BARRON'S

PROFILES OF AMERICAN COLLEGES

20TH EDITION

Descriptions of the Colleges

Twentieth Edition

Compiled and Edited by the College Division
of Barron's Educational Series

Barron's Educational Series, Inc.

All inquiries should be addressed to:
Barron's Educational Series, Inc.
250 Wireless Boulevard
Hauppauge, New York 11788

Library of Congress Catalog Card No. 87-640099

International Standard Book No. 0-8120-1752-8

International Standard Serial No. 1065-5026

PRINTED IN THE UNITED STATES OF AMERICA
4567   100   10987654321

CONTENTS

CONTENTS

PREFACE

Barron's *Profiles of American Colleges* is the most comprehensive, easy-to-use guide available. All four-year institutions that offer bachelor's degrees are described if they are fully accredited or are recognized candidates for accreditation. The comprehensive, readable capsule and detailed essay on each school give an easy-to-absorb, complete picture of the colleges that interest the reader. And the attractive graphic design provides added readability.

The capsule of each profile lists important information for quick reference: enrollment; calendar; fall application deadline; size and salary level of the faculty; percentage of faculty members who hold doctorates; student/faculty ratio; tuition and fees; room and board costs; the number of students who applied to the freshman class, were accepted, and enrolled; the mean SAT* I and/or ACT scores for 1993–94; and finally, the College Admissions Selector Rating for the school. The essay portion of each profile summarizes over 200 questions Barron's asked of the colleges, ranging from information such as available housing and the financial aid climate to the Advanced Placement* tests (APs*) that may be required and the success of graduates. There are twenty-one categories of information under eight main headings: Student Life, Programs of Study, Admissions, Financial Aid, International Students, Computers, Graduates, and Admissions Contact.

We are confident that the features we have added, together with those that have appeared in previous editions of Barron's *Profiles*, will make this twentieth edition the most comprehensive guide available to the college-bound student.

A Word of Thanks

To all the college admissions officers, to many participating high school advisers, to the students, parents, and other supporters of Barron's *Profiles of American Colleges*, we offer our sincere thanks.

Grateful acknowledgment is made to the late Gloria M. Barron, who inspired the editors and production personnel to create a book that would offer every possible assistance in selecting the best college.

We acknowledge, with thanks, the demanding editing task performed by Senior Editor Max Reed and College Division Coordinator Sally Strauss, along with our database designers and our hard-working editorial staff, particularly Assistant Barbara Parkes and the data entry staff, writers, and copy editors.

---

*SAT, Advanced Placement, and AP are registered trademarks owned by the College Entrance Examination Board. No endorsement of this product is implied or given.

AN EXPLANATION OF THE BOOK

You have been thinking about going to college within the next couple of years, and now you're convinced that it's time to get somewhat serious about your plans, and take some steps that will lead to your ultimate college decisions, right?

But how do you go about taking these steps? How much does college cost? How can you and your parents afford it? What about entrance exams? How can you possibly know where you want to go and even if you decide *that* how do you apply, with any degree of assurance that you will be accepted? What if you decide, apply, and then get turned down? How can you ensure that *that* doesn't happen? And if you do get past all those hurdles, how can you determine your college major, when you don't have a clue as to what you want to do *after* college?

But right now—where do you begin? In addition to hundreds of two-year schools, there are nearly 1600 accredited four-year colleges in the United States, and your options are almost unlimited. But Barron's *Profiles of American Colleges* can point you in the right direction, and help you through the coming months of decision making.

You will find articles that will guide you in evaluating your own needs and interests, selecting the college, filling out the application, writing the essay, having the interview, finding the money, and surviving the freshman year.

There is also advice on selecting a major and career and the Index of College Majors, a helpful aid for students who want to know which colleges offer the major they have selected. Over 600 majors are listed, along with the in-state costs and the admissions selector rating in easy-to-read columns.

Profiles of certain large schools in Canada and Mexico and abroad appear. There is advice for international students, as well as a list of schools' in-state costs from least to most expensive. There is also a chart presented geographically that gives students quick information about schools on a state-by-state basis.

The College Admissions Selector ratings give applicants an idea of the competition they will encounter when applying to a particular school. There is also a list of collegiate terms, a key to abbreviations, and an explanation of the actual college entries.

The heart of the book, of course, is the detailed descriptions of the more than 1700 colleges. The college profiles are presented alphabetically by state, and the states are also arranged in alphabetical order. Maps of the states begin each chapter. Actually, Barron's *Profiles of American Colleges* covers more than the fifty states; it also describes colleges in the District of Columbia, Guam, Puerto Rico, the Virgin Islands, Canada, and other countries.

This expanded and updated edition of *Profiles of American Colleges* will answer all of your questions as you embark on this most significant experience—college application, acceptance, and enrollment!

KEY TO ABBREVIATIONS

DEGREES

A.A.—Associate of Arts
A.A.S.—Associate of Applied Science
A.B. or B.A.—Bachelor of Arts
A.B.J.—Bachelor of Arts in Journalism
A.S.—Associate of Science

B.A.A.—Bachelor of Applied Arts
B.A.A.S. or B.Applied A.S.—Bachelor of Applied Arts and Sciences
B.Ac. or B.Acc.—Bachelor of Accountancy
B.A.C.—Bachelor of Science in Air Commerce
B.A.C.V.I.—Bachelor of Arts in Computer and Video Imaging
B.A.E. or B.A.Ed.—Bachelor of Arts in Education
B.A.G.E.—Bachelor of Arts in General Education
B.Agri.—Bachelor of Agriculture
B.A.G.S.—Bachelor of Arts in General Studies
B.A.J.S.—Bachelor of Arts in Judaic Studies
B.A.M.—Bachelor of Arts in Music
B.Applied Sc.—Bachelor of Applied Science
B.A.R.—Bachelor of Religion
B.Arch.—Bachelor of Architecture
B.Arch.Hist.—Bachelor of Architectural History
B.Arch.Tech.—Bachelor of Architectural Technology
B.Ar.Sc.—Baccalaurium Artium et Scientiae (honors college degree) (Bachelor of Arts & Sciences)
B.Art.Ed.—Bachelor of Art Education
B.A.S.—Bachelor of Arts and Sciences
B.A.Sec.Ed.—Bachlor of Arts in Secondary Ed.
B.A.S.W.—B.A. in Social Work
B.A.T.—Bachelor of Arts in Teaching
B.B. or B.Bus.—Bachelor of Business
B.B.A.—Bachelor of Business Administration
B.B.E.—Bachelor of Business Education
B.C. or B.Com. or B.Comm.—Bachelor of Commerce
B.C.A.—Bachelor of Creative Arts
B.C.E.—Bachelor of Civil Engineering
B.C.E.—Bachelor of Computer Engineering
B.Ch. or B.Chem.—Bachelor of Chemistry
B.Ch.E.—Bachelor of Chemical Engineering
B.C.J.—Bachelor of Criminal Justice
B.C.M.—Bachelor of Christian Ministries
B.Church Mus.—Bachelor of Church Music
B.C.S.—Bachelor of College Studies
B.E.—Bachelor of English
B.E. or B.Ed.—Bachelor of Education
B.E.—Bachelor of Engineering
B.E.D.—Bachelor of Environmental Design
B.E.E.—Bachelor of Electrical Engineering
B.En. or B.Eng.—Bachelor of Engineering
B.E.S. or B.Eng.Sc.—Bachelor of Engineering Science
B.E.T.—Bachelor of Engineering Technology
B.F.A.—Bachelor of Fine Arts
B.G.S.—Bachelor of General Studies
B.G.S.—Bachelor of Geological Sciences
B.H.E.—Bachelor of Health Education
B.H.S.—Bachelor of Health Science
B.I.D.—Bachelor of Industrial Design
B.I.M.—Bachelor of Industrial Management
B.Ind.Tech.—Bachelor of Industrial Technology
B.Int.Arch.—Bachelor of Interior Architecture
B.Int.Design—Bachelor of Interior Design
B.I.S.—Bachelor of Industrial Safety
B.I.S.—Bachelor of Interdisciplinary Studies
B.J.—Bachelor of Journalism
B.J.S.—Bachelor of Judaic Studies
B.L.A. or B.Lib.Arts—Bachelor of Liberal Arts
B.L.A. or B.Land.Arch.—Bachelor in Landscape Architecture
B.L.I.—Bachelor of Literary Interpretation
B.L.S.—Bachelor of Liberal Studies
B.M. or B.Mus. or Mus.Bac.—Bachelor of Music
B.M.E.—Bachelor of Mechanical Engineering
B.M.E. or B.M.Ed. or B.Mus.Ed.—Bachelor of Music Education
B.Med.Lab.Sc.—Bachelor of Medical Laboratory Science

B.Min—Bachelor of Ministry
B.M.P. or B.Mu.—Bachelor of Music in Performance
B.Mus.A.—Bachelor of Applied Music
B.M.T.—Bachelor of Music Therapy
B.O.T.—Bachelor of Occupational Therapy
B.P.A.—Bachelor of Public Administration
B.P.E.—Bachelor of Physical Education
B.Perf.Arts—Bachelor of Performing Arts
B.Ph.—Bachelor of Philosophy
B.Pharm.—Bachelor of Pharmacy
B.Phys.Hlth.Ed.—Bachelor of Physical Health Education
B.P.S.—Bachelor of Professional Studies
B.P.T.—Bachelor of Physical Therapy
B.R.E.—Bachelor of Religious Education
B.R.T.—Bachelor of Respiratory Therapy
B.S. or B.Sc. or S.B.—Bachelor of Science
B.S.A. or B.S.Ag. or B.S.Agr.—Bachelor of Science in Agriculture
B.Sacred Mus.—Bachelor of Sacred Music
B.Sacred Theol.—Bachelor of Sacred Theology
B.S.A.E.—Bachelor of Science in Agricultural Engineering
B.S.A.E. or B.S.Art Ed.—Bachelor of Science in Art Education
B.S.Ag.E.—Bachelor of Science in Agricultural Engineering
B.S.A.S.—Bachelor of Science in Administrative Sciences
B.S.B.—Bachelor of Science (business)
B.S.B.A. or B.S.Bus. Adm.—Bachelor of Science in Business Administration
B.S.Bus.—Bachelor of Science in Business
B.S.Bus.Ed.—Bachelor of Science in Business Education
B.S.C.—Bachelor of Science in Commerce
B.S.C.E. or B.S.C.I.E.—Bachelor of Science in Civil Engineering
B.S.C.E.T—B.S. in Computer Engineering Technology
B.S.Ch. or B.S.Chem. or B.S. in Ch.—Bachelor of Science in Chemistry
B.S.Ch.E.—Bachelor of Science in Chemical Engineering
B.S.C.I.S.—Bachelor of Science in Computer Information Sciences
B.S.C.J.—Bachelor of Science in Criminal Justice
B.S.Comp.Eng.—Bachelor of Science in Computer Engineering
B.S.Comp.Sci. or B.S.C.S.—Bachelor of Science in Computer Science
B.S.Comp.Soft—Bachelor of Science in Computer Software
B.S.Comp.Tech.—Bachelor of Science in Computer Technology
B.Sc.(P.T.)—Bachelor of Science in Physical Therapy
B.S.C.S.T.—Bachelor of Science in Computer Science Technology
B.S.D.H.—Bachelor of Science in Dental Hygiene
B.S.Die—Bachelor of Science in Dietetics
B.S.E. or B.S.Ed. or B.S.Educ.—Bachelor of Science in Education
B.S.E. or B.S in E. or B.S. in Eng.—Bachelor of Science in Engineering
B.S.E.E.—Bachelor of Science in Electrical Engineering
B.S.E.E.T.—Bachelor of Science in Electrical Engineering Technology
B.S.E.H.—Bachelor of Science in Environmental Health
B.S.Elect.T.—Bachelor of Science in Electronics Technology
B.S.El.Ed. or B.S. in Elem. Ed.—Bachelor of Science in Elementary Education
B.S.E.P.H.—Bachelor of Science in Environmental and Public Health
B.S.E.S.—Bachelor of Science in Engineering Science
B.S.E.S.—Bachelor of Science in Environmental Studies
B.S.E.T.—Bachelor of Science in Engineering Technology
B.S.F.—Bachelor of Science in Forestry
B.S.F.R.—Bachelor of Science in Forestry Resources
B.S.F.W.—Bachelor of Science in Fisheries and Wildlife
B.S.G.—Bachelor of Science in Geology
B.S.G.—Bachelor of Science in Gerontology
B.S.G.E.—Bachelor of Science in Geological Engineering
B.S.G.S.—Bachelor of Science in General Studies
B.S.H.C.A.—Bachelor of Science in Health Care Administration

B.S.H.E.—Bachelor of Science in Home Economics
B.S.H.S.—Bachelor of Science in Health Sciences
B.S.H.S.—Bachelor of Science in Human Services
B.S.I.A.—Bachelor of Science in Industrial Arts
B.S.I.E.—Bachelor of Science in Industrial Engineering
B.S.I.M.—Bachelor of Science in Industrial Management
B.S. in Biomed.Eng.—Bachelor of Science in Biomedical Engineering
B.S. in C.D.—Bachelor of Science in Communication Disorders
B.S.Ind.Ed.—Bachelor of Science in Industrial Education
B.S.Ind.Tech.—Bachelor of Science in Industrial Technology
B.S. in Sec.Ed.—Bachelor of Science in Secondary Education
B.S.I.T.—Bachelor of Science in Industrial Technology
B.S.J.—Bachelor of Science in Journalism
B.S.L.E.—Bachelor of Science in Law Enforcement
B.S.M.—Bachelor of Science in Management
B.S.M.—Bachelor of Science in Music
B.S.M.E.—Bachelor of Science in Mechanical Engineering
B.S.Med.Tech. or B.S.M.T.—Bachelor of Science in Medical Technology
B.S.Met.E.—Bachelor of Science in Metallurgical Engineering
B.S.M.R.A.—Bachelor of Science in Medical Records Administration
B.S.Mt.E.—Bachelor of Science in Materials Engineering
B.S.Mus.Ed.—Bachelor of Science in Music Education
B.S.N.—Bachelor of Science in Nursing
B.S.Nuc.T.—Bachelor of Science in Nuclear Technology
B.S.O.A.—Bachelor of Science in Office Administration
B.S.O.E.—Bachelor of Science in Occupational Education
B.S.O.T.—Bachelor of Science in Occupational Therapy
B.S.P. or B.S.Pharm—Bachelor of Science in Pharmacy
B.S.P.A.—Bachelor of Science in Public Administration
B.S.Pcs.—Bachelor of Science in Physics
B.S.P.E.—Bachelor of Science in Physical Education
B.S.P.T.—Bachelor of Science in Physical Therapy
B.S.Rad.Tech.—Bachelor of Science in Radiation Technology
B.S.S.—Bachelor of Science in Surveying
B.S.S.—Bachelor of Special Studies
B.S.S.A.—Bachelor of Science in Systems Analysis
B.S.Soc. Work or B.S.S.W.—Bachelor of Science in Social Work
B.S.Sp.—Bachelor of Science in Speech
B.S.S.T.—Bachelor of Science in Surveying and Topography
B.S.T. or B.S.Tech.—Bachelor of Science in Technology
B.S.S.W.E.—Bachelor of Science in Software Engineering
B.S.V.T.E.—Bachelor of Science in Vocational Technical Education
B.S.W.—Bachelor of Social Work
B.T. or B.Tech.—Bachelor of Technology
B.Th.—Bachelor of Theology
B.U.S.—Bachelor of Urban Studies
B.V.M.—Bachelor of Veterinarian Medicine
B.Voc.Arts or B.V.A.—Bachelor of Vocational Arts
B.V.E.D. or B.Voc.Ed.—Bachelor of Vocational Education

D.D.S.—Doctor of Dental Surgery

Ed.S.—Education Specialist

J.D.—Doctor of Jurisprudence

LL.B.—Bachelor of Laws

M.A.—Master of Arts
M.A.Ed.—Master of Arts in Education
M.A.T.—Master of Arts in Teaching
M.B.A.—Master of Business Administration
M.D.—Doctor of Medicine
M.F.A.—Master of Fine Arts
M.P.A.—Master of Public Administration
M.S.—Master of Science
Mus.B. or Mus.Bac.—Bachelor of Music

Ph.D.—Doctor of Philosophy

R.N.—Registered Nurse

S.B. or B.S. or B.Sc.—Bachelor of Science

OTHER ABBREVIATIONS

AACSB—American Assembly of Collegiate Schools of Business
AALS—Association of American Law Schools
ABA—American Bar Association
ABET—Accreditation Board for Engineering and Technology
ABHES—Accrediting Bureau of Health Education Schools
ACBSP—Association of Collegiate Business Schools and Programs
ACCE—American Council for Construction Education
ACE HSA—Accrediting Commission on Education for Health Services Administration
ACE JMC—American Council on Education in Journalism and Mass Communication
ACPE—Association for Clinical Pastoral Education, Inc.
ACPE—American Council on Pharmaceutical Education
ACT—American College Testing Program
ADA—American Dietetic Association
ADA—American Dental Association
AFSA—Application for Federal Student Aid
AHEA—American Home Economics Association
ALA—American Library Association
ALIGU—American Language Institute of Georgetown University
AMAC AHEA—American Medical Association Committee on Allied Health Education and Accreditation
AOA—American Osteopathic Association
AOA—American Optometric Association
AP—Advanced Placement
APA—American Podiatry Association
APA—American Psychological Association
APTA—American Physical Therapy Association
ASLA—American Society of Landscape Architects
ASLHA—American Speech-Language-Hearing Association
AT—Achievement Test
ATP—Admissions Testing Program
ATSUSC—Association of Theological Schools in the United States and Canada
AVMA—American Veterinary Medical Association

BEOG—Basic Educational Opportunity Grant (now Pell Grant)

CAS—Certificate of Advanced Study
CCE—Council on Chiropractic Education
CEEB—College Entrance Examination Board
CELT—Comprehensive English Language Test
CEPH—Council on Education for Public Health
CLEP—College-Level Examination Program
CRDA—Candidates Reply Date Agreement
CRE—Council on Rehabilitation Education
CSAB—Computing Science Accreditation Board
CSS—College Scholarship Service
CSWE—Council on Social Work Education
CWS—College Work-Study

EESL—Examination of English as a Second Language
ELS/ALA—English Language Services/American Language Academy
EMH—Educable Mentally Handicapped
EOP—Equal Opportunity Program
ESL—English as a Second Language
ETS—Educational Testing Service

FAF—Financial Aid Form
FAFSA—Free Application for Federal Student Aid
FFS—Family Financial Statement
FIDER—Foundation for Interior Design Education Research
FISL—Federally Insured Student Loan

GED—General Educational Development (high school equivalency examination)

GPA—Grade Point Average
GRE—Graduate Record Examination
GSLP—Guaranteed Student Loan Program

HEOP—Higher Equal Opportunity Program
HPER—Health, Physical Education, and Recreation

LCME—Liaison Committee on Medical Education

MTELP—Michigan Test of English Language Proficiency

NAA—National Architectural Accrediting
NAPNES—National Association for Practical Nurse Education and Service
NASAD—National Association of Schools of Art and Design
NASDTEC—National Association of State Development Teacher Education
NASM—National Association of Schools of Music
NAST—National Association of Schools of Theatre
NCATE—National Council for Accreditation of Teacher Education
NCCAA—National Christian College Athletic Association
NDEA—National Defense Education Act
NLN—National League for Nursing

PCS—Parents' Confidential Statement
PAIR—PHEAA Aid Information Request
PEP—Proficiency Examination Program
PHEAA—Pennsylvania Higher Education Assistance Agency

PSAT/NMSQT—Preliminary Scholastic Aptitude Test/National Merit Scholarship Qualifying Test

ROTC—Reserve Officers Training Corps
RSE—Regents Scholarship Examination (New York State)

SAAC—Student Aid Application for California
SACU—Service for Admission to College and University (Canada)
SAF—Society of American Foresters
SAM—Single Application Method
SAR—Student Aid Report
SAT—Scholastic Aptitude Test
SCAT—Scholastic College Aptitude Test
SCS—Students' Confidential Statement
SEOG—Supplementary Educational Opportunity Grant

TAP—Tuition Assistance Program (New York State)
TDD—Telecommunication Device for the Deaf
TOEFL—Test of English as a Foreign Language
TTY—Talking Typewriter

UAP—Undergraduate Assessment Program
UP—Undergraduate Program (area tests)

VFAF—Virginia Financial Assistance Form

WPCT—Washington Pre-College Test

PART I
AN INTRODUCTION TO COLLEGE

PART I

AN INTRODUCTION TO COLLEGE

KNOWING YOURSELF

You have in your hands a book that will give you answers to your questions about the qualities and features of over one thousand colleges. But before you start reading the descriptions and getting the answers, you need to know what questions to ask about finding the college that is right for you. Although you need to ask questions about "getting in," i.e., exploring colleges in terms of ease of admission for you, most of your questions should focus on the more significant issue of "fitting in." Fitting in means finding a college where you will be comfortable; where you are compatible with your peers, and where the overall atmosphere encourages your growth as a student and as a person.

This article is designed to help you assess some values and attitudes that will help you determine where you will fit in. It will enable you to ask the right questions. Not all colleges are for everyone; careful thinking about your interests, ideals, and values will lead you to find the college that is right *for you*. Colleges are not "good" or "bad" in a generic sense; they are either good or bad matches for you.

The two tests that follow will be helpful in thinking about yourself as a future college student; they should help you make the right college choice.

THE COLLEGE PLANNING VALUES ASSESSMENT

Students have different reasons for going to college. Ten reasons or values are found to be most important to students as they think about college. Knowing about your values is important as the first step in identifying the colleges where you will fit in and be happy.

To complete the assessment, read through the list of ten values—A–J. Think about the outcomes you hope college will produce for you. Each student will rank them differently; hence, there are no "right" answers. Whereas several, or even most, of these values may be significant for you in one way or another, the goal is to decide the relative importance of each. With 10 being highest and 1 being lowest, *rank* them on the basis of:

What do you want college to do for you?
_____ A. To provide me with an academic challenge.
_____ B. To provide me with opportunities to exchange intellectual ideas with teachers and students.
_____ C. To provide me with lots of fun experiences.
_____ D. To prepare me to make a lot of money.
_____ E. To provide me with recognition for accomplishments.
_____ F. To provide me with opportunities to contribute to others' welfare.
_____ G. To help me prepare for a career.
_____ H. To give me independence.
_____ I. To provide opportunities for me to grow religiously or spiritually.
_____ J. To provide me with a variety of new experiences.

Now go back and circle the values that you have marked with either a 10, 9, or 8. What do your college planning values say about you?

If **A** was among the top three priorities on your list, you will want to explore the academic character of the colleges you are considering. Although all colleges are, by definition, intellectual centers, some put more priority on challenging students and pushing them to their limits. Reading about the academic features of the colleges you are considering will be important. (In the college profiles, pay attention to the *special* section to learn about these features.) Your high ranking of this value says that you will be able to take advantage of intellectual opportunities at college. You may want to select a college where your SAT I scores are similar to or slightly above the ranges of other admitted students: at those colleges, you will be able to shine academically. You may desire to take an active part in classroom discussions and will want a college where the student faculty ratio is low. A word of caution here:

some students select this value because they see the prestige of the college as all-important in their choice. Although it is appropriate to look for a strong faculty and a highly regarded college, you want a college that will give you the greatest chance of academic success. It is success in college, not just academic reputation or prestige, that will lead to admission into graduate school or a broad selection of jobs.

If **B** was among your top three priorities, you feel challenged and stimulated by academics and classroom learning. You will want to find a college where your mind will be stretched. You will want to choose a college where you can explore a range of new academic subjects. A liberal arts and sciences college may give you an enriching breadth of academic offerings. You will want to look for a college where academic clubs are popular and where you have a good chance of knowing professors and sharing ideas with them. Access to faculty is important to you and you will want to look at the student faculty ratio in colleges you consider. Also note the ratio of undergraduate students to graduate students. Primarily undergraduate institutions will be the colleges that may best be able to meet your needs, because you will be the focus of teachers' attention. Teachers at such colleges place their priority on teaching and are not distracted by the needs of graduate students or by pressure to balance teaching and student time with research and writing.

If **C** was circled, you derive satisfaction from social opportunities. You will want a college where the academic demands will not diminish your ability to socialize. You likely will want a good balance between the social and academic sides of campus life. You will want to explore the percentage of students who get involved in intramural sports, clubs, or fraternities and sororities. (This information is listed in each college profile.) Look at your college choices on the basis of school spirit and sporting events offered. The profiles list popular campus events; see if they sound exciting to you. Also look at the percentage of students who stay on campus over the weekend. You will also want a college where it is easy to make friends. Both small and larger colleges would be appropriate for you. Although a larger college would expose you to more students and a larger quantity of potential friends, studies show that students at smaller colleges become more involved in activities and build deep friendships more quickly. Look for supportiveness and camaraderie in the student body.

If **D** is circled, you will want to consider earning potential, advancement opportunities, and the future market for the careers you consider. You will want to consider this value in your career planning. Remember, however, that there is no sure road to riches! You not only must pick a career direction carefully, but must choose a college where the potential for academic success—good grades—is high. The name of a particular college is less important than good grades or contributions to campus life when securing a good job or being admitted to graduate school. Even if you find that a particular career has tremendous earning potential, those earnings may come to only those who are most successful in the profession. Look at average salaries, but also consider your interests, values, and personality before making your final career choice.

If **E** is high on your list, you take pleasure in being known for your success in an area of interest. For instance, you might feel good about being recognized or known in school as a good student, a top athlete, or a leader in a club. No doubt this type of recognition contributes to your confidence. You might look for colleges where you will be able to acquire or continue to receive this recognition. Often, recognition is easier to achieve at smaller colleges where you would not be competing against large numbers of students hoping to achieve the same recognition. You will also want to choose colleges where it is easy to get involved and where the activities offered are appealing to you. You may want to consider the benefits of being a "big fish in a small pond."

If **F** is important, that value will no doubt guide your vocational or avocational pursuits. You may find yourself

choosing a career in which this value can be fulfilled, or you may seek opportunities on a college campus where you can be of service. You will want to choose a college where community service is valued. Look at the *activities* section and note whether community service-related involvements are available.

If **G** was circled, you may know what career you want to pursue or you may be concerned but uncertain about your career decision. If you have tentatively selected a career, you will want to choose a college where you can take courses leading to the attainment of a degree in your chosen field. Explore the *programs of study* section in the profiles to determine whether a college you are considering offers the course work you desire. You will want to make a note of the most popular majors and the strongest majors as they are listed. If you don't yet know what career would suit you, remember, that for most careers, a broad, solid liberal arts foundation is considered good preparation. You will want to look at opportunities for internships and take advantage of the career planning and placement office at your chosen college. Finding a career that will be fulfilling is one of the most important choices you will make in your life. Your selection of a college will be your first step toward achieving your career goal.

If **H** is circled, it suggests that personal autonomy is important to you. College is, in general, a time for independence, and students are often anxious to make their own decisions without parental involvement. If you feel you can handle lots of independence, you will want to look for colleges where there is some freedom in choosing courses and where students are given responsibility for their own lives. Colleges vary in terms of these factors. Note particularly the *required* section under *programs of study*, which tells you the courses that must be fulfilled by all students. Be certain that you will not be stifled by too many rules and regulations. You may also want to look for colleges where the personal development of students receives high priority. A priority on independence also suggests that you will be comfortable being away from home and on your own.

If **I** is one of your top three choices, you will want to look first at the religious affiliation of each of your college options. You may want a college that has a relationship with your particular religious group. Or you may desire a large number of students who belong to the same denomination as you do. The profiles will also give you the percentage of students who are members of the major religious denominations. As you explore colleges, you will also want to see if the college has a commitment to the values and ideals held by you or your family.

If **J** is appealing, you like newness and will likely be stimulated by new experiences and new activities. You may see college-going as an adventure and will want to pick colleges where you can meet your need for stimulation and excitement. Because you value newness, you should not hesitate to attend college in a different part of the country or to experience an environment or a climate that is quite different from your high school. You will also want to look for evidence of diversity in the student body. As you read the descriptions, look for colleges with lots of new opportunities for growth and for personal expansion.

Now that you've read about your top three values, answer the following question on a separate sheet of paper: In your own words, what do your top three values say about what you are looking for in a college? Then, share that information with your college adviser as he or she assists you in finding colleges that are right for you.

SELF-KNOWLEDGE QUESTIONNAIRE

The following seven items—A–G—will help you in thinking about yourself as a college student and the ease with which you will likely proceed through the college selection process. Read each statement and determine whether it is true or not true of you. After each question, you will see numbers ranging from 1 to 5. Circle 1 if the statement is very true of you. Circle 5 if

the statement is not true of you. Use 2, 3, or 4 to reflect varying levels of preference. Be realistic and honest.

A. I am confident about my academic abilities for college (such as reading, writing, and note taking).
Very true of me   1   2   3   4   5   Not true of me

Academic abilities such as reading speed and comprehension, writing, note taking, calculating, speaking, and listening are important for college students. You will be called upon to use such skills in your college classes. If you are confident about your academic skills, you can approach picking a college with the ease of knowing that you will be able to master the academic rigors of college life. If you circled 3, 4, or 5, you will want to work on these skills in your remaining days in high school. You will want to choose colleges where you can work to strengthen these skills. Some colleges provide a learning skills center in which you are able to get help if you are having difficulty writing a paper or understanding the content of a class. If you are less than confident, you might look to colleges where you will not be intimidated by the skills of the other students.

B. My study skills and time management are good.
Very true of me   1   2   3   4   5   Not true of me

Study skills and time management are two of the most important qualities for an efficient and productive college student. Successful college students are average or above in organizing themselves for studying, scheduling, and using study time productively, and differentiating important content of a lecture or a book from supplementary information. In addition, they complete assignments on time and don't get flustered if they have several papers or a couple of tests due on the same day. If you circled 3, 4, or 5, it is important to work on improving these skills during your remaining high school days. You might consider the following:

- Seek help from your parents, a teacher, a counselor, or a learning specialist in becoming more organized.
- Try keeping a calendar. Anticipate each step necessary in preparing for every test and every paper.
- Be responsible for your own appointments.
- Check to see if a study skills course is offered at a local community college or university. Or consider reading a book on study skills.

C. I am motivated to succeed in college.
Very true of me   1   2   3   4   5   Not true of me

Motivation is definitely the most important skill you bring to college. Those students who want to succeed do succeed! Studies show that it is motivation, not your SAT scores, that determines academic success in college. And motivation means knowing not only that you want to go to college, but that you also want to be a student. Some students want to go to college for the fun aspects, but forget that college is primarily an academic experience. So if you circled 1 or 2, great, you're off to a good start. If you circled 3, 4, or 5, it may be an appropriate time to consider your wants and needs in a college. What sort of college would help motivate you? Would a college with a balance between academics and social life be appealing? Would you be more motivated if you were near a large and interesting city? Would nice weather be a distraction rather than an energizer? Is a trade or technical school best for you? Have you considered taking some time off between high school and college? Considering such questions is important, and the time to do that exploration is now.

D. I am a good decision maker.
Very true of me   1   2   3   4   5   Not true of me

Decisions, decisions, decisions. The college selection process is full of decisions! What colleges will I initially consider? To which colleges will I apply for admission? What college will I eventually attend? You will be facing these decisions in the upcoming months. If you circled 1 or 2, you are on your way. If you circled 3, 4, or 5, think about an important decision you made recently. Why didn't it go well? If you can analyze your decision-making weakness in that situation, it may help to avoid any potential pitfalls in your college decision making. The following suggestions will help you improve your ability to make the right college choice:

- Clearly articulate what you're looking for in a college. Write down those features that will make a college right for you.

- List and compare pros and cons of alternative colleges. Every college has both.
- Evaluate each college on the basis of the criteria you set for yourself. Remember, you're looking for a college where you will get in *and* fit in.

E. I'm a good information gatherer; for example, I am usually able to find books, articles, and so on to help me do a history research paper.

Very true of me   1   2   3   4   5   Not true of me

Finding a college requires you to be a good researcher. There is so much information about colleges to sort through and analyze—note the size of this book! If you feel you can do good research, fine, you're on your way. If you circled 3, 4, or 5, the following ideas may be helpful:

- Start with this book and look for colleges that are consistent with what you want. Remember that your primary concern is where you will fit in. Use your college-going values and your responses in this questionnaire to guide your thinking about colleges that will match you.
- Work closely with your college counselor, and seek impressions from students and others with reliable and up-to-date information about colleges of interest. You will make a better decision with credible and extensive input.
- Look for differences in features that are important to you. Is ease of making friends important to you? What about balance between academics and social life? Do you want teachers to know you?

F. I feel I adapt to new situations easily.

Very true of me   1   2   3   4   5   Not true of me

Everyone goes through changes in life. Some move through transition periods with great ease, others find them more difficult. You may have experienced the changes that come after a change of schools (even from middle school to high school), the illness or death of a relative, or the divorce of your parents. If you circled 1 or 2, you are not likely to be intimidated by a college in another part of the country or a college very different from your high school. If you circled 3, 4, or 5, you may want to carefully look at colleges that are a bit closer to home or colleges where the same values, perceptions, and attitudes exist as were true in your high school. Almost everyone has fear and apprehension about leaving for college. But if that fear is significant, you will want to choose a college where you will feel comfortable. Visits to college campuses may be particularly significant in feeling good about potential choices.

6. It is easy for me to meet people and establish friendships.

Very true of me   1   2   3   4   5   Not true of me

Identifying and nurturing friendships is an important skill for college adjustment. If you circled 3, 4, or 5, you will want to look carefully at colleges where there are few cliques, where there is an atmosphere of sharing, and where students report that it is relatively easy to integrate into the campus environment. Your choice of a college is a quest for good social fit. Your thorough review of the profiles and even visits to college campuses will be helpful in assuring your ability to fit in and be comfortable.

FINAL THOUGHTS

If you took time to carefully consider the issues raised in both the Values Assessment and the Self-Knowledge Questionnaire, you should have gained new insights and perspectives about yourself. You will want to share these results with your parents and with your guidance counselor. Elicit their help in getting more insight as to how they see you as a prospective college student. Finally, two suggestions:

- As you research colleges, consider what you have learned about yourself. You want a college that is a good match with your values and interests.
- Spend time on your college search. It will take many hours of organized planning and investigation. But the time spent will result in a better choice and a greater likelihood that you will spend four productive and exciting years in college.

Good luck. There are lots of colleges out there that want you. Let your knowledge of yourself and your objective analysis of potential college options guide you to college environments where you will be able to shine. Success in college is in your hands. Make the most of the opportunity.

Steven R. Antonoff, Ph.D.
Educational Consultant
Antonoff Associates, Inc.
Denver, Colorado

FINDING THE RIGHT COLLEGE

Americans today have more access to college education than any previous generation, anywhere in the world. This is true no matter what your age or what you want to study. Most readers of these profiles are high school seniors or recent high school graduates planning to enroll full-time in four-year colleges or universities. For such students, the choice is especially wide. That makes the task of choosing complicated, but it also gives you the opportunity to get the best possible education for which you are qualified. The choice is yours.

THE BUYERS' MARKET

When your parents graduated from high school, in the 1960s, colleges were crowded with the "baby boom" generation. It was not easy to gain admission. Within the last 10 to 15 years, this situation has changed considerably. Teenaged population has been decreasing, whereas the number and variety of colleges has continued to expand. The law of supply and demand is now on your side.

Since 1960, the number of American four-year colleges and universities has grown from about 1400 to about 2000, of which approximately 600 are specialized institutions, such as music and art conservatories or theological seminaries. Most existing institutions grew larger, and many expanded their programs, offering master's and doctoral degrees as well as bachelor's. The number of two-year colleges expanded dramatically, more than doubling since 1960 from about 600 to about 1400 today.

The total number of graduate and undergraduate students has also grown, from under 4 million in 1960 to over 14 million today. Almost half are part-time students, including many working adults who started attending in large numbers during the 1960s and 1970s. Part-time enrollments are mostly concentrated in the two-year colleges, which enroll about a third of all students.

You Are In Demand

Four-year colleges and universities doubled their enrollments in the 1960s and 1970s, and they still need to fill their classrooms and dormitories with full-time students between 18 and 22 years of age. Such students are getting harder to find. The number of high school seniors hit an all-time high of 3.1 million in 1977. Based on current projections, graduating classes will fall to 2.3 million by 1995. That's why institutions are recruiting so vigorously, sending you mailings, visiting your high school, and setting up displays at college fairs. They need you as much as you need them.

MAKING A SHORT LIST

You have probably already started a list of colleges you know about from friends or relatives who have attended them, from recommendations by teachers, or by their academic or athletic reputations. This list will grow as you read the profiles, receive college mailings, and attend college fairs. If you are interested in preparing for a very specific career, such as engineering, agriculture, health care, or architecture, you should add only institutions that offer that program. If you want to study business, teacher education, or the arts and sciences, almost every college can provide a suitable major. Either way, your list will soon include dozens of institutions. Most students apply to between two and five colleges. In order to narrow your list, you should follow a three-step process:

- **Check your realistic options,** eliminating colleges at which you would not qualify for admission and those that are beyond your family's financial means.
- **Screen the list** according to your preferences, such as institutional size, type, and location.

- **Evaluate the institutions,** using published information and campus visits to make judgments about which colleges can give you the best quality and value.

The following sections will guide you through each of these steps.

REALISTIC OPTIONS

Admissions Competitiveness

The first question most students ask about a college is, "How hard is it to get in?" It should certainly not be the last question. Admissions competitiveness is not the only, or even the most important, measurement of institutional quality. It makes sense to avoid wasting time, money, and useless disappointment applying to institutions for which you clearly are not qualified. Nevertheless, there are many colleges for which you are qualified, and you can make a good choice from among them. The buyer's market has not necessarily forced admission standards down everywhere. The most prestigious institutions are rarely affected by market conditions. Some of the better known public colleges and universities have raised their admission standards in recent years, as their lower prices have attracted larger numbers of applicants. But there remain hundreds of fine public and private colleges, with good local reputations, that will welcome your application.

Use the College Admissions Selector to compare your qualifications to the admissions competitiveness of the institutions of your list. Make sure you read the descriptions of standards very carefully. Even if you meet the stated qualifications for *most competitive* or *highly competitive* institutions, you cannot assume that you will be offered admission. These colleges receive applications from many more students than they can enroll and reject far more than they accept. When considering colleges rated *very competitive* or *competitive*, remember that the median test scores identify the middle of the most recent freshman class; half of the admitted students had scores lower than the median, and half were above. If your high school grades and class rank are within the stated range, and your SAT I and ACT scores are even a little below the stated median, your chances of acceptance are very good. Students in the top quarter of their high school classes who score above 1000 on the SAT I or 25 on the ACT are likely to be accepted at several of the *very competitive* colleges and universities.

Students of average ability are admissible to most of the colleges and universities rated as *competitive* and to virtually all of those rated as *less competitive*. They would need high school grades of C+ or better and SAT I total scores of about 900 or ACT composite scores of about 21.

Cost

The most expensive colleges and universities now cost over $20,000 a year. This is widely publicized and very frightening, especially to your parents. But you don't have to spend that much for a good education. Most private colleges charge between $13,000 and $18,000 a year for tuition and room and board. Public institutions generally cost between $6000 and $8000 a year for in-state residents. Because many states have been cutting budgets in recent years, tuition at public institutions is now rising faster than at private ones. If you can commute to school from home, you can save about $3500 to $4500 in room and board, but should add the cost of transportation. The least expensive option is to attend a local community college for two years, at about $1000 a year, and then transfer to a four-year institution to complete your bachelor's degree. Depending on what you may qualify for in financial aid, and what your family is willing to sacrifice, you may have more choices than you think.

SCREEN BY PREFERENCE

The self-knowledge tests should indicate whether you are more likely to be comfortable far from or near to home, at an urban or rural campus, in a college that is secular or religious, coed or single sex. It is best, however, not to eliminate any options without at least visiting a few campuses of different types to judge their feeling and style at first hand. Choosing the proper institutional size and whether to live on campus or commute from home are more complicated questions.

Large Universities and Small Colleges

Only one-fifth of American colleges and universities have enrollments of 5000 or more, but they account for more than half the 7 million plus students who are pursuing bachelor's degrees. The rest are spread out among more than 1000 smaller schools. There are advantages and disadvantages that go with size.

At a college of 5000 or fewer students, you will get to know the campus quickly. You will not have to compete with many other students for the use of the library or when registering for courses. You can get to know your professors personally and become familiar with most of your fellow students. On the other hand, you may have little privacy and a limited choice of activities. Students at small schools often feel pressure to conform to prevailing customs.

As colleges and universities enroll more students, they offer a greater variety of courses, professors, facilities, and activities. Within a large campus community, you can probably find others who share your special interests and form a circle of good friends. But you may also find the libraries more crowded, many classes closed out, and competition very stiff for athletic teams or musical groups.

Many of the largest institutions are universities offering Ph.Ds., medicine, law, or other doctoral programs as well as bachelor's and master's degrees. Many colleges that do not offer these programs call themselves universities; and a few universities, Dartmouth among them, continue to call themselves colleges. Within the last decade, state colleges in Connecticut, Pennsylvania, and South Carolina have been named universities without a real change in their programs. Don't go by the name, but by the academic program. Universities emphasize research. University faculty need specialized laboratory equipment, computers, library material, and technical assistance for their research.

Because this is very expensive, universities usually charge higher tuition than colleges, even to their undergraduate students. Tuition at public universities can run 25 to 100 percent more than at public colleges in the same state. Private universities generally charge about 50 percent more than similarly located private colleges. In effect, undergraduates at universities subsidize the high cost of graduate programs. Freshmen and sophomores usually receive some instruction from graduate student assistants and fellows, who are paid to be apprentice faculty members.

However, most private universities and many public ones have extensive reputations. They have larger and more up-to-date libraries, laboratories, computers, and other special resources than colleges. They attract students from many states and countries and provide a rich social and cultural environment.

Living On and Off Campus

Deciding whether you will stay in a dormitory or at home is more than a matter of finances or how close to the college you live. You should be aware that students who live on campus, especially during the freshman year, are more likely to pass their courses and graduate than students who commute from home. Campus residents spend more time with faculty members, have more opportunity to use the library and laboratories, and are linked to other students who help one another with their studies. Residence hall life usually helps students mature faster as they participate in social and organizational activities.

About 25 percent of college freshmen live with their parents. If you commute to school, you can get maximum benefits from your college experience by spending time on campus between and after classes. If you need a part-time job, get employment in the college library, offices, or dining halls. Use the library to do homework in an environment that may be less distracting than at home. If possible, have some dinners on campus, to make friends with other students and participate in evening social and cultural events. Get involved in campus activities, participating in athletics, working on the newspaper, attending a meeting, or rehearsing a play.

If you will be living on campus, you may be able to choose among different types of residence buildings. Small dormitories are two to four stories high and house 250 or fewer students. They foster more quiet and privacy than larger buildings. High-rise units can house 1000 or more. They usually offer dining halls, snack bars, game rooms, and laundries all under one roof. Most older halls provide single or double rooms, with shared bathrooms on each floor. Newer halls frequently offer suites, in which a common living/study area and bathroom are shared by eight to twelve students occupying single or double bedrooms. Some students enjoy a larger family group; others prefer having only one roommate.

Campus food is usually wholesome, bland, and laden with carbohydrates to meet the high energy demands of active young people. You may have a choice of food plans between 10 and 21 meals a week. Other plans allow you to prepay a fixed dollar amount and purchase food by the item rather than by the meal. Food services make most of their profits on meals that are paid for but never eaten. Choose a meal plan that fits your own eating habits. Meal plans can usually be supplemented or increased, but they rarely can be reduced or refunded.

Many students live off campus after their freshman or sophomore year, either by choice or because the school does not have room for them on campus. Schools try to provide listings of available off-campus rooms and apartments that meet good standards for safety and cleanliness. Many colleges also offer health care and food services to students who live off campus.

It is usually more expensive to live in an apartment than in a dormitory, especially if you plan to prepare your own meals. Great care must be taken in choosing apartment mates. In addition to the usual problems that may arise through personality conflicts, others may develop because apartment mates share payments for rent and utilities and responsibilities for cleaning, shopping, and cooking. It is much harder to find new people to share an apartment in mid-lease than it is to change roommates on campus.

MAKING QUALITY JUDGMENTS

Once you have narrowed your list, you should decide where to apply on the basis of quality. It is not as difficult as you may think to make such judgments. You have to be willing to read the information in this book and the literature that the schools send out, to visit a few campuses, and to ask plenty of questions. You can usually ask questions of the admissions office, by mail or in person during a campus visit. Sometimes, as indicated in the following sections, it is better to ask questions at the offices most directly involved. Because colleges sincerely are interested in helping you make the right choice, they generally will welcome your questions and answer them politely and honestly.

The Faculty

The most important resources of any college or university are its professors. Admissions brochures usually point out the strengths of the faculty, but provide little detail. You should direct your questions about the faculty and other academic matters to the office of academic affairs. Find out what percentage of the faculty have the Ph.D. or other doctoral degrees. Although there is no fixed right number, it should be at least the majority. Schools start bragging in their brochures when 70 percent or more of the faculty have the Ph.D., so that seems to be a common benchmark of quality.

Recruiting brochures also emphasize faculty research, because the prestige of professors depends largely on the books and articles they have published. Good researchers may or may not make good teachers. Ask how

often the best researchers teach undergraduate courses, and whether they instruct small as well as large classes. For example, a Nobel prize chemist may lecture to 500 students at a time but never show up in the laboratories where graduate assistants actually teach individual students.

Also ask about class size, because this determines the amount of individual attention students get from professors. Student/faculty ratios, which usually range from 10 to 20 students per professor, don't really tell you much. Every school offers a mixture of large and small classes. Here are some general standards:

- Science and technology courses should enroll only 25 to 30 students in each laboratory session, but may combine a number of laboratory classes for large weekly lectures.
- Skill development courses such as speech, foreign language, English composition, and fine and performing arts should have classes of 25 or fewer. Mathematics and computing require considerable graded homework, and classes should be no larger than 35.
- Clinical courses in nursing and other health fields are partly based in hospitals or other health care facilities. In such courses, each 10 students should be supervised by a professor. Similarly, each student teacher should be placed with an experienced elementary or secondary school teacher and visited periodically by a member of the college faculty.
- Most other courses in humanities, social sciences, and professional areas are taught by classroom lectures and discussion. Classes should average 35 to 45 in introductory courses such as general psychology or American government. They should be smaller in advanced or specialized courses, such as Shakespeare or tax accounting.
- Many introductory courses, especially at universities, are taught in lecture classes of 100 or more. This is acceptable, if those courses also include small weekly discussion groups for individual instruction. Sometimes these discussion groups are taught by graduate student assistants rather than regular professors. Although graduate assistants lack teaching experience, they are very often highly capable. You should ask whether the teaching done by graduate assistants is closely supervised by regular faculty members.

Academic Programs

Even colleges and universities that boast fine and well-qualified faculties can be short of professors in certain programs, particularly in business, computing, and engineering. These continue to be popular majors although business, the most popular, has declined slightly since 1990. Some schools depend on instruction by part-time faculty members or fill in with available teachers from other specializations. Many international students are enrolled in technical doctoral programs, so you may find yourself being taught mathematics or engineering by a teaching assistant whose English you cannot understand. If you are interested in these subjects, check to see whether full-time faculty members teach at least 80 percent of the courses.

Other programs may have sufficient faculty but too few student majors. Physics, foreign languages, and philosophy usually have many students in required introductory courses but few taking the major. Because of small enrollments, these departments may not be able to offer their advanced and specialized courses on a regular basis. You should review the college catalog to see whether all of the courses required for majoring in the program are offered at least once every two years.

The academic department gives strength to the program by bringing together faculty members who share a common area of study and make sure their students get the instruction they need. Even at a small college, a department should have at least three full-time professors to offer a major program. Some programs, usually called interdisciplinary, are taught by groups of faculty members from several departments. These programs generally have the word *studies* in their titles; for example, Middle-Eastern Studies, Communication Studies, Women's Studies, or Ethnic Studies. Interdisciplinary committees are usually effective for a few years, after

which the faculty members tend to pay more attention to their own departments. If you enroll in one of these programs, you may not have a regular faculty adviser or a good choice of courses for enrollment.

Sometimes highly specialized programs are offered within more general departments. Examples are semantics or linguistics (within the English department), social work or anthropology (within sociology), or broadcasting (within speech). Such a program may be taught by one faculty specialist, and you could be left stranded if that person leaves. On the other hand, that faculty member may hold tenure and teach the subject successfully for many years.

Accreditation

General standards of academic quality are established by associations of colleges and universities through a process called voluntary accreditation. The criteria include: standards for admission of students; faculty qualifications; content of courses; grading standards; professional success of alumni; adequacy of libraries, laboratories, computers, and other support facilities; administrative systems and policy decision making; and financial support.

Six regional associations (New England, Middle States, Southern, North Central, Northwest, and Western) evaluate and accredit colleges as total institutions. Bible colleges have their own accrediting association. Other organizations evaluate and accredit specific programs, primarily in technical fields, like engineering and architecture; or those that require licensing, such as teaching and health care.

Accreditation must be periodically renewed, usually every five to ten years. Any school that is more than five years old and is not accredited probably has serious quality problems. One that was previously granted accreditation and then lost it is in deep trouble. On the other hand, accreditation means only that the school meets minimum standards. It is not a rating of school quality or a comparison to other schools.

Libraries

Most people judge libraries by the size of the collection, the bigger the better. Collection size is important, but only in relation to the variety and level of programs offered. A small liberal arts college can support its baccalaureate programs with a collection of 200,000 to 300,000 volumes. A university with many professional schools and doctoral programs may require over 2 million. Many books and journals are now available on microfilm or microfiche, so even a small college has money and space to enlarge its collection.

You may often find that the book or journal you need is owned by the library but unavailable. Frequently used material may be misplaced, lost, or out on loan. Many libraries are better at purchasing books than at getting them into the hands of their readers. You can look for some indications of the quality of a library's services.

The main stacks should be open to students, with the possible exception of rare books, bound journals, and other special items. Open stacks encourage browsing and save students from waiting on line while a library assistant fetches a few books at a time. Instead, assistants constantly should be picking up unused materials from reading desks or carts and putting them back on the shelves.

Good circulation policies encourage students to check materials out for short periods and to return them promptly. One week or less loans are appropriate for books regularly used in courses, and four week loans should be the maximum for other materials. A recall system should be available to get back borrowed material when it is needed. Journals, reference material, or books placed on reserve for assigned reading should be used within the library while it is open, and circulated overnight only at closing time.

Much of your reading and research will require work within the library. The library should be open at night and on weekends, at least at those times when it is most likely to be used. Friday and Saturday nights and Sunday mornings are the times when libraries can usually be closed without serious loss of access to students. Professional librarians should be

available to assist you whenever the library is open.

A modern academic library also should offer the following services, free or at a nominal charge:

- Interlibrary loans to get materials from other libraries.
- Online computerized searching of bibliographic databases. These databases automatically provide listings and summaries of books and articles by subject, author, and date.
- Tours and workshops to guide students in using the library.
- Reading lists for various subjects and courses.

Computing

Whatever your courses of study, you should expect to use computers. You will learn to do mathematical and scientific problem solving; to classify, sort, and retrieve information; and to write, revise, and type manuscripts. A few institutions require students to buy personal computers to use as microcomputers or as time-sharing terminals.

Many colleges are still scrambling to catch up with the changing technology and to equip enough classrooms and laboratories for courses that require computing. At a minimum, you should have access to both microcomputers for routine work and terminals connected to a mainframe or minicomputer for more complex instructional and research programs. There should be a number of campus locations where you can do computing, including during evenings and weekends.

During the busy times of the term, particularly around midterms and finals, computer laboratories are likely to be crowded. If you have to wait more than a second or two for a response on a time-sharing terminal, the college is probably trying to serve more students at one time than its computer capacity can handle.

GETTING THE MOST FROM YOUR CAMPUS VISIT

To learn everything important about a college, you need more than the standard presentation and tour given to visiting students and parents. Plan your visit for a weekday during the school term. This will let you see how classes are taught and how students live. It also is the best time to meet faculty and staff members, or to go to a dean's office for information. If the college does not schedule group presentations or tours at the time you want, call the office of admissions to arrange for an individual tour and interview. At the same time, ask the admissions office to make appointments with people you want to meet.

To find out about a specific academic program, ask to meet the department chairperson. If you are interested in athletics, religion, or music, meet the coach, the chaplain, or the conductor of the orchestra. Your parents will also want to talk to a financial aid counselor about scholarships, grants, and loans. The office of academic affairs can help with your questions about courses or the faculty. The office of student affairs is in charge of residence halls, health services, and extracurricular activities. Each of these areas has a dean or vice president and a number of assistants, so you should be able to get your questions answered even if you go in without an appointment.

Take advantage of a group presentation and tour if one is scheduled on the day of your visit. Much of what you learn may be familiar, but other students and parents will ask about some of the same things you want to know. Student tour guides are also good sources of information. They love to talk about their own courses, professors, and campus experiences.

Finally, explore the campus on your own. Visit the library and computing laboratories, to see whether they are

adequate for all the students using them. Check the condition of the buildings and the grounds. If they appear well maintained, the college probably has good overall management. If they look run down, the college may have financial problems that also make it scrimp on the book budget or laboratory supplies. Visit a service office, such as the registrar, career planning, or academic advising. Observe whether they treat students courteously and seem genuinely interested in helping them.

Talk to some of the students who are already enrolled at the college. They will usually speak frankly about weekend activities, whether they find it easy to talk to professors out of class, and how much drinking or drug abuse there is on campus. Most importantly, meeting other students will help you discover how friendly the campus is and whether the college will suit you socially and intellectually.

More than buildings and courses of study, a college is a community of people. Only during a campus visit can you experience the human environment in which you will live and work during four critical years.

CHECKLIST QUESTIONS

The following questions form a checklist to evaluate each college or university you are considering. Use profiles, literature from the colleges, and your own inquiries and observations to get the answers.

I. Identify good possibilities. Only colleges for which all five answers are "Yes" should go on your final list.
1. Is the college accredited by its regional association?
2. Does the college offer the program I want to study?
3. Do I have a good chance to be admitted?
4. Can my family manage the costs? (Read Finding the Money, page 14, before answering this question.)
5. Is the location at an acceptable distance from home?

II. Compare colleges for quality and value. The more questions you answer "Yes," the better that college is for you.

A. Academics
1. Does a majority of the faculty have doctoral degrees?
2. Do the best research professors teach undergraduate courses?
3. Do class sizes meet the standards described in this article?
4. Do regular faculty members teach at least 80 percent of courses?
5. Does the major program have enough full-time faculty members?
6. Does the major program offer its courses on a regular schedule?

B. Support Services
1. Is the library collection adequate for the college programs?
2. Does the library offer good services and accessible hours?
3. Are student computing facilities readily available?
4. Do the people in the admissions, financial aid, and other service offices seem attentive and genuinely interested in helping students?

C. Campus Environment
1. Will I be comfortable with the size and setting of the campus?
2. Will I find activities that meet my interests?
3. Will I find the other students compatible?
4. Will I find the housing and food services suitable?
5. Does the campus seem well maintained and managed?

Sheldon Halpern
Dean of Enrollment Management
Caldwell College

SCORING HIGH ON ENTRANCE EXAMS

WHY COLLEGE ENTRANCE TESTS?

Testing is the only standardized device that may be used to compare candidates from many varied high schools. It is only too well known that marking standards vary from school to school. It is also well known that a student in the top fifth of his class at X high school might very well have fallen into the bottom fifth if he had attended Y school.

Many parents and students are very critical of these standardized tests. It must be noted, however, that they afford equal opportunity to each college-bound student. From the point of view of the college, students who can perform well on this examination will, in all probability, continue to do well in their college studies.

Because college entrance examinations play such an important role in deciding who is admitted and who is rejected, it is necessary to clarify some of their surrounding mystery. These objective tests are scientifically constructed and aim to predict how well a student will perform in college. Their predictive capacity has been excellent. Poor results on these examinations, therefore, may make it difficult for a student to gain acceptance to college, in spite of a relatively good high school record. College admissions officers place a considerable amount of reliance on applicants' scores.

KINDS OF COLLEGE ENTRANCE TESTS

College-bound students must cope with one or more of the following:
- PSAT/NMSQT or the Preliminary SAT/National Merit Scholarship Qualifying Test.
- SAT I: Reasoning Tests.
- SAT II: Subject Tests.
- Advanced Placement (AP) Examinations.
- The ACT Assessment.

The PSAT/NMSQT

The PSAT/NMSQT measures verbal and mathematical ability necessary for success in college. It is a standardized test taken by students in high schools throughout the country, usually in their junior year. The test consists of two parts: four 30-minute verbal sections and two 30-minute math sections. The reading passages with comprehension questions are used to measure critical reading skills and knowledge of vocabulary.

Students taking this preliminary college board examination will find that this is also the qualifying test for the scholarship competition conducted by the National Merit Scholarship Corporation, an independent, nonprofit organization supported by grants from over 600 corporations, private foundations, colleges and universities. Top-scoring PSAT/NMSQT participants in every state are named semifinalists. Those who advance to finalist standing by meeting additional requirements compete for onetime National Merit $2000 Scholarships and renewable four-year Merit Scholarships, which may be worth as much as $8000 a year for four years.

In addition, this test is used by the National Achievement Scholarship Program for outstanding African American students. Top-scoring black students in each of the regional selection units established for the competition continue in the competition for nonrenewable National Achievement $2000 Scholarships and for four-year Achievement Scholarships sponsored by over 175 organizations.

Test-Taking Strategies for the PSAT/NMSQT

1. Know what to expect. In the verbal section of the PSAT you will have sentence completions and analogies but no antonym questions. The math section will have quantitative comparison questions, some multiple-choice questions, as well as questions that will ask you to produce your own responses. For these you will be asked to enter your answers on a grid. Calculators on the math test will be permitted but not required.

2. Don't be guilty of wild guessing. Wild guessing will lower your score because a fraction of your wrong answers is subtracted from the number of correct answers. Because wrong answers count against you on the test, you may think that you should never guess if you aren't sure of the right answer to a question. But even if you guessed wrong four times for every time you guessed right, you would still come out even. A wrong answer costs you only 1/4 of a point (1/3 on the quantitative comparison questions). The best advice is to guess if you can eliminate one or two of the answers. You have a better chance of hitting the right answer when you make this sort of educated guess.

3. Expect easy questions at the beginning of each set of the same question type. Within each set (except for the reading comprehension questions), the questions progress from easy to difficult. In other words, the first antonym question in a set will be easier than the last antonym question in that set; the first quantitative comparison question will be easier than the last one.

4. Take advantage of the easy questions to boost your score. Remember: each question is worth the same number of points. Whether it was easy or difficult, whether it took you ten seconds or two minutes to answer, you get the same number of points for each question you answer correctly. Your job is to answer as many questions as you possibly can without rushing ahead so fast that you make careless errors or lose points for failing to give some questions enough thought. Take enough time to get those easy questions right!

5. For the multiple-choice questions, eliminate as many wrong answers as you can. Deciding between two choices is easier than deciding among five. Even if you have to guess, every answer you eliminate improves your chances of guessing correctly.

The SAT I

The SAT I is a reasoning test consisting of two parts—Verbal Reasoning and Mathematical Reasoning. It is designed to measure your ability to do college work. Part of the test deals with verbal skills with an emphasis on critical reading including a double passage with different points of view. The verbal sections measure the extent of your vocabulary, your ability to interpret and create ideas, and your ability to reason logically and draw conclusions correctly. The mathematics part measures your ability to use and reason with numbers or mathematical concepts. It tests your ability to handle general number concepts rather than specific achievement in mathematics. Some questions require students to produce their own responses in contrast to multiple-choice questions. Calculators are permitted in the test room. For the 60 questions, 70–75 minutes are allowed.

The Verbal Reasoning sections are 30, 30, and 15 minutes in length and include 19 Sentence Completion, 19 Analogy, and 40 Reading Comprehension questions. The Mathematics Reasoning sections are 25, 25, and 15 minutes in length and include 35 Multiple Choice, 15 Quantitative Comparison, and 10 Student-Produced Response questions.

SAT I is usually given in January, March, May, June, October (in some states), November, and December. Applicants may request, for religious reasons, to take the test on the Sunday following the regularly scheduled date.

If a registration form is not available at your school, request one by mail. You can obtain a form from the College Entrance Examination Board, Box 6200, Princeton, New Jersey 08451 or Box 1025, Berkeley, California 94701.

The test is scored on a scale that ranges from 800 (highest) to 200 (lowest). You will get separate grades for the mathematics and verbal sections of the test.

Your score is based on the number of questions you answered correctly, minus points for those you answered incorrectly. Wrong answers on five-choice questions subtract 1/4 point from your raw score. Wrong answers on the four-choice quantitative comparison questions subtract 1/3 of a point from your score. The raw score is then scaled. The scale varies slightly from year to year. Answering 45 of the 60 mathematics questions correctly might give you a score of 650 one year and 660 another year.

Test-Taking Strategies for the SAT

1. Know what to expect. For the critical reading part of the verbal section, be prepared to find 4 passages with content as follows: one in social science, one in natural science, and two in fiction or nonfiction. In the mathematical reasoning section be prepared to find 15 questions on quantitative comparison, 35 multiple-choice questions, and 10 questions for which you will be required to produce a response.

2. Pace yourself. Most school tests don't put a premium on speed. They test achievement, not scholastic aptitude. The test sets a time limit. Therefore, work rapidly but don't give up accuracy. Don't spend too much time on one particular question. Remember, all questions carry the same point value.

3. Read carefully. Make sure you are answering the question asked, not the one that is similar to one you once encountered. Underline key words (i.e., NOT and EXCEPT) to make sure you do not answer the opposite of the question asked. Sometimes data are given for one of two possibilities and you will find that the question deals with a third possibility.

4. Keep calm. Don't get flustered over a single question. Just remind yourself that few people, if any, answer all questions correctly.

5. Know the rules. Learn the directions for the various types of questions. If you know the directions ahead of time you will save time in the examination room.

6. Guessing or not? The SAT I penalizes for guessing. Therefore, leave the question blank if you have no idea of the correct answer. Remember, on the SAT I and the PSAT your test score is based on the number of correct answers minus a fraction of the number of wrong answers. For the ACT, you should give some answer for all questions. The score on the ACT is based on the number of questions answered correctly, with no deductions for wrong answers.

7. Take advantage of the format of the multiple-choice questions which is the format of most of the math questions. One of the answers given has to be the correct one. Always look at all the answers before doing any computations. The correct answer may, by inspection, prove to be the only possible correct answer. Also, you should know that each of the four incorrect responses has been carefully chosen to look plausible or to be the result of a common error. You can make a mistake and still find one of the answers listed. If, after working the problem, you don't find your answer among the choices, you have made an uncommon error. You do, however, have an opportunity to try another method (with the penalty of consuming test time). This is why you should set a time limit in the tests, for the person who gets the correct answer quickly deserves more credit than the one who had to make several trials. Finally, with the multiple-choice format, it is often possible to work back from the answers, eliminating those choices that are contrary to fact.

The SAT II: Subject Tests (formerly known as the Achievement Tests)

These tests are one-hour, multiple-choice question tests. The registration form is the same as the SAT I. The additional fee entitles you to take one, two, or three tests on any one test date. Unlike the SAT I these tests measure knowledge and application of knowledge. Some colleges require specific subject tests whereas others allow applicants to choose the ones they wish to present with the admission application. Those colleges that do require these tests may use them to determine acceptance or placement in college courses. The tests in foreign language not only are used for placement but also for possible exemption from a foreign language requirement. Although many colleges do not require these tests, some not only specify which ones they require but also specify that they would like applicants to take them no later than December or January of their senior year. If the college of your choice does not require these tests and you would like to demonstrate proficiency in a particular field, take the test. The admissions committee will see your scores, along with your SAT I scores.

Tests are given in writing, literature, history, mathematics, sciences, and foreign languages, including Japanese. In the near future, tests will be given in other Asian languages, along with a proficiency test in English-as-a-Second Language.

Advanced Placement (AP) Examinations

The College Board also conducts Advanced Placement tests, given to high school students who have completed advanced or honors courses and wish to get college credit. Many secondary schools offer college level courses in mathematics, European history, American history, Latin, Spanish, French, German, biology, chemistry, and physics. As a result of scores obtained on these tests, colleges grant credit or use the results for placement in advanced college courses.

The ACT Assessment

The registration form for the ACT includes a detailed questionnaire that takes about one hour to complete. As a result of the answers to those questions about your high school courses, personal interests, and career plans, plus the scores on your ACT, an ACT Assessment Student Report is produced. This is made available to you, your high school, and to any college or scholarship source that you request. Decisions regarding college acceptance and award of scholarships are the result. This information is kept confidential and is released only according to your written instructions. To obtain an ACT application form, write or call ACT Registration, P.O. Box 414, Iowa City, Iowa 52243, telephone (319) 337-1270.

The ACT measures knowledge, understanding, and skills acquired in the educational process. The test is made up of four distinct sections: English, mathematics, reading, and science reasoning.

A distinct difference between the ACT and SAT I is that on SAT I, a raw score is obtained by counting the number of correct answers and deducting a fraction of the incorrect answers. The raw score is then converted into a scale in the range of 200 to 800. On the ACT, you are advised to answer all questions, because the score is based on the number of questions answered correctly. There is no penalty for guessing. The ACT score is obtained by counting the number of correct answers with no deduction for wrong answers. For each of the four tests the total number of correct responses yields a *raw score*. A table is used to convert the raw scores to *scaled scores*. The highest possible scaled score for each test is 36. The average of the four scaled scores yields the *composite score*.

The ACT English Test is a 75-item, 45-minute test that measures punctuation, grammar, usage, sentence structure, spelling, and vocabulary. The test consists of five passages, each accompanied by multiple-choice test items. A total score is reported as well as a subscore for the 40 usage questions and a subscore for the 35 questions dealing with the rhetorical skills.

Test-Taking Strategies for the ACT English Test

1. Pace yourself. You have 45 minutes to complete 75 questions.
2. Skim through the whole passage quickly to get the author's view.
3. Read the sentences immediately before and after the one containing an underlined portion.

The ACT Mathematics Test is a 60-question in 60-minute test that emphasizes quantitative reasoning rather than memorized formulas. Five content areas are included in the mathematics test. About 12 questions deal with pre-algebra topics, such as operations with whole numbers, decimals, fractions, and integers. About the same number of questions deal with elementary algebra. Usually 18 questions are based on intermediate algebra and coordinate geometry. About 14 questions are based on plane geometry and usually four items are based on right triangle trigonometry and basic trigonometric identities.

Test-Taking Strategies for the ACT Mathematics Test

1. Spend about one minute on each question.
2. Make sure you answer the question. Incorrect answer choices may be based on incomplete solutions.
3. Make sure your answer is reasonable.

The ACT Reading Test is a 40-item, 35-minute test that measures reading comprehension. Three scores are reported for this test: a total score, a subscore based on the 20 items in the social studies and natural sciences sections, and a subscore on the 20 items in the prose fiction and humanities sections.

Test-Taking Strategies for the ACT Reading Test

1. Read the passage carefully. Underline important ideas in the passage.
2. Pace yourself. You have 40 questions to answer in 35 minutes.
3. Refer to the passage and in particular to your underlined sections when answering the questions.

The ACT Science Reasoning Test presents seven sets of scientific information in three different formats: graphs, tables and other schematic forms (38%); description of experiments (45%); and expression of conflicting viewpoints (17%). The 40 items are to be answered in 35 minutes. The content of the test is drawn from biology, chemistry, physics, geology, astronomy, and meteorology. Background knowledge at the level of a high school general science course is all that is needed to answer these questions. The test emphasizes scientific reasoning skills rather than recall of scientific content, skill in mathematics, or reading ability.

Test-Taking Strategies for the ACT Science Reasoning Test

1. Read the scientific material before you begin answering a question. Read tables and text carefully underlining important ideas.
2. Look for flaws in the experiments and devise ways of improving the experiments.
3. When you are asked to compare viewpoints, make notes in the margin of the printed material summarizing each viewpoint.

A FINAL WORD

Don't walk into the examinations without preparation, even though you will find descriptions of these tests that say they test skills developed over years of study both in and out of school. Don't walk in cold, even though you believe that you meet all the qualities colleges are looking for.

Although the College Board suggests no special preparation, it does distribute to applicants the booklet, "Taking the SAT." It also makes available other publications containing former test questions along with advice on how to cope with the questions. Evidently, all candidates need some form of preparation.

The American College Testing Program furnishes, without cost, a booklet, "Preparing for the ACT Assessment." This gives specific information about the test, test questions, and strategies for taking each of the four parts. It also describes what to expect on the test day and gives practice with typical questions.

College entrance exams are one of the necessities of life for the college-bound student. Whereas they may not be the brightest spot of your high school career, neither should they be approached with anxiety or dread. By knowing what to expect and how to approach the tests, you will stay calm and do your very best in this precollege experience.

Samuel C. Brownstein
Co-author of Barron's *How to Prepare for the Sat,*
Barron's *How to Prepare for the Graduate Record Exam,*
and many other test preparation books.

The college admission process—getting in—begins the minute you start making your first choices in course selection and in cocurricular activities in junior high school, middle school, and high school. These initial and ongoing decisions are crucial to your future well-being. They lay the groundwork for the curriculum you will follow throughout your high school career; they are not easily reversed. These are the decisions that will allow you to market yourself to the colleges of your choice.

STUDENTS TAKE NOTE!

There is a myth prevalent among college-bound students throughout the country that the best way to gain entrance to the selective colleges is to be well rounded. This term usually refers to students who have earned good grades in high school (B+ or better) and participated in a wide range of cocurricular activities.

However, most admission officers at the selective colleges prefer applications from candidates they term angular—students who have demonstrated solid academic achievement in and out of school AND who have developed one or two particularly strong cocurricular skills, interests, and activities. These angular students are very different in character from the well-rounded students who are very good at everything, yet excel at little, if anything.

Bill Fitzsimmons, dean of admission at Harvard, says that Harvard is looking for a well-rounded class, which means Harvard is most interested in admitting angular students—students who have excelled at something. He cautions though that ... *It is a mistake to denigrate or underestimate that persuasive power of high grades, rank, double 700s on SATs and equally impressive achievement scores. The selective colleges take many of these academically high profile applicants. But the numbers game alone often won't get you in! It would be fairly simple for Harvard to enroll an entire freshman class with a superior academic profile and little depth of quality in areas that make up the personality of the class. We just would not do that!*

Dean Fitzsimmons is saying that the majority of the successful applicants to selective colleges must have some major commitment(s) combined with excellent academic qualities. A strong impact results from quality involvements rather than a proliferation of *joinings* and transient interests. Essentially the angular applicant is a committed individual, whereas the well-rounded candidate is merely involved.

STUDENTS AND PARENTS TAKE AN EARLY, ACTIVE ROLE

Students and parents must make time to ensure an early, active role in the college admissions process. Each year, starting in the seventh grade, students and parents should take the time to sit down with the student's guidance counselor and talk meaningfully about:

- Selection and level of courses; projecting through the senior year of high school;
- Cocurricular activities available, i.e., drama, music, athletics, academic clubs, community activities, student government and other special interest groups; and
- Summer study, work, or recreation.

Why is this important to getting in? As sure as death and taxes there is going to come a time in your senior year when you, the college-bound student, will be asked to choose colleges, complete the college application, write your college essay(s), and have an interview, either on the college campus or in your hometown.

You must create the personal marketing process that will take place during the application process in your senior year long before your senior year starts. By the time you reach that long-awaited dream of being a senior, you and you alone have created the person you must market to the colleges of your choice. You must understand that the person you have created is the only person you have to market. There is no Madison Avenue glitz involved in this marketing process! You don't create a pseudo marketing campaign that shows you jumping off a bridge with a bungie cord tied to your sneakers. Admission counselors can tell the difference between a real marketing effort and a pseudo marketing campaign.

THE APPLICATION FORM

Each application form differs with the exception of those colleges that use the common application. When you start to work, be sure to note all deadlines, follow all directions, be complete, be neat, fill out the geographical data with accurate facts, and type all unless you print exceptionally well. Always review the entire application before you start to fill it out, and complete the entire application before you start the next one. Remember the application is *you* to the admissions committee member reading it. Even though "a book should not be judged by its cover," appearances do influence opinions. It is best to work through a rough draft of the application before you actually work on the application copy to be submitted. Remember to make a copy of all parts of the finished application in the event that yours gets lost and a replacement must be sent.

Your high school guidance counselor will fill out the school record data: grades, rank in class, and academic profile. You must fill out the forms from ETS and/or ACT for your SAT I: Reasoning Tests, SAT II: Subject Tests, and ACT scores to be sent directly from each governing body to each college to which you have applied, even if your scores are on your high school transcript. Your college file will not be considered complete, and will not go to the admissions committee for a decision, without the official scores sent directly from the governing body to each college. Also, many colleges want recommendations from one or two teachers. Choose wisely and allow each teacher plenty of time. Request letters from teachers who know you best. If English is your interest, be sure you choose an English teacher. If you are fluent in Spanish and have future interest in Spanish at college, ask the Spanish teacher. Remember, though you have many interests and have participated in many activities, you are developing an admissions package as part of your marketing of yourself. Emphasize your strengths and show how they are integrated into your activities and achievements.

Extracurricular activities usually are athletic or nonathletic. If you have won athletic awards, note them. If you have had the starring role in the spring musical for the last two years, say so. If you are an editor on the school paper, specify this. Admissions people view your activities with special interest. They realize how very time-consuming these activities can be and sometimes with very few accolades. Put these activities in the order of importance to you. Be honest!

Some applications have mini essays. When space is provided, be sure you are concise, clear, and grammatically correct. Here less is more. Your ability to organize your thoughts and present them concisely is being tested. Some colleges have as many as six essays, whereas some large state institutions require none.

Some colleges encourage you to support your application with additional materials. If you are given this option, consider what will strengthen your application. Musical tapes, art or photography portfolios, published writings, an excep-

tional graded term paper, all are additional opportunities for the college to get to know you better and for you to increase your image as an *angular* candidate. Such additions help the admissions committee to get a better handle on you.

Proofread all parts of the application. Be sure you, the student, place your signature where it is required. Then place everything, including the registration fee check, in a large manila envelope and give it to your college guidance counselor. After adding the completed school's record section to the application itself, your guidance counselor will mail it. Your job is now done and the waiting begins!

The Common Application

More than 100 colleges in the United States agreed that students may apply to their colleges by completing one common application instead of individual applications for each college. Many students will face a choice as to whether they will complete the college's individual application or the common application, which substantially reduces the time spent composing different essay answers and neatly typing different application forms. All the colleges participating in the common application agreement sign a statement that they do NOT discriminate among the students who submit the common application instead of the individual application. However, there are those counselors who believe that the individual application may often give the student more of a chance to convey personal information because frequently the individual application requests more essays, long ones and short ones, than does the common application.

THE INTERVIEW

The interview is a contrived situation that few people enjoy, of which many people misunderstand the value, and about which everyone is apprehensive. However, no information from a college catalog, no friend's friend, no high school guidance counselor's comments, and no parental remembrances from bygone days can surpass the value of your college campus visit and interview. This firsthand opportunity to assess your future alma mater will confirm or contradict other impressions and help you make a sound college acceptance.

Many colleges will recommend or request a personal interview. It is best to travel to the campus to meet with a member of the admissions staff if you can; however, if you can't, many colleges will arrange to have one of their representatives, usually an alumnus, interview you in your hometown.

Even though the thought of an interview might give you enough butterflies to lift you to the top of your high school's flagpole, here are some tips that might make it a little easier.

1. **Go prepared.** Read the college's catalog ahead of time so you won't ask "How many books are in your library?" or "How many students do you have?" Ask intelligent questions that introduce a topic of conversation that you want the interviewer to know about you. The key is to distinguish yourself in a positive way from thousands of other applicants. Forge the final steps in the marketing process you have built up since your first choices in the college admission process were taken back in junior high school. The interview is your chance to enhance those decisions.

2. **Nervousness**...is absolutely and entirely normal. The best way to handle it is to admit it, out loud, to the interviewer. Miles Uhrig, director of admission at Tufts University, sometimes relates this true story to his apprehensive applicants: One extremely agitated young applicant sat opposite him for her interview with her legs crossed, wearing loafers on her feet. She swung her top leg back and forth to some inaudible rhythm. The loafer on her top foot flew off her foot, hit him in the head,

ricocheted to the desk lamp and broke it. She looked at him in terror, but when their glances met, they both dissolved in laughter. The moral of the story—the person on the other side of the desk is also a human being and wants to put you at ease. So admit to your anxiety, and don't swing your foot if you're wearing loafers! (By the way, she was admitted.)

3. **Be yourself.** Nobody's perfect, and everyone knows nobody's perfect, so admit to a flaw or two before the interviewer goes hunting for them. The truly impressive candidate will convey a thorough knowledge of self.

4. **Interview the interviewer.** Don't passively sit there and allow the interviewer to ask all the questions and direct the conversation. Participate in this responsibility by assuming an active role. A thoughtful questioner will accomplish three important tasks in a successful interview:
   a. **demonstrate interest**, initiative, and maturity for taking partial responsibility for the content of the conversation;
   b. **guide the conversation** to areas where he/she feels most secure and accomplished; and
   c. **obtain answers.**
   Use your genuine feelings to react to the answers you hear. If you are delighted to learn of a certain program or activity, show it. If you are curious, ask more questions. If you are disappointed by something you learn, try to find a path to a positive answer or...consider yourself lucky that you discovered this particular inadequacy in time.

5. **Parents do belong** in your college decision process as your advisers! Often it is they who spend the megabucks for your next four years, and they can provide psychological support and a stabilizing influence for sensible, rational decisions. In essence, the sage senior will find constructive ways to include parents in the decision-making process as catalysts, without letting them take over (as many are apt to do). You may want your parents to meet and speak briefly to your interviewer. That's fine to do before or after, but not during your interview time.

6. **Practice makes perfect.** Begin your interviews at colleges that are low on your list of preferred choices, and leave your first-choice colleges until last. If you are shy, you will have a chance to practice vocalizing what your usually silent inner voice tells you. Others will have the opportunity to commit their inevitable first blunders where it won't count as much.

7. **Departing impressions.** There is a remarkable tendency for the student to base final college preferences on the quality of the interview only, or on the personal reaction to the interviewer as the personification of the entire institution. Do not do yourself the disservice of letting it influence an otherwise rational selection, one based on institutional programs, students, services, and environment. After the last good-bye and thank you has been smiled, and you exhale deeply on your way out the door, go ahead and congratulate yourself. If you used the interview properly, you will know whether or not you wish to attend that college and why.

8. **Send a thank-you note** to your interviewer. A short and simple handwritten or typed note will do; and if you forgot to mention something important about yourself at the interview, here's your chance.

WRITING THE COLLEGE ESSAY

Do the colleges read the essays you write on their applications? You bet your diploma they do. Here is your chance to "strut your stuff," stand up and be counted, and stylize your way into the hearts of the decision makers.

Write it, edit it, review it, rewrite it. Try to show why you are unique and how the college will benefit having you in its student body. This is not a routine homework assignment, but a college level essay that will be carefully examined for spelling, content and style *of a high school senior*. As strenuous an effort as it may be, by completing the college essays you give the admissions committee a chance to know the real you, a three-dimensional human being with passions and preferences, strengths, weaknesses, imagination, energy, and ambition. Your ability to market yourself will help the deans and directors of admission remember your application from among the sea of thousands that flood their offices each year.

First, maximize your strengths—use your essays to say what you want to say. The answer to a specific question on the college's part still provides an opening for you to furnish background information about yourself, your interests, ambitions, and insights. For example, the essay that asks you to name your favorite book and the reason for your selection could be answered with the title of a Dr. Seuss book because you are considering a career as an elementary school teacher. If you are interested in business, read about a famous businessman you admire and then discuss your interest in business.

Whatever the essay questions are, autobiographical or otherwise, select the person or issue that puts you in the position to discuss the subject in which you are the most well versed. In essence, all of your essay responses are autobiographical in the sense that they will illustrate something important about yourself, your values, and the kind of person you are or hope to become. If personal values are important to you, and they should be, then here is your opportunity to stress their importance.

Because many colleges will ask for more than one essay, make sure that the SUM of the essays in any one college application covers your best points. Do not repeat your answers, even if the questions sound alike. Cover the most important academic and extracurricular activities (most important meaning the ones in which you excelled and/or spent the most time.)

If you are lucky enough to have a cooperative English teacher, you might request a critique of your first draft, but be sure to allow enough time for a careful evaluation and your revision.

Write the essays yourself—no substitutes or stand-ins. College admission professionals can discern mature adult prose from student prose.

PARTING WORDS

Finding and applying to the best colleges for you isn't supposed to be easy, but it can be fun. Parents, guidance counselors, and teachers are there to help you, so don't struggle alone. Keep your sense of humor and a smile on your face as you go about researching, exploring, and discovering your "ideal college."

Anthony F. Capraro, III, Ph.D.
President, Teach...Inc.
College Counseling
Larchmont, New York

FINDING THE MONEY

Postsecondary education is a major American industry. A greater proportion of students pursue postsecondary education in the United States than in any other industrialized country. Annually, more than 13 million students study at over 8000 institutions of higher learning. The diversity of our system of higher education is admired by educators and students throughout the world. There is no reason to believe that this system will change in the future. However, college costs and the resources available to parents and students to meet those costs have changed.

Unfortunately, many high school students and their parents believe either that there is no financial aid available or that they will not qualify for any type of financial assistance from any source. Neither assumption is correct. College costs have increased and will continue to increase. Federal allocations, for some financial aid programs, have decreased. But this decline has been met with generous increases in financial aid from state and school sources.

American students and their parents should realize that they must assume the primary role in planning to meet their future college costs and that the family financial planning process must begin much earlier than has been the case.

COLLEGE COSTS

- Eighty-two percent of all parents believe college costs are too expensive.
- In 1993–94 the average cost at a public school was approximately $8600 and about $18,000 at private colleges.
- While college costs will increase each year, it is important to remember that currently about 4 percent of all college students attend schools with tuition costs exceeding $10,000 and only 50 percent pay the full cost of attendance at these colleges and universities.

STUDENT FINANCIAL AID

- In 1992–93, the total amount of financial aid available from federal, state, and institutional sources to postsecondary students exceeded $28 billion.
- Approximately 60 percent of all students enrolled in higher education receive some type of financial assistance.
- Federal student aid remains the largest source of funding at 75 percent of total aid.
- Financial aid from sources other than parents pays for about 60 percent of the bills of financial aid recipients.
- Ten years ago the majority of federal financial assistance was grants. Today, an equal amount of grant and loan money is awarded from federal sources.

TIMETABLE FOR APPLYING FOR FINANCIAL AID

Sophomore Year of High School

Most families wait until a child has been accepted into a college or university to begin planning on how the family will meet those college costs. However, a family's college financial planning should begin much earlier.

Students, as early as the sophomore year of high school, should begin a systematic search for colleges that offer courses of study that are of interest. There are many computer programs that can be helpful in this process. These programs can match a student's interest with colleges fitting the profile. Considering that half of all students who enter college either drop out or transfer to another school, this type of early selection analysis can be invaluable.

After selecting certain schools for further consideration, you should write to the school and request a viewbook, catalog, and financial aid brochure. After receiving this information, you and your family should compare the schools. Your comparison should include academic considerations as well as financial. Don't rule out a school because you think you can't afford it. Remember the financial aid programs at that school may be more generous than at a lower-priced school. If possible, visit the college and speak with both an admission and financial aid counselor. If it is not possible to visit all the schools, call the schools and obtain answers to your questions about admission, financial aid, and placement after graduation.

Junior Year of High School

The comparative analysis of colleges and universities that you began in your sophomore year should continue in your junior year. By the completion of your junior year, you and your parents should have some idea of what it will cost to attend and the financial aid policies of each of the schools you are considering.

Some colleges and universities offer prospective applicants an early estimate of their financial aid award. This estimate is based upon information supplied by the family and can provide assistance in planning a family's budget. Remember that for most families, financial aid from federal, state, and school sources will probably not meet the total cost of attendance.

Families should remember that college costs can be met over the course of the academic year. It is not necessary to have all of the money needed to attend school available at the beginning of the academic year. Student and family savings, as well as student employment throughout the year, can be used to meet college costs.

Senior Year of High School

January

By January of your senior year of high school you should know which colleges and universities you want to receive your financial aid application forms. Be certain that you have completed not only the federal financial aid application form, but also any necessary state or school forms. Read carefully all of the instructions. Application methods and deadline dates may differ from one college to another. Submit an application clean of erasures or notations in the margins, and sign all of the application forms.

February

Approximately six weeks after you submit your application for financial aid, you will receive a report from the service agency you selected containing information on your family's expected contribution and your eligibility for financial aid. You and your parents should discuss the results of the financial aid application with regard to family contribution, educational costs, and how those costs can be met.

March

Beginning in March, most colleges begin to make financial aid decisions. If your application is complete, your chances of receiving an award letter early are greater than if additional information is required.

The financial aid award letter you receive from your school serves as your official document indicating the amount of financial aid you will receive for the year. You must sign and return a copy of the award letter to your school if you agree to accept their offer of financial aid.

If your family's financial circumstances change and you need additional funding, you should make an appointment to speak with your school's financial aid director or counselor. College financial aid personnel are permitted to exercise professional judgment and make adjustments to a student's financial need. Your letter of appeal should state explicitly how much money you need and why you need it.

TIPS ON APPLYING FOR FINANCIAL AID

1. Families can no longer wait until a child is accepted into college before deciding how they will finance that education. Earlier college financial planning is necessary.

2. Families should assume a much more active role in locating the resources necessary to fund future college costs.

3. Families should assume that college costs will continue to increase.

4. Families should assume that in the future the federal government will not substantially increase financial aid allocations.

5. Families should obtain information on a wide range of colleges, including the many excellent low-cost schools.

6. Families should seek information about all of the available funding sources available at each school they are considering.

7. Families should seek the advice and expertise of financial experts for college financing strategies. College financial planning should specify the amount of money a family should invest or save each month in order to meet future college bills.

8. Families should investigate all of the legitimate ways of reducing their income and assets before filing for financial aid.

9. Families should know how financial aid is awarded and the financial aid policies and programs of each school they are considering.

10. Families should realize that although the job of financing a college education rests primarily with them, they probably will not be able to save the entire cost of their child's college education. They probably will be eligible to receive some type of financial aid from some source and they will have to borrow a portion of their child's college education costs.

11. Families should be advised that the federal government frequently changes the rules and regulations governing financial aid eligibility. Check with your high school guidance counselor or college financial aid administrator for the latest program qualifications.

Marguerite J. Dennis
Dean of Enrollment and Retention Management
Suffolk University
Boston, Massachusetts
and author of Barron's *Complete College Financing Guide,*
Barron's *Guide to Financing a Medical School Education,*
and *Keys to Financing a College Education*

COLLEGE: IT'S DIFFERENT

In college you are likely to hear fellow students say, "I don't know what that prof *wants*, and she won't *tell* me." "I wrote about three papers in high school, and now they want one every week." Though these students may be exaggerating a bit, college *is* different, both in the quality and the amount of work expected. Sometimes in high school the basic concepts of a course are reduced to a set of facts on a study sheet, handed to students to be reviewed and learned for a test.

In college, it is the concepts and ideas that are most important. These can only be grasped through a real understanding of the facts as they interrelate and form larger patterns. Writing papers and answering essay questions on tests can demonstrate a genuine understanding of the concepts, and this is why they are so important to college instructors. Learning to deal with ideas in this way can be a long-term asset, developing your independence, intellectual interests, and self-awareness.

Don't be discouraged; you are not alone. Most of your fellow students are having equally difficult times adjusting to a new learning method. Persist, and you will improve, leading to a lifetime habit of critical thinking and problem solving that can benefit you in many important ways.

College is also different outside of classes. Now that you have the freedom to choose how to spend time and what types of relationships to make, you have a bewildering number of possibilities.

MAKING A GOOD IMPRESSION

Here you are, plopped down in a strange place, feeling a bit like Dorothy transported to Oz. Your first goal is to make a good impression, showing your best self to those who will be important in your life for the next four years and even longer.

Impressing Faculty Members Favorably

Faculty members come in all ranks, from the graduate assistant, who teaches part-time while pursuing a degree, to a lofty full professor, who teaches primarily graduate students. Though different in rank and seniority, they respond to their students in roughly the same ways. They are, after all, people, with families and relationships much like your own. To have a good working relationship with them, try the following suggestions:

- **Make up your own mind about your instructors.** Listening to other students talk about teachers can be confusing. If you listen long enough, you will hear arguments for and against each of them. Don't allow hearsay to affect your own personal opinion.
- **Get to know your instructors firsthand.** Set up a meeting, during regular office hours. Don't try to settle important issues in the few moments before and after class.
- **Approach a discussion of grades carefully.** If you honestly believe that you have been graded too low, schedule a conference. Do not attack your instructor's integrity or judgment. Instead, say that you had expected your work to result in a better grade and would like to know ways to improve. Be serious about overcoming faults.
- **Don't make excuses.** Instructors have heard them all and can rarely be fooled. Accept responsibility for your mistakes, and learn from them.
- **Pay attention in class.** Conversing and daydreaming can insult your instructor and inhibit the learning process.
- **Arrive ahead of time for class.** You will be more relaxed, and you can use these moments to review notes or talk with classmates. You also demonstrate to your instructor a commitment to the class.
- **Participate in class discussions.** Ask questions and give answers to the instructor's questions. Nothing pleases an instructor more than an intelligent question that proves you are interested and prepared.
- **Learn from criticism.** It is an instructor's job to correct your errors in thinking. Don't take in-class criticism personally.

Impressing Fellow Students Favorably

Relationships with other students can be complex, but there are some basic suggestions that may make life easier in the dorms and classrooms:

- **Don't get into the habit of bragging.** Frequent references to your wealth, your outstanding friends, your social status, or your family's successes are offensive to others.
- **Don't pry.** When your fellow students share their feelings and problems, listen carefully and avoid any tendency to intrude or ask embarrassing questions.
- **Don't borrow.** Borrowing a book, a basketball, or a few bucks may seem like a small thing to you, but some people who have trouble saying no may resent your request.
- **Divide chores.** Do your part; agree on a fair division of work in a lab project or a household task.
- **Support others.** Respect your friends' study time and the "Do not disturb" signs on their doors. Helping them to reach their goals will help you as well.
- **Allow others to be upset.** Sometimes, turning someone's anger into a joke, minimizing their difficulties, or belittling their frustration is your worst response. Support them by letting them release their emotions.
- **Don't preach.** Share your opinions when asked for, but don't try to reform the world around you.
- **Tell the truth.** Your reputation is your most important asset. When you make an agreement, keep it.

MANAGING YOUR TIME

Everyone, no matter how prominent or how insignificant, has 168 hours a week to spend. In this one asset we are all equal. There are students on every college campus, however, who seem to accomplish all their goals and still find time for play and socializing. There are others who seem to be alternating between frantic dashes and dull idleness, accomplishing very little. To the first group, college is a happy, fulfilling experience; to the latter, it is maddeningly frustrating. The first group has gained control of time, the second is controlled by that elusive and precious commodity.

- **Know where your time goes.** Unfortunately, we cannot store up time as we do money, to be used when the need is greatest. We use it as it comes, and it is amazing how it sometimes comes slowly (as in the last five minutes of a Friday afternoon class) or quickly (as in the last hour before a final exam). The first step in controlling time is to determine exactly how you use it. For a while, at least, you should carefully record how much time you spend in class, going to and from class, studying, sleeping, eating, listening to music, watching television, and running errands. You need to know what happens to your 168 hours. Only then can you make sensible decisions about managing them.

- **Make a weekly schedule.** You can schedule your routine for the week, using the time plan forms available at most college bookstores or by making your own forms.

- **First schedule the inflexible blocks of time.** Your class periods, transportation time, sleeping, and eating will form relatively routine patterns throughout the week. Trying to shave minutes off these important activities is often a mistake.

- **Plan your study time.** It is preferable, though not always possible, to set your study hours at the same time every weekday. Try to make your study time *prime time*, when you body and mind are ready for a peak performance.

- **Plan time for fun.** No one should plan to spend four years of college as a working robot. Fun and recreation are important, but they can be enjoyed in short periods just as well as long. For example, jogging with friends for thirty minutes can clear the mind, tone up the muscles, and give you those all-important social contacts. Parties and group activities can be scheduled for weekends.

- **Be reasonable in your time allotments.** As you progress through your freshman year, you will learn more precisely how much time is required to write a paper or complete a book report. Until then, schedule some extra minutes for these tasks. You are being unfair to yourself by planning one hour for a job that requires two.

- **Allow flexibility.** The unexpected is to be expected. There will be interruptions to your routine and errands that must be run at certain times. Allow for these unforeseen circumstances.

STUDYING EFFECTIVELY

Your most important activity in college is studying. Efficient study skills separate the inept student (who may spend just as many hours studying as an "A" student) from the excellent student, who thinks while studying and who uses common sense strategies to discover the important core of courses. The following suggested game plan for good study has worked in the past; it can work for you.

Make a commitment. It is universally recommended that you spend two hours studying for every hour in class. At the beginning of your college career, be determined to do just that. It doesn't get easy until you make up your mind to do it.

- **Do the tough jobs first.** If certain courses are boring or particularly difficult, study them first. Don't read the interesting, enjoyable materials first, saving the toughies for the last sleepy twinges of your weary brain.

- **Study in short sessions.** Three two-hour sessions, separated from each other by a different activity, are much better than a long six-hour session.

- **Use your bits of time.** Use those minutes when you're waiting for a bus, a return call, laundry to wash, or a friend to arrive. Some of the best students I know carry 3 x 5 cards filled with definitions, formulas, or equations and learn during brief waiting periods. Most chief executives form the habit early of using bits of time wisely.

Digesting a textbook

1. **Preview chapters.** Before you read a chapter in your textbook, preview it. Quickly examine the introductory paragraphs, headings, tables, illustrations, and other features of the chapter. The purpose is to discover the major topics. Then you can read with increased comprehension because you know where the author is leading.

2. **Underline the important points as you read.** Underlining should never be overdone; it can leave your textbook almost completely marked and less legible to read. Only the major ideas and concepts should be highlighted.

3. **Seven categories of information are commonly found in textbooks.** Be particularly alert when you see the following; get your marking pen ready.
   Definitions of terms.
   Types or *categories* of items.
   Methods of accomplishing certain tasks.
   Sequences of events or stages in a process.
   Reasons or *causes.*
   Results or *effects.*
   Contrasts or *comparisons* between items.

4. **Repeat information you need to learn.** When the object is to learn information, nothing is so effective as reciting the material, either silently or aloud.

5. **Don't read all material the same way.** Decide what you need to learn from the material and read accordingly. You read a work of fiction to learn the characters and the narrative; a poem, to learn an idea, an emotion, or a theme; a work of history, to learn the interrelationships of events. Do not read every sentence with the same speed and concentration; learn when to skim rapidly along. Remember, your study time is limited, and the trick is to discriminate between the most important and the least important. No one can learn *everything* equally well.

6. **The five-minute golden secret.** As soon as possible after class is over—preferably at your desk in the classroom— skim through the chapter that has just been covered, marking the points primarily discussed. Copy what was written on the board. Now you know what the professor thinks is important!

TAKING TESTS SKILLFULLY

Try to predict the test questions. At some college libraries, copies of old examinations are made available to students. If you can legally find out your professor's previous test methods, do so.

Ask your professor to describe the format of the upcoming test: multiple-choice? true-false? essay questions? problems? Adjust your study to the format described.

Listen for clues in the professor's lecture. Sometimes the questions posed in class have a way of reappearing on tests. If a statement is repeated several times or recurs in a subsequent lecture, note it as important.

As you review for the test, devise questions based on the material, and answer them. If you are part of a study group, have members ask questions of the others.

Common Sense Tactics

Arrive on the scene early; relax by breathing deeply. If the instructor gives instructions while distributing the test, listen very carefully.

- **Scan the whole test first.** Notice the point value for each section and budget your time accordingly.

- **Read the directions carefully** and then reread them. Don't lose points because you misread the directions.

- **Answer the short, easy questions first.** A bit of early success stimulates the mind and builds your confidence.

- **Leave space between answers.** You may think of a brilliant comment to add later.

- **Your first instinct is often the best** in answering true-false and multiple-choice questions. Look for qualifiers such as *never, all, often,* or *seldom* in true-false statements. Usually, a qualifier that is absolute (*never, all,* or *none*) will indicate a false statement. Work fast on short-answer questions; they seldom count many points.

- **Open-book tests are no picnic.** Don't think that less study is required for an open-book test. They are often the most difficult of all examinations. If the material is unfamiliar,

you won't have time to locate it and learn it during the test period.

Important Essay Strategies

- **Read the question carefully** and find out exactly what is asked for. If you are asked to *contrast* the French Revolution with the American Revolution and you spend your time describing each, without any contrasting references, your grade will be lowered.

- **Know the definitions of key words** used in essay questions:
  analyze: discuss the component parts.
  compare: examine for similarities.
  criticize: give a judgment or evaluation.
  define: state precise meaning of terms.
  describe: give a detailed picture of qualities and characteristics.
  discuss: give the pros and cons; debate them, and come to a conclusion.
  enumerate: briefly mention a number of ideas, things, or events.
  evaluate: give an opinion, with supporting evidence.
  illustrate: giving examples (illustrations) relating to a general statement.
  interpret: usually means to state in other words, to explain, make clear.
  outline: another way of asking for brief listings of principal ideas or characteristics. Normally the sentence or topic outline format is not required.
  prove: give evidence and facts to support the premise stated in the test.
  summarize: give an abbreviated account, with your conclusions.

- **Write a short outline** before you begin your essay. This organizes your thinking, making you less likely to leave out major topics.

- **Get to the point immediately.** Don't get bogged down in a lengthy introduction.

- **Read your essay over** before you hand it in. Words can be left out or misspelled. Remember that essay answers are graded somewhat subjectively, and papers that are correctly and neatly written make a better impression.

- **Learn from your test paper** when it is returned. Students who look at a test grade and discard the paper are throwing away a valuable tool. Analyze your mistakes honestly; look for clues for improvement in the professor's comments.

WRITING A TERM PAPER

Doing convincing library research and writing a term paper with correct footnotes and bibliography is a complicated procedure. Most first-year English composition courses include this process. Good students will work hard to master this skill because they know that research papers are integral parts of undergraduate and graduate courses.

Many students make the mistake of waiting until near the deadline to begin a term paper. At the busy end of the term,

with final exams approaching, they embark on the uncertain time span of research and writing. Begin your term paper early, when the library staff is unharried and ready to help and when you are under less pressure. It will pay dividends.

REGULATING YOUR RELATIONSHIPS

Find your special friends who believe in your definition of success. In a fast-paced environment like college, it is important to spend most of your time with people who share your attitudes toward learning, where you can be yourself, without defensiveness. To find your kind of friends, first ask yourself: What is success? Is it a secure position and a comfortable home? A life of serving others? A position of power with a commodious executive suite? A challenging job that allows you to be creative? When you have answered honestly, you will have a set of long-range personal goals, and you can begin looking for kindred souls to walk with you on the road to success.

There will be, of course, some persons around you who are determined not to succeed, who for some reason program their lives for failure. About half of all college freshmen never receive a college degree; some may start college with no intention of passing courses. Their goal is to spend one hectic term as a party animal. If you intend to succeed at college, spending time among this type will be a considerable handicap. Consider making friends who will be around longer than the first year.

If possible, steer clear of highly emotional relationships during your first year of college. You don't have time for a broken heart, and relationships that begin with a rush often end that way.

MAINTAINING YOUR HEALTH

Poor health can threaten your success in the first year of college as nothing else can. No matter how busy you are, you must not forget your body and its needs: proper food, sufficient sleep, and healthy exercise. Many students, faced with the stress of college life, find themselves overmunching junk foods and gaining weight. Guard against this. Drugs and alcohol threaten the health and the success of many college students.

A FINAL WORD

So there it is. If you have read this far, you probably have a serious interest in succeeding in your first year of college. You probably have also realized that these suggestions, even if they sound a bit preachy, are practical and workable. They are based on many years of observing college students.

Benjamin W. Griffith
Former Dean of the Graduate School
West Georgia College
Carrollton, Georgia

Author of Barron's *Essentials of English*

PART II

INDEX OF COLLEGE MAJORS

DECIDING ON A MAJOR AND CAREER

What is a major? All four-year colleges require the satisfactory completion of a certain number of courses to graduate. A **major** consists of a concentration of courses in a specialized field of study. Most majors require about one third of your college time and the course work usually is done in the last two years of college. The other two thirds of your college time usually are occupied by general education courses that are required for college graduation and elective courses that you elect, or choose, to enhance and broaden your educational knowledge. After successful completion of the courses in your major, along with the general education and elective requirements, you may be eligible for graduation and receive the undergraduate baccalaureate (bachelor) degree. Your adviser, usually a member of the teaching faculty in your major, helps you to select required courses and plan all requirements for the completion of the major.

What is a minor? A minor usually consists of a number of courses in a field of study other than the major, however, the required units of study are fewer than those required of the major. Many colleges today do not require a formal minor for graduation. Your adviser will inform you if you have to complete one. The more practical reason for a minor is to supplement and strengthen your major. For example: A computer science major may be required to take a certain number of mathematics courses that, when totaled up, meet the definition of a minor, or perhaps a dual major.

Majors And Careers. Deciding upon a major is one of the most important decisions you will have to make. With its emphasis on a structured course of study, a major not only provides for intellectual growth, self-improvement, general knowledge, and a search for truth and understanding, but often provides the required technical training to enter and become successful in the work world. Personal enlightenment is a noble goal, but most students no longer can afford the monetary expenses and the time to pursue courses that do not lead to a major that ties into career goals.

Information on majors and careers is presented here to help you to make college and career decisions. Those decisions should take into consideration the clarification of occupational and personal values, life-style goals and work interests, and the education and training needed for long-range self-satisfaction and job success.

WHAT ARE SOME DIFFERENT APPROACHES TO MAJORS?

Job training. You may want to go to college for one main reason: to acquire specific job skills to qualify for direct job entry. The course work usually is work-related and technical and it is evident that the skills learned in class can be directly applied to a job. For example, if you want to become a professional engineer in one of the many engineering specialties, you will have to complete a four- to five-year engineering curriculum that is quite rigidly prescribed.

Examples of other four-year majors in which you learn technical skills that lead to direct job entry are: accounting, agronomy, architecture, computer science, dance, elementary education, forestry, geology, nursing, and social work.

The generalist approach. You may be the type of person who wants to pursue a more general major that may not directly tie into job entry, but will improve your general knowledge and prepare you as a generalist with intellectual and problem-solving skills rather than technical training. This kind of major is often referred to as liberal arts, humanities, or general studies. Many majors in the social sciences, biological sciences, communications, and the arts are looked at as liberal arts majors in which the bachelor degree will not guarantee direct job entry in a job associated with the major.

Many professional graduate schools (law, medicine, education, business, journalism) prefer candidates who have undergraduate degrees in the liberal arts. Also, many employers prefer to hire the liberal arts major because that person may possess superior analytical skills to apply to problem-solving and innovation.

Special talent/aptitude approach. You may want to select a certain major because you have a special talent and a strong interest in a certain field. It is always a good idea to know your strengths and build on them. Do you have a strong interest in writing? acting? music? art? mathematics? computers? leadership? The list could go on. You can select a major that helps you to further your talents. College life certainly will be more enjoyable if you take courses that will give you personal satisfaction, and in your career planning you might give thought to designing a career that will allow you to enjoy a life-style compatible with your special talents.

Dual major. Many colleges advise dual majors for career preparation. This is true especially in preparing to enter a scientific career, where it is essential to be well-grounded in both the physical and biological sciences.

Individually-designed major. You may have highly divergent interests that cut across traditional lines. Many colleges will allow you to design a major that will satisfy your goals. For example, you may have artistic talents and scientific interests. You might combine the two, and even though the college of your choice does not offer the major, you might design a scientific illustration major that meets faculty approval.

TYING COLLEGE MAJOR PLANNING TO CAREER PLANNING

In the next section we will present relevant educational and career information on nine broad fields of study from which you may choose a major. Relevant facts will be presented to help you to decide upon a major based upon career planning.

Each of the nine fields of study has specific information on majors and careers that you will want to consider carefully when making your decision. Before you begin to look at that information, here is a brief explanation of what you will find within each of the nine fields of study.

• **Representative majors.** The majors listed are the most popular ones in their field.

• **Interests.** Interests that you should have. You will be most successful and fulfilled if you carefully assess your interests and make your plans based upon your interests rather than upon how much money you will make.

• **Job requirements.** These are the most relevant general requirements for careers associated with the field of study.

• **Related jobs.** Consider the present and future job titles associated with the field of study. These job titles come from Occupational Employment Statistics (OES) compiled by the U.S. Department of Labor, Bureau of Labor Statistics.

• **Employment information.** This tells how many people work in the field of study, and, in general terms, where they work.

• **Employment outlook.** The generalized outlook prediction to the year 2005 comes from authoritative *Department of Labor* sources, and can vary greatly depending upon the state of the economy and rapidly changing technological demands. All college graduates should recognize the need to be prepared to meet the challenges of a dynamic and competitive labor market. Job outlook also varies a great deal from region to region.

REPRESENTATIVE MAJORS AND RELATED CAREER INFORMATION

1. AGRICULTURE

The work done by agricultural scientists has played an important part in making American agriculture the most productive in the world. Agricultural scientists study farm crops and animals and develop ways of improving their quantity and quality. They look for ways to increase yields with less labor, control pests and weeds more effectively, and conserve soil and water. Agricultural science is closely related to biological science in that both involve the study of living organisms; agricultural scientists then apply this knowledge to solving practical problems in agriculture.

A high proportion of all agricultural scientists manage or administer research and development projects or marketing or production operations in companies that produce agricultural chemicals or machinery. Many do research and development. Some spend most of their time in laboratories, but some in research and development spend much of their time working with plants and animals in the field. Some agricultural scientists work as consultants to business firms or to government agencies.

Agricultural scientists usually specialize in one area.

Representative majors: agricultural science, agricultural business, agronomy, animal science, dairy science, food science, forestry, horticultural science, ornamental horticulture, plant science, poultry science, range management, soil science.

Interests: interests in plants and animals. These interests can be satisfied in farming, forestry, fishing, and related fields.

Job requirements: leadership/persuasion, helping/instructing others, problem-solving/creativity, initiative, work as part of a team, frequent public contact, manual dexterity.

Related jobs: agronomist, animal scientist, apiculturist, dairy scientist, entomologist, food scientist, horticulturist, poultry scientist.

Employment: 54,000 agricultural, forest, and conservational scientists work in teaching, research, farm and forest management, service companies, seed companies, wholesale distribution, and food product companies.

Employment outlook: employment opportunities for agricultural, forest, and conservational scientists are expected to be good through the year 2005.

Animal Science

Here you will carry out investigations and experiments on breeding, feeding, management, and diseases of farm and domestic animals to improve their health and yield. Some are animal geneticists, breeders, physiologists, or scientists. You probably will do well in such courses as statistics, genetics, anatomy, entomology, ecology, quantitative analysis, botany, zoology, animal breeding, avian science, livestock evaluation. Animal scientists will find job opportunities with the federal government in the Department of Agriculture. Others will find jobs in colleges and universities doing research and teaching. Some jobs can be found in private industry in the pharmaceutical, chemical, food, and agricultural services industries.

Fish and Game Management

You will analyze fish eggs, larvae, fish parasites, and diseases. You will learn to operate fish cultures facilities, tag and mark fish, detect problems of water pollution, analyze, identify, collect, control, and preserve populations of fur and game animals. You probably will do well in such courses as biological sciences, botany, chemistry, mathematics, physics, zoology, ecology, wildlife management. Many jobs in this field can be found with governmental agencies. Some jobs can be found in private industry providing consultation and research. Others will find positions doing research and teaching in colleges and universities.

Forestry

In this major you will learn to manage, protect, and develop forest lands and their resources for economic and recreational purposes; plan and supervise the cutting and harvesting of timber; carry out forestation and reforestation activities; manage parks and camps. You probably will do well in such courses as forest management, botany, forestry, chemistry, ecology, silviculture, dendrology, surveying, aerial photogrammetry, mathematics, geology. Most foresters find employment with federal or state governmental agencies. Others find jobs in private industry. Many foresters are self-employed, running plant nurseries, or have their own large or small tree and plant farms.

Horticulture

In this field you will be concerned with orchards, garden plants, flowers, ornamental plants, and nursery stock. You will study problems of plant production, processing, and disease resistance. You will study soil and climatic conditions. You probably will do well in such courses as biology, botany, chemistry, ecology, zoology, horticulture, plant pathology, soil chemistry, statistics, landscape and design. Horticulturists may find employment with private horticulture service companies. Others will find employment with federal or state agencies. Many are self-employed, running a nursery or a large or small farm. Some will find positions with colleges or universities doing research and teaching.

Natural Resource Management

Deals with the conservation of our forests, our rangeland, and our wildlife; the management, improvement, and development of these great resources; everything from protecting forests from fires, to preserving wildlife native habitats. You probably will do well in such courses as geology, mineralogy, stratigraphy, geochemistry, mathematics, research methods, environmental science, physical science, range and wildlife management. Private industries, such as engineering, manufacturing, and construction provide jobs for graduates of this field. Governmental agencies and colleges and universities employ workers in research, inspection and teaching.

Poultry Science

In this area you will specialize in research, production, management, feeding, and processing of poultry. You will be concerned with egg production, fryer operations, breeder flock management, and hatcheries as well as feeding programs and marketing. You probably will do well in such courses as statistics, genetics, comparative anatomy, entomology, ecology, quantitative analysis, botany, zoology, avian science, mathematics, chemistry, research methods. Most jobs for poultry scientists are found in universities doing research and teaching. Others will find employment with private industries and governmental agencies.

Range Management

Here you will study agronomy, animal science, soil science, botany, geology, and engineering. You will learn about watershed development and timber production as well as setting up recreational areas and support systems for wildlife. You probably will do well in such courses as range management, biological sciences, chemistry, physics, plant sciences, soil science, animal science, wildlife management, ecology, conservation, geology. Most range managers are employed by private ranch and farm owners. Others are employed by federal and state governmental agencies.

Soil Science

Study the physical, chemical, biological characteristics, and behavior of soils, investigate soils both in the field and in the lab, classify soils in terms of their capability of producing crops, grasses, and trees, make land appraisals. You probably will do well in such courses as biological sciences, chemistry, hydrology, physics, mathematics, geology, environmental science, ecology, soil conservation. Most soil scientists are employed by

the federal government. Others find positions with colleges and universities doing research and teaching. Others are employed by private consultation firms providing technical assistance to farmers, ranchers, and others concerned with the conservation of soil, water, and related natural resources.

2. BIOLOGICAL SCIENCE

The biological sciences are concerned with the world of living things—men and microbes, wild and domestic animals, plants and insects, birds and fish. Some scientists in this field conduct research to expand our knowledge about living organisms; others teach in colleges and universities and also conduct research. Still others apply biological knowledge to the solution of practical problems, such as the development of new drugs and vaccines or new strains of plants. Among professional workers in applied fields are agriculturists, conservationists, foresters, and soil scientists.

Biological scientists, who may also be called life scientists, study the structure of living organisms, their life processes and evolutionary development.

Biological scientists may be classified into three broad groups characterized by the type of organism with which they work: botanists study plants, microbiologists work with microorganisms, and zoologists are concerned with animals. Some biological scientists whose work cuts across more than one of these major groupings, as is frequently the case with college teachers, may simply call themselves biologists.

Representative majors: biochemistry, biology, biophysics, biotechnology, cell biology, microbiology, molecular biology, bacteriology, botany, mycology, plant genetics, plant pathology, plant pharmacology, plant physiology, entomology, genetics, pathology, pharmacology, physiology, zoology.

Interests: interests in plants and animals. These interests may be satisfied by doing research and conducting experiments to find out more about plants, animals, and other living things, or conducting research to improve medicine, health, and living conditions for human beings.

Job requirements: problem-solving/creativity, initiative.

Related jobs: aquatic biologist, biochemist, biologist, biophysicist, botanist, cytologist, geneticist, microbiologist, nematologist, physiologist, plant pathologist, zoologist.

Employment: 101,000 biological scientists work in teaching, research and development, management consulting, business and government, and sales and service.

Employment outlook: employment of biological scientists is expected to increase faster than the average through the year 2005.

Biochemistry

Learn how chemical substances enter into or are created in living things; how drugs, foods, hormones, serums, and other substances can influence organisms. You will perform tests to identify, classify, and analyze various chemical reactions. You probably will enjoy courses in chemistry, quantitative analysis, statistics, biology, botany, computer science, foreign language, physics, mathematics, nutrition. About one half of biochemists are employed in colleges and universities doing research and teaching. Others work for the federal government. Many work for the Department of Agriculture, the National Institutes of Health, and the Defense Department. Many positions are available in private industry, mostly in the pharmaceutical, chemical, food, and agricultural services industries.

Biology

You will study the structure of living organisms, their life processes and evolutionary development, and the relation between these organisms and their environment. You may specialize in research centering on plants, animals, or human organisms. You probably will enjoy courses in biological science, chemistry, physics, mathematics, zoology, anatomy, botany, microbiology, biometrics, computer science. Job opportunities are available in high schools, colleges, and universities. Employment opportunities can be found with gov-

ernmental agencies. Many find jobs with the Department of Agriculture, the National Institutes of Health, the Department of Interior. Others find employment in private industry.

Cell and Molecular Biology

This is a challenging study of what cells are, how they are put together, what makes them work, what makes them differ from each other, how they associate and interact, what goes wrong in disease states, and eventually, how you can intervene in these processes in a beneficial way. You probably will enjoy courses in chemistry, physics, mathematics, biology, molecular biology, virology, cytology, genetics, biophysics, physiology, microbiology, immunology. Most molecular biologists are hired as lab technicians or research associates in universities, medical schools, or governmental research labs. Some are employed in large pharmaceutical companies, others operate privately as genetic counselors or teachers.

Ecology

This major is concerned with the interrelationships of organisms and their environments; encompasses many kinds of science. You will study the effect of environmental influences such as rainfall, temperature, altitude, and pollution on the survival of man. You probably will enjoy courses in ecology, biological sciences, chemistry, physics, mathematics, statistics, environmental studies, geology, computer science, public health. Ecologists will find job opportunities with federal and state governmental agencies. Most will find jobs with the Department of Agriculture. Many will find positions with colleges and universities doing research and teaching.

Genetics

Primarily concerned with the nature, transmission, and transplant of genes from one organism to another. You will study their effects on everything from the manufacture of hormones, proteins, and enzymes to curing hereditary diseases. You probably will enjoy courses in genetics, statistics, anatomy, entomology, ecology, quantitative analysis, botany, zoology, animal breeding, computer science, biological sciences. Geneticists may find jobs doing research and conducting experiments to find out more about plants, animals, and other living things for manufacturing plants, governmental agencies, universities, and hospitals.

Marine Biology

Here you will analyze and study plants, fish, and animal species living in the oceanic environment; search for new foods and drugs from the ocean. You will study the life cycles, ecologies, and migration of fish; experiment with underwater farms. You probably will enjoy courses in biology, quantitative analysis, statistics, botany, zoology, computer science, physics, underwater photography. Job opportunities may be found in manufacturing plants, governmental agencies, universities, and production industries doing research and conducting experiments to improve the quality of plants and animals living in water.

Microbiology

You will concentrate on microorganisms, bacteria, yeasts, fungi, protozoa, and one-celled algae; also the application of these organisms in the production of wine, beer, bread, and cheese, as well as antibiotics and industrial chemicals. Many work in clinical laboratories in medical research. You probably will enjoy courses in quantitative analysis, statistics, biology, botany, marine science, computer science, ecology, nutrition. Most microbiologists find employment positions with colleges and universities doing research and teaching. Some find employment with federal and state government agencies. Others work in private industry mostly in pharmaceutical, chemical, food, and agricultural service industries.

Physiology

In this major you will learn about cells, tissues, and organisms and the effects of environmental factors on life processes; as well as growth, respiration, excretion, reproduction, and other

functions of plants and animals; what happens and why. You probably will enjoy courses in quantitative analysis, statistics, biology, botany, marine science, computer science, genetics, zoology, anatomy, physics. Most physiologists may find job positions with colleges and universities doing research and teaching. Some will find opportunities with federal and state government agencies. Others will find jobs in private industry mostly in nonprofit research organizations and foundations.

Zoology

The study encompasses the identification, description, and classification of animals, fish, reptiles, insects, protozoa, and so on; also the life histories, habits, diseases, life processes, and distribution of these species within the environment. You probably will do well in such courses as anatomy, chemistry, embryology, microbiology, zoology, genetics, animal systemics, marine biology, entomology, ornithology, ichthyology. Most job openings may be found with federal and state government agencies. Other opportunities may be found in private industry or nonprofit research organizations and foundations.

3. BUSINESS

Executives, administrators, managers, and their support staff are found in every organization. They establish goals, direct operations, and control major activities of their organizations. As a group, these workers are older, more experienced, more highly trained, and, consequently more highly paid than most other workers. The proportion of these workers with four or more years of college is more than twice that of the total work force; and on the average their salaries are more than 50 percent higher than that of the total work force.

Executives, administrators, and managers must rapidly assess large amounts of information prepared by their support staff. For example, the chief executive officer may base a policy decision upon economic reports developed by budget specialists. Financial managers analyze data meticulously summarized by accountants. Personnel managers monitor information on staffing patterns compiled by personnel specialists. Marketing and sales executives develop strategies to market their firms' products based upon information furnished by buyers.

Representative majors: accounting, banking and finance, business economics, hotel and restaurant management, international business management, marketing, personnel management.

Interests: interest in organized activities and attention to details. These interests may be satisfied in a variety of jobs in business operations. Interests may be satisfied in the fields of business administration, computer science, financial services, office management, or personnel supervision.

Job requirements: leadership/persuasion, helping/instructing others, problem-solving/creativity, initiative, work as part of a team, frequent public contact.

Related jobs: financial institution manager, personnel/labor relations manager, purchasing manager, account executive, advertising manager, marketing manager, department manager, office manager, education administrator, health services manager, property manager, restaurant/food service manager, government legislator, general manager underwriter, accountant, auditor, retail/wholesale buyer.

Employment: 16.1 million business executives, administrators, and management support personnel work in private industry, government agencies, and self-employment.

Employment outlook: employment of business executives, administrators, and management support personnel will be favorable through the year 2005.

Accounting

This major allows you to learn to keep track of expenditures, income, profit and loss, prepare financial reports, and calculate taxes. You may specialize in auditing, taxes, or consulting. Many accountants seek CPA certification after graduation. You probably will enjoy courses in statistical methods, management, accounting, finance, economics, computer science, auditing, taxation, business management, business law. Most accountants are engaged in public accounting as proprietors, partners, or employees of independent accounting firms. Some accountants are self-employed. Others work for the federal, state, or local government agencies, or teach accounting in schools, colleges, and universities.

Actuarial Science

You will learn to calculate the probability of death, illness, disability, retirement, unemployment, and property loss. You will work mainly for insurance or financial institutions. You may want to specialize in health, property, life, or liability insurance, or in pension plans. You probably will do well in such courses as statistics, finance, insurance, accounting, math analysis, differential equations, graph theory, banking. Most actuaries work for life insurance companies. Others work for property and liability companies. Others work for private organizations administering independent pension and welfare plans or for governmental agencies.

Banking and Finance

This is the study of the financial operations and transactions used by banks, other financial institutions, and businesses. The study is related to the fields of real estate, risk management, insurance, international finance, accounting and capital markets. You probably will do well in such courses as finance, business administration, accounting, economics, commercial law, political science, statistics, investment finance, computer science, marketing. The greatest percentage of the graduates in banking and finance will find employment as bank officers in commercial, mutual savings, or federal reserve banks. The remaining will find jobs in establishments, such as credit agencies, savings and loan association, mortgage banking, and agricultural credit agencies.

Business Administration

This study opens the door to many challenges in the world of business. It offers a variety of managerial opportunities in finance and accounting, marketing, information management, operations and production, general management, retailing, and consulting. You probably will enjoy courses in business administration, economics, mathematics, accounting, computer science, marketing, business law, organizational behavior, statistics. The majority of business administration graduates find employment within the manufacturing industries, such as automotive, aerospace, commercial and investment banking, consulting services, retailing, and communications. A smaller percent find jobs in the federal, state, and local government. Some find jobs in private foundations and professional organizations.

Business Economics

This field of study deals with a branch of economics that uses statistical and mathematical models to explain business cycles and the flow of goods and services. You probably will enjoy courses in business, economics, statistics, finance, marketing, business law, mathematics, computer science, business communications. Graduates in this field who are classified as economists will find employment in government agencies. Private industry, manufacturing firms, banks, insurance companies, security and investment companies, economic research firms, and consulting firms offer many job opportunities. Some will find jobs as teachers.

Hotel and Restaurant Management

In this field you will learn to manage the total or partial operation of a hotel or a restaurant; see to it that it is run efficiently and profitably. You will be concerned with personnel, services, supplies, business aspects, decision-making, accounting, and public relations. You probably will enjoy courses in hotel administration, accounting, economics, marketing, computer science, maintenance engineering, food service management, catering, tourism. The largest percentage of graduates will find employment in one of many thousands of hotels, motels, or restaurants throughout the nation in

an organizing or reorganizing capacity. Some will find employment in convention or tourist centers.

International Business

For this field you should have an interest in travel or living in a foreign social, cultural, or business environment. Your work could involve the building of offices or plants in foreign countries. You might be sent as a technical specialist abroad to expand the distribution of a product internationally. You probably will enjoy courses in business administration, economics, accounting, business law, computer science, marketing, foreign language, political science, history, tourism. A large percentage of graduates will find employment in banks as an international officer advising customers with financial dealing in foreign trade. Some will find jobs in the international currency exchange. Others will find jobs with governmental agencies or with importing and exporting firms.

Labor Relations

You will learn to deal with various aspects of employer-employee relations, such as wage and salary negotiations, benefits and welfare, affirmative action, grievances, abuses and demands, labor laws, union organizations, and collective bargaining. You probably will do well in such courses as business administration, business law, personnel administration, psychology, sociology, counseling, political science. Most job opportunities will be with private industry, such as manufacturers, banks, insurance companies, airlines, department stores, labor unions, governmental agencies, and many other business concerns. Some will be self-employed, whereas others will find jobs teaching.

Marketing

The purpose of marketing is to increase sales of products or services. Here you will learn to analyze, compile data, research, and, hopefully, affect the purchasing power of the American public. You will learn about advertising and human relations. You probably will do well in such courses as marketing business management, economics, statistics, computer science, advertising, business law, accounting, finance, psychology, consumer relations. Most jobs for marketing research workers are found in manufacturing companies, advertising agencies, and independent research organizations. Many are employed by stores, radio and television firms, and newspapers. Others work for university research centers and governmental agencies.

Transportation Studies

You will study a variety of traffic management services from air and ocean to rail and truck. You will learn about other related fields, such as urban renewal, development of highways and mass transit systems, airports, communication networks, and sewage systems. You probably will do well in such courses as transportation studies, systems analysis, computer science, economics, engineering, drafting, ecology, mathematics, urban planning, marketing. The greatest percentage of jobs will be found in industries involved with moving people and material. Job opportunities can be found with airlines, bus lines, railroads, and trucking companies. A number of jobs can be found with federal, state, and local government agencies.

4. COMMUNICATIONS AND THE ARTS

The art of communications is as old as humanity. Its importance in modern society becomes apparent when you try to imagine the world without radio, television, newspapers, magazines, or books. From the earliest discoveries of papermaking techniques to today's use of computers and satellites that transmit information around the world instantaneously, people have sought ways of recording the events around them and conveying the information to others. Communication is the process of transmitting information to an audience through a variety of media.

The visual arts occupations include both fine and applied artists. Fine artists create objects of beauty that are appreciated for purely aesthetic reasons. Applied artists create or design objects that are both practical and attractive.

The performing arts include acting, dancing, instrumental music, and singing. These fields have the common goals of entertaining, communicating with, and affecting the emotions of audiences.

Representative majors: advertising, communications, journalism, music, public relations, radio/television, telecommunications, motion picture technology, photographic technology, art conservation, art history, arts management, drawing, fine arts, painting, sculpture, studio art, cinematography, dance, dramatic arts, film arts, jazz, musical theater, visual and performing arts.

Interests: interests in creative expression of feelings or ideas. These interests can be satisfied in several of the creative or performing arts. Interests in communications may be satisfied with jobs on newspapers, in radio and television studios, and in the theater and motion picture industries. Interests in visual arts may be satisfied with jobs for advertising agencies, printing and publishing firms, television and motion picture studios, museums, and restoration laboratories.

Job requirements: persuasion, helping/instructing others, problem-solving/creativity, initiative, work as part of a team, frequent public contact, manual dexterity.

Related jobs: columnist, commentator, writer, playwright, editor, technical writer, lobbyist, public-relations representative, news analyst, announcer, disk jockey, photographer, photojournalist, art director, interior director, illustrator, music director, music composer, music arranger, musician, choreographer.

Employment: 1.5 million work in the communications, art, and entertainment fields.

Employment outlook: employment of workers in the communications and the arts field will have average growth through the year 2005.

Advertising

You will plan and prepare advertisements for newspapers, magazines, radio, TV, billboards, brochures. You may specialize in copywriting, layout, research. You will use creative talents to market a product to prospective clients. You probably will enjoy courses in English, creative writing, technical writing, speech, marketing, economics, public speaking, psychology, statistics, finance, management, sociology, computer science, art. Many workers in advertising are hired by advertising and public relations agencies. Others work for nonprofit organizations and various kinds of businesses. Some are self-employed.

Communications

Communications studies involve the understanding of the role of mass communication in society. You will study the nature, function, content, values, and effects of communication on public policy and opinion, covers the nature of language and communication media. You probably will enjoy courses in English, creative writing, technical writing, speech, marketing, economics, public speaking, psychology, statistics, sociology, foreign language, journalism, research methods, advertising. Many graduates in this field find work with advertising and public relations agencies. Others work for newspapers and radio/television companies. Some work for nonprofit organizations and various kinds of businesses.

Creative Writing

The emphasis here is upon the study and practice of writing as opposed to the traditional English and literature majors. You will learn to communicate experiences and awareness in the special language of fiction, drama, and poetry. You will have to dedicate yourself to developing the craft of creative expression using language as the artistic medium. You probably will do well in such courses as English, American literature, English literature, world literature, humanities, social sciences, short story writing, poetry, playwriting, philosophy, history, psychology. Most creative writers free-lance. That is, they produce articles or books for publication and offer them to publishers,

often through an agent. Radio, television, and cinema companies provide employment for a limited number of talented script writers. Newspapers and magazines also employ columnists and feature writers to do creative writing. Perserverance is required of those who hope to earn a living in this field. However, it can be very personally and financially rewarding.

Design

You will learn to design products, articles, and materials in such a way that they are not only functional but visually pleasing; often set styles and fashion trends; usually specialize in one product or activity from industrial design to fashion design. You probably will enjoy courses in fine arts, arts and crafts, sketching, cinematography, photojournalism, painting process, printing process, drafting, rendering, silk screen process, graphics. Employment opportunities are best in wholesale and retail trade—in florist shops, furniture and home furnishing stores, and apparel stores. Others find jobs in manufacturing industries. Some job opportunities may be found with engineering, architectural, and construction firms. Government agencies employ some designers. Others are self-employed.

Dramatic Arts

You should possess such talents as an actor, dancer, or musician that you might contribute to the cultural enrichment and entertainment of our society. You will undergo long, tedious training and emotional strain in a very competitive field. You probably will do well in such courses as acting techniques, technical theater, dramatic literature, drama, speech, oral interpretation, radio and TV operations, pantomime, stagecraft, technical speaking. Full-time jobs are available at local radio and television stations, and in some community, school, and traveling theatrical companies. Artists are employed by motion picture, television, and radio studios, and by stock companies, theaters, and other places where plays or floor shows are presented.

English

This major deals with the linguistic and literary richness of the English language, as well as some of the cultural history of the English speaking world. You may concentrate on specific areas: creative writing, comparative and American literature, or semantics. You probably will enjoy courses in English, communications, literature, comparative literature, foreign language, writing, poetry, drama, semantics. Jobs are available in cities all over the country. Most are found in areas where motion picture and television studios are located or where large publishing companies have their headquarters. Others are found with newspapers and publishing companies. Many creative writers are self-employed. Teaching positions are found in schools, colleges, and universities.

Film Production

You will study the theory and practice of film production and the techniques used in this medium of communications. This major is for students who recognize the cinema to be an independent, powerful, and unique medium in today's world. You will be called upon to do creative work as well as learn the rapidly changing technology aspects. You probably will enjoy courses in history of films, film production, production laboratory, film aesthetics, film writing, humanities, literature, speech, dramatic arts, music, cinematography. Most filmmakers are employed by private cinema companies at movie capitals around the world. Many work for a time to gain experience and then seek the capital investment to go into business for themselves. Television studios employ a large number of camera technicians and directors to produce everything from soap operas to news documentaries.

Fine Arts

You will draw or design your interpretations of objects, people, and nature using a wide variety of substances, from watercolors and oils to stone and metal. Specialization may range from fashion illustrator or graphic artist to cartoonist. You probably will do well in such courses as art history, fine arts, anatomy, polymer chemistry, sculpturing, foundry, mechanical drawing, arts and crafts, design drafting, architectural rendering. Workers in this field may find jobs with advertising agencies, printing and publishing firms, television and motion picture studios, museums, and restoration laboratories. Some artists work for manufacturers in retail and wholesale trade. Others operate their own commercial art studio.

Journalism

This study embraces the writing, editing, managing, and production of newspapers and magazines; involved also are the fields of advertising, public relations, radio, TV, and motion pictures. You will learn to interview people, review records, observe events, and do journalistic research. You probably will enjoy courses in English, philosophy, economics, social sciences, political science, writing, editing, reporting, mass media, photojournalism. Many workers in this field are employed by newspapers, publishing companies, radio and television stations, networks, and news services. Some work for private industry or for the government.

Music

Deals with the art of sound that expresses ideas and emotions; either classical, jazz, or rock. You may set goals to appear as soloist, become a member of a quartet, a symphony, an opera orchestra, or a dance band. Many specialize in certain kinds of musical instruments. You probably will enjoy courses in music, band, orchestra, instrumental ensembles, choir, chorus, drama, voice, radio and television operation, foreign language, opera, arranging, directing techniques, history of music. Full-time work is found at local radio and television stations, nightclubs, restaurants, and public and private schools. Musicians are also employed by community bands and orchestras, and some work for music publishing firms. Music teachers give private lessons or work for schools.

Photography

Deals with the use of cameras and film to portray people, places, and events. This is both an artistic and technical field. You will be involved in everything from taking motion pictures and video/TV to still, portrait, aerial, and commercial photography. You probably will do well in such courses as photography techniques, photochemistry and processing, photojournalism, cinematography. Full-time jobs are found with photographic or commerical art studios. Other employers include newspapers, magazines, radio and television stations, motion picture companies, government agencies, and manufacturing firms. Teaching positions may be found in schools, colleges, and universities.

Radio and Television

Deals with a wide variety of activities concerning the planning, preparation, and production of radio and television programs; for some it is programming, engineering, or sales. You probably will enjoy courses in radio and television operations, audio visual techniques, film editing, speech, voice, grammar, foreign language, technical speaking, public relations. Workers in this field find employment with motion picture, television, and radio studios. Some find jobs teaching in schools, colleges, and universities.

5. COMPUTER AND PHYSICAL SCIENCE

Mathematics and statistics are sciences that, through the use of quantitative techniques, facilitate our understanding and expression of ideas in many kinds of work. Although mathematics, statistics, and computers are used extensively in many occupations, people in the occupations covered in this section use quantitative techniques to a much greater degree than others, and often devise new techniques to solve problems.

Physical scientists investigate the structure and composition of the earth and the universe. Many physical scientists perform research designed to increase basic scientific knowledge. Others employ the results of research to solve practical

problems in developing new products, locating new sources of oil, or forecasting the weather.

Representative majors: computer graphics, computer and information sciences, computer mathematics, computer programming, data processing, information sciences and systems, microcomputer software, robotics, systems analysis, analytical chemistry, chemistry, inorganic chemistry, organic chemistry, pharmaceutical chemistry, physical chemistry, actuarial sciences, applied mathematics, mathematics statistics, atomic/molecular physics, electron physics, elementary particle physics, fluids and plasmas, nuclear physics, optics, physics, solid state physics.

Interests: interests in discovering, collecting, and analyzing information about the natural world, and in applying scientific research findings to problems. These interests may be satisfied by investigating, discovering, or testing new theories; by developing new or improved materials or processes for use in production and construction; or doing research in such fields as geology, astronomy, oceanography, and computer science.

Job requirements: leadership/persuasion, helping/instructing others, problem-solving/creativity, initiative, work as part of a team.

Related jobs: systems analyst, information scientist, computer programmer, statistician, actuary, financial analyst, mathematician, astronomer, physicist, chemist, meteorologist, geologist, geophysicist, hydrologist, oceanographer, seismologist, environmental analyst.

Employment: 771,000 computer and physical scientists work in research, teaching, government agencies, and private industry.

Employment outlook: Employment of computer and physical scientists is expected to have average growth through the year 2005.

Astronomy

In this major you will study the sizes, shapes, motion, and all other physical properties of the sun, moon, stars, and planets. You may use your knowledge of astronomy in space exploration and the development of space technology. You probably will do well in such courses as mathematics, physics, chemistry, earth science, computer science, biology, astrophysics, astronomical sciences. Most astronomers find jobs in research programs either with aerospace industries manufacturing spacecrafts, or with commercial spacecraft enterprises. A number are employed by governmental agencies, such as the departments of defense and commerce. Jobs may be found with NASA, observatories, and universities.

Chemistry

A study of the science of physical substances; the study of atoms, molecules, elements, and compounds. You will learn to perform chemical tests and develop new chemical products, monitor the air, food, and drugs for pollutions. There are many subfields to specialize in. You probably will do well in such courses as analytical chemistry, inorganic chemistry, organic chemistry, physical chemistry, mathematics, physics, nuclear science. About two thirds of all chemists work for manufacturing firms. Jobs may be found in federal, state, and local governments, such as the departments of defense, health, and human resources, and agriculture. Jobs may be found in research organizations and as teachers.

Computer Science

Here you will learn to design new computers, computer languages, related devices, and research into new ways to use computers effectively; or become involved in aspects of artificial intelligence from pattern recognition to problem-solving. You probably will enjoy courses in mathematics, accounting, physical science, engineering, computer science, logic, linguistics, statistics. Most computer scientists will find job opportunities with manufacturing firms. Others will find jobs as consultants or as teachers in training and college institutions.

Earth Science

This science touches base with geology, geophysics, geography, meteorology, oceanography, hydrology, and so on; everything from the movement of continents to the eruption of volcanoes and the science of earthquakes. There are many specialties. You probably will enjoy courses in mathematics, physical science, geology, meteorology, environmental science, oceanography, geography. Most earth scientists find jobs in the energy and mining industries. Many find teaching and research jobs in educational institutions. Some find careers with governmental agencies such as the U.S. Geological Survey, National Science Foundation, the departments of interior, agriculture, transportation, and NASA.

Geology

A study of the earth's structure, composition, and history. You will examine rocks, minerals, and fossils, record data, and prepare maps; conduct surveys and advise suitability of sites; living conditions can be primitive and physically trying while on field trips. You probably will enjoy courses in physical science, biological science, mathematics, computer science, geological sciences, hydrology, soil science. Forty percent of the geologists find work in oil and gas companies either in service or exploration. Some work for mining and quarrying companies. Some work as consultants or are self-employed. Governmental agencies offer jobs in the Bureau of Mines, U.S. Geological Survey, Bureau of Reclamation. Jobs as teachers may be offered by universities and colleges.

Information Science

You will learn to design information systems to provide management or clients with specific data from computer storage. You will use electronic data processing, mathematics, and computer systems. You probably will do well in such courses as mathematics, computer science, information science, communications, library systems, English, linguistics. Information scientists are employed by electronic semiconductor firms to design microprocessor programs, computers, computer languages, and related devices. Some are employed to do research work in the field of artificial intelligence. Others work in governmental agencies, colleges, and universities, or are self-employed.

Mathematics

This major allows you to learn to solve both theoretical and practical problems that can be explained in mathematical terms. You will study all aspects of algebra, geometry, advanced mathematics, and computer languages. You probably will do well in such courses as advanced mathematics, probability, theory, statistics, mathematical analysis, computer science, physical science, economics, logistics. Most mathematicians find teaching jobs in high schools, colleges, and universities. The remainder work in high technology industries, such as research and development laboratories, engineering, architectural, and surveying services, business services, communications, aircraft and space, and for governmental agencies.

Meteorology

You will concentrate on the phenomena that take place in the Earth's blanket of air and atmosphere. You will study wind, clouds, temperature patterns, and precipitation. The primary concern is to understand and predict weather conditions on Earth and in space. You probably will do well in such courses as meteorology, physics, mathematics, chemistry, computer science, astronomy, geology, geography. Most meteorologists are employed by the National Weather Service. Others find employment working for a public or private television or radio station as a weather forecaster. Some private industries recognize the value of having their own weather meteorological services.

Oceanography

You will use the principles and techniques of natural science, engineering, and mathematics to study oceans, their movements, physical properties, and plant and marine life. You will use your knowledge to develop improved technologies to utilize the vast resources of oceans. You probably will do well in such courses as physics, chemistry, biological science, mathematics, geology, life support and diving technology, photography, engineering. About one half of oceanographers find employment with colleges and universities as teachers and researchers. One fourth find jobs in private industry dealing with research and underwater projects. Others find jobs in governmental agencies.

Physics

Here you will deal with problems relating to matter and energy or the basic laws of nature. You will study everything from the nature and behavior of atoms and their components and relativity theories to light in space. You probably will do well in such courses as physics, chemistry, mathematics, astronomy, mechanics, electromagnetism, electronics, optics, thermodynamics, atomic and molecular physics. Private industry employs about two thirds of all the nonacademic physicists in companies manufacturing electrical equipment, aircraft, and missiles, chemicals, and scientific equipment. A large percentage find positions in universities doing research and teaching. Others find jobs in hospitals and commercial research laboratories.

Systems Analysis

In this field you will learn to devise computerized systems to meet the needs of clients. The system may be in business, science, engineering, or medicine. Computer programming knowledge is essential. You probably will do well in such courses as computer science, mathematics, accounting, business management, physical science, engineering, informational science, statistics. Most systems analysts work for industries that manufacture durable computer goods, governmental agencies, banks, insurance, and data processing service. Some find jobs in research and teaching.

6. EDUCATION

Teaching and counseling are people-oriented fields that involve helping others learn, acquire information, or gain insight into themselves. These professionals usually require a bachelor's degree, although some require a master's or doctoral degree.

Teaching is one of the largest occupations in the United States. By 2005 kindergarten and elementary school teachers will hold about 2.2 million jobs, secondary school teachers will hold 1.7 million, and college and university teachers will hold about 800,000. Many others hold jobs as teachers in preschool programs and nursery schools; in public and private vocational education programs; in dance, music, and art studios; as librarians, counselors, and advisers.

Representative majors: adult education research, curriculum and instruction, education, educational statistics, educational testing, higher education research, comparative education, school psychology, social foundations, student counseling, administration of special education, adult education administration, community college education administration, elementary education, junior high education, early childhood education, secondary education, teacher's aide, teacher education in specific subjects.

Interests: interests in leading and influencing others. These interests may be satisfied by helping others to learn by doing general and specialized teaching; by teaching the skills for a specific trade, or by providing educational and career development counseling services.

Job requirements: leadership/persuasion, helping/instructing others, problem-solving/creativity, initiative, work as part of a team, frequent public contact, physical stamina.

Related jobs: preschool teacher, elementary teacher, secondary school teacher, special education teacher, vocational education teacher, adult education teacher, sports and physical training instructors, college/university faculty member, educational counselor, vocational counselor, educational administrator.

Employment: 5.7 million educators work in teaching, counseling, and library and informational services in public and private educational settings.

Employment outlook: employment of teachers and educational specialists is expected to grow faster than average through the year 2005.

Art Education

You will learn to instruct pupils in art, such as sketching, painting, designing, and sculpturing, or in an applied field: ceramics, weaving, textile design, jewelry making, and such. You will observe pupils' work to make criticism and corrections; plan exhibits and art shows. You probably will enjoy courses in art history, fine arts, anatomy, commercial art, craft arts, educational psychology, sociology, adolescent behavior, teaching methods, survey of architecture. Most job opportunities are found in schools, colleges, and universities. Some jobs may be found in the area of health and recreation. Other employment opportunities are found in manufacturing and wholesale trades.

Developmental Psychology

You will concentrate on the developmental approach to human behavior to prepare yourself for graduate programs in basic research and the teaching of psychology, or you may wish to enter a counseling field in education or social work. This is the undergraduate major that many educational psychologists take. A closely related major is child development. You probably will enjoy courses in psychology, behavioral sciences, social sciences, statistics, adolescent psychology, child psychology, theories of personality, abnormal psychology, psycholinguistics, English, biological sciences. Most developmental psychologists work in the field of education in public schools and colleges either as teachers or as counseling psychologists. Some are self-employed and work as consultants, especially in the field of special education.

Early Childhood Education

You will learn to teach preschool students through art, music, play, poetry, and stories to prepare for learning language, science, numbers, and social studies. You will design programs to develop students mental capacities, learning abilities and emotional growth. You probably will do well in such courses as child development, sociology, anthropology, speech, special education, teaching methods, education psychology, nonacademic tutoring, school health. Most job opportunities are found in private preschools and nurseries. Other teaching positions are found in public and private elementary schools. Some day-care and nursery jobs may be found with large business and industrial firms.

Elementary Education

You will learn to teach pupils the basic academic, social, and manipulative skills; you will also develop in students good study and work habits, as well as an appreciation for learning. You will learn to prepare lesson plans, tests, records, and reports, and how to confer with parents. You probably will enjoy courses in public speaking, educational psychology, child development, reading, mathematics, social studies, science, art, music, teaching methods, school health. Teaching positions are found in preschool and elementary schools. Other job opportunities are found in colleges and universities that train teachers.

Foreign Language

You will learn to teach students and adults to speak and translate a foreign language competently; to prepare them for the growing need for linguists. You may become a translator, journalist, research worker, diplomat, flight attendant, teacher, or a foreign travel consultant. You probably will do well in such subjects as foreign language, literature, area studies, history,

writing, classics, public speaking, educational psychology, teaching methods, philology. Most job openings may be found in public schools and colleges. Some positions may be found in private schools. Some job opportunities may be found in government agencies. A few positions may be found in business.

Guidance

You will learn to help students develop in one or more areas of guidance: academic, social, personal, or career development. Your goal will be to assist students to achieve satisfying and satisfactory life adjustments to their problems. You will also work with parents and authorities. You probably will do well in such courses as psychology, sociology, biology, computer science, counseling techniques, statistics, education, tests and measurements—mental health, community relations, courses in drug and child abuse. Most counselors are employed by public and private schools, colleges, and universities. Other job opportunities may be found with state and local rehabilitation agencies. Veterans Administration rehabilitation programs, and V.A. hospitals. Others work for public and private community mental health and social service agencies and organizations.

Health Education

You will learn to implement strategies related to individual and community health education topics for children and adults. Emphasis is placed on specific health problems of the age group and how the educator can promote good health practices. You probably will enjoy courses in health, first aid procedures, psychology, sociology, anthropology, teaching methods, public health administration, child care, nutrition, drug use and abuse. Most of the workers in this field are hired by government institutions. Some work for schools. Others work for recreational agencies and nonprofit organizations. A few work in businesses.

Music Education

You will learn to teach private, group, or classroom instrumental music or singing lessons. You will learn to organize musicians into bands or orchestras. You may specialize in classical or popular. With an exceptional degree of talent, you may want to perform professionally, as well as teach. You probably will enjoy courses in band, instrumental ensembles, choir, chorus, drama, voice, composition, arranging, foreign language, educational psychology, sociology, teaching methods, history of music. Most musicians work in cities in which entertainment and recording activities are concentrated. Jobs are found with symphony groups, orchestras, churches, clubs, and restaurants. Teaching positions are found in schools, colleges, and universities.

Physical Education

Here you will learn to teach and supervise individual and team sports. You will demonstrate sports techniques, analyze physical capabilities and needs of students, and administer corrective exercises and physical conditioning. A major goal is to provide students with activities to maximize physical fitness. You probably will do well in such courses as sport skills, coaching methods, officiating, teaching methods, psychomotor learning, kinesiology, physiology of exercise, sport rules and regulations, tests and measurements, school health. Most jobs in this field are found in public and private schools, colleges, and universities. Other positions may be found with state and local recreational agencies. Some opportunities may be found in business or in private recreational facilities, such as ski resorts, tennis courts, and gymnasiums.

Secondary Education

You will learn to teach one or more high school subjects using various teaching methods. You will develop and plan teaching materials and assignments and learn to construct tests. You may teach science, math, social studies, English, music, art, physical education, or other subjects. You probably will do well in such courses as specialized subject matter, speech, educational psychology, child development, philosophy, sociology,

anthropology, adolescent behavior, teaching methodologies. Most secondary school teachers are employed in public schools. Others are employed in private schools.

Special Education

You will prepare to work with handicapped children and adults in a variety of settings. You will learn to coordinate the services available to handicapped persons and provide appropriate educational experiences for the deaf, blind, aphasic, physically disabled. You probably will do well in such courses as psychology, philosophy, adolescent behavior, child development, educational methods, speech, nonacademic tutoring, assessment and teaching of educationally handicapped, resources and materials. Employment opportunities are found in public and private schools, colleges, and universities.

7. ENGINEERING AND ENVIRONMENTAL DESIGN

Engineers, surveyors, and architects do planning and design. Engineers design machines, processes, systems, and structures. Surveyors measure and lay out land and building boundaries. Architects design buildings and other structures, as well as outdoor areas.

Architects, engineers, and surveyors often work together on building projects. Architects design the building, concentrating on the visual appearance as well as the needs of owners and occupants; engineers design the building's mechanical, heating, and electric systems; and surveyors lay out the building boundaries and the boundaries of the land it occupies.

Engineers apply scientific and mathematical theories and principles to solve practical technical problems. Most work in one of the more than 25 specialties recognized by professional societies. Electrical, mechanical, civil, industrial, chemical, and aerospace engineering are the largest. Although many engineers work in design and development, others work in testing, production, operations, and maintenance.

Representative majors: architecture, aerospace engineering, agricultural engineering, architectural engineering, biomedical engineering, ceramic engineering, chemical engineering, civil engineering, computer engineering, electrical/electronics engineering, environmental engineering, geological engineering, industrial engineering, materials engineering, mechanical engineering, metallurgical engineering, mining engineering, nuclear engineering, petroleum engineering, surveying and mapping sciences, textile engineering.

Interests: interests in applying mechanical principles to practical situations by use of machines or tools. These interests can be satisfied by planning, designing, and directing the development and construction of buildings, bridges, roads, airports, dams, sewage systems, air conditioning systems, mining machinery, and other structures and equipment.

Job requirements: problem-solving/creativity, initiative, work as part of a team, manual dexterity.

Related jobs: architect, marine architect, landscape architect, surveyor, aeronautical engineer, ceramic engineer, civil engineer, marine engineer, metallurgical engineer, mining engineer, petroleum engineer, chemical engineer, nuclear engineer, waste management engineer, computer engineer, electrical engineer, electronics engineer, industrial engineer, mechanical engineer, design engineer, safety engineer.

Employment: 1.8 million architects, engineers, and surveyors provide developing, managing, and consulting services to business and industrial firms.

Employment outlook: employment of workers in engineering and related fields is expected to grow faster than average through the year 2005.

Aeronautical Engineering

In this field you will study the physics of propulsion, fluid mechanics, and aerodynamic structures, and flight and space mechanics. You will learn to design, test, and build aircraft,

spacecraft, satellites, missiles, and jet and rocket engines. You probably will do well in such courses as higher mathematics, physics, biological science, computer science, general engineering, drafting, aerodynamics, aerothermochemistry. Most are employed in the aircraft and aircraft parts industry. Some work for federal government agencies, primarily for NASA and the Department of Defense. A few work for the commercial airlines, consulting firms, and for colleges and universities.

Architecture

You will learn to plan, design, and supervise the construction of buildings, houses, factories, skyscrapers, schools, and other structures. You will learn to make them attractive, usable, energy efficient, and economical. Eventually you must qualify for state license after graduation. You probably will do well in such courses as architectural theory, design, graphics, computer science, general engineering, urban planning, mathematics, physics, economics, history of art. Most architects work for architectural firms. The remainder work directly for builders, real estate developers, or large construction projects as well as government agencies responsible for housing and community planning, such as the departments of defense, interior, and housing and urban development.

Chemical Engineering

In this major you will learn to turn chemicals into products through research and development and devise economical and efficient production processes. You will learn to work in a number of fields: cosmetics, fertilizers, paints, dyes, pesticides, oil refining, pollution prevention, and others. You probably will do well in such courses as chemistry, physics, mathematics, computer science, general engineering, electrochemical processes, nuclear science. The greatest percent of the chemical engineers work for manufacturing industries, primarily in chemical, petroleum refining, and related industries. About one out of six work for engineering service or consulting firms and the balance work for government agencies.

Civil Engineering

This major teaches you to design and construct buildings, roads and highways, railroads, airports, tunnels and bridges, and sewage systems. Your studies will embrace soil mechanics, hydraulics, and structural engineering. You probably will do well in such courses as mathematics, physics, chemistry, general engineering, computer science, surveying, hydrology, soil mechanics. Most civil engineers work in federal, state, and local government agencies. A number work for firms that provide engineering, design, and architectural consulting services. The remainder work for one of a number of industries as well as public utility and railroad companies.

Computer Engineering

You will learn the fundamentals of electrical and electronic engineering with an emphasis on computer technology. You might major in a specialized branch, such as software engineering, computer design, systems design. You probably will do well in such courses as electronic circuits, data communication, computer structure and language, digital systems, higher mathematics, physics, control systems, solid state electronics, signal processing. Most jobs are in firms that manufacture and develop computers and ancillary hardware. Those who specialize in software will find employment in a growing number of firms that manufacture software. There is a great opportunity in this field to consult, or to start up a new business. Most engineers work in very specialized geographic areas where the electronics and computer industries have concentrated.

Electrical Engineering

This is the largest and fastest growing branch of engineering. It is a diverse field best described by the breadth of the technical societies within the field. Everything from communications and computers, nuclear and plasma science to ultrasonics can be included in the curriculum. You probably will do well in such courses as mathematics, physics, chemistry, general engineering, computer science, power and energy, systems engineer

ing, bioelectronics. Most jobs are in firms that manufacture electrical and electronic equipment, business machines, communications equipment, scientific equipment, and aircraft equipment. Most of the remaining jobs are found in consulting firms, public utility companies, and government agencies.

Engineering Technology

The training is usually more limited in scope than that of general engineering; emphasis is more practical, whereas general engineering is more theoretical. Many serve as direct supporting personnel to engineers and scientists. You probably will do well in such courses as mathematics, physics, chemistry, computer science, engineering analysis, dynamic systems analysis, drafting. The greatest percent of the engineering technicians work in private industry, primarily in the manufacturing sector. Most jobs can be found in electrical or electronic equipment, machinery, and professional and scientific equipment industries. The balance work in a number of different areas, such as wholesale trades, public utilities, and for federal, state, and local government agencies.

General Engineering

You will study the principles of engineering, taking all core courses required of professional engineers. You may have an opportunity to design your major to meet specific career goals in engineering. You probably will do well in such courses as mathematics, physics, chemistry, computer science, energy and power, solar energy, environmental engineering. Most engineers work for manufacturing industries, such as chemical, electrical, and electronic equipment, aircraft, machinery, scientific instruments, and motor vehicle industries. A smaller percent work for federal, state, and local governments. The remainder hold faculty positions in colleges and universities.

Industrial Engineering

Here you will learn to coordinate people, machines, and materials; plan the layout of factories for efficiency, and engage in time, motion, and incentive studies. You will be involved in safety studies, cost and quality control measures, and long-range planning goals. You probably will do well in such courses as mathematics, physics, chemistry, computer science, human engineering, construction and mechanical engineering, operation research. Three out of four jobs are in manufacturing industries. Because of their skills, mechanical engineers can be found in almost any type of organization and are more widely distributed in industry than other engineers. As an example, some work for banks, hospitals, insurance companies, retail organizations, and consulting firms.

Mechanical Engineering

You will be primarily concerned with mechanical devices: everything from can openers to rocket fuel pumps and nuclear reactors. You will learn about heat, machines, and power. Many engineers specialize in various industries: auto, textile, marine, petroleum. You probably will do well in such courses as mathematics, physics, chemistry, computer science, design, manufacturing processes, thermodynamics, fluid mechanics. Three out of five jobs are in manufacturing. Most jobs are in the machinery, transportation equipment, electrical equipment, and fabricated metals industries. Business and engineering consulting services and governmental agencies provide most of the remaining jobs.

Metallurgical Engineering

You will learn about ores, the extraction of metals from them, and the refining, fabricating, alloying, casting, and the heat treatment of metals. You will also learn to design and operate fabricating plants. You probably will do well in such courses as mathematics, physics, chemistry, computer science, general engineering, thermodynamics, physical metallurgy, metallography, chemical metallurgy. Most metallurgical engineers work in one of the three main branches of metallurgy— extractive or chemical, physical, and mechanical or process.

The metal producing industries provide over one fourth of all jobs. Some work in industries that manufacture machinery, aircraft and parts, and electrical equipment. Others work in engineering consulting firms and government agencies.

Nuclear Engineering

This is a field of study emphasizing the use of mathematics and science in the research, design, development, testing, and modification of nuclear energy systems and nuclear power plants. You probably will do well in such courses as mathematics, physics, chemistry, computer science, nuclear engineering, nuclear reactor theory, nuclear materials, neutron scattering theory. About 40 percent of the nuclear engineers work for the federal government, such as the navy department and the Nuclear Regulatory Commission. Other engineers work for the Department of Energy, public utilities, or as consultants. Some work for manufacturers of nuclear power equipment.

Petroleum Engineering

You will learn about the exploration and drilling for fossil fuel both on land and sea, and how to maximize the recovery of oil and gas through engineering processes. Many engineers are involved in looking for new sources of energy, such as geothermal and shale. You probably will do well in such courses as geology, recovery methods, reservoir engineering, stratigraphy and sedimentation, well logging, chemistry, physics, computer science, energy resource engineering. Most jobs are found with major oil companies and hundreds of smaller independent oil exploration, production, and service companies. A number of petroleum engineers work for engineering consulting firms, government agencies, and equipment suppliers. A few work as independent consultants.

8. HEALTH PROFESSIONS

Health practitioners diagnose, treat, and strive to prevent illness and disease. Although all of them practice the art of healing, they differ in methods of treatment and areas of specialization.

Training to become a health practitioner is much more rigorous than training for most other professional occupations, but practice also offers unusual rewards. Incomes of health practitioners greatly exceed the average and generally are higher than those of other professional workers with similar years of graduate education. Furthermore, health practitioners enjoy great prestige within the community, and most derive considerable satisfaction from knowing that their work contributes directly to the well-being of others.

All health practitioners must have the ability and perseverance to complete the years of study required.

They should be emotionally stable, able to make decisions in emergencies, and have a strong desire to help the sick and injured. Sincerity and an ability to gain the confidence of patients also are important qualities.

Representative majors: basic clinical health science, chiropractic, dental specialties, emergency/disaster science, gerontology, health care administration, health sciences, medical laboratory, medical records administration, nurse anesthetist, nursing, optometry, pharmacy, podiatry, family planning, predentistry, premedicine, prepharmacy, preveterinary, public health laboratory science, speech pathology, sports medicine, dental assistant, dental hygiene, geriatric aide, medical assistant, ophthalmic services, practical nursing, veterinarian's assistant.

Interests: interests in discovering, collecting, and analyzing information. These interests may be satisfied in applying scientific research findings to problems in medicine, examining teeth and treating dental problems, planning and carrying out medical care programs, diagnosing illness in animals, giving medical treatment to people, examining eyes and prescribing corrective procedures, or performing surgery to repair injuries or to remove diseased organs.

Job requirements: leadership/persuasion, helping/instructing others, problem-solving/creativity, initiative, work as a part of a team, frequent public contact, manual dexterity.

Related jobs: pathologist, anesthesiologist, cardiologist, dermatologist, gynecologist, internist, neurologist, obstetrician, ophthalmologist, pediatrician, physician, radiologist, surgeon, urologist, allergist, dentist, endodontist, optometrist, podiatrist, chiropractor, veterinarian, respiratory therapist, occupational therapist, audiologist, registered nurse, licensed practical nurse, physician assistant, optician, pharmacist, dietitian, dental hygienist.

Employment: 3.2 million health professionals work in hospitals, clinics, health facilities, industrial plants, and governmental agencies.

Employment outlook: employment opportunities are expected to grow much faster than average through the year 2005.

Dentistry

A field of study dealing with the prevention and treatment of diseases and malformations of the teeth and gums. You probably will do well in such courses as anatomy, physiology, biochemistry, microbiology, toxicology, genetics, pharmacology, chemistry, physics, nutrition, calculus, clinical pathology, dental sciences. Nine out of ten dentists are in private practice. Of the remainder, about half do research, teach, or hold positions in dental schools. Some work in hospitals and clinics.

Dietetics

You will learn to plan and supervise the preparation of nutritious meals to help people maintain or recover good health; plan menus and modify diets for special medical patients; manage personnel and budgets; advise patients on nutrition. You probably will do well in such courses as biology, organic chemistry, human physiology, nutrition, diet and therapy, bacteriology, public speaking, technical writing, food management, statistics, food science. Health care facilities, including hospitals, nursing homes, and clinics, are the major source of jobs in this field. Business firms that provide food services for hospital patients on a contract basis employ a small but growing number of dietitians and nutritionists. Others find jobs in schools, colleges, universities, prisons, and hotel and restaurant chains.

Hospital Administration

You will learn to direct the many activities of a hospital and coordinate the administrative duties with medical services; supervise personnel, budget preparation, accounting procedures, supplies, space needs, staffing, and the policies of the hospital. You probably will enjoy courses in health management, personnel management, gerontology, environmental health and safety, biology, psychology, business administration, computer science, accounting. Almost half of all jobs are in hospitals. Other health services managers find jobs in offices of physicians, nursing homes, offices of dentists, outpatient care facilities, and medical and dental laboratories.

Medical Technology

You will learn to perform complicated chemical, microscopic, and bacteriological tests to provide data for use in treatment and diagnosis of diseases; examine body fluids, make cultures or tissue samples, and check blood samples. You probably will do well in such courses as life science, chemistry, biology, mathematics, computer science, report writing, hematology, microserology, immunology. Most medical technologists and technicians find jobs in hospitals. Others work in independent laboratories, physician's offices, clinics, public health agencies, pharmaceutical firms, and research institutions.

Medicine

You will learn to diagnose and treat people who are ill or in poor health. You will be concerned with the prevention of disease and the rehabilitation of the injured or ill. You may specialize in one of over 30 fields. You probably will do well in such courses as anatomy, physiology, biochemistry, microbiology, toxicology, genetics, pharmacology, chemistry, physics, nutrition, calculus, clinical pathology, physiology, public

health. About half of all physicians are in office-based practice. About one fourth of all physicans are residents or full-time staff members in hospitals. Others find a practice in clinics, urgent care centers, birthing centers, schools, and prisons.

Nursing

In nursing you will learn to give direct nursing care to patients or supervise others who offer care to patients, administer medications and treatments prescribed by the doctors, observe and record symptoms and behaviors of the patients, promote good health. You probably will do well in such courses as nursing (basic, medical-surgical, obstetrics, pediatrics, geriatrics, clinical practice), chemistry, nutrition, physiology, anatomy, psychology, pharmacology. Most nurses find employment in hospitals. Others find jobs in offices of physicians, governmental agencies, nursing and personal care facilities, educational services, personnel supply services, health and allied services, and outpatient care facilities.

Occupational Therapy

You will learn to determine the educational, recreational, vocational, and other activities needed to hasten a patient's recovery. You may also have to design special equipment to do certain tasks, to use artificial limbs, or to regain the use of muscles. You probably will enjoy courses in anatomy, chemistry, physiology, nutrition, biology, neurology, pathology, therapeutic exercises, physics, psychology, arts and crafts. The largest number of jobs are in hospitals, including a substantial number in rehabilitation and psychiatric hospitals. A large number of job opportunities are in school systems and schools for handicapped children. Other job opportunities are found in nursing homes, home health agencies, community mental health centers, adult day-care programs, outpatient clinics, and residential care facilities.

Optometry

You will learn to examine eyes to determine visual efficiency and performance, diseases or other abnormalities, use various instruments and prescribe corrective procedures; some treatments call for glasses, special lenses, vision therapy, or visual training. You probably will do well in such courses as calculus, statistics, geometrical optics, microbiology, ocular anatomy and pathology, neurophysiology, physics, biochemistry. The majority of optometrists are in private practice. Others seek partnership or group practices. Others find salaried jobs with health maintenance organizations and other types of health care clinics. Others work for the Veterans Administration, public and private health agencies, and insurance companies.

Pharmacy

This study emphasizes the science of drugs—their composition, chemical, and physical properties. You must understand the effects of drugs and test for purity and strength. You probably will do well in such courses as organic chemistry, quantitative analysis, calculus, biology, pharmacology, anatomy, physics, microbiology, biochemistry. Most pharmacists practice in community pharmacies independently owned or part of a chain. About one fifth of all pharmacists own their own businesses. Others find jobs in hospitals, pharmaceutical manufacturing companies, wholesaling companies, and government and educational institutions.

Physical Therapy

Physical therapists assist and help persons with muscle/nerve/joint problems, or with burns, bone diseases, or injuries to overcome their disabilities. Following doctors' orders you will use exercise, mechanical equipment, or application of massage/heat/light. You probably will do well in such courses as anatomy, physiology, neuroanatomy, neurophysiology, biomechanics of motion, human growth and development, disease and trauma, therapeutics procedures, and athletic injuries. Hospitals are the largest employer of physical therapists. Other jobs in this field are in rehabilitation facilities, home health agencies, and nursing homes. Other therapists work in residential facilities for handicapped children, school systems, clinics, health maintenance organizations, and physicians' offices.

Public Health

In this field you will learn to plan, organize, and direct health education programs for group and community needs. Sanitation, the prevention of communicable diseases, and how to accomplish it, will be emphasized. You probably will do well in such courses as anatomy, physiology, biochemistry, microbiology, toxicology, genetics, pharmacology, chemistry, physics, nutrition, calculus, clinical pathology, biomedical and environmental health. Many jobs in this field are with federal, state, and local government. Other positions are found with private industrial firms that deal with public sanitation, health, and safety.

Veterinary Medicine

You will learn to diagnose and treat diseases and disorders of animals. You will also give advice on the care and breeding of animals, poultry, and birds. You will learn to perform surgery or prescribe and administer drugs. There are only 18 schools with very demanding admission standards. You probably will do well in such courses as anatomy, physiology, biochemistry, microbiology, toxicology, genetics, pharmacology, chemistry, physics, nutrition, calculus, clinical pathology, zoology. Most veterinarians are in private practice. The federal government employs veterinarians in the Department of Agriculture. Other employers of veterinarians are state and local governments, international health agencies, colleges, research laboratories, and pharmaceutical companies.

9. SOCIAL SCIENCE

Many of the workers described in this section are concerned with the social needs of people. For example, clinical psychologists help the mentally or emotionally disturbed adjust to life through behavior modification programs and other techniques. Social workers in a wide range of settings address the needs of individuals, families, groups, and communities. Their work may involve anything from helping an elderly person adjust to life in a nursing home to organizing fund-raising for community social welfare activities.

Other workers described in this section conduct basic and applied research in the social sciences. They deal primarily with data and things rather than people. They use established methods to assemble a body of fact and theory that contributes to human knowledge. Social scientists investigate all aspects of human society—from an anthropologist studying the origins of the human race or a historian studying an ancient civilization to a political scientist analyzing the results of presidential elections or a market research analyst conducting a survey of consumers' preferences.

Representative majors: anthropology, archaeology, behavioral sciences, criminology, demography, economics, geography, history, international development, international relations, political science, rural sociology, sociology, urban studies, psychology, public affairs, social work, religion, law, legal assistant, prelaw.

Interests: interests in helping others with their mental, spiritual, social, physical, or vocational needs. These interest can be satisfied by conducting research into all aspects of human behavior, language, work, politics, life-style, and cultural expression. Social scientists are employed by museums, schools, and colleges, government agencies, and private research foundations.

Job requirements: leadership/persuasion, problem-solving/creativity, work as part of a team, frequent public contact.

Related jobs: economist, urban planner, psychologist, political scientist, genealogist, historian, sociologist, anthropologist, archaeologist, artifacts conservator, intelligence specialist, medical social worker, psychiatric social worker, probation officer, human service worker, recreation worker, clergy, director of religious activities, lawyer, paralegal.

Employment: 1.3 million social scientists work in education, public, and private agencies.

Employment outlook: employment opportunities for health professions are expected to grow much faster than average through the year 2005.

Anthropology

You will make comparative studies in relation to the distribution, origin, and evolution of man, cultures that man has created and their social and physical characteristics. Studies include primitive as well as modern man. You probably will enjoy courses in cultural anthropology, archeology, linguistics, physical anthropology, social sciences, sociology, foreign language, museology, and moral ritual institutions. Most anthropologists find employment with governmental agencies. Some work for private businesses and others for museums and other nonprofit institutions. Others find research and teaching positions with colleges and universities.

Economics

In economics you will learn to plan, design, and conduct research into activities devoted to satisfying human wants. You will analyze the relationship between supply and demand. You will also study the problems of inflation, unemployment, tariffs, taxation, and foreign trade. You probably will do well in such courses as economics, business history, banking, international economics, marketing, computer science, finance, business law, political science, econometrics, statistics. Opportunities for job placement should be best in business and industry, research organizations, and consulting firms. The need for economic analyses by lawyers, accountants, engineers, health service administrators, and urban planners will increase the number of job opportunities.

History

As a history major you will study the social, economic, and political developments of societies. You will learn to analyze historical happenings and report on their significance as a teacher, writer, or reporter. You probably will do well in such courses as history, research methods, computer science, statistical methods, anthropology, sociology, philosophy. Most historians are employed by colleges and universities in research or teaching. Some work for government agencies. Others work for private institutions, such as museums and other nonprofit institutions.

Humanities

You will explore human thought and expression through aesthetic, historical, philosophical, sociopolitical, psychological, and symbolic contexts. You will be concerned with the relationships among cultural communities and creators with them. The studies serve as a liberal and broad training for professional careers. You probably will enjoy courses in English, literature, history, classics, culture studies, history of art and music, philosophy, psychology, foreign language, social and natural sciences. Those who graduate with just a bachelor's degree will have to apply for those jobs that will accept a liberal arts education as entry-level training, such as management trainee positions in corporations, banks, and government agencies. Many use humanities as an undergraduate degree to become teachers. Some may become writers or communications specialists in humanistic endeavors.

International Relations

You will engage in activities that cross international boundaries. You will learn about alliances and interests all over the globe. You will study contemporary international problems, diplomatic techniques, trade, business, communications, and politics. You probably will do well in such courses as economics, business management, communications, psychology, political science, sociology, linguistics, international law. Most jobs are found with the governmental agencies. Others will find job openings in colleges and universities doing research and teaching. Some will find jobs in banking and consulting firms.

Law

You will learn the law and how to represent a client in court or before a government agency. In general practice you will learn to deal with many legal affairs, or specialize in a specific branch: tax, criminal, patent, labor, or corporation law. You probably will do well in such courses as legal procedures, political science, judicial systems, legal procedures, economic analysis, contract law, labor relations law, statistical methods, criminal procedure, civil procedure, accounting. People in this field either work for others, or set up private law practices. Many find work in private business or with government agencies. Many lawyers go into politics or take management jobs with businesses.

Philosophy

You will seek a balance between vision and self-criticism in the development of a philosophy. You will grope with the philosophical thinking of how the great minds of past and present have answered the most serious questions of the universe. Philosophy is a foundation for teaching, religion, wisdom, and logical thinking. You probably will enjoy courses in philosophy, psychology, sociology, perception, computer science, anthropology, foreign language, education, logic, philosophy of religion, ethics. Most jobs in this field are found in colleges and universities in research and teaching. Other jobs are found in churches and social service agencies.

Political Science

A study of government and the nature of politics. You will study government at every level, analyze the operations of every form of government, attempt to find theoretical and practical solutions to political problems. You probably will do well in such courses as political science, history, international law, statistics, public law, geography, public administration, psychology, economics, computer science, and urban affairs. Many people in this field work for governmental agencies. Many jobs can be found in colleges and universities in research and teaching. Some political scientists are self-employed doing research, or special studies for business, industry, or government.

Psychology

You will seek to understand people and explain their actions; help people to achieve satisfactory personal adjustments; interview patients; give diagnostic tests, and offer therapy. Some work with animal behavior. There are over 30 specialties. You probably will enjoy courses in psychology (developmental, abnormal, child, social, animal, and experimental), computer science, statistical methods, anthropology, sociology, psychobiology. Many people in this field find employment with governmental agencies. Some work for private businesses. Others are self-employed. Jobs may be found in colleges and universities in research and teaching.

Public Administration

The study of public administration deals with at least five areas of specialization: personnel, management, public relations, finance, and planning. Some studies touch base with all areas, along with administrative analysis, research, and engineering. The studies lead to jobs to manage public agencies. You probably will do well in such courses as public administration, psychology, management, finance, sociology, computer science, economics, urban affairs, administrative law, public policy. Most jobs in this field are found in federal, state, and local governmental agencies. Other jobs may be found in nonprofit institutions or organizations, such as museums, the Salvation Army, and the Boy Scouts.

Religious Studies

You must possess a strong religious faith and a desire to help and serve the spiritual needs of others. You will learn to coordinate religious activities and promote religious education. You may learn to provide counseling and guidance services. The studies demand considerable initiative and self-discipline. You probably will enjoy courses in foreign language, music, fine

art, philosophy, psychology, sociology, comparative religion, religious history, education, public speaking, anthropology, origins of Christianity. Jobs in this field are found in schools, churches, hospitals, and social service agencies. Some of these establishments are run by nonprofit organizations and many are operated by federal, state, and local governmental agencies. Self-employment in this kind of work is possible.

Social Work

You must be concerned with many types of social problems and needs—among them poverty, unemployment, illness, broken homes, family maladjustment; also various handicaps, antisocial behavior, and inadequate housing. You will learn to offer a wide range of social services to people in need. You probably will enjoy courses in psychology, sociology, biology, anthropology, interviewing techniques, social legislation, urban studies, political science, counseling, ethnics, geriatrics. Most jobs in this field are found with federal, state and local governmental agencies. Some jobs are found with some nonprofit organizations, churches, and hospitals.

Sociology

In sociology you will study the many groups of human organizations: families, tribes, communities, villages, and states. You will study the behavior and interaction of these groups, and trace their origin and growth. You will analyze the influence of group activities on individual and group behavior. You probably will do well in such courses as sociology, anthropology, geography, political science, psychology, research methods, computer science, statistical methods, criminology, sociological analysis. Most jobs in this field are found in governmental agencies. Some jobs are available in private businesses and others in nonprofit institutions. Jobs in research and teaching are found in colleges and universities. Some sociologists are self-employed doing research or special studies for business, industry, or government.

Urban Studies

You will learn to develop programs to provide for future growth and revitalization of urban, suburban, and rural communities. You will help make decisions on social, economic, and environmental problems. You will deal with personnel, budgets, plans, and civic leaders. You probably will enjoy courses in urban studies (demography, ecology, complex organizations and institutions), regional planning, finance, engineering, architecture, sociology, economics, political science, public policy. Most jobs are found with federal, state, and local governmental agencies. Some urban planners are self-employed doing research or special studies for business, industry, or government.

LOCATING FURTHER JOB INFORMATION RELATED TO YOUR MAJOR

In the previous section you found careers in which you may have an interest within fields of study, and generalized information about those careers. You may now want to go further and find more specific information. Good sources of occupational information are public libraries, high school and college career centers, and standard reference sources. Here are some suggestions in using these sources.

Public libraries. Most public libraries have career/occupational information collections. The *ERIC Digest*, sponsored by the Office of Educational Research, U.S. Department of Education, recommends these topics for occupational research in libraries:

- printed resources including bibliographies, lists of local, state, and federal job opportunities, and descriptions of all types of jobs;
- information about professional associations—directories, joblines or hotlines, employment within professions, training requirements, and job opportunities;

- information on specific careers—salaries, qualifications, benefits, job market outlook, and job descriptions;
- information about potential employers—size of companies, location of offices, types of jobs, specific hiring policies toward women, minorities, the handicapped, mid-life career changers.

High school and college career centers. Many high schools and colleges maintain career centers that cover a variety of topics. Their services usually include:

- a resource room that contains standard occupational information references;
- computerized occupational information systems;
- guidance personnel especially trained to provide professional career guidance;
- specialized workshops and career-related programs;
- résumé writing, job search methods, and interviewing techniques;
- interest inventories that will help you to measure your interests in a valid and reliable way.

Take advantage of what career centers have to offer! They are specialists in career and college planning!

Standard reference sources. Although each library and career center will have its own collection of resources on occupational information, listed below are some standard references you may want to investigate.

The Career Guide. Parsippany, New Jersey: Dun's Employment Opportunities Directory. This guide contains up-to-date, comprehensive, accurate coverage on employers and career opportunities. It includes lists of U.S. companies with 1000 or more employees with the name and address of the company, an overview of the company, what opportunities are available, location of offices, benefits, and the name of a contact person.

U.S. Department of Labor, *Dictionary of Occupational Titles*, 1991. Washington, D.C.: U.S. Employment Service. The DOT gives comprehensive, standardized descriptions of duties of over 12,000 occupations. It is designed to match job requirements and worker skills.

U.S. Department of Labor, *Occupational Outlook Handbook*. Updated biennially. This handbook includes information about specific jobs, working conditions, training and education needed, projected earnings, and job prospects.

Interest inventories. Perhaps you have had the good fortune to take a career interest inventory. If so you may have a pretty good idea of what your career interests are. Interest inventories measure your interests and give you a good idea of what careers might be most satisfying to you. If you have not taken an inventory, or wish to retest your interests, see your counselor or career technician for advice. There are a large number of interest inventories to choose from. A career interest inventory that you can complete on your own and that ties college major decision-making to career planning is *The Major-Minor Finder*. Ask your counselor for it or write to CFKR Career Materials, 11860 Kemper Road, Unit 7, Auburn, California 95603 for information on how you may purchase this instrument.

CHOOSING A COLLEGE TO MATCH YOUR INTERESTS

Your first-choice major and your career plans will become important criteria in choosing a college. Your free choice may be limited by financial or other considerations. However, if at all possible, give high priority to your major and career planning and choose a college that best matches those plans. Your major will have a strong influence in choosing a college. The college major that you choose may influence your final college choice.

- **Some majors are rare and specialized.** Special attention must be given to those majors that are fairly rare and specialized. You will be limited in the number of colleges to choose from. Of the more than 2000 four-year colleges in the United States, only 73 have aeronautical engineering; 51 have agricultural engineering; 24 have architectural engineering majors; 55 have biomedical engineering; 43 have landscape engineering; 28 have petroleum engineering; 57 have business statistics; 71 have astronomy; 26 have oceanography (must be near the ocean); 75 have resource management; 76 have pharmacy; 73 have occupational therapy. This is just a partial listing. If you choose a fairly rare major, you may have to travel a distance to find a college that offers it. Check with your career center or public library for listings of colleges that offer your major.
- **Some majors are traditional and offered widely.** Most colleges offer a common core of traditional majors in business, science, social science, communications, and humanities that by their very title signify a general major. Many students take these general majors as preparation for the job market, or for preparation to a graduate or professional school. Examples of majors that are offered widely by four-year colleges are: business administration, chemistry, mathematics, physics, economics, history, philosophy, political science, psychology, sociology, general biology, art, communications, dramatic arts, music, English, and elementary education. Some colleges also offer majors that include courses in a broad area of studies, such as: liberal arts, humanities, social science, prelaw, environmental science, physical science, urban studies, ethnic studies, international relations.

  If you should choose one of these more general, and commonly offered majors, you will have a much broader choice of colleges. However, an undergraduate degree (B.A. or B.S.) in one of these traditional majors, generally will not prepare you for direct job entry at a professional level. If your goal is to work as a recognized professional in your major field, you will want to make plans to go on to a graduate school to obtain an advanced degree. For example, a B.A. in psychology will not provide sufficient training to become a licensed psychologist; historians, political scientists, sociologists, biologists, and so on, must have advanced degrees to work as professionals. *This is why it is very important that you make your college plans to include your long-range career goals.*
- **Some majors are offered in schools within universities.** Majors in the engineering, business, agriculture, education, and health fields differ from the more traditional majors in that they usually are completed in separate schools within universities. Because these majors are quite specialized and require special labs and equipment and a specialized faculty, not all colleges and universities can afford to staff these majors. Also, there can be a great variance in academic reputation and course requirements from school to school. For example: some universities are noted for their School of Engineering, some for their School of Business Administration, some for their School of Agriculture, School of Medicine, School of Public Health, and so on. If you plan to complete a major in one of these fields you should study carefully the admissions requirements, the courses required to complete the major, and the reputation of the school. Most of the courses you will have to take in the major are technical in content where job skills are acquired for entry into a profession. *Your career opportunities may be enhanced by completing a strong program in a fully-accredited and prestigious school.*

  In addition to the consideration of a major in choosing a four-year college, you should consider the size, location, cost, entrance requirements, social and academic reputations, private or public, accreditation, and scholarship/financial aid offerings.

  It is strongly advised that you go through these steps in your college planning.
- **Read college catalogs and handbooks.** Catalogs are the best source for up-to-date, specific information. Catalogs can reveal the purposes and goals, the academic strengths, and philosophy of universities, as well as the specifics of college majors.

- **Visit college campuses.** At an early date, visit the campuses of preferred colleges to get a firsthand view of what the campuses are like. During the visit, talk to students to get their unbiased views of the college—academic and social. If possible visit the department that offers the major in which you are interested and talk to a faculty member about the major.
- **Financial aids.** If you have financial needs, consider that private colleges usually cost more than public colleges; community colleges offer excellent courses that can be transferred to four-year colleges; transportation costs to out-of-state colleges can be very expensive; out-of-state colleges usually charge additional fees for nonresidents; some colleges are much more endowed and provide more financial aid than others; most colleges have a financial aid office—get as much information as you can; the Armed Forces offer financial aid programs, the ROTC, and the service academies; get all necessary financial aids forms, and file them on time!
- **Write to professional organizations for college and career advice.** Professional organizations may have pertinent information on lists of colleges that are accredited for professional training. You may obtain addresses of professional organizations from libraries and career centers.

MAKING THE FINAL DECISIONS

Making important decisions and setting long range goals is never an easy task. Making a decision on what you will study in college for four or more years, and how this will fit into your lifestyle and your career goals is very important and very personal. In this article, stress was placed upon getting sufficient information for decision-making. You now should have a good idea of what a college major is and the different approaches to majors. You also should have knowledge of the wide range of majors that are offered in nine major fields of study, and related career information.

In your final decision-making, first take a broad view of the nine fields. Look carefully at all career options within the nine fields. Don't just limit yourself to a major or a career that might have been recommended by your family or friends. The final decisions should be yours, and you will have to take responsibility to reach your goals. In the final analysis you will have to look into yourself. As Plato once said, "Know thyself, and to thine own self be true."

- **Assess your aptitudes and interests.** What can you do? What do you like to do? Use the services of your career center and guidance counselors to clarify aptitudes and interests.
- **Assess your career goals.** Tie your career goals to your college planning. Look at all options. Don't limit yourself.
- **Assess your values.** What do you want out of life? What is important to you? Material wealth? Family? The social good? Academic achievement? Advancement? Travel? Creativity? Power? Caring for people? Fame and prestige? Community service? Adventure? Beauty and art? Try to match your college and career planning with your values so that you can have the kind of life-style that will be satisfying and rewarding to you.

The more you know about your aptitudes, interests, career goals, and values the better your decisions will be. In the final analysis, good decision-making is based upon knowing the facts, and being flexible enough to alter decisions when they are not in your best interests.

We wish you well in your college major and the career path that you choose!

Robert Kauk and Francis Ferry authors,
The College Major Handbook
and *The Major-Minor Finder**

INDEX OF COLLEGE MAJORS

This section of *Profiles of American Colleges* will help you quickly determine which schools offer the major you are interested in, what the in-state tuition, room and board costs are, and what the selector rating is. You will be able to compare schools offering those majors that interest you the most and see what their Selector Ratings and in-state costs are before reading their profiles in the main section of the book. You may also discover some new schools or majors that interest you.

ACCOUNTING

School	ST	$IS	SR
Abilene Christian Univ	TX	10,460	NC
Adams State College	CO	4,910	C
Adelphi Univ	NY	18,250	LC
Adrian College	MI	14,340	C
Alabama A&M Univ	AL	4,200	C
Alabama State Univ	AL	3,428	NC
Alaska Pacific Univ	AK	11,350	C
Albany State College	GA	4,481	LC
Albertson College	ID	15,942	C+
Albertus Magnus College	CT	16,280	LC
Albright College	PA	19,260	C
Alcorn State Univ	MS	4,474	C+
Alderson-Broaddus College	WV	12,000	C
Alfred Univ	NY	21,054	VC+
Alice Lloyd College	KY	2,750	VC
Allentown College of St Francis de Sales	PA	13,480	LC
Alvernia College	PA	13,150	LC
American International College	MA	14,029	C
American Univ	DC	21,230	VC+
Anderson Univ	IN	12,920	C
Andrews Univ	MI	14,952	NC
Angelo State Univ	TX	5,176	C
Anna Maria College	MA	15,975	LC
Appalachian State Univ	NC	4,095	C
Aquinas College	MI	14,526	C
Arizona State Univ Main Campus	AZ	6,444	NC
Arkansas State Univ	AR	4,250	NC
Arkansas Tech Univ	AR	4,200	NC
Asbury College	KY	11,105	VC
Ashland Univ	OH	15,508	C
Assumption College	MA	17,095	LC
Atlantic Union College	MA	14,150	LC
Auburn Univ	AL	5,823	C+
Auburn Univ at Montgomery	AL	3,390	C
Augsburg College	MN	15,608	C
Augusta College	GA	1,452	C
Augustana College	IL	16,959	VC
Augustana College	SD	13,420	C
Aurora Univ	IL	13,381	C
Austin Peay State Univ	TN	4,350	C
Averett College	VA	13,610	LC
Avila College	MO	12,130	C
Azusa Pacific Univ	CA	15,034	C
Babson College	MA	23,160	VC
Baker College	MI	6,971	NC
Baker Univ	KS	12,284	C
Baldwin-Wallace College	OH	15,210	C
Ball State Univ	IN	6,032	LC
Barber-Scotia College	NC	6,840	NC
Barry Univ	FL	16,050	C
Bartlesville Wesleyan College	OK	9,400	C
Barton College	NC	10,689	LC
Bayamon Tech Univ College	PR	1,600	
Baylor Univ	TX	10,990	C+
Beaver College	PA	17,660	C
Belhaven College	MS	9,690	C+
Bellarmine College	KY	10,832	C
Bellevue College	NE	3,050	NC
Belmont Abbey College	NC	13,190	C
Belmont Univ	TN	10,540	C
Bemidji State Univ	MN	5,188	C
Benedict College	SC	8,376	LC
Benedictine College	KS	12,830	C
Bennett College	NC	8,920	LC
Bentley College	MA	18,680	C
Berry College	GA	11,990	VC
Bethany College	KS	11,232	C
Bethany College	WV	18,300	C+
Bethel College	IN	11,650	C
Bethel College	KS	11,530	C
Bethel College	MN	15,050	C
Bethel College	TN	9,736	LC
Bethune-Cookman College	FL	8,375	LC
Birmingham-Southern College	AL	15,154	VC+
Black Hills State Univ	SD	4,831	NC
Blackburn College	IL	9,120	C
Bloomfield College	NJ	12,200	LC
Bloomsburg Univ of Penn	PA	6,312	C+
Bluefield State College	WV	1,832	LC
Bluffton College	OH	12,951	C
Boise State Univ	ID	4,909	LC
Boston College	MA	22,706	MC
Boston Univ	MA	24,130	HC
Bowling Green State Univ	OH	6,701	C
Bradley Univ	IL	14,718	C+
Brescia College	KY	9,800	C
Briar Cliff College	IA	13,375	C
Bridgewater State College	MA	7,518	C
Brigham Young Univ	UT	5,625	HC
Brigham Young Univ/Hawaii	HI	6,750	VC
Brooklyn Campus of LIU	NY	15,000	LC
Bryan College	TN	11,465	C
Bryant College	RI	18,335	C
Bucknell Univ	PA	22,320	HC
Buena Vista College	IA	16,150	VC
Butler Univ	IN	16,210	C
Cabrini College	PA	16,012	C
Calif Lutheran Univ	CA	17,240	C
Calif State Polytechnic Univ/ Pomona	CA	6,438	LC
Cal State/Fresno	CA	5,747	C
Cal State/Fullerton	CA	4,850	LC
Cal State/Long Beach	CA	6,057	LC
Cal State/Los Angeles	CA	4,940	VC
Cal State/Northridge	CA	7,122	LC
Cal State/Sacramento	CA	6,387	C
Cal State/San Bernardino	CA	6,055	LC
Calumet College of St. Joseph	IN	3,585	C
Calvin College	MI	13,020	VC
Cameron Univ	OK	3,686	LC
Campbell Univ	NC	10,624	C
Campbellsville College	KY	8,720	C
Canisius College	NY	15,510	C
Capital Univ	OH	16,535	VC
Cardinal Stritch College	WI	11,252	C
Caribbean Univ	PR	2,400	
Carlow College	PA	13,914	C
Carroll College	MT	11,265	C
Carroll College	WI	15,490	C
Carson-Newman College	TN	11,250	C
Carthage College	WI	15,995	C
Case Western Reserve Univ	OH	19,910	HC
Catawba College	NC	12,950	C
Catholic Univ of America	DC	18,856	C
Cedar Crest College	PA	18,930	C
Cedarville College	OH	10,715	C
Centenary College	NJ	17,040	LC
Centenary College of Louisiana	LA	11,826	C+
Central College	IA	14,025	VC
Central Conn State Univ	CT	7,108	C
Central Methodist College	MO	11,410	C
Central Mich Univ	MI	6,737	LC
Central Missouri State Univ	MO	5,138	LC
Central State Univ	OH	7,320	NC
Central Univ of Bayamon	PR	2,430	
Central Washington Univ	WA	5,644	LC
Central Wesleyan College	SC	9,640	C
Chadron State College	NE	4,091	NC
Chaminade Univ of Honolulu	HI	14,290	C
Champlain College	VT	13,637	LC
Chapman Univ	CA	21,842	C
Chatham College	PA	18,010	C
Chestnut Hill College	PA	14,525	C
Chicago State Univ	IL	2,198	C
Christian Brothers Univ	TN	12,120	VC
Christopher Newport Univ	VA	3,196	LC
City Univ	WA	6,400	NC
CUNY/Baruch College	NY	2,562	VC
CUNY/Brooklyn College	NY	2,450	VC
CUNY/College of Staten Island	NY	2,558	NC
CUNY/Herbert H. Lehman College	NY	2,542	C
CUNY/Hunter College	NY	4,101	VC
CUNY/Medgar Evers College	NY	2,577	NC
CUNY/Queens College	NY	2,631	C
CUNY/York College	NY	2,534	NC
Claremont McKenna College	CA	22,150	MC
Clarion Univ of Penn	PA	6,518	C
Clark Atlanta Univ	GA	11,846	C
Clarke College	IA	13,950	C+
Clarkson Univ	NY	20,705	VC+
Clayton State College	GA	1,496	LC
Cleary College	MI	5,095	NC
Clemson Univ	SC	6,564	VC
Cleveland State Univ	OH	7,287	NC
Clinch Valley College/Univ of Virginia	VA	6,364	C
Coastal Carolina Univ	SC	6,010	LC
Coe College	IA	17,085	VC
College Misericordia	PA	15,820	C
College of Charleston	SC	6,250	C
College of Great Falls	MT	6,230	NC
College of Notre Dame	CA	16,480	C
College of Notre Dame of Maryland	MD	16,050	C
College of Our Lady of The Elms	MA	15,639	C
College of St Benedict	MN	15,468	VC
College of St Catherine	MN	14,670	C
College of St Elizabeth	NJ	15,800	C
College of St Francis	IL	13,060	VC
College of St Joseph	VT	12,650	LC
College of St Mary	NE	12,500	C
College of St Rose	NY	14,452	C
College of St Scholastica	MN	14,868	C
College of Santa Fe	NM	14,008	C
College of the Ozarks	MO	2,000	VC+
College of the Southwest	NM	5,720	LC
Colo Christian Univ	CO	9,750	C
Colo State Univ	CO	6,566	VC
Columbia College	MO	11,995	C
Columbia College	SC	13,520	LC
Columbia Union College	MD	13,650	LC
Columbus College	GA	4,892	LC
Concord College	WV	5,104	NC
Concordia College	MN	13,200	C
Concordia College	NE	11,776	NC
Concordia College	OR	12,300	C
Concordia College/Moorhead	MN	12,750	C
Concordia Lutheran College	TX	10,260	C+
Concordia Univ Wisc	WI	12,140	C
Converse College	SC	15,750	C
Coppin State College	MD	7,145	LC
Creighton Univ	NE	14,432	VC
Culver-Stockton College	MO	11,150	C
Cumberland College	KY	9,756	C
D'Youville College	NY	12,850	C
Daemen College	NY	13,020	LC
Dakota Wesleyan Univ	SD	9,770	LC
Dallas Baptist Univ	TX	9,620	LC
Dana College	NE	11,910	C
Daniel Webster College	NH	16,484	LC
Davenport College of Business	MI	8,121	NC
David Lipscomb Univ	TN	7,865	VC
Davis and Elkins College	WV	13,230	LC
Defiance College	OH	13,480	LC
Delaware State College	DE	5,656	C
Delaware Valley College	PA	16,065	LC
Delta State Univ	MS	3,964	LC
DePaul Univ	IL	15,535	VC
Detroit College of Business	MI	5,184	NC
DeVry/Addison (DuPage County)	IL	5,609	LC
DeVry/Atlanta	GA	5,609	LC
DeVry/Chicago	IL	5,609	LC
DeVry/Columbus	OH	5,609	LC
DeVry/Dallas	TX	5,609	LC
DeVry/Kansas City	MO	5,609	LC
DeVry/Los Angeles	CA	5,609	LC
DeVry/Phoenix	AZ	5,609	LC
Dickinson State Univ	ND	3,792	
Dillard Univ	LA	9,950	C
Doane College	NE	12,220	C
Dominican College	NY	13,600	LC
Dominican College of San Rafael	CA	17,860	C
Dordt College	IA	11,690	C
Dowling College	NY	12,730	LC
Drake Univ	IA	17,195	VC
Drexel Univ	PA	15,970	C
Drury College	MO	12,140	VC
Duquesne Univ	PA	16,434	VC
Dyke College	OH	5,200	C
East Carolina Univ	NC	4,498	LC
East Central Univ	OK	3,558	VC
East Tenn State Univ	TN	4,406	LC
East Texas Baptist Univ	TX	7,740	C
East Texas State Univ	TX	4,572	LC
Eastern Conn State Univ	CT	6,966	C
Eastern Illinois Univ	IL	5,548	LC
Eastern Kentucky Univ	KY	4,840	NC
Eastern Mennonite College	VA	12,700	C
Eastern Mich Univ	MI	6,749	C
Eastern Montana College	MT	5,165	LC
Eastern New Mexico Univ	NM	3,950	LC
Eastern Oregon State College	OR	6,090	LC
Eastern Washington Univ	WA	5,439	LC
Edgewood College	WI	11,700	C
Edinboro Univ of Penn	PA	7,181	LC
Edward Waters College	FL	8,300	NC
Elizabeth City State Univ	NC	4,254	LC
Elizabethtown College	PA	17,850	VC
Elmhurst College	IL	12,536	C
Elmira College	NY	18,450	C
Elon College	NC	12,290	LC
Emmanuel College	MA	17,773	LC
Emory and Henry College	VA	12,776	C
Emory Univ	GA	21,930	HC
Emporia State Univ	KS	4,685	NC
Eureka College	IL	14,555	C
Evangel College	MO	10,142	C
Fairfield Univ	CT	20,460	VC
Fairleigh Dickinson Univ	NJ	16,427	C
Fairmont State College	WV	4,640	LC
Fayetteville State Univ	NC	3,926	LC
Ferris State Univ	MI	7,160	NC
Ferrum College	VA	12,800	LC
Fitchburg State College	MA	6,962	C
Flagler College	FL	7,990	C
Florida A&M Univ	FL	4,651	LC
Florida Atlantic Univ	FL	5,525	C
Florida Inst of Tech	FL	16,935	VC
Florida International Univ	FL	4,191	VC
Florida Memorial College	FL	7,600	C+
Florida Southern College	FL	12,260	C
Florida State Univ	FL	5,814	VC
Fontbonne College	MO	12,090	C
Fordham Univ/College of Business Administration	NY	19,875	VC
Fort Hays State Univ	KS	4,675	NC
Fort Lewis College	CO	5,097	C
Fort Valley State College	GA	3,974	LC
Francis Marion Univ	SC	5,878	LC
Franciscan Univ of Steubenville	OH	13,400	C
Franklin and Marshall College	PA	23,655	HC
Franklin College of Indiana	IN	13,970	C
Franklin Pierce College	NH	17,270	LC
Franklin Univ	OH	4,621	NC
Freed-Hardeman Univ	TN	8,585	VC
Fresno Pacific College	CA	13,020	C
Friends Univ	KS	11,205	C
Frostburg State Univ	MD	6,940	C
Furman Univ	SC	16,557	VC
Gallaudet Univ	DC	9,850	SP
Gannon Univ	PA	14,872	C
Gardner-Webb Univ	NC	11,950	LC
Geneva College	PA	13,030	C
George Mason Univ	VA	8,728	C
George Washington Univ	DC	22,470	HC
Georgetown College	KY	10,990	C
Georgetown Univ	DC	24,410	MC
Georgia College	GA	4,310	LC
Georgia Southern Univ	GA	4,988	LC
Georgia Southwestern College	GA	4,338	LC
Georgia State Univ	GA	2,019	C
Georgian Court College	NJ	12,550	C
Glenville State College	WV	4,810	LC
GMI Engineering & Management Inst	MI	14,158	HC
Golden Gate Univ	CA	5,623	VC
Goldey-Beacom College	DE	7,839	C
Gonzaga Univ	WA	16,350	VC
Gordon College	MA	16,790	C
Goshen College	IN	12,360	C
Grace College	IN	12,120	C
Graceland College	IA	11,600	C
Grambling State Univ	LA	4,712	NC
Grand Canyon Univ	AZ	9,680	VC
Grand Rapids Baptist College and Seminary	MI	10,228	C
Grand Valley State Univ	MI	6,822	VC
Grand View College	IA	13,230	NC
Greensboro College	NC	11,496	C
Greenville College	IL	14,190	C
Grove City College	PA	7,870	NC
Guilford College	NC	17,680	C
Gustavus Adolphus College	MN	15,935	VC
Gwynedd-Mercy College	PA	15,450	C
Hampton Univ	VA	10,706	C
Hannibal-LaGrange College	MO	8,400	LC
Hardin-Simmons Univ	TX	9,080	C
Harding Univ	AR	9,050	VC
Hartwick College	NY	20,950	C+
Hastings College	NE	12,426	C
Hawaii Pacific Univ	HI	12,300	C
Heidelberg College	OH	17,160	C
Henderson State Univ	AR	3,860	C
Hendrix College	AR	11,670	C
High Point Univ	NC	12,350	LC
Hillsdale College	MI	15,110	VC
Hofstra Univ	NY	16,580	VC
Holy Family College	PA	8,300	C+
Hope College	MI	15,698	C

School	ST	$IS	SR
Houghton College	NY	13,120	VC
Houston Baptist Univ	TX	11,055	C
Howard Payne Univ	TX	8,052	C
Howard Univ	DC	11,680	C
Humphreys College	CA	9,714	NC
Huntingdon College	AL	11,400	C
Huntington College	IN	13,220	C
Husson College	ME	11,510	NC
Huston-Tillotson College	TX	8,490	C
Idaho State Univ	ID	4,442	C
Illinois Benedictine College	IL	14,170	C
Illinois College	IL	11,200	C
Illinois State Univ	IL	6,413	C
Illinois Wesleyan Univ	IL	18,590	HC+
Immaculata College	PA	14,620	C
Incarnate Word College	TX	12,307	C
Indiana Inst of Tech	IN	11,810	C
Indiana State Univ	IN	6,210	C
Indiana Univ at Kokomo	IN	2,069	C
Indiana Univ Bloomington	IN	6,495	VC
Indiana Univ East	IN	2,044	NC
Indiana Univ Northwest	IN	2,310	C
Indiana Univ Southeast	IN	2,260	LC
Indiana Univ-Purdue Univ at Fort Wayne	IN	2,500	LC
Indiana Univ-Purdue Univ at Indianapolis	IN	5,862	LC
Indiana Univ/South Bend	IN	2,141	LC
Indiana Wesleyan Univ	IN	12,332	C
Inter American Univ of PR/ Aguadilla Regional College	PR	2,290	
Inter American Univ of PR/ Barranquitas Regional College	PR	2,730	
Inter American Univ of PR/ Bayamon Univ College	PR	2,300	
Inter American Univ of PR/ Metropolitan Campus	PR	2,340	
Inter American Univ of PR/ Ponce Regional College	PR	2,300	
Inter American Univ of PR/ San German	PR	4,620	
Inter American Univ/Arecibo Campus	PR	5,666	
Inter-American Univ of PR/ Fajardo Regional College	PR	2,732	
Iona College	NY	16,310	C
Iowa State Univ	IA	5,456	C
Iowa Wesleyan College	IA	13,250	C
Ithaca College	NY	19,679	C
Jackson State Univ	MS	4,996	LC
Jacksonville State Univ	AL	4,080	LC
Jacksonville Univ	FL	13,390	C
James Madison Univ	VA	8,198	HC
Jamestown College	ND	10,250	C
Jarvis Christian College	TX	7,170	LC
Jersey City State College	NJ	7,797	LC
John Brown Univ	AR	9,880	VC
John Carroll Univ	OH	16,510	C
Johnson and Wales Univ	RI	13,995	LC
Judson College	IL	13,625	C
Juniata College	PA	18,390	C+
Kansas Newman College	KS	10,640	C
Kansas State Univ	KS	4,816	NC
Kansas Wesleyan Univ	KS	11,770	C
Kean College of New Jersey	NJ	6,395	LC
Kennesaw State College	GA	1,553	C
Kent State Univ	OH	6,740	LC
Kentucky State Univ	KY	4,282	C+
Kentucky Wesleyan College	KY	11,550	LC
King's College	NY	12,360	LC
King's College	PA	15,420	C
Knoxville College	TN	8,320	LC
Kutztown Univ	PA	6,528	C
La Roche College	PA	12,977	LC
La Salle Univ	PA	16,940	VC
La Sierra Univ	CA	15,472	C
Lake Erie College	OH	13,700	C
Lake Superior State Univ	MI	7,311	C
Lakeland College	WI	12,845	LC
Lamar Univ	TX	3,798	C
Lambuth Univ	TN	8,395	C
Langston Univ	OK	2,907	LC
Lawrence Tech Univ	MI	9,470	C
Le Moyne College	NY	15,180	C
Le Tourneau Univ	TX	12,500	C+
Lebanon Valley College of Penn	PA	18,300	C
Lee College	TN	7,894	LC
Lehigh Univ	PA	23,250	HC
LeMoyne-Owen College	TN	4,500	LC
Lewis Univ	IL	14,797	LC
Lewis-Clark State College	ID	4,040	
Liberty Univ	VA	11,500	LC
Lincoln Memorial Univ	TN	8,218	C
Lincoln Univ	MO	4,638	NC
Lincoln Univ	PA	0	LC
Lindsey Wilson College	KY	9,530	LC
Linfield College	OR	16,670	VC
Livingston Univ	AL	3,979	C
Livingstone College	NC	8,600	LC
LIU/C. W. Post Campus	NY	16,870	C
Loras College	IA	14,160	C
Louisiana State Univ and A&M College	LA	5,605	C
Louisiana State Univ in Shreveport	LA	1,910	NC
Louisiana Tech Univ	LA	4,284	C
Loyola College	MD	18,035	VC
Loyola Marymount Univ	CA	18,560	C
Loyola Univ of Chicago	IL	15,880	C+
Loyola Univ/New Orleans	LA	15,660	C+
Lubbock Christian Univ	TX	9,840	NC
Luther College	IA	15,900	VC
Lycoming College	PA	17,200	LC
Lynchburg College	VA	17,000	C
Lyndon State College	VT	8,394	LC
Lynn Univ	FL	18,300	C
MacMurray College	IL	12,800	C
Madonna Univ	MI	8,546	C
Malone College	OH	12,572	C
Manchester College	IN	13,240	LC
Manhattan College	NY	19,000	C
Mankato State Univ	MN	5,097	LC
Mansfield Univ	PA	6,348	C
Marian College	IN	12,936	C
Marian College of Fond du Lac	WI	12,250	C
Marietta College	OH	16,940	C+
Marist College	NY	16,406	C
Marquette Univ	WI	16,114	VC
Mars Hill College	NC	11,050	C
Marshall Univ	WV	5,762	LC
Martin Univ	IN	4,830	NC
Marygrove College	MI	5,877	VC
Marymount College/ Tarrytown	NY	17,350	C
Marymount Manhattan College	NY	15,450	LC
Marymount Univ	VA	15,930	C
Maryville Univ-St Louis	MO	12,900	VC
Marywood College	PA	14,890	C
McKendree College	IL	10,900	C
McMurry Univ	TX	10,100	C
McNeese State Univ	LA	4,543	NC
McPherson College	KS	11,360	VC
Mercer Univ	GA	15,123	C
Mercy College	NY	11,180	NC
Mercyhurst College	PA	13,488	C
Merrimack College	MA	18,025	C
Mesa State College	CO	5,127	NC
Messiah College	PA	14,664	VC
Methodist College	NC	12,400	C
Metropolitan State College of Denver	CO	1,751	NC
Miami Univ	OH	8,066	VC
Mich State Univ	MI	7,842	C
MidAmerica Nazarene College	KS	10,208	NC
Middle Tenn State Univ	TN	3,857	C
Midland Lutheran College	NE	12,410	LC
Midwestern State Univ	TX	4,542	LC
Millersville Univ of Penn	PA	7,370	VC
Milligan College	TN	10,690	C
Millikin Univ	IL	15,499	C
Millsaps College	MS	15,486	C+
Minot State Univ	ND	3,748	NC
Miss College	MS	8,348	C
Miss State Univ	MS	5,629	VC
Miss Univ for Women	MS	4,456	LC
Missouri Baptist College	MO	9,340	C
Missouri Southern State College	MO	4,272	
Missouri Valley College	MO	14,050	LC
Missouri Western State College	MO	4,384	NC
Molloy College	NY	8,580	LC
Monmouth College	IL	17,300	C+
Monmouth College	NJ	16,820	C
Moorhead State Univ	MN	5,076	C
Moravian College	PA	18,960	VC
Morehead State Univ	KY	4,600	LC
Morehouse College	GA	13,224	LC
Morgan State Univ	MD	7,366	C+
Morningside College	IA	13,896	C
Mount Marty College	SD	10,450	NC
Mount Mary College	WI	10,920	C
Mount Mercy College	IA	13,230	LC
Mount Olive College	NC	9,650	LC
Mount St Clare College	IA	12,870	LC
Mount St Mary College	NY	12,910	C
Mount St Mary's College	CA	16,390	VC
Mount St Mary's College	MD	17,825	LC
Mount Senario College	WI	10,970	C
Mount Union College	OH	15,850	C
Mount Vernon Nazarene College	OH	10,390	C
Muhlenberg College	PA	20,795	VC
Murray State Univ	KY	4,702	C
Muskingum College	OH	16,650	C
National College	SD	9,055	NC
National Univ	CA	6,135	C
National-Louis Univ	IL	13,218	C
Nazareth College of Rochester	NY	15,310	C+
Neumann College	PA	9,950	LC
New Hampshire College	NH	15,242	LC
New Mexico Highlands Univ	NM	3,772	C
New York Inst of Tech/Old Westbury	NY	13,914	LC
New York Univ	NY	24,705	VC+
Newberry College	SC	11,994	LC
Niagara Univ	NY	14,552	C
Nicholls State Univ	LA	4,531	NC
Nichols College	MA	14,200	LC
Norfolk State Univ	VA	6,345	LC
N Car Agricultural and Technical State Univ	NC	4,477	LC
N Car Central Univ	NC	4,347	LC
N Car State Univ	NC	4,984	VC
N Car Wesleyan College	NC	12,480	LC
North Central College	IL	15,498	VC
N Dak State Univ of Agriculture and Applied Science	ND	4,774	VC
North Georgia College	GA	4,103	LC
North Park College	IL	14,310	C
Northeast Louisiana Univ	LA	3,906	NC
Northeast Missouri State Univ	MO	5,654	VC+
Northeastern Illinois Univ	IL	1,955	C
Northeastern State Univ	OK	5,250	C
Northeastern Univ	MA	19,851	C
Northern Arizona Univ	AZ	4,844	C
Northern Illinois Univ	IL	6,408	C
Northern Kentucky Univ	KY	4,620	NC
Northern Mich Univ	MI	6,350	C
Northern State Univ	SD	4,186	LC
Northland College	WI	13,550	LC
Northwest Missouri State Univ	MO	5,010	LC
Northwest Nazarene College	ID	11,750	C
Northwestern College	MN	13,554	C
Northwestern College of Iowa	IA	12,250	C
Northwestern Okla State Univ	OK	3,424	C
Northwestern State Univ of Louisiana	LA	4,287	NC
Northwood Univ	FL	14,569	C
Northwood Univ	MI	13,385	LC
Norwich Univ	VT	18,730	C
Notre Dame College of Ohio	OH	11,370	C
Nova Southeastern Univ	FL	13,244	LC
Oakland City College	IN	10,216	LC
Oakland Univ	MI	6,714	VC
Oakwood College	AL	10,005	C
Oglethorpe Univ	GA	16,360	VC
Ohio Dominican College	OH	11,820	LC
Ohio Northern Univ	OH	18,660	VC
Ohio State Univ	OH	7,218	LC
Ohio Univ	OH	7,341	C
Ohio Wesleyan Univ	OH	21,108	VC+
Okla Baptist Univ	OK	8,486	C
Okla Christian Univ of Science and Arts	OK	8,790	NC
Okla City Univ	OK	9,840	C
Okla Panhandle State Univ	OK	3,155	NC
Okla State Univ	OK	5,086	VC
Old Dominion Univ	VA	8,317	C
Olivet Nazarene Univ	IL	11,976	C
Oral Roberts Univ	OK	10,607	C+
Oregon State Univ	OR	6,175	C
Ottawa Univ	KS	10,490	C+
Otterbein College	OH	16,506	C
Ouachita Baptist Univ	AR	8,940	C
Our Lady of Holy Cross College	LA	4,630	LC
Our Lady of the Lake Univ of San Antonio	TX	11,080	C
Pace Univ	NY	15,540	C
Pacific Univ	OR	17,869	C
Palm Beach Atlantic College	FL	10,720	C
Park College	MO	7,320	C
Paul Quinn College	TX	7,090	LC
Pembroke State Univ	NC	3,538	LC
Penn State Univ at Erie/ Behrend College	PA	8,752	C
Penn State Univ/Univ Park Campus	PA	8,752	HC
Pepperdine Univ	CA	23,720	VC
Peru State College	NE	4,311	NC
Pfeiffer College	NC	11,670	LC
Philadelphia College of Textiles and Science	PA	15,896	C
Phillips Univ	OK	12,744	C
Piedmont College	GA	8,540	LC
Pikeville College	KY	8,500	NC
Pittsburg State Univ	KS	4,478	NC
Plymouth State College	NH	7,166	C
Point Loma Nazarene College	CA	13,532	C
Point Park College	PA	13,922	LC
Pontifical Catholic Univ of PR/Ponce	PR	5,807	
Portland State Univ	OR	7,191	C
Prairie View A&M Univ	TX	4,740	LC
Presbyterian College	SC	15,400	VC
Providence College	RI	19,750	VC
Purdue Univ/Calumet	IN	2,374	NC
Purdue Univ/West Lafayette	IN	6,636	C
Queens College	NC	14,950	C
Quincy Univ	IL	13,646	VC
Quinnipiac College	CT	17,600	C+
Radford Univ	VA	7,034	LC
Ramapo College of New Jersey	NJ	8,027	C+
Regis Univ	CO	17,340	C
Rhode Island College	RI	7,901	LC
Richard Stockton College of New Jersey	NJ	6,950	VC
Rider College	NJ	18,160	C
Rivier College	NH	14,920	LC
Robert Morris College	PA	10,406	LC
Roberts Wesleyan College	NY	13,317	C
Rochester Inst of Tech	NY	18,954	VC
Rockford College	IL	15,300	C
Rockhurst College	MO	12,470	C
Roger Williams Univ	RI	16,750	C
Roosevelt Univ	IL	12,368	C
Rosary College	IL	15,040	C
Rosemont College	PA	16,775	C
Rowan College of New Jersey	NJ	7,358	VC
Russell Sage College	NY	16,790	C
Rutgers Univ/Camden College of A&S	NJ	8,652	VC
Rutgers Univ/Douglass College	NJ	8,795	VC
Rutgers Univ/Livingston College	NJ	8,877	VC
Rutgers Univ/Newark College of A&S	NJ	8,645	C
Rutgers Univ/Rutgers College	NJ	8,841	HC+
Rutgers Univ/Univ College—Camden	NJ	3,506	C
Rutgers Univ/Univ College—New Brunswick	NJ	0	LC
Rutgers Univ/Univ College—Newark	NJ	0	C
Sacred Heart Univ	CT	16,350	C
Saginaw Valley State Univ	MI	6,634	LC
St Ambrose Univ	IA	13,380	C
St Anselm College	NH	17,340	C
St Augustine's College	NC	9,300	C+
St Bonaventure Univ	NY	14,762	C
St Cloud State Univ	MN	5,015	C
St Edward's Univ	TX	12,636	C
St Francis College	IN	11,662	C
St Francis College	NY	6,710	LC
St Francis College	PA	15,744	LC
St John Fisher College	NY	15,415	C
St John's Univ	MN	15,364	C
St John's Univ	NY	8,980	C+
St Joseph's College	IN	14,730	C
St Joseph's College	ME	14,535	C
St Joseph's College	NY	7,322	C
St Joseph's Univ	PA	17,800	VC
St Leo College	FL	13,570	C
St Louis Univ	MO	15,522	VC
St Martin's College	WA	14,965	C
St Mary College	KS	11,250	C
St Mary's College of Calif	CA	18,848	VC
St Mary's College of Minn	MN	13,850	LC
St Mary's Univ	TX	12,064	C
St Mary-of-the-Woods College	IN	14,430	NC
St Michael's College	VT	17,930	C
St Norbert College	WI	15,710	VC
St Peter's College	NJ	14,775	LC
St Thomas Aquinas College	NY	13,550	C
St Thomas Univ	FL	14,280	LC
St Vincent College	PA	13,934	LC
St Xavier Univ	IL	14,700	C
Salem College	NC	16,025	C
Salem State College	MA	6,712	C
Salem-Teikyo Univ	WV	14,527	C
Salisbury State Univ	MD	7,516	C+
Salve Regina Univ	RI	29,100	LC
Sam Houston State Univ	TX	4,506	C
San Diego State Univ	CA	6,692	LC
San Francisco State Univ	CA	7,292	LC
San Jose State Univ	CA	6,680	LC
Santa Clara Univ	CA	18,783	VC
Savannah State College	GA	4,052	C
Schreiner College	TX	14,320	C
Scripps College	CA	23,600	HC
Seattle Pacific Univ	WA	16,503	C
Seattle Univ	WA	16,590	C
Seton Hall Univ	NJ	18,306	LC
Seton Hill College	PA	14,320	C
Shaw Univ	NC	8,936	C+
Shenandoah Univ	VA	11,800	C
Shepherd College	WV	5,540	C
Shippensburg Univ of Penn	PA	7,052	C
Shorter College	GA	10,270	C
Siena College	NY	15,410	VC
Siena Heights College	MI	12,520	C
Silver Lake College	WI	8,280	LC
Simmons College	MA	22,534	C
Simpson College	CA	10,628	C
Simpson College	IA	14,635	VC
Sioux Falls College	SD	11,540	C
Slippery Rock Univ	PA	6,803	C
Sonoma State Univ	CA	6,996	LC
S Car State Univ	SC	5,424	LC
Southeast Missouri State Univ	MO	5,854	C
Southeastern Louisiana Univ	LA	4,230	NC
Southeastern Okla State Univ	OK	3,594	C
Southeastern Univ	DC	6,625	C
Southern Arkansas Univ	AR	3,432	NC
Southern Calif College	CA	12,356	C
Southern College of Seventh-day Adventists	TN	11,348	NC
Southern Conn State Univ	CT	7,532	C

School	ST	$IS	SR
Southern Illinois Univ at Carbondale	IL	6,234	C
Southern Illinois Univ at Edwardsville	IL	6,097	LC
Southern Methodist Univ	TX	18,520	VC
Southern Nazarene Univ	OK	9,206	NC
Southern Oregon State College	OR	6,128	C
Southern Univ and A&M College	LA	4,920	NC
Southern Univ at New Orleans	LA	1,452	NC
Southern Utah Univ	UT	4,104	LC
Southern Vermont College	VT	12,974	C
Southwest Baptist Univ	MO	9,192	NC
Southwest Missouri State Univ	MO	4,956	C
Southwest State Univ	MN	5,400	NC
Southwest Texas State Univ	TX	5,124	C
Southwestern Adventist College	TX	10,530	NC
Southwestern Okla State Univ	OK	3,312	C
Southwestern Univ	TX	15,484	HC
Spring Arbor College	MI	12,256	C
Spring Hill College	AL	16,015	C+
SUNY at Albany	NY	7,059	VC
SUNY at Binghamton	NY	7,921	HC
SUNY at Buffalo	NY	7,896	VC
SUNY/College at Brockport	NY	7,220	C+
SUNY/College at Fredonia	NY	7,159	VC
SUNY/College at Geneseo	NY	6,949	HC
SUNY/College at New Paltz	NY	6,890	VC
SUNY/College at Old Westbury	NY	7,128	LC
SUNY/College at Oneonta	NY	7,878	C
SUNY/College at Oswego	NY	7,330	VC
SUNY/College at Plattsburgh	NY	6,917	C
Stephen F. Austin State Univ	TX	5,117	C
Sterling College	KS	10,990	VC
Stetson Univ	FL	16,435	VC
Stonehill College	MA	17,481	VC
Strayer College	DC	5,850	LC
Suffolk Univ	MA	15,360	LC
Sul Ross State Univ	TX	4,144	NC
Susquehanna Univ	PA	19,950	VC
Syracuse Univ	NY	21,305	HC
Tabor College	KS	11,460	VC
Tarleton State Univ	TX	4,082	LC
Taylor Univ	IN	14,450	VC
Teikyo Marycrest Univ	IA	13,755	VC
Teikyo Post Univ	CT	16,360	LC
Teikyo Westmar Univ	IA	15,920	C
Temple Univ	PA	10,281	C
Tenn State Univ	TN	4,626	C+
Tenn Tech Univ	TN	5,190	C
Texas A&M Univ	TX	5,382	VC
Texas A&M Univ at Kingsville	TX	3,808	LC
Texas Christian Univ	TX	12,180	C
Texas Southern Univ	TX	4,500	NC
Texas Tech Univ	TX	6,008	C
Texas Wesleyan Univ	TX	9,380	LC
Texas Woman's Univ	TX	4,392	C
The Univ of New Mexico	NM	5,304	C
Thiel College	PA	16,282	C
Thomas College	ME	13,450	LC
Thomas More College	KY	12,962	C
Tiffin Univ	OH	10,800	LC
Touro College	NY	11,930	C
Towson State Univ	MD	7,452	C
Trenton State College	NJ	9,085	HC
Trevecca Nazarene College	TN	9,826	NC
Tri-State Univ	IN	13,788	LC
Trinity Christian College	IL	13,260	C
Trinity College	IL	14,010	C
Trinity College of Vermont	VT	16,015	LC
Trinity Univ	TX	16,670	HC
Troy State Univ	AL	4,322	C
Turabo Univ	PR	2,670	
Tuskegee Univ	AL	10,128	C
Union College	KY	9,790	C
Union Univ	TN	7,880	C+
United States International Univ	CA	14,535	LC
Universidad Metropolitana	PR	2,650	
Univ of Akron	OH	6,699	NC
Univ of Alabama	AL	5,702	C
Univ of Alabama at Birmingham	AL	7,533	C
Univ of Alabama at Huntsville	AL	5,868	VC
Univ of Alaska Anchorage	AK	7,131	C
Univ of Alaska Fairbanks	AK	4,718	C
Univ of Alaska Southeast	AK	4,075	LC
Univ of Arizona	AZ	5,808	C
Univ of Arkansas at Fayetteville	AR	5,046	C
Univ of Arkansas at Little Rock	AR	4,419	C
Univ of Arkansas at Monticello	AR	3,832	NC
Univ of Arkansas at Pine Bluff	AR	3,978	LC
Univ of Bridgeport	CT	18,985	C
Univ of Central Arkansas	AR	4,200	LC
Univ of Central Florida	FL	6,061	C+
Univ of Central Okla	OK	3,647	C
Univ of Charleston	WV	12,750	C
Univ of Cincinnati	OH	7,989	C
Univ of Colo at Denver	CO	1,955	VC
Univ of Conn	CT	9,168	C
Univ of Dayton	OH	15,120	C+
Univ of Delaware	DE	8,013	VC
Univ of Denver	CO	19,290	C+
Univ of Detroit Mercy	MI	14,720	C
Univ of Dubuque	IA	14,150	LC
Univ of Evansville	IN	15,300	VC
Univ of Findlay	OH	15,764	C
Univ of Florida	FL	5,850	HC
Univ of Georgia	GA	5,655	VC
Univ of Guam	GU	4,139	NC
Univ of Hartford	CT	19,858	LC
Univ of Hawaii at Hilo	HI	4,141	C
Univ of Hawaii at Manoa	HI	5,626	C
Univ of Houston	TX	5,215	C
Univ of Houston-Downtown	TX	4,034	NC
Univ of Idaho	ID	4,830	C
Univ of Illinois at Chicago	IL	8,443	C
Univ of Illinois at Urbana-Champaign	IL	7,764	HC
Univ of Indianapolis	IN	14,510	C
Univ of Iowa	IA	5,658	VC
Univ of Kansas	KS	5,200	NC
Univ of Kentucky	KY	5,152	VC
Univ of La Verne	CA	17,400	C
Univ of Lowell	MA	8,831	VC
Univ of Maine at Augusta	ME	2,595	NC
Univ of Maine at Machias	ME	6,135	C
Univ of Maine at Presque Isle	ME	6,374	C
Univ of Mary	ND	8,910	C
Univ of Mary Hardin-Baylor	TX	8,120	NC
Univ of Maryland/College Park	MD	8,182	VC
Univ of Maryland/Eastern Shore	MD	6,254	LC
Univ of Maryland/Univ College	MD	4,900	NC
Univ of Mass Dartmouth	MA	8,158	C
Univ of Mass/Amherst	MA	9,364	LC
Univ of Memphis	TN	3,476	C
Univ of Miami	FL	22,107	VC
Univ of Mich/Flint	MI	2,916	C
Univ of Minn/Twin Cities	MN	6,682	VC
Univ of Miss	MS	5,756	C
Univ of Missouri/Columbia	MO	6,254	HC
Univ of Missouri/Kansas City	MO	5,906	VC
Univ of Mobile	AL	9,400	C
Univ of Montana	MT	5,529	C
Univ of Montevallo	AL	5,310	C
Univ of Nebr at Kearney	NE	4,308	LC
Univ of Nebr at Omaha	NE	1,889	LC
Univ of Nebr-Lincoln	NE	5,278	LC
Univ of Nevada/Las Vegas	NV	6,405	C
Univ of Nevada/Reno	NV	5,735	C
Univ of New Haven	CT	14,980	C
Univ of New Orleans	LA	5,468	C
Univ of North Alabama	AL	4,236	NC
Univ of N Car at Asheville	NC	4,791	VC
Univ of N Car at Charlotte	NC	4,597	C
Univ of N Car at Greensboro	NC	5,192	C
Univ of N Car at Wilmington	NC	5,172	C
Univ of N Dak	ND	4,902	NC
Univ of North Florida	FL	5,082	C
Univ of North Texas	TX	4,853	C
Univ of Northern Colo	CO	6,008	C
Univ of Northern Iowa	IA	5,137	C
Univ of Notre Dame	IN	20,150	MC
Univ of Okla	OK	5,427	VC
Univ of Oregon	OR	6,466	VC
Univ of Penn	PA	24,238	MC
Univ of Pittsburgh at Greensburg	PA	8,660	C
Univ of Pittsburgh at Johnstown	PA	8,914	C
Univ of Portland	OR	15,564	C
Univ of PR/Cayey Univ College	PR	900	
Univ of PR/Humacao Univ College	PR	1,494	
Univ of PR/Mayaguez	PR	0	
Univ of PR/Rio Piedras	PR	0	
Univ of Puget Sound	WA	19,520	HC
Univ of Redlands	CA	22,059	VC
Univ of Rhode Island	RI	9,205	C
Univ of Richmond	VA	16,700	HC
Univ of Rio Grande	OH	6,300	NC
Univ of St Thomas	MN	15,785	C+
Univ of St Thomas	TX	11,676	C+
Univ of San Diego	CA	18,970	VC
Univ of San Francisco	CA	18,408	C
Univ of Science and Arts of Okla	OK	3,304	C
Univ of Scranton	PA	17,071	VC
Univ of South Alabama	AL	5,451	C
Univ of S Car	SC	6,158	C
Univ of S Car at Aiken	SC	5,386	C
Univ of S Dak	SD	4,722	C
Univ of South Florida	FL	5,475	C+
Univ of Southern Calif	CA	23,006	VC
Univ of Southern Colo	CO	5,350	LC
Univ of Southern Indiana	IN	3,720	NC
Univ of Southern Maine	ME	7,299	C
Univ of Southern Miss	MS	4,542	C
Univ of Southwestern Louisiana	LA	3,968	NC
Univ of Tampa	FL	16,780	C
Univ of Tenn at Martin	TN	4,550	C
Univ of Tenn/Knoxville	TN	5,668	C
Univ of Texas at Arlington	TX	5,549	LC
Univ of Texas at Austin	TX	5,160	VC
Univ of Texas at Dallas	TX	1,222	VC+
Univ of Texas at El Paso	TX	3,160	LC
Univ of Texas at San Antonio	TX	6,420	C
Univ of Texas-Pan American	TX	3,192	NC
Univ of the District of Columbia	DC	974	NC
Univ of the Ozarks	AR	7,770	C
Univ of the Sacred Heart	PR	3,890	
Univ of the Virgin Islands	VI	5,896	C
Univ of Toledo	OH	6,636	NC
Univ of Tulsa	OK	13,795	VC
Univ of Utah	UT	5,975	C
Univ of Washington	WA	6,618	VC
Univ of West Florida	FL	5,415	C
Univ of Wisc/Eau Claire	WI	4,647	C
Univ of Wisc/Green Bay	WI	4,904	C
Univ of Wisc/La Crosse	WI	4,487	C
Univ of Wisc/Madison	WI	6,400	HC
Univ of Wisc/Milwaukee	WI	6,165	C
Univ of Wisc/Platteville	WI	4,830	C
Univ of Wisc/River Falls	WI	4,655	C
Univ of Wisc/Superior	WI	4,330	C
Univ of Wisc/Whitewater	WI	4,700	C
Univ of Wyoming	WY	4,991	NC
Upper Iowa Univ	IA	11,900	C
Upsala College	NJ	17,200	C
Urbana Univ	OH	12,536	C
Ursinus College	PA	19,165	VC
Ursuline College	OH	13,180	LC
Utah State Univ	UT	4,683	C
Utica College of Syracuse Univ	NY	16,714	LC
Valdosta State Univ	GA	4,670	LC
Valparaiso Univ	IN	14,810	VC
Villanova Univ	PA	21,400	HC
Virginia Commonwealth Univ	VA	7,909	C
Virginia Polytechnic Inst and State Univ	VA	6,828	C
Virginia State Univ	VA	7,040	
Virginia Union Univ	VA	10,555	LC
Virginia Wesleyan College	VA	14,950	VC
Viterbo College	WI	12,670	C
Voorhees College	SC	6,772	LC
Wagner College	NY	17,950	C
Wake Forest Univ	NC	17,280	MC
Walsh Univ	OH	11,640	C
Wartburg College	IA	14,530	VC
Washburn Univ of Topeka	KS	5,802	NC
Washington and Jefferson College	PA	19,360	C
Wayne State Univ	MI	2,680	C
Waynesburg College	PA	11,960	C
Webber College	FL	8,710	C
Weber State Univ	UT	4,398	C
Wesley College	DE	13,745	LC
West Chester Univ of Penn	PA	7,492	C
West Coast Univ	CA	9,120	NC
West Georgia College	GA	4,256	C
West Liberty State College	WV	4,690	LC
West Texas A&M Univ	TX	4,224	C
West Virginia Inst of Tech	WV	5,858	LC
West Virginia State College	WV	5,044	LC
West Virginia Univ	WV	5,774	C
West Virginia Wesleyan College	WV	16,900	C
Westbrook College	ME	15,900	C
Western Carolina Univ	NC	3,811	C
Western Conn State Univ	CT	6,622	C
Western Illinois Univ	IL	5,241	LC
Western International Univ	AZ	3,600	C
Western Kentucky Univ	KY	4,808	C
Western Mich Univ	MI	6,820	C
Western New England College	MA	14,674	LC
Western New Mexico Univ	NM	3,234	LC
Western State College of Colo	CO	5,560	C
Western Washington Univ	WA	6,077	VC
Westminster College	MO	13,750	C+
Westminster College	PA	15,200	C
Westminster College of Salt Lake City	UT	12,100	C
Wheeling Jesuit College	WV	14,370	C
Whitworth College	WA	16,265	C
Wichita State Univ	KS	5,068	NC
Widener Univ	PA	16,840	C
Wilberforce Univ	OH	10,408	C
Wilkes Univ	PA	15,728	LC
William Carey College	MS	7,050	C
William Jewell College	MO	12,500	VC
William Paterson College	NJ	7,438	C+
William Penn College	IA	13,400	C
William Woods Univ	MO	14,025	LC
Wilmington College	DE	5,200	NC
Wilmington College	OH	13,700	LC
Wingate College	NC	10,610	C
Winona State Univ	MN	5,200	VC
Winston-Salem State Univ	NC	4,142	LC
Wofford College	SC	15,360	VC
Women's College of Brenau Univ	GA	14,734	C
Woodbury Univ	CA	17,620	LC
Wright State Univ	OH	6,896	LC
Xavier Univ	OH	15,710	C+
Xavier Univ of Louisiana	LA	10,400	C
Yeshiva Univ	NY	18,200	VC
York College	NE	7,610	C
York College of Penn	PA	8,345	C
Youngstown State Univ	OH	6,447	LC

ACTUARIAL SCIENCE

School	ST	$IS	SR
Ball State Univ	IN	6,032	LC
Bellarmine College	KY	10,832	C
Bryant College	RI	18,335	C
Butler Univ	IN	16,210	C
Central Conn State Univ	CT	7,108	C
Central Mich Univ	MI	6,737	LC
Central Missouri State Univ	MO	5,138	LC
Central Washington Univ	WA	5,644	C
CUNY/Baruch College	NY	2,562	VC
College of Insurance	NY	17,600	VC
Dominican College	NY	13,600	LC
Drake Univ	IA	17,195	VC
Eastern Mich Univ	MI	6,749	C
Florida A&M Univ	FL	4,651	C
Howard Univ	DC	11,680	C
Indiana Univ Northwest	IN	2,310	C
Jamestown College	ND	10,250	C
Le Moyne College	NY	15,180	C
Lebanon Valley College of Penn	PA	18,300	C
Lehigh Univ	PA	23,250	HC
Liberty Univ	VA	11,500	LC
Lincoln Univ	PA	0	LC
Mansfield Univ	PA	6,348	C
Maryville Univ-St Louis	MO	12,900	VC
Mercy College	NY	11,180	NC
Middle Tenn State Univ	TN	3,857	C
Missouri Valley College	MO	14,090	LC
Morehouse College	GA	13,224	LC
New York Univ	NY	24,705	VC+
Ohio State Univ	OH	7,218	LC
Penn State Univ/Univ Park Campus	PA	8,752	HC
Plymouth State College	NH	7,166	C
Purdue Univ/West Lafayette	IN	6,636	C
Rider College	NJ	18,160	C
Roosevelt Univ	IL	12,368	C
Seton Hill College	PA	14,320	C
Temple Univ	PA	10,281	C
Thiel College	PA	16,282	C
Univ of Central Okla	OK	3,647	C
Univ of Conn	CT	9,168	C
Univ of Georgia	GA	5,655	VC
Univ of Hartford	CT	19,858	LC
Univ of Idaho	ID	4,830	C
Univ of Iowa	IA	5,658	VC
Univ of Nebr-Lincoln	NE	5,278	LC
Univ of Northern Colo	CO	6,008	C
Univ of Penn	PA	24,238	MC
Univ of Wisc/Madison	WI	6,400	HC
Utica College of Syracuse Univ	NY	16,714	LC

ADDICTION STUDIES

School	ST	$IS	SR
Alvernia College	PA	13,150	LC
Calumet College of St. Joseph	IN	3,585	C
Graceland College	IA	11,600	C
Kansas Newman College	KS	10,640	C
Kansas Wesleyan Univ	KS	11,770	C
Univ of Mary	ND	8,910	C

ADVERTISING

School	ST	$IS	SR
Abilene Christian Univ	TX	10,460	NC
Adams State College	CO	4,910	C
Anna Maria College	MA	15,975	LC
Appalachian State Univ	NC	4,095	C
Arkansas State Univ	AR	4,250	NC
Art Center College of Design	CA	13,550	SP
Averett College	VA	13,610	LC
Boston Univ	MA	24,130	HC
Brigham Young Univ	UT	5,625	HC
Calif Lutheran Univ	CA	17,240	C
Cal State/Fresno	CA	5,747	C
Cal State/Fullerton	CA	4,850	LC

School	ST	$IS	SR
Center for Creative Studies/College of Art and Design	MI	15,330	SP
Central State Univ	OH	7,320	NC
CUNY/Baruch College	NY	2,562	VC
Clarke College	IA	13,950	C+
Cleveland Inst of Art	OH	15,630	SP
College of St Francis	IL	13,060	VC
Columbia College	MO	11,995	C
Columbus College of Art and Design	OH	14,550	SP
Concordia College/Moorhead	MN	12,750	C
Drake Univ	IA	17,195	VC
Duquesne Univ	PA	16,434	VC
East Texas State Univ	TX	4,572	LC
Eastern Mich Univ	MI	6,749	C
Emerson College	MA	22,678	LC
Fashion Inst of Tech/SUNY	NY	7,135	SP
Ferris State Univ	MI	7,160	NC
Florida Southern College	FL	12,260	C
Florida State Univ	FL	5,814	VC
Franklin College of Indiana	IN	13,970	C
Franklin Pierce College	NH	17,270	LC
Grand Valley State Univ	MI	6,822	VC
Harding Univ	AR	9,050	VC
Iona College	NY	16,310	C
Iowa State Univ	IA	5,456	C
Johnson and Wales Univ	RI	13,995	LC
Kansas State Univ	KS	4,816	NC
Kendall College of Art and Design	MI	9,600	SP
Kent State Univ	OH	6,740	LC
Lamar Univ	TX	3,798	C
Louisiana State Univ and A&M College	LA	5,605	C
Marietta College	OH	16,940	C+
Marquette Univ	WI	16,114	VC
Marshall Univ	WV	5,762	LC
Marywood College	PA	14,890	C
Menlo College	CA	20,375	LC
Mich State Univ	MI	7,842	C
Middle Tenn State Univ	TN	3,857	C
Midland Lutheran College	NE	12,410	LC
Moorhead State Univ	MN	5,076	C
Morehead State Univ	KY	4,600	LC
Murray State Univ	KY	4,702	C
New York Inst of Tech/Old Westbury	NY	13,914	LC
Northeastern State Univ	OK	5,250	C
Northern Arizona Univ	AZ	4,844	C
Northwestern State Univ of Louisiana	LA	4,287	NC
Ohio Univ	OH	7,341	C
Okla Christian Univ of Science and Arts	OK	8,790	NC
Okla City Univ	OK	9,840	C
Okla State Univ	OK	5,086	VC
Parsons School of Design	NY	21,410	SP
Penn State Univ/Univ Park Campus	PA	8,752	HC
Pepperdine Univ	CA	23,720	VC
Portland State Univ	OR	7,191	C
Purdue Univ/West Lafayette	IN	6,636	C
Rider College	NJ	18,160	C
St Cloud State Univ	MN	5,015	C
Salem State College	MA	6,712	C
San Jose State Univ	CA	6,680	LC
School of Visual Arts	NY	17,120	SP
Simmons College	MA	22,534	C
Simpson College	IA	14,635	VC
Southeast Missouri State Univ	MO	5,854	C
Southern Arkansas Univ	AR	3,432	NC
Southern Illinois Univ at Carbondale	IL	6,234	C
Southern Methodist Univ	TX	18,520	VC
Southwest Texas State Univ	TX	5,124	C
Spring Hill College	AL	16,015	C+
Syracuse Univ	NY	21,305	HC
Texas Christian Univ	TX	12,180	C
Texas Tech Univ	TX	6,008	C
Texas Woman's Univ	TX	4,392	C
Univ of Akron	OH	6,699	NC
Univ of Alabama	AL	5,702	C
Univ of Arkansas at Little Rock	AR	4,419	C
Univ of Bridgeport	CT	18,985	C
Univ of Central Okla	OK	3,647	C
Univ of Colo at Boulder	CO	6,410	VC
Univ of Evansville	IN	15,300	VC
Univ of Florida	FL	5,850	HC
Univ of Georgia	GA	5,655	VC
Univ of Illinois at Urbana-Champaign	IL	7,764	HC
Univ of Kansas	KS	5,200	NC
Univ of Kentucky	KY	5,152	VC
Univ of Maryland/College Park	MD	8,182	VC
Univ of Miami	FL	22,107	VC
Univ of Miss	MS	5,756	C
Univ of Missouri/Columbia	MO	6,254	HC
Univ of Nebr at Kearney	NE	4,308	LC
Univ of Nebr-Lincoln	NE	5,278	LC
Univ of N Dak	ND	4,902	NC
Univ of North Texas	TX	4,853	C
Univ of Northern Colo	CO	6,008	C
Univ of Okla	OK	5,427	VC
Univ of St Thomas	MN	15,785	C+
Univ of Scranton	PA	17,071	VC
Univ of S Car	SC	6,158	C
Univ of South Florida	FL	5,475	C+
Univ of Southern Miss	MS	4,542	C
Univ of Southwestern Louisiana	LA	3,968	NC
Univ of Tenn/Knoxville	TN	5,668	C
Univ of Texas at Arlington	TX	5,549	LC
Univ of Texas at Austin	TX	5,160	VC
Univ of the Sacred Heart	PR	3,890	
Univ of Tulsa	OK	13,795	VC
Univ of Wisc/Eau Claire	WI	4,647	C
Univ of Wisc/Superior	WI	4,330	C
Washington State Univ	WA	6,364	C
West Virginia Univ	WV	5,774	C
Western Kentucky Univ	KY	4,808	C
Western Mich Univ	MI	6,820	C
Winona State Univ	MN	5,200	VC
Xavier Univ	OH	15,710	C+
Youngstown State Univ	OH	6,447	LC

AERONAUTICAL ENGINEERING

School	ST	$IS	SR
Arizona State Univ Main Campus	AZ	6,444	C
Auburn Univ	AL	5,823	C+
Bethel College	IN	11,650	C
Boston Univ	MA	24,130	HC
Calif Inst of Tech	CA	20,783	MC
Calif Polytechnic State Univ	CA	6,980	VC+
Calif State Polytechnic Univ/Pomona	CA	6,438	LC
Clarkson Univ	NY	20,705	VC+
Embry-Riddle Aeronautical Univ	AZ	9,896	C+
Embry-Riddle Aeronautical Univ	FL	10,600	C
Florida Inst of Tech	FL	16,935	VC
Georgia Inst of Tech	GA	6,669	HC+
Illinois Inst of Tech	IL	18,290	VC
Iowa State Univ	IA	5,456	C
Mass Inst of Tech	MA	24,800	MC
Middle Tenn State Univ	TN	3,857	C
New York Inst of Tech/Old Westbury	NY	13,914	LC
N Car State Univ	NC	4,984	VC
Ohio State Univ	OH	7,218	LC
Okla State Univ	OK	5,086	VC
Penn State Univ/Univ Park Campus	PA	8,752	HC
Polytechnic Univ/Brooklyn	NY	19,700	HC
Polytechnic Univ/Farmingdale	NY	20,700	VC
Princeton Univ	NJ	24,650	MC
Purdue Univ/West Lafayette	IN	6,636	C
Rensselaer Polytechnic Inst	NY	23,067	HC
St Augustine's College	NC	9,300	C+
St Louis Univ	MO	15,522	VC
St Xavier Univ	IL	14,700	C
San Diego State Univ	CA	6,692	LC
San Jose State Univ	CA	6,680	LC
SUNY at Buffalo	NY	7,896	VC
Syracuse Univ	NY	21,305	HC
Texas A&M Univ	TX	5,382	VC
Tri-State Univ	IN	13,788	LC
Tuskegee Univ	AL	10,128	C
United States Air Force Academy	CO	0	MC
United States Naval Academy	MD	0	MC
Univ of Alabama	AL	5,702	C
Univ of Arizona	AZ	5,808	C
Univ of Calif at Davis	CA	9,534	VC
Univ of Calif at Los Angeles	CA	8,959	HC
Univ of Calif, San Diego	CA	10,028	VC+
Univ of Central Florida	FL	6,061	C+
Univ of Cincinnati	OH	7,989	C
Univ of Colo at Boulder	CO	6,410	VC
Univ of Florida	FL	5,850	HC
Univ of Illinois at Urbana-Champaign	IL	7,764	HC
Univ of Kansas	KS	5,200	NC
Univ of Maryland/College Park	MD	8,182	VC
Univ of Miami	FL	22,107	VC
Univ of Mich/Ann Arbor	MI	9,428	HC+
Univ of Minn/Twin Cities	MN	6,682	VC
Univ of Missouri/Rolla	MO	6,729	VC+
Univ of Notre Dame	IN	20,150	MC
Univ of Okla	OK	5,427	VC
Univ of Southern Calif	CA	23,006	VC
Univ of Tenn/Knoxville	TN	5,668	C
Univ of Texas at Arlington	TX	5,549	LC
Univ of Texas at Austin	TX	5,160	VC
Univ of Washington	WA	6,618	VC
West Virginia Univ	WV	5,774	C
Western Mich Univ	MI	6,820	C
Wichita State Univ	KS	5,068	NC
Worcester Polytechnic Inst	MA	20,350	HC

AERONAUTICAL SCIENCE

School	ST	$IS	SR
College of the Ozarks	MO	2,000	VC+
Dowling College	NY	12,730	LC
Embry-Riddle Aeronautical Univ	AZ	9,896	C+
Embry-Riddle Aeronautical Univ	FL	10,600	C
Florida Inst of Tech	FL	16,935	VC
Hampton Univ	VA	10,706	C
Okla State Univ	OK	5,086	VC
Salem-Teikyo Univ	WV	14,527	C
Univ of Maryland/Eastern Shore	MD	6,254	LC
Univ of Nebr at Kearney	NE	4,308	LC
Univ of N Dak	ND	4,902	NC

AERONAUTICAL TECHNOLOGY

School	ST	$IS	SR
Arizona State Univ Main Campus	AZ	6,444	C
College of Aeronautics	NY	5,870	NC
Dowling College	NY	12,730	LC
Embry-Riddle Aeronautical Univ	FL	10,600	C
Indiana State Univ	IN	6,210	C
Kent State Univ	OH	6,740	LC
Tenn State Univ	TN	4,626	C+

AEROSPACE STUDIES

School	ST	$IS	SR
Case Western Reserve Univ	OH	19,910	HC
Embry-Riddle Aeronautical Univ	AZ	9,896	C+
Embry-Riddle Aeronautical Univ	FL	10,600	C
Florida Inst of Tech	FL	16,935	VC
Miss State Univ	MS	5,629	VC
Rochester Inst of Tech	NY	18,954	VC
Univ of Calif at Los Angeles	CA	8,959	HC
Univ of Virginia	VA	7,964	MC

AFRICAN LANGUAGES

School	ST	$IS	SR
Univ of Calif at Los Angeles	CA	8,959	HC
Univ of Texas at Austin	TX	5,160	VC
Univ of Wisc/Madison	WI	6,400	HC

AFRICAN STUDIES

School	ST	$IS	SR
Boston Univ	MA	24,130	HC
Brandeis Univ	MA	25,585	HC
Bryn Mawr College	PA	24,110	MC
Carleton College	MN	22,155	HC
CUNY/Brooklyn College	NY	2,450	VC
Cornell Univ	NY	13,445	MC
Dartmouth College	NH	24,354	MC
Emory Univ	GA	21,930	HC
Hampshire College	MA	25,320	C
Hofstra Univ	NY	16,580	VC
Kent State Univ	OH	6,740	LC
Rutgers Univ/Rutgers College	NJ	8,841	HC+
Scripps College	CA	23,600	HC
SUNY at Albany	NY	7,059	VC
SUNY at Stony Brook	NY	7,658	VC
SUNY/College at Brockport	NY	7,220	C+
Tenn State Univ	TN	4,626	C+
Univ of Calif at Davis	CA	9,534	VC
Univ of Kansas	KS	5,200	NC
Univ of Mich/Ann Arbor	MI	9,428	HC+
Univ of Minn/Twin Cities	MN	6,682	VC
Univ of N Car at Chapel Hill	NC	5,330	HC
Univ of Texas at Austin	TX	5,160	VC
Vassar College	NY	24,206	HC
Wesleyan Univ	CT	23,770	MC

AFRICAN AMERICAN STUDIES

School	ST	$IS	SR
Amherst College	MA	24,152	MC
Antioch College	OH	19,532	C
Bates College	ME	23,990	MC
Bowdoin College	ME	24,155	MC
Brandeis Univ	MA	25,585	HC
Brown Univ	RI	26,104	MC
Cal State/Fullerton	CA	4,850	LC
Cal State/Los Angeles	CA	4,940	VC
Cal State/Northridge	CA	7,122	LC
Carleton College	MN	22,155	HC
CUNY/City College	NY	2,543	VC
CUNY/College of Staten Island	NY	2,558	NC
CUNY/Herbert H. Lehman College	NY	2,542	C
Claremont McKenna College	CA	22,150	MC
Coe College	IA	17,085	VC
College of Wooster	OH	19,875	VC
Columbia Univ/Columbia College	NY	26,757	MC
Dartmouth College	NH	24,354	MC
Denison Univ	OH	21,150	VC+
Duke Univ	NC	21,271	MC
Earlham College	IN	19,383	VC
Edinboro Univ of Penn	PA	7,181	C
Fordham Univ/College at Lincoln Center	NY	18,150	VC
Fordham Univ/Fordham College	NY	19,875	VC
Harvard Univ/Harvard and Radcliffe Colleges	MA	24,880	MC
Indiana State Univ	IN	6,210	C
Indiana Univ Bloomington	IN	6,495	VC
Indiana Univ Northwest	IN	2,310	C
LeMoyne-Owen College	TN	4,500	LC
Loyola Marymount Univ	CA	18,560	C
Luther College	IA	15,900	VC
Martin Univ	IN	4,830	NC
Metropolitan State College of Denver	CO	1,751	NC
Miami Univ	OH	8,066	VC
Morgan State Univ	MD	7,366	C+
Mount Holyoke College	MA	23,630	VC
Northeastern Univ	MA	19,851	C
Northwestern Univ	IL	21,093	MC
Oakland Univ	MI	6,714	VC
Oberlin College	OH	24,570	HC+
Ohio Wesleyan Univ	OH	21,108	VC+
Purdue Univ/West Lafayette	IN	6,636	C
Roosevelt Univ	IL	12,368	C
Rutgers Univ/Camden College of A&S	NJ	8,652	VC
Rutgers Univ/Douglass College	NJ	8,795	VC
Rutgers Univ/Livingston College	NJ	8,877	VC
Rutgers Univ/Newark College of A&S	NJ	8,645	C
Rutgers Univ/Univ College—Camden	NJ	3,506	C
Rutgers Univ/Univ College—New Brunswick	NJ	0	LC
San Francisco State Univ	CA	7,292	LC
Seton Hall Univ	NJ	18,306	LC
Smith College	MA	24,236	HC
Southern Methodist Univ	TX	18,520	VC
Stanford Univ	CA	24,310	MC
SUNY at Albany	NY	7,059	VC
SUNY at Binghamton	NY	7,921	HC
SUNY at Buffalo	NY	7,896	VC
SUNY/College at Brockport	NY	7,220	C+
Syracuse Univ	NY	21,305	HC
Temple Univ	PA	10,281	C
Univ of Calif at Berkeley	CA	9,962	HC+
Univ of Calif at Los Angeles	CA	8,959	HC
Univ of Calif at Santa Barbara	CA	9,460	C
Univ of Cincinnati	OH	7,989	C
Univ of Colo at Boulder	CO	6,410	VC
Univ of Illinois at Chicago	IL	8,443	C
Univ of Iowa	IA	5,658	VC
Univ of Kansas	KS	5,200	NC
Univ of Maryland/Baltimore County	MD	7,746	VC
Univ of Maryland/College Park	MD	8,182	VC
Univ of Mass/Amherst	MA	9,364	LC
Univ of Mass/Boston	MA	4,253	C
Univ of Mich/Ann Arbor	MI	9,428	HC+
Univ of Minn/Twin Cities	MN	6,682	VC
Univ of Nebr at Omaha	NE	1,889	LC
Univ of N Car at Chapel Hill	NC	5,330	HC
Univ of N Car at Charlotte	NC	4,597	C
Univ of Northern Colo	CO	6,008	C
Univ of Notre Dame	IN	20,150	MC
Univ of Okla	OK	5,427	VC
Univ of Pittsburgh	PA	9,472	C
Univ of S Car	SC	6,158	C
Univ of Tenn/Knoxville	TN	5,668	C
Univ of the Pacific	CA	21,100	C
Univ of Virginia	VA	7,964	MC

School	ST	$IS	SR
Univ of Washington	WA	6,618	VC
Univ of Wisc/Milwaukee	WI	6,165	C
Washington Univ	MO	23,507	HC
Wayne State Univ	MI	2,680	C
Wellesley College	MA	23,815	MC
William Paterson College	NJ	7,438	C+
Yale Univ	CT	25,110	MC
Youngstown State Univ	OH	6,447	LC

AGRICULTURAL BUSINESS MANAGEMENT

School	ST	$IS	SR
Alabama A&M Univ	AL	4,200	C
Arizona State Univ Main Campus	AZ	6,444	C
Arkansas State Univ	AR	4,250	NC
Arkansas Tech Univ	AR	4,200	NC
Auburn Univ	AL	5,823	C+
Calif Polytechnic State Univ	CA	6,980	VC+
Calif State Polytechnic Univ/ Pomona	CA	6,438	LC
Cal State/Chico	CA	6,146	C
Cal State/Fresno	CA	5,747	C
Central Missouri State Univ	MO	5,138	LC
Colo State Univ	CO	6,566	VC
Concordia Univ Wisc	WI	12,140	C
Delaware State College	DE	5,656	C
Dickinson State Univ	ND	3,792	
Eastern New Mexico Univ	NM	3,950	C
Eastern Oregon State College	OR	6,090	C
Freed-Hardeman Univ	TN	8,585	VC
Iowa State Univ	IA	5,456	C
Kansas State Univ	KS	4,816	NC
Louisiana State Univ and A&M College	LA	5,605	C
Louisiana Tech Univ	LA	4,284	C
Lubbock Christian Univ	TX	9,840	NC
McNeese State Univ	LA	4,543	NC
Middle Tenn State Univ	TN	3,857	C
Missouri Valley College	MO	14,050	LC
Montana State Univ	MT	5,534	C
Morningside College	IA	13,896	C
New Mexico State Univ	NM	4,844	LC
Nicholls State Univ	LA	4,531	NC
N Car State Univ	NC	4,984	VC
Northeast Louisiana Univ	LA	3,906	NC
Northwest Missouri State Univ	MO	5,010	LC
Northwestern Okla State Univ	OK	3,424	C
Okla Panhandle State Univ	OK	3,155	NC
Okla State Univ	OK	5,086	VC
Oregon State Univ	OR	6,175	C
Penn State Univ/Univ Park Campus	PA	8,752	HC
S Car State Univ	SC	5,424	LC
S Dak State Univ	SD	4,562	C
Southern Illinois Univ at Carbondale	IL	6,234	C
Southern Univ and A&M College	LA	4,920	NC
Southwest State Univ	MN	5,400	NC
Southwest Texas State Univ	TX	5,124	C
Stephen F. Austin State Univ	TX	5,117	C
Tarleton State Univ	TX	4,082	LC
Texas A&M Univ	TX	5,382	VC
Texas A&M Univ at Kingsville	TX	3,808	LC
Texas Tech Univ	TX	6,008	C
Tuskegee Univ	AL	10,128	C
Univ of Arkansas at Fayetteville	AR	5,046	C
Univ of Calif at Davis	CA	9,534	VC
Univ of Delaware	DE	8,013	VC
Univ of Florida	FL	5,850	HC
Univ of Maine	ME	7,990	C
Univ of Minn/Crookston	MN	6,894	NC
Univ of Minn/Twin Cities	MN	6,682	VC
Univ of Nebr-Lincoln	NE	5,278	LC
Univ of Tenn at Martin	TN	4,550	C
Univ of Wisc/Madison	WI	6,400	HC
Univ of Wisc/Platteville	WI	4,830	C
Univ of Wisc/River Falls	WI	4,655	C
Univ of Wyoming	WY	4,991	NC
Utah State Univ	UT	4,683	C
Virginia State Univ	VA	7,040	
West Virginia Univ	WV	5,774	C
Wilmington College	OH	13,700	LC

AGRICULTURAL ECONOMICS

School	ST	$IS	SR
Alcorn State Univ	MS	4,474	C+
Brigham Young Univ	UT	5,625	HC
Central Missouri State Univ	MO	5,138	LC
Colo State Univ	CO	6,566	VC
Cornell Univ	NY	13,445	MC
East Texas State Univ	TX	4,572	LC
Fort Valley State College	GA	3,974	LC
Langston Univ	OK	2,907	LC
Louisiana State Univ and A&M College	LA	5,605	C
Montana State Univ	MT	5,534	C
N Car Agricultural and Technical State Univ	NC	4,477	LC
N Car State Univ	NC	4,984	VC
N Dak State Univ of Agriculture and Applied Science	ND	4,774	VC
Northeast Missouri State Univ	MO	5,654	VC+
Ohio State Univ	OH	7,218	LC
Okla State Univ	OK	5,086	VC
Oregon State Univ	OR	6,175	C
Penn State Univ/Univ Park Campus	PA	8,752	HC
Southern Univ and A&M College	LA	4,920	NC
Tarleton State Univ	TX	4,082	LC
Tenn Tech Univ	TN	5,190	C
Texas A&M Univ	TX	5,382	VC
Texas Tech Univ	TX	6,008	C
Univ of Arizona	AZ	5,808	C
Univ of Arkansas at Fayetteville	AR	5,046	C
Univ of Arkansas at Pine Bluff	AR	3,978	LC
Univ of Calif at Davis	CA	9,534	VC
Univ of Conn	CT	9,168	C
Univ of Delaware	DE	8,013	VC
Univ of Hawaii at Manoa	HI	5,626	C
Univ of Kentucky	KY	5,152	VC
Univ of Maryland/College Park	MD	8,182	VC
Univ of Minn/Twin Cities	MN	6,682	VC
Univ of Missouri/Columbia	MO	6,254	HC
Univ of Nebr-Lincoln	NE	5,278	LC
Univ of Nevada/Reno	NV	5,735	C
Univ of Tenn/Knoxville	TN	5,668	C
Univ of Wisc/Madison	WI	6,400	HC
Univ of Wisc/Platteville	WI	4,830	C
Univ of Wisc/River Falls	WI	4,655	C
Utah State Univ	UT	4,683	C
Virginia Polytechnic Inst and State Univ	VA	6,828	C

AGRICULTURAL EDUCATION

School	ST	$IS	SR
Alabama A&M Univ	AL	4,200	C
Alcorn State Univ	MS	4,474	C+
Arkansas State Univ	AR	4,250	NC
Cal State/Fresno	CA	5,747	C
Cameron Univ	OK	3,686	LC
Clemson Univ	SC	6,564	VC
Colo State Univ	CO	6,566	VC
Cornell Univ	NY	13,445	MC
Delaware State College	DE	5,656	C
East Texas State Univ	TX	4,572	LC
Fort Valley State College	GA	3,974	LC
Iowa State Univ	IA	5,456	C
Kansas State Univ	KS	4,816	NC
Louisiana State Univ and A&M College	LA	5,605	C
Mich State Univ	MI	7,842	C
Montana State Univ	MT	5,534	C
Morehead State Univ	KY	4,600	LC
Murray State Univ	KY	4,702	C
N Car Agricultural and Technical State Univ	NC	4,477	LC
N Car State Univ	NC	4,984	VC
N Dak State Univ of Agriculture and Applied Science	ND	4,774	VC
Northwest Missouri State Univ	MO	5,010	LC
Ohio State Univ	OH	7,218	LC
Okla State Univ	OK	5,086	VC
Penn State Univ/Univ Park Campus	PA	8,752	HC
S Dak State Univ	SD	4,562	C
Southern Univ and A&M College	LA	4,920	NC
Southwest Missouri State Univ	MO	4,956	C
Southwest Texas State Univ	TX	5,124	C
Stephen F. Austin State Univ	TX	5,117	C
Tarleton State Univ	TX	4,082	LC
Tenn Tech Univ	TN	5,190	C
Texas A&M Univ at Kingsville	TX	3,808	LC
Texas Tech Univ	TX	6,008	C
Univ of Arizona	AZ	5,808	C
Univ of Arkansas at Fayetteville	AR	5,046	C
Univ of Arkansas at Pine Bluff	AR	3,978	LC
Univ of Conn	CT	9,168	C
Univ of Delaware	DE	8,013	VC
Univ of Florida	FL	5,850	HC
Univ of Georgia	GA	5,655	VC
Univ of Idaho	ID	4,830	C
Univ of Illinois at Urbana-Champaign	IL	7,764	HC
Univ of Kentucky	KY	5,152	VC
Univ of Maryland/Eastern Shore	MD	6,254	LC
Univ of Minn/Twin Cities	MN	6,682	VC
Univ of Nebr-Lincoln	NE	5,278	LC
Univ of Nevada/Reno	NV	5,735	C
Univ of Southwestern Louisiana	LA	3,968	NC
Univ of Tenn at Martin	TN	4,550	C
Univ of Tenn/Knoxville	TN	5,668	C
Univ of Wisc/Madison	WI	6,400	HC
Univ of Wisc/Platteville	WI	4,830	C
Univ of Wisc/River Falls	WI	4,655	C
Univ of Wyoming	WY	4,991	NC
Utah State Univ	UT	4,683	C
Virginia Polytechnic Inst and State Univ	VA	6,828	C
West Virginia Univ	WV	5,774	C
Wilmington College	OH	13,700	LC

AGRICULTURAL ENGINEERING

School	ST	$IS	SR
Arkansas State Univ	AR	4,250	NC
Auburn Univ	AL	5,823	C+
Calif Polytechnic State Univ	CA	6,980	VC+
Calif State Polytechnic Univ/ Pomona	CA	6,438	LC
Clemson Univ	SC	6,564	VC
Colo State Univ	CO	6,566	VC
Iowa State Univ	IA	5,456	C
Lakeland College	WI	12,845	LC
Louisiana State Univ and A&M College	LA	5,605	C
Mich State Univ	MI	7,842	C
New Mexico State Univ	NM	4,844	LC
N Car State Univ	NC	4,984	VC
N Dak State Univ of Agriculture and Applied Science	ND	4,774	VC
Ohio State Univ	OH	7,218	LC
Okla State Univ	OK	5,086	VC
Penn State Univ/Univ Park Campus	PA	8,752	HC
Purdue Univ/West Lafayette	IN	6,636	C
St Augustine's College	NC	9,300	C+
S Dak State Univ	SD	4,562	C
Texas A&M Univ	TX	5,382	VC
Texas Tech Univ	TX	6,008	C
Univ of Arkansas at Fayetteville	AR	5,046	C
Univ of Calif at Davis	CA	9,534	VC
Univ of Florida	FL	5,850	HC
Univ of Georgia	GA	5,655	VC
Univ of Idaho	ID	4,830	C
Univ of Illinois at Urbana-Champaign	IL	7,764	HC
Univ of Maryland/College Park	MD	8,182	VC
Univ of Minn/Twin Cities	MN	6,682	VC
Univ of Southwestern Louisiana	LA	3,968	NC
Univ of Tenn/Knoxville	TN	5,668	C
Univ of Wisc/Madison	WI	6,400	HC
Univ of Wisc/River Falls	WI	4,655	C
Utah State Univ	UT	4,683	C
Virginia Polytechnic Inst and State Univ	VA	6,828	C
Washington State Univ	WA	6,364	C

AGRICULTURAL ENGINEERING TECHNOLOGY

School	ST	$IS	SR
Fort Valley State College	GA	3,974	LC
Louisiana State Univ and A&M College	LA	5,605	C
Montana State Univ	MT	5,534	C
S Dak State Univ	SD	4,562	C
Univ of Delaware	DE	8,013	VC
Univ of Wisc/Platteville	WI	4,830	C

AGRICULTURAL MECHANICS

School	ST	$IS	SR
Iowa State Univ	IA	5,456	C
Murray State Univ	KY	4,702	C
N Dak State Univ of Agriculture and Applied Science	ND	4,774	VC
Northern Montana College	MT	4,976	C
Northwest Missouri State Univ	MO	5,010	LC
Penn State Univ/Univ Park Campus	PA	8,752	HC
Southwest Texas State Univ	TX	5,124	C
Tarleton State Univ	TX	4,082	LC
Texas Tech Univ	TX	6,008	C
Univ of Arkansas at Fayetteville	AR	5,046	C
Univ of Idaho	ID	4,830	C
Univ of Nebr-Lincoln	NE	5,278	LC
Univ of Wisc/Madison	WI	6,400	HC

AGRICULTURE

School	ST	$IS	SR
Andrews Univ	MI	14,952	NC
Arkansas State Univ	AR	4,250	NC
Auburn Univ	AL	5,823	C+
Austin Peay State Univ	TN	4,350	C
Berea College	KY	2,883	VC+
Brigham Young Univ	UT	5,625	HC
Calif Polytechnic State Univ	CA	6,980	VC+
Calif State Polytechnic Univ/ Pomona	CA	6,438	LC
Cal State/Chico	CA	6,146	C
Cal State/Fresno	CA	5,747	C
Clemson Univ	SC	6,564	VC
College of the Ozarks	MO	2,000	VC+
Cornell Univ	NY	13,445	MC
Delaware Valley College	PA	16,065	LC
East Texas State Univ	TX	4,572	LC
Eastern Kentucky Univ	KY	4,840	NC
Eastern Oregon State College	OR	6,090	C
Ferrum College	VA	12,800	LC
Hampshire College	MA	25,320	C
Illinois State Univ	IL	6,413	C
Iowa State Univ	IA	5,456	C
Kansas State Univ	KS	4,816	NC
Lincoln Univ	MO	4,638	NC
Louisiana Tech Univ	LA	4,284	C
McNeese State Univ	LA	4,543	NC
Mich State Univ	MI	7,842	C
Miss State Univ	MS	5,629	VC
Morehead State Univ	KY	4,600	LC
Murray State Univ	KY	4,702	C
New Mexico State Univ	NM	4,844	LC
N Car Agricultural and Technical State Univ	NC	4,477	LC
N Car State Univ	NC	4,984	VC
N Dak State Univ of Agriculture and Applied Science	ND	4,774	VC
Northeast Missouri State Univ	MO	5,654	VC+
Northwest Missouri State Univ	MO	5,010	LC
Northwestern Okla State Univ	OK	3,424	C
Okla State Univ	OK	5,086	VC
Oregon State Univ	OR	6,175	C
Penn State Univ/Univ Park Campus	PA	8,752	HC
Rutgers Univ/Cook College	NJ	9,197	HC
Sam Houston State Univ	TX	4,506	C
Southern Illinois Univ at Carbondale	IL	6,234	C
Southern Nazarene Univ	OK	9,206	NC
Southern Univ and A&M College	LA	4,920	NC
Southern Utah Univ	UT	4,104	LC
Southwest Missouri State Univ	MO	4,956	C
Southwest Texas State Univ	TX	5,124	C
Stephen F. Austin State Univ	TX	5,117	C
Tarleton State Univ	TX	4,082	LC
Tenn State Univ	TN	4,626	C+
Tuskegee Univ	AL	10,128	C
Univ of Arkansas at Fayetteville	AR	5,046	C
Univ of Arkansas at Monticello	AR	3,832	NC
Univ of Arkansas at Pine Bluff	AR	3,978	LC
Univ of Conn	CT	9,168	C
Univ of Delaware	DE	8,013	VC
Univ of Georgia	GA	5,655	VC
Univ of Hawaii at Manoa	HI	5,626	C
Univ of Illinois at Urbana-Champaign	IL	7,764	HC
Univ of Kentucky	KY	5,152	VC
Univ of Maine	ME	7,990	C
Univ of Maryland/College Park	MD	8,182	VC
Univ of Maryland/Eastern Shore	MD	6,254	LC
Univ of Missouri/Columbia	MO	6,254	HC
Univ of Nebr-Lincoln	NE	5,278	LC
Univ of Tenn at Martin	TN	4,550	C
Univ of Tenn/Knoxville	TN	5,668	C
Univ of Wisc/River Falls	WI	4,655	C
Univ of Wyoming	WY	4,991	NC
Virginia Polytechnic Inst and State Univ	VA	6,828	C
Virginia State Univ	VA	7,040	
West Texas A&M Univ	TX	4,224	C
Western Illinois Univ	IL	5,241	LC

School	ST	$IS	SR
Western Kentucky Univ	KY	4,808	C
Wilmington College	OH	13,700	LC

AGRONOMY

School	ST	$IS	SR
Iowa State Univ	IA	5,456	C
Miss State Univ	MS	5,629	VC
Montana State Univ	MT	5,534	C
Northeast Missouri State Univ	MO	5,654	VC+
S Dak State Univ	SD	4,562	C
Southwest Missouri State Univ	MO	4,956	C
Univ of Florida	FL	5,850	HC
West Virginia Univ	WV	5,774	C

AIR TRAFFIC CONTROL

School	ST	$IS	SR
Florida Memorial College	FL	7,600	C+

AIRCRAFT MECHANICS

School	ST	$IS	SR
Kent State Univ	OH	6,740	LC

AIRLINE PILOTING AND NAVIGATION

School	ST	$IS	SR
Eastern Kentucky Univ	KY	4,840	NC
Indiana State Univ	IN	6,210	C
Metropolitan State College of Denver	CO	1,751	NC

ALLIED HEALTH

School	ST	$IS	SR
Albany State College	GA	4,481	LC
Clark Atlanta Univ	GA	11,846	C
Dallas Baptist Univ	TX	9,620	LC
East Stroudsburg Univ	PA	6,886	C
Madonna Univ	MI	8,546	C
Malone College	OH	12,572	C
Marian College	IN	12,936	C
Mars Hill College	NC	11,050	C
Marygrove College	MI	5,877	VC
Mass College of Pharmacy and Allied Health Sciences	MA	18,352	C
Merrimack College	MA	18,025	C
Montclair State College	NJ	7,539	C+
Norfolk State Univ	VA	6,345	LC
Roosevelt Univ	IL	12,368	C
St Andrews Presbyterian College	NC	14,240	LC
San Francisco State Univ	CA	7,292	LC
Southwestern Okla State Univ	OK	3,312	C
Trevecca Nazarene College	TN	9,826	NC
Univ of Alabama at Birmingham	AL	7,533	C
Univ of Florida	FL	5,850	HC
Univ of Portland	OR	15,564	C
Univ of Texas at El Paso	TX	3,160	LC
Wingate College	NC	10,610	C
Youngstown State Univ	OH	6,447	LC

AMERICAN INDIAN STUDIES

School	ST	$IS	SR
Pembroke State Univ	NC	3,538	LC
Univ of Minn/Twin Cities	MN	6,682	VC

AMERICAN LITERATURE

School	ST	$IS	SR
Brandeis Univ	MA	25,585	HC
Brown Univ	RI	26,104	MC
Middlebury College	VT	24,400	MC

AMERICAN STUDIES

School	ST	$IS	SR
Albion College	MI	18,264	VC
Albright College	PA	19,260	C
American Univ	DC	21,230	VC+
Amherst College	MA	24,152	MC
Austin College	TX	14,999	VC
Babson College	MA	23,160	VC
Bard College	NY	25,269	HC
Barton College	NC	10,689	LC
Bates College	ME	23,990	MC
Boston Univ	MA	24,130	HC
Brandeis Univ	MA	25,585	HC
Brigham Young Univ	UT	5,625	HC
Cabrini College	PA	16,012	C
Calif State Polytechnic Univ/Pomona	CA	6,438	LC
Cal State/Chico	CA	6,146	C
Carleton College	MN	22,155	HC
Cascade College	OR	9,800	NC
Case Western Reserve Univ	OH	19,910	HC
Cedarville College	OH	10,715	C
Chaminade Univ of Honolulu	HI	14,290	C
CUNY/College of Staten Island	NY	2,558	NC
CUNY/Herbert H. Lehman College	NY	2,542	C
Claremont McKenna College	CA	22,150	MC
Coe College	IA	17,085	VC
Colby College	ME	24,230	HC
College of Our Lady of The Elms	MA	15,639	C
College of St Joseph	VT	12,650	LC
College of St Rose	NY	14,452	C
College of William and Mary	VA	8,602	MC
Columbia Univ/Barnard College	NY	25,492	HC
Cornell Univ	NY	13,445	MC
Creighton Univ	NE	14,432	VC
David Lipscomb Univ	TN	7,865	VC
DePaul Univ	IL	15,535	VC
Dickinson College	PA	22,705	HC
Dominican College	NY	13,600	LC
Drew Univ/College of Liberal Arts	NJ	23,406	HC
Eckerd College	FL	18,855	VC
Elmhurst College	IL	12,536	C
Elmira College	NY	18,450	VC
Florida State Univ	FL	5,814	VC
Fordham Univ/Fordham College	NY	19,875	VC
Franklin and Marshall College	PA	23,655	HC
Georgetown College	KY	10,990	C
Goucher College	MD	20,295	VC
Grinnell College	IA	20,680	HC+
Hamilton College	NY	23,500	HC
Hampshire College	MA	25,320	C
Harvard Univ/Harvard and Radcliffe Colleges	MA	24,880	MC
Hawaii Pacific Univ	HI	12,300	C
Hillsdale College	MI	15,110	VC
Hobart and William Smith Colleges	NY	23,925	VC
Hofstra Univ	NY	16,580	VC
Hollins College	VA	18,484	C
Idaho State Univ	ID	4,442	C
Keene State College	NH	7,081	C
Kendall College	IL	12,651	LC
Kent State Univ	OH	6,740	LC
Knox College	IL	18,990	VC
Kutztown Univ	PA	6,528	C
Lafayette College	PA	23,450	HC
Lebanon Valley College of Penn	PA	18,300	C
Lehigh Univ	PA	23,250	HC
Lynchburg College	VA	17,000	C
Manhattanville College	NY	20,450	LC
Marist College	NY	16,406	C
Marymount College/Tarrytown	NY	17,350	C
Meredith College	NC	9,440	C
Miami Univ	OH	8,066	VC
Mich State Univ	MI	7,842	C
Middlebury College	VT	24,400	MC
Mills College	CA	20,848	VC
Moorhead State Univ	MN	5,076	C
Mount Holyoke College	MA	23,630	VC
Mount St Mary's College	CA	16,390	VC
Mount St Mary's College	MD	17,825	LC
Mount Union College	OH	15,850	C
Muskingum College	OH	16,650	C
Northwestern Univ	IL	21,093	MC
Occidental College	CA	21,792	HC
Oglethorpe Univ	GA	16,360	VC
Olivet College	MI	14,000	C
Oregon State Univ	OR	6,175	C
Our Lady of the Lake Univ of San Antonio	TX	11,080	C
Penn State Univ/Univ Park Campus	PA	8,752	HC
Phillips Univ	OK	12,744	C
Pine Manor College	MA	21,700	LC
Pomona College	CA	23,820	MC
Providence College	RI	19,750	VC
Purdue Univ/West Lafayette	IN	6,636	C
Ramapo College of New Jersey	NJ	8,027	C+
Reed College	OR	24,480	HC+
Rider College	NJ	18,160	C
Roosevelt Univ	IL	12,368	C
Rosary College	IL	15,040	C
Rosemont College	PA	16,775	C
Rutgers Univ/Douglass College	NJ	8,795	VC
Rutgers Univ/Livingston College	NJ	8,877	VC
Rutgers Univ/Newark College of A&S	NJ	8,645	C
Rutgers Univ/Rutgers College	NJ	8,841	HC+
Rutgers Univ/Univ College—Camden	NJ	3,506	C
Rutgers Univ/Univ College—New Brunswick	NJ	0	LC
St Francis College	IN	11,662	C
St Francis College	PA	15,744	LC
St John's Univ	NY	8,980	C+
St Joseph College	CT	16,225	C
St Olaf College	MN	17,200	HC
St Peter's College	NJ	14,775	LC
St Thomas Univ	FL	14,280	LC
Salem College	NC	16,025	C
Salve Regina Univ	RI	29,100	LC
San Francisco State Univ	CA	7,292	LC
Scripps College	CA	23,600	HC
Siena College	NY	15,410	VC
Siena Heights College	MI	12,520	C
Simmons College	MA	22,534	C
Skidmore College	NY	23,230	HC
Smith College	MA	24,236	HC
Southwestern Univ	TX	15,484	HC
Stanford Univ	CA	24,310	MC
SUNY/College at Brockport	NY	7,220	C+
SUNY/College at Old Westbury	NY	7,128	LC
SUNY/College at Oswego	NY	7,330	VC
Sterling College	KS	10,990	VC
Stetson Univ	FL	16,435	VC
Stonehill College	MA	17,481	VC
Syracuse Univ	NY	21,305	HC
Teikyo Marycrest Univ	IA	13,755	VC
Temple Univ	PA	10,281	C
Trinity College	DC	17,660	C
Tufts Univ	MA	24,962	MC
Tulane Univ	LA	24,540	HC
Union College	NY	23,817	HC
United States Military Academy	NY	0	MC
Univ of Alabama	AL	5,702	C
Univ of Alaska Fairbanks	AK	4,718	C
Univ of Calif at Berkeley	CA	9,962	HC+
Univ of Calif at Davis	CA	9,534	VC
Univ of Calif at Santa Cruz	CA	9,060	VC
Univ of Colo at Boulder	CO	6,410	VC
Univ of Dayton	OH	15,120	C+
Univ of Florida	FL	5,850	HC
Univ of Hawaii at Manoa	HI	5,626	C
Univ of Idaho	ID	4,830	C
Univ of Iowa	IA	5,658	VC
Univ of Kansas	KS	5,200	NC
Univ of Louisville	KY	5,948	C
Univ of Lowell	MA	8,831	VC
Univ of Maryland/Baltimore County	MD	7,746	VC
Univ of Maryland/College Park	MD	8,182	VC
Univ of Miami	FL	22,107	VC
Univ of Mich/Ann Arbor	MI	9,428	HC+
Univ of Mich/Dearborn	MI	3,399	HC
Univ of Minn/Duluth	MN	6,512	C
Univ of Minn/Twin Cities	MN	6,682	VC
Univ of N Car at Chapel Hill	NC	5,330	HC
Univ of N Dak	ND	4,902	NC
Univ of Northern Iowa	IA	5,137	C
Univ of Notre Dame	IN	20,150	MC
Univ of Oregon	OR	6,466	VC
Univ of Penn	PA	24,238	MC
Univ of Rio Grande	OH	6,300	NC
Univ of Tenn at Chattanooga	TN	5,375	C
Univ of Tenn/Knoxville	TN	5,668	C
Univ of Texas at Austin	TX	5,160	VC
Univ of Texas at Dallas	TX	1,222	VC+
Univ of Texas at San Antonio	TX	6,420	C
Univ of the South	TN	18,830	HC
Univ of Wisc/River Falls	WI	4,655	C
Univ of Wyoming	WY	4,991	NC
Ursuline College	OH	13,180	LC
Utah State Univ	UT	4,683	C
Valparaiso Univ	IN	14,810	VC
Vassar College	NY	24,206	HC
Warner Pacific College	OR	12,112	C
Washington College	MD	19,270	C+
Wayne State Univ	MI	2,680	C
Wellesley College	MA	23,815	MC
Wells College	NY	19,460	C+
Wesleyan Univ	CT	23,770	MC
Western Conn State Univ	CT	6,622	C
Western Maryland College	MD	18,990	C
Wheaton College	MA	23,840	C+
Williams College	MA	24,390	MC
Wingate College	NC	10,610	C
Wittenberg Univ	OH	19,998	VC
Yale Univ	CT	25,110	MC
Youngstown State Univ	OH	6,447	LC

ANATOMY

School	ST	$IS	SR
Duke Univ	NC	21,271	MC

ANESTHESIOLOGY

School	ST	$IS	SR
Univ of S Dak	SD	4,722	C

ANIMAL SCIENCE

School	ST	$IS	SR
Abilene Christian Univ	TX	10,460	NC
Alabama A&M Univ	AL	4,200	C
Alcorn State Univ	MS	4,474	C+
Angelo State Univ	TX	5,176	C
Arkansas State Univ	AR	4,250	NC
Auburn Univ	AL	5,823	C+
Berry College	GA	11,990	VC
Brigham Young Univ	UT	5,625	HC
Bucknell Univ	PA	22,320	HC
Calif State Polytechnic Univ/Pomona	CA	6,438	LC
Cal State/Fresno	CA	5,747	C
Colo State Univ	CO	6,566	VC
Cornell Univ	NY	13,445	MC
Delaware Valley College	PA	16,065	LC
East Texas State Univ	TX	4,572	LC
Florida A&M Univ	FL	4,651	C
Fort Valley State College	GA	3,974	LC
Hampshire College	MA	25,320	C
Iowa State Univ	IA	5,456	C
Kansas State Univ	KS	4,816	NC
Langston Univ	OK	2,907	LC
Louisiana State Univ and A&M College	LA	5,605	C
Louisiana Tech Univ	LA	4,284	C
Lubbock Christian Univ	TX	9,840	NC
McNeese State Univ	LA	4,543	NC
McPherson College	KS	11,360	VC
Mercy College	NY	11,180	NC
Mich State Univ	MI	7,842	C
Middle Tenn State Univ	TN	3,857	C
Miss State Univ	MS	5,629	VC
Montana State Univ	MT	5,534	C
Murray State Univ	KY	4,702	C
New Mexico State Univ	NM	4,844	LC
N Car Agricultural and Technical State Univ	NC	4,477	LC
N Car State Univ	NC	4,984	VC
N Dak State Univ of Agriculture and Applied Science	ND	4,774	VC
Northeast Missouri State Univ	MO	5,654	VC+
Northwest Missouri State Univ	MO	5,010	LC
Ohio State Univ	OH	7,218	LC
Okla Panhandle State Univ	OK	3,155	NC
Okla State Univ	OK	5,086	VC
Oregon State Univ	OR	6,175	C
Penn State Univ/Univ Park Campus	PA	8,752	HC
Purdue Univ/West Lafayette	IN	6,636	C
Rutgers Univ/Cook College	NJ	9,197	HC
Sam Houston State Univ	TX	4,506	C
S Dak State Univ	SD	4,562	C
Southeast Missouri State Univ	MO	5,854	C
Southern Illinois Univ at Carbondale	IL	6,234	C
Southern Univ and A&M College	LA	4,920	NC
Southwest Missouri State Univ	MO	4,956	C
Southwest Texas State Univ	TX	5,124	C
Southwestern Univ	TX	15,484	HC
SUNY College of Environmental Science and Forestry	NY	9,257	HC+
Stephen F. Austin State Univ	TX	5,117	C
Sul Ross State Univ	TX	4,144	NC
Tabor College	KS	11,460	VC
Tarleton State Univ	TX	4,082	LC
Tenn State Univ	TN	4,626	C+
Tenn Tech Univ	TN	5,190	C
Texas A&M Univ	TX	5,382	VC
Texas A&M Univ at Kingsville	TX	3,808	LC

School	ST	$IS	SR
Texas Tech Univ	TX	6,008	C
Tuskegee Univ	AL	10,128	C
Univ of Arizona	AZ	5,808	C
Univ of Arkansas at Fayetteville	AR	5,046	C
Univ of Arkansas at Pine Bluff	AR	3,978	LC
Univ of Calif at Davis	CA	9,534	VC
Univ of Conn	CT	9,168	C
Univ of Delaware	DE	8,013	VC
Univ of Denver	CO	19,290	C+
Univ of Florida	FL	5,850	HC
Univ of Georgia	GA	5,655	VC
Univ of Hawaii at Hilo	HI	4,141	C
Univ of Hawaii at Manoa	HI	5,626	C
Univ of Idaho	ID	4,830	C
Univ of Illinois at Urbana-Champaign	IL	7,764	HC
Univ of Kentucky	KY	5,152	VC
Univ of Maine	ME	7,990	C
Univ of Maryland/College Park	MD	8,182	VC
Univ of Mass/Amherst	MA	9,364	LC
Univ of Missouri/Columbia	MO	6,254	HC
Univ of Nebr-Lincoln	NE	5,278	LC
Univ of Nevada/Reno	NV	5,735	C
Univ of New Hampshire	NH	8,242	C
Univ of PR/Mayaguez	PR	0	
Univ of Rhode Island	RI	9,205	C
Univ of Southwestern Louisiana	LA	3,968	NC
Univ of Tenn at Martin	TN	4,550	C
Univ of Tenn/Knoxville	TN	5,668	C
Univ of Vermont	VT	10,776	C+
Univ of Wisc/Madison	WI	6,400	HC
Univ of Wisc/Platteville	WI	4,830	C
Univ of Wisc/River Falls	WI	4,655	C
Univ of Wyoming	WY	4,991	NC
Utah State Univ	UT	4,683	C
Virginia Polytechnic Inst and State Univ	VA	6,828	C
Washington State Univ	WA	6,364	C
West Texas A&M Univ	TX	4,224	C
West Virginia Univ	WV	5,774	C

ANTHROPOLOGY

School	ST	$IS	SR
Adelphi Univ	NY	18,250	LC
Agnes Scott College	GA	17,135	VC
Albertson College	ID	15,942	C+
Albion College	MI	18,264	VC
American Univ	DC	21,230	VC+
Amherst College	MA	24,152	MC
Antioch College	OH	19,532	C
Appalachian State Univ	NC	4,095	C
Arizona State Univ Main Campus	AZ	6,444	C
Auburn Univ	AL	5,823	C+
Ball State Univ	IN	6,032	LC
Bard College	NY	25,269	HC
Bates College	ME	23,990	MC
Baylor Univ	TX	10,990	C+
Beloit College	WI	18,950	VC+
Bennington College	VT	24,850	VC+
Bethel College	MN	15,050	C
Bloomsburg Univ of Penn	PA	6,312	C+
Boise State Univ	ID	4,909	LC
Boston Univ	MA	24,130	HC
Bowdoin College	ME	24,155	MC
Brandeis Univ	MA	25,585	HC
Bridgewater State College	MA	7,518	C
Brigham Young Univ	UT	5,625	HC
Brooklyn Campus of LIU	NY	15,000	LC
Brown Univ	RI	26,104	MC
Bryn Mawr College	PA	24,110	MC
Bucknell Univ	PA	22,320	HC
Calif State Polytechnic Univ/Pomona	CA	6,438	LC
Cal State/Bakersfield	CA	5,402	C
Cal State/Chico	CA	6,146	C
Cal State/Dominguez Hills	CA	2,857	LC
Cal State/Fresno	CA	5,747	C
Cal State/Fullerton	CA	4,850	LC
Cal State/Hayward	CA	5,495	C
Cal State/Long Beach	CA	6,057	LC
Cal State/Los Angeles	CA	4,940	LC
Cal State/Northridge	CA	7,122	LC
Cal State/Sacramento	CA	6,387	C
Cal State/San Bernardino	CA	6,055	LC
Cal State/Stanislaus	CA	6,799	C
Calif Univ of Penn	PA	7,370	C
Canisius College	NY	15,510	C
Carleton College	MN	22,155	HC
Case Western Reserve Univ	OH	19,910	HC
Catholic Univ of America	DC	18,856	C
Central College	IA	14,025	VC
Central Conn State Univ	CT	7,108	C
Central Mich Univ	MI	6,737	LC
Central State Univ	OH	7,320	NC
Central Washington Univ	WA	5,644	C
Centre College	KY	15,850	VC+
CUNY/Brooklyn College	NY	2,450	VC
CUNY/City College	NY	2,543	VC
CUNY/Herbert H. Lehman College	NY	2,542	C
CUNY/Hunter College	NY	4,101	VC
CUNY/Queens College	NY	2,631	C
CUNY/York College	NY	2,534	NC
Clarion Univ of Penn	PA	6,518	C
Cleveland State Univ	OH	7,287	NC
Colby College	ME	24,230	HC
Colgate Univ	NY	24,020	HC
College of Charleston	SC	6,250	C
College of William and Mary	VA	8,602	MC
Colo College	CO	20,038	HC
Colo State Univ	CO	6,566	VC
Columbia Univ/Barnard College	NY	25,492	HC
Columbia Univ/Columbia College	NY	26,757	MC
Conn College	CT	24,160	HC
Cornell College	IA	18,425	VC
Cornell Univ	NY	13,445	MC
Dartmouth College	NH	24,354	MC
Davidson College	NC	21,037	MC
Denison Univ	OH	21,150	VC+
DePauw Univ	IN	18,530	VC
Dickinson College	PA	22,705	HC
Dowling College	NY	12,730	LC
Drew Univ/College of Liberal Arts	NJ	23,406	HC
Duke Univ	NC	21,271	MC
Earlham College	IN	19,383	VC
East Carolina Univ	NC	4,498	C
East Stroudsburg Univ	PA	6,886	C
East Texas State Univ	TX	4,572	LC
Eastern Kentucky Univ	KY	4,840	NC
Eastern Mich Univ	MI	6,749	C
Eastern New Mexico Univ	NM	3,950	C
Eastern Oregon State College	OR	6,090	C
Eastern Washington Univ	WA	5,439	LC
Eckerd College	FL	18,855	VC
Edinboro Univ of Penn	PA	7,181	C
Elmira College	NY	18,450	C
Emory Univ	GA	21,930	HC
Evergreen State College	WA	6,306	C
Florida Atlantic Univ	FL	5,525	C
Florida State Univ	FL	5,814	VC
Fordham Univ/College at Lincoln Center	NY	18,150	VC
Fordham Univ/Fordham College	NY	19,875	VC
Fort Lewis College	CO	5,097	C
Franklin and Marshall College	PA	23,655	HC
Franklin Pierce College	NH	17,270	LC
Gannon Univ	PA	14,872	C
George Mason Univ	VA	8,728	C
George Washington Univ	DC	22,470	HC
Georgia Southern Univ	GA	4,988	LC
Grand Valley State Univ	MI	6,822	VC
Grinnell College	IA	20,680	HC+
Gustavus Adolphus College	MN	15,935	VC
Hamilton College	NY	23,500	HC
Hamline Univ	MN	17,122	VC
Hampshire College	MA	25,320	C
Hanover College	IN	10,950	VC
Hartwick College	NY	20,950	C
Harvard Univ/Harvard and Radcliffe Colleges	MA	24,880	MC
Haverford College	PA	23,950	MC
Heidelberg College	OH	17,160	C
Hobart and William Smith Colleges	NY	23,925	VC
Hofstra Univ	NY	16,580	VC
Howard Univ	DC	11,680	C
Humboldt State Univ	CA	5,676	C
Idaho State Univ	ID	4,442	C
Illinois State Univ	IL	6,413	C
Indiana State Univ	IN	6,210	C
Indiana Univ Bloomington	IN	6,495	VC
Indiana Univ of Penn	PA	6,373	C
Indiana Univ-Purdue Univ at Fort Wayne	IN	2,500	LC
Indiana Univ-Purdue Univ at Indianapolis	IN	5,862	LC
Iowa State Univ	IA	5,456	C
Ithaca College	NY	19,679	C
James Madison Univ	VA	8,198	HC
Johns Hopkins Univ	MD	24,360	MC
Johnson State College	VT	8,393	LC
Judson College	IL	13,625	C
Juniata College	PA	18,390	C+
Kalamazoo College	MI	19,974	HC
Kansas State Univ	KS	4,816	NC
Kent State Univ	OH	6,740	LC
Kenyon College	OH	22,430	HC+
Knox College	IL	18,990	VC
Kutztown Univ	PA	6,528	C
La Sierra Univ	CA	15,472	C
Lafayette College	PA	23,450	HC
Lake Forest College	IL	19,960	VC
Lawrence Univ	WI	19,986	HC+
Lehigh Univ	PA	23,250	HC
Lewis and Clark College	OR	19,980	VC
Linfield College	OR	16,670	VC
Longwood College	VA	7,800	C
Louisiana State Univ and A&M College	LA	5,605	C
Loyola Univ of Chicago	IL	15,880	C+
Luther College	IA	15,900	VC
Lycoming College	PA	17,200	LC
Macalester College	MN	19,710	HC
Manchester College	IN	13,240	LC
Mankato State Univ	MN	5,097	LC
Mansfield Univ	PA	6,348	C
Marlboro College	VT	23,305	C+
Marquette Univ	WI	16,114	VC
Mass Inst of Tech	MA	24,800	MC
Mercyhurst College	PA	13,488	C
Mesa State College	CO	5,127	NC
Metropolitan State College of Denver	CO	1,751	NC
Miami Univ	OH	8,066	VC
Mich State Univ	MI	7,842	C
Middle Tenn State Univ	TN	3,857	C
Middlebury College	VT	24,400	MC
Millersville Univ of Penn	PA	7,370	VC
Mills College	CA	20,848	VC
Miss State Univ	MS	5,629	VC
Monmouth College	NJ	16,820	C
Montclair State College	NJ	7,539	C+
Moorhead State Univ	MN	5,076	C
Mount Holyoke College	MA	23,630	VC
National-Louis Univ	IL	13,218	C
Nazareth College of Rochester	NY	15,310	C+
New College of Calif	CA	6,900	NC
New College of the Univ of South Florida	FL	5,697	MC
New Mexico State Univ	NM	4,844	LC
New York Univ	NY	24,705	VC+
N Car Wesleyan College	NC	12,480	LC
North Central College	IL	15,498	VC
North Park College	IL	14,310	C
Northeastern Illinois Univ	IL	1,955	C
Northeastern Univ	MA	19,851	C
Northern Arizona Univ	AZ	4,844	C
Northern Illinois Univ	IL	6,408	C
Northern Kentucky Univ	KY	4,620	NC
Northwestern State Univ of Louisiana	LA	4,287	NC
Northwestern Univ	IL	21,093	MC
Oakland Univ	MI	6,714	VC
Oberlin College	OH	24,570	HC+
Occidental College	CA	21,792	HC
Ohio State Univ	OH	7,218	LC
Ohio Univ	OH	7,341	C
Ohio Wesleyan Univ	OH	21,108	VC+
Old Dominion Univ	VA	8,317	C
Oregon State Univ	OR	6,175	C
Pace Univ	NY	15,540	C
Pacific Lutheran Univ	WA	15,998	VC
Penn State Univ/Univ Park Campus	PA	8,752	HC
Pitzer College	CA	23,780	HC
Plymouth State College	NH	7,166	C
Pomona College	CA	23,820	MC
Portland State Univ	OR	7,191	C
Prescott College	AZ	9,775	C
Princeton Univ	NJ	24,650	MC
Principia College	IL	17,799	C
Purdue Univ/West Lafayette	IN	6,636	C
Radford Univ	VA	7,034	LC
Reed College	OR	24,480	HC+
Rhode Island College	RI	7,901	LC
Rhodes College	TN	19,624	HC
Rice Univ	TX	15,110	MC
Richard Stockton College of New Jersey	NJ	6,950	VC
Ripon College	WI	18,320	C+
Rockford College	IL	15,300	C
Rocky Mountain College	MT	11,320	C
Rollins College	FL	20,875	VC
Rutgers Univ/Douglass College	NJ	8,795	VC
Rutgers Univ/Livingston College	NJ	8,877	VC
Rutgers Univ/Newark College of A&S	NJ	8,645	C
Rutgers Univ/Rutgers College	NJ	8,841	HC
Rutgers Univ/Univ College—New Brunswick	NJ	0	LC
St Cloud State Univ	MN	5,015	C
St Francis College	PA	15,744	LC
St John Fisher College	NY	15,415	C
St John's Univ	NY	8,980	C+
St Lawrence Univ	NY	23,420	VC
St Mary's College of Maryland	MD	8,900	VC+
St Michael's College	VT	17,930	C
St Norbert College	WI	15,710	VC
Salve Regina Univ	RI	29,100	LC
San Diego State Univ	CA	6,692	LC
San Francisco State Univ	CA	7,292	LC
San Jose State Univ	CA	6,680	LC
Santa Clara Univ	CA	18,783	VC
Sarah Lawrence College	NY	24,975	HC
Scripps College	CA	23,600	HC
Seton Hall Univ	NJ	18,306	LC
Shepherd College	WV	5,540	C
Skidmore College	NY	23,230	HC
Slippery Rock Univ	PA	6,803	C
Smith College	MA	24,236	HC
Sonoma State Univ	CA	6,996	LC
Southern Calif College	CA	12,356	C
Southern Illinois Univ at Carbondale	IL	6,234	C
Southern Illinois Univ at Edwardsville	IL	6,097	LC
Southern Methodist Univ	TX	18,520	VC
Southwest Texas State Univ	TX	5,124	C
Stanford Univ	CA	24,310	MC
SUNY at Albany	NY	7,059	VC
SUNY at Binghamton	NY	7,921	HC
SUNY at Buffalo	NY	7,896	VC
SUNY at Stony Brook	NY	7,658	VC
SUNY/College at Brockport	NY	7,220	C+
SUNY/College at Buffalo	NY	7,035	VC
SUNY/College at Cortland	NY	7,326	C+
SUNY/College at Geneseo	NY	6,949	HC
SUNY/College at New Paltz	NY	6,890	VC
SUNY/College at Oneonta	NY	7,878	C
SUNY/College at Oswego	NY	7,330	VC
SUNY/College at Plattsburgh	NY	6,917	C
SUNY/College at Purchase	NY	7,324	C
SUNY/Potsdam College	NY	6,906	C
Swarthmore College	PA	24,136	MC
Sweet Briar College	VA	19,770	C
Syracuse Univ	NY	21,305	HC
Temple Univ	PA	10,281	C
Texas A&M Univ	TX	5,382	VC
Texas Tech Univ	TX	6,008	C
The Univ of New Mexico	NM	5,304	C
Thomas A. Edison State College	NJ	400	
Trinity Univ	TX	16,670	HC
Tufts Univ	MA	24,962	MC
Tulane Univ	LA	24,540	HC
Univ of Akron	OH	6,699	NC
Univ of Alabama	AL	5,702	C
Univ of Alabama at Birmingham	AL	7,533	C
Univ of Alaska Anchorage	AK	7,131	C
Univ of Alaska Fairbanks	AK	4,718	C
Univ of Arizona	AZ	5,808	C
Univ of Arkansas at Fayetteville	AR	5,046	C
Univ of Calif at Berkeley	CA	9,962	HC+
Univ of Calif at Davis	CA	9,534	VC
Univ of Calif at Los Angeles	CA	8,959	HC
Univ of Calif at Santa Barbara	CA	9,460	C
Univ of Calif at Santa Cruz	CA	9,060	VC
Univ of Calif, Riverside	CA	9,178	C
Univ of Calif, San Diego	CA	10,028	VC+
Univ of Calif/Irvine	CA	12,680	VC
Univ of Central Florida	FL	6,061	C+
Univ of Chicago	IL	24,517	MC
Univ of Cincinnati	OH	7,989	C
Univ of Colo at Boulder	CO	6,410	VC
Univ of Colo at Colo Springs	CO	2,269	C
Univ of Colo at Denver	CO	1,955	VC
Univ of Conn	CT	9,168	C
Univ of Delaware	DE	8,013	VC
Univ of Denver	CO	19,290	C+
Univ of Florida	FL	5,850	HC
Univ of Georgia	GA	5,655	VC
Univ of Guam	GU	4,139	NC
Univ of Hawaii at Hilo	HI	4,141	C
Univ of Hawaii at Manoa	HI	5,626	C
Univ of Houston	TX	5,215	C
Univ of Idaho	ID	4,830	C
Univ of Illinois at Chicago	IL	8,443	C
Univ of Indianapolis	IN	14,510	C
Univ of Iowa	IA	5,658	VC
Univ of Kansas	KS	5,200	NC
Univ of Kentucky	KY	5,152	VC
Univ of Louisville	KY	5,948	C
Univ of Maine	ME	7,990	C
Univ of Maryland/College Park	MD	8,182	VC
Univ of Maryland/Univ College	MD	4,900	NC
Univ of Mass Dartmouth	MA	8,158	C
Univ of Mass/Amherst	MA	9,364	LC
Univ of Mass/Boston	MA	4,253	C
Univ of Memphis	TN	3,476	C
Univ of Miami	FL	22,107	VC
Univ of Mich/Dearborn	MI	3,399	HC
Univ of Mich/Flint	MI	2,916	C
Univ of Minn/Duluth	MN	6,512	C
Univ of Minn/Twin Cities	MN	6,682	VC
Univ of Miss	MS	5,756	C
Univ of Missouri/Columbia	MO	6,254	HC
Univ of Missouri/St. Louis	MO	6,378	C
Univ of Montana	MT	5,529	C
Univ of Nebr at Omaha	NE	1,889	LC
Univ of Nebr-Lincoln	NE	5,278	LC
Univ of Nevada/Las Vegas	NV	6,405	C
Univ of Nevada/Reno	NV	5,735	C
Univ of New Hampshire	NH	8,242	C
Univ of New Orleans	LA	5,468	C
Univ of N Car at Chapel Hill	NC	5,330	HC
Univ of N Car at Charlotte	NC	4,597	C
Univ of N Car at Greensboro	NC	5,192	C
Univ of N Car at Wilmington	NC	5,172	C
Univ of N Dak	ND	4,902	NC
Univ of North Texas	TX	4,853	C
Univ of Northern Iowa	IA	5,137	C
Univ of Notre Dame	IN	20,150	MC

School	ST	$IS	SR
Univ of Okla	OK	5,427	VC
Univ of Oregon	OR	6,466	VC
Univ of Penn	PA	24,238	MC
Univ of Pittsburgh	PA	9,472	C
Univ of PR/Rio Piedras	PR	0	
Univ of Redlands	CA	22,059	VC
Univ of Rhode Island	RI	9,205	C
Univ of Rochester	NY	23,696	HC
Univ of San Diego	CA	18,970	VC
Univ of South Alabama	AL	5,451	C
Univ of S Car	SC	6,158	C
Univ of S Dak	SD	4,722	C
Univ of South Florida	FL	5,475	C+
Univ of Southern Calif	CA	23,006	VC
Univ of Southern Maine	ME	7,299	C
Univ of Southern Miss	MS	4,542	C
Univ of Southwestern Louisiana	LA	3,968	NC
Univ of Tenn/Knoxville	TN	5,668	C
Univ of Texas at Arlington	TX	5,549	LC
Univ of Texas at Austin	TX	5,160	VC
Univ of Texas at El Paso	TX	3,160	LC
Univ of Texas at San Antonio	TX	6,420	C
Univ of the Pacific	CA	21,100	C
Univ of the South	TN	18,830	HC
Univ of Toledo	OH	6,636	NC
Univ of Tulsa	OK	13,795	VC
Univ of Utah	UT	5,975	C
Univ of Vermont	VT	10,776	C+
Univ of Virginia	VA	7,964	MC
Univ of Washington	WA	6,618	VC
Univ of Wisc/Madison	WI	6,400	HC
Univ of Wisc/Milwaukee	WI	6,165	C
Univ of Wisc/Oshkosh	WI	4,240	C
Univ of Wyoming	WY	4,991	NC
Upsala College	NJ	17,200	C
Ursinus College	PA	19,165	VC
Utica College of Syracuse Univ	NY	16,714	LC
Valdosta State Univ	GA	4,670	LC
Vanderbilt Univ	TN	23,422	HC+
Vassar College	NY	24,206	HC
Virginia Commonwealth Univ	VA	7,909	C
Wagner College	NY	17,950	C
Wake Forest Univ	NC	17,280	MC
Washburn Univ of Topeka	KS	5,802	NC
Washington and Lee Univ	VA	17,735	MC
Washington State Univ	WA	6,364	C
Washington Univ	MO	23,507	HC
Wayne State Univ	MI	2,680	C
Webster Univ	MO	12,650	C
Wellesley College	MA	23,815	MC
Wesleyan Univ	CT	23,770	MC
West Chester Univ of Penn	PA	7,492	C
West Georgia College	GA	4,256	C
West Virginia Univ	WV	5,774	C
Western Carolina Univ	NC	3,811	C
Western Kentucky Univ	KY	4,808	C
Western Mich Univ	MI	6,820	C
Western Washington Univ	WA	6,077	VC
Westminster College	MO	13,750	C+
Wheaton College	MA	23,840	C+
Whitman College	WA	20,595	HC
Whittier College	CA	21,661	C
Wichita State Univ	KS	5,068	NC
William Paterson College	NJ	7,438	C+
Williams College	MA	24,390	MC
Wright State Univ	OH	6,896	LC
Yale Univ	CT	25,110	MC
Youngstown State Univ	OH	6,447	LC

APPAREL AND ACCESSORIES MARKETING

School	ST	$IS	SR
Albright College	PA	19,260	C
Colo State Univ	CO	6,566	VC
Fashion Inst of Tech/SUNY	NY	7,135	SP
Indiana Univ Bloomington	IN	6,495	VC
Kentucky State Univ	KY	4,282	C+
Laboratory Inst of Merchandising	NY	9,800	SP
S Dak State Univ	SD	4,562	C

APPAREL DESIGN

School	ST	$IS	SR
Bassist College	OR	12,590	SP

APPLIED ART

School	ST	$IS	SR
Charter Oak State College	CT	314	NC
Cleveland Inst of Art	OH	15,630	SP
Oral Roberts Univ	OK	10,607	C+
Point Park College	PA	13,922	LC
Sam Houston State Univ	TX	4,506	C
Southwest Texas State Univ	TX	5,124	C
Univ of Arkansas at Pine Bluff	AR	3,978	LC
Univ of Calif at Berkeley	CA	9,962	HC+
Univ of Denver	CO	19,290	C+
Univ of Illinois at Urbana-Champaign	IL	7,764	HC
Univ of North Texas	TX	4,853	C
Youngstown State Univ	OH	6,447	LC

APPLIED MATHEMATICS

School	ST	$IS	SR
Asbury College	KY	11,105	VC
Auburn Univ	AL	5,823	C+
Bethel College	TN	9,736	LC
Brown Univ	RI	26,104	MC
Case Western Reserve Univ	OH	19,910	HC
Dowling College	NY	12,730	LC
Geneva College	PA	13,030	C
GMI Engineering & Management Inst	MI	14,158	HC
Harvard Univ/Harvard and Radcliffe Colleges	MA	24,880	MC
Kentucky State Univ	KY	4,282	C+
King College	TN	11,500	C
New Jersey Inst of Tech	NJ	9,965	VC
Northwestern Univ	IL	21,093	MC
Pacific Union College	CA	15,075	C
Philadelphia College of Textiles and Science	PA	15,896	C
Purdue Univ/West Lafayette	IN	6,636	C
Rutgers Univ/Newark College of A&S	NJ	8,645	C
San Francisco State Univ	CA	7,292	LC
SUNY at Albany	NY	7,059	VC
SUNY at Stony Brook	NY	7,658	VC
Univ of Calif at Berkeley	CA	9,962	HC+
Univ of Calif at Los Angeles	CA	8,959	HC
Univ of Calif, San Diego	CA	10,028	VC+
Univ of Colo at Boulder	CO	6,410	VC
Univ of Houston-Downtown	TX	4,034	NC
Univ of Mass/Boston	MA	4,253	C
Univ of Miami	FL	22,107	VC
Univ of Mich/Ann Arbor	MI	9,428	HC+
Univ of Missouri/Rolla	MO	6,729	VC+
Univ of Missouri/St. Louis	MO	6,378	C
Univ of New Haven	CT	14,980	C
Univ of Rochester	NY	23,696	HC
Univ of Tenn at Chattanooga	TN	5,375	C
Univ of Texas at Dallas	TX	1,222	VC+
Univ of the Pacific	CA	21,100	C
Univ of Virginia	VA	7,964	MC
Univ of Wisc/Madison	WI	6,400	HC
Univ of Wisc/Milwaukee	WI	6,165	C
Univ of Wisc/Stout	WI	4,719	C
Univ of Wyoming	WY	4,991	NC
Valdosta State Univ	GA	4,670	LC
West Virginia State College	WV	5,044	LC
Wingate College	NC	10,610	C
Yale Univ	CT	25,110	MC

APPLIED MUSIC

School	ST	$IS	SR
Covenant College	GA	13,054	VC
Dallas Baptist Univ	TX	9,620	LC
DePaul Univ	IL	15,535	VC
Geneva College	PA	13,030	C
Grand Canyon Univ	AZ	9,680	VC
Hardin-Simmons Univ	TX	9,080	C
Indiana Wesleyan Univ	IN	12,332	C
Inter American Univ of PR/Aguadilla Regional College	PR	2,290	
Inter American Univ of PR/Bayamon Univ College	PR	2,300	
Inter American Univ of PR/Metropolitan Campus	PR	2,340	
Inter American Univ of PR/Ponce Regional College	PR	2,300	
Inter-American Univ of PR/Fajardo Regional College	PR	2,732	
Lenoir-Rhyne College	NC	14,068	C
Meredith College	NC	9,440	C
Messiah College	PA	14,664	VC
Methodist College	NC	12,400	C
Mich State Univ	MI	7,842	C
Miss College	MS	8,348	C
Nebr Wesleyan Univ	NE	12,240	C
New England Conservatory of Music	MA	21,590	SP
Northwestern Univ	IL	21,093	MC
Sul Ross State Univ	TX	4,144	NC
Univ of Alabama	AL	5,702	C
Univ of Mich/Ann Arbor	MI	9,428	HC+
Univ of Nevada/Reno	NV	5,735	C
Univ of S Dak	SD	4,722	C
Univ of Texas at Austin	TX	5,160	VC
Viterbo College	WI	12,670	C
William Carey College	MS	7,050	C

APPLIED PHYSICS

School	ST	$IS	SR
Hiram College	OH	18,340	VC
Rutgers Univ/Newark College of A&S	NJ	8,645	C

ARABIC

School	ST	$IS	SR
Georgetown Univ	DC	24,410	MC
Howard Univ	DC	11,680	C
Ohio State Univ	OH	7,218	LC
SUNY at Binghamton	NY	7,921	HC
Univ of Calif at Los Angeles	CA	8,959	HC
Univ of Mich/Ann Arbor	MI	9,428	HC+

ARCHEOLOGY

School	ST	$IS	SR
Boston Univ	MA	24,130	HC
Bridgewater State College	MA	7,518	C
Bryn Mawr College	PA	24,110	MC
CUNY/Brooklyn College	NY	2,450	VC
CUNY/Hunter College	NY	4,101	VC
Columbia Univ/Columbia College	NY	26,757	MC
Cornell Univ	NY	13,445	MC
Dartmouth College	NH	24,354	MC
Franklin Pierce College	NH	17,270	LC
Haverford College	PA	23,950	MC
Lycoming College	PA	17,200	LC
Mercyhurst College	PA	13,488	C
Oberlin College	OH	24,570	HC+
Princeton Univ	NJ	24,650	MC
Thomas A. Edison State College	NJ	400	
Tufts Univ	MA	24,962	MC
Univ of Calif at Santa Barbara	CA	9,460	C
Univ of Evansville	IN	15,300	VC
Univ of Missouri/Columbia	MO	6,254	HC
Univ of Texas at Austin	TX	5,160	VC
Univ of Wisc/La Crosse	WI	4,487	C
Washington and Lee Univ	VA	17,735	MC
Washington Univ	MO	23,507	HC
Wellesley College	MA	23,815	MC
Wheaton College	IL	14,710	HC
Yale Univ	CT	25,110	MC

ARCHITECTURAL ENGINEERING

School	ST	$IS	SR
Calif Polytechnic State Univ	CA	6,980	VC+
Catholic Univ of America	DC	18,856	C
Cornell Univ	NY	13,445	MC
Hampton Univ	VA	10,706	C
Kansas State Univ	KS	4,816	NC
Kent State Univ	OH	6,740	LC
Lehigh Univ	PA	23,250	HC
Louisiana Tech Univ	LA	4,284	C
Milwaukee School of Engineering	WI	14,100	C
Morris Brown College	GA	12,234	NC
N Car Agricultural and Technical State Univ	NC	4,477	LC
Penn State Univ/Univ Park Campus	PA	8,752	HC
Prairie View A&M Univ	TX	4,740	LC
Princeton Univ	NJ	24,650	MC
Rice Univ	TX	15,110	MC
Roger Williams Univ	RI	16,750	C
SUNY at Buffalo	NY	7,896	VC
Temple Univ	PA	10,281	C
Tenn State Univ	TN	4,626	C+
Texas Tech Univ	TX	6,008	C
Univ of Arizona	AZ	5,808	C
Univ of Arkansas at Fayetteville	AR	5,046	C
Univ of Cincinnati	OH	7,989	C
Univ of Colo at Boulder	CO	6,410	VC
Univ of Detroit Mercy	MI	14,720	C
Univ of Houston	TX	5,215	C
Univ of Idaho	ID	4,830	C
Univ of Illinois at Chicago	IL	8,443	C
Univ of Kansas	KS	5,200	NC
Univ of Miami	FL	22,107	VC
Univ of Nevada/Las Vegas	NV	6,405	C
Univ of Notre Dame	IN	20,150	MC
Univ of Texas at Arlington	TX	5,549	LC
Univ of Texas at Austin	TX	5,160	VC
Univ of Texas at San Antonio	TX	6,420	C
Univ of Wyoming	WY	4,991	NC
Wellesley College	MA	23,815	MC
Wentworth Inst of Tech	MA	15,250	LC

ARCHITECTURAL TECHNOLOGY

School	ST	$IS	SR
Brown Univ	RI	26,104	MC
Fairmont State College	WV	4,640	LC
Florida International Univ	FL	4,191	VC
Univ of Cincinnati	OH	7,989	C
Univ of Hartford	CT	19,858	LC
Univ of Memphis	TN	3,476	C
Univ of Southern Miss	MS	4,542	C
Univ of Virginia	VA	7,964	MC

ARCHITECTURE

School	ST	$IS	SR
Andrews Univ	MI	14,952	NC
Arizona State Univ Main Campus	AZ	6,444	C
Auburn Univ	AL	5,823	C+
Ball State Univ	IN	6,032	LC
Bennington College	VT	24,850	VC+
Boston Architectural Center	MA	3,372	SP
Calif College of Arts and Crafts	CA	17,378	SP
Calif Polytechnic State Univ	CA	6,980	VC+
Calif State Polytechnic Univ/Pomona	CA	6,438	LC
Case Western Reserve Univ	OH	19,910	HC
Columbia Univ/Barnard College	NY	25,492	HC
Columbia Univ/Columbia College	NY	26,757	MC
Cooper Union for the Advancement of Science and Art	NY	8,430	MC
Cornell Univ	NY	13,445	MC
Drexel Univ	PA	15,970	C
Drury College	MO	12,140	VC
Edward Waters College	FL	8,300	NC
Georgia Inst of Tech	GA	6,669	HC+
Hampton Univ	VA	10,706	C
Hobart and William Smith Colleges	NY	23,925	VC
Howard Univ	DC	11,680	C
Illinois Inst of Tech	IL	18,290	VC
Iowa State Univ	IA	5,456	C
Lawrence Tech Univ	MI	9,470	C
Lehigh Univ	PA	23,250	HC
Louisiana State Univ and A&M College	LA	5,605	C
Mass College of Art	MA	9,447	SP
Mass Inst of Tech	MA	24,800	MC
Miss State Univ	MS	5,629	VC
Montana State Univ	MT	5,534	C
New Jersey Inst of Tech	NJ	9,965	VC
New York Inst of Tech/Old Westbury	NY	13,914	LC
N Car State Univ	NC	4,984	VC
N Dak State Univ of Agriculture and Applied Science	ND	4,774	VC
Norwich Univ	VT	18,730	C
Ohio State Univ	OH	7,218	LC
Okla State Univ	OK	5,086	VC
Philadelphia College of Textiles and Science	PA	15,896	C
Pratt Inst	NY	19,520	C
Princeton Univ	NJ	24,650	MC
Rensselaer Polytechnic Inst	NY	23,067	HC
Rhode Island School of Design	RI	22,315	SP
Roger Williams Univ	RI	16,750	C
Savannah College of Art and Design	GA	14,280	SP
Southern College of Tech	GA	4	C
Southern Illinois Univ at Carbondale	IL	6,234	C
Southern Univ and A&M College	LA	4,920	NC
Syracuse Univ	NY	21,305	HC
Temple Univ	PA	10,281	C
The Univ of New Mexico	NM	5,304	C
Tulane Univ	LA	24,540	HC
Univ of Calif at Berkeley	CA	9,962	HC+
Univ of Florida	FL	5,850	HC
Univ of Hawaii at Manoa	HI	5,626	C
Univ of Illinois at Chicago	IL	8,443	C
Univ of Illinois at Urbana-Champaign	IL	7,764	HC
Univ of Kansas	KS	5,200	NC
Univ of Maryland/College Park	MD	8,182	VC
Univ of Miami	FL	22,107	VC
Univ of Mich/Ann Arbor	MI	9,428	HC+
Univ of Minn/Twin Cities	MN	6,682	VC
Univ of Nebr-Lincoln	NE	5,278	C
Univ of N Car at Charlotte	NC	4,597	C

School	ST	$IS	SR
Kean College of New Jersey	NJ	6,395	LC
Kennesaw State College	GA	1,553	C
Kent State Univ	OH	6,740	LC
Kentucky State Univ	KY	4,282	C+
Kentucky Wesleyan College	KY	11,550	C
Kutztown Univ	PA	6,528	C
LaGrange College	GA	10,602	C
Lamar Univ	TX	3,798	C
Lander Univ	SC	6,180	LC
Lawrence Univ	WI	19,986	HC+
Lenoir-Rhyne College	NC	14,068	C
Lewis Univ	IL	14,797	LC
Limestone College	SC	10,700	LC
Lincoln Univ	MO	4,638	NC
Lincoln Univ	PA	0	LC
Lindenwood College	MO	13,560	C
Linfield College	OR	16,670	VC
Livingston Univ	AL	3,979	C
LIU/C. W. Post Campus	NY	16,870	C
LIU/Southampton Campus	NY	17,280	C
Longwood College	VA	7,800	C
Loras College	IA	14,160	C
Louisiana College	LA	7,518	VC
Louisiana State Univ in Shreveport	LA	1,910	NC
Louisiana Tech Univ	LA	4,284	C
Lubbock Christian Univ	TX	9,840	NC
Luther College	IA	15,900	VC
Madonna Univ	MI	8,546	C
Manchester College	IN	13,240	LC
Manhattanville College	NY	20,450	LC
Mankato State Univ	MN	5,097	LC
Mansfield Univ	PA	6,348	C
Marian College of Fond du Lac	WI	12,250	C
Marietta College	OH	16,940	C+
Mars Hill College	NC	11,050	C
Marshall Univ	WV	5,762	LC
Mary Baldwin College	VA	17,700	LC
Marygrove College	MI	5,877	VC
Marymount College/Tarrytown	NY	17,350	C
Maryville College	TN	14,474	C
Maryville Univ-St Louis	MO	12,900	VC
Marywood College	PA	14,890	C
Mass College of Art	MA	9,447	SP
McKendree College	IL	10,900	C
McNeese State Univ	LA	4,543	NC
McPherson College	KS	11,360	VC
Mercy College	NY	11,180	NC
Mercyhurst College	PA	13,488	C
Messiah College	PA	14,664	VC
Methodist College	NC	12,400	C
Miami Univ	OH	8,066	VC
Mich State Univ	MI	7,842	C
Middle Tenn State Univ	TN	3,857	C
Midland Lutheran College	NE	12,410	LC
Millersville Univ of Penn	PA	7,370	VC
Millikin Univ	IL	15,499	C
Minot State Univ	ND	3,748	NC
Miss College	MS	8,348	C
Miss Univ for Women	MS	4,456	LC
Missouri Southern State College	MO	4,272	
Missouri Western State College	MO	4,384	NC
Molloy College	NY	8,580	LC
Monmouth College	NJ	16,820	C
Moore College of Art and Design	PA	17,947	SP
Moorhead State Univ	MN	5,076	C
Morehead State Univ	KY	4,600	LC
Morris Brown College	GA	12,234	NC
Mount Mary College	WI	10,920	C
Mount Mercy College	IA	13,230	C
Mount St Mary's College	CA	16,390	VC
Mount Senario College	WI	10,970	C
Mount Vernon Nazarene College	OH	10,390	C
Murray State Univ	KY	4,702	C
Nazareth College of Rochester	NY	15,310	C+
New York Inst of Tech/Old Westbury	NY	13,914	LC
New York Univ	NY	24,705	VC+
Nicholls State Univ	LA	4,531	NC
N Car Agricultural and Technical State Univ	NC	4,477	LC
North Georgia College	GA	4,103	LC
Northeast Louisiana Univ	LA	3,906	NC
Northeastern State Univ	OK	5,250	C
Northern Arizona Univ	AZ	4,844	C
Northern Illinois Univ	IL	6,408	C
Northern Kentucky Univ	KY	4,620	NC
Northern Mich Univ	MI	6,350	C
Northern State Univ	SD	4,186	LC
Northland College	WI	13,550	LC
Northwestern College	MN	13,554	C
Northwestern College of Iowa	IA	12,250	C
Northwestern State Univ of Louisiana	LA	4,287	NC
Northwestern Univ	IL	21,093	MC
Notre Dame College	NH	14,220	C
Notre Dame College of Ohio	OH	11,370	C
Oakland City College	IN	10,216	LC
Ohio Dominican College	OH	11,820	LC
Ohio State Univ	OH	7,218	LC
Ohio Univ	OH	7,341	C
Ohio Wesleyan Univ	OH	21,108	VC+
Okla Baptist Univ	OK	8,486	C
Okla Christian Univ of Science and Arts	OK	8,790	NC
Okla State Univ	OK	5,086	VC
Olivet Nazarene Univ	IL	11,976	C
Oral Roberts Univ	OK	10,607	C+
Otterbein College	OH	16,506	C
Ouachita Baptist Univ	AR	8,940	C
Our Lady of the Lake Univ of San Antonio	TX	11,080	C
Palm Beach Atlantic College	FL	10,720	C
Park College	MO	7,320	C
Pembroke State Univ	NC	3,538	LC
Penn State Univ/Univ Park Campus	PA	8,752	HC
Pepperdine Univ	CA	23,720	VC
Peru State College	NE	4,311	NC
Phillips Univ	OK	12,744	C
Piedmont College	GA	8,540	LC
Pittsburg State Univ	KS	4,478	NC
Plymouth State College	NH	7,166	C
Point Loma Nazarene College	CA	13,532	C
Pontifical Catholic Univ of PR/Ponce	PR	5,807	
Pratt Inst	NY	19,520	C
Prescott College	AZ	9,775	C
Purdue Univ/West Lafayette	IN	6,636	C
Quincy Univ	IL	13,646	VC
Radford Univ	VA	7,034	LC
Rhode Island College	RI	7,901	LC
Rivier College	NH	14,920	LC
Roberts Wesleyan College	NY	13,317	C
Rosemont College	PA	16,775	C
Saginaw Valley State Univ	MI	6,634	LC
St Ambrose Univ	IA	13,380	C
St Cloud State Univ	MN	5,015	C
St Francis College	IN	11,662	C
St John's Univ	NY	8,980	C+
St Lawrence Univ	NY	23,420	VC
St Leo College	FL	13,570	C
St Mary's College of Calif	CA	18,848	VC
St Mary-of-the-Woods College	IN	14,430	NC
St Michael's College	VT	17,930	C
St Norbert College	WI	15,710	VC
St Olaf College	MN	17,200	HC
St Thomas Aquinas College	NY	13,550	C
St Vincent College	PA	13,934	LC
St Xavier Univ	IL	14,700	C
Salem State College	MA	6,712	C
Samford Univ	AL	11,400	VC
School of the Art Inst of Chicago	IL	17,610	SP
Schreiner College	TX	14,320	C
Seton Hill College	PA	14,320	C
Shepherd College	WV	5,540	C
Shorter College	GA	10,270	C
Siena Heights College	MI	12,520	C
Silver Lake College	WI	8,280	LC
Simpson College	IA	14,635	VC
Sioux Falls College	SD	11,540	C
Skidmore College	NY	23,230	HC
S Car State Univ	SC	5,424	LC
S Dak State Univ	SD	4,562	C
Southeast Missouri State Univ	MO	5,854	C
Southeastern Louisiana Univ	LA	4,230	NC
Southeastern Okla State Univ	OK	3,594	C
Southern Conn State Univ	CT	7,532	C
Southern Illinois Univ at Carbondale	IL	6,234	C
Southern Illinois Univ at Edwardsville	IL	6,097	LC
Southern Nazarene Univ	OK	9,206	NC
Southern Univ and A&M College	LA	4,920	NC
Southern Univ at New Orleans	LA	1,452	NC
Southern Utah Univ	UT	4,104	LC
Southwest Baptist Univ	MO	9,192	NC
Southwest Missouri State Univ	MO	4,956	C
Southwest State Univ	MN	5,400	NC
Southwest Texas State Univ	TX	5,124	C
Southwestern Okla State Univ	OK	3,312	C
Spelman College	GA	12,942	VC
Spring Hill College	AL	16,015	C+
SUNY/College at Buffalo	NY	7,035	VC
SUNY/College at Cortland	NY	7,326	C+
SUNY/College at New Paltz	NY	6,890	VC
SUNY/College at Oneonta	NY	7,878	C
SUNY/Potsdam College	NY	6,906	C
Sterling College	KS	10,990	VC
Sul Ross State Univ	TX	4,144	NC
Syracuse Univ	NY	21,305	HC
Tarleton State Univ	TX	4,082	LC
Taylor Univ	IN	14,450	VC
Temple Univ	PA	10,281	C
Tenn State Univ	TN	4,626	C+
Texas Christian Univ	TX	12,180	C
Texas College	TX	5,930	NC
Texas Southern Univ	TX	4,500	NC
Texas Tech Univ	TX	6,008	C
The Univ of New Mexico	NM	5,304	C
Thomas More College	KY	12,962	C
Towson State Univ	MD	7,452	C
Trenton State College	NJ	9,085	HC
Trinity Christian College	IL	13,260	C
Trinity Univ	TX	16,670	HC
Troy State Univ	AL	4,322	C
Univ of Akron	OH	6,699	NC
Univ of Alabama	AL	5,702	C
Univ of Alabama at Birmingham	AL	7,533	C
Univ of Alaska Anchorage	AK	7,131	C
Univ of Arizona	AZ	5,808	C
Univ of Arkansas at Fayetteville	AR	5,046	C
Univ of Arkansas at Pine Bluff	AR	3,978	LC
Univ of Bridgeport	CT	18,985	C
Univ of Central Arkansas	AR	4,200	LC
Univ of Central Florida	FL	6,061	C+
Univ of Central Okla	OK	3,647	C
Univ of Charleston	WV	12,750	C
Univ of Cincinnati	OH	7,989	C
Univ of Colo at Boulder	CO	6,410	VC
Univ of Dallas	TX	14,983	VC
Univ of Dayton	OH	15,120	C+
Univ of Detroit Mercy	MI	14,720	C
Univ of Evansville	IN	15,300	VC
Univ of Findlay	OH	15,764	C
Univ of Florida	FL	5,850	HC
Univ of Georgia	GA	5,655	VC
Univ of Guam	GU	4,139	NC
Univ of Hawaii at Manoa	HI	5,626	C
Univ of Houston	TX	5,215	C
Univ of Idaho	ID	4,830	C
Univ of Illinois at Chicago	IL	8,443	C
Univ of Illinois at Urbana-Champaign	IL	7,764	HC
Univ of Indianapolis	IN	14,510	C
Univ of Iowa	IA	5,658	VC
Univ of Kansas	KS	5,200	NC
Univ of Kentucky	KY	5,152	VC
Univ of La Verne	CA	17,400	C
Univ of Louisville	KY	5,948	C
Univ of Maine	ME	7,990	C
Univ of Maine at Presque Isle	ME	6,374	C
Univ of Mary Hardin-Baylor	TX	8,120	NC
Univ of Maryland/College Park	MD	8,182	VC
Univ of Maryland/Eastern Shore	MD	6,254	LC
Univ of Mass Dartmouth	MA	8,158	C
Univ of Mass/Amherst	MA	9,364	LC
Univ of Mich/Ann Arbor	MI	9,428	HC+
Univ of Minn/Duluth	MN	6,512	C
Univ of Minn/Twin Cities	MN	6,682	VC
Univ of Miss	MS	5,756	C
Univ of Missouri/Columbia	MO	6,254	HC
Univ of Montevallo	AL	5,310	C
Univ of Nebr at Kearney	NE	4,308	LC
Univ of Nebr-Lincoln	NE	5,278	LC
Univ of North Alabama	AL	4,236	NC
Univ of N Car at Chapel Hill	NC	5,330	HC
Univ of N Car at Greensboro	NC	5,192	C
Univ of North Florida	FL	5,082	C
Univ of Northern Iowa	IA	5,137	C
Univ of PR/Rio Piedras	PR	0	
Univ of Richmond	VA	16,700	HC
Univ of Science and Arts of Okla	OK	3,304	C
Univ of S Car	SC	6,158	C
Univ of S Dak	SD	4,722	C
Univ of South Florida	FL	5,475	C+
Univ of Southern Indiana	IN	3,720	NC
Univ of Southern Miss	MS	4,542	C
Univ of Southwestern Louisiana	LA	3,968	NC
Univ of Tenn at Chattanooga	TN	5,375	C
Univ of Tenn at Martin	TN	4,550	C
Univ of Tenn/Knoxville	TN	5,668	C
Univ of Texas at Arlington	TX	5,549	LC
Univ of Texas at El Paso	TX	3,160	LC
Univ of the District of Columbia	DC	974	NC
Univ of the Pacific	CA	21,100	C
Univ of Toledo	OH	6,636	NC
Univ of Tulsa	OK	13,795	VC
Univ of Utah	UT	5,975	C
Univ of Vermont	VT	10,776	C+
Univ of West Florida	FL	5,415	C
Univ of Wisc/Eau Claire	WI	4,647	C
Univ of Wisc/Madison	WI	6,600	HC
Univ of Wisc/Milwaukee	WI	6,165	C
Univ of Wisc/Oshkosh	WI	4,240	C
Univ of Wisc/Platteville	WI	4,830	C
Univ of Wisc/River Falls	WI	4,655	C
Univ of Wisc/Stevens Point	WI	5,047	C+
Univ of Wisc/Stout	WI	4,719	C
Univ of Wisc/Superior	WI	4,330	C
Univ of Wisc/Whitewater	WI	4,700	C
Univ of Wyoming	WY	4,991	NC
Ursuline College	OH	13,180	LC
Utah State Univ	UT	4,683	C
Valdosta State Univ	GA	4,670	LC
Valley City State Univ	ND	4,385	LC
Virginia Commonwealth Univ	VA	7,909	C
Virginia Intermont College	VA	12,250	LC
Virginia State Univ	VA	7,040	
Virginia Wesleyan College	VA	14,950	VC
Viterbo College	WI	12,670	C
Wartburg College	IA	14,530	VC
Washburn Univ of Topeka	KS	5,802	NC
Washington and Jefferson College	PA	19,360	C
Wayne State College	NE	4,260	NC
Wayne State Univ	MI	2,680	C
Weber State Univ	UT	4,398	C
Wells College	NY	19,460	C+
West Liberty State College	WV	4,690	LC
West Texas A&M Univ	TX	4,224	C
West Virginia State College	WV	5,044	LC
West Virginia Wesleyan College	WV	16,900	C
Western Carolina Univ	NC	3,811	C
Western Kentucky Univ	KY	4,808	C
Western Mich Univ	MI	6,820	C
Western Montana College of the Univ of Montana	MT	1,646	C
Western New Mexico Univ	NM	3,234	LC
Western State College of Colo	CO	5,560	C
Western Washington Univ	WA	6,077	VC
Westfield State College	MA	7,161	C
Westminster College	MO	13,750	C+
Westmont College	CA	18,732	C
Whitworth College	WA	16,265	C
Wichita State Univ	KS	5,068	NC
Wilkes Univ	PA	15,728	LC
William Penn College	IA	13,400	C
Wilmington College	OH	13,700	LC
Wingate College	NC	10,610	C
Winona State Univ	MN	5,200	VC
Winston-Salem State Univ	NC	4,142	LC
Wittenberg Univ	OH	19,998	VC
Wright State Univ	OH	6,896	LC
Xavier Univ	OH	15,710	C+
Xavier Univ of Louisiana	LA	10,400	C
Youngstown State Univ	OH	6,447	LC

ART HISTORY AND APPRECIATION

School	ST	$IS	SR
Adelphi Univ	NY	18,250	LC
Allegheny College	PA	21,020	VC
American Univ	DC	21,230	VC+
Aquinas College	MI	14,526	C
Arizona State Univ Main Campus	AZ	6,444	C
Art Academy of Cincinnati	OH	8,820	SP
Augustana College	IL	16,959	VC
Baker Univ	KS	12,284	C
Bard College	NY	25,269	HC
Beloit College	WI	18,950	VC+
Bennington College	VT	24,850	VC+
Birmingham-Southern College	AL	15,154	VC+
Bloomsburg Univ of Penn	PA	6,312	C+
Boston College	MA	22,706	MC
Boston Univ	MA	24,130	HC
Bowdoin College	ME	24,155	MC
Bradley Univ	IL	14,718	C+
Brigham Young Univ	UT	5,625	HC
Brown Univ	RI	26,104	MC
Bryn Mawr College	PA	24,110	MC
Cal State/Los Angeles	CA	4,940	VC
Cal State/Northridge	CA	7,122	LC
Calvin College	MI	13,020	VC
Canisius College	NY	15,510	C
Carleton College	MN	22,155	HC
Carlow College	PA	13,914	C
Case Western Reserve Univ	OH	19,910	HC
Charter Oak State College	CT	314	NC
Chatham College	PA	18,010	C
Chestnut Hill College	PA	14,525	C
CUNY/Brooklyn College	NY	2,450	VC
Clark Univ	MA	21,400	VC
Clarke College	IA	13,950	C+
Colby College	ME	24,230	HC
College of Charleston	SC	6,250	C
College of New Rochelle	NY	15,440	LC
College of Notre Dame of Maryland	MD	16,050	C
College of St Benedict	MN	15,468	VC
College of Santa Fe	NM	14,008	C
Columbia Univ/Barnard College	NY	25,492	HC
Columbia Univ/Columbia College	NY	26,757	MC
Conn College	CT	24,160	HC
Cornell Univ	NY	13,445	MC
Dartmouth College	NH	24,354	MC
DePauw Univ	IN	18,530	VC
Dominican College of San Rafael	CA	17,860	C
Drake Univ	IA	17,195	VC
Duke Univ	NC	21,271	MC
Eastern College	PA	15,150	C+
Eastern Washington Univ	WA	5,439	LC

School	ST	$IS	SR
Edinboro Univ of Penn	PA	7,181	C
Emmanuel College	MA	17,773	LC
Emory Univ	GA	21,930	HC
Florida State Univ	FL	5,814	VC
Fordham Univ/College at Lincoln Center	NY	18,150	VC
Fordham Univ/Fordham College	NY	19,875	VC
Framingham State College	MA	6,580	C
Gallaudet Univ	DC	9,850	SP
Georgian Court College	NJ	12,550	C
Hampshire College	MA	25,320	C
Harvard Univ/Harvard and Radcliffe Colleges	MA	24,880	MC
Haverford College	PA	23,950	MC
Hiram College	OH	18,340	VC
Hofstra Univ	NY	16,580	VC
Hollins College	VA	18,484	C
Hood College	MD	19,010	VC
Indiana State Univ	IN	6,210	C
Indiana Univ-Purdue Univ at Indianapolis	IN	5,862	LC
Ithaca College	NY	19,679	C
Jacksonville Univ	FL	13,390	C
James Madison Univ	VA	8,198	HC
John Carroll Univ	OH	16,510	C
Johns Hopkins Univ	MD	24,360	MC
Kent State Univ	OH	6,740	LC
Kenyon College	OH	22,430	HC+
Knox College	IL	18,990	VC
Lawrence Univ	WI	19,986	HC+
Lewis and Clark College	OR	19,980	VC
Lourdes College	OH	6,410	LC
Loyola Marymount Univ	CA	18,560	C
Lycoming College	PA	17,200	LC
Manhattanville College	NY	20,450	LC
Mansfield Univ	PA	6,348	C
Marian College	IN	12,936	C
Mars Hill College	NC	11,050	C
Marymount College/Tarrytown	NY	17,350	C
Mass College of Art	MA	9,447	SP
Messiah College	PA	14,664	VC
Mich State Univ	MI	7,842	C
Mills College	CA	20,848	VC
Moravian College	PA	18,960	VC
Mount Holyoke College	MA	23,630	VC
New College of the Univ of South Florida	FL	5,697	MC
Northeast Missouri State Univ	MO	5,654	VC+
Northwestern Univ	IL	21,093	MC
Oakland Univ	MI	6,714	VC
Occidental College	CA	21,792	HC
Ohio State Univ	OH	7,218	LC
Pacific Union College	CA	15,075	C
Penn State Univ/Univ Park Campus	PA	8,752	HC
Piedmont College	GA	8,540	LC
Pine Manor College	MA	21,700	LC
Plymouth State College	NH	7,166	C
Pratt Inst	NY	19,520	C
Providence College	RI	19,750	VC
Purdue Univ/West Lafayette	IN	6,636	C
Randolph-Macon College	VA	16,980	C
Rockford College	IL	15,300	C
Rollins College	FL	20,875	VC
Roosevelt Univ	IL	12,368	C
Rutgers Univ/Camden College of A&S	NJ	8,652	VC
Rutgers Univ/Douglass College	NJ	8,795	VC
Rutgers Univ/Livingston College	NJ	8,877	VC
Rutgers Univ/Newark College of A&S	NJ	8,645	C
Rutgers Univ/Rutgers College	NJ	8,841	HC+
Rutgers Univ/Univ College—Camden	NJ	3,506	C
Rutgers Univ/Univ College—New Brunswick	NJ	0	LC
St John's Univ	MN	15,364	C
St Joseph College	CT	16,225	C
St Olaf College	MN	17,200	HC
Salem College	NC	16,025	C
Savannah College of Art and Design	GA	14,280	SP
Scripps College	CA	23,600	HC
Skidmore College	NY	23,230	HC
Southern Conn State Univ	CT	7,532	C
Southern Methodist Univ	TX	18,520	VC
Southern Univ and A&M College	LA	4,920	NC
SUNY at Albany	NY	7,059	VC
SUNY at Binghamton	NY	7,921	HC
SUNY at Buffalo	NY	7,896	VC
SUNY at Stony Brook	NY	7,658	VC
SUNY/College at Brockport	NY	7,220	C+
SUNY/College at Plattsburgh	NY	6,917	C
SUNY/College at Purchase	NY	7,324	C
SUNY/Potsdam College	NY	6,906	C
Susquehanna Univ	PA	19,950	VC
Syracuse Univ	NY	21,305	HC
Temple Univ	PA	10,281	C
Texas Christian Univ	TX	12,180	C
Texas Tech Univ	TX	6,008	C
Troy State Univ	AL	4,322	C
Tufts Univ	MA	24,962	MC
Tulane Univ	LA	24,540	HC
Univ of Alabama	AL	5,702	C
Univ of Alabama at Birmingham	AL	7,533	C
Univ of Arizona	AZ	5,808	C
Univ of Arkansas at Little Rock	AR	4,419	C
Univ of Calif at Berkeley	CA	9,962	HC+
Univ of Calif at Davis	CA	9,534	VC
Univ of Calif at Los Angeles	CA	8,959	HC
Univ of Calif at Santa Barbara	CA	9,460	C
Univ of Calif, Riverside	CA	9,178	C
Univ of Calif, San Diego	CA	10,028	VC+
Univ of Calif/Irvine	CA	12,680	VC
Univ of Chicago	IL	24,517	MC
Univ of Colo at Boulder	CO	6,410	VC
Univ of Conn	CT	9,168	C
Univ of Delaware	DE	8,013	VC
Univ of Evansville	IN	15,300	VC
Univ of Florida	FL	5,850	HC
Univ of Hartford	CT	19,858	LC
Univ of Illinois at Chicago	IL	8,443	C
Univ of Illinois at Urbana-Champaign	IL	7,764	HC
Univ of Indianapolis	IN	14,510	C
Univ of Iowa	IA	5,658	VC
Univ of Kansas	KS	5,200	NC
Univ of Kentucky	KY	5,152	VC
Univ of Louisville	KY	5,948	C
Univ of Maryland/College Park	MD	8,182	VC
Univ of Maryland/Univ College	MD	4,900	NC
Univ of Mass Dartmouth	MA	8,158	C
Univ of Mass/Amherst	MA	9,364	LC
Univ of Memphis	TN	3,476	C
Univ of Miami	FL	22,107	VC
Univ of Mich/Ann Arbor	MI	9,428	HC+
Univ of Mich/Dearborn	MI	3,399	HC
Univ of Minn/Morris	MN	6,825	HC
Univ of Minn/Twin Cities	MN	6,682	VC
Univ of Miss	MS	5,756	C
Univ of Missouri/Columbia	MO	6,254	HC
Univ of Missouri/St. Louis	MO	6,378	C
Univ of Nebr-Lincoln	NE	5,278	LC
Univ of N Car at Chapel Hill	NC	5,330	HC
Univ of North Florida	FL	5,082	C
Univ of North Texas	TX	4,853	C
Univ of Oregon	OR	6,466	VC
Univ of Penn	PA	24,238	MC
Univ of PR/Rio Piedras	PR	0	
Univ of Rochester	NY	23,696	HC
Univ of St Thomas	MN	15,785	C+
Univ of South Alabama	AL	5,451	C
Univ of S Car	SC	6,158	C
Univ of Tenn/Knoxville	TN	5,668	C
Univ of Texas at Arlington	TX	5,549	LC
Univ of Texas at Austin	TX	5,160	VC
Univ of the Pacific	CA	21,100	C
Univ of Utah	UT	5,975	C
Univ of Washington	WA	6,618	VC
Univ of Wisc/Madison	WI	6,400	HC
Univ of Wisc/Milwaukee	WI	6,165	C
Univ of Wisc/Whitewater	WI	4,700	C
Wayne State Univ	MI	2,680	C
Wellesley College	MA	23,815	MC
Wheaton College	MA	23,840	C+
William Paterson College	NJ	7,438	C+
Williams College	MA	24,390	MC
Winthrop Univ	SC	6,750	C
Wofford College	SC	15,360	VC
Wright State Univ	OH	6,896	LC
Youngstown State Univ	OH	6,447	LC

ART THERAPY

School	ST	$IS	SR
Anna Maria College	MA	15,975	LC
Barat College	IL	13,990	C
Beaver College	PA	17,660	C
Bowling Green State Univ	OH	6,701	C
Brescia College	KY	9,800	C
Capital Univ	OH	16,535	VC
College of New Rochelle	NY	15,440	LC
College of Our Lady of The Elms	MA	15,639	C
Edgewood College	WI	11,700	C
Emmanuel College	MA	17,773	LC
LIU/C. W. Post Campus	NY	16,870	C
Mercyhurst College	PA	13,488	C
Mount Mary College	WI	10,920	C
Russell Sage College	NY	16,790	C
Seton Hill College	PA	14,320	C
Springfield College	MA	15,200	LC
Univ of Findlay	OH	15,764	C
Univ of Indianapolis	IN	14,510	C
Ursuline College	OH	13,180	LC

ARTS ADMINISTRATION/ MANAGEMENT

School	ST	$IS	SR
Adrian College	MI	14,340	C
Aquinas College	MI	14,526	C
Barry Univ	FL	16,050	C
Buena Vista College	IA	16,150	VC
Butler Univ	IN	16,210	C
Cabrini College	PA	16,012	C
Catawba College	NC	12,950	C
Center for Creative Studies/College of Art and Design	MI	15,330	SP
College of Our Lady of The Elms	MA	15,639	C
Columbia College	IL	7,879	SP
Culver-Stockton College	MO	11,150	C
Elmhurst College	IL	12,536	C
Georgia College	GA	4,310	LC
Linfield College	OR	16,670	VC
LIU/C. W. Post Campus	NY	16,870	C
Mary Baldwin College	VA	17,700	LC
Marywood College	PA	14,890	C
Methodist College	NC	12,400	C
Pembroke State Univ	NC	3,538	LC
Pfeiffer College	NC	11,670	LC
Point Park College	PA	13,922	LC
Quincy Univ	IL	13,646	VC
Randolph-Macon College	VA	16,980	C
Russell Sage College	NY	16,790	C
Salem College	NC	16,025	C
Simmons College	MA	22,534	C
Southeastern Louisiana Univ	LA	4,230	NC
Univ of Charleston	WV	12,750	C
Univ of Kentucky	KY	5,152	VC
Univ of Mich/Dearborn	MI	3,399	HC
Univ of the Pacific	CA	21,100	C
Univ of Wisc/Stevens Point	WI	5,047	C+
Ursuline College	OH	13,180	LC
Viterbo College	WI	12,670	C
Wagner College	NY	17,950	C
Wesleyan College	GA	15,445	C
Wright State Univ	OH	6,896	LC

ASIAN/AMERICAN STUDIES

School	ST	$IS	SR
Univ of Calif at Berkeley	CA	9,962	HC+
Univ of Washington	WA	6,618	VC

ASIAN/ORIENTAL STUDIES

School	ST	$IS	SR
Amherst College	MA	24,152	MC
Bard College	NY	25,269	HC
Bowdoin College	ME	24,155	MC
Brigham Young Univ	UT	5,625	HC
Carleton College	MN	22,155	HC
Case Western Reserve Univ	OH	19,910	HC
CUNY/City College	NY	2,543	VC
Claremont McKenna College	CA	22,150	MC
Coe College	IA	17,085	VC
Colgate Univ	NY	24,020	HC
Columbia Univ/Columbia College	NY	26,757	MC
Conn College	CT	24,160	HC
Cornell Univ	NY	13,445	MC
Dartmouth College	NH	24,354	MC
Florida State Univ	FL	5,814	VC
Furman Univ	SC	16,557	VC
Hamilton College	NY	23,500	HC
Hampshire College	MA	25,320	C
Harvard Univ/Harvard and Radcliffe Colleges	MA	24,880	MC
Hawaii Pacific Univ	HI	12,300	C
Hobart and William Smith Colleges	NY	23,925	VC
Hofstra Univ	NY	16,580	VC
Kenyon College	OH	22,430	HC+
Manhattanville College	NY	20,450	LC
Mount Holyoke College	MA	23,630	VC
Okla City Univ	OK	9,840	C
Pitzer College	CA	23,780	HC
Pomona College	CA	23,820	MC
Rutgers Univ/Livingston College	NJ	8,877	VC
Rutgers Univ/Univ College—New Brunswick	NJ	0	LC
St Lawrence Univ	NY	23,420	VC
St Olaf College	MN	17,200	HC
Sarah Lawrence College	NY	24,975	HC
Scripps College	CA	23,600	HC
Seton Hall Univ	NJ	18,306	LC
Southwest Texas State Univ	TX	5,124	C
SUNY at Albany	NY	7,059	VC
Temple Univ	PA	10,281	C
Tufts Univ	MA	24,962	MC
Tulane Univ	LA	24,540	HC
Univ of Alabama	AL	5,702	C
Univ of Calif at Berkeley	CA	9,962	HC+
Univ of Calif at Santa Barbara	CA	9,460	C
Univ of Calif, Riverside	CA	9,178	C
Univ of Chicago	IL	24,517	MC
Univ of Cincinnati	OH	7,989	C
Univ of Colo at Boulder	CO	6,410	VC
Univ of Florida	FL	5,850	HC
Univ of Hawaii at Manoa	HI	5,626	C
Univ of Iowa	IA	5,658	VC
Univ of Mich/Ann Arbor	MI	9,428	HC+
Univ of Northern Iowa	IA	5,137	C
Univ of Okla	OK	5,427	VC
Univ of Oregon	OR	6,466	VC
Univ of Puget Sound	WA	19,520	HC
Univ of Redlands	CA	22,059	VC
Univ of Tenn/Knoxville	TN	5,668	C
Univ of Texas at Austin	TX	5,160	VC
Univ of Washington	WA	6,618	VC
Univ of Wisc/Madison	WI	6,400	HC
Vassar College	NY	24,206	HC
Washington Univ	MO	23,507	HC
Wellesley College	MA	23,815	MC
Wesleyan Univ	CT	23,770	MC
Wheaton College	MA	23,840	C+
Williams College	MA	24,390	MC

ASTRONOMY

School	ST	$IS	SR
Amherst College	MA	24,152	MC
Benedictine College	KS	12,830	C
Boston Univ	MA	24,130	HC
Bryn Mawr College	PA	24,110	MC
Calif Inst of Tech	CA	20,783	MC
Case Western Reserve Univ	OH	19,910	HC
Colgate Univ	NY	24,020	HC
Columbia Univ/Barnard College	NY	25,492	HC
Columbia Univ/Columbia College	NY	26,757	MC
Cornell Univ	NY	13,445	MC
Eastern College	PA	15,150	C+
Harvard Univ/Harvard and Radcliffe Colleges	MA	24,880	MC
Haverford College	PA	23,950	MC
Indiana Univ Bloomington	IN	6,495	VC
Lycoming College	PA	17,200	LC
Mount Holyoke College	MA	23,630	VC
Mount Union College	OH	15,850	C
Northwestern Univ	IL	21,093	MC
Ohio State Univ	OH	7,218	LC
Penn State Univ/Univ Park Campus	PA	8,752	HC
Smith College	MA	24,236	HC
SUNY at Stony Brook	NY	7,658	VC
Texas Christian Univ	TX	12,180	C
Univ of Arizona	AZ	5,808	C
Univ of Delaware	DE	8,013	VC
Univ of Florida	FL	5,850	HC
Univ of Iowa	IA	5,658	VC
Univ of Kansas	KS	5,200	NC
Univ of Maryland/College Park	MD	8,182	VC
Univ of Mass/Amherst	MA	9,364	LC
Univ of Mich/Ann Arbor	MI	9,428	HC+
Univ of Minn/Twin Cities	MN	6,682	VC
Univ of N Car at Chapel Hill	NC	5,330	HC
Univ of Okla	OK	5,427	VC
Univ of Penn	PA	24,238	MC
Univ of Pittsburgh	PA	9,472	C
Univ of Texas at Austin	TX	5,160	VC
Univ of Virginia	VA	7,964	MC
Univ of Washington	WA	6,618	VC
Univ of Wisc/Madison	WI	6,400	HC
Univ of Wyoming	WY	4,991	HC
Valdosta State Univ	GA	4,670	LC
Valparaiso Univ	IN	14,810	VC
Vanderbilt Univ	TN	23,422	HC+
Villanova Univ	PA	21,400	HC
Wellesley College	MA	23,815	MC
Wesleyan Univ	CT	23,770	MC
Williams College	MA	24,390	MC
Yale Univ	CT	25,110	MC
Youngstown State Univ	OH	6,447	LC

ASTROPHYSICS

School	ST	$IS	SR
Agnes Scott College	GA	17,135	VC
Boston Univ	MA	24,130	HC
Cal State/Northridge	CA	7,122	LC
Columbia Univ/Columbia College	NY	26,757	MC
Mich State Univ	MI	7,842	C
Princeton Univ	NJ	24,650	MC
Univ of Calif at Berkeley	CA	9,962	HC+
Univ of Calif at Los Angeles	CA	8,959	HC

School	ST	$IS	SR
Univ of Minn/Twin Cities	MN	6,682	VC
Univ of Okla	OK	5,427	VC
Villanova Univ	PA	21,400	HC
Williams College	MA	24,390	MC

ATHLETIC TRAINING

School	ST	$IS	SR
Lincoln Memorial Univ	TN	8,218	C

ATMOSPHERIC SCIENCES AND METEOROLOGY

School	ST	$IS	SR
Arizona State Univ Main Campus	AZ	6,444	C
Cornell Univ	NY	13,445	MC
Creighton Univ	NE	14,432	VC
Florida State Univ	FL	5,814	VC
Iowa State Univ	IA	5,456	C
Jackson State Univ	MS	4,996	LC
Lyndon State College	VT	8,394	LC
Mass Inst of Tech	MA	24,800	MC
Metropolitan State College of Denver	CO	1,751	NC
Millersville Univ of Penn	PA	7,370	VC
N Car State Univ	NC	4,984	VC
Northeast Louisiana Univ	LA	3,906	NC
Northern Illinois Univ	IL	6,408	C
Oregon State Univ	OR	6,175	C
Penn State Univ/Univ Park Campus	PA	8,752	HC
Plymouth State College	NH	7,166	C
Purdue Univ/West Lafayette	IN	6,636	C
Rutgers Univ/Cook College	NJ	9,197	HC
Rutgers Univ/Douglass College	NJ	8,795	VC
St Cloud State Univ	MN	5,015	C
SUNY at Stony Brook	NY	7,658	VC
SUNY/College at Brockport	NY	7,220	C+
SUNY/College at Oswego	NY	7,330	VC
SUNY/Maritime College	NY	7,170	C
Texas A&M Univ	TX	5,382	VC
Univ of Arizona	AZ	5,808	C
Univ of Calif at Davis	CA	9,534	VC
Univ of Calif at Los Angeles	CA	8,959	HC
Univ of Hawaii at Manoa	HI	5,626	C
Univ of Kansas	KS	5,200	NC
Univ of Lowell	MA	8,831	VC
Univ of Mich/Ann Arbor	MI	9,428	HC+
Univ of Missouri/Columbia	MO	6,254	HC
Univ of Nebr-Lincoln	NE	5,278	LC
Univ of N Car at Asheville	NC	4,791	VC
Univ of N Dak	ND	4,902	NC
Univ of Northern Colo	CO	6,008	C
Univ of Okla	OK	5,427	VC
Univ of Utah	UT	5,975	C
Univ of Washington	WA	6,618	VC
Univ of Wisc/Madison	WI	6,400	HC
Valparaiso Univ	IN	14,810	VC
Western Conn State Univ	CT	6,622	C

AUDIO TECHNOLOGY

School	ST	$IS	SR
American Univ	DC	21,230	VC+
Barton College	NC	10,689	LC
Five Towns College	NY	11,200	SP
Univ of Hartford	CT	19,858	LC
Univ of Miami	FL	22,107	VC
Univ of New Haven	CT	14,980	C

AUTOMOTIVE TECHNOLOGY

School	ST	$IS	SR
Idaho State Univ	ID	4,442	C
Northern Montana College	MT	4,976	C
Weber State Univ	UT	4,398	C
Western Mich Univ	MI	6,820	C

AVIAN SCIENCES

School	ST	$IS	SR
Univ of Calif at Davis	CA	9,534	VC

AVIATION ADMINISTRATION/ MANAGEMENT

School	ST	$IS	SR
Auburn Univ	AL	5,823	C+
Averett College	VA	13,610	LC
Baker College	MI	6,971	NC
Bridgewater State College	MA	7,518	C
Cal State/Los Angeles	CA	4,940	VC
Dallas Baptist Univ	TX	9,620	LC
Daniel Webster College	NH	16,484	LC
Delta State Univ	MS	3,964	LC
Eastern Mich Univ	MI	6,749	C
Embry-Riddle Aeronautical Univ	AZ	9,896	C+
Florida Memorial College	FL	7,600	C+
Geneva College	PA	13,030	C
Kent State Univ	OH	6,740	LC
Lewis Univ	IL	14,797	LC
Lynn Univ	FL	18,300	C
Metropolitan State College of Denver	CO	1,751	NC
Northeast Louisiana Univ	LA	3,906	NC
Phillips Univ	OK	12,744	C
Rocky Mountain College	MT	11,320	C
St Francis College	NY	6,710	LC
St Martin's College	WA	14,965	C
Southern Nazarene Univ	OK	9,206	NC
Univ of Dubuque	IA	14,150	LC
Univ of New Haven	CT	14,980	C
Univ of N Dak	ND	4,902	NC
Westminster College of Salt Lake City	UT	12,100	C

AVIATION COMPUTER TECHNOLOGY

School	ST	$IS	SR
Delta State Univ	MS	3,964	LC
Eastern Mich Univ	MI	6,749	C
Florida Memorial College	FL	7,600	C+
Kent State Univ	OH	6,740	LC
Le Tourneau Univ	TX	12,500	C+
Metropolitan State College of Denver	CO	1,751	NC
Purdue Univ/West Lafayette	IN	6,636	C
Suffolk Univ	MA	15,360	LC

BACTERIOLOGY

School	ST	$IS	SR
Univ of Calif at Davis	CA	9,534	VC
Univ of Idaho	ID	4,830	C
Univ of Wisc/Madison	WI	6,400	HC

BANKING AND FINANCE

School	ST	$IS	SR
Abilene Christian Univ	TX	10,460	NC
Adelphi Univ	NY	18,250	LC
Alabama State Univ	AL	3,428	NC
Alfred Univ	NY	21,054	VC+
Allentown College of St Francis de Sales	PA	13,480	C
Alvernia College	PA	13,150	LC
American Univ	DC	21,230	VC+
Anderson Univ	IN	12,920	C
Angelo State Univ	TX	5,176	C
Anna Maria College	MA	15,975	LC
Appalachian State Univ	NC	4,095	C
Arizona State Univ Main Campus	AZ	6,444	C
Arkansas State Univ	AR	4,250	NC
Auburn Univ	AL	5,823	C+
Auburn Univ at Montgomery	AL	3,390	C
Augsburg College	MN	15,608	C
Augusta College	GA	1,452	C
Aurora Univ	IL	13,381	C
Austin Peay State Univ	TN	4,350	C
Averett College	VA	13,610	LC
Avila College	MO	12,130	C
Babson College	MA	23,160	VC
Baker Univ	KS	12,284	C
Baldwin-Wallace College	OH	15,210	C
Ball State Univ	IN	6,032	LC
Barry Univ	FL	16,050	C
Baylor Univ	TX	10,990	C+
Beaver College	PA	17,660	C
Bentley College	MA	18,680	C
Berry College	GA	11,990	VC
Bethel College	MN	15,050	C
Bluffton College	OH	12,951	C
Boise State Univ	ID	4,909	LC
Boston College	MA	22,706	MC
Boston Univ	MA	24,130	HC
Bowling Green State Univ	OH	6,701	C
Bradley Univ	IL	14,718	C+
Brescia College	KY	9,800	C
Bridgewater State College	MA	7,518	C
Brigham Young Univ	UT	5,625	HC
Brooklyn Campus of LIU	NY	15,000	LC
Bryant College	RI	18,335	C
Buena Vista College	IA	16,150	VC
Butler Univ	IN	16,210	C
Calif State Polytechnic Univ/ Pomona	CA	6,438	LC
Cal State/Bakersfield	CA	5,402	C
Cal State/Fresno	CA	5,747	C
Cal State/Fullerton	CA	4,850	LC
Cal State/Long Beach	CA	6,057	LC
Cal State/Los Angeles	CA	4,940	VC
Cal State/Northridge	CA	7,122	LC
Cal State/Sacramento	CA	6,387	C
Cal State/San Bernardino	CA	6,055	LC
Cameron Univ	OK	3,686	LC
Canisius College	NY	15,510	C
Caribbean Univ	PR	2,400	
Cedarville College	OH	10,715	C
Central Conn State Univ	CT	7,108	C
Central Mich Univ	MI	6,737	LC
Central Missouri State Univ	MO	5,138	LC
Central State Univ	OH	7,320	NC
Central Washington Univ	WA	5,644	C
Chicago State Univ	IL	2,198	C
Christopher Newport Univ	VA	3,196	LC
City Univ	WA	6,400	NC
CUNY/Brooklyn College	NY	2,450	VC
Clarion Univ of Penn	PA	6,518	C
Clarkson Univ	NY	20,705	VC+
Clemson Univ	SC	6,564	VC
Cleveland State Univ	OH	7,287	NC
Coastal Carolina Univ	SC	6,010	LC
College of Insurance	NY	17,600	VC
College of Notre Dame	CA	16,480	C
College of Notre Dame of Maryland	MD	16,050	C
College of St Francis	IL	13,060	VC
Colo State Univ	CO	6,566	VC
Columbia College	MO	11,995	C
Concord College	WV	5,104	NC
Concordia College	MN	13,200	C
Coppin State College	MD	7,145	LC
Creighton Univ	NE	14,432	VC
Dallas Baptist Univ	TX	9,620	LC
Dana College	NE	11,910	C
David Lipscomb Univ	TN	7,865	VC
Defiance College	OH	13,480	LC
Delta State Univ	MS	3,964	LC
DePaul Univ	IL	15,535	VC
Detroit College of Business	MI	5,184	NC
Dowling College	NY	12,730	LC
Drake Univ	IA	17,195	VC
Drexel Univ	PA	15,970	C
Duquesne Univ	PA	16,434	VC
East Carolina Univ	NC	4,498	C
East Central Univ	OK	3,558	C
East Tenn State Univ	TN	4,406	C
East Texas State Univ	TX	4,572	LC
Eastern Illinois Univ	IL	5,548	C
Eastern Kentucky Univ	KY	4,840	NC
Eastern Mich Univ	MI	6,749	C
Eastern Montana College	MT	5,165	LC
Eastern New Mexico Univ	NM	3,950	C
Eastern Washington Univ	WA	5,439	LC
Elmhurst College	IL	12,536	C
Emory Univ	GA	21,930	HC
Emporia State Univ	KS	4,685	NC
Fairfield Univ	CT	20,460	VC
Fairmont State College	WV	4,640	LC
Fayetteville State Univ	NC	3,926	LC
Ferris State Univ	MI	7,160	NC
Ferrum College	VA	12,800	LC
Florida A&M Univ	FL	4,651	C
Florida Atlantic Univ	FL	5,525	C
Florida International Univ	FL	4,191	VC
Florida Southern College	FL	12,260	C
Florida State Univ	FL	5,814	VC
Fontbonne College	MO	12,090	C
Fordham Univ/College of Business Administration	NY	19,875	VC
Francis Marion Univ	SC	5,878	LC
Franklin College of Indiana	IN	13,970	C
Franklin Pierce College	NH	17,270	LC
Franklin Univ	OH	4,621	NC
Freed-Hardeman Univ	TN	8,585	VC
Gannon Univ	PA	14,872	C
George Mason Univ	VA	8,728	C
George Washington Univ	DC	22,470	HC
Georgetown College	KY	10,990	C
Georgetown Univ	DC	24,410	MC
Georgia Southern Univ	GA	4,988	LC
Georgia State Univ	GA	2,019	C
Golden Gate Univ	CA	5,623	VC
Goldey-Beacom College	DE	7,839	C
Gonzaga Univ	WA	16,350	VC
Grambling State Univ	LA	4,712	NC
Grand Canyon Univ	AZ	9,680	VC
Grand Valley State Univ	MI	6,822	VC
Grove City College	PA	7,870	HC
Hampton Univ	VA	10,706	C
Hannibal-LaGrange College	MO	8,400	LC
Hardin-Simmons Univ	TX	9,080	C
Hillsdale College	MI	15,110	VC
Hofstra Univ	NY	16,580	VC
Houston Baptist Univ	TX	11,055	C
Howard Univ	DC	11,680	C
Husson College	ME	11,510	NC
Idaho State Univ	ID	4,442	C
Illinois Benedictine College	IL	14,170	C
Illinois State Univ	IL	6,413	C
Illinois Wesleyan Univ	IL	18,590	HC+
Incarnate Word College	TX	12,307	C
Indiana State Univ	IN	6,210	C
Indiana Univ Bloomington	IN	6,495	VC
Indiana Univ Southeast	IN	2,260	LC
Indiana Univ-Purdue Univ at Fort Wayne	IN	2,500	LC
Indiana Univ-Purdue Univ at Indianapolis	IN	5,862	LC
Indiana Wesleyan Univ	IN	12,332	C
Inter American Univ of PR/ Aguadilla Regional College	PR	2,290	
Inter American Univ of PR/ Bayamon Univ College	PR	2,300	
Inter American Univ of PR/ Metropolitan Campus	PR	2,340	
Inter American Univ of PR/ Ponce Regional College	PR	2,300	
Inter American Univ of PR/ San German	PR	4,620	
Inter-American Univ of PR/ Fajardo Regional College	PR	2,732	
Iona College	NY	16,310	C
Iowa State Univ	IA	5,456	C
Ithaca College	NY	19,679	C
Jackson State Univ	MS	4,996	LC
Jacksonville State Univ	AL	4,080	LC
Jacksonville Univ	FL	13,390	C
James Madison Univ	VA	8,198	HC
Jersey City State College	NJ	7,797	LC
John Carroll Univ	OH	16,510	C
Juniata College	PA	18,390	C+
Kansas State Univ	KS	4,816	NC
Kean College of New Jersey	NJ	6,395	LC
Kennesaw State College	GA	1,553	C
Kent State Univ	OH	6,740	LC
King's College	PA	15,420	C
La Roche College	PA	12,977	LC
La Salle Univ	PA	16,940	VC
Lawrence Tech Univ	MI	9,470	C
Lehigh Univ	PA	23,250	HC
Lewis Univ	IL	14,797	LC
Liberty Univ	VA	11,500	LC
Lincoln Memorial Univ	TN	8,218	C
Lincoln Univ	PA	0	LC
Linfield College	OR	16,670	VC
LIU/C. W. Post Campus	NY	16,870	C
Loras College	IA	14,160	C
Louisiana State Univ and A&M College	LA	5,605	C
Louisiana State Univ in Shreveport	LA	1,910	NC
Louisiana Tech Univ	LA	4,284	C
Loyola Univ of Chicago	IL	15,880	C+
Loyola Univ/New Orleans	LA	15,660	C+
Lubbock Christian Univ	TX	9,840	NC
Madonna Univ	MI	8,546	C
Manchester College	IN	13,240	LC
Manhattan College	NY	19,000	C
Mankato State Univ	MN	5,097	LC
Marian College	IN	12,936	C
Marquette Univ	WI	16,114	VC
Marshall Univ	WV	5,762	LC
Marymount College/ Tarrytown	NY	17,350	C
Marymount Univ	VA	15,930	C
McMurry Univ	TX	10,100	C
Menlo College	CA	20,375	LC
Mercer Univ	GA	15,123	C
Mercy College	NY	11,180	NC
Mercyhurst College	PA	13,488	C
Mesa State College	CO	5,127	NC
Metropolitan State College of Denver	CO	1,751	NC
Miami Univ	OH	8,066	VC
Middle Tenn State Univ	TN	3,857	C
Midwestern State Univ	TX	4,542	LC
Millersville Univ of Penn	PA	7,370	VC
Millikin Univ	IL	15,499	C
Miss College	MS	8,348	C
Miss State Univ	MS	5,629	VC
Monmouth College	NJ	16,820	C
Moorhead State Univ	MN	5,076	C
Morehead State Univ	KY	4,600	LC
Morehouse College	GA	13,224	LC
Mount St Mary's College	MD	17,825	LC
Murray State Univ	KY	4,702	C
National Univ	CA	6,135	C
New Mexico State Univ	NM	4,844	LC
New York Inst of Tech/Old Westbury	NY	13,914	LC
New York Univ	NY	24,705	VC+
Nicholls State Univ	LA	4,531	NC
Nichols College	MA	14,200	LC
Norfolk State Univ	VA	6,345	LC
North Central College	IL	15,498	VC
North Georgia College	GA	4,103	LC
North Park College	IL	14,310	C

School	ST	$IS	SR
Northeast Louisiana Univ	LA	3,906	NC
Northeastern Illinois Univ	IL	1,955	C
Northeastern State Univ	OK	5,250	C
Northeastern Univ	MA	19,851	C
Northern Arizona Univ	AZ	4,844	C
Northern Illinois Univ	IL	6,408	C
Northern Mich Univ	MI	6,350	C
Northern State Univ	SD	4,186	LC
Northwest Missouri State Univ	MO	5,010	LC
Northwest Nazarene College	ID	11,750	C
Northwestern College	MN	13,554	C
Northwood Univ	FL	14,569	C
Oakland Univ	MI	6,714	VC
Ohio Northern Univ	OH	18,660	VC
Ohio State Univ	OH	7,218	LC
Ohio Univ	OH	7,341	C
Okla Baptist Univ	OK	8,486	C
Okla Christian Univ of Science and Arts	OK	8,790	NC
Okla City Univ	OK	9,840	C
Okla State Univ	OK	5,086	VC
Old Dominion Univ	VA	8,317	C
Olivet Nazarene Univ	IL	11,976	C
Oregon State Univ	OR	6,175	C
Otterbein College	OH	16,506	C
Ouachita Baptist Univ	AR	8,940	C
Pace Univ	NY	15,540	C
Pacific Univ	OR	17,869	C
Palm Beach Atlantic College	FL	10,720	C
Park College	MO	7,320	C
Penn State Univ/Univ Park Campus	PA	8,752	HC
Philadelphia College of Textiles and Science	PA	15,896	C
Phillips Univ	OK	12,744	C
Pittsburg State Univ	KS	4,478	NC
Pontifical Catholic Univ of PR/Ponce	PR	5,807	
Portland State Univ	OR	7,191	C
Prairie View A&M Univ	TX	4,740	LC
Providence College	RI	19,750	VC
Purdue Univ/Calumet	IN	2,374	NC
Quincy Univ	IL	13,646	VC
Quinnipiac College	CT	17,600	C+
Radford Univ	VA	7,034	LC
Ramapo College of New Jersey	NJ	8,027	C+
Richard Stockton College of New Jersey	NJ	6,950	VC
Rider College	NJ	18,160	C
Robert Morris College	PA	10,406	LC
Rochester Inst of Tech	NY	18,954	VC
Rockhurst College	MO	12,470	C
Roosevelt Univ	IL	12,368	C
Rutgers Univ/Douglass College	NJ	8,795	VC
Rutgers Univ/Livingston College	NJ	8,877	VC
Rutgers Univ/Newark College of A&S	NJ	8,645	C
Rutgers Univ/Rutgers College	NJ	8,841	HC+
Rutgers Univ/Univ College—New Brunswick	NJ	0	LC
Rutgers Univ/Univ College—Newark	NJ	0	C
Sacred Heart Univ	CT	16,350	C
Saginaw Valley State Univ	MI	6,634	LC
St Anselm College	NH	17,340	C
St Bonaventure Univ	NY	14,762	C
St Cloud State Univ	MN	5,015	C
St Edward's Univ	TX	12,636	C
St John's Univ	NY	8,980	C+
St Joseph's College	IN	14,730	C
St Joseph's Univ	PA	17,800	VC
St Louis Univ	MO	15,522	VC
St Martin's College	WA	14,965	C
St Mary's College of Calif	CA	18,848	VC
St Mary's Univ	TX	12,064	C
St Thomas Aquinas College	NY	13,550	C
St Thomas Univ	FL	14,280	LC
St Vincent College	PA	13,934	LC
St Xavier Univ	IL	14,700	C
Salem State College	MA	6,712	C
Sam Houston State Univ	TX	4,506	LC
San Francisco State Univ	CA	7,292	LC
San Jose State Univ	CA	6,680	LC
Santa Clara Univ	CA	18,783	VC
Seattle Univ	WA	16,590	C
Seton Hall Univ	NJ	18,306	LC
Seton Hill College	PA	14,320	C
Shorter College	GA	10,270	C
Siena College	NY	15,410	VC
Simmons College	MA	22,534	C
Simpson College	IA	14,635	VC
Sonoma State Univ	CA	6,996	LC
Southeast Missouri State Univ	MO	5,854	C
Southeastern Univ	DC	6,625	C
Southern Arkansas Univ	AR	3,432	NC
Southern Calif College	CA	12,356	C
Southern Conn State Univ	CT	7,532	C
Southern Illinois Univ at Carbondale	IL	6,234	C
Southwest Missouri State Univ	MO	4,956	C

School	ST	$IS	SR
Southwest Texas State Univ	TX	5,124	C
Southwestern Okla State Univ	OK	3,312	C
Spring Hill College	AL	16,015	C+
SUNY/College at New Paltz	NY	6,890	VC
SUNY/College at Old Westbury	NY	7,128	LC
Stephen F. Austin State Univ	TX	5,117	C
Stetson Univ	FL	16,435	VC
Stonehill College	MA	17,481	VC
Suffolk Univ	MA	15,360	LC
Syracuse Univ	NY	21,305	HC
Tarleton State Univ	TX	4,082	LC
Teikyo Marycrest Univ	IA	13,755	VC
Teikyo Post Univ	CT	16,360	LC
Teikyo Westmar Univ	IA	15,920	C
Temple Univ	PA	10,281	C
Texas A&M Univ	TX	5,382	VC
Texas A&M Univ at Kingsville	TX	3,808	LC
Texas Christian Univ	TX	12,180	C
Texas Tech Univ	TX	6,008	C
Texas Wesleyan Univ	TX	9,380	LC
The Univ of New Mexico	NM	5,304	C
Thomas More College	KY	12,962	C
Trenton State College	NJ	9,085	HC
Trinity Christian College	IL	13,260	C
Trinity College of Vermont	VT	16,015	LC
Troy State Univ	AL	4,322	C
Troy State Univ in Montgomery	AL	1,710	NC
Tuskegee Univ	AL	10,128	C
Univ of Akron	OH	6,699	NC
Univ of Alabama	AL	5,702	C
Univ of Alabama at Birmingham	AL	7,533	C
Univ of Alabama at Huntsville	AL	5,868	VC
Univ of Alaska Anchorage	AK	7,131	C
Univ of Arizona	AZ	5,808	C
Univ of Arkansas at Fayetteville	AR	5,046	C
Univ of Arkansas at Little Rock	AR	4,419	C
Univ of Bridgeport	CT	18,985	C
Univ of Central Florida	FL	6,061	C+
Univ of Charleston	WV	12,750	C
Univ of Cincinnati	OH	7,989	C
Univ of Colo at Denver	CO	1,955	VC
Univ of Conn	CT	9,168	C
Univ of Dayton	OH	15,120	C+
Univ of Denver	CO	19,290	C+
Univ of Detroit Mercy	MI	14,720	C
Univ of Evansville	IN	15,300	VC
Univ of Findlay	OH	15,764	C
Univ of Florida	FL	5,850	HC
Univ of Georgia	GA	5,655	VC
Univ of Hawaii at Manoa	HI	5,626	C
Univ of Houston	TX	5,215	C
Univ of Houston-Downtown	TX	4,034	NC
Univ of Idaho	ID	4,830	C
Univ of Illinois at Chicago	IL	8,443	C
Univ of Illinois at Urbana-Champaign	IL	7,764	HC
Univ of Indianapolis	IN	14,510	C
Univ of Iowa	IA	5,658	VC
Univ of Kentucky	KY	5,152	VC
Univ of Lowell	MA	8,831	VC
Univ of Mary Hardin-Baylor	TX	8,120	NC
Univ of Maryland/College Park	MD	8,182	VC
Univ of Maryland/Univ College	MD	4,900	NC
Univ of Mass Dartmouth	MA	8,158	C
Univ of Memphis	TN	3,476	C
Univ of Miami	FL	22,107	VC
Univ of Mich/Flint	MI	2,916	C
Univ of Miss	MS	5,756	C
Univ of Missouri/Columbia	MO	6,254	HC
Univ of Mobile	AL	9,400	C
Univ of Montana	MT	5,529	C
Univ of Nebr at Kearney	NE	4,308	LC
Univ of Nebr at Omaha	NE	1,889	LC
Univ of Nebr-Lincoln	NE	5,278	LC
Univ of Nevada/Las Vegas	NV	6,405	C
Univ of Nevada/Reno	NV	5,735	C
Univ of New Haven	CT	14,980	C
Univ of New Orleans	LA	5,468	C
Univ of North Alabama	AL	4,236	NC
Univ of N Car at Charlotte	NC	4,597	C
Univ of N Car at Greensboro	NC	5,192	C
Univ of N Dak	ND	4,902	NC
Univ of North Florida	FL	5,082	C
Univ of North Texas	TX	4,853	C
Univ of Northern Iowa	IA	5,137	C
Univ of Notre Dame	IN	20,150	MC
Univ of Okla	OK	5,427	VC
Univ of Oregon	OR	6,466	VC
Univ of Penn	PA	24,238	MC
Univ of Pittsburgh at Johnstown	PA	8,914	C
Univ of Portland	OR	15,564	C
Univ of PR/Mayaguez	PR	0	
Univ of PR/Rio Piedras	PR	0	
Univ of Rhode Island	RI	9,205	C
Univ of Richmond	VA	16,700	HC
Univ of St Thomas	MN	15,785	C+

School	ST	$IS	SR
Univ of San Francisco	CA	18,408	C
Univ of Scranton	PA	17,071	VC
Univ of South Alabama	AL	5,451	C
Univ of S Car	SC	6,158	C
Univ of Southern Indiana	IN	3,720	NC
Univ of Southern Miss	MS	4,542	C
Univ of Southwestern Louisiana	LA	3,968	NC
Univ of Tampa	FL	16,780	C
Univ of Tenn at Martin	TN	4,550	C
Univ of Tenn/Knoxville	TN	5,668	C
Univ of Texas at Arlington	TX	5,549	LC
Univ of Texas at El Paso	TX	3,160	LC
Univ of Texas at San Antonio	TX	6,420	C
Univ of Texas-Pan American	TX	3,192	NC
Univ of the District of Columbia	DC	974	NC
Univ of Toledo	OH	6,636	NC
Univ of Tulsa	OK	13,795	VC
Univ of Utah	UT	5,975	C
Univ of Washington	WA	6,618	VC
Univ of West Florida	FL	5,415	C
Univ of Wisc/Eau Claire	WI	4,647	C
Univ of Wisc/La Crosse	WI	4,487	C
Univ of Wisc/Madison	WI	6,400	HC
Univ of Wisc/Milwaukee	WI	6,165	C
Univ of Wisc/Whitewater	WI	4,700	C
Univ of Wyoming	WY	4,991	NC
Urbana Univ	OH	12,536	C
Utah State Univ	UT	4,683	C
Valdosta State Univ	GA	4,670	LC
Valparaiso Univ	IN	14,810	VC
Villanova Univ	PA	21,400	HC
Virginia Polytechnic Inst and State Univ	VA	6,828	C
Virginia Union Univ	VA	10,555	LC
Wagner College	NY	17,950	C
Walsh Univ	OH	11,640	C
Wartburg College	IA	14,530	VC
Washburn Univ of Topeka	KS	5,802	NC
Washington State Univ	WA	6,364	C
Wayne State Univ	MI	2,680	C
Webber College	FL	8,710	C
West Georgia College	GA	4,256	C
West Liberty State College	WV	4,690	LC
West Texas A&M Univ	TX	4,224	C
West Virginia Inst of Tech	WV	5,858	LC
West Virginia State College	WV	5,044	LC
West Virginia Univ	WV	5,774	C
Western Carolina Univ	NC	3,811	C
Western Conn State Univ	CT	6,622	C
Western Illinois Univ	IL	5,241	LC
Western International Univ	AZ	3,600	C
Western Kentucky Univ	KY	4,808	C
Western Mich Univ	MI	6,820	C
Western New England College	MA	14,674	LC
Westminster College	PA	15,200	C
Wichita State Univ	KS	5,068	NC
Widener Univ	PA	16,840	C
Wilberforce Univ	OH	10,408	C
William Paterson College	NJ	7,438	C+
Wilmington College	DE	5,200	NC
Winona State Univ	MN	5,200	VC
Wofford College	SC	15,360	VC
Woodbury Univ	CA	17,620	LC
Wright State Univ	OH	6,896	LC
Xavier Univ of Louisiana	LA	10,400	C
York College of Penn	PA	8,345	C
Youngstown State Univ	OH	6,447	LC

BEHAVIORAL SCIENCE

School	ST	$IS	SR
Andrews Univ	MI	14,952	NC
Bartlesville Wesleyan College	OK	9,400	C
Calif Baptist College	CA	11,294	C
Calif State Polytechnic Univ/Pomona	CA	6,438	LC
Cal State/Dominguez Hills	CA	2,857	LC
Cedarville College	OH	10,715	C
Chaminade Univ of Honolulu	HI	14,290	C
City Univ	WA	6,400	NC
College for Lifelong Learning	NH	3,060	
College of Notre Dame	CA	16,480	C
Concordia College	NE	11,776	NC
Concordia College	NY	0	LC
Concordia College	OR	12,300	C
Concordia Lutheran College	TX	10,260	C+
Concordia Univ	CA	14,675	C
Drew Univ/College of Liberal Arts	NJ	23,406	HC
East Texas Baptist Univ	TX	7,740	C
East-West Univ	IL	5,910	NC
Erskine College	SC	14,310	C
Green Mountain College	VT	14,080	C
Indiana Univ at Kokomo	IN	2,069	C
Indiana Univ East	IN	2,044	NC
King College	TN	11,500	C
La Sierra Univ	CA	15,472	C
Lehigh Univ	PA	23,250	HC
Martin Univ	IN	4,830	NC
Mercy College	NY	11,180	NC
Messiah College	PA	14,664	VC
Metropolitan State College of Denver	CO	1,751	NC
Missouri Baptist College	MO	9,340	C
Mount Mary College	WI	10,920	C
National Univ	CA	6,135	C
North Central Bible College	MN	8,670	LC
Northwest College	WA	9,897	LC
Oglethorpe Univ	GA	16,360	VC
Our Lady of Holy Cross College	LA	4,630	LC
Pacific Union College	CA	15,075	C
Point Park College	PA	13,922	LC
Rice Univ	TX	15,110	MC
Shaw Univ	NC	8,936	C+
Sterling College	KS	10,990	VC
Trevecca Nazarene College	TN	9,826	NC
United States Air Force Academy	CO	0	MC
United States Military Academy	NY	0	MC
Univ of Calif at Davis	CA	9,534	VC
Univ of Maine at Fort Kent	ME	6,285	LC
Univ of Maine at Machias	ME	6,135	C
Univ of Maine at Presque Isle	ME	6,374	C
Univ of Mary	ND	8,910	C
Univ of Maryland/Univ College	MD	4,900	NC
Univ of Mich/Dearborn	MI	3,399	HC
Univ of Mobile	AL	9,400	C
Univ of Penn	PA	24,238	MC
Univ of Wisc/Madison	WI	6,400	HC
Ursuline College	OH	13,180	LC
Western International Univ	AZ	3,600	C
Widener Univ	PA	16,840	C
Wilmington College	DE	5,200	NC
Wilson College	PA	16,630	C
York College of Penn	PA	8,345	C

BIBLICAL LANGUAGES

School	ST	$IS	SR
Asbury College	KY	11,105	VC
Concordia College	MI	13,660	C
Concordia College	MN	13,200	C
Concordia Univ Wisc	WI	12,140	C
David Lipscomb Univ	TN	7,865	VC
Grand Rapids Baptist College and Seminary	MI	10,228	C
Luther College	IA	15,900	VC
North Central Bible College	MN	8,670	LC
Southern Nazarene Univ	OK	9,206	NC
Toccoa Falls College	GA	9,350	C
Univ of Mich/Ann Arbor	MI	9,428	HC+

BIBLICAL STUDIES

School	ST	$IS	SR
Agnes Scott College	GA	17,135	VC
Asbury College	KY	11,105	VC
Azusa Pacific Univ	CA	15,034	C
Bethel College	IN	11,650	C
Biola Univ	CA	16,124	C
Cascade College	OR	9,800	NC
Cedarville College	OH	10,715	C
Christian Heritage College	CA	11,756	C
Clearwater Christian College	FL	8,500	LC
Colo Christian Univ	CO	9,750	C
Covenant College	GA	13,054	VC
Dallas Baptist Univ	TX	9,620	LC
Eastern College	PA	15,150	C+
Eastern Mennonite College	VA	12,700	C
Faulkner Univ	AL	8,630	LC
Geneva College	PA	13,030	C
George Fox College	OR	15,640	LC
Gordon College	MA	16,790	C
Goshen College	IN	12,360	C
Grand Rapids Baptist College and Seminary	MI	10,228	C
Houghton College	NY	13,120	VC
Huntington College	IN	13,220	C
Indiana Wesleyan Univ	IN	12,332	C
John Brown Univ	AR	9,880	VC
King College	TN	11,500	C
Liberty Univ	VA	11,500	LC
Messiah College	PA	14,664	VC
Mich Christian College	MI	8,094	C
Northwest College	WA	9,897	LC
Northwestern College	MN	13,554	C
Nyack College	NY	12,210	LC
Okla Christian Univ of Science and Arts	OK	8,790	NC
Pacific Christian College	CA	12,700	C
Philadelphia College of Bible	PA	11,010	C
Pillsbury Baptist Bible College	MN	7,390	NC
Point Loma Nazarene College	CA	13,532	C
Seattle Pacific Univ	WA	16,503	C

School	ST	$IS	SR
Simpson College	CA	10,628	C
Southern Calif College	CA	12,356	C
Southwest Baptist Univ	MO	9,192	NC
Southwestern Christian College	TX	7,033	NC
Taylor Univ	IN	14,450	VC
Toccoa Falls College	GA	9,350	C
Univ of Mich/Ann Arbor	MI	9,428	HC+
Western Baptist College	OR	12,400	LC
Wheaton College	IL	14,710	HC
York College	NE	7,610	C

BILINGUAL/BICULTURAL EDUCATION

School	ST	$IS	SR
Boston Univ	MA	24,130	HC
Cal State/San Bernardino	CA	6,055	LC
Central Mich Univ	MI	6,737	LC
CUNY/Brooklyn College	NY	2,450	VC
College of Our Lady of The Elms	MA	15,639	C
D'Youville College	NY	12,850	C
Eastern Mich Univ	MI	6,749	C
Hofstra Univ	NY	16,580	VC
Kean College of New Jersey	NJ	6,395	LC
Mount Holyoke College	MA	23,630	VC
Mount Mary College	WI	10,920	C
Northeastern Illinois Univ	IL	1,955	C
St Edward's Univ	TX	12,636	C
St Thomas Aquinas College	NY	13,550	C
SUNY/College at Old Westbury	NY	7,128	LC
The Univ of New Mexico	NM	5,304	C
Univ of Findlay	OH	15,764	C
Univ of Minn/Twin Cities	MN	6,682	VC
Wayne State Univ	MI	2,680	C
Western Illinois Univ	IL	5,241	LC

BIOCHEMISTRY

School	ST	$IS	SR
Abilene Christian Univ	TX	10,460	NC
Adelphi Univ	NY	18,250	LC
Albright College	PA	19,260	C
Allegheny College	PA	21,020	VC
Alma College	MI	16,375	VC+
Alvernia College	PA	13,150	LC
American International College	MA	14,029	C
Andrews Univ	MI	14,952	NC
Atlantic Union College	MA	14,150	LC
Auburn Univ	AL	5,823	C+
Averett College	VA	13,610	LC
Azusa Pacific Univ	CA	15,034	C
Bates College	ME	23,990	MC
Beloit College	WI	18,950	VC+
Benedictine College	KS	12,830	C
Berry College	GA	11,990	VC
Bethany College	WV	18,300	C+
Biola Univ	CA	16,124	C
Bluffton College	OH	12,951	C
Boston College	MA	22,706	MC
Boston Univ	MA	24,130	HC
Bowdoin College	ME	24,155	MC
Bowling Green State Univ	OH	6,701	C
Bradley Univ	IL	14,718	C+
Brandeis Univ	MA	25,585	HC
Bridgewater State College	MA	7,518	C
Brigham Young Univ	UT	5,625	HC
Brown Univ	RI	26,104	MC
Bryn Mawr College	PA	24,110	MC
Bucknell Univ	PA	22,320	HC
Calif Lutheran Univ	CA	17,240	C
Calif Polytechnic State Univ	CA	6,980	VC+
Cal State/Long Beach	CA	6,057	LC
Cal State/Los Angeles	CA	4,940	VC
Cal State/Northridge	CA	7,122	LC
Cal State/San Bernardino	CA	6,055	LC
Calvin College	MI	13,020	VC
Canisius College	NY	15,510	C
Carroll College	MT	11,265	C
Case Western Reserve Univ	OH	19,910	HC
Cedar Crest College	PA	18,930	C
Centenary College of Louisiana	LA	11,826	C+
Centre College	KY	15,850	VC+
Chestnut Hill College	PA	14,525	C
Chicago State Univ	IL	2,198	C
CUNY/City College	NY	2,543	VC
CUNY/College of Staten Island	NY	2,558	NC
CUNY/Queens College	NY	2,631	C
Clark Univ	MA	21,400	VC
Clemson Univ	SC	6,564	VC
Colby College	ME	24,230	HC
Colgate Univ	NY	24,020	HC
College of Charleston	SC	6,250	C
College of Mount St Vincent	NY	16,730	C
College of Notre Dame	CA	16,480	C
College of St Catherine	MN	14,670	C
Colo College	CO	20,038	HC
Colo State Univ	CO	6,566	VC
Columbia Union College	MD	13,650	LC
Columbia Univ/Barnard College	NY	25,492	HC
Columbia Univ/Columbia College	NY	26,757	MC
Conn College	CT	24,160	HC
Dartmouth College	NH	24,354	MC
David Lipscomb Univ	TN	7,865	VC
Denison Univ	OH	21,150	VC+
Duquesne Univ	PA	16,434	VC
East Carolina Univ	NC	4,498	C
East Stroudsburg Univ	PA	6,886	C
Eastern Mich Univ	MI	6,749	C
Eastern Washington Univ	WA	5,439	LC
Edinboro Univ of Penn	PA	7,181	C
Elizabethtown College	PA	17,850	VC
Elmhurst College	IL	12,536	C
Elmira College	NY	18,450	C
Emmanuel College	MA	17,773	LC
Evergreen State College	WA	6,306	C
Fairleigh Dickinson Univ	NJ	16,427	C
Florida Inst of Tech	FL	16,935	VC
Florida State Univ	FL	5,814	VC
Gallaudet Univ	DC	9,850	SP
Georgian Court College	NJ	12,550	C
Grove City College	PA	7,870	HC
Gustavus Adolphus College	MN	15,935	VC
Hamilton College	NY	23,500	HC
Hampden-Sydney College	VA	17,372	C+
Hartwick College	NY	20,950	C
Harvard Univ/Harvard and Radcliffe Colleges	MA	24,880	MC
Hofstra Univ	NY	16,580	VC
Holy Family College	PA	8,300	C
Hood College	MD	19,010	VC
Hope College	MI	15,698	C+
Idaho State Univ	ID	4,442	C
Illinois Benedictine College	IL	14,170	C
Immaculata College	PA	14,620	C
Indiana Univ Bloomington	IN	6,495	VC
Iowa State Univ	IA	5,456	C
Ithaca College	NY	19,679	C
John Brown Univ	AR	9,880	VC
Juniata College	PA	18,390	C+
Kansas State Univ	KS	4,816	NC
Keuka College	NY	13,660	C
Knox College	IL	18,990	VC
La Salle Univ	PA	16,940	VC
La Sierra Univ	CA	15,472	C
Lafayette College	PA	23,450	HC
Lebanon Valley College of Penn	PA	18,300	C
Lehigh Univ	PA	23,250	HC
Lewis and Clark College	OR	19,980	VC
Louisiana State Univ and A&M College	LA	5,605	C
Loyola Marymount Univ	CA	18,560	C
Madonna Univ	MI	8,546	C
Maharishi International Univ	IA	13,666	C
Manchester College	IN	13,240	LC
Manhattan College	NY	19,000	C
Manhattanville College	NY	20,450	LC
Mankato State Univ	MN	5,097	LC
Marietta College	OH	16,940	C+
Marist College	NY	16,406	C
Marlboro College	VT	23,305	C+
Marquette Univ	WI	16,114	VC
Messiah College	PA	14,664	VC
Mich State Univ	MI	7,842	C
Middlebury College	VT	24,400	MC
Millersville Univ of Penn	PA	7,370	VC
Mills College	CA	20,848	VC
Miss College	MS	8,348	C
Miss State Univ	MS	5,629	VC
Montclair State College	NJ	7,539	C+
Mount Holyoke College	MA	23,630	VC
Mount St Mary's College	CA	16,390	VC
Mount St Mary's College	MD	17,825	LC
Murray State Univ	KY	4,702	C
Nazareth College of Rochester	NY	15,310	C+
New Mexico State Univ	NM	4,844	LC
New York Univ	NY	24,705	VC+
Niagara Univ	NY	14,552	C
N Car State Univ	NC	4,984	VC
Northern Mich Univ	MI	6,350	C
Notre Dame College of Ohio	OH	11,370	C
Oakland Univ	MI	6,714	VC
Oakwood College	AL	10,005	C
Oberlin College	OH	24,570	HC+
Occidental College	CA	21,792	HC
Ohio Northern Univ	OH	18,660	VC
Ohio State Univ	OH	7,218	LC
Ohio Wesleyan Univ	OH	21,108	VC+
Okla Christian Univ of Science and Arts	OK	8,790	NC
Okla State Univ	OK	5,086	VC
Old Dominion Univ	VA	8,317	C
Olivet College	MI	14,000	C
Oregon State Univ	OR	6,175	C
Pembroke State Univ	NC	3,538	LC
Penn State Univ/Univ Park Campus	PA	8,752	HC
Philadelphia College of Pharmacy and Science	PA	14,750	VC
Philadelphia College of Textiles and Science	PA	15,896	C
Purdue Univ/West Lafayette	IN	6,636	C
Queens College	NC	14,950	C
Quinnipiac College	CT	17,600	C+
Rhodes College	TN	19,624	HC
Rice Univ	TX	15,110	MC
Rider College	NJ	18,160	C
Ripon College	WI	18,320	C+
Roberts Wesleyan College	NY	13,317	C
Rosary College	IL	15,040	C
Russell Sage College	NY	16,790	C
Rutgers Univ/Camden College of A&S	NJ	8,652	VC
Rutgers Univ/Cook College	NJ	9,197	HC
Rutgers Univ/Douglass College	NJ	8,795	VC
Rutgers Univ/Livingston College	NJ	8,877	VC
Rutgers Univ/Rutgers College	NJ	8,841	HC+
Rutgers Univ/Univ College—Camden	NJ	3,506	C
Rutgers Univ/Univ College—New Brunswick	NJ	0	LC
Saginaw Valley State Univ	MI	6,634	LC
St Andrews Presbyterian College	NC	14,240	LC
St Anselm College	NH	17,340	C
St Joseph College	CT	16,225	C
St Mary's Univ	TX	12,064	C
St Michael's College	VT	17,930	C
St Peter's College	NJ	14,775	LC
St Vincent College	PA	13,934	LC
San Francisco State Univ	CA	7,292	LC
San Jose State Univ	CA	6,680	LC
Schreiner College	TX	14,320	C
Scripps College	CA	23,600	HC
Seton Hill College	PA	14,320	C
Simmons College	MA	22,534	C
Skidmore College	NY	23,230	HC
Smith College	MA	24,236	HC
S Dak State Univ	SD	4,562	C
Southern Conn State Univ	CT	7,532	C
Southern Illinois Univ at Carbondale	IL	6,234	C
Southern Methodist Univ	TX	18,520	VC
Southern Univ and A&M College	LA	4,920	NC
Spelman College	GA	12,942	VC
Spring Arbor College	MI	12,256	C
Springfield College	MA	15,200	LC
SUNY at Albany	NY	7,059	VC
SUNY at Binghamton	NY	7,921	HC
SUNY at Buffalo	NY	7,896	VC
SUNY at Stony Brook	NY	7,658	VC
SUNY/College at Geneseo	NY	6,949	HC
SUNY/College at Plattsburgh	NY	6,917	C
Stevens Inst of Tech	NJ	21,980	VC+
Suffolk Univ	MA	15,360	LC
Susquehanna Univ	PA	19,950	VC
Sweet Briar College	VA	19,770	C
Temple Univ	PA	10,281	C
Tenn Tech Univ	TN	5,190	C
Texas A&M Univ	TX	5,382	VC
Texas Tech Univ	TX	6,008	C
The Univ of New Mexico	NM	5,304	C
Trinity College	CT	24,120	HC
Trinity College	DC	17,660	C
Trinity Univ	TX	16,670	HC
Tulane Univ	LA	24,540	HC
Univ of Arizona	AZ	5,808	C
Univ of Calif at Davis	CA	9,534	VC
Univ of Calif at Los Angeles	CA	8,959	HC
Univ of Calif at Santa Barbara	CA	9,460	C
Univ of Calif at Santa Cruz	CA	9,060	VC
Univ of Calif, Riverside	CA	9,178	C
Univ of Calif, San Diego	CA	10,028	VC+
Univ of Chicago	IL	24,517	MC
Univ of Cincinnati	OH	7,989	C
Univ of Colo at Boulder	CO	6,410	VC
Univ of Dallas	TX	14,983	VC
Univ of Dayton	OH	15,120	C+
Univ of Delaware	DE	8,013	VC
Univ of Denver	CO	19,290	C+
Univ of Detroit Mercy	MI	14,720	C
Univ of Georgia	GA	5,655	VC
Univ of Houston	TX	5,215	C
Univ of Illinois at Chicago	IL	8,443	C
Univ of Illinois at Urbana-Champaign	IL	7,764	HC
Univ of Iowa	IA	5,658	VC
Univ of Kansas	KS	5,200	NC
Univ of Maine	ME	7,990	C
Univ of Maryland/Baltimore County	MD	7,746	VC
Univ of Maryland/College Park	MD	8,182	VC
Univ of Mass/Amherst	MA	9,364	LC
Univ of Miami	FL	22,107	VC
Univ of Mich/Dearborn	MI	3,399	HC
Univ of Minn/Twin Cities	MN	6,682	VC
Univ of Missouri/Columbia	MO	6,254	HC
Univ of Nebr-Lincoln	NE	5,278	LC
Univ of Nevada/Reno	NV	5,735	C
Univ of New Hampshire	NH	8,242	C
Univ of North Texas	TX	4,853	C
Univ of Northern Colo	CO	6,008	C
Univ of Notre Dame	IN	20,150	MC
Univ of Penn	PA	24,238	MC
Univ of PR/Mayaguez	PR	0	
Univ of Rochester	NY	23,696	HC
Univ of Scranton	PA	17,071	VC
Univ of Tampa	FL	16,780	C
Univ of Tenn/Knoxville	TN	5,668	C
Univ of Texas at Arlington	TX	5,549	LC
Univ of Texas at Austin	TX	5,160	VC
Univ of the Pacific	CA	21,100	C
Univ of Vermont	VT	10,776	C+
Univ of Washington	WA	6,618	VC
Univ of Wisc/Eau Claire	WI	4,647	C
Univ of Wisc/Madison	WI	6,400	HC
Univ of Wisc/Milwaukee	WI	6,165	C
Upsala College	NJ	17,200	C
Utah State Univ	UT	4,683	C
Vassar College	NY	24,206	HC
Virginia Polytechnic Inst and State Univ	VA	6,828	C
Virginia Wesleyan College	VA	14,950	VC
Washington State Univ	WA	6,364	C
Washington Univ	MO	23,507	HC
Wellesley College	MA	23,815	MC
Wells College	NY	19,460	C+
Wesleyan Univ	CT	23,770	MC
West Chester Univ of Penn	PA	7,492	C
Western Kentucky Univ	KY	4,808	C
Western Washington Univ	WA	6,077	VC
Wheaton College	MA	23,840	C+
Whittier College	CA	21,661	C
Widener Univ	PA	16,840	C
Wilkes Univ	PA	15,728	LC
Worcester Polytechnic Inst	MA	20,350	HC
Xavier Univ of Louisiana	LA	10,400	C

BIOENGINEERING

School	ST	$IS	SR
Arizona State Univ Main Campus	AZ	6,444	C
Cedar Crest College	PA	18,930	C
Miss State Univ	MS	5,629	VC
Rutgers Univ/College of Engineering	NJ	9,254	HC
Syracuse Univ	NY	21,305	HC
Texas A&M Univ	TX	5,382	VC
Univ of Calif at Berkeley	CA	9,962	HC+
Univ of Calif at Davis	CA	9,534	VC
Univ of Calif, San Diego	CA	10,028	VC+
Univ of Illinois at Chicago	IL	8,443	C
Univ of Maine	ME	7,990	C
Univ of Nebr-Lincoln	NE	5,278	LC
Univ of Penn	PA	24,238	MC
Univ of Wyoming	WY	4,991	NC
Walla Walla College	WA	13,215	C
Western New England College	MA	14,674	LC

BIOLOGY/BIOLOGICAL SCIENCE

School	ST	$IS	SR
Abilene Christian Univ	TX	10,460	NC
Adams State College	CO	4,910	C
Adelphi Univ	NY	18,250	LC
Adrian College	MI	14,340	C
Agnes Scott College	GA	17,135	VC
Alabama A&M Univ	AL	4,200	C
Alabama State Univ	AL	3,428	NC
Albany State College	GA	4,481	LC
Albertson College	ID	15,942	C+
Albertus Magnus College	CT	16,280	LC
Albion College	MI	18,264	VC
Albright College	PA	19,260	C
Alcorn State Univ	MS	4,474	C+
Alderson-Broaddus College	WV	12,000	C
Alfred Univ	NY	21,054	VC+
Alice Lloyd College	KY	2,750	VC
Allegheny College	PA	21,020	VC
Allen Univ	SC	6,705	NC
Allentown College of St Francis de Sales	PA	13,480	C
Alma College	MI	16,375	VC+
Alvernia College	PA	13,150	LC
Alverno College	WI	11,344	C
American International College	MA	14,029	C
American Univ	DC	21,230	VC+
Amherst College	MA	24,152	MC
Anderson Univ	IN	12,920	C
Andrews Univ	MI	14,952	NC
Angelo State Univ	TX	5,176	C
Anna Maria College	MA	15,975	LC
Antioch College	OH	19,532	C
Appalachian State Univ	NC	4,095	C

School	ST	$IS	SR
Aquinas College	MI	14,526	C
Arizona State Univ Main Campus	AZ	6,444	C
Arkansas College	AR	11,626	VC
Arkansas State Univ	AR	4,250	NC
Arkansas Tech Univ	AR	4,200	NC
Armstrong State College	GA	4,874	LC
Asbury College	KY	11,105	VC
Ashland Univ	OH	15,508	C
Assumption College	MA	17,095	C
Atlantic Union College	MA	14,150	C
Auburn Univ	AL	5,823	C+
Auburn Univ at Montgomery	AL	3,390	C
Augsburg College	MN	15,608	C
Augusta College	GA	1,452	C
Augustana College	IL	16,959	VC
Augustana College	SD	13,420	C
Aurora Univ	IL	13,381	C
Austin College	TX	14,999	VC
Austin Peay State Univ	TN	4,350	C
Averett College	VA	13,610	LC
Avila College	MO	12,130	C
Azusa Pacific Univ	CA	15,034	C
Baker Univ	KS	12,284	C
Baldwin-Wallace College	OH	15,210	C
Ball State Univ	IN	6,032	LC
Barat College	IL	13,990	C
Barber-Scotia College	NC	6,840	NC
Bard College	NY	25,269	HC
Barry Univ	FL	16,050	C
Barton College	NC	10,689	LC
Bates College	ME	23,990	MC
Baylor Univ	TX	10,990	C+
Beaver College	PA	17,660	C
Belhaven College	MS	9,690	C+
Bellarmine College	KY	10,832	C
Belmont Abbey College	NC	13,190	C
Belmont Univ	TN	10,540	C
Beloit College	WI	18,950	VC+
Bemidji State Univ	MN	5,188	C
Benedict College	SC	8,376	LC
Benedictine College	KS	12,830	C
Bennett College	NC	8,920	LC
Bennington College	VT	24,850	VC+
Berea College	KY	2,883	VC+
Berry College	GA	11,990	VC
Bethany College	KS	11,232	C
Bethany College	WV	18,300	C+
Bethel College	IN	11,650	C
Bethel College	KS	11,530	C
Bethel College	MN	15,050	C
Bethel College	TN	9,736	LC
Bethune-Cookman College	FL	8,375	LC
Biola Univ	CA	16,124	C
Birmingham-Southern College	AL	15,154	VC+
Black Hills State Univ	SD	4,831	NC
Blackburn College	IL	9,120	C
Bloomfield College	NJ	12,200	LC
Bloomsburg Univ of Penn	PA	6,312	C+
Blue Mountain College	MS	5,958	LC
Bluefield College	VA	10,600	C
Bluefield State College	WV	1,832	LC
Bluffton College	OH	12,951	C
Boise State Univ	ID	4,909	LC
Boston College	MA	22,706	MC
Boston Univ	MA	24,130	HC
Bowdoin College	ME	24,155	MC
Bowie State Univ	MD	7,294	LC
Bowling Green State Univ	OH	6,701	C
Bradley Univ	IL	14,718	C+
Brandeis Univ	MA	25,585	HC
Brescia College	KY	9,800	C
Briar Cliff College	IA	13,375	C
Bridgewater College	VA	15,300	C
Bridgewater State College	MA	7,518	C
Brigham Young Univ	UT	5,625	HC
Brigham Young Univ/Hawaii	HI	6,750	VC
Brooklyn Campus of LIU	NY	15,000	LC
Brown Univ	RI	26,104	MC
Bryan College	TN	11,465	C
Bryn Mawr College	PA	24,110	MC
Bucknell Univ	PA	22,320	HC
Buena Vista College	IA	16,150	VC
Butler Univ	IN	16,210	C
Cabrini College	PA	16,012	C
Caldwell College	NJ	12,860	C
Calif Baptist College	CA	11,294	C
Calif Inst of Tech	CA	20,783	MC
Calif Lutheran Univ	CA	17,240	C
Calif Polytechnic State Univ	CA	6,980	VC+
Calif State Polytechnic Univ/Pomona	CA	6,438	LC
Cal State/Bakersfield	CA	5,402	C
Cal State/Chico	CA	6,146	C
Cal State/Dominguez Hills	CA	2,857	LC
Cal State/Fresno	CA	5,747	C
Cal State/Hayward	CA	5,495	C
Cal State/Long Beach	CA	6,057	LC
Cal State/Los Angeles	CA	4,940	VC
Cal State/Northridge	CA	7,122	LC
Cal State/Sacramento	CA	6,387	C
Cal State/San Bernardino	CA	6,055	LC
Cal State/Stanislaus	CA	6,799	C
Calif Univ of Penn	PA	7,370	C
Calumet College of St. Joseph	IN	3,585	C
Calvin College	MI	13,020	VC
Cameron Univ	OK	3,686	LC
Campbell Univ	NC	10,624	C
Campbellsville College	KY	8,720	C
Canisius College	NY	15,510	C
Capital Univ	OH	16,535	VC
Cardinal Stritch College	WI	11,252	C
Caribbean Univ	PR	2,400	
Carleton College	MN	22,155	HC
Carlow College	PA	13,914	C
Carnegie Mellon Univ	PA	22,560	HC+
Carroll College	MT	11,265	C
Carroll College	WI	15,490	C
Carson-Newman College	TN	11,250	C
Carthage College	WI	15,995	C
Cascade College	OR	9,800	NC
Case Western Reserve Univ	OH	19,910	MC
Catawba College	NC	12,950	C
Catholic Univ of America	DC	18,856	C
Cedar Crest College	PA	18,930	C
Cedarville College	OH	10,715	C
Centenary College of Louisiana	LA	11,826	C+
Central College	IA	14,025	VC
Central Conn State Univ	CT	7,108	C
Central Methodist College	MO	11,410	C
Central Mich Univ	MI	6,737	LC
Central Missouri State Univ	MO	5,138	LC
Central State Univ	OH	7,320	NC
Central Univ of Bayamon	PR	2,430	
Central Washington Univ	WA	5,644	C
Central Wesleyan College	SC	9,640	C
Centre College	KY	15,850	VC+
Chadron State College	NE	4,091	NC
Chaminade Univ of Honolulu	HI	14,290	C
Chapman Univ	CA	21,842	C
Charleston Southern Univ	SC	10,282	LC
Charter Oak State College	CT	314	NC
Chatham College	PA	18,010	C
Chestnut Hill College	PA	14,525	C
Cheyney Univ of Penn	PA	7,005	C
Chicago State Univ	IL	2,198	C
Christian Brothers Univ	TN	12,120	VC
Christopher Newport Univ	VA	3,196	LC
CUNY/Brooklyn College	NY	2,450	VC
CUNY/City College	NY	2,543	VC
CUNY/College of Staten Island	NY	2,558	NC
CUNY/Herbert H. Lehman College	NY	2,542	C
CUNY/Hunter College	NY	4,101	VC
CUNY/Medgar Evers College	NY	2,577	NC
CUNY/Queens College	NY	2,631	C
CUNY/York College	NY	2,534	NC
Claflin College	SC	0	
Claremont McKenna College	CA	22,150	MC
Clarion Univ of Penn	PA	6,518	C
Clark Atlanta Univ	GA	11,846	C
Clark Univ	MA	21,400	VC
Clarke College	IA	13,950	C+
Clarkson Univ	NY	20,705	VC+
Clearwater Christian College	FL	8,500	LC
Clemson Univ	SC	6,564	VC
Cleveland State Univ	OH	7,287	NC
Clinch Valley College/Univ of Virginia	VA	6,364	C
Coastal Carolina Univ	SC	6,010	LC
Coe College	IA	17,085	VC
Coker College	SC	13,790	C
Colby College	ME	24,230	HC
Colby-Sawyer College	NH	18,495	C
Colgate Univ	NY	24,020	HC
College Misericordia	PA	15,820	C
College of Charleston	SC	6,250	C
College of Great Falls	MT	6,230	NC
College of Mount St Joseph	OH	13,272	C
College of Mount St Vincent	NY	16,730	C
College of New Rochelle	NY	15,440	LC
College of Notre Dame	CA	16,480	C
College of Notre Dame of Maryland	MD	16,050	C
College of Our Lady of The Elms	MA	15,639	C
College of St Benedict	MN	15,468	VC
College of St Catherine	MN	14,670	C
College of St Elizabeth	NJ	15,800	C
College of St Francis	IL	13,060	VC
College of St Mary	NE	12,500	C
College of St Rose	NY	14,452	C
College of St Scholastica	MN	14,868	C
College of Santa Fe	NM	14,008	C
College of the Holy Cross	MA	23,850	VC
College of the Ozarks	MO	2,000	VC+
College of the Southwest	NM	5,720	C
College of William and Mary	VA	8,602	MC
College of Wooster	OH	19,875	VC
Colo Christian Univ	CO	9,750	C
Colo College	CO	20,038	VC
Colo State Univ	CO	6,566	VC
Columbia College	MO	11,995	C
Columbia College	SC	13,520	LC
Columbia Univ/Barnard College	NY	25,492	HC
Columbia Univ/Columbia College	NY	26,757	MC
Columbus College	GA	4,892	LC
Concord College	WV	5,104	NC
Concordia College	MI	13,660	VC
Concordia College	MN	13,200	C
Concordia College	NE	11,776	NC
Concordia College	NY	0	LC
Concordia College	OR	12,300	C
Concordia College/Moorhead	MN	12,750	C
Concordia Univ	IL	12,611	C
Concordia Univ	CA	14,675	C
Concordia Univ Wisc	WI	12,140	C
Conn College	CT	24,160	HC
Converse College	SC	15,750	C
Coppin State College	MD	7,145	LC
Cornell College	IA	18,425	VC
Cornell Univ	NY	13,445	MC
Covenant College	GA	13,054	VC
Creighton Univ	NE	14,432	VC
Culver-Stockton College	MO	11,150	C
Cumberland College	KY	9,756	C
Curry College	MA	18,695	LC
D'Youville College	NY	12,850	C
Daemen College	NY	13,020	LC
Dakota State Univ	SD	4,374	LC
Dakota Wesleyan Univ	SD	9,770	C
Dallas Baptist Univ	TX	9,620	C
Dana College	NE	11,910	C
Dartmouth College	NH	24,354	MC
David Lipscomb Univ	TN	7,865	VC
Davidson College	NC	21,037	MC
Davis and Elkins College	WV	13,230	LC
Defiance College	OH	13,480	C
Delaware State College	DE	5,694	C
Delaware Valley College	PA	16,065	LC
Delta State Univ	MS	3,964	LC
Denison Univ	OH	21,150	VC+
DePaul Univ	IL	15,535	VC
DePauw Univ	IN	18,530	VC
Dickinson College	PA	22,705	HC
Dickinson State Univ	ND	3,792	
Dillard Univ	LA	9,950	C
Doane College	NE	12,220	C
Dominican College of San Rafael	CA	17,860	C
Dordt College	IA	11,690	C
Dowling College	NY	12,730	LC
Drake Univ	IA	17,195	VC
Drew Univ/College of Liberal Arts	NJ	23,406	HC
Drexel Univ	PA	15,970	C
Drury College	MO	12,140	VC
Duke Univ	NC	21,271	MC
Duquesne Univ	PA	16,434	VC
Earlham College	IN	19,383	VC
East Carolina Univ	NC	4,498	C
East Central Univ	OK	3,558	C
East Stroudsburg Univ	PA	6,886	C
East Tenn State Univ	TN	4,406	C
East Texas Baptist Univ	TX	7,740	C
East Texas State Univ	TX	4,572	LC
Eastern College	PA	15,150	C+
Eastern Conn State Univ	CT	6,966	C
Eastern Kentucky Univ	KY	4,840	NC
Eastern Mennonite College	VA	12,700	C
Eastern Mich Univ	MI	6,749	C
Eastern Montana College	MT	5,165	LC
Eastern Nazarene College	MA	12,165	LC
Eastern New Mexico Univ	NM	3,950	C
Eastern Oregon State College	OR	6,090	C
Eastern Washington Univ	WA	5,439	VC
Eckerd College	FL	18,855	VC
Edgewood College	WI	11,700	C
Edinboro Univ of Penn	PA	7,181	C
Edward Waters College	FL	8,300	NC
Elizabeth City State Univ	NC	4,254	LC
Elizabethtown College	PA	17,850	VC
Elmhurst College	IL	12,536	C
Elmira College	NY	18,450	C
Elon College	NC	12,290	LC
Emmanuel College	MA	17,773	C
Emory and Henry College	VA	12,776	C
Emory Univ	GA	21,930	HC
Emporia State Univ	KS	4,685	NC
Erskine College	SC	14,310	C
Eureka College	IL	14,555	C
Evangel College	MO	10,142	LC
Evergreen State College	WA	6,306	C
Fairfield Univ	CT	20,460	VC
Fairleigh Dickinson Univ	NJ	16,427	C
Fairmont State College	WV	4,640	LC
Faulkner Univ	AL	8,630	LC
Fayetteville State Univ	NC	3,926	LC
Felician College	NJ	7,900	C
Ferris State Univ	MI	7,160	NC
Ferrum College	VA	12,800	LC
Fisk Univ	TN	0	LC
Fitchburg State College	MA	6,962	C
Florida A&M Univ	FL	4,615	C
Florida Atlantic Univ	FL	5,525	C
Florida Inst of Tech	FL	16,935	VC
Florida International Univ	FL	4,191	VC
Florida Memorial College	FL	7,600	C+
Florida Southern College	FL	12,260	C
Florida State Univ	FL	5,814	VC
Fontbonne College	MO	12,090	C
Fordham Univ/Fordham College	NY	19,875	VC
Fort Hays State Univ	KS	4,675	NC
Fort Lewis College	CO	5,097	C
Fort Valley State College	GA	3,974	LC
Framingham State College	MA	6,580	C
Francis Marion Univ	SC	5,878	LC
Franciscan Univ of Steubenville	OH	13,400	C
Franklin and Marshall College	PA	23,655	HC
Franklin College of Indiana	IN	13,970	C
Franklin Pierce College	NH	17,270	LC
Freed-Hardeman Univ	TN	8,585	VC
Friends Univ	KS	11,205	C
Frostburg State Univ	MD	6,940	C
Furman Univ	SC	16,557	VC
Gallaudet Univ	DC	9,850	SP
Gannon Univ	PA	14,872	C
Gardner-Webb Univ	NC	11,950	LC
Geneva College	PA	13,030	C
George Fox College	OR	15,640	LC
George Mason Univ	VA	8,728	C
George Washington Univ	DC	22,470	HC
Georgetown College	KY	10,990	C
Georgetown Univ	DC	24,410	MC
Georgia College	GA	4,310	LC
Georgia Inst of Tech	GA	6,669	HC+
Georgia Southern Univ	GA	4,988	C
Georgia Southwestern College	GA	4,338	LC
Georgia State Univ	GA	2,019	C
Georgian Court College	NJ	12,550	C
Gettysburg College	PA	22,960	HC
Glenville State College	WV	4,810	LC
Gonzaga Univ	WA	16,350	VC
Gordon College	MA	16,790	C
Goshen College	IN	12,360	C
Goucher College	MD	20,295	VC
Grace College	IN	12,120	C
Graceland College	IA	11,600	C
Grambling State Univ	LA	4,712	NC
Grand Canyon Univ	AZ	9,680	VC
Grand Rapids Baptist College and Seminary	MI	10,228	C
Grand Valley State Univ	MI	6,822	VC
Grand View College	IA	13,230	NC
Greensboro College	NC	11,496	C
Greenville College	IL	14,190	C
Grinnell College	IA	20,680	HC+
Grove City College	PA	7,870	VC
Guilford College	NC	17,680	C
Gustavus Adolphus College	MN	15,935	VC
Gwynedd-Mercy College	PA	15,450	C
Hamilton College	NY	23,560	HC
Hamline Univ	MN	17,122	VC
Hampden-Sydney College	VA	17,372	C+
Hampshire College	MA	25,320	C
Hampton Univ	VA	10,706	C
Hannibal-LaGrange College	MO	8,400	LC
Hanover College	IN	10,950	VC
Hardin-Simmons Univ	TX	9,080	C
Harding Univ	AR	9,050	VC
Hartwick College	NY	20,950	C
Harvard Univ/Harvard and Radcliffe Colleges	MA	24,880	MC
Harvey Mudd College	CA	23,316	MC
Hastings College	NE	12,426	C
Haverford College	PA	23,950	MC
Heidelberg College	OH	17,160	C
Henderson State Univ	AR	3,860	C
Hendrix College	AR	11,670	C
High Point Univ	NC	12,350	LC
Hillsdale College	MI	15,110	VC
Hiram College	OH	18,340	VC
Hobart and William Smith Colleges	NY	23,925	VC
Hofstra Univ	NY	16,580	VC
Hollins College	VA	18,484	C
Holy Family College	PA	8,300	C
Holy Names College	CA	15,660	C
Hood College	MD	19,010	VC
Hope College	MI	15,698	C+
Houghton College	NY	13,120	VC
Houston Baptist Univ	TX	11,055	C
Howard Payne Univ	TX	8,052	C
Humboldt State Univ	CA	5,676	C
Huntingdon College	AL	11,400	C
Huntington College	IN	12,320	C
Huston-Tillotson College	TX	8,490	C
Idaho State Univ	ID	4,442	C
Illinois Benedictine College	IL	14,170	C
Illinois College	IL	11,200	C
Illinois Inst of Tech	IL	18,290	VC
Illinois State Univ	IL	6,413	C
Illinois Wesleyan Univ	IL	18,590	HC+
Immaculata College	PA	14,620	C
Incarnate Word College	TX	12,307	C
Indiana State Univ	IN	6,210	C
Indiana Univ at Kokomo	IN	2,069	C
Indiana Univ Bloomington	IN	6,495	VC
Indiana Univ Northwest	IN	2,310	C
Indiana Univ of Penn	PA	6,373	C
Indiana Univ Southeast	IN	2,260	LC
Indiana Univ-Purdue Univ at Fort Wayne	IN	2,500	LC

School	ST	$IS	SR
Westminster College of Salt Lake City	UT	12,100	C
Westmont College	CA	18,732	C
Wheaton College	IL	14,710	HC
Wheaton College	MA	23,840	C+
Wheeling Jesuit College	WV	14,370	C
Whitman College	WA	20,595	HC
Whittier College	CA	21,661	C
Whitworth College	WA	16,265	C
Wichita State Univ	KS	5,068	NC
Widener Univ	PA	16,840	C
Wilberforce Univ	OH	10,408	C
Wiley College	TX	0	NC
Wilkes Univ	PA	15,728	LC
Willamette Univ	OR	17,995	VC
William Carey College	MS	7,050	C
William Jewell College	MO	12,500	VC
William Paterson College	NJ	7,438	C+
William Penn College	IA	13,400	C
William Woods Univ	MO	14,025	LC
Williams College	MA	24,390	MC
Wilmington College	OH	13,700	LC
Wilson College	PA	16,630	C
Wingate College	NC	10,610	C
Winona State Univ	MN	5,200	VC
Winston-Salem State Univ	NC	4,142	LC
Winthrop Univ	SC	6,750	C
Wittenberg Univ	OH	19,998	VC
Wofford College	SC	15,360	VC
Women's College of Brenau Univ	GA	14,734	C
Worcester Polytechnic Inst	MA	20,350	HC
Worcester State College	MA	6,414	LC
Wright State Univ	OH	6,896	LC
Xavier Univ	OH	15,710	C+
Xavier Univ of Louisiana	LA	10,400	C
Yale Univ	CT	25,110	MC
Yeshiva Univ	NY	18,200	VC
York College of Penn	PA	8,345	C
Youngstown State Univ	OH	6,447	LC

BIOMEDICAL ENGINEERING

School	ST	$IS	SR
Boston Univ	MA	24,130	HC
Case Western Reserve Univ	OH	19,910	HC
Duke Univ	NC	21,271	MC
Johns Hopkins Univ	MD	24,360	MC
Louisiana Tech Univ	LA	4,284	C
Marquette Univ	WI	16,114	VC
Mass Inst of Tech	MA	24,800	MC
Mercer Univ	GA	15,123	C
Mich Tech Univ	MI	7,283	VC+
Milwaukee School of Engineering	WI	14,100	C
Northwestern Univ	IL	21,093	MC
Rensselaer Polytechnic Inst	NY	23,067	HC
Temple Univ	PA	10,281	C
Tulane Univ	LA	24,540	HC
Univ of Iowa	IA	5,658	VC
Univ of Miami	FL	22,107	VC
Vanderbilt Univ	TN	23,422	HC+
Wright State Univ	OH	6,896	LC

BIOMEDICAL SCIENCE

School	ST	$IS	SR
Brown Univ	RI	26,104	MC
LIU/C. W. Post Campus	NY	16,870	C
Oral Roberts Univ	OK	10,607	C+
Rutgers Univ/Cook College	NJ	9,197	HC
Rutgers Univ/Douglass College	NJ	8,795	VC
Rutgers Univ/Livingston College	NJ	8,877	VC
Rutgers Univ/Rutgers College	NJ	8,841	HC+
Rutgers Univ/Univ College—New Brunswick	NJ	0	LC
Texas A&M Univ	TX	5,382	VC
Univ of Mich/Ann Arbor	MI	9,428	HC+
Univ of Miss	MS	5,756	C
Univ of New England	ME	16,075	LC
Univ of South Alabama	AL	5,451	C
West Texas A&M Univ	TX	4,224	C

BIOMETRICS AND BIOSTATISTICS

School	ST	$IS	SR
La Sierra Univ	CA	15,472	C
Rutgers Univ/Douglass College	NJ	8,795	VC
Rutgers Univ/Livingston College	NJ	8,877	VC
Southwestern Adventist College	TX	10,530	NC

BIOPHYSICS

School	ST	$IS	SR
Andrews Univ	MI	14,952	NC
Boston Univ	MA	24,130	HC
Brown Univ	RI	26,104	MC
Centenary College of Louisiana	LA	11,826	C+
Columbia Univ/Columbia College	NY	26,757	MC
Hampden-Sydney College	VA	17,372	C+
Harvard Univ/Harvard and Radcliffe Colleges	MA	24,880	MC
Iowa State Univ	IA	5,456	C
Johns Hopkins Univ	MD	24,360	MC
La Sierra Univ	CA	15,472	C
Oregon State Univ	OR	6,175	C
Pacific Union College	CA	15,075	C
Southwestern Okla State Univ	OK	3,312	C
SUNY at Buffalo	NY	7,896	VC
SUNY/College at Geneseo	NY	6,949	HC
Univ of Calif, San Diego	CA	10,028	VC+
Univ of Conn	CT	9,168	C
Univ of Mich/Ann Arbor	MI	9,428	HC+
Univ of Penn	PA	24,238	MC
Univ of Scranton	PA	17,071	VC
Univ of Southern Indiana	IN	3,720	NC
Wellesley College	MA	23,815	MC

BIOTECHNOLOGY

School	ST	$IS	SR
Bradley Univ	IL	14,718	C+
Calif State Polytechnic Univ/Pomona	CA	6,438	LC
Menlo College	CA	20,375	LC
Millersville Univ of Penn	PA	7,370	VC
N Dak State Univ of Agriculture and Applied Science	ND	4,774	VC
Purdue Univ/Calumet	IN	2,374	NC
Quinnipiac College	CT	17,600	C+
Rutgers Univ/Cook College	NJ	9,197	HC
Rutgers Univ/Douglass College	NJ	8,795	VC
Univ of Lowell	MA	8,831	VC
Univ of Northern Iowa	IA	5,137	C
Univ of PR/Mayaguez	PR	0	
William Paterson College	NJ	7,438	C+
Worcester Polytechnic Inst	MA	20,350	HC

BOTANY

School	ST	$IS	SR
Andrews Univ	MI	14,952	NC
Arizona State Univ Main Campus	AZ	6,444	C
Arkansas State Univ	AR	4,250	NC
Auburn Univ	AL	5,823	C+
Averett College	VA	13,610	LC
Ball State Univ	IN	6,032	LC
Brigham Young Univ	UT	5,625	HC
Calif State Polytechnic Univ/Pomona	CA	6,438	LC
Cal State/Fresno	CA	5,747	C
Cal State/Fullerton	CA	4,850	LC
Cal State/Long Beach	CA	6,057	LC
Colo State Univ	CO	6,566	VC
Conn College	CT	24,160	HC
Cornell Univ	NY	13,445	MC
Delaware State College	DE	5,656	C
East Texas State Univ	TX	4,572	LC
Eastern Illinois Univ	IL	5,548	C
Eastern Washington Univ	WA	5,439	LC
Evergreen State College	WA	6,306	C
Florida Atlantic Univ	FL	5,525	C
Hampshire College	MA	25,320	C
Howard Univ	DC	11,680	C
Humboldt State Univ	CA	5,676	C
Idaho State Univ	ID	4,442	C
Iowa State Univ	IA	5,456	C
Kent State Univ	OH	6,740	LC
Louisiana State Univ and A&M College	LA	5,605	C
Louisiana Tech Univ	LA	4,284	C
Marlboro College	VT	23,305	C+
Mars Hill College	NC	11,050	C
McKendree College	IL	10,900	C
McNeese State Univ	LA	4,543	NC
Miami Univ	OH	8,066	VC
Mich State Univ	MI	7,842	C
N Car State Univ	NC	4,984	VC
N Dak State Univ of Agriculture and Applied Science	ND	4,774	VC
Northeastern State Univ	OK	5,250	C
Northern Arizona Univ	AZ	4,844	C
Northern Mich Univ	MI	6,350	C
Northwest Missouri State Univ	MO	5,010	LC
Ohio Univ	OH	7,341	C
Ohio Wesleyan Univ	OH	21,108	VC+
Okla State Univ	OK	5,086	VC
Olivet Nazarene Univ	IL	11,976	C
Oregon State Univ	OR	6,175	C
Penn State Univ/Univ Park Campus	PA	8,752	HC
Rutgers Univ/Cook College	NJ	9,197	HC
Rutgers Univ/Douglass College	NJ	8,795	VC
Rutgers Univ/Livingston College	NJ	8,877	VC
Rutgers Univ/Newark College of A&S	NJ	8,645	C
Rutgers Univ/Rutgers College	NJ	8,841	HC+
Rutgers Univ/Univ College—New Brunswick	NJ	0	LC
San Francisco State Univ	CA	7,292	LC
San Jose State Univ	CA	6,680	LC
Sonoma State Univ	CA	6,996	LC
S Dak State Univ	SD	4,562	C
Southeastern Louisiana Univ	LA	4,230	NC
Southern Illinois Univ at Carbondale	IL	6,234	C
Southern Univ and A&M College	LA	4,920	NC
Southern Utah Univ	UT	4,104	LC
Southwest Texas State Univ	TX	5,124	C
SUNY College of Environmental Science and Forestry	NY	9,257	HC+
Tabor College	KS	11,460	VC
Texas A&M Univ	TX	5,382	VC
Univ of Akron	OH	6,699	NC
Univ of Arkansas at Fayetteville	AR	5,046	C
Univ of Calif at Davis	CA	9,534	VC
Univ of Calif at Santa Barbara	CA	9,460	C
Univ of Calif, Riverside	CA	9,178	C
Univ of Central Florida	FL	6,061	C+
Univ of Denver	CO	19,290	C+
Univ of Florida	FL	5,850	HC
Univ of Georgia	GA	5,655	VC
Univ of Hawaii at Manoa	HI	5,626	C
Univ of Idaho	ID	4,830	C
Univ of Iowa	IA	5,658	VC
Univ of Kentucky	KY	5,152	VC
Univ of Louisville	KY	5,948	C
Univ of Maine	ME	7,990	C
Univ of Maryland/College Park	MD	8,182	VC
Univ of Mich/Ann Arbor	MI	9,428	HC+
Univ of Minn/Twin Cities	MN	6,682	VC
Univ of Montana	MT	5,529	C
Univ of N Car at Chapel Hill	NC	5,330	HC
Univ of Okla	OK	5,427	VC
Univ of Rhode Island	RI	9,205	C
Univ of South Florida	FL	5,475	C+
Univ of Tenn/Knoxville	TN	5,668	C
Univ of Texas at Austin	TX	5,160	VC
Univ of Texas at El Paso	TX	3,160	LC
Univ of Vermont	VT	10,776	C+
Univ of Washington	WA	6,618	VC
Univ of Wisc/Eau Claire	WI	4,647	C
Univ of Wisc/Madison	WI	6,400	HC
Univ of Wisc/Milwaukee	WI	6,165	C
Univ of Wyoming	WY	4,991	NC
Weber State Univ	UT	4,398	C

BROADCASTING

School	ST	$IS	SR
Abilene Christian Univ	TX	10,460	NC
Adrian College	MI	14,340	C
Alabama State Univ	AL	3,428	NC
Alderson-Broaddus College	WV	12,000	C
Alfred Univ	NY	21,054	VC+
Appalachian State Univ	NC	4,095	C
Arizona State Univ Main Campus	AZ	6,444	C
Arkansas State Univ	AR	4,250	NC
Asbury College	KY	11,105	VC
Ashland Univ	OH	15,508	C
Auburn Univ	AL	5,823	C+
Baldwin-Wallace College	OH	15,210	C
Ball State Univ	IN	6,032	LC
Barry Univ	FL	16,050	C
Baylor Univ	TX	10,990	C+
Bemidji State Univ	MN	5,188	C
Bethune-Cookman College	FL	8,375	LC
Black Hills State Univ	SD	4,831	NC
Boston Univ	MA	24,130	HC
Bowie State Univ	MD	7,294	LC
Bowling Green State Univ	OH	6,701	C
Brigham Young Univ	UT	5,625	HC
Brooklyn Campus of LIU	NY	15,000	LC
Butler Univ	IN	16,210	C
Cal State/Fullerton	CA	4,850	LC
Cal State/Long Beach	CA	6,057	LC
Cal State/Los Angeles	CA	4,940	VC
Cal State/Northridge	CA	7,122	LC
Calif Univ of Penn	PA	7,370	C
Cameron Univ	OK	3,686	LC
Campbell Univ	NC	10,624	C
Cedarville College	OH	10,715	C
Central Mich Univ	MI	6,737	LC
Central Missouri State Univ	MO	5,138	LC
Central State Univ	OH	7,320	NC
Central Washington Univ	WA	5,644	C
Chicago State Univ	IL	2,198	C
CUNY/Brooklyn College	NY	2,450	VC
College of St Francis	IL	13,060	VC
Colo Christian Univ	CO	9,750	C
Columbia College	IL	7,879	SP
Concord College	WV	5,104	NC
Dana College	NE	11,910	C
Dordt College	IA	11,690	C
Drake Univ	IA	17,195	VC
Duquesne Univ	PA	16,434	VC
East Carolina Univ	NC	4,498	C
East Tenn State Univ	TN	4,406	C
East Texas State Univ	TX	4,572	LC
Eastern Kentucky Univ	KY	4,840	NC
Eastern Mich Univ	MI	6,749	C
Eastern Washington Univ	WA	5,439	LC
Elon College	NC	12,290	LC
Emerson College	MA	22,678	LC
Evangel College	MO	10,142	LC
Evergreen State College	WA	6,306	C
Fontbonne College	MO	12,090	C
Fordham Univ/Fordham College	NY	19,875	VC
Franklin College of Indiana	IN	13,970	C
Franklin Pierce College	NH	17,270	LC
Freed-Hardeman Univ	TN	8,585	VC
Geneva College	PA	13,030	C
George Washington Univ	DC	22,470	HC
Gonzaga Univ	WA	16,350	VC
Grambling State Univ	LA	4,712	NC
Grand Valley State Univ	MI	6,822	VC
Grand View College	IA	13,230	NC
Hanover College	IN	10,950	VC
Harding Univ	AR	9,050	VC
Hastings College	NE	12,426	C
Heidelberg College	OH	17,160	C
Hofstra Univ	NY	16,580	VC
Howard Univ	DC	11,680	C
Huntington College	IN	13,220	C
Illinois College	IL	11,200	C
Indiana State Univ	IN	6,210	C
Indiana Univ Bloomington	IN	6,495	VC
Indiana Univ-Purdue Univ at Fort Wayne	IN	2,500	LC
Ithaca College	NY	19,679	C
John Brown Univ	AR	9,880	VC
Kent State Univ	OH	6,740	LC
Lewis Univ	IL	14,797	LC
Liberty Univ	VA	11,500	LC
Lincoln Memorial Univ	TN	8,218	C
LIU/C. W. Post Campus	NY	16,870	C
Loras College	IA	14,160	C
Louisiana State Univ and A&M College	LA	5,605	C
Loyola Univ/New Orleans	LA	15,660	C+
Manchester College	IN	13,240	LC
Mansfield Univ	PA	6,348	C
Marietta College	OH	16,940	C+
Marquette Univ	WI	16,114	VC
Marshall Univ	WV	5,762	LC
McNeese State Univ	LA	4,543	NC
Menlo College	CA	20,375	LC
Mercy College	NY	11,180	NC
Mercyhurst College	PA	13,488	C
Miami Univ	OH	8,066	VC
Middle Tenn State Univ	TN	3,857	C
Millersville Univ of Penn	PA	7,370	VC
Minot State Univ	ND	3,748	NC
Miss Univ for Women	MS	4,456	LC
Missouri Southern State College	MO	4,272	C
Moorhead State Univ	MN	5,076	C
Murray State Univ	KY	4,702	C
New York Univ	NY	24,705	VC+
North Central College	IL	15,498	VC
Northeast Louisiana Univ	LA	3,906	NC
Northeastern State Univ	OK	5,250	C
Northeastern Univ	MA	19,851	C
Northern Arizona Univ	AZ	4,844	C
Northern Mich Univ	MI	6,350	C
Northwest Missouri State Univ	MO	5,010	LC
Northwestern College	MN	13,554	C
Northwestern Okla State Univ	OK	3,424	C
Northwestern State Univ of Louisiana	LA	4,287	NC
Northwestern Univ	IL	21,093	MC
Ohio Northern Univ	OH	18,660	VC
Ohio Univ	OH	7,341	C
Ohio Wesleyan Univ	OH	21,108	VC+
Okla Baptist Univ	OK	8,486	C
Okla Christian Univ of Science and Arts	OK	8,790	NC
Okla City Univ	OK	9,840	C
Okla State Univ	OK	5,086	VC

School	ST	$IS	SR
Olivet Nazarene Univ	IL	11,976	C
Oral Roberts Univ	OK	10,607	C+
Otterbein College	OH	16,506	C
Park College	MO	7,320	C
Pembroke State Univ	NC	3,538	LC
Penn State Univ/Univ Park Campus	PA	8,752	HC
Pepperdine Univ	CA	23,720	VC
Pittsburg State Univ	KS	4,478	NC
Prairie View A&M Univ	TX	4,740	LC
Purdue Univ/Calumet	IN	2,374	NC
Radford Univ	VA	7,034	LC
Roosevelt Univ	IL	12,368	C
Rowan College of New Jersey	NJ	7,358	VC
St Cloud State Univ	MN	5,015	C
Salem-Teikyo Univ	WV	14,527	C
Salisbury State Univ	MD	7,516	C+
San Diego State Univ	CA	6,692	LC
San Francisco State Univ	CA	7,292	LC
San Jose State Univ	CA	6,680	LC
Savannah State College	GA	4,052	C
Shaw Univ	NC	8,936	C+
Shepherd College	WV	5,540	C
Shorter College	GA	10,270	C
Sojourner-Douglass College	MD	5,265	LC
S Dak State Univ	SD	4,562	C
Southern Arkansas Univ	AR	3,432	NC
Southern Calif College	CA	12,356	C
Southern College of Seventh-day Adventists	TN	11,348	NC
Southern Illinois Univ at Carbondale	IL	6,234	C
Southern Illinois Univ at Edwardsville	IL	6,097	LC
Southern Methodist Univ	TX	18,520	VC
Southern Oregon State College	OR	6,128	C
Southern Univ and A&M College	LA	4,920	NC
Southwest Missouri State Univ	MO	4,956	C
Southwest Texas State Univ	TX	5,124	C
Southwestern Adventist College	TX	10,530	NC
Spring Hill College	AL	16,015	C+
SUNY/College at Buffalo	NY	7,035	VC
SUNY/College at Cortland	NY	7,326	C+
SUNY/College at Geneseo	NY	6,949	HC
SUNY/College at New Paltz	NY	6,890	VC
SUNY/College at Oswego	NY	7,330	VC
SUNY/College at Plattsburgh	NY	6,917	C
Stephen F. Austin State Univ	TX	5,117	C
Suffolk Univ	MA	15,360	LC
Syracuse Univ	NY	21,305	HC
Temple Univ	PA	10,281	C
Texas Christian Univ	TX	12,180	C
Texas Tech Univ	TX	6,008	C
Toccoa Falls College	GA	9,350	C
Troy State Univ	AL	4,322	C
Univ of Akron	OH	6,699	NC
Univ of Arizona	AZ	5,808	C
Univ of Calif at Los Angeles	CA	8,959	HC
Univ of Central Florida	FL	6,061	C+
Univ of Central Okla	OK	3,647	C
Univ of Cincinnati	OH	7,989	C
Univ of Colo at Boulder	CO	6,410	VC
Univ of Dayton	OH	15,120	C+
Univ of Findlay	OH	15,764	C
Univ of Georgia	GA	5,655	VC
Univ of Houston	TX	5,215	C
Univ of Indianapolis	IN	14,510	C
Univ of Iowa	IA	5,658	VC
Univ of Kentucky	KY	5,152	VC
Univ of La Verne	CA	17,400	C
Univ of Maryland/College Park	MD	8,182	VC
Univ of Maryland/Univ College	MD	4,900	NC
Univ of Miami	FL	22,107	VC
Univ of Miss	MS	5,756	C
Univ of Missouri/Columbia	MO	6,254	HC
Univ of Montana	MT	5,529	C
Univ of Montevallo	AL	5,310	C
Univ of Nebr at Kearney	NE	4,308	LC
Univ of Nebr at Omaha	NE	1,889	LC
Univ of Nebr-Lincoln	NE	5,278	LC
Univ of North Alabama	AL	4,236	NC
Univ of N Car at Chapel Hill	NC	5,330	HC
Univ of N Car at Greensboro	NC	5,192	C
Univ of N Dak	ND	4,902	NC
Univ of North Texas	TX	4,853	C
Univ of Northern Iowa	IA	5,137	C
Univ of Okla	OK	5,427	VC
Univ of Pittsburgh at Bradford	PA	9,050	C
Univ of S Car	SC	6,158	C
Univ of South Florida	FL	5,475	C+
Univ of Southern Calif	CA	23,006	VC
Univ of Southern Colo	CO	5,350	LC
Univ of Southern Indiana	IN	3,720	NC
Univ of Southern Miss	MS	4,542	C
Univ of Southwestern Louisiana	LA	3,968	NC
Univ of Tenn/Knoxville	TN	5,668	C
Univ of Texas at Arlington	TX	5,549	LC
Univ of Toledo	OH	6,636	NC
Univ of Tulsa	OK	13,795	VC
Univ of Wisc/Eau Claire	WI	4,647	C
Univ of Wisc/Oshkosh	WI	4,240	C
Univ of Wyoming	WY	4,991	NC
Valdosta State Univ	GA	4,670	LC
Valparaiso Univ	IN	14,810	VC
Virginia Wesleyan College	VA	14,950	VC
Wake Forest Univ	NC	17,280	MC
Wartburg College	IA	14,530	VC
Washington State Univ	WA	6,364	C
Wayne State Univ	MI	2,680	C
Webster Univ	MO	12,650	C
West Texas A&M Univ	TX	4,224	C
West Virginia Univ	WV	5,774	C
Western Carolina Univ	NC	3,811	C
Western Kentucky Univ	KY	4,808	C
Westminster College	PA	15,200	C
Winona State Univ	MN	5,200	VC
Women's College of Brenau Univ	GA	14,734	C
York College of Penn	PA	8,345	C

BUSINESS ADMINISTRATION AND MANAGEMENT

School	ST	$IS	SR
Adams State College	CO	4,910	C
Adelphi Univ	NY	18,250	LC
Adrian College	MI	14,340	C
Alabama A&M Univ	AL	4,200	C
Alabama State Univ	AL	3,428	NC
Albertson College	ID	15,942	C+
Albright College	PA	19,260	C
Alcorn State Univ	MS	4,474	C+
Alderson-Broaddus College	WV	12,000	C
Alfred Univ	NY	21,054	VC+
Alice Lloyd College	KY	2,750	VC
Allen Univ	SC	6,705	NC
Allentown College of St Francis de Sales	PA	13,480	C
Alma College	MI	16,375	VC+
Alvernia College	PA	13,150	LC
Alverno College	WI	11,344	C
Ambassador College	TX	4,091	C
American College for the Applied Arts	GA	11,870	SP
American International College	MA	14,029	C
American Univ	DC	21,230	VC+
Anderson Univ	IN	12,920	C
Andrews Univ	MI	14,952	NC
Angelo State Univ	TX	5,176	C
Anna Maria College	MA	15,975	LC
Antioch College	OH	19,532	C
Appalachian State Univ	NC	4,095	C
Aquinas College	MI	14,526	C
Arizona State Univ Main Campus	AZ	6,444	C
Arkansas Baptist College	AR	5,016	NC
Arkansas College	AR	11,626	VC
Arkansas State Univ	AR	4,250	NC
Arkansas Tech Univ	AR	4,200	NC
Asbury College	KY	11,105	VC
Ashland Univ	OH	15,508	C
Assumption College	MA	17,095	LC
Atlantic Union College	MA	14,150	LC
Auburn Univ	AL	5,823	C+
Auburn Univ at Montgomery	AL	3,390	C
Audrey Cohen College	NY	11,184	LC
Augusta College	GA	1,452	C
Augustana College	IL	16,959	VC
Augustana College	SD	13,420	C
Aurora Univ	IL	13,381	C
Austin College	TX	14,999	VC
Austin Peay State Univ	TN	4,350	C
Averett College	VA	13,610	LC
Avila College	MO	12,130	C
Azusa Pacific Univ	CA	15,034	C
Babson College	MA	23,160	VC
Baker College	MI	6,971	NC
Baker Univ	KS	12,284	C
Baldwin-Wallace College	OH	15,210	C
Ball State Univ	IN	6,032	LC
Barat College	IL	13,990	C
Barber-Scotia College	NC	6,840	NC
Bartlesville Wesleyan College	OK	9,400	C
Barton College	NC	10,689	LC
Bayamon Tech Univ College	PR	1,600	
Baylor Univ	TX	10,990	C+
Beaver College	PA	17,660	C
Belhaven College	MS	9,690	C+
Bellarmine College	KY	10,832	C
Bellevue College	NE	3,050	NC
Belmont Abbey College	NC	13,190	C
Beloit College	WI	18,950	VC+
Bemidji State Univ	MN	5,188	C
Benedict College	SC	8,376	LC
Benedictine College	KS	12,830	C
Bennett College	NC	8,920	LC
Berea College	KY	2,883	VC+
Berry College	GA	11,990	VC
Bethany College	KS	11,232	C
Bethel College	IN	11,650	C
Bethel College	KS	11,530	C
Bethel College	MN	15,050	C
Bethel College	TN	9,736	LC
Bethune-Cookman College	FL	8,375	LC
Biola Univ	CA	16,124	C
Birmingham-Southern College	AL	15,154	VC+
Black Hills State Univ	SD	4,831	NC
Blackburn College	IL	9,120	C
Bloomfield College	NJ	12,200	LC
Bloomsburg Univ of Penn	PA	6,312	C+
Bluefield College	VA	10,600	C
Bluefield State College	WV	1,832	LC
Bluffton College	OH	12,951	C
Boise State Univ	ID	4,909	LC
Boricua College	NY	5,920	VC
Boston College	MA	22,706	MC
Boston Univ	MA	24,130	HC
Bowie State Univ	MD	7,294	LC
Bowling Green State Univ	OH	6,701	C
Bradley Univ	IL	14,718	C+
Brescia College	KY	9,800	C
Brewton-Parker College	GA	6,828	NC
Briar Cliff College	IA	13,375	C
Bridgewater College	VA	15,300	C
Brigham Young Univ	UT	5,625	HC
Brigham Young Univ/Hawaii	HI	6,750	VC
Brooklyn Campus of LIU	NY	15,000	LC
Bryan College	TN	11,465	C
Bryant College	RI	18,335	C
Bucknell Univ	PA	22,320	HC
Buena Vista College	IA	16,150	VC
Cabrini College	PA	16,012	C
Caldwell College	NJ	12,860	C
Calif Baptist College	CA	11,294	C
Calif Lutheran Univ	CA	17,240	C
Calif Maritime Academy	CA	7,318	C
Calif Polytechnic State Univ	CA	6,980	VC+
Calif State Polytechnic Univ/Pomona	CA	6,438	LC
Cal State/Bakersfield	CA	5,402	C
Cal State/Chico	CA	6,146	C
Cal State/Dominguez Hills	CA	2,857	LC
Cal State/Fresno	CA	5,747	C
Cal State/Fullerton	CA	4,850	LC
Cal State/Hayward	CA	5,495	C
Cal State/Long Beach	CA	6,057	LC
Cal State/Los Angeles	CA	4,940	VC
Cal State/Northridge	CA	7,122	LC
Cal State/Sacramento	CA	6,387	C
Cal State/San Bernardino	CA	6,055	LC
Cal State/Stanislaus	CA	6,799	C
Calif Univ of Penn	PA	7,370	C
Calumet College of St. Joseph	IN	3,585	C
Calvin College	MI	13,020	VC
Cameron Univ	OK	3,686	LC
Campbell Univ	NC	10,624	C
Campbellsville College	KY	8,720	C
Canisius College	NY	15,510	C
Capital Univ	OH	16,535	VC
Cardinal Stritch College	WI	11,252	C
Caribbean Univ	PR	2,400	
Carlow College	PA	13,914	C
Carnegie Mellon Univ	PA	22,560	HC+
Carroll College	MT	11,265	C
Carroll College	WI	15,490	C
Carson-Newman College	TN	11,250	C
Carthage College	WI	15,995	C
Cascade College	OR	9,800	NC
Case Western Reserve Univ	OH	19,910	HC
Castleton State College	VT	8,378	LC
Catawba College	NC	12,950	C
Cedar Crest College	PA	18,930	C
Cedarville College	OH	10,715	C
Centenary College	NJ	17,040	LC
Centenary College of Louisiana	LA	11,826	C+
Central College	IA	14,025	VC
Central Conn State Univ	CT	7,108	C
Central Methodist College	MO	11,410	C
Central Mich Univ	MI	6,737	LC
Central Missouri State Univ	MO	5,138	LC
Central State Univ	OH	7,320	NC
Central Univ of Bayamon	PR	2,430	
Central Washington Univ	WA	5,644	C
Central Wesleyan College	SC	9,640	C
Chadron State College	NE	4,091	NC
Chaminade Univ of Honolulu	HI	14,290	C
Champlain College	VT	13,637	LC
Chapman Univ	CA	21,842	C
Charleston Southern Univ	SC	10,282	LC
Charter Oak State College	CT	314	NC
Chestnut Hill College	PA	14,525	C
Cheyney Univ of Penn	PA	7,005	C
Chicago State Univ	IL	2,198	C
Christian Brothers Univ	TN	12,120	VC
Christian Heritage College	CA	11,756	C
Christopher Newport Univ	VA	3,196	LC
City Univ	WA	6,400	NC
CUNY/City College	NY	2,543	VC
CUNY/College of Staten Island	NY	2,558	NC
CUNY/Herbert H. Lehman College	NY	2,542	C
CUNY/Medgar Evers College	NY	2,577	NC
CUNY/York College	NY	2,534	NC
Claflin College	SC	0	
Clarion Univ of Penn	PA	6,518	C
Clark Atlanta Univ	GA	11,846	C
Clark Univ	MA	21,400	VC
Clarke College	IA	13,950	C+
Clarkson Univ	NY	20,705	VC+
Clayton State College	GA	1,496	LC
Clearwater Christian College	FL	8,500	LC
Cleary College	MI	5,095	NC
Clemson Univ	SC	6,564	VC
Clinch Valley College/Univ of Virginia	VA	6,364	C
Coastal Carolina Univ	SC	6,010	LC
Coe College	IA	17,085	VC
Coker College	SC	13,790	C
Colby College	ME	24,230	HC
Colby-Sawyer College	NH	18,495	LC
College Misericordia	PA	15,820	C
College of Charleston	SC	6,250	C
College of Great Falls	MT	6,230	NC
College of Insurance	NY	17,600	VC
College of Mount St Joseph	OH	13,272	C
College of Mount St Vincent	NY	16,730	C
College of New Rochelle	NY	15,440	LC
College of Notre Dame	CA	16,480	C
College of St Catherine	MN	14,670	C
College of St Elizabeth	NJ	15,800	C
College of St Francis	IL	13,060	VC
College of St Joseph	VT	12,650	LC
College of St Mary	NE	12,500	C
College of St Rose	NY	14,452	C
College of St Scholastica	MN	14,868	C
College of Santa Fe	NM	14,008	C
College of the Ozarks	MO	2,000	VC+
College of the Southwest	NM	5,720	LC
College of William and Mary	VA	8,602	MC
Colo Christian Univ	CO	9,750	C
Colo State Univ	CO	6,566	VC
Columbia College	MO	11,995	C
Columbia College	SC	13,520	LC
Columbia Union College	MD	13,650	LC
Columbus College	GA	4,892	LC
Concord College	WV	5,104	NC
Concordia College	MN	13,200	C
Concordia College	NE	11,776	NC
Concordia College	NY	0	LC
Concordia College/Moorhead	MN	12,750	C
Concordia Lutheran College	TX	10,260	C+
Concordia Univ	IL	12,611	C
Concordia Univ	CA	14,675	C
Converse College	SC	15,750	C
Coppin State College	MD	7,145	LC
Cornell Univ	NY	13,445	MC
Covenant College	GA	13,054	VC
Creighton Univ	NE	14,432	VC
Crichton College	TN	6,547	NC
Culver-Stockton College	MO	11,150	C
Cumberland College	KY	9,756	C
Cumberland Univ	TN	8,650	C
Curry College	MA	18,695	LC
D'Youville College	NY	12,850	C
Daemen College	NY	13,020	LC
Dakota State Univ	SD	4,374	LC
Dakota Wesleyan Univ	SD	9,770	LC
Dallas Baptist Univ	TX	9,620	LC
Dana College	NE	11,910	C
Daniel Webster College	NH	16,484	LC
Davenport College of Business	MI	8,121	NC
David Lipscomb Univ	TN	7,865	VC
Davis and Elkins College	WV	13,230	LC
Defiance College	OH	13,480	LC
Delaware State College	DE	5,656	C
Delaware Valley College	PA	16,065	LC
Delta State Univ	MS	3,964	LC
DePaul Univ	IL	15,535	VC
DeVry/Addison (DuPage County)	IL	5,609	LC
DeVry/Atlanta	GA	5,609	LC
DeVry/Chicago	IL	5,609	LC
DeVry/Columbus	OH	5,609	LC
DeVry/Dallas	TX	5,609	LC
DeVry/Kansas City	MO	5,609	LC
DeVry/Los Angeles	CA	5,609	LC
DeVry/Phoenix	AZ	5,609	LC
Dickinson State Univ	ND	3,792	
Dillard Univ	LA	9,950	C
Doane College	NE	12,220	C
Dominican College	NY	13,600	LC
Dominican College of San Rafael	CA	17,860	C
Dordt College	IA	11,690	C
Dowling College	NY	12,730	LC
Drake Univ	IA	17,195	VC
Drexel Univ	PA	15,970	C
Drury College	MO	12,140	VC
Duquesne Univ	PA	16,434	VC
Dyke College	OH	5,200	C
Earlham College	IN	19,383	VC
East Carolina Univ	NC	4,498	C
East Central Univ	OK	3,558	C
East Stroudsburg Univ	PA	6,886	C
East Texas Baptist Univ	TX	7,740	C
East Texas State Univ	TX	4,572	LC
East-West Univ	IL	5,910	NC

School	ST	$IS	SR
Eastern College	PA	15,150	C+
Eastern Conn State Univ	CT	6,966	C
Eastern Kentucky Univ	KY	4,840	C
Eastern Mennonite College	VA	12,700	C
Eastern Mich Univ	MI	6,749	C
Eastern Montana College	MT	5,165	HC
Eastern Nazarene College	MA	12,165	C
Eastern New Mexico Univ	NM	3,950	C
Eastern Oregon State College	OR	6,090	C
Eastern Washington Univ	WA	5,439	LC
Edgewood College	WI	11,700	C
Edinboro Univ of Penn	PA	7,181	C
Edward Waters College	FL	8,300	NC
Elizabeth City State Univ	NC	4,254	LC
Elizabethtown College	PA	17,850	VC
Elmhurst College	IL	12,536	C
Elmira College	NY	18,450	C
Elon College	NC	12,290	LC
Embry-Riddle Aeronautical Univ	FL	10,600	C
Emmanuel College	MA	17,773	LC
Emory and Henry College	VA	12,776	C
Emory Univ	GA	21,930	HC
Emporia State Univ	KS	4,685	NC
Erskine College	SC	14,310	C
Eureka College	IL	14,555	C
Fairfield Univ	CT	20,460	VC
Fairleigh Dickinson Univ	NJ	16,427	C
Fairmont State College	WV	4,640	LC
Faulkner Univ	AL	8,630	C
Fayetteville State Univ	NC	3,926	LC
Felician College	NJ	7,900	C
Ferris State Univ	MI	7,160	NC
Ferrum College	VA	12,800	LC
Fisk Univ	TN	0	LC
Fitchburg State College	MA	6,962	C
Flagler College	FL	7,990	C
Florida A&M Univ	FL	4,651	C
Florida Atlantic Univ	FL	5,525	C
Florida Inst of Tech	FL	16,935	VC
Florida International Univ	FL	4,191	VC
Florida Memorial College	FL	7,600	C+
Florida Southern College	FL	12,260	C
Florida State Univ	FL	5,814	VC
Fontbonne College	MO	12,090	C
Fort Hays State Univ	KS	4,675	NC
Fort Lewis College	CO	5,097	C
Fort Valley State College	GA	3,974	LC
Framingham State College	MA	6,580	C
Francis Marion Univ	SC	5,878	LC
Franciscan Univ of Steubenville	OH	13,400	C
Franklin and Marshall College	PA	23,655	HC
Franklin Pierce College	NH	17,270	LC
Franklin Univ	OH	4,621	NC
Freed-Hardeman Univ	TN	8,585	VC
Friends Univ	KS	11,205	C
Frostburg State Univ	MD	6,940	C
Furman Univ	SC	16,557	VC
Gallaudet Univ	DC	9,850	SP
Gannon Univ	PA	14,872	C
Gardner-Webb Univ	NC	11,950	LC
Geneva College	PA	13,030	C
George Mason Univ	VA	8,728	C
George Washington Univ	DC	22,470	HC
Georgetown College	KY	10,590	C
Georgetown Univ	DC	24,410	MC
Georgia College	GA	4,310	LC
Georgia Inst of Tech	GA	6,669	HC+
Georgia Southern Univ	GA	4,988	LC
Georgia Southwestern College	GA	4,338	LC
Georgia State Univ	GA	2,019	C
Georgian Court College	NJ	12,550	C
Gettysburg College	PA	22,960	HC
Glenville State College	WV	4,810	LC
Gonzaga Univ	WA	16,350	VC
Gordon College	MA	16,790	C
Goshen College	IN	12,360	C
Grace College	IN	12,120	C
Graceland College	IA	11,600	C
Grambling State Univ	LA	4,712	NC
Grand Canyon Univ	AZ	9,680	VC
Grand Rapids Baptist College and Seminary	MI	10,228	C
Grand Valley State Univ	MI	6,822	VC
Grand View College	IA	13,230	NC
Green Mountain College	VT	14,080	C
Greensboro College	NC	11,496	C
Grove City College	PA	7,870	HC
Guilford College	NC	17,680	LC
Gustavus Adolphus College	MN	15,935	VC
Gwynedd-Mercy College	PA	15,450	LC
Hamline Univ	MN	17,122	VC
Hampton Univ	VA	10,706	C
Hannibal-LaGrange College	MO	8,400	C
Hanover College	IN	10,950	LC
Hardin-Simmons Univ	TX	9,080	C
Harding Univ	AR	9,050	VC
Hartwick College	NY	20,950	C
Hastings College	NE	12,426	C
Hawaii Pacific Univ	HI	12,300	C
Heidelberg College	OH	17,160	C
Henderson State Univ	AR	3,860	C
Heritage College	WA	5,540	NC
Hillsdale College	MI	15,110	VC
Hofstra Univ	NY	16,580	VC
Holy Family College	PA	8,300	C
Holy Names College	CA	15,660	C
Hood College	MD	19,010	VC
Hope College	MI	15,698	C+
Houghton College	NY	13,120	VC
Howard Payne Univ	TX	8,052	C
Howard Univ	DC	11,680	C
Humboldt State Univ	CA	5,676	C
Humphreys College	CA	9,714	NC
Huntingdon College	AL	11,400	C
Huntington College	IN	13,220	C
Huron Univ	SD	9,790	C
Husson College	ME	11,510	NC
Huston-Tillotson College	TX	8,490	C
Idaho State Univ	ID	4,442	C
Illinois College	IL	11,200	C
Illinois Inst of Tech	IL	18,290	VC
Illinois State Univ	IL	6,413	C
Illinois Wesleyan Univ	IL	18,590	HC+
Immaculata College	PA	14,620	C
Incarnate Word College	TX	12,307	C
Indiana Inst of Tech	IN	11,810	C
Indiana State Univ	IN	6,210	C
Indiana Univ at Kokomo	IN	2,069	C
Indiana Univ Bloomington	IN	6,495	VC
Indiana Univ East	IN	2,044	NC
Indiana Univ Northwest	IN	2,310	C
Indiana Univ of Penn	PA	6,373	C
Indiana Univ Southeast	IN	2,260	LC
Indiana Univ-Purdue Univ at Indianapolis	IN	5,862	LC
Indiana Univ/South Bend	IN	2,141	LC
Indiana Wesleyan Univ	IN	12,332	C
Inter American Univ of PR/ Aguadilla Regional College	PR	2,290	
Inter American Univ of PR/ Barranquitas Regional College	PR	2,730	
Inter American Univ of PR/ Bayamon Univ College	PR	2,300	
Inter American Univ of PR/ Metropolitan Campus	PR	2,340	
Inter American Univ of PR/ Ponce Regional College	PR	2,300	
Inter American Univ of PR/ San German	PR	4,620	
Inter American Univ/Arecibo Campus	PR	5,666	
Inter-American Univ of PR/ Fajardo Regional College	PR	2,732	
Iona College	NY	16,310	C
Iowa State Univ	IA	5,456	C
Iowa Wesleyan College	IA	13,250	C
Ithaca College	NY	19,679	C
Jackson State Univ	MS	4,996	C
Jacksonville Univ	FL	13,390	C
James Madison Univ	VA	8,198	HC
Jamestown College	ND	10,250	C
Jersey City State College	NJ	7,797	LC
John Brown Univ	AR	9,800	LC
John Carroll Univ	OH	16,510	C
Johnson and Wales Univ	RI	13,995	LC
Johnson C. Smith Univ	NC	8,916	LC
Johnson State College	VT	8,393	LC
Judson College	AL	9,060	C
Judson College	IL	13,625	C
Juniata College	PA	18,390	C+
Kalamazoo College	MI	19,974	HC
Kansas Newman College	KS	10,640	C
Kansas State Univ	KS	4,816	NC
Kean College of New Jersey	NJ	6,395	LC
Kendall College	IL	12,651	LC
Kent State Univ	OH	6,740	LC
Kentucky Christian College	KY	7,708	LC
Kentucky State Univ	KY	4,282	C+
Kentucky Wesleyan College	KY	11,550	C
Keuka College	NY	13,660	LC
King College	TN	11,500	C
King's College	NY	12,360	LC
King's College	PA	15,420	C
Knoxville College	TN	8,320	LC
Kutztown Univ	PA	6,528	C
La Roche College	PA	12,977	LC
La Salle Univ	PA	16,940	VC
La Sierra Univ	CA	15,472	C
LaGrange College	GA	10,602	C
Lake Erie College	OH	13,700	C
Lake Superior State Univ	MI	7,311	C
Lakeland College	WI	12,845	LC
Lamar Univ	TX	3,798	C
Lambuth Univ	TN	8,395	C
Lane College	TN	7,628	LC
Langston Univ	OK	2,907	LC
Lawrence Tech Univ	MI	9,470	C
Le Moyne College	NY	15,180	C
Le Tourneau Univ	TX	12,500	C+
Lee College	TN	7,894	C
Lees-McRae College	NC	9,850	LC
LeMoyne-Owen College	TN	4,500	LC
Lenoir-Rhyne College	NC	14,068	C
Lewis and Clark College	OR	19,980	VC
Lewis Univ	IL	14,797	LC
Lewis-Clark State College	ID	4,040	
Liberty Univ	VA	11,500	LC
Limestone College	SC	10,700	LC
Lincoln Memorial Univ	TN	8,218	C
Lincoln Univ	CA	4,400	LC
Lincoln Univ	MO	4,638	NC
Lincoln Univ	PA	0	LC
Lindenwood College	MO	13,560	VC
Lindsey Wilson College	KY	9,530	LC
Linfield College	OR	16,670	VC
Livingston Univ	AL	3,979	C
Livingstone College	NC	8,600	LC
Lock Haven Univ of Penn	PA	7,128	C
LIU/C. W. Post Campus	NY	16,870	LC
Longwood College	VA	7,800	C
Loras College	IA	14,160	C
Louisiana College	LA	7,518	C
Louisiana State Univ and A&M College	LA	5,605	C
Louisiana State Univ in Shreveport	LA	1,910	NC
Louisiana Tech Univ	LA	4,284	C
Lourdes College	OH	6,410	LC
Loyola College	MD	18,035	VC
Loyola Marymount Univ	CA	18,560	C
Loyola Univ of Chicago	IL	15,880	C+
Loyola Univ/New Orleans	LA	15,560	C+
Lubbock Christian Univ	TX	9,840	NC
Lycoming College	PA	17,200	LC
Lyndon State College	VT	8,394	NC
Lynn Univ	FL	18,300	C
MacMurray College	IL	12,800	C
Madonna Univ	MI	8,546	C
Maharishi International Univ	IA	13,666	C
Malone College	OH	12,572	C
Manchester College	IN	13,240	LC
Mankato State Univ	MN	5,097	LC
Mansfield Univ	PA	6,348	C
Marian Univ	IN	12,936	C
Marian College of Fond du Lac	WI	12,250	C
Marietta College	OH	16,940	C+
Marist College	NY	16,406	C
Marquette Univ	WI	16,114	VC
Mars Hill College	NC	11,050	C
Martin Univ	IN	4,830	NC
Mary Baldwin College	VA	17,700	LC
Mary Washington College	VA	7,910	HC
Marygrove College	MI	5,877	NC
Marymount College/ Tarrytown	NY	17,350	C
Marymount Manhattan College	NY	15,450	LC
Marymount Univ	VA	15,930	C
Maryville College	TN	14,474	C
Marywood College	PA	14,890	C
Mass Inst of Tech	MA	24,800	MC
Master's College	CA	12,816	C
Mayville State Univ	ND	4,272	NC
McKendree College	IL	10,900	C
McMurry Univ	TX	10,100	C
McNeese State Univ	LA	4,543	NC
McPherson College	KS	11,360	VC
Medaille College	NY	12,650	C
Menlo College	CA	20,375	LC
Mercer Univ	GA	15,123	C
Mercy College	NY	11,180	NC
Mercyhurst College	PA	13,488	C
Meredith College	NC	9,440	C
Merrimack College	MA	18,025	C
Mesa State College	CO	5,127	NC
Messiah College	PA	14,664	VC
Methodist College	NC	12,400	C
Miami Univ	OH	8,066	VC
Mich Christian College	MI	8,094	C
Mich State Univ	MI	7,842	C
Mich Tech Univ	MI	7,283	VC+
MidAmerica Nazarene College	KS	10,208	NC
Middle Tenn State Univ	TN	3,857	C
Midland Lutheran College	NE	12,410	C
Midwestern State Univ	TX	4,542	LC
Miles College	AL	7,150	NC
Millersville Univ of Penn	PA	7,370	LC
Milligan College	TN	10,690	C
Millikin Univ	IL	15,499	C
Millsaps College	MS	15,486	C+
Milwaukee School of Engineering	WI	14,100	C
Minot State Univ	ND	3,748	NC
Miss College	MS	8,348	C
Miss State Univ	MS	5,629	VC
Miss Univ for Women	MS	4,456	LC
Miss Valley State Univ	MS	4,089	NC
Missouri Baptist College	MO	9,340	C
Missouri Southern State College	MO	4,272	
Missouri Valley College	MO	14,050	LC
Missouri Western State College	MO	4,384	C
Molloy College	NY	8,580	LC
Monmouth College	IL	17,300	C+
Monmouth College	NJ	16,820	C
Montana State Univ	MT	5,534	C
Montclair State College	NJ	7,539	C+
Montreat-Anderson College	NC	10,972	LC
Moorhead State Univ	MN	5,076	C
Morehouse College	GA	13,224	HC
Morgan State Univ	MD	7,366	C+
Morningside College	IA	13,896	C
Morris Brown College	GA	12,234	NC
Morris College	SC	6,880	LC
Mount Ida College	MA	16,700	LC
Mount Mary College	WI	10,920	C
Mount Mercy College	IA	13,230	C
Mount Olive College	NC	9,650	LC
Mount St Clare College	IA	12,870	LC
Mount St Mary College	NY	12,910	C
Mount St Mary's College	CA	16,390	VC
Mount Senario College	WI	10,970	C
Mount Union College	OH	15,850	C
Mount Vernon College	DC	20,668	C
Mount Vernon Nazarene College	OH	10,390	C
Muhlenberg College	PA	20,795	VC
Murray State Univ	KY	4,702	C
National College	SD	9,055	NC
National Univ	CA	6,135	C
National-Louis Univ	IL	13,218	C
Nazareth College of Rochester	NY	15,310	C+
Nebr Wesleyan Univ	NE	12,240	C
Neumann College	PA	9,950	LC
New England College	NH	17,810	C
New Hampshire College	NH	15,242	LC
New Mexico Highlands Univ	NM	3,772	C
New Mexico Inst of Mining and Tech	NM	5,212	C+
New Mexico State Univ	NM	4,844	LC
New York Inst of Tech/Old Westbury	NY	13,914	LC
New York Univ	NY	24,705	VC+
Newberry College	SC	11,994	C
Niagara Univ	NY	14,552	C
Nicholls State Univ	LA	4,531	NC
Nichols College	MA	14,200	C
Norfolk State Univ	VA	6,345	LC
North Adams State College	MA	7,750	C
N Car Agricultural and Technical State Univ	NC	4,477	LC
N Car Central Univ	NC	4,347	LC
N Car State Univ	NC	4,984	VC
N Car Wesleyan College	NC	12,480	LC
North Central College	IL	15,498	VC
N Dak State Univ of Agriculture and Applied Science	ND	4,774	VC
North Georgia College	GA	4,103	LC
North Park College	IL	14,310	C
Northeast Louisiana Univ	LA	3,906	NC
Northeast Missouri State Univ	MO	5,654	VC+
Northeastern Illinois Univ	IL	1,955	C
Northeastern State Univ	OK	5,250	C
Northeastern Univ	MA	19,851	C
Northern Arizona Univ	AZ	4,844	C
Northern Illinois Univ	IL	6,408	C
Northern Mich Univ	MI	6,350	C
Northern State Univ	SD	4,186	LC
Northland College	WI	13,550	C
Northwest College	WA	9,897	LC
Northwest Nazarene College	ID	11,750	C
Northwestern College	MN	13,554	C
Northwestern College of Iowa	IA	12,250	C
Northwestern Okla State Univ	OK	3,424	C
Northwestern State Univ of Louisiana	LA	4,287	NC
Northwood Univ	FL	14,569	C
Northwood Univ	MI	13,385	LC
Norwich Univ	VT	18,730	C
Notre Dame College	NH	14,220	C
Notre Dame College of Ohio	OH	11,370	C
Nova Southeastern Univ	FL	13,244	LC
Nyack College	NY	12,210	LC
Oakland City College	IN	10,216	C
Oakland Univ	MI	6,714	VC
Oglala Lakota College	SD	0	
Oglethorpe Univ	GA	16,360	VC
Ohio Dominican College	OH	11,820	C
Ohio Northern Univ	OH	18,660	VC
Ohio Univ	OH	7,341	C
Ohio Wesleyan Univ	OH	21,108	VC+
Okla Baptist Univ	OK	8,486	C
Okla Christian Univ of Science and Arts	OK	8,790	NC
Okla City Univ	OK	9,840	C
Okla Panhandle State Univ	OK	3,155	NC
Okla State Univ	OK	5,086	VC
Old Dominion Univ	VA	8,317	C
Olivet College	MI	14,000	C
Olivet Nazarene Univ	IL	11,976	C
Oral Roberts Univ	OK	10,607	C+
Oregon State Univ	OR	6,175	C
Ottawa Univ	KS	10,490	C+
Otterbein College	OH	16,506	C
Ouachita Baptist Univ	AR	8,940	C
Our Lady of Holy Cross College	LA	4,630	LC
Pace Univ	NY	15,540	C
Pacific Christian College	CA	12,700	C
Pacific Lutheran Univ	WA	15,998	VC
Pacific Union College	CA	15,075	C
Pacific Univ	OR	17,869	C
Paine College	GA	8,207	LC

School	ST	$IS	SR
Palm Beach Atlantic College	FL	10,720	C
Park College	MO	7,320	C
Parsons School of Design	NY	21,410	SP
Paul Quinn College	TX	7,090	LC
Pembroke State Univ	NC	3,538	LC
Penn State Univ at Erie/ Behrend College	PA	8,752	C
Penn State Univ/Univ Park Campus	PA	8,752	HC
Pepperdine Univ	CA	23,720	VC
Peru State College	NE	4,311	NC
Pfeiffer College	NC	11,670	LC
Philander Smith College	AR	5,434	NC
Phillips Univ	OK	12,744	C
Piedmont College	GA	8,540	LC
Pikeville College	KY	8,500	NC
Pillsbury Baptist Bible College	MN	7,390	NC
Pittsburg State Univ	KS	4,478	NC
Plymouth State College	NH	7,166	C
Point Loma Nazarene College	CA	13,532	C
Point Park College	PA	13,922	LC
Pontifical Catholic Univ of PR/Ponce	PR	5,807	C
Portland State Univ	OR	7,191	C
Prairie View A&M Univ	TX	4,740	LC
Presbyterian College	SC	15,400	VC
Principia College	IL	17,799	C
Providence College	RI	19,750	VC
Queens College	NC	14,950	C
Quincy Univ	IL	13,646	VC
Quinnipiac College	CT	17,600	C+
Radford Univ	VA	7,034	LC
Ramapo College of New Jersey	NJ	8,027	C+
Regis Univ	CO	17,340	C
Rhode Island College	RI	7,901	LC
Rhodes College	TN	19,624	HC
Rider College	NJ	18,160	C
Rivier College	NH	14,920	LC
Roanoke College	VA	16,975	C
Robert Morris College	PA	10,406	LC
Roberts Wesleyan College	NY	13,317	C
Rochester Inst of Tech	NY	18,954	VC
Rockford College	IL	15,300	C
Rockhurst College	MO	12,470	C
Rocky Mountain College	MT	11,320	C
Roger Williams Univ	RI	16,750	C
Roosevelt Univ	IL	12,368	C
Rosary College	IL	15,040	C
Rosemont College	PA	16,775	C
Rowan College of New Jersey	NJ	7,358	VC
Rust College	MS	6,600	LC
Rutgers Univ/Douglass College	NJ	8,795	VC
Rutgers Univ/Livingston College	NJ	8,877	VC
Rutgers Univ/Newark College of A&S	NJ	8,645	C
Rutgers Univ/Univ College—New Brunswick	NJ	0	LC
Rutgers Univ/Univ College—Newark	NJ	0	C
Sacred Heart Univ	CT	16,350	C
Saginaw Valley State Univ	MI	6,634	LC
St Ambrose Univ	IA	13,380	C
St Andrews Presbyterian College	NC	14,240	LC
St Augustine's College	NC	9,300	C+
St Cloud State Univ	MN	5,015	C
St Edward's Univ	TX	12,636	C
St Francis College	IN	11,662	C
St John Fisher College	NY	15,415	C
St John's Univ	NY	8,980	C+
St Joseph College	CT	16,225	C
St Joseph's College	IN	14,730	C
St Joseph's College	ME	14,535	C
St Joseph's College	NY	7,322	C
St Joseph's Univ	PA	17,800	VC
St Leo College	FL	13,570	C
St Louis Univ	MO	15,522	VC
St Mary College	KS	11,250	C
St Mary's College	IN	17,043	VC
St Mary's College	MI	8,350	C
St Mary's College of Calif	CA	18,848	VC
St Mary's College of Minn	MN	13,850	LC
St Mary's Univ	TX	12,064	C
St Mary-of-the-Woods College	IN	14,430	NC
St Michael's College	VT	17,930	C
St Norbert College	WI	15,710	VC
St Paul's College	VA	9,171	C
St Peter's College	NJ	14,775	LC
St Thomas Aquinas College	NY	13,550	C
St Thomas Univ	FL	14,280	LC
St Vincent College	PA	13,934	C
St Xavier Univ	IL	14,700	C
Salem College	NC	16,025	C
Salem State College	MA	6,712	C
Salem-Teikyo Univ	WV	14,527	C
Salisbury State Univ	MD	7,516	C+
San Diego State Univ	CA	6,692	LC
San Francisco State Univ	CA	7,292	LC
Schreiner College	TX	14,320	C
Seattle Pacific Univ	WA	16,503	C
Seattle Univ	WA	16,590	C
Selma Univ	AL	5,785	NC
Seton Hall Univ	NJ	18,306	LC
Seton Hill College	PA	14,320	C
Shaw Univ	NC	8,936	C+
Shawnee State Univ	OH	4,379	NC
Sheldon Jackson College	AK	14,050	NC
Shenandoah Univ	VA	11,800	C
Shepherd College	WV	5,540	C
Shorter College	GA	10,270	C
Siena Heights College	MI	12,520	C
Sierra Nevada College	NV	14,000	NC
Silver Lake College	WI	8,280	LC
Simpson College	CA	10,628	C
Simpson College	IA	14,635	VC
Sioux Falls College	SD	11,540	C
Skidmore College	NY	23,230	HC
Slippery Rock Univ	PA	6,803	C
Sojourner-Douglass College	MD	5,265	LC
S Car State Univ	SC	5,424	LC
Southeastern Louisiana Univ	LA	4,230	NC
Southeastern Okla State Univ	OK	3,594	C
Southeastern Univ	DC	6,625	C
Southern Arkansas Univ	AR	3,432	NC
Southern Calif College	CA	12,356	C
Southern College of Seventh-day Adventists	TN	11,348	NC
Southern Conn State Univ	CT	7,532	C
Southern Illinois Univ at Carbondale	IL	6,234	C
Southern Illinois Univ at Edwardsville	IL	6,097	LC
Southern Methodist Univ	TX	18,520	VC
Southern Nazarene Univ	OK	9,206	NC
Southern Oregon State College	OR	6,128	C
Southern Univ and A&M College	LA	4,920	NC
Southern Univ at New Orleans	LA	1,452	NC
Southern Utah Univ	UT	4,104	LC
Southern Vermont College	VT	12,974	C
Southwest Baptist Univ	MO	9,192	NC
Southwest Missouri State Univ	MO	4,956	C
Southwest State Univ	MN	5,400	NC
Southwest Texas State Univ	TX	5,124	C
Southwestern Adventist College	TX	10,530	NC
Southwestern College	KS	10,032	C
Southwestern Okla State Univ	OK	3,312	C
Southwestern Univ	TX	15,484	HC
Spalding Univ	KY	10,496	LC
Spring Arbor College	MI	12,256	C
Spring Hill College	AL	16,015	C+
Springfield College	MA	15,200	LC
SUNY at Albany	NY	7,059	VC
SUNY at Binghamton	NY	7,921	HC
SUNY at Buffalo	NY	7,896	VC
SUNY at Stony Brook	NY	7,658	VC
SUNY/College at Brockport	NY	7,220	C+
SUNY/College at Buffalo	NY	7,035	VC
SUNY/College at Fredonia	NY	7,159	VC
SUNY/College at Geneseo	NY	6,949	HC
SUNY/College at New Paltz	NY	6,890	VC
SUNY/College at Old Westbury	NY	7,128	LC
SUNY/College at Oswego	NY	7,330	VC
SUNY/Empire State College	NY	2,687	NC
Stephen F. Austin State Univ	TX	5,117	C
Stephens College	MO	18,460	C
Sterling College	KS	10,990	VC
Stetson Univ	FL	16,435	VC
Stillman College	AL	7,213	NC
Strayer College	DC	5,850	LC
Sul Ross State Univ	TX	4,144	NC
Susquehanna Univ	PA	19,950	VC
Syracuse Univ	NY	21,305	HC
Tabor College	KS	11,460	VC
Talladega College	AL	8,124	VC
Tarleton State Univ	TX	4,082	LC
Taylor Univ	IN	14,450	VC
Teikyo Marycrest Univ	IA	13,755	VC
Teikyo Post Univ	CT	16,360	LC
Temple Univ	PA	10,281	C
Tenn State Univ	TN	4,626	C+
Tenn Tech Univ	TN	5,190	C
Tenn Wesleyan College	TN	10,060	C
Texas A&M Univ at Kingsville	TX	3,808	LC
Texas College	TX	5,930	NC
Texas Lutheran College	TX	10,710	C
Texas Southern Univ	TX	4,500	NC
Texas Tech Univ	TX	6,008	C
Texas Wesleyan Univ	TX	9,380	LC
Texas Woman's Univ	TX	4,392	C
The Citadel	SC	6,619	C
The Univ of New Mexico	NM	5,304	C
Thiel College	PA	16,282	C
Thomas A. Edison State College	NJ	400	
Thomas College	ME	13,450	LC
Thomas College	GA	3,123	NC
Thomas More College	KY	12,962	C
Tiffin Univ	OH	10,800	LC
Touro College	NY	11,930	C
Towson State Univ	MD	7,452	C
Transylvania Univ	KY	14,970	VC+
Trenton State College	NJ	9,085	HC
Trevecca Nazarene College	TN	9,826	NC
Tri-State Univ	IN	13,788	LC
Trinity College	DC	17,660	C
Trinity College	IL	14,010	C
Trinity College of Vermont	VT	16,015	LC
Trinity Univ	TX	16,670	HC
Troy State Univ	AL	4,322	C
Troy State Univ at Dothan/ Fort Rucker	AL	2,260	NC
Troy State Univ in Montgomery	AL	1,710	NC
Turabo Univ	PR	2,670	
Tuskegee Univ	AL	10,128	C
Union College	KY	9,790	C
Union College	NE	11,060	NC
United States International Univ	CA	14,535	LC
Universidad Adventista de las Antillas	PR	5,000	
Universidad Metropolitana	PR	2,650	
Universidad Politecnica de PR	PR	6,195	
Univ of Akron	OH	6,699	NC
Univ of Alabama	AL	5,702	C
Univ of Alabama at Huntsville	AL	5,868	VC
Univ of Alaska Anchorage	AK	7,131	C
Univ of Alaska Fairbanks	AK	4,718	C
Univ of Alaska Southeast	AK	4,075	LC
Univ of Arizona	AZ	5,808	C
Univ of Arkansas at Fayetteville	AR	5,046	C
Univ of Arkansas at Little Rock	AR	4,419	C
Univ of Arkansas at Monticello	AR	3,832	NC
Univ of Arkansas at Pine Bluff	AR	3,978	LC
Univ of Bridgeport	CT	18,985	C
Univ of Calif at Berkeley	CA	9,962	HC+
Univ of Calif, Riverside	CA	9,178	C
Univ of Central Arkansas	AR	4,200	LC
Univ of Central Florida	FL	6,061	C+
Univ of Central Okla	OK	3,647	C
Univ of Charleston	WV	12,750	C
Univ of Cincinnati	OH	7,989	C
Univ of Colo at Boulder	CO	6,410	VC
Univ of Colo at Colo Springs	CO	2,269	C
Univ of Colo at Denver	CO	1,955	VC
Univ of Conn	CT	9,168	C
Univ of Delaware	DE	8,013	VC
Univ of Detroit Mercy	MI	14,720	C
Univ of Dubuque	IA	14,150	LC
Univ of Evansville	IN	15,300	VC
Univ of Findlay	OH	15,764	C
Univ of Georgia	GA	5,655	VC
Univ of Guam	GU	4,139	NC
Univ of Hawaii at Hilo	HI	4,141	C
Univ of Hawaii at Manoa	HI	5,626	C
Univ of Houston	TX	5,215	C
Univ of Houston-Downtown	TX	4,034	NC
Univ of Illinois at Chicago	IL	8,443	C
Univ of Illinois at Urbana-Champaign	IL	7,764	HC
Univ of Indianapolis	IN	14,510	C
Univ of Iowa	IA	5,658	VC
Univ of Kansas	KS	5,200	NC
Univ of La Verne	CA	17,400	C
Univ of Lowell	MA	8,831	VC
Univ of Maine	ME	7,990	C
Univ of Maine at Augusta	ME	2,595	NC
Univ of Maine at Fort Kent	ME	6,285	LC
Univ of Maine at Machias	ME	6,135	C
Univ of Maine at Presque Isle	ME	6,374	C
Univ of Mary	ND	8,910	C
Univ of Mary Hardin-Baylor	TX	8,120	NC
Univ of Maryland/College Park	MD	8,182	VC
Univ of Maryland/Eastern Shore	MD	6,254	LC
Univ of Maryland/Univ College	MD	4,900	NC
Univ of Mass Dartmouth	MA	8,158	C
Univ of Mass/Amherst	MA	9,364	LC
Univ of Miami	FL	22,107	VC
Univ of Mich/Ann Arbor	MI	9,428	HC+
Univ of Mich/Dearborn	MI	3,399	HC
Univ of Mich/Flint	MI	2,916	C
Univ of Minn/Duluth	MN	6,512	C
Univ of Minn/Twin Cities	MN	6,682	VC
Univ of Miss	MS	5,756	C
Univ of Missouri/Columbia	MO	6,254	HC
Univ of Missouri/Kansas City	MO	5,906	VC
Univ of Missouri/St. Louis	MO	6,378	C
Univ of Mobile	AL	9,400	C
Univ of Montana	MT	5,529	C
Univ of Nebr at Kearney	NE	4,308	LC
Univ of Nebr at Omaha	NE	1,889	LC
Univ of Nebr-Lincoln	NE	5,278	LC
Univ of New England	ME	16,075	LC
Univ of New Hampshire	NH	8,242	C
Univ of New Haven	CT	14,980	C
Univ of New Orleans	LA	5,468	C
Univ of N Car at Asheville	NC	4,791	VC
Univ of N Car at Chapel Hill	NC	5,330	HC
Univ of N Car at Charlotte	NC	4,597	C
Univ of N Car at Greensboro	NC	5,192	C
Univ of N Car at Wilmington	NC	5,172	C
Univ of N Dak	ND	4,902	NC
Univ of North Florida	FL	5,082	C
Univ of North Texas	TX	4,853	C
Univ of Northern Colo	CO	6,008	C
Univ of Notre Dame	IN	20,150	MC
Univ of Okla	OK	5,427	VC
Univ of Oregon	OR	6,466	VC
Univ of Penn	PA	24,238	MC
Univ of Pittsburgh at Bradford	PA	9,050	C
Univ of Pittsburgh at Johnstown	PA	8,914	C
Univ of PR/Arecibo Tech Univ College	PR	1,302	C
Univ of PR/Cayey Univ College	PR	900	
Univ of PR/Humacao Univ College	PR	1,494	
Univ of PR/Mayaguez	PR	0	
Univ of PR/Rio Piedras	PR	0	
Univ of Puget Sound	WA	19,520	HC
Univ of Redlands	CA	22,059	VC
Univ of Rhode Island	RI	9,205	C
Univ of Richmond	VA	16,700	HC
Univ of Rio Grande	OH	6,300	NC
Univ of St Thomas	MN	15,785	C+
Univ of St Thomas	TX	11,676	C+
Univ of San Diego	CA	18,970	VC
Univ of San Francisco	CA	18,408	C
Univ of Science and Arts of Okla	OK	3,304	C
Univ of Scranton	PA	17,071	VC
Univ of South Alabama	AL	5,451	C
Univ of S Car	SC	6,158	C
Univ of S Car at Spartanburg	SC	2,320	C
Univ of South Florida	FL	5,475	C+
Univ of Southern Calif	CA	23,006	VC
Univ of Southern Colo	CO	5,350	LC
Univ of Southern Indiana	IN	3,720	NC
Univ of Southern Maine	ME	7,299	C
Univ of Southern Miss	MS	4,542	C
Univ of Southwestern Louisiana	LA	3,968	NC
Univ of Tenn at Chattanooga	TN	5,375	C
Univ of Tenn at Martin	TN	4,550	C
Univ of Tenn/Knoxville	TN	5,668	C
Univ of Texas at Arlington	TX	5,549	LC
Univ of Texas at Austin	TX	5,160	VC
Univ of Texas at Dallas	TX	1,222	VC+
Univ of Texas at El Paso	TX	3,160	LC
Univ of Texas-Pan American	TX	3,192	NC
Univ of the District of Columbia	DC	974	NC
Univ of the Ozarks	AR	7,770	C
Univ of the Pacific	CA	21,100	C
Univ of the Sacred Heart	PR	3,890	
Univ of the State of New York/Regents College Degrees	NY	510	
Univ of the Virgin Islands	VI	5,896	C
Univ of Toledo	OH	6,636	NC
Univ of Vermont	VT	10,776	C+
Univ of Washington	WA	6,618	VC
Univ of West Florida	FL	5,415	C
Univ of Wisc/Eau Claire	WI	4,647	C
Univ of Wisc/Green Bay	WI	4,904	C
Univ of Wisc/La Crosse	WI	4,487	C
Univ of Wisc/Madison	WI	6,400	HC
Univ of Wisc/Milwaukee	WI	6,165	C
Univ of Wisc/Oshkosh	WI	4,240	C
Univ of Wisc/Parkside	WI	5,247	C
Univ of Wisc/Platteville	WI	4,830	C
Univ of Wisc/River Falls	WI	4,655	C
Univ of Wisc/Stevens Point	WI	5,047	C+
Univ of Wisc/Stout	WI	4,719	C
Univ of Wisc/Superior	WI	4,330	C
Univ of Wisc/Whitewater	WI	4,700	C
Univ of Wyoming	WY	4,991	NC
Upper Iowa Univ	IA	11,900	C
Upsala College	NJ	17,200	C
Urbana Univ	OH	12,536	C
Ursinus College	PA	19,165	VC
Ursuline College	OH	13,180	LC
Utah State Univ	UT	4,683	C
Utica College of Syracuse Univ	NY	16,714	LC
Valdosta State Univ	GA	4,670	LC
Valley City State Univ	ND	4,385	LC
Valparaiso Univ	IN	14,810	VC
Villa Julie College	MD	9,880	LC
Villanova Univ	PA	21,400	HC
Virginia Commonwealth Univ	VA	7,909	C
Virginia Intermont College	VA	12,250	LC
Virginia State Univ	VA	7,040	C
Virginia Union Univ	VA	10,555	LC
Virginia Wesleyan College	VA	14,950	VC
Viterbo College	WI	12,670	C
Voorhees College	SC	6,772	LC
Wagner College	NY	17,950	C

School	ST	$IS	SR
Wake Forest Univ	NC	17,280	MC
Walla Walla College	WA	13,215	C
Walsh Univ	OH	11,640	C
Warner Pacific College	OR	12,112	C
Wartburg College	IA	14,530	VC
Washburn Univ of Topeka	KS	5,802	NC
Washington and Jefferson College	PA	19,360	C
Washington and Lee Univ	VA	17,735	MC
Washington College	MD	19,270	C+
Washington State Univ	WA	6,364	C
Washington Univ	MO	23,507	HC
Wayland Baptist Univ	TX	7,811	NC
Wayne State College	NE	4,260	NC
Waynesburg College	PA	11,960	C
Webber College	FL	8,710	C
Weber State Univ	UT	4,398	C
Webster Univ	MO	12,650	C
Wesley College	DE	13,745	LC
Wesleyan College	GA	15,445	C
West Chester Univ of Penn	PA	7,492	C
West Coast Univ	CA	9,120	NC
West Liberty State College	WV	4,690	LC
West Texas A&M Univ	TX	4,224	C
West Virginia Inst of Tech	WV	5,858	LC
West Virginia State College	WV	5,044	LC
West Virginia Univ	WV	5,774	C
West Virginia Wesleyan College	WV	16,900	C
Westbrook College	ME	15,900	C
Western Baptist College	OR	12,400	LC
Western Conn State Univ	CT	6,622	C
Western Illinois Univ	IL	5,241	LC
Western Kentucky Univ	KY	4,808	C
Western Maryland College	MD	18,990	C
Western Mich Univ	MI	6,820	C
Western New England College	MA	14,674	LC
Western New Mexico Univ	NM	3,234	LC
Western Oregon State College	OR	6,180	C
Western State College of Colo	CO	5,560	C
Western Washington Univ	WA	6,077	VC
Westfield State College	MA	7,161	C
Westminster College	MO	13,750	C+
Westminster College	PA	15,200	C
Westminster College of Salt Lake City	UT	12,100	C
Whittier College	CA	21,661	C
Whitworth College	WA	16,265	C
Wichita State Univ	KS	5,068	NC
Widener Univ	PA	16,840	C
Wilberforce Univ	OH	10,408	C
Wiley College	TX	0	NC
Wilkes Univ	PA	15,728	LC
William Carey College	MS	7,050	C
William Jewell College	MO	12,500	VC
William Paterson College	NJ	7,438	C+
William Penn College	IA	13,400	C
William Woods Univ	MO	14,025	LC
Williams Baptist College	AR	5,834	LC
Wilmington College	DE	5,200	NC
Wilmington College	OH	13,700	LC
Wingate College	NC	10,610	C
Winona State Univ	MN	5,200	VC
Winston-Salem State Univ	NC	4,142	LC
Winthrop Univ	SC	6,750	C
Wisc Lutheran College	WI	12,180	C
Wittenberg Univ	OH	19,998	VC
Women's College of Brenau Univ	GA	14,734	C
Woodbury Univ	CA	17,620	LC
Worcester State College	MA	6,414	LC
Xavier Univ	OH	15,710	C+
Xavier Univ of Louisiana	LA	10,400	C
Yeshiva Univ	NY	18,200	VC
York College	NE	7,610	C
Youngstown State Univ	OH	6,447	LC

BUSINESS DATA PROCESSING

School	ST	$IS	SR
Cal State/Long Beach	CA	6,057	LC
Faulkner Univ	AL	8,630	LC
Univ of Houston-Downtown	TX	4,034	NC

BUSINESS ECONOMICS

School	ST	$IS	SR
Alabama A&M Univ	AL	4,200	C
Alabama State Univ	AL	3,428	NC
Albertus Magnus College	CT	16,280	LC
Alcorn State Univ	MS	4,474	C+
Alfred Univ	NY	21,054	VC+
American International College	MA	14,029	C
Andrews Univ	MI	14,952	NC
Angelo State Univ	TX	5,176	C
Appalachian State Univ	NC	4,095	C
Arkansas State Univ	AR	4,250	NC
Ashland Univ	OH	15,508	C
Auburn Univ	AL	5,823	C+
Auburn Univ at Montgomery	AL	3,390	C
Augusta College	GA	1,452	C
Aurora Univ	IL	13,381	C
Baker Univ	KS	12,284	C
Ball State Univ	IN	6,032	LC
Baylor Univ	TX	10,990	C+
Bentley College	MA	18,680	C
Bethany College	KS	11,232	C
Bethany College	WV	18,300	C+
Bloomsburg Univ of Penn	PA	6,312	C+
Bluffton College	OH	12,951	C
Boston College	MA	22,706	MC
Boston Univ	MA	24,130	HC
Bowling Green State Univ	OH	6,701	C
Bradley Univ	IL	14,718	C+
Brescia College	KY	9,800	C
Buena Vista College	IA	16,150	VC
Calif Lutheran Univ	CA	17,240	C
Cal State/Fullerton	CA	4,850	LC
Cal State/Los Angeles	CA	4,940	VC
Cal State/San Bernardino	CA	6,055	LC
Calif Univ of Penn	PA	7,370	LC
Calvin College	MI	13,020	VC
Campbell Univ	NC	10,624	C
Carnegie Mellon Univ	PA	22,560	HC+
Carroll College	WI	15,490	C
Carson-Newman College	TN	11,250	C
Centenary College of Louisiana	LA	11,826	C+
Central State Univ	OH	7,320	NC
Central Washington Univ	WA	5,644	C
Chadron State College	NE	4,091	NC
Chaminade Univ of Honolulu	HI	14,290	C
Christian Brothers Univ	TN	12,120	VC
Christopher Newport Univ	VA	3,196	LC
Claremont McKenna College	CA	22,150	MC
Clarion Univ of Penn	PA	6,518	C
Clarkson Univ	NY	20,705	VC+
Cleveland State Univ	OH	7,287	NC
College of Notre Dame	CA	16,480	C
College of Wooster	OH	19,875	VC
Concordia College	MI	13,660	C
Coppin State College	MD	7,145	LC
Creighton Univ	NE	14,432	VC
DePaul Univ	IL	15,535	VC
Dominican College	NY	13,600	LC
Drexel Univ	PA	15,970	C
Duquesne Univ	PA	16,434	VC
East Tenn State Univ	TN	4,406	C
Eastern Kentucky Univ	KY	4,840	NC
Eastern Mich Univ	MI	6,749	C
Eastern Montana College	MT	5,165	LC
Eastern New Mexico Univ	NM	3,950	C
Eastern Washington Univ	WA	5,439	LC
Edinboro Univ of Penn	PA	7,181	C
Elmhurst College	IL	12,536	C
Elmira College	NY	18,450	LC
Emory Univ	GA	21,930	HC
Emporia State Univ	KS	4,685	NC
Fairmont State College	WV	4,640	LC
Fayetteville State Univ	NC	3,926	LC
Florida A&M Univ	FL	4,651	C
Florida Inst of Tech	FL	16,935	VC
Florida Southern College	FL	12,260	C
Fordham Univ/College of Business Administration	NY	19,875	VC
Fort Hays State Univ	KS	4,675	NC
Francis Marion Univ	SC	5,878	LC
Franklin College of Indiana	IN	13,970	C
Gannon Univ	PA	14,872	C
George Fox College	OR	15,640	LC
George Washington Univ	DC	22,470	HC
Georgetown College	KY	10,990	C
Georgia Southern Univ	GA	4,988	LC
Georgia State Univ	GA	2,019	C
Golden Gate Univ	CA	5,623	VC
Graceland College	IA	11,600	C
Grambling State Univ	LA	4,712	NC
Grand Valley State Univ	MI	6,822	VC
Gustavus Adolphus College	MN	15,935	VC
Hampden-Sydney College	VA	17,372	C+
Hanover College	IN	10,950	VC
Harding Univ	AR	9,050	VC
Hastings College	NE	12,426	C
Hawaii Pacific Univ	HI	12,300	C
Heidelberg College	OH	17,160	C
Hendrix College	AR	11,670	C
High Point Univ	NC	12,350	LC
Hollins College	VA	18,484	C
Holy Names College	CA	15,660	C
Houston Baptist Univ	TX	11,055	C
Humboldt State Univ	CA	5,676	C
Huntington College	IN	13,220	C
Illinois Benedictine College	IL	14,170	C
Indiana Univ Bloomington	IN	6,495	VC
Indiana Univ Southeast	IN	2,260	LC
Indiana Univ-Purdue Univ at Fort Wayne	IN	2,500	LC
Inter American Univ of PR/San German	PR	4,620	
Iona College	NY	16,310	C
Jacksonville Univ	FL	13,390	C
James Madison Univ	VA	8,198	HC
Jamestown College	ND	10,250	C
Johnson C. Smith Univ	NC	8,916	LC
Juniata College	PA	18,390	C+
Kansas Wesleyan Univ	KS	11,770	C
Kean College of New Jersey	NJ	6,395	LC
Kennesaw State College	GA	1,553	C
Kent State Univ	OH	6,740	LC
Kentucky State Univ	KY	4,282	C+
Kentucky Wesleyan College	KY	11,550	C
King's College	PA	15,420	C
Kutztown Univ	PA	6,528	C
Lafayette College	PA	23,450	HC
LaGrange College	GA	10,602	C
Lake Forest College	IL	19,960	VC
Lakeland College	WI	12,845	LC
Lamar Univ	TX	3,798	C
Lee College at the Univ of Judaism	CA	15,600	VC
Lehigh Univ	PA	23,250	HC
Lewis Univ	IL	14,797	LC
Liberty Univ	VA	11,500	LC
Lincoln Memorial Univ	TN	8,218	C
Linfield College	OR	16,670	VC
Louisiana State Univ and A&M College	LA	5,605	C
Louisiana State Univ in Shreveport	LA	1,910	NC
Louisiana Tech Univ	LA	4,284	C
Loyola Univ of Chicago	IL	15,880	C+
Loyola Univ/New Orleans	LA	15,660	C+
Manchester College	IN	13,240	LC
Manhattan College	NY	19,000	C
Mansfield Univ	PA	6,348	C
Marist College	NY	16,406	C
Marquette Univ	WI	16,114	VC
Marshall Univ	WV	5,762	LC
Mary Baldwin College	VA	17,700	LC
Marymount College/Tarrytown	NY	17,350	C
Marymount Univ	VA	15,930	C
McMurry Univ	TX	10,100	C
Merrimack College	MA	18,025	C
Mesa State College	CO	5,127	NC
Methodist College	NC	12,400	C
Miami Univ	OH	8,066	VC
Mich Tech Univ	MI	7,283	VC+
Middle Tenn State Univ	TN	3,857	C
Midland Lutheran College	NE	12,410	LC
Midwestern State Univ	TX	4,542	LC
Millikin Univ	IL	15,499	C
Mills College	CA	20,848	VC
Miss College	MS	8,348	C
Missouri Southern State College	MO	4,272	
Monmouth College	IL	17,300	C+
Monmouth College	NJ	16,820	C
Moravian College	PA	18,960	VC
Morehead State Univ	KY	4,600	LC
Morehouse College	GA	13,224	LC
Morris Brown College	GA	12,234	NC
Mount Union College	OH	15,850	C
Murray State Univ	KY	4,702	C
New Mexico State Univ	NM	4,844	LC
New York Inst of Tech/Old Westbury	NY	13,914	LC
New York Univ	NY	24,705	VC+
Niagara Univ	NY	14,552	C
Nicholls State Univ	LA	4,531	NC
Nichols College	MA	14,200	LC
N Car Central Univ	NC	4,347	LC
N Car State Univ	NC	4,984	VC
North Georgia College	GA	4,103	LC
Northeast Louisiana Univ	LA	3,906	NC
Northeastern State Univ	OK	5,250	C
Northern Arizona Univ	AZ	4,844	C
Northern State Univ	SD	4,186	LC
Northland College	WI	13,550	LC
Northwest Missouri State Univ	MO	5,010	LC
Northwestern College of Iowa	IA	12,250	C
Northwood Univ	MI	13,385	LC
Norwich Univ	VT	18,730	C
Oakland Univ	MI	6,714	VC
Ohio Northern Univ	OH	18,660	VC
Ohio Univ	OH	7,341	C
Ohio Wesleyan Univ	OH	21,108	VC+
Okla City Univ	OK	9,840	C
Okla State Univ	OK	5,086	VC
Olivet Nazarene Univ	IL	11,976	C
Ouachita Baptist Univ	AR	8,940	C
Pace Univ	NY	15,540	C
Palm Beach Atlantic College	FL	10,720	C
Park College	MO	7,320	C
Pembroke State Univ	NC	3,538	LC
Penn State Univ at Erie/Behrend College	PA	8,752	C
Penn State Univ/Univ Park Campus	PA	8,752	HC
Philander Smith College	AR	5,434	NC
Phillips Univ	OK	12,744	C
Piedmont College	GA	8,540	LC
Pittsburg State Univ	KS	4,478	NC
Plymouth State College	NH	7,166	C
Pontifical Catholic Univ of PR/Ponce	PR	5,807	
Prairie View A&M Univ	TX	4,740	LC
Principia College	IL	17,799	C
Providence College	RI	19,750	VC
Purdue Univ/Calumet	IN	2,374	NC
Purdue Univ/West Lafayette	IN	6,636	C
Quinnipiac College	CT	17,600	C+
Radford Univ	VA	7,034	LC
Ramapo College of New Jersey	NJ	8,027	C+
Randolph-Macon College	VA	16,980	C
Regis Univ	CO	17,340	C
Rhode Island College	RI	7,901	LC
Rider College	NJ	18,160	C
Rockhurst College	MO	12,470	C
Rocky Mountain College	MT	11,320	C
Roosevelt Univ	IL	12,368	C
Rutgers Univ/Cook College	NJ	9,197	HC
Sacred Heart Univ	CT	16,350	C
Saginaw Valley State Univ	MI	6,634	LC
St Ambrose Univ	IA	13,380	C
St Andrews Presbyterian College	NC	14,240	LC
St Anselm College	NH	17,340	C
St Bonaventure Univ	NY	14,762	C
St Cloud State Univ	MN	5,015	C
St John's Univ	NY	8,980	C+
St Joseph's College	IN	14,730	C
St Louis Univ	MO	15,522	VC
Sam Houston State Univ	TX	4,506	C
Santa Clara Univ	CA	18,783	VC
Seattle Univ	WA	16,590	C
Seton Hall Univ	NJ	18,306	LC
Seton Hill College	PA	14,320	C
Shepherd College	WV	5,540	C
Siena College	NY	15,410	VC
Simpson College	IA	14,635	VC
Sioux Falls College	SD	11,540	C
Skidmore College	NY	23,230	HC
Slippery Rock Univ	PA	6,803	C
Sonoma State Univ	CA	6,996	LC
S Car State Univ	SC	5,424	LC
S Dak State Univ	SD	4,562	C
Southeast Missouri State Univ	MO	5,854	C
Southeastern Louisiana Univ	LA	4,230	NC
Southern Arkansas Univ	AR	3,432	NC
Southern Conn State Univ	CT	7,532	C
Southern Illinois Univ at Carbondale	IL	6,234	C
Southern Illinois Univ at Edwardsville	IL	6,097	LC
Southern Nazarene Univ	OK	9,206	NC
Southwest Texas State Univ	TX	5,124	C
Southwestern Okla State Univ	OK	3,312	C
Spring Arbor College	MI	12,256	C
Spring Hill College	AL	16,015	C+
SUNY/College at Fredonia	NY	7,159	VC
SUNY/College at Geneseo	NY	6,949	HC
SUNY/College at Oneonta	NY	7,878	C
SUNY/College at Plattsburgh	NY	6,917	C
Stephen F. Austin State Univ	TX	5,117	C
Stetson Univ	FL	16,435	VC
Sul Ross State Univ	TX	4,144	NC
Susquehanna Univ	PA	19,950	VC
Tabor College	KS	11,460	VC
Temple Univ	PA	10,281	C
Tenn State Univ	TN	4,626	C+
Texas A&M Univ at Kingsville	TX	3,808	LC
Texas Lutheran College	TX	10,710	C
Texas Tech Univ	TX	6,008	C
Texas Wesleyan Univ	TX	9,380	LC
Thomas College	ME	13,450	LC
Thomas More College	KY	12,962	C
Trenton State College	NJ	9,085	HC
Trinity College	IL	14,010	C
Trinity Univ	TX	16,670	HC
Troy State Univ	AL	4,322	C
Troy State Univ at Dothan/Fort Rucker	AL	2,260	NC
Tuskegee Univ	AL	10,128	C
Univ of Akron	OH	6,699	NC
Univ of Alabama at Birmingham	AL	7,533	C
Univ of Alabama at Huntsville	AL	5,868	VC
Univ of Alaska Fairbanks	AK	4,718	C
Univ of Arizona	AZ	5,808	C
Univ of Arkansas at Fayetteville	AR	5,046	C
Univ of Arkansas at Pine Bluff	AR	3,978	LC
Univ of Bridgeport	CT	18,985	C
Univ of Calif at Santa Barbara	CA	9,460	C
Univ of Calif at Santa Cruz	CA	9,060	VC
Univ of Calif, Riverside	CA	9,178	C
Univ of Central Arkansas	AR	4,200	LC
Univ of Central Okla	OK	3,647	C
Univ of Dayton	OH	15,120	C+
Univ of Denver	CO	19,290	C+
Univ of Detroit Mercy	MI	14,720	C
Univ of Findlay	OH	15,764	C
Univ of Georgia	GA	5,655	VC
Univ of Hawaii at Manoa	HI	5,626	C
Univ of Idaho	ID	4,830	C
Univ of Indianapolis	IN	14,510	C

School	ST	$IS	SR
Univ of Iowa	IA	5,658	VC
Univ of Kentucky	KY	5,152	VC
Univ of La Verne	CA	17,400	C
Univ of Lowell	MA	8,831	VC
Univ of Maine at Farmington	ME	6,700	C
Univ of Mary Hardin-Baylor	TX	8,120	NC
Univ of Maryland/College Park	MD	8,182	VC
Univ of Memphis	TN	3,476	C
Univ of Miami	FL	22,107	VC
Univ of Minn/Morris	MN	6,825	HC
Univ of Miss	MS	5,756	C
Univ of Missouri/Columbia	MO	6,254	HC
Univ of Mobile	AL	9,400	C
Univ of Nebr at Kearney	NE	4,308	LC
Univ of Nebr-Lincoln	NE	5,278	LC
Univ of Nevada/Reno	NV	5,735	C
Univ of New Haven	CT	14,980	C
Univ of New Orleans	LA	5,468	C
Univ of North Alabama	AL	4,236	NC
Univ of N Car at Greensboro	NC	5,192	C
Univ of N Car at Wilmington	NC	5,172	C
Univ of N Dak	ND	4,902	NC
Univ of North Florida	FL	5,082	C
Univ of North Texas	TX	4,853	C
Univ of Okla	OK	5,427	VC
Univ of Pittsburgh at Johnstown	PA	8,914	C
Univ of PR/Mayaguez	PR	0	
Univ of PR/Rio Piedras	PR	0	
Univ of Richmond	VA	16,700	HC
Univ of San Diego	CA	18,970	VC
Univ of Scranton	PA	17,071	VC
Univ of South Alabama	AL	5,451	C
Univ of S Car	SC	6,158	C
Univ of South Florida	FL	5,475	C+
Univ of Southern Colo	CO	5,350	LC
Univ of Southern Indiana	IN	3,720	NC
Univ of Southern Maine	ME	7,299	C
Univ of Southern Miss	MS	4,542	C
Univ of Tampa	FL	16,780	C
Univ of Tenn at Martin	TN	4,550	C
Univ of Tenn/Knoxville	TN	5,668	C
Univ of Texas at Arlington	TX	5,549	LC
Univ of Texas at El Paso	TX	3,160	LC
Univ of Texas at San Antonio	TX	6,420	C
Univ of Texas-Pan American	TX	3,192	NC
Univ of the Pacific	CA	21,100	C
Univ of Toledo	OH	6,636	NC
Univ of Tulsa	OK	13,795	VC
Univ of Virginia	VA	7,964	MC
Univ of Washington	WA	6,618	VC
Univ of West Florida	FL	5,415	C
Univ of Wisc/Eau Claire	WI	4,647	C
Univ of Wisc/Platteville	WI	4,830	C
Univ of Wisc/Superior	WI	4,330	C
Univ of Wisc/Whitewater	WI	4,700	C
Univ of Wyoming	WY	4,991	NC
Urbana Univ	OH	12,536	C
Ursinus College	PA	19,165	VC
Utah State Univ	UT	4,683	C
Utica College of Syracuse Univ	NY	16,714	LC
Valdosta State Univ	GA	4,670	LC
Villanova Univ	PA	21,400	HC
Virginia Commonwealth Univ	VA	7,909	C
Virginia Military Inst	VA	8,630	C
Virginia Polytechnic Inst and State Univ	VA	6,828	C
Virginia State Univ	VA	7,040	
Virginia Wesleyan College	VA	14,950	VC
Wagner College	NY	17,950	C
Wartburg College	IA	14,530	VC
Washburn Univ of Topeka	KS	5,802	NC
Washington State Univ	WA	6,364	C
Wayne State Univ	MI	2,680	C
Weber State Univ	UT	4,398	C
West Chester Univ of Penn	PA	7,492	C
West Georgia College	GA	4,256	C
West Liberty State College	WV	4,690	LC
West Texas A&M Univ	TX	4,224	C
Western Carolina Univ	NC	3,811	C
Western Kentucky Univ	KY	4,808	C
Western Mich Univ	MI	6,820	C
Westmont College	CA	18,732	C
Wheaton College	IL	14,710	HC
Whittier College	CA	21,661	C
Widener Univ	PA	16,840	C
Wilberforce Univ	OH	10,408	C
Willamette Univ	OR	17,995	VC
William Carey College	MS	7,050	C
William Jewell College	MO	12,500	VC
William Penn College	IA	13,400	C
William Woods Univ	MO	14,025	LC
Wilson College	PA	16,630	C
Wingate College	NC	10,610	C
Winona State Univ	MN	5,200	VC
Wofford College	SC	15,360	VC
Wright State Univ	OH	6,896	LC
Xavier Univ	OH	15,710	C+
Xavier Univ of Louisiana	LA	10,400	C

BUSINESS EDUCATION

School	ST	$IS	SR
Abilene Christian Univ	TX	10,460	NC
Adams State College	CO	4,910	C
Alabama State Univ	AL	3,428	NC
Alcorn State Univ	MS	4,474	C+
American International College	MA	14,029	C
Andrews Univ	MI	14,952	NC
Angelo State Univ	TX	5,176	C
Appalachian State Univ	NC	4,095	C
Arkansas State Univ	AR	4,250	NC
Arkansas Tech Univ	AR	4,200	NC
Armstrong State College	GA	4,874	LC
Atlantic Union College	MA	14,150	LC
Auburn Univ	AL	5,823	C+
Austin Peay State Univ	TN	4,350	C
Baker Univ	KS	12,284	C
Ball State Univ	IN	6,032	LC
Bartlesville Wesleyan College	OK	9,400	C
Baylor Univ	TX	10,990	C+
Bethany College	KS	11,232	C
Bethel College	IN	11,650	C
Bethel College	MN	15,050	C
Bethune-Cookman College	FL	8,375	LC
Black Hills State Univ	SD	4,831	NC
Bloomsburg Univ of Penn	PA	6,312	C+
Blue Mountain College	MS	5,958	LC
Bluffton College	OH	12,951	C
Boston Univ	MA	24,130	HC
Bowling Green State Univ	OH	6,701	C
Brigham Young Univ	UT	5,625	HC
Brigham Young Univ/Hawaii	HI	6,750	VC
Brooklyn Campus of LIU	NY	15,000	LC
Buena Vista College	IA	16,150	VC
Cal State/Fresno	CA	5,747	C
Cal State/Los Angeles	CA	4,940	VC
Cal State/Northridge	CA	7,122	LC
Cal State/Sacramento	CA	6,387	C
Calumet College of St. Joseph	IN	3,585	C
Cameron Univ	OK	3,686	LC
Canisius College	NY	15,510	C
Caribbean Univ	PR	2,400	
Castleton State College	VT	8,378	LC
Cedarville College	OH	10,715	C
Central Conn State Univ	CT	7,108	C
Central Mich Univ	MI	6,737	LC
Central Missouri State Univ	MO	5,138	LC
Central State Univ	OH	7,320	NC
Central Washington Univ	WA	5,644	C
Chadron State College	NE	4,091	NC
Chicago State Univ	IL	2,198	C
CUNY/Baruch College	NY	2,562	VC
CUNY/Herbert H. Lehman College	NY	2,542	C
CUNY/York College	NY	2,534	NC
Clark Atlanta Univ	GA	11,846	C
Clarke College	IA	13,950	C+
Columbia College	MO	11,995	C
Concord College	WV	5,104	NC
Concordia College	NE	11,776	NC
Concordia College	NY	0	LC
Concordia College/Moorhead	MN	12,750	C
Concordia Univ Wisc	WI	12,140	C
Crichton College	TN	6,547	NC
Cumberland College	KY	9,756	C
D'Youville College	NY	12,850	C
Daemen College	NY	13,020	LC
Dakota State Univ	SD	4,374	LC
Dana College	NE	11,910	C
David Lipscomb Univ	TN	7,865	VC
Davis and Elkins College	WV	13,230	LC
Defiance College	OH	13,480	LC
Delaware State College	DE	5,656	C
Delta State Univ	MS	3,964	LC
Dickinson State Univ	ND	3,792	
Dordt College	IA	11,690	C
Drake Univ	IA	17,195	VC
East Carolina Univ	NC	4,498	C
East Central Univ	OK	3,558	C
East Texas Baptist Univ	TX	7,740	C
East Texas State Univ	TX	4,572	LC
Eastern Illinois Univ	IL	5,548	C
Eastern Kentucky Univ	KY	4,840	NC
Eastern Mich Univ	MI	6,749	C
Eastern Montana College	MT	5,165	LC
Eastern New Mexico Univ	NM	3,950	C
Eastern Washington Univ	WA	5,439	LC
Elizabeth City State Univ	NC	4,254	LC
Emporia State Univ	KS	4,685	NC
Evangel College	MO	10,142	LC
Fairmont State College	WV	4,640	LC
Fayetteville State Univ	NC	3,926	LC
Ferris State Univ	MI	7,160	NC
Florida A&M Univ	FL	4,651	C
Franklin College of Indiana	IN	13,970	C
Fresno Pacific College	CA	13,020	C
Friends Univ	KS	11,205	C
Frostburg State Univ	MD	6,940	C
Geneva College	PA	13,030	C
Georgia Southwestern College	GA	4,338	LC
Georgia State Univ	GA	2,019	C
Glenville State College	WV	4,810	LC
Goshen College	IN	12,360	C
Grace College	IN	12,120	C
Grambling State Univ	LA	4,712	NC
Grand Canyon Univ	AZ	9,680	VC
Grand Rapids Baptist College and Seminary	MI	10,228	C
Grand View College	IA	13,230	NC
Greenville College	IL	14,190	C
Gustavus Adolphus College	MN	15,935	VC
Gwynedd-Mercy College	PA	15,450	C
Hardin-Simmons Univ	TX	9,080	C
Hastings College	NE	12,426	C
Henderson State Univ	AR	3,860	C
Hofstra Univ	NY	16,580	VC
Hope College	MI	15,698	C+
Howard Payne Univ	TX	8,052	C
Humboldt State Univ	CA	5,676	C
Huntington College	IN	13,220	C
Huron Univ	SD	9,790	C
Husson College	ME	11,510	NC
Idaho State Univ	ID	4,442	C
Illinois State Univ	IL	6,413	C
Incarnate Word College	TX	12,307	C
Indiana State Univ	IN	6,210	C
Indiana Univ of Penn	PA	6,373	C
Jackson State Univ	MS	4,996	LC
John Brown Univ	AR	9,880	VC
Kennesaw State College	GA	1,553	C
Kent State Univ	OH	6,740	LC
Knoxville College	TN	8,320	LC
La Sierra Univ	CA	15,472	C
Lane College	TN	7,628	LC
Langston Univ	OK	2,907	LC
Le Moyne College	NY	15,180	C
Le Tourneau Univ	TX	12,500	C+
Lenoir-Rhyne College	NC	14,068	C
Lewis Univ	IL	14,797	LC
Lincoln Memorial Univ	TN	8,218	C
Lincoln Univ	MO	4,638	NC
Lindenwood College	MO	13,560	C
Livingston Univ	AL	3,979	C
Louisiana College	LA	7,518	VC
Louisiana State Univ and A&M College	LA	5,605	C
Louisiana State Univ in Shreveport	LA	1,910	NC
Louisiana Tech Univ	LA	4,284	C
Lubbock Christian Univ	TX	9,840	NC
Manchester College	IN	13,240	LC
Mankato State Univ	MN	5,097	LC
Marian College of Fond du Lac	WI	12,250	C
Marshall Univ	WV	5,762	LC
Marygrove College	MI	5,877	VC
Mayville State Univ	ND	4,272	NC
McKendree College	IL	10,900	C
McNeese State Univ	LA	4,543	NC
McPherson College	KS	11,360	VC
Mercyhurst College	PA	13,488	C
MidAmerica Nazarene College	KS	10,208	NC
Middle Tenn State Univ	TN	3,857	C
Midland Lutheran College	NE	12,410	LC
Minot State Univ	ND	3,748	NC
Miss College	MS	8,348	C
Miss State Univ	MS	5,629	VC
Missouri Southern State College	MO	4,272	
Montclair State College	NJ	7,539	C+
Moorhead State Univ	MN	5,076	C
Morehead State Univ	KY	4,600	LC
Morgan State Univ	MD	7,366	C+
Morningside College	IA	13,896	C
Morris Brown College	GA	12,234	NC
Mount Mary College	WI	10,920	C
Mount Vernon Nazarene College	OH	10,390	C
Murray State Univ	KY	4,702	C
Nazareth College of Rochester	NY	15,310	C+
New Hampshire College	NH	15,242	LC
New York Inst of Tech/Old Westbury	NY	13,914	LC
Nicholls State Univ	LA	4,531	NC
Norfolk State Univ	VA	6,345	LC
N Car Agricultural and Technical State Univ	NC	4,477	LC
N Car Central Univ	NC	4,347	LC
North Georgia College	GA	4,103	LC
Northeast Louisiana Univ	LA	3,906	NC
Northeastern State Univ	OK	5,250	C
Northern Arizona Univ	AZ	4,844	C
Northern Illinois Univ	IL	6,408	C
Northern Kentucky Univ	KY	4,620	NC
Northern Mich Univ	MI	6,350	C
Northern Montana College	MT	4,976	C
Northern State Univ	SD	4,186	LC
Northland College	WI	13,550	LC
Northwestern College of Iowa	IA	12,250	C
Northwestern Okla State Univ	OK	3,424	C
Northwestern State Univ of Louisiana	LA	4,287	NC
Notre Dame College of Ohio	OH	11,370	C
Oakland City College	IN	10,216	LC
Oakwood College	AL	10,005	C
Ohio State Univ	OH	7,218	LC
Ohio Univ	OH	7,341	C
Okla Baptist Univ	OK	8,486	C
Okla Christian Univ of Science and Arts	OK	8,790	NC
Okla Panhandle State Univ	OK	3,155	NC
Okla State Univ	OK	5,086	VC
Olivet Nazarene Univ	IL	11,976	C
Oral Roberts Univ	OK	10,607	C+
Ouachita Baptist Univ	AR	8,940	C
Our Lady of Holy Cross College	LA	4,630	LC
Pace Univ	NY	15,540	C
Pacific Union College	CA	15,075	C
Pembroke State Univ	NC	3,538	LC
Pikeville College	KY	8,500	NC
Point Loma Nazarene College	CA	13,532	C
Pontifical Catholic Univ of PR/Ponce	PR	5,807	
Rider College	NJ	18,160	C
Rivier College	NH	14,920	LC
Robert Morris College	PA	10,406	LC
Roosevelt Univ	IL	12,368	C
Rust College	MS	6,600	LC
Sacred Heart Univ	CT	16,350	C
St Augustine's College	NC	9,300	C+
St Francis College	IN	11,662	C
St Joseph's College	IN	14,730	C
St Mary's Univ	TX	12,064	C
St Paul's College	VA	9,171	C
Salem State College	MA	6,712	C
Shepherd College	WV	5,540	C
Shippensburg Univ of Penn	PA	7,052	C
Siena Heights College	MI	12,520	C
Simpson College	IA	14,635	VC
S Car State Univ	SC	5,424	LC
S Dak State Univ	SD	4,562	C
Southeast Missouri State Univ	MO	5,854	C
Southeastern Louisiana Univ	LA	4,230	NC
Southeastern Okla State Univ	OK	3,594	C
Southern Arkansas Univ	AR	3,432	NC
Southern Calif College	CA	12,356	C
Southern Illinois Univ at Carbondale	IL	6,234	C
Southern Nazarene Univ	OK	9,206	NC
Southern Univ and A&M College	LA	4,920	NC
Southern Univ at New Orleans	LA	1,452	NC
Southern Utah Univ	UT	4,104	LC
Southwest Baptist Univ	MO	9,192	NC
Southwest Missouri State Univ	MO	4,956	C
Southwest State Univ	MN	5,400	NC
Southwest Texas State Univ	TX	5,124	C
Southwestern College	KS	10,032	C
Southwestern Okla State Univ	OK	3,312	C
SUNY/College at Buffalo	NY	7,035	VC
SUNY/College at Oneonta	NY	7,878	C
SUNY/College at Oswego	NY	7,330	VC
Sterling College	KS	10,990	VC
Suffolk Univ	MA	15,360	LC
Sul Ross State Univ	TX	4,144	NC
Tabor College	KS	11,460	VC
Tarleton State Univ	TX	4,082	LC
Temple Univ	PA	10,281	C
Tenn State Univ	TN	4,626	C+
Texas College	TX	5,930	NC
Texas Tech Univ	TX	6,008	C
The Univ of New Mexico	NM	5,304	C
Thomas College	ME	13,450	LC
Thomas More College	KY	12,962	C
Tri-State Univ	IN	13,788	LC
Trinity Christian College	IL	13,260	C
Trinity College of Vermont	VT	16,015	LC
Troy State Univ	AL	4,322	C
Union College	KY	9,790	C
Union College	NE	11,060	NC
Univ of Akron	OH	6,699	NC
Univ of Alaska Southeast	AK	4,075	LC
Univ of Arkansas at Fayetteville	AR	5,046	C
Univ of Arkansas at Monticello	AR	3,832	NC
Univ of Arkansas at Pine Bluff	AR	3,978	LC
Univ of Central Florida	FL	6,061	C+
Univ of Central Okla	OK	3,647	C
Univ of Cincinnati	OH	7,989	C
Univ of Dayton	OH	15,120	C+
Univ of Detroit Mercy	MI	14,720	C
Univ of Evansville	IN	15,300	VC
Univ of Findlay	OH	15,764	C
Univ of Georgia	GA	5,655	VC
Univ of Houston	TX	5,215	C
Univ of Idaho	ID	4,830	C
Univ of Illinois at Urbana-Champaign	IL	7,764	HC

School	ST	$IS	SR
Univ of Indianapolis	IN	14,510	C
Univ of Kentucky	KY	5,152	VC
Univ of La Verne	CA	17,400	C
Univ of Louisville	KY	5,948	C
Univ of Maine at Machias	ME	6,135	C
Univ of Mary Hardin-Baylor	TX	8,120	NC
Univ of Maryland/College Park	MD	8,182	VC
Univ of Maryland/Eastern Shore	MD	6,254	LC
Univ of Mich/Dearborn	MI	3,399	HC
Univ of Minn/Twin Cities	MN	6,682	VC
Univ of Missouri/Columbia	MO	6,254	HC
Univ of Nebr at Kearney	NE	4,308	LC
Univ of Nebr-Lincoln	NE	5,278	LC
Univ of New Orleans	LA	5,468	C
Univ of North Alabama	AL	4,236	NC
Univ of N Car at Greensboro	NC	5,192	C
Univ of N Dak	ND	4,902	NC
Univ of North Florida	FL	5,082	C
Univ of North Texas	TX	4,853	C
Univ of Northern Iowa	IA	5,137	C
Univ of PR/Rio Piedras	PR	0	
Univ of Rio Grande	OH	6,300	NC
Univ of Science and Arts of Okla	OK	3,304	C
Univ of South Florida	FL	5,475	C+
Univ of Southern Indiana	IN	3,720	NC
Univ of Southern Miss	MS	4,542	C
Univ of Tenn at Martin	TN	4,550	C
Univ of Tenn/Knoxville	TN	5,668	C
Univ of the District of Columbia	DC	974	NC
Univ of the Ozarks	AR	7,770	C
Univ of Toledo	OH	6,636	NC
Univ of Wisc/Eau Claire	WI	4,647	C
Univ of Wisc/Whitewater	WI	4,700	C
Univ of Wyoming	WY	4,991	NC
Utah State Univ	UT	4,683	C
Valdosta State Univ	GA	4,670	LC
Valley City State Univ	ND	4,385	LC
Virginia Polytechnic Inst and State Univ	VA	6,828	C
Virginia Union Univ	VA	10,555	LC
Viterbo College	WI	12,670	C
Walla Walla College	WA	13,215	C
Wayne State College	NE	4,260	NC
Wayne State Univ	MI	2,680	C
Weber State Univ	UT	4,398	C
West Georgia College	GA	4,256	C
West Liberty State College	WV	4,690	LC
West Texas A&M Univ	TX	4,224	C
West Virginia Inst of Tech	WV	5,858	LC
Western Carolina Univ	NC	3,811	C
Western Illinois Univ	IL	5,241	LC
Western Kentucky Univ	KY	4,808	C
Western Mich Univ	MI	6,820	C
Western Montana College of the Univ of Montana	MT	1,646	C
Western State College of Colo	CO	5,560	C
Westfield State College	MA	7,161	C
Wiley College	TX	0	NC
William Carey College	MS	7,050	C
William Penn College	IA	13,400	C
Wilmington College	OH	13,700	LC
Winona State Univ	MN	5,200	VC
Winston-Salem State Univ	NC	4,142	LC
Winthrop Univ	SC	6,750	C
Wittenberg Univ	OH	19,998	VC
Wright State Univ	OH	6,896	LC
York College of Penn	PA	8,345	C
Youngstown State Univ	OH	6,447	LC

BUSINESS LAW

School	ST	$IS	SR
Baylor Univ	TX	10,990	C+
Cal State/Fresno	CA	5,747	C
Duquesne Univ	PA	16,434	VC
Iona College	NY	16,310	C
Lamar Univ	TX	3,798	C
Mankato State Univ	MN	5,097	LC
Marymount Univ	VA	15,930	C
Miss College	MS	8,348	C
Ohio Univ	OH	7,341	C
Okla State Univ	OK	5,086	VC
Southern Arkansas Univ	AR	3,432	NC
Tabor College	KS	11,460	VC
Temple Univ	PA	10,281	C
Union College	KY	9,790	C
Univ of Denver	CO	19,290	C+
Univ of Maryland/Univ College	MD	4,900	NC
Univ of Miami	FL	22,107	VC
Univ of Nebr at Omaha	NE	1,889	LC
Western Carolina Univ	NC	3,811	C
Western New Mexico Univ	NM	3,234	LC

BUSINESS STATISTICS

School	ST	$IS	SR
Univ of Illinois at Chicago	IL	8,443	C
Univ of PR/Rio Piedras	PR	0	
Western Mich Univ	MI	6,820	C

BUSINESS SYSTEMS ANALYSIS

School	ST	$IS	SR
Eastern Mich Univ	MI	6,749	C
Idaho State Univ	ID	4,442	C
Indiana Univ Bloomington	IN	6,495	VC
Louisiana Tech Univ	LA	4,284	C
St John's Univ	NY	8,980	C+
Texas A&M Univ	TX	5,382	VC
Univ of Findlay	OH	15,764	C

CANADIAN STUDIES

School	ST	$IS	SR
Brigham Young Univ	UT	5,625	HC
Franklin College of Indiana	IN	13,970	C
St Lawrence Univ	NY	23,420	VC
SUNY/College at Plattsburgh	NY	6,917	C
Univ of Washington	WA	6,618	VC
Western Washington Univ	WA	6,077	VC

CARIBBEAN STUDIES

School	ST	$IS	SR
Morehouse College	GA	13,224	LC
SUNY at Albany	NY	7,059	VC
SUNY at Binghamton	NY	7,921	HC
Univ of Miami	FL	22,107	VC
Univ of the Virgin Islands	VI	5,896	C

CARTOGRAPHY

School	ST	$IS	SR
Brigham Young Univ	UT	5,625	HC
East Central Univ	OK	3,558	C
Eastern Mich Univ	MI	6,749	C
Salem State College	MA	6,712	C
Southwest Missouri State Univ	MO	4,956	C
Southwest Texas State Univ	TX	5,124	C
Univ of Idaho	ID	4,830	C
Univ of Wisc/Madison	WI	6,400	HC

CELL BIOLOGY

School	ST	$IS	SR
Ball State Univ	IN	6,032	LC
Barton College	NC	10,689	LC
Bucknell Univ	PA	22,320	HC
Cal State/Fullerton	CA	4,850	LC
Cal State/Northridge	CA	7,122	LC
Colby College	ME	24,230	HC
Okla State Univ	OK	5,086	VC
Rutgers Univ/Cook College	NJ	9,197	HC
Rutgers Univ/Douglass College	NJ	8,795	VC
Rutgers Univ/Livingston College	NJ	8,877	VC
Rutgers Univ/Rutgers College	NJ	8,841	HC+
Rutgers Univ/Univ College—New Brunswick	NJ	0	LC
San Francisco State Univ	CA	7,292	LC
Sonoma State Univ	CA	6,996	LC
Southwest Missouri State Univ	MO	4,956	C
Texas Tech Univ	TX	6,008	C
Tulane Univ	LA	24,540	HC
Univ of Calif at Santa Barbara	CA	9,460	C
Univ of Colo at Boulder	CO	6,410	VC
Univ of Kansas	KS	5,200	NC
Univ of Mich/Ann Arbor	MI	9,428	HC+
Univ of Minn/Twin Cities	MN	6,682	VC
Univ of Rochester	NY	23,696	HC

CELTIC STUDIES

School	ST	$IS	SR
Univ of Calif at Berkeley	CA	9,962	HC+

CERAMIC ART AND DESIGN

School	ST	$IS	SR
Arizona State Univ Main Campus	AZ	6,444	C
Barton College	NC	10,689	LC
Center for Creative Studies/College of Art and Design	MI	15,330	SP
Edinboro Univ of Penn	PA	7,181	C
Hofstra Univ	NY	16,580	VC
Indiana Univ-Purdue Univ at Indianapolis	IN	5,862	LC
Kansas City Art Inst	MO	17,000	SP
Maryland Inst, College of Art	MD	18,420	SP
McMurry Univ	TX	10,100	C
Northern Mich Univ	MI	6,350	C
Ohio Northern Univ	OH	18,660	VC
Ohio State Univ	OH	7,218	LC
Otis College of Art and Design	CA	16,686	SP
Pacific Northwest College of Art	OR	7,700	SP
Rhode Island School of Design	RI	22,315	SP
School of the Art Inst of Chicago	IL	17,610	SP
Univ of Mass Dartmouth	MA	8,158	C
Univ of Miami	FL	22,107	VC
Univ of Mich/Ann Arbor	MI	9,428	HC+
Univ of North Texas	TX	4,853	C
Univ of Oregon	OR	6,466	VC
Univ of the Arts	PA	16,150	SP

CERAMIC ENGINEERING

School	ST	$IS	SR
Alfred Univ	NY	21,054	VC+
Clemson Univ	SC	6,564	VC
Georgia Inst of Tech	GA	6,669	HC+
Iowa State Univ	IA	5,456	C
Ohio State Univ	OH	7,218	LC
Penn State Univ/Univ Park Campus	PA	8,752	HC
Rutgers Univ/Camden College of A&S	NJ	8,652	VC
Rutgers Univ/College of Engineering	NJ	9,254	HC
Rutgers Univ/Newark College of A&S	NJ	8,645	C
Univ of Illinois at Urbana-Champaign	IL	7,764	HC
Univ of Missouri/Rolla	MO	6,729	VC+
Univ of Washington	WA	6,618	VC

CERAMIC SCIENCE

School	ST	$IS	SR
Bradley Univ	IL	14,718	C+
Brigham Young Univ	UT	5,625	HC
Maine College of Art	ME	15,673	SP
Penn State Univ/Univ Park Campus	PA	8,752	HC
Syracuse Univ	NY	21,305	HC
Univ of Conn	CT	9,168	C
Univ of Hartford	CT	19,858	LC
Univ of Washington	WA	6,618	VC

CHEMICAL ENGINEERING

School	ST	$IS	SR
Arizona State Univ Main Campus	AZ	6,444	C
Auburn Univ	AL	5,823	C+
Bethel College	IN	11,650	C
Brigham Young Univ	UT	5,625	HC
Bucknell Univ	PA	22,320	HC
Calif Inst of Tech	CA	20,783	MC
Calif State Polytechnic Univ/Pomona	CA	6,438	LC
Cal State/Long Beach	CA	6,057	LC
Carnegie Mellon Univ	PA	22,560	HC+
Case Western Reserve Univ	OH	19,910	HC
Christian Brothers Univ	TN	12,120	VC
CUNY/City College	NY	2,543	VC
Clarkson Univ	NY	20,705	VC+
Clemson Univ	SC	6,564	VC
Cleveland State Univ	OH	7,287	NC
Colo School of Mines	CO	8,436	HC+
Colo State Univ	CO	6,566	VC
Columbia Univ/School of Engineering and Applied Science	NY	24,554	HC
Cooper Union for the Advancement of Science and Art	NY	8,430	MC
Cornell Univ	NY	13,445	MC
Delaware State College	DE	5,656	C
Dordt College	IA	11,690	C
Drexel Univ	PA	15,970	C
Florida A&M Univ	FL	4,651	C
Florida Inst of Tech	FL	16,935	VC
Florida State Univ	FL	5,814	VC
Gannon Univ	PA	14,872	C
Geneva College	PA	13,030	C
Georgia Inst of Tech	GA	6,669	HC+
Hampton Univ	VA	10,706	C
Howard Univ	DC	11,680	C
Illinois Inst of Tech	IL	18,290	VC
Iowa State Univ	IA	5,456	C
Johns Hopkins Univ	MD	24,360	MC
Kansas State Univ	KS	4,816	NC
Lafayette College	PA	23,450	HC
Lakeland College	WI	12,845	LC
Lamar Univ	TX	3,798	C
Lehigh Univ	PA	23,250	HC
Louisiana State Univ and A&M College	LA	5,605	C
Louisiana Tech Univ	LA	4,284	C
Manhattan College	NY	19,000	C
Mass Inst of Tech	MA	24,800	MC
McNeese State Univ	LA	4,543	NC
Mich State Univ	MI	7,842	C
Mich Tech Univ	MI	7,283	VC+
Miss State Univ	MS	5,629	VC
Montana State Univ	MT	5,534	C
Morris Brown College	GA	12,234	NC
New Jersey Inst of Tech	NJ	9,965	VC
New Mexico State Univ	NM	4,844	LC
N Car Agricultural and Technical State Univ	NC	4,477	LC
N Car State Univ	NC	4,984	VC
Northeastern Univ	MA	19,851	C
Northwestern Univ	IL	21,093	MC
Ohio State Univ	OH	7,218	LC
Ohio Univ	OH	7,341	C
Okla State Univ	OK	5,086	VC
Oregon State Univ	OR	6,175	C
Pace Univ	NY	15,540	C
Penn State Univ/Univ Park Campus	PA	8,752	HC
Polytechnic Univ/Brooklyn	NY	19,700	HC
Polytechnic Univ/Farmingdale	NY	20,700	VC
Prairie View A&M Univ	TX	4,740	LC
Princeton Univ	NJ	24,650	MC
Purdue Univ/West Lafayette	IN	6,636	C
Rensselaer Polytechnic Inst	NY	23,067	HC
Rice Univ	TX	15,110	MC
Rose-Hulman Inst of Tech	IN	16,400	HC
Rutgers Univ/Camden College of A&S	NJ	8,652	VC
Rutgers Univ/College of Engineering	NJ	9,254	HC
Rutgers Univ/Newark College of A&S	NJ	8,645	C
St Augustine's College	NC	9,300	C+
St Xavier Univ	IL	14,700	C
San Jose State Univ	CA	6,680	LC
Savannah State College	GA	4,052	C
S Dak School of Mines and Tech	SD	5,329	C
Stanford Univ	CA	24,310	MC
SUNY at Buffalo	NY	7,896	VC
SUNY College of Environmental Science and Forestry	NY	9,257	HC+
SUNY/College at Plattsburgh	NY	6,917	C
Stevens Inst of Tech	NJ	21,980	VC+
Syracuse Univ	NY	21,305	HC
Tenn Tech Univ	TN	5,190	C
Texas A&M Univ	TX	5,382	VC
Texas A&M Univ at Kingsville	TX	3,808	LC
Texas Tech Univ	TX	6,008	C
The Univ of New Mexico	NM	5,304	C
Tri-State Univ	IN	13,788	LC
Tufts Univ	MA	24,962	MC
Tulane Univ	LA	24,540	HC
Tuskegee Univ	AL	10,128	C
United States Military Academy	NY	0	MC
Univ of Akron	OH	6,699	NC
Univ of Alabama	AL	5,702	C
Univ of Alabama at Huntsville	AL	5,868	VC
Univ of Arizona	AZ	5,808	C
Univ of Arkansas at Fayetteville	AR	5,046	C
Univ of Calif at Berkeley	CA	9,962	HC+
Univ of Calif at Davis	CA	9,534	VC
Univ of Calif at Los Angeles	CA	8,959	HC

School	ST	$IS	SR
Univ of Calif at Santa Barbara	CA	9,460	C
Univ of Calif, Riverside	CA	9,178	C
Univ of Calif, San Diego	CA	10,028	VC+
Univ of Cincinnati	OH	7,989	C
Univ of Colo at Boulder	CO	6,410	VC
Univ of Conn	CT	9,168	C
Univ of Dayton	OH	15,120	C+
Univ of Delaware	DE	8,013	VC
Univ of Detroit Mercy	MI	14,720	C
Univ of Florida	FL	5,850	HC
Univ of Houston	TX	5,215	C
Univ of Idaho	ID	4,830	C
Univ of Illinois at Chicago	IL	8,443	C
Univ of Illinois at Urbana-Champaign	IL	7,764	HC
Univ of Iowa	IA	5,658	VC
Univ of Kansas	KS	5,200	NC
Univ of Kentucky	KY	5,152	C
Univ of Louisville	KY	5,948	C
Univ of Lowell	MA	8,831	VC
Univ of Maine	ME	7,990	C
Univ of Maryland/Baltimore County	MD	7,746	VC
Univ of Maryland/College Park	MD	8,182	VC
Univ of Mass/Amherst	MA	9,364	C
Univ of Mich/Ann Arbor	MI	9,428	HC+
Univ of Minn/Duluth	MN	6,512	C
Univ of Minn/Twin Cities	MN	6,682	VC
Univ of Miss	MS	5,756	C
Univ of Missouri/Columbia	MO	6,254	HC
Univ of Missouri/Rolla	MO	6,729	VC+
Univ of Nebr-Lincoln	NE	5,278	LC
Univ of Nevada/Reno	NV	5,735	C
Univ of New Hampshire	NH	8,242	C
Univ of New Haven	CT	14,980	C
Univ of N Dak	ND	4,902	NC
Univ of Notre Dame	IN	20,150	MC
Univ of Okla	OK	5,427	VC
Univ of Penn	PA	24,238	MC
Univ of Pittsburgh	PA	9,472	C
Univ of PR/Mayaguez	PR	0	
Univ of Rhode Island	RI	9,205	C
Univ of Rochester	NY	23,696	HC
Univ of South Alabama	AL	5,451	C
Univ of S Car	SC	6,158	C
Univ of South Florida	FL	5,475	C+
Univ of Southern Calif	CA	23,006	VC
Univ of Southwestern Louisiana	LA	3,968	NC
Univ of Tenn/Knoxville	TN	5,668	C
Univ of Texas at Austin	TX	5,160	VC
Univ of Toledo	OH	6,636	NC
Univ of Tulsa	OK	13,795	VC
Univ of Utah	UT	5,975	C
Univ of Virginia	VA	7,964	MC
Univ of Washington	WA	6,618	VC
Univ of Wisc/Madison	WI	6,400	HC
Univ of Wyoming	WY	4,991	NC
Vanderbilt Univ	TN	23,422	HC+
Villanova Univ	PA	21,400	HC
Virginia Polytechnic Inst and State Univ	VA	6,828	C
Washington State Univ	WA	6,364	C
Washington Univ	MO	23,507	HC
Wayne State Univ	MI	2,680	C
West Virginia Inst of Tech	WV	5,858	LC
West Virginia Univ	WV	5,774	C
Widener Univ	PA	16,840	C
Worcester Polytechnic Inst	MA	20,350	HC
Yale Univ	CT	25,110	MC
Youngstown State Univ	OH	6,447	LC

CHEMICAL TECHNOLOGY

School	ST	$IS	SR
Inter American Univ of PR/ Aguadilla Regional College	PR	2,290	
Inter American Univ of PR/ Bayamon Univ College	PR	2,300	
Inter American Univ of PR/ Metropolitan Campus	PR	2,340	
Inter American Univ of PR/ Ponce Regional College	PR	2,300	
Inter American Univ/Arecibo Campus	PR	5,666	
Inter-American Univ of PR/ Fajardo Regional College	PR	2,732	
Midwestern State Univ	TX	4,542	LC
Philadelphia College of Pharmacy and Science	PA	14,750	VC
Univ of Dayton	OH	15,120	C+
Univ of PR/Arecibo Tech Univ College	PR	1,302	C

CHEMISTRY

School	ST	$IS	SR
Abilene Christian Univ	TX	10,460	NC
Adams State College	CO	4,910	C
Adelphi Univ	NY	18,250	LC
Adrian College	MI	14,340	C
Agnes Scott College	GA	17,135	VC
Alabama A&M Univ	AL	4,200	C
Alabama State Univ	AL	3,428	NC
Albany State College	GA	4,481	LC
Albertson College	ID	15,942	C+
Albion College	MI	18,264	VC
Albright College	PA	19,260	C
Alcorn State Univ	MS	4,474	C+
Alderson-Broaddus College	WV	12,000	C
Alfred Univ	NY	21,054	VC+
Allegheny College	PA	21,020	VC
Allentown College of St Francis de Sales	PA	13,480	C
Alma College	MI	16,375	VC+
Alvernia College	PA	13,150	LC
Alverno College	WI	11,344	C
American International College	MA	14,029	C
American Univ	DC	21,230	VC+
Amherst College	MA	24,152	MC
Anderson Univ	IN	12,920	C
Andrews Univ	MI	14,952	NC
Angelo State Univ	TX	5,176	C
Antioch College	OH	19,532	C
Appalachian State Univ	NC	4,095	C
Aquinas College	MI	14,526	C
Arizona State Univ Main Campus	AZ	6,444	C
Arkansas College	AR	11,626	VC
Arkansas State Univ	AR	4,250	NC
Arkansas Tech Univ	AR	4,200	NC
Armstrong State College	GA	4,874	LC
Asbury College	KY	11,105	VC
Ashland Univ	OH	15,508	C
Assumption College	MA	17,095	LC
Atlantic Union College	MA	14,150	C
Auburn Univ	AL	5,823	C+
Augsburg College	MN	15,608	C
Augusta College	GA	1,452	C
Augustana College	IL	16,959	VC
Augustana College	SD	13,420	C
Aurora Univ	IL	13,381	C
Austin College	TX	14,999	VC
Austin Peay State Univ	TN	4,350	C
Averett College	VA	13,610	LC
Avila College	MO	12,130	C
Azusa Pacific Univ	CA	15,034	C
Baker Univ	KS	12,284	C
Baldwin-Wallace College	OH	15,210	C
Ball State Univ	IN	6,032	LC
Barat College	IL	13,990	C
Barber-Scotia College	NC	6,840	NC
Bard College	NY	25,269	HC
Barry Univ	FL	16,050	C
Bartlesville Wesleyan College	OK	9,400	C
Barton College	NC	10,689	LC
Bates College	ME	23,990	MC
Baylor Univ	TX	10,990	C+
Beaver College	PA	17,660	C
Belhaven College	MS	9,690	C+
Bellarmine College	KY	10,832	C
Belmont Abbey College	NC	13,190	C
Belmont Univ	TN	10,540	C
Beloit College	WI	18,950	VC+
Bemidji State Univ	MN	5,188	C
Benedict College	SC	8,376	LC
Benedictine College	KS	12,830	C
Bennett College	NC	8,920	LC
Bennington College	VT	24,850	VC+
Berea College	KY	2,883	VC+
Berry College	GA	11,990	VC
Bethany College	KS	11,232	C
Bethany College	WV	18,300	C+
Bethel College	IN	11,650	C
Bethel College	KS	11,530	C
Bethel College	MN	15,050	C
Bethel College	TN	9,736	LC
Bethune-Cookman College	FL	8,375	LC
Biola Univ	CA	16,124	C
Birmingham-Southern College	AL	15,154	VC+
Black Hills State Univ	SD	4,831	NC
Blackburn College	IL	9,120	C
Bloomfield College	NJ	12,200	LC
Bloomsburg Univ of Penn	PA	6,312	C
Bluefield College	VA	10,600	C
Bluffton College	OH	12,951	C
Boise State Univ	ID	4,909	LC
Boston College	MA	22,706	MC
Boston Univ	MA	24,130	HC
Bowdoin College	ME	24,155	MC
Bowling Green State Univ	OH	6,701	C
Bradley Univ	IL	14,718	C+
Brandeis Univ	MA	25,585	HC
Brescia College	KY	9,800	C
Briar Cliff College	IA	13,375	C
Bridgewater College	VA	15,300	C
Bridgewater State College	MA	7,518	C
Brigham Young Univ	UT	5,625	HC
Brigham Young Univ/Hawaii	HI	6,750	VC
Brooklyn Campus of LIU	NY	15,000	LC
Brown Univ	RI	26,104	MC
Bryn Mawr College	PA	24,110	MC
Bucknell Univ	PA	22,320	HC
Buena Vista College	IA	16,150	VC
Butler Univ	IN	16,210	C
Cabrini College	PA	16,012	C
Caldwell College	NJ	12,860	C
Calif Inst of Tech	CA	20,783	MC
Calif Lutheran Univ	CA	17,240	C
Calif Polytechnic State Univ	CA	6,980	VC+
Calif State Polytechnic Univ/ Pomona	CA	6,438	LC
Cal State/Bakersfield	CA	5,402	C
Cal State/Chico	CA	6,146	C
Cal State/Dominguez Hills	CA	2,857	C
Cal State/Fresno	CA	5,747	C
Cal State/Fullerton	CA	4,850	C
Cal State/Hayward	CA	5,495	C
Cal State/Long Beach	CA	6,057	C
Cal State/Los Angeles	CA	4,940	VC
Cal State/Northridge	CA	7,122	LC
Cal State/Sacramento	CA	6,387	C
Cal State/San Bernardino	CA	6,055	C
Cal State/Stanislaus	CA	6,799	C
Calif Univ of Penn	PA	7,370	C
Calvin College	MI	13,020	VC
Cameron Univ	OK	3,686	LC
Campbell Univ	NC	10,624	C
Campbellsville College	KY	8,720	C
Canisius College	NY	15,510	C
Capital Univ	OH	16,535	VC
Cardinal Stritch College	WI	11,252	C
Carleton College	MN	22,155	HC
Carnegie Mellon Univ	PA	22,560	HC+
Carroll College	WI	15,490	C
Carthage College	WI	15,995	C
Case Western Reserve Univ	OH	19,910	HC
Catawba College	NC	12,950	C
Catholic Univ of America	DC	18,856	C
Cedar Crest College	PA	18,930	C
Cedarville College	OH	10,715	C
Centenary College of Louisiana	LA	11,826	C+
Central College	IA	14,025	VC
Central Conn State Univ	CT	7,108	C
Central Methodist College	MO	11,410	C
Central Mich Univ	MI	6,737	LC
Central Missouri State Univ	MO	5,138	LC
Central State Univ	OH	7,320	NC
Central Univ of Bayamon	PR	2,430	
Central Washington Univ	WA	5,644	C
Central Wesleyan College	SC	9,640	C
Centre College	KY	15,850	VC+
Chadron State College	NE	4,091	NC
Chaminade Univ of Honolulu	HI	14,290	C
Chapman Univ	CA	21,842	C
Charleston Southern Univ	SC	10,282	LC
Charter Oak State College	CT	314	NC
Chatham College	PA	18,010	C
Chestnut Hill College	PA	14,525	C
Cheyney Univ of Penn	PA	7,005	C
Chicago State Univ	IL	2,198	C
Christian Brothers Univ	TN	12,120	VC
CUNY/Brooklyn College	NY	2,450	VC
CUNY/City College	NY	2,543	C
CUNY/College of Staten Island	NY	2,558	NC
CUNY/Herbert H. Lehman College	NY	2,542	C
CUNY/Hunter College	NY	4,101	VC
CUNY/Queens College	NY	2,631	C
CUNY/York College	NY	2,534	NC
Claflin College	SC	0	
Claremont McKenna College	CA	22,150	MC
Clarion Univ of Penn	PA	6,518	C
Clark Atlanta Univ	GA	11,846	C
Clark Univ	MA	21,400	VC
Clarke College	IA	13,950	C+
Clarkson Univ	NY	20,705	VC+
Clemson Univ	SC	6,564	VC
Cleveland State Univ	OH	7,287	NC
Clinch Valley College/Univ of Virginia	VA	6,364	C
Coe College	IA	17,085	VC
Coker College	SC	13,790	C
Colby College	ME	24,230	HC
Colgate Univ	NY	24,020	HC
College of Charleston	SC	6,250	C
College of Great Falls	MT	6,302	NC
College of Mount St Joseph	OH	13,272	C
College of Mount St Vincent	NY	16,730	C
College of New Rochelle	NY	15,440	LC
College of Notre Dame of Maryland	MD	16,050	C
College of Our Lady of The Elms	MA	15,639	C
College of St Benedict	MN	15,468	VC
College of St Catherine	MN	14,670	C
College of St Elizabeth	NJ	15,800	C
College of St Mary	NE	12,500	C
College of St Rose	NY	14,452	C
College of St Scholastica	MN	14,868	C
College of Santa Fe	NM	14,008	C
College of the Holy Cross	MA	23,850	HC
College of the Ozarks	MO	2,000	VC+
College of William and Mary	VA	8,602	MC
College of Wooster	OH	19,875	VC
Colo College	CO	20,038	HC
Colo School of Mines	CO	8,436	HC+
Colo State Univ	CO	6,566	VC
Columbia College	MO	11,995	C
Columbia College	SC	13,520	LC
Columbia Union College	MD	13,650	LC
Columbia Univ/Barnard College	NY	25,492	HC
Columbia Univ/Columbia College	NY	26,757	MC
Columbus College	GA	4,892	LC
Concord College	WV	5,104	NC
Concordia College	NE	11,776	NC
Concordia College/Moorhead	MN	12,750	C
Concordia Univ	IL	12,611	C
Conn College	CT	24,160	HC
Converse College	SC	15,750	C
Coppin State College	MD	7,145	LC
Cornell College	IA	18,425	VC
Cornell Univ	NY	13,445	MC
Covenant College	GA	13,054	VC
Creighton Univ	NE	14,432	VC
Culver-Stockton College	MO	11,150	C
Cumberland College	KY	9,756	C
Curry College	MA	18,695	LC
Daemen College	NY	13,020	LC
Dakota State Univ	SD	4,374	LC
Dana College	NE	11,910	C
Dartmouth College	NH	24,354	MC
David Lipscomb Univ	TN	7,865	VC
Davidson College	NC	21,037	MC
Davis and Elkins College	WV	13,230	LC
Defiance College	OH	13,480	LC
Delaware State College	DE	5,656	C
Delaware Valley College	PA	16,065	LC
Delta State Univ	MS	3,564	LC
Denison Univ	OH	21,150	VC+
DePaul Univ	IL	15,535	VC
DePauw Univ	IN	18,530	VC
Dickinson College	PA	22,705	HC
Dickinson State Univ	ND	3,792	
Dillard Univ	LA	9,950	C
Doane College	NE	12,220	C
Dordt College	IA	11,690	C
Drake Univ	IA	17,195	VC
Drew Univ/College of Liberal Arts	NJ	23,406	HC
Drexel Univ	PA	15,970	C
Drury College	MO	12,140	VC
Duke Univ	NC	21,271	MC
Duquesne Univ	PA	16,434	VC
Earlham College	IN	19,383	VC
East Carolina Univ	NC	4,498	C
East Central Univ	OK	3,558	C
East Stroudsburg Univ	PA	6,886	C
East Tenn State Univ	TN	4,406	C
East Texas Baptist Univ	TX	7,740	C
East Texas State Univ	TX	4,572	LC
Eastern College	PA	15,150	C+
Eastern Illinois Univ	IL	5,548	C
Eastern Kentucky Univ	KY	4,840	NC
Eastern Mennonite College	VA	12,700	C
Eastern Mich Univ	MI	6,749	C
Eastern Montana College	MT	5,165	LC
Eastern Nazarene College	MA	12,165	LC
Eastern New Mexico Univ	NM	3,950	C
Eastern Oregon State College	OR	6,090	C
Eastern Washington Univ	WA	5,439	LC
Eckerd College	FL	18,855	VC
Edgewood College	WI	11,700	C
Edinboro Univ of Penn	PA	7,181	C
Edward Waters College	FL	8,300	NC
Elizabeth City State Univ	NC	4,254	LC
Elizabethtown College	PA	17,850	VC
Elmhurst College	IL	12,536	C
Elmira College	NY	18,450	C
Elon College	NC	12,290	LC
Emmanuel College	MA	17,773	LC
Emory and Henry College	VA	12,770	C
Emory Univ	GA	21,930	HC
Emporia State Univ	KS	4,685	NC
Erskine College	SC	14,310	C
Eureka College	IL	14,555	C
Evangel College	MO	10,142	LC
Evergreen State College	WA	6,306	C
Fairfield Univ	CT	20,460	VC
Fairleigh Dickinson Univ	NJ	16,427	C
Fairmont State College	WV	4,640	LC
Fayetteville State Univ	NC	3,926	LC
Ferrum College	VA	12,800	C
Fisk Univ	TN	0	LC
Fitchburg State College	MA	6,962	C
Florida A&M Univ	FL	4,651	C
Florida Atlantic Univ	FL	5,525	C
Florida Inst of Tech	FL	16,935	VC
Florida International Univ	FL	4,191	VC
Florida Memorial College	FL	7,600	C+
Florida Southern College	FL	12,260	C
Florida State Univ	FL	5,814	VC

School	ST	$IS	SR
Fordham Univ/Fordham College	NY	19,875	VC
Fort Hays State Univ	KS	4,675	NC
Fort Lewis College	CO	5,097	C
Fort Valley State College	GA	3,974	LC
Framingham State College	MA	6,580	C
Francis Marion Univ	SC	5,878	LC
Franciscan Univ of Steubenville	OH	13,400	C
Franklin and Marshall College	PA	23,655	HC
Franklin College of Indiana	IN	13,970	C
Freed-Hardeman Univ	TN	8,585	NC
Friends Univ	KS	11,205	C
Frostburg State Univ	MD	6,940	C
Furman Univ	SC	16,557	VC
Gallaudet Univ	DC	9,850	SP
Gannon Univ	PA	14,872	C
Gardner-Webb Univ	NC	11,950	C
Geneva College	PA	13,030	C
George Fox College	OR	15,640	LC
George Mason Univ	VA	8,728	C
George Washington Univ	DC	22,470	MC
Georgetown College	KY	10,990	C
Georgetown Univ	DC	24,410	MC
Georgia College	GA	4,310	LC
Georgia Inst of Tech	GA	6,669	HC+
Georgia Southern Univ	GA	4,988	LC
Georgia Southwestern College	GA	4,338	LC
Georgia State Univ	GA	2,019	C
Georgian Court College	NJ	12,550	C
Gettysburg College	PA	22,960	HC
Glenville State College	WV	4,810	LC
Gonzaga Univ	WA	16,350	VC
Gordon College	MA	16,790	C
Goshen College	IN	12,360	C
Goucher College	MD	20,295	VC
Graceland College	IA	11,600	C
Grambling State Univ	LA	4,712	NC
Grand Canyon Univ	AZ	9,680	VC
Grand Valley State Univ	MI	6,822	VC
Greensboro College	NC	11,496	C
Greenville College	IL	14,190	C
Grinnell College	IA	20,680	HC+
Grove City College	PA	7,870	HC
Guilford College	NC	17,680	C
Gustavus Adolphus College	MN	15,935	VC
Hamilton College	NY	23,500	HC
Hamline Univ	MN	17,122	VC
Hampden-Sydney College	VA	17,372	C+
Hampshire College	MA	25,320	C
Hampton Univ	VA	10,706	C
Hanover College	IN	10,950	VC
Hardin-Simmons Univ	TX	9,080	C
Harding Univ	AR	9,050	VC
Hartwick College	NY	20,950	C
Harvard Univ/Harvard and Radcliffe Colleges	MA	24,880	MC
Harvey Mudd College	CA	23,316	MC
Hastings College	NE	12,426	C
Haverford College	PA	23,950	MC
Heidelberg College	OH	17,160	C
Henderson State Univ	AR	3,860	C
Hendrix College	AR	11,670	C
High Point Univ	NC	12,350	LC
Hillsdale College	MI	15,110	VC
Hiram College	OH	18,340	VC
Hobart and William Smith Colleges	NY	23,925	VC
Hofstra Univ	NY	16,580	VC
Hollins College	VA	18,484	C
Holy Family College	PA	8,300	C
Hood College	MD	19,010	VC
Hope College	MI	15,698	C+
Houghton College	NY	13,120	VC
Houston Baptist Univ	TX	11,055	C
Howard Payne Univ	TX	8,052	C
Howard Univ	DC	11,680	C
Humboldt State Univ	CA	5,676	C
Huntingdon College	AL	11,400	C
Huntington College	IN	13,220	C
Huston-Tillotson College	TX	8,490	C
Idaho State Univ	ID	4,442	C
Illinois Benedictine College	IL	14,170	C
Illinois College	IL	11,200	C
Illinois Inst of Tech	IL	18,290	C
Illinois State Univ	IL	6,413	C
Illinois Wesleyan Univ	IL	18,590	HC+
Immaculata College	PA	14,620	C
Incarnate Word College	TX	12,307	C
Indiana State Univ	IN	6,210	C
Indiana Univ Bloomington	IN	6,495	VC
Indiana Univ Northwest	IN	2,310	C
Indiana Univ of Penn	PA	6,373	C
Indiana Univ Southeast	IN	2,260	LC
Indiana Univ-Purdue Univ at Fort Wayne	IN	2,500	LC
Indiana Univ-Purdue Univ at Indianapolis	IN	5,862	LC
Indiana Univ/South Bend	IN	2,141	LC
Indiana Wesleyan Univ	IN	12,332	C
Inter American Univ of PR/ Aguadilla Regional College	PR	2,290	
Inter American Univ of PR/ Bayamon Univ College	PR	2,300	
Inter American Univ of PR/ Metropolitan Campus	PR	2,340	
Inter American Univ of PR/ Ponce Regional College	PR	2,300	
Inter American Univ of PR/ San German	PR	4,620	
Inter American Univ/Arecibo Campus	PR	5,666	
Inter-American Univ of PR/ Fajardo Regional College	PR	2,732	
Iowa State Univ	IA	5,456	C
Iowa Wesleyan College	IA	13,250	C
Ithaca College	NY	19,679	C
Jackson State Univ	MS	4,996	LC
Jacksonville State Univ	AL	4,080	LC
Jacksonville Univ	FL	13,390	C
James Madison Univ	VA	8,198	HC
Jamestown College	ND	10,550	C
Jarvis Christian College	TX	7,170	LC
Jersey City State College	NJ	7,797	LC
John Brown Univ	AR	9,880	VC
John Carroll Univ	OH	16,510	C
Johns Hopkins Univ	MD	24,360	MC
Johnson C. Smith Univ	NC	8,916	LC
Judson College	AL	9,060	C
Juniata College	PA	18,390	C+
Kalamazoo College	MI	19,974	HC
Kansas Newman College	KS	10,640	C
Kansas State Univ	KS	4,816	NC
Kansas Wesleyan Univ	KS	11,770	C
Kean College of New Jersey	NJ	6,395	LC
Keene State College	NH	7,081	C
Kennesaw State College	GA	1,553	C
Kent State Univ	OH	6,740	LC
Kentucky State Univ	KY	4,282	C+
Kentucky Wesleyan College	KY	11,550	C
Kenyon College	OH	22,430	HC+
King College	TN	11,500	C
King's College	NY	12,360	LC
King's College	PA	15,420	C
Knox College	IL	18,990	VC
Knoxville College	TN	8,320	LC
Kutztown Univ	PA	6,528	C
La Roche College	PA	12,977	LC
La Salle Univ	PA	16,940	LC
La Sierra Univ	CA	15,472	C
Lafayette College	PA	23,450	HC
LaGrange College	GA	10,602	C
Lake Erie College	OH	13,370	C
Lake Forest College	IL	19,960	VC
Lakeland College	WI	12,845	LC
Lamar Univ	TX	3,798	LC
Lambuth Univ	TN	8,395	C
Lander Univ	SC	6,180	LC
Lane College	TN	7,628	LC
Langston Univ	OK	2,907	LC
Lawrence Tech Univ	MI	9,470	C
Lawrence Univ	WI	19,986	HC+
Le Moyne College	NY	15,180	C
Le Tourneau Univ	TX	12,500	C+
Lebanon Valley College of Penn	PA	18,300	C
Lee College	TN	7,894	LC
Lehigh Univ	PA	23,250	HC
LeMoyne-Owen College	TN	4,500	LC
Lenoir-Rhyne College	NC	14,068	C
Lewis and Clark College	OR	19,980	VC
Lewis Univ	IL	14,797	LC
Lewis-Clark State College	ID	4,040	C
Liberty Univ	VA	11,500	LC
Limestone College	SC	10,700	LC
Lincoln Memorial Univ	TN	8,218	LC
Lincoln Univ	MO	4,638	NC
Lincoln Univ	PA	0	LC
Lindenwood College	MO	13,560	C
Linfield College	OR	16,670	VC
Livingston Univ	AL	3,979	C
Livingstone College	NC	8,600	LC
Lock Haven Univ of Penn	PA	7,128	C
LIU/C. W. Post Campus	NY	16,870	C
LIU/Southampton Campus	NY	17,280	LC
Longwood College	VA	7,800	C
Loras College	IA	14,160	C
Louisiana College	LA	7,518	VC
Louisiana State Univ and A&M College	LA	5,605	C
Louisiana State Univ in Shreveport	LA	1,910	NC
Louisiana Tech Univ	LA	4,284	C
Loyola College	MD	18,035	VC
Loyola Univ of Chicago	IL	15,880	C+
Loyola Univ/New Orleans	LA	15,660	C+
Lubbock Christian Univ	TX	9,840	NC
Luther College	IA	15,900	VC
Lycoming College	PA	17,200	LC
Lynchburg College	VA	17,000	C
Macalester College	MN	19,710	HC
MacMurray College	IL	12,800	C
Madonna Univ	MI	8,546	C
Maharishi International Univ	IA	13,666	C
Malone College	OH	12,572	C
Manchester College	IN	13,240	LC
Manhattan College	NY	19,000	C
Manhattanville College	NY	20,450	LC
Mankato State Univ	MN	5,097	LC
Mansfield Univ	PA	6,348	C
Marian College	IN	12,936	C
Marian College of Fond du Lac	WI	12,250	C
Marietta College	OH	16,940	C+
Marist College	NY	16,406	C
Marlboro College	VT	23,305	C+
Marquette Univ	WI	16,114	VC
Mars Hill College	NC	11,050	C
Marshall Univ	WV	5,762	LC
Martin Univ	IN	4,830	NC
Mary Baldwin College	VA	17,700	LC
Mary Washington College	VA	7,910	HC
Marygrove College	MI	5,877	VC
Marymount College/ Tarrytown	NY	17,350	C
Maryville College	TN	14,474	C
Maryville Univ-St Louis	MO	12,900	VC
Mass College of Pharmacy and Allied Health Sciences	MA	18,352	C
Mass Inst of Tech	MA	24,800	MC
Mayville State Univ	ND	4,272	NC
McKendree College	IL	10,900	C
McMurry Univ	TX	10,100	C
McNeese State Univ	LA	4,543	NC
McPherson College	KS	11,360	VC
Mercer Univ	GA	15,123	C
Mercyhurst College	PA	13,488	C
Meredith College	NC	9,440	C
Merrimack College	MA	18,025	C
Messiah College	PA	14,664	VC
Methodist College	NC	12,400	C
Metropolitan State College of Denver	CO	1,751	NC
Miami Univ	OH	8,066	VC
Mich State Univ	MI	7,842	C
Mich Tech Univ	MI	7,283	VC+
MidAmerica Nazarene College	KS	10,208	NC
Middle Tenn State Univ	TN	3,857	C
Middlebury College	VT	24,400	MC
Midland Lutheran College	NE	12,410	C
Midwestern State Univ	TX	4,542	LC
Miles College	AL	7,150	NC
Millersville Univ of Penn	PA	7,370	VC
Millikin Univ	IL	15,499	C
Mills College	CA	20,848	VC
Millsaps College	MS	15,486	C+
Minot State Univ	ND	3,748	NC
Miss College	MS	8,348	C
Miss State Univ	MS	5,629	VC
Miss Univ for Women	MS	4,456	LC
Missouri Baptist College	MO	9,340	C
Missouri Southern State College	MO	4,272	
Missouri Western State College	MO	4,384	NC
Monmouth College	IL	17,300	C+
Monmouth College	NJ	16,820	C
Montana College of Mineral Science and Tech	MT	4,977	C
Montana State Univ	MT	5,534	C
Montclair State College	NJ	7,539	C+
Moorhead State Univ	MN	5,076	C
Moravian College	PA	18,960	VC
Morehead State Univ	KY	4,600	LC
Morehouse College	GA	13,224	LC
Morgan State Univ	MD	7,366	C+
Morningside College	IA	13,896	C
Morris Brown College	GA	12,234	NC
Mount Holyoke College	MA	23,630	VC
Mount Marty College	SD	10,450	NC
Mount Mary College	WI	10,920	C
Mount St Mary College	NY	12,910	C
Mount St Mary's College	CA	16,390	VC
Mount St Mary's College	MD	17,825	LC
Mount Union College	OH	15,850	C
Mount Vernon Nazarene College	OH	10,390	C
Muhlenberg College	PA	20,795	VC
Murray State Univ	KY	4,702	C
Muskingum College	OH	16,650	C
Nazareth College of Rochester	NY	15,310	C+
Nebr Wesleyan Univ	NE	12,240	C
New College of the Univ of South Florida	FL	5,697	MC
New Jersey Inst of Tech	NJ	9,965	VC
New Mexico Highlands Univ	NM	3,772	C
New Mexico Inst of Mining and Tech	NM	5,212	C+
New Mexico State Univ	NM	4,844	LC
New York Inst of Tech/Old Westbury	NY	13,914	LC
New York Univ	NY	24,705	VC+
Newberry College	SC	11,994	LC
Niagara Univ	NY	14,552	C
Nicholls State Univ	LA	4,531	NC
Norfolk State Univ	VA	6,345	LC
North Adams State College	MA	7,750	C
N Car Agricultural and Technical State Univ	NC	4,477	LC
N Car Central Univ	NC	4,347	LC
N Car State Univ	NC	4,984	NC
N Car Wesleyan College	NC	12,480	LC
North Central College	IL	15,498	NC
N Dak State Univ of Agriculture and Applied Science	ND	4,774	VC
North Georgia College	GA	4,103	LC
North Park College	IL	14,310	C
Northeast Louisiana Univ	LA	3,906	NC
Northeast Missouri State Univ	MO	5,654	VC+
Northeastern Illinois Univ	IL	1,955	C
Northeastern State Univ	OK	5,250	C
Northern Arizona Univ	AZ	4,844	C
Northern Illinois Univ	IL	6,408	C
Northern Kentucky Univ	KY	4,620	NC
Northern Mich Univ	MI	6,350	C
Northern Montana College	MT	4,976	C
Northern State Univ	SD	4,186	LC
Northland College	WI	13,550	LC
Northwest Missouri State Univ	MO	5,010	LC
Northwest Nazarene College	ID	11,750	C
Northwestern College of Iowa	IA	12,250	C
Northwestern Okla State Univ	OK	3,424	C
Northwestern Univ	IL	21,093	MC
Norwich Univ	VT	18,730	C
Notre Dame College of Ohio	OH	11,370	C
Oakland City College	IN	10,216	LC
Oakland Univ	MI	6,714	VC
Oakwood College	AL	10,005	C
Oberlin College	OH	24,570	HC+
Occidental College	CA	21,792	HC
Oglethorpe Univ	GA	16,360	VC
Ohio Dominican College	OH	11,820	C
Ohio Northern Univ	OH	18,660	VC
Ohio State Univ	OH	7,218	LC
Ohio Univ	OH	7,341	C
Ohio Wesleyan Univ	OH	21,108	VC+
Okla Christian Univ of Science and Arts	OK	8,790	NC
Okla City Univ	OK	9,840	C
Okla Panhandle State Univ	OK	3,155	NC
Okla State Univ	OK	5,086	NC
Old Dominion Univ	VA	8,317	C
Olivet College	MI	14,000	C
Olivet Nazarene Univ	IL	11,976	C
Oral Roberts Univ	OK	10,607	C+
Oregon State Univ	OR	6,175	C
Ottawa Univ	KS	10,490	C+
Otterbein College	OH	16,506	C
Ouachita Baptist Univ	AR	8,940	C
Our Lady of the Lake Univ of San Antonio	TX	11,080	C
Pace Univ	NY	15,540	C
Pacific Lutheran Univ	WA	15,998	VC
Pacific Union College	CA	15,075	C
Pacific Univ	OR	17,869	C
Paine College	GA	8,207	LC
Park College	MO	7,320	C
Pembroke State Univ	NC	3,538	LC
Penn State Univ at Erie/ Behrend College	PA	8,752	C
Penn State Univ/Univ Park Campus	PA	8,752	HC
Pepperdine Univ	CA	23,720	VC
Pfeiffer College	NC	11,670	C
Philadelphia College of Pharmacy and Science	PA	14,750	VC
Philadelphia College of Textiles and Science	PA	15,896	C
Philander Smith College	AR	5,434	NC
Phillips Univ	OK	12,744	C
Piedmont College	GA	8,540	LC
Pikeville College	KY	8,500	NC
Pittsburg State Univ	KS	4,478	NC
Pitzer College	CA	23,780	HC
Plymouth State College	NH	7,166	C
Point Loma Nazarene College	CA	13,532	C
Polytechnic Univ/Brooklyn	NY	19,700	HC
Polytechnic Univ/ Farmingdale	NY	20,700	VC
Pomona College	CA	23,820	MC
Pontifical Catholic Univ of PR/Ponce	PR	5,807	
Portland State Univ	OR	7,191	C
Prairie View A&M Univ	TX	4,740	C
Presbyterian College	SC	15,400	VC
Princeton Univ	NJ	24,650	MC
Principia College	IL	17,799	C
Providence College	RI	19,750	VC
Purdue Univ/Calumet	IN	2,374	NC
Purdue Univ/West Lafayette	IN	6,636	C
Quincy Univ	IL	13,646	VC
Quinnipiac College	CT	17,600	C+
Radford Univ	VA	7,034	LC
Ramapo College of New Jersey	NJ	8,027	C+
Randolph-Macon College	VA	16,980	C
Randolph-Macon Woman's College	VA	19,100	C
Reed College	OR	24,480	HC+
Regis College	MA	17,450	C
Regis Univ	CO	17,340	C
Rensselaer Polytechnic Inst	NY	23,067	VC
Rhode Island College	RI	7,970	LC
Rhodes College	TN	19,624	HC
Rice Univ	TX	15,110	MC

School	ST	$IS	SR
Utah State Univ	UT	4,683	C
Utica College of Syracuse Univ	NY	16,714	LC
Valdosta State Univ	GA	4,670	LC
Valley City State Univ	ND	4,385	LC
Valparaiso Univ	IN	14,810	VC
Vanderbilt Univ	TN	23,422	HC+
Vassar College	NY	24,206	HC
Villanova Univ	PA	21,400	HC
Virginia Commonwealth Univ	VA	7,909	C
Virginia Military Inst	VA	8,630	C
Virginia Polytechnic Inst and State Univ	VA	6,828	C
Virginia State Univ	VA	7,040	
Virginia Union Univ	VA	10,555	LC
Virginia Wesleyan College	VA	14,950	VC
Viterbo College	WI	12,670	C
Wabash College	IN	16,250	VC
Wagner College	NY	17,950	C
Wake Forest Univ	NC	17,280	MC
Walla Walla College	WA	13,215	C
Walsh Univ	OH	11,640	C
Warren Wilson College	NC	10,877	C
Wartburg College	IA	14,530	VC
Washburn Univ of Topeka	KS	5,802	NC
Washington and Jefferson College	PA	19,360	C
Washington and Lee Univ	VA	17,735	MC
Washington College	MD	19,270	C+
Washington State Univ	WA	6,364	C
Washington Univ	MO	23,507	HC
Wayland Baptist Univ	TX	7,811	NC
Wayne State College	NE	4,260	NC
Wayne State Univ	MI	2,680	C
Waynesburg College	PA	11,960	C
Weber State Univ	UT	4,398	C
Wellesley College	MA	23,815	MC
Wells College	NY	19,460	C+
Wesleyan College	GA	15,445	C
Wesleyan Univ	CT	23,770	MC
West Chester Univ of Penn	PA	7,492	C
West Georgia College	GA	4,256	C
West Liberty State College	WV	4,690	LC
West Texas A&M Univ	TX	4,224	C
West Virginia Inst of Tech	WV	5,858	LC
West Virginia State College	WV	5,044	LC
West Virginia Univ	WV	5,774	C
West Virginia Wesleyan College	WV	16,900	C
Western Carolina Univ	NC	3,811	C
Western Conn State Univ	CT	6,622	C
Western Illinois Univ	IL	5,241	LC
Western Kentucky Univ	KY	4,808	C
Western Maryland College	MD	18,990	C
Western Mich Univ	MI	6,820	C
Western New England College	MA	14,674	LC
Western New Mexico Univ	NM	3,234	LC
Western Oregon State College	OR	6,180	C
Western State College of Colo	CO	5,560	C
Western Washington Univ	WA	6,077	VC
Westfield State College	MA	7,161	C
Westminster College	MO	13,750	C+
Westminster College	PA	15,200	C
Westminster College of Salt Lake City	UT	12,100	C
Westmont College	CA	18,732	C
Wheaton College	IL	14,710	HC
Wheaton College	MA	23,840	C+
Wheeling Jesuit College	WV	14,370	C
Whitman College	WA	20,595	HC
Whittier College	CA	21,661	C
Whitworth College	WA	16,265	C
Wichita State Univ	KS	5,068	NC
Widener Univ	PA	16,840	C
Wilberforce Univ	OH	10,408	C
Wiley College	TX	0	NC
Wilkes Univ	PA	15,728	LC
Willamette Univ	OR	17,995	VC
William Carey College	MS	7,050	C
William Jewell College	MO	12,500	VC
William Paterson College	NJ	7,438	C+
William Woods Univ	MO	14,025	LC
Williams College	MA	24,390	MC
Wilmington College	OH	13,700	LC
Wilson College	PA	16,630	C
Wingate College	NC	10,610	C
Winona State Univ	MN	5,200	VC
Winston-Salem State Univ	NC	4,142	LC
Winthrop Univ	SC	6,750	C
Wisc Lutheran College	WI	12,180	C
Wittenberg Univ	OH	19,998	VC
Wofford College	SC	15,360	VC
Worcester Polytechnic Inst	MA	20,350	HC
Worcester State College	MA	6,414	LC
Wright State Univ	OH	6,896	LC
Xavier Univ	OH	15,710	C+
Xavier Univ of Louisiana	LA	10,400	C
Yale Univ	CT	25,110	MC
Yeshiva Univ	NY	18,200	VC
York College of Penn	PA	8,345	C
Youngstown State Univ	OH	6,447	LC

CHILD CARE/CHILD AND FAMILY STUDIES

School	ST	$IS	SR
Albright College	PA	19,260	C
Auburn Univ	AL	5,823	C+
Audrey Cohen College	NY	11,184	LC
Eastern Kentucky Univ	KY	4,840	NC
Florida State Univ	FL	5,814	VC
Georgia Southern Univ	GA	4,988	LC
Indiana State Univ	IN	6,210	C
Iowa State Univ	IA	5,456	C
Miss Univ for Women	MS	4,456	LC
Norfolk State Univ	VA	6,345	LC
N Dak State Univ of Agriculture and Applied Science	ND	4,774	VC
Northeast Louisiana Univ	LA	3,906	NC
Northern Illinois Univ	IL	6,408	C
Okla Christian Univ of Science and Arts	OK	8,790	NC
Southwest Missouri State Univ	MO	4,956	C
Southwest Texas State Univ	TX	5,124	C
SUNY/College at Oneonta	NY	7,878	C
Syracuse Univ	NY	21,305	HC
Texas Tech Univ	TX	6,008	C
Univ of Arkansas at Pine Bluff	AR	3,978	LC
Univ of Nevada/Reno	NV	5,735	C
Univ of N Car at Charlotte	NC	4,597	C
Univ of N Car at Greensboro	NC	5,192	C
Univ of Tenn/Knoxville	TN	5,668	C
Univ of Texas at Austin	TX	5,160	VC
Univ of the District of Columbia	DC	974	NC
Univ of Utah	UT	5,975	C
Univ of Wisc/Madison	WI	6,400	HC
Univ of Wisc/Stout	WI	4,719	C
Ursuline College	OH	13,180	LC
Utah State Univ	UT	4,683	C
Virginia Polytechnic Inst and State Univ	VA	6,828	C
West Virginia Univ	WV	5,774	C
Western Carolina Univ	NC	3,811	C
Wheelock College	MA	18,000	LC

CHILD PSYCHOLOGY/DEVELOPMENT

School	ST	$IS	SR
Bluffton College	OH	12,951	C
Cal State/Los Angeles	CA	4,940	VC
Cal State/Northridge	CA	7,122	LC
Cal State/Stanislaus	CA	6,799	C
Conn College	CT	24,160	HC
Edgewood College	WI	11,700	C
Fort Valley State College	GA	3,974	LC
Iowa State Univ	IA	5,456	C
Kentucky State Univ	KY	4,282	C+
La Sierra Univ	CA	15,472	C
Madonna Univ	MI	8,546	C
Meredith College	NC	9,440	C
Mills College	CA	20,848	VC
N Car Agricultural and Technical State Univ	NC	4,477	LC
Notre Dame College	NH	14,220	C
Pacific Christian College	CA	12,700	C
Southern Univ and A&M College	LA	4,920	NC
Southern Vermont College	VT	12,974	C
Southwestern Univ	TX	15,484	HC
Spelman College	GA	12,942	VC
SUNY/College at Buffalo	NY	7,035	VC
Stephen F. Austin State Univ	TX	5,117	C
Texas Woman's Univ	TX	4,392	C
Univ of Maine	ME	7,990	C
Univ of Minn/Twin Cities	MN	6,682	VC
Univ of North Texas	TX	4,853	C
Univ of Pittsburgh	PA	9,472	C
Univ of Texas at Austin	TX	5,160	VC
Utica College of Syracuse Univ	NY	16,714	LC
Weber State Univ	UT	4,398	C
Whittier College	CA	21,661	C

CHINESE

School	ST	$IS	SR
Arizona State Univ Main Campus	AZ	6,444	C
Ball State Univ	IN	6,032	LC
Bennington College	VT	24,850	VC+
Brigham Young Univ	UT	5,625	HC
CUNY/Hunter College	NY	4,101	VC
Conn College	CT	24,160	HC
Dartmouth College	NH	24,354	MC
George Washington Univ	DC	22,470	HC
Georgetown Univ	DC	24,410	MC
Grinnell College	IA	20,680	HC+
Harvard Univ/Harvard and Radcliffe Colleges	MA	24,880	MC
Hobart and William Smith Colleges	NY	23,925	VC
Middlebury College	VT	24,400	MC
Oakland Univ	MI	6,714	VC
Ohio State Univ	OH	7,218	LC
Pomona College	CA	23,820	MC
Reed College	OR	24,480	HC+
Rutgers Univ/Douglass College	NJ	8,795	VC
Rutgers Univ/Livingston College	NJ	8,877	VC
Rutgers Univ/Rutgers College	NJ	8,841	HC+
Rutgers Univ/Univ College—New Brunswick	NJ	0	LC
San Francisco State Univ	CA	7,292	LC
Scripps College	CA	23,600	HC
Stanford Univ	CA	24,310	MC
SUNY at Albany	NY	7,059	VC
Temple Univ	PA	10,281	C
Univ of Calif at Davis	CA	9,534	VC
Univ of Calif at Los Angeles	CA	8,959	HC
Univ of Calif at Santa Barbara	CA	9,460	C
Univ of Calif, San Diego	CA	10,028	VC+
Univ of Colo at Boulder	CO	6,410	VC
Univ of Hawaii at Manoa	HI	5,626	C
Univ of Maryland/College Park	MD	8,182	VC
Univ of Mass/Amherst	MA	9,364	LC
Univ of Mich/Ann Arbor	MI	9,428	HC+
Univ of Minn/Twin Cities	MN	6,682	VC
Univ of Oregon	OR	6,466	VC
Univ of Pittsburgh	PA	9,472	C
Univ of Rochester	NY	23,696	HC
Univ of Wisc/Madison	WI	6,400	HC
Washington Univ	MO	23,507	HC
Wellesley College	MA	23,815	MC
Wesleyan Univ	CT	23,770	MC
Yale Univ	CT	25,110	MC

CHIROPRACTIC

School	ST	$IS	SR
Dana College	NE	11,910	C
Mercy College	NY	11,180	NC
Univ of Bridgeport	CT	18,985	C

CHRISTIAN EDUCATION

School	ST	$IS	SR
Biola Univ	CA	16,124	C
Columbia College	SC	13,520	LC
Concordia College	NE	11,776	NC
Philander Smith College	AR	5,434	NC
Seattle Pacific Univ	WA	16,503	C
Simpson College	CA	10,628	C
Toccoa Falls College	GA	9,350	C

CHRISTIAN STUDIES

School	ST	$IS	SR
Alderson-Broaddus College	WV	12,000	C
Bryan College	TN	11,465	C
Campbellsville College	KY	8,720	C
Eastern Nazarene College	MA	12,165	LC
Grand Canyon Univ	AZ	9,680	VC
Hillsdale College	MI	15,110	VC
Mich Christian College	MI	8,094	C
Rocky Mountain College	MT	11,320	C
Texas Wesleyan Univ	TX	9,380	LC
Univ of St Thomas	MN	15,785	C+
Wayland Baptist Univ	TX	7,811	NC

CITY/COMMUNITY/REGIONAL PLANNING

School	ST	$IS	SR
Alabama A&M Univ	AL	4,200	C
Calif Polytechnic State Univ	CA	6,980	VC+
Cornell Univ	NY	13,445	MC
Iowa State Univ	IA	5,456	C
Mansfield Univ	PA	6,348	C
Mich State Univ	MI	7,842	C
New Mexico State Univ	NM	4,844	LC
Norfolk State Univ	VA	6,345	LC
Plymouth State College	NH	7,166	C
Southwest Texas State Univ	TX	5,124	C
Univ of Arizona	AZ	5,808	C
Univ of Cincinnati	OH	7,989	C
Univ of Illinois at Urbana-Champaign	IL	7,764	HC
Univ of New Hampshire	NH	8,242	C
Univ of Virginia	VA	7,964	MC
West Virginia Inst of Tech	WV	5,858	LC

CIVIL ENGINEERING

School	ST	$IS	SR
Alabama A&M Univ	AL	4,200	C
Arizona State Univ Main Campus	AZ	6,444	C
Auburn Univ	AL	5,823	C+
Bethel College	IN	11,650	C
Bradley Univ	IL	14,718	C+
Brigham Young Univ	UT	5,625	HC
Bucknell Univ	PA	22,320	HC
Calif Inst of Tech	CA	20,783	MC
Calif Polytechnic State Univ	CA	6,980	VC+
Calif State Polytechnic Univ/Pomona	CA	6,438	LC
Cal State/Chico	CA	6,146	C
Cal State/Fresno	CA	5,747	C
Cal State/Fullerton	CA	4,850	LC
Cal State/Long Beach	CA	6,057	LC
Cal State/Los Angeles	CA	4,940	VC
Cal State/Sacramento	CA	6,387	C
Calvin College	MI	13,020	VC
Caribbean Univ	PR	2,400	
Carnegie Mellon Univ	PA	22,560	HC+
Case Western Reserve Univ	OH	19,910	HC
Catholic Univ of America	DC	18,856	C
Christian Brothers Univ	TN	12,120	VC
CUNY/City College	NY	2,543	VC
Clarkson Univ	NY	20,705	VC+
Clemson Univ	SC	6,564	VC
Cleveland State Univ	OH	7,287	NC
Colo State Univ	CO	6,566	VC
Columbia Univ/School of Engineering and Applied Science	NY	24,554	HC
Cooper Union for the Advancement of Science and Art	NY	8,430	MC
Cornell Univ	NY	13,445	MC
Delaware State College	DE	5,656	C
Drexel Univ	PA	15,970	C
Duke Univ	NC	21,271	MC
Florida A&M Univ	FL	4,651	C
Florida Inst of Tech	FL	16,935	VC
Florida International Univ	FL	4,191	VC
Florida State Univ	FL	5,814	VC
Geneva College	PA	13,030	C
George Washington Univ	DC	22,470	HC
Georgia Inst of Tech	GA	6,669	HC+
Gonzaga Univ	WA	16,350	VC
Howard Univ	DC	11,680	C
Illinois Inst of Tech	IL	18,290	VC
Indiana Inst of Tech	IN	11,810	C
Iowa State Univ	IA	5,456	C
Johns Hopkins Univ	MD	24,360	MC
Kansas State Univ	KS	4,816	NC
Lafayette College	PA	23,450	HC
Lakeland College	WI	12,845	LC
Lamar Univ	TX	3,798	C
Lane College	TN	7,628	LC
Lawrence Tech Univ	MI	9,470	C
Lehigh Univ	PA	23,250	HC
Louisiana State Univ and A&M College	LA	5,605	C
Louisiana Tech Univ	LA	4,284	C
Loyola Marymount Univ	CA	18,560	C
Manhattan College	NY	19,000	C
Marquette Univ	WI	16,114	VC
Mass Inst of Tech	MA	24,800	MC
McNeese State Univ	LA	4,543	NC
Merrimack College	MA	18,025	C
Messiah College	PA	14,664	VC
Mich State Univ	MI	7,842	C
Mich Tech Univ	MI	7,283	VC+
Miss State Univ	MS	5,629	VC
Montana State Univ	MT	5,534	C
Morgan State Univ	MD	7,366	C+
Morris Brown College	GA	12,234	NC
New England College	NH	17,870	LC
New Jersey Inst of Tech	NJ	9,965	VC
New Mexico State Univ	NM	4,844	LC
N Car Agricultural and Technical State Univ	NC	4,477	LC
N Car State Univ	NC	4,984	VC
N Dak State Univ of Agriculture and Applied Science	ND	4,774	VC
Northeastern Univ	MA	19,851	C
Northern Arizona Univ	AZ	6,414	C
Northwestern Univ	IL	21,093	MC
Norwich Univ	VT	18,730	C
Ohio Northern Univ	OH	18,660	VC
Ohio State Univ	OH	7,218	LC
Ohio Univ	OH	7,341	C
Okla State Univ	OK	5,086	VC
Old Dominion Univ	VA	8,317	C

School	ST	$IS	SR
Oregon State Univ	OR	6,175	C
Penn State Univ/Univ Park Campus	PA	8,752	HC
Polytechnic Univ/Brooklyn	NY	19,700	HC
Polytechnic Univ/ Farmingdale	NY	20,700	VC
Portland State Univ	OR	7,191	C
Prairie View A&M Univ	TX	4,740	LC
Princeton Univ	NJ	24,650	MC
Purdue Univ/West Lafayette	IN	6,636	C
Rensselaer Polytechnic Inst	NY	23,067	HC
Rice Univ	TX	15,110	MC
Rose-Hulman Inst of Tech	IN	16,400	HC
Rutgers Univ/Camden College of A&S	NJ	8,652	VC
Rutgers Univ/College of Engineering	NJ	9,254	HC
Rutgers Univ/Newark College of A&S	NJ	8,645	C
St Augustine's College	NC	9,300	C+
St Martin's College	WA	14,965	C
San Diego State Univ	CA	6,692	LC
San Francisco State Univ	CA	7,292	LC
San Jose State Univ	CA	6,680	LC
Santa Clara Univ	CA	18,783	VC
Savannah State College	GA	4,052	C
Seattle Univ	WA	16,590	C
S Car State Univ	SC	5,424	LC
S Dak School of Mines and Tech	SD	5,329	C
S Dak State Univ	SD	4,562	C
Southern Illinois Univ at Carbondale	IL	6,234	C
Southern Illinois Univ at Edwardsville	IL	6,097	LC
Southern Univ and A&M College	LA	4,920	NC
Stanford Univ	CA	24,310	MC
SUNY at Buffalo	NY	7,896	VC
SUNY/College at Plattsburgh	NY	6,917	C
Stevens Inst of Tech	NJ	21,980	VC+
Swarthmore College	PA	24,136	MC
Syracuse Univ	NY	21,305	HC
Temple Univ	PA	10,281	C
Tenn State Univ	TN	4,626	C+
Tenn Tech Univ	TN	5,190	C
Texas A&M Univ	TX	5,382	VC
Texas A&M Univ at Kingsville	TX	3,808	LC
Texas Tech Univ	TX	6,008	C
The Citadel	SC	6,619	C
The Univ of New Mexico	NM	5,304	C
Tri-State Univ	IN	13,788	LC
Tufts Univ	MA	24,962	MC
Tulane Univ	LA	24,540	HC
Union College	NY	23,817	HC
United States Air Force Academy	CO	0	MC
United States Coast Guard Academy	CT	0	MC
United States Military Academy	NY	0	MC
Universidad Politecnica de PR	PR	6,195	
Univ of Akron	OH	6,699	NC
Univ of Alabama	AL	5,702	C
Univ of Alabama at Birmingham	AL	7,533	C
Univ of Alabama at Huntsville	AL	5,868	VC
Univ of Alaska Anchorage	AK	7,131	C
Univ of Alaska Fairbanks	AK	4,718	C
Univ of Arizona	AZ	5,808	C
Univ of Arkansas at Fayetteville	AR	5,046	C
Univ of Calif at Berkeley	CA	9,962	HC+
Univ of Calif at Davis	CA	9,534	VC
Univ of Calif at Los Angeles	CA	8,959	HC
Univ of Calif/Irvine	CA	12,680	VC
Univ of Central Florida	FL	6,061	C+
Univ of Cincinnati	OH	7,989	C
Univ of Colo at Boulder	CO	6,410	VC
Univ of Colo at Denver	CO	1,955	VC
Univ of Conn	CT	9,168	C
Univ of Dayton	OH	15,120	C+
Univ of Delaware	DE	8,013	VC
Univ of Detroit Mercy	MI	14,720	C
Univ of Evansville	IN	15,300	VC
Univ of Florida	FL	5,850	HC
Univ of Hartford	CT	19,858	LC
Univ of Hawaii at Manoa	HI	5,626	C
Univ of Houston	TX	5,215	C
Univ of Idaho	ID	4,830	C
Univ of Illinois at Chicago	IL	8,443	C
Univ of Illinois at Urbana-Champaign	IL	7,764	HC
Univ of Iowa	IA	5,658	VC
Univ of Kansas	KS	5,200	NC
Univ of Kentucky	KY	5,152	VC
Univ of Louisville	KY	5,948	C
Univ of Lowell	MA	8,831	VC
Univ of Maine	ME	7,990	C
Univ of Maryland/College Park	MD	8,182	VC
Univ of Mass Dartmouth	MA	8,158	C
Univ of Mass/Amherst	MA	9,364	LC
Univ of Memphis	TN	3,476	C
Univ of Miami	FL	22,107	VC
Univ of Mich/Ann Arbor	MI	9,428	HC+
Univ of Minn/Twin Cities	MN	6,682	VC
Univ of Miss	MS	5,756	C
Univ of Missouri/Columbia	MO	6,254	HC
Univ of Missouri/Kansas City	MO	5,906	VC
Univ of Missouri/Rolla	MO	6,729	VC+
Univ of Nebr at Omaha	NE	1,889	LC
Univ of Nebr-Lincoln	NE	5,278	LC
Univ of Nevada/Las Vegas	NV	6,405	C
Univ of Nevada/Reno	NV	5,735	C
Univ of New Hampshire	NH	8,242	C
Univ of New Haven	CT	14,980	C
Univ of New Orleans	LA	5,468	C
Univ of N Car at Charlotte	NC	4,597	C
Univ of N Dak	ND	4,902	NC
Univ of Notre Dame	IN	20,150	MC
Univ of Okla	OK	5,427	VC
Univ of Penn	PA	24,238	MC
Univ of Pittsburgh	PA	9,472	C
Univ of Portland	OR	15,564	C
Univ of PR/Mayaguez	PR	0	
Univ of Rhode Island	RI	9,205	C
Univ of South Alabama	AL	5,451	C
Univ of S Car	SC	6,158	C
Univ of South Florida	FL	5,475	C+
Univ of Southern Calif	CA	23,006	VC
Univ of Southwestern Louisiana	LA	3,968	NC
Univ of Tenn at Martin	TN	4,550	C
Univ of Tenn/Knoxville	TN	5,668	C
Univ of Texas at Arlington	TX	5,549	LC
Univ of Texas at Austin	TX	5,160	VC
Univ of Texas at El Paso	TX	3,160	LC
Univ of Texas at San Antonio	TX	6,420	C
Univ of the District of Columbia	DC	974	NC
Univ of the Pacific	CA	21,100	C
Univ of Toledo	OH	6,636	NC
Univ of Utah	UT	5,975	C
Univ of Vermont	VT	10,776	C+
Univ of Virginia	VA	7,964	MC
Univ of Washington	WA	6,618	VC
Univ of Wisc/Madison	WI	6,400	HC
Univ of Wisc/Milwaukee	WI	6,165	C
Univ of Wisc/Platteville	WI	4,830	C
Univ of Wyoming	WY	4,991	NC
Utah State Univ	UT	4,683	C
Valparaiso Univ	IN	14,810	VC
Vanderbilt Univ	TN	23,422	HC+
Villanova Univ	PA	21,400	HC
Virginia Military Inst	VA	8,630	C
Virginia Polytechnic Inst and State Univ	VA	6,828	C
Washington State Univ	WA	6,364	C
Washington Univ	MO	23,507	HC
Wayne State Univ	MI	2,680	C
West Virginia Inst of Tech	WV	5,858	LC
West Virginia Univ	WV	5,774	C
Widener Univ	PA	16,840	C
Worcester Polytechnic Inst	MA	20,350	HC
Youngstown State Univ	OH	6,447	LC

CIVIL ENGINEERING TECHNOLOGY

School	ST	$IS	SR
Alabama A&M Univ	AL	4,200	C
Fairleigh Dickinson Univ	NJ	16,427	C
Fairmont State College	WV	4,640	LC
Georgia Southern Univ	GA	4,988	LC
Idaho State Univ	ID	4,442	C
Metropolitan State College of Denver	CO	1,751	NC
Murray State Univ	KY	4,702	C
Nicholls State Univ	LA	4,531	NC
Northern Montana College	MT	4,976	C
Oregon Inst of Tech	OR	5,985	C
Point Park College	PA	13,922	LC
Rochester Inst of Tech	NY	18,954	VC
Southern College of Tech	GA	4	C
Univ of Pittsburgh at Johnstown	PA	8,914	C
Univ of Tenn at Martin	TN	4,550	C
Wentworth Inst of Tech	MA	15,250	LC
Western Kentucky Univ	KY	4,808	C

CLASSICAL/ANCIENT CIVILIZATION

School	ST	$IS	SR
Boston College	MA	22,706	MC
Bowdoin College	ME	24,155	MC
Carleton College	MN	22,155	HC
CUNY/Herbert H. Lehman College	NY	2,542	C
Clark Univ	MA	21,400	VC
Coe College	IA	17,085	VC
Colby College	ME	24,230	HC
Columbia Univ/Barnard College	NY	25,492	HC
Cornell College	IA	18,425	VC
Creighton Univ	NE	14,432	VC
Denison Univ	OH	21,150	VC+
DePauw Univ	IN	18,530	VC
Duke Univ	NC	21,271	MC
Emory Univ	GA	21,930	HC
Gonzaga Univ	WA	16,350	VC
Hamilton College	NY	23,500	HC
Loyola Marymount Univ	CA	18,560	C
Loyola Univ of Chicago	IL	15,880	C+
Mich State Univ	MI	7,842	C
Middlebury College	VT	24,400	MC
Ohio State Univ	OH	7,218	LC
Rollins College	FL	20,875	VC
St Olaf College	MN	17,200	HC
Seton Hall Univ	NJ	18,306	LC
Smith College	MA	24,236	HC
SUNY at Albany	NY	7,059	VC
SUNY at Binghamton	NY	7,921	HC
Syracuse Univ	NY	21,305	HC
Univ of Calif at Berkeley	CA	9,962	HC+
Univ of Calif at Davis	CA	9,534	VC
Univ of Calif at Los Angeles	CA	8,959	HC
Univ of Calif at Santa Barbara	CA	9,460	C
Univ of Calif/Irvine	CA	12,680	VC
Univ of Cincinnati	OH	7,989	C
Univ of Florida	FL	5,850	HC
Univ of Illinois at Chicago	IL	8,443	C
Univ of Iowa	IA	5,658	VC
Univ of Kansas	KS	5,200	NC
Univ of Maryland/Baltimore County	MD	7,746	VC
Univ of Mich/Ann Arbor	MI	9,428	HC+
Univ of Miss	MS	5,756	C
Univ of Oregon	OR	6,466	VC
Univ of Tenn/Knoxville	TN	5,668	C
Wayne State Univ	MI	2,680	C
Wellesley College	MA	23,815	MC
Wheaton College	MA	23,840	C+
Yale Univ	CT	25,110	MC

CLASSICAL LANGUAGES

School	ST	$IS	SR
Allegheny College	PA	21,020	VC
Berea College	KY	2,883	VC+
Bryn Mawr College	PA	24,110	MC
Carroll College	MT	11,265	C
Concordia College	MI	13,660	C
Concordia College/Moorhead	MN	12,750	C
DePauw Univ	IN	18,530	VC
Fordham Univ/Fordham College	NY	19,875	VC
Mount Holyoke College	MA	23,630	VC
Rockford College	IL	15,300	C
Rutgers Univ/Livingston College	NJ	8,877	VC
Rutgers Univ/Rutgers College	NJ	8,841	HC+
St Peter's College	NJ	14,775	LC
Siena College	NY	15,410	VC
Smith College	MA	24,236	HC
Univ of Calif at Berkeley	CA	9,962	HC+
Univ of Calif, San Diego	CA	10,028	VC+
Univ of Houston	TX	5,215	C
Univ of Kansas	KS	5,200	NC
Univ of Minn/Twin Cities	MN	6,682	VC
Univ of N Car at Chapel Hill	NC	5,330	HC
Vanderbilt Univ	TN	23,422	HC+
Western Washington Univ	WA	6,077	VC
Wright State Univ	OH	6,896	LC
Yeshiva Univ	NY	18,200	VC

CLASSICS

School	ST	$IS	SR
Agnes Scott College	GA	17,135	VC
Albertus Magnus College	CT	16,280	LC
Allegheny College	PA	21,020	VC
Amherst College	MA	24,152	MC
Assumption College	MA	17,095	LC
Augustana College	IL	16,959	VC
Austin College	TX	14,999	VC
Boston College	MA	22,706	MC
Boston Univ	MA	24,130	HC
Bowdoin College	ME	24,155	MC
Brandeis Univ	MA	25,585	HC
Brown Univ	RI	26,104	MC
Bucknell Univ	PA	22,320	HC
Carleton College	MN	22,155	HC
Case Western Reserve Univ	OH	19,910	HC
Catholic Univ of America	DC	18,856	C
CUNY/Brooklyn College	NY	2,450	VC
CUNY/City College	NY	2,543	VC
CUNY/Hunter College	NY	4,101	VC
Claremont McKenna College	CA	22,150	MC
Cleveland State Univ	OH	7,287	NC
Colby College	ME	24,230	HC
College of New Rochelle	NY	15,440	LC
College of St Benedict	MN	15,468	VC
College of the Holy Cross	MA	23,850	HC
College of William and Mary	VA	8,602	MC
Colo College	CO	20,038	HC
Columbia Univ/Barnard College	NY	25,492	HC
Columbia Univ/Columbia College	NY	26,757	MC
Conn College	CT	24,160	HC
Cornell Univ	NY	13,445	MC
Dartmouth College	NH	24,354	MC
Davidson College	NC	21,037	MC
Drew Univ/College of Liberal Arts	NJ	23,406	HC
Elmira College	NY	18,450	C
Emory and Henry College	VA	12,776	C
Emory Univ	GA	21,930	HC
Florida State Univ	FL	5,814	VC
Franklin and Marshall College	PA	23,655	HC
George Mason Univ	VA	8,728	C
George Washington Univ	DC	22,470	HC
Gettysburg College	PA	22,960	HC
Gonzaga Univ	WA	16,350	VC
Grinnell College	IA	20,680	HC+
Gustavus Adolphus College	MN	15,935	VC
Hamilton College	NY	23,500	HC
Hampden-Sydney College	VA	17,372	C+
Harvard Univ/Harvard and Radcliffe Colleges	MA	24,880	MC
Haverford College	PA	23,950	MC
Hellenic College/Holy Cross Greek Orthodox School of Theology	MA	10,295	NC
Hillsdale College	MI	15,110	VC
Hiram College	OH	18,340	VC
Hobart and William Smith Colleges	NY	23,925	VC
Hofstra Univ	NY	16,580	VC
Hollins College	VA	18,484	C
Indiana Univ Bloomington	IN	6,495	VC
Johns Hopkins Univ	MD	24,360	MC
Kenyon College	OH	22,430	HC+
Knox College	IL	18,990	VC
La Salle Univ	PA	16,940	VC
Lawrence Univ	WI	19,986	HC+
Lehigh Univ	PA	23,250	HC
Lenoir-Rhyne College	NC	14,068	C
Macalester College	MN	19,710	HC
Marshall Univ	WV	5,762	LC
Mary Washington College	VA	7,910	HC
Middlebury College	VT	24,400	MC
Millsaps College	MS	15,486	C+
Monmouth College	IL	17,300	C+
Montclair State College	NJ	7,539	C+
Mount St Mary's College	MD	17,825	LC
New College of the Univ of South Florida	FL	5,697	MC
North Central College	IL	15,498	VC
Northwestern Univ	IL	21,093	MC
Oberlin College	OH	24,570	HC+
Ohio State Univ	OH	7,218	LC
Pacific Lutheran Univ	WA	15,998	VC
Penn State Univ/Univ Park Campus	PA	8,752	HC
Pitzer College	CA	23,780	HC
Pomona College	CA	23,820	MC
Princeton Univ	NJ	24,650	MC
Randolph-Macon College	VA	16,980	C
Randolph-Macon Woman's College	VA	19,100	C
Reed College	OR	24,480	HC+
Regis College	MA	17,450	C
Rhodes College	TN	19,624	HC
Rice Univ	TX	15,110	MC
Rutgers Univ/Douglass College	NJ	8,795	VC
Rutgers Univ/Livingston College	NJ	8,877	VC
Rutgers Univ/Newark College of A&S	NJ	8,645	C
Rutgers Univ/Rutgers College	NJ	8,841	HC+
Rutgers Univ/Univ College—New Brunswick	NJ	0	LC
St Anselm College	NH	17,340	C
St Bonaventure Univ	NY	14,762	C
St John's Univ	MN	15,364	C
St Peter's College	NJ	14,775	LC
San Francisco State Univ	CA	7,292	LC
Santa Clara Univ	CA	18,783	VC
Scripps College	CA	23,600	HC
Seattle Pacific Univ	WA	16,503	C
Skidmore College	NY	23,230	HC
Southern Illinois Univ at Carbondale	IL	6,234	C
Southwestern Univ	TX	15,484	HC
Stanford Univ	CA	24,310	MC
SUNY at Binghamton	NY	7,921	HC
Syracuse Univ	NY	21,305	HC
Temple Univ	PA	10,281	C
The Univ of New Mexico	NM	5,304	C
Trinity College	CT	24,120	HC
Tufts Univ	MA	24,962	MC

School	ST	$IS	SR
Fordham Univ/Fordham College	NY	19,875	VC
Fort Hays State Univ	KS	4,675	NC
Fort Valley State College	GA	3,974	LC
Framingham State College	MA	6,580	C
Francis Marion Univ	SC	5,878	LC
Franciscan Univ of Steubenville	OH	13,400	C
Franklin College of Indiana	IN	13,970	C
Franklin Pierce College	NH	17,270	LC
Franklin Univ	OH	4,621	NC
Freed-Hardeman Univ	TN	8,585	VC
Frostburg State Univ	MD	6,940	C
Gallaudet Univ	DC	9,850	SP
Gannon Univ	PA	14,872	C
Gardner-Webb Univ	NC	11,950	LC
Geneva College	PA	13,030	C
George Fox College	OR	15,640	LC
George Mason Univ	VA	8,728	C
George Washington Univ	DC	22,470	HC
Georgetown College	KY	10,990	C
Georgia Southern Univ	GA	4,988	LC
Georgia State Univ	GA	2,019	C
Goldey-Beacom College	DE	7,839	C
Goshen College	IN	12,360	C
Goucher College	MD	20,295	VC
Grace College	IN	12,120	C
Graceland College	IA	11,600	C
Grand Canyon Univ	AZ	9,680	VC
Grand Rapids Baptist College and Seminary	MI	10,228	C
Grand Valley State Univ	MI	6,822	VC
Grand View College	IA	13,230	NC
Greenville College	IL	14,190	C
Grove City College	PA	7,870	HC
Gustavus Adolphus College	MN	15,935	VC
Hamline Univ	MN	17,122	VC
Hampshire College	MA	25,320	C
Hampton Univ	VA	10,706	C
Hannibal-LaGrange College	MO	8,400	LC
Hanover College	IN	10,950	VC
Hardin-Simmons Univ	TX	9,080	C
Harding Univ	AR	9,050	VC
Hastings College	NE	12,426	C
Hawaii Pacific Univ	HI	12,300	C
Heidelberg College	OH	17,160	C
Henderson State Univ	AR	3,860	C
Hiram College	OH	18,340	VC
Hofstra Univ	NY	16,580	VC
Hollins College	VA	18,484	C
Holy Family College	PA	8,300	C
Hood College	MD	19,010	VC
Hope College	MI	15,698	C+
Houghton College	NY	13,120	VC
Houston Baptist Univ	TX	11,055	C
Howard Payne Univ	TX	8,052	C
Howard Univ	DC	11,680	C
Humboldt State Univ	CA	5,676	C
Huntington College	IN	13,220	C
Huron Univ	SD	9,790	C
Huston-Tillotson College	TX	8,490	C
Idaho State Univ	ID	4,442	C
Illinois Benedictine College	IL	14,170	C
Illinois College	IL	11,200	C
Illinois State Univ	IL	6,413	C
Incarnate Word College	TX	12,307	C
Indiana State Univ	IN	6,210	C
Indiana Univ at Kokomo	IN	2,069	C
Indiana Univ Bloomington	IN	6,495	VC
Indiana Univ Northwest	IN	2,310	C
Indiana Univ of Penn	PA	6,373	C
Indiana Univ Southeast	IN	2,260	LC
Indiana Univ-Purdue Univ at Fort Wayne	IN	2,500	LC
Indiana Univ-Purdue Univ at Indianapolis	IN	5,862	LC
Indiana Univ/South Bend	IN	2,141	LC
Indiana Wesleyan Univ	IN	12,332	C
Iona College	NY	16,310	C
Iowa State Univ	IA	5,456	C
Iowa Wesleyan College	IA	13,250	C
Ithaca College	NY	19,679	C
Jackson State Univ	MS	4,996	LC
Jacksonville State Univ	AL	4,080	LC
Jacksonville Univ	FL	13,390	C
James Madison Univ	VA	8,198	HC
John Carroll Univ	OH	16,510	C
Johnson and Wales Univ	RI	13,995	LC
Johnson C. Smith Univ	NC	8,916	LC
Judson College	IL	13,625	C
Juniata College	PA	18,390	C+
Kansas Newman College	KS	10,640	C
Kansas State Univ	KS	4,816	NC
Kansas Wesleyan Univ	KS	11,770	C
Kean College of New Jersey	NJ	6,395	LC
Kendall College	IL	12,651	LC
Kennesaw State College	GA	1,553	C
Kent State Univ	OH	6,740	LC
Kentucky Wesleyan College	KY	11,550	C
King's College	PA	15,420	C
Kutztown Univ	PA	6,528	C
La Roche College	PA	12,977	LC
La Salle Univ	PA	16,940	VC
La Sierra Univ	CA	15,472	C
Lake Erie College	OH	13,700	C
Lamar Univ	TX	3,798	C
Lambuth Univ	TN	8,395	C
Lane College	TN	7,628	LC
Le Moyne College	NY	15,180	C
Lee College	TN	7,894	LC
Lees-McRae College	NC	9,850	LC
Lenoir-Rhyne College	NC	14,068	C
Lewis and Clark College	OR	19,980	VC
Lewis Univ	IL	14,797	LC
Lewis-Clark State College	ID	4,040	C
Lincoln Memorial Univ	TN	8,218	C
Lincoln Univ	PA	0	LC
Lindenwood College	MO	13,560	C
Linfield College	OR	16,670	VC
Lock Haven Univ of Penn	PA	7,128	C
LIU/C. W. Post Campus	NY	16,870	C
LIU/Southampton Campus	NY	17,280	C
Louisiana College	LA	7,518	VC
Louisiana State Univ in Shreveport	LA	1,910	NC
Loyola College	MD	18,035	VC
Loyola Marymount Univ	CA	18,560	C
Loyola Univ of Chicago	IL	15,880	C+
Loyola Univ/New Orleans	LA	15,660	C+
Lubbock Christian Univ	TX	9,840	NC
Luther College	IA	15,900	VC
Lycoming College	PA	17,200	LC
Lynchburg College	VA	17,000	C
Lyndon State College	VT	8,394	LC
Lynn Univ	FL	18,300	C
Macalester College	MN	19,710	HC
Madonna Univ	MI	8,546	C
Malone College	OH	12,572	C
Manchester College	IN	13,240	LC
Manhattan College	NY	19,000	C
Marian College of Fond du Lac	WI	12,250	C
Marietta College	OH	16,940	C+
Marist College	NY	16,406	C
Marquette Univ	WI	16,114	VC
Mars Hill College	NC	11,050	C
Marshall Univ	WV	5,762	LC
Martin Univ	IN	4,830	NC
Mary Baldwin College	VA	17,700	LC
Marylhurst College	OR	6,486	NC
Marymount College/Tarrytown	NY	17,350	C
Marymount Manhattan College	NY	15,450	LC
Marymount Univ	VA	15,930	C
Maryville Univ-St Louis	MO	12,900	VC
Marywood College	PA	14,890	C
Master's College	CA	12,816	C
McKendree College	IL	10,900	C
McMurry Univ	TX	10,100	C
McNeese State Univ	LA	4,543	NC
McPherson College	KS	11,360	VC
Menlo College	CA	20,375	LC
Mercy College	NY	11,180	NC
Mercyhurst College	PA	13,488	C
Mesa State College	CO	5,127	NC
Messiah College	PA	14,664	VC
Methodist College	NC	12,400	C
Metropolitan State College of Denver	CO	1,751	NC
Miami Univ	OH	8,066	VC
Mich State Univ	MI	7,842	C
Mich Tech Univ	MI	7,283	VC+
MidAmerica Nazarene College	KS	10,208	NC
Middle Tenn State Univ	TN	3,857	C
Midland Lutheran College	NE	12,410	C
Midwestern State Univ	TX	4,542	LC
Miles College	AL	7,150	NC
Millersville Univ of Penn	PA	7,370	VC
Milligan College	TN	10,690	C
Millikin Univ	IL	15,499	C
Mills College	CA	20,848	VC
Miss College	MS	8,348	C
Miss State Univ	MS	5,629	VC
Missouri Southern State College	MO	4,272	
Missouri Valley College	MO	14,050	LC
Missouri Western State College	MO	4,384	NC
Molloy College	NY	8,580	LC
Monmouth College	IL	17,300	C+
Moorhead State Univ	MN	5,076	C
Morehead State Univ	KY	4,600	LC
Morningside College	IA	13,896	C
Morris Brown College	GA	12,234	NC
Mount Marty College	SD	10,450	NC
Mount Mary College	WI	10,920	C
Mount St Mary College	NY	12,910	C
Mount St Mary's College	MD	17,825	LC
Mount Union College	OH	15,850	C
Mount Vernon College	DC	20,668	C
Mount Vernon Nazarene College	OH	10,390	C
Muhlenberg College	PA	20,795	VC
Murray State Univ	KY	4,702	C
Muskingum College	OH	16,650	C
Nebr Wesleyan Univ	NE	12,240	C
Neumann College	PA	9,950	LC
New England College	NH	17,870	LC
New Hampshire College	NH	15,242	LC
New Mexico Highlands Univ	NM	3,772	C
New Mexico State Univ	NM	4,844	LC
New York Inst of Tech/Old Westbury	NY	13,914	LC
New York Univ	NY	24,705	VC+
Niagara Univ	NY	14,552	C
Nicholls State Univ	LA	4,531	NC
Norfolk State Univ	VA	6,345	LC
North Adams State College	MA	7,750	C
N Car Agricultural and Technical State Univ	NC	4,477	LC
N Car State Univ	NC	4,984	VC
North Central Bible College	MN	8,670	LC
North Central College	IL	15,498	VC
N Dak State Univ of Agriculture and Applied Science	ND	4,774	VC
North Park College	IL	14,310	C
Northeast Louisiana Univ	LA	3,906	NC
Northeast Missouri State Univ	MO	5,654	VC+
Northeastern State Univ	OK	5,250	C
Northeastern Univ	MA	19,851	C
Northern Arizona Univ	AZ	4,844	C
Northern Illinois Univ	IL	6,408	C
Northern Mich Univ	MI	6,350	C
Northern Montana College	MT	4,976	C
Northwest Missouri State Univ	MO	5,010	LC
Northwestern College	MN	13,554	C
Northwestern College of Iowa	IA	12,250	C
Northwestern Univ	IL	21,093	MC
Norwich Univ	VT	18,730	C
Notre Dame College	NH	14,220	C
Notre Dame College of Ohio	OH	11,370	C
Nyack College	NY	12,210	LC
Oakland Univ	MI	6,714	VC
Oakwood College	AL	10,005	C
Oglethorpe Univ	GA	16,360	VC
Ohio Dominican College	OH	11,820	LC
Ohio Northern Univ	OH	18,660	VC
Ohio State Univ	OH	7,218	LC
Ohio Univ	OH	7,341	C
Okla Baptist Univ	OK	8,486	C
Okla Christian Univ of Science and Arts	OK	8,790	NC
Okla City Univ	OK	9,840	C
Okla Panhandle State Univ	OK	3,155	NC
Okla State Univ	OK	5,086	VC
Olivet College	MI	14,000	C
Olivet Nazarene Univ	IL	11,976	C
Oral Roberts Univ	OK	10,607	C+
Oregon State Univ	OR	6,175	C
Ottawa Univ	KS	10,490	C+
Otterbein College	OH	16,506	C
Ouachita Baptist Univ	AR	8,940	C
Our Lady of the Lake Univ of San Antonio	TX	11,080	C
Pace Univ	NY	15,540	C
Pacific Christian College	CA	12,700	C
Pacific Lutheran Univ	WA	15,998	VC
Pacific Union College	CA	15,075	C
Paine College	GA	8,207	LC
Palm Beach Atlantic College	FL	10,720	C
Park College	MO	7,320	C
Pembroke State Univ	NC	3,538	LC
Penn State Univ at Erie/Behrend College	PA	8,752	C
Penn State Univ/Univ Park Campus	PA	8,752	HC
Pepperdine Univ	CA	23,720	VC
Pfeiffer College	NC	11,670	LC
Phillips Univ	OK	12,744	C
Pine Manor College	MA	21,700	LC
Pittsburg State Univ	KS	4,478	NC
Point Loma Nazarene College	CA	13,532	C
Point Park College	PA	13,922	LC
Pontifical Catholic Univ of PR/Ponce	PR	5,807	
Prairie View A&M Univ	TX	4,740	LC
Pratt Inst	NY	19,520	C
Prescott College	AZ	9,775	C
Principia College	IL	17,799	C
Purdue Univ/Calumet	IN	2,374	NC
Purdue Univ/West Lafayette	IN	6,636	C
Queens College	NC	14,950	C
Quincy Univ	IL	13,646	VC
Quinnipiac College	CT	17,600	C+
Radford Univ	VA	7,034	LC
Ramapo College of New Jersey	NJ	8,027	C+
Randolph-Macon Woman's College	VA	19,100	C
Regis College	MA	17,450	C
Regis Univ	CO	17,340	C
Rensselaer Polytechnic Inst	NY	23,067	HC
Rhode Island College	RI	7,901	LC
Rider College	NJ	18,160	C
Rivier College	NH	14,920	LC
Robert Morris College	PA	10,406	LC
Roberts Wesleyan College	NY	13,317	C
Rochester Inst of Tech	NY	18,954	VC
Rockhurst College	MO	12,470	C
Roger Williams Univ	RI	16,750	C
Rosary College	IL	15,040	C
Rowan College of New Jersey	NJ	7,358	VC
Russell Sage College	NY	16,790	C
Rust College	MS	6,600	LC
Rutgers Univ/Cook College	NJ	9,197	HC
Rutgers Univ/Douglass College	NJ	8,795	VC
Rutgers Univ/Livingston College	NJ	8,877	VC
Rutgers Univ/Rutgers College	NJ	8,841	HC+
Rutgers Univ/Univ College—New Brunswick	NJ	0	LC
Sacred Heart Univ	CT	16,350	C
Saginaw Valley State Univ	MI	6,634	LC
St Ambrose Univ	IA	13,380	C
St Andrews Presbyterian College	NC	14,240	LC
St Augustine's College	NC	9,300	C+
St Cloud State Univ	MN	5,015	C
St Edward's Univ	TX	12,636	C
St Francis College	IN	11,662	C
St Francis College	NY	6,710	LC
St Francis College	PA	15,744	LC
St John Fisher College	NY	15,415	C
St John's Univ	MN	15,364	C
St John's Univ	NY	8,980	C+
St Joseph's College	IN	14,730	C
St Joseph's College	ME	14,535	C
St Louis Univ	MO	15,522	VC
St Mary's College	IN	17,043	VC
St Mary's College	MI	8,350	C
St Mary's College of Calif	CA	18,848	VC
St Mary's College of Minn	MN	13,850	LC
St Mary's Univ	TX	12,064	C
St Norbert College	WI	15,710	VC
St Thomas Aquinas College	NY	13,550	C
St Thomas Univ	FL	14,280	LC
St Vincent College	PA	13,934	LC
St Xavier Univ	IL	14,700	C
Salem College	NC	16,025	C
Salem State College	MA	6,712	C
Salem-Teikyo Univ	WV	14,527	C
Salisbury State Univ	MD	7,516	C+
Samford Univ	AL	11,400	VC
Santa Clara Univ	CA	18,783	VC
Savannah State College	GA	4,052	C
Seattle Pacific Univ	WA	16,503	C
Seattle Univ	WA	16,590	C
Seton Hall Univ	NJ	18,306	LC
Seton Hill College	PA	14,320	C
Shenandoah Univ	VA	11,800	C
Shepherd College	WV	5,540	C
Shippensburg Univ of Penn	PA	7,052	C
Shorter College	GA	10,270	C
Siena Heights College	MI	12,520	C
Simmons College	MA	22,534	C
Simpson College	IA	14,635	VC
Sioux Falls College	SD	11,540	C
Slippery Rock Univ	PA	6,803	C
Sonoma State Univ	CA	6,996	LC
S Dak State Univ	SD	4,562	C
Southeast Missouri State Univ	MO	5,854	C
Southeastern Louisiana Univ	LA	4,230	NC
Southern Arkansas Univ	AR	3,432	NC
Southern Calif College	CA	12,356	C
Southern College of Seventh-day Adventists	TN	11,348	NC
Southern Conn State Univ	CT	7,532	C
Southern Illinois Univ at Edwardsville	IL	6,097	LC
Southern Nazarene Univ	OK	9,206	NC
Southern Oregon State College	OR	6,128	C
Southern Univ and A&M College	LA	4,920	NC
Southern Utah Univ	UT	4,104	LC
Southern Vermont College	VT	12,974	C
Southwest Baptist Univ	MO	9,192	NC
Southwest Missouri State Univ	MO	4,956	C
Southwest State Univ	MN	5,400	NC
Southwest Texas State Univ	TX	5,124	C
Southwestern Adventist College	TX	10,530	NC
Southwestern Univ	TX	15,484	HC
Spalding Univ	KY	10,496	LC
Spring Arbor College	MI	12,256	C
Spring Hill College	AL	16,015	C+
Stanford Univ	CA	24,310	MC
SUNY at Albany	NY	7,059	VC
SUNY at Buffalo	NY	7,896	VC
SUNY/College at Brockport	NY	7,220	C+
SUNY/College at Buffalo	NY	7,035	VC
SUNY/College at Cortland	NY	7,326	C+
SUNY/College at Fredonia	NY	7,159	VC
SUNY/College at Geneseo	NY	6,949	HC
SUNY/College at New Paltz	NY	6,890	VC
SUNY/College at Oswego	NY	7,330	VC
SUNY/College at Plattsburgh	NY	6,917	C
Stephen F. Austin State Univ	TX	5,117	C
Stephens College	MO	18,460	C
Stetson Univ	FL	16,435	VC
Stillman College	AL	7,213	NC
Stonehill College	MA	17,481	VC
Suffolk Univ	MA	15,360	LC
Sul Ross State Univ	TX	4,144	NC

School	ST	$IS	SR
Susquehanna Univ	PA	19,950	VC
Tabor College	KS	11,460	VC
Taylor Univ	IN	14,450	VC
Teikyo Marycrest Univ	IA	13,755	VC
Temple Univ	PA	10,281	C
Tenn State Univ	TN	4,626	C+
Texas A&M Univ at Kingsville	TX	3,808	LC
Texas Christian Univ	TX	12,180	C
Texas Lutheran College	TX	10,710	C
Texas Southern Univ	TX	4,500	NC
Texas Wesleyan Univ	TX	9,380	LC
Texas Woman's Univ	TX	4,392	C
The Univ of New Mexico	NM	5,304	C
Thiel College	PA	16,282	C
Thomas A. Edison State College	NJ	400	
Thomas More College	KY	12,962	C
Toccoa Falls College	GA	9,350	C
Towson State Univ	MD	7,452	C
Trenton State College	NJ	9,085	HC
Trevecca Nazarene College	TN	9,826	NC
Tri-State Univ	IN	13,788	LC
Trinity Christian College	IL	13,260	C
Trinity College	DC	17,660	C
Trinity College	IL	14,010	C
Trinity College of Vermont	VT	16,015	LC
Trinity Univ	TX	16,670	HC
Troy State Univ	AL	4,322	C
Tulane Univ	LA	24,540	HC
Union College	NE	11,060	NC
Union Univ	TN	7,880	C+
Univ of Akron	OH	6,699	NC
Univ of Alabama at Birmingham	AL	7,533	C
Univ of Alabama at Huntsville	AL	5,868	VC
Univ of Arizona	AZ	5,808	C
Univ of Arkansas at Fayetteville	AR	5,046	C
Univ of Bridgeport	CT	18,985	C
Univ of Calif at Berkeley	CA	9,962	HC+
Univ of Calif at Davis	CA	9,534	VC
Univ of Calif at Los Angeles	CA	8,959	HC
Univ of Calif at Santa Barbara	CA	9,460	C
Univ of Calif, San Diego	CA	10,028	VC+
Univ of Central Arkansas	AR	4,200	LC
Univ of Central Florida	FL	6,061	C+
Univ of Central Okla	OK	3,647	C
Univ of Charleston	WV	12,750	C
Univ of Cincinnati	OH	7,989	C
Univ of Colo at Boulder	CO	6,410	VC
Univ of Colo at Colo Springs	CO	2,269	C
Univ of Colo at Denver	CO	1,955	VC
Univ of Conn	CT	9,168	C
Univ of Dayton	OH	15,120	C+
Univ of Delaware	DE	8,013	VC
Univ of Denver	CO	19,290	C+
Univ of Detroit Mercy	MI	14,720	C
Univ of Dubuque	IA	14,150	LC
Univ of Evansville	IN	15,300	VC
Univ of Findlay	OH	15,764	C
Univ of Georgia	GA	5,655	VC
Univ of Guam	GU	4,139	NC
Univ of Hartford	CT	19,858	LC
Univ of Hawaii at Manoa	HI	5,626	C
Univ of Houston	TX	5,215	C
Univ of Houston-Downtown	TX	4,034	NC
Univ of Idaho	ID	4,830	C
Univ of Indianapolis	IN	14,510	C
Univ of Iowa	IA	5,658	VC
Univ of Kansas	KS	5,200	NC
Univ of Kentucky	KY	5,152	VC
Univ of La Verne	CA	17,400	C
Univ of Louisville	KY	5,948	C
Univ of Maine	ME	7,990	C
Univ of Mary	ND	8,910	C
Univ of Mary Hardin-Baylor	TX	8,120	NC
Univ of Maryland/Univ College	MD	4,900	NC
Univ of Mass/Amherst	MA	9,364	LC
Univ of Memphis	TN	3,476	C
Univ of Miami	FL	22,107	VC
Univ of Mich/Ann Arbor	MI	9,428	HC+
Univ of Mich/Flint	MI	2,916	C
Univ of Minn/Duluth	MN	6,512	C
Univ of Missouri/Columbia	MO	6,254	HC
Univ of Missouri/Kansas City	MO	5,906	VC
Univ of Missouri/St. Louis	MO	6,378	C
Univ of Mobile	AL	9,400	C
Univ of Montana	MT	5,529	C
Univ of Nebr at Kearney	NE	4,308	LC
Univ of Nebr at Omaha	NE	1,889	LC
Univ of Nevada/Las Vegas	NV	6,405	C
Univ of New Hampshire	NH	8,242	C
Univ of New Haven	CT	14,980	C
Univ of New Orleans	LA	5,468	C
Univ of North Alabama	AL	4,236	NC
Univ of N Car at Asheville	NC	4,791	VC
Univ of N Car at Greensboro	NC	5,192	C
Univ of N Dak	ND	4,902	NC
Univ of North Florida	FL	5,082	C
Univ of North Texas	TX	4,853	C
Univ of Northern Colo	CO	6,008	C
Univ of Northern Iowa	IA	5,137	C
Univ of Notre Dame	IN	20,150	MC
Univ of Okla	OK	5,427	VC
Univ of Penn	PA	24,238	MC
Univ of Pittsburgh	PA	9,472	C
Univ of Pittsburgh at Bradford	PA	9,050	C
Univ of Pittsburgh at Johnstown	PA	8,914	C
Univ of Portland	OR	15,564	C
Univ of PR/Arecibo Tech Univ College	PR	1,302	C
Univ of PR/Rio Piedras	PR	0	C
Univ of Puget Sound	WA	19,520	HC
Univ of Rio Grande	OH	6,300	NC
Univ of St Thomas	TX	11,676	C+
Univ of San Diego	CA	18,970	VC
Univ of San Francisco	CA	18,408	C
Univ of Science and Arts of Okla	OK	3,304	C
Univ of Scranton	PA	17,071	VC
Univ of South Alabama	AL	5,451	C
Univ of S Car at Spartanburg	SC	2,320	C
Univ of S Dak	SD	4,722	C
Univ of South Florida	FL	5,475	C+
Univ of Southern Calif	CA	23,006	VC
Univ of Southern Colo	CO	5,350	LC
Univ of Southern Indiana	IN	3,720	NC
Univ of Southern Maine	ME	7,299	C
Univ of Southern Miss	MS	4,542	C
Univ of Southwestern Louisiana	LA	3,968	NC
Univ of Tampa	FL	16,780	C
Univ of Tenn at Chattanooga	TN	5,375	C
Univ of Tenn at Martin	TN	4,550	C
Univ of Texas at Arlington	TX	5,549	LC
Univ of Texas at Austin	TX	5,160	VC
Univ of Texas at El Paso	TX	3,160	LC
Univ of Texas-Pan American	TX	3,192	NC
Univ of the Ozarks	AR	7,770	C
Univ of the Pacific	CA	21,100	C
Univ of the Sacred Heart	PR	3,890	
Univ of Toledo	OH	6,636	NC
Univ of Utah	UT	5,975	C
Univ of Virginia	VA	7,964	MC
Univ of Washington	WA	6,618	VC
Univ of West Florida	FL	5,415	C
Univ of Wisc/Eau Claire	WI	4,647	C
Univ of Wisc/Green Bay	WI	4,904	C
Univ of Wisc/La Crosse	WI	4,487	C
Univ of Wisc/Madison	WI	6,400	HC
Univ of Wisc/Milwaukee	WI	6,165	C
Univ of Wisc/Parkside	WI	5,247	
Univ of Wisc/Stevens Point	WI	5,047	C+
Univ of Wisc/Superior	WI	4,330	C
Univ of Wisc/Whitewater	WI	4,700	C
Univ of Wyoming	WY	4,991	NC
Upper Iowa Univ	IA	11,900	C
Upsala College	NJ	17,200	C
Urbana Univ	OH	12,536	C
Ursinus College	PA	19,165	VC
Utica College of Syracuse Univ	NY	16,714	LC
Valdosta State Univ	GA	4,670	LC
Valley City State Univ	ND	4,385	LC
Valparaiso Univ	IN	14,810	VC
Villanova Univ	PA	21,400	HC
Virginia Commonwealth Univ	VA	7,909	C
Virginia Polytechnic Inst and State Univ	VA	6,828	C
Virginia Wesleyan College	VA	14,950	VC
Wake Forest Univ	NC	17,280	MC
Walla Walla College	WA	13,215	C
Walsh Univ	OH	11,640	C
Wartburg College	IA	14,530	VC
Washburn Univ of Topeka	KS	5,802	NC
Washington State Univ	WA	6,364	C
Wayland Baptist Univ	TX	7,811	NC
Wayne State College	NE	4,260	NC
Wayne State Univ	MI	2,680	C
Weber State Univ	UT	4,398	C
Webster Univ	MO	12,650	C
Wesley College	DE	13,745	LC
Wesleyan College	GA	15,445	C
West Chester Univ of Penn	PA	7,492	C
West Georgia College	GA	4,256	C
West Liberty State College	WV	4,690	LC
West Virginia State College	WV	5,044	LC
West Virginia Univ	WV	5,774	C
Western Conn State Univ	CT	6,622	C
Western Illinois Univ	IL	5,241	LC
Western Kentucky Univ	KY	4,808	C
Western Maryland College	MD	18,990	C
Western Mich Univ	MI	6,820	C
Western New England College	MA	14,674	LC
Western State College of Colo	CO	5,560	C
Western Washington Univ	WA	6,077	VC
Westfield State College	MA	7,161	C
Westminster College	PA	15,200	C
Westminster College of Salt Lake City	UT	12,100	C
Westmont College	CA	18,732	C
Wheaton College	IL	14,710	HC
Whitworth College	WA	16,265	C
Wichita State Univ	KS	5,068	NC
Widener Univ	PA	16,840	C
Wilberforce Univ	OH	10,408	C
Wiley College	TX	0	NC
Wilkes Univ	PA	15,728	LC
William Carey College	MS	7,050	C
William Jewell College	MO	12,500	VC
William Paterson College	NJ	7,438	C+
William Tyndale College	MI	7,120	NC
William Woods Univ	MO	14,025	LC
Wilmington College	DE	5,200	NC
Wilmington College	OH	13,700	LC
Wilson College	PA	16,630	C
Wingate College	NC	10,610	C
Winona State Univ	MN	5,200	VC
Winston-Salem State Univ	NC	4,142	LC
Winthrop Univ	SC	6,750	C
Wisc Lutheran College	WI	12,180	C
Women's College of Brenau Univ	GA	14,734	C
Wright State Univ	OH	6,896	LC
Xavier Univ	OH	15,710	C+
Xavier Univ of Louisiana	LA	10,400	C
Yeshiva Univ	NY	18,200	VC
Youngstown State Univ	OH	6,447	LC

COMMUNICATIONS TECHNOLOGY

School	ST	$IS	SR
Black Hills State Univ	SD	4,831	NC
Cedarville College	OH	10,715	C
East Stroudsburg Univ	PA	6,886	C
Lebanon Valley College of Penn	PA	18,300	C
St Mary's College of Minn	MN	13,850	LC
Syracuse Univ	NY	21,305	HC

COMMUNITY HEALTH WORK

School	ST	$IS	SR
Delaware State College	DE	5,656	C
Hofstra Univ	NY	16,580	VC
John Brown Univ	AR	9,880	VC
Morris College	SC	6,880	LC
New Mexico State Univ	NM	4,844	LC
Purdue Univ/West Lafayette	IN	6,636	C
St Joseph's College	NY	7,322	C
Slippery Rock Univ	PA	6,803	C
SUNY/College at Old Westbury	NY	7,128	LC
Univ of Calif at Davis	CA	9,534	VC
Univ of Northern Colo	CO	6,008	C
Waynesburg College	PA	11,960	C
William Paterson College	NJ	7,438	C+

COMMUNITY PSYCHOLOGY

School	ST	$IS	SR
Albertus Magnus College	CT	16,280	LC
Univ of New Haven	CT	14,980	C

COMMUNITY SERVICES

School	ST	$IS	SR
Audrey Cohen College	NY	11,184	LC
Baldwin-Wallace College	OH	15,210	C
Bemidji State Univ	MN	5,188	C
Black Hills State Univ	SD	4,831	NC
Brigham Young Univ	UT	5,625	HC
Cal State/Chico	CA	6,146	C
Central Methodist College	MO	11,410	C
Concord College	WV	5,104	NC
Evergreen State College	WA	6,306	C
Fitchburg State College	MA	6,962	C
Martin Univ	IN	4,830	NC
Midland Lutheran College	NE	12,410	LC
NAES College	IL	4,200	SP
National-Louis Univ	IL	13,218	C
Northern Arizona Univ	AZ	4,844	C
Northern State Univ	SD	4,186	LC
Ohio Univ	OH	7,341	C
Park College	MO	7,320	C
Prescott College	AZ	9,775	C
Rockhurst College	MO	12,470	C
St Martin's College	WA	14,965	C
Samford Univ	AL	11,400	VC
Southern Arkansas Univ	AR	3,432	NC
SUNY at Buffalo	NY	7,896	VC
SUNY/College at Plattsburgh	NY	6,917	C
SUNY/Empire State College	NY	2,687	NC
Tabor College	KS	11,460	VC
Temple Univ	PA	10,281	C
Univ of Calif, Riverside	CA	9,178	C
Univ of Delaware	DE	8,013	VC
Univ of Mary Hardin-Baylor	TX	8,120	NC
Univ of Mass/Boston	MA	4,253	C
Univ of South Florida	FL	5,475	C+
Univ of Southwestern Louisiana	LA	3,968	NC
Univ of Texas at Austin	TX	5,160	VC
Urbana Univ	OH	12,536	C
Virginia Wesleyan College	VA	14,950	VC
Walsh Univ	OH	11,640	C
Wilmington College	OH	13,700	LC
Winona State Univ	MN	5,200	VC

COMPARATIVE LITERATURE

School	ST	$IS	SR
Alaska Pacific Univ	AK	11,350	C
Brandeis Univ	MA	25,585	HC
Brigham Young Univ	UT	5,625	HC
Brown Univ	RI	26,104	MC
Bryn Mawr College	PA	24,110	MC
Cal State/Fullerton	CA	4,850	LC
Cal State/Long Beach	CA	6,057	LC
Case Western Reserve Univ	OH	19,910	HC
Cedar Crest College	PA	18,930	C
CUNY/Brooklyn College	NY	2,450	VC
CUNY/City College	NY	2,543	VC
CUNY/Herbert H. Lehman College	NY	2,542	C
CUNY/Hunter College	NY	4,101	VC
Clark Univ	MA	21,400	VC
Colo College	CO	20,038	HC
Columbia Univ/Columbia College	NY	26,757	MC
Cornell Univ	NY	13,445	MC
Dartmouth College	NH	24,354	MC
DePaul Univ	IL	15,535	VC
Eckerd College	FL	18,855	VC
Fordham Univ/College at Lincoln Center	NY	18,150	VC
Hamilton College	NY	23,500	HC
Hampshire College	MA	25,320	C
Haverford College	PA	23,950	MC
Hillsdale College	MI	15,110	VC
Indiana Univ Bloomington	IN	6,495	VC
Millersville Univ of Penn	PA	7,370	VC
Mills College	CA	20,848	VC
Northwestern Univ	IL	21,093	MC
Oberlin College	OH	24,570	HC+
Occidental College	CA	21,792	HC
Penn State Univ/Univ Park Campus	PA	8,752	HC
Princeton Univ	NJ	24,650	MC
Purdue Univ/West Lafayette	IN	6,636	C
Rutgers Univ/Douglass College	NJ	8,795	VC
Rutgers Univ/Livingston College	NJ	8,877	VC
Rutgers Univ/Rutgers College	NJ	8,841	HC+
Rutgers Univ/Univ College—New Brunswick	NJ	0	LC
San Francisco State Univ	CA	7,292	LC
Scripps College	CA	23,600	HC
Smith College	MA	24,236	HC
Stanford Univ	CA	24,310	MC
SUNY at Binghamton	NY	7,921	HC
SUNY at Stony Brook	NY	7,658	VC
Syracuse Univ	NY	21,305	HC
Univ of Calif at Berkeley	CA	9,962	HC+
Univ of Calif at Davis	CA	9,534	VC
Univ of Calif, Riverside	CA	9,178	C
Univ of Calif/Irvine	CA	12,680	VC
Univ of Cincinnati	OH	7,989	C
Univ of Delaware	DE	8,013	VC
Univ of Denver	CO	19,290	C+
Univ of Iowa	IA	5,658	VC
Univ of Kansas	KS	5,200	NC
Univ of Mass/Amherst	MA	9,364	LC
Univ of Mich/Ann Arbor	MI	9,428	HC+
Univ of N Car at Chapel Hill	NC	5,330	HC
Univ of Oregon	OR	6,466	VC
Univ of Rhode Island	RI	9,205	C
Univ of Rochester	NY	23,696	HC
Univ of Tenn/Knoxville	TN	5,668	C
Univ of the South	TN	18,830	HC
Univ of Washington	WA	6,618	VC
Univ of Wisc/Madison	WI	6,400	HC
Univ of Wisc/Milwaukee	WI	6,165	C
Washington Univ	MO	23,507	HC
Yale Univ	CT	25,110	MC

COMPUTER EDUCATION

School	ST	$IS	SR
College of Great Falls	MT	6,230	NC
Concordia Univ	IL	12,611	C
Eastern Washington Univ	WA	5,439	LC
Northern Mich Univ	MI	6,350	C
St Martin's College	WA	14,965	C

COMPUTER ENGINEERING

School	ST	$IS	SR
Arizona State Univ Main Campus	AZ	6,444	C
Auburn Univ	AL	5,823	C+
Baylor Univ	TX	10,990	C+
Bellarmine College	KY	10,832	C
Boston Univ	MA	24,130	HC
Brigham Young Univ	UT	5,625	HC
Bucknell Univ	PA	22,320	HC
Calif Polytechnic State Univ	CA	6,980	VC+
Cal State/Chico	CA	6,146	C
Cal State/Fresno	CA	5,747	C
Cal State/Long Beach	CA	6,057	LC
Cal State/Sacramento	CA	6,387	C
Calumet College of St. Joseph	IN	3,585	C
Capitol College	MD	10,698	LC
Carnegie Mellon Univ	PA	22,560	HC+
Case Western Reserve Univ	OH	19,910	HC
Central State Univ	OH	7,320	NC
Clarkson Univ	NY	20,705	VC+
Clemson Univ	SC	6,564	VC
Cogswell Polytechnical College	CA	8,000	NC
Colo Technical College	CO	6,005	C
Drexel Univ	PA	15,970	C
Eastern Nazarene College	MA	12,165	LC
Elizabethtown College	PA	17,850	VC
Florida Atlantic Univ	FL	5,525	C
Florida Inst of Tech	FL	16,935	VC
Florida International Univ	FL	4,191	VC
George Washington Univ	DC	22,470	HC
Georgia Inst of Tech	GA	6,669	HC+
GMI Engineering & Management Inst	MI	14,158	HC
Graceland College	IA	11,600	C
Hofstra Univ	NY	16,580	VC
Howard Univ	DC	11,680	C
Illinois Inst of Tech	IL	18,290	VC
Indiana Inst of Tech	IN	11,810	C
Iowa State Univ	IA	5,456	C
Kansas State Univ	KS	4,816	NC
Lehigh Univ	PA	23,250	HC
Louisiana State Univ and A&M College	LA	5,605	C
Louisiana Tech Univ	LA	4,284	C
Marquette Univ	WI	16,114	VC
Mass Inst of Tech	MA	24,800	MC
Merrimack College	MA	18,025	C
Mich State Univ	MI	7,842	C
Millersville Univ of Penn	PA	7,370	VC
Milwaukee School of Engineering	WI	14,100	C
Miss State Univ	MS	5,629	VC
Morris Brown College	GA	12,234	NC
New Jersey Inst of Tech	NJ	9,965	VC
N Car State Univ	NC	4,984	VC
Northeastern Univ	MA	19,851	C
Northern Arizona Univ	AZ	4,844	C
Northwestern Univ	IL	21,093	MC
Norwich Univ	VT	18,730	C
Nova Southeastern Univ	FL	13,244	LC
Oakland Univ	MI	6,714	VC
Ohio Univ	OH	7,341	C
Okla Christian Univ of Science and Arts	OK	8,790	NC
Okla State Univ	OK	5,086	VC
Old Dominion Univ	VA	8,317	C
Oregon State Univ	OR	6,175	C
Pacific Lutheran Univ	WA	15,998	VC
Penn State Univ/Univ Park Campus	PA	8,752	HC
Polytechnic Univ/Brooklyn	NY	19,700	HC
Polytechnic Univ/Farmingdale	NY	20,700	VC
Portland State Univ	OR	7,191	C
Prairie View A&M Univ	TX	4,740	LC
Purdue Univ/Calumet	IN	2,374	NC
Purdue Univ/West Lafayette	IN	6,636	C
Rensselaer Polytechnic Inst	NY	23,067	HC
Rice Univ	TX	15,110	MC
Rochester Inst of Tech	NY	18,954	VC
Rockhurst College	MO	12,470	C
Rose-Hulman Inst of Tech	IN	16,400	HC
St Mary's Univ	TX	12,064	C
San Jose State Univ	CA	6,680	LC
Santa Clara Univ	CA	18,783	VC
S Dak School of Mines and Tech	SD	5,329	C
Southern Methodist Univ	TX	18,520	VC
SUNY/College at New Paltz	NY	6,890	VC
SUNY/College at Plattsburgh	NY	6,917	C
SUNY/Maritime College	NY	7,170	C
Stevens Inst of Tech	NJ	21,980	VC+
Suffolk Univ	MA	15,360	LC
Swarthmore College	PA	24,136	MC
Syracuse Univ	NY	21,305	HC
Texas A&M Univ	TX	5,382	VC
Tufts Univ	MA	24,962	MC
Tulane Univ	LA	24,540	HC
United States Air Force Academy	CO	0	MC
United States Military Academy	NY	0	MC
Univ of Akron	OH	6,699	NC
Univ of Alabama at Huntsville	AL	5,868	VC
Univ of Arizona	AZ	5,808	C
Univ of Arkansas at Fayetteville	AR	5,046	C
Univ of Bridgeport	CT	18,985	C
Univ of Calif at Davis	CA	9,534	VC
Univ of Calif at Los Angeles	CA	8,959	HC
Univ of Calif at Santa Barbara	CA	9,460	C
Univ of Calif at Santa Cruz	CA	9,060	VC
Univ of Calif, San Diego	CA	10,028	VC+
Univ of Central Florida	FL	6,061	C+
Univ of Cincinnati	OH	7,989	C
Univ of Colo at Boulder	CO	6,410	VC
Univ of Conn	CT	9,168	C
Univ of Evansville	IN	15,300	VC
Univ of Florida	FL	5,850	HC
Univ of Hartford	CT	19,858	LC
Univ of Idaho	ID	4,830	C
Univ of Illinois at Chicago	IL	8,443	C
Univ of Illinois at Urbana-Champaign	IL	7,764	HC
Univ of Iowa	IA	5,658	VC
Univ of Kansas	KS	5,200	NC
Univ of La Verne	CA	17,400	C
Univ of Louisville	KY	5,948	C
Univ of Maine	ME	7,990	C
Univ of Mass Dartmouth	MA	8,158	C
Univ of Mass/Amherst	MA	9,364	LC
Univ of Miami	FL	22,107	VC
Univ of Mich/Ann Arbor	MI	9,428	HC+
Univ of Mich/Dearborn	MI	3,399	HC
Univ of Minn/Duluth	MN	6,512	C
Univ of Missouri/Columbia	MO	6,254	HC
Univ of Nebr-Lincoln	NE	5,278	LC
Univ of Nevada/Las Vegas	NV	6,405	C
Univ of New Hampshire	NH	8,242	C
Univ of Notre Dame	IN	20,150	MC
Univ of PR/Mayaguez	PR	0	
Univ of Rhode Island	RI	9,205	C
Univ of S Car	SC	6,158	C
Univ of South Florida	FL	5,475	C+
Univ of Southern Calif	CA	23,006	VC
Univ of Southwestern Louisiana	LA	3,968	NC
Univ of Texas at Arlington	TX	5,549	LC
Univ of the Pacific	CA	21,100	C
Univ of Toledo	OH	6,636	NC
Univ of Utah	UT	5,975	C
Univ of Washington	WA	6,618	VC
Univ of Wyoming	WY	4,991	NC
Valparaiso Univ	IN	14,810	VC
Virginia Polytechnic Inst and State Univ	VA	6,828	C
Washington Univ	MO	23,507	HC
Wentworth Inst of Tech	MA	15,250	LC
West Virginia Univ	WV	5,774	C
Western Mich Univ	MI	6,820	C
Western New England College	MA	14,674	LC
Worcester Polytechnic Inst	MA	20,350	HC
Wright State Univ	OH	6,896	LC

COMPUTER GRAPHICS

School	ST	$IS	SR
Atlanta College of Art	GA	12,495	SP
Cogswell Polytechnical College	CA	8,000	NC
College of St Mary	NE	12,500	C
Jacksonville Univ	FL	13,390	C
Pratt Inst	NY	19,520	C
Ringling School of Art and Design	FL	15,750	SP
Savannah College of Art and Design	GA	14,280	SP
School of Visual Arts	NY	17,120	SP
Syracuse Univ	NY	21,305	HC
Taylor Univ	IN	14,450	VC
Teikyo Marycrest Univ	IA	13,755	VC

COMPUTER MANAGEMENT

School	ST	$IS	SR
Anna Maria College	MA	15,975	LC
Caldwell College	NJ	12,860	C
Cal State/Stanislaus	CA	6,799	C
Campbellsville College	KY	8,720	C
CUNY/Baruch College	NY	2,562	VC
College of Great Falls	MT	6,230	NC
College of St Mary	NE	12,500	C
Colo Christian Univ	CO	9,750	C
Eastern Mennonite College	VA	12,700	C
Emporia State Univ	KS	4,685	NC
Franklin Pierce College	NH	17,270	LC
Franklin Univ	OH	4,621	NC
Friends Univ	KS	11,205	C
Gonzaga Univ	WA	16,350	VC
Indiana Wesleyan Univ	IN	12,332	C
James Madison Univ	VA	8,198	HC
Johnson and Wales Univ	RI	13,995	LC
Louisiana Tech Univ	LA	4,284	C
Metropolitan State College of Denver	CO	1,751	NC
Mount Olive College	NC	9,650	LC
Okla City Univ	OK	9,840	C
Oregon Inst of Tech	OR	5,985	C
Peru State College	NE	4,311	NC
Pfeiffer College	NC	11,670	LC
Rider College	NJ	18,160	C
Texas Lutheran College	TX	10,710	C
Univ of Houston-Downtown	TX	4,034	NC
Univ of Illinois at Chicago	IL	8,443	C
Univ of Portland	OR	15,564	C
Univ of Scranton	PA	17,071	VC
Valdosta State Univ	GA	4,670	LC

COMPUTER MATHEMATICS

School	ST	$IS	SR
Cal State/Northridge	CA	7,122	LC
Carlow College	PA	13,914	C
Dana College	NE	11,910	C
Franklin Pierce College	NH	17,270	LC
Gwynedd-Mercy College	PA	15,450	C
Keene State College	NH	7,081	C
Lewis and Clark College	OR	19,980	VC
Mary Baldwin College	VA	17,700	LC
Rocky Mountain College	MT	11,320	C
Saginaw Valley State Univ	MI	6,634	LC
United States Coast Guard Academy	CT	0	MC
Univ of Maine at Farmington	ME	6,700	C
Univ of Northern Iowa	IA	5,137	C
Univ of S Car at Aiken	SC	5,386	C
Western Conn State Univ	CT	6,622	C
Wofford College	SC	15,360	VC

COMPUTER PROGRAMMING

School	ST	$IS	SR
Alabama State Univ	AL	3,428	NC
Appalachian State Univ	NC	4,095	C
Aquinas College	MI	14,526	C
Augustana College	SD	13,420	C
Aurora Univ	IL	13,381	C
Averett College	VA	13,610	LC
Baker College	MI	6,971	NC
Barat College	IL	13,990	C
Baylor Univ	TX	10,990	C+
Bethel College	MN	15,050	C
Bridgewater College	VA	15,300	C
Brigham Young Univ/Hawaii	HI	6,750	VC
Buena Vista College	IA	16,150	VC
Cal State/Chico	CA	6,146	C
Caribbean Univ	PR	2,400	
Carnegie Mellon Univ	PA	22,560	HC+
Central Washington Univ	WA	5,644	C
City Univ	WA	6,400	NC
Clarion Univ of Penn	PA	6,518	C
Cogswell Polytechnical College	CA	8,000	NC
College of St Francis	IL	13,060	VC
College of St Rose	NY	14,452	C
Columbia College	MO	11,995	C
Concord College	WV	5,104	NC
Concordia Univ	IL	12,611	C
Cumberland College	KY	9,756	C
Dakota State Univ	SD	4,374	LC
Davenport College of Business	MI	8,121	NC
Delta State Univ	MS	3,964	LC
Detroit College of Business	MI	5,184	NC
DeVry/Los Angeles	CA	5,609	LC
DeVry/Phoenix	AZ	5,609	LC
Dickinson State Univ	ND	3,792	C
Dordt College	IA	11,690	C
Dowling College	NY	12,730	LC
East Tenn State Univ	TN	4,406	C
Eastern Kentucky Univ	KY	4,840	NC
Eastern Mich Univ	MI	6,749	C
Emporia State Univ	KS	4,685	NC
Evergreen State College	WA	6,306	C
Felician College	NJ	7,900	C
Ferris State Univ	MI	7,160	NC
Freed-Hardeman Univ	TN	8,585	VC
Georgia Southwestern College	GA	4,338	LC
Goldey-Beacom College	DE	7,839	C
Goshen College	IN	12,360	C
Grand View College	IA	13,230	NC
Hannibal-LaGrange College	MO	8,400	LC
Harding Univ	AR	9,050	VC
Hawaii Pacific Univ	HI	12,300	C
Hofstra Univ	NY	16,580	VC
Howard Univ	DC	11,680	C
Humboldt State Univ	CA	5,676	C
Husson College	ME	11,510	NC
Idaho State Univ	ID	4,442	C
Indiana Inst of Tech	IN	11,810	C
Indiana Univ-Purdue Univ at Fort Wayne	IN	2,500	LC
Ithaca College	NY	19,679	C
Juniata College	PA	18,390	C+
Kansas Newman College	KS	10,640	C
King's College	PA	15,420	C
La Roche College	PA	12,977	LC
Lamar Univ	TX	3,798	C
Lebanon Valley College of Penn	PA	18,300	C
Lee College	TN	7,894	LC
Liberty Univ	VA	11,500	LC
Loyola Univ/New Orleans	LA	15,660	C+
Marshall Univ	WV	5,762	LC
Mayville State Univ	ND	4,272	NC
McMurry Univ	TX	10,100	C
McPherson College	KS	11,360	VC
Menlo College	CA	20,375	LC
Mercy College	NY	11,180	NC
Midland Lutheran College	NE	12,410	LC
Miss College	MS	8,348	C
Miss Univ for Women	MS	4,456	LC
Missouri Southern State College	MO	4,272	
Missouri Western State College	MO	4,384	NC
Monmouth College	IL	17,300	C+
Morgan State Univ	MD	7,366	C+
Morris Brown College	GA	12,234	NC
Mount St Clare College	IA	12,870	LC
Murray State Univ	KY	4,702	C
National College	SD	9,055	NC
New Hampshire College	NH	15,242	LC
New Mexico Highlands Univ	NM	3,772	C
N Car Wesleyan College	NC	12,480	LC
Northeast Louisiana Univ	LA	3,906	NC
Northeastern State Univ	OK	5,250	LC
Northeastern Univ	MA	19,851	C
Northern Mich Univ	MI	6,350	C
Northland College	WI	13,550	LC
Northwestern College	MN	13,554	C
Oakland City College	IN	10,216	LC
Okla State Univ	OK	5,086	VC
Ottawa Univ	KS	10,490	C+
Pacific Lutheran Univ	WA	15,998	VC
Park College	MO	7,320	C
Peru State College	NE	4,311	NC
Pittsburg State Univ	KS	4,478	NC
Plymouth State College	NH	7,166	C
Pontifical Catholic Univ of PR/Ponce	PR	5,807	
Purdue Univ/Calumet	IN	2,374	NC
Purdue Univ/West Lafayette	IN	6,636	C
Rhode Island College	RI	7,901	LC
Richard Stockton College of New Jersey	NJ	6,950	VC
Roger Williams Univ	RI	16,750	C
St John's Univ	NY	8,980	C+
St Joseph's College	IN	14,730	C
St Thomas Univ	FL	14,280	LC
Salem State College	MA	6,712	C
San Diego State Univ	CA	6,692	LC
Shaw Univ	NC	8,936	C+
Shepherd College	WV	5,540	C
S Dak School of Mines and Tech	SD	5,329	C
Southern Arkansas Univ	AR	3,432	NC
Southern Illinois Univ at Carbondale	IL	6,234	C
Southern Oregon State College	OR	6,128	C
Southwestern Okla State Univ	OK	3,312	C
SUNY/College at Plattsburgh	NY	6,917	C
Stephen F. Austin State Univ	TX	5,117	C
Suffolk Univ	MA	15,360	LC
Tabor College	KS	11,460	VC
Tarleton State Univ	TX	4,082	LC
Texas Southern Univ	TX	4,500	NC
Thomas More College	KY	12,962	C
Turabo Univ	PR	2,670	
Union College	KY	9,790	C
Univ of Arkansas at Monticello	AR	3,832	NC
Univ of Bridgeport	CT	18,985	C
Univ of Evansville	IN	15,300	VC
Univ of Louisville	KY	5,948	C
Univ of Mary	ND	8,910	C
Univ of Maryland/College Park	MD	8,182	VC
Univ of Nebr at Kearney	NE	4,308	LC
Univ of Northern Iowa	IA	5,137	C
Univ of Pittsburgh at Bradford	PA	9,050	C
Univ of South Florida	FL	5,475	C+
Univ of the State of New York/Regents College Degrees	NY	510	
Univ of Toledo	OH	6,636	NC
Univ of Tulsa	OK	13,795	VC

School	ST	$IS	SR
Univ of Wisc/Eau Claire	WI	4,647	C
Univ of Wisc/River Falls	WI	4,655	C
Univ of Wisc/Whitewater	WI	4,700	C
Viterbo College	WI	12,670	C
Wartburg College	IA	14,530	VC
Washburn Univ of Topeka	KS	5,802	NC
Weber State Univ	UT	4,398	C
West Coast Univ	CA	9,120	NC
West Liberty State College	WV	4,690	LC
West Virginia Inst of Tech	WV	5,858	LC
Wichita State Univ	KS	5,068	NC
Woodbury Univ	CA	17,620	LC
York College of Penn	PA	8,345	C

COMPUTER SCIENCE

School	ST	$IS	SR
Abilene Christian Univ	TX	10,460	NC
Adelphi Univ	NY	18,250	LC
Adrian College	MI	14,340	C
Alabama A&M Univ	AL	4,200	C
Albany State College	GA	4,481	LC
Albertson College	ID	15,942	C+
Albright College	PA	19,260	C
Alcorn State Univ	MS	4,474	C+
Alderson-Broaddus College	WV	12,000	C
Alfred Univ	NY	21,054	VC+
Allegheny College	PA	21,020	VC
Allentown College of St Francis de Sales	PA	13,480	C
Alma College	MI	16,375	VC+
American Univ	DC	21,230	VC+
Amherst College	MA	24,152	MC
Anderson Univ	IN	12,920	C
Andrews Univ	MI	14,952	NC
Angelo State Univ	TX	5,176	C
Antioch College	OH	19,532	LC
Appalachian State Univ	NC	4,095	C
Arizona State Univ Main Campus	AZ	6,444	C
Arkansas Baptist College	AR	5,016	NC
Arkansas State Univ	AR	4,250	NC
Arkansas Tech Univ	AR	4,200	NC
Armstrong State College	GA	4,874	LC
Asbury College	KY	11,105	VC
Ashland Univ	OH	15,508	C
Assumption College	MA	17,095	LC
Atlantic Union College	MA	14,150	LC
Auburn Univ	AL	5,823	C+
Augsburg College	MN	15,608	C
Augusta College	GA	1,452	C
Augustana College	IL	16,959	VC
Augustana College	SD	13,420	C
Aurora Univ	IL	13,381	C
Averett College	VA	13,610	LC
Avila College	MO	12,130	C
Azusa Pacific Univ	CA	15,034	C
Baker Univ	KS	12,284	C
Baldwin-Wallace College	OH	15,210	C
Ball State Univ	IN	6,032	LC
Barber-Scotia College	NC	6,840	NC
Barry Univ	FL	16,050	C
Bayamon Tech Univ College	PR	1,600	C
Baylor Univ	TX	10,990	C+
Beaver College	PA	17,660	C
Bellarmine College	KY	10,832	C
Belmont Univ	TN	10,540	C
Beloit College	WI	18,950	VC+
Bemidji State Univ	MN	5,188	C
Benedict College	SC	8,376	LC
Benedictine College	KS	12,830	C
Bennett College	NC	8,920	LC
Bennington College	VT	24,850	VC+
Berry College	GA	11,990	VC
Bethany College	WV	18,300	C+
Bethel College	MN	15,050	C
Bethune-Cookman College	FL	8,375	LC
Biola Univ	CA	16,124	C
Birmingham-Southern College	AL	15,154	VC+
Blackburn College	IL	9,120	C
Bloomsburg Univ of Penn	PA	6,312	C+
Bluefield College	VA	10,600	C
Bluefield State College	WV	1,832	LC
Bluffton College	OH	12,951	C
Boston College	MA	22,706	MC
Boston Univ	MA	24,130	HC
Bowdoin College	ME	24,155	MC
Bowie State Univ	MD	7,294	LC
Bowling Green State Univ	OH	6,701	C
Bradley Univ	IL	14,718	C+
Brandeis Univ	MA	25,585	HC
Brescia College	KY	9,800	C
Briar Cliff College	IA	13,375	C
Bridgewater State College	MA	7,518	C
Brigham Young Univ	UT	5,625	HC
Brigham Young Univ/Hawaii	HI	6,750	VC
Brooklyn Campus of LIU	NY	15,000	LC
Brown Univ	RI	26,104	MC
Bryn Mawr College	PA	24,110	MC
Bucknell Univ	PA	22,320	HC
Buena Vista College	IA	16,150	VC
Butler Univ	IN	16,210	C
Cabrini College	PA	16,012	C
Caldwell College	NJ	12,860	C
Calif Lutheran Univ	CA	17,240	C
Calif Polytechnic State Univ	CA	6,980	VC+
Calif State Polytechnic Univ/Pomona	CA	6,438	LC
Cal State/Bakersfield	CA	5,402	C
Cal State/Chico	CA	6,146	C
Cal State/Dominguez Hills	CA	2,857	LC
Cal State/Fresno	CA	5,747	C
Cal State/Fullerton	CA	4,850	LC
Cal State/Hayward	CA	5,495	C
Cal State/Long Beach	CA	6,057	LC
Cal State/Los Angeles	CA	4,940	VC
Cal State/Northridge	CA	7,122	LC
Cal State/Sacramento	CA	6,387	C
Cal State/San Bernardino	CA	6,055	LC
Cal State/Stanislaus	CA	6,799	C
Calif Univ of Penn	PA	7,370	C
Calvin College	MI	13,020	VC
Cameron Univ	OK	3,686	LC
Campbell Univ	NC	10,624	C
Canisius College	NY	15,510	C
Capital Univ	OH	16,535	VC
Cardinal Stritch College	WI	11,252	C
Caribbean Univ	PR	2,400	
Carleton College	MN	22,155	HC
Carnegie Mellon Univ	PA	22,560	HC+
Carroll College	MT	11,265	C
Carroll College	WI	15,490	C
Case Western Reserve Univ	OH	19,910	HC
Catawba College	NC	12,950	C
Catholic Univ of America	DC	18,856	C
Cedar Crest College	PA	18,930	C
Central College	IA	14,025	VC
Central Conn State Univ	CT	7,108	C
Central Methodist College	MO	11,410	C
Central Mich Univ	MI	6,737	LC
Central Missouri State Univ	MO	5,138	LC
Central State Univ	OH	7,320	NC
Central Univ of Bayamon	PR	2,430	
Central Washington Univ	WA	5,644	C
Centre College	KY	15,850	VC+
Chadron State College	NE	4,091	NC
Chaminade Univ of Honolulu	HI	14,290	C
Chapman Univ	CA	21,842	C
Charleston Southern Univ	SC	10,282	LC
Charter Oak State College	CT	314	NC
Chestnut Hill College	PA	14,525	C
Cheyney Univ of Penn	PA	7,005	C
Chicago State Univ	IL	2,198	C
Christian Brothers Univ	TN	12,120	VC
Christopher Newport Univ	VA	3,196	LC
City Univ	WA	6,400	NC
CUNY/Brooklyn College	NY	2,450	VC
CUNY/City College	NY	2,543	VC
CUNY/College of Staten Island	NY	2,558	NC
CUNY/Herbert H. Lehman College	NY	2,542	C
CUNY/Hunter College	NY	4,101	VC
CUNY/Queens College	NY	2,631	C
CUNY/York College	NY	2,534	NC
Claflin College	SC	0	
Clarion Univ of Penn	PA	6,518	C
Clark Univ	MA	21,400	VC
Clarke College	IA	13,950	C+
Clarkson Univ	NY	20,705	VC+
Clemson Univ	SC	6,564	VC
Cleveland State Univ	OH	7,287	NC
Coastal Carolina Univ	SC	6,010	LC
Coe College	IA	17,085	VC
Colby College	ME	24,230	HC
Colgate Univ	NY	24,020	HC
College Misericordia	PA	15,820	C
College of Charleston	SC	6,250	C
College of Great Falls	MT	6,230	NC
College of Mount St Joseph	OH	13,272	C
College of Mount St Vincent	NY	16,730	C
College of Notre Dame	CA	16,480	C
College of Notre Dame of Maryland	MD	16,050	C
College of Our Lady of The Elms	MA	15,639	C
College of St Benedict	MN	15,468	VC
College of St Elizabeth	NJ	15,800	C
College of St Francis	IL	13,060	VC
College of St Joseph	VT	12,650	LC
College of St Scholastica	MN	14,868	C
College of Santa Fe	NM	14,008	C
College of the Ozarks	MO	2,000	VC+
College of William and Mary	VA	8,602	MC
College of Wooster	OH	19,875	VC
Colo State Univ	CO	6,566	VC
Colo Technical College	CO	6,005	C
Columbia Union College	MD	13,650	LC
Columbia Univ/Barnard College	NY	25,492	HC
Columbia Univ/Columbia College	NY	26,757	MC
Columbia Univ/School of Engineering and Applied Science	NY	24,554	HC
Columbus College	GA	4,892	LC
Concord College	WV	5,104	NC
Concordia College	NE	11,776	NC
Concordia College/Moorhead	MN	12,750	C
Concordia Univ	IL	12,611	C
Converse College	SC	15,750	C
Coppin State College	MD	7,145	LC
Cornell College	IA	18,425	VC
Cornell Univ	NY	13,445	MC
Covenant College	GA	13,054	VC
Creighton Univ	NE	14,432	VC
Dakota State Univ	SD	4,374	LC
Dallas Baptist Univ	TX	9,620	LC
Daniel Webster College	NH	16,484	LC
Dartmouth College	NH	24,354	MC
David Lipscomb Univ	TN	7,865	VC
Davis and Elkins College	WV	13,230	LC
Defiance College	OH	13,480	LC
Delaware State College	DE	5,656	C
Delaware Valley College	PA	16,065	LC
Denison Univ	OH	21,150	VC+
DePaul Univ	IL	15,535	VC
DePauw Univ	IN	18,530	VC
Dickinson College	PA	22,705	HC
Dickinson State Univ	ND	3,792	
Dillard Univ	LA	9,950	C
Doane College	NE	12,220	C
Dordt College	IA	11,690	C
Dowling College	NY	12,730	LC
Drake Univ	IA	17,195	VC
Drew Univ/College of Liberal Arts	NJ	23,406	HC
Drexel Univ	PA	15,970	C
Duke Univ	NC	21,271	MC
Duquesne Univ	PA	16,434	VC
Earlham College	IN	19,383	VC
East Carolina Univ	NC	4,498	C
East Central Univ	OK	3,558	C
East Stroudsburg Univ	PA	6,886	C
East Tenn State Univ	TN	4,406	C
East Texas State Univ	TX	4,572	LC
East-West Univ	IL	5,910	NC
Eastern Conn State Univ	CT	6,966	C
Eastern Kentucky Univ	KY	4,840	NC
Eastern Mennonite College	VA	12,700	C
Eastern Mich Univ	MI	6,749	C
Eastern Nazarene College	MA	12,165	LC
Eastern New Mexico Univ	NM	3,950	C
Eastern Washington Univ	WA	5,439	LC
Eckerd College	FL	18,855	VC
Edgewood College	WI	11,700	C
Edinboro Univ of Penn	PA	7,181	C
Edward Waters College	FL	8,300	NC
Elizabeth City State Univ	NC	4,254	LC
Elizabethtown College	PA	17,850	VC
Elmhurst College	IL	12,536	C
Elon College	NC	12,290	LC
Embry-Riddle Aeronautical Univ	AZ	9,896	C+
Embry-Riddle Aeronautical Univ	FL	10,600	C
Emory and Henry College	VA	12,776	C
Emory Univ	GA	21,930	HC
Emporia State Univ	KS	4,685	NC
Eureka College	IL	14,555	C
Evangel College	MO	10,142	LC
Evergreen State College	WA	6,306	C
Fairfield Univ	CT	20,460	VC
Fairleigh Dickinson Univ	NJ	16,427	C
Fairmont State College	WV	4,640	LC
Ferrum College	VA	12,800	LC
Fitchburg State College	MA	6,962	C
Florida A&M Univ	FL	4,651	C
Florida Atlantic Univ	FL	5,525	C
Florida Inst of Tech	FL	16,935	VC
Florida International Univ	FL	4,191	VC
Florida Memorial College	FL	7,600	C+
Florida State Univ	FL	5,814	VC
Fontbonne College	MO	12,090	C
Fordham Univ/College at Lincoln Center	NY	18,150	VC
Fordham Univ/Fordham College	NY	19,875	VC
Fort Hays State Univ	KS	4,675	NC
Fort Valley State College	GA	3,974	LC
Framingham State College	MA	6,580	C
Francis Marion Univ	SC	5,878	LC
Franciscan Univ of Steubenville	OH	13,400	C
Franklin College of Indiana	IN	13,970	C
Franklin Pierce College	NH	17,270	LC
Franklin Univ	OH	4,621	NC
Freed-Hardeman Univ	TN	8,585	VC
Friends Univ	KS	11,205	C
Frostburg State Univ	MD	6,940	C
Furman Univ	SC	16,557	VC
Gallaudet Univ	DC	9,850	SP
Gannon Univ	PA	14,872	C
Gardner-Webb Univ	NC	11,950	LC
Geneva College	PA	13,030	C
George Fox College	OR	15,640	LC
George Mason Univ	VA	8,728	C
George Washington Univ	DC	22,470	HC
Georgetown College	KY	10,990	C
Georgetown Univ	DC	24,410	MC
Georgia College	GA	4,310	LC
Georgia Inst of Tech	GA	6,669	HC+
Georgia Southern Univ	GA	4,988	LC
Georgia Southwestern College	GA	4,338	LC
Georgia State Univ	GA	2,019	C
Gettysburg College	PA	22,960	HC
Glenville State College	WV	4,810	LC
Gonzaga Univ	WA	16,350	VC
Gordon College	MA	16,790	C
Graceland College	IA	11,600	C
Grambling State Univ	LA	4,712	NC
Grand Canyon Univ	AZ	9,680	VC
Grand Valley State Univ	MI	6,822	VC
Grand View College	IA	13,230	NC
Greenville College	IL	14,190	C
Grinnell College	IA	20,680	HC+
Grove City College	PA	7,870	HC
Gustavus Adolphus College	MN	15,935	VC
Hamilton College	NY	23,500	HC
Hampden-Sydney College	VA	17,372	C+
Hampshire College	MA	25,320	C
Hampton Univ	VA	10,706	C
Hanover College	IN	10,950	VC
Hardin-Simmons Univ	TX	9,080	C
Harding Univ	AR	9,050	VC
Hartwick College	NY	20,950	C
Harvard Univ/Harvard and Radcliffe Colleges	MA	24,880	MC
Harvey Mudd College	CA	23,316	MC
Hastings College	NE	12,426	C
Hawaii Pacific Univ	HI	12,300	C
Heidelberg College	OH	17,160	C
Henderson State Univ	AR	3,860	C
Heritage College	WA	5,540	NC
Hiram College	OH	18,340	VC
Hobart and William Smith Colleges	NY	23,925	VC
Hofstra Univ	NY	16,580	VC
Hollins College	VA	18,484	C
Hood College	MD	19,010	VC
Hope College	MI	15,698	C+
Howard Payne Univ	TX	8,052	C
Howard Univ	DC	11,680	C
Humphreys College	CA	9,714	NC
Huntingdon College	AL	11,400	C
Huntington College	IN	13,220	C
Huron Univ	SD	9,790	C
Huston-Tillotson College	TX	8,490	C
Idaho State Univ	ID	4,442	C
Illinois Benedictine College	IL	14,170	C
Illinois College	IL	11,200	C
Illinois Inst of Tech	IL	18,290	VC
Illinois State Univ	IL	6,413	C
Illinois Wesleyan Univ	IL	18,590	HC+
Indiana Inst of Tech	IN	11,810	C
Indiana State Univ	IN	6,210	C
Indiana Univ Bloomington	IN	6,495	VC
Indiana Univ of Penn	PA	6,373	C
Indiana Univ Southeast	IN	2,260	LC
Indiana Univ-Purdue Univ at Fort Wayne	IN	2,500	LC
Indiana Univ-Purdue Univ at Indianapolis	IN	5,862	LC
Indiana Univ/South Bend	IN	2,141	LC
Inter American Univ of PR/Aguadilla Regional College	PR	2,290	
Inter American Univ of PR/Bayamon Univ College	PR	2,300	
Inter American Univ of PR/Metropolitan Campus	PR	2,340	
Inter American Univ of PR/Ponce Regional College	PR	2,300	
Inter American Univ of PR/San German	PR	4,620	
Inter American Univ/Arecibo Campus	PR	5,666	
Inter-American Univ of PR/Fajardo Regional College	PR	2,732	
Iona College	NY	16,310	C
Iowa State Univ	IA	5,456	C
Iowa Wesleyan College	IA	13,250	C
Ithaca College	NY	19,679	C
Jackson State Univ	MS	4,996	LC
Jacksonville State Univ	AL	4,080	LC
Jacksonville Univ	FL	13,390	C
James Madison Univ	VA	8,198	HC
Jamestown College	ND	10,250	C
Jarvis Christian College	TX	7,170	LC
Jersey City State College	NJ	7,797	LC
John Carroll Univ	OH	16,510	C
Johns Hopkins Univ	MD	24,360	MC
Johnson and Wales Univ	RI	13,995	LC
Johnson C. Smith Univ	NC	8,916	LC
Judson College	AL	9,060	C
Judson College	IL	13,625	C
Juniata College	PA	18,390	C+
Kalamazoo College	MI	19,974	HC
Kansas State Univ	KS	4,816	NC
Kansas Wesleyan Univ	KS	11,770	C
Kean College of New Jersey	NJ	6,395	LC
Keene State College	NH	7,081	C
Kennesaw State College	GA	1,553	C
Kent State Univ	OH	6,740	LC
Kentucky State Univ	KY	4,282	C+
Kentucky Wesleyan College	KY	11,550	C
King's College	NY	12,360	LC
King's College	PA	15,420	C
Knox College	IL	18,990	VC
La Salle Univ	PA	16,940	VC
La Sierra Univ	CA	15,472	C
Lafayette College	PA	23,450	HC
LaGrange College	GA	10,602	C

School	ST	$IS	SR
Troy State Univ at Dothan/ Fort Rucker	AL	2,260	NC
Tufts Univ	MA	24,962	MC
Tulane Univ	LA	24,540	HC
Tusculum College	TN	10,400	LC
Tuskegee Univ	AL	10,128	C
Union College	NE	11,060	NC
Union College	NY	23,817	HC
Union Univ	TN	7,880	C+
United States Air Force Academy	CO	0	MC
United States Military Academy	NY	0	MC
United States Naval Academy	MD	0	MC
Universidad Adventista de las Antillas	PR	5,000	
Univ of Akron	OH	6,699	NC
Univ of Alabama	AL	5,702	C
Univ of Alabama at Birmingham	AL	7,533	C
Univ of Alabama at Huntsville	AL	5,868	VC
Univ of Alaska Anchorage	AK	7,131	C
Univ of Alaska Fairbanks	AK	4,718	C
Univ of Alaska Southeast	AK	4,075	LC
Univ of Arizona	AZ	5,808	C
Univ of Arkansas at Fayetteville	AR	5,046	C
Univ of Arkansas at Little Rock	AR	4,419	C
Univ of Arkansas at Monticello	AR	3,832	NC
Univ of Arkansas at Pine Bluff	AR	3,978	LC
Univ of Bridgeport	CT	18,985	C
Univ of Calif at Berkeley	CA	9,962	HC+
Univ of Calif at Davis	CA	9,534	VC
Univ of Calif at Los Angeles	CA	8,959	HC
Univ of Calif at Santa Barbara	CA	9,460	C
Univ of Calif, Riverside	CA	9,178	C
Univ of Calif, San Diego	CA	10,028	VC+
Univ of Central Arkansas	AR	4,200	LC
Univ of Central Florida	FL	6,061	C+
Univ of Central Okla	OK	3,647	C
Univ of Cincinnati	OH	7,989	C
Univ of Colo at Boulder	CO	6,410	VC
Univ of Colo at Colo Springs	CO	2,269	C
Univ of Colo at Denver	CO	1,955	VC
Univ of Dayton	OH	15,120	C+
Univ of Delaware	DE	8,013	VC
Univ of Denver	CO	19,290	C+
Univ of Detroit Mercy	MI	14,720	C
Univ of Dubuque	IA	14,150	LC
Univ of Evansville	IN	15,300	VC
Univ of Findlay	OH	15,764	C
Univ of Florida	FL	5,850	HC
Univ of Georgia	GA	5,655	VC
Univ of Hartford	CT	19,858	LC
Univ of Hawaii at Hilo	HI	4,141	C
Univ of Hawaii at Manoa	HI	5,626	C
Univ of Houston	TX	5,215	C
Univ of Houston-Downtown	TX	4,034	NC
Univ of Idaho	ID	4,830	C
Univ of Illinois at Chicago	IL	8,443	C
Univ of Illinois at Urbana-Champaign	IL	7,764	HC
Univ of Iowa	IA	5,658	VC
Univ of Kansas	KS	5,200	NC
Univ of Kentucky	KY	5,152	VC
Univ of La Verne	CA	17,400	C
Univ of Louisville	KY	5,948	C
Univ of Lowell	MA	8,831	VC
Univ of Maine	ME	7,990	C
Univ of Maine at Fort Kent	ME	6,285	LC
Univ of Mary Hardin-Baylor	TX	8,120	NC
Univ of Maryland/Baltimore County	MD	7,746	VC
Univ of Maryland/College Park	MD	8,182	VC
Univ of Maryland/Eastern Shore	MD	6,254	LC
Univ of Maryland/Univ College	MD	4,900	NC
Univ of Mass Dartmouth	MA	8,158	C
Univ of Mass/Amherst	MA	9,364	LC
Univ of Mass/Boston	MA	4,253	C
Univ of Memphis	TN	3,476	C
Univ of Miami	FL	22,107	VC
Univ of Mich/Ann Arbor	MI	9,428	HC+
Univ of Mich/Dearborn	MI	3,399	HC
Univ of Mich/Flint	MI	2,916	C
Univ of Minn/Duluth	MN	6,512	C
Univ of Minn/Morris	MN	6,825	HC
Univ of Minn/Twin Cities	MN	6,682	VC
Univ of Miss	MS	5,756	C
Univ of Missouri/Columbia	MO	6,254	HC
Univ of Missouri/Kansas City	MO	5,906	VC
Univ of Missouri/Rolla	MO	6,729	VC+
Univ of Missouri/St. Louis	MO	6,378	C
Univ of Mobile	AL	9,400	C
Univ of Montana	MT	5,529	C
Univ of Nebr at Kearney	NE	4,308	LC
Univ of Nebr at Omaha	NE	1,889	LC
Univ of Nebr-Lincoln	NE	5,278	LC
Univ of Nevada/Las Vegas	NV	6,405	C
Univ of Nevada/Reno	NV	5,735	C
Univ of New Hampshire	NH	8,242	C
Univ of New Haven	CT	14,980	C
Univ of New Orleans	LA	5,468	C
Univ of North Alabama	AL	4,236	NC
Univ of N Car at Asheville	NC	4,791	VC
Univ of N Car at Charlotte	NC	4,597	C
Univ of N Car at Wilmington	NC	5,172	C
Univ of N Dak	ND	4,902	NC
Univ of North Florida	FL	5,082	C
Univ of North Texas	TX	4,853	C
Univ of Northern Colo	CO	6,008	C
Univ of Northern Iowa	IA	5,137	C
Univ of Notre Dame	IN	20,150	MC
Univ of Okla	OK	5,427	VC
Univ of Oregon	OR	6,466	VC
Univ of Penn	PA	24,238	MC
Univ of Pittsburgh	PA	9,472	C
Univ of Pittsburgh at Bradford	PA	9,050	C
Univ of Pittsburgh at Johnstown	PA	8,914	C
Univ of Portland	OR	15,564	C
Univ of PR/Mayaguez	PR	0	
Univ of PR/Rio Piedras	PR	0	
Univ of Puget Sound	WA	19,520	HC
Univ of Redlands	CA	22,059	VC
Univ of Rhode Island	RI	9,205	C
Univ of Richmond	VA	16,700	HC
Univ of Rochester	NY	23,696	HC
Univ of St Thomas	MN	15,785	C+
Univ of San Diego	CA	18,970	VC
Univ of San Francisco	CA	18,408	C
Univ of Science and Arts of Okla	OK	3,304	C
Univ of Scranton	PA	17,071	VC
Univ of South Alabama	AL	5,451	C
Univ of S Car	SC	6,158	C
Univ of S Car at Spartanburg	SC	2,320	C
Univ of S Dak	SD	4,722	C
Univ of South Florida	FL	5,475	C+
Univ of Southern Calif	CA	23,006	VC
Univ of Southern Colo	CO	5,350	LC
Univ of Southern Maine	ME	7,299	C
Univ of Southern Miss	MS	4,542	C
Univ of Southwestern Louisiana	LA	3,968	NC
Univ of Tenn at Chattanooga	TN	5,375	C
Univ of Tenn at Martin	TN	4,550	C
Univ of Tenn/Knoxville	TN	5,668	C
Univ of Texas at Arlington	TX	5,549	LC
Univ of Texas at Austin	TX	5,160	VC
Univ of Texas at Dallas	TX	1,222	VC+
Univ of Texas at El Paso	TX	3,160	LC
Univ of Texas at San Antonio	TX	6,420	C
Univ of the District of Columbia	DC	974	NC
Univ of the Pacific	CA	21,100	C
Univ of the Sacred Heart	PR	3,890	
Univ of the South	TN	18,830	HC
Univ of Toledo	OH	6,636	NC
Univ of Tulsa	OK	13,795	VC
Univ of Utah	UT	5,975	C
Univ of Vermont	VT	10,776	C+
Univ of Virginia	VA	7,964	MC
Univ of Washington	WA	6,618	VC
Univ of West Florida	FL	5,415	C
Univ of Wisc/Eau Claire	WI	4,647	C
Univ of Wisc/La Crosse	WI	4,487	C
Univ of Wisc/Madison	WI	6,400	HC
Univ of Wisc/Milwaukee	WI	6,165	C
Univ of Wisc/Oshkosh	WI	4,240	C
Univ of Wisc/Parkside	WI	5,247	
Univ of Wisc/Platteville	WI	4,830	C
Univ of Wisc/Superior	WI	4,330	C
Univ of Wyoming	WY	4,991	NC
Upper Iowa Univ	IA	11,900	C
Upsala College	NJ	17,200	C
Ursinus College	PA	19,165	VC
Utah State Univ	UT	4,683	C
Utica College of Syracuse Univ	NY	16,714	LC
Valdosta State Univ	GA	4,670	LC
Valley City State Univ	ND	4,385	LC
Valparaiso Univ	IN	14,810	VC
Vanderbilt Univ	TN	23,422	HC+
Vassar College	NY	24,206	HC
Villanova Univ	PA	21,400	HC
Virginia Commonwealth Univ	VA	7,909	C
Virginia Military Inst	VA	8,630	C
Virginia Polytechnic Inst and State Univ	VA	6,828	C
Virginia Wesleyan College	VA	14,950	VC
Viterbo College	WI	12,670	C
Voorhees College	SC	6,772	LC
Wagner College	NY	17,950	C
Wake Forest Univ	NC	17,280	MC
Walla Walla College	WA	13,215	C
Walsh Univ	OH	11,640	C
Wartburg College	IA	14,530	VC
Washington and Jefferson College	PA	19,360	C
Washington and Lee Univ	VA	17,735	MC
Washington State Univ	WA	6,364	C
Washington Univ	MO	23,507	HC
Wayne State College	NE	4,260	NC
Wayne State Univ	MI	2,680	C
Waynesburg College	PA	11,960	C
Weber State Univ	UT	4,398	C
Webster Univ	MO	12,650	C
Wellesley College	MA	23,815	MC
Wells College	NY	19,460	C+
Wentworth Inst of Tech	MA	15,250	LC
Wesley College	DE	13,745	LC
Wesleyan Univ	CT	23,770	MC
West Chester Univ of Penn	PA	7,492	C
West Coast Univ	CA	9,120	NC
West Georgia College	GA	4,256	C
West Texas A&M Univ	TX	4,224	C
West Virginia Inst of Tech	WV	5,858	LC
West Virginia Univ	WV	5,774	C
West Virginia Wesleyan College	WV	16,900	C
Western Carolina Univ	NC	3,811	C
Western Conn State Univ	CT	6,622	C
Western Illinois Univ	IL	5,241	LC
Western Kentucky Univ	KY	4,808	C
Western Mich Univ	MI	6,820	C
Western New England College	MA	14,674	LC
Western New Mexico Univ	NM	3,234	LC
Western Oregon State College	OR	6,180	C
Western Washington Univ	WA	6,077	VC
Westfield State College	MA	7,161	C
Westminster College	PA	15,200	C
Westminster College of Salt Lake City	UT	12,100	C
Westmont College	CA	18,732	C
Wheaton College	IL	14,710	HC
Wheeling Jesuit College	WV	14,370	C
Whitman College	WA	20,595	HC
Whitworth College	WA	16,265	C
Wichita State Univ	KS	5,068	NC
Widener Univ	PA	16,840	C
Wiley College	TX	0	NC
Wilkes Univ	PA	15,728	LC
Willamette Univ	OR	17,995	VC
William Jewell College	MO	12,500	VC
William Paterson College	NJ	7,438	C+
William Penn College	IA	13,400	C
William Woods Univ	MO	14,025	LC
Williams College	MA	24,390	MC
Wilmington College	OH	13,700	LC
Winona State Univ	MN	5,200	VC
Winston-Salem State Univ	NC	4,142	LC
Winthrop Univ	SC	6,750	C
Wittenberg Univ	OH	19,998	VC
Worcester Polytechnic Inst	MA	20,350	HC
Worcester State College	MA	6,414	LC
Wright State Univ	OH	6,896	LC
Xavier Univ	OH	15,710	C+
Xavier Univ of Louisiana	LA	10,400	C
Yale Univ	CT	25,110	MC
Yeshiva Univ	NY	18,200	VC
Youngstown State Univ	OH	6,447	LC

COMPUTER TECHNOLOGY

School	ST	$IS	SR
Andrews Univ	MI	14,952	NC
Bowie State Univ	MD	7,294	LC
Daniel Webster College	NH	16,484	LC
Eastern Washington Univ	WA	5,439	LC
Georgia Southwestern College	GA	4,338	LC
Indiana State Univ	IN	6,210	C
Indiana Univ-Purdue Univ at Indianapolis	IN	5,862	LC
Martin Univ	IN	4,830	NC
Murray State Univ	KY	4,702	C
New Mexico Highlands Univ	NM	3,772	C
Oregon Inst of Tech	OR	5,985	C
Purdue Univ/Calumet	IN	2,374	NC
Rochester Inst of Tech	NY	18,954	VC
Shawnee State Univ	OH	4,379	NC
Southern College of Tech	GA	4	C
Univ of Arkansas at Little Rock	AR	4,419	C
Univ of Houston	TX	5,215	C
Univ of Memphis	TN	3,476	C
Univ of Southern Miss	MS	4,542	C
Univ of the State of New York/Regents College Degrees	NY	510	
Youngstown State Univ	OH	6,447	LC

CONSERVATION AND REGULATION

School	ST	$IS	SR
Central Missouri State Univ	MO	5,138	LC
Kent State Univ	OH	6,740	LC
LIU/C. W. Post Campus	NY	16,870	C
N Car State Univ	NC	4,984	VC
Northwest Missouri State Univ	MO	5,010	LC
Northwestern Okla State Univ	OK	3,424	C
Southeastern Okla State Univ	OK	3,594	C
Southwest Missouri State Univ	MO	4,956	C
Unity College	ME	12,885	LC
Univ of Calif at Berkeley	CA	9,962	HC+
Univ of Wisc/Milwaukee	WI	6,165	C
Univ of Wisc/River Falls	WI	4,655	C
Upper Iowa Univ	IA	11,900	C

CONSUMER SERVICES

School	ST	$IS	SR
Norfolk State Univ	VA	6,345	LC
Oregon State Univ	OR	6,175	C
S Dak State Univ	SD	4,562	C
Southwest Texas State Univ	TX	5,124	C
Univ of Wisc/Madison	WI	6,400	HC

CONSTRUCTION ENGINEERING

School	ST	$IS	SR
Andrews Univ	MI	14,952	NC
Arizona State Univ Main Campus	AZ	6,444	C
Bradley Univ	IL	14,718	C+
Cal State/Fresno	CA	5,747	C
Iowa State Univ	IA	5,456	C
Louisiana Tech Univ	LA	4,284	C
Moorhead State Univ	MN	5,076	C
N Dak State Univ of Agriculture and Applied Science	ND	4,774	VC
Northeast Louisiana Univ	LA	3,906	NC
Purdue Univ/West Lafayette	IN	6,636	C
Southern College of Tech	GA	4	C
Southern Illinois Univ at Edwardsville	IL	6,097	LC
Texas A&M Univ	TX	5,382	VC
Tuskegee Univ	AL	10,128	C
Univ of Calif, San Diego	CA	10,028	VC+
Univ of Florida	FL	5,850	HC
Univ of Northern Iowa	IA	5,137	C
Univ of Okla	OK	5,427	VC
Univ of the District of Columbia	DC	974	NC
Univ of Washington	WA	6,618	VC

CONSTRUCTION MANAGEMENT

School	ST	$IS	SR
Auburn Univ	AL	5,823	C+
Boise State Univ	ID	4,909	LC
Brigham Young Univ	UT	5,625	HC
Calif Polytechnic State Univ	CA	6,980	VC+
Clemson Univ	SC	6,564	VC
Colo State Univ	CO	6,566	VC
Ferris State Univ	MI	7,160	NC
Florida International Univ	FL	4,191	VC
Georgia Inst of Tech	GA	6,669	HC+
Georgia Southern Univ	GA	4,988	LC
John Brown Univ	AR	9,880	VC
Mich State Univ	MI	7,842	C
N Car State Univ	NC	4,984	VC
N Dak State Univ of Agriculture and Applied Science	ND	4,774	VC
Okla State Univ	OK	5,086	VC
Oregon State Univ	OR	6,175	C
Pratt Inst	NY	19,520	C
Southwest Missouri State Univ	MO	4,956	C
SUNY College of Environmental Science and Forestry	NY	9,257	HC+
Univ of Cincinnati	OH	7,989	C
Univ of Denver	CO	19,290	C+
Univ of Nebr-Lincoln	NE	5,278	LC
Univ of Wisc/Madison	WI	6,400	HC
Utica College of Syracuse Univ	NY	16,714	LC
Virginia Polytechnic Inst and State Univ	VA	6,828	C
Washington State Univ	WA	6,364	C
Wentworth Inst of Tech	MA	15,250	LC
West Texas A&M Univ	TX	4,224	C

CONSTRUCTION TECHNOLOGY

School	ST	$IS	SR
Bowling Green State Univ	OH	6,701	C
Central Conn State Univ	CT	7,108	C
Eastern Kentucky Univ	KY	4,840	NC
Fairleigh Dickinson Univ	NJ	16,427	C
Hampton Univ	VA	10,706	C
Indiana State Univ	IN	6,210	C
Indiana Univ-Purdue Univ at Indianapolis	IN	5,862	LC
Montana State Univ	MT	5,534	C
Murray State Univ	KY	4,702	C
Norfolk State Univ	VA	6,345	LC
N Dak State Univ of Agriculture and Applied Science	ND	4,774	VC
Northern Kentucky Univ	KY	4,620	NC
Northern Mich Univ	MI	6,350	C
Northern Montana College	MT	4,976	C
Peru State College	NE	4,311	NC
Purdue Univ/Calumet	IN	2,374	NC
Texas Tech Univ	TX	6,008	C
Univ of Arkansas at Little Rock	AR	4,419	C
Univ of Houston	TX	5,215	C
Univ of Maine	ME	7,990	C
Univ of Maryland/Eastern Shore	MD	6,254	LC
Univ of Nebr-Lincoln	NE	5,278	LC
Univ of North Florida	FL	5,082	C
Univ of Southern Miss	MS	4,542	C
Univ of Wisc/Stout	WI	4,719	C
Wentworth Inst of Tech	MA	15,250	LC

CORRECTIONS

School	ST	$IS	SR
CUNY/John Jay College of Criminal Justice	NY	2,501	LC
Eastern Kentucky Univ	KY	4,840	NC
Northern Mich Univ	MI	6,350	C
Okla City Univ	OK	9,840	C
Roger Williams Univ	RI	16,750	C
Southwest Texas State Univ	TX	5,124	C
Tiffin Univ	OH	10,800	LC
Western Illinois Univ	IL	5,241	LC
Western Oregon State College	OR	6,180	C

COUNSELING PSYCHOLOGY

School	ST	$IS	SR
Christian Heritage College	CA	11,756	C
College of Great Falls	MT	6,230	NC
Dallas Baptist Univ	TX	9,620	LC
Geneva College	PA	13,030	C
Goddard College	VT	17,990	LC
Grace College	IN	12,120	C
Martin Univ	IN	4,830	NC
Mich Christian College	MI	8,094	C
Mount Ida College	MA	16,700	LC
National-Louis Univ	IL	13,218	C
Southern Calif College	CA	12,356	C
Toccoa Falls College	GA	9,350	C
Univ of North Texas	TX	4,853	C
Wayne State College	NE	4,260	NC

COURT REPORTING

School	ST	$IS	SR
Central Mich Univ	MI	6,737	LC
Concordia Univ Wisc	WI	12,140	C
Husson College	ME	11,510	NC
Johnson and Wales Univ	RI	13,995	LC
Univ of Miss	MS	5,756	C

CRAFTS

School	ST	$IS	SR
Bridgewater State College	MA	7,518	C
Kent State Univ	OH	6,740	LC
Kutztown Univ	PA	6,528	C
Pacific Northwest College of Art	OR	7,700	SP
Rochester Inst of Tech	NY	18,954	VC
Univ of Illinois at Urbana-Champaign	IL	7,764	HC
Univ of North Texas	TX	4,853	C

CREATIVE WRITING

School	ST	$IS	SR
Agnes Scott College	GA	17,135	VC
Alderson-Broaddus College	WV	12,000	C
Antioch College	OH	19,532	C
Arkansas Tech Univ	AR	4,200	NC
Bennington College	VT	24,850	VC+
Carlow College	PA	13,914	C
Carroll College	MT	11,265	C
CUNY/Brooklyn College	NY	2,450	VC
CUNY/City College	NY	2,543	VC
CUNY/Hunter College	NY	4,101	VC
College of Santa Fe	NM	14,008	C
Columbia College	IL	7,879	SP
Dartmouth College	NH	24,354	MC
Dominican College of San Rafael	CA	17,860	C
Eastern College	PA	15,150	C+
Eastern Washington Univ	WA	5,439	LC
Eckerd College	FL	18,855	VC
Edinboro Univ of Penn	PA	7,181	C
Emerson College	MA	22,678	LC
Emory and Henry College	VA	12,776	C
Emory Univ	GA	21,930	HC
Eugene Lang College of the New School for Social Research	NY	21,145	C+
Fordham Univ/College at Lincoln Center	NY	18,150	VC
Geneva College	PA	13,030	C
Goddard College	VT	17,990	LC
Hamilton College	NY	23,500	HC
Hampshire College	MA	25,320	C
Harvard Univ/Harvard and Radcliffe Colleges	MA	24,880	MC
Houghton College	NY	13,120	VC
Indiana Wesleyan Univ	IN	12,332	C
Knox College	IL	18,990	VC
Lakeland College	WI	12,845	LC
Linfield College	OR	16,670	VC
Loyola College	MD	18,035	VC
Marlboro College	VT	23,305	C+
Mass Inst of Tech	MA	24,800	MC
Methodist College	NC	12,400	C
Millikin Univ	IL	15,499	C
Mills College	CA	20,848	VC
New York Univ	NY	24,705	VC+
Oberlin College	OH	24,570	HC+
Okla Christian Univ of Science and Arts	OK	8,790	NC
Pacific Univ	OR	17,869	C
Purdue Univ/West Lafayette	IN	6,636	C
Roger Williams Univ	RI	16,750	C
Sarah Lawrence College	NY	24,975	HC
Southern Methodist Univ	TX	18,520	VC
Southern Nazarene Univ	OK	9,206	NC
Southwest State Univ	MN	5,400	NC
Trinity College	IL	14,010	C
Univ of Arizona	AZ	5,808	C
Univ of Calif, Riverside	CA	9,178	C
Univ of Evansville	IN	15,300	VC
Univ of Findlay	OH	15,764	C
Univ of Maine at Farmington	ME	6,700	C
Univ of Mich/Ann Arbor	MI	9,428	HC+
Univ of New Haven	CT	14,980	C
Univ of Pittsburgh at Greensburg	PA	8,660	C
Univ of Pittsburgh at Johnstown	PA	8,914	C
Univ of Tampa	FL	16,780	C
Wheaton College	MA	23,840	C+

CRIMINAL JUSTICE

School	ST	$IS	SR
Abilene Christian Univ	TX	10,460	NC
Adrian College	MI	14,340	C
Alabama State Univ	AL	3,428	NC
Albany State College	GA	4,481	LC
Alfred Univ	NY	21,054	VC+
Allentown College of St Francis de Sales	PA	13,480	C
Alvernia College	PA	13,150	LC
American International College	MA	14,029	C
American Univ	DC	21,230	VC+
Anderson Univ	IN	12,920	C
Angelo State Univ	TX	5,176	C
Anna Maria College	MA	15,975	LC
Appalachian State Univ	NC	4,095	C
Arizona State Univ Main Campus	AZ	6,444	C
Arkansas State Univ	AR	4,250	NC
Armstrong State College	GA	4,874	LC
Ashland Univ	OH	15,508	C
Auburn Univ	AL	5,823	C+
Aurora Univ	IL	13,381	C
Averett College	VA	13,610	LC
Baldwin-Wallace College	OH	15,210	C
Ball State Univ	IN	6,032	LC
Barry Univ	FL	16,050	C
Bellevue College	NE	3,050	NC
Belmont Univ	TN	10,540	C
Bemidji State Univ	MN	5,188	C
Benedict College	SC	8,376	LC
Bethune-Cookman College	FL	8,375	LC
Bluefield College	VA	10,600	C
Bluefield State College	WV	1,832	LC
Bluffton College	OH	12,951	C
Boise State Univ	ID	4,909	LC
Bowie State Univ	MD	7,294	LC
Bowling Green State Univ	OH	6,701	C
Bradley Univ	IL	14,718	C+
Buena Vista College	IA	16,150	VC
Calif Lutheran Univ	CA	17,240	C
Cal State/Bakersfield	CA	5,402	C
Cal State/Fullerton	CA	4,850	LC
Cal State/Hayward	CA	5,495	C
Cal State/Long Beach	CA	6,057	LC
Cal State/Los Angeles	CA	4,940	VC
Cal State/Sacramento	CA	6,387	C
Cal State/San Bernardino	CA	6,055	LC
Cal State/Stanislaus	CA	6,799	C
Calumet College of St. Joseph	IN	3,585	C
Calvin College	MI	13,020	VC
Cameron Univ	OK	3,686	LC
Capital Univ	OH	16,535	VC
Caribbean Univ	PR	2,400	
Carroll College	WI	15,490	C
Carthage College	WI	15,995	C
Castleton State College	VT	8,378	LC
Cedarville College	OH	10,715	C
Central Missouri State Univ	MO	5,138	LC
Central Washington Univ	WA	5,644	C
Chadron State College	NE	4,091	NC
Chaminade Univ of Honolulu	HI	14,290	C
Chapman Univ	CA	21,842	C
Charleston Southern Univ	SC	10,282	LC
Chatham College	PA	18,010	C
Chicago State Univ	IL	2,198	C
Christopher Newport Univ	VA	3,196	LC
City Univ	WA	6,400	NC
CUNY/Herbert H. Lehman College	NY	2,542	C
CUNY/John Jay College of Criminal Justice	NY	2,501	LC
College of Great Falls	MT	6,230	NC
College of the Ozarks	MO	2,000	VC+
Columbia College	MO	11,995	C
Columbus State Univ	GA	4,892	LC
Concordia College/Moorhead	MN	12,750	C
Coppin State College	MD	7,145	LC
Culver-Stockton College	MO	11,150	C
Dallas Baptist Univ	TX	9,620	LC
Defiance College	OH	13,480	LC
Delaware Valley College	PA	16,065	LC
Delta State Univ	MS	3,964	LC
Dillard Univ	LA	9,950	C
Drury College	MO	12,140	VC
Duquesne Univ	PA	16,434	VC
East Carolina Univ	NC	4,498	C
East Central Univ	OK	3,558	C
East Tenn State Univ	TN	4,406	C
East Texas State Univ	TX	4,572	LC
Eastern Mich Univ	MI	6,749	C
Eastern Washington Univ	WA	5,439	LC
Edgewood College	WI	11,700	C
Edinboro Univ of Penn	PA	7,181	C
Edward Waters College	FL	8,300	NC
Elizabeth City State Univ	NC	4,254	LC
Elmira College	NY	18,450	C
Fairmont State College	WV	4,640	LC
Fayetteville State Univ	NC	3,926	LC
Ferris State Univ	MI	7,160	NC
Florida A&M Univ	FL	4,651	C
Florida Atlantic Univ	FL	5,525	C
Florida International Univ	FL	4,191	VC
Florida Memorial College	FL	7,600	C+
Florida Southern College	FL	12,260	C
Fordham Univ/Fordham College	NY	19,875	VC
Fort Valley State College	GA	3,974	LC
Franciscan Univ of Steubenville	OH	13,400	C
Gannon Univ	PA	14,872	C
George Washington Univ	DC	22,470	HC
Georgia Southern Univ	GA	4,988	LC
Gonzaga Univ	WA	16,350	VC
Grace College	IN	12,120	C
Grambling State Univ	LA	4,712	NC
Grand Canyon Univ	AZ	9,680	VC
Grand Valley State Univ	MI	6,822	VC
Guilford College	NC	17,680	C
Gustavus Adolphus College	MN	15,935	VC
Hannibal-LaGrange College	MO	8,400	LC
Hardin-Simmons Univ	TX	9,080	C
Hawaii Pacific Univ	HI	12,300	C
Holy Family College	PA	8,300	C
Howard Univ	DC	11,680	C
Huron Univ	SD	9,790	C
Illinois State Univ	IL	6,413	C
Indiana Univ Bloomington	IN	6,495	VC
Indiana Univ Northwest	IN	2,310	C
Indiana Univ of Penn	PA	6,373	C
Indiana Univ-Purdue Univ at Fort Wayne	IN	2,500	LC
Indiana Univ-Purdue Univ at Indianapolis	IN	5,862	LC
Indiana Univ/South Bend	IN	2,141	LC
Indiana Wesleyan Univ	IN	12,332	C
Inter American Univ of PR/ Aguadilla Regional College	PR	2,290	
Inter American Univ of PR/ Barranquitas Regional College	PR	2,730	
Inter American Univ of PR/ Bayamon Univ College	PR	2,300	
Inter American Univ of PR/ Metropolitan Campus	PR	2,340	
Inter American Univ of PR/ Ponce Regional College	PR	2,300	
Inter American Univ/Arecibo Campus	PR	5,666	
Inter-American Univ of PR/ Fajardo Regional College	PR	2,732	
Iona College	NY	16,310	C
Iowa Wesleyan College	IA	13,250	C
Jackson State Univ	MS	4,996	LC
Jacksonville State Univ	AL	4,080	LC
Jarvis Christian College	TX	7,170	LC
Jersey City State College	NJ	7,797	LC
Kansas Wesleyan Univ	KS	11,770	C
Kean College of New Jersey	NJ	6,395	LC
Kent State Univ	OH	6,740	LC
Kentucky State Univ	KY	4,282	C+
Kentucky Wesleyan College	KY	11,550	C
King's College	PA	15,420	C
Kutztown Univ	PA	6,528	C
La Salle Univ	PA	16,940	VC
Lake Superior State Univ	MI	7,311	C
Lamar Univ	TX	3,798	C
Langston Univ	OK	2,907	LC
Le Moyne College	NY	15,180	C
Lees-McRae College	NC	9,850	LC
Lewis Univ	IL	14,797	LC
Lewis-Clark State College	ID	4,040	
Liberty Univ	VA	11,500	LC
Lincoln Univ	MO	4,638	NC
Lincoln Univ	PA	0	LC
LIU/C. W. Post Campus	NY	16,870	C
Louisiana College	LA	7,518	VC
Loyola Univ of Chicago	IL	15,880	C+
Loyola Univ/New Orleans	LA	15,660	C+
Lycoming College	PA	17,200	LC
MacMurray College	IL	12,800	C
Madonna Univ	MI	8,546	C
Manchester College	IN	13,240	LC
Mansfield Univ	PA	6,348	C
Marian College of Fond du Lac	WI	12,250	C
Marist College	NY	16,406	C
Marquette Univ	WI	16,114	VC
Marshall Univ	WV	5,762	LC
Martin Univ	IN	4,830	NC
Marymount Univ	VA	15,930	C
McKendree College	IL	10,900	C
McNeese State Univ	LA	4,543	NC
Mercy College	NY	11,180	NC
Mercyhurst College	PA	13,488	C
Metropolitan State College of Denver	CO	1,751	NC
Mich State Univ	MI	7,842	C
Middle Tenn State Univ	TN	3,857	C
Midwestern State Univ	TX	4,542	LC
Minot State Univ	ND	3,748	NC
Miss College	MS	8,348	C
Miss Valley State Univ	MS	4,089	NC
Missouri Southern State College	MO	4,272	
Missouri Western State College	MO	4,384	NC
Monmouth College	NJ	16,820	C
Moorhead State Univ	MN	5,076	C
Moravian College	PA	18,960	VC
Morehouse College	GA	13,224	LC
Morningside College	IA	13,896	C
Morris Brown College	GA	12,234	NC
Morris College	SC	6,880	LC
Mount Ida College	MA	16,700	LC
Mount Mercy College	IA	13,230	C
Mount Senario College	WI	10,970	C
Murray State Univ	KY	4,702	C
National Univ	CA	6,135	C
New Mexico State Univ	NM	4,844	LC
Niagara Univ	NY	14,552	C
N Car Central Univ	NC	4,347	LC
N Car State Univ	NC	4,984	VC
N Car Wesleyan College	NC	12,480	LC
North Georgia College	GA	4,103	LC
Northeast Louisiana Univ	LA	3,906	NC
Northeast Missouri State Univ	MO	5,654	VC+
Northeastern Illinois Univ	IL	1,955	C
Northeastern State Univ	OK	5,250	C
Northeastern Univ	MA	19,851	C
Northern Arizona Univ	AZ	4,844	C
Northern Mich Univ	MI	6,350	C
Northern State Univ	SD	4,186	LC
Northwestern College of Iowa	IA	12,250	C

School	ST	$IS	SR
Northwestern Okla State Univ	OK	3,424	C
Norwich Univ	VT	18,730	C
Ohio Dominican College	OH	11,820	LC
Ohio Northern Univ	OH	18,660	VC
Ohio Univ	OH	7,341	C
Okla City Univ	OK	9,840	C
Old Dominion Univ	VA	8,317	C
Pace Univ	NY	15,540	C
Park College	MO	7,320	C
Pembroke State Univ	NC	3,538	LC
Penn State Univ/Univ Park Campus	PA	8,752	HC
Pfeiffer College	NC	11,670	LC
Portland State Univ	OR	7,191	C
Prairie View A&M Univ	TX	4,740	LC
Purdue Univ/Calumet	IN	2,374	NC
Purdue Univ/West Lafayette	IN	6,636	C
Radford Univ	VA	7,034	LC
Richard Stockton College of New Jersey	NJ	6,950	VC
Roanoke College	VA	16,975	C
Roberts Wesleyan College	NY	13,317	C
Rochester Inst of Tech	NY	18,954	VC
Rockford College	IL	15,300	C
Rowan College of New Jersey	NJ	7,358	VC
Russell Sage College	NY	16,790	C
Rutgers Univ/Livingston College	NJ	8,877	VC
Rutgers Univ/Newark College of A&S	NJ	8,645	C
Rutgers Univ/Rutgers College	NJ	8,841	HC+
Rutgers Univ/Univ College—New Brunswick	NJ	0	LC
Rutgers Univ/Univ College—Newark	NJ	0	C
Sacred Heart Univ	CT	16,350	C
Saginaw Valley State Univ	MI	6,634	LC
St Ambrose Univ	IA	13,380	C
St Anselm College	NH	17,340	C
St Augustine's College	NC	9,300	C+
St Cloud State Univ	MN	5,015	C
St Edward's Univ	TX	12,636	C
St Francis College	PA	15,744	LC
St John's Univ	NY	8,980	C+
St Joseph's Univ	PA	17,800	VC
St Louis Univ	MO	15,522	VC
St Martin's College	WA	14,965	C
St Mary's College of Minn	MN	13,850	LC
St Mary's Univ	TX	12,064	C
St Thomas Aquinas College	NY	13,550	C
St Thomas Univ	FL	14,280	LC
St Xavier Univ	IL	14,700	C
Salem State College	MA	6,712	C
Salem-Teikyo Univ	WV	14,527	C
Salve-Regina Univ	RI	29,100	LC
Sam Houston State Univ	TX	4,506	C
San Diego State Univ	CA	6,692	LC
San Jose State Univ	CA	6,680	LC
Seattle Univ	WA	16,590	C
Seton Hall Univ	NJ	18,306	LC
Shaw Univ	NC	8,936	C+
Shippensburg Univ of Penn	PA	7,052	C
Siena Heights College	MI	12,520	C
Simpson College	IA	14,635	VC
Sojourner-Douglass College	MD	5,265	LC
Sonoma State Univ	CA	6,996	LC
S Car State Univ	SC	5,424	LC
Southeast Missouri State Univ	MO	5,854	C
Southeastern Louisiana Univ	LA	4,230	NC
Southeastern Okla State Univ	OK	3,594	C
Southern Illinois Univ at Carbondale	IL	6,234	C
Southern Nazarene Univ	OK	9,206	NC
Southern Univ at New Orleans	LA	1,452	NC
Southern Vermont College	VT	12,974	C
Southwest Texas State Univ	TX	5,124	C
Southwestern Okla State Univ	OK	3,312	C
SUNY at Albany	NY	7,059	VC
SUNY/College at Brockport	NY	7,220	C+
SUNY/College at Buffalo	NY	7,035	VC
SUNY/College at Plattsburgh	NY	6,917	C
Stephen F. Austin State Univ	TX	5,117	C
Stonehill College	MA	17,481	VC
Suffolk Univ	MA	15,360	LC
Sul Ross State Univ	TX	4,144	NC
Tarleton State Univ	TX	4,082	LC
Taylor Univ	IN	14,450	VC
Temple Univ	PA	10,281	C
Tenn State Univ	TN	4,626	C+
Texas Christian Univ	TX	12,180	C
Texas Southern Univ	TX	4,500	NC
Texas Wesleyan Univ	TX	9,380	LC
Texas Woman's Univ	TX	4,392	C
The Univ of New Mexico	NM	5,304	C
Trenton State College	NJ	9,085	HC
Tri-State Univ	IN	13,788	LC
Trinity College of Vermont	VT	16,015	LC
Troy State Univ	AL	4,322	C

School	ST	$IS	SR
Troy State Univ at Dothan/Fort Rucker	AL	2,260	NC
Union College	KY	9,790	C
Univ of Akron	OH	6,699	NC
Univ of Alabama	AL	5,702	C
Univ of Alabama at Birmingham	AL	7,533	C
Univ of Alaska Anchorage	AK	7,131	C
Univ of Alaska Fairbanks	AK	4,718	C
Univ of Arizona	AZ	5,808	C
Univ of Arkansas at Fayetteville	AR	5,046	C
Univ of Arkansas at Little Rock	AR	4,419	C
Univ of Arkansas at Pine Bluff	AR	3,978	LC
Univ of Calif at Santa Barbara	CA	9,460	C
Univ of Central Florida	FL	6,061	C+
Univ of Central Okla	OK	3,647	C
Univ of Cincinnati	OH	7,989	C
Univ of Dayton	OH	15,120	C+
Univ of Delaware	DE	8,013	VC
Univ of Detroit Mercy	MI	14,720	C
Univ of Findlay	OH	15,764	C
Univ of Florida	FL	5,850	HC
Univ of Georgia	GA	5,655	VC
Univ of Guam	GU	4,139	NC
Univ of Hartford	CT	19,858	LC
Univ of Hawaii at Hilo	HI	4,141	C
Univ of Houston-Downtown	TX	4,034	NC
Univ of Idaho	ID	4,830	C
Univ of Illinois at Chicago	IL	8,443	C
Univ of Indianapolis	IN	14,510	C
Univ of La Verne	CA	17,400	C
Univ of Lowell	MA	8,831	VC
Univ of Mary Hardin-Baylor	TX	8,120	NC
Univ of Maryland/College Park	MD	8,182	VC
Univ of Maryland/Eastern Shore	MD	6,254	LC
Univ of Maryland/Univ College	MD	4,900	NC
Univ of Mass Dartmouth	MA	8,158	C
Univ of Mass/Boston	MA	4,253	C
Univ of Memphis	TN	3,476	C
Univ of Miami	FL	22,107	VC
Univ of Mich/Flint	MI	2,916	C
Univ of Missouri/Kansas City	MO	5,906	VC
Univ of Missouri/St. Louis	MO	6,378	C
Univ of Nebr at Kearney	NE	4,308	LC
Univ of Nebr at Omaha	NE	1,889	LC
Univ of Nebr-Lincoln	NE	5,278	LC
Univ of Nevada/Las Vegas	NV	6,405	C
Univ of Nevada/Reno	NV	5,735	C
Univ of New Haven	CT	14,980	C
Univ of North Alabama	AL	4,236	NC
Univ of N Car at Chapel Hill	NC	5,330	HC
Univ of N Car at Charlotte	NC	4,597	C
Univ of N Car at Wilmington	NC	5,172	C
Univ of N Dak	ND	4,902	NC
Univ of North Florida	FL	5,082	C
Univ of North Texas	TX	4,853	C
Univ of Northern Colo	CO	6,008	C
Univ of Northern Iowa	IA	5,137	C
Univ of Pittsburgh at Greensburg	PA	8,660	C
Univ of Portland	OR	15,564	C
Univ of Richmond	VA	16,700	HC
Univ of St Thomas	MN	15,785	C+
Univ of Scranton	PA	17,071	VC
Univ of South Alabama	AL	5,451	C
Univ of S Car	SC	6,158	C
Univ of S Car at Spartanburg	SC	2,320	C
Univ of S Dak	SD	4,722	C
Univ of South Florida	FL	5,475	C+
Univ of Southern Colo	CO	5,350	LC
Univ of Southern Indiana	IN	3,720	NC
Univ of Southern Maine	ME	7,299	C
Univ of Southern Miss	MS	4,542	C
Univ of Southwestern Louisiana	LA	3,968	NC
Univ of Tampa	FL	16,780	C
Univ of Tenn at Chattanooga	TN	5,375	C
Univ of Tenn at Martin	TN	4,550	C
Univ of Texas at Arlington	TX	5,549	LC
Univ of Texas at El Paso	TX	3,160	LC
Univ of Texas at San Antonio	TX	6,420	C
Univ of the District of Columbia	DC	974	NC
Univ of the Sacred Heart	PR	3,890	
Univ of Toledo	OH	6,636	NC
Univ of West Florida	FL	5,415	C
Univ of Wisc/Eau Claire	WI	4,647	C
Univ of Wisc/Milwaukee	WI	6,165	C
Univ of Wisc/Oshkosh	WI	4,240	C
Univ of Wisc/Platteville	WI	4,830	C
Univ of Wisc/Superior	WI	4,330	C
Univ of Wyoming	WY	4,991	NC
Utica College of Syracuse Univ	NY	16,714	LC
Valdosta State Univ	GA	4,670	LC
Virginia Commonwealth Univ	VA	7,909	C
Voorhees College	SC	6,772	LC

School	ST	$IS	SR
Washburn Univ of Topeka	KS	5,802	NC
Washington State Univ	WA	6,364	C
Wayne State College	NE	4,260	NC
Wayne State Univ	MI	2,806	C
Waynesburg College	PA	11,960	C
Weber State Univ	UT	4,398	C
West Chester Univ of Penn	PA	7,492	C
West Liberty State College	WV	4,690	LC
West Texas A&M Univ	TX	4,224	C
West Virginia State College	WV	5,044	LC
Western Carolina Univ	NC	3,811	C
Western Illinois Univ	IL	5,241	LC
Western Mich Univ	MI	6,820	C
Western New England College	MA	14,674	LC
Westfield State College	MA	7,161	C
Westminster College	PA	15,200	C
Wheeling Jesuit College	WV	14,370	C
Wichita State Univ	KS	5,068	NC
Widener Univ	PA	16,840	C
Wilberforce Univ	OH	10,408	C
William Penn College	IA	13,400	C
Wilmington College	DE	5,200	NC
Wilmington College	OH	13,700	LC
Winona State Univ	MN	5,200	VC
Women's College of Brenau Univ	GA	14,734	C
Xavier Univ	OH	15,710	C+
York College of Penn	PA	8,345	C
Youngstown State Univ	OH	6,447	LC

CRIMINOLOGY

School	ST	$IS	SR
Albertus Magnus College	CT	16,280	LC
Auburn Univ	AL	5,823	C+
Bridgewater State College	MA	7,518	C
Cal State/Fresno	CA	5,747	C
Cal State/Northridge	CA	7,122	LC
CUNY/John Jay College of Criminal Justice	NY	2,501	LC
Florida State Univ	FL	5,814	VC
Indiana State Univ	IN	6,210	C
Marquette Univ	WI	16,114	VC
Ohio State Univ	OH	7,218	LC
Pontifical Catholic Univ of PR/Ponce	PR	5,807	
St Leo College	FL	13,570	C
Southern Oregon State College	OR	6,128	C
SUNY/College at Old Westbury	NY	7,128	LC
Turabo Univ	PR	2,670	
Univ of Illinois at Chicago	IL	8,443	C
Univ of Minn/Duluth	MN	6,512	C
Univ of New Haven	CT	14,980	C

CROSSCULTURAL STUDIES

School	ST	$IS	SR
Antioch College	OH	19,532	C
Azusa Pacific Univ	CA	15,034	C
Biola Univ	CA	16,124	C
Bridgewater State College	MA	7,518	C
CUNY/Herbert H. Lehman College	NY	2,542	C
Emory and Henry College	VA	12,776	C
Goddard College	VT	17,990	LC
Hofstra Univ	NY	16,580	VC
John Brown Univ	AR	9,880	VC
Lee College	TN	7,894	LC
Montreat-Anderson College	NC	10,972	LC
Mount Union College	OH	15,850	C
National-Louis Univ	IL	13,218	C
Nyack College	NY	12,210	LC
St Olaf College	MN	17,200	HC
Simpson College	CA	10,628	C
Trevecca Nazarene College	TN	9,826	NC
Trinity College of Vermont	VT	16,015	LC
Univ of Calif at Los Angeles	CA	8,959	HC
Univ of Calif, San Diego	CA	10,028	VC+
Univ of Maine at Fort Kent	ME	6,285	LC
Univ of the Pacific	CA	21,100	C
Western Baptist College	OR	12,400	LC
William Tyndale College	MI	7,120	NC

CURRICULUM AND INSTRUCTION

School	ST	$IS	SR
Northwest Nazarene College	ID	11,750	C

CYBERNETICS

School	ST	$IS	SR
Univ of Calif at Los Angeles	CA	8,959	HC

CYTOTECHNOLOGY

School	ST	$IS	SR
Alderson-Broaddus College	WV	12,000	C
Barry Univ	FL	16,050	C
Edgewood College	WI	11,700	C
Indiana Univ Bloomington	IN	6,495	VC
Indiana Univ-Purdue Univ at Indianapolis	IN	5,862	LC
Kansas Newman College	KS	10,640	C
Kent State Univ	OH	6,740	LC
Marian College of Fond du Lac	WI	12,250	C
Mount St Clare College	IA	12,870	LC
Northern Mich Univ	MI	6,350	C
Roosevelt Univ	IL	12,368	C
St Mary's College of Minn	MN	13,850	LC
Southern Univ and A&M College	LA	4,920	NC
Suffolk Univ	MA	15,360	LC
Thiel College	PA	16,282	C
Univ of Alabama at Birmingham	AL	7,533	C
Univ of Conn	CT	9,168	C
Univ of Kansas	KS	5,200	NC
Univ of Miami	FL	22,107	VC
Univ of N Dak	ND	4,902	NC
Univ of North Texas	TX	4,853	C
Ursuline College	OH	13,180	LC

DAIRY SCIENCE

School	ST	$IS	SR
Calif Polytechnic State Univ	CA	6,980	VC+
Delaware Valley College	PA	16,065	LC
Iowa State Univ	IA	5,456	C
S Dak State Univ	SD	4,562	C
Texas A&M Univ	TX	5,382	VC
Univ of Arizona	AZ	5,808	C
Univ of Arkansas at Fayetteville	AR	5,046	C
Univ of Florida	FL	5,850	HC
Univ of Georgia	GA	5,655	VC
Univ of New Hampshire	NH	8,242	C
Univ of Wisc/Madison	WI	6,400	HC
Utah State Univ	UT	4,683	C
Virginia Polytechnic Inst and State Univ	VA	6,828	C

DANCE

School	ST	$IS	SR
Adelphi Univ	NY	18,250	LC
Allentown College of St Francis de Sales	PA	13,480	C
Alma College	MI	16,375	VC+
Amherst College	MA	24,152	MC
Antioch College	OH	19,532	C
Arizona State Univ Main Campus	AZ	6,444	C
Baldwin-Wallace College	OH	15,210	C
Ball State Univ	IN	6,032	LC
Barat College	IL	13,990	C
Bard College	NY	25,269	HC
Bennington College	VT	24,850	VC+
Birmingham-Southern College	AL	15,154	VC+
Boston Conservatory	MA	17,900	SP
Bowling Green State Univ	OH	6,701	C
Brigham Young Univ	UT	5,625	HC
Butler Univ	IN	16,210	C
Calif Inst of the Arts	CA	16,400	SP
Cal State/Fresno	CA	5,747	C
Cal State/Fullerton	CA	4,854	LC
Cal State/Long Beach	CA	6,057	LC
Cal State/Los Angeles	CA	4,940	VC
Cal State/Northridge	CA	7,122	LC
Centenary College of Louisiana	LA	11,826	C+
CUNY/Brooklyn College	NY	2,450	VC
CUNY/City College	NY	2,543	VC
CUNY/Herbert H. Lehman College	NY	2,542	C
CUNY/Hunter College	NY	4,101	VC
CUNY/Queens College	NY	2,631	C
Coker College	SC	13,790	C
Colo College	CO	20,038	HC
Columbia College	IL	7,879	SP
Columbia College	SC	13,520	LC
Columbia Univ/Barnard College	NY	25,492	HC
Columbia Univ/Columbia College	NY	26,757	MC
Conn College	CT	24,160	HC
Cornell Univ	NY	13,445	MC
Cornish College of the Arts	WA	9,300	SP
Denison Univ	OH	21,150	VC+

School	ST	$IS	SR
Eastern Mich Univ	MI	6,749	C
Eastern Washington Univ	WA	5,439	LC
Evergreen State College	WA	6,306	C
Florida International Univ	FL	4,191	VC
Florida State Univ	FL	5,814	VC
Friends Univ	KS	11,205	C
George Mason Univ	VA	8,728	C
George Washington Univ	DC	22,470	HC
Goucher College	MD	20,295	VC
Gustavus Adolphus College	MN	15,935	VC
Hamilton College	NY	23,500	HC
Hobart and William Smith Colleges	NY	23,925	VC
Hofstra Univ	NY	16,580	VC
Hope College	MI	15,698	C+
Howard Univ	DC	11,680	C
Huntingdon College	AL	11,400	C
Illinois State Univ	IL	6,413	C
Incarnate Word College	TX	12,307	C
Indiana Univ Bloomington	IN	6,495	VC
Jacksonville Univ	FL	13,390	C
James Madison Univ	VA	8,198	HC
Juilliard School	NY	18,050	SP
Kent State Univ	OH	6,740	LC
Kenyon College	OH	22,430	HC+
Lake Erie College	OH	13,700	C
Lees-McRae College	NC	9,850	LC
Loyola Marymount Univ	CA	18,560	C
Luther College	IA	15,900	VC
Manhattanville College	NY	20,450	LC
Marlboro College	VT	23,305	C+
Mary Washington College	VA	7,910	HC
Marygrove College	MI	5,877	VC
Marymount Manhattan College	NY	15,450	LC
Mercyhurst College	PA	13,488	C
Meredith College	NC	9,440	C
Middlebury College	VT	24,400	MC
Mills College	CA	20,848	VC
Montclair State College	NJ	7,539	C+
Mount Holyoke College	MA	23,630	VC
New York Univ	NY	24,705	VC+
N Car School of the Arts	NC	5,375	SP
Oberlin College	OH	24,570	HC+
Ohio State Univ	OH	7,218	LC
Ohio Univ	OH	7,341	C
Okla City Univ	OK	9,840	C
Old Dominion Univ	VA	8,317	C
Otterbein College	OH	16,506	C
Point Park College	PA	13,922	LC
Radford Univ	VA	7,034	LC
Randolph-Macon Woman's College	VA	19,100	C
Reed College	OR	24,480	HC+
Richard Stockton College of New Jersey	NJ	6,950	VC
Roger Williams Univ	RI	16,750	C
Rutgers Univ/Douglass College	NJ	8,795	VC
Rutgers Univ/Livingston College	NJ	8,877	VC
Rutgers Univ/Mason Gross School of the Arts	NJ	8,877	SP
Rutgers Univ/Rutgers College	NJ	8,841	HC+
Rutgers Univ/Univ College—New Brunswick	NJ	0	LC
St Olaf College	MN	17,200	HC
Sam Houston State Univ	TX	4,506	C
San Diego State Univ	CA	6,692	LC
San Francisco State Univ	CA	7,292	LC
San Jose State Univ	CA	6,680	LC
Sarah Lawrence College	NY	24,975	HC
Scripps College	CA	23,600	HC
Shenandoah Univ	VA	11,800	C
Skidmore College	NY	23,230	HC
Slippery Rock Univ	PA	6,803	C
Smith College	MA	24,236	HC
Sonoma State Univ	CA	6,996	LC
Southeastern Louisiana Univ	LA	4,230	NC
Southern Illinois Univ at Edwardsville	IL	6,097	LC
Southern Methodist Univ	TX	18,520	VC
Southern Univ and A&M College	LA	4,920	NC
Southern Utah Univ	UT	4,104	LC
Southwest Missouri State Univ	MO	4,956	C
Southwest Texas State Univ	TX	5,124	C
SUNY/College at Brockport	NY	7,220	C+
SUNY/College at Purchase	NY	7,324	C
SUNY/Potsdam College	NY	6,906	C
Stephens College	MO	18,460	C
Sweet Briar College	VA	19,770	C
Temple Univ	PA	10,281	C
Texas Christian Univ	TX	12,180	C
Texas Tech Univ	TX	6,008	C
Texas Woman's Univ	TX	4,392	C
The Univ of New Mexico	NM	5,304	C
Thomas A. Edison State College	NJ	400	
Towson State Univ	MD	7,452	C
Trinity College	CT	24,120	HC
Univ of Akron	OH	6,699	NC
Univ of Alabama	AL	5,702	C
Univ of Alabama at Birmingham	AL	7,533	C
Univ of Arizona	AZ	5,808	C
Univ of Arkansas at Fayetteville	AR	5,046	C
Univ of Calif at Berkeley	CA	9,962	HC+
Univ of Calif at Los Angeles	CA	8,959	HC
Univ of Calif at Santa Barbara	CA	9,460	C
Univ of Calif, Riverside	CA	9,178	C
Univ of Calif/Irvine	CA	12,680	VC
Univ of Central Okla	OK	3,647	C
Univ of Cincinnati	OH	7,989	C
Univ of Colo at Boulder	CO	6,410	VC
Univ of Hartford	CT	19,858	LC
Univ of Hawaii at Manoa	HI	5,626	C
Univ of Idaho	ID	4,830	C
Univ of Illinois at Urbana-Champaign	IL	7,764	HC
Univ of Iowa	IA	5,658	VC
Univ of Kansas	KS	5,200	NC
Univ of Maryland/College Park	MD	8,182	VC
Univ of Mass/Amherst	MA	9,364	LC
Univ of Mich/Ann Arbor	MI	9,428	HC+
Univ of Minn/Twin Cities	MN	6,682	VC
Univ of Missouri/Kansas City	MO	5,906	VC
Univ of Montana	MT	5,529	C
Univ of Nebr-Lincoln	NE	5,278	LC
Univ of Nevada/Las Vegas	NV	6,405	C
Univ of N Car at Charlotte	NC	4,597	C
Univ of N Car at Greensboro	NC	5,192	C
Univ of North Texas	TX	4,853	C
Univ of Northern Colo	CO	6,008	C
Univ of Okla	OK	5,427	VC
Univ of Oregon	OR	6,466	VC
Univ of South Florida	FL	5,475	C+
Univ of Southern Miss	MS	4,542	C
Univ of Southwestern Louisiana	LA	3,968	NC
Univ of Texas at Austin	TX	5,160	VC
Univ of Texas at El Paso	TX	3,160	LC
Univ of the Arts	PA	16,150	SP
Univ of Toledo	OH	6,636	NC
Univ of Utah	UT	5,975	C
Univ of Washington	WA	6,618	VC
Univ of Wisc/Milwaukee	WI	6,165	C
Univ of Wisc/Stevens Point	WI	5,047	C+
Utah State Univ	UT	4,683	C
Virginia Commonwealth Univ	VA	7,909	C
Virginia Intermont College	VA	12,250	LC
Washburn Univ of Topeka	KS	5,802	NC
Washington Univ	MO	23,507	HC
Wayne State Univ	MI	2,680	C
Webster Univ	MO	12,650	C
Wells College	NY	19,460	C+
Wesleyan Univ	CT	23,770	MC
West Texas A&M Univ	TX	4,224	C
Western Mich Univ	MI	6,820	C
Wichita State Univ	KS	5,068	NC
Winthrop Univ	SC	6,750	C
Women's College of Brenau Univ	GA	14,734	C
Wright State Univ	OH	6,896	LC

DANCE EDUCATION

School	ST	$IS	SR
Columbia College	SC	13,520	LC

DANCE THERAPY

School	ST	$IS	SR
Barat College	IL	13,990	C

DATA PROCESSING

School	ST	$IS	SR
Chicago State Univ	IL	2,198	C
Indiana Univ at Kokomo	IN	2,069	C
Indiana Univ Northwest	IN	2,310	C
Morehead State Univ	KY	4,600	LC
Wayne State Univ	MI	2,680	C

DENTAL HYGIENE

School	ST	$IS	SR
Armstrong State College	GA	4,874	LC
Bloomsburg Univ of Penn	PA	6,312	C+
East Texas State Univ	TX	4,572	LC
Eastern Washington Univ	WA	5,439	LC
Idaho State Univ	ID	4,442	C
Indiana Univ Bloomington	IN	6,495	VC
Indiana Univ-Purdue Univ at Indianapolis	IN	5,862	LC
Indiana Univ/South Bend	IN	2,141	LC
Marquette Univ	WI	16,114	VC
Midwestern State Univ	TX	4,542	LC
Northeast Louisiana Univ	LA	3,906	NC
Ohio State Univ	OH	7,218	LC
Oregon Inst of Tech	OR	5,985	C
Southern Illinois Univ at Carbondale	IL	6,234	C
Tenn State Univ	TN	4,626	C+
Univ of Alabama at Birmingham	AL	7,533	C
Univ of Bridgeport	CT	18,985	C
Univ of Hawaii at Manoa	HI	5,626	C
Univ of Louisville	KY	5,948	C
Univ of Mich/Ann Arbor	MI	9,428	HC+
Univ of Minn/Twin Cities	MN	6,682	VC
Univ of Nebr-Lincoln	NE	5,278	LC
Univ of New Orleans	LA	5,468	C
Univ of N Car at Chapel Hill	NC	5,330	HC
Univ of Rhode Island	RI	9,205	C
Univ of S Dak	SD	4,722	C
Univ of Washington	WA	6,618	VC
Univ of Wyoming	WY	4,991	NC
West Liberty State College	WV	4,690	LC
West Virginia Univ	WV	5,774	C
Westbrook College	ME	15,900	C

DENTAL LABORATORY TECHNOLOGY

School	ST	$IS	SR
Boston Univ	MA	24,130	HC
Idaho State Univ	ID	4,442	C
Southern Illinois Univ at Carbondale	IL	6,234	C

DESIGN

School	ST	$IS	SR
Abilene Christian Univ	TX	10,460	NC
Adelphi Univ	NY	18,250	LC
Alfred Univ	NY	21,054	VC+
Alma College	MI	16,375	VC+
American Univ	DC	21,230	VC+
Arizona State Univ Main Campus	AZ	6,444	C
Arkansas State Univ	AR	4,250	NC
Art Center College of Design	CA	13,550	SP
Atlanta College of Art	GA	12,495	SP
Auburn Univ	AL	5,823	C+
Baylor Univ	TX	10,990	C+
Beaver College	PA	17,660	C
Brigham Young Univ	UT	5,625	HC
Calif College of Arts and Crafts	CA	17,378	SP
Cal State/Fullerton	CA	4,850	LC
Cal State/Long Beach	CA	6,057	LC
Cal State/Northridge	CA	7,122	LC
Cal State/San Bernardino	CA	6,055	LC
Carnegie Mellon Univ	PA	22,560	HC+
Carthage College	WI	15,995	C
Centenary College	NJ	17,040	LC
Central Missouri State Univ	MO	5,138	LC
Clemson Univ	SC	6,564	VC
Cleveland Inst of Art	OH	15,630	SP
Colby-Sawyer College	NH	18,495	LC
College of Santa Fe	NM	14,008	C
Columbus College of Art and Design	OH	14,550	SP
Converse College	SC	15,750	C
Cornell Univ	NY	13,445	MC
Cornish College of the Arts	WA	9,300	SP
Daemen College	NY	13,020	LC
Drake Univ	IA	17,195	VC
Drexel Univ	PA	15,970	C
Duke Univ	NC	21,271	MC
East Carolina Univ	NC	4,498	C
East Tenn State Univ	TN	4,406	C
Eastern Mich Univ	MI	6,749	C
Evangel College	MO	10,142	LC
Fashion Inst of Tech/SUNY	NY	7,135	SP
Grand Valley State Univ	MI	6,822	VC
Harding Univ	AR	9,050	VC
Hofstra Univ	NY	16,580	VC
Howard Univ	DC	11,680	C
Illinois Inst of Tech	IL	18,290	VC
Iowa State Univ	IA	5,456	C
Jacksonville Univ	FL	13,390	C
Jersey City State College	NJ	7,797	LC
John Brown Univ	AR	9,880	VC
Kansas City Art Inst	MO	17,000	SP
Kean College of New Jersey	NJ	6,395	LC
Kendall College of Art and Design	MI	9,600	SP
Kent State Univ	OH	6,740	LC
Kutztown Univ	PA	6,528	C
Lamar Univ	TX	3,798	C
Lambuth Univ	TN	8,395	C
Louisiana State Univ and A&M College	LA	5,605	C
Loyola Univ/New Orleans	LA	15,660	C+
Lynn Univ	FL	18,300	C
Manhattanville College	NY	20,450	LC
Marywood College	PA	14,890	C
Mass College of Art	MA	9,447	SP
Memphis College of Art	TN	13,140	SP
Middle Tenn State Univ	TN	3,857	C
Minneapolis College of Art and Design	MN	15,512	SP
Miss College	MS	8,348	C
Montserrat College of Art	MA	12,500	SP
Mount Senario College	WI	10,970	C
N Car State Univ	NC	4,984	VC
N Dak State Univ of Agriculture and Applied Science	ND	4,774	VC
Northern Arizona Univ	AZ	4,844	C
Northern Mich Univ	MI	6,350	C
Northwestern College	MN	13,554	C
Ohio Univ	OH	7,341	C
Okla Christian Univ of Science and Arts	OK	8,790	NC
Okla State Univ	OK	5,086	VC
Otis College of Art and Design	CA	16,686	SP
Pacific Union College	CA	15,075	C
Paier College of Art	CT	10,120	SP
Park College	MO	7,320	C
Parsons School of Design	NY	21,410	SP
Pittsburg State Univ	KS	4,478	NC
Radford Univ	VA	7,034	LC
Rhode Island School of Design	RI	22,315	SP
Richard Stockton College of New Jersey	NJ	6,950	VC
Rivier College	NH	14,920	LC
Rochester Inst of Tech	NY	18,954	VC
Saginaw Valley State Univ	MI	6,634	LC
St Mary's College of Minn	MN	13,850	LC
St Vincent College	PA	13,934	LC
Salem State College	MA	6,712	C
Samford Univ	AL	11,400	VC
San Jose State Univ	CA	6,680	LC
School of the Art Inst of Chicago	IL	17,610	SP
Seton Hill College	PA	14,320	C
Shepherd College	WV	5,540	C
S Dak State Univ	SD	4,562	C
Southern Illinois Univ at Carbondale	IL	6,234	C
Southwest Missouri State Univ	MO	4,956	C
SUNY at Buffalo	NY	7,896	VC
SUNY/College at Buffalo	NY	7,035	VC
SUNY/College at Fredonia	NY	7,159	VC
SUNY/College at New Paltz	NY	6,890	VC
SUNY/College at Purchase	NY	7,324	C
Syracuse Univ	NY	21,305	HC
Texas Christian Univ	TX	12,180	C
Texas Woman's Univ	TX	4,392	C
Univ of Akron	OH	6,699	NC
Univ of Bridgeport	CT	18,985	C
Univ of Calif at Davis	CA	9,534	VC
Univ of Calif at Los Angeles	CA	8,959	HC
Univ of Cincinnati	OH	7,989	C
Univ of Conn	CT	9,168	C
Univ of Dayton	OH	15,120	C+
Univ of Georgia	GA	5,655	VC
Univ of Hartford	CT	19,858	LC
Univ of Idaho	ID	4,830	C
Univ of Illinois at Chicago	IL	8,443	C
Univ of Iowa	IA	5,658	VC
Univ of Kansas	KS	5,200	NC
Univ of Maryland/College Park	MD	8,182	VC
Univ of Mass Dartmouth	MA	8,158	C
Univ of Mass/Amherst	MA	9,364	LC
Univ of Mich/Ann Arbor	MI	9,428	HC+
Univ of Miss	MS	5,756	C
Univ of Missouri/Columbia	MO	6,254	HC
Univ of Nebr-Lincoln	NE	5,278	LC
Univ of N Car at Greensboro	NC	5,192	C
Univ of Notre Dame	IN	20,150	MC
Univ of San Francisco	CA	18,408	C
Univ of Southern Miss	MS	4,542	C
Univ of Texas at Austin	TX	5,160	VC
Univ of Tulsa	OK	13,795	VC
Univ of Wisc/Superior	WI	4,330	C
Virginia Commonwealth Univ	VA	7,909	C
Wayne State Univ	MI	2,680	C
Weber State Univ	UT	4,398	C
Western Kentucky Univ	KY	4,808	C
William Woods Univ	MO	14,025	LC
Women's College of Brenau Univ	GA	14,734	C
Woodbury Univ	CA	17,620	LC

DEVELOPMENTAL PSYCHOLOGY

School	ST	$IS	SR
La Sierra Univ	CA	15,472	C
Univ of Calif at Los Angeles	CA	8,959	HC
Univ of Kansas	KS	5,200	NC

DIETETICS

School	ST	$IS	SR
Auburn Univ	AL	5,823	C+
Ball State Univ	IN	6,032	LC
Baylor Univ	TX	10,990	C+
Bennett College	NC	8,920	LC
Berea College	KY	2,883	VC+
Bluffton College	OH	12,951	C
Bowling Green State Univ	OH	6,701	C
Brigham Young Univ	UT	5,625	HC
Cal State/Chico	CA	6,146	C
Cal State/Fresno	CA	5,747	C
Cal State/Long Beach	CA	6,057	LC
Cal State/Los Angeles	CA	4,940	VC
Cal State/Northridge	CA	7,122	LC
Central Missouri State Univ	MO	5,138	LC
Cheyney Univ of Penn	PA	7,005	C
Chicago State Univ	IL	2,198	C
CUNY/Herbert H. Lehman College	NY	2,542	C
CUNY/Queens College	NY	2,631	C
College of St Benedict	MN	15,468	VC
College of St Scholastica	MN	14,868	C
College of the Ozarks	MO	2,000	VC+
Concordia College/Moorhead	MN	12,750	C
D'Youville College	NY	12,850	C
David Lipscomb Univ	TN	7,865	VC
Drexel Univ	PA	15,970	C
East Tenn State Univ	TN	4,406	C
Eastern Illinois Univ	IL	5,548	C
Eastern Kentucky Univ	KY	4,840	NC
Eastern Mennonite College	VA	12,700	C
Eastern Mich Univ	MI	6,749	C
Florida International Univ	FL	4,191	VC
Fontbonne College	MO	12,090	C
Framingham State College	MA	6,580	C
Gannon Univ	PA	14,872	C
Hampton Univ	VA	10,706	C
Harding Univ	AR	9,050	VC
Howard Univ	DC	11,680	C
Idaho State Univ	ID	4,442	C
Immaculata College	PA	14,620	C
Incarnate Word College	TX	12,307	C
Indiana State Univ	IN	6,210	C
Indiana Univ Bloomington	IN	6,495	VC
Iowa State Univ	IA	5,456	C
James Madison Univ	VA	8,198	HC
Kansas State Univ	KS	4,816	NC
Keene State College	NH	7,081	C
Kent State Univ	OH	6,740	LC
Louisiana State Univ and A&M College	LA	5,605	C
Louisiana Tech Univ	LA	4,284	C
Madonna Univ	MI	8,546	C
Mankato State Univ	MN	5,097	LC
Marian College	IN	12,936	C
Marshall Univ	WV	5,762	LC
Marywood College	PA	14,890	C
Mercyhurst College	PA	13,488	C
Messiah College	PA	14,664	VC
Miami Univ	OH	8,066	VC
Mich State Univ	MI	7,842	C
Middle Tenn State Univ	TN	3,857	C
Morehead State Univ	KY	4,600	LC
Mount Mary College	WI	10,920	C
Murray State Univ	KY	4,702	C
New York Univ	NY	24,705	VC+
Nicholls State Univ	LA	4,531	NC
Northern Arizona Univ	AZ	4,844	C
Northern Illinois Univ	IL	6,408	C
Northern Mich Univ	MI	6,350	C
Northwest Nazarene College	ID	11,750	C
Notre Dame College of Ohio	OH	11,370	C
Ohio State Univ	OH	7,218	LC
Ohio Univ	OH	7,341	C
Okla State Univ	OK	5,086	VC
Olivet Nazarene Univ	IL	11,976	C
Oregon State Univ	OR	6,175	C
Ouachita Baptist Univ	AR	8,940	C
Purdue Univ/West Lafayette	IN	6,636	C
Rochester Inst of Tech	NY	18,954	VC
Rosary College	IL	15,040	C
St John's Univ	MN	15,364	C
St Joseph College	CT	16,225	C
St Vincent College	PA	13,934	LC
San Francisco State Univ	CA	7,292	LC
Seton Hill College	PA	14,320	C
S Dak State Univ	SD	4,562	C
Southeast Missouri State Univ	MO	5,854	C
Southern Illinois Univ at Carbondale	IL	6,234	C
Southern Univ and A&M College	LA	4,920	NC
Southwest Missouri State Univ	MO	4,956	C
SUNY/College at Buffalo	NY	7,035	VC
SUNY/College at Oneonta	NY	7,878	C
SUNY/College at Plattsburgh	NY	6,917	C
Stephen F. Austin State Univ	TX	5,117	C
Syracuse Univ	NY	21,305	HC
Teikyo Marycrest Univ	IA	13,755	VC
Texas Tech Univ	TX	6,008	C
Texas Woman's Univ	TX	4,392	C
The Univ of New Mexico	NM	5,304	C
Tuskegee Univ	AL	10,128	C
Univ of Akron	OH	6,699	NC
Univ of Arkansas at Fayetteville	AR	5,046	C
Univ of Arkansas at Pine Bluff	AR	3,978	LC
Univ of Calif at Davis	CA	9,534	VC
Univ of Central Okla	OK	3,647	C
Univ of Conn	CT	9,168	C
Univ of Dayton	OH	15,120	C+
Univ of Delaware	DE	8,013	VC
Univ of Georgia	GA	5,655	VC
Univ of Idaho	ID	4,830	C
Univ of Kentucky	KY	5,152	VC
Univ of Missouri/Columbia	MO	6,254	HC
Univ of Nebr at Kearney	NE	4,308	LC
Univ of Nebr-Lincoln	NE	5,278	LC
Univ of New Haven	CT	14,980	C
Univ of N Car at Greensboro	NC	5,192	C
Univ of N Dak	ND	4,902	NC
Univ of Northern Colo	CO	6,008	C
Univ of Northern Iowa	IA	5,137	C
Univ of PR/Rio Piedras	PR	0	NC
Univ of Rhode Island	RI	9,205	C
Univ of Southwestern Louisiana	LA	3,968	NC
Univ of Tenn at Martin	TN	4,550	C
Univ of Texas-Pan American	TX	3,192	NC
Univ of Vermont	VT	10,776	C+
Univ of Wisc/Green Bay	WI	4,904	C
Univ of Wisc/Madison	WI	6,400	HC
Univ of Wisc/Stevens Point	WI	5,047	C+
Univ of Wisc/Stout	WI	4,719	C
Viterbo College	WI	12,670	C
Washington State Univ	WA	6,364	C
Wayne State Univ	MI	2,680	C
Western Carolina Univ	NC	3,811	C
Western Kentucky Univ	KY	4,808	C
Western Mich Univ	MI	6,820	C
Youngstown State Univ	OH	6,447	LC

DRAFTING AND DESIGN

School	ST	$IS	SR
Central Missouri State Univ	MO	5,138	LC
Southwest Missouri State Univ	MO	4,956	C

DRAFTING AND DESIGN TECHNOLOGY

School	ST	$IS	SR
Baker College	MI	6,971	NC
Idaho State Univ	ID	4,442	C
Northern Montana College	MT	4,976	C
Univ of Central Florida	FL	6,061	C+
Univ of Houston	TX	5,215	C
Univ of Nebr-Lincoln	NE	5,278	LC

DRAMA EDUCATION

School	ST	$IS	SR
Boston Univ	MA	24,130	HC
Culver-Stockton College	MO	11,150	C
Palm Beach Atlantic College	FL	10,720	C

DRAMATIC ARTS

School	ST	$IS	SR
Abilene Christian Univ	TX	10,460	NC
Adelphi Univ	NY	18,250	LC
Agnes Scott College	GA	17,135	VC
Albany State College	GA	4,481	LC
Albertus Magnus College	CT	16,280	LC
Alfred Univ	NY	21,054	VC+
Allegheny College	PA	21,020	VC
Allentown College of St Francis de Sales	PA	13,480	C
Alma College	MI	16,375	VC+
American Univ	DC	21,230	VC+
Anderson Univ	IN	12,920	C
Angelo State Univ	TX	5,176	C
Antioch College	OH	19,532	C
Appalachian State Univ	NC	4,095	C
Arizona State Univ Main Campus	AZ	6,444	C
Arkansas College	AR	11,626	VC
Arkansas State Univ	AR	4,250	NC
Armstrong State College	GA	4,874	LC
Auburn Univ	AL	5,823	C+
Auburn Univ at Montgomery	AL	3,390	C
Augsburg College	MN	15,608	C
Augustana College	IL	16,959	VC
Averett College	VA	13,610	LC
Avila College	MO	12,130	C
Baker Univ	KS	12,284	C
Baldwin-Wallace College	OH	15,210	C
Ball State Univ	IN	6,032	LC
Bard College	NY	25,269	HC
Barry Univ	FL	16,050	C
Bates College	ME	23,990	MC
Baylor Univ	TX	10,990	C+
Beaver College	PA	17,660	C
Bennington College	VT	24,850	VC+
Berry College	GA	11,990	VC
Bethany College	KS	11,232	C
Bethel College	KS	11,530	C
Bethel College	MN	15,050	C
Birmingham-Southern College	AL	15,154	VC+
Black Hills State Univ	SD	4,831	NC
Bloomsburg Univ of Penn	PA	6,312	C+
Boise State Univ	ID	4,909	LC
Boston College	MA	22,706	MC
Boston Univ	MA	24,130	HC
Bowie State Univ	MD	7,294	LC
Bowling Green State Univ	OH	6,701	C
Bradley Univ	IL	14,718	C+
Brandeis Univ	MA	25,585	HC
Briar Cliff College	IA	13,375	C
Bridgewater State College	MA	7,518	C
Brigham Young Univ	UT	5,625	HC
Bucknell Univ	PA	22,320	HC
Butler Univ	IN	16,210	C
Calif Inst of the Arts	CA	16,400	SP
Calif Lutheran Univ	CA	17,240	C
Calif State Polytechnic Univ/Pomona	CA	6,438	LC
Cal State/Dominguez Hills	CA	2,857	LC
Cal State/Fresno	CA	5,747	C
Cal State/Fullerton	CA	4,850	LC
Cal State/Hayward	CA	5,495	C
Cal State/Long Beach	CA	6,057	LC
Cal State/Los Angeles	CA	4,940	VC
Cal State/Northridge	CA	7,122	LC
Cal State/Sacramento	CA	6,387	C
Cal State/San Bernardino	CA	6,055	LC
Cal State/Stanislaus	CA	6,799	C
Calif Univ of Penn	PA	7,370	LC
Calvin College	MI	13,020	VC
Cameron Univ	OK	3,686	LC
Campbell Univ	NC	10,624	C
Capital Univ	OH	16,535	VC
Cardinal Stritch College	WI	11,252	C
Carnegie Mellon Univ	PA	22,560	HC+
Carroll College	MT	11,265	C
Carroll College	WI	15,490	C
Carthage College	WI	15,995	C
Case Western Reserve Univ	OH	19,910	HC
Castleton State College	VT	8,378	LC
Catawba College	NC	12,950	C
Catholic Univ of America	DC	18,856	C
Cedar Crest College	PA	18,930	C
Central College	IA	14,025	VC
Central Conn State Univ	CT	7,108	C
Central Methodist College	MO	11,410	C
Central Mich Univ	MI	6,737	LC
Central Missouri State Univ	MO	5,138	LC
Central Washington Univ	WA	5,644	C
Centre College	KY	15,850	VC+
Chadron State College	NE	4,091	NC
Charleston Southern Univ	SC	10,282	LC
Chatham College	PA	18,010	C
Cheyney Univ of Penn	PA	7,005	C
Christian Brothers Univ	TN	12,120	VC
CUNY/Brooklyn College	NY	2,450	VC
CUNY/City College	NY	2,543	VC
CUNY/College of Staten Island	NY	2,558	NC
CUNY/Hunter College	NY	4,101	VC
CUNY/Queens College	NY	2,631	C
Claremont McKenna College	CA	22,150	MC
Clarion Univ of Penn	PA	6,518	C
Clark Univ	MA	21,400	VC
Clarke College	IA	13,950	C+
Cleveland State Univ	OH	4,074	C
Clinch Valley College/Univ of Virginia	VA	6,364	C
Coe College	IA	17,085	VC
Coker College	SC	13,790	C
College of Charleston	SC	6,250	C
College of Notre Dame	CA	16,480	C
College of St Benedict	MN	15,468	VC
College of Santa Fe	NM	14,008	C
College of the Holy Cross	MA	23,850	HC
College of Wooster	OH	19,875	VC
Colo Christian Univ	CO	9,750	C
Colo College	CO	20,038	HC
Columbia College	IL	7,879	SP
Columbia College	SC	13,520	LC
Columbia Univ/Barnard College	NY	25,492	HC
Columbia Univ/Columbia College	NY	26,757	MC
Columbus College	GA	4,892	LC
Concordia College	NE	11,776	NC
Concordia College	OR	12,300	C
Concordia College/Moorhead	MN	12,750	C
Conn College	CT	24,160	HC
Cornell College	IA	18,425	VC
Cornell Univ	NY	13,445	MC
Cornish College of the Arts	WA	9,300	SP
Creighton Univ	NE	14,432	VC
Culver-Stockton College	MO	11,150	C
Cumberland College	KY	9,756	C
Dana College	NE	11,910	C
Dartmouth College	NH	24,354	MC
Davis and Elkins College	WV	13,230	LC
Denison Univ	OH	21,150	VC+
DePaul Univ	IL	15,535	VC
Dickinson College	PA	22,705	HC
Dillard Univ	LA	9,950	C
Dordt College	IA	11,690	C
Drake Univ	IA	17,195	VC
Drew Univ/College of Liberal Arts	NJ	23,406	HC
Drury College	MO	12,140	VC
Earlham College	IN	19,383	VC
East Stroudsburg Univ	PA	6,886	C
East Tenn State Univ	TN	4,406	C
East Texas Baptist Univ	TX	7,740	C
East Texas State Univ	TX	4,572	LC
Eastern Illinois Univ	IL	5,548	C
Eastern Kentucky Univ	KY	4,840	NC
Eastern Mich Univ	MI	6,749	C
Eastern New Mexico Univ	NM	3,950	C
Eastern Oregon State College	OR	6,090	C
Eastern Washington Univ	WA	5,439	LC
Eckerd College	FL	18,855	VC
Edinboro Univ of Penn	PA	7,181	C
Elmhurst College	IL	12,536	C
Elmira College	NY	18,450	C
Elon College	NC	12,290	LC
Emerson College	MA	22,678	LC
Emory Univ	GA	21,930	HC
Emporia State Univ	KS	4,685	NC
Eugene Lang College of the New School for Social Research	NY	21,145	C+
Eureka College	IL	14,555	C
Evergreen State College	WA	6,306	C
Fayetteville State Univ	NC	3,926	LC
Ferrum College	VA	12,800	LC
Fisk Univ	TN	0	LC
Flagler College	FL	7,990	C
Florida A&M Univ	FL	4,651	C
Florida Atlantic Univ	FL	5,525	C
Florida International Univ	FL	4,191	VC
Florida Southern College	FL	12,260	C
Florida State Univ	FL	5,814	VC
Fontbonne College	MO	12,090	C
Fordham Univ/College at Lincoln Center	NY	18,150	VC
Francis Marion Univ	SC	5,878	LC
Franklin and Marshall College	PA	23,655	HC
Franklin Pierce College	NH	17,270	LC
Freed-Hardeman Univ	TN	8,585	VC
Frostburg State Univ	MD	6,940	C
Furman Univ	SC	16,557	VC
George Mason Univ	VA	8,728	C
George Washington Univ	DC	22,470	HC
Georgetown College	KY	10,990	C
Georgia Southwestern College	GA	4,338	LC
Gettysburg College	PA	22,960	HC
Gonzaga Univ	WA	16,350	VC
Goshen College	IN	12,360	C
Graceland College	IA	11,600	C
Grand Canyon Univ	AZ	9,680	VC
Grand Valley State Univ	MI	6,822	VC
Greensboro College	NC	11,496	C
Grinnell College	IA	20,680	HC+
Guilford College	NC	17,680	C
Gustavus Adolphus College	MN	15,935	VC
Hamilton College	NY	23,500	HC
Hampshire College	MA	25,320	C
Hampton Univ	VA	10,706	C
Hanover College	IN	10,950	VC
Harding Univ	AR	9,050	VC
Hartwick College	NY	20,950	C
Hastings College	NE	12,426	C
Heidelberg College	OH	17,160	C
Hendrix College	AR	11,670	C
High Point Univ	NC	12,350	LC
Hillsdale College	MI	15,110	VC
Hiram College	OH	18,340	VC
Hofstra Univ	NY	16,580	VC
Hollins College	VA	18,484	C
Howard Payne Univ	TX	8,052	C
Howard Univ	DC	11,680	C
Humboldt State Univ	CA	5,676	C
Huntingdon College	AL	11,400	C
Idaho State Univ	ID	4,442	C
Illinois College	IL	11,200	C
Illinois State Univ	IL	6,413	C
Illinois Wesleyan Univ	IL	18,590	HC+
Incarnate Word College	TX	12,307	C
Indiana State Univ	IN	6,210	C
Indiana Univ Bloomington	IN	6,495	VC
Indiana Univ Northwest	IN	2,310	C

School	ST	$IS	SR
Indiana Univ of Penn	PA	6,373	C
Indiana Univ of Penn	PA	6,373	C
Indiana Univ/South Bend	IN	2,141	LC
Iona College	NY	16,310	C
Ithaca College	NY	19,679	C
Jacksonville State Univ	AL	4,080	LC
Jacksonville Univ	FL	13,390	LC
James Madison Univ	VA	8,198	HC
Jamestown College	ND	10,250	C
Judson College	IL	13,625	C
Juilliard School	NY	18,050	SP
Kalamazoo College	MI	19,974	HC
Kansas State Univ	KS	4,816	NC
Kansas Wesleyan Univ	KS	11,770	C
Kean College of New Jersey	NJ	6,395	LC
Keene State College	NH	7,081	C
Kent State Univ	OH	6,740	LC
Kentucky Wesleyan College	KY	11,550	C
Kenyon College	OH	22,430	HC+
King's College	PA	15,420	C
Knox College	IL	18,990	VC
Kutztown Univ	PA	6,528	C
LaGrange College	GA	10,602	C
Lamar Univ	TX	3,798	C
Lander Univ	SC	6,180	LC
Langston Univ	OK	2,907	LC
Lawrence Univ	WI	19,986	HC+
Le Moyne College	NY	15,180	C
Lees-McRae College	NC	9,850	LC
Lehigh Univ	PA	23,250	HC
Lenoir-Rhyne College	NC	14,068	C
Lewis and Clark College	OR	19,980	VC
Liberty Univ	VA	11,500	LC
Lindenwood College	MO	13,560	C
Linfield College	OR	16,670	VC
LIU/C. W. Post Campus	NY	16,870	C
Longwood College	VA	7,800	C
Louisiana College	LA	7,518	VC
Louisiana State Univ and A&M College	LA	5,605	C
Loyola Marymount Univ	CA	18,560	C
Loyola Univ of Chicago	IL	15,880	C+
Loyola Univ/New Orleans	LA	15,660	C+
Lycoming College	PA	17,200	LC
Macalester College	MN	19,710	HC
Manchester College	IN	13,240	LC
Manhattanville College	NY	20,450	LC
Mansfield Univ	PA	6,348	C
Marian College	IN	12,936	C
Marlboro College	VT	23,305	C+
Marquette Univ	WI	16,114	VC
Mars Hill College	NC	11,050	LC
Marshall Univ	WV	5,762	LC
Mary Baldwin College	VA	17,700	LC
Mary Washington College	VA	7,910	HC
Marymount College/Tarrytown	NY	17,350	C
Marymount Manhattan College	NY	15,450	LC
Marywood College	PA	14,890	C
McMurry Univ	TX	10,100	C
McNeese State Univ	LA	4,543	NC
Meredith College	NC	9,440	C
Mesa State College	CO	5,127	NC
Messiah College	PA	14,664	VC
Methodist College	NC	12,400	C
Miami Univ	OH	8,066	VC
Middle Tenn State Univ	TN	3,857	C
Middlebury College	VT	24,400	MC
Midwestern State Univ	TX	4,542	LC
Millikin Univ	IL	15,499	C
Mills College	CA	20,848	VC
Millsaps College	MS	15,486	C+
Missouri Southern State College	MO	4,272	C
Missouri Valley College	MO	14,050	LC
Monmouth College	IL	17,300	C+
Montclair State College	NJ	7,539	C+
Moorhead State Univ	MN	5,076	C
Moravian College	PA	18,960	VC
Morehead State Univ	KY	4,600	LC
Morehouse College	GA	13,224	LC
Morgan State Univ	MD	7,366	C+
Morningside College	IA	13,896	C
Mount Holyoke College	MA	23,630	VC
Mount Union College	OH	15,850	C
Muhlenberg College	PA	20,795	VC
Murray State Univ	KY	4,702	C
Muskingum College	OH	16,650	C
National-Louis Univ	IL	13,218	C
Nebr Wesleyan Univ	NE	12,240	C
New College of Calif	CA	6,900	NC
New England College	NH	17,870	LC
New Mexico State Univ	NM	4,844	LC
New York Univ	NY	24,705	VC+
Newberry College	SC	11,994	LC
Niagara Univ	NY	14,552	C
N Car Agricultural and Technical State Univ	NC	4,477	LC
N Car Central Univ	NC	4,347	LC
N Car School of the Arts	NC	5,375	SP
N Dak State Univ of Agriculture and Applied Science	ND	4,774	VC
Northeast Missouri State Univ	MO	5,654	VC+
Northern Arizona Univ	AZ	4,844	C
Northern Illinois Univ	IL	6,408	C
Northern Kentucky Univ	KY	4,620	NC
Northern Mich Univ	MI	6,350	C
Northern Montana College	MT	4,976	C
Northwest Missouri State Univ	MO	5,010	LC
Northwest Nazarene College	ID	11,750	C
Northwestern College of Iowa	IA	12,250	C
Northwestern Okla State Univ	OK	3,424	C
Northwestern Univ	IL	21,093	MC
Oberlin College	OH	24,570	HC+
Occidental College	CA	21,792	HC
Ohio Northern Univ	OH	18,660	VC
Ohio State Univ	OH	7,218	LC
Ohio Univ	OH	7,341	C
Ohio Wesleyan Univ	OH	21,108	VC+
Okla Baptist Univ	OK	8,486	C
Okla City Univ	OK	9,840	C
Old Dominion Univ	VA	8,317	C
Oral Roberts Univ	OK	10,607	C+
Oregon State Univ	OR	6,175	C
Ottawa Univ	KS	10,490	C+
Otterbein College	OH	16,506	C
Pace Univ	NY	15,540	C
Pacific Univ	OR	17,869	C
Palm Beach Atlantic College	FL	10,720	C
Pepperdine Univ	CA	23,720	VC
Peru State College	NE	4,311	NC
Pfeiffer College	NC	11,670	LC
Phillips Univ	OK	12,744	C
Pittsburg State Univ	KS	4,478	NC
Pitzer College	CA	23,780	HC
Plymouth State College	NH	7,166	C
Point Loma Nazarene College	CA	13,532	C
Point Park College	PA	13,922	LC
Pomona College	CA	23,820	MC
Portland State Univ	OR	7,191	C
Prairie View A&M Univ	TX	4,740	LC
Presbyterian College	SC	15,400	VC
Principia College	IL	17,799	C
Providence College	RI	19,750	VC
Purdue Univ/West Lafayette	IN	6,636	C
Queens College	NC	14,950	C
Radford Univ	VA	7,034	LC
Ramapo College of New Jersey	NJ	8,027	C+
Randolph-Macon College	VA	16,980	C
Randolph-Macon Woman's College	VA	19,100	C
Reed College	OR	24,480	HC+
Rhode Island College	RI	7,901	LC
Rhodes College	TN	19,624	HC
Richard Stockton College of New Jersey	NJ	6,950	VC
Roanoke College	VA	16,975	C
Rockford College	IL	15,300	C
Rocky Mountain College	MT	11,320	C
Roger Williams Univ	RI	16,750	C
Rollins College	FL	20,875	VC
Roosevelt Univ	IL	12,368	C
Rowan College of New Jersey	NJ	7,358	VC
Rutgers Univ/Camden College of A&S	NJ	8,652	VC
Rutgers Univ/Douglass College	NJ	8,795	VC
Rutgers Univ/Livingston College	NJ	8,877	VC
Rutgers Univ/Mason Gross School of the Arts	NJ	8,877	SP
Rutgers Univ/Newark College of A&S	NJ	8,645	C
Rutgers Univ/Rutgers College	NJ	8,841	HC+
Rutgers Univ/Univ College—Camden	NJ	3,506	C
Rutgers Univ/Univ College—New Brunswick	NJ	0	LC
Saginaw Valley State Univ	MI	6,634	LC
St Andrews Presbyterian College	NC	14,240	LC
St Cloud State Univ	MN	5,015	C
St Edward's Univ	TX	12,636	C
St John's Univ	MN	15,364	C
St Mary College	KS	11,250	C
St Mary's College	IN	17,043	VC
St Mary's College of Maryland	MD	8,900	VC+
St Mary's College of Minn	MN	13,850	LC
St Michael's College	VT	17,930	C
St Vincent College	PA	13,934	LC
Salem State College	MA	6,712	C
Salisbury State Univ	MD	7,516	C+
Salve Regina Univ	RI	29,100	LC
Sam Houston State Univ	TX	4,506	C
Samford Univ	AL	11,400	VC
San Diego State Univ	CA	6,692	LC
San Francisco State Univ	CA	7,292	LC
San Jose State Univ	CA	6,680	LC
Santa Clara Univ	CA	18,783	VC
Sarah Lawrence College	NY	24,975	HC
Scripps College	CA	23,600	HC
Seattle Pacific Univ	WA	16,503	C
Seattle Univ	WA	16,590	C
Seton Hill College	PA	14,320	C
Shaw Univ	NC	8,936	C+
Shenandoah Univ	VA	11,800	C
Shepherd College	WV	5,540	C
Shorter College	GA	10,270	C
Simpson College	IA	14,635	VC
Skidmore College	NY	23,230	HC
Smith College	MA	24,236	HC
Sonoma State Univ	CA	6,996	LC
S Car State Univ	SC	5,424	LC
Southeastern Louisiana Univ	LA	4,230	NC
Southeastern Okla State Univ	OK	3,594	C
Southern Calif College	CA	12,356	C
Southern Conn State Univ	CT	7,532	C
Southern Illinois Univ at Carbondale	IL	6,234	C
Southern Illinois Univ at Edwardsville	IL	6,097	LC
Southern Methodist Univ	TX	18,520	VC
Southern Oregon State College	OR	6,128	C
Southern Univ and A&M College	LA	4,920	NC
Southern Utah Univ	UT	4,104	LC
Southwest Baptist Univ	MO	9,192	NC
Southwest Missouri State Univ	MO	4,956	C
Southwest Texas State Univ	TX	5,124	C
Southwestern Okla State Univ	OK	3,312	C
Southwestern Univ	TX	15,484	HC
Spelman College	GA	12,942	VC
Stanford Univ	CA	24,310	MC
SUNY at Binghamton	NY	7,921	HC
SUNY at Buffalo	NY	7,896	VC
SUNY/College at Brockport	NY	7,220	C+
SUNY/College at Buffalo	NY	7,035	VC
SUNY/College at Cortland	NY	7,326	C+
SUNY/College at Fredonia	NY	7,159	VC
SUNY/College at Geneseo	NY	6,949	HC
SUNY/College at New Paltz	NY	6,890	VC
SUNY/College at Oneonta	NY	7,878	C
SUNY/College at Oswego	NY	7,330	VC
SUNY/College at Plattsburgh	NY	6,917	C
SUNY/College at Purchase	NY	7,324	C
SUNY/Potsdam College	NY	6,906	C
Stephen F. Austin State Univ	TX	5,117	C
Stephens College	MO	18,460	C
Sterling College	KS	10,990	VC
Stetson Univ	FL	16,435	VC
Suffolk Univ	MA	15,360	LC
Sul Ross State Univ	TX	4,144	NC
Syracuse Univ	NY	21,305	HC
Tarleton State Univ	TX	4,082	LC
Teikyo Marycrest Univ	IA	13,755	VC
Texas A&M Univ at Kingsville	TX	3,808	LC
Texas Christian Univ	TX	12,180	C
Texas Tech Univ	TX	6,008	C
Texas Wesleyan Univ	TX	9,380	LC
Texas Woman's Univ	TX	4,392	C
The Univ of New Mexico	NM	5,304	C
Thomas A. Edison State College	NJ	400	
Thomas More College	KY	12,962	C
Towson State Univ	MD	7,452	C
Transylvania Univ	KY	14,970	VC+
Trenton State College	NJ	9,085	HC
Trevecca Nazarene College	TN	9,826	NC
Trinity College	CT	24,120	HC
Trinity Univ	TX	16,670	HC
Troy State Univ	AL	4,322	NC
Tufts Univ	MA	24,962	MC
Tulane Univ	LA	24,540	HC
Union College	KY	9,790	C
Univ of Akron	OH	6,699	NC
Univ of Alabama at Birmingham	AL	7,533	C
Univ of Alaska Anchorage	AK	7,131	C
Univ of Alaska Fairbanks	AK	4,718	C
Univ of Arizona	AZ	5,808	C
Univ of Arkansas at Fayetteville	AR	5,046	C
Univ of Arkansas at Little Rock	AR	4,419	C
Univ of Calif at Berkeley	CA	9,962	HC+
Univ of Calif at Davis	CA	9,534	VC
Univ of Calif at Los Angeles	CA	8,959	HC
Univ of Calif at Santa Barbara	CA	9,460	C
Univ of Calif at Santa Cruz	CA	9,060	VC
Univ of Calif, Riverside	CA	9,178	C
Univ of Calif, San Diego	CA	10,028	VC+
Univ of Calif/Irvine	CA	12,680	VC
Univ of Central Arkansas	AR	4,200	LC
Univ of Central Florida	FL	6,061	C+
Univ of Central Okla	OK	3,647	C
Univ of Cincinnati	OH	7,989	C
Univ of Colo at Boulder	CO	6,410	VC
Univ of Conn	CT	9,168	C
Univ of Dallas	TX	14,983	VC
Univ of Dayton	OH	15,120	C+
Univ of Denver	CO	19,290	C+
Univ of Detroit Mercy	MI	14,720	C
Univ of Evansville	IN	15,300	VC
Univ of Findlay	OH	15,764	C
Univ of Georgia	GA	5,655	VC
Univ of Hartford	CT	19,858	LC
Univ of Houston	TX	5,215	C
Univ of Idaho	ID	4,830	C
Univ of Illinois at Urbana-Champaign	IL	7,764	HC
Univ of Iowa	IA	5,658	VC
Univ of Kansas	KS	5,200	NC
Univ of Kentucky	KY	5,152	VC
Univ of La Verne	CA	17,400	C
Univ of Louisville	KY	5,948	C
Univ of Maine at Farmington	ME	6,700	C
Univ of Maine at Presque Isle	ME	6,374	C
Univ of Maryland/Baltimore County	MD	7,746	VC
Univ of Maryland/College Park	MD	8,182	VC
Univ of Mass/Amherst	MA	9,364	LC
Univ of Mass/Boston	MA	4,253	C
Univ of Memphis	TN	3,476	C
Univ of Miami	FL	22,107	VC
Univ of Mich/Ann Arbor	MI	9,428	HC+
Univ of Mich/Flint	MI	2,916	C
Univ of Minn/Duluth	MN	6,512	C
Univ of Minn/Morris	MN	6,825	HC
Univ of Miss	MS	5,756	C
Univ of Missouri/Columbia	MO	6,254	HC
Univ of Missouri/Kansas City	MO	5,906	VC
Univ of Montana	MT	5,529	C
Univ of Montevallo	AL	5,310	C
Univ of Nebr at Kearney	NE	4,308	LC
Univ of Nebr at Omaha	NE	1,889	LC
Univ of Nebr-Lincoln	NE	5,278	LC
Univ of Nevada/Las Vegas	NV	6,405	C
Univ of Nevada/Reno	NV	5,735	C
Univ of New Hampshire	NH	8,242	C
Univ of New Orleans	LA	5,468	C
Univ of North Alabama	AL	4,236	NC
Univ of N Car at Asheville	NC	4,791	VC
Univ of N Car at Chapel Hill	NC	5,330	HC
Univ of N Car at Charlotte	NC	4,597	C
Univ of N Car at Greensboro	NC	5,192	C
Univ of N Dak	ND	4,902	NC
Univ of North Texas	TX	4,853	C
Univ of Northern Colo	CO	6,008	C
Univ of Northern Iowa	IA	5,137	C
Univ of Notre Dame	IN	20,150	MC
Univ of Okla	OK	5,427	VC
Univ of Penn	PA	24,238	MC
Univ of Pittsburgh at Johnstown	PA	8,914	C
Univ of Portland	OR	15,564	C
Univ of PR/Rio Piedras	PR	0	
Univ of Puget Sound	WA	19,520	HC
Univ of Rhode Island	RI	9,205	C
Univ of St Thomas	MN	15,785	C+
Univ of St Thomas	TX	11,676	C+
Univ of Science and Arts of Okla	OK	3,304	C
Univ of South Alabama	AL	5,451	C
Univ of S Car	SC	6,158	C
Univ of S Dak	SD	4,722	C
Univ of South Florida	FL	5,475	C+
Univ of Southern Calif	CA	23,006	VC
Univ of Southern Indiana	IN	3,720	NC
Univ of Southern Maine	ME	7,299	C
Univ of Southern Miss	MS	4,542	LC
Univ of Southwestern Louisiana	LA	3,968	NC
Univ of Tenn/Knoxville	TN	5,668	C
Univ of Texas at Austin	TX	5,160	VC
Univ of Texas at El Paso	TX	3,160	LC
Univ of the District of Columbia	DC	974	NC
Univ of the Pacific	CA	21,100	C
Univ of Toledo	OH	6,636	NC
Univ of Tulsa	OK	13,795	VC
Univ of Utah	UT	5,975	C
Univ of Vermont	VT	10,776	C+
Univ of Virginia	VA	7,964	MC
Univ of Washington	WA	6,618	VC
Univ of Wisc/Eau Claire	WI	4,647	C
Univ of Wisc/Green Bay	WI	4,904	C
Univ of Wisc/La Crosse	WI	4,487	C
Univ of Wisc/Madison	WI	6,400	HC
Univ of Wisc/Milwaukee	WI	6,165	C
Univ of Wisc/Parkside	WI	5,247	C
Univ of Wisc/Stevens Point	WI	5,047	C+
Univ of Wisc/Superior	WI	4,330	C
Univ of Wisc/Whitewater	WI	4,700	C
Univ of Wyoming	WY	4,991	NC
Utah State Univ	UT	4,683	C
Utica College of Syracuse Univ	NY	16,714	LC
Valdosta State Univ	GA	4,670	LC
Valparaiso Univ	IN	14,810	VC
Vanderbilt Univ	TN	23,422	HC+
Vassar College	NY	24,206	HC
Virginia Commonwealth Univ	VA	7,909	C
Virginia Polytechnic Inst and State Univ	VA	6,828	C
Virginia Polytechnic Inst and State Univ	VA	6,828	C
Virginia Wesleyan College	VA	14,950	VC

School	ST	$IS	SR
Viterbo College	WI	12,670	C
Wabash College	IN	16,250	VC
Wagner College	NY	17,950	C
Wake Forest Univ	NC	17,280	MC
Washburn Univ of Topeka	KS	5,802	NC
Washington and Lee Univ	VA	17,735	MC
Washington College	MD	19,270	C+
Washington State Univ	WA	6,364	C
Washington Univ	MO	23,507	HC
Wayland Baptist Univ	TX	7,811	NC
Wayne State College	NE	4,260	NC
Wayne State Univ	MI	2,680	C
Weber State Univ	UT	4,398	C
Webster Univ	MO	12,650	C
Wellesley College	MA	23,815	MC
Wells College	NY	19,460	C+
Wesleyan Univ	CT	23,770	MC
West Chester Univ of Penn	PA	7,492	C
West Virginia Univ	WV	5,774	C
West Virginia Wesleyan College	WV	16,900	C
Western Carolina Univ	NC	3,811	C
Western Conn State Univ	CT	6,622	C
Western Illinois Univ	IL	5,241	LC
Western Kentucky Univ	KY	4,808	C
Western Mich Univ	MI	6,820	C
Western State College of Colo	CO	5,560	C
Western Washington Univ	WA	6,077	VC
Westminster College	MO	13,750	C+
Westminster College of Salt Lake City	UT	12,100	C
Westmont College	CA	18,732	C
Whitman College	WA	20,595	HC
Whittier College	CA	21,661	C
Wichita State Univ	KS	5,068	NC
Wilkes Univ	PA	15,728	LC
Willamette Univ	OR	17,995	VC
William Carey College	MS	7,050	C
William Paterson College	NJ	7,438	C+
Williams College	MA	24,390	MC
Wilmington College	OH	13,700	LC
Winona State Univ	MN	5,200	VC
Winthrop Univ	SC	6,750	C
Wittenberg Univ	OH	19,998	VC
Women's College of Brenau Univ	GA	14,734	C
Wright State Univ	OH	6,896	LC
Yale Univ	CT	25,110	MC
Youngstown State Univ	OH	6,447	LC

DRAWING

School	ST	$IS	SR
Aquinas College	MI	14,526	C
Arizona State Univ Main Campus	AZ	6,444	C
Art Inst of Southern Calif	CA	16,000	SP
Atlanta College of Art	GA	12,495	SP
Barton College	NC	10,689	LC
Cooper Union for the Advancement of Science and Art	NY	8,430	MC
Edinboro Univ of Penn	PA	7,181	C
Louisiana State Univ and A&M College	LA	5,605	C
Maryland Inst, College of Art	MD	18,420	SP
Milwaukee Inst of Art and Design	WI	9,800	SP
Miss Univ for Women	MS	4,456	LC
Moore College of Art and Design	PA	17,947	SP
Northern Mich Univ	MI	6,350	C
Ohio State Univ	OH	7,218	LC
Pacific Northwest College of Art	OR	7,700	SP
Plymouth State College	NH	7,166	C
Univ of Hartford	CT	19,858	LC
Univ of North Texas	TX	4,853	C
Univ of Texas at El Paso	TX	3,160	LC
William Carey College	MS	7,050	C

DRIVER AND SAFETY EDUCATION

School	ST	$IS	SR
N Car Agricultural and Technical State Univ	NC	4,477	LC

DUTCH

School	ST	$IS	SR
Calvin College	MI	13,020	VC
Univ of Calif at Berkeley	CA	9,962	HC+

EARLY CHILDHOOD EDUCATION

School	ST	$IS	SR
Abilene Christian Univ	TX	10,460	NC
Adrian College	MI	14,340	C
Alabama A&M Univ	AL	4,200	C
Alabama State Univ	AL	3,428	NC
Albany State College	GA	4,481	LC
Alcorn State Univ	MS	4,474	C+
Alverno College	WI	11,344	C
American International College	MA	14,029	C
Andrews Univ	MI	14,952	NC
Angelo State Univ	TX	5,176	C
Anna Maria College	MA	15,975	LC
Appalachian State Univ	NC	4,095	C
Arizona State Univ Main Campus	AZ	6,444	C
Arkansas State Univ	AR	4,250	NC
Ashland Univ	OH	15,508	C
Atlantic Union College	MA	14,150	LC
Auburn Univ	AL	5,823	C+
Auburn Univ at Montgomery	AL	3,390	C
Audrey Cohen College	NY	11,184	LC
Augusta College	GA	1,452	C
Augustana College	SD	13,420	C
Averett College	VA	13,610	LC
Ball State Univ	IN	6,032	LC
Barber-Scotia College	NC	6,840	NC
Barry Univ	FL	16,050	C
Bayamon Tech Univ College	PR	1,600	
Baylor Univ	TX	10,990	C+
Beaver College	PA	17,660	C
Bemidji State Univ	MN	5,188	C
Benedict College	SC	8,376	LC
Bennett College	NC	8,920	LC
Bennington College	VT	24,850	VC+
Berea College	KY	2,883	VC+
Berry College	GA	11,990	VC
Bethany College	WV	18,300	C+
Bethel College	MN	15,050	C
Birmingham-Southern College	AL	15,154	VC+
Bloomsburg Univ of Penn	PA	6,312	C+
Bluffton College	OH	12,951	C
Boston College	MA	22,706	MC
Boston Univ	MA	24,130	HC
Bowie State Univ	MD	7,294	LC
Bowling Green State Univ	OH	6,701	C
Bradley Univ	IL	14,718	C+
Brewton-Parker College	GA	6,828	NC
Bridgewater State College	MA	7,518	C
Brigham Young Univ	UT	5,625	HC
Brooklyn Campus of LIU	NY	15,000	LC
Bucknell Univ	PA	22,320	HC
Calif Lutheran Univ	CA	17,240	C
Cal State/Bakersfield	CA	5,402	C
Cal State/Fresno	CA	5,747	C
Cal State/Fullerton	CA	4,850	LC
Cal State/Sacramento	CA	6,387	C
Calif Univ of Penn	PA	7,370	C
Cameron Univ	OK	3,686	LC
Cardinal Stritch College	WI	11,252	C
Carlow College	PA	13,914	C
Carroll College	WI	15,490	C
Carson-Newman College	TN	11,250	C
Central Conn State Univ	CT	7,108	C
Central Methodist College	MO	11,410	C
Central Mich Univ	MI	6,737	LC
Central Missouri State Univ	MO	5,138	LC
Central Washington Univ	WA	5,644	C
Chadron State College	NE	4,091	NC
Chaminade Univ of Honolulu	HI	14,290	C
Charleston Southern Univ	SC	10,282	LC
Chatham College	PA	18,010	C
Chestnut Hill College	PA	14,525	C
Cheyney Univ of Penn	PA	7,005	C
Chicago State Univ	IL	2,198	C
Christian Heritage College	CA	11,756	C
CUNY/Baruch College	NY	2,562	VC
CUNY/Brooklyn College	NY	2,450	VC
CUNY/City College	NY	2,543	VC
CUNY/Herbert H. Lehman College	NY	2,542	C
CUNY/Hunter College	NY	4,101	VC
CUNY/Queens College	NY	2,631	C
CUNY/York College	NY	2,534	NC
Clarion Univ of Penn	PA	6,518	C
Clarke College	IA	13,950	C+
Clemson Univ	SC	6,564	VC
Cleveland State Univ	OH	7,287	NC
Coastal Carolina Univ	SC	6,010	LC
Coker College	SC	13,790	C
Colby-Sawyer College	NH	18,495	LC
College Misericordia	PA	15,820	C
College of Charleston	SC	6,250	C
College of New Rochelle	NY	15,440	LC
College of Notre Dame of Maryland	MD	16,050	C
College of Our Lady of The Elms	MA	15,639	C
College of St Catherine	MN	14,670	C
College of St Elizabeth	NJ	15,800	C
College of St Joseph	VT	12,650	LC
College of St Mary	NE	12,500	C
College of St Scholastica	MN	14,868	C
Columbia College	SC	13,520	LC
Columbia Union College	MD	13,650	LC
Columbus College	GA	4,892	LC
Concord College	WV	5,104	NC
Concordia College	MN	13,200	C
Concordia College	NE	11,776	NC
Concordia College	NY	0	LC
Concordia College	OR	12,300	C
Concordia Univ	IL	12,611	C
Concordia Univ	CA	14,675	C
Converse College	SC	15,750	C
Cumberland College	KY	9,756	C
Delaware State College	DE	5,656	C
DePaul Univ	IL	15,535	VC
Dickinson State Univ	ND	3,792	
Drake Univ	IA	17,195	VC
Duquesne Univ	PA	16,434	VC
East Carolina Univ	NC	4,498	C
East Central Univ	OK	3,558	C
East Stroudsburg Univ	PA	6,886	C
East Tenn State Univ	TN	4,406	C
East Texas State Univ	TX	4,572	LC
Eastern Conn State Univ	CT	6,966	C
Eastern Illinois Univ	IL	5,548	C
Eastern Kentucky Univ	KY	4,840	NC
Eastern Mennonite College	VA	12,700	C
Eastern Mich Univ	MI	6,749	C
Eastern Montana College	MT	5,165	LC
Eastern Nazarene College	MA	12,165	LC
Edgewood College	WI	11,700	C
Edinboro Univ of Penn	PA	7,181	C
Edward Waters College	FL	8,300	NC
Elizabeth City State Univ	NC	4,254	LC
Elizabethtown College	PA	17,850	VC
Elmhurst College	IL	12,536	C
Emory and Henry College	VA	12,776	C
Emory Univ	GA	21,930	HC
Erskine College	SC	14,310	C
Evangel College	MO	10,142	LC
Fairmont State College	WV	4,640	LC
Fayetteville State Univ	NC	3,926	LC
Fitchburg State College	MA	6,962	C
Florida A&M Univ	FL	4,651	C
Florida Atlantic Univ	FL	5,525	C
Florida Southern College	FL	12,260	C
Florida State Univ	FL	5,814	VC
Fontbonne College	MO	12,090	C
Fort Valley State College	GA	3,974	LC
Framingham State College	MA	6,580	C
Francis Marion Univ	SC	5,878	LC
Freed-Hardeman Univ	TN	8,585	VC
Friends Univ	KS	11,205	C
Frostburg State Univ	MD	6,940	C
Gallaudet Univ	DC	9,850	SP
Gannon Univ	PA	14,872	C
Georgia College	GA	4,310	LC
Georgia Southern Univ	GA	4,988	LC
Georgia Southwestern College	GA	4,338	LC
Glenville State College	WV	4,810	LC
Gordon College	MA	16,790	C
Goshen College	IN	12,360	C
Grambling State Univ	LA	4,712	NC
Greenville College	IL	14,190	C
Gwynedd-Mercy College	PA	15,450	C
Hampton Univ	VA	10,706	C
Hannibal-LaGrange College	MO	8,400	LC
Hardin-Simmons Univ	TX	9,080	C
Harding Univ	AR	9,050	VC
Harris-Stowe State College	MO	1,888	LC
Hillsdale College	MI	15,110	VC
Hofstra Univ	NY	16,580	VC
Holy Family College	PA	8,300	C
Hood College	MD	19,010	VC
Houston Baptist Univ	TX	11,055	C
Howard Payne Univ	TX	8,052	LC
Howard Univ	DC	11,680	C
Humboldt State Univ	CA	5,676	C
Huntingdon College	AL	11,400	C
Idaho State Univ	ID	4,442	C
Illinois State Univ	IL	6,413	C
Immaculata College	PA	14,620	C
Incarnate Word College	TX	12,307	C
Indiana State Univ	IN	6,210	C
Indiana Univ Bloomington	IN	6,495	VC
Indiana Univ of Penn	PA	6,373	C
Indiana Univ/South Bend	IN	2,141	LC
Inter American Univ of PR/ Aguadilla Regional College	PR	2,290	
Inter American Univ of PR/ Barranquitas Regional College	PR	2,730	
Inter American Univ of PR/ Bayamon Univ College	PR	2,300	
Inter American Univ of PR/ Metropolitan Campus	PR	2,340	
Inter American Univ of PR/ Ponce Regional College	PR	2,300	
Inter American Univ of PR/ San German	PR	4,620	
Inter-American Univ of PR/ Fajardo Regional College	PR	2,732	
Iowa State Univ	IA	5,456	C
Iowa Wesleyan College	IA	13,250	C
Jacksonville State Univ	AL	4,080	LC
Jacksonville Univ	FL	13,390	C
Jersey City State College	NJ	7,797	LC
John Brown Univ	AR	9,880	VC
John Carroll Univ	OH	16,510	C
Juniata College	PA	18,390	C+
Kansas State Univ	KS	4,816	NC
Kean College of New Jersey	NJ	6,395	LC
Keene State College	NH	7,081	C
Kendall College	IL	12,651	LC
Kent State Univ	OH	6,740	LC
Kentucky State Univ	KY	4,282	C+
Knoxville College	TN	8,320	LC
Kutztown Univ	PA	6,528	C
La Salle Univ	PA	16,940	VC
LaGrange College	GA	10,602	C
Lakeland College	WI	12,845	LC
Lamar Univ	TX	3,798	C
Lander Univ	SC	6,180	LC
Lenoir-Rhyne College	NC	14,068	C
Lesley College	MA	17,120	LC
Limestone College	SC	10,700	LC
Lincoln Memorial Univ	TN	8,218	C
Lincoln Univ	PA	0	LC
Lindenwood College	MO	13,560	C
Linfield College	OR	16,670	VC
Livingston Univ	AL	3,979	C
Livingstone College	NC	8,600	LC
Lock Haven Univ of Penn	PA	7,128	C
LIU/C. W. Post Campus	NY	16,870	C
Loras College	IA	14,160	C
Louisiana Tech Univ	LA	4,284	C
Lourdes College	OH	6,410	LC
Loyola Univ of Chicago	IL	15,880	C+
Loyola Univ/New Orleans	LA	15,660	C+
Luther College	IA	15,900	VC
Lynchburg College	VA	17,000	C
Lyndon State College	VT	8,394	LC
Lynn Univ	FL	18,300	C
Manchester College	IN	13,240	LC
Manhattan College	NY	19,000	C
Manhattanville College	NY	20,450	LC
Mankato State Univ	MN	5,097	LC
Mansfield Univ	PA	6,348	C
Marian College	IN	12,936	C
Marian College of Fond du Lac	WI	12,250	LC
Marshall Univ	WV	5,762	LC
Martin Univ	IN	4,830	NC
Mary Baldwin College	VA	17,700	LC
Marygrove College	MI	5,877	VC
Marymount College/ Tarrytown	NY	17,350	C
Marymount Manhattan College	NY	15,450	LC
Maryville Univ-St Louis	MO	12,900	VC
Marywood College	PA	14,890	C
McNeese State Univ	LA	4,543	NC
McPherson College	KS	11,360	VC
Mercer Univ	GA	15,123	C
Mercy College	NY	11,180	NC
Mercyhurst College	PA	13,488	C
Messiah College	PA	14,664	VC
Methodist College	NC	12,400	C
Miami Univ	OH	8,066	VC
Mich State Univ	MI	7,842	C
MidAmerica Nazarene College	KS	10,208	NC
Middle Tenn State Univ	TN	3,857	C
Midland Lutheran College	NE	12,410	LC
Miles College	AL	7,150	NC
Millersville Univ of Penn	PA	7,370	VC
Mills College	CA	20,848	VC
Miss College	MS	8,348	C
Missouri Southern State College	MO	4,272	
Missouri Western State College	MO	4,384	NC
Monmouth College	NJ	16,820	C
Moorhead State Univ	MN	5,076	C
Morehouse College	GA	13,224	LC
Morningside College	IA	13,896	C
Morris Brown College	GA	12,234	NC
Morris College	SC	6,880	LC
Mount Holyoke College	MA	23,630	VC
Mount Ida College	MA	16,700	LC
Mount Mary College	WI	10,920	C
Mount Senario College	WI	10,970	LC
Mount Vernon College	DC	20,668	C
Mount Vernon Nazarene College	OH	10,390	C
Murray State Univ	KY	4,702	C
Muskingum College	OH	16,650	C
National-Louis Univ	IL	13,218	C
Neumann College	PA	9,950	LC
New York Univ	NY	24,705	VC+
Newberry College	SC	11,994	LC
Nicholls State Univ	LA	4,531	NC
Norfolk State Univ	VA	6,345	LC
North Adams State College	MA	7,750	C
N Car Agricultural and Technical State Univ	NC	4,477	LC
North Georgia College	GA	4,103	LC
North Park College	IL	14,310	C
Northeast Louisiana Univ	LA	3,906	NC
Northeastern Illinois Univ	IL	1,955	C
Northeastern State Univ	OK	5,250	C
Northeastern Univ	MA	19,851	C

School	ST	$IS	SR
Northern Arizona Univ	AZ	4,844	C
Northern Illinois Univ	IL	6,408	C
Northern Mich Univ	MI	6,350	C
Northern State Univ	SD	4,186	LC
Northland College	WI	13,550	LC
Northwest Missouri State Univ	MO	5,010	LC
Northwest Nazarene College	ID	11,750	C
Northwestern College of Iowa	IA	12,250	C
Northwestern Okla State Univ	OK	3,424	C
Northwestern State Univ of Louisiana	LA	4,287	NC
Notre Dame College	NH	14,220	C
Notre Dame College of Ohio	OH	11,370	C
Nyack College	NY	12,210	LC
Occidental College	CA	21,792	HC
Oglethorpe Univ	GA	16,360	VC
Ohio Univ	OH	7,341	C
Ohio Wesleyan Univ	OH	21,108	VC+
Okla Baptist Univ	OK	8,486	C
Okla Christian Univ of Science and Arts	OK	8,790	NC
Okla City Univ	OK	9,840	C
Okla State Univ	OK	5,086	VC
Old Dominion Univ	VA	8,317	C
Olivet Nazarene Univ	IL	11,976	C
Otterbein College	OH	16,506	C
Ouachita Baptist Univ	AR	8,940	C
Pace Univ	NY	15,540	C
Pacific Christian College	CA	12,700	C
Pacific Union College	CA	15,075	C
Paine College	GA	8,207	LC
Park College	MO	7,320	C
Pembroke State Univ	NC	3,538	LC
Penn State Univ/Univ Park Campus	PA	8,752	HC
Piedmont College	GA	8,540	LC
Pikeville College	KY	8,500	NC
Pine Manor College	MA	21,700	LC
Pittsburg State Univ	KS	4,478	NC
Plymouth State College	NH	7,166	C
Point Park College	PA	13,922	LC
Prescott College	AZ	9,775	C
Purdue Univ/Calumet	IN	2,374	NC
Purdue Univ/West Lafayette	IN	6,636	C
Rhode Island College	RI	7,901	LC
Rider College	NJ	18,160	C
Ripon College	WI	18,320	C+
Rivier College	NH	14,920	LC
Rockford College	IL	15,300	C
Roosevelt Univ	IL	12,368	C
Rowan College of New Jersey	NJ	7,358	VC
Sacred Heart Univ	CT	16,350	C
St Augustine's College	NC	9,300	C+
St Cloud State Univ	MN	5,015	C
St John's Univ	NY	8,980	C+
St Joseph College	CT	16,225	C
St Joseph's College	NY	7,322	C
St Louis Univ	MO	15,522	VC
St Mary's College of Calif	CA	18,848	VC
St Mary's College of Minn	MN	13,850	LC
St Mary-of-the-Woods College	IN	14,430	NC
St Thomas Aquinas College	NY	13,550	C
St Xavier Univ	IL	14,700	C
Samford Univ	AL	11,400	VC
San Francisco State Univ	CA	7,292	LC
San Jose State Univ	CA	6,680	LC
Sarah Lawrence College	NY	24,975	HC
Seton Hill College	PA	14,320	C
Shaw Univ	NC	8,936	C+
Shepherd College	WV	5,540	C
Shorter College	GA	10,270	C
Silver Lake College	WI	8,280	LC
Simpson College	IA	14,635	VC
Sinte Gleska Univ	SD	1,580	NC
Sioux Falls College	SD	11,540	C
Slippery Rock Univ	PA	6,803	C
Smith College	MA	24,236	HC
Sojourner-Douglass College	MD	5,265	LC
S Car State Univ	SC	5,424	LC
S Dak State Univ	SD	4,562	C
Southeast Missouri State Univ	MO	5,854	C
Southeastern College of the Assemblies of God	FL	6,618	NC
Southeastern Louisiana Univ	LA	4,230	NC
Southeastern Okla State Univ	OK	3,594	C
Southern Arkansas Univ	AR	3,432	NC
Southern Conn State Univ	CT	7,532	C
Southern Illinois Univ at Carbondale	IL	6,234	C
Southern Illinois Univ at Edwardsville	IL	6,097	LC
Southern Nazarene Univ	OK	9,206	NC
Southern Univ and A&M College	LA	4,920	NC
Southwest Baptist Univ	MO	9,192	NC
Southwest Texas State Univ	TX	5,124	C
Southwestern Okla State Univ	OK	3,312	C
Spalding Univ	KY	10,496	LC
Spring Hill College	AL	16,015	C+
Springfield College	MA	15,200	LC
SUNY/College at Cortland	NY	7,326	C+
SUNY/College at Fredonia	NY	7,159	VC
SUNY/College at Geneseo	NY	6,949	HC
SUNY/College at New Paltz	NY	6,890	VC
SUNY/Potsdam College	NY	6,906	C
Stephen F. Austin State Univ	TX	5,117	C
Stephens College	MO	18,460	C
Syracuse Univ	NY	21,305	HC
Teikyo Marycrest Univ	IA	13,755	VC
Temple Univ	PA	10,281	C
Tenn State Univ	TN	4,626	C+
Tenn Tech Univ	TN	5,190	C
Texas College	TX	5,930	NC
Texas Southern Univ	TX	4,500	NC
Texas Tech Univ	TX	6,008	C
Texas Wesleyan Univ	TX	9,380	LC
Thomas College	GA	3,123	NC
Toccoa Falls College	GA	9,350	C
Towson State Univ	MD	7,452	C
Trenton State College	NJ	9,085	HC
Trevecca Nazarene College	TN	9,826	NC
Trinity College	DC	17,660	C
Trinity College of Vermont	VT	16,015	LC
Troy State Univ	AL	4,322	C
Troy State Univ at Dothan/Fort Rucker	AL	2,260	NC
Tufts Univ	MA	24,962	MC
Tulane Univ	LA	24,540	HC
Tuskegee Univ	AL	10,128	C
Union College	KY	9,790	C
Univ of Akron	OH	6,699	NC
Univ of Alabama	AL	5,702	C
Univ of Alabama at Birmingham	AL	7,533	C
Univ of Alaska Southeast	AK	4,075	LC
Univ of Arizona	AZ	5,808	C
Univ of Arkansas at Fayetteville	AR	5,046	C
Univ of Arkansas at Little Rock	AR	4,419	C
Univ of Arkansas at Pine Bluff	AR	3,978	LC
Univ of Central Arkansas	AR	4,200	LC
Univ of Central Florida	FL	6,061	C+
Univ of Central Okla	OK	3,647	C
Univ of Cincinnati	OH	7,989	C
Univ of Dayton	OH	15,120	C+
Univ of Delaware	DE	8,013	VC
Univ of Detroit Mercy	MI	14,720	C
Univ of Dubuque	IA	14,150	LC
Univ of Georgia	GA	5,655	VC
Univ of Guam	GU	4,139	NC
Univ of Hartford	CT	19,858	LC
Univ of Houston	TX	5,215	C
Univ of Idaho	ID	4,830	C
Univ of Illinois at Urbana-Champaign	IL	7,764	HC
Univ of Kentucky	KY	5,152	VC
Univ of La Verne	CA	17,400	C
Univ of Louisville	KY	5,948	C
Univ of Maine	ME	7,990	C
Univ of Maine at Farmington	ME	6,700	C
Univ of Maine at Machias	ME	6,135	C
Univ of Mary	ND	8,910	C
Univ of Mary Hardin-Baylor	TX	8,120	NC
Univ of Maryland/Baltimore County	MD	7,746	VC
Univ of Maryland/College Park	MD	8,182	VC
Univ of Mass/Amherst	MA	9,364	LC
Univ of Memphis	TN	3,476	C
Univ of Mich/Dearborn	MI	3,399	HC
Univ of Mich/Flint	MI	2,916	C
Univ of Minn/Twin Cities	MN	6,682	VC
Univ of Miss	MS	5,756	C
Univ of Missouri/Columbia	MO	6,254	HC
Univ of Missouri/St. Louis	MO	6,378	C
Univ of Mobile	AL	9,400	C
Univ of Montevallo	AL	5,310	C
Univ of Nebr at Kearney	NE	4,308	LC
Univ of Nebr at Omaha	NE	1,889	LC
Univ of Nebr-Lincoln	NE	5,278	LC
Univ of North Alabama	AL	4,236	NC
Univ of N Car at Chapel Hill	NC	5,330	HC
Univ of N Car at Greensboro	NC	5,192	C
Univ of N Dak	ND	4,902	NC
Univ of North Florida	FL	5,082	C
Univ of North Texas	TX	4,853	C
Univ of Northern Iowa	IA	5,137	C
Univ of Okla	OK	5,427	VC
Univ of PR/Rio Piedras	PR	0	
Univ of Richmond	VA	16,700	HC
Univ of Science and Arts of Okla	OK	3,304	C
Univ of South Alabama	AL	5,451	C
Univ of S Car at Aiken	SC	5,386	C
Univ of S Car at Spartanburg	SC	2,320	C
Univ of South Florida	FL	5,475	C+
Univ of Southern Indiana	IN	3,720	NC
Univ of Southern Miss	MS	4,542	C
Univ of Tenn at Chattanooga	TN	5,375	C
Univ of Tenn at Martin	TN	4,550	C
Univ of Texas at El Paso	TX	3,160	LC
Univ of Texas at San Antonio	TX	6,420	C
Univ of the District of Columbia	DC	974	NC
Univ of Toledo	OH	6,636	NC
Univ of Utah	UT	5,975	C
Univ of Vermont	VT	10,776	C+
Univ of West Florida	FL	5,415	C
Univ of Wisc/River Falls	WI	4,655	C
Univ of Wisc/Stout	WI	4,719	C
Univ of Wisc/Whitewater	WI	4,700	C
Utah State Univ	UT	4,683	C
Valdosta State Univ	GA	4,670	LC
Vanderbilt Univ	TN	23,422	HC+
Virginia Intermont College	VA	12,250	LC
Virginia Polytechnic Inst and State Univ	VA	6,828	C
Virginia Union Univ	VA	10,555	LC
Viterbo College	WI	12,670	C
Walsh Univ	OH	11,640	C
Washburn Univ of Topeka	KS	5,802	NC
Washington State Univ	WA	6,364	C
Washington Univ	MO	23,507	HC
Wayne State Univ	MI	2,680	C
Weber State Univ	UT	4,398	C
Wesleyan College	GA	15,445	C
West Chester Univ of Penn	PA	7,492	C
West Georgia College	GA	4,256	C
West Liberty State College	WV	4,690	LC
West Virginia State College	WV	5,044	LC
Westbrook College	ME	15,900	C
Western Carolina Univ	NC	3,811	C
Western Illinois Univ	IL	5,241	LC
Western Montana College of the Univ of Montana	MT	1,646	C
Western Washington Univ	WA	6,077	VC
Westfield State College	MA	7,161	C
Westminster College	MO	13,750	C+
Westminster College of Salt Lake City	UT	12,100	C
Wheelock College	MA	18,000	LC
Wichita State Univ	KS	5,068	NC
Widener Univ	PA	16,840	C
Wilkes Univ	PA	15,728	LC
William Penn College	IA	13,400	C
William Tyndale College	MI	7,120	NC
William Woods Univ	MO	14,025	LC
Wilmington College	DE	5,200	NC
Winona State Univ	MN	5,200	VC
Winston-Salem State Univ	NC	4,142	LC
Winthrop Univ	SC	6,750	C
Women's College of Brenau Univ	GA	14,734	C
Worcester State College	MA	6,414	LC
Xavier Univ	OH	15,710	C+
Xavier Univ of Louisiana	LA	10,400	C
Youngstown State Univ	OH	6,447	LC

EARLY CHILDHOOD STUDIES

School	ST	$IS	SR
Kentucky Wesleyan College	KY	11,550	C
Langston Univ	OK	2,907	LC
Univ of Minn/Duluth	MN	6,512	C
Wayne State College	NE	4,260	NC

EARTH SCIENCE

School	ST	$IS	SR
Adelphi Univ	NY	18,250	LC
Adrian College	MI	14,340	C
Auburn Univ	AL	5,823	C+
Augustana College	IL	16,959	VC
Augustana College	SD	13,420	C
Austin Peay State Univ	TN	4,350	C
Baldwin-Wallace College	OH	15,210	C
Baylor Univ	TX	10,990	C+
Bemidji State Univ	MN	5,188	C
Bloomsburg Univ of Penn	PA	6,312	C+
Bowling Green State Univ	OH	6,701	C
Bridgewater State College	MA	7,518	C
Calif State Polytechnic Univ/Pomona	CA	6,438	LC
Cal State/Long Beach	CA	6,057	LC
Cal State/Los Angeles	CA	4,940	VC
Cal State/Northridge	CA	7,122	LC
Cal State/Stanislaus	CA	6,799	C
Calif Univ of Penn	PA	7,370	C
Central Conn State Univ	CT	7,108	C
Central Mich Univ	MI	6,737	LC
Central Missouri State Univ	MO	5,138	LC
Central Washington Univ	WA	5,644	C
Chadron State College	NE	4,091	NC
CUNY/Brooklyn College	NY	2,450	VC
CUNY/City College	NY	2,543	VC
CUNY/York College	NY	2,534	NC
Clarion Univ of Penn	PA	6,518	C
Colby College	ME	24,230	HC
Columbia Univ/Columbia College	NY	26,757	MC
Concordia College	MI	13,660	C
Concordia Univ	IL	12,611	C
Dartmouth College	NH	24,354	MC
DePauw Univ	IN	18,530	VC
Dickinson State Univ	ND	3,792	C
Drake Univ	IA	17,195	VC
East Stroudsburg Univ	PA	6,886	C
East Texas State Univ	TX	4,572	LC
Eastern Mich Univ	MI	6,749	C
Edinboro Univ of Penn	PA	7,181	C
Emporia State Univ	KS	4,685	NC
Evergreen State College	WA	6,306	C
Fitchburg State College	MA	6,962	C
Fort Hays State Univ	KS	4,675	NC
Framingham State College	MA	6,580	C
Gannon Univ	PA	14,872	C
Indiana Univ of Penn	PA	6,373	C
Indiana Univ-Purdue Univ at Fort Wayne	IN	2,500	LC
Iowa State Univ	IA	5,456	C
Jersey City State College	NJ	7,797	LC
Johns Hopkins Univ	MD	24,360	MC
Juniata College	PA	18,390	C+
Kean College of New Jersey	NJ	6,395	LC
Kent State Univ	OH	6,740	LC
Lehigh Univ	PA	23,250	HC
Lewis-Clark State College	ID	4,040	C
Lock Haven Univ of Penn	PA	7,128	C
Mankato State Univ	MN	5,097	LC
Mass Inst of Tech	MA	24,800	MC
Mercyhurst College	PA	13,488	C
Mich State Univ	MI	7,842	C
Middle Tenn State Univ	TN	3,857	C
Millersville Univ of Penn	PA	7,370	VC
Minot State Univ	ND	3,748	NC
Montana State Univ	MT	5,534	C
Moorhead State Univ	MN	5,076	C
Morehead State Univ	KY	4,600	LC
Murray State Univ	KY	4,702	C
N Car State Univ	NC	4,984	VC
N Dak State Univ of Agriculture and Applied Science	ND	4,774	VC
Northeastern Illinois Univ	IL	1,955	C
Northern Mich Univ	MI	6,350	C
Northland College	WI	13,550	LC
Northwest Missouri State Univ	MO	5,010	LC
Norwich Univ	VT	18,730	C
Ohio Wesleyan Univ	OH	21,108	VC+
Pacific Lutheran Univ	WA	15,998	VC
Penn State Univ/Univ Park Campus	PA	8,752	HC
Prescott College	AZ	9,775	C
Purdue Univ/West Lafayette	IN	6,636	C
Rutgers Univ/Cook College	NJ	9,197	HC
St Cloud State Univ	MN	5,015	C
St Louis Univ	MO	15,522	VC
St Mary's Univ	TX	12,064	C
Salem State College	MA	6,712	C
Salisbury State Univ	MD	7,516	C+
Sarah Lawrence College	NY	24,975	HC
Shepherd College	WV	5,540	C
Shippensburg Univ of Penn	PA	7,052	C
Slippery Rock Univ	PA	6,803	C
Southeast Missouri State Univ	MO	5,854	C
Southeastern Louisiana Univ	LA	4,230	NC
Southern Arkansas Univ	AR	3,432	NC
Southern Conn State Univ	CT	7,532	C
Southwest Missouri State Univ	MO	4,956	C
Southwest Texas State Univ	TX	5,124	C
Stanford Univ	CA	24,310	MC
SUNY at Stony Brook	NY	7,658	VC
SUNY/College at Brockport	NY	7,220	C+
SUNY/College at Fredonia	NY	7,159	VC
SUNY/College at Geneseo	NY	6,949	HC
SUNY/College at Oneonta	NY	7,878	C
SUNY/College at Oswego	NY	7,330	VC
SUNY/College at Plattsburgh	NY	6,917	C
Tarleton State Univ	TX	4,082	LC
Texas Wesleyan Univ	TX	9,380	LC
Trinity Univ	TX	16,670	HC
Tulane Univ	LA	24,540	HC
Univ of Akron	OH	6,699	NC
Univ of Alaska Fairbanks	AK	4,718	C
Univ of Arizona	AZ	5,808	C
Univ of Arkansas at Fayetteville	AR	5,046	C
Univ of Calif at Berkeley	CA	9,962	HC+
Univ of Calif at Los Angeles	CA	8,959	HC
Univ of Calif at Santa Cruz	CA	9,060	VC
Univ of Calif, San Diego	CA	10,028	VC+
Univ of Dubuque	IA	14,150	LC
Univ of Indianapolis	IN	14,510	C
Univ of Memphis	TN	3,476	C
Univ of Mich/Flint	MI	2,916	C
Univ of Minn/Duluth	MN	6,512	C
Univ of Missouri/Kansas City	MO	5,906	VC
Univ of Nebr at Kearney	NE	4,308	LC
Univ of Nevada/Las Vegas	NV	6,405	C
Univ of New Hampshire	NH	8,242	C
Univ of N Car at Charlotte	NC	4,597	C
Univ of N Car at Greensboro	NC	5,192	C
Univ of N Dak	ND	4,902	NC
Univ of North Texas	TX	4,853	C

School	ST	$IS	SR
Univ of Northern Colo	CO	6,008	C
Univ of Northern Iowa	IA	5,137	C
Univ of South Alabama	AL	5,451	C
Univ of S Dak	SD	4,722	C
Univ of South Florida	FL	5,475	C+
Univ of Tulsa	OK	13,795	VC
Univ of Wisc/Green Bay	WI	4,904	C
Utah State Univ	UT	4,683	C
Valley City State Univ	ND	4,385	LC
Virginia State Univ	VA	7,040	C
Washington Univ	MO	23,507	HC
Wayne State College	NE	4,260	NC
Weber State Univ	UT	4,398	C
Wesleyan Univ	CT	23,770	MC
West Chester Univ of Penn	PA	7,492	C
West Georgia College	GA	4,256	C
Western Carolina Univ	NC	3,811	C
Western Conn State Univ	CT	6,622	C
Western Kentucky Univ	KY	4,808	C
Western Mich Univ	MI	6,820	C
Whittier College	CA	21,661	C
Wilkes Univ	PA	15,728	LC
William Penn College	IA	13,400	C
Winona State Univ	MN	5,200	VC
Wittenberg Univ	OH	19,998	VC
Youngstown State Univ	OH	6,447	LC

EAST ASIAN LANGUAGES AND LITERATURE

School	ST	$IS	SR
Bates College	ME	23,990	MC
Univ of Calif at Berkeley	CA	9,962	HC+
Univ of Kansas	KS	5,200	NC

EAST ASIAN STUDIES

School	ST	$IS	SR
Augsburg College	MN	15,608	C
Boston Univ	MA	24,130	HC
Brown Univ	RI	26,104	MC
Bryn Mawr College	PA	24,110	MC
Bucknell Univ	PA	22,320	HC
Central Conn State Univ	CT	7,108	C
Colby College	ME	24,230	HC
Columbia Univ/Barnard College	NY	25,492	HC
Columbia Univ/Columbia College	NY	26,757	MC
Denison Univ	OH	21,150	VC+
Dickinson College	PA	22,705	HC
Haverford College	PA	23,950	MC
Indiana Univ Bloomington	IN	6,495	VC
Lawrence Univ	WI	19,986	HC+
Lehigh Univ	PA	23,250	HC
Macalester College	MN	19,710	HC
Middlebury College	VT	24,400	MC
Oakland Univ	MI	6,714	VC
Oberlin College	OH	24,570	HC+
Penn State Univ/Univ Park Campus	PA	8,752	HC
Princeton Univ	NJ	24,650	MC
Rutgers Univ/Douglass College	NJ	8,795	VC
Rutgers Univ/Livingston College	NJ	8,877	VC
Rutgers Univ/Rutgers College	NJ	8,841	HC+
Stanford Univ	CA	24,310	MC
Union College	NY	23,817	HC
Univ of Arizona	AZ	5,808	C
Univ of Calif at Davis	CA	9,534	VC
Univ of Calif at Los Angeles	CA	8,959	HC
Univ of Florida	FL	5,850	HC
Univ of Minn/Twin Cities	MN	6,682	VC
Univ of N Car at Chapel Hill	NC	5,330	HC
Washington and Lee Univ	VA	17,735	MC
Western Washington Univ	WA	6,077	VC
Wittenberg Univ	OH	19,998	VC
Yale Univ	CT	25,110	MC

EASTERN EUROPEAN STUDIES

School	ST	$IS	SR
Boston Univ	MA	24,130	HC
Florida State Univ	FL	5,814	VC
Kent State Univ	OH	6,740	LC
Rutgers Univ/Douglass College	NJ	8,795	VC
Rutgers Univ/Livingston College	NJ	8,877	VC
Rutgers Univ/Newark College of A&S	NJ	8,645	C
SUNY at Albany	NY	7,059	VC
Univ of Colo at Boulder	CO	6,410	VC
Univ of Conn	CT	9,168	C
Univ of Kansas	KS	5,200	NC
Yale Univ	CT	25,110	MC

ECOLOGY

School	ST	$IS	SR
Cal State/Fullerton	CA	4,850	LC
Cal State/Hayward	CA	5,495	C
Colo State Univ	CO	6,566	VC
Hampshire College	MA	25,320	C
Idaho State Univ	ID	4,442	C
Iona College	NY	16,310	C
McNeese State Univ	LA	4,543	NC
Morehead State Univ	KY	4,600	LC
Northern Mich Univ	MI	6,350	C
Northern Montana College	MT	4,976	C
Northwestern Univ	IL	21,093	MC
Rutgers Univ/Cook College	NJ	9,197	HC
Rutgers Univ/Douglass College	NJ	8,795	VC
Rutgers Univ/Livingston College	NJ	8,877	VC
Rutgers Univ/Rutgers College	NJ	8,841	HC+
Rutgers Univ/Univ College—New Brunswick	NJ	0	LC
San Francisco State Univ	CA	7,292	LC
Sierra Nevada College	NV	14,000	NC
SUNY College of Environmental Science and Forestry	NY	9,257	HC+
Tulane Univ	LA	24,540	HC
Unity College	ME	12,885	LC
Univ of Calif, San Diego	CA	10,028	VC+
Univ of Kansas	KS	5,200	NC
Univ of Miami	FL	22,107	VC
Univ of Minn/Twin Cities	MN	6,682	VC
Univ of Rochester	NY	23,696	HC

ECONOMICS

School	ST	$IS	SR
Adelphi Univ	NY	18,250	LC
Adrian College	MI	14,340	C
Agnes Scott College	GA	17,135	VC
Alabama A&M Univ	AL	4,200	C
Albertson College	ID	15,942	C+
Albertus Magnus College	CT	16,280	LC
Albion College	MI	18,264	VC
Albright College	PA	19,260	C
Alcorn State Univ	MS	4,474	C+
Alfred Univ	NY	21,054	VC+
Allegheny College	PA	21,020	VC
Alma College	MI	16,375	VC+
American International College	MA	14,029	C
American Univ	DC	21,230	VC+
Amherst College	MA	24,152	MC
Anderson Univ	IN	12,920	C
Andrews Univ	MI	14,952	NC
Angelo State Univ	TX	5,176	C
Antioch College	OH	19,532	C
Appalachian State Univ	NC	4,095	C
Aquinas College	MI	14,526	C
Arizona State Univ Main Campus	AZ	6,444	C
Arkansas College	AR	11,626	VC
Arkansas State Univ	AR	4,250	NC
Arkansas Tech Univ	AR	4,200	NC
Assumption College	MA	17,095	LC
Auburn Univ	AL	5,823	C+
Augsburg College	MN	15,608	C
Augustana College	IL	16,959	VC
Augustana College	SD	13,420	C
Austin College	TX	14,999	VC
Austin Peay State Univ	TN	4,350	C
Babson College	MA	23,160	VC
Baker Univ	KS	12,284	C
Baldwin-Wallace College	OH	15,210	C
Ball State Univ	IN	6,032	LC
Barat College	IL	13,990	C
Bard College	NY	25,269	HC
Barry Univ	FL	16,050	C
Bates College	ME	23,990	MC
Baylor Univ	TX	10,990	C+
Bellarmine College	KY	10,832	C
Belmont Abbey College	NC	13,190	C
Belmont Univ	TN	10,540	C
Beloit College	WI	18,950	VC+
Bemidji State Univ	MN	5,188	C
Benedictine College	KS	12,830	C
Bennington College	VT	24,850	VC+
Bentley College	MA	18,680	C
Berea College	KY	2,883	VC+
Berry College	GA	11,990	VC
Bethany College	KS	11,232	C
Bethany College	WV	18,300	C+
Bethel College	MN	15,050	C
Birmingham-Southern College	AL	15,154	VC+
Bloomfield College	NJ	12,200	LC
Bloomsburg Univ of Penn	PA	6,312	C+
Bluffton College	OH	12,951	C
Boise State Univ	ID	4,909	LC
Boston College	MA	22,706	MC
Boston Univ	MA	24,130	HC
Bowdoin College	ME	24,155	MC
Bowling Green State Univ	OH	6,701	C
Bradley Univ	IL	14,718	C+
Brandeis Univ	MA	25,585	HC
Bridgewater College	VA	15,300	C
Brigham Young Univ	UT	5,625	HC
Brooklyn Campus of LIU	NY	15,000	LC
Brown Univ	RI	26,104	MC
Bryant College	RI	18,335	C
Bryn Mawr College	PA	24,110	MC
Bucknell Univ	PA	22,320	HC
Buena Vista College	IA	16,150	VC
Butler Univ	IN	16,210	C
Calif Inst of Tech	CA	20,783	MC
Calif Polytechnic State Univ	CA	6,980	VC+
Calif State Polytechnic Univ/Pomona	CA	6,438	LC
Cal State/Bakersfield	CA	5,402	C
Cal State/Chico	CA	6,146	C
Cal State/Dominguez Hills	CA	2,857	LC
Cal State/Fresno	CA	5,747	C
Cal State/Fullerton	CA	4,850	LC
Cal State/Hayward	CA	5,495	C
Cal State/Long Beach	CA	6,057	LC
Cal State/Los Angeles	CA	4,940	VC
Cal State/Northridge	CA	7,122	LC
Cal State/Sacramento	CA	6,387	C
Cal State/San Bernardino	CA	6,055	LC
Cal State/Stanislaus	CA	6,799	C
Calif Univ of Penn	PA	7,370	C
Calumet College of St. Joseph	IN	3,585	C
Calvin College	MI	13,020	VC
Canisius College	NY	15,510	C
Capital Univ	OH	16,535	VC
Carleton College	MN	22,155	HC
Carnegie Mellon Univ	PA	22,560	HC+
Carroll College	WI	15,490	C
Carson-Newman College	TN	11,250	C
Carthage College	WI	15,995	C
Case Western Reserve Univ	OH	19,910	HC
Catholic Univ of America	DC	18,856	C
Centenary College of Louisiana	LA	11,826	C+
Central College	IA	14,025	VC
Central Conn State Univ	CT	7,108	C
Central Methodist College	MO	11,410	C
Central Mich Univ	MI	6,737	LC
Central Missouri State Univ	MO	5,138	LC
Central State Univ	OH	7,320	NC
Central Washington Univ	WA	5,644	C
Centre College	KY	15,850	VC+
Chapman Univ	CA	21,842	C
Charleston Southern Univ	SC	10,282	LC
Charter Oak State College	CT	314	NC
Chatham College	PA	18,010	C
Chestnut Hill College	PA	14,525	C
Cheyney Univ of Penn	PA	7,005	C
Chicago State Univ	IL	2,198	C
Christopher Newport Univ	VA	3,196	LC
CUNY/Baruch College	NY	2,562	VC
CUNY/Brooklyn College	NY	2,450	VC
CUNY/City College	NY	2,543	VC
CUNY/College of Staten Island	NY	2,558	NC
CUNY/Herbert H. Lehman College	NY	2,542	C
CUNY/Hunter College	NY	4,101	VC
CUNY/Queens College	NY	2,631	C
CUNY/York College	NY	2,534	NC
Claremont McKenna College	CA	22,150	MC
Clarion Univ of Penn	PA	6,518	C
Clark Atlanta Univ	GA	11,846	C
Clark Univ	MA	21,400	VC
Clarkson Univ	NY	20,705	VC+
Clemson Univ	SC	6,564	VC
Cleveland State Univ	OH	7,287	NC
Clinch Valley College/Univ of Virginia	VA	6,364	C
Coe College	IA	17,085	VC
Colby College	ME	24,230	HC
Colgate Univ	NY	24,020	HC
College of Charleston	SC	6,250	C
College of Mount St Vincent	NY	16,730	C
College of New Rochelle	NY	15,440	LC
College of Notre Dame of Maryland	MD	16,050	LC
College of St Benedict	MN	15,468	VC
College of St Catherine	MN	14,670	C
College of St Elizabeth	NJ	15,800	C
College of the Holy Cross	MA	23,850	HC
College of William and Mary	VA	8,602	MC
College of Wooster	OH	19,875	VC
Colo College	CO	20,038	HC
Colo State Univ	CO	6,566	VC
Columbia Univ/Barnard College	NY	25,492	HC
Columbia Univ/Columbia College	NY	26,757	MC
Concordia College	MN	13,200	C
Concordia College/Moorhead	MN	12,750	C
Conn College	CT	24,160	HC
Converse College	SC	15,750	C
Cornell College	IA	18,425	VC
Cornell Univ	NY	13,445	MC
Creighton Univ	NE	14,432	VC
Dallas Baptist Univ	TX	9,620	LC
Dana College	NE	11,910	C
Dartmouth College	NH	24,354	MC
Davidson College	NC	21,037	MC
Davis and Elkins College	WV	13,230	LC
Delaware State College	DE	5,656	C
Denison Univ	OH	21,150	VC+
DePaul Univ	IL	15,535	VC
DePauw Univ	IN	18,530	VC
Dickinson College	PA	22,705	HC
Dillard Univ	LA	9,950	C
Doane College	NE	12,220	C
Dowling College	NY	12,730	LC
Drake Univ	IA	17,195	VC
Drew Univ/College of Liberal Arts	NJ	23,406	HC
Drury College	MO	12,140	VC
Duke Univ	NC	21,271	MC
Duquesne Univ	PA	16,434	VC
Dyke College	OH	5,200	C
Earlham College	IN	19,383	VC
East Carolina Univ	NC	4,498	C
East Stroudsburg Univ	PA	6,886	C
East Tenn State Univ	TN	4,406	C
East Texas State Univ	TX	4,572	LC
Eastern Conn State Univ	CT	6,966	C
Eastern Illinois Univ	IL	5,548	C
Eastern Kentucky Univ	KY	4,840	NC
Eastern Mich Univ	MI	6,749	C
Eastern New Mexico Univ	NM	3,950	C
Eastern Washington Univ	WA	5,439	LC
Eckerd College	FL	18,855	VC
Edgewood College	WI	11,700	C
Edinboro Univ of Penn	PA	7,181	C
Elizabethtown College	PA	17,850	VC
Elmhurst College	IL	12,536	C
Elon College	NC	12,290	LC
Emmanuel College	MA	17,773	LC
Emory and Henry College	VA	12,776	C
Emory Univ	GA	21,930	HC
Emporia State Univ	KS	4,685	NC
Eugene Lang College of the New School for Social Research	NY	21,145	C+
Eureka College	IL	14,555	C
Evergreen State College	WA	6,306	C
Fairfield Univ	CT	20,460	VC
Fairleigh Dickinson Univ	NJ	16,427	C
Fayetteville State Univ	NC	3,926	LC
Fisk Univ	TN	0	LC
Fitchburg State College	MA	6,962	C
Florida A&M Univ	FL	4,651	C
Florida Atlantic Univ	FL	5,525	C
Florida International Univ	FL	4,191	VC
Florida Southern College	FL	12,260	C
Florida State Univ	FL	5,814	VC
Fordham Univ/College at Lincoln Center	NY	18,150	VC
Fordham Univ/Fordham College	NY	19,875	VC
Fort Hays State Univ	KS	4,675	NC
Fort Lewis College	CO	5,097	C
Fort Valley State College	GA	3,974	LC
Framingham State College	MA	6,580	C
Francis Marion Univ	SC	5,878	LC
Franklin and Marshall College	PA	23,655	HC
Franklin College of Indiana	IN	13,970	C
Franklin Pierce College	NH	17,270	LC
Frostburg State Univ	MD	6,940	C
Furman Univ	SC	16,557	VC
Gallaudet Univ	DC	9,850	SP
George Fox College	OR	15,640	LC
George Mason Univ	VA	8,728	C
George Washington Univ	DC	22,470	HC
Georgetown College	KY	10,990	C
Georgetown Univ	DC	24,410	MC
Georgia College	GA	4,310	LC
Georgia Inst of Tech	GA	6,669	HC+
Georgia Southern Univ	GA	4,988	LC
Gettysburg College	PA	22,960	HC
Gonzaga Univ	WA	16,350	VC
Gordon College	MA	16,790	C
Goshen College	IN	12,360	C
Goucher College	MD	20,295	VC
Graceland College	IA	11,600	C
Grand Canyon Univ	AZ	9,680	VC
Grand Valley State Univ	MI	6,822	VC
Grinnell College	IA	20,680	HC+
Grove City College	PA	7,870	HC
Guilford College	NC	17,680	C
Gustavus Adolphus College	MN	15,935	VC
Hamilton College	NY	23,500	HC
Hamline Univ	MN	17,122	VC
Hampden-Sydney College	VA	17,372	C+
Hampshire College	MA	25,320	C
Hampton Univ	VA	10,706	C
Hanover College	IN	10,950	VC
Harding Univ	AR	9,050	VC
Hartwick College	NY	20,950	C
Harvard Univ/Harvard and Radcliffe Colleges	MA	24,880	MC
Hastings College	NE	12,426	C
Haverford College	PA	23,950	MC
Hawaii Pacific Univ	HI	12,300	C

School	ST	$IS	SR
Univ of Calif at Santa Cruz	CA	9,060	VC
Univ of Calif, Riverside	CA	9,178	C
Univ of Calif, San Diego	CA	10,028	VC+
Univ of Calif/Irvine	CA	12,680	VC
Univ of Central Arkansas	AR	4,200	LC
Univ of Central Florida	FL	6,061	C+
Univ of Central Okla	OK	3,647	C
Univ of Chicago	IL	24,517	MC
Univ of Cincinnati	OH	7,989	C
Univ of Colo at Boulder	CO	6,410	VC
Univ of Colo at Colo Springs	CO	2,269	C
Univ of Colo at Denver	CO	1,955	VC
Univ of Conn	CT	9,168	C
Univ of Dallas	TX	14,983	VC
Univ of Dayton	OH	15,120	C+
Univ of Delaware	DE	8,013	VC
Univ of Denver	CO	19,290	C+
Univ of Detroit Mercy	MI	14,720	C
Univ of Dubuque	IA	14,150	LC
Univ of Evansville	IN	15,300	VC
Univ of Findlay	OH	15,764	C
Univ of Florida	FL	5,850	HC
Univ of Georgia	GA	5,655	VC
Univ of Hartford	CT	19,858	LC
Univ of Hawaii at Hilo	HI	4,141	C
Univ of Hawaii at Manoa	HI	5,626	C
Univ of Houston	TX	5,215	C
Univ of Idaho	ID	4,830	C
Univ of Illinois at Chicago	IL	8,443	C
Univ of Illinois at Urbana-Champaign	IL	7,764	HC
Univ of Iowa	IA	5,658	VC
Univ of Kansas	KS	5,200	NC
Univ of Kentucky	KY	5,152	VC
Univ of La Verne	CA	17,400	C
Univ of Louisville	KY	5,948	C
Univ of Lowell	MA	8,831	VC
Univ of Maine	ME	7,990	C
Univ of Mary Hardin-Baylor	TX	8,120	NC
Univ of Maryland/Baltimore County	MD	7,746	VC
Univ of Maryland/College Park	MD	8,182	VC
Univ of Maryland/Univ College	MD	4,900	NC
Univ of Mass Dartmouth	MA	8,158	C
Univ of Mass/Amherst	MA	9,364	LC
Univ of Mass/Boston	MA	4,253	C
Univ of Memphis	TN	3,476	C
Univ of Miami	FL	22,107	VC
Univ of Mich/Ann Arbor	MI	9,428	HC+
Univ of Mich/Dearborn	MI	3,399	HC
Univ of Mich/Flint	MI	2,916	C
Univ of Minn/Duluth	MN	6,512	C
Univ of Minn/Morris	MN	6,825	HC
Univ of Minn/Twin Cities	MN	6,682	VC
Univ of Miss	MS	5,756	C
Univ of Missouri/Columbia	MO	6,254	HC
Univ of Missouri/Kansas City	MO	5,906	VC
Univ of Missouri/Rolla	MO	6,729	VC+
Univ of Missouri/St. Louis	MO	6,378	C
Univ of Mobile	AL	9,400	C
Univ of Montana	MT	5,529	C
Univ of Nebr at Kearney	NE	4,308	LC
Univ of Nebr at Omaha	NE	1,889	LC
Univ of Nebr-Lincoln	NE	5,278	LC
Univ of Nevada/Las Vegas	NV	6,405	C
Univ of New Hampshire	NH	8,242	C
Univ of New Haven	CT	14,980	C
Univ of New Orleans	LA	5,468	C
Univ of N Car at Asheville	NC	4,791	VC
Univ of N Car at Chapel Hill	NC	5,330	HC
Univ of N Car at Charlotte	NC	4,597	C
Univ of N Car at Greensboro	NC	5,192	C
Univ of N Dak	ND	4,902	NC
Univ of North Florida	FL	5,082	C
Univ of North Texas	TX	4,853	C
Univ of Northern Colo	CO	6,008	C
Univ of Northern Iowa	IA	5,137	C
Univ of Notre Dame	IN	20,150	MC
Univ of Okla	OK	5,427	VC
Univ of Oregon	OR	6,466	VC
Univ of Penn	PA	24,238	MC
Univ of Pittsburgh	PA	9,472	C
Univ of Pittsburgh at Bradford	PA	9,050	C
Univ of Pittsburgh at Johnstown	PA	8,914	C
Univ of PR/Cayey Univ College	PR	900	
Univ of PR/Mayaguez	PR	0	
Univ of PR/Rio Piedras	PR	0	
Univ of Puget Sound	WA	19,520	HC
Univ of Redlands	CA	22,059	VC
Univ of Rhode Island	RI	9,205	C
Univ of Richmond	VA	16,700	HC
Univ of Rio Grande	OH	6,300	NC
Univ of Rochester	NY	23,696	HC
Univ of St Thomas	MN	15,785	C+
Univ of St Thomas	TX	11,676	C+
Univ of San Diego	CA	18,970	VC
Univ of San Francisco	CA	18,408	C
Univ of Science and Arts of Okla	OK	3,304	C
Univ of Scranton	PA	17,071	VC
Univ of South Alabama	AL	5,451	C
Univ of S Car	SC	6,158	C
Univ of S Car at Aiken	SC	5,386	C
Univ of S Dak	SD	4,722	C
Univ of South Florida	FL	5,475	C+
Univ of Southern Calif	CA	23,006	VC
Univ of Southern Indiana	IN	3,720	NC
Univ of Southern Maine	ME	7,299	C
Univ of Southern Miss	MS	4,542	C
Univ of Southwestern Louisiana	LA	3,968	NC
Univ of Tenn at Chattanooga	TN	5,375	C
Univ of Tenn at Martin	TN	4,550	C
Univ of Tenn/Knoxville	TN	5,668	C
Univ of Texas at Arlington	TX	5,549	LC
Univ of Texas at Austin	TX	5,160	VC
Univ of Texas at Dallas	TX	1,222	VC+
Univ of Texas at El Paso	TX	3,160	LC
Univ of Texas at San Antonio	TX	6,420	C
Univ of the District of Columbia	DC	974	NC
Univ of the Pacific	CA	21,100	C
Univ of the South	TN	18,830	HC
Univ of Toledo	OH	6,636	NC
Univ of Tulsa	OK	13,795	VC
Univ of Utah	UT	5,975	C
Univ of Vermont	VT	10,776	C+
Univ of Virginia	VA	7,964	MC
Univ of Washington	WA	6,618	VC
Univ of Wisc/Eau Claire	WI	4,647	C
Univ of Wisc/Green Bay	WI	4,904	C
Univ of Wisc/La Crosse	WI	4,487	C
Univ of Wisc/Madison	WI	6,400	HC
Univ of Wisc/Milwaukee	WI	6,165	C
Univ of Wisc/Oshkosh	WI	4,240	C
Univ of Wisc/Parkside	WI	5,247	
Univ of Wisc/Platteville	WI	4,830	C
Univ of Wisc/River Falls	WI	4,655	C
Univ of Wisc/Stevens Point	WI	5,047	C+
Univ of Wisc/Whitewater	WI	4,700	C
Univ of Wyoming	WY	4,991	NC
Upsala College	NJ	17,200	C
Ursinus College	PA	19,165	VC
Utah State Univ	UT	4,683	C
Utica College of Syracuse Univ	NY	16,714	LC
Valparaiso Univ	IN	14,810	VC
Vanderbilt Univ	TN	23,422	HC+
Vassar College	NY	24,206	HC
Villanova Univ	PA	21,400	HC
Virginia Commonwealth Univ	VA	7,909	C
Virginia Military Inst	VA	8,630	C
Virginia Polytechnic Inst and State Univ	VA	6,828	C
Virginia Wesleyan College	VA	14,950	VC
Wabash College	IN	16,250	VC
Wake Forest Univ	NC	17,280	MC
Warren Wilson College	NC	10,877	C
Wartburg College	IA	14,530	VC
Washburn Univ of Topeka	KS	5,802	NC
Washington and Jefferson College	PA	19,360	C
Washington and Lee Univ	VA	17,735	MC
Washington College	MD	19,270	C+
Washington Univ	MO	23,507	HC
Wayne State College	NE	4,260	NC
Wayne State Univ	MI	2,680	C
Waynesburg College	PA	11,960	C
Weber State Univ	UT	4,398	C
Wellesley College	MA	23,815	MC
Wells College	NY	19,460	C+
Wesley College	DE	13,745	LC
Wesleyan Univ	CT	23,770	MC
West Chester Univ of Penn	PA	7,492	C
West Georgia College	GA	4,256	C
West Liberty State College	WV	4,690	LC
West Virginia State College	WV	5,044	LC
West Virginia Univ	WV	5,774	C
West Virginia Wesleyan College	WV	16,900	C
Western Carolina Univ	NC	3,811	C
Western Conn State Univ	CT	6,622	C
Western Illinois Univ	IL	5,241	LC
Western Kentucky Univ	KY	4,808	C
Western Maryland College	MD	18,990	C
Western Mich Univ	MI	6,820	C
Western New England College	MA	14,674	LC
Western Oregon State College	OR	6,180	C
Western State College of Colo	CO	5,560	C
Western Washington Univ	WA	6,077	VC
Westfield State College	MA	7,161	C
Westminster College	MO	13,750	C+
Westminster College	PA	15,200	C
Westminster College of Salt Lake City	UT	12,100	C
Wheaton College	IL	14,710	HC
Wheaton College	MA	23,840	C+
Whitman College	WA	20,595	HC
Whittier College	CA	21,661	C
Whitworth College	WA	16,265	C
Wichita State Univ	KS	5,068	NC
Widener Univ	PA	16,840	C
Wilberforce Univ	OH	10,408	C
Wilkes Univ	PA	15,728	LC
Willamette Univ	OR	17,995	VC
William Paterson College	NJ	7,438	C+
William Penn College	IA	13,400	C
Williams College	MA	24,390	MC
Wilmington College	OH	13,700	LC
Winona State Univ	MN	5,200	VC
Wittenberg Univ	OH	19,998	VC
Wofford College	SC	15,360	VC
Worcester Polytechnic Inst	MA	20,350	HC
Worcester State College	MA	6,414	LC
Wright State Univ	OH	6,896	LC
Xavier Univ	OH	15,710	C+
Yale Univ	CT	25,110	MC
Yeshiva Univ	NY	18,200	VC
Youngstown State Univ	OH	6,447	LC

EDUCATION

School	ST	$IS	SR
Academy of the New Church	PA	7,341	NC
Belmont Abbey College	NC	13,190	C
Boise State Univ	ID	4,909	LC
Brown Univ	RI	26,104	MC
Cabrini College	PA	16,012	C
Catawba College	NC	12,950	C
Central Mich Univ	MI	6,737	LC
Christian Heritage College	CA	11,756	C
CUNY/College of Staten Island	NY	2,558	NC
Coker College	SC	13,790	C
Colgate Univ	NY	24,020	HC
College of St Mary	NE	12,500	C
College of Santa Fe	NM	14,008	C
Concordia College	NY	0	LC
Culver-Stockton College	MO	11,150	C
Dartmouth College	NH	24,354	MC
Drexel Univ	PA	15,970	C
Earlham College	IN	19,383	VC
Eastern Nazarene College	MA	12,165	LC
Eastern Oregon State College	OR	6,090	C
Emory Univ	GA	21,930	HC
Eureka College	IL	14,555	C
Ferrum College	VA	12,800	LC
Furman Univ	SC	16,557	VC
Goddard College	VT	17,990	LC
Hampshire College	MA	25,320	C
Huntington College	IN	13,220	C
Huston-Tillotson College	TX	8,490	C
Indiana Univ of Penn	PA	6,373	C
LeMoyne-Owen College	TN	4,500	LC
Lynn Univ	FL	18,300	C
Martin Univ	IN	4,830	NC
Miss State Univ	MS	5,629	VC
N Car State Univ	NC	4,984	VC
Northwest College	WA	9,897	LC
Northwestern Univ	IL	21,093	MC
Philadelphia College of Bible	PA	11,010	C
St Mary's College	MI	8,350	C
St Mary's College of Minn	MN	13,850	LC
Salem State College	MA	6,712	C
Selma Univ	AL	5,785	NC
Simmons College	MA	22,534	C
Southern Calif College	CA	12,356	C
SUNY/Empire State College	NY	2,687	NC
Temple Univ	PA	10,281	C
Texas Tech Univ	TX	6,008	C
Towson State Univ	MD	7,452	C
Univ of Alabama at Huntsville	AL	5,868	VC
Univ of Delaware	DE	8,013	VC
Univ of Denver	CO	19,290	C+
Univ of Findlay	OH	15,764	C
Univ of Illinois at Chicago	IL	8,443	C
Univ of Missouri/Columbia	MO	6,254	HC
Univ of Nebr-Lincoln	NE	5,278	LC
Univ of N Car at Chapel Hill	NC	5,330	HC
Univ of Penn	PA	24,238	MC
Univ of Wisc/Milwaukee	WI	6,165	C
Univ of Wisc/Parkside	WI	5,247	
Wake Forest Univ	NC	17,280	MC
Washington Univ	MO	23,507	HC
Webster Univ	MO	12,650	C
Western Baptist College	OR	12,400	LC
Williams Baptist College	AR	5,834	LC
Winthrop Univ	SC	6,750	C
York College	NE	7,610	C

EDUCATION OF THE DEAF AND HEARING IMPAIRED

School	ST	$IS	SR
Adelphi Univ	NY	18,250	LC
Ball State Univ	IN	6,032	LC
Barton College	NC	10,689	LC
Boston Univ	MA	24,130	HC
CUNY/Brooklyn College	NY	2,450	VC
Eastern Kentucky Univ	KY	4,840	NC
Flagler College	FL	7,990	C
Fontbonne College	MO	12,090	C
Ithaca College	NY	19,679	C
Kent State Univ	OH	6,740	LC
Lenoir-Rhyne College	NC	14,068	C
MacMurray College	IL	12,800	C
Mercy College	NY	11,180	NC
Minot State Univ	ND	3,748	NC
St John's Univ	NY	8,980	C+
Southern Univ at New Orleans	LA	1,452	NC
SUNY/College at Plattsburgh	NY	6,917	C
Stephen F. Austin State Univ	TX	5,117	C
Texas Christian Univ	TX	12,180	C
Univ of Arkansas at Little Rock	AR	4,419	C
Univ of Montevallo	AL	5,310	C
Univ of Tulsa	OK	13,795	VC
Washington Univ	MO	23,507	HC

EDUCATION OF THE EMOTIONALLY HANDICAPPED

School	ST	$IS	SR
Marygrove College	MI	5,877	VC
Univ of Maine at Farmington	ME	6,700	C

EDUCATION OF THE EXCEPTIONAL CHILD

School	ST	$IS	SR
Bethune-Cookman College	FL	8,375	LC
Idaho State Univ	ID	4,442	C
Jacksonville Univ	FL	13,390	C
Nova Southeastern Univ	FL	13,244	LC
Univ of Central Arkansas	AR	4,200	LC
Univ of Central Florida	FL	6,061	C+
Univ of Wisc/Stevens Point	WI	5,047	C+

EDUCATION OF THE MENTALLY HANDICAPPED

School	ST	$IS	SR
Calif Univ of Penn	PA	7,370	C
Clarke College	IA	13,950	C+
Florida State Univ	FL	5,814	VC
Marygrove College	MI	5,877	VC
Northern Mich Univ	MI	6,350	C
Northwest Missouri State Univ	MO	5,010	LC
Univ of Georgia	GA	5,655	VC
Univ of Illinois at Urbana-Champaign	IL	7,764	HC
Univ of Maine at Farmington	ME	6,700	C

EDUCATION OF THE MULTIPLY HANDICAPPED

School	ST	$IS	SR
Kent State Univ	OH	6,740	LC

EDUCATION OF THE PHYSICALLY HANDICAPPED

School	ST	$IS	SR
Calif Univ of Penn	PA	7,370	C

EDUCATION OF THE VISUALLY HANDICAPPED

School	ST	$IS	SR
D'Youville College	NY	12,850	C
Florida State Univ	FL	5,814	VC
Stephen F. Austin State Univ	TX	5,117	C

EDUCATIONAL MEDIA

School	ST	$IS	SR
Indiana State Univ	IN	6,210	C

INDEX OF COLLEGE MAJORS

EDUCATIONAL STATISTICS AND RESEARCH

School	ST	$IS	SR
Bucknell Univ	PA	22,320	HC

ELECTRICAL/ELECTRONICS ENGINEERING

School	ST	$IS	SR
Alfred Univ	NY	21,054	VC+
Andrews Univ	MI	14,952	NC
Arizona State Univ Main Campus	AZ	6,444	C
Auburn Univ	AL	5,823	C+
Baylor Univ	TX	10,990	C+
Bethel College	IN	11,650	C
Boston Univ	MA	24,130	HC
Bradley Univ	IL	14,718	C+
Bridgeport Engineering Inst	CT	6,135	NC
Brigham Young Univ	UT	5,625	HC
Bucknell Univ	PA	22,320	HC
Calif Inst of Tech	CA	20,783	MC
Calif Polytechnic State Univ	CA	6,980	VC+
Calif State Polytechnic Univ/Pomona	CA	6,438	LC
Cal State/Chico	CA	6,146	C
Cal State/Fresno	CA	5,747	C
Cal State/Fullerton	CA	4,850	LC
Cal State/Long Beach	CA	6,057	LC
Cal State/Los Angeles	CA	4,940	VC
Cal State/Sacramento	CA	6,387	C
Calvin College	MI	13,020	VC
Capitol College	MD	10,698	LC
Carnegie Mellon Univ	PA	22,560	HC+
Case Western Reserve Univ	OH	19,910	HC
Catholic Univ of America	DC	18,856	C
Cedarville College	OH	10,715	C
Central Washington Univ	WA	5,644	C
Christian Brothers Univ	TN	12,120	VC
CUNY/City College	NY	2,543	VC
Clarkson Univ	NY	20,705	VC+
Clemson Univ	SC	6,564	VC
Cleveland State Univ	OH	7,287	NC
Cogswell College North	WA	7,200	NC
Cogswell Polytechnical College	CA	8,000	NC
Colo State Univ	CO	6,566	VC
Colo Technical College	CO	6,005	C
Columbia Univ/School of Engineering and Applied Science	NY	24,554	HC
Concordia Univ Wisc	WI	12,140	C
Cooper Union for the Advancement of Science and Art	NY	8,430	MC
Cornell Univ	NY	13,445	MC
Delaware State College	DE	5,656	C
Dordt College	IA	11,690	C
Drexel Univ	PA	15,970	C
Duke Univ	NC	21,271	MC
Edward Waters College	FL	8,300	NC
Embry-Riddle Aeronautical Univ	AZ	9,896	C+
Embry-Riddle Aeronautical Univ	FL	10,600	C
Fairleigh Dickinson Univ	NJ	16,427	C
Florida A&M Univ	FL	4,651	C
Florida Atlantic Univ	FL	5,525	C
Florida Inst of Tech	FL	16,935	VC
Florida International Univ	FL	4,191	VC
Florida State Univ	FL	5,814	VC
Gannon Univ	PA	14,872	C
Geneva College	PA	13,030	C
George Washington Univ	DC	22,470	HC
Georgia Inst of Tech	GA	6,669	HC+
GMI Engineering & Management Inst	MI	14,158	HC
Gonzaga Univ	WA	16,350	VC
Grove City College	PA	7,870	HC
Hampton Univ	VA	10,706	C
Hofstra Univ	NY	16,580	VC
Howard Univ	DC	11,680	C
Illinois Inst of Tech	IL	18,290	VC
Indiana Inst of Tech	IN	11,810	C
Indiana Univ-Purdue Univ at Fort Wayne	IN	2,500	LC
Indiana Univ-Purdue Univ at Indianapolis	IN	5,862	LC
Iowa State Univ	IA	5,456	C
John Brown Univ	AR	9,880	VC
Johns Hopkins Univ	MD	24,360	MC
Kansas State Univ	KS	4,816	NC
Kean College of New Jersey	NJ	6,395	LC
Lafayette College	PA	23,450	HC
Lakeland College	WI	12,845	LC
Lamar Univ	TX	3,798	C
Lane College	TN	7,628	LC
Lawrence Tech Univ	MI	9,470	C
Le Tourneau Univ	TX	12,500	C+
Lehigh Univ	PA	23,250	HC
Louisiana State Univ and A&M College	LA	5,605	C
Loyola College	MD	18,035	VC
Loyola Marymount Univ	CA	18,560	C
Maharishi International Univ	IA	13,666	C
Manhattan College	NY	19,000	C
Mankato State Univ	MN	5,097	LC
Marquette Univ	WI	16,114	VC
Mass Inst of Tech	MA	24,800	MC
McNeese State Univ	LA	4,543	NC
Mercer Univ	GA	15,123	C
Merrimack College	MA	18,025	C
Messiah College	PA	14,664	VC
Mich State Univ	MI	7,842	C
Mich Tech Univ	MI	7,283	VC+
Milwaukee School of Engineering	WI	14,100	C
Miss State Univ	MS	5,629	VC
Montana State Univ	MT	5,534	C
Morgan State Univ	MD	7,366	C+
Morris Brown College	GA	12,234	NC
New Jersey Inst of Tech	NJ	9,965	VC
New Mexico Inst of Mining and Tech	NM	5,212	C+
New Mexico State Univ	NM	4,844	LC
New York Inst of Tech/Old Westbury	NY	13,914	LC
N Car Agricultural and Technical State Univ	NC	4,477	LC
N Car State Univ	NC	4,984	VC
N Dak State Univ of Agriculture and Applied Science	ND	4,774	VC
Northeastern Univ	MA	19,851	C
Northern Arizona Univ	AZ	4,844	C
Northern Illinois Univ	IL	6,408	C
Northwestern Univ	IL	21,093	MC
Norwich Univ	VT	18,730	C
Oakland Univ	MI	6,714	VC
Occidental College	CA	21,792	HC
Ohio State Univ	OH	7,218	LC
Ohio Univ	OH	7,341	C
Okla Christian Univ of Science and Arts	OK	8,790	NC
Okla State Univ	OK	5,086	VC
Old Dominion Univ	VA	8,317	C
Oral Roberts Univ	OK	10,607	C+
Pace Univ	NY	15,540	C
Pacific Lutheran Univ	WA	15,998	VC
Penn State Univ/Univ Park Campus	PA	8,752	HC
Polytechnic Univ/Brooklyn	NY	19,700	HC
Polytechnic Univ/Farmingdale	NY	20,700	VC
Portland State Univ	OR	7,191	C
Prairie View A&M Univ	TX	4,740	LC
Princeton Univ	NJ	24,650	MC
Purdue Univ/Calumet	IN	2,374	NC
Purdue Univ/West Lafayette	IN	6,636	C
Rensselaer Polytechnic Inst	NY	23,067	HC
Rice Univ	TX	15,110	MC
Rochester Inst of Tech	NY	18,954	VC
Rose-Hulman Inst of Tech	IN	16,400	HC
Rutgers Univ/Camden College of A&S	NJ	8,652	VC
Rutgers Univ/College of Engineering	NJ	9,254	HC
Rutgers Univ/Newark College of A&S	NJ	8,645	C
Saginaw Valley State Univ	MI	6,634	LC
St Augustine's College	NC	9,300	C+
St Cloud State Univ	MN	5,015	C
St Louis Univ	MO	15,522	VC
St Mary's Univ	TX	12,064	C
San Diego State Univ	CA	6,692	LC
San Francisco State Univ	CA	7,292	LC
San Jose State Univ	CA	6,680	LC
Santa Clara Univ	CA	18,783	VC
Seattle Pacific Univ	WA	16,503	C
Seattle Univ	WA	16,590	C
S Dak School of Mines and Tech	SD	5,329	C
S Dak State Univ	SD	4,562	C
Southern Illinois Univ at Carbondale	IL	6,234	C
Southern Illinois Univ at Edwardsville	IL	6,097	LC
Southern Methodist Univ	TX	18,520	VC
Southern Univ and A&M College	LA	4,920	NC
Stanford Univ	CA	24,310	MC
SUNY at Binghamton	NY	7,921	HC
SUNY at Buffalo	NY	7,896	VC
SUNY at Stony Brook	NY	7,658	VC
SUNY/College at New Paltz	NY	6,890	VC
SUNY/Maritime College	NY	7,170	C
Stevens Inst of Tech	NJ	21,980	VC+
Suffolk Univ	MA	15,360	LC
Swarthmore College	PA	24,136	MC
Syracuse Univ	NY	21,305	HC
Temple Univ	PA	10,281	C
Tenn State Univ	TN	4,626	C+
Tenn Tech Univ	TN	5,190	C
Texas A&M Univ	TX	5,382	VC
Texas A&M Univ at Kingsville	TX	3,808	LC
Texas Tech Univ	TX	6,008	C
The Citadel	SC	6,619	C
The Univ of New Mexico	NM	5,304	C
Tri-State Univ	IN	13,788	LC
Tufts Univ	MA	24,962	MC
Tulane Univ	LA	24,540	HC
Tuskegee Univ	AL	10,128	C
Union College	NY	23,817	HC
United States Air Force Academy	CO	0	MC
United States Coast Guard Academy	CT	0	MC
United States Military Academy	NY	0	MC
United States Naval Academy	MD	0	MC
Universidad Politecnica de PR	PR	6,195	C
Univ of Akron	OH	6,699	NC
Univ of Alabama	AL	5,702	C
Univ of Alabama at Birmingham	AL	7,533	C
Univ of Alabama at Huntsville	AL	5,868	VC
Univ of Alaska Fairbanks	AK	4,718	C
Univ of Arizona	AZ	5,808	C
Univ of Arkansas at Fayetteville	AR	5,046	C
Univ of Bridgeport	CT	18,985	C
Univ of Calif at Berkeley	CA	9,962	HC+
Univ of Calif at Davis	CA	9,534	VC
Univ of Calif at Los Angeles	CA	8,959	HC
Univ of Calif at Santa Barbara	CA	9,460	C
Univ of Calif, Riverside	CA	9,178	C
Univ of Calif, San Diego	CA	10,028	VC+
Univ of Calif/Irvine	CA	12,680	VC
Univ of Central Florida	FL	6,061	C+
Univ of Cincinnati	OH	7,989	C
Univ of Colo at Boulder	CO	6,410	VC
Univ of Colo at Colo Springs	CO	2,269	C
Univ of Colo at Denver	CO	1,955	VC
Univ of Conn	CT	9,168	C
Univ of Dayton	OH	15,120	C+
Univ of Delaware	DE	8,013	VC
Univ of Denver	CO	19,290	C+
Univ of Detroit Mercy	MI	14,720	C
Univ of Evansville	IN	15,300	VC
Univ of Florida	FL	5,850	HC
Univ of Hartford	CT	19,858	LC
Univ of Hawaii at Manoa	HI	5,626	C
Univ of Houston	TX	5,215	C
Univ of Houston-Downtown	TX	4,034	NC
Univ of Idaho	ID	4,830	C
Univ of Illinois at Chicago	IL	8,443	C
Univ of Illinois at Urbana-Champaign	IL	7,764	HC
Univ of Indianapolis	IN	14,510	C
Univ of Iowa	IA	5,658	VC
Univ of Kansas	KS	5,200	NC
Univ of Kentucky	KY	5,152	VC
Univ of La Verne	CA	17,400	C
Univ of Louisville	KY	5,948	C
Univ of Lowell	MA	8,831	VC
Univ of Maine	ME	7,990	C
Univ of Maryland/College Park	MD	8,182	VC
Univ of Mass Dartmouth	MA	8,158	C
Univ of Mass/Amherst	MA	9,364	LC
Univ of Memphis	TN	3,476	C
Univ of Miami	FL	22,107	VC
Univ of Mich/Ann Arbor	MI	9,428	HC+
Univ of Mich/Dearborn	MI	3,399	HC
Univ of Minn/Twin Cities	MN	6,682	VC
Univ of Miss	MS	5,756	C
Univ of Missouri/Columbia	MO	6,254	HC
Univ of Missouri/Kansas City	MO	5,906	VC
Univ of Missouri/Rolla	MO	6,729	VC+
Univ of Missouri/St. Louis	MO	6,378	C
Univ of Nebr-Lincoln	NE	5,278	LC
Univ of Nevada/Las Vegas	NV	6,405	C
Univ of Nevada/Reno	NV	5,735	C
Univ of New Hampshire	NH	8,242	C
Univ of New Haven	CT	14,980	C
Univ of New Orleans	LA	5,468	C
Univ of N Car at Charlotte	NC	4,597	C
Univ of N Dak	ND	4,902	NC
Univ of North Florida	FL	5,082	C
Univ of Notre Dame	IN	20,150	MC
Univ of Okla	OK	5,427	VC
Univ of Penn	PA	24,238	MC
Univ of Pittsburgh	PA	9,472	C
Univ of Portland	OR	15,564	C
Univ of PR/Mayaguez	PR	0	
Univ of Rhode Island	RI	9,205	C
Univ of Rochester	NY	23,696	HC
Univ of San Diego	CA	18,970	VC
Univ of Scranton	PA	17,071	VC
Univ of South Alabama	AL	5,451	C
Univ of S Car	SC	6,158	C
Univ of South Florida	FL	5,475	C+
Univ of Southern Calif	CA	23,006	VC
Univ of Southern Maine	ME	7,299	C
Univ of Southwestern Louisiana	LA	3,968	NC
Univ of Tenn/Knoxville	TN	5,668	C
Univ of Texas at Arlington	TX	5,549	LC
Univ of Texas at Austin	TX	5,160	VC
Univ of Texas at Dallas	TX	1,222	VC+
Univ of Texas at El Paso	TX	3,160	LC
Univ of Texas at San Antonio	TX	6,420	C
Univ of the District of Columbia	DC	974	NC
Univ of the Pacific	CA	21,100	C
Univ of Toledo	OH	6,636	NC
Univ of Tulsa	OK	13,795	VC
Univ of Utah	UT	5,975	C
Univ of Vermont	VT	10,776	C+
Univ of Virginia	VA	7,964	MC
Univ of Washington	WA	6,618	VC
Univ of Wisc/Madison	WI	6,400	HC
Univ of Wisc/Milwaukee	WI	6,165	C
Univ of Wisc/Platteville	WI	4,830	C
Univ of Wyoming	WY	4,991	NC
Utah State Univ	UT	4,683	C
Utica College of Syracuse Univ	NY	16,714	LC
Valparaiso Univ	IN	14,810	VC
Vanderbilt Univ	TN	23,422	HC+
Villanova Univ	PA	21,400	HC
Virginia Military Inst	VA	8,630	C
Virginia Polytechnic Inst and State Univ	VA	6,828	C
Washington State Univ	WA	6,364	C
Washington Univ	MO	23,507	HC
Wayne State Univ	MI	2,680	C
West Coast Univ	CA	9,120	NC
West Virginia Inst of Tech	WV	5,858	LC
West Virginia Univ	WV	5,774	C
Western Mich Univ	MI	6,820	C
Western New England College	MA	14,674	LC
Wichita State Univ	KS	5,068	NC
Widener Univ	PA	16,840	C
Wilkes Univ	PA	15,728	LC
Worcester Polytechnic Inst	MA	20,350	HC
Wright State Univ	OH	6,896	LC
Yale Univ	CT	25,110	MC
Youngstown State Univ	OH	6,447	LC

ELECTRICAL/ELECTRONICS ENGINEERING TECHNOLOGY

School	ST	$IS	SR
Alabama A&M Univ	AL	4,200	C
Andrews Univ	MI	14,952	NC
Arizona State Univ Main Campus	AZ	6,444	C
Baker College	MI	6,971	NC
Bowling Green State Univ	OH	6,701	C
Brigham Young Univ	UT	5,625	HC
Calif Univ of Penn	PA	7,370	C
Central Missouri State Univ	MO	5,138	LC
Cogswell College North	WA	7,200	NC
Colo Technical College	CO	6,005	C
DeVry/Addison (DuPage County)	IL	5,609	LC
DeVry/Atlanta	GA	5,609	LC
DeVry/Chicago	IL	5,609	LC
DeVry/Columbus	OH	5,609	LC
DeVry/Dallas	TX	5,609	LC
DeVry/Kansas City	MO	5,609	LC
DeVry/Los Angeles	CA	5,609	LC
DeVry/Phoenix	AZ	5,609	LC
East-West Univ	IL	5,910	NC
Fairleigh Dickinson Univ	NJ	16,427	C
Fairmont State College	WV	4,640	LC
Fort Valley State College	GA	3,974	LC
Franklin Univ	OH	4,621	NC
Georgia Southern Univ	GA	4,988	LC
Idaho State Univ	ID	4,442	C
Indiana Inst of Tech	IN	11,810	C
Indiana State Univ	IN	6,210	C
Indiana Univ-Purdue Univ at Indianapolis	IN	5,862	LC
Inter American Univ of PR/Aguadilla Regional College	PR	2,290	
Inter American Univ of PR/Bayamon Univ College	PR	2,300	
Inter American Univ of PR/Metropolitan Campus	PR	2,340	
Inter American Univ of PR/Ponce Regional College	PR	2,300	
Inter-American Univ of PR/Fajardo Regional College	PR	2,732	
Louisiana Tech Univ	LA	4,284	C
Maharishi International Univ	IA	13,666	C
Metropolitan State College of Denver	CO	1,751	NC
Midwestern State Univ	TX	4,542	LC
Montana State Univ	MT	5,534	C
Murray State Univ	KY	4,702	C
New Mexico Highlands Univ	NM	3,772	C
Nicholls State Univ	LA	4,531	NC
Norfolk State Univ	VA	6,345	LC
Northeastern Univ	MA	19,851	C
Northern Kentucky Univ	KY	4,620	NC
Northern Mich Univ	MI	6,350	C

School	ST	$IS	SR
Northern Montana College	MT	4,976	C
Okla State Univ	OK	5,086	VC
Oregon Inst of Tech	OR	5,985	C
Point Park College	PA	13,922	LC
Purdue Univ/Calumet	IN	2,374	NC
Purdue Univ/West Lafayette	IN	6,636	C
Rochester Inst of Tech	NY	18,954	VC
Roosevelt Univ	IL	12,368	C
S Car State Univ	SC	5,424	LC
Southern College of Tech	GA	4	C
Southern Utah Univ	UT	4,104	LC
Southwest Missouri State Univ	MO	4,956	C
Southwest State Univ	MN	5,400	NC
Temple Univ	PA	10,281	C
Texas Tech Univ	TX	6,008	C
Univ of Arkansas at Little Rock	AR	4,419	C
Univ of Central Florida	FL	6,061	C+
Univ of Cincinnati	OH	7,989	C
Univ of Dayton	OH	15,120	C+
Univ of Hartford	CT	19,858	LC
Univ of Mass Dartmouth	MA	8,158	C
Univ of Memphis	TN	3,476	C
Univ of Nebr-Lincoln	NE	5,278	LC
Univ of Pittsburgh at Johnstown	PA	8,914	C
Univ of Southern Miss	MS	4,542	C
Univ of Tenn at Martin	TN	4,550	C
Univ of the State of New York/Regents College Degrees	NY	510	
Wentworth Inst of Tech	MA	15,250	LC
West Virginia Inst of Tech	WV	5,858	C
Western Carolina Univ	NC	3,811	C
Western Kentucky Univ	KY	4,808	C
Western Washington Univ	WA	6,077	VC

ELECTROMECHANICAL TECHNOLOGY

School	ST	$IS	SR
Cleveland State Univ	OH	7,287	NC
Idaho State Univ	ID	4,442	C
Maharishi International Univ	IA	13,666	C
Peru State College	NE	4,311	NC
Univ of Northern Iowa	IA	5,137	C
Univ of the District of Columbia	DC	974	NC
Wentworth Inst of Tech	MA	15,250	LC

ELECTRON PHYSICS

School	ST	$IS	SR
Univ of San Francisco	CA	18,408	C

ELEMENTARY EDUCATION

School	ST	$IS	SR
Abilene Christian Univ	TX	10,460	NC
Adams State College	CO	4,910	C
Adelphi Univ	NY	18,250	LC
Adrian College	MI	14,340	C
Alabama A&M Univ	AL	4,200	C
Alaska Pacific Univ	AK	11,350	C
Albertson College	ID	15,942	C+
Albright College	PA	19,260	C
Alcorn State Univ	MS	4,474	C+
Alderson-Broaddus College	WV	12,000	C
Alfred Univ	NY	21,054	VC+
Alice Lloyd College	KY	2,750	VC
Allegheny College	PA	21,020	VC
Alma College	MI	16,375	VC+
Alvernia College	PA	13,150	LC
Alverno College	WI	11,344	C
American International College	MA	14,029	C
American Univ	DC	21,230	VC+
Anderson Univ	IN	12,920	C
Andrews Univ	MI	14,952	NC
Angelo State Univ	TX	5,176	C
Anna Maria College	MA	15,975	LC
Antioch College	OH	19,532	C
Appalachian State Univ	NC	4,095	C
Aquinas College	MI	14,526	C
Arizona State Univ Main Campus	AZ	6,444	C
Arkansas Baptist College	AR	5,016	NC
Arkansas College	AR	11,626	VC
Arkansas State Univ	AR	4,250	NC
Arkansas Tech Univ	AR	4,200	NC
Armstrong State College	GA	4,874	LC
Asbury College	KY	11,105	VC
Ashland Univ	OH	15,508	C
Atlantic Union College	MA	14,150	LC
Auburn Univ	AL	5,823	C+
Auburn Univ at Montgomery	AL	3,390	C
Augsburg College	MN	15,608	C
Augusta College	GA	1,452	C
Augustana College	IL	16,959	VC
Augustana College	SD	13,420	C
Aurora Univ	IL	13,381	C
Austin Peay State Univ	TN	4,350	C
Averett College	VA	13,610	LC
Avila College	MO	12,130	C
Baker Univ	KS	12,284	C
Baldwin-Wallace College	OH	15,210	C
Ball State Univ	IN	6,032	LC
Barber-Scotia College	NC	6,840	NC
Bartlesville Wesleyan College	OK	9,400	C
Barton College	NC	10,689	LC
Bayamon Tech Univ College	PR	1,600	
Baylor Univ	TX	10,990	C+
Beaver College	PA	17,660	C
Belhaven College	MS	9,690	C+
Bellarmine College	KY	10,832	C
Belmont Abbey College	NC	13,190	C
Belmont Univ	TN	10,540	C
Beloit College	WI	18,950	VC+
Bemidji State Univ	MN	5,188	C
Benedict College	SC	8,376	LC
Benedictine College	KS	12,830	C
Bennett College	NC	8,920	LC
Berea College	KY	2,883	VC+
Bethany College	KS	11,232	C
Bethany College	WV	18,300	C+
Bethel College	IN	11,650	C
Bethel College	KS	11,530	C
Bethel College	MN	15,050	C
Bethel College	TN	9,736	LC
Bethune-Cookman College	FL	8,375	LC
Biola Univ	CA	16,124	C
Birmingham-Southern College	AL	15,154	VC+
Black Hills State Univ	SD	4,831	NC
Blackburn College	IL	9,120	C
Bloomsburg Univ of Penn	PA	6,312	C+
Blue Mountain College	MS	5,958	LC
Bluefield State College	WV	1,832	LC
Bluffton College	OH	12,951	C
Boise State Univ	ID	4,909	LC
Boricua College	NY	5,920	VC
Boston College	MA	22,706	MC
Boston Univ	MA	24,130	HC
Bowie State Univ	MD	7,294	LC
Bowling Green State Univ	OH	6,701	C
Bradley Univ	IL	14,718	C+
Brescia College	KY	9,800	C
Briar Cliff College	IA	13,375	C
Bridgewater State College	MA	7,518	C
Brigham Young Univ	UT	5,625	HC
Brigham Young Univ/Hawaii	HI	6,750	VC
Brooklyn Campus of LIU	NY	15,000	LC
Bryan College	TN	11,465	C
Bucknell Univ	PA	22,320	HC
Buena Vista College	IA	16,150	VC
Butler Univ	IN	16,210	C
Caldwell College	NJ	12,860	C
Calif Baptist College	CA	11,294	C
Calif Lutheran Univ	CA	17,240	C
Cal State/Chico	CA	6,146	C
Cal State/Fresno	CA	5,747	C
Calif Univ of Penn	PA	7,370	C
Calumet College of St. Joseph	IN	3,585	C
Calvin College	MI	13,020	VC
Cameron Univ	OK	3,686	LC
Campbell Univ	NC	10,624	C
Campbellsville College	KY	8,720	C
Canisius College	NY	15,510	C
Capital Univ	OH	16,535	VC
Cardinal Stritch College	WI	11,252	C
Caribbean Univ	PR	2,400	
Carlow College	PA	13,914	C
Carroll College	MT	11,265	C
Carroll College	WI	15,490	C
Carson-Newman College	TN	11,250	C
Carthage College	WI	15,995	C
Castleton State College	VT	8,378	LC
Catawba College	NC	12,950	C
Catholic Univ of America	DC	18,856	C
Cedar Crest College	PA	18,930	C
Cedarville College	OH	10,715	C
Centenary College	NJ	17,040	LC
Centenary College of Louisiana	LA	11,826	C+
Central College	IA	14,025	VC
Central Conn State Univ	CT	7,108	C
Central Methodist College	MO	11,410	C
Central Mich Univ	MI	6,737	LC
Central Missouri State Univ	MO	5,138	LC
Central State Univ	OH	7,320	NC
Central Univ of Bayamon	PR	2,430	
Central Washington Univ	WA	5,644	C
Central Wesleyan College	SC	9,640	C
Centre College	KY	15,850	VC+
Chadron State College	NE	4,091	NC
Chaminade Univ of Honolulu	HI	14,290	C
Charleston Southern Univ	SC	10,282	LC
Chatham College	PA	18,010	C
Chestnut Hill College	PA	14,525	C
Cheyney Univ of Penn	PA	7,005	C
Chicago State Univ	IL	2,198	C
Christian Brothers Univ	TN	12,120	VC
Christian Heritage College	CA	11,756	C
City Univ	WA	6,400	NC
CUNY/Baruch College	NY	2,562	VC
CUNY/Brooklyn College	NY	2,450	VC
CUNY/City College	NY	2,543	VC
CUNY/Herbert H. Lehman College	NY	2,542	C
CUNY/Hunter College	NY	4,101	VC
CUNY/Medgar Evers College	NY	2,577	NC
CUNY/Queens College	NY	2,631	C
CUNY/York College	NY	2,534	NC
Claflin College	SC	0	
Clarion Univ of Penn	PA	6,518	C
Clarke College	IA	13,950	C+
Clearwater Christian College	FL	8,500	LC
Clemson Univ	SC	6,564	VC
Cleveland State Univ	OH	7,287	NC
Coastal Carolina Univ	SC	6,010	LC
Coe College	IA	17,085	VC
Coker College	SC	13,790	C
College Misericordia	PA	15,820	C
College of Charleston	SC	6,250	C
College of Great Falls	MT	6,230	NC
College of Mount St Joseph	OH	13,272	C
College of New Rochelle	NY	15,440	LC
College of Notre Dame of Maryland	MD	16,050	C
College of Our Lady of The Elms	MA	15,639	C
College of St Benedict	MN	15,468	VC
College of St Catherine	MN	14,670	C
College of St Elizabeth	NJ	15,800	C
College of St Joseph	VT	12,650	LC
College of St Rose	NY	14,452	C
College of St Scholastica	MN	14,868	C
College of the Ozarks	MO	2,000	VC+
College of the Southwest	NM	5,720	LC
Colo Christian Univ	CO	9,750	C
Columbia College	MO	11,995	C
Columbia College	SC	13,520	LC
Columbia Union College	MD	13,650	LC
Columbia Univ/Barnard College	NY	25,492	HC
Concord College	WV	5,104	NC
Concordia College	MI	13,660	C
Concordia College	MN	13,200	C
Concordia College	NE	11,776	NC
Concordia College	NY	0	LC
Concordia College	OR	12,300	C
Concordia College/Moorhead	MN	12,750	C
Concordia Lutheran College	TX	10,260	C+
Concordia Univ	IL	12,611	C
Concordia Univ Wisc	WI	12,140	C
Converse College	SC	15,750	C
Coppin State College	MD	7,145	LC
Cornell College	IA	18,425	VC
Covenant College	GA	13,054	VC
Creighton Univ	NE	14,432	VC
Crichton College	TN	6,547	NC
Cumberland College	KY	9,756	C
Cumberland Univ	TN	8,650	C
Curry College	MA	18,695	LC
D'Youville College	NY	12,850	C
Daemen College	NY	13,020	LC
Dakota State Univ	SD	4,374	LC
Dakota Wesleyan Univ	SD	9,770	LC
Dana College	NE	11,910	C
David Lipscomb Univ	TN	7,865	VC
Davis and Elkins College	WV	13,230	LC
Defiance College	OH	13,480	LC
Delaware State College	DE	5,656	C
Delta State Univ	MS	3,964	LC
DePaul Univ	IL	15,535	VC
DePauw Univ	IN	18,530	VC
Dickinson State Univ	ND	3,792	C
Dillard Univ	LA	9,950	C
Doane College	NE	12,220	C
Dominican College	NY	13,600	LC
Dordt College	IA	11,690	C
Dowling College	NY	12,730	LC
Drake Univ	IA	17,195	VC
Drury College	MO	12,140	VC
Duquesne Univ	PA	16,434	VC
East Carolina Univ	NC	4,498	C
East Central Univ	OK	3,558	C
East Stroudsburg Univ	PA	6,886	C
East Tenn State Univ	TN	4,406	C
East Texas Baptist Univ	TX	7,740	C
East Texas State Univ	TX	4,572	LC
Eastern College	PA	15,150	C+
Eastern Conn State Univ	CT	6,966	C
Eastern Illinois Univ	IL	5,548	C
Eastern Kentucky Univ	KY	4,840	NC
Eastern Mennonite College	VA	12,700	C
Eastern Mich Univ	MI	6,749	C
Eastern Montana College	MT	5,165	LC
Eastern Nazarene College	MA	12,165	LC
Eastern New Mexico Univ	NM	3,950	C
Eastern Washington Univ	WA	5,439	LC
Eckerd College	FL	18,855	VC
Edgewood College	WI	11,700	C
Edinboro Univ of Penn	PA	7,181	C
Edward Waters College	FL	8,300	NC
Elizabeth City State Univ	NC	4,254	LC
Elizabethtown College	PA	17,850	VC
Elmhurst College	IL	12,536	C
Elmira College	NY	18,450	C
Elon College	NC	12,290	LC
Emmanuel College	MA	17,773	LC
Emory Univ	GA	21,930	HC
Emporia State Univ	KS	4,685	NC
Erskine College	SC	14,310	C
Eureka College	IL	14,555	C
Evangel College	MO	10,142	LC
Fairmont State College	WV	4,640	LC
Faulkner Univ	AL	8,630	LC
Fayetteville State Univ	NC	3,926	LC
Felician College	NJ	7,900	C
Fitchburg State College	MA	6,962	C
Flagler College	FL	7,990	C
Florida A&M Univ	FL	4,651	C
Florida Atlantic Univ	FL	5,525	C
Florida International Univ	FL	4,191	VC
Florida Memorial College	FL	7,600	C+
Florida Southern College	FL	12,260	C
Florida State Univ	FL	5,814	VC
Fontbonne College	MO	12,090	C
Fordham Univ/College at Lincoln Center	NY	18,150	VC
Fort Hays State Univ	KS	4,675	NC
Framingham State College	MA	6,580	C
Francis Marion Univ	SC	5,878	LC
Franciscan Univ of Steubenville	OH	13,400	C
Franklin College of Indiana	IN	13,970	C
Franklin Pierce College	NH	17,270	LC
Freed-Hardeman Univ	TN	8,585	VC
Friends Univ	KS	11,205	C
Furman Univ	SC	16,557	VC
Gallaudet Univ	DC	9,850	SP
Gannon Univ	PA	14,872	C
Gardner-Webb Univ	NC	11,950	LC
Geneva College	PA	13,030	C
George Fox College	OR	15,640	LC
Georgetown College	KY	10,990	C
Georgia Southwestern College	GA	4,338	LC
Georgia State Univ	GA	2,019	C
Gettysburg College	PA	22,960	HC
Glenville State College	WV	4,810	LC
Gordon College	MA	16,790	C
Goshen College	IN	12,360	C
Goucher College	MD	20,295	VC
Grace College	IN	12,120	C
Graceland College	IA	11,600	C
Grambling State Univ	LA	4,712	NC
Grand Canyon Univ	AZ	9,680	VC
Grand Rapids Baptist College and Seminary	MI	10,228	C
Grand Valley State Univ	MI	6,822	VC
Grand View College	IA	13,230	NC
Green Mountain College	VT	14,080	C
Greensboro College	NC	11,496	C
Greenville College	IL	14,190	C
Grove City College	PA	7,870	HC
Guilford College	NC	17,680	C
Gustavus Adolphus College	MN	15,935	VC
Gwynedd-Mercy College	PA	15,450	C
Hamline Univ	MN	17,122	VC
Hampton Univ	VA	10,706	C
Hannibal-LaGrange College	MO	8,400	LC
Hanover College	IN	10,950	VC
Hardin-Simmons Univ	TX	9,080	C
Harding Univ	AR	9,050	VC
Harris-Stowe State College	MO	1,888	LC
Hastings College	NE	12,426	C
Heidelberg College	OH	17,160	C
Hellenic College/Holy Cross Greek Orthodox School of Theology	MA	10,295	NC
Henderson State Univ	AR	3,860	C
Hendrix College	AR	11,670	C
Heritage College	WA	5,540	NC
High Point Univ	NC	12,350	LC
Hillsdale College	MI	15,110	VC
Hiram College	OH	18,340	VC
Hofstra Univ	NY	16,580	VC
Holy Family College	PA	8,300	C
Hope College	MI	15,698	C+
Houghton College	NY	13,120	VC
Houston Baptist Univ	TX	11,055	C
Howard Payne Univ	TX	8,052	C
Howard Univ	DC	11,680	C
Humboldt State Univ	CA	5,676	C
Huntingdon College	AL	11,400	C
Huntington College	IN	13,220	C
Huron Univ	SD	9,790	C
Huston-Tillotson College	TX	8,490	C
Idaho State Univ	ID	4,442	C
Illinois Benedictine College	IL	14,170	C
Illinois College	IL	11,200	C
Illinois State Univ	IL	6,413	C
Illinois Wesleyan Univ	IL	18,590	HC+
Immaculata College	PA	14,620	C
Incarnate Word College	TX	12,307	C
Indiana State Univ	IN	6,210	C
Indiana Univ at Kokomo	IN	2,069	C
Indiana Univ Bloomington	IN	6,495	VC
Indiana Univ East	IN	2,044	NC
Indiana Univ Northwest	IN	2,310	C
Indiana Univ of Penn	PA	6,373	C
Indiana Univ Southeast	IN	2,260	LC

School	ST	$IS	SR
Indiana Univ-Purdue Univ at Fort Wayne	IN	2,500	LC
Indiana Univ-Purdue Univ at Indianapolis	IN	5,862	LC
Indiana Univ/South Bend	IN	2,141	LC
Indiana Wesleyan Univ	IN	12,332	C
Inter American Univ of PR/ Aguadilla Regional College	PR	2,290	
Inter American Univ of PR/ Barranquitas Regional College	PR	2,730	
Inter American Univ of PR/ Bayamon Univ College	PR	2,300	
Inter American Univ of PR/ Metropolitan Campus	PR	2,340	
Inter American Univ of PR/ Ponce Regional College	PR	2,300	
Inter American Univ of PR/ San German	PR	4,620	
Inter American Univ/Arecibo Campus	PR	5,666	
Inter-American Univ of PR/ Fajardo Regional College	PR	2,732	
Iona College	NY	16,310	C
Iowa State Univ	IA	5,456	C
Iowa Wesleyan College	IA	13,250	C
Jackson State Univ	MS	4,996	LC
Jacksonville State Univ	AL	4,080	LC
Jacksonville Univ	FL	13,390	LC
Jamestown College	ND	10,250	C
Jarvis Christian College	TX	7,170	LC
Jersey City State College	NJ	7,797	LC
John Brown Univ	AR	9,880	VC
John Carroll Univ	OH	16,510	C
Johnson C. Smith Univ	NC	8,916	LC
Johnson State College	VT	8,393	LC
Judson College	AL	9,060	C
Judson College	IL	13,625	C
Juniata College	PA	18,390	C+
Kansas Newman College	KS	10,640	C
Kansas State Univ	KS	4,816	NC
Kean College of New Jersey	NJ	6,395	LC
Keene State College	NH	7,081	C
Kennesaw State College	GA	1,553	LC
Kent State Univ	OH	6,740	LC
Kentucky Christian College	KY	7,708	LC
Kentucky State Univ	KY	4,282	C+
Kentucky Wesleyan College	KY	11,550	C
Keuka College	NY	13,660	C
King's College	NY	12,360	LC
King's College	PA	15,420	C
Knox College	IL	18,990	VC
Knoxville College	TN	8,320	LC
Kutztown Univ	PA	6,528	C
La Salle Univ	PA	16,940	VC
Lake Erie College	OH	13,700	C
Lake Forest College	IL	19,960	VC
Lakeland College	WI	12,845	LC
Lamar Univ	TX	3,798	C
Lambuth Univ	TN	8,395	C
Lander Univ	SC	6,180	LC
Lane College	TN	7,628	LC
Langston Univ	OK	2,907	LC
Le Moyne College	NY	15,180	C
Lebanon Valley College of Penn	PA	18,300	C
Lee Univ	TN	7,894	C
LeMoyne-Owen College	TN	4,500	LC
Lenoir-Rhyne College	NC	14,068	LC
Lesley College	MA	17,120	LC
Lewis Univ	IL	14,797	LC
Lewis-Clark State College	ID	4,040	
Liberty Univ	VA	11,500	LC
Limestone College	SC	10,700	LC
Lincoln Memorial Univ	TN	8,218	C
Lincoln Univ	MO	4,638	NC
Lincoln Univ	PA	0	LC
Lindenwood College	MO	13,560	C
Lindsey Wilson College	KY	9,530	LC
Linfield College	OR	16,670	VC
Livingston Univ	AL	3,979	C
Livingstone College	NC	8,600	LC
Lock Haven Univ of Penn	PA	7,128	C
LIU/C. W. Post Campus	NY	16,870	C
LIU/Southampton Campus	NY	17,280	C
Longwood College	VA	7,800	C
Loras College	IA	14,160	C
Louisiana College	LA	7,518	VC
Louisiana State Univ and A&M College	LA	5,605	C
Louisiana State Univ in Shreveport	LA	1,910	NC
Louisiana Tech Univ	LA	4,284	C
Loyola College	MD	18,035	VC
Loyola Univ of Chicago	IL	15,880	C+
Loyola Univ/New Orleans	LA	15,660	C+
Lubbock Christian Univ	TX	9,840	NC
Luther College	IA	15,900	VC
Lyndon State College	VT	8,394	C
Lynn Univ	FL	18,300	VC
MacMurray College	IL	12,800	C
Malone College	OH	12,572	C
Manchester College	IN	13,240	LC
Manhattan College	NY	19,000	C
Manhattanville College	NY	20,450	LC
Mankato State Univ	MN	5,097	LC
Mansfield Univ	PA	6,348	C
Marian College	IN	12,936	C
Marian College of Fond du Lac	WI	12,250	C
Marietta College	OH	16,940	C+
Marist College	NY	16,406	C
Marquette Univ	WI	16,114	VC
Mars Hill College	NC	11,050	C
Marshall Univ	WV	5,762	LC
Marygrove College	MI	5,877	VC
Marymount College/ Tarrytown	NY	17,350	C
Marymount Manhattan College	NY	15,450	LC
Maryville College	TN	14,474	C
Maryville Univ-St Louis	MO	12,900	VC
Marywood College	PA	14,890	C
Master's College	CA	12,816	C
Mayville State Univ	ND	4,272	NC
McKendree College	IL	10,900	C
McMurry Univ	TX	10,100	C
McNeese State Univ	LA	4,543	NC
McPherson College	KS	11,360	VC
Medaille College	NY	12,650	C
Mercer Univ	GA	15,123	C
Mercy College	NY	11,180	NC
Mercyhurst College	PA	13,488	C
Merrimack College	MA	18,025	C
Messiah College	PA	14,664	VC
Methodist College	NC	12,400	C
Miami Univ	OH	8,066	VC
Mich State Univ	MI	7,842	C
MidAmerica Nazarene College	KS	10,208	NC
Middle Tenn State Univ	TN	3,857	C
Midland Lutheran College	NE	12,410	LC
Miles College	AL	7,150	NC
Millersville Univ of Penn	PA	7,370	C
Milligan College	TN	10,690	C
Millikin Univ	IL	15,499	C
Millsaps College	MS	15,486	C+
Minot State Univ	ND	3,748	NC
Miss College	MS	8,348	C
Miss State Univ	MS	5,629	VC
Miss Univ for Women	MS	4,456	LC
Miss Valley State Univ	MS	4,089	NC
Missouri Baptist College	MO	9,340	C
Missouri Southern State College	MO	4,272	
Missouri Valley College	MO	14,050	LC
Missouri Western State College	MO	4,384	NC
Molloy College	NY	8,580	LC
Monmouth College	IL	17,300	C+
Monmouth College	NJ	16,820	C
Montana State Univ	MT	5,534	C
Moorhead State Univ	MN	5,076	C
Moravian College	PA	18,960	VC
Morehead State Univ	KY	4,600	LC
Morehouse College	GA	13,224	LC
Morgan State Univ	MD	7,366	C
Morningside College	IA	13,896	C
Morris Brown College	GA	12,234	NC
Morris College	SC	6,880	LC
Mount Holyoke College	MA	23,630	VC
Mount Marty College	SD	10,450	NC
Mount Mary College	WI	10,920	C
Mount Mercy College	IA	13,230	C
Mount St Mary College	NY	12,910	C
Mount St Mary's College	CA	16,390	VC
Mount St Mary's College	MD	17,825	LC
Mount Senario College	WI	10,970	C
Mount Union College	OH	15,850	C
Mount Vernon Nazarene College	OH	10,390	C
Murray State Univ	KY	4,702	C
Muskingum College	OH	16,650	C
National-Louis Univ	IL	13,218	C
Nazareth College of Rochester	NY	15,310	C+
Nebr Wesleyan Univ	NE	12,240	C
Neumann College	PA	9,950	LC
New England College	NH	17,870	VC
New Mexico Highlands Univ	NM	3,772	C
New Mexico State Univ	NM	4,844	LC
Newberry College	SC	11,994	LC
Niagara Univ	NY	14,552	C
Nicholls State Univ	LA	4,531	NC
North Adams State College	MA	7,750	C
N Car Central Univ	NC	4,347	LC
N Car Wesleyan College	NC	12,480	LC
North Central Bible College	MN	8,670	C
North Central College	IL	15,498	VC
North Georgia College	GA	4,103	LC
North Park College	IL	14,310	C
Northeast Louisiana Univ	LA	3,906	NC
Northeastern Illinois Univ	IL	1,955	C
Northeastern State Univ	OK	5,250	C
Northeastern Univ	MA	19,851	C
Northern Arizona Univ	AZ	4,844	VC
Northern Illinois Univ	IL	6,408	C
Northern Kentucky Univ	KY	4,620	NC
Northern Mich Univ	MI	6,350	C
Northern Montana College	MT	4,976	C
Northern State Univ	SD	4,186	LC
Northland College	WI	13,550	LC
Northwest Missouri State Univ	MO	5,010	LC
Northwest Nazarene College	ID	11,750	C
Northwestern College	MN	13,554	C
Northwestern College of Iowa	IA	12,250	C
Northwestern Okla State Univ	OK	3,424	C
Northwestern State Univ of Louisiana	LA	4,287	NC
Notre Dame College	NH	14,220	C
Notre Dame College of Ohio	OH	11,370	C
Nova Southeastern Univ	FL	13,244	LC
Nyack College	NY	12,210	LC
Oakland City College	IN	10,216	LC
Oakland Univ	MI	6,714	VC
Oakwood College	AL	10,005	C
Occidental College	CA	21,792	HC
Oglala Lakota College	SD	0	
Ohio Dominican College	OH	11,820	LC
Ohio Northern Univ	OH	18,660	VC
Ohio State Univ	OH	7,218	LC
Ohio State Univ at Lima	OH	2,835	NC
Ohio State Univ at Mansfield	OH	2,835	NC
Ohio State Univ at Marion	OH	2,835	NC
Ohio State Univ at Newark	OH	2,835	NC
Ohio Univ	OH	7,341	VC
Ohio Wesleyan Univ	OH	21,108	VC+
Okla Baptist Univ	OK	8,486	C
Okla Christian Univ of Science and Arts	OK	8,790	NC
Okla City Univ	OK	9,840	C
Okla Panhandle State Univ	OK	3,155	NC
Okla State Univ	OK	5,086	VC
Old Dominion Univ	VA	8,317	C
Olivet Nazarene Univ	IL	11,976	C
Oral Roberts Univ	OK	10,607	C+
Ottawa Univ	KS	10,490	C+
Otterbein College	OH	16,506	C
Ouachita Baptist Univ	AR	8,940	C
Our Lady of Holy Cross College	LA	4,630	LC
Our Lady of the Lake Univ of San Antonio	TX	11,080	C
Pace Univ	NY	15,540	LC
Pacific Christian College	CA	12,700	C
Pacific Univ	OR	17,869	C
Palm Beach Atlantic College	FL	10,720	C
Park College	MO	7,320	C
Pembroke State Univ	NC	3,538	LC
Penn State Univ/Univ Park Campus	PA	8,752	HC
Pepperdine Univ	CA	23,720	VC
Peru State College	NE	4,311	NC
Pfeiffer College	NC	11,670	LC
Philander Smith College	AR	5,434	NC
Phillips Univ	OK	12,744	C
Pikeville College	KY	8,500	NC
Pillsbury Baptist Bible College	MN	7,390	NC
Pine Manor College	MA	21,700	LC
Pittsburg State College	KS	4,478	NC
Plymouth State College	NH	7,166	C
Point Park College	PA	13,922	LC
Pontifical Catholic Univ of PR/Ponce	PR	5,807	
Presbyterian College	SC	15,400	VC
Prescott College	AZ	9,775	C
Principia College	IL	17,799	C
Providence College	RI	19,750	VC
Purdue Univ/Calumet	IN	2,374	NC
Purdue Univ/West Lafayette	IN	6,636	C
Queens College	NC	14,950	C
Quincy Univ	IL	13,646	VC
Rhode Island College	RI	7,901	LC
Rider College	NJ	18,160	C
Ripon College	WI	18,320	C+
Rivier College	NH	14,920	LC
Roberts Wesleyan College	NY	13,317	C
Rockford College	IL	15,300	C
Rockhurst College	MO	12,470	C
Rocky Mountain College	MT	11,320	C
Rollins College	FL	20,875	VC
Roosevelt Univ	IL	12,368	C
Rosemont College	PA	16,775	C
Rowan College of New Jersey	NJ	7,358	VC
Russell Sage College	NY	16,790	C
Rust College	MS	6,600	LC
Rutgers Univ/Camden College of A&S	NJ	8,652	VC
Sacred Heart Univ	CT	16,350	C
Saginaw Valley State Univ	MI	6,634	LC
St Ambrose Univ	IA	13,380	C
St Andrews Presbyterian College	NC	14,240	LC
St Augustine's College	NC	9,300	C+
St Bonaventure Univ	NY	14,762	C
St Cloud State Univ	MN	5,015	C
St Edward's Univ	TX	12,636	C
St Francis College	IN	11,662	C
St Francis College	NY	6,710	LC
St Francis College	PA	15,744	LC
St John Fisher College	NY	15,415	C
St John's College	MN	15,364	C
St John's Univ	NY	8,980	C
St Joseph's College	IN	14,730	C
St Joseph's College	ME	14,535	C
St Joseph's College	NY	7,322	C
St Joseph's Univ	PA	17,800	VC
St Leo College	FL	13,570	C
St Louis Univ	MO	15,522	VC
St Martin's College	WA	14,965	C
St Mary College	KS	11,250	C
St Mary's College	IN	17,043	VC
St Mary's College of Calif	CA	18,848	VC
St Mary's College of Minn	MN	13,850	C
St Mary's Univ	TX	12,064	VC
St Mary-of-the-Woods College	IN	14,430	NC
St Michael's College	VT	17,930	C
St Norbert College	WI	15,710	VC
St Paul's College	VA	9,171	C
St Peter's College	NJ	14,775	LC
St Thomas Aquinas College	NY	13,550	C
St Thomas Univ	FL	14,280	LC
St Xavier Univ	IL	14,700	C
Salem-Teikyo Univ	WV	14,527	C
Salisbury State Univ	MD	7,516	C+
Salve Regina Univ	RI	29,100	C
Samford Univ	AL	11,400	VC
San Francisco State Univ	CA	7,292	LC
Schreiner College	TX	14,320	C
Seton Hall Univ	NJ	18,306	LC
Seton Hill College	PA	14,320	C
Shaw Univ	NC	8,936	C+
Shawnee State Univ	OH	4,379	NC
Sheldon Jackson College	AK	14,050	NC
Shenandoah Univ	VA	11,800	C
Shepherd College	WV	5,540	C
Shippensburg Univ of Penn	PA	7,052	C
Shorter College	GA	10,270	C
Siena Heights College	MI	12,520	C
Silver Lake College	WI	8,280	C
Simpson College	CA	10,628	C
Simpson College	IA	14,635	VC
Sinte Gleska Univ	SD	1,580	NC
Sioux Falls College	SD	11,540	C
Skidmore College	NY	23,230	HC
Slippery Rock Univ	PA	6,803	C
Smith College	MA	24,236	HC
S Car State Univ	SC	5,424	LC
Southeast Missouri State Univ	MO	5,854	C
Southeastern College of the Assemblies of God	FL	6,618	NC
Southeastern Louisiana Univ	LA	4,230	NC
Southeastern Okla State Univ	OK	3,594	C
Southern Arkansas Univ	AR	3,432	NC
Southern Calif College	CA	12,356	C
Southern College of Seventh-day Adventists	TN	11,348	NC
Southern Conn State Univ	CT	7,532	C
Southern Illinois Univ at Carbondale	IL	6,234	C
Southern Illinois Univ at Edwardsville	IL	6,097	C
Southern Nazarene Univ	OK	9,206	NC
Southern Oregon State College	OR	6,128	C
Southern Univ and A&M College	LA	4,920	NC
Southern Univ at New Orleans	LA	1,452	NC
Southern Utah Univ	UT	4,104	LC
Southwest Baptist Univ	MO	9,192	NC
Southwest Missouri State Univ	MO	4,956	C
Southwest State Univ	MN	5,400	NC
Southwest Texas State Univ	TX	5,124	C
Southwestern Adventist College	TX	10,530	NC
Southwestern College	KS	10,032	C
Southwestern Okla State Univ	OK	3,312	C
Spring Hill College	AL	16,015	C
Springfield College	MA	15,200	LC
SUNY at Albany	NY	7,059	VC
SUNY/College at Buffalo	NY	7,035	VC
SUNY/College at Cortland	NY	7,326	C+
SUNY/College at Fredonia	NY	7,159	VC
SUNY/College at Geneseo	NY	6,949	VC
SUNY/College at New Paltz	NY	6,890	VC
SUNY/College at Old Westbury	NY	7,128	LC
SUNY/College at Oneonta	NY	7,878	C
SUNY/College at Oswego	NY	7,330	VC
SUNY/College at Plattsburgh	NY	6,917	C
SUNY/Potsdam College	NY	6,906	C
Stephens College	MO	18,460	C
Sterling College	KS	10,990	VC
Stetson Univ	FL	16,435	VC
Stillman College	AL	7,213	NC
Suffolk Univ	MA	15,360	LC
Sul Ross State Univ	TX	4,144	NC
Susquehanna Univ	PA	19,950	VC
Syracuse Univ	NY	21,305	HC
Tabor College	KS	11,460	VC
Taylor Univ	IN	14,450	VC
Teikyo Marycrest Univ	IA	13,755	VC
Temple Univ	PA	10,281	C
Tenn Tech Univ	TN	5,190	C
Tenn Wesleyan College	TN	10,060	C
Texas A&M Univ	TX	5,382	VC

School	ST	$IS	SR
Texas A&M Univ at Kingsville	TX	3,808	LC
Texas Christian Univ	TX	12,180	C
Texas College	TX	5,930	NC
Texas Southern Univ	TX	4,500	NC
Texas Tech Univ	TX	6,008	C
Texas Wesleyan Univ	TX	9,380	LC
The Univ of New Mexico	NM	5,304	C
Thiel College	PA	16,282	C
Thomas More College	KY	12,962	C
Toccoa Falls College	GA	9,350	C
Tougaloo College	MS	7,480	LC
Touro College	NY	11,930	C
Towson State Univ	MD	7,452	C
Transylvania Univ	KY	14,970	VC+
Trenton State College	NJ	9,085	HC
Trevecca Nazarene College	TN	9,826	NC
Tri-State Univ	IN	13,788	LC
Trinity Christian College	IL	13,260	C
Trinity College	DC	17,660	C
Trinity College	IL	14,010	C
Trinity College of Vermont	VT	16,015	LC
Troy State Univ	AL	4,322	C
Troy State Univ at Dothan/ Fort Rucker	AL	2,260	NC
Turabo Univ	PR	2,670	
Tusculum College	TN	10,400	LC
Tuskegee Univ	AL	10,128	C
Union College	KY	9,790	C
Union College	NE	11,060	NC
Union Univ	TN	7,880	C+
United States International Univ	CA	14,535	LC
Universidad Adventista de las Antillas	PR	5,000	
Universidad Metropolitana	PR	2,650	
Univ of Akron	OH	6,699	NC
Univ of Alabama	AL	5,702	C
Univ of Alabama at Birmingham	AL	7,533	C
Univ of Alaska Anchorage	AK	7,131	C
Univ of Alaska Fairbanks	AK	4,718	C
Univ of Alaska Southeast	AK	4,075	LC
Univ of Arizona	AZ	5,808	C
Univ of Arkansas at Fayetteville	AR	5,046	C
Univ of Arkansas at Little Rock	AR	4,419	C
Univ of Arkansas at Monticello	AR	3,832	NC
Univ of Arkansas at Pine Bluff	AR	3,978	LC
Univ of Central Arkansas	AR	4,200	LC
Univ of Central Florida	FL	6,061	C+
Univ of Central Okla	OK	3,647	C
Univ of Charleston	WV	12,750	C
Univ of Cincinnati	OH	7,989	C
Univ of Conn	CT	9,168	C
Univ of Dallas	TX	14,983	VC
Univ of Dayton	OH	15,120	C+
Univ of Delaware	DE	8,013	VC
Univ of Detroit Mercy	MI	14,720	C
Univ of Dubuque	IA	14,150	LC
Univ of Evansville	IN	15,300	VC
Univ of Findlay	OH	15,764	C
Univ of Florida	FL	5,850	HC
Univ of Georgia	GA	5,655	VC
Univ of Guam	GU	4,139	NC
Univ of Hartford	CT	19,858	LC
Univ of Hawaii at Hilo	HI	4,141	C
Univ of Hawaii at Manoa	HI	5,626	C
Univ of Houston	TX	5,215	C
Univ of Idaho	ID	4,830	C
Univ of Illinois at Chicago	IL	8,443	C
Univ of Illinois at Urbana-Champaign	IL	7,764	HC
Univ of Indianapolis	IN	14,510	C
Univ of Iowa	IA	5,658	VC
Univ of Kansas	KS	5,200	NC
Univ of Kentucky	KY	5,152	VC
Univ of La Verne	CA	17,400	C
Univ of Louisville	KY	5,948	C
Univ of Maine	ME	7,990	C
Univ of Maine at Farmington	ME	6,700	C
Univ of Maine at Fort Kent	ME	6,285	LC
Univ of Maine at Machias	ME	6,135	C
Univ of Maine at Presque Isle	ME	6,374	C
Univ of Mary	ND	8,910	C
Univ of Mary Hardin-Baylor	TX	8,120	NC
Univ of Maryland/Baltimore County	MD	7,746	VC
Univ of Maryland/College Park	MD	8,182	VC
Univ of Maryland/Eastern Shore	MD	6,254	LC
Univ of Mass/Amherst	MA	9,364	LC
Univ of Miami	FL	22,107	VC
Univ of Mich/Ann Arbor	MI	9,428	HC+
Univ of Mich/Dearborn	MI	3,399	HC
Univ of Mich/Flint	MI	2,916	C
Univ of Minn/Duluth	MN	6,512	C
Univ of Minn/Morris	MN	6,825	HC
Univ of Minn/Twin Cities	MN	6,682	VC
Univ of Miss	MS	5,756	C
Univ of Missouri/Columbia	MO	6,254	HC

School	ST	$IS	SR
Univ of Missouri/Kansas City	MO	5,906	VC
Univ of Missouri/St. Louis	MO	6,378	C
Univ of Mobile	AL	9,400	C
Univ of Montana	MT	5,529	C
Univ of Montevallo	AL	5,310	C
Univ of Nebr at Kearney	NE	4,308	LC
Univ of Nebr at Omaha	NE	1,889	LC
Univ of Nebr-Lincoln	NE	5,278	LC
Univ of Nevada/Las Vegas	NV	6,405	C
Univ of Nevada/Reno	NV	5,735	C
Univ of New England	ME	16,075	LC
Univ of New Orleans	LA	5,468	C
Univ of North Alabama	AL	4,236	NC
Univ of N Car at Chapel Hill	NC	5,330	HC
Univ of N Car at Charlotte	NC	4,597	C
Univ of N Car at Greensboro	NC	5,192	C
Univ of N Car at Wilmington	NC	5,172	C
Univ of N Dak	ND	4,902	NC
Univ of North Florida	FL	5,082	C
Univ of North Texas	TX	4,853	C
Univ of Northern Iowa	IA	5,137	C
Univ of Okla	OK	5,427	VC
Univ of Penn	PA	24,238	MC
Univ of Pittsburgh at Bradford	PA	9,050	C
Univ of Pittsburgh at Johnstown	PA	8,914	C
Univ of Portland	OR	15,564	C
Univ of PR/Arecibo Tech Univ College	PR	1,302	C
Univ of PR/Cayey Univ College	PR	900	
Univ of PR/Humacao Univ College	PR	1,494	
Univ of PR/Rio Piedras	PR	0	
Univ of Redlands	CA	22,059	VC
Univ of Rhode Island	RI	9,205	C
Univ of Rio Grande	OH	6,300	NC
Univ of St Thomas	MN	15,785	C+
Univ of St Thomas	TX	11,676	C+
Univ of San Diego	CA	18,970	VC
Univ of San Francisco	CA	18,408	C
Univ of Science and Arts of Okla	OK	3,304	C
Univ of Scranton	PA	17,071	VC
Univ of South Alabama	AL	5,451	C
Univ of S Car at Aiken	SC	5,386	C
Univ of S Car at Spartanburg	SC	2,320	C
Univ of S Dak	SD	4,722	C
Univ of South Florida	FL	5,475	C+
Univ of Southern Calif	CA	23,006	VC
Univ of Southern Indiana	IN	3,720	NC
Univ of Southern Miss	MS	4,542	C
Univ of Southwestern Louisiana	LA	3,968	NC
Univ of Tampa	FL	16,780	C
Univ of Tenn at Chattanooga	TN	5,375	C
Univ of Tenn at Martin	TN	4,550	C
Univ of Tenn/Knoxville	TN	5,668	C
Univ of Texas at Arlington	TX	5,549	LC
Univ of Texas at El Paso	TX	3,160	LC
Univ of Texas at San Antonio	TX	6,420	C
Univ of Texas-Pan American	TX	3,192	NC
Univ of the District of Columbia	DC	974	NC
Univ of the Ozarks	AR	7,770	C
Univ of the Pacific	CA	21,100	C
Univ of the Sacred Heart	PR	3,890	
Univ of the Virgin Islands	VI	5,896	C
Univ of Toledo	OH	6,636	NC
Univ of Tulsa	OK	13,795	VC
Univ of Utah	UT	5,975	C
Univ of Vermont	VT	10,776	C+
Univ of West Florida	FL	5,415	C
Univ of Wisc/Eau Claire	WI	4,647	C
Univ of Wisc/La Crosse	WI	4,487	C
Univ of Wisc/Madison	WI	6,400	HC
Univ of Wisc/Oshkosh	WI	4,240	C
Univ of Wisc/Platteville	WI	4,830	C
Univ of Wisc/River Falls	WI	4,655	C
Univ of Wisc/Stevens Point	WI	5,047	C+
Univ of Wisc/Superior	WI	4,330	C
Univ of Wisc/Whitewater	WI	4,700	C
Univ of Wyoming	WY	4,991	NC
Upper Iowa Univ	IA	11,900	C
Urbana Univ	OH	12,536	C
Ursuline College	OH	13,180	LC
Utah State Univ	UT	4,683	C
Valdosta State Univ	GA	4,670	LC
Valley City State Univ	ND	4,385	LC
Valparaiso Univ	IN	14,810	VC
Vanderbilt Univ	TN	23,422	HC+
Villanova Univ	PA	21,400	HC
Virginia Commonwealth Univ	VA	7,909	C
Virginia Intermont College	VA	12,250	LC
Virginia State Univ	VA	7,040	C
Virginia Union Univ	VA	10,555	LC
Virginia Wesleyan College	VA	14,950	VC
Viterbo College	WI	12,670	C
Wagner College	NY	17,950	C
Walla Walla College	WA	13,215	C
Walsh Univ	OH	11,640	C
Warner Pacific College	OR	12,112	C
Warren Wilson College	NC	10,877	C

School	ST	$IS	SR
Wartburg College	IA	14,530	VC
Washburn Univ of Topeka	KS	5,802	NC
Washington State Univ	WA	6,364	C
Washington Univ	MO	23,507	HC
Wayne State College	NE	4,260	NC
Wayne State Univ	MI	2,680	C
Waynesburg College	PA	11,960	C
Weber State Univ	UT	4,398	C
Wells College	NY	19,460	C+
Wesley College	DE	13,745	LC
West Chester Univ of Penn	PA	7,492	C
West Liberty State College	WV	4,690	LC
West Texas A&M Univ	TX	4,224	C
West Virginia State College	WV	5,044	LC
West Virginia Univ	WV	5,774	C
West Virginia Wesleyan College	WV	16,900	C
Westbrook College	ME	15,900	C
Western Carolina Univ	NC	3,811	C
Western Conn State Univ	CT	6,622	C
Western Illinois Univ	IL	5,241	LC
Western Kentucky Univ	KY	4,808	C
Western Mich Univ	MI	6,820	C
Western Montana College of the Univ of Montana	MT	1,646	C
Western New Mexico Univ	NM	3,234	LC
Western Oregon State College	OR	6,180	C
Western State College of Colo	CO	5,560	C
Western Washington Univ	WA	6,077	VC
Westfield State College	MA	7,161	C
Westminster College	MO	13,750	C+
Westminster College	PA	15,200	C
Westminster College of Salt Lake City	UT	12,100	C
Westmont College	CA	18,732	C
Wheaton College	IL	14,710	HC
Wheelock College	MA	18,000	LC
Whitworth College	WA	16,265	C
Wichita State Univ	KS	5,068	NC
Widener Univ	PA	16,840	C
Wiley College	TX	0	NC
Wilkes Univ	PA	15,728	LC
William Carey College	MS	7,050	C
William Jewell College	MO	12,500	VC
William Woods Univ	MO	14,025	LC
Wilmington College	DE	5,200	NC
Wilmington College	OH	13,700	LC
Wilson College	PA	16,630	C
Wingate College	NC	10,610	C
Winona State Univ	MN	5,200	VC
Winston-Salem State Univ	NC	4,142	LC
Winthrop Univ	SC	6,750	C
Wittenberg Univ	OH	19,998	VC
Worcester State College	MA	6,414	LC
Wright State Univ	OH	6,896	LC
Xavier Univ	OH	15,710	C+
Xavier Univ of Louisiana	LA	10,400	C
York College of Penn	PA	8,345	C
Youngstown State Univ	OH	6,447	LC

ELEMENTARY PARTICLE PHYSICS

School	ST	$IS	SR
Georgia State Univ	GA	2,019	C

EMERGENCY/DISASTER SCIENCE

School	ST	$IS	SR
Univ of Maryland/Baltimore County	MD	7,746	VC
Univ of North Texas	TX	4,853	C
Western Carolina Univ	NC	3,811	C

EMERGENCY MEDICAL TECHNOLOGIES

School	ST	$IS	SR
Springfield College	MA	15,200	LC

ENERGY MANAGEMENT TECHNOLOGY

School	ST	$IS	SR
Bridgewater State College	MA	7,518	C
Jordan College	MI	5,760	LC
Moorhead State Univ	MN	5,076	C
Univ of Northern Iowa	IA	5,137	C

ENGINEERING

School	ST	$IS	SR
Alabama State Univ	AL	3,428	NC
Alcorn State Univ	MS	4,474	C+
Alfred Univ	NY	21,054	VC+
Arizona State Univ Main Campus	AZ	6,444	C
Arkansas State Univ	AR	4,250	NC
Arkansas Tech Univ	AR	4,200	NC
Aurora Univ	IL	13,381	C
Baldwin-Wallace College	OH	15,210	C
Baylor Univ	TX	10,990	C+
Boston Univ	MA	24,130	HC
Brigham Young Univ	UT	5,625	HC
Brown Univ	RI	26,104	MC
Bucknell Univ	PA	22,320	HC
Calif Inst of Tech	CA	20,783	MC
Calif Polytechnic State Univ	CA	6,980	VC+
Cal State/Long Beach	CA	6,057	LC
Cal State/Northridge	CA	7,122	LC
Calvin College	MI	13,020	VC
Caribbean Univ	PR	2,400	
Carnegie Mellon Univ	PA	22,560	HC+
Carroll College	WI	15,490	C
Case Western Reserve Univ	OH	19,910	HC
Catholic Univ of America	DC	18,856	C
CUNY/College of Staten Island	NY	2,558	NC
Cleveland State Univ	OH	7,287	NC
Cogswell Polytechnical College	CA	8,000	NC
Colgate Univ	NY	24,020	HC
Colo School of Mines	CO	8,436	HC+
Cooper Union for the Advancement of Science and Art	NY	8,430	MC
Cornell Univ	NY	13,445	MC
Dartmouth College	NH	24,354	MC
David Lipscomb Univ	TN	7,865	VC
Davis and Elkins College	WV	13,230	LC
Dillard Univ	LA	9,950	C
Dordt College	IA	11,690	C
East Stroudsburg Univ	PA	6,886	C
Elizabethtown College	PA	17,850	VC
Florida Inst of Tech	FL	16,935	VC
Franciscan Univ of Steubenville	OH	13,400	C
Franklin College of Indiana	IN	13,970	C
Geneva College	PA	13,030	C
George Washington Univ	DC	22,470	HC
Georgetown Univ	DC	24,410	MC
Grand Valley State Univ	MI	6,822	VC
Harvard Univ/Harvard and Radcliffe Colleges	MA	24,880	MC
Harvey Mudd College	CA	23,316	MC
Hofstra Univ	NY	16,580	VC
Idaho State Univ	ID	4,442	C
Illinois Benedictine College	IL	14,170	C
Indiana Inst of Tech	IN	11,810	C
Indiana Univ-Purdue Univ at Fort Wayne	IN	2,500	LC
Indiana Univ-Purdue Univ at Indianapolis	IN	5,862	LC
Iowa State Univ	IA	5,456	C
John Brown Univ	AR	9,880	VC
Johns Hopkins Univ	MD	24,360	MC
Kansas State Univ	KS	4,816	NC
Le Tourneau Univ	TX	12,500	C+
Lebanon Valley College of Penn	PA	18,300	C
LeMoyne-Owen College	TN	4,500	LC
Lincoln Univ	MO	4,638	NC
Loyola College	MD	18,035	VC
Maine Maritime Academy	ME	8,336	C
Manchester College	IN	13,240	LC
Marquette Univ	WI	16,114	VC
Merrimack College	MA	18,025	C
Miami Univ	OH	8,066	VC
Mich State Univ	MI	7,842	C
Mich Tech Univ	MI	7,283	VC+
Montana College of Mineral Science and Tech	MT	4,977	C
Morehouse College	GA	13,224	LC
Morningside College	IA	13,896	C
Morris Brown College	GA	12,234	NC
New Jersey Inst of Tech	NJ	9,965	VC
New Mexico Highlands Univ	NM	3,772	C
New Mexico Inst of Mining and Tech	NM	5,212	C+
N Car State Univ	NC	4,984	VC
North Park College	IL	14,310	C
Northeastern Univ	MA	19,851	C
Northern Arizona Univ	AZ	4,844	C
Northwestern Univ	IL	21,093	MC
Norwich Univ	VT	18,730	C
Okla State Univ	OK	5,086	VC
Olivet Nazarene Univ	IL	11,976	C
Oral Roberts Univ	OK	10,607	C+
Penn State Univ at Erie/ Behrend College	PA	8,752	C
Penn State Univ/Univ Park Campus	PA	8,752	HC
Polytechnic Univ/Brooklyn	NY	19,700	HC

School	ST	$IS	SR
Keuka College	NY	13,660	C
King College	TN	11,500	C
King's College	NY	12,360	LC
King's College	PA	15,420	C
Knox College	IL	18,990	VC
Knoxville College	TN	8,320	LC
Kutztown Univ	PA	6,528	C
La Roche College	PA	12,977	LC
La Salle Univ	PA	16,940	VC
La Sierra Univ	CA	15,472	C
Lafayette College	PA	23,450	HC
LaGrange College	GA	10,602	C
Lake Erie College	OH	13,700	C
Lake Forest College	IL	19,960	VC
Lake Superior State Univ	MI	7,311	C
Lakeland College	WI	12,845	LC
Lamar Univ	TX	3,798	C
Lambuth Univ	TN	8,395	C
Lander Univ	SC	6,180	LC
Lane College	TN	7,628	LC
Langston Univ	OK	2,907	LC
Lawrence Univ	WI	19,986	HC+
Le Moyne College	NY	15,180	C
Le Tourneau Univ	TX	12,500	C+
Lebanon Valley College of Penn	PA	18,300	C
Lee College	TN	7,894	LC
Lees-McRae College	NC	9,850	LC
Lehigh Univ	PA	23,250	HC
LeMoyne-Owen College	TN	4,500	LC
Lenoir-Rhyne College	NC	14,068	C
Lewis and Clark College	OR	19,980	VC
Lewis Univ	IL	14,797	LC
Lewis-Clark State College	ID	4,040	C
Liberty Univ	VA	11,500	LC
Limestone College	SC	10,700	LC
Lincoln Memorial Univ	TN	8,218	C
Lincoln Univ	MO	4,638	NC
Lincoln Univ	PA	0	LC
Lindenwood College	MO	13,560	C
Lindsey Wilson College	KY	9,530	LC
Linfield College	OR	16,670	VC
Livingston Univ	AL	3,979	C
Livingstone College	NC	8,600	LC
Lock Haven Univ of Penn	PA	7,128	C
LIU/C. W. Post Campus	NY	16,870	C
LIU/Southampton Campus	NY	17,280	C
Longwood College	VA	7,800	C
Loras College	IA	14,160	C
Louisiana State Univ and A&M College	LA	5,605	C
Louisiana State Univ in Shreveport	LA	1,910	NC
Louisiana Tech Univ	LA	4,284	C
Lourdes College	OH	6,410	LC
Loyola College	MD	18,035	VC
Loyola Marymount Univ	CA	18,560	C
Loyola Univ of Chicago	IL	15,880	C+
Loyola Univ/New Orleans	LA	15,660	C+
Lubbock Christian Univ	TX	9,840	NC
Luther College	IA	15,900	VC
Lycoming College	PA	17,200	LC
Lynchburg College	VA	17,000	C
Lyndon State College	VT	8,394	C
Macalester College	MN	19,710	HC
MacMurray College	IL	12,800	C
Madonna Univ	MI	8,546	C
Malone College	OH	12,572	C
Manchester College	IN	13,240	LC
Manhattan College	NY	19,000	C
Manhattanville College	NY	20,450	LC
Mankato State Univ	MN	5,097	LC
Mansfield Univ	PA	6,348	C
Marian College	IN	12,936	C
Marian College of Fond du Lac	WI	12,250	C
Marietta College	OH	16,940	C+
Marist College	NY	16,406	C
Marlboro College	VT	23,305	C+
Marquette Univ	WI	16,114	VC
Mars Hill College	NC	11,050	LC
Marshall Univ	WV	5,762	LC
Martin Univ	IN	4,830	NC
Mary Baldwin College	VA	17,700	LC
Mary Washington College	VA	7,910	HC
Marygrove College	MI	5,877	VC
Marymount College/ Tarrytown	NY	17,350	C
Marymount Manhattan College	NY	15,450	LC
Marymount Univ	VA	15,930	C
Maryville College	TN	14,474	C
Marywood College	PA	14,890	C
Mayville State Univ	ND	4,272	NC
McKendree College	IL	10,900	C
McMurry Univ	TX	10,100	C
McNeese State Univ	LA	4,543	NC
McPherson College	KS	11,360	LC
Mercer Univ	GA	15,123	C
Mercy College	NY	11,180	NC
Mercyhurst College	PA	13,488	C
Meredith College	NC	9,440	C
Merrimack College	MA	18,025	C
Mesa State College	CO	5,127	NC
Messiah College	PA	14,664	VC
Methodist College	NC	12,400	C

School	ST	$IS	SR
Metropolitan State College of Denver	CO	1,751	NC
Miami Univ	OH	8,066	VC
Mich State Univ	MI	7,842	C
MidAmerica Nazarene College	KS	10,208	NC
Middle Tenn State Univ	TN	3,857	C
Middlebury College	VT	24,400	MC
Midland Lutheran College	NE	12,410	LC
Midwestern State Univ	TX	4,542	LC
Miles College	AL	7,150	NC
Millersville Univ of Penn	PA	7,370	VC
Milligan College	TN	10,690	LC
Millikin Univ	IL	15,499	C
Mills College	CA	20,848	VC
Millsaps College	MS	15,486	C+
Miss College	MS	8,348	C
Miss State Univ	MS	5,629	VC
Miss Univ for Women	MS	4,456	LC
Miss Valley State Univ	MS	4,089	NC
Missouri Southern State College	MO	4,272	
Missouri Valley College	MO	14,050	LC
Missouri Western State College	MO	4,384	NC
Molloy College	NY	8,580	LC
Monmouth College	IL	17,300	C+
Monmouth College	NJ	16,820	C
Montana State Univ	MT	5,534	C
Montclair State College	NJ	7,539	C+
Montreat-Anderson College	NC	10,972	LC
Moorhead State Univ	MN	5,076	C
Moravian College	PA	18,960	VC
Morehead State Univ	KY	4,600	LC
Morehouse College	GA	13,224	LC
Morgan State Univ	MD	7,366	C+
Morningside College	IA	13,896	C
Morris Brown College	GA	12,234	NC
Morris College	SC	6,880	LC
Mount Holyoke College	MA	23,630	VC
Mount Marty College	SD	10,450	NC
Mount Mary College	WI	10,920	C
Mount Mercy College	IA	13,230	C
Mount Olive College	NC	9,650	LC
Mount St Mary College	NY	12,910	C
Mount St Mary's College	CA	16,390	VC
Mount St Mary's College	MD	17,825	LC
Mount Senario College	WI	10,970	C
Mount Union College	OH	15,850	C
Mount Vernon Nazarene College	OH	10,390	C
Muhlenberg College	PA	20,795	VC
Murray State Univ	KY	4,702	C
Muskingum College	OH	16,650	C
National-Louis Univ	IL	13,218	C
Nazareth College of Rochester	NY	15,310	C+
Nebr Wesleyan Univ	NE	12,240	C
Neumann College	PA	9,950	LC
New College of Calif	CA	6,900	NC
New England College	NH	17,870	LC
New Hampshire College	NH	15,242	LC
New Mexico Highlands Univ	NM	3,772	C
New Mexico State Univ	NM	4,844	LC
New York Univ	NY	24,705	VC+
Newberry College	SC	11,994	C
Niagara Univ	NY	14,552	C
Nicholls State Univ	LA	4,531	NC
Norfolk State Univ	VA	6,345	LC
North Adams State College	MA	7,750	C
N Car Agricultural and Technical State Univ	NC	4,477	LC
N Car Central Univ	NC	4,347	LC
N Car State Univ	NC	4,984	VC
N Car Wesleyan College	NC	12,480	LC
North Central College	IL	15,498	VC
N Dak State Univ of Agriculture and Applied Science	ND	4,774	VC
North Georgia College	GA	4,103	LC
North Park College	IL	14,310	C
Northeast Louisiana Univ	LA	3,906	NC
Northeast Missouri State Univ	MO	5,654	VC+
Northeastern Illinois Univ	IL	1,955	C
Northeastern State Univ	OK	5,250	C
Northeastern Univ	MA	19,851	C
Northern Arizona Univ	AZ	4,844	VC
Northern Illinois Univ	IL	6,408	C
Northern Kentucky Univ	KY	4,620	NC
Northern Mich Univ	MI	6,350	C
Northern Montana College	MT	4,976	C
Northern State Univ	SD	4,186	LC
Northland College	WI	13,550	LC
Northwest Missouri State Univ	MO	5,510	LC
Northwest Nazarene College	ID	11,750	C
Northwestern College	MN	13,554	C
Northwestern College of Iowa	IA	12,250	C
Northwestern Okla State Univ	OK	3,424	C
Northwestern State Univ of Louisiana	LA	4,287	NC
Northwestern Univ	IL	21,093	MC
Norwich Univ	VT	18,730	C
Notre Dame College	NH	14,220	C

School	ST	$IS	SR
Notre Dame College of Ohio	OH	11,370	C
Nyack College	NY	12,210	C
Oakland City College	IN	10,216	LC
Oakland Univ	MI	6,714	VC
Oakwood College	AL	10,005	C
Oberlin College	OH	24,570	HC+
Oglethorpe Univ	GA	16,360	VC
Ohio Dominican College	OH	11,820	C
Ohio Northern Univ	OH	18,660	VC
Ohio State Univ	OH	7,218	LC
Ohio Univ	OH	7,341	C
Ohio Wesleyan Univ	OH	21,108	VC+
Okla Baptist Univ	OK	8,486	C
Okla Christian Univ of Science and Arts	OK	8,790	NC
Okla City Univ	OK	9,840	C
Okla Panhandle State Univ	OK	3,155	NC
Okla State Univ	OK	5,086	VC
Old Dominion Univ	VA	8,317	C
Olivet College	MI	14,000	C
Olivet Nazarene Univ	IL	11,976	C
Oral Roberts Univ	OK	10,607	C+
Oregon State Univ	OR	6,175	C
Ottawa Univ	KS	10,490	C+
Otterbein College	OH	16,506	C
Ouachita Baptist Univ	AR	8,940	C
Our Lady of Holy Cross College	LA	4,630	LC
Our Lady of the Lake Univ of San Antonio	TX	11,080	C
Pace Univ	NY	15,540	C
Pacific Christian College	CA	12,700	C
Pacific Lutheran Univ	WA	15,998	VC
Pacific Union College	CA	15,075	C
Paine College	GA	8,207	LC
Palm Beach Atlantic College	FL	10,720	C
Paul Quinn College	TX	7,090	LC
Pembroke State Univ	NC	3,538	LC
Penn State Univ at Erie/ Behrend College	PA	8,752	C
Penn State Univ/Univ Park Campus	PA	8,752	HC
Pepperdine Univ	CA	23,720	VC
Peru State College	NE	4,311	NC
Philander Smith College	AR	5,434	NC
Phillips Univ	OK	12,744	C
Piedmont College	GA	8,540	LC
Pikeville College	KY	8,500	NC
Pillsbury Baptist Bible College	MN	7,390	NC
Pine Manor College	MA	21,700	LC
Pittsburg State Univ	KS	4,478	NC
Pitzer College	CA	23,780	HC
Plymouth State College	NH	7,166	C
Point Loma Nazarene College	CA	13,532	C
Point Park College	PA	13,922	LC
Pomona College	CA	23,820	MC
Pontifical Catholic Univ of PR/Ponce	PR	5,807	
Portland State Univ	OR	7,191	C
Prairie View A&M Univ	TX	4,740	LC
Presbyterian College	SC	15,400	VC
Prescott College	AZ	9,775	C
Princeton Univ	NJ	24,650	MC
Principia College	IL	17,799	C
Providence College	RI	19,750	VC
Purdue Univ/Calumet	IN	2,374	NC
Purdue Univ/West Lafayette	IN	6,636	C
Queens College	NC	14,950	C
Quincy Univ	IL	13,646	VC
Quinnipiac College	CT	17,600	C+
Radford Univ	VA	7,034	C
Randolph-Macon College	VA	16,980	C
Randolph-Macon Woman's College	VA	19,100	C
Reed College	OR	24,480	HC+
Regis College	MA	17,450	C
Regis Univ	CO	17,340	C
Rhode Island College	RI	7,901	LC
Rhodes College	TN	19,624	HC
Rice Univ	TX	15,110	MC
Rider College	NJ	18,160	C
Ripon College	WI	18,320	C+
Rivier College	NH	14,920	LC
Roanoke College	VA	16,975	C
Robert Morris College	PA	10,406	LC
Roberts Wesleyan College	NY	13,317	C
Rockford College	IL	15,300	C
Rockhurst College	MO	12,470	C
Rocky Mountain College	MT	11,320	C
Roger Williams Univ	RI	16,750	C
Rollins College	FL	20,875	VC
Roosevelt Univ	IL	12,368	C
Rosary College	IL	15,040	C
Rosemont College	PA	16,775	C
Rowan College of New Jersey	NJ	7,358	VC
Russell Sage College	NY	16,790	C
Rust College	MS	6,600	LC
Rutgers Univ/Camden College of A&S	NJ	8,652	C
Rutgers Univ/Douglass College	NJ	8,795	C
Rutgers Univ/Livingston College	NJ	8,877	VC

School	ST	$IS	SR
Rutgers Univ/Newark College of A&S	NJ	8,645	C
Rutgers Univ/Rutgers College	NJ	8,841	HC+
Rutgers Univ/Univ College— Camden	NJ	3,506	C
Rutgers Univ/Univ College— New Brunswick	NJ	0	LC
Rutgers Univ/Univ College— Newark	NJ	0	C
Sacred Heart Univ	CT	16350	C
Saginaw Valley State Univ	MI	6634	LC
St Ambrose Univ	IA	13380	C
St Andrews Presbyterian College	NC	14,025	LC
St Anselm College	NH	17340	C
St Augustine's College	NC	9,300	C+
St Bonaventure Univ	NY	14,762	C
St Cloud State Univ	MN	5,015	C
St Edward's Univ	TX	12,636	C
St Francis College	IN	11,662	C
St Francis College	NY	6,710	LC
St Francis College	PA	15,744	LC
St John Fisher College	NY	15,415	C
St John's Univ	MN	15,364	C
St John's Univ	NY	8,980	C+
St Joseph College	CT	16,225	C
St Joseph's College	IN	14,730	C
St Joseph's College	ME	14,535	C
St Joseph's College	NY	7,322	C
St Joseph's Univ	PA	17,800	VC
St Lawrence Univ	NY	23,420	VC
St Leo College	FL	13,570	C
St Louis Univ	MO	15,522	VC
St Martin's College	WA	14,965	C
St Mary College	KS	11,250	C
St Mary's College	IN	17,043	VC
St Mary's College	MI	8,350	C
St Mary's College of Calif	CA	18,848	VC
St Mary's College of Maryland	MD	8,900	VC+
St Mary's College of Minn	MN	13,850	LC
St Mary's Univ	TX	12,064	C
St Mary-of-the-Woods College	IN	14,430	NC
St Meinrad College	IN	10,302	C
St Michael's College	VT	17,930	C
St Norbert College	WI	15,710	VC
St Olaf College	MN	17,200	HC
St Paul's College	VA	9,171	C
St Peter's College	NJ	14,775	LC
St Thomas Aquinas College	NY	13,550	C
St Thomas Univ	FL	14,280	LC
St Vincent College	PA	13,934	LC
St Xavier Univ	IL	14,700	C
Salem College	NC	16,025	C
Salem State College	MA	6,712	C
Salisbury State Univ	MD	7,516	C+
Salve Regina Univ	RI	29,100	LC
Sam Houston State Univ	TX	4,506	C
Samford Univ	AL	11,400	VC
San Diego State Univ	CA	6,692	LC
San Francisco State Univ	CA	7,292	C
San Jose State Univ	CA	6,680	LC
Santa Clara Univ	CA	18,783	VC
Sarah Lawrence College	NY	24,975	HC
Savannah State College	GA	4,052	C
Schreiner College	TX	14,320	C
Scripps College	CA	23,600	HC
Seattle Pacific Univ	WA	16,503	C
Seattle Univ	WA	16,590	C
Selma Univ	AL	5,785	NC
Seton Hall Univ	NJ	18,306	LC
Seton Hill College	PA	14,320	C
Shaw Univ	NC	8,936	C+
Shawnee State Univ	OH	4,379	NC
Shenandoah Univ	VA	11,800	C
Shepherd College	WV	5,540	C
Shippensburg Univ of Penn	PA	7,052	C
Shorter College	GA	10,270	C
Siena College	NY	15,410	C
Siena Heights College	MI	12,520	C
Silver Lake College	WI	8,280	LC
Simmons College	MA	22,534	C
Simpson College	CA	10,628	C
Simpson College	IA	14,635	VC
Sioux Falls College	SD	11,540	C
Skidmore College	NY	23,230	HC
Slippery Rock Univ	PA	6,803	C
Smith College	MA	24,236	HC
Sonoma State Univ	CA	6,996	LC
S Car State Univ	SC	5,424	LC
S Dak State Univ	SD	4,562	C
Southeast Missouri State Univ	MO	5,854	C
Southeastern Louisiana Univ	LA	4,230	NC
Southeastern Okla State Univ	OK	3,594	C
Southern Arkansas Univ	AR	3,432	NC
Southern Calif College	CA	12,356	C
Southern College of Seventh- day Adventists	TN	11,348	LC
Southern Conn State Univ	CT	7,532	C
Southern Illinois Univ at Carbondale	IL	6,234	C
Southern Illinois Univ at Edwardsville	IL	6,097	LC

ENGLISH AS A SECOND/FOREIGN LANGUAGE

School	ST	$IS	SR
CUNY/Queens College	NY	2,631	C
Doane College	NE	12,220	C
Florida Inst of Tech	FL	16,935	VC
Holy Names College	CA	15,660	C
La Sierra Univ	CA	15,472	C
Univ of Findlay	OH	15,764	C

ENGLISH EDUCATION

School	ST	$IS	SR
Adelphi Univ	NY	18,250	LC
Albertson College	ID	15,942	C+
Andrews Univ	MI	14,952	NC
Bartlesville Wesleyan College	OK	9,400	C
Bennett College	NC	8,920	LC
Bethany College	WV	18,300	C+
Bethune-Cookman College	FL	8,375	LC
Blackburn College	IL	9,120	C
Boise State Univ	ID	4,909	LC
Boston Univ	MA	24,130	HC
Calif Univ of Penn	PA	7,370	C
Canisius College	NY	15,510	C
Central Univ of Bayamon	PR	2,430	
Christian Heritage College	CA	11,756	C
Coastal Carolina Univ	SC	6,010	LC
Coker College	SC	13,790	C
College of St Rose	NY	14,452	C
College of Santa Fe	NM	14,008	C
Columbia Union College	MD	13,650	LC
Concordia College	MN	13,200	C
Coppin State College	MD	7,145	LC
Daemen College	NY	13,020	LC
Drake Univ	IA	17,195	VC
East Texas Baptist Univ	TX	7,740	C
Eastern College	PA	15,150	C+
Edinboro Univ of Penn	PA	7,181	C
Florida Atlantic Univ	FL	5,525	C
Florida International Univ	FL	4,191	VC
Fresno Pacific College	CA	13,020	C
Georgia Southwestern College	GA	4,338	LC
Georgia State Univ	GA	2,019	C
Grace College	IN	12,120	C
Gwynedd-Mercy College	PA	15,450	C
Hood College	MD	19,010	VC
Humboldt State Univ	CA	5,676	C
Huntington College	IN	13,220	C
Indiana Wesleyan Univ	IN	12,332	C
Judson College	IL	13,625	C
Kennesaw State College	GA	1,553	C
Kent State Univ	OH	6,740	LC
Lincoln Univ	PA	0	LC
LIU/C. W. Post Campus	NY	16,870	C
Lyndon State College	VT	8,394	LC
Mansfield Univ	PA	6,348	C
Mary Baldwin College	VA	17,700	LC
Montreat-Anderson College	NC	10,972	LC
Morningside College	IA	13,896	C
Morris College	SC	6,880	LC
New Hampshire College	NH	15,242	LC
Niagara Univ	NY	14,552	C
N Car Agricultural and Technical State Univ	NC	4,477	LC
Northeast Louisiana Univ	LA	3,906	NC
Northwestern College	MN	13,554	C
Northwestern Okla State Univ	OK	3,424	C
Northwestern Univ	IL	21,093	MC
Oakwood College	AL	10,005	C
Ohio State Univ	OH	7,218	LC
Okla Christian Univ of Science and Arts	OK	8,790	NC
Okla State Univ	OK	5,086	VC
Pembroke State Univ	NC	3,538	LC
Pillsbury Baptist Bible College	MN	7,390	NC
Plymouth State College	NH	7,166	C
Point Loma Nazarene College	CA	13,532	C
Queens College	NC	14,950	C
Rivier College	NH	14,920	LC
St Francis College	IN	11,662	C
St Mary's College of Minn	MN	13,850	LC
St Olaf College	MN	17,200	HC
Southeastern College of the Assemblies of God	FL	6,618	NC
Southeastern Louisiana Univ	LA	4,230	NC
Southern Calif College	CA	12,356	C
Southern Univ and A&M College	LA	4,920	NC
Southern Univ at New Orleans	LA	1,452	NC
Southwestern Okla State Univ	OK	3,312	C
SUNY/College at Plattsburgh	NY	6,917	C
Temple Univ	PA	10,281	C
Trevecca Nazarene College	TN	9,826	NC
Troy State Univ	AL	4,322	C
Troy State Univ at Dothan/Fort Rucker	AL	2,260	NC
Turabo Univ	PR	2,670	
Univ of Arkansas at Pine Bluff	AR	3,978	LC
Univ of Central Florida	FL	6,061	C+
Univ of Conn	CT	9,168	C
Univ of Delaware	DE	8,013	VC
Univ of Evansville	IN	15,300	VC
Univ of Illinois at Chicago	IL	8,443	C
Univ of Illinois at Urbana-Champaign	IL	7,764	HC
Univ of Maine at Farmington	ME	6,700	C
Univ of Maine at Presque Isle	ME	6,374	C
Univ of Minn/Duluth	MN	6,512	C
Univ of Minn/Twin Cities	MN	6,682	VC
Univ of New Hampshire	NH	8,242	C
Univ of New Orleans	LA	5,468	C
Univ of Pittsburgh at Johnstown	PA	8,914	C
Univ of Southwestern Louisiana	LA	3,968	NC
Whitworth College	WA	16,265	C
Wiley College	TX	0	NC
Wingate College	NC	10,610	C
Xavier Univ of Louisiana	LA	10,400	C

ENGLISH LITERATURE

School	ST	$IS	SR
Blackburn College	IL	9,120	C
Brandeis Univ	MA	25,585	HC
Claremont McKenna College	CA	22,150	MC
DePauw Univ	IN	18,530	VC
Dominican College of San Rafael	CA	17,860	C
Eastern College	PA	15,150	C+
Edinboro Univ of Penn	PA	7,181	C
Elmira College	NY	18,450	C
Pfeiffer College	NC	11,670	LC
St Edward's Univ	TX	12,636	C
Syracuse Univ	NY	21,305	HC
Univ of Pittsburgh	PA	9,472	C
Univ of Pittsburgh at Greensburg	PA	8,660	C
Wilmington College	OH	13,700	LC

ENTOMOLOGY

School	ST	$IS	SR
Auburn Univ	AL	5,823	C+
Brigham Young Univ	UT	5,625	HC
Clemson Univ	SC	6,564	VC
Cornell Univ	NY	13,445	MC
Iowa State Univ	IA	5,456	C
Mich State Univ	MI	7,842	C
Miss State Univ	MS	5,629	VC
N Dak State Univ of Agriculture and Applied Science	ND	4,774	VC
Ohio State Univ	OH	7,218	LC
Oregon State Univ	OR	6,175	C
Penn State Univ/Univ Park Campus	PA	8,752	HC
Purdue Univ/West Lafayette	IN	6,636	C
Rutgers Univ/Cook College	NJ	9,197	HC
SUNY College of Environmental Science and Forestry	NY	9,257	HC+
Texas A&M Univ	TX	5,382	VC
Texas Tech Univ	TX	6,008	C
Univ of Calif at Berkeley	CA	9,962	HC+
Univ of Calif at Davis	CA	9,534	VC
Univ of Calif, Riverside	CA	9,178	C
Univ of Delaware	DE	8,013	VC
Univ of Florida	FL	5,850	HC
Univ of Hawaii at Manoa	HI	5,626	C
Univ of Idaho	ID	4,830	C
Univ of Kentucky	KY	5,152	VC
Univ of Maryland/College Park	MD	8,182	VC
Univ of Mass/Amherst	MA	9,364	LC
Univ of New Hampshire	NH	8,242	C
Univ of Wisc/Madison	WI	6,400	HC
Univ of Wyoming	WY	4,991	NC
Washington State Univ	WA	6,364	C

ENTREPRENEURIAL STUDIES

School	ST	$IS	SR
Jacksonville Univ	FL	13,390	C
Univ of Miami	FL	22,107	VC
Univ of St Thomas	MN	15,785	C+

ENVIRONMENTAL BIOLOGY

School	ST	$IS	SR
Cal State/Fresno	CA	5,747	C
Cal State/Northridge	CA	7,122	LC
Eastern Illinois Univ	IL	5,548	C
Grand Canyon Univ	AZ	9,680	VC
Lock Haven Univ of Penn	PA	7,128	C
Millersville Univ of Penn	PA	7,370	VC
Plymouth State College	NH	7,166	C
St Mary's College of Minn	MN	13,850	LC
SUNY College of Environmental Science and Forestry	NY	9,257	HC+
Univ of Calif at Davis	CA	9,534	VC
Univ of Colo at Boulder	CO	6,410	VC
Univ of North Alabama	AL	4,236	NC

ENVIRONMENTAL DESIGN

School	ST	$IS	SR
Art Center College of Design	CA	13,550	SP
Ball State Univ	IN	6,032	LC
Hampshire College	MA	25,320	C
Harvard Univ/Harvard and Radcliffe Colleges	MA	24,880	MC
Miami Univ	OH	8,066	VC
N Car State Univ	NC	4,984	VC
Otis College of Art and Design	CA	16,686	SP
Rutgers Univ/Cook College	NJ	9,197	HC
Southern College of Tech	GA	4	C
SUNY at Buffalo	NY	7,896	VC
SUNY College of Environmental Science and Forestry	NY	9,257	HC+
Syracuse Univ	NY	21,305	HC
Texas A&M Univ	TX	5,382	VC
Univ of Colo at Boulder	CO	6,410	VC
Univ of Mass/Amherst	MA	9,364	LC
Univ of Mich/Ann Arbor	MI	9,428	HC+
Univ of Minn/Twin Cities	MN	6,682	VC
Univ of Okla	OK	5,427	VC
Univ of Penn	PA	24,238	MC
Univ of Wisc/Green Bay	WI	4,904	C

ENVIRONMENTAL EDUCATION

School	ST	$IS	SR
Florida International Univ	FL	4,191	VC
Mich State Univ	MI	7,842	C
Ohio State Univ	OH	7,218	LC
Prescott College	AZ	9,775	C
SUNY College of Environmental Science and Forestry	NY	9,257	HC+
Unity College	ME	12,885	LC
Univ of Mich/Ann Arbor	MI	9,428	HC+

ENVIRONMENTAL ENGINEERING

School	ST	$IS	SR
Calif Polytechnic State Univ	CA	6,980	VC+
Florida Inst of Tech	FL	16,935	VC
Humboldt State Univ	CA	5,676	C
Johns Hopkins Univ	MD	24,360	MC
Manhattan College	NY	19,000	C
Marquette Univ	WI	16,114	VC
Mass Maritime Academy	MA	7,410	C
Mercer Univ	GA	15,123	C
Mich Tech Univ	MI	7,283	VC+
Montana College of Mineral Science and Tech	MT	4,977	C
New Mexico Inst of Mining and Tech	NM	5,212	C+
N Car State Univ	NC	4,984	VC
Northern Arizona Univ	AZ	4,844	C
Northwestern Univ	IL	21,093	MC
Polytechnic Univ/Brooklyn	NY	19,700	HC
Polytechnic Univ/Farmingdale	NY	20,700	VC
Rensselaer Polytechnic Inst	NY	23,067	HC
Rutgers Univ/Camden College of A&S	NJ	8,652	VC
SUNY College of Environmental Science and Forestry	NY	9,257	HC+
Stevens Inst of Tech	NJ	21,980	VC+
Syracuse Univ	NY	21,305	HC
Texas Tech Univ	TX	6,008	C
Tulane Univ	LA	24,540	HC
United States Military Academy	NY	0	MC
Univ of Calif, Riverside	CA	9,178	C
Univ of Central Florida	FL	6,061	C+
Univ of Florida	FL	5,850	HC
Univ of Iowa	IA	5,658	VC
Univ of Mich/Ann Arbor	MI	9,428	HC+
Univ of Notre Dame	IN	20,150	MC
Vanderbilt Univ	TN	23,422	HC+
Wentworth Inst of Tech	MA	15,250	LC
Wilkes Univ	PA	15,728	LC
Worcester Polytechnic Inst	MA	20,350	HC

ENVIRONMENTAL ENGINEERING TECHNOLOGY

School	ST	$IS	SR
Cornell Univ	NY	13,445	MC
Humboldt State Univ	CA	5,676	C
Mesa State College	CO	5,127	NC
Rochester Inst of Tech	NY	18,954	VC
Temple Univ	PA	10,281	C
Univ of Dayton	OH	15,120	C+
Univ of Miami	FL	22,107	VC
Univ of Minn/Crookston	MN	6,894	NC
Univ of Mobile	AL	9,400	C

ENVIRONMENTAL HEALTH SCIENCE

School	ST	$IS	SR
Anna Maria College	MA	15,975	LC
Benedict College	SC	8,376	LC
Boise State Univ	ID	4,909	LC
Cal State/Sacramento	CA	6,387	C
Cal State/San Bernardino	CA	6,055	LC
Colo State Univ	CO	6,566	VC
Delaware State College	DE	5,656	C
Eastern Kentucky Univ	KY	4,840	NC
Illinois State Univ	IL	6,413	C
Indiana State Univ	IN	6,210	C
Indiana Univ-Purdue Univ at Indianapolis	IN	5,862	LC
Miss Valley State Univ	MS	4,089	NC
Oakland Univ	MI	6,714	VC
Ohio Northern Univ	OH	18,660	VC
Salisbury State Univ	MD	7,516	C+
Springfield College	MA	15,200	LC
Univ of Arkansas at Little Rock	AR	4,419	C
Univ of Miami	FL	22,107	VC
Univ of Washington	WA	6,618	VC
Western Carolina Univ	NC	3,811	C
Wright State Univ	OH	6,896	LC

ENVIRONMENTAL SCIENCE

School	ST	$IS	SR
Adrian College	MI	14,340	C
Alabama A&M Univ	AL	4,200	C
Alaska Pacific Univ	AK	11,350	C
Albright College	PA	19,260	C
Alfred Univ	NY	21,054	VC+
Allegheny College	PA	21,020	VC
Antioch College	OH	19,532	C
Aquinas College	MI	14,526	C
Auburn Univ	AL	5,823	C+
Augustana College	IL	16,959	VC
Aurora Univ	IL	13,381	C
Averett College	VA	13,610	LC
Bard College	NY	25,269	HC
Barton College	NC	10,689	LC
Boston College	MA	22,706	MC
Boston Univ	MA	24,130	HC
Bowdoin College	ME	24,155	MC
Bowling Green State Univ	OH	6,701	C
Bradley Univ	IL	14,718	C+
Brown Univ	RI	26,104	MC
Butler Univ	IN	16,210	C
Cal State/Bakersfield	CA	5,402	C
Cal State/Hayward	CA	5,495	C
Calif Univ of Penn	PA	7,370	C
Central College	IA	14,025	VC
Chatham College	PA	18,010	C
CUNY/Hunter College	NY	4,101	VC
Claremont McKenna College	CA	22,150	MC
Clark Univ	MA	21,400	VC
Clarkson Univ	NY	20,705	VC+
Cleveland State Univ	OH	7,287	NC
Clinch Valley College/Univ of Virginia	VA	6,364	C
Colby College	ME	24,230	HC
College of St Francis	IL	13,060	VC
College of Santa Fe	NM	14,008	C
Colo College	CO	20,038	HC
Columbia Univ/Barnard College	NY	25,492	HC
Columbia Univ/Columbia College	NY	26,757	MC
Concordia College	MN	13,200	C

School	ST	$IS	SR
Concordia College	NY	0	LC
Concordia Lutheran College	TX	10,260	C+
Cornell College	IA	18,425	VC
Dana College	NE	11,910	C
Dartmouth College	NH	24,354	MC
Davis and Elkins College	WV	13,230	LC
Defiance College	OH	13,480	LC
Delta State Univ	MS	3,964	LC
DePaul Univ	IL	15,535	VC
Doane College	NE	12,220	C
Drake Univ	IA	17,195	VC
Duke Univ	NC	21,271	MC
Earlham College	IN	19,383	VC
Eastern Kentucky Univ	KY	4,840	NC
Eckerd College	FL	18,855	VC
Edinboro Univ of Penn	PA	7,181	C
Elizabethtown College	PA	17,850	VC
Elmira College	NY	18,450	C
Fairleigh Dickinson Univ	NJ	16,427	C
Ferrum College	VA	12,800	LC
Florida Inst of Tech	FL	16,935	VC
Florida International Univ	FL	4,191	VC
Florida Southern College	FL	12,260	C
Franklin Pierce College	NH	17,270	LC
Frostburg State Univ	MD	6,940	C
George Washington Univ	DC	22,470	HC
Georgetown College	KY	10,990	C
Goddard College	VT	17,990	LC
Harvard Univ/Harvard and Radcliffe Colleges	MA	24,880	MC
Heritage College	WA	5,540	NC
Hillsdale College	MI	15,110	VC
Hobart and William Smith Colleges	NY	23,925	VC
Hood College	MD	19,010	VC
Howard Payne Univ	TX	8,052	C
Incarnate Word College	TX	12,307	C
Indiana Univ Bloomington	IN	6,495	VC
Indiana Univ-Purdue Univ at Indianapolis	IN	5,862	LC
Iowa State Univ	IA	5,456	C
Jacksonville Univ	FL	13,390	C
Johnson State College	VT	8,393	LC
Juniata College	PA	18,390	C+
Keene State College	NH	7,081	C
Kenyon College	OH	22,430	HC+
Kutztown Univ	PA	6,528	C
Lake Erie College	OH	13,700	C
Lake Superior State Univ	MI	7,311	C
Lawrence Univ	WI	19,986	HC+
Lehigh Univ	PA	23,250	HC
Lincoln Memorial Univ	TN	8,218	C
Linfield College	OR	16,670	VC
Lynchburg College	VA	17,000	C
Macalester College	MN	19,710	HC
Manhattanville College	NY	20,450	LC
Mansfield Univ	PA	6,348	C
Marist College	NY	16,406	C
Mary Washington College	VA	7,910	HC
Marymount Univ	VA	15,930	C
Mass Inst of Tech	MA	24,800	MC
Mercyhurst College	PA	13,488	C
Middlebury College	VT	24,400	MC
Monmouth College	IL	17,300	C+
Muskingum College	OH	16,650	C
New College of the Univ of South Florida	FL	5,697	MC
New England College	NH	17,870	LC
New Mexico Highlands Univ	NM	3,772	C
New Mexico Inst of Mining and Tech	NM	5,212	C+
N Car State Univ	NC	4,984	VC
N Car Wesleyan College	NC	12,480	LC
Northeastern Illinois Univ	IL	1,955	C
Northern Montana College	MT	4,976	C
Northern State Univ	SD	4,186	LC
Northwestern Univ	IL	21,093	MC
Norwich Univ	VT	18,730	C
Oberlin College	OH	24,570	HC+
Ohio Wesleyan Univ	OH	21,108	VC+
Penn State Univ/Univ Park Campus	PA	8,752	HC
Philadelphia College of Textiles and Science	PA	15,896	C
Pitzer College	CA	23,780	HC
Point Park College	PA	13,922	LC
Prescott College	AZ	9,775	C
Principia College	IL	17,799	C
Purdue Univ/West Lafayette	IN	6,636	C
Ramapo College of New Jersey	NJ	8,027	C+
Randolph-Macon College	VA	16,980	C
Rice Univ	TX	15,110	MC
Richard Stockton College of New Jersey	NJ	6,950	VC
Rollins College	FL	20,875	VC
Roosevelt Univ	IL	12,368	C
Rutgers Univ/Cook College	NJ	9,197	HC
St Francis College	IN	11,662	C
St John's Univ	NY	8,980	C+
St Joseph's College	ME	14,535	C
St Lawrence Univ	NY	23,420	VC
St Michael's College	VT	17,930	C
St Norbert College	WI	15,710	VC
St Paul's College	VA	9,171	C
St Vincent College	PA	13,934	LC
Sam Houston State Univ	TX	4,506	C
Savannah State College	GA	4,052	C
Scripps College	CA	23,600	HC
Sierra Nevada College	NV	14,000	NC
Simmons College	MA	22,534	C
Simon's Rock College of Bard	MA	23,760	VC+
Sonoma State Univ	CA	6,996	LC
Southern Univ and A&M College	LA	4,920	NC
Southern Vermont College	VT	12,974	C
Southwest Texas State Univ	TX	5,124	C
SUNY College of Environmental Science and Forestry	NY	9,257	HC+
SUNY/College at Oneonta	NY	7,878	C
SUNY/College at Plattsburgh	NY	6,917	C
SUNY/College at Purchase	NY	7,324	C
Stephen F. Austin State Univ	TX	5,117	C
Susquehanna Univ	PA	19,950	VC
Taylor Univ	IN	14,450	VC
Teikyo Marycrest Univ	IA	13,755	VC
Texas A&M Univ	TX	5,382	VC
Texas Christian Univ	TX	12,180	C
Thiel College	PA	16,282	C
Thomas A. Edison State College	NJ	400	
Tri-State Univ	IN	13,788	LC
Trinity College	DC	17,660	C
Trinity College of Vermont	VT	16,015	LC
Tufts Univ	MA	24,962	MC
Tulane Univ	LA	24,540	HC
Tusculum College	TN	10,400	LC
Union College	NY	23,817	HC
United States Military Academy	NY	0	MC
Unity College	ME	12,885	LC
Univ of Calif at Berkeley	CA	9,962	HC+
Univ of Calif at Davis	CA	9,534	VC
Univ of Calif at Santa Barbara	CA	9,460	C
Univ of Calif, Riverside	CA	9,178	C
Univ of Calif/Irvine	CA	12,680	VC
Univ of Charleston	WV	12,750	C
Univ of Colo at Boulder	CO	6,410	VC
Univ of Delaware	DE	8,013	VC
Univ of Denver	CO	19,290	C+
Univ of Dubuque	IA	14,150	LC
Univ of Evansville	IN	15,300	VC
Univ of Findlay	OH	15,764	C
Univ of Kansas	KS	5,200	NC
Univ of La Verne	CA	17,400	C
Univ of Lowell	MA	8,831	VC
Univ of Maine at Farmington	ME	6,700	C
Univ of Maine at Fort Kent	ME	6,285	LC
Univ of Maine at Machias	ME	6,135	C
Univ of Maine at Presque Isle	ME	6,374	C
Univ of Maryland/Eastern Shore	MD	6,254	LC
Univ of Mass/Amherst	MA	9,364	LC
Univ of Miami	FL	22,107	VC
Univ of Mich/Ann Arbor	MI	9,428	HC+
Univ of Mich/Dearborn	MI	3,399	HC
Univ of Nebr-Lincoln	NE	5,278	LC
Univ of New England	ME	16,075	LC
Univ of New Hampshire	NH	8,242	C
Univ of New Haven	CT	14,980	C
Univ of N Car at Asheville	NC	4,791	VC
Univ of N Car at Wilmington	NC	5,172	C
Univ of Okla	OK	5,427	VC
Univ of Penn	PA	24,238	MC
Univ of Rhode Island	RI	9,205	C
Univ of San Francisco	CA	18,408	C
Univ of Southern Maine	ME	7,299	C
Univ of Tenn at Chattanooga	TN	5,375	C
Univ of the District of Columbia	DC	974	NC
Univ of Tulsa	OK	13,795	VC
Univ of Vermont	VT	10,776	C+
Univ of Virginia	VA	7,964	MC
Univ of Washington	WA	6,618	VC
Univ of Wisc/Green Bay	WI	4,904	C
Utah State Univ	UT	4,683	C
Vassar College	NY	24,206	HC
Virginia Polytechnic Inst and State Univ	VA	6,828	C
Warren Wilson College	NC	10,877	C
Wells College	NY	19,460	C+
Wesley College	DE	13,745	LC
Wesleyan Univ	CT	23,770	MC
West Virginia Univ	WV	5,774	C
Western Conn State Univ	CT	6,622	C
Western Kentucky Univ	KY	4,808	C
Wheaton College	IL	14,710	HC
Widener Univ	PA	16,840	C
Willamette Univ	OR	17,995	VC
William Paterson College	NJ	7,438	C+
Winston-Salem State Univ	NC	4,142	LC

EQUESTRIAN SCIENCE

School	ST	$IS	SR
Averett College	VA	13,610	LC
Centenary College	NJ	17,040	LC
Colo State Univ	CO	6,566	VC
Johnson and Wales Univ	RI	13,995	LC
Lake Erie College	OH	13,700	C
Northeast Missouri State Univ	MO	5,654	VC+
Otterbein College	OH	16,506	C
Rocky Mountain College	MT	11,320	C
Salem-Teikyo Univ	WV	14,527	C
Stephens College	MO	18,460	C
Univ of Findlay	OH	15,764	C
Univ of New Hampshire	NH	8,242	C
Univ of PR/Rio Piedras	PR	0	C
Virginia Intermont College	VA	12,250	LC
William Woods Univ	MO	14,025	LC
Wilson College	PA	16,630	C

ESKIMO

School	ST	$IS	SR
Univ of Alaska Fairbanks	AK	4,718	C

ETHICS, POLITICS, AND SOCIAL POLICY

School	ST	$IS	SR
Bloomsburg Univ of Penn	PA	6,312	C+
Dickinson College	PA	22,705	HC
Univ of Mass/Amherst	MA	9,364	LC
Wells College	NY	19,460	C+
Wheeling Jesuit College	WV	14,370	C

ETHNIC STUDIES

School	ST	$IS	SR
Cal State/Chico	CA	6,146	C
Cal State/Hayward	CA	5,495	C
Kent State Univ	OH	6,740	LC
Mills College	CA	20,848	VC
St John's Univ	NY	8,980	C+
Univ of Calif at Berkeley	CA	9,962	HC+
Univ of Calif, Riverside	CA	9,178	C
Univ of Calif, San Diego	CA	10,028	VC+
Univ of Texas at Austin	TX	5,160	VC
Univ of Virginia	VA	7,964	MC
Univ of Washington	WA	6,618	VC
Villanova Univ	PA	21,400	HC

EUROPEAN STUDIES

School	ST	$IS	SR
Amherst College	MA	24,152	MC
Boston Univ	MA	24,130	HC
Brandeis Univ	MA	25,585	HC
Brigham Young Univ	UT	5,625	HC
Chatham College	PA	18,010	C
Claremont McKenna College	CA	22,150	MC
College of the Holy Cross	MA	23,850	HC
Columbia Univ/Barnard College	NY	25,492	HC
Emory Univ	GA	21,930	HC
Georgetown College	KY	10,990	C
Goucher College	MD	20,295	VC
Harvard Univ/Harvard and Radcliffe Colleges	MA	24,880	MC
Hillsdale College	MI	15,110	VC
Loyola Marymount Univ	CA	18,560	C
Lynchburg College	VA	17,000	C
Millsaps College	MS	15,486	C+
Mount Holyoke College	MA	23,630	VC
Phillips Univ	OK	12,744	C
Pitzer College	CA	23,780	HC
Rosary College	IL	15,040	C
Scripps College	CA	23,600	HC
Seattle Pacific Univ	WA	16,503	C
Southwest Texas State Univ	TX	5,124	C
Univ of Minn/Morris	MN	6,825	HC
Univ of Northern Iowa	IA	5,137	C
Univ of Okla	OK	5,427	VC
Univ of S Car	SC	6,158	C
Wellesley College	MA	23,815	MC

EVOLUTIONARY BIOLOGY

School	ST	$IS	SR
Cornell Univ	NY	13,445	MC
Rutgers Univ/Cook College	NJ	9,197	HC
Rutgers Univ/Douglass College	NJ	8,795	VC
Rutgers Univ/Rutgers College	NJ	8,841	HC+
Rutgers Univ/Univ College—New Brunswick	NJ	0	LC
Univ of Calif at Santa Barbara	CA	9,460	C
Univ of Minn/Twin Cities	MN	6,682	VC
Wellesley College	MA	23,815	MC

EXPERIMENTAL PSYCHOLOGY

School	ST	$IS	SR
Southern Calif College	CA	12,356	C
Tufts Univ	MA	24,962	MC

FAMILY AND COMMUNITY SERVICES

School	ST	$IS	SR
Iowa State Univ	IA	5,456	C
John Brown Univ	AR	9,880	VC
Liberty Univ	VA	11,500	LC
SUNY/College at Plattsburgh	NY	6,917	C
Syracuse Univ	NY	21,305	HC
Univ of Northern Iowa	IA	5,137	C

FAMILY/CONSUMER RESOURCE MANAGEMENT

School	ST	$IS	SR
Arizona State Univ Main Campus	AZ	6,444	C
Iowa State Univ	IA	5,456	C
Mich State Univ	MI	7,842	C
N Dak State Univ of Agriculture and Applied Science	ND	4,774	VC
Northwest Missouri State Univ	MO	5,010	LC
Ohio State Univ	OH	7,218	LC
St Olaf College	MN	17,200	HC
Texas Tech Univ	TX	6,008	C
Univ of Arizona	AZ	5,808	C
Univ of Hawaii at Manoa	HI	5,626	C
West Virginia Univ	WV	5,774	C

FAMILY/CONSUMER STUDIES

School	ST	$IS	SR
Berry College	GA	11,990	VC
Brigham Young Univ	UT	5,625	HC
Christian Heritage College	CA	11,756	C
CUNY/Herbert H. Lehman College	NY	2,542	C
College of St Catherine	MN	14,670	C
Framingham State College	MA	6,580	C
Georgia Southern Univ	GA	4,988	LC
Hampshire College	MA	25,320	C
Iowa State Univ	IA	5,456	C
Madonna Univ	MI	8,546	C
Mercyhurst College	PA	13,488	C
Messiah College	PA	14,664	VC
New Mexico State Univ	NM	4,844	LC
Oregon State Univ	OR	6,175	C
Pacific Union College	CA	15,075	C
St Joseph College	CT	16,225	C
Seattle Pacific Univ	WA	16,503	C
Seton Hill College	PA	14,320	C
Southeastern Louisiana Univ	LA	4,230	NC
SUNY/College at Buffalo	NY	7,035	VC
Syracuse Univ	NY	21,305	HC
Univ of Alabama	AL	5,702	C
Univ of Illinois at Urbana-Champaign	IL	7,764	HC
Univ of Mass/Amherst	MA	9,364	LC
Univ of Nebr at Kearney	NE	4,308	LC
Univ of Nebr at Omaha	NE	1,889	LC
Univ of New Hampshire	NH	8,242	C
Univ of Utah	UT	5,975	C
Univ of Wisc/Madison	WI	6,400	HC
Weber State Univ	UT	4,398	C
Western Mich Univ	MI	6,820	C

FASHION DESIGN AND TECHNOLOGY

School	ST	$IS	SR
American College for the Applied Arts	GA	11,870	SP
Brigham Young Univ	UT	5,625	HC
Centenary College	NJ	17,040	LC
Columbia College	MO	11,995	C
Davis and Elkins College	WV	13,230	LC
Drexel Univ	PA	15,970	C
Eastern Kentucky Univ	KY	4,840	NC
Fashion Inst of Tech/SUNY	NY	7,135	SP
Georgia Southern Univ	GA	4,988	LC
Illinois State Univ	IL	6,413	C
Incarnate Word College	TX	12,307	C
Iowa State Univ	IA	5,456	C
Kent State Univ	OH	6,740	LC
Marist College	NY	16,406	C
Marymount College/Tarrytown	NY	17,350	C
Marymount Univ	VA	15,930	C
Mass College of Art	MA	9,447	SP
Moore College of Art and Design	PA	17,947	SP
Mount Ida College	MA	16,700	LC
Oregon State Univ	OR	6,175	C
Otis College of Art and Design	CA	16,686	SP
Parsons School of Design	NY	21,410	SP
Philadelphia College of Textiles and Science	PA	15,896	C
Pratt Inst	NY	19,520	C
Rosary College	IL	15,040	C
Savannah College of Art and Design	GA	14,280	SP
School of the Art Inst of Chicago	IL	17,610	SP
Stephens College	MO	18,460	C
Syracuse Univ	NY	21,305	HC
Texas Christian Univ	TX	12,180	C
Texas Tech Univ	TX	6,008	C
Univ of Arkansas at Fayetteville	AR	5,046	C
Univ of Delaware	DE	8,013	VC
Univ of North Texas	TX	4,853	C
Univ of San Francisco	CA	18,408	C
Univ of Wisc/Stout	WI	4,719	C
Ursuline College	OH	13,180	LC
Washington Univ	MO	23,507	HC
Woodbury Univ	CA	17,620	LC

FASHION MERCHANDISING

School	ST	$IS	SR
American College for the Applied Arts	GA	11,870	SP
Auburn Univ	AL	5,823	C+
Bennett College	NC	8,920	LC
Berry College	GA	11,990	VC
Brigham Young Univ	UT	5,625	HC
Central Missouri State Univ	MO	5,138	LC
College of St Catherine	MN	14,670	C
David Lipscomb Univ	TN	7,865	VC
Delaware State College	DE	5,656	C
Delta State Univ	MS	3,964	LC
Drexel Univ	PA	15,970	C
Eastern Kentucky Univ	KY	4,840	NC
Eastern Mich Univ	MI	6,749	C
Georgia Southern Univ	GA	4,988	LC
Immaculata College	PA	14,620	C
Iowa State Univ	IA	5,456	C
James Madison Univ	VA	8,198	HC
Johnson and Wales Univ	RI	13,995	LC
Kent State Univ	OH	6,740	LC
Laboratory Inst of Merchandising	NY	9,800	SP
Liberty Univ	VA	11,500	LC
Lindenwood College	MO	13,560	C
Louisiana Tech Univ	LA	4,284	C
Lynn Univ	FL	18,300	C
Madonna Univ	MI	8,546	C
Mansfield Univ	PA	6,348	C
Marian College	IN	12,936	C
Marist College	NY	16,406	C
Mars Hill College	NC	11,050	C
Marshall Univ	WV	5,762	LC
Marymount College/Tarrytown	NY	17,350	C
Marymount Univ	VA	15,930	C
Marywood College	PA	14,890	C
Mercyhurst College	PA	13,488	C
Meredith College	NC	9,440	C
Mount Ida College	MA	16,700	LC
New Mexico State Univ	NM	4,844	LC
Northeast Louisiana Univ	LA	3,906	NC
Northern Mich Univ	MI	6,350	C
Northwest Nazarene College	ID	11,750	C
Ohio Dominican College	OH	11,820	LC
Pacific Union College	CA	15,075	C
Philadelphia College of Textiles and Science	PA	15,896	C
Point Park College	PA	13,922	LC
Pratt Inst	NY	19,520	C
Rosary College	IL	15,040	C
St Vincent College	PA	13,934	LC
Seton Hill College	PA	14,320	C
Siena Heights College	MI	12,520	C
Southern Nazarene Univ	OK	9,206	NC
Southwest Texas State Univ	TX	5,124	C
SUNY/College at Oneonta	NY	7,878	C
Stephen F. Austin State Univ	TX	5,117	C
Stephens College	MO	18,460	C
Tarleton State Univ	TX	4,082	LC
Texas Christian Univ	TX	12,180	C
Univ of Alabama	AL	5,702	C
Univ of Arkansas at Fayetteville	AR	5,046	C
Univ of Arkansas at Pine Bluff	AR	3,978	LC
Univ of Bridgeport	CT	18,985	C
Univ of Hawaii at Manoa	HI	5,626	C
Univ of Southwestern Louisiana	LA	3,968	NC
Univ of Wisc/Stevens Point	WI	5,047	C+
Univ of Wisc/Stout	WI	4,719	C
Ursuline College	OH	13,180	LC
Utah State Univ	UT	4,683	C
West Virginia Univ	WV	5,774	C
West Virginia Wesleyan College	WV	16,900	C
William Woods Univ	MO	14,025	LC
Woodbury Univ	CA	17,620	LC
Youngstown State Univ	OH	6,447	LC

FIBER/TEXTILES/WEAVING

School	ST	$IS	SR
Edinboro Univ of Penn	PA	7,181	C
Fashion Inst of Tech/SUNY	NY	7,135	SP
Kansas City Art Inst	MO	17,000	SP
Maryland Inst, College of Art	MD	18,420	SP
Savannah College of Art and Design	GA	14,280	SP
School of the Art Inst of Chicago	IL	17,610	SP
Syracuse Univ	NY	21,305	HC
Univ of Mass Dartmouth	MA	8,158	C
Univ of Miami	FL	22,107	VC
Univ of North Texas	TX	4,853	C
Univ of the Arts	PA	16,150	SP
Univ of Washington	WA	6,618	VC

FILM ARTS

School	ST	$IS	SR
American Univ	DC	21,230	VC+
Art Center College of Design	CA	13,550	SP
Asbury College	KY	11,105	VC
Ball State Univ	IN	6,032	LC
Bard College	NY	25,269	HC
Baylor Univ	TX	10,990	C+
Boston Univ	MA	24,130	HC
Bowling Green State Univ	OH	6,701	C
Brigham Young Univ	UT	5,625	HC
Calif College of Arts and Crafts	CA	17,378	SP
Calif Inst of the Arts	CA	16,400	SP
Cal State/Fullerton	CA	4,850	LC
Cal State/Long Beach	CA	6,057	LC
Cal State/Northridge	CA	7,122	LC
Central Missouri State Univ	MO	5,138	LC
Chapman Univ	CA	21,842	C
CUNY/Brooklyn College	NY	2,450	VC
CUNY/City College	NY	2,543	VC
CUNY/College of Staten Island	NY	2,558	NC
CUNY/Hunter College	NY	4,101	VC
CUNY/Queens College	NY	2,631	C
Claremont McKenna College	CA	22,150	MC
Clark Univ	MA	21,400	VC
College of Santa Fe	NM	14,008	C
Columbia College	IL	7,879	SP
Columbia Univ/Columbia College	NY	26,757	MC
Dartmouth College	NH	24,354	MC
Denison Univ	OH	21,150	VC+
Eastern Mich Univ	MI	6,749	C
Edinboro Univ of Penn	PA	7,181	C
Emerson College	MA	22,678	LC
Evergreen State College	WA	6,306	C
Florida State Univ	FL	5,814	VC
Fordham Univ/College at Lincoln Center	NY	18,150	VC
Fordham Univ/Fordham College	NY	19,875	VC
Grand Valley State Univ	MI	6,822	VC
Hampshire College	MA	25,320	C
Hanover College	IN	10,950	VC
Hofstra Univ	NY	16,580	VC
Howard Univ	DC	11,680	C
Indiana State Univ	IN	6,210	C
Iona College	NY	16,310	C
Ithaca College	NY	19,679	C
Kent State Univ	OH	6,740	LC
LIU/C. W. Post Campus	NY	16,870	C
Marist College	NY	16,406	C
Mass College of Art	MA	9,447	SP
Middlebury College	VT	24,400	MC
Minneapolis College of Art and Design	MN	15,512	SP
New College of Calif	CA	6,900	NC
New York Univ	NY	24,705	VC+
N Car School of the Arts	NC	5,375	SP
Northeast Louisiana Univ	LA	3,906	NC
Northern Mich Univ	MI	6,350	C
Northwestern Univ	IL	21,093	MC
Ohio Univ	OH	7,341	C
Oral Roberts Univ	OK	10,607	C+
Penn State Univ/Univ Park Campus	PA	8,752	HC
Pitzer College	CA	23,780	HC
Pratt Inst	NY	19,520	C
Purdue Univ/West Lafayette	IN	6,636	C
Rhode Island College	RI	7,901	LC
Rhode Island School of Design	RI	22,315	SP
Rochester Inst of Tech	NY	18,954	VC
Sacred Heart Univ	CT	16,350	C
San Francisco Art Inst	CA	12,900	SP
San Francisco State Univ	CA	7,292	LC
San Jose State Univ	CA	6,680	LC
Sarah Lawrence College	NY	24,975	HC
School of the Art Inst of Chicago	IL	17,610	SP
School of Visual Arts	NY	17,120	SP
Scripps College	CA	23,600	HC
Southern Illinois Univ at Carbondale	IL	6,234	C
Southern Methodist Univ	TX	18,520	VC
Southwest Missouri State Univ	MO	4,956	C
Southwestern College	KS	10,032	C
SUNY at Binghamton	NY	7,921	HC
SUNY/College at Purchase	NY	7,324	C
Syracuse Univ	NY	21,305	HC
Temple Univ	PA	10,281	C
Texas Christian Univ	TX	12,180	C
Univ of Bridgeport	CT	18,985	C
Univ of Calif at Berkeley	CA	9,962	HC+
Univ of Calif at Los Angeles	CA	8,959	HC
Univ of Calif at Santa Barbara	CA	9,460	C
Univ of Calif at Santa Cruz	CA	9,060	VC
Univ of Calif/Irvine	CA	12,680	VC
Univ of Central Florida	FL	6,061	C+
Univ of Colo at Boulder	CO	6,410	VC
Univ of Georgia	GA	5,655	VC
Univ of Hartford	CT	19,858	LC
Univ of Iowa	IA	5,658	VC
Univ of Maryland/College Park	MD	8,182	VC
Univ of Miami	FL	22,107	VC
Univ of Mich/Ann Arbor	MI	9,428	HC+
Univ of Minn/Twin Cities	MN	6,682	VC
Univ of N Car at Greensboro	NC	5,192	C
Univ of North Texas	TX	4,853	C
Univ of Notre Dame	IN	20,150	MC
Univ of Okla	OK	5,427	VC
Univ of Pittsburgh	PA	9,472	C
Univ of Rochester	NY	23,696	HC
Univ of South Florida	FL	5,475	C+
Univ of Southern Calif	CA	23,006	VC
Univ of Tenn/Knoxville	TN	5,668	C
Univ of the Arts	PA	16,150	SP
Univ of Toledo	OH	6,636	NC
Univ of Utah	UT	5,975	C
Univ of Wisc/Milwaukee	WI	6,165	C
Vassar College	NY	24,206	HC
Wake Forest Univ	NC	17,280	MC
Wayne State Univ	MI	2,680	C
Wesleyan Univ	CT	23,770	MC
Wright State Univ	OH	6,896	LC
Yale Univ	CT	25,110	MC

FINE ARTS

School	ST	$IS	SR
Abilene Christian Univ	TX	10,460	NC
Adams State College	CO	4,910	C
Adelphi Univ	NY	18,250	LC
Adrian College	MI	14,340	C
Agnes Scott College	GA	17,135	VC
Alabama State Univ	AL	3,428	NC
Albany State College	GA	4,481	LC
Albertus Magnus College	CT	16,280	LC
Albion College	MI	18,264	VC
Alfred Univ	NY	21,054	VC+
Alma College	MI	16,375	VC+
Alverno College	WI	11,344	C
American Univ	DC	21,230	VC+
Amherst College	MA	24,152	MC
Anderson Univ	IN	12,920	C
Andrews Univ	MI	14,952	NC
Angelo State Univ	TX	5,176	C
Anna Maria College	MA	15,975	LC
Antioch College	OH	19,532	C
Appalachian State Univ	NC	4,095	C
Aquinas College	MI	14,526	C
Arizona State Univ Main Campus	AZ	6,444	C
Arkansas State Univ	AR	4,250	NC
Art Center College of Design	CA	13,550	SP
Atlanta College of Art	GA	12,495	SP
Auburn Univ at Montgomery	AL	3,390	C
Augsburg College	MN	15,608	C
Augusta College	GA	1,452	C
Augustana College	SD	13,420	C
Austin College	TX	14,999	VC
Austin Peay State Univ	TN	4,350	C
Averett College	VA	13,610	LC
Baker Univ	KS	12,284	C
Baldwin-Wallace College	OH	15,210	C
Ball State Univ	IN	6,032	LC
Bard College	NY	25,269	HC
Barry Univ	FL	16,050	C
Baylor Univ	TX	10,990	C+
Beaver College	PA	17,660	C
Bellarmine College	KY	10,832	C
Bellevue College	NE	3,050	NC
Bemidji State Univ	MN	5,188	C
Bennington College	VT	24,850	VC+
Bethany College	KS	11,232	C
Bethany College	WV	18,300	C+
Bethel College	MN	15,050	C
Biola Univ	CA	16,124	C
Birmingham-Southern College	AL	15,154	VC+
Black Hills State Univ	SD	4,831	NC
Bloomfield College	NJ	12,200	LC
Blue Mountain College	MS	5,958	LC
Bluefield College	VA	10,600	C
Bluffton College	OH	12,951	C
Boise State Univ	ID	4,909	LC
Boston College	MA	22,706	MC
Boston Univ	MA	24,130	HC
Bowie State Univ	MD	7,294	LC
Bowling Green State Univ	OH	6,701	C
Bradford College	MA	19,600	C
Brandeis Univ	MA	25,585	HC
Briar Cliff College	IA	13,375	C
Bridgewater State College	MA	7,518	C
Brigham Young Univ	UT	5,625	HC
Brigham Young Univ/Hawaii	HI	6,750	VC
Brooklyn Campus of LIU	NY	15,000	LC
Bryn Mawr College	PA	24,110	MC
Bucknell Univ	PA	22,320	HC
Burlington College	VT	6,150	NC
Caldwell College	NJ	12,860	C
Calif Baptist College	CA	11,294	C
Calif College of Arts and Crafts	CA	17,378	SP
Calif Inst of the Arts	CA	16,400	SP
Calif Lutheran Univ	CA	17,240	C
Calif State Polytechnic Univ/Pomona	CA	6,438	LC
Cal State/Bakersfield	CA	5,402	C
Cal State/Chico	CA	6,146	C
Cal State/Dominguez Hills	CA	2,857	LC
Cal State/Fresno	CA	5,747	C
Cal State/Fullerton	CA	4,850	LC
Cal State/Los Angeles	CA	4,940	VC
Cal State/Northridge	CA	7,122	LC
Cal State/Stanislaus	CA	6,799	C
Calif Univ of Penn	PA	7,370	C
Calumet College of St. Joseph	IN	3,585	C
Calvin College	MI	13,020	VC
Cameron Univ	OK	3,686	LC
Capital Univ	OH	16,535	VC
Cardinal Stritch College	WI	11,252	C
Carnegie Mellon Univ	PA	22,560	HC+
Carroll College	WI	15,490	C
Carson-Newman College	TN	11,250	C
Carthage College	WI	15,995	C
Castleton State College	VT	8,378	LC
Cazenovia College	NY	14,655	LC
Cedar Crest College	PA	18,930	C
Centenary College of Louisiana	LA	11,826	C+
Center for Creative Studies/College of Art and Design	MI	15,330	SP
Central College	IA	14,025	VC
Central Mich Univ	MI	6,737	LC
Central Missouri State Univ	MO	5,138	LC
Central Washington Univ	WA	5,644	C
Centre College	KY	15,850	VC+
Chapman Univ	CA	21,842	C
Charleston Southern Univ	SC	10,282	LC
Cheyney Univ of Penn	PA	7,005	C
Christopher Newport Univ	VA	3,196	LC
CUNY/City College	NY	2,543	VC
CUNY/College of Staten Island	NY	2,558	NC
CUNY/Herbert H. Lehman College	NY	2,542	C
CUNY/Queens College	NY	2,631	C
Claflin College	SC	0	
Clarion Univ of Penn	PA	6,518	C
Clark Atlanta Univ	GA	11,846	C
Clark Univ	MA	21,400	VC

School	ST	$IS	SR
St Mary's College of Maryland	MD	8,900	VC+
St Mary's College of Minn	MN	13,850	LC
St Mary-of-the-Woods College	IN	14,430	NC
St Michael's College	VT	17,930	C
St Norbert College	WI	15,710	VC
St Olaf College	MN	17,200	HC
St Peter's College	NJ	14,775	LC
St Thomas Aquinas College	NY	13,550	C
St Vincent College	PA	13,934	LC
St Xavier Univ	IL	14,700	C
Salem State College	MA	6,712	C
Salisbury State Univ	MD	7,516	C+
Salve Regina Univ	RI	29,100	LC
Samford Univ	AL	11,400	VC
San Diego State Univ	CA	6,692	LC
San Francisco Art Inst	CA	12,900	SP
San Francisco State Univ	CA	7,292	LC
San Jose State Univ	CA	6,680	LC
Santa Clara Univ	CA	18,783	VC
Sarah Lawrence College	NY	24,975	HC
School of Visual Arts	NY	17,120	SP
Schreiner College	TX	14,320	C
Seattle Pacific Univ	WA	16,503	C
Seattle Univ	WA	16,590	C
Seton Hill College	PA	14,320	C
Shenandoah Univ	VA	11,800	C
Shepherd College	WV	5,540	C
Siena Heights College	MI	12,520	C
Sierra Nevada College	NV	14,000	NC
Silver Lake College	WI	8,280	LC
Simpson College	IA	14,635	VC
Skidmore College	NY	23,230	HC
Slippery Rock Univ	PA	6,803	C
Sonoma State Univ	CA	6,996	LC
S Car State Univ	SC	5,424	LC
S Dak State Univ	SD	4,562	C
Southeastern Louisiana Univ	LA	4,230	NC
Southeastern Okla State Univ	OK	3,594	C
Southern Calif College	CA	12,356	C
Southern Conn State Univ	CT	7,532	C
Southern Illinois Univ at Carbondale	IL	6,234	C
Southern Illinois Univ at Edwardsville	IL	6,097	LC
Southern Nazarene Univ	OK	9,206	NC
Southern Oregon State College	OR	6,128	C
Southern Univ and A&M College	LA	4,920	NC
Southern Univ at New Orleans	LA	1,452	NC
Southwest Texas State Univ	TX	5,124	C
Southwestern Okla State Univ	OK	3,312	C
Spelman College	GA	12,942	VC
Spring Arbor College	MI	12,256	C
Spring Hill College	AL	16,015	C+
Springfield College	MA	15,200	LC
Stanford Univ	CA	24,310	MC
SUNY at Albany	NY	7,059	VC
SUNY at Binghamton	NY	7,921	HC
SUNY at Buffalo	NY	7,896	VC
SUNY/College at Brockport	NY	7,220	C+
SUNY/College at Buffalo	NY	7,035	VC
SUNY/College at Cortland	NY	7,326	C+
SUNY/College at Fredonia	NY	7,159	VC
SUNY/College at Geneseo	NY	6,949	HC
SUNY/College at New Paltz	NY	6,890	VC
SUNY/College at Oneonta	NY	7,878	C
SUNY/College at Oswego	NY	7,330	VC
SUNY/College at Purchase	NY	7,324	C
SUNY/Potsdam College	NY	6,906	C
Stephen F. Austin State Univ	TX	5,117	C
Stephens College	MO	18,460	C
Sterling College	KS	10,990	VC
Stetson Univ	FL	16,435	VC
Swarthmore College	PA	24,136	MC
Syracuse Univ	NY	21,305	HC
Tarleton State Univ	TX	4,082	LC
Teikyo Westmar Univ	IA	15,920	C
Temple Univ	PA	10,281	C
Tenn Tech Univ	TN	5,190	C
Texas A&M Univ at Kingsville	TX	3,808	LC
Texas Christian Univ	TX	12,180	C
Texas Southern Univ	TX	4,500	NC
Texas Tech Univ	TX	6,008	C
Texas Wesleyan Univ	TX	9,380	LC
Texas Woman's Univ	TX	4,392	C
The Univ of New Mexico	NM	5,304	C
Thomas A. Edison State College	NJ	400	C
Thomas More College	KY	12,962	C
Towson State Univ	MD	7,452	C
Trenton State College	NJ	9,085	HC
Trinity Christian College	IL	13,260	C
Trinity College	CT	24,120	HC
Tulane Univ	LA	24,540	HC
Tusculum College	TN	10,400	LC
Union College	KY	9,790	C
Union College	NY	23,817	HC
Univ of Akron	OH	6,699	NC
Univ of Alabama at Birmingham	AL	7,533	C

School	ST	$IS	SR
Univ of Alabama at Huntsville	AL	5,868	VC
Univ of Alaska Anchorage	AK	7,131	C
Univ of Arizona	AZ	5,808	C
Univ of Arkansas at Fayetteville	AR	5,046	C
Univ of Arkansas at Monticello	AR	3,832	NC
Univ of Bridgeport	CT	18,985	C
Univ of Calif at Davis	CA	9,534	VC
Univ of Calif at Los Angeles	CA	8,959	HC
Univ of Calif at Santa Barbara	CA	9,460	C
Univ of Calif at Santa Cruz	CA	9,060	VC
Univ of Calif, Riverside	CA	9,178	C
Univ of Calif/Irvine	CA	12,680	VC
Univ of Central Florida	FL	6,061	C+
Univ of Central Okla	OK	3,647	C
Univ of Chicago	IL	24,517	MC
Univ of Cincinnati	OH	7,989	C
Univ of Colo at Boulder	CO	6,410	VC
Univ of Colo at Colo Springs	CO	2,269	C
Univ of Colo at Denver	CO	1,955	VC
Univ of Conn	CT	9,168	C
Univ of Dallas	TX	14,983	VC
Univ of Dayton	OH	15,120	C+
Univ of Delaware	DE	8,013	VC
Univ of Evansville	IN	15,300	VC
Univ of Findlay	OH	15,764	C
Univ of Georgia	GA	5,655	VC
Univ of Guam	GU	4,139	NC
Univ of Hartford	CT	19,858	LC
Univ of Hawaii at Hilo	HI	4,141	C
Univ of Hawaii at Manoa	HI	5,626	C
Univ of Houston	TX	5,215	C
Univ of Idaho	ID	4,830	C
Univ of Indianapolis	IN	14,510	C
Univ of Iowa	IA	5,658	VC
Univ of Kentucky	KY	5,152	VC
Univ of La Verne	CA	17,400	C
Univ of Louisville	KY	5,948	C
Univ of Lowell	MA	8,831	VC
Univ of Mary Hardin-Baylor	TX	8,120	NC
Univ of Maryland/Baltimore County	MD	7,746	VC
Univ of Maryland/College Park	MD	8,182	VC
Univ of Maryland/Univ College	MD	4,900	NC
Univ of Mass Dartmouth	MA	8,158	C
Univ of Mass/Amherst	MA	9,364	LC
Univ of Mass/Boston	MA	4,253	C
Univ of Memphis	TN	3,476	C
Univ of Miami	FL	22,107	VC
Univ of Mich/Dearborn	MI	3,399	HC
Univ of Missouri/Columbia	MO	6,254	HC
Univ of Missouri/Kansas City	MO	5,906	VC
Univ of Mobile	AL	9,400	C
Univ of Montana	MT	5,529	C
Univ of Nebr at Kearney	NE	4,308	LC
Univ of Nebr at Omaha	NE	1,889	LC
Univ of Nebr-Lincoln	NE	5,278	LC
Univ of Nevada/Las Vegas	NV	6,405	C
Univ of New Hampshire	NH	8,242	C
Univ of New Haven	CT	14,980	C
Univ of New Orleans	LA	5,468	C
Univ of N Car at Asheville	NC	4,791	VC
Univ of N Car at Charlotte	NC	4,597	C
Univ of N Car at Greensboro	NC	5,192	C
Univ of N Car at Wilmington	NC	5,172	C
Univ of N Dak	ND	4,902	NC
Univ of North Florida	FL	5,082	C
Univ of North Texas	TX	4,853	C
Univ of Northern Colo	CO	6,008	C
Univ of Northern Iowa	IA	5,137	C
Univ of Notre Dame	IN	20,150	MC
Univ of Okla	OK	5,427	VC
Univ of Oregon	OR	6,466	VC
Univ of Pittsburgh	PA	9,472	C
Univ of PR/Mayaguez	PR	0	NC
Univ of PR/Rio Piedras	PR	0	C
Univ of Puget Sound	WA	19,520	HC
Univ of Rhode Island	RI	9,205	C
Univ of Rio Grande	OH	6,300	NC
Univ of Rochester	NY	23,696	HC
Univ of St Thomas	TX	11,676	C+
Univ of San Diego	CA	18,970	VC
Univ of San Francisco	CA	18,408	C
Univ of South Alabama	AL	5,451	C
Univ of S Car	SC	6,158	C
Univ of South Florida	FL	5,475	C+
Univ of Southern Calif	CA	23,006	VC
Univ of Southern Colo	CO	5,350	LC
Univ of Southern Maine	ME	7,299	C
Univ of Southern Miss	MS	4,542	C
Univ of Southwestern Louisiana	LA	3,968	NC
Univ of Tampa	FL	16,780	C
Univ of Tenn at Chattanooga	TN	5,375	C
Univ of Tenn at Martin	TN	4,550	C
Univ of Tenn/Knoxville	TN	5,668	C
Univ of Texas at Arlington	TX	5,549	LC
Univ of Texas at El Paso	TX	3,160	LC
Univ of Texas at San Antonio	TX	6,420	C
Univ of Texas-Pan American	TX	3,192	NC

School	ST	$IS	SR
Univ of the District of Columbia	DC	974	NC
Univ of the Ozarks	AR	7,770	C
Univ of the South	TN	18,830	HC
Univ of Toledo	OH	6,636	NC
Univ of Tulsa	OK	13,795	VC
Univ of Wisc/Eau Claire	WI	4,647	C
Univ of Wisc/Green Bay	WI	4,904	C
Univ of Wisc/La Crosse	WI	4,487	C
Univ of Wisc/Milwaukee	WI	6,165	C
Univ of Wisc/Oshkosh	WI	4,240	C
Univ of Wisc/Parkside	WI	5,247	C
Univ of Wisc/Platteville	WI	4,830	C
Univ of Wisc/River Falls	WI	4,655	C
Univ of Wisc/Stevens Point	WI	5,047	C+
Univ of Wisc/Stout	WI	4,719	C
Univ of Wisc/Superior	WI	4,330	C
Univ of Wyoming	WY	4,991	NC
Upper Iowa Univ	IA	11,900	C
Upsala College	NJ	17,200	C
Utah State Univ	UT	4,683	C
Utica College of Syracuse Univ	NY	16,714	LC
Valdosta State Univ	GA	4,670	LC
Valley City State Univ	ND	4,385	LC
Valparaiso Univ	IN	14,810	VC
Vanderbilt Univ	TN	23,422	HC+
Vassar College	NY	24,206	HC
Virginia Commonwealth Univ	VA	7,909	C
Virginia Intermont College	VA	12,250	LC
Virginia Polytechnic Inst and State Univ	VA	6,828	C
Virginia Wesleyan College	VA	14,950	VC
Viterbo College	WI	12,670	C
Wabash College	IN	16,250	VC
Wagner College	NY	17,950	C
Walla Walla College	WA	13,215	C
Washington and Lee Univ	VA	17,735	MC
Washington College	MD	19,270	C+
Washington State Univ	WA	6,364	C
Washington Univ	MO	23,507	HC
Wayland Baptist Univ	TX	7,811	NC
Wayne State College	NE	4,260	NC
Wayne State Univ	MI	2,680	C
Weber State Univ	UT	4,398	C
Wellesley College	MA	23,815	MC
Wells College	NY	19,460	C+
Wesleyan Univ	CT	23,770	MC
West Chester Univ of Penn	PA	7,492	C
West Georgia College	GA	4,256	C
West Liberty State College	WV	4,690	LC
West Virginia State College	WV	5,044	LC
Western Carolina Univ	NC	3,811	C
Western Conn State Univ	CT	6,622	C
Western Illinois Univ	IL	5,241	LC
Western Kentucky Univ	KY	4,808	C
Western Maryland College	MD	18,990	C
Western Mich Univ	MI	6,820	C
Western New Mexico Univ	NM	3,234	LC
Western Oregon State College	OR	6,180	C
Western State College of Colo	CO	5,560	C
Western Washington Univ	WA	6,077	VC
Westfield State College	MA	7,161	C
Westminster College	MO	13,750	C+
Westminster College	PA	15,200	C
Westminster College of Salt Lake City	UT	12,100	C
Westmont College	CA	18,732	C
Wheaton College	IL	14,710	HC
Wheaton College	MA	23,840	C+
Whitman College	WA	20,595	HC
Whittier College	CA	21,661	C
Whitworth College	WA	16,265	C
Wichita State Univ	KS	5,068	NC
Wilberforce Univ	OH	10,408	C
Wilkes Univ	PA	15,728	LC
Willamette Univ	OR	17,995	VC
William Paterson College	NJ	7,438	C+
William Woods Univ	MO	14,025	LC
Williams College	MA	24,390	MC
Wilmington College	OH	13,700	LC
Wilson College	PA	16,630	C
Winona State Univ	MN	5,200	VC
Winston-Salem State Univ	NC	4,142	LC
Winthrop Univ	SC	6,750	C
Wittenberg Univ	OH	19,998	VC
Women's College of Brenau Univ	GA	14,734	C
Wright State Univ	OH	6,896	LC
Xavier Univ	OH	15,710	C+
Xavier Univ of Louisiana	LA	10,400	C
York College of Penn	PA	8,345	C

FIRE CONTROL AND SAFETY TECHNOLOGY

School	ST	$IS	SR
Charter Oak State College	CT	314	NC
Cogswell Polytechnical College	CA	8,000	NC
Idaho State Univ	ID	4,442	C
Okla State Univ	OK	5,086	VC

FIRE PROTECTION

School	ST	$IS	SR
Cal State/Los Angeles	CA	4,940	C
Cogswell Polytechnical College	CA	8,000	NC
Eastern Kentucky Univ	KY	4,840	NC
Western Oregon State College	OR	6,180	C

FIRE PROTECTION ENGINEERING

School	ST	$IS	SR
Univ of Maryland/College Park	MD	8,182	VC
Univ of New Haven	CT	14,980	C

FIRE SCIENCE

School	ST	$IS	SR
CUNY/John Jay College of Criminal Justice	NY	2,501	LC
Madonna Univ	MI	8,546	C
Univ of New Haven	CT	14,980	C
Univ of the District of Columbia	DC	974	NC

FISH AND GAME MANAGEMENT

School	ST	$IS	SR
Delaware State College	DE	5,656	C
Eastern Kentucky Univ	KY	4,840	NC
Lake Superior State Univ	MI	7,311	C
Ohio State Univ	OH	7,218	LC
Texas A&M Univ	TX	5,382	VC
Univ of Nebr-Lincoln	NE	5,278	LC

FISHING AND FISHERIES

School	ST	$IS	SR
Auburn Univ	AL	5,823	C+
Ball State Univ	IN	6,032	LC
Colo State Univ	CO	6,566	VC
Florida Inst of Tech	FL	16,935	VC
Humboldt State Univ	CA	5,676	C
Iowa State Univ	IA	5,456	C
Louisiana State Univ and A&M College	LA	5,605	C
Mansfield Univ	PA	6,348	C
Miss State Univ	MS	5,629	VC
Murray State Univ	KY	4,702	C
New Mexico State Univ	NM	4,844	LC
N Car State Univ	NC	4,984	VC
Oregon State Univ	OR	6,175	C
Penn State Univ/Univ Park Campus	PA	8,752	HC
Rutgers Univ/Cook College	NJ	9,197	HC
Sheldon Jackson College	AK	14,050	NC
Southwest Texas State Univ	TX	5,124	C
Texas A&M Univ	TX	5,382	VC
Texas A&M Univ at Galveston	TX	4,874	LC
Unity College	ME	12,885	LC
Univ of Alaska Fairbanks	AK	4,718	C
Univ of Arkansas at Pine Bluff	AR	3,978	LC
Univ of Idaho	ID	4,830	C
Univ of Maine	ME	7,990	C
Univ of Mich/Ann Arbor	MI	9,428	HC+
Univ of Minn/Twin Cities	MN	6,682	VC
Univ of Rhode Island	RI	9,205	C
Univ of Tenn/Knoxville	TN	5,668	C
Univ of Washington	WA	6,618	VC
West Virginia Univ	WV	5,774	C

FLUID AND THERMAL SCIENCE

School	ST	$IS	SR
Case Western Reserve Univ	OH	19,910	HC

FOLKLORE AND MYTHOLOGY

School	ST	$IS	SR
Harvard Univ/Harvard and Radcliffe Colleges	MA	24,880	MC
Indiana Univ Bloomington	IN	6,495	VC
Pitzer College	CA	23,780	HC

FOOD PRODUCTION/MANAGEMENT/SERVICES

School	ST	$IS	SR
Ball State Univ	IN	6,032	LC
Berry College	GA	11,990	VC
Cornell Univ	NY	13,445	MC
David Lipscomb Univ	TN	7,865	VC
Delaware Valley College	PA	16,065	LC
Eastern Kentucky Univ	KY	4,840	NC
Eastern Mennonite College	VA	12,700	C
Eastern Mich Univ	MI	6,749	C
Georgia Southern Univ	GA	4,988	LC
Iowa State Univ	IA	5,456	C
Johnson and Wales Univ	RI	13,995	LC
Kansas State Univ	KS	4,816	NC
Mich State Univ	MI	7,842	C
Morehead State Univ	KY	4,600	LC
New Hampshire College	NH	15,242	LC
Rochester Inst of Tech	NY	18,954	VC
Rosary College	IL	15,040	C
St Vincent College	PA	13,934	LC
Seton Hill College	PA	14,320	C
S Dak State Univ	SD	4,562	C
SUNY/College at Buffalo	NY	7,035	VC
Stephen F. Austin State Univ	TX	5,117	C
Syracuse Univ	NY	21,305	HC
Texas Tech Univ	TX	6,008	C
Univ of Illinois at Urbana-Champaign	IL	7,764	HC
Univ of Wisc/Stevens Point	WI	5,047	C+
Univ of Wisc/Stout	WI	4,719	C
Wayne State College	NE	4,260	NC
Western Carolina Univ	NC	3,811	C

FOOD SCIENCE

School	ST	$IS	SR
Alabama A&M Univ	AL	4,200	C
Auburn Univ	AL	5,823	C+
Ball State Univ	IN	6,032	LC
Bluffton College	OH	12,951	C
Bowling Green State Univ	OH	6,701	C
Brigham Young Univ	UT	5,625	HC
Calif Polytechnic State Univ	CA	6,980	VC+
Calif State Polytechnic Univ/Pomona	CA	6,438	LC
Cal State/Fresno	CA	5,747	C
Cal State/San Bernardino	CA	6,055	LC
Central Washington Univ	WA	5,644	C
Chapman Univ	CA	21,842	C
Clemson Univ	SC	6,564	VC
Colo State Univ	CO	6,566	VC
Cornell Univ	NY	13,445	MC
Delaware Valley College	PA	16,065	LC
Fontbonne College	MO	12,090	C
Framingham State College	MA	6,580	C
Immaculata College	PA	14,620	C
Indiana State Univ	IN	6,210	C
Indiana Univ of Penn	PA	6,373	C
Iowa State Univ	IA	5,456	C
Kansas State Univ	KS	4,816	NC
Louisiana State Univ and A&M College	LA	5,605	C
Madonna Univ	MI	8,546	C
Marymount College/Tarrytown	NY	17,350	C
Mich State Univ	MI	7,842	C
Miss State Univ	MS	5,629	VC
Morehead State Univ	KY	4,600	LC
N Car State Univ	NC	4,984	VC
N Dak State Univ of Agriculture and Applied Science	ND	4,774	VC
Northwest Missouri State Univ	MO	5,010	LC
Ohio State Univ	OH	7,218	LC
Ohio Univ	OH	7,341	C
Oregon State Univ	OR	6,175	C
Pacific Union College	CA	15,075	C
Penn State Univ/Univ Park Campus	PA	8,752	HC
Purdue Univ/West Lafayette	IN	6,636	C
Radford Univ	VA	7,034	LC
Rutgers Univ/Cook College	NJ	9,197	HC
Rutgers Univ/Douglass College	NJ	8,795	VC
Rutgers Univ/Univ College—New Brunswick	NJ	0	LC
Samford Univ	AL	11,400	VC
San Jose State Univ	CA	6,680	LC
Seattle Pacific Univ	WA	16,503	C
S Car State Univ	SC	5,424	LC
S Dak State Univ	SD	4,562	C
Southeast Missouri State Univ	MO	5,854	C
Southern Illinois Univ at Carbondale	IL	6,234	C
Southwest Texas State Univ	TX	5,124	C
SUNY/College at Plattsburgh	NY	6,917	C
Texas Tech Univ	TX	6,008	C
Tuskegee Univ	AL	10,128	C
Univ of Arizona	AZ	5,808	C
Univ of Arkansas at Fayetteville	AR	5,046	C
Univ of Arkansas at Pine Bluff	AR	3,978	LC
Univ of Calif at Berkeley	CA	9,962	HC+
Univ of Calif at Davis	CA	9,534	VC
Univ of Delaware	DE	8,013	VC
Univ of Florida	FL	5,850	HC
Univ of Georgia	GA	5,655	VC
Univ of Hawaii at Manoa	HI	5,626	C
Univ of Idaho	ID	4,830	C
Univ of Illinois at Urbana-Champaign	IL	7,764	HC
Univ of Kentucky	KY	5,152	VC
Univ of Maine	ME	7,990	C
Univ of Maryland/College Park	MD	8,182	VC
Univ of Mass/Amherst	MA	9,364	LC
Univ of Minn/Twin Cities	MN	6,682	VC
Univ of Missouri/Columbia	MO	6,254	HC
Univ of Nebr-Lincoln	NE	5,278	LC
Univ of Rhode Island	RI	9,205	C
Univ of Tenn/Knoxville	TN	5,668	C
Univ of the District of Columbia	DC	974	NC
Univ of Vermont	VT	10,776	C+
Univ of Washington	WA	6,618	VC
Univ of Wisc/Madison	WI	6,400	HC
Univ of Wisc/River Falls	WI	4,655	C
Univ of Wyoming	WY	4,991	NC
Utah State Univ	UT	4,683	C
Virginia Polytechnic Inst and State Univ	VA	6,828	C
Washington State Univ	WA	6,364	C
Wayne State Univ	MI	2,680	C
Winthrop Univ	SC	6,750	C

FOOD SERVICES TECHNOLOGY

School	ST	$IS	SR
Austin Peay State Univ	TN	4,350	C
Delaware Valley College	PA	16,065	LC
Iowa State Univ	IA	5,456	C
Johnson and Wales Univ	RI	13,995	LC
Kent State Univ	OH	6,740	LC
Mount Mary College	WI	10,920	C
N Dak State Univ of Agriculture and Applied Science	ND	4,774	VC

FOREIGN LANGUAGES EDUCATION

School	ST	$IS	SR
Abilene Christian Univ	TX	10,460	NC
Adams State College	CO	4,910	C
Adelphi Univ	NY	18,250	LC
Adrian College	MI	14,340	C
Alabama State Univ	AL	3,428	NC
American International College	MA	14,029	C
Anderson Univ	IN	12,920	C
Andrews Univ	MI	14,952	NC
Angelo State Univ	TX	5,176	C
Appalachian State Univ	NC	4,095	C
Arkansas State Univ	AR	4,250	NC
Ashland Univ	OH	15,508	C
Auburn Univ	AL	5,823	C+
Augsburg College	MN	15,608	C
Augustana College	SD	13,420	C
Baldwin-Wallace College	OH	15,210	C
Ball State Univ	IN	6,032	LC
Baylor Univ	TX	10,990	C+
Bemidji State Univ	MN	5,188	C
Berea College	KY	2,883	VC+
Bethany College	WV	18,300	C+
Bethel College	MN	15,050	LC
Bethune-Cookman College	FL	8,375	LC
Bluffton College	OH	12,951	C
Boston Univ	MA	24,130	HC
Bowling Green State Univ	OH	6,701	C
Bradley Univ	IL	14,718	C+
Bridgewater State College	MA	7,518	C
Brigham Young Univ	UT	5,625	HC
Buena Vista College	IA	16,150	VC
Calif Lutheran Univ	CA	17,240	C
Cal State/Chico	CA	6,146	C
Cal State/Fresno	CA	5,747	C
Calif Univ of Penn	PA	7,370	C
Canisius College	NY	15,510	C
Capital Univ	OH	16,535	VC
Carroll College	WI	15,490	C
Carson-Newman College	TN	11,250	C
Carthage College	WI	15,995	C
Castleton State College	VT	8,378	LC
Cedarville College	OH	10,715	C
Centenary College of Louisiana	LA	11,826	C+
Central Methodist College	MO	11,410	C
Central Mich Univ	MI	6,737	LC
Central Missouri State Univ	MO	5,138	LC
Central Washington Univ	WA	5,644	C
Christopher Newport Univ	VA	3,196	LC
CUNY/City College	NY	2,543	VC
CUNY/Herbert H. Lehman College	NY	2,542	C
CUNY/Hunter College	NY	4,101	VC
CUNY/Queens College	NY	2,631	C
CUNY/York College	NY	2,534	NC
Clarion Univ of Penn	PA	6,518	C
College of New Rochelle	NY	15,440	LC
College of Notre Dame of Maryland	MD	16,050	C
College of Our Lady of The Elms	MA	15,639	C
College of St Rose	NY	14,452	C
College of the Ozarks	MO	2,000	VC+
Concordia College/Moorhead	MN	12,750	C
Converse College	SC	15,750	C
Cornell College	IA	18,425	VC
Dana College	NE	11,910	C
David Lipscomb Univ	TN	7,865	VC
Delta State Univ	MS	3,964	LC
DePaul Univ	IL	15,535	VC
Dordt College	IA	11,690	C
Drake Univ	IA	17,195	VC
Duquesne Univ	PA	16,434	VC
East Stroudsburg Univ	PA	6,886	C
East Tenn State Univ	TN	4,406	C
Eastern Kentucky Univ	KY	4,840	NC
Eastern Mich Univ	MI	6,749	C
Eastern Montana College	MT	5,165	LC
Eastern Washington Univ	WA	5,439	LC
Edinboro Univ of Penn	PA	7,181	C
Elmira College	NY	18,450	C
Emporia State Univ	KS	4,685	NC
Erskine College	SC	14,310	C
Evangel College	MO	10,142	LC
Evergreen State College	WA	6,306	C
Fairmont State College	WV	4,640	LC
Florida Atlantic Univ	FL	5,525	C
Florida International Univ	FL	4,191	VC
Florida Southern College	FL	12,260	C
Fort Hays State Univ	KS	4,675	NC
Franklin Pierce College	NH	17,270	LC
Friends Univ	KS	11,205	C
Gardner-Webb Univ	NC	11,950	LC
George Mason Univ	VA	8,728	C
Georgetown College	KY	10,990	C
Georgetown Univ	DC	24,410	MC
Georgia Southwestern College	GA	4,338	LC
Georgia State Univ	GA	2,019	C
Gettysburg College	PA	22,960	HC
Gordon College	MA	16,790	C
Goshen College	IN	12,360	C
Grace College	IN	12,120	C
Grambling State Univ	LA	4,712	NC
Grand Valley State Univ	MI	6,822	VC
Gustavus Adolphus College	MN	15,935	VC
Hamline Univ	MN	17,122	VC
Hanover College	IN	10,950	VC
Hardin-Simmons Univ	TX	9,080	C
Harding Univ	AR	9,050	VC
Hastings College	NE	12,426	C
Heidelberg College	OH	17,160	C
Hillsdale College	MI	15,110	VC
Hofstra Univ	NY	16,580	VC
Holy Family College	PA	8,300	C
Hood College	MD	19,010	VC
Hope College	MI	15,698	C+
Houghton College	NY	13,120	VC
Houston Baptist Univ	TX	11,055	C
Howard Payne Univ	TX	8,052	C
Illinois College	IL	11,200	C
Immaculata College	PA	14,620	C
Indiana State Univ	IN	6,210	C
Indiana Univ-Purdue Univ at Fort Wayne	IN	2,500	LC
Iona College	NY	16,310	C
Ithaca College	NY	19,679	C
Jacksonville Univ	FL	13,390	C
Juniata College	PA	18,390	C+
Kansas State Univ	KS	4,816	NC
Kean College of New Jersey	NJ	6,395	LC
Keene State College	NH	7,081	C
Kennesaw State College	GA	1,553	C
Kent State Univ	OH	6,740	LC
King College	TN	11,500	C
King's College	PA	15,420	C
La Salle Univ	PA	16,940	VC
Lakeland College	WI	12,845	LC
Lamar Univ	TX	3,798	C
Le Moyne College	NY	15,180	C
Lenoir-Rhyne College	NC	14,068	C
Lincoln Univ	PA	0	LC
Linfield College	OR	16,670	VC
Lock Haven Univ of Penn	PA	7,128	C
LIU/C. W. Post Campus	NY	16,870	C
Loras College	IA	14,160	C
Louisiana Tech Univ	LA	4,284	C
Luther College	IA	15,900	VC
Manchester College	IN	13,240	LC
Manhattan College	NY	19,000	C
Mankato State Univ	MN	5,097	LC
Mansfield Univ	PA	6,348	C
Mars Hill College	NC	11,050	C
Marshall Univ	WV	5,762	LC
Mary Baldwin College	VA	17,700	LC
Marymount College/Tarrytown	NY	17,350	C
McNeese State Univ	LA	4,543	NC
McPherson College	KS	11,360	VC
Mercy College	NY	11,180	NC
Methodist College	NC	12,400	C
Miami Univ	OH	8,066	VC
Mich State Univ	MI	7,842	C
Millikin Univ	IL	15,499	C
Minot State Univ	ND	3,748	NC
Miss College	MS	8,348	C
Missouri Western State College	MO	4,384	NC
Molloy College	NY	8,580	LC
Monmouth College	NJ	16,820	C
Moorhead State Univ	MN	5,076	C
Morris Brown College	GA	12,234	NC
Mount Mary College	WI	10,920	C
Mount St Mary's College	CA	16,390	VC
Mount Union College	OH	15,850	C
Murray State Univ	KY	4,702	C
Muskingum College	OH	16,650	C
Nazareth College of Rochester	NY	15,310	C+
Niagara Univ	NY	14,552	C
Nicholls State Univ	LA	4,531	NC
N Car State Univ	NC	4,984	VC
North Georgia College	GA	4,103	LC
Northeast Louisiana Univ	LA	3,906	NC
Northern Arizona Univ	AZ	4,844	C
Northern Mich Univ	MI	6,350	LC
Northern State Univ	SD	4,186	LC
Northwestern College of Iowa	IA	12,250	C
Northwestern Univ	IL	21,093	MC
Notre Dame College of Ohio	OH	11,370	C
Occidental College	CA	21,792	HC
Ohio Univ	OH	7,341	C
Ohio Wesleyan Univ	OH	21,108	VC+
Okla Baptist Univ	OK	8,486	C
Okla City Univ	OK	9,840	C
Okla State Univ	OK	5,086	VC
Olivet College	MI	14,000	C
Olivet Nazarene Univ	IL	11,976	C
Otterbein College	OH	16,506	C
Ouachita Baptist Univ	AR	8,940	C
Pepperdine Univ	CA	23,720	VC
Piedmont College	GA	8,540	LC
Pittsburg State Univ	KS	4,478	NC
Plymouth State College	NH	7,166	C
Prescott College	AZ	9,775	C
Purdue Univ/Calumet	IN	2,374	NC
Queens College	NC	14,950	C
Radford Univ	VA	7,034	LC
Rhode Island College	RI	7,901	LC
Rider College	NJ	18,160	C
Rivier College	NH	14,920	LC
Rockhurst College	MO	12,470	C
Rosemont College	PA	16,775	C
Rowan College of New Jersey	NJ	7,358	VC
Saginaw Valley State Univ	MI	6,634	LC
St Cloud State Univ	MN	5,015	C
St John's Univ	NY	8,980	C+
St Mary's College of Minn	MN	13,850	LC
St Mary-of-the-Woods College	IN	14,430	NC
St Michael's College	VT	17,930	C
St Olaf College	MN	17,200	HC
St Thomas Aquinas College	NY	13,550	C
St Vincent College	PA	13,934	LC
St Xavier Univ	IL	14,700	C
Salisbury State Univ	MD	7,516	C+
Samford Univ	AL	11,400	VC
Simpson College	IA	14,635	VC
Slippery Rock Univ	PA	6,803	C
S Dak State Univ	SD	4,562	C
Southeastern Louisiana Univ	LA	4,230	NC
Southeastern Okla State Univ	OK	3,594	C
Southern Conn State Univ	CT	7,532	C
Southern Illinois Univ at Carbondale	IL	6,234	C
Southern Nazarene Univ	OK	9,206	NC
Southern Univ and A&M College	LA	4,920	NC
Southern Univ at New Orleans	LA	1,452	NC
Southern Utah Univ	UT	4,104	LC

School	ST	$IS	SR
Southwest Missouri State Univ	MO	4,956	C
Southwest Texas State Univ	TX	5,124	C
Southwestern College	KS	10,032	C
SUNY at Albany	NY	7,059	VC
SUNY at Buffalo	NY	7,896	VC
SUNY/College at Buffalo	NY	7,035	VC
SUNY/College at Cortland	NY	7,326	C+
SUNY/College at Fredonia	NY	7,159	VC
SUNY/College at Geneseo	NY	6,949	HC
SUNY/College at New Paltz	NY	6,890	VC
SUNY/College at Old Westbury	NY	7,128	LC
SUNY/College at Oneonta	NY	7,878	C
SUNY/College at Oswego	NY	7,330	VC
SUNY/College at Plattsburgh	NY	6,917	C
SUNY/Potsdam College	NY	6,906	C
Syracuse Univ	NY	21,305	HC
Temple Univ	PA	10,281	C
Trinity Univ	TX	16,670	HC
Troy State Univ	AL	4,322	C
Turabo Univ	PR	2,670	
Univ of Akron	OH	6,699	NC
Univ of Arizona	AZ	5,808	C
Univ of Central Arkansas	AR	4,200	LC
Univ of Central Florida	FL	6,061	C+
Univ of Central Okla	OK	3,647	C
Univ of Cincinnati	OH	7,989	C
Univ of Colo at Boulder	CO	6,410	VC
Univ of Conn	CT	9,168	C
Univ of Delaware	DE	8,013	VC
Univ of Denver	CO	19,290	C+
Univ of Findlay	OH	15,764	C
Univ of Georgia	GA	5,655	VC
Univ of Idaho	ID	4,830	C
Univ of Illinois at Chicago	IL	8,443	C
Univ of Illinois at Urbana-Champaign	IL	7,764	HC
Univ of Indianapolis	IN	14,510	C
Univ of Iowa	IA	5,658	VC
Univ of Kentucky	KY	5,152	VC
Univ of La Verne	CA	17,400	C
Univ of Louisville	KY	5,948	C
Univ of Maine at Presque Isle	ME	6,374	C
Univ of Mary Hardin-Baylor	TX	8,120	NC
Univ of Maryland/College Park	MD	8,182	VC
Univ of Mass Dartmouth	MA	8,158	C
Univ of Mich/Flint	MI	2,916	C
Univ of Minn/Duluth	MN	6,512	C
Univ of Missouri/Columbia	MO	6,254	HC
Univ of Nebr at Kearney	NE	4,308	LC
Univ of Nebr-Lincoln	NE	5,278	LC
Univ of New Orleans	LA	5,468	C
Univ of North Alabama	AL	4,236	NC
Univ of N Car at Chapel Hill	NC	5,330	HC
Univ of N Car at Greensboro	NC	5,192	C
Univ of Northern Iowa	IA	5,137	C
Univ of Notre Dame	IN	20,150	MC
Univ of Okla	OK	5,427	VC
Univ of PR/Mayaguez	PR	0	
Univ of PR/Rio Piedras	PR	0	
Univ of South Florida	FL	5,475	C+
Univ of Southern Miss	MS	4,542	C
Univ of Southwestern Louisiana	LA	3,968	NC
Univ of Tenn at Martin	TN	4,550	C
Univ of the Pacific	CA	21,100	C
Univ of Toledo	OH	6,636	NC
Univ of Tulsa	OK	13,795	VC
Univ of Vermont	VT	10,776	C+
Univ of Wisc/Eau Claire	WI	4,647	C
Univ of Wisc/River Falls	WI	4,655	C
Univ of Wisc/Whitewater	WI	4,700	C
Ursuline College	OH	13,180	LC
Utah State Univ	UT	4,683	C
Valley City State Univ	ND	4,385	LC
Valparaiso Univ	IN	14,810	VC
Vassar College	NY	24,206	HC
Virginia Wesleyan College	VA	14,950	VC
Wartburg College	IA	14,530	VC
Washington and Jefferson College	PA	19,360	C
Washington State Univ	WA	6,364	C
Wayne State College	NE	4,260	NC
Wayne State Univ	MI	2,680	C
Weber State Univ	UT	4,398	C
Wells College	NY	19,460	C+
West Chester Univ of Penn	PA	7,492	C
West Liberty State College	WV	4,690	LC
Western Carolina Univ	NC	3,811	C
Western Mich Univ	MI	6,820	C
Western Oregon State College	OR	6,180	C
Western State College of Colo	CO	5,560	C
Western Washington Univ	WA	6,077	VC
Westfield State College	MA	7,161	C
Westminster College	MO	13,750	C+
Wheaton College	IL	14,710	HC
Whitworth College	WA	16,265	C
Widener Univ	PA	16,840	C
Wilkes Univ	PA	15,728	LC
Wilmington College	OH	13,700	LC
Winona State Univ	MN	5,200	VC
Wittenberg Univ	OH	19,998	VC
Wright State Univ	OH	6,896	LC
Youngstown State Univ	OH	6,447	LC

FORENSIC STUDIES

School	ST	$IS	SR
CUNY/John Jay College of Criminal Justice	NY	2,501	LC
Eastern Kentucky Univ	KY	4,840	NC
Univ of Central Florida	FL	6,061	C+
Univ of New Haven	CT	14,980	C

FOREST ENGINEERING

School	ST	$IS	SR
Auburn Univ	AL	5,823	C+
Oregon State Univ	OR	6,175	C
SUNY College of Environmental Science and Forestry	NY	9,257	HC+
Univ of Maine	ME	7,990	C
Univ of Washington	WA	6,618	VC

FORESTRY PRODUCTION AND PROCESSING

School	ST	$IS	SR
Auburn Univ	AL	5,823	C+
Clemson Univ	SC	6,564	VC
Oregon State Univ	OR	6,175	C
Penn State Univ/Univ Park Campus	PA	8,752	HC
Stephen F. Austin State Univ	TX	5,117	C
Univ of Calif at Berkeley	CA	9,962	HC+
Univ of Idaho	ID	4,830	C
Univ of Minn/Twin Cities	MN	6,682	VC
Univ of Washington	WA	6,618	VC

FORESTRY AND RELATED SCIENCES

School	ST	$IS	SR
Alabama A&M Univ	AL	4,200	C
Austin Peay State Univ	TN	4,350	C
Catawba College	NC	12,950	C
Clemson Univ	SC	6,564	VC
Colo State Univ	CO	6,566	VC
Eastern Mich Univ	MI	6,749	C
Eastern Oregon State College	OR	6,090	C
Georgia State Univ	GA	2,019	C
High Point Univ	NC	12,350	LC
Humboldt State Univ	CA	5,676	C
Iowa State Univ	IA	5,456	C
Kansas State Univ	KS	4,816	NC
Louisiana Tech Univ	LA	4,284	C
Mich State Univ	MI	7,842	C
Mich Tech Univ	MI	7,283	VC+
Miss State Univ	MS	5,629	VC
N Car State Univ	NC	4,984	VC
Northern Arizona Univ	AZ	4,844	C
Northwest Missouri State Univ	MO	5,010	LC
Okla Panhandle State Univ	OK	3,155	NC
Oregon State Univ	OR	6,175	C
Penn State Univ/Univ Park Campus	PA	8,752	HC
Peru State College	NE	4,311	NC
Southern Illinois Univ at Carbondale	IL	6,234	C
SUNY College of Environmental Science and Forestry	NY	9,257	HC+
Texas A&M Univ	TX	5,382	VC
Univ of Arkansas at Monticello	AR	3,832	NC
Univ of Calif at Berkeley	CA	9,962	HC+
Univ of Florida	FL	5,850	HC
Univ of Georgia	GA	5,655	VC
Univ of Illinois at Urbana-Champaign	IL	7,764	HC
Univ of Kentucky	KY	5,152	VC
Univ of Maine	ME	7,990	C
Univ of Mass/Amherst	MA	9,364	LC
Univ of Mich/Ann Arbor	MI	9,428	HC+
Univ of Minn/Twin Cities	MN	6,682	VC
Univ of Montana	MT	5,529	C
Univ of New Hampshire	NH	8,242	C
Univ of Tenn/Knoxville	TN	5,668	C
Univ of Wisc/Madison	WI	6,400	HC
Univ of Wisc/Stevens Point	WI	5,047	C+
Utah State Univ	UT	4,683	C
Virginia Polytechnic Inst and State Univ	VA	6,828	C
Washington and Lee Univ	VA	17,735	MC
West Virginia Univ	WV	5,774	C
Western Illinois Univ	IL	5,241	LC
Western New Mexico Univ	NM	3,234	LC
Youngstown State Univ	OH	6,447	LC

FRENCH

School	ST	$IS	SR
Abilene Christian Univ	TX	10,460	NC
Adelphi Univ	NY	18,250	LC
Adrian College	MI	14,340	C
Agnes Scott College	GA	17,135	VC
Alabama A&M Univ	AL	4,200	C
Alabama State Univ	AL	3,428	NC
Albany State College	GA	4,481	LC
Albertson College	ID	15,942	C+
Albertus Magnus College	CT	16,280	LC
Albion College	MI	18,264	VC
Albright College	PA	19,260	C
Alfred Univ	NY	21,054	VC+
Allegheny College	PA	21,020	VC
Allentown College of St Francis de Sales	PA	13,480	C
Alma College	MI	16,375	VC+
American Univ	DC	21,230	VC+
Amherst College	MA	24,152	MC
Anderson Univ	IN	12,920	C
Andrews Univ	MI	14,952	NC
Angelo State Univ	TX	5,176	C
Appalachian State Univ	NC	4,095	C
Aquinas College	MI	14,526	C
Arizona State Univ Main Campus	AZ	6,444	C
Arkansas State Univ	AR	4,250	NC
Asbury College	KY	11,105	VC
Assumption College	MA	17,095	LC
Atlantic Union College	MA	14,150	LC
Auburn Univ	AL	5,823	C+
Augsburg College	MN	15,608	C
Augustana College	IL	16,959	VC
Austin College	TX	14,999	VC
Austin Peay State Univ	TN	4,350	C
Baker Univ	KS	12,284	C
Baldwin-Wallace College	OH	15,210	C
Ball State Univ	IN	6,032	LC
Barry Univ	FL	16,050	C
Barton College	NC	10,689	LC
Bates College	ME	23,990	MC
Baylor Univ	TX	10,990	C+
Belmont Univ	TN	10,540	C
Beloit College	WI	18,950	VC+
Bemidji State Univ	MN	5,188	C
Benedictine College	KS	12,830	C
Bennington College	VT	24,850	VC+
Berea College	KY	2,883	VC+
Berry College	GA	11,990	VC
Bethany College	WV	18,300	C+
Birmingham-Southern College	AL	15,154	VC+
Bloomfield College	NJ	12,200	LC
Bloomsburg Univ of Penn	PA	6,312	C+
Boston College	MA	22,706	MC
Boston Univ	MA	24,130	HC
Bowdoin College	ME	24,155	MC
Bowling Green State Univ	OH	6,701	C
Bradley Univ	IL	14,718	C+
Brandeis Univ	MA	25,585	HC
Bridgewater College	VA	15,300	C
Bridgewater State College	MA	7,518	C
Brigham Young Univ	UT	5,625	HC
Brown Univ	RI	26,104	MC
Bryn Mawr College	PA	24,110	MC
Bucknell Univ	PA	22,320	HC
Butler Univ	IN	16,210	C
Cabrini College	PA	16,012	C
Caldwell College	NJ	12,860	C
Calif Lutheran Univ	CA	17,240	C
Cal State/Chico	CA	6,146	C
Cal State/Dominguez Hills	CA	2,857	LC
Cal State/Fresno	CA	5,747	C
Cal State/Fullerton	CA	4,850	LC
Cal State/Hayward	CA	5,495	C
Cal State/Long Beach	CA	6,057	LC
Cal State/Los Angeles	CA	4,940	VC
Cal State/Northridge	CA	7,122	LC
Cal State/Sacramento	CA	6,387	C
Cal State/San Bernardino	CA	6,055	LC
Cal State/Stanislaus	CA	6,799	C
Calif Univ of Penn	PA	7,370	C
Calvin College	MI	13,020	VC
Campbell Univ	NC	10,624	C
Canisius College	NY	15,510	C
Capital Univ	OH	16,535	VC
Cardinal Stritch College	WI	11,252	C
Carleton College	MN	22,155	HC
Carnegie Mellon Univ	PA	22,560	HC+
Carroll College	MT	11,265	C
Carroll College	WI	15,490	C
Carson-Newman College	TN	11,250	C
Carthage College	WI	15,995	C
Case Western Reserve Univ	OH	19,910	HC
Catawba College	NC	12,950	C
Catholic Univ of America	DC	18,856	C
Cedar Crest College	PA	18,930	C
Central College	IA	14,025	VC
Central Conn State Univ	CT	7,108	C
Central Methodist College	MO	11,410	C
Central Mich Univ	MI	6,737	LC
Central Missouri State Univ	MO	5,138	LC
Central State Univ	OH	7,320	NC
Central Washington Univ	WA	5,644	C
Centre College	KY	15,850	VC+
Chapman Univ	CA	21,842	C
Chatham College	PA	18,010	C
Chestnut Hill College	PA	14,525	C
Christendom College	VA	11,750	VC
Christopher Newport Univ	VA	3,196	LC
CUNY/Brooklyn College	NY	2,450	VC
CUNY/City College	NY	2,543	VC
CUNY/Herbert H. Lehman College	NY	2,542	C
CUNY/Hunter College	NY	4,101	VC
CUNY/Queens College	NY	2,631	C
CUNY/York College	NY	2,534	NC
Claremont McKenna College	CA	22,150	MC
Clarion Univ of Penn	PA	6,518	C
Clark Univ	MA	21,400	VC
Clarke College	IA	13,950	C+
Clemson Univ	SC	6,564	VC
Cleveland State Univ	OH	7,287	NC
Coe College	IA	17,085	VC
Coker College	SC	13,790	C
Colby College	ME	24,230	HC
Colgate Univ	NY	24,020	HC
College of Charleston	SC	6,250	C
College of Mount St Vincent	NY	16,730	C
College of New Rochelle	NY	15,440	LC
College of Notre Dame	CA	16,480	C
College of Our Lady of The Elms	MA	15,639	C
College of St Benedict	MN	15,468	VC
College of St Catherine	MN	14,670	C
College of St Elizabeth	NJ	15,800	C
College of the Holy Cross	MA	23,850	HC
College of William and Mary	VA	8,602	MC
College of Wooster	OH	19,875	VC
Colo College	CO	20,038	HC
Colo State Univ	CO	6,566	VC
Columbia College	SC	13,520	LC
Columbia Univ/Barnard College	NY	25,492	HC
Columbia Univ/Columbia College	NY	26,757	MC
Concordia College/Moorhead	MN	12,750	C
Conn College	CT	24,160	HC
Converse College	SC	15,750	C
Cornell College	IA	18,425	VC
Cornell Univ	NY	13,445	MC
Creighton Univ	NE	14,432	VC
Daemen College	NY	13,020	LC
Dartmouth College	NH	24,354	MC
David Lipscomb Univ	TN	7,865	VC
Davidson College	NC	21,037	MC
Davis and Elkins College	WV	13,230	LC
Delaware State College	DE	5,656	C
Denison Univ	OH	21,150	VC+
DePaul Univ	IL	15,535	VC
DePauw Univ	IN	18,530	VC
Dickinson College	PA	22,705	HC
Dillard Univ	LA	9,950	C
Drake Univ	IA	17,195	VC
Drew Univ/College of Liberal Arts	NJ	23,406	HC
Drury College	MO	12,140	VC
Duke Univ	NC	21,271	MC
Duquesne Univ	PA	16,434	VC
Earlham College	IN	19,383	VC
East Carolina Univ	NC	4,498	C
East Stroudsburg Univ	PA	6,886	C
East Texas State Univ	TX	4,572	LC
Eastern College	PA	15,150	C+
Eastern Illinois Univ	IL	5,548	C
Eastern Kentucky Univ	KY	4,840	NC
Eastern Mennonite College	VA	12,700	C
Eastern Mich Univ	MI	6,749	C
Eastern Nazarene College	MA	12,165	LC
Eastern New Mexico Univ	NM	3,950	C
Eastern Washington Univ	WA	5,439	LC
Eckerd College	FL	18,855	VC
Edgewood College	WI	11,700	C
Edinboro Univ of Penn	PA	7,181	C
Elizabethtown College	PA	17,850	VC
Elmhurst College	IL	12,536	C
Elmira College	NY	18,450	C
Elon College	NC	12,290	LC
Emmanuel College	MA	17,773	LC
Emory and Henry College	VA	12,776	C
Emory Univ	GA	21,930	HC
Evergreen State College	WA	6,306	C
Fairfield Univ	CT	20,460	VC
Fairleigh Dickinson Univ	NJ	16,427	C
Fairmont State College	WV	4,640	LC
Ferrum College	VA	12,800	LC
Fisk Univ	TN	0	LC
Florida Atlantic Univ	FL	5,525	C
Florida International Univ	FL	4,191	VC
Florida Southern College	FL	12,260	C

INDEX OF COLLEGE MAJORS

School	ST	$IS	SR
Univ of Louisville	KY	5,948	C
Univ of Lowell	MA	8,831	VC
Univ of Maine	ME	7,990	C
Univ of Maine at Fort Kent	ME	6,285	LC
Univ of Maine at Presque Isle	ME	6,374	C
Univ of Maryland/Baltimore County	MD	7,746	VC
Univ of Maryland/College Park	MD	8,182	VC
Univ of Mass Dartmouth	MA	8,158	C
Univ of Mass/Amherst	MA	9,364	LC
Univ of Mass/Boston	MA	4,253	C
Univ of Memphis	TN	3,476	C
Univ of Miami	FL	22,107	VC
Univ of Mich/Ann Arbor	MI	9,428	HC+
Univ of Minn/Duluth	MN	6,512	C
Univ of Minn/Morris	MN	6,825	HC
Univ of Minn/Twin Cities	MN	6,682	VC
Univ of Miss	MS	5,756	C
Univ of Missouri/Columbia	MO	6,254	HC
Univ of Missouri/St. Louis	MO	6,378	C
Univ of Montana	MT	5,529	C
Univ of Montevallo	AL	5,310	C
Univ of Nebr at Kearney	NE	4,308	LC
Univ of Nebr at Omaha	NE	1,889	LC
Univ of Nebr-Lincoln	NE	5,278	LC
Univ of Nevada/Las Vegas	NV	6,405	C
Univ of Nevada/Reno	NV	5,735	C
Univ of New Hampshire	NH	8,242	C
Univ of New Orleans	LA	5,468	C
Univ of North Alabama	AL	4,236	NC
Univ of N Car at Asheville	NC	4,791	VC
Univ of N Car at Chapel Hill	NC	5,330	HC
Univ of N Car at Charlotte	NC	4,597	C
Univ of N Car at Greensboro	NC	5,192	C
Univ of N Car at Wilmington	NC	5,172	C
Univ of N Dak	ND	4,902	NC
Univ of North Texas	TX	4,853	C
Univ of Northern Colo	CO	6,008	C
Univ of Northern Iowa	IA	5,137	C
Univ of Notre Dame	IN	20,150	MC
Univ of Okla	OK	5,427	VC
Univ of Oregon	OR	6,466	VC
Univ of Pittsburgh	PA	9,472	C
Univ of Portland	OR	15,564	C
Univ of PR/Mayaguez	PR	0	
Univ of PR/Rio Piedras	PR	0	
Univ of Puget Sound	WA	19,520	HC
Univ of Redlands	CA	22,059	VC
Univ of Rhode Island	RI	9,205	C
Univ of Richmond	VA	16,700	HC
Univ of Rochester	NY	23,696	HC
Univ of St Thomas	MN	15,785	C+
Univ of San Diego	CA	18,970	VC
Univ of San Francisco	CA	18,408	C
Univ of Scranton	PA	17,071	VC
Univ of South Alabama	AL	5,451	C
Univ of S Car	SC	6,158	C
Univ of S Car at Spartanburg	SC	2,320	C
Univ of S Dak	SD	4,722	C
Univ of South Florida	FL	5,475	C+
Univ of Southern Maine	ME	7,299	C
Univ of Southwestern Louisiana	LA	3,968	NC
Univ of Tampa	FL	16,780	C
Univ of Tenn at Chattanooga	TN	5,375	C
Univ of Tenn at Martin	TN	4,550	C
Univ of Tenn/Knoxville	TN	5,668	C
Univ of Texas at Arlington	TX	5,549	LC
Univ of Texas at Austin	TX	5,160	VC
Univ of Texas at El Paso	TX	3,160	LC
Univ of Texas at San Antonio	TX	6,420	C
Univ of the District of Columbia	DC	974	NC
Univ of the Pacific	CA	21,100	C
Univ of the South	TN	18,830	HC
Univ of Toledo	OH	6,636	NC
Univ of Tulsa	OK	13,795	VC
Univ of Utah	UT	5,975	C
Univ of Vermont	VT	10,776	C+
Univ of Virginia	VA	7,964	MC
Univ of Washington	WA	6,618	VC
Univ of West Florida	FL	5,415	C
Univ of Wisc/Eau Claire	WI	4,647	C
Univ of Wisc/Green Bay	WI	4,904	C
Univ of Wisc/La Crosse	WI	4,487	C
Univ of Wisc/Madison	WI	6,400	HC
Univ of Wisc/Milwaukee	WI	6,165	C
Univ of Wisc/Oshkosh	WI	4,240	C
Univ of Wisc/Parkside	WI	5,247	C
Univ of Wisc/Platteville	WI	4,830	C
Univ of Wisc/River Falls	WI	4,655	C
Univ of Wisc/Stevens Point	WI	5,047	C+
Univ of Wisc/Whitewater	WI	4,700	C
Univ of Wyoming	WY	4,991	NC
Ursinus College	PA	19,165	VC
Utah State Univ	UT	4,683	C
Valdosta State Univ	GA	4,670	LC
Valparaiso Univ	IN	14,810	VC
Vanderbilt Univ	TN	23,422	HC+
Villanova Univ	PA	21,400	HC
Virginia Polytechnic Inst and State Univ	VA	6,828	C
Virginia Union Univ	VA	10,555	LC
Virginia Wesleyan College	VA	14,950	VC
Wabash College	IN	16,250	VC
Wake Forest Univ	NC	17,280	MC
Walla Walla College	WA	13,215	C
Walsh Univ	OH	11,640	C
Washburn Univ of Topeka	KS	5,802	NC
Washington and Jefferson College	PA	19,360	C
Washington and Lee Univ	VA	17,735	MC
Washington College	MD	19,270	C+
Washington State Univ	WA	6,364	C
Washington Univ	MO	23,507	HC
Wayne State College	NE	4,260	NC
Wayne State Univ	MI	2,680	C
Weber State Univ	UT	4,398	C
Wellesley College	MA	23,815	MC
Wells College	NY	19,460	C+
Wesleyan College	GA	15,445	C
Wesleyan Univ	CT	23,770	MC
West Chester Univ of Penn	PA	7,492	C
West Georgia College	GA	4,256	C
Western Carolina Univ	NC	3,811	C
Western Illinois Univ	IL	5,241	LC
Western Kentucky Univ	KY	4,808	C
Western Maryland College	MD	18,990	C
Western Mich Univ	MI	6,820	C
Western State College of Colo	CO	5,560	C
Western Washington Univ	WA	6,077	VC
Westfield State College	MA	7,161	C
Westminster College	PA	15,200	C
Westmont College	CA	18,732	C
Wheaton College	IL	14,710	HC
Wheaton College	MA	23,840	C+
Wheeling Jesuit College	WV	14,370	C
Whitman College	WA	20,595	HC
Whittier College	CA	21,661	C
Whitworth College	WA	16,265	C
Wichita State Univ	KS	5,068	NC
Wilkes Univ	PA	15,728	LC
Willamette Univ	OR	17,995	VC
William Jewell College	MO	12,500	VC
William Woods Univ	MO	14,025	LC
Williams College	MA	24,390	MC
Wilmington College	OH	13,700	LC
Winona State Univ	MN	5,200	VC
Winthrop Univ	SC	6,750	C
Wittenberg Univ	OH	19,998	VC
Wofford College	SC	15,360	VC
Worcester State College	MA	6,414	LC
Wright State Univ	OH	6,896	LC
Xavier Univ	OH	15,710	C+
Xavier Univ of Louisiana	LA	10,400	C
Yale Univ	CT	25,110	MC
Yeshiva Univ	NY	18,200	VC
Youngstown State Univ	OH	6,447	LC

FRENCH STUDIES

School	ST	$IS	SR
Scripps College	CA	23,600	HC
Smith College	MA	24,236	HC

FURNITURE DESIGN

School	ST	$IS	SR
Center for Creative Studies/College of Art and Design	MI	15,330	SP
Kendall College of Art and Design	MI	9,600	SP
N Car State Univ	NC	4,984	VC
Northern Mich Univ	MI	6,350	C
Savannah College of Art and Design	GA	14,280	SP

GENETICS

School	ST	$IS	SR
Ball State Univ	IN	6,032	LC
Cal State/Fullerton	CA	4,850	LC
Cedar Crest College	PA	18,930	C
Cornell Univ	NY	13,445	MC
Iowa State Univ	IA	5,456	C
Ohio Wesleyan Univ	OH	21,108	VC+
Rutgers Univ/Cook College	NJ	9,197	HC
Rutgers Univ/Douglass College	NJ	8,795	VC
Rutgers Univ/Livingston College	NJ	8,877	VC
Rutgers Univ/Rutgers College	NJ	8,841	HC+
Rutgers Univ/Univ College—New Brunswick	NJ	0	LC
Texas A&M Univ	TX	5,382	VC
Univ of Calif at Davis	CA	9,534	VC
Univ of Georgia	GA	5,655	VC
Univ of Kansas	KS	5,200	NC
Univ of Minn/Twin Cities	MN	6,682	VC
Univ of Wisc/Madison	WI	6,400	HC
Western Kentucky Univ	KY	4,808	C

GEOCHEMISTRY

School	ST	$IS	SR
Calif Inst of Tech	CA	20,783	MC
Columbia Univ/Columbia College	NY	26,757	MC
Occidental College	CA	21,792	HC
SUNY/College at Cortland	NY	7,326	C+
SUNY/College at Geneseo	NY	6,949	HC
SUNY/College at Oswego	NY	7,330	VC
Univ of Maine at Farmington	ME	6,700	C

GEODETIC SCIENCE

School	ST	$IS	SR
Ohio State Univ	OH	7,218	LC
Univ of Calif at Berkeley	CA	9,962	HC+

GEOGRAPHY

School	ST	$IS	SR
Appalachian State Univ	NC	4,095	C
Aquinas College	MI	14,526	C
Arizona State Univ Main Campus	AZ	6,444	C
Arkansas State Univ	AR	4,250	NC
Auburn Univ	AL	5,823	C+
Augustana College	IL	16,959	VC
Augustana College	SD	13,420	C
Austin Peay State Univ	TN	4,350	C
Ball State Univ	IN	6,032	LC
Bellevue College	NE	3,050	NC
Bemidji State Univ	MN	5,188	C
Bloomsburg Univ of Penn	PA	6,312	C+
Boston Univ	MA	24,130	HC
Bowling Green State Univ	OH	6,701	C
Bridgewater State College	MA	7,518	C
Brigham Young Univ	UT	5,625	HC
Bucknell Univ	PA	22,320	HC
Calif State Polytechnic Univ/Pomona	CA	6,438	LC
Cal State/Chico	CA	6,146	C
Cal State/Dominguez Hills	CA	2,857	LC
Cal State/Fresno	CA	5,747	C
Cal State/Fullerton	CA	4,850	LC
Cal State/Hayward	CA	5,495	C
Cal State/Long Beach	CA	6,057	LC
Cal State/Los Angeles	CA	4,940	C
Cal State/Northridge	CA	7,122	LC
Cal State/Sacramento	CA	6,387	C
Cal State/San Bernardino	CA	6,055	LC
Cal State/Stanislaus	CA	6,799	C
Calif Univ of Penn	PA	7,370	C
Calvin College	MI	13,020	VC
Carroll College	WI	15,490	C
Carthage College	WI	15,995	C
Central Conn State Univ	CT	7,108	C
Central Mich Univ	MI	6,737	LC
Central Missouri State Univ	MO	5,138	C
Central Washington Univ	WA	5,644	C
Charleston Southern Univ	SC	10,282	LC
Charter Oak State College	CT	314	NC
Cheyney Univ of Penn	PA	7,005	C
Chicago State Univ	IL	2,198	C
CUNY/City College	NY	2,543	VC
CUNY/Herbert H. Lehman College	NY	2,542	C
CUNY/Hunter College	NY	4,101	VC
CUNY/York College	NY	2,534	NC
Clarion Univ of Penn	PA	6,518	C
Clark Univ	MA	21,400	VC
Colgate Univ	NY	24,020	HC
Concord College	WV	5,104	NC
Concordia College	NE	11,776	NC
Concordia Univ	IL	12,611	C
Dartmouth College	NH	24,354	MC
DePaul Univ	IL	15,535	VC
DePauw Univ	IN	18,530	VC
Dickinson State Univ	ND	3,792	
Drake Univ	IA	17,195	VC
East Carolina Univ	NC	4,498	C
East Stroudsburg Univ	PA	6,886	C
East Tenn State Univ	TN	4,406	C
East Texas State Univ	TX	4,572	LC
Eastern Kentucky Univ	KY	4,840	NC
Eastern Mich Univ	MI	6,749	C
Eastern Washington Univ	WA	5,439	LC
Edinboro Univ of Penn	PA	7,181	C
Elmhurst College	IL	12,536	C
Emory and Henry College	VA	12,776	C
Fayetteville State Univ	NC	3,926	LC
Fitchburg State College	MA	6,962	C
Florida Atlantic Univ	FL	5,525	C
Florida State Univ	FL	5,814	VC
Framingham State College	MA	6,580	C
Francis Marion Univ	SC	5,878	LC
Frostburg State Univ	MD	6,940	C
George Mason Univ	VA	8,728	C
George Washington Univ	DC	22,470	HC
Grambling State Univ	LA	4,712	NC
Grand Valley State Univ	MI	6,822	VC
Gustavus Adolphus College	MN	15,935	VC
Heidelberg College	OH	17,160	C
Hofstra Univ	NY	16,580	VC
Humboldt State Univ	CA	5,676	C
Illinois State Univ	IL	6,413	C
Indiana State Univ	IN	6,210	C
Indiana Univ Bloomington	IN	6,495	VC
Indiana Univ of Penn	PA	6,373	C
Indiana Univ Southeast	IN	2,260	LC
Indiana Univ-Purdue Univ at Indianapolis	IN	5,862	LC
Jacksonville State Univ	AL	4,080	LC
Jacksonville Univ	FL	13,390	C
James Madison Univ	VA	8,198	HC
Jersey City State College	NJ	7,797	LC
Kansas State Univ	KS	4,816	NC
Keene State College	NH	7,081	C
Kent State Univ	OH	6,740	LC
Kutztown Univ	PA	6,528	C
Lock Haven Univ of Penn	PA	7,128	C
LIU/C. W. Post Campus	NY	16,870	C
Louisiana State Univ and A&M College	LA	5,605	C
Louisiana Tech Univ	LA	4,284	C
Macalester College	MN	19,710	HC
Mankato State Univ	MN	5,097	LC
Mansfield Univ	PA	6,348	C
Marshall Univ	WV	5,762	LC
Mary Washington College	VA	7,910	HC
Miami Univ	OH	8,066	VC
Mich State Univ	MI	7,842	C
Middle Tenn State Univ	TN	3,857	C
Middlebury College	VT	24,400	MC
Millersville Univ of Penn	PA	7,370	VC
Montclair State College	NJ	7,539	C+
Moorhead State Univ	MN	5,076	C
Morehead State Univ	KY	4,600	LC
Mount Holyoke College	MA	23,630	VC
Murray State Univ	KY	4,702	C
New Mexico State Univ	NM	4,844	LC
Norfolk State Univ	VA	6,345	LC
N Car Central Univ	NC	4,347	LC
Northeast Louisiana Univ	LA	3,906	NC
Northeastern Illinois Univ	IL	1,955	C
Northeastern State Univ	OK	5,250	C
Northern Arizona Univ	AZ	4,844	C
Northern Illinois Univ	IL	6,408	C
Northern Kentucky Univ	KY	4,620	NC
Northern Mich Univ	MI	6,350	C
Northwest Missouri State Univ	MO	5,010	LC
Northwestern Univ	IL	21,093	MC
Ohio State Univ	OH	7,218	LC
Ohio Univ	OH	7,341	C
Ohio Wesleyan Univ	OH	21,108	VC+
Okla State Univ	OK	5,086	VC
Old Dominion Univ	VA	8,317	C
Oregon State Univ	OR	6,175	C
Penn State Univ/Univ Park Campus	PA	8,752	HC
Pittsburg State Univ	KS	4,478	NC
Plymouth State College	NH	7,166	C
Portland State Univ	OR	7,191	C
Prairie View A&M Univ	TX	4,740	LC
Radford Univ	VA	7,034	LC
Rhode Island College	RI	7,901	LC
Rockhurst College	MO	12,470	C
Rutgers Univ/Cook College	NJ	9,197	HC
Rutgers Univ/Douglass College	NJ	8,795	VC
Rutgers Univ/Livingston College	NJ	8,877	VC
Rutgers Univ/Rutgers College	NJ	8,841	HC+
Rutgers Univ/Univ College—New Brunswick	NJ	0	LC
St Cloud State Univ	MN	5,015	C
Salem State College	MA	6,712	C
Salisbury State Univ	MD	7,516	C+
Sam Houston State Univ	TX	4,506	C
San Diego State Univ	CA	6,692	LC
San Francisco State Univ	CA	7,292	LC
San Jose State Univ	CA	6,680	LC
Shepherd College	WV	5,540	C
Shippensburg Univ of Penn	PA	7,052	C
Slippery Rock Univ	PA	6,803	C
Sonoma State Univ	CA	6,996	LC
S Dak State Univ	SD	4,562	C
Southeast Missouri State Univ	MO	5,854	C
Southern Arkansas Univ	AR	3,432	NC
Southern Conn State Univ	CT	7,532	C
Southern Illinois Univ at Carbondale	IL	6,234	C
Southern Illinois Univ at Edwardsville	IL	6,097	LC
Southern Oregon State College	OR	6,128	C

School	ST	$IS	SR
Southwest Missouri State Univ	MO	4,956	C
Southwest Texas State Univ	TX	5,124	C
Southwestern Okla State Univ	OK	3,312	C
SUNY at Albany	NY	7,059	VC
SUNY at Binghamton	NY	7,921	HC
SUNY at Buffalo	NY	7,896	VC
SUNY/College at Buffalo	NY	7,035	VC
SUNY/College at Cortland	NY	7,326	C+
SUNY/College at Geneseo	NY	6,949	HC
SUNY/College at New Paltz	NY	6,890	VC
SUNY/College at Oneonta	NY	7,878	C
SUNY/College at Plattsburgh	NY	6,917	C
Stephen F. Austin State Univ	TX	5,117	C
Stetson Univ	FL	16,435	VC
Syracuse Univ	NY	21,305	HC
Temple Univ	PA	10,281	C
Texas A&M Univ at Kingsville	TX	3,808	LC
Texas Tech Univ	TX	6,008	C
The Univ of New Mexico	NM	5,304	C
Thomas A. Edison State College	NJ	400	
Towson State Univ	MD	7,452	C
United States Air Force Academy	CO	0	MC
United States Military Academy	NY	0	MC
Univ of Akron	OH	6,699	NC
Univ of Alabama	AL	5,702	C
Univ of Alaska Fairbanks	AK	4,718	C
Univ of Arizona	AZ	5,808	C
Univ of Arkansas at Fayetteville	AR	5,046	C
Univ of Calif at Berkeley	CA	9,962	HC+
Univ of Calif at Davis	CA	9,534	VC
Univ of Calif at Los Angeles	CA	8,959	HC
Univ of Calif at Santa Barbara	CA	9,460	C
Univ of Calif, Riverside	CA	9,178	C
Univ of Central Arkansas	AR	4,200	LC
Univ of Central Okla	OK	3,647	C
Univ of Chicago	IL	24,517	MC
Univ of Cincinnati	OH	7,989	C
Univ of Colo at Boulder	CO	6,410	VC
Univ of Colo at Colo Springs	CO	2,269	C
Univ of Colo at Denver	CO	1,955	VC
Univ of Conn	CT	9,168	C
Univ of Delaware	DE	8,013	VC
Univ of Denver	CO	19,290	C+
Univ of Florida	FL	5,850	HC
Univ of Georgia	GA	5,655	VC
Univ of Hawaii at Hilo	HI	4,141	C
Univ of Hawaii at Manoa	HI	5,626	C
Univ of Idaho	ID	4,830	C
Univ of Illinois at Chicago	IL	8,443	C
Univ of Iowa	IA	5,658	VC
Univ of Kansas	KS	5,200	NC
Univ of Kentucky	KY	5,152	VC
Univ of Louisville	KY	5,948	C
Univ of Maine at Farmington	ME	6,700	C
Univ of Maryland/Baltimore County	MD	7,746	VC
Univ of Maryland/College Park	MD	8,182	VC
Univ of Maryland/Univ College	MD	4,900	NC
Univ of Mass/Amherst	MA	9,364	LC
Univ of Mass/Boston	MA	4,253	C
Univ of Memphis	TN	3,476	C
Univ of Miami	FL	22,107	VC
Univ of Mich/Ann Arbor	MI	9,428	HC+
Univ of Mich/Flint	MI	2,916	C
Univ of Minn/Duluth	MN	6,512	C
Univ of Minn/Twin Cities	MN	6,682	VC
Univ of Missouri/Columbia	MO	6,254	HC
Univ of Missouri/Kansas City	MO	5,906	VC
Univ of Montana	MT	5,529	C
Univ of Nebr at Kearney	NE	4,308	LC
Univ of Nebr at Omaha	NE	1,889	LC
Univ of Nebr-Lincoln	NE	5,278	LC
Univ of Nevada/Reno	NV	5,735	C
Univ of New Hampshire	NH	8,242	C
Univ of New Orleans	LA	5,468	C
Univ of North Alabama	AL	4,236	NC
Univ of N Car at Chapel Hill	NC	5,330	HC
Univ of N Car at Charlotte	NC	4,597	C
Univ of N Car at Greensboro	NC	5,192	C
Univ of N Car at Wilmington	NC	5,172	C
Univ of N Dak	ND	4,902	NC
Univ of North Texas	TX	4,853	C
Univ of Northern Colo	CO	6,008	C
Univ of Northern Iowa	IA	5,137	C
Univ of Okla	OK	5,427	VC
Univ of Oregon	OR	6,466	VC
Univ of Pittsburgh at Johnstown	PA	8,914	C
Univ of PR/Rio Piedras	PR	0	
Univ of Rhode Island	RI	9,205	C
Univ of St Thomas	MN	15,785	C+
Univ of South Alabama	AL	5,451	C
Univ of S Car	SC	6,158	C
Univ of South Florida	FL	5,475	C+
Univ of Southern Calif	CA	23,006	VC
Univ of Southern Maine	ME	7,299	C
Univ of Southern Miss	MS	4,542	C
Univ of Southwestern Louisiana	LA	3,968	NC
Univ of Tenn at Martin	TN	4,550	C
Univ of Tenn/Knoxville	TN	5,668	C
Univ of Texas at Austin	TX	5,160	VC
Univ of Texas at San Antonio	TX	6,420	C
Univ of the District of Columbia	DC	974	NC
Univ of Toledo	OH	6,636	NC
Univ of Utah	UT	5,975	C
Univ of Vermont	VT	10,776	C+
Univ of Washington	WA	6,618	VC
Univ of Wisc/Eau Claire	WI	4,647	C
Univ of Wisc/Green Bay	WI	4,904	C
Univ of Wisc/La Crosse	WI	4,487	C
Univ of Wisc/Madison	WI	6,400	HC
Univ of Wisc/Milwaukee	WI	6,165	C
Univ of Wisc/Oshkosh	WI	4,240	C
Univ of Wisc/Parkside	WI	5,247	C
Univ of Wisc/Platteville	WI	4,830	C
Univ of Wisc/River Falls	WI	4,655	C
Univ of Wisc/Stevens Point	WI	5,047	C+
Univ of Wisc/Whitewater	WI	4,700	C
Univ of Wyoming	WY	4,991	NC
Utah State Univ	UT	4,683	C
Valparaiso Univ	IN	14,810	VC
Vassar College	NY	24,206	HC
Villanova Univ	PA	21,400	HC
Virginia Polytechnic Inst and State Univ	VA	6,828	C
Wayne State College	NE	4,260	NC
Wayne State Univ	MI	2,680	C
Weber State Univ	UT	4,398	C
West Chester Univ of Penn	PA	7,492	C
West Georgia College	GA	4,256	C
West Liberty State College	WV	4,690	LC
West Texas A&M Univ	TX	4,224	C
West Virginia Univ	WV	5,774	C
Western Carolina Univ	NC	3,811	C
Western Illinois Univ	IL	5,241	LC
Western Kentucky Univ	KY	4,808	C
Western Mich Univ	MI	6,820	C
Western Oregon State College	OR	6,180	C
Western Washington Univ	WA	6,077	VC
Westfield State College	MA	7,161	C
William Paterson College	NJ	7,438	C+
William Woods Univ	MO	14,025	LC
Winona State Univ	MN	5,200	VC
Wittenberg Univ	OH	19,998	VC
Worcester State College	MA	6,414	LC
Wright State Univ	OH	6,896	LC
Youngstown State Univ	OH	6,447	LC

GEOLOGICAL ENGINEERING

School	ST	$IS	SR
Arizona State Univ Main Campus	AZ	6,444	C
Auburn Univ	AL	5,823	C+
Brigham Young Univ	UT	5,625	HC
Colo School of Mines	CO	8,436	HC+
Lakeland College	WI	12,845	LC
Mich Tech Univ	MI	7,283	VC+
Montana College of Mineral Science and Tech	MT	4,977	C
New Mexico Inst of Mining and Tech	NM	5,212	C+
New Mexico State Univ	NM	4,844	LC
S Dak School of Mines and Tech	SD	5,329	C
Univ of Alaska Fairbanks	AK	4,718	C
Univ of Idaho	ID	4,830	C
Univ of Minn/Twin Cities	MN	6,682	VC
Univ of Miss	MS	5,756	C
Univ of Missouri/Rolla	MO	6,729	VC+
Univ of Nevada/Reno	NV	5,735	C
Univ of N Dak	ND	4,902	NC
Univ of Okla	OK	5,427	VC
Univ of Rochester	NY	23,696	HC
Univ of Utah	UT	5,975	C
Univ of Wisc/Madison	WI	6,400	HC
Washington Univ	MO	23,507	HC

GEOLOGY

School	ST	$IS	SR
Adams State College	CO	4,910	C
Alfred Univ	NY	21,054	VC+
Allegheny College	PA	21,020	VC
Amherst College	MA	24,152	MC
Angelo State Univ	TX	5,176	C
Appalachian State Univ	NC	4,095	C
Arizona State Univ Main Campus	AZ	6,444	C
Arkansas Tech Univ	AR	4,200	NC
Ashland Univ	OH	15,508	C
Auburn Univ	AL	5,823	C+
Augustana College	IL	16,959	VC
Austin Peay State Univ	TN	4,350	C
Baldwin-Wallace College	OH	15,210	C
Ball State Univ	IN	6,032	LC
Bates College	ME	23,990	MC
Baylor Univ	TX	10,990	C+
Beloit College	WI	18,950	VC+
Bemidji State Univ	MN	5,188	C
Bloomsburg Univ of Penn	PA	6,312	C+
Boise State Univ	ID	4,909	LC
Boston College	MA	22,706	MC
Boston Univ	MA	24,130	HC
Bowdoin College	ME	24,155	MC
Bowling Green State Univ	OH	6,701	C
Bradley Univ	IL	14,718	C+
Bridgewater State College	MA	7,518	C
Brigham Young Univ	UT	5,625	HC
Brown Univ	RI	26,104	MC
Bryn Mawr College	PA	24,110	MC
Bucknell Univ	PA	22,320	HC
Calif Inst of Tech	CA	20,783	MC
Calif Lutheran Univ	CA	17,240	C
Calif State Polytechnic Univ/Pomona	CA	6,438	LC
Cal State/Bakersfield	CA	5,402	C
Cal State/Chico	CA	6,146	C
Cal State/Dominguez Hills	CA	2,857	LC
Cal State/Fresno	CA	5,747	C
Cal State/Fullerton	CA	4,850	LC
Cal State/Hayward	CA	5,495	C
Cal State/Long Beach	CA	6,057	LC
Cal State/Los Angeles	CA	4,940	VC
Cal State/Northridge	CA	7,122	LC
Cal State/Sacramento	CA	6,387	C
Cal State/San Bernardino	CA	6,055	LC
Cal State/Stanislaus	CA	6,799	C
Calif Univ of Penn	PA	7,370	C
Calvin College	MI	13,020	VC
Carleton College	MN	22,155	HC
Case Western Reserve Univ	OH	19,910	HC
Central Mich Univ	MI	6,737	LC
Central Washington Univ	WA	5,644	C
Charleston Southern Univ	SC	10,282	LC
Charter Oak State College	CT	314	NC
CUNY/Brooklyn College	NY	2,450	VC
CUNY/City College	NY	2,543	VC
CUNY/Herbert H. Lehman College	NY	2,542	C
CUNY/Hunter College	NY	4,101	VC
CUNY/Queens College	NY	2,631	C
CUNY/York College	NY	2,534	NC
Clarion Univ of Penn	PA	6,518	C
Clemson Univ	SC	6,564	VC
Cleveland State Univ	OH	7,287	NC
Colby College	ME	24,230	HC
Colgate Univ	NY	24,020	HC
College of Charleston	SC	6,250	C
College of the Southwest	NM	5,720	LC
College of William and Mary	VA	8,602	MC
College of Wooster	OH	19,875	VC
Colo College	CO	20,038	HC
Colo State Univ	CO	6,566	VC
Columbia Univ/Columbia College	NY	26,757	MC
Columbus College	GA	4,892	LC
Cornell College	IA	18,425	VC
Cornell Univ	NY	13,445	MC
Dartmouth College	NH	24,354	MC
Denison Univ	OH	21,150	VC+
DePauw Univ	IN	18,530	VC
Dickinson College	PA	22,705	HC
Duke Univ	NC	21,271	MC
Earlham College	IN	19,383	VC
East Carolina Univ	NC	4,498	C
East Tenn State Univ	TN	4,406	C
East Texas State Univ	TX	4,572	LC
Eastern Kentucky Univ	KY	4,840	NC
Eastern Mich Univ	MI	6,749	C
Eastern New Mexico Univ	NM	3,950	C
Eastern Washington Univ	WA	5,439	LC
Edinboro Univ of Penn	PA	7,181	C
Elizabeth City State Univ	NC	4,254	LC
Emory Univ	GA	21,930	HC
Evergreen State College	WA	6,306	C
Florida Atlantic Univ	FL	5,525	C
Florida International Univ	FL	4,191	VC
Florida State Univ	FL	5,814	VC
Fort Lewis College	CO	5,097	C
Franklin and Marshall College	PA	23,655	HC
Furman Univ	SC	16,557	VC
George Mason Univ	VA	8,728	C
George Washington Univ	DC	22,470	HC
Georgia Southern Univ	GA	4,988	LC
Georgia Southwestern College	GA	4,338	LC
Grand Valley State Univ	MI	6,822	VC
Guilford College	NC	17,680	C
Gustavus Adolphus College	MN	15,935	VC
Hamilton College	NY	23,500	HC
Hampshire College	MA	25,320	C
Hanover College	IN	10,950	VC
Hardin-Simmons Univ	TX	9,080	C
Hartwick College	NY	20,950	C
Harvard Univ/Harvard and Radcliffe Colleges	MA	24,880	MC
Haverford College	PA	23,950	MC
Hofstra Univ	NY	16,580	VC
Hope College	MI	15,698	C+
Humboldt State Univ	CA	5,676	C
Idaho State Univ	ID	4,442	C
Illinois State Univ	IL	6,413	C
Indiana State Univ	IN	6,210	C
Indiana Univ Bloomington	IN	6,495	VC
Indiana Univ Northwest	IN	2,310	C
Indiana Univ of Penn	PA	6,373	C
Indiana Univ-Purdue Univ at Fort Wayne	IN	2,500	LC
Indiana Univ-Purdue Univ at Indianapolis	IN	5,862	LC
Iowa State Univ	IA	5,456	C
James Madison Univ	VA	8,198	HC
Jersey City State College	NJ	7,797	LC
Juniata College	PA	18,390	C+
Kansas State Univ	KS	4,816	NC
Kean College of New Jersey	NJ	6,395	LC
Keene State College	NH	7,081	C
Kent State Univ	OH	6,740	LC
Kutztown Univ	PA	6,528	C
La Salle Univ	PA	16,940	VC
Lafayette College	PA	23,450	HC
Lake Superior State Univ	MI	7,311	C
Lamar Univ	TX	3,798	C
Lawrence Univ	WI	19,986	HC+
Lehigh Univ	PA	23,250	HC
Lewis-Clark State College	ID	4,040	
Lock Haven Univ of Penn	PA	7,128	C
LIU/C. W. Post Campus	NY	16,870	C
LIU/Southampton Campus	NY	17,280	C
Louisiana State Univ and A&M College	LA	5,605	C
Louisiana Tech Univ	LA	4,284	C
Macalester College	MN	19,710	HC
Mansfield Univ	PA	6,348	C
Marietta College	OH	16,940	C+
Marshall Univ	WV	5,762	LC
Mary Washington College	VA	7,910	HC
McNeese State Univ	LA	4,543	NC
Mercyhurst College	PA	13,488	C
Mesa State College	CO	5,127	NC
Miami Univ	OH	8,066	VC
Mich State Univ	MI	7,842	C
Mich Tech Univ	MI	7,283	VC+
Middle Tenn State Univ	TN	3,857	C
Middlebury College	VT	24,400	MC
Midwestern State Univ	TX	4,542	LC
Millersville Univ of Penn	PA	7,370	VC
Millsaps College	MS	15,486	C+
Miss State Univ	MS	5,629	VC
Moravian College	PA	18,960	VC
Morehead State Univ	KY	4,600	LC
Mount Holyoke College	MA	23,630	VC
Mount Union College	OH	15,850	C
Murray State Univ	KY	4,702	C
Muskingum College	OH	16,650	C
New Mexico Inst of Mining and Tech	NM	5,212	C+
New Mexico State Univ	NM	4,844	LC
Nicholls State Univ	LA	4,531	NC
N Car State Univ	NC	4,984	VC
Northeast Louisiana Univ	LA	3,906	NC
Northeastern Illinois Univ	IL	1,955	C
Northeastern State Univ	OK	5,250	C
Northeastern Univ	MA	19,851	C
Northern Arizona Univ	AZ	4,844	C
Northern Illinois Univ	IL	6,408	C
Northern Kentucky Univ	KY	4,620	NC
Northland College	WI	13,550	LC
Northwest Missouri State Univ	MO	5,010	LC
Northwestern Univ	IL	21,093	MC
Oberlin College	OH	24,570	HC+
Occidental College	CA	21,792	HC
Ohio State Univ	OH	7,218	LC
Ohio Univ	OH	7,341	C
Ohio Wesleyan Univ	OH	21,108	VC+
Okla State Univ	OK	5,086	VC
Old Dominion Univ	VA	8,317	C
Olivet Nazarene Univ	IL	11,976	C
Oregon State Univ	OR	6,175	C
Pacific Lutheran Univ	WA	15,998	VC
Phillips Univ	OK	12,744	C
Pomona College	CA	23,820	MC
Portland State Univ	OR	7,191	C
Prescott College	AZ	9,775	C
Princeton Univ	NJ	24,650	MC
Purdue Univ/West Lafayette	IN	6,636	C
Radford Univ	VA	7,034	LC
Rensselaer Polytechnic Inst	NY	23,067	HC
Rice Univ	TX	15,110	MC
Rider College	NJ	18,160	C
Rocky Mountain College	MT	11,320	C
Rutgers Univ/Cook College	NJ	9,197	HC
Rutgers Univ/Douglass College	NJ	8,795	VC
Rutgers Univ/Livingston College	NJ	8,877	VC
Rutgers Univ/Newark College of A&S	NJ	8,645	C
Rutgers Univ/Rutgers College	NJ	8,841	HC+
Rutgers Univ/Univ College—New Brunswick	NJ	0	LC

School	ST	$IS	SR
St Cloud State Univ	MN	5,015	C
St Lawrence Univ	NY	23,420	VC
St Louis Univ	MO	15,522	VC
Salem State College	MA	6,712	C
Sam Houston State Univ	TX	4,506	C
San Diego State Univ	CA	6,692	LC
San Francisco State Univ	CA	7,292	LC
San Jose State Univ	CA	6,680	LC
Sarah Lawrence College	NY	24,975	HC
Scripps College	CA	23,600	HC
Skidmore College	NY	23,230	HC
Slippery Rock Univ	PA	6,803	C
Smith College	MA	24,236	HC
Sonoma State Univ	CA	6,996	LC
S Dak School of Mines and Tech	SD	5,329	C
Southern Illinois Univ at Carbondale	IL	6,234	C
Southern Methodist Univ	TX	18,520	VC
Southern Oregon State College	OR	6,128	C
Southern Utah Univ	UT	4,104	LC
Southwest Missouri State Univ	MO	4,956	C
Stanford Univ	CA	24,310	MC
SUNY at Albany	NY	7,059	VC
SUNY at Binghamton	NY	7,921	HC
SUNY at Buffalo	NY	7,896	VC
SUNY at Stony Brook	NY	7,658	VC
SUNY/College at Brockport	NY	7,220	C+
SUNY/College at Buffalo	NY	7,035	VC
SUNY/College at Cortland	NY	7,326	C+
SUNY/College at Fredonia	NY	7,159	VC
SUNY/College at Geneseo	NY	6,949	HC
SUNY/College at New Paltz	NY	6,890	VC
SUNY/College at Oneonta	NY	7,878	C
SUNY/College at Oswego	NY	7,330	VC
SUNY/College at Plattsburgh	NY	6,917	C
SUNY/Potsdam College	NY	6,906	C
Stephen F. Austin State Univ	TX	5,117	C
Sul Ross State Univ	TX	4,144	NC
Syracuse Univ	NY	21,305	HC
Tarleton State Univ	TX	4,082	LC
Temple Univ	PA	10,281	C
Tenn Tech Univ	TN	5,190	C
Texas A&M Univ	TX	5,382	VC
Texas A&M Univ at Kingsville	TX	3,808	LC
Texas Christian Univ	TX	12,180	C
Texas Tech Univ	TX	6,008	C
The Univ of New Mexico	NM	5,304	C
Thiel College	PA	16,282	C
Thomas A. Edison State College	NJ	400	
Trinity Univ	TX	16,670	HC
Tufts Univ	MA	24,962	MC
Tulane Univ	LA	24,540	HC
Union College	NY	23,817	HC
Univ of Akron	OH	6,699	NC
Univ of Alabama	AL	5,702	C
Univ of Alabama at Birmingham	AL	7,533	C
Univ of Alaska Fairbanks	AK	4,718	C
Univ of Arizona	AZ	5,808	C
Univ of Arkansas at Fayetteville	AR	5,046	C
Univ of Arkansas at Little Rock	AR	4,419	C
Univ of Calif at Berkeley	CA	9,962	HC+
Univ of Calif at Davis	CA	9,534	VC
Univ of Calif at Los Angeles	CA	8,959	HC
Univ of Calif at Santa Barbara	CA	9,460	C
Univ of Calif at Santa Cruz	CA	9,060	VC
Univ of Calif, Riverside	CA	9,178	C
Univ of Cincinnati	OH	7,989	C
Univ of Colo at Boulder	CO	6,410	VC
Univ of Colo at Denver	CO	1,955	VC
Univ of Conn	CT	9,168	C
Univ of Dayton	OH	15,120	C+
Univ of Delaware	DE	8,013	VC
Univ of Florida	FL	5,850	HC
Univ of Georgia	GA	5,655	VC
Univ of Hawaii at Hilo	HI	4,141	C
Univ of Hawaii at Manoa	HI	5,626	C
Univ of Houston	TX	5,215	C
Univ of Idaho	ID	4,830	C
Univ of Illinois at Chicago	IL	8,443	C
Univ of Illinois at Urbana-Champaign	IL	7,764	HC
Univ of Iowa	IA	5,658	VC
Univ of Kansas	KS	5,200	NC
Univ of Kentucky	KY	5,152	VC
Univ of Louisville	KY	5,948	C
Univ of Lowell	MA	8,831	VC
Univ of Maine	ME	7,990	C
Univ of Maryland/College Park	MD	8,182	VC
Univ of Maryland/Univ College	MD	4,900	NC
Univ of Mass/Amherst	MA	9,364	LC
Univ of Miami	FL	22,107	VC
Univ of Mich/Ann Arbor	MI	9,428	HC+
Univ of Minn/Duluth	MN	6,512	C
Univ of Minn/Morris	MN	6,825	HC
Univ of Minn/Twin Cities	MN	6,682	VC
Univ of Miss	MS	5,756	C
Univ of Missouri/Columbia	MO	6,254	HC
Univ of Missouri/Kansas City	MO	5,906	VC
Univ of Missouri/Rolla	MO	6,729	VC+
Univ of Montana	MT	5,529	C
Univ of Nebr at Omaha	NE	1,889	LC
Univ of Nebr-Lincoln	NE	5,278	LC
Univ of Nevada/Las Vegas	NV	6,405	C
Univ of New Hampshire	NH	8,242	C
Univ of New Orleans	LA	5,468	C
Univ of N Car at Chapel Hill	NC	5,330	HC
Univ of N Car at Wilmington	NC	5,172	C
Univ of N Dak	ND	4,902	NC
Univ of Northern Colo	CO	6,008	C
Univ of Northern Iowa	IA	5,137	C
Univ of Okla	OK	5,427	VC
Univ of Oregon	OR	6,466	VC
Univ of Penn	PA	24,238	MC
Univ of Pittsburgh	PA	9,472	C
Univ of Pittsburgh at Bradford	PA	9,050	C
Univ of Pittsburgh at Johnstown	PA	8,914	C
Univ of PR/Mayaguez	PR	0	
Univ of Puget Sound	WA	19,520	HC
Univ of Rhode Island	RI	9,205	C
Univ of Rochester	NY	23,696	HC
Univ of St Thomas	MN	15,785	C+
Univ of South Alabama	AL	5,451	C
Univ of S Car	SC	6,158	C
Univ of South Florida	FL	5,475	C+
Univ of Southern Calif	CA	23,006	VC
Univ of Southern Maine	ME	7,299	C
Univ of Southern Miss	MS	4,542	C
Univ of Southwestern Louisiana	LA	3,968	NC
Univ of Tenn at Chattanooga	TN	5,375	C
Univ of Tenn at Martin	TN	4,550	C
Univ of Tenn/Knoxville	TN	5,668	C
Univ of Texas at Arlington	TX	5,549	LC
Univ of Texas at Austin	TX	5,160	VC
Univ of Texas at El Paso	TX	3,160	LC
Univ of Texas at San Antonio	TX	6,420	C
Univ of the Pacific	CA	21,100	C
Univ of the South	TN	18,830	HC
Univ of Toledo	OH	6,636	NC
Univ of Tulsa	OK	13,795	VC
Univ of Utah	UT	5,975	C
Univ of Vermont	VT	10,776	C+
Univ of Washington	WA	6,618	VC
Univ of Wisc/Eau Claire	WI	4,647	C
Univ of Wisc/Madison	WI	6,400	HC
Univ of Wisc/Milwaukee	WI	6,165	C
Univ of Wisc/Oshkosh	WI	4,240	C
Univ of Wisc/Parkside	WI	5,247	
Univ of Wisc/River Falls	WI	4,655	C
Univ of Wyoming	WY	4,991	NC
Utah State Univ	UT	4,683	C
Valparaiso Univ	IN	14,810	VC
Vanderbilt Univ	TN	23,422	HC+
Vassar College	NY	24,206	HC
Virginia Polytechnic Inst and State Univ	VA	6,828	C
Virginia State Univ	VA	7,040	
Washington and Lee Univ	VA	17,735	MC
Washington State Univ	WA	6,364	C
Wayne State Univ	MI	2,680	C
Weber State Univ	UT	4,398	C
Wellesley College	MA	23,815	MC
Wesleyan Univ	CT	23,770	MC
West Chester Univ of Penn	PA	7,492	C
West Georgia College	GA	4,256	C
West Texas A&M Univ	TX	4,224	C
West Virginia Univ	WV	5,774	C
Western Carolina Univ	NC	3,811	C
Western Illinois Univ	IL	5,241	LC
Western Kentucky Univ	KY	4,808	C
Western Mich Univ	MI	6,820	C
Western State College of Colo	CO	5,560	C
Western Washington Univ	WA	6,077	VC
Wheaton College	IL	14,710	HC
Whitman College	WA	20,595	HC
Whittier College	CA	21,661	C
Wichita State Univ	KS	5,068	NC
Williams College	MA	24,390	MC
Winona State Univ	MN	5,200	VC
Wittenberg Univ	OH	19,998	VC
Wright State Univ	OH	6,896	LC
Youngstown State Univ	OH	6,447	LC

GEOPHYSICAL ENGINEERING

School	ST	$IS	SR
Colo School of Mines	CO	8,436	HC+
Montana College of Mineral Science and Tech	MT	4,977	C

GEOPHYSICS AND SEISMOLOGY

School	ST	$IS	SR
Boise State Univ	ID	4,909	LC
Boston College	MA	22,706	MC
Calif Inst of Tech	CA	20,783	MC
Cal State/Northridge	CA	7,122	LC
Colgate Univ	NY	24,020	HC
Columbia Univ/Columbia College	NY	26,757	MC
Harvard Univ/Harvard and Radcliffe Colleges	MA	24,880	MC
Lehigh Univ	PA	23,250	HC
Mich Tech Univ	MI	7,283	VC+
New Mexico Inst of Mining and Tech	NM	5,212	C+
Occidental College	CA	21,792	HC
Purdue Univ/West Lafayette	IN	6,636	C
Rice Univ	TX	15,110	MC
Southern Methodist Univ	TX	18,520	VC
SUNY at Binghamton	NY	7,921	HC
Texas A&M Univ	TX	5,382	VC
Texas Tech Univ	TX	6,008	C
Univ of Calif at Berkeley	CA	9,962	HC+
Univ of Calif at Los Angeles	CA	8,959	HC
Univ of Calif at Santa Barbara	CA	9,460	C
Univ of Calif, Riverside	CA	9,178	C
Univ of Delaware	DE	8,013	VC
Univ of Kansas	KS	5,200	NC
Univ of Minn/Twin Cities	MN	6,682	VC
Univ of New Orleans	LA	5,468	C
Univ of Okla	OK	5,427	VC
Univ of Texas at El Paso	TX	3,160	LC
Univ of the Pacific	CA	21,100	C
Univ of Utah	UT	5,975	C
Univ of Wyoming	WY	4,991	NC
Virginia Polytechnic Inst and State Univ	VA	6,828	C
Washington and Lee Univ	VA	17,735	MC
Wright State Univ	OH	6,896	C

GEOSCIENCE

School	ST	$IS	SR
Albion College	MI	18,264	VC
Hobart and William Smith Colleges	NY	23,925	VC
Indiana Univ of Penn	PA	6,373	C
Montclair State College	NJ	7,539	C
Penn State Univ/Univ Park Campus	PA	8,752	HC
Stanford Univ	CA	24,310	MC
SUNY/College at Geneseo	NY	6,949	HC
Susquehanna Univ	PA	19,950	VC
Texas Tech Univ	TX	6,008	C
Univ of Arizona	AZ	5,808	C
Univ of Notre Dame	IN	20,150	MC
Univ of Okla	OK	5,427	VC
Univ of the District of Columbia	DC	974	NC
Univ of Tulsa	OK	13,795	VC
Univ of Wisc/Milwaukee	WI	6,165	C

GERMAN

School	ST	$IS	SR
Abilene Christian Univ	TX	10,460	NC
Adrian College	MI	14,340	C
Agnes Scott College	GA	17,135	VC
Albion College	MI	18,264	VC
Allegheny College	PA	21,020	VC
Alma College	MI	16,375	VC+
American Univ	DC	21,230	VC+
Amherst College	MA	24,152	MC
Anderson Univ	IN	12,920	C
Andrews Univ	MI	14,952	NC
Aquinas College	MI	14,526	C
Arizona State Univ Main Campus	AZ	6,444	C
Auburn Univ	AL	5,823	C+
Augsburg College	MN	15,608	C
Augustana College	IL	16,959	VC
Austin College	TX	14,999	VC
Austin Peay State Univ	TN	4,350	C
Baker Univ	KS	12,284	C
Baldwin-Wallace College	OH	15,210	C
Ball State Univ	IN	6,032	LC
Bates College	ME	23,990	MC
Baylor Univ	TX	10,990	C+
Beloit College	WI	18,950	VC+
Bemidji State Univ	MN	5,188	C
Bennington College	VT	24,850	VC+
Berea College	KY	2,883	VC+
Berry College	GA	11,990	VC
Bethany College	WV	18,300	C+
Bethel College	KS	11,530	C
Birmingham-Southern College	AL	15,154	VC+
Bloomsburg Univ of Penn	PA	6,312	C+
Boston College	MA	22,706	MC
Boston Univ	MA	24,130	HC
Bowdoin College	ME	24,155	MC
Bowling Green State Univ	OH	6,701	C
Bradley Univ	IL	14,718	C+
Brandeis Univ	MA	25,585	HC
Bridgewater College	VA	15,300	C
Brigham Young Univ	UT	5,625	HC
Brown Univ	RI	26,104	MC
Bryn Mawr College	PA	24,110	MC
Bucknell Univ	PA	22,320	HC
Butler Univ	IN	16,210	C
Calif Lutheran Univ	CA	17,240	C
Cal State/Chico	CA	6,146	C
Cal State/Fresno	CA	5,747	C
Cal State/Fullerton	CA	4,850	LC
Cal State/Hayward	CA	5,495	C
Cal State/Northridge	CA	7,122	LC
Cal State/Sacramento	CA	6,387	C
Cal State/Stanislaus	CA	6,799	C
Calif Univ of Penn	PA	7,370	C
Calvin College	MI	13,020	VC
Canisius College	NY	15,510	C
Carleton College	MN	22,155	HC
Carnegie Mellon Univ	PA	22,560	HC+
Carroll College	WI	15,490	C
Carson-Newman College	TN	11,250	C
Carthage College	WI	15,995	C
Case Western Reserve Univ	OH	19,910	HC
Catholic Univ of America	DC	18,856	C
Cedar Crest College	PA	18,930	C
Central College	IA	14,025	VC
Central Conn State Univ	CT	7,108	C
Central Methodist College	MO	11,410	C
Central Mich Univ	MI	6,737	LC
Central Missouri State Univ	MO	5,138	LC
Central Washington Univ	WA	5,644	C
Centre College	KY	15,850	VC+
Chestnut Hill College	PA	14,525	C
Christopher Newport Univ	VA	3,196	LC
CUNY/Brooklyn College	NY	2,450	VC
CUNY/Herbert H. Lehman College	NY	2,542	C
CUNY/Hunter College	NY	4,101	VC
CUNY/Queens College	NY	2,631	C
Claremont McKenna College	CA	22,150	MC
Clarion Univ of Penn	PA	6,518	C
Clark Univ	MA	21,400	VC
Clemson Univ	SC	6,564	VC
Cleveland State Univ	OH	7,287	NC
Coe College	IA	17,085	VC
Colby College	ME	24,230	HC
Colgate Univ	NY	24,020	HC
College of Charleston	SC	6,250	C
College of St Benedict	MN	15,468	VC
College of the Holy Cross	MA	23,850	HC
College of William and Mary	VA	8,602	MC
College of Wooster	OH	19,875	VC
Colo College	CO	20,038	HC
Colo State Univ	CO	6,566	VC
Columbia Univ/Barnard College	NY	25,492	HC
Columbia Univ/Columbia College	NY	26,757	MC
Concordia College/Moorhead	MN	12,750	C
Conn College	CT	24,160	HC
Cornell College	IA	18,425	VC
Cornell Univ	NY	13,445	MC
Creighton Univ	NE	14,432	VC
Dana College	NE	11,910	C
Dartmouth College	NH	24,354	MC
David Lipscomb Univ	TN	7,865	VC
Davidson College	NC	21,037	MC
Denison Univ	OH	21,150	VC+
DePaul Univ	IL	15,535	VC
DePauw Univ	IN	18,530	VC
Dickinson College	PA	22,705	HC
Dillard Univ	LA	9,950	C
Doane College	NE	12,220	C
Drake Univ	IA	17,195	VC
Drew Univ/College of Liberal Arts	NJ	23,406	HC
Drury College	MO	12,140	VC
Duke Univ	NC	21,271	MC
Duquesne Univ	PA	16,434	VC
Earlham College	IN	19,383	VC
East Carolina Univ	NC	4,498	C
East Stroudsburg Univ	PA	6,886	C
East Texas State Univ	TX	4,572	LC
Eastern Illinois Univ	IL	5,548	C
Eastern Kentucky Univ	KY	4,840	NC
Eastern Mennonite College	VA	12,700	C
Eastern Mich Univ	MI	6,749	C
Eastern Montana College	MT	5,165	LC
Eastern Washington Univ	WA	5,439	LC
Eckerd College	FL	18,855	VC
Edinboro Univ of Penn	PA	7,181	C
Elizabethtown College	PA	17,850	VC
Elmhurst College	IL	12,536	C
Elmira College	NY	18,450	C
Emory and Henry College	VA	12,776	C
Emory Univ	GA	21,930	HC
Fairfield Univ	CT	20,460	VC

School	ST	$IS	SR
Florida Atlantic Univ	FL	5,525	C
Florida International Univ	FL	4,191	VC
Florida Southern College	FL	12,260	C
Florida State Univ	FL	5,814	VC
Fordham Univ/Fordham College	NY	19,875	VC
Franklin and Marshall College	PA	23,655	HC
Furman Univ	SC	16,557	VC
Gallaudet Univ	DC	9,850	SP
George Mason Univ	VA	8,728	C
George Washington Univ	DC	22,470	HC
Georgetown College	KY	10,990	C
Georgetown Univ	DC	24,410	MC
Georgia Southern Univ	GA	4,988	LC
Gettysburg College	PA	22,960	HC
Gonzaga Univ	WA	16,350	VC
Goshen College	IN	12,360	C
Grace College	IN	12,120	C
Graceland College	IA	11,600	C
Grinnell College	IA	20,680	HC+
Guilford College	NC	17,680	C
Gustavus Adolphus College	MN	15,935	VC
Hamilton College	NY	23,500	HC
Hampden-Sydney College	VA	17,372	C+
Hanover College	IN	10,950	VC
Hardin-Simmons Univ	TX	9,080	C
Harvard Univ/Harvard and Radcliffe Colleges	MA	24,880	MC
Hastings College	NE	12,426	C
Haverford College	PA	23,950	MC
Heidelberg College	OH	17,160	C
Hendrix College	AR	11,670	C
Hillsdale College	MI	15,110	VC
Hiram College	OH	18,340	VC
Hobart and William Smith Colleges	NY	23,925	VC
Hollins College	VA	18,484	C
Hood College	MD	19,010	VC
Hope College	MI	15,698	C+
Howard Univ	DC	11,680	C
Humboldt State Univ	CA	5,676	C
Idaho State Univ	ID	4,442	C
Illinois College	IL	11,200	C
Illinois State Univ	IL	6,413	C
Illinois Wesleyan Univ	IL	18,590	HC+
Immaculata College	PA	14,620	C
Indiana State Univ	IN	6,210	C
Indiana Univ Bloomington	IN	6,495	VC
Indiana Univ of Penn	PA	6,373	C
Indiana Univ-Purdue Univ at Fort Wayne	IN	2,500	LC
Indiana Univ-Purdue Univ at Indianapolis	IN	5,862	LC
Indiana Univ/South Bend	IN	2,141	LC
Iowa State Univ	IA	5,456	C
Ithaca College	NY	19,679	C
James Madison Univ	VA	8,198	HC
John Carroll Univ	OH	16,510	C
Johns Hopkins Univ	MD	24,360	MC
Juniata College	PA	18,390	C+
Kalamazoo College	MI	19,974	HC
Kansas State Univ	KS	4,816	NC
Kent State Univ	OH	6,740	LC
Kenyon College	OH	22,430	HC+
Knox College	IL	18,990	VC
Kutztown Univ	PA	6,528	C
La Salle Univ	PA	16,940	VC
Lafayette College	PA	23,450	HC
Lake Erie College	OH	13,700	C
Lake Forest College	IL	19,960	VC
Lakeland College	WI	12,845	LC
Lawrence Univ	WI	19,986	HC+
Lebanon Valley College of Penn	PA	18,300	C
Lee College	TN	7,894	LC
Lehigh Univ	PA	23,250	HC
Lenoir-Rhyne College	NC	14,068	C
Lewis and Clark College	OR	19,980	VC
Linfield College	OR	16,670	VC
Lock Haven Univ of Penn	PA	7,128	C
LIU/C. W. Post Campus	NY	16,870	C
Longwood College	VA	7,800	C
Louisiana State Univ and A&M College	LA	5,605	C
Loyola College	MD	18,035	VC
Loyola Univ of Chicago	IL	15,880	C+
Loyola Univ/New Orleans	LA	15,660	C+
Luther College	IA	15,900	VC
Lycoming College	PA	17,200	LC
Lynchburg College	VA	17,000	C
Macalester College	MN	19,710	HC
Manchester College	IN	13,240	LC
Manhattanville College	NY	20,450	LC
Mansfield Univ	PA	6,348	C
Marian College	IN	12,936	C
Marlboro College	VT	23,305	C+
Marquette Univ	WI	16,114	VC
Marshall Univ	WV	5,762	LC
Mary Washington College	VA	7,910	HC
McPherson College	KS	11,360	VC
Mercer Univ	GA	15,123	C
Messiah College	PA	14,664	VC
Miami Univ	OH	8,066	VC
Mich State Univ	MI	7,842	C
Middle Tenn State Univ	TN	3,857	C
Middlebury College	VT	24,400	MC
Millersville Univ of Penn	PA	7,370	VC
Mills College	CA	20,848	VC
Minot State Univ	ND	3,748	NC
Montclair State College	NJ	7,539	C+
Moorhead State Univ	MN	5,076	C
Moravian College	PA	18,960	VC
Morehouse College	GA	13,224	LC
Mount Holyoke College	MA	23,630	VC
Mount Mary College	WI	10,920	C
Mount St Mary's College	MD	17,825	LC
Muhlenberg College	PA	20,795	VC
Murray State Univ	KY	4,702	C
Muskingum College	OH	16,650	C
Nazareth College of Rochester	NY	15,310	C+
Nebr Wesleyan Univ	NE	12,240	C
New College of the Univ of South Florida	FL	5,697	MC
New Mexico State Univ	NM	4,844	LC
New York Univ	NY	24,705	VC+
North Central College	IL	15,498	VC
N Dak State Univ of Agriculture and Applied Science	ND	4,774	VC
North Park College	IL	14,310	C
Northeast Missouri State Univ	MO	5,654	VC+
Northeastern Univ	MA	19,851	C
Northern Illinois Univ	IL	6,408	C
Northern Mich Univ	MI	6,350	C
Northern State Univ	SD	4,186	LC
Northwestern Univ	IL	21,093	MC
Oakland Univ	MI	6,714	VC
Oberlin College	OH	24,570	HC+
Occidental College	CA	21,792	HC
Ohio State Univ	OH	7,218	LC
Ohio Wesleyan Univ	OH	21,108	VC+
Okla Baptist Univ	OK	8,486	C
Okla City Univ	OK	9,840	C
Okla State Univ	OK	5,086	VC
Old Dominion Univ	VA	8,317	C
Oral Roberts Univ	OK	10,607	C+
Oregon State Univ	OR	6,175	C
Pacific Lutheran Univ	WA	15,998	VC
Pacific Univ	OR	17,869	C
Penn State Univ/Univ Park Campus	PA	8,752	HC
Pepperdine Univ	CA	23,720	VC
Phillips Univ	OK	12,744	C
Pitzer College	CA	23,780	HC
Pomona College	CA	23,820	MC
Portland State Univ	OR	7,191	C
Presbyterian College	SC	15,400	VC
Principia College	IL	17,799	C
Purdue Univ/Calumet	IN	2,374	NC
Purdue Univ/West Lafayette	IN	6,636	C
Randolph-Macon College	VA	16,980	C
Randolph-Macon Woman's College	VA	19,100	C
Reed College	OR	24,480	HC+
Regis College	MA	17,450	C
Rhodes College	TN	19,624	HC
Rice Univ	TX	15,110	MC
Rider College	NJ	18,160	C
Ripon College	WI	18,320	C+
Rockford College	IL	15,300	C
Rollins College	FL	20,875	VC
Rosary College	IL	15,040	C
Rosemont College	PA	16,775	C
Rutgers Univ/Camden College of A&S	NJ	8,652	VC
Rutgers Univ/Douglass College	NJ	8,795	VC
Rutgers Univ/Livingston College	NJ	8,877	VC
Rutgers Univ/Newark College of A&S	NJ	8,645	C
Rutgers Univ/Rutgers College	NJ	8,841	HC+
Rutgers Univ/Univ College—Camden	NJ	3,506	C
Rutgers Univ/Univ College—New Brunswick	NJ	0	LC
St Ambrose Univ	IA	13,380	C
St Bonaventure Univ	NY	14,762	C
St John Fisher College	NY	15,415	C
St John's Univ	MN	15,364	C
St John's Univ	NY	8,980	C+
St Joseph's Univ	PA	17,800	VC
St Lawrence Univ	NY	23,420	VC
St Louis Univ	MO	15,522	VC
St Mary's Univ	TX	12,064	C
St Norbert College	WI	15,710	VC
St Olaf College	MN	17,200	HC
Salem College	NC	16,025	C
Sam Houston State Univ	TX	4,506	C
Samford Univ	AL	11,400	VC
San Francisco State Univ	CA	7,292	LC
San Jose State Univ	CA	6,680	LC
Santa Clara Univ	CA	18,783	VC
Sarah Lawrence College	NY	24,975	HC
Scripps College	CA	23,600	HC
Seattle Univ	WA	16,590	C
Shippensburg Univ of Penn	PA	7,052	C
Simpson College	IA	14,635	VC
Skidmore College	NY	23,230	HC
Slippery Rock Univ	PA	6,803	C
Sonoma State Univ	CA	6,996	LC
S Dak State Univ	SD	4,562	C
Southern College of Seventh-day Adventists	TN	11,348	NC
Southern Conn State Univ	CT	7,532	C
Southern Illinois Univ at Edwardsville	IL	6,097	LC
Southern Methodist Univ	TX	18,520	VC
Southern Nazarene Univ	OK	9,206	NC
Southern Utah Univ	UT	4,104	LC
Southwest Missouri State Univ	MO	4,956	C
Southwest Texas State Univ	TX	5,124	C
Southwestern Univ	TX	15,484	HC
SUNY at Albany	NY	7,059	VC
SUNY at Binghamton	NY	7,921	HC
SUNY at Buffalo	NY	7,896	VC
SUNY at Stony Brook	NY	7,658	VC
SUNY/College at Fredonia	NY	7,159	VC
SUNY/College at New Paltz	NY	6,890	VC
SUNY/College at Oswego	NY	7,330	VC
Stetson Univ	FL	16,435	VC
Susquehanna Univ	PA	19,950	VC
Swarthmore College	PA	24,136	MC
Syracuse Univ	NY	21,305	HC
Teikyo Westmar Univ	IA	15,920	C
Tenn Tech Univ	TN	5,190	C
Texas A&M Univ	TX	5,382	VC
Texas Lutheran College	TX	10,710	C
Texas Tech Univ	TX	6,008	C
The Citadel	SC	6,619	C
The Univ of New Mexico	NM	5,304	C
Towson State Univ	MD	7,452	C
Trinity College	CT	24,120	HC
Trinity Univ	TX	16,670	HC
Tufts Univ	MA	24,962	MC
Tulane Univ	LA	24,540	HC
Univ of Akron	OH	6,699	NC
Univ of Alabama	AL	5,702	C
Univ of Alabama at Birmingham	AL	7,533	C
Univ of Alabama at Huntsville	AL	5,868	VC
Univ of Alaska Fairbanks	AK	4,718	C
Univ of Arizona	AZ	5,808	C
Univ of Arkansas at Fayetteville	AR	5,046	C
Univ of Calif at Berkeley	CA	9,962	HC+
Univ of Calif at Davis	CA	9,534	VC
Univ of Calif at Los Angeles	CA	8,959	HC
Univ of Calif at Santa Barbara	CA	9,460	C
Univ of Calif at Santa Cruz	CA	9,060	VC
Univ of Calif, Riverside	CA	9,178	C
Univ of Calif, San Diego	CA	10,028	VC+
Univ of Calif/Irvine	CA	12,680	VC
Univ of Central Okla	OK	3,647	C
Univ of Chicago	IL	24,517	MC
Univ of Cincinnati	OH	7,989	C
Univ of Colo at Boulder	CO	6,410	VC
Univ of Colo at Denver	CO	1,955	VC
Univ of Conn	CT	9,168	C
Univ of Dallas	TX	14,983	VC
Univ of Dayton	OH	15,120	C+
Univ of Delaware	DE	8,013	VC
Univ of Denver	CO	19,290	C+
Univ of Evansville	IN	15,300	VC
Univ of Findlay	OH	15,764	C
Univ of Florida	FL	5,850	HC
Univ of Hawaii at Manoa	HI	5,626	C
Univ of Houston	TX	5,215	C
Univ of Idaho	ID	4,830	C
Univ of Illinois at Chicago	IL	8,443	C
Univ of Indianapolis	IN	14,510	C
Univ of Iowa	IA	5,658	VC
Univ of Kansas	KS	5,200	NC
Univ of Kentucky	KY	5,152	VC
Univ of La Verne	CA	17,400	C
Univ of Louisville	KY	5,948	C
Univ of Maine	ME	7,990	C
Univ of Maryland/Baltimore County	MD	7,746	VC
Univ of Maryland/College Park	MD	8,182	VC
Univ of Mass/Amherst	MA	9,364	C
Univ of Mass/Boston	MA	4,253	C
Univ of Memphis	TN	3,476	C
Univ of Miami	FL	22,107	VC
Univ of Mich/Ann Arbor	MI	9,428	HC+
Univ of Minn/Duluth	MN	6,512	C
Univ of Minn/Morris	MN	6,825	HC
Univ of Minn/Twin Cities	MN	6,682	VC
Univ of Miss	MS	5,756	C
Univ of Missouri/Columbia	MO	6,254	HC
Univ of Missouri/St. Louis	MO	6,378	C
Univ of Montana	MT	5,529	C
Univ of Nebr at Kearney	NE	4,308	LC
Univ of Nebr at Omaha	NE	1,889	LC
Univ of Nebr-Lincoln	NE	5,278	LC
Univ of Nevada/Las Vegas	NV	6,405	C
Univ of Nevada/Reno	NV	5,735	C
Univ of New Hampshire	NH	8,242	C
Univ of North Alabama	AL	4,236	NC
Univ of N Car at Asheville	NC	4,791	VC
Univ of N Car at Chapel Hill	NC	5,330	HC
Univ of N Car at Charlotte	NC	4,597	C
Univ of N Car at Greensboro	NC	5,192	C
Univ of N Dak	ND	4,902	NC
Univ of North Texas	TX	4,853	C
Univ of Northern Colo	CO	6,008	C
Univ of Northern Iowa	IA	5,137	C
Univ of Notre Dame	IN	20,150	MC
Univ of Okla	OK	5,427	VC
Univ of Oregon	OR	6,466	VC
Univ of Penn	PA	24,238	MC
Univ of Pittsburgh	PA	9,472	C
Univ of Portland	OR	15,564	C
Univ of Puget Sound	WA	19,520	HC
Univ of Redlands	CA	22,059	VC
Univ of Rhode Island	RI	9,205	C
Univ of Richmond	VA	16,700	HC
Univ of Rochester	NY	23,696	HC
Univ of St Thomas	MN	15,785	C+
Univ of Scranton	PA	17,071	VC
Univ of South Alabama	AL	5,451	C
Univ of S Car	SC	6,158	C
Univ of S Dak	SD	4,722	C
Univ of South Florida	FL	5,475	C+
Univ of Southern Indiana	IN	3,720	NC
Univ of Tenn/Knoxville	TN	5,668	C
Univ of Texas at Arlington	TX	5,549	LC
Univ of Texas at Austin	TX	5,160	VC
Univ of Texas at San Antonio	TX	6,420	C
Univ of the Pacific	CA	21,100	C
Univ of the South	TN	18,830	HC
Univ of Toledo	OH	6,636	NC
Univ of Utah	UT	5,975	C
Univ of Vermont	VT	10,776	C+
Univ of Virginia	VA	7,964	MC
Univ of Wisc/Eau Claire	WI	4,647	C
Univ of Wisc/Green Bay	WI	4,904	C
Univ of Wisc/Madison	WI	6,400	HC
Univ of Wisc/Milwaukee	WI	6,165	C
Univ of Wisc/Oshkosh	WI	4,240	C
Univ of Wisc/Parkside	WI	5,247	
Univ of Wisc/Platteville	WI	4,830	C
Univ of Wisc/River Falls	WI	4,655	C
Univ of Wisc/Stevens Point	WI	5,047	C+
Univ of Wisc/Whitewater	WI	4,700	C
Univ of Wyoming	WY	4,991	NC
Ursinus College	PA	19,165	VC
Utah State Univ	UT	4,683	C
Valparaiso Univ	IN	14,810	VC
Vanderbilt Univ	TN	23,422	HC+
Villanova Univ	PA	21,400	HC
Virginia Polytechnic Inst and State Univ	VA	6,828	C
Wabash College	IN	16,250	VC
Wake Forest Univ	NC	17,280	MC
Walla Walla College	WA	13,215	C
Washburn Univ of Topeka	KS	5,802	NC
Washington and Jefferson College	PA	19,360	C
Washington and Lee Univ	VA	17,735	MC
Washington College	MD	19,270	C+
Washington State Univ	WA	6,364	C
Washington Univ	MO	23,507	HC
Wayne State College	NE	4,260	NC
Wayne State Univ	MI	2,680	C
Weber State Univ	UT	4,398	C
Wellesley College	MA	23,815	MC
Wells College	NY	19,460	C+
Wesleyan Univ	CT	23,770	MC
West Chester Univ of Penn	PA	7,492	C
Western Carolina Univ	NC	3,811	C
Western Illinois Univ	IL	5,241	LC
Western Kentucky Univ	KY	4,808	C
Western Maryland College	MD	18,990	C
Western Mich Univ	MI	6,820	C
Western Washington Univ	WA	6,077	VC
Westminster College	PA	15,200	C
Wheaton College	IL	14,710	HC
Wheaton College	MA	23,840	C+
Whitman College	WA	20,595	HC
Wichita State Univ	KS	5,068	NC
Wilkes Univ	PA	15,728	LC
Willamette Univ	OR	17,995	VC
William Woods Univ	MO	14,025	LC
Williams College	MA	24,390	MC
Winona State Univ	MN	5,200	VC
Wittenberg Univ	OH	19,998	VC
Wofford College	SC	15,360	VC
Wright State Univ	OH	6,896	LC
Xavier Univ	OH	15,710	C+
Yale Univ	CT	25,110	MC
Youngstown State Univ	OH	6,447	LC

GERMANIC LANGUAGES AND LITERATURE

School	ST	$IS	SR
Columbia Univ/Columbia College	NY	26,757	MC
Gonzaga Univ	WA	16,350	VC
Princeton Univ	NJ	24,650	MC
Scripps College	CA	23,600	HC
Smith College	MA	24,236	HC
Temple Univ	PA	10,281	C
Univ of Washington	WA	6,618	VC

GERMAN AREA STUDIES

School	ST	$IS	SR
Case Western Reserve Univ	OH	19,910	HC
Knox College	IL	18,990	VC
Univ of the South	TN	18,830	HC

GERONTOLOGY

School	ST	$IS	SR
Alfred Univ	NY	21,054	VC+
Audrey Cohen College	NY	11,184	LC
Black Hills State Univ	SD	4,831	NC
Bowling Green State Univ	OH	6,701	C
Calif Univ of Penn	PA	7,370	C
Case Western Reserve Univ	OH	19,910	HC
College of Mount St Joseph	OH	13,272	C
Greenville College	IL	14,190	C
Gwynedd-Mercy College	PA	15,450	C
Hampton Univ	VA	10,706	C
Kent State Univ	OH	6,740	LC
King's College	PA	15,420	C
Langston Univ	OK	2,907	LC
Lourdes College	OH	6,410	LC
Madonna Univ	MI	8,546	C
Northern Mich Univ	MI	6,350	C
Pontifical Catholic Univ of PR/Ponce	PR	5,807	
Quinnipiac College	CT	17,600	C+
Roberts Wesleyan College	NY	13,317	C
Shaw Univ	NC	8,936	C+
Sojourner-Douglass College	MD	5,265	LC
Southeastern Okla State Univ	OK	3,594	C
Southern Nazarene Univ	OK	9,206	NC
Southern Vermont College	VT	12,974	C
Southwest Missouri State Univ	MO	4,956	C
Springfield College	MA	15,200	LC
SUNY/College at Oneonta	NY	7,878	C
Stephen F. Austin State Univ	TX	5,117	C
Univ of Arkansas at Pine Bluff	AR	3,978	LC
Univ of Mass/Boston	MA	4,253	C
Univ of North Texas	TX	4,853	C
Univ of Northern Colo	CO	6,008	C
Univ of Scranton	PA	17,071	VC
Wagner College	NY	17,950	C
Weber State Univ	UT	4,398	C

GLASS

School	ST	$IS	SR
Center for Creative Studies/College of Art and Design	MI	15,330	SP
Ohio State Univ	OH	7,218	LC
Rhode Island School of Design	RI	22,315	SP

GRAPHIC ARTS TECHNOLOGY

School	ST	$IS	SR
Bridgewater State College	MA	7,518	C
Calif Univ of Penn	PA	7,370	C
Central Missouri State Univ	MO	5,138	LC
College of the Ozarks	MO	2,000	VC+
Idaho State Univ	ID	4,442	C
Purdue Univ/West Lafayette	IN	6,636	C

GRAPHIC DESIGN

School	ST	$IS	SR
Anderson Univ	IN	12,920	C
Art Academy of Cincinnati	OH	8,820	SP
Art Center College of Design	CA	13,550	SP
Art Inst of Southern Calif	CA	16,000	SP
Atlanta College of Art	GA	12,495	SP
Avila College	MO	12,130	C
Ball State Univ	IN	6,032	LC
Beaver College	PA	17,660	C
Boston Univ	MA	24,130	HC
Bradley Univ	IL	14,718	C+
Brescia College	KY	9,800	C
Brigham Young Univ	UT	5,625	HC
Calif Polytechnic State Univ	CA	6,980	VC+
Cal State/Fresno	CA	5,747	C
Cazenovia College	NY	14,655	LC
Center for Creative Studies/College of Art and Design	MI	15,330	SP
Cleveland Inst of Art	OH	15,630	SP
Coker College	SC	13,790	C
College of Notre Dame	CA	16,480	C
College of Notre Dame of Maryland	MD	16,050	C
College of St Rose	NY	14,452	C
Cooper Union for the Advancement of Science and Art	NY	8,430	MC
Corcoran School of Art	DC	14,480	SP
Daemen College	NY	13,020	LC
Dana College	NE	11,910	C
Drake Univ	IA	17,195	VC
Eastern Mich Univ	MI	6,749	C
Eastern Washington Univ	WA	5,439	LC
Edinboro Univ of Penn	PA	7,181	C
Escuela de Artes Plasticas	PR	4,024	
Fashion Inst of Tech/SUNY	NY	7,135	SP
Frostburg State Univ	MD	6,940	C
Grace College	IN	12,120	C
Graceland College	IA	11,600	C
Grand Canyon Univ	AZ	9,680	VC
Indiana Univ-Purdue Univ at Indianapolis	IN	5,862	LC
Iowa State Univ	IA	5,456	C
Kansas Newman College	KS	10,640	C
Kendall College of Art and Design	MI	9,600	SP
Kent State Univ	OH	6,740	LC
La Roche College	PA	12,977	LC
LIU/Southampton Campus	NY	17,280	C
Louisiana State Univ and A&M College	LA	5,605	C
Lynn Univ	FL	18,300	C
Maine College of Art	ME	15,673	SP
Maryland Inst, College of Art	MD	18,420	SP
Marymount Univ	VA	15,930	C
Mercy College	NY	11,180	NC
Mercyhurst College	PA	13,488	C
Milwaukee Inst of Art and Design	WI	9,800	SP
Miss Univ for Women	MS	4,456	LC
Moore College of Art and Design	PA	17,947	SP
Moravian College	PA	18,960	VC
Mount Ida College	MA	16,700	LC
New Mexico Highlands Univ	NM	3,772	C
N Car State Univ	NC	4,984	VC
Northern Kentucky Univ	KY	4,620	NC
Northern Mich Univ	MI	6,350	C
Notre Dame College of Ohio	OH	11,370	C
Ohio Northern Univ	OH	18,660	VC
Otis College of Art and Design	CA	16,686	SP
Pacific Northwest College of Art	OR	7,700	SP
Paier College of Art	CT	10,120	SP
Philadelphia College of Textiles and Science	PA	15,896	C
Plymouth State College	NH	7,166	C
Point Loma Nazarene College	CA	13,532	C
Rhode Island School of Design	RI	22,315	SP
Ringling School of Art and Design	FL	15,750	SP
Sacred Heart Univ	CT	16,350	C
St Vincent College	PA	13,934	LC
Sam Houston State Univ	TX	4,506	C
Savannah College of Art and Design	GA	14,280	SP
School of Visual Arts	NY	17,120	SP
Simmons College	MA	22,534	C
S Dak State Univ	SD	4,562	C
Texas Christian Univ	TX	12,180	C
Univ of Conn	CT	9,168	C
Univ of Evansville	IN	15,300	VC
Univ of Florida	FL	5,850	HC
Univ of Illinois at Chicago	IL	8,443	C
Univ of Illinois at Urbana-Champaign	IL	7,764	HC
Univ of Mass Dartmouth	MA	8,158	C
Univ of Miami	FL	22,107	VC
Univ of Mich/Ann Arbor	MI	9,428	HC+
Univ of New Haven	CT	14,980	C
Univ of Northern Colo	CO	6,008	C
Univ of Northern Iowa	IA	5,137	C
Univ of Tenn/Knoxville	TN	5,668	C
Univ of Texas at El Paso	TX	3,160	LC
Univ of the Arts	PA	16,150	SP
Univ of the Pacific	CA	21,100	C
Univ of Washington	WA	6,618	VC
Wayne State College	NE	4,260	NC
West Liberty State College	WV	4,690	LC
West Texas A&M Univ	TX	4,224	C
Western Conn State Univ	CT	6,622	C
Woodbury Univ	CA	17,620	LC

GRAPHIC AND PRINTING PRODUCTION

School	ST	$IS	SR
CUNY/New York City Technical College	NY	2,405	NC
Rochester Inst of Tech	NY	18,954	VC

GREEK

School	ST	$IS	SR
Abilene Christian Univ	TX	10,460	NC
Boston College	MA	22,706	MC
Brigham Young Univ	UT	5,625	HC
Bryn Mawr College	PA	24,110	MC
Bucknell Univ	PA	22,320	HC
Butler Univ	IN	16,210	C
Calvin College	MI	13,020	VC
Carleton College	MN	22,155	HC
Catholic Univ of America	DC	18,856	C
CUNY/Brooklyn College	NY	2,450	VC
CUNY/City College	NY	2,543	VC
CUNY/Herbert H. Lehman College	NY	2,542	C
CUNY/Hunter College	NY	4,101	VC
CUNY/Queens College	NY	2,631	C
Colgate Univ	NY	24,020	HC
College of the Holy Cross	MA	23,850	HC
Columbia Univ/Barnard College	NY	25,492	HC
Columbia Univ/Columbia College	NY	26,757	MC
Cornell Univ	NY	13,445	MC
Creighton Univ	NE	14,432	VC
Dartmouth College	NH	24,354	MC
Dickinson College	PA	22,705	HC
Duke Univ	NC	21,271	MC
Duquesne Univ	PA	16,434	VC
Emory Univ	GA	21,930	HC
Evergreen State College	WA	6,306	C
Florida State Univ	FL	5,814	VC
Fordham Univ/Fordham College	NY	19,875	VC
Franklin and Marshall College	PA	23,655	HC
Furman Univ	SC	16,557	VC
Gettysburg College	PA	22,960	HC
Gonzaga Univ	WA	16,350	VC
Hampden-Sydney College	VA	17,372	C+
Harvard Univ/Harvard and Radcliffe Colleges	MA	24,880	MC
Hellenic College/Holy Cross Greek Orthodox School of Theology	MA	10,295	NC
Howard Univ	DC	11,680	C
John Carroll Univ	OH	16,510	C
Kenyon College	OH	22,430	HC+
Loyola Marymount Univ	CA	18,560	C
Loyola Univ of Chicago	IL	15,880	C+
Luther College	IA	15,900	VC
Marlboro College	VT	23,305	C+
Mercer Univ	GA	15,123	C
Miami Univ	OH	8,066	VC
Millersville Univ of Penn	PA	7,370	VC
Monmouth College	IL	17,300	C+
Moravian College	PA	18,960	VC
Mount Holyoke College	MA	23,630	VC
Muhlenberg College	PA	20,795	VC
New York Univ	NY	24,705	VC+
Northwestern Univ	IL	21,093	MC
Randolph-Macon College	VA	16,980	C
Rutgers Univ/Douglass College	NJ	8,795	VC
Rutgers Univ/Livingston College	NJ	8,877	VC
Rutgers Univ/Univ College—New Brunswick	NJ	0	LC
St Louis Univ	MO	15,522	VC
St Mary's College of Calif	CA	18,848	VC
St Olaf College	MN	17,200	HC
Sarah Lawrence College	NY	24,975	HC
Scripps College	CA	23,600	HC
Smith College	MA	24,236	HC
SUNY at Albany	NY	7,059	VC
Susquehanna Univ	PA	19,950	VC
Swarthmore College	PA	24,136	MC
Temple Univ	PA	10,281	C
Tufts Univ	MA	24,962	MC
Tulane Univ	LA	24,540	HC
Univ of Arizona	AZ	5,808	C
Univ of Calif at Berkeley	CA	9,962	HC+
Univ of Calif at Davis	CA	9,534	VC
Univ of Calif at Los Angeles	CA	8,959	HC
Univ of Calif at Santa Barbara	CA	9,460	C
Univ of Iowa	IA	5,658	VC
Univ of Mich/Ann Arbor	MI	9,428	HC+
Univ of Minn/Twin Cities	MN	6,682	VC
Univ of Nebr-Lincoln	NE	5,278	LC
Univ of New Hampshire	NH	8,242	C
Univ of N Car at Chapel Hill	NC	5,330	HC
Univ of N Car at Greensboro	NC	5,192	C
Univ of Notre Dame	IN	20,150	MC
Univ of Oregon	OR	6,466	VC
Univ of Scranton	PA	17,071	VC
Univ of S Car	SC	6,158	C
Univ of S Dak	SD	4,722	C
Univ of South Florida	FL	5,475	C+
Univ of Tenn at Chattanooga	TN	5,375	C
Univ of Texas at Austin	TX	5,160	VC
Univ of the Pacific	CA	21,100	C
Univ of the South	TN	18,830	HC
Univ of Vermont	VT	10,776	C+
Univ of Wisc/Madison	WI	6,400	HC
Valparaiso Univ	IN	14,810	VC
Wabash College	IN	16,250	VC
Wayne State Univ	MI	2,680	C
Wellesley College	MA	23,815	MC
Wesleyan Univ	CT	23,770	MC

GREEK (CLASSICAL)

School	ST	$IS	SR
Agnes Scott College	GA	17,135	VC
Allegheny College	PA	21,020	VC
Boston Univ	MA	24,130	HC
College of Wooster	OH	19,875	VC
Rutgers Univ/Rutgers College	NJ	8,841	HC+
Univ of Mass/Boston	MA	4,253	C

GREEK (MODERN)

School	ST	$IS	SR
Boston Univ	MA	24,130	HC
Ohio State Univ	OH	7,218	LC

GUIDANCE EDUCATION

School	ST	$IS	SR
Angelo State Univ	TX	5,176	C
Auburn Univ	AL	5,823	C+
Calif Lutheran Univ	CA	17,240	C
Cal State/Chico	CA	6,146	C
Central Mich Univ	MI	6,737	LC
East Texas State Univ	TX	4,572	LC
Eastern Montana College	MT	5,165	LC
Eastern Washington Univ	WA	5,439	LC
Lenoir-Rhyne College	NC	14,068	C
Marshall Univ	WV	5,762	LC
McNeese State Univ	LA	4,543	NC
Middle Tenn State Univ	TN	3,857	C
Northwestern Okla State Univ	OK	3,424	C
Northwestern State Univ of Louisiana	LA	4,287	NC
Plymouth State College	NH	7,166	C
Prescott College	AZ	9,775	C
St Cloud State Univ	MN	5,015	C
S Car State Univ	SC	5,424	LC
Southern Arkansas Univ	AR	3,432	NC
Texas Southern Univ	TX	4,500	NC
Univ of Central Arkansas	AR	4,200	LC
Univ of Central Okla	OK	3,647	C
Univ of Cincinnati	OH	7,989	C
Univ of Detroit Mercy	MI	14,720	C
Univ of Guam	GU	4,139	NC
Univ of Missouri/Columbia	MO	6,254	HC
Univ of Nebr-Lincoln	NE	5,278	LC
Univ of Southern Miss	MS	4,542	C
Univ of Southwestern Louisiana	LA	3,968	NC
Valdosta State Univ	GA	4,670	LC
Westminster College	PA	15,200	C
Wichita State Univ	KS	5,068	NC

GUITAR

School	ST	$IS	SR
Boston Conservatory	MA	17,900	SP
Temple Univ	PA	10,281	C

HAWAIIAN

School	ST	$IS	SR
Univ of Hawaii at Manoa	HI	5,626	C

HAWAIIAN STUDIES

School	ST	$IS	SR
Univ of Hawaii at Hilo	HI	4,141	C

HEALTH

School	ST	$IS	SR
Aquinas College	MI	14,526	C
Azusa Pacific Univ	CA	15,034	C
Bloomsburg Univ of Penn	PA	6,312	C+
Boston Univ	MA	24,130	HC
Cal State/Northridge	CA	7,122	LC
Central College	IA	14,025	VC
Concordia College	NE	11,776	NC
Concordia College/Moorhead	MN	12,750	C
Cumberland College	KY	9,756	C
Eastern Oregon State College	OR	6,090	C
Hampton Univ	VA	10,706	C
Miami Univ	OH	8,066	VC
New Mexico Highlands Univ	NM	3,772	C
Oregon State Univ	OR	6,175	C
Southwestern Adventist College	TX	10,530	NC
Tarleton State Univ	TX	4,082	LC
Towson State Univ	MD	7,452	C
Wayne State College	NE	4,260	NC
West Chester Univ of Penn	PA	7,492	C
Youngstown State Univ	OH	6,447	LC

HEALTH CARE ADMINISTRATION

School	ST	$IS	SR
Albertus Magnus College	CT	16,280	LC
Alfred Univ	NY	21,054	VC+
Arkansas State Univ	AR	4,250	NC
Auburn Univ	AL	5,823	C+
Austin Peay State Univ	TN	4,350	C
Baker College	MI	6,971	NC
Beaver College	PA	17,660	C
Benedictine College	KS	12,830	C
Cal State/Northridge	CA	7,122	LC
City Univ	WA	6,400	NC
CUNY/Herbert H. Lehman College	NY	2,542	C
College of Great Falls	MT	6,230	NC
College of Mount St Joseph	OH	13,272	C
College of St Scholastica	MN	14,868	C
Concordia College	MI	13,660	C
Concordia College	OR	12,300	C
Concordia College/Moorhead	MN	12,750	C
Dana College	NE	11,910	C
Davis and Elkins College	WV	13,230	LC
Detroit College of Business	MI	5,184	NC
Dyke College	OH	5,200	C
Eastern Kentucky Univ	KY	4,840	NC
Eastern Washington Univ	WA	5,439	LC
Ferris State Univ	MI	7,160	NC
Florida Atlantic Univ	FL	5,525	C
Florida International Univ	FL	4,191	VC
Friends Univ	KS	11,205	C
Hastings College	NE	12,426	C
Idaho State Univ	ID	4,442	C
Illinois Benedictine College	IL	14,170	C
Illinois State Univ	IL	6,413	C
Indiana Univ-Purdue Univ at Indianapolis	IN	5,862	LC
Iona College	NY	16,310	C
Ithaca College	NY	19,679	C
Johnson and Wales Univ	RI	13,995	LC
King's College	PA	15,420	C
Knoxville College	TN	8,320	LC
Lake Erie College	OH	13,700	C
Langston Univ	OK	2,907	LC
LIU/C. W. Post Campus	NY	16,870	C
Lynn Univ	FL	18,300	C
Madonna Univ	MI	8,546	C
Marshall Univ	WV	5,762	LC
Marymount Univ	VA	15,930	C
Maryville Univ-St Louis	MO	12,900	VC
Marywood College	PA	14,890	C
Metropolitan State College of Denver	CO	1,751	NC
National-Louis Univ	IL	13,218	C
Ohio Dominican College	OH	11,820	LC
Oregon State Univ	OR	6,175	C
Penn State Univ/Univ Park Campus	PA	8,752	HC
Point Park College	PA	13,922	LC
Presentation College	SD	9,116	NC
Providence College	RI	19,750	VC
Quinnipiac College	CT	17,600	C+
Robert Morris College	PA	10,406	LC
St Francis College	NY	6,710	LC
St John's Univ	NY	8,980	C+
St Joseph's College	NY	7,322	C
St Joseph's Univ	PA	17,800	VC
St Peter's College	NJ	14,775	LC
Sojourner-Douglass College	MD	5,265	LC
Southern Univ at New Orleans	LA	1,452	NC
Southwestern Adventist College	TX	10,530	NC
Southwestern Okla State Univ	OK	3,312	C
Springfield College	MA	15,200	LC
SUNY/College at Cortland	NY	7,326	C+
Stonehill College	MA	17,481	VC
Temple Univ	PA	10,281	C
Univ of Alabama	AL	5,702	C
Univ of Arizona	AZ	5,808	C
Univ of Central Florida	FL	6,061	C+
Univ of Illinois at Chicago	IL	8,443	C
Univ of Kansas	KS	5,200	NC
Univ of Maryland/Univ College	MD	4,900	NC
Univ of Nevada/Las Vegas	NV	6,405	C
Univ of New England	ME	16,075	LC
Univ of New Hampshire	NH	8,242	C
Univ of New Haven	CT	14,980	C
Univ of Northern Colo	CO	6,008	C
Univ of Northern Iowa	IA	5,137	C
Univ of Scranton	PA	17,071	VC
Univ of S Dak	SD	4,722	C
Univ of Washington	WA	6,618	VC
Univ of Wisc/Eau Claire	WI	4,647	C
Univ of Wisc/Milwaukee	WI	6,165	C
Upper Iowa Univ	IA	11,900	C
Ursuline College	OH	13,180	LC
Viterbo College	WI	12,670	C
West Virginia Inst of Tech	WV	5,858	LC
Western Carolina Univ	NC	3,811	C
Western Kentucky Univ	KY	4,808	C
Wilberforce Univ	OH	10,408	C
York College of Penn	PA	8,345	C

HEALTH EDUCATION

School	ST	$IS	SR
Adrian College	MI	14,340	C
Albany State College	GA	4,481	LC
Arkansas Tech Univ	AR	4,200	NC
Auburn Univ	AL	5,823	C+
Augsburg College	MN	15,608	C
Augusta College	GA	1,452	C
Austin Peay State Univ	TN	4,350	C
Averett College	VA	13,610	LC
Baldwin-Wallace College	OH	15,210	LC
Ball State Univ	IN	6,032	LC
Baylor Univ	TX	10,990	C+
Bemidji State Univ	MN	5,188	C
Bethel College	MN	15,050	C
Bethel College	TN	9,736	LC
Black Hills State Univ	SD	4,831	NC
Bluffton College	OH	12,951	C
Bowling Green State Univ	OH	6,701	C
Brewton-Parker College	GA	6,828	NC
Briar Cliff College	IA	13,375	C
Bridgewater State College	MA	7,518	C
Calif Lutheran Univ	CA	17,240	C
Cal State/Chico	CA	6,146	C
Cal State/Fresno	CA	5,747	C
Cal State/Long Beach	CA	6,057	LC
Cal State/Los Angeles	CA	4,940	VC
Cal State/Sacramento	CA	6,387	C
Cal State/San Bernardino	CA	6,055	LC
Cameron Univ	OK	3,686	LC
Capital Univ	OH	16,535	VC
Carson-Newman College	TN	11,250	C
Central Mich Univ	MI	6,737	LC
Central State Univ	OH	7,320	NC
Central Washington Univ	WA	5,644	C
Chadron State College	NE	4,091	NC
CUNY/City College	NY	2,543	VC
CUNY/Herbert H. Lehman College	NY	2,542	C
CUNY/Hunter College	NY	4,101	VC
CUNY/Queens College	NY	2,631	C
Cleveland State Univ	OH	7,287	NC
College of Mount St Vincent	NY	16,730	C
Concordia College/Moorhead	MN	12,750	C
Cumberland College	KY	9,756	C
Cumberland Univ	TN	8,650	C
Dakota State Univ	SD	4,374	LC
Davis and Elkins College	WV	13,230	LC
Delaware State College	DE	5,656	C
Delta State Univ	MS	3,964	LC
Dillard Univ	LA	9,950	C
East Central Univ	OK	3,558	C
East Tenn State Univ	TN	4,406	C
East Texas State Univ	TX	4,572	LC
Eastern College	PA	15,150	C+
Eastern Illinois Univ	IL	5,548	C
Eastern Kentucky Univ	KY	4,840	NC
Eastern Mich Univ	MI	6,749	C
Eastern Montana College	MT	5,165	LC
Eastern Washington Univ	WA	5,439	LC
Edinboro Univ of Penn	PA	7,181	C
Edward Waters College	FL	8,300	NC
Elon College	NC	12,290	LC
Emporia State Univ	KS	4,685	NC
Fairmont State College	WV	4,640	LC
Florida International Univ	FL	4,191	VC
Freed-Hardeman Univ	TN	8,585	VC
Friends Univ	KS	11,205	C
Gardner-Webb Univ	NC	11,950	LC
George Fox College	OR	15,640	LC
George Mason Univ	VA	8,728	C
Georgia College	GA	4,310	LC
Georgia Southern Univ	GA	4,988	LC
Georgia State Univ	GA	2,019	C
Gustavus Adolphus College	MN	15,935	VC
Hardin-Simmons Univ	TX	9,080	C
Hillsdale College	MI	15,110	VC
Idaho State Univ	ID	4,442	C
Illinois State Univ	IL	6,413	C
Indiana State Univ	IN	6,210	C
Indiana Univ of Penn	PA	6,373	C
Inter American Univ of PR/San German	PR	4,620	
Iowa State Univ	IA	5,456	C
Ithaca College	NY	19,679	C
Jackson State Univ	MS	4,996	LC
Jacksonville State Univ	AL	4,080	LC
Jersey City State College	NJ	7,797	LC
Johnson C. Smith Univ	NC	8,916	LC
Kean College of New Jersey	NJ	6,395	LC
Kennesaw State College	GA	1,553	C
Kent State Univ	OH	6,740	LC
Knoxville College	TN	8,320	LC
Lamar Univ	TX	3,798	C
Lambuth Univ	TN	8,395	C
LeMoyne-Owen College	TN	4,500	LC
Lenoir-Rhyne College	NC	14,068	C
Liberty Univ	VA	11,500	LC
Lincoln Memorial Univ	TN	8,218	C
Lincoln Univ	PA	0	LC
Linfield College	OR	16,670	VC
Livingston Univ	AL	3,979	C
Lock Haven Univ of Penn	PA	7,128	C
LIU/C. W. Post Campus	NY	16,870	C
Louisiana College	LA	7,518	VC
Louisiana Tech Univ	LA	4,284	C
Loyola Univ/New Orleans	LA	15,660	C+
Luther College	IA	15,900	VC
Manchester College	IN	13,240	LC
Manhattan College	NY	19,000	C
Mankato State Univ	MN	5,097	LC
Marshall Univ	WV	5,762	LC
McNeese State Univ	LA	4,543	NC
McPherson College	KS	11,360	VC
Messiah College	PA	14,664	VC
Miami Univ	OH	8,066	VC
Miss Valley State Univ	MS	4,089	NC
Montclair State College	NJ	7,539	C+
Moorhead State Univ	MN	5,076	C
Morehead State Univ	KY	4,600	LC
Morgan State Univ	MD	7,366	C+
Mount Union College	OH	15,850	C
Murray State Univ	KY	4,702	C
New York Inst of Tech/Old Westbury	NY	13,914	LC
Nicholls State Univ	LA	4,531	NC
Norfolk State Univ	VA	6,345	LC
N Car Central Univ	NC	4,347	LC
Northeastern State Univ	OK	5,250	C
Northeastern Univ	MA	19,851	C
Northern Arizona Univ	AZ	4,844	C
Northern Mich Univ	MI	6,350	C
Northern State Univ	SD	4,186	LC
Northwest Nazarene College	ID	11,750	C
Ohio Northern Univ	OH	18,660	VC
Ohio State Univ	OH	7,218	C
Ohio Univ	OH	7,341	C
Okla City Univ	OK	9,840	C
Okla State Univ	OK	5,086	VC
Olivet College	MI	14,000	C
Olivet Nazarene Univ	IL	11,976	C
Oral Roberts Univ	OK	10,607	C+
Oregon State Univ	OR	6,175	C
Ouachita Baptist Univ	AR	8,940	C
Penn State Univ/Univ Park Campus	PA	8,752	HC
Peru State College	NE	4,311	NC
Philander Smith College	AR	5,434	NC
Phillips Univ	OK	12,744	C
Plymouth State College	NH	7,166	C
Portland State Univ	OR	7,191	C
Purdue Univ/West Lafayette	IN	6,636	C
Rhode Island College	RI	7,901	LC
St Cloud State Univ	MN	5,015	C
St Francis College	IN	11,662	C
St Olaf College	MN	17,200	HC
Samford Univ	AL	11,400	VC
Shepherd College	WV	5,540	C
Simpson College	IA	14,635	VC
Slippery Rock Univ	PA	6,803	C
S Car State Univ	SC	5,424	LC
S Dak State Univ	SD	4,562	C
Southern Arkansas Univ	AR	3,432	NC
Southern Conn State Univ	CT	7,532	C
Southern Illinois Univ at Carbondale	IL	6,234	C
Southern Illinois Univ at Edwardsville	IL	6,097	LC
Southern Univ and A&M College	LA	4,920	NC
Southwest Missouri State Univ	MO	4,956	C
Southwest State Univ	MN	5,400	NC
Southwest Texas State Univ	TX	5,124	C
Southwestern College	KS	10,032	C
Southwestern Okla State Univ	OK	3,312	C
Springfield College	MA	15,200	LC
SUNY/College at Cortland	NY	7,326	C+
Stephen F. Austin State Univ	TX	5,117	C
Tabor College	KS	11,460	VC
Temple Univ	PA	10,281	C
Texas A&M Univ	TX	5,382	VC
Texas A&M Univ at Kingsville	TX	3,808	LC
Texas Christian Univ	TX	12,180	C
Texas Southern Univ	TX	4,500	NC
The Citadel	SC	6,619	C
The Univ of New Mexico	NM	5,304	C
Trenton State College	NJ	9,085	HC
Trevecca Nazarene College	TN	9,826	NC
Troy State Univ	AL	4,322	C
Univ of Akron	OH	6,699	NC
Univ of Alabama	AL	5,702	C
Univ of Alabama at Birmingham	AL	7,533	C
Univ of Arizona	AZ	5,808	C
Univ of Arkansas at Fayetteville	AR	5,046	C
Univ of Arkansas at Little Rock	AR	4,419	C
Univ of Central Arkansas	AR	4,200	LC
Univ of Central Okla	OK	3,647	C
Univ of Cincinnati	OH	7,989	C
Univ of Dayton	OH	15,120	C+
Univ of Detroit Mercy	MI	14,720	C
Univ of Florida	FL	5,850	HC
Univ of Georgia	GA	5,655	VC
Univ of Hawaii at Manoa	HI	5,626	C
Univ of Houston	TX	5,215	C
Univ of Illinois at Urbana-Champaign	IL	7,764	HC
Univ of Iowa	IA	5,658	VC
Univ of Kansas	KS	5,200	NC
Univ of Kentucky	KY	5,152	VC
Univ of Louisville	KY	5,948	C
Univ of Lowell	MA	8,831	VC
Univ of Maine	ME	7,990	C
Univ of Maine at Farmington	ME	6,700	C
Univ of Maine at Machias	ME	6,135	C
Univ of Maine at Presque Isle	ME	6,374	C
Univ of Mary Hardin-Baylor	TX	8,120	NC
Univ of Maryland/College Park	MD	8,182	VC
Univ of Maryland/Eastern Shore	MD	6,254	LC
Univ of Memphis	TN	3,476	C
Univ of Minn/Duluth	MN	6,512	C
Univ of Missouri/Kansas City	MO	5,906	VC
Univ of Mobile	AL	9,400	C
Univ of Montevallo	AL	5,310	C
Univ of Nebr at Kearney	NE	4,308	LC
Univ of Nebr at Omaha	NE	1,889	LC
Univ of Nebr-Lincoln	NE	5,278	LC
Univ of Nevada/Las Vegas	NV	6,405	C
Univ of Nevada/Reno	NV	5,735	C
Univ of North Alabama	AL	4,236	NC
Univ of N Car at Greensboro	NC	5,192	C
Univ of N Dak	ND	4,902	NC
Univ of North Florida	FL	5,082	C
Univ of North Texas	TX	4,853	C
Univ of Northern Iowa	IA	5,137	C
Univ of Okla	OK	5,427	VC
Univ of Richmond	VA	16,700	HC
Univ of St Thomas	MN	15,785	C+
Univ of South Alabama	AL	5,451	C
Univ of South Florida	FL	5,475	C+
Univ of Southern Miss	MS	4,542	C
Univ of Southwestern Louisiana	LA	3,968	NC
Univ of Tenn at Martin	TN	4,550	C
Univ of Tenn/Knoxville	TN	5,668	C
Univ of Texas at Arlington	TX	5,549	LC
Univ of Texas at El Paso	TX	3,160	LC
Univ of Texas at San Antonio	TX	6,420	C
Univ of Texas-Pan American	TX	3,192	NC
Univ of Toledo	OH	6,636	NC
Univ of Utah	UT	5,975	C
Univ of Vermont	VT	10,776	C+
Univ of Virginia	VA	7,964	MC
Univ of West Florida	FL	5,415	C
Univ of Wisc/La Crosse	WI	4,487	C
Univ of Wyoming	WY	4,991	NC
Utah State Univ	UT	4,683	C
Valdosta State Univ	GA	4,670	LC
Valley City State Univ	ND	4,385	LC
Virginia Commonwealth Univ	VA	7,909	C
Virginia Polytechnic Inst and State Univ	VA	6,828	C
Walla Walla College	WA	13,215	C
Warner Pacific College	OR	12,112	C
Wayne State College	NE	4,260	NC
Wayne State Univ	MI	2,680	C
Weber State Univ	UT	4,398	C
West Chester Univ of Penn	PA	7,492	C
West Texas A&M Univ	TX	4,224	C
West Virginia Inst of Tech	WV	5,858	LC
Western Carolina Univ	NC	3,811	C
Western Conn State Univ	CT	6,622	C

School	ST	$IS	SR
Western Illinois Univ	IL	5,241	LC
Western Kentucky Univ	KY	4,808	C
Western Mich Univ	MI	6,820	C
Western Oregon State College	OR	6,180	C
Western Washington Univ	WA	6,077	VC
William Paterson College	NJ	7,438	C+
Wilmington College	OH	13,700	LC
Winona State Univ	MN	5,200	C
Xavier Univ	OH	15,710	C+
Youngstown State Univ	OH	6,447	LC

HEALTH SCIENCE

School	ST	$IS	SR
Barat College	IL	13,990	C
Boise State Univ	ID	4,909	LC
Boston Univ	MA	24,130	HC
Bridgewater College	VA	15,300	C
Brigham Young Univ	UT	5,625	HC
Cal State/Dominguez Hills	CA	2,857	LC
Cal State/Hayward	CA	5,495	C
Carlow College	PA	13,914	C
CUNY/Brooklyn College	NY	2,450	VC
College of Our Lady of The Elms	MA	15,639	C
Columbia Union College	MD	13,650	LC
Columbus College	GA	4,892	LC
Florida Atlantic Univ	FL	5,525	C
Florida State Univ	FL	5,814	VC
Furman Univ	SC	16,557	VC
Grand Valley State Univ	MI	6,822	VC
Gwynedd-Mercy College	PA	15,450	C
Hampshire College	MA	25,320	C
Illinois Benedictine College	IL	14,170	C
James Madison Univ	VA	8,198	HC
Johnson State College	VT	8,393	C
Kalamazoo College	MI	19,974	HC
Kansas Newman College	KS	10,640	C
La Sierra Univ	CA	15,472	C
Maryville College	TN	14,474	C
Meredith College	NC	9,440	C
Mount St Mary's College	CA	16,390	VC
Mount Vernon College	DC	20,668	C
Northeast Missouri State Univ	MO	5,654	VC+
Oakland Univ	MI	6,714	VC
Our Lady of Holy Cross College	LA	4,630	LC
St Ambrose Univ	IA	13,380	C
St Francis College	NY	6,710	LC
St Mary's College	MI	8,350	C
San Francisco State Univ	CA	7,292	LC
Southern Univ and A&M College	LA	4,920	NC
SUNY/College at Brockport	NY	7,220	C+
Stephen F. Austin State Univ	TX	5,117	C
Univ of Arkansas at Little Rock	AR	4,419	C
Univ of Central Florida	FL	6,061	C+
Univ of Maryland/Baltimore County	MD	7,746	VC
Univ of Miami	FL	22,107	VC
Univ of Tenn/Knoxville	TN	5,668	C
Univ of Wisc/Milwaukee	WI	6,165	C
Western Illinois Univ	IL	5,241	LC
William Paterson College	NJ	7,438	C+
Yeshiva Univ	NY	18,200	VC

HEBREW

School	ST	$IS	SR
CUNY/Baruch College	NY	2,562	VC
CUNY/Brooklyn College	NY	2,450	VC
CUNY/City College	NY	2,543	VC
CUNY/Herbert H. Lehman College	NY	2,542	VC
CUNY/Hunter College	NY	4,101	VC
CUNY/Queens College	NY	2,631	VC
Harvard Univ/Harvard and Radcliffe Colleges	MA	24,880	MC
New York Univ	NY	24,705	VC+
Ohio State Univ	OH	7,218	LC
Scripps College	CA	23,600	HC
SUNY at Albany	NY	7,059	VC
SUNY at Binghamton	NY	7,921	HC
Temple Univ	PA	10,281	C
Univ of Calif at Los Angeles	CA	8,959	HC
Univ of Mich/Ann Arbor	MI	9,428	HC+
Univ of Minn/Twin Cities	MN	6,682	VC
Univ of Texas at Austin	TX	5,160	VC
Univ of Wisc/Milwaukee	WI	6,165	C
Wayne State Univ	MI	2,680	LC
Wesleyan Univ	CT	23,770	MC
Yeshiva Univ	NY	18,200	VC

HISPANIC AMERICAN STUDIES

School	ST	$IS	SR
Adams State College	CO	4,910	C
Brown Univ	RI	26,104	MC
CUNY/Brooklyn College	NY	2,450	VC
CUNY/City College	NY	2,543	VC
CUNY/Herbert H. Lehman College	NY	2,542	VC
CUNY/Hunter College	NY	4,101	VC
Conn College	CT	24,160	HC
Fordham Univ/College at Lincoln Center	NY	18,150	VC
Lewis and Clark College	OR	19,980	VC
Mills College	CA	20,848	VC
Mount St Mary College	NY	12,910	C
Northwestern Univ	IL	21,093	MC
Rutgers Univ/Douglass College	NJ	8,795	VC
Rutgers Univ/Livingston College	NJ	8,877	VC
Rutgers Univ/Newark College of A&S	NJ	8,645	C
Rutgers Univ/Rutgers College	NJ	8,841	HC+
Rutgers Univ/Univ College—New Brunswick	NJ	0	LC
St Olaf College	MN	17,200	HC
Scripps College	CA	23,600	HC
Univ of Mich/Ann Arbor	MI	9,428	HC+
Univ of Northern Colo	CO	6,008	C
Univ of PR/Cayey Univ College	PR	900	C
Western New Mexico Univ	NM	3,234	LC

HISTORIC PRESERVATION

School	ST	$IS	SR
Fashion Inst of Tech/SUNY	NY	7,135	SP
Goucher College	MD	20,295	VC
Roger Williams Univ	RI	16,750	C
Savannah College of Art and Design	GA	14,280	SP
Univ of Delaware	DE	8,013	VC

HISTORY

School	ST	$IS	SR
Abilene Christian Univ	TX	10,460	NC
Adams State College	CO	4,910	C
Adelphi Univ	NY	18,250	LC
Adrian College	MI	14,340	C
Agnes Scott College	GA	17,135	VC
Alabama A&M Univ	AL	4,200	C
Alabama State Univ	AL	3,428	NC
Alaska Pacific Univ	AK	11,350	C
Albany State College	GA	4,481	LC
Albertson College	ID	15,942	C+
Albertus Magnus College	CT	16,280	LC
Albion College	MI	18,264	VC
Albright College	PA	19,260	C
Alcorn State Univ	MS	4,474	C
Alderson-Broaddus College	WV	12,000	C
Alfred Univ	NY	21,054	VC+
Alice Lloyd College	KY	2,750	VC
Allegheny College	PA	21,020	VC
Allen Univ	SC	6,705	NC
Alma College	MI	16,375	VC+
Alvernia College	PA	13,150	LC
Alverno College	WI	11,344	C
American International College	MA	14,029	C
American Univ	DC	21,230	VC+
Amherst College	MA	24,152	MC
Anderson Univ	IN	12,920	C
Andrews Univ	MI	14,952	NC
Angelo State Univ	TX	5,176	C
Antioch College	OH	19,532	C
Appalachian State Univ	NC	4,095	C
Aquinas College	MI	14,526	C
Arizona State Univ Main Campus	AZ	6,444	C
Arkansas College	AR	11,626	VC
Arkansas State Univ	AR	4,250	NC
Armstrong State College	GA	4,874	LC
Asbury College	KY	11,105	VC
Ashland Univ	OH	15,508	C
Assumption College	MA	17,095	LC
Atlantic Union College	MA	14,150	LC
Auburn Univ	AL	5,823	C+
Auburn Univ at Montgomery	AL	3,390	C
Augsburg College	MN	15,608	C
Augusta College	GA	1,452	C
Augustana College	IL	16,959	VC
Augustana College	SD	13,420	C
Aurora Univ	IL	13,381	C
Austin College	TX	14,999	VC
Austin Peay State Univ	TN	4,350	C
Averett College	VA	13,610	LC
Avila College	MO	12,130	C
Azusa Pacific Univ	CA	15,034	C
Baker Univ	KS	12,284	C
Baldwin-Wallace College	OH	15,210	C
Ball State Univ	IN	6,032	LC
Bard College	NY	25,269	HC
Barry Univ	FL	16,050	C
Bartlesville Wesleyan College	OK	9,400	C
Barton College	NC	10,689	LC
Bates College	ME	23,990	MC
Baylor Univ	TX	10,990	C+
Beaver College	PA	17,660	VC
Belhaven College	MS	9,690	C+
Bellarmine College	KY	10,832	C
Bellevue College	NE	3,050	NC
Belmont Abbey College	NC	13,190	C
Belmont Univ	TN	10,540	C
Beloit College	WI	18,950	VC+
Bemidji State Univ	MN	5,188	C
Benedictine College	KS	12,830	C
Bennington College	VT	24,850	VC+
Bentley College	MA	18,680	C
Berea College	KY	2,883	VC+
Berry College	GA	11,990	VC
Bethany College	WV	18,300	C+
Bethel College	KS	11,530	C
Bethel College	MN	15,050	C
Bethel College	TN	9,736	LC
Bethune-Cookman College	FL	8,375	LC
Biola Univ	CA	16,124	C
Birmingham-Southern College	AL	15,154	VC+
Black Hills State Univ	SD	4,831	NC
Blackburn College	IL	9,120	C
Bloomfield College	NJ	12,200	C
Bloomsburg Univ of Penn	PA	6,312	C+
Blue Mountain College	MS	5,958	LC
Bluefield College	VA	10,600	C
Bluffton College	OH	12,951	C
Boise State Univ	ID	4,909	LC
Boston College	MA	22,706	MC
Boston Univ	MA	24,130	HC
Bowdoin College	ME	24,155	MC
Bowie State Univ	MD	7,294	LC
Bowling Green State Univ	OH	6,701	C
Bradley Univ	IL	14,718	C+
Brandeis Univ	MA	25,585	HC
Brescia College	KY	9,800	C
Briar Cliff College	IA	13,375	C
Bridgewater College	VA	15,300	C
Bridgewater State College	MA	7,518	C
Brigham Young Univ	UT	5,625	HC
Brigham Young Univ/Hawaii	HI	6,750	VC
Brooklyn Campus of LIU	NY	15,000	C
Brown Univ	RI	26,104	MC
Bryan College	TN	11,465	C
Bryant College	RI	18,335	C
Bryn Mawr College	PA	24,110	HC
Bucknell Univ	PA	22,320	HC
Buena Vista College	IA	16,150	VC
Butler Univ	IN	16,210	C
Cabrini College	PA	16,012	C
Caldwell College	NJ	12,860	C
Calif Baptist College	CA	11,294	C
Calif Inst of Tech	CA	20,783	MC
Calif Lutheran Univ	CA	17,240	C
Calif Polytechnic State Univ	CA	6,980	VC+
Calif State Polytechnic Univ/Pomona	CA	6,438	LC
Cal State/Bakersfield	CA	5,402	C
Cal State/Chico	CA	6,146	C
Cal State/Dominguez Hills	CA	2,857	LC
Cal State/Fresno	CA	5,747	C
Cal State/Fullerton	CA	4,850	LC
Cal State/Hayward	CA	5,495	C
Cal State/Long Beach	CA	6,057	LC
Cal State/Los Angeles	CA	4,940	VC
Cal State/Northridge	CA	7,122	C
Cal State/Sacramento	CA	6,387	C
Cal State/San Bernardino	CA	6,055	LC
Cal State/Stanislaus	CA	6,799	C
Calif Univ of Penn	PA	7,370	C
Calumet College of St. Joseph	IN	3,585	C
Calvin College	MI	13,020	VC
Cameron Univ	OK	3,686	LC
Campbell Univ	NC	10,624	C
Campbellsville College	KY	8,720	C
Canisius College	NY	15,510	C
Capital Univ	OH	16,535	VC
Cardinal Stritch College	WI	11,252	C
Carleton College	MN	22,155	HC
Carlow College	PA	13,914	C
Carnegie Mellon Univ	PA	22,560	HC+
Carroll College	MT	11,265	C
Carroll College	WI	15,490	C
Carson-Newman College	TN	11,250	C
Carthage College	WI	15,995	C
Cascade College	OR	9,800	NC
Case Western Reserve Univ	OH	19,910	HC
Castleton State College	VT	8,378	C
Catawba College	NC	12,950	C
Catholic Univ of America	DC	18,856	C
Cedar Crest College	PA	18,930	C
Cedarville College	OH	10,715	C
Centenary College	NJ	17,040	LC
Centenary College of Louisiana	LA	11,826	C+
Central College	IA	14,025	VC
Central Conn State Univ	CT	7,108	C
Central Methodist College	MO	11,410	C
Central Mich Univ	MI	6,737	LC
Central Missouri State Univ	MO	5,138	LC
Central State Univ	OH	7,320	NC
Central Washington Univ	WA	5,644	C
Central Wesleyan College	SC	9,640	C
Centre College	KY	15,850	VC+
Chadron State College	NE	4,091	NC
Chaminade Univ of Honolulu	HI	14,290	C
Chapman Univ	CA	21,842	C
Charleston Southern Univ	SC	10,282	LC
Charter Oak State College	CT	314	NC
Chatham College	PA	18,010	C
Chestnut Hill College	PA	14,525	C
Cheyney Univ of Penn	PA	7,005	C
Chicago State Univ	IL	2,198	C
Christendom College	VA	11,750	VC
Christian Brothers Univ	TN	12,120	VC
Christian Heritage College	CA	11,756	C
Christopher Newport Univ	VA	3,196	LC
CUNY/Baruch College	NY	2,562	VC
CUNY/Brooklyn College	NY	2,450	VC
CUNY/City College	NY	2,543	VC
CUNY/College of Staten Island	NY	2,558	VC
CUNY/Herbert H. Lehman College	NY	2,542	C
CUNY/Hunter College	NY	4,101	VC
CUNY/Queens College	NY	2,631	C
CUNY/York College	NY	2,534	NC
Claflin College	SC	0	C
Claremont McKenna College	CA	22,150	MC
Clarion Univ of Penn	PA	6,518	C
Clark Atlanta Univ	GA	11,846	C
Clark Univ	MA	21,400	HC
Clarke College	IA	13,950	C+
Clarkson Univ	NY	20,705	VC+
Clemson Univ	SC	6,564	VC
Cleveland State Univ	OH	7,287	NC
Clinch Valley College/Univ of Virginia	VA	6,364	C
Coastal Carolina Univ	SC	6,010	LC
Coe College	IA	17,085	VC
Coker College	SC	13,790	C
Colby College	ME	24,230	HC
Colgate Univ	NY	24,020	HC
College Misericordia	PA	15,820	C
College of Charleston	SC	6,250	C
College of Great Falls	MT	6,230	NC
College of Mount St Joseph	OH	13,272	C
College of Mount St Vincent	NY	16,730	C
College of New Rochelle	NY	15,440	LC
College of Notre Dame	CA	16,480	C
College of Notre Dame of Maryland	MD	16,050	C
College of St Benedict	MN	15,468	VC
College of St Catherine	MN	14,670	C
College of St Elizabeth	NJ	15,800	C
College of St Francis	IL	13,060	VC
College of St Joseph	VT	12,650	C
College of St Mary	NE	12,500	C
College of St Rose	NY	14,452	C
College of St Scholastica	MN	14,868	C
College of the Holy Cross	MA	23,850	HC
College of the Ozarks	MO	2,000	VC+
College of the Southwest	NM	5,720	LC
College of William and Mary	VA	8,602	MC
College of Wooster	OH	19,875	VC
Colo Christian Univ	CO	9,750	C
Colo College	CO	20,038	HC
Colo State Univ	CO	6,566	VC
Columbia College	MO	11,995	C
Columbia College	SC	13,520	C
Columbia Union College	MD	13,650	LC
Columbia Univ/Barnard College	NY	25,492	HC
Columbia Univ/Columbia College	NY	26,757	MC
Columbus College	GA	4,892	LC
Concord College	WV	5,104	NC
Concordia College	MI	13,660	C
Concordia College	MN	13,200	C
Concordia College	NE	11,776	NC
Concordia College	NY	0	LC
Concordia College/Moorhead	MN	12,750	C
Concordia Univ	IL	12,611	C
Concordia Univ	CA	14,675	C
Concordia Univ Wisc	WI	12,140	C
Conn College	CT	24,160	HC
Converse College	SC	15,750	C
Coppin State College	MD	7,145	LC
Cornell College	IA	18,425	VC
Cornell Univ	NY	13,445	MC
Covenant College	GA	13,054	VC
Creighton Univ	NE	14,432	VC
Culver-Stockton College	MO	11,150	C
Cumberland College	KY	9,756	C
Curry College	MA	18,695	LC
D'Youville College	NY	12,850	C
Daemen College	NY	13,020	VC
Dakota Wesleyan Univ	SD	9,770	LC

School	ST	$IS	SR
Dallas Baptist Univ	TX	9,620	LC
Dana College	NE	11,910	C
Dartmouth College	NH	24,354	MC
David Lipscomb Univ	TN	7,865	C
Davidson College	NC	21,037	MC
Davis and Elkins College	WV	13,230	LC
Defiance College	OH	13,480	LC
Delaware State College	DE	5,656	C
Delta State Univ	MS	3,964	LC
Denison Univ	OH	21,150	VC+
DePaul Univ	IL	15,535	VC
DePauw Univ	IN	18,530	VC
Dickinson College	PA	22,705	HC
Dickinson State Univ	ND	3,792	
Dillard Univ	LA	9,950	C
Doane College	NE	12,220	C
Dominican College	NY	13,600	C
Dominican College of San Rafael	CA	17,860	C
Dordt College	IA	11,690	C
Dowling College	NY	12,730	LC
Drake Univ	IA	17,195	C
Drew Univ/College of Liberal Arts	NJ	23,406	HC
Drexel Univ	PA	15,970	C
Drury College	MO	12,140	VC
Duke Univ	NC	21,271	MC
Duquesne Univ	PA	16,434	VC
Earlham College	IN	19,383	VC
East Carolina Univ	NC	4,498	LC
East Stroudsburg Univ	PA	6,886	C
East Tenn State Univ	TN	4,406	LC
East Texas Baptist Univ	TX	7,740	C
East Texas State Univ	TX	4,512	LC
Eastern College	PA	15,150	C+
Eastern Conn State Univ	CT	6,966	C
Eastern Illinois Univ	IL	5,548	LC
Eastern Kentucky Univ	KY	4,840	NC
Eastern Mennonite College	VA	12,700	C
Eastern Mich Univ	MI	6,749	LC
Eastern Montana College	MT	5,165	LC
Eastern Nazarene College	MA	12,163	LC
Eastern New Mexico Univ	NM	3,950	LC
Eastern Oregon State College	OR	6,090	C
Eastern Washington Univ	WA	5,439	LC
Eckerd College	FL	18,855	VC
Edgewood College	WI	11,700	C
Edinboro Univ of Penn	PA	7,181	C
Edward Waters College	FL	8,300	C
Elizabeth City State Univ	NC	4,254	LC
Elizabethtown College	PA	17,850	VC
Elmhurst College	IL	12,536	C
Elmira College	NY	18,450	C
Elon College	NC	12,290	LC
Emmanuel College	MA	17,773	LC
Emory and Henry College	VA	12,776	C
Emory Univ	GA	21,930	HC
Emporia State Univ	KS	4,685	NC
Erskine College	SC	14,310	C
Eugene Lang College of the New School for Social Research	NY	21,145	C+
Eureka College	IL	14,555	C
Evangel College	MO	10,142	C
Evergreen State College	WA	6,306	C
Fairfield Univ	CT	20,460	VC
Fairleigh Dickinson Univ	NJ	16,427	C
Fairmont State College	WV	4,640	LC
Fayetteville State Univ	NC	3,926	LC
Felician College	NJ	7,900	C
Ferrum College	VA	12,800	LC
Fisk Univ	TN	0	LC
Fitchburg State College	MA	6,962	C
Flagler College	FL	7,990	C
Florida A&M Univ	FL	4,651	C
Florida Atlantic Univ	FL	5,525	C
Florida International Univ	FL	4,191	VC
Florida Southern College	FL	12,260	C
Florida State Univ	FL	5,814	VC
Fontbonne College	MO	12,090	C
Fordham Univ/College at Lincoln Center	NY	18,150	VC
Fordham Univ/Fordham College	NY	19,875	VC
Fort Hays State Univ	KS	4,675	NC
Fort Lewis College	CO	5,097	C
Framingham State College	MA	6,580	C
Francis Marion Univ	SC	5,878	LC
Franciscan Univ of Steubenville	OH	13,400	C
Franklin and Marshall College	PA	23,655	HC
Franklin College of Indiana	IN	13,970	C
Franklin Pierce College	NH	17,270	LC
Freed-Hardeman Univ	TN	8,585	VC
Friends Univ	KS	11,205	C
Frostburg State Univ	MD	6,940	C
Furman Univ	SC	16,557	VC
Gallaudet Univ	DC	9,850	SP
Gannon Univ	PA	14,872	C
Gardner-Webb College	NC	11,950	LC
Geneva College	PA	13,030	C
George Fox College	OR	15,640	VC
George Mason Univ	VA	8,728	C
George Washington Univ	DC	22,470	HC
Georgetown College	KY	10,990	C
Georgetown Univ	DC	24,410	MC
Georgia College	GA	4,310	LC
Georgia Southern Univ	GA	4,988	LC
Georgia Southwestern College	GA	4,338	LC
Georgia State Univ	GA	2,019	C
Georgian Court College	NJ	12,550	C
Gettysburg College	PA	22,960	HC
Glenville State College	WV	4,810	LC
Gonzaga Univ	WA	16,350	VC
Gordon College	MA	16,790	C
Goshen College	IN	12,360	C
Goucher College	MD	20,295	VC
Graceland College	IA	11,600	C
Grambling State Univ	LA	4,712	NC
Grand Canyon Univ	AZ	9,680	VC
Grand Rapids Baptist College and Seminary	MI	10,228	C
Grand Valley State Univ	MI	6,822	VC
Grand View College	IA	13,230	NC
Greensboro College	NC	11,496	C
Greenville College	IL	14,190	C
Grinnell College	IA	20,680	HC+
Grove City College	PA	7,870	HC
Guilford College	NC	17,680	C
Gustavus Adolphus College	MN	15,935	VC
Gwynedd-Mercy College	PA	15,450	C
Hamilton College	NY	23,500	HC
Hamline Univ	MN	17,122	VC
Hampden-Sydney College	VA	17,372	C+
Hampshire College	MA	25,320	C
Hampton Univ	VA	10,706	C
Hanover College	IN	10,950	VC
Hardin-Simmons Univ	TX	9,080	C
Harding Univ	AR	9,050	VC
Hartwick College	NY	20,950	C
Harvard Univ/Harvard and Radcliffe Colleges	MA	24,880	MC
Hastings College	NE	12,426	C
Haverford College	PA	23,950	HC
Hawaii Pacific Univ	HI	12,300	C
Heidelberg College	OH	17,160	C
Henderson State Univ	AR	3,860	C
Hendrix College	AR	11,670	C
High Point Univ	NC	12,350	LC
Hillsdale College	MI	15,110	VC
Hiram College	OH	18,340	VC
Hobart and William Smith Colleges	NY	23,925	VC
Hofstra Univ	NY	16,580	VC
Hollins College	VA	18,484	C
Holy Family College	PA	8,300	C
Holy Names College	CA	15,660	C
Hood College	MD	19,010	VC
Hope College	MI	15,698	C+
Houghton College	NY	13,120	VC
Houston Baptist Univ	TX	11,055	C
Howard Payne Univ	TX	8,052	C
Howard Univ	DC	11,680	C
Humboldt State Univ	CA	5,676	C
Huntingdon College	AL	11,400	C
Huntington College	IN	13,220	C
Huron Univ	SD	9,790	C
Idaho State Univ	ID	4,442	LC
Illinois Benedictine College	IL	14,170	C
Illinois College	IL	11,200	C
Illinois Inst of Tech	IL	18,290	VC
Illinois State Univ	IL	6,413	C
Illinois Wesleyan Univ	IL	18,590	HC+
Immaculata College	PA	14,620	C
Incarnate Word College	TX	12,307	C
Indiana State Univ	IN	6,210	C
Indiana Univ Bloomington	IN	6,495	VC
Indiana Univ Northwest	IN	2,310	C
Indiana Univ of Penn	PA	6,373	C
Indiana Univ Southeast	IN	2,260	LC
Indiana Univ-Purdue Univ at Fort Wayne	IN	2,500	LC
Indiana Univ-Purdue Univ at Indianapolis	IN	5,862	LC
Indiana Univ/South Bend	IN	2,141	LC
Indiana Wesleyan Univ	IN	12,332	C
Inter American Univ of PR/Aguadilla Regional College	PR	2,290	
Inter American Univ of PR/Bayamon Univ College	PR	2,300	
Inter American Univ of PR/Metropolitan Campus	PR	2,340	
Inter American Univ of PR/Ponce Regional College	PR	2,300	
Inter American Univ of PR/San German	PR	4,620	
Inter-American Univ of PR/Fajardo Regional College	PR	2,732	
Iona College	NY	16,310	C
Iowa State Univ	IA	5,456	C
Ithaca College	NY	19,679	C
Jackson State Univ	MS	4,996	LC
Jacksonville State Univ	AL	4,080	LC
Jacksonville Univ	FL	13,390	C
James Madison Univ	VA	8,198	HC
Jamestown College	ND	10,250	C
Jarvis Christian College	TX	7,170	LC
Jersey City State College	NJ	7,797	LC
John Brown Univ	AR	9,850	VC
John Carroll Univ	OH	16,510	C
Johns Hopkins Univ	MD	24,360	MC
Johnson C. Smith Univ	NC	8,916	LC
Johnson State College	VT	8,393	LC
Judson College	IL	13,625	C
Juniata College	PA	18,390	C+
Kalamazoo College	MI	19,974	HC
Kansas Newman College	KS	10,640	C
Kansas State Univ	KS	4,816	NC
Kansas Wesleyan Univ	KS	11,770	C
Kean College of New Jersey	NJ	6,395	LC
Keene State College	NH	7,081	C
Kennesaw State College	GA	1,553	C
Kent State Univ	OH	6,740	LC
Kentucky State Univ	KY	4,282	C+
Kentucky Wesleyan College	KY	11,550	C
Kenyon College	OH	22,430	HC+
Keuka College	NY	13,660	C
King College	TN	11,500	C
King's College	PA	15,420	C
Knox College	IL	18,990	VC
Kutztown Univ	PA	6,528	C
La Roche College	PA	12,977	LC
La Salle Univ	PA	16,940	VC
La Sierra Univ	CA	15,472	C
Lafayette College	PA	23,450	HC
Lake Forest College	IL	19,960	VC
Lake Superior State Univ	MI	7,311	C
Lakeland College	WI	12,845	LC
Lamar Univ	TX	3,798	C
Lander Univ	SC	6,180	LC
Lane College	TN	7,628	LC
Langston Univ	OK	2,907	LC
Lawrence Univ	WI	19,986	HC+
Le Moyne College	NY	15,180	C
Lebanon Valley College of Penn	PA	18,300	C
Lee College	TN	7,894	LC
Lees-McRae College	NC	9,850	LC
Lehigh Univ	PA	23,250	HC
LeMoyne-Owen College	TN	4,500	LC
Lenoir-Rhyne College	NC	14,068	C
Lewis and Clark College	OR	19,980	VC
Lewis Univ	IL	14,797	LC
Lewis-Clark State College	ID	4,040	
Liberty Univ	VA	11,500	C
Limestone College	SC	10,700	LC
Lincoln Memorial Univ	TN	8,218	C
Lincoln Univ	MO	4,638	NC
Lincoln Univ	PA	0	C
Lindenwood College	MO	13,560	C
Lindsey Wilson College	KY	9,530	LC
Linfield College	OR	16,670	VC
Livingston Univ	AL	3,979	C
Livingstone College	NC	8,600	LC
Lock Haven Univ of Penn	PA	7,128	C
LIU/C. W. Post Campus	NY	16,870	C
LIU/Southampton Campus	NY	17,280	C
Longwood College	VA	7,800	C
Louisiana College	LA	7,518	VC
Louisiana State Univ and A&M College	LA	5,605	C
Louisiana Tech Univ	LA	4,284	C
Lourdes College	OH	6,410	LC
Loyola College	MD	18,035	VC
Loyola Marymount Univ	CA	18,560	C
Loyola Univ of Chicago	IL	15,880	C+
Loyola Univ/New Orleans	LA	15,660	C+
Lubbock Christian Univ	TX	9,840	NC
Luther College	IA	15,900	VC
Lycoming College	PA	17,200	LC
Lynchburg College	VA	17,000	C
Lynn Univ	FL	18,300	C
Macalester College	MN	19,710	HC
MacMurray College	IL	12,800	C
Madonna Univ	MI	8,546	C
Malone College	OH	12,572	C
Manchester College	IN	13,240	LC
Manhattan College	NY	19,000	C
Manhattanville College	NY	20,450	C
Mankato State Univ	MN	5,097	LC
Mansfield Univ	PA	6,348	C
Marian College	IN	12,936	C
Marian College of Fond du Lac	WI	12,250	C
Marietta College	OH	16,940	C+
Marist College	NY	16,406	C
Marlboro College	VT	23,305	C+
Marquette Univ	WI	16,114	VC
Mars Hill College	NC	11,050	C
Marshall Univ	WV	5,762	LC
Martin Univ	IN	4,830	NC
Mary Washington College	VA	7,910	VC
Marygrove College	MI	5,877	C
Marymount College/Tarrytown	NY	17,350	C
Marymount Manhattan College	NY	15,450	C
Marymount Univ	VA	15,930	C
Maryville College	TN	14,474	C
Maryville Univ-St Louis	MO	12,900	VC
Mass Inst of Tech	MA	24,800	MC
Master's College	CA	12,816	C
McMurry Univ	TX	10,100	C
McNeese State Univ	LA	4,543	NC
McPherson College	KS	11,360	VC
Menlo College	CA	20,375	LC
Mercer Univ	GA	15,123	C
Mercy College	NY	11,180	NC
Mercyhurst College	PA	13,488	C
Meredith College	NC	9,440	C
Merrimack College	MA	18,025	C
Mesa State College	CO	5,127	NC
Messiah College	PA	14,664	VC
Methodist College	NC	12,400	C
Metropolitan State College of Denver	CO	1,751	NC
Miami Univ	OH	8,066	VC
Mich State Univ	MI	7,842	C
MidAmerica Nazarene College	KS	10,208	NC
Middle Tenn State Univ	TN	3,857	C
Middlebury College	VT	24,400	MC
Midland Lutheran College	NE	12,410	C
Midwestern State Univ	TX	4,542	LC
Millersville Univ of Penn	PA	7,370	VC
Milligan College	TN	10,690	C
Millikin Univ	IL	15,499	C
Mills College	CA	20,848	VC
Millsaps College	MS	15,486	C+
Minot State Univ	ND	3,748	NC
Miss College	MS	8,348	C
Miss State Univ	MS	5,629	VC
Miss Univ for Women	MS	4,456	LC
Missouri Baptist College	MO	9,340	C
Missouri Southern State College	MO	4,272	
Missouri Valley College	MO	14,050	LC
Missouri Western State College	MO	4,384	NC
Molloy College	NY	8,580	LC
Monmouth College	IL	17,300	C+
Monmouth College	NJ	16,820	C
Montana State Univ	MT	5,534	C
Montclair State College	NJ	7,539	C+
Montreat-Anderson College	NC	10,972	LC
Moorhead State Univ	MN	5,076	C
Moravian College	PA	18,960	VC
Morehead State Univ	KY	4,600	LC
Morehouse College	GA	13,224	LC
Morgan State Univ	MD	7,366	C+
Morningside College	IA	13,896	C
Morris Brown College	GA	12,234	NC
Morris College	SC	6,880	C
Mount Holyoke College	MA	23,630	VC
Mount Mary College	WI	10,920	C
Mount Mercy College	IA	13,230	C
Mount Olive College	NC	9,650	LC
Mount St Mary College	NY	12,910	C
Mount St Mary's College	CA	16,390	VC
Mount St Mary's College	MD	17,825	LC
Mount Senario College	WI	10,970	C
Mount Union College	OH	15,850	C
Mount Vernon Nazarene College	OH	10,390	C
Muhlenberg College	PA	20,795	VC
Murray State Univ	KY	4,702	C
Muskingum College	OH	16,650	C
Nazareth College of Rochester	NY	15,310	C+
Nebr Wesleyan Univ	NE	12,240	C
New College of the Univ of South Florida	FL	5,697	MC
New England College	NH	17,870	LC
New Mexico Highlands Univ	NM	3,772	C
New Mexico State Univ	NM	4,844	LC
New York Univ	NY	24,705	VC+
Newberry College	SC	11,994	LC
Niagara Univ	NY	14,552	C
Nicholls State Univ	LA	4,531	NC
Nichols College	MA	14,200	LC
Norfolk State Univ	VA	6,345	LC
North Adams State College	MA	7,750	C
N Car Agricultural and Technical State Univ	NC	4,477	LC
N Car Central Univ	NC	4,347	LC
N Car State Univ	NC	4,984	C
N Car Wesleyan College	NC	12,480	LC
North Central College	IL	15,498	VC
N Dak State Univ of Agriculture and Applied Science	ND	4,774	VC
North Georgia College	GA	4,103	LC
North Park College	IL	14,310	C
Northeast Louisiana Univ	LA	3,906	NC
Northeast Missouri State Univ	MO	5,654	VC+
Northeastern Illinois Univ	IL	1,955	C
Northeastern State Univ	OK	5,250	C
Northeastern Univ	MA	19,851	C
Northern Arizona Univ	AZ	4,844	C
Northern Illinois Univ	IL	6,408	C
Northern Kentucky Univ	KY	4,620	NC
Northern Mich Univ	MI	6,350	C
Northern Montana College	MT	4,976	C
Northern State Univ	SD	4,186	LC
Northland College	WI	13,550	LC
Northwest Missouri State Univ	MO	5,010	LC
Northwest Nazarene College	ID	11,750	C
Northwestern College of Iowa	IA	12,250	C
Northwestern Okla State Univ	OK	3,424	C

School	ST	$IS	SR
Univ of New Orleans	LA	5,468	C
Univ of North Alabama	AL	4,236	NC
Univ of N Car at Asheville	NC	4,791	VC
Univ of N Car at Chapel Hill	NC	5,330	HC
Univ of N Car at Charlotte	NC	4,597	C
Univ of N Car at Greensboro	NC	5,192	C
Univ of N Car at Wilmington	NC	5,172	C
Univ of N Dak	ND	4,902	NC
Univ of North Florida	FL	5,082	C
Univ of North Texas	TX	4,853	C
Univ of Northern Colo	CO	6,008	C
Univ of Northern Iowa	IA	5,137	C
Univ of Notre Dame	IN	20,150	MC
Univ of Okla	OK	5,427	VC
Univ of Oregon	OR	6,466	VC
Univ of Penn	PA	24,238	MC
Univ of Pittsburgh	PA	9,472	C
Univ of Pittsburgh at Bradford	PA	9,050	C
Univ of Pittsburgh at Johnstown	PA	8,914	C
Univ of Portland	OR	15,564	C
Univ of PR/Cayey Univ College	PR	900	
Univ of PR/Mayaguez	PR	0	
Univ of PR/Rio Piedras	PR	0	C
Univ of Puget Sound	WA	19,520	HC
Univ of Redlands	CA	22,059	VC
Univ of Rhode Island	RI	9,205	C
Univ of Richmond	VA	16,700	HC
Univ of Rio Grande	OH	6,300	NC
Univ of Rochester	NY	23,696	HC
Univ of St Thomas	MN	15,785	C+
Univ of St Thomas	TX	11,676	C+
Univ of San Diego	CA	18,970	VC
Univ of San Francisco	CA	18,408	C
Univ of Science and Arts of Okla	OK	3,304	C
Univ of Scranton	PA	17,071	VC
Univ of South Alabama	AL	5,451	C
Univ of S Car	SC	6,158	C
Univ of S Car at Aiken	SC	5,386	C
Univ of S Car at Spartanburg	SC	2,320	C
Univ of S Dak	SD	4,722	C
Univ of South Florida	FL	5,475	C+
Univ of Southern Calif	CA	23,006	VC
Univ of Southern Colo	CO	5,350	LC
Univ of Southern Indiana	IN	3,720	NC
Univ of Southern Maine	ME	7,299	C
Univ of Southern Miss	MS	4,542	C
Univ of Southwestern Louisiana	LA	3,968	NC
Univ of Tampa	FL	16,780	C
Univ of Tenn at Chattanooga	TN	5,375	C
Univ of Tenn at Martin	TN	4,550	C
Univ of Tenn/Knoxville	TN	5,668	C
Univ of Texas at Arlington	TX	5,549	LC
Univ of Texas at Austin	TX	5,160	VC
Univ of Texas at Dallas	TX	1,222	VC+
Univ of Texas at El Paso	TX	3,160	LC
Univ of Texas at San Antonio	TX	6,420	C
Univ of Texas-Pan American	TX	3,192	NC
Univ of the District of Columbia	DC	974	NC
Univ of the Ozarks	AR	7,770	C
Univ of the Pacific	CA	21,100	C
Univ of the South	TN	18,830	HC
Univ of Toledo	OH	6,636	NC
Univ of Tulsa	OK	13,795	VC
Univ of Utah	UT	5,975	C
Univ of Vermont	VT	10,776	C+
Univ of Virginia	VA	7,964	MC
Univ of Washington	WA	6,618	VC
Univ of West Florida	FL	5,415	C
Univ of Wisc/Eau Claire	WI	4,647	C
Univ of Wisc/Green Bay	WI	4,904	C
Univ of Wisc/La Crosse	WI	4,487	C
Univ of Wisc/Madison	WI	6,400	HC
Univ of Wisc/Milwaukee	WI	6,165	C
Univ of Wisc/Oshkosh	WI	4,240	C
Univ of Wisc/Parkside	WI	5,247	
Univ of Wisc/Platteville	WI	4,830	C
Univ of Wisc/River Falls	WI	4,655	C
Univ of Wisc/Stevens Point	WI	5,047	C+
Univ of Wisc/Superior	WI	4,330	C
Univ of Wisc/Whitewater	WI	4,700	C
Univ of Wyoming	WY	4,991	NC
Upsala College	NJ	17,200	C
Ursinus College	PA	19,165	VC
Ursuline College	OH	13,180	LC
Utah State Univ	UT	4,683	C
Utica College of Syracuse Univ	NY	16,714	LC
Valdosta State Univ	GA	4,670	LC
Valley City State Univ	ND	4,385	LC
Valparaiso Univ	IN	14,810	VC
Vanderbilt Univ	TN	23,422	HC+
Vassar College	NY	24,206	HC
Villanova Univ	PA	21,400	HC
Virginia Commonwealth Univ	VA	7,909	C
Virginia Intermont College	VA	12,250	LC
Virginia Military Inst	VA	8,630	C
Virginia Polytechnic Inst and State Univ	VA	6,828	C
Virginia State Univ	VA	7,040	
Virginia Union Univ	VA	10,555	LC
Virginia Wesleyan College	VA	14,950	VC
Wabash College	IN	16,250	VC
Wagner College	NY	17,950	C
Wake Forest Univ	NC	17,280	MC
Walla Walla College	WA	13,215	C
Walsh Univ	OH	11,640	C
Warner Pacific College	OR	12,112	C
Warren Wilson College	NC	10,877	C
Wartburg College	IA	14,530	VC
Washburn Univ of Topeka	KS	5,802	NC
Washington and Jefferson College	PA	19,360	C
Washington and Lee Univ	VA	17,735	MC
Washington College	MD	19,270	C+
Washington State Univ	WA	6,364	C
Washington Univ	MO	23,507	HC
Wayland Baptist Univ	TX	7,811	NC
Wayne State College	NE	4,260	NC
Wayne State Univ	MI	2,680	C
Waynesburg College	PA	11,960	C
Weber State Univ	UT	4,398	C
Webster Univ	MO	12,650	C
Wellesley College	MA	23,815	MC
Wells College	NY	19,460	C+
Wesley College	DE	13,745	LC
Wesleyan College	GA	15,445	C
Wesleyan Univ	CT	23,770	MC
West Chester Univ of Penn	PA	7,492	C
West Georgia College	GA	4,256	C
West Liberty State College	WV	4,690	LC
West Texas A&M Univ	TX	4,224	C
West Virginia Inst of Tech	WV	5,858	LC
West Virginia State College	WV	5,044	LC
West Virginia Univ	WV	5,774	C
West Virginia Wesleyan College	WV	16,900	C
Western Carolina Univ	NC	3,811	C
Western Conn State Univ	CT	6,622	C
Western Illinois Univ	IL	5,241	LC
Western Kentucky Univ	KY	4,808	C
Western Maryland College	MD	18,990	C
Western Mich Univ	MI	6,820	C
Western New England College	MA	14,674	LC
Western New Mexico Univ	NM	3,234	LC
Western Oregon State College	OR	6,180	C
Western State College of Colo	CO	5,560	C
Western Washington Univ	WA	6,077	VC
Westfield State College	MA	7,161	C
Westminster College	MO	13,750	C+
Westminster College	PA	15,200	C
Westminster College of Salt Lake City	UT	12,100	C
Westmont College	CA	18,732	C
Wheaton College	IL	14,710	HC
Wheaton College	MA	23,840	C+
Wheeling Jesuit College	WV	14,370	C
Whitman College	WA	20,595	HC
Whittier College	CA	21,661	C
Whitworth College	WA	16,265	C
Wichita State Univ	KS	5,068	NC
Widener Univ	PA	16,840	C
Wiley College	TX	0	NC
Wilkes Univ	PA	15,728	LC
Willamette Univ	OR	17,995	VC
William Carey College	MS	7,050	C
William Jewell College	MO	12,500	VC
William Paterson College	NJ	7,438	C+
William Penn College	IA	13,400	C
William Woods Univ	MO	14,025	LC
Williams College	MA	24,390	MC
Wilmington College	OH	13,700	LC
Wingate College	NC	10,610	C
Winona State Univ	MN	5,200	VC
Winston-Salem State Univ	NC	4,142	LC
Winthrop Univ	SC	6,750	C
Wittenberg Univ	OH	19,998	VC
Wofford College	SC	15,360	VC
Women's College of Brenau Univ	GA	14,734	C
Worcester Polytechnic Inst	MA	20,350	HC
Worcester State College	MA	6,414	LC
Wright State Univ	OH	6,896	LC
Xavier Univ	OH	15,710	C+
Xavier Univ of Louisiana	LA	10,400	C
Yale Univ	CT	25,110	MC
Yeshiva Univ	NY	18,200	VC
York College of Penn	PA	8,345	C
Youngstown State Univ	OH	6,447	LC

HISTORY OF PHILOSOPHY

School	ST	$IS	SR
Brandeis Univ	MA	25,585	HC
Bryn Mawr College	PA	24,110	MC
Rocky Mountain College	MT	11,320	C

HISTORY OF SCIENCE

School	ST	$IS	SR
Bard College	NY	25,269	HC
Case Western Reserve Univ	OH	19,910	HC
Johns Hopkins Univ	MD	24,360	MC
Univ of Wisc/Madison	WI	6,400	HC
Yale Univ	CT	25,110	MC

HOME ECONOMICS

School	ST	$IS	SR
Ambassador College	TX	4,091	C
Bridgewater College	VA	15,300	C
Chadron State College	NE	4,091	NC
College of St Scholastica	MN	14,868	C
Colo State Univ	CO	6,566	VC
David Lipscomb Univ	TN	7,865	VC
East Carolina Univ	NC	4,498	C
East Central Univ	OK	3,558	C
Florida State Univ	FL	5,814	VC
George Fox College	OR	15,640	LC
Idaho State Univ	ID	4,442	C
Illinois State Univ	IL	6,413	C
Indiana State Univ	IN	6,210	C
Langston Univ	OK	2,907	LC
Madonna Univ	MI	8,546	C
Mars Hill College	NC	11,050	C
Marygrove College	MI	5,877	VC
Marymount College/ Tarrytown	NY	17,350	C
Marywood College	PA	14,890	C
Meredith College	NC	9,440	C
Messiah College	PA	14,664	VC
Miss State Univ	MS	5,629	VC
Montana State Univ	MT	5,534	C
Morgan State Univ	MD	7,366	C+
Nicholls State Univ	LA	4,531	NC
Norfolk State Univ	VA	6,345	LC
N Dak State Univ of Agriculture and Applied Science	ND	4,774	VC
Northwest Missouri State Univ	MO	5,010	LC
Oakwood College	AL	10,005	C
Oregon State Univ	OR	6,175	C
Philander Smith College	AR	5,434	NC
Sam Houston State Univ	TX	4,506	C
S Dak State Univ	SD	4,562	C
Southeastern Okla State Univ	OK	3,594	C
Southern Utah Univ	UT	4,104	LC
Southwest Texas State Univ	TX	5,124	C
Southwestern Okla State Univ	OK	3,312	C
SUNY/College at Oneonta	NY	7,878	C
Stephen F. Austin State Univ	TX	5,117	C
Sterling College	KS	10,990	VC
Tarleton State Univ	TX	4,082	LC
Texas A&M Univ at Kingsville	TX	3,808	LC
Texas Tech Univ	TX	6,008	C
Tuskegee Univ	AL	10,128	C
Univ of Akron	OH	6,699	NC
Univ of Arkansas at Fayetteville	AR	5,046	C
Univ of Florida	FL	5,850	HC
Univ of Illinois at Urbana-Champaign	IL	7,764	HC
Univ of Maryland/Eastern Shore	MD	6,254	LC
Univ of Montevallo	AL	5,310	C
Univ of Nebr at Omaha	NE	1,889	LC
Univ of Rhode Island	RI	9,205	C
Univ of Tenn at Chattanooga	TN	5,375	C
Univ of Texas at Austin	TX	5,160	VC
Utah State Univ	UT	4,683	C
Western Carolina Univ	NC	3,811	C
Winthrop Univ	SC	6,750	C
Youngstown State Univ	OH	6,447	LC

HOME ECONOMICS EDUCATION

School	ST	$IS	SR
Abilene Christian Univ	TX	10,460	NC
Alabama A&M Univ	AL	4,200	C
Alcorn State Univ	MS	4,474	C+
Appalachian State Univ	NC	4,095	C
Ashland Univ	OH	15,508	C
Auburn Univ	AL	5,823	C+
Baldwin-Wallace College	OH	15,210	C
Ball State Univ	IN	6,032	LC
Baylor Univ	TX	10,990	C+
Berea College	KY	2,883	VC+
Berry College	GA	11,990	VC
Blue Mountain College	MS	5,958	LC
Bluffton College	OH	12,951	C
Bowling Green State Univ	OH	6,701	C
Bradley Univ	IL	14,718	C+
Brigham Young Univ	UT	5,625	HC
Cal State/Fresno	CA	5,747	C
Cal State/Northridge	CA	7,122	LC
Cameron Univ	OK	3,686	LC
Carson-Newman College	TN	11,250	C
Central Mich Univ	MI	6,737	LC
Central Missouri State Univ	MO	5,138	LC
Central Washington Univ	WA	5,644	C
Chadron State College	NE	4,091	NC
Cheyney Univ of Penn	PA	7,005	C
Christian Heritage College	CA	11,756	C
CUNY/Brooklyn College	NY	2,450	VC
CUNY/Herbert H. Lehman College	NY	2,542	C
CUNY/Queens College	NY	2,631	C
College of St Catherine	MN	14,670	C
College of St Elizabeth	NJ	15,800	C
College of the Ozarks	MO	2,000	VC+
Colo State Univ	CO	6,566	VC
Concordia College	NE	11,776	NC
Concordia College/Moorhead	MN	12,750	C
Delaware State College	DE	5,656	C
East Carolina Univ	NC	4,498	C
East Tenn State Univ	TN	4,406	C
Eastern Illinois Univ	IL	5,548	C
Eastern Kentucky Univ	KY	4,840	NC
Eastern Mich Univ	MI	6,749	C
Eastern New Mexico Univ	NM	3,950	C
Fairmont State College	WV	4,640	LC
Florida International Univ	FL	4,191	VC
Florida State Univ	FL	5,814	VC
Fontbonne College	MO	12,090	C
Fort Hays State Univ	KS	4,675	NC
Fort Valley State College	GA	3,974	LC
Gallaudet Univ	DC	9,850	SP
George Fox College	OR	15,640	LC
Harding Univ	AR	9,050	VC
Henderson State Univ	AR	3,860	C
Hood College	MD	19,010	VC
Idaho State Univ	ID	4,442	C
Immaculata College	PA	14,620	C
Indiana State Univ	IN	6,210	C
Indiana Univ of Penn	PA	6,373	C
Iowa State Univ	IA	5,456	C
Jacksonville State Univ	AL	4,080	LC
Keene State College	NH	7,081	C
Lamar Univ	TX	3,798	C
Lambuth Univ	TN	8,395	C
Langston Univ	OK	2,907	LC
Lincoln Univ	MO	4,638	NC
Louisiana State Univ and A&M College	LA	5,605	C
Louisiana Tech Univ	LA	4,284	C
Lubbock Christian Univ	TX	9,840	NC
Madonna Univ	MI	8,546	C
Mankato State Univ	MN	5,097	LC
Mars Hill College	NC	11,050	C
Marshall Univ	WV	5,762	LC
Marymount College/ Tarrytown	NY	17,350	C
McNeese State Univ	LA	4,543	NC
Mercyhurst College	PA	13,488	C
Messiah College	PA	14,664	VC
Miami Univ	OH	8,066	VC
Mich State Univ	MI	7,842	C
Middle Tenn State Univ	TN	3,857	C
Miss College	MS	8,348	C
Miss Univ for Women	MS	4,456	LC
Montclair State College	NJ	7,539	C+
Morehead State Univ	KY	4,600	LC
Mount Mary College	WI	10,920	C
Mount Vernon Nazarene College	OH	10,390	C
Murray State Univ	KY	4,702	C
New Mexico State Univ	NM	4,844	C
Nicholls State Univ	LA	4,531	NC
Norfolk State Univ	VA	6,345	LC
N Car Agricultural and Technical State Univ	NC	4,477	LC
N Dak State Univ of Agriculture and Applied Science	ND	4,774	VC
Northeast Louisiana Univ	LA	3,906	NC
Northeastern State Univ	OK	5,250	C
Northern Arizona Univ	AZ	4,844	C
Northern Illinois Univ	IL	6,408	C
Northern Mich Univ	MI	6,350	C
Northwest Nazarene College	ID	11,750	C
Northwestern Okla State Univ	OK	3,424	C
Northwestern State Univ of Louisiana	LA	4,287	NC
Oakwood College	AL	10,005	C
Ohio State Univ	OH	7,218	LC
Ohio Univ	OH	7,341	C
Okla Panhandle State Univ	OK	3,155	NC
Olivet Nazarene Univ	IL	11,976	C
Ouachita Baptist Univ	AR	8,940	C
Penn State Univ/Univ Park Campus	PA	8,752	HC
Pillsbury Baptist Bible College	MN	7,390	NC
Pittsburg State Univ	KS	4,478	NC

School	ST	$IS	SR
Point Loma Nazarene College	CA	13,532	C
Pontifical Catholic Univ of PR/Ponce	PR	5,807	
Purdue Univ/West Lafayette	IN	6,636	C
Rosary College	IL	15,040	C
St Joseph College	CT	16,225	C
St Vincent College	PA	13,934	LC
Samford Univ	AL	11,400	VC
San Diego State Univ	CA	6,692	LC
San Francisco State Univ	CA	7,292	LC
Seton Hill College	PA	14,320	C
Shepherd College	WV	5,540	C
S Car State Univ	SC	5,424	LC
S Dak State Univ	SD	4,562	C
Southeastern Louisiana Univ	LA	4,230	NC
Southern Illinois Univ at Carbondale	IL	6,234	C
Southern Univ and A&M College	LA	4,920	NC
Southern Utah Univ	UT	4,104	LC
Southwest Missouri State Univ	MO	4,956	C
Southwest Texas State Univ	TX	5,124	C
Southwestern Okla State Univ	OK	3,312	C
SUNY/College at Oneonta	NY	7,878	C
Stephen F. Austin State Univ	TX	5,117	C
Sterling College	KS	10,990	VC
Tarleton State Univ	TX	4,082	LC
Temple Univ	PA	10,281	C
Tenn State Univ	TN	4,626	C+
Tenn Tech Univ	TN	5,190	C
Texas Southern Univ	TX	4,500	NC
Texas Tech Univ	TX	6,008	C
The Univ of New Mexico	NM	5,304	C
Tuskegee Univ	AL	10,128	C
Univ of Akron	OH	6,699	NC
Univ of Alabama	AL	5,702	C
Univ of Arizona	AZ	5,808	C
Univ of Arkansas at Fayetteville	AR	5,046	C
Univ of Arkansas at Pine Bluff	AR	3,978	LC
Univ of Central Arkansas	AR	4,200	LC
Univ of Central Okla	OK	3,647	C
Univ of Delaware	DE	8,013	VC
Univ of Georgia	GA	5,655	VC
Univ of Idaho	ID	4,830	C
Univ of Illinois at Urbana-Champaign	IL	7,764	HC
Univ of Kentucky	KY	5,152	VC
Univ of Mary Hardin-Baylor	TX	8,120	NC
Univ of Maryland/College Park	MD	8,182	VC
Univ of Maryland/Eastern Shore	MD	6,254	LC
Univ of Mass/Amherst	MA	9,364	LC
Univ of Memphis	TN	3,476	C
Univ of Minn/Duluth	MN	6,512	C
Univ of Minn/Twin Cities	MN	6,682	VC
Univ of Miss	MS	5,756	C
Univ of Missouri/Columbia	MO	6,254	HC
Univ of Montevallo	AL	5,310	C
Univ of Nebr at Kearney	NE	4,308	LC
Univ of Nebr-Lincoln	NE	5,278	LC
Univ of North Alabama	AL	4,236	NC
Univ of N Car at Greensboro	NC	5,192	C
Univ of N Dak	ND	4,902	NC
Univ of PR/Rio Piedras	PR	0	
Univ of Science and Arts of Okla	OK	3,304	C
Univ of Southern Miss	MS	4,542	C
Univ of Southwestern Louisiana	LA	3,968	NC
Univ of Tenn at Martin	TN	4,550	C
Univ of Tenn/Knoxville	TN	5,668	C
Univ of the District of Columbia	DC	974	NC
Univ of Utah	UT	5,975	C
Univ of Wisc/Stevens Point	WI	5,047	C+
Univ of Wisc/Stout	WI	4,719	C
Univ of Wyoming	WY	4,991	NC
Utah State Univ	UT	4,683	C
Virginia Polytechnic Inst and State Univ	VA	6,828	C
Virginia State Univ	VA	7,040	
Washington State Univ	WA	6,364	C
Wayne State College	NE	4,260	NC
Weber State Univ	UT	4,398	C
West Virginia Univ	WV	5,774	C
Western Carolina Univ	NC	3,811	C
Western Illinois Univ	IL	5,241	LC
Western Kentucky Univ	KY	4,808	C
Western Mich Univ	MI	6,820	C
William Penn College	IA	13,400	C
Winthrop Univ	SC	6,750	C
Youngstown State Univ	OH	6,447	LC

HOME FURNISHINGS AND EQUIPMENT MANAGEMENT/PRODUCTION/SERVICES

School	ST	$IS	SR
Southwestern Okla State Univ	OK	3,312	C
Univ of North Texas	TX	4,853	C

HORTICULTURE

School	ST	$IS	SR
Alabama A&M Univ	AL	4,200	C
Andrews Univ	MI	14,952	NC
Arkansas State Univ	AR	4,250	NC
Auburn Univ	AL	5,823	C+
Berry College	GA	11,990	VC
Brigham Young Univ	UT	5,625	HC
Calif Polytechnic State Univ	CA	6,980	VC+
Calif State Polytechnic Univ/Pomona	CA	6,438	LC
Cal State/Chico	CA	6,146	C
Christopher Newport Univ	VA	3,196	LC
Clemson Univ	SC	6,564	VC
Colo State Univ	CO	6,566	VC
Delaware Valley College	PA	16,065	LC
Eastern Kentucky Univ	KY	4,840	NC
Florida A&M Univ	FL	4,651	C
Florida Southern College	FL	12,260	C
Fort Valley State College	GA	3,974	LC
Iowa State Univ	IA	5,456	C
Kansas State Univ	KS	4,816	NC
Louisiana State Univ and A&M College	LA	5,605	C
Louisiana Tech Univ	LA	4,284	C
Mich State Univ	MI	7,842	C
Middle Tenn State Univ	TN	3,857	C
Miss State Univ	MS	5,629	VC
Montana State Univ	MT	5,534	C
Murray State Univ	KY	4,702	C
New Mexico State Univ	NM	4,844	LC
N Car State Univ	NC	4,984	VC
N Dak State Univ of Agriculture and Applied Science	ND	4,774	VC
Northeastern State Univ	OK	5,250	C
Northwest Missouri State Univ	MO	5,010	LC
Ohio State Univ	OH	7,218	LC
Okla Panhandle State Univ	OK	3,155	NC
Okla State Univ	OK	5,086	VC
Oregon State Univ	OR	6,175	C
Penn State Univ/Univ Park Campus	PA	8,752	HC
Purdue Univ/West Lafayette	IN	6,636	C
Rutgers Univ/Cook College	NJ	9,197	HC
Sam Houston State Univ	TX	4,506	C
S Dak State Univ	SD	4,562	C
Southeast Missouri State Univ	MO	5,854	C
Southeastern Louisiana Univ	LA	4,230	NC
Southern Illinois Univ at Carbondale	IL	6,234	C
Southwest Missouri State Univ	MO	4,956	C
Southwest Texas State Univ	TX	5,124	C
Stephen F. Austin State Univ	TX	5,117	C
Tarleton State Univ	TX	4,082	LC
Temple Univ	PA	10,281	C
Texas A&M Univ	TX	5,382	VC
Texas Tech Univ	TX	6,008	C
Tuskegee Univ	AL	10,128	C
Univ of Arkansas at Fayetteville	AR	5,046	C
Univ of Conn	CT	9,168	C
Univ of Florida	FL	5,850	HC
Univ of Georgia	GA	5,655	VC
Univ of Hawaii at Hilo	HI	4,141	C
Univ of Hawaii at Manoa	HI	5,626	C
Univ of Idaho	ID	4,830	C
Univ of Illinois at Urbana-Champaign	IL	7,764	HC
Univ of Kentucky	KY	5,152	VC
Univ of Maine	ME	7,990	C
Univ of Maryland/College Park	MD	8,182	VC
Univ of Missouri/Columbia	MO	6,254	HC
Univ of Nebr-Lincoln	NE	5,278	LC
Univ of New Hampshire	NH	8,242	C
Univ of PR/Mayaguez	PR	0	
Univ of Rhode Island	RI	9,205	C
Univ of Southwestern Louisiana	LA	3,968	NC
Univ of Tenn/Knoxville	TN	5,668	C
Univ of the District of Columbia	DC	974	NC
Univ of Wisc/Madison	WI	6,400	HC
Univ of Wisc/River Falls	WI	4,655	C
Virginia Polytechnic Inst and State Univ	VA	6,828	C
Washington State Univ	WA	6,364	C
West Virginia Univ	WV	5,774	C

HOSPICE CARE

School	ST	$IS	SR
Madonna Univ	MI	8,546	C

HOSPITAL ADMINISTRATION

School	ST	$IS	SR
Univ of Penn	PA	24,238	MC

HOSPITALITY MANAGEMENT SERVICES

School	ST	$IS	SR
Alaska Pacific Univ	AK	11,350	C
Eastern Mich Univ	MI	6,749	C
Ferris State Univ	MI	7,160	NC
Florida Inst of Tech	FL	16,935	VC
Florida International Univ	FL	4,191	VC
Idaho State Univ	ID	4,442	C
Johnson and Wales Univ	RI	13,995	LC
Johnson State College	VT	8,393	LC
Kendall College	IL	12,651	LC
Lakeland College	WI	12,845	LC
Madonna Univ	MI	8,546	C
Metropolitan State College of Denver	CO	1,751	NC
Mount Ida College	MA	16,700	LC
New Hampshire College	NH	15,242	LC
Ohio State Univ	OH	7,218	LC
Sierra Nevada College	NV	14,000	NC
Tuskegee Univ	AL	10,128	C
Univ of Alabama	AL	5,702	C
Univ of Central Florida	FL	6,061	C+
Univ of Denver	CO	19,290	C+
Univ of Nebr-Lincoln	NE	5,278	LC
Univ of San Francisco	CA	18,408	C
Univ of Wisc/Stout	WI	4,719	C

HOTEL/MOTEL AND RESTAURANT MANAGEMENT

School	ST	$IS	SR
Appalachian State Univ	NC	4,095	C
Arkansas Tech Univ	AR	4,200	NC
Ashland Univ	OH	15,508	C
Auburn Univ	AL	5,823	C+
Barber-Scotia College	NC	6,840	NC
Belmont Univ	TN	10,540	C
Berea College	KY	2,883	VC+
Berry College	GA	11,990	VC
Bethune-Cookman College	FL	8,375	LC
Black Hills State Univ	SD	4,831	NC
Boston Univ	MA	24,130	HC
Bowling Green State Univ	OH	6,701	C
Brigham Young Univ/Hawaii	HI	6,750	VC
Calif State Polytechnic Univ/Pomona	CA	6,438	LC
Central Missouri State Univ	MO	5,138	LC
Cheyney Univ of Penn	PA	7,005	C
Chicago State Univ	IL	2,198	C
CUNY/New York City Technical College	NY	2,405	NC
College of the Ozarks	MO	2,000	VC+
Colo State Univ	CO	6,566	VC
Concord College	WV	5,104	NC
Cornell Univ	NY	13,445	MC
Davenport College of Business	MI	8,121	NC
Davis and Elkins College	WV	13,230	LC
Delaware State College	DE	5,656	C
Drexel Univ	PA	15,970	C
East Stroudsburg Univ	PA	6,886	C
Eastern Illinois Univ	IL	5,548	C
Fairleigh Dickinson Univ	NJ	16,427	C
Florida Southern College	FL	12,260	C
Florida State Univ	FL	5,814	VC
Georgia Southern Univ	GA	4,988	LC
Golden Gate Univ	CA	5,623	VC
Grambling State Univ	LA	4,712	NC
Grand Valley State Univ	MI	6,822	VC
Howard Univ	DC	11,680	C
Huron Univ	SD	9,790	C
Huston-Tillotson College	TX	8,490	C
Incarnate Word College	TX	12,307	C
Indiana State Univ	IN	6,210	C
Indiana Univ of Penn	PA	6,373	C
Iowa State Univ	IA	5,456	C
James Madison Univ	VA	8,198	HC
Johnson and Wales Univ	RI	13,995	LC
Kansas State Univ	KS	4,816	NC
Kendall College	IL	12,651	LC
Lake Superior State Univ	MI	7,311	C
Lebanon Valley College of Penn	PA	18,300	C
Lynn Univ	FL	18,300	C
Marywood College	PA	14,890	C
Mercy College	NY	11,180	NC
Mercyhurst College	PA	13,488	C
Moorhead State Univ	MN	5,076	C
Mount Mary College	WI	10,920	C
New Hampshire College	NH	15,242	LC
New York Inst of Tech/Old Westbury	NY	13,914	LC
New York Univ	NY	24,705	VC+
Niagara Univ	NY	14,552	C
Norfolk State Univ	VA	6,345	LC
N Car Wesleyan College	NC	12,480	LC
N Dak State Univ of Agriculture and Applied Science	ND	4,774	VC
Northeastern State Univ	OK	5,250	C
Northern Arizona Univ	AZ	4,844	C
Okla State Univ	OK	5,086	VC
Olivet Nazarene Univ	IL	11,976	C
Oregon State Univ	OR	6,175	C
Penn State Univ/Univ Park Campus	PA	8,752	HC
Purdue Univ/Calumet	IN	2,374	NC
Purdue Univ/West Lafayette	IN	6,636	C
Rochester Inst of Tech	NY	18,954	VC
Roosevelt Univ	IL	12,368	C
St Leo College	FL	13,570	C
St Thomas Univ	FL	14,280	LC
Shepherd College	WV	5,540	C
Siena Heights College	MI	12,520	C
S Dak State Univ	SD	4,562	C
Southern Illinois Univ at Carbondale	IL	6,234	C
Southern Vermont College	VT	12,974	C
Southwest Missouri State Univ	MO	4,956	C
Southwest State Univ	MN	5,400	NC
SUNY/College at Plattsburgh	NY	6,917	C
Tenn State Univ	TN	4,626	C+
Texas Tech Univ	TX	6,008	C
Tiffin Univ	OH	10,800	LC
United States International Univ	CA	14,535	LC
Univ of Arkansas at Pine Bluff	AR	3,978	LC
Univ of Central Okla	OK	3,647	C
Univ of Delaware	DE	8,013	VC
Univ of Georgia	GA	5,655	VC
Univ of Houston	TX	5,215	C
Univ of Illinois at Urbana-Champaign	IL	7,764	HC
Univ of Kentucky	KY	5,152	VC
Univ of Maryland/Eastern Shore	MD	6,254	LC
Univ of Mass/Amherst	MA	9,364	LC
Univ of Minn/Crookston	MN	6,894	NC
Univ of Missouri/Columbia	MO	6,254	HC
Univ of Nevada/Las Vegas	NV	6,405	C
Univ of New Hampshire	NH	8,242	C
Univ of New Haven	CT	14,980	C
Univ of New Orleans	LA	5,468	C
Univ of N Car at Greensboro	NC	5,192	C
Univ of North Texas	TX	4,853	C
Univ of S Car	SC	6,158	C
Univ of Southern Miss	MS	4,542	C
Univ of Southwestern Louisiana	LA	3,968	NC
Univ of Tenn/Knoxville	TN	5,668	C
Virginia Polytechnic Inst and State Univ	VA	6,828	C
Virginia State Univ	VA	7,040	
Washington State Univ	WA	6,364	C
Webber College	FL	8,710	C
Western Kentucky Univ	KY	4,808	C
Widener Univ	PA	16,840	C
Wiley College	TX	0	NC
Youngstown State Univ	OH	6,447	LC

HUMAN DEVELOPMENT

School	ST	$IS	SR
Boston College	MA	22,706	MC
Bradford College	MA	19,600	C
Brescia College	KY	9,800	C
Brigham Young Univ	UT	5,625	HC
Cal State/Hayward	CA	5,495	C
Colo State Univ	CO	6,566	VC
Cornell Univ	NY	13,445	MC
Earlham College	IN	19,383	VC
Eckerd College	FL	18,855	VC
Indiana Univ Bloomington	IN	6,495	VC
Mount Vernon College	DC	20,668	C
National-Louis Univ	IL	13,218	C
Northwestern Univ	IL	21,093	MC
Oregon State Univ	OR	6,175	C
Radford Univ	VA	7,034	LC
Rivier College	NH	14,920	LC

School	ST	$IS	SR
St Mary College	KS	11,250	C
St Mary's College of Maryland	MD	8,900	VC+
SUNY/Empire State College	NY	2,687	NC
Suffolk Univ	MA	15,360	LC
Tusculum College	TN	10,400	LC
Univ of Alabama	AL	5,702	C
Univ of Arkansas at Fayetteville	AR	5,046	C
Univ of Calif at Davis	CA	9,534	VC
Univ of Calif at Los Angeles	CA	8,959	HC
Univ of Calif, Riverside	CA	9,178	C
Univ of Conn	CT	9,168	C
Univ of Delaware	DE	8,013	VC
Univ of Mass/Amherst	MA	9,364	LC
Univ of Nebr at Kearney	NE	4,308	LC
Univ of Nebr-Lincoln	NE	5,278	LC
Univ of the Pacific	CA	21,100	C
Univ of Wisc/Green Bay	WI	4,904	C
Utah State Univ	UT	4,683	C
Vanderbilt Univ	TN	23,422	HC+
Warner Pacific College	OR	12,112	C
Wayne State Univ	MI	2,680	C
Westminster College of Salt Lake City	UT	12,100	C
Wheelock College	MA	18,000	LC

HUMAN ECOLOGY

School	ST	$IS	SR
Allegheny College	PA	21,020	VC
Aquinas College	MI	14,526	C
College of the Atlantic	ME	17,147	VC
Liberty Univ	VA	11,500	LC
Marywood College	PA	14,890	C
Rutgers Univ/Cook College	NJ	9,197	HC
St Norbert College	WI	15,710	VC
Seton Hill College	PA	14,320	C
SUNY at Binghamton	NY	7,921	HC
Univ of Miami	FL	22,107	VC
Univ of Mich/Ann Arbor	MI	9,428	HC+
Univ of St Thomas	MN	15,785	C+

HUMAN RESOURCES

School	ST	$IS	SR
Bartlesville Wesleyan College	OK	9,400	C
Bluefield College	VA	10,600	C
Boston College	MA	22,706	MC
Briar Cliff College	IA	13,375	C
Brigham Young Univ	UT	5,625	HC
Cabrini College	PA	16,012	C
Calif State Polytechnic Univ/Pomona	CA	6,438	LC
Cal State/Los Angeles	CA	4,940	VC
College of St Mary	NE	12,500	C
Colo Christian Univ	CO	9,750	C
Concordia College	MI	13,660	C
Drexel Univ	PA	15,970	C
Friends Univ	KS	11,205	C
Geneva College	PA	13,030	C
Grand Canyon Univ	AZ	9,680	VC
Hawaii Pacific Univ	HI	12,300	C
Indiana Univ-Purdue Univ at Indianapolis	IN	5,862	LC
Kentucky Wesleyan College	KY	11,550	C
Le Moyne College	NY	15,180	C
Marquette Univ	WI	16,114	VC
Medaille College	NY	12,650	C
Menlo College	CA	20,375	LC
Mich Christian College	MI	8,094	C
National Univ	CA	6,135	C
Niagara Univ	NY	14,552	C
Northeastern Univ	MA	19,851	C
Northwestern College	MN	13,554	C
Notre Dame College of Ohio	OH	11,370	C
Oakland Univ	MI	6,714	VC
Ohio State Univ	OH	7,218	LC
Our Lady of the Lake Univ of San Antonio	TX	11,080	C
Palm Beach Atlantic College	FL	10,720	C
Point Park College	PA	13,922	LC
Quincy Univ	IL	13,646	VC
Robert Morris College	PA	10,406	LC
Roberts Wesleyan College	NY	13,317	C
St Francis College	PA	15,744	LC
St Mary's Univ	TX	12,064	C
St Thomas Univ	FL	14,280	LC
Simpson College	CA	10,628	C
Tarleton State Univ	TX	4,082	LC
Temple Univ	PA	10,281	C
Univ of Alabama	AL	5,702	C
Univ of Miami	FL	22,107	VC
Univ of New Haven	CT	14,980	C
Univ of North Texas	TX	4,853	C
Western Mich Univ	MI	6,820	C
Xavier Univ	OH	15,710	C+
York College	NE	7,610	C

HUMAN SERVICES

School	ST	$IS	SR
Albertus Magnus College	CT	16,280	LC
Asbury College	KY	11,105	VC
Audrey Cohen College	NY	11,184	LC
Boricua College	NY	5,920	VC
Boston Univ	MA	24,130	HC
Burlington College	VT	6,150	NC
Cal State/Dominguez Hills	CA	2,857	LC
Cal State/San Bernardino	CA	6,055	LC
Charter Oak State College	CT	314	NC
Chatham College	PA	18,010	C
College of Great Falls	MT	6,230	NC
College of St Joseph	VT	12,650	LC
College of St Mary	NE	12,500	C
College of Santa Fe	NM	14,008	C
Cornell Univ	NY	13,445	MC
Doane College	NE	12,220	C
East Central Univ	OK	3,558	C
Elmira College	NY	18,450	C
Elon College	NC	12,290	LC
Fitchburg State College	MA	6,962	C
Fontbonne College	MO	12,090	C
Friends Univ	KS	11,205	C
George Washington Univ	DC	22,470	HC
Hastings College	NE	12,426	C
Hawaii Pacific Univ	HI	12,300	C
Henderson State Univ	AR	3,860	C
Holy Names College	CA	15,660	C
Indiana Inst of Tech	IN	11,810	C
La Roche College	PA	12,977	LC
Lake Superior State Univ	MI	7,311	C
Lesley College	MA	17,120	LC
Limestone College	SC	10,700	LC
Lincoln Univ	PA	0	LC
Lindsey Wilson College	KY	9,530	LC
Lyndon State College	VT	8,394	LC
Lynn Univ	FL	18,300	C
Marian College of Fond du Lac	WI	12,250	C
Medaille College	NY	12,650	C
Mesa State College	CO	5,127	NC
Metropolitan State College of Denver	CO	1,751	NC
Missouri Valley College	MO	14,050	LC
Mount St Mary College	NY	12,910	C
National-Louis Univ	IL	13,218	C
Northeastern Univ	MA	19,851	C
Northwest Nazarene College	ID	11,750	C
Oglala Lakota College	SD	0	
Ottawa Univ	KS	10,490	C+
Peru State College	NE	4,311	NC
Russell Sage College	NY	16,790	C
St John's Univ	NY	8,980	C+
St Joseph's Univ	PA	17,800	VC
St Mary College	KS	11,250	C
St Mary's College	MI	8,350	C
St Mary's College of Minn	MN	13,850	LC
Simmons College	MA	22,534	C
Sinte Gleska Univ	SD	1,580	NC
S Car State Univ	SC	5,424	LC
S Dak State Univ	SD	4,562	C
Southern Vermont College	VT	12,974	C
Southwest Baptist Univ	MO	9,192	NC
Springfield College	MA	15,200	LC
SUNY/College at Plattsburgh	NY	6,917	C
Teikyo Westmar Univ	IA	15,920	C
Thomas A. Edison State College	NJ	400	
Trinity College of Vermont	VT	16,015	LC
Troy State Univ	AL	4,322	C
Univ of Alaska Fairbanks	AK	4,718	C
Univ of Bridgeport	CT	18,985	C
Univ of Hartford	CT	19,858	LC
Univ of Maine at Machias	ME	6,135	C
Univ of Mass/Boston	MA	4,253	C
Univ of N Car at Charlotte	NC	4,597	C
Univ of Scranton	PA	17,071	VC
Univ of Tenn at Chattanooga	TN	5,375	C
Univ of Tenn/Knoxville	TN	5,668	C
Univ of Wisc/Oshkosh	WI	4,240	C
Upper Iowa Univ	IA	11,900	C
Villanova Univ	PA	21,400	HC
Viterbo College	WI	12,670	C
Wayland Baptist Univ	TX	7,811	NC
Western Mich Univ	MI	6,820	C
Western New Mexico Univ	NM	3,234	LC
Wingate College	NC	10,610	C

HUMANITIES

School	ST	$IS	SR
Albertus Magnus College	CT	16,280	LC
Alderson-Broaddus College	WV	12,000	C
Arizona State Univ Main Campus	AZ	6,444	C
Augustana College	IL	16,959	VC
Aurora Univ	IL	13,381	C
Barat College	IL	13,990	C
Belhaven College	MS	9,690	C+
Biola Univ	CA	16,124	C
Bloomsburg Univ of Penn	PA	6,312	C+
Bluefield State College	WV	1,832	LC
Bluffton College	OH	12,951	C
Bradford College	MA	19,600	C
Brigham Young Univ	UT	5,625	HC
Burlington College	VT	6,150	NC
Calif State Polytechnic Univ/Pomona	CA	6,438	LC
Cal State/Chico	CA	6,146	C
Cazenovia College	NY	14,655	LC
Chaminade Univ of Honolulu	HI	14,290	C
Charleston Southern Univ	SC	10,282	LC
Charter Oak State College	CT	314	NC
Christian Brothers Univ	TN	12,120	VC
Clarkson Univ	NY	20,705	VC+
Clearwater Christian College	FL	8,500	LC
College of Mount St Joseph	OH	13,272	C
College of Notre Dame	CA	16,480	C
College of St Benedict	MN	15,468	VC
College of St Mary	NE	12,500	C
College of Santa Fe	NM	14,008	C
Colo State Univ	CO	6,566	VC
Concordia College	MI	13,660	C
Concordia College	OR	12,300	C
Concordia College/Moorhead	MN	12,750	C
Concordia Univ	CA	14,675	C
Concordia Univ Wisc	WI	12,140	C
Daemen College	NY	13,020	LC
Dana College	NE	11,910	C
Dominican College	NY	13,600	LC
Dominican College of San Rafael	CA	17,860	C
Dowling College	NY	12,730	LC
Drexel Univ	PA	15,970	C
Eastern Washington Univ	WA	5,439	LC
Eckerd College	FL	18,855	VC
Edinboro Univ of Penn	PA	7,181	C
Fairleigh Dickinson Univ	NJ	16,427	C
Felician College	NJ	7,900	C
Florida Inst of Tech	FL	16,935	VC
Florida International Univ	FL	4,191	VC
Florida State Univ	FL	5,814	VC
Fort Lewis College	CO	5,097	C
Georgian Court College	NJ	12,550	C
Guilford College	NC	17,680	C
Hampden-Sydney College	VA	17,372	C+
Hampshire College	MA	25,320	C
Harvard Univ/Harvard and Radcliffe Colleges	MA	24,880	MC
Hawaii Pacific Univ	HI	12,300	C
Hofstra Univ	NY	16,580	VC
Holy Names College	CA	15,660	C
Houghton College	NY	13,120	VC
Indiana Univ at Kokomo	IN	2,069	C
John Carroll Univ	OH	16,510	C
Lawrence Tech Univ	MI	9,470	C
Lees-McRae College	NC	9,850	LC
LeMoyne-Owen College	TN	4,500	LC
Linfield College	OR	16,670	VC
Loyola Marymount Univ	CA	18,560	C
Lynn Univ	FL	18,300	C
Marshall Univ	WV	5,762	LC
Martin Univ	IN	4,830	NC
Marygrove College	MI	5,877	VC
Marylhurst College	OR	6,486	NC
Mass Inst of Tech	MA	24,800	MC
Medaille College	NY	12,650	C
Menlo College	CA	20,375	LC
Messiah College	PA	14,664	VC
Mich State Univ	MI	7,842	C
Midwestern State Univ	TX	4,542	LC
Montclair State College	NJ	7,539	C+
Mount Vernon College	DC	20,668	C
New College of the Univ of South Florida	FL	5,697	MC
New Hampshire College	NH	15,242	LC
N Dak State Univ of Agriculture and Applied Science	ND	4,774	VC
Northern Montana College	MT	4,976	C
Northwest Missouri State Univ	MO	5,010	LC
Okla City Univ	OK	9,840	C
Pacific Univ	OR	17,869	C
Pepperdine Univ	CA	23,720	VC
Plymouth State College	NH	7,166	C
Polytechnic Univ/Brooklyn	NY	19,700	HC
Providence College	RI	19,750	VC
Quincy Univ	IL	13,646	VC
Rockford College	IL	15,300	C
Rutgers Univ/Livingston College	NJ	8,877	VC
Rutgers Univ/Newark College of A&S	NJ	8,645	C
Rutgers Univ/Rutgers College	NJ	8,841	HC+
Rutgers Univ/Univ College—New Brunswick	NJ	0	LC
St John's Univ	MN	15,364	C
St Joseph College	CT	16,226	C
St Joseph's Univ	PA	17,800	VC
St Martin's College	WA	14,965	C
St Mary's College	IN	17,043	VC
St Norbert College	WI	15,710	VC
St Peter's College	NJ	14,775	LC
Sam Houston State Univ	TX	4,506	C
San Francisco State Univ	CA	7,292	LC
Schreiner College	TX	14,320	C
Shawnee State Univ	OH	4,379	NC
Shimer College	IL	12,850	NC
Siena Heights College	MI	12,520	C
Sierra Nevada College	NV	14,000	NC
Southern Methodist Univ	TX	18,520	VC
Stanford Univ	CA	24,310	MC
SUNY at Stony Brook	NY	7,658	VC
SUNY/College at Buffalo	NY	7,035	VC
SUNY/College at Old Westbury	NY	7,128	LC
SUNY/Maritime College	NY	7,170	C
Stephen F. Austin State Univ	TX	5,117	C
Suffolk Univ	MA	15,360	LC
Texas Wesleyan Univ	TX	9,380	LC
Thomas A. Edison State College	NJ	400	
Turabo Univ	PR	2,670	
United States Air Force Academy	CO	0	MC
Universidad Metropolitana	PR	2,650	
Univ of Akron	OH	6,699	NC
Univ of Alaska Fairbanks	AK	4,718	C
Univ of Calif at Berkeley	CA	9,962	HC+
Univ of Calif, Riverside	CA	9,178	C
Univ of Calif/Irvine	CA	12,680	VC
Univ of Central Florida	FL	6,061	C+
Univ of Charleston	WV	12,750	C
Univ of Colo at Boulder	CO	6,410	VC
Univ of Houston-Downtown	TX	4,034	NC
Univ of Kansas	KS	5,200	NC
Univ of Louisville	KY	5,948	C
Univ of Maine at Presque Isle	ME	6,374	C
Univ of Maryland/Univ College	MD	4,900	NC
Univ of Mass Dartmouth	MA	8,158	C
Univ of Mich/Ann Arbor	MI	9,428	HC+
Univ of Mich/Dearborn	MI	3,399	HC
Univ of Minn/Twin Cities	MN	6,682	VC
Univ of New Hampshire	NH	8,242	C
Univ of N Dak	ND	4,902	NC
Univ of Northern Iowa	IA	5,137	C
Univ of Penn	PA	24,238	MC
Univ of Pittsburgh	PA	9,472	C
Univ of Pittsburgh at Greensburg	PA	8,660	C
Univ of PR/Cayey Univ College	PR	900	
Univ of Redlands	CA	22,059	VC
Univ of Rio Grande	OH	6,300	NC
Univ of San Diego	CA	18,970	VC
Univ of S Dak	SD	4,722	C
Univ of Tenn at Chattanooga	TN	5,375	C
Univ of Texas at Austin	TX	5,160	VC
Univ of Texas at San Antonio	TX	6,420	C
Univ of the Virgin Islands	VI	5,896	C
Univ of Wisc/Green Bay	WI	4,904	C
Univ of Wisc/Madison	WI	6,400	HC
Univ of Wisc/Parkside	WI	5,247	C
Univ of Wyoming	WY	4,991	NC
Ursuline College	OH	13,180	LC
Warren Wilson College	NC	10,877	C
Washington College	MD	19,270	C+
Washington Univ	MO	23,507	HC
Wayne State Univ	MI	2,680	C
Western Baptist College	OR	12,400	LC
Western New Mexico Univ	NM	3,234	LC
Western Oregon State College	OR	6,180	C
Widener Univ	PA	16,840	C
Willamette Univ	OR	17,995	VC
Wofford College	SC	15,360	VC
Wright State Univ	OH	6,896	LC
Yale Univ	CT	25,110	MC
York College of Penn	PA	8,345	C

HUMANITIES AND SOCIAL SCIENCE

School	ST	$IS	SR
Franciscan Univ of Steubenville	OH	13,400	C
Lock Haven Univ of Penn	PA	7,128	C
SUNY/Empire State College	NY	2,687	NC
Univ of Okla	OK	5,427	VC

HYDROLOGY

School	ST	$IS	SR
Univ of New Hampshire	NH	8,242	C

ILLUSTRATION

School	ST	$IS	SR
Anna Maria College	MA	15,975	LC
Art Academy of Cincinnati	OH	8,820	SP
Art Center College of Design	CA	13,550	SP
Art Inst of Southern Calif	CA	16,000	SP
Atlanta College of Art	GA	12,495	SP
Brigham Young Univ	UT	5,625	HC
Center for Creative Studies/ College of Art and Design	MI	15,330	SP
Columbia College	MO	11,995	C
Columbus College of Art and Design	OH	14,550	SP
Fashion Inst of Tech/SUNY	NY	7,135	SP
Iowa State Univ	IA	5,456	C
Kendall College of Art and Design	MI	9,600	SP
Milwaukee Inst of Art and Design	WI	9,800	SP
Montserrat College of Art	MA	12,500	SP
Moore College of Art and Design	PA	17,947	SP
Northern Mich Univ	MI	6,350	C
Otis College of Art and Design	CA	16,686	SP
Pacific Northwest College of Art	OR	7,700	SP
Paier College of Art	CT	10,120	SP
Parsons School of Design	NY	21,410	SP
Rhode Island School of Design	RI	22,315	SP
Ringling School of Art and Design	FL	15,750	SP
Sacred Heart Univ	CT	16,350	C
Savannah College of Art and Design	GA	14,280	SP
School of Visual Arts	NY	17,120	SP
Syracuse Univ	NY	21,305	HC
Univ of Hartford	CT	19,858	LC
Univ of Mass Dartmouth	MA	8,158	C
Univ of San Francisco	CA	18,408	C
Univ of the Arts	PA	16,150	SP
Western Conn State Univ	CT	6,622	C

INDIC LANGUAGES

School	ST	$IS	SR
Univ of La Verne	CA	17,400	C

INDUSTRIAL ADMINISTRATION/ MANAGEMENT

School	ST	$IS	SR
Aurora Univ	IL	13,381	C
Brigham Young Univ	UT	5,625	HC
Calumet College of St. Joseph	IN	3,585	C
Central Mich Univ	MI	6,737	LC
Central Missouri State Univ	MO	5,138	LC
Cheyney Univ of Penn	PA	7,005	C
Clarion Univ of Penn	PA	6,518	C
Clarkson Univ	NY	20,705	VC+
Clemson Univ	SC	6,564	VC
Detroit College of Business	MI	5,184	NC
Dyke College	OH	5,200	C
Edinboro Univ of Penn	PA	7,181	C
Gannon Univ	PA	14,872	C
Gardner-Webb Univ	NC	11,950	LC
Grove City College	PA	7,870	HC
Indiana Univ/South Bend	IN	2,141	LC
Kansas Newman College	KS	10,640	C
Kent State Univ	OH	6,740	LC
Lawrence Tech Univ	MI	9,470	C
Le Tourneau Univ	TX	12,500	C+
Metropolitan State College of Denver	CO	1,751	NC
Mich State Univ	MI	7,842	C
Middle Tenn State Univ	TN	3,857	C
N Dak State Univ of Agriculture and Applied Science	ND	4,774	VC
Northeast Louisiana Univ	LA	3,906	NC
Northern State Univ	SD	4,186	LC
Northwood Univ	FL	14,569	C
Northwood Univ	MI	13,385	LC
Oregon Inst of Tech	OR	5,985	C
Pace Univ	NY	15,540	C
Peru State College	NE	4,311	NC
Rochester Inst of Tech	NY	18,954	VC
Saginaw Valley State Univ	MI	6,634	LC
St Augustine's College	NC	9,300	C+
San Francisco State Univ	CA	7,292	LC
Southern College of Tech	GA	4	C
Southwest Missouri State Univ	MO	4,956	C
Southwest Texas State Univ	TX	5,124	C
SUNY/Potsdam College	NY	6,906	C
Syracuse Univ	NY	21,305	HC
Tri-State Univ	IN	13,788	LC
Universidad Politecnica de PR	PR	6,195	C
Univ of Alabama	AL	5,702	C
Univ of Alabama at Birmingham	AL	7,533	C
Univ of Arkansas at Fayetteville	AR	5,046	C
Univ of Cincinnati	OH	7,989	C
Univ of Indianapolis	IN	14,510	C
Univ of Iowa	IA	5,658	VC
Univ of N Car at Chapel Hill	NC	5,330	HC
Univ of N Car at Charlotte	NC	4,597	C
Univ of North Texas	TX	4,853	C
Univ of Wisc/Milwaukee	WI	6,165	C
Univ of Wisc/Parkside	WI	5,247	
Wayland Baptist Univ	TX	7,811	NC
West Virginia Inst of Tech	WV	5,858	LC
Western New England College	MA	14,674	LC
Xavier Univ	OH	15,710	C+
Youngstown State Univ	OH	6,447	LC

INDUSTRIAL ARTS EDUCATION

School	ST	$IS	SR
Abilene Christian Univ	TX	10,460	NC
Alabama A&M Univ	AL	4,200	C
Alcorn State Univ	MS	4,474	C+
Appalachian State Univ	NC	4,095	C
Auburn Univ	AL	5,823	C+
Ball State Univ	IN	6,032	LC
Bemidji State Univ	MN	5,188	C
Berea College	KY	2,883	VC+
Black Hills State Univ	SD	4,831	NC
Brigham Young Univ	UT	5,625	HC
Calif Polytechnic State Univ	CA	6,980	VC+
Cal State/Fresno	CA	5,747	C
Cal State/Long Beach	CA	6,057	LC
Cal State/Los Angeles	CA	4,940	VC
Calif Univ of Penn	PA	7,370	C
Central Mich Univ	MI	6,737	LC
Central Missouri State Univ	MO	5,138	LC
Central State Univ	OH	7,320	NC
Central Washington Univ	WA	5,644	C
Chicago State Univ	IL	2,198	C
CUNY/City College	NY	2,543	VC
Clemson Univ	SC	6,564	VC
College of the Ozarks	MO	2,000	VC+
Concordia College	NE	11,776	NC
East Central Univ	OK	3,558	C
East Texas State Univ	TX	4,572	LC
Eastern Kentucky Univ	KY	4,840	NC
Eastern Mich Univ	MI	6,749	C
Elizabeth City State Univ	NC	4,254	LC
Fitchburg State College	MA	6,962	C
Florida A&M Univ	FL	4,651	C
Fort Hays State Univ	KS	4,675	NC
George Mason Univ	VA	8,728	C
Grambling State Univ	LA	4,712	NC
Humboldt State Univ	CA	5,676	C
Indiana State Univ	IN	6,210	C
Iowa State Univ	IA	5,456	C
Jackson State Univ	MS	4,996	LC
Kean College of New Jersey	NJ	6,395	LC
Keene State College	NH	7,081	C
Langston Univ	OK	2,907	LC
Livingston Univ	AL	3,979	C
Louisiana State Univ and A&M College	LA	5,605	C
Mankato State Univ	MN	5,097	LC
McPherson College	KS	11,360	VC
Middle Tenn State Univ	TN	3,857	C
Miss Valley State Univ	MS	4,089	NC
Missouri Southern State College	MO	4,272	
Moorhead State Univ	MN	5,076	C
Morehead State Univ	KY	4,600	LC
Murray State Univ	KY	4,702	C
Norfolk State Univ	VA	6,345	LC
N Car Agricultural and Technical State Univ	NC	4,477	LC
N Car State Univ	NC	4,984	VC
Northeastern State Univ	OK	5,250	C
Northern Arizona Univ	AZ	4,844	C
Northern Illinois Univ	IL	6,408	C
Northern Kentucky Univ	KY	4,620	NC
Northern Mich Univ	MI	6,350	C
Northern Montana College	MT	4,976	C
Northern State Univ	SD	4,186	LC
Northwestern Okla State Univ	OK	3,424	C
Northwestern State Univ of Louisiana	LA	4,287	NC
Ohio Univ	OH	7,341	C
Okla Panhandle State Univ	OK	3,155	NC
Okla State Univ	OK	5,086	VC
Penn State Univ/Univ Park Campus	PA	8,752	HC
Peru State College	NE	4,311	NC
Pittsburg State Univ	KS	4,478	NC
Rhode Island College	RI	7,901	LC
St Cloud State Univ	MN	5,015	C
San Francisco State Univ	CA	7,292	LC
S Car State Univ	SC	5,424	LC
Southeast Missouri State Univ	MO	5,854	C
Southeastern Louisiana Univ	LA	4,230	NC
Southeastern Okla State Univ	OK	3,594	C
Southern Univ and A&M College	LA	4,920	NC
Southwest Missouri State Univ	MO	4,956	C
Southwest Texas State Univ	TX	5,124	C
Southwestern Okla State Univ	OK	3,312	C
SUNY/College at Buffalo	NY	7,035	VC
SUNY/College at Oswego	NY	7,330	VC
Sul Ross State Univ	TX	4,144	NC
Tarleton State Univ	TX	4,082	LC
Temple Univ	PA	10,281	C
Texas Southern Univ	TX	4,500	NC
The Univ of New Mexico	NM	5,304	C
Univ of Arkansas at Fayetteville	AR	5,046	C
Univ of Arkansas at Pine Bluff	AR	3,978	LC
Univ of Central Arkansas	AR	4,200	LC
Univ of Central Okla	OK	3,647	C
Univ of Cincinnati	OH	7,989	C
Univ of Georgia	GA	5,655	VC
Univ of Idaho	ID	4,830	C
Univ of Kentucky	KY	5,152	VC
Univ of Maryland/College Park	MD	8,182	VC
Univ of Maryland/Eastern Shore	MD	6,254	LC
Univ of Minn/Twin Cities	MN	6,682	VC
Univ of Missouri/Columbia	MO	6,254	HC
Univ of Nebr at Kearney	NE	4,308	LC
Univ of Nebr-Lincoln	NE	5,278	LC
Univ of New Hampshire	NH	8,242	C
Univ of N Dak	ND	4,902	NC
Univ of PR/Rio Piedras	PR	0	
Univ of South Florida	FL	5,475	C+
Univ of Southern Maine	ME	7,299	C
Univ of Southern Miss	MS	4,542	C
Univ of Southwestern Louisiana	LA	3,968	NC
Univ of Tenn/Knoxville	TN	5,668	C
Univ of Wyoming	WY	4,991	NC
Utah State Univ	UT	4,683	C
Valley City State Univ	ND	4,385	LC
Virginia State Univ	VA	7,040	
Walla Walla College	WA	13,215	C
Wayne State College	NE	4,260	NC
Wayne State Univ	MI	2,680	C
West Virginia Inst of Tech	WV	5,858	LC
Western Illinois Univ	IL	5,241	LC
Western Kentucky Univ	KY	4,808	C
Western Mich Univ	MI	6,820	C
Western Montana College of the Univ of Montana	MT	1,646	C
Western State College of Colo	CO	5,560	C
Wichita State Univ	KS	5,068	NC
William Penn College	IA	13,400	C

INDUSTRIAL DESIGN

School	ST	$IS	SR
Arizona State Univ Main Campus	AZ	6,444	C
Art Center College of Design	CA	13,550	SP
Auburn Univ	AL	5,823	C+
Bassist College	OR	12,590	SP
Brigham Young Univ	UT	5,625	HC
Center for Creative Studies/ College of Art and Design	MI	15,330	SP
Cleveland Inst of Art	OH	15,630	SP
Columbus College of Art and Design	OH	14,550	SP
Georgia Inst of Tech	GA	6,669	HC+
Kendall College of Art and Design	MI	9,600	SP
Kent State Univ	OH	6,740	LC
Mass College of Art	MA	9,447	SP
Metropolitan State College of Denver	CO	1,751	NC
Milwaukee Inst of Art and Design	WI	9,800	SP
N Car State Univ	NC	4,984	VC
Pratt Inst	NY	19,520	C
Rhode Island School of Design	RI	22,315	SP
Rochester Inst of Tech	NY	18,954	VC
Syracuse Univ	NY	21,305	HC
Univ of Bridgeport	CT	18,985	C
Univ of Illinois at Chicago	IL	8,443	C
Univ of Illinois at Urbana-Champaign	IL	7,764	HC
Univ of Mich/Ann Arbor	MI	9,428	HC+
Univ of the Arts	PA	16,150	SP
Univ of Washington	WA	6,618	VC
Wentworth Inst of Tech	MA	15,250	LC

INDUSTRIAL ENGINEERING

School	ST	$IS	SR
Albertus Magnus College	CT	16,280	LC
Alfred Univ	NY	21,054	VC+
Arizona State Univ Main Campus	AZ	6,444	C
Boston Univ	MA	24,130	HC
Bradley Univ	IL	14,718	C+
Calif Polytechnic State Univ	CA	6,980	VC+
Calif State Polytechnic Univ/ Pomona	CA	6,438	LC
Cal State/Fresno	CA	5,747	C
Case Western Reserve Univ	OH	19,910	HC
Central State Univ	OH	7,320	NC
Clemson Univ	SC	6,564	VC
Cleveland State Univ	OH	7,287	NC
Eastern Kentucky Univ	KY	4,840	NC
Elizabethtown College	PA	17,850	VC
Florida A&M Univ	FL	4,651	C
Florida International Univ	FL	4,191	VC
Florida State Univ	FL	5,814	VC
Geneva College	PA	13,030	C
Georgia Inst of Tech	GA	6,669	HC+
GMI Engineering & Management Inst	MI	14,158	HC
Hofstra Univ	NY	16,580	VC
Indiana Univ-Purdue Univ at Fort Wayne	IN	2,500	LC
Lakeland College	WI	12,845	LC
Lamar Univ	TX	3,798	C
Lehigh Univ	PA	23,250	HC
Louisiana State Univ and A&M College	LA	5,605	C
Louisiana Tech Univ	LA	4,284	C
Marietta College	OH	16,940	C+
Mass Maritime Academy	MA	7,410	C
Mercer Univ	GA	15,123	C
Milwaukee School of Engineering	WI	14,100	C
Miss State Univ	MS	5,629	VC
Montana State Univ	MT	5,534	C
Morris Brown College	GA	12,234	NC
New Jersey Inst of Tech	NJ	9,965	VC
New Mexico State Univ	NM	4,844	LC
New York Inst of Tech/Old Westbury	NY	13,914	LC
N Car Agricultural and Technical State Univ	NC	4,477	LC
N Car State Univ	NC	4,984	VC
Northeastern Univ	MA	19,851	C
Northern Illinois Univ	IL	6,408	C
Northwestern Univ	IL	21,093	MC
Oakland Univ	MI	6,714	VC
Ohio State Univ	OH	7,218	LC
Ohio Univ	OH	7,341	C
Okla State Univ	OK	5,086	VC
Purdue Univ/West Lafayette	IN	6,636	C
Rensselaer Polytechnic Inst	NY	23,067	HC
Rochester Inst of Tech	NY	18,954	VC
Rutgers Univ/Camden College of A&S	NJ	8,652	VC
Rutgers Univ/College of Engineering	NJ	9,254	HC
Rutgers Univ/Newark College of A&S	NJ	8,645	C
St Ambrose Univ	IA	13,380	C
St Augustine's College	NC	9,300	C+
St Mary's Univ	TX	12,064	C
San Jose State Univ	CA	6,680	LC
S Dak School of Mines and Tech	SD	5,329	C
Southern Illinois Univ at Edwardsville	IL	6,097	LC
Stanford Univ	CA	24,310	MC
SUNY at Buffalo	NY	7,896	VC
Tenn Tech Univ	TN	5,190	C
The Univ of New Mexico	NM	5,304	C
Universidad Politecnica de PR	PR	6,195	C
Univ of Alabama	AL	5,702	C
Univ of Alabama at Huntsville	AL	5,868	VC
Univ of Arizona	AZ	5,808	C
Univ of Arkansas at Fayetteville	AR	5,046	C
Univ of Calif at Berkeley	CA	9,962	HC+
Univ of Houston	TX	5,215	C
Univ of Houston-Downtown	TX	4,034	NC
Univ of Iowa	IA	5,658	VC
Univ of Mass/Amherst	MA	9,364	LC
Univ of Miami	FL	22,107	VC
Univ of Mich/Ann Arbor	MI	9,428	HC+
Univ of Mich/Dearborn	MI	3,399	HC
Univ of Minn/Duluth	MN	6,512	C
Univ of Minn/Twin Cities	MN	6,682	VC
Univ of Missouri/Columbia	MO	6,254	HC
Univ of Nebr at Omaha	NE	1,889	LC
Univ of Nebr-Lincoln	NE	5,278	LC
Univ of New Haven	CT	14,980	C
Univ of Okla	OK	5,427	VC
Univ of Pittsburgh	PA	9,472	C
Univ of PR/Mayaguez	PR	0	
Univ of Rhode Island	RI	9,205	C

School	ST	$IS	SR
Univ of Southern Colo	CO	5,350	LC
Univ of Southwestern Louisiana	LA	3,968	NC
Univ of Wisc/Madison	WI	6,400	HC
Univ of Wisc/Milwaukee	WI	6,165	C
Univ of Wisc/Platteville	WI	4,830	C
Utah State Univ	UT	4,683	C
West Coast Univ	CA	9,120	NC
West Virginia Univ	WV	5,774	C
Western Mich Univ	MI	6,820	C
Western New England College	MA	14,674	LC
Wheeling Jesuit College	WV	14,370	C
Wichita State Univ	KS	5,068	NC
Worcester Polytechnic Inst	MA	20,350	HC
Youngstown State Univ	OH	6,447	LC

INDUSTRIAL AND ORGANIZATIONAL PSYCHOLOGY

School	ST	$IS	SR
Albertus Magnus College	CT	16,280	LC
Bridgewater State College	MA	7,518	C
CUNY/Baruch College	NY	2,562	VC
High Point Univ	NC	12,350	LC
La Sierra Univ	CA	15,472	C
Nichols College	MA	14,200	LC
St Joseph's Univ	PA	17,800	VC
Suffolk Univ	MA	15,360	LC
Univ of New Haven	CT	14,980	C

INDUSTRIAL ENGINEERING TECHNOLOGY

School	ST	$IS	SR
Arizona State Univ Main Campus	AZ	6,444	C
Bemidji State Univ	MN	5,188	C
Cal State/Chico	CA	6,146	C
Cal State/Los Angeles	CA	4,940	VC
Caribbean Univ	PR	2,400	
Central Conn State Univ	CT	7,108	C
Chadron State College	NE	4,091	NC
Cheyney Univ of Penn	PA	7,005	C
Colo State Univ	CO	6,566	VC
Columbia Univ/School of Engineering and Applied Science	NY	24,554	HC
Elizabeth City State Univ	NC	4,254	LC
Fitchburg State College	MA	6,962	C
Gannon Univ	PA	14,872	C
Georgia Southern Univ	GA	4,988	LC
GMI Engineering & Management Inst	MI	14,158	HC
Grand Valley State Univ	MI	6,822	VC
Humboldt State Univ	CA	5,676	C
Illinois State Univ	IL	6,413	C
Indiana State Univ	IN	6,210	C
Iowa State Univ	IA	5,456	C
Jackson State Univ	MS	4,996	LC
Kansas State Univ	KS	4,816	NC
Keene State College	NH	7,081	C
Kent State Univ	OH	6,740	LC
Lamar Univ	TX	3,798	C
Langston Univ	OK	2,907	LC
Louisiana State Univ and A&M College	LA	5,605	C
Marquette Univ	WI	16,114	VC
Metropolitan State College of Denver	CO	1,751	NC
Millersville Univ of Penn	PA	7,370	VC
Miss State Univ	MS	5,629	VC
Morehead State Univ	KY	4,600	LC
Morgan State Univ	MD	7,366	C+
Northern Kentucky Univ	KY	4,620	NC
Northern Mich Univ	MI	6,350	C
Northern State Univ	SD	4,186	LC
Ohio Northern Univ	OH	18,660	VC
Oregon State Univ	OR	6,175	C
Pacific Union College	CA	15,075	C
Penn State Univ/Univ Park Campus	PA	8,752	HC
Peru State College	NE	4,311	NC
Pittsburg State Univ	KS	4,478	NC
Prairie View A&M Univ	TX	4,740	LC
Purdue Univ/Calumet	IN	2,374	NC
Purdue Univ/West Lafayette	IN	6,636	C
Rhode Island College	RI	7,901	LC
Salem-Teikyo Univ	WV	14,527	C
Southern College of Tech	GA	4	C
Southern Illinois Univ at Carbondale	IL	6,234	C
Southwest Texas State Univ	TX	5,124	C
Southwestern Okla State Univ	OK	3,312	C
SUNY/College at Buffalo	NY	7,035	VC
Sul Ross State Univ	TX	4,144	NC
Tarleton State Univ	TX	4,082	LC
Tenn Tech Univ	TN	5,190	C
Texas A&M Univ	TX	5,382	VC
Texas A&M Univ at Kingsville	TX	3,808	LC
Texas Tech Univ	TX	6,008	C
Univ of Arkansas at Pine Bluff	AR	3,978	LC
Univ of Central Florida	FL	6,061	C+
Univ of Cincinnati	OH	7,989	C
Univ of Dayton	OH	15,120	C+
Univ of Florida	FL	5,850	HC
Univ of Houston	TX	5,215	C
Univ of Illinois at Chicago	IL	8,443	C
Univ of Illinois at Urbana-Champaign	IL	7,764	HC
Univ of Louisville	KY	5,948	C
Univ of Lowell	MA	8,831	VC
Univ of Nebr at Kearney	NE	4,308	LC
Univ of Nebr-Lincoln	NE	5,278	LC
Univ of Northern Iowa	IA	5,137	C
Univ of Rio Grande	OH	6,300	NC
Univ of South Florida	FL	5,475	C+
Univ of Southern Calif	CA	23,006	VC
Univ of Southern Maine	ME	7,299	C
Univ of Texas at Arlington	TX	5,549	LC
Univ of Texas at El Paso	TX	3,160	LC
Univ of Toledo	OH	6,636	NC
Univ of Washington	WA	6,618	VC
Univ of Wisc/Platteville	WI	4,830	C
Univ of Wisc/Stout	WI	4,719	C
Utah State Univ	UT	4,683	C
Valley City State Univ	ND	4,385	LC
Wayne State Univ	MI	2,680	C
West Coast Univ	CA	9,120	NC
West Virginia Inst of Tech	WV	5,858	LC
Western Illinois Univ	IL	5,241	LC

INDUSTRIAL HYGIENE

School	ST	$IS	SR
Oakland Univ	MI	6,714	VC
Univ of North Alabama	AL	4,236	NC

INFORMATION SCIENCES AND SYSTEMS

School	ST	$IS	SR
Abilene Christian Univ	TX	10,460	NC
Alma College	MI	16,375	VC+
Alvernia College	PA	13,150	LC
American Univ	DC	21,230	VC+
Andrews Univ	MI	14,952	NC
Appalachian State Univ	NC	4,095	C
Auburn Univ at Montgomery	AL	3,390	C
Augustana College	SD	13,420	C
Avila College	MO	12,130	C
Azusa Pacific Univ	CA	15,034	C
Barat College	IL	13,990	C
Baylor Univ	TX	10,990	C+
Bellevue College	NE	3,050	NC
Benedictine College	KS	12,830	C
Bentley College	MA	18,680	C
Bethune-Cookman College	FL	8,375	LC
Birmingham-Southern College	AL	15,154	VC+
Boise State Univ	ID	4,909	LC
Boston College	MA	22,706	MC
Boston Univ	MA	24,130	HC
Bridgewater State College	MA	7,518	C
Brooklyn Campus of LIU	NY	15,000	LC
Bryant College	RI	18,335	C
Calif Lutheran Univ	CA	17,240	C
Calif State Polytechnic Univ/Pomona	CA	6,438	LC
Cal State/Los Angeles	CA	4,940	VC
Cal State/San Bernardino	CA	6,055	LC
Cal State/Stanislaus	CA	6,799	C
Calumet College of St. Joseph	IN	3,585	C
Carlow College	PA	13,914	C
Carnegie Mellon Univ	PA	22,560	HC+
Castleton State College	VT	8,378	LC
Catawba College	NC	12,950	C
Cedarville College	OH	10,715	C
Central Missouri State Univ	MO	5,138	LC
Central State Univ	OH	7,320	NC
Central Washington Univ	WA	5,644	C
Chadron State College	NE	4,091	NC
Chatham College	PA	18,010	C
Chicago State Univ	IL	2,198	C
Christian Brothers Univ	TN	12,120	VC
Christopher Newport Univ	VA	3,196	LC
CUNY/Brooklyn College	NY	2,450	VC
CUNY/John Jay College of Criminal Justice	NY	2,501	LC
CUNY/York College	NY	2,534	NC
Claremont McKenna College	CA	22,150	MC
Clarion Univ of Penn	PA	6,518	C
Clarke College	IA	13,950	C+
Clayton State College	GA	1,496	LC
Clemson Univ	SC	6,564	VC
Cleveland State Univ	OH	7,287	NC
Clinch Valley College/Univ of Virginia	VA	6,364	C
College Misericordia	PA	15,820	C
College of Notre Dame of Maryland	MD	16,050	C
College of St Catherine	MN	14,670	C
College of St Francis	IL	13,060	VC
College of Santa Fe	NM	14,008	C
Colo State Univ	CO	6,566	VC
Columbia Union College	MD	13,650	LC
Concord College	WV	5,104	NC
Dakota State Univ	SD	4,374	LC
Dana College	NE	11,910	C
DePaul Univ	IL	15,535	VC
Detroit College of Business	MI	5,184	NC
DeVry/Addison (DuPage County)	IL	5,609	LC
DeVry/Atlanta	GA	5,609	LC
DeVry/Chicago	IL	5,609	LC
DeVry/Columbus	OH	5,609	LC
DeVry/Dallas	TX	5,609	LC
DeVry/Kansas City	MO	5,609	LC
DeVry/Los Angeles	CA	5,609	LC
DeVry/Phoenix	AZ	5,609	LC
Dordt College	IA	11,690	C
Duquesne Univ	PA	16,434	VC
Dyke College	OH	5,200	C
East Tenn State Univ	TN	4,406	C
East Texas Baptist Univ	TX	7,740	C
Eastern Kentucky Univ	KY	4,840	NC
Eastern Mich Univ	MI	6,749	C
Eastern Montana College	MT	5,165	LC
Eastern New Mexico Univ	NM	3,950	C
Eastern Washington Univ	WA	5,439	LC
Edgewood College	WI	11,700	C
Embry-Riddle Aeronautical Univ	FL	10,600	C
Fairfield Univ	CT	20,460	VC
Florida Atlantic Univ	FL	5,525	C
Florida Southern College	FL	12,260	C
Fontbonne College	MO	12,090	C
Fordham Univ/College of Business Administration	NY	19,875	VC
Fordham Univ/Fordham College	NY	19,875	VC
Fort Lewis College	CO	5,097	C
Fort Valley State College	GA	3,974	LC
Francis Marion Univ	SC	5,878	LC
Franklin College of Indiana	IN	13,970	C
Freed-Hardeman Univ	TN	8,585	VC
Gannon Univ	PA	14,872	C
Gardner-Webb Univ	NC	11,950	LC
George Fox College	OR	15,640	LC
George Mason Univ	VA	8,728	C
George Washington Univ	DC	22,470	HC
Georgetown College	KY	10,990	C
Georgia Southern Univ	GA	4,988	LC
Georgia State Univ	GA	2,019	C
Golden Gate Univ	CA	5,623	VC
Gonzaga Univ	WA	16,350	VC
Graceland College	IA	11,600	C
Grambling State Univ	LA	4,712	NC
Grand Rapids Baptist College and Seminary	MI	10,228	C
Gwynedd-Mercy College	PA	15,450	C
Hampton Univ	VA	10,706	C
Hartwick College	NY	20,950	C
High Point Univ	NC	12,350	LC
Hofstra Univ	NY	16,580	VC
Holy Family College	PA	8,300	C
Hood College	MD	19,010	VC
Howard Univ	DC	11,680	C
Humboldt State Univ	CA	5,676	C
Huntingdon College	AL	11,400	C
Idaho State Univ	ID	4,442	C
Illinois College	IL	11,200	C
Immaculata College	PA	14,620	C
Incarnate Word College	TX	12,307	C
Indiana Inst of Tech	IN	11,810	C
Indiana Univ at Kokomo	IN	2,069	C
Indiana Univ-Purdue Univ at Fort Wayne	IN	2,500	LC
Iona College	NY	16,310	C
Jamestown College	ND	10,250	C
Juniata College	PA	18,390	C+
Kansas State Univ	KS	4,816	NC
Kean College of New Jersey	NJ	6,395	LC
Kennesaw State College	GA	1,553	C
King's College	PA	15,420	C
La Sierra Univ	CA	15,472	C
Lamar Univ	TX	3,798	C
Lincoln Memorial Univ	TN	8,218	C
Lincoln Univ	MO	4,638	NC
Lock Haven Univ of Penn	PA	7,128	C
Lynchburg College	VA	17,000	C
Madonna Univ	MI	8,546	C
Manhattan College	NY	19,000	C
Mansfield Univ	PA	6,348	C
Marietta College	OH	16,940	C+
Marist College	NY	16,406	C
Marquette Univ	WI	16,114	VC
Mars Hill College	NC	11,050	C
Marshall Univ	WV	5,762	LC
Marymount College/Tarrytown	NY	17,350	C
Maryville Univ-St Louis	MO	12,900	VC
Marywood College	PA	14,890	C
McNeese State Univ	LA	4,543	NC
Mercy College	NY	11,180	NC
Metropolitan State College of Denver	CO	1,751	NC
Middle Tenn State Univ	TN	3,857	C
Millikin Univ	IL	15,499	C
Miss State Univ	MS	5,629	VC
Missouri Baptist College	MO	9,340	C
Missouri Southern State College	MO	4,272	
Missouri Western State College	MO	4,384	NC
Moravian College	PA	18,960	VC
Morgan State Univ	MD	7,366	C+
Mount Union College	OH	15,850	C
Mount Vernon College	DC	20,668	C
Muhlenberg College	PA	20,795	VC
National-Louis Univ	IL	13,218	C
Neumann College	PA	9,950	LC
New Jersey Inst of Tech	NJ	9,965	VC
Niagara Univ	NY	14,552	C
Nicholls State Univ	LA	4,531	NC
Northeast Louisiana Univ	LA	3,906	NC
Northeastern Illinois Univ	IL	1,955	C
Northeastern State Univ	OK	5,250	C
Northeastern Univ	MA	19,851	C
Northern Arizona Univ	AZ	4,844	C
Northern Kentucky Univ	KY	4,620	NC
Northern Mich Univ	MI	6,350	C
Northland College	WI	13,550	LC
Northwest Missouri State Univ	MO	5,010	LC
Northwestern State Univ of Louisiana	LA	4,287	NC
Northwestern Univ	IL	21,093	MC
Northwood Univ	FL	14,569	C
Northwood Univ	MI	13,385	LC
Norwich Univ	VT	18,730	C
Nova Southeastern Univ	FL	13,244	LC
Oakland Univ	MI	6,714	VC
Ohio State Univ	OH	7,218	LC
Okla Baptist Univ	OK	8,486	C
Okla Christian Univ of Science and Arts	OK	8,790	NC
Okla State Univ	OK	5,086	VC
Olivet Nazarene Univ	IL	11,976	C
Ottawa Univ	KS	10,490	C+
Our Lady of the Lake Univ of San Antonio	TX	11,080	C
Pace Univ	NY	15,540	C
Philadelphia College of Textiles and Science	PA	15,896	C
Piedmont College	GA	8,540	LC
Pittsburg State Univ	KS	4,478	NC
Point Loma Nazarene College	CA	13,532	C
Polytechnic Univ/Brooklyn	NY	19,700	HC
Polytechnic Univ/Farmingdale	NY	20,700	VC
Portland State Univ	OR	7,191	C
Purdue Univ/Calumet	IN	2,374	NC
Quincy Univ	IL	13,646	VC
Radford Univ	VA	7,034	LC
Rhode Island College	RI	7,901	LC
Richard Stockton College of New Jersey	NJ	6,950	VC
Roanoke College	VA	16,975	C
Rockhurst College	MO	12,470	C
Roosevelt Univ	IL	12,368	C
Rutgers Univ/Newark College of A&S	NJ	8,645	C
Rutgers Univ/Univ College—Newark	NJ	0	C
St Joseph's Univ	PA	17,800	VC
St Mary College	KS	11,250	C
St Mary's College of Minn	MN	13,850	LC
St Mary-of-the-Woods College	IN	14,430	NC
St Norbert College	WI	15,710	VC
St Vincent College	PA	13,934	LC
Salisbury State Univ	MD	7,516	C+
Salve Regina Univ	RI	29,100	LC
San Francisco State Univ	CA	7,292	LC
Santa Clara Univ	CA	18,783	VC
Selma Univ	AL	5,785	NC
Seton Hall Univ	NJ	18,306	LC
Shepherd College	WV	5,540	C
Siena Heights College	MI	12,520	C
Slippery Rock Univ	PA	6,803	C
Southeastern Okla State Univ	OK	3,594	C
Southeastern Univ	DC	6,625	C
Southwest Missouri State Univ	MO	4,956	C
Southwest Texas State Univ	TX	5,124	C
Southwestern Adventist College	TX	10,530	NC
Southwestern Okla State Univ	OK	3,312	C
Spring Hill College	AL	16,015	C+
Springfield College	MA	15,200	LC
SUNY at Albany	NY	7,059	VC
SUNY at Stony Brook	NY	7,658	VC
SUNY/College at Buffalo	NY	7,035	VC
SUNY/College at Oswego	NY	7,330	VC
Strayer College	DC	5,850	LC
Susquehanna Univ	PA	19,950	VC

School	ST	$IS	SR
Syracuse Univ	NY	21,305	HC
Tarleton State Univ	TX	4,082	LC
Texas Wesleyan Univ	TX	9,380	LC
Thomas College	ME	13,450	LC
Tiffin Univ	OH	10,800	LC
Trevecca Nazarene College	TN	9,826	NC
Tri-State Univ	IN	13,788	LC
Trinity College	IL	14,010	C
Tulane Univ	LA	24,540	HC
Union College	KY	9,790	C
United States International Univ	CA	14,535	LC
Univ of Arkansas at Little Rock	AR	4,419	C
Univ of Calif at Santa Cruz	CA	9,060	VC
Univ of Calif, San Diego	CA	10,028	VC+
Univ of Calif/Irvine	CA	12,680	VC
Univ of Central Arkansas	AR	4,200	LC
Univ of Charleston	WV	12,750	C
Univ of Cincinnati	OH	7,989	C
Univ of Conn	CT	9,168	C
Univ of Dayton	OH	15,120	C+
Univ of Delaware	DE	8,013	VC
Univ of Detroit Mercy	MI	14,720	C
Univ of Houston	TX	5,215	C
Univ of Idaho	ID	4,830	C
Univ of Illinois at Chicago	IL	8,443	C
Univ of Indianapolis	IN	14,510	C
Univ of Iowa	IA	5,658	VC
Univ of Louisville	KY	5,948	C
Univ of Mary Hardin-Baylor	TX	8,120	NC
Univ of Mass Dartmouth	MA	8,158	C
Univ of Memphis	TN	3,476	C
Univ of Miami	FL	22,107	VC
Univ of Nebr at Kearney	NE	4,308	LC
Univ of Nevada/Reno	NV	5,735	C
Univ of North Alabama	AL	4,236	NC
Univ of N Car at Greensboro	NC	5,192	C
Univ of N Dak	ND	4,902	NC
Univ of North Florida	FL	5,082	C
Univ of North Texas	TX	4,853	C
Univ of Northern Colo	CO	6,008	C
Univ of Northern Iowa	IA	5,137	C
Univ of Notre Dame	IN	20,150	MC
Univ of Pittsburgh at Greensburg	PA	8,660	C
Univ of PR/Mayaguez	PR	0	LC
Univ of San Francisco	CA	18,408	C
Univ of South Florida	FL	5,475	C+
Univ of Southern Miss	MS	4,542	C
Univ of Tampa	FL	16,780	C
Univ of Texas at Arlington	TX	5,549	LC
Univ of the Pacific	CA	21,100	C
Univ of Washington	WA	6,618	VC
Univ of Wisc/Eau Claire	WI	4,647	C
Univ of Wisc/Green Bay	WI	4,904	C
Univ of Wisc/Madison	WI	6,400	HC
Univ of Wisc/Superior	WI	4,330	C
Upsala College	NJ	17,200	C
Utah State Univ	UT	4,683	C
Villa Julie College	MD	9,880	LC
Virginia Commonwealth Univ	VA	7,909	C
Washburn Univ of Topeka	KS	5,802	NC
Wayne State Univ	MI	2,680	C
Webster Univ	MO	12,650	C
Wesley College	DE	13,745	LC
West Coast Univ	CA	9,120	NC
Western International Univ	AZ	3,600	C
Western Kentucky Univ	KY	4,808	C
Western Mich Univ	MI	6,820	C
Western New England College	MA	14,674	LC
Westfield State College	MA	7,161	C
Widener Univ	PA	16,840	C
Wilberforce Univ	OH	10,408	C
Wilkes Univ	PA	15,728	LC
William Carey College	MS	7,050	C
Wingate College	NC	10,610	C
Winona State Univ	MN	5,200	VC
Worcester Polytechnic Inst	MA	20,350	HC
Xavier Univ	OH	15,710	C+

INSTITUTIONAL MANAGEMENT

School	ST	$IS	SR
Johnson and Wales Univ	RI	13,995	LC
Southwest Missouri State Univ	MO	4,956	C

INSURANCE

School	ST	$IS	SR
Ball State Univ	IN	6,032	LC
Cal State/Sacramento	CA	6,387	C
College of Insurance	NY	17,600	VC
Delta State Univ	MS	3,964	LC
Drake Univ	IA	17,195	VC
Eastern Kentucky Univ	KY	4,840	NC
Ferris State Univ	MI	7,160	NC
Florida State Univ	FL	5,814	VC
Georgia Southern Univ	GA	4,988	LC
Howard Univ	DC	11,680	C
Indiana State Univ	IN	6,210	C
Indiana Univ Bloomington	IN	6,495	VC
Indiana Univ-Purdue Univ at Indianapolis	IN	5,862	LC
Inter American Univ of PR/ Aguadilla Regional College	PR	2,290	
Inter American Univ of PR/ Bayamon Univ College	PR	2,300	
Inter American Univ of PR/ Metropolitan Campus	PR	2,340	
Inter American Univ of PR/ Ponce Regional College	PR	2,300	
Inter-American Univ of PR/ Fajardo Regional College	PR	2,732	
Martin Univ	IN	4,830	NC
Middle Tenn State Univ	TN	3,857	C
Miss State Univ	MS	5,629	VC
Northeast Louisiana Univ	LA	3,906	NC
Penn State Univ/Univ Park Campus	PA	8,752	HC
Southwest Missouri State Univ	MO	4,956	C
Univ of Alabama	AL	5,702	C
Univ of Florida	FL	5,850	HC
Univ of Hartford	CT	19,858	LC
Univ of Miss	MS	5,756	C
Univ of Nebr at Omaha	NE	1,889	LC
Univ of North Texas	TX	4,853	C
Univ of S Car	SC	6,158	C
Western Mich Univ	MI	6,820	C

INSURANCE AND RISK MANAGEMENT

School	ST	$IS	SR
Mercyhurst College	PA	13,488	C
Univ of Conn	CT	9,168	C
Univ of Memphis	TN	3,476	C
Univ of North Florida	FL	5,082	C
Univ of Wisc/Madison	WI	6,400	HC

INTERDISCIPLINARY STUDIES

School	ST	$IS	SR
Academy of the New Church	PA	7,341	NC
Angelo State Univ	TX	5,176	C
Arizona State Univ Main Campus	AZ	6,444	C
Austin College	TX	14,999	VC
Berry College	GA	11,990	VC
Bloomfield College	NJ	12,200	LC
Bluefield College	VA	10,600	C
Boise State Univ	ID	4,909	LC
Boston Univ	MA	24,130	HC
Cal State/Dominguez Hills	CA	2,857	LC
Cal State/Long Beach	CA	6,057	LC
Centenary College	NJ	17,040	LC
Charter Oak State College	CT	314	NC
Coe College	IA	17,085	VC
College of St Rose	NY	14,452	C
College of William and Mary	VA	8,602	MC
Covenant College	GA	13,054	VC
Dallas Baptist Univ	TX	9,620	LC
Davidson College	NC	21,037	MC
DePauw Univ	IN	18,530	VC
Felician College	NJ	7,900	C
Ferrum College	VA	12,800	LC
Friends World Program	NY	17,150	LC
Goddard College	VT	17,990	LC
Gonzaga Univ	WA	16,350	VC
Grand Rapids Baptist College and Seminary	MI	10,228	C
Heritage College	WA	5,540	NC
Hofstra Univ	NY	16,580	VC
Indiana State Univ	IN	6,210	C
John Brown Univ	AR	9,880	VC
Lafayette College	PA	23,450	HC
Lander Univ	SC	6,180	LC
Lees-McRae College	NC	9,850	LC
Lewis and Clark College	OR	19,980	VC
Liberty Univ	VA	11,500	LC
Lyndon State College	VT	8,394	LC
Marist College	NY	16,406	C
Marlboro College	VT	23,305	C+
Marquette Univ	WI	16,114	VC
Marylhurst College	OR	6,486	NC
Marymount College/ Tarrytown	NY	17,350	C
Mercy College	NY	11,180	NC
Miami Univ	OH	8,066	VC
Midwestern State Univ	TX	4,542	LC
Minneapolis College of Art and Design	MN	15,512	SP
Molloy College	NY	8,580	LC
Mount St Mary College	NY	12,910	C
Mount Vernon College	DC	20,668	C
National Univ	CA	6,135	C
N Car State Univ	NC	4,984	VC
Northern Montana College	MT	4,976	C
Northwest College	WA	9,897	LC
Nyack College	NY	12,210	LC
Pacific Union College	CA	15,075	C
Plymouth State College	NH	7,166	C
Radford Univ	VA	7,034	LC
Rensselaer Polytechnic Inst	NY	23,067	HC
Russell Sage College	NY	16,790	C
St John Fisher College	NY	15,415	C
San Francisco State Univ	CA	7,292	LC
Santa Clara Univ	CA	18,783	VC
Sheldon Jackson College	AK	14,050	NC
Simon's Rock College of Bard	MA	23,760	VC+
SUNY/Empire State College	NY	2,687	NC
SUNY/Potsdam College	NY	6,906	C
Stephen F. Austin State Univ	TX	5,117	C
Tarleton State Univ	TX	4,082	LC
Texas Woman's Univ	TX	4,392	C
Toccoa Falls College	GA	9,350	C
Towson State Univ	MD	7,452	C
Trinity College of Vermont	VT	16,015	LC
Union College	NY	23,817	HC
Unity College	ME	12,885	LC
Univ of Alabama	AL	5,702	C
Univ of Calif at Berkeley	CA	9,962	HC+
Univ of Colo at Boulder	CO	6,410	VC
Univ of Florida	FL	5,850	HC
Univ of Kentucky	KY	5,152	VC
Univ of Maryland/Baltimore County	MD	7,746	VC
Univ of Maryland/Univ College	MD	4,900	NC
Univ of Mass Dartmouth	MA	8,158	C
Univ of Minn/Duluth	MN	6,512	C
Univ of Nebr at Omaha	NE	1,889	LC
Univ of Nevada/Las Vegas	NV	6,405	C
Univ of North Texas	TX	4,853	C
Univ of Northern Colo	CO	6,008	C
Univ of Portland	OR	15,564	C
Univ of S Car	SC	6,158	C
Univ of S Car at Aiken	SC	5,386	C
Univ of Texas at Arlington	TX	5,549	LC
Univ of Texas at Dallas	TX	1,222	VC+
Univ of Virginia	VA	7,964	MC
Wayland Baptist Univ	TX	7,811	NC
Wayne State College	NE	4,260	NC
Wesleyan College	GA	15,445	C
West Liberty State College	WV	4,690	LC
West Virginia Univ	WV	5,774	C
Western Oregon State College	OR	6,180	C
Wheaton College	IL	14,710	HC

INTERIOR DESIGN

School	ST	$IS	SR
Alabama A&M Univ	AL	4,200	C
American College for the Applied Arts	GA	11,870	SP
Anna Maria College	MA	15,975	LC
Arizona State Univ Main Campus	AZ	6,444	C
Atlanta College of Art	GA	12,495	SP
Atlantic Union College	MA	14,150	LC
Auburn Univ	AL	5,823	C+
Baker College	MI	6,971	NC
Bassist College	OR	12,590	SP
Beaver College	PA	17,660	C
Boston Architectural Center	MA	3,372	SP
Brigham Young Univ	UT	5,625	HC
Cal State/Fresno	CA	5,747	C
Cazenovia College	NY	14,655	LC
Centenary College	NJ	17,040	LC
Center for Creative Studies/ College of Art and Design	MI	15,330	SP
Chadron State College	NE	4,091	NC
Chaminade Univ of Honolulu	HI	14,290	C
College of Notre Dame	CA	16,480	C
Colo State Univ	CO	6,566	VC
Columbus College of Art and Design	OH	14,550	SP
Concordia Univ Wisc	WI	12,140	C
Drake Univ	IA	17,195	VC
Eastern Kentucky Univ	KY	4,840	NC
Eastern Mich Univ	MI	6,749	C
Fashion Inst of Tech/SUNY	NY	7,135	SP
Florida International Univ	FL	4,191	VC
Florida State Univ	FL	5,814	VC
Georgia Southern Univ	GA	4,988	LC
Hampton Univ	VA	10,706	C
Harding Univ	AR	9,050	VC
Indiana State Univ	IN	6,210	C
Indiana Univ Bloomington	IN	6,495	VC
Iowa State Univ	IA	5,456	C
Judson College	AL	9,060	C
Kendall College of Art and Design	MI	9,600	SP
Kent State Univ	OH	6,740	LC
La Roche College	PA	12,977	LC
Louisiana State Univ and A&M College	LA	5,605	C
Maryland Inst, College of Art	MD	18,420	SP
Marymount College/ Tarrytown	NY	17,350	C
Marymount Univ	VA	15,930	C
Maryville Univ-St Louis	MO	12,900	VC
Mercyhurst College	PA	13,488	C
Meredith College	NC	9,440	C
Miami Univ	OH	8,066	VC
Mich State Univ	MI	7,842	C
Milwaukee Inst of Art and Design	WI	9,800	SP
Miss College	MS	8,348	C
Miss Univ for Women	MS	4,456	LC
Montana State Univ	MT	5,534	C
Moore College of Art and Design	PA	17,947	SP
Morehead State Univ	KY	4,600	LC
Mount Ida College	MA	16,700	LC
Mount Vernon College	DC	20,668	C
N Dak State Univ of Agriculture and Applied Science	ND	4,774	VC
Northeast Louisiana Univ	LA	3,906	NC
Ohio State Univ	OH	7,218	LC
Okla Christian Univ of Science and Arts	OK	8,790	NC
Pacific Union College	CA	15,075	C
Paier College of Art	CT	10,120	SP
Parsons School of Design	NY	21,410	SP
Philadelphia College of Textiles and Science	PA	15,896	C
Pratt Inst	NY	19,520	C
Purdue Univ/West Lafayette	IN	6,636	C
Rhode Island School of Design	RI	22,315	SP
Ringling School of Art and Design	FL	15,750	SP
Rochester Inst of Tech	NY	18,954	VC
Roosevelt Univ	IL	12,368	C
St Vincent College	PA	13,934	LC
Salem College	NC	16,025	C
San Francisco State Univ	CA	7,292	LC
Savannah College of Art and Design	GA	14,280	SP
School of the Art Inst of Chicago	IL	17,610	SP
School of Visual Arts	NY	17,120	SP
S Dak State Univ	SD	4,562	C
Southern Nazarene Univ	OK	9,206	NC
Southern Univ and A&M College	LA	4,920	NC
Southwest Missouri State Univ	MO	4,956	C
Southwest Texas State Univ	TX	5,124	C
Stephen F. Austin State Univ	TX	5,117	C
Syracuse Univ	NY	21,305	HC
Texas Christian Univ	TX	12,180	C
Texas Tech Univ	TX	6,008	C
Univ of Alabama	AL	5,702	C
Univ of Arkansas at Fayetteville	AR	5,046	C
Univ of Bridgeport	CT	18,985	C
Univ of Charleston	WV	12,750	C
Univ of Florida	FL	5,850	HC
Univ of Maryland/College Park	MD	8,182	VC
Univ of Mich/Ann Arbor	MI	9,428	HC+
Univ of Minn/Twin Cities	MN	6,682	VC
Univ of New Haven	CT	14,980	C
Univ of North Texas	TX	4,853	C
Univ of Okla	OK	5,427	VC
Univ of San Francisco	CA	18,408	C
Univ of Southwestern Louisiana	LA	3,968	NC
Univ of Tenn/Knoxville	TN	5,668	C
Univ of Texas at Arlington	TX	5,549	LC
Univ of Texas at Austin	TX	5,160	VC
Univ of Texas at San Antonio	TX	6,420	C
Univ of Wisc/Madison	WI	6,400	HC
Univ of Wisc/Stevens Point	WI	5,047	C+
Ursuline College	OH	13,180	LC
Utah State Univ	UT	4,683	C
Virginia Polytechnic Inst and State Univ	VA	6,828	C
Wentworth Inst of Tech	MA	15,250	LC
West Virginia Univ	WV	5,774	C
Western Carolina Univ	NC	3,811	C
Western Kentucky Univ	KY	4,808	C
William Carey College	MS	7,050	C
William Woods Univ	MO	14,025	LC
Woodbury Univ	CA	17,620	LC

INTERNATIONAL AGRICULTURE

School	ST	$IS	SR
Calif State Polytechnic Univ/ Pomona	CA	6,438	LC
Cornell Univ	NY	13,445	MC
Eastern Mennonite College	VA	12,700	C
Iowa State Univ	IA	5,456	C
Univ of Calif at Davis	CA	9,534	VC
Univ of Wyoming	WY	4,991	NC
Utah State Univ	UT	4,683	C

INTERNATIONAL BUSINESS MANAGEMENT

School	ST	$IS	SR
Adrian College	MI	14,340	C
Alaska Pacific Univ	AK	11,350	C
Alfred Univ	NY	21,054	VC+
Alma College	MI	16,375	VC+
American International College	MA	14,029	C
American Univ	DC	21,230	VC+
Appalachian State Univ	NC	4,095	C
Aquinas College	MI	14,526	C
Arkansas State Univ	AR	4,250	NC
Assumption College	MA	17,095	LC
Auburn Univ	AL	5,823	C+
Augsburg College	MN	15,608	C
Avila College	MO	12,130	C
Babson College	MA	23,160	VC
Baker Univ	KS	12,284	C
Ball State Univ	IN	6,032	LC
Barry Univ	FL	16,050	C
Baylor Univ	TX	10,990	C+
Birmingham-Southern College	AL	15,154	VC+
Boston Univ	MA	24,130	HC
Bowling Green State Univ	OH	6,701	C
Bradley Univ	IL	14,718	C+
Brigham Young Univ/Hawaii	HI	6,750	VC
Buena Vista College	IA	16,150	VC
Calif Lutheran Univ	CA	17,240	C
Cal State/Fresno	CA	5,747	C
Cal State/Fullerton	CA	4,850	LC
Cal State/Los Angeles	CA	4,940	VC
Cal State/Sacramento	CA	6,387	C
Cal State/San Bernardino	CA	6,055	LC
Cardinal Stritch College	WI	11,252	C
Carthage College	WI	15,995	C
Catawba College	NC	12,950	C
Cedarville College	OH	10,715	C
Central College	IA	14,025	VC
Central Conn State Univ	CT	7,108	C
Central Washington Univ	WA	5,644	C
Chatham College	PA	18,010	C
Christian Heritage College	CA	11,756	C
Christopher Newport Univ	VA	3,196	LC
College of Notre Dame	CA	16,480	C
College of Notre Dame of Maryland	MD	16,050	C
College of Our Lady of The Elms	MA	15,639	C
College of St Francis	IL	13,060	VC
College of St Scholastica	MN	14,868	C
Concordia College/Moorhead	MN	12,750	C
Cornell College	IA	18,425	VC
Davis and Elkins College	WV	13,230	LC
Dominican College	NY	13,600	LC
Dominican College of San Rafael	CA	17,860	C
Drexel Univ	PA	15,970	C
Duquesne Univ	PA	16,434	VC
Eastern Mich Univ	MI	6,749	C
Eckerd College	FL	18,855	VC
Elizabethtown College	PA	17,850	VC
Elmhurst College	IL	12,536	C
Elmira College	NY	18,450	C
Emporia State Univ	KS	4,685	NC
Fairfield Univ	CT	20,460	VC
Ferris State Univ	MI	7,160	NC
Florida Atlantic Univ	FL	5,525	C
Florida International Univ	FL	4,191	VC
Florida Southern College	FL	12,260	C
Florida State Univ	FL	5,814	VC
Fordham Univ/College of Business Administration	NY	19,875	VC
Franklin College of Indiana	IN	13,970	C
Franklin Pierce College	NH	17,270	LC
Friends Univ	KS	11,205	C
Gannon Univ	PA	14,872	C
George Washington Univ	DC	22,470	HC
Georgetown College	KY	10,990	C
Georgetown Univ	DC	24,410	MC
Golden Gate Univ	CA	5,623	VC
Goldey-Beacom College	DE	7,839	C
Gonzaga Univ	WA	16,350	VC
Grand Canyon Univ	AZ	9,680	VC
Grand Valley State Univ	MI	6,822	VC
Grove City College	PA	7,870	HC
Gustavus Adolphus College	MN	15,935	VC
Hamline Univ	MN	17,122	VC
Harding Univ	AR	9,050	VC
Hawaii Pacific Univ	HI	12,300	C
Heidelberg College	OH	17,160	C
High Point Univ	NC	12,350	LC
Hillsdale College	MI	15,110	VC
Hofstra Univ	NY	16,580	VC
Holy Family College	PA	8,300	C
Howard Univ	DC	11,680	C
Huntingdon College	AL	11,400	C
Illinois Benedictine College	IL	14,170	C
Illinois State Univ	IL	6,413	C
Illinois Wesleyan Univ	IL	18,590	HC+
Incarnate Word College	TX	12,307	C
Ithaca College	NY	19,679	C
Jacksonville Univ	FL	13,390	C
James Madison Univ	VA	8,198	HC
Johnson and Wales Univ	RI	13,995	LC
Judson College	IL	13,625	C
Kean College of New Jersey	NJ	6,395	LC
King's College	PA	15,420	C
Kutztown Univ	PA	6,528	C
La Roche College	PA	12,977	LC
Lake Erie College	OH	13,700	C
Lebanon Valley College of Penn	PA	18,300	C
Lenoir-Rhyne College	NC	14,068	C
Linfield College	OR	16,670	VC
Louisiana State Univ and A&M College	LA	5,605	C
Lynchburg College	VA	17,000	C
Madonna Univ	MI	8,546	C
Manchester College	IN	13,240	LC
Manhattan College	NY	19,000	C
Mankato State Univ	MN	5,097	LC
Marietta College	OH	16,940	C+
Marquette Univ	WI	16,114	VC
Marymount College/Tarrytown	NY	17,350	C
Marymount Manhattan College	NY	15,450	LC
Marymount Univ	VA	15,930	C
Marywood College	PA	14,890	C
Menlo College	CA	20,375	LC
Merrimack College	MA	18,025	C
Messiah College	PA	14,664	VC
Millikin Univ	IL	15,499	C
Monmouth College	NJ	16,820	C
Moorhead State Univ	MN	5,076	C
Moravian College	PA	18,960	VC
Mount St Mary's College	CA	16,390	VC
Mount Union College	OH	15,850	C
Muskingum College	OH	16,650	C
New England College	NH	17,870	LC
New Hampshire College	NH	15,242	LC
New Mexico State Univ	NM	4,844	LC
North Central College	IL	15,498	VC
North Park College	IL	14,310	C
Northeastern Univ	MA	19,851	C
Northern State Univ	SD	4,186	LC
Northwest Missouri State Univ	MO	5,010	LC
Northwestern College	MN	13,554	C
Notre Dame College of Ohio	OH	11,370	C
Ohio Dominican College	OH	11,820	LC
Ohio State Univ	OH	7,218	LC
Ohio Univ	OH	7,341	C
Ohio Wesleyan Univ	OH	21,108	VC+
Okla State Univ	OK	5,086	VC
Oregon State Univ	OR	6,175	C
Otterbein College	OH	16,506	C
Pace Univ	NY	15,540	C
Palm Beach Atlantic College	FL	10,720	C
Park College	MO	7,320	C
Penn State Univ/Univ Park Campus	PA	8,752	HC
Philadelphia College of Textiles and Science	PA	15,896	C
Quinnipiac College	CT	17,600	C+
Ramapo College of New Jersey	NJ	8,027	C+
Regis Univ	CO	17,340	C
Rochester Inst of Tech	NY	18,954	VC
Rosary College	IL	15,040	C
Sacred Heart Univ	CT	16,350	C
St Cloud State Univ	MN	5,015	C
St Edward's Univ	TX	12,636	C
St Louis Univ	MO	15,522	VC
St Martin's College	WA	14,965	C
St Mary's College of Calif	CA	18,848	VC
St Mary's Univ	TX	12,064	C
St Norbert College	WI	15,710	VC
St Thomas Univ	FL	14,280	LC
St Xavier Univ	IL	14,700	C
Sam Houston State Univ	TX	4,506	C
Samford Univ	AL	11,400	VC
San Francisco State Univ	CA	7,292	LC
San Jose State Univ	CA	6,680	LC
Seattle Univ	WA	16,590	C
Seton Hill College	PA	14,320	C
Shenandoah Univ	VA	11,800	C
Simmons College	MA	22,534	C
Simpson College	IA	14,635	VC
Slippery Rock Univ	PA	6,803	C
Sonoma State Univ	CA	6,996	LC
Southern Illinois Univ at Carbondale	IL	6,234	C
Spring Hill College	AL	16,015	C+
SUNY/College at Brockport	NY	7,220	C+
SUNY/College at Geneseo	NY	6,949	HC
SUNY/College at Plattsburgh	NY	6,917	C
Teikyo Marycrest Univ	IA	13,755	VC
Temple Univ	PA	10,281	C
Texas Tech Univ	TX	6,008	C
Texas Wesleyan Univ	TX	9,380	LC
The Univ of New Mexico	NM	5,304	C
Thiel College	PA	16,282	C
United States International Univ	CA	14,535	LC
Univ of Arkansas at Fayetteville	AR	5,046	C
Univ of Bridgeport	CT	18,985	C
Univ of Colo at Denver	CO	1,955	VC
Univ of Denver	CO	19,290	C+
Univ of Evansville	IN	15,300	VC
Univ of Georgia	GA	5,655	VC
Univ of Hawaii at Manoa	HI	5,626	C
Univ of Indianapolis	IN	14,510	C
Univ of La Verne	CA	17,400	C
Univ of Miami	FL	22,107	VC
Univ of Nebr-Lincoln	NE	5,278	LC
Univ of New Haven	CT	14,980	C
Univ of N Car at Charlotte	NC	4,597	C
Univ of Okla	OK	5,427	VC
Univ of Penn	PA	24,238	MC
Univ of St Thomas	MN	15,785	C+
Univ of San Francisco	CA	18,408	C
Univ of Southern Miss	MS	4,542	C
Univ of Tampa	FL	16,780	C
Univ of Tenn at Martin	TN	4,550	C
Univ of Texas at Austin	TX	5,160	VC
Univ of the Pacific	CA	21,100	C
Univ of Toledo	OH	6,636	NC
Univ of Washington	WA	6,618	VC
Upsala College	NJ	17,200	C
Utah State Univ	UT	4,683	C
Virginia Wesleyan College	VA	14,950	VC
Wartburg College	IA	14,530	VC
Washington State Univ	WA	6,364	C
Webber College	FL	8,710	C
Western International Univ	AZ	3,600	C
Western New Mexico Univ	NM	3,234	LC
Western Washington Univ	WA	6,077	VC
Westminster College	PA	15,200	C
Whitworth College	WA	16,265	C
Wichita State Univ	KS	5,068	NC
Widener Univ	PA	16,840	C
William Jewell College	MO	12,500	VC
Woodbury Univ	CA	17,620	LC

INTERNATIONAL ECONOMICS

School	ST	$IS	SR
Bryn Mawr College	PA	24,110	MC
College of St Catherine	MN	14,670	C
Hiram College	OH	18,340	VC
Kent State Univ	OH	6,740	LC
Middlebury College	VT	24,400	MC
St Norbert College	WI	15,710	VC
Suffolk Univ	MA	15,360	LC
Univ of Calif at Los Angeles	CA	8,959	HC
Valparaiso Univ	IN	14,810	VC

INTERNATIONAL PUBLIC SERVICE

School	ST	$IS	SR
Georgetown Univ	DC	24,410	MC
Valparaiso Univ	IN	14,810	VC

INTERNATIONAL RELATIONS

School	ST	$IS	SR
Abilene Christian Univ	TX	10,460	NC
Agnes Scott College	GA	17,135	VC
American International College	MA	14,029	C
Antioch College	OH	19,532	C
Augsburg College	MN	15,608	C
Augustana College	IL	16,959	VC
Baldwin-Wallace College	OH	15,210	C
Beloit College	WI	18,950	VC+
Bethel College	MN	15,050	C
Birmingham-Southern College	AL	15,154	VC+
Boston Univ	MA	24,130	HC
Bridgewater State College	MA	7,518	C
Brigham Young Univ	UT	5,625	HC
Brown Univ	RI	26,104	MC
Bucknell Univ	PA	22,320	HC
Cal State/Chico	CA	6,146	C
Cal State/Sacramento	CA	6,387	C
Canisius College	NY	15,510	C
Capital Univ	OH	16,535	VC
Carleton College	MN	22,155	HC
Carroll College	MT	11,265	C
Carroll College	WI	15,490	C
Chaminade Univ of Honolulu	HI	14,290	C
Chatham College	PA	18,010	C
CUNY/Herbert H. Lehman College	NY	2,542	C
CUNY/Hunter College	NY	4,101	VC
Claremont McKenna College	CA	22,150	MC
Clark Univ	MA	21,400	VC
Cleveland State Univ	OH	7,287	NC
Colgate Univ	NY	24,020	HC
College of New Rochelle	NY	15,440	LC
College of Notre Dame of Maryland	MD	16,050	C
College of St Catherine	MN	14,670	C
College of William and Mary	VA	8,602	MC
College of Wooster	OH	19,875	VC
Concordia College/Moorhead	MN	12,750	C
Conn College	CT	24,160	HC
Cornell College	IA	18,425	VC
Drake Univ	IA	17,195	VC
Duquesne Univ	PA	16,434	VC
Earlham College	IN	19,383	VC
Eastern Mich Univ	MI	6,749	C
Eastern Washington Univ	WA	5,439	LC
Eckerd College	FL	18,855	VC
Evergreen State College	WA	6,306	C
Florida Atlantic Univ	FL	5,525	C
Florida International Univ	FL	4,191	VC
Florida State Univ	FL	5,814	VC
Gannon Univ	PA	14,872	C
George Mason Univ	VA	8,728	C
George Washington Univ	DC	22,470	HC
Georgetown Univ	DC	24,410	MC
Georgia Inst of Tech	GA	6,669	HC+
Georgia State Univ	GA	2,019	C
Gettysburg College	PA	22,960	HC
Goucher College	MD	20,295	VC
Grand Valley State Univ	MI	6,822	VC
Hamilton College	NY	23,500	HC
Hamline Univ	MN	17,122	VC
Hanover College	IN	10,950	VC
Hawaii Pacific Univ	HI	12,300	C
Hendrix College	AR	11,670	C
Holy Names College	CA	15,660	C
Hope College	MI	15,698	C+
Howard Univ	DC	11,680	C
Illinois College	IL	11,200	C
Immaculata College	PA	14,620	C
Iona College	NY	16,310	C
Iowa State Univ	IA	5,456	C
Jacksonville Univ	FL	13,390	C
Juniata College	PA	18,390	C+
Kent State Univ	OH	6,740	LC
Knox College	IL	18,990	VC
Lafayette College	PA	23,450	HC
Lake Forest College	IL	19,960	VC
Lambuth Univ	TN	8,395	C
Lawrence Univ	WI	19,986	HC+
Lehigh Univ	PA	23,250	HC
Lewis and Clark College	OR	19,980	VC
Lincoln Univ	PA	0	LC
Luther College	IA	15,900	VC
Lycoming College	PA	17,200	LC
Lynchburg College	VA	17,000	C
Macalester College	MN	19,710	HC
Manhattanville College	NY	20,450	LC
Marlboro College	VT	23,305	C+
Marquette Univ	WI	16,114	VC
Marshall Univ	WV	5,762	LC
Mary Baldwin College	VA	17,700	LC
Mary Washington College	VA	7,910	HC
Maryville College	TN	14,474	C
McKendree College	IL	10,900	C
Miami Univ	OH	8,066	VC
Mich State Univ	MI	7,842	C
Middle Tenn State Univ	TN	3,857	C
Middlebury College	VT	24,400	MC
Mills College	CA	20,848	VC
Morehouse College	GA	13,224	LC
Mount Holyoke College	MA	23,630	VC
Muskingum College	OH	16,650	C
New College of the Univ of South Florida	FL	5,697	MC
New York Univ	NY	24,705	VC+
North Park College	IL	14,310	C
Northern Arizona Univ	AZ	4,844	C
Norwich Univ	VT	18,730	C
Occidental College	CA	21,792	HC
Ohio Univ	OH	7,341	C
Ohio Wesleyan Univ	OH	21,108	VC+
Okla State Univ	OK	5,086	VC
Old Dominion Univ	VA	8,317	C
Otterbein College	OH	16,506	C
Penn State Univ/Univ Park Campus	PA	8,752	HC
Pitzer College	CA	23,780	HC
Pomona College	CA	23,820	MC
Princeton Univ	NJ	24,650	MC
Principia College	IL	17,799	C
Purdue Univ/Calumet	IN	2,374	NC
Randolph-Macon College	VA	16,980	C
Randolph-Macon Woman's College	VA	19,100	C
Ripon College	WI	18,320	C+
Roanoke College	VA	16,975	C
Rockhurst College	MO	12,470	C
Rollins College	FL	20,875	VC
Sacred Heart Univ	CT	16,350	C
St Cloud State Univ	MN	5,015	C
St Joseph's Univ	PA	17,800	VC
St Leo College	FL	13,570	C
St Mary's Univ	TX	12,064	C
St Thomas Univ	FL	14,280	LC
Salem College	NC	16,025	C
Samford Univ	AL	11,400	VC
San Francisco State Univ	CA	7,292	LC
Sarah Lawrence College	NY	24,975	HC

School	ST	$IS	SR
Scripps College	CA	23,600	HC
Shaw Univ	NC	8,936	C+
Simmons College	MA	22,534	C
Simpson College	IA	14,635	VC
Southern College of Seventh-day Adventists	TN	11,348	NC
Southern Illinois Univ at Carbondale	IL	6,234	C
Southwest Texas State Univ	TX	5,124	C
Southwestern Adventist College	TX	10,530	NC
Stanford Univ	CA	24,310	MC
SUNY at Buffalo	NY	7,896	VC
SUNY/College at Geneseo	NY	6,949	HC
SUNY/College at New Paltz	NY	6,890	VC
SUNY/College at Plattsburgh	NY	6,917	C
Stonehill College	MA	17,481	VC
Swarthmore College	PA	24,136	MC
Sweet Briar College	VA	19,770	C
Syracuse Univ	NY	21,305	HC
Temple Univ	PA	10,281	C
Texas College	TX	5,930	NC
Trinity Univ	TX	16,670	HC
Troy State Univ	AL	4,322	C
Tufts Univ	MA	24,962	MC
Tulane Univ	LA	24,540	HC
United States International Univ	CA	14,535	LC
Univ of Calif at Davis	CA	9,534	VC
Univ of Calif at Los Angeles	CA	8,959	HC
Univ of Colo at Boulder	CO	6,410	VC
Univ of Delaware	DE	8,013	VC
Univ of Denver	CO	19,290	C+
Univ of Detroit Mercy	MI	14,720	C
Univ of Idaho	ID	4,830	C
Univ of La Verne	CA	17,400	C
Univ of Memphis	TN	3,476	C
Univ of Miami	FL	22,107	VC
Univ of Minn/Twin Cities	MN	6,682	VC
Univ of Nebr-Lincoln	NE	5,278	LC
Univ of Nevada/Reno	NV	5,735	C
Univ of Northern Colo	CO	6,008	C
Univ of Notre Dame	IN	20,150	MC
Univ of Penn	PA	24,238	MC
Univ of Puget Sound	WA	19,520	HC
Univ of Redlands	CA	22,059	VC
Univ of Richmond	VA	16,700	HC
Univ of St Thomas	TX	11,676	C+
Univ of San Diego	CA	18,970	VC
Univ of Scranton	PA	17,071	VC
Univ of South Alabama	AL	5,451	C
Univ of S Car	SC	6,158	C
Univ of South Florida	FL	5,475	C+
Univ of Southern Calif	CA	23,006	VC
Univ of Southern Miss	MS	4,542	C
Univ of the Pacific	CA	21,100	C
Univ of Toledo	OH	6,636	NC
Univ of Virginia	VA	7,964	MC
Univ of Washington	WA	6,618	VC
Univ of Wisc/Madison	WI	6,400	HC
Ursinus College	PA	19,165	VC
Utah State Univ	UT	4,683	C
Utica College of Syracuse Univ	NY	16,714	LC
Virginia State Univ	VA	7,040	C
Virginia Wesleyan College	VA	14,950	VC
Washington Univ	MO	23,507	HC
Webster Univ	MO	12,650	C
Wellesley College	MA	23,815	MC
Wesleyan College	GA	15,445	C
Wesleyan Univ	CT	23,770	MC
Westminster College	MO	13,750	C+
Westminster College	PA	15,200	C
Wheaton College	MA	23,840	C+
Wheeling Jesuit College	WV	14,370	C
Whitworth College	WA	16,265	C
Widener Univ	PA	16,840	C
Willamette Univ	OR	17,995	VC
William Jewell College	MO	12,500	VC
Winona State Univ	MN	5,200	VC
Wittenberg Univ	OH	19,998	VC
Wright State Univ	OH	6,896	LC
Xavier Univ	OH	15,710	C+

INTERNATIONAL STUDIES

School	ST	$IS	SR
Albion College	MI	18,264	VC
Alfred Univ	NY	21,054	VC+
Allegheny College	PA	21,020	VC
American Univ	DC	21,230	VC+
Antioch College	OH	19,532	C
Aquinas College	MI	14,526	C
Assumption College	MA	17,095	LC
Austin College	TX	14,999	VC
Azusa Pacific Univ	CA	15,034	C
Barry Univ	FL	16,050	C
Barton College	NC	10,689	LC
Berry College	GA	11,990	VC
Bethel College	KS	11,530	C
Bowie State Univ	MD	7,294	LC
Bridgewater College	VA	15,300	C
Bryant College	RI	18,335	C
Butler Univ	IN	16,210	C
Case Western Reserve Univ	OH	19,910	HC
Centenary College	NJ	17,040	LC
Central College	IA	14,025	VC
Chatham College	PA	18,010	C
CUNY/City College	NY	2,543	VC
CUNY/College of Staten Island	NY	2,558	NC
Colby College	ME	24,230	HC
College of Our Lady of The Elms	MA	15,639	C
College of William and Mary	VA	8,602	MC
Columbia Univ/Barnard College	NY	25,492	HC
Cornell Univ	NY	13,445	MC
DePaul Univ	IL	15,535	VC
Dickinson College	PA	22,705	HC
Doane College	NE	12,220	C
Dominican College of San Rafael	CA	17,860	C
Drexel Univ	PA	15,970	C
Elmira College	NY	18,450	C
Emory Univ	GA	21,930	HC
Evangel College	MO	10,142	LC
Fairleigh Dickinson Univ	NJ	16,427	C
Ferrum College	VA	12,800	LC
Fort Lewis College	CO	5,097	C
Frostburg State Univ	MD	6,940	C
Gallaudet Univ	DC	9,850	SP
Gannon Univ	PA	14,872	C
George Fox College	OR	15,640	LC
Gordon College	MA	16,790	C
Graceland College	IA	11,600	C
Guilford College	NC	17,680	C
Hampshire College	MA	25,320	C
Harding Univ	AR	9,050	VC
Hawaii Pacific Univ	HI	12,300	C
Heidelberg College	OH	17,160	C
High Point Univ	NC	12,350	LC
Houghton College	NY	13,120	VC
Idaho State Univ	ID	4,442	C
Illinois Wesleyan Univ	IL	18,590	HC+
James Madison Univ	VA	8,198	HC
John Brown Univ	AR	9,880	VC
Johns Hopkins Univ	MD	24,360	MC
Kenyon College	OH	22,430	HC+
LIU/C. W. Post Campus	NY	16,870	C
Manhattan College	NY	19,000	C
Mansfield Univ	PA	6,348	C
Mars Hill College	NC	11,050	C
Marymount College/Tarrytown	NY	17,350	C
Marymount Manhattan College	NY	15,450	LC
Meredith College	NC	9,440	C
Millersville Univ of Penn	PA	7,370	VC
Mount St Mary College	NY	12,910	C
Mount St Mary's College	MD	17,825	LC
Mount Vernon College	DC	20,668	C
Nazareth College of Rochester	NY	15,310	C+
Nebr Wesleyan Univ	NE	12,240	C
Niagara Univ	NY	14,552	C
Northern Kentucky Univ	KY	4,620	NC
Northern Mich Univ	MI	6,350	C
Northwest Nazarene College	ID	11,750	C
Northwestern Univ	IL	21,093	MC
Nova Southeastern Univ	FL	13,244	LC
Oglethorpe Univ	GA	16,360	VC
Ohio Northern Univ	OH	18,660	VC
Ohio State Univ	OH	7,218	LC
Pacific Lutheran Univ	WA	15,998	VC
Pepperdine Univ	CA	23,720	VC
Point Park College	PA	13,922	LC
Portland State Univ	OR	7,191	C
Quincy Univ	IL	13,646	VC
Ramapo College of New Jersey	NJ	8,027	C+
Randolph-Macon College	VA	16,980	C
Reed College	OR	24,480	HC+
Rhodes College	TN	19,624	HC
Roosevelt Univ	IL	12,368	C
Russell Sage College	NY	16,790	C
Rutgers Univ/Cook College	NJ	9,197	HC
St Edward's Univ	TX	12,636	C
St Francis College	PA	15,744	LC
St John Fisher College	NY	15,415	C
St Mary's Univ	TX	12,064	C
St Norbert College	WI	15,710	VC
Southern Methodist Univ	TX	18,520	VC
Southern Nazarene Univ	OK	9,206	NC
Southern Oregon State College	OR	6,128	C
Southwest Texas State Univ	TX	5,124	C
Southwestern Univ	TX	15,484	HC
SUNY/College at Brockport	NY	7,220	C+
SUNY/College at Cortland	NY	7,326	C+
SUNY/College at Old Westbury	NY	7,128	LC
SUNY/College at Oneonta	NY	7,878	C
Stillman College	AL	7,213	NC
Susquehanna Univ	PA	19,950	VC
Taylor Univ	IN	14,450	VC
Teikyo Marycrest Univ	IA	13,755	VC
Texas A&M Univ	TX	5,382	VC
Thomas College	ME	13,450	LC
Thomas More College	KY	12,962	C
Towson State Univ	MD	7,452	C
Trinity College	DC	17,660	C
Univ of Alabama	AL	5,702	C
Univ of Alabama at Birmingham	AL	7,533	C
Univ of Arkansas at Little Rock	AR	4,419	C
Univ of Cincinnati	OH	7,989	C
Univ of Dayton	OH	15,120	C+
Univ of Dubuque	IA	14,150	LC
Univ of Evansville	IN	15,300	VC
Univ of Maine at Farmington	ME	6,700	C
Univ of Miami	FL	22,107	VC
Univ of Mich/Dearborn	MI	3,399	HC
Univ of Minn/Duluth	MN	6,512	C
Univ of Nebr at Kearney	NE	4,308	LC
Univ of N Car at Chapel Hill	NC	5,330	HC
Univ of Oregon	OR	6,466	VC
Univ of St Thomas	MN	15,785	C+
Univ of Tampa	FL	16,780	C
Univ of the Pacific	CA	21,100	C
Univ of Wisc/Oshkosh	WI	4,240	C
Univ of Wisc/Parkside	WI	5,247	C
Univ of Wisc/Platteville	WI	4,830	C
Univ of Wisc/Stevens Point	WI	5,047	C+
Univ of Wisc/Whitewater	WI	4,700	C
Univ of Wyoming	WY	4,991	NC
Vassar College	NY	24,206	HC
Villanova Univ	PA	21,400	HC
Virginia Military Inst	VA	8,630	C
Virginia Polytechnic Inst and State Univ	VA	6,828	C
Walsh Univ	OH	11,640	C
Washington College	MD	19,270	C+
Wayne State College	NE	4,260	NC
Wayne State Univ	MI	2,680	C
Wells College	NY	19,460	C+
West Virginia Univ	WV	5,774	C
West Virginia Wesleyan College	WV	16,900	C
Western International Univ	AZ	3,600	C
Western Oregon State College	OR	6,180	C
Westmont College	CA	18,732	C
Whittier College	CA	21,661	C
Whitworth College	WA	16,265	C
Wilkes Univ	PA	15,728	LC
Wilson College	PA	16,630	C

INTERPRETER FOR THE DEAF

School	ST	$IS	SR
Bloomsburg Univ of Penn	PA	6,312	C+
Gallaudet Univ	DC	9,850	SP
Madonna Univ	MI	8,546	C
Maryville College	TN	14,474	C
Western Oregon State College	OR	6,180	C
William Woods Univ	MO	14,025	LC

INVESTMENTS AND SECURITIES

School	ST	$IS	SR
Babson College	MA	23,160	VC
CUNY/Baruch College	NY	2,562	VC
Illinois Inst of Tech	IL	18,290	VC

ISLAMIC STUDIES

School	ST	$IS	SR
Ohio State Univ	OH	7,218	LC
Univ of Mich/Ann Arbor	MI	9,428	HC+
Villanova Univ	PA	21,400	HC

ITALIAN

School	ST	$IS	SR
Albertus Magnus College	CT	16,280	LC
Arizona State Univ Main Campus	AZ	6,444	C
Boston College	MA	22,706	MC
Boston Univ	MA	24,130	HC
Brigham Young Univ	UT	5,625	HC
Brown Univ	RI	26,104	MC
Bryn Mawr College	PA	24,110	MC
Central Conn State Univ	CT	7,108	C
CUNY/Brooklyn College	NY	2,450	VC
CUNY/Herbert H. Lehman College	NY	2,542	C
CUNY/Hunter College	NY	4,101	VC
CUNY/Queens College	NY	2,631	C
CUNY/York College	NY	2,534	NC
College of New Rochelle	NY	15,440	LC
Columbia Univ/Barnard College	NY	25,492	HC
Columbia Univ/Columbia College	NY	26,757	MC
Cornell Univ	NY	13,445	MC
Dartmouth College	NH	24,354	MC
DePaul Univ	IL	15,535	VC
Duke Univ	NC	21,271	MC
Fairfield Univ	CT	20,460	VC
Florida State Univ	FL	5,814	VC
Fordham Univ/College at Lincoln Center	NY	18,150	VC
Fordham Univ/Fordham College	NY	19,875	VC
Georgetown Univ	DC	24,410	MC
Gonzaga Univ	WA	16,350	VC
Harvard Univ/Harvard and Radcliffe Colleges	MA	24,880	MC
Haverford College	PA	23,950	MC
Indiana Univ Bloomington	IN	6,495	VC
Iona College	NY	16,310	C
La Salle Univ	PA	16,940	VC
Lake Erie College	OH	13,700	C
LIU/C. W. Post Campus	NY	16,870	C
Loyola Univ of Chicago	IL	15,880	C+
Marlboro College	VT	23,305	C+
Mercy College	NY	11,180	NC
Middlebury College	VT	24,400	MC
Montclair State College	NJ	7,539	C+
Mount Holyoke College	MA	23,630	VC
Nazareth College of Rochester	NY	15,310	C+
New York Univ	NY	24,705	VC+
Northeastern Univ	MA	19,851	C
Northwestern Univ	IL	21,093	MC
Ohio State Univ	OH	7,218	LC
Ohio Wesleyan Univ	OH	21,108	VC+
Penn State Univ/Univ Park Campus	PA	8,752	HC
Pepperdine Univ	CA	23,720	VC
Providence College	RI	19,750	VC
Rosary College	IL	15,040	C
Rutgers Univ/Douglass College	NJ	8,795	VC
Rutgers Univ/Livingston College	NJ	8,877	VC
Rutgers Univ/Newark College of A&S	NJ	8,645	C
Rutgers Univ/Rutgers College	NJ	8,841	HC+
Rutgers Univ/Univ College—New Brunswick	NJ	0	LC
St John Fisher College	NY	15,415	C
St John's Univ	NY	8,980	C+
San Francisco State Univ	CA	7,292	LC
Santa Clara Univ	CA	18,783	VC
Sarah Lawrence College	NY	24,975	HC
Scripps College	CA	23,600	HC
Seton Hall Univ	NJ	18,306	LC
Smith College	MA	24,236	HC
Southern Conn State Univ	CT	7,532	C
Stanford Univ	CA	24,310	MC
SUNY at Albany	NY	7,059	VC
SUNY at Binghamton	NY	7,921	HC
SUNY at Buffalo	NY	7,896	VC
SUNY at Stony Brook	NY	7,658	VC
SUNY/College at Buffalo	NY	7,035	VC
SUNY/College at Purchase	NY	7,324	C
Syracuse Univ	NY	21,305	HC
Temple Univ	PA	10,281	C
Trinity College	CT	24,120	HC
Tulane Univ	LA	24,540	HC
Univ of Arizona	AZ	5,808	C
Univ of Calif at Berkeley	CA	9,962	HC+
Univ of Calif at Davis	CA	9,534	VC
Univ of Calif at Los Angeles	CA	8,959	HC
Univ of Calif at Santa Barbara	CA	9,460	C
Univ of Calif at Santa Cruz	CA	9,060	VC
Univ of Calif, San Diego	CA	10,028	VC+
Univ of Colo at Boulder	CO	6,410	VC
Univ of Conn	CT	9,168	C
Univ of Delaware	DE	8,013	VC
Univ of Georgia	GA	5,655	VC
Univ of Illinois at Chicago	IL	8,443	C
Univ of Iowa	IA	5,658	VC
Univ of Kansas	KS	5,200	NC
Univ of Kentucky	KY	5,152	VC
Univ of Mass/Amherst	MA	9,364	LC
Univ of Mass/Boston	MA	4,253	C
Univ of Mich/Ann Arbor	MI	9,428	HC+
Univ of Minn/Twin Cities	MN	6,682	VC
Univ of N Car at Chapel Hill	NC	5,330	HC
Univ of Notre Dame	IN	20,150	MC
Univ of Oregon	OR	6,466	VC
Univ of Pittsburgh	PA	9,472	C
Univ of Rhode Island	RI	9,205	C
Univ of S Car	SC	6,158	C
Univ of South Florida	FL	5,475	C+
Univ of Tenn/Knoxville	TN	5,668	C
Univ of Texas at Austin	TX	5,160	VC
Univ of Virginia	VA	7,964	MC
Univ of Washington	WA	6,618	VC
Univ of Wisc/Madison	WI	6,400	HC
Univ of Wisc/Milwaukee	WI	6,165	C
Washington Univ	MO	23,507	HC
Wayne State Univ	MI	2,680	C

School	ST	$IS	SR
Wellesley College	MA	23,815	MC
Wells College	NY	19,460	C+
Wesleyan Univ	CT	23,770	MC
Wheaton College	MA	23,840	C+
Yale Univ	CT	25,110	MC
Youngstown State Univ	OH	6,447	LC

ITALIAN STUDIES

School	ST	$IS	SR
Dickinson College	PA	22,705	HC
Rosemont College	PA	16,775	C

JAPANESE

School	ST	$IS	SR
Arizona State Univ Main Campus	AZ	6,444	C
Brigham Young Univ	UT	5,625	HC
Bucknell Univ	PA	22,320	HC
Cal State/Los Angeles	CA	4,940	VC
Conn College	CT	24,160	HC
Earlham College	IN	19,383	VC
Eastern Mich Univ	MI	6,749	C
Evergreen State College	WA	6,306	C
Georgetown Univ	DC	24,410	MC
Harvard Univ/Harvard and Radcliffe Colleges	MA	24,880	MC
Hobart and William Smith Colleges	NY	23,925	VC
Illinois Wesleyan Univ	IL	18,590	HC+
North Central College	IL	15,498	VC
Oakland Univ	MI	6,714	VC
Ohio State Univ	OH	7,218	LC
Pacific Univ	OR	17,869	C
Pepperdine Univ	CA	23,720	VC
Pomona College	CA	23,820	MC
Portland State Univ	OR	7,191	C
San Francisco State Univ	CA	7,292	LC
Scripps College	CA	23,600	HC
Stanford Univ	CA	24,310	MC
Univ of Calif at Davis	CA	9,534	VC
Univ of Calif at Los Angeles	CA	8,959	HC
Univ of Calif at Santa Barbara	CA	9,460	C
Univ of Calif at Santa Cruz	CA	9,060	VC
Univ of Colo at Boulder	CO	6,410	VC
Univ of Findlay	OH	15,764	C
Univ of Hawaii at Hilo	HI	4,141	C
Univ of Hawaii at Manoa	HI	5,626	C
Univ of Maryland/College Park	MD	8,182	VC
Univ of Mass/Amherst	MA	9,364	LC
Univ of Mich/Ann Arbor	MI	9,428	HC+
Univ of Minn/Twin Cities	MN	6,682	VC
Univ of Montana	MT	5,529	C
Univ of Notre Dame	IN	20,150	MC
Univ of Oregon	OR	6,466	VC
Univ of Pittsburgh	PA	9,472	C
Univ of Rochester	NY	23,696	HC
Univ of the Pacific	CA	21,100	C
Univ of Washington	WA	6,618	VC
Univ of Wisc/Madison	WI	6,400	HC
Washington Univ	MO	23,507	HC
Wellesley College	MA	23,815	MC
Wesleyan Univ	CT	23,770	MC
Yale Univ	CT	25,110	MC

JAZZ

School	ST	$IS	SR
DePaul Univ	IL	15,535	VC
Five Towns College	NY	11,200	SP
Ithaca College	NY	19,679	C
Manhattan School of Music	NY	12,000	SP
New England Conservatory of Music	MA	21,590	SP
Ohio State Univ	OH	7,218	LC
Temple Univ	PA	10,281	C
Univ of Cincinnati	OH	7,989	C
Univ of Miami	FL	22,107	VC
Univ of Mich/Ann Arbor	MI	9,428	HC+
Univ of Minn/Duluth	MN	6,512	C
Univ of North Texas	TX	4,853	C
Univ of the Arts	PA	16,150	SP
Univ of Washington	WA	6,618	VC
Webster Univ	MO	12,650	C
Western Mich Univ	MI	6,820	C

JOURNALISM

School	ST	$IS	SR
Abilene Christian Univ	TX	10,460	NC
Adams State College	CO	4,910	C
Adrian College	MI	14,340	C
Alabama State Univ	AL	3,428	NC
American Univ	DC	21,230	VC+
Andrews Univ	MI	14,952	NC
Angelo State Univ	TX	5,176	C
Antioch College	OH	19,532	C
Appalachian State Univ	NC	4,095	C
Arizona State Univ Main Campus	AZ	6,444	C
Arkansas State Univ	AR	4,250	NC
Arkansas Tech Univ	AR	4,200	NC
Asbury College	KY	11,105	VC
Ashland Univ	OH	15,508	C
Auburn Univ	AL	5,823	C+
Augusta College	GA	1,452	C
Augustana College	SD	13,420	C
Averett College	VA	13,610	LC
Ball State Univ	IN	6,032	LC
Baylor Univ	TX	10,990	C+
Bemidji State Univ	MN	5,188	C
Benedict College	SC	8,376	LC
Benedictine College	KS	12,830	C
Bethany College	WV	18,300	C+
Black Hills State Univ	SD	4,831	NC
Boston Univ	MA	24,130	HC
Bowie State Univ	MD	7,294	LC
Bowling Green State Univ	OH	6,701	C
Brigham Young Univ	UT	5,625	HC
Brooklyn Campus of LIU	NY	15,000	LC
Butler Univ	IN	16,210	C
Calif Polytechnic State Univ	CA	6,980	VC+
Cal State/Chico	CA	6,146	C
Cal State/Fresno	CA	5,747	C
Cal State/Fullerton	CA	4,850	LC
Cal State/Long Beach	CA	6,057	LC
Cal State/Los Angeles	CA	4,940	VC
Cal State/Northridge	CA	7,122	LC
Cal State/Sacramento	CA	6,387	C
Cameron Univ	OK	3,686	LC
Campbell Univ	NC	10,624	C
Carnegie Mellon Univ	PA	22,560	HC+
Carroll College	WI	15,490	C
Cedarville College	OH	10,715	C
Central Mich Univ	MI	6,737	LC
Central Missouri State Univ	MO	5,138	LC
Central State Univ	OH	7,320	NC
Central Univ of Bayamon	PR	2,430	
Central Washington Univ	WA	5,644	C
Christian Brothers Univ	TN	12,120	VC
Christopher Newport Univ	VA	3,196	LC
CUNY/Baruch College	NY	2,562	VC
CUNY/Brooklyn College	NY	2,450	VC
College of St Francis	IL	13,060	VC
Colo State Univ	CO	6,566	VC
Columbia College	IL	7,879	SP
Columbia Union College	MD	13,650	LC
Creighton Univ	NE	14,432	VC
Davis and Elkins College	WV	13,230	LC
Delaware State College	DE	5,656	C
Dickinson State Univ	ND	3,792	
Dordt College	IA	11,690	C
Drake Univ	IA	17,195	VC
Duquesne Univ	PA	16,434	VC
East Central Univ	OK	3,558	C
East Tenn State Univ	TN	4,406	C
East Texas State Univ	TX	4,572	LC
Eastern Illinois Univ	IL	5,548	C
Eastern Kentucky Univ	KY	4,840	NC
Eastern Mich Univ	MI	6,749	C
Eastern New Mexico Univ	NM	3,950	C
Eastern Washington Univ	WA	5,439	LC
Elon College	NC	12,290	LC
Emerson College	MA	22,678	LC
Emory and Henry College	VA	12,776	C
Evangel College	MO	10,142	LC
Evergreen State College	WA	6,306	C
Florida A&M Univ	FL	4,651	C
Florida Atlantic Univ	FL	5,525	C
Florida Southern College	FL	12,260	C
Fordham Univ/College at Lincoln Center	NY	18,150	VC
Fordham Univ/Fordham College	NY	19,875	VC
Franklin College of Indiana	IN	13,970	C
George Mason Univ	VA	8,728	C
George Washington Univ	DC	22,470	HC
Georgia College	GA	4,310	LC
Georgia Southern Univ	GA	4,988	LC
Georgia State Univ	GA	2,019	C
Gonzaga Univ	WA	16,350	VC
Grambling State Univ	LA	4,712	NC
Grand Valley State Univ	MI	6,822	VC
Grand View College	IA	13,230	NC
Hampshire College	MA	25,320	C
Hastings College	NE	12,426	C
Henderson State Univ	AR	3,860	C
Hofstra Univ	NY	16,580	VC
Howard Univ	DC	11,680	C
Humboldt State Univ	CA	5,676	C
Indiana State Univ	IN	6,210	C
Indiana Univ Bloomington	IN	6,495	VC
Indiana Univ of Penn	PA	6,373	C
Indiana Univ-Purdue Univ at Indianapolis	IN	5,862	LC
Iona College	NY	16,310	C
Iowa State Univ	IA	5,456	C
Ithaca College	NY	19,679	C
John Brown Univ	AR	9,880	VC
Kansas State Univ	KS	4,816	NC
Keene State College	NH	7,081	C
Kennesaw State College	GA	1,553	C
Kent State Univ	OH	6,740	LC
La Sierra Univ	CA	15,472	C
Lehigh Univ	PA	23,250	HC
Lewis Univ	IL	14,797	LC
Liberty Univ	VA	11,500	LC
Lincoln Univ	MO	4,638	NC
Lincoln Univ	PA	0	LC
Lock Haven Univ of Penn	PA	7,128	C
LIU/C. W. Post Campus	NY	16,870	C
Loras College	IA	14,160	C
Louisiana State Univ and A&M College	LA	5,605	C
Louisiana Tech Univ	LA	4,284	C
Loyola Univ/New Orleans	LA	15,660	C+
Lubbock Christian Univ	TX	9,840	NC
Lyndon State College	VT	8,394	LC
MacMurray College	IL	12,800	C
Madonna Univ	MI	8,546	C
Mankato State Univ	MN	5,097	LC
Mansfield Univ	PA	6,348	C
Marietta College	OH	16,940	C+
Marist College	NY	16,406	C
Marquette Univ	WI	16,114	VC
Marshall Univ	WV	5,762	LC
Marymount College/Tarrytown	NY	17,350	C
Maryville College	TN	14,474	C
Menlo College	CA	20,375	LC
Mercy College	NY	11,180	NC
Mercyhurst College	PA	13,488	C
Messiah College	PA	14,664	VC
Metropolitan State College of Denver	CO	1,751	NC
Mich State Univ	MI	7,842	C
Middle Tenn State Univ	TN	3,857	C
Midland Lutheran College	NE	12,410	LC
Millersville Univ of Penn	PA	7,370	VC
Miss College	MS	8,348	C
Miss Univ for Women	MS	4,456	LC
Moorhead State Univ	MN	5,076	C
Moravian College	PA	18,960	VC
Morehead State Univ	KY	4,600	LC
Mount Ida College	MA	16,700	LC
Murray State Univ	KY	4,702	C
New England College	NH	17,870	LC
New Mexico Highlands Univ	NM	3,772	C
New Mexico State Univ	NM	4,844	LC
New York Inst of Tech/Old Westbury	NY	13,914	LC
New York Univ	NY	24,705	VC+
Norfolk State Univ	VA	6,345	LC
Northeast Louisiana Univ	LA	3,906	NC
Northeast Missouri State Univ	MO	5,654	VC+
Northeastern State Univ	OK	5,250	C
Northeastern Univ	MA	19,851	C
Northern Arizona Univ	AZ	4,844	C
Northern Illinois Univ	IL	6,408	C
Northern Kentucky Univ	KY	4,620	NC
Northwest Missouri State Univ	MO	5,010	LC
Northwestern Okla State Univ	OK	3,424	C
Northwestern State Univ of Louisiana	LA	4,287	NC
Northwestern Univ	IL	21,093	MC
Oakland Univ	MI	6,714	VC
Ohio State Univ	OH	7,218	LC
Ohio Univ	OH	7,341	C
Ohio Wesleyan Univ	OH	21,108	VC+
Okla Baptist Univ	OK	8,486	C
Okla Christian Univ of Science and Arts	OK	8,790	NC
Okla City Univ	OK	9,840	C
Okla State Univ	OK	5,086	VC
Old Dominion Univ	VA	8,317	C
Olivet College	MI	14,000	C
Olivet Nazarene Univ	IL	11,976	C
Oregon State Univ	OR	6,175	C
Otterbein College	OH	16,506	C
Pace Univ	NY	15,540	C
Pacific Christian College	CA	12,700	C
Pacific Union College	CA	15,075	C
Park College	MO	7,320	C
Pembroke State Univ	NC	3,538	LC
Penn State Univ/Univ Park Campus	PA	8,752	HC
Pepperdine Univ	CA	23,720	VC
Point Loma Nazarene College	CA	13,532	C
Point Park College	PA	13,922	LC
Polytechnic Univ/Brooklyn	NY	19,700	HC
Polytechnic Univ/Farmingdale	NY	20,700	VC
Prairie View A&M Univ	TX	4,740	LC
Prescott College	AZ	9,775	C
Radford Univ	VA	7,034	LC
Rider College	NJ	18,160	C
Roosevelt Univ	IL	12,368	C
Rowan College of New Jersey	NJ	7,358	VC
Rutgers Univ/Cook College	NJ	9,197	HC
Rutgers Univ/Douglass College	NJ	8,795	VC
Rutgers Univ/Livingston College	NJ	8,877	VC
Rutgers Univ/Newark College of A&S	NJ	8,645	C
Rutgers Univ/Rutgers College	NJ	8,841	HC+
Rutgers Univ/Univ College—New Brunswick	NJ	0	LC
St Bonaventure Univ	NY	14,762	C
St Cloud State Univ	MN	5,015	C
St John Fisher College	NY	15,415	C
St John's Univ	NY	8,980	C+
St Joseph's College	IN	14,730	C
St Mary-of-the-Woods College	IN	14,430	NC
St Michael's College	VT	17,930	C
Sam Houston State Univ	TX	4,506	C
Samford Univ	AL	11,400	VC
San Diego State Univ	CA	6,692	LC
San Francisco State Univ	CA	7,292	LC
San Jose State Univ	CA	6,680	LC
Seattle Univ	WA	16,590	C
Seton Hill College	PA	14,320	C
Shorter College	GA	10,270	C
S Dak State Univ	SD	4,562	C
Southern Arkansas Univ	AR	3,432	NC
Southern Calif College	CA	12,356	C
Southern College of Seventh-day Adventists	TN	11,348	NC
Southern Conn State Univ	CT	7,532	C
Southern Illinois Univ at Carbondale	IL	6,234	C
Southern Illinois Univ at Edwardsville	IL	6,097	LC
Southern Methodist Univ	TX	18,520	VC
Southern Nazarene Univ	OK	9,206	NC
Southern Univ and A&M College	LA	4,920	NC
Southern Univ at New Orleans	LA	1,452	NC
Southwest Texas State Univ	TX	5,124	C
Southwestern Adventist College	TX	10,530	NC
Spring Hill College	AL	16,015	C+
SUNY/College at Buffalo	NY	7,035	VC
SUNY/College at New Paltz	NY	6,890	VC
SUNY/College at Plattsburgh	NY	6,917	C
Stephen F. Austin State Univ	TX	5,117	C
Suffolk Univ	MA	15,360	LC
Syracuse Univ	NY	21,305	HC
Talladega College	AL	8,124	VC
Temple Univ	PA	10,281	C
Tenn Tech Univ	TN	5,190	C
Texas A&M Univ	TX	5,382	VC
Texas Christian Univ	TX	12,180	C
Texas Southern Univ	TX	4,500	NC
Texas Tech Univ	TX	6,008	C
The Univ of New Mexico	NM	5,304	C
Thomas A. Edison State College	NJ	400	
Toccoa Falls College	GA	9,350	C
Trinity Univ	TX	16,670	HC
Troy State Univ	AL	4,322	C
Union College	KY	9,790	C
Union Univ	TN	7,880	C+
Univ of Alabama	AL	5,702	C
Univ of Alaska Anchorage	AK	7,131	C
Univ of Alaska Fairbanks	AK	4,718	C
Univ of Arizona	AZ	5,808	C
Univ of Arkansas at Fayetteville	AR	5,046	C
Univ of Arkansas at Little Rock	AR	4,419	C
Univ of Bridgeport	CT	18,985	C
Univ of Central Arkansas	AR	4,200	LC
Univ of Central Florida	FL	6,061	C+
Univ of Central Okla	OK	3,647	C
Univ of Colo at Boulder	CO	6,410	VC
Univ of Conn	CT	9,168	C
Univ of Dayton	OH	15,120	C+
Univ of Delaware	DE	8,013	VC
Univ of Detroit Mercy	MI	14,720	C
Univ of Evansville	IN	15,300	VC
Univ of Findlay	OH	15,764	C
Univ of Florida	FL	5,850	HC
Univ of Georgia	GA	5,655	VC
Univ of Hawaii at Manoa	HI	5,626	C
Univ of Houston	TX	5,215	C
Univ of Houston-Downtown	TX	4,034	NC
Univ of Idaho	ID	4,830	C
Univ of Illinois at Urbana-Champaign	IL	7,764	HC
Univ of Indianapolis	IN	14,510	C
Univ of Iowa	IA	5,658	VC
Univ of Kansas	KS	5,200	NC
Univ of Kentucky	KY	5,152	VC
Univ of La Verne	CA	17,400	C

School	ST	$IS	SR
Univ of Maine	ME	7,990	C
Univ of Maryland/College Park	MD	8,182	VC
Univ of Maryland/Univ College	MD	4,900	NC
Univ of Mass/Amherst	MA	9,364	LC
Univ of Memphis	TN	3,476	C
Univ of Miami	FL	22,107	VC
Univ of Mich/Ann Arbor	MI	9,428	HC+
Univ of Miss	MS	5,756	C
Univ of Missouri/Columbia	MO	6,254	HC
Univ of Montana	MT	5,529	LC
Univ of Nebr at Kearney	NE	4,308	LC
Univ of Nebr at Omaha	NE	1,889	LC
Univ of Nebr-Lincoln	NE	5,278	LC
Univ of Nevada/Reno	NV	5,735	C
Univ of New Hampshire	NH	8,242	C
Univ of North Alabama	AL	4,236	NC
Univ of N Car at Chapel Hill	NC	5,330	HC
Univ of N Dak	ND	4,902	NC
Univ of North Texas	TX	4,853	C
Univ of Northern Colo	CO	6,008	C
Univ of Okla	OK	5,427	VC
Univ of Oregon	OR	6,466	VC
Univ of Pittsburgh at Johnstown	PA	8,914	C
Univ of Portland	OR	15,564	C
Univ of Rhode Island	RI	9,205	C
Univ of Richmond	VA	16,700	HC
Univ of Rio Grande	OH	6,300	NC
Univ of St Thomas	MN	15,785	C+
Univ of S Car	SC	6,158	C
Univ of South Florida	FL	5,475	C+
Univ of Southern Calif	CA	23,006	VC
Univ of Southern Colo	CO	5,350	LC
Univ of Southern Indiana	IN	3,720	NC
Univ of Southern Miss	MS	4,542	C
Univ of Southwestern Louisiana	LA	3,968	NC
Univ of Tenn/Knoxville	TN	5,668	C
Univ of Texas at Arlington	TX	5,549	LC
Univ of Texas at Austin	TX	5,160	VC
Univ of Texas at El Paso	TX	3,160	LC
Univ of the District of Columbia	DC	974	NC
Univ of the Sacred Heart	PR	3,890	
Univ of Toledo	OH	6,636	NC
Univ of Tulsa	OK	13,795	VC
Univ of Wisc/Eau Claire	WI	4,647	C
Univ of Wisc/Madison	WI	6,400	HC
Univ of Wisc/Oshkosh	WI	4,240	C
Univ of Wisc/River Falls	WI	4,655	C
Univ of Wisc/Whitewater	WI	4,700	C
Univ of Wyoming	WY	4,991	NC
Utah State Univ	UT	4,683	C
Utica College of Syracuse Univ	NY	16,714	LC
Valparaiso Univ	IN	14,810	VC
Virginia Union Univ	VA	10,555	LC
Virginia Wesleyan College	VA	14,950	VC
Wartburg College	IA	14,530	VC
Washington and Lee Univ	VA	17,735	MC
Washington State Univ	WA	6,364	C
Wayne State Univ	MI	2,680	C
Wesleyan College	GA	15,445	C
West Texas A&M Univ	TX	4,224	C
West Virginia Univ	WV	5,774	C
Western Kentucky Univ	KY	4,808	C
Western New England College	MA	14,674	LC
Western Washington Univ	WA	6,077	VC
Whitworth College	WA	16,265	C
Wilmington College	OH	13,700	LC
Winona State Univ	MN	5,200	VC
Women's College of Brenau Univ	GA	14,734	C

JOURNALISM EDUCATION

School	ST	$IS	SR
Auburn Univ	AL	5,823	C+
Drake Univ	IA	17,195	VC

JUDAIC STUDIES

School	ST	$IS	SR
American Univ	DC	21,230	VC+
Brandeis Univ	MA	25,585	HC
Brown Univ	RI	26,104	MC
CUNY/Brooklyn College	NY	2,450	VC
CUNY/City College	NY	2,543	VC
CUNY/Hunter College	NY	4,101	VC
Concordia College	NY	0	LC
DePaul Univ	IL	15,535	VC
Dickinson College	PA	22,705	HC
Emory Univ	GA	21,930	HC
George Washington Univ	DC	22,470	HC
Gratz College	PA	4,620	NC
Hampshire College	MA	25,320	C
Hofstra Univ	NY	16,580	VC
Indiana Univ Bloomington	IN	6,495	VC
Lee College at the Univ of Judaism	CA	15,600	VC
Mount Holyoke College	MA	23,630	VC
Oberlin College	OH	24,570	HC+
Ohio State Univ	OH	7,218	LC
Rutgers Univ/Douglass College	NJ	8,795	VC
Rutgers Univ/Livingston College	NJ	8,877	VC
Rutgers Univ/Newark College of A&S	NJ	8,645	C
Rutgers Univ/Rutgers College	NJ	8,841	HC+
Rutgers Univ/Univ College—New Brunswick	NJ	0	LC
SUNY at Binghamton	NY	7,921	HC
Tulane Univ	LA	24,540	HC
Univ of Arizona	AZ	5,808	C
Univ of Calif at Los Angeles	CA	8,959	HC
Univ of Calif, San Diego	CA	10,028	VC+
Univ of Cincinnati	OH	7,989	C
Univ of Florida	FL	5,850	HC
Univ of Illinois at Chicago	IL	8,443	C
Univ of Maryland/College Park	MD	8,182	VC
Univ of Mass/Amherst	MA	9,364	LC
Univ of Miami	FL	22,107	VC
Univ of Mich/Ann Arbor	MI	9,428	HC+
Univ of Washington	WA	6,618	VC
Univ of Wisc/Madison	WI	6,400	HC
Washington Univ	MO	23,507	HC
Wellesley College	MA	23,815	MC
Yale Univ	CT	25,110	MC

KOREAN

School	ST	$IS	SR
Brigham Young Univ	UT	5,625	HC

LABOR STUDIES

School	ST	$IS	SR
Cal State/Dominguez Hills	CA	2,857	LC
Cal State/Los Angeles	CA	4,940	VC
CUNY/Queens College	NY	2,631	C
Cleveland State Univ	OH	7,287	NC
Cornell Univ	NY	13,445	MC
Indiana Univ at Kokomo	IN	2,069	C
Indiana Univ Northwest	IN	2,310	C
Indiana Univ-Purdue Univ at Indianapolis	IN	5,862	LC
Northern Kentucky Univ	KY	4,620	NC
Penn State Univ/Univ Park Campus	PA	8,752	HC
Rutgers Univ/Douglass College	NJ	8,795	VC
Rutgers Univ/Livingston College	NJ	8,877	VC
Rutgers Univ/Rutgers College	NJ	8,841	HC+
Rutgers Univ/Univ College—New Brunswick	NJ	0	LC
St Joseph's Univ	PA	17,800	VC
San Francisco State Univ	CA	7,292	LC
Thomas A. Edison State College	NJ	400	
Univ of Calif at Los Angeles	CA	8,959	HC
Univ of Mass/Boston	MA	4,253	C
Univ of PR/Rio Piedras	PR	0	
Wayne State Univ	MI	2,680	C
Youngstown State Univ	OH	6,447	LC

LANDSCAPE ARCHITECTURE/ DESIGN

School	ST	$IS	SR
Arizona State Univ Main Campus	AZ	6,444	C
Auburn Univ	AL	5,823	C+
Augustana College	IL	16,959	VC
Ball State Univ	IN	6,032	LC
Calif Polytechnic State Univ	CA	6,980	VC+
Calif State Polytechnic Univ/Pomona	CA	6,438	LC
Colo State Univ	CO	6,566	VC
Cornell Univ	NY	13,445	MC
Iowa State Univ	IA	5,456	C
Louisiana State Univ and A&M College	LA	5,605	C
Mich State Univ	MI	7,842	C
Miss State Univ	MS	5,629	VC
N Car Agricultural and Technical State Univ	NC	4,477	LC
N Car State Univ	NC	4,984	VC
N Dak State Univ of Agriculture and Applied Science	ND	4,774	VC
Ohio State Univ	OH	7,218	LC
Oregon State Univ	OR	6,175	C
Penn State Univ/Univ Park Campus	PA	8,752	HC
Purdue Univ/West Lafayette	IN	6,636	C
Rhode Island School of Design	RI	22,315	SP
Rutgers Univ/Cook College	NJ	9,197	HC
S Dak State Univ	SD	4,562	C
SUNY College of Environmental Science and Forestry	NY	9,257	HC+
Temple Univ	PA	10,281	C
Texas A&M Univ	TX	5,382	VC
Texas Tech Univ	TX	6,008	C
Univ of Arkansas at Fayetteville	AR	5,046	C
Univ of Calif at Berkeley	CA	9,962	HC+
Univ of Calif at Davis	CA	9,534	VC
Univ of Conn	CT	9,168	C
Univ of Florida	FL	5,850	HC
Univ of Illinois at Urbana-Champaign	IL	7,764	HC
Univ of Kentucky	KY	5,152	VC
Univ of Maryland/College Park	MD	8,182	VC
Univ of Mass/Amherst	MA	9,364	LC
Univ of Mich/Ann Arbor	MI	9,428	HC+
Univ of Minn/Twin Cities	MN	6,682	VC
Univ of Oregon	OR	6,466	VC
Univ of Rhode Island	RI	9,205	C
Univ of Texas at Arlington	TX	5,549	LC
Univ of Washington	WA	6,618	VC
Univ of Wisc/Madison	WI	6,400	HC
Utah State Univ	UT	4,683	C
Virginia Polytechnic Inst and State Univ	VA	6,828	C
West Virginia Univ	WV	5,774	C

LAND USE MANAGEMENT AND RECLAMATION

School	ST	$IS	SR
Cal State/Bakersfield	CA	5,402	C
College of the Southwest	NM	5,720	LC
Eastern Mich Univ	MI	6,749	C
Metropolitan State College of Denver	CO	1,751	NC
Montana State Univ	MT	5,534	C
Northern Mich Univ	MI	6,350	C
Unity College	ME	12,885	LC
Univ of Evansville	IN	15,300	VC
Univ of Okla	OK	5,427	VC
Univ of Southwestern Louisiana	LA	3,968	NC
Univ of Wisc/Platteville	WI	4,830	C
Univ of Wisc/River Falls	WI	4,655	C

LANGUAGES

School	ST	$IS	SR
Adelphi Univ	NY	18,250	LC
American Univ	DC	21,230	VC+
Assumption College	MA	17,095	LC
Auburn Univ	AL	5,823	C+
Augusta College	GA	1,452	C
Austin Peay State Univ	TN	4,350	C
Bard College	NY	25,269	HC
Baylor Univ	TX	10,990	C+
Belmont Univ	TN	10,540	C
Beloit College	WI	18,950	VC+
Bemidji State Univ	MN	5,188	C
Benedictine College	KS	12,830	C
Bennington College	VT	24,850	VC+
Berry College	GA	11,990	VC
Bethany College	WV	18,300	C+
Bethune-Cookman College	FL	8,375	LC
Brooklyn Campus of LIU	NY	15,000	LC
Canisius College	NY	15,510	C
Carnegie Mellon Univ	PA	22,560	HC+
Carroll College	MT	11,265	C
Carroll College	WI	15,490	C
Carson-Newman College	TN	11,250	C
Carthage College	WI	15,995	C
Castleton State College	VT	8,378	LC
Cedar Crest College	PA	18,930	C
Central College	IA	14,025	VC
Central Methodist College	MO	11,410	C
Central Mich Univ	MI	6,737	LC
Charter Oak State College	CT	314	NC
CUNY/Brooklyn College	NY	2,450	VC
CUNY/City College	NY	2,543	VC
CUNY/College of Staten Island	NY	2,558	NC
CUNY/Herbert H. Lehman College	NY	2,542	C
CUNY/Hunter College	NY	4,101	VC
Clark Atlanta Univ	GA	11,846	C
Clark Univ	MA	21,400	VC
College of St Mary	NE	12,500	C
Columbia College	SC	13,520	LC
Columbia Univ/Barnard College	NY	25,492	HC
Columbia Univ/Columbia College	NY	26,757	MC
Concordia College	MN	13,200	C
Conn College	CT	24,160	HC
Converse College	SC	15,750	C
Cornell College	IA	18,425	VC
Cornell Univ	NY	13,445	MC
Creighton Univ	NE	14,432	VC
Daemen College	NY	13,020	LC
Dana College	NE	11,910	C
Dartmouth College	NH	24,354	MC
David Lipscomb Univ	TN	7,865	VC
Davis and Elkins College	WV	13,230	LC
Denison Univ	OH	21,150	VC+
DePauw Univ	IN	18,530	VC
Dillard Univ	LA	9,950	C
Dominican College	NY	13,600	LC
Dordt College	IA	11,690	C
Dowling College	NY	12,730	LC
Drake Univ	IA	17,195	VC
East Texas State Univ	TX	4,572	LC
Emmanuel College	MA	17,773	LC
Flagler College	FL	7,990	C
Frostburg State Univ	MD	6,940	C
Georgetown Univ	DC	24,410	MC
Grand Valley State Univ	MI	6,822	VC
Hamilton College	NY	23,500	HC
Hartwick College	NY	20,950	C
Hofstra Univ	NY	16,580	VC
Jacksonville Univ	FL	13,390	C
King's College	PA	15,420	C
Le Moyne College	NY	15,180	C
Lewis and Clark College	OR	19,980	VC
Mary Washington College	VA	7,910	HC
McNeese State Univ	LA	4,543	NC
Miss State Univ	MS	5,629	VC
Murray State Univ	KY	4,702	C
New College of the Univ of South Florida	FL	5,697	MC
New York Univ	NY	24,705	VC+
Norfolk State Univ	VA	6,345	LC
North Georgia College	GA	4,103	LC
Occidental College	CA	21,792	HC
Ohio Univ	OH	7,341	C
Pittsburg State Univ	KS	4,478	NC
Pomona College	CA	23,820	MC
Portland State Univ	OR	7,191	C
Presbyterian College	SC	15,400	VC
Radford Univ	VA	7,034	LC
Rhodes College	TN	19,624	HC
St Andrews Presbyterian College	NC	14,240	LC
St Anselm College	NH	17,340	C
St Cloud State Univ	MN	5,015	C
St Mary's College of Maryland	MD	8,900	VC+
St Mary's College of Minn	MN	13,850	LC
St Mary-of-the-Woods College	IN	14,430	NC
Southern Illinois Univ at Carbondale	IL	6,234	C
Southern Methodist Univ	TX	18,520	VC
SUNY/College at Cortland	NY	7,326	C+
Stonehill College	MA	17,481	VC
Sweet Briar College	VA	19,770	C
Thomas A. Edison State College	NJ	400	
United States Military Academy	NY	0	MC
Univ of Alabama	AL	5,702	C
Univ of Alabama at Huntsville	AL	5,868	VC
Univ of Calif, Riverside	CA	9,178	C
Univ of Central Florida	FL	6,061	C+
Univ of Denver	CO	19,290	C+
Univ of Detroit Mercy	MI	14,720	C
Univ of Hartford	CT	19,858	LC
Univ of Maryland/Baltimore County	MD	7,746	VC
Univ of Maryland/Univ College	MD	4,900	NC
Univ of Mich/Dearborn	MI	3,399	HC
Univ of Minn/Twin Cities	MN	6,682	VC
Univ of Missouri/Kansas City	MO	5,906	VC
Univ of Nebr-Lincoln	NE	5,278	LC
Univ of New Orleans	LA	5,468	C
Univ of Oregon	OR	6,466	VC
Univ of Penn	PA	24,238	MC
Univ of Southern Calif	CA	23,006	VC
Univ of Southern Colo	CO	5,350	LC
Univ of Southern Miss	MS	4,542	C
Univ of Texas at El Paso	TX	3,160	LC
Vassar College	NY	24,206	HC
Virginia Commonwealth Univ	VA	7,909	C
Virginia State Univ	VA	7,040	
Washington Univ	MO	23,507	HC
Webster Univ	MO	12,650	C
Wellesley College	MA	23,815	MC
West Virginia Univ	WV	5,774	C
Western Mich Univ	MI	6,820	C

School	ST	$IS	SR
Western Oregon State College	OR	6,180	C
Westminster College	MO	13,750	C+
Wheaton College	IL	14,710	HC
Wilson College	PA	16,630	C

LASER ELECTRO-OPTICS TECHNOLOGY

School	ST	$IS	SR
Idaho State Univ	ID	4,442	C
Oregon Inst of Tech	OR	5,985	C

LATIN

School	ST	$IS	SR
Agnes Scott College	GA	17,135	VC
Allegheny College	PA	21,020	VC
Amherst College	MA	24,152	MC
Austin Peay State Univ	TN	4,350	C
Ball State Univ	IN	6,032	LC
Baylor Univ	TX	10,990	C+
Benedictine College	KS	12,830	C
Boston College	MA	22,706	MC
Boston Univ	MA	24,130	HC
Brigham Young Univ	UT	5,625	HC
Bryn Mawr College	PA	24,110	MC
Bucknell Univ	PA	22,320	HC
Butler Univ	IN	16,210	C
Calvin College	MI	13,020	VC
Carleton College	MN	22,155	HC
Catholic Univ of America	DC	18,856	C
CUNY/Brooklyn College	NY	2,450	VC
CUNY/Herbert H. Lehman College	NY	2,542	C
CUNY/Hunter College	NY	4,101	VC
CUNY/Queens College	NY	2,631	C
Colgate Univ	NY	24,020	HC
College of St Benedict	MN	15,468	VC
College of the Holy Cross	MA	23,850	HC
College of Wooster	OH	19,875	VC
Columbia Univ/Barnard College	NY	25,492	HC
Columbia Univ/Columbia College	NY	26,757	MC
Concordia College/Moorhead	MN	12,750	C
Cornell Univ	NY	13,445	MC
Creighton Univ	NE	14,432	VC
Dartmouth College	NH	24,354	MC
Denison Univ	OH	21,150	VC+
DePauw Univ	IN	18,530	VC
Dickinson College	PA	22,705	HC
Duke Univ	NC	21,271	MC
Duquesne Univ	PA	16,434	VC
Emory Univ	GA	21,930	HC
Evergreen State College	WA	6,306	C
Florida State Univ	FL	5,814	VC
Fordham Univ/Fordham College	NY	19,875	VC
Franklin and Marshall College	PA	23,655	HC
Furman Univ	SC	16,557	VC
Gettysburg College	PA	22,960	HC
Gonzaga Univ	WA	16,350	VC
Hampden-Sydney College	VA	17,372	C+
Harvard Univ/Harvard and Radcliffe Colleges	MA	24,880	MC
Howard Univ	DC	11,680	C
Indiana State Univ	IN	6,210	C
John Carroll Univ	OH	16,510	C
Kent State Univ	OH	6,740	LC
Kenyon College	OH	22,430	HC+
Louisiana State Univ and A&M College	LA	5,605	C
Loyola College	MD	18,035	VC
Loyola Marymount Univ	CA	18,560	C
Loyola Univ of Chicago	IL	15,880	C+
Luther College	IA	15,900	VC
Marlboro College	VT	23,305	C+
Mary Washington College	VA	7,910	HC
Mercer Univ	GA	15,123	C
Miami Univ	OH	8,066	VC
Mich State Univ	MI	7,842	C
Millersville Univ of Penn	PA	7,370	VC
Monmouth College	IL	17,300	C+
Montclair State College	NJ	7,539	C+
Moravian College	PA	18,960	VC
Mount Holyoke College	MA	23,630	VC
Muhlenberg College	PA	20,795	VC
New York Univ	NY	24,705	VC+
Northwestern Univ	IL	21,093	MC
Randolph-Macon College	VA	16,980	C
Rutgers Univ/Douglass College	NJ	8,795	VC
Rutgers Univ/Livingston College	NJ	8,877	VC
Rutgers Univ/Rutgers College	NJ	8,841	HC+
Rutgers Univ/Univ College—New Brunswick	NJ	0	LC
St John's Univ	MN	15,364	C
St Louis Univ	MO	15,522	VC
St Mary's College of Calif	CA	18,848	VC
St Olaf College	MN	17,200	HC
Sarah Lawrence College	NY	24,975	HC
Scripps College	CA	23,600	HC
Smith College	MA	24,236	HC
Southwest Missouri State Univ	MO	4,956	C
Southwestern Univ	TX	15,484	HC
SUNY at Albany	NY	7,059	VC
Susquehanna Univ	PA	19,950	VC
Swarthmore College	PA	24,136	MC
Syracuse Univ	NY	21,305	HC
Temple Univ	PA	10,281	C
Texas Tech Univ	TX	6,008	C
Troy State Univ	AL	4,322	C
Tufts Univ	MA	24,962	MC
Tulane Univ	LA	24,540	HC
Univ of Arizona	AZ	5,808	C
Univ of Calif at Berkeley	CA	9,962	HC+
Univ of Calif at Davis	CA	9,534	VC
Univ of Calif at Los Angeles	CA	8,959	HC
Univ of Calif at Santa Barbara	CA	9,460	C
Univ of Delaware	DE	8,013	VC
Univ of Georgia	GA	5,655	VC
Univ of Idaho	ID	4,830	C
Univ of Iowa	IA	5,658	VC
Univ of Kentucky	KY	5,152	VC
Univ of Maine	ME	7,990	C
Univ of Mass/Boston	MA	4,253	C
Univ of Memphis	TN	3,476	C
Univ of Mich/Ann Arbor	MI	9,428	HC+
Univ of Minn/Twin Cities	MN	6,682	VC
Univ of Montana	MT	5,529	C
Univ of Nebr-Lincoln	NE	5,278	LC
Univ of New Hampshire	NH	8,242	C
Univ of N Car at Chapel Hill	NC	5,330	HC
Univ of N Car at Greensboro	NC	5,192	C
Univ of N Dak	ND	4,902	NC
Univ of Notre Dame	IN	20,150	MC
Univ of Oregon	OR	6,466	VC
Univ of St Thomas	MN	15,785	C+
Univ of Scranton	PA	17,071	VC
Univ of S Car	SC	6,158	C
Univ of S Dak	SD	4,722	C
Univ of South Florida	FL	5,475	C+
Univ of Tenn at Chattanooga	TN	5,375	C
Univ of Texas at Austin	TX	5,160	VC
Univ of the Pacific	CA	21,100	C
Univ of the South	TN	18,830	HC
Univ of Vermont	VT	10,776	C+
Univ of Wisc/Madison	WI	6,400	HC
Valparaiso Univ	IN	14,810	VC
Wabash College	IN	16,250	VC
Washington Univ	MO	23,507	HC
Wayne State Univ	MI	2,680	C
Wellesley College	MA	23,815	MC
Wesleyan Univ	CT	23,770	MC
West Chester Univ of Penn	PA	7,492	C
Western Mich Univ	MI	6,820	C
Westminster College	PA	15,200	C
Wichita State Univ	KS	5,068	NC
Youngstown State Univ	OH	6,447	LC

LATIN AMERICAN STUDIES

School	ST	$IS	SR
Adelphi Univ	NY	18,250	LC
Agnes Scott College	GA	17,135	VC
Austin College	TX	14,999	VC
Boston Univ	MA	24,130	HC
Brandeis Univ	MA	25,585	HC
Brigham Young Univ	UT	5,625	HC
Brown Univ	RI	26,104	MC
Bucknell Univ	PA	22,320	HC
Cal State/Fullerton	CA	4,850	LC
Cal State/Hayward	CA	5,495	C
Cal State/Los Angeles	CA	4,940	VC
Carleton College	MN	22,155	HC
CUNY/City College	NY	2,543	VC
CUNY/Herbert H. Lehman College	NY	2,542	C
CUNY/Hunter College	NY	4,101	VC
College of Notre Dame	CA	16,480	C
Cornell College	IA	18,425	VC
Denison Univ	OH	21,150	VC+
DePaul Univ	IL	15,535	VC
Drake Univ	IA	17,195	VC
Emory Univ	GA	21,930	HC
Flagler College	FL	7,990	C
Florida Atlantic Univ	FL	5,525	C
Florida State Univ	FL	5,814	VC
Hood College	MD	19,010	VC
Johns Hopkins Univ	MD	24,360	MC
Kent State Univ	OH	6,740	LC
Lock Haven Univ of Penn	PA	7,128	C
Macalester College	MN	19,710	HC
Mount Holyoke College	MA	23,630	VC
New Mexico State Univ	NM	4,844	LC
Oakland Univ	MI	6,714	VC
Oberlin College	OH	24,570	HC+
Penn State Univ/Univ Park Campus	PA	8,752	HC
Pitzer College	CA	23,780	HC
Providence College	RI	19,750	VC
Rhodes College	TN	19,624	HC
Rollins College	FL	20,875	VC
Rosary College	IL	15,040	C
Rutgers Univ/Douglass College	NJ	8,795	VC
Rutgers Univ/Livingston College	NJ	8,877	VC
Rutgers Univ/Rutgers College	NJ	8,841	HC+
Rutgers Univ/Univ College—New Brunswick	NJ	0	LC
St Mary's Univ	TX	12,064	C
Smith College	MA	24,236	HC
Southern Methodist Univ	TX	18,520	VC
Stanford Univ	CA	24,310	MC
SUNY at Albany	NY	7,059	VC
SUNY at Binghamton	NY	7,921	HC
SUNY/College at Plattsburgh	NY	6,917	C
Stetson Univ	FL	16,435	VC
Syracuse Univ	NY	21,305	HC
Texas Christian Univ	TX	12,180	C
Texas Tech Univ	TX	6,008	C
Tulane Univ	LA	24,540	HC
Union College	NY	23,817	HC
Univ of Alabama	AL	5,702	C
Univ of Calif at Berkeley	CA	9,962	HC+
Univ of Calif at Los Angeles	CA	8,959	HC
Univ of Calif at Santa Barbara	CA	9,460	C
Univ of Calif at Santa Cruz	CA	9,060	VC
Univ of Calif, Riverside	CA	9,178	C
Univ of Chicago	IL	24,517	MC
Univ of Cincinnati	OH	7,989	C
Univ of Colo at Boulder	CO	6,410	VC
Univ of Conn	CT	9,168	C
Univ of Delaware	DE	8,013	VC
Univ of Denver	CO	19,290	C+
Univ of Illinois at Chicago	IL	8,443	C
Univ of Kansas	KS	5,200	NC
Univ of Kentucky	KY	5,152	VC
Univ of Miami	FL	22,107	VC
Univ of Mich/Ann Arbor	MI	9,428	HC+
Univ of Minn/Morris	MN	6,825	HC
Univ of Missouri/Columbia	MO	6,254	HC
Univ of Nebr-Lincoln	NE	5,278	LC
Univ of N Car at Chapel Hill	NC	5,330	HC
Univ of Northern Iowa	IA	5,137	C
Univ of Okla	OK	5,427	VC
Univ of Rhode Island	RI	9,205	C
Univ of S Car	SC	6,158	C
Univ of Tenn/Knoxville	TN	5,668	C
Univ of Texas at Austin	TX	5,160	VC
Univ of Texas at El Paso	TX	3,160	LC
Univ of Wisc/Eau Claire	WI	4,647	C
Washington Univ	MO	23,507	HC
Wellesley College	MA	23,815	MC
Whittier College	CA	21,661	C
Yale Univ	CT	25,110	MC
York College of Penn	PA	8,345	C

LAW

School	ST	$IS	SR
Bridgewater State College	MA	7,518	C
Claremont McKenna College	CA	22,150	MC
Oberlin College	OH	24,570	HC+
Pacific Lutheran Univ	WA	15,998	VC
Ramapo College of New Jersey	NJ	8,027	C+
Sacred Heart Univ	CT	16,350	C
Southeastern Univ	DC	6,625	C
Texas Wesleyan Univ	TX	9,380	LC
United States Military Academy	NY	0	MC
Univ of Calif at Santa Barbara	CA	9,460	C
Univ of Central Florida	FL	6,061	C+
Univ of Miami	FL	22,107	VC
Univ of Nebr-Lincoln	NE	5,278	LC
Univ of Penn	PA	24,238	MC
Univ of Wisc/Milwaukee	WI	6,165	C

LAW ENFORCEMENT AND CORRECTIONS

School	ST	$IS	SR
CUNY/John Jay College of Criminal Justice	NY	2,501	LC
Eastern Kentucky Univ	KY	4,840	NC
Hardin-Simmons Univ	TX	9,080	C
Okla City Univ	OK	9,840	C
St Paul's College	VA	9,171	C
Sam Houston State Univ	TX	4,506	C
Southwest Texas State Univ	TX	5,124	C
Tarleton State Univ	TX	4,082	LC
Tiffin Univ	OH	10,800	LC
Urbana Univ	OH	12,536	C
Western Conn State Univ	CT	6,622	C
Western New England College	MA	14,674	LC
Western Oregon State College	OR	6,180	C

LIBERAL ARTS/GENERAL STUDIES

School	ST	$IS	SR
Adelphi Univ	NY	18,250	LC
Alabama A&M Univ	AL	4,200	C
Albertus Magnus College	CT	16,280	LC
Alderson-Broaddus College	WV	12,000	C
Allentown College of St Francis de Sales	PA	13,480	C
Alvernia College	PA	13,150	LC
Ambassador College	TX	4,091	C
American International College	MA	14,029	C
Anna Maria College	MA	15,975	LC
Averett College	VA	13,610	LC
Avila College	MO	12,130	C
Azusa Pacific Univ	CA	15,034	C
Belmont Abbey College	NC	13,190	C
Bentley College	MA	18,680	C
Bethune-Cookman College	FL	8,375	LC
Boricua College	NY	5,920	VC
Bowling Green State Univ	OH	6,701	C
Brescia College	KY	9,800	C
Brewton-Parker College	GA	6,828	NC
Cabrini College	PA	16,012	C
Calif Baptist College	CA	11,294	C
Cal State/Dominguez Hills	CA	2,857	LC
Cal State/Fullerton	CA	4,850	LC
Cal State/Hayward	CA	5,495	C
Cal State/Los Angeles	CA	4,940	VC
Cal State/Northridge	CA	7,122	LC
Cal State/Stanislaus	CA	6,799	C
Calumet College of St. Joseph	IN	3,585	C
Carlow College	PA	13,914	C
Cascade College	OR	9,800	NC
Chapman Univ	CA	21,842	C
City Univ	WA	6,400	NC
CUNY/College of Staten Island	NY	2,558	NC
Cleveland State Univ	OH	7,287	NC
College Misericordia	PA	15,820	C
College of Great Falls	MT	6,230	NC
College of Mount St Joseph	OH	13,272	C
College of Mount St Vincent	NY	16,730	C
College of Notre Dame	CA	16,480	C
College of Notre Dame of Maryland	MD	16,050	C
College of St Benedict	MN	15,468	VC
College of St Mary	NE	12,500	C
Colo Christian Univ	CO	9,750	C
Colo College	CO	20,038	HC
Concordia Lutheran College	TX	10,260	C+
Concordia Univ	CA	14,675	C
D'Youville College	NY	12,850	C
Dana College	NE	11,910	C
Eastern Mennonite College	VA	12,700	C
Eastern Nazarene College	MA	12,165	LC
Eastern Oregon State College	OR	6,090	C
Edinboro Univ of Penn	PA	7,181	C
Faulkner Univ	AL	8,630	LC
Ferrum College	VA	12,800	LC
Florida International Univ	FL	4,191	VC
Gonzaga Univ	WA	16,350	VC
Graceland College	IA	11,600	C
Green Mountain College	VT	14,080	C
Harding Univ	AR	9,050	VC
Hofstra Univ	NY	16,580	VC
Holy Names College	CA	15,660	C
Humboldt State Univ	CA	5,676	C
Idaho State Univ	ID	4,442	C
Indiana State Univ	IN	6,210	C
Indiana Univ at Kokomo	IN	2,069	C
Indiana Univ East	IN	2,044	NC
Indiana Univ Southeast	IN	2,260	LC
Indiana Univ-Purdue Univ at Indianapolis	IN	5,862	LC
Iowa State Univ	IA	5,456	C
James Madison Univ	VA	8,198	HC
Jordan College	MI	5,760	LC
La Sierra Univ	CA	15,472	C
Lesley College	MA	17,120	LC
Lewis Univ	IL	14,797	LC
Lewis-Clark State College	ID	4,040	
Lindsey Wilson College	KY	9,530	LC
Linfield College	OR	16,670	VC
Lock Haven Univ of Penn	PA	7,128	C
Longwood College	VA	7,800	C
Louisiana State Univ and A&M College	LA	5,605	C
Loyola Marymount Univ	CA	18,560	C
Malone College	OH	12,572	C
Mansfield Univ	PA	6,348	C

School	ST	$IS	SR
Marymount College/Tarrytown	NY	17,350	C
Marymount Manhattan College	NY	15,450	LC
Marymount Univ	VA	15,930	C
Mayville State Univ	ND	4,272	NC
Medaille College	NY	12,650	C
Mesa State College	CO	5,127	NC
Methodist College	NC	12,400	C
Mich Tech Univ	MI	7,283	VC+
Montreat-Anderson College	NC	10,972	LC
Mount Ida College	MA	16,700	LC
Mount Mercy College	IA	13,230	C
Mount Olive College	NC	9,650	LC
Mount St Clare College	IA	12,870	LC
New Mexico Inst of Mining and Tech	NM	5,212	C+
Northern Illinois Univ	IL	6,408	C
Northwest Nazarene College	ID	11,750	C
Nova Southeastern Univ	FL	13,244	LC
Ohio Dominican College	OH	11,820	LC
Okla Christian Univ of Science and Arts	OK	8,790	NC
Oregon State Univ	OR	6,175	C
Pacific Union College	CA	15,075	C
Penn State Univ/Univ Park Campus	PA	8,752	HC
Pepperdine Univ	CA	23,720	VC
Point Park College	PA	13,922	LC
Radford Univ	VA	7,034	LC
Richard Stockton College of New Jersey	NJ	6,950	VC
Rivier College	NH	14,920	LC
Rosemont College	PA	16,775	C
St Anselm College	NH	17,340	C
St Edward's Univ	TX	12,636	C
St John's College	MD	21,800	VC+
St John's College	NM	21,750	VC+
St John's Univ	MN	15,364	C
St Mary College	KS	11,250	C
St Meinrad College	IN	10,302	C
San Francisco State Univ	CA	7,292	LC
Seattle Pacific Univ	WA	16,503	C
Seattle Univ	WA	16,590	C
Seton Hall Univ	NJ	18,306	LC
Sheldon Jackson College	AK	14,050	NC
Siena Heights College	MI	12,520	C
Simpson College	CA	10,628	C
S Dak State Univ	SD	4,562	C
Southern Illinois Univ at Carbondale	IL	6,234	C
Southern Methodist Univ	TX	18,520	VC
Southern Oregon State College	OR	6,128	C
Southern Vermont College	VT	12,974	C
Spalding Univ	KY	10,496	LC
SUNY at Stony Brook	NY	7,658	VC
SUNY/College at Brockport	NY	7,220	C+
SUNY/Empire State College	NY	2,687	NC
Teikyo Post Univ	CT	16,360	LC
Thomas Aquinas College	CA	17,900	HC
Thomas College	GA	3,123	NC
Univ of Arkansas at Little Rock	AR	4,419	C
Univ of Calif, Riverside	CA	9,178	C
Univ of Charleston	WV	12,750	C
Univ of Evansville	IN	15,300	VC
Univ of Houston-Downtown	TX	4,034	NC
Univ of Illinois at Urbana-Champaign	IL	7,764	HC
Univ of Iowa	IA	5,658	VC
Univ of Kansas	KS	5,200	NC
Univ of Maine at Farmington	ME	6,700	C
Univ of Maine at Fort Kent	ME	6,285	LC
Univ of Maryland/Eastern Shore	MD	6,254	LC
Univ of Mass/Amherst	MA	9,364	LC
Univ of Mich/Ann Arbor	MI	9,428	HC+
Univ of Mich/Dearborn	MI	3,399	HC
Univ of Minn/Morris	MN	6,825	HC
Univ of Mobile	AL	9,400	C
Univ of Montana	MT	5,529	C
Univ of New Hampshire	NH	8,242	C
Univ of New Haven	CT	14,980	C
Univ of N Car at Chapel Hill	NC	5,330	HC
Univ of North Texas	TX	4,853	C
Univ of Northern Iowa	IA	5,137	C
Univ of Okla	OK	5,427	VC
Univ of Penn	PA	24,238	MC
Univ of Pittsburgh	PA	9,472	C
Univ of San Diego	CA	18,970	VC
Univ of S Dak	SD	4,722	C
Univ of Texas at Arlington	TX	5,549	LC
Univ of Texas at Austin	TX	5,160	VC
Univ of the Ozarks	AR	7,770	C
Univ of the State of New York/Regents College Degrees	NY	510	
Univ of Washington	WA	6,618	VC
Univ of Wisc/Oshkosh	WI	4,240	C
Urbana Univ	OH	12,536	C
Utah State Univ	UT	4,683	C
Virginia Polytechnic Inst and State Univ	VA	6,828	C
Warner Pacific College	OR	12,112	C
Wayne State Univ	MI	2,680	C
West Georgia College	GA	4,256	C
West Virginia Univ	WV	5,774	C
Western International Univ	AZ	3,600	C
Westmont College	CA	18,732	C
Wilberforce Univ	OH	10,408	C
Wiley College	TX	0	NC
William Carey College	MS	7,050	C
William Paterson College	NJ	7,438	C+
Wingate College	NC	10,610	C
York College	NE	7,610	C

LIBRARY SCIENCE

School	ST	$IS	SR
Kutztown Univ	PA	6,528	C
Lock Haven Univ of Penn	PA	7,128	C
Northeast Louisiana Univ	LA	3,906	NC
Northwestern Okla State Univ	OK	3,424	C
Ohio Dominican College	OH	11,820	LC
Phillips Univ	OK	12,744	C
Southern Conn State Univ	CT	7,532	C
Southwestern Okla State Univ	OK	3,312	C
Spalding Univ	KY	10,496	LC
Univ of Central Arkansas	AR	4,200	LC
Univ of N Dak	ND	4,902	NC
Univ of North Texas	TX	4,853	C
Univ of the District of Columbia	DC	974	NC

LIFE SCIENCE

School	ST	$IS	SR
Azusa Pacific Univ	CA	15,034	C
Iowa Wesleyan College	IA	13,250	C
James Madison Univ	VA	8,198	HC
Niagara Univ	NY	14,552	C
United States Military Academy	NY	0	MC
Univ of Missouri/Rolla	MO	6,729	VC+
Wayland Baptist Univ	TX	7,811	NC
Wayne State College	NE	4,260	NC

LIMNOLOGY

School	ST	$IS	SR
Univ of Central Florida	FL	6,061	C+

LINGUISTICS

School	ST	$IS	SR
Boston College	MA	22,706	MC
Boston Univ	MA	24,130	HC
Brandeis Univ	MA	25,585	HC
Brigham Young Univ	UT	5,625	HC
Brown Univ	RI	26,104	MC
Cal State/Fullerton	CA	4,850	LC
Cal State/Northridge	CA	7,122	LC
Central College	IA	14,025	VC
CUNY/Brooklyn College	NY	2,450	VC
CUNY/Herbert H. Lehman College	NY	2,542	C
Cleveland State Univ	OH	7,287	NC
Columbia Univ/Barnard College	NY	25,492	HC
Cornell Univ	NY	13,445	MC
Emporia State Univ	KS	4,685	NC
Florida Atlantic Univ	FL	5,525	C
Georgetown Univ	DC	24,410	MC
Hamilton College	NY	23,500	HC
Hampshire College	MA	25,320	C
Harvard Univ/Harvard and Radcliffe Colleges	MA	24,880	MC
Indiana Univ Bloomington	IN	6,495	VC
Iowa State Univ	IA	5,456	C
Lawrence Univ	WI	19,986	HC+
Liberty Univ	VA	11,500	LC
Loyola Univ of Chicago	IL	15,880	C+
Macalester College	MN	19,710	HC
Marlboro College	VT	23,305	C+
Mich State Univ	MI	7,842	C
Millersville Univ of Penn	PA	7,370	VC
Montclair State College	NJ	7,539	C+
Northeastern Illinois Univ	IL	1,955	C
Northeastern Univ	MA	19,851	C
Northwestern Univ	IL	21,093	MC
Oakland Univ	MI	6,714	VC
Ohio State Univ	OH	7,218	LC
Pitzer College	CA	23,780	HC
Pomona College	CA	23,820	MC
Portland State Univ	OR	7,191	C
Purdue Univ/West Lafayette	IN	6,636	C
Reed College	OR	24,480	HC+
Rice Univ	TX	15,110	MC
Rutgers Univ/Douglass College	NJ	8,795	VC
Rutgers Univ/Livingston College	NJ	8,877	VC
Rutgers Univ/Rutgers College	NJ	8,841	HC+
Rutgers Univ/Univ College—New Brunswick	NJ	0	LC
Scripps College	CA	23,600	HC
Southern Illinois Univ at Carbondale	IL	6,234	C
Stanford Univ	CA	24,310	MC
SUNY at Albany	NY	7,059	VC
SUNY at Buffalo	NY	7,896	VC
SUNY at Stony Brook	NY	7,658	VC
SUNY/College at Oswego	NY	7,330	VC
Syracuse Univ	NY	21,305	HC
Temple Univ	PA	10,281	C
Tulane Univ	LA	24,540	HC
Univ of Alabama at Birmingham	AL	7,533	C
Univ of Alaska Fairbanks	AK	4,718	C
Univ of Arizona	AZ	5,808	C
Univ of Calif at Berkeley	CA	9,962	HC+
Univ of Calif at Davis	CA	9,534	VC
Univ of Calif at Los Angeles	CA	8,959	HC
Univ of Calif at Santa Barbara	CA	9,460	C
Univ of Calif at Santa Cruz	CA	9,060	VC
Univ of Calif, Riverside	CA	9,178	C
Univ of Calif, San Diego	CA	10,028	VC+
Univ of Calif/Irvine	CA	12,680	VC
Univ of Chicago	IL	24,517	MC
Univ of Cincinnati	OH	7,989	C
Univ of Colo at Boulder	CO	6,410	VC
Univ of Conn	CT	9,168	C
Univ of Florida	FL	5,850	HC
Univ of Hawaii at Hilo	HI	4,141	C
Univ of Iowa	IA	5,658	VC
Univ of Kansas	KS	5,200	NC
Univ of Kentucky	KY	5,152	VC
Univ of Louisville	KY	5,948	C
Univ of Maryland/College Park	MD	8,182	VC
Univ of Mass/Amherst	MA	9,364	LC
Univ of Mich/Ann Arbor	MI	9,428	HC+
Univ of Minn/Twin Cities	MN	6,682	VC
Univ of New Hampshire	NH	8,242	C
Univ of N Car at Chapel Hill	NC	5,330	HC
Univ of Okla	OK	5,427	VC
Univ of Oregon	OR	6,466	VC
Univ of Penn	PA	24,238	MC
Univ of Pittsburgh	PA	9,472	C
Univ of Rhode Island	RI	9,205	C
Univ of Rochester	NY	23,696	HC
Univ of Tenn/Knoxville	TN	5,668	C
Univ of Texas at Austin	TX	5,160	VC
Univ of the Pacific	CA	21,100	C
Univ of Utah	UT	5,975	C
Univ of Wisc/Madison	WI	6,400	HC
Univ of Wisc/Milwaukee	WI	6,165	C
Washington Univ	MO	23,507	HC
Wayne State Univ	MI	2,680	C
Western Mich Univ	MI	6,820	C
Yale Univ	CT	25,110	MC

LITERATURE

School	ST	$IS	SR
Agnes Scott College	GA	17,135	VC
Antioch College	OH	19,532	C
Aurora Univ	IL	13,381	C
Bennington College	VT	24,850	VC+
Calif Inst of Tech	CA	20,783	MC
Case Western Reserve Univ	OH	19,910	HC
Castleton State College	VT	8,378	LC
Charter Oak State College	CT	314	NC
Claremont McKenna College	CA	22,150	MC
Coe College	IA	17,085	VC
Concordia College	MN	13,200	C
D'Youville College	NY	12,850	C
Dartmouth College	NH	24,354	MC
Davis and Elkins College	WV	13,230	LC
Drexel Univ	PA	15,970	C
Duke Univ	NC	21,271	MC
Eastern Washington Univ	WA	5,439	LC
Emory and Henry College	VA	12,776	C
Emory Univ	GA	21,930	HC
Florida State Univ	FL	5,814	VC
George Fox College	OR	15,640	LC
Gonzaga Univ	WA	16,350	VC
Hampshire College	MA	25,320	C
Harvard Univ/Harvard and Radcliffe Colleges	MA	24,880	MC
Hawaii Pacific Univ	HI	12,300	C
John Carroll Univ	OH	16,510	C
Johnson State College	VT	8,393	LC
Knox College	IL	18,990	VC
Lee College at the Univ of Judaism	CA	15,600	VC
Lycoming College	PA	17,200	LC
Maharishi International Univ	IA	13,666	C
Mass Inst of Tech	MA	24,800	MC
Middlebury College	VT	24,400	MC
New College of the Univ of South Florida	FL	5,697	MC
Oral Roberts Univ	OK	10,607	C+
Pacific Univ	OR	17,869	C
Penn State Univ/Univ Park Campus	PA	8,752	HC
Plymouth State College	NH	7,166	C
Pomona College	CA	23,820	MC
Ramapo College of New Jersey	NJ	8,027	C+
Reed College	OR	24,480	HC+
St Andrews Presbyterian College	NC	14,240	LC
St Mary's College of Minn	MN	13,850	LC
Scripps College	CA	23,600	HC
Southwest State Univ	MN	5,400	NC
SUNY/College at Purchase	NY	7,324	C
Stevens Inst of Tech	NJ	21,980	VC+
Thomas A. Edison State College	NJ	400	
Thomas Moore College of Liberal Arts	NH	11,900	NC
United States Military Academy	NY	0	MC
Univ of Calif, San Diego	CA	10,028	VC+
Univ of Evansville	IN	15,300	VC
Univ of Illinois at Chicago	IL	8,443	C
Univ of Mich/Ann Arbor	MI	9,428	HC+
Univ of North Florida	FL	5,082	C
Univ of Notre Dame	IN	20,150	MC
Univ of Rhode Island	RI	9,205	C
Univ of St Thomas	MN	15,785	C+
Univ of Texas at Dallas	TX	1,222	VC+
Univ of Virginia	VA	7,964	MC
Webster Univ	MO	12,650	C
Wheaton College	MA	23,840	C+
Wilberforce Univ	OH	10,408	C
Williams College	MA	24,390	MC
Yale Univ	CT	25,110	MC

LUSO-BRAZILIAN STUDIES

School	ST	$IS	SR
Smith College	MA	24,236	HC

MANAGEMENT ENGINEERING

School	ST	$IS	SR
Boston College	MA	22,706	MC
Cal State/Chico	CA	6,146	C
Claremont McKenna College	CA	22,150	MC
New England College	NH	17,870	LC
Pitzer College	CA	23,780	HC
Univ of Nebr at Kearney	NE	4,308	LC
Valdosta State Univ	GA	4,670	LC

MANAGEMENT INFORMATION SYSTEMS

School	ST	$IS	SR
Adelphi Univ	NY	18,250	LC
Adrian College	MI	14,340	C
Alderson-Broaddus College	WV	12,000	C
Ambassador College	TX	4,091	C
American Univ	DC	21,230	VC+
Augsburg College	MN	15,608	C
Babson College	MA	23,160	VC
Barry Univ	FL	16,050	C
Boston Univ	MA	24,130	HC
Brigham Young Univ	UT	5,625	HC
Cal State/Fullerton	CA	4,850	LC
Cal State/Northridge	CA	7,122	LC
Cal State/Sacramento	CA	6,387	C
Canisius College	NY	15,510	C
Central Conn State Univ	CT	7,108	C
Clarkson Univ	NY	20,705	VC+
Colo Christian Univ	CO	9,750	C
Colo Technical College	CO	6,005	C
Creighton Univ	NE	14,432	VC
Elmhurst College	IL	12,536	C
Ferrum College	VA	12,800	LC
Fitchburg State College	MA	6,962	C
Florida International Univ	FL	4,191	VC
Florida State Univ	FL	5,814	VC
Georgetown College	KY	10,990	C
Georgia College	GA	4,310	LC
GMI Engineering & Management Inst	MI	14,158	HC
Grace College	IN	12,120	C
Greenville College	IL	14,190	C
Grove City College	PA	7,870	HC
Hofstra Univ	NY	16,580	VC
Indiana State Univ	IN	6,210	C
Inter American Univ of PR/Aguadilla Regional College	PR	2,290	

MARINE BIOLOGY

School	ST	$IS	SR
Auburn Univ	AL	5,823	C+
Boston Univ	MA	24,130	HC
Cal State/Fullerton	CA	4,850	LC
College of Charleston	SC	6,250	LC
Dowling College	NY	12,730	LC
Fairleigh Dickinson Univ	NJ	16,427	C
Florida Atlantic Univ	FL	5,525	C
Florida Inst of Tech	FL	16,935	VC
Hampshire College	MA	25,320	C
Millersville Univ of Penn	PA	7,370	VC
Nicholls State Univ	LA	4,531	NC
Roger Williams Univ	RI	16,750	C
San Francisco State Univ	CA	7,292	LC
Savannah State College	GA	4,052	C
Sonoma State Univ	CA	6,996	LC
Southwest Texas State Univ	TX	5,124	C
Southwestern College	KS	10,032	C
Spring Hill College	AL	16,015	C+
Texas A&M Univ at Galveston	TX	4,874	LC
Troy State Univ	AL	4,322	C
Univ of Calif at Santa Cruz	CA	9,060	VC
Univ of Maine at Machias	ME	6,135	C
Univ of Mass Dartmouth	MA	8,158	C
Univ of New England	ME	16,075	LC
Univ of North Alabama	AL	4,236	NC
Univ of N Car at Wilmington	NC	5,172	C
Univ of PR/Humacao Univ College	PR	1,494	
Univ of the Virgin Islands	VI	5,896	C

MARINE ENGINEERING

School	ST	$IS	SR
Calif Maritime Academy	CA	7,318	C
Maine Maritime Academy	ME	8,336	C
Mass Maritime Academy	MA	7,410	C
Texas A&M Univ at Galveston	TX	4,874	LC
United States Merchant Marine Academy	NY	4,090	HC
United States Naval Academy	MD	0	MC
Univ of New Orleans	LA	5,468	C

MARINE SCIENCE

School	ST	$IS	SR
Cal State/Stanislaus	CA	6,799	C
CUNY/City College	NY	2,543	VC
Coastal Carolina Univ	SC	6,010	LC
Drake Univ	IA	17,195	VC
East Stroudsburg Univ	PA	6,886	C
Eckerd College	FL	18,855	VC
Hawaii Pacific Univ	HI	12,300	C
Jacksonville Univ	FL	13,390	C
Kutztown Univ	PA	6,528	C
LIU/Southampton Campus	NY	17,280	C
Richard Stockton College of New Jersey	NJ	6,950	VC
Rider College	NJ	18,160	C
Salisbury State Univ	MD	7,516	C+
Suffolk Univ	MA	15,360	LC
Texas A&M Univ at Galveston	TX	4,874	LC
United States Coast Guard Academy	CT	0	MC
Univ of Alabama	AL	5,702	C
Univ of Hawaii at Hilo	HI	4,141	C
Univ of Miami	FL	22,107	VC
Univ of Rhode Island	RI	9,205	C
Univ of San Diego	CA	18,970	VC
Univ of S Car	SC	6,158	C
Univ of Tampa	FL	16,780	C

MARITIME SCIENCE

School	ST	$IS	SR
Hampton Univ	VA	10,706	C
Maine Maritime Academy	ME	8,336	C

MARKETING AND DISTRIBUTION

School	ST	$IS	SR
Indiana State Univ	IN	6,210	C
Inter American Univ/Arecibo Campus	PR	5,666	
Johnson and Wales Univ	RI	13,995	LC
National Univ	CA	6,135	C
Ohio State Univ	OH	7,218	LC
Ouachita Baptist Univ	AR	8,940	C
Tarleton State Univ	TX	4,082	LC
West Virginia Univ	WV	5,774	C
Youngstown State Univ	OH	6,447	LC

MARKETING AND DISTRIBUTION EDUCATION

School	ST	$IS	SR
Central Conn State Univ	CT	7,108	C
Eastern Washington Univ	WA	5,439	LC
Indiana Univ of Penn	PA	6,373	C
James Madison Univ	VA	8,198	HC
Johnson and Wales Univ	RI	13,995	LC
New Hampshire College	NH	15,242	LC
N Car State Univ	NC	4,984	VC
Rider College	NJ	18,160	C
Temple Univ	PA	10,281	C
Univ of Georgia	GA	5,655	VC
Univ of Tenn/Knoxville	TN	5,668	C
Univ of Wisc/Stout	WI	4,719	C
Virginia Polytechnic Inst and State Univ	VA	6,828	C

MARKETING MANAGEMENT

School	ST	$IS	SR
Alaska Pacific Univ	AK	11,350	C
Assumption College	MA	17,095	LC
Baker College	MI	6,971	NC
Bentley College	MA	18,680	C
CUNY/Baruch College	NY	2,562	VC
Clarke College	IA	13,950	C+
Colo Christian Univ	CO	9,750	C
Coppin State College	MD	7,145	LC
Golden Gate Univ	CA	5,623	VC
Hawaii Pacific Univ	HI	12,300	C
Johnson and Wales Univ	RI	13,995	LC
La Sierra Univ	CA	15,472	C
Menlo College	CA	20,375	LC
Mich Christian College	MI	8,094	C
Mich State Univ	MI	7,842	C
Miss State Univ	MS	5,629	VC
Morehead State Univ	KY	4,600	LC
Northwood Univ	FL	14,569	C
Oregon State Univ	OR	6,175	C
Rochester Inst of Tech	NY	18,954	VC
Shippensburg Univ of Penn	PA	7,052	C
Siena College	NY	15,410	VC
Simmons College	MA	22,534	C
Sul Ross State Univ	TX	4,144	NC
Syracuse Univ	NY	21,305	HC
Thomas College	ME	13,450	LC
Union Univ	TN	7,880	C+
Univ of Arkansas at Fayetteville	AR	5,046	C
Virginia State Univ	VA	7,040	C
Weber State Univ	UT	4,398	C
Western International Univ	AZ	3,600	C
Youngstown State Univ	OH	6,447	LC

MARKETING/RETAILING/MERCHANDISING

School	ST	$IS	SR
Abilene Christian Univ	TX	10,460	NC
Adams State College	CO	4,910	C
Adrian College	MI	14,340	C
Alabama A&M Univ	AL	4,200	C
Alabama State Univ	AL	3,428	NC
Albany State College	GA	4,481	LC
Alfred Univ	NY	21,054	VC+
Allentown College of St Francis de Sales	PA	13,480	C
American International College	MA	14,029	C
American Univ	DC	21,230	VC+
Anderson Univ	IN	12,920	C
Andrews Univ	MI	14,952	NC
Angelo State Univ	TX	5,176	C
Anna Maria College	MA	15,975	LC
Appalachian State Univ	NC	4,095	C
Arizona State Univ Main Campus	AZ	6,444	C
Arkansas State Univ	AR	4,250	NC
Ashland Univ	OH	15,508	C
Auburn Univ	AL	5,823	C+
Auburn Univ at Montgomery	AL	3,390	C
Augsburg College	MN	15,608	C
Augusta College	GA	1,452	C
Aurora Univ	IL	13,381	C
Austin Peay State Univ	TN	4,350	C
Averett College	VA	13,610	LC
Avila College	MO	12,130	C
Azusa Pacific Univ	CA	15,034	C
Babson College	MA	23,160	VC
Baldwin-Wallace College	OH	15,210	C
Ball State Univ	IN	6,032	LC
Barber-Scotia College	NC	6,840	NC
Barry Univ	FL	16,050	C
Bayamon Tech Univ College	PR	1,600	
Baylor Univ	TX	10,990	C+
Beaver College	PA	17,660	C
Belmont Univ	TN	10,540	C
Berry College	GA	11,990	VC
Bethel College	MN	15,050	C
Birmingham-Southern College	AL	15,154	VC+
Bluffton College	OH	12,951	C
Boise State Univ	ID	4,909	LC
Boston College	MA	22,706	MC
Boston Univ	MA	24,130	HC
Bowling Green State Univ	OH	6,701	C
Bradley Univ	IL	14,718	C+
Bridgewater State College	MA	7,518	C
Brooklyn Campus of LIU	NY	15,000	LC
Bryant College	RI	18,335	C
Buena Vista College	IA	16,150	VC
Butler Univ	IN	16,210	C
Cabrini College	PA	16,012	C
Calif Lutheran Univ	CA	17,240	C
Calif State Polytechnic Univ/Pomona	CA	6,438	LC
Cal State/Fresno	CA	5,747	C
Cal State/Fullerton	CA	4,850	LC
Cal State/Long Beach	CA	6,057	LC
Cal State/Los Angeles	CA	4,940	VC
Cal State/Northridge	CA	7,122	LC
Cal State/Sacramento	CA	6,387	C
Cal State/San Bernardino	CA	6,055	LC
Cameron Univ	OK	3,686	LC
Canisius College	NY	15,510	C
Caribbean Univ	PR	2,400	
Carnegie Mellon Univ	PA	22,560	HC+
Carroll College	WI	15,490	C
Carthage College	WI	15,995	C
Cedarville College	OH	10,715	C
Central Conn State Univ	CT	7,108	C
Central Mich Univ	MI	6,737	LC
Central Missouri State Univ	MO	5,138	LC
Central State Univ	OH	7,320	NC
Central Univ of Bayamon	PR	2,430	
Central Washington Univ	WA	5,644	C
Chadron State College	NE	4,091	NC
Chaminade Univ of Honolulu	HI	14,290	C
Chestnut Hill College	PA	14,525	C
Chicago State Univ	IL	2,198	C
Christian Brothers Univ	TN	12,120	VC
Christopher Newport Univ	VA	3,196	LC
City Univ	WA	6,400	NC
CUNY/Baruch College	NY	2,562	VC
CUNY/York College	NY	2,534	NC
Clarion Univ of Penn	PA	6,518	C
Clarkson Univ	NY	20,705	VC+
Cleary College	MI	5,095	NC
Clemson Univ	SC	6,564	VC
Cleveland State Univ	OH	7,287	NC
Coastal Carolina Univ	SC	6,010	LC
College Misericordia	PA	15,820	C
College of Great Falls	MT	6,230	NC
College of Notre Dame	CA	16,480	C
College of Notre Dame of Maryland	MD	16,050	C
College of Our Lady of The Elms	MA	15,639	C
College of St Francis	IL	13,060	VC
College of St Scholastica	MN	14,868	C
College of the Southwest	NM	5,720	LC
Colo State Univ	CO	6,566	VC
Columbia College	MO	11,995	C
Columbus College	GA	4,892	LC
Concord College	WV	5,104	NC
Concordia College	MN	13,200	C
Concordia College	OR	12,300	C
Creighton Univ	NE	14,432	VC
D'Youville College	NY	12,850	C
Dallas Baptist Univ	TX	9,620	LC
Dana College	NE	11,910	C
Davenport College of Business	MI	8,121	NC
David Lipscomb Univ	TN	7,865	VC
Davis and Elkins College	WV	13,230	LC
Defiance College	OH	13,480	LC
Delaware State College	DE	5,656	C
Delaware Valley College	PA	16,065	LC
Delta State Univ	MS	3,964	LC
DePaul Univ	IL	15,535	VC
Detroit College of Business	MI	5,184	NC
Dominican College	NY	13,600	LC
Dowling College	NY	12,730	LC
Drake Univ	IA	17,195	VC
Drexel Univ	PA	15,970	C
Duquesne Univ	PA	16,434	VC
Dyke College	OH	5,200	C
East Central Univ	OK	3,558	C
East Tenn State Univ	TN	4,406	C
East Texas State Univ	TX	4,572	LC
Eastern Illinois Univ	IL	5,548	C
Eastern Kentucky Univ	KY	4,840	NC
Eastern Mich Univ	MI	6,749	C
Eastern New Mexico Univ	NM	3,950	C
Eastern Washington Univ	WA	5,439	LC
Edgewood College	WI	11,700	C
Elmhurst College	IL	12,536	C
Elmira College	NY	18,450	C
Emory Univ	GA	21,930	HC
Emporia State Univ	KS	4,685	NC
Evangel College	MO	10,142	LC
Evergreen State College	WA	6,306	C
Fairfield Univ	CT	20,460	VC
Fairleigh Dickinson Univ	NJ	16,427	C
Fairmont State College	WV	4,640	LC
Fashion Inst of Tech/SUNY	NY	7,135	SP
Fayetteville State Univ	NC	3,926	LC
Ferris State Univ	MI	7,160	NC
Ferrum College	VA	12,800	LC
Fitchburg State College	MA	6,962	C
Flagler College	FL	7,990	C
Florida Atlantic Univ	FL	5,525	C
Florida Inst of Tech	FL	16,935	VC
Florida International Univ	FL	4,191	VC
Florida Southern College	FL	12,260	C
Florida State Univ	FL	5,814	VC
Fordham Univ/College of Business Administration	NY	19,875	VC
Fort Hays State Univ	KS	4,675	NC
Fort Lewis College	CO	5,097	C
Fort Valley State College	GA	3,974	LC
Francis Marion Univ	SC	5,878	LC
Franklin College of Indiana	IN	13,970	C
Franklin Pierce College	NH	17,270	LC
Franklin Univ	OH	4,621	NC
Freed-Hardeman Univ	TN	8,585	VC
Gannon Univ	PA	14,872	C
George Mason Univ	VA	8,728	C
George Washington Univ	DC	22,476	HC
Georgetown College	KY	10,990	C
Georgetown Univ	DC	24,410	MC
Georgia College	GA	4,310	LC
Georgia Southern Univ	GA	4,988	LC
Georgia Southwestern College	GA	4,338	LC
Georgia State Univ	GA	2,019	C
Glenville State College	WV	4,810	LC
GMI Engineering & Management Inst	MI	14,158	HC
Goldey-Beacom College	DE	7,839	C
Gonzaga Univ	WA	16,350	VC
Grambling State Univ	LA	4,712	NC
Grand Canyon Univ	AZ	9,680	VC
Grand Rapids Baptist College and Seminary	MI	10,228	C
Grand Valley State Univ	MI	6,822	VC
Greenville College	IL	14,190	C
Grove City College	PA	7,870	HC
Hampton Univ	VA	10,706	C
Hannibal-LaGrange College	MO	8,400	LC
Hardin-Simmons Univ	TX	9,080	C
Harding Univ	AR	9,050	VC
Heidelberg College	OH	17,160	C
Hillsdale College	MI	15,110	VC
Hofstra Univ	NY	16,580	VC
Holy Family College	PA	8,300	C
Houston Baptist Univ	TX	11,055	C
Howard Univ	DC	11,680	C
Husson College	ME	11,510	NC
Huston-Tillotson College	TX	8,490	C
Idaho State Univ	ID	4,442	C
Illinois Benedictine College	IL	14,170	C
Illinois State Univ	IL	6,413	C
Incarnate Word College	TX	12,307	C
Indiana State Univ	IN	6,210	C
Indiana Univ Bloomington	IN	6,495	VC
Indiana Univ of Penn	PA	6,373	C
Indiana Univ Southeast	IN	2,260	LC
Indiana Univ-Purdue Univ at Fort Wayne	IN	2,500	LC
Indiana Univ-Purdue Univ at Indianapolis	IN	5,862	LC
Indiana Univ/South Bend	IN	2,141	LC
Indiana Wesleyan Univ	IN	12,332	C
Inter American Univ of PR/Aguadilla Regional College	PR	2,290	
Inter American Univ of PR/Bayamon Univ College	PR	2,300	
Inter American Univ of PR/Metropolitan Campus	PR	2,340	
Inter American Univ of PR/Ponce Regional College	PR	2,300	
Inter American Univ of PR/San German	PR	4,620	
Inter-American Univ of PR/Fajardo Regional College	PR	2,732	
Iona College	NY	16,310	C
Iowa State Univ	IA	5,456	C
Ithaca College	NY	19,679	C
Jackson State Univ	MS	4,996	LC
Jacksonville State Univ	AL	4,080	LC
Jacksonville Univ	FL	13,390	C
James Madison Univ	VA	8,198	HC
Jarvis Christian College	TX	7,170	LC
Jersey City State College	NJ	7,797	LC
John Carroll Univ	OH	16,510	C
Johnson and Wales Univ	RI	13,995	LC
Juniata College	PA	18,390	C+
Kansas Newman College	KS	10,640	C
Kansas State Univ	KS	4,816	NC
Kean College of New Jersey	NJ	6,395	LC

School	ST	$IS	SR
Western Mich Univ	MI	6,820	C
Western New England College	MA	14,674	LC
Western New Mexico Univ	NM	3,234	C
Western Washington Univ	WA	6,077	VC
Westminster College	PA	15,200	C
Westminster College of Salt Lake City	UT	12,100	C
Wheeling Jesuit College	WV	14,370	C
Wichita State Univ	KS	5,068	NC
Wilberforce Univ	OH	10,408	C
William Woods Univ	MO	14,025	C
Wilmington College	OH	13,700	LC
Winona State Univ	MN	5,200	VC
Woodbury Univ	CA	17,620	C
Wright State Univ	OH	6,896	LC
Xavier Univ	OH	15,710	C+
Xavier Univ of Louisiana	LA	10,400	C
Yeshiva Univ	NY	18,200	VC
York College of Penn	PA	8,345	C
Youngstown State Univ	OH	6,447	LC

MATERIALS ENGINEERING

School	ST	$IS	SR
Drexel Univ	PA	15,970	C
Georgia Inst of Tech	GA	6,669	HC+
Johns Hopkins Univ	MD	24,360	MC
Lakeland College	WI	12,845	LC
Lehigh Univ	PA	23,250	HC
Mass Inst of Tech	MA	24,800	MC
Mich State Univ	MI	7,842	C
New Mexico Inst of Mining and Tech	NM	5,212	C+
Purdue Univ/West Lafayette	IN	6,636	C
Rensselaer Polytechnic Inst	NY	23,067	HC
St Augustine's College	NC	9,300	C+
San Jose State Univ	CA	6,680	LC
Stevens Inst of Tech	NJ	21,980	VC+
Univ of Alabama at Birmingham	AL	7,533	C
Univ of Calif at Berkeley	CA	9,962	HC+
Univ of Calif at Davis	CA	9,534	VC
Univ of Calif at Los Angeles	CA	8,959	HC
Univ of Cincinnati	OH	7,989	C
Univ of Florida	FL	5,850	VC
Univ of Kentucky	KY	5,152	VC
Univ of Minn/Twin Cities	MN	6,682	VC
Univ of Penn	PA	24,238	MC
Univ of Rhode Island	RI	9,205	C
Univ of Tenn/Knoxville	TN	5,668	C
Univ of Utah	UT	5,975	C
Univ of Wisc/Milwaukee	WI	6,165	C
Virginia Polytechnic Inst and State Univ	VA	6,828	C
Wilkes Univ	PA	15,728	LC
Winona State Univ	MN	5,200	VC
Wright State Univ	OH	6,896	LC
Youngstown State Univ	OH	6,447	LC

MATERIALS SCIENCE

School	ST	$IS	SR
Arizona State Univ Main Campus	AZ	6,444	C
Case Western Reserve Univ	OH	19,910	HC
Columbia Univ/School of Engineering and Applied Science	NY	24,554	HC
Cornell Univ	NY	13,445	MC
Duke Univ	NC	21,271	MC
N Car State Univ	NC	4,984	VC
Northwestern Univ	IL	21,093	MC
Rice Univ	TX	15,110	MC
Stanford Univ	CA	24,310	MC
Stevens Inst of Tech	NJ	21,980	VC+
Univ of Arizona	AZ	5,808	C
Univ of Calif at Los Angeles	CA	8,959	HC
Univ of Illinois at Chicago	IL	8,443	C
Univ of Minn/Twin Cities	MN	6,682	VC
Univ of Pittsburgh	PA	9,472	C
Univ of Tenn/Knoxville	TN	5,668	C
Univ of Washington	WA	6,618	VC
Western Mich Univ	MI	6,820	C

MATHEMATICS

School	ST	$IS	SR
Abilene Christian Univ	TX	10,460	NC
Adams State College	CO	4,910	C
Adelphi Univ	NY	18,250	LC
Adrian College	MI	14,340	C
Agnes Scott College	GA	17,135	VC
Alabama A&M Univ	AL	4,200	C
Alabama State Univ	AL	3,428	NC
Albany State College	GA	4,481	LC
Albertson College	ID	15,942	C+
Albertus Magnus College	CT	16,280	LC
Albion College	MI	18,264	VC
Albright College	PA	19,260	C
Alcorn State Univ	MS	4,474	C+
Alderson-Broaddus College	WV	12,000	C
Alfred Univ	NY	21,054	VC+
Alice Lloyd College	KY	2,750	VC
Allegheny College	PA	21,020	VC
Allen Univ	SC	6,705	NC
Allentown College of St Francis de Sales	PA	13,480	C
Alma College	MI	16,375	VC+
Alvernia College	PA	13,150	LC
Alverno College	WI	11,344	C
American International College	MA	14,029	C
American Univ	DC	21,230	VC+
Anderson Univ	IN	12,920	C
Andrews Univ	MI	14,952	NC
Angelo State Univ	TX	5,176	C
Antioch College	OH	19,532	C
Appalachian State Univ	NC	4,095	C
Aquinas College	MI	14,526	C
Arizona State Univ Main Campus	AZ	6,444	C
Arkansas College	AR	11,626	VC
Arkansas State Univ	AR	4,250	NC
Arkansas Tech Univ	AR	4,200	NC
Armstrong State College	GA	4,874	LC
Asbury College	KY	11,105	VC
Ashland Univ	OH	15,508	C
Assumption College	MA	17,095	LC
Atlantic Union College	MA	14,150	LC
Auburn Univ	AL	5,823	C+
Auburn Univ at Montgomery	AL	3,390	C
Augsburg College	MN	15,608	C
Augusta College	GA	1,452	C
Augustana College	IL	16,959	VC
Augustana College	SD	13,420	C
Aurora Univ	IL	13,381	C
Austin College	TX	14,999	VC
Austin Peay State Univ	TN	4,350	C
Averett College	VA	13,610	LC
Avila College	MO	12,130	C
Azusa Pacific Univ	CA	15,034	C
Baker Univ	KS	12,284	C
Baldwin-Wallace College	OH	15,312	C
Ball State Univ	IN	6,032	LC
Barat College	IL	13,990	C
Barber-Scotia College	NC	6,840	NC
Bard College	NY	25,269	HC
Barry Univ	FL	16,050	C
Bartlesville Wesleyan College	OK	9,400	C
Barton College	NC	10,689	LC
Bates College	ME	23,990	MC
Baylor Univ	TX	10,990	C+
Beaver College	PA	17,660	C
Belhaven College	MS	9,690	C+
Bellarmine College	KY	10,832	C
Belmont Abbey College	NC	13,190	C
Belmont Univ	TN	10,540	C
Beloit College	WI	18,950	VC+
Bemidji State Univ	MN	5,188	C
Benedict College	SC	8,376	LC
Benedictine College	KS	12,830	C
Bennett College	NC	8,920	LC
Bennington College	VT	24,850	VC+
Berea College	KY	2,883	VC+
Berry College	GA	11,990	VC
Bethany College	KS	11,232	C
Bethany College	WV	18,300	C+
Bethel College	IN	11,650	C
Bethel College	KS	11,530	C
Bethel College	MN	15,050	C
Bethune-Cookman College	FL	8,375	LC
Biola Univ	CA	16,124	C
Birmingham-Southern College	AL	15,154	VC
Black Hills State Univ	SD	4,831	NC
Blackburn College	IL	9,120	C
Bloomsburg Univ of Penn	PA	6,312	C+
Blue Mountain College	MS	5,958	LC
Bluefield College	VA	10,600	C
Bluefield State College	WV	1,832	LC
Bluffton College	OH	12,951	C
Boise State Univ	ID	4,909	LC
Boston College	MA	22,706	MC
Boston Univ	MA	24,130	HC
Bowdoin College	ME	24,155	MC
Bowling Green State Univ	OH	6,701	C
Bradford College	MA	19,600	C
Bradley Univ	IL	14,718	C+
Brandeis Univ	MA	25,585	HC
Brescia College	KY	9,800	C
Briar Cliff College	IA	13,375	C
Bridgewater College	VA	15,300	C
Bridgewater State College	MA	7,518	C
Brigham Young Univ	UT	5,625	VC
Brigham Young Univ/Hawaii	HI	6,750	VC
Brooklyn Campus of LIU	NY	15,000	LC
Brown Univ	RI	26,104	MC
Bryan College	TN	11,465	C
Bryn Mawr College	PA	24,110	MC
Bucknell Univ	PA	22,320	HC
Buena Vista College	IA	16,150	VC
Butler Univ	IN	16,210	C
Cabrini College	PA	16,012	C
Caldwell College	NJ	12,860	C
Calif Inst of Tech	CA	20,783	MC
Calif Lutheran Univ	CA	17,240	C
Calif Polytechnic State Univ	CA	6,980	VC+
Calif State Polytechnic Univ/Pomona	CA	6,438	LC
Cal State/Bakersfield	CA	5,402	C
Cal State/Chico	CA	6,146	C
Cal State/Dominguez Hills	CA	2,857	LC
Cal State/Fresno	CA	5,747	C
Cal State/Fullerton	CA	4,850	LC
Cal State/Hayward	CA	5,495	C
Cal State/Long Beach	CA	6,057	LC
Cal State/Los Angeles	CA	4,940	VC
Cal State/Northridge	CA	7,122	LC
Cal State/Sacramento	CA	6,387	C
Cal State/San Bernardino	CA	6,055	C
Cal State/Stanislaus	CA	6,799	C
Calif Univ of Penn	PA	7,370	C
Calvin College	MI	13,020	VC
Cameron Univ	OK	3,686	LC
Campbell Univ	NC	10,624	C
Campbellsville College	KY	8,720	C
Canisius College	NY	15,510	C
Capital Univ	OH	16,535	VC
Cardinal Stritch College	WI	11,252	C
Caribbean Univ	PR	2,400	
Carleton College	MN	22,155	HC
Carlow College	PA	13,914	C
Carnegie Mellon Univ	PA	22,560	HC+
Carroll College	MT	11,265	C
Carroll College	WI	15,490	C
Carthage College	WI	15,995	C
Case Western Reserve Univ	OH	19,910	HC
Castleton State College	VT	8,378	C
Catawba College	NC	12,950	C
Catholic Univ of America	DC	18,856	C
Cedar Crest College	PA	18,930	C
Cedarville College	OH	10,715	C
Centenary College	NJ	17,040	LC
Centenary College of Louisiana	LA	11,826	C+
Central College	IA	14,025	VC
Central Conn State Univ	CT	7,108	C
Central Methodist College	MO	11,410	C
Central Mich Univ	MI	6,737	LC
Central Missouri State Univ	MO	5,138	LC
Central State Univ	OH	7,320	NC
Central Washington Univ	WA	5,644	C
Central Wesleyan College	SC	9,640	C
Centre College	KY	15,850	VC+
Chadron State College	NE	4,091	NC
Chaminade Univ of Honolulu	HI	14,290	C
Chapman Univ	CA	21,842	C
Charleston Southern Univ	SC	10,282	LC
Charter Oak State College	CT	314	NC
Chatham College	PA	18,010	C
Chestnut Hill College	PA	14,525	C
Cheyney Univ of Penn	PA	7,005	C
Chicago State Univ	IL	2,198	C
Christian Brothers Univ	TN	12,120	VC
Christopher Newport Univ	VA	3,196	LC
CUNY/Baruch College	NY	2,562	VC
CUNY/Brooklyn College	NY	2,450	LC
CUNY/City College	NY	2,543	VC
CUNY/College of Staten Island	NY	2,558	NC
CUNY/Herbert H. Lehman College	NY	2,542	C
CUNY/Hunter College	NY	4,101	VC
CUNY/Queens College	NY	2,631	C
CUNY/York College	NY	2,534	NC
Claflin College	SC	0	
Claremont McKenna College	CA	22,150	MC
Clarion Univ of Penn	PA	6,518	C
Clark Atlanta Univ	GA	11,846	C
Clark Univ	MA	21,400	VC
Clarke College	IA	13,950	C+
Clarkson Univ	NY	20,705	VC+
Clearwater Christian College	FL	8,500	LC
Clemson Univ	SC	6,564	VC
Cleveland State Univ	OH	7,287	NC
Clinch Valley College/Univ of Virginia	VA	6,364	C
Coastal Carolina Univ	SC	6,010	LC
Coe College	IA	17,085	VC
Coker College	SC	13,790	C
Colby College	ME	24,230	HC
Colgate Univ	NY	24,020	HC
College Misericordia	PA	15,820	C
College of Charleston	SC	6,250	C
College of Great Falls	MT	6,230	NC
College of Mount St Joseph	OH	13,272	C
College of Mount St Vincent	NY	16,730	C
College of New Rochelle	NY	15,440	LC
College of Notre Dame of Maryland	MD	16,050	C
College of Our Lady of The Elms	MA	15,639	C
College of St Benedict	MN	15,468	VC
College of St Catherine	MN	14,670	C
College of St Elizabeth	NJ	15,800	C
College of St Francis	IL	13,060	VC
College of St Mary	NE	12,500	C
College of St Rose	NY	14,452	C
College of St Scholastica	MN	14,868	C
College of Santa Fe	NM	14,008	C
College of the Holy Cross	MA	23,850	HC
College of the Ozarks	MO	2,000	VC+
College of the Southwest	NM	5,720	LC
College of William and Mary	VA	8,602	MC
College of Wooster	OH	19,875	VC
Colo Christian Univ	CO	9,750	C
Colo College	CO	20,038	HC
Colo School of Mines	CO	8,436	HC+
Colo State Univ	CO	6,566	VC
Columbia College	SC	13,520	LC
Columbia Union College	MD	13,650	LC
Columbia Univ/Barnard College	NY	25,492	HC
Columbia Univ/Columbia College	NY	26,757	MC
Columbus College	GA	4,892	LC
Concord College	WV	5,104	NC
Concordia College	MI	13,660	C
Concordia College	NY	13,200	C
Concordia College	NE	11,776	NC
Concordia College	NY	0	LC
Concordia College/Moorhead	MN	12,750	C
Concordia Univ	IL	12,611	C
Concordia Univ	CA	14,675	C
Concordia Univ Wisc	WI	12,140	C
Conn College	CT	24,160	C
Converse College	SC	15,750	C
Coppin State College	MD	7,145	LC
Cornell College	IA	18,425	VC
Cornell Univ	NY	13,445	MC
Creighton Univ	NE	14,432	VC
Culver-Stockton College	MO	11,150	C
Cumberland College	KY	9,756	C
Daemen College	NY	13,020	LC
Dakota State Univ	SD	4,374	C
Dakota Wesleyan Univ	SD	9,770	LC
Dallas Baptist Univ	TX	9,620	LC
Dana College	NE	11,910	C
Dartmouth College	NH	24,354	MC
David Lipscomb Univ	TN	7,865	VC
Davidson College	NC	21,037	MC
Davis and Elkins College	WV	13,230	LC
Defiance College	OH	13,480	C
Delaware State College	DE	5,656	C
Delaware Valley College	PA	16,065	LC
Delta State Univ	MS	3,964	LC
Denison Univ	OH	21,150	VC+
DePaul Univ	IL	15,165	VC
DePauw Univ	IN	18,530	VC
Dickinson College	PA	22,705	HC
Dickinson State Univ	ND	3,792	
Dillard Univ	LA	9,950	C
Doane College	NE	12,220	C
Dominican College	NY	13,600	LC
Dominican College of San Rafael	CA	17,860	C
Dordt College	IA	11,690	C
Dowling College	NY	12,730	LC
Drake Univ	IA	17,195	VC
Drew Univ/College of Liberal Arts	NJ	23,406	HC
Drexel Univ	PA	15,970	C
Drury College	MO	12,140	VC
Duke Univ	NC	21,271	MC
Duquesne Univ	PA	16,434	VC
Earlham College	IN	19,383	VC
East Carolina Univ	NC	4,498	C
East Central Univ	OK	3,558	C
East Stroudsburg Univ	PA	6,886	C
East Tenn State Univ	TN	4,406	C
East Texas Baptist Univ	TX	7,740	C
East Texas State Univ	TX	4,572	LC
Eastern College	PA	15,150	C+
Eastern Conn State Univ	CT	6,966	C
Eastern Illinois Univ	IL	5,548	C
Eastern Kentucky Univ	KY	4,840	NC
Eastern Mennonite College	VA	12,700	C
Eastern Mich Univ	MI	6,749	C
Eastern Montana College	MT	5,165	LC
Eastern Nazarene College	MA	12,165	C
Eastern New Mexico Univ	NM	3,950	C
Eastern Oregon State College	OR	6,090	C
Eastern Washington Univ	WA	5,439	LC
Eckerd College	FL	18,855	VC
Edgewood College	WI	11,700	C
Edinboro Univ of Penn	PA	7,181	C
Edward Waters College	FL	8,300	NC
Elizabeth City State Univ	NC	4,254	LC
Elizabethtown College	PA	17,850	VC
Elmhurst College	IL	12,536	C
Elmira College	NY	18,450	C
Elon College	NC	12,290	VC
Emmanuel College	MA	17,773	C
Emory and Henry College	VA	12,776	C
Emory Univ	GA	21,930	HC
Emporia State Univ	KS	4,685	NC
Erskine College	SC	14,310	C
Eureka College	IL	14,555	C
Evangel College	MO	10,142	C
Evergreen State College	WA	6,306	C
Fairfield Univ	CT	20,460	C
Fairleigh Dickinson Univ	NJ	16,427	C
Fairmont State College	WV	4,640	LC
Fayetteville State Univ	NC	3,926	LC
Felician College	NJ	7,900	C

School	ST	$IS	SR
Univ of Southern Miss	MS	4,542	C
Univ of Southwestern Louisiana	LA	3,968	NC
Univ of Tampa	FL	16,780	C
Univ of Tenn at Chattanooga	TN	5,375	C
Univ of Tenn at Martin	TN	4,550	C
Univ of Tenn/Knoxville	TN	5,668	C
Univ of Texas at Arlington	TX	5,549	LC
Univ of Texas at Austin	TX	5,160	VC
Univ of Texas at Dallas	TX	1,222	VC+
Univ of Texas at El Paso	TX	3,160	LC
Univ of Texas at San Antonio	TX	6,420	C
Univ of the District of Columbia	DC	974	NC
Univ of the Ozarks	AR	7,770	C
Univ of the Pacific	CA	21,100	C
Univ of the Sacred Heart	PR	3,890	C
Univ of the South	TN	18,830	HC
Univ of the Virgin Islands	VI	5,896	C
Univ of Toledo	OH	6,636	NC
Univ of Tulsa	OK	13,795	VC
Univ of Utah	UT	5,975	C
Univ of Vermont	VT	10,776	C+
Univ of Virginia	VA	7,964	MC
Univ of Washington	WA	6,618	VC
Univ of West Florida	FL	5,415	C
Univ of Wisc/Eau Claire	WI	4,647	C
Univ of Wisc/Green Bay	WI	4,904	C
Univ of Wisc/La Crosse	WI	4,487	C
Univ of Wisc/Madison	WI	6,400	HC
Univ of Wisc/Milwaukee	WI	6,165	C
Univ of Wisc/Oshkosh	WI	4,240	C
Univ of Wisc/Parkside	WI	5,247	C
Univ of Wisc/Platteville	WI	4,830	C
Univ of Wisc/River Falls	WI	4,655	C
Univ of Wisc/Stevens Point	WI	5,047	C+
Univ of Wisc/Superior	WI	4,330	C
Univ of Wisc/Whitewater	WI	4,700	C
Univ of Wyoming	WY	4,991	NC
Upper Iowa Univ	IA	11,900	C
Upsala College	NJ	17,200	C
Ursinus College	PA	19,165	VC
Ursuline College	OH	13,180	LC
Utah State Univ	UT	4,683	C
Utica College of Syracuse Univ	NY	16,714	LC
Valdosta State Univ	GA	4,670	LC
Valley City State Univ	ND	4,385	LC
Valparaiso Univ	IN	14,810	VC
Vanderbilt Univ	TN	23,422	HC+
Vassar College	NY	24,206	HC
Villanova Univ	PA	21,400	HC
Virginia Commonwealth Univ	VA	7,909	C
Virginia Military Inst	VA	8,630	C
Virginia Polytechnic Inst and State Univ	VA	6,828	C
Virginia State Univ	VA	7,040	C
Virginia Union Univ	VA	10,555	LC
Virginia Wesleyan College	VA	14,950	VC
Viterbo College	WI	12,670	C
Voorhees College	SC	6,772	LC
Wabash College	IN	16,250	VC
Wagner College	NY	17,950	C
Wake Forest Univ	NC	17,280	MC
Walla Walla College	WA	13,215	C
Walsh Univ	OH	11,640	C
Warner Pacific College	OR	12,112	C
Warren Wilson College	NC	10,877	C
Wartburg College	IA	14,530	VC
Washburn Univ of Topeka	KS	5,802	NC
Washington and Jefferson College	PA	19,360	C
Washington and Lee Univ	VA	17,735	MC
Washington College	MD	19,270	C+
Washington State Univ	WA	6,364	C
Washington Univ	MO	23,507	HC
Wayland Baptist Univ	TX	7,811	NC
Wayne State College	NE	4,260	NC
Wayne State Univ	MI	2,680	C
Waynesburg College	PA	11,960	C
Weber State Univ	UT	4,398	C
Webster Univ	MO	12,650	C
Wellesley College	MA	23,815	MC
Wells College	NY	19,460	C+
Wesleyan College	GA	15,445	C
Wesleyan Univ	CT	23,770	MC
West Chester Univ of Penn	PA	7,492	C
West Georgia College	GA	4,256	C
West Liberty State College	WV	4,690	LC
West Texas A&M Univ	TX	4,224	C
West Virginia State College	WV	5,044	LC
West Virginia Univ	WV	5,774	C
West Virginia Wesleyan College	WV	16,900	C
Western Baptist College	OR	12,400	C
Western Carolina Univ	NC	3,811	C
Western Conn State Univ	CT	6,622	C
Western Illinois Univ	IL	5,241	LC
Western Kentucky Univ	KY	4,808	C
Western Maryland College	MD	18,990	C
Western Mich Univ	MI	6,820	C
Western New England College	MA	14,674	LC
Western New Mexico Univ	NM	3,234	LC
Western Oregon State College	OR	6,180	C
Western State College of Colo	CO	5,560	C
Western Washington Univ	WA	6,077	VC
Westfield State College	MA	7,161	C
Westminster College	MO	13,750	C+
Westminster College	PA	15,200	C
Westminster College of Salt Lake City	UT	12,100	C
Westmont College	CA	18,732	C
Wheaton College	IL	14,710	HC
Wheaton College	MA	23,840	C+
Wheeling Jesuit College	WV	14,370	C
Whitman College	WA	20,595	HC
Whittier College	CA	21,661	C
Whitworth College	WA	16,265	C
Wichita State Univ	KS	5,068	NC
Widener Univ	PA	16,840	C
Wilberforce Univ	OH	10,408	C
Wiley College	TX	0	NC
Wilkes Univ	PA	15,728	LC
Willamette Univ	OR	17,995	VC
William Carey College	MS	7,050	C
William Paterson College	NJ	7,438	C+
William Penn College	IA	13,400	C
William Woods Univ	MO	14,025	LC
Williams College	MA	24,390	MC
Wilmington College	OH	13,700	LC
Wilson College	PA	16,630	C
Wingate College	NC	10,610	C
Winona State Univ	MN	5,200	VC
Winston-Salem State Univ	NC	4,142	LC
Winthrop Univ	SC	6,750	C
Wisc Lutheran College	WI	12,180	C
Wittenberg Univ	OH	19,998	VC
Worcester Polytechnic Inst	MA	20,350	HC
Worcester State College	MA	6,414	LC
Wright State Univ	OH	6,896	LC
Xavier Univ	OH	15,710	C+
Xavier Univ of Louisiana	LA	10,400	C
Yale Univ	CT	25,110	MC
Yeshiva Univ	NY	18,200	VC
York College of Penn	PA	8,345	C
Youngstown State Univ	OH	6,447	LC

MATHEMATICS EDUCATION

School	ST	$IS	SR
Adelphi Univ	NY	18,250	LC
Albertson College	ID	15,942	C+
Bartlesville Wesleyan College	OK	9,400	C
Barton College	NC	10,689	LC
Bennett College	NC	8,920	LC
Berry College	GA	11,990	VC
Bethune-Cookman College	FL	8,375	LC
Boston Univ	MA	24,130	HC
Calif Univ of Penn	PA	7,370	C
Canisius College	NY	15,510	C
Castleton State College	VT	8,378	LC
Charleston Southern Univ	SC	10,282	LC
CUNY/Brooklyn College	NY	2,450	VC
CUNY/Queens College	NY	2,631	C
Coastal Carolina Univ	SC	6,010	LC
Coker College	SC	13,790	C
College of St Rose	NY	14,452	C
College of Santa Fe	NM	14,008	C
Columbia Union College	MD	13,650	LC
Concordia College	MN	13,200	C
Daemen College	NY	13,020	LC
Defiance College	OH	13,480	LC
Drake Univ	IA	17,195	VC
East Texas Baptist Univ	TX	7,740	C
Eastern Kentucky Univ	KY	4,840	NC
Eastern Washington Univ	WA	5,439	LC
Elmhurst College	IL	12,536	C
Ferris State Univ	MI	7,160	NC
Florida International Univ	FL	4,191	VC
Fort Valley State College	GA	3,974	LC
Fresno Pacific College	CA	13,020	C
Geneva College	PA	13,030	C
George Fox College	OR	15,640	LC
Georgia Southwestern College	GA	4,338	LC
Georgia State Univ	GA	2,019	C
Grace College	IN	12,120	C
Gwynedd-Mercy College	PA	15,450	C
Hood College	MD	19,010	VC
Humboldt State Univ	CA	5,676	C
Huntington College	IN	13,220	C
Indiana Univ of Penn	PA	6,373	C
John Carroll Univ	OH	16,510	C
Judson College	IL	13,625	C
Keene State College	NH	7,081	C
Kennesaw State College	GA	1,553	C
Kent State Univ	OH	6,740	LC
Knoxville College	TN	8,320	LC
Langston Univ	OK	2,907	LC
Lincoln Univ	PA	0	LC
Mansfield Univ	PA	6,348	C
Mary Baldwin College	VA	17,700	LC
Marymount Univ	VA	15,930	C
Mercyhurst College	PA	13,488	C
Messiah College	PA	14,664	VC
MidAmerica Nazarene College	KS	10,208	NC
Morris College	SC	6,880	LC
Mount Holyoke College	MA	23,630	VC
New Hampshire College	NH	15,242	LC
Niagara Univ	NY	14,552	C
N Car Agricultural and Technical State Univ	NC	4,477	LC
N Car State Univ	NC	4,984	VC
Northeast Louisiana Univ	LA	3,906	NC
Northwestern College	MN	13,554	C
Northwestern Okla State Univ	OK	3,424	C
Okla Christian Univ of Science and Arts	OK	8,790	NC
Pembroke State Univ	NC	3,538	LC
Pillsbury Baptist Bible College	MN	7,390	NC
Plymouth State College	NH	7,166	C
Pontifical Catholic Univ of PR/Ponce	PR	5,807	
Queens College	NC	14,950	C
Rivier College	NH	14,920	LC
St Olaf College	MN	17,200	HC
Seattle Pacific Univ	WA	16,503	C
Sheldon Jackson College	AK	14,050	NC
Southeastern College of the Assemblies of God	FL	6,618	NC
Southeastern Louisiana Univ	LA	4,230	NC
Southern Univ and A&M College	LA	4,920	NC
Southern Univ at New Orleans	LA	1,452	NC
Southern Utah Univ	UT	4,104	LC
Southwest State Univ	MN	5,400	NC
SUNY/College at Old Westbury	NY	7,128	LC
SUNY/College at Plattsburgh	NY	6,917	C
Syracuse Univ	NY	21,305	HC
Temple Univ	PA	10,281	C
Trevecca Nazarene College	TN	9,826	NC
Tri-State Univ	IN	13,788	LC
Troy State Univ	AL	4,322	C
Troy State Univ at Dothan/Fort Rucker	AL	2,260	NC
Turabo Univ	PR	2,670	
Univ of Arkansas at Pine Bluff	AR	3,978	LC
Univ of Central Florida	FL	6,061	C+
Univ of Charleston	WV	12,750	C
Univ of Conn	CT	9,168	C
Univ of Delaware	DE	8,013	VC
Univ of Evansville	IN	15,300	VC
Univ of Illinois at Chicago	IL	8,443	C
Univ of Illinois at Urbana-Champaign	IL	7,764	HC
Univ of Kentucky	KY	5,152	VC
Univ of Maine at Farmington	ME	6,700	C
Univ of Maine at Presque Isle	ME	6,374	C
Univ of Maryland/Eastern Shore	MD	6,254	LC
Univ of Minn/Duluth	MN	6,512	C
Univ of Minn/Twin Cities	MN	6,682	VC
Univ of New Hampshire	NH	8,242	C
Univ of New Orleans	LA	5,468	C
Univ of North Florida	FL	5,082	C
Univ of Okla	OK	5,427	VC
Univ of Pittsburgh at Johnstown	PA	8,914	C
Univ of Southwestern Louisiana	LA	3,968	NC
Utah State Univ	UT	4,683	C
Wayne State Univ	MI	2,680	C
Waynesburg College	PA	11,960	C
Western Oregon State College	OR	6,180	C
Whitworth College	WA	16,265	C
Wiley College	TX	0	NC
Wilmington College	OH	13,700	LC
Wingate College	NC	10,610	C
Xavier Univ of Louisiana	LA	10,400	C

MECHANICAL DESIGN TECHNOLOGY

School	ST	$IS	SR
Alabama A&M Univ	AL	4,200	C
Lincoln Univ	MO	4,638	NC

MECHANICAL ENGINEERING

School	ST	$IS	SR
Alfred Univ	NY	21,054	VC+
Arizona State Univ Main Campus	AZ	6,444	C
Auburn Univ	AL	5,823	C+
Baylor Univ	TX	10,990	C+
Bethel College	IN	11,650	C
Boston Univ	MA	24,130	HC
Bradley Univ	IL	14,718	C+
Bridgeport Engineering Inst	CT	6,135	NC
Brigham Young Univ	UT	5,625	HC
Bucknell Univ	PA	22,320	HC
Calif Inst of Tech	CA	20,783	MC
Calif Maritime Academy	CA	7,318	C
Calif Polytechnic State Univ	CA	6,980	VC+
Calif State Polytechnic Univ/Pomona	CA	6,438	LC
Cal State/Chico	CA	6,146	C
Cal State/Fresno	CA	5,747	C
Cal State/Fullerton	CA	4,850	LC
Cal State/Long Beach	CA	6,057	LC
Cal State/Los Angeles	CA	4,940	VC
Cal State/Sacramento	CA	6,387	C
Calvin College	MI	13,020	VC
Carnegie Mellon Univ	PA	22,560	HC+
Case Western Reserve Univ	OH	19,910	HC
Catholic Univ of America	DC	18,856	C
Cedarville College	OH	10,715	C
Central Washington Univ	WA	5,644	C
Christian Brothers Univ	TN	12,120	VC
CUNY/City College	NY	2,543	VC
Clarkson Univ	NY	20,705	VC+
Clemson Univ	SC	6,564	VC
Cleveland State Univ	OH	7,287	NC
Cogswell Polytechnical College	CA	8,000	NC
Colo State Univ	CO	6,566	VC
Columbia Univ/School of Engineering and Applied Science	NY	24,554	HC
Cooper Union for the Advancement of Science and Art	NY	8,430	MC
Cornell Univ	NY	13,445	MC
Delaware State College	DE	5,656	C
Dordt College	IA	11,690	C
Drexel Univ	PA	15,970	C
Duke Univ	NC	21,271	MC
Florida A&M Univ	FL	4,651	C
Florida Inst of Tech	FL	16,935	VC
Florida International Univ	FL	4,191	VC
Florida State Univ	FL	5,814	VC
Geneva College	PA	13,030	C
George Washington Univ	DC	22,470	HC
Georgia Inst of Tech	GA	6,669	HC+
GMI Engineering & Management Inst	MI	14,158	HC
Gonzaga Univ	WA	16,350	VC
Grove City College	PA	7,870	HC
Hofstra Univ	NY	16,580	VC
Howard Univ	DC	11,680	C
Illinois Inst of Tech	IL	18,290	VC
Indiana Inst of Tech	IN	11,810	C
Indiana Univ-Purdue Univ at Fort Wayne	IN	2,500	LC
Indiana Univ-Purdue Univ at Indianapolis	IN	5,862	LC
Iowa State Univ	IA	5,456	C
Johns Hopkins Univ	MD	24,360	MC
Kansas State Univ	KS	4,816	NC
Lafayette College	PA	23,450	HC
Lakeland College	WI	12,845	LC
Lamar Univ	TX	3,798	C
Lawrence Tech Univ	MI	9,470	C
Le Tourneau Univ	TX	12,500	C+
Lehigh Univ	PA	23,250	HC
Louisiana State Univ and A&M College	LA	5,605	C
Louisiana Tech Univ	LA	4,284	C
Loyola Marymount Univ	CA	18,560	C
Manhattan College	NY	19,000	C
Mankato State Univ	MN	5,097	LC
Marquette Univ	WI	16,114	VC
Mass Inst of Tech	MA	24,800	MC
McNeese State Univ	LA	4,543	NC
Mercer Univ	GA	15,123	C
Messiah College	PA	14,664	VC
Mich State Univ	MI	7,842	C
Mich Tech Univ	MI	7,283	VC+
Milwaukee School of Engineering	WI	14,100	C
Miss State Univ	MS	5,629	VC
Montana State Univ	MT	5,534	C
Morris Brown College	GA	12,234	NC
New Jersey Inst of Tech	NJ	9,965	VC
New Mexico State Univ	NM	4,844	LC
New York Inst of Tech/Old Westbury	NY	13,914	LC
N Car Agricultural and Technical State Univ	NC	4,477	LC
N Car State Univ	NC	4,984	VC
N Dak State Univ of Agriculture and Applied Science	ND	4,774	VC
Northeastern Univ	MA	19,851	C
Northern Arizona Univ	AZ	4,844	C
Northern Illinois Univ	IL	6,408	C
Northwestern Univ	IL	21,093	MC
Norwich Univ	VT	18,730	C
Oakland Univ	MI	6,714	VC
Occidental College	CA	21,792	HC
Ohio Northern Univ	OH	18,660	VC
Ohio State Univ	OH	7,218	LC
Ohio Univ	OH	7,341	C
Okla Christian Univ of Science and Arts	OK	8,790	NC

School	ST	$IS	SR
Okla State Univ	OK	5,086	VC
Old Dominion Univ	VA	8,317	C
Oral Roberts Univ	OK	10,607	C+
Oregon State Univ	OR	6,175	C
Penn State Univ/Univ Park Campus	PA	8,752	HC
Polytechnic Univ/Brooklyn	NY	19,700	HC
Polytechnic Univ/ Farmingdale	NY	20,700	VC
Portland State Univ	OR	7,191	C
Prairie View A&M Univ	TX	4,740	LC
Princeton Univ	NJ	24,650	MC
Purdue Univ/Calumet	IN	2,374	NC
Purdue Univ/West Lafayette	IN	6,636	C
Rensselaer Polytechnic Inst	NY	23,067	HC
Rice Univ	TX	15,110	MC
Rochester Inst of Tech	NY	18,954	VC
Rose-Hulman Inst of Tech	IN	16,400	HC
Rutgers Univ/Camden College of A&S	NJ	8,652	VC
Rutgers Univ/College of Engineering	NJ	9,254	HC
Rutgers Univ/Newark College of A&S	NJ	8,645	C
Saginaw Valley State Univ	MI	6,634	LC
St Augustine's College	NC	9,300	C+
St Martin's College	WA	14,965	C
St Xavier Univ	IL	14,700	C
San Diego State Univ	CA	6,692	LC
San Francisco State Univ	CA	7,292	LC
San Jose State Univ	CA	6,680	LC
Santa Clara Univ	CA	18,783	VC
Savannah State College	GA	4,052	C
Seattle Univ	WA	16,590	C
S Dak School of Mines and Tech	SD	5,329	C
S Dak State Univ	SD	4,562	C
Southern Illinois Univ at Carbondale	IL	6,234	C
Southern Illinois Univ at Edwardsville	IL	6,097	LC
Southern Methodist Univ	TX	18,520	VC
Southern Univ and A&M College	LA	4,920	NC
Stanford Univ	CA	24,310	MC
SUNY at Binghamton	NY	7,921	HC
SUNY at Buffalo	NY	7,896	VC
SUNY at Stony Brook	NY	7,658	VC
SUNY/College at Plattsburgh	NY	6,917	C
SUNY/Maritime College	NY	7,170	C
Stevens Inst of Tech	NJ	21,980	VC+
Swarthmore College	PA	24,136	MC
Syracuse Univ	NY	21,305	HC
Temple Univ	PA	10,281	C
Tenn State Univ	TN	4,626	C+
Tenn Tech Univ	TN	5,190	C
Texas A&M Univ	TX	5,382	VC
Texas A&M Univ at Kingsville	TX	3,808	LC
Texas Tech Univ	TX	6,008	C
The Univ of New Mexico	NM	5,304	C
Tri-State Univ	IN	13,788	LC
Tufts Univ	MA	24,962	MC
Tulane Univ	LA	24,540	HC
Tuskegee Univ	AL	10,128	C
Union College	NY	23,817	HC
United States Coast Guard Academy	CT	0	MC
United States Military Academy	NY	0	MC
United States Naval Academy	MD	0	MC
Universidad Politecnica de PR	PR	6,195	C
Univ of Akron	OH	6,699	NC
Univ of Alabama	AL	5,702	C
Univ of Alabama at Birmingham	AL	7,533	C
Univ of Alabama at Huntsville	AL	5,868	VC
Univ of Alaska Fairbanks	AK	4,718	C
Univ of Arizona	AZ	5,808	C
Univ of Arkansas at Fayetteville	AR	5,046	C
Univ of Bridgeport	CT	18,985	C
Univ of Calif at Berkeley	CA	9,962	HC+
Univ of Calif at Davis	CA	9,534	VC
Univ of Calif at Los Angeles	CA	8,959	HC
Univ of Calif at Santa Barbara	CA	9,460	C
Univ of Calif, San Diego	CA	10,028	VC+
Univ of Calif/Irvine	CA	12,680	VC
Univ of Central Florida	FL	6,061	C+
Univ of Cincinnati	OH	7,989	C
Univ of Colo at Boulder	CO	6,410	VC
Univ of Colo at Denver	CO	1,955	VC
Univ of Conn	CT	9,168	C
Univ of Dayton	OH	15,120	C+
Univ of Delaware	DE	8,013	VC
Univ of Denver	CO	19,290	C+
Univ of Detroit Mercy	MI	14,720	C
Univ of Evansville	IN	15,300	VC
Univ of Florida	FL	5,850	HC
Univ of Hartford	CT	19,858	LC
Univ of Hawaii at Manoa	HI	5,626	C
Univ of Houston	TX	5,215	C
Univ of Idaho	ID	4,830	C
Univ of Illinois at Chicago	IL	8,443	C
Univ of Illinois at Urbana-Champaign	IL	7,764	HC
Univ of Iowa	IA	5,658	VC
Univ of Kansas	KS	5,200	NC
Univ of Kentucky	KY	5,152	VC
Univ of Louisville	KY	5,948	C
Univ of Lowell	MA	8,831	VC
Univ of Maine	ME	7,990	C
Univ of Maryland/Baltimore County	MD	7,746	VC
Univ of Maryland/College Park	MD	8,182	VC
Univ of Mass Dartmouth	MA	8,158	C
Univ of Mass/Amherst	MA	9,364	LC
Univ of Memphis	TN	3,476	C
Univ of Miami	FL	22,107	VC
Univ of Mich/Ann Arbor	MI	9,428	HC+
Univ of Mich/Dearborn	MI	3,399	HC
Univ of Minn/Twin Cities	MN	6,682	VC
Univ of Miss	MS	5,756	C
Univ of Missouri/Columbia	MO	6,254	HC
Univ of Missouri/Kansas City	MO	5,906	VC
Univ of Missouri/Rolla	MO	6,729	VC+
Univ of Missouri/St. Louis	MO	6,378	C
Univ of Nebr at Omaha	NE	1,889	LC
Univ of Nebr-Lincoln	NE	5,278	LC
Univ of Nevada/Las Vegas	NV	6,405	C
Univ of Nevada/Reno	NV	5,735	C
Univ of New Hampshire	NH	8,242	C
Univ of New Haven	CT	14,980	C
Univ of New Orleans	LA	5,468	C
Univ of N Car at Charlotte	NC	4,597	C
Univ of N Dak	ND	4,902	NC
Univ of Notre Dame	IN	20,150	MC
Univ of Okla	OK	5,427	VC
Univ of Penn	PA	24,238	MC
Univ of Pittsburgh	PA	9,472	C
Univ of Portland	OR	15,564	C
Univ of PR/Mayaguez	PR	0	
Univ of Rhode Island	RI	9,205	C
Univ of Rochester	NY	23,696	HC
Univ of South Alabama	AL	5,451	C
Univ of S Car	SC	6,158	C
Univ of South Florida	FL	5,475	C+
Univ of Southern Calif	CA	23,006	VC
Univ of Southwestern Louisiana	LA	3,968	NC
Univ of Tenn/Knoxville	TN	5,668	C
Univ of Texas at Arlington	TX	5,549	LC
Univ of Texas at Austin	TX	5,160	VC
Univ of Texas at El Paso	TX	3,160	LC
Univ of Texas at San Antonio	TX	6,420	C
Univ of the District of Columbia	DC	974	NC
Univ of the Pacific	CA	21,100	C
Univ of Toledo	OH	6,636	NC
Univ of Tulsa	OK	13,795	VC
Univ of Utah	UT	5,975	C
Univ of Vermont	VT	10,776	C+
Univ of Virginia	VA	7,964	MC
Univ of Wisc/Madison	WI	6,400	HC
Univ of Wisc/Milwaukee	WI	6,165	C
Univ of Wisc/Platteville	WI	4,830	C
Univ of Wyoming	WY	4,991	NC
Utah State Univ	UT	4,683	C
Valparaiso Univ	IN	14,810	VC
Vanderbilt Univ	TN	23,422	HC+
Villanova Univ	PA	21,400	HC
Virginia Military Inst	VA	8,630	C
Virginia Polytechnic Inst and State Univ	VA	6,828	C
Washington State Univ	WA	6,364	C
Washington Univ	MO	23,507	HC
Wayne State Univ	MI	2,680	C
Weber State Univ	UT	4,398	C
West Coast Univ	CA	9,120	NC
West Virginia Inst of Tech	WV	5,858	LC
West Virginia Univ	WV	5,774	C
Western Mich Univ	MI	6,820	C
Western New England College	MA	14,674	LC
Wichita State Univ	KS	5,068	NC
Widener Univ	PA	16,840	C
Wilkes Univ	PA	15,728	LC
Worcester Polytechnic Inst	MA	20,350	HC
Wright State Univ	OH	6,896	LC
Yale Univ	CT	25,110	MC
Youngstown State Univ	OH	6,447	LC

MECHANICAL ENGINEERING TECHNOLOGY

School	ST	$IS	SR
Alabama A&M Univ	AL	4,200	C
Arizona State Univ Main Campus	AZ	6,444	C
Central Conn State Univ	CT	7,108	C
Cogswell College North	WA	7,200	NC
Eastern Washington Univ	WA	5,439	LC
Fairleigh Dickinson Univ	NJ	16,427	C
Fairmont State College	WV	4,640	LC
Franklin Univ	OH	4,621	NC
Georgia Southern Univ	GA	4,988	LC
Indiana State Univ	IN	6,210	C
Indiana Univ-Purdue Univ at Indianapolis	IN	5,862	LC
Metropolitan State College of Denver	CO	1,751	NC
Montana State Univ	MT	5,534	C
Northeastern Univ	MA	19,851	C
Okla State Univ	OK	5,086	VC
Oregon Inst of Tech	OR	5,985	C
Penn State Univ at Erie/ Behrend College	PA	8,752	C
Point Park College	PA	13,922	LC
Purdue Univ/Calumet	IN	2,374	NC
Purdue Univ/West Lafayette	IN	6,636	C
Rochester Inst of Tech	NY	18,954	VC
S Car State Univ	SC	5,424	LC
Southern College of Tech	GA	4	C
Southern Univ and A&M College	LA	4,920	NC
Southwest State Univ	MN	5,400	NC
Temple Univ	PA	10,281	C
Texas Tech Univ	TX	6,008	C
Univ of Akron	OH	6,699	NC
Univ of Arkansas at Little Rock	AR	4,419	C
Univ of Cincinnati	OH	7,989	C
Univ of Dayton	OH	15,120	C+
Univ of Hartford	CT	19,858	LC
Univ of Pittsburgh at Johnstown	PA	8,914	C
Univ of Southern Miss	MS	4,542	C
Univ of Tenn at Martin	TN	4,550	C
Wentworth Inst of Tech	MA	15,250	LC
Western Kentucky Univ	KY	4,808	C

MEDIA ARTS

School	ST	$IS	SR
Antioch College	OH	19,532	C
Arizona State Univ Main Campus	AZ	6,444	C
East Stroudsburg Univ	PA	6,886	C
Edinboro Univ of Penn	PA	7,181	C
Goddard College	VT	17,990	LC
Jersey City State College	NJ	7,797	LC
Menlo College	CA	20,375	LC
Montana State Univ	MT	5,534	C
Mount Ida College	MA	16,700	LC
Pomona College	CA	23,820	MC
Southern Methodist Univ	TX	18,520	VC
SUNY at Buffalo	NY	7,896	VC
SUNY/College at Old Westbury	NY	7,128	LC
Tulane Univ	LA	24,540	HC
Univ of Arizona	AZ	5,808	C
Univ of Illinois at Urbana-Champaign	IL	7,764	HC
Univ of Kansas	KS	5,200	NC
Univ of Mich/Ann Arbor	MI	9,428	HC+
Univ of S Car	SC	6,158	C
Webster Univ	MO	12,650	C
Worcester State College	MA	6,414	LC

MEDICAL LABORATORY SCIENCE

School	ST	$IS	SR
Oakland Univ	MI	6,714	VC
Quinnipiac College	CT	17,600	C+
S Dak State Univ	SD	4,562	C
Univ of Illinois at Chicago	IL	8,443	C
Univ of Mass Dartmouth	MA	8,158	C

MEDICAL LABORATORY TECHNOLOGY

School	ST	$IS	SR
Adams State College	CO	4,910	C
Alabama A&M Univ	AL	4,200	C
Albright College	PA	19,260	C
Alderson-Broaddus College	WV	12,000	C
Alfred Univ	NY	21,054	VC+
Alvernia College	PA	13,150	LC
American International College	MA	14,029	C
Anderson Univ	IN	12,920	C
Andrews Univ	MI	14,952	NC
Angelo State Univ	TX	5,176	C
Anna Maria College	MA	15,975	LC
Appalachian State Univ	NC	4,095	C
Aquinas College	MI	14,526	C
Arkansas State Univ	AR	4,250	NC
Arkansas Tech Univ	AR	4,200	NC
Armstrong State College	GA	4,874	LC
Asbury College	KY	11,105	VC
Ashland Univ	OH	15,508	C
Atlantic Union College	MA	14,150	LC
Auburn Univ	AL	5,823	C+
Augustana College	SD	13,420	C
Aurora Univ	IL	13,381	C
Austin Peay State Univ	TN	4,350	C
Averett College	VA	13,610	LC
Avila College	MO	12,130	C
Baldwin-Wallace College	OH	15,210	C
Ball State Univ	IN	6,032	LC
Barber-Scotia College	NC	6,840	NC
Barry Univ	FL	16,050	C
Barton College	NC	10,689	LC
Baylor Univ	TX	10,990	C+
Belmont Abbey College	NC	13,190	C
Bemidji State Univ	MN	5,188	C
Bethany College	KS	11,232	C
Bethune-Cookman College	FL	8,375	LC
Blackburn College	IL	9,120	C
Bloomsburg Univ of Penn	PA	6,312	C+
Boise State Univ	ID	4,909	LC
Boston Univ	MA	24,130	HC
Bowling Green State Univ	OH	6,701	C
Bradley Univ	IL	14,718	C+
Brescia College	KY	9,800	C
Briar Cliff College	IA	13,375	C
Bridgewater College	VA	15,300	C
Brigham Young Univ	UT	5,625	HC
Cabrini College	PA	16,012	C
Caldwell College	NJ	12,860	C
Cal State/Los Angeles	CA	4,940	VC
Cal State/Northridge	CA	7,122	LC
Cal State/Sacramento	CA	6,387	C
Calif Univ of Penn	PA	7,370	C
Calumet College of St. Joseph	IN	3,585	C
Calvin College	MI	13,020	VC
Cameron Univ	OK	3,686	LC
Campbell Univ	NC	10,624	C
Campbellsville College	KY	8,720	C
Canisius College	NY	15,510	C
Carroll College	MT	11,265	C
Carthage College	WI	15,995	C
Case Western Reserve Univ	OH	19,910	HC
Catholic Univ of America	DC	18,856	C
Cedar Crest College	PA	18,930	C
Central Missouri State Univ	MO	5,138	LC
Central Wesleyan College	SC	9,640	C
Chadron State College	NE	4,091	NC
Cheyney Univ of Penn	PA	7,005	C
Christian Brothers Univ	TN	12,120	VC
CUNY/College of Staten Island	NY	2,558	NC
CUNY/Hunter College	NY	4,101	VC
CUNY/York College	NY	2,534	NC
Clarion Univ of Penn	PA	6,518	C
Clarke College	IA	13,950	C+
Clemson Univ	SC	6,564	VC
Clinch Valley College/Univ of Virginia	VA	6,364	C
Coe College	IA	17,085	VC
Coker College	SC	13,790	C
College Misericordia	PA	15,820	C
College of Mount St Joseph	OH	13,272	C
College of Our Lady of The Elms	MA	15,639	C
College of St Benedict	MN	15,468	VC
College of St Francis	IL	13,060	VC
College of St Mary	NE	12,500	C
College of St Rose	NY	14,452	C
College of St Scholastica	MN	14,868	C
Colo College	CO	20,038	HC
Columbia College	SC	13,520	LC
Columbia Union College	MD	13,650	LC
Columbus College	GA	4,892	LC
Concord College	WV	5,104	NC
Concordia College	NE	11,776	NC
Concordia College/Moorhead	MN	12,750	C
Cumberland College	KY	9,756	C
Daemen College	NY	13,020	LC
Dakota State Univ	SD	4,374	LC
Dana College	NE	11,910	C
Davis and Elkins College	WV	13,230	LC
Defiance College	OH	13,480	LC
Delta State Univ	MS	3,964	LC
DePaul Univ	IL	15,535	VC
Dordt College	IA	11,690	C
Drake Univ	IA	17,195	VC
East Central Univ	OK	3,558	C
East Stroudsburg Univ	PA	6,886	C
East Texas Baptist Univ	TX	7,740	C
East Texas State Univ	TX	4,572	LC
Eastern College	PA	15,150	C+
Eastern Illinois Univ	IL	5,548	C
Eastern Kentucky Univ	KY	4,840	NC
Eastern Mennonite College	VA	12,700	C
Eastern Mich Univ	MI	6,749	C
Eastern New Mexico Univ	NM	3,950	C
Eastern Washington Univ	WA	5,439	LC
Edgewood College	WI	11,700	C
Edinboro Univ of Penn	PA	7,181	C
Elizabethtown College	PA	17,850	VC
Elmira College	NY	18,450	C
Elon College	NC	12,290	LC
Emmanuel College	MA	17,773	LC

MEDICAL RECORDS ADMINISTRATION/SERVICES

School	ST	$IS	SR
Western Carolina Univ	NC	3,811	C
Wilkes Univ	PA	15,728	LC
York College of Penn	PA	8,345	C

MEDICAL TECHNOLOGY

School	ST	$IS	SR
Barry Univ	FL	16,050	C
Cal State/Bakersfield	CA	5,402	C
Catawba College	NC	12,950	C
Christian Brothers Univ	TN	12,120	VC
CUNY/College of Staten Island	NY	2,558	NC
Culver-Stockton College	MO	11,150	C
DePauw Univ	IN	18,530	VC
Eastern Kentucky Univ	KY	4,840	NC
Georgia Southern Univ	GA	4,988	LC
Hartwick College	NY	20,950	C
Indiana Univ Bloomington	IN	6,495	VC
Inter American Univ of PR/Aguadilla Regional College	PR	2,290	
Inter American Univ of PR/Bayamon Univ College	PR	2,300	
Inter American Univ of PR/Metropolitan Campus	PR	2,340	
Inter American Univ of PR/Ponce Regional College	PR	2,300	
Inter-American Univ of PR/Fajardo Regional College	PR	2,732	
La Roche College	PA	12,977	LC
Lincoln Univ	MO	4,638	NC
Miami Univ	OH	8,066	VC
Miss State Univ	MS	5,629	VC
Northeast Missouri State Univ	MO	5,654	VC+
Ohio State Univ	OH	7,218	LC
Peru State College	NE	4,311	NC
Rockhurst College	MO	12,470	C
Southwest State Univ	MN	5,400	NC
Stonehill College	MA	17,481	VC
Univ of Alabama at Birmingham	AL	7,533	C
Univ of Findlay	OH	15,764	C
Univ of New Haven	CT	14,980	C
Univ of Texas at Austin	TX	5,160	VC
Univ of Wisc/Stevens Point	WI	5,047	C+
West Virginia Univ	WV	5,774	C
Youngstown State Univ	OH	6,447	LC

MEDICAL SCIENCE

School	ST	$IS	SR
Alderson-Broaddus College	WV	12,000	C
Cedarville College	OH	10,715	C
Dana College	NE	11,910	C
Univ of Central Florida	FL	6,061	C+
Univ of Louisville	KY	5,948	C
Univ of S Dak	SD	4,722	C
Univ of Wisc/Madison	WI	6,400	HC
Univ of Wisc/Milwaukee	WI	6,165	C

MEDIEVAL STUDIES

School	ST	$IS	SR
Brown Univ	RI	26,104	MC
Catholic Univ of America	DC	18,856	C
College of St Benedict	MN	15,468	VC
Columbia Univ/Barnard College	NY	25,492	HC
Cornell College	IA	18,425	VC
Duke Univ	NC	21,271	MC
Emory Univ	GA	21,930	HC
Fordham Univ/Fordham College	NY	19,875	VC
Manhattanville College	NY	20,450	LC
Mount Holyoke College	MA	23,630	VC
Ohio State Univ	OH	7,218	LC
Penn State Univ/Univ Park Campus	PA	8,752	HC
Plymouth State College	NH	7,166	C
Purdue Univ/West Lafayette	IN	6,636	C
Reed College	OR	24,480	HC+
St John's Univ	MN	15,364	C
St Olaf College	MN	17,200	HC
Smith College	MA	24,236	HC
SUNY at Albany	NY	7,059	VC
SUNY at Binghamton	NY	7,921	HC
Syracuse Univ	NY	21,305	HC
Tulane Univ	LA	24,540	HC
Univ of Calif at Davis	CA	9,534	VC
Univ of Calif at Santa Barbara	CA	9,460	C
Univ of Chicago	IL	24,517	MC
Univ of Mich/Ann Arbor	MI	9,428	HC+
Univ of Notre Dame	IN	20,150	MC
Univ of Tenn/Knoxville	TN	5,668	C
Univ of the South	TN	18,830	HC
Washington Univ	MO	23,507	HC
Wellesley College	MA	23,815	MC

MENTAL HEALTH/HUMAN SERVICES

School	ST	$IS	SR
Audrey Cohen College	NY	11,184	LC
Franciscan Univ of Steubenville	OH	13,400	C
Gannon Univ	PA	14,872	C
Morgan State Univ	MD	7,366	C+
Northern Kentucky Univ	KY	4,620	NC
Sinte Gleska Univ	SD	1,580	NC

METAL/JEWELRY

School	ST	$IS	SR
Arizona State Univ Main Campus	AZ	6,444	C
Center for Creative Studies/College of Art and Design	MI	15,330	SP
Edinboro Univ of Penn	PA	7,181	C
Maine College of Art	ME	15,673	SP
Moore College of Art and Design	PA	17,947	SP
Northern Mich Univ	MI	6,350	C
Rhode Island School of Design	RI	22,315	SP
Savannah College of Art and Design	GA	14,280	SP
Syracuse Univ	NY	21,305	HC
Univ of Mich/Ann Arbor	MI	9,428	HC+
Univ of North Texas	TX	4,853	C
Univ of Oregon	OR	6,466	VC
Univ of Texas at El Paso	TX	3,160	LC
Univ of the Arts	PA	16,150	SP
Univ of Washington	WA	6,618	VC

METALLURGICAL ENGINEERING

School	ST	$IS	SR
Bethel College	IN	11,650	C
Calif Polytechnic State Univ	CA	6,980	VC+
Colo School of Mines	CO	8,436	HC+
Columbia Univ/School of Engineering and Applied Science	NY	24,554	HC
Illinois Inst of Tech	IL	18,290	VC
Iowa State Univ	IA	5,456	C
Mich Tech Univ	MI	7,283	VC+
Montana College of Mineral Science and Tech	MT	4,977	C
New Mexico Inst of Mining and Tech	NM	5,212	C+
Ohio State Univ	OH	7,218	LC
Polytechnic Univ/Brooklyn	NY	19,700	HC
Polytechnic Univ/Farmingdale	NY	20,700	VC
S Dak School of Mines and Tech	SD	5,329	C
Univ of Alabama	AL	5,702	C
Univ of Cincinnati	OH	7,989	C
Univ of Idaho	ID	4,830	C
Univ of Illinois at Chicago	IL	8,443	C
Univ of Illinois at Urbana-Champaign	IL	7,764	HC
Univ of Minn/Twin Cities	MN	6,682	VC
Univ of Missouri/Rolla	MO	6,729	VC+
Univ of Pittsburgh	PA	9,472	C
Univ of Texas at El Paso	TX	3,160	LC
Univ of Utah	UT	5,975	C
Univ of Wisc/Madison	WI	6,400	HC
Wayne State Univ	MI	2,680	C

METALLURGY

School	ST	$IS	SR
Penn State Univ/Univ Park Campus	PA	8,752	HC

MEXICAN-AMERICAN/CHICANO STUDIES

School	ST	$IS	SR
Cal State/Dominguez Hills	CA	2,857	LC
Cal State/Fullerton	CA	4,850	LC
Cal State/Los Angeles	CA	4,940	VC
Cal State/Northridge	CA	7,122	LC
Claremont McKenna College	CA	22,150	MC
Concordia Lutheran College	TX	10,260	C+
Loyola Marymount Univ	CA	18,560	C
Metropolitan State College of Denver	CO	1,751	NC
New Mexico State Univ	NM	4,844	LC
Pitzer College	CA	23,780	HC
Scripps College	CA	23,600	HC
Southern Methodist Univ	TX	18,520	VC
Univ of Arizona	AZ	5,808	C
Univ of Calif at Berkeley	CA	9,962	HC+
Univ of Calif at Los Angeles	CA	8,959	HC
Univ of Calif at Santa Barbara	CA	9,460	C
Univ of Calif, San Diego	CA	10,028	VC+
Univ of Minn/Twin Cities	MN	6,682	VC
Univ of Texas at El Paso	TX	3,160	LC
Wayne State Univ	MI	2,680	C

MICROBIOLOGY

School	ST	$IS	SR
Abilene Christian Univ	TX	10,460	NC
Arizona State Univ Main Campus	AZ	6,444	C
Auburn Univ	AL	5,823	C+
Austin Peay State Univ	TN	4,350	C
Ball State Univ	IN	6,032	LC
Bowling Green State Univ	OH	6,701	C
Brigham Young Univ	UT	5,625	HC
Calif Polytechnic State Univ	CA	6,980	VC+
Calif State Polytechnic Univ/Pomona	CA	6,438	LC
Cal State/Chico	CA	6,146	C
Cal State/Fresno	CA	5,747	C
Cal State/Fullerton	CA	4,850	LC
Cal State/Long Beach	CA	6,057	LC
Cal State/Los Angeles	CA	4,940	VC
Cal State/Northridge	CA	7,122	LC
Cal State/Sacramento	CA	6,387	C
Clemson Univ	SC	6,564	VC
Colo State Univ	CO	6,566	VC
Columbia Univ/Columbia College	NY	26,757	MC
Cornell Univ	NY	13,445	MC
Duquesne Univ	PA	16,434	VC
East Tenn State Univ	TN	4,406	C
Eastern Kentucky Univ	KY	4,840	NC
Eastern Mich Univ	MI	6,749	C
Eastern Washington Univ	WA	5,439	LC
Florida Atlantic Univ	FL	5,525	C
Florida Inst of Tech	FL	16,935	VC
Howard Univ	DC	11,680	C
Idaho State Univ	ID	4,442	C
Indiana Univ Bloomington	IN	6,495	VC
Inter American Univ/Arecibo Campus	PR	5,666	
Iowa State Univ	IA	5,456	C
Kansas State Univ	KS	4,816	NC
Louisiana State Univ and A&M College	LA	5,605	C
Louisiana Tech Univ	LA	4,284	C
Marlboro College	VT	23,305	C+
McKendree College	IL	10,900	C
McNeese State Univ	LA	4,543	NC
Miami Univ	OH	8,066	VC
Mich State Univ	MI	7,842	C
Miss State Univ	MS	5,629	VC
Miss Univ for Women	MS	4,456	LC
Montana State Univ	MT	5,534	C
New Mexico State Univ	NM	4,844	LC
N Car State Univ	NC	4,984	VC
N Dak State Univ of Agriculture and Applied Science	ND	4,774	VC
Northeastern State Univ	OK	5,250	C
Northern Arizona Univ	AZ	4,844	C
Northern Mich Univ	MI	6,350	C
Notre Dame College	NH	14,220	C
Ohio State Univ	OH	7,218	LC
Ohio Univ	OH	7,341	C
Ohio Wesleyan Univ	OH	21,108	VC+
Okla State Univ	OK	5,086	VC
Oregon State Univ	OR	6,175	C
Penn State Univ/Univ Park Campus	PA	8,752	HC
Philadelphia College of Pharmacy and Science	PA	14,750	VC
Purdue Univ/Calumet	IN	2,374	NC
Purdue Univ/West Lafayette	IN	6,636	C
Quinnipiac College	CT	17,600	C+
Rutgers Univ/Cook College	NJ	9,197	HC
Rutgers Univ/Douglass College	NJ	8,795	VC
Rutgers Univ/Livingston College	NJ	8,877	VC
Rutgers Univ/Newark College of A&S	NJ	8,645	C
Rutgers Univ/Rutgers College	NJ	8,841	HC+
Rutgers Univ/Univ College—New Brunswick	NJ	0	LC
San Francisco State Univ	CA	7,292	LC
San Jose State Univ	CA	6,680	LC
Sonoma State Univ	CA	6,996	LC
S Dak State Univ	SD	4,562	C
Southeastern Louisiana Univ	LA	4,230	NC
Southern Illinois Univ at Carbondale	IL	6,234	C
Southern Univ and A&M College	LA	4,920	NC
Southwest Texas State Univ	TX	5,124	C
Stanford Univ	CA	24,310	MC
SUNY College of Environmental Science and Forestry	NY	9,257	HC+
Texas A&M Univ	TX	5,382	VC
Texas Tech Univ	TX	6,008	C
Univ of Akron	OH	6,699	NC
Univ of Alabama	AL	5,702	C
Univ of Arizona	AZ	5,808	C
Univ of Arkansas at Fayetteville	AR	5,046	C
Univ of Calif at Davis	CA	9,534	VC
Univ of Calif at Los Angeles	CA	8,959	HC
Univ of Calif at Santa Barbara	CA	9,460	C
Univ of Calif, San Diego	CA	10,028	VC+
Univ of Central Florida	FL	6,061	C+
Univ of Florida	FL	5,850	HC
Univ of Georgia	GA	5,655	VC
Univ of Hawaii at Manoa	HI	5,626	C
Univ of Houston-Downtown	TX	4,034	NC
Univ of Iowa	IA	5,658	VC
Univ of Kansas	KS	5,200	NC
Univ of Kentucky	KY	5,152	VC
Univ of Maine	ME	7,990	C
Univ of Maryland/College Park	MD	8,182	VC
Univ of Maryland/Univ College	MD	4,900	NC
Univ of Mass/Amherst	MA	9,364	LC
Univ of Miami	FL	22,107	VC
Univ of Mich/Ann Arbor	MI	9,428	HC+
Univ of Mich/Dearborn	MI	3,399	HC
Univ of Minn/Twin Cities	MN	6,682	VC
Univ of Montana	MT	5,529	C
Univ of New Hampshire	NH	8,242	C
Univ of Notre Dame	IN	20,150	MC
Univ of Okla	OK	5,427	VC
Univ of Pittsburgh	PA	9,472	C
Univ of PR/Arecibo Tech Univ College	PR	1,302	C
Univ of PR/Humacao Univ College	PR	1,494	
Univ of PR/Mayaguez	PR	0	
Univ of Rhode Island	RI	9,205	C
Univ of Rochester	NY	23,696	HC
Univ of South Florida	FL	5,475	C+
Univ of Tenn/Knoxville	TN	5,668	C
Univ of Texas at Arlington	TX	5,549	LC
Univ of Texas at Austin	TX	5,160	VC
Univ of Texas at El Paso	TX	3,160	LC
Univ of Vermont	VT	10,776	C+
Univ of Washington	WA	6,618	VC
Univ of Wisc/La Crosse	WI	4,487	C
Univ of Wisc/Madison	WI	6,400	HC
Univ of Wisc/Milwaukee	WI	6,165	C
Univ of Wisc/Oshkosh	WI	4,240	C
Utah State Univ	UT	4,683	C
Wagner College	NY	17,950	C
Washington State Univ	WA	6,364	C
Weber State Univ	UT	4,398	C
West Chester Univ of Penn	PA	7,492	C
Xavier Univ of Louisiana	LA	10,400	C

MIDDLE EASTERN STUDIES

School	ST	$IS	SR
Columbia Univ/Barnard College	NY	25,492	HC
Columbia Univ/Columbia College	NY	26,757	MC
Fordham Univ/College at Lincoln Center	NY	18,150	VC
Fordham Univ/Fordham College	NY	19,875	VC
Hampshire College	MA	25,320	C
Harvard Univ/Harvard and Radcliffe Colleges	MA	24,880	MC
Northwestern Univ	IL	21,093	MC
Rutgers Univ/Douglass College	NJ	8,795	VC
Rutgers Univ/Livingston College	NJ	8,877	VC
Rutgers Univ/Rutgers College	NJ	8,841	HC+
Rutgers Univ/Univ College—New Brunswick	NJ	0	LC
Southwest Texas State Univ	TX	5,124	C
Univ of Calif at Berkeley	CA	9,962	HC+
Univ of Conn	CT	9,168	C
Univ of Minn/Twin Cities	MN	6,682	VC
Univ of Texas at Austin	TX	5,160	VC
Univ of Utah	UT	5,975	C

MIDDLE SCHOOL EDUCATION

School	ST	$IS	SR
Abilene Christian Univ	TX	10,460	NC
Alabama A&M Univ	AL	4,200	LC
Albany State College	GA	4,481	LC
Alcorn State Univ	MS	4,474	C+
Alderson-Broaddus College	WV	12,000	C
Alice Lloyd College	KY	2,750	VC
American International College	MA	14,029	C
Angelo State Univ	TX	5,176	C
Appalachian State Univ	NC	4,095	C
Armstrong State College	GA	4,874	LC
Auburn Univ	AL	5,823	C+
Augusta College	GA	1,452	C
Averett College	VA	13,610	LC
Ball State Univ	IN	6,032	LC
Bartlesville Wesleyan College	OK	9,400	C
Barton College	NC	10,689	LC
Bellarmine College	KY	10,832	C
Bemidji State Univ	MN	5,188	C
Bennett College	NC	8,920	LC
Berea College	KY	2,883	VC+
Berry College	GA	11,990	VC
Bethany College	KS	11,232	C
Blue Mountain College	MS	5,958	LC
Bluefield College	VA	10,600	C
Bluefield State College	WV	1,832	LC
Brewton-Parker College	GA	6,828	NC
Bridgewater State College	MA	7,518	C
Brigham Young Univ	UT	5,625	HC
Buena Vista College	IA	16,150	VC
Calif Lutheran Univ	CA	17,240	C
Campbell Univ	NC	10,624	C
Campbellsville College	KY	8,720	C
Capital Univ	OH	16,535	VC
Cardinal Stritch College	WI	11,252	C
Caribbean Univ	PR	2,400	C
Carson-Newman College	TN	11,250	LC
Carthage College	WI	15,995	C
Catawba College	NC	12,950	LC
Cedar Crest College	PA	18,930	C
Centenary College of Louisiana	LA	11,826	C+
Central Methodist College	MO	11,410	C
Central Mich Univ	MI	6,737	LC
Central Missouri State Univ	MO	5,138	LC
Central Washington Univ	WA	5,644	C
Chadron State College	NE	4,091	NC
Christopher Newport Univ	VA	3,196	LC
City Univ	WA	6,400	NC
CUNY/Hunter College	NY	4,101	VC
CUNY/York College	NY	2,534	NC
Clayton State College	GA	1,496	LC
College of Great Falls	MT	6,230	NC
College of New Rochelle	NY	15,440	LC
College of Our Lady of The Elms	MA	15,639	C
Columbus College	GA	4,892	LC
Concord College	WV	5,104	NC
Concordia College	MN	13,200	LC
Concordia College	NE	11,776	NC
Concordia College/Moorhead	MN	12,750	C
Concordia Univ	IL	12,611	C
Covenant College	GA	13,054	VC
Cumberland Univ	TN	8,650	LC
Davis and Elkins College	WV	13,230	LC
Dickinson State Univ	ND	3,792	C
Drake Univ	IA	17,195	VC
Duquesne Univ	PA	16,434	VC
East Carolina Univ	NC	4,498	C
East Tenn State Univ	TN	4,406	C
East Texas Baptist Univ	TX	7,740	C
Eastern Conn State Univ	CT	6,966	C
Eastern Illinois Univ	IL	5,548	C
Eastern Kentucky Univ	KY	4,840	NC
Eastern Mich Univ	MI	6,749	C
Eastern Montana College	MT	5,165	LC
Eastern Washington Univ	WA	5,439	LC
Edgewood College	WI	11,700	C
Elizabeth City State Univ	NC	4,254	LC
Elon College	NC	12,290	LC
Emory and Henry College	VA	12,776	C
Fairmont State College	WV	4,640	LC
Fayetteville State Univ	NC	3,926	LC
Fitchburg State College	MA	6,962	C
Flagler College	FL	7,990	C
Florida Southern College	FL	12,260	C
Fontbonne College	MO	12,090	C
Fort Valley State College	GA	3,974	LC
Franklin College of Indiana	IN	13,970	C
Freed-Hardeman Univ	TN	8,585	VC
Gardner-Webb Univ	NC	11,950	LC
George Fox College	OR	15,640	LC
Georgia College	GA	4,310	LC
Georgia Southern Univ	GA	4,988	LC
Georgia Southwestern College	GA	4,338	LC
Georgia State Univ	GA	2,019	C
Glenville State College	WV	4,810	LC
Gordon College	MA	16,790	C
Goshen College	IN	12,360	C
Grand Rapids Baptist College and Seminary	MI	10,228	C
Grand Valley State Univ	MI	6,822	VC
Grand View College	IA	13,230	NC
Greensboro College	NC	11,496	C
Gustavus Adolphus College	MN	15,935	VC
Harris-Stowe State College	MO	1,888	LC
Heidelberg College	OH	17,160	C
High Point Univ	NC	12,350	LC
Hillsdale College	MI	15,110	VC
Humboldt State Univ	CA	5,676	C
Huntington College	IN	13,220	C
Idaho State Univ	ID	4,442	C
Illinois State Univ	IL	6,413	C
Immaculata College	PA	14,620	C
Incarnate Word College	TX	12,307	C
Indiana State Univ	IN	6,210	C
Indiana Univ at Kokomo	IN	2,069	C
Indiana Univ Bloomington	IN	6,495	VC
Indiana Univ/South Bend	IN	2,141	LC
Iona College	NY	16,310	C
Iowa State Univ	IA	5,456	C
Jamestown College	ND	10,250	C
Johnson C. Smith Univ	NC	8,916	LC
Judson College	AL	9,060	C
Kansas Newman College	KS	10,640	C
Kennesaw State College	GA	1,553	C
Kentucky Christian College	KY	7,708	LC
Kentucky Wesleyan College	KY	11,550	C
King's College	PA	15,420	LC
LaGrange College	GA	10,602	C
Lenoir-Rhyne College	NC	14,068	C
Lesley College	MA	17,120	LC
Lewis Univ	IL	14,797	LC
Lincoln Memorial Univ	TN	8,218	C
Lindenwood College	MO	13,560	C
Linfield College	OR	16,670	VC
Livingston Univ	AL	3,979	C
Loras College	IA	14,160	C
Louisiana Tech Univ	LA	4,284	C
Loyola Univ/New Orleans	LA	15,660	C+
Lubbock Christian Univ	TX	9,840	NC
Lynchburg College	VA	17,000	LC
Manchester College	IN	13,240	LC
Manhattan College	NY	19,000	LC
Manhattanville College	NY	20,450	LC
Mankato State Univ	MN	5,097	LC
Marian College of Fond du Lac	WI	12,250	C
Marietta College	OH	16,940	C+
Mars Hill College	NC	11,050	C
Marshall Univ	WV	5,762	LC
Mary Baldwin College	VA	17,700	LC
Marymount College/Tarrytown	NY	17,350	LC
McPherson College	KS	11,360	VC
Mercy College	NY	11,180	NC
Methodist College	NC	12,400	C
Miami Univ	OH	8,066	VC
Midland Lutheran College	NE	12,410	LC
Millikin Univ	IL	15,499	C
Monmouth College	NJ	16,820	C
Morehead State Univ	KY	4,600	LC
Morehouse College	GA	13,224	LC
Mount Marty College	SD	10,450	NC
Murray State Univ	KY	4,702	C
National-Louis Univ	IL	13,218	C
Nazareth College of Rochester	NY	15,310	C+
Nebr Wesleyan Univ	NE	12,240	C
North Adams State College	MA	7,750	C
N Car Central Univ	NC	4,347	LC
N Car State Univ	NC	4,984	VC
N Car Wesleyan College	NC	12,480	LC
North Georgia College	GA	4,103	LC
Northern Kentucky Univ	KY	4,620	NC
Northern State Univ	SD	4,186	LC
Northland College	WI	13,550	LC
Northwest Missouri State Univ	MO	5,010	LC
Northwestern College of Iowa	IA	12,250	C
Northwestern Okla State Univ	OK	3,424	C
Notre Dame College	NH	14,220	C
Oakland City College	IN	10,216	LC
Occidental College	CA	21,792	HC
Oglethorpe Univ	GA	16,360	VC
Ohio Univ	OH	7,341	C
Ohio Wesleyan Univ	OH	21,108	VC+
Okla Christian Univ of Science and Arts	OK	8,790	NC
Okla State Univ	OK	5,086	VC
Old Dominion Univ	VA	8,317	C
Otterbein College	OH	16,506	C
Ouachita Baptist Univ	AR	8,940	C
Paine College	GA	8,207	LC
Park College	MO	7,320	C
Pembroke State Univ	NC	3,538	LC
Piedmont College	GA	8,540	LC
Pikeville College	KY	8,500	NC
Pittsburg State Univ	KS	4,478	NC
Plymouth State College	NH	7,166	C
Prescott College	AZ	9,775	C
Purdue Univ/West Lafayette	IN	6,636	C
Rhode Island College	RI	7,901	LC
Ripon College	WI	18,320	C+
Sacred Heart Univ	CT	16,350	C
St Augustine's College	NC	9,300	C+
St Francis College	NY	6,710	LC
St John's Univ	NY	8,980	C+
St Joseph's College	IN	14,730	C
St Mary's College of Minn	MN	13,850	LC
St Mary-of-the-Woods College	IN	14,430	NC
St Thomas Aquinas College	NY	13,550	C
St Xavier Univ	IL	14,700	C
Samford Univ	AL	11,400	VC
Shepherd College	WV	5,540	C
Shorter College	GA	10,270	C
Simpson College	IA	14,635	VC
Sioux Falls College	SD	11,540	C
S Dak State Univ	SD	4,562	C
Southeastern College of the Assemblies of God	FL	6,618	NC
Southern Arkansas Univ	AR	3,432	NC
Southern Univ and A&M College	LA	4,920	NC
Southwest Texas State Univ	TX	5,124	C
Spalding Univ	KY	10,496	LC
Spring Hill College	AL	16,015	C+
Springfield College	MA	15,200	LC
SUNY at Albany	NY	7,059	VC
SUNY/College at Cortland	NY	7,326	C+
SUNY/College at Fredonia	NY	7,159	VC
SUNY/College at New Paltz	NY	6,890	VC
SUNY/College at Oneonta	NY	7,878	C
SUNY/Potsdam College	NY	6,906	C
Syracuse Univ	NY	21,305	HC
Tabor College	KS	11,460	VC
Temple Univ	PA	10,281	C
Texas Wesleyan Univ	TX	9,380	LC
Thomas More College	KY	12,962	C
Toccoa Falls College	GA	9,350	C
Transylvania Univ	KY	14,970	VC+
Trinity Christian College	IL	13,260	C
Troy State Univ	AL	4,322	C
Troy State Univ at Dothan/Fort Rucker	AL	2,260	NC
Union College	KY	9,790	C
Univ of Central Arkansas	AR	4,200	LC
Univ of Cincinnati	OH	7,989	C
Univ of Colo at Boulder	CO	6,410	VC
Univ of Detroit Mercy	MI	14,720	C
Univ of Evansville	IN	15,300	VC
Univ of Georgia	GA	5,655	VC
Univ of Indianapolis	IN	14,510	C
Univ of Iowa	IA	5,658	VC
Univ of Kentucky	KY	5,152	VC
Univ of Louisville	KY	5,948	C
Univ of Maine at Fort Kent	ME	6,285	LC
Univ of Maine at Machias	ME	6,135	C
Univ of Mary Hardin-Baylor	TX	8,120	NC
Univ of Mass/Amherst	MA	9,364	LC
Univ of Missouri/Columbia	MO	6,254	HC
Univ of Mobile	AL	9,400	C
Univ of Nebr at Kearney	NE	4,308	LC
Univ of Nebr-Lincoln	NE	5,278	LC
Univ of N Car at Chapel Hill	NC	5,330	HC
Univ of N Car at Charlotte	NC	4,597	C
Univ of N Car at Greensboro	NC	5,192	C
Univ of N Car at Wilmington	NC	5,172	C
Univ of N Dak	ND	4,902	NC
Univ of Northern Iowa	IA	5,137	C
Univ of Richmond	VA	16,700	HC
Univ of San Francisco	CA	18,408	C
Univ of South Alabama	AL	5,451	C
Univ of South Florida	FL	5,475	C+
Univ of Southern Indiana	IN	3,720	NC
Univ of Southern Miss	MS	4,542	C
Univ of the Pacific	CA	21,100	C
Univ of Toledo	OH	6,636	NC
Univ of Tulsa	OK	13,795	VC
Univ of West Florida	FL	5,415	C
Univ of Wisc/Platteville	WI	4,830	C
Univ of Wisc/River Falls	WI	4,655	C
Univ of Wisc/Whitewater	WI	4,700	C
Urbana Univ	OH	12,536	C
Valdosta State Univ	GA	4,670	LC
Valley City State Univ	ND	4,385	LC
Valparaiso Univ	IN	14,810	VC
Virginia Intermont College	VA	12,250	LC
Virginia Wesleyan College	VA	14,950	VC
Wagner College	NY	17,950	C
Walsh Univ	OH	11,640	C
Warner Pacific College	OR	12,112	C
Warren Wilson College	NC	10,877	C
Wartburg College	IA	14,530	VC
Weber State Univ	UT	4,398	C
Wesleyan College	GA	15,445	C
West Georgia College	GA	4,256	C
West Liberty State College	WV	4,690	LC
West Virginia Inst of Tech	WV	5,858	LC
Western Carolina Univ	NC	3,811	C
Western Kentucky Univ	KY	4,808	C
Western Mich Univ	MI	6,820	C
Western Montana College of the Univ of Montana	MT	1,646	C
Westfield State College	MA	7,161	C
William Penn College	IA	13,400	C
Wingate College	NC	10,610	C
Winston-Salem State Univ	NC	4,142	LC
Wittenberg Univ	OH	19,998	VC
Women's College of Brenau Univ	GA	14,734	C

MILITARY SCIENCE

School	ST	$IS	SR
Campbell Univ	NC	10,624	C
Cumberland College	KY	9,756	C
Drake Univ	IA	17,195	VC
Eastern Washington Univ	WA	5,439	LC
Elizabeth City State Univ	NC	4,254	LC
United States Military Academy	NY	0	MC
Univ of Central Arkansas	AR	4,200	LC
Univ of Charleston	WV	12,750	C

MINING AND MINERAL ENGINEERING

School	ST	$IS	SR
Colo School of Mines	CO	8,436	HC+
Columbia Univ/School of Engineering and Applied Science	NY	24,554	HC
Mich Tech Univ	MI	7,283	VC+
Montana College of Mineral Science and Tech	MT	4,977	C
New Mexico Inst of Mining and Tech	NM	5,212	C+
Ohio State Univ	OH	7,218	LC
Penn State Univ/Univ Park Campus	PA	8,752	HC
S Dak School of Mines and Tech	SD	5,329	C
Southern Illinois Univ at Carbondale	IL	6,234	C
Univ of Alabama	AL	5,702	C
Univ of Alaska Fairbanks	AK	4,718	C
Univ of Calif at Berkeley	CA	9,962	HC+
Univ of Idaho	ID	4,830	C
Univ of Kentucky	KY	5,152	VC
Univ of Missouri/Rolla	MO	6,729	VC+
Univ of Utah	UT	5,975	C
Virginia Polytechnic Inst and State Univ	VA	6,828	C
West Virginia Univ	WV	5,774	C

MINING AND PETROLEUM TECHNOLOGY

School	ST	$IS	SR
Calif Univ of Penn	PA	7,370	C
West Virginia Univ	WV	5,774	C

MINISTRIES

School	ST	$IS	SR
Alabama A&M Univ	AL	4,200	C
Asbury College	KY	11,105	VC
Averett College	VA	13,610	LC
Azusa Pacific Univ	CA	15,034	C
Bethel College	IN	11,650	C
Brescia College	KY	9,800	C
Cascade College	OR	9,800	NC
Claflin College	SC	0	
College of St Scholastica	MN	14,868	C
Concordia College	NY	0	LC
Concordia Univ Wisc	WI	12,140	C
Crichton College	TN	6,547	NC
Dana College	NE	11,910	C
Defiance College	OH	13,480	LC
Eastern Mennonite College	VA	12,700	C
Eastern Nazarene College	MA	12,165	LC
Florida State Univ	FL	5,814	VC
Fresno Pacific College	CA	13,020	C
Geneva College	PA	13,030	C
George Fox College	OR	15,640	LC
Grace College	IN	12,120	C
Greenville College	IL	14,190	C
Hardin-Simmons Univ	TX	9,080	C
Harding Univ	AR	9,050	VC
Huntington College	IN	13,220	C
Indiana Wesleyan Univ	IN	12,332	C
John Brown Univ	AR	9,880	VC
Kentucky Christian College	KY	7,708	LC
La Sierra Univ	CA	15,472	C
Liberty Univ	VA	11,500	LC
Malone College	OH	12,572	C
Marylhurst College	OR	6,486	NC
Messiah College	PA	14,664	VC
Mich Christian College	MI	8,094	C
Mount Olive College	NC	9,650	LC
North Central Bible College	MN	8,670	LC
Northwest College	WA	9,897	LC
Northwestern College	MN	13,554	C
Northwestern College	WI	5,218	C
Nyack College	NY	12,210	LC

School	ST	$IS	SR
Oakwood College	AL	10,005	C
Okla Christian Univ of Science and Arts	OK	8,790	NC
Oral Roberts Univ	OK	10,607	C+
Pacific Christian College	CA	12,700	C
Point Loma Nazarene College	CA	13,532	C
St Mary's College of Minn	MN	13,850	LC
Shaw Univ	NC	8,936	C+
Simpson College	CA	10,628	C
Southeastern College of the Assemblies of God	FL	6,618	NC
Southern Calif College	CA	12,356	C
Southwest Baptist Univ	MO	9,192	NC
Spring Arbor College	MI	12,256	C
Toccoa Falls College	GA	9,350	C
Trevecca Nazarene College	TN	9,826	NC
Union Univ	TN	7,880	C+
Univ of the Pacific	CA	21,100	C
Viterbo College	WI	12,670	C
Warner Pacific College	OR	12,112	C

MISSIONS

School	ST	$IS	SR
Cedarville College	OH	10,715	C
Colo Christian Univ	CO	9,750	C
Fresno Pacific College	CA	13,020	C
Liberty Univ	VA	11,500	LC
Mich Christian College	MI	8,094	C
Nyack College	NY	12,210	LC
Okla Christian Univ of Science and Arts	OK	8,790	NC
Pillsbury Baptist Bible College	MN	7,390	NC
Simpson College	CA	10,628	C
Toccoa Falls College	GA	9,350	C

MODERN LANGUAGE

School	ST	$IS	SR
College of Mount St Vincent	NY	16,730	C
Converse College	SC	15,750	C
Emory Univ	GA	21,930	HC
Fordham Univ/College at Lincoln Center	NY	18,150	VC
Fordham Univ/Fordham College	NY	19,875	VC
James Madison Univ	VA	8,198	HC
Judson College	AL	9,060	C
Kenyon College	OH	22,430	HC+
King College	TN	11,500	C
Knox College	IL	18,990	VC
Liberty Univ	VA	11,500	LC
Metropolitan State College of Denver	CO	1,751	NC
Miss College	MS	8,348	C
Montana State Univ	MT	5,534	C
St Francis College	PA	15,744	LC
St Mary's College	MI	8,350	C
Seton Hall Univ	NJ	18,306	LC
Southeastern Okla State Univ	OK	3,594	C
Trinity College	CT	24,120	HC
Trinity College of Vermont	VT	16,015	LC
Union College	NY	23,817	HC
Univ of Lowell	MA	8,831	VC
Univ of Maine	ME	7,990	C
Univ of Portland	OR	15,564	C
Virginia Military Inst	VA	8,630	C
Westmont College	CA	18,732	C
Widener Univ	PA	16,840	C
Wright State Univ	OH	6,896	LC

MOLECULAR BIOLOGY

School	ST	$IS	SR
Auburn Univ	AL	5,823	C+
Ball State Univ	IN	6,032	LC
Centre College	KY	15,850	VC+
Chestnut Hill College	PA	14,525	C
Clarke College	IA	13,950	C+
Colgate Univ	NY	24,020	HC
Lehigh Univ	PA	23,250	HC
LIU/C. W. Post Campus	NY	16,870	C
Marquette Univ	WI	16,114	VC
Middlebury College	VT	24,400	MC
Millersville Univ of Penn	PA	7,370	VC
Montclair State College	NJ	7,539	C+
Northwestern Univ	IL	21,093	MC
Penn State Univ/Univ Park Campus	PA	8,752	HC
Pomona College	CA	23,820	MC
Purdue Univ/West Lafayette	IN	6,636	C
Rutgers Univ/Cook College	NJ	9,197	HC
Rutgers Univ/Rutgers College	NJ	8,841	HC+
Rutgers Univ/Univ College—New Brunswick	NJ	0	LC
SUNY at Albany	NY	7,059	VC
SUNY College of Environmental Science and Forestry	NY	9,257	HC+
Sweet Briar College	VA	19,770	C
Univ of Calif at Berkeley	CA	9,962	HC+
Univ of Calif, San Diego	CA	10,028	VC+
Univ of Colo at Boulder	CO	6,410	VC
Univ of Conn	CT	9,168	C
Univ of Maine	ME	7,990	C
Univ of North Texas	TX	4,853	C
Univ of Wisc/Madison	WI	6,400	HC
Univ of Wyoming	WY	4,991	NC

MUSEUM STUDIES

School	ST	$IS	SR
Tusculum College	TN	10,400	LC

MUSIC

School	ST	$IS	SR
Abilene Christian Univ	TX	10,460	NC
Adams State College	CO	4,910	C
Adelphi Univ	NY	18,250	LC
Adrian College	MI	14,340	C
Agnes Scott College	GA	17,135	VC
Alabama State Univ	AL	3,428	NC
Alaska Pacific Univ	AK	11,350	C
Albany State College	GA	4,481	LC
Albertson College	ID	15,942	C+
Albion College	MI	18,264	VC
Alderson-Broaddus College	WV	12,000	C
Allegheny College	PA	21,020	VC
Allen Univ	SC	6,705	NC
Alma College	MI	16,375	VC+
Alverno College	WI	11,344	C
American Univ	DC	21,230	VC+
Amherst College	MA	24,152	MC
Andrews Univ	MI	14,952	NC
Angelo State Univ	TX	5,176	C
Antioch College	OH	19,532	C
Appalachian State Univ	NC	4,095	C
Aquinas College	MI	14,526	C
Arizona State Univ Main Campus	AZ	6,444	C
Arkansas College	AR	11,626	VC
Arkansas State Univ	AR	4,250	NC
Arkansas Tech Univ	AR	4,200	NC
Armstrong State College	GA	4,874	LC
Asbury College	KY	11,105	VC
Ashland Univ	OH	15,508	C
Atlantic Union College	MA	14,150	LC
Auburn Univ	AL	5,823	C+
Augsburg College	MN	15,608	C
Augusta College	GA	1,452	C
Augustana College	IL	16,959	VC
Augustana College	SD	13,420	C
Austin College	TX	14,999	VC
Austin Peay State Univ	TN	4,350	C
Averett College	VA	13,610	LC
Avila College	MO	12,130	C
Azusa Pacific Univ	CA	15,034	C
Baker Univ	KS	12,284	C
Ball State Univ	IN	6,032	LC
Bard College	NY	25,269	HC
Barton College	NC	10,689	LC
Bates College	ME	23,990	MC
Baylor Univ	TX	10,990	C+
Belhaven College	MS	9,690	C+
Bellarmine College	KY	10,832	C
Belmont Univ	TN	10,540	C
Beloit College	WI	18,950	VC+
Bemidji State Univ	MN	5,188	C
Benedict College	SC	8,376	LC
Benedictine College	KS	12,830	C
Bennington College	VT	24,850	VC+
Berea College	KY	2,883	VC+
Berklee College of Music	MA	17,530	SP
Berry College	GA	11,990	VC
Bethany College	KS	11,232	C
Bethel College	IN	11,650	C
Bethel College	KS	11,530	C
Bethel College	MN	15,050	C
Bethel College	TN	9,736	LC
Bethune-Cookman College	FL	8,375	LC
Biola Univ	CA	16,124	C
Birmingham-Southern College	AL	15,154	VC+
Black Hills State Univ	SD	4,831	NC
Bloomsburg Univ of Penn	PA	6,312	C+
Blue Mountain College	MS	5,958	LC
Bluefield College	VA	10,600	C
Bluffton College	OH	12,951	C
Boise State Univ	ID	4,909	LC
Boston College	MA	22,706	MC
Boston Conservatory	MA	17,900	SP
Bowdoin College	ME	24,155	MC
Bowie State Univ	MD	7,294	LC
Bowling Green State Univ	OH	6,701	C
Bradley Univ	IL	14,718	C+
Brandeis Univ	MA	25,585	HC
Brewton-Parker College	GA	6,828	NC
Briar Cliff College	IA	13,375	C
Bridgewater College	VA	15,300	C
Brigham Young Univ	UT	5,625	HC
Brooklyn Campus of LIU	NY	15,000	LC
Brown Univ	RI	26,104	MC
Bryan College	TN	11,465	C
Bryn Mawr College	PA	24,110	MC
Bucknell Univ	PA	22,320	HC
Buena Vista College	IA	16,150	VC
Butler Univ	IN	16,210	C
Caldwell College	NJ	12,860	C
Calif Baptist College	CA	11,294	C
Calif Inst of the Arts	CA	16,400	SP
Calif Lutheran Univ	CA	17,240	C
Calif State Polytechnic Univ/Pomona	CA	6,438	LC
Cal State/Chico	CA	6,146	C
Cal State/Dominguez Hills	CA	2,857	LC
Cal State/Fresno	CA	5,747	C
Cal State/Fullerton	CA	4,850	LC
Cal State/Hayward	CA	5,495	C
Cal State/Long Beach	CA	6,057	LC
Cal State/Los Angeles	CA	4,940	VC
Cal State/Northridge	CA	7,122	LC
Cal State/Sacramento	CA	6,387	C
Cal State/San Bernardino	CA	6,055	LC
Cal State/Stanislaus	CA	6,799	C
Calvin College	MI	13,020	VC
Cameron Univ	OK	3,686	LC
Campbell Univ	NC	10,624	C
Campbellsville College	KY	8,720	C
Capital Univ	OH	16,535	VC
Carleton College	MN	22,155	HC
Carnegie Mellon Univ	PA	22,560	HC+
Carroll College	WI	15,490	C
Carson-Newman College	TN	11,250	C
Carthage College	WI	15,995	C
Cascade College	OR	9,800	NC
Case Western Reserve Univ	OH	19,910	HC
Castleton State College	VT	8,378	LC
Catawba College	NC	12,950	C
Catholic Univ of America	DC	18,856	C
Cedar Crest College	PA	18,930	C
Cedarville College	OH	10,715	C
Centenary College of Louisiana	LA	11,826	C+
Central College	IA	14,025	VC
Central Conn State Univ	CT	7,108	C
Central Methodist College	MO	11,410	C
Central Mich Univ	MI	6,737	LC
Central Missouri State Univ	MO	5,138	LC
Central State Univ	OH	7,320	NC
Central Washington Univ	WA	5,644	C
Central Wesleyan College	SC	9,640	C
Centre College	KY	15,850	VC+
Chadron State College	NE	4,091	NC
Chapman Univ	CA	21,842	C
Charleston Southern Univ	SC	10,282	LC
Charter Oak State College	CT	314	NC
Chatham College	PA	18,010	C
Chestnut Hill College	PA	14,525	C
Cheyney Univ of Penn	PA	7,005	C
Chicago State Univ	IL	2,198	C
Christian Heritage College	CA	11,756	C
Christopher Newport Univ	VA	3,196	LC
CUNY/Baruch College	NY	2,562	VC
CUNY/Brooklyn College	NY	2,450	VC
CUNY/City College	NY	2,543	VC
CUNY/College of Staten Island	NY	2,558	NC
CUNY/Herbert H. Lehman College	NY	2,542	C
CUNY/Hunter College	NY	4,101	VC
CUNY/Queens College	NY	2,631	C
CUNY/York College	NY	2,534	NC
Claflin College	SC	0	C
Clarion Univ of Penn	PA	6,518	C
Clark Atlanta Univ	GA	11,846	C
Clark Univ	MA	21,400	VC
Clarke College	IA	13,950	C+
Clayton State College	GA	1,496	LC
Cleveland Inst of Music	OH	18,177	SP
Cleveland State Univ	OH	7,287	NC
Coe College	IA	17,085	VC
Coker College	SC	13,790	C
Colby College	ME	24,230	HC
Colgate Univ	NY	24,020	HC
College of Charleston	SC	6,250	C
College of Mount St Joseph	OH	13,272	C
College of Notre Dame	CA	16,480	C
College of Notre Dame of Maryland	MD	16,050	C
College of St Benedict	MN	15,468	VC
College of St Catherine	MN	14,670	C
College of St Elizabeth	NJ	15,800	C
College of St Rose	NY	14,452	C
College of St Scholastica	MN	14,868	C
College of Santa Fe	NM	14,008	C
College of the Holy Cross	MA	23,850	HC
College of the Ozarks	MO	2,000	VC+
College of William and Mary	VA	8,602	MC
College of Wooster	OH	19,875	VC
Colo Christian Univ	CO	9,750	C
Colo College	CO	20,038	HC
Colo State Univ	CO	6,566	VC
Columbia College	SC	13,520	LC
Columbia Union College	MD	13,650	LC
Columbia Univ/Barnard College	NY	25,492	HC
Columbia Univ/Columbia College	NY	26,757	MC
Columbus College	GA	4,892	LC
Concordia College	MI	13,660	C
Concordia College	MN	13,200	C
Concordia College	NE	11,776	NC
Concordia College	NY	0	LC
Concordia College/Moorhead	MN	12,750	C
Concordia Lutheran College	TX	10,260	C+
Concordia Univ	IL	12,611	C
Concordia Univ	CA	14,675	C
Concordia Univ Wisc	WI	12,140	C
Conn College	CT	24,160	HC
Converse College	SC	15,750	C
Cornell College	IA	18,425	VC
Cornell Univ	NY	13,445	MC
Cornish College of the Arts	WA	9,300	SP
Covenant College	GA	13,054	VC
Culver-Stockton College	MO	11,150	C
Cumberland College	KY	9,756	C
Curtis Inst of Music	PA	0	SP
Dakota State Univ	SD	4,374	LC
Dallas Baptist Univ	TX	9,620	LC
Dana College	NE	11,910	C
Dartmouth College	NH	24,354	MC
David Lipscomb Univ	TN	7,865	VC
Davidson College	NC	21,037	MC
Davis and Elkins College	WV	13,230	LC
Defiance College	OH	13,480	LC
Delaware State College	DE	5,656	C
Delta State Univ	MS	3,964	LC
Denison Univ	OH	21,150	VC+
DePaul Univ	IL	15,535	VC
DePauw Univ	IN	18,530	VC
Dickinson College	PA	22,705	HC
Dickinson State Univ	ND	3,792	C
Dillard Univ	LA	9,950	C
Doane College	NE	12,220	C
Dominican College of San Rafael	CA	17,860	C
Dordt College	IA	11,690	C
Dowling College	NY	12,730	LC
Drake Univ	IA	17,195	VC
Drew Univ/College of Liberal Arts	NJ	23,406	HC
Drexel Univ	PA	15,970	C
Drury College	MO	12,140	VC
Duke Univ	NC	21,271	MC
Duquesne Univ	PA	16,434	VC
Earlham College	IN	19,383	VC
East Carolina Univ	NC	4,498	C
East Central Univ	OK	3,558	C
East Tenn State Univ	TN	4,406	C
East Texas Baptist Univ	TX	7,740	C
East Texas State Univ	TX	4,572	LC
Eastern College	PA	15,150	C+
Eastern Illinois Univ	IL	5,548	C
Eastern Kentucky Univ	KY	4,840	NC
Eastern Mennonite College	VA	12,700	C
Eastern Mich Univ	MI	6,749	C
Eastern Montana College	MT	5,165	LC
Eastern Nazarene College	MA	12,165	LC
Eastern New Mexico Univ	NM	3,950	C
Eastern Oregon State College	OR	6,090	C
Eastern Washington Univ	WA	5,439	LC
Eastman School of Music	NY	21,794	SP
Eckerd College	FL	18,855	VC
Edgewood College	WI	11,700	C
Edinboro Univ of Penn	PA	7,181	C
Elizabeth City State Univ	NC	4,254	LC
Elizabethtown College	PA	17,850	VC
Elmhurst College	IL	12,536	C
Elmira College	NY	18,450	C
Elon College	NC	12,290	LC
Emory Univ	GA	21,930	HC
Emporia State Univ	KS	4,685	NC
Erskine College	SC	14,310	C
Eureka College	IL	14,555	C
Evangel College	MO	10,142	LC
Evergreen State College	WA	6,306	C
Fisk Univ	TN	0	LC
Florida A&M Univ	FL	4,651	C
Florida Atlantic Univ	FL	5,525	C
Florida International Univ	FL	4,191	VC
Florida Memorial College	FL	7,600	C+
Florida Southern College	FL	12,260	C
Florida State Univ	FL	5,814	VC
Fordham Univ/Fordham College	NY	19,875	VC
Fort Hays State Univ	KS	4,675	NC
Fort Lewis College	CO	5,097	C
Franklin and Marshall College	PA	23,655	HC
Franklin Pierce College	NH	17,270	LC
Fresno Pacific College	CA	13,020	C
Friends Univ	KS	11,205	C
Frostburg State Univ	MD	6,940	C
Furman Univ	SC	16,557	VC

School	ST	$IS	SR
Southern College of Seventh-day Adventists	TN	11,348	NC
Southern Illinois Univ at Carbondale	IL	6,234	C
Southern Illinois Univ at Edwardsville	IL	6,097	LC
Southern Nazarene Univ	OK	9,206	NC
Southern Oregon State College	OR	6,128	C
Southern Univ and A&M College	LA	4,920	NC
Southern Utah Univ	UT	4,104	LC
Southwest Baptist Univ	MO	9,192	NC
Southwest Missouri State Univ	MO	4,956	C
Southwest State Univ	MN	5,400	NC
Southwest Texas State Univ	TX	5,124	C
Southwestern College	KS	10,032	C
Southwestern Okla State Univ	OK	3,312	C
Southwestern Univ	TX	15,484	HC
Spelman College	GA	12,942	VC
Spring Arbor College	MI	12,256	C
Stanford Univ	CA	24,310	MC
SUNY at Albany	NY	7,059	VC
SUNY at Binghamton	NY	7,921	HC
SUNY at Buffalo	NY	7,896	VC
SUNY at Stony Brook	NY	7,658	VC
SUNY/College at Buffalo	NY	7,035	VC
SUNY/College at Cortland	NY	7,326	C+
SUNY/College at Fredonia	NY	7,159	VC
SUNY/College at Geneseo	NY	6,949	HC
SUNY/College at New Paltz	NY	6,890	VC
SUNY/College at Oneonta	NY	7,878	C
SUNY/College at Oswego	NY	7,330	VC
SUNY/College at Purchase	NY	7,324	C
SUNY/Potsdam College	NY	6,906	C
Stephen F. Austin State Univ	TX	5,117	C
Sterling College	KS	10,990	VC
Stetson Univ	FL	16,435	VC
Stillman College	AL	7,213	NC
Susquehanna Univ	PA	19,950	VC
Swarthmore College	PA	24,136	MC
Syracuse Univ	NY	21,305	HC
Tabor College	KS	11,460	VC
Tarleton State Univ	TX	4,082	LC
Taylor Univ	IN	14,450	VC
Teikyo Westmar Univ	IA	15,920	C
Temple Univ	PA	10,281	C
Tenn State Univ	TN	4,626	C+
Tenn Wesleyan College	TN	10,060	C
Texas A&M Univ at Kingsville	TX	3,808	LC
Texas Christian Univ	TX	12,180	C
Texas College	TX	5,930	NC
Texas Lutheran College	TX	10,710	C
Texas Southern Univ	TX	4,500	NC
Texas Tech Univ	TX	6,008	C
Texas Wesleyan Univ	TX	9,380	LC
Texas Woman's Univ	TX	4,392	LC
The Univ of New Mexico	NM	5,304	C
Thomas A. Edison State College	NJ	400	
Toccoa Falls College	GA	9,350	C
Tougaloo College	MS	7,480	LC
Towson State Univ	MD	7,452	C
Transylvania Univ	KY	14,970	VC+
Trenton State College	NJ	9,085	HC
Trevecca Nazarene College	TN	9,826	NC
Trinity Christian College	IL	13,260	C
Trinity College	CT	24,120	HC
Trinity College	IL	14,010	C
Trinity Univ	TX	16,670	HC
Tufts Univ	MA	24,962	MC
Tulane Univ	LA	24,540	HC
Union College	KY	9,790	C
Union College	NE	11,060	NC
Union Univ	TN	7,880	C+
Universidad Adventista de las Antillas	PR	5,000	
Univ of Akron	OH	6,699	NC
Univ of Alabama	AL	5,702	C
Univ of Alabama at Birmingham	AL	7,533	C
Univ of Alabama at Huntsville	AL	5,868	VC
Univ of Alaska Anchorage	AK	7,131	C
Univ of Alaska Fairbanks	AK	4,718	C
Univ of Arizona	AZ	5,808	C
Univ of Arkansas at Fayetteville	AR	5,046	C
Univ of Arkansas at Little Rock	AR	4,419	C
Univ of Arkansas at Monticello	AR	3,832	NC
Univ of Arkansas at Pine Bluff	AR	3,978	LC
Univ of Bridgeport	CT	18,985	C
Univ of Calif at Berkeley	CA	9,962	HC+
Univ of Calif at Davis	CA	9,534	VC
Univ of Calif at Los Angeles	CA	8,959	HC
Univ of Calif at Santa Barbara	CA	9,460	C
Univ of Calif at Santa Cruz	CA	9,060	VC
Univ of Calif, Riverside	CA	9,178	C
Univ of Calif, San Diego	CA	10,028	VC+
Univ of Calif/Irvine	CA	12,680	VC

School	ST	$IS	SR
Univ of Central Arkansas	AR	4,200	LC
Univ of Central Florida	FL	6,061	C+
Univ of Central Okla	OK	3,647	C
Univ of Charleston	WV	12,750	C
Univ of Chicago	IL	24,517	MC
Univ of Cincinnati	OH	7,989	C
Univ of Colo at Boulder	CO	6,410	VC
Univ of Colo at Denver	CO	1,955	VC
Univ of Conn	CT	9,168	C
Univ of Dayton	OH	15,120	C+
Univ of Delaware	DE	8,013	VC
Univ of Denver	CO	19,290	C+
Univ of Evansville	IN	15,300	VC
Univ of Florida	FL	5,850	HC
Univ of Georgia	GA	5,655	VC
Univ of Hartford	CT	19,858	LC
Univ of Hawaii at Hilo	HI	4,141	C
Univ of Hawaii at Manoa	HI	5,626	VC
Univ of Houston	TX	5,215	C
Univ of Idaho	ID	4,830	C
Univ of Illinois at Chicago	IL	8,443	C
Univ of Illinois at Urbana-Champaign	IL	7,764	HC
Univ of Indianapolis	IN	14,510	C
Univ of Iowa	IA	5,658	VC
Univ of Kansas	KS	5,200	NC
Univ of Kentucky	KY	5,152	VC
Univ of La Verne	CA	17,400	C
Univ of Louisville	KY	5,948	C
Univ of Lowell	MA	8,831	VC
Univ of Maine	ME	7,990	C
Univ of Maine at Augusta	ME	2,595	NC
Univ of Maine at Farmington	ME	6,700	C
Univ of Mary	ND	8,910	C
Univ of Mary Hardin-Baylor	TX	8,120	NC
Univ of Maryland/Baltimore County	MD	7,746	VC
Univ of Maryland/College Park	MD	8,182	VC
Univ of Mass Dartmouth	MA	8,158	C
Univ of Mass/Amherst	MA	9,364	LC
Univ of Mass/Boston	MA	4,253	C
Univ of Memphis	TN	3,476	C
Univ of Miami	FL	22,107	VC
Univ of Mich/Ann Arbor	MI	9,428	HC+
Univ of Mich/Dearborn	MI	3,399	HC
Univ of Mich/Flint	MI	2,916	C
Univ of Minn/Duluth	MN	6,512	C
Univ of Minn/Morris	MN	6,825	HC
Univ of Minn/Twin Cities	MN	6,682	VC
Univ of Miss	MS	5,756	C
Univ of Missouri/Columbia	MO	6,254	HC
Univ of Missouri/Kansas City	MO	5,906	VC
Univ of Missouri/St. Louis	MO	6,378	C
Univ of Mobile	AL	9,400	C
Univ of Montana	MT	5,529	C
Univ of Montevallo	AL	5,310	C
Univ of Nebr at Kearney	NE	4,308	LC
Univ of Nebr at Omaha	NE	1,889	LC
Univ of Nebr-Lincoln	NE	5,278	LC
Univ of Nevada/Las Vegas	NV	6,405	C
Univ of Nevada/Reno	NV	5,735	C
Univ of New Hampshire	NH	8,242	C
Univ of New Haven	CT	14,980	C
Univ of New Orleans	LA	5,468	C
Univ of North Alabama	AL	4,236	NC
Univ of N Car at Asheville	NC	4,791	VC
Univ of N Car at Chapel Hill	NC	5,330	HC
Univ of N Car at Charlotte	NC	4,597	C
Univ of N Car at Greensboro	NC	5,192	C
Univ of N Dak	ND	4,902	NC
Univ of North Florida	FL	5,082	C
Univ of North Texas	TX	4,853	C
Univ of Northern Colo	CO	6,008	C
Univ of Northern Iowa	IA	5,137	C
Univ of Notre Dame	IN	20,150	MC
Univ of Okla	OK	5,427	VC
Univ of Oregon	OR	6,466	VC
Univ of Penn	PA	24,238	MC
Univ of Pittsburgh	PA	9,472	C
Univ of Portland	OR	15,564	C
Univ of PR/Rio Piedras	PR	0	
Univ of Puget Sound	WA	19,520	HC
Univ of Redlands	CA	22,059	VC
Univ of Rhode Island	RI	9,205	C
Univ of Richmond	VA	16,700	HC
Univ of Rio Grande	OH	6,300	NC
Univ of Rochester	NY	23,696	HC
Univ of St Thomas	MN	15,785	C+
Univ of St Thomas	TX	11,676	C+
Univ of San Diego	CA	18,970	VC
Univ of Science and Arts of Okla	OK	3,304	C
Univ of South Alabama	AL	5,451	C
Univ of S Car	SC	6,158	C
Univ of S Dak	SD	4,722	C
Univ of South Florida	FL	5,475	C+
Univ of Southern Calif	CA	23,006	VC
Univ of Southern Colo	CO	5,350	LC
Univ of Southern Maine	ME	7,299	C
Univ of Southern Miss	MS	4,542	C
Univ of Southwestern Louisiana	LA	3,968	NC
Univ of Tampa	FL	16,780	C
Univ of Tenn at Chattanooga	TN	5,375	C
Univ of Tenn at Martin	TN	4,550	C

School	ST	$IS	SR
Univ of Tenn/Knoxville	TN	5,668	C
Univ of Texas at Arlington	TX	5,549	LC
Univ of Texas at Austin	TX	5,160	VC
Univ of Texas at El Paso	TX	3,160	LC
Univ of Texas at San Antonio	TX	6,420	C
Univ of the District of Columbia	DC	974	NC
Univ of the Ozarks	AR	7,770	C
Univ of the Pacific	CA	21,100	C
Univ of the South	TN	18,830	HC
Univ of Toledo	OH	6,636	NC
Univ of Tulsa	OK	13,795	VC
Univ of Utah	UT	5,975	C
Univ of Vermont	VT	10,776	C+
Univ of Virginia	VA	7,964	MC
Univ of West Florida	FL	5,415	C
Univ of Wisc/Eau Claire	WI	4,647	C
Univ of Wisc/Green Bay	WI	4,904	C
Univ of Wisc/La Crosse	WI	4,487	C
Univ of Wisc/Madison	WI	6,400	HC
Univ of Wisc/Milwaukee	WI	6,165	C
Univ of Wisc/Oshkosh	WI	4,240	C
Univ of Wisc/Parkside	WI	5,247	
Univ of Wisc/Platteville	WI	4,830	C
Univ of Wisc/River Falls	WI	4,655	C
Univ of Wisc/Stevens Point	WI	5,047	C+
Univ of Wisc/Superior	WI	4,330	C
Univ of Wisc/Whitewater	WI	4,700	C
Univ of Wyoming	WY	4,991	NC
Upper Iowa Univ	IA	11,900	C
Ursinus College	PA	19,165	VC
Utah State Univ	UT	4,683	C
Valdosta State Univ	GA	4,670	LC
Valley City State Univ	ND	4,385	LC
Valparaiso Univ	IN	14,810	VC
Vanderbilt Univ	TN	23,422	HC+
Vassar College	NY	24,206	HC
Virginia Commonwealth Univ	VA	7,909	C
Virginia Intermont College	VA	12,250	LC
Virginia Polytechnic Inst and State Univ	VA	6,828	C
Virginia State Univ	VA	7,040	C
Virginia Union Univ	VA	10,555	LC
Virginia Wesleyan College	VA	14,950	VC
Viterbo College	WI	12,670	C
Wabash College	IN	16,250	VC
Wagner College	NY	17,950	C
Wake Forest Univ	NC	17,280	MC
Walla Walla College	WA	13,215	C
Warner Pacific College	OR	12,112	C
Wartburg College	IA	14,530	VC
Washburn Univ of Topeka	KS	5,802	NC
Washington and Lee Univ	VA	17,735	MC
Washington College	MD	19,270	C+
Washington State Univ	WA	6,364	C
Washington Univ	MO	23,507	HC
Wayland Baptist Univ	TX	7,811	NC
Wayne State College	NE	4,260	NC
Wayne State Univ	MI	2,680	C
Weber State Univ	UT	4,398	C
Webster Univ	MO	12,650	C
Wellesley College	MA	23,815	MC
Wells College	NY	19,460	C+
Wesleyan College	GA	15,445	C
Wesleyan Univ	CT	23,770	MC
West Chester Univ of Penn	PA	7,492	C
West Georgia College	GA	4,256	C
West Liberty State College	WV	4,690	LC
West Virginia Inst of Tech	WV	5,858	LC
West Virginia Univ	WV	5,774	C
West Virginia Wesleyan College	WV	16,900	C
Western Carolina Univ	NC	3,811	C
Western Conn State Univ	CT	6,622	C
Western Illinois Univ	IL	5,241	LC
Western Kentucky Univ	KY	4,808	C
Western Maryland College	MD	18,990	C
Western Mich Univ	MI	6,820	C
Western New Mexico Univ	NM	3,234	LC
Western Oregon State College	OR	6,180	C
Western State College of Colo	CO	5,560	C
Western Washington Univ	WA	6,077	VC
Westfield State College	MA	7,161	C
Westminster Choir College	NJ	18,585	SP
Westminster College	PA	15,200	C
Wheaton College	IL	14,710	HC
Wheaton College	MA	23,840	C+
Whitman College	WA	20,595	HC
Whittier College	CA	21,661	C
Whitworth College	WA	16,265	C
Wichita State Univ	KS	5,068	NC
Wilberforce Univ	OH	10,408	C
Wiley College	TX	0	NC
Wilkes Univ	PA	15,728	LC
Willamette Univ	OR	17,995	VC
William Carey College	MS	7,050	C
William Jewell College	MO	12,500	VC
William Paterson College	NJ	7,438	C+
William Penn College	IA	13,400	C
William Tyndale College	MI	7,120	NC
Williams Baptist College	AR	5,834	LC
Williams College	MA	24,390	MC
Wingate College	NC	10,610	C
Winona State Univ	MN	5,200	VC

School	ST	$IS	SR
Winthrop Univ	SC	6,750	C
Wittenberg Univ	OH	19,998	VC
Women's College of Brenau Univ	GA	14,734	C
Wright State Univ	OH	6,896	LC
Xavier Univ	OH	15,710	C+
Xavier Univ of Louisiana	LA	10,400	C
Yale Univ	CT	25,110	MC
Yeshiva Univ	NY	18,200	VC
York College of Penn	PA	8,345	C
Youngstown State Univ	OH	6,447	LC

MUSIC BUSINESS MANAGEMENT

School	ST	$IS	SR
Anderson Univ	IN	12,920	C
Baldwin-Wallace College	OH	15,210	C
Blackburn College	IL	9,120	C
Butler Univ	IN	16,210	C
DePaul Univ	IL	15,535	VC
DePauw Univ	IN	18,530	VC
Drake Univ	IA	17,195	VC
Eastern Washington Univ	WA	5,439	LC
Elmhurst College	IL	12,536	C
Five Towns College	NY	11,200	SP
Fontbonne College	MO	12,090	C
Geneva College	PA	13,030	C
Grove City College	PA	7,870	HC
Incarnate Word College	TX	12,307	C
Johnson C. Smith Univ	NC	8,916	LC
Mansfield Univ	PA	6,348	C
Methodist College	NC	12,400	C
New York Univ	NY	24,705	VC+
Peru State College	NE	4,311	NC
Quincy Univ	IL	13,646	VC
Shorter College	GA	10,270	C
S Car State Univ	SC	5,424	LC
S Dak State Univ	SD	4,562	C
Southern Oregon State College	OR	6,128	C
Syracuse Univ	NY	21,305	HC
Trevecca Nazarene College	TN	9,826	NC
Univ of Charleston	WV	12,750	C
Univ of Evansville	IN	15,300	VC
Univ of Miami	FL	22,107	VC
Univ of the Pacific	CA	21,100	C
Wayne State Univ	MI	2,680	C
West Texas A&M Univ	TX	4,224	C
West Virginia Inst of Tech	WV	5,858	LC
Wingate College	NC	10,610	C

MUSIC EDUCATION

School	ST	$IS	SR
Abilene Christian Univ	TX	10,460	NC
Adams State College	CO	4,910	C
Adelphi Univ	NY	18,250	LC
Adrian College	MI	14,340	C
Alabama A&M Univ	AL	4,200	C
Alabama State Univ	AL	3,428	NC
Albany State College	GA	4,481	LC
Albion College	MI	18,264	VC
Alcorn State Univ	MS	4,474	C+
Alderson-Broaddus College	WV	12,000	C
Alverno College	WI	11,344	C
Anderson Univ	IN	12,920	C
Andrews Univ	MI	14,952	NC
Angelo State Univ	TX	5,176	C
Anna Maria College	MA	15,975	LC
Appalachian State Univ	NC	4,095	C
Arkansas State Univ	AR	4,250	NC
Arkansas Tech Univ	AR	4,200	NC
Armstrong State College	GA	4,874	LC
Asbury College	KY	11,105	VC
Ashland Univ	OH	15,508	C
Atlantic Union College	MA	14,150	LC
Augsburg College	MN	15,608	C
Augustana College	IL	16,959	VC
Augustana College	SD	13,420	C
Avila College	MO	12,130	C
Azusa Pacific Univ	CA	15,034	C
Baker Univ	KS	12,284	C
Baldwin-Wallace College	OH	15,210	C
Ball State Univ	IN	6,032	LC
Barton College	NC	10,689	LC
Berea College	KY	2,883	VC+
Berry College	GA	11,990	VC
Bethel College	IN	11,650	C
Bethel College	MN	15,050	C
Bethune-Cookman College	FL	8,375	LC
Biola Univ	CA	16,124	C
Birmingham-Southern College	AL	15,154	VC+
Black Hills State Univ	SD	4,831	NC
Blackburn College	IL	9,120	C
Blue Mountain College	MS	5,958	LC
Bluffton College	OH	12,951	C
Boise State Univ	ID	4,909	LC
Boston Conservatory	MA	17,900	SP
Boston Univ	MA	24,130	HC

School	ST	$IS	SR
Bowling Green State Univ	OH	6,701	C
Bradley Univ	IL	14,718	C+
Brigham Young Univ	UT	5,625	HC
Brooklyn Campus of LIU	NY	15,000	LC
Bucknell Univ	PA	22,320	HC
Buena Vista College	IA	16,150	VC
Butler Univ	IN	16,210	C
Calif Lutheran Univ	CA	17,240	C
Cal State/Chico	CA	6,146	C
Cal State/Fresno	CA	5,747	C
Cal State/Fullerton	CA	4,850	LC
Cal State/Los Angeles	CA	4,940	VC
Cal State/Northridge	CA	7,122	LC
Cal State/San Bernardino	CA	6,055	LC
Cameron Univ	OK	3,686	LC
Capital Univ	OH	16,535	VC
Carnegie Mellon Univ	PA	22,560	HC+
Carroll College	WI	15,490	C
Carson-Newman College	TN	11,250	C
Carthage College	WI	15,995	C
Case Western Reserve Univ	OH	19,910	HC
Catawba College	NC	12,950	C
Cedarville College	OH	10,715	C
Centenary College of Louisiana	LA	11,826	C+
Central College	IA	14,025	VC
Central Conn State Univ	CT	7,108	C
Central Mich Univ	MI	6,737	LC
Central Missouri State Univ	MO	5,138	LC
Central State Univ	OH	7,320	NC
Central Washington Univ	WA	5,644	C
Central Wesleyan College	SC	9,640	C
Chadron State College	NE	4,091	NC
Chestnut Hill College	PA	14,525	C
Chicago State Univ	IL	2,198	C
Christian Heritage College	CA	11,756	C
Christopher Newport Univ	VA	3,196	LC
CUNY/Brooklyn College	NY	2,450	VC
CUNY/City College	NY	2,543	VC
CUNY/Herbert H. Lehman College	NY	2,542	C
CUNY/Hunter College	NY	4,101	VC
CUNY/Queens College	NY	2,631	C
Claflin College	SC	0	
Clarion Univ of Penn	PA	6,518	C
Clarke College	IA	13,950	C+
Clearwater Christian College	FL	8,500	LC
Coastal Carolina Univ	SC	6,010	LC
Coe College	IA	17,085	VC
Coker College	SC	13,790	C
College of Mount St Joseph	OH	13,272	C
College of Notre Dame of Maryland	MD	16,050	C
College of St Catherine	MN	14,670	C
College of St Rose	NY	14,452	C
Colo Christian Univ	CO	9,750	C
Columbia College	SC	13,520	LC
Columbus College	GA	4,892	LC
Concord College	WV	5,104	NC
Concordia College	MN	13,200	C
Concordia College	NE	11,776	NC
Concordia College	NY	0	LC
Concordia College/Moorhead	MN	12,750	C
Concordia Univ	IL	12,611	C
Converse College	SC	15,750	LC
Cornell College	IA	18,425	VC
Covenant College	GA	13,054	VC
Crichton College	TN	6,547	NC
Culver-Stockton College	MO	11,150	C
Cumberland College	KY	9,756	C
Dakota State Univ	SD	4,374	LC
Dana College	NE	11,910	C
David Lipscomb Univ	TN	7,865	VC
Defiance College	OH	13,480	LC
Delaware State College	DE	5,656	C
Delta State Univ	MS	3,964	LC
DePaul Univ	IL	15,535	VC
DePauw Univ	IN	18,530	VC
Dickinson State Univ	ND	3,792	C
Dordt College	IA	11,690	C
Drake Univ	IA	17,195	VC
Drury College	MO	12,140	VC
Duquesne Univ	PA	16,434	VC
East Central Univ	OK	3,558	C
East Tenn State Univ	TN	4,406	C
East Texas Baptist Univ	TX	7,740	C
East Texas State Univ	TX	4,572	LC
Eastern Illinois Univ	IL	5,548	C
Eastern Kentucky Univ	KY	4,840	NC
Eastern Mich Univ	MI	6,749	C
Eastern Montana College	MT	5,165	LC
Eastern Nazarene College	MA	12,165	LC
Eastern New Mexico Univ	NM	3,950	C
Eastern Washington Univ	WA	5,439	LC
Eastman School of Music	NY	21,794	SP
Edinboro Univ of Penn	PA	7,181	C
Elizabethtown College	PA	17,850	VC
Elmhurst College	IL	12,536	C
Elon College	NC	12,290	LC
Emmanuel College	MA	17,773	LC
Emporia State Univ	KS	4,685	NC
Erskine College	SC	14,310	C
Evangel College	MO	10,142	LC
Fairmont State College	WV	4,640	LC
Fayetteville State Univ	NC	3,926	LC
Fisk Univ	TN	0	LC
Five Towns College	NY	11,200	SP
Florida A&M Univ	FL	4,651	C
Florida Atlantic Univ	FL	5,525	C
Florida International Univ	FL	4,191	VC
Florida Southern College	FL	12,260	C
Florida State Univ	FL	5,814	VC
Fort Hays State Univ	KS	4,675	NC
Freed-Hardeman Univ	TN	8,585	VC
Fresno Pacific College	CA	13,020	C
Friends Univ	KS	11,205	C
Frostburg State Univ	MD	6,940	C
Furman Univ	SC	16,557	VC
Gardner-Webb Univ	NC	11,950	LC
Geneva College	PA	13,030	C
George Fox College	OR	15,640	LC
Georgetown College	KY	10,990	C
Georgia College	GA	4,310	LC
Georgia Southern Univ	GA	4,988	LC
Georgia Southwestern College	GA	4,338	LC
Georgia State Univ	GA	2,019	C
Gettysburg College	PA	22,960	HC
Glenville State College	WV	4,810	LC
Gonzaga Univ	WA	16,350	VC
Gordon College	MA	16,790	C
Goshen College	IN	12,360	C
Grace College	IN	12,120	C
Graceland College	IA	11,600	C
Grambling State Univ	LA	4,712	NC
Grand Canyon Univ	AZ	9,680	VC
Grand Rapids Baptist College and Seminary	MI	10,228	C
Grand Valley State Univ	MI	6,822	VC
Greenville College	IL	14,190	C
Grove City College	PA	7,870	HC
Gustavus Adolphus College	MN	15,935	VC
Hamline Univ	MN	17,122	VC
Hannibal-LaGrange College	MO	8,400	LC
Hanover College	IN	10,950	VC
Hardin-Simmons Univ	TX	9,080	C
Harding Univ	AR	9,050	VC
Hartwick College	NY	20,950	C
Hastings College	NE	12,426	C
Heidelberg College	OH	17,160	C
Henderson State Univ	AR	3,860	C
Hendrix College	AR	11,670	C
Hillsdale College	MI	15,110	VC
Hofstra Univ	NY	16,580	VC
Hope College	MI	15,698	C+
Houghton College	NY	13,120	VC
Houston Baptist Univ	TX	11,055	C
Howard Payne Univ	TX	8,052	C
Howard Univ	DC	11,680	C
Humboldt State Univ	CA	5,676	C
Huntingdon College	AL	11,400	C
Huntington College	IN	13,220	C
Idaho State Univ	ID	4,442	C
Illinois State Univ	IL	6,413	C
Immaculata College	PA	14,620	C
Incarnate Word College	TX	12,307	C
Indiana State Univ	IN	6,210	C
Indiana Univ of Penn	PA	6,373	C
Indiana Univ-Purdue Univ at Fort Wayne	IN	2,500	LC
Indiana Univ/South Bend	IN	2,141	LC
Indiana Wesleyan Univ	IN	12,332	C
Inter American Univ of PR/ Aguadilla Regional College	PR	2,290	
Inter American Univ of PR/ Bayamon Univ College	PR	2,300	
Inter American Univ of PR/ Metropolitan Campus	PR	2,340	
Inter American Univ of PR/ Ponce Regional College	PR	2,300	
Inter American Univ of PR/ San German	PR	4,620	
Inter-American Univ of PR/ Fajardo Regional College	PR	2,732	
Iowa State Univ	IA	5,456	C
Iowa Wesleyan College	IA	13,250	C
Ithaca College	NY	19,679	C
Jackson State Univ	MS	4,996	LC
Jacksonville State Univ	AL	4,080	LC
Jacksonville Univ	FL	13,390	C
Jarvis Christian College	TX	7,170	LC
Jersey City State College	NJ	7,797	LC
John Brown Univ	AR	9,880	VC
Judson College	AL	9,060	C
Judson College	IL	13,625	C
Kansas State Univ	KS	4,816	NC
Kansas Wesleyan Univ	KS	11,770	C
Kean College of New Jersey	NJ	6,395	LC
Keene State College	NH	7,081	C
Kennesaw State College	GA	1,553	C
Kent State Univ	OH	6,740	LC
Kentucky State Univ	KY	4,282	C+
Kentucky Wesleyan College	KY	11,550	C
King's College	NY	12,360	LC
Knoxville College	TN	8,320	LC
La Sierra Univ	CA	15,472	C
Lakeland College	WI	12,845	LC
Lamar Univ	TX	3,798	C
Lambuth Univ	TN	8,395	C
Lander Univ	SC	6,180	LC
Lawrence Univ	WI	19,986	HC+
Lebanon Valley College of Penn	PA	18,300	C
Lee College	TN	7,894	LC
Lewis Univ	IL	14,797	LC
Limestone College	SC	10,700	LC
Lincoln Univ	MO	4,638	NC
Lincoln Univ	PA	0	LC
Lindenwood College	MO	13,560	C
Linfield College	OR	16,670	VC
Livingston Univ	AL	3,979	C
Livingstone College	NC	8,600	LC
LIU/C. W. Post Campus	NY	16,870	C
Longwood College	VA	7,800	C
Loras College	IA	14,160	C
Louisiana State Univ and A&M College	LA	5,605	C
Louisiana Tech Univ	LA	4,284	C
Loyola Univ/New Orleans	LA	15,660	C+
Lubbock Christian Univ	TX	9,840	NC
Luther College	IA	15,900	VC
MacMurray College	IL	12,800	C
Madonna Univ	MI	8,546	C
Malone College	OH	12,572	C
Manchester College	IN	13,240	LC
Manhattanville College	NY	20,450	LC
Mankato State Univ	MN	5,097	LC
Mansfield Univ	PA	6,348	C
Marian College of Fond du Lac	WI	12,250	C
Marietta College	OH	16,940	C+
Mars Hill College	NC	11,050	C
Marshall Univ	WV	5,762	LC
Marygrove College	MI	5,877	VC
Maryville College	TN	14,474	C
Marywood College	PA	14,890	C
McMurry Univ	TX	10,100	C
McPherson College	KS	11,360	VC
Mercer Univ	GA	15,123	C
Mercy College	NY	11,180	NC
Mercyhurst College	PA	13,488	C
Meredith College	NC	9,440	C
Messiah College	PA	14,664	VC
Methodist College	NC	12,400	C
Metropolitan State College of Denver	CO	1,751	NC
Miami Univ	OH	8,066	VC
Mich State Univ	MI	7,842	C
MidAmerica Nazarene College	KS	10,208	NC
Middle Tenn State Univ	TN	3,857	C
Midland Lutheran College	NE	12,410	LC
Midwestern State Univ	TX	4,542	LC
Millersville Univ of Penn	PA	7,370	VC
Milligan College	TN	10,690	C
Millikin Univ	IL	15,499	C
Minot State Univ	ND	3,748	NC
Miss College	MS	8,348	C
Miss State Univ	MS	5,629	VC
Miss Univ for Women	MS	4,456	LC
Missouri Southern State College	MO	4,272	
Missouri Western State College	MO	4,384	NC
Monmouth College	NJ	16,820	C
Montana State Univ	MT	5,534	C
Moorhead State Univ	MN	5,076	C
Moravian College	PA	18,960	VC
Morehead State Univ	KY	4,600	LC
Morningside College	IA	13,896	C
Morris Brown College	GA	12,234	NC
Mount Marty College	SD	10,450	NC
Mount Mary College	WI	10,920	C
Mount Mercy College	IA	13,230	C
Mount St Mary's College	CA	16,390	VC
Mount Senario College	WI	10,970	C
Mount Union College	OH	15,850	C
Mount Vernon Nazarene College	OH	10,390	C
Murray State Univ	KY	4,702	C
Muskingum College	OH	16,650	C
Nazareth College of Rochester	NY	15,310	C+
Nebr Wesleyan Univ	NE	12,240	C
New England Conservatory of Music	MA	21,590	SP
New Mexico Highlands Univ	NM	3,772	C
New Mexico State Univ	NM	4,844	C
New York Univ	NY	24,705	VC+
Newberry College	SC	11,994	LC
Nicholls State Univ	LA	4,531	NC
Norfolk State Univ	VA	6,345	LC
N Car Agricultural and Technical State Univ	NC	4,477	LC
North Georgia College	GA	4,103	LC
Northeast Louisiana Univ	LA	3,906	NC
Northeastern State Univ	OK	5,250	C
Northern Arizona Univ	AZ	4,844	C
Northern Illinois Univ	IL	6,408	C
Northern Kentucky Univ	KY	4,620	NC
Northern Mich Univ	MI	6,350	C
Northern State Univ	SD	4,186	LC
Northland College	WI	13,550	LC
Northwestern College	MN	13,554	C
Northwestern College of Iowa	IA	12,250	C
Northwestern Okla State Univ	OK	3,424	C
Northwestern State Univ of Louisiana	LA	4,287	NC
Northwestern Univ	IL	21,093	MC
Oakland City College	IN	10,216	LC
Oakland Univ	MI	6,714	VC
Oakwood College	AL	10,005	C
Oberlin College	OH	24,570	HC+
Occidental College	CA	21,792	HC
Ohio Northern Univ	OH	18,660	VC
Ohio State Univ	OH	7,218	LC
Ohio Univ	OH	7,341	C
Ohio Wesleyan Univ	OH	21,108	VC+
Okla Baptist Univ	OK	8,486	C
Okla Christian Univ of Science and Arts	OK	8,790	NC
Okla City Univ	OK	9,840	C
Okla Panhandle State Univ	OK	3,155	NC
Olivet College	MI	14,000	C
Olivet Nazarene Univ	IL	11,976	C
Oral Roberts Univ	OK	10,607	C+
Otterbein College	OH	16,506	C
Ouachita Baptist Univ	AR	8,940	C
Pacific Lutheran Univ	WA	15,998	VC
Paine College	GA	8,207	LC
Pembroke State Univ	NC	3,538	LC
Penn State Univ/Univ Park Campus	PA	8,752	HC
Pepperdine Univ	CA	23,720	VC
Peru State College	NE	4,311	NC
Pfeiffer College	NC	11,670	LC
Phillips Univ	OK	12,744	C
Piedmont College	GA	8,540	LC
Pillsbury Baptist Bible College	MN	7,390	NC
Pittsburg State Univ	KS	4,478	NC
Plymouth State College	NH	7,166	C
Point Loma Nazarene College	CA	13,532	C
Pontifical Catholic Univ of PR/Ponce	PR	5,807	
Presbyterian College	SC	15,400	VC
Quincy Univ	IL	13,646	VC
Radford Univ	VA	7,034	LC
Rhode Island College	RI	7,901	LC
Roberts Wesleyan College	NY	13,317	C
Rocky Mountain College	MT	11,320	C
Rowan College of New Jersey	NJ	7,358	VC
Rutgers Univ/Mason Gross School of the Arts	NJ	8,877	SP
Saginaw Valley State Univ	MI	6,634	LC
St Ambrose Univ	IA	13,380	C
St Cloud State Univ	MN	5,015	C
St Joseph's College	IN	14,730	C
St Mary's College of Minn	MN	13,850	LC
St Mary-of-the-Woods College	IN	14,430	NC
St Norbert College	WI	15,710	VC
St Vincent College	PA	13,934	LC
St Xavier Univ	IL	14,700	C
Salisbury State Univ	MD	7,516	C+
Salve Regina Univ	RI	29,100	LC
Samford Univ	AL	11,400	VC
Seattle Pacific Univ	WA	16,503	C
Seton Hill College	PA	14,320	C
Shenandoah Univ	VA	11,800	C
Shepherd College	WV	5,540	C
Shorter College	GA	10,270	C
Siena Heights College	MI	12,520	C
Silver Lake College	WI	8,280	LC
Simpson College	CA	10,628	C
Simpson College	IA	14,635	VC
Sioux Falls College	SD	11,540	C
Slippery Rock Univ	PA	6,803	C
S Car State Univ	SC	5,424	LC
S Dak State Univ	SD	4,562	C
Southeast Missouri State Univ	MO	5,854	C
Southeastern College of the Assemblies of God	FL	6,618	NC
Southeastern Louisiana Univ	LA	4,230	NC
Southeastern Okla State Univ	OK	3,594	C
Southern Arkansas Univ	AR	3,432	NC
Southern Calif College	CA	12,356	C
Southern College of Seventh-day Adventists	TN	11,348	NC
Southern Illinois Univ at Carbondale	IL	6,234	C
Southern Illinois Univ at Edwardsville	IL	6,097	LC
Southern Methodist Univ	TX	18,520	VC
Southern Nazarene Univ	OK	9,206	NC
Southern Univ and A&M College	LA	4,920	NC
Southern Univ at New Orleans	LA	1,452	NC
Southern Utah Univ	UT	4,104	LC
Southwest Baptist Univ	MO	9,192	NC
Southwest Missouri State Univ	MO	4,956	C
Southwest State Univ	MN	5,400	NC
Southwest Texas State Univ	TX	5,124	C
Southwestern College	KS	10,032	C
Southwestern Okla State Univ	OK	3,312	C
SUNY at Albany	NY	7,059	VC
SUNY at Buffalo	NY	7,896	VC
SUNY/College at Fredonia	NY	7,159	VC

MUSIC HISTORY AND APPRECIATION

MUSIC PERFORMANCE

MUSIC THEORY AND COMPOSITION

MUSIC THERAPY

School	ST	$IS	SR
Augsburg College	MN	15,608	C
Baldwin-Wallace College	OH	15,210	C
Cleveland State Univ	OH	7,287	NC
Dillard Univ	LA	9,950	C
Elizabethtown College	PA	17,850	VC
Florida State Univ	FL	5,814	VC
Georgia College	GA	4,310	LC
Mansfield Univ	PA	6,348	C
Maryville Univ-St Louis	MO	12,900	VC
Marywood College	PA	14,890	C
Mich State Univ	MI	7,842	C
Molloy College	NY	8,580	LC
Montclair State College	NJ	7,539	C+
Sam Houston State Univ	TX	4,506	C
Southern Methodist Univ	TX	18,520	VC
Southwestern Okla State Univ	OK	3,312	C
Temple Univ	PA	10,281	C
Tenn Tech Univ	TN	5,190	C
Univ of Alabama	AL	5,702	C
Univ of Dayton	OH	15,120	C+
Univ of Evansville	IN	15,300	VC
Univ of Georgia	GA	5,655	VC
Univ of Kansas	KS	5,200	NC
Univ of Miami	FL	22,107	VC
Univ of Minn/Twin Cities	MN	6,682	VC
Univ of the Pacific	CA	21,100	C
Univ of Wisc/Eau Claire	WI	4,647	C
Univ of Wisc/Oshkosh	WI	4,240	C
Utah State Univ	UT	4,683	C
Wartburg College	IA	14,530	VC
Wayne State Univ	MI	2,680	C
West Texas A&M Univ	TX	4,224	C
William Carey College	MS	7,050	C

MUSICAL THEATER

School	ST	$IS	SR
Boston Conservatory	MA	17,900	SP
Elon College	NC	12,290	LC
Lees-McRae College	NC	9,850	LC
Roosevelt Univ	IL	12,368	C
Shorter College	GA	10,270	C
SUNY/College at Old Westbury	NY	7,128	LC
Univ of Miami	FL	22,107	VC
Univ of Mich/Ann Arbor	MI	9,428	HC+
Webster Univ	MO	12,650	C

NATIVE AMERICAN STUDIES

School	ST	$IS	SR
Colgate Univ	NY	24,020	HC
Dartmouth College	NH	24,354	MC
Humboldt State Univ	CA	5,676	C
Morningside College	IA	13,896	C
Northern Montana College	MT	4,976	C
Univ of Calif at Berkeley	CA	9,962	HC+
Univ of Calif at Davis	CA	9,534	VC
Univ of Okla	OK	5,427	VC

NATURAL RESOURCE MANAGEMENT

School	ST	$IS	SR
Alaska Pacific Univ	AK	11,350	C
Arizona State Univ Main Campus	AZ	6,444	C
Ball State Univ	IN	6,032	LC
Brigham Young Univ	UT	5,625	HC
Calif Polytechnic State Univ	CA	6,980	VC+
Colo State Univ	CO	6,566	VC
Cornell Univ	NY	13,445	MC
Delaware State College	DE	5,656	C
Hofstra Univ	NY	16,580	VC
Humboldt State Univ	CA	5,676	C
Jordan College	MI	5,760	LC
N Car State Univ	NC	4,984	VC
Penn State Univ/Univ Park Campus	PA	8,752	HC
Peru State College	NE	4,311	NC
Rutgers Univ/Cook College	NJ	9,197	HC
Sheldon Jackson College	AK	14,050	NC
SUNY College of Environmental Science and Forestry	NY	9,257	HC+
Univ of Alaska Fairbanks	AK	4,718	C
Univ of Arizona	AZ	5,808	C
Univ of Calif at Berkeley	CA	9,962	HC+
Univ of Conn	CT	9,168	C
Univ of Florida	FL	5,850	HC
Univ of Maine	ME	7,990	C
Univ of Mass/Amherst	MA	9,364	LC
Univ of Mich/Ann Arbor	MI	9,428	HC+
Univ of Minn/Crookston	MN	6,894	NC
Univ of Minn/Twin Cities	MN	6,682	VC
Univ of Nevada/Reno	NV	5,735	C
Univ of the South	TN	18,830	HC
Univ of Wisc/Stevens Point	WI	5,047	C+
Utah State Univ	UT	4,683	C
West Virginia Univ	WV	5,774	C
Western Carolina Univ	NC	3,811	C

NATURAL SCIENCES

School	ST	$IS	SR
Adelphi Univ	NY	18,250	LC
Arkansas Tech Univ	AR	4,200	NC
Avila College	MO	12,130	C
Bloomsburg Univ of Penn	PA	6,312	C+
Bradford College	MA	19,600	C
Calif Univ of Penn	PA	7,370	C
Carthage College	WI	15,995	C
Case Western Reserve Univ	OH	19,910	HC
Castleton State College	VT	8,378	LC
Charleston Southern Univ	SC	10,282	LC
Charter Oak State College	CT	314	NC
College of St Benedict	MN	15,468	VC
College of St Mary	NE	12,500	C
College of the Southwest	NM	5,720	LC
Concordia College	MN	13,200	C
Concordia College	NE	11,776	NC
Covenant College	GA	13,054	VC
Daemen College	NY	13,020	LC
Dowling College	NY	12,730	LC
Edgewood College	WI	11,700	C
Edinboro Univ of Penn	PA	7,181	C
Erskine College	SC	14,310	C
Felician College	NJ	7,900	C
Fordham Univ/College at Lincoln Center	NY	18,150	VC
Fresno Pacific College	CA	13,020	C
Goshen College	IN	12,360	C
Hofstra Univ	NY	16,580	VC
Illinois Wesleyan Univ	IL	18,590	HC+
La Roche College	PA	12,977	LC
LeMoyne-Owen College	TN	4,500	LC
Lewis-Clark State College	ID	4,040	
Lyndon State College	VT	8,394	LC
Madonna Univ	MI	8,546	C
Marygrove College	MI	5,877	VC
McMurry Univ	TX	10,100	C
Mercer Univ	GA	15,123	C
Messiah College	PA	14,664	VC
Miles College	AL	7,150	NC
Missouri Western State College	MO	4,384	NC
New College of the Univ of South Florida	FL	5,697	MC
Northwest Nazarene College	ID	11,750	C
Oakwood College	AL	10,005	C
St Anselm College	NH	17,340	C
St John's Univ	MN	15,364	C
St Joseph College	CT	16,225	C
St Joseph's College	ME	14,535	C
St Mary's College of Maryland	MD	8,900	VC+
St Meinrad College	IN	10,302	C
St Peter's College	NJ	14,775	LC
Shawnee State Univ	OH	4,379	NC
Shimer College	IL	12,850	NC
Shorter College	GA	10,270	C
Siena Heights College	MI	12,520	C
Simon's Rock College of Bard	MA	23,760	VC+
Southern Univ and A&M College	LA	4,920	NC
Spelman College	GA	12,942	VC
Taylor Univ	IN	14,450	VC
Thomas A. Edison State College	NJ	400	
Towson State Univ	MD	7,452	C
Turabo Univ	PR	2,670	
Universidad Metropolitana	PR	2,650	
Univ of Akron	OH	6,699	NC
Univ of Alabama at Birmingham	AL	7,533	C
Univ of Arkansas at Fayetteville	AR	5,046	C
Univ of Hawaii at Hilo	HI	4,141	C
Univ of Houston-Downtown	TX	4,034	NC
Univ of La Verne	CA	17,400	C
Univ of New Haven	CT	14,980	C
Univ of N Dak	ND	4,902	NC
Univ of Pittsburgh	PA	9,472	C
Univ of Pittsburgh at Greensburg	PA	8,660	C
Univ of PR/Cayey Univ College	PR	900	
Univ of Puget Sound	WA	19,520	HC
Univ of Wisc/Stevens Point	WI	5,047	C+
Univ of Wyoming	WY	4,991	NC
Western Oregon State College	OR	6,180	C
Westmont College	CA	18,732	C
Worcester State College	MA	6,414	LC
Xavier Univ	OH	15,710	C+

NAVAL ARCHITECTURE AND MARINE ENGINEERING

School	ST	$IS	SR
Mass Inst of Tech	MA	24,800	MC
SUNY/Maritime College	NY	7,170	C
United States Coast Guard Academy	CT	0	MC
United States Naval Academy	MD	0	MC
Univ of Calif at Berkeley	CA	9,962	HC+
Univ of Mich/Ann Arbor	MI	9,428	HC+
Univ of New Orleans	LA	5,468	C
Webb Inst of Naval Architecture	NY	4,800	MC

NAVAL SCIENCE

School	ST	$IS	SR
Iowa State Univ	IA	5,456	C

NEAR EASTERN STUDIES

School	ST	$IS	SR
Brandeis Univ	MA	25,585	HC
Brigham Young Univ	UT	5,625	HC
Cornell Univ	NY	13,445	MC
Indiana Univ Bloomington	IN	6,495	VC
Johns Hopkins Univ	MD	24,360	MC
Oberlin College	OH	24,570	HC+
Princeton Univ	NJ	24,650	MC
Univ of Arizona	AZ	5,808	C
Univ of Calif at Berkeley	CA	9,962	HC+
Univ of Calif at Los Angeles	CA	8,959	HC
Univ of Chicago	IL	24,517	MC
Univ of Mass/Amherst	MA	9,364	LC
Univ of Mich/Ann Arbor	MI	9,428	HC+
Univ of Washington	WA	6,618	VC
Wayne State Univ	MI	2,680	C
Yale Univ	CT	25,110	MC

NEUROSCIENCES

School	ST	$IS	SR
Amherst College	MA	24,152	MC
Bowdoin College	ME	24,155	MC
Brandeis Univ	MA	25,585	HC
Brown Univ	RI	26,104	MC
Bryn Mawr College	PA	24,110	MC
Colgate Univ	NY	24,020	HC
Cornell Univ	NY	13,445	MC
Kenyon College	OH	22,430	HC+
Lawrence Univ	WI	19,986	HC+
Muskingum College	OH	16,650	C
Northwestern Univ	IL	21,093	MC
Oberlin College	OH	24,570	HC+
Purdue Univ/West Lafayette	IN	6,636	C
Rutgers Univ/Douglass College	NJ	8,795	VC
Texas Christian Univ	TX	12,180	C
Trinity College	CT	24,120	HC
Univ of Calif at Los Angeles	CA	8,959	HC
Univ of Pittsburgh	PA	9,472	C
Univ of Rochester	NY	23,696	HC
Univ of Scranton	PA	17,071	VC
Washington and Lee Univ	VA	17,735	MC

NUCLEAR ENGINEERING

School	ST	$IS	SR
American Technical Inst	TN	0	SP
Georgia Inst of Tech	GA	6,669	HC+
Kansas State Univ	KS	4,816	NC
Lakeland College	WI	12,845	LC
Mass Inst of Tech	MA	24,800	MC
Miss State Univ	MS	5,629	VC
N Car State Univ	NC	4,984	VC
Oregon State Univ	OR	6,175	C
Penn State Univ/Univ Park Campus	PA	8,752	HC
Purdue Univ/West Lafayette	IN	6,636	C
Rensselaer Polytechnic Inst	NY	23,067	HC
Texas A&M Univ	TX	5,382	VC
United States Military Academy	NY	0	MC
Univ of Arizona	AZ	5,808	C
Univ of Calif at Berkeley	CA	9,962	HC+
Univ of Calif at Santa Barbara	CA	9,460	C
Univ of Cincinnati	OH	7,989	C
Univ of Florida	FL	5,850	HC
Univ of Illinois at Urbana-Champaign	IL	7,764	HC
Univ of Lowell	MA	8,831	VC
Univ of Mich/Ann Arbor	MI	9,428	HC+
Univ of Missouri/Rolla	MO	6,729	VC+
Univ of Tenn/Knoxville	TN	5,668	C
Univ of Wisc/Madison	WI	6,400	HC

NUCLEAR ENGINEERING TECHNOLOGY

School	ST	$IS	SR
American Technical Inst	TN	0	SP
Univ of Florida	FL	5,850	HC

NUCLEAR MEDICAL TECHNOLOGY

School	ST	$IS	SR
Alverno College	WI	11,344	C
Aquinas College	MI	14,526	C
Barry Univ	FL	16,050	C
Cedar Crest College	PA	18,930	C
Edinboro Univ of Penn	PA	7,181	C
Ferris State Univ	MI	7,160	NC
Illinois Benedictine College	IL	14,170	C
Incarnate Word College	TX	12,307	C
Indiana Univ-Purdue Univ at Indianapolis	IN	5,862	LC
Kansas Newman College	KS	10,640	C
Mass College of Pharmacy and Allied Health Sciences	MA	18,352	C
Millersville Univ of Penn	PA	7,370	VC
Peru State College	NE	4,311	NC
Rochester Inst of Tech	NY	18,954	VC
Roosevelt Univ	IL	12,368	C
St Mary's College of Minn	MN	13,850	LC
SUNY at Buffalo	NY	7,896	VC
Univ of Alabama at Birmingham	AL	7,533	C
Univ of Cincinnati	OH	7,989	C
Univ of Dayton	OH	15,120	C+
Univ of Iowa	IA	5,658	VC
Univ of Miami	FL	22,107	VC
Univ of Wisc/La Crosse	WI	4,487	C
Wheeling Jesuit College	WV	14,370	C
York College of Penn	PA	8,345	C

NUCLEAR TECHNOLOGY

School	ST	$IS	SR
Peru State College	NE	4,311	NC
Univ of the State of New York/Regents College Degrees	NY	510	

NURSING

School	ST	$IS	SR
Abilene Christian Univ	TX	10,460	NC
Adelphi Univ	NY	18,250	LC
Albany State College	GA	4,481	LC
Alcorn State Univ	MS	4,474	C+
Alderson-Broaddus College	WV	12,000	C
Allentown College of St Francis de Sales	PA	13,480	C
Alvernia College	PA	13,150	LC
Alverno College	WI	11,344	C
American International College	MA	14,029	C
Anderson Univ	IN	12,920	C
Andrews Univ	MI	14,952	NC
Angelo State Univ	TX	5,176	C
Arizona State Univ Main Campus	AZ	6,444	C
Arkansas State Univ	AR	4,250	NC
Arkansas Tech Univ	AR	4,200	NC
Armstrong State College	GA	4,874	LC
Ashland Univ	OH	15,508	C
Atlantic Union College	MA	14,150	LC
Auburn Univ	AL	5,823	C+
Auburn Univ at Montgomery	AL	3,390	C
Augusta College	GA	1,452	C
Augustana College	SD	13,420	C
Aurora Univ	IL	13,381	C
Austin Peay State Univ	TN	4,350	C
Avila College	MO	12,130	C
Azusa Pacific Univ	CA	15,034	C
Ball State Univ	IN	6,032	LC
Barat College	IL	13,990	C
Barnes College	MO	7,000	VC
Barry Univ	FL	16,050	C
Barton College	NC	10,689	LC

School	ST	$IS	SR
Baylor Univ	TX	10,990	C+
Bellarmine College	KY	10,832	C
Belmont Univ	TN	10,540	C
Bemidji State Univ	MN	5,188	C
Berea College	KY	2,883	VC+
Beth-El College of Nursing	CO	4,660	VC
Bethel College	IN	11,650	LC
Bethel College	KS	11,530	C
Bethel College	MN	15,050	C
Bethune-Cookman College	FL	8,375	LC
Biola Univ	CA	16,124	C
Bloomfield College	NJ	12,200	LC
Bloomsburg Univ of Penn	PA	6,312	C+
Blue Mountain College	MS	5,958	LC
Bluefield State College	WV	1,832	LC
Boise State Univ	ID	4,909	LC
Boston College	MA	22,706	MC
Bowie State Univ	MD	7,294	LC
Bowling Green State Univ	OH	6,701	C
Bradley Univ	IL	14,718	C+
Briar Cliff College	IA	13,375	C
Brigham Young Univ	UT	5,625	HC
Brooklyn Campus of LIU	NY	15,000	LC
Cal State/Bakersfield	CA	5,402	C
Cal State/Chico	CA	6,146	C
Cal State/Dominguez Hills	CA	2,857	LC
Cal State/Fresno	CA	5,747	C
Cal State/Fullerton	CA	4,850	LC
Cal State/Hayward	CA	5,495	LC
Cal State/Long Beach	CA	6,057	LC
Cal State/Los Angeles	CA	4,940	VC
Cal State/Northridge	CA	7,122	LC
Cal State/Sacramento	CA	6,387	C
Cal State/San Bernardino	CA	6,055	LC
Cal State/Stanislaus	CA	6,799	C
Calif Univ of Penn	PA	7,370	C
Calvin College	MI	13,020	VC
Cameron Univ	OK	3,686	LC
Capital Univ	OH	16,535	VC
Cardinal Stritch College	WI	11,252	C
Caribbean Univ	PR	2,400	
Carlow College	PA	13,914	C
Carroll College	MT	11,265	C
Carroll College	WI	15,490	C
Carson-Newman College	TN	11,250	C
Case Western Reserve Univ	OH	19,910	HC
Catholic Univ of America	DC	18,856	C
Cedar Crest College	PA	18,930	C
Cedarville College	OH	10,715	C
Central Conn State Univ	CT	7,108	C
Central Methodist College	MO	11,410	C
Central Missouri State Univ	MO	5,138	LC
Central Univ of Bayamon	PR	2,430	
Chicago State Univ	IL	2,198	C
Christopher Newport Univ	VA	3,196	LC
CUNY/City College	NY	2,543	VC
CUNY/College of Staten Island	NY	2,558	NC
CUNY/Herbert H. Lehman College	NY	2,542	C
CUNY/Hunter College	NY	4,101	VC
CUNY/York College	NY	2,534	NC
Clarion Univ of Penn	PA	6,518	C
Clarke College	IA	13,950	C+
Clarkson College	NE	7,582	C
Clayton State College	GA	1,496	LC
Clemson Univ	SC	6,564	VC
Cleveland State Univ	OH	7,287	NC
Clinch Valley College/Univ of Virginia	VA	6,364	C
Coe College	IA	17,085	VC
Colby-Sawyer College	NH	18,495	LC
College Misericordia	PA	15,820	C
College of Mount St Joseph	OH	13,272	C
College of Mount St Vincent	NY	16,730	LC
College of New Rochelle	NY	15,440	LC
College of Notre Dame of Maryland	MD	16,050	C
College of Our Lady of The Elms	MA	15,639	C
College of St Benedict	MN	15,468	VC
College of St Catherine	MN	14,670	C
College of St Elizabeth	NJ	15,800	C
College of St Mary	NE	12,500	C
College of St Scholastica	MN	14,868	C
College of the Ozarks	MO	2,000	VC+
Columbia College of Nursing	WI	15,200	C
Columbia Union College	MD	13,650	LC
Columbus College	GA	4,892	LC
Concordia College/Moorhead	MN	12,750	C
Concordia Univ	IL	12,611	C
Concordia Univ Wisc	WI	12,140	C
Coppin State College	MD	7,145	LC
Creighton Univ	NE	14,432	VC
Culver-Stockton College	MO	11,150	C
Cumberland Univ	TN	8,650	C
Curry College	MA	18,695	LC
D'Youville College	NY	12,850	C
Daemen College	NY	13,020	LC
Davis and Elkins College	WV	13,230	LC
Deaconess College of Nursing	MO	9,360	VC
Delaware State College	DE	5,656	C
Delta State Univ	MS	3,964	LC
Dickinson State Univ	ND	3,792	C
Dillard Univ	LA	9,950	C
Dominican College	NY	13,600	LC
Dominican College of San Rafael	CA	17,860	C
Drake Univ	IA	17,195	VC
Drury College	MO	12,140	VC
Duquesne Univ	PA	16,434	VC
East Carolina Univ	NC	4,498	C
East Central Univ	OK	3,558	C
East Stroudsburg Univ	PA	6,886	C
East Tenn State Univ	TN	4,406	C
East Texas Baptist Univ	TX	7,740	C
East Texas State Univ	TX	4,572	LC
Eastern College	PA	15,150	C+
Eastern Kentucky Univ	KY	4,840	NC
Eastern Mennonite College	VA	12,700	C
Eastern Mich Univ	MI	6,749	C
Eastern Oregon State College	OR	6,090	C
Eastern Washington Univ	WA	5,439	LC
Edgewood College	WI	11,700	C
Edinboro Univ of Penn	PA	7,181	C
Elmhurst College	IL	12,536	C
Elmira College	NY	18,450	C
Emmanuel College	MA	17,773	LC
Emory Univ	GA	21,930	HC
Emporia State Univ	KS	4,685	NC
Fairfield Univ	CT	20,460	VC
Fairleigh Dickinson Univ	NJ	16,427	C
Fayetteville State Univ	NC	3,926	LC
Felician College	NJ	7,900	C
Ferris State Univ	MI	7,160	NC
Fitchburg State College	MA	6,962	C
Florida A&M Univ	FL	4,651	C
Florida Atlantic Univ	FL	5,525	C
Florida International Univ	FL	4,191	VC
Florida State Univ	FL	5,814	VC
Fort Hays State Univ	KS	4,675	NC
Framingham State College	MA	6,580	C
Franciscan Univ of Steubenville	OH	13,400	C
Franklin College of Indiana	IN	13,970	C
Franklin Univ	OH	4,621	NC
Gannon Univ	PA	14,872	C
Gardner-Webb Univ	NC	11,950	LC
Geneva College	PA	13,030	C
Georgetown College	KY	10,990	C
Georgetown Univ	DC	24,410	MC
Georgia College	GA	4,310	LC
Georgia Southern Univ	GA	4,988	LC
Georgia Southwestern College	GA	4,338	LC
Georgia State Univ	GA	2,019	C
Glenville State College	WV	4,810	LC
Gonzaga Univ	WA	16,350	VC
Goshen College	IN	12,360	C
Graceland College	IA	11,600	C
Grambling State Univ	LA	4,712	NC
Grand Canyon Univ	AZ	9,680	VC
Grand Valley State Univ	MI	6,822	VC
Grand View College	IA	13,230	NC
Gustavus Adolphus College	MN	15,935	VC
Gwynedd-Mercy College	PA	15,450	C
Hampton Univ	VA	10,706	C
Hannibal-LaGrange College	MO	8,400	LC
Hardin-Simmons Univ	TX	9,080	C
Harding Univ	AR	9,050	VC
Hartwick College	NY	20,950	C
Hawaii Pacific Univ	HI	12,300	C
Holy Family College	PA	8,300	C
Holy Names College	CA	15,660	C
Hope College	MI	15,698	C+
Houston Baptist Univ	TX	11,055	C
Howard Univ	DC	11,680	C
Humboldt State Univ	CA	5,676	C
Husson College	ME	11,510	NC
Idaho State Univ	ID	4,442	C
Illinois Benedictine College	IL	14,170	C
Immaculata College	PA	14,620	C
Incarnate Word College	TX	12,307	C
Indiana State Univ	IN	6,210	C
Indiana Univ at Kokomo	IN	2,069	C
Indiana Univ Bloomington	IN	6,495	VC
Indiana Univ East	IN	2,044	NC
Indiana Univ Northwest	IN	2,310	C
Indiana Univ of Penn	PA	6,373	C
Indiana Univ Southeast	IN	2,260	LC
Indiana Univ-Purdue Univ at Fort Wayne	IN	2,500	LC
Indiana Univ-Purdue Univ at Indianapolis	IN	5,862	LC
Indiana Univ/South Bend	IN	2,141	LC
Inter American Univ of PR/ Aguadilla Regional College	PR	2,290	
Inter American Univ of PR/ Bayamon Univ College	PR	2,300	
Inter American Univ of PR/ Metropolitan Campus	PR	2,340	
Inter American Univ of PR/ Ponce Regional College	PR	2,300	
Inter American Univ of PR/ San German	PR	4,620	
Inter American Univ/Arecibo Campus	PR	5,666	
Inter-American Univ of PR/ Fajardo Regional College	PR	2,732	
Iowa Wesleyan College	IA	13,250	C
Jacksonville State Univ	AL	4,080	LC
Jacksonville Univ	FL	13,390	C
James Madison Univ	VA	8,198	HC
Jamestown College	ND	10,250	C
Jersey City State College	NJ	7,797	LC
Judson College	IL	13,625	C
Juniata College	PA	18,390	C+
Kansas Newman College	KS	10,640	C
Kansas Wesleyan Univ	KS	11,770	C
Kean College of New Jersey	NJ	6,395	LC
Kennesaw State College	GA	1,553	C
Kent State Univ	OH	6,740	LC
Kentucky Wesleyan College	KY	11,550	C
Keuka College	NY	13,660	C
King's College	NY	12,360	LC
Kutztown Univ	PA	6,528	C
La Roche College	PA	12,977	LC
Lake Forest College	IL	19,960	VC
Lake Superior State Univ	MI	7,311	C
Lamar Univ	TX	3,798	C
Lander Univ	SC	6,180	LC
Lane College	TN	7,628	LC
Langston Univ	OK	2,907	LC
Lebanon Valley College of Penn	PA	18,300	C
Lenoir-Rhyne College	NC	14,068	C
Lewis Univ	IL	14,797	LC
Lewis-Clark State College	ID	4,040	
Liberty Univ	VA	11,500	LC
Lincoln Memorial Univ	TN	8,218	C
Lincoln Univ	MO	4,638	NC
Linfield College	OR	16,670	VC
LIU/C. W. Post Campus	NY	16,870	C
Louisiana College	LA	7,518	VC
Lourdes College	OH	6,410	LC
Loyola Univ of Chicago	IL	15,880	C+
Luther College	IA	15,900	VC
Lycoming College	PA	17,200	LC
Lynchburg College	VA	17,000	C
MacMurray College	IL	12,800	C
Madonna Univ	MI	8,546	C
Malone College	OH	12,572	C
Manchester College	IN	13,240	LC
Mankato State Univ	MN	5,097	LC
Mansfield Univ	PA	6,348	C
Marian College	IN	12,936	C
Marian College of Fond du Lac	WI	12,250	C
Marquette Univ	WI	16,114	VC
Marshall Univ	WV	5,762	LC
Martin Univ	IN	4,830	NC
Marymount Univ	VA	15,930	C
Maryville College	TN	14,474	C
Maryville Univ-St Louis	MO	12,900	VC
Marywood College	PA	14,890	C
Mass College of Pharmacy and Allied Health Sciences	MA	18,352	C
McKendree College	IL	10,900	C
McMurry Univ	TX	10,100	C
McNeese State Univ	LA	4,543	NC
Mercy College	NY	11,180	NC
Mesa State College	CO	5,127	NC
Messiah College	PA	14,664	VC
Metropolitan State College of Denver	CO	1,751	NC
Mich State Univ	MI	7,842	C
Middle Tenn State Univ	TN	3,857	C
Midland Lutheran College	NE	12,410	LC
Midwestern State Univ	TX	4,542	LC
Millersville Univ of Penn	PA	7,370	VC
Milligan College	TN	10,690	LC
Millikin Univ	IL	15,499	C
Minot State Univ	ND	3,748	NC
Miss College	MS	8,348	C
Miss Univ for Women	MS	4,456	LC
Missouri Baptist College	MO	9,340	C
Missouri Southern State College	MO	4,272	
Missouri Western State College	MO	4,384	NC
Molloy College	NY	8,580	LC
Monmouth College	NJ	16,820	C
Montana State Univ	MT	5,534	C
Moorhead State Univ	MN	5,076	C
Morehead State Univ	KY	4,600	LC
Morningside College	IA	13,896	C
Morris Brown College	GA	12,234	NC
Mount Marty College	SD	10,450	NC
Mount Mercy College	IA	13,230	C
Mount St Mary College	NY	12,910	C
Mount St Mary's College	CA	16,390	VC
Murray State Univ	KY	4,702	C
Nazareth College of Rochester	NY	15,310	C+
Nebr Methodist College of Nursing and Allied Health	NE	4,360	C
Nebr Wesleyan Univ	NE	12,240	C
Neumann College	PA	9,950	LC
New Mexico State Univ	NM	4,844	LC
New York Univ	NY	24,705	VC+
Niagara Univ	NY	14,552	C
Nicholls State Univ	LA	4,531	NC
Norfolk State Univ	VA	6,345	LC
N Car Agricultural and Technical State Univ	NC	4,477	LC
N Car Central Univ	NC	4,347	LC
North Central College	IL	15,498	VC
N Dak State Univ of Agriculture and Applied Science	ND	4,774	VC
North Georgia College	GA	4,103	LC
North Park College	IL	14,310	C
Northeast Louisiana Univ	LA	3,906	NC
Northeast Missouri State Univ	MO	5,654	VC+
Northeastern State Univ	OK	5,250	C
Northeastern Univ	MA	19,851	C
Northern Arizona Univ	AZ	4,844	C
Northern Illinois Univ	IL	6,408	C
Northern Kentucky Univ	KY	4,620	NC
Northern Mich Univ	MI	6,350	C
Northern Montana College	MT	4,976	C
Northwest Nazarene College	ID	11,750	C
Northwestern Okla State Univ	OK	3,424	C
Northwestern State Univ of Louisiana	LA	4,287	NC
Norwich Univ	VT	18,730	C
Oakland Univ	MI	6,714	VC
Oakwood College	AL	10,005	C
Ohio State Univ	OH	7,218	LC
Ohio Univ	OH	7,341	C
Okla Baptist Univ	OK	8,486	C
Okla City Univ	OK	9,840	C
Old Dominion Univ	VA	8,317	C
Olivet Nazarene Univ	IL	11,976	C
Oral Roberts Univ	OK	10,607	C+
Oregon Inst of Tech	OR	5,985	C
Oregon State Univ	OR	6,175	C
Otterbein College	OH	16,506	C
Our Lady of Holy Cross College	LA	4,630	LC
Pace Univ	NY	15,540	C
Pacific Lutheran Univ	WA	15,998	VC
Pacific Union College	CA	15,075	C
Penn State Univ/Univ Park Campus	PA	8,752	HC
Peru State College	NE	4,311	NC
Phillips Univ	OK	12,744	C
Pikeville College	KY	8,500	NC
Pittsburg State Univ	KS	4,478	NC
Point Loma Nazarene College	CA	13,532	C
Pontifical Catholic Univ of PR/Ponce	PR	5,807	
Prairie View A&M Univ	TX	4,740	LC
Presentation College	SD	9,116	NC
Purdue Univ/Calumet	IN	2,374	NC
Purdue Univ/West Lafayette	IN	6,636	C
Queens College	NC	14,950	C
Quinnipiac College	CT	17,600	C+
Radford Univ	VA	7,034	LC
Ramapo College of New Jersey	NJ	8,027	C+
Regis College	MA	17,450	C
Regis Univ	CO	17,340	C
Research College of Nursing	MO	13,360	C
Rhode Island College	RI	7,901	LC
Richard Stockton College of New Jersey	NJ	6,950	VC
Rivier College	NH	14,920	LC
Roberts Wesleyan College	NY	13,317	C
Rockford College	IL	15,300	C
Rockhurst College	MO	12,470	C
Russell Sage College	NY	16,790	C
Rutgers Univ/Camden College of A&S	NJ	8,652	VC
Rutgers Univ/College of Nursing	NJ	8,638	VC+
Sacred Heart Univ	CT	16,350	C
Saginaw Valley State Univ	MI	6,634	LC
St Anselm College	NH	17,340	C
St Francis College	IN	11,662	C
St Francis College	PA	15,744	LC
St John Fisher College	NY	15,415	C
St John's Univ	MN	15,364	C
St Joseph College	CT	16,225	C
St Joseph's College	IN	14,730	C
St Joseph's College	ME	14,535	C
St Joseph's College	NY	7,322	C
St Louis Univ	MO	15,522	VC
St Martin's College	WA	14,965	C
St Mary College	KS	11,250	C
St Mary's College	IN	17,043	VC
St Mary's College of Calif	CA	18,848	VC
St Olaf College	MN	17,200	HC
St Peter's College	NJ	14,775	LC
St Xavier Univ	IL	14,700	C
Salem State College	MA	6,712	C
Salisbury State Univ	MD	7,516	C+
Salve Regina Univ	RI	29,100	LC
Samford Univ	AL	11,400	VC
Samuel Merritt College	CA	17,450	C
San Diego State Univ	CA	6,692	LC
San Francisco State Univ	CA	7,292	LC
San Jose State Univ	CA	6,680	LC
Seattle Pacific Univ	WA	16,503	C
Seattle Univ	WA	16,590	C
Seton Hall Univ	NJ	18,306	LC
Seton Hill College	PA	14,320	C
Shenandoah Univ	VA	11,800	C
Shepherd College	WV	5,540	C
Simmons College	MA	22,534	C
Simpson College	IA	14,635	VC

School	ST	$IS	SR
Rockhurst College	MO	12,470	C
Russell Sage College	NY	16,790	C
Saginaw Valley State Univ	MI	6,634	LC
Samford Univ	AL	11,400	VC
San Jose State Univ	CA	6,680	LC
Southern Univ and A&M College	LA	4,920	NC
SUNY at Buffalo	NY	7,896	VC
Temple Univ	PA	10,281	C
Tenn State Univ	TN	4,626	C+
Texas Woman's Univ	TX	4,392	C
Touro College	NY	11,930	C
Towson State Univ	MD	7,452	C
Tuskegee Univ	AL	10,128	C
Univ of Alabama at Birmingham	AL	7,533	C
Univ of Central Arkansas	AR	4,200	LC
Univ of Florida	FL	5,850	HC
Univ of Hartford	CT	19,858	LC
Univ of Houston-Downtown	TX	4,034	NC
Univ of Illinois at Chicago	IL	8,443	C
Univ of Indianapolis	IN	14,510	C
Univ of Kansas	KS	5,200	NC
Univ of Minn/Twin Cities	MN	6,682	VC
Univ of Missouri/Columbia	MO	6,254	HC
Univ of New England	ME	16,075	LC
Univ of New Hampshire	NH	8,242	C
Univ of N Dak	ND	4,902	NC
Univ of Pittsburgh	PA	9,472	C
Univ of Puget Sound	WA	19,520	HC
Univ of Scranton	PA	17,071	VC
Univ of Southern Calif	CA	23,006	VC
Univ of Texas at San Antonio	TX	6,420	C
Univ of Washington	WA	6,618	VC
Univ of Wisc/Madison	WI	6,400	HC
Univ of Wisc/Milwaukee	WI	6,165	C
Utica College of Syracuse Univ	NY	16,714	LC
Virginia Commonwealth Univ	VA	7,909	C
Wartburg College	IA	14,530	VC
Wayne State Univ	MI	2,680	C
Western Mich Univ	MI	6,820	C
Wilmington College	OH	13,700	LC
Worcester State College	MA	6,414	LC
Xavier Univ	OH	15,710	C+

OCEAN ENGINEERING

School	ST	$IS	SR
Florida Atlantic Univ	FL	5,525	C
Florida Inst of Tech	FL	16,935	VC
Mass Inst of Tech	MA	24,800	MC
United States Naval Academy	MD	0	MC
Univ of Miami	FL	22,107	VC
Univ of Washington	WA	6,618	VC
Virginia Polytechnic Inst and State Univ	VA	6,828	C

OCEANOGRAPHY

School	ST	$IS	SR
Humboldt State Univ	CA	5,676	C
Maine Maritime Academy	ME	8,336	C
Millersville Univ of Penn	PA	7,370	VC
Rutgers Univ/Cook College	NJ	9,197	HC
SUNY/Maritime College	NY	7,170	C
United States Naval Academy	MD	0	MC
Univ of Mich/Ann Arbor	MI	9,428	HC+
Univ of Rhode Island	RI	9,205	C
Univ of San Diego	CA	18,970	VC
Univ of Washington	WA	6,618	VC

OFFICE SUPERVISION AND MANAGEMENT

School	ST	$IS	SR
Albany State College	GA	4,481	LC
Arkansas Tech Univ	AR	4,200	NC
Atlantic Union College	MA	14,150	LC
Baker College	MI	6,971	NC
Black Hills State Univ	SD	4,831	NC
Bloomsburg Univ of Penn	PA	6,312	C+
Cabrini College	PA	16,012	C
Campbellsville College	KY	8,720	C
Central Conn State Univ	CT	7,108	C
College of Mount St Vincent	NY	16,730	C
Concord College	WV	5,104	NC
David Lipscomb Univ	TN	7,865	VC
Davis and Elkins College	WV	13,230	LC
Delta State Univ	MS	3,964	LC
Detroit College of Business	MI	5,184	NC
Dyke College	OH	5,200	C
Emporia State Univ	KS	4,685	NC
Evangel College	MO	10,142	LC
Fayetteville State Univ	NC	3,926	LC
Ferris State Univ	MI	7,160	NC
Fort Valley State College	GA	3,974	LC
Georgia College	GA	4,310	LC
Goldey-Beacom College	DE	7,839	C
Indiana State Univ	IN	6,210	C
Indiana Univ-Purdue Univ at Indianapolis	IN	5,862	LC
Jackson State Univ	MS	4,996	LC
James Madison Univ	VA	8,198	HC
John Brown Univ	AR	9,880	VC
Johnson and Wales Univ	RI	13,995	LC
La Sierra Univ	CA	15,472	C
Lincoln Univ	MO	4,638	NC
Miss College	MS	8,348	C
Moorhead State Univ	MN	5,076	C
Morningside College	IA	13,896	C
Mount St Clare College	IA	12,870	LC
Mount Vernon Nazarene College	OH	10,390	C
Northwestern College	MN	13,554	C
Northwestern Okla State Univ	OK	3,424	C
Oakwood College	AL	10,005	C
Okla Christian Univ of Science and Arts	OK	8,790	NC
Ouachita Baptist Univ	AR	8,940	C
Pacific Union College	CA	15,075	C
Pembroke State Univ	NC	3,538	LC
Philander Smith College	AR	5,434	NC
Point Loma Nazarene College	CA	13,532	C
St Augustine's College	NC	9,300	C+
Shippensburg Univ of Penn	PA	7,052	C
S Car State Univ	SC	5,424	LC
Southeastern Louisiana Univ	LA	4,230	NC
Southern Nazarene Univ	OK	9,206	NC
Southwestern Adventist College	TX	10,530	NC
SUNY/College at Buffalo	NY	7,035	VC
Stephen F. Austin State Univ	TX	5,117	C
Sul Ross State Univ	TX	4,144	NC
Tarleton State Univ	TX	4,082	LC
Tri-State Univ	IN	13,788	LC
Union College	KY	9,790	C
Univ of Houston-Downtown	TX	4,034	NC
Univ of S Car	SC	6,158	C
Univ of the District of Columbia	DC	974	NC
Univ of Wisc/Whitewater	WI	4,700	C
Virginia Intermont College	VA	12,250	LC
West Liberty State College	WV	4,690	LC
Western Carolina Univ	NC	3,811	C
Wiley College	TX	0	NC
York College of Penn	PA	8,345	C

OPERA

School	ST	$IS	SR
Boston Conservatory	MA	17,900	SP

OPERATIONS RESEARCH

School	ST	$IS	SR
Boston College	MA	22,706	MC
Boston Univ	MA	24,130	HC
CUNY/Baruch College	NY	2,562	VC
Columbia Univ/School of Engineering and Applied Science	NY	24,554	HC
Cornell Univ	NY	13,445	MC
Le Moyne College	NY	15,180	C
United States Air Force Academy	CO	0	MC
United States Military Academy	NY	0	MC
Univ of Scranton	PA	17,071	VC

OPTICAL ENGINEERING

School	ST	$IS	SR
Univ of Alabama at Huntsville	AL	5,868	VC
Univ of Arizona	AZ	5,808	C
Univ of La Verne	CA	17,400	C

OPTICS

School	ST	$IS	SR
Capitol College	MD	10,698	LC
Rose-Hulman Inst of Tech	IN	16,400	HC
Saginaw Valley State Univ	MI	6,634	LC
Univ of Alabama at Huntsville	AL	5,868	VC
Univ of Rochester	NY	23,696	HC

OPTOMETRY

School	ST	$IS	SR
Auburn Univ	AL	5,823	C+
Austin Peay State Univ	TN	4,350	C
Berry College	GA	11,990	VC
Cedarville College	OH	10,715	C
East Texas State Univ	TX	4,572	LC
Faulkner Univ	AL	8,630	LC
Ferris State Univ	MI	7,160	NC
Indiana Univ Bloomington	IN	6,495	VC
Indiana Wesleyan Univ	IN	12,332	C
Northeast Missouri State Univ	MO	5,654	VC+
Northwest Nazarene College	ID	11,750	C
Oral Roberts Univ	OK	10,607	C+
Peru State College	NE	4,311	NC
Phillips Univ	OK	12,744	C
Purdue Univ/Calumet	IN	2,374	NC
Simpson College	IA	14,635	VC
Southeastern Louisiana Univ	LA	4,230	NC
Spring Hill College	AL	16,015	C+
Univ of Calif at Berkeley	CA	9,962	HC+
Univ of Hartford	CT	19,858	LC
Univ of Houston	TX	5,215	C
Univ of Houston-Downtown	TX	4,034	NC
Villanova Univ	PA	21,400	HC
William Carey College	MS	7,050	C
Youngstown State Univ	OH	6,447	LC

ORGANIZATIONAL BEHAVIOR

School	ST	$IS	SR
Barton College	NC	10,689	LC
Brown Univ	RI	26,104	MC
Covenant College	GA	13,054	VC
Eastern College	PA	15,150	C+
Edward Waters College	FL	8,300	NC
La Salle Univ	PA	16,940	VC
Northern Kentucky Univ	KY	4,620	NC
Pitzer College	CA	23,780	HC
Rider College	NJ	18,160	C
St Francis College	PA	15,744	LC
Santa Clara Univ	CA	18,783	VC
Southern Methodist Univ	TX	18,520	VC
Univ of Calif at Davis	CA	9,534	VC
Univ of Calif at Los Angeles	CA	8,959	HC
Univ of Georgia	GA	5,655	VC
Univ of Penn	PA	24,238	MC

PACIFIC AREA STUDIES

School	ST	$IS	SR
Brigham Young Univ/Hawaii	HI	6,750	VC
Hawaii Pacific Univ	HI	12,300	C
Univ of Georgia	GA	5,655	VC

PAINTING

School	ST	$IS	SR
Aquinas College	MI	14,526	C
Arizona State Univ Main Campus	AZ	6,444	C
Art Academy of Cincinnati	OH	8,820	SP
Art Inst of Southern Calif	CA	16,000	SP
Atlanta College of Art	GA	12,495	SP
Barton College	NC	10,689	LC
Birmingham-Southern College	AL	15,154	VC+
Boston Univ	MA	24,130	HC
Bradley Univ	IL	14,718	C+
Brigham Young Univ	UT	5,625	HC
Center for Creative Studies/College of Art and Design	MI	15,330	SP
Cleveland Inst of Art	OH	15,630	SP
Cooper Union for the Advancement of Science and Art	NY	8,430	MC
Edinboro Univ of Penn	PA	7,181	C
Escuela de Artes Plasticas	PR	4,024	
Hofstra Univ	NY	16,580	VC
Indiana Univ-Purdue Univ at Indianapolis	IN	5,862	LC
Kansas City Art Inst	MO	17,000	SP
Louisiana State Univ and A&M College	LA	5,605	C
Maine College of Art	ME	15,673	SP
Maryland Inst, College of Art	MD	18,420	SP
Milwaukee Inst of Art and Design	WI	9,800	SP
Montserrat College of Art	MA	12,500	SP
Moore College of Art and Design	PA	17,947	SP
Northern Mich Univ	MI	6,350	C
Ohio Northern Univ	OH	18,660	VC
Pacific Northwest College of Art	OR	7,700	SP
Plymouth State College	NH	7,166	C
Rhode Island School of Design	RI	22,315	SP
Sacred Heart Univ	CT	16,350	C
San Francisco Art Inst	CA	12,900	SP
Savannah College of Art and Design	GA	14,280	SP
School of the Art Inst of Chicago	IL	17,610	SP
Syracuse Univ	NY	21,305	HC
Univ of Conn	CT	9,168	C
Univ of Hartford	CT	19,858	LC
Univ of Illinois at Urbana-Champaign	IL	7,764	HC
Univ of Kansas	KS	5,200	NC
Univ of Mass Dartmouth	MA	8,158	C
Univ of Miami	FL	22,107	VC
Univ of Mich/Ann Arbor	MI	9,428	HC+
Univ of North Texas	TX	4,853	C
Univ of Oregon	OR	6,466	VC
Univ of Texas at El Paso	TX	3,160	LC
Univ of the Arts	PA	16,150	SP
Univ of Washington	WA	6,618	VC
William Carey College	MS	7,050	C

PALEONTOLOGY

School	ST	$IS	SR
Purdue Univ/West Lafayette	IN	6,636	C
Univ of Calif at Los Angeles	CA	8,959	HC

PAPER AND PULP SCIENCE

School	ST	$IS	SR
Miami Univ	OH	8,066	VC
N Car State Univ	NC	4,984	VC
SUNY College of Environmental Science and Forestry	NY	9,257	HC+
Univ of Maine	ME	7,990	C
Univ of Washington	WA	6,618	VC
Univ of Wisc/Stevens Point	WI	5,047	C+
West Virginia Inst of Tech	WV	5,858	LC
Western Mich Univ	MI	6,820	C

PAPER ENGINEERING

School	ST	$IS	SR
SUNY College of Environmental Science and Forestry	NY	9,257	HC+
Western Mich Univ	MI	6,820	C

PARALEGAL STUDIES

School	ST	$IS	SR
Anna Maria College	MA	15,975	LC
Avila College	MO	12,130	C
Boston Univ	MA	24,130	HC
Bridgewater State College	MA	7,518	C
Cedar Crest College	PA	18,930	C
CUNY/John Jay College of Criminal Justice	NY	2,501	LC
College of Great Falls	MT	6,230	NC
College of Mount St Joseph	OH	13,272	C
College of Our Lady of The Elms	MA	15,639	C
College of St Mary	NE	12,500	C
Concordia Univ Wisc	WI	12,140	C
Dyke College	OH	5,200	C
Eastern Kentucky Univ	KY	4,840	NC
Gannon Univ	PA	14,872	C
Georgia College	GA	4,310	LC
Humphreys College	CA	9,714	NC
Johnson and Wales Univ	RI	13,995	LC
Lake Erie College	OH	13,700	C
Madonna Univ	MI	8,546	C
Marymount Univ	VA	15,930	C
Marywood College	PA	14,890	C
McMurry Univ	TX	10,100	C
Miss College	MS	8,348	C
Miss Univ for Women	MS	4,456	LC
Moorhead State Univ	MN	5,076	C
Morehead State Univ	KY	4,600	LC

School	ST	$IS	SR
Mount Ida College	MA	16,700	LC
National College	SD	9,055	NC
Notre Dame College	NH	14,220	C
Point Park College	PA	13,922	LC
Rivier College	NH	14,920	LC
Roger Williams Univ	RI	16,750	LC
Sacred Heart Univ	CT	16,350	C
St John's Univ	NY	8,980	C+
Southern Illinois Univ at Carbondale	IL	6,234	C
Suffolk Univ	MA	15,360	LC
Univ of Calif at Berkeley	CA	9,962	HC+
Univ of Evansville	IN	15,300	VC
Univ of Maryland/Univ College	MD	4,900	NC
Univ of Memphis	TN	3,476	C
Valdosta State Univ	GA	4,670	LC
Villa Julie College	MD	9,880	LC
Virginia Intermont College	VA	12,250	LC
Winona State Univ	MN	5,200	VC

PARKS AND RECREATION MANAGEMENT

School	ST	$IS	SR
Appalachian State Univ	NC	4,095	C
Arizona State Univ Main Campus	AZ	6,444	C
Arkansas Tech Univ	AR	4,200	NC
Auburn Univ	AL	5,823	C+
Aurora Univ	IL	13,381	C
Averett College	VA	13,610	LC
Ball State Univ	IN	6,032	LC
Belmont Abbey College	NC	13,190	C
Bemidji State Univ	MN	5,188	C
Bethany College	KS	11,232	C
Bethel College	IN	11,650	LC
Bluffton College	OH	12,951	C
Bowling Green State Univ	OH	6,701	C
Calif State Polytechnic Univ/Pomona	CA	6,438	LC
Cal State/Chico	CA	6,146	C
Cal State/Fresno	CA	5,747	C
Cal State/Long Beach	CA	6,057	LC
Cal State/Sacramento	CA	6,387	C
Calif Univ of Penn	PA	7,370	C
Central Mich Univ	MI	6,737	LC
Central Missouri State Univ	MO	5,138	LC
Central Washington Univ	WA	5,644	C
Cheyney Univ of Penn	PA	7,005	C
Christopher Newport Univ	VA	3,196	LC
Clemson Univ	SC	6,564	VC
College of St Francis	IL	13,060	VC
Columbus College	GA	4,892	LC
Concord College	WV	5,104	NC
Delaware State College	DE	5,656	C
East Stroudsburg Univ	PA	6,886	C
Eastern Kentucky Univ	KY	4,840	NC
Eastern Mich Univ	MI	6,749	C
Eastern Washington Univ	WA	5,439	LC
Evangel College	MO	10,142	LC
Evergreen State College	WA	6,306	C
Florida International Univ	FL	4,191	VC
Franklin Pierce College	NH	17,270	LC
George Mason Univ	VA	8,728	C
Grambling State Univ	LA	4,712	NC
Huntington College	IN	13,220	C
Illinois State Univ	IL	6,413	C
Indiana Inst of Tech	IN	11,810	C
Indiana State Univ	IN	6,210	C
Indiana Univ Bloomington	IN	6,495	VC
Ithaca College	NY	19,679	C
Johnson and Wales Univ	RI	13,995	LC
Kansas State Univ	KS	4,816	NC
Kent State Univ	OH	6,740	LC
Lake Superior State Univ	MI	7,311	C
Mankato State Univ	MN	5,097	LC
Marshall Univ	WV	5,762	LC
Mesa State College	CO	5,127	NC
Midland Lutheran College	NE	12,410	LC
Missouri Western State College	MO	4,384	NC
Montclair State College	NJ	7,539	C+
Morningside College	IA	13,896	C
Murray State Univ	KY	4,702	C
N Car Central Univ	NC	4,347	LC
N Car State Univ	NC	4,984	VC
Northeastern State Univ	OK	5,250	C
Northeastern Univ	MA	19,851	C
Northern Arizona Univ	AZ	4,844	C
Northern Mich Univ	MI	6,350	C
Northland College	WI	13,550	LC
Northwest Nazarene College	ID	11,750	C
Northwestern College of Iowa	IA	12,250	C
Ohio State Univ	OH	7,218	LC
Ohio Univ	OH	7,341	C
Pembroke State Univ	NC	3,538	LC
Purdue Univ/West Lafayette	IN	6,636	C
Radford Univ	VA	7,034	LC
Sheldon Jackson College	AK	14,050	NC
Shepherd College	WV	5,540	LC
Shorter College	GA	10,270	C
Slippery Rock Univ	PA	6,803	C
S Dak State Univ	SD	4,562	C
Southeast Missouri State Univ	MO	5,854	C
Southern Illinois Univ at Carbondale	IL	6,234	C
Southwest Missouri State Univ	MO	4,956	C
Springfield College	MA	15,200	LC
SUNY/College at Cortland	NY	7,326	C+
Temple Univ	PA	10,281	C
Texas A&M Univ	TX	5,382	VC
Texas Tech Univ	TX	6,008	C
Unity College	ME	12,885	LC
Univ of Arkansas at Pine Bluff	AR	3,978	LC
Univ of Delaware	DE	8,013	VC
Univ of Georgia	GA	5,655	VC
Univ of Idaho	ID	4,830	C
Univ of Iowa	IA	5,658	VC
Univ of Maine	ME	7,990	C
Univ of Mary Hardin-Baylor	TX	8,120	NC
Univ of Memphis	TN	3,476	C
Univ of Missouri/Columbia	MO	6,254	HC
Univ of Nebr-Lincoln	NE	5,278	LC
Univ of N Car at Greensboro	NC	5,192	C
Univ of N Car at Wilmington	NC	5,172	C
Univ of N Dak	ND	4,902	NC
Univ of Southern Miss	MS	4,542	C
Univ of Tenn at Martin	TN	4,550	C
Univ of Vermont	VT	10,776	C+
Univ of Wisc/La Crosse	WI	4,487	C
Univ of Wyoming	WY	4,991	NC
Utah State Univ	UT	4,683	C
Virginia Wesleyan College	VA	14,950	VC
Warren Wilson College	NC	10,877	C
Washington State Univ	WA	6,364	C
Wayne State College	NE	4,260	NC
Wayne State Univ	MI	2,680	C
West Georgia College	GA	4,256	C
West Virginia Univ	WV	5,774	C
Western Carolina Univ	NC	3,811	C
Western Illinois Univ	IL	5,241	LC
Western Kentucky Univ	KY	4,808	C
Western Washington Univ	WA	6,077	VC
Wingate College	NC	10,610	C
Winona State Univ	MN	5,200	VC
York College of Penn	PA	8,345	C

PASTORAL STUDIES

School	ST	$IS	SR
Alabama A&M Univ	AL	4,200	C
Clearwater Christian College	FL	8,500	LC
College of St Scholastica	MN	14,868	C
Dallas Baptist Univ	TX	9,620	LC
John Brown Univ	AR	9,880	VC
Kansas Newman College	KS	10,640	C
Liberty Univ	VA	11,500	LC
Madonna Univ	MI	8,546	C
North Central Bible College	MN	8,670	LC
Northwestern College	MN	13,554	C
Nyack College	NY	12,210	LC
Simpson College	CA	10,628	C
Toccoa Falls College	GA	9,350	C
Universidad Adventista de las Antillas	PR	5,000	

PEACE STUDIES

School	ST	$IS	SR
Antioch College	OH	19,532	C
Bryn Mawr College	PA	24,110	MC
Colgate Univ	NY	24,020	HC
College of St Benedict	MN	15,468	VC
Earlham College	IN	19,383	VC
Fordham Univ/Fordham College	NY	19,875	VC
Juniata College	PA	18,390	C+
Kent State Univ	OH	6,740	LC
Manhattan College	NY	19,000	C
St John's Univ	MN	15,364	C
Syracuse Univ	NY	21,305	HC
Univ of Calif at Berkeley	CA	9,962	HC+
Univ of N Car at Chapel Hill	NC	5,330	HC
Univ of St Thomas	MN	15,785	C+
Univ of Washington	WA	6,618	VC
Villanova Univ	PA	21,400	HC
Wayne State Univ	MI	2,680	C
Wellesley College	MA	23,815	MC
William Penn College	IA	13,400	C

PERCUSSION

School	ST	$IS	SR
Northwestern Univ	IL	21,093	MC
Temple Univ	PA	10,281	C
Univ of Mich/Ann Arbor	MI	9,428	HC+

PERFORMING ARTS

School	ST	$IS	SR
Adelphi Univ	NY	18,250	LC
Barat College	IL	13,990	C
Brigham Young Univ	UT	5,625	HC
Brown Univ	RI	26,104	MC
Butler Univ	IN	16,210	C
Cal State/Los Angeles	CA	4,940	VC
Colby College	ME	24,230	HC
Colo State Univ	CO	6,566	VC
Columbia College	SC	13,520	LC
Cornish College of the Arts	WA	9,300	SP
Davidson College	NC	21,037	MC
Eastern Kentucky Univ	KY	4,840	NC
Edgewood College	WI	11,700	C
Georgia Southern Univ	GA	4,988	LC
Hollins College	VA	18,484	C
Johnson State College	VT	8,393	LC
Marywood College	PA	14,890	C
N Car School of the Arts	NC	5,375	SP
Northern Kentucky Univ	KY	4,620	NC
Northwestern Univ	IL	21,093	MC
Oakland Univ	MI	6,714	VC
St Mary College	KS	11,250	C
St Olaf College	MN	17,200	HC
Seton Hill College	PA	14,320	C
Temple Univ	PA	10,281	C
Univ of Florida	FL	5,850	HC
Univ of Mich/Ann Arbor	MI	9,428	HC+
Univ of New Hampshire	NH	8,242	C
Univ of the Arts	PA	16,150	SP
Univ of the South	TN	18,830	HC
Webster Univ	MO	12,650	C

PERSONNEL MANAGEMENT

School	ST	$IS	SR
Alabama State Univ	AL	3,428	NC
American International College	MA	14,029	C
Auburn Univ	AL	5,823	C+
Auburn Univ at Montgomery	AL	3,390	C
Avila College	MO	12,130	C
Baldwin-Wallace College	OH	15,210	C
Ball State Univ	IN	6,032	LC
Baylor Univ	TX	10,990	C+
Beaver College	PA	17,660	C
Bellevue College	NE	3,050	NC
Bluffton College	OH	12,951	C
Bowling Green State Univ	OH	6,701	C
Cal State/Fresno	CA	5,747	C
Cal State/Long Beach	CA	6,057	LC
Carroll College	WI	15,490	C
Central Missouri State Univ	MO	5,138	LC
Central Wesleyan College	SC	9,640	C
CUNY/Baruch College	NY	2,562	VC
Columbia Union College	MD	13,650	LC
Coppin State College	MD	7,145	LC
Creighton Univ	NE	14,432	VC
Dickinson State Univ	ND	3,792	C
Duquesne Univ	PA	16,434	VC
East Texas State Univ	TX	4,572	LC
Eastern Kentucky Univ	KY	4,840	NC
Eastern Mich Univ	MI	6,749	G
Eastern New Mexico Univ	NM	3,950	C
Eastern Washington Univ	WA	5,439	LC
Elmhurst College	IL	12,536	C
Faulkner Univ	AL	8,630	LC
Ferris State Univ	MI	7,160	NC
Florida Atlantic Univ	FL	5,525	C
Florida International Univ	FL	4,191	VC
Florida Southern College	FL	12,260	C
Florida State Univ	FL	5,814	VC
Franklin Univ	OH	4,621	NC
George Fox College	OR	15,640	LC
George Washington Univ	DC	22,470	HC
Golden Gate Univ	CA	5,623	VC
Grand Canyon Univ	AZ	9,680	VC
Grand Valley State Univ	MI	6,822	VC
Hannibal-LaGrange College	MO	8,400	LC
Hastings College	NE	12,426	C
Hawaii Pacific Univ	HI	12,300	C
Husson College	ME	11,510	NC
Idaho State Univ	ID	4,442	C
Indiana Univ Bloomington	IN	6,495	VC
Indiana Univ-Purdue Univ at Fort Wayne	IN	2,500	LC
Ithaca College	NY	19,679	C
Juniata College	PA	18,390	C+
Kent State Univ	OH	6,740	LC
Keuka College	NY	13,660	C
King's College	PA	15,420	C
Kutztown Univ	PA	6,528	C
La Salle Univ	PA	16,940	VC
Lamar Univ	TX	3,798	C
Lewis-Clark State College	ID	4,040	
Loras College	IA	14,160	C
Louisiana Tech Univ	LA	4,284	C
Loyola Univ of Chicago	IL	15,880	C+
Mansfield Univ	PA	6,348	C
Marietta College	OH	16,940	C+
Marquette Univ	WI	16,114	VC
Marymount College/Tarrytown	NY	17,350	C
Marymount Univ	VA	15,930	C
Mesa State College	CO	5,127	NC
Messiah College	PA	14,664	VC
Miami Univ	OH	8,066	VC
Mich State Univ	MI	7,842	C
Middle Tenn State Univ	TN	3,857	C
Millikin Univ	IL	15,499	C
Murray State Univ	KY	4,702	C
Nicholls State Univ	LA	4,531	NC
Northeastern Univ	MA	19,851	C
Northern Illinois Univ	IL	6,408	C
Northern State Univ	SD	4,186	LC
Northwest Missouri State Univ	MO	5,010	LC
Northwestern College	MN	13,554	C
Northwestern State Univ of Louisiana	LA	4,287	NC
Oakland Univ	MI	6,714	VC
Ohio Univ	OH	7,341	C
Okla State Univ	OK	5,086	VC
Portland State Univ	OR	7,191	C
Radford Univ	VA	7,034	LC
Rhode Island College	RI	7,901	LC
Rider College	NJ	18,160	C
Rockhurst College	MO	12,470	C
Roosevelt Univ	IL	12,368	C
Rowan College of New Jersey	NJ	7,358	VC
St Cloud State Univ	MN	5,015	C
St Leo College	FL	13,570	C
St Louis Univ	MO	15,522	VC
St Xavier Univ	IL	14,700	C
San Francisco State Univ	CA	7,292	LC
Seton Hill College	PA	14,320	C
Silver Lake College	WI	8,280	LC
Sonoma State Univ	CA	6,996	LC
Southern Arkansas Univ	AR	3,432	NC
Southern Calif College	CA	12,356	C
Southern Illinois Univ at Carbondale	IL	6,234	C
Southern Oregon State College	OR	6,128	C
Southwest Texas State Univ	TX	5,124	C
SUNY/College at Geneseo	NY	6,949	HC
Tarleton State Univ	TX	4,082	LC
Temple Univ	PA	10,281	C
Texas A&M Univ	TX	5,382	VC
Texas Woman's Univ	TX	4,392	C
The Univ of New Mexico	NM	5,304	C
Tiffin Univ	OH	10,800	LC
Trinity College	IL	14,010	C
Troy State Univ at Dothan/Fort Rucker	AL	2,260	NC
Univ of Akron	OH	6,699	NC
Univ of Alabama at Birmingham	AL	7,533	C
Univ of Arizona	AZ	5,808	C
Univ of Arkansas at Fayetteville	AR	5,046	C
Univ of Colo at Boulder	CO	6,410	VC
Univ of Houston	TX	5,215	C
Univ of Idaho	ID	4,830	C
Univ of Lowell	MA	8,831	VC
Univ of Mary Hardin-Baylor	TX	8,120	NC
Univ of Maryland/College Park	MD	8,182	VC
Univ of Maryland/Univ College	MD	4,900	NC
Univ of Montana	MT	5,529	C
Univ of Nebr at Kearney	NE	4,308	LC
Univ of N Car at Asheville	NC	4,791	VC
Univ of N Car at Greensboro	NC	5,192	C
Univ of North Texas	TX	4,853	C
Univ of PR/Humacao Univ College	PR	1,494	
Univ of PR/Rio Piedras	PR	0	
Univ of St Thomas	MN	15,785	C+
Univ of South Florida	FL	5,475	C+
Univ of Southern Miss	MS	4,542	C
Univ of Southwestern Louisiana	LA	3,968	NC
Univ of Tenn at Martin	TN	4,550	C
Univ of Texas at Arlington	TX	5,549	LC
Univ of Texas at San Antonio	TX	6,420	C
Univ of the Sacred Heart	PR	3,890	
Univ of Toledo	OH	6,636	NC
Univ of Washington	WA	6,618	VC
Univ of Wisc/Whitewater	WI	4,700	C
Upsala College	NJ	17,200	C
Urbana Univ	OH	12,536	C
Utah State Univ	UT	4,683	C
Valparaiso Univ	IN	14,810	VC
Virginia Wesleyan College	VA	14,950	VC
Viterbo College	WI	12,670	C
Washington State Univ	WA	6,364	C
Weber State Univ	UT	4,398	C
Western Illinois Univ	IL	5,241	LC
Western New England College	MA	14,674	LC
Wichita State Univ	KS	5,068	NC
Wilmington College	DE	5,200	NC
Winona State Univ	MN	5,200	VC

School	ST	$IS	SR
Woodbury Univ	CA	17,620	LC
Xavier Univ of Louisiana	LA	10,400	C

PETROLEUM/NATURAL GAS ENGINEERING

School	ST	$IS	SR
Cal State/Bakersfield	CA	5,402	C
Colo School of Mines	CO	8,436	HC+
Louisiana State Univ and A&M College	LA	5,605	C
Louisiana Tech Univ	LA	4,284	C
Marietta College	OH	16,940	C+
Miss State Univ	MS	5,629	VC
Montana College of Mineral Science and Tech	MT	4,977	C
New Mexico Inst of Mining and Tech	NM	5,212	C+
Savannah State College	GA	4,052	C
Stanford Univ	CA	24,310	MC
Texas A&M Univ	TX	5,382	VC
Texas A&M Univ at Kingsville	TX	3,808	LC
Texas Tech Univ	TX	6,008	C
Univ of Alaska Fairbanks	AK	4,718	C
Univ of Arizona	AZ	5,808	C
Univ of Calif at Berkeley	CA	9,962	HC+
Univ of Houston-Downtown	TX	4,034	NC
Univ of Kansas	KS	5,200	NC
Univ of Missouri/Rolla	MO	6,729	VC+
Univ of Okla	OK	5,427	VC
Univ of Southwestern Louisiana	LA	3,968	NC
Univ of Texas at Austin	TX	5,160	VC
Univ of Tulsa	OK	13,795	VC
Univ of Wyoming	WY	4,991	NC
West Virginia Univ	WV	5,774	C

PHARMACY

School	ST	$IS	SR
Albany College of Pharmacy	NY	13,000	VC
Auburn Univ	AL	5,823	C+
Brooklyn Campus of LIU	NY	15,000	LC
Butler Univ	IN	16,210	C
Creighton Univ	NE	14,432	VC
Drake Univ	IA	17,195	VC
Duquesne Univ	PA	16,434	VC
Ferris State Univ	MI	7,160	NC
Florida A&M Univ	FL	4,651	C
Henderson State Univ	AR	3,860	C
Howard Univ	DC	11,680	C
Idaho State Univ	ID	4,442	C
Lamar Univ	TX	3,798	C
Mass College of Pharmacy and Allied Health Sciences	MA	18,352	C
Miss College	MS	8,348	C
N Dak State Univ of Agriculture and Applied Science	ND	4,774	VC
Northeast Louisiana Univ	LA	3,906	NC
Northeastern Univ	MA	19,851	C
Ohio Northern Univ	OH	18,660	VC
Ohio State Univ	OH	7,218	LC
Oregon State Univ	OR	6,175	C
Philadelphia College of Pharmacy and Science	PA	14,750	VC
Purdue Univ/West Lafayette	IN	6,636	NC
Rutgers Univ/College of Pharmacy	NJ	9,254	HC
St John's Univ	NY	8,980	C+
St Louis College of Pharmacy	MO	11,590	VC
Samford Univ	AL	11,400	VC
S Dak State Univ	SD	4,562	C
Southwestern Okla State Univ	OK	3,312	C
SUNY at Buffalo	NY	7,896	VC
Temple Univ	PA	10,281	C
Texas Southern Univ	TX	4,500	NC
The Univ of New Mexico	NM	5,304	C
Thomas More College	KY	12,962	C
Univ of Arizona	AZ	5,808	C
Univ of Calif at Santa Barbara	CA	9,460	C
Univ of Cincinnati	OH	7,989	C
Univ of Colo at Boulder	CO	6,410	VC
Univ of Conn	CT	9,168	C
Univ of Florida	FL	5,850	HC
Univ of Georgia	GA	5,655	VC
Univ of Iowa	IA	5,658	VC
Univ of Kansas	KS	5,200	NC
Univ of Mich/Ann Arbor	MI	9,428	HC+
Univ of Minn/Twin Cities	MN	6,682	VC
Univ of Miss	MS	5,756	C
Univ of Missouri/Kansas City	MO	5,906	VC
Univ of Montana	MT	5,529	C
Univ of Nebr-Lincoln	NE	5,278	LC
Univ of N Car at Chapel Hill	NC	5,330	HC
Univ of Pittsburgh	PA	9,472	C
Univ of Rhode Island	RI	9,205	C
Univ of S Car	SC	6,158	C
Univ of Texas at Austin	TX	5,160	VC
Univ of the Pacific	CA	21,100	C
Univ of Toledo	OH	6,636	NC
Univ of Utah	UT	5,975	C
Univ of Washington	WA	6,618	VC
Univ of Wisc/Madison	WI	6,400	HC
Univ of Wisc/Milwaukee	WI	6,165	C
Univ of Wyoming	WY	4,991	NC
Virginia Commonwealth Univ	VA	7,909	C
Washington State Univ	WA	6,364	C
Wayne State Univ	MI	2,680	C
West Virginia Univ	WV	5,774	C
Western New England College	MA	14,674	LC
Xavier Univ of Louisiana	LA	10,400	C

PHILOSOPHY

School	ST	$IS	SR
Adelphi Univ	NY	18,250	LC
Adrian College	MI	14,340	C
Agnes Scott College	GA	17,135	VC
Alaska Pacific Univ	AK	11,350	C
Albertson College	ID	15,942	C+
Albertus Magnus College	CT	16,280	LC
Albion College	MI	18,264	VC
Albright College	PA	19,260	C
Alfred Univ	NY	21,054	VC+
Allegheny College	PA	21,020	VC
Alma College	MI	16,375	VC+
Alvernia College	PA	13,150	LC
Alverno College	WI	11,344	C
American International College	MA	14,029	C
American Univ	DC	21,230	VC+
Amherst College	MA	24,152	MC
Anderson Univ	IN	12,920	C
Antioch College	OH	19,532	C
Appalachian State Univ	NC	4,095	C
Aquinas College	MI	14,526	C
Arizona State Univ Main Campus	AZ	6,444	C
Arkansas Baptist College	AR	5,016	NC
Arkansas State Univ	AR	4,250	NC
Asbury College	KY	11,105	VC
Ashland Univ	OH	15,508	C
Assumption College	MA	17,095	LC
Auburn Univ	AL	5,823	C+
Augsburg College	MN	15,608	C
Augustana College	IL	16,959	VC
Augustana College	SD	13,420	C
Aurora Univ	IL	13,381	C
Austin College	TX	14,999	VC
Austin Peay State Univ	TN	4,350	C
Azusa Pacific Univ	CA	15,034	C
Baker Univ	KS	12,284	C
Baldwin-Wallace College	OH	15,210	C
Ball State Univ	IN	6,032	LC
Bard College	NY	25,269	HC
Barry Univ	FL	16,050	C
Bates College	ME	23,990	MC
Baylor Univ	TX	10,990	C+
Beaver College	PA	17,660	C
Belhaven College	MS	9,690	C+
Bellarmine College	KY	10,832	C
Bellevue College	NE	3,050	NC
Belmont Abbey College	NC	13,190	C
Belmont Univ	TN	10,540	C
Beloit College	WI	18,950	VC+
Bemidji State Univ	MN	5,188	C
Benedict College	SC	8,376	LC
Benedictine College	KS	12,830	C
Bennington College	VT	24,850	VC+
Bentley College	MA	18,680	C
Berea College	KY	2,883	VC+
Berry College	GA	11,990	VC
Bethany College	WV	18,300	C+
Bethel College	MN	15,050	C
Biola Univ	CA	16,124	C
Birmingham-Southern College	AL	15,154	VC+
Bloomfield College	NJ	12,200	LC
Bloomsburg Univ of Penn	PA	6,312	C+
Boise State Univ	ID	4,909	LC
Boston College	MA	22,706	MC
Boston Univ	MA	24,130	HC
Bowdoin College	ME	24,155	MC
Bowling Green State Univ	OH	6,701	C
Bradley Univ	IL	14,718	C+
Brandeis Univ	MA	25,585	HC
Bridgewater College	VA	15,300	C
Bridgewater State College	MA	7,518	C
Brigham Young Univ	UT	5,625	HC
Brooklyn Campus of LIU	NY	15,000	LC
Brown Univ	RI	26,104	MC
Bryn Mawr College	PA	24,110	MC
Bucknell Univ	PA	22,320	HC
Buena Vista College	IA	16,150	VC
Butler Univ	IN	16,210	C
Cabrini College	PA	16,012	C
Calif Lutheran Univ	CA	17,240	C
Calif State Polytechnic Univ/Pomona	CA	6,438	LC
Cal State/Bakersfield	CA	5,402	C
Cal State/Chico	CA	6,146	C
Cal State/Dominguez Hills	CA	2,857	LC
Cal State/Fresno	CA	5,747	C
Cal State/Fullerton	CA	4,850	LC
Cal State/Hayward	CA	5,495	C
Cal State/Long Beach	CA	6,057	LC
Cal State/Los Angeles	CA	4,940	VC
Cal State/Northridge	CA	7,122	LC
Cal State/Sacramento	CA	6,387	C
Cal State/San Bernardino	CA	6,055	LC
Cal State/Stanislaus	CA	6,799	C
Calif Univ of Penn	PA	7,370	C
Calumet College of St. Joseph	IN	3,585	C
Calvin College	MI	13,020	VC
Canisius College	NY	15,510	C
Carleton College	MN	22,155	HC
Carlow College	PA	13,914	C
Carnegie Mellon Univ	PA	22,560	HC+
Carroll College	MT	11,265	C
Carroll College	WI	15,490	C
Carson-Newman College	TN	11,250	C
Carthage College	WI	15,995	C
Case Western Reserve Univ	OH	19,910	HC
Catawba College	NC	12,950	C
Catholic Univ of America	DC	18,856	C
Cedar Crest College	PA	18,930	C
Cedarville College	OH	10,715	C
Centenary College of Louisiana	LA	11,826	C+
Central College	IA	14,025	VC
Central Conn State Univ	CT	7,108	C
Central Methodist College	MO	11,410	C
Central Mich Univ	MI	6,737	LC
Central State Univ	OH	7,320	NC
Central Univ of Bayamon	PR	2,430	C
Central Washington Univ	WA	5,644	C
Centre College	KY	15,850	VC+
Chaminade Univ of Honolulu	HI	14,290	C
Chapman Univ	CA	21,842	C
Charter Oak State College	CT	314	NC
Chatham College	PA	18,010	C
Christendom College	VA	11,750	VC
Christopher Newport Univ	VA	3,196	LC
CUNY/Baruch College	NY	2,562	VC
CUNY/Brooklyn College	NY	2,450	VC
CUNY/City College	NY	2,543	VC
CUNY/College of Staten Island	NY	2,558	NC
CUNY/Herbert H. Lehman College	NY	2,542	C
CUNY/Hunter College	NY	4,101	VC
CUNY/Queens College	NY	2,631	C
CUNY/York College	NY	2,534	NC
Claremont McKenna College	CA	22,150	MC
Clarion Univ of Penn	PA	6,518	C
Clark Atlanta Univ	GA	11,846	C
Clark Univ	MA	21,400	VC
Clarke College	IA	13,950	C+
Clemson Univ	SC	6,564	VC
Cleveland State Univ	OH	7,287	NC
Coe College	IA	17,085	VC
Colby College	ME	24,230	HC
Colgate Univ	NY	24,020	HC
College of Charleston	SC	6,250	C
College of New Rochelle	NY	15,440	LC
College of Notre Dame	CA	16,480	C
College of St Benedict	MN	15,468	VC
College of St Catherine	MN	14,670	C
College of St Elizabeth	NJ	15,800	C
College of the Holy Cross	MA	23,850	HC
College of the Ozarks	MO	2,000	VC+
College of William and Mary	VA	8,602	MC
College of Wooster	OH	19,875	VC
Colo College	CO	20,038	HC
Colo State Univ	CO	6,566	VC
Columbia Univ/Barnard College	NY	25,492	HC
Columbia Univ/Columbia College	NY	26,757	MC
Concordia College/Moorhead	MN	12,750	C
Concordia Univ	IL	12,611	C
Conn College	CT	24,160	HC
Cornell College	IA	18,425	VC
Cornell Univ	NY	13,445	MC
Creighton Univ	NE	14,432	VC
Curry College	MA	18,695	LC
D'Youville College	NY	12,850	C
Dakota Wesleyan Univ	SD	9,770	LC
Dallas Baptist Univ	TX	9,620	LC
Dartmouth College	NH	24,354	MC
Davidson College	NC	21,037	MC
Davis and Elkins College	WV	13,230	LC
Defiance College	OH	13,480	LC
Denison Univ	OH	21,150	VC+
DePaul Univ	IL	15,535	VC
DePauw Univ	IN	18,530	VC
Dickinson College	PA	22,705	HC
Dillard Univ	LA	9,950	C
Dordt College	IA	11,690	C
Drake Univ	IA	17,195	VC
Drew Univ/College of Liberal Arts	NJ	23,406	HC
Drury College	MO	12,140	VC
Duke Univ	NC	21,271	MC
Duquesne Univ	PA	16,434	VC
Earlham College	IN	19,383	VC
East Carolina Univ	NC	4,498	C
East Stroudsburg Univ	PA	6,886	C
East Tenn State Univ	TN	4,406	C
Eastern College	PA	15,150	C+
Eastern Illinois Univ	IL	5,548	C
Eastern Kentucky Univ	KY	4,840	NC
Eastern Mich Univ	MI	6,749	C
Eastern Washington Univ	WA	5,439	LC
Eckerd College	FL	18,855	VC
Edinboro Univ of Penn	PA	7,181	C
Edward Waters College	FL	8,300	NC
Elizabethtown College	PA	17,850	VC
Elmhurst College	IL	12,536	C
Elmira College	NY	18,450	C
Elon College	NC	12,290	LC
Emory and Henry College	VA	12,776	C
Emory Univ	GA	21,930	HC
Eureka College	IL	14,555	C
Evergreen State College	WA	6,306	C
Fairfield Univ	CT	20,460	VC
Fairleigh Dickinson Univ	NJ	16,427	C
Ferrum College	VA	12,800	LC
Fisk Univ	TN	0	LC
Flagler College	FL	7,990	C
Florida Atlantic Univ	FL	5,525	C
Florida International Univ	FL	4,191	VC
Florida Memorial College	FL	7,600	C+
Florida State Univ	FL	5,814	VC
Fordham Univ/College at Lincoln Center	NY	18,150	VC
Fordham Univ/Fordham College	NY	19,875	VC
Fort Hays State Univ	KS	4,675	NC
Fort Lewis College	CO	5,097	C
Framingham State College	MA	6,580	C
Franciscan Univ of Steubenville	OH	13,400	C
Franklin and Marshall College	PA	23,655	HC
Franklin College of Indiana	IN	13,970	C
Frostburg State Univ	MD	6,940	C
Furman Univ	SC	16,557	VC
Gallaudet Univ	DC	9,850	SP
Gannon Univ	PA	14,872	C
Geneva College	PA	13,030	C
George Mason Univ	VA	8,728	C
George Washington Univ	DC	22,470	HC
Georgetown College	KY	10,990	C
Georgetown Univ	DC	24,410	MC
Gettysburg College	PA	22,960	HC
Gonzaga Univ	WA	16,350	VC
Gordon College	MA	16,790	C
Goucher College	MD	20,295	VC
Graceland College	IA	11,600	C
Grambling State Univ	LA	4,712	NC
Grand Valley State Univ	MI	6,822	VC
Greenville College	IL	14,190	C
Grinnell College	IA	20,680	HC+
Grove City College	PA	7,870	HC
Guilford College	NC	17,680	C
Gustavus Adolphus College	MN	15,935	VC
Hamilton College	NY	23,500	HC
Hamline Univ	MN	17,122	VC
Hampden-Sydney College	VA	17,372	C+
Hampshire College	MA	25,320	C
Hanover College	IN	10,950	VC
Hardin-Simmons Univ	TX	9,080	C
Hartwick College	NY	20,950	C
Harvard Univ/Harvard and Radcliffe Colleges	MA	24,880	MC
Hastings College	NE	12,426	C
Haverford College	PA	23,950	MC
Hendrix College	AR	11,670	C
High Point Univ	NC	12,350	LC
Hiram College	OH	18,340	VC
Hobart and William Smith Colleges	NY	23,925	VC
Hofstra Univ	NY	16,580	VC
Hollins College	VA	18,484	C
Holy Family College	PA	8,300	C
Holy Names College	CA	15,660	C
Hood College	MD	19,010	VC
Hope College	MI	15,698	C+
Houghton College	NY	13,120	VC
Howard Payne Univ	TX	8,052	C
Howard Univ	DC	11,680	C
Humboldt State Univ	CA	5,676	C
Huntingdon College	AL	11,400	C
Huntington College	IN	13,220	C
Idaho State Univ	ID	4,442	C
Illinois Benedictine College	IL	14,170	C
Illinois College	IL	11,200	C
Illinois State Univ	IL	6,413	C
Illinois Wesleyan Univ	IL	18,590	HC+
Incarnate Word College	TX	12,307	C
Indiana State Univ	IN	6,210	C
Indiana Univ Bloomington	IN	6,495	VC
Indiana Univ Northwest	IN	2,310	C
Indiana Univ of Penn	PA	6,373	C
Indiana Univ Southeast	IN	2,260	LC
Indiana Univ-Purdue Univ at Fort Wayne	IN	2,500	LC

School	ST	$IS	SR
Indiana Univ-Purdue Univ at Indianapolis	IN	5,862	LC
Indiana Univ/South Bend	IN	2,141	LC
Iona College	NY	16,310	C
Iowa State Univ	IA	5,456	C
Ithaca College	NY	19,679	C
Jacksonville Univ	FL	13,390	C
James Madison Univ	VA	8,198	HC
Jamestown College	ND	10,250	C
Jersey City State College	NJ	7,797	LC
John Carroll Univ	OH	16,510	C
Johns Hopkins Univ	MD	24,360	HC
Juniata College	PA	18,390	C+
Kalamazoo College	MI	19,974	HC
Kansas State Univ	KS	4,816	NC
Kean College of New Jersey	NJ	6,395	LC
Kent State Univ	OH	6,740	LC
Kenyon College	OH	22,430	HC+
King's College	PA	15,420	C
Knox College	IL	18,990	C
Kutztown Univ	PA	6,528	C
La Salle Univ	PA	16,940	LC
Lafayette College	PA	23,450	HC
Lake Forest College	IL	19,960	VC
Lakeland College	WI	12,845	LC
Lawrence Univ	WI	19,986	HC+
Le Moyne College	NY	15,180	C
Lebanon Valley College of Penn	PA	18,300	C
Lehigh Univ	PA	23,250	HC
Lenoir-Rhyne College	NC	14,068	C
Lewis and Clark College	OR	19,980	VC
Lewis Univ	IL	14,797	C
Liberty Univ	VA	11,500	LC
Lincoln Univ	MO	4,638	NC
Lincoln Univ	PA	0	LC
Linfield College	OR	16,670	VC
Lock Haven Univ of Penn	PA	7,128	C
LIU/C. W. Post Campus	NY	16,870	L
Louisiana Tech Univ	LA	7,518	VC
Louisiana State Univ and A&M College	LA	5,605	C
Loyola College	MD	18,035	VC
Loyola Marymount Univ	CA	18,560	VC
Loyola Univ of Chicago	IL	15,880	C+
Loyola Univ/New Orleans	LA	15,660	C+
Lycoming College	PA	17,200	LC
Lynchburg College	VA	17,000	C
Macalester College	MN	19,710	HC
MacMurray College	IL	12,800	C
Manchester College	IN	13,240	LC
Manhattan College	NY	19,000	C
Manhattanville College	NY	20,450	LC
Mankato State Univ	MN	5,097	LC
Mansfield Univ	PA	6,348	C
Marian College	IN	12,936	C
Marietta College	OH	16,940	C+
Marlboro College	VT	23,305	C+
Marquette Univ	WI	16,114	VC
Marshall Univ	WV	5,762	LC
Mary Baldwin College	VA	17,700	LC
Mary Washington College	VA	7,910	HC
Marygrove College	MI	5,877	VC
Marymount College/Tarrytown	NY	17,350	C
Marymount Univ	VA	15,930	C
Mass Inst of Tech	MA	24,800	MC
McMurry Univ	TX	10,100	C
McPherson College	KS	11,360	VC
Menlo College	CA	20,375	LC
Mercer Univ	GA	15,123	C
Merrimack College	MA	18,025	C
Metropolitan State College of Denver	CO	1,751	NC
Miami Univ	OH	8,066	VC
Mich State Univ	MI	7,842	C
Middle Tenn State Univ	TN	3,857	C
Middlebury College	VT	24,400	MC
Millersville Univ of Penn	PA	7,370	C
Millikin Univ	IL	15,499	C
Mills College	CA	20,848	VC
Millsaps College	MS	15,486	C+
Miss State Univ	MS	5,629	NC
Missouri Valley College	MO	14,050	LC
Molloy College	NY	8,580	LC
Monmouth College	IL	17,300	C+
Monmouth College	NJ	16,820	C
Montana State Univ	MT	5,534	C
Montclair State College	NJ	7,539	C+
Moorhead State Univ	MN	5,076	C
Moravian College	PA	18,960	LC
Morehead State Univ	KY	4,600	NC
Morehouse College	GA	13,224	LC
Morgan State Univ	MD	7,366	C+
Morningside College	IA	13,896	C
Morris Brown College	GA	12,234	NC
Mount Holyoke College	MA	23,630	HC
Mount Mary College	WI	10,920	C
Mount St Mary's College	CA	16,390	VC
Mount St Mary's College	MD	17,825	C
Mount Union College	OH	15,850	C
Mount Vernon Nazarene College	OH	10,390	C
Muhlenberg College	PA	20,795	VC
Murray State Univ	KY	4,702	C
Muskingum College	OH	16,650	C

School	ST	$IS	SR
Nazareth College of Rochester	NY	15,310	C+
Nebr Wesleyan Univ	NE	12,240	C
New College of the Univ of South Florida	FL	5,697	MC
New England College	NH	17,870	LC
New Mexico State Univ	NM	4,844	C
New York Univ	NY	24,705	VC+
Newberry College	SC	11,994	C
Niagara Univ	NY	14,552	C
North Adams State College	MA	7,750	C
N Car Central Univ	NC	4,347	LC
N Car State Univ	NC	4,984	VC
N Car Wesleyan College	NC	12,480	LC
North Central College	IL	15,498	VC
North Park College	IL	14,310	C
Northeast Missouri State Univ	MO	5,654	VC+
Northeastern Illinois Univ	IL	1,955	C
Northeastern Univ	MA	19,851	C
Northern Arizona Univ	AZ	4,844	C
Northern Illinois Univ	IL	6,408	C
Northern Kentucky Univ	KY	4,620	NC
Northern Mich Univ	MI	6,350	C
Northwest Missouri State Univ	MO	5,010	LC
Northwest Nazarene College	ID	11,750	C
Northwestern College of Iowa	IA	12,250	C
Northwestern Univ	IL	21,093	MC
Nyack College	NY	12,210	LC
Oakland Univ	MI	6,714	VC
Oberlin College	OH	24,570	HC+
Occidental College	CA	21,792	HC
Oglethorpe Univ	GA	16,360	VC
Ohio Dominican College	OH	11,820	LC
Ohio Northern Univ	OH	18,660	VC
Ohio State Univ	OH	7,218	LC
Ohio Univ	OH	7,341	C
Ohio Wesleyan Univ	OH	21,108	VC
Okla City Univ	OK	9,840	C
Okla State Univ	OK	5,086	VC
Old Dominion Univ	VA	8,317	C
Olivet Nazarene Univ	IL	11,976	C
Oral Roberts Univ	OK	10,607	C+
Oregon State Univ	OR	6,175	C
Ottawa Univ	KS	10,240	C+
Otterbein College	OH	16,506	C
Ouachita Baptist Univ	AR	8,940	C
Our Lady of the Lake Univ of San Antonio	TX	11,080	C
Pacific Lutheran Univ	WA	15,998	VC
Pacific Univ	OR	17,869	C
Paine College	GA	8,207	LC
Pembroke State Univ	NC	3,538	LC
Penn State Univ/Univ Park Campus	PA	8,752	HC
Pepperdine Univ	CA	23,720	VC
Philander Smith College	AR	5,434	NC
Phillips Univ	OK	12,744	C
Pitzer College	CA	23,780	HC
Plymouth State College	NH	7,166	C
Point Loma Nazarene College	CA	13,532	C
Pomona College	CA	23,820	MC
Pontifical Catholic Univ of PR/Ponce	PR	5,807	C
Portland State Univ	OR	7,191	C
Princeton Univ	NJ	24,650	MC
Principia College	IL	17,799	C
Providence College	RI	19,750	VC
Purdue Univ/Calumet	IN	2,374	NC
Purdue Univ/West Lafayette	IN	6,636	C
Quincy Univ	IL	13,646	VC
Radford Univ	VA	7,034	LC
Ramapo College of New Jersey	NJ	8,027	C+
Randolph-Macon College	VA	16,980	C
Randolph-Macon Woman's College	VA	19,100	C
Reed College	OR	24,480	HC+
Regis Univ	CO	17,340	C
Rensselaer Polytechnic Inst	NY	23,067	HC
Rhode Island College	RI	7,901	LC
Rhodes College	TN	19,624	HC
Rice Univ	TX	15,110	HC
Richard Stockton College of New Jersey	NJ	6,950	LC
Rider College	NJ	18,160	C
Ripon College	WI	18,320	C+
Roanoke College	VA	16,975	C
Rockford College	IL	15,300	C
Rockhurst College	MO	12,470	C
Rocky Mountain College	MT	11,320	C
Roger Williams Univ	RI	16,750	C
Rollins College	FL	20,875	VC
Roosevelt Univ	IL	12,368	C
Rosary College	IL	15,040	C
Rosemont College	PA	16,775	C
Rutgers Univ/Camden College of A&S	NJ	8,652	VC
Rutgers Univ/Douglass College	NJ	8,795	VC
Rutgers Univ/Livingston College	NJ	8,877	VC
Rutgers Univ/Newark College of A&S	NJ	8,645	C

School	ST	$IS	SR
Rutgers Univ/Rutgers College	NJ	8,841	HC+
Rutgers Univ/Univ College— Camden	NJ	3,506	C
Rutgers Univ/Univ College— New Brunswick	NJ	0	LC
Rutgers Univ/Univ College— Newark	NJ	0	C
Sacred Heart Univ	CT	16,350	C
St Ambrose Univ	IA	13,380	C
St Andrews Presbyterian College	NC	14,240	LC
St Anselm College	NH	17,340	C
St Bonaventure Univ	NY	14,762	C
St Cloud State Univ	MN	5,015	C
St Edward's Univ	TX	12,636	C
St Francis College	PA	15,744	C
St John Fisher College	NY	15,415	C
St John's Univ	MN	15,364	C
St John's Univ	NY	8,980	C+
St Joseph College	CT	16,225	C
St Joseph's College	ME	14,535	C
St Joseph's Univ	PA	17,800	VC
St Lawrence Univ	NY	23,420	VC
St Louis Univ	MO	15,522	VC
St Mary's College	IN	17,043	VC
St Mary's College	MI	8,350	C
St Mary's College of Calif	CA	18,848	VC
St Mary's College of Maryland	MD	8,900	VC+
St Mary's College of Minn	MN	13,850	C
St Mary's Univ	TX	12,064	C
St Mary-of-the-Woods College	IN	14,430	NC
St Meinrad College	IN	10,302	C
St Michael's College	VT	17,930	C
St Norbert College	WI	15,710	VC
St Olaf College	MN	17,200	HC
St Peter's College	NJ	14,775	LC
St Thomas Aquinas College	NY	13,550	C
St Vincent College	PA	13,934	LC
St Xavier Univ	IL	14,700	C
Salem College	NC	16,025	C
Salisbury State Univ	MD	7,516	C+
Salve Regina Univ	RI	29,100	LC
Sam Houston State Univ	TX	4,506	C
San Diego State Univ	CA	6,692	LC
San Francisco State Univ	CA	7,292	LC
San Jose State Univ	CA	6,680	LC
Santa Clara Univ	CA	18,783	VC
Sarah Lawrence College	NY	24,975	HC
Schreiner College	TX	14,320	C
Scripps College	CA	23,600	HC
Seattle Pacific Univ	WA	16,503	C
Seattle Univ	WA	16,590	C
Seton Hall Univ	NJ	18,306	LC
Seton Hill College	PA	14,320	C
Shimer College	IL	12,850	NC
Shorter College	GA	10,270	C
Siena College	NY	15,410	VC
Siena Heights College	MI	12,520	C
Simmons College	MA	22,534	C
Simpson College	IA	14,635	VC
Sioux Falls College	SD	11,540	C
Skidmore College	NY	23,230	HC
Slippery Rock Univ	PA	6,803	C
Smith College	MA	24,236	HC
Sonoma State Univ	CA	6,996	C
Southeast Missouri State Univ	MO	5,854	C
Southern Conn State Univ	CT	7,532	C
Southern Illinois Univ at Carbondale	IL	6,234	C
Southern Illinois Univ at Edwardsville	IL	6,097	LC
Southern Methodist Univ	TX	18,520	VC
Southern Nazarene Univ	OK	9,206	NC
Southwest Missouri State Univ	MO	4,956	C
Southwest Texas State Univ	TX	5,124	C
Southwestern College	KS	10,032	C
Southwestern Univ	TX	15,484	HC
Spalding Univ	KY	10,496	C
Spelman College	GA	12,942	VC
Spring Arbor College	MI	12,256	C
Spring Hill College	AL	16,015	C+
Stanford Univ	CA	24,310	MC
SUNY at Albany	NY	7,059	VC
SUNY at Binghamton	NY	7,921	HC
SUNY at Buffalo	NY	7,896	VC
SUNY at Stony Brook	NY	7,658	VC
SUNY/College at Brockport	NY	7,220	C+
SUNY/College at Buffalo	NY	7,035	VC
SUNY/College at Cortland	NY	7,326	C+
SUNY/College at Fredonia	NY	7,159	VC
SUNY/College at Geneseo	NY	6,949	VC
SUNY/College at New Paltz	NY	6,890	VC
SUNY/College at Old Westbury	NY	7,128	LC
SUNY/College at Oneonta	NY	7,878	C
SUNY/College at Oswego	NY	7,330	VC
SUNY/College at Plattsburgh	NY	6,917	C
SUNY/College at Purchase	NY	7,324	C
SUNY/Potsdam College	NY	6,906	C
Stephens College	MO	18,460	C
Stetson Univ	FL	16,435	VC

School	ST	$IS	SR
Stevens Inst of Tech	NJ	21,980	VC+
Stonehill College	MA	17,481	VC
Suffolk Univ	MA	15,360	LC
Susquehanna Univ	PA	19,950	VC
Swarthmore College	PA	24,136	MC
Sweet Briar College	VA	19,770	C
Syracuse Univ	NY	21,305	HC
Tabor College	KS	11,460	VC
Taylor Univ	IN	14,450	VC
Temple Univ	PA	10,281	C
Texas A&M Univ	TX	5,382	VC
Texas Christian Univ	TX	12,180	C
Texas Lutheran College	TX	10,710	C
Texas Tech Univ	TX	6,008	C
The Univ of New Mexico	NM	5,304	C
Thiel College	PA	16,282	C
Thomas A. Edison State College	NJ	400	
Thomas Moore College of Liberal Arts	NH	11,900	NC
Thomas More College	KY	12,962	C
Toccoa Falls College	GA	9,350	C
Towson State Univ	MD	7,452	C
Transylvania Univ	KY	14,970	VC+
Trenton State College	NJ	9,085	HC
Trevecca Nazarene College	TN	9,826	NC
Trinity Christian College	IL	13,260	C
Trinity College	CT	24,120	HC
Trinity College	DC	14,010	C
Trinity College of Vermont	VT	16,015	LC
Trinity Univ	TX	16,670	HC
Tufts Univ	MA	24,962	MC
Tulane Univ	LA	24,540	HC
Union College	NY	23,817	HC
United States Military Academy	NY	0	MC
Univ of Akron	OH	6,699	NC
Univ of Alabama	AL	5,702	C
Univ of Alabama at Birmingham	AL	7,533	C
Univ of Alaska Fairbanks	AK	4,718	C
Univ of Arizona	AZ	5,808	C
Univ of Arkansas at Fayetteville	AR	5,046	C
Univ of Arkansas at Little Rock	AR	4,419	C
Univ of Calif at Berkeley	CA	9,962	HC+
Univ of Calif at Davis	CA	9,534	VC
Univ of Calif at Los Angeles	CA	8,959	VC
Univ of Calif at Santa Barbara	CA	9,460	C
Univ of Calif at Santa Cruz	CA	9,060	VC
Univ of Calif, Riverside	CA	9,178	C
Univ of Calif, San Diego	CA	10,028	VC+
Univ of Calif/Irvine	CA	12,680	VC
Univ of Central Arkansas	AR	4,200	LC
Univ of Central Florida	FL	6,061	C+
Univ of Central Okla	OK	3,647	C
Univ of Chicago	IL	24,517	MC
Univ of Cincinnati	OH	7,989	C
Univ of Colo at Boulder	CO	6,410	C
Univ of Colo at Colo Springs	CO	2,269	C
Univ of Colo at Denver	CO	1,955	VC
Univ of Conn	CT	9,168	C
Univ of Dallas	TX	14,983	C
Univ of Dayton	OH	15,120	C+
Univ of Delaware	DE	8,013	VC
Univ of Denver	CO	19,290	C+
Univ of Detroit Mercy	MI	14,720	C
Univ of Dubuque	IA	14,150	LC
Univ of Evansville	IN	15,300	VC
Univ of Findlay	OH	15,764	C
Univ of Florida	FL	5,850	HC
Univ of Georgia	GA	5,695	VC
Univ of Hartford	CT	19,858	LC
Univ of Hawaii at Hilo	HI	4,141	C
Univ of Hawaii at Manoa	HI	5,626	C
Univ of Houston	TX	5,215	C
Univ of Idaho	ID	4,830	C
Univ of Illinois at Chicago	IL	8,443	C
Univ of Indianapolis	IN	14,510	C
Univ of Iowa	IA	5,658	VC
Univ of Kansas	KS	5,200	NC
Univ of Kentucky	KY	5,152	VC
Univ of La Verne	CA	17,400	C
Univ of Louisville	KY	5,948	C
Univ of Lowell	MA	8,831	VC
Univ of Maine	ME	7,990	C
Univ of Maryland/Baltimore County	MD	7,746	VC
Univ of Maryland/College Park	MD	8,182	VC
Univ of Maryland/Univ College	MD	4,900	NC
Univ of Mass Dartmouth	MA	8,158	C
Univ of Mass/Amherst	MA	9,364	LC
Univ of Mass/Boston	MA	4,253	C
Univ of Memphis	TN	3,476	C
Univ of Miami	FL	22,107	VC
Univ of Mich/Ann Arbor	MI	9,428	HC+
Univ of Mich/Dearborn	MI	3,399	C
Univ of Mich/Flint	MI	2,916	C
Univ of Minn/Duluth	MN	6,512	C
Univ of Minn/Morris	MN	6,825	HC
Univ of Minn/Twin Cities	MN	6,682	VC
Univ of Miss	MS	5,756	C
Univ of Missouri/Columbia	MO	6,254	HC

School	ST	$IS	SR
Univ of Missouri/Kansas City	MO	5,906	VC
Univ of Missouri/Rolla	MO	6,729	VC+
Univ of Missouri/St. Louis	MO	6,378	C
Univ of Montana	MT	5,529	C
Univ of Nebr at Omaha	NE	1,889	LC
Univ of Nebr-Lincoln	NE	5,278	LC
Univ of Nevada/Las Vegas	NV	6,405	C
Univ of Nevada/Reno	NV	5,735	C
Univ of New Hampshire	NH	8,242	C
Univ of New Orleans	LA	5,468	C
Univ of N Car at Asheville	NC	4,791	VC
Univ of N Car at Chapel Hill	NC	5,330	HC
Univ of N Car at Charlotte	NC	4,597	C
Univ of N Car at Greensboro	NC	5,192	C
Univ of N Dak	ND	4,902	NC
Univ of North Texas	TX	4,853	C
Univ of Northern Colo	CO	6,008	C
Univ of Northern Iowa	IA	5,137	C
Univ of Notre Dame	IN	20,150	MC
Univ of Okla	OK	5,427	VC
Univ of Oregon	OR	6,466	VC
Univ of Penn	PA	24,238	MC
Univ of Pittsburgh	PA	9,472	C
Univ of Portland	OR	15,564	C
Univ of PR/Mayaguez	PR	0	
Univ of PR/Rio Piedras	PR	0	
Univ of Puget Sound	WA	19,520	HC
Univ of Redlands	CA	22,059	VC
Univ of Rhode Island	RI	9,205	C
Univ of Richmond	VA	16,700	HC
Univ of Rochester	NY	23,696	HC
Univ of St Thomas	MN	15,785	C+
Univ of St Thomas	TX	11,676	C+
Univ of San Diego	CA	18,970	VC
Univ of San Francisco	CA	18,408	C
Univ of Scranton	PA	17,071	VC
Univ of South Alabama	AL	5,451	C
Univ of S Car	SC	6,158	C
Univ of S Dak	SD	4,722	C
Univ of South Florida	FL	5,475	C+
Univ of Southern Calif	CA	23,006	VC
Univ of Southern Indiana	IN	3,720	NC
Univ of Southern Maine	ME	7,299	C
Univ of Southern Miss	MS	4,542	C
Univ of Southwestern Louisiana	LA	3,968	NC
Univ of Tampa	FL	16,780	C
Univ of Tenn at Chattanooga	TN	5,375	C
Univ of Tenn/Knoxville	TN	5,668	C
Univ of Texas at Arlington	TX	5,549	LC
Univ of Texas at Austin	TX	5,160	VC
Univ of Texas at El Paso	TX	3,160	LC
Univ of Texas-Pan American	TX	3,192	NC
Univ of the District of Columbia	DC	974	NC
Univ of the Ozarks	AR	7,770	C
Univ of the Pacific	CA	21,100	C
Univ of the South	TN	18,830	HC
Univ of Toledo	OH	6,636	NC
Univ of Tulsa	OK	13,795	VC
Univ of Utah	UT	5,975	C
Univ of Vermont	VT	10,776	C+
Univ of Virginia	VA	7,964	MC
Univ of Washington	WA	6,618	VC
Univ of West Florida	FL	5,415	C
Univ of Wisc/Eau Claire	WI	4,647	C
Univ of Wisc/Green Bay	WI	4,904	C
Univ of Wisc/La Crosse	WI	4,487	C
Univ of Wisc/Madison	WI	6,400	HC
Univ of Wisc/Milwaukee	WI	6,165	C
Univ of Wisc/Oshkosh	WI	4,240	C
Univ of Wisc/Parkside	WI	5,247	C
Univ of Wisc/Platteville	WI	4,830	C
Univ of Wisc/Stevens Point	WI	5,047	C+
Urbana Univ	OH	12,536	C
Ursuline College	OH	13,180	LC
Utah State Univ	UT	4,683	C
Utica College of Syracuse Univ	NY	16,714	LC
Valdosta State Univ	GA	4,670	LC
Valparaiso Univ	IN	14,810	VC
Vanderbilt Univ	TN	23,422	HC+
Vassar College	NY	24,206	HC
Villanova Univ	PA	21,400	HC
Virginia Polytechnic Inst and State Univ	VA	6,828	C
Virginia Union Univ	VA	10,555	LC
Virginia Wesleyan College	VA	14,950	VC
Wabash College	IN	16,250	VC
Wagner College	NY	17,950	C
Wake Forest Univ	NC	17,280	MC
Walsh Univ	OH	11,640	C
Wartburg College	IA	14,530	VC
Washburn Univ of Topeka	KS	5,802	NC
Washington and Jefferson College	PA	19,360	C
Washington and Lee Univ	VA	17,735	MC
Washington College	MD	19,270	C+
Washington State Univ	WA	6,364	C
Washington Univ	MO	23,507	HC
Wayland Baptist Univ	TX	7,811	NC
Wayne State Univ	MI	2,680	C
Webster Univ	MO	12,650	C
Wellesley College	MA	23,815	MC
Wells College	NY	19,460	C+
Wesleyan College	GA	15,445	C
Wesleyan Univ	CT	23,770	MC
West Chester Univ of Penn	PA	7,492	C
West Georgia College	GA	4,256	C
West Virginia Univ	WV	5,774	C
West Virginia Wesleyan College	WV	16,900	C
Western Illinois Univ	IL	5,241	LC
Western Kentucky Univ	KY	4,808	C
Western Maryland College	MD	18,990	C
Western Mich Univ	MI	6,820	C
Western Washington Univ	WA	6,077	VC
Westminster College	MO	13,750	C+
Westminster College	PA	15,200	C
Westminster College of Salt Lake City	UT	12,100	C
Westmont College	CA	18,732	C
Wheaton College	IL	14,710	HC
Wheaton College	MA	23,840	C+
Wheeling Jesuit College	WV	14,370	C
Whitman College	WA	20,595	HC
Whittier College	CA	21,661	C
Whitworth College	WA	16,265	C
Wichita State Univ	KS	5,068	NC
Wiley College	TX	0	NC
Wilkes Univ	PA	15,728	LC
Willamette Univ	OR	17,995	VC
William Jewell College	MO	12,500	VC
William Paterson College	NJ	7,438	C+
William Woods Univ	MO	14,025	LC
Williams College	MA	24,390	MC
Winthrop Univ	SC	6,750	C
Wittenberg Univ	OH	19,998	VC
Wofford College	SC	15,360	VC
Worcester Polytechnic Inst	MA	20,350	HC
Wright State Univ	OH	6,896	LC
Xavier Univ	OH	15,710	C+
Xavier Univ of Louisiana	LA	10,400	C
Yale Univ	CT	25,110	MC
Yeshiva Univ	NY	18,200	VC
Youngstown State Univ	OH	6,447	LC

PHOTOGRAPHY

School	ST	$IS	SR
Alfred Univ	NY	21,054	VC+
Aquinas College	MI	14,526	C
Arizona State Univ Main Campus	AZ	6,444	C
Arkansas State Univ	AR	4,250	NC
Art Academy of Cincinnati	OH	8,820	SP
Art Center College of Design	CA	13,550	SP
Atlanta College of Art	GA	12,495	SP
Ball State Univ	IN	6,032	LC
Bard College	NY	25,269	HC
Barry Univ	FL	16,050	C
Barton College	NC	10,689	LC
Beaver College	PA	17,660	C
Bellevue College	NE	3,050	NC
Bennington College	VT	24,850	VC+
Bradley Univ	IL	14,718	C+
Brescia College	KY	9,800	C
Brigham Young Univ	UT	5,625	HC
Calif College of Arts and Crafts	CA	17,378	SP
Cal State/Fresno	CA	5,747	C
Cal State/Fullerton	CA	4,850	LC
Cal State/Long Beach	CA	6,057	LC
Center for Creative Studies/ College of Art and Design	MI	15,330	SP
Central Missouri State Univ	MO	5,138	LC
CUNY/City College	NY	2,543	VC
Cleveland Inst of Art	OH	15,630	SP
Coker College	SC	13,790	C
College of Notre Dame of Maryland	MD	16,050	C
Columbia College	IL	7,879	SP
Columbus College of Art and Design	OH	14,550	SP
Cooper Union for the Advancement of Science and Art	NY	8,430	MC
Corcoran School of Art	DC	14,480	SP
Cornell Univ	NY	13,445	MC
Drexel Univ	PA	15,970	C
East Tenn State Univ	TN	4,406	C
East Texas State Univ	TX	4,572	LC
Eastern Washington Univ	WA	5,439	LC
Edinboro Univ of Penn	PA	7,181	C
Evergreen State College	WA	6,306	C
Fitchburg State College	MA	6,962	C
George Washington Univ	DC	22,470	HC
Grand Valley State Univ	MI	6,822	VC
Hampshire College	MA	25,320	C
Hofstra Univ	NY	16,580	VC
Howard Univ	DC	11,680	C
Indiana Univ-Purdue Univ at Indianapolis	IN	5,862	LC
Ithaca College	NY	19,679	C
Jersey City State College	NJ	7,797	LC
Kansas City Art Inst	MO	17,000	SP
Kent State Univ	OH	6,740	LC
LIU/C. W. Post Campus	NY	16,870	C
Louisiana Tech Univ	LA	4,284	C
Maine College of Art	ME	15,673	SP
Manhattanville College	NY	20,450	LC
Maryland Inst, College of Art	MD	18,420	SP
Mass College of Art	MA	9,447	SP
Middle Tenn State Univ	TN	3,857	C
Milwaukee Inst of Art and Design	WI	9,800	SP
Minneapolis College of Art and Design	MN	15,512	SP
Montserrat College of Art	MA	12,500	SP
New York Univ	NY	24,705	VC+
Northern Mich Univ	MI	6,350	C
Ohio Univ	OH	7,341	C
Ohio Wesleyan Univ	OH	21,108	VC+
Otis College of Art and Design	CA	16,686	SP
Ouachita Baptist Univ	AR	8,940	C
Pacific Northwest College of Art	OR	7,700	SP
Parsons School of Design	NY	21,410	SP
Pratt Inst	NY	19,520	C
Prescott College	AZ	9,775	C
Purdue Univ/West Lafayette	IN	6,636	C
Rhode Island College	RI	7,901	LC
Rhode Island School of Design	RI	22,315	SP
Rochester Inst of Tech	NY	18,954	VC
St Edward's Univ	TX	12,636	C
St John's Univ	NY	8,980	C+
St Vincent College	PA	13,934	LC
Salem State College	MA	6,712	C
Sam Houston State Univ	TX	4,506	C
San Francisco Art Inst	CA	12,900	SP
Sarah Lawrence College	NY	24,975	HC
Savannah College of Art and Design	GA	14,280	SP
School of the Art Inst of Chicago	IL	17,610	SP
School of Visual Arts	NY	17,120	SP
Scripps College	CA	23,600	HC
Seton Hill College	PA	14,320	C
Shepherd College	WV	5,540	C
Southern Illinois Univ at Carbondale	IL	6,234	C
SUNY/College at Buffalo	NY	7,035	VC
SUNY/College at New Paltz	NY	6,890	VC
SUNY/College at Purchase	NY	7,324	C
Syracuse Univ	NY	21,305	HC
Temple Univ	PA	10,281	C
Texas Tech Univ	TX	6,008	C
Texas Woman's Univ	TX	4,392	C
Thomas A. Edison State College	NJ	400	
Univ of Akron	OH	6,699	NC
Univ of Arizona	AZ	5,808	C
Univ of Bridgeport	CT	18,985	C
Univ of Calif at Santa Cruz	CA	9,060	VC
Univ of Central Okla	OK	3,647	C
Univ of Conn	CT	9,168	C
Univ of Dayton	OH	15,120	C+
Univ of Florida	FL	5,850	HC
Univ of Georgia	GA	5,655	VC
Univ of Hartford	CT	19,858	LC
Univ of Idaho	ID	4,830	C
Univ of Illinois at Chicago	IL	8,443	C
Univ of Illinois at Urbana-Champaign	IL	7,764	HC
Univ of Mass Dartmouth	MA	8,158	C
Univ of Miami	FL	22,107	VC
Univ of Mich/Ann Arbor	MI	9,428	HC+
Univ of Montevallo	AL	5,310	C
Univ of North Texas	TX	4,853	C
Univ of Notre Dame	IN	20,150	MC
Univ of Okla	OK	5,427	VC
Univ of San Francisco	CA	18,408	C
Univ of South Florida	FL	5,475	C+
Univ of Southern Calif	CA	23,006	VC
Univ of the Arts	PA	16,150	SP
Univ of Washington	WA	6,618	VC
Univ of Wisc/Eau Claire	WI	4,647	C
Univ of Wisc/Superior	WI	4,330	C
Valparaiso Univ	IN	14,810	VC
Virginia Intermont College	VA	12,250	LC
Washington Univ	MO	23,507	HC
Wesleyan Univ	CT	23,770	MC
Western Conn State Univ	CT	6,622	C

PHYSICAL CHEMISTRY

School	ST	$IS	SR
Elizabethtown College	PA	17,850	VC
Hampden-Sydney College	VA	17,372	C+
Saginaw Valley State Univ	MI	6,634	LC

PHYSICAL EDUCATION

School	ST	$IS	SR
Adelphi Univ	NY	18,250	LC
Alabama A&M Univ	AL	4,200	C
Albany State College	GA	4,481	LC
Albertson College	ID	15,942	C+
Albion College	MI	18,264	VC
Alice Lloyd College	KY	2,750	VC
Anderson Univ	IN	12,920	C
Aquinas College	MI	14,526	C
Arizona State Univ Main Campus	AZ	6,444	C
Arkansas State Univ	AR	4,250	NC
Armstrong State College	GA	4,874	LC
Asbury College	KY	11,105	VC
Atlantic Union College	MA	14,150	LC
Auburn Univ	AL	5,823	C+
Augustana College	IL	16,959	VC
Aurora Univ	IL	13,381	C
Austin College	TX	14,999	VC
Austin Peay State Univ	TN	4,350	C
Averett College	VA	13,610	LC
Azusa Pacific Univ	CA	15,034	C
Barber-Scotia College	NC	6,840	NC
Barry Univ	FL	16,050	C
Bartlesville Wesleyan College	OK	9,400	C
Barton College	NC	10,689	LC
Bellevue College	NE	3,050	NC
Belmont Univ	TN	10,540	C
Berea College	KY	2,883	VC+
Berry College	GA	11,990	VC
Bethany College	WV	18,300	C+
Bethel College	TN	9,736	LC
Bethune-Cookman College	FL	8,375	LC
Blackburn College	IL	9,120	C
Bluefield College	VA	10,600	C
Bluefield State College	WV	1,832	LC
Bluffton College	OH	12,951	C
Boise State Univ	ID	4,909	LC
Boston Univ	MA	24,130	HC
Brewton-Parker College	GA	6,828	NC
Bridgewater College	VA	15,300	C
Bridgewater State College	MA	7,518	C
Brigham Young Univ	UT	5,625	HC
Calif Baptist College	CA	11,294	C
Calif Lutheran Univ	CA	17,240	C
Calif Polytechnic State Univ	CA	6,980	VC+
Calif State Polytechnic Univ/ Pomona	CA	6,438	LC
Cal State/Dominguez Hills	CA	2,857	LC
Cal State/Hayward	CA	5,495	C
Cal State/Los Angeles	CA	4,940	VC
Cal State/Northridge	CA	7,122	LC
Cal State/San Bernardino	CA	6,055	LC
Cal State/Stanislaus	CA	6,799	C
Calvin College	MI	13,020	VC
Campbellsville College	KY	8,720	C
Canisius College	NY	15,510	C
Capital Univ	OH	16,535	VC
Carroll College	MT	11,265	C
Carthage College	WI	15,995	C
Cascade College	OR	9,800	NC
Castleton State College	VT	8,378	LC
Catawba College	NC	12,950	C
Cedarville College	OH	10,715	C
Central Conn State Univ	CT	7,108	C
Central Methodist College	MO	11,410	C
Central Wesleyan College	SC	9,640	C
Chapman Univ	CA	21,842	C
Charleston Southern Univ	SC	10,282	LC
Chicago State Univ	IL	2,198	C
Christian Heritage College	CA	11,756	C
CUNY/Brooklyn College	NY	2,450	VC
CUNY/City College	NY	2,543	VC
CUNY/Queens College	NY	2,631	C
Claflin College	SC	0	
Clarke College	IA	13,950	C+
Cleveland State Univ	OH	7,287	NC
Coastal Carolina Univ	SC	6,010	LC
Coe College	IA	17,085	VC
Coker College	SC	13,790	C
College of Charleston	SC	6,250	C
College of Great Falls	MT	6,230	NC
College of the Ozarks	MO	2,000	VC+
College of the Southwest	NM	5,720	LC
College of William and Mary	VA	8,602	MC
Colo State Univ	CO	6,566	VC
Columbia College	SC	13,520	LC
Concordia College	MI	13,660	C
Concordia College	MN	13,200	C
Concordia College	NE	11,776	NC
Concordia College/Moorhead	MN	12,750	C
Concordia Univ	CA	14,675	C
Coppin State College	MD	7,145	LC
Culver-Stockton College	MO	11,150	C
Cumberland College	KY	9,756	C
Dallas Baptist Univ	TX	9,620	LC
Dana College	NE	11,910	C
David Lipscomb Univ	TN	7,865	VC
Defiance College	OH	13,480	LC
Delaware State College	DE	5,656	C
Denison Univ	OH	21,150	VC+
DePaul Univ	IL	15,535	VC
DePauw Univ	IN	18,530	VC
Dillard Univ	LA	9,950	C
Doane College	NE	12,220	C
Drury College	MO	12,140	VC
East Stroudsburg Univ	PA	6,886	C
East Texas Baptist Univ	TX	7,740	C
Eastern Conn State Univ	CT	6,966	C
Eastern Kentucky Univ	KY	4,840	NC
Eastern Mennonite College	VA	12,700	C

School	ST	$IS	SR
Eastern Mich Univ	MI	6,749	C
Eastern New Mexico Univ	NM	3,950	C
Eastern Oregon State College	OR	6,090	C
Eastern Washington Univ	WA	5,439	LC
Elizabeth City State Univ	NC	4,254	LC
Elmhurst College	IL	12,536	C
Elon College	NC	12,290	LC
Emory and Henry College	VA	12,776	C
Emporia State Univ	KS	4,685	NC
Erskine College	SC	14,310	C
Eureka College	IL	14,555	C
Evangel College	MO	10,142	LC
Faulkner Univ	AL	8,630	LC
Ferrum College	VA	12,800	LC
Flagler College	FL	7,990	C
Florida International Univ	FL	4,191	VC
Florida Memorial College	FL	7,600	C+
Florida State Univ	FL	5,814	VC
Fort Valley State College	GA	3,974	LC
Fresno Pacific College	CA	13,020	C
Frostburg State Univ	MD	6,940	C
Gallaudet Univ	DC	9,850	SP
George Fox College	OR	15,640	LC
Georgetown College	KY	10,990	C
Georgia College	GA	4,310	LC
Georgia Southern Univ	GA	4,988	LC
Glenville State College	WV	4,810	LC
Gonzaga Univ	WA	16,350	VC
Goshen College	IN	12,360	C
Grace College	IN	12,120	C
Graceland College	IA	11,600	C
Grand Canyon Univ	AZ	9,680	VC
Grand Rapids Baptist College and Seminary	MI	10,228	C
Greensboro College	NC	11,496	C
Greenville College	IL	14,190	C
Guilford College	NC	17,680	C
Hampton Univ	VA	10,706	C
Hanover College	IN	10,950	VC
Hardin-Simmons Univ	TX	9,080	C
Heidelberg College	OH	17,160	C
Henderson State Univ	AR	3,860	C
High Point Univ	NC	12,350	LC
Hofstra Univ	NY	16,580	VC
Humboldt State Univ	CA	5,676	C
Huntington College	IN	13,220	C
Huston-Tillotson College	TX	8,490	C
Idaho State Univ	ID	4,442	C
Illinois Benedictine College	IL	14,170	C
Illinois College	IL	11,200	C
Illinois State Univ	IL	6,413	C
Indiana State Univ	IN	6,210	C
Indiana Univ Bloomington	IN	6,495	VC
Indiana Univ-Purdue Univ at Indianapolis	IN	5,862	LC
Indiana Wesleyan Univ	IN	12,332	C
Iowa State Univ	IA	5,456	C
Iowa Wesleyan College	IA	13,250	C
Ithaca College	NY	19,679	C
John Brown Univ	AR	9,880	VC
John Carroll Univ	OH	16,510	C
Johnson C. Smith Univ	NC	8,916	LC
Judson College	IL	13,625	C
Kansas Wesleyan Univ	KS	11,770	C
Keene State College	NH	7,081	C
Kennesaw State College	GA	1,553	C
Kent State Univ	OH	6,740	LC
Kentucky State Univ	KY	4,282	C+
Kentucky Wesleyan College	KY	11,550	C
King's College	NY	12,360	LC
Knoxville College	TN	8,320	LC
La Sierra Univ	CA	15,472	C
Lander Univ	SC	6,180	LC
Langston Univ	OK	2,907	LC
Le Tourneau Univ	TX	12,500	C+
Lee College	TN	7,894	LC
LeMoyne-Owen College	TN	4,500	LC
Liberty Univ	VA	11,500	LC
Lincoln Univ	MO	4,638	NC
Linfield College	OR	16,670	VC
Lock Haven Univ of Penn	PA	7,128	C
Longwood College	VA	7,800	C
Louisiana Tech Univ	LA	4,284	C
Lubbock Christian Univ	TX	9,840	NC
Lyndon State College	VT	8,394	LC
Malone College	OH	12,572	C
Manhattan College	NY	19,000	C
Marian College	IN	12,936	C
Mars Hill College	NC	11,050	C
Marywood College	PA	14,890	C
McKendree College	IL	10,900	C
McMurry Univ	TX	10,100	C
Messiah College	PA	14,664	VC
Methodist College	NC	12,400	C
Metropolitan State College of Denver	CO	1,751	NC
Miami Univ	OH	8,066	VC
Mich State Univ	MI	7,842	C
MidAmerica Nazarene College	KS	10,208	NC
Midwestern State Univ	TX	4,542	LC
Millikin Univ	IL	15,499	C
Miss State Univ	MS	5,629	VC
Miss Univ for Women	MS	4,456	LC
Miss Valley State Univ	MS	4,089	NC
Missouri Baptist College	MO	9,340	C
Missouri Valley College	MO	14,050	LC
Monmouth College	IL	17,300	C+
Montana State Univ	MT	5,534	C
Montclair State College	NJ	7,539	C+
Morehead State Univ	KY	4,600	LC
Morehouse College	GA	13,224	LC
Morgan State Univ	MD	7,366	C+
Morningside College	IA	13,896	C
Mount Vernon Nazarene College	OH	10,390	C
Muskingum College	OH	16,650	C
Nebr Wesleyan Univ	NE	12,240	C
New England College	NH	17,870	LC
New Mexico State Univ	NM	4,844	LC
Nicholls State Univ	LA	4,531	NC
Norfolk State Univ	VA	6,345	LC
N Car Agricultural and Technical State Univ	NC	4,477	LC
N Car Central Univ	NC	4,347	LC
N Car Wesleyan College	NC	12,480	LC
N Dak State Univ of Agriculture and Applied Science	ND	4,774	VC
Northeast Missouri State Univ	MO	5,654	VC+
Northeastern Illinois Univ	IL	1,955	C
Northeastern Univ	MA	19,851	C
Northern Kentucky Univ	KY	4,620	NC
Northern Mich Univ	MI	6,350	C
Northern Montana College	MT	4,976	C
Northern State Univ	SD	4,186	LC
Northwest Missouri State Univ	MO	5,010	LC
Northwest Nazarene College	ID	11,750	C
Northwestern College	MN	13,554	C
Northwestern College of Iowa	IA	12,250	C
Northwestern Okla State Univ	OK	3,424	C
Norwich Univ	VT	18,730	C
Oakwood College	AL	10,005	C
Ohio Northern Univ	OH	18,660	VC
Ohio State Univ	OH	7,218	LC
Ohio Wesleyan Univ	OH	21,108	VC+
Okla Christian Univ of Science and Arts	OK	8,790	NC
Olivet College	MI	14,000	C
Pacific Christian College	CA	12,700	C
Pacific Lutheran Univ	WA	15,998	VC
Pacific Union College	CA	15,075	C
Pacific Univ	OR	17,869	C
Palm Beach Atlantic College	FL	10,720	C
Paul Quinn College	TX	7,090	LC
Pembroke State Univ	NC	3,538	LC
Pepperdine Univ	CA	23,720	VC
Peru State College	NE	4,311	NC
Pfeiffer College	NC	11,670	LC
Phillips Univ	OK	12,744	C
Pillsbury Baptist Bible College	MN	7,390	NC
Plymouth State College	NH	7,166	C
Point Loma Nazarene College	CA	13,532	C
Pontifical Catholic Univ of PR/Ponce	PR	5,807	C
Purdue Univ/West Lafayette	IN	6,636	C
Quincy Univ	IL	13,646	VC
Radford Univ	VA	7,034	LC
Roanoke College	VA	16,975	C
Rockford College	IL	15,300	C
Rocky Mountain College	MT	11,320	C
Russell Sage College	NY	16,790	C
Rust College	MS	6,600	LC
Rutgers Univ/Cook College	NJ	9,197	HC
Rutgers Univ/Douglass College	NJ	8,795	VC
St Ambrose Univ	IA	13,380	C
St Andrews Presbyterian College	NC	14,240	LC
St Augustine's College	NC	9,300	C+
St Bonaventure Univ	NY	14,762	C
St Joseph's College	ME	14,535	C
St Leo College	FL	13,570	C
St Olaf College	MN	17,200	HC
Salisbury State Univ	MD	7,516	C+
Sam Houston State Univ	TX	4,506	C
San Francisco State Univ	CA	7,292	LC
Seattle Pacific Univ	WA	16,503	C
Selma Univ	AL	5,785	NC
Seton Hall Univ	NJ	18,306	LC
Shaw Univ	NC	8,936	C+
Shenandoah Univ	VA	11,800	C
Skidmore College	NY	23,230	HC
S Car State Univ	SC	5,424	LC
Southeastern Louisiana Univ	LA	4,230	NC
Southeastern Okla State Univ	OK	3,594	C
Southern Calif College	CA	12,356	C
Southern Conn State Univ	CT	7,532	C
Southern Illinois Univ at Carbondale	IL	6,234	C
Southern Nazarene Univ	OK	9,206	NC
Southern Univ and A&M College	LA	4,920	NC
Southern Univ at New Orleans	LA	1,452	NC
Southern Utah Univ	UT	4,104	LC
Southwest Baptist Univ	MO	9,192	NC
Southwest Missouri State Univ	MO	4,956	C
Southwest State Univ	MN	5,400	NC
Southwest Texas State Univ	TX	5,124	C
Southwestern Okla State Univ	OK	3,312	C
Springfield College	MA	15,200	LC
SUNY/College at Brockport	NY	7,220	C+
Sterling College	KS	10,990	VC
Syracuse Univ	NY	21,305	HC
Tabor College	KS	11,460	VC
Tarleton State Univ	TX	4,082	LC
Taylor Univ	IN	14,450	VC
Temple Univ	PA	10,281	C
Tenn Tech Univ	TN	5,190	C
Tenn Wesleyan College	TN	10,060	C
Texas A&M Univ	TX	5,382	VC
Texas A&M Univ at Kingsville	TX	3,808	LC
Texas Christian Univ	TX	12,180	C
Texas College	TX	5,930	NC
Texas Tech Univ	TX	6,008	C
Texas Wesleyan Univ	TX	9,380	LC
The Citadel	SC	6,619	C
Towson State Univ	MD	7,452	C
Trenton State College	NJ	9,085	HC
Trevecca Nazarene College	TN	9,826	NC
Tri-State Univ	IN	13,788	LC
Troy State Univ	AL	4,322	C
Turabo Univ	PR	2,670	
Tusculum College	TN	10,400	LC
Tuskegee Univ	AL	10,128	C
Union Univ	TN	7,880	C+
Univ of Alabama	AL	5,702	C
Univ of Alabama at Birmingham	AL	7,533	C
Univ of Alaska Anchorage	AK	7,131	C
Univ of Alaska Fairbanks	AK	4,718	C
Univ of Arizona	AZ	5,808	C
Univ of Arkansas at Fayetteville	AR	5,046	C
Univ of Arkansas at Monticello	AR	3,832	NC
Univ of Arkansas at Pine Bluff	AR	3,978	LC
Univ of Calif at Berkeley	CA	9,962	HC+
Univ of Calif at Davis	CA	9,534	VC
Univ of Central Arkansas	AR	4,200	LC
Univ of Central Florida	FL	6,061	C+
Univ of Charleston	WV	12,750	C
Univ of Conn	CT	9,168	C
Univ of Delaware	DE	8,013	VC
Univ of Dubuque	IA	14,150	LC
Univ of Evansville	IN	15,300	VC
Univ of Findlay	OH	15,764	C
Univ of Hawaii at Manoa	HI	5,626	C
Univ of Houston	TX	5,215	C
Univ of Idaho	ID	4,830	C
Univ of Illinois at Chicago	IL	8,443	C
Univ of Illinois at Urbana-Champaign	IL	7,764	HC
Univ of Indianapolis	IN	14,510	C
Univ of Iowa	IA	5,658	VC
Univ of Kansas	KS	5,200	NC
Univ of Kentucky	KY	5,152	VC
Univ of Louisville	KY	5,948	C
Univ of Maine	ME	7,990	C
Univ of Maine at Presque Isle	ME	6,374	C
Univ of Mary	ND	8,910	C
Univ of Maryland/College Park	MD	8,182	VC
Univ of Maryland/Eastern Shore	MD	6,254	LC
Univ of Mass/Boston	MA	4,253	C
Univ of Memphis	TN	3,476	C
Univ of Mich/Ann Arbor	MI	9,428	HC+
Univ of Minn/Duluth	MN	6,512	C
Univ of Minn/Twin Cities	MN	6,682	VC
Univ of Missouri/St. Louis	MO	6,378	C
Univ of Mobile	AL	9,400	C
Univ of Montana	MT	5,529	C
Univ of Nebr at Kearney	NE	4,308	LC
Univ of Nebr at Omaha	NE	1,889	LC
Univ of Nevada/Las Vegas	NV	6,405	C
Univ of New Hampshire	NH	8,242	C
Univ of New Orleans	LA	5,468	C
Univ of N Car at Wilmington	NC	5,172	C
Univ of North Texas	TX	4,853	C
Univ of Northern Colo	CO	6,008	C
Univ of Northern Iowa	IA	5,137	C
Univ of Puget Sound	WA	19,520	HC
Univ of Rhode Island	RI	9,205	C
Univ of Rio Grande	OH	6,300	NC
Univ of St Thomas	MN	15,785	C+
Univ of San Francisco	CA	18,408	C
Univ of South Alabama	AL	5,451	C
Univ of S Car	SC	6,158	C
Univ of S Car at Spartanburg	SC	2,320	C
Univ of S Dak	SD	4,722	C
Univ of Tampa	FL	16,780	C
Univ of Tenn/Knoxville	TN	5,668	C
Univ of Texas at Arlington	TX	5,549	LC
Univ of Texas at El Paso	TX	3,160	LC
Univ of Texas at San Antonio	TX	6,420	C
Univ of the District of Columbia	DC	974	NC
Univ of the Ozarks	AR	7,770	C
Univ of the Pacific	CA	21,100	C
Univ of the Sacred Heart	PR	3,890	
Univ of Wisc/Eau Claire	WI	4,647	C
Univ of Wisc/La Crosse	WI	4,487	C
Univ of Wisc/Madison	WI	6,400	HC
Univ of Wisc/Oshkosh	WI	4,240	C
Univ of Wisc/Platteville	WI	4,830	C
Univ of Wisc/River Falls	WI	4,655	C
Univ of Wisc/Stevens Point	WI	5,047	C+
Univ of Wisc/Superior	WI	4,330	C
Univ of Wisc/Whitewater	WI	4,700	C
Univ of Wyoming	WY	4,991	NC
Upper Iowa Univ	IA	11,900	C
Urbana Univ	OH	12,536	C
Utah State Univ	UT	4,683	C
Valdosta State Univ	GA	4,670	LC
Virginia Polytechnic Inst and State Univ	VA	6,828	C
Virginia State Univ	VA	7,040	
Walla Walla College	WA	13,215	C
Walsh Univ	OH	11,640	C
Wayland Baptist Univ	TX	7,811	NC
Wayne State Univ	MI	2,680	C
Weber State Univ	UT	4,398	C
Wesley College	DE	13,745	LC
West Georgia College	GA	4,256	C
West Texas A&M Univ	TX	4,224	C
West Virginia Univ	WV	5,774	C
West Virginia Wesleyan College	WV	16,900	C
Western Baptist College	OR	12,400	LC
Western Carolina Univ	NC	3,811	C
Western Kentucky Univ	KY	4,808	C
Western Maryland College	MD	18,990	C
Western New Mexico Univ	NM	3,234	LC
Western Oregon State College	OR	6,180	C
Westmont College	CA	18,732	C
Wheaton College	IL	14,710	HC
Whittier College	CA	21,661	C
Wiley College	TX	0	NC
William Carey College	MS	7,050	C
William Paterson College	NJ	7,438	C+
William Woods Univ	MO	14,025	LC
Wilmington College	OH	13,700	LC
Winston-Salem State Univ	NC	4,142	LC
Winthrop Univ	SC	6,750	C
Wright State Univ	OH	6,896	LC
Xavier Univ of Louisiana	LA	10,400	C
Youngstown State Univ	OH	6,447	LC

PHYSICAL FITNESS/MOVEMENT

School	ST	$IS	SR
Adams State College	CO	4,910	C
Adelphi Univ	NY	18,250	LC
Albertson College	ID	15,942	C+
Arizona State Univ Main Campus	AZ	6,444	C
Auburn Univ	AL	5,823	C+
Baldwin-Wallace College	OH	15,210	C
Ball State Univ	IN	6,032	LC
Black Hills State Univ	SD	4,831	NC
Boston Univ	MA	24,130	HC
Bridgewater State College	MA	7,518	C
Calif Univ of Penn	PA	7,370	C
Carroll College	WI	15,490	C
College of St Catherine	MN	14,670	C
Concordia College	NE	11,776	NC
Concordia Univ	IL	12,611	C
Eastern Nazarene College	MA	12,165	LC
Eureka College	IL	14,555	C
Fort Lewis College	CO	5,097	C
George Washington Univ	DC	22,470	HC
Gordon College	MA	16,790	C
Grand Canyon Univ	AZ	9,680	VC
Hardin-Simmons Univ	TX	9,080	C
Ithaca College	NY	19,679	C
James Madison Univ	VA	8,198	HC
Kansas Newman College	KS	10,640	C
Liberty Univ	VA	11,500	LC
Limestone College	SC	10,700	LC
Marshall Univ	WV	5,762	LC
Marymount Univ	VA	15,930	C
Miami Univ	OH	8,066	VC
New Mexico Highlands Univ	NM	3,772	C
N Dak State Univ of Agriculture and Applied Science	ND	4,774	VC
Northeast Missouri State Univ	MO	5,654	VC+
Northeastern Univ	MA	19,851	C
Northern Kentucky Univ	KY	4,620	NC
Northern Mich Univ	MI	6,350	C
Northwest Nazarene College	ID	11,750	C
Occidental College	CA	21,792	HC
Penn State Univ/Univ Park Campus	PA	8,752	HC
Rice Univ	TX	15,110	MC

School	ST	$IS	SR
Rutgers Univ/Cook College	NJ	9,197	HC
Rutgers Univ/Douglass College	NJ	8,795	VC
Rutgers Univ/Livingston College	NJ	8,877	VC
Rutgers Univ/Rutgers College	NJ	8,841	HC+
Rutgers Univ/Univ College—New Brunswick	NJ	0	LC
Salisbury State Univ	MD	7,516	C+
Seattle Pacific Univ	WA	16,503	C
Southwest Texas State Univ	TX	5,124	C
Southwestern Univ	TX	15,484	HC
Spring Arbor College	MI	12,256	C
Springfield College	MA	15,200	LC
SUNY at Buffalo	NY	7,896	VC
Stetson Univ	FL	16,435	VC
Tarleton State Univ	TX	4,082	LC
Texas Christian Univ	TX	12,180	C
Texas Tech Univ	TX	6,008	C
Texas Woman's Univ	TX	4,392	C
Univ of Alabama	AL	5,702	C
Univ of Colo at Boulder	CO	6,410	VC
Univ of Dayton	OH	15,120	C+
Univ of Evansville	IN	15,300	VC
Univ of Florida	FL	5,850	HC
Univ of Iowa	IA	5,658	VC
Univ of Maryland/College Park	MD	8,182	VC
Univ of Mass/Amherst	MA	9,364	LC
Univ of Mich/Ann Arbor	MI	9,428	HC+
Univ of N Dak	ND	4,902	NC
Univ of North Texas	TX	4,853	C
Univ of Northern Colo	CO	6,008	C
Univ of St Thomas	MN	15,785	C+
Univ of Tenn at Chattanooga	TN	5,375	C
Univ of Texas at Austin	TX	5,160	VC
Univ of Texas-Pan American	TX	3,192	NC
Univ of Toledo	OH	6,636	NC
Univ of Utah	UT	5,975	C
West Virginia Univ	WV	5,774	C
Western State College of Colo	CO	5,560	C
Westmont College	CA	18,732	C
Winona State Univ	MN	5,200	VC

PHYSICAL SCIENCES

School	ST	$IS	SR
Albertus Magnus College	CT	16,280	LC
Arkansas Tech Univ	AR	4,200	NC
Armstrong State College	GA	4,874	LC
Asbury College	KY	11,105	VC
Bridgewater College	VA	15,300	C
Calif Baptist College	CA	11,294	C
Cal State/Hayward	CA	5,495	C
Cal State/Los Angeles	CA	4,940	VC
Cal State/Sacramento	CA	6,387	C
Cal State/Stanislaus	CA	6,799	C
Central Conn State Univ	CT	7,108	C
Central Mich Univ	MI	6,737	LC
Colo State Univ	CO	6,566	VC
Concordia College	MI	13,660	C
Concordia College	MN	13,200	C
Concordia College	NE	11,776	NC
Doane College	NE	12,220	C
East Stroudsburg Univ	PA	6,886	C
Emporia State Univ	KS	4,685	NC
Eureka College	IL	14,555	C
Harvard Univ/Harvard and Radcliffe Colleges	MA	24,880	MC
La Sierra Univ	CA	15,472	C
Mayville State Univ	ND	4,272	NC
Mich State Univ	MI	7,842	C
Midwestern State Univ	TX	4,542	LC
Miss Univ for Women	MS	4,456	LC
Northwest Nazarene College	ID	11,750	C
Pacific Union College	CA	15,075	C
Peru State College	NE	4,311	NC
Radford Univ	VA	7,034	LC
St John's Univ	NY	8,980	C+
Shawnee State Univ	OH	4,379	NC
Southern Utah Univ	UT	4,104	LC
Texas Wesleyan Univ	TX	9,380	LC
Tri-State Univ	IN	13,788	LC
Troy State Univ at Dothan/Fort Rucker	AL	2,260	NC
Union Univ	TN	7,880	C+
Univ of Calif at Berkeley	CA	9,962	HC+
Univ of Calif, Riverside	CA	9,178	C
Univ of Dayton	OH	15,120	C+
Univ of Maryland/College Park	MD	8,182	VC
Univ of N Dak	ND	4,902	NC
Univ of the Ozarks	AR	7,770	C
Univ of the Pacific	CA	21,100	C
Univ of Wisc/Eau Claire	WI	4,647	C
Univ of Wisc/Platteville	WI	4,830	C
Univ of Wisc/River Falls	WI	4,655	C
Warner Pacific College	OR	12,112	C
Washington Univ	MO	23,507	HC
Weber State Univ	UT	4,398	C
Winston-Salem State Univ	NC	4,142	LC
York College of Penn	PA	8,345	C

PHYSICAL THERAPY

School	ST	$IS	SR
American International College	MA	14,029	C
Andrews Univ	MI	14,952	NC
Auburn Univ	AL	5,823	C+
Austin Peay State Univ	TN	4,350	C
Bowling Green State Univ	OH	6,701	C
Briar Cliff College	IA	13,375	C
Brooklyn Campus of LIU	NY	15,000	LC
Cal State/Fresno	CA	5,747	C
Cal State/Long Beach	CA	6,057	LC
Cal State/Northridge	CA	7,122	LC
Carson-Newman College	TN	11,250	C
Carthage College	WI	15,995	C
Cedarville College	OH	10,715	C
Centenary College of Louisiana	LA	11,826	C+
CUNY/Hunter College	NY	4,101	VC
Cleveland State Univ	OH	7,287	NC
College of St Mary	NE	12,500	C
College of St Scholastica	MN	14,868	C
Coppin State College	MD	7,145	LC
Creighton Univ	NE	14,432	VC
Cumberland College	KY	9,756	C
D'Youville College	NY	12,850	C
Daemen College	NY	13,020	LC
East Carolina Univ	NC	4,498	C
East Tenn State Univ	TN	4,406	C
Eastern Washington Univ	WA	5,439	LC
Florida A&M Univ	FL	4,651	C
Florida International Univ	FL	4,191	VC
Gannon Univ	PA	14,872	C
Grambling State Univ	LA	4,712	NC
Grand Valley State Univ	MI	6,822	VC
Gustavus Adolphus College	MN	15,935	VC
Hardin-Simmons Univ	TX	9,080	C
Howard Univ	DC	11,680	C
Huntingdon College	AL	11,400	C
Indiana Univ Bloomington	IN	6,495	VC
Indiana Univ-Purdue Univ at Indianapolis	IN	5,862	LC
Ithaca College	NY	19,679	C
Juniata College	PA	18,390	C+
Kean College of New Jersey	NJ	6,395	LC
Lamar Univ	TX	3,798	C
Langston Univ	OK	2,907	LC
Lebanon Valley College of Penn	PA	18,300	C
Lewis Univ	IL	14,797	LC
Louisiana State Univ in Shreveport	LA	1,910	NC
Luther College	IA	15,900	VC
Marquette Univ	WI	16,114	VC
Maryville College	TN	14,474	C
Maryville Univ-St Louis	MO	12,900	VC
Miss College	MS	8,348	C
New York Univ	NY	24,705	VC+
North Park College	IL	14,310	C
Northeast Missouri State Univ	MO	5,654	VC+
Northeastern Univ	MA	19,851	C
Northern Illinois Univ	IL	6,408	C
Northwest Nazarene College	ID	11,750	C
Oakland Univ	MI	6,714	VC
Ohio State Univ	OH	7,218	LC
Ohio Univ	OH	7,341	C
Ohio Wesleyan Univ	OH	21,108	VC+
Okla Baptist Univ	OK	8,486	C
Oregon State Univ	OR	6,175	C
Peru State College	NE	4,311	NC
Phillips Univ	OK	12,744	C
Purdue Univ/Calumet	IN	2,374	NC
Quinnipiac College	CT	17,600	C+
Richard Stockton College of New Jersey	NJ	6,950	VC
Rockhurst College	MO	12,470	C
Russell Sage College	NY	16,790	C
St Ambrose Univ	IA	13,380	C
St Augustine's College	NC	9,300	C+
St Francis College	PA	15,744	LC
St Louis Univ	MO	15,522	VC
St Mary's College of Minn	MN	13,850	LC
San Francisco State Univ	CA	7,292	LC
Shepherd College	WV	5,540	C
Simmons College	MA	22,534	C
Simpson College	IA	14,635	VC
Southeastern Louisiana Univ	LA	4,230	NC
Southeastern Okla State Univ	OK	3,594	C
Southern Illinois Univ at Carbondale	IL	6,234	C
Southern Univ and A&M College	LA	4,920	NC
Southwest Baptist Univ	MO	9,192	NC
Springfield College	MA	15,200	LC
SUNY at Buffalo	NY	7,896	VC
SUNY at Stony Brook	NY	7,658	VC
Tarleton State Univ	TX	4,082	LC
Teikyo Westmar Univ	IA	15,920	C
Temple Univ	PA	10,281	C
Tenn State Univ	TN	4,626	C+
The Univ of New Mexico	NM	5,304	C
Thiel College	PA	16,282	C
Touro College	NY	11,930	C
Univ of Central Arkansas	AR	4,200	LC
Univ of Central Florida	FL	6,061	C+
Univ of Conn	CT	9,168	C
Univ of Evansville	IN	15,300	VC
Univ of Florida	FL	5,850	HC
Univ of Houston-Downtown	TX	4,034	NC
Univ of Illinois at Chicago	IL	8,443	C
Univ of Indianapolis	IN	14,510	C
Univ of Kentucky	KY	5,152	VC
Univ of Louisville	KY	5,948	C
Univ of Maryland/Eastern Shore	MD	6,254	LC
Univ of Mich/Flint	MI	2,916	C
Univ of Minn/Twin Cities	MN	6,682	VC
Univ of Missouri/Columbia	MO	6,254	HC
Univ of Montana	MT	5,529	C
Univ of Nebr-Lincoln	NE	5,278	LC
Univ of New England	ME	16,075	LC
Univ of New Orleans	LA	5,468	C
Univ of N Car at Chapel Hill	NC	5,330	HC
Univ of N Dak	ND	4,902	NC
Univ of North Florida	FL	5,082	C
Univ of Northern Iowa	IA	5,137	C
Univ of Scranton	PA	17,071	VC
Univ of South Alabama	AL	5,451	C
Univ of Tenn at Chattanooga	TN	5,375	C
Univ of Tenn/Knoxville	TN	5,668	C
Univ of Texas at San Antonio	TX	6,420	C
Univ of Texas-Pan American	TX	3,192	NC
Univ of Toledo	OH	6,636	NC
Univ of Utah	UT	5,975	C
Univ of Vermont	VT	10,776	C+
Univ of Washington	WA	6,618	VC
Univ of Wisc/La Crosse	WI	4,487	C
Univ of Wisc/Madison	WI	6,400	HC
Utica College of Syracuse Univ	NY	16,714	LC
Villanova Univ	PA	21,400	HC
Virginia Commonwealth Univ	VA	7,909	C
Wartburg College	IA	14,530	VC
Wayne State Univ	MI	2,680	C
West Virginia Univ	WV	5,774	C
Western State College of Colo	CO	5,560	C
Wichita State Univ	KS	5,068	NC
William Carey College	MS	7,050	C
William Penn College	IA	13,400	C
Winona State Univ	MN	5,200	VC
Winston-Salem State Univ	NC	4,142	LC

PHYSICIAN'S ASSISTANT

School	ST	$IS	SR
CUNY/College of Staten Island	NY	2,558	NC
D'Youville College	NY	12,850	C
Dana College	NE	11,910	C
East Texas State Univ	TX	4,572	LC
Gannon Univ	PA	14,872	C
George Washington Univ	DC	22,470	HC
Howard Univ	DC	11,680	C
Idaho State Univ	ID	4,442	C
King's College	PA	15,420	C
Lenoir-Rhyne College	NC	14,068	C
Mars Hill College	NC	11,050	C
Peru State College	NE	4,311	NC
Rochester Inst of Tech	NY	18,954	VC
Rutgers Univ/Livingston College	NJ	8,877	VC
St Francis College	PA	15,744	LC
St John's Univ	NY	8,980	C+
Salem College	NC	16,025	C
Springfield College	MA	15,200	LC
SUNY at Stony Brook	NY	7,658	VC
Trevecca Nazarene College	TN	9,826	NC
Univ of Alabama at Birmingham	AL	7,533	C
Univ of Florida	FL	5,850	HC
Univ of Houston-Downtown	TX	4,034	NC
Univ of Kentucky	KY	5,152	VC
Univ of Wisc/Madison	WI	6,400	HC
Wagner College	NY	17,950	C

PHYSICS

School	ST	$IS	SR
Abilene Christian Univ	TX	10,460	NC
Adams State College	CO	4,910	C
Adelphi Univ	NY	18,250	LC
Adrian College	MI	14,340	C
Agnes Scott College	GA	17,135	VC
Alabama A&M Univ	AL	4,200	C
Alabama State Univ	AL	3,428	NC
Albertson College	ID	15,942	C+
Albion College	MI	18,264	VC
Alfred Univ	NY	21,054	VC+
Allegheny College	PA	21,020	VC
Alma College	MI	16,375	VC+
American Univ	DC	21,230	VC+
Amherst College	MA	24,152	MC
Anderson Univ	IN	12,920	C
Andrews Univ	MI	14,952	NC
Angelo State Univ	TX	5,176	C
Antioch College	OH	19,532	C
Appalachian State Univ	NC	4,095	C
Arizona State Univ Main Campus	AZ	6,444	C
Arkansas State Univ	AR	4,250	NC
Ashland Univ	OH	15,508	C
Auburn Univ	AL	5,823	C+
Augsburg College	MN	15,608	C
Augusta College	GA	1,452	C
Augustana College	IL	16,959	VC
Augustana College	SD	13,420	C
Aurora Univ	IL	13,381	C
Austin College	TX	14,999	VC
Austin Peay State Univ	TN	4,350	C
Azusa Pacific Univ	CA	15,034	C
Baker Univ	KS	12,284	C
Baldwin-Wallace College	OH	15,210	C
Ball State Univ	IN	6,032	LC
Bard College	NY	25,269	HC
Bates College	ME	23,990	MC
Baylor Univ	TX	10,990	C+
Belmont Univ	TN	10,540	C
Beloit College	WI	18,950	VC+
Bemidji State Univ	MN	5,188	C
Benedict College	SC	8,376	LC
Benedictine College	KS	12,830	C
Bennington College	VT	24,850	VC+
Berea College	KY	2,883	VC+
Berry College	GA	11,990	VC
Bethany College	WV	18,300	C+
Bethel College	KS	11,530	C
Bethel College	MN	15,050	C
Bethune-Cookman College	FL	8,375	LC
Birmingham-Southern College	AL	15,154	VC+
Bloomsburg Univ of Penn	PA	6,312	C+
Boise State Univ	ID	4,909	LC
Boston College	MA	22,706	MC
Boston Univ	MA	24,130	HC
Bowdoin College	ME	24,155	MC
Bowling Green State Univ	OH	6,701	C
Bradley Univ	IL	14,718	C+
Brandeis Univ	MA	25,585	HC
Bridgewater College	VA	15,300	C
Bridgewater State College	MA	7,518	C
Brigham Young Univ	UT	5,625	HC
Brown Univ	RI	26,104	MC
Bryn Mawr College	PA	24,110	MC
Bucknell Univ	PA	22,320	HC
Buena Vista College	IA	16,150	VC
Butler Univ	IN	16,210	C
Calif Inst of Tech	CA	20,783	MC
Calif Lutheran Univ	CA	17,240	C
Calif Polytechnic State Univ	CA	6,980	VC+
Calif State Polytechnic Univ/Pomona	CA	6,438	LC
Cal State/Bakersfield	CA	5,402	C
Cal State/Chico	CA	6,146	C
Cal State/Dominguez Hills	CA	2,857	LC
Cal State/Fresno	CA	5,747	C
Cal State/Fullerton	CA	4,850	LC
Cal State/Hayward	CA	5,495	C
Cal State/Long Beach	CA	6,057	LC
Cal State/Los Angeles	CA	4,940	VC
Cal State/Northridge	CA	7,122	LC
Cal State/Sacramento	CA	6,387	C
Cal State/San Bernardino	CA	6,055	LC
Cal State/Stanislaus	CA	6,799	C
Calif Univ of Penn	PA	7,370	C
Calvin College	MI	13,020	VC
Cameron Univ	OK	3,686	LC
Canisius College	NY	15,510	C
Carleton College	MN	22,155	HC
Carnegie Mellon Univ	PA	22,560	HC+
Carroll College	WI	15,490	C
Carthage College	WI	15,995	C
Case Western Reserve Univ	OH	19,910	HC
Catholic Univ of America	DC	18,856	C
Centenary College of Louisiana	LA	11,826	C+
Central College	IA	14,025	VC
Central Conn State Univ	CT	7,108	C
Central Mich Univ	MI	6,737	LC
Central Missouri State Univ	MO	5,138	LC
Central State Univ	OH	7,320	NC
Central Washington Univ	WA	5,644	C
Centre College	KY	15,850	VC+
Chadron State College	NE	4,091	NC
Charleston Southern Univ	SC	10,282	LC
Charter Oak State College	CT	314	NC
Chicago State Univ	IL	2,198	C
Christian Brothers Univ	TN	12,120	VC
Christian Heritage College	CA	11,756	C
Christopher Newport Univ	VA	3,196	LC
CUNY/Brooklyn College	NY	2,450	VC
CUNY/City College	NY	2,543	VC
CUNY/College of Staten Island	NY	2,558	NC
CUNY/Herbert H. Lehman College	NY	2,542	C
CUNY/Hunter College	NY	4,101	VC

School	ST	$IS	SR
CUNY/Queens College	NY	2,631	C
CUNY/York College	NY	2,534	NC
Claremont McKenna College	CA	22,150	MC
Clarion Univ of Penn	PA	6,518	C
Clark Atlanta Univ	GA	11,846	C
Clark Univ	MA	21,400	VC
Clarkson Univ	NY	20,705	VC+
Clemson Univ	SC	6,564	VC
Cleveland State Univ	OH	7,287	NC
Coe College	IA	17,085	VC
Colby College	ME	24,230	HC
Colgate Univ	NY	24,020	HC
College of Charleston	SC	6,250	C
College of New Rochelle	NY	15,440	LC
College of Notre Dame of Maryland	MD	16,050	C
College of St Benedict	MN	15,468	VC
College of St Catherine	MN	14,670	C
College of the Holy Cross	MA	23,850	HC
College of William and Mary	VA	8,602	MC
College of Wooster	OH	19,875	VC
Colo College	CO	20,038	HC
Colo School of Mines	CO	8,436	HC+
Colo State Univ	CO	6,566	VC
Columbia Univ/Barnard College	NY	25,492	HC
Columbia Univ/Columbia College	NY	26,757	MC
Concordia College/Moorhead	MN	12,750	C
Conn College	CT	24,160	HC
Cornell College	IA	18,425	VC
Cornell Univ	NY	13,445	MC
Creighton Univ	NE	14,432	VC
Cumberland College	KY	9,756	C
Curry College	MA	18,695	LC
Dakota State Univ	SD	4,374	LC
Dartmouth College	NH	24,354	MC
David Lipscomb Univ	TN	7,865	VC
Davidson College	NC	21,037	MC
Davis and Elkins College	WV	13,230	LC
Defiance College	OH	13,480	LC
Delaware State College	DE	5,656	C
Denison Univ	OH	21,150	VC+
DePaul Univ	IL	15,535	VC
DePauw Univ	IN	18,530	VC
Dickinson College	PA	22,705	HC
Dillard Univ	LA	9,950	C
Dordt College	IA	11,690	C
Drake Univ	IA	17,195	VC
Drew Univ/College of Liberal Arts	NJ	23,406	HC
Drexel Univ	PA	15,970	C
Drury College	MO	12,140	VC
Duke Univ	NC	21,271	MC
Duquesne Univ	PA	16,434	VC
Earlham College	IN	19,383	VC
East Carolina Univ	NC	4,498	C
East Central Univ	OK	3,558	C
East Tenn State Univ	TN	4,406	C
East Texas State Univ	TX	4,572	LC
Eastern Illinois Univ	IL	5,548	C
Eastern Mich Univ	MI	6,749	C
Eastern Nazarene College	MA	12,165	LC
Eastern New Mexico Univ	NM	3,950	C
Eastern Oregon State College	OR	6,090	C
Eastern Washington Univ	WA	5,439	LC
Eckerd College	FL	18,855	VC
Edinboro Univ of Penn	PA	7,181	C
Edward Waters College	FL	8,300	NC
Elizabeth City State Univ	NC	4,254	LC
Elizabethtown College	PA	17,850	VC
Elmhurst College	IL	12,536	C
Elon College	NC	12,290	LC
Emmanuel College	MA	17,773	LC
Emory and Henry College	VA	12,776	C
Emory Univ	GA	21,930	HC
Emporia State Univ	KS	4,685	NC
Erskine College	SC	14,310	C
Evergreen State College	WA	6,306	C
Fairfield Univ	CT	20,460	VC
Fisk Univ	TN	0	LC
Florida A&M Univ	FL	4,651	C
Florida Atlantic Univ	FL	5,525	C
Florida Inst of Tech	FL	16,935	VC
Florida International Univ	FL	4,191	VC
Florida Southern College	FL	12,260	C
Florida State Univ	FL	5,814	VC
Fordham Univ/Fordham College	NY	19,875	VC
Fort Lewis College	CO	5,097	C
Francis Marion Univ	SC	5,878	LC
Franklin and Marshall College	PA	23,655	HC
Franklin College of Indiana	IN	13,970	C
Frostburg State Univ	MD	6,940	C
Furman Univ	SC	16,557	VC
Gallaudet Univ	DC	9,850	SP
Gannon Univ	PA	14,872	C
Geneva College	PA	13,030	C
George Mason Univ	VA	8,728	C
George Washington Univ	DC	22,470	HC
Georgetown College	KY	10,990	C
Georgetown Univ	DC	24,410	MC
Georgia Inst of Tech	GA	6,669	HC+
Georgia Southern Univ	GA	4,988	LC
Georgian Court College	NJ	12,550	C
Gettysburg College	PA	22,960	HC
Gonzaga Univ	WA	16,350	VC
Gordon College	MA	16,790	C
Goshen College	IN	12,360	C
Graceland College	IA	11,600	C
Grambling State Univ	LA	4,712	NC
Grand Valley State Univ	MI	6,822	VC
Greenville College	IL	14,190	C
Grinnell College	IA	20,680	HC+
Grove City College	PA	7,870	HC
Guilford College	NC	17,680	C
Gustavus Adolphus College	MN	15,935	VC
Hamilton College	NY	23,500	HC
Hamline Univ	MN	17,122	VC
Hampden-Sydney College	VA	17,372	C+
Hampshire College	MA	25,320	C
Hampton Univ	VA	10,706	C
Hanover College	IN	10,950	VC
Hardin-Simmons Univ	TX	9,080	C
Harding Univ	AR	9,050	VC
Hartwick College	NY	20,950	C
Harvard Univ/Harvard and Radcliffe Colleges	MA	24,880	MC
Harvey Mudd College	CA	23,316	MC
Hastings College	NE	12,426	C
Haverford College	PA	23,950	MC
Heidelberg College	OH	17,160	C
Henderson State Univ	AR	3,860	C
Hendrix College	AR	11,670	C
Hillsdale College	MI	15,110	VC
Hobart and William Smith Colleges	NY	23,925	VC
Hofstra Univ	NY	16,580	VC
Hollins College	VA	18,484	C
Hope College	MI	15,698	C+
Houghton College	NY	13,120	VC
Howard Univ	DC	11,680	C
Humboldt State Univ	CA	5,676	C
Idaho State Univ	ID	4,442	C
Illinois Benedictine College	IL	14,170	C
Illinois College	IL	11,200	C
Illinois Inst of Tech	IL	18,290	VC
Illinois State Univ	IL	6,413	C
Illinois Wesleyan Univ	IL	18,590	HC+
Indiana State Univ	IN	6,210	C
Indiana Univ Bloomington	IN	6,495	VC
Indiana Univ of Penn	PA	6,373	C
Indiana Univ-Purdue Univ at Fort Wayne	IN	2,500	LC
Indiana Univ-Purdue Univ at Indianapolis	IN	5,862	LC
Indiana Univ/South Bend	IN	2,141	LC
Iona College	NY	16,310	C
Iowa State Univ	IA	5,456	C
Ithaca College	NY	19,679	C
Jackson State Univ	MS	4,996	LC
Jacksonville State Univ	AL	4,080	LC
Jacksonville Univ	FL	13,390	C
James Madison Univ	VA	8,198	HC
John Carroll Univ	OH	16,510	C
Johns Hopkins Univ	MD	24,360	MC
Johnson C. Smith Univ	NC	8,916	LC
Juniata College	PA	18,390	C+
Kalamazoo College	MI	19,974	HC
Kansas State Univ	KS	4,816	NC
Kansas Wesleyan Univ	KS	11,770	C
Kent State Univ	OH	6,740	LC
Kentucky Wesleyan College	KY	11,550	C
Kenyon College	OH	22,430	HC+
King College	TN	11,500	C
King's College	PA	15,420	C
Knox College	IL	18,990	VC
Kutztown Univ	PA	6,528	C
La Salle Univ	PA	16,940	VC
La Sierra Univ	CA	15,472	C
Lafayette College	PA	23,450	HC
LaGrange College	GA	10,602	C
Lake Forest College	IL	19,960	VC
Lamar Univ	TX	3,798	C
Lambuth Univ	TN	8,395	C
Lawrence Tech Univ	MI	9,470	C
Lawrence Univ	WI	19,986	HC+
Le Moyne College	NY	15,180	C
Lebanon Valley College of Penn	PA	18,300	C
Lehigh Univ	PA	23,250	HC
Lenoir-Rhyne College	NC	14,068	C
Lewis and Clark College	OR	19,980	VC
Lewis Univ	IL	14,797	LC
Lincoln Univ	MO	4,638	NC
Lincoln Univ	PA	0	LC
Linfield College	OR	16,670	VC
Livingston Univ	AL	3,979	C
Lock Haven Univ of Penn	PA	7,128	C
LIU/C. W. Post Campus	NY	16,870	C
Longwood College	VA	7,800	C
Loras College	IA	14,160	C
Louisiana State Univ and A&M College	LA	5,605	C
Louisiana State Univ in Shreveport	LA	1,910	NC
Louisiana Tech Univ	LA	4,284	C
Loyola College	MD	18,035	VC
Loyola Marymount Univ	CA	18,560	C
Loyola Univ of Chicago	IL	15,880	C+
Loyola Univ/New Orleans	LA	15,660	C+
Luther College	IA	15,900	VC
Lycoming College	PA	17,200	LC
Lynchburg College	VA	17,000	C
Macalester College	MN	19,710	HC
MacMurray College	IL	12,800	C
Maharishi International Univ	IA	13,666	C
Manchester College	IN	13,240	LC
Manhattan College	NY	19,000	C
Manhattanville College	NY	20,450	LC
Mankato State Univ	MN	5,097	LC
Mansfield Univ	PA	6,348	C
Marietta College	OH	16,940	C+
Marlboro College	VT	23,305	C+
Marquette Univ	WI	16,114	VC
Marshall Univ	WV	5,762	LC
Mary Washington College	VA	7,910	HC
Mass Inst of Tech	MA	24,800	MC
McNeese State Univ	LA	4,543	NC
Mercer Univ	GA	15,123	C
Merrimack College	MA	18,025	C
Mesa State College	CO	5,127	NC
Messiah College	PA	14,664	VC
Metropolitan State College of Denver	CO	1,751	NC
Miami Univ	OH	8,066	VC
Mich State Univ	MI	7,842	C
Mich Tech Univ	MI	7,283	VC+
MidAmerica Nazarene College	KS	10,208	NC
Middle Tenn State Univ	TN	3,857	C
Middlebury College	VT	24,400	MC
Midwestern State Univ	TX	4,542	LC
Millersville Univ of Penn	PA	7,370	VC
Millikin Univ	IL	15,499	C
Millsaps College	MS	15,486	C+
Minot State Univ	ND	3,748	NC
Miss College	MS	8,348	C
Miss State Univ	MS	5,629	VC
Missouri Southern State College	MO	4,272	C
Monmouth College	IL	17,300	C+
Monmouth College	NJ	16,820	C
Montana State Univ	MT	5,534	C
Montclair State College	NJ	7,539	C+
Moorhead State Univ	MN	5,076	C
Moravian College	PA	18,960	VC
Morehead State Univ	KY	4,600	LC
Morehouse College	GA	13,224	LC
Morgan State Univ	MD	7,366	C+
Morningside College	IA	13,896	C
Morris Brown College	GA	12,234	NC
Mount Holyoke College	MA	23,630	VC
Mount Union College	OH	15,850	C
Muhlenberg College	PA	20,795	VC
Murray State Univ	KY	4,702	C
Muskingum College	OH	16,650	C
Nebr Wesleyan Univ	NE	12,240	C
New College of the Univ of South Florida	FL	5,697	MC
New Jersey Inst of Tech	NJ	9,965	VC
New Mexico Inst of Mining and Tech	NM	5,212	C+
New Mexico State Univ	NM	4,844	LC
New York Inst of Tech/Old Westbury	NY	13,914	LC
New York Univ	NY	24,705	VC+
North Adams State College	MA	7,750	C
N Car Agricultural and Technical State Univ	NC	4,477	LC
N Car Central Univ	NC	4,347	LC
N Car State Univ	NC	4,984	VC
North Central College	IL	15,498	VC
N Dak State Univ of Agriculture and Applied Science	ND	4,774	VC
North Georgia College	GA	4,103	LC
North Park College	IL	14,310	C
Northeast Louisiana Univ	LA	3,906	NC
Northeast Missouri State Univ	MO	5,654	VC+
Northeastern Illinois Univ	IL	1,955	C
Northeastern State Univ	OK	5,250	C
Northeastern Univ	MA	19,851	C
Northern Arizona Univ	AZ	4,844	C
Northern Illinois Univ	IL	6,408	C
Northern Kentucky Univ	KY	4,620	NC
Northern Mich Univ	MI	6,350	C
Northland College	WI	13,550	LC
Northwest Missouri State Univ	MO	5,010	LC
Northwest Nazarene College	ID	11,750	C
Northwestern Okla State Univ	OK	3,424	C
Northwestern State Univ of Louisiana	LA	4,287	NC
Northwestern Univ	IL	21,093	MC
Norwich Univ	VT	18,730	C
Oakland Univ	MI	6,714	VC
Oberlin College	OH	24,570	HC+
Occidental College	CA	21,792	HC
Oglethorpe Univ	GA	16,360	VC
Ohio Northern Univ	OH	18,660	VC
Ohio State Univ	OH	7,218	LC
Ohio Univ	OH	7,341	C
Ohio Wesleyan Univ	OH	21,108	VC+
Okla Baptist Univ	OK	8,486	C
Okla City Univ	OK	9,840	C
Okla State Univ	OK	5,086	VC
Old Dominion Univ	VA	8,317	C
Olivet Nazarene Univ	IL	11,976	C
Oral Roberts Univ	OK	10,607	C+
Oregon State Univ	OR	6,175	C
Otterbein College	OH	16,506	C
Ouachita Baptist Univ	AR	8,940	C
Pace Univ	NY	15,540	C
Pacific Lutheran Univ	WA	15,998	VC
Pacific Union College	CA	15,075	C
Pacific Univ	OR	17,869	C
Penn State Univ at Erie/Behrend College	PA	8,752	C
Penn State Univ/Univ Park Campus	PA	8,752	HC
Pittsburg State Univ	KS	4,478	NC
Pitzer College	CA	23,780	HC
Point Loma Nazarene College	CA	13,532	C
Polytechnic Univ/Brooklyn	NY	19,700	HC
Polytechnic Univ/Farmingdale	NY	20,700	VC
Pomona College	CA	23,820	MC
Pontifical Catholic Univ of PR/Ponce		5,807	
Portland State Univ	OR	7,191	C
Prairie View A&M Univ	TX	4,740	LC
Presbyterian College	SC	15,400	VC
Princeton Univ	NJ	24,650	MC
Principia College	IL	17,799	C
Purdue Univ/Calumet	IN	2,374	NC
Purdue Univ/West Lafayette	IN	6,636	C
Ramapo College of New Jersey	NJ	8,027	C+
Randolph-Macon College	VA	16,980	C
Randolph-Macon Woman's College	VA	19,100	C
Reed College	OR	24,480	HC+
Rensselaer Polytechnic Inst	NY	23,067	HC
Rhode Island College	RI	7,901	LC
Rhodes College	TN	19,624	HC
Rice Univ	TX	15,110	MC
Richard Stockton College of New Jersey	NJ	6,950	VC
Rider College	NJ	18,160	C
Ripon College	WI	18,320	C+
Roanoke College	VA	16,975	C
Roberts Wesleyan College	NY	13,317	C
Rochester Inst of Tech	NY	18,954	VC
Rockhurst College	MO	12,470	C
Rollins College	FL	20,875	VC
Rose-Hulman Inst of Tech	IN	16,400	HC
Rowan College of New Jersey	NJ	7,358	VC
Rust College	MS	6,600	LC
Rutgers Univ/Camden College of A&S	NJ	8,652	VC
Rutgers Univ/Douglass College	NJ	8,795	VC
Rutgers Univ/Livingston College	NJ	8,877	VC
Rutgers Univ/Newark College of A&S	NJ	8,645	C
Rutgers Univ/Rutgers College	NJ	8,841	HC+
Rutgers Univ/Univ College—Camden	NJ	3,506	C
Rutgers Univ/Univ College—New Brunswick	NJ	0	LC
Saginaw Valley State Univ	MI	6,634	LC
St Ambrose Univ	IA	13,380	C
St Andrews Presbyterian College	NC	14,240	LC
St Augustine's College	NC	9,300	C+
St Bonaventure Univ	NY	14,762	C
St Cloud State Univ	MN	5,015	C
St John Fisher College	NY	15,415	C
St John's Univ	MN	15,364	C
St John's Univ	NY	8,980	C+
St Joseph's Univ	PA	17,800	VC
St Lawrence Univ	NY	23,420	VC
St Louis Univ	MO	15,522	VC
St Mary's College of Maryland	MD	8,900	VC+
St Mary's College of Minn	MN	13,850	LC
St Mary's Univ	TX	12,064	C
St Michael's College	VT	17,930	C
St Norbert College	WI	15,710	VC
St Olaf College	MN	17,200	HC
St Peter's College	NJ	14,775	LC
St Vincent College	PA	13,934	LC
Salisbury State Univ	MD	7,516	C+
Sam Houston State Univ	TX	4,506	C
Samford Univ	AL	11,400	VC
San Diego State Univ	CA	6,692	LC
San Francisco State Univ	CA	7,292	LC
San Jose State Univ	CA	6,680	LC
Santa Clara Univ	CA	18,783	VC
Sarah Lawrence College	NY	24,975	HC
Savannah State College	GA	4,052	C
Scripps College	CA	23,600	HC
Seattle Pacific Univ	WA	16,503	C
Seattle Univ	WA	16,590	C
Selma Univ	AL	5,785	NC
Seton Hall Univ	NJ	18,306	LC
Seton Hill College	PA	14,320	C
Shippensburg Univ of Penn	PA	7,052	C

School	ST	$IS	SR
Siena College	NY	15,410	VC
Skidmore College	NY	23,230	HC
Slippery Rock Univ	PA	6,803	C
Smith College	MA	24,236	HC
Sonoma State Univ	CA	6,996	LC
S Car State Univ	SC	5,424	LC
S Dak School of Mines and Tech	SD	5,329	C
S Dak State Univ	SD	4,562	C
Southeast Missouri State Univ	MO	5,854	C
Southeastern Louisiana Univ	LA	4,230	NC
Southeastern Okla State Univ	OK	3,594	C
Southern College of Seventh-day Adventists	TN	11,348	NC
Southern College of Tech	GA	4	C
Southern Conn State Univ	CT	7,532	C
Southern Illinois Univ at Carbondale	IL	6,234	C
Southern Illinois Univ at Edwardsville	IL	6,097	LC
Southern Methodist Univ	TX	18,520	VC
Southern Nazarene Univ	OK	9,206	NC
Southern Oregon State College	OR	6,128	C
Southern Univ and A&M College	LA	4,920	NC
Southern Univ at New Orleans	LA	1,452	NC
Southwest Missouri State Univ	MO	4,956	C
Southwest State Univ	MN	5,400	NC
Southwest Texas State Univ	TX	5,124	C
Southwestern Adventist College	TX	10,530	NC
Southwestern College	KS	10,032	C
Southwestern Okla State Univ	OK	3,312	C
Southwestern Univ	TX	15,484	HC
Spelman College	GA	12,942	VC
Spring Arbor College	MI	12,256	C
Stanford Univ	CA	24,310	MC
SUNY at Albany	NY	7,059	VC
SUNY at Binghamton	NY	7,921	HC
SUNY at Buffalo	NY	7,896	VC
SUNY at Stony Brook	NY	7,658	VC
SUNY/College at Brockport	NY	7,220	C+
SUNY/College at Buffalo	NY	7,035	VC
SUNY/College at Cortland	NY	7,326	C+
SUNY/College at Fredonia	NY	7,159	VC
SUNY/College at Geneseo	NY	6,949	HC
SUNY/College at New Paltz	NY	6,890	VC
SUNY/College at Oneonta	NY	7,878	C
SUNY/College at Oswego	NY	7,330	VC
SUNY/College at Plattsburgh	NY	6,917	C
SUNY/College at Purchase	NY	7,324	C
SUNY/Potsdam College	NY	6,906	C
Stephen F. Austin State Univ	TX	5,117	C
Stetson Univ	FL	16,435	VC
Stevens Inst of Tech	NJ	21,980	VC+
Stillman College	AL	7,213	NC
Suffolk Univ	MA	15,360	LC
Susquehanna Univ	PA	19,950	VC
Swarthmore College	PA	24,136	MC
Sweet Briar College	VA	19,770	C
Syracuse Univ	NY	21,305	HC
Tabor College	KS	11,460	VC
Talladega College	AL	8,124	VC
Tarleton State Univ	TX	4,082	LC
Taylor Univ	IN	14,450	VC
Temple Univ	PA	10,281	C
Tenn State Univ	TN	4,626	C+
Tenn Tech Univ	TN	5,190	C
Texas A&M Univ	TX	5,382	VC
Texas A&M Univ at Kingsville	TX	3,808	LC
Texas Christian Univ	TX	12,180	C
Texas Southern Univ	TX	4,500	NC
Texas Tech Univ	TX	6,008	C
The Citadel	SC	6,619	C
The Univ of New Mexico	NM	5,304	C
Thiel College	PA	16,282	C
Thomas A. Edison State College	NJ	400	
Thomas More College	KY	12,962	C
Tougaloo College	MS	7,480	LC
Touro College	NY	11,930	C
Towson State Univ	MD	7,452	C
Transylvania Univ	KY	14,970	VC+
Trenton State College	NJ	9,085	HC
Trinity College	CT	24,120	HC
Trinity Univ	TX	16,670	HC
Tufts Univ	MA	24,962	MC
Tulane Univ	LA	24,540	HC
Tuskegee Univ	AL	10,128	C
Union College	KY	9,790	C
Union College	NE	11,060	NC
Union College	NY	23,817	HC
Union Univ	TN	7,880	C+
United States Air Force Academy	CO	0	MC
United States Military Academy	NY	0	MC
United States Naval Academy	MD	0	MC
Univ of Akron	OH	6,699	NC
Univ of Alabama	AL	5,702	C
Univ of Alabama at Birmingham	AL	7,533	C
Univ of Alabama at Huntsville	AL	5,868	VC
Univ of Alaska Fairbanks	AK	4,718	C
Univ of Arizona	AZ	5,808	C
Univ of Arkansas at Fayetteville	AR	5,046	C
Univ of Arkansas at Little Rock	AR	4,419	C
Univ of Arkansas at Pine Bluff	AR	3,978	LC
Univ of Bridgeport	CT	18,985	C
Univ of Calif at Berkeley	CA	9,962	HC+
Univ of Calif at Davis	CA	9,534	VC
Univ of Calif at Los Angeles	CA	8,959	HC
Univ of Calif at Santa Barbara	CA	9,460	C
Univ of Calif at Santa Cruz	CA	9,060	VC
Univ of Calif, Riverside	CA	9,178	C
Univ of Calif, San Diego	CA	10,028	VC+
Univ of Calif/Irvine	CA	12,680	VC
Univ of Central Arkansas	AR	4,200	LC
Univ of Central Florida	FL	6,061	C+
Univ of Central Okla	OK	3,647	C
Univ of Chicago	IL	24,517	MC
Univ of Cincinnati	OH	7,989	C
Univ of Colo at Boulder	CO	6,410	VC
Univ of Colo at Colo Springs	CO	2,269	C
Univ of Colo at Denver	CO	1,955	VC
Univ of Conn	CT	9,168	C
Univ of Dallas	TX	14,983	VC
Univ of Dayton	OH	15,120	C+
Univ of Delaware	DE	8,013	VC
Univ of Denver	CO	19,290	C+
Univ of Dubuque	IA	14,150	LC
Univ of Evansville	IN	15,300	VC
Univ of Florida	FL	5,850	HC
Univ of Georgia	GA	5,655	VC
Univ of Hartford	CT	19,858	LC
Univ of Hawaii at Hilo	HI	4,141	C
Univ of Hawaii at Manoa	HI	5,626	C
Univ of Houston	TX	5,215	C
Univ of Houston-Downtown	TX	4,034	NC
Univ of Idaho	ID	4,830	C
Univ of Illinois at Chicago	IL	8,443	C
Univ of Illinois at Urbana-Champaign	IL	7,764	HC
Univ of Indianapolis	IN	14,510	C
Univ of Iowa	IA	5,658	VC
Univ of Kansas	KS	5,200	NC
Univ of Kentucky	KY	5,152	VC
Univ of La Verne	CA	17,400	C
Univ of Louisville	KY	5,948	C
Univ of Lowell	MA	8,831	VC
Univ of Maine	ME	7,990	C
Univ of Maryland/Baltimore County	MD	7,746	VC
Univ of Maryland/College Park	MD	8,182	VC
Univ of Mass Dartmouth	MA	8,158	C
Univ of Mass/Amherst	MA	9,364	LC
Univ of Mass/Boston	MA	4,253	C
Univ of Memphis	TN	3,476	C
Univ of Miami	FL	22,107	VC
Univ of Mich/Ann Arbor	MI	9,428	HC+
Univ of Mich/Dearborn	MI	3,399	HC
Univ of Mich/Flint	MI	2,916	C
Univ of Minn/Duluth	MN	6,512	C
Univ of Minn/Morris	MN	6,825	HC
Univ of Minn/Twin Cities	MN	6,682	VC
Univ of Miss	MS	5,756	C
Univ of Missouri/Columbia	MO	6,254	HC
Univ of Missouri/Kansas City	MO	5,906	VC
Univ of Missouri/Rolla	MO	6,729	VC+
Univ of Missouri/St. Louis	MO	6,378	C
Univ of Montana	MT	5,529	C
Univ of Nebr at Kearney	NE	4,308	LC
Univ of Nebr at Omaha	NE	1,889	LC
Univ of Nebr-Lincoln	NE	5,278	LC
Univ of Nevada/Las Vegas	NV	6,405	C
Univ of Nevada/Reno	NV	5,735	C
Univ of New Hampshire	NH	8,242	C
Univ of New Orleans	LA	5,468	C
Univ of North Alabama	AL	4,236	NC
Univ of N Car at Asheville	NC	4,791	VC
Univ of N Car at Chapel Hill	NC	5,330	HC
Univ of N Car at Charlotte	NC	4,597	C
Univ of N Car at Greensboro	NC	5,192	C
Univ of N Car at Wilmington	NC	5,172	C
Univ of N Dak	ND	4,902	NC
Univ of North Texas	TX	4,853	C
Univ of Northern Colo	CO	6,008	C
Univ of Northern Iowa	IA	5,137	C
Univ of Notre Dame	IN	20,150	MC
Univ of Okla	OK	5,427	VC
Univ of Oregon	OR	6,466	VC
Univ of Penn	PA	24,238	MC
Univ of Pittsburgh	PA	9,472	C
Univ of Portland	OR	15,564	C
Univ of PR/Humacao Univ College	PR	1,494	
Univ of PR/Mayaguez	PR	0	
Univ of PR/Rio Piedras	PR	0	
Univ of Puget Sound	WA	19,520	HC
Univ of Redlands	CA	22,059	VC
Univ of Rhode Island	RI	9,205	C
Univ of Richmond	VA	16,700	HC
Univ of Rio Grande	OH	6,300	NC
Univ of Rochester	NY	23,696	HC
Univ of St Thomas	MN	15,785	C+
Univ of San Diego	CA	18,970	VC
Univ of San Francisco	CA	18,408	C
Univ of Science and Arts of Okla	OK	3,304	C
Univ of Scranton	PA	17,071	VC
Univ of South Alabama	AL	5,451	C
Univ of S Car	SC	6,158	C
Univ of S Dak	SD	4,722	C
Univ of South Florida	FL	5,475	C+
Univ of Southern Calif	CA	23,006	VC
Univ of Southern Colo	CO	5,350	LC
Univ of Southern Indiana	IN	3,720	NC
Univ of Southern Maine	ME	7,299	C
Univ of Southern Miss	MS	4,542	C
Univ of Southwestern Louisiana	LA	3,968	NC
Univ of Tenn at Chattanooga	TN	5,375	C
Univ of Tenn/Knoxville	TN	5,668	C
Univ of Texas at Arlington	TX	5,549	LC
Univ of Texas at Austin	TX	5,160	VC
Univ of Texas at Dallas	TX	1,222	VC+
Univ of Texas at El Paso	TX	3,160	LC
Univ of Texas at San Antonio	TX	6,420	C
Univ of the District of Columbia	DC	974	NC
Univ of the Pacific	CA	21,100	C
Univ of the South	TN	18,830	HC
Univ of Toledo	OH	6,636	NC
Univ of Tulsa	OK	13,795	VC
Univ of Utah	UT	5,975	C
Univ of Vermont	VT	10,776	C+
Univ of Virginia	VA	7,964	MC
Univ of Washington	WA	6,618	VC
Univ of West Florida	FL	5,415	C
Univ of Wisc/Eau Claire	WI	4,647	C
Univ of Wisc/Green Bay	WI	4,904	C
Univ of Wisc/La Crosse	WI	4,487	C
Univ of Wisc/Madison	WI	6,400	HC
Univ of Wisc/Milwaukee	WI	6,165	C
Univ of Wisc/Oshkosh	WI	4,240	C
Univ of Wisc/Parkside	WI	5,247	
Univ of Wisc/Platteville	WI	4,830	C
Univ of Wisc/River Falls	WI	4,655	C
Univ of Wisc/Stevens Point	WI	5,047	C+
Univ of Wisc/Whitewater	WI	4,700	C
Univ of Wyoming	WY	4,991	NC
Ursinus College	PA	19,165	VC
Utah State Univ	UT	4,683	C
Utica College of Syracuse Univ	NY	16,714	LC
Valdosta State Univ	GA	4,670	LC
Valparaiso Univ	IN	14,810	VC
Vanderbilt Univ	TN	23,422	HC+
Vassar College	NY	24,206	HC
Villanova Univ	PA	21,400	HC
Virginia Commonwealth Univ	VA	7,909	C
Virginia Military Inst	VA	8,630	C
Virginia Polytechnic Inst and State Univ	VA	6,828	C
Virginia State Univ	VA	7,040	
Virginia Wesleyan College	VA	14,950	VC
Wabash College	IN	16,250	VC
Wagner College	NY	17,950	C
Wake Forest Univ	NC	17,280	MC
Walla Walla College	WA	13,215	C
Wartburg College	IA	14,530	VC
Washburn Univ of Topeka	KS	5,802	NC
Washington and Jefferson College	PA	19,360	C
Washington and Lee Univ	VA	17,735	MC
Washington College	MD	19,270	C+
Washington State Univ	WA	6,364	C
Washington Univ	MO	23,507	HC
Wayland Baptist Univ	TX	7,811	NC
Wayne State Univ	MI	2,680	C
Weber State Univ	UT	4,398	C
Wellesley College	MA	23,815	MC
Wesleyan Univ	CT	23,770	MC
West Chester Univ of Penn	PA	7,492	C
West Georgia College	GA	4,256	C
West Texas A&M Univ	TX	4,224	C
West Virginia Inst of Tech	WV	5,858	LC
West Virginia Univ	WV	5,774	C
West Virginia Wesleyan College	WV	16,900	C
Western Carolina Univ	NC	3,811	C
Western Illinois Univ	IL	5,241	LC
Western Kentucky Univ	KY	4,808	C
Western Maryland College	MD	18,990	C
Western Mich Univ	MI	6,820	C
Western State College of Colo	CO	5,560	C
Western Washington Univ	WA	6,077	VC
Westminster College	MO	13,750	C+
Westminster College	PA	15,200	C
Westminster College of Salt Lake City	UT	12,100	C
Westmont College	CA	18,732	C
Wheaton College	IL	14,710	HC
Wheaton College	MA	23,840	C+
Wheeling Jesuit College	WV	14,370	C
Whitman College	WA	20,595	HC
Whittier College	CA	21,661	C
Whitworth College	WA	16,265	C
Wichita State Univ	KS	5,068	NC
Widener Univ	PA	16,840	C
Wiley College	TX	0	NC
Wilkes Univ	PA	15,728	LC
Willamette Univ	OR	17,995	VC
William Jewell College	MO	12,500	VC
William Woods Univ	MO	14,025	LC
Williams College	MA	24,390	MC
Winona State Univ	MN	5,200	VC
Wittenberg Univ	OH	19,998	VC
Wofford College	SC	15,360	VC
Worcester Polytechnic Inst	MA	20,350	HC
Worcester State College	MA	6,414	LC
Wright State Univ	OH	6,896	LC
Xavier Univ	OH	15,710	C+
Xavier Univ of Louisiana	LA	10,400	C
Yale Univ	CT	25,110	MC
Youngstown State Univ	OH	6,447	LC

PHYSIOLOGY

School	ST	$IS	SR
Boston Univ	MA	24,130	HC
Northern Mich Univ	MI	6,350	C
Rutgers Univ/Cook College	NJ	9,197	HC
Rutgers Univ/Douglass College	NJ	8,795	VC
Rutgers Univ/Livingston College	NJ	8,877	VC
Rutgers Univ/Rutgers College	NJ	8,841	HC+
Rutgers Univ/Univ College—New Brunswick	NJ	0	LC
San Francisco State Univ	CA	7,292	LC
Southern Illinois Univ at Carbondale	IL	6,234	C
Southwest Texas State Univ	TX	5,124	C
Univ of Calif at Davis	CA	9,534	VC
Univ of Calif at Los Angeles	CA	8,959	HC
Univ of Calif, San Diego	CA	10,028	VC+
Univ of Conn	CT	9,168	C
Univ of Minn/Twin Cities	MN	6,682	VC
Univ of Texas at Arlington	TX	5,549	LC
Univ of Wyoming	WY	4,991	NC

PIANO/ORGAN

School	ST	$IS	SR
Avila College	MO	12,130	C
Belhaven College	MS	9,690	C+
Boston Conservatory	MA	17,900	SP
Columbia College	SC	13,520	LC
Furman Univ	SC	16,557	VC
Grand Canyon Univ	AZ	9,680	VC
Indiana Univ/South Bend	IN	2,141	LC
Juilliard School	NY	18,050	SP
Martin Univ	IN	4,830	NC
Nicholls State Univ	LA	4,531	NC
Northwestern Univ	IL	21,093	MC
Nyack College	NY	12,210	LC
Ohio State Univ	OH	7,218	LC
Pacific Lutheran Univ	WA	15,998	VC
Peru State College	NE	4,311	NC
Point Loma Nazarene College	CA	13,532	C
St Mary College	KS	11,250	C
Shorter College	GA	10,270	C
Southern Methodist Univ	TX	18,520	VC
Southern Nazarene Univ	OK	9,206	NC
Temple Univ	PA	10,281	C
Univ of Cincinnati	OH	7,989	C
Univ of Mich/Ann Arbor	MI	9,428	HC+
Univ of North Texas	TX	4,853	C
Westminster Choir College	NJ	18,585	SP

PLANETARY AND SPACE SCIENCE

School	ST	$IS	SR
Boston Univ	MA	24,130	HC
Calif Inst of Tech	CA	20,783	MC
Mass Inst of Tech	MA	24,800	MC
SUNY at Stony Brook	NY	7,658	VC

PLANT GENETICS

School	ST	$IS	SR
SUNY College of Environmental Science and Forestry	NY	9,257	HC+

PLANT PATHOLOGY

School	ST	$IS	SR
Clemson Univ	SC	6,564	VC
Iowa State Univ	IA	5,456	C
N Dak State Univ of Agriculture and Applied Science	ND	4,774	VC
Ohio State Univ	OH	7,218	LC
Oregon State Univ	OR	6,175	C
Univ of Florida	FL	5,850	HC
Univ of Georgia	GA	5,655	VC
Univ of Mass/Amherst	MA	9,364	LC
Univ of Wisc/Madison	WI	6,400	HC

PLANT PHYSIOLOGY

School	ST	$IS	SR
Purdue Univ/West Lafayette	IN	6,636	C
SUNY College of Environmental Science and Forestry	NY	9,257	HC+

PLANT PROTECTION (PEST MANAGEMENT)

School	ST	$IS	SR
Auburn Univ	AL	5,823	C+
Iowa State Univ	IA	5,456	C
Univ of Arkansas at Fayetteville	AR	5,046	C
Univ of Georgia	GA	5,655	VC
Univ of Mass/Amherst	MA	9,364	LC

PLANT SCIENCE

School	ST	$IS	SR
Arkansas State Univ	AR	4,250	NC
Cal State/Fresno	CA	5,747	C
Cornell Univ	NY	13,445	MC
Fort Valley State College	GA	3,974	LC
Indiana Univ Bloomington	IN	6,495	VC
Iowa State Univ	IA	5,456	C
Rutgers Univ/Cook College	NJ	9,197	HC
Southern Univ and A&M College	LA	4,920	NC
SUNY College of Environmental Science and Forestry	NY	9,257	HC+
Tarleton State Univ	TX	4,082	LC
Tenn Tech Univ	TN	5,190	C
Texas A&M Univ at Kingsville	TX	3,808	LC
Univ of Arizona	AZ	5,808	C
Univ of Calif at Berkeley	CA	9,962	HC+
Univ of Calif at Davis	CA	9,534	VC
Univ of Delaware	DE	8,013	VC
Univ of Florida	FL	5,850	HC
Univ of Mass/Amherst	MA	9,364	LC
Univ of New Hampshire	NH	8,242	C
Utah State Univ	UT	4,683	C
West Texas A&M Univ	TX	4,224	C
West Virginia Univ	WV	5,774	C

PLASTICS ENGINEERING

School	ST	$IS	SR
Univ of Lowell	MA	8,831	VC

PLASTICS TECHNOLOGY

School	ST	$IS	SR
Eastern Mich Univ	MI	6,749	C
Ferris State Univ	MI	7,160	NC
Penn State Univ at Erie/Behrend College	PA	8,752	C
Shawnee State Univ	OH	4,379	NC
Univ of Detroit Mercy	MI	14,720	C

POLISH

School	ST	$IS	SR
Univ of Illinois at Chicago	IL	8,443	C
Wayne State Univ	MI	2,680	C

POLITICAL SCIENCE/GOVERNMENT

School	ST	$IS	SR
Abilene Christian Univ	TX	10,460	NC
Adelphi Univ	NY	18,250	LC
Adrian College	MI	14,340	C
Agnes Scott College	GA	17,135	VC
Alabama A&M Univ	AL	4,200	C
Alabama State Univ	AL	3,428	NC
Albany State College	GA	4,481	LC
Albertson College	ID	15,942	C+
Albertus Magnus College	CT	16,280	LC
Albion College	MI	18,264	VC
Albright College	PA	19,260	C
Alcorn State Univ	MS	4,474	C+
Alderson-Broaddus College	WV	12,000	C
Alfred Univ	NY	21,054	VC+
Allegheny College	PA	21,020	VC
Allen Univ	SC	6,705	NC
Allentown College of St Francis de Sales	PA	13,480	C
Alma College	MI	16,375	VC+
Alvernia College	PA	13,150	LC
Alverno College	WI	11,344	C
American International College	MA	14,029	C
American Univ	DC	21,230	VC+
Amherst College	MA	24,152	MC
Anderson Univ	IN	12,920	C
Angelo State Univ	TX	5,176	C
Antioch College	OH	19,532	C
Appalachian State Univ	NC	4,095	C
Aquinas College	MI	14,526	C
Arizona State Univ Main Campus	AZ	6,444	C
Arkansas State Univ	AR	4,250	NC
Armstrong State College	GA	4,874	LC
Ashland Univ	OH	15,508	C
Assumption College	MA	17,095	LC
Auburn Univ	AL	5,823	C+
Auburn Univ at Montgomery	AL	3,390	C
Augsburg College	MN	15,608	C
Augusta College	GA	1,452	C
Augustana College	IL	16,959	VC
Augustana College	SD	13,420	C
Aurora Univ	IL	13,381	C
Austin College	TX	14,999	VC
Austin Peay State Univ	TN	4,350	C
Averett College	VA	13,610	LC
Avila College	MO	12,130	C
Azusa Pacific Univ	CA	15,034	C
Baker Univ	KS	12,284	C
Baldwin-Wallace College	OH	15,210	C
Ball State Univ	IN	6,032	LC
Barat College	IL	13,990	C
Bard College	NY	25,269	HC
Barry Univ	FL	16,050	C
Bartlesville Wesleyan College	OK	9,400	C
Barton College	NC	10,689	LC
Bates College	ME	23,990	MC
Baylor Univ	TX	10,990	C+
Beaver College	PA	17,660	C
Bellarmine College	KY	10,832	C
Bellevue College	NE	3,050	NC
Belmont Abbey College	NC	13,190	C
Belmont Univ	TN	10,540	C
Beloit College	WI	18,950	VC+
Bemidji State Univ	MN	5,188	C
Benedictine College	KS	12,830	C
Bennett College	NC	8,920	LC
Bennington College	VT	24,850	VC+
Berea College	KY	2,883	VC+
Berry College	GA	11,990	VC
Bethany College	WV	18,300	C+
Bethel College	MN	15,050	C
Bethune-Cookman College	FL	8,375	LC
Birmingham-Southern College	AL	15,154	VC+
Black Hills State Univ	SD	4,831	NC
Blackburn College	IL	9,120	C
Bloomfield College	NJ	12,200	LC
Bloomsburg Univ of Penn	PA	6,312	C+
Boise State Univ	ID	4,909	LC
Boston College	MA	22,706	MC
Boston Univ	MA	24,130	HC
Bowdoin College	ME	24,155	MC
Bowie State Univ	MD	7,294	LC
Bowling Green State Univ	OH	6,701	C
Bradley Univ	IL	14,718	C+
Brandeis Univ	MA	25,585	HC
Bridgewater College	VA	15,300	C
Bridgewater State College	MA	7,518	C
Brigham Young Univ	UT	5,625	HC
Brigham Young Univ/Hawaii	HI	6,750	VC
Brooklyn Campus of LIU	NY	15,000	LC
Brown Univ	RI	26,104	MC
Bryn Mawr College	PA	24,110	MC
Bucknell Univ	PA	22,320	HC
Buena Vista College	IA	16,150	VC
Butler Univ	IN	16,210	C
Cabrini College	PA	16,012	C
Calif Baptist College	CA	11,294	C
Calif Inst of Tech	CA	20,783	MC
Calif Lutheran Univ	CA	17,240	C
Calif Polytechnic State Univ	CA	6,980	VC+
Calif State Polytechnic Univ/Pomona	CA	6,438	LC
Cal State/Bakersfield	CA	5,402	C
Cal State/Chico	CA	6,146	C
Cal State/Dominguez Hills	CA	2,857	LC
Cal State/Fresno	CA	5,747	C
Cal State/Fullerton	CA	4,850	LC
Cal State/Hayward	CA	5,495	C
Cal State/Long Beach	CA	6,057	LC
Cal State/Los Angeles	CA	4,940	VC
Cal State/Northridge	CA	7,122	LC
Cal State/San Bernardino	CA	6,055	LC
Calif Univ of Penn	PA	7,370	C
Calumet College of St. Joseph	IN	3,585	C
Calvin College	MI	13,020	VC
Cameron Univ	OK	3,686	LC
Campbell Univ	NC	10,624	C
Campbellsville College	KY	8,720	C
Canisius College	NY	15,510	C
Capital Univ	OH	16,535	VC
Carleton College	MN	22,155	HC
Carnegie Mellon Univ	PA	22,560	HC+
Carroll College	MT	11,265	C
Carroll College	WI	15,490	C
Carthage College	WI	15,995	C
Case Western Reserve Univ	OH	19,910	HC
Catawba College	NC	12,950	C
Catholic Univ of America	DC	18,856	C
Cedar Crest College	PA	18,930	C
Cedarville College	OH	10,715	C
Centenary College of Louisiana	LA	11,826	C+
Central College	IA	14,025	VC
Central Conn State Univ	CT	7,108	C
Central Methodist College	MO	11,410	C
Central Mich Univ	MI	6,737	LC
Central Missouri State Univ	MO	5,138	LC
Central State Univ	OH	7,320	NC
Central Washington Univ	WA	5,644	C
Centre College	KY	15,850	VC+
Chadron State College	NE	4,091	NC
Chaminade Univ of Honolulu	HI	14,290	C
Chapman Univ	CA	21,842	C
Charleston Southern Univ	SC	10,282	LC
Charter Oak State College	CT	314	NC
Chatham College	PA	18,010	C
Chestnut Hill College	PA	14,525	C
Cheyney Univ of Penn	PA	7,005	C
Chicago State Univ	IL	2,198	C
Christendom College	VA	11,750	VC
Christopher Newport Univ	VA	3,196	LC
CUNY/Baruch College	NY	2,562	VC
CUNY/Brooklyn College	NY	2,450	VC
CUNY/City College	NY	2,543	VC
CUNY/College of Staten Island	NY	2,558	NC
CUNY/Herbert H. Lehman College	NY	2,542	C
CUNY/Hunter College	NY	4,101	VC
CUNY/Queens College	NY	2,631	C
CUNY/York College	NY	2,534	NC
Claflin College	SC	0	LC
Claremont McKenna College	CA	22,150	MC
Clarion Univ of Penn	PA	6,518	C
Clark Atlanta Univ	GA	11,846	LC
Clarke College	IA	13,950	C+
Clarkson Univ	NY	20,705	VC+
Clemson Univ	SC	6,564	VC
Cleveland State Univ	OH	7,287	NC
Clinch Valley College/Univ of Virginia	VA	6,364	C
Coastal Carolina Univ	SC	6,010	LC
Coe College	IA	17,085	VC
Coker College	SC	13,790	C
Colby College	ME	24,230	HC
Colgate Univ	NY	24,020	HC
College of Charleston	SC	6,250	C
College of Great Falls	MT	6,230	NC
College of New Rochelle	NY	15,440	LC
College of Notre Dame	CA	16,480	C
College of Notre Dame of Maryland	MD	16,050	C
College of St Benedict	MN	15,468	VC
College of St Catherine	MN	14,670	C
College of St Francis	IL	13,060	VC
College of St Joseph	VT	12,650	LC
College of the Holy Cross	MA	23,850	HC
College of the Ozarks	MO	2,000	VC+
College of the Southwest	NM	5,720	LC
College of William and Mary	VA	8,602	MC
College of Wooster	OH	19,875	VC
Colo Christian Univ	CO	9,750	C
Colo College	CO	20,038	HC
Colo State Univ	CO	6,566	VC
Columbia College	SC	13,520	LC
Columbia Univ/Barnard College	NY	25,492	HC
Columbia Univ/Columbia College	NY	26,757	MC
Columbus College	GA	4,892	LC
Concord College	WV	5,104	NC
Concordia College/Moorhead	MN	12,750	C
Concordia Univ	IL	12,611	C
Conn College	CT	24,160	HC
Converse College	SC	15,750	C
Cornell College	IA	18,425	VC
Cornell Univ	NY	13,445	MC
Creighton Univ	NE	14,432	VC
Cumberland College	KY	9,756	C
Dartmouth College	NH	24,354	MC
David Lipscomb Univ	TN	7,865	VC
Davidson College	NC	21,037	MC
Davis and Elkins College	WV	13,230	LC
Delaware State College	DE	5,656	C
Delta State Univ	MS	3,964	LC
Denison Univ	OH	21,150	VC+
DePaul Univ	IL	15,535	VC
DePauw Univ	IN	18,530	VC
Dickinson College	PA	22,705	HC
Dickinson State Univ	ND	3,792	
Dillard Univ	LA	9,950	C
Doane College	NE	12,220	C
Dominican College of San Rafael	CA	17,860	C
Dordt College	IA	11,690	C
Drake Univ	IA	17,195	VC
Drew Univ/College of Liberal Arts	NJ	23,406	HC
Drexel Univ	PA	15,970	C
Drury College	MO	12,140	VC
Duke Univ	NC	21,271	MC
Duquesne Univ	PA	16,434	VC
Earlham College	IN	19,383	VC
East Stroudsburg Univ	PA	6,886	C
East Tenn State Univ	TN	4,406	C
East Texas State Univ	TX	4,572	LC
Eastern College	PA	15,150	C+
Eastern Conn State Univ	CT	6,966	C
Eastern Illinois Univ	IL	5,548	C
Eastern Kentucky Univ	KY	4,840	NC
Eastern Mich Univ	MI	6,749	C
Eastern New Mexico Univ	NM	3,950	C
Eastern Washington Univ	WA	5,439	LC
Eckerd College	FL	18,855	VC
Edgewood College	WI	11,700	C
Edinboro Univ of Penn	PA	7,181	C
Edward Waters College	FL	8,300	NC
Elizabeth City State Univ	NC	4,254	LC
Elizabethtown College	PA	17,850	VC
Elmhurst College	IL	12,536	C
Elmira College	NY	18,450	C
Elon College	NC	12,290	LC
Emmanuel College	MA	17,773	LC
Emory and Henry College	VA	12,776	C
Emory Univ	GA	21,930	HC
Emporia State Univ	KS	4,685	NC
Eugene Lang College of the New School for Social Research	NY	21,145	C+
Evangel College	MO	10,142	LC
Evergreen State College	WA	6,306	C
Fairfield Univ	CT	20,460	VC
Fairleigh Dickinson Univ	NJ	16,427	C
Fairmont State College	WV	4,640	LC
Fayetteville State Univ	NC	3,926	LC
Ferrum College	VA	12,800	LC
Fisk Univ	TN	0	LC
Florida A&M Univ	FL	4,651	C
Florida Atlantic Univ	FL	5,525	C
Florida International Univ	FL	4,191	VC
Florida Memorial College	FL	7,600	C+
Florida Southern College	FL	12,260	C
Florida State Univ	FL	5,814	VC
Fordham Univ/College at Lincoln Center	NY	18,150	VC
Fordham Univ/Fordham College	NY	19,875	VC
Fort Hays State Univ	KS	4,675	NC
Fort Lewis College	CO	5,097	C
Fort Valley State College	GA	3,974	LC
Framingham State College	MA	6,580	C
Francis Marion Univ	SC	5,878	LC
Franciscan Univ of Steubenville	OH	13,400	C
Franklin and Marshall College	PA	23,655	HC
Franklin College of Indiana	IN	13,970	C
Friends Univ	KS	11,205	C
Frostburg State Univ	MD	6,940	C
Furman Univ	SC	16,557	VC
Gallaudet Univ	DC	9,850	SP
Gannon Univ	PA	14,872	C
Geneva College	PA	13,030	C
George Mason Univ	VA	8,728	C
George Washington Univ	DC	22,470	HC
Georgetown College	KY	10,990	C
Georgetown Univ	DC	24,410	MC
Georgia College	GA	4,310	LC
Georgia Southern Univ	GA	4,988	LC
Georgia Southwestern College	GA	4,338	LC
Georgia State Univ	GA	2,019	C
Gettysburg College	PA	22,960	HC
Golden Gate Univ	CA	5,623	VC
Gonzaga Univ	WA	16,350	VC
Gordon College	MA	16,790	C
Goucher College	MD	20,295	VC
Grambling State Univ	LA	4,712	NC
Grand Valley State Univ	MI	6,822	VC
Grand View College	IA	13,230	NC
Greensboro College	NC	11,496	C

School	ST	$IS	SR
Grinnell College	IA	20,680	HC+
Grove City College	PA	7,870	HC
Guilford College	NC	17,680	C
Gustavus Adolphus College	MN	15,935	VC
Hamilton College	NY	23,500	HC
Hamline Univ	MN	17,122	VC
Hampden-Sydney College	VA	17,372	C+
Hampshire College	MA	25,320	C
Hampton Univ	VA	10,706	C
Hanover College	IN	10,950	VC
Hardin-Simmons Univ	TX	9,080	C
Harding Univ	AR	9,050	VC
Hartwick College	NY	20,950	C
Harvard Univ/Harvard and Radcliffe Colleges	MA	24,880	MC
Hastings College	NE	12,426	C
Haverford College	PA	23,950	MC
Hawaii Pacific Univ	HI	12,300	C
Heidelberg College	OH	17,160	C
Henderson State Univ	AR	3,860	C
Hendrix College	AR	11,670	C
High Point Univ	NC	12,350	LC
Hillsdale College	MI	15,110	VC
Hiram College	OH	18,340	VC
Hobart and William Smith Colleges	NY	23,925	VC
Hofstra Univ	NY	16,580	VC
Hollins College	VA	18,484	C
Hood College	MD	19,010	VC
Hope College	MI	15,698	C+
Houghton College	NY	13,120	VC
Howard Payne Univ	TX	8,052	C
Howard Univ	DC	11,680	C
Humboldt State Univ	CA	5,676	C
Huston-Tillotson College	TX	8,490	C
Idaho State Univ	ID	4,442	C
Illinois Benedictine College	IL	14,170	C
Illinois College	IL	11,200	C
Illinois Inst of Tech	IL	18,290	VC
Illinois State Univ	IL	6,413	C
Illinois Wesleyan Univ	IL	18,590	HC+
Incarnate Word College	TX	12,307	C
Indiana State Univ	IN	6,210	C
Indiana Univ Bloomington	IN	6,495	VC
Indiana Univ Northwest	IN	2,310	C
Indiana Univ of Penn	PA	6,373	C
Indiana Univ Southeast	IN	2,260	LC
Indiana Univ-Purdue Univ at Fort Wayne	IN	2,500	LC
Indiana Univ-Purdue Univ at Indianapolis	IN	5,862	LC
Indiana Univ/South Bend	IN	2,141	LC
Indiana Wesleyan Univ	IN	12,332	C
Inter American Univ of PR/Aguadilla Regional College	PR	2,290	
Inter American Univ of PR/Bayamon Univ College	PR	2,300	
Inter American Univ of PR/Metropolitan Campus	PR	2,340	
Inter American Univ of PR/Ponce Regional College	PR	2,300	
Inter American Univ of PR/San German	PR	4,620	
Inter-American Univ of PR/Fajardo Regional College	PR	2,732	
Iona College	NY	16,310	C
Iowa State Univ	IA	5,456	C
Ithaca College	NY	19,679	C
Jackson State Univ	MS	4,996	LC
Jacksonville State Univ	AL	4,080	LC
Jacksonville Univ	FL	13,390	C
James Madison Univ	VA	8,198	HC
Jamestown College	ND	10,250	C
Jarvis Christian College	TX	7,170	LC
Jersey City State College	NJ	7,797	LC
John Carroll Univ	OH	16,510	C
Johns Hopkins Univ	MD	24,360	MC
Johnson C. Smith Univ	NC	8,916	LC
Johnson State College	VT	8,393	LC
Juniata College	PA	18,390	C+
Kalamazoo College	MI	19,974	HC
Kansas State Univ	KS	4,816	NC
Kean College of New Jersey	NJ	6,395	LC
Keene State College	NH	7,081	C
Kennesaw State College	GA	1,553	C
Kent State Univ	OH	6,740	LC
Kentucky State Univ	KY	4,282	C+
Kentucky Wesleyan College	KY	11,550	C
Kenyon College	OH	22,430	HC+
Keuka College	NY	13,660	C
King College	TN	11,500	C
King's College	PA	15,420	C
Knox College	IL	18,990	VC
Knoxville College	TN	8,320	LC
Kutztown Univ	PA	6,528	C
La Salle Univ	PA	16,940	VC
Lafayette College	PA	23,450	HC
LaGrange College	GA	10,602	C
Lake Forest College	IL	19,960	VC
Lake Superior State Univ	MI	7,311	C
Lamar Univ	TX	3,798	C
Lambuth Univ	TN	8,395	C
Lander Univ	SC	6,180	LC
Lawrence Univ	WI	19,986	HC+
Le Moyne College	NY	15,180	C
Lebanon Valley College of Penn	PA	18,300	C
Lee College at the Univ of Judaism	CA	15,600	VC
Lehigh Univ	PA	23,250	HC
LeMoyne-Owen College	TN	4,500	LC
Lenoir-Rhyne College	NC	14,068	C
Lewis and Clark College	OR	19,980	VC
Lewis Univ	IL	14,797	LC
Liberty Univ	VA	11,500	LC
Lincoln Univ	MO	4,638	NC
Lincoln Univ	PA	0	LC
Lindenwood College	MO	13,560	C
Linfield College	OR	16,670	VC
Livingston Univ	AL	3,979	C
Livingstone College	NC	8,600	LC
Lock Haven Univ of Penn	PA	7,128	C
LIU/C. W. Post Campus	NY	16,870	C
LIU/Southampton Campus	NY	17,280	C
Longwood College	VA	7,800	C
Louisiana State Univ and A&M College	LA	5,605	C
Louisiana Tech Univ	LA	4,284	C
Loyola College	MD	18,035	VC
Loyola Marymount Univ	CA	18,560	C
Loyola Univ of Chicago	IL	15,880	C+
Loyola Univ/New Orleans	LA	15,660	C+
Luther College	IA	15,900	VC
Lycoming College	PA	17,200	LC
Lynchburg College	VA	17,000	C
Lynn Univ	FL	18,300	C
Macalester College	MN	19,710	HC
MacMurray College	IL	12,800	C
Maharishi International Univ	IA	13,666	C
Manchester College	IN	13,240	LC
Manhattan College	NY	19,000	C
Manhattanville College	NY	20,450	LC
Mankato State Univ	MN	5,097	LC
Mansfield Univ	PA	6,348	C
Marist College	NY	16,406	C
Marlboro College	VT	23,305	C+
Marquette Univ	WI	16,114	VC
Mars Hill College	NC	11,050	C
Marshall Univ	WV	5,762	LC
Martin Univ	IN	4,830	NC
Mary Baldwin College	VA	17,700	LC
Mary Washington College	VA	7,910	HC
Marygrove College	MI	5,877	VC
Marymount College/Tarrytown	NY	17,350	C
Marymount Manhattan College	NY	15,450	LC
Marymount Univ	VA	15,930	C
Maryville College	TN	14,474	C
Maryville Univ-St Louis	MO	12,900	VC
Mass Inst of Tech	MA	24,800	MC
Master's College	CA	12,816	C
McKendree College	IL	10,900	C
McMurry Univ	TX	10,100	C
Mercer Univ	GA	15,123	C
Mercy College	NY	11,180	NC
Mercyhurst College	PA	13,488	C
Meredith College	NC	9,440	C
Merrimack College	MA	18,025	C
Mesa State College	CO	5,127	NC
Messiah College	PA	14,664	VC
Methodist College	NC	12,400	C
Metropolitan State College of Denver	CO	1,751	NC
Miami Univ	OH	8,066	VC
Mich State Univ	MI	7,842	C
Middle Tenn State Univ	TN	3,857	C
Middlebury College	VT	24,400	MC
Midwestern State Univ	TX	4,542	LC
Miles College	AL	7,150	NC
Millersville Univ of Penn	PA	7,370	VC
Millikin Univ	IL	15,499	C
Mills College	CA	20,848	VC
Millsaps College	MS	15,486	C+
Miss College	MS	8,348	C
Miss State Univ	MS	5,629	VC
Miss Valley State Univ	MS	4,089	NC
Missouri Southern State College	MO	4,272	
Missouri Valley College	MO	14,050	LC
Missouri Western State College	MO	4,384	NC
Monmouth College	IL	17,300	C+
Monmouth College	NJ	16,820	C
Montana State Univ	MT	5,534	C
Montclair State College	NJ	7,539	C+
Moorhead State Univ	MN	5,076	C
Moravian College	PA	18,960	VC
Morehead State Univ	KY	4,600	LC
Morehouse College	GA	13,224	LC
Morgan State Univ	MD	7,366	C+
Morningside College	IA	13,896	C
Morris Brown College	GA	12,234	NC
Morris College	SC	6,880	LC
Mount Holyoke College	MA	23,630	VC
Mount Mercy College	IA	13,230	C
Mount St Mary College	NY	12,910	C
Mount St Mary's College	CA	16,390	VC
Mount St Mary's College	MD	17,825	LC
Mount Union College	OH	15,850	C
Mount Vernon College	DC	20,668	C
Muhlenberg College	PA	20,795	VC
Murray State Univ	KY	4,702	C
Muskingum College	OH	16,650	C
Nazareth College of Rochester	NY	15,310	C+
Nebr Wesleyan Univ	NE	12,240	C
Neumann College	PA	9,950	LC
New College of Calif	CA	6,900	NC
New College of the Univ of South Florida	FL	5,697	MC
New England College	NH	17,870	LC
New Mexico Highlands Univ	NM	3,772	C
New Mexico State Univ	NM	4,844	LC
New York Inst of Tech/Old Westbury	NY	13,914	LC
New York Univ	NY	24,705	VC+
Newberry College	SC	11,994	LC
Niagara Univ	NY	14,552	C
Nicholls State Univ	LA	4,531	NC
Norfolk State Univ	VA	6,345	LC
N Car Agricultural and Technical State Univ	NC	4,477	LC
N Car Central Univ	NC	4,347	LC
N Car State Univ	NC	4,984	VC
North Central College	IL	15,498	VC
N Dak State Univ of Agriculture and Applied Science	ND	4,774	VC
North Georgia College	GA	4,103	LC
North Park College	IL	14,310	C
Northeast Louisiana Univ	LA	3,906	NC
Northeast Missouri State Univ	MO	5,654	VC+
Northeastern Illinois Univ	IL	1,955	C
Northeastern State Univ	OK	5,250	C
Northeastern Univ	MA	19,851	C
Northern Arizona Univ	AZ	4,844	C
Northern Illinois Univ	IL	6,408	C
Northern Kentucky Univ	KY	4,620	NC
Northern Mich Univ	MI	6,350	C
Northern State Univ	SD	4,186	LC
Northwest Missouri State Univ	MO	5,010	LC
Northwest Nazarene College	ID	11,750	C
Northwestern College of Iowa	IA	12,250	C
Northwestern Okla State Univ	OK	3,424	C
Northwestern State Univ of Louisiana	LA	4,287	NC
Northwestern Univ	IL	21,093	MC
Norwich Univ	VT	18,730	C
Notre Dame College of Ohio	OH	11,370	C
Oakland Univ	MI	6,714	VC
Oberlin College	OH	24,570	HC+
Occidental College	CA	21,792	HC
Ohio Dominican College	OH	11,820	LC
Ohio Northern Univ	OH	18,660	VC
Ohio State Univ	OH	7,218	LC
Ohio Univ	OH	7,341	C
Ohio Wesleyan Univ	OH	21,108	VC+
Okla Baptist Univ	OK	8,486	C
Okla City Univ	OK	9,840	C
Okla State Univ	OK	5,086	VC
Old Dominion Univ	VA	8,317	C
Olivet Nazarene Univ	IL	11,976	C
Oral Roberts Univ	OK	10,607	C+
Oregon State Univ	OR	6,175	C
Ottawa Univ	KS	10,490	C+
Otterbein College	OH	16,506	C
Ouachita Baptist Univ	AR	8,940	C
Pace Univ	NY	15,540	C
Pacific Lutheran Univ	WA	15,998	VC
Pacific Univ	OR	17,869	C
Palm Beach Atlantic College	FL	10,720	C
Park College	MO	7,320	C
Pembroke State Univ	NC	3,538	LC
Penn State Univ at Erie/Behrend College	PA	8,752	C
Penn State Univ/Univ Park Campus	PA	8,752	HC
Pepperdine Univ	CA	23,720	VC
Philander Smith College	AR	5,434	NC
Phillips Univ	OK	12,744	C
Pittsburg State Univ	KS	4,478	NC
Plymouth State College	NH	7,166	C
Point Loma Nazarene College	CA	13,532	C
Point Park College	PA	13,922	LC
Pomona College	CA	23,820	MC
Pontifical Catholic Univ of PR/Ponce	PR	5,807	
Portland State Univ	OR	7,191	C
Prairie View A&M Univ	TX	4,740	LC
Presbyterian College	SC	15,400	VC
Princeton Univ	NJ	24,650	MC
Principia College	IL	17,799	C
Providence College	RI	19,750	VC
Purdue Univ/Calumet	IN	2,374	NC
Purdue Univ/West Lafayette	IN	6,636	C
Queens College	NC	14,950	C
Quincy Univ	IL	13,646	VC
Quinnipiac College	CT	17,600	C+
Radford Univ	VA	7,034	LC
Ramapo College of New Jersey	NJ	8,027	C+
Randolph-Macon College	VA	16,980	C
Randolph-Macon Woman's College	VA	19,100	C
Reed College	OR	24,480	HC+
Regis College	MA	17,450	C
Regis Univ	CO	17,340	C
Rhode Island College	RI	7,901	LC
Rhodes College	TN	19,624	HC
Rice Univ	TX	15,110	MC
Richard Stockton College of New Jersey	NJ	6,950	VC
Rider College	NJ	18,160	C
Ripon College	WI	18,320	C+
Rivier College	NH	14,920	LC
Roanoke College	VA	16,975	C
Rockford College	IL	15,300	C
Rockhurst College	MO	12,470	C
Rocky Mountain College	MT	11,320	C
Roger Williams Univ	RI	16,750	C
Rollins College	FL	20,875	VC
Roosevelt Univ	IL	12,368	C
Rosary College	IL	15,040	C
Rosemont College	PA	16,775	C
Rowan College of New Jersey	NJ	7,358	VC
Rust College	MS	6,600	LC
Rutgers Univ/Camden College of A&S	NJ	8,652	VC
Rutgers Univ/Douglass College	NJ	8,795	VC
Rutgers Univ/Livingston College	NJ	8,877	VC
Rutgers Univ/Newark College of A&S	NJ	8,645	C
Rutgers Univ/Rutgers College	NJ	8,841	HC+
Rutgers Univ/Univ College—Camden	NJ	3,506	C
Rutgers Univ/Univ College—New Brunswick	NJ	0	LC
Rutgers Univ/Univ College—Newark	NJ	0	C
Sacred Heart Univ	CT	16,350	C
Saginaw Valley State Univ	MI	6,634	LC
St Ambrose Univ	IA	13,380	C
St Andrews Presbyterian College	NC	14,240	LC
St Anselm College	NH	17,340	C
St Augustine's College	NC	9,300	C+
St Bonaventure Univ	NY	14,762	C
St Cloud State Univ	MN	5,015	C
St Edward's Univ	TX	12,636	C
St Francis College	NY	6,710	LC
St Francis College	PA	15,744	LC
St John Fisher College	NY	15,415	C
St John's Univ	MN	15,364	C
St John's Univ	NY	8,980	C+
St Joseph College	CT	16,225	C
St Joseph's College	IN	14,730	C
St Joseph's Univ	PA	17,800	VC
St Lawrence Univ	NY	23,420	VC
St Leo College	FL	13,570	C
St Louis Univ	MO	15,522	VC
St Martin's College	WA	14,965	C
St Mary College	KS	11,250	C
St Mary's College	IN	17,043	VC
St Mary's College of Calif	CA	18,848	VC
St Mary's College of Maryland	MD	8,900	VC+
St Mary's College of Minn	MN	13,850	LC
St Mary's Univ	TX	12,064	C
St Mary-of-the-Woods College	IN	14,430	NC
St Michael's College	VT	17,930	C
St Norbert College	WI	15,710	VC
St Olaf College	MN	17,200	HC
St Paul's College	VA	9,171	C
St Peter's College	NJ	14,775	LC
St Thomas Univ	FL	14,280	LC
St Vincent College	PA	13,934	LC
St Xavier Univ	IL	14,700	C
Salisbury State Univ	MD	7,516	C+
Salve Regina Univ	RI	29,100	LC
Sam Houston State Univ	TX	4,506	C
San Diego State Univ	CA	6,692	LC
San Francisco State Univ	CA	7,292	LC
San Jose State Univ	CA	6,680	LC
Santa Clara Univ	CA	18,783	VC
Sarah Lawrence College	NY	24,975	HC
Scripps College	CA	23,600	HC
Seattle Pacific Univ	WA	16,503	C
Seattle Univ	WA	16,590	C
Selma Univ	AL	5,785	NC
Seton Hall Univ	NJ	18,306	LC
Seton Hill College	PA	14,320	C
Shepherd College	WV	5,540	C
Shorter College	GA	10,270	C
Siena College	NY	15,410	VC
Simmons College	MA	22,534	C
Simpson College	IA	14,635	VC
Sioux Falls College	SD	11,540	C
Skidmore College	NY	23,230	HC
Slippery Rock Univ	PA	6,803	C
Smith College	MA	24,236	HC
Sonoma State Univ	CA	6,996	LC
S Car State Univ	SC	5,424	LC
S Dak State Univ	SD	4,562	C
Southeast Missouri State Univ	MO	5,854	C
Southeastern Louisiana Univ	LA	4,230	NC

School	ST	$IS	SR
The Univ of New Mexico	NM	5,304	C
Tulane Univ	LA	24,540	HC
Univ of Arizona	AZ	5,808	C
Univ of Calif at Los Angeles	CA	8,959	HC
Univ of Calif at Santa Barbara	CA	9,460	C
Univ of Conn	CT	9,168	C
Univ of Florida	FL	5,850	HC
Univ of Iowa	IA	5,658	VC
Univ of Mass Dartmouth	MA	8,158	C
Univ of Mass/Amherst	MA	9,364	LC
Univ of N Car at Chapel Hill	NC	5,330	HC
Univ of Texas at Austin	TX	5,160	VC
Univ of Wisc/Madison	WI	6,400	HC
Vanderbilt Univ	TN	23,422	HC+

POULTRY SCIENCE

School	ST	$IS	SR
Auburn Univ	AL	5,823	C+
Miss State Univ	MS	5,629	VC
N Car State Univ	NC	4,984	VC
Oregon State Univ	OR	6,175	C
Texas A&M Univ	TX	5,382	VC
Univ of Arkansas at Fayetteville	AR	5,046	C
Univ of Florida	FL	5,850	HC
Univ of Georgia	GA	5,655	VC
Univ of Maryland/Eastern Shore	MD	6,254	LC
Univ of Wisc/Madison	WI	6,400	HC
Virginia Polytechnic Inst and State Univ	VA	6,828	C

PREDENTISTRY

School	ST	$IS	SR
Abilene Christian Univ	TX	10,460	NC
Albertus Magnus College	CT	16,280	LC
Alderson-Broaddus College	WV	12,000	C
Alfred Univ	NY	21,054	VC+
Allegheny College	PA	21,020	HC
Alvernia College	PA	13,150	LC
Alverno College	WI	11,344	C
American International College	MA	14,029	C
Anderson Univ	IN	12,920	C
Andrews Univ	MI	14,952	NC
Angelo State Univ	TX	5,176	C
Anna Maria College	MA	15,975	LC
Appalachian State Univ	NC	4,095	C
Aquinas College	MI	14,526	C
Arkansas State Univ	AR	4,250	LC
Ashland Univ	OH	15,508	C
Auburn Univ	AL	5,823	C+
Augsburg College	MN	15,608	C
Augustana College	IL	16,959	VC
Augustana College	SD	13,420	C
Aurora Univ	IL	13,381	C
Austin Peay State Univ	TN	4,350	C
Averett College	VA	13,610	C
Azusa Pacific Univ	CA	15,034	C
Baker Univ	KS	12,284	C
Baldwin-Wallace College	OH	15,210	C
Ball State Univ	IN	6,032	LC
Bard College	NY	25,269	HC
Barry Univ	FL	16,050	C
Bartlesville Wesleyan College	OK	9,400	C
Baylor Univ	TX	10,990	C+
Beaver College	PA	17,660	C
Bellarmine College	KY	10,832	C
Belmont Abbey College	NC	13,190	C
Belmont Univ	TN	10,540	C
Bemidji State Univ	MN	5,188	C
Bennett College	NC	8,920	LC
Berry College	GA	11,990	C
Bethany College	KS	11,232	C
Bethany College	WV	18,300	C+
Bethel College	IN	11,650	C
Bethel College	MN	15,050	C
Boise State Univ	ID	4,909	LC
Boston Univ	MA	24,130	HC
Bowling Green State Univ	OH	6,701	C
Briar Cliff College	IA	13,375	C
Bridgewater College	MA	7,518	C
Brigham Young Univ/Hawaii	HI	6,750	VC
Brooklyn Campus of LIU	NY	15,000	C
Calif Lutheran Univ	CA	17,240	C
Cal State/Bakersfield	CA	5,402	C
Cal State/Chico	CA	6,146	C
Cal State/Fresno	CA	5,747	C
Calif Univ of Penn	PA	7,370	C
Calvin College	MI	13,020	VC
Canisius College	NY	15,510	C
Capital Univ	OH	16,535	VC
Carroll College	MT	11,265	C
Carroll College	WI	15,490	C
Carthage College	WI	15,995	C
Catawba College	NC	12,950	C
Cedarville College	OH	10,715	C

School	ST	$IS	SR
Centenary College of Louisiana	LA	11,826	C+
Central Missouri State Univ	MO	5,138	LC
Central State Univ	OH	7,320	NC
Chadron State College	NE	4,091	NC
Chicago State Univ	IL	2,198	C
Christian Brothers Univ	TN	12,120	VC
Christopher Newport Univ	VA	3,196	LC
CUNY/Brooklyn College	NY	2,450	VC
CUNY/City College	NY	2,543	VC
CUNY/Herbert H. Lehman College	NY	2,542	VC
CUNY/Hunter College	NY	4,101	VC
CUNY/Queens College	NY	2,631	C
CUNY/York College	NY	2,534	NC
Claflin College	SC	0	
Clark Univ	MA	21,400	VC
Clemson Univ	SC	6,564	VC
Coastal Carolina Univ	SC	6,010	LC
Coe College	IA	17,085	VC
College Misericordia	PA	15,820	C
College of Charleston	SC	6,250	C
College of Great Falls	MT	6,230	NC
College of New Rochelle	NY	15,440	LC
College of Notre Dame	CA	16,480	C
College of Notre Dame of Maryland	MD	16,050	C
College of Our Lady of The Elms	MA	15,639	C
College of St Benedict	MN	15,468	VC
College of St Elizabeth	NJ	15,800	C
College of St Francis	IL	13,060	NC
College of St Mary	NE	12,500	C
College of St Scholastica	MN	14,868	C
Columbia College	NY	11,995	C
Columbia Union College	MD	13,650	LC
Concord College	WV	5,104	NC
Concordia College	NE	11,776	NC
Concordia College/Moorhead	MN	12,750	C
Concordia Univ	IL	12,611	C
Converse College	SC	15,750	C
Coppin State College	MD	7,145	LC
Creighton Univ	NE	14,432	VC
Cumberland College	KY	9,756	C
D'Youville College	NY	12,850	C
Dakota Wesleyan Univ	SD	9,770	LC
Dana College	NE	11,910	C
David Lipscomb Univ	TN	7,865	VC
Davis and Elkins College	WV	13,230	LC
Defiance College	OH	13,480	VC
Delta State Univ	MS	3,964	LC
Dominican College of San Rafael	CA	17,860	C
Dordt College	IA	11,690	C
Drake Univ	IA	17,195	VC
Drexel Univ	PA	15,970	C
Duquesne Univ	PA	16,434	VC
East Texas State Univ	TX	4,572	LC
Eastern Mich Univ	MI	6,749	C
Eastern Oregon State College	OR	6,090	C
Eastern Washington Univ	WA	5,439	LC
Eckerd College	FL	18,855	VC
Edinboro Univ of Penn	PA	7,181	C
Elmira College	NY	18,450	C
Emmanuel College	MA	17,773	LC
Erskine College	SC	14,310	C
Fairleigh Dickinson Univ	NJ	16,427	C
Fisk Univ	TN	0	LC
Florida A&M Univ	FL	4,651	C
Florida Inst of Tech	FL	16,935	VC
Florida State Univ	FL	5,814	VC
Fordham Univ/College at Lincoln Center	NY	18,150	VC
Franklin College of Indiana	IN	13,970	C
Franklin Pierce College	NH	17,270	LC
Freed-Hardeman Univ	TN	8,585	VC
Gannon Univ	PA	14,872	C
George Fox College	OR	15,640	LC
Georgetown Univ	DC	24,410	HC
Georgia State Univ	GA	2,019	C
Gettysburg College	PA	22,960	HC
Gonzaga Univ	WA	16,350	VC
Goshen College	IN	12,360	C
Grace College	IN	12,120	C
Graceland College	IA	11,600	C
Grambling State Univ	LA	4,712	NC
Grand Rapids Baptist College and Seminary	MI	10,228	C
Grand Valley State Univ	MI	6,822	VC
Grand View College	IA	13,230	NC
Grove City College	PA	7,870	NC
Gustavus Adolphus College	MN	15,935	VC
Hamline Univ	MN	17,122	VC
Hanover College	IN	10,950	VC
Harding Univ	AR	9,050	VC
Heidelberg College	OH	17,160	VC
Henderson State Univ	AR	3,860	C
Hendrix College	AR	11,670	C
Hillsdale College	MI	15,110	VC
Hofstra Univ	NY	16,580	VC
Holy Family College	PA	8,300	C
Hope College	MI	15,698	VC
Houghton College	NY	13,050	C
Houston Baptist Univ	TX	11,055	LC
Howard Univ	DC	11,680	C

School	ST	$IS	SR
Humboldt State Univ	CA	5,676	C
Huntingdon College	AL	11,400	C
Huron Univ	SD	9,790	C
Illinois Benedictine College	IL	14,170	C
Incarnate Word College	TX	12,307	C
Indiana State Univ	IN	6,210	C
Indiana Univ Bloomington	IN	6,495	VC
Indiana Univ-Purdue Univ at Fort Wayne	IN	2,500	LC
Indiana Univ/South Bend	IN	2,141	LC
Indiana Wesleyan Univ	IN	12,332	C
Iona College	NY	16,310	C
Iowa Wesleyan College	IA	13,250	C
Ithaca College	NY	19,679	C
Jackson State Univ	MS	4,996	LC
Jacksonville State Univ	AL	4,080	LC
Jacksonville Univ	FL	13,390	C
Jamestown College	ND	10,250	C
Jersey City State College	NJ	7,797	LC
Johnson C. Smith Univ	NC	8,916	LC
Judson College	AL	9,060	C
Judson College	IL	13,625	C
Juniata College	PA	18,390	C+
Kalamazoo College	MI	19,974	NC
Kansas Newman College	KS	10,640	C
Kansas State Univ	KS	4,816	NC
Kennesaw State College	GA	1,553	C
Kent State Univ	OH	6,740	LC
Kentucky Wesleyan College	KY	11,550	C
King's College	PA	15,420	C
La Salle Univ	PA	16,940	VC
Lafayette College	PA	23,450	HC
LaGrange College	GA	10,602	C
Lake Superior State Univ	MI	7,311	C
Lamar Univ	TX	3,798	C
Lander Univ	SC	6,180	LC
Lane College	TN	7,628	LC
Le Moyne College	NY	15,180	C
Lebanon Valley College of Penn	PA	18,300	C
Lehigh Univ	PA	23,250	HC
Lenoir-Rhyne College	NC	14,068	C
Lewis Univ	IL	14,797	LC
Limestone College	SC	10,700	LC
Lincoln Memorial Univ	TN	8,218	C
Linfield College	OR	16,670	VC
Livingston Univ	AL	3,979	C
Livingstone College	NC	8,600	LC
LIU/C. W. Post Campus	NY	16,870	C
Loras College	IA	14,160	C
Louisiana College	LA	7,518	VC
Louisiana State Univ and A&M Univ	LA	5,605	C
Louisiana State Univ in Shreveport	LA	1,910	NC
Louisiana Tech Univ	LA	4,284	C
Loyola Univ of Chicago	IL	15,880	C+
Lubbock Christian Univ	TX	9,840	NC
Luther College	IA	15,900	VC
MacMurray College	IL	12,800	C
Manhattan College	NY	19,000	C
Manhattanville College	NY	20,450	LC
Marietta College	OH	16,940	C+
Marist College	NY	16,406	C
Mars Hill College	NC	11,050	C
Marshall Univ	WV	5,762	LC
Mary Washington College	VA	7,910	HC
Marygrove College	MI	5,877	VC
Maryville College	TN	14,474	C
Maryville Univ-St Louis	MO	12,900	VC
McKendree College	IL	10,900	C
McMurry Univ	TX	10,100	C
McNeese State Univ	LA	4,543	NC
McPherson College	KS	11,360	VC
Mercer Univ	GA	15,123	C
Mercy College	NY	11,180	NC
Mercyhurst College	PA	13,488	C
Merrimack College	MA	18,025	C
Messiah College	PA	14,664	VC
Methodist College	NC	12,400	C
Mich State Univ	MI	7,842	VC
Middle Tenn State Univ	TN	3,857	C
Middlebury College	VT	24,400	MC
Midland Lutheran College	NE	12,410	C
Midwestern State Univ	TX	4,542	LC
Miles College	AL	7,150	NC
Milligan College	TN	10,690	C
Millikin Univ	IL	15,499	VC
Miss College	MS	8,348	C
Missouri Southern State College	MO	4,272	
Molloy College	NY	8,580	LC
Moorhead State Univ	MN	5,076	C
Morehouse College	GA	13,224	VC
Morgan State Univ	MD	7,366	C+
Mount Mary College	WI	10,920	C
Mount St Mary College	NY	12,910	C
Murray State Univ	KY	4,702	C
New Mexico Highlands Univ	NM	3,772	C
New York Univ	NY	24,705	VC+
Newberry College	SC	11,994	LC
Niagara Univ	NY	14,552	C
Nicholls State Univ	LA	4,531	NC
N Car State Univ	NC	4,984	VC
North Central College	IL	15,498	VC
North Georgia College	GA	4,103	LC
North Park College	IL	14,310	C

School	ST	$IS	SR
Northeast Louisiana Univ	LA	3,906	NC
Northeast Missouri State Univ	MO	5,654	VC+
Northeastern State Univ	OK	5,250	C
Northern Arizona Univ	AZ	4,844	C
Northern Kentucky Univ	KY	4,620	NC
Northern Mich Univ	MI	6,350	C
Northern State Univ	SD	4,186	LC
Northland College	WI	13,550	C
Northwest Missouri State Univ	MO	5,010	LC
Northwest Nazarene College	ID	11,750	C
Northwestern College of Iowa	IA	12,250	C
Northwestern Univ	IL	21,093	MC
Norwich Univ	VT	18,730	C
Notre Dame College of Ohio	OH	11,370	C
Oakland Univ	MI	6,714	VC
Occidental College	CA	21,792	HC
Oglethorpe Univ	GA	16,360	VC
Ohio Univ	OH	7,341	C
Ohio Wesleyan Univ	OH	21,108	VC+
Okla Baptist Univ	OK	8,486	C
Olivet Nazarene Univ	IL	11,976	C
Oral Roberts Univ	OK	10,607	C
Oregon State Univ	OR	6,175	C
Otterbein College	OH	16,506	C
Ouachita Baptist Univ	AR	8,940	C
Pace Univ	NY	15,540	C
Park College	MO	7,320	C
Pembroke State Univ	NC	3,538	LC
Peru State College	NE	4,311	NC
Phillips Univ	OK	12,744	C
Pittsburg State Univ	KS	4,478	NC
Point Loma Nazarene College	CA	13,532	C
Purdue Univ/Calumet	IN	2,374	NC
Purdue Univ/West Lafayette	IN	6,636	C
Queens College	NC	14,950	C
Quinnipiac College	CT	17,600	C+
Rensselaer Polytechnic Inst	NY	23,067	HC
Rider College	NJ	18,160	C
Rivier College	NH	14,920	LC
Rockford College	IL	15,300	C
Rockhurst College	MO	12,470	C
Roosevelt Univ	IL	12,368	C
Rosemont College	PA	16,775	C
Russell Sage College	NY	16,790	C
Rutgers Univ/Camden College of A&S	NJ	8,652	VC
Rutgers Univ/Cook College	NJ	9,197	HC
Rutgers Univ/Douglass College	NJ	8,795	VC
Rutgers Univ/Livingston College	NJ	8,877	VC
Rutgers Univ/Newark College of A&S	NJ	8,645	C
Rutgers Univ/Rutgers College	NJ	8,841	HC+
Rutgers Univ/Univ College—Camden	NJ	3,506	LC
Rutgers Univ/Univ College—New Brunswick	NJ	0	LC
Rutgers Univ/Univ College—Newark	NJ	0	LC
Sacred Heart Univ	CT	16,350	C
Saginaw Valley State Univ	MI	6,634	LC
St Anselm College	NH	17,340	C
St Cloud State Univ	MN	5,015	C
St Francis College	IN	11,662	C
St John Fisher College	NY	15,415	C
St John's College	MN	15,364	C
St John's Univ	NY	8,980	C
St Joseph's College	IN	14,730	C
St Joseph's College	ME	14,535	C
St Leo College	FL	13,570	C
St Martin's College	WA	14,965	C
St Mary's College of Calif	CA	18,848	VC
St Mary's College of Minn	MN	13,850	LC
St Mary's Univ	TX	12,064	C
St Mary-of-the-Woods College	IN	14,430	NC
St Michael's College	VT	17,930	C
St Norbert College	WI	15,710	VC
St Olaf College	MN	17,200	HC
St Peter's College	NJ	14,775	LC
St Thomas Univ	FL	14,280	LC
St Vincent College	PA	13,934	LC
St Xavier Univ	IL	14,700	C
Salisbury State Univ	MD	7,516	C+
Savannah State College	GA	4,052	C
Schreiner College	TX	14,320	C
Seattle Univ	WA	16,590	C
Seton Hall Univ	NJ	18,306	C
Seton Hill College	PA	14,320	C
Shaw Univ	NC	8,936	C+
Shepherd College	WV	5,540	C
Simpson College	IA	14,635	VC
Southeastern Louisiana Univ	LA	4,230	NC
Southern Arkansas Univ	AR	3,432	NC
Southern College of Seventh-day Adventists	TN	11,348	NC
Southern Illinois Univ at Carbondale	IL	6,234	C
Southern Nazarene Univ	OK	9,206	NC
Southwest Missouri State Univ	MO	4,956	C

School	ST	$IS	SR
Southwest Texas State Univ	TX	5,124	C
Southwestern Okla State Univ	OK	3,312	C
Spring Hill College	AL	16,015	C+
Springfield College	MA	15,200	LC
SUNY at Albany	NY	7,059	VC
SUNY College of Environmental Science and Forestry	NY	9,257	HC+
SUNY/College at Cortland	NY	7,326	C+
SUNY/College at Fredonia	NY	7,159	VC
SUNY/College at Geneseo	NY	6,949	HC
SUNY/College at Oneonta	NY	7,878	C
SUNY/College at Oswego	NY	7,330	VC
SUNY/College at Plattsburgh	NY	6,917	C
Sterling College	KS	10,990	VC
Susquehanna Univ	PA	19,950	VC
Syracuse Univ	NY	21,305	HC
Tarleton State Univ	TX	4,082	LC
Taylor Univ	IN	14,450	VC
Temple Univ	PA	10,281	C
Texas A&M Univ at Kingsville	TX	3,808	LC
The Citadel	SC	6,619	C
Thiel College	PA	16,282	C
Thomas More College	KY	12,962	C
Touro College	NY	11,930	C
Trinity Christian College	IL	13,260	C
Trinity College	IL	14,010	C
Trinity Univ	TX	16,670	HC
Troy State Univ	AL	4,322	C
Union Univ	TN	7,880	C+
Univ of Akron	OH	6,699	NC
Univ of Alabama	AL	5,702	C
Univ of Arizona	AZ	5,808	C
Univ of Arkansas at Pine Bluff	AR	3,978	LC
Univ of Bridgeport	CT	18,985	C
Univ of Central Arkansas	AR	4,200	LC
Univ of Charleston	WV	12,750	C
Univ of Cincinnati	OH	7,989	C
Univ of Dayton	OH	15,120	C+
Univ of Denver	CO	19,290	C+
Univ of Detroit Mercy	MI	14,720	C
Univ of Georgia	GA	5,655	VC
Univ of Houston	TX	5,215	C
Univ of Houston-Downtown	TX	4,034	NC
Univ of Illinois at Chicago	IL	8,443	C
Univ of Indianapolis	IN	14,510	C
Univ of Iowa	IA	5,658	VC
Univ of La Verne	CA	17,400	C
Univ of Maryland/College Park	MD	8,182	VC
Univ of Mass/Amherst	MA	9,364	LC
Univ of Memphis	TN	3,476	C
Univ of Mich/Flint	MI	2,916	C
Univ of Minn/Twin Cities	MN	6,682	VC
Univ of Montana	MT	5,529	C
Univ of Nebr at Kearney	NE	4,308	LC
Univ of Nebr-Lincoln	NE	5,278	LC
Univ of Nevada/Reno	NV	5,735	C
Univ of New England	ME	16,075	LC
Univ of New Haven	CT	14,980	C
Univ of New Orleans	LA	5,468	C
Univ of N Car at Greensboro	NC	5,192	C
Univ of North Texas	TX	4,853	C
Univ of Notre Dame	IN	20,150	MC
Univ of Pittsburgh at Bradford	PA	9,050	C
Univ of Pittsburgh at Johnstown	PA	8,914	C
Univ of Portland	OR	15,564	C
Univ of St Thomas	TX	11,676	C+
Univ of Scranton	PA	17,071	VC
Univ of S Car at Aiken	SC	5,386	C
Univ of South Florida	FL	5,475	C+
Univ of Southern Calif	CA	23,006	VC
Univ of Southern Colo	CO	5,350	LC
Univ of Southern Indiana	IN	3,720	NC
Univ of Southern Miss	MS	4,542	C
Univ of Southwestern Louisiana	LA	3,968	NC
Univ of Tenn at Martin	TN	4,550	C
Univ of Tenn/Knoxville	TN	5,668	C
Univ of Texas at Arlington	TX	5,549	LC
Univ of the Pacific	CA	21,100	C
Univ of Toledo	OH	6,636	NC
Univ of Tulsa	OK	13,795	VC
Univ of West Florida	FL	5,415	C
Univ of Wisc/Milwaukee	WI	6,165	C
Univ of Wisc/River Falls	WI	4,655	C
Univ of Wisc/Stevens Point	WI	5,047	C+
Utah State Univ	UT	4,683	C
Utica College of Syracuse Univ	NY	16,714	LC
Valparaiso Univ	IN	14,810	VC
Virginia Commonwealth Univ	VA	7,909	C
Virginia Intermont College	VA	12,250	LC
Virginia Wesleyan College	VA	14,950	VC
Wagner College	NY	17,950	C
Walla Walla College	WA	13,215	C
Walsh Univ	OH	11,640	C
Washington and Jefferson College	PA	19,360	C
Washington State Univ	WA	6,364	C
Wayland Baptist Univ	TX	7,811	NC
Waynesburg College	PA	11,960	C
Weber State Univ	UT	4,398	C
Wells College	NY	19,460	C+
West Chester Univ of Penn	PA	7,492	C
West Liberty State College	WV	4,690	LC
West Texas A&M Univ	TX	4,224	C
Western Illinois Univ	IL	5,241	LC
Western Kentucky Univ	KY	4,808	C
Western Mich Univ	MI	6,820	C
Western New Mexico Univ	NM	3,234	LC
Western State College of Colo	CO	5,560	C
Westminster College	MO	13,750	C+
Westminster College	PA	15,200	C
Whitworth College	WA	16,265	C
Wichita State Univ	KS	5,068	NC
Widener Univ	PA	16,840	C
Wilberforce Univ	OH	10,408	C
Wilkes Univ	PA	15,728	LC
Willamette Univ	OR	17,995	VC
William Carey College	MS	7,050	C
William Jewell College	MO	12,500	VC
William Penn College	IA	13,400	C
Wilmington College	OH	13,700	LC
Wingate College	NC	10,610	C
Winona State Univ	MN	5,200	VC
Wittenberg Univ	OH	19,998	VC
Women's College of Brenau Univ	GA	14,734	C
Worcester Polytechnic Inst	MA	20,350	HC
Wright State Univ	OH	6,896	LC
Xavier Univ	OH	15,710	C+
Xavier Univ of Louisiana	LA	10,400	C
Youngstown State Univ	OH	6,447	LC

PREENGINEERING

School	ST	$IS	SR
Alice Lloyd College	KY	2,750	VC
Appalachian State Univ	NC	4,095	C
Aquinas College	MI	14,526	C
Augustana College	IL	16,959	VC
Aurora Univ	IL	13,381	C
Barry Univ	FL	16,050	C
Bellarmine College	KY	10,832	C
Belmont Abbey College	NC	13,190	C
Belmont Univ	TN	10,540	C
Berry College	GA	11,990	VC
Bethel College	MN	15,050	C
Briar Cliff College	IA	13,375	C
Cal State/Bakersfield	CA	5,402	C
Canisius College	NY	15,510	C
Carroll College	MT	11,265	C
Carthage College	WI	15,995	C
Cedarville College	OH	10,715	C
Centenary College of Louisiana	LA	11,826	C+
Central College	IA	14,025	VC
CUNY/Hunter College	NY	4,101	VC
Coe College	IA	17,085	VC
College of Charleston	SC	6,250	C
College of Notre Dame of Maryland	MD	16,050	C
College of St Benedict	MN	15,468	VC
Concordia College/Moorhead	MN	12,750	C
Coppin State College	MD	7,145	LC
David Lipscomb Univ	TN	7,865	VC
DePauw Univ	IN	18,530	VC
Dillard Univ	LA	9,950	C
Dominican College	NY	13,600	LC
East Texas State Univ	TX	4,572	LC
Eastern Mich Univ	MI	6,749	C
Emmanuel College	MA	17,773	LC
Fisk Univ	TN	0	LC
Framingham State College	MA	6,580	C
Freed-Hardeman Univ	TN	8,585	VC
Furman Univ	SC	16,557	VC
George Fox College	OR	15,640	LC
Georgia State Univ	GA	2,019	C
Goshen College	IN	12,360	C
Harvard Univ/Harvard and Radcliffe Colleges	MA	24,880	MC
Heidelberg College	OH	17,160	C
Henderson State Univ	AR	3,860	C
Hendrix College	AR	11,670	C
Huron Univ	SD	9,790	C
Illinois Benedictine College	IL	14,170	C
Indiana State Univ	IN	6,210	C
Iowa Wesleyan College	IA	13,250	C
Johnson C. Smith Univ	NC	8,916	LC
Judson College	IL	13,625	C
Juniata College	PA	18,390	C+
Kennesaw State College	GA	1,553	C
Kentucky Wesleyan College	KY	11,550	C
Le Moyne College	NY	15,180	C
Lewis Univ	IL	14,797	LC
Lincoln Univ	PA	0	LC
LIU/C. W. Post Campus	NY	16,870	C
Longwood College	VA	7,800	C
Louisiana College	LA	7,518	VC
Luther College	IA	15,900	VC
MacMurray College	IL	12,800	C
Mansfield Univ	PA	6,348	C
Maryville College	TN	14,474	C
Midwestern State Univ	TX	4,542	LC
Miles College	AL	7,150	NC
Morehouse College	GA	13,224	LC
Morgan State Univ	MD	7,366	C+
New Mexico Highlands Univ	NM	3,772	C
Niagara Univ	NY	14,552	C
North Central College	IL	15,498	VC
Northeast Missouri State Univ	MO	5,654	VC+
Northern Kentucky Univ	KY	4,620	NC
Northwest Missouri State Univ	MO	5,010	LC
Notre Dame College of Ohio	OH	11,370	C
Oral Roberts Univ	OK	10,607	C+
Peru State College	NE	4,311	NC
Pfeiffer College	NC	11,670	LC
Phillips Univ	OK	12,744	C
Richard Stockton College of New Jersey	NJ	6,950	VC
Rockford College	IL	15,300	C
St Edward's Univ	TX	12,636	C
St John Fisher College	NY	15,415	C
St John's Univ	MN	15,364	C
St John's Univ	NY	8,980	C+
St Lawrence Univ	NY	23,420	VC
St Mary's College of Minn	MN	13,850	LC
St Olaf College	MN	17,200	HC
Scripps College	CA	23,600	HC
Shaw Univ	NC	8,936	C+
Simpson College	IA	14,635	VC
Southern Nazarene Univ	OK	9,206	NC
Southern Univ and A&M College	LA	4,920	NC
Spring Hill College	AL	16,015	C+
Stephen F. Austin State Univ	TX	5,117	C
Taylor Univ	IN	14,450	VC
Thiel College	PA	16,282	C
Thomas More College	KY	12,962	C
Union College	KY	9,790	C
Univ of Arkansas at Pine Bluff	AR	3,978	LC
Univ of Central Arkansas	AR	4,200	LC
Univ of North Texas	TX	4,853	C
Univ of Oregon	OR	6,666	VC
Univ of Scranton	PA	17,071	VC
Valdosta State Univ	GA	4,670	LC
West Liberty State College	WV	4,690	LC
Western Illinois Univ	IL	5,241	LC
Western State College of Colo	CO	5,560	C
Wilberforce Univ	OH	10,408	C
William Carey College	MS	7,050	C
Wingate College	NC	10,610	C
Yeshiva Univ	NY	18,200	VC

PRELAW

School	ST	$IS	SR
Abilene Christian Univ	TX	10,460	NC
Albertus Magnus College	CT	16,280	LC
Alcorn State Univ	MS	4,474	C+
Alderson-Broaddus College	WV	12,000	C
Alfred Univ	NY	21,054	VC+
Allegheny College	PA	21,020	VC
Alvernia College	PA	13,150	LC
Alverno College	WI	11,344	C
American International College	MA	14,029	C
Anderson Univ	IN	12,920	C
Andrews Univ	MI	14,952	NC
Anna Maria College	MA	15,975	LC
Antioch College	OH	19,532	C
Appalachian State Univ	NC	4,095	C
Arkansas State Univ	AR	4,250	NC
Asbury College	KY	11,105	VC
Ashland Univ	OH	15,508	C
Audrey Cohen College	NY	11,184	LC
Augsburg College	MN	15,608	C
Augustana College	SD	13,420	C
Aurora Univ	IL	13,381	C
Austin Peay State Univ	TN	4,350	C
Averett College	VA	13,610	LC
Baker Univ	KS	12,284	C
Baldwin-Wallace College	OH	15,210	C
Ball State Univ	IN	6,032	LC
Bard College	NY	25,269	HC
Barry Univ	FL	16,050	C
Bartlesville Wesleyan College	OK	9,400	C
Baylor Univ	TX	10,990	C+
Beaver College	PA	17,660	C
Bellarmine College	KY	10,832	C
Belmont Abbey College	NC	13,190	C
Bemidji State Univ	MN	5,188	C
Berry College	GA	11,990	VC
Bethany College	KS	11,232	C
Bethany College	WV	18,300	C+
Bethel College	MN	15,050	C
Black Hills State Univ	SD	4,831	NC
Blue Mountain College	MS	5,958	LC
Boston Univ	MA	24,130	HC
Bowling Green State Univ	OH	6,701	C
Briar Cliff College	IA	13,375	C
Bridgewater State College	MA	7,518	C
Brooklyn Campus of LIU	NY	15,000	LC
Calif Lutheran Univ	CA	17,240	C
Cal State/Bakersfield	CA	5,402	C
Cal State/Chico	CA	6,146	C
Cal State/Fresno	CA	5,747	C
Cal State/Los Angeles	CA	4,940	VC
Calvin College	MI	13,020	VC
Cameron Univ	OK	3,686	LC
Canisius College	NY	15,510	C
Capital Univ	OH	16,535	VC
Cardinal Stritch College	WI	11,252	C
Caribbean Univ	PR	2,400	
Carroll College	MT	11,265	C
Carroll College	WI	15,490	C
Carthage College	WI	15,995	C
Catawba College	NC	12,950	C
Catholic Univ of America	DC	18,856	C
Cedarville College	OH	10,715	C
Centenary College of Louisiana	LA	11,826	C+
Central College	IA	14,025	VC
Central Methodist College	MO	11,410	C
Central Missouri State Univ	MO	5,138	LC
Central State Univ	OH	7,320	NC
Chadron State College	NE	4,091	NC
Chatham College	PA	18,010	C
Chicago State Univ	IL	2,198	C
Christian Brothers Univ	TN	12,120	VC
Christopher Newport Univ	VA	3,196	LC
CUNY/Brooklyn College	NY	2,450	VC
CUNY/City College	NY	2,543	VC
CUNY/Herbert H. Lehman College	NY	2,542	C
CUNY/Hunter College	NY	4,101	VC
CUNY/Queens College	NY	2,631	C
CUNY/York College	NY	2,534	NC
Claflin College	SC	0	
Clark Univ	MA	21,400	VC
Clemson Univ	SC	6,564	VC
Coastal Carolina Univ	SC	6,010	LC
Coe College	IA	17,085	VC
College Misericordia	PA	15,820	C
College of Great Falls	MT	6,230	NC
College of Mount St Joseph	OH	13,272	C
College of New Rochelle	NY	15,440	LC
College of Notre Dame	CA	16,480	C
College of Notre Dame of Maryland	MD	16,050	C
College of Our Lady of The Elms	MA	15,639	C
College of St Benedict	MN	15,468	VC
College of St Elizabeth	NJ	15,800	C
College of St Francis	IL	13,060	VC
College of St Joseph	VT	12,650	LC
College of St Mary	NE	12,500	VC
College of St Scholastica	MN	14,868	C
College of the Southwest	NM	5,720	LC
Colo Christian Univ	CO	9,750	C
Columbia College	MO	11,995	C
Columbia Union College	MD	13,650	LC
Columbia Univ/Columbia College	NY	26,757	MC
Columbus College	GA	4,892	LC
Concord College	WV	5,104	NC
Concordia College	MN	13,200	C
Concordia College	NE	11,776	NC
Concordia College/Moorhead	MN	12,750	C
Concordia Univ	IL	12,611	C
Converse College	SC	15,750	C
Creighton Univ	NE	14,432	VC
Cumberland College	KY	9,756	C
Cumberland Univ	TN	8,650	C
D'Youville College	NY	12,850	C
Dakota Wesleyan Univ	SD	9,770	LC
Dana College	NE	11,910	C
David Lipscomb Univ	TN	7,865	VC
Davis and Elkins College	WV	13,230	LC
Defiance College	OH	13,480	LC
Dominican College	NY	13,600	LC
Dordt College	IA	11,690	C
Drake Univ	IA	17,195	VC
Drexel Univ	PA	15,970	C
Drury College	MO	12,140	VC
Duquesne Univ	PA	16,434	VC
East Central Univ	OK	3,558	C
East Texas State Univ	TX	4,572	LC
Eastern Conn State Univ	CT	6,966	C
Eastern Mich Univ	MI	6,749	C
Eastern Oregon State College	OR	6,090	C
Eastern Washington Univ	WA	5,439	LC
Eckerd College	FL	18,855	VC
Edinboro Univ of Penn	PA	7,181	C
Elmira College	NY	18,450	C
Emerson College	MA	22,678	LC
Emmanuel College	MA	17,773	LC
Emory and Henry College	VA	12,776	C
Eugene Lang College of the New School for Social Research	NY	21,145	C+
Evergreen State College	WA	6,306	C
Fairleigh Dickinson Univ	NJ	16,427	C
Faulkner Univ	AL	8,630	LC
Felician College	NJ	7,900	C
Fisk Univ	TN	0	LC
Fitchburg State College	MA	6,962	C

INDEX OF COLLEGE MAJORS

School	ST	$IS	SR
Flagler College	FL	7,990	C
Florida Atlantic Univ	FL	5,525	C
Florida State Univ	FL	5,814	VC
Fontbonne College	MO	12,090	C
Fordham Univ/College at Lincoln Center	NY	18,150	VC
Franklin College of Indiana	IN	13,970	C
Franklin Pierce College	NH	17,270	LC
Fresno Pacific College	CA	13,020	C
Gannon Univ	PA	14,872	C
Geneva College	PA	13,030	C
George Fox College	OR	15,640	LC
George Mason Univ	VA	8,728	C
Georgetown Univ	DC	24,410	MC
Georgia State Univ	GA	2,019	C
Gettysburg College	PA	22,960	HC
Golden Gate Univ	CA	5,623	VC
Gonzaga Univ	WA	16,350	VC
Goucher College	MD	20,295	VC
Grace College	IN	12,120	C
Graceland College	IA	11,600	C
Grambling State Univ	LA	4,712	NC
Grand Rapids Baptist College and Seminary	MI	10,228	C
Grand Valley State Univ	MI	6,822	VC
Grove City College	PA	7,870	HC
Gustavus Adolphus College	MN	15,935	VC
Hamline Univ	MN	17,122	VC
Hanover College	IN	10,950	VC
Harding Univ	AR	9,050	VC
Heidelberg College	OH	17,160	C
Henderson State Univ	AR	3,860	C
Hendrix College	AR	11,670	C
Hillsdale College	MI	15,110	VC
Hofstra Univ	NY	16,580	VC
Holy Family College	PA	8,300	C
Hope College	MI	15,698	C+
Houghton College	NY	13,120	VC
Howard Payne Univ	TX	8,052	C
Humboldt State Univ	CA	5,676	C
Huntingdon College	AL	11,400	C
Huntington College	IN	13,220	C
Huron Univ	SD	9,790	C
Illinois Benedictine College	IL	14,170	C
Illinois College	IL	11,200	C
Illinois Inst of Tech	IL	18,290	VC
Immaculata College	PA	14,620	C
Incarnate Word College	TX	12,307	C
Indiana State Univ	IN	6,210	C
Indiana Univ of Penn	PA	6,373	C
Indiana Univ-Purdue Univ at Fort Wayne	IN	2,500	LC
Indiana Univ/South Bend	IN	2,141	LC
Iona College	NY	16,310	C
Iowa Wesleyan College	IA	13,250	C
Ithaca College	NY	19,679	C
Jacksonville State Univ	AL	4,080	LC
Jamestown College	ND	10,250	C
Jersey City State College	NJ	7,797	LC
John Brown Univ	AR	9,880	VC
Johns Hopkins Univ	MD	24,360	MC
Johnson C. Smith Univ	NC	8,916	LC
Judson College	AL	9,060	C
Judson College	IL	13,625	C
Juniata College	PA	18,390	C+
Kalamazoo College	MI	19,974	HC
Kansas Newman College	KS	10,640	C
Kansas Wesleyan Univ	KS	11,770	C
Kennesaw State College	GA	1,553	C
Kentucky Wesleyan College	KY	11,550	C
King's College	NY	12,360	LC
King's College	PA	15,420	C
La Salle Univ	PA	16,940	VC
Lafayette College	PA	23,450	HC
LaGrange College	GA	10,602	C
Lake Superior State Univ	MI	7,311	C
Lamar Univ	TX	3,798	C
Lander Univ	SC	6,180	LC
Lane College	TN	7,628	LC
Le Moyne College	NY	15,180	C
Lebanon Valley College of Penn	PA	18,300	C
Lehigh Univ	PA	23,250	HC
Lenoir-Rhyne College	NC	14,068	C
Lewis Univ	IL	14,797	LC
Liberty Univ	VA	11,500	LC
Limestone College	SC	10,700	LC
Lincoln Memorial Univ	TN	8,218	C
Lindenwood College	MO	13,560	C
Linfield College	OR	16,670	VC
Livingston Univ	AL	3,979	C
Livingstone College	NC	8,600	LC
LIU/C. W. Post Campus	NY	16,870	C
LIU/Southampton Campus	NY	17,280	C
Louisiana College	LA	7,518	VC
Louisiana Tech Univ	LA	4,284	C
Loyola Univ/New Orleans	LA	15,660	C+
Lubbock Christian Univ	TX	9,840	NC
Luther College	IA	15,900	VC
Lynn Univ	FL	18,300	C
MacMurray College	IL	12,800	C
Manhattan College	NY	19,000	C
Manhattanville College	NY	20,450	LC
Marietta College	OH	16,940	C+
Marist College	NY	16,406	C
Marlboro College	VT	23,305	C+
Mars Hill College	NC	11,050	C
Marshall Univ	WV	5,762	LC
Mary Washington College	VA	7,910	HC
Maryville College	TN	14,474	C
Maryville Univ-St Louis	MO	12,900	VC
McKendree College	IL	10,900	C
McMurry Univ	TX	10,100	C
McNeese State Univ	LA	4,543	NC
McPherson College	KS	11,360	VC
Mercer Univ	GA	15,123	C
Mercy College	NY	11,180	NC
Mercyhurst College	PA	13,488	C
Merrimack College	MA	18,025	C
Messiah College	PA	14,664	VC
Methodist College	NC	12,400	C
Miami Univ	OH	8,066	VC
Mich State Univ	MI	7,842	C
Middle Tenn State Univ	TN	3,857	C
Midland Lutheran College	NE	12,410	LC
Midwestern State Univ	TX	4,542	LC
Milligan College	TN	10,690	C
Millikin Univ	IL	15,499	C
Mills College	CA	20,848	VC
Miss College	MS	8,348	C
Missouri Southern State College	MO	4,272	C
Molloy College	NY	8,580	LC
Monmouth College	NJ	16,820	C
Moorhead State Univ	MN	5,076	C
Moravian College	PA	18,960	VC
Morehouse College	GA	13,224	LC
Morgan State Univ	MD	7,366	C+
Morris Brown College	GA	12,234	NC
Mount Mary College	WI	10,920	C
Mount St Mary College	NY	12,910	C
Mount St Mary's College	CA	16,390	VC
Murray State Univ	KY	4,702	C
National Univ	CA	6,135	C
Neumann College	PA	9,950	LC
New Mexico Highlands Univ	NM	3,772	C
New York Univ	NY	24,705	VC+
Newberry College	SC	11,994	LC
Niagara Univ	NY	14,552	C
Nicholls State Univ	LA	4,531	NC
Norfolk State Univ	VA	6,345	LC
North Adams State College	MA	7,750	C
N Car State Univ	NC	4,984	VC
North Central College	IL	15,498	VC
North Georgia College	GA	4,103	LC
North Park College	IL	14,310	C
Northeast Louisiana Univ	LA	3,906	NC
Northeast Missouri State Univ	MO	5,654	VC+
Northeastern State Univ	OK	5,250	C
Northern Arizona Univ	AZ	4,844	C
Northern Kentucky Univ	KY	4,620	NC
Northern Mich Univ	MI	6,350	C
Northern State Univ	SD	4,186	LC
Northland College	WI	13,550	LC
Northwest Missouri State Univ	MO	5,010	LC
Northwest Nazarene College	ID	11,750	C
Northwestern College of Iowa	IA	12,250	LC
Northwestern Univ	IL	21,093	MC
Norwich Univ	VT	18,730	C
Notre Dame College	NH	14,220	C
Notre Dame College of Ohio	OH	11,370	C
Oakland City College	IN	10,216	LC
Oglethorpe Univ	GA	16,360	VC
Ohio Univ	OH	7,341	C
Ohio Wesleyan Univ	OH	21,108	VC+
Okla Baptist Univ	OK	8,486	C
Okla Christian Univ of Science and Arts	OK	8,790	NC
Okla City Univ	OK	9,840	C
Okla State Univ	OK	5,086	VC
Olivet Nazarene Univ	IL	11,976	C
Oral Roberts Univ	OK	10,607	C+
Otterbein College	OH	16,506	C
Ouachita Baptist Univ	AR	8,940	C
Park College	MO	7,320	C
Pembroke State Univ	NC	3,538	LC
Penn State Univ/Univ Park Campus	PA	8,752	HC
Peru State College	NE	4,311	NC
Pfeiffer College	NC	11,670	LC
Philadelphia College of Textiles and Science	PA	15,896	C
Phillips Univ	OK	12,744	C
Pittsburg State Univ	KS	4,478	NC
Point Loma Nazarene College	CA	13,532	C
Purdue Univ/Calumet	IN	2,374	NC
Purdue Univ/West Lafayette	IN	6,636	C
Queens College	NC	14,950	C
Quinnipiac College	CT	17,600	C+
Regis Univ	CO	17,340	C
Rensselaer Polytechnic Inst	NY	23,067	HC
Rhode Island College	RI	7,901	LC
Rider College	NJ	18,160	C
Rivier College	NH	14,920	LC
Roberts Wesleyan College	NY	13,317	C
Rockford College	IL	15,300	C
Rockhurst College	MO	12,470	C
Roger Williams Univ	RI	16,750	C
Roosevelt Univ	IL	12,368	C
Rosemont College	PA	16,775	C
Rutgers Univ/Camden College of A&S	NJ	8,652	VC
Rutgers Univ/Douglass College	NJ	8,795	VC
Rutgers Univ/Livingston College	NJ	8,877	VC
Rutgers Univ/Newark College of A&S	NJ	8,645	C
Rutgers Univ/Rutgers College	NJ	8,841	HC+
Rutgers Univ/Univ College—Camden	NJ	3,506	C
Rutgers Univ/Univ College—New Brunswick	NJ	0	LC
Rutgers Univ/Univ College—Newark	NJ	0	C
Sacred Heart Univ	CT	16,350	C
Saginaw Valley State Univ	MI	6,634	LC
St Anselm College	NH	17,340	C
St Augustine's College	NC	9,300	C+
St Bonaventure Univ	NY	14,762	C
St Cloud State Univ	MN	5,015	C
St Edward's Univ	TX	12,636	C
St Francis College	IN	11,662	C
St John Fisher College	NY	15,415	C
St John's Univ	MN	15,364	C
St John's Univ	NY	8,980	C+
St Joseph College	CT	16,225	C
St Joseph's College	IN	14,730	C
St Joseph's College	ME	14,535	C
St Leo College	FL	13,570	C
St Martin's College	WA	14,965	C
St Mary's College	MI	8,350	C
St Mary's College of Calif	CA	18,848	VC
St Mary's College of Minn	MN	13,850	LC
St Mary's Univ	TX	12,064	C
St Mary-of-the-Woods College	IN	14,430	NC
St Michael's College	VT	17,930	C
St Norbert College	WI	15,710	VC
St Olaf College	MN	17,200	HC
St Peter's College	NJ	14,775	LC
St Thomas Aquinas College	NY	13,550	C
St Thomas Univ	FL	14,280	LC
St Vincent College	PA	13,934	LC
St Xavier Univ	IL	14,700	C
Samford Univ	AL	11,400	VC
Sarah Lawrence College	NY	24,975	HC
Schreiner College	TX	14,320	C
Scripps College	CA	23,600	HC
Seattle Univ	WA	16,590	C
Seton Hall Univ	NJ	18,306	LC
Seton Hill College	PA	14,320	C
Shawnee State Univ	OH	4,379	NC
Shepherd College	WV	5,540	C
Shimer College	IL	12,850	NC
Simmons College	MA	22,534	C
Simpson College	IA	14,635	VC
Sioux Falls College	SD	11,540	C
Southeastern Louisiana Univ	LA	4,230	NC
Southern Calif College	CA	12,356	C
Southern College of Seventh-day Adventists	TN	11,348	NC
Southern Illinois Univ at Carbondale	IL	6,234	C
Southern Nazarene Univ	OK	9,206	NC
Southern Oregon State College	OR	6,128	C
Southern Univ and A&M College	LA	4,920	NC
Southwest Missouri State Univ	MO	4,956	C
Southwestern College	KS	10,032	C
Southwestern Okla State Univ	OK	3,312	C
Spring Hill College	AL	16,015	C+
Springfield College	MA	15,200	LC
SUNY at Albany	NY	7,059	VC
SUNY College of Environmental Science and Forestry	NY	9,257	HC+
SUNY/College at Cortland	NY	7,326	C+
SUNY/College at Geneseo	NY	6,949	HC
SUNY/College at Oneonta	NY	7,878	C
SUNY/College at Oswego	NY	7,330	VC
SUNY/College at Plattsburgh	NY	6,917	C
Stephens College	MO	18,460	C
Sterling College	KS	10,990	VC
Stetson Univ	FL	16,435	VC
Susquehanna Univ	PA	19,950	VC
Syracuse Univ	NY	21,305	HC
Tarleton State Univ	TX	4,082	LC
Taylor Univ	IN	14,450	VC
Teikyo Marycrest Univ	IA	13,755	VC
Temple Univ	PA	10,281	C
Texas A&M Univ at Kingsville	TX	3,808	LC
Texas College	TX	5,930	NC
Texas Tech Univ	TX	6,008	C
Thiel College	PA	16,282	C
Thomas More College	KY	12,962	C
Touro College	NY	11,930	C
Trevecca Nazarene College	TN	9,826	NC
Trinity Christian College	IL	13,260	C
Trinity College	DC	17,660	C
Trinity College	IL	14,010	C
Trinity Univ	TX	16,670	HC
Troy State Univ	AL	4,322	C
Tulane Univ	LA	24,540	HC
Union College	KY	9,790	C
Union Univ	TN	7,880	C+
United States International Univ	CA	14,535	LC
Unity College	ME	12,885	LC
Univ of Akron	OH	6,699	NC
Univ of Arkansas at Monticello	AR	3,832	NC
Univ of Bridgeport	CT	18,985	C
Univ of Central Okla	OK	3,647	C
Univ of Charleston	WV	12,750	LC
Univ of Cincinnati	OH	7,989	C
Univ of Denver	CO	19,290	C+
Univ of Detroit Mercy	MI	14,720	C
Univ of Dubuque	IA	14,150	LC
Univ of Evansville	IN	15,300	VC
Univ of Houston	TX	5,215	C
Univ of Indianapolis	IN	14,510	C
Univ of Iowa	IA	5,658	VC
Univ of La Verne	CA	17,400	C
Univ of Mary	ND	8,910	C
Univ of Mary Hardin-Baylor	TX	8,120	NC
Univ of Mass/Amherst	MA	9,364	LC
Univ of Memphis	TN	3,476	C
Univ of Mich/Flint	MI	2,916	C
Univ of Minn/Morris	MN	6,825	HC
Univ of Minn/Twin Cities	MN	6,682	VC
Univ of Montana	MT	5,529	C
Univ of Nebr at Kearney	NE	4,308	LC
Univ of Nebr at Omaha	NE	1,889	LC
Univ of New England	ME	16,075	LC
Univ of N Car at Greensboro	NC	5,192	C
Univ of N Dak	ND	4,902	NC
Univ of North Florida	FL	5,082	C
Univ of Notre Dame	IN	20,150	MC
Univ of Pittsburgh at Bradford	PA	9,050	C
Univ of Pittsburgh at Johnstown	PA	8,914	C
Univ of Portland	OR	15,564	C
Univ of PR/Rio Piedras	PR	0	
Univ of St Thomas	TX	11,676	C+
Univ of Scranton	PA	17,071	VC
Univ of S Car at Aiken	SC	5,386	C
Univ of S Car at Spartanburg	SC	2,320	C
Univ of South Florida	FL	5,475	C+
Univ of Southern Colo	CO	5,350	LC
Univ of Southern Indiana	IN	3,720	NC
Univ of Southern Miss	MS	4,542	C
Univ of Southwestern Louisiana	LA	3,968	NC
Univ of Tenn at Martin	TN	4,550	C
Univ of Texas at Arlington	TX	5,549	LC
Univ of the Pacific	CA	21,100	C
Univ of Toledo	OH	6,636	NC
Univ of Tulsa	OK	13,795	VC
Univ of West Florida	FL	5,415	C
Univ of Wisc/Milwaukee	WI	6,165	C
Univ of Wisc/River Falls	WI	4,655	C
Univ of Wisc/Whitewater	WI	4,700	C
Urbana Univ	OH	12,536	C
Ursinus College	PA	19,165	VC
Ursuline College	OH	13,180	LC
Utah State Univ	UT	4,683	C
Utica College of Syracuse Univ	NY	16,714	LC
Valdosta State Univ	GA	4,670	LC
Valparaiso Univ	IN	14,810	VC
Vassar College	NY	24,206	HC
Virginia Intermont College	VA	12,250	LC
Virginia Polytechnic Inst and State Univ	VA	6,828	C
Virginia Wesleyan College	VA	14,950	VC
Wagner College	NY	17,950	C
Walla Walla College	WA	13,215	C
Walsh Univ	OH	11,640	C
Washington and Jefferson College	PA	19,360	C
Washington State Univ	WA	6,364	C
Wayne State College	NE	4,260	NC
Waynesburg College	PA	11,960	C
Wells College	NY	19,460	C+
West Chester Univ of Penn	PA	7,492	C
West Liberty State College	WV	4,690	LC
Western Illinois Univ	IL	5,241	LC
Western Kentucky Univ	KY	4,808	C
Western Mich Univ	MI	6,820	C
Western State College of Colo	CO	5,560	C
Western Washington Univ	WA	6,077	VC
Westminster College	PA	15,200	C
Whitman College	WA	20,595	HC
Whitworth College	WA	16,265	C
Wichita State Univ	KS	5,068	NC
Widener Univ	PA	16,840	C
Wilberforce Univ	OH	10,408	C
Wilkes Univ	PA	15,728	LC
Willamette Univ	OR	17,995	VC
William Jewell College	MO	12,500	VC
William Penn College	IA	13,400	C
William Woods Univ	MO	14,025	LC
Wilmington College	OH	13,700	LC
Wingate College	NC	10,610	C

School	ST	$IS	SR
Winona State Univ	MN	5,200	VC
Wittenberg Univ	OH	19,998	VC
Wofford College	SC	15,360	VC
Women's College of Brenau Univ	GA	14,734	C
Wright State Univ	OH	6,896	VC
Xavier Univ of Louisiana	LA	10,400	C
York College of Penn	PA	8,345	C
Youngstown State Univ	OH	6,447	LC

PREMEDICINE

School	ST	$IS	SR
Abilene Christian Univ	TX	10,460	NC
Albertus Magnus College	CT	16,280	LC
Alcorn State Univ	MS	4,474	C+
Alderson-Broaddus College	WV	12,000	C
Alfred Univ	NY	21,054	VC+
Allegheny College	PA	21,020	VC
Alvernia College	PA	13,150	LC
Alverno College	WI	11,344	C
American International College	MA	14,029	C
Anderson Univ	IN	12,920	C
Andrews Univ	MI	14,952	NC
Angelo State Univ	TX	5,176	C
Anna Maria College	MA	15,975	LC
Antioch College	OH	19,532	C
Appalachian State Univ	NC	4,095	C
Aquinas College	MI	14,526	C
Arkansas State Univ	AR	4,250	NC
Asbury College	KY	11,105	VC
Ashland Univ	OH	15,508	C
Auburn Univ	AL	5,823	C+
Augsburg College	MN	15,608	C
Augustana College	IL	16,959	VC
Augustana College	SD	13,420	C
Aurora Univ	IL	13,381	C
Austin Peay State Univ	TN	4,350	C
Averett College	VA	13,610	LC
Avila College	MO	12,130	C
Azusa Pacific Univ	CA	15,034	C
Baker Univ	KS	12,284	C
Baldwin-Wallace College	OH	15,210	LC
Ball State Univ	IN	6,032	LC
Bard College	NY	25,269	HC
Barry Univ	FL	16,050	C
Bartlesville Wesleyan College	OK	9,400	C
Baylor Univ	TX	10,990	C+
Beaver College	PA	17,660	C
Bellarmine College	KY	10,832	C
Belmont Abbey College	NC	13,190	C
Belmont Univ	TN	10,540	C
Bemidji State Univ	MN	5,188	C
Bennett College	NC	8,920	LC
Berry College	GA	11,990	VC
Bethany College	KS	11,232	C
Bethany College	WV	18,300	C+
Bethel College	IN	11,650	C
Bethel College	TN	15,050	LC
Blue Mountain College	MS	5,958	LC
Boise State Univ	ID	4,909	LC
Boston Univ	MA	24,130	HC
Bowling Green State Univ	OH	6,701	C
Briar Cliff College	IA	13,375	C
Bridgewater State College	MA	7,518	C
Brigham Young Univ/Hawaii	HI	6,750	VC
Brooklyn Campus of LIU	NY	15,000	VC
Calif Lutheran Univ	CA	17,240	C
Cal State/Bakersfield	CA	5,402	C
Cal State/Chico	CA	6,146	C
Cal State/Fresno	CA	5,747	C
Calif Univ of Penn	PA	7,370	C
Calvin College	MI	13,020	VC
Canisius College	NY	15,510	C
Capital Univ	OH	16,535	VC
Cardinal Stritch College	WI	11,252	C
Caribbean Univ	PR	2,400	
Carroll College	MT	11,265	C
Carroll College	WI	15,490	C
Carthage College	WI	15,995	C
Catawba College	NC	12,920	VC
Catholic Univ of America	DC	18,856	C
Cedarville College	OH	10,715	C
Centenary College of Louisiana	LA	11,826	C+
Central Missouri State Univ	MO	5,138	LC
Central State Univ	OH	7,320	NC
Central Univ of Bayamon	PR	2,430	
Chadron State College	NE	4,091	NC
Chatham College	PA	18,010	C
Chicago State Univ	IL	2,198	C
Christian Brothers Univ	TN	12,120	C
Christopher Newport Univ	VA	3,196	LC
CUNY/Brooklyn College	NY	2,450	VC
CUNY/City College	NY	2,543	VC
CUNY/Herbert H. Lehman College	NY	2,542	LC
CUNY/Hunter College	NY	4,101	VC
CUNY/Queens College	NY	2,631	C
CUNY/York College	NY	2,534	NC
Claremont McKenna College	CA	22,150	MC
Clark Univ	MA	21,400	HC
Clarkson Univ	NY	20,705	VC+

School	ST	$IS	SR
Clemson Univ	SC	6,564	VC
Cleveland State Univ	OH	7,287	NC
Coastal Carolina Univ	SC	6,010	LC
Coe College	IA	17,085	VC
College Misericordia	PA	15,820	C
College of Charleston	SC	6,250	C
College of Great Falls	MT	6,230	C
College of Mount St Joseph	OH	13,272	C
College of New Rochelle	NY	15,440	LC
College of Notre Dame	CA	16,480	C
College of Notre Dame of Maryland	MD	16,050	C
College of Our Lady of The Elms	MA	15,639	C
College of St Benedict	MN	15,468	VC
College of St Elizabeth	NJ	15,800	C
College of St Francis	IL	13,060	VC
College of St Mary	NE	12,500	C
College of St Scholastica	MN	14,868	C
Colo Christian Univ	CO	9,750	C
Columbia College	MO	11,995	C
Columbia Union College	MD	13,650	LC
Concord College	WV	5,104	NC
Concordia College	MN	13,200	C
Concordia College	NE	11,776	NC
Concordia College/Moorhead	MN	12,750	C
Concordia Univ	IL	12,611	C
Converse College	SC	15,750	C
Creighton Univ	NE	14,432	VC
Cumberland College	KY	9,756	C
Cumberland Univ	TN	8,650	C
D'Youville College	NY	12,850	C
Dakota State Univ	SD	4,374	LC
Dakota Wesleyan Univ	SD	9,770	LC
Dana College	NE	11,910	C
David Lipscomb Univ	TN	7,865	VC
Davis and Elkins College	WV	13,230	LC
Defiance College	OH	13,480	LC
Delaware Valley College	PA	16,065	LC
Delta State Univ	MS	3,964	LC
Dillard Univ	LA	9,950	C
Dominican College of San Rafael	CA	17,860	C
Dordt College	IA	11,690	C
Drake Univ	IA	17,195	VC
Drexel Univ	PA	15,970	C
Drury College	MO	12,140	VC
Duquesne Univ	PA	16,434	VC
East Stroudsburg Univ	PA	6,886	C
East Texas State Univ	TX	4,572	LC
Eastern Mich Univ	MI	6,749	C
Eastern Oregon State College	OR	6,090	C
Eastern Washington Univ	WA	5,439	LC
Eckerd College	FL	18,855	VC
Edinboro Univ of Penn	PA	7,181	C
Elmira College	NY	18,450	C
Emmanuel College	MA	17,773	LC
Emory and Henry College	VA	12,776	C
Erskine College	SC	14,310	C
Evergreen State College	WA	6,306	C
Fairleigh Dickinson Univ	NJ	16,427	C
Felician College	NJ	7,900	C
Fisk Univ	TN	0	LC
Fitchburg State College	MA	6,962	C
Florida A&M Univ	FL	4,651	LC
Florida Inst of Tech	FL	16,935	VC
Fontbonne College	MO	12,090	C
Fordham Univ/College at Lincoln Center	NY	18,150	C
Franklin College of Indiana	IN	13,970	C
Franklin Pierce College	NH	17,270	LC
Freed-Hardeman Univ	TN	8,585	VC
Fresno Pacific College	CA	13,020	C
Friends Univ	KS	11,205	C
Gannon Univ	PA	14,872	C
Geneva College	PA	13,030	C
George Fox College	OR	15,640	LC
George Mason Univ	VA	8,728	C
Georgetown Univ	DC	24,410	MC
Georgia State Univ	GA	2,019	C
Gettysburg College	PA	22,960	HC
Gonzaga Univ	WA	16,350	VC
Goshen College	IN	12,360	C
Grace College	IN	12,120	C
Graceland College	IA	11,600	C
Grambling State Univ	LA	4,712	NC
Grand Rapids Baptist College and Seminary	MI	10,228	C
Grand Valley State Univ	MI	6,822	VC
Grand View College	IA	13,230	NC
Grove City College	PA	7,870	NC
Gustavus Adolphus College	MN	15,935	VC
Gwynedd-Mercy College	PA	15,450	LC
Hamline Univ	MN	17,122	VC
Hampshire College	MA	25,320	C
Hanover College	IN	10,950	VC
Harding Univ	AR	9,050	VC
Heidelberg College	OH	17,160	C
Henderson State Univ	AR	3,860	LC
Hendrix College	AR	11,670	C
Hillsdale College	MI	15,110	VC
Hofstra Univ	NY	16,580	VC
Holy Family College	PA	8,300	C
Hope College	MI	15,698	C+
Houghton College	NY	13,120	VC

School	ST	$IS	SR
Houston Baptist Univ	TX	11,055	C
Howard Payne Univ	TX	8,052	C
Howard Univ	DC	11,680	C
Humboldt State Univ	CA	5,676	C
Huntingdon College	AL	11,400	C
Huntington College	IN	13,220	C
Huron Univ	SD	9,790	C
Illinois Benedictine College	IL	14,170	C
Illinois Inst of Tech	IL	18,290	VC
Immaculata College	PA	14,620	C
Incarnate Word College	TX	12,307	C
Indiana State Univ	IN	6,210	C
Indiana Univ of Penn	PA	6,373	C
Indiana Univ-Purdue Univ at Fort Wayne	IN	2,500	LC
Indiana Univ/South Bend	IN	2,141	LC
Indiana Wesleyan Univ	IN	12,332	C
Inter American Univ of PR/ San German	PR	4,620	
Iona College	NY	16,310	C
Ithaca College	NY	19,679	C
Jackson State Univ	MS	4,996	LC
Jacksonville State Univ	AL	4,080	LC
Jacksonville Univ	FL	13,390	C
Jamestown College	ND	10,250	C
Jarvis Christian College	TX	7,170	C
Jersey City State College	NJ	7,797	LC
Johns Hopkins Univ	MD	24,360	MC
Johnson C. Smith Univ	NC	8,916	LC
Judson College	AL	9,060	C
Judson College	IL	13,625	C
Juniata College	PA	18,390	C+
Kansas Newman College	KS	10,640	C
Kansas State Univ	KS	4,816	NC
Kennesaw State College	GA	1,553	C
Kent State Univ	OH	6,740	LC
Kentucky Wesleyan College	KY	11,550	C
King's College	NY	12,360	C
King's College	PA	15,420	C
La Salle Univ	PA	16,940	VC
LaGrange College	GA	10,602	C
Lake Superior State Univ	MI	7,311	C
Lamar Univ	TX	3,798	C
Lander Univ	SC	6,180	C
Lane College	TN	7,628	LC
Le Moyne College	NY	15,180	C
Lebanon Valley College of Penn	PA	18,300	C
Lee College at the Univ of Judaism	CA	15,600	VC
Lehigh Univ	PA	23,250	HC
Lenoir-Rhyne College	NC	14,068	C
Lewis Univ	IL	14,797	LC
Limestone College	SC	10,700	VC
Lincoln Memorial Univ	TN	8,218	C
Linfield College	OR	16,670	VC
Livingston Univ	AL	3,979	C
Livingstone College	NC	8,600	LC
LIU/C. W. Post Campus	NY	16,870	C
Longwood College	VA	7,800	C
Loras College	IA	14,160	C
Louisiana College	LA	7,518	VC
Louisiana State Univ and A&M College	LA	5,605	C
Louisiana State Univ in Shreveport	LA	1,910	NC
Louisiana Tech Univ	LA	4,284	C
Loyola Univ of Chicago	IL	15,880	C+
Loyola Univ/New Orleans	LA	15,660	C+
Lubbock Christian Univ	TX	9,840	NC
Luther College	IA	15,900	VC
MacMurray College	IL	12,800	C
Malone College	OH	12,572	C
Manhattan College	NY	19,000	C
Manhattanville College	NY	20,450	LC
Marietta College	OH	16,940	C
Marist College	NY	16,406	C
Marlboro College	VT	23,305	C+
Mars Hill College	NC	11,050	C
Marshall Univ	WV	5,762	LC
Mary Washington College	VA	7,910	HC
Marygrove College	MI	5,877	C
Marymount Manhattan College	NY	15,450	LC
Maryville College	TN	14,474	C
Maryville Univ-St Louis	MO	12,900	VC
Mass College of Pharmacy and Allied Health Sciences	MA	18,352	C
McKendree College	IL	10,900	C
McMurry Univ	TX	10,100	C
McNeese State Univ	LA	4,543	NC
McPherson College	KS	11,360	VC
Menlo College	CA	20,375	LC
Mercer Univ	GA	15,123	C
Mercy College	NY	11,180	NC
Mercyhurst College	PA	13,488	C
Merrimack College	MA	18,025	C
Messiah College	PA	14,664	VC
Miami Univ	OH	8,066	VC
Mich State Univ	MI	7,842	C
Middle Tenn State Univ	TN	3,857	C
Middlebury College	VT	24,400	MC
Midland Lutheran College	NE	12,410	C
Midwestern State Univ	TX	4,542	LC
Milligan College	TN	10,690	C
Millikin Univ	IL	15,499	C
Miss College	MS	8,348	C

School	ST	$IS	SR
Missouri Southern State College	MO	4,272	C
Molloy College	NY	8,580	LC
Monmouth College	NJ	16,820	C
Moorhead State Univ	MN	5,076	C
Morehouse College	GA	13,224	LC
Morgan State Univ	MD	7,366	C+
Morris Brown College	GA	12,234	NC
Mount Mary College	WI	10,920	C
Mount St Mary College	NY	12,910	C
Mount St Mary's College	CA	16,390	VC
Murray State Univ	KY	4,702	C
New Mexico Highlands Univ	NM	3,772	C
New York Univ	NY	24,705	VC+
Newberry College	SC	11,994	C
Niagara Univ	NY	14,552	C
Nicholls State Univ	LA	4,531	NC
N Car State Univ	NC	4,984	VC
North Central College	IL	15,498	VC
North Georgia College	GA	4,103	LC
North Park College	IL	14,310	C
Northeast Louisiana Univ	LA	3,906	NC
Northeast Missouri State Univ	MO	5,654	VC+
Northeastern State Univ	OK	5,250	C
Northern Arizona Univ	AZ	4,844	C
Northern Kentucky Univ	KY	4,620	NC
Northern Mich Univ	MI	6,350	C
Northern State Univ	SD	4,186	LC
Northland College	WI	13,550	LC
Northwest Missouri State Univ	MO	5,010	LC
Northwest Nazarene College	ID	11,750	C
Northwestern College of Iowa	IA	12,250	C
Northwestern Univ	IL	21,093	MC
Norwich Univ	VT	18,730	C
Notre Dame College of Ohio	OH	11,370	C
Nova Southeastern Univ	FL	13,244	LC
Oakland City College	IN	10,216	VC
Occidental College	CA	21,792	HC
Oglethorpe Univ	GA	16,360	VC
Ohio Univ	OH	7,341	C
Ohio Wesleyan Univ	OH	21,108	VC+
Okla Baptist Univ	OK	8,486	C
Okla Christian Univ of Science and Arts	OK	8,790	NC
Okla City Univ	OK	9,840	C
Okla State Univ	OK	5,086	VC
Old Dominion Univ	VA	8,317	C
Olivet Nazarene Univ	IL	11,976	C
Oral Roberts Univ	OK	10,607	C+
Oregon State Univ	OR	6,175	C
Otterbein College	OH	16,506	C
Ouachita Baptist Univ	AR	8,940	C
Pace Univ	NY	15,540	C
Park College	MO	7,320	C
Pembroke State Univ	NC	3,538	LC
Penn State Univ/Univ Park Campus	PA	8,752	HC
Peru State College	NE	4,311	NC
Pfeiffer College	NC	11,670	LC
Philadelphia College of Textiles and Science	PA	15,896	C
Phillips Univ	OK	12,744	C
Pittsburg State Univ	KS	4,478	NC
Point Loma Nazarene College	CA	13,532	C
Purdue Univ/Calumet	IN	2,374	NC
Purdue Univ/West Lafayette	IN	6,636	C
Queens College	NC	14,950	C
Quinnipiac College	CT	17,600	C+
Rensselaer Polytechnic Inst	NY	23,067	HC
Rider College	NJ	18,160	C
Rivier College	NH	14,920	LC
Roberts Wesleyan College	NY	13,317	C
Rockford College	IL	15,300	C
Rockhurst College	MO	12,470	C
Roosevelt Univ	IL	12,368	C
Rosemont College	PA	16,775	C
Russell Sage College	NY	16,790	C
Rutgers Univ/Camden College of A&S	NJ	8,652	VC
Rutgers Univ/Cook College	NJ	9,197	HC
Rutgers Univ/Douglass College	NJ	8,795	VC
Rutgers Univ/Livingston College	NJ	8,877	VC
Rutgers Univ/Newark College of A&S	NJ	8,645	C
Rutgers Univ/Rutgers College	NJ	8,841	HC+
Rutgers Univ/Univ College— Camden	NJ	3,506	C
Rutgers Univ/Univ College— New Brunswick	NJ	0	LC
Rutgers Univ/Univ College— Newark	NJ	0	C
Sacred Heart Univ	CT	16,350	C
Saginaw Valley State Univ	MI	6,634	LC
St Anselm College	NH	17,340	C
St Augustine's College	NC	9,300	C+
St Bonaventure Univ	NY	14,762	C
St Cloud State Univ	MN	5,015	C
St Edward's Univ	TX	12,636	C
St Francis College	IN	11,662	C
St Francis College	NY	6,710	LC

School	ST	$IS	SR
St John Fisher College	NY	15,415	C
St John's Univ	MN	15,364	C
St John's Univ	NY	8,980	C+
St Joseph College	CT	16,225	C
St Joseph's College	IN	14,730	C
St Joseph's College	ME	14,535	C
St Leo College	FL	13,570	C
St Martin's College	WA	14,965	C
St Mary's College	MI	8,350	C
St Mary's College of Calif	CA	18,848	VC
St Mary's College of Minn	MN	13,850	LC
St Mary's Univ	TX	12,064	C
St Mary-of-the-Woods College	IN	14,430	NC
St Michael's College	VT	17,930	C
St Norbert College	WI	15,710	VC
St Olaf College	MN	17,200	HC
St Peter's College	NJ	14,775	LC
St Thomas Aquinas College	NY	13,550	C
St Thomas Univ	FL	14,280	LC
St Vincent College	PA	13,934	LC
St Xavier Univ	IL	14,700	C
Salisbury State Univ	MD	7,516	C+
Sarah Lawrence College	NY	24,975	HC
Savannah State College	GA	4,052	C
Schreiner College	TX	14,320	C
Seattle Univ	WA	16,590	C
Seton Hall Univ	NJ	18,306	LC
Seton Hill College	PA	14,320	C
Shaw Univ	NC	8,936	C+
Shawnee State Univ	OH	4,379	NC
Shepherd College	WV	5,540	C
Siena Heights College	MI	12,520	C
Simmons College	MA	22,534	C
Simpson College	IA	14,635	VC
Sioux Falls College	SD	11,540	C
Southeastern Louisiana Univ	LA	4,230	NC
Southern Arkansas Univ	AR	3,432	NC
Southern Calif College	CA	12,356	C
Southern College of Seventh-day Adventists	TN	11,348	NC
Southern Illinois Univ at Carbondale	IL	6,234	C
Southern Nazarene Univ	OK	9,206	NC
Southern Oregon State College	OR	6,128	C
Southern Univ and A&M College	LA	4,920	NC
Southwest Missouri State Univ	MO	4,956	C
Southwest Texas State Univ	TX	5,124	C
Southwestern College	KS	10,032	C
Southwestern Okla State Univ	OK	3,312	C
Spring Hill College	AL	16,015	C+
Springfield College	MA	15,200	LC
SUNY at Albany	NY	7,059	VC
SUNY College of Environmental Science and Forestry	NY	9,257	HC+
SUNY/College at Cortland	NY	7,326	C+
SUNY/College at Fredonia	NY	7,159	VC
SUNY/College at Geneseo	NY	6,949	HC
SUNY/College at New Paltz	NY	6,890	VC
SUNY/College at Oneonta	NY	7,878	C
SUNY/College at Oswego	NY	7,330	VC
SUNY/College at Plattsburgh	NY	6,917	C
Sterling College	KS	10,090	VC
Susquehanna Univ	PA	19,950	VC
Syracuse Univ	NY	21,305	HC
Tarleton State Univ	TX	4,082	LC
Taylor Univ	IN	14,450	VC
Teikyo Marycrest Univ	IA	13,755	VC
Temple Univ	PA	10,281	C
Texas A&M Univ at Kingsville	TX	3,808	LC
Texas Southern Univ	TX	4,500	NC
The Citadel	SC	6,619	C
The Univ of New Mexico	NM	5,304	C
Thiel College	PA	16,282	C
Thomas More College	KY	12,962	C
Touro College	NY	11,930	C
Tri-State Univ	IN	13,788	LC
Trinity Christian College	IL	13,260	C
Trinity College	DC	17,660	C
Trinity College	IL	14,010	C
Trinity Univ	TX	16,670	HC
Troy State Univ	AL	4,322	C
Tulane Univ	LA	24,540	HC
Union Univ	TN	7,880	C+
Univ of Akron	OH	6,699	NC
Univ of Alabama	AL	5,702	C
Univ of Arizona	AZ	5,808	C
Univ of Arkansas at Monticello	AR	3,832	NC
Univ of Arkansas at Pine Bluff	AR	3,978	LC
Univ of Bridgeport	CT	18,985	C
Univ of Calif, Riverside	CA	9,178	C
Univ of Charleston	WV	12,750	C
Univ of Cincinnati	OH	7,989	C
Univ of Dayton	OH	15,120	C+
Univ of Denver	CO	19,290	C+
Univ of Detroit Mercy	MI	14,720	C
Univ of Dubuque	IA	14,150	LC
Univ of Evansville	IN	15,300	VC
Univ of Findlay	OH	15,764	C
Univ of Georgia	GA	5,655	VC
Univ of Houston	TX	5,215	C
Univ of Houston-Downtown	TX	4,034	NC
Univ of Indianapolis	IN	14,510	C
Univ of Iowa	IA	5,658	VC
Univ of La Verne	CA	17,400	C
Univ of Mary	ND	8,910	C
Univ of Mary Hardin-Baylor	TX	8,120	NC
Univ of Mass Dartmouth	MA	8,158	C
Univ of Mass/Amherst	MA	9,364	LC
Univ of Memphis	TN	3,476	C
Univ of Mich/Flint	MI	2,916	C
Univ of Minn/Morris	MN	6,825	HC
Univ of Minn/Twin Cities	MN	6,682	VC
Univ of Montana	MT	5,529	C
Univ of Nebr at Kearney	NE	4,308	LC
Univ of Nebr at Omaha	NE	1,889	LC
Univ of Nevada/Reno	NV	5,735	C
Univ of New England	ME	16,075	LC
Univ of New Haven	CT	14,980	C
Univ of New Orleans	LA	5,468	C
Univ of N Car at Greensboro	NC	5,192	C
Univ of N Dak	ND	4,902	NC
Univ of North Texas	TX	4,853	C
Univ of Notre Dame	IN	20,150	MC
Univ of Pittsburgh at Bradford	PA	9,050	C
Univ of Pittsburgh at Johnstown	PA	8,914	C
Univ of Portland	OR	15,564	C
Univ of PR/Mayaguez	PR	0	
Univ of Scranton	PA	17,071	VC
Univ of South Alabama	AL	5,451	C
Univ of S Car at Aiken	SC	5,386	C
Univ of S Car at Spartanburg	SC	2,320	C
Univ of South Florida	FL	5,475	C+
Univ of Southern Colo	CO	5,350	LC
Univ of Southern Indiana	IN	3,720	NC
Univ of Southern Miss	MS	4,542	C
Univ of Southwestern Louisiana	LA	3,968	NC
Univ of Tenn at Martin	TN	4,550	C
Univ of Tenn/Knoxville	TN	5,668	C
Univ of Texas at Arlington	TX	5,549	LC
Univ of Toledo	OH	6,636	NC
Univ of Tulsa	OK	13,795	VC
Univ of West Florida	FL	5,415	C
Univ of Wisc/Milwaukee	WI	6,165	C
Univ of Wisc/River Falls	WI	4,655	C
Univ of Wisc/Stevens Point	WI	5,047	C+
Urbana Univ	OH	12,536	C
Ursinus College	PA	19,165	VC
Ursuline College	OH	13,180	LC
Utah State Univ	UT	4,683	C
Utica College of Syracuse Univ	NY	16,714	LC
Valley City State Univ	ND	4,385	LC
Valparaiso Univ	IN	14,810	VC
Vassar College	NY	24,206	HC
Villanova Univ	PA	21,400	HC
Virginia Commonwealth Univ	VA	7,909	C
Virginia Intermont College	VA	12,250	LC
Virginia Polytechnic Inst and State Univ	VA	6,828	C
Virginia Wesleyan College	VA	14,950	VC
Wagner College	NY	17,950	C
Walla Walla College	WA	13,215	C
Walsh Univ	OH	11,640	C
Washington and Jefferson College	PA	19,360	C
Washington State Univ	WA	6,364	C
Wayland Baptist Univ	TX	7,811	NC
Waynesburg College	PA	11,960	C
Weber State Univ	UT	4,398	C
Wells College	NY	19,460	C+
West Chester Univ of Penn	PA	7,492	C
West Liberty State College	WV	4,690	LC
West Texas A&M Univ	TX	4,224	C
Western Illinois Univ	IL	5,241	LC
Western Kentucky Univ	KY	4,808	C
Western Mich Univ	MI	6,820	C
Western New Mexico Univ	NM	3,234	LC
Western Washington Univ	WA	6,077	VC
Westminster College	MO	13,750	C+
Westminster College	PA	15,200	C
Whitworth College	WA	16,265	C
Wichita State Univ	KS	5,068	NC
Widener Univ	PA	16,840	C
Wilberforce Univ	OH	10,408	C
Wilkes Univ	PA	15,728	LC
Willamette Univ	OR	17,995	VC
William Carey College	MS	7,050	C
William Jewell College	MO	12,500	VC
William Penn College	IA	13,400	C
William Woods Univ	MO	14,025	LC
Wilmington College	OH	13,700	LC
Wingate College	NC	10,610	C
Winona State Univ	MN	5,200	VC
Wittenberg Univ	OH	19,998	VC
Women's College of Brenau Univ	GA	14,734	C
Worcester Polytechnic Inst	MA	20,350	HC
Wright State Univ	OH	6,896	LC
Xavier Univ	OH	15,710	C+
Xavier Univ of Louisiana	LA	10,400	C
York College of Penn	PA	8,345	C
Youngstown State Univ	OH	6,447	LC

PREOSTEOPATHY

School	ST	$IS	SR
Peru State College	NE	4,311	NC
Youngstown State Univ	OH	6,447	LC

PREPHARMACY

School	ST	$IS	SR
Alice Lloyd College	KY	2,750	VC
Appalachian State Univ	NC	4,095	C
Austin Peay State Univ	TN	4,350	C
Ball State Univ	IN	6,032	LC
Barry Univ	FL	16,050	C
Bellarmine College	KY	10,832	C
Belmont Abbey College	NC	13,190	C
Belmont Univ	TN	10,540	C
Berry College	GA	11,990	VC
Briar Cliff College	IA	13,375	C
Cal State/Bakersfield	CA	5,402	C
Cal State/Fresno	CA	5,747	C
Carthage College	WI	15,995	C
Christian Brothers Univ	TN	12,120	VC
Clemson Univ	SC	6,564	VC
College of Notre Dame	CA	16,480	C
College of Notre Dame of Maryland	MD	16,050	C
College of St Benedict	MN	15,468	VC
Concord College	WV	5,104	NC
Coppin State College	MD	7,145	LC
Cumberland College	KY	9,756	C
Dana College	NE	11,910	C
David Lipscomb Univ	TN	7,865	VC
Davis and Elkins College	WV	13,230	LC
East Texas State Univ	TX	4,572	LC
Eastern Mich Univ	MI	6,749	C
Edinboro Univ of Penn	PA	7,181	C
Fisk Univ	TN	0	LC
Florida State Univ	FL	5,814	VC
Gannon Univ	PA	14,872	C
Georgia State Univ	GA	2,019	C
Goshen College	IN	12,360	C
Hendrix College	AR	11,670	C
Illinois Benedictine College	IL	14,170	C
Indiana State Univ	IN	6,210	C
Indiana Wesleyan Univ	IN	12,332	C
Iona College	NY	16,310	C
Jacksonville State Univ	AL	4,080	LC
Kennesaw State College	GA	1,553	C
Lebanon Valley College of Penn	PA	18,300	C
Lewis Univ	IL	14,797	LC
LIU/C. W. Post Campus	NY	16,870	C
Louisiana State Univ in Shreveport	LA	1,910	NC
Mercer Univ	GA	15,123	C
Mercy College	NY	11,180	NC
Mercyhurst College	PA	13,488	C
Messiah College	PA	14,664	VC
Methodist College	NC	12,400	C
Middle Tenn State Univ	TN	3,857	C
Midwestern State Univ	TX	4,542	LC
Miles College	AL	7,150	NC
Moorhead State Univ	MN	5,076	C
Morgan State Univ	MD	7,366	C+
Northeast Missouri State Univ	MO	5,654	VC+
Northern Kentucky Univ	KY	4,620	NC
Northwest Missouri State Univ	MO	5,010	LC
Notre Dame College	NH	14,220	C
Oglethorpe Univ	GA	16,360	VC
Peru State College	NE	4,311	NC
Phillips Univ	OK	12,744	C
Purdue Univ/Calumet	IN	2,374	NC
Roberts Wesleyan College	NY	13,317	C
Rockford College	IL	15,300	C
Roosevelt Univ	IL	12,368	C
Sacred Heart Univ	CT	16,350	C
St John Fisher College	NY	15,415	C
St John's Univ	MN	15,364	C
St Joseph's College	ME	14,535	C
St Martin's College	WA	14,965	C
St Norbert College	WI	15,710	VC
St Vincent College	PA	13,934	LC
St Xavier Univ	IL	14,700	C
Salisbury State Univ	MD	7,516	C+
Southeastern Louisiana Univ	LA	4,230	NC
Southern Nazarene Univ	OK	9,206	NC
SUNY College of Environmental Science and Forestry	NY	9,257	HC+
Tarleton State Univ	TX	4,082	LC
Texas A&M Univ at Kingsville	TX	3,808	LC
Thiel College	PA	16,282	C
Univ of Akron	OH	6,699	NC
Univ of Arkansas at Pine Bluff	AR	3,978	LC
Univ of Houston	TX	5,215	C
Univ of Houston-Downtown	TX	4,034	NC
Univ of Maryland/College Park	MD	8,182	VC
Univ of Minn/Twin Cities	MN	6,682	VC
Univ of Nebr-Lincoln	NE	5,278	LC
Univ of New England	ME	16,075	LC
Univ of Portland	OR	15,564	C
Univ of Tenn at Martin	TN	4,550	C
Univ of Wisc/River Falls	WI	4,655	C
West Liberty State College	WV	4,690	LC
Western Illinois Univ	IL	5,241	LC
Western New Mexico Univ	NM	3,234	LC
William Carey College	MS	7,050	C
Wingate College	NC	10,610	C
Xavier Univ	OH	15,710	C+
Youngstown State Univ	OH	6,447	LC

PREPODIATRIC

School	ST	$IS	SR
Peru State College	NE	4,311	NC

PREVETERINARY SCIENCE

School	ST	$IS	SR
Alabama A&M Univ	AL	4,200	C
Albertus Magnus College	CT	16,280	LC
Anderson-Broaddus College	WV	12,000	C
Alfred Univ	NY	21,054	VC+
Alvernia College	PA	13,150	LC
Auburn Univ	AL	5,823	C+
Aurora Univ	IL	13,381	C
Bellarmine College	KY	10,832	C
Berry College	GA	11,990	VC
Cal State/Bakersfield	CA	5,402	C
Cal State/Fresno	CA	5,747	C
Clemson Univ	SC	6,564	VC
College of Notre Dame	CA	16,480	C
College of St Benedict	MN	15,468	VC
College of St Mary	NE	12,500	C
Concordia College/Moorhead	MN	12,750	C
Cumberland College	KY	9,756	C
D'Youville College	NY	12,850	C
Dana College	NE	11,910	C
Defiance College	OH	13,480	LC
Eastern Oregon State College	OR	6,090	C
Eastern Washington Univ	WA	5,439	LC
Edinboro Univ of Penn	PA	7,181	C
Fairleigh Dickinson Univ	NJ	16,427	C
Florida State Univ	FL	5,814	VC
Franklin Pierce College	NH	17,270	LC
Gannon Univ	PA	14,872	C
George Fox College	OR	15,640	LC
George Mason Univ	VA	8,728	C
Georgia State Univ	GA	2,019	C
Goshen College	IN	12,360	C
Grand Rapids Baptist College and Seminary	MI	10,228	C
Hillsdale College	MI	15,110	VC
Illinois Benedictine College	IL	14,170	C
Indiana State Univ	IN	6,210	C
Indiana Univ of Penn	PA	6,373	C
Indiana Wesleyan Univ	IN	12,332	C
Iona College	NY	16,310	C
Jacksonville State Univ	AL	4,080	LC
Judson College	AL	9,060	C
Juniata College	PA	18,390	C+
Kennesaw State College	GA	1,553	C
Kent State Univ	OH	6,740	LC
Lebanon Valley College of Penn	PA	18,300	C
Louisiana College	LA	7,518	VC
Loyola Univ of Chicago	IL	15,880	C+
MacMurray College	IL	12,800	C
Marshall Univ	WV	5,762	LC
Mary Washington College	VA	7,910	HC
Mercyhurst College	PA	13,488	C
Messiah College	PA	14,664	VC
Middlebury College	VT	24,400	MC
Midwestern State Univ	TX	4,542	LC
Miles College	AL	7,150	NC
Miss State Univ	MS	5,629	VC
Moorhead State Univ	MN	5,076	C
Mount St Mary College	NY	12,910	C
New Mexico Highlands Univ	NM	3,772	C
N Car State Univ	NC	4,984	VC
North Central College	IL	15,498	VC
Northeast Missouri State Univ	MO	5,654	VC+
Northern Kentucky Univ	KY	4,620	NC
Northern Mich Univ	MI	6,350	C
Northwest Missouri State Univ	MO	5,010	LC
Northwest Nazarene College	ID	11,750	C
Ohio Wesleyan Univ	OH	21,108	VC+

School	ST	$IS	SR
Okla State Univ	OK	5,086	VC
Peru State College	NE	4,311	NC
Phillips Univ	OK	12,744	C
Purdue Univ/Calumet	IN	2,374	NC
Purdue Univ/West Lafayette	IN	6,636	C
Queens College	NC	14,950	C
Rivier College	NH	14,920	LC
Roberts Wesleyan College	NY	13,317	C
Rockford College	IL	15,300	C
Roosevelt Univ	IL	12,368	C
Rutgers Univ/Cook College	NJ	9,197	HC
Sacred Heart Univ	CT	16,350	C
St John's Univ	MN	15,364	C
St Leo College	FL	13,570	C
St Martin's College	WA	14,965	C
St Mary's College of Minn	MN	13,850	LC
St Norbert College	WI	15,710	VC
St Vincent College	PA	13,934	LC
Salisbury State Univ	MD	7,516	C+
Seton Hill College	PA	14,320	C
Shawnee State Univ	OH	4,379	NC
Shepherd College	WV	5,540	C
Simpson College	IA	14,635	VC
Southern Illinois Univ at Carbondale	IL	6,234	C
Southern Univ and A&M College	LA	4,920	NC
Susquehanna Univ	PA	19,950	VC
Tarleton State Univ	TX	4,082	LC
Texas A&M Univ at Kingsville	TX	3,808	LC
Thiel College	PA	16,282	C
Thomas More College	KY	12,962	C
Trinity Univ	TX	16,670	HC
Univ of Akron	OH	6,699	NC
Univ of Denver	CO	19,290	C+
Univ of Findlay	OH	15,764	C
Univ of Houston	TX	5,215	C
Univ of Minn/Twin Cities	MN	6,682	VC
Univ of New Haven	CT	14,980	C
Univ of New Orleans	LA	5,468	C
Univ of Portland	OR	15,564	C
Univ of Tenn/Knoxville	TN	5,668	C
Univ of Tulsa	OK	13,795	VC
Virginia Polytechnic Inst and State Univ	VA	6,828	C
Walsh Univ	OH	11,640	C
Wells College	NY	19,460	C+
Western Illinois Univ	IL	5,241	LC
William Carey College	MS	7,050	C
Wilmington College	OH	13,700	LC
Wingate College	NC	10,610	C
Worcester Polytechnic Inst	MA	20,350	HC
Youngstown State Univ	OH	6,447	LC

PRINTMAKING

School	ST	$IS	SR
Aquinas College	MI	14,526	C
Arizona State Univ Main Campus	AZ	6,444	C
Art Academy of Cincinnati	OH	8,820	SP
Atlanta College of Art	GA	12,495	SP
Barton College	NC	10,689	LC
Birmingham-Southern College	AL	15,154	VC+
Bradley Univ	IL	14,718	C+
Brigham Young Univ	UT	5,625	HC
Center for Creative Studies/College of Art and Design	MI	15,330	SP
Cooper Union for the Advancement of Science and Art	NY	8,430	MC
East Texas State Univ	TX	4,572	LC
Edinboro Univ of Penn	PA	7,181	C
Indiana Univ-Purdue Univ at Indianapolis	IN	5,862	LC
Kansas City Art Inst	MO	17,000	SP
Louisiana State Univ and A&M College	LA	5,605	C
Maine College of Art	ME	15,673	SP
Maryland Inst, College of Art	MD	18,420	SP
Milwaukee Inst of Art and Design	WI	9,800	SP
Miss Univ for Women	MS	4,456	LC
Montserrat College of Art	MA	12,500	SP
Moore College of Art and Design	PA	17,947	SP
Northern Mich Univ	MI	6,350	C
Ohio Northern Univ	OH	18,660	VC
Pacific Northwest College of Art	OR	7,700	SP
Plymouth State College	NH	7,166	C
Rhode Island School of Design	RI	22,315	SP
Rochester Inst of Tech	NY	18,954	VC
San Francisco Art Inst	CA	12,900	SP
School of the Art Inst of Chicago	IL	17,610	SP
Syracuse Univ	NY	21,305	HC
Univ of Conn	CT	9,168	C
Univ of Hartford	CT	19,858	LC
Univ of Kansas	KS	5,200	NC
Univ of Mass Dartmouth	MA	8,158	C
Univ of Miami	FL	22,107	VC
Univ of Mich/Ann Arbor	MI	9,428	HC+
Univ of North Texas	TX	4,853	C
Univ of Oregon	OR	6,466	VC
Univ of Texas at El Paso	TX	3,160	LC
Univ of the Arts	PA	16,150	SP
Univ of Washington	WA	6,618	VC

PRINTING TECHNOLOGY

School	ST	$IS	SR
Arkansas State Univ	AR	4,250	NC
Pittsburg State Univ	KS	4,478	NC
Rochester Inst of Tech	NY	18,954	VC
S Dak State Univ	SD	4,562	C

PSYCHOBIOLOGY

School	ST	$IS	SR
Agnes Scott College	GA	17,135	VC
Albright College	PA	19,260	C
Beaver College	PA	17,660	C
Centre College	KY	15,850	VC+
Drew Univ/College of Liberal Arts	NJ	23,406	HC
Hamilton College	NY	23,500	HC
Hiram College	OH	18,340	VC
Hood College	MD	19,010	VC
La Roche College	PA	12,977	LC
La Sierra Univ	CA	15,472	C
Lebanon Valley College of Penn	PA	18,300	C
Mount Holyoke College	MA	23,630	VC
Pine Manor College	MA	21,700	LC
Pitzer College	CA	23,780	HC
Quinnipiac College	CT	17,600	C+
Scripps College	CA	23,600	HC
Simmons College	MA	22,534	C
SUNY at Binghamton	NY	7,921	HC
Tufts Univ	MA	24,962	MC
Univ of Calif at Los Angeles	CA	8,959	HC
Univ of Calif at Santa Barbara	CA	9,460	C
Univ of Calif at Santa Cruz	CA	9,060	VC
Univ of Calif, Riverside	CA	9,178	C
Univ of Evansville	IN	15,300	VC
Univ of Miami	FL	22,107	VC
Vassar College	NY	24,206	HC
Wellesley College	MA	23,815	MC
Wheaton College	MA	23,840	C+
Wilson College	PA	16,630	C

PSYCHOLOGY

School	ST	$IS	SR
Abilene Christian Univ	TX	10,460	NC
Adams State College	CO	4,910	C
Adelphi Univ	NY	18,250	LC
Adrian College	MI	14,340	C
Agnes Scott College	GA	17,135	VC
Alabama A&M Univ	AL	4,200	C
Alabama State Univ	AL	3,428	NC
Alaska Pacific Univ	AK	11,350	C
Albany State College	GA	4,481	LC
Albertson College	ID	15,942	C+
Albertus Magnus College	CT	16,280	LC
Albion College	MI	18,264	VC
Albright College	PA	19,260	C
Alderson-Broaddus College	WV	12,000	C
Alfred Univ	NY	21,054	VC+
Allegheny College	PA	21,020	VC
Allentown College of St Francis de Sales	PA	13,480	C
Alma College	MI	16,375	VC+
Alvernia College	PA	13,150	LC
Alverno College	WI	11,344	C
American International College	MA	14,029	C
American Univ	DC	21,230	VC+
Amherst College	MA	24,152	MC
Anderson Univ	IN	12,920	C
Andrews Univ	MI	14,952	NC
Angelo State Univ	TX	5,176	C
Anna Maria College	MA	15,975	LC
Antioch College	OH	19,532	C
Appalachian State Univ	NC	4,095	C
Aquinas College	MI	14,526	C
Arizona State Univ Main Campus	AZ	6,444	C
Arkansas College	AR	11,626	VC
Arkansas State Univ	AR	4,250	NC
Arkansas Tech Univ	AR	4,200	NC
Armstrong State College	GA	4,874	LC
Asbury College	KY	11,105	VC
Ashland Univ	OH	15,508	C
Assumption College	MA	17,095	LC
Atlantic Union College	MA	14,150	LC
Auburn Univ	AL	5,823	C+
Auburn Univ at Montgomery	AL	3,390	LC
Audrey Cohen College	NY	11,184	LC
Augsburg College	MN	15,608	C
Augusta College	GA	1,452	LC
Augustana College	IL	16,959	VC
Augustana College	SD	13,420	C
Aurora Univ	IL	13,381	C
Austin College	TX	14,999	VC
Austin Peay State Univ	TN	4,350	C
Averett College	VA	13,610	LC
Avila College	MO	12,130	C
Azusa Pacific Univ	CA	15,034	C
Baker Univ	KS	12,284	C
Baldwin-Wallace College	OH	15,210	C
Ball State Univ	IN	6,032	LC
Barat College	IL	13,990	C
Bard College	NY	25,269	HC
Barry Univ	FL	16,050	C
Barton College	NC	10,689	LC
Bates College	ME	23,990	MC
Baylor Univ	TX	10,990	C+
Beaver College	PA	17,660	C
Belhaven College	MS	9,690	C+
Bellarmine College	KY	10,832	C
Bellevue College	NE	3,050	NC
Belmont Abbey College	NC	13,190	C
Belmont Univ	TN	10,540	C
Beloit College	WI	18,950	VC+
Bemidji State Univ	MN	5,188	C
Benedictine College	KS	12,830	C
Bennett College	NC	8,920	LC
Bennington College	VT	24,850	VC+
Berea College	KY	2,883	VC+
Berry College	GA	11,990	VC
Bethany College	KS	11,232	C
Bethany College	WV	18,300	C+
Bethel College	IN	11,650	C
Bethel College	KS	11,530	C
Bethel College	MN	15,050	C
Bethel College	TN	9,736	LC
Bethune-Cookman College	FL	8,375	LC
Biola Univ	CA	16,124	C
Birmingham-Southern College	AL	15,154	VC+
Black Hills State Univ	SD	4,831	NC
Blackburn College	IL	9,120	C
Bloomfield College	NJ	12,200	LC
Bloomsburg Univ of Penn	PA	6,312	C+
Blue Mountain College	MS	5,958	LC
Bluefield College	VA	10,600	C
Bluffton College	OH	12,951	C
Boise State Univ	ID	4,909	LC
Boston College	MA	22,706	MC
Boston Univ	MA	24,130	HC
Bowdoin College	ME	24,155	MC
Bowie State Univ	MD	7,294	LC
Bowling Green State Univ	OH	6,701	C
Bradley Univ	IL	14,718	C+
Brandeis Univ	MA	25,585	HC
Brescia College	KY	9,800	C
Briar Cliff College	IA	13,375	C
Bridgewater College	VA	15,300	C
Bridgewater State College	MA	7,518	C
Brigham Young Univ	UT	5,625	HC
Brigham Young Univ/Hawaii	HI	6,750	VC
Brooklyn Campus of LIU	NY	15,000	LC
Brown Univ	RI	26,104	MC
Bryan College	TN	11,465	C
Bryn Mawr College	PA	24,110	MC
Bucknell Univ	PA	22,320	HC
Buena Vista College	IA	16,150	VC
Burlington College	VT	6,150	NC
Butler Univ	IN	16,210	C
Cabrini College	PA	16,012	C
Caldwell College	NJ	12,860	C
Calif Baptist College	CA	11,294	C
Calif Lutheran Univ	CA	17,240	C
Calif State Polytechnic Univ/Pomona	CA	6,438	LC
Cal State/Bakersfield	CA	5,402	C
Cal State/Chico	CA	6,146	C
Cal State/Dominguez Hills	CA	2,857	LC
Cal State/Fresno	CA	5,747	C
Cal State/Fullerton	CA	4,850	LC
Cal State/Hayward	CA	5,495	C
Cal State/Long Beach	CA	6,057	LC
Cal State/Los Angeles	CA	4,940	VC
Cal State/Northridge	CA	7,122	LC
Cal State/Sacramento	CA	6,387	C
Cal State/San Bernardino	CA	6,055	LC
Cal State/Stanislaus	CA	6,799	C
Calif Univ of Penn	PA	7,370	C
Calumet College of St. Joseph	IN	3,585	C
Calvin College	MI	13,020	VC
Cameron Univ	OK	3,686	LC
Campbell Univ	NC	10,624	C
Campbellsville College	KY	8,720	C
Canisius College	NY	15,510	C
Capital Univ	OH	16,535	VC
Cardinal Stritch College	WI	11,252	C
Carleton College	MN	22,155	HC
Carlow College	PA	13,914	C
Carnegie Mellon Univ	PA	22,560	HC+
Carroll College	MT	11,265	C
Carroll College	WI	15,490	C
Carson-Newman College	TN	11,250	C
Carthage College	WI	15,995	C
Cascade College	OR	9,800	NC
Case Western Reserve Univ	OH	19,910	HC
Castleton State College	VT	8,378	LC
Catawba College	NC	12,950	C
Catholic Univ of America	DC	18,856	C
Cedar Crest College	PA	18,930	C
Cedarville College	OH	10,715	C
Centenary College	NJ	17,040	LC
Centenary College of Louisiana	LA	11,826	C+
Central College	IA	14,025	VC
Central Conn State Univ	CT	7,108	C
Central Methodist College	MO	11,410	C
Central Mich Univ	MI	6,737	LC
Central Missouri State Univ	MO	5,138	LC
Central State Univ	OH	7,320	NC
Central Univ of Bayamon	PR	2,430	
Central Washington Univ	WA	5,644	C
Central Wesleyan College	SC	9,640	C
Centre College	KY	15,850	VC+
Chadron State College	NE	4,091	NC
Chaminade Univ of Honolulu	HI	14,290	C
Chapman Univ	CA	21,842	C
Charleston Southern Univ	SC	10,282	LC
Charter Oak State College	CT	314	NC
Chatham College	PA	18,010	C
Chestnut Hill College	PA	14,525	C
Cheyney Univ of Penn	PA	7,005	C
Chicago State Univ	IL	2,198	C
Christian Brothers Univ	TN	12,120	VC
Christopher Newport Univ	VA	3,196	LC
CUNY/Baruch College	NY	2,562	VC
CUNY/Brooklyn College	NY	2,450	VC
CUNY/City College	NY	2,543	VC
CUNY/College of Staten Island	NY	2,558	NC
CUNY/Herbert H. Lehman College	NY	2,542	C
CUNY/Hunter College	NY	4,101	VC
CUNY/Medgar Evers College	NY	2,577	NC
CUNY/Queens College	NY	2,631	C
CUNY/York College	NY	2,534	NC
Claremont McKenna College	CA	22,150	MC
Clarion Univ of Penn	PA	6,518	C
Clark Atlanta Univ	GA	11,846	C
Clark Univ	MA	21,400	VC
Clarke College	IA	13,950	C+
Clarkson Univ	NY	20,705	VC+
Clearwater Christian College	FL	8,500	LC
Clemson Univ	SC	6,564	VC
Cleveland State Univ	OH	7,287	NC
Coastal Carolina Univ	SC	6,010	LC
Coe College	IA	17,085	VC
Coker College	SC	13,790	C
Colby College	ME	24,230	HC
Colby-Sawyer College	NH	18,495	LC
Colgate Univ	NY	24,020	HC
College of Charleston	SC	6,250	C
College of Mount St Vincent	NY	16,730	C
College of New Rochelle	NY	15,440	LC
College of Notre Dame	CA	16,480	C
College of Notre Dame of Maryland	MD	16,050	C
College of Our Lady of The Elms	MA	15,639	C
College of St Benedict	MN	15,468	VC
College of St Catherine	MN	14,670	C
College of St Elizabeth	NJ	15,800	C
College of St Francis	IL	13,060	VC
College of St Joseph	VT	12,650	LC
College of St Scholastica	MN	14,868	C
College of Santa Fe	NM	14,008	C
College of the Holy Cross	MA	23,850	HC
College of the Ozarks	MO	2,000	VC+
College of the Southwest	NM	5,720	LC
College of William and Mary	VA	8,602	MC
College of Wooster	OH	19,875	VC
Colo Christian Univ	CO	9,750	C
Colo College	CO	20,038	HC
Colo State Univ	CO	6,566	VC
Columbia College	MO	11,995	C
Columbia College	SC	13,520	LC
Columbia Union College	MD	13,650	LC
Columbia Univ/Barnard College	NY	25,492	HC
Columbia Univ/Columbia College	NY	26,757	MC
Columbus College	GA	4,892	LC
Concord College	WV	5,104	NC
Concordia College	MI	13,660	C
Concordia College	MN	13,200	C
Concordia College	NE	11,776	NC
Concordia College/Moorhead	MN	12,750	C
Concordia Univ	IL	12,611	C
Concordia Univ	CA	14,675	C
Concordia Univ Wisc	WI	12,140	C
Conn College	CT	24,160	HC
Converse College	SC	15,750	C
Coppin State College	MD	7,145	LC
Cornell College	IA	18,425	VC
Cornell Univ	NY	13,445	MC
Covenant College	GA	13,054	VC
Creighton Univ	NE	14,432	VC
Crichton College	TN	6,547	NC

School	ST	$IS	SR
Culver-Stockton College	MO	11,150	C
Cumberland College	KY	9,756	C
Curry College	MA	18,695	LC
Daemen College	NY	13,020	LC
Dakota Wesleyan Univ	SD	9,770	LC
Dallas Baptist Univ	TX	9,620	LC
Dana College	NE	11,910	C
Dartmouth College	NH	24,354	MC
David Lipscomb Univ	TN	7,865	VC
Davidson College	NC	21,037	MC
Davis and Elkins College	WV	13,230	LC
Defiance College	OH	13,480	LC
Delaware State College	DE	5,656	C
Delta State Univ	MS	3,964	LC
Denison Univ	OH	21,150	VC+
DePaul Univ	IL	15,535	VC
DePauw Univ	IN	18,530	VC
Dickinson College	PA	22,705	HC
Dillard Univ	LA	9,950	C
Doane College	NE	12,220	C
Dominican College	NY	13,600	LC
Dominican College of San Rafael	CA	17,860	C
Dordt College	IA	11,690	C
Dowling College	NY	12,730	LC
Drake Univ	IA	17,195	VC
Drew Univ/College of Liberal Arts	NJ	23,406	HC
Drury College	MO	12,140	VC
Duke Univ	NC	21,271	MC
Duquesne Univ	PA	16,434	VC
Earlham College	IN	19,383	VC
East Carolina Univ	NC	4,498	C
East Central Univ	OK	3,558	C
East Stroudsburg Univ	PA	6,886	C
East Tenn State Univ	TN	4,406	C
East Texas Baptist Univ	TX	7,740	C
East Texas State Univ	TX	4,572	LC
Eastern College	PA	15,150	C+
Eastern Conn State Univ	CT	6,966	C
Eastern Illinois Univ	IL	5,548	C
Eastern Kentucky Univ	KY	4,840	NC
Eastern Mennonite College	VA	12,700	C
Eastern Mich Univ	MI	6,749	C
Eastern Montana College	MT	5,165	LC
Eastern Nazarene College	MA	12,165	LC
Eastern New Mexico Univ	NM	3,950	C
Eastern Oregon State College	OR	6,090	C
Eastern Washington Univ	WA	5,439	LC
Eckerd College	FL	18,855	VC
Edgewood College	WI	11,700	C
Edinboro Univ of Penn	PA	7,181	C
Edward Waters College	FL	8,300	NC
Elizabeth City State Univ	NC	4,254	LC
Elizabethtown College	PA	17,850	VC
Elmhurst College	IL	12,536	C
Elmira College	NY	18,450	C
Elon College	NC	12,290	LC
Emmanuel College	MA	17,773	LC
Emory and Henry College	VA	12,776	C
Emory Univ	GA	21,930	HC
Emporia State Univ	KS	4,685	NC
Erskine College	SC	14,310	C
Eugene Lang College of the New School for Social Research	NY	21,145	C+
Eureka College	IL	14,555	C
Evangel College	MO	10,142	LC
Evergreen State College	WA	6,306	C
Fairfield Univ	CT	20,460	VC
Fairleigh Dickinson Univ	NJ	16,427	C
Fairmont State College	WV	4,640	LC
Fayetteville State Univ	NC	3,926	LC
Felician College	NJ	7,900	C
Ferrum College	VA	12,800	C
Fisk Univ	TN	0	LC
Fitchburg State College	MA	6,962	C
Flagler College	FL	7,990	C
Florida A&M Univ	FL	4,651	C
Florida Atlantic Univ	FL	5,525	C
Florida Inst of Tech	FL	16,935	VC
Florida International Univ	FL	4,191	VC
Florida Memorial College	FL	7,600	C+
Florida Southern College	FL	12,260	C
Florida State Univ	FL	5,814	VC
Fordham Univ/College at Lincoln Center	NY	18,150	VC
Fordham Univ/Fordham College	NY	19,875	VC
Fort Hays State Univ	KS	4,675	NC
Fort Lewis College	CO	5,097	C
Fort Valley State College	GA	3,974	LC
Framingham State College	MA	6,580	C
Francis Marion Univ	SC	5,878	LC
Franciscan Univ of Steubenville	OH	13,400	C
Franklin and Marshall College	PA	23,655	HC
Franklin College of Indiana	IN	13,970	C
Franklin Pierce College	NH	17,270	LC
Freed-Hardeman Univ	TN	8,585	VC
Fresno Pacific College	CA	13,020	C
Friends Univ	KS	11,205	C
Frostburg State Univ	MD	6,940	C
Furman Univ	SC	16,557	VC
Gannon Univ	PA	14,872	C
Gardner-Webb Univ	NC	11,950	LC
Geneva College	PA	13,030	C
George Fox College	OR	15,640	LC
George Mason Univ	VA	8,728	C
George Washington Univ	DC	22,470	HC
Georgetown College	KY	10,990	C
Georgetown Univ	DC	24,410	MC
Georgia College	GA	4,310	LC
Georgia Inst of Tech	GA	6,669	HC+
Georgia Southern Univ	GA	4,988	LC
Georgia Southwestern College	GA	4,338	LC
Georgia State Univ	GA	2,019	C
Georgian Court College	NJ	12,550	C
Gettysburg College	PA	22,960	HC
Gonzaga Univ	WA	16,350	VC
Gordon College	MA	16,790	C
Goshen College	IN	12,360	C
Goucher College	MD	20,295	VC
Grace College	IN	12,120	C
Graceland College	IA	11,600	C
Grambling State Univ	LA	4,712	NC
Grand Canyon Univ	AZ	9,680	VC
Grand Rapids Baptist College and Seminary	MI	10,228	C
Grand Valley State Univ	MI	6,822	VC
Greensboro College	NC	11,496	C
Greenville College	IL	14,190	C
Grinnell College	IA	20,680	HC+
Grove City College	PA	7,870	HC
Guilford College	NC	17,680	C
Gustavus Adolphus College	MN	15,935	VC
Gwynedd-Mercy College	PA	15,450	C
Hamilton College	NY	23,500	HC
Hamline Univ	MN	17,122	VC
Hampden-Sydney College	VA	17,372	C+
Hampshire College	MA	25,320	C
Hampton Univ	VA	10,706	C
Hanover College	IN	10,950	VC
Hardin-Simmons Univ	TX	9,080	C
Harding Univ	AR	9,050	VC
Hartwick College	NY	20,950	LC
Harvard Univ/Harvard and Radcliffe Colleges	MA	24,880	MC
Hastings College	NE	12,426	C
Haverford College	PA	23,950	MC
Hawaii Pacific Univ	HI	12,300	C
Heidelberg College	OH	17,160	C
Henderson State Univ	AR	3,860	C
Hendrix College	AR	11,670	C
Heritage College	WA	5,540	NC
High Point Univ	NC	12,350	LC
Hillsdale College	MI	15,110	VC
Hiram College	OH	18,340	VC
Hobart and William Smith Colleges	NY	23,925	VC
Hofstra Univ	NY	16,580	VC
Hollins College	VA	18,484	C
Holy Family College	PA	8,300	C
Holy Names College	CA	15,660	C
Hood College	MD	19,010	VC
Hope College	MI	15,698	C+
Houghton College	NY	13,120	VC
Houston Baptist Univ	TX	11,055	C
Howard Payne Univ	TX	8,052	C
Howard Univ	DC	11,680	C
Humboldt State Univ	CA	5,676	C
Huntingdon College	AL	11,400	C
Huntington College	IN	13,220	C
Huron Univ	SD	9,790	C
Idaho State Univ	ID	4,442	C
Illinois Benedictine College	IL	14,170	C
Illinois College	IL	11,200	C
Illinois Inst of Tech	IL	18,290	VC
Illinois State Univ	IL	6,413	C
Illinois Wesleyan Univ	IL	18,590	HC+
Immaculata College	PA	14,620	C
Incarnate Word College	TX	12,307	C
Indiana State Univ	IN	6,210	C
Indiana Univ Bloomington	IN	6,495	VC
Indiana Univ Northwest	IN	2,310	C
Indiana Univ of Penn	PA	6,373	C
Indiana Univ Southeast	IN	2,260	LC
Indiana Univ-Purdue Univ at Fort Wayne	IN	2,500	LC
Indiana Univ-Purdue Univ at Indianapolis	IN	5,862	LC
Indiana Univ/South Bend	IN	2,141	LC
Indiana Wesleyan Univ	IN	12,332	C
Inter American Univ of PR/ Aguadilla Regional College	PR	2,290	
Inter American Univ of PR/ Bayamon Univ College	PR	2,300	
Inter American Univ of PR/ Metropolitan Campus	PR	2,340	
Inter American Univ of PR/ Ponce Regional College	PR	2,300	
Inter American Univ of PR/ San German	PR	4,620	
Inter-American Univ of PR/ Fajardo Regional College	PR	2,732	
Iona College	NY	16,310	C
Iowa State Univ	IA	5,456	C
Iowa Wesleyan College	IA	13,250	LC
Ithaca College	NY	19,679	C
Jackson State Univ	MS	4,996	LC
Jacksonville State Univ	AL	4,080	LC
Jacksonville Univ	FL	13,390	C
James Madison Univ	VA	8,198	HC
Jamestown College	ND	10,250	C
Jersey City State College	NJ	7,797	LC
John Brown Univ	AR	9,880	VC
John Carroll Univ	OH	16,510	C
Johns Hopkins Univ	MD	24,360	MC
Johnson C. Smith Univ	NC	8,916	LC
Johnson State College	VT	8,393	LC
Judson College	AL	9,060	C
Judson College	IL	13,625	C
Juniata College	PA	18,390	C+
Kalamazoo College	MI	19,974	HC
Kansas Newman College	KS	10,640	C
Kansas State Univ	KS	4,816	NC
Kansas Wesleyan Univ	KS	11,770	C
Kean College of New Jersey	NJ	6,395	LC
Keene State College	NH	7,081	C
Kennesaw State College	GA	1,553	C
Kent State Univ	OH	6,740	LC
Kentucky Christian College	KY	7,708	LC
Kentucky State Univ	KY	4,282	C+
Kentucky Wesleyan College	KY	11,550	LC
Kenyon College	OH	22,430	HC+
King College	TN	11,500	C
King's College	NY	12,360	LC
King's College	PA	15,420	C
Knox College	IL	18,990	VC
Knoxville College	TN	8,320	LC
Kutztown Univ	PA	6,528	C
La Roche College	PA	12,977	LC
La Salle Univ	PA	16,940	VC
La Sierra Univ	CA	15,472	C
Lafayette College	PA	23,450	HC
LaGrange College	GA	10,602	C
Lake Erie College	OH	13,700	C
Lake Forest College	IL	19,960	VC
Lake Superior State Univ	MI	7,311	C
Lakeland College	WI	12,845	LC
Lamar Univ	TX	3,798	C
Lambuth Univ	TN	8,395	C
Lander Univ	SC	6,180	LC
Langston Univ	OK	2,907	LC
Lawrence Univ	WI	19,986	HC+
Le Moyne College	NY	15,180	C
Lebanon Valley College of Penn	PA	18,300	C
Lee College	TN	7,894	LC
Lee College at the Univ of Judaism	CA	15,600	VC
Lehigh Univ	PA	23,250	HC
Lenoir-Rhyne College	NC	14,068	C
Lewis and Clark College	OR	19,980	VC
Lewis Univ	IL	14,797	LC
Liberty Univ	VA	11,500	LC
Limestone College	SC	10,700	LC
Lincoln Memorial Univ	TN	8,218	C
Lincoln Univ	MO	4,638	NC
Lincoln Univ	PA	0	LC
Lindenwood College	MO	13,560	C
Linfield College	OR	16,670	VC
Livingstone College	NC	8,600	LC
Lock Haven Univ of Penn	PA	7,128	C
LIU/C. W. Post Campus	NY	16,870	C
LIU/Southampton Campus	NY	17,280	C
Longwood College	VA	7,800	C
Louisiana College	LA	7,518	VC
Louisiana State Univ and A&M College	LA	5,605	C
Louisiana Tech Univ	LA	4,284	C
Lourdes College	OH	6,410	LC
Loyola College	MD	18,035	VC
Loyola Marymount Univ	CA	18,560	C
Loyola Univ of Chicago	IL	15,880	C+
Loyola Univ/New Orleans	LA	15,660	C+
Lubbock Christian Univ	TX	9,840	NC
Luther College	IA	15,900	VC
Lycoming College	PA	17,200	LC
Lynchburg College	VA	17,000	C
Lyndon State College	VT	8,394	LC
Lynn Univ	FL	18,300	C
Macalester College	MN	19,710	HC
MacMurray College	IL	12,800	C
Madonna Univ	MI	8,546	C
Maharishi International Univ	IA	13,666	C
Malone College	OH	12,572	C
Manchester College	IN	13,240	LC
Manhattan College	NY	19,000	C
Manhattanville College	NY	20,450	LC
Mankato State Univ	MN	5,097	LC
Mansfield Univ	PA	6,348	C
Marian College	IN	12,936	C
Marian College of Fond du Lac	WI	12,250	C
Marietta College	OH	16,940	C+
Marist College	NY	16,406	C
Marlboro College	VT	23,305	C+
Marquette Univ	WI	16,114	VC
Mars Hill College	NC	11,050	C
Marshall Univ	WV	5,762	LC
Martin Univ	IN	4,830	NC
Mary Baldwin College	VA	17,700	LC
Mary Washington College	VA	7,910	HC
Marygrove College	MI	5,877	VC
Marymount College/ Tarrytown	NY	17,350	C
Marymount Manhattan College	NY	15,450	LC
Marymount Univ	VA	15,930	C
Maryville College	TN	14,474	C
Maryville Univ-St Louis	MO	12,900	VC
Mass College of Pharmacy and Allied Health Sciences	MA	18,352	C
McKendree College	IL	10,900	C
McMurry Univ	TX	10,100	C
McNeese State Univ	LA	4,543	NC
McPherson College	KS	11,360	VC
Menlo College	CA	20,375	LC
Mercer Univ	GA	15,123	C
Mercy College	NY	11,180	NC
Mercyhurst College	PA	13,488	C
Meredith College	NC	9,440	C
Merrimack College	MA	18,025	C
Mesa State College	CO	5,127	NC
Messiah College	PA	14,664	VC
Methodist College	NC	12,400	C
Metropolitan State College of Denver	CO	1,751	NC
Miami Univ	OH	8,066	VC
Mich Christian College	MI	8,094	C
Mich State Univ	MI	7,842	C
MidAmerica Nazarene College	KS	10,208	NC
Middle Tenn State Univ	TN	3,857	C
Middlebury College	VT	24,400	MC
Midland Lutheran College	NE	12,410	LC
Midwestern State Univ	TX	4,542	LC
Millersville Univ of Penn	PA	7,370	VC
Milligan College	TN	10,690	C
Millikin Univ	IL	15,499	C
Mills College	CA	20,848	VC
Millsaps College	MS	15,486	C+
Minot State Univ	ND	3,748	NC
Miss College	MS	8,348	C
Miss State Univ	MS	5,629	VC
Missouri Baptist College	MO	9,340	C
Missouri Southern State College	MO	4,272	
Missouri Valley College	MO	14,050	LC
Missouri Western State College	MO	4,384	NC
Molloy College	NY	8,580	LC
Monmouth College	IL	17,300	C+
Monmouth College	NJ	16,820	C
Montana State Univ	MT	5,534	C
Montclair State College	NJ	7,539	C+
Moorhead State Univ	MN	5,076	C
Moravian College	PA	18,960	VC
Morehead State Univ	KY	4,600	LC
Morehouse College	GA	13,224	LC
Morgan State Univ	MD	7,366	C+
Morningside College	IA	13,896	C
Morris Brown College	GA	12,234	NC
Mount Holyoke College	MA	23,630	VC
Mount Mercy College	IA	13,230	C
Mount Olive College	NC	9,650	LC
Mount St Mary College	NY	12,910	C
Mount St Mary's College	CA	16,390	VC
Mount St Mary's College	MD	17,825	LC
Mount Senario College	WI	10,970	C
Mount Union College	OH	15,850	C
Mount Vernon Nazarene College	OH	10,390	C
Muhlenberg College	PA	20,795	VC
Murray State Univ	KY	4,702	C
Muskingum College	OH	16,650	C
National Univ	CA	6,135	C
National-Louis Univ	IL	13,218	C
Nazareth College of Rochester	NY	15,310	C+
Nebr Wesleyan Univ	NE	12,240	C
Neumann College	PA	9,950	LC
New College of Calif	CA	6,900	NC
New College of the Univ of South Florida	FL	5,697	MC
New England College	NH	17,870	LC
New Mexico Highlands Univ	NM	3,772	C
New Mexico Inst of Mining and Tech	NM	5,212	C+
New Mexico State Univ	NM	4,844	LC
New York Univ	NY	24,705	VC+
Niagara Univ	NY	14,552	C
Nicholls State Univ	LA	4,531	NC
Nichols College	MA	14,200	LC
Norfolk State Univ	VA	6,345	LC
North Adams State College	MA	7,750	C
N Car Agricultural and Technical State Univ	NC	4,477	LC
N Car Central Univ	NC	4,347	LC
N Car State Univ	NC	4,984	VC
N Car Wesleyan College	NC	12,480	LC
North Central College	IL	15,498	VC
N Dak State Univ of Agriculture and Applied Science	ND	4,774	VC
North Georgia College	GA	4,103	LC
North Park College	IL	14,310	C
Northeast Louisiana Univ	LA	3,906	NC
Northeast Missouri State Univ	MO	5,654	VC+
Northeastern Illinois Univ	IL	1,955	C
Northeastern State Univ	OK	5,250	C
Northeastern Univ	MA	19,851	C

School	ST	$IS	SR
Northern Arizona Univ	AZ	4,844	C
Northern Illinois Univ	IL	6,408	C
Northern Kentucky Univ	KY	4,620	NC
Northern Mich Univ	MI	6,350	C
Northern State Univ	SD	4,186	LC
Northland College	WI	13,550	C
Northwest Missouri State Univ	MO	5,010	C
Northwest Nazarene College	ID	11,750	C
Northwestern College	MN	13,554	C
Northwestern College of Iowa	IA	12,250	C
Northwestern Okla State Univ	OK	3,424	C
Northwestern State Univ of Louisiana	LA	4,287	NC
Northwestern Univ	IL	21,093	MC
Norwich Univ	VT	18,730	C
Notre Dame College	NH	14,220	C
Notre Dame College of Ohio	OH	11,370	C
Nova Southeastern Univ	FL	13,244	LC
Nyack College	NY	12,210	C
Oakwood College	AL	10,005	C
Oberlin College	OH	24,570	HC+
Occidental College	CA	21,792	HC
Oglethorpe Univ	GA	16,360	VC
Ohio Dominican College	OH	11,820	C
Ohio Northern Univ	OH	18,660	VC
Ohio State Univ	OH	7,218	LC
Ohio Univ	OH	7,341	C
Ohio Wesleyan Univ	OH	21,108	VC+
Okla Baptist Univ	OK	8,486	C
Okla Christian Univ of Science and Arts	OK	8,790	NC
Okla City Univ	OK	9,840	C
Okla Panhandle State Univ	OK	3,155	NC
Okla State Univ	OK	5,086	C
Old Dominion Univ	VA	8,317	C
Olivet College	MI	14,000	C
Olivet Nazarene Univ	IL	11,976	C
Oral Roberts Univ	OK	10,607	C+
Oregon State Univ	OR	6,175	C
Ottawa Univ	KS	10,490	C+
Otterbein College	OH	16,506	C
Ouachita Baptist Univ	AR	8,940	C
Our Lady of the Lake Univ of San Antonio	TX	11,080	C
Pace Univ	NY	15,540	C
Pacific Christian College	CA	12,700	C
Pacific Lutheran Univ	WA	15,998	VC
Pacific Union College	CA	15,075	C
Pacific Univ	OR	17,869	C
Paine College	GA	8,207	LC
Palm Beach Atlantic College	FL	10,720	C
Park College	MO	7,320	C
Pembroke State Univ	NC	3,538	LC
Penn State Univ at Erie/ Behrend College	PA	8,752	C
Penn State Univ/Univ Park Campus	PA	8,752	HC
Pepperdine Univ	CA	23,720	VC
Peru State College	NE	4,831	NC
Pfeiffer College	NC	11,670	C
Philadelphia College of Textiles and Science	PA	15,896	C
Philander Smith College	AR	5,434	NC
Phillips Univ	OK	12,744	C
Piedmont College	GA	8,540	LC
Pine Manor College	MA	21,700	LC
Pittsburg State Univ	KS	4,478	NC
Pitzer College	CA	23,780	HC
Plymouth State College	NH	7,166	C
Point Loma Nazarene College	CA	13,532	C
Point Park College	PA	13,922	LC
Pomona College	CA	23,820	MC
Pontifical Catholic Univ of PR/Ponce	PR	5,807	C
Portland State Univ	OR	7,191	C
Prairie View A&M Univ	TX	4,740	C
Presbyterian College	SC	15,400	VC
Prescott College	AZ	9,775	C
Princeton Univ	NJ	24,650	MC
Providence College	RI	19,750	VC
Purdue Univ/Calumet	IN	2,374	NC
Purdue Univ/West Lafayette	IN	6,636	C
Queens College	NC	14,950	C
Quincy Univ	IL	13,646	VC
Quinnipiac College	CT	17,600	C+
Radford Univ	VA	7,034	LC
Ramapo College of New Jersey	NJ	8,823	C+
Randolph-Macon College	VA	16,980	C
Randolph-Macon Woman's College	VA	19,100	C
Reed College	OR	24,480	HC+
Regis College	MA	17,450	C
Regis Univ	CO	17,340	C
Rensselaer Polytechnic Inst	NY	23,067	HC
Rhode Island College	RI	7,901	LC
Rhodes College	TN	19,624	HC
Rice Univ	TX	15,110	MC
Richard Stockton College of New Jersey	NJ	6,950	VC
Rider Univ	NJ	18,160	C
Ripon College	WI	18,320	C+
Rivier College	NH	14,920	LC

School	ST	$IS	SR
Roanoke College	VA	16,975	C
Roberts Wesleyan College	NY	13,317	C
Rockford College	IL	15,300	C
Rockhurst College	MO	12,470	C
Rocky Mountain College	MT	11,320	C
Roger Williams Univ	RI	16,750	C
Rollins College	FL	20,875	VC
Roosevelt Univ	IL	12,368	C
Rosary College	IL	15,040	C
Rosemont College	PA	16,775	C
Rowan College of New Jersey	NJ	7,358	C
Russell Sage College	NY	16,790	C
Rutgers Univ/Camden College of A&S	NJ	8,652	C
Rutgers Univ/Douglass College	NJ	8,795	VC
Rutgers Univ/Livingston College	NJ	8,877	VC
Rutgers Univ/Newark College of A&S	NJ	8,645	C
Rutgers Univ/Rutgers College	NJ	8,841	HC+
Rutgers Univ/Univ College— Camden	NJ	3,506	C
Rutgers Univ/Univ College— New Brunswick	NJ	0	LC
Rutgers Univ/Univ College— Newark	NJ	0	C
Sacred Heart Univ	CT	16,350	C
Saginaw Valley State Univ	MI	6,634	LC
St Ambrose Univ	IA	13,380	C
St Andrews Presbyterian College	NC	14,240	LC
St Anselm College	NH	17,340	C
St Augustine's College	NC	9,300	C+
St Bonaventure Univ	NY	14,762	C
St Cloud State Univ	MN	5,015	C
St Edward's Univ	TX	12,636	C
St Francis College	IN	11,662	C
St Francis College	NY	6,710	LC
St Francis College	PA	15,744	LC
St John Fisher College	NY	15,415	C
St John's Univ	MN	15,364	C
St John's Univ	NY	8,980	C+
St Joseph College	CT	16,225	C
St Joseph's College	IN	14,730	C
St Joseph's College	ME	14,535	C
St Joseph's College	NY	7,322	C
St Joseph's Univ	PA	17,800	VC
St Lawrence Univ	NY	23,420	VC
St Leo College	FL	13,570	C
St Louis Univ	MO	15,522	VC
St Martin's College	WA	14,965	C
St Mary College	KS	11,250	C
St Mary's College	IN	17,043	VC
St Mary's College	MI	8,350	C
St Mary's College of Calif	CA	18,848	VC
St Mary's College of Maryland	MD	8,900	VC+
St Mary's College of Minn	MN	13,850	LC
St Mary's Univ	TX	12,064	C
St Mary-of-the-Woods College	IN	14,430	NC
St Meinrad College	IN	10,302	C
St Michael's College	VT	17,930	C
St Norbert College	WI	15,710	VC
St Olaf College	MN	17,200	HC
St Peter's College	NJ	14,775	LC
St Thomas Aquinas College	NY	13,550	C
St Thomas Univ	FL	14,280	LC
St Vincent College	PA	13,934	LC
St Xavier Univ	IL	14,700	C
Salem College	NC	16,025	C
Salem State College	MA	6,712	C
Salisbury State Univ	MD	7,516	C+
Salve Regina Univ	RI	29,100	LC
Sam Houston State Univ	TX	4,506	C
Samford Univ	AL	11,400	VC
San Diego State Univ	CA	6,692	LC
San Francisco State Univ	CA	7,292	LC
San Jose State Univ	CA	6,680	LC
Santa Clara Univ	CA	18,783	VC
Sarah Lawrence College	NY	24,975	HC
Schreiner College	TX	14,320	C
Scripps College	CA	23,600	HC
Seattle Pacific Univ	WA	16,503	C
Seattle Univ	WA	16,590	C
Seton Hall Univ	NJ	18,306	C
Seton Hill College	PA	14,320	C
Shenandoah Univ	VA	11,800	C
Shepherd College	WV	5,540	C
Shippensburg Univ of Penn	PA	7,052	C
Shorter College	GA	10,270	C
Siena College	NY	15,410	VC
Siena Heights College	MI	12,520	C
Simmons College	MA	22,534	C
Simpson College	CA	10,628	C
Simpson College	IA	14,635	VC
Sioux Falls College	SD	11,540	C
Skidmore College	NY	23,230	HC
Slippery Rock Univ	PA	6,803	C
Smith College	MA	24,236	HC
Sojourner-Douglass College	MD	5,265	LC
Sonoma State Univ	CA	6,996	LC
S Car State Univ	SC	5,424	LC
S Dak State Univ	SD	4,562	C

School	ST	$IS	SR
Southeast Missouri State Univ	MO	5,854	C
Southeastern College of the Assemblies of God	FL	6,618	NC
Southeastern Louisiana Univ	LA	4,230	NC
Southeastern Okla State Univ	OK	3,594	C
Southern Calif College	CA	12,356	C
Southern College of Seventh-day Adventists	TN	11,348	NC
Southern Conn State Univ	CT	7,532	C
Southern Illinois Univ at Carbondale	IL	6,234	C
Southern Illinois Univ at Edwardsville	IL	6,097	LC
Southern Methodist Univ	TX	18,520	VC
Southern Nazarene Univ	OK	9,206	NC
Southern Oregon State College	OR	6,128	C
Southern Univ and A&M College	LA	4,920	NC
Southern Univ at New Orleans	LA	1,452	NC
Southern Utah Univ	UT	4,104	LC
Southwest Baptist Univ	MO	9,192	NC
Southwest Missouri State Univ	MO	4,956	C
Southwest State Univ	MN	5,400	NC
Southwest Texas State Univ	TX	5,124	C
Southwestern Adventist College	TX	10,530	NC
Southwestern College	KS	10,032	C
Southwestern Okla State Univ	OK	3,312	C
Southwestern Univ	TX	15,484	HC
Spalding Univ	KY	10,496	C
Spelman College	GA	12,942	VC
Spring Arbor College	MI	12,256	C
Spring Hill College	AL	16,015	C+
Springfield College	MA	15,200	LC
Stanford Univ	CA	24,310	MC
SUNY at Albany	NY	7,059	VC
SUNY at Binghamton	NY	7,921	HC
SUNY at Buffalo	NY	7,896	VC
SUNY at Stony Brook	NY	7,658	VC
SUNY/College at Brockport	NY	7,220	C+
SUNY/College at Buffalo	NY	7,035	VC
SUNY/College at Cortland	NY	7,326	C+
SUNY/College at Fredonia	NY	7,159	VC
SUNY/College at Geneseo	NY	6,949	HC
SUNY/College at New Paltz	NY	6,890	C
SUNY/College at Old Westbury	NY	7,128	LC
SUNY/College at Oneonta	NY	7,878	C
SUNY/College at Oswego	NY	7,330	VC
SUNY/College at Plattsburgh	NY	6,917	C
SUNY/College at Purchase	NY	7,324	C
SUNY/Potsdam College	NY	6,906	C
Stephen F. Austin State Univ	TX	5,117	C
Stetson Univ	FL	16,435	VC
Stonehill College	MA	17,481	VC
Sul Ross State Univ	TX	4,144	NC
Susquehanna Univ	PA	19,950	VC
Swarthmore College	PA	24,136	MC
Sweet Briar College	VA	19,770	C
Syracuse Univ	NY	21,305	HC
Tabor College	KS	11,460	C
Talladega College	AL	8,124	VC
Taylor Univ	IN	14,450	VC
Teikyo Marycrest Univ	IA	13,755	NC
Teikyo Post Univ	CT	16,360	LC
Teikyo Westmar Univ	IA	15,920	C
Temple Univ	PA	10,281	C
Tenn State Univ	TN	4,626	C+
Tenn Tech Univ	TN	5,190	C
Tenn Wesleyan College	TN	10,060	C
Texas A&M Univ	TX	5,382	VC
Texas A&M Univ at Kingsville	TX	3,808	LC
Texas Christian Univ	TX	12,180	C
Texas Lutheran College	TX	10,710	C
Texas Southern Univ	TX	4,500	NC
Texas Tech Univ	TX	6,008	C
Texas Wesleyan Univ	TX	9,380	LC
The Citadel	SC	6,619	C
The Univ of New Mexico	NM	5,304	C
Thiel College	PA	16,282	C
Thomas A. Edison State College	NJ	400	
Thomas More College	KY	12,962	C
Tougaloo College	MS	7,480	LC
Touro College	NY	11,930	C
Towson State Univ	MD	7,452	C
Transylvania Univ	KY	14,970	VC+
Trenton State College	NJ	9,085	HC
Trevecca Nazarene College	TN	9,826	NC
Trinity Christian College	IL	13,260	C
Trinity College	CT	24,120	HC
Trinity College	DC	17,660	C
Trinity College	IL	14,010	C
Trinity College of Vermont	VT	16,015	LC
Trinity Univ	TX	16,670	HC
Troy State Univ	AL	4,322	C
Troy State Univ at Dothan/ Fort Rucker	AL	2,260	NC

School	ST	$IS	SR
Troy State Univ in Montgomery	AL	1,710	NC
Tufts Univ	MA	24,962	MC
Tulane Univ	LA	24,540	HC
Turabo Univ	PR	2,670	
Tusculum College	TN	10,400	LC
Tuskegee Univ	AL	10,128	C
Union College	KY	9,790	C
Union College	NY	23,817	HC
Union Univ	TN	7,880	C+
United States Air Force Academy	CO	0	MC
United States International Univ	CA	14,535	LC
Universidad Metropolitana	PR	2,650	
Univ of Akron	OH	6,699	NC
Univ of Alabama	AL	5,702	C
Univ of Alabama at Birmingham	AL	7,533	C
Univ of Alabama at Huntsville	AL	5,868	VC
Univ of Alaska Anchorage	AK	7,131	C
Univ of Alaska Fairbanks	AK	4,718	C
Univ of Arizona	AZ	5,808	C
Univ of Arkansas at Fayetteville	AR	5,046	C
Univ of Arkansas at Little Rock	AR	4,419	C
Univ of Arkansas at Monticello	AR	3,832	NC
Univ of Arkansas at Pine Bluff	AR	3,978	LC
Univ of Bridgeport	CT	18,985	C
Univ of Calif at Berkeley	CA	9,962	HC+
Univ of Calif at Davis	CA	9,534	VC
Univ of Calif at Los Angeles	CA	8,959	HC
Univ of Calif at Santa Barbara	CA	9,460	C
Univ of Calif at Santa Cruz	CA	9,060	VC
Univ of Calif, Riverside	CA	9,178	C
Univ of Calif, San Diego	CA	10,028	VC+
Univ of Calif/Irvine	CA	12,680	VC
Univ of Central Arkansas	AR	4,200	LC
Univ of Central Florida	FL	6,061	C+
Univ of Central Okla	OK	3,647	C
Univ of Charleston	WV	12,750	C
Univ of Chicago	IL	24,517	MC
Univ of Cincinnati	OH	7,989	C
Univ of Colo at Boulder	CO	6,410	VC
Univ of Colo at Colo Springs	CO	2,269	C
Univ of Colo at Denver	CO	1,955	NC
Univ of Conn	CT	9,168	C
Univ of Dallas	TX	14,983	VC
Univ of Dayton	OH	15,120	C+
Univ of Delaware	DE	8,013	C
Univ of Denver	CO	19,290	C+
Univ of Detroit Mercy	MI	14,720	C
Univ of Dubuque	IA	14,150	LC
Univ of Evansville	IN	15,300	VC
Univ of Findlay	OH	15,764	C
Univ of Florida	FL	5,850	HC
Univ of Georgia	GA	5,655	VC
Univ of Guam	GU	4,139	NC
Univ of Hartford	CT	19,858	LC
Univ of Hawaii at Hilo	HI	4,141	C
Univ of Hawaii at Manoa	HI	5,626	C
Univ of Houston	TX	5,215	C
Univ of Idaho	ID	4,830	C
Univ of Illinois at Chicago	IL	8,443	C
Univ of Indianapolis	IN	14,510	C
Univ of Iowa	IA	5,658	VC
Univ of Kansas	KS	5,200	VC
Univ of Kentucky	KY	5,152	VC
Univ of La Verne	CA	17,400	C
Univ of Louisville	KY	5,948	C
Univ of Lowell	MA	8,831	C
Univ of Maine	ME	7,990	C
Univ of Maine at Farmington	ME	6,700	C
Univ of Maine at Machias	ME	6,135	C
Univ of Mary Hardin-Baylor	TX	8,120	NC
Univ of Maryland/Baltimore County	MD	7,746	VC
Univ of Maryland/College Park	MD	8,182	VC
Univ of Maryland/Univ College	MD	4,900	NC
Univ of Mass Dartmouth	MA	8,158	C
Univ of Mass/Amherst	MA	9,364	VC
Univ of Mass/Boston	MA	4,253	C
Univ of Memphis	TN	3,476	C
Univ of Miami	FL	22,107	VC
Univ of Mich/Ann Arbor	MI	9,428	HC+
Univ of Mich/Dearborn	MI	3,399	NC
Univ of Mich/Flint	MI	2,916	C
Univ of Minn/Duluth	MN	6,512	C
Univ of Minn/Morris	MN	6,825	VC
Univ of Minn/Twin Cities	MN	6,682	VC
Univ of Miss	MS	5,756	C
Univ of Missouri/Columbia	MO	6,254	VC
Univ of Missouri/Kansas City	MO	5,906	VC
Univ of Missouri/Rolla	MO	6,729	VC+
Univ of Missouri/St. Louis	MO	6,378	C
Univ of Mobile	AL	9,400	C
Univ of Montana	MT	5,529	C
Univ of Montevallo	AL	5,310	C
Univ of Nebr at Kearney	NE	4,308	LC

School	ST	$IS	SR
Univ of Nebr at Omaha	NE	1,889	LC
Univ of Nebr-Lincoln	NE	5,278	LC
Univ of Nevada/Las Vegas	NV	6,405	C
Univ of Nevada/Reno	NV	5,735	C
Univ of New England	ME	16,075	LC
Univ of New Hampshire	NH	8,242	C
Univ of New Haven	CT	14,980	C
Univ of New Orleans	LA	5,468	C
Univ of North Alabama	AL	4,236	NC
Univ of N Car at Asheville	NC	4,791	VC
Univ of N Car at Chapel Hill	NC	5,330	HC
Univ of N Car at Charlotte	NC	4,597	C
Univ of N Car at Greensboro	NC	5,192	C
Univ of N Car at Wilmington	NC	5,172	C
Univ of N Dak	ND	4,902	NC
Univ of North Florida	FL	5,082	C
Univ of North Texas	TX	4,853	C
Univ of Northern Colo	CO	6,008	C
Univ of Northern Iowa	IA	5,137	C
Univ of Notre Dame	IN	20,150	MC
Univ of Okla	OK	5,427	VC
Univ of Oregon	OR	6,466	VC
Univ of Penn	PA	24,238	MC
Univ of Pittsburgh	PA	9,472	C
Univ of Pittsburgh at Bradford	PA	9,050	C
Univ of Pittsburgh at Greensburg	PA	8,660	C
Univ of Pittsburgh at Johnstown	PA	8,914	C
Univ of Portland	OR	15,564	C
Univ of PR/Cayey Univ College	PR	900	
Univ of PR/Mayaguez	PR	0	
Univ of PR/Rio Piedras	PR	0	
Univ of Puget Sound	WA	19,520	HC
Univ of Redlands	CA	22,059	VC
Univ of Rhode Island	RI	9,205	C
Univ of Richmond	VA	16,700	HC
Univ of Rochester	NY	23,696	HC
Univ of St Thomas	MN	15,785	C+
Univ of St Thomas	TX	11,676	C+
Univ of San Diego	CA	18,970	VC
Univ of San Francisco	CA	18,408	C
Univ of Science and Arts of Okla	OK	3,304	C
Univ of Scranton	PA	17,071	VC
Univ of South Alabama	AL	5,451	C
Univ of S Car	SC	6,158	C
Univ of S Car at Aiken	SC	5,386	C
Univ of S Car at Spartanburg	SC	2,320	C
Univ of S Dak	SD	4,722	C
Univ of South Florida	FL	5,475	C+
Univ of Southern Calif	CA	23,006	VC
Univ of Southern Colo	CO	5,350	LC
Univ of Southern Indiana	IN	3,720	NC
Univ of Southern Maine	ME	7,299	C
Univ of Southern Miss	MS	4,542	C
Univ of Southwestern Louisiana	LA	3,968	NC
Univ of Tampa	FL	16,780	C
Univ of Tenn at Chattanooga	TN	5,375	C
Univ of Tenn at Martin	TN	4,550	C
Univ of Tenn/Knoxville	TN	5,668	C
Univ of Texas at Arlington	TX	5,549	LC
Univ of Texas at Austin	TX	5,160	VC
Univ of Texas at Dallas	TX	1,222	VC+
Univ of Texas at El Paso	TX	3,160	LC
Univ of Texas at San Antonio	TX	6,420	C
Univ of Texas-Pan American	TX	3,192	NC
Univ of the District of Columbia	DC	974	NC
Univ of the Pacific	CA	21,100	C
Univ of the Sacred Heart	PR	3,890	C
Univ of the South	TN	18,830	HC
Univ of the Virgin Islands	VI	5,896	C
Univ of Toledo	OH	6,636	NC
Univ of Tulsa	OK	13,795	VC
Univ of Utah	UT	5,975	C
Univ of Vermont	VT	10,776	C+
Univ of Virginia	VA	7,964	MC
Univ of Washington	WA	6,618	VC
Univ of West Florida	FL	5,415	C
Univ of Wisc/Eau Claire	WI	4,647	C
Univ of Wisc/Green Bay	WI	4,904	C
Univ of Wisc/La Crosse	WI	4,487	C
Univ of Wisc/Madison	WI	6,400	HC
Univ of Wisc/Milwaukee	WI	6,165	C
Univ of Wisc/Oshkosh	WI	4,240	C
Univ of Wisc/Parkside	WI	5,247	
Univ of Wisc/Platteville	WI	4,830	C
Univ of Wisc/River Falls	WI	4,655	C
Univ of Wisc/Stevens Point	WI	5,047	C+
Univ of Wisc/Stout	WI	4,719	C
Univ of Wisc/Superior	WI	4,330	C
Univ of Wisc/Whitewater	WI	4,700	C
Univ of Wyoming	WY	4,991	NC
Upper Iowa Univ	IA	11,900	C
Upsala College	NJ	17,200	C
Urbana Univ	OH	12,536	C
Ursinus College	PA	19,165	VC
Ursuline College	OH	13,180	LC
Utah State Univ	UT	4,683	C
Utica College of Syracuse Univ	NY	16,714	LC
Valdosta State Univ	GA	4,670	LC
Valparaiso Univ	IN	14,810	VC
Vanderbilt Univ	TN	23,422	HC+
Vassar College	NY	24,206	HC
Villanova Univ	PA	21,400	HC
Virginia Commonwealth Univ	VA	7,909	C
Virginia Intermont College	VA	12,250	LC
Virginia Polytechnic Inst and State Univ	VA	6,828	C
Virginia State Univ	VA	7,040	
Virginia Union Univ	VA	10,555	LC
Virginia Wesleyan College	VA	14,950	VC
Viterbo College	WI	12,670	C
Wabash College	IN	16,250	VC
Wagner College	NY	17,950	C
Wake Forest Univ	NC	17,280	MC
Walla Walla College	WA	13,215	C
Walsh Univ	OH	11,640	C
Warner Pacific College	OR	12,112	C
Warren Wilson College	NC	10,877	C
Wartburg College	IA	14,530	VC
Washburn Univ of Topeka	KS	5,802	NC
Washington and Jefferson College	PA	19,360	C
Washington College	MD	19,270	C+
Washington State Univ	WA	6,364	C
Washington Univ	MO	23,507	HC
Wayland Baptist Univ	TX	7,811	NC
Wayne State College	NE	4,260	NC
Wayne State Univ	MI	2,680	C
Waynesburg College	PA	11,960	C
Weber State Univ	UT	4,398	C
Webster Univ	MO	12,650	C
Wellesley College	MA	23,815	MC
Wells College	NY	19,460	C+
Wesley College	DE	13,745	LC
Wesleyan College	GA	15,445	C
West Chester Univ of Penn	PA	7,492	C
West Georgia College	GA	4,256	C
West Liberty State College	WV	4,690	LC
West Texas A&M Univ	TX	4,224	C
West Virginia State College	WV	5,044	LC
West Virginia Univ	WV	5,774	C
West Virginia Wesleyan College	WV	16,900	C
Western Baptist College	OR	12,400	LC
Western Carolina Univ	NC	3,811	C
Western Conn State Univ	CT	6,622	C
Western Illinois Univ	IL	5,241	LC
Western Kentucky Univ	KY	4,808	C
Western Maryland College	MD	18,990	C
Western Mich Univ	MI	6,820	C
Western New England College	MA	14,674	LC
Western New Mexico Univ	NM	3,234	LC
Western Oregon State College	OR	6,180	C
Western State College of Colo	CO	5,560	C
Western Washington Univ	WA	6,077	VC
Westfield State College	MA	7,161	C
Westminster College	MO	13,750	C+
Westminster College	PA	15,200	C
Westminster College of Salt Lake City	UT	12,100	C
Westmont College	CA	18,732	C
Wheaton College	IL	14,710	HC
Wheaton College	MA	23,840	C+
Wheeling Jesuit College	WV	14,370	C
Whitman College	WA	20,595	HC
Whittier College	CA	21,661	C
Whitworth College	WA	16,265	C
Wichita State Univ	KS	5,068	NC
Widener Univ	PA	16,840	C
Wilberforce Univ	OH	10,408	C
Wilkes Univ	PA	15,728	LC
Willamette Univ	OR	17,995	VC
William Carey College	MS	7,050	C
William Jewell College	MO	12,500	VC
William Paterson College	NJ	7,438	C+
William Tyndale College	MI	7,120	NC
William Woods Univ	MO	14,025	LC
Williams Baptist College	AR	5,834	LC
Williams College	MA	24,390	MC
Wilmington College	OH	13,700	LC
Wingate College	NC	10,610	C
Winona State Univ	MN	5,200	VC
Winston-Salem State Univ	NC	4,142	LC
Winthrop Univ	SC	6,750	C
Wisc Lutheran College	WI	12,180	C
Wittenberg Univ	OH	19,998	VC
Wofford College	SC	15,360	VC
Women's College of Brenau Univ	GA	14,734	C
Worcester State College	MA	6,414	LC
Wright State Univ	OH	6,896	LC
Xavier Univ	OH	15,710	C+
Xavier Univ of Louisiana	LA	10,400	C
Yale Univ	CT	25,110	MC
Yeshiva Univ	NY	18,200	VC
York College of Penn	PA	8,345	C
Youngstown State Univ	OH	6,447	LC

PSYCHOLOGY EDUCATION

School	ST	$IS	SR
Barat College	IL	13,990	C
Huntington College	IN	13,220	C
MidAmerica Nazarene College	KS	10,208	NC
Univ of Delaware	DE	8,013	VC

PUBLIC ADMINISTRATION

School	ST	$IS	SR
Alfred Univ	NY	21,054	VC+
American International College	MA	14,029	C
Antioch College	OH	19,532	C
Appalachian State Univ	NC	4,095	C
Ashland Univ	OH	15,508	C
Auburn Univ	AL	5,823	C+
Auburn Univ at Montgomery	AL	3,390	C
Augustana College	IL	16,959	VC
Bethany College	WV	18,300	C+
Blackburn College	IL	9,120	C
Bowling Green State Univ	OH	6,701	C
Calif Baptist College	CA	11,294	C
Cal State/Bakersfield	CA	5,402	C
Cal State/Chico	CA	6,146	C
Cal State/Dominguez Hills	CA	2,857	LC
Cal State/Fresno	CA	5,747	C
Cal State/Los Angeles	CA	4,940	VC
Cal State/Sacramento	CA	6,387	C
Cal State/San Bernardino	CA	6,055	LC
Cal State/Stanislaus	CA	6,799	C
Capital Univ	OH	16,535	VC
Carnegie Mellon Univ	PA	22,560	HC+
Carroll College	MT	11,265	C
Cedar Crest College	PA	18,930	C
Cedarville College	OH	10,715	C
Central State Univ	OH	7,320	NC
Central Washington Univ	WA	5,644	C
Christopher Newport Univ	VA	3,196	LC
City Univ	WA	6,400	NC
CUNY/Baruch College	NY	2,562	VC
CUNY/John Jay College of Criminal Justice	NY	2,501	LC
CUNY/Medgar Evers College	NY	2,577	NC
College of Santa Fe	NM	14,008	C
Columbus College	GA	4,892	LC
Dallas Baptist Univ	TX	9,620	LC
Doane College	NE	12,220	C
Dominican College	NY	13,600	LC
Drake Univ	IA	17,195	VC
Dyke College	OH	5,200	LC
East Carolina Univ	NC	4,498	C
Eastern Mich Univ	MI	6,749	C
Eastern Washington Univ	WA	5,439	LC
Edgewood College	WI	11,700	C
Edward Waters College	FL	8,300	NC
Elon College	NC	12,290	LC
Evangel College	MO	10,142	LC
Evergreen State College	WA	6,306	C
Fayetteville State Univ	NC	3,926	LC
Florida A&M Univ	FL	4,651	C
Florida Atlantic Univ	FL	5,525	C
Florida International Univ	FL	4,191	VC
Florida Memorial College	FL	7,600	C+
Franklin Univ	OH	4,621	NC
George Mason Univ	VA	8,728	C
Georgia College	GA	4,310	LC
Grambling State Univ	LA	4,712	NC
Grand Valley State Univ	MI	6,822	VC
Hamline Univ	MN	17,122	VC
Hastings College	NE	12,426	C
Hawaii Pacific Univ	HI	12,300	C
Heidelberg College	OH	17,160	C
Heritage College	WA	5,540	NC
Indiana Univ Bloomington	IN	6,495	VC
Indiana Univ Northwest	IN	2,310	C
Indiana Univ-Purdue Univ at Fort Wayne	IN	2,500	LC
Inter American Univ of PR/ Aguadilla Regional College	PR	2,290	
Inter American Univ of PR/ Bayamon Univ College	PR	2,300	
Inter American Univ of PR/ Metropolitan Campus	PR	2,340	
Inter American Univ of PR/ Ponce Regional College	PR	2,300	
Inter American Univ of PR/ San German	PR	4,620	
Inter-American Univ of PR/ Fajardo Regional College	PR	2,732	
Jacksonville Univ	FL	13,390	C
James Madison Univ	VA	8,198	HC
John Carroll Univ	OH	16,510	C
Juniata College	PA	18,390	C+
Kean College of New Jersey	NJ	6,395	LC
Kentucky State Univ	KY	4,282	C+
Kutztown Univ	PA	6,528	C
La Salle Univ	PA	16,940	VC
Lakeland College	WI	12,845	LC
Lamar Univ	TX	3,798	C
Le Tourneau Univ	TX	12,500	C+
Liberty Univ	VA	11,500	LC
Lincoln Univ	MO	4,638	NC
LIU/C. W. Post Campus	NY	16,870	C
Louisiana College	LA	7,518	VC
Madonna Univ	MI	8,546	C
Miami Univ	OH	8,066	VC
Mich State Univ	MI	7,842	C
Middle Tenn State Univ	TN	3,857	C
Missouri Valley College	MO	14,050	LC
Mount Ida College	MA	16,700	LC
New York Univ	NY	24,705	VC+
Nichols College	MA	14,200	LC
Northeastern Univ	MA	19,851	C
Northern Arizona Univ	AZ	4,844	C
Northern Kentucky Univ	KY	4,620	NC
Northern Mich Univ	MI	6,350	C
Northland College	WI	13,550	LC
Oakland Univ	MI	6,714	VC
Ohio Univ	OH	7,341	C
Old Dominion Univ	VA	8,317	C
Our Lady of the Lake Univ of San Antonio	TX	11,080	C
Pembroke State Univ	NC	3,538	LC
Plymouth State College	NH	7,166	C
Point Park College	PA	13,922	LC
Pontifical Catholic Univ of PR/Ponce	PR	5,807	C
Rhode Island College	RI	7,901	LC
Roosevelt Univ	IL	12,368	C
Saginaw Valley State Univ	MI	6,634	LC
St Ambrose Univ	IA	13,380	C
St Bonaventure Univ	NY	14,762	C
St Cloud State Univ	MN	5,015	C
St Francis College	PA	15,744	LC
St John's Univ	NY	8,980	C+
St Joseph's Univ	PA	17,800	VC
St Leo College	FL	13,570	C
St Louis Univ	MO	15,522	VC
St Mary's College of Minn	MN	13,850	LC
St Thomas Univ	FL	14,280	LC
Samford Univ	AL	11,400	VC
San Diego State Univ	CA	6,692	LC
Seattle Univ	WA	16,590	C
Shaw Univ	NC	8,936	C+
Shippensburg Univ of Penn	PA	7,052	C
Siena Heights College	MI	12,520	C
Slippery Rock Univ	PA	6,803	C
Sojourner-Douglass College	MD	5,265	LC
Southeastern Univ	DC	6,625	C
Southwest Missouri State Univ	MO	4,956	C
SUNY/College at Cortland	NY	7,326	C+
SUNY/College at Geneseo	NY	6,949	HC
Stephen F. Austin State Univ	TX	5,117	C
Stonehill College	MA	17,481	VC
Suffolk Univ	MA	15,360	LC
Syracuse Univ	NY	21,305	HC
Talladega College	AL	8,124	VC
Temple Univ	PA	10,281	C
Texas A&M Univ at Kingsville	TX	3,808	LC
Texas Southern Univ	TX	4,500	NC
Turabo Univ	PR	2,670	
Univ of Akron	OH	6,699	NC
Univ of Alaska Southeast	AK	4,075	LC
Univ of Arizona	AZ	5,808	C
Univ of Arkansas at Fayetteville	AR	5,046	C
Univ of Central Arkansas	AR	4,200	LC
Univ of Central Florida	FL	6,061	C+
Univ of Central Okla	OK	3,647	C
Univ of Detroit Mercy	MI	14,720	C
Univ of Guam	GU	4,139	NC
Univ of La Verne	CA	17,400	C
Univ of Louisville	KY	5,948	C
Univ of Maine	ME	7,990	C
Univ of Mich/Dearborn	MI	3,399	HC
Univ of Mich/Flint	MI	2,916	C
Univ of Miss	MS	5,756	C
Univ of Missouri/St. Louis	MO	6,378	C
Univ of Nebr at Omaha	NE	1,889	LC
Univ of Nevada/Las Vegas	NV	6,405	C
Univ of New Haven	CT	14,980	C
Univ of N Car at Greensboro	NC	5,192	C
Univ of N Dak	ND	4,902	NC
Univ of Northern Iowa	IA	5,137	C
Univ of Pittsburgh	PA	9,472	C
Univ of Puget Sound	WA	19,520	HC
Univ of St Thomas	MN	15,785	C+
Univ of San Francisco	CA	18,408	C
Univ of Scranton	PA	17,071	VC
Univ of S Car	SC	6,158	C
Univ of Southern Calif	CA	23,006	VC
Univ of Tenn at Martin	TN	4,550	C
Univ of Tenn/Knoxville	TN	5,668	C
Univ of Texas at Dallas	TX	1,222	VC+
Univ of the District of Columbia	DC	974	NC
Univ of the Ozarks	AR	7,770	C
Univ of the Pacific	CA	21,100	C
Univ of Wisc/Green Bay	WI	4,904	C
Univ of Wisc/La Crosse	WI	4,487	C
Univ of Wisc/Stevens Point	WI	5,047	C+
Univ of Wisc/Whitewater	WI	4,700	C
Upper Iowa Univ	IA	11,900	C

School	ST	$IS	SR
Valdosta State Univ	GA	4,670	LC
Virginia Polytechnic Inst and State Univ	VA	6,828	C
Virginia State Univ	VA	7,040	
Wagner College	NY	17,950	C
Washburn Univ of Topeka	KS	5,802	NC
Washington and Lee Univ	VA	17,735	MC
Waynesburg College	PA	11,960	C
Wesleyan Univ	CT	23,770	MC
West Chester Univ of Penn	PA	7,492	C
West Liberty State College	WV	4,690	LC
West Texas A&M Univ	TX	4,224	C
West Virginia Inst of Tech	WV	5,858	LC
West Virginia Wesleyan College	WV	16,900	C
Western Mich Univ	MI	6,820	C
Western New Mexico Univ	NM	3,234	LC
Wichita State Univ	KS	5,068	NC
Winona State Univ	MN	5,200	VC
Winston-Salem State Univ	NC	4,142	LC
Women's College of Brenau Univ	GA	14,734	C
Youngstown State Univ	OH	6,447	LC

PUBLIC AFFAIRS

School	ST	$IS	SR
Brigham Young Univ	UT	5,625	HC
Columbia College	SC	13,520	LC
Cornell Univ	NY	13,445	MC
Duke Univ	NC	21,271	MC
Hamilton College	NY	23,500	HC
Hampshire College	MA	25,320	C
Indiana Univ/South Bend	IN	2,141	LC
Lincoln Univ	PA	0	LC
Muskingum College	OH	16,650	C
Northwest Nazarene College	ID	11,750	C
Pomona College	CA	23,820	MC
Rice Univ	TX	15,110	MC
St Mary College	KS	11,250	C
St Mary's College of Maryland	MD	8,900	VC+
Stanford Univ	CA	24,310	MC
Syracuse Univ	NY	21,305	HC
Trinity College	CT	24,120	HC
Univ of Denver	CO	19,290	C+
Univ of N Car at Chapel Hill	NC	5,330	HC
Univ of Okla	OK	5,427	VC
Univ of Penn	PA	24,238	MC
Wayne State Univ	MI	2,680	C
Wells College	NY	19,460	C+
Western Oregon State College	OR	6,180	C

PUBLIC HEALTH

School	ST	$IS	SR
Cal State/Bakersfield	CA	5,402	C
Cal State/Fresno	CA	5,747	C
Central Washington Univ	WA	5,644	C
CUNY/Herbert H. Lehman College	NY	2,542	C
CUNY/Hunter College	NY	4,101	VC
East Stroudsburg Univ	PA	6,886	C
East Tenn State Univ	TN	4,406	C
Evergreen State College	WA	6,306	C
George Mason Univ	VA	8,728	C
Indiana Univ Bloomington	IN	6,495	VC
Jersey City State College	NJ	7,797	LC
Johns Hopkins Univ	MD	24,360	MC
Liberty Univ	VA	11,500	LC
Mankato State Univ	MN	5,097	LC
Old Dominion Univ	VA	8,317	C
Richard Stockton College of New Jersey	NJ	6,950	VC
Rutgers Univ/Cook College	NJ	9,197	HC
Rutgers Univ/Douglass College	NJ	8,795	VC
Rutgers Univ/Livingston College	NJ	8,877	VC
Rutgers Univ/Rutgers College	NJ	8,841	HC+
Rutgers Univ/Univ College—New Brunswick	NJ	0	LC
St Cloud State Univ	MN	5,015	C
San Francisco State Univ	CA	7,292	LC
Southern Conn State Univ	CT	7,532	C
Texas Southern Univ	TX	4,500	NC
Univ of Kentucky	KY	5,152	VC
Univ of Nebr-Lincoln	NE	5,278	LC
Univ of N Car at Chapel Hill	NC	5,330	HC
Univ of N Car at Greensboro	NC	5,192	C
Univ of Northern Iowa	IA	5,137	C
Univ of Wisc/Eau Claire	WI	4,647	C
Utah State Univ	UT	4,683	C
West Chester Univ of Penn	PA	7,492	C
Western Kentucky Univ	KY	4,808	C
Western New Mexico Univ	NM	3,234	LC
Winona State Univ	MN	5,200	VC

PUBLIC RELATIONS

School	ST	$IS	SR
Arkansas State Univ	AR	4,250	NC
Auburn Univ	AL	5,823	C+
Barry Univ	FL	16,050	C
Boston Univ	MA	24,130	HC
Bowie State Univ	MD	7,294	LC
Brigham Young Univ	UT	5,625	HC
Capital Univ	OH	16,535	VC
Carroll College	MT	11,265	C
Central Missouri State Univ	MO	5,138	C
College of St Rose	NY	14,452	C
David Lipscomb Univ	TN	7,865	VC
Drake Univ	IA	17,195	VC
Eastern Kentucky Univ	KY	4,840	NC
Emerson College	MA	22,678	LC
Ferris State Univ	MI	7,160	NC
Florida Southern College	FL	12,260	C
Freed-Hardeman Univ	TN	8,585	VC
Gonzaga Univ	WA	16,350	VC
Heidelberg College	OH	17,160	C
Illinois State Univ	IL	6,413	C
John Brown Univ	AR	9,880	VC
Kent State Univ	OH	6,740	LC
LIU/C. W. Post Campus	NY	16,870	C
Mansfield Univ	PA	6,348	C
Marietta College	OH	16,940	C+
Marquette Univ	WI	16,114	VC
Millersville Univ of Penn	PA	7,370	VC
Moorhead State Univ	MN	5,076	C
Mount Mercy College	IA	13,230	C
Mount St Mary College	NY	12,910	C
Northern Mich Univ	MI	6,350	C
Northwest Missouri State Univ	MO	5,010	LC
Northwestern Okla State Univ	OK	3,424	C
Ohio Dominican College	OH	11,820	LC
Ohio Northern Univ	OH	18,660	VC
Otterbein College	OH	16,506	C
Pacific Union College	CA	15,075	C
Pepperdine Univ	CA	23,720	VC
Pontifical Catholic Univ of PR/Ponce	PR	5,807	
Purdue Univ/West Lafayette	IN	6,636	C
Roosevelt Univ	IL	12,368	C
Rosary College	IL	15,040	C
St Mary's College of Minn	MN	13,850	LC
Shorter College	GA	10,270	C
Simmons College	MA	22,534	C
Southern Methodist Univ	TX	18,520	VC
Suffolk Univ	MA	15,360	LC
Syracuse Univ	NY	21,305	HC
Taylor Univ	IN	14,450	VC
Texas Tech Univ	TX	6,008	C
Toccoa Falls College	GA	9,350	C
Univ of Alabama	AL	5,702	C
Univ of Dayton	OH	15,120	C+
Univ of Evansville	IN	15,300	VC
Univ of Florida	FL	5,850	HC
Univ of Miami	FL	22,107	VC
Univ of New Haven	CT	14,980	C
Univ of North Alabama	AL	4,236	NC
Univ of N Dak	ND	4,902	NC
Univ of Northern Colo	CO	6,008	C
Univ of Northern Iowa	IA	5,137	C
Univ of St Thomas	MN	15,785	C+
Univ of S Car	SC	6,158	C
Univ of Southwestern Louisiana	LA	3,968	NC
Univ of Texas at Arlington	TX	5,549	LC
Univ of Wisc/Whitewater	WI	4,700	C
Ursuline College	OH	13,180	LC
Utica College of Syracuse Univ	NY	16,714	LC
Wartburg College	IA	14,530	VC
Wayne State Univ	MI	2,680	C
West Virginia Univ	WV	5,774	C
West Virginia Wesleyan College	WV	16,900	C
Western Kentucky Univ	KY	4,808	C
William Carey College	MS	7,050	C
Xavier Univ	OH	15,710	C+

PUBLISHING

School	ST	$IS	SR
Emerson College	MA	22,678	LC
Syracuse Univ	NY	21,305	HC

PURCHASING/INVENTORY MANAGEMENT

School	ST	$IS	SR
Arizona State Univ Main Campus	AZ	6,444	C
Florida Inst of Tech	FL	16,935	VC
Southern Oregon State College	OR	6,128	C
Univ of Alabama at Huntsville	AL	5,868	VC
Univ of Houston-Downtown	TX	4,034	NC
Western Mich Univ	MI	6,820	C

QUANTITATIVE METHODS

School	ST	$IS	SR
Babson College	MA	23,160	VC
Cleveland State Univ	OH	7,287	NC
Coppin State College	MD	7,145	LC
La Salle Univ	PA	16,940	VC
Louisiana State Univ and A&M College	LA	5,605	C
Penn State Univ/Univ Park Campus	PA	8,752	HC
Simon's Rock College of Bard	MA	23,760	VC+
Univ of Calif, San Diego	CA	10,028	VC+
Univ of Central Arkansas	AR	4,200	LC
Univ of Cincinnati	OH	7,989	C
Univ of Houston-Downtown	TX	4,034	NC
Univ of PR/Rio Piedras	PR	0	
Univ of Washington	WA	6,618	VC
Univ of Wisc/Madison	WI	6,400	HC
Western New England College	MA	14,674	LC

RADIATION THERAPY

School	ST	$IS	SR
Indiana Univ-Purdue Univ at Indianapolis	IN	5,862	LC
National-Louis Univ	IL	13,218	C
Nebr Methodist College of Nursing and Allied Health	NE	4,360	C

RADIO/TELEVISION TECHNOLOGY

School	ST	$IS	SR
La Sierra Univ	CA	15,472	C
Marywood College	PA	14,890	C
New Mexico Highlands Univ	NM	3,772	C
Northern Kentucky Univ	KY	4,620	NC
Northwestern Univ	IL	21,093	MC
Southern Calif College	CA	12,356	C
Univ of Arkansas at Little Rock	AR	4,419	C
Univ of North Texas	TX	4,853	C

RADIOGRAPH MEDICAL TECHNOLOGY

School	ST	$IS	SR
Alderson-Broaddus College	WV	12,000	C
Clarkson College	NE	7,582	C
Howard Univ	DC	11,680	C
La Roche College	PA	12,977	LC
Madonna Univ	MI	8,546	C
Southwest Missouri State Univ	MO	4,956	C
Univ of Lowell	MA	8,831	VC
Univ of the Ozarks	AR	7,770	C

RADIOLOGICAL SCIENCE

School	ST	$IS	SR
Dana College	NE	11,910	C
George Washington Univ	DC	22,470	HC
Indiana Univ Bloomington	IN	6,495	VC
Malone College	OH	12,572	C
Manhattan College	NY	19,000	C
Midwestern State Univ	TX	4,542	LC
Quinnipiac College	CT	17,600	C+
Univ of Alabama at Birmingham	AL	7,533	C
Univ of Central Arkansas	AR	4,200	LC
Univ of Central Florida	FL	6,061	C+

School	ST	$IS	SR
Univ of Charleston	WV	12,750	C
Univ of Kentucky	KY	5,152	VC
Univ of Missouri/Columbia	MO	6,254	HC
Univ of N Car at Chapel Hill	NC	5,330	HC

RADIOLOGICAL TECHNOLOGY

School	ST	$IS	SR
Austin Peay State Univ	TN	4,350	C
Avila College	MO	12,130	C
Bloomsburg Univ of Penn	PA	6,312	C+
Boise State Univ	ID	4,909	LC
Cal State/Northridge	CA	7,122	LC
Clarkson College	NE	7,582	C
Emory Univ	GA	21,930	HC
Friends Univ	KS	11,205	C
Idaho State Univ	ID	4,442	C
LIU/C. W. Post Campus	NY	16,870	C
Marian College of Fond du Lac	WI	12,250	C
Mass College of Pharmacy and Allied Health Sciences	MA	18,352	C
McNeese State Univ	LA	4,543	NC
Minot State Univ	ND	3,748	NC
National-Louis Univ	IL	13,218	C
Northeast Louisiana Univ	LA	3,906	NC
Northern Kentucky Univ	KY	4,620	NC
Ohio State Univ	OH	7,218	LC
Peru State College	NE	4,311	NC
St Joseph's College	ME	14,535	C
St Mary's College	MI	8,350	C
Southern Illinois Univ at Carbondale	IL	6,234	C
Univ of Hartford	CT	19,858	LC
Univ of Mary	ND	8,910	C
Univ of Nevada/Las Vegas	NV	6,405	C
Wayne State Univ	MI	2,680	C
William Carey College	MS	7,050	C

RANGE/FARM MANAGEMENT

School	ST	$IS	SR
Colo State Univ	CO	6,566	VC
Humboldt State Univ	CA	5,676	C
Montana State Univ	MT	5,534	C
New Mexico State Univ	NM	4,844	LC
N Dak State Univ of Agriculture and Applied Science	ND	4,774	VC
Oregon State Univ	OR	6,175	C
S Dak State Univ	SD	4,562	C
Tarleton State Univ	TX	4,082	LC
Texas A&M Univ	TX	5,382	VC
Texas A&M Univ at Kingsville	TX	3,808	LC
Texas Tech Univ	TX	6,008	C
Univ of Arizona	AZ	5,808	C
Univ of Calif at Davis	CA	9,534	VC
Univ of Nebr-Lincoln	NE	5,278	LC
Univ of Wisc/River Falls	WI	4,655	C
Univ of Wyoming	WY	4,991	NC
Utah State Univ	UT	4,683	C

READING EDUCATION

School	ST	$IS	SR
Drake Univ	IA	17,195	VC
Hardin-Simmons Univ	TX	9,080	C
Jarvis Christian College	TX	7,170	LC
Muskingum College	OH	16,650	C
S Car State Univ	SC	5,424	LC
Southwest Texas State Univ	TX	5,124	C
Texas Wesleyan Univ	TX	9,380	LC
Univ of Texas at Arlington	TX	5,549	LC

REAL ESTATE

School	ST	$IS	SR
Arizona State Univ Main Campus	AZ	6,444	C
Arkansas State Univ	AR	4,250	NC
Calif State Polytechnic Univ/Pomona	CA	6,438	LC
Cal State/Los Angeles	CA	4,940	VC
Cal State/Northridge	CA	7,122	LC
Cal State/Sacramento	CA	6,387	C
Christopher Newport Univ	VA	3,196	LC
Coastal Carolina Univ	SC	6,010	LC
Columbia College	MO	11,995	C
Dyke College	OH	5,200	C
Eastern Kentucky Univ	KY	4,840	NC
Eastern Mich Univ	MI	6,749	C
Florida Atlantic Univ	FL	5,525	C

School	ST	$IS	SR
Florida State Univ	FL	5,814	VC
Franklin Univ	OH	4,621	NC
Indiana Univ Bloomington	IN	6,495	VC
Indiana Univ-Purdue Univ at Indianapolis	IN	5,862	LC
Kent State Univ	OH	6,740	LC
Miss State Univ	MS	5,629	VC
Morehead State Univ	KY	4,600	LC
Northeast Louisiana Univ	LA	3,906	NC
Pace Univ	NY	15,540	C
Penn State Univ/Univ Park Campus	PA	8,752	HC
San Francisco State Univ	CA	7,292	LC
Schreiner College	TX	14,320	C
Shippensburg Univ of Penn	PA	7,052	C
Southern Methodist Univ	TX	18,520	VC
Temple Univ	PA	10,281	C
Texas A&M Univ at Kingsville	TX	3,808	LC
Univ of Alabama	AL	5,702	C
Univ of Cincinnati	OH	7,989	C
Univ of Conn	CT	9,168	C
Univ of Denver	CO	19,290	C+
Univ of Florida	FL	5,850	HC
Univ of Hawaii at Manoa	HI	5,626	C
Univ of Houston-Downtown	TX	4,034	NC
Univ of Memphis	TN	3,476	C
Univ of Miami	FL	22,107	VC
Univ of Miss	MS	5,756	C
Univ of Missouri/Columbia	MO	6,254	HC
Univ of North Texas	TX	4,853	C
Univ of Okla	OK	5,427	VC
Univ of Penn	PA	24,238	MC
Univ of S Car	SC	6,158	C
Univ of Texas at Arlington	TX	5,549	LC
Univ of Texas at El Paso	TX	3,160	LC
Univ of Wisc/Madison	WI	6,400	HC
Univ of Wisc/Milwaukee	WI	6,165	C
Western Mich Univ	MI	6,820	C

RECREATION AND LEISURE SERVICES

School	ST	$IS	SR
Aquinas College	MI	14,526	C
Arizona State Univ Main Campus	AZ	6,444	C
Arkansas Tech Univ	AR	4,200	NC
Asbury College	KY	11,105	VC
Austin Peay State Univ	TN	4,350	C
Boston Univ	MA	24,130	HC
Calif Polytechnic State Univ	CA	6,980	VC+
Cal State/Hayward	CA	5,495	C
Cal State/Northridge	CA	7,122	LC
Calvin College	MI	13,020	VC
Catawba College	NC	12,950	C
Central Washington Univ	WA	5,644	C
Davis and Elkins College	WV	13,230	LC
Defiance College	OH	13,480	LC
Eastern Washington Univ	WA	5,439	LC
Emporia State Univ	KS	4,685	NC
Ferrum College	VA	12,800	LC
Florida State Univ	FL	5,814	VC
Frostburg State Univ	MD	6,940	C
Gallaudet Univ	DC	9,850	SP
Georgetown College	KY	10,990	C
Georgia Southern Univ	GA	4,988	LC
Gordon College	MA	16,790	C
Graceland College	IA	11,600	C
Green Mountain College	VT	14,080	C
Greenville College	IL	14,190	C
Houghton College	NY	13,120	VC
Indiana State Univ	IN	6,210	C
Indiana Univ Bloomington	IN	6,495	VC
Iowa State Univ	IA	5,456	C
Ithaca College	NY	19,679	C
Johnson and Wales Univ	RI	13,995	LC
Liberty Univ	VA	11,500	LC
Lincoln Univ	PA	0	LC
Lyndon State College	VT	8,394	LC
Mars Hill College	NC	11,050	C
Mesa State College	CO	5,127	NC
Metropolitan State College of Denver	CO	1,751	NC
Montreat-Anderson College	NC	10,972	LC
Morgan State Univ	MD	7,366	C+
Morris College	SC	6,880	LC
Mount Olive College	NC	9,650	LC
New Mexico Highlands Univ	NM	3,772	C
N Car State Univ	NC	4,984	VC
N Dak State Univ of Agriculture and Applied Science	ND	4,774	VC
Northeastern Illinois Univ	IL	1,955	C
Pacific Union College	CA	15,075	C
Penn State Univ/Univ Park Campus	PA	8,752	HC
St Thomas Aquinas College	NY	13,550	C
Salisbury State Univ	MD	7,516	C+
Seattle Pacific Univ	WA	16,503	C
Southeastern Okla State Univ	OK	3,594	C
Southern Conn State Univ	CT	7,532	C
Southwest Missouri State Univ	MO	4,956	C
Southwest Texas State Univ	TX	5,124	C
SUNY/College at Brockport	NY	7,220	C+
Taylor Univ	IN	14,450	VC
Texas Tech Univ	TX	6,008	C
Univ of Arkansas at Pine Bluff	AR	3,978	LC
Univ of Florida	FL	5,850	HC
Univ of Illinois at Urbana-Champaign	IL	7,764	HC
Univ of Iowa	IA	5,658	VC
Univ of Maine at Presque Isle	ME	6,374	C
Univ of Maryland/College Park	MD	8,182	VC
Univ of Mich/Ann Arbor	MI	9,428	HC+
Univ of Minn/Twin Cities	MN	6,682	VC
Univ of New Hampshire	NH	8,242	C
Univ of N Car at Chapel Hill	NC	5,330	HC
Univ of North Texas	TX	4,853	C
Univ of Northern Iowa	IA	5,137	C
Univ of Oregon	OR	6,466	VC
Univ of S Dak	SD	4,722	C
Univ of Tenn at Chattanooga	TN	5,375	C
Univ of Utah	UT	5,975	C
Univ of Wisc/Madison	WI	6,400	HC
Univ of Wisc/Milwaukee	WI	6,165	C
Urbana Univ	OH	12,536	C
Wartburg College	IA	14,530	VC
Western State College of Colo	CO	5,560	C

RECREATION EDUCATION

School	ST	$IS	SR
Alderson-Broaddus College	WV	12,000	C
Bridgewater State College	MA	7,518	C
Campbellsville College	KY	8,720	C
Eastern Mich Univ	MI	6,749	C
Eastern Washington Univ	WA	5,439	LC
Emory and Henry College	VA	12,776	C
Emporia State Univ	KS	4,685	NC
Georgia Southwestern College	GA	4,338	LC
Henderson State Univ	AR	3,860	C
Knoxville College	TN	8,320	LC
Lyndon State College	VT	8,394	LC
Northwest Missouri State Univ	MO	5,010	LC
Ohio State Univ	OH	7,218	LC
Plymouth State College	NH	7,166	C
Prescott College	AZ	9,775	C
San Francisco State Univ	CA	7,292	LC
Southern Univ and A&M College	LA	4,920	NC
Southern Univ at New Orleans	LA	1,452	NC
Southwestern Okla State Univ	OK	3,312	C
Texas Christian Univ	TX	12,180	C
Univ of Arkansas at Fayetteville	AR	5,046	C
Univ of Conn	CT	9,168	C
Univ of Hawaii at Manoa	HI	5,626	C
Univ of Idaho	ID	4,830	C
Univ of Nevada/Las Vegas	NV	6,405	C
Univ of Tenn/Knoxville	TN	5,668	C
Univ of the Pacific	CA	21,100	C
Upper Iowa Univ	IA	11,900	C
Virginia Union Univ	VA	10,555	LC

RECREATION THERAPY

School	ST	$IS	SR
Belmont Abbey College	NC	13,190	C
Cal State/Northridge	CA	7,122	LC
Catawba College	NC	12,950	C
Defiance College	OH	13,480	LC
Eastern Washington Univ	WA	5,439	LC
Gannon Univ	PA	14,872	C
Green Mountain College	VT	14,080	C
Indiana Inst of Tech	IN	11,810	C
Indiana Univ Bloomington	IN	6,495	VC
Lake Superior State Univ	MI	7,311	C
Lincoln Univ	PA	0	LC
Longwood College	VA	7,800	C
Northeastern Univ	MA	19,851	C
Shepherd College	WV	5,540	C
Southwestern Okla State Univ	OK	3,312	C
Springfield College	MA	15,200	LC
SUNY/College at Cortland	NY	7,326	C+
Univ of Southern Maine	ME	7,299	C
Univ of Wisc/La Crosse	WI	4,487	C
Utica College of Syracuse Univ	NY	16,714	LC
Virginia Wesleyan College	VA	14,950	VC
West Virginia State College	WV	5,044	LC
Winston-Salem State Univ	NC	4,142	LC

RECREATIONAL FACILITIES MANAGEMENT

School	ST	$IS	SR
Bluffton College	OH	12,951	C
Colo State Univ	CO	6,566	VC
Culver-Stockton College	MO	11,150	C
Elmhurst College	IL	12,536	C
Green Mountain College	VT	14,080	C
Indiana Wesleyan Univ	IN	12,332	C
Johnson and Wales Univ	RI	13,995	LC
Lynn Univ	FL	18,300	C
New Mexico State Univ	NM	4,844	LC
Pembroke State Univ	NC	3,538	LC
Shorter College	GA	10,270	C
Sierra Nevada College	NV	14,000	NC
Univ of Maine at Machias	ME	6,135	C
Univ of Minn/Twin Cities	MN	6,682	VC
Webber College	FL	8,710	C

REHABILITATION THERAPY

School	ST	$IS	SR
Assumption College	MA	17,095	LC
Cal State/Los Angeles	CA	4,940	VC
East Stroudsburg Univ	PA	6,886	C
Emporia State Univ	KS	4,685	NC
Florida International Univ	FL	4,191	VC
Florida State Univ	FL	5,814	VC
Penn State Univ/Univ Park Campus	PA	8,752	HC
Southern Univ and A&M College	LA	4,920	NC
Springfield College	MA	15,200	LC
Stephen F. Austin State Univ	TX	5,117	C
Syracuse Univ	NY	21,305	HC
Univ of Georgia	GA	5,655	VC
Univ of Maine at Farmington	ME	6,700	C
Univ of Maryland/Eastern Shore	MD	6,254	LC
Univ of North Texas	TX	4,853	C
Univ of Northern Colo	CO	6,008	C
Univ of Wisc/Stout	WI	4,719	C
West Virginia Wesleyan College	WV	16,900	C
Wilberforce Univ	OH	10,408	C
Wright State Univ	OH	6,896	LC

RELIGION

School	ST	$IS	SR
Abilene Christian Univ	TX	10,460	NC
Academy of the New Church	PA	7,341	NC
Adrian College	MI	14,340	C
Albertson College	ID	15,942	C+
Albertus Magnus College	CT	16,280	LC
Albion College	MI	18,264	VC
Albright College	PA	19,260	C
Allegheny College	PA	21,020	VC
Alma College	MI	16,375	VC+
American Univ	DC	21,230	VC+
Amherst College	MA	24,152	MC
Anderson Univ	IN	12,920	C
Andrews Univ	MI	14,952	NC
Angelo State Univ	TX	5,176	C
Appalachian State Univ	NC	4,095	C
Aquinas College	MI	14,526	C
Arizona State Univ Main Campus	AZ	6,444	C
Arkansas Baptist College	AR	5,016	NC
Arkansas College	AR	11,626	VC
Assumption College	MA	17,095	LC
Atlantic Union College	MA	14,150	LC
Auburn Univ	AL	5,823	C+
Augsburg College	MN	15,608	C
Augustana College	IL	16,959	VC
Augustana College	SD	13,420	C
Aurora Univ	IL	13,381	C
Austin College	TX	14,999	VC
Averett College	VA	13,610	LC
Azusa Pacific Univ	CA	15,034	C
Baker Univ	KS	12,284	C
Baldwin-Wallace College	OH	15,210	C
Ball State Univ	IN	6,032	LC
Bard College	NY	25,269	HC
Bartlesville Wesleyan College	OK	9,400	C
Barton College	NC	10,689	LC
Bates College	ME	23,990	MC
Baylor Univ	TX	10,990	C+
Belhaven College	MS	9,690	C+
Belmont Univ	TN	10,540	C
Beloit College	WI	18,950	VC+
Benedict College	SC	8,376	LC
Benedictine College	KS	12,830	C
Berea College	KY	2,883	VC+
Berry College	GA	11,990	VC
Bethany College	WV	18,300	C+
Bethel College	IN	11,650	C
Bethel College	KS	11,530	C
Bethel College	MN	15,050	C
Bethel College	TN	9,736	LC
Bethune-Cookman College	FL	8,375	LC
Bloomfield College	NJ	12,200	LC
Bluefield College	VA	10,600	C
Bluffton College	OH	12,951	C
Boston Univ	MA	24,130	HC
Bowdoin College	ME	24,155	MC
Bradley Univ	IL	14,718	C+
Brescia College	KY	9,800	C
Brewton-Parker College	GA	6,828	NC
Bridgewater State College	MA	7,518	C
Bryan College	TN	11,465	C
Bucknell Univ	PA	22,320	HC
Buena Vista College	IA	16,150	VC
Butler Univ	IN	16,210	C
Cabrini College	PA	16,012	C
Caldwell College	NJ	12,860	LC
Calif Baptist College	CA	11,294	C
Calif Lutheran Univ	CA	17,240	C
Cal State/Bakersfield	CA	5,402	LC
Cal State/Chico	CA	6,146	C
Cal State/Fresno	CA	5,747	C
Cal State/Fullerton	CA	4,850	LC
Cal State/Long Beach	CA	6,057	LC
Cal State/Northridge	CA	7,122	LC
Calvin College	MI	13,020	VC
Campbell Univ	NC	10,624	C
Canisius College	NY	15,510	C
Capital Univ	OH	16,535	VC
Cardinal Stritch College	WI	11,252	C
Carleton College	MN	22,155	HC
Carroll College	MT	11,265	C
Carroll College	WI	15,490	C
Carson-Newman College	TN	11,250	C
Carthage College	WI	15,995	C
Case Western Reserve Univ	OH	19,910	HC
Catawba College	NC	12,950	C
Catholic Univ of America	DC	18,856	C
Cedarville College	OH	10,715	C
Central College	IA	14,025	VC
Central Methodist College	MO	11,410	C
Central Mich Univ	MI	6,737	LC
Central Univ of Bayamon	PR	2,430	
Central Wesleyan College	SC	9,640	C
Centre College	KY	15,850	VC+
Chaminade Univ of Honolulu	HI	14,290	C
Charleston Southern Univ	SC	10,282	LC
Christendom College	VA	11,750	VC
Christopher Newport Univ	VA	3,196	LC
CUNY/Brooklyn College	NY	2,450	VC
CUNY/Hunter College	NY	4,101	VC
Claflin College	SC	0	
Claremont McKenna College	CA	22,150	MC
Clark Atlanta Univ	GA	11,846	C
Clarke College	IA	13,950	C+
Cleveland State Univ	OH	7,287	NC
Coe College	IA	17,085	VC
Coker College	SC	13,790	C
Colby College	ME	24,230	HC
Colgate Univ	NY	24,020	HC
College of Great Falls	MT	6,230	NC
College of Mount St Joseph	OH	13,272	C
College of New Rochelle	NY	15,440	LC
College of Notre Dame	CA	16,480	C
College of Notre Dame of Maryland	MD	16,050	C
College of Our Lady of The Elms	MA	15,639	C
College of St Catherine	MN	14,670	C
College of St Francis	IL	13,060	VC
College of St Rose	NY	14,452	C
College of St Scholastica	MN	14,868	C
College of Santa Fe	NM	14,008	C
College of the Holy Cross	MA	23,850	HC
College of William and Mary	VA	8,602	MC
College of Wooster	OH	19,875	VC
Colo Christian Univ	CO	9,750	C
Colo College	CO	20,038	HC
Columbia College	SC	13,520	LC
Columbia Union College	MD	13,650	LC
Columbia Univ/Barnard College	NY	25,492	HC
Columbia Univ/Columbia College	NY	26,757	MC
Concordia College	MI	13,660	C
Concordia College	MN	13,200	C
Concordia College	OR	12,300	C
Concordia College/Moorhead	MN	12,750	C
Concordia Univ	IL	12,611	C
Concordia Univ	CA	14,675	C
Concordia Univ Wisc	WI	12,140	C
Conn College	CT	24,160	HC
Converse College	SC	15,750	C
Cornell College	IA	18,425	VC
Cornell Univ	NY	13,445	MC
Creighton Univ	NE	14,432	VC
Culver-Stockton College	MO	11,150	C
Cumberland College	KY	9,756	C
Daemen College	NY	13,020	LC
Dakota Wesleyan Univ	SD	9,770	LC
Dana College	NE	11,910	C
Dartmouth College	NH	24,354	MC
David Lipscomb Univ	TN	7,865	VC

School	ST	$IS	SR
Davidson College	NC	21,037	MC
Davis and Elkins College	WV	13,230	LC
Defiance College	OH	13,480	LC
Denison Univ	OH	21,150	VC+
DePaul Univ	IL	15,535	VC
DePauw Univ	IN	18,530	VC
Dickinson College	PA	22,705	HC
Dillard Univ	LA	9,950	C
Dominican College of San Rafael	CA	17,860	C
Dordt College	IA	11,690	C
Drake Univ	IA	17,195	VC
Drew Univ/College of Liberal Arts	NJ	23,406	HC
Duke Univ	NC	21,271	MC
Duquesne Univ	PA	16,434	VC
Earlham College	IN	19,383	VC
East Texas Baptist Univ	TX	7,740	C
East Texas State Univ	TX	4,572	LC
Eastern Kentucky Univ	KY	4,840	NC
Eastern Mennonite College	VA	12,700	C
Eastern Nazarene College	MA	12,165	LC
Eastern New Mexico Univ	NM	3,950	C
Eckerd College	FL	18,855	VC
Edgewood College	WI	11,700	C
Edward Waters College	FL	8,300	NC
Elizabethtown College	PA	17,850	VC
Elmhurst College	IL	12,536	C
Elon College	NC	12,290	LC
Emmanuel College	MA	17,773	LC
Emory Univ	GA	21,930	HC
Erskine College	SC	14,310	C
Eureka College	IL	14,555	C
Evangel College	MO	10,142	LC
Fairfield Univ	CT	20,460	VC
Felician College	NJ	7,900	C
Ferrum College	VA	12,800	LC
Fisk Univ	TN	0	LC
Flagler College	FL	7,990	C
Florida International Univ	FL	4,191	VC
Florida Memorial College	FL	7,600	C+
Florida Southern College	FL	12,260	C
Florida State Univ	FL	5,814	VC
Fordham Univ/College at Lincoln Center	NY	18,150	VC
Franklin and Marshall College	PA	23,655	HC
Franklin College of Indiana	IN	13,970	C
Freed-Hardeman Univ	TN	8,585	VC
Fresno Pacific College	CA	13,020	C
Friends Univ	KS	11,205	C
Furman Univ	SC	16,557	VC
Gallaudet Univ	DC	9,850	SP
Gannon Univ	PA	14,872	C
Gardner-Webb Univ	NC	11,950	LC
George Fox College	OR	15,640	LC
George Washington Univ	DC	22,470	HC
Georgetown College	KY	10,990	C
Georgetown Univ	DC	24,410	MC
Georgian Court College	NJ	12,550	C
Gettysburg College	PA	22,960	HC
Gonzaga Univ	WA	16,350	VC
Goshen College	IN	12,360	C
Goucher College	MD	20,295	VC
Grace College	IN	12,120	C
Graceland College	IA	11,600	C
Grand Rapids Baptist College and Seminary	MI	10,228	C
Gratz College	PA	4,620	NC
Greensboro College	NC	11,496	C
Greenville College	IL	14,190	C
Grinnell College	IA	20,680	HC+
Grove City College	PA	7,870	HC
Guilford College	NC	17,680	C
Gustavus Adolphus College	MN	15,935	VC
Hamilton College	NY	23,500	HC
Hamline Univ	MN	17,122	VC
Hampden-Sydney College	VA	17,372	C+
Hanover College	IN	10,950	VC
Hardin-Simmons Univ	TX	9,080	C
Harding Univ	AR	9,050	VC
Hartwick College	NY	20,950	C
Harvard Univ/Harvard and Radcliffe Colleges	MA	24,880	MC
Hastings College	NE	12,426	C
Haverford College	PA	23,950	MC
Heidelberg College	OH	17,160	C
Hellenic College/Holy Cross Greek Orthodox School of Theology	MA	10,295	NC
Hendrix College	AR	11,670	C
High Point Univ	NC	12,350	LC
Hillsdale College	MI	15,110	VC
Hiram College	OH	18,340	VC
Hobart and William Smith Colleges	NY	23,925	VC
Hollins College	VA	18,484	C
Holy Family College	PA	8,300	C
Holy Names College	CA	15,660	C
Hood College	MD	19,010	VC
Hope College	MI	15,698	C+
Houghton College	NY	13,120	VC
Howard Payne Univ	TX	8,052	C
Humboldt State Univ	CA	5,676	C
Huntingdon College	AL	11,400	C
Huntington College	IN	13,220	C
Illinois Benedictine College	IL	14,170	C
Illinois College	IL	11,200	C
Illinois Wesleyan Univ	IL	18,590	HC+
Incarnate Word College	TX	12,307	C
Indiana State Univ	IN	6,210	C
Indiana Univ Bloomington	IN	6,495	VC
Indiana Univ of Penn	PA	6,373	C
Indiana Univ-Purdue Univ at Indianapolis	IN	5,862	LC
Indiana Wesleyan Univ	IN	12,332	C
Iona College	NY	16,310	C
Iowa State Univ	IA	5,456	C
Ithaca College	NY	19,679	C
James Madison Univ	VA	8,198	HC
Jamestown College	ND	10,250	C
Jarvis Christian College	TX	7,170	LC
Jewish Theological Seminary of America/List College of Jewish Studies	NY	12,795	HC
John Carroll Univ	OH	16,510	C
Judson College	AL	9,060	C
Juniata College	PA	18,390	C+
Kalamazoo College	MI	19,974	HC
Kansas Newman College	KS	10,640	C
Kansas Wesleyan Univ	KS	11,770	C
Kenyon College	OH	22,430	HC+
King College	TN	11,500	C
King's College	NY	12,360	LC
La Roche College	PA	12,977	LC
La Salle Univ	PA	16,940	VC
La Sierra Univ	CA	15,472	C
Lafayette College	PA	23,450	HC
LaGrange College	GA	10,602	C
Lakeland College	WI	12,845	LC
Lambuth Univ	TN	8,395	C
Lane College	TN	7,628	LC
Lawrence Univ	WI	19,986	HC+
Le Moyne College	NY	15,180	C
Le Tourneau Univ	TX	12,500	C+
Lebanon Valley College of Penn	PA	18,300	C
Lees-McRae College	NC	9,850	LC
Lehigh Univ	PA	23,250	HC
Lewis and Clark College	OR	19,980	VC
Lewis Univ	IL	14,797	LC
Lincoln Univ	PA	0	LC
Linfield College	OR	16,670	VC
Louisiana College	LA	7,518	VC
Louisiana State Univ and A&M College	LA	5,605	C
Lourdes College	OH	6,410	LC
Loyola Univ of Chicago	IL	15,880	C+
Loyola Univ/New Orleans	LA	15,660	C+
Lubbock Christian Univ	TX	9,840	NC
Lycoming College	PA	17,200	LC
Lynchburg College	VA	17,000	C
Macalester College	MN	19,710	HC
Madonna Univ	MI	8,546	C
Manchester College	IN	13,240	LC
Manhattan College	NY	19,000	C
Manhattanville College	NY	20,450	LC
Marietta College	OH	16,940	C+
Marquette Univ	WI	16,114	VC
Mars Hill College	NC	11,050	C
Marshall Univ	WV	5,762	LC
Martin Univ	IN	4,830	NC
Mary Washington College	VA	7,910	HC
Marygrove College	MI	5,877	VC
Maryville College	TN	14,474	C
Maryville Univ-St Louis	MO	12,900	VC
Marywood College	PA	14,890	C
McKendree College	IL	10,900	C
McMurry Univ	TX	10,100	C
McPherson College	KS	11,360	VC
Mercer Univ	GA	15,123	C
Meredith College	NC	9,440	C
Merrimack College	MA	18,025	C
Messiah College	PA	14,664	VC
Methodist College	NC	12,400	C
Miami Univ	OH	8,066	VC
Mich State Univ	MI	7,842	C
MidAmerica Nazarene College	KS	10,208	NC
Middlebury College	VT	24,400	MC
Midland Lutheran College	NE	12,410	LC
Milligan College	TN	10,690	C
Millikin Univ	IL	15,499	C
Millsaps College	MS	15,486	C+
Miss College	MS	8,348	C
Missouri Baptist College	MO	9,340	C
Missouri Valley College	MO	14,050	LC
Molloy College	NY	8,580	LC
Monmouth College	IL	17,300	C+
Moravian College	PA	18,960	VC
Morehouse College	GA	13,224	LC
Morgan State Univ	MD	7,366	C+
Morningside College	IA	13,896	C
Morris Brown College	GA	12,234	NC
Mount Holyoke College	MA	23,630	VC
Mount Marty College	SD	10,450	NC
Mount Mercy College	IA	13,230	C
Mount Olive College	NC	9,650	LC
Mount St Mary's College	CA	16,390	VC
Mount Union College	OH	15,850	C
Mount Vernon Nazarene College	OH	10,390	C
Muhlenberg College	PA	20,795	VC
Muskingum College	OH	16,650	C
Nazareth College of Rochester	NY	15,310	C+
Nebr Wesleyan Univ	NE	12,240	C
Neumann College	PA	9,950	LC
New College of the Univ of South Florida	FL	5,697	MC
Newberry College	SC	11,994	LC
Niagara Univ	NY	14,552	C
N Car State Univ	NC	4,984	VC
N Car Wesleyan College	NC	12,480	LC
North Central Bible College	MN	8,670	LC
North Central College	IL	15,498	VC
North Park College	IL	14,310	C
Northeast Missouri State Univ	MO	5,654	VC+
Northern Arizona Univ	AZ	4,844	C
Northland College	WI	13,550	LC
Northwest College	WA	9,897	LC
Northwest Nazarene College	ID	11,750	C
Northwestern College of Iowa	IA	12,250	C
Northwestern Univ	IL	21,093	MC
Norwich Univ	VT	18,730	C
Notre Dame College	NH	14,220	C
Nyack College	NY	12,210	LC
Oakland City College	IN	10,216	LC
Oakwood College	AL	10,005	C
Occidental College	CA	21,792	HC
Ohio Northern Univ	OH	18,660	VC
Ohio State Univ	OH	7,218	LC
Ohio Valley College	WV	8,780	LC
Ohio Wesleyan Univ	OH	21,108	VC+
Okla Baptist Univ	OK	8,486	C
Okla Christian Univ of Science and Arts	OK	8,790	NC
Okla City Univ	OK	9,840	C
Old Dominion Univ	VA	8,317	C
Olivet Nazarene Univ	IL	11,976	C
Oral Roberts Univ	OK	10,607	C+
Oregon State Univ	OR	6,175	C
Ottawa Univ	KS	10,490	C+
Otterbein College	OH	16,506	C
Ouachita Baptist Univ	AR	8,940	C
Our Lady of the Lake Univ of San Antonio	TX	11,080	C
Pacific Lutheran Univ	WA	15,998	VC
Pacific Union College	CA	15,075	C
Palm Beach Atlantic College	FL	10,720	C
Paul Quinn College	TX	7,090	LC
Penn State Univ/Univ Park Campus	PA	8,752	HC
Pepperdine Univ	CA	23,720	VC
Pfeiffer College	NC	11,670	LC
Phillips Univ	OK	12,744	C
Pikeville College	KY	8,500	NC
Point Loma Nazarene College	CA	13,532	C
Pomona College	CA	23,820	MC
Pontifical Catholic Univ of PR/Ponce	PR	5,807	
Presbyterian College	SC	15,400	VC
Princeton Univ	NJ	24,650	MC
Principia College	IL	17,799	C
Providence College	RI	19,750	VC
Purdue Univ/West Lafayette	IN	6,636	C
Radford Univ	VA	7,034	LC
Randolph-Macon College	VA	16,980	C
Randolph-Macon Woman's College	VA	19,100	C
Reed College	OR	24,480	HC+
Regis Univ	CO	17,340	C
Rhodes College	TN	19,624	HC
Rice Univ	TX	15,110	MC
Ripon College	WI	18,320	C
Roanoke College	VA	16,975	C
Rockhurst College	MO	12,470	C
Rocky Mountain College	MT	11,320	C
Rollins College	FL	20,875	VC
Rosary College	IL	15,040	C
Rosemont College	PA	16,775	C
Rutgers Univ/Douglass College	NJ	8,795	VC
Rutgers Univ/Livingston College	NJ	8,877	VC
Rutgers Univ/Rutgers College	NJ	8,841	HC+
Rutgers Univ/Univ College—New Brunswick	NJ	0	LC
Sacred Heart Univ	CT	16,350	C
St Andrews Presbyterian College	NC	14,240	LC
St Bonaventure Univ	NY	14,762	C
St Edward's Univ	TX	12,636	C
St Francis College	IN	11,662	C
St Francis College	PA	15,744	LC
St John Fisher College	NY	15,415	C
St John's Univ	NY	8,980	C+
St Joseph College	CT	16,225	C
St Joseph's College	IN	14,730	C
St Joseph's College	ME	14,535	C
St Joseph's Univ	PA	17,800	VC
St Lawrence Univ	NY	23,420	VC
St Leo College	FL	13,570	C
St Louis Univ	MO	15,522	VC
St Martin's College	WA	14,965	C
St Mary's College	IN	17,043	VC
St Mary's College of Calif	CA	18,848	VC
St Michael's College	VT	17,930	C
St Norbert College	WI	15,710	VC
St Olaf College	MN	17,200	HC
St Peter's College	NJ	14,775	LC
St Thomas Aquinas College	NY	13,550	C
St Thomas Univ	FL	14,280	LC
St Vincent College	PA	13,934	LC
St Xavier Univ	IL	14,700	C
Salem College	NC	16,025	C
Salve Regina Univ	RI	29,100	LC
Samford Univ	AL	11,400	VC
San Diego State Univ	CA	6,692	LC
San Jose State Univ	CA	6,680	LC
Santa Clara Univ	CA	18,783	VC
Sarah Lawrence College	NY	24,975	HC
Schreiner College	TX	14,320	C
Scripps College	CA	23,600	HC
Seattle Pacific Univ	WA	16,503	C
Seattle Univ	WA	16,590	C
Selma Univ	AL	5,785	NC
Seton Hall Univ	NJ	18,306	C
Seton Hill College	PA	14,320	C
Shaw Univ	NC	8,936	C+
Shenandoah Univ	VA	11,800	C
Shorter College	GA	10,270	C
Siena College	NY	15,410	VC
Siena Heights College	MI	12,520	C
Silver Lake College	WI	8,280	LC
Simpson College	CA	10,628	C
Simpson College	IA	14,635	VC
Sioux Falls College	SD	11,540	C
Smith College	MA	24,236	HC
Southeastern College of the Assemblies of God	FL	6,618	NC
Southern College of Seventh-day Adventists	TN	11,348	NC
Southern Methodist Univ	TX	18,520	VC
Southern Nazarene Univ	OK	9,206	NC
Southwest Baptist Univ	MO	9,192	NC
Southwest Missouri State Univ	MO	4,956	C
Southwestern Adventist College	TX	10,530	NC
Southwestern College	KS	10,032	C
Southwestern Univ	TX	15,484	HC
Spalding Univ	KY	10,496	LC
Spelman College	GA	12,942	VC
Spring Arbor College	MI	12,256	C
Spring Hill College	AL	16,015	C+
Stanford Univ	CA	24,310	MC
SUNY at Albany	NY	7,059	VC
SUNY at Stony Brook	NY	7,658	VC
Stonehill College	MA	17,481	VC
Susquehanna Univ	PA	19,950	VC
Swarthmore College	PA	24,136	MC
Sweet Briar College	VA	19,770	C
Syracuse Univ	NY	21,305	HC
Tabor College	KS	11,460	VC
Taylor Univ	IN	14,450	VC
Teikyo Westmar Univ	IA	15,920	C
Temple Univ	PA	10,281	C
Texas Christian Univ	TX	12,180	C
Texas Wesleyan Univ	TX	9,380	LC
Thiel College	PA	16,282	C
Thomas A. Edison State College	NJ	400	
Thomas More College	KY	12,962	C
Toccoa Falls College	GA	9,350	C
Transylvania Univ	KY	14,970	VC+
Trevecca Nazarene College	TN	9,826	NC
Trinity Christian College	IL	13,260	C
Trinity College	CT	24,120	HC
Trinity College	IL	14,010	C
Trinity Univ	TX	16,670	HC
Tufts Univ	MA	24,962	MC
Union Univ	TN	7,880	C+
Universidad Adventista de las Antillas	PR	5,000	
Univ of Alabama	AL	5,702	C
Univ of Arizona	AZ	5,808	C
Univ of Calif at Berkeley	CA	9,962	HC+
Univ of Calif at Davis	CA	9,534	VC
Univ of Calif at Los Angeles	CA	8,959	HC
Univ of Calif at Santa Barbara	CA	9,460	C
Univ of Calif at Santa Cruz	CA	9,060	VC
Univ of Calif, Riverside	CA	9,178	C
Univ of Charleston	WV	12,750	C
Univ of Chicago	IL	24,517	MC
Univ of Colo at Boulder	CO	6,410	VC
Univ of Dayton	OH	15,120	C+
Univ of Denver	CO	19,290	C+
Univ of Detroit Mercy	MI	14,720	C
Univ of Evansville	IN	15,300	VC
Univ of Findlay	OH	15,764	C
Univ of Florida	FL	5,850	HC
Univ of Georgia	GA	5,655	VC
Univ of Hawaii at Manoa	HI	5,626	C
Univ of Indianapolis	IN	14,510	C
Univ of Iowa	IA	5,658	VC
Univ of Kansas	KS	5,200	NC
Univ of La Verne	CA	17,400	C
Univ of Mary	ND	8,910	C
Univ of Mary Hardin-Baylor	TX	8,120	NC
Univ of Miami	FL	22,107	VC
Univ of Mich/Ann Arbor	MI	9,428	HC+
Univ of Missouri/Columbia	MO	6,254	HC

School	ST	$IS	SR
Univ of Mobile	AL	9,400	C
Univ of N Car at Chapel Hill	NC	5,330	HC
Univ of N Car at Charlotte	NC	4,597	C
Univ of N Car at Greensboro	NC	5,192	C
Univ of N Car at Wilmington	NC	5,172	C
Univ of N Dak	ND	4,902	NC
Univ of Northern Iowa	IA	5,137	C
Univ of Okla	OK	5,427	VC
Univ of Oregon	OR	6,466	VC
Univ of Penn	PA	24,238	MC
Univ of Pittsburgh	PA	9,472	C
Univ of Puget Sound	WA	19,520	HC
Univ of Redlands	CA	22,059	VC
Univ of Richmond	VA	16,700	HC
Univ of Rochester	NY	23,696	HC
Univ of St Thomas	TX	11,676	C+
Univ of San Diego	CA	18,970	VC
Univ of San Francisco	CA	18,408	C
Univ of S Car	SC	6,158	C
Univ of South Florida	FL	5,475	C+
Univ of Southern Calif	CA	23,006	VC
Univ of Tenn/Knoxville	TN	5,668	C
Univ of the Pacific	CA	21,100	C
Univ of the South	TN	18,830	HC
Univ of Vermont	VT	10,776	C+
Univ of Virginia	VA	7,964	MC
Univ of Washington	WA	6,618	VC
Univ of West Florida	FL	5,415	C
Univ of Wisc/Eau Claire	WI	4,647	C
Univ of Wisc/Milwaukee	WI	6,165	C
Univ of Wisc/Oshkosh	WI	4,240	C
Upsala College	NJ	17,200	C
Urbana Univ	OH	12,536	C
Ursinus College	PA	19,165	VC
Ursuline College	OH	13,180	LC
Valparaiso Univ	IN	14,810	VC
Vanderbilt Univ	TN	23,422	HC+
Vassar College	NY	24,206	HC
Villanova Univ	PA	21,400	HC
Virginia Commonwealth Univ	VA	7,909	C
Virginia Intermont College	VA	12,250	LC
Virginia Union Univ	VA	10,555	LC
Virginia Wesleyan College	VA	14,950	VC
Viterbo College	WI	12,670	C
Wabash College	IN	16,250	VC
Wagner College	NY	17,950	C
Wake Forest Univ	NC	17,280	MC
Walla Walla College	WA	13,215	C
Walsh Univ	OH	11,640	C
Warner Pacific College	OR	12,112	C
Wartburg College	IA	14,530	VC
Washington and Lee Univ	VA	17,735	MC
Washington Univ	MO	23,507	HC
Wayland Baptist Univ	TX	7,811	NC
Webster Univ	MO	12,650	C
Wellesley College	MA	23,815	MC
Wells College	NY	19,460	C+
Wesleyan College	GA	15,445	C
West Chester Univ of Penn	PA	7,492	C
West Virginia Wesleyan College	WV	16,900	C
Western Kentucky Univ	KY	4,808	C
Western Maryland College	MD	18,990	C
Western Mich Univ	MI	6,820	C
Westminster College	MO	13,750	C+
Westminster College	PA	15,200	C
Westmont College	CA	18,732	C
Wheaton College	IL	14,710	HC
Wheaton College	MA	23,840	C+
Wheeling Jesuit College	WV	14,370	C
Whittier College	CA	21,661	C
Whitworth College	WA	16,265	C
Wiley College	TX	0	NC
Willamette Univ	OR	17,995	VC
William Carey College	MS	7,050	C
William Jewell College	MO	12,500	VC
William Penn College	IA	13,400	C
William Tyndale College	MI	7,120	NC
Williams Baptist College	AR	5,834	LC
Williams College	MA	24,390	MC
Wilmington College	OH	13,700	LC
Wingate College	NC	10,610	C
Winthrop Univ	SC	6,750	C
Wittenberg Univ	OH	19,998	VC
Wofford College	SC	15,360	VC
Wright State Univ	OH	6,896	LC
Xavier Univ	OH	15,710	C+
Yale Univ	CT	25,110	MC
Yeshiva Univ	NY	18,200	VC
Youngstown State Univ	OH	6,447	LC

RELIGIOUS EDUCATION

School	ST	$IS	SR
Bethune-Cookman College	FL	8,375	LC
Biola Univ	CA	16,124	C
Campbellsville College	KY	8,720	C
Christian Heritage College	CA	11,756	C
Concordia College	MN	13,200	C
Concordia College	OR	12,300	C
Dallas Baptist Univ	TX	9,620	LC
Defiance College	OH	13,480	LC
Grand Rapids Baptist College and Seminary	MI	10,228	C
Huntingdon College	AL	11,400	C
Indiana Wesleyan Univ	IN	12,332	C
Kansas Wesleyan Univ	KS	11,770	C
La Roche College	PA	12,977	LC
Lee College	TN	7,894	LC
Lenoir-Rhyne College	NC	14,068	C
Marian College	IN	12,936	C
Mercyhurst College	PA	13,488	C
Messiah College	PA	14,664	VC
Missouri Baptist College	MO	9,340	C
Morris College	SC	6,880	LC
Mount Vernon Nazarene College	OH	10,390	C
Muskingum College	OH	16,650	C
North Central Bible College	MN	8,670	LC
Notre Dame College of Ohio	OH	11,370	C
Nyack College	NY	12,210	LC
Oakwood College	AL	10,005	C
Okla Christian Univ of Science and Arts	OK	8,790	NC
Oral Roberts Univ	OK	10,607	C+
Pfeiffer College	NC	11,670	LC
Pillsbury Baptist Bible College	MN	7,390	NC
Point Loma Nazarene College	CA	13,532	C
Quincy Univ	IL	13,646	VC
St Mary's College	MI	8,350	C
Southern Calif College	CA	12,356	C
Southern Nazarene Univ	OK	9,206	NC
Southwest Baptist Univ	MO	9,192	NC
Southwestern Christian College	TX	7,033	NC
Sterling College	KS	10,990	VC
Taylor Univ	IN	14,450	VC
Tenn Wesleyan College	TN	10,060	C
Thiel College	PA	16,282	C
Toccoa Falls College	GA	9,350	C
Trevecca Nazarene College	TN	9,826	NC
Wayland Baptist Univ	TX	7,811	NC
West Virginia Wesleyan College	WV	16,900	C
William Tyndale College	MI	7,120	NC
Wingate College	NC	10,610	C
York College	NE	7,610	C

RELIGIOUS MUSIC

School	ST	$IS	SR
Alverno College	WI	11,344	C
Arizona State Univ Main Campus	AZ	6,444	C
Campbellsville College	KY	8,720	C
Clearwater Christian College	FL	8,500	LC
Columbia College	SC	13,520	LC
Eastern Nazarene College	MA	12,165	LC
Elmhurst College	IL	12,536	C
Emory and Henry College	VA	12,776	C
Evangel College	MO	10,142	LC
Furman Univ	SC	16,557	VC
Georgetown College	KY	10,990	C
Grand Canyon Univ	AZ	9,680	VC
Greenville College	IL	14,190	C
Grove City College	PA	7,870	HC
Indiana Wesleyan Univ	IN	12,332	C
La Sierra Univ	CA	15,472	C
Liberty Univ	VA	11,500	LC
Madonna Univ	MI	8,546	C
Mars Hill College	NC	11,050	C
Marywood College	PA	14,890	C
North Central Bible College	MN	8,670	LC
Northwest College	WA	9,897	LC
Nyack College	NY	12,210	LC
Oral Roberts Univ	OK	10,607	C+
Pfeiffer College	NC	11,670	LC
Pillsbury Baptist Bible College	MN	7,390	NC
Seton Hill College	PA	14,320	C
Shorter College	GA	10,270	C
Southwest Baptist Univ	MO	9,192	NC
Spring Arbor College	MI	12,256	C
Susquehanna Univ	PA	19,950	VC
Trevecca Nazarene College	TN	9,826	NC
Union Univ	TN	7,880	C+
Univ of Puget Sound	WA	19,520	HC
Viterbo College	WI	12,670	C
Wayland Baptist Univ	TX	7,811	NC
Westminster Choir College	NJ	18,585	SP
William Carey College	MS	7,050	C

RESPIRATORY THERAPY

School	ST	$IS	SR
Avila College	MO	12,130	C
Boise State Univ	ID	4,909	LC
Dakota State Univ	SD	4,374	LC
Gannon Univ	PA	14,872	C
Indiana Univ Bloomington	IN	6,495	VC
Indiana Univ of Penn	PA	6,373	C
Indiana Univ-Purdue Univ at Indianapolis	IN	5,862	LC
La Roche College	PA	12,977	LC
Mansfield Univ	PA	6,348	C
Millersville Univ of Penn	PA	7,370	VC
National-Louis Univ	IL	13,218	C
Nebr Methodist College of Nursing and Allied Health	NE	4,360	C
Northeastern Univ	MA	19,851	C
Northern Kentucky Univ	KY	4,620	NC
Ohio State Univ	OH	7,218	LC
Peru State College	NE	4,311	NC
Salisbury State Univ	MD	7,516	C+
Shenandoah Univ	VA	11,800	C
Southern Illinois Univ at Carbondale	IL	6,234	C
Southwest Missouri State Univ	MO	4,956	C
Southwest Texas State Univ	TX	5,124	C
Southwestern College	KS	10,032	C
Tenn State Univ	TN	4,626	C+
Thiel College	PA	16,282	C
Univ of Bridgeport	CT	18,985	C
Univ of Central Arkansas	AR	4,200	LC
Univ of Central Florida	FL	6,061	C+
Univ of Charleston	WV	12,750	C
Univ of Hartford	CT	19,858	LC
Univ of Houston-Downtown	TX	4,034	NC
Univ of Kansas	KS	5,200	NC
Univ of Mary	ND	8,910	C
Univ of Missouri/Columbia	MO	6,254	HC
Univ of the Ozarks	AR	7,770	C
Wheeling Jesuit College	WV	14,370	C
York College of Penn	PA	8,345	C

RETAILING

School	ST	$IS	SR
Auburn Univ	AL	5,823	C+
Bassist College	OR	12,590	SP
Cal State/Los Angeles	CA	4,940	VC
Cazenovia College	NY	14,655	LC
Central Mich Univ	MI	6,737	LC
Dyke College	OH	5,200	C
Hood College	MD	19,010	VC
Jersey City State College	NJ	7,797	LC
Johnson and Wales Univ	RI	13,995	LC
Mount Ida College	MA	16,700	LC
New Hampshire College	NH	15,242	LC
Philadelphia College of Textiles and Science	PA	15,896	C
St Vincent College	PA	13,934	LC
Simmons College	MA	22,534	C
Southwestern Okla State Univ	OK	3,312	C
Thomas College	ME	13,450	LC
Univ of Arkansas at Fayetteville	AR	5,046	C
Univ of Minn/Twin Cities	MN	6,682	VC
Univ of N Dak	ND	4,902	NC
Univ of S Car	SC	6,158	C
Univ of Wisc/Madison	WI	6,400	HC
Univ of Wisc/Stout	WI	4,719	C
Western Mich Univ	MI	6,820	C

ROMANCE LANGUAGES

School	ST	$IS	SR
Albertus Magnus College	CT	16,280	LC
Boston College	MA	22,706	MC
Bowdoin College	ME	24,155	MC
Bryn Mawr College	PA	24,110	MC
Cameron Univ	OK	3,686	LC
Carleton College	MN	22,155	HC
Clark Univ	MA	21,400	VC
Dartmouth College	NH	24,354	MC
DePauw Univ	IN	18,530	VC
Dowling College	NY	12,730	LC
Mount Holyoke College	MA	23,630	VC
Princeton Univ	NJ	24,650	MC
St Thomas Aquinas College	NY	13,550	C
Univ of Georgia	GA	5,655	VC
Univ of Maine	ME	7,990	C
Univ of Maryland/College Park	MD	8,182	VC
Univ of Mich/Ann Arbor	MI	9,428	HC+
Univ of Nevada/Las Vegas	NV	6,405	C
Univ of Oregon	OR	6,466	VC
Univ of Penn	PA	24,238	MC
Washington and Lee Univ	VA	17,735	MC
Wheeling Jesuit College	WV	14,370	C

RURAL SOCIOLOGY

School	ST	$IS	SR
Auburn Univ	AL	5,823	C+
Cornell Univ	NY	13,445	MC
Univ of Alaska Fairbanks	AK	4,718	C
Univ of Missouri/Columbia	MO	6,254	HC
Univ of Wisc/Madison	WI	6,400	HC

RUSSIAN

School	ST	$IS	SR
Allegheny College	PA	21,020	VC
American Univ	DC	21,230	VC+
Amherst College	MA	24,152	MC
Arizona State Univ Main Campus	AZ	6,444	C
Bates College	ME	23,990	MC
Baylor Univ	TX	10,990	C+
Beloit College	WI	18,950	VC+
Boston Univ	MA	24,130	HC
Bowdoin College	ME	24,155	MC
Bowling Green State Univ	OH	6,701	C
Brandeis Univ	MA	25,585	HC
Brigham Young Univ	UT	5,625	HC
Bryn Mawr College	PA	24,110	MC
Bucknell Univ	PA	22,320	HC
Cal State/Fresno	CA	5,747	C
Carleton College	MN	22,155	HC
CUNY/Brooklyn College	NY	2,450	VC
CUNY/Herbert H. Lehman College	NY	2,542	C
CUNY/Hunter College	NY	4,101	VC
CUNY/Queens College	NY	2,631	C
Colgate Univ	NY	24,020	HC
College of the Holy Cross	MA	23,850	HC
Columbia Univ/Barnard College	NY	25,492	HC
Columbia Univ/Columbia College	NY	26,757	MC
Cornell College	IA	18,425	VC
Cornell Univ	NY	13,445	MC
Dartmouth College	NH	24,354	MC
Davidson College	NC	21,037	MC
Dickinson College	PA	22,705	HC
Drew Univ/College of Liberal Arts	NJ	23,406	HC
Eckerd College	FL	18,855	VC
Edinboro Univ of Penn	PA	7,181	C
Emory Univ	GA	21,930	HC
Evergreen State College	WA	6,306	C
Ferrum College	VA	12,800	LC
Florida State Univ	FL	5,814	VC
Fordham Univ/Fordham College	NY	19,875	VC
Gallaudet Univ	DC	9,850	SP
George Washington Univ	DC	22,470	HC
Georgetown Univ	DC	24,410	MC
Goucher College	MD	20,295	VC
Grace College	IN	12,120	C
Grinnell College	IA	20,680	HC+
Gustavus Adolphus College	MN	15,935	VC
Harvard Univ/Harvard and Radcliffe Colleges	MA	24,880	MC
Haverford College	PA	23,950	MC
Hobart and William Smith Colleges	NY	23,925	VC
Howard Univ	DC	11,680	C
Illinois Wesleyan Univ	IL	18,590	HC+
Indiana State Univ	IN	6,210	C
Iowa State Univ	IA	5,456	C
James Madison Univ	VA	8,198	HC
Juniata College	PA	18,390	C+
Kent State Univ	OH	6,740	LC
Knox College	IL	18,990	VC
Kutztown Univ	PA	6,528	C
La Salle Univ	PA	16,940	VC
Lincoln Univ	PA	0	LC
Loyola Univ/New Orleans	LA	15,660	C+
Macalester College	MN	19,710	HC
Marist College	NY	16,406	C
Marlboro College	VT	23,305	C+
Miami Univ	OH	8,066	VC
Mich State Univ	MI	7,842	C
Middlebury College	VT	24,400	MC
Millersville Univ of Penn	PA	7,370	VC
Mount Holyoke College	MA	23,630	VC
New College of the Univ of South Florida	FL	5,697	MC
New Mexico State Univ	NM	4,844	LC
New York Univ	NY	24,705	VC+
Northeast Missouri State Univ	MO	5,654	VC+
Northeastern Univ	MA	19,851	C
Northern Illinois Univ	IL	6,408	C
Norwich Univ	VT	18,730	C
Oakland Univ	MI	6,714	VC
Oberlin College	OH	24,570	HC+
Okla State Univ	OK	5,086	VC
Old Dominion Univ	VA	8,317	C

School	ST	$IS	SR
Penn State Univ/Univ Park Campus	PA	8,752	HC
Pomona College	CA	23,820	MC
Portland State Univ	OR	7,191	C
Purdue Univ/West Lafayette	IN	6,636	C
Reed College	OR	24,480	HC+
Rider College	NJ	18,160	C
Rutgers Univ/Douglass College	NJ	8,795	VC
Rutgers Univ/Livingston College	NJ	8,877	VC
Rutgers Univ/Newark College of A&S	NJ	8,645	C
Rutgers Univ/Rutgers College	NJ	8,841	HC+
Rutgers Univ/Univ College—New Brunswick	NJ	0	LC
St Louis Univ	MO	15,522	VC
St Olaf College	MN	17,200	HC
San Francisco State Univ	CA	7,292	LC
Sarah Lawrence College	NY	24,975	HC
Scripps College	CA	23,600	HC
Smith College	MA	24,236	HC
Southern Illinois Univ at Carbondale	IL	6,234	C
Southern Methodist Univ	TX	18,520	VC
SUNY at Albany	NY	7,059	VC
SUNY at Stony Brook	NY	7,658	VC
SUNY/College at Oswego	NY	7,330	VC
Stetson Univ	FL	16,435	VC
Swarthmore College	PA	24,136	MC
Syracuse Univ	NY	21,305	HC
Temple Univ	PA	10,281	C
Texas A&M Univ	TX	5,382	VC
Trinity College	CT	24,120	HC
Trinity Univ	TX	16,670	HC
Tufts Univ	MA	24,962	MC
Tulane Univ	LA	24,540	HC
Univ of Akron	OH	6,699	NC
Univ of Alabama	AL	5,702	C
Univ of Arizona	AZ	5,808	C
Univ of Calif at Davis	CA	9,534	VC
Univ of Calif at Santa Cruz	CA	9,060	VC
Univ of Calif, Riverside	CA	9,178	C
Univ of Calif, San Diego	CA	10,028	VC+
Univ of Calif/Irvine	CA	12,680	VC
Univ of Chicago	IL	24,517	MC
Univ of Colo at Boulder	CO	6,410	VC
Univ of Delaware	DE	8,013	VC
Univ of Florida	FL	5,850	HC
Univ of Hawaii at Manoa	HI	5,626	C
Univ of Illinois at Chicago	IL	8,443	C
Univ of Iowa	IA	5,658	VC
Univ of Kansas	KS	5,200	NC
Univ of Kentucky	KY	5,152	VC
Univ of Louisville	KY	5,948	C
Univ of Maryland/Baltimore County	MD	7,746	VC
Univ of Maryland/College Park	MD	8,182	VC
Univ of Mass/Amherst	MA	9,364	LC
Univ of Mass/Boston	MA	4,253	C
Univ of Memphis	TN	3,476	C
Univ of Mich/Ann Arbor	MI	9,428	HC+
Univ of Minn/Twin Cities	MN	6,682	VC
Univ of Missouri/Columbia	MO	6,254	HC
Univ of Montana	MT	5,529	C
Univ of Nebr-Lincoln	NE	5,278	LC
Univ of New Hampshire	NH	8,242	C
Univ of N Car at Chapel Hill	NC	5,330	HC
Univ of Notre Dame	IN	20,150	MC
Univ of Okla	OK	5,427	VC
Univ of Oregon	OR	6,466	VC
Univ of Pittsburgh	PA	9,472	C
Univ of Rhode Island	RI	9,205	C
Univ of Richmond	VA	16,700	HC
Univ of Rochester	NY	23,696	HC
Univ of South Alabama	AL	5,451	C
Univ of South Florida	FL	5,475	C+
Univ of Tenn/Knoxville	TN	5,668	C
Univ of Texas at Arlington	TX	5,549	LC
Univ of Texas at Austin	TX	5,160	VC
Univ of the South	TN	18,830	HC
Univ of Utah	UT	5,975	C
Univ of Vermont	VT	10,776	C+
Univ of Wisc/Madison	WI	6,400	HC
Univ of Wisc/Milwaukee	WI	6,165	C
Univ of Wyoming	WY	4,991	NC
Vanderbilt Univ	TN	23,422	HC+
Washington State Univ	WA	6,364	C
Washington Univ	MO	23,507	HC
Wayne State Univ	MI	2,680	C
Wellesley College	MA	23,815	MC
Wells College	NY	19,460	C+
Wesleyan Univ	CT	23,770	MC
West Chester Univ of Penn	PA	7,492	C
Wheaton College	MA	23,840	C+
Williams College	MA	24,390	MC
Wittenberg Univ	OH	19,998	VC
Yale Univ	CT	25,110	MC
Youngstown State Univ	OH	6,447	LC

RUSSIAN AND SLAVIC STUDIES

School	ST	$IS	SR
Boston College	MA	22,706	MC
Boston Univ	MA	24,130	HC
Brown Univ	RI	26,104	MC
Cal State/Fullerton	CA	4,850	LC
Colby College	ME	24,230	HC
Colgate Univ	NY	24,020	HC
Columbia Univ/Columbia College	NY	26,757	MC
Cornell College	IA	18,425	VC
Cornell Univ	NY	13,445	MC
Dartmouth College	NH	24,354	MC
DePauw Univ	IN	18,530	VC
Dickinson College	PA	22,705	HC
Drew Univ/College of Liberal Arts	NJ	23,406	HC
Florida State Univ	FL	5,814	VC
Fordham Univ/Fordham College	NY	19,875	VC
Hamilton College	NY	23,500	HC
Harvard Univ/Harvard and Radcliffe Colleges	MA	24,880	MC
Hobart and William Smith Colleges	NY	23,925	VC
Illinois State Univ	IL	6,413	C
Indiana Univ Bloomington	IN	6,495	VC
Kent State Univ	OH	6,740	LC
Kenyon College	OH	22,430	HC+
Knox College	IL	18,990	VC
Lafayette College	PA	23,450	HC
Lehigh Univ	PA	23,250	HC
Louisiana State Univ and A&M College	LA	5,605	C
Macalester College	MN	19,710	HC
Manhattanville College	NY	20,450	LC
Middlebury College	VT	24,400	MC
Oakland Univ	MI	6,714	VC
Principia College	IL	17,799	C
Randolph-Macon Woman's College	VA	19,100	C
Rhodes College	TN	19,624	HC
Rice Univ	TX	15,110	MC
Rutgers Univ/Newark College of A&S	NJ	8,645	C
Rutgers Univ/Rutgers College	NJ	8,841	HC+
Rutgers Univ/Univ College—New Brunswick	NJ	0	LC
Sarah Lawrence College	NY	24,975	HC
Smith College	MA	24,236	HC
Southern Methodist Univ	TX	18,520	VC
SUNY at Albany	NY	7,059	VC
Stetson Univ	FL	16,435	VC
Syracuse Univ	NY	21,305	HC
Texas Tech Univ	TX	6,008	C
Tufts Univ	MA	24,962	MC
Tulane Univ	LA	24,540	HC
Univ of Alabama	AL	5,702	C
Univ of Alabama at Huntsville	AL	5,868	VC
Univ of Alaska Fairbanks	AK	4,718	C
Univ of Calif at Los Angeles	CA	8,959	HC
Univ of Conn	CT	9,168	C
Univ of Denver	CO	19,290	C+
Univ of Iowa	IA	5,658	VC
Univ of Kansas	KS	5,200	NC
Univ of Louisville	KY	5,948	C
Univ of Mass/Amherst	MA	9,364	LC
Univ of Mich/Ann Arbor	MI	9,428	HC+
Univ of Minn/Twin Cities	MN	6,682	VC
Univ of N Car at Chapel Hill	NC	5,330	HC
Univ of Northern Iowa	IA	5,137	C
Univ of Okla	OK	5,427	VC
Univ of Tenn/Knoxville	TN	5,668	C
Univ of Texas at Austin	TX	5,160	VC
Univ of the South	TN	18,830	HC
Univ of Washington	WA	6,618	VC
Wheaton College	MA	23,840	C+

SAFETY AND SECURITY TECHNOLOGY

School	ST	$IS	SR
Eastern Kentucky Univ	KY	4,840	NC
Madonna Univ	MI	8,546	C
Marshall Univ	WV	5,762	LC
National Univ	CA	6,135	C
Univ of Wisc/Whitewater	WI	4,700	C

SAFETY MANAGEMENT

School	ST	$IS	SR
Illinois State Univ	IL	6,413	C
Indiana State Univ	IN	6,210	C
Keene State College	NH	7,081	C
Madonna Univ	MI	8,546	C
National Univ	CA	6,135	C
St John's Univ	NY	8,980	C+

SANSKRIT AND INDIAN STUDIES

School	ST	$IS	SR
Harvard Univ/Harvard and Radcliffe Colleges	MA	24,880	MC

SCANDINAVIAN LANGUAGES

School	ST	$IS	SR
Augsburg College	MN	15,608	C
Augustana College	IL	16,959	VC
Gustavus Adolphus College	MN	15,935	VC
Pacific Lutheran Univ	WA	15,998	VC
St Olaf College	MN	17,200	HC
Univ of Calif at Berkeley	CA	9,962	HC+
Univ of Calif at Los Angeles	CA	8,959	HC
Univ of Minn/Twin Cities	MN	6,682	VC
Univ of N Dak	ND	4,902	NC
Univ of Texas at Austin	TX	5,160	VC
Univ of Washington	WA	6,618	VC

SCANDINAVIAN STUDIES

School	ST	$IS	SR
Luther College	IA	15,900	VC
Pacific Lutheran Univ	WA	15,998	VC
Univ of Mich/Ann Arbor	MI	9,428	HC+
Univ of Wisc/Madison	WI	6,400	HC

SCHOOL PSYCHOLOGY

School	ST	$IS	SR
Boston Univ	MA	24,130	HC

SCIENCE

School	ST	$IS	SR
Alfred Univ	NY	21,054	VC+
Alvernia College	PA	13,150	LC
American International College	MA	14,029	C
Augustana College	SD	13,420	C
Barat College	IL	13,990	C
Barton College	NC	10,689	LC
Beaver College	PA	17,660	C
Belhaven College	MS	9,690	C+
Brandeis Univ	MA	25,585	HC
Brescia College	KY	9,800	C
Bridgewater College	VA	15,300	C
Calumet College of St. Joseph	IN	3,585	C
Cedarville College	OH	10,715	C
Central Conn State Univ	CT	7,108	C
Cheyney Univ of Penn	PA	7,005	C
Claremont McKenna College	CA	22,150	MC
Coe College	IA	17,085	VC
College of Great Falls	MT	6,230	NC
Colo Christian Univ	CO	9,750	C
Dana College	NE	11,910	C
Drexel Univ	PA	15,970	C
East Stroudsburg Univ	PA	6,886	C
Eastern Nazarene College	MA	12,165	LC
Elizabethtown College	PA	17,850	VC
Fairleigh Dickinson Univ	NJ	16,427	C
Ferrum College	VA	12,800	LC
Fort Lewis College	CO	5,097	C
Geneva College	PA	13,030	C
George Fox College	OR	15,640	LC
Gonzaga Univ	WA	16,350	VC
Grace College	IN	12,120	C
Graceland College	IA	11,600	C
Grinnell College	IA	20,680	HC+
Hampshire College	MA	25,320	C
Hawaii Pacific Univ	HI	12,300	C
Heritage College	WA	5,540	NC
Houghton College	NY	13,120	VC
Indiana Wesleyan Univ	IN	12,332	C
John Brown Univ	AR	9,880	VC
King's College	PA	15,420	C
Le Moyne College	NY	15,180	C
Lee College	TN	7,894	LC
Linfield College	OR	16,670	VC
Malone College	OH	12,572	C
Marylhurst College	OR	6,486	NC
Mayville State Univ	ND	4,272	NC
Methodist College	NC	12,400	C
Mich State Univ	MI	7,842	C
National-Louis Univ	IL	13,218	C
Northwest Missouri State Univ	MO	5,010	LC
Notre Dame College	NH	14,220	C
Okla City Univ	OK	9,840	C
Oregon State Univ	OR	6,175	C
Pacific Univ	OR	17,869	C
Penn State Univ at Erie/Behrend College	PA	8,752	C
Pitzer College	CA	23,780	HC
Pomona College	CA	23,820	MC
Portland State Univ	OR	7,191	C
Rockford College	IL	15,300	C
Rutgers Univ/Camden College of A&S	NJ	8,652	VC
Rutgers Univ/Newark College of A&S	NJ	8,645	C
Rutgers Univ/Univ College—Camden	NJ	3,506	C
St Francis College	IN	11,662	C
San Francisco State Univ	CA	7,292	LC
Santa Clara Univ	CA	18,783	VC
Seattle Pacific Univ	WA	16,503	C
Sierra Nevada College	NV	14,000	NC
Southern Univ and A&M College	LA	4,920	NC
SUNY/Empire State College	NY	2,687	NC
Stevens Inst of Tech	NJ	21,980	VC+
Trevecca Nazarene College	TN	9,826	NC
Troy State Univ	AL	4,322	C
Troy State Univ at Dothan/Fort Rucker	AL	2,260	NC
United States Air Force Academy	CO	0	MC
United States Naval Academy	MD	0	MC
Univ of Alaska Fairbanks	AK	4,718	C
Univ of Denver	CO	19,290	C+
Univ of Dubuque	IA	14,150	LC
Univ of Findlay	OH	15,764	C
Univ of Mich/Dearborn	MI	3,399	HC
Univ of Mobile	AL	9,400	C
Univ of N Car at Chapel Hill	NC	5,330	HC
Univ of Northern Iowa	IA	5,137	C
Univ of Wisc/Parkside	WI	5,247	C
Univ of Wisc/Platteville	WI	4,830	C
Upper Iowa Univ	IA	11,900	C
Urbana Univ	OH	12,536	C
Warner Pacific College	OR	12,112	C
Wayland Baptist Univ	TX	7,811	NC
Webster Univ	MO	12,650	C
West Virginia Univ	WV	5,774	C
Western New Mexico Univ	NM	3,234	LC
Western Oregon State College	OR	6,180	C
Wheeling Jesuit College	WV	14,370	C
Wilberforce Univ	OH	10,408	C
Youngstown State Univ	OH	6,447	LC

SCIENCE AND MANAGEMENT

School	ST	$IS	SR
Claremont McKenna College	CA	22,150	MC
Elizabethtown College	PA	17,850	VC

SCIENCE EDUCATION

School	ST	$IS	SR
Abilene Christian Univ	TX	10,460	NC
Adams State College	CO	4,910	C
Adelphi Univ	NY	18,250	LC
Alabama A&M Univ	AL	4,200	C
Albany State College	GA	4,481	LC
Alice Lloyd College	KY	2,750	VC
Alverno College	WI	11,344	C
American International College	MA	14,029	C
Anderson Univ	IN	12,920	C
Andrews Univ	MI	14,952	NC
Angelo State Univ	TX	5,176	C
Appalachian State Univ	NC	4,095	C
Arkansas State Univ	AR	4,250	NC
Ashland Univ	OH	15,508	C
Auburn Univ	AL	5,823	C+
Augsburg College	MN	15,608	C
Averett College	VA	13,610	LC
Baldwin-Wallace College	OH	15,210	C
Ball State Univ	IN	6,032	LC
Bartlesville Wesleyan College	OK	9,400	C
Barton College	NC	10,689	LC
Baylor Univ	TX	10,990	C+
Belmont Univ	TN	10,540	C
Beloit College	WI	18,950	VC+
Bemidji State Univ	MN	5,188	C
Bennett College	NC	8,920	LC
Bethany College	KS	11,232	C
Bethany College	WV	18,300	C+
Bethel College	IN	11,650	C
Bethel College	MN	15,050	C

School	ST	$IS	SR
Bethune-Cookman College	FL	8,375	LC
Black Hills State Univ	SD	4,831	NC
Bloomsburg Univ of Penn	PA	6,312	C+
Blue Mountain College	MS	5,958	LC
Bluefield State College	WV	1,832	LC
Bluffton College	OH	12,951	C
Boston Univ	MA	24,130	HC
Bowling Green State Univ	OH	6,701	C
Bridgewater State College	MA	7,518	C
Brigham Young Univ	UT	5,625	HC
Brigham Young Univ/Hawaii	HI	6,750	VC
Brooklyn Campus of LIU	NY	15,000	LC
Bryan College	TN	11,465	C
Buena Vista College	IA	16,150	VC
Calif Lutheran Univ	CA	17,240	C
Cal State/Chico	CA	6,146	C
Cal State/Fresno	CA	5,747	C
Calif Univ of Penn	PA	7,370	C
Calumet College of St. Joseph	IN	3,585	C
Cameron Univ	OK	3,686	LC
Canisius College	NY	15,510	C
Capital Univ	OH	16,535	VC
Caribbean Univ	PR	2,400	
Carroll College	WI	15,490	C
Carson-Newman College	TN	11,250	C
Carthage College	WI	15,995	C
Castleton State College	VT	8,378	LC
Cedar Crest College	PA	18,930	C
Cedarville College	OH	10,715	C
Centenary College of Louisiana	LA	11,826	C+
Central Methodist College	MO	11,410	C
Central Mich Univ	MI	6,737	LC
Central Missouri State Univ	MO	5,138	LC
Central Univ of Bayamon	PR	2,430	
Central Washington Univ	WA	5,644	C
Chadron State College	NE	4,091	NC
Charleston Southern Univ	SC	10,282	LC
Christian Heritage College	CA	11,756	C
Christopher Newport Univ	VA	3,196	LC
CUNY/City College	NY	2,543	VC
CUNY/Herbert H. Lehman College	NY	2,542	C
CUNY/Hunter College	NY	4,101	VC
CUNY/Queens College	NY	2,631	C
College of Great Falls	MT	6,230	NC
College of Mount St Joseph	OH	13,272	C
College of Notre Dame of Maryland	MD	16,050	C
College of Our Lady of The Elms	MA	15,639	C
College of St Rose	NY	14,452	C
Columbia College	MO	11,995	C
Concord College	WV	5,104	NC
Concordia College	MN	13,200	C
Concordia College	NE	11,776	NC
Concordia Univ	IL	12,611	C
Converse College	SC	15,750	C
Cornell College	IA	18,425	VC
Cumberland College	KY	9,756	C
Daemen College	NY	13,020	LC
Dana College	NE	11,910	C
David Lipscomb Univ	TN	7,865	VC
Davis and Elkins College	WV	13,230	LC
Defiance College	OH	13,480	LC
Delaware State College	DE	5,656	C
Delta State Univ	MS	3,964	LC
Dickinson State Univ	ND	3,792	
Doane College	NE	12,220	C
Dominican College	NY	13,600	LC
Drake Univ	IA	17,195	VC
Duquesne Univ	PA	16,434	VC
East Central Univ	OK	3,558	C
East Stroudsburg Univ	PA	6,886	C
East Tenn State Univ	TN	4,406	C
East Texas Baptist Univ	TX	7,740	LC
East Texas State Univ	TX	4,572	LC
Eastern Kentucky Univ	KY	4,840	NC
Eastern Mich Univ	MI	6,749	C
Eastern Montana College	MT	5,165	LC
Eastern Nazarene College	MA	12,165	LC
Eastern Washington Univ	WA	5,439	LC
Edinboro Univ of Penn	PA	7,181	C
Elizabeth City State Univ	NC	4,254	LC
Elmhurst College	IL	12,536	C
Elmira College	NY	18,450	VC
Elon College	NC	12,290	LC
Emory and Henry College	VA	12,776	C
Eureka College	IL	14,555	C
Evangel College	MO	10,142	LC
Evergreen State College	WA	6,306	C
Fairmont State College	WV	4,640	LC
Ferris State Univ	MI	7,160	NC
Florida A&M Univ	FL	4,651	C
Florida Atlantic Univ	FL	5,525	C
Florida Inst of Tech	FL	16,935	VC
Florida International Univ	FL	4,191	VC
Florida Southern College	FL	12,260	C
Fontbonne College	MO	12,090	C
Franklin Pierce College	NH	17,270	LC
Freed-Hardeman Univ	TN	8,585	VC
Fresno Pacific College	CA	13,020	C
Friends Univ	KS	11,205	C
George Fox College	OR	15,640	LC
Georgia Southwestern College	GA	4,338	LC
Georgia State Univ	GA	2,019	C
Gettysburg College	PA	22,960	HC
Glenville State College	WV	4,810	LC
Goshen College	IN	12,360	C
Grace College	IN	12,120	C
Grambling State Univ	LA	4,712	NC
Grand Canyon Univ	AZ	9,680	VC
Grand Rapids Baptist College and Seminary	MI	10,228	C
Grand Valley State Univ	MI	6,822	VC
Grand View College	IA	13,230	NC
Grove City College	PA	7,870	HC
Gustavus Adolphus College	MN	15,935	VC
Gwynedd-Mercy College	PA	15,450	C
Hamline Univ	MN	17,122	VC
Hanover College	IN	10,950	VC
Hardin-Simmons Univ	TX	9,080	C
Harding Univ	AR	9,050	VC
Hastings College	NE	12,426	C
Heidelberg College	OH	17,160	C
Hendrix College	AR	11,670	C
Heritage College	WA	5,540	NC
Hillsdale College	MI	15,110	VC
Hofstra Univ	NY	16,580	VC
Holy Family College	PA	8,300	C
Hood College	MD	19,010	VC
Hope College	MI	15,698	C+
Houghton College	NY	13,120	VC
Houston Baptist Univ	TX	11,055	C
Howard Payne Univ	TX	8,052	C
Humboldt State Univ	CA	5,676	C
Huntington College	IN	13,220	C
Illinois College	IL	11,200	C
Immaculata College	PA	14,620	C
Incarnate Word College	TX	12,307	C
Indiana State Univ	IN	6,210	C
Indiana Univ of Penn	PA	6,373	C
Indiana Univ-Purdue Univ at Fort Wayne	IN	2,500	LC
Indiana Univ/South Bend	IN	2,141	LC
Indiana Wesleyan Univ	IN	12,332	C
Inter American Univ of PR/San German	PR	4,620	
Iona College	NY	16,310	C
Iowa State Univ	IA	5,456	C
Iowa Wesleyan College	IA	13,250	C
Ithaca College	NY	19,679	C
Jacksonville State Univ	AL	4,080	LC
Jacksonville Univ	FL	13,390	C
John Brown Univ	AR	9,880	VC
Johnson C. Smith Univ	NC	8,916	LC
Judson College	AL	9,060	C
Judson College	IL	13,625	C
Juniata College	PA	18,390	C+
Kean College of New Jersey	NJ	6,395	LC
Keene State College	NH	7,081	C
Kennesaw State College	GA	1,553	C
Kent State Univ	OH	6,740	LC
King's College	PA	15,420	C
Knoxville College	TN	8,320	LC
La Roche College	PA	12,977	LC
La Salle Univ	PA	16,940	VC
Lamar Univ	TX	3,798	C
Lander Univ	SC	6,180	LC
Langston Univ	OK	2,907	LC
Le Moyne College	NY	15,180	C
Le Tourneau Univ	TX	12,500	C+
Lenoir-Rhyne College	NC	14,068	C
Limestone College	SC	10,700	LC
Lincoln Memorial Univ	TN	8,218	C
Lincoln Univ	PA	0	LC
Lindenwood College	MO	13,560	C
Linfield College	OR	16,670	VC
Livingston Univ	AL	3,979	C
Livingstone College	NC	8,600	LC
Lock Haven Univ of Penn	PA	7,128	C
LIU/C. W. Post Campus	NY	16,870	C
Loras College	IA	14,160	C
Louisiana College	LA	7,518	VC
Louisiana Tech Univ	LA	4,284	C
Lubbock Christian Univ	TX	9,840	NC
Luther College	IA	15,900	VC
Lyndon State College	VT	8,394	LC
MacMurray College	IL	12,800	C
Malone College	OH	12,572	C
Manchester College	IN	13,240	LC
Manhattan College	NY	19,000	C
Manhattanville College	NY	20,450	LC
Mankato State Univ	MN	5,097	LC
Mansfield Univ	PA	6,348	C
Marietta College	OH	16,940	C+
Marist College	NY	16,406	C
Mars Hill College	NC	11,050	C
Marshall Univ	WV	5,762	LC
Mary Baldwin College	VA	17,700	LC
Marymount College/Tarrytown	NY	17,350	C
Maryville College	TN	14,474	C
Maryville Univ-St Louis	MO	12,900	VC
Marywood College	PA	14,890	C
Mayville State Univ	ND	4,272	NC
McNeese State Univ	LA	4,543	NC
McPherson College	KS	11,360	VC
Mercy College	NY	11,180	NC
Mercyhurst College	PA	13,488	C
Merrimack College	MA	18,025	C
Mesa State College	CO	5,127	NC
Messiah College	PA	14,664	VC
Methodist College	NC	12,400	C
Miami Univ	OH	8,066	VC
Mich State Univ	MI	7,842	C
Middle Tenn State Univ	TN	3,857	C
Midland Lutheran College	NE	12,410	LC
Millikin Univ	IL	15,499	C
Miss College	MS	8,348	C
Missouri Southern State College	MO	4,272	C
Monmouth College	NJ	16,820	C
Moorhead State Univ	MN	5,076	C
Mount Holyoke College	MA	23,630	VC
Mount Marty College	SD	10,450	NC
Mount Mary College	WI	10,920	C
Mount St Mary's College	CA	16,390	VC
Mount Senario College	WI	10,970	C
Mount Vernon Nazarene College	OH	10,390	C
Muskingum College	OH	16,650	C
New York Univ	NY	24,705	VC+
Niagara Univ	NY	14,552	C
Nicholls State Univ	LA	4,531	NC
N Car Agricultural and Technical State Univ	NC	4,477	LC
N Car State Univ	NC	4,984	VC
North Georgia College	GA	4,103	LC
Northeast Louisiana Univ	LA	3,906	NC
Northeastern State Univ	OK	5,250	C
Northern Arizona Univ	AZ	4,844	C
Northern Kentucky Univ	KY	4,620	NC
Northern Mich Univ	MI	6,350	C
Northern Montana College	MT	4,976	C
Northern State Univ	SD	4,186	LC
Northland College	WI	13,550	LC
Northwest Missouri State Univ	MO	5,010	LC
Northwestern College of Iowa	IA	12,250	C
Northwestern Okla State Univ	OK	3,424	C
Northwestern State Univ of Louisiana	LA	4,287	NC
Northwestern Univ	IL	21,093	MC
Notre Dame College	NH	14,220	C
Notre Dame College of Ohio	OH	11,370	C
Oakland City College	IN	10,216	LC
Oakwood College	AL	10,005	C
Occidental College	CA	21,792	HC
Ohio State Univ	OH	7,218	LC
Ohio Univ	OH	7,341	C
Ohio Wesleyan Univ	OH	21,108	VC+
Okla Baptist Univ	OK	8,486	C
Okla Christian Univ of Science and Arts	OK	8,790	NC
Okla City Univ	OK	9,840	C
Okla Panhandle State Univ	OK	3,155	NC
Okla State Univ	OK	5,086	VC
Olivet Nazarene Univ	IL	11,976	C
Otterbein College	OH	16,506	C
Ouachita Baptist Univ	AR	8,940	C
Park College	MO	7,320	C
Pembroke State Univ	NC	3,538	LC
Pepperdine Univ	CA	23,720	VC
Peru State College	NE	4,311	NC
Pfeiffer College	NC	11,670	LC
Phillips Univ	OK	12,744	C
Pikeville College	KY	8,500	NC
Pillsbury Baptist Bible College	MN	7,390	NC
Pittsburg State Univ	KS	4,478	NC
Plymouth State College	NH	7,166	C
Pontifical Catholic Univ of PR/Ponce	PR	5,807	C
Purdue Univ/Calumet	IN	2,374	NC
Purdue Univ/West Lafayette	IN	6,636	C
Queens College	NC	14,950	C
Quincy Univ	IL	13,646	VC
Radford Univ	VA	7,034	LC
Rhode Island College	RI	7,901	LC
Rider College	NJ	18,160	C
Rivier College	NH	14,920	LC
Roosevelt Univ	IL	12,368	C
Rowan College of New Jersey	NJ	7,358	VC
Russell Sage College	NY	16,790	C
Sacred Heart Univ	CT	16,350	C
St Cloud State Univ	MN	5,015	C
St Francis College	IN	11,662	C
St John Fisher College	NY	15,415	C
St John's Univ	NY	8,980	C+
St Joseph's College	IN	14,730	C
St Mary's College of Minn	MN	13,850	LC
St Mary's Univ	TX	12,064	C
St Mary-of-the-Woods College	IN	14,430	NC
St Michael's College	VT	17,930	C
St Olaf College	MN	17,200	HC
St Thomas Aquinas College	NY	13,550	C
St Xavier Univ	IL	14,700	C
Salem State College	MA	6,712	C
Salisbury State Univ	MD	7,516	C+
Samford Univ	AL	11,400	VC
Sheldon Jackson College	AK	14,050	NC
Shepherd College	WV	5,540	C
Shorter College	GA	10,270	C
Simpson College	IA	14,635	VC
Sioux Falls College	SD	11,540	C
Slippery Rock Univ	PA	6,803	C
S Dak State Univ	SD	4,562	C
Southeastern College of the Assemblies of God	FL	6,618	NC
Southeastern Louisiana Univ	LA	4,230	NC
Southeastern Okla State Univ	OK	3,594	C
Southern Arkansas Univ	AR	3,432	NC
Southern Calif College	CA	12,356	C
Southern Conn State Univ	CT	7,532	C
Southern Illinois Univ at Carbondale	IL	6,234	C
Southern Univ and A&M College	LA	4,920	NC
Southern Univ at New Orleans	LA	1,452	NC
Southwest Missouri State Univ	MO	4,956	C
Southwest Texas State Univ	TX	5,124	C
Southwestern Okla State Univ	OK	3,312	C
Springfield College	MA	15,200	LC
SUNY at Albany	NY	7,059	LC
SUNY at Buffalo	NY	7,896	VC
SUNY College of Environmental Science and Forestry	NY	9,257	HC+
SUNY/College at Buffalo	NY	7,035	VC
SUNY/College at Cortland	NY	7,326	C+
SUNY/College at Fredonia	NY	7,159	VC
SUNY/College at Geneseo	NY	6,949	HC
SUNY/College at New Paltz	NY	6,890	VC
SUNY/College at Old Westbury	NY	7,128	LC
SUNY/College at Oneonta	NY	7,878	C
SUNY/College at Plattsburgh	NY	6,917	C
SUNY/Potsdam College	NY	6,906	C
Syracuse Univ	NY	21,305	HC
Tabor College	KS	11,460	VC
Teikyo Marycrest Univ	IA	13,755	VC
Temple Univ	PA	10,281	C
Tenn Wesleyan College	TN	10,060	C
Texas Southern Univ	TX	4,500	NC
The Univ of New Mexico	NM	5,304	C
Thomas More College	KY	12,962	C
Tri-State Univ	IN	13,788	LC
Trinity Christian College	IL	13,260	C
Trinity College	IL	14,010	C
Trinity College of Vermont	VT	16,015	LC
Trinity Univ	TX	16,670	HC
Troy State Univ	AL	4,322	C
Troy State Univ at Dothan/Fort Rucker	AL	2,260	NC
Turabo Univ	PR	2,670	
Union College	KY	9,790	C
Univ of Akron	OH	6,699	NC
Univ of Alaska Southeast	AK	4,075	LC
Univ of Arizona	AZ	5,808	C
Univ of Arkansas at Pine Bluff	AR	3,978	LC
Univ of Central Arkansas	AR	4,200	LC
Univ of Central Florida	FL	6,061	C+
Univ of Central Okla	OK	3,647	C
Univ of Charleston	WV	12,750	C
Univ of Cincinnati	OH	7,989	C
Univ of Delaware	DE	8,013	VC
Univ of Denver	CO	19,290	C+
Univ of Detroit Mercy	MI	14,720	C
Univ of Evansville	IN	15,300	VC
Univ of Georgia	GA	5,655	VC
Univ of Houston	TX	5,215	C
Univ of Idaho	ID	4,830	C
Univ of Illinois at Chicago	IL	8,443	C
Univ of Illinois at Urbana-Champaign	IL	7,764	HC
Univ of Indianapolis	IN	14,510	C
Univ of Iowa	IA	5,658	VC
Univ of Kentucky	KY	5,152	VC
Univ of Louisville	KY	5,948	C
Univ of Maine at Farmington	ME	6,700	C
Univ of Maine at Presque Isle	ME	6,374	C
Univ of Mary	ND	8,910	C
Univ of Mary Hardin-Baylor	TX	8,120	NC
Univ of Maryland/College Park	MD	8,182	VC
Univ of Maryland/Eastern Shore	MD	6,254	LC
Univ of Mich/Dearborn	MI	3,399	HC
Univ of Mich/Flint	MI	2,916	C
Univ of Minn/Duluth	MN	6,512	C
Univ of Minn/Twin Cities	MN	6,682	VC
Univ of Missouri/Kansas City	MO	5,906	VC
Univ of Montana	MT	5,529	C
Univ of Nebr at Kearney	NE	4,308	LC
Univ of Nebr-Lincoln	NE	5,278	LC
Univ of New England	ME	16,075	LC
Univ of New Orleans	LA	5,468	C
Univ of North Alabama	AL	4,236	NC
Univ of N Car at Chapel Hill	NC	5,330	HC
Univ of N Car at Greensboro	NC	5,192	C
Univ of North Florida	FL	5,082	C
Univ of Northern Colo	CO	6,008	C
Univ of Northern Iowa	IA	5,137	C

School	ST	$IS	SR
Univ of Notre Dame	IN	20,150	MC
Univ of Okla	OK	5,427	VC
Univ of Pittsburgh at Johnstown	PA	8,914	C
Univ of PR/Rio Piedras	PR	0	
Univ of Richmond	VA	16,700	HC
Univ of Science and Arts of Okla	OK	3,304	C
Univ of Scranton	PA	17,071	VC
Univ of S Car at Aiken	SC	5,386	C
Univ of South Florida	FL	5,475	C+
Univ of Southern Indiana	IN	3,720	NC
Univ of Southern Miss	MS	4,542	C
Univ of Southwestern Louisiana	LA	3,968	NC
Univ of Tenn at Martin	TN	4,550	C
Univ of Texas at Arlington	TX	5,549	LC
Univ of the Pacific	CA	21,100	C
Univ of Toledo	OH	6,636	NC
Univ of Tulsa	OK	13,795	VC
Univ of Wisc/Eau Claire	WI	4,647	C
Univ of Wisc/Platteville	WI	4,830	C
Univ of Wisc/River Falls	WI	4,655	C
Univ of Wisc/Superior	WI	4,330	C
Univ of Wisc/Whitewater	WI	4,700	C
Ursuline College	OH	13,180	LC
Utah State Univ	UT	4,683	C
Valdosta State Univ	GA	4,670	LC
Valley City State Univ	ND	4,385	LC
Valparaiso Univ	IN	14,810	VC
Virginia Wesleyan College	VA	14,950	VC
Warner Pacific College	OR	12,112	C
Wartburg College	IA	14,530	VC
Wayland Baptist Univ	TX	7,811	NC
Wayne State College	NE	4,260	NC
Wayne State Univ	MI	2,680	C
Weber State Univ	UT	4,398	C
Wells College	NY	19,460	C+
West Liberty State College	WV	4,690	LC
West Virginia Inst of Tech	WV	5,858	LC
Western Carolina Univ	NC	3,811	C
Western Kentucky Univ	KY	4,808	C
Western Mich Univ	MI	6,820	C
Western Montana College of the Univ of Montana	MT	1,646	C
Western Oregon State College	OR	6,180	C
Western State College of Colo	CO	5,560	C
Western Washington Univ	WA	6,077	VC
Westfield State College	MA	7,161	C
Westminster College	MO	13,750	C+
Westmont College	CA	18,732	C
Wheaton College	IL	14,710	HC
Whitworth College	WA	16,265	C
Wichita State Univ	KS	5,068	NC
Widener Univ	PA	16,840	C
Wilkes Univ	PA	15,728	LC
William Jewell College	MO	12,500	VC
William Penn College	IA	13,400	C
Wilmington College	OH	13,700	LC
Wingate College	NC	10,610	C
Winona State Univ	MN	5,200	VC
Wittenberg Univ	OH	19,998	VC
Wright State Univ	OH	6,896	LC
Xavier Univ	OH	15,710	C+
Xavier Univ of Louisiana	LA	10,400	C
York College of Penn	PA	8,345	C
Youngstown State Univ	OH	6,447	LC

SCIENCE TECHNOLOGY

School	ST	$IS	SR
Cazenovia College	NY	14,655	LC
Charter Oak State College	CT	314	NC
James Madison Univ	VA	8,198	HC
Mass Inst of Tech	MA	24,800	MC
Northwest Nazarene College	ID	11,750	C
Rensselaer Polytechnic Inst	NY	23,067	HC
Thomas A. Edison State College	NJ	400	

SCULPTURE

School	ST	$IS	SR
Aquinas College	MI	14,526	C
Arizona State Univ Main Campus	AZ	6,444	C
Art Academy of Cincinnati	OH	8,820	SP
Atlanta College of Art	GA	12,495	SP
Barton College	NC	10,689	LC
Birmingham-Southern College	AL	15,154	VC+
Boston Univ	MA	24,130	HC
Bradley Univ	IL	14,718	C+
Brigham Young Univ	UT	5,625	HC
Center for Creative Studies/College of Art and Design	MI	15,330	SP
Cooper Union for the Advancement of Science and Art	NY	8,430	MC
Edinboro Univ of Penn	PA	7,181	C
Escuela de Artes Plasticas	PR	4,024	
Hofstra Univ	NY	16,580	VC
Indiana Univ-Purdue Univ at Indianapolis	IN	5,862	LC
Kansas City Art Inst	MO	17,000	SP
Louisiana State Univ and A&M College	LA	5,605	C
Lycoming College	PA	17,200	LC
Maine College of Art	ME	15,673	SP
Maryland Inst, College of Art	MD	18,420	SP
Milwaukee Inst of Art and Design	WI	9,800	SP
Montserrat College of Art	MA	12,500	SP
Moore College of Art and Design	PA	17,947	SP
Northern Mich Univ	MI	6,350	C
Ohio Northern Univ	OH	18,660	VC
Ohio State Univ	OH	7,218	LC
Pacific Northwest College of Art	OR	7,700	SP
Plymouth State College	NH	7,166	C
Rhode Island School of Design	RI	22,315	SP
San Francisco Art Inst	CA	12,900	SP
School of the Art Inst of Chicago	IL	17,610	SP
Syracuse Univ	NY	21,305	HC
Univ of Conn	CT	9,168	C
Univ of Hartford	CT	19,858	LC
Univ of Illinois at Urbana-Champaign	IL	7,764	HC
Univ of Kansas	KS	5,200	NC
Univ of Mass Dartmouth	MA	8,158	C
Univ of Miami	FL	22,107	VC
Univ of Mich/Ann Arbor	MI	9,428	HC+
Univ of North Texas	TX	4,853	C
Univ of Oregon	OR	6,466	VC
Univ of Texas at El Paso	TX	3,160	LC
Univ of the Arts	PA	16,150	SP
Univ of Washington	WA	6,618	VC

SECONDARY EDUCATION

School	ST	$IS	SR
Abilene Christian Univ	TX	10,460	NC
Adams State College	CO	4,910	C
Adelphi Univ	NY	18,250	LC
Adrian College	MI	14,340	C
Alabama A&M Univ	AL	4,200	C
Alabama State Univ	AL	3,428	NC
Albright College	PA	19,260	C
Alcorn State Univ	MS	4,474	C+
Alderson-Broaddus College	WV	12,000	C
Alfred Univ	NY	21,054	VC+
Alice Lloyd College	KY	2,750	VC
Allegheny College	PA	21,020	VC
Alma College	MI	16,375	VC+
Alvernia College	PA	13,150	LC
Alverno College	WI	11,344	C
American International College	MA	14,029	C
Angelo State Univ	TX	5,176	C
Antioch College	OH	19,532	C
Appalachian State Univ	NC	4,095	C
Aquinas College	MI	14,526	C
Arizona State Univ Main Campus	AZ	6,444	C
Arkansas Baptist College	AR	5,016	NC
Arkansas State Univ	AR	4,250	NC
Arkansas Tech Univ	AR	4,200	NC
Armstrong State College	GA	4,874	LC
Asbury College	KY	11,105	VC
Ashland Univ	OH	15,508	C
Atlantic Union College	MA	14,150	LC
Auburn Univ	AL	5,823	C+
Auburn Univ at Montgomery	AL	3,390	C
Augsburg College	MN	15,608	C
Augusta College	GA	1,452	C
Augustana College	IL	16,959	VC
Augustana College	SD	13,420	C
Averett College	VA	13,610	LC
Baker Univ	KS	12,284	C
Baldwin-Wallace College	OH	15,210	C
Ball State Univ	IN	6,032	LC
Bartlesville Wesleyan College	OK	9,400	C
Baylor Univ	TX	10,990	C+
Beaver College	PA	17,660	C
Bellarmine College	KY	10,832	C
Belmont Abbey College	NC	13,190	C
Beloit College	WI	18,950	VC+
Bemidji State Univ	MN	5,188	C
Bennett College	NC	8,920	LC
Berea College	KY	2,883	VC+
Bethany College	KS	11,232	C
Bethany College	WV	18,300	C+
Bethel College	IN	11,650	C
Bethel College	KS	11,530	C
Bethel College	MN	15,050	C
Biola Univ	CA	16,124	C
Black Hills State Univ	SD	4,831	NC
Blackburn College	IL	9,120	C
Bloomsburg Univ of Penn	PA	6,312	C+
Blue Mountain College	MS	5,958	LC
Bluefield College	VA	10,600	C
Bluefield State College	WV	1,832	LC
Bluffton College	OH	12,951	C
Boise State Univ	ID	4,909	LC
Boston College	MA	22,706	MC
Boston Univ	MA	24,130	HC
Bowling Green State Univ	OH	6,701	C
Bradley Univ	IL	14,718	C+
Briar Cliff College	IA	13,375	C
Bridgewater State College	MA	7,518	C
Brigham Young Univ	UT	5,625	HC
Brigham Young Univ/Hawaii	HI	6,750	VC
Brooklyn Campus of LIU	NY	15,000	LC
Bucknell Univ	PA	22,320	HC
Buena Vista College	IA	16,150	VC
Butler Univ	IN	16,210	C
Calif Baptist College	CA	11,294	C
Calif Lutheran Univ	CA	17,240	C
Cal State/Chico	CA	6,146	C
Cal State/Fresno	CA	5,747	C
Cal State/Stanislaus	CA	6,799	C
Calif Univ of Penn	PA	7,370	C
Calumet College of St. Joseph	IN	3,585	C
Calvin College	MI	13,020	VC
Canisius College	NY	15,510	C
Capital Univ	OH	16,535	VC
Cardinal Stritch College	WI	11,252	C
Caribbean Univ	PR	2,400	
Carroll College	MT	11,265	C
Carroll College	WI	15,490	C
Carson-Newman College	TN	11,250	C
Carthage College	WI	15,995	C
Castleton State College	VT	8,378	LC
Catholic Univ of America	DC	18,856	C
Cedar Crest College	PA	18,930	C
Cedarville College	OH	10,715	C
Centenary College	NJ	17,040	LC
Centenary College of Louisiana	LA	11,826	C+
Central College	IA	14,025	VC
Central Methodist College	MO	11,410	C
Central Mich Univ	MI	6,737	LC
Central Missouri State Univ	MO	5,138	LC
Central State Univ	OH	7,320	NC
Central Univ of Bayamon	PR	2,430	
Central Washington Univ	WA	5,644	C
Chadron State College	NE	4,091	NC
Chaminade Univ of Honolulu	HI	14,290	C
Chatham College	PA	18,010	C
Cheyney Univ of Penn	PA	7,005	C
Chicago State Univ	IL	2,198	C
Christian Brothers Univ	TN	12,120	VC
Christian Heritage College	CA	11,756	C
Christopher Newport Univ	VA	3,196	LC
CUNY/Brooklyn College	NY	2,450	VC
CUNY/City College	NY	2,543	VC
CUNY/Herbert H. Lehman College	NY	2,542	C
CUNY/Hunter College	NY	4,101	VC
CUNY/Queens College	NY	2,631	C
CUNY/York College	NY	2,534	NC
Claflin College	SC	0	
Clarion Univ of Penn	PA	6,518	C
Clarke College	IA	13,950	C+
Clearwater Christian College	FL	8,500	LC
Clemson Univ	SC	6,564	VC
Coastal Carolina Univ	SC	6,010	LC
Coe College	IA	17,085	VC
Coker College	SC	13,790	C
Colby-Sawyer College	NH	18,495	LC
College Misericordia	PA	15,820	C
College of Great Falls	MT	6,230	NC
College of Mount St Joseph	OH	13,272	C
College of New Rochelle	NY	15,440	LC
College of Notre Dame of Maryland	MD	16,050	C
College of Our Lady of The Elms	MA	15,639	C
College of St Francis	IL	13,060	VC
College of St Joseph	VT	12,650	LC
College of St Scholastica	MN	14,868	C
College of the Southwest	NM	5,720	LC
Colo Christian Univ	CO	9,750	C
Columbia College	MO	11,995	C
Columbia Univ/Barnard College	NY	25,492	HC
Columbus College	GA	4,892	LC
Concord College	WV	5,104	NC
Concordia College	MI	13,660	C
Concordia College	MN	13,260	C
Concordia College	NE	11,776	NC
Concordia College	NY	0	LC
Concordia College	OR	12,300	C
Concordia College/Moorhead	MN	12,750	C
Concordia Lutheran College	TX	10,260	C+
Concordia Univ	IL	12,611	C
Concordia Univ Wisc	WI	12,140	C
Converse College	SC	15,750	C
Cornell College	IA	18,425	VC
Creighton Univ	NE	14,432	VC
Crichton College	TN	6,547	NC
Cumberland College	KY	9,756	C
Cumberland Univ	TN	8,650	C
D'Youville College	NY	12,850	C
Daemen College	NY	13,020	LC
Dakota State Univ	SD	4,374	LC
Dakota Wesleyan Univ	SD	9,770	LC
Dana College	NE	11,910	C
Davis and Elkins College	WV	13,230	LC
Defiance College	OH	13,480	LC
Delaware Valley College	PA	16,065	LC
Delta State Univ	MS	3,964	LC
DePaul Univ	IL	15,535	VC
Dickinson State Univ	ND	3,792	
Dillard Univ	LA	9,950	C
Doane College	NE	12,220	C
Dominican College	NY	13,600	LC
Dordt College	IA	11,690	C
Dowling College	NY	12,730	LC
Drake Univ	IA	17,195	VC
Drury College	MO	12,140	VC
Duquesne Univ	PA	16,434	VC
East Carolina Univ	NC	4,498	C
East Central Univ	OK	3,558	C
East Stroudsburg Univ	PA	6,886	C
East Tenn State Univ	TN	4,406	C
East Texas Baptist Univ	TX	7,740	C
East Texas State Univ	TX	4,572	LC
Eastern College	PA	15,150	C+
Eastern Conn State Univ	CT	6,966	C
Eastern Illinois Univ	IL	5,548	C
Eastern Kentucky Univ	KY	4,840	NC
Eastern Mennonite College	VA	12,700	C
Eastern Mich Univ	MI	6,749	C
Eastern Montana College	MT	5,165	LC
Eastern Washington Univ	WA	5,439	LC
Edinboro Univ of Penn	PA	7,181	C
Elizabeth City State Univ	NC	4,254	LC
Elizabethtown College	PA	17,850	VC
Elmhurst College	IL	12,536	C
Elmira College	NY	18,450	C
Elon College	NC	12,290	LC
Emmanuel College	MA	17,773	LC
Emory and Henry College	VA	12,776	C
Emory Univ	GA	21,930	HC
Emporia State Univ	KS	4,685	NC
Erskine College	SC	14,310	C
Eureka College	IL	14,555	C
Evangel College	MO	10,142	LC
Fairmont State College	WV	4,640	LC
Faulkner Univ	AL	8,630	LC
Fayetteville State Univ	NC	3,926	LC
Fitchburg State College	MA	6,962	C
Flagler College	FL	7,990	C
Florida Memorial College	FL	7,600	C+
Florida Southern College	FL	12,260	C
Florida State Univ	FL	5,814	VC
Fontbonne College	MO	12,090	C
Fordham Univ/College at Lincoln Center	NY	18,150	VC
Fort Lewis College	CO	5,097	C
Fort Valley State College	GA	3,974	LC
Franciscan Univ of Steubenville	OH	13,400	C
Franklin College of Indiana	IN	13,970	C
Franklin Pierce College	NH	17,270	LC
Freed-Hardeman Univ	TN	8,585	VC
Friends Univ	KS	11,205	C
Gallaudet Univ	DC	9,850	SP
Gannon Univ	PA	14,872	C
Gardner-Webb Univ	NC	11,950	LC
George Fox College	OR	15,640	LC
Georgia Southern Univ	GA	4,988	C
Georgia State Univ	GA	2,019	C
Gettysburg College	PA	22,960	HC
Glenville State College	WV	4,810	LC
Goshen College	IN	12,360	C
Goucher College	MD	20,295	VC
Grand Canyon Univ	AZ	9,680	VC
Grand Rapids Baptist College and Seminary	MI	10,228	C
Grand Valley State Univ	MI	6,822	VC
Grand View College	IA	13,230	NC
Greensboro College	NC	11,496	C
Greenville College	IL	14,190	C
Grove City College	PA	7,870	HC
Guilford College	NC	17,680	C
Gustavus Adolphus College	MN	15,935	VC
Gwynedd-Mercy College	PA	15,450	C
Hamline Univ	MN	17,122	VC
Hannibal-LaGrange College	MO	8,400	LC
Hanover College	IN	10,950	VC
Hardin-Simmons Univ	TX	9,080	C
Harding Univ	AR	9,050	VC
Hastings College	NE	12,426	C
Heidelberg College	OH	17,160	C
Henderson State Univ	AR	3,860	C
Heritage College	WA	5,540	NC
High Point Univ	NC	12,350	LC
Hillsdale College	MI	15,110	VC
Hofstra Univ	NY	16,580	VC
Holy Family College	PA	8,300	C
Hood College	MD	19,010	VC
Hope College	MI	15,698	C+
Houghton College	NY	13,120	VC
Houston Baptist Univ	TX	11,055	C
Howard Payne Univ	TX	8,052	
Humboldt State Univ	CA	5,676	
Huntingdon College	AL	11,400	

School	ST	$IS	SR
Huntington College	IN	13,220	C
Huron Univ	SD	9,790	C
Idaho State Univ	ID	4,442	C
Illinois College	IL	11,200	C
Immaculata College	PA	14,620	C
Incarnate Word College	TX	12,307	C
Indiana State Univ	IN	6,210	C
Indiana Univ Bloomington	IN	6,495	VC
Indiana Univ East	IN	2,044	NC
Indiana Univ Northwest	IN	2,310	C
Indiana Univ of Penn	PA	6,373	C
Indiana Univ Southeast	IN	2,260	LC
Indiana Univ-Purdue Univ at Fort Wayne	IN	2,500	LC
Indiana Univ-Purdue Univ at Indianapolis	IN	5,862	LC
Indiana Univ/South Bend	IN	2,141	LC
Inter American Univ of PR/ Aguadilla Regional College	PR	2,290	
Inter American Univ of PR/ Barranquitas Regional College	PR	2,730	
Inter American Univ of PR/ Bayamon Univ College	PR	2,300	
Inter American Univ of PR/ Metropolitan Campus	PR	2,340	
Inter American Univ of PR/ Ponce Regional College	PR	2,300	
Inter American Univ of PR/ San German	PR	4,620	
Inter American Univ/Arecibo Campus	PR	5,666	
Inter-American Univ of PR/ Fajardo Regional College	PR	2,732	
Iona College	NY	16,310	C
Iowa State Univ	IA	5,456	C
Iowa Wesleyan College	IA	13,250	C
Ithaca College	NY	19,679	C
Jacksonville State Univ	AL	4,080	LC
Jacksonville Univ	FL	13,390	C
Jamestown College	ND	10,250	C
Jarvis Christian College	TX	7,170	LC
Jersey City State College	NJ	7,797	LC
John Brown Univ	AR	9,880	VC
John Carroll Univ	OH	16,510	C
Johnson C. Smith Univ	NC	8,916	LC
Judson College	AL	9,060	C
Judson College	IL	13,625	C
Juniata College	PA	18,390	C+
Kansas Newman College	KS	10,640	C
Kansas State Univ	KS	4,816	NC
Kansas Wesleyan Univ	KS	11,770	C
Kean College of New Jersey	NJ	6,395	LC
Keene State College	NH	7,081	C
Kennesaw State College	GA	1,553	C
Kent State Univ	OH	6,740	LC
Kentucky Christian College	KY	7,708	LC
Kentucky State Univ	KY	4,282	C+
Kentucky Wesleyan College	KY	11,550	C
Keuka College	NY	13,660	C
King's College	PA	15,420	C
Knox College	IL	18,990	VC
Kutztown Univ	PA	6,528	C
La Salle Univ	PA	16,940	VC
LaGrange College	GA	10,602	C
Lake Forest College	IL	19,960	VC
Lakeland College	WI	12,845	LC
Lamar Univ	TX	3,798	C
Lambuth Univ	TN	8,395	C
Lawrence Univ	WI	19,986	HC+
Le Moyne College	NY	15,180	C
Le Tourneau Univ	TX	12,500	C+
Lebanon Valley College of Penn	PA	18,300	C
Lenoir-Rhyne College	NC	14,068	C
Lewis Univ	IL	14,797	LC
Lewis-Clark State College	ID	4,040	
Lincoln Memorial Univ	TN	8,218	C
Lincoln Univ	PA	0	LC
Lindenwood College	MO	13,560	C
Lindsey Wilson College	KY	9,530	LC
Linfield College	OR	16,670	VC
Livingston Univ	AL	3,979	C
Livingstone College	NC	8,600	LC
Lock Haven Univ of Penn	PA	7,128	C
LIU/C. W. Post Campus	NY	16,870	C
Longwood College	VA	7,800	C
Loras College	IA	14,160	C
Louisiana College	LA	7,518	VC
Louisiana State Univ in Shreveport	LA	1,910	NC
Louisiana Tech Univ	LA	4,284	C
Loyola College	MD	18,035	VC
Loyola Univ/New Orleans	LA	15,660	C+
Lubbock Christian Univ	TX	9,840	NC
Luther College	IA	15,900	VC
Lynn Univ	FL	18,300	C
MacMurray College	IL	12,800	C
Madonna Univ	MI	8,546	C
Malone College	OH	12,572	C
Manchester College	IN	13,240	LC
Manhattan College	NY	19,000	C
Manhattanville College	NY	20,450	LC
Mankato State Univ	MN	5,097	LC
Mansfield Univ	PA	6,348	C
Marian College of Fond du Lac	WI	12,250	C
Marietta College	OH	16,940	C+
Marist College	NY	16,406	C
Marquette Univ	WI	16,114	VC
Mars Hill College	NC	11,050	C
Mary Baldwin College	VA	17,700	LC
Marygrove College	MI	5,877	VC
Marymount College/ Tarrytown	NY	17,350	C
Marymount Manhattan College	NY	15,450	LC
Maryville College	TN	14,474	C
Maryville Univ-St Louis	MO	12,900	VC
Marywood College	PA	14,890	C
Master's College	CA	12,816	C
Mayville State Univ	ND	4,272	NC
McKendree College	IL	10,900	C
McMurry Univ	TX	10,100	C
McPherson College	KS	11,360	VC
Mercer Univ	GA	15,123	C
Mercy College	NY	11,180	NC
Mercyhurst College	PA	13,488	C
Merrimack College	MA	18,025	C
Mesa State College	CO	5,127	NC
Messiah College	PA	14,664	VC
Methodist College	NC	12,400	C
Miami Univ	OH	8,066	VC
Mich State Univ	MI	7,842	C
MidAmerica Nazarene College	KS	10,208	NC
Middle Tenn State Univ	TN	3,857	C
Midland Lutheran College	NE	12,410	LC
Miles College	AL	7,150	NC
Milligan College	TN	10,690	C
Millikin Univ	IL	15,499	C
Miss State Univ	MS	5,629	VC
Miss Univ for Women	MS	4,456	LC
Missouri Southern State College	MO	4,272	
Missouri Western State College	MO	4,384	NC
Molloy College	NY	8,580	LC
Monmouth College	IL	17,300	C+
Monmouth College	NJ	16,820	C
Montana State Univ	MT	5,534	C
Montreat-Anderson College	NC	10,972	LC
Moorhead State Univ	MN	5,076	C
Moravian College	PA	18,960	VC
Morehouse College	GA	13,224	LC
Mount Marty College	SD	10,450	NC
Mount Mary College	WI	10,920	C
Mount St Mary College	NY	12,910	C
Mount St Mary's College	CA	16,390	VC
Mount Senario College	WI	10,970	C
Mount Union College	OH	15,850	C
Mount Vernon Nazarene College	OH	10,390	C
Murray State Univ	KY	4,702	C
Muskingum College	OH	16,650	C
New England College	NH	17,870	LC
New Mexico State Univ	NM	4,844	LC
New York Inst of Tech/Old Westbury	NY	13,914	LC
New York Univ	NY	24,705	VC+
Niagara Univ	NY	14,552	C
Norfolk State Univ	VA	6,345	LC
N Car State Univ	NC	4,984	VC
North Central College	IL	15,498	VC
N Dak State Univ of Agriculture and Applied Science	ND	4,774	VC
North Georgia College	GA	4,103	LC
North Park College	IL	14,310	C
Northeastern Illinois Univ	IL	1,955	C
Northeastern State Univ	OK	5,250	C
Northern Arizona Univ	AZ	4,844	C
Northern Kentucky Univ	KY	4,620	NC
Northern Mich Univ	MI	6,350	C
Northern Montana College	MT	4,976	C
Northern State Univ	SD	4,186	LC
Northland College	WI	13,550	LC
Northwest Missouri State Univ	MO	5,010	LC
Northwest Nazarene College	ID	11,750	C
Northwestern College	MN	13,554	C
Northwestern College of Iowa	IA	12,250	C
Northwestern Okla State Univ	OK	3,424	C
Northwestern State Univ of Louisiana	LA	4,287	NC
Northwestern Univ	IL	21,093	MC
Norwich Univ	VT	18,730	C
Notre Dame College	NH	14,220	C
Notre Dame College of Ohio	OH	11,370	C
Nova Southeastern Univ	FL	13,244	LC
Nyack College	NY	12,210	LC
Oakland City College	IN	10,216	LC
Occidental College	CA	21,792	HC
Oglethorpe Univ	GA	16,360	VC
Ohio Dominican College	OH	11,820	LC
Ohio Univ	OH	7,341	C
Ohio Wesleyan Univ	OH	21,108	VC+
Okla Baptist Univ	OK	8,486	C
Okla City Univ	OK	9,840	C
Okla Panhandle State Univ	OK	3,155	NC
Okla State Univ	OK	5,086	VC
Old Dominion Univ	VA	8,317	C
Olivet Nazarene Univ	IL	11,976	C
Oral Roberts Univ	OK	10,607	C+
Otterbein College	OH	16,506	C
Ouachita Baptist Univ	AR	8,940	C
Our Lady of Holy Cross College	LA	4,630	LC
Pace Univ	NY	15,540	C
Pacific Christian College	CA	12,700	C
Park College	MO	7,320	C
Paul Quinn College	TX	7,090	LC
Pembroke State Univ	NC	3,538	LC
Penn State Univ/Univ Park Campus	PA	8,752	HC
Pepperdine Univ	CA	23,720	VC
Peru State College	NE	4,311	NC
Pfeiffer College	NC	11,670	LC
Phillips Univ	OK	12,744	C
Pikeville College	KY	8,500	NC
Pillsbury Baptist Bible College	MN	7,390	NC
Pittsburg State Univ	KS	4,478	NC
Plymouth State College	NH	7,166	C
Point Park College	PA	13,922	LC
Pontifical Catholic Univ of PR/Ponce	PR	5,807	
Presbyterian College	SC	15,400	VC
Prescott College	AZ	9,775	C
Principia College	IL	17,799	C
Providence College	RI	19,750	VC
Purdue Univ/Calumet	IN	2,374	NC
Purdue Univ/West Lafayette	IN	6,636	C
Queens College	NC	14,950	C
Quincy Univ	IL	13,646	VC
Rhode Island College	RI	7,901	LC
Rider College	NJ	18,160	C
Ripon College	WI	18,320	C+
Rivier College	NH	14,920	LC
Rockhurst College	MO	12,470	C
Roosevelt Univ	IL	12,368	C
Rosemont College	PA	16,775	C
Russell Sage College	NY	16,790	C
Rutgers Univ/Camden College of A&S	NJ	8,652	VC
Sacred Heart Univ	CT	16,350	C
Saginaw Valley State Univ	MI	6,634	LC
St Ambrose Univ	IA	13,380	C
St Anselm College	NH	17,340	C
St Bonaventure Univ	NY	14,762	C
St Cloud State Univ	MN	5,015	C
St Edward's Univ	TX	12,636	C
St Francis College	IN	11,662	C
St Francis College	NY	6,710	LC
St Francis College	PA	15,744	LC
St John Fisher College	NY	15,415	C
St John's Univ	NY	8,980	C+
St Joseph's College	IN	14,730	C
St Joseph's College	ME	14,535	C
St Joseph's College	NY	7,322	C
St Joseph's Univ	PA	17,800	VC
St Leo College	FL	13,570	C
St Louis Univ	MO	15,522	VC
St Mary's College of Calif	CA	18,848	VC
St Mary's College of Minn	MN	13,850	LC
St Mary's Univ	TX	12,064	C
St Mary-of-the-Woods College	IN	14,430	NC
St Michael's College	VT	17,930	C
St Norbert College	WI	15,710	VC
St Olaf College	MN	17,200	HC
St Paul's College	VA	9,171	C
St Peter's College	NJ	14,775	LC
St Thomas Aquinas College	NY	13,550	C
St Thomas Univ	FL	14,280	LC
St Xavier Univ	IL	14,700	C
Salem State College	MA	6,712	C
Salem-Teikyo Univ	WV	14,527	C
Salisbury State Univ	MD	7,516	C+
Salve Regina Univ	RI	29,100	LC
Samford Univ	AL	11,400	VC
San Francisco State Univ	CA	7,292	LC
Schreiner College	TX	14,320	C
Seton Hall Univ	NJ	18,306	LC
Seton Hill College	PA	14,320	C
Shaw Univ	NC	8,936	C+
Sheldon Jackson College	AK	14,050	NC
Shenandoah Univ	VA	11,800	C
Shepherd College	WV	5,540	C
Shorter College	GA	10,270	C
Silver Lake College	WI	8,280	LC
Simmons College	MA	22,534	C
Simpson College	CA	10,628	C
Simpson College	IA	14,435	VC
Sioux Falls College	SD	11,540	C
Slippery Rock Univ	PA	6,803	C
S Dak State Univ	SD	4,562	C
Southeast Missouri State Univ	MO	5,854	C
Southeastern College of the Assemblies of God	FL	6,618	NC
Southeastern Okla State Univ	OK	3,594	C
Southern Arkansas Univ	AR	3,432	NC
Southern Calif College	CA	12,356	C
Southern Conn State Univ	CT	7,532	C
Southern Illinois Univ at Carbondale	IL	6,234	C
Southern Illinois Univ at Edwardsville	IL	6,097	LC
Southern Nazarene Univ	OK	9,206	NC
Southern Univ and A&M College	LA	4,920	NC
Southern Univ at New Orleans	LA	1,452	NC
Southwest Missouri State Univ	MO	4,956	C
Southwest Texas State Univ	TX	5,124	C
Southwestern College	KS	10,032	C
Southwestern Okla State Univ	OK	3,312	C
Spalding Univ	KY	10,496	LC
Spring Hill College	AL	16,015	C+
Springfield College	MA	15,200	LC
SUNY at Albany	NY	7,059	VC
SUNY at Buffalo	NY	7,896	VC
SUNY/College at Brockport	NY	7,220	C+
SUNY/College at Buffalo	NY	7,035	VC
SUNY/College at Cortland	NY	7,326	C+
SUNY/College at Fredonia	NY	7,159	VC
SUNY/College at Geneseo	NY	6,949	HC
SUNY/College at New Paltz	NY	6,890	VC
SUNY/College at Old Westbury	NY	7,128	LC
SUNY/College at Oneonta	NY	7,878	C
SUNY/College at Oswego	NY	7,330	VC
SUNY/College at Plattsburgh	NY	6,917	C
SUNY/Potsdam College	NY	6,906	C
Sterling College	KS	10,990	VC
Stetson Univ	FL	16,435	VC
Susquehanna Univ	PA	19,950	VC
Syracuse Univ	NY	21,305	HC
Tabor College	KS	11,460	VC
Taylor Univ	IN	14,450	VC
Teikyo Marycrest Univ	IA	13,755	VC
Teikyo Westmar Univ	IA	15,920	C
Temple Univ	PA	10,281	C
Tenn Tech Univ	TN	5,190	C
Tenn Wesleyan College	TN	10,060	C
Texas A&M Univ	TX	5,382	VC
Texas A&M Univ at Kingsville	TX	3,808	LC
Texas Christian Univ	TX	12,180	C
Texas College	TX	5,930	NC
Texas Southern Univ	TX	4,500	NC
Texas Wesleyan Univ	TX	9,380	LC
The Citadel	SC	6,619	C
Thiel College	PA	16,282	C
Thomas More College	KY	12,962	C
Toccoa Falls College	GA	9,350	C
Transylvania Univ	KY	14,970	VC+
Tri-State Univ	IN	13,788	LC
Trinity Christian College	IL	13,260	C
Trinity College	IL	14,010	C
Trinity College of Vermont	VT	16,015	LC
Troy State Univ	AL	4,322	C
Troy State Univ at Dothan/ Fort Rucker	AL	2,260	NC
Turabo Univ	PR	2,670	
Tuskegee Univ	AL	10,128	C
Union College	KY	9,790	C
Union College	NE	11,060	NC
United States International Univ	CA	14,535	LC
Universidad Adventista de las Antillas	PR	5,000	
Universidad Metropolitana	PR	2,650	
Univ of Akron	OH	6,699	NC
Univ of Alabama	AL	5,702	C
Univ of Alabama at Birmingham	AL	7,533	C
Univ of Alaska Anchorage	AK	7,131	C
Univ of Alaska Fairbanks	AK	4,718	C
Univ of Alaska Southeast	AK	4,075	LC
Univ of Arizona	AZ	5,808	C
Univ of Arkansas at Fayetteville	AR	5,046	C
Univ of Central Arkansas	AR	4,200	LC
Univ of Central Okla	OK	3,647	C
Univ of Charleston	WV	12,750	C
Univ of Cincinnati	OH	7,989	C
Univ of Dallas	TX	14,983	VC
Univ of Dayton	OH	15,120	C+
Univ of Delaware	DE	8,013	VC
Univ of Detroit Mercy	MI	14,720	C
Univ of Dubuque	IA	14,150	LC
Univ of Evansville	IN	15,300	VC
Univ of Georgia	GA	5,655	VC
Univ of Guam	GU	4,139	NC
Univ of Hartford	CT	19,858	LC
Univ of Hawaii at Manoa	HI	5,626	C
Univ of Houston	TX	5,215	C
Univ of Idaho	ID	4,830	C
Univ of Illinois at Chicago	IL	8,443	C
Univ of Illinois at Urbana-Champaign	IL	7,764	HC
Univ of Indianapolis	IN	14,510	C
Univ of Iowa	IA	5,658	VC
Univ of Kansas	KS	5,200	NC
Univ of Kentucky	KY	5,152	VC
Univ of La Verne	CA	17,000	C
Univ of Louisville	KY	5,948	C
Univ of Maine	ME	7,990	C
Univ of Maine at Farmington	ME	6,700	C

School	ST	$IS	SR
Univ of Maine at Machias	ME	6,135	C
Univ of Maine at Presque Isle	ME	6,374	C
Univ of Mary	ND	8,910	C
Univ of Mary Hardin-Baylor	TX	8,120	NC
Univ of Maryland/Baltimore County	MD	7,746	VC
Univ of Maryland/College Park	MD	8,182	VC
Univ of Maryland/Eastern Shore	MD	6,254	LC
Univ of Mass/Amherst	MA	9,364	LC
Univ of Miami	FL	22,107	VC
Univ of Mich/Ann Arbor	MI	9,428	HC+
Univ of Mich/Dearborn	MI	3,399	HC
Univ of Mich/Flint	MI	2,916	C
Univ of Minn/Morris	MN	6,825	HC
Univ of Missouri/Columbia	MO	6,254	HC
Univ of Missouri/Kansas City	MO	5,906	VC
Univ of Missouri/St. Louis	MO	6,378	C
Univ of Mobile	AL	9,400	C
Univ of Montana	MT	5,529	C
Univ of Nebr at Kearney	NE	4,308	LC
Univ of Nebr at Omaha	NE	1,889	LC
Univ of Nebr-Lincoln	NE	5,278	LC
Univ of Nevada/Las Vegas	NV	6,405	C
Univ of Nevada/Reno	NV	5,735	C
Univ of New England	ME	16,075	LC
Univ of New Orleans	LA	5,468	C
Univ of North Alabama	AL	4,236	NC
Univ of N Car at Chapel Hill	NC	5,330	HC
Univ of N Car at Wilmington	NC	5,172	C
Univ of North Florida	FL	5,082	C
Univ of Notre Dame	IN	20,150	MC
Univ of Pittsburgh at Bradford	PA	9,050	C
Univ of Pittsburgh at Johnstown	PA	8,914	C
Univ of Portland	OR	15,564	C
Univ of PR/Cayey Univ College	PR	900	
Univ of PR/Rio Piedras	PR	0	
Univ of Redlands	CA	22,059	VC
Univ of Rhode Island	RI	9,205	C
Univ of Richmond	VA	16,700	HC
Univ of Rio Grande	OH	6,300	NC
Univ of St Thomas	TX	11,676	C+
Univ of San Diego	CA	18,970	VC
Univ of San Francisco	CA	18,408	C
Univ of Scranton	PA	17,071	VC
Univ of South Alabama	AL	5,451	C
Univ of S Car at Aiken	SC	5,386	C
Univ of S Car at Spartanburg	SC	2,320	C
Univ of S Dak	SD	4,722	C
Univ of South Florida	FL	5,475	C+
Univ of Southern Indiana	IN	3,720	NC
Univ of Southern Miss	MS	4,542	C
Univ of Southwestern Louisiana	LA	3,968	NC
Univ of Tampa	FL	16,780	C
Univ of Tenn at Chattanooga	TN	5,375	C
Univ of Tenn at Martin	TN	4,550	C
Univ of Texas at Arlington	TX	5,549	LC
Univ of Texas at El Paso	TX	3,160	LC
Univ of Texas-Pan American	TX	3,192	NC
Univ of the Pacific	CA	21,100	C
Univ of Toledo	OH	6,636	NC
Univ of Tulsa	OK	13,795	VC
Univ of Vermont	VT	10,776	C+
Univ of West Florida	FL	5,415	C
Univ of Wisc/Eau Claire	WI	4,647	C
Univ of Wisc/La Crosse	WI	4,487	C
Univ of Wisc/Madison	WI	6,400	HC
Univ of Wisc/Oshkosh	WI	4,240	C
Univ of Wisc/Platteville	WI	4,830	C
Univ of Wisc/River Falls	WI	4,655	C
Univ of Wisc/Superior	WI	4,330	C
Univ of Wisc/Whitewater	WI	4,700	C
Univ of Wyoming	WY	4,991	NC
Upper Iowa Univ	IA	11,900	C
Urbana Univ	OH	12,536	C
Ursinus College	PA	19,165	VC
Ursuline College	OH	13,180	LC
Utah State Univ	UT	4,683	C
Valdosta State Univ	GA	4,670	LC
Valley City State Univ	ND	4,385	LC
Valparaiso Univ	IN	14,810	VC
Vanderbilt Univ	TN	23,422	HC+
Villanova Univ	PA	21,400	HC
Virginia Intermont College	VA	12,250	LC
Virginia Union Univ	VA	10,555	LC
Virginia Wesleyan College	VA	14,950	VC
Wagner College	NY	17,950	C
Walsh Univ	OH	11,640	C
Warner Pacific College	OR	12,112	C
Wartburg College	IA	14,530	VC
Washburn Univ of Topeka	KS	5,802	NC
Washington and Jefferson College	PA	19,360	C
Washington State Univ	WA	6,364	C
Washington Univ	MO	23,507	HC
Wayne State Univ	MI	2,680	C
Waynesburg College	PA	11,960	C
Weber State Univ	UT	4,398	C
Wellesley College	MA	23,815	MC
Wells College	NY	19,460	C+
Wesley College	DE	13,745	LC
Wesleyan College	GA	15,445	C
West Chester Univ of Penn	PA	7,492	C
West Georgia College	GA	4,256	C
West Liberty State College	WV	4,690	LC
West Texas A&M Univ	TX	4,224	C
West Virginia Inst of Tech	WV	5,858	LC
West Virginia State College	WV	5,044	LC
West Virginia Univ	WV	5,774	C
West Virginia Wesleyan College	WV	16,900	C
Western Carolina Univ	NC	3,811	C
Western Conn State Univ	CT	6,622	C
Western Illinois Univ	IL	5,241	LC
Western Mich Univ	MI	6,820	C
Western Montana College of the Univ of Montana	MT	1,646	C
Western New Mexico Univ	NM	3,234	LC
Western Oregon State College	OR	6,180	C
Western State College of Colo	CO	5,560	C
Western Washington Univ	WA	6,077	VC
Westfield State College	MA	7,161	C
Westminster College	MO	13,750	C+
Westminster College	PA	15,200	C
Westminster College of Salt Lake City	UT	12,100	C
Westmont College	CA	18,732	C
Wheaton College	IL	14,710	HC
Whitworth College	WA	16,265	C
Wichita State Univ	KS	5,068	NC
Widener Univ	PA	16,840	C
Wiley College	TX	0	NC
Wilkes Univ	PA	15,728	LC
William Jewell College	MO	12,500	VC
William Penn College	IA	13,400	C
William Woods Univ	MO	14,025	LC
Wilmington College	OH	13,700	LC
Winona State Univ	MN	5,200	VC
Winthrop Univ	SC	6,750	C
Wittenberg Univ	OH	19,998	VC
Wright State Univ	OH	6,896	LC
Xavier Univ	OH	15,710	C+
Xavier Univ of Louisiana	LA	10,400	C
York College of Penn	PA	8,345	C
Youngstown State Univ	OH	6,447	LC

SECRETARIAL STUDIES/OFFICE MANAGEMENT

School	ST	$IS	SR
Cleary College	MI	5,095	NC
Dyke College	OH	5,200	C
Ferris State Univ	MI	7,160	NC
Grand Rapids Baptist College and Seminary	MI	10,228	C
Husson College	ME	11,510	NC
Idaho State Univ	ID	4,442	C
Inter American Univ of PR/Aguadilla Regional College	PR	2,290	
Inter American Univ of PR/Barranquitas Regional College	PR	2,730	
Inter American Univ of PR/Bayamon Univ College	PR	2,300	
Inter American Univ of PR/Metropolitan Campus	PR	2,340	
Inter American Univ of PR/Ponce Regional College	PR	2,300	
Inter American Univ of PR/San German	PR	4,620	
Inter-American Univ of PR/Fajardo Regional College	PR	2,372	
Johnson and Wales Univ	RI	13,995	LC
Pillsbury Baptist Bible College	MN	7,390	NC
Selma Univ	AL	5,785	NC
Southeastern Okla State Univ	OK	3,594	C
Southern Univ at New Orleans	LA	1,452	NC
Turabo Univ	PR	2,670	
Univ of PR/Arecibo Tech Univ College	PR	1,302	C
Univ of PR/Humacao Univ College	PR	1,494	
Univ of PR/Rio Piedras	PR	0	
Univ of Southwestern Louisiana	LA	3,968	NC
Univ of the Sacred Heart	PR	3,890	
Univ of Wisc/Eau Claire	WI	4,647	C

SLAVIC LANGUAGES

School	ST	$IS	SR
Brown Univ	RI	26,104	MC
Duke Univ	NC	21,271	MC
Lawrence Univ	WI	19,986	HC+
Northwestern Univ	IL	21,093	MC
Ohio State Univ	OH	7,218	LC
Princeton Univ	NJ	24,650	MC
Univ of Calif at Berkeley	CA	9,962	HC+
Univ of Calif at Los Angeles	CA	8,959	HC
Univ of Calif at Santa Barbara	CA	9,460	C
Univ of Georgia	GA	5,655	VC
Univ of N Car at Chapel Hill	NC	5,330	HC
Univ of Penn	PA	24,238	MC
Univ of Texas at Austin	TX	5,160	VC
Univ of Virginia	VA	7,964	MC
Univ of Washington	WA	6,618	VC
Wayne State Univ	MI	2,680	C

SMALL BUSINESS MANAGEMENT

School	ST	$IS	SR
Concord College	WV	5,104	NC
Ferris State Univ	MI	7,160	NC
Florida Atlantic Univ	FL	5,525	C
Hawaii Pacific Univ	HI	12,300	C
Johnson and Wales Univ	RI	13,995	LC
Lawrence Tech Univ	MI	9,470	C
Mount Ida College	MA	16,700	LC
Northeastern Univ	MA	19,851	C
Pacific Univ	OR	17,869	C
Rowan College of New Jersey	NJ	7,358	VC
Univ of Maine at Augusta	ME	2,595	NC
Univ of Montana	MT	5,529	C
Univ of North Texas	TX	4,853	C
Univ of Penn	PA	24,238	MC
Univ of Wyoming	WY	4,991	NC
Waynesburg College	PA	11,960	C

SOCIAL FOUNDATIONS

School	ST	$IS	SR
Boston Univ	MA	24,130	HC
Marquette Univ	WI	16,114	VC

SOCIAL PSYCHOLOGY

School	ST	$IS	SR
Tufts Univ	MA	24,962	MC
Univ of Nevada/Reno	NV	5,735	C
Wheaton College	MA	23,840	C+

SOCIAL SCIENCE

School	ST	$IS	SR
Abilene Christian Univ	TX	10,460	NC
Adelphi Univ	NY	18,250	LC
Adrian College	MI	14,340	C
Alabama A&M Univ	AL	4,200	C
Alcorn State Univ	MS	4,474	C+
Alverno College	WI	11,344	C
Antioch College	OH	19,532	C
Appalachian State Univ	NC	4,095	C
Aquinas College	MI	14,526	C
Arkansas Baptist College	AR	5,016	NC
Ashland Univ	OH	15,508	C
Augustana College	SD	13,420	C
Azusa Pacific Univ	CA	15,034	C
Bard College	NY	25,269	HC
Bartlesville Wesleyan College	OK	9,400	C
Bellevue College	NE	3,050	NC
Bemidji State Univ	MN	5,188	C
Benedict College	SC	8,376	LC
Benedictine College	KS	12,830	C
Berry College	GA	11,990	VC
Bethany College	KS	11,232	C
Bethel College	IN	11,650	C
Bethel College	KS	11,530	C
Bethel College	MN	15,050	C
Bethel College	TN	9,736	LC
Biola Univ	CA	16,124	C
Black Hills State Univ	SD	4,831	NC
Bloomsburg Univ of Penn	PA	6,312	C+
Blue Mountain College	MS	5,958	LC
Bluefield State College	WV	1,832	LC
Bluffton College	OH	12,951	C
Boise State Univ	ID	4,909	LC
Boston Univ	MA	24,130	HC
Bowling Green State Univ	OH	6,701	C
Brooklyn Campus of LIU	NY	15,000	LC
Buena Vista College	IA	16,150	VC
Calif Baptist College	CA	11,294	C
Calif Inst of Tech	CA	20,783	MC
Calif Lutheran Univ	CA	17,240	C
Calif Polytechnic State Univ	CA	6,980	VC+
Calif State Polytechnic Univ/Pomona	CA	6,438	LC
Cal State/Chico	CA	6,146	C
Cal State/Fresno	CA	5,747	C
Cal State/Los Angeles	CA	4,940	VC
Cal State/Sacramento	CA	6,387	C
Cal State/San Bernardino	CA	6,055	LC
Cal State/Stanislaus	CA	6,799	C
Calif Univ of Penn	PA	7,370	C
Calumet College of St. Joseph	IN	3,585	C
Calvin College	MI	13,020	VC
Cardinal Stritch College	WI	11,252	C
Caribbean Univ	PR	2,400	
Carnegie Mellon Univ	PA	22,560	HC+
Carroll College	MT	11,265	C
Carson-Newman College	TN	11,250	C
Carthage College	WI	15,995	C
Castleton State College	VT	8,378	LC
Catholic Univ of America	DC	18,856	C
Cazenovia College	NY	14,655	LC
Cedarville College	OH	10,715	C
Central Conn State Univ	CT	7,108	C
Central Methodist College	MO	11,410	C
Central Missouri State Univ	MO	5,138	LC
Central Washington Univ	WA	5,644	C
Central Wesleyan College	SC	9,640	C
Chadron State College	NE	4,091	NC
Chaminade Univ of Honolulu	HI	14,290	C
Chapman Univ	CA	21,842	C
Charleston Southern Univ	SC	10,282	LC
Charter Oak State College	CT	314	NC
Cheyney Univ of Penn	PA	7,005	C
CUNY/Hunter College	NY	4,101	VC
Claflin College	SC	0	
Clarion Univ of Penn	PA	6,518	C
Clarkson Univ	NY	20,705	VC+
Cleveland State Univ	OH	7,287	NC
Clinch Valley College/Univ of Virginia	VA	6,364	C
Coker College	SC	13,790	C
Colgate Univ	NY	24,020	HC
College of Great Falls	MT	6,230	NC
College of Notre Dame	CA	16,480	C
College of St Benedict	MN	15,468	VC
College of St Catherine	MN	14,670	C
College of St Joseph	VT	12,650	LC
College of St Mary	NE	12,500	C
Colo Christian Univ	CO	9,750	C
Colo State Univ	CO	6,566	VC
Columbia Univ/Columbia College	NY	26,757	MC
Concord College	WV	5,104	NC
Concordia College	MI	13,660	C
Concordia College	MN	13,200	C
Concordia Univ	IL	12,611	C
Concordia Univ Wisc	WI	12,140	C
Coppin State College	MD	7,145	LC
Cornell Univ	NY	13,445	MC
Cumberland Univ	TN	8,650	C
Dana College	NE	11,910	C
Dartmouth College	NH	24,354	MC
Delta State Univ	MS	3,964	LC
DePaul Univ	IL	15,535	VC
Doane College	NE	12,220	C
Dominican College	NY	13,600	LC
Dordt College	IA	11,690	C
Dowling College	NY	12,730	LC
Drake Univ	IA	17,195	VC
Duquesne Univ	PA	16,434	VC
Dyke College	OH	5,200	C
Earlham College	IN	19,383	VC
East Stroudsburg Univ	PA	6,886	C
East Tenn State Univ	TN	4,406	C
Eastern Illinois Univ	IL	5,548	C
Eastern Mennonite College	VA	12,700	C
Eastern Mich Univ	MI	6,749	C
Eastern Montana College	MT	5,165	LC
Eastern Washington Univ	WA	5,439	LC
Edinboro Univ of Penn	PA	7,181	C
Elizabeth City State Univ	NC	4,254	LC
Elon College	NC	12,290	LC
Emory and Henry College	VA	12,776	C
Emporia State Univ	KS	4,685	NC
Eugene Lang College of the New School for Social Research	NY	21,145	C+
Eureka College	IL	14,555	C
Evangel College	MO	10,142	LC
Evergreen State College	WA	6,306	C
Fayetteville State Univ	NC	3,926	LC
Felician College	NJ	7,900	C
Flagler College	FL	7,990	C
Florida A&M Univ	FL	4,651	C
Florida Atlantic Univ	FL	5,525	C
Florida Southern College	FL	12,260	C
Fordham Univ/College at Lincoln Center	NY	18,150	VC
Fresno Pacific College	CA	13,020	C
Frostburg State Univ	MD	6,940	C
Gannon Univ	PA	14,872	C
Gardner-Webb Univ	NC	11,950	LC
Georgia College	GA	4,310	LC
Goddard College	VT	17,990	LC
Graceland College	IA	11,600	C
Grambling State Univ	LA	4,712	NC
Grand Canyon Univ	AZ	9,680	VC

School	ST	$IS	SR
Grand Valley State Univ	MI	6,822	VC
Grand View College	IA	13,230	NC
Gustavus Adolphus College	MN	15,935	VC
Hamline Univ	MN	17,122	VC
Hardin-Simmons Univ	TX	9,080	C
Harding Univ	AR	9,050	VC
Harvard Univ/Harvard and Radcliffe Colleges	MA	24,880	MC
Hastings College	NE	12,426	C
Hawaii Pacific Univ	HI	12,300	C
Heidelberg College	OH	17,160	C
Hendrix College	AR	11,670	C
Hillsdale College	MI	15,110	VC
Hiram College	OH	18,340	VC
Hofstra Univ	NY	16,580	VC
Holy Family College	PA	8,300	C
Houghton College	NY	13,120	VC
Howard Payne Univ	TX	8,052	C
Humboldt State Univ	CA	5,676	C
Huron Univ	SD	9,790	C
Illinois Benedictine College	IL	14,170	C
Illinois State Univ	IL	6,413	C
Immaculata College	PA	14,620	C
Indiana Univ at Kokomo	IN	2,069	C
Indiana Univ Bloomington	IN	6,495	VC
Indiana Univ of Penn	PA	6,373	C
Indiana Univ-Purdue Univ at Fort Wayne	IN	2,500	LC
Iona College	NY	16,310	C
Jackson State Univ	MS	4,996	LC
James Madison Univ	VA	8,198	HC
Johnson C. Smith Univ	NC	8,916	LC
Judson College	AL	9,060	C
Juniata College	PA	18,390	C+
Kendall College	IL	12,651	LC
Lake Erie College	OH	13,700	C
Lake Superior State Univ	MI	7,311	C
Lamar Univ	TX	3,798	C
Langston Univ	OK	2,907	LC
Lee College	TN	7,894	LC
Lehigh Univ	PA	23,250	HC
LeMoyne-Owen College	TN	4,500	LC
Lewis-Clark State College	ID	4,040	
Liberty Univ	VA	11,500	LC
Lincoln Memorial Univ	TN	8,218	C
Livingston Univ	AL	3,979	C
Lock Haven Univ of Penn	PA	7,128	C
LIU/Southampton Campus	NY	17,280	C
Loyola Univ/New Orleans	LA	15,660	C+
Lyndon State College	VT	8,394	LC
Madonna Univ	MI	8,546	C
Malone College	OH	12,572	C
Manhattan College	NY	19,000	C
Mansfield Univ	PA	6,348	C
Marlboro College	VT	23,305	C+
Marquette Univ	WI	16,114	VC
Marygrove College	MI	5,877	VC
Marylhurst College	OR	6,486	NC
Maryville College	TN	14,474	C
Marywood College	PA	14,890	C
Mayville State Univ	ND	4,272	NC
McKendree College	IL	10,900	C
McMurry Univ	TX	10,100	C
McPherson College	KS	11,360	VC
Medaille College	NY	12,650	C
Mercer Univ	GA	15,123	C
Mercy College	NY	11,180	NC
Mesa State College	CO	5,127	NC
Methodist College	NC	12,400	C
Miami Univ	OH	8,066	VC
Mich State Univ	MI	7,842	C
Mich Tech Univ	MI	7,283	VC+
Middle Tenn State Univ	TN	3,857	C
Midland Lutheran College	NE	12,410	LC
Miles College	AL	7,150	NC
Millikin Univ	IL	15,499	C
Minot State Univ	ND	3,748	NC
Miss College	MS	8,348	C
Miss Univ for Women	MS	4,456	LC
Missouri Baptist College	MO	9,340	C
Missouri Southern State College	MO	4,272	C
Missouri Valley College	MO	14,050	LC
Moorhead State Univ	MN	5,076	C
Moravian College	PA	18,960	VC
Morehead State Univ	KY	4,600	LC
Morris Brown College	GA	12,234	NC
Mount Marty College	SD	10,450	NC
Mount St Mary College	NY	12,910	C
Mount Senario College	WI	10,970	C
Mount Union College	OH	15,850	C
Muhlenberg College	PA	20,795	VC
Muskingum College	OH	16,650	C
National-Louis Univ	IL	13,218	C
Nazareth College of Rochester	NY	15,310	C+
New College of Calif	CA	6,900	NC
New College of the Univ of South Florida	FL	5,697	MC
New Hampshire College	NH	15,242	LC
New York Univ	NY	24,705	VC+
Niagara Univ	NY	14,552	C
Nichols College	MA	14,200	LC
Norfolk State Univ	VA	6,345	LC
N Car Central Univ	NC	4,347	LC
N Car State Univ	NC	4,984	VC
North Central College	IL	15,498	VC
N Dak State Univ of Agriculture and Applied Science	ND	4,774	VC
North Park College	IL	14,310	C
Northeastern Illinois Univ	IL	1,955	C
Northeastern State Univ	OK	5,250	C
Northern Arizona Univ	AZ	4,844	C
Northern Kentucky Univ	KY	4,620	NC
Northern Montana College	MT	4,976	C
Northern State Univ	SD	4,186	LC
Northland College	WI	13,550	LC
Northwest Missouri State Univ	MO	5,010	LC
Northwest Nazarene College	ID	11,750	C
Northwestern College	MN	13,554	C
Northwestern Okla State Univ	OK	3,424	C
Northwestern State Univ of Louisiana	LA	4,287	NC
Notre Dame College of Ohio	OH	11,370	C
Nyack College	NY	12,210	LC
Ohio Dominican College	OH	11,820	LC
Ohio Univ	OH	7,341	C
Ohio Wesleyan Univ	OH	21,108	VC+
Okla Baptist Univ	OK	8,486	C
Old Dominion Univ	VA	8,317	C
Olivet Nazarene Univ	IL	11,976	C
Otterbein College	OH	16,506	C
Our Lady of Holy Cross College	LA	4,630	LC
Pace Univ	NY	15,540	C
Pacific Christian College	CA	12,700	C
Pepperdine Univ	CA	23,720	VC
Peru State College	NE	4,311	NC
Pittsburg State Univ	KS	4,478	NC
Plymouth State College	NH	7,166	C
Polytechnic Univ/Brooklyn	NY	19,700	HC
Polytechnic Univ/Farmingdale	NY	20,700	VC
Pontifical Catholic Univ of PR/Ponce	PR	5,807	
Portland State Univ	OR	7,191	C
Presbyterian College	SC	15,400	VC
Providence College	RI	19,750	VC
Quinnipiac College	CT	17,600	C+
Radford Univ	VA	7,034	LC
Ramapo College of New Jersey	NJ	8,027	C+
Rhode Island College	RI	7,901	LC
Rockford College	IL	15,300	C
Roosevelt Univ	IL	12,368	C
Rosary College	IL	15,040	C
Rosemont College	PA	16,775	C
St Bonaventure Univ	NY	14,762	C
St Cloud State Univ	MN	5,015	C
St Francis College	IN	11,662	C
St John's Univ	MN	15,364	C
St John's Univ	NY	8,980	C+
St Joseph College	CT	16,225	C
St Joseph's College	NY	7,322	C
St Mary's College	MI	8,350	C
St Mary's College of Minn	MN	13,850	LC
St Mary-of-the-Woods College	IN	14,430	NC
St Paul's College	VA	9,171	C
St Peter's College	NJ	14,775	LC
St Thomas Aquinas College	NY	13,550	C
St Xavier Univ	IL	14,700	C
Salve Regina Univ	RI	29,100	LC
San Diego State Univ	CA	6,692	LC
San Jose State Univ	CA	6,680	LC
Scripps College	CA	23,600	HC
Seton Hall Univ	NJ	18,306	LC
Shawnee State Univ	OH	4,379	NC
Shepherd College	WV	5,540	C
Shimer College	IL	12,850	NC
Shorter College	GA	10,270	C
Siena Heights College	MI	12,520	C
Silver Lake College	WI	8,280	LC
Simon's Rock College of Bard	MA	23,760	VC+
Simpson College	CA	10,628	C
Slippery Rock Univ	PA	6,803	C
Southeastern Okla State Univ	OK	3,594	C
Southern Illinois Univ at Carbondale	IL	6,234	C
Southern Methodist Univ	TX	18,520	VC
Southern Nazarene Univ	OK	9,206	NC
Southern Oregon State College	OR	6,128	C
Southern Univ and A&M College	LA	4,920	NC
Southern Utah Univ	UT	4,104	LC
Southwest Baptist Univ	MO	9,192	NC
Southwest Missouri State Univ	MO	4,956	C
Southwest Texas State Univ	TX	5,124	C
Southwestern Adventist College	TX	10,530	NC
Southwestern College	KS	10,032	C
Southwestern Okla State Univ	OK	3,312	C
Spring Arbor College	MI	12,256	C
Spring Hill College	AL	16,015	C+
SUNY at Binghamton	NY	7,921	HC
SUNY at Buffalo	NY	7,896	VC
SUNY at Stony Brook	NY	7,658	VC
SUNY/College at Cortland	NY	7,326	C+
SUNY/College at New Paltz	NY	6,890	VC
SUNY/College at Plattsburgh	NY	6,917	C
Stephens College	MO	18,460	C
Stetson Univ	FL	16,435	VC
Suffolk Univ	MA	15,360	LC
Sul Ross State Univ	TX	4,144	NC
Sweet Briar College	VA	19,770	C
Syracuse Univ	NY	21,305	HC
Teikyo Marycrest Univ	IA	13,755	VC
Temple Univ	PA	10,281	C
Tenn Wesleyan College	TN	10,060	C
Texas College	TX	5,930	NC
Texas Wesleyan Univ	TX	9,380	LC
Thomas A. Edison State College	NJ	400	
Touro College	NY	11,930	C
Towson State Univ	MD	7,452	C
Tri-State Univ	IN	13,788	LC
Troy State Univ	AL	4,322	C
Troy State Univ at Dothan/Fort Rucker	AL	2,260	NC
Troy State Univ in Montgomery	AL	1,710	NC
Turabo Univ	PR	2,670	
Union College	KY	9,790	C
Union College	NE	11,060	NC
United States Air Force Academy	CO	0	MC
United States International Univ	CA	14,535	LC
Universidad Metropolitana	PR	2,650	
Univ of Akron	OH	6,699	NC
Univ of Arkansas at Monticello	AR	3,832	NC
Univ of Calif at Berkeley	CA	9,962	HC+
Univ of Calif at Davis	CA	9,534	VC
Univ of Calif, Riverside	CA	9,178	C
Univ of Calif/Irvine	CA	12,680	VC
Univ of Central Florida	FL	6,061	C+
Univ of Charleston	WV	12,750	C
Univ of Cincinnati	OH	7,989	C
Univ of Denver	CO	19,290	C+
Univ of Guam	GU	4,139	NC
Univ of Houston	TX	5,215	C
Univ of Houston-Downtown	TX	4,034	NC
Univ of Indianapolis	IN	14,510	C
Univ of Iowa	IA	5,658	VC
Univ of La Verne	CA	17,400	C
Univ of Maine at Augusta	ME	2,595	NC
Univ of Maine at Fort Kent	ME	6,285	LC
Univ of Maine at Machias	ME	6,135	C
Univ of Maine at Presque Isle	ME	6,374	C
Univ of Mary	ND	8,910	C
Univ of Mary Hardin-Baylor	TX	8,120	NC
Univ of Maryland/College Park	MD	8,182	VC
Univ of Mich/Ann Arbor	MI	9,428	HC+
Univ of Mich/Dearborn	MI	3,399	HC
Univ of Mich/Flint	MI	2,916	C
Univ of Minn/Morris	MN	6,825	HC
Univ of Missouri/Columbia	MO	6,254	HC
Univ of Montevallo	AL	5,310	C
Univ of Nebr at Kearney	NE	4,308	LC
Univ of Nebr-Lincoln	NE	5,278	LC
Univ of Nevada/Las Vegas	NV	6,405	C
Univ of N Car at Greensboro	NC	5,192	C
Univ of N Car at Wilmington	NC	5,172	C
Univ of N Dak	ND	4,902	NC
Univ of North Texas	TX	4,853	C
Univ of Northern Colo	CO	6,008	C
Univ of Northern Iowa	IA	5,137	C
Univ of Penn	PA	24,238	MC
Univ of Pittsburgh at Greensburg	PA	8,660	C
Univ of Pittsburgh at Johnstown	PA	8,914	C
Univ of PR/Cayey Univ College	PR	900	
Univ of PR/Mayaguez	PR	0	
Univ of PR/Rio Piedras	PR	0	
Univ of Puget Sound	WA	19,520	HC
Univ of Rio Grande	OH	6,300	NC
Univ of South Florida	FL	5,475	C+
Univ of Southern Calif	CA	23,006	VC
Univ of Southern Colo	CO	5,350	LC
Univ of Southern Miss	MS	4,542	C
Univ of Tampa	FL	16,780	C
Univ of the District of Columbia	DC	974	NC
Univ of the Pacific	CA	21,100	C
Univ of the South	TN	18,830	HC
Univ of the Virgin Islands	VI	5,896	C
Univ of Utah	UT	5,975	C
Univ of West Florida	FL	5,415	C
Univ of Wisc/Eau Claire	WI	4,647	C
Univ of Wisc/Platteville	WI	4,830	C
Univ of Wisc/Stevens Point	WI	5,047	C+
Upper Iowa Univ	IA	11,900	C
Ursuline College	OH	13,180	LC
Utica College of Syracuse Univ	NY	16,714	LC
Valdosta State Univ	GA	4,670	LC
Virginia Wesleyan College	VA	14,950	VC
Wagner College	NY	17,950	C
Warner Pacific College	OR	12,112	C
Washington State Univ	WA	6,364	C
Wayland Baptist Univ	TX	7,811	NC
Wayne State College	NE	4,260	NC
Waynesburg College	PA	11,960	C
Weber State Univ	UT	4,398	C
Webster Univ	MO	12,650	C
Wesleyan Univ	CT	23,770	MC
West Liberty State College	WV	4,690	LC
West Texas A&M Univ	TX	4,224	C
West Virginia Wesleyan College	WV	16,900	C
Western Baptist College	OR	12,400	LC
Western Carolina Univ	NC	3,811	C
Western Conn State Univ	CT	6,622	C
Western Kentucky Univ	KY	4,808	C
Western Mich Univ	MI	6,820	C
Western New Mexico Univ	NM	3,234	LC
Western Oregon State College	OR	6,180	C
Westfield State College	MA	7,161	C
Westminster College	PA	15,200	C
Westminster College of Salt Lake City	UT	12,100	C
Westmont College	CA	18,732	C
Widener Univ	PA	16,840	C
Wilberforce Univ	OH	10,408	C
Wiley College	TX	0	NC
William Carey College	MS	7,050	C
William Penn College	IA	13,400	C
William Tyndale College	MI	7,120	NC
Wilmington College	OH	13,700	LC
Winona State Univ	MN	5,200	VC
Youngstown State Univ	OH	6,447	LC

SOCIAL SCIENCE EDUCATION

School	ST	$IS	SR
Armstrong State College	GA	4,874	LC
Blackburn College	IL	9,120	C
Calif Univ of Penn	PA	7,370	C
Calumet College of St. Joseph	IN	3,585	C
Central Methodist College	MO	11,410	C
Chadron State College	NE	4,091	NC
Drake Univ	IA	17,195	VC
Eastern Nazarene College	MA	12,165	LC
Eastern Washington Univ	WA	5,439	LC
Franklin Pierce College	NH	17,270	LC
Fresno Pacific College	CA	13,020	C
Georgia Southwestern College	GA	4,338	LC
Humboldt State Univ	CA	5,676	C
Indiana Univ of Penn	PA	6,373	C
Lincoln Univ	MO	4,638	NC
Marquette Univ	WI	16,114	VC
Mercyhurst College	PA	13,488	C
Miles College	AL	7,150	NC
Miss Valley State Univ	MS	4,089	NC
Mount Holyoke College	MA	23,630	VC
N Car Agricultural and Technical State Univ	NC	4,477	LC
Northern Montana College	MT	4,976	C
Northwestern Univ	IL	21,093	MC
Oakwood College	AL	10,005	C
Plymouth State College	NH	7,166	C
St Mary's College of Minn	MN	13,850	LC
Seattle Pacific Univ	WA	16,503	C
Sheldon Jackson College	AK	14,050	NC
Southwestern Okla State Univ	OK	3,312	C
Tri-State Univ	IN	13,788	LC
Troy State Univ	AL	4,322	C
Troy State Univ at Dothan/Fort Rucker	AL	2,260	NC
Turabo Univ	PR	2,670	
Univ of Arkansas at Pine Bluff	AR	3,978	LC
Univ of Central Florida	FL	6,061	C+
Univ of Maine at Farmington	ME	6,700	C
Univ of Maine at Presque Isle	ME	6,374	C
Univ of Maryland/Eastern Shore	MD	6,254	LC
Univ of North Florida	FL	5,082	C
Univ of Wisc/Milwaukee	WI	6,165	C
Univ of Wisc/Oshkosh	WI	4,240	C
Wiley College	TX	0	NC

SOCIAL STUDIES

School	ST	$IS	SR
Alvernia College	PA	13,150	LC
Barton College	NC	10,689	LC
Bluefield College	VA	10,600	C
Brescia College	KY	9,800	C
Caldwell College	NJ	12,860	C
Carlow College	PA	13,914	C
Cleveland State Univ	OH	7,287	NC

School	ST	$IS	SR
College of St Catherine	MN	14,670	C
Colo Christian Univ	CO	9,750	C
Defiance College	OH	13,480	LC
DePaul Univ	IL	15,535	VC
Eastern Nazarene College	MA	12,165	LC
Eastern New Mexico Univ	NM	3,950	C
Elizabethtown College	PA	17,850	VC
Ferrum College	VA	12,800	LC
Grand Canyon Univ	AZ	9,680	VC
Harvard Univ/Harvard and Radcliffe Colleges	MA	24,880	MC
Indiana Wesleyan Univ	IN	12,332	C
Ithaca College	NY	19,679	C
John Brown Univ	AR	9,880	VC
Lees-McRae College	NC	9,850	LC
Limestone College	SC	10,700	LC
Morris College	SC	6,880	LC
Northern Mich Univ	MI	6,350	C
Olivet College	MI	14,000	C
Our Lady of the Lake Univ of San Antonio	TX	11,080	C
Pacific Union College	CA	15,075	C
Pfeiffer College	NC	11,670	LC
St Augustine's College	NC	9,300	C+
St Francis College	NY	6,710	LC
St Joseph's Univ	PA	17,800	VC
S Car State Univ	SC	5,424	LC
Tusculum College	TN	10,400	LC
Union Univ	TN	7,880	C+
Univ of Calif at Los Angeles	CA	8,959	HC
Univ of Nebr-Lincoln	NE	5,278	LC
Univ of St Thomas	MN	15,785	C+
Univ of Wisc/River Falls	WI	4,655	C
Univ of Wisc/Superior	WI	4,330	C
Vassar College	NY	24,206	HC
William Woods Univ	MO	14,025	LC

SOCIAL STUDIES EDUCATION

School	ST	$IS	SR
Adelphi Univ	NY	18,250	LC
Albertson College	ID	15,942	C+
Alice Lloyd College	KY	2,750	VC
Alverno College	WI	11,344	C
Augsburg College	MN	15,608	C
Baldwin-Wallace College	OH	15,210	C
Bethune-Cookman College	FL	8,375	LC
Bloomsburg Univ of Penn	PA	6,312	C+
Boston Univ	MA	24,130	HC
Canisius College	NY	15,510	C
Carthage College	WI	15,995	C
CUNY/Queens College	NY	2,631	C
Coastal Carolina Univ	SC	6,010	LC
College of St Rose	NY	14,452	C
Concordia College	MN	13,200	C
Concordia College/Moorhead	MN	12,750	C
Daemen College	NY	13,020	LC
Delta State Univ	MS	3,964	LC
Drake Univ	IA	17,195	VC
Florida International Univ	FL	4,191	VC
George Fox College	OR	15,640	LC
Georgia State Univ	GA	2,019	C
Gwynedd-Mercy College	PA	15,450	C
Heritage College	WA	5,540	NC
Huntington College	IN	13,220	C
Indiana State Univ	IN	6,210	C
Indiana Univ-Purdue Univ at Indianapolis	IN	5,862	LC
Indiana Wesleyan Univ	IN	12,332	C
Johnson C. Smith Univ	NC	8,916	LC
Kennesaw State College	GA	1,553	C
Kent State Univ	OH	6,740	LC
Kentucky State Univ	KY	4,282	C+
La Salle Univ	PA	16,940	VC
Lewis and Clark College	OR	19,980	VC
Lincoln Univ	PA	0	LC
Mansfield Univ	PA	6,348	C
Mary Baldwin College	VA	17,700	LC
Messiah College	PA	14,664	VC
MidAmerica Nazarene College	KS	10,208	NC
Millersville Univ of Penn	PA	7,370	VC
Montreat-Anderson College	NC	10,972	LC
Moorhead State Univ	MN	5,076	C
Morris College	SC	6,880	LC
Niagara Univ	NY	14,552	C
Nicholls State Univ	LA	4,531	NC
N Car State Univ	NC	4,984	VC
Northeast Louisiana Univ	LA	3,906	NC
Northwestern College	MN	13,554	C
Ohio State Univ	OH	7,218	LC
Okla Christian Univ of Science and Arts	OK	8,790	NC
Pembroke State Univ	NC	3,538	LC
Pontifical Catholic Univ of PR/Ponce	PR	5,807	
Purdue Univ/West Lafayette	IN	6,636	C
Queens College	NC	14,950	C
Rider College	NJ	18,160	C
Rivier College	NH	14,920	LC
St Francis College	IN	11,662	C
St Martin's College	WA	14,965	C
St Olaf College	MN	17,200	HC
St Thomas Univ	FL	14,280	LC
Southeastern College of the Assemblies of God	FL	6,618	NC
Southeastern Louisiana Univ	LA	4,230	NC
Southern Illinois Univ at Carbondale	IL	6,234	C
Southern Univ and A&M College	LA	4,920	NC
Southern Univ at New Orleans	LA	1,452	NC
Syracuse Univ	NY	21,305	HC
Temple Univ	PA	10,281	C
Univ of Charleston	WV	12,750	C
Univ of Evansville	IN	15,300	VC
Univ of Illinois at Chicago	IL	8,443	C
Univ of Illinois at Urbana-Champaign	IL	7,764	HC
Univ of Kentucky	KY	5,152	VC
Univ of Mich/Dearborn	MI	3,399	HC
Univ of Minn/Duluth	MN	6,512	C
Univ of Minn/Twin Cities	MN	6,682	VC
Univ of Okla	OK	5,427	VC
Univ of Southwestern Louisiana	LA	3,968	NC
Univ of Wisc/La Crosse	WI	4,487	C
Univ of Wisc/Whitewater	WI	4,700	C
Ursuline College	OH	13,180	LC
West Texas A&M Univ	TX	4,224	C
Western Oregon State College	OR	6,180	C
Whitworth College	WA	16,265	C
Xavier Univ of Louisiana	LA	10,400	C

SOCIAL WORK

School	ST	$IS	SR
Abilene Christian Univ	TX	10,460	NC
Adelphi Univ	NY	18,250	LC
Adrian College	MI	14,340	C
Alabama A&M Univ	AL	4,200	C
Alabama State Univ	AL	3,428	NC
Albany State College	GA	4,481	LC
Alvernia College	PA	13,150	LC
Anderson Univ	IN	12,920	C
Andrews Univ	MI	14,952	NC
Anna Maria College	MA	15,975	LC
Antioch College	OH	19,532	C
Appalachian State Univ	NC	4,095	C
Arizona State Univ Main Campus	AZ	6,444	C
Arkansas State Univ	AR	4,250	NC
Asbury College	KY	11,105	VC
Ashland Univ	OH	15,508	C
Atlantic Union College	MA	14,150	LC
Auburn Univ	AL	5,823	C+
Audrey Cohen College	NY	11,184	LC
Augsburg College	MN	15,608	C
Augustana College	SD	13,420	C
Aurora Univ	IL	13,381	C
Austin Peay State Univ	TN	4,350	C
Averett College	VA	13,610	LC
Avila College	MO	12,130	C
Azusa Pacific Univ	CA	15,034	C
Ball State Univ	IN	6,032	LC
Barton College	NC	10,689	LC
Baylor Univ	TX	10,990	C+
Belmont Univ	TN	10,540	C
Bemidji State Univ	MN	5,188	C
Benedict College	SC	8,376	LC
Bennett College	NC	8,920	LC
Bethany College	KS	11,232	C
Bethany College	WV	18,300	C+
Bethel College	KS	11,530	C
Bethel College	MN	15,050	C
Bloomsburg Univ of Penn	PA	6,312	C+
Bluffton College	OH	12,951	C
Boise State Univ	ID	4,909	LC
Boston Univ	MA	24,130	HC
Bowie State Univ	MD	7,294	LC
Bowling Green State Univ	OH	6,701	C
Bradley Univ	IL	14,718	C+
Brescia College	KY	9,800	C
Briar Cliff College	IA	13,375	C
Bridgewater State College	MA	7,518	C
Brigham Young Univ	UT	5,625	HC
Brigham Young Univ/Hawaii	HI	6,750	VC
Buena Vista College	IA	16,150	VC
Cabrini College	PA	16,012	C
Cal State/Chico	CA	6,146	C
Cal State/Fresno	CA	5,747	C
Cal State/Long Beach	CA	6,057	LC
Cal State/Los Angeles	CA	4,940	VC
Cal State/Northridge	CA	7,122	LC
Cal State/Sacramento	CA	6,387	C
Cal State/San Bernardino	CA	6,055	LC
Calif Univ of Penn	PA	7,370	C
Calumet College of St. Joseph	IN	3,585	C
Calvin College	MI	13,020	VC
Campbell Univ	NC	10,624	C
Capital Univ	OH	16,535	VC
Caribbean Univ	PR	2,400	
Carroll College	MT	11,265	C
Carroll College	WI	15,490	C
Carthage College	WI	15,995	C
Castleton State College	VT	8,378	LC
Catholic Univ of America	DC	18,856	C
Cedar Crest College	PA	18,930	C
Cedarville College	OH	10,715	C
Central Conn State Univ	CT	7,108	C
Central Missouri State Univ	MO	5,138	LC
Central State Univ	OH	7,320	NC
Central Univ of Bayamon	PR	2,430	
Central Washington Univ	WA	5,644	C
Chadron State College	NE	4,091	NC
Christopher Newport Univ	VA	3,196	LC
CUNY/Herbert H. Lehman College	NY	2,542	C
CUNY/York College	NY	2,534	NC
Clark Atlanta Univ	GA	11,846	C
Clarke College	IA	13,950	C+
Cleveland State Univ	OH	7,287	NC
College Misericordia	PA	15,820	C
College of Mount St Joseph	OH	13,272	C
College of New Rochelle	NY	15,440	LC
College of Our Lady of The Elms	MA	15,639	C
College of St Benedict	MN	15,468	VC
College of St Catherine	MN	14,670	C
College of St Francis	IL	13,060	VC
College of St Scholastica	MN	14,868	C
Colo State Univ	CO	6,566	VC
Columbia College	MO	11,995	C
Columbia College	SC	13,520	LC
Concord College	WV	5,104	NC
Concordia College	NY	0	LC
Concordia College	OR	12,300	C
Concordia College/Moorhead	MN	12,750	C
Concordia Univ Wisc	WI	12,140	C
Coppin State College	MD	7,145	LC
Creighton Univ	NE	14,432	VC
D'Youville College	NY	12,850	C
Daemen College	NY	13,020	LC
Dana College	NE	11,910	C
David Lipscomb Univ	TN	7,865	VC
Defiance College	OH	13,480	LC
Delaware State College	DE	5,656	C
Delta State Univ	MS	3,964	LC
Dickinson State Univ	ND	3,792	
Dillard Univ	LA	9,950	C
Dominican College	NY	13,600	LC
Dordt College	IA	11,690	C
East Carolina Univ	NC	4,498	C
East Central Univ	OK	3,558	C
East Tenn State Univ	TN	4,406	C
East Texas State Univ	TX	4,572	LC
Eastern College	PA	15,150	C+
Eastern Kentucky Univ	KY	4,840	NC
Eastern Mennonite College	VA	12,700	C
Eastern Mich Univ	MI	6,749	C
Eastern Nazarene College	MA	12,165	LC
Eastern Washington Univ	WA	5,439	LC
Edinboro Univ of Penn	PA	7,181	C
Edward Waters College	FL	8,300	NC
Elizabeth City State Univ	NC	4,254	LC
Elizabethtown College	PA	17,850	VC
Evangel College	MO	10,142	LC
Evergreen State College	WA	6,306	C
Ferris State Univ	MI	7,160	NC
Ferrum College	VA	12,800	LC
Florida A&M Univ	FL	4,651	C
Florida International Univ	FL	4,191	VC
Florida State Univ	FL	5,814	VC
Fontbonne College	MO	12,090	C
Fort Hays State Univ	KS	4,675	NC
Fort Valley State College	GA	3,974	LC
Franklin Pierce College	NH	17,270	LC
Freed-Hardeman Univ	TN	8,585	VC
Fresno Pacific College	CA	13,020	C
Frostburg State Univ	MD	6,940	C
Gallaudet Univ	DC	9,850	SP
Gannon Univ	PA	14,872	C
George Fox College	OR	15,640	LC
George Mason Univ	VA	8,728	C
Georgia State Univ	GA	2,019	C
Georgian Court College	NJ	12,550	C
Gordon College	MA	16,790	C
Goshen College	IN	12,360	C
Grambling State Univ	LA	4,712	NC
Grand Rapids Baptist College and Seminary	MI	10,228	C
Grand Valley State Univ	MI	6,822	VC
Grand View College	IA	13,230	NC
Greenville College	IL	14,190	C
Hampton Univ	VA	10,706	C
Hardin-Simmons Univ	TX	9,080	C
Harding Univ	AR	9,050	VC
Holy Family College	PA	8,300	C
Hood College	MD	19,010	VC
Hope College	MI	15,698	C+
Howard Payne Univ	TX	8,052	C
Humboldt State Univ	CA	5,676	C
Huron Univ	SD	9,790	C
Idaho State Univ	ID	4,442	C
Illinois College	IL	11,200	C
Illinois State Univ	IL	6,413	C
Indiana State Univ	IN	6,210	C
Indiana Univ Bloomington	IN	6,495	VC
Indiana Univ-Purdue Univ at Indianapolis	IN	5,862	LC
Indiana Wesleyan Univ	IN	12,332	C
Inter American Univ of PR/ Aguadilla Regional College	PR	2,290	
Inter American Univ of PR/ Bayamon Univ College	PR	2,300	
Inter American Univ of PR/ Metropolitan Campus	PR	2,340	
Inter American Univ of PR/ Ponce Regional College	PR	2,300	
Inter American Univ/Arecibo Campus	PR	5,666	
Inter-American Univ of PR/ Fajardo Regional College	PR	2,732	
Iona College	NY	16,310	C
Iowa State Univ	IA	5,456	C
Jackson State Univ	MS	4,996	LC
Jacksonville State Univ	AL	4,080	LC
James Madison Univ	VA	8,198	HC
Johnson C. Smith Univ	NC	8,916	LC
Judson College	AL	9,060	C
Juniata College	PA	18,390	C+
Kansas State Univ	KS	4,816	NC
Kean College of New Jersey	NJ	6,395	LC
Kendall College	IL	12,651	LC
Kentucky Christian College	KY	7,708	LC
Kentucky State Univ	KY	4,282	C+
Keuka College	NY	13,660	C
Kutztown Univ	PA	6,528	C
La Salle Univ	PA	16,940	VC
La Sierra Univ	CA	15,472	C
LaGrange College	GA	10,602	C
Lakeland College	WI	12,845	LC
Lamar Univ	TX	3,798	C
LeMoyne-Owen College	TN	4,500	LC
Lewis Univ	IL	14,797	LC
Lewis-Clark State College	ID	4,040	
Limestone College	SC	10,700	LC
Lincoln Memorial Univ	TN	8,218	C
Lindsey Wilson College	KY	9,530	LC
Livingstone College	NC	8,600	LC
Lock Haven Univ of Penn	PA	7,128	C
Longwood College	VA	7,800	C
Louisiana College	LA	7,518	VC
Louisiana Tech Univ	LA	4,284	C
Lourdes College	OH	6,410	LC
Loyola Univ of Chicago	IL	15,880	C+
Lubbock Christian Univ	TX	9,840	NC
Luther College	IA	15,900	VC
MacMurray College	IL	12,800	C
Madonna Univ	MI	8,546	C
Malone College	OH	12,572	C
Manchester College	IN	13,240	LC
Manhattan College	NY	19,000	C
Mankato State Univ	MN	5,097	LC
Mansfield Univ	PA	6,348	C
Marian College of Fond du Lac	WI	12,250	C
Marist College	NY	16,406	C
Marquette Univ	WI	16,114	VC
Mars Hill College	NC	11,050	C
Marshall Univ	WV	5,762	LC
Mary Baldwin College	VA	17,700	LC
Marygrove College	MI	5,877	VC
Marymount College/ Tarrytown	NY	17,350	C
Marywood College	PA	14,890	C
Mercy College	NY	11,180	NC
Mercyhurst College	PA	13,488	C
Meredith College	NC	9,440	C
Messiah College	PA	14,664	VC
Methodist College	NC	12,400	C
Metropolitan State College of Denver	CO	1,751	NC
Mich Christian College	MI	8,094	C
Mich State Univ	MI	7,842	C
Middle Tenn State Univ	TN	3,857	C
Midwestern State Univ	TX	4,542	LC
Miles College	AL	7,150	NC
Millersville Univ of Penn	PA	7,370	VC
Minot State Univ	ND	3,748	NC
Miss College	MS	8,348	C
Miss State Univ	MS	5,629	VC
Miss Valley State Univ	MS	4,089	NC
Missouri Western State College	MO	4,384	NC
Molloy College	NY	8,580	LC
Monmouth College	NJ	16,820	C
Moorhead State Univ	MN	5,076	C
Morehead State Univ	KY	4,600	LC
Morehouse College	GA	13,224	LC
Morgan State Univ	MD	7,366	C+
Mount Mary College	WI	10,920	C
Mount Mercy College	IA	13,230	C
Mount Senario College	WI	10,970	C
Muhlenberg College	PA	20,795	VC
Murray State Univ	KY	4,702	C
Nazareth College of Rochester	NY	15,310	C+
Nebr Wesleyan Univ	NE	12,240	C
New Mexico Highlands Univ	NM	3,772	C
New Mexico State Univ	NM	4,844	LC
New York Univ	NY	24,705	VC+
Niagara Univ	NY	14,552	C
Norfolk State Univ	VA	6,345	LC
N Car Agricultural and Technical State Univ	NC	4,477	LC
N Car State Univ	NC	4,984	VC

INDEX OF COLLEGE MAJORS

School	ST	$IS	SR
North Georgia College	GA	4,103	LC
Northeast Louisiana Univ	LA	3,906	NC
Northeastern Illinois Univ	IL	1,955	C
Northeastern State Univ	OK	5,250	C
Northern Arizona Univ	AZ	4,844	C
Northern Kentucky Univ	KY	4,620	NC
Northern Mich Univ	MI	6,350	C
Northwest Nazarene College	ID	11,750	C
Northwestern College of Iowa	IA	12,250	C
Northwestern Okla State Univ	OK	3,424	C
Northwestern State Univ of Louisiana	LA	4,287	NC
Oakwood College	AL	10,005	C
Oglethorpe Univ	GA	16,360	VC
Ohio Dominican College	OH	11,820	LC
Ohio State Univ	OH	7,218	LC
Ohio Univ	OH	7,341	C
Okla Baptist Univ	OK	8,486	C
Okla Christian Univ of Science and Arts	OK	8,790	NC
Okla State Univ	OK	5,086	VC
Olivet Nazarene Univ	IL	11,976	C
Oral Roberts Univ	OK	10,607	C+
Our Lady of the Lake Univ of San Antonio	TX	11,080	C
Pacific Christian College	CA	12,700	C
Pacific Lutheran Univ	WA	15,998	VC
Pacific Union College	CA	15,075	C
Pacific Univ	OR	17,869	C
Paul Quinn College	TX	7,090	LC
Pembroke State Univ	NC	3,538	LC
Philadelphia College of Bible	PA	11,010	C
Philander Smith College	AR	5,434	NC
Phillips Univ	OK	12,744	C
Pikeville College	KY	8,500	NC
Pittsburg State Univ	KS	4,478	NC
Plymouth State College	NH	7,166	C
Pontifical Catholic Univ of PR/Ponce	PR	5,807	
Prairie View A&M Univ	TX	4,740	LC
Prescott College	AZ	9,775	C
Presentation College	SD	9,116	NC
Providence College	RI	19,750	VC
Purdue Univ/Calumet	IN	2,374	NC
Quincy Univ	IL	13,646	VC
Radford Univ	VA	7,034	LC
Ramapo College of New Jersey	NJ	8,027	C+
Regis College	MA	17,450	C
Rhode Island College	RI	7,901	LC
Richard Stockton College of New Jersey	NJ	6,950	VC
Rivier College	NH	14,920	LC
Roberts Wesleyan College	NY	13,317	C
Rochester Inst of Tech	NY	18,954	VC
Rust College	MS	6,600	LC
Rutgers Univ/Camden College of A&S	NJ	8,652	VC
Rutgers Univ/Livingston College	NJ	8,877	VC
Rutgers Univ/Newark College of A&S	NJ	8,645	C
Rutgers Univ/Univ College—Camden	NJ	3,506	C
Rutgers Univ/Univ College—Newark	NJ	0	C
Sacred Heart Univ	CT	16,350	C
Saginaw Valley State Univ	MI	6,634	LC
St Anselm College	NH	17,340	C
St Bonaventure Univ	NY	14,762	C
St Cloud State Univ	MN	5,015	C
St Edward's Univ	TX	12,636	C
St Francis College	IN	11,662	C
St Francis College	PA	15,744	LC
St John's Univ	MN	15,364	C
St Joseph College	CT	16,225	C
St Leo College	FL	13,570	C
St Louis Univ	MO	15,522	VC
St Mary's College	IN	17,043	VC
St Mary-of-the-Woods College	IN	14,430	NC
St Olaf College	MN	17,200	HC
St Vincent College	PA	13,934	LC
Salem State College	MA	6,712	C
Salisbury State Univ	MD	7,516	C+
Salve Regina Univ	RI	29,100	LC
San Diego State Univ	CA	6,692	LC
San Francisco State Univ	CA	7,292	LC
San Jose State Univ	CA	6,680	LC
Seton Hall Univ	NJ	18,306	LC
Seton Hill College	PA	14,320	C
Shepherd College	WV	5,540	C
Shippensburg Univ of Penn	PA	7,052	C
Siena College	NY	15,410	VC
Sioux Falls College	SD	11,540	C
Skidmore College	NY	23,230	HC
Slippery Rock Univ	PA	6,803	C
Sojourner-Douglass College	MD	5,265	LC
S Car State Univ	SC	5,424	LC
Southeast Missouri State Univ	MO	5,854	C
Southeastern Louisiana Univ	LA	4,230	NC
Southern College of Seventh-day Adventists	TN	11,348	NC
Southern Conn State Univ	CT	7,532	C
Southern Illinois Univ at Carbondale	IL	6,234	C
Southern Illinois Univ at Edwardsville	IL	6,097	LC
Southern Univ and A&M College	LA	4,920	NC
Southern Univ at New Orleans	LA	1,452	NC
Southern Vermont College	VT	12,974	C
Southwest Missouri State Univ	MO	4,956	C
Southwest State Univ	MN	5,400	NC
Southwest Texas State Univ	TX	5,124	C
Southwestern Adventist College	TX	10,530	NC
Southwestern College	KS	10,032	C
Southwestern Okla State Univ	OK	3,312	C
Spalding Univ	KY	10,496	LC
Spring Arbor College	MI	12,256	C
SUNY at Albany	NY	7,059	VC
SUNY at Stony Brook	NY	7,658	VC
SUNY/College at Brockport	NY	7,220	C+
SUNY/College at Buffalo	NY	7,035	VC
SUNY/College at Plattsburgh	NY	6,917	C
Stephen F. Austin State Univ	TX	5,117	C
Syracuse Univ	NY	21,305	HC
Tabor College	KS	11,460	VC
Talladega College	AL	8,124	VC
Tarleton State Univ	TX	4,082	LC
Taylor Univ	IN	14,450	VC
Teikyo Marycrest Univ	IA	13,755	VC
Temple Univ	PA	10,281	C
Tenn State Univ	TN	4,626	C+
Tenn Wesleyan College	TN	10,060	C
Texas Christian Univ	TX	12,180	C
Texas College	TX	5,930	NC
Texas Lutheran College	TX	10,710	C
Texas Southern Univ	TX	4,500	NC
Texas Tech Univ	TX	6,008	C
Texas Woman's Univ	TX	4,392	C
Trevecca Nazarene College	TN	9,826	NC
Trinity College of Vermont	VT	16,015	LC
Troy State Univ	AL	4,322	C
Tuskegee Univ	AL	10,128	C
Union College	NE	11,060	NC
Univ of Akron	OH	6,699	NC
Univ of Alabama	AL	5,702	C
Univ of Alabama at Birmingham	AL	7,533	C
Univ of Alaska Anchorage	AK	7,131	C
Univ of Alaska Fairbanks	AK	4,718	C
Univ of Arkansas at Fayetteville	AR	5,046	C
Univ of Arkansas at Pine Bluff	AR	3,978	LC
Univ of Calif at Berkeley	CA	9,962	HC+
Univ of Central Florida	FL	6,061	C+
Univ of Cincinnati	OH	7,989	C
Univ of Detroit Mercy	MI	14,720	C
Univ of Dubuque	IA	14,150	LC
Univ of Findlay	OH	15,764	C
Univ of Georgia	GA	5,655	VC
Univ of Guam	GU	4,139	NC
Univ of Hawaii at Manoa	HI	5,626	C
Univ of Illinois at Chicago	IL	8,443	C
Univ of Illinois at Urbana-Champaign	IL	7,764	HC
Univ of Indianapolis	IN	14,510	C
Univ of Iowa	IA	5,658	VC
Univ of Kansas	KS	5,200	NC
Univ of Kentucky	KY	5,152	VC
Univ of Maine	ME	7,990	C
Univ of Maine at Machias	ME	6,135	C
Univ of Mary	ND	8,910	C
Univ of Mary Hardin-Baylor	TX	8,120	NC
Univ of Maryland/Baltimore County	MD	7,746	VC
Univ of Mass Dartmouth	MA	8,158	C
Univ of Memphis	TN	3,476	C
Univ of Mich/Flint	MI	2,916	C
Univ of Miss	MS	5,756	C
Univ of Missouri/Columbia	MO	6,254	HC
Univ of Missouri/St. Louis	MO	6,378	C
Univ of Montana	MT	5,529	C
Univ of Montevallo	AL	5,310	C
Univ of Nebr at Kearney	NE	4,308	LC
Univ of Nebr at Omaha	NE	1,889	LC
Univ of Nebr-Lincoln	NE	5,278	LC
Univ of Nevada/Las Vegas	NV	6,405	C
Univ of Nevada/Reno	NV	5,735	C
Univ of New Hampshire	NH	8,242	C
Univ of North Alabama	AL	4,236	NC
Univ of N Car at Charlotte	NC	4,597	C
Univ of N Car at Greensboro	NC	5,192	C
Univ of N Car at Wilmington	NC	5,172	C
Univ of N Dak	ND	4,902	NC
Univ of North Texas	TX	4,853	C
Univ of Northern Colo	CO	6,008	C
Univ of Northern Iowa	IA	5,137	C
Univ of Okla	OK	5,427	VC
Univ of Pittsburgh	PA	9,472	C
Univ of Portland	OR	15,564	C
Univ of PR/Humacao Univ College	PR	1,494	
Univ of PR/Rio Piedras	PR	0	
Univ of Rio Grande	OH	6,300	NC
Univ of St Thomas	MN	15,785	C+
Univ of S Dak	SD	4,722	C
Univ of South Florida	FL	5,475	C+
Univ of Southern Colo	CO	5,350	LC
Univ of Southern Indiana	IN	3,720	NC
Univ of Southern Maine	ME	7,299	C
Univ of Southern Miss	MS	4,542	C
Univ of Tampa	FL	16,780	C
Univ of Tenn at Chattanooga	TN	5,375	C
Univ of Tenn at Martin	TN	4,550	C
Univ of Tenn/Knoxville	TN	5,668	C
Univ of Texas at Arlington	TX	5,549	LC
Univ of Texas at El Paso	TX	3,160	LC
Univ of the Sacred Heart	PR	3,890	
Univ of the Virgin Islands	VI	5,896	C
Univ of Toledo	OH	6,636	NC
Univ of Vermont	VT	10,776	C+
Univ of Washington	WA	6,618	VC
Univ of West Florida	FL	5,415	C
Univ of Wisc/Eau Claire	WI	4,647	C
Univ of Wisc/Green Bay	WI	4,904	C
Univ of Wisc/La Crosse	WI	4,487	C
Univ of Wisc/Madison	WI	6,400	HC
Univ of Wisc/Milwaukee	WI	6,165	C
Univ of Wisc/Oshkosh	WI	4,240	C
Univ of Wisc/Superior	WI	4,330	C
Univ of Wisc/Whitewater	WI	4,700	C
Univ of Wyoming	WY	4,991	NC
Upsala College	NJ	17,200	C
Urbana Univ	OH	12,536	C
Ursuline College	OH	13,180	LC
Utah State Univ	UT	4,683	C
Valparaiso Univ	IN	14,810	VC
Virginia Commonwealth Univ	VA	7,909	C
Virginia Intermont College	VA	12,250	LC
Virginia State Univ	VA	7,040	C
Virginia Union Univ	VA	10,555	LC
Virginia Wesleyan College	VA	14,950	VC
Wagner College	NY	17,950	C
Walla Walla College	WA	13,215	C
Warner Pacific College	OR	12,112	C
Warren Wilson College	NC	10,877	C
Wartburg College	IA	14,530	VC
Washburn Univ of Topeka	KS	5,802	NC
Wayne State Univ	MI	2,680	C
Weber State Univ	UT	4,398	C
West Chester Univ of Penn	PA	7,492	C
West Texas A&M Univ	TX	4,224	C
West Virginia State College	WV	5,044	LC
West Virginia Univ	WV	5,774	C
Western Carolina Univ	NC	3,811	C
Western Conn State Univ	CT	6,622	C
Western Kentucky Univ	KY	4,808	C
Western Maryland College	MD	18,990	C
Western Mich Univ	MI	6,820	C
Western New England College	MA	14,674	LC
Wheelock College	MA	18,000	LC
Whittier College	CA	21,661	C
Wichita State Univ	KS	5,068	NC
Widener Univ	PA	16,840	C
William Woods Univ	MO	14,025	LC
Winona State Univ	MN	5,200	VC
Winthrop Univ	SC	6,750	C
Wright State Univ	OH	6,896	LC
Xavier Univ	OH	15,710	C+
Youngstown State Univ	OH	6,447	LC

SOCIOLOGY

School	ST	$IS	SR
Adams State College	CO	4,910	C
Adelphi Univ	NY	18,250	LC
Adrian College	MI	14,340	C
Agnes Scott College	GA	17,135	VC
Alabama A&M Univ	AL	4,200	C
Alabama State Univ	AL	3,428	NC
Albany State College	GA	4,481	LC
Albertson College	ID	15,942	C+
Albertus Magnus College	CT	16,280	LC
Albion College	MI	18,264	VC
Alderson-Broaddus College	WV	12,000	C
Alfred Univ	NY	21,054	VC+
Allegheny College	PA	21,020	VC
Allen Univ	SC	6,705	NC
Alma College	MI	16,375	VC+
American International College	MA	14,029	C
American Univ	DC	21,230	VC+
Amherst College	MA	24,152	MC
Anderson Univ	IN	12,920	C
Andrews Univ	MI	14,952	NC
Angelo State Univ	TX	5,176	C
Antioch College	OH	19,532	C
Appalachian State Univ	NC	4,095	C
Aquinas College	MI	14,526	C
Arizona State Univ Main Campus	AZ	6,444	C
Arkansas State Univ	AR	4,250	NC
Arkansas Tech Univ	AR	4,200	NC
Asbury College	KY	11,105	VC
Ashland Univ	OH	15,508	C
Assumption College	MA	17,095	LC
Auburn Univ	AL	5,823	C+
Auburn Univ at Montgomery	AL	3,390	C
Augsburg College	MN	15,608	C
Augusta College	GA	1,452	C
Augustana College	IL	16,959	VC
Augustana College	SD	13,420	C
Aurora Univ	IL	13,381	C
Austin College	TX	14,999	VC
Austin Peay State Univ	TN	4,350	C
Averett College	VA	13,610	LC
Avila College	MO	12,130	C
Azusa Pacific Univ	CA	15,034	C
Baker Univ	KS	12,284	C
Baldwin-Wallace College	OH	15,210	C
Ball State Univ	IN	6,032	LC
Barat College	IL	13,990	C
Barber-Scotia College	NC	6,840	NC
Bard College	NY	25,269	HC
Barry Univ	FL	16,050	C
Bartlesville Wesleyan College	OK	9,400	C
Barton College	NC	10,689	LC
Bates College	ME	23,990	MC
Baylor Univ	TX	10,990	C+
Beaver College	PA	17,660	C
Bellarmine College	KY	10,832	C
Bellevue College	NE	3,050	NC
Belmont Abbey College	NC	13,190	C
Beloit College	WI	18,950	VC+
Bemidji State Univ	MN	5,188	C
Benedictine College	KS	12,830	C
Bennett College	NC	8,920	LC
Berea College	KY	2,883	VC+
Berry College	GA	11,990	VC
Bethany College	KS	11,232	C
Bethel College	MN	15,050	C
Bethune-Cookman College	FL	8,375	LC
Biola Univ	CA	16,124	C
Birmingham-Southern College	AL	15,154	VC+
Black Hills State Univ	SD	4,831	NC
Bloomfield College	NJ	12,200	LC
Bloomsburg Univ of Penn	PA	6,312	C+
Bluffton College	OH	12,951	C
Boise State Univ	ID	4,909	LC
Boston College	MA	22,706	MC
Boston Univ	MA	24,130	HC
Bowdoin College	ME	24,155	MC
Bowie State Univ	MD	7,294	LC
Bowling Green State Univ	OH	6,701	C
Bradley Univ	IL	14,718	C+
Brandeis Univ	MA	25,585	HC
Brescia College	KY	9,800	C
Briar Cliff College	IA	13,375	C
Bridgewater College	VA	15,300	C
Bridgewater State College	MA	7,518	C
Brigham Young Univ	UT	5,625	HC
Brigham Young Univ/Hawaii	HI	6,750	VC
Brooklyn Campus of LIU	NY	15,000	LC
Brown Univ	RI	26,104	MC
Bryn Mawr College	PA	24,110	MC
Bucknell Univ	PA	22,320	HC
Butler Univ	IN	16,210	C
Cabrini College	PA	16,012	C
Caldwell College	NJ	12,860	C
Calif Baptist College	CA	11,294	C
Calif Lutheran Univ	CA	17,240	C
Calif State Polytechnic Univ/Pomona	CA	6,438	LC
Cal State/Bakersfield	CA	5,402	C
Cal State/Chico	CA	6,146	C
Cal State/Dominguez Hills	CA	2,857	LC
Cal State/Fresno	CA	5,747	C
Cal State/Fullerton	CA	4,850	LC
Cal State/Hayward	CA	5,495	C
Cal State/Long Beach	CA	6,057	LC
Cal State/Los Angeles	CA	4,940	VC
Cal State/Northridge	CA	7,122	LC
Cal State/Sacramento	CA	6,637	C
Cal State/San Bernardino	CA	6,055	LC
Cal State/Stanislaus	CA	6,799	C
Calif Univ of Penn	PA	7,370	C
Calumet College of St. Joseph	IN	3,585	C
Calvin College	MI	13,020	VC
Cameron Univ	OK	3,686	LC
Campbellsville College	KY	8,720	C
Canisius College	NY	15,510	C
Capital Univ	OH	16,535	VC
Cardinal Stritch College	WI	11,252	C
Carleton College	MN	22,155	HC
Carroll College	MT	11,265	C
Carroll College	WI	15,490	C
Carson-Newman College	TN	11,250	C
Carthage College	WI	15,995	C
Case Western Reserve Univ	OH	19,910	HC
Castleton State College	VT	8,378	LC
Catawba College	NC	12,950	C
Catholic Univ of America	DC	18,856	C
Cedar Crest College	PA	18,930	C
Cedarville College	OH	10,715	C
Centenary College of Louisiana	LA	11,826	C+
Central College	IA	14,025	VC
Central Conn State Univ	CT	7,108	C
Central Mich Univ	MI	6,737	LC
Central Missouri State Univ	MO	5,138	LC
Central State Univ	OH	7,320	NC

School	ST	$IS	SR
Nicholls State Univ	LA	4,531	NC
Norfolk State Univ	VA	6,345	LC
North Adams State College	MA	7,750	C
N Car Agricultural and Technical State Univ	NC	4,477	LC
N Car Central Univ	NC	4,347	LC
N Car State Univ	NC	4,984	LC
N Car Wesleyan College	NC	12,480	LC
North Central College	IL	15,498	VC
N Dak State Univ of Agriculture and Applied Science	ND	4,774	VC
North Georgia College	GA	4,103	LC
North Park College	IL	14,310	C
Northeast Louisiana Univ	LA	3,906	NC
Northeast Missouri State Univ	MO	5,654	VC+
Northeastern Illinois Univ	IL	1,955	C
Northeastern State Univ	OK	5,250	C
Northeastern Univ	MA	19,851	C
Northern Arizona Univ	AZ	4,844	C
Northern Illinois Univ	IL	6,408	C
Northern Kentucky Univ	KY	4,620	NC
Northern Mich Univ	MI	6,350	C
Northern State Univ	SD	4,186	LC
Northland College	WI	13,550	LC
Northwest Missouri State Univ	MO	5,010	LC
Northwest Nazarene College	ID	11,750	C
Northwest College of Iowa	IA	12,250	C
Northwestern Okla State Univ	OK	3,424	C
Northwestern State Univ of Louisiana	LA	4,287	NC
Northwestern Univ	IL	21,093	MC
Notre Dame College of Ohio	OH	24,550	HC+
Nyack College	NY	12,210	LC
Oakland Univ	MI	6,714	VC
Oberlin College	OH	24,570	HC+
Occidental College	CA	21,792	HC
Oglethorpe Univ	GA	16,360	VC
Ohio Dominican College	OH	11,820	C
Ohio Northern Univ	OH	18,660	VC
Ohio State Univ	OH	7,218	LC
Ohio Univ	OH	7,341	C
Ohio Wesleyan Univ	OH	21,108	VC+
Okla Baptist Univ	OK	8,486	C
Okla Christian Univ of Science and Arts	OK	8,790	NC
Okla City Univ	OK	9,840	C
Okla State Univ	OK	5,086	VC
Old Dominion Univ	VA	8,317	C
Olivet College	MI	14,000	C
Olivet Nazarene Univ	IL	11,976	C
Oregon State Univ	OR	6,175	C
Ottawa Univ	KS	10,490	C+
Otterbein College	OH	16,506	C
Ouachita Baptist Univ	AR	8,940	C
Our Lady of the Lake Univ of San Antonio	TX	11,080	C
Pace Univ	NY	15,540	C
Pacific Lutheran Univ	WA	15,998	VC
Pacific Union College	CA	15,075	C
Pacific Univ	OR	17,869	C
Paine College	GA	8,207	LC
Park College	MO	7,320	C
Paul Quinn College	TX	7,090	LC
Pembroke State Univ	NC	3,538	LC
Penn State Univ/Univ Park Campus	PA	8,752	HC
Pepperdine Univ	CA	23,720	VC
Peru State College	NE	4,311	NC
Pfeiffer College	NC	11,670	VC
Philander Smith College	AR	5,434	NC
Phillips Univ	OK	12,744	C
Piedmont College	GA	8,540	LC
Pittsburg State Univ	KS	4,478	NC
Pitzer College	CA	23,780	HC
Plymouth State College	NH	7,166	C
Point Loma Nazarene College	CA	13,532	C
Pomona College	CA	23,820	MC
Pontifical Catholic Univ of PR/Ponce	PR	5,807	
Portland State Univ	OR	7,191	C
Prairie View A&M Univ	TX	4,740	LC
Presbyterian College	SC	15,400	VC
Prescott College	AZ	9,775	C
Princeton Univ	NJ	24,650	MC
Principia College	IL	17,799	C
Providence College	RI	19,750	VC
Purdue Univ/Calumet	IN	2,374	NC
Purdue Univ/West Lafayette	IN	6,636	C
Queens College	NC	14,950	C
Quincy Univ	IL	13,646	VC
Quinnipiac College	CT	17,600	C+
Radford Univ	VA	7,034	LC
Ramapo College of New Jersey	NJ	8,027	C+
Randolph-Macon College	VA	19,100	C
Randolph-Macon Woman's College	VA	19,100	C
Reed College	OR	24,480	HC+
Regis College	MA	17,450	C
Regis Univ	CO	17,340	C
Rhode Island College	RI	7,901	LC

School	ST	$IS	SR
Rice Univ	TX	15,110	MC
Rider College	NJ	18,160	C
Ripon College	WI	18,320	C+
Rivier College	NH	14,920	LC
Roanoke College	VA	16,975	C
Roberts Wesleyan College	NY	13,317	C
Rockford College	IL	15,300	C
Rockhurst College	MO	12,470	C
Rocky Mountain College	MT	11,320	C
Rollins College	FL	20,875	VC
Roosevelt Univ	IL	12,368	C
Rosary College	IL	15,040	C
Rosemont College	PA	16,775	C
Rowan College of New Jersey	NJ	7,358	VC
Russell Sage College	NY	16,790	C
Rust College	MS	6,600	LC
Rutgers Univ/Camden College of A&S	NJ	8,652	VC
Rutgers Univ/Douglass College	NJ	8,795	VC
Rutgers Univ/Livingston College	NJ	8,877	VC
Rutgers Univ/Newark College of A&S	NJ	8,645	C
Rutgers Univ/Rutgers College	NJ	8,841	HC+
Rutgers Univ/Univ College—Camden	NJ	3,506	C
Rutgers Univ/Univ College—New Brunswick	NJ	0	LC
Rutgers Univ/Univ College—Newark	NJ	0	C
Sacred Heart Univ	CT	16,350	C
Saginaw Valley State Univ	MI	6,634	LC
St Ambrose Univ	IA	13,380	C
St Anselm College	NH	17,340	C
St Augustine's College	NC	9,300	C+
St Bonaventure Univ	NY	14,762	C
St Cloud State Univ	MN	5,015	C
St Edward's Univ	TX	12,636	C
St Francis College	NY	6,710	C
St Francis College	PA	15,744	LC
St John Fisher College	NY	15,415	C
St John's Univ	MN	15,364	C
St John's Univ	NY	8,980	C+
St Joseph College	CT	16,225	C
St Joseph's College	ME	14,535	C
St Joseph's Univ	PA	17,800	VC
St Lawrence Univ	NY	23,420	VC
St Leo College	FL	13,570	C
St Louis Univ	MO	15,522	VC
St Mary College	KS	11,250	C
St Mary's College	IN	17,043	VC
St Mary's College	MI	8,350	C
St Mary's College of Minn	MN	13,850	LC
St Mary's Univ	TX	12,064	C
St Michael's College	VT	17,930	C
St Norbert College	WI	15,710	VC
St Olaf College	MN	17,200	HC
St Paul's College	VA	9,171	C
St Peter's College	NJ	14,775	LC
St Thomas Univ	FL	14,280	LC
St Vincent College	PA	13,934	LC
St Xavier Univ	IL	14,700	C
Salem College	NC	16,025	C
Salem State College	MA	6,712	C
Salisbury State Univ	MD	7,516	C+
Salve Regina Univ	RI	29,100	LC
Sam Houston State Univ	TX	4,506	C
Samford Univ	AL	11,400	VC
San Diego State Univ	CA	6,692	LC
San Francisco State Univ	CA	7,292	C
San Jose State Univ	CA	6,680	LC
Santa Clara Univ	CA	18,783	VC
Sarah Lawrence College	NY	24,975	HC
Scripps College	CA	23,600	HC
Seattle Pacific Univ	WA	16,503	C
Seattle Univ	WA	16,590	C
Selma Univ	AL	5,785	NC
Seton Hall Univ	NJ	18,306	LC
Seton Hill College	PA	14,320	C
Shepherd College	WV	5,540	C
Shippensburg Univ of Penn	PA	7,052	C
Shorter College	GA	10,270	C
Siena College	NY	15,410	VC
Siena Heights College	MI	12,520	C
Simmons College	MA	22,534	C
Simpson College	IA	14,635	VC
Sioux Falls College	SD	11,540	C
Skidmore College	NY	23,230	HC
Slippery Rock Univ	PA	6,803	C
Smith College	MA	24,236	HC
Sonoma State Univ	CA	6,996	C
S Car State Univ	SC	5,424	LC
S Dak State Univ	SD	4,562	C
Southeast Missouri State Univ	MO	5,854	C
Southeastern Louisiana Univ	LA	4,230	NC
Southeastern Okla State Univ	OK	3,594	C
Southern Calif College	CA	12,356	C
Southern Conn State Univ	CT	7,532	C
Southern Illinois Univ at Carbondale	IL	6,234	C
Southern Illinois Univ at Edwardsville	IL	6,097	LC

School	ST	$IS	SR
Southern Methodist Univ	TX	18,520	VC
Southern Nazarene Univ	OK	9,206	NC
Southern Oregon State College	OR	6,128	C
Southern Univ and A&M College	LA	4,920	NC
Southern Univ at New Orleans	LA	1,452	NC
Southern Utah Univ	UT	4,104	LC
Southwest Baptist Univ	MO	9,192	NC
Southwest Missouri State Univ	MO	4,956	C
Southwest State Univ	MN	5,400	NC
Southwest Texas State Univ	TX	5,124	C
Southwestern Okla State Univ	OK	3,312	C
Southwestern Univ	TX	15,484	HC
Spalding Univ	KY	10,496	LC
Spelman College	GA	12,942	VC
Spring Arbor College	MI	12,256	C
Spring Hill College	AL	16,015	C+
Springfield College	MA	15,200	LC
Stanford Univ	CA	24,310	MC
SUNY at Albany	NY	7,059	HC
SUNY at Binghamton	NY	7,921	HC
SUNY at Buffalo	NY	7,896	VC
SUNY at Stony Brook	NY	7,658	VC
SUNY/College at Brockport	NY	7,220	C+
SUNY/College at Buffalo	NY	7,035	VC
SUNY/College at Cortland	NY	7,326	C+
SUNY/College at Fredonia	NY	7,159	VC
SUNY/College at Geneseo	NY	6,949	VC
SUNY/College at New Paltz	NY	6,890	VC
SUNY/College at Old Westbury	NY	7,128	LC
SUNY/College at Oneonta	NY	7,878	C
SUNY/College at Oswego	NY	7,330	VC
SUNY/College at Plattsburgh	NY	6,917	C
SUNY/College at Purchase	NY	7,324	C
SUNY/Empire State College	NY	2,687	NC
SUNY/Potsdam College	NY	6,906	C
Stephen F. Austin State Univ	TX	5,117	C
Stetson Univ	FL	16,435	VC
Stillman College	AL	7,213	NC
Stonehill College	MA	17,481	VC
Suffolk Univ	MA	15,360	LC
Susquehanna Univ	PA	19,950	VC
Swarthmore College	PA	24,136	MC
Sweet Briar College	VA	19,770	C
Syracuse Univ	NY	21,305	HC
Tabor College	KS	11,460	C
Talladega College	AL	8,124	VC
Tarleton State Univ	TX	4,082	LC
Taylor Univ	IN	14,450	VC
Teikyo Post Univ	CT	16,360	LC
Teikyo Westmar Univ	IA	15,920	C
Temple Univ	PA	10,281	C
Tenn State Univ	TN	4,626	C+
Tenn Tech Univ	TN	5,190	C
Texas A&M Univ	TX	5,382	VC
Texas A&M Univ at Kingsville	TX	3,808	LC
Texas Christian Univ	TX	12,180	C
Texas College	TX	5,930	NC
Texas Lutheran College	TX	10,710	C
Texas Southern Univ	TX	4,500	NC
Texas Tech Univ	TX	6,008	C
Texas Woman's Univ	TX	4,392	C
The Univ of New Mexico	NM	5,304	C
Thiel College	PA	16,282	C
Thomas A. Edison State College	NJ	400	
Tougaloo College	MS	7,480	LC
Touro College	NY	11,930	C
Towson State Univ	MD	7,452	C
Transylvania Univ	KY	14,970	VC+
Trenton State College	NJ	9,085	HC
Trinity Christian College	IL	13,260	C
Trinity College	CT	24,120	HC
Trinity College	IL	14,010	C
Trinity Univ	TX	16,670	HC
Troy State Univ	AL	4,322	C
Troy State Univ at Dothan/Fort Rucker	AL	2,260	NC
Tufts Univ	MA	24,962	MC
Tulane Univ	LA	24,540	HC
Turabo Univ	PR	2,670	
Tuskegee Univ	AL	10,128	C
Union College	KY	9,790	C
Union College	NY	23,817	HC
Union Univ	TN	7,880	C+
Universidad Metropolitana	PR	2,650	
Univ of Akron	OH	6,699	NC
Univ of Alabama	AL	5,702	C
Univ of Alabama at Birmingham	AL	7,533	C
Univ of Alabama at Huntsville	AL	5,868	VC
Univ of Alaska Anchorage	AK	7,131	C
Univ of Alaska Fairbanks	AK	4,718	C
Univ of Arizona	AZ	5,808	C
Univ of Arkansas at Fayetteville	AR	5,046	C
Univ of Arkansas at Little Rock	AR	4,419	C

School	ST	$IS	SR
Univ of Arkansas at Pine Bluff	AR	3,978	LC
Univ of Calif at Berkeley	CA	9,962	HC+
Univ of Calif at Davis	CA	9,534	VC
Univ of Calif at Los Angeles	CA	8,959	HC
Univ of Calif at Santa Barbara	CA	9,460	C
Univ of Calif at Santa Cruz	CA	9,060	VC
Univ of Calif, Riverside	CA	9,178	C
Univ of Calif, San Diego	CA	10,028	VC+
Univ of Calif/Irvine	CA	12,680	VC
Univ of Central Arkansas	AR	4,200	LC
Univ of Central Florida	FL	6,061	C+
Univ of Central Okla	OK	3,647	C
Univ of Chicago	IL	24,517	MC
Univ of Cincinnati	OH	7,989	C
Univ of Colo at Boulder	CO	6,410	VC
Univ of Colo at Colo Springs	CO	2,269	C
Univ of Colo at Denver	CO	1,955	VC
Univ of Conn	CT	9,168	C
Univ of Dayton	OH	15,120	C+
Univ of Delaware	DE	8,013	VC
Univ of Denver	CO	19,290	C+
Univ of Detroit Mercy	MI	14,720	C
Univ of Dubuque	IA	14,150	LC
Univ of Evansville	IN	15,300	VC
Univ of Findlay	OH	15,764	C
Univ of Florida	FL	5,850	HC
Univ of Georgia	GA	5,655	VC
Univ of Guam	GU	4,139	NC
Univ of Hartford	CT	19,858	LC
Univ of Hawaii at Hilo	HI	4,141	C
Univ of Hawaii at Manoa	HI	5,626	C
Univ of Houston	TX	5,215	C
Univ of Idaho	ID	4,830	C
Univ of Illinois at Chicago	IL	8,443	C
Univ of Indianapolis	IN	14,510	C
Univ of Iowa	IA	5,658	VC
Univ of Kansas	KS	5,200	NC
Univ of Kentucky	KY	5,152	VC
Univ of La Verne	CA	17,400	C
Univ of Louisville	KY	5,948	C
Univ of Lowell	MA	8,831	LC
Univ of Maine	ME	7,990	C
Univ of Maine at Farmington	ME	6,700	C
Univ of Maine at Presque Isle	ME	6,374	C
Univ of Mary Hardin-Baylor	TX	8,120	NC
Univ of Maryland/Baltimore County	MD	7,746	C
Univ of Maryland/College Park	MD	8,182	VC
Univ of Maryland/Eastern Shore	MD	6,254	C
Univ of Maryland/Univ College	MD	4,900	C
Univ of Mass Dartmouth	MA	8,158	C
Univ of Mass/Amherst	MA	9,364	LC
Univ of Mass/Boston	MA	4,253	C
Univ of Memphis	TN	3,476	C
Univ of Miami	FL	22,107	VC
Univ of Mich/Ann Arbor	MI	9,428	HC+
Univ of Mich/Dearborn	MI	3,399	HC
Univ of Mich/Flint	MI	2,916	C
Univ of Minn/Duluth	MN	6,512	C
Univ of Minn/Morris	MN	6,825	HC
Univ of Minn/Twin Cities	MN	6,682	VC
Univ of Miss	MS	5,756	C
Univ of Missouri/Columbia	MO	6,254	VC
Univ of Missouri/Kansas City	MO	5,906	VC
Univ of Missouri/St. Louis	MO	6,378	C
Univ of Mobile	AL	9,400	C
Univ of Montana	MT	5,529	C
Univ of Montevallo	AL	5,310	C
Univ of Nebr at Kearney	NE	4,308	C
Univ of Nebr at Omaha	NE	1,889	LC
Univ of Nebr-Lincoln	NE	5,278	C
Univ of Nevada/Las Vegas	NV	6,405	C
Univ of Nevada/Reno	NV	5,735	C
Univ of New Hampshire	NH	8,242	C
Univ of New Orleans	LA	5,468	C
Univ of North Alabama	AL	4,236	NC
Univ of N Car at Asheville	NC	4,791	VC
Univ of N Car at Chapel Hill	NC	5,330	HC
Univ of N Car at Charlotte	NC	4,597	C
Univ of N Car at Greensboro	NC	5,192	C
Univ of N Car at Wilmington	NC	5,172	C
Univ of N Dak	ND	4,902	NC
Univ of North Florida	FL	5,082	C
Univ of North Texas	TX	4,853	C
Univ of Northern Colo	CO	6,008	C
Univ of Northern Iowa	IA	5,137	C
Univ of Notre Dame	IN	20,150	MC
Univ of Okla	OK	5,427	VC
Univ of Oregon	OR	6,466	VC
Univ of Penn	PA	24,238	MC
Univ of Pittsburgh	PA	9,472	C
Univ of Pittsburgh at Bradford	PA	9,050	C
Univ of Pittsburgh at Johnstown	PA	8,914	C
Univ of Portland	OR	15,564	C
Univ of PR/Cayey Univ College	PR	900	
Univ of PR/Mayaguez	PR	0	
Univ of PR/Rio Piedras	PR	0	

SOIL SCIENCE

SOUTH ASIAN STUDIES

SOUTHWEST AMERICAN STUDIES

SPANISH

School	ST	$IS	SR
Southeastern Okla State Univ	OK	3,594	C
Southern Arkansas Univ	AR	3,432	NC
Southern College of Seventh-day Adventists	TN	11,348	NC
Southern Conn State Univ	CT	7,532	C
Southern Illinois Univ at Carbondale	IL	6,234	C
Southern Illinois Univ at Edwardsville	IL	6,097	LC
Southern Methodist Univ	TX	18,520	VC
Southern Nazarene Univ	OK	9,206	NC
Southern Oregon State College	OR	6,128	C
Southern Univ and A&M College	LA	4,920	NC
Southern Univ at New Orleans	LA	1,452	NC
Southern Utah Univ	UT	4,104	LC
Southwest Baptist Univ	MO	9,192	NC
Southwest Missouri State Univ	MO	4,956	C
Southwest Texas State Univ	TX	5,124	C
Southwestern Univ	TX	15,484	HC
Spelman College	GA	12,942	VC
Spring Arbor College	MI	12,256	C
Stanford Univ	CA	24,310	MC
SUNY at Albany	NY	7,059	VC
SUNY at Binghamton	NY	7,921	HC
SUNY at Buffalo	NY	7,896	VC
SUNY at Stony Brook	NY	7,658	VC
SUNY/College at Brockport	NY	7,220	C+
SUNY/College at Buffalo	NY	7,035	VC
SUNY/College at Fredonia	NY	7,159	VC
SUNY/College at Geneseo	NY	6,949	HC
SUNY/College at New Paltz	NY	6,890	VC
SUNY/College at Old Westbury	NY	7,128	LC
SUNY/College at Oneonta	NY	7,878	C
SUNY/College at Oswego	NY	7,330	VC
SUNY/College at Plattsburgh	NY	6,917	C
SUNY/College at Purchase	NY	7,324	C
SUNY/Potsdam College	NY	6,906	C
Stephen F. Austin State Univ	TX	5,117	C
Stetson Univ	FL	16,435	VC
Suffolk Univ	MA	15,360	LC
Sul Ross State Univ	TX	4,144	NC
Susquehanna Univ	PA	19,950	VC
Swarthmore College	PA	24,136	MC
Syracuse Univ	NY	21,305	HC
Tarleton State Univ	TX	4,082	LC
Taylor Univ	IN	14,450	VC
Temple Univ	PA	10,281	C
Tenn Tech Univ	TN	5,190	C
Texas A&M Univ	TX	5,382	VC
Texas A&M Univ at Kingsville	TX	3,808	LC
Texas Christian Univ	TX	12,180	C
Texas Lutheran College	TX	10,710	C
Texas Southern Univ	TX	4,500	NC
Texas Tech Univ	TX	6,008	C
Texas Wesleyan Univ	TX	9,380	LC
Texas Woman's Univ	TX	4,392	C
The Citadel	SC	6,619	C
The Univ of New Mexico	NM	5,304	C
Thiel College	PA	16,282	C
Towson State Univ	MD	7,452	C
Transylvania Univ	KY	14,970	VC+
Trinity College	CT	24,120	HC
Trinity College	DC	17,660	C
Trinity College of Vermont	VT	16,015	LC
Trinity Univ	TX	16,670	HC
Troy State Univ	AL	4,322	C
Tufts Univ	MA	24,962	MC
Tulane Univ	LA	24,540	HC
Turabo Univ	PR	2,670	
Union Univ	TN	7,880	C+
Universidad Adventista de las Antillas	PR	5,000	
Univ of Akron	OH	6,699	NC
Univ of Alabama	AL	5,702	C
Univ of Alabama at Birmingham	AL	7,533	C
Univ of Alaska Fairbanks	AK	4,718	C
Univ of Arizona	AZ	5,808	C
Univ of Arkansas at Fayetteville	AR	5,046	C
Univ of Arkansas at Little Rock	AR	4,419	C
Univ of Calif at Berkeley	CA	9,962	HC+
Univ of Calif at Davis	CA	9,534	VC
Univ of Calif at Los Angeles	CA	8,959	HC
Univ of Calif at Santa Barbara	CA	9,460	C
Univ of Calif at Santa Cruz	CA	9,060	VC
Univ of Calif, Riverside	CA	9,178	C
Univ of Calif, San Diego	CA	10,028	VC+
Univ of Calif/Irvine	CA	12,680	VC
Univ of Central Arkansas	AR	4,200	LC
Univ of Central Florida	FL	6,061	C+
Univ of Central Okla	OK	3,647	C
Univ of Cincinnati	OH	7,989	C
Univ of Colo at Boulder	CO	6,410	VC
Univ of Colo at Colo Springs	CO	2,269	C
Univ of Colo at Denver	CO	1,955	VC
Univ of Conn	CT	9,168	C
Univ of Dallas	TX	14,983	VC
Univ of Dayton	OH	15,120	C+
Univ of Delaware	DE	8,013	VC
Univ of Denver	CO	19,290	C+
Univ of Dubuque	IA	14,150	LC
Univ of Evansville	IN	15,300	VC
Univ of Findlay	OH	15,764	C
Univ of Florida	FL	5,850	HC
Univ of Hawaii at Manoa	HI	5,626	C
Univ of Houston	TX	5,215	C
Univ of Idaho	ID	4,830	C
Univ of Illinois at Chicago	IL	8,443	C
Univ of Indianapolis	IN	14,510	C
Univ of Iowa	IA	5,658	VC
Univ of Kansas	KS	5,200	NC
Univ of Kentucky	KY	5,152	VC
Univ of La Verne	CA	17,400	C
Univ of Louisville	KY	5,948	C
Univ of Lowell	MA	8,831	VC
Univ of Maine	ME	7,990	C
Univ of Mary Hardin-Baylor	TX	8,120	NC
Univ of Maryland/Baltimore County	MD	7,746	VC
Univ of Maryland/College Park	MD	8,182	VC
Univ of Mass Dartmouth	MA	8,158	C
Univ of Mass/Amherst	MA	9,364	LC
Univ of Mass/Boston	MA	4,253	C
Univ of Memphis	TN	3,476	C
Univ of Miami	FL	22,107	VC
Univ of Mich/Ann Arbor	MI	9,428	HC+
Univ of Minn/Duluth	MN	6,512	C
Univ of Minn/Morris	MN	6,825	HC
Univ of Minn/Twin Cities	MN	6,682	VC
Univ of Miss	MS	5,756	C
Univ of Missouri/Columbia	MO	6,254	HC
Univ of Missouri/St. Louis	MO	6,378	C
Univ of Montana	MT	5,529	C
Univ of Montevallo	AL	5,310	C
Univ of Nebr at Kearney	NE	4,308	LC
Univ of Nebr at Omaha	NE	1,889	LC
Univ of Nebr-Lincoln	NE	5,278	LC
Univ of Nevada/Las Vegas	NV	6,405	C
Univ of Nevada/Reno	NV	5,735	C
Univ of New Hampshire	NH	8,242	C
Univ of New Orleans	LA	5,468	C
Univ of North Alabama	AL	4,236	NC
Univ of N Car at Asheville	NC	4,791	VC
Univ of N Car at Chapel Hill	NC	5,330	HC
Univ of N Car at Charlotte	NC	4,597	C
Univ of N Car at Greensboro	NC	5,192	C
Univ of N Car at Wilmington	NC	5,172	C
Univ of N Dak	ND	4,902	NC
Univ of North Florida	FL	5,082	C
Univ of North Texas	TX	4,853	C
Univ of Northern Colo	CO	6,008	C
Univ of Northern Iowa	IA	5,137	C
Univ of Notre Dame	IN	20,150	MC
Univ of Okla	OK	5,427	VC
Univ of Oregon	OR	6,466	VC
Univ of Pittsburgh	PA	9,472	C
Univ of Portland	OR	15,564	C
Univ of PR/Rio Piedras	PR	0	
Univ of Puget Sound	WA	19,520	HC
Univ of Redlands	CA	22,059	VC
Univ of Rhode Island	RI	9,205	C
Univ of Richmond	VA	16,700	HC
Univ of Rochester	NY	23,696	HC
Univ of St Thomas	MN	15,785	C+
Univ of San Diego	CA	18,970	VC
Univ of San Francisco	CA	18,408	C
Univ of Scranton	PA	17,071	VC
Univ of South Alabama	AL	5,451	C
Univ of S Car	SC	6,158	C
Univ of S Car at Spartanburg	SC	2,320	C
Univ of S Dak	SD	4,722	C
Univ of South Florida	FL	5,475	C+
Univ of Southern Indiana	IN	3,720	NC
Univ of Southwestern Louisiana	LA	3,968	NC
Univ of Tampa	FL	16,780	C
Univ of Tenn at Chattanooga	TN	5,375	C
Univ of Tenn at Martin	TN	4,550	C
Univ of Tenn/Knoxville	TN	5,668	C
Univ of Texas at Arlington	TX	5,549	LC
Univ of Texas at Austin	TX	5,160	VC
Univ of Texas at El Paso	TX	3,160	LC
Univ of Texas at San Antonio	TX	6,420	C
Univ of Texas-Pan American	TX	3,192	NC
Univ of the District of Columbia	DC	974	NC
Univ of the Pacific	CA	21,100	C
Univ of the South	TN	18,830	HC
Univ of the Virgin Islands	VI	5,896	C
Univ of Toledo	OH	6,636	NC
Univ of Tulsa	OK	13,795	VC
Univ of Utah	UT	5,975	C
Univ of Vermont	VT	10,776	C+
Univ of Virginia	VA	7,964	MC
Univ of Washington	WA	6,618	VC
Univ of West Florida	FL	5,415	C
Univ of Wisc/Eau Claire	WI	4,647	C
Univ of Wisc/Green Bay	WI	4,904	C
Univ of Wisc/La Crosse	WI	4,487	C
Univ of Wisc/Madison	WI	6,400	HC
Univ of Wisc/Milwaukee	WI	6,165	C
Univ of Wisc/Oshkosh	WI	4,240	C
Univ of Wisc/Parkside	WI	5,247	
Univ of Wisc/Platteville	WI	4,830	C
Univ of Wisc/Stevens Point	WI	5,047	C+
Univ of Wisc/Whitewater	WI	4,700	C
Univ of Wyoming	WY	4,991	NC
Upsala College	NJ	17,200	C
Ursinus College	PA	19,165	VC
Utah State Univ	UT	4,683	C
Valdosta State Univ	GA	4,670	LC
Valley City State Univ	ND	4,385	LC
Valparaiso Univ	IN	14,810	VC
Vanderbilt Univ	TN	23,422	HC+
Villanova Univ	PA	21,400	HC
Virginia Polytechnic Inst and State Univ	VA	6,828	C
Virginia Wesleyan College	VA	14,950	VC
Wabash College	IN	16,250	VC
Wake Forest Univ	NC	17,280	MC
Walla Walla College	WA	13,215	C
Walsh Univ	OH	11,640	C
Washburn Univ of Topeka	KS	5,802	NC
Washington and Jefferson College	PA	19,360	C
Washington and Lee Univ	VA	17,735	MC
Washington College	MD	19,270	C+
Washington State Univ	WA	6,364	C
Washington Univ	MO	23,507	HC
Wayne State College	NE	4,260	NC
Wayne State Univ	MI	2,680	C
Weber State Univ	UT	4,398	C
Wellesley College	MA	23,815	MC
Wells College	NY	19,460	C+
Wesleyan College	GA	15,445	C
Wesleyan Univ	CT	23,770	MC
West Chester Univ of Penn	PA	7,492	C
West Georgia College	GA	4,256	C
West Texas A&M Univ	TX	4,224	C
Western Carolina Univ	NC	3,811	C
Western Conn State Univ	CT	6,622	C
Western Illinois Univ	IL	5,241	LC
Western Kentucky Univ	KY	4,808	C
Western Maryland College	MD	18,990	C
Western Mich Univ	MI	6,820	C
Western Oregon State College	OR	6,180	C
Western State College of Colo	CO	5,560	C
Western Washington Univ	WA	6,077	VC
Westfield State College	MA	7,161	C
Westminster College	PA	15,200	C
Westmont College	CA	18,732	C
Wheaton College	IL	14,710	HC
Wheaton College	MA	23,840	C+
Wheeling Jesuit College	WV	14,370	C
Whitman College	WA	20,595	HC
Whittier College	CA	21,661	C
Whitworth College	WA	16,265	C
Wichita State Univ	KS	5,068	NC
Wilkes Univ	PA	15,728	LC
Willamette Univ	OR	17,995	VC
William Carey College	MS	7,050	C
William Jewell College	MO	12,500	VC
William Paterson College	NJ	7,438	C+
William Woods Univ	MO	14,025	LC
Williams College	MA	24,390	MC
Wilmington College	OH	13,700	LC
Winona State Univ	MN	5,200	VC
Winston-Salem State Univ	NC	4,142	LC
Winthrop Univ	SC	6,750	C
Wittenberg Univ	OH	19,998	VC
Wofford College	SC	15,360	VC
Worcester State College	MA	6,414	LC
Wright State Univ	OH	6,896	LC
Xavier Univ	OH	15,710	C+
Xavier Univ of Louisiana	LA	10,400	C
Yale Univ	CT	25,110	MC
Youngstown State Univ	OH	6,447	LC

SPANISH STUDIES

School	ST	$IS	SR
Scripps College	CA	23,600	HC

SPECIAL EDUCATION

School	ST	$IS	SR
Alabama A&M Univ	AL	4,200	C
Alabama State Univ	AL	3,428	NC
Albany State College	GA	4,481	LC
Alfred Univ	NY	21,054	VC+
American International College	MA	14,029	C
Angelo State Univ	TX	5,176	C
Appalachian State Univ	NC	4,095	C
Arizona State Univ Main Campus	AZ	6,444	C
Arkansas State Univ	AR	4,250	NC
Auburn Univ	AL	5,823	C+
Auburn Univ at Montgomery	AL	3,390	C
Augustana College	SD	13,420	C
Austin Peay State Univ	TN	4,350	C
Avila College	MO	12,130	C
Baldwin-Wallace College	OH	15,210	C
Ball State Univ	IN	6,032	LC
Baylor Univ	TX	10,990	C+
Beaver College	PA	17,660	C
Bellarmine College	KY	10,832	C
Belmont Abbey College	NC	13,190	C
Benedictine College	KS	12,830	C
Bethany College	WV	18,300	C+
Black Hills State Univ	SD	4,831	NC
Bloomsburg Univ of Penn	PA	6,312	C+
Blue Mountain College	MS	5,958	LC
Bluefield State College	WV	1,832	LC
Boston College	MA	22,706	MC
Boston Univ	MA	24,130	HC
Bowling Green State Univ	OH	6,701	C
Bradley Univ	IL	14,718	C+
Brescia College	KY	9,800	C
Brigham Young Univ	UT	5,625	HC
Brooklyn Campus of LIU	NY	15,000	LC
Buena Vista College	IA	16,150	VC
Calif Lutheran Univ	CA	17,240	C
Cal State/Chico	CA	6,146	C
Cal State/Fresno	CA	5,747	C
Calif Univ of Penn	PA	7,370	C
Cardinal Stritch College	WI	11,252	C
Caribbean Univ	PR	2,400	
Carlow College	PA	13,914	C
Catawba College	NC	12,950	C
Central Conn State Univ	CT	7,108	C
Central Mich Univ	MI	6,737	LC
Central Missouri State Univ	MO	5,138	LC
Central State Univ	OH	7,320	NC
Central Washington Univ	WA	5,644	C
Central Wesleyan College	SC	9,640	C
Cheyney Univ of Penn	PA	7,005	C
Chicago State Univ	IL	2,198	C
CUNY/Baruch College	NY	2,562	VC
CUNY/Brooklyn College	NY	2,450	VC
CUNY/City College	NY	2,543	VC
CUNY/Medgar Evers College	NY	2,577	NC
Clarion Univ of Penn	PA	6,518	C
Clarke College	IA	13,950	C+
Clemson Univ	SC	6,564	VC
Cleveland State Univ	OH	7,287	NC
College Misericordia	PA	15,820	C
College of Charleston	SC	6,250	C
College of Mount St Vincent	NY	16,730	C
College of Notre Dame of Maryland	MD	16,050	C
College of Our Lady of The Elms	MA	15,639	C
College of St Elizabeth	NJ	15,800	C
College of St Joseph	VT	12,650	LC
College of St Mary	NE	12,500	LC
College of St Rose	NY	14,452	C
College of the Southwest	NM	5,720	LC
Columbia College	SC	13,520	LC
Columbus College	GA	4,892	LC
Concord College	WV	5,104	NC
Concordia College	NE	11,776	NC
Coppin State College	MD	7,145	LC
Creighton Univ	NE	14,432	VC
Cumberland College	KY	9,756	C
D'Youville College	NY	12,850	C
Daemen College	NY	13,020	LC
Dana College	NE	11,910	C
Defiance College	OH	13,480	LC
Delaware State College	DE	5,656	C
Delta State Univ	MS	3,964	LC
Dillard Univ	LA	9,950	C
Doane College	NE	12,220	C
Dominican College	NY	13,600	LC
Dowling College	NY	12,730	LC
Drury College	MO	12,140	VC
Duquesne Univ	PA	16,434	VC
East Carolina Univ	NC	4,498	C
East Central Univ	OK	3,558	C
East Stroudsburg Univ	PA	6,886	C
East Tenn State Univ	TN	4,406	C
Eastern Illinois Univ	IL	5,548	C
Eastern Kentucky Univ	KY	4,840	NC
Eastern Mennonite College	VA	12,700	C
Eastern Mich Univ	MI	6,749	C
Eastern New Mexico Univ	NM	3,950	C
Edinboro Univ of Penn	PA	7,181	C
Elizabeth City State Univ	NC	4,254	LC
Elmhurst College	IL	12,536	C
Erskine College	SC	14,310	C
Evangel College	MO	10,142	LC
Felician College	NJ	7,900	C
Fitchburg State College	MA	6,962	C
Flagler College	FL	7,990	C
Florida Atlantic Univ	FL	5,525	C
Florida International Univ	FL	4,191	VC
Florida Southern College	FL	12,260	C
Fontbonne College	MO	12,090	C
Franciscan Univ of Steubenville	OH	13,400	C
Gannon Univ	PA	14,872	C
Georgia College	GA	4,310	LC
Georgia Southern Univ	GA	4,988	LC
Georgia Southwestern College	GA	4,338	LC

School	ST	$IS	SR
Georgian Court College	NJ	12,550	C
Glenville State College	WV	4,810	LC
Gonzaga Univ	WA	16,350	VC
Gordon College	MA	16,790	C
Goucher College	MD	20,295	VC
Grambling State Univ	LA	4,712	NC
Grand Canyon Univ	AZ	9,680	VC
Green Mountain College	VT	14,080	C
Greensboro College	NC	11,496	C
Greenville College	IL	14,190	C
Gwynedd-Mercy College	PA	15,450	C
Hampton Univ	VA	10,706	C
Hastings College	NE	12,426	C
High Point Univ	NC	12,350	LC
Holy Family College	PA	8,300	C
Hood College	MD	19,010	VC
Hope College	MI	15,698	C+
Houston Baptist Univ	TX	11,055	C
Idaho State Univ	ID	4,442	C
Illinois Benedictine College	IL	14,170	C
Illinois State Univ	IL	6,413	C
Incarnate Word College	TX	12,307	C
Indiana State Univ	IN	6,210	C
Indiana Univ Bloomington	IN	6,495	VC
Indiana Univ of Penn	PA	6,373	C
Indiana Univ Southeast	IN	2,260	LC
Indiana Univ/South Bend	IN	2,141	LC
Inter American Univ of PR/ Aguadilla Regional College	PR	2,290	
Inter American Univ of PR/ Bayamon Univ College	PR	2,300	
Inter American Univ of PR/ Metropolitan Campus	PR	2,340	
Inter American Univ of PR/ Ponce Regional College	PR	2,300	
Inter American Univ of PR/ San German	PR	4,620	
Inter American Univ/Arecibo Campus	PR	5,666	
Inter-American Univ of PR/ Fajardo Regional College	PR	2,732	
Jackson State Univ	MS	4,996	LC
Jacksonville State Univ	AL	4,080	LC
Jarvis Christian College	TX	7,170	LC
Jersey City State College	NJ	7,797	LC
Kansas State Univ	KS	4,816	NC
Kansas Wesleyan Univ	KS	11,770	C
Kean College of New Jersey	NJ	6,395	LC
Keene State College	NH	7,081	C
Kent State Univ	OH	6,740	LC
Keuka College	NY	13,660	C
Kutztown Univ	PA	6,528	C
La Salle Univ	PA	16,940	VC
Lamar Univ	TX	3,798	C
Lambuth Univ	TN	8,395	C
Lander Univ	SC	6,180	LC
Le Moyne College	NY	15,180	C
Lesley College	MA	17,120	LC
Lewis-Clark State College	ID	4,040	
Lincoln Univ	MO	4,638	NC
Livingston Univ	AL	3,979	C
Lock Haven Univ of Penn	PA	7,128	C
Longwood College	VA	7,800	C
Loras College	IA	14,160	C
Louisiana College	LA	7,518	VC
Louisiana Tech Univ	LA	4,284	C
Loyola Univ of Chicago	IL	15,880	C+
Luther College	IA	15,900	VC
Lynchburg College	VA	17,000	C
MacMurray College	IL	12,800	C
Madonna Univ	MI	8,546	C
Manhattan College	NY	19,000	C
Manhattanville College	NY	20,450	LC
Mansfield Univ	PA	6,348	C
Marian College	IN	12,936	C
Marist College	NY	16,406	C
Marshall Univ	WV	5,762	LC
Marygrove College	MI	5,877	VC
Marymount College/ Tarrytown	NY	17,350	C
Marymount Manhattan College	NY	15,450	LC
Marywood College	PA	14,890	C
Mercer Univ	GA	15,123	C
Mercy College	NY	11,180	NC
Mercyhurst College	PA	13,488	C
Methodist College	NC	12,400	C
Miami Univ	OH	8,066	VC
Mich State Univ	MI	7,842	C
Millersville Univ of Penn	PA	7,370	VC
Miss College	MS	8,348	C
Miss State Univ	MS	5,629	VC
Miss Univ for Women	MS	4,456	LC
Missouri Southern State College	MO	4,272	
Molloy College	NY	8,580	LC
Monmouth College	IL	17,300	C+
Moorhead State Univ	MN	5,076	C
Morehead State Univ	KY	4,600	LC
Morningside College	IA	13,896	C
Mount Marty College	SD	10,450	NC
Mount St Mary College	NY	12,910	C
Mount Vernon Nazarene College	OH	10,390	C
Muskingum College	OH	16,650	C
Nebr Wesleyan Univ	NE	12,240	C
New Mexico State Univ	NM	4,844	LC
New York Univ	NY	24,705	VC+
Norfolk State Univ	VA	6,345	LC
N Car Agricultural and Technical State Univ	NC	4,477	LC
N Car Central Univ	NC	4,347	LC
North Georgia College	GA	4,103	LC
Northeast Louisiana Univ	LA	3,906	NC
Northeast Missouri State Univ	MO	5,654	VC+
Northeastern Illinois Univ	IL	1,955	C
Northeastern State Univ	OK	5,250	C
Northern State Univ	SD	4,186	LC
Northwest Missouri State Univ	MO	5,010	LC
Northwest Nazarene College	ID	11,750	C
Northwestern College of Iowa	IA	12,250	C
Northwestern Okla State Univ	OK	3,424	C
Notre Dame College	NH	14,220	C
Ohio Dominican College	OH	11,820	LC
Okla Christian Univ of Science and Arts	OK	8,790	NC
Okla State Univ	OK	5,086	VC
Pembroke State Univ	NC	3,538	LC
Penn State Univ/Univ Park Campus	PA	8,752	HC
Peru State College	NE	4,311	NC
Pfeiffer College	NC	11,670	LC
Philander Smith College	AR	5,434	NC
Piedmont College	GA	8,540	LC
Pikeville College	KY	8,500	NC
Pillsbury Baptist Bible College	MN	7,390	NC
Plymouth State College	NH	7,166	C
Pontifical Catholic Univ of PR/Ponce	PR	5,807	
Presbyterian College	SC	15,400	VC
Prescott College	AZ	9,775	C
Providence College	RI	19,750	VC
Purdue Univ/West Lafayette	IN	6,636	C
Quincy Univ	IL	13,646	VC
Rhode Island College	RI	7,901	LC
Rivier College	NH	14,920	LC
St Francis College	IN	11,662	C
St Francis College	NY	6,710	LC
St John's Univ	NY	8,980	C+
St Joseph College	CT	16,225	C
St Joseph's College	NY	7,322	C
St Leo College	FL	13,570	C
St Louis Univ	MO	15,522	VC
St Martin's College	WA	14,965	C
St Mary-of-the-Woods College	IN	14,430	NC
St Thomas Aquinas College	NY	13,550	C
Salve Regina Univ	RI	29,100	LC
San Francisco State Univ	CA	7,292	LC
Seattle Pacific Univ	WA	16,503	C
Simmons College	MA	22,534	C
S Car State Univ	SC	5,424	LC
Southeast Missouri State Univ	MO	5,854	C
Southeastern Louisiana Univ	LA	4,230	NC
Southern Conn State Univ	CT	7,532	C
Southern Illinois Univ at Carbondale	IL	6,234	C
Southern Illinois Univ at Edwardsville	IL	6,097	LC
Southern Univ and A&M College	LA	4,920	NC
Southern Utah Univ	UT	4,104	LC
Southwest Texas State Univ	TX	5,124	C
Southwestern Okla State Univ	OK	3,312	C
SUNY at Albany	NY	7,059	VC
SUNY/College at Buffalo	NY	7,035	VC
SUNY/College at Geneseo	NY	6,949	HC
SUNY/College at Old Westbury	NY	7,128	LC
SUNY/College at Plattsburgh	NY	6,917	C
SUNY/Potsdam College	NY	6,906	C
Syracuse Univ	NY	21,305	HC
Tenn State Univ	TN	4,626	C+
Tenn Tech Univ	TN	5,190	C
Texas Christian Univ	TX	12,180	C
Texas Southern Univ	TX	4,500	NC
The Univ of New Mexico	NM	5,304	C
Trenton State College	NJ	9,085	HC
Trinity Christian College	IL	13,260	C
Trinity College of Vermont	VT	16,015	LC
Troy State Univ	AL	4,322	C
Turabo Univ	PR	2,670	
Tusculum College	TN	10,400	LC
Tuskegee Univ	AL	10,128	C
Union College	KY	9,790	C
Univ of Akron	OH	6,699	NC
Univ of Alabama	AL	5,702	C
Univ of Alabama at Birmingham	AL	7,533	C
Univ of Arkansas at Fayetteville	AR	5,046	C
Univ of Arkansas at Monticello	AR	3,832	NC
Univ of Arkansas at Pine Bluff	AR	3,978	LC
Univ of Central Arkansas	AR	4,200	LC
Univ of Central Florida	FL	6,061	C+
Univ of Cincinnati	OH	7,989	C
Univ of Conn	CT	9,168	C
Univ of Dayton	OH	15,120	C+
Univ of Delaware	DE	8,013	VC
Univ of Detroit Mercy	MI	14,720	C
Univ of Dubuque	IA	14,150	LC
Univ of Evansville	IN	15,300	VC
Univ of Florida	FL	5,850	HC
Univ of Hartford	CT	19,858	LC
Univ of Houston	TX	5,215	C
Univ of Idaho	ID	4,830	C
Univ of Kentucky	KY	5,152	VC
Univ of Maine at Farmington	ME	6,700	C
Univ of Mary Hardin-Baylor	TX	8,120	NC
Univ of Memphis	TN	3,476	C
Univ of Miami	FL	22,107	VC
Univ of Mich/Ann Arbor	MI	9,428	HC+
Univ of Miss	MS	5,756	C
Univ of Missouri/Columbia	MO	6,254	HC
Univ of Missouri/St. Louis	MO	6,378	C
Univ of Nebr at Kearney	NE	4,308	LC
Univ of Nebr at Omaha	NE	1,889	LC
Univ of Nebr-Lincoln	NE	5,278	LC
Univ of Nevada/Las Vegas	NV	6,405	C
Univ of Nevada/Reno	NV	5,735	C
Univ of N Car at Charlotte	NC	4,597	C
Univ of N Car at Wilmington	NC	5,172	C
Univ of North Florida	FL	5,082	C
Univ of Northern Iowa	IA	5,137	C
Univ of Okla	OK	5,427	VC
Univ of PR/Rio Piedras	PR	0	
Univ of South Alabama	AL	5,451	C
Univ of S Dak	SD	4,722	C
Univ of Southwestern Louisiana	LA	3,968	NC
Univ of Tenn at Chattanooga	TN	5,375	C
Univ of Tenn/Knoxville	TN	5,668	C
Univ of the District of Columbia	DC	974	NC
Univ of the Pacific	CA	21,100	C
Univ of Toledo	OH	6,636	NC
Univ of Utah	UT	5,975	C
Univ of Vermont	VT	10,776	C+
Univ of Wisc/Eau Claire	WI	4,647	C
Univ of Wisc/Oshkosh	WI	4,240	C
Univ of Wisc/Whitewater	WI	4,700	C
Univ of Wyoming	WY	4,991	NC
Utah State Univ	UT	4,683	C
Valdosta State Univ	GA	4,670	LC
Vanderbilt Univ	TN	23,422	HC+
Villanova Univ	PA	21,400	HC
Virginia State Univ	VA	7,040	
Virginia Union Univ	VA	10,555	LC
Walsh Univ	OH	11,640	C
Washington State Univ	WA	6,364	C
Wayne State College	NE	4,260	NC
Wayne State Univ	MI	2,680	C
West Chester Univ of Penn	PA	7,492	C
West Georgia College	GA	4,256	C
West Liberty State College	WV	4,690	LC
Western Carolina Univ	NC	3,811	C
Western Illinois Univ	IL	5,241	LC
Western Kentucky Univ	KY	4,808	C
Western Mich Univ	MI	6,820	C
Western New Mexico Univ	NM	3,234	LC
Westfield State College	MA	7,161	C
Wheelock College	MA	18,000	LC
Wichita State Univ	KS	5,068	NC
Wiley College	TX	0	NC
William Carey College	MS	7,050	C
William Paterson College	NJ	7,438	C+
Winona State Univ	MN	5,200	VC
Winston-Salem State Univ	NC	4,142	LC
Winthrop Univ	SC	6,750	C
Wittenberg Univ	OH	19,998	VC
Women's College of Brenau Univ	GA	14,734	C
Wright State Univ	OH	6,896	LC
Xavier Univ	OH	15,710	C+
Youngstown State Univ	OH	6,447	LC

SPECIFIC LEARNING DISABILITIES

School	ST	$IS	SR
Florida International Univ	FL	4,191	VC
Florida State Univ	FL	5,814	VC
Northwest Missouri State Univ	MO	5,010	LC

SPEECH CORRECTION

School	ST	$IS	SR
Boston Univ	MA	24,130	HC
Columbia College	SC	13,520	LC
Okla Christian Univ of Science and Arts	OK	8,790	NC
Univ of Illinois at Urbana-Champaign	IL	7,764	HC
Western Carolina Univ	NC	3,811	C
Xavier Univ of Louisiana	LA	10,400	C

SPEECH/DEBATE/RHETORIC

School	ST	$IS	SR
Abilene Christian Univ	TX	10,460	NC
Adrian College	MI	14,340	C
Albany State College	GA	4,481	LC
Alderson-Broaddus College	WV	12,000	C
Allegheny College	PA	21,020	VC
Angelo State Univ	TX	5,176	C
Appalachian State Univ	NC	4,095	C
Arkansas State Univ	AR	4,250	NC
Arkansas Tech Univ	AR	4,200	NC
Armstrong State College	GA	4,874	LC
Asbury College	KY	11,105	VC
Ashland Univ	OH	15,508	C
Auburn Univ	AL	5,823	C+
Augsburg College	MN	15,608	C
Augustana College	IL	16,959	VC
Augustana College	SD	13,420	C
Averett College	VA	13,610	LC
Baldwin-Wallace College	OH	15,210	C
Ball State Univ	IN	6,032	LC
Bates College	ME	23,990	MC
Baylor Univ	TX	10,990	C+
Bethel College	MN	15,050	C
Black Hills State Univ	SD	4,831	NC
Bloomsburg Univ of Penn	PA	6,312	C+
Bowling Green State Univ	OH	6,701	C
Bridgewater State College	MA	7,518	C
Brigham Young Univ	UT	5,625	HC
Brooklyn Campus of LIU	NY	15,000	LC
Buena Vista College	IA	16,150	VC
Butler Univ	IN	16,210	C
Calif Lutheran Univ	CA	17,240	C
Cal State/Chico	CA	6,146	C
Cal State/Fresno	CA	5,747	C
Cal State/Fullerton	CA	4,850	LC
Cal State/Hayward	CA	5,495	C
Cal State/Long Beach	CA	6,057	LC
Cal State/Los Angeles	CA	4,940	VC
Cal State/Northridge	CA	7,122	LC
Cal State/Stanislaus	CA	6,799	C
Calif Univ of Penn	PA	7,370	C
Cameron Univ	OK	3,686	LC
Capital Univ	OH	16,535	VC
Catawba College	NC	12,950	C
Cedar Crest College	PA	18,930	C
Centenary College of Louisiana	LA	11,826	C+
Central Missouri State Univ	MO	5,138	LC
Central State Univ	OH	7,320	NC
Central Washington Univ	WA	5,644	C
Chadron State College	NE	4,091	NC
Charleston Southern Univ	SC	10,282	LC
Chicago State Univ	IL	2,198	C
CUNY/Brooklyn College	NY	2,450	VC
CUNY/Herbert H. Lehman College	NY	2,542	C
CUNY/York College	NY	2,534	NC
Clarion Univ of Penn	PA	6,518	C
Clark Atlanta Univ	GA	11,846	C
College of St Catherine	MN	14,670	C
College of William and Mary	VA	8,602	MC
Colo State Univ	CO	6,566	VC
Columbus College	GA	4,892	LC
Concordia College	MN	13,200	C
Concordia College	NE	11,776	NC
Cornell College	IA	18,425	VC
Cumberland College	KY	9,756	C
Dana College	NE	11,910	C
David Lipscomb Univ	TN	7,865	VC
Defiance College	OH	13,480	LC
Denison Univ	OH	21,150	VC+
Dickinson State Univ	ND	3,792	
Dillard Univ	LA	9,950	C
Dordt College	IA	11,690	C
Dowling College	NY	12,730	LC
Drake Univ	IA	17,195	VC
Duquesne Univ	PA	16,434	VC
East Central Univ	OK	3,558	C
East Stroudsburg Univ	PA	6,886	C
East Tenn State Univ	TN	4,406	C
East Texas Baptist Univ	TX	7,740	C
Eastern Kentucky Univ	KY	4,840	NC
Eastern Mich Univ	MI	6,749	C
Eastern New Mexico Univ	NM	3,950	C
Eastern Washington Univ	WA	5,439	LC
Elmhurst College	IL	12,536	C
Emerson College	MA	22,678	LC
Emporia State Univ	KS	4,685	NC
Eureka College	IL	14,555	C
Evangel College	MO	10,142	LC
Evergreen State College	WA	6,306	C
Fairmont State College	WV	4,640	LC
Fayetteville State Univ	NC	3,926	LC
Fisk Univ	TN	0	LC
Florida State Univ	FL	5,814	VC
Fontbonne College	MO	12,090	C
Freed-Hardeman Univ	TN	8,585	VC
Frostburg State Univ	MD	6,940	C
Geneva College	PA	13,030	C
George Mason Univ	VA	8,728	C
George Washington Univ	DC	22,470	HC
Gonzaga Univ	WA	16,350	VC

School	ST	$IS	SR
Graceland College	IA	11,600	C
Grambling State Univ	LA	4,712	NC
Grand Canyon Univ	AZ	9,680	VC
Grand Rapids Baptist College and Seminary	MI	10,228	C
Gustavus Adolphus College	MN	15,935	VC
Hastings College	NE	12,426	C
Henderson State Univ	AR	3,860	C
Hillsdale College	MI	15,110	VC
Hofstra Univ	NY	16,580	VC
Houston Baptist Univ	TX	11,055	C
Humboldt State Univ	CA	5,676	C
Huntingdon College	AL	11,400	C
Idaho State Univ	ID	4,442	C
Illinois College	IL	11,200	C
Illinois State Univ	IL	6,413	C
Incarnate Word College	TX	12,307	C
Indiana Univ at Kokomo	IN	2,069	C
Indiana Univ Bloomington	IN	6,495	VC
Indiana Univ-Purdue Univ at Fort Wayne	IN	2,500	LC
Indiana Univ/South Bend	IN	2,141	LC
Iowa State Univ	IA	5,456	C
Ithaca College	NY	19,679	C
Jackson State Univ	MS	4,996	LC
Judson College	IL	13,625	C
Kansas State Univ	KS	4,816	NC
Kansas Wesleyan Univ	KS	11,770	C
Kent State Univ	OH	6,740	LC
Kutztown Univ	PA	6,528	C
Lamar Univ	TX	3,798	C
Lander Univ	SC	6,180	LC
Langston Univ	OK	2,907	LC
Lewis Univ	IL	14,797	LC
Liberty Univ	VA	11,500	LC
Lock Haven Univ of Penn	PA	7,128	C
Loras College	IA	14,160	C
Louisiana College	LA	7,518	VC
Louisiana State Univ and A&M College	LA	5,605	C
Louisiana State Univ in Shreveport	LA	1,910	NC
Louisiana Tech Univ	LA	4,284	C
Lubbock Christian Univ	TX	9,840	NC
Luther College	IA	15,900	VC
Marian College	IN	12,936	C
Marietta College	OH	16,940	C+
Marquette Univ	WI	16,114	VC
Maryville College	TN	14,474	C
McKendree College	IL	10,900	C
McNeese State Univ	LA	4,543	NC
McPherson College	KS	11,360	VC
Mercy College	NY	11,180	NC
Meredith College	NC	9,440	C
Methodist College	NC	12,400	C
Miami Univ	OH	8,066	VC
Middle Tenn State Univ	TN	3,857	C
Midwestern State Univ	TX	4,542	LC
Millersville Univ of Penn	PA	7,370	VC
Miss College	MS	8,348	C
Miss Valley State Univ	MS	4,089	NC
Missouri Valley College	MO	14,050	LC
Missouri Western State College	MO	4,384	NC
Molloy College	NY	8,580	LC
Monmouth College	NJ	16,820	C
Montana State Univ	MT	5,534	C
Moorhead State Univ	MN	5,076	C
Morehead State Univ	KY	4,600	LC
Morehouse College	GA	13,224	LC
Morgan State Univ	MD	7,366	C+
Mount Mercy College	IA	13,230	C
Mount Union College	OH	15,850	C
Murray State Univ	KY	4,702	C
Muskingum College	OH	16,650	C
New York Univ	NY	24,705	VC+
Nicholls State Univ	LA	4,531	NC
N Car Agricultural and Technical State Univ	NC	4,477	LC
North Central College	IL	15,498	VC
Northeast Louisiana Univ	LA	3,906	NC
Northeast Missouri State Univ	MO	5,654	VC+
Northeastern Illinois Univ	IL	1,955	C
Northeastern State Univ	OK	5,250	C
Northern Arizona Univ	AZ	4,844	C
Northern Kentucky Univ	KY	4,620	NC
Northern Mich Univ	MI	6,350	C
Northwest Missouri State Univ	MO	5,010	LC
Northwest Nazarene College	ID	11,750	C
Northwestern Okla State Univ	OK	3,424	C
Northwestern Univ	IL	21,093	MC
Ohio Northern Univ	OH	18,660	VC
Ohio Univ	OH	7,341	C
Okla Baptist Univ	OK	8,486	C
Okla Christian Univ of Science and Arts	OK	8,790	NC
Okla City Univ	OK	9,840	C
Okla Panhandle State Univ	OK	3,155	NC
Okla State Univ	OK	5,086	VC
Old Dominion Univ	VA	8,317	C
Olivet College	MI	14,000	C
Olivet Nazarene Univ	IL	11,976	C
Oregon State Univ	OR	6,175	C
Ottawa Univ	KS	10,490	C+

School	ST	$IS	SR
Otterbein College	OH	16,506	C
Ouachita Baptist Univ	AR	8,940	C
Our Lady of the Lake Univ of San Antonio	TX	11,080	C
Palm Beach Atlantic College	FL	10,720	C
Penn State Univ/Univ Park Campus	PA	8,752	HC
Pepperdine Univ	CA	23,720	VC
Pittsburg State Univ	KS	4,478	NC
Point Loma Nazarene College	CA	13,532	C
Portland State Univ	OR	7,191	C
Prairie View A&M Univ	TX	4,740	LC
Radford Univ	VA	7,034	LC
Rider College	NJ	18,160	C
Ripon College	WI	18,320	C+
Roosevelt Univ	IL	12,368	C
Rowan College of New Jersey	NJ	7,358	VC
St Ambrose Univ	IA	13,380	C
St Cloud State Univ	MN	5,015	C
St John's Univ	NY	8,980	C+
St Joseph's College	NY	7,322	C
St Mary's College of Minn	MN	13,850	LC
St Mary's Univ	TX	12,064	C
St Olaf College	MN	17,200	HC
Salisbury State Univ	MD	7,516	C+
Sam Houston State Univ	TX	4,506	C
Samford Univ	AL	11,400	VC
San Francisco State Univ	CA	7,292	LC
San Jose State Univ	CA	6,680	LC
Shaw Univ	NC	8,936	C+
Shepherd College	WV	5,540	C
Shorter College	GA	10,270	C
Sioux Falls College	SD	11,540	C
S Dak State Univ	SD	4,562	C
Southeastern Louisiana Univ	LA	4,230	NC
Southeastern Okla State Univ	OK	3,594	C
Southern Arkansas Univ	AR	3,432	NC
Southern Illinois Univ at Carbondale	IL	6,234	C
Southern Illinois Univ at Edwardsville	IL	6,097	LC
Southern Nazarene Univ	OK	9,206	NC
Southern Univ and A&M College	LA	4,920	NC
Southern Univ at New Orleans	LA	1,452	NC
Southwest Missouri State Univ	MO	4,956	C
Southwest Texas State Univ	TX	5,124	C
Southwestern Okla State Univ	OK	3,312	C
Spring Arbor College	MI	12,256	C
SUNY/College at Brockport	NY	7,220	C+
SUNY/College at Buffalo	NY	7,035	VC
SUNY/College at Cortland	NY	7,326	C+
SUNY/College at New Paltz	NY	6,890	VC
SUNY/College at Oneonta	NY	7,878	C
SUNY/College at Plattsburgh	NY	6,917	C
SUNY/Potsdam College	NY	6,906	C
Stephen F. Austin State Univ	TX	5,117	C
Sterling College	KS	10,990	VC
Stetson Univ	FL	16,435	VC
Suffolk Univ	MA	15,360	LC
Syracuse Univ	NY	21,305	HC
Tarleton State Univ	TX	4,082	LC
Teikyo Westmar Univ	IA	15,920	C
Temple Univ	PA	10,281	C
Tenn State Univ	TN	4,626	C+
Texas A&M Univ	TX	5,382	VC
Texas Southern Univ	TX	4,500	NC
Texas Tech Univ	TX	6,008	C
Towson State Univ	MD	7,452	C
Trevecca Nazarene College	TN	9,826	NC
Trinity Univ	TX	16,670	HC
Troy State Univ	AL	4,322	C
Union College	KY	9,790	C
Univ of Akron	OH	6,699	NC
Univ of Alabama	AL	5,702	C
Univ of Alaska Fairbanks	AK	4,718	C
Univ of Arizona	AZ	5,808	C
Univ of Arkansas at Fayetteville	AR	5,046	C
Univ of Arkansas at Pine Bluff	AR	3,978	LC
Univ of Calif at Berkeley	CA	9,962	HC+
Univ of Calif at Davis	CA	9,534	VC
Univ of Central Arkansas	AR	4,200	LC
Univ of Central Okla	OK	3,647	C
Univ of Denver	CO	19,290	C+
Univ of Dubuque	IA	14,150	LC
Univ of Florida	FL	5,850	HC
Univ of Georgia	GA	5,655	VC
Univ of Hawaii at Hilo	HI	4,141	C
Univ of Hawaii at Manoa	HI	5,626	C
Univ of Houston	TX	5,215	C
Univ of Illinois at Chicago	IL	8,443	C
Univ of Indianapolis	IN	14,510	C
Univ of Iowa	IA	5,658	VC
Univ of Maine	ME	7,990	C
Univ of Maine at Presque Isle	ME	6,374	C
Univ of Mary Hardin-Baylor	TX	8,120	NC

School	ST	$IS	SR
Univ of Maryland/College Park	MD	8,182	VC
Univ of Maryland/Univ College	MD	4,900	NC
Univ of Miami	FL	22,107	VC
Univ of Mich/Ann Arbor	MI	9,428	HC+
Univ of Minn/Morris	MN	6,825	HC
Univ of Minn/Twin Cities	MN	6,682	VC
Univ of Missouri/Kansas City	MO	5,906	VC
Univ of Montevallo	AL	5,310	C
Univ of Nebr at Kearney	NE	4,308	LC
Univ of Nebr at Omaha	NE	1,889	LC
Univ of Nebr-Lincoln	NE	5,278	LC
Univ of Nevada/Reno	NV	5,735	C
Univ of N Car at Chapel Hill	NC	5,330	HC
Univ of N Car at Greensboro	NC	5,192	C
Univ of N Car at Wilmington	NC	5,172	C
Univ of N Dak	ND	4,902	NC
Univ of Northern Iowa	IA	5,137	C
Univ of Oregon	OR	6,466	VC
Univ of Pittsburgh	PA	9,472	C
Univ of PR/Rio Piedras	PR	0	
Univ of Rhode Island	RI	9,205	C
Univ of Richmond	VA	16,700	HC
Univ of St Thomas	MN	15,785	C+
Univ of S Car	SC	6,158	C
Univ of S Dak	SD	4,722	C
Univ of South Florida	FL	5,475	C+
Univ of Southern Colo	CO	5,350	LC
Univ of Southern Indiana	IN	3,720	NC
Univ of Southern Miss	MS	4,542	C
Univ of Southwestern Louisiana	LA	3,968	NC
Univ of Tenn/Knoxville	TN	5,668	C
Univ of Texas at Arlington	TX	5,549	LC
Univ of Texas at Austin	TX	5,160	VC
Univ of Texas at El Paso	TX	3,160	LC
Univ of Toledo	OH	6,636	NC
Univ of Utah	UT	5,975	C
Univ of Washington	WA	6,618	VC
Univ of Wisc/Eau Claire	WI	4,647	C
Univ of Wisc/La Crosse	WI	4,487	C
Univ of Wisc/Oshkosh	WI	4,240	C
Univ of Wisc/Platteville	WI	4,830	C
Univ of Wisc/River Falls	WI	4,655	C
Univ of Wisc/Superior	WI	4,330	C
Univ of Wisc/Whitewater	WI	4,700	C
Utica College of Syracuse Univ	NY	16,714	LC
Valdosta State Univ	GA	4,670	LC
Valley City State Univ	ND	4,385	LC
Wabash College	IN	16,250	VC
Wagner College	NY	17,950	C
Wake Forest Univ	NC	17,280	MC
Walla Walla College	WA	13,215	C
Washington State Univ	WA	6,364	C
Wayne State College	NE	4,260	NC
Wayne State Univ	MI	2,680	C
Weber State Univ	UT	4,398	C
West Chester Univ of Penn	PA	7,492	C
West Georgia College	GA	4,256	C
West Texas A&M Univ	TX	4,224	C
West Virginia Wesleyan College	WV	16,900	C
Western Kentucky Univ	KY	4,808	C
Western Oregon State College	OR	6,180	C
Western Washington Univ	WA	6,077	VC
Whitworth College	WA	16,265	C
Willamette Univ	OR	17,995	VC
William Carey College	MS	7,050	C
William Woods Univ	MO	14,025	LC
Winona State Univ	MN	5,200	VC
Winthrop Univ	SC	6,750	C
Yeshiva Univ	NY	18,200	VC
York College of Penn	PA	8,345	C
Youngstown State Univ	OH	6,447	LC

SPEECH PATHOLOGY/AUDIOLOGY

School	ST	$IS	SR
Abilene Christian Univ	TX	10,460	NC
Adelphi Univ	NY	18,250	LC
Alabama A&M Univ	AL	4,200	C
Andrews Univ	MI	14,952	NC
Appalachian State Univ	NC	4,095	C
Arizona State Univ Main Campus	AZ	6,444	C
Arkansas State Univ	AR	4,250	NC
Auburn Univ	AL	5,823	C+
Augustana College	IL	16,959	VC
Baldwin-Wallace College	OH	15,210	C
Ball State Univ	IN	6,032	LC
Baylor Univ	TX	10,990	C+
Bloomsburg Univ of Penn	PA	6,312	C+
Boston Univ	MA	24,130	HC
Bowling Green State Univ	OH	6,701	C
Brescia College	KY	9,800	C
Bridgewater State College	MA	7,518	C
Brigham Young Univ	UT	5,625	HC
Butler Univ	IN	16,210	C
Cal State/Chico	CA	6,146	C
Cal State/Fresno	CA	5,747	C
Cal State/Fullerton	CA	4,850	LC
Cal State/Hayward	CA	5,495	C
Cal State/Long Beach	CA	6,057	LC
Cal State/Los Angeles	CA	4,940	VC
Cal State/Northridge	CA	7,122	LC
Cal State/Sacramento	CA	6,387	C
Calif Univ of Penn	PA	7,370	C
Calvin College	MI	13,020	VC
Case Western Reserve Univ	OH	19,910	HC
Central Mich Univ	MI	6,737	LC
Central Missouri State Univ	MO	5,138	LC
CUNY/Brooklyn College	NY	2,450	VC
CUNY/Herbert H. Lehman College	NY	2,542	C
CUNY/Queens College	NY	2,631	C
Clarion Univ of Penn	PA	6,518	C
College of Our Lady of The Elms	MA	15,639	C
College of St Rose	NY	14,452	C
Delta State Univ	MS	3,964	LC
East Stroudsburg Univ	PA	6,886	C
East Tenn State Univ	TN	4,406	C
Eastern Illinois Univ	IL	5,548	C
Eastern Mich Univ	MI	6,749	C
Eastern Washington Univ	WA	5,439	LC
Edinboro Univ of Penn	PA	7,181	C
Elmhurst College	IL	12,536	C
Emerson College	MA	22,678	LC
Florida State Univ	FL	5,814	VC
Fontbonne College	MO	12,090	C
Geneva College	PA	13,030	C
Grambling State Univ	LA	4,712	NC
Hampton Univ	VA	10,706	C
Hanover College	IN	10,950	VC
Hardin-Simmons Univ	TX	9,080	C
Harding Univ	AR	9,050	VC
Henderson State Univ	AR	3,860	C
Hofstra Univ	NY	16,580	VC
Howard Univ	DC	11,680	C
Idaho State Univ	ID	4,442	C
Illinois State Univ	IL	6,413	C
Indiana State Univ	IN	6,210	C
Indiana Univ-Purdue Univ at Fort Wayne	IN	2,500	LC
Iona College	NY	16,310	C
Ithaca College	NY	19,679	C
James Madison Univ	VA	8,198	HC
Kansas State Univ	KS	4,816	NC
Kent State Univ	OH	6,740	LC
Kutztown Univ	PA	6,528	C
Lamar Univ	TX	3,798	C
LIU/C. W. Post Campus	NY	16,870	C
Longwood College	VA	7,800	C
Louisiana State Univ and A&M College	LA	5,605	C
Louisiana Tech Univ	LA	4,284	C
Loyola College	MD	18,035	VC
Mankato State Univ	MN	5,097	LC
Marist College	NY	16,406	C
Marquette Univ	WI	16,114	VC
Marymount Manhattan College	NY	15,450	LC
Marywood College	PA	14,890	C
Mercy College	NY	11,180	NC
Miami Univ	OH	8,066	VC
Mich State Univ	MI	7,842	C
Middle Tenn State Univ	TN	3,857	C
Minot State Univ	ND	3,748	NC
Miss Univ for Women	MS	4,456	LC
Montclair State College	NJ	7,539	C+
Moorhead State Univ	MN	5,076	C
Murray State Univ	KY	4,702	C
Nazareth College of Rochester	NY	15,310	C+
New York Univ	NY	24,705	VC+
Nicholls State Univ	LA	4,531	NC
N Car State Univ	NC	4,984	NC
Northeast Louisiana Univ	LA	3,906	NC
Northeast Missouri State Univ	MO	5,654	VC+
Northern Arizona Univ	AZ	4,844	C
Northern Illinois Univ	IL	6,408	C
Northern Mich Univ	MI	6,350	C
Northwest Nazarene College	ID	11,750	C
Northwestern State Univ of Louisiana	LA	4,287	NC
Northwestern Univ	IL	21,093	MC
Ohio Univ	OH	7,341	C
Okla State Univ	OK	5,086	VC
Old Dominion Univ	VA	8,317	C
Ouachita Baptist Univ	AR	8,940	C
Pace Univ	NY	15,540	C
Penn State Univ/Univ Park Campus	PA	8,752	HC
Peru State College	NE	4,311	NC
Point Loma Nazarene College	CA	13,532	C
Purdue Univ/West Lafayette	IN	6,636	C
Radford Univ	VA	7,034	LC
Richard Stockton College of New Jersey	NJ	6,950	VC
St Cloud State Univ	MN	5,015	C
St John's Univ	NY	8,980	C+
St Louis Univ	MO	15,522	VC
St Xavier Univ	IL	14,700	C
San Diego State Univ	CA	6,692	LC
San Francisco State Univ	CA	7,292	LC

School	ST	$IS	SR
San Jose State Univ	CA	6,680	LC
Shaw Univ	NC	8,936	C+
S Car State Univ	SC	5,424	LC
S Dak State Univ	SD	4,562	C
Southeast Missouri State Univ	MO	5,854	C
Southern Illinois Univ at Carbondale	IL	6,234	C
Southern Illinois Univ at Edwardsville	IL	6,097	LC
Southern Univ and A&M College	LA	4,920	NC
Southwest Missouri State Univ	MO	4,956	C
Southwest Texas State Univ	TX	5,124	C
SUNY at Buffalo	NY	7,896	VC
SUNY/College at Buffalo	NY	7,035	VC
SUNY/College at Cortland	NY	7,326	C+
SUNY/College at Fredonia	NY	7,159	VC
SUNY/College at Geneseo	NY	6,949	HC
SUNY/College at New Paltz	NY	6,890	VC
SUNY/College at Plattsburgh	NY	6,917	C
Tenn State Univ	TN	4,626	C+
Texas A&M Univ at Kingsville	TX	3,808	LC
Texas Christian Univ	TX	12,180	C
Thiel College	PA	16,282	C
Towson State Univ	MD	7,452	C
Trenton State College	NJ	9,085	HC
Univ of Akron	OH	6,699	NC
Univ of Alabama	AL	5,702	C
Univ of Arizona	AZ	5,808	C
Univ of Arkansas at Fayetteville	AR	5,046	C
Univ of Arkansas at Little Rock	AR	4,419	C
Univ of Central Arkansas	AR	4,200	LC
Univ of Central Florida	FL	6,061	C+
Univ of Central Okla	OK	3,647	C
Univ of Cincinnati	OH	7,989	C
Univ of Colo at Boulder	CO	6,410	VC
Univ of Florida	FL	5,850	HC
Univ of Georgia	GA	5,655	VC
Univ of Hawaii at Manoa	HI	5,626	C
Univ of Illinois at Urbana-Champaign	IL	7,764	HC
Univ of Iowa	IA	5,658	VC
Univ of Kansas	KS	5,200	NC
Univ of Maine at Farmington	ME	6,700	C
Univ of Mass/Amherst	MA	9,364	LC
Univ of Minn/Duluth	MN	6,512	C
Univ of Minn/Twin Cities	MN	6,682	VC
Univ of Miss	MS	5,756	C
Univ of Missouri/Columbia	MO	6,254	HC
Univ of Montevallo	AL	5,310	C
Univ of Nebr-Lincoln	NE	5,278	LC
Univ of Nevada/Reno	NV	5,735	C
Univ of New Hampshire	NH	8,242	C
Univ of N Car at Greensboro	NC	5,192	C
Univ of N Dak	ND	4,902	NC
Univ of North Texas	TX	4,853	C
Univ of Northern Colo	CO	6,008	C
Univ of Northern Iowa	IA	5,137	C
Univ of Redlands	CA	22,059	VC
Univ of South Alabama	AL	5,451	C
Univ of S Dak	SD	4,722	C
Univ of South Florida	FL	5,475	C+
Univ of Southern Miss	MS	4,542	C
Univ of Southwestern Louisiana	LA	3,968	NC
Univ of Tenn/Knoxville	TN	5,668	C
Univ of Texas at Dallas	TX	1,222	VC+
Univ of the District of Columbia	DC	974	NC
Univ of the Pacific	CA	21,100	C
Univ of Toledo	OH	6,636	NC
Univ of Tulsa	OK	13,795	VC
Univ of Utah	UT	5,975	C
Univ of Virginia	VA	7,964	MC
Univ of Washington	WA	6,618	VC
Univ of Wisc/Eau Claire	WI	4,647	C
Univ of Wisc/Madison	WI	6,400	HC
Univ of Wisc/Milwaukee	WI	6,165	C
Univ of Wisc/Oshkosh	WI	4,240	C
Univ of Wisc/River Falls	WI	4,655	C
Univ of Wisc/Stevens Point	WI	5,047	C+
Univ of Wyoming	WY	4,991	NC
Utah State Univ	UT	4,683	C
Valdosta State Univ	GA	4,670	LC
Valparaiso Univ	IN	14,810	VC
Washington State Univ	WA	6,364	C
West Chester Univ of Penn	PA	7,492	C
West Virginia Univ	WV	5,774	C
Western Illinois Univ	IL	5,241	LC
Western Kentucky Univ	KY	4,808	C
Western Mich Univ	MI	6,820	C
Western Washington Univ	WA	6,077	VC
Whittier College	CA	21,661	C
Wichita State Univ	KS	5,068	NC
William Paterson College	NJ	7,438	C+
Worcester State College	MA	6,414	LC
Xavier Univ of Louisiana	LA	10,400	C

SPEECH THERAPY

School	ST	$IS	SR
Cleveland State Univ	OH	7,287	NC
Southern Univ and A&M College	LA	4,920	NC

SPORTS MANAGEMENT

School	ST	$IS	SR
Alaska Pacific Univ	AK	11,350	C
Albertson College	ID	15,942	C+
Allentown College of St Francis de Sales	PA	13,480	C
Anderson Univ	IN	12,920	C
Aquinas College	MI	14,526	C
Auburn Univ	AL	5,823	C+
Averett College	VA	13,610	LC
Baldwin-Wallace College	OH	15,210	C
Barry Univ	FL	16,050	C
Barton College	NC	10,689	LC
Belmont Abbey College	NC	13,190	C
Bluffton College	OH	12,951	C
Bridgewater State College	MA	7,518	C
Brigham Young Univ	UT	5,625	HC
Canisius College	NY	15,510	C
Carthage College	WI	15,995	C
Colby-Sawyer College	NH	18,495	LC
Concordia College	NE	11,776	NC
Defiance College	OH	13,480	LC
Elon College	NC	12,290	LC
Faulkner Univ	AL	8,630	LC
Georgia Southern Univ	GA	4,988	LC
Guilford College	NC	17,680	C
Husson College	ME	11,510	NC
Indiana State Univ	IN	6,210	C
Ithaca College	NY	19,679	C
Johnson and Wales Univ	RI	13,995	LC
Keene State College	NH	7,081	C
La Roche College	PA	12,977	LC
Liberty Univ	VA	11,500	LC
Lincoln Memorial Univ	TN	8,218	C
Lyndon State College	VT	8,394	LC
Lynn Univ	FL	18,300	C
Marian College of Fond du Lac	WI	12,250	LC
Marshall Univ	WV	5,762	LC
Miami Univ	OH	8,066	VC
Mount Union College	OH	15,850	C
National-Louis Univ	IL	13,218	C
New Hampshire College	NH	15,242	LC
Ohio Northern Univ	OH	18,660	VC
Peru State College	NE	4,311	NC
Pfeiffer College	NC	11,670	LC
Principia College	IL	17,799	C
Quincy Univ	IL	13,646	VC
Robert Morris College	PA	10,406	LC
St Edward's Univ	TX	12,636	C
St Leo College	FL	13,570	C
St Thomas Univ	FL	14,280	LC
Shepherd College	WV	5,540	C
Southwest Baptist Univ	MO	9,192	NC
Springfield College	MA	15,200	LC
Temple Univ	PA	10,281	C
Tulane Univ	LA	24,540	HC
Tusculum College	TN	10,400	LC
Union College	KY	9,790	C
Univ of Conn	CT	9,168	C
Univ of Dayton	OH	15,120	C+
Univ of Idaho	ID	4,830	C
Univ of Indianapolis	IN	14,510	C
Univ of Mass/Amherst	MA	9,364	LC
Univ of Miami	FL	22,107	VC
Univ of Mich/Ann Arbor	MI	9,428	HC+
Univ of New England	ME	16,075	LC
Univ of New Haven	CT	14,980	C
Univ of S Car	SC	6,158	C
Univ of the Pacific	CA	21,100	C
Wayne State College	NE	4,260	NC
West Virginia Univ	WV	5,774	C
Wingate College	NC	10,610	C
Winston-Salem State Univ	NC	4,142	LC
Xavier Univ	OH	15,710	C+

SPORTS MEDICINE

School	ST	$IS	SR
Alderson-Broaddus College	WV	12,000	C
Averett College	VA	13,610	LC
Baldwin-Wallace College	OH	15,210	C
Barry Univ	FL	16,050	C
Barton College	NC	10,689	LC
Boston Univ	MA	24,130	HC
Capital Univ	OH	16,535	VC
Catawba College	NC	12,950	C
Central Mich Univ	MI	6,737	LC
Colby-Sawyer College	NH	18,495	LC
College of St Scholastica	MN	14,868	C
Defiance College	OH	13,480	LC
Eastern Nazarene College	MA	12,165	LC
Elon College	NC	12,290	LC
Guilford College	NC	17,680	C
Heidelberg College	OH	17,160	C
High Point Univ	NC	12,350	LC
John Brown Univ	AR	9,880	VC
Judson College	IL	13,625	C
Keene State College	NH	7,081	C
Marietta College	OH	16,940	C+
Messiah College	PA	14,664	VC
Mount Union College	OH	15,850	C
Northwestern College	MN	13,554	C
Norwich Univ	VT	18,730	C
Ohio Northern Univ	OH	18,660	VC
Otterbein College	OH	16,506	C
Park College	MO	7,320	C
Pepperdine Univ	CA	23,720	VC
Pfeiffer College	NC	11,670	LC
Quincy Univ	IL	13,646	VC
Shepherd College	WV	5,540	C
Southeast Missouri State Univ	MO	5,854	C
Tulane Univ	LA	24,540	HC
Univ of Alabama	AL	5,702	C
Univ of Charleston	WV	12,750	C
Univ of Lowell	MA	8,831	VC
Univ of Southern Colo	CO	5,350	LC
Univ of the Pacific	CA	21,100	C
Univ of Tulsa	OK	13,795	VC
Urbana Univ	OH	12,536	C
Valdosta State Univ	GA	4,670	LC
Waynesburg College	PA	11,960	C
Wingate College	NC	10,610	C
Xavier Univ	OH	15,710	C+

STATISTICS

School	ST	$IS	SR
American Univ	DC	21,230	VC+
Baylor Univ	TX	10,990	C+
Boston Univ	MA	24,130	HC
Bowling Green State Univ	OH	6,701	C
Brigham Young Univ	UT	5,625	HC
Calif Polytechnic State Univ	CA	6,980	VC+
Cal State/Fullerton	CA	4,850	LC
Cal State/Hayward	CA	5,495	C
Carnegie Mellon Univ	PA	22,560	HC+
Case Western Reserve Univ	OH	19,910	HC
Central Mich Univ	MI	6,737	LC
CUNY/Baruch College	NY	2,562	VC
Colo State Univ	CO	6,566	VC
Columbia Univ/Barnard College	NY	25,492	HC
Columbia Univ/Columbia College	NY	26,757	MC
Cornell Univ	NY	13,445	MC
Creighton Univ	NE	14,432	VC
Delaware Valley College	PA	16,065	LC
Eastern Kentucky Univ	KY	4,840	NC
Eastern New Mexico Univ	NM	3,950	C
Eastern Washington Univ	WA	5,439	LC
Florida International Univ	FL	4,191	VC
Florida State Univ	FL	5,814	VC
George Washington Univ	DC	22,470	HC
Grambling State Univ	LA	4,712	NC
Harvard Univ/Harvard and Radcliffe Colleges	MA	24,880	MC
Iowa State Univ	IA	5,456	C
Kansas Newman College	KS	10,640	C
Kansas State Univ	KS	4,816	NC
La Salle Univ	PA	16,940	VC
Le Moyne College	NY	15,180	C
Marlboro College	VT	23,305	C+
Marquette Univ	WI	16,114	VC
McNeese State Univ	LA	4,543	NC
Miami Univ	OH	8,066	VC
Mich State Univ	MI	7,842	C
Mount Holyoke College	MA	23,630	VC
New Jersey Inst of Tech	NJ	9,965	VC
New York Univ	NY	24,705	VC+
N Car State Univ	NC	4,984	VC
N Dak State Univ of Agriculture and Applied Science	ND	4,774	VC
Northwestern Univ	IL	21,093	MC
Oakland Univ	MI	6,714	VC
Ohio State Univ	OH	7,218	LC
Okla State Univ	OK	5,086	VC
Purdue Univ/West Lafayette	IN	6,636	C
Radford Univ	VA	7,034	LC
Rice Univ	TX	15,110	MC
Rochester Inst of Tech	NY	18,954	VC
Rutgers Univ/Douglass College	NJ	8,795	VC
Rutgers Univ/Livingston College	NJ	8,877	VC
Rutgers Univ/Rutgers College	NJ	8,841	HC+
Rutgers Univ/Univ College—New Brunswick	NJ	0	LC
St Cloud State Univ	MN	5,015	C
St John's Univ	NY	8,980	C+
St Mary's College of Minn	MN	13,850	LC
San Francisco State Univ	CA	7,292	LC
San Jose State Univ	CA	6,680	LC
Sarah Lawrence College	NY	24,975	HC
Southern Methodist Univ	TX	18,520	VC
SUNY at Buffalo	NY	7,896	VC
SUNY/College at Oneonta	NY	7,878	C
Stevens Inst of Tech	NJ	21,980	VC+
Syracuse Univ	NY	21,305	HC
Temple Univ	PA	10,281	C
Trenton State College	NJ	9,085	HC
Univ of Akron	OH	6,699	NC
Univ of Alabama	AL	5,702	C
Univ of Alaska Fairbanks	AK	4,718	C
Univ of Calif at Berkeley	CA	9,962	HC+
Univ of Calif at Davis	CA	9,534	VC
Univ of Calif at Santa Barbara	CA	9,460	C
Univ of Calif, Riverside	CA	9,178	C
Univ of Central Florida	FL	6,061	C+
Univ of Chicago	IL	24,517	MC
Univ of Conn	CT	9,168	C
Univ of Delaware	DE	8,013	VC
Univ of Denver	CO	19,290	C+
Univ of Florida	FL	5,850	HC
Univ of Georgia	GA	5,655	VC
Univ of Houston	TX	5,215	C
Univ of Illinois at Chicago	IL	8,443	C
Univ of Iowa	IA	5,658	VC
Univ of Lowell	MA	8,831	VC
Univ of Maryland/College Park	MD	8,182	VC
Univ of Memphis	TN	3,476	C
Univ of Mich/Ann Arbor	MI	9,428	HC+
Univ of Minn/Twin Cities	MN	6,682	VC
Univ of Missouri/Columbia	MO	6,254	HC
Univ of Nebr at Kearney	NE	4,308	LC
Univ of Nebr at Omaha	NE	1,889	LC
Univ of Nebr-Lincoln	NE	5,278	LC
Univ of New Haven	CT	14,980	C
Univ of N Car at Chapel Hill	NC	5,330	HC
Univ of N Car at Greensboro	NC	5,192	C
Univ of North Florida	FL	5,082	C
Univ of Northern Colo	CO	6,008	C
Univ of Pittsburgh	PA	9,472	C
Univ of Rhode Island	RI	9,205	C
Univ of Rochester	NY	23,696	HC
Univ of South Alabama	AL	5,451	C
Univ of S Car	SC	6,158	C
Univ of S Dak	SD	4,722	C
Univ of Southern Miss	MS	4,542	C
Univ of Southwestern Louisiana	LA	3,968	NC
Univ of Tenn/Knoxville	TN	5,668	C
Univ of Texas at Dallas	TX	1,222	VC+
Univ of Texas at El Paso	TX	3,160	LC
Univ of Texas at San Antonio	TX	6,420	C
Univ of Vermont	VT	10,776	C+
Univ of Washington	WA	6,618	VC
Univ of West Florida	FL	5,415	C
Univ of Wisc/Eau Claire	WI	4,647	C
Univ of Wisc/Madison	WI	6,400	HC
Univ of Wyoming	WY	4,991	NC
Utah State Univ	UT	4,683	C
Virginia Polytechnic Inst and State Univ	VA	6,828	C
West Virginia Univ	WV	5,774	C
Western Mich Univ	MI	6,820	C
Winona State Univ	MN	5,200	VC
Worcester Polytechnic Inst	MA	20,350	HC
Xavier Univ of Louisiana	LA	10,400	C

STRINGS

School	ST	$IS	SR
Juilliard School	NY	18,050	SP
Temple Univ	PA	10,281	C
Univ of Mich/Ann Arbor	MI	9,428	HC+

STUDIO ART

School	ST	$IS	SR
Allegheny College	PA	21,020	VC
American Univ	DC	21,230	VC+
Augustana College	IL	16,959	VC
Baker Univ	KS	12,284	C
Barat College	IL	13,990	C
Barton College	NC	10,689	LC
Beloit College	WI	18,950	VC+
Berry College	GA	11,990	VC
Bloomsburg Univ of Penn	PA	6,312	C+
Boston College	MA	22,706	MC
Bowdoin College	ME	24,155	MC
Cal State/Los Angeles	CA	4,940	VC
Cal State/Stanislaus	CA	6,799	C
Carleton College	MN	22,155	HC
Catholic Univ of America	DC	18,856	C
Chestnut Hill College	PA	14,525	C
Clark Univ	MA	21,400	VC

School	ST	$IS	SR
Clarke College	IA	13,950	C+
Cleveland Inst of Art	OH	15,630	SP
Colby College	ME	24,230	HC
College of Charleston	SC	6,250	C
College of Notre Dame	CA	16,480	C
College of Notre Dame of Maryland	MD	16,050	C
College of St Rose	NY	14,452	C
Columbia College	SC	13,520	LC
Conn College	CT	24,160	HC
DePauw Univ	IN	18,530	VC
Eastern College	PA	15,150	C+
Eastern Washington Univ	WA	5,439	LC
Emmanuel College	MA	17,773	LC
Fordham Univ/College at Lincoln Center	NY	18,150	VC
Graceland College	IA	11,600	C
Grand Canyon Univ	AZ	9,680	VC
Hood College	MD	19,010	VC
Indiana State Univ	IN	6,210	C
Indiana Wesleyan Univ	IN	12,332	C
Johnson State College	VT	8,393	LC
Kansas Wesleyan Univ	KS	11,770	C
Kean College of New Jersey	NJ	6,395	LC
Kentucky State Univ	KY	4,282	C+
Kenyon College	OH	22,430	HC+
Knox College	IL	18,990	VC
La Sierra Univ	CA	15,472	C
Lawrence Univ	WI	19,986	HC+
Lewis and Clark College	OR	19,980	VC
Limestone College	SC	10,700	LC
Loyola Marymount Univ	CA	18,560	C
Lycoming College	PA	17,200	LC
Mansfield Univ	PA	6,348	C
Marian College	IN	12,936	C
Mars Hill College	NC	11,050	C
Maryville Univ-St Louis	MO	12,900	VC
Marywood College	PA	14,890	C
Mass College of Art	MA	9,447	SP
Mercyhurst College	PA	13,488	C
Mich State Univ	MI	7,842	C
Mills College	CA	20,848	VC
Moravian College	PA	18,960	VC
Mount Holyoke College	MA	23,630	VC
Northern Kentucky Univ	KY	4,620	NC
Notre Dame College of Ohio	OH	11,370	C
Pacific Union College	CA	15,075	C
Palm Beach Atlantic College	FL	10,720	C
Parsons School of Design	NY	21,410	SP
Plymouth State College	NH	7,166	C
Randolph-Macon College	VA	16,980	C
Rivier College	NH	14,920	LC
Rollins College	FL	20,875	VC
St Vincent College	PA	13,934	LC
Salem College	NC	16,025	C
Salve Regina Univ	RI	29,100	LC
Scripps College	CA	23,600	HC
Seton Hill College	PA	14,320	C
Sierra Nevada College	NV	14,000	NC
Southern Conn State Univ	CT	7,532	C
Southern Univ and A&M College	LA	4,920	NC
Southwest Texas State Univ	TX	5,124	C
SUNY at Buffalo	NY	7,896	VC
SUNY at Stony Brook	NY	7,658	VC
SUNY/College at Brockport	NY	7,220	C+
SUNY/College at Plattsburgh	NY	6,917	C
SUNY/Potsdam College	NY	6,906	C
Texas Christian Univ	TX	12,180	C
Texas College	TX	5,930	NC
Texas Tech Univ	TX	6,008	C
Transylvania Univ	KY	14,970	VC+
Tulane Univ	LA	24,540	HC
Univ of Alabama	AL	5,702	C
Univ of Calif at Davis	CA	9,534	VC
Univ of Calif, San Diego	CA	10,028	VC+
Univ of Calif/Irvine	CA	12,680	VC
Univ of Colo at Boulder	CO	6,410	VC
Univ of Evansville	IN	15,300	VC
Univ of Illinois at Chicago	IL	8,443	C
Univ of Kentucky	KY	5,152	VC
Univ of Minn/Morris	MN	6,825	HC
Univ of Minn/Twin Cities	MN	6,682	VC
Univ of N Car at Chapel Hill	NC	5,330	HC
Univ of Pittsburgh	PA	9,472	C
Univ of Rochester	NY	23,696	HC
Univ of South Alabama	AL	5,451	C
Univ of Tenn/Knoxville	TN	5,668	C
Univ of Texas at Arlington	TX	5,549	LC
Univ of Texas at Austin	TX	5,160	VC
Univ of the Pacific	CA	21,100	C
Univ of Washington	WA	6,618	VC
Wellesley College	MA	23,815	MC
West Texas A&M Univ	TX	4,224	C
Western Conn State Univ	CT	6,622	C
William Paterson College	NJ	7,438	C+
Youngstown State Univ	OH	6,447	LC

SURVEY AND MAPPING TECHNOLOGY

School	ST	$IS	SR
Ohio State Univ	OH	7,218	LC
SUNY College of Environmental Science and Forestry	NY	9,257	HC+

SURVEYING ENGINEERING

School	ST	$IS	SR
Cal State/Fresno	CA	5,747	C
Ferris State Univ	MI	7,160	NC
Metropolitan State College of Denver	CO	1,751	NC
Mich Tech Univ	MI	7,283	VC+
Miss State Univ	MS	5,629	VC
Oregon Inst of Tech	OR	5,985	C
Purdue Univ/West Lafayette	IN	6,636	C
Universidad Metropolitana	PR	2,650	
Universidad Politecnica de PR	PR	6,195	
Univ of Arkansas at Little Rock	AR	4,419	C
Univ of Florida	FL	5,850	HC
Univ of Houston	TX	5,215	C
Univ of Maine	ME	7,990	C
Univ of PR/Mayaguez	PR	0	

SYSTEMS ANALYSIS

School	ST	$IS	SR
George Washington Univ	DC	22,470	HC
Johnson and Wales Univ	RI	13,995	LC
Univ of Miami	FL	22,107	VC

SYSTEMS ENGINEERING

School	ST	$IS	SR
Boston Univ	MA	24,130	HC
Bridgeport Engineering Inst	CT	6,135	NC
Case Western Reserve Univ	OH	19,910	HC
Oakland Univ	MI	6,714	VC
Texas A&M Univ at Galveston	TX	4,874	LC
United States Military Academy	NY	0	MC
United States Naval Academy	MD	0	MC
Univ of Arizona	AZ	5,808	C
Univ of Calif, San Diego	CA	10,028	VC+
Univ of Virginia	VA	7,964	MC
Washington Univ	MO	23,507	HC
Wright State Univ	OH	6,896	LC

SYSTEMS SCIENCE

School	ST	$IS	SR
Colo Technical College	CO	6,005	C
Johnson and Wales Univ	RI	13,995	LC
Providence College	RI	19,750	VC
Stanford Univ	CA	24,310	MC
Washington Univ	MO	23,507	HC
West Georgia College	GA	4,256	C

TEACHING ENGLISH AS A SECOND LANGUAGE/FOREIGN LANGUAGE

School	ST	$IS	SR
Abilene Christian Univ	TX	10,460	NC
Andrews Univ	MI	14,952	NC
Boston Univ	MA	24,130	HC
Brigham Young Univ	UT	5,625	HC
Brigham Young Univ/Hawaii	HI	6,750	VC
Brooklyn Campus of LIU	NY	15,000	LC
Cal State/Fresno	CA	5,747	C
Caribbean Univ	PR	2,400	
Carroll College	MT	11,265	C
Cedarville College	OH	10,715	C
Central Missouri State Univ	MO	5,138	LC
City Univ	WA	6,400	NC
College of Our Lady of The Elms	MA	15,639	C
Doane College	NE	12,220	C
Eastern Mich Univ	MI	6,749	C
Friends Univ	KS	11,205	C
George Mason Univ	VA	8,728	C
Goshen College	IN	12,360	C
Hawaii Pacific Univ	HI	12,300	C
Houston Baptist Univ	TX	11,055	C
Inter American Univ of PR/San German	PR	4,620	
Inter American Univ/Arecibo Campus	PR	5,666	
Lincoln Univ	CA	4,400	LC
Mercy College	NY	11,180	NC
Methodist College	NC	12,400	C
Millersville Univ of Penn	PA	7,370	VC
Northern Arizona Univ	AZ	4,844	C
Notre Dame College	NH	14,220	C
Occidental College	CA	21,792	HC
Ohio Dominican College	OH	11,820	LC
Ohio Univ	OH	7,341	C
Okla Christian Univ of Science and Arts	OK	8,790	NC
Old Dominion Univ	VA	8,317	C
Pittsburg State Univ	KS	4,478	NC
Pontifical Catholic Univ of PR/Ponce	PR	5,807	
Rider College	NJ	18,160	C
San Jose State Univ	CA	6,680	LC
Southern Arkansas Univ	AR	3,432	NC
SUNY at Albany	NY	7,059	VC
Texas Wesleyan Univ	TX	9,380	LC
The Univ of New Mexico	NM	5,304	C
Toccoa Falls College	GA	9,350	C
Univ of Arizona	AZ	5,808	C
Univ of Hawaii at Manoa	HI	5,626	C
Univ of Houston	TX	5,215	C
Univ of Louisville	KY	5,948	C
Univ of Minn/Twin Cities	MN	6,682	VC
Univ of Nebr at Kearney	NE	4,308	LC
Univ of Northern Iowa	IA	5,137	C
Univ of PR/Mayaguez	PR	0	
Univ of PR/Rio Piedras	PR	0	
Univ of South Florida	FL	5,475	C+
Univ of Texas at Arlington	TX	5,549	LC
Univ of the Pacific	CA	21,100	C
Valley City State Univ	ND	4,385	LC

TECHNICAL AND BUSINESS WRITING

School	ST	$IS	SR
Alderson-Broaddus College	WV	12,000	C
Allentown College of St Francis de Sales	PA	13,480	C
Clarkson Univ	NY	20,705	VC+
Colo State Univ	CO	6,566	VC
Florida Inst of Tech	FL	16,935	VC
Geneva College	PA	13,030	C
Indiana Inst of Tech	IN	11,810	C
Louisiana Tech Univ	LA	4,284	C
Madonna Univ	MI	8,546	C
Milwaukee School of Engineering	WI	14,100	C
New Mexico Inst of Mining and Tech	NM	5,212	C+
Point Loma Nazarene College	CA	13,532	C
Polytechnic Univ/Brooklyn	NY	19,700	HC
Polytechnic Univ/Farmingdale	NY	20,700	VC
Rosary College	IL	15,040	C
Southern College of Tech	GA	4	C
Southwest Missouri State Univ	MO	4,956	C
Tenn Tech Univ	TN	5,190	C
Univ of Arkansas at Little Rock	AR	4,419	C
Univ of Miami	FL	22,107	VC
Univ of Washington	WA	6,618	VC
Wentworth Inst of Tech	MA	15,250	LC
Wheeling Jesuit College	WV	14,370	C
Youngstown State Univ	OH	6,447	LC

TECHNICAL EDUCATION

School	ST	$IS	SR
Calif Univ of Penn	PA	7,370	C
Central Conn State Univ	CT	7,108	C
Eastern Kentucky Univ	KY	4,840	NC
Ferris State Univ	MI	7,160	NC
Kean College of New Jersey	NJ	6,395	LC
Montana State Univ	MT	5,534	C
Montclair State College	NJ	7,539	C+
National Univ	CA	6,135	C
New Mexico Highlands Univ	NM	3,772	C
N Car State Univ	NC	4,984	VC
Southern Utah Univ	UT	4,104	LC
Tuskegee Univ	AL	10,128	C
Univ of Central Florida	FL	6,061	C+
Univ of Northern Iowa	IA	5,137	C
Univ of Southern Maine	ME	7,299	C
Univ of Wisc/Platteville	WI	4,830	C
Univ of Wisc/Stout	WI	4,719	C
Virginia Polytechnic Inst and State Univ	VA	6,828	C

TECHNOLOGICAL MANAGEMENT

School	ST	$IS	SR
Charter Oak State College	CT	314	NC
Montana College of Mineral Science and Tech	MT	4,977	C
New Hampshire College	NH	15,242	LC
Southern College of Tech	GA	4	C
Univ of Minn/Crookston	MN	6,894	NC
Wayne State College	NE	4,260	NC
Wentworth Inst of Tech	MA	15,250	LC
Western State College of Colo	CO	5,560	C

TECHNOLOGY AND PUBLIC AFFAIRS

School	ST	$IS	SR
Montana College of Mineral Science and Tech	MT	4,977	C
Pomona College	CA	23,820	MC
Wheeling Jesuit College	WV	14,370	C

TELECOMMUNICATIONS

School	ST	$IS	SR
Alabama A&M Univ	AL	4,200	C
Ball State Univ	IN	6,032	LC
Cal State/Chico	CA	6,146	C
Cal State/Fresno	CA	5,747	C
Cal State/Los Angeles	CA	4,940	VC
Capitol College	MD	10,698	LC
Cheyney Univ of Penn	PA	7,005	C
City Univ	WA	6,400	NC
DeVry/Addison (DuPage County)	IL	5,609	LC
DeVry/Kansas City	MO	5,609	LC
DeVry/Los Angeles	CA	5,609	LC
Evergreen State College	WA	6,306	C
Fitchburg State College	MA	6,962	C
George Fox College	OR	15,640	LC
Golden Gate Univ	CA	5,623	VC
Hanover College	IN	10,950	VC
Indiana Univ Bloomington	IN	6,495	VC
Indiana Univ-Purdue Univ at Fort Wayne	IN	2,500	LC
Ithaca College	NY	19,679	C
Kent State Univ	OH	6,740	LC
Kutztown Univ	PA	6,528	C
Liberty Univ	VA	11,500	LC
Loyola Univ/New Orleans	LA	15,660	C+
Marietta College	OH	16,940	C+
Miami Univ	OH	8,066	VC
Mich State Univ	MI	7,842	C
Morgan State Univ	MD	7,366	C+
New York Inst of Tech/Old Westbury	NY	13,914	LC
Northern Arizona Univ	AZ	4,844	C
Ohio Univ	OH	7,341	C
Okla Baptist Univ	OK	8,486	C
Oral Roberts Univ	OK	10,607	C+
Penn State Univ/Univ Park Campus	PA	8,752	HC
Pepperdine Univ	CA	23,720	VC
Purdue Univ/West Lafayette	IN	6,636	C
Rochester Inst of Tech	NY	18,954	VC
St Mary's College of Minn	MN	13,850	LC
Southwest Baptist Univ	MO	9,192	NC
Temple Univ	PA	10,281	C
Texas Tech Univ	TX	6,008	C
Univ of Alabama	AL	5,702	C
Univ of Evansville	IN	15,300	VC
Univ of Florida	FL	5,850	HC
Univ of Georgia	GA	5,655	VC
Univ of Idaho	ID	4,830	C
Univ of Kentucky	KY	5,152	VC
Univ of Miami	FL	22,107	VC
Univ of Miss	MS	5,756	C
Univ of Nebr at Kearney	NE	4,308	LC
Univ of Northern Colo	CO	6,008	C
Univ of St Thomas	MN	15,785	C+
Univ of Southwestern Louisiana	LA	3,968	NC
Univ of Texas at Dallas	TX	1,222	VC+
Univ of the Sacred Heart	PR	3,890	
Univ of Wisc/Eau Claire	WI	4,647	C
Valdosta State Univ	GA	4,670	LC
Woodbury Univ	CA	17,620	LC
Youngstown State Univ	OH	6,447	LC

TEXTILE ENGINEERING

School	ST	$IS	SR
Auburn Univ	AL	5,823	C+
Georgia Inst of Tech	GA	6,669	HC+
N Car State Univ	NC	4,984	VC
Philadelphia College of Textiles and Science	PA	15,896	C
Texas Tech Univ	TX	6,008	C
Univ of Delaware	DE	8,013	VC

TEXTILE TECHNOLOGY

School	ST	$IS	SR
Auburn Univ	AL	5,823	C+
Clemson Univ	SC	6,564	VC
Philadelphia College of Textiles and Science	PA	15,896	C
Texas Tech Univ	TX	6,008	C
Univ of Mass Dartmouth	MA	8,158	C
Univ of Mich/Ann Arbor	MI	9,428	HC+
Univ of Wisc/Madison	WI	6,400	HC

TEXTILES AND CLOTHING

School	ST	$IS	SR
Albright College	PA	19,260	C
Auburn Univ	AL	5,823	C+
Center for Creative Studies/ College of Art and Design	MI	15,330	SP
Cornell Univ	NY	13,445	MC
Edinboro Univ of Penn	PA	7,181	C
Fashion Inst of Tech/SUNY	NY	7,135	SP
Framingham State College	MA	6,580	C
Georgia Inst of Tech	GA	6,669	HC+
Indiana State Univ	IN	6,210	C
Iowa State Univ	IA	5,456	C
Kentucky State Univ	KY	4,282	C+
Louisiana State Univ and A&M College	LA	5,605	C
Moore College of Art and Design	PA	17,947	SP
Morehead State Univ	KY	4,600	C
N Car State Univ	NC	4,984	VC
N Dak State Univ of Agriculture and Applied Science	ND	4,774	VC
Ohio State Univ	OH	7,218	LC
Oregon State Univ	OR	6,175	C
Philadelphia College of Textiles and Science	PA	15,896	C
Rhode Island School of Design	RI	22,315	SP
Syracuse Univ	NY	21,305	HC
Univ of Alabama	AL	5,702	C
Univ of Calif at Davis	CA	9,534	VC
Univ of Delaware	DE	8,013	VC
Univ of Kentucky	KY	5,152	VC
Univ of Minn/Twin Cities	MN	6,682	VC
Univ of Nebr at Omaha	NE	1,889	LC
Univ of Nebr-Lincoln	NE	5,278	LC
Univ of Rhode Island	RI	9,205	C
Univ of Tenn/Knoxville	TN	5,668	C
Univ of Texas at Austin	TX	5,160	VC
Univ of Wisc/Madison	WI	6,400	HC
Virginia Polytechnic Inst and State Univ	VA	6,828	C
West Virginia Univ	WV	5,774	C
Western Kentucky Univ	KY	4,808	C

THEATER DESIGN

School	ST	$IS	SR
Albertson College	ID	15,942	C+
Berea College	KY	2,883	VC+
Boston Univ	MA	24,130	HC
College of the Ozarks	MO	2,000	VC+
Cornish College of the Arts	WA	9,300	SP
Davis and Elkins College	WV	13,230	LC
DePaul Univ	IL	15,535	VC
Franklin Pierce College	NH	17,270	LC
Lynchburg College	VA	17,000	C
N Car School of the Arts	NC	5,375	SP
Northwestern Univ	IL	21,093	MC
Pace Univ	NY	15,540	C
Shenandoah Univ	VA	11,800	C
Univ of Alabama	AL	5,702	C
Univ of Cincinnati	OH	7,989	C
Univ of Conn	CT	9,168	C
Univ of Evansville	IN	15,300	VC
Univ of Florida	FL	5,850	HC
Univ of Hawaii at Manoa	HI	5,626	C
Univ of Indianapolis	IN	14,510	C
Univ of Kansas	KS	5,200	NC

School	ST	$IS	SR
Univ of Northern Iowa	IA	5,137	C
Webster Univ	MO	12,650	C
Western Maryland College	MD	18,990	C
Wright State Univ	OH	6,896	LC

THEATER MANAGEMENT

School	ST	$IS	SR
Barry Univ	FL	16,050	C
Hardin-Simmons Univ	TX	9,080	C
Univ of Delaware	DE	8,013	VC
Univ of Evansville	IN	15,300	VC
Univ of Portland	OR	15,564	C

THEOLOGICAL STUDIES

School	ST	$IS	SR
Allentown College of St Francis de Sales	PA	13,480	C
Alvernia College	PA	13,150	LC
Avila College	MO	12,130	C
Barry Univ	FL	16,050	C
Bellarmine College	KY	10,832	C
Belmont Abbey College	NC	13,190	C
Berry College	GA	11,990	C
Boston College	MA	22,706	MC
Briar Cliff College	IA	13,375	C
Calumet College of St. Joseph	IN	3,585	C
Carlow College	PA	13,914	C
Christendom College	VA	11,750	VC
College of St Benedict	MN	15,468	VC
Concordia College	NE	11,776	NC
Fordham Univ/Fordham College	NY	19,875	VC
Franciscan Univ of Steubenville	OH	13,400	C
Hardin-Simmons Univ	TX	9,080	C
Huntingdon College	AL	11,400	C
John Brown Univ	AR	9,880	VC
King's College	PA	15,420	C
Lenoir-Rhyne College	NC	14,068	C
Loyola College	MD	18,035	VC
Loyola Marymount Univ	CA	18,560	C
Loyola Univ of Chicago	IL	15,880	VC+
Marian College	IN	12,936	C
Marian College of Fond du Lac	WI	12,250	C
Mount Mary College	WI	10,920	C
Mount St Mary's College	MD	17,825	LC
Ohio Dominican College	OH	11,820	LC
Pacific Union College	CA	15,075	C
Point Loma Nazarene College	CA	13,532	C
Pontifical Catholic Univ of PR/Ponce	PR	5,807	C
Providence College	RI	19,750	VC
Quincy Univ	IL	13,646	VC
Rockhurst College	MO	12,470	C
St Anselm College	NH	17,340	C
St Bonaventure Univ	NY	14,762	C
St John's Univ	MN	15,364	C
St Mary College	KS	11,250	C
St Mary's College	MI	8,350	C
St Mary's College of Minn	MN	13,850	LC
St Mary's Univ	TX	12,064	C
Seattle Pacific Univ	WA	16,503	C
Southwestern Adventist College	TX	10,530	NC
Sterling College	KS	10,990	VC
Tarleton State Univ	TX	4,082	LC
Texas Lutheran College	TX	10,710	C
Thomas More College	KY	12,962	C
Toccoa Falls College	GA	9,350	C
Universidad Adventista de las Antillas	PR	5,000	C
Univ of Calif at Berkeley	CA	9,962	HC+
Univ of Dallas	TX	14,983	VC
Univ of Evansville	IN	15,300	VC
Univ of Notre Dame	IN	20,150	MC
Univ of Portland	OR	15,564	C
Univ of St Thomas	MN	15,785	C+
Univ of San Francisco	CA	18,408	C
Univ of Scranton	PA	17,071	VC
Wisc Lutheran College	WI	12,180	C
Xavier Univ of Louisiana	LA	10,400	C

THIRD WORLD STUDIES

School	ST	$IS	SR
Univ of the South	TN	18,830	HC

TOURISM

School	ST	$IS	SR
Arizona State Univ Main Campus	AZ	6,444	C
Brigham Young Univ	UT	5,625	HC
Eastern Mich Univ	MI	6,749	C
Fort Lewis College	CO	5,097	C
Hawaii Pacific Univ	HI	12,300	C
Johnson and Wales Univ	RI	13,995	LC
Lynn Univ	FL	18,300	C
Mansfield Univ	PA	6,348	C
New Mexico Highlands Univ	NM	3,772	C
Niagara Univ	NY	14,552	C
Sojourner-Douglass College	MD	5,265	LC
Univ of Hawaii at Manoa	HI	5,626	C
Univ of Nebr at Kearney	NE	4,308	LC
Univ of New Haven	CT	14,980	C
Univ of New Orleans	LA	5,468	C
Univ of the Sacred Heart	PR	3,890	C
Webber College	FL	8,710	C
Western Mich Univ	MI	6,820	C

TOXICOLOGY

School	ST	$IS	SR
CUNY/John Jay College of Criminal Justice	NY	2,501	LC
Montclair State College	NJ	7,539	C+
Northeast Louisiana Univ	LA	3,906	NC
Northeastern Univ	MA	19,851	C
Philadelphia College of Pharmacy and Science	PA	14,750	VC
St John's Univ	NY	8,980	C+
Univ of Miami	FL	22,107	VC
Univ of Wisc/Madison	WI	6,400	HC

TOY DESIGN

School	ST	$IS	SR
Fashion Inst of Tech/SUNY	NY	7,135	SP

TRADE AND INDUSTRIAL EDUCATION

School	ST	$IS	SR
Alabama A&M Univ	AL	4,200	C
James Madison Univ	VA	8,198	HC
Ohio State Univ	OH	7,218	LC
Pacific Union College	CA	15,075	C
Univ of Georgia	GA	5,655	VC
Univ of Houston	TX	5,215	C
Univ of Wyoming	WY	4,991	NC

TRADE AND INDUSTRIAL SUPERVISION AND MANAGEMENT

School	ST	$IS	SR
Gannon Univ	PA	14,872	C
Moorhead State Univ	MN	5,076	C

TRANSPORTATION ENGINEERING

School	ST	$IS	SR
N Dak State Univ of Agriculture and Applied Science	ND	4,774	VC
Univ of Arkansas at Fayetteville	AR	5,046	C
Western Mich Univ	MI	6,820	C

TRANSPORTATION MANAGEMENT

School	ST	$IS	SR
Arizona State Univ Main Campus	AZ	6,444	C
Arkansas State Univ	AR	4,250	NC
Auburn Univ	AL	5,823	C+
Bridgewater State College	MA	7,518	C
Calif Maritime Academy	CA	7,318	C
Cal State/Los Angeles	CA	4,940	VC
Daemen College	NY	13,020	LC
Eastern Kentucky Univ	KY	4,840	NC

School	ST	$IS	SR
Elmhurst College	IL	12,536	C
Embry-Riddle Aeronautical Univ	FL	10,600	C
Florida Memorial College	FL	7,600	C+
Indiana Univ Bloomington	IN	6,495	VC
Iowa State Univ	IA	5,456	C
Mass Maritime Academy	MA	7,410	C
Miss State Univ	MS	5,629	VC
Niagara Univ	NY	14,552	C
Northeastern Univ	MA	19,851	C
Ohio State Univ	OH	7,218	LC
Robert Morris College	PA	10,406	LC
St John's Univ	NY	8,980	C+
San Francisco State Univ	CA	7,292	LC
Southern Univ at New Orleans	LA	1,452	NC
Syracuse Univ	NY	21,305	HC
United States Merchant Marine Academy	NY	4,090	HC
Univ of Maryland/College Park	MD	8,182	VC
Univ of Memphis	TN	3,476	C
Univ of North Florida	FL	5,082	C
Univ of Penn	PA	24,238	MC
Univ of Tenn/Knoxville	TN	5,668	C
Western Illinois Univ	IL	5,241	C

TRANSPORTATION AND TRAVEL MARKETING

School	ST	$IS	SR
Columbia College	MO	11,995	C
Johnson and Wales Univ	RI	13,995	LC

TRANSPORTATION TECHNOLOGY

School	ST	$IS	SR
Central Missouri State Univ	MO	5,138	LC
Idaho State Univ	ID	4,442	C
Maine Maritime Academy	ME	8,336	C
Peru State College	NE	4,311	NC

ULTRASOUND TECHNOLOGY

School	ST	$IS	SR
Barry Univ	FL	16,050	C
Nebr Methodist College of Nursing and Allied Health	NE	4,360	C
Rochester Inst of Tech	NY	18,954	VC
Univ of Miami	FL	22,107	VC

URBAN DESIGN

School	ST	$IS	SR
Arizona State Univ Main Campus	AZ	6,444	C
Oregon State Univ	OR	6,175	C
Univ of Arkansas at Fayetteville	AR	5,046	C

URBAN PLANNING TECHNOLOGY

School	ST	$IS	SR
Arizona State Univ Main Campus	AZ	6,444	C
Ball State Univ	IN	6,032	LC
Southwest Missouri State Univ	MO	4,956	C
Univ of Utah	UT	5,975	C

URBAN STUDIES

School	ST	$IS	SR
Albertus Magnus College	CT	16,280	LC
Aquinas College	MI	14,526	C
Arkansas State Univ	AR	4,250	NC
Auburn Univ at Montgomery	AL	3,390	C
Augsburg College	MN	15,608	C
Baylor Univ	TX	10,990	C+
Bellevue College	NE	3,050	NC
Boston Univ	MA	24,130	HC
Brown Univ	RI	26,104	MC
Bryn Mawr College	PA	24,110	MC
Calif State Polytechnic Univ/ Pomona	CA	6,438	LC
Cal State/Fresno	CA	5,747	C
Cal State/Northridge	CA	7,122	LC

School	ST	$IS	SR
Calif Univ of Penn	PA	7,370	C
Canisius College	NY	15,510	C
Carnegie Mellon Univ	PA	22,560	HC+
Central College	IA	14,025	VC
Central Washington Univ	WA	5,644	C
CUNY/Brooklyn College	NY	2,450	VC
CUNY/Hunter College	NY	4,101	VC
CUNY/Queens College	NY	2,631	C
Cleveland State Univ	OH	7,287	NC
College of Charleston	SC	6,250	C
College of Wooster	OH	19,875	VC
Columbia Univ/Barnard College	NY	25,492	HC
Columbia Univ/Columbia College	NY	26,757	MC
Conn College	CT	24,160	HC
Cornell College	IA	18,425	VC
David Lipscomb Univ	TN	7,865	VC
DePaul Univ	IL	15,535	VC
Dillard Univ	LA	9,950	C
Eastern Washington Univ	WA	5,439	LC
Elmhurst College	IL	12,536	C
Eugene Lang College of the New School for Social Research	NY	21,145	C+
Evergreen State College	WA	6,306	C
Florida Atlantic Univ	FL	5,525	C
Fordham Univ/College at Lincoln Center	NY	18,150	VC
Fordham Univ/Fordham College	NY	19,875	VC
Furman Univ	SC	16,557	VC
Hamline Univ	MN	17,122	VC
Hampshire College	MA	25,320	C
Haverford College	PA	23,950	MC
Hobart and William Smith Colleges	NY	23,925	VC
Indiana State Univ	IN	6,210	C
Indiana Univ Bloomington	IN	6,495	VC
Iona College	NY	16,310	C
Jackson State Univ	MS	4,996	LC
Johns Hopkins Univ	MD	24,360	MC
Langston Univ	OK	2,907	LC
Lehigh Univ	PA	23,250	HC
Loyola Marymount Univ	CA	18,560	C
Macalester College	MN	19,710	HC
Manhattan College	NY	19,000	C
Mankato State Univ	MN	5,097	LC
Mass Inst of Tech	MA	24,800	MC
Mercy College	NY	11,180	NC
Metropolitan State College of Denver	CO	1,751	NC
Miami Univ	OH	8,066	VC
Middle Tenn State Univ	TN	3,857	C
Morehouse College	GA	13,224	LC
Mount Vernon College	DC	20,668	C
New York Univ	NY	24,705	VC+
Northwestern Univ	IL	21,093	MC
Occidental College	CA	21,792	HC
Ramapo College of New Jersey	NJ	8,027	C+
Rhode Island College	RI	7,901	LC
Rhodes College	TN	19,624	HC
Rockford College	IL	15,300	C
Rutgers Univ/Camden College of A&S	NJ	8,652	VC
Rutgers Univ/Douglass College	NJ	8,795	VC
Rutgers Univ/Livingston College	NJ	8,877	VC
Rutgers Univ/Rutgers College	NJ	8,841	HC+
Rutgers Univ/Univ College—New Brunswick	NJ	0	LC
St Augustine's College	NC	9,300	C+
St Cloud State Univ	MN	5,015	C
St Louis Univ	MO	15,522	VC
St Olaf College	MN	17,200	HC
St Peter's College	NJ	14,775	LC
San Diego State Univ	CA	6,692	LC
San Francisco State Univ	CA	7,292	LC
Sarah Lawrence College	NY	24,975	HC
Shippensburg Univ of Penn	PA	7,052	C
Southern Univ at New Orleans	LA	1,452	NC
Stanford Univ	CA	24,310	MC
SUNY at Buffalo	NY	7,896	VC
SUNY/College at Buffalo	NY	7,035	VC
Stetson Univ	FL	16,435	VC
Temple Univ	PA	10,281	C
Trinity Univ	TX	16,670	HC
Univ of Alabama	AL	5,702	C
Univ of Calif at Los Angeles	CA	8,959	HC
Univ of Calif, San Diego	CA	10,028	VC+
Univ of Cincinnati	OH	7,989	C
Univ of Conn	CT	9,168	C
Univ of Louisville	KY	5,948	C
Univ of Mich/Flint	MI	2,916	C
Univ of Minn/Duluth	MN	6,512	C
Univ of Minn/Twin Cities	MN	6,682	VC
Univ of Missouri/Kansas City	MO	5,906	VC
Univ of Nebr at Omaha	NE	1,889	LC
Univ of Notre Dame	IN	20,150	MC
Univ of Penn	PA	24,238	MC
Univ of Pittsburgh	PA	9,472	C
Univ of Rhode Island	RI	9,205	C
Univ of Richmond	VA	16,700	HC
Univ of South Florida	FL	5,475	C+
Univ of Southwestern Louisiana	LA	3,968	NC
Univ of Tampa	FL	16,780	C
Univ of Tenn/Knoxville	TN	5,668	C
Univ of Texas at Arlington	TX	5,549	LC
Univ of the Pacific	CA	21,100	C
Univ of the Sacred Heart	PR	3,890	
Univ of Toledo	OH	6,636	NC
Univ of Wisc/Green Bay	WI	4,904	C
Univ of Wisc/Oshkosh	WI	4,240	C
Univ of Wisc/River Falls	WI	4,655	C
Vassar College	NY	24,206	HC
Virginia Commonwealth Univ	VA	7,909	C
Virginia Polytechnic Inst and State Univ	VA	6,828	C
Washington Univ	MO	23,507	HC
Wayne State Univ	MI	2,680	C
Wesleyan Univ	CT	23,770	MC
Western Washington Univ	WA	6,077	VC
Westfield State College	MA	7,161	C
Whittier College	CA	21,661	C
Wichita State Univ	KS	5,068	NC
William Tyndale College	MI	7,120	NC
Winston-Salem State Univ	NC	4,142	LC
Worcester State College	MA	6,414	LC
Wright State Univ	OH	6,896	LC

VETERINARY SCIENCE

School	ST	$IS	SR
East Texas State Univ	TX	4,572	LC
Fort Valley State College	GA	3,974	LC
Lincoln Memorial Univ	TN	8,218	C
Mercy College	NY	11,180	NC
Mount Ida College	MA	16,700	LC
Murray State Univ	KY	4,702	C
N Dak State Univ of Agriculture and Applied Science	ND	4,774	VC
Tuskegee Univ	AL	10,128	C
Univ of Arizona	AZ	5,808	C
Univ of Houston-Downtown	TX	4,034	NC
Univ of Idaho	ID	4,830	C
Univ of Nebr-Lincoln	NE	5,278	LC
Univ of Nevada/Reno	NV	5,735	C
Utah State Univ	UT	4,683	C
Washington State Univ	WA	6,364	C
Wilson College	PA	16,630	C

VIDEO

School	ST	$IS	SR
Atlanta College of Art	GA	12,495	SP
Five Towns College	NY	11,200	SP
Kansas City Art Inst	MO	17,000	SP
Madonna Univ	MI	8,546	C
Minneapolis College of Art and Design	MN	15,512	SP
Point Park College	PA	13,922	LC
San Francisco Art Inst	CA	12,900	SP
Savannah College of Art and Design	GA	14,280	SP
School of Visual Arts	NY	17,120	SP
Univ of Calif at Los Angeles	CA	8,959	HC
Univ of Hartford	CT	19,858	LC
Univ of Miami	FL	22,107	VC
Univ of Okla	OK	5,427	VC

VISUAL AND PERFORMING ARTS

School	ST	$IS	SR
Albion College	MI	18,264	VC
Bennett College	NC	8,920	LC
Cabrini College	PA	16,012	C
Carthage College	WI	15,995	C
Chatham College	PA	18,010	C
Clark Univ	MA	21,400	VC
College of Santa Fe	NM	14,008	C
Columbia Univ/Columbia College	NY	26,757	MC
Curry College	MA	18,695	LC
Dartmouth College	NH	24,354	MC
Eckerd College	FL	18,855	VC
Fayetteville State Univ	NC	3,926	LC
Goddard College	VT	17,990	LC
Gordon College	MA	16,790	C
Grand View College	IA	13,230	NC
Inter American Univ of PR/Aguadilla Regional College	PR	2,290	
Inter American Univ of PR/Bayamon Univ College	PR	2,300	
Inter American Univ of PR/Metropolitan Campus	PR	2,340	
Inter American Univ of PR/Ponce Regional College	PR	2,300	
Inter-American Univ of PR/Fajardo Regional College	PR	2,732	
Ithaca College	NY	19,679	C
Lander Univ	SC	6,180	LC
Longwood College	VA	7,800	C
New England Conservatory of Music	MA	21,590	SP
Oregon State Univ	OR	6,175	C
Pine Manor College	MA	21,700	LC
Presbyterian College	SC	15,400	VC
Rutgers Univ/Douglass College	NJ	8,795	VC
Rutgers Univ/Livingston College	NJ	8,877	VC
Rutgers Univ/Mason Gross School of the Arts	NJ	8,877	SP
Rutgers Univ/Rutgers College	NJ	8,841	HC+
Rutgers Univ/Univ College—Camden	NJ	3,506	C
Rutgers Univ/Univ College—New Brunswick	NJ	0	LC
St Norbert College	WI	15,710	VC
St Vincent College	PA	13,934	LC
School of the Art Inst of Chicago	IL	17,610	SP
Seattle Pacific Univ	WA	16,503	C
SUNY/College at Old Westbury	NY	7,128	LC
Teikyo Marycrest Univ	IA	13,755	VC
Univ of Arkansas at Little Rock	AR	4,419	C
Univ of Calif, San Diego	CA	10,028	VC+
Univ of Maine at Farmington	ME	6,700	C
Univ of Maryland/Baltimore County	MD	7,746	VC
Univ of N Dak	ND	4,902	NC
Univ of North Texas	TX	4,853	C
Univ of Texas at Austin	TX	5,160	VC
Univ of the Sacred Heart	PR	3,890	
West Virginia Univ	WV	5,774	C
William Woods Univ	MO	14,025	LC

VOCATIONAL EDUCATION

School	ST	$IS	SR
Auburn Univ	AL	5,823	C+
Calif Polytechnic State Univ	CA	6,980	VC+
Cal State/Long Beach	CA	6,057	LC
Cal State/Los Angeles	CA	4,940	VC
Cal State/Stanislaus	CA	6,799	C
Central Conn State Univ	CT	7,108	C
Chicago State Univ	IL	2,198	C
CUNY/City College	NY	2,543	VC
Eastern Kentucky Univ	KY	4,840	NC
Florida International Univ	FL	4,191	VC
Idaho State Univ	ID	4,442	C
Keene State College	NH	7,081	C
Martin Univ	IN	4,830	NC
National Univ	CA	6,135	C
N Car State Univ	NC	4,984	VC
Rutgers Univ/Univ College—New Brunswick	NJ	0	LC
Rutgers Univ/Univ College—Newark	NJ	0	C
San Francisco State Univ	CA	7,292	LC
Southern Illinois Univ at Carbondale	IL	6,234	C
Southern Univ and A&M College	LA	4,920	NC
Southwest Texas State Univ	TX	5,124	C
Southwestern Okla State Univ	OK	3,312	C
SUNY/College at Oswego	NY	7,330	VC
Univ of Arkansas at Fayetteville	AR	5,046	C
Univ of Arkansas at Pine Bluff	AR	3,978	LC
Univ of New Hampshire	NH	8,242	C
Univ of North Texas	TX	4,853	C
Univ of Pittsburgh	PA	9,472	C
Univ of the District of Columbia	DC	974	NC
Univ of the Virgin Islands	VI	5,896	C
Univ of Wisc/Stout	WI	4,719	C
Virginia Polytechnic Inst and State Univ	VA	6,828	C
Wayland Baptist Univ	TX	7,811	NC
Western Mich Univ	MI	6,820	C
Wilmington College	OH	13,700	LC

VOICE

School	ST	$IS	SR
Avila College	MO	12,130	C
Belhaven College	MS	9,690	C+
Georgia College	GA	4,310	LC
Grand Canyon Univ	AZ	9,680	VC
Juilliard School	NY	18,050	SP
Manhattan School of Music	NY	12,000	SP
Mannes College of Music	NY	17,200	SP
Northwestern Univ	IL	21,093	MC
Nyack College	NY	12,210	LC
Ohio State Univ	OH	7,218	LC
Pacific Lutheran Univ	WA	15,998	VC
Point Loma Nazarene College	CA	13,532	C
Rollins College	FL	20,875	VC
St Mary College	KS	11,250	C
Shorter College	GA	10,270	C
Southern Nazarene Univ	OK	9,206	NC
Temple Univ	PA	10,281	C
Univ of Cincinnati	OH	7,989	C
Univ of Kansas	KS	5,200	NC
Univ of Mich/Ann Arbor	MI	9,428	HC+
Westminster Choir College	NJ	18,585	SP
William Carey College	MS	7,050	C

WATER RESOURCES

School	ST	$IS	SR
Montana State Univ	MT	5,534	C
Northern Mich Univ	MI	6,350	C
SUNY/College at Brockport	NY	7,220	C+
Tarleton State Univ	TX	4,082	LC
Univ of Arizona	AZ	5,808	C
Univ of New Hampshire	NH	8,242	C
Univ of Rhode Island	RI	9,205	C
Univ of Wisc/Stevens Point	WI	5,047	C+
Western Mich Univ	MI	6,820	C

WATER AND WASTEWATER TECHNOLOGY

School	ST	$IS	SR
Wright State Univ	OH	6,896	LC

WELDING ENGINEERING

School	ST	$IS	SR
Arizona State Univ Main Campus	AZ	6,444	C
Le Tourneau Univ	TX	12,500	C+
Ohio State Univ	OH	7,218	LC

WESTERN EUROPEAN STUDIES

School	ST	$IS	SR
Boston Univ	MA	24,130	HC
St John's College	MD	21,800	VC+
Univ of Mich/Ann Arbor	MI	9,428	HC+
Univ of Nebr-Lincoln	NE	5,278	LC
Washington Univ	MO	23,507	HC

WESTERN CIVILIZATION/CULTURE

School	ST	$IS	SR
St John's College	MD	21,800	VC+
Univ of Calif at Santa Cruz	CA	9,060	VC
Virginia Wesleyan College	VA	14,950	VC

WILDLIFE BIOLOGY

School	ST	$IS	SR
Arizona State Univ Main Campus	AZ	6,444	C
Auburn Univ	AL	5,823	C+
Ball State Univ	IN	6,032	LC
Colo State Univ	CO	6,566	VC
Humboldt State Univ	CA	5,676	C
Iowa State Univ	IA	5,456	C
Midwestern State Univ	TX	4,542	LC
Murray State Univ	KY	4,702	C
New Mexico State Univ	NM	4,844	LC
Northern Mich Univ	MI	6,350	C
Oregon State Univ	OR	6,175	C
Penn State Univ/Univ Park Campus	PA	8,752	HC
Southwest Texas State Univ	TX	5,124	C
Unity College	ME	12,885	LC
Univ of Calif at Davis	CA	9,534	VC
Univ of Florida	FL	5,850	HC
Univ of Mass/Amherst	MA	9,364	LC
Univ of Mich/Ann Arbor	MI	9,428	HC+
Univ of Minn/Twin Cities	MN	6,682	VC
Univ of Montana	MT	5,529	C
Univ of Wisc/Madison	WI	6,400	HC

INDEX OF COLLEGE MAJORS

School	ST	$IS	SR
Univ of Wisc/Stevens Point	WI	5,047	C+
Washington State Univ	WA	6,364	C
West Virginia Univ	WV	5,774	C

WILDLIFE MANAGEMENT

School	ST	$IS	SR
Arkansas State Univ	AR	4,250	NC
Brigham Young Univ	UT	5,625	HC
East Texas State Univ	TX	4,572	LC
Eastern Kentucky Univ	KY	4,840	NC
Eastern New Mexico Univ	NM	3,950	C
Frostburg State Univ	MD	6,940	C
Lake Superior State Univ	MI	7,311	C
Lincoln Memorial Univ	TN	8,218	C
Louisiana Tech Univ	LA	4,284	C
McNeese State Univ	LA	4,543	NC
Ohio State Univ	OH	7,218	LC
Peru State College	NE	4,311	NC
Purdue Univ/West Lafayette	IN	6,636	C
Rutgers Univ/Cook College	NJ	9,197	HC
Southwest Missouri State Univ	MO	4,956	C
Sul Ross State Univ	TX	4,144	NC
Tenn Tech Univ	TN	5,190	C
Texas Tech Univ	TX	6,008	C
Univ of Alaska Fairbanks	AK	4,718	C
Univ of Idaho	ID	4,830	C
Univ of Maine	ME	7,990	C
Univ of Miami	FL	22,107	VC
Univ of New Hampshire	NH	8,242	C
Univ of N Dak	ND	4,902	NC
Univ of Rhode Island	RI	9,205	C
Univ of Southwestern Louisiana	LA	3,968	NC
Univ of Wyoming	WY	4,991	NC
Utah State Univ	UT	4,683	C

WINDS

School	ST	$IS	SR
Northwestern Univ	IL	21,093	MC
Temple Univ	PA	10,281	C
Univ of Mich/Ann Arbor	MI	9,428	HC+

WOMEN'S STUDIES

School	ST	$IS	SR
Amherst College	MA	24,152	MC
Antioch College	OH	19,532	C
Arizona State Univ Main Campus	AZ	6,444	C
Bates College	ME	23,990	MC
Brown Univ	RI	26,104	MC
Bucknell Univ	PA	22,320	HC
Burlington College	VT	6,150	NC
Chatham College	PA	18,010	C
CUNY/College of Staten Island	NY	2,558	NC
CUNY/Hunter College	NY	4,101	VC
Claremont McKenna College	CA	22,150	MC
Colgate Univ	NY	24,020	HC
College of Mount St Joseph	OH	13,272	C
College of Wooster	OH	19,875	VC
Columbia Univ/Barnard College	NY	25,492	HC
Columbia Univ/Columbia College	NY	26,757	MC
Cornell College	IA	18,425	VC
Dartmouth College	NH	24,354	MC
Denison Univ	OH	21,150	VC+
DePaul Univ	IL	15,535	VC
Earlham College	IN	19,383	VC
Eckerd College	FL	18,855	VC
Emory Univ	GA	21,930	HC
Eugene Lang College of the New School for Social Research	NY	21,145	C+
Fordham Univ/Fordham College	NY	19,875	VC
Goddard College	VT	17,990	VC
Goucher College	MD	20,295	VC
Hamilton College	NY	23,500	HC
Hobart and William Smith Colleges	NY	23,925	VC
Kenyon College	OH	22,430	HC+
Middlebury College	VT	24,400	VC
Mills College	CA	20,848	VC
Mount Holyoke College	MA	23,630	VC
Oberlin College	OH	24,570	HC+
Ohio State Univ	OH	7,218	LC
Ohio Wesleyan Univ	OH	21,108	VC+
Old Dominion Univ	VA	8,317	C
Pitzer College	CA	23,780	HC
Pomona College	CA	23,820	MC
Rutgers Univ/Douglass College	NJ	8,795	VC
Rutgers Univ/Livingston College	NJ	8,877	VC
Rutgers Univ/Newark College of A&S	NJ	8,645	C
Rutgers Univ/Rutgers College	NJ	8,841	HC+
Rutgers Univ/Univ College—New Brunswick	NJ	0	LC
St Olaf College	MN	17,200	HC
San Francisco State Univ	CA	7,292	LC
Sarah Lawrence College	NY	24,975	HC
Scripps College	CA	23,600	HC
Simmons College	MA	22,534	C
Simon's Rock College of Bard	MA	23,760	VC+
Smith College	MA	24,236	HC
Southwestern Univ	TX	15,484	HC
SUNY at Albany	NY	7,059	VC
SUNY at Buffalo	NY	7,896	VC
Temple Univ	PA	10,281	C
Towson State Univ	MD	7,452	C
Tulane Univ	LA	24,540	HC
Union College	NY	23,817	HC
Univ of Arizona	AZ	5,808	C
Univ of Calif at Berkeley	CA	9,962	HC
Univ of Calif at Davis	CA	9,534	VC
Univ of Calif at Los Angeles	CA	8,959	HC
Univ of Calif at Santa Barbara	CA	9,460	C
Univ of Calif, Riverside	CA	9,178	C
Univ of Colo at Boulder	CO	6,410	VC
Univ of Conn	CT	9,168	C
Univ of Delaware	DE	8,013	VC
Univ of Denver	CO	19,290	C+
Univ of Hawaii at Manoa	HI	5,626	C
Univ of Kansas	KS	5,200	NC
Univ of Mass/Amherst	MA	9,364	LC
Univ of Mass/Boston	MA	4,253	C
Univ of Mich/Ann Arbor	MI	9,428	HC+
Univ of Minn/Duluth	MN	6,512	C
Univ of Minn/Twin Cities	MN	6,682	VC
Univ of Montana	MT	5,529	C
Univ of Nebr-Lincoln	NE	5,278	LC
Univ of New Hampshire	NH	8,242	C
Univ of N Car at Chapel Hill	NC	5,330	HC
Univ of Okla	OK	5,427	VC
Univ of Penn	PA	24,238	MC
Univ of Pittsburgh	PA	9,472	C
Univ of Rhode Island	RI	9,205	C
Univ of Rochester	NY	23,696	HC
Univ of St Thomas	MN	15,785	C+
Univ of Tenn/Knoxville	TN	5,668	C
Univ of Toledo	OH	6,636	NC
Univ of Washington	WA	6,618	VC
Univ of Wisc/Madison	WI	6,400	HC
Univ of Wisc/Whitewater	WI	4,700	C
Vassar College	NY	24,206	HC
Washington Univ	MO	23,507	HC
Wayne State Univ	MI	2,680	C
Wellesley College	MA	23,815	MC
Wells College	NY	19,460	C+
Wesleyan Univ	CT	23,770	MC
Yale Univ	CT	25,110	MC

WOOD SCIENCE

School	ST	$IS	SR
N Car State Univ	NC	4,984	VC
Univ of Maine	ME	7,990	C
Univ of Washington	WA	6,618	VC
West Virginia Univ	WV	5,774	C

WOODWORKING

School	ST	$IS	SR
Indiana Univ-Purdue Univ at Indianapolis	IN	5,862	LC
Kansas Newman College	KS	10,640	C
Rochester Inst of Tech	NY	18,954	VC

YIDDISH

School	ST	$IS	SR
CUNY/Queens College	NY	2,631	C

YOUTH MINISTRY

School	ST	$IS	SR
Colo Christian Univ	CO	9,750	C
Eastern College	PA	15,150	C+
Eastern Mennonite College	VA	12,700	C
Gordon College	MA	16,790	C
John Brown Univ	AR	9,880	VC
Mich Christian College	MI	8,094	C
Okla Christian Univ of Science and Arts	OK	8,790	NC
Trinity College	IL	14,010	C

ZOOLOGY

School	ST	$IS	SR
Alabama A&M Univ	AL	4,200	C
Andrews Univ	MI	14,952	NC
Arizona State Univ Main Campus	AZ	6,444	C
Arkansas State Univ	AR	4,250	NC
Auburn Univ	AL	5,823	C+
Averett College	VA	13,610	C
Ball State Univ	IN	6,032	LC
Brigham Young Univ	UT	5,625	HC
Calif State Polytechnic Univ/Pomona	CA	6,438	LC
Cal State/Fresno	CA	5,747	C
Cal State/Fullerton	CA	4,850	LC
Cal State/Long Beach	CA	6,057	LC
Central Washington Univ	WA	5,644	C
Colo State Univ	CO	6,566	VC
Conn College	CT	24,160	HC
Eastern Illinois Univ	IL	5,548	C
Eastern Washington Univ	WA	5,439	LC
Evergreen State College	WA	6,306	C
Florida Atlantic Univ	FL	5,525	C
Fort Valley State College	GA	3,974	LC
Friends Univ	KS	11,205	C
Howard Univ	DC	11,680	C
Humboldt State Univ	CA	5,676	C
Idaho State Univ	ID	4,442	C
Iowa State Univ	IA	5,456	C
Kent State Univ	OH	6,740	LC
Louisiana State Univ and A&M College	LA	5,605	C
Louisiana Tech Univ	LA	4,284	C
Mars Hill College	NC	11,050	C
McNeese State Univ	LA	4,543	NC
Miami Univ	OH	8,066	C
Mich State Univ	MI	7,842	C
N Car State Univ	NC	4,984	VC
North Central College	IL	15,498	VC
N Dak State Univ of Agriculture and Applied Science	ND	4,774	VC
Northeastern State Univ	OK	3,424	C
Northern Arizona Univ	AZ	4,844	C
Northern Mich Univ	MI	6,350	C
Northwest Missouri State Univ	MO	5,010	LC
Northwestern Okla State Univ	OK	3,424	C
Ohio State Univ	OH	7,218	LC
Ohio Univ	OH	7,341	C
Ohio Wesleyan Univ	OH	21,108	VC+
Okla State Univ	OK	5,086	VC
Olivet Nazarene Univ	IL	11,976	C
Oregon State Univ	OR	6,175	C
Purdue Univ/Calumet	IN	2,374	C
Purdue Univ/West Lafayette	IN	6,636	C
Rutgers Univ/Newark College of A&S	NJ	8,645	C
San Francisco State Univ	CA	7,292	LC
San Jose State Univ	CA	6,680	LC
Sonoma State Univ	CA	6,996	LC
Southeastern Louisiana Univ	LA	4,230	VC
Southern Illinois Univ at Carbondale	IL	6,234	C
Southern Univ and A&M College	LA	4,920	NC
Southern Utah Univ	UT	4,104	LC
Southwest Texas State Univ	TX	5,124	C
SUNY/College at Oswego	NY	7,330	VC
Texas A&M Univ	TX	5,382	VC
Texas Tech Univ	TX	6,008	C
Univ of Akron	OH	6,699	NC
Univ of Arkansas at Fayetteville	AR	5,046	C
Univ of Calif at Davis	CA	9,534	VC
Univ of Calif at Santa Barbara	CA	9,460	C
Univ of Central Florida	FL	6,061	C+
Univ of Florida	FL	5,850	VC
Univ of Georgia	GA	5,655	VC
Univ of Hawaii at Manoa	HI	5,626	C
Univ of Idaho	ID	4,830	C
Univ of Kentucky	KY	5,152	VC
Univ of Louisville	KY	5,948	C
Univ of Maine	ME	7,990	C
Univ of Maryland/College Park	MD	8,182	VC
Univ of Mich/Ann Arbor	MI	9,428	HC+
Univ of Montana	MT	5,529	C
Univ of New Hampshire	NH	8,242	C
Univ of N Dak	ND	4,902	NC
Univ of Okla	OK	5,427	VC
Univ of Rhode Island	RI	9,205	C
Univ of South Florida	FL	5,475	C+
Univ of Tenn/Knoxville	TN	5,668	C
Univ of Texas at Austin	TX	5,160	VC
Univ of Texas at El Paso	TX	3,160	LC
Univ of Vermont	VT	10,776	C
Univ of Washington	WA	6,618	VC
Univ of Wisc/Eau Claire	WI	4,647	C
Univ of Wisc/Madison	WI	6,400	HC
Univ of Wisc/Milwaukee	WI	6,165	C
Univ of Wyoming	WY	4,991	NC
Washington State Univ	WA	6,364	C
Weber State Univ	UT	4,398	C

ST = State $IS = In-state Costs SR = Selector Rating

PART III
COLLEGE FACTS AND FINANCES

COLLEGES AT A GLANCE

The charts on these pages present some of the basic data that initially concerns many students. All of the four-year accredited schools in the United States are listed here alphabetically by state. The type of college environment (from urban to rural) is given, followed by degrees offered and whether the institution is public or private. Information about whether the student body is coed or primarily men or women, and whether fraternities or sororities are on campus follows. The undergraduate enrollment for the fall of 1993 is given as well as the median test scores for those 1993-94 freshmen who took the ACT or SAT I. Finally, the fall admissions deadline is shown. "Open" usually indicates that admission applications will be accepted until a few weeks before classes begin.

Legend:
ENVIRONMENT: U-Urban, R-Rural, Su-Suburban, Sm-Small Town •
DEGREES AWARDED: A-Associate, B-Bachelor, M-Master, D-Doctorate •
CONTROL: Pri-Private, Pub-Public •
FRATERNITIES AND SORORITIES: F-Fraternities, S-Sororities, F,S-Both, No-Neither •
STUDENTS: C-Coed, M-Men, W-Women, PM-Primarily Men, PW-Primarily Women

Name of School	Town	Env	Deg	Ctrl	Frat	Stu	Enroll Fall '93	ACT Med	ACT Below 21	ACT 21-23	ACT 24-26	ACT 27-28	ACT Above 28	SATV Med	SATV Below 500	SATV 500-599	SATV 600-700	SATV Above 700	SATM Med	SATM Below 500	SATM 500-599	SATM 600-700	SATM Above 700	Application Deadline
Alabama																								
Alabama Agricultural and Mechanical University	Normal	SU	B,M,D	Pub	F,S	C	4,263	17																
Alabama State University	Montgomery	U	A,B,M	Pub	F,S	C	5,242																	Open
Auburn University	Auburn University	SM	B,M,D	Pub	F,S	C	18,349	24	24	27	25	11	13	501	49	38	12	1	575	17	41	34	8	8/1
Auburn University at Montgomery	Montgomery	SU	B,M,D	Pub	F,S	C	5,416	21																9/1
Birmingham-Southern College	Birmingham	U	B,M	Pri	F,S	C	1,582	26	10	18	21	21	30	515	41	38	16	5	535	19	43	30	8	9/1
Faulkner University	Montgomery	U	A,B	Pri	F,S	C	1,705	23																3/1
Huntingdon College	Montgomery	SU	A,B	Pri	F,S	C	790	23																6/1
Jacksonville State University	Jacksonville	SM	B,M	Pub	F,S	C	6,635	19																Open
Judson College	Marion	SM	B	Pri	No	W	431	22	38	32	17	8	5											8/30
Livingston University	Livingston	SM	A,B,M	Pub	F,S	C	1,759	19	71	16	10	3												Open
Miles College	Fairfield	U	A,B	Pri	F,S	C	864																	Open
Oakwood College	Huntsville	SU	A,B	Pri	No	C	1,451	17	82	13	4	1	1	378	90	5	5		382	83	13	4		Open
Samford University	Birmingham	SU	A,B,M,D	Pri	F,S	C	3,359		14	33	29	17	7			80	20				20	80		Open
Selma University	Selma	SU	A,B	Pri	No	C	264																	Open
Spring Hill College	Mobile	SU	B,M	Pri	F,S	C	1,145	24	22	32	23	15	8	545	59	30	10		500	39	43	17		8/15
Stillman College	Tuscaloosa	SM	B	Pri	F,S	C	953	17	89	8	3													6/15
Talladega College	Talladega	SM	B	Pri	F,S	C	1,027																	6/15
Troy State University	Troy	SM	A,B,M	Pub	F,S	C	4,769	22						460					490					Open
Troy State University at Dothan/Fort Rucker	Dothan	U	A,B,M	Pub	No	C	1,702																	Open
Troy State University in Montgomery	Montgomery	U	A,B,M	Pub	No	C	2,921																	Open
Tuskegee University	Tuskegee	R	B,M,D	Pri	F,S	C	2,990	18						374					409					3/1
University of Alabama	Tuscaloosa	SM	B,M,D	Pub	F,S	C	15,343	23	27	31	23	8	11											4/15
University of Alabama at Birmingham	Birmingham	U	B,M,D	Pub	F,S	C	11,658		49	26	15	5	5											Open
University of Alabama at Huntsville	Huntsville	U	B,M,D	Pub	F,S	C	6,171																	8/13
University of Mobile	Mobile	SU	A,B,M	Pri	No	C	1,544	23	25	26	26	11	13	450	62	23	13	2	550	30	36	25	8	7/1
University of Montevallo	Montevallo	SM	B,M	Pub	F,S	C	2,717	21	39	27	22	10	2											8/1
University of North Alabama	Florence	U	B,M	Pub	F,S	C	4,806																	7/1
University of South Alabama	Mobile	U	B,M,D	Pub	F,S	C	10,459	23																9/10
Alaska																								
Alaska Pacific University	Anchorage	SU	A,B,M	Pri	No	C	447	19																8/15
Sheldon Jackson College	Sitka	SM	A,B	Pri	No	C	303	20	62	17	3	10	7	485	58	33	5	3	470	56	31	11	3	Open
University of Alaska Anchorage	Anchorage	U	A,B,M	Pub	No	C	14,350																	7/1
University of Alaska Fairbanks	Fairbanks	SM	A,B,M,D	Pub	F,S	C	8,464	22																8/1
University of Alaska Southeast	Juneau	SU	A,B,M	Pub	No	C	1,667							463					490					Open
Arizona																								
Arizona State University Main Campus	Tempe	SU	B,M,D	Pub	F,S	C	30,178	22	31	29	24	9	7	450	69	25	5	1	520	38	39	18	5	4/15
DeVry Institute of Technology/Phoenix	Phoenix	SU	A,B	Pri	No	C	2,645																	Open
Embry-Riddle Aeronautical University	Prescott	R	A,B	Pri	F,S	C	4,178	24	18	26	27	17	13	470	62	30	7	1	550	30	41	26	4	Open
Grand Canyon University	Phoenix	SU	B,M	Pri	No	C	1,837	21	39	31	21	3	5	441	74	21	4	1	485	53	34	13	1	8/1
Northern Arizona University	Flagstaff	SM	B,M,D	Pub	F,S	C	13,931	21						450					480					4/1
Prescott College	Prescott	SM	B,M	Pri	No	C	368																	Open
University of Arizona	Tuscon	U	B,M,D		F,S	C	26,558	23	27	27	26	10	10	470	60	31	8	1	530	39	35	21	5	4/1
Western International University	Phoenix	U	A,B,M	Pri	No	C	1,169																	Open
Arkansas																								
Arkansas Baptist College	Little Rock	U	A,B	Pri			266																	Open
Arkansas College	Batesville	SM	B	Pri	F,S	C	718	25	14	25	31	17	13											8/1
Arkansas State University	State University	SM	A,B,M,D	Pub	F,S	C	8,919	20																7/31
Arkansas Tech University	Russellville	SM	A,B,M		F,S	C	4,541	20	53	24	18	3	2											Open
Harding University	Searcy	SM	B,M	Pri		C	3,263	24	15	20	30	20	15											5/1
Henderson State University	Arkadelphia	SM	A,B,M	Pub	F,S	C	3,445	21	63	21	11	3	2											Open
Hendrix College	Conway	SU	B	Pri	No	C	954																	Open
John Brown University	Siloam Springs	SM	A,B	Pri	No	C	1,061	23																Open
Ouachita Baptist University	Arkadelphia	SM	B	Pri	F,S	C	1,371	23	31	25	24	8	12											Open
Philander Smith College	Little Rock	U	B	Pri	F,S		915	18	99															6/15
Southern Arkansas University	Magnolia	SM	A,B,M	Pub	F,S	C	2,648		71	18	9	1												Open
University of Arkansas at Fayetteville	Fayetteville	U	A,B,M,D	Pub	F,S	C	11,508																	8/15
University of Arkansas at Little Rock	Little Rock	U	A,B,M,D	Pub	F,S	C	9,991	19	65	18	12	3	1											8/1
University of Arkansas at Monticello	Monticello	SM	A,B	Pub	F,S	C	2,450	18																8/15
University of Arkansas at Pine Bluff	Pine Bluff	SM	A,B,M	Pub	F,S	C	4,015																	
University of Central Arkansas	Conway	SM	A,B,M	Pub	F,S	C	8,521	20																Open

Key to column codes — ENVIRONMENT: U-Urban, R-Rural, Su-Suburban, Sm-Small Town · DEGREES AWARDED: A-Associate, B-Bachelor, M-Master, D-Doctorate · CONTROL: Pri-Private, Pub-Public · FRATERNITIES AND SORORITIES: F-Fraternities, S-Sororities, No-Neither · STUDENTS: C-Coed, M-Men, W-Women, PW-Primarily Women, PM-Primarily Men

Name of School	Town	Environment	Degrees Awarded	Control	Fraternities and Sororities	Students	Undergrad Enrollment Fall '93	ACT Median	ACT Below 21	ACT 21-23	ACT 24-26	ACT 27-28	ACT Above 28	SAT I Verbal Median	SAT I Verbal Below 500	SAT I Verbal 500-599	SAT I Verbal 600-700	SAT I Verbal Above 700	SAT I Math Median	SAT I Math Below 500	SAT I Math 500-599	SAT I Math 600-700	SAT I Math Above 700	Application Deadline
University of the Ozarks	Clarksville	SM	A,B,M	Pri	No	C	563	23	30	27	25	13	5											7/1
Williams Baptist College	Walnut Ridge	SM	A,B	Pri	No	C	604	19	64	18	17	1												Open
California																								
Art Center College of Design	Pasadena	SU	B,M	Pri	No	C	1,254																	Open
Art Institute of Southern California	Laguna Beach	SM	B	Pri	No	C	150																	Open
Azusa Pacific University	Azusa	SM	B,M,D	Pri	No	C	2,268	18	36	32	23	7	2	428	59	28	11	3	474	77	18	4		Open
Biola University	La Mirada	SU	B,M,D	Pri	No	C	2,001	22						440					500					6/1
California Baptist College	Riverside	SU	B,M	Pri	No	C	863								67	26	4	3		48	30	15	7	Open
California College of Arts and Crafts	Oakland	U	B,M	Pri	No	C	1,071									16	63	21				7	93	1/1
California Institute of Technology	Pasadena	SU	B,M,D	Pri	No	C	884																	2/1
California Institute of the Arts	Valencia	SU	B,M	Pri	No	C	679																	Open
California Lutheran University	Thousand Oaks	U	B,M	Pri	No	C	1,859							436	76	19	4		495	47	37	14	2	3/15
California Maritime Academy	Vallejo	SU	B	Pub	No	C	487								61	29	7	2	553					11/30
California Polytechnic State University	San Luis Obispo	SU	B,M	Pub	F,S	C	14,104							451										11/30
California State Polytechnic University/Pomona	Pomona	SU	B,M	Pub	F,S	C	15,348	20	49	27	13	9	2	380	86	11	2	1	510	44	35	17	4	11/1
California State University/Bakersfield	Bakersfield	U	B,M	Pub	F,S	C	3,961	21						404					433					9/14
California State University/Chico	Chico	SM	B,M	Pub	F,S	C	13,171	20	51	30	15	2	2	420	83	15	2		480	55	34	10	1	Open
California State University/Dominguez Hills	Carson	U	B,M	Pub	F,S	C	8,487							360	89	7	4		430	82	15	2		5/15
California State University/Fresno	Fresno	SU	B,M,D	Pub	F,S	C	15,279	19																Open
California State University/Fullerton	Fullerton	SU	B,M	Pub	F,S	C	20,313	19	58	25	12	2	3	390	87	11	2		460	60	29	10	1	5/1
California State University/Hayward	Hayward	SU	B,M	Pub	F,S	C	9,749							362	93	7			438	73	22	5		11/30
California State University/Long Beach	Long Beach	SU	B,D	Pub	F,S	C	21,424																	8/7
California State University/Los Angeles	Los Angeles	U	B,M,D	Pub	F,S	C	13,509							365	92	7	1	1	444	70	23	6	1	11/30
California State University/Northridge	Northridge	SU	B,M	Pub	F,S	C	21,681							408	82	15	3		476	55	33	11	1	11/30
California State University/Sacramento	Sacramento	U	B,M	Pub	F,S	C	19,406																	11/30
California State University/San Bernardino	San Bernardino	SU	B,M	Pub	F,S	C	9,198							400					449					12/1
California State University/Stanislaus	Turlock	R	M	Pub			4,579																	3/1
Chapman University	Orange	SU	B,M	Pri	F,S	C	1,871	21	43	27	18	6	6	440	73	22	5		485	53	33	11	3	Open
Christian Heritage College	El Cajon	SU	A,B	Pri	No	C	350	20	90	7	2	1		443	97	2	1		456	95	3	1		2/1
Claremont McKenna College	Claremont	SM	B	Pri	No	C	888	28		9	25	25	41	600	6	38	52	4	670	2	16	45	37	8/25
Cogswell Polytechnic College	Cupertino	SU	A,B	Pri	No	C	368																	6/1
College of Notre Dame	Belmont	SU	A,B,M	Pri	No	C	831							420	75	22	3		485	51	33	14	2	7/1
Concordia University	Irvine	SU	B,M	Pri	No	C	742	22																Open
DeVry Institute of Technology/Los Angeles	Pomona	SU	A,B	Pri	No	C	2,620																	Open
Dominican College of San Rafael	San Rafael	SU	B,M	Pri	No	C	798							432	79	17	4		452	68	27	5		Open
Fresno Pacific College	Fresno	SU	A,B,M	Pri	No	C	909	20	57	20	17	6		477	60	32	8		532	34	42	19	4	7/31
Golden Gate University	San Francisco	U	A,B,M,D	Pri	No	C	2,066								3	23	58	16				20	80	2/1
Harvey Mudd College	Claremont	SU	B	Pri	No	C	659							448	92	8			450	67	33			8/1
Holy Names College	Oakland	U	B,M	Pri	No	C	590							460					510					11
Humboldt State University	Arcata	SM	B,M	Pub	F,S	C	6,315	21						360	90	10			380	87	13			9/27
Humphreys College	Stockton	SU	A,B,D	Pri	No	C	652								72	20	5	3		78	14	6	2	8/15
La Sierra University	Riverside	SU	A,B,M,D	Pri	No	C	1,242																	
Lee College at the University of Judaism	Los Angeles	SU	B,M	Pri	No	C	100							565	28	36	36		565	21	43	29	7	1/31
Lincoln University	San Francisco	U	B,M	Pri	No	C	188																	Open
Loyola Marymount University	Los Angeles	SU	B,M,D	Pri	F,S	C	3,824							473	63	29	8	1	535	32	46	18	4	8/1
Master's College	Santa Clarita	R	B,M	Pri	No	C	773	21	25	28	27	15	5	449	68	23	9		474	59	30	10	1	8/1
Menlo College	Atherton	SU	A,B	Pri	F	C	568	19	93	4	2	1		450	70	24	3	3	380	77	18	4	1	3/1
Mills College	Oakland	U	B,M	Pri	No	W	828	25	11	30	21	10	28	540	33	38	25	3	530	31	40	23	6	2/1
Mount Saint Mary's College	Los Angeles	U	A,B,M	Pri	S	PW	1,156	21							64	26	9	1		46	39	10	4	3/1
National University	San Diego	U	A,B,M,D	Pri	No	C	3,892																	9/1
New College of California	San Francisco	U	B,M	Pri	No	C	900								42	41	16	1		22	38	28	12	2/1
Occidental College	Los Angeles	U	B,M	Pri	F,S	C	1,621							500	47	50	3		467	65	34	1		8/15
Otis College of Art and Design	Los Angeles	U	A,B,M	Pri	No	C	726	22	8	22	50	20		436	41	33	19	4	477	20	37	30	11	7/1
Pacific Christian College	Fullerton	SM	A,B,M	Pri	No	C	599	22	37	25	21	12	5											Open
Pacific Union College	Angwin	SU	B,M,D	Pri	No	C	1,455	25	5	21	37	20	17	514	29	57	12	2	582	28	50	20	2	2/1
Pepperdine University	Malibu	SU	B,M,D	Pri	F,S	C	2,759	26	6	17	25	39	13	560	14	50	27	9	580	10	51	31	8	2/1
Pitzer College	Claremont	SU	B	Pri	No	C	760	21	52	27	13	3		425	77	19	4	1	472	59	28	11	2	Open
Point Loma Nazarene College	San Diego	SU	B,M	Pri	F,S	C	2,107	21																1/15
Pomona College	Claremont	SU	B	Pri	F	C	1,382	31						640	4	22	59	15	700	2	8	39	51	3/1
Saint Mary's College of California	Moraga	SU	B,M	Pri	No	C	2,881							493	48	39	12		539	35	43	19	3	7/15
Samuel Merritt College	Oakland	U	B	Pri	No	C	301							453	83	17			459	83	17			11/30
San Diego State University	San Diego	U	B,M	Pub	F,S	C	21,957	19	63	24	10	1	2	390	86	12	2		460	65	26	8	1	Open
San Francisco Art Institute	San Francisco	U	B,M	Pri	No	C	505																	7/1
San Francisco Conservatory of Music	San Francisco	U	B,M	Pri	No	C	166							468		87	9	3	547		66	25	8	11/30
San Francisco State University	San Francisco	U	A,B,M,D	Pub	F,S	C	19,102							360	89	9			460	60	28	12	1	11/1
San Jose State University	San Jose	U	A,B	Pub	F,S	C	21,655	18	66	18	11	4	1		53	36	10	1		16	43	33	8		2/1
Santa Clara University	Santa Clara	SU	B,M,D	Pri	F,S	C	4,019							562	19	45	29	6	590	9	38	42	10	2/1
Scripps College	Claremont	SU	B	Pri	No	W	612										60							Open
Simpson College	Redding	SU	A,B,M	Pri	No	C	518	22						486	78	18	4	1	482	52	36	11	1	Open
Sonoma State University	Rohnert Park	SU	B,M	Pub	F,S	C	5,498	22	47	27	15	4		410	80	15	4	1	460	66	23	10	1	7/31
Southern California College	Costa Mesa	SU	B,M	Pri	No	C	900																	12/15
Stanford University	Stanford	SU	B,M,D	Pri	F,S	C	6,573								6	22	50	22		1	10	30	59	Open
Thomas Aquinas College	Santa Paula	R	B	Pri	No	C	208	27		11	28	33	28	580	20	36	30	14	570	12	42	36	10	Open
United States International University	San Diego	SU	B,M,D	Pri	No	C	1,450																	11/30
University of California at Berkeley	Berkeley	U	B,M,D	Pub	F,S	C	21,713							490	51	36	12	1	590	16	34	37	13	11/30
University of California at Davis	Davis	SU	B,M,D	Pub	F,S	C	17,206	24																11/30

Key to columns

- **ENVIRONMENT:** U-Urban, R-Rural, Su-Suburban, Sm-Small Town
- **DEGREES AWARDED:** A-Associate, B-Bachelor, M-Master, D-Doctorate
- **CONTROL:** Pri-Private, Pub-Public
- **FRATERNITIES AND SORORITIES:** F-Fraternities, S-Sororities, F,S-Both, No-Neither
- **STUDENTS:** C-Coed, M-Men, W-Women, PM-Primarily Men, PW-Primarily Women
- **TEST SCORES:** ACT (Median, Below 21, 21-23, 24-26, 27-28, Above 28); SAT I Verbal Reasoning (Median, Below 500, 500-599, 600-700, Above 700); SAT I Mathematical Reasoning (Median, Below 500, 500-599, 600-700, Above 700)
- **APPLICATION DEADLINE:** Month/Day

Name of School	Town	Env	Deg	Ctrl	Frat	Std	Enroll '93	ACT Med	ACT <21	21-23	24-26	27-28	>28	V Med	V<500	V500-599	V600-700	V>700	M Med	M<500	M500-599	M600-700	M>700	Deadline
University of California at Los Angeles	Los Angeles	U	B,M,D	Pub	F,S	C	22,892																	11/30
University of California at Santa Barbara	Santa Barbara	SU	B,M,D	Pub	F,S	C	16,277								38	39	21	2		12	24	38	26	11/30
University of California at Santa Cruz	Santa Cruz	SM	B,M,D	Pub	No	C	9,466							459	65	29	6		547	26	44	25	6	11/30
University of California/Irvine	Irvine	SU	B,M,D	Pub	F,S	C	13,541							515	43	36	16	3	560	25	39	27	7	11/30
University of California, Riverside	Riverside	SU	B,M,D	Pub	F,S	C	7,187							450					580					11/30
University of California, San Diego	La Jolla	SU	B,M,D	Pub	F,S	C	14,360							440	69	23	7	1	541	33	36	22	9	11/30
University of La Verne	La Verne	SU	B,M,D	Pri	F,S	C	1,347		53	32	12	2	1	515	11	35	39	16	616	1	9	33	57	3/1
University of Redlands	Redlands	SM	B,M	Pri	F,S	C	1,500							420	64	31	4	1	460	58	37	4	1	3/1
University of San Diego	San Diego	U	B,M,D	Pri	F,S	C	3,915							510					540					3/1
University of San Francisco	San Francisco	U	B,M,D	Pri	F,S	C	3,315							506	56	31	12	1	548	30	44	23	3	1/15
University of Southern California	Los Angeles	U	B,M,D	Pri	F,S	C	15,847	21	42	28	22	2	6	450	64	24	11	1	500	46	31	18	5	3/2
University of the Pacific	Stockton	SU	B,M,D	Pri	F,S	C	3,558	25	15	24	23	13	25	480	50	32	16	2	580	15	37	35	13	2/1
West Coast University	Los Angeles	U	A,B,M	Pri	No	C	500							440					530					3/1
Westmont College	Santa Barbara	SU	B	Pri	No	C	1,285	24	10	34	33	9	13	501	44	43	12	1	550	29	40	25	7	Open
Whittier College	Whittier	SU	B,M,D	Pri	F,S	C	1,261							450	70	23	6	1	510	44	37	13	3	2/15
Woodbury University	Burbank	SU	B,M	Pri	F,S	C	956	20	60	30	10			381	89	9	2		441	70	22	8		Open

Colorado

Name of School	Town	Env	Deg	Ctrl	Frat	Std	Enroll '93	ACT Med	ACT <21	21-23	24-26	27-28	>28	V Med	V<500	V500-599	V600-700	V>700	M Med	M<500	M500-599	M600-700	M>700	Deadline
Adams State College	Alamosa	SM	A,B,M	Pub	No	C	2,017	21	40	40	14	4	2	442					478					8/1
Beth-El College of Nursing	Colorado Springs	U	B,M	Pub	No	C	355	22		100														4/15
Colorado Christian University	Lakewood	SU	A,B,M	Pri	F	C	1,066	21						422					445					Open
Colorado College	Colorado Springs	SU	B,M	Pri	F,S	C	1,897		5	9	26	23	37		19	46	31	4		8	33	45	14	1/15
Colorado School of Mines	Golden	SM	B,M,D	Pub	F,S	C	2,122	28		5	25	40	30	550	23	65	11	1	650		20	70	10	5/1
Colorado State University	Fort Collins	SU	B,M,D	Pub	F,S	C	17,475	24	9	30	35	14	12	470	59	33	6	2	540	27	43	16	13	7/1
Colorado Technical College	Colorado Springs	SU	A,B,M	Pri	No	C	1,170							407	100				600			25	75	10/1
Fort Lewis College	Durango	SM	A,B	Pub	No	C	4,279	20	38	24	23	10	5											8/1
Mesa State College	Grand Junction	SM	A,B	Pub	No	C	4,600	19						407										8/1
Metropolitan State College of Denver	Denver	U	B	Pub	No	C	17,520	19	67	21	9	2	1	404	84	13	2		439					8/1
Regis University	Denver	SU	B,M	Pri	No	C	1,169	21	40	29	19	7	4	480	76	16	6	2	439	70	21	8	1	Open
United States Air Force Academy	USAFA	SU	B	Pub	No	C	4,236	27	2	4	34	27	33	569	7	61	31		663		15	61	24	1/31
University of Colorado at Boulder	Boulder	SU	B,M,D	Pub	F,S	C	20,006		11	24	32	18	16		48	40	11			19	38	33	9	2/15
University of Colorado at Colorado Springs	Colorado Springs	U	B,M,D	Pub	No	C	4,139	23						448					510					7/1
University of Colorado at Denver	Denver	U	B,M,D	Pub	No	C	6,054								59	26	12	3		40	35	22	3	7/22
University of Denver	Denver	SU	B,M,D	Pri	F,S	C	3,207	24	24	23	23	16	14	500	63	28	8	1	510	36	43	19	2	3/1
University of Northern Colorado	Greeley	SU	B,M,D	Pub	F,S	C	8,786	22	37	31	23	7	2	430	78	18	4		480	55	35	8	2	3/1
University of Southern Colorado	Pueblo	U	B,M	Pub	No	C	4,145																	8/1
Western State College of Colorado	Gunnison	R	B	Pub	F,S	C	2,455	21	53	29	13	4	1	420	82	15	2	1	470	65	29	6		7/21

Connecticut

Name of School	Town	Env	Deg	Ctrl	Frat	Std	Enroll '93	ACT Med	ACT <21	21-23	24-26	27-28	>28	V Med	V<500	V500-599	V600-700	V>700	M Med	M<500	M500-599	M600-700	M>700	Deadline
Albertus Magnus College	New Haven	SU	A,B,M	Pri	No	C	450																	Open
Bridgeport Engineering Institute	Fairfield	SM	A,B	Pri		C	327																	Open
Central Connecticut State University	New Britain	SU	B,M	Pub	F,S	C	10,275							414	86	13	1		457	67	26	6	1	Open
Charter Oak State College	Farmington	SU	A,B	Pub		C	1,144																	5/1
Connecticut College	New London	SM	B,M		No	C	1,862	27						600	11	40	45	5	620	6	28	52	15	1/15
Eastern Connecticut State University	Willimantic	SU	A,B,M	Pub	No	C	4,285							430	80	16	3	1	460	67	27	5	1	5/1
Fairfield University	Fairfield	SU	B,M	Pri	No	C	4,021							498	47	45	7	1	560	18	49	29	4	5/1
Paier College of Art	Hamden	U	A,B	Pri	No	C	253							410					410					3/1
Quinnipiac College	Hamden	SU	B,M	Pri	F,S	C	3,406							510	48	34	14	4	535	35	45	14	6	8/20
Sacred Heart University	Fairfield	SU	A,B,M	Pri	F,S	C	3,596							420	78	19	3		480	54	35	10	1	3/1
Saint Joseph College	West Hartford	SU	B,M	Pri	No	W	1,255							420	75	23	2		450	66	29	4	1	5/1
Southern Connecticut State University	New Haven	U	A,B,M	Pub	F,S	C	8,370							427					462					5/1
Teikyo Post University	Waterbury	SU	A,B	Pri	No	C	1,843																	Open
Trinity College	Hartford	U	B,M		F,S	C	1,946		2	22	44	23	9		19	54	25	2		7	36	46	11	1/15
United States Coast Guard Academy	New London	SU	B	Pub	No	C	930							542	25	50	23	2	643		24	49	27	12/15
University of Bridgeport	Bridgeport	U	A,B,M,D	Pri	F,S	C	839							420					510					4/1
University of Connecticut	Storrs	R	B,M,D	Pub	F,S	C	12,059							480	58	34	7	1	500	26	42	25	7	4/1
University of Hartford	West Hartford	SU	A,B,M,D	Pri	F,S	C	5,454							450	73	22	5		500	49	35	15		4/1
University of New Haven	West Haven	SU	A,B,M,D	Pri	F,S	C	3,110							434	91	6	3		495	48	50	2		9/1
Wesleyan University	Middletown	SU	B,M,D	Pri	F,S	C	2,741	30						630	10	25	50	12	660	4	17	48	32	1/15
Western Connecticut State University	Danbury	SU	A,B,M	Pub	F,S	C	4,679							424	82	15	3		470	64	28	8	1	4/1
Yale University	New Haven	U	B,M,D	Pri	F,S	C	5,287								3	17	44	36		1	8	35	57	12/31

Delaware

Name of School	Town	Env	Deg	Ctrl	Frat	Std	Enroll '93	ACT Med	ACT <21	21-23	24-26	27-28	>28	V Med	V<500	V500-599	V600-700	V>700	M Med	M<500	M500-599	M600-700	M>700	Deadline
Delaware State College	Dover	SU	B,M	Pub	F,S	C	3,051																	6/1
Goldey-Beacom College	Wilmington	SU	A,B,M	Pri	F,S	C	1,795																	Open
University of Delaware	Newark	SM	A,B,M,D	Pri	F,S	C	14,932							425	92	7	1		486	60	32	8		3/1
Wesley College	Dover	SM	A,B,M	Pri	F,S	C	1,320																	Open
Wilmington College	New Castle		A,B,M,D	Pri	F,S	C	2,386							380	96		1		410	85	12	3		Open

District of Columbia

Name of School	Town	Env	Deg	Ctrl	Frat	Std	Enroll '93	ACT Med	ACT <21	21-23	24-26	27-28	>28	V Med	V<500	V500-599	V600-700	V>700	M Med	M<500	M500-599	M600-700	M>700	Deadline
American University	Washington	SU	B,M,D	Pri	F,S	C	4,999	26	7	16	26	29	22	540	25	47	26	2	580	11	47	35	7	2/15
Catholic University of America	Washington	U	B,M,D	Pri	F,S	C	2,370								45	38	15	2		25	44	25	6	2/15
Corcoran School of Art	Washington	U	B	Pri	No	C	296	22																Open
Gallaudet University	Washington	U	A,B,M,D	Pri	F,S	C	1,660							460	60	29	10	1						Open
George Washington University	Washington	U	A,B,M,D	Pri	F,S	C	5,900		5	17	27	23	28		27	45	25	3		10	40	39	11	12/1

Legend (from column headings):

- **ENVIRONMENT:** U-Urban, R-Rural, SU-Suburban, Sm-Small Town
- **DEGREES AWARDED:** A-Associate, B-Bachelor, M-Master, D-Doctorate
- **CONTROL:** Pri-Private, Pub-Public
- **FRATERNITIES AND SORORITIES:** F-Fraternities, S-Sororities, T-S-Both, No-Neither
- **STUDENTS:** C-Coed, M-Men, W-Women, PM-Primarily Men, PW-Primarily Women
- **TEST SCORES** percentages shown under ACT (Median, Below 21, 21-23, 24-26, 27-28, Above 28), SAT I Verbal Reasoning and SAT I Mathematical Reasoning (Median, Below 500, 500-599, 600-700, Above 700)
- **APPLICATION DEADLINE** (Month/Day)

Name of School	Town	Env	Deg	Ctrl	Frat	Stu	Enroll	ACT Med	ACT <21	ACT 21-23	ACT 24-26	ACT 27-28	ACT >28	SATV Med	SATV <500	SATV 500-599	SATV 600-700	SATV >700	SATM Med	SATM <500	SATM 500-599	SATM 600-700	SATM >700	Deadline
Georgetown University	Washington	U	B,M,D	Pri	No	C	6,287		1	6	14	15	64		13	34	45	8		4	20	51	25	1/10; 4/1
Howard University	Washington	U	B,M,D	Pri	F,S	C	7,579								20	75	5			20	75	5	Open
Mount Vernon College	Washington	SU	A,B,M	Pri	No	W	245	21	20	75	5													Open
Southeastern University	Washington	U	A,B,M	Pri	F		650																	Open
Strayer College	Washington	U	A,B,M	Pri	No	C	5,324																	Open
Trinity College	Washington	U	B,M	Pri	No	W	945	24						500					510					6/15
University of the District of Columbia	Washington	SU	A,B,M	Pub	F,S	C	9,985																	

Florida

Name of School	Town	Env	Deg	Ctrl	Frat	Stu	Enroll	ACT Med	ACT <21	ACT 21-23	ACT 24-26	ACT 27-28	ACT >28	SATV Med	SATV <500	SATV 500-599	SATV 600-700	SATV >700	SATM Med	SATM <500	SATM 500-599	SATM 600-700	SATM >700	Deadline
Barry University	Miami Shores	SU	B,M,D	Pri	F,S	C	4,955	20	65	17	12	5	1	425	82	15	4		465	62	30	10	1	5/1
Bethune-Cookman College	Daytona Beach	U	B	Pri	F,S	C	2,210	16	92	5	2	1		367	98	2			408	93	7			7/30
Clearwater Christian College	Clearwater	SM	A,B	Pri		C	441							433					442					Open
Eckerd College	St. Petersburg	SU	B	Pri	No	C	1,418	25	8	28	25	19	20	517	43	41	15	1	559	22	47	26	5	8/1
Edward Waters College	Jacksonville	U	B	Pri	F,S	C	850																	7/21
Embry-Riddle Aeronautical University	Daytona Beach	U	A,B,M	Pri	F,S	C	4,178	23	27	26	27	10	9	450	72	25	3		530	33	42	23	2	3/15
Flagler College	St. Augustine	SM	B	Pri	No	C	1,389	22	31	36	22	5	6	470	66	29	4	1	510	43	42	13	2	
Florida Agricultural and Mechanical University	Tallahassee	U	A,B,M,D	Pub	F,S	C	8,838	20	71	20	6	2	1	439	78	17	5		489	59	29	11	1	6/1
Florida Atlantic University	Boca Raton	SU	A,B,M,D	Pub	F,S	C	11,690	22						462	67	27	5		528	35	45	18	2	4/1
Florida Institute of Technology	Melbourne	SM	B,M,D	Pri	F,S	C	2,096							500	47	42	11		596	13	35	39	14	6/1
Florida International University	Miami	U	A,B,M,D	Pub	F,S	C	19,518	24	15	42	24	11	9	470	63	31	5		542	30	45	21	4	Open
Florida Memorial College	Miami	U	B	Pri	F,S	C	1,463																	8/1
Florida Southern College	Lakeland	SU	B,M	Pri	F,S	C	2,417	22	15	75	8	2		470	75	20	5		470	80	17	3		3/1
Florida State University	Tallahassee	SU	B,M,D	Pub	F,S	C	21,318								44	42	13	1		19	42	32	7	4/1
Jacksonville University	Jacksonville	SU	B,M	Pri	F,S	C	2,073							440					470					Open
Lynn University	Boca Raton	SU	A,B,M	Pri	F	C	1,469	21																5/1
New College of the University of South Florida	Sarasota	SU	B	Pub	No	C	536				20	22	57		3	36	46	15		3	23	47	27	8/1
Northwood University	West Palm Beach	SU	A,B	Pri	No	C	525							435	84	12	4		480	63	30	7		Open
Nova Southeastern University	Fort Lauderdale	SU	B,M,D	Pri	F,S	C	3,509	21	46	24	16	7	7	440	71	23	6		490	50	34	14	2	
Palm Beach Atlantic College	West Palm Beach	U	B,M	Pri	No	C	1,747																	Open
Ringling School of Art and Design	Sarasota	U	B	Pri	F	C	640		23	25	22	17	13		45	43	11	1		20	52	23	5	2/15
Rollins College	Winter Park	R	A,B,M	Pri	F,S	C	1,035	21	49	20	21	5	5	407	84	14	1	1	446	76	22	1	1	8/1
Saint Leo College	Saint Leo	SU	B,M	Pri		C	1,607	19	70	19	8	2	1	390	90	8	2		440	92	6	1	1	Open
Saint Thomas University	Miami	SM	B	Pri	No	C	1,147																	8/1
Southeastern College of the Assemblies of God	Lakeland	SM	B,M		F,S	C	2,045	23	23	28	23	13	13	464	57	32	10	1	533	32	40	24	3	3/1
Stetson University	Deland	U	A,B,M,D	Pub	F,S	C	20,313	23	32	31	20	9	6		67	23	6	1		36	39	17	8	3/15
University of Central Florida	Orlando	SU	B,M,D	Pub	F,S	C	27,473		12	22	28	19	18		48	37	13	1		17	38	37	8	2/1
University of Florida	Gainesville	SU	B,M,D	Pri	F,S	C	8,352		30	23	24	17	6		54	32	12	2		28	34	29	9	3/1
University of Miami	Coral Gables	U	B,M,D	Pub	F,S	C	7,869								43	43	14			43	43	14		7/1
University of North Florida	Jacksonville	SU	B,M,D	Pub	F,S	C	21,670	23	25	30	23	10	12	492	53	33	12	2	553	25	43	26	6	6/1
University of South Florida	Tampa	U	A,B,M	Pri	F,S	C	2,460							420					471					Open
University of Tampa	Tampa	SU	A,B,M	Pub	F,S	C	5,456																	6/1
University of West Florida	Pensacola	SM	A,B	Pri	F	C	437	18																Open
Webber College	Babson Park																							

Georgia

Name of School	Town	Env	Deg	Ctrl	Frat	Stu	Enroll	ACT Med	ACT <21	ACT 21-23	ACT 24-26	ACT 27-28	ACT >28	SATV Med	SATV <500	SATV 500-599	SATV 600-700	SATV >700	SATM Med	SATM <500	SATM 500-599	SATM 600-700	SATM >700	Deadline
Agnes Scott College	Decatur	U	B,M		No	PW	573							540	33	39	23	5	554	27	37	33	3	2/1
Albany State College	Albany	SM	A,B,M	Pub	F,S	C	2,939								94	6				92	8			9/1
American College for the Applied Arts	Atlanta	U	A,B	Pri	No	C	662																	Open
Armstrong State College	Savannah	U	A,B,M	Pub	S		5,187																	8/1
Atlanta College of Art	Atlanta	U	B	Pri	No	C	435																	Open
Augusta College	Augusta	U	A,B,M	Pub	F,S	C	4,760																	8/18
Berry College	Rome	R	B,M	Pri	No	C	1,675		18	25	27	17	13		54	33	13	1		31	41	24	4	2/1
Brewton-Parker College	Mt. Vernon	R	A,B	Pri	F,S	C	2,142																	Open
Clark Atlanta University	Atlanta	U	B,M,D	Pri	F,S	C	4,100	20						460	85	15			420	85	15			8/30
Clayton State College	Morrow	SU	A,B	Pub	No	C	4,760																	9/1
Columbus College	Columbus	SU	A,B,M	Pub	F,S	C	4,454							420	87	11	2		464	70	24	6		8/27
Covenant College	Lookout Mountain	SU	A,B,M	Pri	No	C	639	25	12	26	27	16	19	500	48	28	21	3	540	28	41	23	8	5/1
DeVry Institute of Technology/Atlanta	Decatur	SU	A,B	Pri	No	C	2,825																	Open
Emory University	Atlanta	SU	A,B,M,D	Pri	F,S	C	4,837	28		5	30	26	39	570	8	55	33	4	650		23	56	21	8/27
Fort Valley State College	Fort Valley	SM	A,B,M	Pub	F,S	C	2,357																	8/31
Georgia College	Milledgeville		B,M	Pub	F,S	C	4,634	19	80	12	4	4		460	83	14	3		480	55	35	10		2/1
Georgia Institute of Technology	Atlanta	U	B,M,D	Pub	F,S	C	9,182							559					673					9/1
Georgia Southern University	Statesboro	SM	A,B,M,D	Pub	F,S	C	12,411							404					446					8/10
Georgia Southwestern College	Americus	SM	A,B,M	Pub	F,S	C	2,176							424					468					9/1
Georgia State University	Atlanta	U	A,B,M,D	Pub	F,S	C	16,786	20						467	77	20	3		493	58	31	10	1	9/1
Kennesaw State College	Marietta	SU	A,B,M	Pub	F,S	C	10,994							410	90	10	1		370	75	20	5		8/1
LaGrange College	LaGrange	U	A,B,M	Pri	F,S	C	963	24						473	60	33	7	1	529	34	43	20	3	Open
Mercer University	Macon	SU	B,M,D	Pri	F		4,203																	2/15
Morehouse College	Atlanta	U	B	Pri	F	M	3,150																	8/15
Morris Brown College	Atlanta	U	B	Pri	F,S	C	1,858							437					475					9/1
North Georgia College	Dahlonega	SM	A,B,M	Pub	F,S	C	2,539	27	4	16	27	19	34	549	28	46	25	1	570	18	44	31	7	8/1
Oglethorpe University	Atlanta	U	B,M	Pri	F,S	C	1,148																	7/15
Paine College	Augusta	U	B	Pri	F,S	C	723	17						340	89	9	2		342	89	9	2		7/1
Piedmont College	Demorest	SM	B	Pri	F,S	C	704							452	81	16	3		499	71	21	8		Open
Savannah College of Art and Design	Savannah	U	B,M	Pri	No	C	2,056	21	37	22	23	15	3	470	56	29	13	2	492	47	32	19	2	8/15
Savannah State College	Savannah	SU	A,B,M	Pub	F,S	C	3,198								67	28	6		500	46	37	16		Open
Shorter College	Rome	SM	B,M	Pri	F,S	C	1,188	22	38	26	26	3	9											

TEST SCORES

Column key:
- **ENVIRONMENT:** U-Urban, R-Rural, Su-Suburban, Sm-Small Town
- **DEGREES AWARDED:** A-Associate, B-Bachelor, M-Master, D-Doctorate
- **CONTROL:** Pri-Private, Pub-Public
- **FRATERNITIES AND SORORITIES:** F-Fraternities, S-Sororities
- **STUDENTS:** C-Coed, M-Men, W-Women, PM-Primary Men, PW-Primary Women, B-Both, No-Neither

Name of School	Town	Env.	Degrees	Control	Frat./Sor.	Students	Undergrad Enroll. Fall '93	ACT Median	ACT Below 21	ACT 21-23	ACT 24-26	ACT 27-28	ACT Above 28	SAT V Median	V Below 500	V 500-599	V 600-700	V Above 700	SAT M Median	M Below 500	M 500-599	M 600-700	M Above 700	Appl. Deadline
Southern College of Technology	Marietta	SU	A,B,M	Pub	F,S	C	3,519	22	17	67	17			430	86	12	2		510	40	46	13	2	8/31
Spelman College	Atlanta	U	B	Pri	S	W	2,075	23						490					520					2/1
Thomas College	Thomasville	SU	A,B	Pri	No	C	601							360	89	11			390	85	15			Open
Toccoa Falls College	Toccoa Falls	SM	A,B	Pri	No	C	873	21	49	27	12	9	3	433	71	24	5		450	70	22	8		Open
University of Georgia	Athens	SM	A,B,M,D	Pub	F,S	C	22,301							540	45	39	14	2	570	16	47	29	8	2/1
Valdosta State University	Valdosta	SM	A,B,M	Pub	F,S	C	7,400							396					434					2/1
Wesleyan College	Macon	SU	B	Pri	No	W	456							510	40	28	26	6	480	56	25	18	1	3/1
West Georgia College	Carrollton	SU	A,B,M	Pub	F,S	C	5,727	20	62	23	11	3	1	400	89	9	2		450	77	17	5		9/1
Women's College of Brenau University	Gainesville	SM	B,M	Pri	S	PW	1,396																	Open

Guam

Name of School	Town	Env.	Degrees	Control	Frat./Sor.	Students	Undergrad Enroll. Fall '93	Appl. Deadline
University of Guam	Mangilao	R	A,B,M	Pub	No	C	3,327	8/4

Hawaii

Name of School	Town	Env.	Degrees	Control	Frat./Sor.	Students	Undergrad Enroll. Fall '93	ACT Median	ACT Below 21	ACT 21-23	ACT 24-26	ACT 27-28	ACT Above 28	SAT V Median	V Below 500	V 500-599	V 600-700	V Above 700	SAT M Median	M Below 500	M 500-599	M 600-700	M Above 700	Appl. Deadline
Brigham Young University/Hawaii	Oahu	SM	A,B	Pri	No	C	2,028	21	13	42	32	11	2											3/31
Chaminade University of Honolulu	Honolulu	SU	A,B,M	Pri	No	C	1,920	19						440					480					8/1
Hawaii Pacific University	Honolulu	U	A,B,M	Pri	No	C	6,140	23						479	70	20	10		525	60	35	5		Open
University of Hawaii at Hilo	Hilo	SM	B	Pub	No	C	2,953							401	85	12	3	1	473	58	29	11	2	5/15
University of Hawaii at Manoa	Honolulu	U	B,M,D	Pub	F,S	C	13,226							440	75	20	5		540	34	38	24	4	5/1

Idaho

Name of School	Town	Env.	Degrees	Control	Frat./Sor.	Students	Undergrad Enroll. Fall '93	ACT Median	ACT Below 21	ACT 21-23	ACT 24-26	ACT 27-28	ACT Above 28	SAT V Median	V Below 500	V 500-599	V 600-700	V Above 700	SAT M Median	M Below 500	M 500-599	M 600-700	M Above 700	Appl. Deadline
Albertson College	Caldwell	SM	B,M	Pri	F,S	C	719	24	27	25	19	14	14	487	56	28	15	1	524	39	38	16	7	Open
Boise State University	Boise	U	A,B,M,D	Pub	F,S	C	12,997	21	52	26	14	5	3	435	77	19	4		474	60	28	11	1	7/27
Idaho State University	Pocatello	SM	A,B,M,D	Pub	F,S	C	9,011	18	53	25	15	5	2											Open
Lewis-Clark State College	Lewiston	U	A,B	Pub	No	C	3,226	20	62	21	10	5	2											Open
Northwest Nazarene College	Nampa	SM	A,B,M			C	1,229	24	40	25	11													9/15
University of Idaho	Moscow	SM	B,M,D	Pub	F,S	C	8,673	23	22	34	29	11	5	460	66	26	7	1	520	42	33	20	5	8/1

Illinois

Name of School	Town	Env.	Degrees	Control	Frat./Sor.	Students	Undergrad Enroll. Fall '93	ACT Median	ACT Below 21	ACT 21-23	ACT 24-26	ACT 27-28	ACT Above 28	SAT V Median	V Below 500	V 500-599	V 600-700	V Above 700	SAT M Median	M Below 500	M 500-599	M 600-700	M Above 700	Appl. Deadline
Augustana College	Rock Island	U	B	Pri	F,S	C	2,080	25	14	27	27	15	17											Open
Aurora University	Aurora	SU	B,M	Pri	F,S	C	1,493	21																Open
Barat College	Lake Forest	SU	B	Pri	No	C	710							488	70	30			495	66	34			Open
Blackburn College	Carlinville	R	B	Pri	No	C	499	21	56	20	16	5	3											Open
Bradley University	Peoria	U	B,M	Pri	F,S	C	5,174	25	15	42	36	7		530	36	38	22	4	590	13	38	34	15	8/20
Chicago State University	Chicago	U	B,M	Pub	F,S	C	7,235	17	91	8	1													6/1
College of Saint Francis	Joliet	SU	B,M	Pri	No	C	1,073	23	31	29	24	8	8											Open
Columbia College	Chicago	U	B,M	Pri	No	C	6,843																	6/1
Concordia University	River Forest	SU	B,M	Pri	No	C	1,313	23	33	23	23	12	9											Open
DePaul University	Chicago	U	B,M,D	Pri	F,S	C	9,783	25	18	32	24	12	14											Open
DeVry Institute of Technology/Addison (DuPage County)	Addison	SU	A,B	Pri	No	C	2,779							520	49	39	10	1	560	34	37	22	6	8/15
DeVry Institute of Technology/Chicago	Chicago	U	A,B	Pri	No	C	3,025																	Open
East-West University	Chicago	U	A,B	Pri	No	C	281																	Open
Eastern Illinois University	Charleston	SM	B,M	Pub	F,S	C	10,006	21	39	36	18	5	2											Open
Elmhurst College	Elmhurst	SU	B	Pri	F,S	C	2,687		51	23	15	5	2											8/15
Eureka College	Eureka	SM	B	Pri	F,S	C	524		26	40	15	15	4											Open
Greenville College	Greenville	SM	B	Pri	No	C	830	22	40	25	22	8	5											Open
Illinois Benedictine College	Lisle	SU	B,M	Pri	No	C	1,670	23	34	23	25	9		500	46	29	22	2	530	32	37	27	2	Open
Illinois College	Jacksonville	R	B	Pri	F,S	C	937	23	24	35	21	13	7	470	53	35	8	4	545	42	15	27	16	8/15
Illinois Institute of Technology	Chicago	U	B,M,D	Pri	F,S	C	2,537	25	16	22	27	23	12	510	41	44	13	2	610	10	32	39	19	3/15
Illinois State University	Normal	SM	B,M,D	Pub	F,S	C	17,404	22	33	34	22	7	4											Open
Illinois Wesleyan University	Bloomington	SU	B	Pri	F,S	C	1,841	28		7	26	28	39	534	34	36	28	2	617	7	32	41	20	3/1
Judson College	Elgin	SU	B	Pri	No	C	602	21	47	26	24	2												3/1
Kendall College	Evanston	U	A,B	Pri	No	C	560																	Open
Knox College	Galesburg	SM	B	Pri	F,S	C	991		7	19	26	24	24		31	43	22	4		23	28	37	12	
Lake Forest College	Lake Forest	SU	B,M	Pri	F,S	C	1,004	25	16	23	30	17	14	510	46	36	16	2	530	40	36	19	5	2/15
Lewis University	Romeoville	SU	A,B,M	Pri	F,S	C	3,614																	3/1
Loyola University of Chicago	Chicago	U	B,M,D	Pri	F,S	C	8,661	24	17	32	29	13	9	480	55	33	11	1	520	37	40	21	2	7/13
MacMurray College	Jacksonville	SM	A,B	Pri	F	C	691	20	61	18	12	5	4											7/15
McKendree College	Lebanon	SM	A,B	Pri	F,S	C	1,450	21	51	26	13	4	6											Open
Millikin University	Decatur	SU	B	Pri	F,S	C	1,883	23	16	36	21	16	11	500					530					Open
Monmouth College	Monmouth	SM	B	Pri	F,S	C	677	24	18	21	43	10		500					530					Open
NAES College	Chicago	U	B	Pri	No	C	88																	Open
National-Louis University	Evanston	SU	B,M,D	Pri	S	C	3,013		91	9														Open
North Central College	Naperville	SU	B,M	Pri	No	C	2,076	24	20	22	24	22	12	483	51	37	12		556	25	34	25	7	Open
North Park College	Chicago	U	B,M,D	Pri	No	C	1,034	21	47	21	15	9	8	465	66	26			535	43	21	31	5	8/1
Northeastern Illinois University	Chicago	U	B,M	Pub	F,S	C	7,454		52	42	3	1												8/1
Northern Illinois University	DeKalb	SM	B,M,D	Pub	F,S	C	16,805	22	28	39	26	9	5											8/1
Northwestern University	Evanston	SU	B,M,D	Pri	F,S	C	7,496	29		4	14	21	61	600	13	43	38	6	670	5	18	44	33	1/1
Olivet Nazarene University	Kankakee	SM	A,B,M	Pri	No	C	1,915	22																8/1
Principia College	Elsah	R	B	Pri	No	C	546							496	60	25	17	1	548	26	36	27	8	8/1
Quincy University	Quincy	SM	A,B	Pri	No	C	1,154	23	16	15	37	20	12		24	60	15	1		8	64	24	4	8/1
Rockford College	Rockford	SU	A,B,M	Pri	No	C	1,262	21	21	55	24			500	88	5	7		536	59	29	12		Open
Roosevelt University	Chicago	U	B,M,D	Pri	No	C	4,596	20	68	18	5	7	9	440	71	29			440	57	43			Open
Rosary College	River Forest	SU	B,M	Pri	No	C	891	22	47	21	20	7	3											Open
Saint Xavier University	Chicago	U	B,M	Pri	No	C	2,396																	8/15

| | | | | | | | | TEST SCORES | | | | | | | | | | | | | | | | |
| | | | | | | | | ACT | | | | | | SAT I VERBAL REASONING | | | | | SAT I MATHEMATICAL REASONING | | | | | APPLICATION DEADLINE |
NAME OF SCHOOL	TOWN	ENVIRONMENT	DEGREES AWARDED	CONTROL	FRATERNITIES AND SORORITIES	STUDENTS	UNDERGRADUATE ENROLLMENT FALL '93	Median	Below 21	21-23	24-26	27-28	Above 28	Median	Below 500	500-599	600-700	Above 700	Median	Below 500	500-599	600-700	Above 700	Month/Day
School of the Art Institute of Chicago	Chicago	U	B,M	Pri	No	C	1,370																	8/15
Shimer College	Waukegan	SU	B	Pri	No	C	119																	8/1
Southern Illinois University at Carbondale	Carbondale	SM	A,B,M,D	Pub	F,S	C	19,402	22	39	35	16	9	1											Open
Southern Illinois University at Edwardsville	Edwardsville	R	B,M	Pub	F,S	C	8,613	21	50	26	15	6	3											8/1
Trinity Christian College	Palos Heights	SU	B	Pri	No	C	608	22																8/15
Trinity College	Deerfield	SU	B	Pri	No	C	739	22	37	33	25	5	3											Open
University of Chicago	Chicago	U	B,M,D	Pri	F,S	C	3,417			2	9	45	44		9	23	49	19		2	13	38	47	1/15
University of Illinois at Chicago	Chicago	U	B,M,D	Pub	F,S	C	16,434	21	49	28	15	5	3											2/28
University of Illinois at Urbana-Champaign	Urbana	SM	B,M,D	Pub	F,S	C	26,333		5	12	29	32	22											1/1
VanderCook College of Music	Chicago	U	B,M	Pri	F,S	C	52	20																6/1
West Suburban College of Nursing	Oak Park	SU	B	Pri	No	C	238	23																Open
Western Illinois University	Macomb	R	B,M	Pub	F,S	C	10,464	22	54	28	12	4	2											8/10
Wheaton College	Wheaton	SU	B,M,D	Pri	No	C	2,256		1	11	25	22	39		20	41	32	5		5	36	41	17	2/15

Indiana

NAME OF SCHOOL	TOWN	ENVIRONMENT	DEGREES AWARDED	CONTROL	FRATERNITIES AND SORORITIES	STUDENTS	UNDERGRADUATE ENROLLMENT FALL '93	ACT Median	ACT Below 21	ACT 21-23	ACT 24-26	ACT 27-28	ACT Above 28	SATV Median	SATV Below 500	SATV 500-599	SATV 600-700	SATV Above 700	SATM Median	SATM Below 500	SATM 500-599	SATM 600-700	SATM Above 700	App
Anderson University	Anderson	SU	A,B,M	Pri	No	C	2,101	21	47	26	15	7	5	423	77	19	4		462	62	27	10	1	Open
Ball State University	Muncie	U	A,B,M,D	Pub	F,S	C	18,355	21	49	21	16	8	6	422	81	16	2	1	473	61	28	10	1	3/1
Bethel College	Mishawaka	SU	A,B,M	Pri	No	C	1,135	22	44	20	16	8	12	453					490					Open
Butler University	Indianapolis	SU	B,M	Pri	F,S	C	2,739	25	14	25	29	16	16		54	35	9	2		30	40	26	4	8/1
Calumet College of St. Joseph	Whiting	U	A,B	Pri	No	C	1,097																	2/15
DePauw University	Greencastle	SM	B	Pri	F,S	C	1,983		5	20	31	22	22	540	40	39	20	1	560	18	36	36	10	2/15
Earlham College	Richmond	SU	B	Pri	No	C	1,041	26	13	17	22	29	19	481	32	40	24	4	532	25	38	29	8	Open
Franklin College of Indiana	Franklin	SM	A,B	Pri	F,S	C	908	22						487	55	35	10	1	519	45	32	16	7	8/15
Goshen College	Goshen	SM	B	Pri	No	C	1,122							487										8/1
Grace College	Winona Lake	R	A,B	Pri	No	C	731	22																3/15
Hanover College	Hanover	R	B	Pri	F,S	C	1,062	25	5	20	53	19	3	505	41	50	1		535	36	54	8	2	Open
Huntington College	Huntington	SM	A,B,M	Pri	F,S	C	531	21	61	31	5	2	1	450	65	34	1		450	59	38	2	1	Open
Indiana Institute of Technology	Fort Wayne	U	A,B	Pri	F,S	C	1,079							446					491					8/15
Indiana State University	Terre Haute	U	A,B,M,D	Pub	F,S	C	10,548																	
Indiana University at Kokomo	Kokomo	SM	A,B,M	Pub		C		24						466	63	29	7	1	530	35	39	22	5	2/15
Indiana University Bloomington	Bloomington	SM	A,B,M,D	Pub	F,S	C	26,243							374	94	5	1		411	79	16	5		8/11
Indiana University East	Richmond	SM	A,B	Pub	F	C	2,376	19	66	25	5	4												7/15
Indiana University Northwest	Gary	U	A,B,M	Pub	F,S	C	4,865							406					457					
Indiana University-Purdue University at Fort Wayne	Fort Wayne	SU	A,B,M	Pub	F,S	C	11,701							406					457					8/1
Indiana University-Purdue University at Indianapolis	Indianapolis	U	A,B,M,D	Pub	F,S	C	20,392	19	68	20	8	3	1	380	89	9	2		420	75	19	5	1	6/1
Indiana University/South Bend	South Bend	SU	A,B,M	Pub	F	C	6,106							420	88	11	1		437	74	19	6	1	7/1
Indiana University Southeast	New Albany	SU	A,B,M	Pub	F	C	5,478							390					420					Open
Indiana Wesleyan University	Marion	SU	A,B,M	Pri	No	C		21						408					455					Open
Manchester College	North Manchester	SM	A,B,M	Pri	No	C	983	22	45	25	19	7	5	432	74	20	5	1	512	45	37	17	1	Open
Marian College	Indianapolis	U	A,B	Pri	No	C	1,350							420	87	10	3		466	65	25	9	1	Open
Martin University	Indianapolis	U	B,M	Pri	No	C	700							370					370	85	11	4		Open
Oakland City College	Oakland City	SM	A,B,M	Pri	No	C	888	20	67	21	5	3	4	370	77	17	6		425					Open
Purdue University/Calumet	Hammond	U	A,B,M	Pub	No	C	8,570							450					545	31	36	27	7	Open
Purdue University/West Lafayette	West Lafayette	SU	A,B,M,D	Pub	F,S	C	28,464	24	17	25	29	14	14	453	69	25	6		545	31	36	27	7	3/1
Rose-Hulman Institute of Technology	Terre Haute	SU	B,M	Pri	F	M	1,300					5	95	540	31	47	18	4	670	19	47	34		8
Saint Francis College	Fort Wayne	SU	A,B,M	Pri	S	C	760	21	34	44	12	9		400	93	7			450	64	32	4		Open
Saint Joseph's College	Rensselaer	SM	A,B,M	Pri	No	W	1,042	23	9	50	34	7		432	83	15	1		500	59	28	11	1	Open
Saint Mary-of-the-Woods College	St. Mary-of-the-Woods	R	A,B,M	Pri	No	W	1,050							489	54	39	6		538	28	45	26	1	3/1
Saint Mary's College	Notre Dame	SU	B	Pri		W	1,565	25	8	23	38	19	12											7/1
Saint Meinrad College	St. Meinrad	R	B	Pri	No	M	134		46	36	4	11	4	546	27	38	31		556	28	37	29	6	Open
Taylor University	Upland	R	A,B	Pri	No	C	1,849	25						410	84	13	3		510	42	36	19	3	Open
Tri-State University	Angola	R	A,B	Pri	F,S	C	1,074	22	43	27	20	8	2	498	48	37	14	1	538	29	44	24	3	2/15
University of Evansville	Evansville	U	A,B,M	Pri	F,S	C	2,898	25	13	25	28	18	16	432					487					
University of Indianapolis	Indianapolis	SU	A,B,M	Pri	No	C	3,060	21						580	13	48	34	5	670	3	19	48	30	1/6
University of Notre Dame	Notre Dame	SU	B,M,D	Pri	F,S	C	7,600							392	98	8	3		436	75	20	5		Open
University of Southern Indiana	Evansville	SU	A,B,M	Pub	F,S	C	6,765	17							43	36	19	3		17	33	35	15	Open
Valparaiso University	Valparaiso	SM	A,B,M,D	Pri	F,S	M	2,738		3	18	29	20	30	510	40	38	20	2	600	15	35	36	14	3/1
Wabash College	Crawfordsville	SM	B		F	M	809																	

Iowa

NAME OF SCHOOL	TOWN	ENVIRONMENT	DEGREES AWARDED	CONTROL	FRATERNITIES AND SORORITIES	STUDENTS	UNDERGRADUATE ENROLLMENT FALL '93	ACT Median	ACT Below 21	ACT 21-23	ACT 24-26	ACT 27-28	ACT Above 28	SATV Median	SATV Below 500	SATV 500-599	SATV 600-700	SATV Above 700	SATM Median	SATM Below 500	SATM 500-599	SATM 600-700	SATM Above 700	App
Briar Cliff College	Sioux City	SU	A,B	Pri	No	C	1,168	22	35	29	23	6	7	385	83		17		410	83		17		9/1
Buena Vista College	Storm Lake	SM	B	Pri	F,S	C	1,023	24	10	34	26	18	12	515	35	61	3	1	585	28	64	8		5/1
Central College	Pella	SU	B	Pri	F,S	C	1,395		21	24	28	15	12											7/1
Clarke College	Dubuque	U	A,B,M	Pri	No	C	954	24	23	31	27	11	8											Open
Coe College	Cedar Rapids	U	B,M	Pri	F,S	C	1,332	25	15	29	30	13	13	520	48	38	14		560	29	36	27	8	3/1
Cornell College	Mount Vernon	SM	B	Pri	F,S	C	1,150	25	10	17	34	18	21	520	40	35	21	4	560	25	45	22	8	8/15
Dordt College	Sioux Center	R	A,B	Pri	No	C	1,160	23	20	31	21	9							550					3/1
Drake University	Des Moines	SU	B,M,D	Pri	F,S	C	4,260	25	12	22	28	17	21	490					502	50	32	16	2	8/15
Graceland College	Lamoni	SM	B	Pri	No	C	1,105	22	43	39	14	4		447	68	23	9							8/15
Grand View College	Des Moines	SU	A,B	Pri	No	C	1,383		35	40	15	5												2/1
Grinnell College	Grinnell	SM	B	Pri	No	C	1,322	29	1	5	14	23	53	600	8	36	46	10	650	4	21	52	23	8/19
Iowa State University	Ames	SU	B,M,D	Pub	F,S	C	20,629		17	26	30	13	14			64	24	11	1		35	29	24	12	Open
Iowa Wesleyan College	Mount Pleasant	SM	B	Pri	F,S	C	928	21																Open
Loras College	Dubuque	U	A,B,M	Pri	No	C	1,914	22																Open
Luther College	Decorah	SM	B	Pri	F,S	C	2,354	25	8	25	28	22	17	520	36	43	19	2	590	14	37	36	13	3/1

TEST SCORES

Legend — ENVIRONMENT: U-Urban, R-Rural, Su-Suburban, Sm-Small Town · DEGREES AWARDED: A-Associate, B-Bachelor, M-Master, D-Doctorate · CONTROL: Pri-Private, Pub-Public · FRATERNITIES AND SORORITIES: F-Fraternities, S-Sororities, B-Both, No-Neither · STUDENTS: C-Coed, M-Men, W-Women, PM-Primarily Men, PW-Primarily Women · APPLICATION DEADLINE: Month/Day

Name of School	Town	Env	Degrees	Control	Frat/Sor	Students	Undergrad Enroll Fall '93	ACT Med	ACT Below 21	ACT 21-23	ACT 24-26	ACT 27-28	ACT Above 28	SAT V Med	SAT V Below 500	SAT V 500-599	SAT V 600-700	SAT V Above 700	SAT M Med	SAT M Below 500	SAT M 500-599	SAT M 600-700	SAT M Above 700	App Deadline
Maharishi International University	Fairfield	SM	A,B,M,D	Pri	No	C	378																	
Morningside College	Sioux City	SU	A,B,M	Pri		C	1,180	22	34	32	20	8	7											Open
Mount Mercy College	Cedar Rapids	U	B	Pri	No	C	1,349	22	31	33	22	6	1											Open
Mount Saint Clare College	Clinton	SM	A,B	Pri	No	C	459	20	60	20	13	8	6											8/15
Northwestern College of Iowa	Orange City	SM	A,B,M	Pri	No	C	1,092	20	34	24	24	11	7											Open
Saint Ambrose University	Davenport	U	B,M	Pri	No	C	1,739	22																8/15
Simpson College	Indianola	SU	B	Pri	F,S	C	1,718	24	13	33	30	12	12											Open
Teikyo Marycrest University	Davenport	U	A,B,M	Pri	No	C	1,078	23																Open
Teikyo Westmar University	Le Mars	SM	B	Pri	No	C	757		53	28	14	4	1											Open
University of Dubuque	Dubuque	SU	A,B,M	Pri	F,S	C	793	21	34	32	28	5	1	410	86	14			500	45	50	5		Open
University of Iowa	Iowa City	U	B,M,D	Pub	F,S	C	18,290		13	28	30	14	15											8/1
University of Northern Iowa	Cedar Falls	SM	B,M,D	Pub	F,S	C	11,467	23	25	33	25	10	7											5/15
Upper Iowa University	Fayette	R	B	Pri	F,S	C	586	20	48	26	14	8	4											8/15
Wartburg College	Waverly	SM	B	Pri	No	C	1,400	24	21	24	25	15	14	430	54	44	2		400	61	37	2		8/1
William Penn College	Oskaloosa	R	B	Pri	F,S	C	693	19							50	39	11			25	28	36	11	8/1
																								8/15

Kansas

Name of School	Town	Env	Degrees	Control	Frat/Sor	Students	Undergrad Enroll Fall '93	ACT Med	ACT Below 21	ACT 21-23	ACT 24-26	ACT 27-28	ACT Above 28	SAT V Med	SAT V Below 500	SAT V 500-599	SAT V 600-700	SAT V Above 700	SAT M Med	SAT M Below 500	SAT M 500-599	SAT M 600-700	SAT M Above 700	App Deadline
Baker University	Baldwin City	R	B	Pri	F,S	C	859	22	29	31	25	7	8											Open
Benedictine College	Atchison	SM	A,B,M	Pri	No	C	1,246	22	36	27	19	9	9											8/1
Bethany College	Lindsborg	SM	B	Pri	F,S	C	774	23	34	25	22	12	7	435	70	29	1		560	50	35	13	1	7/1
Bethel College	North Newton	SU	B	Pri	No	C	638	22	9	30	33	18	10											8/15
Emporia State University	Emporia	SM	B,M,D	Pub	F,S	C	4,545	20	57	25	12	4	2											Open
Fort Hays State University	Hays	SM	A,B,M	Pub	F,S	C	4,318	21																Open
Friends University	Wichita	U	A,B,M	Pri	F,S	C	960	21																8/10
Kansas Newman College	Wichita	U	A,B,M	Pri	No	C	1,813	21	45	29	17	2	6	442										Open
Kansas State University	Manhattan	SU	A,B,M,D	Pub	F,S	C	17,160	22	34	24	21	10	11						498					Open
Kansas Wesleyan University	Salina	SM	A,B	Pri	F,S	C	732	21	50	31	12	6	1											Open
McPherson College	McPherson	SM	A,B	Pri	No	C	426		43	23	19	12	3											8/1
MidAmerica Nazarene College	Olathe	SU	A,B,M	Pri	No	C	1,476																	
Ottawa University	Ottawa	SM	B	Pri	No	C	574	21	45	32	19	3	1											Open
Pittsburg State University	Pittsburg	SM	A,B,M	Pub	F,S	C	5,202	20	63	15	7	3	5											Open
Saint Mary College	Leavenworth	SM	A,B	Pri	No	C	854	21	24	34	11	9												Open
Southwestern College	Winfield	SM	B,M	Pri	F,S	C	577	21	45	20	21	10	3	390	86	14			444	57	29	14		Open
Sterling College	Sterling	R	A,B	Pri	No	C	517	22																8/1
Tabor College	Hillsboro	R	A,B	Pri	No	C	448	23	40	20	18	15	7											2/15
University of Kansas	Lawrence	SM	B,M,D	Pub	F,S	C	19,553	23	27	26	24	11	12											8/15
Washburn University of Topeka	Topeka	U	B,M,D	Pub	F,S	C	5,862	20																2/1
Wichita State University	Wichita	U	A,B,M,D	Pub	F,S	C	12,015	21																7/1
																								Open

Kentucky

Name of School	Town	Env	Degrees	Control	Frat/Sor	Students	Undergrad Enroll Fall '93	ACT Med	ACT Below 21	ACT 21-23	ACT 24-26	ACT 27-28	ACT Above 28	SAT V Med	SAT V Below 500	SAT V 500-599	SAT V 600-700	SAT V Above 700	SAT M Med	SAT M Below 500	SAT M 500-599	SAT M 600-700	SAT M Above 700	App Deadline
Alice Lloyd College	Pippa Passes	R	A,B	Pri	No	C	617	21	29	31	19	12	10											
Asbury College	Wilmore	R	B		No	C	1,157	24	20	34	31	8	7											Open
Bellarmine College	Louisville	SU	B,M	Pri	F		1,803	23	25	28	23	13	11	480	59	29	12		530	37	42	18	3	8/1
Berea College	Berea	SM	B	Pri	No	C	1,591	22						465	63	29	8		514	43	34	21	2	8/15
Brescia College	Owensboro	U	A,B,M	Pri	No	C	701		36	32	19	11	3											Open
Campbellsville College	Campbellsville	SM	A,B,M	Pri	No	C	1,119	21						420					450					Open
Centre College	Danville	SM	B	Pri	F,S	C	956	27	4	16	28	25	27	534					575					8/1
Cumberland College	Williamsburg	SM	B,M	Pri	No	C	1,428	21	50	24	17	6	3	420	83	17	1		470	68	27	5		3/1
Eastern Kentucky University	Richmond	SM	A,B,M	Pub	F,S	C	4,700	19	68	19	7	4	2											Open
Georgetown College	Georgetown	SM	B,M	Pri	F,S	C	1,111		36	31	19	7	7											Open
Kentucky Christian College	Grayson	R	A,B	Pri	No	C	476	20	56	19	12	8	5	390	75	25			450	63	31	6		Open
Kentucky State University	Frankfort	SM	A,B,M		F,S	C	2,414		81	12	1	1												8/1
Kentucky Wesleyan College	Owensboro	SU	A,B	Pri	F,S	C	783	22	29	30	29	5	7	425	77	19	4		470	59	33	8		4/15
Lindsey Wilson College	Columbia	SM	A,B	Pri	No	C	1,168	18	40	39	10	10	1											Open
Morehead State University	Morehead	SM	A,B,M	Pub	F,S	C	7,532	19	66	20	9	3	1											Open
Murray State University	Murray	SM	A,B,M	Pub	F,S	C	6,972	22	43	28	19	7	3											Open
Northern Kentucky University	Highland Heights	SU	A,B,M	Pub	F,S	C	10,285	19	60	25	11	3	1											8/1
Pikeville College	Pikeville	SM	A,B	Pri	No	C	950	20	31	50	11	5	3											Open
Spalding University	Louisville	U	A,B,M	Pri	No	C	852	19	67	19	5	5												9/1
Thomas More College	Crestview Hills	SU	A,B	Pri	F	C	1,299																	8/15
Transylvania University	Lexington	U	B	Pri	F,S	C	918	26	9	18	25	16	32	530	41	31	22	6	560	28	32	29	11	8/15
Union College	Barbourville	SM	A,B,M	Pri	No	C	723	20	47	29	17	6	1	420	87	9	4		460	75	17	8		3/15
University of Kentucky	Lexington	SU	B,M,D	Pub	F,S	C	4,220	25																7/15
University of Louisville	Louisville	U	A,B,M,D	Pub	F,S	C	21,864	25																6/1
Western Kentucky University	Bowling Green	SU	A,B,M	Pub	F,S	C	13,711	21	51	26	13	6	4											Open
																								8/1

Louisiana

Name of School	Town	Env	Degrees	Control	Frat/Sor	Students	Undergrad Enroll Fall '93	ACT Med	ACT Below 21	ACT 21-23	ACT 24-26	ACT 27-28	ACT Above 28	SAT V Med	SAT V Below 500	SAT V 500-599	SAT V 600-700	SAT V Above 700	SAT M Med	SAT M Below 500	SAT M 500-599	SAT M 600-700	SAT M Above 700	App Deadline
Centenary College of Louisiana	Shreveport	SU	B,M	Pri	F,S	C	819	25	15	31	20	18	16	500	47	37	14	2	550	32	34	33	1	2/15
Dillard University	New Orleans	U	B	Pri	F,S	C	1,584	20																7/1
Grambling State University	Grambling	SM	A,B,M,D	Pub	F,S	C	8,162	16	95	3	1	1												7/15
Louisiana College	Pineville	SM	A,B	Pri	F,S	C	1,070	22	35	27	22	10	6											7/15
Louisiana State University and Agricultural and Mechanical College	Baton Rouge	U	B,M,D	Pub	F,S	C	20,040	23	27	26	23	12	11											9/6
Louisiana State University in Shreveport	Shreveport	U	B,M	Pub	F,S	C	3,890	20																6/1
Louisiana Tech University	Ruston	SM	A,B,M,D	Pub	F,S	C	8,585		39	26	18	9	8											7/15
Loyola University/New Orleans	New Orleans	U	B,M	Pri	F,S	C	3,501	25		37	32	16	15											7/15
McNeese State University	Lake Charles	SU	A,B,M	Pub	F,S	C	7,347	19						510	47	36	16	1	540	32	43	21	4	8/1
																								7/1

NAME OF SCHOOL	TOWN	ENVIRONMENT	DEGREES AWARDED	CONTROL	FRAT/SOR	STUDENTS	UNDERGRAD ENROLL FALL '93	ACT Median	ACT Below 21	ACT 21-23	ACT 24-26	ACT 27-28	ACT Above 28	SAT I VERBAL Median	SAT V Below 500	SAT V 500-599	SAT V 600-700	SAT V Above 700	SAT I MATH Median	SAT M Below 500	SAT M 500-599	SAT M 600-700	SAT M Above 700	APPLICATION DEADLINE
Nicholls State University	Thibodaux	SM	A,B,M	Pub	F,S	C	6,259	18	69	18	10	3	1											8/27
Northeast Louisiana University	Monroe	U	A,B,M,D	Pub	F,S	C	10,425	19	70	17	9	3	1											Open
Northwestern State University of Louisiana	Natchitoches	SM	A,B,M	Pub	F,S	C	7,711	19																8/12
Our Lady of Holy Cross College	New Orleans	U	A,B,M	Pri	No	C	1,146																	7/15
Southeastern Louisiana University	Hammond	SM	A,B,M	Pub	F,S	C	11,973	19																7/1
Southern University and A&M College	Baton Rouge	SU	A,B,M,D	Pub	F,S	C	8,550																	7/1
Southern University at New Orleans	New Orleans	SU	A,B,M	Pub	F,S	C								556	28	40	26	6	612	8	35	40	17	1/15
Tulane University	New Orleans	U	A,B,M,D	Pri	F,S	C	6,475																	7/1
University of New Orleans	New Orleans	U	A,B,M,D	Pub	F,S	C	11,801	21	51	28	13	5	3											Open
University of Southwestern Louisiana	Lafayette	U	A,B,M,D	Pub	F,S	C	15,157	20	50	19	19	12		445	74	22	4		480	59	31	10		3/1
Xavier University of Louisiana	New Orleans	U	B,M,D	Pri	F,S	C	2,978																	3/1

Maine

NAME OF SCHOOL	TOWN	ENVIRONMENT	DEGREES AWARDED	CONTROL	FRAT/SOR	STUDENTS	UNDERGRAD ENROLL FALL '93	ACT Median	ACT Below 21	ACT 21-23	ACT 24-26	ACT 27-28	ACT Above 28	SAT I VERBAL Median	SAT V Below 500	SAT V 500-599	SAT V 600-700	SAT V Above 700	SAT I MATH Median	SAT M Below 500	SAT M 500-599	SAT M 600-700	SAT M Above 700	APPLICATION DEADLINE
Bates College	Lewiston	SU	B	Pri	No	C	1,550							590	4	52	40	4	640	1	24	56	19	2/1
Bowdoin College	Brunswick	SM	B	Pri	F	C	1,498							570	14	47	36	3	640	5	27	44	24	1/15
Colby College	Waterville	SM	B	Pri	No	C	1,755	27	3	8	29	29	31	580	10	50	37	3	620					1/15
College of the Atlantic	Bar Harbor	SM	B,M	Pri	No	C	224							563	11	60	29		560	22	47	22	9	3/1
Husson College	Bangor	U	A,B,M	Pri	F,S	C	1,621							383	94	6			435	73	22	5		Open
Maine College of Art	Portland	U	B	Pri	No	C	330							460	66	28	3	3	450	72	16	7	4	7/1
Maine Maritime Academy	Castine	R	A,B,M	Pub	F	C	690							440					510					6/1
Saint Joseph's College	Windham	R	A,B,M	Pri	F,S	C	889							425	83	16	1		475	66	28	6		Open
Thomas College	Waterville	R	A,B	Pri	No	C	139							370					460					Open
Unity College	Unity	R	A,B	Pri	No	C	470																	2/1
University of Maine	Orono	SM	A,B,M,D	Pub	F,S	C	9,161							464	69	25	5	1	525	38	40	18	4	
University of Maine at Augusta	Augusta	SM	A,B	Pub	F	C	5,080							437					475					4/15
University of Maine at Farmington	Farmington	SM	B	Pub	No	C	2,250							430	68	27	5		390	90	10			8/15
University of Maine at Fort Kent	Fort Kent	SM	A,B	Pub	F,S	C	629							440					470					Open
University of Maine at Machias	Machias	R	A,B	Pub	F,S	C	950																	8/15
University of Maine at Presque Isle	Presque Isle	R	A,B,M	Pub	F,S	C	1,454							430	80	17	3		470	62	29	9		Open
University of New England	Biddeford	R	A,B,M,D	Pri	No	C	845							440	76	19	4	1	500	47	41	11	1	7/15
University of Southern Maine	Gorham	SM	A,B,M	Pub	F,S	C	7,813							406					438					Open
Westbrook College	Portland	SU	A,B	Pri	No	C	354																	

Maryland

NAME OF SCHOOL	TOWN	ENVIRONMENT	DEGREES AWARDED	CONTROL	FRAT/SOR	STUDENTS	UNDERGRAD ENROLL FALL '93	ACT Median	ACT Below 21	ACT 21-23	ACT 24-26	ACT 27-28	ACT Above 28	SAT I VERBAL Median	SAT V Below 500	SAT V 500-599	SAT V 600-700	SAT V Above 700	SAT I MATH Median	SAT M Below 500	SAT M 500-599	SAT M 600-700	SAT M Above 700	APPLICATION DEADLINE
Bowie State University	Bowie	SU	B,M	Pub	F,S	C	3,268							357					384					4/1
Capitol College	Laurel	R	A,B,M	Pri	No	C	613																	2/15
College of Notre Dame of Maryland	Baltimore	SU	B,M	Pri	No	PW	2,650								65	24	10	1		50	32	17	1	8/1
Columbia Union College	Takoma Park	SU	A,B	Pri	No	C	980	23	38	17	32	10	3	410	81	18	1		420	78	15	6	1	7/15
Coppin State College	Baltimore	U	B,M	Pub	No	C	2,300							376					406					Open
Frostburg State University	Frostburg	SM	B,M	Pub	F,S	C	4,620	23						540	48	33	15	4	570	32	41	18	9	2/1
Goucher College	Baltimore	SU	B,M	Pri	No	C	933								53	37	10			41	39	19	1	3/15
Hood College	Frederick	U	B,M	Pri	No	W	1,109		19	26	19	16	19	610	8	32	52	7	700	1	10	46	44	1/1
Johns Hopkins University	Baltimore	U	B,M,D	Pri	F,S	C	3,371	30	1	3	8	29	59	507	47	39	13	1	563	20	46	28	7	2/1
Loyola College	Baltimore	SU	B,M,D	Pri	No	C	3,247																	3/1
Maryland Institute, College of Art	Baltimore	U	B,M	Pri	No	C	827							410	93	7	1		440	83	15	2		4/15
Morgan State University	Baltimore	SU	B,M,D	Pub	F,S	C	5,262							450	68	23	8	1	500	44	41	12	3	3/1
Mount Saint Mary's College	Emmitsburg	SM	B,M	Pri	No	C	1,322							630	9	20	53	18	600	16	32	38	14	3/1
Saint John's College	Annapolis	R	B	Pub	No	C	397							590	14	39	43	4	620	9	28	54	9	1/15
Saint Mary's College of Maryland	St. Mary's City	SM	B	Pub	No	C	1,524	22	22	49	20	5	4	490	55	36	8	1	560	18	54	27	1	1/15
Salisbury State University	Salisbury	SM	B,M	Pub	F,S	C	5,323																	Open
Sojourner-Douglass College	Baltimore	U	B	Pri	No	C	218							467	71	25	4		516	44	44	11	1	3/1
Towson State University	Towson	SU	B,M	Pub	F,S	C	12,831																	3/1
United States Naval Academy	Annapolis	SM	B	Pub	No	C	4,125																	
University of Maryland/Baltimore County	Baltimore	SU	B,M,D	Pub	F,S	C	9,068	22						500	49	32	16	3	570	16	42	32	10	5/1
University of Maryland/College Park	College Park	SU	B,M,D	Pub	F,S	C	23,331							500	49	37	12	2	580	15	41	33	11	12/1
University of Maryland/Eastern Shore	Princess Anne	R	B,M,D	Pub	F,S	C	2,412							400					368					Open
University of Maryland/University College	College Park	U	A,B,M	Pub	No	C	10,795							436					484					Open
Villa Julie College	Stevenson	SU	A,B		S	C	1,858							516	51	35	11	3	551	42	36	20	2	2/15
Washington College	Chestertown	SM	B,M	Pri	F,S	C	873	25						470	59	29	11	1	520	35	42	19	4	3/15
Western Maryland College	Westminster	SM	B,M	Pri	F,S	C	1,169																	

Massachusetts

NAME OF SCHOOL	TOWN	ENVIRONMENT	DEGREES AWARDED	CONTROL	FRAT/SOR	STUDENTS	UNDERGRAD ENROLL FALL '93	ACT Median	ACT Below 21	ACT 21-23	ACT 24-26	ACT 27-28	ACT Above 28	SAT I VERBAL Median	SAT V Below 500	SAT V 500-599	SAT V 600-700	SAT V Above 700	SAT I MATH Median	SAT M Below 500	SAT M 500-599	SAT M 600-700	SAT M Above 700	APPLICATION DEADLINE
American International College	Springfield	U	A,B,M,D	Pri	F,S	C	1,336							426	68	29	2	1	451	65	33	1	1	Open
Amherst College	Amherst	SM	B	Pri	No	C	1,585	29						639	5	20	51	24	684	1	13	35	51	12/1
Anna Maria College	Paxton	SU	A,B,M	Pri	No	C	660							418	60	40			415	60	40	4		Open
Assumption College	Worcester	SU	A,B,M	Pri	No	C	2,397																	8/1
Atlantic Union College	South Lancaster	SM	A,B,M	Pri	No	C	616	21	47	9	21	12	12	410	77	13	10		430	70	23	5	2	2/1
Babson College	Babson Park	SU	B,M	Pri	F,S	C	1,680								54	38	7			15	44	34	7	2/5
Bentley College	Waltham	SU	B,M	Pri	F,S	C	4,628							460	75	22	3		550	24	46	25	5	Open
Berklee College of Music	Boston	U	B	Pri	No	C	2,553							435	34	60	5	1	475	42	54	20	4	Open
Boston Architectural Center	Boston	U	B	Pri	No	C	620																	1/10
Boston College	Chestnut Hill	SU	B,M,D	Pri	No	C	8,807								17	49	32	2		2	23	54	21	6/1
Boston Conservatory	Boston	U	B	Pri	No	C	291							496	95	5			456	98	2			1/15
Boston University	Boston	U	B,M,D	Pri	F,S	C	14,495	27	3	15	30	22	30	550	25	47	25	3	600	9	38	40	13	Open
Bradford College	Bradford	SU	B	Pri	No	C	519																	Open

TEST SCORES

Column key:
- **ENVIRONMENT:** U-Urban, R-Rural, Su-Suburban, Sm-Small Town
- **DEGREES AWARDED:** A-Associate, B-Bachelor, M-Master, D-Doctorate
- **CONTROL:** Pri-Private, Pub-Public
- **FRATERNITIES AND SORORITIES:** F-Fraternities, S-Sororities
- **STUDENTS:** C-Coed, M-Men, W-Women, PM-Primary Men, PW-Primary Women, B-Both, No-Neither

Name of School	Town	Env	Degrees	Control	Frat/Sor	Students	Undergrad Enroll Fall '93	ACT Med	ACT <21	ACT 21-23	ACT 24-26	ACT 27-28	ACT >28	SAT V Med	SAT V <500	SAT V 500-599	SAT V 600-700	SAT V >700	SAT M Med	SAT M <500	SAT M 500-599	SAT M 600-700	SAT M >700	App Deadline
Brandeis University	Waltham	SU	B,M,D	Pri	No	C	2,881																	2/1
Bridgewater State College	Bridgewater	SM	B,M	Pub	F,S	C	5,560							570	18	43	34	5	610	9	34	39	18	3/1
Clark University	Worcester	U	B,M,D	Pri	No	C	1,922																	3/1
College of Our Lady of The Elms	Chicopee	SU	A,B,M	Pri	No	PW	1,000							440					420					2/15
College of the Holy Cross	Worcester	SU	B	Pri	No	C	2,675							570	9	53	35	3	630	3	30	50	17	2/1
Curry College	Milton	SU	B,M	Pri	No	C	944							380	62	6	1		420	59	9	1		4/1
Eastern Nazarene College	Quincy	SU	A,B,M	Pri	No	C	688																	
Emerson College	Boston	U	B,M,D	Pri	F,S	C	2,205							443	73	18	8		477	55	27	14	5	Open
Emmanuel College	Boston	U	A,B,M	Pri	No	PW	1,316																	2/1
Fitchburg State College	Fitchburg	SM	B,M	Pub	F,S	C	4,291																	Open
Framingham State College	Framingham	SU	B,M	Pub	No	C	4,850								80	17	2							3/1
Gordon College	Wenham	SM	B	Pri	No	C	1,190							428	83	15	2	2	469	65	28	7		3/1
Hampshire College	Amherst	R	B	Pri	No	C	1,079							483	59	29	11	1	509	42	44	12	2	4/15
Harvard University/Harvard and Radcliffe Colleges	Cambridge	U	B,M	Pri	No	C	6,799																	2/1
Hebrew College	Brookline	SU	B,M	Pri	No	C	25																	1/1
Hellenic College/Holy Cross Greek Orthodox School of Theology	Brookline	U	B,M	Pri	No	C	69																	Open
Lesley College	Cambridge	U	A,B,M,D	Pri	No	PW	496																	Open
Massachusetts College of Art	Boston	U	B,M	Pub	No	C	1,128							410					410					4/1
Massachusetts College of Pharmacy and Allied Health Sciences	Boston	U	A,M,D	Pri	F,S	C	1,387							467					470					4/1
Massachusetts Institute of Technology	Cambridge	U	B,M,D	Pri	F,S	C	4,509				8	19	72											3/1
Massachusetts Maritime Academy	Buzzards Bay	SM	B	Pub	No	C	749														1	14	83	1/1
Merrimack College	North Andover	SU	B	Pri	F,S	C	3,021																	6/1
Montserrat College of Art	Beverly	SM	B	Pri	No	C	272																	3/1
Mount Holyoke College	South Hadley	SM	B,M,D	Pri	No	W	1,931	26						549					571					Open
Mount Ida College	Newton Center	SU	A,B	Pri	F	C	1,901																	2/1
New England Conservatory of Music	Boston	U	B,M,D	Pri	F,S	C	397																	Open
Nichols College	Dudley	R	A,B,M	Pri	No	C	1,334																	1/15
North Adams State College	North Adams	R	B	Pub	F,S	C	1,516							427					470					Open
Northeastern University	Boston	U	A,B,M,D	Pri	F,S	C	21,381	22	32	29	18	17	4	460	66	25	8	1	530	35	40	20	5	6/1
Pine Manor College	Chestnut Hill	SU	A,B,M	Pri	No	W	450		50	50				383	85	15			396	84	16			Open
Regis College	Weston	SU	B	Pri		W	1,114							440					450					Open
Salem State College	Salem	U	B,M	Pub	No	C	15,222																	5/1
Simmons College	Boston	U	B,M,D	Pri	No	W	1,305							421					454					3/1
Simon's Rock College of Bard	Great Barrington	SM	A,B	Pri	No	C	317																	2/1
Smith College	Northampton	SM	B,M,D	Pri	No	W	2,554							570	19	41	32	10	590	10	45	26	21	6/30
Springfield College	Springfield	SU	B,M,D	Pri	No	C	2,631								17	39	36	8		9	39	42	10	1/15
Stonehill College	North Easton	SU	B	Pri	No	C	2,023	24																4/1
Suffolk University	Boston	U	A,B,M	Pri	No	C	3,021							480	62	32	6		530	28	50	20	2	2/15
Tufts University	Medford	SU	B,M,D	Pri	F,S	C	4,596							400	84	14	2		440	69	25	6		5/1
University of Lowell	Lowell	U	A,B,M,D	Pub	No	C	6,312							580	7	50	40	3	660	1	17	53	29	1/1
University of Massachusetts/Amherst	Amherst	SM	A,B,M,D		F,S	C	16,906																	
University of Massachusetts/Boston	Boston	U	B,M,D	Pub	No	C	9,808								66	27	7			36	40	20	4	2/15
University of Massachusetts Dartmouth	North Dartmouth	SU	B,M	Pri	No	C	4,884							420	78	18	4		465	64	28	7	1	6/15
Wellesley College	Wellesley	SU	B	Pri	No	W	2,349							423					482					Open
Wentworth Institute of Technology	Boston	U	A,B	Pri	No	C	2,387							610	9	32	49	10	640	6	22	49	23	1/15
Western New England College	Springfield	SU	A,B,M,D	Pri	F,S	C	2,919							370	92	7	1		460	62	28	10		6/1
Westfield State College	Westfield	R	B,M	Pub	No	C	4,248								90	9	1			68	26	6		Open
Wheaton College	Norton	R	B	Pri	No	C	1,365								86	13	1			70	26	4	1	3/1
Wheelock College	Boston	U	B,M	Pri	No	PW	765	24			43	57		530	30	55	14	1	550	25	50	23	2	2/1
Williams College	Williamstown	SM	B,M	Pri	No	C	2,013				16	9	75	420	87	11	2		440	76	20	3		2/15
Worcester Polytechnic Institute	Worcester	SU	B,M,D	Pri	F,S	C	2,888								5	19	45	31		3	10	35	52	1/1
Worcester State College	Worcester	SU	B,M	Pub	No		3,675							400					436					2/15, 7/15

Michigan

Name of School	Town	Env	Degrees	Control	Frat/Sor	Students	Undergrad Enroll Fall '93	ACT Med	ACT <21	ACT 21-23	ACT 24-26	ACT 27-28	ACT >28	SAT V Med	SAT V <500	SAT V 500-599	SAT V 600-700	SAT V >700	SAT M Med	SAT M <500	SAT M 500-599	SAT M 600-700	SAT M >700	App Deadline
Adrian College	Adrian	SM	A,B	Pri	F,S	C	1,135	23	41	32	20	3	4											8/15
Albion College	Albion	SM	B	Pri	F,S	C	1,674	25	16	20	23	18	23	530	26	43	28	3	580	16	34	33	17	Open
Alma College	Alma	SM	B	Pri	F,S	C	1,334	26	13	21	27	18	21											Open
Andrews University	Berrien Springs	R	A,B,M,D	Pri	F,S	C	1,912	20	43	20	18	10	9											
Aquinas College	Grand Rapids	SU	A,B,M	Pri	No	C	2,018	22	38	25	20	11	6											8/1
Baker College	Flint	U	A,B	Pri	No	C	4,147																	9/19
Calvin College	Grand Rapids	SU	B,M	Pri	No	C	3,538	24	16	25	28	14	18	500	45	35	17	3	560	26	32	27	15	Open
Center for Creative Studies/College of Art and Design	Detroit	U	B	Pri	No	C	795	20	52	22	20	2	4	450	69	26	5		480	53	31	16		4/1
Central Michigan University	Mount Pleasant	SM	B,M,D	Pub	F,S	C	14,515	21	48	30	15	2	5											4/1
Cleary College	Ypsilanti		A,B	Pri	No	C	761																	3/1
Concordia College	Ann Arbor	SU	A,B	Pri	No	C	580	20	53	23	17	5	2	485	56	41	3		500	43	25	32		Open
Davenport College of Business	Grand Rapids	SU	A,B	Pri	S	C	3,455	19																Open
Detroit College of Business	Dearborn	SU	A,B		F,S	C	5,135																	Open
Eastern Michigan University	Ypsilanti	SU	B,M,D	Pub	F,S	C	18,954	21	49	31	11	6	3		70	25	5							9/15
Ferris State University	Big Rapids	SM	A,B,M,D	Pub	F,S	C	11,188	18	76	16	6	2								56	38	6		7/1
GMI Engineering & Management Institute	Flint	SU	B,M	Pri	F,S	C	2,367																	Open
Grand Rapids Baptist College and Seminary	Grand Rapids	SU	A,B,M	Pri	No	C	710	26	2	12	38	25	23	510	46	42	11	1	640	5	25	54	16	Open
Grand Valley State University	Allendale	SM	B,M	Pub	No	C	10,853	21	40	26	20	9	5											Open
Hillsdale College	Hillsdale	SU	B	Pri	F,S	C	1,139	23	18	38	28	10	6											7/31
Hope College	Holland	SU	B	Pri	F,S	C	2,713	25	18	27	26	14	15	520	43	40	15	3	550	27	49	18	6	7/15
Jordan College	Cedar Springs		A,B	Pri	No	C	2,115	25	13	24	19		19	500	53	32	11	3	580	31	32	8		Open

NAME OF SCHOOL	TOWN	ENVIRONMENT	DEGREES AWARDED	CONTROL	FRATERNITIES AND SORORITIES	STUDENTS	UNDERGRADUATE ENROLLMENT FALL '93	ACT Median	Below 21	21-23	24-26	27-28	Above 28	SAT I VERBAL REASONING Median	Below 500	500-599	600-700	Above 700	SAT I MATHEMATICAL REASONING Median	Below 500	500-599	600-700	Above 700	APPLICATION DEADLINE Month/Day
Kalamazoo College	Kalamazoo	SU	B		No	C	1,218	1	13	31	23	32		15	41	39	5	390	7	24	46	23	2/15
Kendall College of Art and Design	Grand Rapids	U	B		No	C	593	19	69	20	8	2	390	89	11			390	67	33			Open
Lake Superior State University	Sault Sainte Marie	SM	A,B,M	Pub	F,S	C	3,024	54	24	15		5											8/12
Lawrence Technological University	Southfield	SU	A,B,M	Pri	F,S	C	4,239	22															8/1
Madonna University	Livonia	SU	A,B,M	Pri	No	C	4,000	21															Open
Marygrove College	Detroit	U	A,B,M	Pri	No	C	1,000																8/15
Michigan Christian College	Rochester Hills	SU	A,B	Pri	No	C	374																Open
Michigan State University	East Lansing	SU	B,M,D		F,S	C	30,760	23	24	33	27	9	7	458	68	23	8	1	524	40	35	20	5	7/30
Michigan Technological University	Houghton	SM	A,B,M,D	Pub	F,S	C	5,938	26	6	19	30	21	24	520	41	37	21	1	630	8	29	45	18	Open
Northern Michigan University	Marquette	U	A,B,M	Pub	F,S	C	7,889																Open
Northwood University	Midland	SU	A,B,M	Pri	No	C	1,303	20															7/15
Oakland University	Rochester	SU	B,M,D	Pub	F,S	C	10,423	23	18	31	38	8	5										Open
Olivet College	Olivet	R	B	Pri	F,S	C	776	18	68	19	10	2	1										Open
Saginaw Valley State University	University Center	SU	B,M	Pub	No	C	5,682	21	54	27	13	3	2										9/1
Saint Mary's College	Orchard Lake	SU	B		F,S	C	291																8/15
Siena Heights College	Adrian	SM	A,B,M	Pri	F,S	C	954	21	53	28	12	5	2										Open
Spring Arbor College	Spring Arbor	SM	A,B	Pri	No	C	919		49	24	16	5	6										Open
University of Detroit Mercy	Detroit	U	A,B,M,D	Pri	F,S	C	4,366	22	45	17	22	10	7	440	72	22	7		510	47	27	26		4/1
University of Michigan/Ann Arbor	Ann Arbor	SU	B,M,D	Pub	F,S	C	23,384		4	10	24	29	33		27	44	26	3		7	23	43	27	2/1
University of Michigan/Dearborn	Dearborn	SU	B,M	Pub	F,S	C	6,912		2	48		47	3											Open
University of Michigan/Flint	Flint	U	B,M	Pub	F,S	C	6,026		32	37	24	5	2										8/27
Wayne State University	Detroit	U	B,M,D	Pub	F,S	C	20,865	20	66	18	10	3	3										8/1
Western Michigan University	Kalamazoo	U	B,M,D	Pub	F,S	C	20,017	23	30	31	12	8	7										Open
William Tyndale College	Farmington Hills	SU	A,B	Pri	No	C	542	18	30	50	15	3	2										7/30

Minnesota

Augsburg College	Minneapolis	U	B,M	Pri	No	C	1,648		53	21														8/15
Bemidji State University	Bemidji	SM	A,B,M	Pub	F,S	C	4,656	21	44	34	16	4	2	491					542					Open
Bethel College	St. Paul	SU	A,B	Pri	No	C	1,796	23															Open
Carleton College	Northfield	SM	B	Pri	No	C	1,678		2	6	16	24	52	490	7	30	50	13	530	3	17	46	34	2/1
College of Saint Benedict	St. Joseph	SM	B	Pri	No	W	1,767	23	24	32	24	11	9	490	56	34	9	1	530	36	33	29	1	Open
College of Saint Catherine	St. Paul	U	B,M	Pri	S		2,251	22	9	53	35	3	6	483	56	23	21		468	63	23	14		8/15
College of Saint Scholastica	Duluth	SU	B,M	Pri	No	C	1,622	23	42	22	23	9	4	435	77	19	4		480	61	31	8		Open
Concordia College	St. Paul	U	A,B,M	Pri	No	C	1,230																	8/15
Concordia College/Moorhead	Moorhead	U	B	Pri	No	C	2,999		23	29	23	13	12		54	34	10	2		37	33	23	7	Open
Gustavus Adolphus College	St. Peter	SM	B	Pri	F,S	C	2,316	25	10	25	32	14	19	520	44	29	24	3	590	21	31	33	15	4/1
Hamline University	St. Paul	U	B,M	Pri	F,S	C	1,562	25	11	26	27	18	18	530	36	36	20	8	580	13	47	32	8	4/1
Macalester College	St. Paul	SU	B	Pri	No	C	1,836		2	4	14	27	54		8	34	49	9		5	29	43	23	1/15
Mankato State University	Mankato	R	A,B,M	Pub	F,S	C	12,338																	Open
Minneapolis College of Art and Design	Minneapolis	U	B,M	Pri	No	C	537		58	16	12	8	6		53	27	13	7		66	20	7	7	3/15
Moorhead State University	Moorhead	SU	A,B,M	Pub	F,S	C	6,905	22	32	37	20	6	5										8/15
North Central Bible College	Minneapolis	U	A,B	Pri	No	C	1,054	21															9/1
Northwestern College	St. Paul	SU	A,B	Pri	No	C	1,242	22	27	26	24	7	16										8/15
Pillsbury Baptist Bible College	Owatonna	SM	A,B	Pri	No	C	278	20															8/25
Saint Cloud State University	St. Cloud	SU	A,B,M	Pub	F,S	C	14,475	21	45	31	17	5	2	465	59	34	6	1	555	25	41	27	7	8/10
Saint John's University	Collegeville	R	B,M	Pri	No	C	1,763	23	23	27	26	14	10		70	23		2		55	34	9	2	Open
Saint Mary's College of Minnesota	Winona	SM	B,M	Pri	F,S	C	1,315																	Open
Saint Olaf College	Northfield	SM	B	Pri	No	C	2,993	26	9	22	29	20	20	530	38	39	21	2	580	19	39	31	11	Open
Southwest State University	Marshall	R	A,B	Pub	No	C	2,637	20	57	25	12	3	3										9/1
University of Minnesota/Crookston	Crookston	R	A	Pub	No	C	1,457																	2/1
University of Minnesota/Duluth	Duluth	SU	B,M	Pub	No	C	7,141	22	16	55	13	12	3	550	29	34	30	7	650	20	30	32	18	3/15
University of Minnesota/Morris	Morris	SM	B	Pub	F,S	C	1,933	26	8	18	34	23	17	492	51	33	14	2	570	25	30	32	14	12/15
University of Minnesota/Twin Cities	Minneapolis	U	B,M,D	Pub	F,S	C	25,837	24	21	25	25	13	12	470	61	29	10		535	33	42	21	4	4/1
University of Saint Thomas	St. Paul	U	B,M,D	Pri	F,S	C	5,088	24	27	31	25	13	9	470					490					2/15
Winona State University	Winona	SM	A,B,M	Pub	F,S	C	6,700	22	10	35	30	15	10	460										

Mississippi

Alcorn State University	Lorman	R	A,B,M	Pub	F,S	C	2,561	18	45	40	10	5	2											Open
Belhaven College	Jackson	U	B	Pri	No	C	1,083	24																Open
Blue Mountain College	Blue Mountain	R	B	Pri	No	W	395	24																7/31
Delta State University	Cleveland	SM	B,M,D	Pub	F,S	C	3,332	19	63	22	9	4	1											Open
Jackson State University	Jackson	U	B,M,D	Pub	F,S	C	5,455																	8/15
Millsaps College	Jackson	U	B,M	Pri	F,S	C	1,252	26						550					570					2/1
Mississippi College	Clinton	SU	B,M	Pri	No	C	2,416	23						450					450					8/15
Mississippi State University	Mississippi State	SM	B,M,D	Pub	F,S	C	11,619	24	35	22	17	10	16											8/1
Mississippi University for Women	Columbus	SM	A,B,M	Pub	F,S	PW	2,687																	8/20
Mississippi Valley State University	Itta Bena	SM	B,M	Pub	F,S	C	2,519	16	91	6	2	1												7/15
Rust College	Holly Springs	SM	A,B	Pri	F,S	C	1,180	16																Open
Tougaloo College	Tougaloo	SU	A,B	Pri	F,S	C	1,153	18	82	12	5	1												8/1
University of Mississippi	University	SM	B,M,D	Pub	F,S	C	8,157																	Open
University of Southern Mississippi	Hattiesburg	SU	B,M,D	Pub	F,S	C	9,605	21	51	23	14	7	5											8/15
William Carey College	Hattiesburg	SM	B,M	Pri	F,S	C	1,957	20	37	34	16	9	4											

Missouri

Avila College	Kansas City	SU	B,M	Pri	No	C	1,141	21	49	23	15	7	9	430	65	29	6		430	59	35	6		Open
Barnes College	St. Louis	U	B	Pri	No	C	455	21																Open
Central Methodist College	Fayette	SM	A,B	Pri	F,S	C	1,068	21	57	20	16	4	3											8/24

TEST SCORES

Column key:
- **ENVIRONMENT:** U-Urban R-Rural Su-Suburban Sm-Small Town
- **DEGREES AWARDED:** A-Associate B-Bachelor M-Master D-Doctorate
- **CONTROL:** Pri-Private, Pub-Public
- **FRATERNITIES AND SORORITIES:** F-Fraternities S-Sororities; S-Both No-Neither
- **STUDENTS:** C-Coed M-Men W-Women PM-Primary Men PW-Primary Women

Name of School	Town	Env.	Degrees	Control	Frat/Sor	Students	Undergrad Enroll. Fall '93	ACT Median	ACT Below 21	ACT 21-23	ACT 24-26	ACT 27-28	ACT Above 28	SAT V Median	SAT V Below 500	SAT V 500-599	SAT V 600-700	SAT V Above 700	SAT M Median	SAT M Below 500	SAT M 500-599	SAT M 600-700	SAT M Above 700	Application Deadline
Central Missouri State University	Warrensburg	SM	A,B,M	Pub	F,S	C	9,690	21	55	24	13	4	2											
College of the Ozarks	Point Lookout	SM	B	Pri	No	C	1,472	21																Open
Columbia College	Columbia	SM	A,B	Pri	F	C	836	21																Open
Culver-Stockton College	Canton	R	B	Pri	F,S	C	1,102	22	31	33	23	10	3											Open
Deaconess College of Nursing	St. Louis	U	A,B	Pri	No	C	391	22	33	39	21	6	1											5/1
DeVry Institute of Technology/ Kansas City	Kansas City	SU	A,B	Pri	No	C	1,907																	Open
Drury College	Springfield	U	A,B,M	Pri	F,S	C	1,113	25	20	28	23	13	16											Open
Evangel College	Springfield	U	A,B	Pri	No	C	1,503	22																8/1
Fontbonne College	St. Louis	SU	B,M	Pri	F	C	1,530	21	31	48	19	2	3											8/1
Hannibal-LaGrange College	Hannibal	SM	A,B	Pri	No	C	875	20																8/1
Harris-Stowe State College	St Louis	U	B	Pub	F,S	C	1,771																	Open
Kansas City Art Institute	Kansas City	U	B	Pri	No	C	559	22																Open
Lincoln University	Jefferson City	SM	A,B,M	Pub	F,S	C	3,300	18	72	16	8	3	1											2/15
Lindenwood College	St. Charles	SU	B,M	Pri	F,S	C	2,346	22	39	34	15	8	4											Open
Maryville University-Saint Louis	St. Louis	SU	B,M	Pri	No	C	3,094	24	25	25	21	16	13											Open
Missouri Baptist College	St. Louis	SU	A,B	Pri	No	C	1,752	20																Open
Missouri Southern State College	Joplin	SM	A,B	Pub	F,S	C	5,666	20	15	40	25	15	5											
Missouri Valley College	Marshall	SM	A,B	Pub	F,S	C	1,103	19	50	38	12			380					380					8/23
Missouri Western State College	St. Joseph	SU	A,B	Pub	F,S	C	5,121	19	69	18	9	2	1											Open
Northeast Missouri State University	Kirksville	SM	B,M	Pub	F,S	C	5,906	26	4	25	34	16	21											8/1
Northwest Missouri State University	Maryville	R	B,M	Pub	F,S	C	5,149	21	50	22	15	7	6											11/15
Park College	Parkville	SU	B,M	Pri	No	C	840	20	53	29	12	4	2											8
Research College of Nursing	Kansas City	U	B	Pri	F,S	C	308	23	37	28	17	9	9											Open
Rockhurst College	Kansas City	U	B,M	Pri	F	C	1,881	23																6/30
Saint Louis College of Pharmacy	St. Louis	U	B,M,D	Pri	F,S	C	811		10	29	33	16	12											6/1
Saint Louis University	St. Louis	U	A,B,M,D	Pri	F,S	C	7,030	25	9	21	25	20	25	480	57	30	10		550					8/1
Southeast Missouri State University	Cape Girardeau	R	A,B,M	Pub	F,S	C	7,330		37	29	17	7	10											6/1
Southwest Baptist University	Bolivar	R	A,B,M	Pri	No	C	2,737	21																
Southwest Missouri State University	Springfield	SU	A,B,M	Pub	F,S	PW	16,505	22	45	28	15	5	7											Open
Stephens College	Columbia	U	A,B	Pri	S	PW	1,002	21	49	21	14	8	8	460	64	23	12	1	460	60	24	15	1	8/1
University of Missouri/Columbia	Columbia	SM	B,M,D		F,S	C	16,365	25	13	28	27	13	20	502					564					8/1
University of Missouri/Kansas City	Kansas City	U	B,M,D	Pub	F,S	C	5,400	25	22	23	23	12	20											5/15
University of Missouri/Rolla	Rolla	SM	B,M,D	Pub	F,S	C	4,487	27	4	14	27	17	38	547	35	42	21	2	655	8	23	47	22	7/1
University of Missouri/St. Louis	St. Louis	U	B,M,D	Pub	F	C	9,345	22	35	31	22	5	7											7/1
Washington University	St. Louis	U	B,M,D	Pri	F,S	C	6,153			5	20	21	53		20	44	31	4		4	18	50	26	1/15
Webster University	St. Louis	SU	B,M,D	Pri	No	C	3,289	23	29	27	29	10	5	511	39	40	20	1	494	48	43	9		8/1
Westminster College	Fulton	SM	B	Pri	F,S	C	731	24	23	29	22	11	15	480	60	27	11	2	520	38	33	25	4	Open
William Jewell College	Liberty	SU	B	Pri	F,S	C	1,354	24	22	24	24	15	15	500	43	44	12	1	550	25	45	23	7	Open
William Woods University	Fulton	SM	A,B	Pri	S	W	816	21	52	22	21	4	1	436	73	21	4	2	445	73	21	5		Open

Montana

Name of School	Town	Env.	Degrees	Control	Frat/Sor	Students	Undergrad Enroll. Fall '93	ACT Median	ACT Below 21	ACT 21-23	ACT 24-26	ACT 27-28	ACT Above 28	SAT V Median	SAT V Below 500	SAT V 500-599	SAT V 600-700	SAT V Above 700	SAT M Median	SAT M Below 500	SAT M 500-599	SAT M 600-700	SAT M Above 700	Application Deadline
Carroll College	Helena	SM	A,B	Pri	No	C	1,415	23	32	19	27	12	10											
College of Great Falls	Great Falls	U	A,B,M	Pri	No	C	1,304																	7/1
Eastern Montana College	Billings	U	A,B,M	Pub	F,S	C	3,347	20	59	26	12	3		421					464					Open
Montana College of Mineral Science and Technology	Butte	SM	A,B,M	Pub	No	C	1,886	22	28	28	24	11	9	456	65	26	9		554	32	34	29	5	8/25
Montana State University	Bozeman	SM	B,M,D		F,S	C	9,914	23	28	30	25	11	7	440	69	26	9	5	520	41	34	21	4	8/1
Northern Montana College	Havre	SM	A,B,M	Pub	No	C	1,572																	7/1
Rocky Mountain College	Billings	SM	A,B	Pri	No	C	854																	
University of Montana	Missoula	U	A,B,M,D	Pub	F,S	C	8,768	22	5	50	21	18	6	458					489					8/15
Western Montana College of the University of Montana	Dillon	SM	A,B	Pub	No	C	1,070	17																3/1

Nebraska

Name of School	Town	Env.	Degrees	Control	Frat/Sor	Students	Undergrad Enroll. Fall '93	ACT Median	ACT Below 21	ACT 21-23	ACT 24-26	ACT 27-28	ACT Above 28	SAT V Median	SAT V Below 500	SAT V 500-599	SAT V 600-700	SAT V Above 700	SAT M Median	SAT M Below 500	SAT M 500-599	SAT M 600-700	SAT M Above 700	Application Deadline
Bellevue College	Bellevue	SU	B,M	Pri	No	C	2,039	21																
Chadron State College	Chadron	SM	A,B,M	Pub	No	C	2,371																	Open
Clarkson College	Omaha	U	A,B,M	Pri	S	C	523	19	66	22	11		1											Open
College of Saint Mary	Omaha	SU	A,B	Pri	No	W	1,168	21	61	20	12	6	1											5/1
Concordia College	Seward	SM	B,M	Pri	No	C	857	23																8/22
Creighton University	Omaha	U	B,M,D	Pri	F,S	C	4,094	25	14	25	30	15	16											8/1
Dana College	Blair	SM	B	Pri	No	C	616	23	43	27	21	6	3											8/1
Doane College	Crete	SM	B,M	Pri	F,S	C	851	23	27	27	29	10	7											Open
Hastings College	Hastings	R	B,M	Pri	F,S	C	972	22																6/1
Midland Lutheran College	Fremont	SM	A,B	Pri	F,S	C	1,017	21	45	25	20	6	4											7/1
Nebraska Methodist College of Nursing and Allied Health	Omaha	U	A,B	Pri	No	C	450	21																Open
Nebraska Wesleyan University	Lincoln	SU	B	Pri	F,S	C	1,703	23	23	31	26	12	8											4/1
Peru State College	Peru	R	A,B,M	Pub	F,S	C																		3/15
Union College	Lincoln	SU	A,B	Pri	No	C	574	21	44	22	23	5	6											Open
University of Nebraska at Kearney	Kearney	SM	B,M	Pub	F,S	C	6,940																	7/30
University of Nebraska at Omaha	Omaha	SU	A,B,M,D	Pub	F,S	C	13,312	20																8/1
University of Nebraska-Lincoln	Lincoln	U	A,B,M,D	Pub	F,S	C	19,829	22																8/1
Wayne State College	Wayne	R	B,M	Pub	F,S	C	3,180	20	54	24	15	4	3	447	64	26	7	3	513	40	33	19	8	8/1
York College	York	SM	A,B	Pri	F,S	C	481	20																Open 4/15

Nevada

Name of School	Town	Env.	Degrees	Control	Frat/Sor	Students	Undergrad Enroll. Fall '93	ACT Median	ACT Below 21	ACT 21-23	ACT 24-26	ACT 27-28	ACT Above 28	SAT V Median	SAT V Below 500	SAT V 500-599	SAT V 600-700	SAT V Above 700	SAT M Median	SAT M Below 500	SAT M 500-599	SAT M 600-700	SAT M Above 700	Application Deadline
Sierra Nevada College	Incline Village	R	B	Pri	No	C	500	23																Open

Legend:
- ENVIRONMENT: U:Urban, R:Rural, Su:Suburban, Sm:Small Town
- DEGREES AWARDED: A:Associate, B:Bachelor, M:Master, D:Doctorate
- CONTROL: Pri:Private, Pub:Public
- FRATERNITIES AND SORORITIES: F:Fraternities, S:Sororities, No:Neither
- STUDENTS: C:Coed, M:Men, W:Women, PM:Primarily Men, PW:Primarily Women

NAME OF SCHOOL	TOWN	ENV	DEGREES	CONTROL	FRAT	STUD	UNDERGRAD ENROLL FALL '93	ACT Median	ACT Below 21	ACT 21-23	ACT 24-26	ACT 27-28	ACT Above 28	SAT I Verbal Median	Below 500	500-599	600-700	Above 700	SAT I Math Median	Below 500	500-599	600-700	Above 700	APPLICATION DEADLINE
University of Nevada/Las Vegas	Las Vegas	U	B,M,D	Pub	F,S	C	16,820	21						418					487					8/16
University of Nevada/Reno	Reno	U	B,M,D	Pub	F,S	C	8,609	22	36	34	17	10	3	432	64	26	8	1	488	61	26	8	5	7/1

New Hampshire

NAME OF SCHOOL	TOWN	ENV	DEGREES	CONTROL	FRAT	STUD	UNDERGRAD ENROLL FALL '93	ACT Median	ACT Below 21	ACT 21-23	ACT 24-26	ACT 27-28	ACT Above 28	SAT I Verbal Median	Below 500	500-599	600-700	Above 700	SAT I Math Median	Below 500	500-599	600-700	Above 700	APPLICATION DEADLINE
Colby-Sawyer College	New London	SM	A,B	Pri	No	C	670	20						440					443					5
College for Lifelong Learning	Durham	SM	A,B	Pub	No	C	1,749							438					490					Open
Daniel Webster College	Nashua	SU	A,B	Pri	No	C	460																	Open
Dartmouth College	Hanover	SM	B,M,D	Pri	F,S	C	4,275							640	4	24	55	17	710	1	9	34	56	1/1
Franklin Pierce College	Rindge	R	B	Pri	No	C	1,239							403	86	13	1		424	77	18	4	1	Open
Keene State College	Keene	SU	A,B,M	Pub	F,S	C	4,405							424	87	12	1		463	72	23	5		4/1
New England College	Henniker	R	B,M		F,S	C	950							405	93	7			455	77	19	3	1	Open
New Hampshire College	Manchester	SU	A,B,M	Pri	F,S	C	4,530							440					442					Open
Notre Dame College	Manchester	SU	A,B,M	Pri	No	C	804							450	80	18	2		449	66	27	6		4/1
Plymouth State College	Plymouth	SM	A,B,M	Pub	F,S	C	4,000							430	80	16	3	1	467	73	23	4		Open
Rivier College	Nashua	SU	A,B,M	Pri	No	C	1,786							481	62	34	4		512	45	43	12		3/15
Saint Anselm College	Manchester	SU	A,B	Pri	F,S	C	1,967							526	35	35	24	6	513	53	18	18	11	Open
Thomas Moore College of Liberal Arts	Merrimack	R	B	Pri	No	C	59																	
University of New Hampshire	Durham	R	A,B,M,D		F,S	C	10,831							476	61	33	6		536	32	43	3	2	2/1

New Jersey

NAME OF SCHOOL	TOWN	ENV	DEGREES	CONTROL	FRAT	STUD	UNDERGRAD ENROLL FALL '93	ACT Median	ACT Below 21	ACT 21-23	ACT 24-26	ACT 27-28	ACT Above 28	SAT I Verbal Median	Below 500	500-599	600-700	Above 700	SAT I Math Median	Below 500	500-599	600-700	Above 700	APPLICATION DEADLINE
Bloomfield College	Bloomfield	SU	B		F,S	C	1,994							450					470					Open
Caldwell College	Caldwell	SU	B,M	Pri	No	C	1,562							470	80	15	5		500	73	22	5		Open
Centenary College	Hackettstown	SM	A,B	Pri	F,S	C	920							450	66	26	8		470	57	30	12	1	8/15
College of Saint Elizabeth	Morristown	SU	B	Pri	No	PW	1,465							450					470					
Drew University/College of Liberal Arts	Madison	SM	B,M,D	Pri	No	C	1,214							580	19	38	35	8	630	12	29	39	20	2/15
Fairleigh Dickinson University	Teaneck	SU	A,B,M,D		F,S	C	4,977							432					496					6/1
Felician College	Lodi	SU	A,B	Pri	F,S	C	1,145							450					450					Open
Georgian Court College	Lakewood	SU	B,M	Pri	No	PW	1,880							441	86	11	4		473	66	28	6		8/1
Jersey City State College	Jersey City	U	B,M	Pub	F,S	C	5,611							430	85	13	2		400	80	15	5		5/1
Kean College of New Jersey	Union	SU	B,M	Pub	F,S	C	10,233							409	91	9			470	65	30	5		6/15
Monmouth College	West Long Branch	SU	B,M	Pri	F,S	C	2,740							430	80	14	5	1	490	51	35	13	1	3/1
Montclair State College	Upper Montclair	SU	B,M	Pub	F,S	C	9,588							460	70	27	3		520	32	55	12	1	3/1
New Jersey Institute of Technology	Newark	U	B,M,D	Pub	No	C	4,957							466	64	29	7		600	4	47	39	10	4/1
Princeton University	Princeton	SM	B,M,D	Pri	No	C	4,538								2	19	52	27			6	31	63	1/2
Ramapo College of New Jersey	Mahwah	SU	B	Pub	F,S	C	4,683							450	73	22	5		510	45	37	17	1	3/15
Richard Stockton College of New Jersey	Pomona	SU	B	Pub	F,S	C	5,782							490	56	37	6	1	560	21	52	23	4	5/1
Rider College	Lawrenceville	SU	A,B,M	Pri	F,S	C	4,060							439	81	15	3	1	501	53	32	12	4	Open
Rowan College of New Jersey	Glassboro	SM	B,M	Pub	F,S	C	9,368							486	58	34	6	1	538	28	50	19	1	3/15
Rutgers University/Camden College of Arts and Sciences	Camden	U	B	Pub	F,S	C	2,567							492	55	37	8		551	19	58	21	2	5/1
Rutgers University/College of Engineering	New Brunswick	SU	B,M,D	Pub	F,S	C	2,407							514	43	39	17	1	667	1	13	53	33	1/15
Rutgers University/College of Nursing	Newark	U	B,M,D	Pub	F,S	C	428							508	44	52	4		575	18	52	26	4	1/15
Rutgers University/College of Pharmacy	New Brunswick	SU	B,M,D	Pub	F,S	C	875							531	34	47	19		662	1	16	55	28	1/15
Rutgers University/Cook College	New Brunswick	SM	B	Pub	F,S	C	2,931							514	42	47	10	1	588	11	44	37	8	1/15
Rutgers University/Douglass College	New Brunswick	SU	B	Pub	S	W	2,990							497	51	37	11	1	550	24	53	21	2	1/15
Rutgers University/Livingston College	New Brunswick	SU	B	Pub	F,S	C	3,686							487	56	38	5	1	556	22	49	26	3	1/15
Rutgers University/Mason Gross School of the Arts	New Brunswick	SM	B,M,D	Pub	F,S	C	410							496	52	39	9		530	35	44	18	3	
Rutgers University/Newark College of Arts and Sciences	Newark	U	B	Pub	F,S	C	3,643							455	74	21	5		529	33	48	17	2	5/1
Rutgers University/Rutgers College	New Brunswick	SU	B	Pub	F,S	C	8,582							539	32	43	23	2	617	9	33	42	16	1/15
Rutgers University/University College—Camden	Camden	U	B	Pub	No	C	830																	5/1
Rutgers University/University College—New Brunswick	New Brunswick	SM	B	Pub	No	C	3,249																	7/21
Rutgers University/University College—Newark	Newark	U	B	Pub	No	C	1,820																	8/1
Saint Peter's College	Jersey City	U	A,B,M	Pri	F,S	C	3,189							450	73	21	5	1	490	53	35	11	1	3/1
Seton Hall University	South Orange	SU	B,M,D	Pri	F,S	C	5,318							442	76	19	4	1	496	52	34	13	1	3/1
Stevens Institute of Technology	Hoboken	U	B,M,D	Pri	F,S	C	1,274							521					652					3/1
Thomas A. Edison State College	Trenton	U	A,B	Pub		C	8,768																	Open
Trenton State College	Trenton	SU	B,M	Pub	F,S	C	6,067							520	38	48	13	1	590	10	42	38	11	3/1
Upsala College	East Orange	U	A,B	Pri	F,S	C	1,488							420					440					6/1
Westminster Choir College	Princeton	SU	B,M	Pri	No	C	259	22	57		14	14	15	490	55	35	10		510	47	31	18	4	Open
William Paterson College	Wayne	SU	B,M	Pub	F,S	C	8,044	21						428	80	15	2		485	59	37	7		6/30

New Mexico

NAME OF SCHOOL	TOWN	ENV	DEGREES	CONTROL	FRAT	STUD	UNDERGRAD ENROLL FALL '93	ACT Median	ACT Below 21	ACT 21-23	ACT 24-26	ACT 27-28	ACT Above 28	SAT I Verbal Median	Below 500	500-599	600-700	Above 700	SAT I Math Median	Below 500	500-599	600-700	Above 700	APPLICATION DEADLINE
College of Santa Fe	Santa Fe	SU	B,M	Pri	No	C	784	21	26	47	17	5	4	480	28	57	13	2	490	35	52	12	1	Open
College of the Southwest	Hobbs	SM	B	Pri	No	C	367	19	74	10	10		6	390					460					Open
Eastern New Mexico University	Portales	SM	A,B,M	Pub	F,S	C	3,352	20																Open
New Mexico Highlands University	Las Vegas	SM	A,B,M	Pub	F	C	2,014	18																Open
New Mexico Institute of Mining and Technology	Socorro	SM	A,B,M,D	Pub	No	C	1,423	26	9	19	24	23	25	506	45	34	19	3	594	19	28	35	18	8/1
New Mexico State University	Las Cruces	SU	A,B,M,D	Pub	F,S	C	13,154																	

Column legend

- ENVIRONMENT: U/Urban, R/Rural, Su/Suburban, Sm/Small Town
- DEGREES AWARDED: A/Associate, B/Bachelor, M/Master, D/Doctorate
- CONTROL: Pri/Private, Pub/Public
- FRATERNITIES AND SORORITIES: F/Fraternities, S/Sororities
- STUDENTS: C/Co-ed, M/Men, W/Women, PM/Primarily Men, PW/Primarily Women
- TEST SCORES — ACT / SAT I Verbal Reasoning / SAT I Mathematical Reasoning
- APPLICATION DEADLINE: Month/Day

Name of School	Town	Environment	Degrees Awarded	Control	Frat./Soror.	Students	Undergrad Enrollment Fall '93	ACT Median	ACT Below 21	ACT 21–23	ACT 24–26	ACT 27–28	ACT Above 28	SAT V Median	SAT V Below 500	SAT V 500–599	SAT V 600–700	SAT V Above 700	SAT M Median	SAT M Below 500	SAT M 500–599	SAT M 600–700	SAT M Above 700	Application Deadline
Saint John's College	Santa Fe	SM	B,M	Pri	No	C	413	27			9	40	39	610	6	42	46	6	600	11	43	38	8	3/1
The University of New Mexico	Albuquerque	U	A,B,M,D	Pub	F,S	C	20,004	22	38	30	18			462					506					
Western New Mexico University	Silver City	SM	A,B,M	Pub	No	C	661																	9/1
New York																								
Adelphi University	Garden City	SU	A,B,M,D	Pri	F	C	3,910							449	74	25	1		488	75	23	2		3/1
Albany College of Pharmacy	Albany	U	B	Pri	F,S	C	672							460	72	22	6		550	21	53	24	2	Open
Alfred University	Alfred	U R	B,M,D	Pri	F,S	C	1,940	27	11	29	26	23	12	580	43	37	15	5	660	11	40	35	14	2/15
Audrey Cohen College	New York	U	B,M	Pri	No	C	988																	8/1
Bard College	Annandale-on-Hudson	R	B,M	Pri	No	C	1,068																	
Boricua College	New York	U	A,B	Pri		C	1,211								1	43	46	10		1	40	51	8	2/15
Brooklyn Campus of Long Island University	Brooklyn	U	A,B,M,D	Pri	F,S	C	5,976																	8/15
Canisius College	Buffalo	U	A,B,M	Pri	F,S	C	3,525																	Open
Cazenovia College	Cazenovia	R	A,B	Pri	No	C	1,036	23	5	64	29	3		448	73	21	5		510	46	34	16	3	Open
City University of New York/Baruch College	New York	U	B,M,D	Pub	No	C	12,575								71	23	5	1		74	21	4	1	Open
City University of New York/Brooklyn College	Brooklyn	U	B,M	Pub	F,S	C	10,836																	1/16
City University of New York/City College	New York	U	B,M	Pub	F	C	11,700																	6/1
City University of New York/College of Staten Island	Staten Island	U	A,B,M,D	Pub	No	C	11,836																	1/15
City University of New York/Herbert H. Lehman College	Bronx	U	B,M	Pub	S	C	8,667																	9/1
City University of New York/Hunter College	New York	U	B,M	Pub	F,S	C	13,966																	8
City University of New York/John Jay College of Criminal Justice	New York	U	A,B,M,D	Pub	No	C	8,317																	1/15
City University of New York/Medgar Evers College	Brooklyn	U	A,B	Pub	No	C	5,011																	
City University of New York/New York City Technical College	Brooklyn	U	A,B	Pub	No	C	10,786																	Open
City University of New York/Queens College	Flushing	U	B,M	Pub	F	C	14,100																	1/15
City University of New York/York College	Jamaica	U	B	Pub	F,S	C	6,869																	3/15
Clarkson University	Potsdam	R R	B,M,D	Pri	F,S	C	2,385	28						518	43	35	18	4	612	6	34	49	12	3/1
Colgate University	Hamilton	R R	B,M	Pri	F,S	C	2,675		1	6	28	25	40		17	46	35			6	27	54	12	2/1
College of Aeronautics	Flushing	U	A,B	Pri	No	C	1,170							400	60	30	8		420	70	23	5		1/15
College of Insurance	New York	U	A,B,M	Pri	F	C	733								43	47				7	40	47	9	Open
College of Mount Saint Vincent	Riverdale	SU	A,B,M	Pri	No	C	1,152	22	38	38	13	13		454	79	17		4	474	65	28	6	1	5/1
College of New Rochelle	New Rochelle	SU	B,M	Pri	No	C	975							410	88	10	1	1	420	78	19	3		2/1
College of Saint Rose	Albany	SU	B,M	Pri	No	C	2,592							480	71	24	4	1	500					8/15
Columbia University/Barnard College	New York	U U	B	Pri	S	W	2,190																	8/1
Columbia University/Columbia College	New York	U	B	Pri	S	C	3,447	27		5	28	37	30	600	6	44	46	4	620	2	32	55	11	1/1
Columbia University/School of Engineering and Applied Science	New York	U	B,M,D	Pri	F,S	C	1,008																	1/1
Concordia College	Bronxville	SU	A,B	Pri	No	C	590												625					1/1
Cooper Union for the Advancement of Science and Art	New York	U	B,M	Pri	F,S	C	964												740				73	Open
Cornell University	Ithaca	U R	B,M,D	Pri	F,S	C	12,813							600	16	38	39	7				25	75	1/1
Daemen College	Amherst	SU	B,M	Pri	F,S	C	1,790																	1/1
Dominican College	Orangeburg	SM	A,B	Pri	No	C	1,601																	Open
Dowling College	Oakdale	SU	B,M	Pri	No	C	3,517	18	74	19	4	2	1	370	65	30	5		385	55	38	7		Open
D'Youville College	Buffalo	U U	B,M	Pri	No	C	1,410	22	31	28	25	16		420	90	7	1	1	450	70	25	3	1	Open
Eastman School of Music	Rochester	U U	B,M,D	Pri	F,S	C	478	22						435	80	19	1		497	45	45	10		Open
Elmira College	Elmira	SU	B	Pri	No	C	1,099		28	35	15	9	13		63	30	6	1		52	30	16	2	2/1
Eugene Lang College of the New School for Social Research	New York	U	B,M,D	Pri	No	C	267								26	44	28	2		31	43	23	3	12/15
Fashion Institute of Technology/State University of New York	New York	U	A,B,M	Pub	No	C	12,118	21						420					400					2/1
Five Towns College	Dix Hills	SU	A,B	Pri	No	C	744							440	75	20	5		450	75	19	5		1/15
Fordham University/College at Lincoln Center	New York	U	B,M,D	Pri	No	C	2,253							511	46	39	14	1	556	26	49	20	5	Open
Fordham University/College of Business Administration	Bronx	U	B,M,D	Pri	No	C	1,272							510	44	40	15	1	552	26	48	21	5	2/1
Fordham University/Fordham College	Bronx	U	B,M,D	Pri	No	C	2,861							511	44	40	15	1	554	27	48	20	5	2/1
Friends World Program	Southampton	R R	B	Pri	No	C	126																	2/1
Hamilton College	Clinton	R	B	Pri	F,S	C	1,670							560	28	52	19	1	610	8	43	39	10	Open
Hartwick College	Oneonta	SM	B	Pri	F,S	C	1,534	23	22	36	24	5	13	478	64	28	7	1	524	36	47	15	2	1/15
Hobart and William Smith Colleges	Geneva	SM	B	Pri	F	C	1,797		14	33	28	13	12		52	39	8			25	47	24	4	2/15
Hofstra University	Hempstead	SU	A,B,M,D	Pri	F,S	C	7,884	25	11	15	48	18	7	480	44	45	10	1	545	25	47	24	4	2/15
Houghton College	Houghton	R	A,B	Pri	No	C	1,236	24	13	35	33	12	7	500	48	36	14	2	535	33	39	24	4	2/15
Iona College	New Rochelle	SU	A,B,M	Pri	F,S	C	5,382							402	86	11	3		450	68	25	6	1	8/1
Ithaca College	Ithaca	SM	B,M	Pri	No	C	5,778								52	38	9	1		24	50	24	2	3/15
Jewish Theological Seminary of America/List College of Jewish Studies	New York	U	B,M,D	Pri	F,S	C	127	28						580	4	54	36	4	600	4	27	54	13	3/1
Juilliard School	New York	U	B,M,D	Pri	No	C	487																	2/15

Legend
- ENVIRONMENT: U–Urban, R–Rural, SU–Suburban, Sm–Small Town
- DEGREES AWARDED: A–Associate, B–Bachelor, M–Master, D–Doctorate
- CONTROL: Pri–Private, Pub–Public
- FRATERNITIES AND SORORITIES: F–Fraternities, S–Sororities
- STUDENTS: C–Coed, M–Men, W–Women, PM–Primarily Men, PW–Primarily Women

Name of School	Town	Env.	Degrees Awarded	Control	Frat./Sor.	Students	Undergrad. Enroll. Fall '93	ACT Median	ACT Below 21	ACT 21–23	ACT 24–26	ACT 27–28	ACT Above 28	SAT-V Median	SAT-V Below 500	SAT-V 500–599	SAT-V 600–700	SAT-V Above 700	SAT-M Median	SAT-M Below 500	SAT-M 500–599	SAT-M 600–700	SAT-M Above 700	App. Deadline
Keuka College	Keuka Park	R	B	Pri	No	C	825							451	77	21	3		495	50	40	9	1	Open
King's College	Briarcliff Manor	SU	A,B	Pri	No	C	239	25						442	76	19	6		465	67	21	12		Open
Laboratory Institute of Merchandising	New York	U	A,B	Pri	No	C	173																	Open
Le Moyne College	Syracuse	SU	B,M	Pri	No	C	2,402		14	24	30	16	16		66	29	5			31	46	20	3	3/15
Long Island University/ C. W. Post Campus	Brookville	SU	A,B,M,D	Pri	F,S	C	4,757							479	60	31	10		547	28	41	27	4	Open
Long Island University/ Southampton Campus	Southampton	R	B,M	Pri	No	C	1,342	27						468	65	26	8	1	495					Open
Manhattan College	New York	SU	A,B,M	Pri	F,S	C	2,834							467	59	34	7		539	38	41	20	1	3/1
Manhattan School of Music	New York	U	B,M,D	Pri	No	C	426																	3/15
Manhattanville College	Purchase	SU	B,M	Pri	No	C	980							413	77	18	5		471	59	32	9	1	3/15
Mannes College of Music	New York	U	B,M	Pri	No	C	110																	3/1
Marist College	Poughkeepsie	SU	B,M	Pri	F,S	C	3,665								57	39	4			49	43	6	2	
Marymount College/Tarrytown	Tarrytown	SU	B	Pri	No	W	1,101							460	77	20	3		460	73	20	7		5/1
Marymount Manhattan College	New York	U	B	Pri	S	C	1,759							460	69	20	10	1	500	60	29	11		Open
Medaille College	Buffalo	U	A,B	Pri	No	C	1,146																	8/15
Mercy College	Dobbs Ferry	SU	A,B,M	Pri	No	C	6,078							396					416					Open
Molloy College	Rockville Centre	SU	A,B,M	Pri	No	PW	1,981	19																Open
Mount Saint Mary College	Newburgh	SU	B,M	Pri	No	C	1,599	20																Open
Nazareth College of Rochester	Rochester	SU	B,M	Pri	No	C	1,738	24						494	52	35	12	2	540	28	49	20	3	6/1
New York Institute of Technology/ Old Westbury	Old Westbury	SU	A,B,M	Pri	F,S	C	6,737																	Open
New York University	New York	U	A,B,M,D	Pri	F,S	C	15,225								22	48	26	4		12	34	41	13	2/1
Niagara University	Niagara University	SU	A,B,M	Pri	F	C	2,253																	8/15
Nyack College	Nyack	SU	A,B	Pri	No	C																		Open
Pace University	New York	SM	A,B,M,D	Pri	F,S	C	10,188							441	74	22	3	1	517	41	38	19	2	7/15
Parsons School of Design	New York	U	A,B,M	Pri	No	C	1,687																	Open
Polytechnic University/Brooklyn	Brooklyn	U	B,M,D	Pri	F	C	1,199							460	71	22	7		630	3	31	46	20	Open
Polytechnic University/Farmingdale	Farmingdale	SU	B,M,D	Pri	F	C	394							490	52	36	12		630	2	31	52	15	2/1
Pratt Institute	Brooklyn	U	A,B,M	Pri	F,S	C	1,848							460	77	16	7		520	60	24	14	2	1/15
Rensselaer Polytechnic Institute	Troy	U	B,M,D	Pri	F,S	C	4,307								29	45	22	3		2	15	51	32	8/1
Roberts Wesleyan College	Rochester	SU	A,B,M	Pri	No	C	1,039	23	33	27	27	6	6	464	69	27	4		503	47	39	13	1	8/1
Rochester Institute of Technology	Rochester	SU	A,B,M,D	Pri	F,S	C	10,335		20	21	19	25	15		54	34	11	1		21	37	32	10	
Russell Sage College	Troy	U	B	Pri	No	W	1,128							446	75	22	3		483	55	40	5		8/1
Saint Bonaventure University	St. Bonaventure	R	B,M	Pri	No	C	1,895	23	23	31	26	10	10	473	63	28	9		525	35	44	21	2	4/15
Saint Francis College	Brooklyn	U	A,B	Pri	No	C	2,256																	Open
Saint John Fisher College	Rochester	SU	B,M	Pri	No	C	4,869	22	32	36	20	8	4	465	70	25	5		525	40	40	19	1	Open
Saint John's University	Jamaica	SU	A,B,M,D	Pri	F,S	C	12,973							430					500					Open
Saint Joseph's College	Brooklyn	U	B	Pri	F,S	C	1,144							426	77	19	3		460	61	34	4		2/1
Saint Lawrence University	Canton	R	B,M	Pri	F,S	C	1,978							510	42	45	13	1	560	11	54	31	4	2/1
Saint Thomas Aquinas College	Sparkill	SU	B,M	Pri	No	C	1,932																	Open
Sarah Lawrence College	Bronxville	SU	B,M	Pri	No	C	1,020							590	17	37	39	7	560	26	42	28	4	Open
School of Visual Arts	New York	U	B,M	Pri	No	C	4,759																	3/1
Siena College	Loudonville	SU	B	Pri	No	C	3,492		14	33	34	9	10	491	58	36	6		560	21	51	25	3	2/1
Skidmore College	Saratoga Springs	SM	B,M	Pri	No	C	2,128								29	46	24	2		10	40	40	8	2/15
State University of New York at Albany	Albany	SU	B,M,D	Pub	F,S	C	11,406							506	45	44	10	1	580	11	49	34	6	2/15
State University of New York at Binghamton	Binghamton	SU	B,M,D	Pub	F,S	C	9,225	26	5	39	45	11		530	29	51	18	2	620	6	32	49	13	1/15
State University of New York at Buffalo	Buffalo	SU	B,M,D	Pub	F,S	C	17,087	24						480	59	33	7	1	575	17	44	31	8	1/5
State University of New York at Stony Brook	Stony Brook	SU	B,M,D	Pub	F,S	C	11,095							469	63	31	6		537	28	45	22	5	7/15
State University of New York/ College at Brockport	Brockport	SM	B,M	Pub	F,S	C	7,121	22	27	48	14	11		449	79	18	3		504	48	41	11		3/1
State University of New York/ College at Buffalo	Buffalo	U	B,M	Pub	F,S	C	9,848																	
State University of New York/ College at Cortland	Cortland	SM	B,M	Pub	F,S	C	5,359	24	11	38	39	10	2	460	82	17	1		524	43	49	9		2/1
State University of New York/ College at Fredonia	Fredonia	SM	B,M	Pub	F,S	C	4,422	23	20	42	27	8	3		69	27	4			35	48	15	1	3/1
State University of New York/ College at Geneseo	Geneseo	SM	B,M	Pub	F,S	C	5,162	25	4	5	30	48	13	541	27	53	19	1	608	4	38	48	10	1/15
State University of New York/ College at New Paltz	New Paltz	R	B,M	Pub	F,S	C	6,175	24						479	62	31	6	1	537	32	48	20	2	5/1
State University of New York/ College at Old Westbury	Westbury	SU	B	Pub	F,S	C	3,947																	6/1
State University of New York/ College at Oneonta	Oneonta	R	B,M	Pub	F,S	C	5,132	22	25	50	25			463	68	30	2		509	33	53	14		4/1
State University of New York/ College at Oswego	Oswego	SM	B,M	Pub	F,S	C	7,605	23	14	39	28	14	5	480	66	29	5		550	24	55	20	1	1/15
State University of New York/ College at Plattsburgh	Plattsburgh	SU	B,M	Pub	F,S	C	5,535	23	27	41	23	6	3	450	72	26	2		540	37	50	13		3/15
State University of New York/ College at Purchase	Purchase	SU	B,M	Pub	No	C	3,927							470	60	31	9	1	490	51	36	13		8/1
State University of New York/ College of Agriculture and Technology at Cobleskill	Cobleskill	R	A,B	Pub	No	C	2,697	19																Open
State University of New York/ College of Environmental Science and Forestry	Syracuse	U	A,B,M,D	Pub	F,S	C	1,197							519	36	48	15	1	584	11	41	41	7	Open
State University of New York/ Empire State College	Saratoga Springs		A,B,M	Pub	No	C	5,929																	Open
State University of New York/ Maritime College	Throgs Neck	SU	B,M	Pub	No	C	723							450	68	22	10		520	30	46	20	2	Open

TEST SCORES

NAME OF SCHOOL	TOWN	ENVIRONMENT (U-Urban, R-Rural, Su-Suburban, Sm-Small Town)	DEGREES AWARDED (A-Associate, B-Bachelor, M-Master, D-Doctorate)	CONTROL (Pri-Private, Pub-Public)	FRATERNITIES AND SORORITIES (F-Fraternities, S-Sororities, No-Neither)	STUDENTS (C-Coed, M-Men, W-Women, PM-Primarily Men, PW-Primarily Women)	UNDERGRADUATE ENROLLMENT FALL '93	ACT Median	ACT Below 21	ACT 21-23	ACT 24-26	ACT 27-28	ACT Above 28	SAT I Verbal Median	SAT I Verbal Below 500	SAT I Verbal 500-599	SAT I Verbal 600-700	SAT I Verbal Above 700	SAT I Math Median	SAT I Math Below 500	SAT I Math 500-599	SAT I Math 600-700	SAT I Math Above 700	APPLICATION DEADLINE Month/Day
State University of New York/ Potsdam College	Potsdam	R	B,M	Pub	F,S	C	3,854	22						480	68	28	4		520	35	51	12	2	4/1
Syracuse University	Syracuse	U	B,M,D	Pri	F,S	C	10,259								32	54	12	2		13	51	29	7	2/1
Touro College	New York	U	A,B,M	Pri	No	C	8,382																	Open
Union College	Schenectady	SM	B,M,D	Pri	F,S	C	2,015	28																2/1
United States Merchant Marine Academy	Kings Point	SU	B	Pub	No	C	987							530	35	39	19	7	590		56	39	4	
United States Military Academy	West Point	SM	B	Pub	No	C	4,273	28						558	20	51	26	3	653	1	19	52	29	3/1
University of Rochester	Rochester	SU	B,M,D	Pri	F,S	C	5,270		6	20	24	20	30		37	41	19	3		12	30	42	16	1/15
University of the State of New York/ Regents College Degrees	Albany		A,B	Pri	No	C	15,300																	Open
Utica College of Syracuse University	Utica	SU	B	Pri	F,S	C	1,308								80	17	3			52	36	11	1	
Vassar College	Poughkeepsie	SU	B,M	Pri	No	C	2,241							600	9	41	47	4	620	7	31	51	11	1/15
Wagner College	Staten Island	U	B,M	Pri	F,S	C	1,441							480	52	37	9	1	510	36	47	12	3	2/15
Webb Institute of Naval Architecture	Glen Cove	SU	B	Pri	No	PM	83							620		44	48	8	700			48	52	2/15
Wells College	Aurora	SM	B	Pri	No	W	415																	3/1
Yeshiva University	New York	U	A,B	Pri	No	C	1,990							559	35	39	19	7	629	18	37	31	14	2/15

North Carolina

NAME OF SCHOOL	TOWN	ENVIRONMENT	DEGREES AWARDED	CONTROL	FRATERNITIES AND SORORITIES	STUDENTS	UNDERGRADUATE ENROLLMENT FALL '93	ACT Median	ACT Below 21	ACT 21-23	ACT 24-26	ACT 27-28	ACT Above 28	SAT I Verbal Median	SAT I Verbal Below 500	SAT I Verbal 500-599	SAT I Verbal 600-700	SAT I Verbal Above 700	SAT I Math Median	SAT I Math Below 500	SAT I Math 500-599	SAT I Math 600-700	SAT I Math Above 700	APPLICATION DEADLINE
Appalachian State University	Boone	SM	B,M,D	Pub	F,S	C	10,693	22						471	67	26	6	1	519					1/31
Barber-Scotia College	Concord	SU	A,B	Pri	F,S	C	732							280					310					Open
Barton College	Wilson	SU	B	Pri	F,S	C	1,614							396	92	8			444	75	20	5		Open
Belmont Abbey College	Belmont	SU	B,M	Pri	F,S	C	867							449	84	14	2		499	70	24	6		7/31
Bennett College	Greensboro	U	B	Pri	S	W	664	17	90	5			5	385					395					Open
Campbell University	Buies Creek	R	A,B,M,D	Pri	No	C	2,183							439	75	20	4	1	476	59	29	11	1	Open
Catawba College	Salisbury	SM	B,M	Pri	No	C	995							420	78	19	3		480	57	32	11		Open
Davidson College	Davidson	SU	B	Pri	F	C	1,607	29						580	12	41	41	6	650	3	20	52	25	2/1
Duke University	Durham	SU	B,M,D	Pri	F,S	C	6,135							620	7	28	51	14	700	2	10	36	52	1/2
East Carolina University	Greenville	SU	B,M,D	Pub	F,S	C	14,776							434	82	15	3		487	57	35	7	1	3/15
Elizabeth City State University	Elizabeth City	SM	B	Pub	F,S	C	2,130							360	94	6			410	85	14	1		8/1
Elon College	Elon College	SM	B,M	Pri	F,S	C	3,141							439	80	17	3		483	57	35	7	1	
Fayetteville State University	Fayetteville	U	A,B,M	Pub	F,S	C	3,249							390	88	11	1		426	79	18	2	1	Open
Gardner-Webb University	Boiling Springs	SM	A,B,M	Pri	No	C	1,977	18	65	25	10			400	66	33	1		445	66	33	1		8/1
Greensboro College	Greensboro	U	B	Pri	No	C	963							430	81	17	2		460	66	28	5	1	Open
Guilford College	Greensboro	SU	A,B	Pri	No	C	1,225							498	54	31	12	2	531	30	45	21	4	3/1
High Point University	High Point	SU	B,M	Pri	F,S	C	2,399							420	83	15	2		450	65	28	7		Open
Johnson C. Smith University	Charlotte	U	B	Pri	F,S	C	1,393							339					362					7/1
Lees-McRae College	Banner Elk	R	B	Pri	No	C	659																	3/15
Lenoir-Rhyne College	Hickory	SM	B,M	Pri	F,S	C	1,339	21	10	79	3	5	3	451	77	19	4		496	61	28	10	1	Open
Livingstone College	Salisbury	SM	B	Pri	F,S	C	628		100					304	98	2			340	98	2			4/30
Mars Hill College	Mars Hill	R	B	Pri	F,S	C	1,024							406	66	28	5	1	442	51	38	10	1	Open
Meredith College	Raleigh	SU	B,M	Pri	No	W	2,190							440					480					2/15
Methodist College	Fayetteville	SU	A,B	Pri	No	C	1,508	20	46	40	6	8		398	93	5	2		459	81	15	3	1	Open
Montreat-Anderson College	Montreat	R	A,B	Pri	No	C	356							372					401					Open
Mount Olive College	Mount Olive	SM	A,B	Pri	No	C	863							370	91	8	1	1	430	76	18	6		Open
North Carolina Agricultural and Technical State University	Greensboro	U	B,M	Pub	F,S	C	7,033							384					441					6/1
North Carolina Central University	Durham	U	B,M	Pub	F,S	C	4,318	21						371					410	89	9	2		7/1
North Carolina School of the Arts	Winston-Salem	U	B,M	Pub	No		690																	4/1
North Carolina State University	Raleigh	U	A,B,M,D		F,S	C	21,408							493	55	34	10	1	578	15	44	30	10	2/1
North Carolina Wesleyan College	Rocky Mount	SU	B	Pri	F,S	C	730	21						420	87	11	2		430	83	13	4		7/15
Pembroke State University	Pembroke	SM	B,M	Pub	F,S	C	2,703							380	92	6	1		430	81	17	2		7/15
Pfeiffer College	Misenheimer	R	B,M	Pri	No	C	815							390	90	7	1		441	71	19	6	1	Open
Queens College	Charlotte	SU	B,M	Pri	F,S	C	1,179	25						500	62	24	11		510	46	38	13		Open
Saint Andrews Presbyterian College	Laurinburg	SM	B	Pri	No	C	761																	Open
Saint Augustine's College	Raleigh	U	B	Pri	F,S		1,745																	Open
Salem College	Winston-Salem	U	B,M	Pri	No	PW	757							530	20	50	25	5	510	15	55	24	6	8/10
Shaw University	Raleigh	U	A,B	Pri	No	C	2,504																	Open
University of North Carolina at Asheville	Asheville	SU	B,M	Pub	F,S	C	3,111	24		46	39	15		500	48	38	13	1	540	24	46	27	3	4/1
University of North Carolina at Chapel Hill	Chapel Hill	SM	B,M,D	Pub	F,S	C	15,709							527					594					1/15
University of North Carolina at Charlotte	Charlotte	U	B,M,D	Pub	F,S	C	13,216							435	79	18	2	1	491	51	38	10	1	7/1
University of North Carolina at Greensboro	Greensboro	U	B,M,D	Pub	F,S	C	9,379							450	72	21	6	1	490	51	38	9	2	8/1
University of North Carolina at Wilmington	Wilmington	SU	B,M	Pub	F,S	C	7,780	22	26	48	26			441	78	18	3	1	494	49	41	9	1	2/15
Wake Forest University	Winston-Salem	SU	B,M,D	Pri	F,S	C	3,693								17	48	32	3		5	24	49	22	1/15
Warren Wilson College	Asheville	SM	B,M	Pri	No	C	489		30	20	30	7	13		40	38	20	2		40	38	21	1	3/15
Western Carolina University	Cullowhee	R	B,M	Pub	F,S	C	5,517							400	87	11	2	1	450	70	24	5	1	8/15
Wingate College	Wingate	SM	A,B,M	Pri	F,S	C	1,393							398	89	9	2	1	444	74	19	7	1	Open
Winston-Salem State University	Winston-Salem	SU	B,M,D	Pub	F,S	C	2,817							369	96	3	1		405	93	6	1		Open

North Dakota

NAME OF SCHOOL	TOWN	ENVIRONMENT	DEGREES AWARDED	CONTROL	FRATERNITIES AND SORORITIES	STUDENTS	UNDERGRADUATE ENROLLMENT FALL '93	ACT Median	ACT Below 21	ACT 21-23	ACT 24-26	ACT 27-28	ACT Above 28	SAT I Verbal Median	SAT I Verbal Below 500	SAT I Verbal 500-599	SAT I Verbal 600-700	SAT I Verbal Above 700	SAT I Math Median	SAT I Math Below 500	SAT I Math 500-599	SAT I Math 600-700	SAT I Math Above 700	APPLICATION DEADLINE
Dickinson State University	Dickinson	R	A,B	Pub	S	C	1,613	20	69	13	13	2	3											8/15
Jamestown College	Jamestown	SM	B	Pri	No	C	1,066	22	39	31	20	5	5											Open
Mayville State University	Mayville	R	A,B	Pub	S	C	716																	Open
Minot State University	Minot	SM	A,B,M	Pub	F,S	C	3,901		61	23	13	3												Open

Column key: ENVIRONMENT: U-Urban, R-Rural, Su-Suburban, Sm-Small Town · DEGREES AWARDED: A-Associate, B-Bachelor, M-Master, D-Doctorate · CONTROL: Pri-Private, Pub-Public · FRATERNITIES AND SORORITIES: F-Fraternities, S-Sororities · STUDENTS: C-Coed, M-Men, W-Women, PM-Primarily Men, PW-Primarily Women

NAME OF SCHOOL	TOWN	ENV	DEGREES	CONTROL	FRAT/SOR	STUD	ENROLL FALL '93	ACT Med	<21	21-23	24-26	27-28	>28	SATV Med	<500	500-599	600-700	>700	SATM Med	<500	500-599	600-700	>700	DEADLINE
North Dakota State University of Agriculture and Applied Science	Fargo	U	B,M,D	Pub	F,S	C	8,496	23	30	45	20		5											Open
University of Mary	Bismarck	SU	B,M	Pri	No	C	1,758	21	50	26	18	4	2											7
University of North Dakota	Grand Forks	U	B,M,D	Pub	F,S	C	9,769		15		27	41	17	465	68	22	7	3	535					
Valley City State University	Valley City	SM	B	Pub	F,S	C	1,052	21																Open

Ohio

NAME OF SCHOOL	TOWN	ENV	DEGREES	CONTROL	FRAT/SOR	STUD	ENROLL FALL '93	ACT Med	<21	21-23	24-26	27-28	>28	SATV Med	<500	500-599	600-700	>700	SATM Med	<500	500-599	600-700	>700	DEADLINE
Antioch College	Yellow Springs	SM	B		No	C	778	24	22	29	27	11	11	520	39	40	20	1	500	44	35	20	1	2/1
Art Academy of Cincinnati	Cincinnati	U	A,B	Pri	No	C	208	18	90	5	5			420	90	10			420	90	10			8/15
Ashland University	Ashland	SM	A,B,M,D	Pri	F,S	C	2,631	21	22	47	4	6	21	410	84	13	2		438	67	22	10		7/1
Baldwin-Wallace College	Berea	SU	B,M	Pri	F,S	C	4,178	23	28	31	25	8	7	460	62	33	5	1	530	36	39	21	4	8/15
Bluffton College	Bluffton	SM	B	Pri	No	C	841	22	42	48			10	438	69	27	4		512	44	33	17	6	2/1
Bowling Green State University	Bowling Green	SM	A,B,M,D	Pub	F,S	C	14,813	22	32	37	21	6	4	440	73	21	5	1	500	49	36	13	2	8/1
Capital University	Columbus	U	B,M	Pri	F,S	C	1,605	23	23	32	26	11	8	465	64	29	7		510	44	36	15	5	2/15
Case Western Reserve University	Cleveland	U	B,M,D	Pri	F,S	C	3,564		1	6	20	20	53		21	36	34	9		3	17	36	44	2/15
Cedarville College	Cedarville	SM	A,B	Pri	No	C	2,278	23	19	31	26	12	12	480	57	30	12	1	520	41	31	23	4	Open
Central State University	Wilberforce	R	A,B,M	Pub	F,S	C	3,068																	6/15
Cincinnati College of Mortuary Science	Cincinnati	U	A,B	Pri	No	C	171																	10/1
Cleveland Institute of Art	Cleveland	U	B		F,S	C	518	22	47	16	22	14	1	464	64	24	8	4	474	53	35	12		
Cleveland Institute of Music	Cleveland	U	B,M,D	Pri	No	C	181							570					550					1/15
Cleveland State University	Cleveland	U	B,M,D	Pub	F,S	C	11,966	19	61	23	11	3	2	410	82	16	2	1	430	70	20	9	1	Open
College of Mount Saint Joseph	Cincinnati	SU	A,B,M	Pri	No	C	2,420	21	45	27	18	6	4	440	70	25	5		480	55	35	10		Open
College of Wooster	Wooster	SU	B		F,S	C	1,704	25	9		37	39	15	520	39	40	18	3	560	23	44	24	9	2/15
Columbus College of Art and Design	Columbus	U	B	Pri	No	C	1,695	21	46		40		14	440	62	30	8		438	63	28	9		8/15
Defiance College	Defiance	SM	A,B,M	Pri	F,S	C	934	21	67	10	15	7	1	400	91	8	1		438	68	26	8		8/15
Denison University	Granville	SM	B	Pri	F,S	C	1,940	27	11	27	28	15	19	510	54	36	9	1	570	26	45	23	6	2/1
DeVry Institute of Technology/Columbus	Columbus	U	A,B	Pri	No	C	2,798																	Open
Dyke College	Cleveland	U	A,B	Pri	F	C	1,426																	8/1
Franciscan University of Steubenville	Steubenville	SU	A,B,M	Pri	F,S	C	1,543	23	26	27	22	13	12	488	51	34	14	1	516	41	34	22	3	7/31
Franklin University	Columbus	U	A,B	Pri	No	C	3,825																	6/1
Heidelberg College	Tiffin	SM	B,M	Pri	F,S	C	1,094	21	27	31	17	13	12	416	32	50	15	3	460	25	55	15	5	4/15
Hiram College	Hiram	R	B	Pri	No	C	840	25	17	26	27	16	14	510	49	37	14		540	36	44	21	2	6/1
John Carroll University	University Heights	SU	B,M	Pri	F,S	C	3,560	23	35	22	29	9	5	502	46	39	14	1	561	22	42	30	6	3/15
Kent State University	Kent	SM	B,M,D	Pub	F,S	C	17,812																	2/15
Kenyon College	Gambier	SM	B	Pri	F,S	C	1,454	27		21	29	23	27	570	24	43	27	6	593	9	48	34	9	2/15
Lake Erie College	Painesville	SM	B,M	Pri	No	C	670	21	38	40	9	7	6	434					473					Open
Lourdes College	Sylvania	SU	A,B	Pri	S	C	1,605	20	66	14	10	10												8/10
Malone College	Canton	U	A,B,M	Pri	No	C	1,433	21	51	26	15	3	5	430	72	20	8		466	65	17	18		7/1
Marietta College	Marietta	SM	A,B,M	Pri	F,S	C	1,235	24						500					540					1/31
Miami University	Oxford	SM	B,M,D	Pub	F,S	C	14,379		7	24	38	18	13		41	46	12	1		10	43	40	7	Open
Mount Union College	Alliance	SU	B	Pri	F,S	C	1,407	23	31	28	21	13	7											8/1
Mount Vernon Nazarene College	Mt. Vernon	SM	A,B,M	Pri	No	C	1,208	22	44	25	20	8	3											
Muskingum College	New Concord	SM	B,M	Pri	F,S	C	1,188	22	45	21	20	9	5	430	73	22	3	2	500	45	39	15	1	6/30
Notre Dame College of Ohio	South Euclid	SU	A,B,M	Pri		W	750	19	58	29	13		3	450	84	16			440	84	16			1/15
Oberlin College	Oberlin	SM	B,M		No	C	2,669	28	6	9	23	18	47	610	10	35	48	8	630	6	27	51	17	Open
Ohio Dominican College	Columbus	SU	A,B	Pri	No	C	1,594							441					509					Open
Ohio Northern University	Ada	SU	B,D	Pri	F,S	C	2,569	24	24	30	26	12	8											2/15
Ohio State University	Columbus	U	B,M,D	Pub	F,S	C	37,044		30	28	21	10	11											7/1
Ohio State University at Lima	Lima	SU	A,B	Pub	No	C	1,191		52	27	14	5	2		75	25				55	35	10		7/1
Ohio State University at Mansfield	Mansfield	SU	A,B	Pub	No	C	1,306		56	27	12	3	2		72	28				59	31	3	7	7/1
Ohio State University at Marion	Marion	R	A,B	Pub	No	C	1,021		59	22	14	4	1		87	10	3			67	23	10		7/1
Ohio State University at Newark	Newark	SU	A,B	Pub	No	C	1,587	18	54	24	17	3	2		72	25	3			63	27	9	1	3/1
Ohio University	Athens	SM	A,B,M,D	Pub	F,S	C	15,323	23	17	36	29	10	8	470	62	30	7	1	520	40	41	17	2	3/1
Ohio Wesleyan University	Delaware	SM	B	Pri	F,S	C	1,828	26	16	18	24	16	26	523	39	38	22	1	580	13	43	32	12	4/20
Otterbein College	Westerville	SU	B,M	Pri	F,S	C	2,465	23						430	69	23	7	1	430	44	38	14	4	Open
Shawnee State University	Portsmouth	SM	A,B	Pub	F,S	C	3,312		67	23	7	2	1											Open
Tiffin University	Tiffin	SM	A,B,M	Pri	F,S	C	1,013	19	78	13	6													10/15
Union Institute	Cincinnati		B,D	Pri		C	412																	8/12
University of Akron	Akron	U	A,B,M,D	Pub	F,S	C	21,782	23						464	65	28	7		533	34	36	30		Open
University of Cincinnati	Cincinnati	U	A,B,M,D	Pub	F,S	C	13,047	23						504	48	38	13	2	578	17	41	32	11	Open
University of Dayton	Dayton	SU	A,B,M,D	Pri	F,S	C	6,562	25	8	41	39	13		439	76	16	8		473	58	25	15	2	Open
University of Findlay	Findlay	SM	A,B,M	Pri	F,S	C	2,337	20																8/15
University of Rio Grande	Rio Grande	R	A,B,M	Pri	F,S	C	2,032	19	50	25	15	7	3											8/1
University of Toledo	Toledo	SU	A,B,M,D	Pub	F,S	C	20,798	21	45	25	16	6	8	440	67	20	10	3	510	42	29	18	11	Open
Urbana University	Urbana	SM	A,B	Pri	F	C	911	19																Open
Ursuline College	Pepper Pike	SU	A,B,M	Pri	No	PW	1,416	20	50	29	10	6	5	390	82	13	5		410	68	25	7		Open
Walsh University	North Canton	SM	A,B,M	Pri	No	C	1,356	22																6/1
Wilberforce University	Wilberforce	R	B	Pri	F,S	C	845	17																Open
Wilmington College	Wilmington	SM	B	Pri	F,S	C	889	21	55	21	15	6	3	522	30	50	17	3	575	16	45	33	6	3/15
Wittenberg University	Springfield	SU	B	Pri	F,S	C	2,217	24	8	12	37	29	14											Open
Wright State University	Dayton	SU	B,M,D	Pub	F,S	C	12,727																	Open
Xavier University	Cincinnati	SU	A,B,M	Pri	No	C	3,956	24	25	23	24	14	14	480	59	32	8	1	520	41	33	21	5	Open
Youngstown State University	Youngstown	U	A,B,M,D	Pub	F,S	C	13,295	19	61	20	10	4	4											8/15

Oklahoma

NAME OF SCHOOL	TOWN	ENV	DEGREES	CONTROL	FRAT/SOR	STUD	ENROLL FALL '93	ACT Med	<21	21-23	24-26	27-28	>28	SATV Med	<500	500-599	600-700	>700	SATM Med	<500	500-599	600-700	>700	DEADLINE
Bartlesville Wesleyan College	Bartlesville	SU	A,B	Pri	No	C	508	21	45	23	26	5	2											Open
Cameron University	Lawton	SM	A,B	Pub	F,S	C	5,614	19	74	17	6	3	1											Open
East Central University	Ada	SM	B,M	Pub	F,S	C	3,841	20	1	61	31	6	1											Open

NAME OF SCHOOL	TOWN	ENV.	DEGREES	CONTROL	FRAT.	STUD.	ENROLL. '93	ACT Med.	<21	21-23	24-26	27-28	>28	SAT V Med.	<500	500-599	600-700	>700	SAT M Med.	<500	500-599	600-700	>700	DEADLINE
Langston University	Langston	R	A,B,M	Pub	F,S	C	2,100																	Open
Northeastern State University	Tahlequah	SM	B,M,D	Pub	F,S	C	6,745	20	78	15	4	2	1											Open
Northwestern Oklahoma State University	Alva	SM	B,M	Pub	F,S	C	1,624		58	25	11	5	1											Open
Oklahoma Baptist University	Shawnee	SM	A,B		F,S	C	2,412	23	28	24	17	19	12											Open
Oklahoma Christian University of Science and Arts	Oklahoma City	SU	B,M	Pri	No	C	1,647		41	21	18	7	13											Open
Oklahoma City University	Oklahoma City	U	A,B,M,D	Pri	F,S	C	2,154	23	32	24	21	12	11	501	44	36	16	4	531	33	33	31	2	Open
Oklahoma Panhandle State University	Goodwell	R	A,B	Pub	No	C	1,197																	9/15
Oklahoma State University	Stillwater	SM	B,M,D	Pub	F,S	C	14,488	23	23	30	24	12	12											Open
Oral Roberts University	Tulsa	SU	B,M,D	Pri	No	C	2,787	24	45	22	17	8	8	500	68	25	7		500	54	28	16	2	3/1
Phillips University	Enid	SM	A,B,M	Pri	No	C	730	21	42	28	17	7	6	430					470					8/23
Southeastern Oklahoma State University	Durant	R	B,M	Pub	F,S	C	3,754	19	62	22	10	4	2											Open
Southern Nazarene University	Bethany	SU	A,B,M	Pri	No	C	1,536	21	43	24	17	8	8											8/1
Southwestern Oklahoma State University	Weatherford	SM	A,B,M	Pub	F,S	C	4,423																	
University of Central Oklahoma	Edmond	SU	B,M	Pub	F,S	C	12,192	20	56	25	13	5	1											Open
University of Oklahoma	Norman	SU	B,M,D	Pub	F,S	C	14,832	24	20	31	21	11	16											8/15
University of Science and Arts of Oklahoma	Chickasha	SM	B	Pub	No	C	1,613	19	58	20	14	5	3											Open
University of Tulsa	Tulsa	U	B,M,D	Pri	F,S	C	3,369	24	20	25	26	14	15	527	34	46	18	3	580	18	39	32	11	Open

Oregon

NAME OF SCHOOL	TOWN	ENV.	DEGREES	CONTROL	FRAT.	STUD.	ENROLL. '93	ACT Med.	<21	21-23	24-26	27-28	>28	SAT V Med.	<500	500-599	600-700	>700	SAT M Med.	<500	500-599	600-700	>700	DEADLINE
Bassist College	Portland	U	A,B	Pri	No	C	174																	
Cascade College	Portland	U	B	Pri	F,S	C																		9/1
Concordia College	Portland	SU	A,B	Pri	No	C	1,017	19	50	40	10			434	78	13	7	2	466	65	21	10	4	Open
Eastern Oregon State College	La Grande	R	A,B,M	Pub	No	C	1,820																	Open
George Fox College	Newberg	SM	B,M,D	Pri	No	C	1,326							470	59	32	8	1	500	46	30	19	3	8/1
Lewis and Clark College	Portland	SU	B,M		F	C	1,795		8	18	34	22	18		29	46	21	4		15	45	31	9	6/1
Linfield College	McMinnville	SM	B,M	Pri	F,S	C	1,632	25	7	34	23	16	21	495	54	30	11	4	556	24	43	26	7	2/1
Marylhurst College	Marylhurst	SU	B,M	Pri	No	C	1,035																	2/15
Oregon Institute of Technology	Klamath Falls	SM	A,B	Pub	F,S	C	2,500							447	79	17	4		482	60	28	10	2	Open
Oregon State University	Corvallis	SM	B,M,D	Pub	F,S	C	11,430	22	34	23	21	12	10	440	65	30	6		520	38	35	22	4	7/1
Pacific Northwest College of Art	Portland	U	B	Pri	No	C	264																	3/1
Pacific University	Forest Grove	SM	B,M,D	Pri	F,S	C	1,027	24	21	34	25	10	10	480	67	28	4	1	530	37	40	21	2	8/15
Portland State University	Portland	U	B,M,D	Pub	F,S	C	10,277	22	34	40	14	8	4	420	78	18	4		480	57	29	12	2	3/1
Reed College	Portland	U	B,M	Pri	No	C	1,260							610	10	30	48	12	640	6	25	44	25	6/1
Southern Oregon State College	Ashland	SM	A,B,M	Pub	No	C	4,162	21						440					473					2/1
University of Oregon	Eugene	SU	B,M,D	Pub	F,S	C	13,074																	Open
University of Portland	Portland	SU	B,M	Pri	No	C	2,213							470					530					3/1
Warner Pacific College	Portland	U	A,B,M	Pri	No	C	640		50	40	10				86	7	7			57	39	4		8/15
Western Baptist College	Salem	U	A,B	Pri	No	C	536							404	78	18	4		429	62	34	4		Open
Western Oregon State College	Monmouth	R	A,B,M	Pub	No	C	3,715																	4/15
Willamette University	Salem	SU	B,M,D		F,S	C	1,638	26	6	23	33	19	16	520	36	42	18	3	580	16	40	34	9	2/1

Pennsylvania

NAME OF SCHOOL	TOWN	ENV.	DEGREES	CONTROL	FRAT.	STUD.	ENROLL. '93	ACT Med.	<21	21-23	24-26	27-28	>28	SAT V Med.	<500	500-599	600-700	>700	SAT M Med.	<500	500-599	600-700	>700	DEADLINE
Academy of the New Church	Bryn Athyn	SU	A,B,M	Pri	No	C	125																	
Albright College	Reading	SU	B	Pri	F,S	C	1,279	22						500	48	28	21	3	530	41	33	23	3	3/1
Allegheny College	Meadville	SM	B	Pri	F,S	C	1,790		13	20	31	23	13	480					540					2/15
Allentown College of Saint Francis de Sales	Center Valley	R	B,M	Pri	S	C	2,031								43	43	13	1		14	48	32	6	2/15
Alvernia College	Reading	SU	A,B		No	C	1,261							460	65	26	8	1	510	44	37	17	2	8/1
Beaver College	Glenside	SU	A,B,M	Pri	No	C	1,398							460	71	27	2	1	505	42	42	13	3	Open
Bloomsburg University of Pennsylvania	Bloomsburg	SM	A,B,M	Pub	F,S	C	6,793							459	69	28	3		520	34	51	14	1	Open
Bryn Mawr College	Bryn Mawr	SU	B,M,D	Pri	No	PW	1,309																	1/15
Bucknell University	Lewisburg	SM	B,M	Pri	F,S	C	3,357								25	52	21	1		4	31	47	18	1/1
Cabrini College	Radnor	SU	B,M	Pri	No	C	1,463							448	76	18	6		468	65	28	6	1	8/15
California University of Pennsylvania	California	SM	A,B,M	Pub	F,S	C	5,383							409					449					Open
Carlow College	Pittsburgh	U	B,M	Pri	No	PW	1,820																	8/1
Carnegie Mellon University	Pittsburgh	SU	B,M,D	Pri	F,S	C	4,556							469	67	25	7	1	489	58	35	5	2	Open
Cedar Crest College	Allentown	SU	B	Pri	No	W	1,545	22	37	33	11	15	4	491	56	28	16		481	50	34	10	6	2/1
Chatham College	Pittsburgh	U	B,M	Pri		W	621							495	46	44	10		483	45	42	13		Open
Chestnut Hill College	Philadelphia	SU	A,B,M	Pri	No	PW	815							429					474					3/15
Cheyney University of Pennsylvania	Cheyney	SU	B,M	Pub	F,S	C	1,195							460	23	67	10		480	20	65	15		6/30
Clarion University of Pennsylvania	Clarion	SM	A,B,M	Pub	F,S	C	5,691																	
College Misericordia	Dallas	SM	A,B,M	Pri	No	C	1,614							440	78	19	3	1	470	59	31	8	1	4/1
Curtis Institute of Music	Philadelphia	U	B,M	Pri	No	C	120								23	44	14	1		23	46	29	2	Open
Delaware Valley College	Doylestown	SU	A,B	Pri	No	C	1,468							460	66	26	7	1	550	30	38	25	7	1/15
Dickinson College	Carlisle	SU	B	Pri	F,S	C	1,951	24	11	47	35		6	490					520	40	40	17	3	Open
Drexel University	Philadelphia	U	B,M,D	Pri	F,S	C	7,272							421	88	11	1		475	63	31	5	1	2/20
Duquesne University	Pittsburgh	U	B,M,D	Pri	F,S	C	5,179	23	20	40		40		450	68	27	5	1	476	56	30	13	1	3/1
East Stroudsburg University	East Stroudsburg	SM	B,M	Pub	F,S	C	4,569							490	54	38	8	1	540	27	46	22	5	7/1
Eastern College	St. Davids	SM	A,B,M	Pri	No	C	1,412								22	51	25	2		5	36	44	15	3/1
Edinboro University of Pennsylvania	Edinboro	SM	A,B,M	Pub	F,S	C	7,135	23	31	30	27	5	7	450	66	28	5	1	510	40	41	17	2	Open
Elizabethtown College	Elizabethtown	SM	B	Pri	No	C	1,788	22						460	68	25	7		490	52	30	17	2	Open
Franklin and Marshall College	Lancaster	SU	B	Pri	S	C	1,844		21	24	35	20			24	59	15	2		9	51	35	5	2/15
Gannon University	Erie	U	A,B,M	Pri	F,S	C	3,384																	2/1
Geneva College	Beaver Falls	SM	A,B,M	Pri	No	C	1,347																	Open
Gettysburg College	Gettysburg	SM	B	Pri	F,S	C	1,985																	2/15

KEY: ENVIRONMENT: U-Urban, R-Rural, Su-Suburban, Sm-Small Town · DEGREES AWARDED: A-Associate, B-Bachelor, M-Master, D-Doctorate · CONTROL: Pri-Private, Pub-Public · FRATERNITIES AND SORORITIES: F-Fraternities, S-Sororities, T-Both, N-Neither · STUDENTS: C-Coed, M-Men, W-Women, PM-Primarily Men, PW-Primarily Women

Name of School	Town	Environ.	Degrees	Control	Frat./Soror.	Students	Undergrad Enroll. Fall '93	ACT Med.	ACT <21	ACT 21–23	ACT 24–26	ACT 27–28	ACT >28	SAT V Med.	SATV <500	SATV 500–599	SATV 600–700	SATV >700	SAT M Med.	SATM <500	SATM 500–599	SATM 600–700	SATM >700	App. Deadline
Gratz College	Melrose Park	SU	B,M	Pri	No	C	78	27	4	16	28	22	30	537	28	52	18	2	607	7	35	45	13	2/15
Grove City College	Grove City	SM	B	Pri	F,S	C	2,248							470	69	23	7	1	500	57	32	10	1	Open
Gwynedd-Mercy College	Gwynedd Valley	SU	A,B,M	Pri	No	C	1,824								5	24	58	13		3	11	47	39	1/15
Haverford College	Haverford	SU	B	Pri	No	C	1,084							427					456					7/1
Holy Family College	Philadelphia	SU	A,B,M	Pri	No	C	2,204							440					450					5/1
Immaculata College	Immaculata	SU	A,B,M,D	Pri	No	PW	1,799							444					495					12/31
Indiana University of Pennsylvania	Indiana	SM	A,B,M,D	Pub	F,S	C	12,507							510					560					3/1
Juniata College	Huntingdon	SM	B	Pri	No	C	1,281																	8/1
King's College	Wilkes Barre	U	A,B,M	Pri	No	C	2,257																	Open
Kutztown University	Kutztown	R	B,M	Pub	F,S	C	6,857							420	89	11			420	85	14	1		Open
La Roche College	Pittsburgh	SU	B,M	Pri	S	C	1,469							500	40	41	10	9	560	20	50	20	10	8/15
La Salle University	Philadelphia	U	A,B,M	Pri	F,S	C	4,707								29	50	20	1		4	32	49	16	1/15
Lafayette College	Easton	SU	B	Pri	F,S	C	2,244																	Open
Lebanon Valley College of Pennsylvania	Annville	R	A,B,M	Pri	F,S	C	1,467							467	65	28	7		521	42	39	15	4	2/15
Lehigh University	Bethlehem	SU	B,M,D	Pri	F,S	C	4,483								37	47	15	1		5	29	53	13	1/1
Lincoln University	Lincoln University	R	B,M	Pub	F,S	C	1,260							460	72	26	2		520	41	45	13	1	6/1
Lock Haven University of Pennsylvania	Lock Haven	SM	A,B,M	Pub	F,S	C	3,895							470	72	22	6		520	52	35	12	2	4/1
Lycoming College	Williamsport	SM	B	Pri	F,S	C	1,453							421	83	16	1		461	66	26	7	1	7/1
Mansfield University	Mansfield	R	A,B,M	Pub	F,S	C	2,891	24						440	75	21	4		460	64	29	7		Open
Marywood College	Scranton	SU	B,M	Pri	No	C	1,854	23	19	48	29	3	1	450	46	38	16		570	41	43	15	1	Open
Mercyhurst College	Erie	SU	A,B,M	Pri	No	C	2,238	24	14	48	19	12	7	509	46	41	12	1	555	26	43	24	7	4/1
Messiah College	Grantham	SM	B	Pri	No	C	2,331	24							61	33	6			26	53	19	2	Open
Millersville University of Pennsylvania	Millersville	SM	A,B,M	Pub	F,S	C	6,678		80					410	80					80				3/1
Moore College of Art and Design	Philadelphia	U	B	Pri		W	380		80						55	35	10			30	48	20	2	2/15
Moravian College	Bethlehem	SU	B,M	Pri	F,S	C	1,204	23	8	46	46			506	44	46	9	1	565	16	51	29	4	Open
Muhlenberg College	Allentown	SU	B	Pri	F	C	2,006	25	4	41	46	7	2	410	86	12	2		440	75	20	5		Open
Neumann College	Aston	SM	A,B,M	Pri		C	1,242																	Open
Penn State University at Erie/Behrend College	Erie	SU	A,B,M	Pub	F,S	C	3,081							446	76	21	3		510	43	38	18	1	Open
Penn State University/University Park Campus	University Park	SU	A,B,M,D		F,S	C	30,963							506	45	40	13	2	591	14	37	37	12	11/30
Philadelphia College of Bible	Langhorne	SU	A,B,M	Pri	No	C	880	21	32	26	30	11	1	460	70	23	7		468	63	26	10	1	Open
Philadelphia College of Pharmacy and Science	Philadelphia	U	B,M,D	Pri	F,S	C	1,729							470	61	32	6	1	570	19	51	27	3	Open
Philadelphia College of Textiles and Science	Philadelphia	SU	A,B,M	Pri	F,S	C	2,706	21						455					520					Open
Point Park College	Pittsburgh	U	A,B,M	Pri	F,S	C	2,575	21						418	84	15	1		424	78	20	2		Open
Robert Morris College	Coraopolis	SU	A,B,M	Pri	F,S	C	4,429							396	90	7	2	1	451	66	27	5	2	Open
Rosemont College	Rosemont	SU	B,M	Pri	No	W	630							505					502					Open
Saint Francis College	Loretto	R	B,M	Pri	F,S	C	1,674								79	15	4			57	30	10	2	Open
Saint Joseph's University	Philadelphia	SU	A,B,M	Pri	F,S	C	3,793							500	50	38	11	1	540	24	51	20	5	5/1
Saint Vincent College	Latrobe	SM	B,M	Pri	No	C	1,217								64	28	8			45	35	17	3	Open
Seton Hill College	Greensburg	SM	B	Pri	No	PW	962																	Open
Shippensburg University of Pennsylvania	Shippensburg	R	B,M	Pub	F,S	C	5,557							460	68	29	3		520	31	54	15	1	4/1
Slippery Rock University	Slippery Rock	SM	B,M	Pub	F,S	C	6,919		18	40	38	3	1		56	33	10	1		25	50	22	3	3/15
Susquehanna University	Selinsgrove	SM	A,B		F,S	C	1,515								7	22	49	23		2	12	41	45	2/1
Swarthmore College	Swarthmore	SU	A,B	Pri	F	C	1,388							455					508					6/15
Temple University	Philadelphia	U	A,B,M,D	Pub	F,S	C	24,939	20						418					444					1/1
Thiel College	Greenville	R	A,B	Pri	F,S	C	931																	Open
University of Pennsylvania	Philadelphia	U	A,B,M,D	Pri	F,S	C	11,448	29						599	11	34	47	8	670	2	11	40	47	1/1
University of Pittsburgh	Pittsburgh	U	B,M,D	Pub	F,S	C	17,607							480	57	32	10	1	540	27	46	23	4	7/1
University of Pittsburgh at Bradford	Bradford	SM	A,B	Pri	F,S	C	1,261							440					487					Open
University of Pittsburgh at Greensburg	Greensburg	SU	B	Pri	No	C	1,447							422	72	26	2		474	59	29	10	2	Open
University of Pittsburgh at Johnstown	Johnstown	SU	A,B	Pub	F,S	C	3,008							509	44	44	11	1	561	15	56	26	4	3/1
University of Scranton	Scranton	U	A,B,M	Pri	No	C	4,167							443	74	20	6		452	66	24	10		Open
University of the Arts	Philadelphia	U	A,B,M	Pri	No	C	1,184								42	45	12	1		14	48	35	3	2/15
Ursinus College	Collegeville	SU	B	Pri	F,S	C	1,148								35	49	14	1		8	45	37	10	1/15
Villanova University	Villanova	SU	A,B,M,D	Pri	F,S	C	7,643								35					35	43	18	4	3/1
Washington and Jefferson College	Washington	SM	B	Pri	F,S	C	1,129								44	47	7	2						Open
Waynesburg College	Waynesburg	SM	A,B,M	Pri	F,S	C	1,342																	Open
West Chester University of Pennsylvania	West Chester	SM	A,B,M	Pub	F,S	C	9,782							450	76	21	2	1	500	50	40	9	1	11/15
Westminster College	New Wilmington	R	B,M	Pri	F,S	C	1,483	24						466	68	24	7	1	491	49	32	15	4	4/1
Widener University	Chester	SU	B,M,D	Pri	F,S	C	2,125							420	77	16	6		470	59	26	11	3	Open
Wilkes University	Wilkes Barre	U	B,M,D	Pri	No	C	2,406							465	67	22	11		500	49	35	16	2	8/1
Wilson College	Chambersburg	SM	A,B	Pri	No	W	193							469					517	27	56	15	2	Open
York College of Pennsylvania	York	SU	A,B,M	Pri	F,S	C	4,714																	Open

Puerto Rico

Name of School	Town	Environ.	Degrees	Control	Frat./Soror.	Students	Undergrad Enroll. Fall '93	ACT Med.	ACT <21	ACT 21–23	ACT 24–26	ACT 27–28	ACT >28	SAT V Med.	SATV <500	SATV 500–599	SATV 600–700	SATV >700	SAT M Med.	SATM <500	SATM 500–599	SATM 600–700	SATM >700	App. Deadline
Bayamon Technological University College	Bayamon	SU	A,B	Pub	No	C	4,282																	12/20
Caribbean University	Bayamon	U	A,B				3,041																	8/31
Central University of Bayamon	Bayamon	U	A,B,M	Pri	No	C	805																	4/15
Conservatory of Music of Puerto Rico	Hato Rey	U	B	Pub	No	C	283								10	90				60	35	5		4/15
Escuela de Artes Plasticas	San Juan	U	B	Pub	No	C	192																	5/16
Inter American University/Arecibo Campus	Arecibo	SU	A,B	Pri	F,S	C	4,379																	5/1
Inter American University of Puerto Rico/Aguadilla Regional College	Aguadilla	U	A,B,M,D	Pri		C																		5/1

TEST SCORES

Legend:
- ENVIRONMENT: U-Urban R-Rural Sub-Suburban Sm-Small Town
- DEGREES AWARDED: A-Associate B-Bachelor M-Master D-Doctorate
- CONTROL: Pri-Private, Pub-Public
- FRATERNITIES AND SORORITIES: F-Fraternities S-Sororities F,S-Both No-Neither
- STUDENTS: C-Coed M-Men W-Women PM-Primarily Men PW-Primarily Women

Name of School	Town	Env.	Degrees Awarded	Control	Frat./Sor.	Students	Undergrad Enroll. Fall '93	ACT Median	ACT Below 21	ACT 21-23	ACT 24-26	ACT 27-28	ACT Above 28	SAT I V Median	SAT I V Below 500	SAT I V 500-599	SAT I V 600-700	SAT I V Above 700	SAT I M Median	SAT I M Below 500	SAT I M 500-599	SAT I M 600-700	SAT I M Above 700	App. Deadline Month/Day
Inter American University of Puerto Rico/Barranquitas Regional College	Barranquitas	SM	A,B	Pri	No	C	1,618																	Open
Inter American University of Puerto Rico/Bayamon University College	Bayamon	U	A,B,M,D	Pri		C																		5/1
Inter-American University of Puerto Rico/Fajardo Regional College	Fajardo	U	A,B,M,D	Pri		C	1,974																	5/15
Inter American University of Puerto Rico/Metropolitan Campus	Hato Rey		A,B,M,D	Pri		C																		5/1
Inter American University of Puerto Rico/Ponce Regional College	Ponce	U	A,B,M,D	Pri		C	3,379																	5/1
Inter American University of Puerto Rico/San German	San German	R	A,B,M	Pri	F,S	C	5,161																	5/15
Pontifical Catholic University of Puerto Rico/Ponce	Ponce	U	A,B,M	Pri	F,S	C	11,091							487					509					7/15
Turabo University	Gurabo		A,B,M	Pri	No	C	14,800							453	71	24	5		490	68	27	5		Open
Universidad Adventista de las Antillas	Mayaguez	SM	A,B	Pri	F,S	C	795																	7/15
Universidad Metropolitana	Rio Piedras	U	A,B,M	Pri	No	C																		Open
Universidad Politecnica de Puerto Rico	Hato Rey	U	B,M	Pri	F	C	4,987																	7/30
University of Puerto Rico/Arecibo Technological University College	Arecibo	SU	A,B	Pub	F,S	C	3,537																	12/15
University of Puerto Rico/Cayey University College	Cayey	U	A,B	Pub	F	C	3,132																	12/15
University of Puerto Rico/Humacao University College	Humacao	SU	A,B	Pub	F	C	3,825																	12/15
University of Puerto Rico/Mayaguez	Mayaguez	U	A,B,M,D	Pub	F,S	C	10,322							549	23	58	20		565	17	51	29	3	12/18
University of Puerto Rico/Rio Piedras	Rio Piedras	U	A,B,M,D	Pub	No	C	16,710							647			63	37	704			40	60	12/15
University of the Sacred Heart	Santurce	U	A,B,M	Pri	No	C	5,404																	6/30

Rhode Island

Name of School	Town	Env.	Degrees Awarded	Control	Frat./Sor.	Students	Undergrad Enroll. Fall '93	ACT Median	ACT Below 21	ACT 21-23	ACT 24-26	ACT 27-28	ACT Above 28	SAT I V Median	SAT I V Below 500	SAT I V 500-599	SAT I V 600-700	SAT I V Above 700	SAT I M Median	SAT I M Below 500	SAT I M 500-599	SAT I M 600-700	SAT I M Above 700	App. Deadline Month/Day
Brown University	Providence	U	B,M,D	Pri	F,S	C	5,992	31	3		23	46	28	620	7	26	51	16	680	2	11	41	46	1/1
Bryant College	Smithfield	SU	A,B,M	Pri	F,S	C	3,568							450	78	20	2		540	31	48	18	3	8/1
Johnson and Wales University	Providence	U	A,M	Pri	F,S	C	8,884																	Open
Providence College	Providence	U	B,M,D	Pri	No	C	5,299	25						499	54	39	7		559	25	50	23	2	2/1
Rhode Island College	Providence	U	B,M	Pub	F,S	C	6,861							411	83	12	5		441	72	23	5		5/1
Rhode Island School of Design	Providence	U	B,M	Pri	No	C	1,844								47	39	12	2		28	39	24	10	2/15
Roger Williams University	Bristol	SM	B,M	Pri	No	C	2,100							414					458					Open
Salve Regina University	Newport	SU	A,B,M,D	Pri	No	C	1,689																	8/8
University of Rhode Island	Kingston	SM	B,M,D	Pub	F,S	C	11,350							440	77	19	3	1	510	41	44	14	1	3/1

South Carolina

Name of School	Town	Env.	Degrees Awarded	Control	Frat./Sor.	Students	Undergrad Enroll. Fall '93	ACT Median	ACT Below 21	ACT 21-23	ACT 24-26	ACT 27-28	ACT Above 28	SAT I V Median	SAT I V Below 500	SAT I V 500-599	SAT I V 600-700	SAT I V Above 700	SAT I M Median	SAT I M Below 500	SAT I M 500-599	SAT I M 600-700	SAT I M Above 700	App. Deadline Month/Day
Allen University	Columbia	SM	A,B	Pri	F,S	C	308																	
Benedict College	Columbia	U	B	Pri	F,S	C	1,266																	Open
Central Wesleyan College	Central	R	A,B,M	Pri	No	C	1,277																	Open
Charleston Southern University	Charleston	SU	A,B,M	Pri	F,S	C	2,267																	8/10
Claflin College	Orangeburg	SU	B	Pri	F,S	C	850																	Open
Clemson University	Clemson	SM	B,M,D	Pub	F,S	C	12,525																	Open
Coastal Carolina University	Myrtle Beach	SU	A,B	Pub	F,S	C	4,159							470	57	35	8	1	550	19	47	28	6	Open
Coker College	Hartsville	SM	B	Pri	No	C	912																	8/15
College of Charleston	Charleston	U	B,M	Pub	F,S	C	8,051							431	78	13	8		469	61	33	5		8/1
Columbia College	Columbia	U	B,M	Pri	No	W	1,209	20	41	51	8			489	59	32	9		532	41	45	13	1	6/1
Converse College	Spartanburg	U	B,M	Pri	No	W	738																	Open
Erskine College	Due West	R	B,M,D	Pri	F,S	C	567																	4/1
Francis Marion University	Florence	R	B,M	Pub	F,S	C	3,660							482	58	27	14	1	532	38	39	21	2	Open
Furman University	Greenville	SU	B,M	Pri	F,S	C	2,546		7	25	36	14	18		39	38	19	4		16	40	33	11	2/1
Lander University	Greenwood	SM	B,M	Pub	F,S	C	2,563							396	91	8	2		441	75	20	5		Open
Limestone College	Gaffney	U	B	Pri	F,S	C	324																	8/7
Morris College	Sumter	SM	B	Pri	F,S	C	938	19						420					380					Open
Newberry College	Newberry	SM	B	Pri	F,S	C	651																	Open
Presbyterian College	Clinton	SM	B	Pri	F,S	C	1,180	21	67	17	10	4	2	431	61	22	12	5	452	57	27	14	2	Open
South Carolina State University	Orangeburg	SM	B,M,D	Pub	F,S	C	4,626							530	30	48	18		570	10	57	26	7	Open
The Citadel	Charleston	SU	B	Pub	No	M	2,000	17						340					384					7/31
University of South Carolina	Columbia	U	B,M,D	Pub	F,S	C	15,802	22	32	29	23	10	7	460	65	26	8	1	510	40	39	18	3	Open
University of South Carolina at Aiken	Aiken	SM	A,B,M	Pub	F,S	C	3,284							413	88	9	2		473	62	28	8	1	8/1
University of South Carolina at Spartanburg	Spartanburg	U	A,B	Pub	F,S	C	3,265							400	86	12	2		450	69	26	5		8/1
Voorhees College	Denmark	R	B	Pri	F,S	C	723	15						326	99	1			330	99	1			Open
Winthrop University	Rock Hill	SM	B,M	Pub	F,S	C	4,065	18	78	21	1			460	65	26	8	1	510	42	40	15	3	5/1
Wofford College	Spartanburg	U	B	Pri	F,S	C	1,108	24							47	34	16	3		19	45	30	6	2/1

South Dakota

Name of School	Town	Env.	Degrees Awarded	Control	Frat./Sor.	Students	Undergrad Enroll. Fall '93	ACT Median	ACT Below 21	ACT 21-23	ACT 24-26	ACT 27-28	ACT Above 28	SAT I V Median	SAT I V Below 500	SAT I V 500-599	SAT I V 600-700	SAT I V Above 700	SAT I M Median	SAT I M Below 500	SAT I M 500-599	SAT I M 600-700	SAT I M Above 700	App. Deadline Month/Day
Augustana College	Sioux Falls	SU	A,B,M	Pri	No	C	1,692		30	29	18	13	10											
Black Hills State University	Spearfish	SM	A,B,M	Pub	F,S	C	2,803	19	68	20	9	2	1											8/15
Dakota State University	Madison	SM	A,B	Pub	No	C	1,563	20	58	25	11	4	1											Open
Dakota Wesleyan University	Mitchell	SM	A,B,M	Pri	No	C	668	20	63	19	13	4	1											Open
Huron University	Huron	SM	A,B,M	Pri	No	C	477	18	76	16	4	1	1											8/26

NAME OF SCHOOL	TOWN	ENVIRONMENT U-Urban R-Rural Su-Suburban Sm-Small Town	DEGREES AWARDED A-Associate B-Bachelor M-Master D-Doctorate	CONTROL Pri-Private, Pub-Public	FRATERNITIES AND SORORITIES F-Fraternities S-Sororities F, S-Both No-Neither	STUDENTS: C-Coed M-Men W-Women PM-Primarily Men PW-Primarily Women	UNDERGRADUATE ENROLLMENT FALL '93	TEST SCORES: ACT Median	ACT Below 21	ACT 21-23	ACT 24-26	ACT 27-28	ACT Above 28	SAT I VERBAL REASONING Median	Below 500	500-599	600-700	Above 700	SAT I MATHEMATICAL REASONING Median	Below 500	500-599	600-700	Above 700	APPLICATION DEADLINE Month / Day
Mount Marty College	Yankton	SM	A,B,M	Pri	No	C	1,052	22	19	42	23	12	4											8/15
National College	Rapid City	SM	A,B	Pri	F,S	C	263																	Open
Northern State University	Aberdeen	U	A,B,M	Pub	No	C	2,756	20																8/15
Oglala Lakota College	Kyle	R	A,B	Pri		C	1,100																	Open
Presentation College	Aberdeen	SM	A,B	Pri	No	C	435																	Open
Sinte Gleska University	Rosebud	R	A,B,M	Pri	No	C	677																	9/1
Sioux Falls College	Sioux Falls	SU	A,B,M	Pri	No	C	885	21		26	48	15	11											Open
South Dakota School of Mines and Technology	Rapid City	SU	B,M,D	Pub	F,S	C	2,248		11	30	36	15	8											8/15
South Dakota State University	Brookings	R	A,B,M,D	Pub	F,S	C	8,103	23	39	31	18	8	4											8/30
University of South Dakota	Vermillion	R	A,B,M,D	Pub	F,S	C	5,952	22	40	28	19	8	5											Open

Tennessee

NAME OF SCHOOL	TOWN	ENVIRONMENT	DEGREES AWARDED	CONTROL	FRATERNITIES AND SORORITIES	STUDENTS	UNDERGRADUATE ENROLLMENT FALL '93	ACT Median	ACT Below 21	ACT 21-23	ACT 24-26	ACT 27-28	ACT Above 28	SAT I Verbal Median	Below 500	500-599	600-700	Above 700	SAT I Math Median	Below 500	500-599	600-700	Above 700	APPLICATION DEADLINE
American Technical Institute	Brunswick	U	B			C	1,977																	Open
Austin Peay State University	Clarksville	U	A,B,M	Pub	F,S	C	6,350																	8/19
Belmont University	Nashville	U	B,M	Pri	F,S	C	2,587	23	21	35	21	14	9	479	46	41	13		501	45	39	16	1	8/1
Bethel College	McKenzie	R	B,M	Pri	F,S	C	400		65	19	8	5	3											9/15
Bryan College	Dayton	SM	A,B	Pri	No	C	429	23	30	31	20	14	5	453	69	25	6		471	59	31	10		7/31
Carson-Newman College	Jefferson City	SM	A,B,M	Pri	F,S	C	2,015	23	42	23	20	4	11											5/1
Christian Brothers University	Memphis	U	B,M	Pri	F,S	C	1,307	24	24	28	20	14	15	462	63	38			530	42	25	33		8/1
Crichton College	Memphis	SU	B	Pri	No	C	354	18	49	30	15	4	2											Open
Cumberland University	Lebanon	SM	A,B,M	Pri	F,S	C	1,001	21	46	27	20	8	2											Open
David Lipscomb University	Nashville	SU	B,M	Pri	F,S	C	2,335	23	28	16	22	18	16		52	28	18	2		30	36	30	4	5/15
East Tennessee State University	Johnson City	SM	A,B,M,D	Pub	F,S	C	9,458	20	40	20	24	14	2	400					450					7/1
Fisk University	Nashville	U	B,M	Pri	F,S	C	900																	6/15
Freed-Hardeman University	Henderson	R	B,M	Pri	No	C	1,180	23	38	25	19	9	9	480	53	32	15		540	39	39	22		Open
King College	Bristol	SU	B	Pri	No	C	561	23	11	42	27	16	5	450	60	31	8	1	500	42	31	24	3	Open
Knoxville College	Knoxville	U	A,B		F,S	C	844	13						550	15	50	30	5	440					
Lambuth University	Jackson	U	B	Pri	F,S	C	1,165	22	20	28	36	8	8											Open
Lane College	Jackson	SM	B	Pri	F,S	C	744	16	90	7	1													8/1
Lee College	Cleveland	SU	B	Pri	F,S	C	2,011																	Open
LeMoyne-Owen College	Memphis	U	B	Pri	F,S	C	1,321	18																6/15
Lincoln Memorial University	Harrogate	R	A,B,M	Pri	F,S	C	1,530	22	35	31	17	6	11											Open
Maryville College	Maryville	SU	B	Pri	No	C	752	22	27	35	22	10	6	440	71	21	8		500	49	30	20	1	Open
Memphis College of Art	Memphis	U	B,M	Pri	No	C	216	19	66	23	7	3		426	63	27	10		433	61	27	10	2	Open
Middle Tennessee State University	Murfreesboro	SU	A,B,M,D	Pub	F,S	C	15,426	20																7/1
Milligan College	Milligan College	SU	A,B,M	Pri	No	C	663	23						500					500					Open
Rhodes College	Memphis	SU	B,M	Pri	F,S	C	1,403			7	15	46	32		14	45	34	7		6	33	43	18	2/1
Southern College of Seventh-day Adventists	Collegedale	SM	A,B	Pri	No	C	1,527																	Open
Tennessee State University	Nashville	U	A,B,M,D	Pub	F,S	C	6,617	19	67	21	10	1	1											8/1
Tennessee Technological University	Cookeville	SM	A,B,M,D	Pub	F,S	C	7,371	22	35	26	21	11	7											7/21
Tennessee Wesleyan College	Athens	U	B	Pri	S	C	639	20	73	12	12	1	1											7/31
Trevecca Nazarene College	Nashville	U	A,B,M	Pri	No	C	932	21	22	31	36	10	1											Open
Tusculum College	Greeneville	SU	B,M	Pri	No	C	1,023	18	72	22	3	2		370	93	6	1		420	78	19	3		5/1
Union University	Jackson	SU	B,M	Pri	F,S	C	1,913	24	28	19	28	15	10											Open
University of Memphis	Memphis	U	B,M,D	Pub	F,S	C	15,485	22	36	30	18	9	7											8/1
University of Tennessee at Chattanooga	Chattanooga	U	B,M	Pub	F,S	C	7,117																	8/15
University of Tennessee at Martin	Martin	SM	B,M	Pub	F,S	C	5,344	22	39	31	24	6												8/1
University of Tennessee/Knoxville	Knoxville	U	B,M,D	Pub	F,S	C	18,988	23	26	49	20	6		468	63	28	8	1	525	38	39	18	5	7/1
University of the South	Sewanee	SM	B,M,D		F,S	C	1,153	27		10	35	25	30	557	24	45	28	3	601	4	46	41	9	2/1
Vanderbilt University	Nashville	U	B,M,D	Pri	F,S	C	5,652	28			2	22	76	559	19	50	27	4	640	3	23	52	22	1/15

Texas

NAME OF SCHOOL	TOWN	ENVIRONMENT	DEGREES AWARDED	CONTROL	FRATERNITIES AND SORORITIES	STUDENTS	UNDERGRADUATE ENROLLMENT FALL '93	ACT Median	ACT Below 21	ACT 21-23	ACT 24-26	ACT 27-28	ACT Above 28	SAT I Verbal Median	Below 500	500-599	600-700	Above 700	SAT I Math Median	Below 500	500-599	600-700	Above 700	APPLICATION DEADLINE
Abilene Christian University	Abilene	SU	A,B,M,D	Pri	No	C	3,385	21	45	27	15	6	7	430	71	20	8	1	490	48	32	16	4	Open
Ambassador College	Big Sandy	R	A,B	Pri	No	C	1,110							490	58	30	11	1	520	42	36	20	2	2/1
Angelo State University	San Angelo	SM	A,B,M	Pub	F,S	C	5,702	22	43	28	17	5	7	439	74	19	6	1	507	46	34	18	2	8/5
Austin College	Sherman	SU	B,M	Pri	F,S	C	1,135	24	15	28	29	19	9	498	51	35	12	2	554	24	45	23	8	
Baylor University	Waco	U	B,M,D	Pri	F,S	C	10,403																	Open
Concordia Lutheran College	Austin	U	A,B	Pri	No	C	706	20	57	25	13	2	3	410	84	14	2		475	63	22	14	1	8/15
Dallas Baptist University	Dallas	U	A,B,M	Pri	No	C	2,390	22						435	70	27	3		495	51	31	15	3	Open
DeVry Institute of Technology/Dallas	Irving	SU	A,B	Pri	No	C	2,033																	Open
East Texas Baptist University	Marshall	SM	A,B,M	Pri	F,S	C	1,202																	Open
East Texas State University	Commerce	SM	B,M,D	Pub	F,S	C	5,472		50	26	18	3	3											8/10
Hardin-Simmons University	Abilene	U	A,B,M	Pri	F,S	C	1,699	22	38	23	23	9	7	470	65	25	9	1	510	46	32	19	2	Open
Houston Baptist University	Houston	U	A,B,M	Pri	F,S	C	1,703	21	40	31	18	6	4	420	82	14	4		500	50	37	9	4	Open
Howard Payne University	Brownwood	SM	B	Pri	No	C	1,467	20	54	25	12	5	4	405	84	12	3	1	458	62	25	12	1	8/15
Huston-Tillotson College	Austin	U	B	Pri	F,S	C	539	16	97	3														3/1
Incarnate Word College	San Antonio	U	B,M	Pri	F,S	C	2,241	21						441					480					Open
Jarvis Christian College	Hawkins	R	B	Pri	F,S	C	496	14	99	1				307	100				361	100				8/8
Lamar University	Beaumont	U	A,B,M,D	Pub	F,S	C	8,824							413					459					8/10
Le Tourneau University	Longview	U	A,B,M	Pri	No	C	1,611	24	29	23	27	11	10	491	51	32	15	2	552	31	26	30	12	8/15
Lubbock Christian University	Lubbock	SU	A,B,M	Pri	No	C	1,098	21																Open
McMurry University	Abilene	SU	A,B	Pri	F,S	C	1,357	21	42	31	17	6	5	410	82	16	2		500	50	27	15	8	8/15
Midwestern State University	Wichita Falls	U	A,B,M	Pub	F,S	C	5,138	20						400					435					8/7
Our Lady of the Lake University of San Antonio	San Antonio	U	B,M,D	Pri	No	C	2,144							415	83	14	3		420	84	13	3		Open
Paul Quinn College	Dallas	U	B		F,S	C	670																	8/1
Prairie View A&M University	Prairie View	SM	B,M		F,S	C	5,419	19						335					380					Open

TEST SCORES

Name of School	Town	Environment	Degrees Awarded	Control	Frat./Sor.	Students	Undergrad Enrollment Fall '93	ACT Median	ACT Below 21	ACT 21-23	ACT 24-26	ACT 27-28	ACT Above 28	SAT I Verbal Median	V Below 500	V 500-599	V 600-700	V Above 700	SAT I Math Median	M Below 500	M 500-599	M 600-700	M Above 700	Application Deadline (Month/Day)
Rice University	Houston	SU	B,M,D		No	C	2,674								7	17	51	25		3	9	28	60	1/3
Saint Edward's University	Austin	U	B,M	Pri	No	C	2,668	22	39	30	24	6	1	430	76	22	2		480					8/1
Saint Mary's University	San Antonio	SU	B,M,D		F,S	C	2,567																	8/15
Sam Houston State University	Huntsville	SM	B,M,D	Pub	F,S	C	11,140	20	58	28	10	3	1											8/15
Schreiner College	Kerrville	SM	A,B		No	C	620	21						400					460					Open
Southern Methodist University	Dallas	SU	B,M,D		F,S	C	5,279																	8/15
Southwest Texas State University	San Marcos	SM	A,B,M	Pub	F,S	C	18,497	22	31	40	22	5	2											1/15
Southwestern Adventist College	Keene	R	A,B,M	Pri	No	C	913	22	45	26	14	9	6	390	79	18	3	1	410	75	20	5	1	Open
Southwestern Christian College	Terrell	R	A,B	Pri	No	C	254																	7/31
Southwestern University	Georgetown	SM	B	Pri	F,S	C	1,220	25	4	27	33	17	19	526	38	42	18	2	577	14	43	33	9	2/15
Stephen F. Austin State University	Nacogdoches	SM	B,M,D	Pub	F,S	C	11,140	21	49	39	6	4	2	430	85	12	2		470	62	31	6	1	9/1
Sul Ross State University	Alpine	R	A,B,M	Pub	No	C	1,574	17	88	11	2			340	94	6	1		390	85	14	1		Open
Tarleton State University	Stephenville	SM	A,B,M	Pub	F,S	C	5,580	20	66	23	8	2	1	391	90	9	1		441	74	20	6	1	Open
Texas A&M University	College Station	SM	B,M,D		F,S	C	34,441	24	12	28	29	16	15	490	74	20	5	1	580	37	39	21	3	3/1
Texas A&M University at Galveston	Galveston	SU	B	Pub	No	C	1,166																	3/1
Texas A&M University at Kingsville	Kingsville	SM	B,M,D	Pub	F,S	C	5,402																	Open
Texas Christian University	Fort Worth	SU	B,M,D	Pri	F,S	C	5,724																	Open
Texas College	Tyler	U	B	Pri	F,S	C	452	15																2/15
Texas Lutheran College	Seguin	SM	A,B	Pri	F,S	C	1,023																	5/15
Texas Southern University	Houston	U	B,M,D	Pub	F,S	C	8,685	22	35	26	21	14	4	435	75	20	4	2	498	50	33	14	3	8/1
Texas Tech University	Lubbock	U	B,M,D	Pub	F,S	C	19,565	22	31	35	21	8	5	439	78	18	4		507	46	37	14	3	8/5
Texas Wesleyan University	Fort Worth	U	B,M	Pri	F,S	C	1,596	20	64	20	10	5	1	430	79	16	5		460	65	25	10		7/15
Texas Woman's University	Denton	U	B,M,D	Pub	S	PW	5,757																	Open
Trinity University	San Antonio	U	B,M	Pri	F,S	C	2,208	28	1	10	27	40	22	575	17	48	32	3	635	4	31	35	20	7/15
University of Dallas	Irving	SU	B,M,D	Pri	No	C	1,131	26	3	21	30	22	24	530	26	49	22	3	580	16	41	36	7	2/1
University of Houston	Houston	U	B,M,D	Pub	F,S	C	22,386																	2/1
University of Houston-Downtown	Houston	U	B	Pub	S	C	6,961																	7/15
University of Mary Hardin-Baylor	Belton	SM	B,M	Pri	No	C	1,886	21	48	25	16	8	4	424	84	14	2		462	61	32	6		8/18
University of North Texas	Denton	U	B,M,D	Pub	F,S	C	19,181	23	16					467					526					Open
University of Saint Thomas	Houston	U	B,M,D	Pri	No	C	1,403	25	16	22	28	9	25	500	53	36	11		560	27	49	22	2	6/15
University of Texas at Arlington	Arlington	SU	B,M,D	Pub	F,S	C	19,396												486					2/1
University of Texas at Austin	Austin	U	B,M,D	Pub	F,S	C	35,206	25	7	21	36	15	20	523	39	39	19	3						8/1
University of Texas at Dallas	Richardson	SU	B,M,D	Pub	F,S	C	4,726	27						553					631					3/1
University of Texas at El Paso	El Paso	U	B,M,D	Pub	F,S	C	14,503																	3/1
University of Texas at San Antonio	San Antonio	SU	B,M,D	Pub	F,S	C	14,832	20						416										5/1
University of Texas-Pan American	Edinburg	SM	A,B,M	Pub	F,S	C	12,764	16	90	7	2	1	1	475										7/1
Wayland Baptist University	Plainview	SM	A,B,M	Pri	No	C	2,888	20																8/7
West Texas A&M University	Canyon	SM	B,M	Pub	F,S	C	5,409	22						450					426					Open
Wiley College	Marshall	SM	B		F,S		410																	6/1

Utah

Name of School	Town	Environment	Degrees Awarded	Control	Frat./Sor.	Students	Undergrad Enrollment Fall '93	ACT Median	ACT Below 21	ACT 21-23	ACT 24-26	ACT 27-28	ACT Above 28	SAT I Verbal Median	V Below 500	V 500-599	V 600-700	V Above 700	SAT I Math Median	M Below 500	M 500-599	M 600-700	M Above 700	Application Deadline (Month/Day)
Brigham Young University	Provo	SU	A,B,M,D	Pri	No	C	27,631	27	3	10	26	21	39											2/15
Southern Utah University	Cedar City	R	A,B,M	Pub	F,S	C	4,048	21																7/1
University of Utah	Salt Lake City	U	B,M,D	Pub	F,S	C	21,192	23	26	23	26	10	15	480	55	28	15	2	550	34	32	26	8	7/1
Utah State University	Logan	SM	A,B,M,D	Pub	F,S	C	13,612	22	35	29	16	9	11											7/1
Weber State University	Ogden	U	A,B,M	Pub	F,S	C	14,289	21	46	26	19	7	3											7/1
Westminster College of Salt Lake City	Salt Lake City	U	B,M	Pri	No	C	1,759	23	29	27	31	9	4	500	47	47	6		570	37	30	30	3	Open

Vermont

Name of School	Town	Environment	Degrees Awarded	Control	Frat./Sor.	Students	Undergrad Enrollment Fall '93	ACT Median	ACT Below 21	ACT 21-23	ACT 24-26	ACT 27-28	ACT Above 28	SAT I Verbal Median	V Below 500	V 500-599	V 600-700	V Above 700	SAT I Math Median	M Below 500	M 500-599	M 600-700	M Above 700	Application Deadline (Month/Day)
Bennington College	Bennington	SM	B,M	Pri	No	C	459	25						601					551					
Burlington College	Burlington	U	A,B	Pri	No	C	161																	1/1
Castleton State College	Castleton	R	A,B,M	Pub	No	C	1,869	21						416					459					Open
Champlain College	Burlington	SU	A,B	Pri	No	C	2,047																	Open
College of Saint Joseph	Rutland	R	A,B,M	Pri	No	C	395							370	92	7			390	82	15	3		Open
Goddard College	Plainfield	R	B,M	Pri	No	C	225							473					464					
Green Mountain College	Poultney	SM	B	Pri	No	C	592		25	45	18	10	2	460	68	24	5	3	440	75	18	6	1	
Johnson State College	Johnson	R	A,B,M	Pub	No	C	1,622							390	89	10	1		410	77	21	2		Open
Lyndon State College	Lyndonville	SM	A,B,M	Pub	No	C	1,050																	Open
Marlboro College	Marlboro	R	B,M	Pri	No	C	271																	Open
Middlebury College	Middlebury	SM	B,M,D	Pri	No	C	1,960							580					530					8/1
Norwich University	Northfield	SM	A,B,M	Pri	No	C	2,244	23	16				4	465	73	31	55	7	510	53	36	10	1	12/15
Saint Michael's College	Colchester	SU	B,M	Pri	No	C	1,719							487	65	31	4		540	36	48	15	1	2/15
Southern Vermont College	Bennington	SM	A,B	Pri	No	C	701																	Open
Trinity College of Vermont	Burlington	U	A,B,M	Pri	No	PW	1,016							410	88	10	2		420	80	18	2		Open
University of Vermont	Burlington	SM	A,B,M,D	Pub	F,S	C	7,751							480	55	37	8	1	550	24	45	28	3	2/1

Virgin Islands

Name of School	Town	Environment	Degrees Awarded	Control	Frat./Sor.	Students	Undergrad Enrollment Fall '93	ACT Median	ACT Below 21	ACT 21-23	ACT 24-26	ACT 27-28	ACT Above 28	SAT I Verbal Median	V Below 500	V 500-599	V 600-700	V Above 700	SAT I Math Median	M Below 500	M 500-599	M 600-700	M Above 700	Application Deadline (Month/Day)
University of the Virgin Islands	St Thomas	SU	A,B,M	Pub	No	C	2,668																	4/15

Virginia

Name of School	Town	Environment	Degrees Awarded	Control	Frat./Sor.	Students	Undergrad Enrollment Fall '93	ACT Median	ACT Below 21	ACT 21-23	ACT 24-26	ACT 27-28	ACT Above 28	SAT I Verbal Median	V Below 500	V 500-599	V 600-700	V Above 700	SAT I Math Median	M Below 500	M 500-599	M 600-700	M Above 700	Application Deadline (Month/Day)
Averett College	Danville	SU	A,B,M	Pri	F,S	C	1,365																	8/1
Bluefield College	Bluefield	SM	A,B	Pri	F,S	C	765	21						432	72	20	6	2	465	58	32	8	2	8/1
Bridgewater College	Bridgewater	SM	B	Pri	No	C	935																	Open
Christendom College	Front Royal	R	A,B	Pri	No	C	145																	
Christopher Newport University	Newport News	SU	B,M	Pub	F,S	C	4,659	21	45	20	14	7	14	575	27	27	36	10	550	28	36	24	12	4/1
Clinch Valley College/University of Virginia	Wise	SM	B	Pub	F,S	C	1,547							415	85	12	3		445	74	20	5	1	8/15

TEST SCORES

Column legend:

- **ENVIRONMENT:** U-Urban, R-Rural, SU-Suburban, SM-Small Town
- **DEGREES AWARDED:** A-Associate, B-Bachelor, M-Master, D-Doctorate
- **CONTROL:** Pri-Private, Pub-Public
- **FRATERNITIES AND SORORITIES:** F-Fraternities, S-Sororities, F,S-Both, No-Neither
- **STUDENTS:** C-Coed, M-Men, W-Women, PM-Primarily Men, PW-Primarily Women
- **UNDERGRADUATE ENROLLMENT FALL '93**
- **ACT / SAT I VERBAL REASONING / SAT I MATHEMATICAL REASONING:** Median, Below 21 / Below 500, 21-23 / 500-599, 24-26 / 600-700, 27-28 / Above 700, Above 28
- **APPLICATION DEADLINE:** Month/Day

Name of School	Town	Env	Degrees	Control	Frat/Sor	Students	Undergrad Enroll Fall '93	ACT Med	ACT <21	ACT 21-23	ACT 24-26	ACT 27-28	ACT >28	SATV Med	SATV <500	SATV 500-599	SATV 600-700	SATV >700	SATM Med	SATM <500	SATM 500-599	SATM 600-700	SATM >700	App Deadline
College of William and Mary	Williamsburg	SM	B,M,D	Pub	F,S	C	5,320							600	13	35	44	8	640	4	22	48	27	1/15
Eastern Mennonite College	Harrisonburg	SM	A,B,M	Pri	No	C	962	22	39	15	24	15	7	468	55	28	15	3	510	40	32	21	6	Open
Emory and Henry College	Emory	R	B	Pri	No	C	841	23						443										Open
Ferrum College	Ferrum	R	B	Pri	No	C	1,128							387	93	6	1		433	82	15	3		2/1
George Mason University	Fairfax	SU	B,M,D	Pub	F,S	C	13,351							510	42	41	16	1	560	18	47	27	8	3/1
Hampden-Sydney College	Hampden-Sydney	R	B	Pri	F	M	946																	3/15
Hampton University	Hampton	U	B,M	Pri	F,S	C	4,740																	3/15
Hollins College	Roanoke	SU	B,M	Pri	No	W	842	22	27	38	25	10		505	50	34	15	1	502	50	37	12	1	1/15
James Madison University	Harrisonburg	SU	A,B,M,D	Pub	No	C	9,927							521	41	47	11	1	587	13	44	38	5	8/1
Liberty University	Lynchberg	SU	A,B,M,D	Pri	No	C	4,641							450	72	26	2		490	50	43	5	2	3/1
Longwood College	Farmville	SM	B,M	Pub	F,S	C	2,992																	6/1
Lynchburg College	Lynchburg	SU	B,M	Pri	No	C	1,869																	4/15
Mary Baldwin College	Staunton	SM	A,B	Pri	No	W	1,169								31	51	18			15	48	37		2/1
Mary Washington College	Fredericksburg	SM	B,M	Pub	No	C	3,733							440	73	27			467	62	32	6		Open
Marymount University	Arlington	SU	A,B,M	Pri	No	C	2,098							430	75	20	4	1	490	60	30	7	3	8/1
Norfolk State University	Norfolk	U	A,B,M	Pub	F,S	C	7,552							417	87	12	1		453	72	24	4		5/1
Old Dominion University	Norfolk	SU	B,M,D	Pub	F,S	C	11,624	21																4/1
Radford University	Radford	SM	B,M	Pub	F,S	C	8,527																	3/1
Randolph-Macon College	Ashland	SM	B	Pri	F,S	C	1,119							502	50	32		1	517	38	46	15	2	3/1
Randolph-Macon Woman's College	Lynchburg	SU	B	Pri	No	W	709	25	14	30	22	16	18	480	57	34	17	9	530	31	47	19	3	3/1
Roanoke College	Salem	SU	B	Pri	F,S	C	1,699																	Open
Saint Paul's College	Lawrenceville	R	A,B,M	Pri	No	C	609							438	72	23	5		477	57	27	14	2	Open
Shenandoah University	Winchester	SM	A,B,M	Pri	No	C	1,180																	2/15
Sweet Briar College	Sweet Briar	SM	B	Pri	No	W	568		8	9	21	18	43		14	50	32	4		3	24	53	20	2/1
University of Richmond	Richmond	SU	B,M	Pri	F,S	C	3,465							570	17	42	36	5	650	5	21	48	26	1/2
University of Virginia	Charlottesville	SU	B,M,D	Pub	F,S	C	11,371							485	60	30	10		525	39	42	16	3	2/1
Virginia Commonwealth University	Richmond	U	A,B,M,D	Pub	F,S	C	15,329																	Open
Virginia Intermont College	Bristol	U	A,B	Pri	No	C	718							484					543					4/1
Virginia Military Institute	Lexington	SM	B	Pub	No	M	1,191	22																2/1
Virginia Polytechnic Institute and State University	Blacksburg	R	A,B,M,D	Pub	F,S	C	19,115								51	37	11	1		17	40	34	9	2/1 / 5/1
Virginia State University	Petersburg	SU	B,M	Pub	F,S	C	3,300							317					343					Open
Virginia Union University	Richmond	U	B,M,D	Pri	F,S	C	1,365																	
Virginia Wesleyan College	Norfolk/Virginia Beach	U	B	Pri	F,S	C	1,547								34	35	26	5		27	37	31	5	3/1
Washington and Lee University	Lexington	SM	B	Pri	F,S	C	1,587	29						600					650					2/15

Washington

Name of School	Town	Env	Degrees	Control	Frat/Sor	Students	Undergrad Enroll Fall '93	ACT Med	ACT <21	ACT 21-23	ACT 24-26	ACT 27-28	ACT >28	SATV Med	SATV <500	SATV 500-599	SATV 600-700	SATV >700	SATM Med	SATM <500	SATM 500-599	SATM 600-700	SATM >700	App Deadline
Central Washington University	Ellensburg	SM	B,M	Pub	No	C	8,122							414	84	14	2		463	66	25	8	1	3/1
City University	Bellevue	SU	A,B,M	Pri	No	C	1,949																	Open
Cogswell College North	Kirkland	SU	A,B	Pri	No	C	219																	Open
Cornish College of the Arts	Seattle	U	B	Pri	No	C	607																	8/15
Eastern Washington University	Cheney	SM	B,M	Pub	F,S	C	7,737																	2/15
Evergreen State College	Olympia	SM	B,M	Pub	No	C	3,398																	3/1
Gonzaga University	Spokane	U	B,M,D	Pri	No	C	2,935	25	11	44	35	10		499	53	36	10	1	548	27	45	22	6	4/1
Heritage College	Toppenish	R	B	Pri	No	C	519							470					440					Open
Northwest College	Kirkland	SU	A,B	Pri	No	C	757	21						470					440					8/1
Pacific Lutheran University	Tacoma	SU	B,M	Pri	No	C	2,882							460	65	26	9		510	43	36	17	4	Open
Saint Martin's College	Lacey	SU	A,B,M	Pri	F,S	C	1,071	21	10	40	30	10	10	460	60	30	10		480	70	25	5		9/1
Seattle Pacific University	Seattle	U	B,M,D	Pri	No	C	2,272							467	62	29	8	1	506	50	29	17	4	6/1
Seattle University	Seattle	U	B,M,D	Pri	No	C	3,340							457	56	37	6	1	533	35	38	22	5	3/1
University of Puget Sound	Tacoma	SU	B,M	Pri	F,S	C	2,855	25	9	18	34	19	20	520	40	41	17	2	581	16	39	37	8	2/1
University of Washington	Seattle	U	B,M,D	Pub	F,S	C									58	27	13			25	35	30	10	8/1
Walla Walla College	College Place	SM	A,B,M	Pri	No	C	1,620								50	33	15	2						5/1
Washington State University	Pullman	SM	B,M,D	Pub	F,S	C	15,712	24						470	78	19	3		530	34	44	20	2	3/1
Western Washington University	Bellingham	SM	B,M	Pub	No	C	9,412							470	63	29	8							2/15
Whitman College	Walla Walla	SM	B	Pri	F,S	C	1,266	28						550	26	42	25	8	600	11	35	41	13	
Whitworth College	Spokane	SU	B,M	Pri	No	C	1,430																	

West Virginia

Name of School	Town	Env	Degrees	Control	Frat/Sor	Students	Undergrad Enroll Fall '93	ACT Med	ACT <21	ACT 21-23	ACT 24-26	ACT 27-28	ACT >28	SATV Med	SATV <500	SATV 500-599	SATV 600-700	SATV >700	SATM Med	SATM <500	SATM 500-599	SATM 600-700	SATM >700	App Deadline
Alderson-Broaddus College	Philippi	SM	A,B,M	Pri	F,S	C	877																	8/15
Bethany College	Bethany	SM	B	Pri	F,S	C	777		16	39	30	11	4		58	33	8	1		48	37	12	1	Open
Bluefield State College	Bluefield	SM	A,B	Pub	F,S	C	2,613	18	62	31	4	2	1	390	91	8	1		410	92	7	1		Open
Concord College	Athens	SM	A,B	Pub	F,S	C	2,960		72	19	7	1		396	88	9	3		426	74	20	5	1	Open
Davis and Elkins College	Elkins	SM	A,B	Pri	F,S	C	941																	6/15
Fairmont State College	Fairmont	SU	A,B	Pub	F,S	C	6,329																	Open
Glenville State College	Glenville	R	A,B	Pub	F,S	C	2,294							480					450					9/1
Marshall University	Huntington	U	A,B,M,D	Pub	F,S	C	10,042	21	53	26	13	5	3	480										Open
Ohio Valley College	Parkersburg	SU	A,B	Pri	No	C	289	20																Open
Salem-Teikyo University	Salem	R	A,B,M	Pri	F,S	C	767	22	54	15	15	13	3		63	26	6	5		59	25	14	2	2/1
Shepherd College	Shepherdstown	SM	A,B	Pub	F,S	C	3,566																	8/1
University of Charleston	Charleston	U	A,B,M	Pri	F,S	C	1,382	21	47	31	15	4	3	443	76	15	9		505	51	31	9	9	8/1
West Liberty State College	West Liberty	R	A,B	Pub	F,S	C	2,377	19	69	21	4	4	2											8/1
West Virginia Institute of Technology	Montgomery	SM	A,B,M	Pub	F,S	C	2,824		21	21	13	4	5											8/10
West Virginia State College	Institute	SU	A,B	Pub	F,S	C	4,756	18						430					500					Open
West Virginia University	Morgantown	SM	B,M,D	Pub	F,S	C	15,577								75	20	5	2		54	31	11	4	Open
West Virginia Wesleyan College	Buckhannon	SM	A,B,M	Pri	F,S	C	1,679		27	25	25	11	12											Open
Wheeling Jesuit College	Wheeling	SU	B,M	Pri	No	C	1,277	22	46	28	19	4		433	79	19	2		479	61	28	10	1	5/15

Column key (rotated headers):
- **Environment:** U-Urban, R-Rural, Su-Suburban, Sm-Small Town
- **Degrees Awarded:** A-Associate, B-Bachelor, M-Master, D-Doctorate
- **Control:** Pri-Private, Pub-Public
- **Fraternities and Sororities:** F-Fraternities, S-Sororities, N-Neither
- **Students:** C-Coed, M-Men, W-Women, PM-Primarily Men, PW-Primarily Women

Wisconsin

Name of School	Town	Environ.	Degrees	Control	Frat/Sor.	Students	Undergrad Enroll. Fall '93	ACT Median	ACT Below 21	ACT 21-23	ACT 24-26	ACT 27-28	ACT Above 28	SAT V Median	SAT V Below 500	SAT V 500-599	SAT V 600-700	SAT V Above 700	SAT M Median	SAT M Below 500	SAT M 500-599	SAT M 600-700	SAT M Above 700	Application Deadline
Alverno College	Milwaukee	SU	B		No	W	2,552	20																8/1
Beloit College	Beloit	SM	B,M	Pri	F,S	C	1,206	26	10	18	26	22	25	550	25	42	30	3	580	15	44	30	11	3/15
Cardinal Stritch College	Milwaukee	SU	A,B,M	Pri	No	C	2,764	21	33	35	20	7	6											8/15
Carroll College	Waukesha	SU	B,M		F,S	C	2,094	23	36	33	20	6	5											Open
Carthage College	Kenosha	SU	B,M		F,S	C	1,974	22	40	23	20	12	5											Open
Columbia College of Nursing	Milwaukee	U	B	Pri	F,S	C	386	20																5/1
Concordia University Wisconsin	Mequon	SU	A,B,M	Pri	No	C	1,970		55	23	13	5	5											Open
Edgewood College	Madison	SU	A,B,M	Pri	No	C	1,392	21	44	27	17	5	3											8/1
Lakeland College	Sheboygan	R	B,M	Pri	F,S	C	741	20	51	28	14	4	3											8/1
Lawrence University	Appleton	U	B		F,S	C	1,211	28	5	17	18	17	44	540	28	36	32	4	610	16	30	38	16	8/15
Marian College of Fond du Lac	Fond du Lac	SM	B,M	Pri	F,S	C	1,819	20	39	53	8													2/1
Marquette University	Milwaukee	U	A,B,M,D	Pri	F,S	C	7,820	25	6	24	32	19	17	490	59	32	8	1	560	28	41	25	6	Open
Milwaukee Institute of Art and Design	Milwaukee	U	B	Pri	No	C	505																	Open
Milwaukee School of Engineering	Milwaukee	U	A,B,M	Pri	F,S	C	2,634																	4/1
Mount Mary College	Milwaukee	SU	B,M	Pri	No		1,433							510					520					Open
Mount Senario College	Ladysmith	R	A,B	Pri	No	C	1,162												510					8/15
Northland College	Ashland	SM	B	Pri	F,S	C	738	23						495					510					Open
Northwestern College	Watertown	SM	B	Pri		M	187		22	30	22	14	14											8/1
Ripon College	Ripon	SM	B		F,S	C	768	24	23	27	30	10	11											8/1
Saint Norbert College	De Pere	SU	B,M	Pri	F,S	C	2,041	24	24	29	22	14	11	513	34	47	16	2	557	24	35	35	6	3/15
Silver Lake College	Manitowoc		A,B,M	Pri	No		829	19	56	22	13		9											Open
University of Wisconsin/Eau Claire	Eau Claire	U	A,B,M	Pub	F,S	C	9,780	22	26	36	24	8	6											Open
University of Wisconsin/Green Bay	Green Bay	R	A,B,M	Pub	F,S	C	5,168	22	32	34	24	7	3	455	69	20	7	4	520	38	39	17	6	3/1
University of Wisconsin/La Crosse	La Crosse	SM	A,B,M	Pub	F,S	C	7,470	22	27	39	23	8	3											2/1
University of Wisconsin/Madison	Madison	U	B,M,D	Pub	F,S	C	26,638		2	24	33	20	21		35	39	20	6		14	33	35	18	9/15
University of Wisconsin/Milwaukee	Milwaukee	U	A,B,M,D	Pub	F,S	C	19,116	22	35	35	19	6	5											2/1
University of Wisconsin/Oshkosh	Oshkosh	U	A,B,M	Pub	F,S	C	9,281	22	42	31	18	6	3											6/30
University of Wisconsin/Parkside	Kenosha	SU	B,M	Pub	No	C	4,983	20																Open
University of Wisconsin/Platteville	Platteville	SM	A,B,M	Pub	F,S	C	4,910	23																8/14
University of Wisconsin/River Falls	River Falls	SM	A,B,M	Pub	F,S	C	5,263	22	35	35	20	7	3											1/1
University of Wisconsin/Stevens Point	Stevens Point	SM	A,B,M	Pub	F,S	C	8,059	24																1/1
University of Wisconsin/Stout	Menomonie	R	B,M	Pub	F,S	C	6,803	21	46	37	13	3	1											Open
University of Wisconsin/Superior	Superior	SM	A,B,M	Pub	No	C	2,185	21	6	65	21	6	2											5/1
University of Wisconsin/Whitewater	Whitewater	SM	A,B,M	Pub	F,S	C	9,296	22																Open
Viterbo College	LaCrosse	SM	B,M	Pri	No	C	1,401	22																Open
Wisconsin Lutheran College	Milwaukee	SU	B	Pri	No	C	304	22	36	19	23	15	7											8/15 / 4/1

Wyoming

Name of School	Town	Environ.	Degrees	Control	Frat/Sor.	Students	Undergrad Enroll. Fall '93	ACT Median	ACT Below 21	ACT 21-23	ACT 24-26	ACT 27-28	ACT Above 28	SAT V Median	SAT V Below 500	SAT V 500-599	SAT V 600-700	SAT V Above 700	SAT M Median	SAT M Below 500	SAT M 500-599	SAT M 600-700	SAT M Above 700	Application Deadline
University of Wyoming	Laramie	SM	B,M,D	Pub	F,S	C	9,293	23	31	24	24	10	11											8/10

IN-STATE COST RANGES DIRECTORY

The breakdown of in-state tuition, room and board costs for the 1993-94 academic year are arranged form least expensive to most expensive. Within each range are lists of schools that don't charge for tuition or for room and board, and those that do.

Less Than $2000

Colleges Without Tuition or Room and Board

American Technical Inst, TN (no R & B)
Augusta College, GA (no R & B)
Bayamon Tech Univ College, PR (no R & B)
Bluefield State College, WV (no R & B)
Charter Oak State College, CT (no R & B)
Claflin College, SC
Clayton State College, GA (no R & B)
Concordia College, NY
Conservatory of Music of PR, PR (no R & B)
Curtis Inst of Music, PA
Fisk Univ, TN
Harris-Stowe State College, MO (no R & B)
Kennesaw State College, GA (no R & B)
Lincoln Univ, PA
Louisiana State Univ in Shreveport, LA (no R & B)
Metropolitan State College of Denver, CO (no R & B)
Northeastern Illinois Univ, IL (no R & B)
Oglala Lakota College, SD
Rutgers Univ/Univ College—New Brunswick, NJ
Rutgers Univ/Univ College—Newark, NJ
Sinte Gleska Univ, SD (no R & B)
Southern Univ at New Orleans, LA (no R & B)
Thomas A. Edison State College, NJ (no R & B)
Troy State Univ in Montgomery, AL (no R & B)
United States Air Force Academy, CO
United States Coast Guard Academy, CT
United States Military Academy, NY
United States Naval Academy, MD
Univ of Colo at Denver, CO (no R & B)
Univ of Nebr at Omaha, NE (no R & B)
Univ of PR/Arecibo Tech Univ College, PR (no R & B)
Univ of PR/Cayey Univ College, PR (no R & B)
Univ of PR/Humacao Univ College, PR
Univ of PR/Mayaguez, PR
Univ of PR/Rio Piedras, PR
Univ of Texas at Dallas, TX (no R & B)
Univ of the District of Columbia, DC (no R & B)
Univ of the State of New York/Regents College Degrees, NY (no R & B)
Western Montana College of the Univ of Montana, MT (no R & B)
Wiley College, TX

Colleges with Tuition, Room, and Board

Southern College of Technology, GA

$2000-$3999

Colleges Without Tuition or Room and Board

Bellevue College, NE (no R & B)
Berea College, KY
Boston Architectural Center, MA (no R & B)
Calumet College of St. Joseph, IN (no R & B)
Caribbean Univ, PR (no R & B)
Central Univ of Bayamon, PR (no R & B)
Chicago State Univ, IL (no R & B)
Christopher Newport Univ, VA (no R & B)
CUNY/Baruch College, NY (no R & B)
CUNY/Brooklyn College, NY (no R & B)
CUNY/City College, NY (no R & B)
CUNY/College of Staten Island, NY (no R & B)
CUNY/Herbert H. Lehman College, NY (no R & B)
CUNY/John Jay College of Criminal Justice, NY (no R & B)
CUNY/Medgar Evers College, NY (no R & B)
CUNY/New York City Technical College, NY (no R & B)
CUNY/Queens College, NY (no R & B)
CUNY/York College, NY (no R & B)
College for Lifelong Learning, NH (no R & B)
Georgia State Univ, GA (no R & B)
Indiana Univ at Kokomo, IN
Indiana Univ East, IN (no R & B)
Indiana Univ Northwest, IN (no R & B)
Indiana Univ-Purdue Univ at Fort Wayne, IN (no R & B)
Indiana Univ/South Bend, IN (no R & B)
Indiana Univ Southeast, IN (no R & B)
Inter American Univ of PR/Aguadilla Regional College, PR (no R & B)
Inter American Univ of PR/Barranquitas Regional College, PR (no R & B)
Inter American Univ of PR/Bayamon Univ College, PR (no R & B)
Inter-American Univ of PR/Fajardo Regional College, PR (no R & B)
Inter American Univ of PR/Metropolitan Campus, PR (no R & B)
Inter American Univ of PR/Ponce Regional College, PR (no R & B)
Ohio State Univ at Lima, OH (no R & B)
Ohio State Univ at Mansfield, OH (no R & B)
Ohio State Univ at Marion, OH (no R & B)
Ohio State Univ at Newark, OH (no R & B)
Purdue Univ/Calumet, IN (no R & B)
Rutgers Univ/Univ College—Camden, NJ
SUNY/Empire State College, NY (no R & B)
Thomas College, GA (no R & B)
Troy State Univ at Dothan/Fort Rucker, AL (no R & B)
Turabo Univ, PR (no R & B)
Universidad Metropolitana, PR (no R & B)
Univ of Colo at Colo Springs, CO (no R & B)
Univ of Maine at Augusta, ME (no R & B)
Univ of Mich/Dearborn, MI (no R & B)
Univ of Mich/Flint, MI (no R & B)
Univ of S Car at Spartanburg, SC (no R & B)
Wayne State Univ, MI (no R & B)
Western International Univ, AZ (no R & B)

Colleges with Tuition, Room, and Board

Alabama State Univ, AL
Alice Lloyd College, KY
Auburn Univ at Montgomery, AL
Cal State/Dominguez Hills, CA
Cameron Univ, OK
College of the Ozarks, MO
Delta State Univ, MS
Dickinson State Univ, ND
East Central Univ, OK
Eastern New Mexico Univ, NM
Fayetteville State Univ, NC
Fort Valley State College, GA
Henderson State Univ, AR
Lamar Univ, TX
Langston Univ, OK
Livingston Univ, AL
Middle Tenn State Univ, TN
Minot State Univ, ND
New Mexico Highlands Univ, NM
Northeast Louisiana Univ, LA
Northwestern Okla State Univ, OK
Okla Panhandle State Univ, OK
Pembroke State Univ, NC
Southeastern Okla State Univ, OK
Southern Arkansas Univ, AR
Southwestern Okla State Univ, OK
Texas A&M Univ at Kingsville, TX
Univ of Arkansas at Monticello, AR
Univ of Arkansas at Pine Bluff, AR
Univ of Central Okla, OK
Univ of Memphis, TN
Univ of Science and Arts of Okla, OK
Univ of Southern Indiana, IN
Univ of Southwestern Louisiana, LA
Univ of Texas at El Paso, TX
Univ of Texas-Pan American, TX
Univ of the Sacred Heart, PR
Western Carolina Univ, NC
Western New Mexico Univ, NM

$4000-$5999

Colleges Without Tuition or Room and Board

Beth-El College of Nursing, CO (no R & B)
Boricua College, NY (no R & B)
Cleary College, MI (no R & B)
College of Aeronautics, NY (no R & B)
Detroit College of Business, MI (no R & B)
DeVry/Addison (DuPage County), IL (no R & B)
DeVry/Atlanta, GA (no R & B)
DeVry/Chicago, IL (no R & B)
DeVry/Columbus, OH (no R & B)
DeVry/Dallas, TX (no R & B)
DeVry/Kansas City, MO (no R & B)
DeVry/Los Angeles, CA (no R & B)
DeVry/Phoenix, AZ (no R & B)
Dyke College, OH (no R & B)
East-West Univ, IL (no R & B)
Franklin Univ, OH (no R & B)
Golden Gate Univ, CA (no R & B)
Gratz College, PA (no R & B)
Hebrew College, MA (no R & B)
Heritage College, WA (no R & B)
Jordan College, MI (no R & B)
Kentucky State Univ, KY
LeMoyne-Owen College, TN (no R & B)
Lincoln Univ, CA (no R & B)
Martin Univ, IN (no R & B)
NAES College, IL (no R & B)
North Georgia College, GA
Our Lady of Holy Cross College, LA (no R & B)
Sojourner-Douglass College, MD (no R & B)
Strayer College, DC (no R & B)
United States Merchant Marine Academy, NY
Univ of Maryland/Univ College, MD (no R & B)
Univ of Mass/Boston, MA (no R & B)
Webb Inst of Naval Architecture, NY
Wilmington College, DE (no R & B)

Colleges with Tuition, Room, and Board

Adams State College, CO
Alabama A&M Univ, AL

Albany State College, GA
Alcorn State Univ, MS
Ambassador College, TX
Angelo State Univ, TX
Appalachian State Univ, NC
Arkansas Baptist College, AR
Arkansas State Univ, AR
Arkansas Tech Univ, AR
Armstrong State College, GA
Auburn Univ, AL
Austin Peay State Univ, TN
Bemidji State Univ, MN
Black Hills State Univ, SD
Blue Mountain College, MS
Boise State Univ, ID
Brigham Young Univ, UT
Cal State/Bakersfield, CA
Cal State/Fresno, CA
Cal State/Fullerton, CA
Cal State/Hayward, CA
Cal State/Los Angeles, CA
Central Missouri State Univ, MO
Central Washington Univ, WA
Chadron State College, NE
CUNY/Hunter College, NY
College of the Southwest, NM
Columbus College, GA
Concord College, WV
Dakota State Univ, SD
Delaware State College, DE
East Carolina Univ, NC
East Tenn State Univ, TN
East Texas State Univ, TX
Eastern Illinois Univ, IL
Eastern Kentucky Univ, KY
Eastern Montana College, MT
Eastern Washington Univ, WA
Elizabeth City State Univ, NC
Emporia State Univ, KS
Escuela de Artes Plasticas, PR
Fairmont State College, WV
Florida A&M Univ, FL
Florida Atlantic Univ, FL
Florida International Univ, FL
Florida State Univ, FL
Fort Hays State Univ, KS
Fort Lewis College, CO
Francis Marion Univ, SC
Georgia College, GA
Georgia Southern Univ, GA
Georgia Southwestern College, GA
Glenville State College, WV
Grambling State Univ, LA
Humboldt State Univ, CA
Idaho State Univ, ID
Indiana Univ-Purdue Univ at Indianapolis, IN
Inter American Univ/Arecibo Campus, PR
Inter American Univ of PR/San German, PR
Iowa State Univ, IA
Jackson State Univ, MS
Jacksonville State Univ, AL
Kansas State Univ, KS
Lewis-Clark State College, ID
Lincoln Univ, MO
Louisiana State Univ and A&M College, LA
Louisiana Tech Univ, LA
Mankato State Univ, MN
Marshall Univ, WV
Marygrove College, MI
Mayville State Univ, ND
McNeese State Univ, LA
Mesa State College, CO
Midwestern State Univ, TX
Miss State Univ, MS
Miss Univ for Women, MS
Miss Valley State Univ, MS
Missouri Southern State College, MO
Missouri Western State College, MO
Montana College of Mineral Science and Technology, MT
Montana State Univ, MT
Moorhead State Univ, MN
Morehead State Univ, KY
Murray State Univ, KY
Nebr Methodist College of Nursing and Allied Health, NE
New College of the Univ of South Florida, FL

New Mexico Inst of Mining and
Technology, NM
New Mexico State Univ, NM
Nicholls State Univ, LA
N Car Agricultural and Technical
State Univ, NC
N Car Central Univ, NC
N Car School of the Arts, NC
N Car State Univ, NC
N Dak State Univ of Agriculture and
Applied Science, ND
Northeast Missouri State Univ, MO
Northeastern State Univ, OK
Northern Arizona Univ, AZ
Northern Kentucky Univ, KY
Northern Montana College, MT
Northern State Univ, SD
Northwest Missouri State Univ, MO
Northwestern College, WI
Northwestern State Univ of
Louisiana, LA
Okla State Univ, OK
Oregon Inst of Technology, OR
Peru State College, NE
Philander Smith College, AR
Pittsburg State Univ, KS
Pontifical Catholic Univ of
PR/Ponce, PR
Prairie View A&M Univ, TX
St. Cloud State Univ, MN
Sam Houston State Univ, TX
Savannah State College, GA
Selma Univ, AL
Shawnee State Univ, OH
Shepherd College, WV
S Car State Univ, SC
S Dak School of Mines and
Technology, SD
S Dak State Univ, SD
Southeast Missouri State Univ, MO
Southeastern Louisiana Univ, LA
Southern Univ and A&M College, LA
Southern Utah Univ, UT
Southwest Missouri State Univ, MO
Southwest State Univ, MN
Southwest Texas State Univ, TX
SUNY/College of Agriculture and
Technology at Cobleskill, NY
Stephen F. Austin State Univ, TX
Sul Ross State Univ, TX
Tarleton State Univ, TX
Tenn State Univ, TN
Tenn Tech Univ, TN
Texas A&M Univ, TX
Texas A&M Univ at Galveston, TX
Texas College, TX
Texas Southern Univ, TX
Texas Woman's Univ, TX
The Univ of New Mexico, NM
Troy State Univ, AL
Universidad Adventista de las
Antillas, PR
Univ of Alabama, AL
Univ of Alabama at Huntsville, AL
Univ of Alaska Fairbanks, AK
Univ of Alaska Southeast, AK
Univ of Arizona, AZ
Univ of Arkansas at Fayetteville, AR
Univ of Arkansas at Little Rock, AR
Univ of Central Arkansas, AR
Univ of Florida, FL
Univ of Georgia, GA
Univ of Guam, GU
Univ of Hawaii at Hilo, HI
Univ of Hawaii at Manoa, HI
Univ of Houston, TX
Univ of Houston-Downtown, TX
Univ of Idaho, ID
Univ of Iowa, IA
Univ of Kansas, KS
Univ of Kentucky, KY
Univ of Louisville, KY
Univ of Miss, MS
Univ of Missouri/Kansas City, MO
Univ of Montana, MT
Univ of Montevallo, AL
Univ of Nebr at Kearney, NE
Univ of Nebr-Lincoln, NE
Univ of Nevada/Reno, NV
Univ of New Orleans, LA
Univ of North Alabama, AL
Univ of N Car at Asheville, NC
Univ of N Car at Chapel Hill, NC
Univ of N Car at Charlotte, NC
Univ of N Car at Greensboro, NC
Univ of N Car at Wilmington, NC
Univ of N Dak, ND
Univ of North Florida, FL

Univ of North Texas, TX
Univ of Northern Iowa, IA
Univ of Okla, OK
Univ of South Alabama, AL
Univ of S Car at Aiken, SC
Univ of S Dak, SD
Univ of South Florida, FL
Univ of Southern Colo, CO
Univ of Southern Miss, MS
Univ of Tenn at Chattanooga, TN
Univ of Tenn at Martin, TN
Univ of Tenn/Knoxville, TN
Univ of Texas at Arlington, TX
Univ of Texas at Austin, TX
Univ of the Virgin Islands, VI
Univ of Utah, UT
Univ of West Florida, FL
Univ of Wisc/Eau Claire, WI
Univ of Wisc/Green Bay, WI
Univ of Wisc/La Crosse, WI
Univ of Wisc/Oshkosh, WI
Univ of Wisc/Parkside, WI
Univ of Wisc/Platteville, WI
Univ of Wisc/River Falls, WI
Univ of Wisc/Stevens Point, WI
Univ of Wisc/Stout, WI
Univ of Wisc/Superior, WI
Univ of Wisc/Whitewater, WI
Univ of Wyoming, WY
Utah State Univ, UT
Valdosta State Univ, GA
Valley City State Univ, ND
Washburn Univ of Topeka, KS
Wayne State College, NE
Weber State Univ, UT
West Georgia College, GA
West Liberty State College, WV
West Texas A&M Univ, TX
West Virginia Inst of Technology, WV
West Virginia State College, WV
West Virginia Univ, WV
Western Illinois Univ, IL
Western Kentucky Univ, KY
Western State College of Colo, CO
Wichita State Univ, KS
Williams Baptist College, AR
Winona State Univ, MN
Winston-Salem State Univ, NC

$6000-$7999

Colleges Without Tuition or Room and Board

Bridgeport Engineering Inst, CT
(no R & B)
Burlington College, VT (no R & B)
Cincinnati College of Mortuary
Science, OH (no R & B)
City Univ, WA (no R & B)
Cogswell College North, WA
(no R & B)
Colo Technical College, CO
(no R & B)
Felician College, NJ (no R & B)
Lourdes College, OH (no R & B)
Marylhurst College, OR (no R & B)
National Univ, CA (no R & B)
New College of Calif, CA (no R & B)
Pacific Northwest College of Art, OR
(no R & B)
St. Francis College, NY (no R & B)
St. Joseph's College, NY (no R & B)
Southeastern Univ, DC
(no R & B)
The Citadel, SC (no R & B)
Union Inst, OH (no R & B)

Colleges with Tuition, Room, and Board

Academy of the New Church, PA
Allen Univ, SC
Arizona State Univ Main Campus, AZ
Baker College, MI
Ball State Univ, IN
Barber-Scotia College, NC
Barnes College, MO
Bloomsburg Univ of Pennsylvania, PA
Bowie State Univ, MD
Bowling Green State Univ, OH
Brewton-Parker College, GA
Bridgewater State College, MA
Brigham Young Univ/Hawaii, HI
Calif Maritime Academy, CA
Calif Polytechnic State Univ, CA

Calif State Polytechnic
Univ/Pomona, CA
Cal State/Chico, CA
Cal State/Long Beach, CA
Cal State/Northridge, CA
Cal State/Sacramento, CA
Cal State/San Bernardino, CA
Cal State/Stanislaus, CA
Calif Univ of Pennsylvania, PA
Central Conn State Univ, CT
Central Mich Univ, MI
Central State Univ, OH
Cheyney Univ of Pennsylvania, PA
Clarion Univ of Pennsylvania, PA
Clarkson College, NE
Clemson Univ, SC
Cleveland State Univ, OH
Clinch Valley College/Univ of
Virginia, VA
Coastal Carolina Univ, SC
College of Charleston, SC
College of Great Falls, MT
Colo State Univ, CO
Columbia College, IL
Coppin State College, MD
Crichton College, TN
David Lipscomb Univ, TN
East Stroudsburg Univ, PA
East Texas Baptist Univ, TX
Eastern Conn State Univ, CT
Eastern Mich Univ, MI
Eastern Oregon State College, OR
Edinboro Univ of Pennsylvania, PA
Evergreen State College, WA
Fashion Inst of Technology/
SUNY, NY
Ferris State Univ, MI
Fitchburg State College, MA
Flagler College, FL
Florida Memorial College, FL
Framingham State College, MA
Frostburg State Univ, MD
Georgia Inst of Technology, GA
Goldey-Beacom College, DE
Grand Valley State Univ, MI
Grove City College, PA
Illinois State Univ, IL
Indiana State Univ, IN
Indiana Univ Bloomington, IN
Indiana Univ of Pennsylvania, PA
Jarvis Christian College, TX
Jersey City State College, NJ
Kean College of New Jersey, NJ
Keene State College, NH
Kent State Univ, OH
Kentucky Christian College, KY
Kutztown Univ, PA
Lake Superior State Univ, MI
Lander Univ, SC
Lane College, TN
Lee College, TN
Lock Haven Univ of Pennsylvania, PA
Longwood College, VA
Louisiana College, LA
Mansfield Univ, PA
Mary Washington College, VA
Mass Maritime Academy, MA
Mich State Univ, MI
Mich Tech Univ, MI
Miles College, AL
Millersville Univ of Pennsylvania, PA
Montclair State College, NJ
Morgan State Univ, MD
Morris College, SC
Norfolk State Univ, VA
North Adams State College, MA
Northern Illinois Univ, IL
Northern Mich Univ, MI
Oakland Univ, MI
Ohio State Univ, OH
Ohio Univ, OH
Oregon State Univ, OR
Park College, MO
Paul Quinn College, TX
Pillsbury Baptist Bible College, MN
Plymouth State College, NH
Portland State Univ, OR
Purdue Univ/West Lafayette, IN
Radford Univ, VA
Rhode Island College, RI
Richard Stockton College of New
Jersey, NJ
Rowan College of New Jersey, NJ
Rust College, MS
Saginaw Valley State Univ, MI
Salem State College, MA
Salisbury State Univ, MD
San Diego State Univ, CA

San Francisco State Univ, CA
San Jose State Univ, CA
Shippensburg Univ of Pennsylvania,
PA
Slippery Rock Univ, PA
Sonoma State Univ, CA
Southeastern College of the
Assemblies of God, FL
Southern Conn State Univ, CT
Southern Illinois Univ at Carbondale,
IL
Southern Illinois Univ at
Edwardsville, IL
Southern Oregon State College, OR
Southwestern Christian College, TX
SUNY at Albany, NY
SUNY at Binghamton, NY
SUNY at Buffalo, NY
SUNY at Stony Brook, NY
SUNY/College at Brockport, NY
SUNY/College at Buffalo, NY
SUNY/College at Cortland, NY
SUNY/College at Fredonia, NY
SUNY/College at Geneseo, NY
SUNY/College at New Paltz, NY
SUNY/College at
Old Westbury, NY
SUNY/College at Oneonta, NY
SUNY/College at Oswego, NY
SUNY/College at Plattsburgh, NY
SUNY/College at Purchase, NY
SUNY/Maritime College, NY
SUNY/Potsdam College, NY
Stillman College, AL
Texas Tech Univ, TX
Tougaloo College, MS
Towson State Univ, MD
Union Univ, TN
Universidad Politecnica de PR, PR
Univ of Akron, OH
Univ of Alabama at Birmingham, AL
Univ of Alaska Anchorage, AK
Univ of Central Florida, FL
Univ of Cincinnati, OH
Univ of Colo at Boulder, CO
Univ of Illinois at
Urbana-Champaign, IL
Univ of Maine, ME
Univ of Maine at Farmington, ME
Univ of Maine at Fort Kent, ME
Univ of Maine at Machias, ME
Univ of Maine at Presque Isle, ME
Univ of Maryland/Baltimore County,
MD
Univ of Maryland/
Eastern Shore, MD
Univ of Minn/Crookston, MN
Univ of Minn/Duluth, MN
Univ of Minn/Morris, MN
Univ of Minn/Twin Cities, MN
Univ of Missouri/Columbia, MO
Univ of Missouri/Rolla, MO
Univ of Missouri/St. Louis, MO
Univ of Nevada/Las Vegas, NV
Univ of Northern Colo, CO
Univ of Oregon, OR
Univ of Rio Grande, OH
Univ of S Car, SC
Univ of Southern Maine, ME
Univ of Texas at San Antonio, TX
Univ of the Ozarks, AR
Univ of Toledo, OH
Univ of Virginia, VA
Univ of Washington, WA
Univ of Wisc/Madison, WI
Univ of Wisc/Milwaukee, WI
Virginia Commonwealth Univ, VA
Virginia Polytechnic Inst and State
Univ, VA
Virginia State Univ, VA
Voorhees College, SC
Washington State Univ, WA
Wayland Baptist Univ, TX
West Chester Univ of Pennsylvania,
PA
Western Conn State Univ, CT
Western Mich Univ, MI
Western Oregon State College, OR
Western Washington Univ, WA
Westfield State College, MA
William Carey College, MS
William Paterson College, NJ
William Tyndale College, MI
Winthrop Univ, SC
Worcester State College, MA
Wright State Univ, OH
York College, NE
Youngstown State Univ, OH

$8000-$9999

Colleges Without Tuition or Room and Board

Art Academy of Cincinnati, OH (no R & B)
Cascade College, OR
Cornish College of the Arts, WA (no R & B)
Holy Family College, PA (no R & B)
Kendall College of Art and Design, MI (no R & B)
Laboratory Inst of Merchandising, NY (no R & B)
Milwaukee Inst of Art and Design, WI (no R & B)
Molloy College, NY (no R & B)
Neumann College, PA (no R & B)
Prescott College, AZ (no R & B)
St. John's Univ, NY (no R & B)
Silver Lake College, WI (no R & B)
West Coast Univ, CA (no R & B)

Colleges with Tuition, Room, and Board

Bartlesville Wesleyan College, OK
Belhaven College, MS
Benedict College, SC
Bennett College, NC
Bethel College, TN
Bethune-Cookman College, FL
Blackburn College, IL
Brescia College, KY
Campbellsville College, KY
Castleton State College, VT
Central Wesleyan College, SC
Clearwater Christian College, FL
Cogswell Polytechnical College, CA
College of William and Mary, VA
Colo Christian Univ, CO
Colo School of Mines, CO
Cooper Union for the Advancement of Science and Art, NY
Cumberland College, KY
Cumberland Univ, TN
Dakota Wesleyan Univ, SD
Dallas Baptist Univ, TX
Davenport College of Business, MI
Deaconess College of Nursing, MO
Dillard Univ, LA
Edward Waters College, FL
Embry-Riddle Aeronautical Univ, AZ
Faulkner Univ, AL
Freed-Hardeman Univ, TN
Gallaudet Univ, DC
George Mason Univ, VA
Grand Canyon Univ, AZ
Hannibal-LaGrange College, MO
Hardin-Simmons Univ, TX
Harding Univ, AR
Howard Payne Univ, TX
Humphreys College, CA
Huron Univ, SD
Huston-Tillotson College, TX
James Madison Univ, VA
John Brown Univ, AR
Johnson C. Smith Univ, NC
Johnson State College, VT
Judson College, AL
Knoxville College, TN
Lambuth Univ, TN
Lawrence Tech Univ, MI
Lees-McRae College, NC
Lincoln Memorial Univ, TN
Lindsey Wilson College, KY
Livingstone College, NC
Lubbock Christian Univ, TX
Lyndon State College, VT
Madonna Univ, MI
Maine Maritime Academy, ME
Mass College of Art, MA
Meredith College, NC
Miami Univ, OH
Mich Christian College, MI
Miss College, MS
Missouri Baptist College, MO
Mount Olive College, NC
National College, SD
New Jersey Inst of Technology, NJ
North Central Bible College, MN
Northwest College, WA
Ohio Valley College, WV
Okla Baptist Univ, OK
Okla Christian Univ of Science and Arts, OK

Okla City Univ, OK
Old Dominion Univ, VA
Ouachita Baptist Univ, AR
Paine College, GA
Penn State Univ at Erie/Behrend College, PA
Penn State Univ/Univ Park Campus, PA
Piedmont College, GA
Pikeville College, KY
Presentation College, SD
Ramapo College of New Jersey, NJ
Rutgers Univ/Camden College of A&S, NJ
Rutgers Univ/College of Engineering, NJ
Rutgers Univ/College of Nursing, NJ
Rutgers Univ/College of Pharmacy, NJ
Rutgers Univ/Cook College, NJ
Rutgers Univ/Douglass College, NJ
Rutgers Univ/Livingston College, NJ
Rutgers Univ/Mason Gross School of the Arts, NJ
Rutgers Univ/Newark College of A&S, NJ
Rutgers Univ/Rutgers College, NJ
St. Augustine's College, NC
St. Mary's College, MI
St. Mary's College of Maryland, MD
St. Paul's College, VA
Shaw Univ, NC
Southern Nazarene Univ, OK
Southwest Baptist Univ, MO
SUNY College of Environmental Science and Forestry, NY
Talladega College, AL
Texas Wesleyan Univ, TX
Toccoa Falls College, GA
Trenton State College, NJ
Trevecca Nazarene College, TN
Union College, KY
Univ of Calif at Berkeley, CA
Univ of Calif at Davis, CA
Univ of Calif at Los Angeles, CA
Univ of Calif at Santa Barbara, CA
Univ of Calif at Santa Cruz, CA
Univ of Calif, Riverside, CA
Univ of Conn, CT
Univ of Delaware, DE
Univ of Illinois at Chicago, IL
Univ of Lowell, MA
Univ of Mary, ND
Univ of Mary Hardin-Baylor, TX
Univ of Maryland/College Park, MD
Univ of Mass/Amherst, MA
Univ of Mass Dartmouth, MA
Univ of Mich/Ann Arbor, MI
Univ of Mobile, AL
Univ of New Hampshire, NH
Univ of Pittsburgh, PA
Univ of Pittsburgh at Bradford, PA
Univ of Pittsburgh at Greensburg, PA
Univ of Pittsburgh at Johnstown, PA
Univ of Rhode Island, RI
Villa Julie College, MD
Virginia Military Inst, VA
Webber College, FL
York College of Pennsylvania, PA

$10,000-$11,999

Colleges Without Tuition or Room and Board

Audrey Cohen College, NY (no R & B)
Paier College of Art, CT (no R & B)
Shenandoah Univ, VA
Sterling College, KS
Warren Wilson College, NC (no R & B)

Colleges with Tuition, Room, and Board

Abilene Christian Univ, TX
Alaska Pacific Univ, AK
Alverno College, WI
American College for the Applied Arts, GA
Arkansas College, AR
Asbury College, KY
Barton College, NC
Baylor Univ, TX
Bellarmine College, KY
Belmont Univ, TN

Berry College, GA
Bethany College, KS
Bethel College, IN
Bethel College, KS
Bluefield College, VA
Bryan College, TN
Calif Baptist College, CA
Campbell Univ, NC
Capitol College, MD
Cardinal Stritch College, WI
Carroll College, MT
Carson-Newman College, TN
Cedarville College, OH
Centenary College of Louisiana, LA
Central Methodist College, MO
Charleston Southern Univ, SC
Christendom College, VA
Christian Heritage College, CA
Clark Atlanta Univ, GA
Columbia College, MO
Concordia College, NE
Concordia Lutheran College, TX
Culver-Stockton College, MO
Dana College, NE
Dordt College, IA
Edgewood College, WI
Embry-Riddle Aeronautical Univ, FL
Evangel College, MO
Five Towns College, NY
Friends Univ, KS
Gardner-Webb Univ, NC
Georgetown College, KY
Graceland College, IA
Grand Rapids Baptist College and Seminary, MI
Greensboro College, NC
Hampton Univ, VA
Hanover College, IN
Hellenic College/Holy Cross Greek Orthodox School of Theology, MA
Hendrix College, AR
Houston Baptist Univ, TX
Howard Univ, DC
Huntingdon College, AL
Husson College, ME
Illinois College, IL
Indiana Inst of Technology, IN
Jamestown College, ND
Kansas Newman College, KS
Kansas Wesleyan Univ, KS
Kentucky Wesleyan College, KY
King College, TN
LaGrange College, GA
Liberty Univ, VA
Limestone College, SC
Mars Hill College, NC
McKendree College, IL
McMurry Univ, TX
McPherson College, KS
Mercy College, NY
MidAmerica Nazarene College, KS
Milligan College, TN
Montreat-Anderson College, NC
Mount Marty College, SD
Mount Mary College, WI
Mount Senario College, WI
Mount Vernon Nazarene College, OH
Newberry College, SC
Northwest Nazarene College, ID
Notre Dame College of Ohio, OH
Oakland City College, IN
Oakwood College, AL
Ohio Dominican College, OH
Olivet Nazarene Univ, IL
Oral Roberts Univ, OK
Ottawa Univ, KS
Our Lady of the Lake Univ of San Antonio, TX
Palm Beach Atlantic College, FL
Pfeiffer College, NC
Philadelphia College of Bible, PA
Robert Morris College, PA
Rocky Mountain College, MT
St. Francis College, IN
St. Louis College of Pharmacy, MO
St. Mary College, KS
St. Meinrad College, IN
Samford Univ, AL
Shorter College, GA
Simpson College, CA
Sioux Falls College, SD
Southern College of Seventh-day Adventists, TN
Southwestern Adventist College, TX
Southwestern College, KS
Spalding Univ, KY
Tabor College, KS
Temple Univ, PA

Tenn Wesleyan College, TN
Texas Lutheran College, TX
Thomas Moore College of Liberal Arts, NH
Tiffin Univ, OH
Touro College, NY
Tusculum College, TN
Tuskegee Univ, AL
Union College, NE
Univ of Calif, San Diego, CA
Univ of St. Thomas, TX
Univ of Vermont, VT
Upper Iowa Univ, IA
Virginia Union Univ, VA
Walsh Univ, OH
Waynesburg College, PA
Wilberforce Univ, OH
Wingate College, NC
Xavier Univ of Louisiana, LA

$12,000-$13,999

Colleges Without Tuition or Room and Board

Art Center College of Design, CA (no R & B)
Indiana Wesleyan Univ, IN
Le Tourneau Univ, TX
Manhattan School of Music, NY
Nova Southeastern Univ, FL
St. Mary's College of Minn, MN
San Francisco Art Inst, CA (no R & B)
San Francisco Conservatory of Music, CA (no R & B)

Colleges with Tuition, Room, and Board

Albany College of Pharmacy, NY
Alderson-Broaddus College, WV
Allentown College of St. Francis de Sales, PA
Alvernia College, PA
Anderson Univ, IN
Atlanta College of Art, GA
Augustana College, SD
Aurora Univ, IL
Averett College, VA
Avila College, MO
Baker Univ, KS
Barat College, IL
Bassist College, OR
Belmont Abbey College, NC
Benedictine College, KS
Bloomfield College, NJ
Bluffton College, OH
Briar Cliff College, IA
Caldwell College, NJ
Calvin College, MI
Carlow College, PA
Catawba College, NC
Champlain College, VT
Christian Brothers Univ, TN
Clarke College, IA
Coker College, SC
College of Mount St. Joseph, OH
College of St. Francis, IL
College of St. Joseph, VT
College of St. Mary, NE
Columbia College, SC
Columbia Union College, MD
Concordia College, MI
Concordia College, MN
Concordia College, OR
Concordia College/Moorhead, MN
Concordia Univ, IL
Concordia Univ Wisc, WI
Cornell Univ, NY
Covenant College, GA
Daemen College, NY
Davis and Elkins College, WV
Defiance College, OH
Doane College, NE
Dominican College, NY
Dowling College, NY
Drury College, MO
D'Youville College, NY
Eastern Mennonite College, VA
Eastern Nazarene College, MA
Elmhurst College, IL
Elon College, NC
Emory and Henry College, VA
Ferrum College, VA
Florida Southern College, FL
Fontbonne College, MO

Franciscan Univ of Steubenville, OH
Franklin College of Indiana, IN
Fresno Pacific College, CA
Geneva College, PA
Georgian Court College, NJ
Goshen College, IN
Grace College, IN
Grand View College, IA
Hastings College, NE
Hawaii Pacific Univ, HI
High Point Univ, NC
Houghton College, NY
Huntington College, IN
Incarnate Word College, TX
Iowa Wesleyan College, IA
Jacksonville Univ, FL
Jewish Theological Seminary of America/List College of Jewish Studies, NY
Johnson and Wales Univ, RI
Judson College, IL
Kendall College, IL
Keuka College, NY
King's College, NY
La Roche College, PA
Lake Erie College, OH
Lakeland College, WI
Lindenwood College, MO
MacMurray College, IL
Maharishi International Univ, IA
Malone College, OH
Manchester College, IN
Marian College, IN
Marian College of Fond du Lac, WI
Maryville Univ-St. Louis, MO
Master's College, CA
Medaille College, NY
Memphis College of Art, TN
Mercyhurst College, PA
Methodist College, NC
Midland Lutheran College, NE
Montserrat College of Art, MA
Morehouse College, GA
Morningside College, IA
Morris Brown College, GA
Mount Mercy College, IA
Mount St. Clare College, IA
Mount St. Mary College, NY
National-Louis Univ, IL
Nebr Wesleyan Univ, NE
New York Inst of Technology/Old Westbury, NY
N Car Wesleyan College, NC
Northland College, WI
Northwestern College, MN
Northwestern College of Iowa, IA
Northwood Univ, MI
Nyack College, NY
Pacific Christian College, CA
Phillips Univ, OK
Point Loma Nazarene College, CA
Point Park College, PA
Quincy Univ, IL
Research College of Nursing, MO
Roberts Wesleyan College, NY
Rockhurst College, MO
Roosevelt Univ, IL
St. Ambrose Univ, IA
St. Edward's Univ, TX
St. Leo College, FL
St. Mary's Univ, TX
St. Thomas Aquinas College, NY
St. Vincent College, PA
Shimer College, IL
Siena Heights College, MI
Southern Calif College, CA
Southern Vermont College, VT
Spelman College, GA
Spring Arbor College, MI
Teikyo Marycrest Univ, IA
Texas Christian Univ, TX
Thomas College, ME
Thomas More College, KY
Tri-State Univ, IN
Trinity Christian College, IL
Unity College, ME
Univ of Calif/Irvine, CA
Univ of Charleston, WV
Univ of Tulsa, OK
Urbana Univ, OH
Ursuline College, OH
VanderCook College of Music, IL
Virginia Intermont College, VA
Viterbo College, WI
Walla Walla College, WA
Warner Pacific College, OR
Webster Univ, MO
Wesley College, DE

West Suburban College of Nursing, IL
Western Baptist College, OR
Westminster College, MO
Westminster College of Salt Lake City, UT
William Jewell College, MO
William Penn Univ, IA
Wilmington College, OH
Wisc Lutheran College, WI

$14,000-$15,999

Colleges Without Tuition or Room and Board
Eureka College, IL
Hope College, MI

Colleges with Tuition, Room, and Board
Adrian College, MI
Albertson College, ID
American International College, MA
Andrews Univ, MI
Anna Maria College, MA
Aquinas College, MI
Ashland Univ, OH
Atlantic Union College, MA
Augsburg College, MN
Austin College, TX
Azusa Pacific Univ, CA
Baldwin-Wallace College, OH
Bethel College, MN
Birmingham-Southern College, AL
Bradley Univ, IL
Bridgewater College, VA
Brooklyn Campus of LIU, NY
Canisius College, NY
Carroll College, WI
Carthage College, WI
Cazenovia College, NY
Center for Creative Studies/College of Art and Design, MI
Central College, IA
Centre College, KY
Chaminade Univ of Honolulu, HI
Chestnut Hill College, PA
Cleveland Inst of Art, OH
College Misericordia, PA
College of New Rochelle, NY
College of Our Lady of The Elms, MA
College of St. Benedict, MN
College of St. Catherine, MN
College of St. Elizabeth, NJ
College of St. Rose, NY
College of St. Scholastica, MN
College of Santa Fe, NM
Columbia College of Nursing, WI
Columbus College of Art and Design, OH
Concordia Univ, CA
Converse College, SC
Corcoran School of Art, DC
Creighton Univ, NE
DePaul Univ, IL
Drexel Univ, PA
Eastern College, PA
Erskine College, SC
Gannon Univ, PA
George Fox College, OR
GMI Engineering & Management Inst, MI
Green Mountain College, VT
Greenville College, IL
Gustavus Adolphus College, MN
Gwynedd-Mercy College, PA
Hillsdale College, MI
Holy Names College, CA
Illinois Benedictine College, IL
Immaculata College, PA
King's College, PA
La Sierra Univ, CA
Le Moyne College, NY
Lee College at the Univ of Judaism, CA
Lenoir-Rhyne College, NC
Lewis Univ, IL
Loras College, IA
Loyola Univ/New Orleans, LA
Loyola Univ of Chicago, IL
Luther College, IA
Maine College of Art, ME
Marymount Manhattan College, NY
Marymount Univ, VA
Maryville College, TN
Marywood College, PA

Mercer Univ, GA
Messiah College, PA
Millikin Univ, IL
Millsaps College, MS
Milwaukee School of Engineering, WI
Minneapolis College of Art and Design, MN
Missouri Valley College, MO
Mount Union College, OH
Nazareth College of Rochester, NY
New Hampshire College, NH
Niagara Univ, NY
Nichols College, MA
North Central College, IL
North Park College, IL
Northwood Univ, FL
Notre Dame College, NH
Olivet College, MI
Pace Univ, NY
Pacific Lutheran Univ, WA
Pacific Union College, CA
Philadelphia College of Pharmacy and Science, PA
Philadelphia College of Textiles and Science, PA
Presbyterian College, SC
Queens College, NC
Rice Univ, TX
Ringling School of Art and Design, FL
Rivier College, NH
Rockford College, IL
Rosary College, IL
St. Andrews Presbyterian College, NC
St. Bonaventure Univ, NY
St. Francis College, PA
St. John Fisher College, NY
St. John's Univ, MN
St. Joseph's College, IN
St. Joseph's College, ME
St. Louis Univ, MO
St. Martin's College, WA
St. Mary-of-the-Woods College, IN
St. Norbert College, WI
St. Peter's College, NJ
St. Thomas Univ, FL
St. Xavier Univ, IL
Salem-Teikyo Univ, WV
Savannah College of Art and Design, GA
Schreiner College, TX
Seton Hill College, PA
Sheldon Jackson College, AK
Siena College, NY
Sierra Nevada College, NV
Simpson College, IA
Southwestern Univ, TX
Springfield College, MA
Suffolk Univ, MA
Taylor Univ, IN
Teikyo Westmar Univ, IA
Transylvania Univ, KY
Trinity College, IL
United States International Univ, CA
Univ of Dallas, TX
Univ of Dayton, OH
Univ of Detroit Mercy, MI
Univ of Dubuque, IA
Univ of Evansville, IN
Univ of Findlay, OH
Univ of Indianapolis, IN
Univ of New Haven, CT
Univ of Portland, OR
Univ of St. Thomas, MN
Valparaiso Univ, IN
Virginia Wesleyan College, VA
Wartburg College, IA
Wentworth Inst of Technology, MA
Wesleyan College, GA
Westbrook College, ME
Western New England College, MA
Westminster College, PA
Wheaton College, IL
Wheeling Jesuit College, WV
Wilkes Univ, PA
William Woods Univ, MO
Wofford College, SC
Women's College of Brenau Univ, GA
Xavier Univ, OH

$16,000-$17,999

Colleges Without Tuition or Room and Board
New England College, NH

Colleges with Tuition, Room, and Board
Agnes Scott College, GA
Albertus Magnus College, CT
Alma College, MI
Art Inst of Southern Calif, CA
Assumption College, MA
Augustana College, IL
Barry Univ, FL
Beaver College, PA
Berklee College of Music, MA
Biola Univ, CA
Boston Conservatory, MA
Buena Vista College, IA
Butler Univ, IN
Cabrini College, PA
Calif College of Arts and Crafts, CA
Calif Inst of the Arts, CA
Calif Lutheran Univ, CA
Capital Univ, OH
Centenary College, NJ
Coe College, IA
College of Insurance, NY
College of Mount St. Vincent, NY
College of Notre Dame, CA
College of Notre Dame of Maryland, MD
College of the Atlantic, ME
Daniel Webster College, NH
Delaware Valley College, PA
Dominican College of San Rafael, CA
Drake Univ, IA
Duquesne Univ, PA
Elizabethtown College, PA
Emmanuel College, MA
Fairleigh Dickinson Univ, NJ
Florida Inst of Technology, FL
Franklin Pierce College, NH
Friends World Program, NY
Furman Univ, SC
Goddard College, VT
Gonzaga Univ, WA
Gordon College, MA
Guilford College, NC
Hamline Univ, MN
Hampden-Sydney College, VA
Heidelberg College, OH
Hofstra Univ, NY
Iona College, NY
John Carroll Univ, OH
Kansas City Art Inst, MO
La Salle Univ, PA
Lesley College, MA
Linfield College, OR
LIU/C. W. Post Campus, NY
LIU/Southampton Campus, NY
Lycoming College, PA
Lynchburg College, VA
Mannes College of Music, NY
Marietta College, OH
Marist College, NY
Marquette Univ, WI
Mary Baldwin College, VA
Marymount College/Tarrytown, NY
Monmouth College, IL
Monmouth College, NJ
Moore College of Art and Design, PA
Mount Ida College, MA
Mount St. Mary's College, CA
Mount St. Mary's College, MD
Muskingum College, OH
Oglethorpe Univ, GA
Otis College of Art and Design, CA
Otterbein College, OH
Pacific Univ, OR
Principia College, IL
Quinnipiac College, CT
Randolph-Macon College, VA
Regis College, MA
Regis Univ, CO
Roanoke College, VA
Roger Williams Univ, RI
Rose-Hulman Inst of Technology, IN
Rosemont College, PA
Russell Sage College, NY
Sacred Heart Univ, CT
St. Anselm College, NH
St. Joseph College, CT
St. Joseph's Univ, PA
St. Mary's College, IN
St. Michael's College, VT
St. Olaf College, MN
Salem College, NC
Samuel Merritt College, CA
School of the Art Inst of Chicago, IL
School of Visual Arts, NY

Seattle Pacific Univ, WA
Seattle Univ, WA
Spring Hill College, AL
Stetson Univ, FL
Stonehill College, MA
Teikyo Post Univ, CT
Thiel College, PA
Thomas Aquinas College, CA
Trinity College, DC
Trinity College of Vermont, VT
Trinity Univ, TX
Univ of La Verne, CA
Univ of New England, ME
Univ of Richmond, VA
Univ of Scranton, PA
Univ of Tampa, FL
Univ of the Arts, PA
Upsala College, NJ
Utica College of Syracuse Univ, NY
Wabash College, IN
Wagner College, NY
Wake Forest Univ, NC
Washington and Lee Univ, VA
West Virginia Wesleyan College, WV
Whitworth College, WA
Widener Univ, PA
Willamette Univ, OR
Wilson College, PA
Woodbury Univ, CA

Over $18,000

Colleges Without Tuition or Room and Board

Bates College, ME
Bennington College, VT
Curry College, MA
Eastman School of Music, NY
Franklin and Marshall College, PA
Gettysburg College, PA
Grinnell College, IA
Middlebury College, VT (no R & B)
Norwich Univ, VT
Western Maryland College, MD

Colleges with Tuition, Room, and Board

Adelphi Univ, NY
Albion College, MI
Albright College, PA
Alfred Univ, NY
Allegheny College, PA
American Univ, DC
Amherst College, MA
Antioch College, OH
Babson College, MA
Bard College, NY
Beloit College, WI
Bentley College, MA
Bethany College, WV
Boston College, MA
Boston Univ, MA
Bowdoin College, ME
Bradford College, MA
Brandeis Univ, MA
Brown Univ, RI
Bryant College, RI
Bryn Mawr College, PA
Bucknell Univ, PA
Calif Inst of Technology, CA
Carleton College, MN
Carnegie Mellon Univ, PA
Case Western Reserve Univ, OH
Catholic Univ of America, DC
Cedar Crest College, PA
Chapman Univ, CA
Chatham College, PA
Claremont McKenna College, CA
Clark Univ, MA
Clarkson Univ, NY
Cleveland Inst of Music, OH
Colby College, ME
Colby-Sawyer College, NH
Colgate Univ, NY
College of the Holy Cross, MA
College of Wooster, OH
Colo College, CO
Columbia Univ/Barnard College, NY
Columbia Univ/Columbia College, NY
Columbia Univ/School of
  Engineering and Applied Science,
  NY
Conn College, CT
Cornell Univ, IA
Dartmouth College, NH

Davidson College, NC
Denison Univ, OH
DePauw Univ, IN
Dickinson College, PA
Drew Univ/College of Liberal Arts, NJ
Duke Univ, NC
Earlham College, IN
Eckerd College, FL
Elmira College, NY
Emerson College, MA
Emory Univ, GA
Eugene Lang College of the New
  School for Social Research, NY
Fairfield Univ, CT
Fordham Univ/College at Lincoln
  Center, NY
Fordham Univ/College of Business
  Administration, NY
Fordham Univ/Fordham College, NY
George Washington Univ, DC
Georgetown Univ, DC
Goucher College, MD
Hamilton College, NY
Hampshire College, MA
Hartwick College, NY
Harvard Univ/Harvard and Radcliffe
  Colleges, MA
Harvey Mudd College, CA
Haverford College, PA
Hiram College, OH
Hobart and William Smith Colleges,
  NY
Hollins College, VA
Hood College, MD
Illinois Inst of Technology, IL
Illinois Wesleyan Univ, IL
Ithaca College, NY
Johns Hopkins Univ, MD
Juilliard School, NY
Juniata College, PA
Kalamazoo College, MI
Kenyon College, OH
Knox College, IL
Lafayette College, PA
Lake Forest College, IL
Lawrence Univ, WI
Lebanon Valley College of
  Pennsylvania, PA
Lehigh Univ, PA
Lewis and Clark College, OR
Loyola College, MD
Loyola Marymount Univ, CA
Lynn Univ, FL
Macalester College, MN
Manhattan College, NY
Manhattanville College, NY
Marlboro College, VT
Maryland Inst, College of Art, MD
Mass College of Pharmacy and Allied
  Health Sciences, MA
Mass Inst of Technology, MA
Menlo College, CA
Merrimack College, MA
Mills College, CA
Moravian College, PA
Mount Holyoke College, MA
Mount Vernon College, DC
Muhlenberg College, PA
New England Conservatory of Music,
  MA
New York Univ, NY
Northeastern Univ, MA
Northwestern Univ, IL
Oberlin College, OH
Occidental College, CA
Ohio Northern Univ, OH
Ohio Wesleyan Univ, OH
Parsons School of Design, NY
Pepperdine Univ, CA
Pine Manor College, MA
Pitzer College, CA
Polytechnic Univ/Brooklyn, NY
Polytechnic Univ/Farmingdale, NY
Pomona College, CA
Pratt Inst, NY
Princeton Univ, NJ
Providence College, RI
Randolph-Macon Woman's College,
  VA
Reed College, OR
Rensselaer Polytechnic Inst, NY
Rhode Island School of Design, RI
Rhodes College, TN
Rider College, NJ
Ripon College, WI
Rochester Inst of Technology, NY
Rollins College, FL
St. John's College, MD

St. John's College, NM
St. Lawrence Univ, NY
St. Mary's College of Calif, CA
Salve Regina Univ, RI
Santa Clara Univ, CA
Sarah Lawrence College, NY
Scripps College, CA
Seton Hall Univ, NJ
Simmons College, MA
Simon's Rock College of Bard, MA
Skidmore College, NY
Smith College, MA
Southern Methodist Univ, TX
Stanford Univ, CA
Stephens College, MO
Stevens Inst of Technology, NJ
Susquehanna Univ, PA
Swarthmore College, PA
Sweet Briar College, VA
Syracuse Univ, NY
Trinity College, CT
Tufts Univ, MA
Tulane Univ, LA
Union College, NY
Univ of Bridgeport, CT
Univ of Chicago, IL
Univ of Denver, CO
Univ of Hartford, CT
Univ of Miami, FL
Univ of Notre Dame, IN
Univ of Pennsylvania, PA
Univ of Puget Sound, WA
Univ of Redlands, CA
Univ of Rochester, NY
Univ of San Diego, CA
Univ of San Francisco, CA
Univ of Southern Calif, CA
Univ of the Pacific, CA
Univ of the South, TN
Ursinus College, PA
Vanderbilt Univ, TN
Vassar College, NY
Villanova Univ, PA
Washington and Jefferson College, PA
Washington College, MD
Washington Univ, MO
Wellesley College, MA
Wells College, NY
Wesleyan Univ, CT
Westminster Choir College, NJ
Westmont College, CA
Wheaton College, MA
Wheelock College, MA
Whitman College, WA
Whittier College, CA
Williams College, MA
Wittenberg Univ, OH
Worcester Polytechnic Inst, MA
Yale Univ, CT
Yeshiva Univ, NY

PART IV

A CLOSE LOOK AT THE COLLEGES

COLLEGE ADMISSIONS SELECTOR

This index groups all the colleges listed in this book according to degree of admissions competitiveness. The *Selector* is not a rating of colleges by academic standards or quality of education; it is rather an attempt to describe, in general terms, the situation a prospective student will meet when applying for admission.

THE CRITERIA USED

The factors used in determining the category for each college were: median entrance examination scores for the 1993-94 freshman class (the SAT I score used was derived by averaging the median verbal reasoning and the median mathematics reasoning scores; the ACT score used was the median composite score); percentages of 1993-94 freshmen scoring 500 and above and 600 and above on both the verbal reasoning and mathematics reasoning sections of SAT I; percentages of 1993-94 freshmen scoring 21 and above and 27 and above on the ACT; percentage of 1993-94 freshmen who ranked in the upper fifth and the upper two-fifths of their high school graduating classes; minimum class rank and grade point average required for admission (if any); and percentage of applicants to the 1993-94 freshman class who were accepted. The Selector cannot, and does not, take into account all the other factors that each college considers when making admissions decisions. Colleges place varying degrees of emphasis on the factors that comprise each of these categories.

USING THE SELECTOR

To use the *Selector* effectively, the prospective student's records should be compared realistically with the freshmen enrolled by the colleges in each category, as shown by the SAT I or ACT scores, the quality of high school record emphasized by the colleges in each category, and the kinds of risks that the applicant wishes to take.

The student should also be aware of what importance a particular school places on various nonacademic factors; when available, this information is presented in the profile of the school. If a student has unusual qualifications that may compensate for exam scores or high school record, the student should examine admissions policies of the colleges in the next higher category than the one that encompasses his or her score and consider those colleges that give major consideration to factors other than exam scores and high school grades. The "safety" college should usually be chosen from the next lower category, where the student can be reasonably sure that his or her scores and high school record will fall above the median scores and records of the freshmen enrolled in the college.

The listing within each category is alphabetical and not in any qualitative order. State-supported institutions have been classified according to the requirements for state residents, but standards for admission of out-of-state students are usually higher. Colleges that are experimenting with the admission of students of higher potential but lower achievement may appear in a less competitive category because of this fact.

A WORD OF CAUTION

The *Selector* is intended primarily for preliminary screening, to eliminate the majority of colleges that are not suitable for a particular student. Be sure to examine the admissions policies spelled out in the *Admissions* section of each profile. And remember that many colleges have to reject *qualified* students; the *Selector* will tell you what your chances are, not which college will accept you.

MOST COMPETITIVE

Even superior students will encounter a great deal of competition for admission to the colleges in this category. In general, these colleges require high school rank in the top 10% to 20% and grade averages of A to B+. Median freshman test scores at these colleges are generally between 625 and 800 on the SAT I and 29 and above on the Act. In addition, many of these colleges admit only a small percentage of those who apply—usually fewer than one third.

Amherst College, MA
Bates College, ME
Boston College, MA
Bowdoin College, ME
Brown University, RI
Bryn Mawr College, PA
California Institute of Technology, CA
Claremont McKenna College, CA
College of William and Mary, VA
Columbia University/Columbia College, NY
Cooper Union for the Advancement of Science and Art, NY
Cornell University, NY
Dartmouth College, NH
Davidson College, NC
Duke University, NC
Georgetown University, DC

Harvard University/Harvard and Radcliffe Colleges, MA
Harvey Mudd College, CA
Haverford College, PA
Johns Hopkins University, MD
Massachusetts Institute of Technology, MA
Middlebury College, VT
New College of the University of South Florida, FL
Northwestern University, IL
Pomona College, CA
Princeton University, NJ
Rice University, TX
Stanford University, CA
Swarthmore College, PA
Tufts University, MA
United States Air Force Academy, CO

United States Coast Guard Academy, CT
United States Military Academy, NY
United States Naval Academy, MD
University of Chicago, IL
University of Notre Dame, IN
University of Pennsylvania, PA
University of Virginia, VA
Wake Forest University, NC
Washington and Lee University, VA
Webb Institute of Naval Architecture, NY
Wellesley College, MA
Wesleyan University, CT
Williams College, MA
Yale University, CT

HIGHLY COMPETITIVE

Colleges in this group look for students with grade averages of B+ to B and accept most of their students from the top 20% to 35% of the high school class. Median freshman test scores at these colleges range from 575 to 625 on the SAT I and 27 or 28 on the ACT. These schools generally accept between one third and one half of their applicants.

To provide for finer distinctions within this admissions category, a plus (+) symbol has been placed before some entries. These are colleges with median freshman scores of 615 or more on the SAT I *or* 28 or more on the ACT (depending on which test the college prefers), and colleges that accept fewer than one quarter of their applicants.

Bard College, NY
Boston University, MA
Brandeis University, MA

Brigham Young University, UT
Bucknell University, PA
Carleton College, MN

+Carnegie Mellon University, PA
Case Western Reserve University, OH
Colby College, ME

Colgate University, NY
College of the Holy Cross, MA
Colorado College, CO
+Colorado School of Mines, CO
Columbia University/Barnard College, NY
Columbia University/School of Engineering and Applied Science, NY
Connecticut College, CT
Dickinson College, PA
Drew University/College of Liberal Arts, NJ
Emory University, GA
Franklin and Marshall College, PA
George Washington University, DC
+Georgia Institute of Technology, GA
Gettysburg College, PA
GMI Engineering & Management Institute, MI
+Grinnell College, IA
Grove City College, PA
Hamilton College, NY
+Illinois Wesleyan University, IL
James Madison University, VA
Jewish Theological Seminary of America/List College of Jewish Studies, NY
Kalamazoo College, MI
+Kenyon College, OH
Lafayette College, PA
+Lawrence University, WI
Lehigh University, PA

Macalester College, MN
Mary Washington College, VA
+Oberlin College, OH
Occidental College, CA
Penn State University/University Park Campus, PA
Pitzer College, CA
Polytechnic University/Brooklyn, NY
+Reed College, OR
Rensselaer Polytechnic Institute, NY
Rhodes College, TN
Rose-Hulman Institute of Technology, IN
Rutgers University/College of Engineering, NJ
Rutgers University/College of Pharmacy, NJ
Rutgers University/Cook College, NJ
+Rutgers University/Rutgers College, NJ
Saint Olaf College, MN
Sarah Lawrence College, NY
Scripps College, CA
Skidmore College, NY
Smith College, MA
Southwestern University, TX
State University of New York at Binghamton, NY
+State University of New York College of Environmental Science and Forestry, NY
State University of New York/College at Geneseo, NY
Syracuse University, NY

Thomas Aquinas College, CA
Trenton State College, NJ
Trinity College, CT
Trinity University, TX
Tulane University, LA
Union College, NY
United States Merchant Marine Academy, NY
+University of California at Berkeley, CA
University of California at Los Angeles, CA
University of Florida, FL
University of Illinois at Urbana-Champaign, IL
+University of Michigan/Ann Arbor, MI
University of Michigan/Dearborn, MI
University of Minnesota/Morris, MN
University of Missouri/Columbia, MO
University of North Carolina at Chapel Hill, NC
University of Puget Sound, WA
University of Richmond, VA
University of Rochester, NY
University of the South, TN
University of Wisconsin/Madison, WI
+Vanderbilt University, TN
Vassar College, NY
Villanova University, PA
Washington University, MO
Wheaton College, IL
Whitman College, WA
Worcester Polytechnic Institute, MA

VERY COMPETITIVE

The colleges in this category admit students whose averages are no less than B- and who rank in the top 35% to 50% of thei r graduating class. They report median freshman test scores in the 525 to 575 range on the SAT I and from 24 to 26 on the ACT. The schools in this category generally accept between one half and three quarters of their applicants.

The plus (+) has been placed before colleges with median freshman scores of 565 or above on the SAT I or 26 or better on the ACT (depending on which test the college prefers), and colleges that accept fewer than one third of their applicants.

Agnes Scott College, GA
Albany College of Pharmacy, NY
Albion College, MI
+Alfred University, NY
Alice Lloyd College, KY
Allegheny College, PA
+Alma College, MI
+American University, DC
Arkansas College, AR
Asbury College, KY
Augustana College, IL
Austin College, TX
Babson College, MA
Barnes College, MO
+Beloit College, WI
+Bennington College, VT
+Berea College, KY
Berry College, GA
Beth-El College of Nursing, CO
+Birmingham-Southern College, AL
Boricua College, NY
Brigham Young University/Hawaii, HI
Buena Vista College, IA
+California Polytechnic State University, CA
California State University/Los Angeles, CA
Calvin College, MI
Capital University, OH
Central College, IA
+Centre College, KY
Christendom College, VA
Christian Brothers University, TN
City University of New York/Baruch College, NY
City University of New York/Brooklyn College, NY
City University of New York/City College, NY
City University of New York/Hunter College, NY

Clark University, MA
+Clarkson University, NY
Clemson University, SC
Coe College, IA
College of Insurance, NY
College of Saint Benedict, MN
College of Saint Francis, IL
College of the Atlantic, ME
+College of the Ozarks, MO
College of Wooster, OH
Colorado State University, CO
Cornell College, IA
Covenant College, GA
Creighton University, NE
David Lipscomb University, TN
Deaconess College of Nursing, MO
+Denison University, OH
DePaul University, IL
DePauw University, IN
Drake University, IA
Drury College, MO
Duquesne University, PA
Earlham College, IN
Eckerd College, FL
Elizabethtown College, PA
Fairfield University, CT
Florida Institute of Technology, FL
Florida International University, FL
Florida State University, FL
Fordham University/College at Lincoln Center, NY
Fordham University/College of Business Administration, NY
Fordham University/Fordham College, NY
Freed-Hardeman University, TN
Furman University, SC
Golden Gate University, CA
Gonzaga University, WA
Goucher College, MD
Grand Canyon University, AZ

Grand Valley State University, MI
Gustavus Adolphus College, MN
Hamline University, MN
Hanover College, IN
Harding University, AR
Hillsdale College, MI
Hiram College, OH
Hobart and William Smith Colleges, NY
Hofstra University, NY
Hood College, MD
Houghton College, NY
Illinois Institute of Technology, IL
Indiana University Bloomington, IN
John Brown University, AR
Knox College, IL
La Salle University, PA
Lake Forest College, IL
Lee College at the University of Judaism, CA
Lewis and Clark College, OR
Linfield College, OR
Louisiana College, LA
Loyola College, MD
Luther College, IA
Marquette University, WI
Marygrove College, MI
Maryville University-Saint Louis, MO
McPherson College, KS
Messiah College, PA
Miami University, OH
+Michigan Technological University, MI
Millersville University of Pennsylvania, PA
Mills College, CA
Mississippi State University, MS
Moravian College, PA
Mount Holyoke College, MA
Mount Saint Mary's College, CA
Muhlenberg College, PA
New Jersey Institute of Technology, NJ
+New York University, NY

North Carolina State University, NC
North Central College, IL
North Dakota State University of Agriculture and Applied Science, ND
+Northeast Missouri State University, MO
Oakland University, MI
Oglethorpe University, GA
Ohio Northern University, OH
+Ohio Wesleyan University, OH
Oklahoma State University, OK
Pacific Lutheran University, WA
Pepperdine University, CA
Philadelphia College of Pharmacy and Science, PA
Polytechnic University/Farmingdale, NY
Presbyterian College, SC
Providence College, RI
Quincy University, IL
Richard Stockton College of New Jersey, NJ
Rochester Institute of Technology, NY
Rollins College, FL
Rowan College of New Jersey, NJ
Rutgers University/Camden College of Arts and Sciences, NJ
+Rutgers University/College of Nursing, NJ
Rutgers University/Douglass College, NJ
Rutgers University/Livingston College, NJ
+Saint John's College, MD
+Saint John's College, NM
Saint Joseph's University, PA
Saint Lawrence University, NY
Saint Louis College of Pharmacy, MO
Saint Louis University, MO
Saint Mary's College, IN
Saint Mary's College of California, CA
+Saint Mary's College of Maryland, MD

Saint Norbert College, WI
Samford University, AL
Santa Clara University, CA
Siena College, NY
+Simon's Rock College of Bard, MA
Simpson College, IA
Southern Methodist University, TX
Spelman College, GA
State University of New York at Albany, NY
State University of New York at Buffalo, NY
State University of New York at Stony Brook, NY
State University of New York/College at Buffalo, NY
State University of New York/College at Fredonia, NY
State University of New York/College at New Paltz, NY
State University of New York/College at Oswego, NY
Sterling College, KS
Stetson University, FL
+Stevens Institute of Technology, NJ
Stonehill College, MA
Susquehanna University, PA
Tabor College, KS
Talladega College, AL
Taylor University, IN
Teikyo Marycrest University, IA
Texas A&M University, TX
+Transylvania University, KY
University of Alabama at Huntsville, AL
University of California at Davis, CA
University of California at Santa Cruz, CA
+University of California, San Diego, CA
University of California/Irvine, CA
University of Colorado at Boulder, CO
University of Colorado at Denver, CO

University of Dallas, TX
*University of Delaware, DE
University of Evansville, IN
University of Georgia, GA
University of Iowa, IA
University of Kentucky, KY
University of Lowell, MA
University of Maryland/Baltimore County, MD
*University of Maryland/College Park, MD
University of Miami, FL
University of Minnesota/Twin Cities, MN
University of Missouri/Kansas City, MO
+University of Missouri/Rolla, MO
University of North Carolina at Asheville, NC
University of Oklahoma, OK
University of Oregon, OR
University of Redlands, CA
University of San Diego, CA
University of Scranton, PA
University of Southern California, CA
University of Texas at Austin, TX
+University of Texas at Dallas, TX
University of Tulsa, OK
University of Washington, WA
Ursinus College, PA
Valparaiso University, IN
Virginia Wesleyan College, VA
Wabash College, IN
Wartburg College, IA
West Suburban College of Nursing, IL
Western Washington University, WA
Willamette University, OR
William Jewell College, MO
Winona State University, MN
Wittenberg University, OH
Wofford College, SC
Yeshiva University, NY

COMPETITIVE

This category is a very broad one, covering colleges that generally have median freshman test scores between 450 and 525 on the SAT I and between 21 and 23 on the ACT. Some of these colleges require that students have high school averages of B- or better, although others state a minimum of C+ or C. Generally, these colleges prefer student in the top 50% to 65% of the graduating class and accept between 75% and 85% of their applicants.

Colleges with a plus (+) are those with median freshman SAT I scores of 515 or more or median freshman ACT scores of 24 or more (depending on which test the colleges prefers), and those that admit fewer than half of their applicants.

Adams State College, CO
Adrian College, MI
Alabama Agricultural and Mechanical University, AL
Alaska Pacific University, AK
+Albertson College, ID
Albright College, PA
+Alcorn State University, MS
Alderson-Broaddus College, WV
Allentown College of Saint Francis de Sales, PA
Alverno College, WI
Ambassador College, TX
American International College, MA
Anderson University, IN
Angelo State University, TX
Antioch College, OH
Appalachian State University, NC
Aquinas College, MI
Arizona State University Main Campus, AZ
Ashland University, OH
+Auburn University, AL
Auburn University at Montgomery, AL
Augsburg College, MN
Augusta College, GA
Augustana College, SD
Aurora University, IL
Austin Peay State University, TN
Avila College, MO
Azusa Pacific University, CA
Baker University, KS

Baldwin-Wallace College, OH
Barat College, IL
Barry University, FL
Bartlesville Wesleyan College, OK
+Baylor University, TX
Beaver College, PA
+Belhaven College, MS
Bellarmine College, KY
Belmont Abbey College, NC
Belmont University, TN
Bemidji State University, MN
Benedictine College, KS
Bentley College, MA
Bethany College, KS
+Bethany College, WV
Bethel College, IN
Bethel College, KS
Bethel College, MN
Biola University, CA
Blackburn College, IL
+Bloomsburg University of Pennsylvania, PA
Bluefield College, VA
Bluffton College, OH
Bowling Green State University, OH
Bradford College, MA
+Bradley University, IL
Brescia College, KY
Briar Cliff College, IA
Bridgewater College, VA
Bridgewater State College, MA
Bryan College, TN

Bryant College, RI
Butler University, IN
Cabrini College, PA
Caldwell College, NJ
California Baptist College, CA
California Lutheran University, CA
California Maritime Academy, CA
California State University/Bakersfield, CA
California State University/Chico, CA
California State University/Fresno, CA
California State University/Hayward, CA
California State University/Sacramento, CA
California State University/Stanislaus, CA
California University of Pennsylvania, PA
Calumet College of St. Joseph, IN
Campbell University, NC
Campbellsville College, KY
Canisius College, NY
Cardinal Stritch College, WI
Carlow College, PA
Carroll College, MT
Carroll College, WI
Carson-Newman College, TN
Carthage College, WI
Catawba College, NC
Catholic University of America, DC
Cedar Crest College, PA

Cedarville College, OH
+Centenary College of Louisiana, LA
Central Connecticut State University, CT
Central Methodist College, MO
Central Washington University, WA
Central Wesleyan College, SC
Chaminade University of Honolulu, HI
Chapman University, CA
Chatham College, PA
Chestnut Hill College, PA
Cheyney University of Pennsylvania, PA
Chicago State University, IL
Christian Heritage College, CA
City University of New York/Herbert H. Lehman College, NY
City University of New York/Queens College, NY
Clarion University of Pennsylvania, PA
Clark Atlanta University, GA
+Clarke College, IA
Clarkson College, NE
Clinch Valley College/University of Virginia, VA
Coker College, SC
College Misericordia, PA
College of Charleston, SC
College of Mount Saint Joseph, OH
College of Mount Saint Vincent, NY
College of Notre Dame, CA
College of Notre Dame of Maryland, MD
College of Our Lady of The Elms, MA
College of Saint Catherine, MN
College of Saint Elizabeth, NJ
College of Saint Mary, NE
College of Saint Rose, NY
College of Saint Scholastica, MN
College of Santa Fe, NM
Colorado Christian University, CO
Colorado Technical College, CO
Columbia College, MO
Columbia College of Nursing, WI
Concordia College, MI
Concordia College, MN
Concordia College, OR
Concordia College/Moorhead, MN
+Concordia Lutheran College, TX
Concordia University, IL
Concordia University, CA
Concordia University Wisconsin, WI
Converse College, SC
Culver-Stockton College, MO
Cumberland College, KY
Cumberland University, TN
D'Youville College, NY
Dana College, NE
Delaware State College, DE
Dillard University, LA
Doane College, NE
Dominican College of San Rafael, CA
Dordt College, IA
Drexel University, PA
Dyke College, OH
East Carolina University, NC
East Central University, OK
East Stroudsburg University, PA
East Tennessee State University, TN
East Texas Baptist University, TX
+Eastern College, PA
Eastern Connecticut State University, CT
Eastern Illinois University, IL
Eastern Mennonite College, VA
Eastern Michigan University, MI
Eastern New Mexico University, NM
Eastern Oregon State College, OR
Edgewood College, WI
Edinboro University of Pennsylvania, PA
Elmhurst College, IL
Elmira College, NY
+Embry-Riddle Aeronautical University, AZ
Embry-Riddle Aeronautical University, FL
Emory and Henry College, VA
Erskine College, SC

+Eugene Lang College of the New School for Social Research, NY
Eureka College, IL
Evergreen State College, WA
Fairleigh Dickinson University, NJ
Felician College, NJ
Fitchburg State College, MA
Flagler College, FL
Florida Agricultural and Mechanical University, FL
Florida Atlantic University, FL
+Florida Memorial College, FL
Florida Southern College, FL
Fontbonne College, MO
Fort Lewis College, CO
Framingham State College, MA
Franciscan University of Steubenville, OH
Franklin College of Indiana, IN
Fresno Pacific College, CA
Friends University, KS
Frostburg State University, MD
Gannon University, PA
Geneva College, PA
George Mason University, VA
Georgetown College, KY
Georgia State University, GA
Georgian Court College, NJ
Goldey-Beacom College, DE
Gordon College, MA
Goshen College, IN
Grace College, IN
Graceland College, IA
Grand Rapids Baptist College and Seminary, MI
Green Mountain College, VT
Greensboro College, NC
Greenville College, IL
Guilford College, NC
Gwynedd-Mercy College, PA
+Hampden-Sydney College, VA
Hampshire College, MA
Hampton University, VA
Hardin-Simmons University, TX
Hartwick College, NY
Hastings College, NE
Hawaii Pacific University, HI
Heidelberg College, OH
Henderson State University, AR
Hendrix College, AR
Hollins College, VA
Holy Family College, PA
Holy Names College, CA
+Hope College, MI
Houston Baptist University, TX
Howard Payne University, TX
Howard University, DC
Humboldt State University, CA
Huntingdon College, AL
Huntington College, IN
Huron University, SD
Huston-Tillotson College, TX
Idaho State University, ID
Illinois Benedictine College, IL
Illinois College, IL
Illinois State University, IL
Immaculata College, PA
Incarnate Word College, TX
Indiana Institute of Technology, IN
Indiana State University, IN
Indiana University at Kokomo, IN
Indiana University Northwest, IN
Indiana University of Pennsylvania, PA
Indiana Wesleyan University, IN
Iona College, NY
Iowa State University, IA
Iowa Wesleyan College, IA
Ithaca College, NY
Jacksonville University, FL
Jamestown College, ND
John Carroll University, OH
Judson College, AL
Judson College, IL
+Juniata College, PA
Kansas Newman College, KS
Kansas Wesleyan University, KS
Keene State College, NH
Kennesaw State College, GA
+Kentucky State University, KY

Kentucky Wesleyan College, KY
Keuka College, NY
King College, TN
King's College, PA
Kutztown University, PA
La Sierra University, CA
LaGrange College, GA
Lake Erie College, OH
Lake Superior State University, MI
Lamar University, TX
Lambuth University, TN
Lawrence Technological University, MI
Le Moyne College, NY
+Le Tourneau University, TX
Lebanon Valley College of Pennsylvania, PA
Lenoir-Rhyne College, NC
Lincoln Memorial University, TN
Lindenwood College, MO
Livingston University, AL
Lock Haven University of Pennsylvania, PA
Long Island University/C. W. Post Campus, NY
Long Island University/Southampton Campus, NY
Longwood College, VA
Loras College, IA
Louisiana State University and Agricultural and Mechanical College, LA
Louisiana Tech University, LA
Loyola Marymount University, CA
+Loyola University of Chicago, IL
+Loyola University/New Orleans, LA
Lynchburg College, VA
Lynn University, FL
MacMurray College, IL
Madonna University, MI
Maharishi International University, IA
Maine Maritime Academy, ME
Malone College, OH
Manhattan College, NY
Mansfield University, PA
Marian College, IN
Marian College of Fond du Lac, WI
+Marietta College, OH
Marist College, NY
+Marlboro College, VT
Mars Hill College, NC
Marymount College/Tarrytown, NY
Marymount University, VA
Maryville College, TN
Marywood College, PA
Massachusetts College of Pharmacy and Allied Health Sciences, MA
Massachusetts Maritime Academy, MA
Master's College, CA
McKendree College, IL
McMurry University, TX
Medaille College, NY
Mercer University, GA
Mercyhurst College, PA
Meredith College, NC
Merrimack College, MA
Methodist College, NC
Michigan Christian College, MI
Michigan State University, MI
Middle Tennessee State University, TN
Milligan College, TN
Millikin University, IL
+Millsaps College, MS
Milwaukee School of Engineering, WI
Mississippi College, MS
Missouri Baptist College, MO
+Monmouth College, IL
Monmouth College, NJ
Montana College of Mineral Science and Technology, MT
Montana State University, MT
+Montclair State College, NJ
Moorhead State University, MN
+Morgan State University, MD
Morningside College, IA
Mount Mary College, WI
Mount Mercy College, IA
Mount Saint Mary College, NY
Mount Senario College, WI

Mount Union College, OH
Mount Vernon College, DC
Mount Vernon Nazarene College, OH
Murray State University, KY
Muskingum College, OH
National University, CA
National-Louis University, IL
+Nazareth College of Rochester, NY
Nebraska Methodist College of
    Nursing and Allied Health, NE
Nebraska Wesleyan University, NE
New Mexico Highlands University, NM
+New Mexico Institute of Mining and
    Technology, NM
Niagara University, NY
North Adams State College, MA
North Park College, IL
Northeastern Illinois University, IL
Northeastern State University, OK
Northeastern University, MA
Northern Arizona University, AZ
Northern Illinois University, IL
Northern Michigan University, MI
Northern Montana College, MT
Northwest Nazarene College, ID
Northwestern College, MN
Northwestern College, WI
Northwestern College of Iowa, IA
Northwestern Oklahoma State
    University, OK
Northwood University, FL
Norwich University, VT
Notre Dame College, NH
Notre Dame College of Ohio, OH
Oakwood College, AL
Ohio University, OH
Oklahoma Baptist University, OK
Oklahoma City University, OK
Old Dominion University, VA
Olivet College, MI
Olivet Nazarene University, IL
+Oral Roberts University, OK
Oregon Institute of Technology, OR
Oregon State University, OR
+Ottawa University, KS
Otterbein College, OH
Ouachita Baptist University, AR
Our Lady of the Lake University of San
    Antonio, TX
Pace University, NY
Pacific Christian College, CA
Pacific Union College, CA
Pacific University, OR
Palm Beach Atlantic College, FL
Park College, MO
Penn State University at Erie/Behrend
    College, PA
Philadelphia College of Bible, PA
Philadelphia College of Textiles and
    Science, PA
Phillips University, OK
Plymouth State College, NH
Point Loma Nazarene College, CA
Portland State University, OR
Pratt Institute, NY
Prescott College, AZ
Principia College, IL
Purdue University/West Lafayette,
    IN
Queens College, NC
+Quinnipiac College, CT
+Ramapo College of New Jersey, NJ
Randolph-Macon College, VA
Randolph-Macon Woman's College,
    VA
Regis College, MA
Regis University, CO
Research College of Nursing, MO
Rider College, NJ
+Ripon College, WI
Roanoke College, VA
Roberts Wesleyan College, NY
Rockford College, IL
Rockhurst College, MO
Rocky Mountain College, MT
Roger Williams University, RI
Roosevelt University, IL
Rosary College, IL

Rosemont College, PA
Russell Sage College, NY
Rutgers University/Newark College of
    Arts and Sciences, NJ
Rutgers University/University
    College—Camden, NJ
Rutgers University/University
    College—Newark, NJ
Sacred Heart University, CT
Saint Ambrose University, IA
Saint Anselm College, NH
+Saint Augustine's College, NC
Saint Bonaventure University, NY
Saint Cloud State University, MN
Saint Edward's University, TX
Saint Francis College, IN
Saint John Fisher College, NY
Saint John's University, MN
+Saint John's University, NY
Saint Joseph College, CT
Saint Joseph's College, IN
Saint Joseph's College, ME
Saint Joseph's College, NY
Saint Leo College, FL
Saint Martin's College, WA
Saint Mary College, KS
Saint Mary's College, MI
Saint Mary's University, TX
Saint Meinrad College, IN
Saint Michael's College, VT
Saint Paul's College, VA
Saint Thomas Aquinas College, NY
Saint Xavier University, IL
Salem College, NC
Salem State College, MA
Salem-Teikyo University, WV
+Salisbury State University, MD
Sam Houston State University, TX
Samuel Merritt College, CA
Savannah State College, GA
Schreiner College, TX
Seattle Pacific University, WA
Seattle University, WA
Seton Hill College, PA
+Shaw University, NC
Shenandoah University, VA
Shepherd College, WV
Shippensburg University of
    Pennsylvania, PA
Shorter College, GA
Siena Heights College, MI
Simmons College, MA
Simpson College, CA
Sioux Falls College, SD
Slippery Rock University, PA
South Dakota School of Mines and
    Technology, SD
South Dakota State University, SD
Southeast Missouri State University, MO
Southeastern Oklahoma State
    University, OK
Southeastern University, DC
Southern California College, CA
Southern College of Technology, GA
Southern Connecticut State University,
    CT
Southern Illinois University at
    Carbondale, IL
Southern Oregon State College, OR
Southern Vermont College, VT
Southwest Missouri State University,
    MO
Southwest Texas State University, TX
Southwestern College, KS
Southwestern Oklahoma State
    University, OK
Spring Arbor College, MI
+Spring Hill College, AL
+State University of New York/College
    at Brockport, NY
+State University of New York/College
    at Cortland, NY
State University of New York/College
    at Oneonta, NY
State University of New York/College
    at Plattsburgh, NY
State University of New York/College
    at Purchase, NY

State University of New York/Maritime
    College, NY
State University of New York/Potsdam
    College, NY
Stephen F. Austin State University, TX
Stephens College, MO
Sweet Briar College, VA
Teikyo Westmar University, IA
Temple University, PA
+Tennessee State University, TN
Tennessee Technological University, TN
Tennessee Wesleyan College, TN
Texas Christian University, TX
Texas Lutheran College, TX
Texas Tech University, TX
Texas Woman's University, TX
The Citadel, SC
The University of New Mexico, NM
Thiel College, PA
Thomas More College, KY
Toccoa Falls College, GA
Touro College, NY
Towson State University, MD
Trinity Christian College, IL
Trinity College, DC
Trinity College, IL
Troy State University, AL
Tuskegee University, AL
Union College, KY
+Union University, TN
University of Alabama, AL
University of Alabama at Birmingham,
    AL
University of Alaska Anchorage, AK
University of Alaska Fairbanks, AK
University of Arizona, AZ
University of Arkansas at Fayetteville,
    AR
University of Arkansas at Little Rock,
    AR
University of Bridgeport, CT
University of California at Santa
    Barbara, CA
University of California, Riverside, CA
+University of Central Florida, FL
University of Central Oklahoma, OK
University of Charleston, WV
University of Cincinnati, OH
University of Colorado at Colorado
    Springs, CO
University of Connecticut, CT
+University of Dayton, OH
+University of Denver, CO
University of Detroit Mercy, MI
University of Findlay, OH
University of Hawaii at Hilo, HI
University of Hawaii at Manoa, HI
University of Houston, TX
University of Idaho, ID
University of Illinois at Chicago, IL
University of Indianapolis, IN
University of La Verne, CA
University of Louisville, KY
University of Maine, ME
University of Maine at Farmington,
    ME
University of Maine at Machias, ME
University of Maine at Presque Isle, ME
University of Mary, ND
University of Massachusetts
    Dartmouth, MA
University of Massachusetts/Boston,
    MA
University of Memphis, TN
University of Michigan/Flint, MI
University of Minnesota/Duluth, MN
University of Mississippi, MS
University of Missouri/St. Louis, MO
University of Mobile, AL
University of Montana, MT
University of Montevallo, AL
University of Nevada/Las Vegas, NV
University of Nevada/Reno, NV
University of New Hampshire, NH
University of New Haven, CT
University of New Orleans, LA
University of North Carolina at
    Charlotte, NC

University of North Carolina at
Greensboro, NC
University of North Carolina at
Wilmington, NC
University of North Florida, FL
University of North Texas, TX
University of Northern Colorado, CO
University of Northern Iowa, IA
University of Pittsburgh, PA
University of Pittsburgh at Bradford, PA
University of Pittsburgh at Greensburg,
PA
University of Pittsburgh at Johnstown,
PA
University of Portland, OR
University of Puerto Rico/Arecibo
Technological University College,
PR
University of Rhode Island, RI
+University of Saint Thomas, MN
+University of Saint Thomas, TX
University of San Francisco, CA
University of Science and Arts of
Oklahoma, OK
University of South Alabama, AL
University of South Carolina, SC
University of South Carolina at Aiken,
SC
University of South Carolina at
Spartanburg, SC
University of South Dakota, SD
+University of South Florida, FL
University of Southern Maine, ME
University of Southern Mississippi, MS
University of Tampa, FL
University of Tennessee at
Chattanooga, TN
University of Tennessee at Martin, TN
University of Tennessee/Knoxville, TN
University of Texas at San Antonio, TX
University of the Ozarks, AR
University of the Pacific, CA
University of the Virgin Islands, VI

University of Utah, UT
+University of Vermont, VT
University of West Florida, FL
University of Wisconsin/Eau Claire, WI
University of Wisconsin/Green Bay, WI
University of Wisconsin/La Crosse, WI
University of Wisconsin/Milwaukee, WI
University of Wisconsin/Oshkosh, WI
University of Wisconsin/Platteville, WI
University of Wisconsin/River Falls, WI
+University of Wisconsin/Stevens Point,
WI
University of Wisconsin/Stout, WI
University of Wisconsin/Superior, WI
University of Wisconsin/Whitewater,
WI
Upper Iowa University, IA
Upsala College, NJ
Urbana University, OH
Utah State University, UT
Virginia Commonwealth University,
VA
Virginia Military Institute, VA
Virginia Polytechnic Institute and State
University, VA
Viterbo College, WI
Wagner College, NY
Walla Walla College, WA
Walsh University, OH
Warner Pacific College, OR
Warren Wilson College, NC
Washington and Jefferson College, PA
+Washington College, MD
Washington State University, WA
Wayne State University, MI
Waynesburg College, PA
Webber College, FL
Weber State University, UT
Webster University, MO
+Wells College, NY
Wesleyan College, GA
West Chester University of
Pennsylvania, PA

West Georgia College, GA
West Texas A&M University, TX
West Virginia University, WV
West Virginia Wesleyan College, WV
Westbrook College, ME
Western Carolina University, NC
Western Connecticut State University,
CT
Western International University, AZ
Western Kentucky University, KY
Western Maryland College, MD
Western Michigan University, MI
Western Montana College of the
University of Montana, MT
Western Oregon State College, OR
Western State College of Colorado,
CO
Westfield State College, MA
+Westminster College, MO
Westminster College, PA
Westminster College of Salt Lake City,
UT
Westmont College, CA
+Wheaton College, MA
Wheeling Jesuit College, WV
Whittier College, CA
Whitworth College, WA
Widener University, PA
Wilberforce University, OH
William Carey College, MS
+William Paterson College, NJ
William Penn College, IA
Wilson College, PA
Wingate College, NC
Winthrop University, SC
Wisconsin Lutheran College, WI
Women's College of Brenau University,
GA
+Xavier University, OH
Xavier University of Louisiana, LA
York College, NE
York College of Pennsylvania, PA

LESS COMPETITIVE

Included in this category are colleges with median fresh-man test scores below 450 on the SAT I and below 21 on the ACT; some colleges that require entrance examinations but do not report median scores; and colleges that admit students with averages below C who rank in the top 65% of the graduating class. These colleges usually admit 85% or more of their applicants.

Adelphi University, NY
Albany State College, GA
Albertus Magnus College, CT
Alvernia College, PA
Anna Maria College, MA
Armstrong State College, GA
Assumption College, MA
Atlantic Union College, MA
Audrey Cohen College, NY
Averett College, VA
Ball State University, IN
Barton College, NC
Benedict College, SC
Bennett College, NC
Bethel College, TN
Bethune-Cookman College, FL
Bloomfield College, NJ
Blue Mountain College, MS
Bluefield State College, WV
Boise State University, ID
Bowie State University, MD
Brooklyn Campus of Long Island
University, NY
California State Polytechnic
University/Pomona, CA
California State University/Dominguez
Hills, CA
California State University/Fullerton,
CA
California State University/Long
Beach, CA
California State University/Northridge,
CA

California State University/San
Bernardino, CA
Cameron University, OK
Capitol College, MD
Castleton State College, VT
Cazenovia College, NY
Centenary College, NJ
Central Michigan University, MI
Central Missouri State University, MO
Champlain College, VT
Charleston Southern University, SC
Christopher Newport University, VA
Cincinnati College of Mortuary
Science, OH
City University of New York/John Jay
College of Criminal Justice, NY
Clayton State College, GA
Clearwater Christian College, FL
Coastal Carolina University, SC
Colby-Sawyer College, NH
College of New Rochelle, NY
College of Saint Joseph, VT
College of the Southwest, NM
Columbia College, SC
Columbia Union College, MD
Columbus College, GA
Concordia College, NY
Coppin State College, MD
Curry College, MA
Daemen College, NY
Dakota State University, SD
Dakota Wesleyan University, SD
Dallas Baptist University, TX

Daniel Webster College, NH
Davis and Elkins College, WV
Defiance College, OH
Delaware Valley College, PA
Delta State University, MS
DeVry Institute of
Technology/Addison (DuPage
County), IL
DeVry Institute of Technology/Atlanta,
GA
DeVry Institute of
Technology/Chicago, IL
DeVry Institute of
Technology/Columbus, OH
DeVry Institute of Technology/Dallas,
TX
DeVry Institute of Technology/Kansas
City, MO
DeVry Institute of Technology/Los
Angeles, CA
DeVry Institute of
Technology/Phoenix, AZ
Dominican College, NY
Dowling College, NY
East Texas State University, TX
Eastern Montana College, MT
Eastern Nazarene College, MA
Eastern Washington University, WA
Elizabeth City State University, NC
Elon College, NC
Emerson College, MA
Emmanuel College, MA
Evangel College, MO

Fairmont State College, WV
Faulkner University, AL
Fayetteville State University, NC
Ferrum College, VA
Fisk University, TN
Fort Valley State College, GA
Francis Marion University, SC
Franklin Pierce College, NH
Friends World Program, NY
Gardner-Webb University, NC
George Fox College, OR
Georgia College, GA
Georgia Southern University, GA
Georgia Southwestern College, GA
Glenville State College, WV
Goddard College, VT
Hannibal-LaGrange College, MO
Harris-Stowe State College, MO
Hebrew College, MA
High Point University, NC
Indiana University Southeast, IN
Indiana University-Purdue University
    at Fort Wayne, IN
Indiana University-Purdue University
    at Indianapolis, IN
Indiana University/South Bend, IN
Jackson State University, MS
Jacksonville State University, AL
Jarvis Christian College, TX
Jersey City State College, NJ
Johnson and Wales University, RI
Johnson C. Smith University, NC
Johnson State College, VT
Jordan College, MI
Kean College of New Jersey, NJ
Kendall College, IL
Kent State University, OH
Kentucky Christian College, KY
King's College, NY
Knoxville College, TN
La Roche College, PA
Lakeland College, WI
Lander University, SC
Lane College, TN
Langston University, OK
Lee College, TN
Lees-McRae College, NC
LeMoyne-Owen College, TN
Lesley College, MA
Lewis University, IL
Liberty University, VA
Limestone College, SC
Lincoln University, CA
Lincoln University, PA
Lindsey Wilson College, KY
Livingstone College, NC
Lourdes College, OH
Lycoming College, PA
Lyndon State College, VT
Manchester College, IN
Manhattanville College, NY
Mankato State University, MN
Marshall University, WV
Mary Baldwin College, VA
Marymount Manhattan College, NY
Menlo College, CA
Midland Lutheran College, NE
Midwestern State University, TX
Mississippi University for Women, MS
Missouri Valley College, MO
Molloy College, NY

Montreat-Anderson College, NC
Morehead State University, KY
Morehouse College, GA
Morris College, SC
Mount Ida College, MA
Mount Olive College, NC
Mount Saint Clare College, IA
Mount Saint Mary's College, MD
Neumann College, PA
New England College, NH
New Hampshire College, NH
New Mexico State University, NM
New York Institute of Technology/Old
    Westbury, NY
Newberry College, SC
Nichols College, MA
Norfolk State University, VA
North Carolina Agricultural and
    Technical State University, NC
North Carolina Central University, NC
North Carolina Wesleyan College, NC
North Central Bible College, MN
North Georgia College, GA
Northern State University, SD
Northland College, WI
Northwest College, WA
Northwest Missouri State University,
    MO
Northwood University, MI
Nova Southeastern University, FL
Nyack College, NY
Oakland City College, IN
Ohio Dominican College, OH
Ohio State University, OH
Ohio Valley College, WV
Our Lady of Holy Cross College, LA
Paine College, GA
Paul Quinn College, TX
Pembroke State University, NC
Pfeiffer College, NC
Piedmont College, GA
Pine Manor College, MA
Point Park College, PA
Prairie View A&M University, TX
Radford University, VA
Rhode Island College, RI
Rivier College, NH
Robert Morris College, PA
Rust College, MS
Rutgers University/University
    College—New Brunswick, NJ
Saginaw Valley State University, MI
Saint Andrews Presbyterian College,
    NC
Saint Francis College, NY
Saint Francis College, PA
Saint Mary's College of Minnesota, MN
Saint Peter's College, NJ
Saint Thomas University, FL
Saint Vincent College, PA
Salve Regina University, RI
San Diego State University, CA
San Francisco State University, CA
San Jose State University, CA
Seton Hall University, NJ
Silver Lake College, WI
Sojourner-Douglass College, MD
Sonoma State University, CA
South Carolina State University, SC
Southern Illinois University at
    Edwardsville, IL

Southern Utah University, UT
Spalding University, KY
Springfield College, MA
State University of New York/College
    at Old Westbury, NY
State University of New York/College
    of Agriculture and Technology at
    Cobleskill, NY
Strayer College, DC
Suffolk University, MA
Tarleton State University, TX
Teikyo Post University, CT
Texas A&M University at Galveston, TX
Texas A&M University at Kingsville, TX
Texas Wesleyan University, TX
Thomas College, ME
Tiffin University, OH
Tougaloo College, MS
Tri-State University, IN
Trinity College of Vermont, VT
Tusculum College, TN
United States International University,
    CA
Unity College, ME
University of Alaska Southeast, AK
University of Arkansas at Pine Bluff, AR
University of Central Arkansas, AR
University of Dubuque, IA
University of Hartford, CT
University of Maine at Fort Kent, ME
University of Maryland/Eastern Shore,
    MD
University of Massachusetts/Amherst,
    MA
University of Nebraska at Kearney, NE
University of Nebraska at Omaha, NE
University of Nebraska-Lincoln, NE
University of New England, ME
University of Southern Colorado, CO
University of Texas at Arlington, TX
University of Texas at El Paso, TX
Ursuline College, OH
Utica College of Syracuse University,
    NY
Valdosta State University, GA
Valley City State University, ND
Villa Julie College, MD
Virginia Intermont College, VA
Virginia Union University, VA
Voorhees College, SC
Wentworth Institute of Technology, MA
Wesley College, DE
West Liberty State College, WV
West Virginia Institute of Technology,
    WV
West Virginia State College, WV
Western Baptist College, OR
Western Illinois University, IL
Western New England College, MA
Western New Mexico University, NM
Wheelock College, MA
Wilkes University, PA
William Woods University, MO
Williams Baptist College, AR
Wilmington College, OH
Winston-Salem State University, NC
Woodbury University, CA
Worcester State College, MA
Wright State University, OH
Youngstown State University, OH

NONCOMPETITIVE

The colleges in this category generally only require evidence of graduation from an accredited high school (although they may also require completion of a certain number of high school units). Some require that entrance examinations be taken for placement purposes only, or only by graduates of unaccredited high schools or only by out-of-state students. In some cases, insufficient capacity may compel a college in this category to limit the number of students that are accepted; generally, however, if a college accepts 98% or more of its applicants, if automatically falls in this category. Colleges are rated Noncompetitive if they admit all state residents, but have some requirements for nonresidents.

Abilene Christian University, TX
Academy of the New Church, PA
Alabama State University, AL
Allen University, SC
Andrews University, MI
Arkansas Baptist College, AR
Arkansas State University, AR
Arkansas Tech University, AR
Baker College, MI
Barber-Scotia College, NC
Bellevue College, NE
Black Hills State University, SD
Brewton-Parker College, GA
Bridgeport Engineering Institute, CT
Burlington College, VT
Cascade College, OR
Central State University, OH
Chadron State College, NE
Charter Oak State College, CT
City University, WA
City University of New York/College of
    Staten Island, NY
City University of New York/Medgar
    Evers College, NY
City University of New York/New York
    City Technical College, NY
City University of New York/York
    College, NY
Cleary College, MI
Cleveland State University, OH
Cogswell College North, WA
Cogswell Polytechnical College, CA
College of Aeronautics, NY
College of Great Falls, MT
Concord College, WV
Concordia College, NE
Crichton College, TN
Davenport College of Business, MI
Detroit College of Business, MI
East-West University, IL
Eastern Kentucky University, KY
Edward Waters College, FL
Emporia State University, KS
Ferris State University, MI
Fort Hays State University, KS
Franklin University, OH
Grambling State University, LA
Grand View College, IA
Gratz College, PA
Hellenic College/Holy Cross Greek
    Orthodox School of Theology, MA
Heritage College, WA
Humphreys College, CA
Husson College, ME
Indiana University East, IN

Kansas State University, KS
Lincoln University, MO
Louisiana State University in
    Shreveport, LA
Lubbock Christian University, TX
Martin University, IN
Marylhurst College, OR
Mayville State University, ND
McNeese State University, LA
Mercy College, NY
Mesa State College, CO
Metropolitan State College of Denver,
    CO
MidAmerica Nazarene College, KS
Miles College, AL
Minot State University, ND
Mississippi Valley State University, MS
Missouri Western State College, MO
Morris Brown College, GA
Mount Marty College, SD
National College, SD
New College of California, CA
Nicholls State University, LA
Northeast Louisiana University, LA
Northern Kentucky University, KY
Northwestern State University of
    Louisiana, LA
Ohio State University at Lima, OH
Ohio State University at Mansfield, OH
Ohio State University at Marion, OH
Ohio State University at Newark, OH
Oklahoma Christian University of
    Science and Arts, OK
Oklahoma Panhandle State University,
    OK
Peru State College, NE
Philander Smith College, AR
Pikeville College, KY
Pillsbury Baptist Bible College, MN
Pittsburg State University, KS
Presentation College, SD
Purdue University/Calumet, IN
Saint Mary-of-the-Woods College, IN
Selma University, AL
Shawnee State University, OH
Sheldon Jackson College, AK
Shimer College, IL
Sierra Nevada College, NV
Sinte Gleska University, SD
Southeastern College of the Assemblies
    of God, FL
Southeastern Louisiana University, LA
Southern Arkansas University, AR
Southern College of Seventh-day
    Adventists, TN

Southern Nazarene University, OK
Southern University and A&M College,
    LA
Southern University at New Orleans, LA
Southwest Baptist University, MO
Southwest State University, MN
Southwestern Adventist College, TX
Southwestern Christian College, TX
State University of New York/Empire
    State College, NY
Stillman College, AL
Sul Ross State University, TX
Texas College, TX
Texas Southern University, TX
Thomas College, GA
Thomas Moore College of Liberal Arts,
    NH
Trevecca Nazarene College, TN
Troy State University at Dothan/Fort
    Rucker, AL
Troy State University in Montgomery,
    AL
Union College, NE
University of Akron, OH
University of Arkansas at Monticello,
    AR
University of Guam, GU
University of Houston-Downtown, TX
University of Kansas, KS
University of Maine at Augusta, ME
University of Mary Hardin-Baylor, TX
University of Maryland/University
    College, MD
University of Minnesota/Crookston,
    MN
University of North Alabama, AL
University of North Dakota, ND
University of Rio Grande, OH
University of Southern Indiana, IN
University of Southwestern Louisiana,
    LA
University of Texas-Pan American, TX
University of the District of Columbia,
    DC
University of Toledo, OH
University of Wyoming, WY
Washburn University of Topeka, KS
Wayland Baptist University, TX
Wayne State College, NE
West Coast University, CA
Wichita State University, KS
Wiley College, TX
William Tyndale College, MI
Wilmington College, DE

SPECIAL

Listed here are colleges whose programs of study are specialized; professional schools of art, music, or theater arts. In general, the admissions requirements are not based primarily on academic criteria, but on evidence of talent or special interest in the field. Many other colleges and universities offer special-interest programs *in addition* to regular academic curricula, but such institutions have been given a regular competitive rating based on academic criteria. Other schools with this rating may be oriented toward working adults.

American College for the Applied Arts, GA
American Technical Institute, TN
Art Academy of Cincinnati, OH
Art Center College of Design, CA
Art Institute of Southern California, CA
Atlanta College of Art, GA
Bassist College, OR
Berklee College of Music, MA
Boston Architectural Center, MA
Boston Conservatory, MA
California College of Arts and Crafts, CA
California Institute of the Arts, CA
Center for Creative Studies/College of Art and Design, MI
Cleveland Institute of Art, OH
Cleveland Institute of Music, OH
Columbia College, IL
Columbus College of Art and Design, OH
Corcoran School of Art, DC
Cornish College of the Arts, WA

Curtis Institute of Music, PA
Eastman School of Music, NY
Fashion Institute of Technology/State University of New York, NY
Five Towns College, NY
Gallaudet University, DC
Juilliard School, NY
Kansas City Art Institute, MO
Kendall College of Art and Design, MI
Laboratory Institute of Merchandising, NY
Maine College of Art, ME
Manhattan School of Music, NY
Mannes College of Music, NY
Maryland Institute, College of Art, MD
Massachusetts College of Art, MA
Memphis College of Art, TN
Milwaukee Institute of Art and Design, WI
Minneapolis College of Art and Design, MN
Montserrat College of Art, MA
Moore College of Art and Design, PA

NAES College, IL
New England Conservatory of Music, MA
North Carolina School of the Arts, NC
Otis College of Art and Design, CA
Pacific Northwest College of Art, OR
Paier College of Art, CT
Parsons School of Design, NY
Rhode Island School of Design, RI
Ringling School of Art and Design, FL
Rutgers University/Mason Gross School of the Arts, NJ
San Francisco Art Institute, CA
San Francisco Conservatory of Music, CA
Savannah College of Art and Design, GA
School of the Art Institute of Chicago, IL
School of Visual Arts, NY
Union Institute, OH
University of the Arts, PA
VanderCook College of Music, IL
Westminster Choir College, NJ

AIR FORCE

In the Air Force ROTC program, young men and women may earn commissions by participating in the 2- or 4-year program while attending college. The amount of academic credit given for Air Force ROTC varies from school to school.

In the 4-year program, students spend their first two years in the General Military Course, studying the organization, mission, and history of the Air Force in one hour of instruction and one hour of leadership laboratory each week. Students may register for this as they register for any other course and incur no military obligation (except scholarship students). After two years, they may compete for the Professional Officer Course on the basis of standardized tests, majors, gradepoint averages, physical examinations, and other factors. This course involves three hours of classes a week in leadership and defense policy, plus a one-hour leadership laboratory. POC candidates attend a 4-week field training course between the sophomore and junior years.

The 2-year program, for students with junior standing and above, allows direct entrance into the Professional Officer Course, but students must complete a 6-week field training course.

All cadets enrolled in the Professional Officer Course receive a $100 monthly allowance during the school year. They also are paid during field training. The Air Force provides all uniforms and textbooks required for the Air Force ROTC program.

Air Force ROTC offers scholarships to high school seniors and graduates. Type I, Type II, and Targeted scholarships are available, based on the needs of the Air Force. Type I scholarships pay full college tuition, incidental and lab fees, and a textbook allowance. Type II scholarships pay the same benefits, except tuition is capped at $8000 per year. The entitlement for the Targeted Scholarship is full tuition and most required fees at a particular school based on the school preference listed by the applicant on the scholarship application. These scholarships also carry a $100 monthly allowance during the school year. Most AFROTC scholarships are awarded in technical and scientific academic degree areas. Selections are made on the basis of scores on the SAT I or ACT, academic record, an interview with an Air Force officer, extracurricular activities record, and recommendations from high school officials.

Scholarships for 2 to 3 1/2 years also are available to students already in college. Special scholarships are available through the Pre-health Professions Program for students in premedical programs. There are also 2- and 3-year nursing scholarships.

Cadets in the Professional Officer Course agree to serve four years on active duty if assigned to nonflying duties. Pilots must serve at least 8 years after training and navigators must serve 5 years. Those in the Health Professions Program must serve 7 or 8 years, depending on the length of their training. After leaving active duty, officers may be required to serve in the Air Force Reserve.

Applicants for the Air Force ROTC must be U.S. citizens in good physical condition and meet Air Force physical requirements (which are more rigorous for light aircraft training candidates). Applicants for the General Military Course must be at least 14 years old, or at least 17 to qualify for a scholarship. Further information can be obtained from the professor of aerospace studies at any of the institutions listed below. These schools represent only the main campuses where Air Force ROTC is located. However, there are hundreds of other schools with crosstown agreements, making Air Force ROTC accessible to more of their students. Check with the nearest listed school for further information, or write Air Force ROTC RROO, Maxwell Air Force Base, Alabama 36112-6016.

ALABAMA

Alabama State University
Auburn University
Samford University
Troy State University
Tuskegee University
University of Alabama
University of South Alabama

ARIZONA

Arizona State University
Embry-Riddle Aeronautical University
Northern Arizona University
University of Arizona

ARKANSAS

University of Arkansas at Fayetteville

CALIFORNIA

California State University at Fresno
California State University at Long
   Beach
California State University at
   Sacramento
Loyola Marymount University
San Diego State University
San Jose State University
University of California at Berkeley
University of California at Los Angeles
University of Southern California

COLORADO

Colorado State University
University of Colorado at Boulder

CONNECTICUT

University of Connecticut

DELAWARE

University of Delaware

DISTRICT OF COLUMBIA

Howard University

FLORIDA

Embry-Riddle Aeronautical
   University
Florida State University
University of Central Florida
University of Florida
University of Miami
University of South Florida

GEORGIA

Georgia Institute of Technology
University of Georgia
Valdosta State College

HAWAII

University of Hawaii at Manoa

ILLINOIS

Illinois Institute of Technology
Parks College of St. Louis University
Southern Illinois University at
   Carbondale
University of Illinois at Urbana

INDIANA

Indiana State University
Indiana University/Bloomington
Purdue University
University of Notre Dame

IOWA

University of Iowa

KANSAS

Kansas State University
University of Kansas

KENTUCKY

University of Kentucky
University of Louisville

LOUISIANA

Grambling State University
Louisiana State University and
    Agricultural & Mechanical College
Louisiana Tech University
Tulane University

MAINE

University of Maine

MARYLAND

University of Maryland

MASSACHUSETTS

Boston University
Massachusetts Institute of Technology
University of Lowell
University of Massachusetts
University of Massachusetts at Lowell
Worcester Polytechnic Institute

MICHIGAN

Michigan State University
Michigan Technological University
University of Michigan

MINNESOTA

University of Minnesota/Duluth
University of Minnesota/Twin Cities
    (Minneapolis)
University of Saint Thomas

MISSISSIPPI

Mississippi State University
Mississippi Valley State University
University of Mississippi
University of Southern Mississippi

MISSOURI

Southeast Missouri State University
University of Missouri/Columbia
University of Missouri/Rolla

MONTANA

Montana State University

NEBRASKA

University of Nebraska at Lincoln
University of Nebraska at Omaha

NEW HAMPSHIRE

University of New Hampshire

NEW JERSEY

New Jersey Institute of Technology
Rutgers, The State University of New
    Jersey

NEW MEXICO

New Mexico State University
University of New Mexico

NEW YORK

Clarkson University College
Cornell University
Manhattan College
Rensselaer Polytechnic Institute
Rochester Institute of Technology
Syracuse University

NORTH CAROLINA

Duke University
East Carolina University
Fayetteville State University
North Carolina Agricultural &
Technical State University
North Carolina State University
University of North Carolina at Chapel
    Hill
University of North Carolina at
    Charlotte

NORTH DAKOTA

North Dakota State University

OHIO

Bowling Green State University
Kent State University
Miami University
Ohio State University
Ohio University
University of Akron
University of Cincinnati
Wright State University

OKLAHOMA

Oklahoma State University
University of Oklahoma

OREGON

Oregon State University
University of Portland

PENNSYLVANIA

Lehigh University
Pennsylvania State University
    Park Campus
Saint Joseph's University
University of Pittsburgh
Wilkes College

PUERTO RICO

University of Puerto Rico/Mayaguez
University of Puerto Rico/Río Piedras

SOUTH CAROLINA

The Citadel
Clemson University
University of South Carolina

SOUTH DAKOTA

South Dakota State University

TENNESSEE

Memphis State University
Tennessee State University
University of Tennessee at Knoxville

TEXAS

Angelo State University
Baylor University
Southwest Texas State University
Texas A & M University
Texas Christian University
Texas Tech University
University of North Texas
University of Texas at El Paso
University of Texas at San Antonio

UTAH

Brigham Young University
University of Utah
Utah State University

VERMONT

Norwich University
Saint Michael's College

VIRGINIA

University of Virginia
Virginia Military Institute
Virginia Polytechnic Institute

WASHINGTON

Central Washington University
University of Washington
Washington State University

WEST VIRGINIA

West Virginia University

WISCONSIN

University of Wisconsin/Madison

WYOMING

University of Wyoming

ARMY

The Army Reserve Officers' Training Corps (ROTC) is a program of college electives that gives students a chance to earn a college degree and an officer's commission at the same time. Upon graduation and commissioning, they'll serve in either the Active Army, Army National Guard, or U.S. Army Reserve.

The 4-year Army ROTC program is divided into two parts: the basic course and the advanced course. The basic course is usually taken during the first two years of college and covers such subjects as management principles, national defense, and military history. All necessary ROTC textbooks, uniforms, and other essential materials for the basic course are furnished to students at no cost. After completion of the basic course, students who have demonstrated the potential to become officers and who have met the physical and scholastic requirements are eligible to enroll in the advanced course.

The advanced course is usually taken during the last two years of college and includes instruction in organization and management, tactics, ethics, and professionalism and leadership development.

During the summer between their junior and senior years of college, advanced-course cadets attend a paid 6-week advanced camp. This camp gives cadets the chance to practice what they've learned in the classroom.

Nursing students enrolled in the program may attend a Nurse Summer Training Program instead of the regular advanced camp. This program provides them with the opportunity to work in an Army hospital under the supervision of an Army Nurse Corps officer.

Army ROTC also offers a 2-year program designed for junior and community college graduates, students at four-year colleges who did not take ROTC during their first two years of school, and students entering a 2-year post-graduate course of study. To enter the 2-year program, students must first attend and successfully complete a paid six-week basic camp, normally held during the summer between the sophomore and junior years of college.

Army ROTC scholarships are offered for four, three, and two years and are awarded on a competitive basis to the most outstanding students who apply. The 4-year scholarships are awarded to students who will be entering college as freshmen. The 3- and 2-year scholarships are awarded to students already enrolled in college and to Army enlisted personnel on active duty. Students who attend the basic camp of the 2-year program may compete for 2-year scholarships while at camp.

Each scholarship pays annual college tuition and mandatory educational fees up to the limit set by U.S. Army Cadet Command. The scholarship will also pay an annual amount for miscellaneous fees, a flat rate for text books and classroom supplies, and a tax-free stipend of $100 per academic month for the duration of the scholarship.

All non-scholarship cadets in the Advanced Course will also receive the stipend mentioned above for each of the two years.

Applications for four-year scholarships are available between February 1 and October 15 of each year. Two- and three-year scholarships may be obtained from the Professor of Military Science at a college or university offering Army ROTC. For more information and scholarship applications, call 1-800-USA-ROTC or write to College Army ROTC, Gold QUEST Center, P.O. Box 3279, Warminster, PA 13974-0128.

The program is currently hosted by more than 200 colleges and universities across the country, and offered at more than 1,000 other schools through extension center and cross-enrollment agreements.

The following list shows the colleges and universities currently hosting Army ROTC units.

ALABAMA

Alabama Agricultural and
   Mechanical University
Auburn University
Auburn University at Montgomery
Jacksonville State University
Tuskegee University
University of Alabama
University of Alabama at Birmingham
University of North Alabama
University of South Alabama

ALASKA

University of Alaska/Fairbanks

ARIZONA

Arizona State University
Northern Arizona University
University of Arizona

ARKANSAS

Arkansas State University
University of Arkansas at Fayetteville
University of Arkansas at Little Rock
University of Arkansas at Pine Bluff

CALIFORNIA

California Polytechnic State University
California State University at Fresno
California State University at Fullerton
California State University at Long
   Beach
Claremont Colleges/Claremont
   McKenna College
San Diego State University
San Jose State University
Santa Clara University
University of California/Berkeley
University of California/Los Angeles
University of California/Santa Barbara
University of San Francisco
University of Southern California

COLORADO

Colorado State University
Metropolitan State College
University of Colorado at Boulder
University of Colorado at Colorado
   Springs

CONNECTICUT

University of Bridgeport
University of Connecticut

DELAWARE

University of Delaware

DISTRICT OF COLUMBIA

Georgetown University
Howard University

FLORIDA

Embry-Riddle Aeronautical University
Florida A & M University
Florida Institute of Technology
Florida Southern College
Florida State University
University of Central Florida
University of Florida
University of Miami
University of North Florida
University of South Florida
University of Tampa
University of West Florida

GEORGIA

Albany State College
Armstrong State College
Augusta College
Columbus College
Fort Valley State College
Georgia Institute of Technology
Georgia Southern University
Georgia State University
North Georgia College
University of Georgia

GUAM

University of Guam

HAWAII

University of Hawaii

IDAHO

Boise State University
University of Idaho

ILLINOIS

Chicago State University
Eastern Illinois University
Illinois State University
Northern Illinois University
Southern Illinois University at
  Carbondale
Southern Illinois University at
  Edwardsville
University of Illinois at Chicago
University of Illinois at Urbana—
  Champaign
Western Illinois University
Wheaton College

INDIANA

Ball State University
Indiana University at Bloomington
Indiana University/Purdue
Purdue University/West Lafayette
Rose-Hulman Institute of Technology
University of Notre Dame

IOWA

Drake University
Iowa State University of Science and
  Technology
University of Iowa
University of Northern Iowa

KANSAS

Emporia State University
Kansas State University
Pittsburg State University
University of Kansas

KENTUCKY

Eastern Kentucky University
Morehead State University
Murray State University
University of Kentucky
University of Louisville
Western Kentucky University

LOUISIANA

Dillard University
Grambling State University
Louisiana State University and
  Agricultural & Mechanical College
Louisiana State University at
  Shreveport
McNeese State University
Northeast Louisiana University
Northwestern State University of
  Louisiana
Southeastern Louisiana University
Southern University and A & M
  College
Tulane University

MAINE

University of Maine at Orono

MARYLAND

Bowie State College
Frostburg State University
Johns Hopkins University
Loyola College
Morgan State University
Mount Saint Mary's College
Salisbury State College
Western Maryland College

MASSACHUSETTS

Boston University
Fitchburg State College
Massachusetts Institute of Technology
Northeastern University
Stonehill College
University of Massachusetts at
  Amherst
Western New England College
Worcester Polytechnic Institute

MICHIGAN

Central Michigan University
Eastern Michigan University
Michigan State University
Michigan Technological University
Northern Michigan University
University of Michigan/Ann Arbor
Western Michigan University

MINNESOTA

Mankato State University
Saint Cloud State University
Saint John's University
University of Minnesota/Twin Cities

MISSISSIPPI

Alcorn State University
Delta State University
Jackson State University
Mississippi State University
University of Mississippi
University of Southern Mississippi

MISSOURI

Central Missouri State University
Lincoln University
Missouri Western State University
Northeast Missouri State University
Northwest Missouri State University
Southeast Missouri State University
Southwest Missouri State University
University of Missouri/Columbia
University of Missouri/Rolla
Washington University

MONTANA

Montana State University
University of Montana

NEBRASKA

Creighton University
Kearney State College
University of Nebraska at Lincoln

NEVADA

University of Nevada/Reno

NEW HAMPSHIRE

University of New Hampshire

NEW JERSEY

Princeton University
Rider College
Rutgers, The State University of New
  Jersey
Seton Hall University

NEW MEXICO

Eastern New Mexico University
New Mexico Institute of Mining and
  Technology
New Mexico State University
University of New Mexico

NEW YORK

Canisius College
Clarkson College
Cornell University
Fordham University
Hofstra University
Niagara University
Polytechnic University
Rochester Institute of Technology
Saint Bonaventure University
Saint John's University
Siena College
State University of New
  York/Brockport
State University of New York/Oswego
Syracuse University

NORTH CAROLINA

Appalachian State University
Campbell University
Davidson College
Duke University
East Carolina University
Elizabeth City State University
Elon College
North Carolina Agricultural and
  Technical State University
North Carolina State University
Saint Augustine's College
University of North Carolina at
  Charlotte
University of North Carolina at Chapel
  Hill
Wake Forest University
Western Carolina University

NORTH DAKOTA

North Dakota State University
University of North Dakota

OHIO

Bowling Green State University
Capital University
Central State University
Franklin University
John Carroll University
Kent State University
Ohio State University
Ohio University
University of Akron
University of Cincinnati
University of Dayton
University of Toledo
Wright State University
Xavier University

OKLAHOMA

Cameron University
East Central Oklahoma State
University
Oklahoma State University
University of Central Oklahoma
University of Oklahoma
University of Tulsa

OREGON

Oregon State University
Portland State University
University of Oregon

PENNSYLVANIA

Bloomsburg University of
Pennsylvania
Bucknell University
California University of Pennsylvania
Dickinson College
Drexel University
Duquesne University
East Stroudsburg University
Edinboro University of Pennsylvania
Gannon University
Indiana University of Pennsylvania
Lehigh University
Lock Haven University of
Pennsylvania
Millersville University of Pennsylvania
Pennsylvania State University Park
Campus
Shippensburg University
of Pennsylvania
Slippery Rock University
Temple University
University of Pennsylvania
University of Pittsburgh
University of Scranton
Washington and Jefferson College
Widener University

PUERTO RICO

University of Puerto Rico/Mayaguez
University of Puerto Rico/Río Piedras
University of Puerto Rico/Cayey
University of Puerto Rico/Humacao

RHODE ISLAND

Bryant College
Providence College
University of Rhode Island

SOUTH CAROLINA

Benedict College
The Citadel
Clemson University
Francis Marion College
Furman University
Presbyterian College
South Carolina State College
University of South Carolina
Wofford College

SOUTH DAKOTA

South Dakota School of Mines and
Technology
South Dakota State University
University of South Dakota

TENNESSEE

Austin Peay State University
Carson-Newman College
East Tennessee State University
Memphis State University
Middle Tennessee State University
Tennessee Technological University
University of Tennessee at
Chattanooga
University of Tennessee at Knoxville
University of Tennessee at Martin
Vanderbilt University

TEXAS

Hardin-Simmons University
Lamar University
Prairie View A & M University
Saint Mary's University
Sam Houston State University
Southwestern Texas State University
Stephen F. Austin State University
Tarleton State University
Texas A & I University
Texas A & M University
Texas Tech University
Texas Christian University
Texas Woman's University
Trinity University

University of Houston
University of Texas at Arlington
University of Texas at Austin
University of Texas at El Paso
University of Texas at San Antonio
University of Texas-Pan American

UTAH

Brigham Young University
University of Utah
Utah State University
Weber State College

VERMONT

Norwich University
University of Vermont

VIRGINIA

Christopher Newport College
College of William and Mary
George Mason University
James Madison University
Longwood College
Marshall University
Norfolk State University
Old Dominion University
Radford University
University of Richmond
University of Virginia
Virginia Commonwealth University
Virginia Military Institute
Virginia Polytechnic Institute and
State University
Virginia State University
West Virginia State College
West Virginia University

WASHINGTON

Central Washington University
Eastern Washington University
Gonzaga University
Seattle University
University of Washington
Washington State University

WISCONSIN

Marquette University
University of Wisconsin/La Crosse
University of Wisconsin/Madison
University of Wisconsin/Oshkosh
University of Wisconsin/Stevens Point
University of Wisconsin/Whitewater

WYOMING

University of Wyoming

NAVY

The Naval Reserve Officers Training Corps gives young men and women an opportunity to earn commissions in the Navy and the Marine Corps while attending college. Two types of NROTC programs are available: a scholarship program of two, three, or four years, and a nonsubsidized program.

Under the scholarship program, which is highly competitive, students are granted full costs of tuition, fees, and textbooks, receive a subsistence allowance of $100 per month for up to 40 months and are paid for summer training periods. Scholarship recipients can major in engineering, the sciences, or other fields of interest to the Navy or Marine Corps. They must agree to serve a minimum of four years on active duty and the remainder of their 8-year commitment on inactive duty after graduation.

In the nonsubsidized program, called the College Program, students undergo the same training as scholarship students, but attend college at their own expense. During their junior and senior years, they receive $100 per month for up to twenty months. College Program students also receive the uniforms and books required for naval-science courses. Students may enroll in either a 2- or 4-year College Program. Those entering the 2-year program must complete a 6-week paid Naval Science Institute program in the summer before their junior year. Graduates of the College Program agree to serve on active duty for three years.

In addition to their normal studies, all NROTC program students take courses in naval science and management and participate in drills. Scholarship students also participate in three summer training programs of four to six weeks each, conducted between the academic years. College Program students participate in one summer training program between the junior and senior years.

Applicants for 4-year scholarship programs must apply before December 1, take the SAT I or ACT and have their scores released to the NROTC scholarship program. Those who qualify as finalists will be notified by the Navy or Marine Corps Recruiting Activity in their area and asked to complete an application package. The minimum scores required to ensure qualification as a finalist were: Navy—SAT I verbal 450 and math 500, or ACT English 22 and math 22; Marines—SAT I composite of 1000 or ACT total of 45. Navy and Marine Corps selection boards select scholarship recipients on the basis of academic achievement, test scores, demonstrated leadership ability, extracurricular activities, and aptitude for service. Some of those not selected for 4-year scholarships receive guarantees of 3-year scholarships, provided they enroll in an NROTC College Program and meet minimum academic and aptitude standards during their freshman year. Students seeking 2-year scholarships for their third or fourth years of college should write to the Navy Opportunity Information Center, P.O. Box 5000, Clifton, N.J. 07012 for further information.

Admissions for the College Program are handled by the professor of naval science at each school. Those who apply for NROTC must be United States citizens between the ages of 17 and 21, possess a high school diploma or equivalency certificate, and meet standards of physical fitness, height, and weight. Further information on NROTC and initial application forms for NROTC scholarships are available from high school guidance offices, colleges and universities that offer the NROTC Program, Navy and Marine Corps recruiting stations, and the Naval Recruiting Command, Code 314, 801 North Randolph Street, Arlington, Virginia 22203-1991.

The following list shows the colleges and universities included in this book that have an NROTC unit on campus. Many more institutions offer the program through cross-town agreements. If the school of your choice does not appear below, you may want to check with that school about cross-town possibilities.

ALABAMA

Auburn University

ARIZONA

University of Arizona

CALIFORNIA

University of California/Berkeley
University of California/Los Angeles
University of California/San Diego
University of Southern California

COLORADO

University of Colorado at Boulder

DISTRICT OF COLUMBIA

George Washington University

FLORIDA

Florida A & M University
Jacksonville University
University of Florida

GEORGIA

Georgia Institute of Technology
Savannah State College

IDAHO

University of Idaho

ILLINOIS

Illinois Institute of Technology
Northwestern University
University of Illinois at Urbana-
    Champaign

INDIANA

Purdue University/West Lafayette
University of Notre Dame

IOWA

Iowa State University

KANSAS

University of Kansas

LOUISIANA

Southern University and A & M College
Tulane University

MAINE

Maine Maritime Academy

MASSACHUSETTS

Boston University
College of the Holy Cross
Massachusetts Institute of Technology

MICHIGAN

University of Michigan/Ann Arbor

MISSISSIPPI

University of Mississippi

NEBRASKA

University of Nebraska at Lincoln

NEW YORK

Cornell University
Rensselaer Polytechnic Institute
State University of New York/Maritime
    College
University of Rochester

NORTH CAROLINA

Duke University
North Carolina State University
University of North Carolina at Chapel
    Hill

OHIO

Miami University
Ohio State University

OKLAHOMA

University of Oklahoma

OREGON

Oregon State University

PENNSYLVANIA

Carnegie Mellon University
Pennsylvania State University Park
    Campus
University of Pennsylvania
Villanova University

SOUTH CAROLINA

The Citadel
University of South Carolina

TENNESSEE

Memphis State University
Vanderbilt University

TEXAS

Prairie View A & M University
Rice University
Texas A & M University
University of Texas at Austin

VERMONT

Norwich University

VIRGINIA

Hampton University
Norfolk State University
Old Dominion University
University of Virginia
Virginia Military Institute
Virginia Polytechnic Institute and State
    University

WASHINGTON

University of Washington

WISCONSIN

Marquette University
University of Wisconsin/Madison

AN EXPLANATION OF THE COLLEGE ENTRIES

THE BASICS

More than 1700 U.S. colleges and universities, Canadian universities, Mexican and other foreign schools are described in detail in the profiles that follow.

The Choice of Schools

Colleges and universities in this country may achieve recognition from a number of professional organizations, but we have based our choice of U.S. colleges on accreditation from one of the six U.S. regional accrediting associations.

Accreditation amounts to a stamp of approval given to a college. The accreditation process evaluates institutions and programs to determine whether they meet established standards of educational quality. The regional associations listed below supervise an aspect of the accrediting procedure—the study of a detailed report submitted by the institution applying for accreditation, and then an inspection visit by members of the accrediting agency. The six agencies are associated with the Commission on Recognition of Postsecondary Accreditation (CORPA). They include:

Middle States Association of Colleges and Schools
New England Association of Schools and Colleges
North Central Association of Colleges and Schools
Northwest Association of Colleges and Schools
Southern Association of Colleges and Schools
Western Association of Schools and Colleges

Getting accreditation for the first time can take a school several years. To acknowledge that schools have begun this process, the agencies accord them candidate status. Most candidates eventually are awarded full accreditation.

The U.S. schools included in this book are fully accredited or are candidates for that status. If the latter is the case, it is indicated below the address of the school. Because the U.S. regional accrediting bodies do not officially accredit Canadian colleges and universities, and because there is no equivalent accrediting system in Canada, we have chosen to include only the larger, English-language Canadian schools—those with total full-time undergraduate enrollment of more than 10,000. It should be understood that size in no way relates to quality; there are many excellent Canadian colleges and universities with fewer than 10,000 students.

Four-Year Colleges Only

This book presents profiles for all accredited four-year colleges that grant bachelor's degrees and admit freshmen with no previous college experience. Most of these colleges also accept transfer students. Profiles of upper division schools, which offer only the junior or senior year of undergraduate study, are not included.

Consistent Entries

Each profile of a U.S. college is organized in the same way; the only profiles that vary are those of Canada, Mexico, schools abroad, and religious schools. The following discussion applies to the U.S. college profiles, but refers to the other profiles as well.

Every profile begins with a capsule and is followed by separate sections covering the campus environment, student life, programs of study, admissions, financial aid, information for international students, computers, graduates, and the admissions contact. These categories are always introduced in the same sequence, so you can find data and compare specific points easily. The following commentary will help you evaluate and interpret the information given for each college.

Data Collection

Barron's *Profiles of American Colleges* was first published in 1964. Since then, it has been revised almost every year; comprehensive revisions are undertaken every two years. Such frequent updating is necessary because so much information about colleges—particularly enrollment figures, costs, programs of study, and admissions standards—changes rapidly.

The facts included in this edition were gathered in the fall of 1993 and apply to the 1993–94 academic year. You should expect all the entries in this edition to become somewhat dated, but some facts will change faster than others. Figures on tuition and room-and-board costs generally change soon after the book is published. For the most up-to-date information on such items, you should always check with the colleges. Other information—such as the basic nature of the school, its campus, and the educational goals of its students—changes less rapidly. A few new programs of study might be added or new services made available, but the basic educational offerings generally will remain constant.

THE CAPSULE

The capsule of each profile provides basic information about the college at a glance. An explanation of the standard capsule is shown in the accompanying box.

A former name is given only if the name has been changed since the previous edition of *Profiles*. To use the map code to the right of the college name, turn to the appropriate college-locator map at the beginning of each chapter. Wherever "n/av" is used in the capsule, it means the information was not available. The abbreviation "n/app" means not applicable.

Full-time, Part-time, Graduate

Enrollment figures are the clearest indication of the size of a

---

COMPLETE NAME OF SCHOOL
(former Name, if any)
City, State, Zip Code
(Accreditation Status, if a candidate)

MAP CODE

Phone Number

Full-time: Full-time undergraduate enrollment
Part-time: Part-time undergraduate enrollment
Graduate: Graduate enrollment
Year: Type of calendar, whether there is a summer session
Application deadline: fall admission deadline
Freshman Class: Number of students who applied, number accepted, number enrolled
SAT I: Median Verbal, Median Math

Faculty: Number of full-time faculty; AAUP category of school, salary-level symbol
Ph.Ds: Percentage of faculty holding Ph.D. or highest terminal degree
Student/Faculty: Full-time student/full-time faculty ratio
Tuition: Yearly tuition and fees (out-of-state tuition and fees if different)
Room & Board: Yearly room and board costs
ACT: Median composite of ACT

ADMISSIONS SELECTOR RATING

college, and show whether or not it is coeducational and what the male-female ratio is. Graduate enrollment is presented to give a better idea of the size of the entire student body; some schools have far more graduate students enrolled than undergraduates.

Year

Some of the more innovative college calendars include the 4-1-4, 3-2-3, 3-3-1, and 1-3-1-4-3 terms. College administrators sometimes utilize various intersessions or interims—special short terms—for projects, independent study, short courses, or travel programs. The early semester calendar, which allows students to finish spring semesters earlier than those of the traditional semester calendar, gives students a head start on finding summer jobs. A modified semester (4-1-4) system provides a January or winter term, approximately four weeks long, for special projects that usually earn the same credit as one semester-long course. The trimester calendar divides the year into three equal parts; students may attend college during all three but generally take a vacation during any one. The quarter calendar divides the year into four equal parts; students usually attend for three quarters each year. The term calendar is essentially the same as the quarter calendar without the summer quarter; it has three sessions between September and June. The capsule also indicates schools that offer a summer session.

Application Deadline

Indicated here is the deadline for applications for admission to the fall semester. If there are no specific deadlines, it will say "open." Application deadlines for admission to other semesters are, where available, given in the admissions section of the profile.

Faculty

The first number given refers to the number of full-time faculty members at the college or university.

The Roman numeral and symbol that follow represent the salary level of faculty at the school as compared with faculty salaries nationally. This information is based on the salary report* published by the American Association of University Professors (AAUP). The Roman numeral refers to the AAUP category to which the particular college or university is assigned (this allows for comparison of faculty salaries at the same types of schools). Category I includes "institutions that offer the doctorate degree, and that conferred in the most recent three years an annual average of fifteen or more earned doctorates covering a minimum of three nonrelated disciplines." Category IIA includes "institutions awarding degrees above the baccalaureate, but not included in Category I." Category IIB includes "institutions awarding only the baccalaureate or equivalent degree." Category III includes "institutions with academic ranks, mostly two-year institutions." IV includes "institutions without academic ranks (with the exception of a few liberal arts colleges, this category includes mostly two-year institutions)."

The symbol that follows the Roman numeral indicates into which percentile range the average salary of professors, associate professors, assistant professors, and instructors at the school falls, as compared with other schools in the same AAUP category. The symbols used in this book represent the following:

++$ 80th percentile
+$ 60th percentile
av$ 40th percentile
-$ 20th percentile
--$ lower than 20th percentile

If the school is not a member of AAUP, nothing will appear.

Ph.D.s

The figure here indicates the percentage of full-time faculty who have Ph.D.s.

*Source: Annual Report on the Economic Status of the Profession published in the March-April 1993 issue of *Academe:* Bulletin of the AAUP 1012 Fourteenth St., N.W. Suite 500 Washington D.C. 20005.

Student/faculty

Student/faculty ratios may be deceptive because the faculties of many large universities include scholars and scientists who do little or no teaching. Nearly every college has some large lecture classes, usually in required or popular subjects, and many small classes in advanced or specialized fields. Here, the ratio reflects full-time students and faculty, and some colleges utilize the services of a large part-time faculty. In general, a student/faculty ratio of 10 to 1 is very good.

If the faculty and student body are both mostly part-time, the entry will say "n/app."

Tuition

It is important to remember that tuition costs change continually and that in many cases, these changes are substantial. Particularly heavy increases have occurred recently and will continue to occur; students are therefore urged to contact individual colleges for the most current tuition figures.

The figure given here includes tuition and student fees for the school's standard academic year. If costs differ for state residents and out-of-state residents, the figure for nonresidents is given in parenthesis. Where tuition costs are listed per credit hour (p/c), per course (p/course), or per unit (p/unit), student fees are not included. In some university systems, tuition is the same for all schools. However, student fees, and therefore the total tuition figure, may vary from school to school.

Room and Board

It is suggested that students check with individual schools for the most current room-and-board figures because, like tuition figures, they increase continually. The room-and-board figures given here represent the annual cost of a double room and all meals. The word "none" indicates that the college does not charge for room and board; "n/app" indicates that room and board are not provided.

Freshman class

The numbers apply to the number of students who applied, were accepted, and enrolled in the 1993–94 freshman class or in a recent class.

SAT I, ACT

Whenever available, the median SAT I scores—both Verbal and Mathematics—and the median ACT composite score for the 1993–94 freshman class are given. If the school has not reported median SAT I or ACT scores, the capsule indicates whether the SAT I or ACT is required.

Admissions Selector Rating

The College Admissions Selector indicates degree of competitiveness of admission to the college.

THE GENERAL DESCRIPTION

The Introductory Paragraph

This paragraph indicates, in general, what types of programs the college offers, when it was founded, whether it is public or private, and its religious affiliation. Baccalaureate program accreditation and information on the size of the school's library collection are also provided.

In evaluating the size of the collection, keep in mind the difference between college and university libraries: A university's graduate and professional schools require many specialized books that would be of no value to an undergraduate. For a university, a ratio of one undergraduate to 500 books generally means an outstanding library, one to 200 an adequate library, one to 100 an inferior library. For a college, a ratio of one to 400 is outstanding, one to 300 superior, one to 200 adequate, one to 50 inferior.

These figures are somewhat arbitrary, because a large university with many professional schools or campuses requires more books than a smaller university. Furthermore, a recently founded college would be expected to have fewer books than an older school, since it has not inherited from the

past what might be a great quantity of outdated and use-less books. Most libraries can make up for deficiencies through interlibrary loans.

The ratio of students to the number of subscriptions to periodicals is less meaningful, and again, a university requires more periodicals than a college. But for a university, subscription to more than 15,000 periodicals is outstanding, and 6000 is generally more than adequate. For a college, 15,000 subscriptions are exceptional, 700 very good, and 400 adequate. Subscription to fewer than 200 periodicals generally implies an inferior library with a very tight budget. Microform items are assuming greater importance within a library's holdings, and this information is included when available. Services of a Learning Resource Center and special facilities, such as a museum, and radio or TV station are also described in this paragraph.

This paragraph also provides information on the campus: its size, the type of area in which it is located, and its proximity to a large city.

At most institutions, the existence of classrooms, administrative offices, and dining facilities may be taken for granted, and they generally are not mentioned in the entries unless they have been recently constructed or are considered exceptional.

Student Life

This section, with subdivisions that detail housing, campus activities, sports, facilities for handicapped students, and services offered to students, concentrates on the everyday life of students.

The introductory paragraph, which includes various characteristics of the student body, gives an idea of the mix of attitudes and backgrounds. It includes, where available, percentages of students from out-of-state and from private or public high schools. It also indicates what percentage of the students belong to minority groups and what percentages are Protestant, Catholic, and Jewish. Finally, it tells the average age of all enrolled freshmen and of all undergraduates, and gives data on the freshman dropout rate and the percentage of freshmen who remain to graduate.

Housing. Availability of on-campus housing is described here. If you plan to live on campus, note the type, quantity, and capacity of the dormitory accommodations. Some colleges provide dormitory rooms for freshmen, but require upperclass students to make their own arrangements to live in fraternity or sorority houses, off-campus apartments, or rented rooms in private houses. Many small colleges require all students who do not live with parents or other relatives to live on campus. Some colleges have no residence halls.

This paragraph tells whether special housing is available and whether campus housing is single-sex or coed. It gives the percentage of those who live on campus and those who remain on campus on weekends. Finally, it states if alcohol is not permitted on campus and whether students may keep cars on campus.

Activities. Campus organizations play a vital part in students' social lives. This subsection lists types of activities, including student government, special interest or academic clubs, fraternities and sororities, and cultural and popular campus events sponsored at the college.

Sports. Sports are becoming increasingly important on campus again, so we indicate the extent of the athletic program by giving the number of intercollegiate and intramural sports offered for men and for women. We have also included the athletic and recreation facilities and campus stadium seating capacity.

Disabled Students. The colleges' own estimates of how accessible their campuses are to the physically disabled also are provided. This information should be considered along with the specific kinds of special facilities available. If a profile does not include a subsection on the disabled, the college did not provide the information.

Services. Services that may be available to students—free or for a fee—include health care, birth control information, day-care services, psychological, vocational, personal, and military students counseling, tutoring, remedial instruction, and reader service for the blind.

Programs of Study

Listed here are the bachelor's degrees granted, strongest and most popular majors, and whether associate, master's, and doctoral degrees are awarded. Major areas of study have been included under broader general areas (shown in capital letters in the profiles) for quicker reference; however, the general areas do not necessarily correspond to the academic divisions of the college or university but are more career-oriented.

Required. Wherever possible, information on specific required courses and distribution requirements is supplied, in addition to the number of credits or hours required for graduation. If the college requires students to maintain a certain grade-point average (GPA) or pass comprehensive exams to graduate, that also is given. Whether a computer course or physical education is required is mentioned here.

Special. Special programs are described here. Students at almost every college now have the opportunity to study abroad, either through their college or through other institutions. Internships with businesses, schools, hospitals, and public agencies permit students to gain work experience as they learn. The pass/fail grading option, now quite prevalent, allows students to take courses in unfamiliar areas without threatening their academic average. Many schools offer students the opportunity to earn a combined B.A.-B.S. degree, pursue a general studies (no major) degree, or design their own major. Frequently students may take advantage of a cooperative program offered by two or more universities. Such a program might be referred to, for instance, as a 3-2 engineering program; a student in this program would spend three years at one institution and two at another. The number of national honor societies represented on campus is included. Schools also may conduct honors programs for qualified students, either university-wide or in specific major fields, and these also are listed.

Faculty/Classroom. The percentage of male and female faculty are mentioned here if provided by the college. Also, the percentage of introductory courses taught by graduate students, if any. The average class size in an introductory lecture, laboratory, and regular class offering may also be indicated.

Admissions

The admissions section gives detailed information on standards so you can evaluate your chances for acceptance. Where the SAT I or ACT scores of the 1993–94 freshman class are broken down, you may compare your own scores. Because the role of standardized tests in the admissions process has been subject to criticism, more colleges are considering other factors such as recommendations from high school officials, leadership record, special talents, extracurricular activities, and advanced placement or honors courses completed. A few schools may consider education of parents, ability to pay for college, and relationship to alumni. Some give preference to state residents; others seek a geographically diverse student body.

If a college indicates that it follows an open admissions policy, it is noncompetitive and generally accepts all applicants who meet certain basic requirements, such as graduation from an accredited high school. If a college has rolling admissions, it decides on each application as soon as possible if the applicant's file is complete and does not specify a notification deadline. As a general rule, it is best to submit applications as early as possible.

Some colleges offer special admissions programs for nontraditional applicants. Early admissions programs allow students to begin college either during the summer before their freshman year or during what would have been their last year of high school; in the latter case, a high school diploma is not required. These programs are designed for students who are emotionally and educationally prepared for college at an earlier age than usual.

Deferred admissions plans permit students to spend a year at another activity, such as working or traveling, before beginning college. Students who take advantage of this option can relax during the year off, because they already have been accepted at a college and have a space

reserved. During the year off from study, many students become clearer about their educational goals, and they perform better when they do begin study.

Early decision plans allow students to be notified by their first-choice school during the first term of the senior year. This plan may eliminate the anxiety of deciding whether or not to send a deposit to a second-choice college that offers admission before the first-choice college responds.

The Ivy League institutions, along with the Massachusetts Institute of Technology, have adopted an early evaluation procedure under which applicants receive, between November 1 and February 15, an evaluation of their chances for admission. They are told that acceptance is likely, possible, or unlikely, or that the colleges have received insufficient evidence for evaluation. This information helps applicants decide whether to concentrate on another school. Final notification is made on a common date in April.

Requirements. This subsection indicates the minimum high school class rank and GPA required by the college for freshmen applicants. It indicates what standardized tests, if any, are required; if an essay, interview, or audition is necessary; and if AP/CLEP credit is given. Other factors used by the school in the admissions decision are also listed.

Procedure. This subsection indicates when you should take entrance exams, the application deadlines for various sessions, the application fee, and when students are notified of the admissions decision. Some schools note that their application deadlines are open; this can mean either that they will consider applications until a class is filled, or that applications are considered right up until registration for the term in which the student wishes to enroll. If a waiting list is an active part of the admissions procedure, the college may indicate what percentage of applicants are placed on that list.

Transfer. Nearly every college admits some transfer students. These students may have earned associate degrees at two-year colleges and want to continue their education at a four-year college or wish to attend a different school. One important thing to consider when transferring is how many credits earned at one school will be accepted at another, so entire semesters won't be spent making up lost work. Because most schools require students to spend a specified number of hours in residence to earn a degree, it is best not to wait too long to transfer if you decide to do so.

Visiting. Some colleges hold special orientation programs for prospective students to give them a better idea of what the school is like. Many also will provide guides for informal visits, often allowing students to spend a night in the residence halls. You should make arrangements with the college before visiting.

Financial Aid

This paragraph in each profile describes the availability of financial aid. It includes the percentage of freshmen and continuing students who receive aid, the average scholarship, loan, and work contract aid to freshmen, the average amount of need-based scholarships from all sources and the types and sources of aid available, such as scholarships, grants, loans, and work-study. It indicates if there is a formal appeal process for obtaining more money for the second semester. Aid application deadlines and required forms are also indicated.

International Students

This section begins by telling how many of the school's students come from outside the United States. It tells which English proficiency exam, if any, applicants must take and the minimum score required, if there is one. Any necessary college entrance exams, including SAT II: Subject tests, are listed, as are any minimum scores required on those exams.

Computers

This section details the make and model of the mainframe and the scope of computerized facilities that are available for academic use. Limitations (if any) on student use of computer facilities are outlined. It also gives information on the required or recommended ownership of a personal computer.

Graduates

This section gives the number of graduates in the 1992–93 class, the most popular majors and percentage of graduates earning degrees in those fields, and the percentages of men and women in the 1991–92 class who enrolled in graduate school or found employment within 6 months of graduation.

Admissions Contact

This is the name or title of the person to whom all correspondence regarding your application should be sent.

STUDY ABROAD

Study abroad programs are now available in over 60 countries in fields that range from Costa Rican tropical biology to Finnish architecture. Program directors have responded to the vocational interests of the student of the 1990s by organizing programs in international management, health care administration, and other career-oriented fields.

In fact, study in both traditional and nontraditional fields is enriched by overseas experience. An international perspective can benefit study of environmental sciences, anthropology, political science, urban planning, oceanography, hotel administration, psychology, social work, journalism, marketing and law, as well as film, art history, theater, music and dance.

The vast majority of U.S. students enter European schools through organized, ongoing programs sponsored and managed by the colleges and universities in which they are already enrolled. In this way, they automatically earn U.S. academic credit from their home institution for their overseas course work. Academic credit *directly* earned at a foreign institution is often not acceptable toward a U.S. degree. Applying directly to a foreign school is not difficult, but unusual.

There are colleges and universities located in foreign nations that are organized on the U.S. system and accredited by U.S. accrediting agencies, e.g., American University of Paris. A list of accredited U.S. institutions overseas is provided in the annual *Accredited Institutions of Postsecondary Education*, published for the Council on Postsecondary Accreditation by the American Council on Education and available from Macmillan Publishing Company, Front and Brown Streets, Riverside, NJ 08075.

According to a study by the Institute of International Education (IIE) about 75% of foreign study is done in western Europe—about 30% in the United Kingdom, 12% in France, and 5% in Mexico. Most students are women (64%), and the most popular programs are in the liberal arts (18%). The study showed that, unlike American students, international students coming to the U.S. are primarily interested in engineering, physical and life sciences, and mathematics and computer sciences, and account for 38% of the international student population. Unlike their U.S. counterparts, most of the international students coming to this country are male (66%).

A Productive Experience

If you are interested in study abroad, plan ahead by taking the following steps to ensure that the experience is productive:

- **Assess the ways in which study abroad will benefit your educational and career plans**. Study abroad can be a casual choice or a pleasant way to spend a semester, but you will derive the greatest benefit if you bring more thought to it: How will the overseas experience complement your other courses or your educational major? Can you maximize its value by seeking language as well as academic study, or by combining independent study or an internship with traditional course work?

- **Consult your campus study-abroad adviser.** Most colleges and universities have a person or an office charged with the responsibility of counseling students on overseas study. The study-abroad adviser is best qualified to help you make the right choices.

- **Make sure your college will accept credit earned at the study-abroad program you have chosen.** Speak with both your academic adviser and your study-abroad adviser, and resolve any issues before you leave. Many students have assumed incorrectly that credit is granted automatically for another institution's program. You cannot take this for granted.

- **Be realistic about your foreign language proficiency.** It is one thing to be able to order a meal or buy a train ticket in a foreign language. It is quite another to follow a professor lecturing on a complex subject. If you discover that your linguistic ability is inadequate, it is quite possible that you can find abroad the subject matter you want taught in English. You will get more out of the overseas experience; however, if you make the effort to function in the language of the chosen country.

- **Look carefully at costs.** If you are dealing with a program sponsor that is not your home institution, it is wise to read program literature carefully. Ask questions before you go if you have any qualms! Are charges clearly specified? Does the literature specify what services *are* covered and, more important, what services are *not* covered? What is the refund policy, if any? Is there a clearly-identified organization with an official base in the United States which would be legally responsible in the event of disaster?

    While drawing up your budget, think about the extras. You will want to make the small side trips to new places that help to make overseas living rewarding. Try to give yourself some financial flexibility in working out your budget.

- **Think about what it means to live abroad.** Be sure to arrange for substitutes for the support systems you take for granted at home. Will your medical insurance cover you? Do you need vaccinations or a doctor who can manage your specific health problems while you are living abroad? What about visas?

    It is critically important to find out about housing before you leave. Student housing is difficult to find almost everywhere. Be sure to find out whether securing housing abroad is your responsibility, and what the alternatives are in the country in which you plan to live.

- **Don't assume that you can work abroad.** Because of foreign labor laws, students should not plan to seek paid employment. The practice of working one's way through college is not common abroad, nor are the relatively high-paying part-time jobs that make it possible in the United States. However, increasing numbers of students are looking to combine practical work experience with study abroad. There are many work exchanges, volunteer opportunities, and internships available. Contact the Council on International Exchange, 205 East 42nd Street, New York, NY 10017, for further information.

- **Find out what you can about the sponsoring agency, especially if it is not an accredited U.S. college or university.** Talk to your study-abroad adviser if you have any doubts. Most private agencies engaged in study abroad are legitimate organizations, but their basic purposes may not match yours. Does the organization have experience in placing students in an academic environment, not just in arranging travel? Are descriptions of its study program specific or vague? Does it make unverifiable claims about the academic reputation of its programs, or their recognition by U.S. higher educational institutions?

For further information, consult:

Institute of International Education
IIE Books
809 United Nations Plaza
New York, NY 10017
(publications include *Basic Facts on Study Abroad, Academic Year Abroad 1992/93, Vacation Study Abroad 1992.*)

Council on International Educational Exchange
Publications Department
205 East 42nd Street
New York, NY 10017

Ed Battle
Director of Communications
Institute of International Education
New York, New York

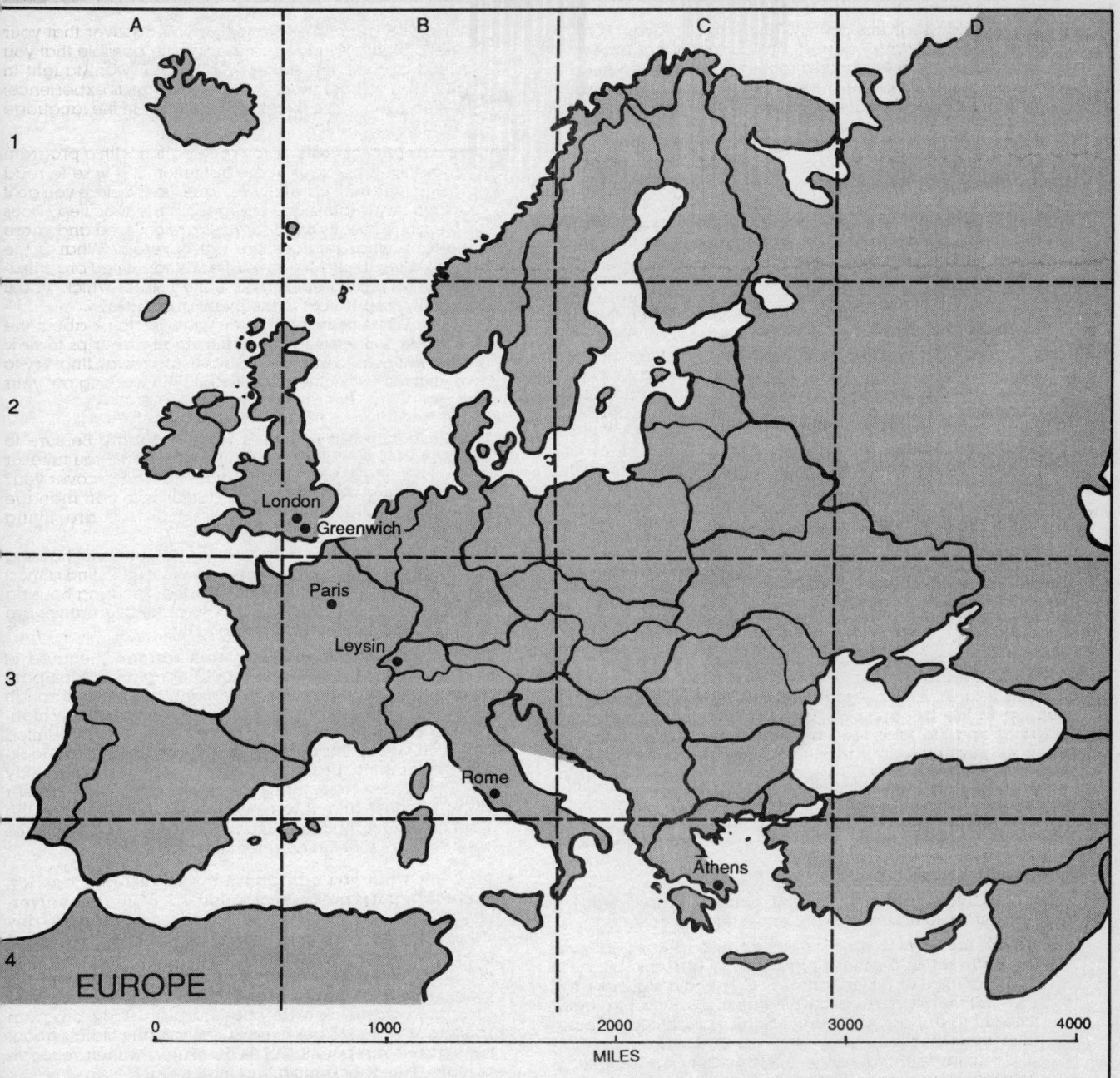

A B C D

1

2

London
Greenwich

Paris

Leysin

3

Rome

Athens

4

EUROPE

| 0 | 1000 | 2000 | 3000 | 4000 |

MILES

AMERICAN COLLEGE OF GREECE
DEREE COLLEGE

C-4

Athens, Greece 15342 (30)(1) 600–9814 or 600–9800, ext. 1317 and 1318

Full-time: 891 men, 2118 women	**Faculty:** 68
Part-time: 306 men, 830 women	**Ph.D.s:** 65%
Graduate: none	**Student/Faculty:** 44 to 1
Year: 4–1-4, summer session	**Tuition:** $3463
Application Deadline: July 10	**Room & Board:** n/app

Freshman Class: 749 applied, 672 accepted, 599 enrolled
SAT I: required

Deree College, the upper division of the American College of Greece, was founded in Asia Minor in 1875 as the American College for Girls. In 1961, the college opened its campus in Athens, where it offers English/American- style liberal arts programs. The library contains 42,000 volumes, 1975 microform items, and 745 audiovisual forms, and subscribes to 292 periodicals. Special learning facilities include a museum of the history of the college. The 60-acre campus is in a suburban area 15 miles northeast of Athens. There is one building on campus. There are no residence halls.

Student Life: About 89% of undergraduates are from Greece. Students come from 43 countries. Fifty percent are from public schools; 31% from private. All are white. The average age of freshmen is 18; all undergraduates, 21. Fifteen percent drop out by the end of their first year; 68% remain to graduate.

Housing: There are no residence halls. Alcohol is not permitted.

Activities: There are no fraternities or sororities on campus. There are many groups and organizations on campus, including art, band, computers, dance, drama, ethnic, international, literary magazine, newspaper, photography, professional, social service, student government, and yearbook. Popular campus events include Club's Day, company visitation day, and Professional Week.

Sports: There are 3 intercollegiate sports for men and 2 for women, and 12 intramural sports for men and 8 for women. Athletic and recreation facilities include a 600-seat stadium, a 1000-seat gymnasium, a 400-meter track, a soccer field, outdoor basketball/volleyball courts, a minisoccer arena, a dance studio, a fitness center, and an Olympic-size pool.

Campus Safety and Security: Campus safety and security measures include 24-hour foot and vehicle patrol, pamphlets, posters, films, and lighted pathways and sidewalks.

Programs of Study: Deree awards the B.A. and B.S. degrees. Associate degrees also are awarded. Bachelor's degrees are awarded in BUSINESS (accounting, business administration and management, management information systems, marketing/retailing/ merchandising, and organizational behavior), COMMUNICATIONS AND THE ARTS (dance, English, and music), ENGINEERING AND ENVIRONMENTAL DESIGN (preengineering), SOCIAL SCIENCE (economics, history, philosophy, psychology, social science, and sociology). Marketing management has the largest enrollment.

Required: All students must maintain a minimum GPA of 2.0 and complete 128 semester hours, of which the last 30 must be earned in residence. Distribution requirements vary with the major, and include composition, literature, public speaking, humanities, ethics, aesthetics, history, music, and political science.

Special: Study abroad, work-study programs, B.A.-B.S. degrees, dual majors, self-directed study, and interdisciplinary programs are offered. Nondegree study and pass/fail options are available.

Faculty/Classroom: All teach undergraduates.

Admissions: About 90% of the 1993–94 applicants were accepted. The SAT I scores for the 1993–94 freshman class were as follows: Verbal—78% below 500, 11% between 500 and 599, and 11% between 600 and 700; Math—67% below 500, 22% between 500 and 599, and 11% between 600 and 700.

Requirements: A minimum GPA of 2.0 is required. The SAT I is required for native English speakers, with minimum scores of 450 on each section. Applicants must be graduates of an accredited secondary school. The GED is accepted. AP and CLEP credits are accepted. Important factors used in the admissions decision are recommendations by school officials, recommendations by alumni, personality, intangible qualities, leadership record, and parents or siblings attending the school.

Procedure: Freshmen are admitted to all sessions. Applications should be filed by July 10 for fall entry, December 15 for winter entry, January 10 for spring entry, and May 15 for summer entry, along with an application fee of $110. Notification is sent on a rolling basis. There is a deferred admissions plan. A waiting list is an active part of the admissions procedure.

Transfer: About 25 transfer students enrolled in 1993–94. Applicants must have a minimum GPA of 2.0 and submit high school transcripts and a diploma if they have fewer than 30 credits. English proficiency also must be demonstrated. At least 36 credits out of 128 must be completed at Deree.

Visiting: There are guides for informal visits and visitors may sit in on classes. To arrange for a visit, contact the Office of Admissions at 600–9814 or 600–9800, ext. 1317, 1318, or 1322.

Financial Aid: In 1993–94, 62% of continuing students received some form of financial aid. About 83% of freshmen and 16% of continuing students received need-based aid. The average freshman award was $2186. Of that total, scholarships or need-based grants averaged $2186 ($3174 maximum). Two percent of undergraduate students work part-time. Deree is a member of CSS. The college's own financial statement and Internal Revenue statement are required. The deadline for financial aid applications is July 15.

International Students: There are currently 434 international students enrolled. They must take the TOEFL or the University of Michigan Language Test and achieve a minimum score on the TOEFL of 500. Native English speakers must also take the SAT I.

Computers: The college provides computer facilities for student use. The mainframes are a Wang VS 65 and an IBM AS400. Senior computer information systems students and marketing research students may use the Wang mainframe; 4 terminals are in the computer laboratories. Microcomputers are used for all courses that require computer work. Only students taking computer-related courses may access the system. It may be used 8:30 A.M. to 10 P.M. daily. Students may access the system 1 to 5 hours per week (varies according to course). The fees are $24 per laboratory unit, with the number of units varying according to the course.

Graduates: In 1992–93, 647 bachelor's degrees were awarded. The most popular majors among graduates were business administration (67%) and arts (33%). Some 220 companies recruited on campus in a recent year. In the 1992 graduating class, 15% of the men and 45% of the women had found employment within 6 months of graduation.

Admissions Contact: Yanna Papaconstantinou, Dean.

AMERICAN UNIVERSITY IN CAIRO
Cairo, Egypt   (212) 421–6320

Full-time: 1674 men, 1529 women	Faculty: 222
Part-time: 68 men, 86 women	Ph.D.s: 71%
Graduate: 300 men, 400 women	Student/Faculty: 14 to 1
Year: semesters, summer session	Tuition: $7900
Application Deadline: June 15	Room & Board: $2080
Freshman Class: 2408 applied, 1501 accepted, 1036 enrolled	
SAT I or ACT: see profile	

The American University in Cairo, founded in 1919, is a private liberal arts institution offering accredited American undergraduate and graduate programs in Egypt. There is one graduate school. The 2 libraries contain 225,000 volumes, 75,000 microform items, and 2000 audiovisual forms, and subscribe to 2190 periodicals. Computerized library sources and services include the card catalog, interlibrary loans, and database searching. Special learning facilities include a learning resource center, art gallery, and TV station. The 26-acre campus is in an urban area in Cairo. Including residence halls, there are 12 buildings on campus.

Student Life: Students come from 50 foreign counties and Canada. Seventy-two percent are white; 17% African American. The average age of freshmen is 18; all undergraduates, 20. Nineteen percent drop out by the end of their first year; 78% remain to graduate.

Housing: A total of 351 students can be accommodated in college housing. College-sponsored living facilities include single-sex dormitories. On-campus housing is available on a first-come, first-served basis. Alcohol is not permitted. All students may keep cars on campus.

Activities: There are no fraternities or sororities on campus. There are many groups and organizations on campus, including chess, chorus, dance, drama, ethnic, literary magazine, musical theater, newspaper, photography, radio and TV, social, student government, and yearbook. Popular campus events include International Day, National University Competition, variety show, Model UN, Family Night, Alumni and Homecoming, and Model Arab League.

Sports: There are 14 intercollegiate sports for men and 7 for women and 5 intramural sports for men and 5 for women. Athletic and recreation facilities include tennis courts, multipurpose courts, an exercise gymnasium, a weight room, and a 200-seat stadium. There are also private clubs in the area and provisions for horseback riding, rowing, swimming and diving, track and field, and water polo.

Services: There is a reader service for the blind.

Campus Safety and Security: Campus safety and security measures include 24-hour foot and vehicle patrol, shuttle buses, and lighted pathways and sidewalks.

Programs of Study: AUC awards the B.A. and B.S. degrees. Master's degrees also are awarded. Bachelor's degrees are awarded in BUSINESS (business administration and management), COMMUNICATIONS AND THE ARTS (communications, comparative literature, dramatic arts, English, and journalism), COMPUTER AND PHYSICAL SCIENCE (chemistry, computer science, mathematics, and physics), ENGINEERING AND ENVIRONMENTAL DESIGN (construction engineering, engineering, and mechanical engineering), SOCIAL SCIENCE (anthropology, economics, Middle Eastern studies, political science/government, psychology, and sociology). Economics, business administration, mechanical engineering, political science, computer science, and mass communications have the largest enrollments.

Required: All students must maintain a C average while taking 120 to 162 semester credits, depending on the major. Distribution requirements include 9 hours of English, 7 of humanities, 6 each of seminar and social science, and 3 each in philosophy and sciences. Required courses include a writing program, an interdisciplinary seminar in humanities, natural science, and social science, a scientific thinking course, and Arabic literature, history, and society.

Special: Study abroad through a consortium of U.S. schools, work-study programs with the university, and nondegree study are available.

Faculty/Classroom: Fifty-four percent of faculty are male; 46%, female. The average class size in an introductory lecture is 35; in a laboratory, 15; and in a regular course offering, 27.

Admissions: About 62% of the 1993–94 applicants were accepted. About 90% of the current freshmen were in the top fifth of their class; 95% were in the top two fifths.

Requirements: A minimum GPA of 2.0 is required. Applicants must be graduates of an accredited secondary high school. Students with a U.S. high school diploma must submit SAT I or ACT scores. The Egyptian Thanawiya Amma Certificate or a foreign secondary education certificate that requires an end-of-program certifying examination may be used in place of SAT I or ACT scores. Students should have taken courses in 3 of the following subjects: languages and humanities, mathematics, social studies, and biological and physical sciences. AP credits are accepted. Important factors used in the admissions decision are ability to finance college education, evidence of special

alent, parents or siblings attending the school, geographic diversity, and recommendations by school officials.

Procedure: Freshmen are admitted in the fall and spring. Applications should be filed by June 15 for fall entry and December 1 for spring entry, along with an application fee of $30. Notification is sent on a rolling basis.

Transfer: One transfer student enrolled in a recent year. Transfer students must have at least a C average on secondary school and college transcripts. At least 45 credits out of 120 must be completed at AUC.

Financial Aid: In a recent year, 48% of all freshmen and 27% of continuing students received some form of financial aid. The average freshman award was $3400. Of that total, work contracts averaged $340 ($850 maximum). Two percent of undergraduate students work part-time. AUC is a member of CSS. The FAF is required. The deadline for financial aid applications is September 15.

International Students: There are currently 903 international students enrolled. The school actively recruits these students.

Computers: The college provides computer facilities for student use. The mainframe is an IBM 4361. Students may access the mainframe through 338 terminals in computer laboratories throughout the campus. Only students with computer-related classes may access the system. It may be used from 8 A.M. to 9 P.M., 6 days a week. There are no fees.

Graduates: In a recent year, 385 bachelor's degrees were awarded. The most popular majors among graduates were mass communication (20%), economics (19%), and business administration (16%). Some 80 companies recruited on campus in a recent year.

Admissions Contact: Mary Davidson, Director of Admission/USA.

AMERICAN UNIVERSITY OF PARIS
B-3
Paris, France 75007   (212) 677-4870

Full-time: 626 men and women | Faculty: 40
Part-time: 73 men and women | Ph.D.s: 76%
Graduate: none | Student/Faculty: 16 to 1
Year: semesters, summer session | Tuition: $14,756
Application Deadline: May 1 | Room & Board: n/app
Freshman Class: 422 applied, 330 accepted, 129 enrolled
SAT I Verbal/Math: 480/556

The American University of Paris, founded in 1962, is a private coeducational institution providing a liberal arts program in an international context. It has regional U.S. accreditation and is recognized by the French government as an institute of higher learning. Classes are in English except for foreign language and literature courses. The library contains 130,000 volumes and 3000 microform items, and subscribes to 700 periodicals. The campus is in an urban area in Paris. There are 15 buildings on campus. There are no residence halls.

Student Life: Students come from 80 countries. Sixty percent are from public schools; 40% from private. The average age of freshmen is 19; all undergraduates, 22.

Housing: There are no residence halls. Living accommodations are arranged with the assistance of the housing office. Students may choose from a wide variety of off-campus housing arrangements, including living with French families, au pair positions, and studios. All students may keep cars on campus.

Activities: There are no fraternities or sororities on campus. There are some groups and organizations on campus, including drama, film, international, literary magazine, newspaper, political, professional, student government, and yearbook. Popular campus events include International Day.

Sports: There are 2 intercollegiate sports for men, and 5 intramural sports for men and 5 for women. Students may join the University of Paris sports club for a modest fee.

Disabled Students: Twenty percent of the campus is accessible to disabled students. Special class scheduling is available.

Services: In addition to many counseling and information services, tutoring is available in every subject. There is also remedial writing.

Programs of Study: AUP awards the B.A. and B.S. degrees. Bachelor's degrees are awarded in BUSINESS (international business administration and international economics), COMMUNICATIONS AND THE ARTS (art history and appreciation and comparative literature), COMPUTER AND PHYSICAL SCIENCE (computer science), SOCIAL SCIENCE (European studies, French studies, and international affairs). Art history, international affairs, and comparative literature are the strongest academically. International business administration, international affairs, and international economics have the largest enrollments.

Required: Students must maintain a minimum GPA of 2.0 while taking at least 120 semester credits, including an average of 50 in the major. Distribution requirements include 6 semester hours each of English composition, humanities, and social sciences, 16 of French, and 8 of laboratory science or mathematics.

Special: There are co-op programs with George Washington University, Boston University, the Ringling School of Art and Design in Florida, Bentley, Mills, Rollins, and Wells colleges, and Universite de Paris-Sorbonne. Cross-registration is available in foreign language programs at 3 other French colleges and through the Parsons School of Design in Paris. Juniors and seniors with good academic standing are encouraged to undertake internships. Work-study programs, a B.A.-B.F.A. degree in conjunction with Parsons, second degrees, non-degree study, and pass/fail options also are offered. There is a 5-year engineering degree offered with the University of Alabama at Huntsville. There are 3 national honor societies on campus. Three departments have honors programs.

Faculty/Classroom: The average class size in a regular course offering is 16.

Admissions: About 78% of the 1993–94 applicants were accepted. The SAT scores for the 1993–94 freshman class were as follows: Verbal—45% below 500, 35% between 500 and 599, and 20% between 600 and 700; Math—23% below 500, 35% between 500 and 599, 30% between 600 and 700, and 10% above 700.

Requirements: The SAT I or ACT is required. In addition, candidates must be graduates of an accredited secondary school. The GED is not accepted. An essay and 2 letters of recommendation are also needed. Knowledge of French is not required. Applicants in the New York area are encouraged to interview at that office. AP and CLEP credits are accepted. Important factors used in the admissions decision are advanced placement or honor courses, personality, intangible qualities, recommendations by school officials, evidence of special talent, and geographic diversity.

Procedure: Freshmen are admitted in the fall and spring. Entrance exams should be taken by April 1. Applications should be filed by May 1 for fall entry and December 1 for spring entry, along with an application fee of $40. Notification is sent on a rolling basis. There is a deferred admissions plan.

Transfer: Transfer applicants must submit college and high school transcripts, and SAT I or ACT scores if they have fewer than 45 credits. An interview, 2 letters of recommendation, and an essay are required. At least 30 credits out of 120 must be completed at AUP.

Visiting: There are regularly scheduled orientations for prospective students. There are guides for informal visits, and visitors may sit in on classes. To arrange for a visit, contact the Admissions Office at (212) 677-4870 (New York office).

Financial Aid: Scholarships or need-based grants averaged $6700 ($12,000 maximum); and work contracts averaged $1600. AUP is a member of CSS. The FAF is required. The deadline for financial aid applications is May 1.

International Students: There are currently 403 international students enrolled. The school actively recruits these students. Non-native English speakers must take the TOEFL or the University of Michigan Language Test and achieve a minimum score on the TOEFL of 500. They must also take the SAT I.

Computers: The college provides computer facilities for student use. PCs and PC-based graphic workstations are available in the computer center. Students enrolled in computer-related courses may access the system. Other students may use the laboratory only to print out material from their own disks; an Apple Laserwriter and Imagewriter II are available. There are no time limits on using the system. The fees are $35.

Graduates: In 1992–93, 148 bachelor's degrees were awarded. Some 25 companies recruited on campus in a recent year.

Admissions Contact: Thelma Bullock, Director, U.S. Office.

FRANKLIN COLLEGE SWITZERLAND
B-3
Lugano Switzerland 011–41–55–01.01   (212) 772-2090

Full-time: 90 men, 130 women | Faculty: 17
Part-time: 3 men, 3 women | Ph.D.s: 65%
Graduate: none | Student/Faculty: 13 to 1
Year: semesters, summer session | Tuition: $18,602
Application Deadline: May 1 | Room: $5000
Freshman Class: 140 applied, 120 accepted, 72 enrolled
SAT I Verbal/Math: 510/540

Franklin College Switzerland, founded in 1969, is a private coeducational institution providing a liberal education through courses that are international in perspective and cross cultural in content. The baccalaureate degree offers concentrations in international management, art history, modern languages, French and Italian area studies, international relations, and modern European civilization. The library contains 24,000 volumes. Computerized library sources and services include the card catalog, interlibrary loans, and database searching. The 4.5 acre campus is in a suburban area in the southern section of Switzerland called the Ticino (Southern Alps). Including residence halls, there are 8 buildings on campus.

Student Life: Students come from 25 U.S. states and 39 foreign countries. Fifty percent are from public schools; 50% from private. Forty percent are Protestant; 30% Catholic. The average age of fresh-

men is 19; all undergraduates, 22. Fifteen percent drop out by the end of their first year; 70% remain to graduate.

Housing: A total of 200 students can be accommodated in college housing. College-sponsored living facilities include single-sex on-campus apartments and off-campus apartments. On-campus housing is guaranteed for all 4 years. Ninety percent of students live on campus; of those, 75% remain on campus on weekends. All students may keep cars on campus.

Activities: There are no fraternities or sororities on campus. There are some groups and organizations on campus, including art, computers, ethnic, international, newspaper, social, student government, and yearbook. Popular campus events include Charter Day (Homecoming), Christmas Prom, Spring Prom, and academic travel.

Sports: A sports program includes play with local Swiss teams. Athletic and recreational activities include soccer, basketball, volleyball, tennis, skiing, and hiking.

Campus Safety and Security: Campus safety and security measures include lighted pathways and sidewalks. The city is known for its safety; there is no problem with crime on campus.

Programs of Study: Franklin College Switzerland awards the B.A. degree. Associate degrees also are awarded. Bachelor's degrees are awarded in BUSINESS (international business management and international economics), COMMUNICATIONS AND THE ARTS (art history and appreciation, literature, and modern language), SOCIAL SCIENCE (international relations). International management and international relations have the largest enrollments.

Required: All students must complete 120 credit hours. A general core requirement of 42 credit hours includes 12 each in foreign languages and mathematics and sciences, 9 in humanities, 6 in history, and 3 in English. Academic travel is required each year. A minimum overall GPA of 2.0 and at least 24 credits in the major with a C or better are also required. Each major requires a thesis.

Special: Cross-registration with most U.S. colleges having an international management major, internships, study abroad as part of the academic travel requirement, accelerated degree programs in any major, and dual majors are offered.

Faculty/Classroom: Sixty-five percent of faculty are male; 35%, female. All teach undergraduates and 10% do research as well. The average class size in an introductory lecture is 15; in a laboratory, 10; and in a regular course offering, 12.

Admissions: About 86% of the 1993–94 applicants were accepted. The SAT scores for the 1993–94 freshman class were as follows: Verbal—10% below 500, 80% between 500 and 599, and 10% between 600 and 700; Math—27% below 500, 55% between 500 and 599, 12% between 600 and 700, and 6% above 700. About 15% of the current freshmen were in the top fifth of their class; 40% were in the top two fifths. There was 1 National Merit semifinalist.

Requirements: Franklin College Switzerland requires applicants to be in the upper 60% of their class. A minimum GPA of 2.0 is required. The SAT I or ACT is required. In addition, the college requires applicants to have completed 4 years of English, 3 each of history and a foreign language, and 2 each of science and mathematics. Electives in art, music, and computers are recommended. An essay, a personal statement, and 3 personal and academic references are required. An interview is strongly encouraged. AP credits are accepted. Important factors used in the admissions decision are recommendations by school officials, personality, intangible qualities, extracurricular activities record, evidence of special talent, and ability to finance college education.

Procedure: Freshmen are admitted to all sessions. Entrance exams should be taken in the fall prior to the desired entrance. There are early decision, early admissions, and deferred admissions plans. Early decision applications should be filed by December 15; regular applications, by May 1 for fall entry, November 15 for spring entry, and May 1 for summer entry, along with an application fee of $40. Notification of early decision is sent January 1; regular decision, on a rolling basis. Two early decision candidates were accepted for the 1993–94 class.

Transfer: About 20 transfer students enrolled in 1993–94. Transfer applicants must have a C average and provide one recommendation. A total of 45 credits out of 120 must be completed at Franklin College Switzerland.

Visiting: There are guides for informal visits and visitors may sit in on classes. To arrange for a visit, contact the New York Admissions Office at (212) 772-2090.

Financial Aid: In 1993–94, 20% of all students received some form of financial aid. About 20% of students received need-based aid. The average freshman award was $9000. Of that total, scholarships or need-based grants averaged $9000 ($14,000 maximum); and work contracts averaged $1000 ($1300 maximum). Thirty percent of undergraduate students work part-time. Average earnings from campus work for the school year are $1000. Franklin College Switzerland is a member of CSS. The FAF and the college's own financial statement are required. The deadline for financial aid applications is May 1.

International Students: There are currently 120 international students enrolled. The school actively recruits these students. They must take the TOEFL and achieve a minimum score of 550. The student must also take the SAT I or the ACT and SAT II: Subject tests.

Computers: The college provides computer facilities for student use. The mainframe is an IBM 486. Ten terminals are available for academic use. All students may access the system. There are no time limits and no fees.

Graduates: In 1992–93, 38 bachelor's degrees were awarded. The most popular majors among graduates were international management (60%), international relations (15%), and modern language (10%). Within an average freshman class, 20% graduate in 3 years and 80% in 4 years. In the 1992 graduating class, 25% of all graduates were enrolled in graduate school within 6 months of graduation; 70% had found employment.

Admissions Contact: Susan D. Hendricks, U.S. Director of Admissions.

RICHMOND COLLEGE, THE AMERICAN INTERNATIONAL UNIVERSITY IN LONDON

B-?

Richmond, Surrey, U.K. TW10 6JP   (203) 869–9090, ext. 609
(800) 727-AIFS

Full-time: 500 men, 600 women	**Faculty:** 38
Part-time: none	**Ph.D.s:** 50%
Graduate: 60 men and women	**Student/Faculty:** 29 to 1
Year: semesters, summer session	**Tuition:** $10,500
Application Deadline: open	**Room & Board:** $5000
Freshman Class: 425 applied, 400 accepted, 262 enrolled	
SAT I or ACT: required for U.S. students	

Richmond College was founded in 1843 as part of London University and reincorporated in 1972 as a private international university affiliated with the American Institute for Foreign Study. The university's degree programs in the liberal and fine arts and business are designed for students interested in international, multicultural careers. There is one graduate school. The library contains 60,000 volumes, and subscribes to 300 periodicals. The 5-acre campus is in a suburban area 5 miles southwest of London.

Student Life: Students come from 80 countries. The average age of freshmen is 19; all undergraduates, 22.

Housing: College-sponsored living facilities include dormitories and off-campus apartments. On-campus housing is guaranteed for all 4 years. Sixty-five percent of students live on campus; of those, 60% remain on campus on weekends. Alcohol is not permitted.

Activities: There are no fraternities or sororities on campus. There are 8 groups on campus, including dance, drama, film, international literary magazine, newspaper, student government, and yearbook. Popular campus events include International Night and Gala Night.

Sports: There are 4 intercollegiate sports for men and 2 for women and 12 intramural sports for men and 9 for women. Athletic and recreation facilities include a weight room and an all-weather sports court.

Services: There is remedial math and writing. The English Language Development Program for international students offers intensive language development courses for credit and noncredit.

Programs of Study: The university awards the B.A. degree. Associate and master's degrees also are awarded. Bachelor's degrees are awarded in BUSINESS (business administration and management and international business management), COMMUNICATIONS AND THE ARTS (art history and appreciation, English literature, fine arts, performing arts, and studio art), COMPUTER AND PHYSICAL SCIENCE (computer science and mathematics), ENGINEERING AND ENVIRONMENTAL DESIGN (engineering), SOCIAL SCIENCE (anthropology, British Studies, economics, history, political science/government, psychology, and social science). Business and economics have the largest enrollments.

Required: Students must complete 12 courses in 7 fields: English, humanities, social science, intercultural studies, mathematics, science, and the creative arts. Proficiency in English composition, mathematics, and computer skills is required. A 2.0 minimum GPA and 120 credit hours are needed to graduate.

Special: The International Internship Program utilizes London-based businesses and institutions. Study abroad at the university's Florence Study Center and at Leningrad State Technical University is offered. A field study project in a developing country may be arranged during the summer. A limited number of students can be placed in family helper/au pair positions with British families. Joint degrees are offered in engineering and in mathematical sciences from Richmond and George Washington University.

Faculty/Classroom: The average class size in an introductory lecture is 18 and in a regular course offering, 18.

Admissions: About 94% of the 1993–94 applicants were accepted.

Requirements: The SAT I or ACT is required for American students. U.S. applicants should have completed secondary school with a 2.5 minimum GPA. A GED is acceptable. An autobiographical essay is an important part of the application. AP and CLEP credits are accepted. Important factors used in the admissions decision are advanced placement or honor courses, recommendations by school officials, and geographic diversity.

Procedure: Freshmen are admitted in the fall and winter. Application deadlines are open. Application fee is $35. Notification is sent on a rolling basis. There is a deferred admissions plan.

Transfer: About 70 transfer students enrolled in an earlier year. A 2.0 minimum GPA, official transcripts from all previous institutions, and 2 references are required for admission. At least 45 credits out of 120 must be completed at the university.

Visiting: There are regularly scheduled orientations for prospective students. There are guides for informal visits, and visitors may sit in on classes. To arrange for a visit, contact an Admissions Counselor at (203) 869–9090 or (800) 727-AIFS.

Financial Aid: The college's own financial statement is required.

International Students: The school actively recruits these students.

Computers: The college provides computer facilities for student use. The mainframe is a DEC VAX 11/750. There are also 40 Tandon, PCX 10 and 20, and Rainbow PCs available. All students may access the system daily from 8:30 A.M. to 10 P.M. There are no fees.

Graduates: In an earlier year, 150 bachelor's degrees were awarded.

Admissions Contact: Sharman Hedayati, Director of Admissions.

THE AMERICAN UNIVERSITY OF ROME   B-3
Rome, Italy 00153   00 39 6 58330919

Full-time: 106 men, 176 women	**Faculty:** 7
Part-time: 12 men, 21 women	**Ph.D.s:** 67%
Graduate: none	**Student/Faculty:** 40 to 1
Year: semesters, summer session	**Tuition:** $7528
Application Deadline: May 1	**Room & Board:** $6100
Freshman Class: n/av	
SAT I or ACT: recommended	

The American University of Rome, founded in 1969, is a private institution offering programs in liberal arts, international business, and international relations. The library contains 5000 volumes and 30 audiovisual forms, and subscribes to 15 periodicals. Computerized library sources and services include database searching. The campus is in an urban area. Including residence halls, there is 1 building on campus.

Student Life: About 90% of undergraduates are from outside Italy, mostly the Middle Atlantic States. Students come from 15 states and 23 foreign countries. Twenty percent are from public schools; 80% from private. Eighty-three percent are white. The average age of freshmen is 18; all undergraduates, 20. About 26% of freshmen remain to graduate.

Housing: A total of 140 students can be accommodated in college housing. College-sponsored living facilities include off-campus apartments. Alcohol is not permitted.

Activities: There are no fraternities or sororities on campus. There are some groups on campus, including art, dance, film, honors, international, literary magazine, newspaper, student government, and yearbook. Popular campus events include Charter Day (Homecoming), the Distinguished Lecture Series, liberal arts excursions, business excursions, and international relations debates.

Sports: There is 1 intercollegiate sport for men, and 3 intramural sports each for men and women. Athletic and recreation facilities include off-campus access to soccer, tennis, and swimming facilities.

Disabled Students: Thirty percent of the campus is accessible to disabled students.

Services: Remedial writing is available.

Campus Safety and Security: Campus safety and security measures include informal discussions.

Programs of Study: The American University of Rome awards the B.A. and B.B.A. degrees. Associate degrees also are awarded. Bachelor's degrees are awarded in BUSINESS (business administration and management) and SOCIAL SCIENCE (international relations, international studies, and Italian Studies). Business administration and international relations have the largest enrollments.

Required: To graduate, students must complete 120 credits, 45 to 66 in the major, with a minimum GPA of 2.0. Distribution requirements include English composition and courses in humanities, social sciences, and science/mathematics.

Special: Internships in business, international relations, and Italian studies are available. Study abroad is possible by special arrangement and work-study is available with AUR. There is one national honor society on campus.

Faculty/Classroom: Fifty-four percent of faculty are male; 46%, female. All teach undergraduates. The average class size in an introductory lecture is 17 and in a regular course offering, 12.

Requirements: The SAT I or ACT is recommended. A high school diploma and transcript or the nonAmerican equivalent is required. A letter of recommendation, an interview (if possible), and an essay are recommended. AP and CLEP credits are accepted. Important factors used in the admissions decision are recommendations by school officials, advanced placement or honor courses, personality, intangible qualities, parents or siblings attending the school, and recommendations by alumni.

Procedure: Freshmen are admitted to all sessions. Applications should be filed by May 1 for fall entry and December 1 for spring entry, along with an application fee of $40. There is a deferred admissions plan.

Transfer: Nearly 200 transfer students enrolled in 1993–94. A total of 45 credits out of 120 must be completed at AUR.

Visiting: There are regularly scheduled orientations for prospective students organized by AUR directly and through its agents in many U.S. states and in other countries. Orientation is assisted by use of audio visual materials. There are guides for informal visits and visitors may sit in on classes. To arrange for a visit, contact Dean Mary Handley at 00 39 6 58330919.

Financial Aid: Four percent of undergraduate students work part-time. Average earnings from campus work for the school year are $3764.

International Students: There are currently 79 international students enrolled. The school actively recruits these students. They must take the TOEFL, the University of Michigan Language Test, or the college's own test and achieve a minimum score on the TOEFL of 550.

Computers: The college provides computer facilities for student use. PCs are available. All students may access the system. There are no time limits and no fees.

Graduates: In 1992–93, 19 bachelor's degrees were awarded. The most popular majors among graduates were business administration (70%), international relations (20%), and Italian studies (5%). Within an average freshman class, 90% graduate in 4 years and 10% in 5 years. In the 1992 graduating class, 33% of the men were enrolled in graduate school within 6 months of graduation; 33% of the men and 60% of the women had found employment.

Admissions Contact: Dean Mary B. Handley, Dean of Administration.

STUDY IN THE UNITED STATES

More and more American colleges and universities are welcoming students from foreign countries. Did you know that there are nearly 500,000 international students enrolled in U.S. institutions of higher learning, and that number continues to increase?

Why Colleges and Universities Seek International Students

There are a number of reasons why American colleges and universities seek international students. First, they recognize that international students help educate the American students on campus by introducing them to different ideas and cultures. Second, the number of college-age American students is declining, and international students can fill places that otherwise would go unfilled. Third, the money that international students spend on tuition and other expenses helps the U.S. economy; education is becoming a valuable export for the United States. And fourth, education has long been an important part of America's foreign aid program, providing foreign nationals with skills that they can use to improve life in their homelands.

Why International Students Seek to Study in the United States

There are also a number of reasons why international students seek to study in the United States. For some students, colleges and universities in the United States offer opportunities to study major fields that are not available in their own countries. For other students, American colleges and universities offer an alternative to colleges and universities in their own countries where places may not be available for all of the qualified students who wish to attend. For still other students, study in the United States provides them not only with an education but also with experiences in living in another culture and in exchanging ideas with students from many nations.

Whatever your reason may be for studying in the United States, this chapter will help you make decisions and plans.

Investigating a College or University

Although most of the colleges and universities in the United States are very honest about their programs and services, a few have been known to misrepresent themselves. When choosing a college or university, as when making any other major purchase, you should investigate carefully. In addition to checking whether your exact major field is offered, you should compare the special services for international students offered by the schools that you are considering. You will want to know whether a representative of the school will pick you up at the airport when you arrive, whether dormitories or other housing is available, and whether there is a foreign student adviser to help you with decisions that you will have to make and problems that you may have to solve after you arrive.

The Difference Between a College and a University

Most international students want to know the difference between a college and a university. This is a difficult question because there is more than one correct answer. In fact, there are three definitions for the word *college* (as it refers to a college in the United States) listed in the *American Heritage Dictionary of the English Language*.

According to the dictionary, a *college* is (1) a school of higher learning that grants a bachelor's degree (undergraduate degree) in arts or sciences or both; (2) an undergraduate division of a university that offers courses and grants undergraduate degrees in a particular field of study; or (3) a technical or professional school, often affiliated with a university, that grants a bachelor's or master's degree in that field.

A *university* is a school of higher learning that grants a bachelor's degree (undergraduate degree), master's degree, and doctorate (Ph.D.) through various colleges within the university.

The Comparison of a College and a University

Many international students ask whether a university is better than a college. The answer is that a university has advantages and disadvantages for an international student, and a college has advantages and disadvantages.

The advantages of a university are that there are usually more research and recreational facilities, and more different kinds of courses offered. The disadvantages of a university are that courses taught to first-year students are often taught by teaching assistants who are graduate students themselves, and that the classes can be very large. The advantages of a college are that the courses are almost always taught by professors, and that the classes are usually small. The disadvantages of a college are that there are usually fewer research and recreational facilities.

Remember, as you decide what is best for you, that there are excellent colleges and there are excellent universities.

Accreditation

Unlike most countries, the United States does not have a national ministry of education that approves the programs at colleges and universities throughout the country. Instead, programs are approved by professional organizations and regional associations. This approval is called accreditation.

All of the schools listed in this book are accredited or are in the process of being accredited.

Requirements for Admission

Academic Preparation

To study in the United States, an international student should begin preparing in secondary school. A good secondary school report is one of the most important requirements for admission to a college or university. When applying to a college or university, you must submit an English translation of your grades with a seal and signature on it. This grade report is called a transcript. In addition, most colleges and universities require undergraduate students to submit standardized test scores. Some of the most common tests are the Cambridge O Level Examination, the Cambridge A Level Examination, the SAT I, and the ACT (American College Test). Each test is described below.

Cambridge O Level	A series of examinations to test your ability in subjects that you have studied in secondary school.
Cambridge A Level	A series of examinations to test your ability in subjects that you have studied in secondary school and junior college. The A Level is graded at a higher level than the O Level.
SAT I	A test of your English language proficiency in grammar and vocabulary and your skills in mathematics from secondary school.
ACT	A test of your general educational development in English, mathematics, social studies, and natural sciences.

Some highly selective schools also ask applicants to take as many as three SAT II: Subject tests, which are offered in specific subject areas such as French, physics, European history, and mathematics on two levels. SAT I and SAT II: Subject tests, which are given only in English, are part of the Scholastic Assessment Testing Program. Both are administered by the Educational Testing Service for the sponsoring organization, the College Board. You can take SAT I and SAT II: Subject tests at established test centers or you may be able to arrange for a special testing location. The completed registration form for testing at test centers must be received by the Educational Testing Service about six weeks prior to the test date; requests for special locations must be received eight to ten weeks prior to the test date. (Note that you cannot take

both SAT I and one or more of SAT II: Subject tests on the same date.) For more information write to The Office of International Education, Suite 402, 1717 Massachusetts Avenue, N.W., Washington, D.C. 20036.

The ACT, which is given in English only, is administered by the American College Testing Program. You can take the ACT at an established test center or may be able to arrange for a special testing location. You may register at a particular test center up to a week before the test is given there; requests for special locations should be directed to the American College Testing Program as soon as possible before a particular test date. For more information, write to the American College Testing Program, P.O. Box 168, Iowa City, Iowa 52243, USA, and ask for the Overseas Registration Packet.

The following books are available from Barron's Educational Series, Inc., 250 Wireless Boulevard, Hauppauge, NY 11788, USA, to help you prepare for SAT I and SAT II: Subject tests. *How to Prepare for SAT I, Pass Key to SAT I, SAT II: Subject tests* (in many subject areas), *Mathematics Workbook for SAT I, Verbal Workbook for SAT I, Hot Words for SAT I, 14 Days to Higher SAT I Scores, After the SAT, How to Prepare for the ACT, Pass Key to the ACT,* and *How to Prepare for the Advanced Placement Examination* series. *Barron's Computer Study Program for SAT I* and *Barron's Computer Study Program for the ACT,* complete software packages for IBM, IBM-compatibles, and Macintosh, are also available from this source.

English Language Proficiency

In addition, if your native language is not English, you will probably have to take a test of your ability to use English. The most widely used of these tests is the TOEFL (Test of English as a Foreign Language), given at 1250 test centers throughout the world. Other English exams include the MTELP (Michigan Test of English Language Proficiency), the Test of Written English (TWE), and the Test of Spoken English (TSE).

Each test is described as follows:

TOEFL   A test of listening comprehension, structure and written expression, reading comprehension, and vocabulary.

MTELP   A test battery that may include a listening test and a composition and always includes grammar, vocabulary, and reading.

TWE   An essay test, given with the TOEFL at the August, September, October, February, and May administrations.

TSE   A test of listening and speaking, often required for graduate students seeking an assistantship.

You can take TOEFL and TWE as well as the TSE at an established center, or you may be able to set up a special testing location if there is no test center in your country. Completed registration forms for testing at test centers must be received about four weeks prior to the test date. These forms must be sent to either the appropriate international TOEFL agent or the TOEFL organization in the United States, depending on where you will take the test. Requests for special testing locations, together with the application form and either the test fee or proof of fee payment, must be received by an official TOEFL organization. For more information, write to TOEFL, Box 6151, Princeton, NJ 08541-6151, USA.

When the Michigan test is required, the administrators must receive a letter from either the applicant or the college that has accepted the applicant, requesting an administration. The letter should include the name, address, and birth date of the applicant along with a $30 application fee to English Language Institute, Testing and Certification, The University of Michigan, Ann Arbor, MI 48109-1057, USA. Arrangements will then be made for taking the test at one of the official sites, at which time an additional $20 fee must be paid.

The following books with accompanying records and cassettes are available from Barron's Educational Series, Inc., 250 Wireless Boulevard, Hauppauge, NY 11788, USA, to help you prepare for the TOEFL and the MTELP: *Barron's How to Prepare for the TOEFL (Test of English as a Foreign Language), Barron's Practice Exercises for the TOEFL, Barron's* *Hints for the TOEFL, TOEFL Strategies, Classroom TOEFL,* and *Barron's How to Prepare for the Michigan Test Battery.*

Financial Guarantees

All schools require that international students show proof of their ability to pay tuition, fees, and living expenses. Most schools require a statement from a bank that shows adequate finances for one year's study. If the name on the account is not the same as the name of the student, a signed letter from the person who has the account must accompany the bank statement. In the letter this person promises to support the international student while the student is in the United States. This person is called the student's sponsor.

Application Procedures

Select a few schools and write for information

When you are ready to apply—usually about a year before the date on which you hope to enter college—write to the schools that interest you for application materials. You can send completed copies of the *Request for Application Materials from U.S. Colleges and Universities,* usually available at counseling centers, or letters that include the name of your country, the field you wish to study, a brief outline of your previous education, the number of years you have studied English, the amount of money you can spend, and the proposed date of enrollment. The college admissions officers will review this information and should let you know if the college cannot meet your needs. You should also ask the schools for information about special programs and organizations for international students.

Remember, this book provides general information about the requirements for admission to colleges and universities, but each school has the authority to set its own standards for admission. For the specific requirements for admission, you must write directly to the schools that most interest you. Some schools will be glad to send you a catalog free of charge; other schools will charge you a fee for the catalog.

Libraries of college catalogs also can be found at the offices of the Institute of International Education, a private, nonprofit, international educational exchange agency (located in New York, Bangkok, Hong Kong, Jakarta, Budapest, Sri Lanka, Addis Ababa, and Mexico City), and the U.S. Information Service counseling centers, generally located at U.S. embassies, and at the offices of binational and Fulbright commissions.

Apply to more than one school

Remember, most American students apply to more than one college or university, and you should, too, especially if you are interested in competitive schools with very high admissions standards. By using this book and by reviewing catalogs from the schools that interest you, you can select several colleges and universities to which you can apply. Because the application fees are almost always nonrefundable, you should truly be serious about the schools where you make application.

Be sure that you have selected some schools where you are likely to be accepted. If you were an average student in high school and your standardized test scores are average, you have little chance of being accepted by a highly competitive school. Evaluate yourself realistically.

Remember, too, that the rating of colleges and universities in this book is based upon information about American students only. Although it is usually accurate for international students as well, some large state universities that are listed as noncompetitive have open admission for state residents. This means that anyone with a high school diploma who is a resident of that state may attend the state school. These schools, listed as noncompetitive, may actually be very competitive for students from other states and for international students. Nevertheless, the rating scale will be useful to you, especially for schools that are not large state universities.

Be sure that you submit all of the documents that the schools require along with application fees. The most common reason for delays in admission to American colleges and universities is because international students do not send everything that is required along with their application forms.

When you are ready to apply to the schools of your choice, consider the following points:

1. Be sure that the schools offer your major field of study.
2. Be sure that the schools are accredited.
3. Be sure that you apply to more than one school.
4. Be sure that you apply to schools where you meet the requirements for admission.
5. Be sure that you submit all of the documents and fees with your application to avoid delays.

Make a decision

Some international students choose a school in the United States because their friends are going there. It is nice to have friends on campus, but the right school for your friend may not be the right school for you. There is no list of the best schools in the United States. A school may be the best in one major field and only average in another major field. It may have famous professors who only do research and do not teach. It may be well known but not academically excellent.

Consider the following points in making a decision where you will go to school.

1. Be sure that the school offers your major field of study or a premajor for your major field of study.
2. Be sure that the school is accredited.
3. Be sure that the school offers an English program if you need one.
4. Be sure that you understand how much credit you will receive if you are transferring from another school.
5. Be sure that the school has a foreign student adviser or someone assigned to help international students.
6. Be sure that the expenses for the school are within your budget.

Going to the United States

You should start investigating requirements for visas from the United States and from your home country (if applicable) as soon as you decide to study overseas. You cannot apply for an American visa, however, until you have been accepted by a school in the United States. You must apply for the visa at a U.S. embassy or consulate. You will need the following items.

1. A passport (except for Canadians) from your own country.
2. A Form I-20A (Certificate of Eligibility for Non-Immigrant Student Status) from the school that has accepted you.
3. Evidence that you are in good health, including a recent chest X-ray and, in some countries, proof that you have been vaccinated against small pox within the past three years.
4. A notarized bank statement or other proof that you have enough money available and/or financial aid promised to cover your expenses for the entire term of your program. (If you have been accepted to a bachelor's degree program, for instance, the term is four years.)

Most students are admitted to the United States under an F-1 (foreign student) visa. Those who come under certain grant or scholarship programs may qualify for a J-1 (exchange visitor) visa. After you have qualified for your visa, any spouse and children of yours may be admitted under F-2 or J-2 visas. You must provide evidence that there is enough money to support them while you are studying.

You may want to consider participating in predeparture orientation programs offered by education services abroad and by the U.S. Information Service. Information about these programs is available from the agency or from any U.S. embassy or consulate.

Many schools send representatives to meet students at local airports and bus and train stations, if they have correct arrival information. If your school offers this service, take advantage of it. Send your travel plans to the foreign student adviser on your campus.

Arriving on Campus

As soon as you arrive on campus, you should visit the foreign-student adviser, an official who is responsible for the welfare of students from other countries. If your college has no such official, you should see the dean of students. Bring your passport and immigration documents.

Your university also will assign a faculty member to advise you on your academic program. Other services available through the school may include psychological counseling and health-care services. Although some schools provide limited health care to students at no charge, you should keep in mind that, in the United States, medical care is the responsibility of the individual, not the government. You would be wise to obtain health insurance. Many colleges offer such plans (some *require* foreign students to have health insurance), and your foreign-student adviser can provide information on them.

Most colleges and universities offer campus orientation programs for all new students; some also hold special orientations for foreign students. The latter are generally held during the summer and may continue on after the academic year has begun. On- and off-campus tours and placement exams may be included.

English Language and Cultural Orientation Programs

Many American colleges and universities provide English language instruction, often in conjunction with courses and activities that orient foreign students to the various phases of life in the United States. Full-time English language programs generally involve at least 15 hours of intensive instruction per week and usually include orientation activities. Single courses involve fewer hours and are generally taken to help students engaged in academic courses.

You should know that your ability to speak and write English will affect your admission to most American colleges and universities. If your ability falls below that required for admission, you may be accepted conditionally, with the understanding that you will participate in an intensive English course or program. Some schools require that all foreign students enroll in such a course or program.

For more information, you should refer to the booklet *English Language and Orientation Programs in the United States* ($42.95 U.S.), published by the Institue of International Education, 809 United Nations Plaza, New York, NY 10017 and available in their overseas offices and many U.S. embassy libraries. This publication gives detailed information on the intensive English-language courses and/or programs at many of the institutions in the accompanying chart.

Expenses

Most colleges will expect you to pay all fixed costs—tuition, room and board if you live and eat in college facilities and student fees—in U.S. dollars at the beginning of each academic term. Some colleges provide installment plans, under which these costs may be paid monthly over the course of the term.

Keep in mind when determining your probable expenses that personal expenses, including travel, entertainment, and textbooks, may be considerable and generally are not listed as part of a college's tuition schedule. While some colleges will provide an estimate of a typical student's personal expenses, you should generally expect to spend considerably more.

International students generally are not permitted to hold jobs in the United States. Work permits are issued only when there is unexpected economic need. Part-time jobs on campus, however, are permitted and do not require government approval.

Financial aid may be available from your government, the U.S. government, cultural exchange programs, corporations, the college you attend, or religious, fraternal, or special-interest groups. For information, contact a U.S. embassy or consulate and your government's ministry or department of education. If you are already in the United States, see your foreign student adviser.

Pamela J. Sharpe, Ph.D.
Northern Arizona University in Yuma

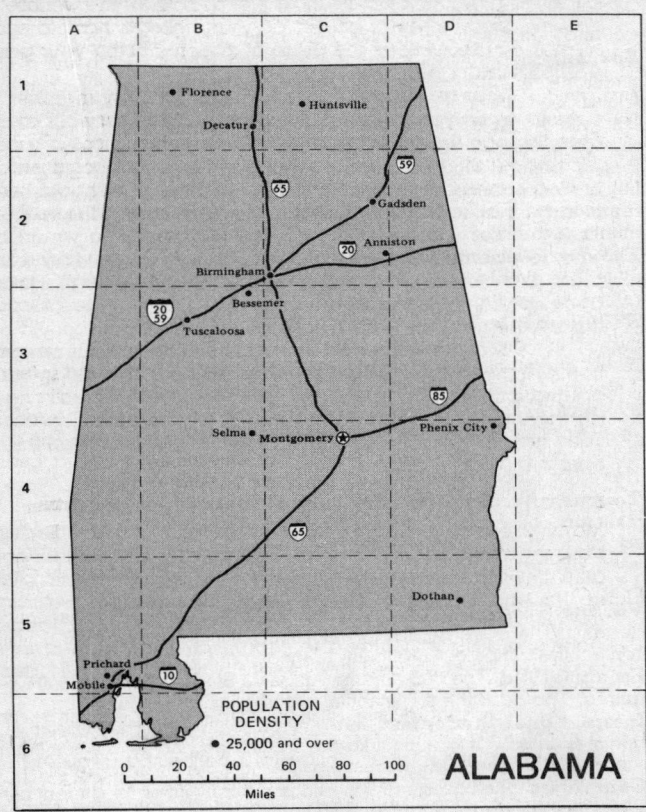

POPULATION
DENSITY

● 25,000 and over

0 20 40 60 80 100
Miles

ALABAMA

ALABAMA AGRICULTURAL AND MECHANICAL UNIVERSITY

C-1

Normal, AL 35762   (205) 851-5245; (800) 553-0816 (in-state)

Full-time: 1899 men, 2074 women	Faculty: 295; IIA, --$
Part-time: 128 men, 162 women	Ph.D.s: 59%
Graduate: 547 men, 783 women	Student/Faculty: 13 to 1
Year: semesters, summer session	Tuition: $1650 ($3200)
Application Deadline: open	Room & Board: $2550
Freshman Class: 2830 applied, 1929 accepted, 985 enrolled	
ACT: 17	**COMPETITIVE**

Alabama Agricultural and Mechanical University, founded in 1875, is a public, land-grant institution offering undergraduate and graduate studies in agriculture, home economics, arts and sciences, business, education, and engineering and technology. There are 6 undergraduate schools and one graduate school. In addition to regional accreditation, A&M has baccalaureate program accreditation with ABET, CAHEA, CSWE, and NCATE. The library contains 339,272 volumes, 488,759 microform items, and 3606 audiovisual forms, and subscribes to 1606 periodicals. Computerized library sources and services include the card catalog, interlibrary loans, and database searching. Special learning facilities include a learning resource center, art gallery, radio station, and the State Black Archives. The 2001-acre campus is in a suburban area 90 miles north of Birmingham. Including residence halls, there are 51 buildings on campus.

Student Life: About 64% of undergraduates are from Alabama. Students come from 37 states and 41 foreign countries. Ninety-two percent are from public schools; 8% from private. Seventy-eight percent are African American; 12% white. The average age of freshmen is 18; all undergraduates, 19. Thirty percent drop out by the end of their first year; 60% remain to graduate.

Housing: A total of 2430 students can be accommodated in college housing. College-sponsored living facilities include single-sex dormitories and on-campus apartments. On-campus housing is guaranteed for the freshman year only. Sixty-two percent of students commute. Alcohol is not permitted. Upperclassmen may keep cars on campus.

Activities: About 23% of men belong to 4 national fraternities; about 25% of women belong to 3 national sororities. There are 40 groups on campus, including art, band, cheerleading, choir, computers, dance, drama, drill team, ethnic, honors, international, jazz band, marching band, newspaper, orchestra, pep band, professional, radio and TV, religious, social, student government, and yearbook. Popular

campus events include Homecoming, Magic City Classic, Women's Week, Men's Week, and Greek Organization Initiation Week.

Sports: Athletic and recreation facilities include a 7000-seat gymnasium, an Olympic-size pool, and track and playing fields.

Disabled Students: Thirty-one percent of the campus is accessible to disabled students. The following facilities are available: wheelchair ramps, elevators, special parking, and specially equipped rest rooms.

Services: In addition to many counseling and information services, tutoring is available in most subjects. In addition, there is remedial math, reading, and writing.

Campus Safety and Security: Campus safety and security measures include 24-hour foot and vehicle patrol, pamphlets, posters, and films, and lighted pathways and sidewalks.

Programs of Study: A&M awards the B.A. and B.S. degrees. Master's and doctoral degrees also are awarded. Bachelor's degrees are awarded in AGRICULTURE (agricultural business management, animal science, forestry and related sciences, horticulture, and soil science), BIOLOGICAL SCIENCE (biology/biological science and zoology), BUSINESS (accounting, business administration and management, business economics, and marketing/retailing/merchandising), COMMUNICATIONS AND THE ARTS (English, French, and telecommunications), COMPUTER AND PHYSICAL SCIENCE (chemistry, computer science, mathematics, and physics), EDUCATION (agricultural, art, early childhood, elementary, home economics, industrial arts, middle school, music, physical, science, secondary, special, and trade and industrial), ENGINEERING AND ENVIRONMENTAL DESIGN (city/community/regional planning, civil engineering, civil engineering technology, electrical/electronics engineering technology, environmental science, interior design, mechanical design technology, and mechanical engineering technology), HEALTH PROFESSIONS (medical laboratory technology, preveterinary science, and speech pathology/audiology), SOCIAL SCIENCE (economics, food science, history, liberal arts/general studies, ministries, pastoral studies, political science/government, psychology, social science, social work, and sociology). Physics, food science, and teacher education are the strongest academically. Business administration has the largest enrollment.

Required: All students are required to take at least 52 hours of general studies, including physical education, and to maintain a minimum GPA of 2.0. Students must complete a total of 128 to 140 credit hours, with 30 to 36 in the major. A comprehensive exam is required for some majors.

Special: Co-op programs with Georgia Institute of Technology and Tuskegee University, cross-registration with the University of Alabama in Huntsville, Oakwood College, Calhoun Community College, and Athens State College, internships with various government agencies, and work-study programs are available. In addition, B.A.-B.S degrees and dual majors are offered. The university also offers a 3-2 engineering degree with the Georgia Institute of Technology. There is a freshman honors program on campus, as well as 5 national honor societies. Five departments have honors programs.

Faculty/Classroom: Sixty-four percent of faculty are male; 36%, female. Ninety-nine percent teach undergraduates. No introductory courses are taught by graduate students. The average class size in an introductory lecture is 30.

Admissions: About 68% of the 1993-94 applicants were accepted.

Requirements: A minimum GPA of 2.0 is required. The SAT I or ACT is required. Applicants must have 4 years each of English, mathematics, science, social studies and history. An interview is recommended. The GED is accepted. AP and CLEP credits are accepted. Important factors used in the admissions decision are advanced placement or honor courses, leadership record, recommendations by school officials, extracurricular activities record, and recommendations by alumni.

Procedure: Freshmen are admitted to all sessions. Application deadlines are open. The application fee is $10. Notification is sent on a rolling basis. There are early decision, early admissions, and deferred admissions plans.

Transfer: About 190 transfer students enrolled in 1993-94. Transfer students must have a minimum GPA of 2.0 and have earned at least 12 credit hours. A total of 30 credits out of 128 to 140 must be completed at A&M.

Visiting: There are regularly scheduled orientations for prospective students, consisting of sessions in June, July, and November. There are guides for informal visits. To arrange for a visit, contact James Heyward, Director of Admissions at (205) 851-5245.

Financial Aid: In 1993-94, 66% of all current freshmen and 76% of continuing students received some form of financial aid. About 55% of freshmen received need-based aid. The average freshman

award was $3339. Of that total, scholarships or need-based grants averaged $1877 ($2300 maximum); loans averaged $2954 ($5500 maximum); and work contracts averaged $958. Sixteen percent of undergraduate students work part-time. Average earnings from campus work for the school year are $958. The average financial indebtedness of the 1992–93 graduate was $17,000. The FAF, FFS or SFS and the college's own financial statement are required. The deadline for financial aid applications is April 1.

International Students: There are currently 364 international students enrolled. They must take the TOEFL and achieve a minimum score of 500. The student must also take the SAT I or the ACT.

Computers: The college provides computer facilities for student use. The mainframe is an IBM. Computer science and business majors may access the system. There are no time limits on using the system and no fees.

Graduates: In 1992–93, 433 bachelor's degrees were awarded. The most popular majors among graduates were business administration (13%), computer science (7%), and education (6%). Within an average freshman class, 7% graduate in 4 years and 36% in 5 years. Some 225 companies recruited on campus in 1992–93.

Admissions Contact: James O. Heyward, Director of Admissions.

ALABAMA STATE UNIVERSITY
Montgomery, AL 36101–0271

C-4

(205) 293–4291
(800) 253–5037 (out-of-state)

Full-time: 2108 men, 2604 women	Faculty: 204; IIA, --$
Part-time: 220 men, 310 women	Ph.D.s: 44%
Graduate: 113 men, 396 women	Student/Faculty: 23 to 1
Year: semesters, summer session	Tuition: $1608 ($3108)
Application Deadline: August 1	Room & Board: $1820
Freshman Class: n/av	
SAT I or ACT: required	NONCOMPETITIVE

Alabama State University, founded in 1874, is a state-supported, coeducational institution offering undergraduate programs in liberal arts and sciences, business administration, education, music, and aerospace studies. There are 5 undergraduate schools and one graduate school. In addition to regional accreditation, ASU has baccalaureate program accreditation with NASM and NCATE. The library contains 146,820 volumes and 222,272 microform items, and subscribes to 1101 periodicals. Special learning facilities include a learning resource center, art gallery, and radio station. The 83-acre campus is in an urban area 91 miles south of Birmingham. Including residence halls, there are 26 buildings on campus.

Student Life: About 63% of undergraduates are from Alabama. Students come from 35 states, 12 foreign countries, and Canada. Ninety-seven percent are African American. The average age of freshmen is 18.

Housing: A total of 1449 students can be accommodated in college housing. College-sponsored living facilities include single-sex dormitories, on-campus apartments, and married-student housing. In addition, there are honors houses. On-campus housing is available on a first-come, first-served basis. Alcohol is not permitted. All students may keep cars on campus.

Activities: There are 5 national fraternities and 4 national sororities. There are 39 groups on campus, including art, cheerleading, choir, chorus, drama, drum and bugle corps, honors, jazz band, marching band, newspaper, orchestra, radio and TV, social service, student government, symphony, and yearbook. Popular campus events include Founders Day and Homecoming.

Sports: There are 7 intercollegiate sports for men and 5 for women. Athletic and recreation facilities include a 5000-seat arena, a stadium, a gymnasium, tennis courts, and a swimming pool.

Disabled Students: The entire campus is accessible to disabled students. The following facilities are available: wheelchair ramps, elevators, special parking, specially equipped rest rooms, special class scheduling, lowered drinking fountains, and lowered telephones.

Services: In addition to many counseling and information services, tutoring is available in some subjects, including mathematics and English. In addition, there is remedial math, reading, and writing.

Campus Safety and Security: Campus safety and security measures include a campus police department with 12 security officers.

Programs of Study: ASU awards the B.A., B.S., B.F.A., B.M.E., and B.S.W. degrees. Associate and master's degrees also are awarded. Bachelor's degrees are awarded in BIOLOGICAL SCIENCE (biology/biological science), BUSINESS (accounting, banking and finance, business administration and management, business economics, marketing/retailing/merchandising, and personnel management), COMMUNICATIONS AND THE ARTS (broadcasting, communications, English, fine arts, French, journalism, music, and Spanish), COMPUTER AND PHYSICAL SCIENCE (chemistry, computer programming, mathematics, and physics), EDUCATION (art, business, early childhood, foreign languages, music, secondary, and special), ENGINEERING AND ENVIRONMENTAL DESIGN (engineering), SOCIAL SCIENCE (criminal justice, history, political

science/government, psychology, social work, and sociology). Business is the strongest program academically. Computer information systems has the largest enrollment.

Required: All students must complete a 59-hour core curriculum and pass an English proficiency examination and a senior comprehensive examination. A total of 128 semester hours, with at least 32 in the major, and a minimum GPA of 2.0 are required for graduation.

Special: Cooperative programs are offered in engineering and mathematics with Auburn University and in marine biology with Dauphin Island Sea Laboratory. The Division of Aerospace Studies, in conjunction with the AFROTC curriculum, offers programs leading to a commission in the U.S. Air Force. Internships, B.A.-B.S. degrees, dual majors, a general studies degree, nondegree study, and credit for military experience are available. There is a freshman honors program on campus, as well as 18 national honor societies. Nine departments have honors programs.

Faculty/Classroom: Fifty-three percent of faculty are male; 47%, female. The average class size in an introductory lecture is 40; in a laboratory, 40; and in a regular course offering, 40.

Requirements: The SAT I or ACT is required. Applicants should be high school graduates with at least 3 units of English and 8 units combined in mathematics, natural sciences, social sciences, and foreign languages. An interview is recommended.

Procedure: Entrance exams should be taken in the fall of the senior year. Applications should be filed by August 1 for fall entry. The college accepts all applicants. Notification is sent on a rolling basis. There are early admissions and deferred admissions plans.

Transfer: About 164 transfer students enrolled in an earlier year. A minimum college GPA of 2.0 is required. An interview is recommended. No more than 64 semester hours are accepted for credit from 2-year colleges. A total of 64 credits out of 128 must be completed at ASU.

Visiting: There are regularly scheduled orientations for prospective students. There are guides for informal visits. To arrange for a visit, contact the Office of Enrollment Management at (205) 293–4291.

Financial Aid: The FFS and the Alabama Student Data Form are required. The deadline for financial aid applications is June 1.

International Students: There are currently 28 international students enrolled. They must take the TOEFL and achieve a minimum score of 500. The student must also take the SAT I or the ACT.

Computers: The college provides computer facilities for student use. The mainframe is an IBM 4381/P13. About 100 IBM, IBM-compatible, and Apple-compatible microcomputers are available in student laboratories. All students may access the system 24 hours a day. There are no time limits on using the system and no fees.

Graduates: In an earlier year, 249 bachelor's degrees were awarded.

Admissions Contact: Samuel L. Mitchell, Coordinator of Admissions and Recruitment.

AUBURN UNIVERSITY

Auburn University, established in 1856, is a public system in Alabama. It is governed by a board of trustees, whose chief administrator is the president. The primary goal of the system is service through its instruction, research, and extension divisions. The main priorities are to provide an outstanding, economical instruction to its undergraduate, graduate, and professional students, to expand and diversify overall research effort, and to disseminate and apply knowledge through extension and public service programs. The total enrollment in fall 1993 of both campuses was 27,803; there were 1571 faculty members. Altogether there are 168 baccalaureate, 78 master's, and 39 doctoral programs offered in Auburn University. There are 4-year campuses located in Auburn and Montgomery. Profiles of the 4-year campuses are included in this chapter in alphabetical order with other Alabama schools.

AUBURN UNIVERSITY
Auburn University, AL 36849–3501

D-3

(205) 844–4080
(800) 392–8051 (in-state)

Full-time: 8911 men, 7720 women	Faculty: 1109; I, --$
Part-time: 1120 men, 598 women	Ph.D.s: 90%
Graduate: 1795 men, 1219 women	Student/Faculty: 15 to 1
Year: quarters, summer session	Tuition: $1950 ($5850)
Application Deadline: September 1	Room & Board: $3873
Freshman Class: 7548 applied, 6791 accepted, 3070 enrolled	
SAT I Verbal/Math: 501/575	ACT: 24 COMPETITIVE +

Auburn University, founded in 1856, is a state-supported, coeducational institution, offering undergraduate and graduate degrees in agriculture, business, education, engineering, liberal arts, sciences and mathematics, veterinary medicine, architecture, forestry, human sciences, nursing, and pharmacy. There are 12 undergraduate schools and one graduate school. In addition to regional accreditation, Auburn has baccalaureate program accreditation with AACSB, ABET,

ACPE, ADA, AHEA, ASLA, CSWE, FIDER, NAAB, NASAD, NASM, NCATE, NLN, and SAF. The 3 libraries contain 2,140,856 volumes, 2,811,499 microform items, and 18,284 audiovisual forms, and subscribe to 21,611 periodicals. Computerized library sources and services include the card catalog, interlibrary loans, and database searching. Special learning facilities include a learning resource center, a radio station, a nuclear science center, an arboretum, and electron microscopy laboratories. The 1871-acre campus is in a small town 110 miles southwest of Atlanta, Georgia. Including residence halls, there are 141 buildings on campus.

Student Life: About 64% of undergraduates are from Alabama. Students come from 50 states, 79 foreign countries, and Canada. Seventy-eight percent are from public schools; 18% from private. Eighty-nine percent are white. The average age of freshmen is 18; all undergraduates, 21. Eight percent drop out by the end of their first year; 65% remain to graduate.

Housing: A total of 3280 students can be accommodated in college housing. College-sponsored living facilities include single-sex dormitories, on-campus apartments, married-student housing, and fraternity houses. In addition there are honors houses. On-campus housing is available on a first-come, first-served basis. Alcohol is not permitted. All students may keep cars on campus.

Activities: About 20% of men and about 1% of women belong to 32 national fraternities; about 29% of women belong to 18 national sororities. There are 300 groups on campus, including art, band, cheerleading, choir, chorale, chorus, computers, dance, drama, drill team, ethnic, film, gay, honors, international, jazz band, literary magazine, marching band, musical theater, newspaper, opera, orchestra, pep band, photography, political, professional, radio and TV, religious, social, social service, student government, symphony, and yearbook. Popular campus events include Hey Day, ODK Cake Race, Homecoming, Burn the Bulldogs Parade, SGA Blood Drive, Freshmen Picnic, International Fair, Splash into Spring, A-Day, step shows, Step Sing, Fine Arts Week, Greek Week, and sports victory celebrations.

Sports: There are 7 intercollegiate sports for men and 8 for women, and 15 intramural sports for men and 15 for women. Athletic and recreation facilities include a stadium, a coliseum, an athletic complex, a sports arena, a track, a park, a student activities center, intramural field houses, racquetball courts, tennis courts, and a swim center.

Disabled Students: Seventy percent of the campus is accessible to disabled students. The following facilities are available: wheelchair ramps, elevators, special parking, specially equipped rest rooms, special class scheduling, lowered drinking fountains, braille elevators, and wheelchair lifts.

Services: In addition to many counseling and information services, tutoring is available in most subjects. There is also a reader service for the blind.

Campus Safety and Security: Campus safety and security measures include 24-hour foot and vehicle patrol, self-defense education, escort service, and informal discussions. In addition, there are pamphlets, posters, films and lighted pathways and sidewalks.

Programs of Study: Auburn awards the B.A., B.S., B.Arch., B.En., B.F.A., B.I.D., B.Int.Design, B.Land.Arch., and B.Mus.Ed. degrees. Master's and doctoral degrees also are awarded. Bachelor's degrees are awarded in AGRICULTURE (agricultural business management, agriculture, animal science, fishing and fisheries, forest engineering, forestry production and processing, horticulture, plant protection (pest management), poultry science, and soil science), BIOLOGICAL SCIENCE (biochemistry, biology/biological science, botany, entomology, marine biology, microbiology, molecular biology, nutrition, wildlife biology, and zoology), BUSINESS (accounting, banking and finance, business administration and management, business economics, fashion merchandising, hotel/motel and restaurant management, international business management, marketing/retailing/merchandising, personnel management, retailing, sports management, and transportation management), COMMUNICATIONS AND THE ARTS (broadcasting, communications, design, dramatic arts, English, French, German, industrial design, journalism, languages, music, public relations, Spanish, and speech/debate/rhetoric), COMPUTER AND PHYSICAL SCIENCE (applied mathematics, chemistry, computer science, earth science, geology, mathematics, and physics), EDUCATION (business, early childhood, elementary, foreign languages, guidance, health, home economics, industrial arts, journalism, middle school, physical, science, secondary, special, and vocational), ENGINEERING AND ENVIRONMENTAL DESIGN (aeronautical engineering, agricultural engineering, architecture, aviation administration/management, chemical engineering, civil engineering, computer engineering, construction management, electrical/electronics engineering, environmental science, geological engineering, interior design, landscape architecture/design, mechanical engineering, textile engineering, and textile technology), HEALTH PROFESSIONS (health care administration, medical laboratory technology, nursing, optometry, pharmacy, physical therapy, predentistry, premedicine, preveterinary science, and speech pathology/audiology), SOCIAL SCIENCE (anthropology, child care/

child and family studies, criminal justice, criminology, dietetics, economics, food science, geography, history, parks and recreation management, philosophy, physical fitness/movement, political science/government, psychology, public administration, religion, rural sociology, social work, sociology, and textiles and clothing). Engineering, architecture, agricultural sciences, pharmacy, and veterinary medicine are the strongest academically. Liberal arts, engineering, and business have the largest enrollments.

Required: All students msut complete a core curriculum of 10 quarter hours each in English composition, literature, and science, 9 each in history and social science, 5 each in mathematics and philosophy, and 3 in fine arts. A total of 192 to 257 quarter hours, with a minimum overall GPA of 2.0, is required in order to graduate. Two upper-level writing reinforcement courses are required within various fields of study that include extensive writing assignments and are evaluated for both content and writing mechanics.

Special: Opportunities are available for co-op programs in most majors, and there are internships, work-study programs, and dual majors. A 3–2 engineering degree with several area institutions, credit by examination, nondegree study, pass/fail options, credit for life experience, and study abroad in more than 25 countries are also available. There is a freshman honors program on campus, as well as 74 national honor societies. Three departments have honors programs and there is also a university-wide honors program.

Faculty/Classroom: Seventy-eight percent of faculty are male; 22%, female. Ninety-eight percent both teach and do research. The average class size in a regular course offering is 26.

Admissions: About 90% of the 1993–94 applicants were accepted. The SAT scores for the 1993–94 freshman class were as follows: Verbal—49% below 500, 38% between 500 and 599, 12% between 600 and 700, and 1% above 700; Math—17% below 500, 41% between 500 and 599, 34% between 600 and 700, and 8% above 700. The ACT scores were 24% below 21, 27% between 21 and 23, 25% between 24 and 26, 11% between 27 and 28, and 13% above 28. About 46% of the current freshmen were in the top fifth of their class; 75% were in the top two fifths. There were 22 National Merit finalists and 22 semifinalists.

Requirements: The SAT I or the ACT is required. Graduation from an accredited secondary school is required; a GED will be accepted. Applicants must have completed 4 years of high school English, 3 each of mathematics and social studies, and 2 of science. It is recommended that students also complete 1 year each of a foreign language, an additional science course, and an additional social science. Admission is equally based on test scores and the GPA in completed core requirements. AP and CLEP credits are accepted. Important factors used in the admissions decision are parents or siblings attending the school, evidence of special talent, advanced placement or honor courses, recommendations by school officials, and recommendations by alumni.

Procedure: Freshmen are admitted to all sessions. Entrance exams should be taken in the spring of the junior year. Applications should be filed by September 1 for fall entry, December 10 for winter entry, March 1 for spring entry, and June 1 for summer entry, along with an application fee of $25. Notification is sent on a rolling basis. There are early admissions and deferred admissions plans.

Transfer: About 1858 transfer students enrolled in 1993–94. Applicants for transfer must have maintained a cumulative GPA of 2.5 in previous college courses. The number of required credit hours depends on eligibility for admission to Auburn after graduating from high school. If not eligible, student must present a minimum of 48 quarter hours of college work, including 30 credit hours of standard academic courses, with at least 3 quarter hours each in English, history, mathematics, and natural sciences. A total of 45 quarter hours out of 192 must be completed at Auburn.

Visiting: There are regularly scheduled orientations for prospective students, including 3 War Eagle Days held on Saturdays, minority recruitment weekends, and informal visits. Agendas vary, but normally include campus tours, meeting with an admissions counselor, a tour of housing, and meeting with faculty in various academic areas as desired. There are guides for informal visits and visitors may sit in on classes and stay overnight at the school. To arrange for a visit, contact Admissions Office at (205) 844-4080.

Financial Aid: In 1993–94, 47% of all current freshmen and 47% of continuing students received some form of financial aid. About 32% of freshmen and 32% of continuing students received need-based aid. The average freshman award was $4804. Of that total, scholarships or need-based grants averaged $1607 ($5850 maximum); loans averaged $2625 ($4425 maximum); and work contracts averaged $1500 ($2250 maximum). Ten percent of undergraduate students work part-time. Average earnings from campus work for the school year are $1800. Auburn is a member of CSS. The FAFSA financial statement is required. The deadline for financial aid applications is April 15.

International Students: There are currently 691 international students enrolled. They must take the TOEFL and achieve a minimum score of 550. The student must also take the SAT I.

Computers: The college provides computer facilities for student use. The mainframe is an IBM ES/9121 610. More than 700 networked microcomputers and terminals are available in various academic buildings and the library. Student computer labs include spreadsheet, word processing, statistical, and other software programs. Students may also access the university's mainframe computers, external networks such as Bitnet and Internet, and the Alabama Supercomputer. All students may access the system. It may be used 24 hours a day. There are no time limits on using the system. Most facilities are available free of charge, but a few services have minimal charges based on usage.

Graduates: In 1992–93, 4104 bachelor's degrees were awarded. The most popular majors among graduates were business (25%), engineering (16%), and education (11%). Within an average freshman class, 1% graduate in 3 years, 32% in 4 years, 60% in 5 years, and 67% in 6 years. Some 448 companies recruited on campus in 1992–93. In the 1992 graduating class, 30% of the men and 30% of the women were enrolled in graduate school within 6 months of graduation; 65% of the men and 70% of the women had found employment.

Admissions Contact: Dr. Charles F. Reeder, Director of Admissions.

AUBURN UNIVERSITY AT MONTGOMERY   C-4
Montgomery, AL 36117-3596   (205) 244-3611
(800) 227-2649 (in-state)

Full-time: 1405 men, 2070 women	**Faculty:** 201; IIA, --$
Part-time: 807 men, 1134 women	**Ph.D.s:** 74%
Graduate: 403 men, 588 women	**Student/Faculty:** 17 to 1
Year: quarters, summer session	**Tuition:** $1800 ($5400)
Application Deadline: September 1	**Room:** $1590
Freshman Class: 985 applied, 868 accepted, 645 enrolled	
ACT: 21	**COMPETITIVE**

Auburn University at Montgomery, founded in 1967, is a public, coeducational institution. There are 5 undergraduate and 4 graduate schools. In addition to regional accreditation, AUM has baccalaureate program accreditation with AACSB, CAHEA, NCATE, and NLN. The library contains 235,258 volumes, 1,005,525 microform items, and 23,238 audiovisual forms, and subscribes to 1537 periodicals. Computerized library sources and services include the card catalog, interlibrary loans, and database searching. The 500-acre campus is in a suburban area. Including residence halls, there are 42 buildings on campus.

Student Life: About 98% of undergraduates are from Alabama. Seventy-seven percent are white; 20% African American. The average age of freshmen is 20; all undergraduates, 24.

Housing: A total of 576 students can be accommodated in college housing. College-sponsored living facilities include coed on-campus apartments and married-student housing. On-campus housing is available on a first-come, first-served basis. Ninety-one percent of students commute. Alcohol is not permitted. All students may keep cars on campus.

Activities: About 3% of men belong to 5 national fraternities; about 4% of women belong to 6 national sororities. There are 40 groups on campus, including cheerleading, choir, chorus, drama, honors, literary magazine, newspaper, pep band, social, student government, and yearbook. Popular campus events include the Harvest Moon Festival, the Easter Egg Hunt, Black History Week, and lectures.

Sports: There are 4 intercollegiate sports for men and 2 for women, and 8 intramural sports for men and 8 for women. Athletic and recreation facilities are few because the campus primarily serves a commuting student body.

Disabled Students: The entire campus is accessible to disabled students. The following facilities are available: wheelchair ramps, elevators, special parking, specially equipped rest rooms, special class scheduling, lowered drinking fountains, and lowered telephones.

Services: In addition to many counseling and information services, tutoring is available in every subject. There is also a reader service for the blind, and remedial math, reading, and writing.

Campus Safety and Security: Campus safety and security measures include 24-hour foot and vehicle patrol, escort service, informal discussions, and pamphlets, posters, and films. In addition, there are emergency telephones and lighted pathways and sidewalks.

Programs of Study: AUM awards the B.A., B.S., B.G.Sc., B.S.B.A., and B.S.N. degrees. Master's and doctoral degrees also are awarded. Bachelor's degrees are awarded in BIOLOGICAL SCIENCE (biology/biological science), BUSINESS (accounting, banking and finance, business administration and management, business economics, marketing/retailing/merchandising, and personnel management), COMMUNICATIONS AND THE ARTS (communications, dramatic arts, English, and fine arts), COMPUTER AND PHYSICAL

SCIENCE (information sciences and systems and mathematics), EDUCATION (art, early childhood, elementary, secondary, and special), HEALTH PROFESSIONS (nursing), SOCIAL SCIENCE (history, political science/government, psychology, public administration, sociology, and urban studies). Biology and mathematics are the strongest academically. Business administration has the largest enrollment.

Required: To graduate, students must complete 200 quarter hours of passing credit within the identified field of study. Distribution requirements include 10 hours each of English composition, world history, and natural or physical sciences, 5 hours of mathematics, plus a minimum of 20 hours in liberal education electives.

Special: The university offers cross-registration with Faulkner University and Huntingdon College. Study abroad, co-op programs, a general studies degree, student-designed majors, and nondegree study are available. There is a freshman honors program on campus, as well as 13 national honor societies. Eleven departments have honors programs.

Faculty/Classroom: Sixty-four percent of faculty are male; 36%, female. The average class size in a regular course offering is 20.

Admissions: About 88% of the 1993–94 applicants were accepted.

Requirements: A minimum GPA of 2.0 is required. The ACT is recommended. In addition, applicants must be graduates of an accredited secondary school. The GED is accepted. Admission is by test score and grade average of the 5 subjects of English, mathematics, foreign language, social studies, and science. There are special criteria for older applicants who are not high school graduates. AP and CLEP credits are accepted.

Procedure: Freshmen are admitted to all sessions. Entrance exams should be taken late in the junior year or early in the senior year. Early decision applications should be filed by June 1; regular applications, by September 1 for fall entry, along with an application fee of $15. Notification is sent on a rolling basis. There are early decision and early admissions plans.

Transfer: Applicants for transfer must have a C average and be in good standing at their last school. A total of 45 quarter credit hours out of 200 must be completed at AUM.

Visiting: There are regularly scheduled orientations for prospective students. There are guides for informal visits and visitors may sit in on classes. To arrange for a visit, contact the Admissions Office at (205) 244-3611 or (800) 227-2649 (in-state).

Financial Aid: Scholarships or need-based grants averaged $835; loans averaged $1800; and work contracts averaged $1500. Seven percent of undergraduate students work part-time. Average earnings from campus work for the school year are $4420. The college's own financial statement and FAFSA are required. The deadline for financial aid applications is April 15.

International Students: There are currently 80 international students enrolled. The school actively recruits these students. They must take the TOEFL and achieve a minimum score of 500. The student must also take the SAT I or the ACT and achieve a minimum combined score of 780 on the SAT I or 19 on the ACT.

Computers: The university provides computer facilities for student use. All students may access the system 8 A.M. to midnight. There are no time limits on using the system and no fees.

Graduates: In 1992–93, 828 bachelor's degrees were awarded. The most popular majors among graduates were business management and administrative services (30%), education (24%), and social sciences and history (8%).

Admissions Contact: Lee Davis, Director of Admissions.

BIRMINGHAM-SOUTHERN COLLEGE   C-2
Birmingham, AL 35254   (205) 226-4686; (800) 523-5793 (in-state)

Full-time: 627 men, 749 women	**Faculty:** 92; IIB, av$
Part-time: 65 men, 141 women	**Ph.D.s:** 78%
Graduate: 50 men, 41 women	**Student/Faculty:** 15 to 1
Year: 4-1-4, summer session	**Tuition:** $11,014
Application Deadline: March 1	**Room & Board:** $4140
Freshman Class: 804 applied, 587 accepted, 287 enrolled	
SAT I: 515/535	**ACT:** 26 **VERY COMPETITIVE +**

Birmingham-Southern College, founded in 1856, is a private, coeducational liberal arts college affiliated with the United Methodist Church. There is one graduate school. In addition to regional accreditation, BSC has baccalaureate program accreditation with NASM and NCATE. The library contains 167,391 volumes, 33,184 microform items, and 22,708 audiovisual forms and subscribes to 819 periodicals. Computerized library sources and services include the card catalog, interlibrary loans, and database searching. Special learning facilities include a learning resource center, art gallery, and planetarium. The 185-acre campus is in an urban area 3 miles west of downtown Birmingham. Including residence halls, there are 28 buildings on campus.

Student Life: About 76% of undergraduates are from Alabama. Students come from 36 states and 12 foreign countries. Sixty-seven percent are from public schools; 33% from private. Eighty-four percent

are white; 13% African American. Most are Protestant. The average age of freshmen is 18; all undergraduates, 24. Eight percent drop out by the end of their first year; 70% remain to graduate.

Housing: A total of 1220 students can be accommodated in college housing. College-sponsored living facilities include single-sex dormitories, on-campus apartments, married-student housing, fraternity houses, and sorority houses. In addition there are honors houses. On-campus housing is guaranteed for all 4 years. Priority is given to out-of-town students. Eighty-eight percent of students live on campus; of those, 70% remain on campus on weekends. All students may keep cars on campus.

Activities: About 65% of men belong to 6 national fraternities; about 70% of women belong to 7 national sororities. There are 70 groups on campus, including art, band, cheerleading, choir, chorale, chorus, computers, dance, drama, drill team, ethnic, honors, international, jazz band, literary magazine, musical theater, newspaper, opera, pep band, political, professional, religious, social, social service, student government, and yearbook. Popular campus events include Southern Comfort, Entertainment Festival, Homecoming, Greek Weekend, Miss BSC, and Christmas on the Quad.

Sports: There are 4 intercollegiate sports for men and 1 for women, and 17 intramural sports for men and 17 for women. Athletic and recreation facilities include a coliseum, a baseball field, racquetball and tennis courts, a soccer field, a gymnasium, a weight room, and an intramural athletic field.

Disabled Students: Eighty percent of the campus is accessible to disabled students. The following facilities are available: wheelchair ramps, elevators, special parking, specially equipped rest rooms, special class scheduling, and lowered drinking fountains.

Services: In addition to many counseling and information services, tutoring is available in some subjects, including mathematics, English, computer science, and other subjects as requested. Tutoring is arranged on an individual basis; assistance in finding teachers is provided upon request.

Campus Safety and Security: Campus safety and security measures include 24-hour foot and vehicle patrol, self defense education, escort service, and informal discussions. In addition, there are pamphlets, posters, films, emergency telephones, and lighted pathways and sidewalks.

Programs of Study: BSC awards the B.A., B.S., B.F.A., B.Mus., and B.Mus.Ed. degrees. Master's degrees also are awarded. Bachelor's degrees are awarded in BIOLOGICAL SCIENCE (biology/biological science), BUSINESS (accounting, business administration and management, international business management, and marketing/retailing/merchandising), COMMUNICATIONS AND THE ARTS (art history and appreciation, dance, dramatic arts, English, fine arts, French, German, music, painting, printmaking, sculpture, and Spanish), COMPUTER AND PHYSICAL SCIENCE (chemistry, computer science, information sciences and systems, mathematics, and physics), EDUCATION (art, early childhood, elementary, and music), SOCIAL SCIENCE (economics, history, international relations, philosophy, political science/government, psychology, and sociology). Biology, English, psychology, and the arts are the strongest academically. Business administration has the largest enrollment.

Required: All students must complete 32 regular units with courses in English composition and literature, laboratory sciences, mathematics, fine arts, foreign language, social sciences, history, philosophy, and religion as well as 4 interim (January) experiences. A total of 128 credits with a GPA of at least 2.0 is required in order to graduate.

Special: There is cross-registration with the University of Alabama at Birmingham and Samford University. Student-designed majors, dual majors, a Washington semester, internships, work-study programs, and study abroad in England, France, Africa, and Latin America are offered. A 3–2 engineering degree is offered with the University of Alabama at Birmingham, Auburn University, Columbia University, and Washington University at St. Louis. Limited pass/fail options and B.A.-B.S. degrees are available. Credit for life experience is evaluated by faculty. There is a freshman honors program on campus, as well as 22 national honor societies, including Phi Beta Kappa. One department has an honors program.

Faculty/Classroom: Sixty-one percent of faculty are male; 39%, female. Ninety-four percent teach undergraduates and 80% both teach and do research. No introductory courses are taught by graduate students. The average class size in an introductory lecture is 30; in a laboratory, 15; and in a regular course offering, 17.

Admissions: About 73% of the 1993–94 applicants were accepted. The SAT scores for the 1993–94 freshman class were as follows: Verbal—41% below 500, 38% between 500 and 599, 16% between 600 and 700, and 5% above 700; Math—19% below 500, 43% between 500 and 599, 30% between 600 and 700, and 8% above 700. The ACT scores were 10% below 21, 18% between 21 and 23, 21% between 24 and 26, 21% between 27 and 28, and 30% above 28. About 30% of the current freshmen were in the top fifth of their class; 65% were in the top two fifths. There were 10 National Merit finalists

and 21 semifinalists. Twenty-six freshmen graduated first in their class.

Requirements: A minimum GPA of 2.2 is required. SAT I or the ACT is required. The minimum SAT I score should be 800, 400 verbal and 400 math, and the minimum ACT score, 21. Applicants should have graduated from an accredited secondary school with 12 academic credits and 16 Carnegie units, including 4 courses in English, 2 or more each in mathematics, science, history, and social studies, and a recommended 2 in foreign language. The GED is also accepted. An essay and interview are required. Fine arts majors are advised to submit a portfolio or arrange an audition. AP and CLEP credits are accepted. Important factors used in the admissions decision are advanced placement or honor courses, evidence of special talent, ability to finance college education, extracurricular activities record, and geographic diversity.

Procedure: Freshmen are admitted in the fall, spring, and summer. Entrance exams should be taken in the spring of the junior year. Applications should be filed by March 1 for fall entry, December 15 for winter entry, January 15 for spring entry, and May 1 for summer entry, along with an application fee of $25. There are early admissions and deferred admissions plans. A waiting list is an active part of the admissions procedure, with about 10% of applicants on the list.

Transfer: About 63 transfer students enrolled in 1993–94. Transfer applicants must have a minimum GPA of 2.0 and leave their former school in good standing. An interview, 1 essay, and a school recommendation are required. A total of 64 credits out of 128 must be completed at BSC.

Visiting: There are regularly scheduled orientations for prospective students, including Preview Days, Scholarship Days, and individual visits. There are guides for informal visits and visitors may sit in on classes and stay overnight at the school. To arrange for a visit, contact the Office of Admissions at (205) 226–4696.

Financial Aid: In 1993–94 77% of all current freshmen and 80% of continuing students received some form of financial aid. About 46% of freshmen and 47% of continuing students received need-based aid. The average freshman award was $8173. Of that total, scholarships or need-based grants averaged $3500 ($10,900 maximum); loans averaged $2500 ($3000 maximum); and work contracts averaged $1500 ($2000 maximum). Fifteen percent of undergraduate students work part-time. Average earnings from campus work for the school year are $1000. The average financial indebtedness of the 1992–93 graduate was $10,000. BSC is a member of CSS. The FAF, FFS, or SFS is required. The deadline for financial aid applications is March 31.

International Students: There are currently 21 international students enrolled. The school actively recruits these students. They must take the TOEFL or the University of Michigan Language Test and achieve a minimum score on the TOEFL of 550. The student must also take the SAT I or the ACT and achieve a minimum sore of 20 on the ACT.

Computers: The college provides computer facilities for student use. The mainframe is an HP 9000/Series 835. There are 114 microcomputers in the computer center and other buildings on campus. All students may access the system from 8 A.M. to 2 A.M. every day. There are no time limits and no fees.

Graduates: In a recent year 332 bachelor's degrees were awarded. The most popular majors among graduates were business administration (30%), psychology (8%), and English (6%). Within an average freshman class, 69% graduate in 4 years and 70% in 5 years. Some 31 companies recruited on campus in 1992–93. In an earlier graduating class, 42% of the men and 40% of the women were enrolled in graduate school within 6 months of graduation.

Admissions Contact: Robert D. Dortch, Vice-President for Admissions Services.

FAULKNER UNIVERSITY
C-4

Montgomery, AL 36109–3398   (205) 272–5820; (800) 828–8110

Full-time: 490 men, 665 women	Faculty: 21
Part-time: 260 men, 290 women	Ph.D.s: 33%
Graduate: 180 men, 95 women	Student/Faculty: 55 to 1
Year: semesters, summer session	Tuition: $5580
Application Deadline: open	Room & Board: $3050
Freshman Class: 372 applied, 340 accepted, 171 enrolled	
SAT I or ACT: required	LESS COMPETITIVE

Faulkner University, founded in 1942, is a private, coeducational multicampus university affiliated with the Church of Christ, offering undergraduate programs in Bible studies, business, education, and liberal arts and sciences. There are 3 undergraduate schools and one graduate school. The 2 libraries contain 80,000 volumes, 857 microform items, and 1857 audiovisual forms, and subscribe to 550 periodicals. Computerized library sources and services include the card catalog, interlibrary loans, and database searching. Special learning facilities include a learning resource center. The 92-acre campus is in

an urban area. Including residence halls, there are 12 buildings on campus.

Student Life: About 94% of undergraduates are from Alabama. Students come from 16 states and 3 foreign countries. Ninety-two percent are from public schools; 8% from private. Seventy-four percent are white; 24% African American.

Housing: College-sponsored living facilities include single-sex dormitories. In addition there are honors houses. On-campus housing is available on a first-come, first-served basis. Priority is given to out-of-town students. Alcohol is not permitted. All students may keep cars on campus.

Activities: There are 6 local fraternities and 6 local sororities . There are many groups and organizations on campus, including cheerleading, chorus, drama, literary magazine, musical theater, newspaper, religious, social, social service, student government, and yearbook. Popular campus events include the Annual Bible Lectureship, Homecoming, Jamboree, and Fall Visitation Weekend.

Sports: There are 2 intercollegiate sports for men and 1 for women, and 6 intramural sports for men and 6 for women. Athletic and recreation facilities include a gymnasium, a weight room, baseball and softball fields, and lighted tennis courts.

Disabled Students: The entire campus is accessible to disabled students. Wheelchair ramps and special parking are available.

Services: In addition to many counseling and information services, tutoring is available in some subjects, including basic mathematics, English, and reading comprehension. There is also remedial math, reading, and writing.

Campus Safety and Security: Campus safety and security measures include 24-hour foot and vehicle patrol, informal discussions, and pamphlets, posters, and films.

Programs of Study: Faulkner awards the B.A. and B.S. degrees. Associate degrees also are awarded. Bachelor's degrees are awarded in BIOLOGICAL SCIENCE (biology/biological science), BUSINESS (business administration and management, business data processing, personnel management, and sports management), COMMUNICATIONS AND THE ARTS (English), EDUCATION (elementary, physical, and secondary), HEALTH PROFESSIONS (optometry), SOCIAL SCIENCE (biblical studies, liberal arts/general studies, and prelaw).

Required: Students must complete a 52-semester-hour core curriculum, including courses in Bible history, social science, English composition, literature, art/music appreciation, speech communication, physical and natural science, mathematics, computer literacy, and physical education. B.A. students must take 2 semesters of foreign language. At least 120 semester hours with a minimum GPA of 2.0 are required to graduate.

Special: A second bachelor's degree in a separate major may be completed with a minimum of 24 semester hours earned beyond the first degree. Dual majors, credit for life/military/work experience, and nondegree study are offered.

Admissions: About 91% of the 1993–94 applicants were accepted.

Requirements: A minimum GPA of 2.0 is required. The SAT I or ACT is required, with minimum composite scores of 735 on the SAT I or 16 on the ACT. Candidates must be graduates of an accredited secondary school, or have the GED equivalent, with a minimum of 15 academic units, including 3 in English. AP and CLEP credits are accepted.

Procedure: Application deadlines are open. Application fee is $15.

Transfer: Applicants must be in good academic standing from another accredited college.

Financial Aid: In 1993–94, all students received some form of financial aid. All students received need-based aid. The average freshman award was $1000. Of that total, scholarships or need-based grants averaged $1000 ($2000 maximum); loans averaged $2625 (maximum); and work contracts averaged $500 ($1000 maximum). Fifty-nine percent of undergraduate students work part-time. Average earnings from campus work for the school year were $1200. The average financial indebtedness of the 1992–93 graduate was $5700. The FFS is required. The deadline for financial aid applications is May 1.

International Students: International students must take the TOEFL and achieve a minimum score of 450.

Computers: The university provides computer facilities for student use. IBM and Apple PCs are available in the computer laboratory. There are no time limits on using the system and no fees.

Graduates: In 1992–93, 340 bachelor's degrees were awarded. The most popular majors among graduates were business administration (75%), management of human resources (17%), and education (5%).

Admissions Contact: Joey Wiginton, Director of Admissions.

HUNTINGDON COLLEGE
C-4
Montgomery, AL 36106-2148

(205) 834-3300
(800) 763-0313 (out-of-state)

Full-time: 282 men, 382 women	Faculty: 43; IIB, --$
Part-time: 32 men, 94 women	Ph.D.s: 70%
Graduate: none	Student/Faculty: 15 to 1
Year: semesters, summer session	Tuition: $7640
Application Deadline: June 1	Room & Board: $3760
Freshman Class: 473 applied, 406 accepted, 130 enrolled	
ACT: 23	**COMPETITIVE**

Huntingdon College, founded in 1854, is a private, coeducational liberal arts institution affiliated with the United Methodist Church. In addition to regional accreditation, Huntingdon has baccalaureate program accreditation with NASM. The library contains 95,000 volumes, 6000 microform items, and 1000 audiovisual forms and subscribes to 318 periodicals. Computerized library sources and services include database searching. Special learning facilities include an art gallery. The 58-acre campus is in a suburban area 90 miles south of Birmingham. Including residence halls, there are 17 buildings on campus.

Student Life: About 70% of undergraduates are from Alabama. Students come from 14 states, 11 foreign countries, and Canada. Seventy-five percent are from public schools; 25% private. Eighty-two percent are white. Eighty-seven percent are Protestant; 10% Catholic. The average age of freshmen is 18; all undergraduates, 20. Twenty-five percent drop out by the end of their first year; 44% remain to graduate.

Housing: A total of 443 students can be accommodated in college housing. College-sponsored living facilities include single-sex dormitories. On-campus housing is guaranteed for all 4 years. Fifty-eight percent of students live on campus. Alcohol is not permitted. All students may keep cars on campus.

Activities: About 26% of men belong to 2 national fraternities; about 28% of women belong to 2 national sororities. There are 35 groups on campus, including band, choir, chorus, computers, dance, drama, ethnic, honors, international, jazz band, literary magazine, musical theater, newspaper, professional, religious, social, social service, student government, and yearbook. Popular campus events include Homecoming and the Miss Huntingdon and Mr. Huntindgon pageant.

Sports: There are 4 intercollegiate sports for men and 4 for women, and 7 intramural sports for men and 7 for women. Athletic and recreation facilities include a student center with a 1500-seat gymnasium, a swimming pool, and a weight room.

Disabled Students: Ten percent of the campus is accessible to disabled students. The following facilities are available: wheelchair ramps and special parking.

Services: In addition to many counseling and information services, tutoring is available in most subjects.

Campus Safety and Security: Campus safety and security measures include 24-hour foot and vehicle patrol, self-defense education, escort service, and informal discussions. In addition, there are emergency telephones and lighted pathways and sidewalks.

Programs of Study: Huntingdon awards the B.A. degree. Associate degrees also are awarded. Bachelor's degrees are awarded in BIOLOGICAL SCIENCE (biology/biological science), BUSINESS (accounting, business administration and management, and international business), COMMUNICATIONS AND THE ARTS (dance, dramatic arts, English, fine arts, music, and speech/debate/rhetoric), COMPUTER AND PHYSICAL SCIENCE (chemistry, computer science, information sciences and systems, and mathematics), EDUCATION (art, early childhood, elementary, music, and secondary), HEALTH PROFESSIONS (predentistry, premedicine, and prephysical therapy), SOCIAL SCIENCE (history, philosophy, prelaw, psychology, religion, religious education, and theological studies). Chemistry, business, psychology, and music are the strongest academically. Business, education, mathematics, and physical education have the largest enrollments.

Required: All students are required to complete a core curriculum, including 12 semester hours in English, 12 in religion and philosophy, 6 each in science and history, 3 each in mathematics, fine arts, and speech, and 2 in physical education. A total of 124 semester hours, with a minimum GPA of 2.0, is required in order to graduate.

Special: Huntingdon offers cross-registration and a 3–2 engineering degree with Auburn University at Montgomery. Internships are available in business, chemistry, psychology, and biology. Dual majors, student-designed majors, and pass/fail options are available. There is a freshman honors program on campus, as well as 2 national honor societies. Twelve departments have honors programs.

Faculty/Classroom: Sixty-nine percent of faculty are male; 31%, female. All teach undergraduates. The average class size in an introductory lecture is 31; in a laboratory, 13; and in a regular course offering, 17.

Admissions: About 86% of the 1993–94 applicants were accepted. *Requirements:* A minimum GPA of 2.3 is required. The SAT I or ACT is required. Applicants should have completed 4 years of high school English, 3 credits each in mathematics and history, and 2 credits of science. An interview is recommended. A portfolio or audition may be required. AP and CLEP credits are accepted. Important factors used in the admissions decision are advanced placement or honor courses, leadership record, recommendations by school officials, personality, intangible qualities, and extracurricular activities record. *Procedure:* Freshmen are admitted to all sessions. Applications should be filed by June 1 for fall entry and January 10 for winter entry, along with an application fee of $25. Notification is sent on a rolling basis. There is an early admissions plan.

Transfer: About 47 transfer students enrolled in 1993–94. Transfer applicants must have a minimum GPA of 2.0. An interview is recommended.

Visiting: There are regularly scheduled orientations for prospective students, consisting of class visitation, a campus tour, and a meeting with an admissions counselor. There are guides for informal visits and visitors may sit in on classes and stay overnight at the school. To arrange for a visit, contact the Office of Admissions at (205) 834–3300 or (800) 763–0313.

Financial Aid: Twelve percent of undergraduate students work part-time. Average earnings from campus work for the school year are $1275. The average financial indebtedness of a recent year's graduate was $2500. Huntingdon is a member of CSS. The FAF or FFS and the college's own financial statement are required. The deadline for financial aid applications is May 1.

International Students: There are currently 19 international students enrolled. The school actively recruits these students. They must take the TOEFL and achieve a minimum score of 500. The student must also take the SAT I or the ACT.

Computers: The college provides computer facilities for student use. The mainframe is a DEC VAX 8250. There are 16 IBM PS/2 and Apple Macintosh microcomputers for academic use, available in the Wilson Center. All students may access the system 24 hours a day, 7 days a week. There are no time limits on using the system and no fees.

Graduates: In 1992–93 145 bachelor's degrees were awarded. The most popular majors among graduates were business administration (23%), English (10%), and history (8%). Within an average freshman class, 4% graduate in 3 years, 44% in 4 years, 47% in 5 years, and 50% in 6 years. Some 19 companies recruited on campus in 1992–93. In the 1992 graduating class, 37% of the graduates were enrolled in graduate school within 6 months of graduation; 63% had found employment.

Admissions Contact: Paul Mittelhammer, Dean of Enrollment Management.

JACKSONVILLE STATE UNIVERSITY

D-2

Jacksonville, AL 36265

(205) 782–5000

Full-time: 2390 men, 2770 women	Faculty: 270; IIA, --$
Part-time: 769 men, 706 women	Ph.D.s: 52%
Graduate: 356 men, 515 women	Student/Faculty: 19 to 1
Year: semesters, summer session	Tuition: $1680 ($2520)
Application Deadline: open	Room & Board: $2400
Freshman Class: 1850 applied, 1650 accepted, 1101 enrolled	
ACT: 19	**LESS COMPETITIVE**

Jacksonville State University, founded in 1883, is a public, coeducational institution offering programs in business, arts and sciences, criminal justice, education, and nursing. There are 6 undergraduate schools and one graduate school. In addition to regional accreditation, JSU has baccalaureate program accreditation with CSWE, NASM, NCATE, and NLN. The library contains 594,943 volumes, 896,576 microform items, and 24,539 audiovisual forms, and subscribes to 2120 periodicals. Computerized library sources and services include the card catalog, interlibrary loans, and database searching. Special learning facilities include a learning resource center, radio station, a stellar observatory, and the Center for Southern Studies. The 345-acre campus is in a small town 75 miles east of Birmingham. Including residence halls, there are 51 buildings on campus.

Student Life: About 82% of undergraduates are from Alabama. Students come from 33 states, 65 foreign countries, and Canada. Eighty-five percent are from public schools; 5% from private. Eighty-one percent are white; 17% African American. The average age of freshmen is 20.3; all undergraduates, 23.3. Thirty-eight percent drop out by the end of their first year; 22% remain to graduate.

Housing: A total of 2100 students can be accommodated in college housing. College-sponsored living facilities include single-sex and coed dormitories, off-campus apartments, and married-student housing. There is an International House available for students on Rotary Club International scholarships. On-campus housing is guaranteed for all 4 years. Seventy percent of students commute. Alcohol is not permitted. All students may keep cars on campus.

Activities: About 12% of men belong to 1 local fraternity and 9 national fraternities; about 12% of women belong to 8 national sororities. There are 70 groups on campus, including art, band, cheerleading, choir, chorus, computers, dance, drama, drill team, ethnic, honors, international, jazz band, marching band, musical theater, newspaper, pep band, political, professional, radio and TV, religious, social, social service, student government, symphony, and yearbook. Popular campus events include Homecoming and Visitation Day.

Sports: There are 5 intercollegiate sports for men and 4 for women, and 15 intramural sports for men and 8 for women. Athletic and recreation facilities include a 15,000-seat football stadium, indoor and outdoor courts, athletic fields, a 5,000-seat indoor gymnasium, an indoor pool, a weight room, and a fitness center.

Disabled Students: Sixty percent of the campus is accessible to disabled students. The following facilities are available: wheelchair ramps, elevators, special parking, specially equipped rest rooms, lowered drinking fountains, and lowered telephones.

Services: In addition to many counseling and information services, tutoring is available in most subjects. There is also remedial math, reading, and writing.

Campus Safety and Security: Campus safety and security measures include 24-hour foot and vehicle patrol, escort service, informal discussions, and pamphlets, posters, and films. In addition, there are lighted pathways and sidewalks.

Programs of Study: JSU awards the B.A., B.S., B.F.A., B.M., B.S.Ed., and B.S.W. degrees. Master's degrees also are awarded. Bachelor's degrees are awarded in BIOLOGICAL SCIENCE (biology/biological science), BUSINESS (accounting, banking and finance, and marketing/retailing/merchandising), COMMUNICATIONS AND THE ARTS (communications, dramatic arts, English, and music), COMPUTER AND PHYSICAL SCIENCE (chemistry, computer science, mathematics, and physics), EDUCATION (early childhood, elementary, health, home economics, music, science, secondary, and special), HEALTH PROFESSIONS (nursing, predentistry, premedicine, prepharmacy, and preveterinary science), SOCIAL SCIENCE (criminal justice, economics, geography, history, political science/government, prelaw, psychology, social work, and sociology). Education is the strongest academically. Business has the largest enrollment.

Required: All students are required to complete a core curriculum of 46 semester hours, including 15 hours in fine arts and humanities, 8 each in communications and natural sciences, 6 each in analysis and social sciences, and 3 in wellness. English competency and courses in computer literacy are required. A total of 128 semester hours, with a minimum GPA of 2.2, is required in order to graduate.

Special: Co-op programs with major area employers are available. The university has cross-registration with the Marine Environmental Sciences Consortium, and internships in education, political science, communication, journalism, and criminal justice. Work-study programs and credit for military experience are offered. There are 8 national honor societies on campus.

Faculty/Classroom: Sixty-two percent of faculty are male; 38%, female. Ninety-nine percent teach undergraduates, 1% do research, and 70% do both. No introductory courses are taught by graduate students. The average class size in an introductory lecture is 50; in a laboratory, 25; and in a regular course offering, 25.

Admissions: About 89% of the 1993–94 applicants were accepted. *Requirements:* The SAT I or ACT is required. Applicants should be graduates of an accredited high school; the GED is also accepted. AP and CLEP credits are accepted. Important factors used in the admissions decision are advanced placement or honor courses, recommendations by school officials, leadership record, evidence of special talent, and extracurricular activities record.

Procedure: Freshmen are admitted to all sessions. Application deadlines are open. The application fee is $20. Notification is sent on a rolling basis.

Transfer: A total of 715 transfer students enrolled in a recent year. Transfer applicants must be eligible to return to the last institution attended. A total of 32 credits out of 128 must be completed at JSU.

Visiting: There are regularly scheduled orientations for prospective students, consisting of 2-day orientations scheduled during the summer. There are guides for informal visits. To arrange for a visit, contact Teresa Stricklin, Coordinator of Recruiting, Information Center, JSU, at (205) 782–5260.

Financial Aid: In 1993–94, 52% of all current freshmen and 48% of continuing students received some form of financial aid. About 48% of freshmen and 46% of continuing students received need-based aid. The average freshman award was $1500. Of that total, scholarships or need-based grants averaged $1000 ($4000 maximum); loans averaged $2000 ($2625 maximum); and work contracts averaged $2100 ($2300 maximum). Thirty percent of undergraduate students work part-time. Average earnings from campus work for the school year are $2300. The FAFSA financial statement is required. The deadline for financial aid applications is April 1.

International Students: There are currently 126 international students enrolled. They must take the TOEFL and achieve a minimum score of 500. The student must also take the SAT I or the ACT.

Computers: The university provides computer facilities for student use. The mainframe is an IBM 9121. The mainframe is accessed via computer laboratories at various locations on campus. All students may access the system during specific laboratory hours. There are no time limits on using the system. There are no fees.

Graduates: In 1992–93, 1101 bachelor's degrees were awarded. The most popular majors among graduates were elementary education (12%), secondary education (9%), and criminal justice (3%). Some 150 companies recruited on campus in an earlier year.

Admissions Contact: Jerry D. Smith, Dean of Admissions and Records.

JUDSON COLLEGE
Marion, AL 36756

B-3

(205) 683-6161, ext. 834
(800) 447-9472 (out-of-state)

Full-time: 263 women	Faculty: 27
Part-time: 168 women	Ph.D.s: 59%
Graduate: none	Student/Faculty: 10 to 1
Year: 2–2–1, summer session	Tuition: $5560
Application Deadline: August 30	Room & Board: $3500
Freshman Class: 299 applied, 222 accepted, 112 enrolled	
ACT: 22	**COMPETITIVE**

Judson College, founded in 1838, is a private women's liberal arts college affiliated with the Alabama Baptist Convention. In addition to regional accreditation, Judson has baccalaureate program accreditation with NCATE. The library contains 66,000 volumes, 501 microform items, and 2500 audiovisual forms, and subscribes to 358 periodicals. Computerized library sources and services include the card catalog and database searching. Special learning facilities include a learning resource center. The 83-acre campus is in a small town 27 miles west of Selma. Including residence halls, there are 18 buildings on campus.

Student Life: About 74% of undergraduates are from Alabama. Students come from 6 states and 2 foreign countries. Ninety-seven percent are from public schools; 3% from private. Ninety-two percent are white. Most are Protestant. The average age of freshmen is 18; all undergraduates, 20. Forty-three percent drop out by the end of their first year; 50% remain to graduate.

Housing: A total of 310 students can be accommodated in college housing. College-sponsored living facilities include dormitories. On-campus housing is guaranteed for all 4 years. Eighty-five percent of students live on campus; of those, 40% remain on campus on weekends. Alcohol is not permitted. All students may keep cars on campus.

Activities: There are no fraternities on campus. There are 21 groups on campus, including choir, chorale, chorus, computers, dance, drama, drill team, honors, musical theater, newspaper, photography, political, religious, social service, student government, and yearbook. Popular campus events include Parents Day, Christmas Tea, Concert Lecture Series, J-Day, Winter Ball, Old South Ball, and Junior-Sophomore Weekend.

Sports: Athletic and recreation facilities include a swimming pool, riding stables, and tennis courts.

Disabled Students: Thirty percent of the campus is accessible to disabled students. The following facilities are available: elevators, special parking, and lowered telephones.

Services: In addition to many counseling and information services, tutoring is available in most subjects.

Campus Safety and Security: Campus safety and security measures include 24-hour foot and vehicle patrol, self defense education, pamphlets, posters, and films, and lighted pathways and sidewalks.

Programs of Study: Judson awards the B.A. and B.S degrees. Bachelor's degrees are awarded in BIOLOGICAL SCIENCE (biology/biological science), BUSINESS (business administration and management), COMMUNICATIONS AND THE ARTS (English, modern language, music, and Spanish), COMPUTER AND PHYSICAL SCIENCE (chemistry, computer science, and mathematics), EDUCATION (elementary, middle school, music, science, and secondary), ENGINEERING AND ENVIRONMENTAL DESIGN (interior design), HEALTH PROFESSIONS (predentistry, premedicine, and preveterinary science), SOCIAL SCIENCE (prelaw, psychology, religion, social science, social work, and sociology). Equine science, biology, education, psychology, and history are the strongest academically. Biology has the largest enrollment.

Required: All students are required to complete courses in English, history, science, religion, mathematics, fine arts, computer literacy, and health/physical education. A total of 128 credit hours, with a minimum GPA of 2.0, is required in order to graduate.

Special: Cross-registration with the Marion Military Institution is available for ROTC students. B.A.-B.S. degrees are offered in criminal justice, mathematics, biology, business, chemistry, and computer information systems. Study abroad in 4 countries, dual majors in education and music, 3–2 engineering degrees, work-study programs, and internships are offered. The External Degree Program offers credit for prior learning experience and provides individually paced instruction leading to a baccalaureate degree. There are 6 national honor societies on campus. Six departments have honors programs.

Faculty/Classroom: Forty-seven percent of faculty are male; 53%, female. All teach undergraduates. The average class size in an introductory lecture is 25 and in a regular course offering, 15.

Admissions: About 74% of the 1993–94 applicants were accepted. The ACT scores for the 1993–94 freshman class were as follows: 38% below 21, 32% between 21 and 23, 17% between 24 and 26, 8% between 27 and 28, and 5% above 28. About 41% of the current freshmen were in the top fifth of their class; 92% were in the top two fifths. Six freshmen graduated first in their class.

Requirements: A minimum GPA of 2.0 is required. The SAT I or ACT is required, with a minimum composite score of 20 on the ACT. Applicants should have completed 12 high school credits, including 4 in English, or the GED equivalent. An interview is recommended. AP and CLEP credits are accepted. Important factors used in the admissions decision are advanced placement or honor courses, extracurricular activities record, evidence of special talent, leadership record, personality, and intangible qualities.

Procedure: Freshmen are admitted fall and winter. Entrance exams should be taken in the spring of the junior year. Applications should be filed by August 30 for fall entry and January 1 for winter entry, along with an application fee of $20. Notification is sent on a rolling basis. There is an early admissions plan.

Transfer: Fifteen transfer students enrolled in 1993–94. Transfer students must have a minimum GPA of 2.0 and be eligible to return to the school from which they transfer. A total of 30 credits out of 128 must be completed at Judson.

Visiting: There are regularly scheduled orientations for prospective students, consisting of 2 college Pre View Days in the fall and spring. There are guides for informal visits and visitors may sit in on classes and stay overnight at the school. To arrange for a visit, contact Admissions at (205) 683-6363, ext. 1.

Financial Aid: In 1993–94, 98% of all current freshmen and 94% of continuing students received some form of financial aid. About 67% of freshmen and 52% of continuing students received need-based aid. The average freshman award was $7246. Of that total, scholarships or need-based grants averaged $3821 ($6550 maximum); loans averaged $2625; and work contracts averaged $800 ($1000 maximum). Forty-three percent of undergraduate students work part-time. Average earnings from campus work for the school year are $500. The average financial indebtedness of the 1992–93 graduate was $8034. The FFS is required. The deadline for financial aid applications is April 1.

International Students: There are currently 3 international students enrolled. They must take the TOEFL and achieve a minimum score of 500. The student must also take the SAT I or the ACT, with a minimum composite score of 20 required on the ACT.

Computers: The college provides computer facilities for student use. The mainframe is an IBM S/36 and Novell network 486's. There are 24 microcomputers available for students use in the computer center. Other computer facilities are available in each academic department. All students may access the system. It may be used Monday through Friday from 8 A.M. to 10 P.M. Saturday afternoon and Sunday night. There are no time limits on using the system.

Graduates: In 1992–93, 57 bachelor's degrees were awarded. The most popular majors among graduates were business (20%), education (13%), and psychology (11%). Within an average freshman class, 18% graduate in 3 years, 22% in 4 years, and 3% in 5 years. Some 36 companies recruited on campus in 1992–93. In the 1992 graduating class, 34% were enrolled in graduate school within 6 months of graduation; 59% had found employment.

Admissions Contact: Ginger Bagby, Director of Admissions.

LIVINGSTON UNIVERSITY
Livingston, AL 35470

A-3

(205) 652-9661
(800) 621-8044 (out-of-state)

Full-time: 744 men, 883 women	Faculty: 87; IIB, --$
Part-time: 57 men, 75 women	Ph.D.s: 65%
Graduate: 61 men, 165 women	Student/Faculty: 19 to 1
Year: quarters, summer session	Tuition: $1728
Application Deadline: open	Room & Board: $2251
Freshman Class: 1206 applied, 957 accepted, 444 enrolled	
ACT: 19	**COMPETITIVE**

Livingston University, founded in 1835, is a state-controlled, coeducational institution offering programs in liberal arts and sciences, business and commerce, general studies, and education. There are 5 undergraduate schools and one graduate school. In addition to regional accreditation, Livingston has baccalaureate program accreditation with NLN. The library contains 120,000 volumes, 485,657 microform

items, and 7500 audiovisual forms, and subscribes to 700 periodicals. Computerized library sources and services include interlibrary loans. Special learning facilities include an art gallery and radio station. The 600-acre campus is in a small town 35 miles east of Meridian. Including residence halls, there are 36 buildings on campus.

Student Life: About 80% of undergraduates are from Alabama. Students come from 27 states and 6 foreign countries. Sixty-eight percent are white; 31% African American. The average age of freshmen is 18; all undergraduates, 21. Thirty-five percent drop out by the end of their first year; 35% remain to graduate.

Housing: A total of 903 students can be accommodated in college housing. College-sponsored living facilities include single-sex dormitories, on-campus apartments, and married-student housing. In addition there are honors houses. On-campus housing is guaranteed for all 4 years. Alcohol is not permitted. All students may keep cars on campus.

Activities: About 10% of men belong to 6 national fraternities; about 6% of women belong to 4 national sororities. There are 30 groups on campus, including band, cheerleading, choir, chorus, drama, drill team, ethnic, honors, international, jazz band, marching band, newspaper, pep band, photography, political, professional, radio and TV, religious, social, student government, symphony, and yearbook. Popular campus events include Springfest and Club Luie.

Sports: There are 4 intercollegiate sports for men and 4 for women, and 8 intramural sports for men and 8 for women. Athletic and recreation facilities include an 800-seat gymnasium, a 7500-seat football stadium, a baseball field, tennis and racquetball courts, a pool, weight rooms, a lake, and hiking trails.

Disabled Students: Ninety-five percent of the campus is accessible to disabled students. The following facilities are available: wheelchair ramps, elevators, special parking, specially equipped rest rooms, special class scheduling, and lowered drinking fountains.

Services: In addition to many counseling and information services, tutoring is available in most subjects. There is also remedial math, reading, and writing.

Campus Safety and Security: Campus safety and security measures include 24-hour foot and vehicle patrol, informal discussions, pamphlets, posters, films, and lighted pathways and sidewalks.

Programs of Study: Livingston awards the B.A., B.S., B.M.Ed., and B.T. degrees. Associate and master's degrees also are awarded. Bachelor's degrees are awarded in BIOLOGICAL SCIENCE (biology/biological science), BUSINESS (accounting, business administration and management, and marketing/retailing/merchandising), COMMUNICATIONS AND THE ARTS (English and music), COMPUTER AND PHYSICAL SCIENCE (chemistry, computer science, mathematics, and physics), EDUCATION (art, business, early childhood, elementary, health, industrial arts, middle school, music, science, secondary, and special), HEALTH PROFESSIONS (medical laboratory technology, predentistry, and premedicine), SOCIAL SCIENCE (history, political science/government, prelaw, social science, and sociology). English, business, and sciences are the strongest academically. Education and business have the largest enrollments.

Required: All students must complete at least 192 quarter hours with a minimum GPA of 2.0 in order to graduate.

Special: There is a 3–2 engineering program with Auburn University. The 2-year technical division offers programs leading to a possible B.T. degree. B.A.-B.S. degrees, a co-op program in environmental science, and an accelerated degree are available. Nondegree study is possible. There is a freshman honors program on campus, as well as 5 national honor societies. Four departments have honors programs.

Faculty/Classroom: Sixty percent of faculty are male; 40%, female. Graduate students teach 4% of introductory courses. The average class size in an introductory lecture is 30; in a laboratory, 18; and in a regular course offering, 15.

Admissions: About 79% of the 1993–94 applicants were accepted. The ACT scores for the 1993–94 freshman class were as follows: 71% below 21, 16% between 21 and 23, 10% between 24 and 26, and 3% between 27 and 28.

Requirements: A minimum GPA of 2.0 is required. The SAT I or ACT is required, with a minimum composite score of 17 on the ACT for unconditional admission. In addition, applicants should have completed 15 high school credits or the GED equivalent. AP and CLEP credits are accepted.

Procedure: Freshmen are admitted to all sessions. Entrance exams should be taken during the junior or senior year. Application deadlines are open. The application fee is $15. Notification is sent on a rolling basis. There are early admissions and deferred admissions plans.

Transfer: About 173 transfer students enrolled in 1993–94. Transfer applicants must have maintained a minimum GPA of 2.0 in all previous college courses. A total of 48 quarter hours out of 192 must be completed at Livingston.

Visiting: There are regularly scheduled orientations for prospective students. There are guides for informal visits and visitors may sit in on classes and stay overnight at the school. To arrange for a visit, contact Ervin Wood at (205) 652–9661, ext. 352.

Financial Aid: In an earlier year 75% of all students received some form of financial aid. The FAF, FFS or SFS is required. The deadline for financial aid applications is May 1.

International Students: There are currently 18 international students enrolled. They must take the TOEFL and achieve a minimum score of 500. The student must also take the ACT.

Computers: The college provides computer facilities for student use. The mainframe is an IBM 9375. All students may access the system. There are no time limits on using the system. The fee is $20.

Graduates: In 1992–93 247 bachelor's degrees were awarded. The most popular majors among graduates were elementary education (19%), business administration (15%), and environmental science (6%). Within an average freshman class, 17% graduate in 3 years, 28% in 4 years, 33% in 5 years, and 37% in 6 years. Some 25 companies usually recruited on campus.

Admissions Contact: Richard Hester, Director of Admissions.

MILES COLLEGE
C-2

Fairfield, AL 35064

Full-time, part-time: 864

Graduate: none

Year: semesters, summer session

Application Deadline: open

(205) 923–2771, ext. 226 or 221

Faculty: 40

Ph.D.s: 37%

Student/Faculty: 22 to 1

Tuition: $3875

Room & Board: $3275

Freshman Class: n/av

ACT: required

NONCOMPETITIVE

Miles College, founded in 1908, is a private, coeducational institution affiliated with and controlled by the Christian Methodist Episcopal Church. The college offers undergraduate programs in the liberal arts and sciences, business, and education. There are 5 undergraduate schools. The library contains 180,000 volumes and 850 microform items, and subscribes to 250 periodicals. Special learning facilities include a learning resource center, an African-American materials center, and a media center. The 35-acre campus is in an urban area 7 miles from downtown Birmingham. Including residence halls, there are 17 buildings on campus.

Student Life: About 85% of undergraduates are from Alabama. Ninety-eight percent are African American. The average age of freshmen is 18; all undergraduates, 22. Fifteen percent drop out by the end of their first year.

Housing: A total of 318 students can be accommodated in college housing. College-sponsored living facilities include single-sex dormitories. On-campus housing is available on a first-come, first-served basis. Priority is given to out-of-town students. Alcohol is not permitted. All students may keep cars on campus.

Activities: About 15% of men belong to 4 local and 4 national fraternities; about 15% of women belong to 4 local and 4 national sororities. There are many groups and organizations on campus, including choir, drama, ethnic, honors, international, literary magazine, newspaper, professional, radio and tv, religious, student government, and yearbook. Popular campus events include Founders Day, Homecoming, Senior Class Day, Spring Festival, Matriculation Day, and Honors Day.

Sports: There are 6 intercollegiate sports for men and 4 for women, and 5 intramural sports for men and for women. Athletic and recreation facilities include a 2000-seat football field, a 1500-seat gymnasium, a weight room, and a baseball field.

Services: In addition to many counseling and information services, tutoring is available in every subject. There is also remedial math, reading, and writing. Miles offers a Student Support Services Program for students with an academically challenged developmental background.

Programs of Study: Miles awards the B.A. and B.S. degrees. Associate degrees are also awarded. Bachelor's degrees are awarded in BIOLOGICAL SCIENCE (biology/biological science), BUSINESS (business administration and management), COMMUNICATIONS AND THE ARTS (communications, English, and music), COMPUTER AND PHYSICAL SCIENCE (chemistry, mathematics, and natural sciences), EDUCATION (early childhood, elementary, secondary, and social science), ENGINEERING AND ENVIRONMENTAL DESIGN (preengineering), HEALTH PROFESSIONS (predentistry, prepharmacy, and preveterinary science), SOCIAL SCIENCE (political science/government, social science, and social work). Business is the strongest academically. Early childhood education, elementary education, political science, and social science have the largest enrollments.

Required: To graduate, all students must complete the 59-hour general education requirement and a computer course. Attendance at chapel services is required at least once a week. At least 124 semester hours must be completed for a bachelor's degree. Students must

be able to pass a relevant graduate-level examination, either the GRE, the GMAT, or, for education majors, the Alabama Initial Certification Test.

Special: Miles offers a B.A.-B.S. degree, internships for business majors, dual majors, nondegree study, and work-study programs. Co-op programs are available in allied health science with the University of Alabama at Birmingham, and in engineering, physics, or veterinary medicine with Tuskegee Institute and Alabama A&M University. There is a freshman honors program on campus, as well as one national honor society.

Requirements: The SAT I or ACT is required. In addition, students should be graduates of an accredited high school or hold a GED. A personal interview is recommended.

Procedure: Freshmen are admitted to all sessions. Application deadlines are open. Application fee is $25. The college accepts all applicants.

Transfer: A total of 32 credits out of 124 must be completed at Miles.

Visiting: There are guides for informal visits and visitors may sit in on classes. To arrange for a visit, contact Admissions at (205) 923–2771.

Financial Aid: Miles is a member of CSS. The FAF or FFS is required. The deadline for financial aid applications is June 15.

International Students: There are currently 9 international students enrolled. They must take the TOEFL or the University of Michigan Language Test and achieve a minimum score on the TOEFL of 450. The student must also take the SAT I or the ACT.

Computers: The college provides computer facilities for student use. All students may access the system. There are no time limits on using the system. The fees are $20.

Admissions Contact: Gloria Beverly, Admissions Director.

MOBILE COLLEGE
(See University of Mobile)

OAKWOOD COLLEGE
C-1
Huntsville, AL 35896 (205) 726–7000; (800) 824–5312 (out-of-state)

Full-time: 547 men, 769 women	Faculty: 77; IIB, --$
Part-time: 66 men, 69 women	Ph.D.s: 52%
Graduate: none	Student/Faculty: 17 to 1
Year: quarters, summer session	Tuition: $6519
Application Deadline: open	Room & Board: $3486
Freshman Class: 949 applied, 605 accepted, 385 enrolled	
SAT I Verbal/Math: 378/382	ACT: 17 **COMPETITIVE**

Oakwood College, founded in 1896, is an historically black, coeducational Seventh-day Adventist institution offering undergraduate programs in business and education, humanities, natural sciences and mathematics, religion and theology, and social sciences. In addition to regional accreditation, Oakwood has baccalaureate program accreditation with ADA, CSWE, NCATE, and NLN. The library contains 109,317 volumes, 1500 microform items, and 2780 audiovisual forms, and subscribes to 530 periodicals. Special learning facilities include a learning resource center, radio station, and a black history museum. The 1185-acre campus is in a suburban area 5 miles northwest of Huntsville. Including residence halls, there are 30 buildings on campus.

Student Life: About 82% of undergraduates are from out-of-state, mostly the Northeast. Students come from 38 states, 31 foreign countries, and Canada. Sixty-one percent are from public schools; 39% from private. Eighty-seven percent are African American; 12% foreign nationals. The average age of freshmen is 19; all undergraduates, 22. Thirty-four percent drop out by the end of their first year.

Housing: A total of 1142 students can be accommodated in college housing. College-sponsored living facilities include single-sex dormitories and married-student housing. On-campus housing is guaranteed for all 4 years. Seventy percent of students live on campus; of those, 98% remain on campus on weekends. Alcohol is not permitted. Upperclassmen may keep cars on campus.

Activities: There are no fraternities or sororities on campus. There are some groups and organizations on campus, including band, choir, chorale, international, newspaper, radio and TV, religious, student government, and yearbook. Popular campus events include Convocations, the Arts and Lecture Series, and Homecoming Weekend.

Sports: There are 4 intramural sports for men and 3 for women. Athletic and recreation facilities include a gymnasium, a skating rink, an Olympic-size pool, tennis courts, playing fields, racquetball courts, and a weight room.

Disabled Students: The following facilities are available: wheelchair ramps, elevators, special parking, and specially equipped rest rooms.

Services: In addition to many counseling and information services, tutoring is available in every subject. There is also remedial math, reading, and writing, and remedial psychology. Testing, counseling, and developmental guidance services are available through the counseling center.

Campus Safety and Security: Campus safety and security measures include 24-hour foot and vehicle patrol, escort service, shuttle buses, and informal discussions. In addition, there are pamphlets, posters, films and lighted pathways and sidewalks.

Programs of Study: Oakwood awards the B.A., B.S., and B.S.W. degrees. Associate degrees also are awarded. Bachelor's degrees are awarded in BIOLOGICAL SCIENCE (biochemistry and biology/ biological science), BUSINESS (accounting and office supervision and management), COMMUNICATIONS AND THE ARTS (communications, English, music, and music performance), COMPUTER AND PHYSICAL SCIENCE (chemistry, computer science, mathematics, and natural sciences), EDUCATION (business, elementary, English, home economics, music, physical, science, and social science), HEALTH PROFESSIONS (nursing), SOCIAL SCIENCE (economics, history, home economics, ministries, psychology, religion, religious education, and social work). Biochemistry, chemistry, and nursing are the strongest academically. Business has the largest enrollment.

Required: To graduate, students must complete 192 quarter hours, including 45 in the major and 40 in upper-division courses, with a GPA of 2.0. Regular chapel attendance is required. All students must complete 70 to 82 quarter credits in a liberal arts core, as well as 8 to 12 credits in foreign language (for B.A. candidates) and 6 in health and education. Specific coursework is required in writing, speech, and religion. All students must pass an English proficiency examination and the senior exit examination for graduation.

Special: Students may cross-register with Alabama A&M, Athens State, or the University of Alabama at Huntsville. The college offers a student missionary abroad program as well as a study abroad program through the Adventist College consortium. Internships, work-study, dual and student-designed majors, independent study, life experience credit, and pass/fail options are also available. A second bachelor's degree is offered to students completing at least 240 quarter credits.

Faculty/Classroom: Fifty-three percent of faculty are male; 47%, female. All teach undergraduates. The average class size in an introductory lecture, a laboratory, and in a regular course offering is 30.

Admissions: About 64% of the 1993–94 applicants were accepted. The SAT scores for the 1993–94 freshman class were as follows: Verbal—90% below 500, 5% between 500 and 599, and 5% between 600 and 700; Math—83% below 500, 13% between 500 and 599, and 4% between 600 and 700. The ACT scores were 82% below 21, 13% between 21 and 23, 4% between 24 and 26, 1% between 27 and 28, and 1% above 28.

Requirements: A minimum GPA of 2.0 is required. The SAT I or ACT is recommended. Applicants should be high school graduates with a minimum GPA of 2.0 and at least 11 academic units, distributed as follows: 4 in English, 2 each in mathematics, science, and social studies, and 1 in typing. The GED is accepted. Two character references are required. Students with GPAs between 1.7 and 2.0 may be admitted on probation. Applicants admitted without test scores must take the ACT during freshman orientation. CLEP credit is accepted.

Procedure: Freshmen are admitted to all sessions. Entrance exams should be taken before high school graduation. Application deadlines are open. The application fee is $15 for U.S. residents and $25 for international students. Notification is sent on a rolling basis. There is an early decision plan.

Transfer: About 90 transfer students enrolled in 1993–94. Applicants must submit a college transcript and a statement of honorable dismissal. Grades of C minus or better transfer for credit. A total of 48 quarter hour credits out of 192 must be completed at Oakwood.

Visiting: There are guides for informal visits and visitors may sit in on classes. To arrange for a visit, contact Enrollment Management at (800) 824–5312.

Financial Aid: In 1993–94, 66% of all current freshmen and 60% of continuing students received some form of financial aid. The average freshman award was $6125. Of that total, scholarships or need-based grants averaged $900 ($5178 maximum); loans averaged $2625 ($6625 maximum); and work contracts averaged $800 ($1200 maximum). The average financial indebtedness of the 1992–93 graduate was $15,500. Oakwood is a member of CSS. The FAF, the college's own financial statement and the student and parent federal income tax returns are required. The deadline for financial aid applications is March 15.

International Students: There are currently 157 international students enrolled. Students must submit SAT I or ACT scores, or they may take the ACT on campus prior to registration..

Computers: The college provides computer facilities for student use. Microcomputer facilities are available in various departmental computer laboratories. There are no time limits on using the system and no fees.

Graduates: In 1992–93, 168 bachelor's degrees were awarded. The most popular majors among graduates were biology (11%), theology (10%), and psychology (10%). Some 100 companies recruited on campus in 1992–93.

Admissions Contact: Trevor Fraser, Enrollment Management Director.

SAMFORD UNIVERSITY
Birmingham, AL 35229

C-2

(205) 870–2901
(800) 888–7218 (out-of-state)

Full-time: 1155 men, 1802 women	Faculty: 172; IIA, av$
Part-time: 123 men, 279 women	Ph.D.s: 83%
Graduate: 689 men, 498 women	Student/Faculty: 17 to 1
Year: 4–1–4, summer session	Tuition: $7770
Application Deadline: open	Room & Board: $3630
Freshman Class: 1511 applied, 1396 accepted, 692 enrolled	
SAT I or ACT: required	**VERY COMPETITIVE**

Samford University, founded in 1841, is a private, coeducational liberal arts school and an agency of the Alabama Baptist Convention. There are 6 undergraduate and 2 graduate schools. In addition to regional accreditation, Samford has baccalaureate program accreditation with ACPE, ADA, AHEA, NASM, NCATE, and NLN. The 3 libraries contain 752,501 volumes, 236,588 microform items, and 46,904 audiovisual forms, and subscribe to 2600 periodicals. Computerized library sources and services include the card catalog and database searching. Special learning facilities include a learning resource center, art gallery, and radio station. The 280-acre campus is in a suburban area 4 miles south of Birmingham. Including residence halls, there are 50 buildings on campus.

Student Life: About 56% of undergraduates are from Alabama. Students come from 43 states, 42 foreign countries, and Canada. Seventy-one percent are from public schools; 29% from private. Ninety percent are white. Eighty-one percent are Protestant; 13% claim no religious affiliation. The average age of freshmen is 18; all undergraduates, 23. Seven percent drop out by the end of their first year.

Housing: A total of 1760 students can be accommodated in college housing. College-sponsored living facilities include single-sex dormitories, married-student housing, fraternity houses, and sorority houses. In addition, there are fraternity chapter houses, and a hotel in London for study abroad plans. On-campus housing is available on a first-come, first-served basis. Sixty percent of students live on campus; of those, 50% remain on campus on weekends. Alcohol is not permitted. All students may keep cars on campus.

Activities: About 30% of men belong to 4 national fraternities; about 30% of women belong to 6 national sororities. There are 110 groups on campus, including band, cheerleading, choir, chorus, computers, drama, drill team, ethnic, honors, international, jazz band, literary magazine, marching band, newspaper, opera, pep band, political, professional, radio and TV, religious, social, social service, student government, and yearbook. Popular campus events include Step Sing, Homecoming, and Spring Fling/Picnic.

Sports: There are 8 intercollegiate sports for men and 7 for women, and 31 intramural sports for men and women. Athletic and recreation facilities include a 6000-seat stadium, a 4000-seat gymnasium, intramural fields, tennis and racquetball courts, practice fields, and a swimming pool.

Disabled Students: Fifty percent of the campus is accessible to disabled students. The following facilities are available: wheelchair ramps, elevators, special parking, specially equipped rest rooms, special class scheduling, lowered drinking fountains, and dormitory rooms with wheelchair access.

Services: In addition to many counseling and information services, tutoring is available in most subjects. There is also a reader service for the blind, and remedial math, reading, and writing.

Campus Safety and Security: Campus safety and security measures include 24-hour foot and vehicle patrol, self defense education, informal discussions, and pamphlets, posters, and films. In addition, there are lighted pathways and sidewalks.

Programs of Study: Samford awards the B.A., B.S., B.B.A., B.Mus., B.Pharm., B.S.E.D, and B.S.N. degrees. Associate, master's, and doctoral degrees also are awarded. Bachelor's degrees are awarded in BIOLOGICAL SCIENCE (biology/biological science), BUSINESS (international business management and marketing/retailing/merchandising), COMMUNICATIONS AND THE ARTS (communications, design, dramatic arts, English, fine arts, French, German, journalism, music, Spanish, and speech/debate/rhetoric), COMPUTER AND PHYSICAL SCIENCE (chemistry, computer science, mathematics, and physics), EDUCATION (art, early childhood, elementary, foreign languages, health, home economics, middle school, music, science, and secondary), HEALTH PROFESSIONS (medical laboratory technology, nursing, occupational therapy, and pharmacy), SOCIAL SCIENCE (community services, food science, history, international relations, prelaw, psychology, public administration, religion, and sociology). Pharmacy, business, and nursing are the strongest academically. Business, pharmacy, and education have the largest enrollments.

Required: All students must receive an overall GPA of at least 2.0 and take at least 128 credits, including 30 semester hours in their major. Distribution requirements include 8 semester hours in laboratory science, 6 each in composition, mathematics, history, and religion, and 4 hours each in physical education and humanities. Students also must demonstrate writing proficiency.

Special: Co-op programs are offered in public administration, graphic design, business, computer science, art, journalism, and fashion merchandise. A 3–2 engineering degree is available with Auburn University, Georgia Institute of Technology, Washington University (St. Louis), and Mercer University. The School of Arts and Sciences offers an interdisciplinary core curriculum with team teaching. Cross-registration with Birmingham-Southern College and the University of Alabama at Birmingham, study abroad in London, additional major options, internships, work-study programs, credit for life experience, and pass/fail options are offered. There is a freshman honors program on campus, as well as 11 national honor societies. One department has an honors program.

Faculty/Classroom: Seventy-five percent of faculty are male; 25%, female. Eighty-two percent teach undergraduates. No introductory courses are taught by graduate students. The average class size in an introductory lecture is 35; in a laboratory, 25; and in a regular course offering, 20.

Admissions: About 92% of the 1993–94 applicants were accepted. The ACT scores for the 1993–94 freshman class were as follows: 14% below 21, 33% between 21 and 23, 29% between 24 and 26, 17% between 27 and 28, and 7% above 28. About 59% of the current freshmen were in the top fifth of their class; 85% were in the top two fifths. There were 12 National Merit finalists. Twenty freshmen graduated first in their class.

Requirements: A minimum GPA of 3.0 is required. The SAT I or ACT is required. Applicants need 18 academic credits and 16 Carnegie units, including 4 in English. The university also recommends that students have 2 units each in foreign language, mathematics, science, and social studies. In addition, an essay is required and an interview suggested. The GED is accepted. AP and CLEP credits are accepted. Important factors used in the admissions decision are advanced placement or honor courses, leadership record, recommendations by school officials, recommendations by alumni, and evidence of special talent.

Procedure: Freshmen are admitted fall, spring, and summer. Entrance exams should be taken in the junior year. Application deadlines are open. Application fee is $25. Notification of early decision is sent December 10; regular decision, on a rolling basis. There are early decision and early admissions plans. A waiting list is an active part of the admissions procedure, with about 6% of applicants on the list.

Transfer: Transfer applicants need 24 semester hours of credit with a minimum GPA of 2.5. A total of 32 credits out of 128 must be completed at Samford.

Visiting: There are regularly scheduled orientations for prospective students, consisting of interviews and campus tours daily by appointment. There are guides for informal visits and visitors may sit in on classes. To arrange for a visit, contact the Admissions Office at (800) 888–7218.

Financial Aid: In an earlier year, 80% of all current freshmen and 80% of continuing students received some form of financial aid. About 45% of freshmen and 55% of continuing students received need-based aid. The average freshman award was $3600. Of that total, scholarships or need-based grants averaged $1600 ($10,200 maximum); loans averaged $1250 ($4125 maximum); and work contracts averaged $600 ($2550 maximum). Twenty-five percent of undergraduate students work part-time. Average earnings from campus work for the school year are $934. The average financial indebtedness of the 1992–93 graduate was $2800. Samford is a member of CSS. The FAF is required. The deadline for financial aid applications is March 1.

International Students: There are currently 46 international students enrolled. The school actively recruits these students. They must take the TOEFL and achieve a minimum score of 550.

Computers: The college provides computer facilities for student use. The mainframe is an Amdahl. Ten computer laboratories are available for academic and student use. One is available 24 hours per day. Microcomputers include IBM, Zenith, and Macintosh. Computers are used in all instruction programs. Computer science majors with personal computers may access the system. There are no time limits on using the system and no fees.

Graduates: In 1992–93, 642 bachelor's degrees were awarded. The most popular majors among graduates were pharmacy (14%), management (11%), and elementary education (4%). Within an average freshman class, 68% graduate in 3 years. Some 111 companies recruited on campus in 1992–93.

Admissions Contact: Don Belcher, Dean of Admissions and Financial Aid.

SELMA UNIVERSITY

B-4

Selma, AL 36701 (205) 874-9009

Full-time: 117 men, 95 women | Faculty: 19
Part-time: 41 men, 11 women | Ph.D.s: 47%
Graduate: none | Student/Faculty: 11 to 1
Year: semesters, summer session | Tuition: $4045
Application Deadline: open | Room & Board: $1740
Freshman Class: 275 applied, 263 accepted, 184 enrolled
SAT I or ACT: not required | **NONCOMPETITIVE**

Selma University, founded in 1878, is a small, coeducational liberal arts institution affiliated with the Baptist Convention. Special learning facilities include a computer-aided writing laboratory. The campus is in a suburban area 50 miles east of Montgomery. Including residence halls, there are 16 buildings on campus.

Student Life: About 90% of undergraduates are from Alabama. Students come from 13 states and 1 foreign country. All are from public schools. Ninety-nine percent are African American. The average age of freshmen is 19; all undergraduates, 21. Ten percent drop out by the end of their first year; 75% remain to graduate.

Housing: A total of 200 students can be accommodated in college housing. College-sponsored living facilities include single-sex dormitories. On-campus housing is guaranteed for all 4 years. Alcohol is not permitted. All students may keep cars on campus.

Activities: There are no fraternities or sororities on campus. There are some groups and organizations on campus, including cheerleading, choir, chorus, drama, newspaper, religious, student government, and yearbook. Popular campus events include Religious Emphasis Week, Founders Day, Freshman Sophomore Ball, Coronation Ball, and the Lyceum Series.

Sports: There are 2 intercollegiate sports for men and 1 for women, and 4 intramural sports for men and 3 for women. Athletic and recreation facilities include a gymnasium and a 400-seat stadium.

Disabled Students: Ten percent of the campus is accessible to disabled students. The following facilities are available: special parking and specially equipped rest rooms.

Programs of Study: SU awards the B.A. and B.S. degrees. Associate degrees also are awarded. Bachelor's degrees are awarded in BIOLOGICAL SCIENCE (biology/biological science), BUSINESS (business administration and management, management information systems, and secretarial studies/office management), COMMUNICATIONS AND THE ARTS (English and music), COMPUTER AND PHYSICAL SCIENCE (chemistry, computer science, information sciences and systems, mathematics, and physics), EDUCATION (education and physical), SOCIAL SCIENCE (history, political science/government, religion, and sociology).

Required: To graduate, all students must complete at least 126 semester hours, including 38 core curriculum credits and 12 general education electives, with a GPA of 2.0. Regular chapel attendance is required. All students must pass the English proficiency writing and oral communications tests. B.S. candidates must pass a technical writing course and a comprehensive exam in the major.

Special: The university offers work-study programs and a general education degree.

Faculty/Classroom: Seventy-five percent of faculty are male; 25%, female.

Admissions: About 96% of the 1993–94 applicants were accepted. The SAT scores for the 1993–94 freshman class were as follows: Verbal—80% below 500 and 20% between 500 and 599; Math—20% below 500 and 80% between 500 and 599. About 12% of the current freshmen were in the top fifth of their class; 42% were in the top two fifths.

Requirements: Applicants should be graduates of an accredited secondary school with 20 to 22 Carnegie units. The GED is accepted. AP credits are accepted.

Procedure: Freshmen are admitted fall and spring. Application deadlines are open. The university accepts all applicants. Notification is sent on a rolling basis. There is an early decision plan.

Transfer: Applicants should present a GPA of 2.0 in all college work. At least 33 hours of upper-division courses must be completed at the university.

Visiting: There are regularly scheduled orientations for prospective students. There are guides for informal visits and visitors may sit in on classes and stay overnight at the school. To arrange for a visit, contact the Admissions Office.

Financial Aid: In 1993–94, 95% of continuing students received some form of financial aid. SU is a member of CSS. The FFS is required.

International Students: The school actively recruits international students. They must take the TOEFL. The student must also take the university's English placement test prior to registration.

Computers: The university provides computer facilities for student use. The mainframe is an IBM. The are also Apple microcomputers available in the science laboratory. All students may access the system 8 A.M. to 9:30 P.M. Monday through Thursday for 1 hour. The fees are $10.

Admissions Contact: Raymond C. Brown, Director of Admissions.

SPRING HILL COLLEGE

A-5

Mobile, AL 36608 (205) 460-2130

Full-time: 415 men, 518 women | Faculty: 64; IIB, -$
Part-time: 70 men, 142 women | Ph.D.s: 84%
Graduate: 43 men, 101 women | Student/Faculty: 15 to 1
Year: semesters, summer session | Tuition: $11,425
Application Deadline: August 15 | Room & Board: $4590
Freshman Class: 773 applied, 694 accepted, 230 enrolled
SAT I Verbal/Math: 545/500 | ACT: 24 | **COMPETITIVE +**

Spring Hill College, founded in 1830, is a private, coeducational liberal arts and sciences college operated by the Jesuits. There are 3 graduate schools. The library contains 150,000 volumes and 51,000 microform items, and subscribes to 764 periodicals. Computerized library sources and services include interlibrary loans and database searching. Special learning facilities include a radio station and a learning theater, and the Dauphin Island Sea Lab. The 500-acre campus is in a suburban area in Mobile. Including residence halls, there are 27 buildings on campus.

Student Life: About 56% of undergraduates are from out-of-state, mostly the South. Students come from 32 states, 8 foreign countries, and Canada. Thirty-two percent are from public schools; 68% from private. Eighty-six percent are white. Sixty-four percent are Catholic. The average age of freshmen is 18; all undergraduates, 20. Fourteen percent drop out by the end of their first year; 80% remain to graduate.

Housing: A total of 800 students can be accommodated in college housing. College-sponsored living facilities include single-sex and coed dormitories and on-campus apartments. In addition, there are honors houses and freshman dorms. On-campus housing is guaranteed for all 4 years. Seventy percent of students live on campus; of those, 90% remain on campus on weekends. All students may keep cars on campus.

Activities: About 35% of men belong to 2 local and 4 national fraternities; about 35% of women belong to 1 local and 4 national sororities. There are 40 groups on campus, including art, cheerleading, choir, chorale, computers, drama, ethnic, honors, international, literary magazine, musical theater, newspaper, political, professional, radio and TV, religious, social, social service, student government, and yearbook. Popular campus events include Mardi Gras, Oktoberfest, Hurricane Party, Art Shows, film festivals, Special Olympics, Greek Week, Powder-Puff Day and Badger Open.

Sports: There are 7 intercollegiate sports for men and 5 for women, and 10 intramural sports for men and 8 for women. Athletic and recreation facilities include an 18-hole golf course; tennis and basketball courts; baseball, football, and soccer fields; a 1000-seat gymnasium; a weight room; a sailing complex; and an outdoor sand volleyball area.

Disabled Students: Eighty percent of the campus is accessible to disabled students. The following facilities are available: wheelchair ramps, elevators, special parking, specially equipped rest rooms, special class scheduling, specially equipped dorm rooms and additional railings in classrooms.

Services: In addition to many counseling and information services, tutoring is available in most subjects, including all introductory courses. In addition, there is remedial math, reading, and writing.

Campus Safety and Security: Campus safety and security measures include 24-hour foot and vehicle patrol, self defense education, escort service, and pamphlets, posters, and films. In addition, there are emergency telephones and lighted pathways and sidewalks.

Programs of Study: Spring Hill awards the B.A., B.S., and B.G.S. degrees. Master's degrees are also awarded. Bachelor's degrees are awarded in BIOLOGICAL SCIENCE (biology/biological science and marine biology), BUSINESS (accounting, banking and finance, business administration and management, business economics, international business management, management science, and marketing/retailing/merchandising), COMMUNICATIONS AND THE ARTS (advertising, broadcasting, communications, English, fine arts, and journalism), COMPUTER AND PHYSICAL SCIENCE (chemistry, computer science, information sciences and systems, and mathematics), EDUCATION (art, early childhood, elementary, middle school, and secondary), ENGINEERING AND ENVIRONMENTAL DESIGN (preengineering), HEALTH PROFESSIONS (predentistry, premedicine, and preoptometry), SOCIAL SCIENCE (economics, history, philosophy, political science/government, prelaw, psychology, religion, social science, and sociology). Premedicine, political science, English, business administration and management, and computer science are the strongest academically. Communications/fine arts, social sciences, business management, and premedicine have the largest enrollments.

Required: All students must take courses in English composition and literature, history, philosophy, theology, mathematics, science, social science, fine arts, and a foreign language. A minimum of 128 credits, with 30 to 36 semester hours in the major, and a GPA of 2.0 or better are required in order to graduate.

Special: There are 3–2 engineering programs with Georgia Institute of Technology and Auburn University. Spring Hill is a member of the Marine Environmental Sciences Consortium and offers marine biology courses at the Dauphin Island Sea Lab. Study abroad is available throughout the world. Work-study programs and internships are possible with many companies, including IBM, International Paper, and WKRG-TV. The bachelor's degree may be earned in 3 years. Also available are B.A.-B.S. degrees, dual majors, student-designed majors, a Washington semester, and pass/fail options. Credit for life experience is offered. Nondegree study is possible. There is a freshman honors program on campus, as well as 6 national honor societies.

Faculty/Classroom: Seventy-four percent of faculty are male; 26%, female. All teach undergraduates, and do research. No introductory courses are taught by graduate students. The average class size in an introductory lecture is 25; in a laboratory, 18; and in a regular course offering, 22.

Admissions: About 90% of the 1993–94 applicants were accepted. The SAT scores for the 1993–94 freshman class were as follows: Verbal—59% below 500, 30% between 500 and 599, and 10% between 600 and 700; Math—39% below 500, 43% between 500 and 599, and 17% between 600 and 700. The ACT scores were 22% below 21, 32% between 21 and 23, 23% between 24 and 26, 15% between 27 and 28, and 8% above 28. About 47% of the current freshmen were in the top fifth of their class; 71% were in the top two fifths. Four freshmen graduated first in their class.

Requirements: Spring Hill requires applicants to be in the upper 50% of their class. A minimum GPA of 2.5 is required. The SAT or ACT is required. Applicants should have completed 16 high school units, including 4 in English, 2 each in mathematics, science, and social studies, and at least 2 in another academic area, or the GED equivalent. An essay and interview are recommended. AP and CLEP credits are accepted. Important factors used in the admissions decision are advanced placement or honor courses, recommendations by school officials, leadership record, parents or siblings attending the school, and extracurricular activities record.

Procedure: Freshmen are admitted to all sessions. Applications should be filed by August 15 for fall entry and December 15 for spring entry, along with an application fee of $25. Notification is sent on a rolling basis. There is an early admissions plan.

Transfer: About 49 transfer students enrolled in 1993–94. To apply as a transfer, applicants must have at least 20 semester or 30 quarter hours of credit and a minimum GPA of 2.0. An interview is recommended. A total of 24 credits out of 128 must be completed at Spring Hill.

Visiting: There are regularly scheduled orientations for prospective students, consisting of an admissions counselor appointment, faculty appointment, and lunch. There are guides for informal visits and visitors may sit in on classes and stay overnight at the school. To arrange for a visit, contact the Office of Admissions at (205) 460–2130.

Financial Aid: In 1993–94, 83% of all current freshmen and 84% of continuing students received some form of financial aid. About 66% of freshmen and 59% of continuing students received need-based aid. The average freshman award was $10,149. Of that total, scholarships or need-based grants averaged $7026 ($16,315 maximum); loans averaged $2570 ($4625 maximum); and work contracts averaged $559 ($1530 maximum). All undergraduate students work part-time. Average earnings from campus work for the school year are $559. The average financial indebtedness of the 1992–93 graduate was $5500. Spring Hill is a member of CSS. The FAFSA financial statement is required. The deadline for financial aid applications is March 1.

International Students: There are currently 24 international students enrolled. The school actively recruits these students. They must take the TOEFL or the University of Michigan Language Test and achieve a minimum score on the TOEFL of 500. Students with English as their first language must also take the SAT I or the ACT.

Computers: The college provides computer facilities for student use. The mainframe is a DEC VAX 3100. Twenty terminals in a centralized laboratory provide access to the mainframe and modems allow access from remote sites. Fifty IBM-compatible and 20 Macintosh microcomputers are available for student use in 4 laboratories. All students may access the system. It may be used from 8 A.M. to midnight 24 hours per day via modem. There are no time limits on using the system and no fees.

Graduates: In 1992–93, 187 bachelor's degrees were awarded. The most popular majors among graduates were social sciences (23%), business (21%), and communications (13%). Within an average freshman class, 2% graduate in 3 years, 74% in 4 years, 19% in 5 years, and 2% in 6 years. Some 25 companies recruited on campus in 1992–93. In the 1992 graduating class, 25% of the men and 35% of

the women were enrolled in graduate school within 6 months of graduation; 70% of the men and 60% of the women had found employment.

Admissions Contact: Timothy Williams, Director of Admissions.

STILLMAN COLLEGE
Tuscaloosa, AL 35403–9990

B-3

(205) 349–4240, ext. 411
(800) 841–5722 (out-of-state)

Full-time: 286 men, 646 women	Faculty: 50; IIB, --$
Part-time: 13 men, 8 women	Ph.D.s: 46%
Graduate: n/av	Student/Faculty: 17 to 1
Year: semesters, summer session	Tuition: $4460
Application Deadline: June 15	Room & Board: $2753
Freshman Class: 726 applied, 593 accepted, 240 enrolled	
SAT I or ACT: recommended	**NONCOMPETITIVE**

Stillman College, founded in 1876, is a small, private, coeducational liberal arts institution affiliated with the Presbyterian Church. The library contains 96,094 volumes and 1025 audiovisual forms, and subscribes to 384 periodicals. Computerized library sources and services include the card catalog. Special learning facilities include a learning resource center, an art gallery, and a radio station. The 100-acre campus is in a small town 60 miles from Birmingham.

Student Life: About 75% of undergraduates are from Alabama. Ninety-five percent are from public schools. The average age of freshmen is 18. Thirty-six percent drop out by the end of their first year; 44% remain to graduate.

Housing: A total of 623 students can be accommodated in college housing. College-sponsored living facilities include single-sex dormitories. On-campus housing is available on a first-come, first-served basis. Alcohol is not permitted. All students may keep cars on campus.

Activities: About 10% of men belong to 4 local fraternities; about 20% of women belong to 4 local sororities. There are some groups and organizations on campus, including band, chorus, drama, newspaper, pep band, religious, student government, and yearbook.

Disabled Students: Wheelchair ramps are available.

Services: In addition to many counseling and information services, tutoring is available in some subjects. In addition, there is remedial math, reading, and writing.

Programs of Study: Stillman awards the B.A. and B.S. degrees. Bachelor's degrees are awarded in BIOLOGICAL SCIENCE (biology/biological science), BUSINESS (business administration and management), COMMUNICATIONS AND THE ARTS (communications and music), COMPUTER AND PHYSICAL SCIENCE (chemistry, computer science, mathematics, and physics), EDUCATION (elementary), SOCIAL SCIENCE (history, international studies, and sociology).

Required: Students must take courses in Bible, history, political studies, world civilizations, literature, mathematics, humanities, physical education, psychology, science, computer science, and writing. At least 124 semester hours, including a maximum of 30 hours in the major and at least a 2.0 GPA, are required for graduation.

Special: Stillman offers independent and nondegree study, interdepartmental and interdisciplinary majors, co-op programs in business, communications, computer science, and sociology, and courses in African American history and literature. Cross-registration with the University of Alabama and work-study programs with Stillman College are offered. Exchange, nursing, and 3–2 engineering programs with the University of Alabama and an exchange program with the University of Nebraska are offered, as well as a 3–2 degree program in architectural science and a 2–4 degree program in veterinary medicine with Tuskegee Institute. Internships in communications and B.A.-B.S. degrees are possible. There are 2 national honor societies on campus.

Admissions: About 82% of the 1993–94 applicants were accepted. The ACT scores for the 1993–94 freshman class were as follows: 89% below 21, 8% between 21 and 23, and 3% between 24 and 26.

Requirements: A minimum GPA of 2.0 is required. Students may be admitted conditionally with a 1.6 GPA. The SAT I or ACT is recommended. In addition, applicants should be high school graduates or have earned the GED. Secondary preparation should include 4 units of English and 1 each of mathematics, science, and history. All applicants must have an interview. Music majors must audition.

Procedure: Freshmen are admitted to all sessions. Applications should be filed by June 15 for fall entry, along with an application fee of $10. The college accepts all applicants Notification is sent on a rolling basis.

Transfer: Transfer applicants should present at least a C average in previous college work and must plan to spend at least a year in residence. Priority is given to applications received by May 1.

Visiting: There are regularly scheduled orientations for prospective students. To arrange for a visit, contact Mason Bonner, Director of Recruitment at (205) 349–4240, ext. 346.

Financial Aid: The FAF, FFS or SFS and an application for federal student aid are required. The deadline for financial aid applications is June 15.

International Students: There are currently 3 international students enrolled. The school actively recruits these students. They must take the TOEFL or the college's own test and achieve a minimum score on the TOEFL of 500. The student must also take the SAT I or the ACT.

Computers: The college provides computer facilities for student use. The mainframe is a DEC VAX 11/750. All students may access the system. It may be used 8 A.M. to 5 P.M., Monday through Friday, 8 A.M. to noon Saturday, and 1 P.M. to 5 P.M. on Sunday. Students may access the system 69 hours per week. There are no fees.

Graduates: In a recent year, 126 bachelor's degrees were awarded. The most popular majors among graduates were business administration (50%), communications (25%), and computer science (25%). Some 25 companies recruited on campus.

Admissions Contact: Myrtes D. Green, Assistant to President for Institutional Effectiveness.

TALLADEGA COLLEGE
C-2

Talladega, AL 35160   (205) 362-0206, ext. 273
(800) 633-2440 (out-of-state)

Full-time: 321 men, 587 women	Faculty: 45
Part-time: 105 men, 14 women	Ph.D.s: 64%
Graduate: none	Student/Faculty: 20 to 1
Year: semesters	Tuition: $5584
Application Deadline: June 15	Room & Board: $2540
Freshman Class: 4230 applied, 1432 accepted, 379 enrolled	
SAT I or ACT: recommended	COMPETITIVE +

Talladega College, founded in 1867, is a private, coeducational liberal arts institution offering emphases on business, sciences, and social work. In addition to regional accreditation, Talladega has baccalaureate program accreditation with CSWE. The library contains 91,500 volumes, 1767 microform items, and 160 audiovisual forms, and subscribes to 487 periodicals. Computerized library sources and services include interlibrary loans. Special learning facilities include a learning resource center and art gallery. The 130-acre campus is in a small town 55 miles southeast of Birmingham. Including residence halls, there are 26 buildings on campus.

Student Life: About 52% of undergraduates are from Alabama. Students come from 30 states and 2 foreign countries. Ninety-seven percent are African American. The average age of freshmen is 18; all undergraduates, 20.

Housing: A total of 582 students can be accommodated in college housing. College-sponsored living facilities include single-sex dormitories and on-campus apartments. In addition, there are honors houses. On-campus housing is guaranteed for all 4 years. Seventy-one percent of students live on campus; of those, 85% remain on campus on weekends. Alcohol is not permitted. All students may keep cars on campus.

Activities: About 14% of men belong to 4 local and 4 national fraternities; about 40% of women belong to 3 local and 3 national sororities. There are 22 groups on campus, including art, choir, chorus, computers, dance, drama, honors, jazz band, newspaper, social, student government, and yearbook. Popular campus events include Spring Concert, Carnival, Coronation, Alumni Weekend, Parents Day, Religious Emphasis Week, Arts Festival, and Founders Day.

Sports: There are 2 intercollegiate sports for men, and 8 intramural sports for men and 3 for women. Athletic and recreation facilities include a swimming pool, a 150-seat gymnasium, lounges, locker and shower rooms, and game rooms.

Disabled Students: Fifty percent of the campus is accessible to disabled students. The following facilities are available: wheelchair ramps, elevators, special parking, and specially equipped rest rooms.

Services: In addition to many counseling and information services, tutoring is available in every subject. There also is remedial math, reading, and writing.

Campus Safety and Security: Campus safety and security measures include 24-hour foot and vehicle patrol, pamphlets, posters, and films, and lighted pathways and sidewalks.

Programs of Study: Talladega awards the B.A. degree in BIOLOGICAL SCIENCE (biology/biological science), BUSINESS (business administration and management), COMMUNICATIONS AND THE ARTS (English, journalism, and music performance), COMPUTER AND PHYSICAL SCIENCE (chemistry, computer science, mathematics, and physics), EDUCATION (music), SOCIAL SCIENCE (history, psychology, public administration, social work, and sociology). Business, biology, chemistry, and physics are the strongest academically. Business has the largest enrollment.

Required: All students are required to maintain a minimum GPA of 2.5 while taking 124 to 127 total semester hours, including 60 hours in the major. Distribution requirements include 6 semester hours each in communications and humanities, 8 each in natural sciences, mathematics, and social sciences, and 3 in physical education.

Special: Co-op programs with other schools through individual departments, internships involving historic preservation work, work-study plans with Adopt-a-Family and Adult Literacy, B.A.-B.S. degrees in biology, business administration, chemistry, and computer science, and dual majors in law, nursing, engineering, and allied health are offered. There are 4 national honor societies on campus.

Faculty/Classroom: Sixty percent of faculty are male; 40%, female. All teach undergraduates and 25% both teach and do research. The average class size in an introductory lecture is 30 and in a laboratory, 20.

Admissions: About 34% of the 1993–94 applicants were accepted. The ACT scores for the 1993–94 freshman class were as follows: 84% below 21, 10% between 21 and 23, 4% between 24 and 26, and 2% between 27 and 28. Seven freshmen graduated first in their class.

Requirements: A minimum GPA of 2.5 is required. The ACT is recommended. Applicants must have 4 units in English, 3 in social studies, and 2 each in mathematics, science, health/physical education, and electives. An essay and interview are recommended. An audition is required for music majors. CLEP credit is accepted. Important factors used in the admissions decision are advanced placement or honor courses, recommendations by school officials, and recommendations by alumni.

Procedure: Freshmen are admitted fall and spring. Entrance exams should be taken in the junior year. Applications should be filed by June 15 for fall entry, along with an application fee of $10. Notification is sent on a rolling basis. There are early decision, early admissions, and deferred admissions plans.

Transfer: A total of 47 transfer students enrolled in a recent year. Applicants must have a cumulative GPA of 2.0 in college work. The SAT I or ACT is recommended. A total of 60 credit hours out of 124 to 127 must be completed at Talladega.

Visiting: There are guides for informal visits and visitors may sit in on classes and stay overnight at the school. To arrange for a visit, contact the Admissions Office at (800) 762-2468 (in-state) or (800) 633-2440 (out-of-state).

Financial Aid: In an earlier year, 82% of all current freshmen received some form of financial aid. Scholarships or need-based grants averaged $2950 ($5811 maximum); loans averaged $2625 ($4000 maximum); and work contracts averaged $828 ($900 maximum). The FAF, FFS, or SFS and the college's own financial statement are required. The deadline for financial aid applications is May 1.

International Students: There is currently 1 international student enrolled. The school actively recruits these students. They must take the TOEFL or the college's own test. The student must also take the SAT I or the ACT.

Computers: The college provides computer facilities for student use. The mainframes are a DEC VAX 750 and an HP 835/41. Student computer laboratories in the library and in a classroom building provide 30 microcomputers and 3 mainframe terminals for use. All students may access the system. It may be used from 8 A.M. to 4:30 P.M. and 7 P.M. to 10 P.M. daily. There are no time limits on using the system and no fees.

Graduates: In a recent year, 95 bachelor's degrees were awarded. The most popular majors among graduates were business (27%), English (10%), and biology (9%). Within an average freshman class, 50% graduate in 4 years. In a recent graduating class, 17% of the men and 31% of the women were enrolled in graduate school within 6 months of graduation; 6% of the men and 9% of the women had found employment.

Admissions Contact: Monroe Thornton, Acting Director of Admissions.

TROY STATE UNIVERSITY SYSTEM

The Troy State University system, established in 1887, is a public system in Alabama. It is governed by a board of trustees, whose chief administrator is chancellor. The primary goal of the system is to provide an academic, cultural, and social environment conducive to the development of students as well as productive, individual members of society. The main priorities are the preprofessional and professional preparation of students in the arts and sciences, fine arts, business, education, communication, applied science, nursing, and allied health sciences. The total enrollment in fall 1993 of the main campus was approximately 6,400; there were 654 faculty members at the 12-campus system. Altogether there are 20 baccalaureate and 7 master's programs offered in the system. Four-year campuses are located in Troy, Phoenix City, Montgomery, and Dothan/Fort Rucker. Profiles of those campuses are included in this chapter in alphabetical order with other Alabama schools.

TROY STATE UNIVERSITY

C-4

Troy, AL 36082   (205) 670–3179; (800) 551–9716 (in-state)

Full-time: 2015 men, 2570 women	**Faculty:** 206
Part-time: 81 men, 103 women	**Ph.D.s:** 60%
Graduate: 156 men, 247 women	**Student/Faculty:** 22 to 1
Year: quarters, summer session	**Tuition:** $1722 ($2950)
Application Deadline: open	**Room & Board:** $2600
Freshman Class: 2675 applied, 2015 accepted, 1650 enrolled	
SAT I Verbal/Math: 460/490	**ACT:** 22 COMPETITIVE

Troy State University, founded in 1887, is a coeducational liberal arts institution that is part of the public Troy State University system. There are 7 undergraduate and 3 graduate schools. In addition to regional accreditation, TSU has baccalaureate program accreditation with CSWE, NCATE, and NLN. The library contains 267,761 volumes and 500,000 microform items, and subscribes to 1500 periodicals. Computerized library sources and services include the card catalog, interlibrary loans, and database searching. Special learning facilities include a learning resource center, art gallery, radio station, TV station, and arboretum. The 500-acre campus is in a small town 40 miles south of Montgomery. Including residence halls, there are 53 buildings on campus.

Student Life: About 74% of undergraduates are from Alabama. Students come from 41 states and 15 foreign countries. Seventy-seven percent are from public schools. Eighty-one percent are white; 18% African American. The average age of freshmen is 18; all undergraduates, 20. Twenty-four percent drop out by the end of their first year; 68% remain to graduate.

Housing: A total of 2750 students can be accommodated in college housing. College-sponsored living facilities include single-sex and coed dormitories, on-campus apartments, off-campus apartments, married-student housing, and fraternity houses. In addition, there are special interest houses and an international house. On-campus housing is guaranteed for all 4 years. Fifty-five percent of students commute. Alcohol is not permitted. All students may keep cars on campus.

Activities: About 27% of men belong to 8 national fraternities; about 26% of women belong to 8 national sororities. There are 111 groups on campus, including art, band, cheerleading, choir, chorale, chorus, computers, dance, drama, drill team, ethnic, film, honors, international, jazz band, literary magazine, marching band, musical theater, newspaper, opera, orchestra, pep band, photography, political, professional, radio and TV, religious, social, social service, student government, symphony, and yearbook. Popular campus events include Homecoming, Greek Rush, Greek Week, winter formals, and spring beach weekends.

Sports: There are 6 intercollegiate sports for men and 4 for women, and 11 intramural sports for men and 11 for women. Athletic and recreation facilities include a 15,000-seat football stadium, a 3500-seat gymnasium, a natatorium, bowling lanes, a baseball field, a golf course, and tennis courts.

Disabled Students: Ninety-five percent of the campus is accessible to disabled students. The following facilities are available: wheelchair ramps, elevators, special parking, specially equipped rest rooms, special class scheduling, lowered drinking fountains, lowered telephones, graded inclines, and specially equipped apartments.

Services: In addition to many counseling and information services, tutoring is available in most subjects. There is a reader service for the blind, and remedial math, reading, and writing.

Campus Safety and Security: Campus safety and security measures include 24-hour foot and vehicle patrol, escort service, pamphlets, posters, and films, and lighted pathways and sidewalks.

Programs of Study: TSU awards the B.A., B.S., B.A.Ed., B.Applied Sc., B.S.Ed., and B.S.N. degrees. Associate and master's degrees also are awarded. Bachelor's degrees are awarded in BIOLOGICAL SCIENCE (biology/biological science and marine biology), BUSINESS (accounting, banking and finance, business administration and management, business economics, and marketing/retailing/merchandising), COMMUNICATIONS AND THE ARTS (art history and appreciation, broadcasting, communications, dramatic arts, English, French, journalism, Latin, Spanish, and speech/debate/rhetoric), COMPUTER AND PHYSICAL SCIENCE (chemistry, computer science, mathematics, and science), EDUCATION (art, business, early childhood, elementary, English, foreign languages, health, mathematics, middle school, music, physical, science, secondary, social science, and special), HEALTH PROFESSIONS (medical laboratory technology, nursing, predentistry, and premedicine), SOCIAL SCIENCE (criminal justice, economics, history, human services, international relations, political science/government, prelaw, psychology, social science, social work, and sociology). Business and education are the strongest academically. Business has the largest enrollment.

Required: All students must maintain a minimum GPA of 2.0 while taking at least 180 total quarter credit hours, 45 of which must be in their major field. Distribution requirements include 72 hours of gener-

al studies covering such subjects as English, mathematics, history, science, and fine arts, and 3 hours of physical education.

Special: Cross-registration with the Marine Biological Consortium, internships in education, journalism, and nursing, study abroad in 2 countries, work-study programs at the university, and student-designed majors in public relations, advertising, and other fields are available. Credit for life experience and nondegree study are also offered. There is a freshman honors program on campus, as well as 19 national honor societies. Seven departments have honors programs.

Faculty/Classroom: The average class size in an introductory lecture is 35; in a laboratory, 25; and in a regular course offering, 35.

Admissions: About 75% of the 1993–94 applicants were accepted. About 30% of the current freshmen were in the top fifth of their class; 50% were in the top two fifths.

Requirements: TSU requires applicants to be in the upper 30% of their class. A minimum GPA of 2.0 is required. The SAT I or ACT is required with recommended composite scores of 740 and 18, respectively. Applicants must have earned 11 academic credits, including 4 years of English, and 15 Carnegie units. An interview is recommended, along with a portfolio or audition for some programs. The GED is accepted. AP and CLEP credits are accepted. Important factors used in the admissions decision are ability to finance college education, evidence of special talent, extracurricular activities record, recommendations by alumni, and recommendations by school officials.

Procedure: Freshmen are admitted to all sessions. Entrance exams should be taken early in the senior year. The application fee is $15. Application deadlines are open. Notification is sent on a rolling basis.

Transfer: Transfer applicants need 30 quarter hours at their previous institution, with an overall GPA of at least 2.0. A total of 90 quarter credits out of 180 must be completed at TSU.

Visiting: There are regularly scheduled orientations for prospective students. There are guides for informal visits, and visitors may sit in on classes. To arrange for a visit, contact the Office of Enrollment Services at (800)551–9716 (in-state and FL) or (205)670–3179.

Financial Aid: In a recent year, 70% of all current freshmen and 70% of continuing students received some form of financial aid. About 70% of freshmen and 70% of continuing students received need-based aid. The average freshman award was $2666. Of that total, scholarships or need-based grants averaged $1780 ($2400 maximum); loans averaged $1000 ($1500 maximum); and work contracts averaged $1500 (maximum). Twelve percent of undergraduate students work part-time. Average earnings from campus work for the school year are $2000. The average financial indebtedness of a recent year's graduate was $12,000. TSU is a member of CSS. The FAF, FFS, or SFS and the college's own financial statement are required. The deadline for financial aid applications is May 1.

International Students: There are currently 41 international students enrolled. The school actively recruits these students. They must take the TOEFL and achieve a minimum score of 525. Students must also take the SAT I or ACT if they are transferring from another school. The minimum composite scores are 750 on the SAT I, with at least 375 on verbal, and 18 on the ACT, with at least 18 on English.

Computers: The college provides computer facilities for student use. The mainframe is an IBM 4300. Terminals and microcomputers are available 7 days a week. All students may access the system. There are no time limits on using the system. There are no fees.

Graduates: In a recent year, 762 bachelor's degrees were awarded. In a recent graduating class, 80% of the men and 80% of the women had found employment within 6 months of graduation.

Admissions Contact: Jim Hutto, Dean of Enrollment Services.

TROY STATE UNIVERSITY AT DOTHAN FORT RUCKER

D-5

Dothan, AL 36304   (205) 983–6556

Full-time: 358 men, 418 women	**Faculty:** 45; IIA, --$
Part-time: 337 men, 589 women	**Ph.D.s:** 76%
Graduate: 321 men, 258 women	**Student/Faculty:** 17 to 1
Year: quarters, summer session	**Tuition:** $2260 ($3702)
Application Deadline: open	**Room & Board:** n/app
Freshman Class: n/av	
SAT I or ACT: not required	NONCOMPETITIVE

Troy State University at Dothan, founded in 1955, is a public, coeducational liberal arts school. As part of the Troy State University System, it established a permanent campus in Dothan in 1977 to serve the tristate region. It continues to offer degree completion studies for the military at Fort Rucker. There are 3 undergraduate and 3 graduate schools. The library contains 71,952 volumes, 133,587 microform items, and 7300 audiovisual forms, and subscribes to 830 periodicals. Computerized library sources and services include interlibrary loans. The 250-acre campus is in an urban area 100 miles southeast of Montgomery. There are 2 buildings on campus.

Student Life: About 84% of undergraduates are from Alabama. Students come from 6 states and 4 foreign countries. Eighty-nine percent are white. The average age of freshmen is 31; all undergraduates, 30.

Housing: There are no residence halls; all students commute.

Activities: There are no fraternities or sororities. There are 8 groups on campus, including band, newspaper, and student government.

Sports: There is no sports program at TSU Dothan.

Disabled Students: The entire campus is accessible to disabled students. The following facilities are available: wheelchair ramps, elevators, special parking, specially equipped rest rooms, and lowered drinking fountains.

Services: In addition to many counseling and information services, tutoring is available in some subjects. There is remedial math.

Campus Safety and Security: Campus safety and security measures include lighted pathways and sidewalks and security from 5 P.M. to 8 A.M.

Programs of Study: TSU Dothan awards the B.S., B.A.E., and B.Applied Sc. degrees. Associate and master's degrees are also awarded. Bachelor's degrees are awarded in BIOLOGICAL SCIENCE (biology/biological science), BUSINESS (business administration and management, business economics, and personnel management), COMMUNICATIONS AND THE ARTS (English), COMPUTER AND PHYSICAL SCIENCE (computer science, mathematics, physical sciences, and science), EDUCATION (early childhood, elementary, English, mathematics, middle school, science, secondary, and social science), SOCIAL SCIENCE (criminal justice, psychology, social science, and sociology). Business has the largest enrollment.

Required: All students must take a minimum of 185 quarter hours, including 45 in their major, and must maintain an overall GPA of at least 2.0. Distribution requirements include English composition I and II, 10 hours each of literature, history, and social science, 6 each of music and art, and microcomputing and speech, and 5 each of mathematics, biology, philosophy, and science.

Special: Internships in the business and education programs, an accelerated degree program, nondegree study, and pass/fail options are available. There is one national honor society on campus.

Faculty/Classroom: Sixty percent of faculty are male; 40%, female. All teach undergraduates. No introductory courses are taught by graduate students. The average class size in a regular course offering is 23.

Requirements: A minimum GPA of 2.0 is required. The SAT I or ACT is not required, but may be requested if the high school performance seems inadequate. The recommended scores vary with student GPAs. Applicants need 11 academic credits and 15 Carnegie units, including 4 English units. The GED is accepted. AP and CLEP credits are accepted.

Procedure: Entrance exams should be taken during the junior year. Application deadlines are open; the fee is $15. The college accepts all applicants. Notification is sent on a rolling basis. There is an early admissions plan.

Transfer: More than 500 transfer students enrolled in a recent year. Transfer applicants will receive unconditional acceptance if their GPA is 2.0 or above. The minimum number of credit hours necessary is 15. A total of 45 quarter hours out of 185 must be completed at TSU Dothan.

Visiting: There are regularly scheduled orientations for prospective students. There are guides for informal visits and visitors may sit in on classes. To arrange for a visit, contact Pamela Williamson at (205) 983-6556.

Financial Aid: Only 1% of undergraduate students work part-time. The application for federal student aid financial statement is required. The deadline for financial aid applications is August 1.

International Students: There are currently 2 international students enrolled. They must take the TOEFL and achieve a minimum score of 500.

Computers: The college provides computer facilities for student use. The mainframe is an IBM 4331. There are 40 microcomputers in 2 laboratories. Computer and information science majors may access the system. It may be used between 9 A.M. and 10 P.M., Monday through Thursday. There are no time limits on using the system and no fees.

Graduates: In a recent year, 281 bachelor's degrees were awarded. The most popular majors among graduates were general business and management (44%), elementary education (11%), and psychology (6%). Some 41 companies recruited on campus that year.

Admissions Contact: Bob Willis, Director of Admissions.

TROY STATE UNIVERSITY IN MONTGOMERY   C-4

Montgomery, AL 36103-4419   (205) 241-9508

Full-time: 253 men, 366 women	Faculty: 30; IIA, --$
Part-time: 931 men, 1371 women	Ph.D.s: 74%
Graduate: 282 men, 266 women	Student/Faculty: 21 to 1
Year: quarters, summer session	Tuition: $1710 ($2565)
Application Deadline: open	Room & Board: n/app
Freshman Class: 1093 applied, 1093 accepted, 1093 enrolled	
SAT I or ACT: see profile	**NONCOMPETITIVE**

Troy State University in Montgomery, founded in 1965 as a branch of the Troy State University system, is a public, coeducational evening commuter institution offering undergraduate and graduate degrees in arts and sciences, education, and business. There are 4 undergraduate schools and one graduate school. The library contains 22,238 volumes, and subscribes to 312 periodicals. Computerized library sources and services include the card catalog, interlibrary loans, and database searching. Special learning facilities include a learning resource center, planetarium, radio station, and TV station. The 3-acre campus is in an urban area in Montgomery. There are 5 buildings on campus.

Student Life: All undergraduates are from Alabama. The average age of freshmen is 27; all undergraduates, 31.

Housing: There are no residence halls. Alcohol is not permitted.

Activities: There are no fraternities or sororities on campus.

Sports: There is no sports program at TSUM.

Disabled Students: Ninety-five percent of the campus is accessible to disabled students. The following facilities are available: wheelchair ramps, elevators, special parking, specially equipped rest rooms, lowered drinking fountains, and lowered telephones.

Services: In addition to many counseling and information services, tutoring is available in some subjects. In addition, there is a reader service for the blind, and remedial math, reading, and writing. Tutors may be provided for students upon request.

Campus Safety and Security: Campus safety and security measures include escort service, informal discussions, pamphlets, posters, and films, and lighted pathways and sidewalks. In addition, there are foot and vehicle patrols during class hours.

Programs of Study: TSUM awards the B.A. and B.S. degrees. Associate and master's degrees also are awarded. Bachelor's degrees are awarded in BUSINESS (banking and finance and business administration and management), COMMUNICATIONS AND THE ARTS (English), COMPUTER AND PHYSICAL SCIENCE (mathematics), SOCIAL SCIENCE (history, political science/government, psychology, and social science).

Required: Students must complete a minimum of 185 quarter hours, with 15 quarter hours within the TSU system in the major area, and maintain a minimum GPA of 2.0. At least half the required total hours must be composed of traditional credits, excluding credit by correspondence or by examination.

Special: TSUM offers an external degree program in professional studies for those unable to attend regularly scheduled classes because of handicap, work, or family restrictions. An ROTC program is available through Auburn and Alabama State universities. Credit may be granted for military service and experiential learning. Guided independent study/research, nondegree study, and pass/fail options are possible. Flexible schedules and televised courses are available to meet the needs of adult students. There are 2 national honor societies on campus.

Faculty/Classroom: No introductory courses are taught by graduate students. The average class size in a regular course offering is 20.

Admissions: All of the 1993–94 applicants were accepted.

Requirements: Graduates from accredited secondary schools should have 15 Carnegie units, with 3 or more in English and 11 others in academic courses. Graduates from nonaccredited secondary schools may be admitted if they meet the same requirements and are deemed capable of performing satisfactorily. The GED is accepted. Other applicants may be admitted as unclassified, nondegree-seeking students. For students under 21, the high school GPA and SAT I or ACT scores are used in a formula to determine admissions eligibility; those applicants not having a test score may be admitted with conditional status. For students over 21, requirements include a minimum high school GPA of 2.0. Applicants with a lower GPA may be admitted conditionally.

Procedure: Freshmen are admitted to all sessions. Entrance exams should be taken by the fall of the senior year. Application deadlines are open. The application fee is $10. The college accepts all applicants. Notification is sent on a rolling basis. There is an early admissions plan.

Transfer: Transfer students must submit college transcripts from each college attended. Those with fewer than 15 quarter hours (or 9 semester hours) of credit are required to submit a high school transcript as well. Applicants should have a college GPA of at least 2.0 and be

in good standing; others may be admitted conditionally. A total of 15 quarter hours out of 185 must be completed within the TSU system.
Visiting: There are guides for informal visits and visitors may sit in on classes.
Graduates: In a recent year, 160 bachelor's degrees were awarded. The most popular majors among graduates were business and management (58%), computer science (13%), and social science (11%).
Admissions Contact: Kay Webb, Director of Admissions.

TUSKEGEE UNIVERSITY D-4

Tuskegee, AL 36088   (205) 727-8500; (800) 622-6531
Full-time: 1350 men, 1504 women   Faculty: 254
Part-time: 72 men, 64 women   Ph.D.s: 62%
Graduate: 174 men, 207 women   Student/Faculty: 11 to 1
Year: semesters, summer session   Tuition: $6734
Application Deadline: March 1   Room & Board: $3394
Freshman Class: 3098 applied, 2305 accepted, 685 enrolled
SAT I Verbal/Math: 374/409   ACT: 18   **COMPETITIVE**

Tuskegee University, founded in 1881 by Booker T. Washington, is an independent, coeducational, professional and technical institution offering undergraduate and graduate programs in liberal arts and sciences, agriculture, architecture, business, education, engineering, and health professions. There are 7 undergraduate and 5 graduate schools. In addition to regional accreditation, Tuskegee has baccalaureate program accreditation with ABET, CSWE, NAAB, NCATE, and NLN. The 3 libraries contain 293,656 volumes and 297 microform items, and subscribe to 1150 periodicals. Special learning facilities include a learning resource center, the Carver Museum, and the home of Booker T. Washington. The 4500-acre campus is in a rural area 40 miles east of Montgomery. Including residence halls, there are 150 buildings on campus.
Student Life: About 76% of undergraduates are from out-of-state, mostly the South. Students come from 42 states and 34 foreign countries. Eighty-eight percent are from public schools; 12% from private. Ninety-two percent are African American. The average age of freshmen is 18; all undergraduates, 22. Thirty-five percent drop out by the end of their first year; 45% remain to graduate.
Housing: A total of 2000 students can be accommodated in college housing. College-sponsored living facilities include single-sex dormitories and married-student housing. In addition there are honors houses. On-campus housing is guaranteed for the freshman year only. Sixty-four percent of students live on campus. Alcohol is not permitted. All students may keep cars on campus.
Activities: About 4% of men belong to 6 local and 4 national fraternities; about 4% of women belong to 5 local and 4 national sororities. There are 60 groups on campus, including band, choir, chorus, drama, honors, international, jazz band, marching band, newspaper, orchestra, religious, social service, and student government. Popular campus events include Homecoming, Spring Pageant, Campus All-Star Challenge, and Student Leadership Retreat.
Sports: There are 5 intercollegiate sports for men and 5 for women, and 7 intramural sports for men and 6 for women. Athletic and recreation facilities include a 10,000-seat stadium, a 5000-seat arena, a student center, tennis courts, a rifle range, playing fields, and an Olympic-size natatorium.
Disabled Students: The following facilities are available: wheelchair ramps and elevators.
Services: In addition to many counseling and information services, tutoring is available in some subjects. In addition, there is a reader service for the blind.
Campus Safety and Security: Campus safety and security measures include 24-hour foot and vehicle patrol, escort service, informal discussions, and lighted pathways and sidewalks.
Programs of Study: Tuskegee awards the B.A., B.S., and B.S.N. degrees. Master's and doctoral degrees also are awarded. Bachelor's degrees are awarded in AGRICULTURE (agricultural business management, agriculture, animal science, and horticulture), BIOLOGICAL SCIENCE (biology/biological science), BUSINESS (accounting, banking and finance, business administration and management, business economics, hospitality management services, management science, and marketing/retailing/merchandising), COMMUNICATIONS AND THE ARTS (English), COMPUTER AND PHYSICAL SCIENCE (chemistry, computer science, mathematics, and physics), EDUCATION (early childhood, elementary, home economics, physical, secondary, special, and technical), ENGINEERING AND ENVIRONMENTAL DESIGN (aeronautical engineering, chemical engineering, construction engineering, electrical/electronics engineering, and mechanical engineering), HEALTH PROFESSIONS (medical laboratory technology, nursing, occupational therapy, and veterinary science), SOCIAL SCIENCE (dietetics, food science, history, home economics, political science/government, psychology, social work, and sociology). Engineering, biology, and veterinary medicine have the largest enrollments.

Required: All students must complete a general education curriculum, including courses in history, sociology, philosophy, art, English, humanities, political science, mathematics, natural sciences, and physical education. A minimum of 124 semester credits with a GPA of 2.0 is required for graduation.

Special: A cooperative program in engineering, internships, work-study programs, nondegree study, and a B.A.-B.S. degree are offered. There is a freshman honors program on campus, as well as 17 national honor societies. Nine departments have honors programs.

Faculty/Classroom: Sixty-nine percent of faculty are male; 31%, female.

Admissions: About 74% of the 1993-94 applicants were accepted. About 50% of the current freshmen were in the top fifth of their class; 50% were in the top two fifths.

Requirements: The SAT I (preferred) or ACT is required, with a recommended minimum composite score of 900 on the SAT I or 18 on the ACT. Applicants should be graduates of an accredited secondary school or hold the GED. A high school GPA of 2.5 is recommended, along with 4 units of English, 3 each of social science and mathematics, and 1 each of physical science and biological science. SAT II: Subject tests in mathematics (level I or II) and one other subject are recommended. An essay is required. CLEP credit is accepted.

Procedure: Freshmen are admitted to all sessions. Applications should be filed by March 1 for fall entry and November 31 for spring entry, along with an application fee of $25. Notification is sent on a rolling basis. There is an early admissions plan.

Transfer: Transfer applicants must be in good standing at all previously attended institutions and have completed 12 or more semester hours with a GPA of 2.0. A total of 44 to 59 credits out of 124 to 139 must be completed at Tuskegee.

Visiting: Visitors may sit in on classes and stay overnight at the school. To arrange for a visit, contact the Office of Admissions at (800) 622-6531.

Financial Aid: In 1993-94, 70% of all current freshmen and 80% of continuing students received some form of financial aid. About 65% of freshmen and 75% of continuing students received need-based aid. The average freshman award was $7529. Of that total, scholarships or need-based grants averaged $1633 ($3367 maximum); loans averaged $1500 ($3000 maximum); and work contracts averaged $1581 (maximum). The average financial indebtedness of the 1992-93 graduate was $22,250. Tuskegee is a member of CSS. The FAF and federal tax returns are required. The deadline for financial aid applications is March 31.

International Students: There are currently 134 international students enrolled. They must take the TOEFL. The student must also take the SAT I or the ACT.

Computers: The university provides computer facilities for student use. The mainframe is a DEC VAX 6420. There are 10 microcomputers and terminals in various campus departments. There are no time limits on using the system and no fees.

Graduates: In 1992-93, 506 bachelor's degrees were awarded. The most popular majors among graduates were electrical engineering (10%), biology (8%), and mechanical engineering (7%). Within an average freshman class, 21% graduate in 4 years, 45% in 5 years, and 62% in 6 years. Some 382 companies recruited on campus in 1992-93.

Admissions Contact: Lee Young, Director of Admissions and Enrollment Services.

UNIVERSITY OF ALABAMA SYSTEM

The University of Alabama System, established in 1969, is a public system in Alabama comprised of three research universities: The University of Alabama (Tuscaloosa); The University of Alabama at Birmingham; and The University of Alabama in Huntsville. It is governed by a board of trustees, whose chief administrator is the chancellor. The primary goal of the system is to serve all the people of the state through teaching, research, and public service. The main priorities are to promote the economic, cultural, and social welfare of Alabama through higher education; to educate and train the leaders and citizens of tomorrow; and to conduct research in all fields that address the critical needs of mankind. The total enrollment in a recent year of all 3 campuses exceeded 44,000; there were nearly 3,400 faculty members. Altogether there are approximately 190 baccalaureate, 170 master's, and 90 doctoral programs offered in the University of Alabama System. Profiles of the 4-year campuses are included in this chapter in alphabetical order with other Alabama schools.

UNIVERSITY OF ALABAMA
B-3

Tuscaloosa, AL 35487   (205) 348-5666; (800) 933-BAMA (in-state)

Full-time: 6928 men, 6821 women	Faculty: 666; I, --$
Part-time: 731 men, 863 women	Ph.D.s: 89%
Graduate: 2005 men, 2146 women	Student/Faculty: 21 to 1
Year: semesters, summer session	Tuition: $2172 ($5424)
Application Deadline: April 15	Room & Board: $3530

Freshman Class: 7677 applied, 6007 accepted, 2628 enrolled
ACT: 23   **COMPETITIVE**

The University of Alabama, founded in 1831, is a public coeducational liberal arts institution and part of the University of Alabama System. There are 10 undergraduate and 3 graduate schools. In addition to regional accreditation, UA has baccalaureate program accreditation with AACSB, ABET, ACEJMC, ADA, AHEA, CSWE, FIDER, NASM, NCATE, and NLN. The 8 libraries contain 1,902,029 volumes, 2,723,168 microform items, and 17,255 audiovisual forms, and subscribe to 16,878 periodicals. Special learning facilities include a learning resource center, art gallery, natural history museum, radio station, TV station, special collections department, and a map library. The 1000-acre campus is in a small town. Including residence halls, there are 90 buildings on campus.

Student Life: About 66% of undergraduates are from Alabama. Students come from 49 states, 66 foreign countries, and Canada. Eighty-four percent are white; 11% African American. The average age of freshmen is 18; all undergraduates, 22. Nineteen percent drop out by the end of their first year; 48% remain to graduate.

Housing: A total of 4900 students can be accommodated in college housing. College-sponsored living facilities include single-sex dormitories, on-campus apartments, married-student housing, fraternity houses, and sorority houses. In addition, there are honors houses, language houses, and special interest houses. On-campus housing is guaranteed for all 4 years. Seventy percent of students commute. All students may keep cars on campus.

Activities: About 14% of men belong to 27 national fraternities; about 26% of women belong to 18 national sororities. There are 253 groups on campus, including art, band, cheerleading, chorus, computers, dance, drama, drill team, ethnic, film, gay, honors, international, jazz band, literary magazine, marching band, musical theater, newspaper, opera, orchestra, pep band, photography, political, professional, radio and TV, religious, social, social service, student government, symphony, and yearbook. Popular campus events include Homecoming, Radio-free Tuscaloosa, Honors Week, Get on Board Day, Bama Triathlon, A-Day, and Unity Day.

Sports: There are 8 intercollegiate sports for men and 8 for women, and 15 intramural sports for men and 15 for women. Athletic and recreation facilities include A 72,000-seat football stadium, 15,053-seat coliseum, track and field areas, intramural fields, tennis courts, a golf course, and an aquatic center. The student recreation center provides a swimming pool, racquetball courts, weight and exercise rooms, and basketball courts.

Disabled Students: Ninety percent of the campus is accessible to disabled students. The following facilities are available: wheelchair ramps, elevators, special parking, specially equipped rest rooms, special class scheduling, lowered drinking fountains, and lowered telephones.

Services: In addition to many counseling and information services, tutoring is available in some subjects, including mathematics, chemistry, physics, computer science, accounting, finance, economics, and foreign languages. In addition, there is remedial reading and writing.

Campus Safety and Security: Campus safety and security measures include 24-hour foot and vehicle patrol, self defense education, escort service, and pamphlets, posters, and films. In addition, there are emergency telephones and lighted pathways and sidewalks.

Programs of Study: UA awards the B.A., B.S., B.F.A, B.M. and B.S.Ed degrees. Master's and doctoral degrees also are awarded. Bachelor's degrees are awarded in BIOLOGICAL SCIENCE (biology/biological science, marine science, microbiology, and nutrition), BUSINESS (accounting, banking and finance, business administration and management, fashion merchandising, hospitality management services, human resources, insurance, management science, marketing/retailing/merchandising, and real estate), COMMUNICATIONS AND THE ARTS (advertising, applied music, art history and appreciation, classics, dance, English, French, German, journalism, languages, music, music theory and composition, public relations, Russian, Spanish, speech/debate/rhetoric, studio art, telecommunications, and theater design), COMPUTER AND PHYSICAL SCIENCE (chemistry, computer science, geology, mathematics, physics, and statistics), EDUCATION (art, early childhood, elementary, health, home economics, music, physical, secondary, and special), ENGINEERING AND ENVIRONMENTAL DESIGN (aeronautical engineering, chemical engineering, civil engineering, electrical/electronics engineering, industrial administration/management, industrial engineering, interior design, mechanical engineering, metallurgical engi-

neering, and mining and mineral engineering), HEALTH PROFESSIONS (health care administration, medical laboratory technology, music therapy, nursing, predentistry, premedicine, speech pathology/audiology, and sports medicine), SOCIAL SCIENCE (American studies, anthropology, Asian/Oriental studies, clothing and textiles management/production/services, criminal justice, economics, family/consumer studies, geography, history, human development, interdisciplinary studies, international studies, Latin American studies, philosophy, physical fitness/movement, political science/government, psychology, religion, Russian and Slavic studies, social work, sociology, textiles and clothing, and urban studies). Humanities, fine arts, accounting, engineering, natural sciences mathematics, and communication are the strongest academically. Engineering, humanities, fine arts, accounting, natural sciences mathematics, business, and communication have the largest enrollments.

Required: All students must take 128 to 137 total semester hours including 30 to 35 in their major field. They must maintain a minimum GPA of 2.0. Distribution requirements include English, mathematics, natural sciences, social science, humanities, and foreign language. Two semesters of freshmen composition also are required.

Special: Cross-registration with Stillman College is offered. Internships, international study programs, a Washington semester, work-study and co-op programs are possible. An accelerated 3–2 degree in business administration, B.A.-B.S. degrees, dual majors, and student-designed majors in arts and sciences and in interdisciplinary programs are available. The university also offers credit for life experiences, nondegree study, and pass/fail options. There is a freshman honors program on campus, as well as 7 national honor societies, including Phi Beta Kappa. Five departments have honors programs.

Faculty/Classroom: Sixty-nine percent of faculty are male; 31%, female. Seventy-nine percent teach undergraduates, 52% do research, and 38% do both. Graduate students teach 56% of introductory courses. The average class size in an introductory lecture is 43; in a laboratory, 18; and in a regular course offering, 28.

Admissions: About 78% of the 1993–94 applicants were accepted. The ACT scores for the 1993–94 freshman class were as follows: 27% below 21, 31% between 21 and 23, 23% between 24 and 26, 8% between 27 and 28, and 11% above 28. There were 59 National Merit finalists.

Requirements: A minimum GPA of 2.0 is required. The SAT I or ACT is required. The GED is accepted. AP and CLEP credits are accepted. Important factors used in the admissions decision are advanced placement or honor courses, leadership record, evidence of special talent, recommendations by school officials, and parents or siblings attending the school.

Procedure: Entrance exams should be taken in the spring of the junior year. Applications should be filed by April 15 for fall entry and April 15 for summer entry, along with an application fee of $20. Notification is sent on a rolling basis.

Transfer: About 1300 transfer students enrolled in 1993–94. Transfer applicants need an overall minimum GPA of 2.0 with a minimum of 24 semester hours earned. A total of 32 credits out of 128 must be completed at UA.

Visiting: There are regularly scheduled orientations for prospective students, consisting of a campus tour followed by meeting with admissions counselors and faculty and staff. Customized visits to suit student and parent needs are possible. There are guides for informal visits and visitors may sit in on classes and stay overnight at the school. To arrange for a visit, contact the Office of Admission Services at (205) 348-5666.

Financial Aid: In 1993–94, 38% of all current freshmen and 47% of continuing students received some form of financial aid. About 30% of freshmen and 34% of continuing students received need-based aid. The average freshman award was $4161. Seven percent of undergraduate students work part-time. Average earnings from campus work for the school year are $1700. The average financial indebtedness of the 1992–93 graduate was $7700. UA is a member of CSS. The FAF or FFS and the college's own financial statement are required. The deadline for financial aid applications is March 1.

International Students: There are currently 780 international students enrolled. The school actively recruits these students. They must take the TOEFL and achieve a minimum score of 500.

Computers: The college provides computer facilities for student use. The mainframe is an IBM 3090/400E. There are also 854 IBM, IBM clones, Apple IIs, and Apple Macintosh microcomputers available campuswide. Anyone with department permission may access the system. It may be used 24 hours daily. There are no time limits on using the system and no fees.

Graduates: In 1992–93, 3062 bachelor's degrees were awarded. The most popular majors among graduates were marketing (8%), accounting (7%), and banking and finance (6%). Within an average freshman class, 1% graduate in 3 years, 25% in 4 years, and 22% in 5 years. Some 300 companies recruited on campus in 1992–93.

Admissions Contact: Dr. Roy C. Smith, Director-Registrar.

UNIVERSITY OF ALABAMA AT BIRMINGHAM   C-2

Birmingham, AL 35294   (205) 934–8221; (800) 421–8743 (in-state)

Full-time: 3144 men, 3816 women	Faculty: 1683; I, --$
Part-time: 2235 men, 2463 women	Ph.D.s: 86%
Graduate: 1859 men, 2396 women	Student/Faculty: 4 to 1
Year: quarters, summer session	Tuition: $2358 ($4458)
Application Deadline: open	Room & Board: $5175
Freshman Class: 2153 applied, 1524 accepted, 1140 enrolled	
ACT: required	COMPETITIVE

The University of Alabama at Birmingham, founded in 1969, is a public, coeducational institution offering undergraduate and graduate degrees in the arts and humanities, business, education, engineering, natural sciences and mathematics, health-related professions, and social and behavioral sciences. There are 10 undergraduate and 13 graduate schools. In addition to regional accreditation, UAB has baccalaureate program accreditation with AACSB, ABET, ADA, APTA, CAHEA, CSWE, NASAD, NASM, NCATE, and NLN. The 2 libraries contain 1,471,689 volumes, 1,073,622 microform items, and 50,361 audiovisual forms, and subscribe to 5577 periodicals. Computerized library sources and services include the card catalog, interlibrary loans, and database searching. Special learning facilities include a radio station. The 180-acre campus is in an urban area located in Birmingham. Including residence halls, there are 105 buildings on campus.

Student Life: About 95% of undergraduates are from Alabama. Students come from 39 states, 50 foreign countries, and Canada. Seventy-two percent are white; 21% African American. The average age of freshmen is 19.6; all undergraduates, 25.2. Twenty-eight percent drop out by the end of their first year.

Housing: A total of 1600 students can be accommodated in college housing. College-sponsored living facilities include single-sex and coed dormitories, on-campus apartments, and married-student housing. In addition, a limited amount of housing is available to students on a first-come, first-served basis. Ninety-two percent of students commute. Alcohol is not permitted. All students may keep cars on campus.

Activities: About 6% of men belong to 10 national fraternities; about 5% of women belong to 7 national sororities. There are 200 groups on campus, including cheerleading, chess, choir, dance, ethnic, honors, international, jazz band, literary magazine, musical theater, newspaper, pep band, political, professional, religious, social, social service, and student government. Popular campus events include Springfest and Homecoming.

Sports: Athletic and recreation facilities include the UAB arena, baseball and soccer fields, and a gymnasium housing basketball and racquetball courts, a weight room, a track, and a swimming pool.

Disabled Students: Eighty percent of the campus is accessible to disabled students. The following facilities are available: wheelchair ramps, elevators, special parking, specially equipped rest rooms, lowered drinking fountains, and lowered telephones.

Services: In addition to many counseling and information services, tutoring is available in most subjects. In addition, there is a reader service for the blind, and remedial math, reading, and writing.

Campus Safety and Security: Campus safety and security measures include 24-hour foot and vehicle patrol, self defense education, escort service, and shuttle buses. In addition, there are informal discussions, pamphlets, posters, and films, emergency telephones, lighted pathways and sidewalks, a bike and mounted patrol, and a campus watch program.

Programs of Study: UAB awards the B.A., B.S., B.F.A., B.S.C.E., B.S.E.E., B.S.M.E., B.S.Mt.E., B.S.N., B.S.S.W., and B.S. in Physiological Optics degrees. Master's and doctoral degrees also are awarded. Bachelor's degrees are awarded in BIOLOGICAL SCIENCE (biology/biological science), BUSINESS (accounting, banking and finance, business economics, marketing/retailing/merchandising, and personnel management), COMMUNICATIONS AND THE ARTS (art history and appreciation, communications, dance, dramatic arts, English, fine arts, French, German, linguistics, music, and Spanish), COMPUTER AND PHYSICAL SCIENCE (chemistry, computer science, geology, mathematics, natural sciences, and physics), EDUCATION (art, early childhood, elementary, health, music, physical, secondary, and special), ENGINEERING AND ENVIRONMENTAL DESIGN (civil engineering, electrical/electronics engineering, industrial administration/management, materials engineering, and mechanical engineering), HEALTH PROFESSIONS (allied health, cytotechnology, dental hygiene, medical records administration/services, medical technology, nuclear medical technology, nursing, occupational therapy, physician's assistant, and radiological science), SOCIAL SCIENCE (anthropology, criminal justice, economics, history, international studies, philosophy, political science/government, psychology, social work, and sociology). Biology, nursing, and psychology have the largest enrollments.

Required: All students must complete a core curriculum which includes courses in mathematics, computers, English, history, science, economics/political science, foreign culture, creative expression, and ethical reasoning. To receive a bachelor's degree, students must complete 128 semester hours for most programs, with a GPA of at least 2.0.

Special: Student-designed majors, cross-registration, internships, study abroad in the Bahamas, Brazil, England, and Mexico, work-study programs, and pass/fail options are available. Cooperative education programs in the student's area of interest provide full-time or part-time work. Credit by examination and for life experience is offered. Nondegree study is possible. There is a freshman honors program on campus, as well as 28 national honor societies.

Faculty/Classroom: Seventy-one percent of faculty are male; 29%, female.

Admissions: About 71% of the 1993–94 applicants were accepted. The ACT scores for the 1993–94 freshman class were as follows: 49% below 21, 26% between 21 and 23, 15% between 24 and 26, 5% between 27 and 28, and 5% above 28.

Requirements: A minimum GPA of 2.0 is required. The ACT is required, with a minimum score of 20. Applicants should have completed 12 Carnegie units, including 4 in English and 2 each in mathematics, science, and social studies. The GED, with an average score of 52, is accepted. AP and CLEP credits are accepted.

Procedure: Freshmen are admitted to all sessions. Entrance exams should be taken by the beginning of the senior year. Application deadlines are open. The application fee is $20. Notification is sent on a rolling basis. There are early admissions and deferred admissions plans.

Transfer: About 1180 transfer students enrolled in 1993–94. Transfer applicants should have earned a minimum of 24 semester hours at an accredited institution with a minimum GPA of 2.0. A total of 32 credits out of 128 must be completed at UAB.

Visiting: There are regularly scheduled orientations for prospective students, including a question and answer session, academic advising and sessions for parents. There are guides for informal visits and visitors may sit in on classes. To arrange for a visit, contact Shirley Anderson at (205) 934–8221.

Financial Aid: In 1993–94, 47% of all current freshmen and 31% of continuing students received some form of financial aid. About 37% of freshmen and 31% of continuing students received need-based aid. The average freshman award was $4600. Of that total, scholarships or need-based grants averaged $1500 ($6000 maximum); loans averaged $2000 ($5500 maximum); and work contracts averaged $1100 ($3200 maximum). Forty percent of undergraduate students work part-time. Average earnings from campus work for the school year are $2500. The average financial indebtedness of the 1992–93 graduate was $7500. UAB is a member of CSS. The FAF, FFS, SFS and FAFSA are required. The deadline for financial aid applications is June 1.

International Students: There are currently 148 international students enrolled. They must take the TOEFL and achieve a minimum score of 500.

Computers: The college provides computer facilities for student use. Microcomputers are available in various schools and laboratories around the campus. There are no time limits on using the system and no fees.

Graduates: In 1992–93, 1604 bachelor's degrees were awarded. The most popular majors among graduates were nursing (10%), marketing (6%), and accounting (6%). Within an average freshman class, 7% graduate in 3 years, 14% in 4 years, 26% in 5 years, and 32% in 6 years. Some 105 companies recruited on campus in 1992–93. In the 1992 graduating class, 50% found employment within 6 months of graduation.

Admissions Contact: Office of Undergraduate Admissions.

UNIVERSITY OF ALABAMA AT HUNTSVILLE   C-1

Huntsville, AL 35899   (205) 895–6070
(800) UAH-CALL (out-of-state)

Full-time: 1499 men, 1278 women	Faculty: 282; IIA, -$
Part-time: 1694 men, 1700 women	Ph.D.s: 90%
Graduate: 1282 men, 776 women	Student/Faculty: 10 to 1
Year: terms, summer session	Tuition: $2418 ($4836)
Application Deadline: August 13	Room & Board: $3450
Freshman Class: 1376 applied, 957 accepted, 478 enrolled	
SAT I Verbal/Math: 450/550	ACT: 23 VERY COMPETITIVE

The University of Alabama in Huntsville, founded in 1950 and part of the University of Alabama system, is a public, coeducational institution offering programs in liberal arts and sciences, business administration, nursing and engineering. There are 5 undergraduate schools and one graduate school. In addition to regional accreditation, UAH has baccalaureate program accreditation with ABET and NLN. The 2 libraries contain 300,000 volumes and 300,000 microform items, and subscribe to 3000 periodicals. Computerized library sources and ser-

vices include the card catalog and interlibrary loans. Special learning facilities include an art gallery and radio station. The 337-acre campus is in an urban area 100 miles north of Birmingham and 100 miles south of Nashville, Tennessee. Including residence halls, there are 28 buildings on campus.

Student Life: About 88% of undergraduates are from Alabama. Students come from 38 states, 42 foreign countries, and Canada. Eighty-nine percent are from public schools; 11% from private. Eighty-two percent are white. Seventy percent are Protestant; 16% claim no religious affiliation. The average age of freshmen is 20; all undergraduates, 26. About 53% of freshmen remain to graduate.

Housing: A total of 800 students can be accommodated in college housing. College-sponsored living facilities include coed dormitories, on-campus apartments, and married-student housing. On-campus housing is available on a first-come, first-served basis. Ninety-two percent of students commute. Alcohol is not permitted. All students may keep cars on campus.

Activities: About 11% of men belong to 5 national fraternities; about 7% of women belong to 5 national sororities. There are 90 groups on campus, including art, band, cheerleading, chess, choir, chorale, chorus, computers, dance, drama, ethnic, film, honors, international, jazz band, literary magazine, musical theater, newspaper, opera, pep band, photography, political, professional, religious, social, social service, student government, symphony, and yearbook. Popular campus events include FallFest, SpringFest, Homecoming, and Black History Month.

Sports: There are 5 intercollegiate sports for men and 4 for women, and 6 intramural sports for men and 6 for women. Athletic and recreation facilities include a 2800-seat gymnasium, a swimming pool, handball and tennis courts, soccer fields, and softball diamonds.

Disabled Students: Eighty percent of the campus is accessible to disabled students. The following facilities are available: wheelchair ramps, elevators, special parking, specially equipped rest rooms, special class scheduling, lowered drinking fountains, and a swimming pool lift.

Services: In addition to many counseling and information services, tutoring is available in most subjects. In addition, there is a reader service for the blind, and remedial math, reading, and writing, and study skills classes.

Campus Safety and Security: Campus safety and security measures include 24-hour foot and vehicle patrol and lighted pathways and sidewalks.

Programs of Study: UAH awards the B.A., B.S., B.S.B.A., B.S.E., and B.S.N. degrees. Master's and doctoral degrees also are awarded. Bachelor's degrees are awarded in BIOLOGICAL SCIENCE (biology/biological science), BUSINESS (accounting, banking and finance, business administration and management, business economics, management information systems, marketing/retailing/merchandising, and purchasing/inventory management), COMMUNICATIONS AND THE ARTS (communications, English, fine arts, French, German, languages, and music), COMPUTER AND PHYSICAL SCIENCE (chemistry, computer science, mathematics, optics, and physics), EDUCATION (education), ENGINEERING AND ENVIRONMENTAL DESIGN (chemical engineering, civil engineering, computer engineering, electrical/electronics engineering, industrial engineering, mechanical engineering, and optical engineering), HEALTH PROFESSIONS (nursing), SOCIAL SCIENCE (economics, history, political science/government, psychology, Russian and Slavic studies, and sociology). Electrical engineering, accounting, computer science, and nursing have the largest enrollments.

Required: All students must earn a minimum GPA of 2.0 over 128 to 134 credit hours, including 21 to 36 in their major. The core curriculum includes courses in English composition, literature, history, foreign language and communications, fine arts, mathematics, science, and social sciences.

Special: Co-op programs are available in accounting, engineering, nursing, computer science, and physics. Cross-registration for visiting students is offered at Alabama Agricultural and Mechanical University and Athens State and Calhoun Community colleges. Internships in administrative science, education, and political science are available. Dual majors, B.A.-B.S. degrees, nondegree study, and a pass/fail option are also offered. There is a freshman honors program on campus, as well as 23 national honor societies. Three departments have honors programs.

Faculty/Classroom: Seventy-two percent of faculty are male; 28%, female. The average class size in a regular course offering is 34.

Admissions: About 70% of the 1993–94 applicants were accepted. The SAT scores for the 1993–94 freshman class were as follows: Verbal—62% below 500, 23% between 500 and 599, 13% between 600 and 700, and 2% above 700; Math—30% below 500, 36% between 500 and 599, 25% between 600 and 700, and 8% above 700. The ACT scores were 25% below 21, 26% between 21 and 23, 26% between 24 and 26, 11% between 27 and 28, and 13% above 28. There were 2 National Merit finalists and 2 semifinalists.

Requirements: The SAT I or ACT is required. A sliding scale determines the minimum score needed. For example, with a 3.25 GPA, 17 is needed on the ACT or 750 on the SAT. The GED is accepted. Students should present a minimum of 20 Carnegie units, including 4 years of English, 3 each of mathematics and social studies, and 2 of science. AP and CLEP credits are accepted.

Procedure: Entrance exams should be taken during the junior year. Applications should be filed by August 13 for fall entry, December for winter entry, March for spring entry, and May for summer entry, along with an application fee of $20. Notification is sent on a rolling basis. There is an early admissions plan.

Transfer: About 530 transfer students enrolled in 1993–94. Transfer students need a minimum GPA of 2.0. A total of 32 credits out of 128 to 134 must be completed at UAH.

Visiting: There are regularly scheduled orientations for prospective students. There are guides for informal visits and visitors may stay overnight at the school. To arrange for a visit, contact the Admissions Office at (205) 895–6070.

Financial Aid: In an earlier year, 31% of all current freshmen and 35% of continuing students received some form of financial aid. About 24% of freshmen and 29% of continuing students received need-based aid. The average freshman award was $1600. Of that total, scholarships or need-based grants averaged $1800 ($4200 maximum); loans averaged $1900 ($4000 maximum); and work contracts averaged $2100 ($3000 maximum). Fifty percent of undergraduate students work part-time. Average earnings from campus work for the school year are $2100. The average financial indebtedness of recent year graduates was $3700. UAH is a member of CSS. The FAFSA financial statement is required. The deadline for financial aid applications is July 1.

International Students: There are currently 308 international students enrolled. They must take the TOEFL and achieve a minimum score of 500. The student must also take the SAT I or the ACT.

Computers: The college provides computer facilities for student use. The mainframe is a Unisys UNIVAC 2200/402, an HP 9000, and a DEC MicroVAX 3100, 8530/8250, and Station 5000. Terminals are located in 8 buildings across campus. The campus is served by Ethernet and provides access to the Alabama Supercomputer Cray X-MP 24. Those students enrolled in classes that require a computer laboratory may access the system. It may be used 24 hours daily. There are no fees.

Graduates: In 1992–93, 674 bachelor's degrees were awarded. The most popular majors among graduates were electrical engineering (24%), nursing (11%), and accounting (9%). Some 129 companies recruited on campus in 1992–93.

Admissions Contact: Dr. Ron Koger, Assistant Vice President for Enrollment Services.

UNIVERSITY OF MOBILE   A-5
(Formerly Mobile College)

Mobile, AL 36663–0220   (205) 675–5990; (800) 423–1089 (in-state)

Full-time: 506 men, 770 women	Faculty: 65; n/av
Part-time: 81 men, 187 women	Ph.D.s: 69%
Graduate: 57 men, 102 women	Student/Faculty: 20 to 1
Year: semesters, summer session	Tuition: $5920
Application Deadline: July 1	Room & Board: $3480
Freshman Class: 452 applied, 331 accepted, 269 enrolled	
ACT: 21	COMPETITIVE

University of Mobile, founded in 1961, is a private, coeducational liberal arts institution affiliated with the Southern Baptists. There are 3 undergraduate and 4 graduate schools. In addition to regional accreditation, Mobile has baccalaureate program accreditation with NASM and NLN. The library contains 130,633 volumes, 78,046 microform items, and 3376 audiovisual forms, and subscribes to 532 periodicals. Computerized library sources and services include the card catalog, interlibrary loans, and database searching. Special learning facilities include a learning resource center, art gallery, and a forest learning center. The 780-acre campus is in a suburban area 10 miles northwest of Mobile. Including residence halls, there are 52 buildings on campus.

Student Life: About 87% of undergraduates are from Alabama. Students come from 21 states, 30 foreign countries, and Canada. Eighty-six percent are from public schools; 14% from private. Eighty-three percent are white; 12% African American. Most are Protestant. Forty-five percent drop out by the end of their first year; 33% remain to graduate.

Housing: A total of 400 students can be accommodated in college housing. College-sponsored living facilities include single-sex dormitories. In addition, there are honors houses. On-campus housing is guaranteed for the freshman year only and is available on a first-come, first-served basis. Seventy-five percent of students commute. Alcohol is not permitted. All students may keep cars on campus.

Activities: There are no fraternities or sororities on campus. There are 52 groups on campus, including art, band, cheerleading, choir, chorus, computers, dance, drama, ethnic, film, honors, international, musical theater, newspaper, orchestra, pep band, political, professional, radio and TV, religious, social, social service, student government, and symphony. Popular campus events include Homecoming, Boar's Head Festival, Music Festival, College Preview Day, International Business Conference, and Spring Festival of the Arts.

Sports: There are 6 intercollegiate sports for men and 7 for women, and 7 intramural sports for men and 5 for women. Athletic and recreation facilities include a 1000-seat gymnasium, a tennis complex with 10 courts, a swimming pool, a track, baseball, softball, and soccer fields, and a golf driving range with 2 putting greens.

Disabled Students: Ninety percent of the campus is accessible to disabled students. The following facilities are available: wheelchair ramps, elevators, special parking, specially equipped rest rooms, special class scheduling, and lowered drinking fountains.

Services: In addition to many counseling and information services, tutoring is available in some subjects, including writing, English, and mathematics. There is also remedial math, reading, and writing.

Campus Safety and Security: Campus safety and security measures include 24-hour foot and vehicle patrol, self defense education, informal discussions, and pamphlets, posters, and films. In addition, there are emergency telephones, lighted pathways and sidewalks, and a professional campus security service available 24 hours per day.

Programs of Study: Mobile awards the B.A., B.S., and B.S.N. degrees. Associate and master's degrees also are awarded. Bachelor's degrees are awarded in BIOLOGICAL SCIENCE (biology/biological science), BUSINESS (accounting, banking and finance, business administration and management, business economics, and marketing/retailing/merchandising), COMMUNICATIONS AND THE ARTS (communications, English, fine arts, and music), COMPUTER AND PHYSICAL SCIENCE (chemistry, computer science, mathematics, and science), EDUCATION (early childhood, elementary, health, middle school, physical, and secondary), ENVIRONMENTAL DESIGN (environmental engineering technology), HEALTH PROFESSIONS (nursing), SOCIAL SCIENCE (behavioral science, economics, history, liberal arts/general studies, psychology, religion, and sociology). Education and nursing are the strongest academically. Business administration, religion, elementary education, and nursing have the largest enrollments.

Required: All students are required to complete 128 credit hours, with at least 30 in their major field, and earn a minimum GPA of 2.0. Distribution requirements include 12 hours in English, 8 hours in laboratory science, 6 hours each in religion and history, 6 hours from the following subjects: business, computer science, economics, political science, psychology, and sociology, 4 hours in health/physical education and recreation, 3 hours each in speech and mathematics, and 3 hours in art, music, or philosophy. Chapel attendance is also required.

Special: There are co-op programs, internships in many areas, study abroad in Nicaragua, work-study programs, B.A.-B.S. degrees in several majors, dual majors and a 3–2 engineering degree with Auburn University. There is also a freshman honors program on campus, as well as 5 national honor societies. Seven departments have honors programs.

Faculty/Classroom: Forty percent of faculty are male; 60%, female. All teach undergraduates, and 5% also do research. The average class size in an introductory lecture is 25; in a laboratory, 16; and in a regular course offering, 20.

Admissions: About 73% of the 1993–94 applicants were accepted. The ACT scores for the 1993–94 freshman class were as follows: 39% below 21, 27% between 21 and 23, 22% between 24 and 26, 10% between 27 and 28, and 2% above 28. About 25% of the current freshmen were in the top fifth of their class; 73% were in the top two fifths. Ten freshmen graduated first in their class.

Requirements: A minimum GPA of 2.0 is required. Applicants must have 22 Carnegie units and submit ACT results with a minimum composite score of 18. An essay, portfolio, and interview are recommended. AP and CLEP credits are accepted. Important factors used in the admissions decision are recommendations by school officials, advanced placement or honor courses, ability to finance college education, evidence of special talents, and leadership record.

Procedure: Freshmen are admitted to all sessions. Entrance exams should be taken in August before the junior year. Early decision applications should be filed by June 1; regular applications, by July 1 for fall entry, December 1 for spring entry, and May 1 for summer entry, along with an application fee of $30. Notification of early decision is sent June 15; regular decision, on a rolling basis. There are early decision, early admissions, and deferred admissions plans. A waiting list is an active part of the admissions procedure, with about 19% of applicants on the list.

Transfer: About 224 transfer students enrolled in an earlier year. Transfer students need to have earned a minimum GPA of 2.0 for previous college work. If fewer than 30 hours are accepted, a minimum score of 18 on the ACT and a high school transcript are required. A total of 30 credits out of 128 must be completed at Mobile.

Visiting: There are regularly scheduled orientations for prospective students, including financial aid seminars, academic seminars, faculty advising, campus tours, and admissions counseling. There are guides for informal visits and visitors may sit in on classes and stay overnight at the school. To arrange for a visit, contact Kim Leousis, Director of Admissions at (205) 675–5990 or (800) 423–1089 (in-state).

Financial Aid: In an earlier year 91% of all current freshmen and 88% of continuing students received some form of financial aid. About 33% of freshmen and 31% of continuing students received need-based aid. The average freshman award was $4200. Of that total, scholarships or need-based grants averaged $1125 ($5010 maximum); loans averaged $1800 ($2625 maximum); and work contracts averaged $1275 ($12,750 maximum). Sixteen percent of undergraduate students work part-time. Average earnings from campus work for the school year are $1275. The average financial indebtedness of an earlier year's graduate was $7060. Mobile is a member of CSS. The FFS and the college's own financial statement are required. The deadline for financial aid applications is March 31.

International Students: There are currently 37 international students enrolled. The school actively recruits these students. They must take the TOEFL or the college's own test and achieve a minimum score on the TOEFL of 500. The student must also take the ACT.

Computers: The college provides computer facilities for student use. The mainframe is a DEC VAX 11/750. About 200 students use the 12 terminals located in the minicomputer laboratory and 17 microcomputers in the microcomputer laboratory. Nine microcomputers are in a Novell network, 5 are in the psychology laboratory, and 5 in the accounting laboratory. All students may access the system. It may be used 8 A.M. to 9 P.M. Monday through Friday and a half day Saturday. There are no time limits and no fees.

Graduates: In 1992–93 183 bachelor's degrees were awarded. The most popular majors among graduates were nursing (20%), education (16%), and business/management (14%). Some 62 companies recruited on campus in a recent year. In the 1992 graduating class, 15% of the men and 13% of the women were enrolled in graduate school within 6 months of graduation; 70% of the men and 88% of the women had found employment.

Admissions Contact: Kim Leousius, Director of Admissions.

UNIVERSITY OF MONTEVALLO
C-3
Montevallo, AL 35115–6030
(205) 665–6030
(800) 292–4349 (in-state)

Full-time: 777 men, 1609 women	**Faculty:** 127
Part-time: 119 men, 212 women	**Ph.D.s:** 68%
Graduate: 135 men, 463 women	**Student/Faculty:** 19 to 1
Year: semesters, summer session	**Tuition:** $2280 ($4500)
Application Deadline: August 1	**Room & Board:** $3030
Freshman Class: 1351 applied, 1027 accepted, 571 enrolled	
SAT I or ACT: required	**COMPETITIVE**

The University of Montevallo, founded in 1896, is a public, coeducational liberal arts institution offering courses in business, fine arts, music, professional training, and teacher preparation. There are 4 undergraduate schools and one graduate school. In addition to regional accreditation, UM has baccalaureate program accreditation with AACSB, ADA, AHEA, CSWE, NASAD, NASM, and NCATE. The library contains 238,658 volumes, 337,222 microform items, and 1845 audiovisual forms, and subscribes to 1232 periodicals. Computerized library sources and services include the card catalog, interlibrary loans, and database searching. Special learning facilities include an art gallery, a TV station, and a university theater. The 160-acre campus is in a small town 35 miles south of Birmingham. Including residence halls, there are 37 buildings on campus.

Student Life: About 96% of undergraduates are from Alabama. Students come from 24 states and 12 foreign countries. Ninety-four percent are from public schools; 6% from private. Eighty-eight percent are white; 10% African American. Eighty-one percent are Protestant; 10% claim no religious affiliation. The average age of freshmen is 18; all undergraduates, 21. Twenty-nine percent drop out by the end of their first year.

Housing: A total of 1285 students can be accommodated in college housing. College-sponsored living facilities include single-sex and coed dormitories and on-campus apartments. On-campus housing is available on a first-come, first-served basis. Fifty-eight percent of students commute. All students may keep cars on campus.

Activities: About 23% of men belong to 7 national fraternities; about 23% of women belong to 7 national sororities. There are 65 groups on campus, including art, cheerleading, choir, chorus, dance, drama, ethnic, gay, honors, international, jazz band, literary magazine, musical theater, newspaper, orchestra, pep band, photography, political,

professional, radio and TV, religious, social, social service, student government, and yearbook. Popular campus events include College Night and Elite Night.

Sports: There are 3 intercollegiate sports for men and 2 for women, and 6 intramural sports for men and 6 for women. Athletic and recreation facilities include a 2200-seat gymnasium, a swimming pool, bowling lanes, playing fields, a golf course, a walking track, a soccer field, and handball courts.

Disabled Students: Ninety percent of the campus is accessible to disabled students. The following facilities are available: wheelchair ramps, elevators, special parking, specially equipped rest rooms, special class scheduling, lowered drinking fountains, and lowered telephones.

Services: In addition to many counseling and information services, tutoring is available in some subjects, including note taking (study skills). In addition, there is remedial math, reading, and writing, and a speech and hearing center.

Campus Safety and Security: Campus safety and security measures include 24-hour foot and vehicle patrol, escort service, informal discussions, and pamphlets, posters, and films.

Programs of Study: UM awards the B.A., B.S., B.B.A., B.F.A., B.M., and B.M.E. degrees. Master's degrees also are awarded. Bachelor's degrees are awarded in BIOLOGICAL SCIENCE (biology/biological science), BUSINESS (accounting, management science, and marketing/retailing/merchandising), COMMUNICATIONS AND THE ARTS (broadcasting, dramatic arts, English, French, music, photography, Spanish, and speech/debate/rhetoric), COMPUTER AND PHYSICAL SCIENCE (chemistry and mathematics), EDUCATION (art, early childhood, education of the deaf and hearing impaired, elementary, health, home economics, and music), HEALTH PROFESSIONS (medical laboratory technology and speech pathology/audiology), SOCIAL SCIENCE (history, home economics, political science/government, psychology, social science, social work, and sociology). Elementary/early childhood education, business administration, home economics, art, and English have the largest enrollments.

Required: To graduate, students must complete a minimum of 130 semester hours with an overall 2.0 GPA while meeting core requirements, major requirements, and minor requirements. Core requirements include 12 hours of writing reinforcement courses (usually met with literature and major/minor courses), 7 hours of sciences (two branches), 6 hours each of foundations in writing, world literature, world civilizations, and institutions and issues courses, 3 hours each of oral communications, mathematics, fine arts, and human behavior and inquiry courses, 4 hours of health/physical education, and 1 to 3 hours of computer science.

Special: A 3-2 engineering degree is offered with Auburn University and the University of Alabama at Birmingham. Internships, study abroad, work-study, an accelerated degree plan, B.A.-B.S. degrees, dual degrees, and pass/fail options are available. There is a freshman honors program on campus. Three departments have honors programs.

Faculty/Classroom: Fifty-two percent of faculty are male; 48%, female. All teach undergraduates. No introductory courses are taught by graduate students. The average class size in an introductory lecture is 35; in a laboratory, 24; and in a regular course offering, 35.

Admissions: About 76% of the 1993-94 applicants were accepted. About 35% of the current freshmen were in the top fifth of their class; 80% were in the top two fifths. There was 1 National Merit finalist and 7 semifinalists. Forty-one freshmen graduated first in their class.

Requirements: UM requires applicants to be in the upper 50% of their class. A minimum GPA of 2.0 is required. The SAT I or ACT is required. Applicants must be high school graduates with 16 academic credits, including 4 units each of English and social studies, 2 each of mathematics and science, and 4 academic electives. One year each of algebra and plane geometry is recommended. The GED is accepted. AP and CLEP credits are accepted. Important factors used in the admissions decision are advanced placement or honor courses, evidence of special talent, geographic diversity, leadership record, and extracurricular activities record.

Procedure: Freshmen are admitted to all sessions. Entrance exams should be taken in April or June of the junior year, or October of the senior year. Applications should be filed by August 1 for fall entry, January 1 for spring entry, and June 1 for summer entry, along with an application fee of $15. Notification is sent on a rolling basis. There are early admissions and deferred admissions plans.

Transfer: About 290 transfer students enrolled in 1993-94. Transfer students need a minimum GPA of 2.0 on previous college study attempted. One year of residency and at least 30 semester hours out of 130 must be completed at UM.

Visiting: There are regularly scheduled orientations for prospective students, consisting of 1 day of registration (pre-orientation) and orientation, including on-site visits, mentor groups, play activities, career assessments, and learning style assessments. There are guides for informal visits, and visitors may sit in on classes and stay overnight at the school. To arrange for a visit, contact the Office of Admissions at (205) 665-6030 or (800) 292-4349 (in-state).

Financial Aid: In 1993-94, 62% of all current freshmen and 46% of continuing students received some form of financial aid. About 56% of freshmen and 42% of continuing students received need-based aid. Scholarships or need-based grants averaged $1600 ($5500 maximum); loans averaged $3000 ($7500 maximum); and work contracts averaged $1600. The average financial indebtedness of the 1992-93 graduate was $11,000. The FAF, FFS, or SFS is required. The deadline for financial aid applications is August 1.

International Students: There are currently 19 international students enrolled. They must take the TOEFL and achieve a minimum score of 525.

Computers: The college provides computer facilities for student use. The mainframe is a DEC VAX 6410. About 125 IBM, Zenith, Leading Edge, and Tandy PCs, 10 Apple Macintoshes, and other microcomputers are available. All students may access the system. It may be used 8 A.M. to 11 P.M. Monday through Friday; hours vary on weekends. There are no time limits on using the system and no fees.

Admissions Contact: Robert A. Doyle, Director of Admissions.

UNIVERSITY OF NORTH ALABAMA
Florence, AL 35632-0001

B-1
(205) 760-4221

Full-time: 1566 men, 2206 women	Faculty: 202
Part-time: 451 men, 583 women	Ph.D.s: 62%
Graduate: 174 men, 429 women	Student/Faculty: 19 to 1
Year: semesters, summer session	Tuition: $1576 ($2176)
Application Deadline: July 1	Room & Board: $2660
Freshman Class: 916 applied, 916 accepted, 707 enrolled	
SAT I or ACT: required	NONCOMPETITIVE

The University of North Alabama, founded in 1872, is a public institution offering degree programs in arts and sciences, business, education, and nursing. There are 4 undergraduate and 2 graduate schools. In addition to regional accreditation, UNA has baccalaureate program accreditation with CSWE, NASAD, NASM, NCATE, and NLN. The library contains 265,608 volumes, 616,374 microform items, and 4693 audiovisual forms, and subscribes to 2046 periodicals. Computerized library sources and services include the card catalog, interlibrary loans, and database searching. Special learning facilities include a learning resource center, art gallery, and planetarium. The 100-acre campus is in an urban area 116 miles north of Birmingham. Including residence halls, there are 37 buildings on campus.

Student Life: About 17% of undergraduates are from out-of-state, mostly the South. Students come from 33 states, 19 foreign countries, and Canada. Eighty-nine percent are from public schools; 5% from private. Ninety-one percent are white. Most are Protestant. The average age of freshmen is 18; all undergraduates, 23. Twenty-seven percent drop out by the end of their first year.

Housing: A total of 1010 students can be accommodated in college housing. College-sponsored living facilities include single-sex dormitories and married-student housing. On-campus housing is available on a first-come, first-served basis. Eighty-five percent of students commute. Alcohol is not permitted. All students may keep cars on campus.

Activities: About 10% of men belong to 6 national fraternities; about 9% of women belong to 6 national sororities. There are 91 groups on campus, including band, cheerleading, choir, chorus, computers, drama, drill team, ethnic, film, honors, international, jazz band, literary magazine, marching band, musical theater, newspaper, opera, political, radio and TV, religious, social, social service, student government, and yearbook. Popular campus events include Homecoming and Spring Fling.

Sports: There are 7 intercollegiate sports for men and 5 for women, and 19 intramural sports for men and 19 for women. Athletic and recreation facilities include a 13,500-seat football stadium, a 4,000-seat gymnasium, a baseball field, an outdoor track, an indoor swimming pool, and tennis courts.

Disabled Students: Ninety-six percent of the campus is accessible to disabled students. The following facilities are available: wheelchair ramps, elevators, special parking, specially equipped rest rooms, special class scheduling, lowered drinking fountains, and lowered telephones.

Services: In addition to many counseling and information services, tutoring is available in some subjects, including mathematics, English, history, biology, chemistry, accounting, finance, economics, and physics. In addition, there is a reader service for the blind.

Campus Safety and Security: Campus safety and security measures include 24-hour foot and vehicle patrol, informal discussions, pamphlets, posters, and films, and emergency telephones. In addition, there are lighted pathways and sidewalks.

Programs of Study: UNA awards the B.A., B.S., B.A.M., B.F.A., B.G.S., B.M., B.M.M.Ed., B.S.Ed., B.S.M., and B.S.N. degrees. Master's degrees also are awarded. Bachelor's degrees are awarded in

BIOLOGICAL SCIENCE (biology/biological science, environmental biology, and marine biology), BUSINESS (accounting, banking and finance, business economics, management science, and marketing/retailing/merchandising), COMMUNICATIONS AND THE ARTS (art, broadcasting, communications, dramatic arts, English, French, German, journalism, music, public relations, and Spanish), COMPUTER AND PHYSICAL SCIENCE (chemistry, computer science, information sciences and systems, mathematics, and physics), EDUCATION (art, business, early childhood, elementary, foreign languages, health, home economics, music, science, and secondary), HEALTH PROFESSIONS (industrial hygiene and nursing), SOCIAL SCIENCE (criminal justice, geography, history, political science/government, psychology, social work, and sociology). Physical sciences, biological sciences, and mathematics are the strongest academically. Management, accounting, and marketing have the largest enrollments.

Required: Students must complete a core curriculum, which includes 14 semester hours in language and literature, 12 in social and behavioral science, 12 in science and mathematics, 2 in physical education, and 3 in art, military science, music, or theater. Passing grades in 1 writing emphasis course and 1 computer course also are needed. A minimum of 128 semester hours and a minimum GPA of 2.0 are required in order to graduate.

Special: UNA offers cooperative programs in all majors, work-study programs, various B.A.-B.S. degrees, dual majors, and a general studies degree. Nondegree study is possible. There are 13 national honor societies on campus, including Phi Beta Kappa. Two departments have honors programs.

Faculty/Classroom: Sixty-three percent of faculty are male; 37%, female. All teach undergraduates. No introductory courses are taught by graduate students.

Admissions: All of the 1993–94 applicants were accepted. About 37% of the current freshmen were in the top fifth of their class; 72% were in the top two fifths.

Requirements: UNA requires applicants to be in the upper 50% of their class. A minimum GPA of 2.0 is required. The SAT I or ACT is required. Applicants should be graduates of an accredited high school or have earned a GED. AP and CLEP credits are accepted.

Procedure: Freshmen are admitted to all sessions. Entrance exams should be taken in the senior year. Applications should be filed by July 1 for fall entry, December 1 for spring entry, and May 25 for summer entry, along with an application fee of $25. Notification is sent on a rolling basis. There is a deferred admissions plan.

Transfer: About 680 transfer students enrolled in a recent year. Applicants should be eligible to return to the school last attended. A total of 30 credits out of 128 must be completed at UNA.

Visiting: There are regularly scheduled orientations for prospective students, consisting of orientation programs conducted each summer prior to the fall semester. There are guides for informal visits. To arrange for a visit, contact Joe Wallace, Director of University Events, at (205) 760-4608.

Financial Aid: In a recent year, 40% of all current freshmen and 45% of continuing students received some form of financial aid. About 30% of freshmen and 35% of continuing students received need-based aid. The average freshman award was $1800. Of that total, scholarships or need-based grants averaged $1200 ($4200 maximum); loans averaged $1000 ($2625 maximum); and work contracts averaged $1300 ($1700 maximum). Forty-nine percent of undergraduate students work part-time. Average earnings from campus work for the school year are $1400. The average financial indebtedness of a recent graduate was $7200. The FFS is required. The deadline for financial aid applications is April 1.

International Students: There are currently 30 international students enrolled. The school actively recruits these students. They must take the TOEFL and achieve a minimum overall score of 500, with at least 55 on the listening comprehension sections.

Computers: The college provides computer facilities for student use. The mainframe is an IBM 4300 series. Terminals are located in the Computer Center and in a computer laboratory in the School of Business. There are Apple Macintosh and IBM microcomputers available in the new Academic Resource Center, with additional IBM, Apple, and Zenith units available in faculty or departmental offices. All students may access the system. There are no time limits on using the system and no fees.

Graduates: In a recent year, 722 bachelor's degrees were awarded. The most popular majors among graduates were marketing (9%), accounting (9%), and management (8%). Within an average freshman class, 30% graduate in 5 years. Some 58 companies recruited on campus in a recent year.

Admissions Contact: Dr. G. Daniel Howard, Acting Dean of Enrollment Management.

UNIVERSITY OF SOUTH ALABAMA
A-5

Mobile, AL 36688   (205) 460–6141; (800) 872–5247 (out-of-state)

Full-time: 3385 men, 4131 women	Faculty: 444; IIA, -$
Part-time: 1287 men, 1656 women	Ph.D.s: 81%
Graduate: 694 men, 1107 women	Student/Faculty: 17 to 1
Year: quarters, summer session	Tuition: $2391 ($3291)
Application Deadline: September 10	Room & Board: $3060
Freshman Class: 2328 applied, 2110 accepted, 1047 enrolled	
ACT: 23	COMPETITIVE

The University of South Alabama, a state-supported coeducational institution established in 1963, offers undergraduate and graduate degrees in the allied health professions, arts and sciences, business and management studies, education, engineering, and nursing, and computer and information sciences. There are 8 undergraduate and 9 graduate schools. In addition to regional accreditation, USA has baccalaureate program accreditation with AACSB, ABET, AHEA, APTA, NCATE, and NLN. The 2 libraries contain 327,934 volumes, 1,015,992 microform items, and 343 audiovisual forms, and subscribe to 4694 periodicals. Computerized library sources and services include the card catalog and interlibrary loans. The 1585-acre campus is in an urban area. Including residence halls, there are 124 buildings on campus.

Student Life: About 75% of undergraduates are from Alabama. Students come from 41 states, 69 foreign countries, and Canada. Ninety percent are from public schools; 10% from private. Eighty-one percent are white; 10% African American. The average freshman age is 19; all other undergraduates, 25.5. Thirty-five percent drop out by the end of their first year; 37% remain to graduate.

Housing: A total of 1800 students can be accommodated in college housing. College-sponsored living facilities include dormitories, on-campus apartments, married-student housing, and fraternity houses. On-campus housing is available on a first-come, first-served basis. About 77% of students commute and all may keep cars on campus. Alcohol is not permitted.

Activities: About 5% of men belong to 12 national fraternities; about 3% of women belong to 9 national sororities. There are 150 groups on campus, including band, cheerleading, chess, choir, chorale, chorus, computers, dance, drama, ethnic, honors, international, jazz band, musical theater, newspaper, orchestra, pep band, political, professional, religious, social, social service, and student government. Popular campus events include Homecoming, Club South, Mayfest, Greek Week, and Chi Omega Songfest.

Sports: There are 9 intramural sports for men and 9 for women. Athletic and recreation facilities include a 3000-seat stadium, a 3500-seat gymnasium, and athletic fields.

Disabled Students: Nearly 85% of the campus is accessible to disabled students. The following facilities are available: wheelchair ramps, elevators, special parking, specially equipped rest rooms, and lowered drinking fountains and telephones.

Services: In addition to many counseling and information services, tutoring is available in most subjects. There is also remedial math, reading, and writing.

Campus Safety and Security: Campus safety and security measures include 24-hour foot and vehicle patrol, escort service, and lighted pathways and sidewalks.

Programs of Study: USA awards the B.A.and B.S. degree. Master's and doctoral degrees also are awarded. Bachelor's degrees are awarded in BIOLOGICAL SCIENCE (biology/biological science), BUSINESS (accounting, banking and finance, business administration and management, business economics, management science, and marketing/retailing/merchandising), COMMUNICATIONS AND THE ARTS (art, art history and appreciation, communications, dramatic arts, English, fine arts, French, German, music, Russian, Spanish, and studio art), COMPUTER AND PHYSICAL SCIENCE (chemistry, computer science, earth science, geology, mathematics, physics, and statistics), EDUCATION (early childhood, elementary, health, middle school, music, physical, secondary, and special), ENGINEERING AND ENVIRONMENTAL DESIGN (chemical engineering, civil engineering, electrical/electronics engineering, and mechanical engineering), HEALTH PROFESSIONS (biomedical science, medical laboratory technology, nursing, physical therapy, premedicine, and speech pathology/audiology), SOCIAL SCIENCE (anthropology, criminal justice, economics, geography, history, international relations, philosophy, political science/government, psychology, and sociology). Engineering is the strongest academically. Business administration has the largest enrollment.

Required: Distribution requirements for all students include 6 quarter hours of physical education or ROTC, English, mathematics, communication, and computer science. A minimum of 192 quarter hours and a GPA of at least 2.0 are required in order to graduate.

Special: A cooperative program in education is offered in conjunction with Auburn University. The university offers cross registration with the Marine Environmental Sciences consortium at Dauphin Is-

land for students majoring in marine biology. Work-study programs, medicine internships, study abroad, credit for life experience, and pass/fail options are available. Nondegree study, interdisciplinary majors, including African American studies and international studies, and a personalized studies program are possible. There is a freshman honors program on campus, as well as 14 national honor societies.

Faculty/Classroom: Seventy-two percent of faculty are male; 28%, female. The average class size in an introductory lecture is 60; in a laboratory, 20; and in a regular course offering, 22.

Admissions: About 91% of the 1993–94 applicants were accepted.

Requirements: A minimum GPA of 2.0 is required; 2.5 is necessary for some programs. The SAT I or ACT (preferred) is required. Applicants should be high school graduates or GED equivalent with a minimum composite score of 16. An interview is recommended. AP and CLEP credits are accepted. Important factors used in the admissions decision are advanced placement or honor courses, leadership record, extracurricular activities record, evidence of special talent, and recommendations by school officials.

Procedure: Freshmen are admitted to all sessions. Entrance exams should be taken during the junior year. Applications should be filed by September 10 for fall entry, along with an application fee of $20. Notification is sent on a rolling basis. There are early decision, early admissions, and deferred admissions plans.

Transfer: About 1170 transfer students enrolled recently. Transfer applicants must have at least a 2.0 GPA. A total of 48 quarter hours out of 192 must be completed at USA.

Visiting: There are regularly scheduled orientations for prospective students, including 3 Saturday visiting days in February, November, and April. There are guides for informal visits and visitors may sit in on classes. To arrange for a visit, contact Catherine King, Admissions, at (205) 460–6141 or (800) 872–5247 (out-of-state).

Financial Aid: In an earlier year, 45% of all students received some form of financial aid. Scholarships or need-based grants averaged $1759 ($2400 maximum); loans averaged $3045; and work contracts averaged $2103. About 60% of undergraduate students work part-time. The FFS is required. The deadline for financial aid applications is July 15.

International Students: There are currently 543 international students enrolled. The school actively recruits these students. They must take the TOEFL and achieve a minimum score of 500.

Computers: The college provides computer facilities for student use. The mainframe is an IBM 4341 and there is a DEC VAX 8250 minicomputer. There are also 130 IBM and Apple microcomputers available in academic areas and some dormitories. All students may access the system. It may be used at various times.

Graduates: Recently, 1280 bachelor's degrees were awarded. Within an average freshman class, 13% graduate in 4 years, 11% in 5 years, and 6% in 6 years.

Admissions Contact: Catherine P. King, Director of Admissions.

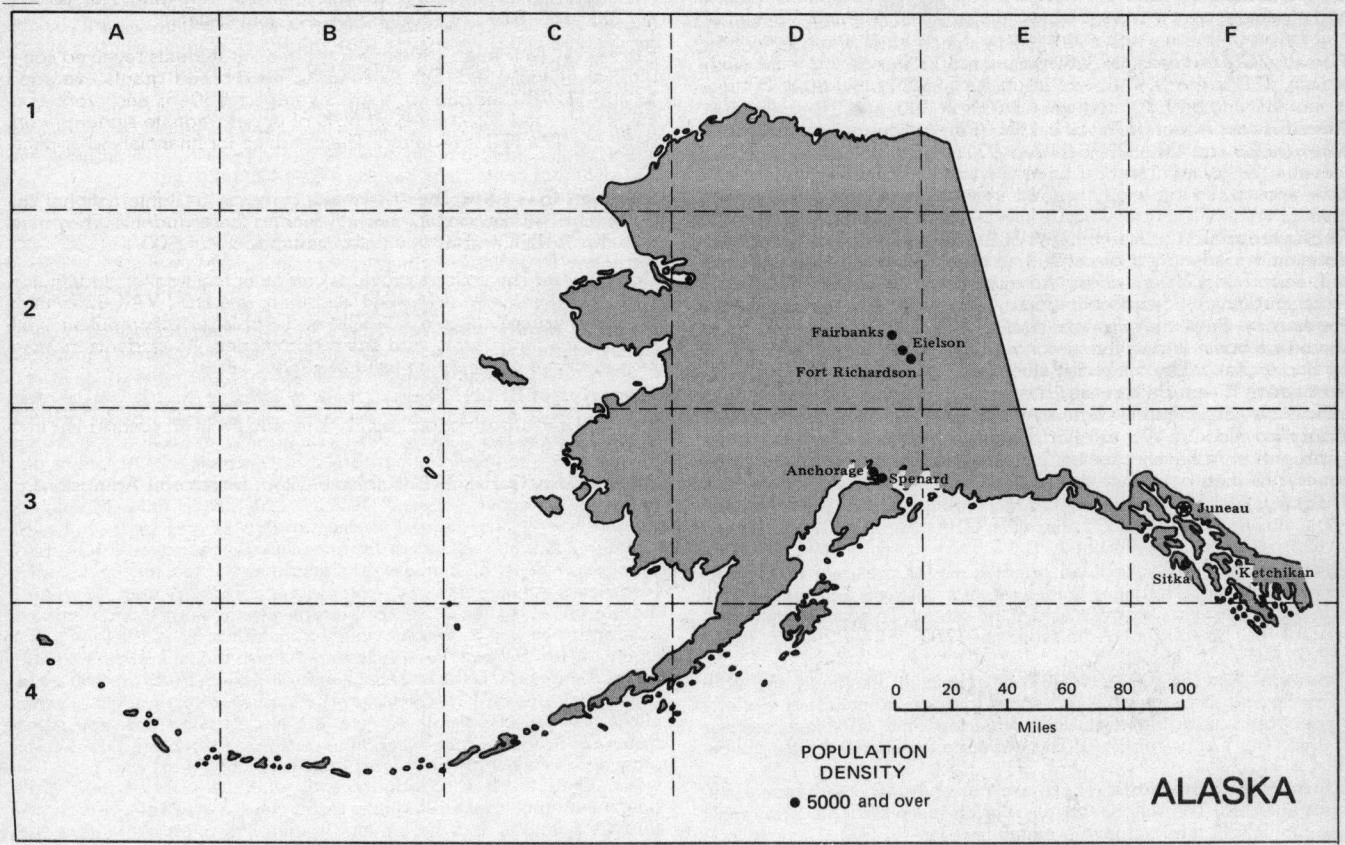

POPULATION DENSITY
● 5000 and over

ALASKA

ALASKA PACIFIC UNIVERSITY

D-3

Anchorage, AK 99508-4672

(907) 564-8248
(800) ALASKA-U (out-of-state)

Full-time: 82 men, 181 women	**Faculty:** 22
Part-time: 78 men, 106 women	**Ph.D.s:** 72%
Graduate: 83 men, 151 women	**Student/Faculty:** 12 to 1
Year: semesters, summer session	**Tuition:** $7330
Application Deadline: August 15	**Room & Board:** $4020

Freshman Class: 193 applied, 146 accepted, 55 enrolled

SAT I Verbal/Math: 485/470   **ACT:** 19   **COMPETITIVE**

Alaska Pacific University, founded in 1957, is a private, coeducational institution affiliated with the United Methodist Church, offering undergraduate programs in education, humanities, environmental science and mathematics, management, and social sciences. There are 7 graduate schools. The library contains 384,698 volumes, 37,619 microform items, and 7080 audiovisual forms, and subscribes to 3479 periodicals. Computerized library sources and services include the card catalog and interlibrary loans. Special learning facilities include a learning resource center, a radio station, and a tv station. The 270-acre campus is in midtown Anchorage. Including residence halls, there are 7 buildings on campus.

Student Life: About 91% of undergraduates are from Alaska. Students come from 17 states, 6 foreign countries, and Canada. Seventy-one percent are white. Fifty-one percent are Protestant; 30% claim no religious affiliation; 18% are Catholic. The average age of freshmen is 18.7; all undergraduates, 30. Sixty-one percent drop out by the end of their first year; 11% remain to graduate.

Housing: A total of 125 students can be accommodated in college housing. College-sponsored living facilities include coed dormitories, on-campus apartments, off-campus apartments, and married-student housing. In addition, there are special interest houses. On-campus housing is available on a first-come, first-served basis. Eighty-eight percent of students commute. Alcohol is not permitted. All students may keep cars on campus.

Activities: There are no fraternities or sororities on campus. There are 15 groups on campus, including chorus, drama, ethnic, gay, international, literary magazine, newspaper, religious, student government, and yearbook. Popular campus events include the Outdoor Program.

Sports: There are 5 intramural sports for men and for women. Athletic and recreation facilities include a 300-seat sports center, an indoor swimming pool, cross-country skiing and running trails, a climbing wall, a soccer field, a lake for boating, and a weight/exercise room.

Disabled Students: Fifty percent of the campus is accessible to disabled students. The following facilities are available: wheelchair ramps, elevators, special parking, specially equipped rest rooms, lowered drinking fountains, and lowered telephones.

Services: In addition to many counseling and information services, tutoring is available in most subjects, including mathematics, writing, and other subjects as needed.

Campus Safety and Security: Campus safety and security measures include 24-hour foot and vehicle patrol, informal discussions, pamphlets, posters, and films, and emergency telephones. In addition, there are lighted pathways and sidewalks.

Programs of Study: APU awards the B.A. degree. Associate and master's degrees also are awarded. Bachelor's degrees are awarded in AGRICULTURE (natural resource management), BUSINESS (accounting, hospitality management services, international business management, marketing management, and sports management), COMMUNICATIONS AND THE ARTS (art, comparative literature, and music), EDUCATION (elementary), ENGINEERING AND ENVIRONMENTAL DESIGN (environmental science), SOCIAL SCIENCE (history, philosophy, and psychology). Management/organizational management has the largest enrollment.

Required: Competency in writing, speech, and college-level mathematics is required. Distribution requirements include a 2-semester course in world civilization, a laboratory science, 2 semesters of a foreign language, and an integrative elective in humanities and social sciences. All students must complete a core curriculum that includes courses in the individual, social, natural, and spiritual environments and integration; students also must take a physical education activity and lecture course in fitness for life. A total of 128 credits with a minimum GPA of 2.0, a senior comprehensive examination or project, and a 3-semester-hour practicum are required in order to graduate.

Special: Study abroad is possible. The Degree Completion Program for working adults leads to a B.A. in management/organizational management.

Faculty/Classroom: Fifty-two percent of faculty are male; 48%, female. Eighty-six percent teach undergraduates. The average class size in an introductory lecture is 12; in a laboratory, 13; and in a regular course offering, 12.

Admissions: About 76% of the 1993–94 applicants were accepted. The SAT I scores for the 1993–94 freshman class were as follows: Verbal—58% below 500, 33% between 500 and 599, 5% between 600 and 700, and 3% above 700; Math—56% below 500, 31% between 500 and 599, 11% between 600 and 700, and 3% above 700. The ACT scores were 62% below 21, 17% between 21 and 23, 3% between 24 and 26, 10% between 27 and 28, and 7% above 28. About 35% of the current freshmen were in the top fifth of their class; 70% were in the top two fifths. Two freshmen graduated first in their class.

Requirements: A minimum GPA of 2.5 is required. The SAT I, with a minimum composite score of 800, or the ACT, with a minimum composite score of 17, is required. An interview is also required. AP and CLEP credits are accepted. Important factors used in the admissions decision are evidence of special talent, advanced placement or honor courses, recommendations by school officials, recommendations by alumni, and parents or siblings attending the school.

Procedure: Freshmen are admitted to all sessions. Entrance exams should be taken before January of the senior year. Applications should be filed by August 15 for fall entry and December 15 for spring entry. Notification is sent on a rolling basis. There is an early admissions plan.

Transfer: About 100 transfer students enrolled in 1993–94. Transfer applicants must have a 2.0 cumulative GPA. The final 32 credits out of 128 must be completed at APU.

Visiting: Regularly scheduled orientations for prospective students vary by program. There are guides for informal visits and visitors may sit in on classes and stay overnight at the school. To arrange for a visit, contact the Director of Admissions at (907) 564–8248 or (800) ALASKA-U.

Financial Aid: In 1993–94, 93% of all current freshmen and 48% of continuing students received some form of financial aid. Twenty percent of undergraduate students work part-time. APU is a member of CSS. The FAF is required. The deadline for financial aid applications is July 1.

International Students: There are currently 28 international students enrolled. The school actively recruits these students. They must take the TOEFL and achieve a minimum score of 500.

Computers: The college provides computer facilities for student use. The mainframe is an AS 400. The Academic Support Center provides 26 PCs for student and faculty use. There are no time limits on using the system and no fees.

Graduates: In 1992–93, 93 bachelor's degrees were awarded. The most popular majors among graduates were management/organizational management (59%), management/marketing (10%), and elementary education (9%). Within an average freshman class, 10% graduate in 4 years and 2% in 5 years.

Admissions Contact: Karon Jahn, Acting Director of Admissions.

SHELDON JACKSON COLLEGE   F-3
Sitka, AK 99835   (907) 747–5221; (800) 544–2231 (out-of-state)

Full-time: 104 men, 100 women	Faculty: 26
Part-time: 27 men, 72 women	Ph.D.s: 46%
Graduate: none	Student/Faculty: 8 to 1
Year: 4–1–4	Tuition: $9250
Application Deadline: open	Room & Board: $4800
Freshman Class: 160 applied, 160 accepted, 90 enrolled	
ACT: 20	NONCOMPETITIVE

Sheldon Jackson College, founded in 1878, is a private liberal arts college, affiliated with the Presbyterian Church, offering an academic program with an emphasis in natural and aquatic resource science, marine biology, business, elementary and secondary education, and interdisciplinary studies. The library contains 70,000 volumes and subscribes to 500 periodicals. Computerized library sources and services include the card catalog and interlibrary loans. Special learning facilities include a learning resource center and a state-owned museum, a 60-foot research vessel, and a salmon hatchery. The 345-acre campus is in a small town 800 miles north of Seattle. Including residence halls, there are 23 buildings on campus.

Student Life: About 70% of undergraduates are from out-of-state, mostly the Northwest. Students come from 35 states, 4 foreign countries, and Canada. Ninety-nine percent are from public schools. Seventy percent are white; 26% Native American/Eskimo. Eighteen percent drop out by the end of their first year; 21% remain to graduate.

Housing: A total of 240 students can be accommodated in college housing. College-sponsored living facilities include single-sex dormitories, on-campus apartments, and married-student housing. On-campus housing is guaranteed for all 4 years. Seventy-five percent of students live on campus; of those, all remain on campus on week-

ends. Alcohol is not permitted. All students may keep cars on campus.

Activities: There are no fraternities or sororities on campus. There are 10 groups on campus, including chorus, computers, drama, ethnic, musical theater, photography, political, religious, social, social service, student government, and yearbook. Popular campus events include Alaska Day and Gathering of the People (Alaska native dances and dinner).

Sports: There are 10 intramural sports for men and 10 for women. Athletic and recreation facilities include a 3-court gymnasium, a 25-meter pool, a weight room, two racquetball courts, a wilderness center, a student center, sea kayaks, and a climbing wall.

Disabled Students: The entire campus is accessible to disabled students. The following facilities are available: wheelchair ramps, special parking, specially equipped rest rooms, and special class scheduling.

Services: In addition to many counseling and information services, tutoring is available in every subject. There is remedial math, reading, and writing.

Campus Safety and Security: Campus safety and security measures include self defense education, informal discussions, pamphlets, posters, and films, and lighted pathways and sidewalks.

Programs of Study: Sheldon Jackson College awards the B.A. and B.S. degrees. Associate degrees also are awarded. Bachelor's degrees are awarded in AGRICULTURE (fishing and fisheries and natural resource management), BUSINESS (business administration and management), EDUCATION (elementary, mathematics, science, secondary, and social science), SOCIAL SCIENCE (interdisciplinary studies, liberal arts/general studies, and parks and recreation management). Aquatic resources/fisheries/marine biology are the strongest academically. Elementary education has the largest enrollment.

Required: All students must complete a core curriculum in writing, mathematics, speech, computer competence, and multicultural awareness, as well as specific courses, including World Role of Christianity, Social Science Perspectives, Arts and Ideas, and Scientific Inquiry. A minimum GPA of 2.0, a major of more than 30 credits, a total number of at least 130 credits, and a survival course of either swimming, first aid, or outdoor survival are also required for graduation.

Special: Business and education internships are required, and co-op programs, work-study programs with the U.S. Forest and Park Services, combined B.A.-B.S. degrees, a general studies degree, and a dual major in natural and aquatic resources are available. Nondegree study is possible, and the January interim allows for exchanges with other colleges and study abroad.

Faculty/Classroom: Fifty-nine percent of faculty are male; 41%, female. All teach undergraduates. The average class size in an introductory lecture is 32; in a laboratory, 11; and in a regular course offering, 13.

Admissions: All 1993–94 applicants were accepted.

Requirements: The SAT I or ACT is recommended. AP and CLEP credits are accepted.

Procedure: Freshmen are admitted fall and spring. Application deadlines are open. The fee is $30. The college accepts all applicants. Notification is sent on a rolling basis.

Transfer: The college follows an open admissions policy for transfer applicants. A total of 32 credits out of 130 must be completed at Sheldon Jackson College.

Visiting: There are guides for informal visits, and visitors may sit in on classes and stay overnight at the school. To arrange for a visit, contact the Admissions Office at (907) 747–5221.

Financial Aid: In a recent year, 89% of all freshmen and 91% of continuing students received some form of financial aid. Thirty-four percent of undergraduate students work part-time. Average earnings from campus work for the school year are $1500. The FAF, FFS, or SFS is required. The deadline for financial aid applications is July 15.

International Students: There are currently 4 international students enrolled. They must take the TOEFL and achieve a minimum score of 550.

Computers: The college provides computer facilities for student use. A 20-unit microcomputer center housing IBM, IBM-compatible, and Apple Macintosh PCs is open from 8 A.M. to 10 P.M. weekdays, and part of the weekend. All students may access the system. There are no time limits on using the system and no fees.

Graduates: The most popular majors among recent graduates were aquatic resources (30%), elementary education (28%), and liberal arts/natural resources (14%). Within an average freshman class, 13% graduate in 4 years, 22% in 5 years, and 27% in 6 years.

Admissions Contact: Dennis Trotter, Director of Admissions.

UNIVERSITY OF ALASKA SYSTEM

The University of Alaska System, established in 1975, is a private system in Alaska. It is governed by a board of regents, whose chief administrator is president. The primary goal of the system is teaching, research, and public service. The main priorities are maintaining open access to students to prepare them for rigorous postsecondary pro-

grams; providing the cultural populations of Alaska with appropriate vocational and academic education; and conducting research with emphasis on arctic areas and issues. The total enrollment in fall 1991 of all 4 campuses was 26,601; there were 1992 faculty members. Altogether there are 120 baccalaureate, 85 master's, and 13 doctoral programs offered in University of Alaska System. Profiles of the 4-year campuses are included in this chapter in alphabetical order with other Alaska schools.

UNIVERSITY OF ALASKA ANCHORAGE   D-3
Anchorage, AK 99508   **(907) 786-1529**

Full-time: 2250 men, 3000 women	Faculty: 362; IIA, +$
Part-time: 3700 men, 5400 women	Ph.D.s: 41%
Graduate: 180 men, 340 women	Student/Faculty: 15 to 1
Year: semesters, summer session	Tuition: $1721 ($5106)
Application Deadline: July 1	Room & Board: $5410
Freshman Class: 1800 applied, 1300 accepted	
SAT I or ACT: required	**COMPETITIVE**

The University of Alaska Anchorage, founded in 1954, is a public, coeducational institution and a major unit of the University of Alaska statewide system. Its baccalaureate programs are administered through the colleges of arts and sciences, nursing and health sciences, and career and vocational education, and the schools of business, education, and public affairs and engineering. There are 7 undergraduate and 9 graduate schools. In addition to regional accreditation, UAA has baccalaureate program accreditation with ABET, ACEJMC, CSWE, NASAD, and NLN. The library contains 384,698 volumes, 37,619 microform items, and 7080 audiovisual forms, and subscribes to 3479 periodicals. Computerized library sources and services include interlibrary loans and database searching. Special learning facilities include a learning resource center, art gallery, radio station, TV station, dental clinic, welding laboratory, auto-diesel garage, theater, and photography laboratories. The 350-acre campus is in an urban area of Anchorage. Including residence halls, there are 27 buildings on campus.
Student Life: About 85% of undergraduates are from Alaska. Students come from 50 states, 41 foreign countries, and Canada. Eighty-three percent are white. The average age of all undergraduates is 29.
Housing: A total of 400 students can be accommodated in college housing. College-sponsored living facilities include single-sex and coed on-campus apartments. On-campus housing is available on a first-come, first-served basis. Priority is given to out-of-town students. Ninety-nine percent of students commute. Alcohol is not permitted. All students may keep cars on campus.
Activities: There are no fraternities or sororities on campus. There are 75 groups on campus, including art, band, cheerleading, chess, choir, chorus, computers, dance, drama, ethnic, film, gay, honors, international, jazz band, literary magazine, newspaper, orchestra, photography, political, professional, radio and TV, religious, social, social service, student government, and yearbook. Popular campus events include Freshmen Early Admit Program, Great Alaska Shoot-Out, Northern Lights Invitational, Student Showcase, Leadership Honors, Bartlett Lectures, and Alaska College and Career Fair.
Sports: There are 6 intercollegiate sports for men and 6 for women, and 6 intramural sports for men and 6 for women. Athletic and recreation facilities include an ice rink, an indoor jogging track, a gymnasium, a swimming/diving pool, a weight room, and racquetball/squash courts.
Disabled Students: The entire campus is accessible to disabled students. The following facilities are available: wheelchair ramps, elevators, special parking, specially equipped rest rooms, lowered drinking fountains, and lowered telephones.
Services: In addition to many counseling and information services, tutoring is available in most subjects. In addition, there is a reader service for the blind, and remedial math, reading, and writing. Sign language, interpreters, and note takers are available.
Campus Safety and Security: Campus safety and security measures include 24-hour foot and vehicle patrol, self defense education, escort service, and informal discussions. In addition, there are pamphlets, posters, and films, emergency telephones, and lighted pathways and sidewalks.
Programs of Study: UAA awards the B.A., B.S., B.B.A., B.Ed., B.F.A., B.Mus., and B.S.W. degrees. Associate and master's degrees also are awarded. Bachelor's degrees are awarded in BIOLOGICAL SCIENCE (biology/biological science), BUSINESS (accounting, banking and finance, business administration and management, management information systems, and marketing/retailing/merchandising), COMMUNICATIONS AND THE ARTS (dramatic arts, English, fine arts, journalism, and music), COMPUTER AND PHYSICAL SCIENCE (chemistry, computer science, and mathematics), EDUCATION (art, elementary, music, physical, and secondary), ENGINEERING AND ENVIRONMENTAL DESIGN (civil engineering), HEALTH PROFESSIONS (nursing), SOCIAL SCIENCE (anthropology, criminal justice, economics, history, political science/government, psychology, social work, and sociology). Education,

nursing, and engineering are the strongest academically. Elementary education, accounting, and nursing have the largest enrollments.
Required: General education requirements include 7 credits in natural science, 6 each in written communications, humanities, and social sciences, and 3 each in speech reasoning, quantitative skills, and fine arts. A total of 120 credits, with 48 upper-division courses, and a minimum GPA of 2.0 are required to graduate.
Special: There is a National Student Exchange Program and study abroad in London. UAA also offers B.A.-B.S. degrees, student-designed and dual majors, internships, pass/fail options, a general studies degree, nondegree study, and credit for life experience. The College of Career and Vocational Education provides educational and vocational courses for career development. There are 2 national honor societies on campus. Three departments have honors programs.
Faculty/Classroom: Sixty percent of faculty are male; 40%, female. The average class size in an introductory lecture is 50; in a laboratory, 20; and in a regular course offering, 35.
Admissions: About 72% of the 1993-94 applicants were accepted.
Requirements: A minimum GPA of 2.5 is required. The SAT I or ACT is required. In addition, applicants should be graduates of an accredited secondary school or have a high school or GED certificate. AP and CLEP credits are accepted.
Procedure: Freshmen are admitted to all sessions. Entrance exams should be taken by May of the senior year. Applications should be filed by July 1 for fall entry and November 1 for spring entry, along with an application fee of $35. Notification is sent on a rolling basis. There are early admissions and deferred admissions plans.
Transfer: Transfer applicants must have a minimum GPA of 2.0 and at least 30 credit hours earned. A total of 30 credits out of 120 must be completed at UAA.
Visiting: There are regularly scheduled orientations for prospective students, consisting of registration orientation, application process, campus tours, student appointments, and classes. There are guides for informal visits and visitors may sit in on classes. To arrange for a visit, contact the Office of Admissions at (907) 786-1529 or 786-1480.
Financial Aid: In a recent year, 34% of all current freshmen and 60% of continuing students received some form of financial aid. The average financial indebtedness of a recent graduate was $3725. UAA is a member of CSS. The university's own financial statement and the FAF, FFS, SFS, and the FAFSA are required. The deadline for financial aid applications is May 15.
International Students: There are currently 110 international students enrolled. They must take the TOEFL and achieve a minimum score of 450. The student must also take the SAT I or the ACT.
Computers: The university provides computer facilities for student use. The mainframe is a DEC VAX VMS 8800. There are also 75 Apple Macintosh, IBM, and IBM-compatible microcomputers available in various academic departments, the Learning Resource Center, the Reading and Writing Center, and the campus center. All students may access the system. There are no time limits on using the system and no fees.
Graduates: In a recent year, 433 bachelor's degrees were awarded. The most popular majors among graduates were elementary education (14%), nursing (11%), and accounting (10%). Some 25 companies recruited on campus in 1992-93.
Admissions Contact: Linda Berg Smith, Associate Vice Chancellor of Student Services.

UNIVERSITY OF ALASKA FAIRBANKS   D-2
Fairbanks, AK 99775-7480   **(907) 474-7822**
                                            (800) 478-IUAF (in-state)

Full-time: 1881 men, 1768 women	Faculty: 524; I, --$
Part-time: 1642 men, 3173 women	Ph.D.s: 66%
Graduate: 439 men, 317 women	Student/Faculty: 7 to 1
Year: semesters, summer session	Tuition: $1698 ($4714)
Application Deadline: August 1	Room & Board: $3020
Freshman Class: 1849 applied, 1432 accepted, 928 enrolled	
SAT I Verbal/Math: 463/490	ACT: 22 **COMPETITIVE**

The University of Alaska Fairbanks, a land-, space-, and sea-grant coeducational institution founded in 1917, is part of the statewide system and offers undergraduate and graduate programs in agriculture and land resource management, engineering, fisheries and ocean sciences, liberal arts, natural sciences, management, mineral engineering, behavioral sciences, and education. There are 9 undergraduate and 8 graduate schools. In addition to regional accreditation, UAF has baccalaureate program accreditation with AACSB, ABET, ACEJMC, CSWE, NASM, and NCATE. The 4 libraries contain 800,000 volumes, 400,000 microform items, and 25,000 audiovisual forms, and subscribe to 6000 periodicals. Computerized library sources and services include the card catalog, interlibrary loans, and database searching. Special learning facilities include a learning resource center, natural history museum, radio station, and TV station.

Several research institutes and laboratories for study in the physical and natural sciences are associated with the university. The 2250-acre campus is in a small town 4 miles northwest of Fairbanks. Including residence halls, there are 138 buildings on campus.

Student Life: About 86% of undergraduates are from Alaska. Students come from 49 states, 47 foreign countries, and Canada. Seventy percent are white; 17% Native American/Eskimo. The average age of freshmen is 19; all undergraduates, 31. Thirty-nine percent drop out by the end of their first year.

Housing: A total of 1554 students can be accommodated in college housing. College-sponsored living facilities include single-sex and coed dormitories, on-campus apartments, and married-student housing. In addition there are honors houses and language houses. On-campus housing is available on a first-come, first-served basis. Eighty-one percent of students commute. All students may keep cars on campus.

Activities: There is 1 national fraternity and 1 national sorority. There are 67 groups on campus, including art, band, cheerleading, chess, choir, computers, ethnic, gay, honors, international, jazz band, newspaper, orchestra, political, radio and TV, religious, and student government. Popular campus events include Starvation Gulch, All-Campus Day, Alcohol Awareness Week, and Meltdown (spring event).

Sports: There are 5 intercollegiate sports for men and 5 for women, and 16 intramural sports for men and 16 for women. Athletic and recreation facilities include a 2500-seat arena, a 2000-seat gymnasium, a 1500-seat skating rink, 2 racquetball courts, 2 weight rooms, a basketball court, an Olympic-size swimming pool, a small-bore rifle range, and a lighted 30-mile ski trail.

Disabled Students: Ninety percent of the campus is accessible to disabled students. The following facilities are available: wheelchair ramps, elevators, special parking, specially equipped rest rooms, special class scheduling, lowered drinking fountains, lowered telephones, a shuttle bus, and a swimming pool equipped with hydraulic lifts. Special residence hall accommodations are coordinated by the Disabled Student Service Office.

Services: In addition to many counseling and information services, tutoring is available in some subjects. In addition, there is a reader service for the blind, and remedial math, reading, and writing.

Campus Safety and Security: Campus safety and security measures include self defense education, escort service, shuttle buses, and informal discussions. In addition, there are pamphlets, posters, and films, emergency telephones, lighted pathways and sidewalks, 24-hour dormitory lockup, a 24-hour crisis line, evening patrols inside dormitories, and residence hall check-in.

Programs of Study: UAF awards the B.A., B.S., B.B.A., B.Ed., B.F.A., and B.Tech. degrees. Associate, master's, and doctoral degrees also are awarded. Bachelor's degrees are awarded in AGRICULTURE (fishing and fisheries, natural resource management, and wildlife management), BIOLOGICAL SCIENCE (biology/biological science), BUSINESS (accounting, business administration and management, and business economics), COMMUNICATIONS AND THE ARTS (dramatic arts, English, Eskimo, German, journalism, linguistics, music, Spanish, and speech/debate/rhetoric), COMPUTER AND PHYSICAL SCIENCE (chemistry, computer science, earth science, geology, mathematics, physics, science, and statistics), EDUCATION (elementary, physical, and secondary), ENGINEERING AND ENVIRONMENTAL DESIGN (civil engineering, electrical/electronics engineering, geological engineering, mechanical engineering, mining and mineral engineering, and petroleum/natural gas engineering), SOCIAL SCIENCE (American studies, anthropology, criminal justice, geography, history, human services, humanities, philosophy, political science/government, psychology, rural sociology, Russian and Slavic studies, social work, and sociology). Engineering, fisheries, wildlife management, biology, business administration, journalism, and broadcasting are the strongest academically. Business administration and education have the largest enrollments.

Required: All students must complete core courses in English and oral communication, library skills, humanities, social science, natural science, and mathematics. A minimum of 120 credit hours, with 30 in the major, and a 2.0 GPA are required for graduation.

Special: There is a freshman honors program on campus, as well as 5 national honor societies, including Phi Beta Kappa.

Faculty/Classroom: Sixty-nine percent of faculty are male; 31%, female. The average class size in an introductory lecture is 50; in a laboratory, 21; and in a regular course offering, 24.

Admissions: About 77% of the 1993–94 applicants were accepted. There were 13 National Merit finalists.

Requirements: A minimum GPA of 2.0 is required. The SAT I or ACT is required. In addition, applicants should be graduates of an accredited secondary school or have the GED equivalent with 16 academic credits, including 4 in English and 3 each in mathematics, science, social studies, and electives. AP and CLEP credits are accepted.

Procedure: Freshmen are admitted to all sessions. Applications should be filed by August 1 for fall entry and December 1 for spring entry, along with an application fee of $30. Notification is sent on a rolling basis.

Transfer: About 350 transfer students enrolled in a recent year. A GPA of 2.0 in all previous college work and an honorable dismissal from all schools attended are required. Applicants with fewer than 30 semester hours of transferable credit also must have a high school GPA of 2.0 and ACT or SAT I scores. A total of 30 credits out of a minimum of 120 must be completed at UAF.

Visiting: There are regularly scheduled orientations for prospective students. There are guides for informal visits and visitors may sit in on classes. To arrange for a visit, contact the Admissions Counseling Office at (907) 474–7822.

Financial Aid: In an earlier year, 65% of all current freshmen and 68% of continuing students received some form of financial aid. Fifteen percent of undergraduate students work part-time. UAF is a member of CSS. The FAF, FFS, SFS and the FAFSA are required. The deadline for financial aid applications is May 15.

International Students: There are currently 303 international students enrolled. They must take the TOEFL and achieve a minimum score of 550. The student must also take the SAT I or the ACT.

Computers: The university provides computer facilities for student use. The mainframes are 2 DEC VAX 8800s and a DEC VAX 860, supported by various smaller VAXes. Terminal facilities are available at several campus locations. Students may use these terminals for any of the mainframe computers for any purpose, though academic use takes precedence. All students may access the system 24 hours per day. There are no time limits on using the system and no fees.

Graduates: In 1992–93, 427 bachelor's degrees were awarded. The most popular majors among graduates were education (14%), business management (8%), and accounting (7%).

Admissions Contact: James Mansfield, Associate Director of Admissions.

UNIVERSITY OF ALASKA SOUTHEAST F-3
Juneau, AK 99801 (907) 789–4550

Full-time: 235 men, 286 women	Faculty: 83; IIA, -$
Part-time: 516 men, 630 women	Ph.D.s: 36%
Graduate: 22 men, 36 women	Student/Faculty: 6 to 1
Year: semesters	Tuition: $1681 ($5009)
Application Deadline: open	Room: $2394
SAT I: required	**LESS COMPETITIVE**

The University of Alaska Southeast, a multicampus, coeducational institution founded in 1972, is part of the University of Alaska statewide system, with baccalaureate programs offered in business and public administration, education, and liberal arts and science. There are 3 undergraduate and 2 graduate schools. The library contains 100,000 volumes, 250,000 microform items, and 1850 audiovisual forms, and subscribes to 1500 periodicals. Computerized library sources and services include the card catalog, interlibrary loans, and database searching. Special learning facilities include a learning resource center and media and educational technology classrooms. The 198-acre campus is in a suburban area 10 miles north of Juneau. Including residence halls, there are 18 buildings on campus.

Student Life: About 90% of undergraduates are from Alaska. Students come from Canada. Ninety-five percent are from public schools. Seventy percent are white; 17% Native American/Eskimo. The average age of freshmen is 18.

Housing: A total of 200 students can be accommodated in college housing. College-sponsored living facilities include single-sex on-campus apartments and married-student housing. On-campus housing is available on a first-come, first-served basis. Priority is given to out-of-town students. Ninety percent of students commute. All students may keep cars on campus.

Activities: There are no fraternities or sororities on campus. There are 10 groups on campus, including band, choir, drama, ethnic, honors, literary magazine, newspaper, orchestra, political, religious, student government, and symphony. Popular campus events include At the Hop Dance and Ski Day.

Sports: There are 3 intramural sports for men and 3 for women. Athletic and recreation facilities include community gymnasiums, a pool, and recreational equipment.

Disabled Students: The following facilities are available: wheelchair ramps, elevators, special parking, and specially equipped rest rooms.

Services: In addition to various counseling and information services, there is a reader service for the blind, and remedial math, reading, and writing.

Campus Safety and Security: Campus safety and security measures include 24-hour foot and vehicle patrol, self-defense education, escort service, and informal discussions. In addition, there are pamphlets, posters, and films, and lighted pathways and sidewalks.

Programs of Study: UAS awards the B.A., B.S., B.B.A., B.Ed., and B.L.A. degrees. Associate and master's degrees also are awarded. Bachelor's degrees are awarded in BIOLOGICAL SCIENCE (biology/biological science), BUSINESS (accounting and business administration and management), COMPUTER AND PHYSICAL SCIENCE (computer science), EDUCATION (business, early childhood, elementary, music, science, and secondary), SOCIAL SCIENCE (public administration). Accounting and education are the strongest academically. Liberal arts has the largest enrollment.

Required: All students are required to complete general education courses, including 15 credits in humanities and social science, 10 in mathematics and natural sciences, 6 in written communication skills, and 3 in speech. A total of 120 semester credits, with 36 in the major, and a minimum GPA of 2.0 are required in order to graduate.

Special: Internships with the state government, dual majors, credit/no credit options, and credit for military experience are available. The School of Career and Continuing Education offers courses and certificate programs in technological skills.

Faculty/Classroom: The average class size in an introductory lecture is 20 and in a laboratory, 12.

Admissions: About 95% of the 1993–94 applicants were accepted.

Requirements: A minimum GPA of 2.0 is required. The SAT I is required. Applicants should be graduates of an accredited secondary school or have the GED. AP and CLEP credits are accepted.

Procedure: Freshmen are admitted fall and spring. Application deadlines are open. The application fee is $20. Notification is sent on a rolling basis. There is a deferred admissions plan.

Transfer: Nine transfer students enrolled in a recent year. A minimum GPA of 2.0 from an accredited institution is required. A total of 30 credits out of 120 must be completed at UAS.

Visiting: There are regularly scheduled orientations for prospective students. There are guides for informal visits and visitors may sit in on classes. To arrange for a visit, contact Greg Wagner at (907) 789–4550.

Financial Aid: In an earlier year, 15% of continuing students received some form of financial aid. Loans averaged $2500 ($5000 maximum). UAS is a member of CSS. The FAF, the college's own financial statement, and FAFSA are required. The deadline for financial aid applications is May 1.

International Students: They must take the TOEFL and achieve a minimum score of 500. The student must also take the SAT I or the ACT.

Computers: The college provides computer facilities for student use. The mainframe is a DEC VAX 8600. There are 2 computer laboratories with 15 terminals each. There are also 68 IBM and Apple Macintosh microcomputers. All students may access the system. There are no time limits on using the system and no fees.

Graduates: In an earlier year, 52 bachelor's degrees were awarded. The most popular majors among graduates were education (38%), accounting (23%), and management (12%). Within an average freshman class, 11% graduate in 5 years and 5% in 6 years. Some 25 companies recruited on campus in a recent year. In a recent graduating class, 10% of the men and 15% of the women were enrolled in graduate school within 6 months of graduation.

Admissions Contact: Greg Wagner, Admissions.

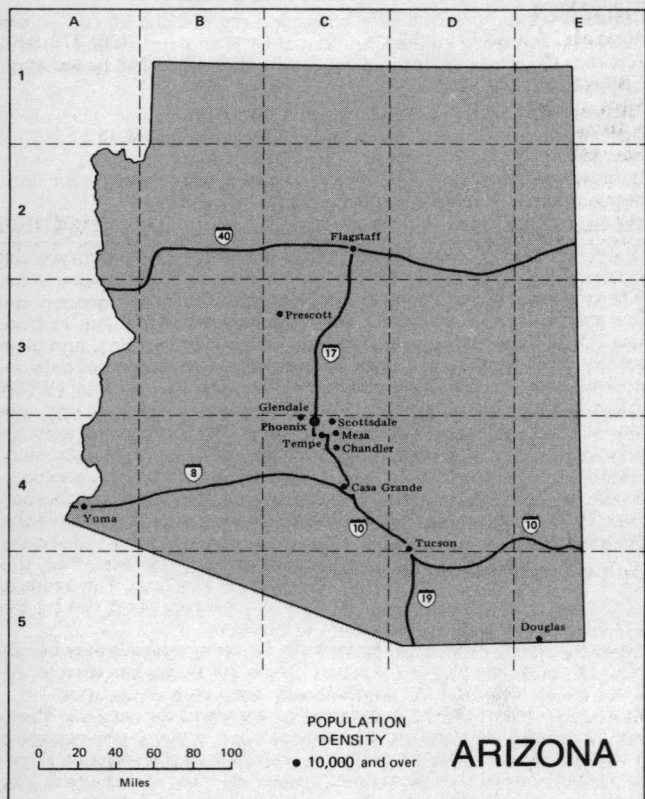

POPULATION
DENSITY

0 20 40 60 80 100
Miles

● 10,000 and over   **ARIZONA**

ARIZONA STATE UNIVERSITY MAIN CAMPUS
C-4
Tempe, AZ 85287-0112   (602) 965-7788
(800) 252-ASU1 (out-of-state)

Full-time: 11,664 men, 10,929 women   **Faculty:** 1623; I, --$
Part-time: 3876 men, 3709 women   **Ph.D's:** 93%
Graduate: 5450 men, 5622 women   **Student/Faculty:** 14 to 1
Year: semesters, summer session   **Tuition:** $1844 ($7350)
Application Deadline: April 15   **Room & Board:** $4600
Freshman Class: 12,809 applied, 10,308 accepted, 3761 enrolled
SAT I: 450/520   **ACT:** 22   **COMPETITIVE**

Arizona State University Main Campus, founded in 1885, is a public-ly funded institution offering undergraduate programs in the arts and sciences, business, education, engineering, nursing, public pro-grams, architecture and environmental design, and social work. There are 10 undergraduate and 11 graduate schools. In addition to regional accreditation, ASU has baccalaureate program accreditation with AACSB, ABET, ACCE, ACEJMC, CSWE, FIDER, NAAB, NASM, NCATE, and NLN. The 6 libraries contain 2,698,607 volumes and 4,684,743 microform items, and subscribe to 29,084 periodicals. Computerized library sources and services include the card catalog, interlibrary loans, and database searching. Special learning facilities include an art gallery, planetarium, radio station, and TV station. The 700-acre campus is in a suburban area 10 miles east of Phoenix. In-cluding residence halls, there are 110 buildings on campus.

Student Life: About 79% of undergraduates are from Arizona. Stu-dents come from 50 states, 82 foreign countries, and Canada. Seventy-six percent are white. The average age of freshmen is 18; all undergraduates, 23. Thirty percent drop out by the end of their first year; 70% remain to graduate.

Housing: A total of 5428 students can be accommodated in college housing. College-sponsored living facilities include single-sex and coed dormitories, on-campus apartments, fraternity houses, and soror-ity houses. In addition there are honors houses. On-campus housing is available on a first-come, first-served basis. Eighty-seven percent of students commute. All students may keep cars on campus.

Activities: About 12% of men belong to 25 national fraternities; about 10% of women belong to 15 national sororities. There are 330 groups on campus, including art, band, cheerleading, chess, choir, chorus, computers, dance, drama, ethnic, gay, honors, international, jazz band, literary magazine, marching band, musical theater, news-paper, opera, orchestra, political, professional, radio and TV, reli-gious, social, social service, student government, symphony, and yearbook. Popular campus events include Homecoming and the World Fest international food and cultural festival.

Sports: There are 10 intercollegiate sports for men and 10 for wo-men, and 35 intramural sports for men and 34 for women. Athletic and recreation facilities include 4 stadiums (including football and baseball), a tennis center, an aquatic complex, a golf course, 2 activi-ty centers, a student recreation complex, and a track.

Disabled Students: Ninety-five percent of the campus is accessible to disabled students. The following facilities are available: wheelchair ramps, elevators, special parking, specially equipped rest rooms, spe-cial class scheduling, lowered drinking fountains, lowered tele-phones, flashing alarms for the deaf, braille maps, modified residence hall rooms, and an adaptive exercise program and facility.

Services: In addition to many counseling and information services, tutoring is available in most subjects. In addition, there is a reader ser-vice for the blind, and remedial math, reading, and writing. Student legal aid and child-care assistance are offered.

Campus Safety and Security: Campus safety and security mea-sures include 24-hour foot and vehicle patrol, self-defense education, escort service, and shuttle buses. In addition, there are informal dis-cussions, pamphlets, posters, and films, emergency telephones, and lighted pathways and sidewalks.

Programs of Study: ASU awards the B.A., B.S., B.A.E., B.F.A., B.Mus., B.S.D., B.S.E., B.S. in Landscape Architecture, B.S. in Plan-ning, B.S.N., and B.S.W. degrees. Master's and doctoral degrees also are awarded. Bachelor's degrees are awarded in AGRICULTURE (agricultural business management and natural resource manage-ment), BIOLOGICAL SCIENCE (biology/biological science, botany, microbiology, nutrition, wildlife biology, and zoology), BUSINESS (ac-counting, banking and finance, business administration and manage-ment, marketing/retailing/merchandising, purchasing/inventory management, real estate, recreation and leisure services, tourism, and transportation management), COMMUNICATIONS AND THE ARTS (art history and appreciation, broadcasting, ceramic art and design, Chinese, communications, dance, design, dramatic arts, drawing, En-glish, fine arts, French, German, industrial design, Italian, Japanese, journalism, media arts, metal/jewelry, music, music performance, mu-sic theory and composition, painting, photography, printmaking, Rus-sian, sculpture, and Spanish), COMPUTER AND PHYSICAL SCI-ENCE (atmospheric sciences and meteorology, chemistry, computer science, geology, mathematics, and physics), EDUCATION (early childhood, elementary, physical, secondary, and special), ENGI-NEERING AND ENVIRONMENTAL DESIGN (aeronautical engineer-ing, aeronautical technology, architecture, bioengineering, chemical engineering, civil engineering, computer engineering, construction engineering, electrical engineering, electronics engineering technol-ogy, engineering, geological engineering, industrial engineering, in-dustrial engineering technology, interior design, landscape architecture/design, manufacturing technology, materials science, mechanical engineering, mechanical engineering technology, urban design, urban planning technology, and welding engineering), HEALTH PROFESSIONS (clinical science, music therapy, nursing, and speech pathology/audiology), SOCIAL SCIENCE (anthropolo-gy, criminal justice, economics, family/consumer resource manage-ment, geography, history, humanities, interdisciplinary studies, parks and recreation management, philosophy, physical fitness/movement, political science/government, psychology, religion, religious music, social work, sociology, and women's studies). Engineering, architec-ture, and computer science are the strongest academically. Finance, management, and marketing have the largest enrollments.

Required: To graduate, students must have a minimum GPA of 2.0 and a total of at least 126 credit hours, including 50 hours of upper-level work. The number of hours in the major varies by degree pro-gram. All students must take English composition and fulfill the gener-al studies requirement of 35 hours in the areas of numeracy, literacy and critical inquiry, humanities and fine arts, social and behavioral sciences, natural sciences, global awareness, and historical aware-ness.

Special: ASU offers internships in many disciplines, study abroad in 5 countries, and a variety of interdisciplinary undergraduate pro-grams. Students may participate in educational programs supported by several institutes and centers, such as the National Center for Elec-tron Microscopy, the American Indian Institute, and the Center for Medieval and Renaissance Studies. Also available are continuing ed-ucation programs and a summer mathematics and science program for high school students. There is a freshman honors program on cam-pus, as well as 50 national honor societies, including Phi Beta Kappa. All colleges offer honors courses through the Honors College.

Faculty/Classroom: Seventy-one percent of faculty are male; 29%, female. The average class size in an introductory lecture is 42; in a laboratory, 20.

Admissions: About 80% of the 1993–94 applicants were accepted. The SAT scores for the 1993–94 freshman class were as follows: Verbal—69% below 500, 25% between 500 and 599, 5% between 600 and 700, and 1% above 700; Math—38% below 500, 39% between 500 and 599, 18% between 600 and 700, and 5% above 700. The ACT scores were 31% below 21, 29% between 21 and 23, 24% between 24 and 26, 9% between 27 and 28, and 7% above 28. About 42% of the current freshmen were in the top fifth of their class; 70% were in the top two fifths. There were 26 National Merit finalists.

Requirements: ASU requires applicants to be in the upper 25% of their class. A minimum GPA of 3.0 is required. The SAT I or ACT is required. The minimum composite score on the ACT is 22 for in-state students, 24 for out-of-state students; on the SAT I, 930 for in-state students, 1010 for out-of-state students. Graduation from an accredited secondary school must include 4 years of English, 3 years of mathematics, and 2 years each of laboratory science and social science (including American history). The GED, minimum score 50, is also accepted. AP and CLEP credits are accepted.

Procedure: Freshmen are admitted to all sessions. Entrance exams should be taken late in the junior year. Applications should be filed by April 15 for fall entry and November 15 for spring entry, along with an application fee of $35. Notification is sent on a rolling basis.

Transfer: About 4400 transfer students enrolled in 1993–94. Applicants with fewer than 36 transferable hours must meet the requirements for freshman admission. A minimum GPA of 2.0 is required for in-state applicants; 2.5 for out-of-state applicants. A total of 30 credits out of 126 must be completed at ASU.

Visiting: There are regularly scheduled orientations for prospective students. There are guides for informal visits and visitors may sit in on classes. To arrange for a visit, contact Undergraduate Admissions at (602) 965–7788 or (800) 252–2781 (out-of-state).

Financial Aid: In a recent year, 60% of all current freshmen and 51% of continuing students received some form of financial aid. Scholarships or need-based grants averaged $1960 ($14,000 maximum); and loans averaged $2400 ($6625 maximum). Eighty percent of undergraduate students work part-time. Average earnings from campus work for the school year are $1900. The average financial indebtedness of the 1992–93 graduate was $6500. ASU is a member of CSS. The FAF, FFS, or SFS, and FAFSA are required. The deadline for financial aid applications is March 1.

International Students: There are currently 1042 international students enrolled. They must take the TOEFL and achieve a minimum score of 500.

Computers: The college provides computer facilities for student use. The mainframes are an IBM 3090 Processor Complex Model 500E, an IBM 3084 Processor Model C8, a DEC VAX 6000/430, an academic workstation cluster of 3 RS/6000 Model 580s and 1 RS/6000 Model 53H, a MasPar Massively Parallel Computer Model MP2, and a DEC VAX cluster post office configuration with 2 VAX 4000/300 units. There are 771 Rycom, MAG, HAL, Zenith, and Apple Macintosh microcomputers available in 8 areas on campus. All students may access the system. One site is open 24 hours per day. There are no time limits on using the system and no fees.

Graduates: In 1992–93, 6244 bachelor's degrees were awarded. The most popular majors among graduates were marketing (6%), management (6%), and finance (5%). Within an average freshman class, 1% graduate in 3 years, 15% in 4 years, 38% in 5 years, and 46% in 6 years. Some 500 companies recruited on campus in 1992–93.

Admissions Contact: Susan Dolbert, Director of Undergraduate Admissions.

ARIZONA UNIVERSITY SYSTEM

The Arizona University system, established in 1945, is a public system in Arizona. It is governed by a board of regents, whose chief administrator is the executive director. The primary goal of the system is teaching, research, and service. The main priorities are to provide outstanding undergraduate, graduate, and professional instruction; basic and applied research; and public service for Arizona and the nation. The total enrollment in fall 1993 of all 3 campuses was 99,841; there were 3500 faculty members. Altogether there are 325 baccalaureate, 250 master's, and 140 doctoral programs offered in the Arizona University System. Profiles of the 4-year campuses are included in this chapter in alphabetical order with other Arizona schools.

DEVRY INSTITUTE OF TECHNOLOGY
PHOENIX
C-4
Phoenix, AZ 85021–2995

(602) 870–9201
(800) 528–0250 (out-of-state)

Full-time: 1767 men, 407 women	**Faculty:** 60
Part-time: 373 men, 98 women	**Ph.D.s:** n/av
Graduate: none	**Student/Faculty:** 36 to 1
Year: trimesters, summer session	**Tuition:** $5609
Application Deadline: open	**Room & Board:** n/app

Freshman Class: 1442 applied, 1339 accepted, 634 enrolled
SAT I or ACT: see profile
LESS COMPETITIVE

The DeVry Institute of Technology/Phoenix is a private coeducational institution opened in 1967; there are 10 other DeVry Institutes in the U.S. and Canada owned by Keller Graduate School of Management. The school offers a hands-on technology-based curriculum in business operations, computer information systems, accounting, and electronics. In addition to regional accreditation, DeVry has baccalaureate program accreditation with ABET. The library contains 12,885 volumes, 140 microform items, and 157 audiovisual forms, and subscribes to 213 periodicals. Computerized library sources and services include the card catalog, interlibrary loans, and database searching. Special learning facilities include a learning resource center and electronics and other laboratories. The 18-acre campus is in a suburban area. There is one building on campus. There are no residence halls.

Student Life: About 52% of undergraduates are from out-of-state, mostly the Southwest. Students come from 6 foreign countries and Canada. Seventy-one percent are white; 11% Hispanic. The average age of all undergraduates is 25. Fifty-four percent drop out by the end of their first year; 36% remain to graduate.

Housing: There are no residence halls. Housing referrals may be obtained through the Student Housing Office. All students commute. Alcohol is not permitted. All students may keep cars on campus.

Activities: There are no fraternities or sororities on campus. There are 14 groups on campus, including ethnic, honors, photography, professional, radio and TV, religious, and student government. Popular campus events include survival games, ski trips, horseback riding, cookouts, casino nights, Thanksgiving Dinner, and Club Day.

Sports: There are 6 intramural sports for men and 6 for women. Athletic and recreation facilities include a game room.

Disabled Students: Ninety percent of the campus is accessible to disabled students. The following facilities are available: wheelchair ramps, elevators, special parking, specially equipped rest rooms, lowered drinking fountains, and lowered telephones.

Services: In addition to many counseling and information services, tutoring is available in every subject.

Campus Safety and Security: Campus safety and security measures include informal discussions, pamphlets, posters, and films, emergency telephones, and lighted pathways and sidewalks. In addition, there is security guard service Monday through Friday 7 A.M. to 10:30 P.M. and from 12 noon to 6 P.M. on Sunday. The building is guarded during hours of closure by a motion-detector system.

Programs of Study: DeVry awards the B.S. degree. Associate degrees also are awarded. Bachelor's degrees are awarded in BUSINESS (accounting and business administration and management), COMPUTER AND PHYSICAL SCIENCE (computer programming and information sciences and systems), ENGINEERING AND ENVIRONMENTAL DESIGN (electrical/electronics engineering technology). Electronics has the largest enrollment.

Required: In order to graduate, students must complete between 143 and 158 credit hours with a 2.0 minimum GPA. Course requirements vary according to program. All first-semester students take courses in business organization, computer applications, algebra, psychology, and student success strategies.

Special: Nondegree study and evening classes are possible. There are 2 national honor societies on campus.

Faculty/Classroom: Eighty percent of faculty are male; 20%, female. All teach undergraduates. The average class size in an introductory lecture is 30; in a laboratory, 30; and in a regular course offering, 30.

Admissions: About 93% of the 1993–94 applicants were accepted.

Requirements: Admissions requirements include graduation from a secondary school; the GED is also accepted. Applicants from accredited postsecondary schools must pass the DeVry entrance exam or present satisfactory ACT, SAT I, or WPCT scores. CLEP credit is accepted.

Procedure: Freshmen are admitted to all sessions. Application deadlines are open. Application fee is $25. Notification is sent on a rolling basis. There are early decision and deferred admissions plans.

Transfer: About 390 transfer students enrolled in 1993–94. Transfer students must take the DeVry entrance exam. It is recommended that applicants have math scores of at least 23 on the ACT or 480 on the SAT. A minimum of 35 credits out of 143 to 158 must be completed at DeVry.

Visiting: There are regularly scheduled orientations for prospective students. There are guides for informal visits and visitors may sit in on classes. To arrange for a visit, contact Paul Lau, New Student Coordinator at (602) 870–0981.

Financial Aid: In 1993–94, 80% of all students received some form of financial aid. About 80% of students received need-based aid. DeVry is a member of CSS. The FAFSA financial statement is required.

International Students: International students must take the TOEFL and achieve a minimum score of 550. The student must also take the college's own entrance exam. The ACT, SAT, or WPCT may be accepted in lieu of the DeVry entrance exam.

Computers: The college provides computer facilities for student use. The mainframe is an IBM 3081K. Laboratory facilities include IBM and IBM-compatible PCs in stand-alone and network configurations with access to the mainframe. LANs provide access to a wide range of applications software. Hard copy from the mainframe is provided through a local minicomputer and medium- and high-speed printers. It may be used during published laboratory hours. There are no time limits on using the system and no fees.

Graduates: In 1992–93, 326 bachelor's degrees were awarded. The most popular majors among graduates were electronics technology (68%), business administration and management (22%), and information systems and science (10%). Within an average freshman class, 36% graduate in 5 years. Some 182 companies recruited on campus in 1992–93. In the 1992 graduating class, 96% of the men and women had found employment within 6 months of graduation.

Admissions Contact: Kim Galetti, Director of Admissions.

EMBRY-RIDDLE AERONAUTICAL UNIVERSITY

Prescott, AZ 86301–8662

C-3

(904) 239–6129
(800) 222-ERAU (out-of-state)

Full-time: 3102 men, 401 women	Faculty: 69; IIA, --$
Part-time: 599 men, 76 women	Ph.D.s: 68%
Graduate: 152 men, 27 women	Student/Faculty: 51 to 1
Year: semesters, summer session	Tuition: $6700
Application Deadline: 30 days before fall entry	Room & Board: $3196

Freshman Class: 3042 applied, 2468 accepted, 1065 enrolled
SAT I Verbal/Math: 470/550 | **ACT:** 24 | **COMPETITIVE +**

Embry-Riddle Aeronautical University, founded in 1926, is a private, coeducational institution offering undergraduate programs in aviation, engineering, business, and professional training on 2 campuses: the Prescott campus, founded in 1978, and the Daytona Beach, Florida, campus. Graduate programs are offered at the Daytona Beach campus. There are 2 undergraduate schools. In addition to regional accreditation, Embry-Riddle has baccalaureate program accreditation with ABET. The library contains 21,663 volumes, 107,005 microform items, and 1367 audiovisual forms, and subscribes to 408 periodicals. Computerized library sources and services include the card catalog, interlibrary loans, and database searching. Special learning facilities include a learning resource center and 4 wind tunnels, an aviation safety center, and an aircraft structures lab. The Flight Training Center at Ernest A. Love Field offers a simulator laboratory and flight operations center. The 510-acre campus is in a rural area 100 miles north of Phoenix. Including residence halls, there are 55 buildings on campus.

Student Life: About 90% of undergraduates are from out-of-state, mostly the Southwest. Students also come from Canada. Eighty-three percent are from public schools; 17% from private. Eighty-six percent are white. Thirty-nine percent are Protestant; 25% Catholic; 23% claim no religious affiliation. The average age of freshmen is 18; all undergraduates, 20.

Housing: A total of 450 students can be accommodated in college housing. College-sponsored living facilities include coed dormitories and off-campus apartments. On-campus housing is guaranteed for the freshman year only and is available on a first-come, first-served basis. Alcohol is not permitted. All students may keep cars on campus.

Activities: There are 3 national fraternities and 2 national sororities. There are 55 groups on campus, including drama, ethnic, international, literary magazine, newspaper, political, professional, radio and TV, religious, social, student government, and yearbook. Popular campus events include concerts, performing arts, and theme events.

Sports: There are 3 intercollegiate sports for men; 13 intramural sports for men and 2 for women.

Services: In addition to many counseling and information services, tutoring is available in most subjects. There is also remedial math, reading, and writing.

Campus Safety and Security: Campus safety and security measures include 24-hour foot and vehicle patrol, shuttle buses, and lighted pathways and sidewalks.

Programs of Study: Embry-Riddle awards the B.S. degree. Associate degrees also are awarded. Bachelor's degrees are awarded in COMPUTER AND PHYSICAL SCIENCE (computer science), ENGINEERING AND ENVIRONMENTAL DESIGN (aeronautical engineering, aeronautical science, aerospace studies, aviation administration/management, and electrical/electronics engineering). Engineering is the strongest academically. Aeronautical science has the largest enrollment.

Required: All students must complete 36 credits of general education requirements, including courses in communication skills, technical report writing, humanities/social sciences, mathematics, physical science, economics, and computer science. A total of 126 to 136 credit hours with a minimum GPA of 2.0 is required in order to graduate.

Special: Cooperative work-study programs are offered. Flight training may be taken in conjunction with aeronautical science and other degree programs. Credit is given for military experience.

Faculty/Classroom: Eighty-eight percent of faculty are male; 12%, female. All teach undergraduates. No introductory courses are taught by graduate students. The average class size in a regular course offering is 22.

Admissions: About 81% of the 1993–94 applicants were accepted. The SAT scores for the 1993–94 freshman class were as follows: Verbal—62% below 500, 30% between 500 and 599, 7% between 600 and 700, and 1% above 700; Math—30% below 500, 41% between 500 and 599, 26% between 600 and 700, and 4% above 700. The ACT scores were 18% below 21, 26% between 21 and 23, 27% between 24 and 26, 17% between 27 and 28, and 13% above 28. About 32% of the current freshmen were in the top fifth of their class; 66% were in the top two fifths.

Requirements: A minimum GPA of 2.0 is required. The SAT I or ACT is required. Applicants must be graduates of an accredited secondary school or have a GED equivalent. All admission items are processed at Daytona Beach headquarters. AP and CLEP credits are accepted. Important factors used in the admissions decision are recommendations by alumni, personality, intangible qualities, parents or siblings attending the school, leadership record, and geographic diversity.

Procedure: Freshmen are admitted fall, spring, and summer. Entrance exams should be taken during the fall of the senior year. Applications should be filed 30 days before fall entry. The application fee is $30. Notification is sent on a rolling basis. A waiting list is an active part of the admissions procedure.

Transfer: About 144 transfer students enrolled in a recent year. Applicant must have a minimum GPA of 2.0 in at least 12 credit hours earned. A total of 30 credits out of 126 to 136 credits must be completed at Embry-Riddle.

Visiting: To arrange for a visit, contact Betty Campbell at (904) 239–6100.

Financial Aid: Twenty-seven percent of undergraduate students worked part-time in a recent year. Average earnings from campus work for that school year were $2200. The FAF or FFS is required. The deadline for financial aid applications is as early as possible for fall entry.

International Students: There are currently 17 international students enrolled. They must take the TOEFL and achieve a minimum score of 500. The student must also take the SAT I or the ACT.

Computers: The college provides computer facilities for student use. The computer laboratory houses 58 IBM PCs. In addition, there are 10 terminals connected to a Network File Server running UNIX, and 25 Apple Macintosh microcomputers available. All students may access the system. There are no time limits and no fees.

Graduates: In a recent year 150 bachelor's degrees were awarded. The most popular majors among graduates were aeronautical science (37%), aeronautical studies (22%), and aviation business administration (16%). Within an average freshman class, 36% graduate in 5 years and 37% in 6 years.

Admissions Contact: Director of Admissions.

GRAND CANYON UNIVERSITY

Phoenix, AZ 85017

C-4

(602) 589–2441; 800–9776 (out-of-state)

Full-time: 522 men, 896 women	Faculty: 66; IIB, --$
Part-time: 126 men, 293 women	Ph.D.s: 53%
Graduate: 51 men, 75 women	Student/Faculty: 21 to 1
Year: semesters, summer session	Tuition: $6730
Application Deadline: August 1	Room & Board: $2950

Freshman Class: 1348 applied, 957 accepted, 212 enrolled
SAT I Verbal/Math: 441/485 | **ACT:** 21 | **VERY COMPETITIVE**

Grand Canyon University, founded in 1949 by the Arizona Southern Baptist Convention, is a small, private, coeducational, Christian liberal arts institution. There are 5 undergraduate and 2 graduate schools. In addition to regional accreditation, Canyon has baccalaureate program accreditation with NLN. The library contains 166,000 volumes,

34,200 microform items, and 4100 audiovisual forms, and subscribes to 700 periodicals. Computerized library sources and services include interlibrary loans and database searching. Special learning facilities include an art gallery. The 70-acre campus is in a suburban area of Phoenix. Including residence halls, there are 32 buildings on campus.

Student Life: About 13% of undergraduates are from out-of-state, mostly the Southwest. Students come from 35 states, 6 foreign countries, and Canada. Eighty percent are white. Forty-nine percent are Protestant; 21% claim no religious affiliation; 10% are Catholic. The average age of freshmen is 22; all undergraduates, 24.

Housing: A total of 600 students can be accommodated in college housing. College-sponsored living facilities include single-sex dormitories and on-campus apartments. On-campus housing is available on a first-come, first-served basis. Alcohol is not permitted. All students may keep cars on campus.

Activities: There are no fraternities or sororities on campus. There are many groups and organizations on campus, including art, band, cheerleading, choir, chorale, chorus, computers, drama, ethnic, honors, international, jazz band, literary magazine, musical theater, newspaper, opera, pep band, photography, political, professional, religious, social service, student government, and yearbook. Popular campus events include Hanging of the Green, Spiritual Emphasis Week, Harvest Festival, Basketball Homecoming, and Spring Formal.

Sports: Athletic and recreation facilities include a baseball field, a 500-seat gymnasium, a 3000-seat stadium, 6 tennis courts, a weight room, and a swimming pool.

Disabled Students: All of the campus is accessible to disabled students. The following facilities are available: wheelchair ramps, elevators, special parking, and specially equipped rest rooms.

Services: In addition to many counseling and information services, tutoring is available in most subjects. In addition, there is a reader service for the blind and remedial reading and writing.

Campus Safety and Security: Campus safety and security measures include 24-hour foot and vehicle patrol, self-defense education, escort service, and informal discussions. In addition, there are emergency telephones, lighted pathways and sidewalks, and a university safety committee that provides controlled after-hours access to residence halls.

Programs of Study: Canyon awards the B.A., B.S., B.G.S., B.M., and B.S.N. degrees. Master's degrees also are awarded. Bachelor's degrees are awarded in BIOLOGICAL SCIENCE (biology/biological science and environmental biology), BUSINESS (accounting, banking and finance, business administration and management, human resources, international business management, marketing/retailing/merchandising, and personnel management), COMMUNICATIONS AND THE ARTS (applied music, communications, dramatic arts, English, fine arts, graphic design, music, piano/organ, Spanish, speech/debate/rhetoric, studio art, and voice), COMPUTER AND PHYSICAL SCIENCE (chemistry, computer science, and mathematics), EDUCATION (art, business, elementary, music, physical, science, secondary, and special), HEALTH PROFESSIONS (nursing), SOCIAL SCIENCE (Christian studies, criminal justice, economics, history, physical fitness/movement, psychology, religious music, social science, social studies, and sociology). Natural sciences, elementary education, nursing, and performing arts are the strongest academically. Elementary education has the largest enrollment.

Required: A total of 128 semester hours, with a minimum GPA of 2.0 and a writing proficiency examination are required in order to graduate. All students are required to complete 39 hours of general studies, including 10 hours in science, 9 in social studies, 6 each in English and humanities, 3 each in Old and New Testament history, and 2 in physical education. Chapel attendance is required.

Special: Co-op programs with several schools in the Christian College Coalition are available. Internships are offered for most majors through organizations, corporations, and agencies in the Phoenix area. Dual majors, study abroad in 5 countries, and a Washington semester are possible. A 3-2 engineering degree with Arizona State University is available. There is a freshman honors program on campus, as well as one national honor society, Phi Beta Kappa. One department has an honors program.

Faculty/Classroom: Fifty-one percent of faculty are male; 49%, female. Ninety-nine percent teach undergraduates, 17% do research, and 1% do both. The average class size in an introductory lecture is 25; in a laboratory, 10; and in a regular course offering, 25.

Admissions: About 71% of the 1993-94 applicants were accepted. The SAT scores for the 1993-94 freshman class were as follows: Verbal—74% below 500, 21% between 500 and 599, 4% between 600 and 700, and 1% above 700; Math—53% below 500, 34% between 500 and 599, 13% between 600 and 700, and 1% above 700. The ACT scores were 39% below 21, 31% between 21 and 23, 21% between 24 and 26, 3% between 27 and 28, and 5% above 28.

Requirements: Canyon requires applicants to be in the upper 25% of their class. A minimum GPA of 2.5 is required. The SAT I or ACT is required. In addition, applicants should be graduates of an accred-

ited high school or have a GED. AP and CLEP credits are accepted. Important factors used in the admissions decision are evidence of special talent, extracurricular activities record, leadership record, recommendations by school officials, and parents or siblings attending the school.

Procedure: Freshmen are admitted to all sessions. Entrance exams should be taken during the junior or senior year. Applications should be filed by August 1 for fall entry, January 1 for spring entry, and May 1 for summer entry, along with an application fee of $25. Notification is sent on a rolling basis. There is an early admissions plan.

Transfer: Transfer applicants must have a minimum GPA of 2.0 and a minimum of 24 transferable hours. A total of 30 credits out of 128 must be completed at Canyon.

Visiting: There are regularly scheduled orientations for prospective students, including High School Preview Days in February and Transfer Preview Days in March. There are guides for informal visits and visitors may sit in on classes and stay overnight at the school. To arrange for a visit, contact the Admissions Office at (602) 589-2441 or (800) 800-9776.

Financial Aid: In an earlier year, 85% of all current freshmen and 85% of continuing students received some form of financial aid. About 80% of freshmen and continuing students received need-based aid. The average freshman award was $5900. Of that total, scholarships or need-based grants averaged $3275 ($7200 maximum); loans averaged $2625; and work contracts averaged $1500 ($3000 maximum). Seventy-three percent of undergraduate students work part-time. Average earnings from campus work for the school year are $3000. The average financial indebtedness of the 1992-93 graduate was $10,000. The FAF, FFS or SFS is required, and the FAFSA is recommended. The deadline for financial aid applications is March 15.

International Students: There are currently 43 international students enrolled. The school actively recruits these students. They must take the TOEFL and achieve a minimum score of 500. Students with English as their first language must take the SAT I or ACT, and a 50 national percentile score or higher is required.

Computers: The college provides computer facilities for student use. The mainframe is a DEC VAX 6000-410. The computer laboratory facilities also include a large network of IBM-compatible PCs, Apple and Macintosh microcomputers, and a Motorola 6000 system running the UNIX operating system. All students may access the system. It may usually be used from morning until midnight. There are no time limits on using the system. The fees are $85 per semester.

Graduates: In a recent year, 326 bachelor's degrees were awarded. The most popular majors among graduates were elementary education (16%), psychology (8%), and nursing (8%). Within an average freshman class, 34% graduate in 4 years and 22% in 5 years. Some 39 companies recruited on campus in a recent year.

Admissions Contact: Michelle Sedgwick, Assistant Director of Admissions.

NORTHERN ARIZONA UNIVERSITY   C-2

Flagstaff, AZ 86001   (602) 523-5511; (800) 345-1987 (in-state)

Full-time: 5315 men, 5934 women	Faculty: 566; I, --$
Part-time: 1099 men, 1583 women	Ph.D.s: 80%
Graduate: 1484 men, 3402 women	Student/Faculty: 20 to 1
Year: semesters, summer session	Tuition: $1844 ($6596)
Application Deadline: April 1	Room & Board: $3000
Freshman Class: 5891 applied, 4931 accepted, 1973 enrolled	
SAT I: 450/480	ACT: 21 COMPETITIVE

Northern Arizona University, founded in 1899, is a public institution offering undergraduate and graduate degrees in a full range of disciplines from liberal arts and sciences to professional and career-related fields. There are 9 undergraduate and 7 graduate schools. In addition to regional accreditation, NAU has baccalaureate program accreditation with AACSB, ABET, ADA, AHEA, APTA, NASM, NCATE, NLN, and SAF. The 2 libraries contain 1,023,658 volumes, 348,339 microform items, and 18,749 audiovisual forms, and subscribe to 5398 periodicals. Computerized library sources and services include the card catalog and database searching. Special learning facilities include a learning resource center, art gallery, radio station, TV station, and an observatory, research centers, and the Institute for Human Development. The 730-acre campus is in a small town 140 miles north of Phoenix. Including residence halls, there are 79 buildings on campus.

Student Life: About 84% of undergraduates are from Arizona. Students come from 50 states, 65 foreign countries, and Canada. Eighty percent are white. The average age of freshmen is 18.7; all undergraduates, 22. Thirty-one percent drop out by the end of their first year; 40% remain to graduate.

Housing: A total of 6106 students can be accommodated in college housing. College-sponsored living facilities include single-sex and coed dormitories, on-campus apartments, married-student housing, fraternity houses, and sorority houses. In addition there are honors

houses. On-campus housing is guaranteed for all 4 years. Fifty-seven percent of students live on campus; of those, 90% remain on campus on weekends. All students may keep cars on campus.

Activities: About 3% of men belong to 8 national fraternities; about 4% of women belong to 5 national sororities. There are 160 groups on campus, including art, band, cheerleading, chess, choir, chorale, chorus, computers, dance, drama, ethnic, film, gay, honors, international, jazz band, marching band, musical theater, newspaper, opera, orchestra, pep band, photography, political, professional, radio and TV, religious, social, social service, student government, and symphony. Popular campus events include Martin Luther King Day, Luminario Lighting, Homecoming, and Parents Day.

Sports: There are 7 intercollegiate sports for men and 7 for women, and 30 intramural sports for men and 30 for women. Athletic and recreation facilities include the Skydome for football, basketball, and indoor track and field, 3 recreation centers with basketball and racquetball courts and weight rooms, and a 50-meter indoor pool with diving facilities.

Disabled Students: Ninety percent of the campus is accessible to disabled students. The following facilities are available: wheelchair ramps, elevators, special parking, specially equipped rest rooms, lowered drinking fountains, and lowered telephones.

Services: In addition to many counseling and information services, tutoring is available in most subjects. Most counseling and tutoring is done by volunteers and student interns. In addition, there is remedial math, reading, and writing.

Campus Safety and Security: Campus safety and security measures include 24-hour foot and vehicle patrol, self-defense education, escort service, and shuttle buses. In addition, there are informal discussions, pamphlets, posters, and films, emergency telephones, and lighted pathways and sidewalks.

Programs of Study: NAU awards the B.A., B.S., B.F.A., B.Mus., B.Mus.Ed., and B.S.N. degrees. Master's and doctoral degrees also are awarded. Bachelor's degrees are awarded in AGRICULTURE (forestry and related sciences), BIOLOGICAL SCIENCE (biology/biological science, botany, microbiology, and zoology), BUSINESS (accounting, banking and finance, business administration and management, business economics, hotel/restaurant management, and marketing/retailing/merchandising), COMMUNICATIONS AND THE ARTS (advertising, broadcasting, communications, design, dramatic arts, English, fine arts, French, journalism, music, Spanish, speech/debate/rhetoric, and telecommunications), COMPUTER AND PHYSICAL SCIENCE (chemistry, computer science, geology, information sciences and systems, mathematics, and physics), EDUCATION (art, business, early childhood, elementary, foreign languages, health, home economics, industrial arts, music, science, secondary, and teaching English as a second language/foreign language), ENGINEERING AND ENVIRONMENTAL DESIGN (civil engineering, computer engineering, electrical/electronics engineering, engineering, environmental engineering, and mechanical engineering), HEALTH PROFESSIONS (nursing, predentistry, premedicine, and speech pathology/audiology), SOCIAL SCIENCE (anthropology, community services, criminal justice, dietetics, economics, geography, history, international relations, parks and recreation management, philosophy, political science/government, prelaw, psychology, public administration, religion, social science, social work, and sociology). Health professions, hotel/restaurant management, engineering, and forestry are the strongest academically. Education, hotel/restaurant management, and psychology have the largest enrollments.

Required: To graduate, students must have at least 125 credit hours, including 45 to 60 in the major, with a minimum GPA of 2.0; some majors require a higher GPA. Students must complete a 44-hour liberal studies curriculum, consisting of foundation courses (6 hours of English and 3 hours of college algebra) and discipline courses (8 hours of natural science and mathematics and 9 hours each of creative arts, letters, and behavioral science).

Special: NAU offers cross-registration with many universities through the Western Interstate Commission for Higher Education (WICHE) and the National Student Exchange. Internships are available in student teaching, nursing, and physical therapy. Legislative internships are offered through the Arizona State Senate and House of Representatives. Students may study abroad in 11 countries. Work-study programs are available in engineering, business, park services, and arts management. A general studies degree, dual and student-designed majors, nondegree study, and pass/fail options are possible. There is a freshman honors program on campus, as well as 2 national honor societies.

Faculty/Classroom: Seventy percent of faculty are male; 30%, female. All teach and do research. The average class size in an introductory lecture is 45; in a laboratory, 25; and in a regular course offering, 35.

Admissions: About 84% of the 1993-94 applicants were accepted.

Requirements: The SAT I or ACT is required. Students must have a minimum GPA of 2.5 or rank in the top 50% of their class, or have minimum composite SAT I scores of 930 for in-state and 1010 for out-of-state applicants, or minimum ACT scores of 22 for in-state and 24 for out-of-state applicants. Students should be graduates of an accredited secondary school or hold the GED. Requirements include 11 academic credits, with a grade of C or better in each class, including 4 years of English, 2 each of algebra and laboratory science, and 1 each of geometry, social studies, and American history. AP and CLEP credits are accepted.

Procedure: Freshmen are admitted to all sessions. Entrance exams should be taken before the last semester of the senior year. Applications should be filed by April 1 for fall entry, December 1 for spring entry, and May 20 for summer entry. There is an application fee of $35 for out-of-state applicants. Notification is sent on a rolling basis. There is an early admissions plan.

Transfer: About 1900 transfer students enrolled in 1993-94. Transfer students must be eligible to reenter the institution last attended. Requirements vary with the number of college credits being transferred. Generally, in-state applicants must have a minimum GPA of 2.0 and submit high school and/or college transcripts. Nonresident transfer students with a GPA below 2.5 are admitted on a space-available basis. A total of 60 credits out of 125 must be completed at NAU.

Visiting: There are regularly scheduled orientations for prospective students, including eight 1 1/2-day orientation/registration sessions for new students held mid-June through mid-July, and a 4-day program held the week before the fall and spring semesters. There are guides for informal visits and visitors may stay overnight at the school. To arrange for a visit, contact the Office of Undergraduate Admissions at (602) 523-2491.

Financial Aid: In 1993-94, 60% of all current freshmen and 60% of continuing students received some form of financial aid. Scholarships or need-based grants averaged $1700; loans averaged $1700; and work contracts averaged $1500. Sixty-five percent of undergraduate students work part-time. Average earnings from campus work for the school year are $1400. NAU is a member of CSS. The FAF or FFS is required. The deadline for financial aid applications is April 15.

International Students: There are currently 393 international students enrolled. They must take the TOEFL or the University of Michigan Language Test and achieve a minimum score on the TOEFL of 500.

Computers: The college provides computer facilities for student use. The mainframes are a DEC VAX and an IBM 3083 and 9375-60. Microcomputers are available to students at various campus locations. Mainframes are sponsored by the faculty. All students may access the system. Computer usage, including access and amount of time, may be limited by academic level and major. There are no fees.

Graduates: In 1992-93, 2591 bachelor's degrees were awarded. The most popular majors among graduates were elementary education (10%), hotel/restaurant management (3%), and special education (3%). Within an average freshman class, 31% graduate in 4 years and 41% in 5 years. Some 325 companies recruited on campus in 1992-93.

Admissions Contact: Molly S. Carder, Director of Admissions.

PRESCOTT COLLEGE
Prescott, AZ 86301

C-3
(602) 776-5180

Full-time: 198 men, 158 women	Faculty: 40
Part-time: 7 men, 5 women	Ph.D.s: 47%
Graduate: none	Student/Faculty: 9 to 1
Year: see profile	Tuition: $9775
Application Deadline: open	Room & Board: n/app
Freshman Class: 321 applied, 227 accepted, 129 enrolled	
SAT I or ACT: recommended	COMPETITIVE

Prescott College, founded in 1966, is a private, coeducational commuter institution offering a nontraditional undergraduate program in the liberal arts. The school year consists of 3 blocks and 2 quarters. The curriculum is organized into multidisciplinary courses that allow students to pursue individual areas of competency. Evaluations of a student's work are conducted through a portfolio/contract system and an ongoing series of student self-evaluations. There are 3 undergraduate schools and one graduate school. The library contains 12,000 volumes, 100 microform items, and 600 audiovisual forms, and subscribes to 325 periodicals. Computerized library sources and services include the card catalog, interlibrary loans, and database searching. Special learning facilities include a learning resource center, greenhouse, weather station, and recycling center. The 4-acre campus is in a small town 100 miles north of Phoenix. There are 14 buildings on campus.

Student Life: About 96% of undergraduates are from out-of-state, mostly the Northeast. Students come from 43 states, 3 foreign countries, and Canada. Ninety-five percent are white. The average age of freshmen is 21; all undergraduates, 22. Five percent drop out by the end of their first year; 78% remain to graduate.

Housing: There are no residence halls. All students commute. Alcohol is not permitted. All students may keep cars on campus.

Activities: There are no fraternities or sororities on campus. There are 18 groups on campus, including art, dance, drama, literary magazine, newspaper, photography, political, social, social service, and student government. Popular campus events include Earth Day, Southwest Writers Series, Student-Directed Days, Coffee House, and PC Environmental Award.

Sports: There is no sports program at Prescott. There are no facilities on campus, but students have access to the local community pool, weight room, gymnasium, and city league sports.

Disabled Students: Fifty percent of the campus is accessible to disabled students. Wheelchair ramps are available.

Services: There is remedial math and writing. There is a learning specialist on staff, and untimed tests are available.

Campus Safety and Security: Campus safety and security measures include self defense education, informal discussions, and pamphlets, posters, and films.

Programs of Study: Prescott awards the B.A. degree. Master's degrees also are awarded. Bachelor's degrees are awarded in BIOLOGICAL SCIENCE (biology/biological science), COMMUNICATIONS AND THE ARTS (communications, English, fine arts, journalism, photography, and Spanish), COMPUTER AND PHYSICAL SCIENCE (earth science and geology), EDUCATION (art, early childhood, elementary, environmental, foreign languages, guidance, middle school, recreation, secondary, and special), ENGINEERING AND ENVIRONMENTAL DESIGN (environmental science), SOCIAL SCIENCE (anthropology, community services, psychology, social work, and sociology). Enviromental studies is the strongest academically. Outdoor action/wilderness leadership has the largest enrollment.

Required: Prescott does not specify any formal graduation requirements. Students may design an individual program of studies within 5 multidisciplinary areas: environmental studies, human development, outdoor action, cultural and regional studies, and humanities. Each student is required to submit a graduation proposal at the end of the junior year to the Graduation Review Committee.

Special: Internships, study abroad in almost any country, dual majors, a general studies degree, pass/fail options, and credit for life experience are offered. All majors are student-designed.

Faculty/Classroom: Sixty-three percent of faculty are male; 37%, female. All teach undergraduates. The average class size in an introductory lecture is 12; in a laboratory, 12; and in a regular course offering, 12.

Admissions: About 71% of the 1993–94 applicants were accepted.

Requirements: The SAT I or ACT is recommended. The GED is accepted. The school requires essays, transcripts, and letters of recommendation. Students may also submit portfolios and writing samples.

Procedure: Freshmen are admitted fall and spring. Application deadlines are open. Application fee is $25. Notification is sent on a rolling basis. A waiting list is an active part of the admissions procedure.

Transfer: A total of 97 transfer students enrolled in 1993–94. Transfer applicants must meet the same requirements as entering freshmen and must also submit official college transcripts. Students who successfully completed 2 years of college work (60 semester hours or 90 quarter credits) need not submit high school transcripts. There is a 2-year residency requirement.

Visiting: There are regularly scheduled orientations for prospective students, including a college video, a campus tour, and an interview with an admissions counselor. There are guides for informal visits and visitors may sit in on classes. To arrange for a visit, contact the RDP Admissions Office at (602) 776–5180.

Financial Aid: In 1993–94, 65% of all current freshmen and 53% of continuing students received some form of financial aid. About 65% of freshmen and 58% of continuing students received need-based aid. The average freshman award was $4200. Of that total, scholarships or need-based grants averaged $2494 ($4600 maximum); loans averaged $2637 ($10,500 maximum); and work contracts averaged $1995 ($2400 maximum). Forty-two percent of undergraduate students work part-time. Average earnings from campus work for the school year are $1995. The average financial indebtedness of the 1992–93 graduate was $12,000. Prescott is a member of CSS. The FAFSA financial statement is required. The deadline for financial aid applications is April 15.

International Students: There are currently 8 international students enrolled. They must take the TOEFL and achieve a minimum score of 500.

Computers: The college provides computer facilities for student use. The Learning Center has 20 personal computers for student use. All students may access the system 100 hours per week. There are no time limits on using the system and no fees.

Graduates: In 1992–93, 76 bachelor's degrees were awarded. Within an average freshman class, 6% graduate in 3 years, 17% in 4 years, 25% in 5 years, and 2% in 6 years. One company recruited on campus in 1992–93.

Admissions Contact: Shari Sterling, Director of RDP Admissions.

UNIVERSITY OF ARIZONA D-4
Tuscon, AZ 85721 (602) 621–3237

Full-time: 11,009 men, 10,662 women	Faculty: 1576; I, --$
Part-time: 2483 men, 2404 women	Ph.Ds: 95%
Graduate: 4579 men, 4142 women	Student/Faculty: 14 to 1
Year: semesters, summer session	Tuition: $1840 ($7346)
Application Deadline: April 1	Room & Board: $3968
Freshman Class: 14,000 applied, 12,200 accepted, 4529 enrolled	
SAT I Verbal/Math: 470/530	ACT: 23 **COMPETITIVE**

The University of Arizona, founded in 1885, is a public, coeducational, land-grant institution controlled by the state of Arizona. Undergraduate programs are offered in agriculture, architecture, arts and sciences, business and public administration, education, engineering and mines, law, medicine, nursing, pharmacy, and other health-related professions. There are 14 undergraduate schools and one graduate school. In addition to regional accreditation, U of A has baccalaureate program accreditation with AACSB, ABET, ACPE, ADA, ASLA, NAAB, NASAD, NASM, NCATE, and NLN. The 5 libraries contain 3,800,000 volumes, 4,100,000 microform items, and 141,000 audiovisual forms, and subscribe to 31,919 periodicals. Computerized library sources and services include the card catalog, interlibrary loans, and database searching. Special learning facilities include a learning resource center, art gallery, natural history museum, planetarium, radio station, TV station, and the Ansel Adams Center for creative photography. The 325-acre campus is in an urban area in Tucson. Including residence halls, there are 136 buildings on campus.

Student Life: About 71% of undergraduates are from Arizona. Students come from 50 states, 122 foreign countries, and Canada. Ninety percent are from public schools; 10% from private. Eighty-four percent are white; 11% Hispanic. The average age of freshmen is 19; all undergraduates, 22. Twenty-three percent drop out by the end of their first year; 60% remain to graduate.

Housing: A total of 5200 students can be accommodated in college housing. College-sponsored living facilities include single-sex and coed dormitories, off-campus apartments, married-student housing, fraternity houses, and sorority houses. In addition there are honors houses, special interest houses, and an international house. On-campus housing is available on a first-come, first-served basis. Priority is given to out-of-town students. Alcohol is not permitted. All students may keep cars on campus.

Activities: About 12% of men belong to 24 national fraternities; about 12% of women belong to 16 national sororities. There are 260 groups on campus, including art, band, cheerleading, chess, choir, chorale, chorus, computers, dance, drama, drill team, ethnic, film, gay, honors, international, jazz band, marching band, musical theater, newspaper, orchestra, pep band, photography, political, professional, radio and TV, religious, social, social service, student government, and yearbook. Popular campus events include the Spring Fling carnival and cultural programs.

Sports: There are 8 intercollegiate sports for men and 9 for women, and 27 intramural sports for men and 26 for women. Athletic and recreation facilities include an athletic center, a 53,000-seat stadium, a 13,500-seat arena, and a student recreation facility with a weight room, racquetball, squash, and handball courts, a waveless swimming pool, two gymnasiums, aerobics facilities, treadmills, stairclimbers, and stationary bicycles. Hiking, backpacking, and skiing trails, as well as facilities for kayaking, caving, and scuba diving are available.

Disabled Students: Nearly all of the campus is accessible to disabled students. The following facilities are available: wheelchair ramps, elevators, special parking, specially equipped rest rooms, lowered drinking fountains, and lowered telephones.

Services: In addition to many counseling and information services, tutoring is available in most subjects. There is also a reader service for the blind available.

Campus Safety and Security: Campus safety and security measures include 24-hour foot and vehicle patrol, self-defense education, escort service, and shuttle buses. In addition, there are lighted pathways and sidewalks.

Programs of Study: U of A awards the B.A., B.S., B.Arch., B.F.A., B.L.A., B.M., B.S.B.A., B.S.H.S., B.S.N., and B.S.P.A. degrees. Master's and doctoral degrees also are awarded. Bachelor's degrees are awarded in AGRICULTURE (agricultural economics, animal science, dairy science, natural resource management, plant science, range/farm management, and soil science), BIOLOGICAL SCIENCE (biochemistry, biology/biological science, microbiology, and nutrition), BUSINESS (accounting, banking and finance, business administration and management, business economics, management information systems, management science, marketing/retailing/merchandising, and personnel management), COMMUNICATIONS AND THE ARTS (art

history and appreciation, broadcasting, communications, creative writing, dance, dramatic arts, English, fine arts, French, German, Greek, Italian, journalism, Latin, linguistics, media arts, music, photography, Portuguese, Russian, Spanish, and speech/debate/rhetoric), COMPUTER AND PHYSICAL SCIENCE (astronomy, atmospheric sciences and meteorology, chemistry, computer science, earth science, geology, geoscience, mathematics, and physics), EDUCATION (agricultural, art, early childhood, elementary, foreign languages, health, home economics, music, physical, science, secondary, and teaching English as a second language/foreign language), ENGINEERING AND ENVIRONMENTAL DESIGN (aeronautical engineering, architectural engineering, chemical engineering, city/community/regional planning, civil engineering, computer engineering, electrical/electronics engineering, engineering, industrial engineering, materials science, mechanical engineering, nuclear engineering, optical engineering, petroleum/natural gas engineering, and systems engineering), HEALTH PROFESSIONS (health care administration, medical laboratory technology, nursing, pharmacy, predentistry, premedicine, speech pathology/audiology, and veterinary science), SOCIAL SCIENCE (anthropology, criminal justice, East Asian studies, economics, family/consumer resource management, food science, geography, history, Judaic studies, Mexican-American/Chicano studies, Near Eastern studies, philosophy, political science/government, psychology, public administration, religion, sociology, water resources, and women's studies). Sciences and social sciences are the strongest academically. Social sciences and business have the largest enrollments.

Required: All students must complete requirements in English, mathematics, and science. A total of 125 credits, with a minimum GPA of 2.0, is required in order to graduate.

Special: Co-op programs are available in almost all majors. B.A.-B.S. degrees, dual majors, interdisciplinary degrees such as engineering mathematics and theater arts education, and student-designed majors are offered. Internships in almost all disciplines, study abroad in numerous countries, work-study programs on campus, a general studies degree, and pass/fail options are offered. Nondegree study is possible. There is a freshman honors program on campus, as well as 16 national honor societies, including Phi Beta Kappa.

Faculty/Classroom: Seventy-nine percent of faculty are male; 21%, female. Graduate students teach 25% of introductory courses. The average class size in an introductory lecture is 20; in a laboratory, 20; and in a regular course offering, 22.

Admissions: About 87% of the 1993–94 applicants were accepted. The SAT scores for the 1993–94 freshman class were as follows: Verbal—60% below 500, 31% between 500 and 599, 8% between 600 and 700, and 1% above 700; Math—39% below 500, 35% between 500 and 599, 21% between 600 and 700, and 5% above 700. The ACT scores were 27% below 21, 27% between 21 and 23, 26% between 24 and 26, 10% between 27 and 28, and 10% above 28. About 52% of the current freshmen were in the top fifth of their class; 80% were in the top two fifths. There were 42 National Merit finalists and 123 semifinalists. More than 200 freshmen graduated first in their class.

Requirements: U of A requires applicants to be in the upper 25% of their class. A minimum GPA of 3.0 is required. The SAT I or ACT is required. Applicants should have completed 4 years in high school English, 3 in mathematics, 2 in science, and 1 each in history and social studies. AP and CLEP credits are accepted. Important factors used in the admissions decision are advanced placement or honor courses, leadership record, extracurricular activities record, evidence of special talents, and recommendations by school officials.

Procedure: Freshmen are admitted to all sessions. Entrance exams should be taken from June through February. Early action applications should be filed by November 1 and December 1; regular applications, by April 1 for fall entry, December 1 for spring entry, and April 1 for summer entry, along with an application fee of $35. Notification of early action is sent December 1 and January 15; regular decision, on a rolling basis. There are early admissions and deferred admissions plans.

Transfer: About 2491 transfer students enrolled in 1993–94. Resident transfer applicants must have a minimum GPA of 2.0; nonresidents, 2.5. Some university divisions have higher requirements. A total of 30 credits out of 125 must be completed at U of A.

Visiting: There are regularly scheduled orientations for prospective students, consisting of an admissions presentation and tour. There are guides for informal visits and visitors may sit in on classes. To arrange for a visit, contact the Visitation Coordinator at (602) 621–3641.

Financial Aid: In a recent year 48% of continuing students received some form of financial aid. About 31% of freshmen and 26% of continuing students received need-based aid. Scholarships or need-based grants averaged $2000 ($3400 maximum); loans averaged $1918 ($5625 maximum); and work contracts averaged $1500 ($1800 maximum). Twenty-four percent of undergraduate students work part-time. Average earnings from campus work for the school year are $1877. The average financial indebtedness of a recent

year's graduate was $7518. U of A is a member of CSS. The FAF, FFS or SFS is required. The deadline for financial aid applications is March 1.

International Students: There are currently 2045 international students enrolled. They must take the TOEFL and achieve a minimum score of 500. The student must also take the SAT I or ACT, only if the applicant is a graduate of a U.S. high school.

Computers: The college provides computer facilities for student use. The mainframe is an IBM 3090 Model 300 and a DEC VAX/VMS. There are 1700 microcomputers and 250 terminals available for student use. All students may access the system. It may be used 18 hours a day. Students may access the system depending on course work. There are no fees.

Graduates: In 1992–93 4848 bachelor's degrees were awarded. The most popular majors among graduates were political science (7%), psychology (6%), and finance (4%). Within an average freshman class, 17% graduate in 4 years, 44% in 5 years, and 60% in 6 years. More than 250 companies recruited on campus in 1992–93.

Admissions Contact: Loyd Bell, Director of Admissions.

WESTERN INTERNATIONAL UNIVERSITY   C-4
Phoenix, AZ 85021   (602) 943–2311

Full-time: 702 men, 467 women	Faculty: 85
Part-time: none	Ph.D.s: 62%
Graduate: 282 men, 172 women	Student/Faculty: 19 to 1
Year: see profile	Tuition: $3600
Application Deadline: open	Room & Board: n/app
Freshman Class: 30 applied, 26 accepted, 21 enrolled	
SAT I or ACT: see profile	**COMPETITIVE**

Western International University, founded in 1978, is a private, coeducational arts and sciences institution designed to serve adult students and professionals. WIU offers two-month semesters and evening and weekend courses. The library contains 7500 volumes, 100 microform items, and 20 audiovisual forms, and subscribes to 106 periodicals. Computerized library sources and services include the card catalog and database searching. Special learning facilities include a learning resource center. The 4-acre main campus is in Phoenix. There is one building on campus.

Student Life: About 78% of undergraduates are from Arizona. Students come from 52 foreign countries and Canada. Fifty-seven percent are white; 25% foreign nationals; 6% African American; 5% Hispanic; and 5% Asian American. The average age of all undergraduates is 33.

Housing: There are no residence halls. All students commute. Alcohol is not permitted. All students may keep cars on campus.

Activities: There are no fraternities or sororities on campus. The 6 groups on campus include honors, international, professional, social, social service, and student government. Popular campus events include International Day and cultural activities off and on campus, the Annual Alumni Dinner, and student association activities.

Sports: There is no sports program at WIU.

Disabled Students: The entire campus is accessible to disabled students. The following facilities are available: wheelchair ramps, elevators, special parking, specially equipped rest rooms, and lowered telephones.

Services: In addition to many counseling and information services, tutoring is available in some subjects, including accounting, finance, statistics, and operations management. In addition, there is remedial writing.

Campus Safety and Security: Campus safety and security measures include lighted pathways, sidewalks, and parking lots.

Programs of Study: WIU awards the B.A. and B.S. degrees. Associate and master's degrees also are awarded. Bachelor's degrees are awarded in BUSINESS (accounting, banking and finance, international business management, management science, and marketing management), COMPUTER AND PHYSICAL SCIENCE (information sciences and systems), SOCIAL SCIENCE (behavioral science, international studies, and liberal arts/general studies). Management has the largest enrollment.

Required: All students must demonstrate competence or satisfactorily complete courses in a 33-hour concentration, a 30-hour business core, and a 63-hour general curriculum, which includes competencies in communications, world cultures, interpersonal relations, community service, self-knowledge, science/technology/environment, and personal competence. A 2.0 GPA and 126 credit hours are required to graduate.

Special: Corporate internships, college work-study programs, executive development programs and study abroad at the United Kingdom campus are available. An accelerated degree program, dual and student-designed majors, credit by exam, and nondegree study are possible. Credit for life and work experience is an integral part of the degree program. Course offerings are also available at Fort Huachuca and 11 corporate teaching sites. There is a freshman honors program on campus.

Faculty/Classroom: Seventy-eight percent of faculty are male; 22%, female. Seventy-two percent teach undergraduates and 27% do research. No introductory courses are taught by graduate students. The average class size in an introductory lecture is 18; and in a regular course offering, 18.

Admissions: About 87% of the 1993–94 applicants were accepted.

Requirements: A minimum GPA of 2.5 is required. High School graduates from an accredited secondary school must meet one of the following requirements: a 2.5 cumulative GPA, a rank in the upper half of the class, a composite score of 22 on the ACT, or a combined score of 950 on the SAT I. The GED is accepted with a minimun average score of 50 and minimum standard scores of 35 in each section. AP and CLEP credits are accepted. Important factors used in the admissions decision are evidence of special talent, leadership record, geographic diversity, ability to finance college education, and recommendations by school officials.

Procedure: Freshmen are admitted to all sessions. Application deadlines are open. The application fee is $50. Notification is sent on a rolling basis. There is a deferred admissions plan.

Transfer: Applicants must have a cumulative college GPA of at least 2.0. Those with fewer than 12 transferable semester credits also must meet requirements for new freshmen. A total of 36 credits out of 126 must be completed at WIU.

Visiting: There are guides for informal visits and visitors may sit in on classes. To arrange for a visit, contact Kathie WesterField, Director of Admission at (602) 943-2311.

Financial Aid: In 1993–94, 20% of all current freshman and 20% of continuing students received some form of financial aid. About 5% of freshmen and 20% of continuing students received need-based aid. The average freshman award was $3000. Of that total, scholarships or need-based grants averaged $800 ($2400 maximum); loans averaged $1350 ($4000 maximum); and work contracts averaged $400 ($3000 maximum). One percent of undergraduate students work part-time. Average earnings from campus work for the school year are $3000. The average financial indebtedness of the 1992–93 graduate was $9000. The FAF, FFS, or SFS is required.

International Students: There are currently 143 international students enrolled. The school actively recruits these students. International students may either participate in an intensive English program, or submit scores of 500 on the TOEFL, or 75 on the Michigan English test.

Computers: The college provides computer facilities for student use. The computer facility includes 13 Easy-PC terminals, a 286 Zenith terminal with 40MB, 2 Citizen MSP-50s a Panasonic K-X-P112 printer, 8 Everex Tempo 386/25 terminals, an Everex Tempo 386/25 terminal with 85M, an HP Laser Jet Series II, and an 11241 Panasonic 24 pin printer. Word processing, dBASE IV, Lotus 1-2-3, Windows, and other software are available, and all microcomputers are networked to an Everex Tempo 386. All students may access the system. There are no time limits on using the system and no fees.

Graduates: In 1992–93, 246 bachelor's degrees were awarded. The most popular majors among graduates were management (29%), information systems (28)%, and liberal arts (19)%. Within an average freshman class, 79% graduate in 3 years.

Admissions Contact: Kathie WesterField, Director of Admissions.

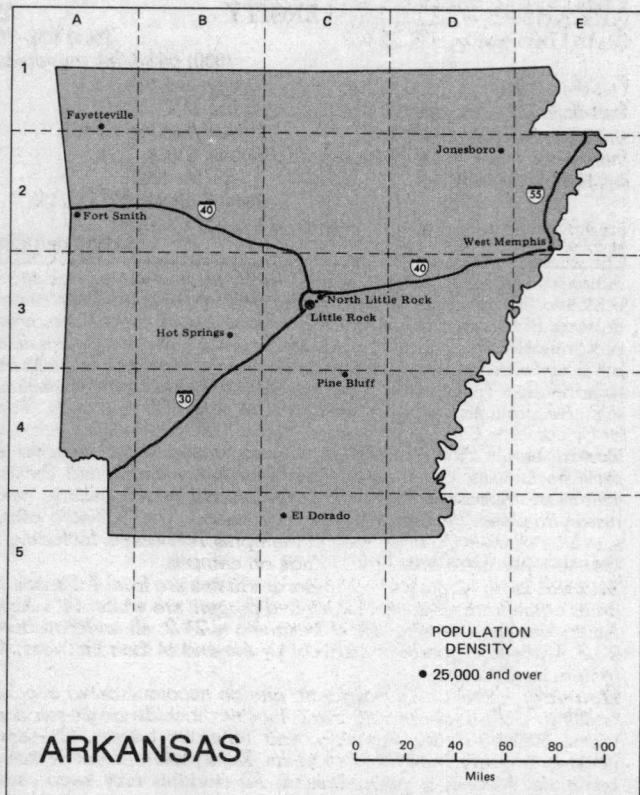

ARKANSAS

POPULATION
DENSITY

● 25,000 and over

| 0 | 20 | 40 | 60 | 80 | 100 |
Miles

ARKANSAS BAPTIST COLLEGE

Little Rock, AR 72202

C-3

(501) 374–7856, ext. 19

Full-time, part-time: 266 men and women	Faculty: 28
	Ph.D.s: 17%
Graduate: none	Student/Faculty: 10 to 1
Year: semesters, summer session	Tuition: $2090
Application Deadline: open	Room & Board: $2926
Freshman Class: 76 applied, 76 accepted, 76 enrolled	
SAT I or ACT: not required	**NONCOMPETITIVE**

Arkansas Baptist College, founded in 1884, is a private, liberal arts institution affiliated with American Baptist Churches, U.S.A. The library contains 23,000 volumes, and subscribes to 6 periodicals. The campus is in an urban area in downtown Little Rock.

Student Life: About 95% of undergraduates are from Arkansas. The average age of freshmen is 24; all undergraduates, 35. Twenty-five percent drop out by the end of their first year.

Housing: On-campus housing is guaranteed for all 4 years and 98% of students commute.

Activities: There are 2 groups on campus, including choir and student government. Popular campus events include Homecoming.

Programs of Study: The college awards the B.A. and B.S. degrees. Associate degrees also are awarded. Bachelor's degrees are awarded in BUSINESS (business administration and management), COMPUTER AND PHYSICAL SCIENCE (computer science), EDUCATION (elementary and secondary), SOCIAL SCIENCE (philosophy, religion, and social science).

Required: Students must complete 124 hours, with 72 in the major. Courses in English, history, mathematics, philosophy/religion, biological/physical science, social science and physical education are required.

Special: The college offers a co-op program with Ouachita Baptist University, work-study programs, combined B.A.-B.S. degrees, dual majors, and the general studies degree.

Admissions: All of the 1993–94 applicants were accepted.

Requirements: The SAT I or ACT is not required. Placement tests are given on campus. The only requirement for admission is a minimum high school GPA of 1.5. Students must have 18 units, including 4 each in English and mathematics, and 1 in biology and physical and social science.

Procedure: Freshmens are admitted to all sessions. Application deadlines are open and the application fee is $10. The college accepts all in-state residents who apply. Notification is sent on a rolling basis.

Financial Aid: Recently, 43% of all current freshmen and 94% of continuing students received some form of financial aid. The deadline for financial aid applications is May 1.

Graduates: In an earlier year, 36 bachelor's degrees were awarded. The most popular majors among graduates were educaton (36%), business and management (34%), and social science (16%).

Admissions Contact: Annie A. Hightower, Registrar.

ARKANSAS COLLEGE

C-2

Batesville, AR 72503   (501) 698–4250; (800) 423–2542 (out-of-state)

Full-time: 233 men, 297 women	Faculty: 42; IIB, av$
Part-time: 72 men, 116 women	Ph.D.s: 76%
Graduate: none	Student/Faculty: 13 to 1
Year: 4–1–4, summer session	Tuition: $8090
Application Deadline: August 1	Room & Board: $3536
Freshman Class: 420 applied, 334 accepted, 168 enrolled	
ACT: 25	**VERY COMPETITIVE**

Arkansas College, founded in 1872, is an independent, coeducational, liberal arts institution affiliated with the Presbyterian Church (USA). In addition to regional accreditation, AC has baccalaureate program accreditation with CSWE and NCATE. The library contains 105,000 volumes, 6000 microform items, and 2200 audiovisual forms, and subscribes to 900 periodicals. Computerized library sources and services include the card catalog, interlibrary loans, and database searching. Special learning facilities include a learning resource center and art gallery. The 136-acre campus is in a small town 90 miles north of Little Rock and 120 miles west of Memphis. Including residence halls, there are 25 buildings on campus.

Student Life: About 82% of undergraduates are from Arkansas. Students come from 20 states, 3 foreign countries, and Canada. Ninety-eight percent are from public schools; 2% from private. Ninety-four percent are white. Seventy-nine percent are Protestant; 16% claim no religious affiliation. The average age of freshmen is 18; all undergraduates, 23. Twenty-seven percent drop out by the end of their first year; 35% remain to graduate.

Housing: A total of 407 students can be accommodated in college housing. College-sponsored living facilities include single-sex dormitories and on-campus apartments. In addition, there is freshman-only housing. On-campus housing is guaranteed for all 4 years and is available on a lottery system for upperclassmen. Seventy-two percent of students live on campus; of those, 80% remain on campus on weekends. All students may keep cars on campus.

Activities: About 25% of men belong to 2 local and 2 national fraternities; about 21% of women belong to 1 local and 2 national sororities. There are 40 groups on campus, including art, bagpipe band, band, cheerleading, choir, computers, drama, ethnic, honors, literary magazine, newspaper, pep band, photography, political, professional, radio and TV, religious, social, social service, student government, and yearbook. Popular campus events include Founders Day, Honors Day, Scottish Festival, Homecoming, Kirkin 'O' the Tartans, Service Day, Parents Weekend, Alumni Weekend, and Arkansas Business Leaders' Symposium.

Sports: There are 6 intercollegiate sports for men and 5 for women, and 14 intramural sports for men and 14 for women. Athletic and recreation facilities include a 2500-seat gymnasium, softball and soccer fields, a cross-country track, a swimming pool, basketball and tennis courts, a hiking trail, and an off-campus baseball field.

Disabled Students: Ninety percent of the campus is accessible to disabled students. The following facilities are available: wheelchair ramps, elevators, special parking, specially equipped rest rooms, special class scheduling, and lowered drinking fountains.

Services: In addition to many counseling and information services, tutoring is available in every subject. There is also a reader service for the blind. Writing and mathematics laboratories are also available.

Campus Safety and Security: Campus safety and security measures include self defense education, escort service, informal discussions, and pamphlets, posters, and films. In addition, there are emergency telephones and lighted pathways and sidewalks. Security assistance is available at all times, with foot and vehicle patrol on weekends and evenings.

Programs of Study: AC awards the B.A. and B.S. degrees. Bachelor's degrees are awarded in BIOLOGICAL SCIENCE (biology/biological science), BUSINESS (business administration and management), COMMUNICATIONS AND THE ARTS (art, dramatic arts, English, and music), COMPUTER AND PHYSICAL SCIENCE (chemistry and mathematics), EDUCATION (elementary), SOCIAL SCIENCE

(economics, history, psychology, and religion). Chemistry, biology, business, English, history, philosophy, and religion are the strongest academically. Education, business, biology, and English have the largest enrollments.

Required: All students are required to complete a liberal arts core curriculum, including 8 credits in mathematics and science, 6 each in English, social sciences, and history, 3 each in college algebra, fine arts, and religion and philosophy, 1 in freshman orientation, plus 2 semesters of physical education. A total of 120 credits, with a minimum GPA of 2.0, is required to graduate.

Special: Co-op programs and internships are offered. A 2–2 engineering program is offered with the University of Missouri in Rolla and a 3–2 program is offered with the University of Arkansas at Fayetteville. Work-study courses, study abroad, dual majors, student-designed majors, pass/fail options, and credit for military experience are available. There are 4 national honor societies on campus.

Faculty/Classroom: Seventy-four percent of faculty are male; 26%, female. All teach undergraduates and do research. The average class size in an introductory lecture is 21; in a laboratory, 19; and in a regular course offering, 13.

Admissions: About 80% of the 1993–94 applicants were accepted. The ACT scores for the 1993–94 freshman class were as follows: 14% below 21, 25% between 21 and 23, 31% between 24 and 26, 17% between 27 and 28, and 13% above 28. About 67% of the current freshmen were in the top fifth of their class; 92% were in the top two fifths. There were 2 National Merit finalists and 6 semifinalists. Sixteen freshmen graduated first in their class.

Requirements: The SAT I or ACT (preferred) is required. Applicants should have completed a minimum of 15 high school units, including 4 in English, 3 to 4 each in science and mathematics, 3 in social sciences, and 1 to 2 in a foreign language. A letter of recommendation and an admission interview are recommended. AP and CLEP credits are accepted. Important factors used in the admissions decision are advanced placement or honor courses, leadership record, evidence of special talent, extracurricular activities record, and recommendations by school officials.

Procedure: Freshmen are admitted fall and spring. Entrance exams should be taken in the spring of junior year and the fall of senior year. Applications should be filed by August 1 for fall entry and January 15 for spring entry, along with an application fee of $15. Notification is sent on a rolling basis. There are early admissions and deferred admissions plans. A waiting list is an active part of the admissions procedure, with about 5% of applicants on the list.

Transfer: About 29 transfer students enrolled in 1993–94. Transfer applicants with 24 or more semester hours earned must submit transcripts from each college attended; those with fewer hours must submit their final high school transcript as well. A total of 60 credits out of 120 must be completed at AC.

Visiting: There are regularly scheduled orientations for prospective students, consisting of a campus tour, admission and financial aid orientation, and information sessions with faculty and students. There are guides for informal visits and visitors may sit in on classes and stay overnight at the school. To arrange for a visit, contact the Admission Center at (800) 423–2542.

Financial Aid: In 1993–94, 98% of all current freshmen and 89% of continuing students received some form of financial aid. About 72% of freshmen and 87% of continuing students received need-based aid. The average freshman award was $9948. Of that total, scholarships or need-based grants averaged $7213 ($13,376 maximum); loans averaged $1924 ($2625 maximum); and work contracts averaged $811 ($1360 maximum). Fifty-four percent of undergraduate students work part-time. Average earnings from campus work for the school year are $1137. The average financial indebtedness of the 1992–93 graduate was $9244. AC is a member of CSS. The FAFSA is required. The deadline for financial aid applications is April 1.

International Students: There are currently 2 international students enrolled. The school actively recruits these students. They must take the TOEFL or the college's own test and achieve a minimum score on the TOEFL of 550. The student must also take the SAT I or the ACT.

Computers: The college provides computer facilities for student use. The mainframes are an IBM System/38, an IBM RISC 6000, and 3 DEC VAXs. The DEC VAX computers are accessed through a 12-terminal laboratory in the science building. The RISC 6000 is accessed through 16 workstations in the library. A new computer laboratory contains 32 networked IBM-compatible microcomputers and 28 networked Apple Macintosh microcomputers utilizing a VAX server. Access to Internet is available. All students may access the system. There are no time limits and no fees.

Graduates: In 1992–93 119 bachelor's degrees were awarded. The most popular majors among graduates were business (14%), elementary education (14%), and English (10%). Within an average freshman class, 35% graduate in 4 years, 35% in 5 years, and 37% in 6 years. Some 16 companies recruited on campus in 1992–93. In the 1992 graduating class, 11% of all students were enrolled in graduate school within 6 months of graduation; 74% of the men and 86% of the

women had found employment.

Admissions Contact: Jonathan Stroud, Dean of Admission/ Financial Aid.

ARKANSAS STATE UNIVERSITY
D-2
State University, AR 72467
(501) 972–3024
(800) 643–0080 (out-of-state)

Full-time: 3266 men, 3946 women	**Faculty:** 345; IIA, --$
Part-time: 682 men, 1025 women	**Ph.D.s:** 74%
Graduate: 338 men, 631 women	**Student/Faculty:** 21 to 1
Year: semesters, summer session	**Tuition:** $1920–2370
Application Deadline: July 31	($3750–4200)
	Room & Board: $2330–2410

Freshman Class: 2688 applied, 2633 accepted, 1573 enrolled
ACT: 20
NONCOMPETITIVE

Arkansas State University, founded in 1909, is a state-supported co-educational institution, offering undergraduate and graduate degrees in agriculture, arts and sciences, business, communications, education, engineering, fine arts, and nursing and health professions. There are 8 undergraduate schools and one graduate school. In addition to regional accreditation, ASU has baccalaureate program accreditation with AACSB, ACEJMC, CSWE, NASM, NCATE, and NLN. The library contains 1.2 million volumes and 300,000 microform items, and subscribes to 2500 periodicals. Computerized library sources and services include the card catalog, interlibrary loans, and database searching. Special learning facilities include an art gallery, natural history museum, radio station, and TV station. The 800-acre campus is in a small town 70 miles west of Memphis, Tennessee. Including residence halls, there are 37 buildings on campus.

Student Life: About 84% of undergraduates are from Arkansas. Students come from 46 states. Eighty-five percent are white; 11% African American. The average age of freshmen is 21.2; all undergraduates, 23.3. Thirty-three percent drop out by the end of their first year; 40% remain to graduate.

Housing: A total of 2359 students can be accommodated in college housing. College-sponsored living facilities include single-sex dormitories, married-student housing, and fraternity houses. On-campus housing is guaranteed for all 4 years. Eighty-two percent of students commute. Alcohol is not permitted. All students may keep cars on campus.

Activities: About 5% of men belong to 13 national fraternities; about 5% of women belong to 8 national sororities. There are more than 140 groups on campus, including art, cheerleading, choir, computers, dance, drama, ethnic, honors, international, marching band, musical theater, newspaper, pep band, photography, political, professional, radio and TV, religious, student government, symphony, and yearbook. Popular campus events include Springfest, Homecoming, Convocation of Scholars Week and International Night.

Sports: There are 9 intercollegiate sports for men and 6 for women, and 13 intramural sports for men and 12 for women. Athletic and recreation facilities include a convocation center and physical education complex with an 18,709-seat stadium and a 10,529-seat auditorium/arena.

Disabled Students: Ninety percent of the campus is accessible to disabled students. The following facilities are available: wheelchair ramps, elevators, special parking, specially equipped rest rooms, special class scheduling, lowered drinking fountains, and lowered telephones.

Services: In addition to many counseling and information services, tutoring is available in some subjects. In addition, there is remedial math, reading, and writing. Tutoring is available in basic general education courses.

Campus Safety and Security: Campus safety and security measures include 24-hour foot and vehicle patrol, pamphlets, posters, and films, emergency telephones, and lighted pathways and sidewalks.

Programs of Study: ASU awards the B.A., B.S., B.F.A., B.G.S., B.Mus., B.Mus.Ed., B.S.Ag., B.S.Ag.E., B.S.Ed., B.S. in Eng., and B.S.N. degrees. Associate, master's, and doctoral degrees also are awarded. Bachelor's degrees are awarded in AGRICULTURE (agricultural business management, agriculture, animal science, horticulture, plant science, and wildlife management), BIOLOGICAL SCIENCE (biology/biological science, botany, and zoology), BUSINESS (accounting, banking and finance, business administration and management, business economics, international business management, marketing/retailing/merchandising, real estate, and transportation management), COMMUNICATIONS AND THE ARTS (advertising, broadcasting, communications, design, dramatic arts, English, fine arts, French, journalism, music, photography, public relations, Spanish, and speech/debate/rhetoric), COMPUTER AND PHYSICAL SCIENCE (chemistry, computer science, mathematics, and physics), EDUCATION (agricultural, art, business, early childhood, elementary, foreign languages, music, physical, science, secondary, and special), ENGINEERING AND ENVIRONMENTAL DESIGN (agricultural engineering, engineering, and printing technology), HEALTH PROFES-

SIONS (health care administration, medical laboratory technology, nursing, predentistry, premedicine, and speech pathology/audiology), SOCIAL SCIENCE (criminal justice, economics, geography, history, philosophy, political science/government, prelaw, psychology, social work, sociology, and urban studies). Business and education have the largest enrollments.

Required: All students must complete a 45-credit distribution of general education courses. A total of at least 124 credits, with a minimum GPA of 2.0, is required to graduate.

Special: B.A.-B.S. degrees, a general studies degree, and limited pass/fail options are offered. There are internships in marketing, journalism, and international business. Nondegree study is possible. There is a freshman honors program on campus, as well as 23 national honor societies, including Phi Beta Kappa. Six departments have honors programs.

Faculty/Classroom: Sixty-five percent of faculty are male; 35%, female. Seventy-five percent teach undergraduates, 25% do research, and 35% do both. Graduate students teach 10% of introductory courses. The average class size in an introductory lecture is 25; in a laboratory, 40; and in a regular course offering, 22.

Admissions: About 98% of the 1993–94 applicants were accepted.

Requirements: A minimum GPA of 2.0 is required. The ACT is required. Applicants should have completed 18 high school units, including 4 in English, 3 in social studies, and 2 each in mathematics and science. The university places those applicants scoring below 19 on the ACT into developmental or remedial courses. AP and CLEP credits are accepted. Important factors used in the admissions decision are recommendations by school officials, parents or siblings attending the school, recommendations by alumni, advanced placement or honor courses, and evidence of special talent.

Procedure: Freshmen are admitted to all sessions. Applications should be filed by July 31 for fall entry, July 30 for winter entry, November 30 for spring entry, and March 31 for summer entry. There are early decision and early admissions plans. About 10 early decision candidates were accepted for the 1993–94 class.

Transfer: About 821 transfer students enrolled in 1993–94. Transfer applicants should have a minimum GPA of 2.0. Those having completed fewer than 24 credit hours will be admitted on the same basis as freshmen. A total of 32 credits out of 124 must be completed at ASU.

Visiting: There are regularly scheduled orientations for prospective students, consisting of every second and third Wednesday in June and July. There are guides for informal visits and visitors may sit in on classes and stay overnight at the school. To arrange for a visit, contact the Office of Admissions and Records at (501) 972-3024.

Financial Aid: In 1993–94, 60% of all current freshmen and 65% of continuing students received some form of financial aid. About 60% of freshmen and 60% of continuing students received need-based aid. The average freshman award was $3000. Of that total, scholarships or need-based grants averaged $500 ($2400 maximum); loans averaged $2000 ($4000 maximum); and work contracts averaged $500 ($2000 maximum). Eighty percent of undergraduate students work part-time. Average earnings from campus work for the school year are $2000. The average financial indebtedness of the 1992–93 graduate was $12,000. The FFS, CSS, and USAF or CSX are required. The deadline for financial aid applications is May 1.

International Students: There are currently 321 international students enrolled. They must take the TOEFL and achieve a minimum score of 500. The student must also take the SAT I or the ACT and achieve a minimum score of 700 on the SAT I or 19 on the ACT.

Computers: The college provides computer facilities for student use. The mainframe is an IBM 4381. Students enrolled in computer courses may access the system. It may be used during the day and evening on weekdays and weekends. A schedule is posted. There are no time limits on using the system and no fees.

Graduates: In 1992–93, 1220 bachelor's degrees were awarded. The most popular majors among graduates were accounting (9%), elementary education, early childhood (8%), and elementary education, general (7%).

Admissions Contact: Leonard McDaniel, Director of Admissions.

ARKANSAS TECH UNIVERSITY

Russellville, AR 72801-2222

B-2

(501) 968-0343

(800) 582-6953 (in-state)

Full-time: 1704 men, 1898 women	Faculty: 180; IIB, -$
Part-time: 327 men, 612 women	Ph.D.s: 60%
Graduate: 53 men, 136 women	Student/Faculty: 20 to 1
Year: semesters, summer session	Tuition: $1710 ($3360)
Application Deadline: open	Room & Board: $2490
Freshman Class: 1733 applied, 1733 accepted, 953 enrolled	
ACT: 20	NONCOMPETITIVE

Arkansas Tech University, founded in 1909, is a state-supported coeducational institution offering undergraduate and graduate instruction in the liberal and fine arts, business, education, physical life

sciences, information technology and systems, and various other technical fields. There are 5 undergraduate and 8 graduate schools. In addition to regional accreditation, ATU has baccalaureate program accreditation with AACSB, CAHEA, NASM, NCATE, and NLN. The library contains 203,487 volumes and 659,685 microform items, and subscribes to 1198 periodicals. Computerized library sources and services include the card catalog. Special learning facilities include an art gallery, natural history museum, radio station, TV station, and TV project. The 517-acre campus is in a small town 75 miles east of Little Rock. Including residence halls, there are 41 buildings on campus.

Student Life: About 96% of undergraduates are from Arkansas. Students come from 30 states, 21 foreign countries, and Canada. Ninety-seven percent are from public schools. Ninety-four percent are white. The average age of freshmen is 18; all undergraduates, 24. Fifteen percent drop out by the end of their first year.

Housing: A total of 1056 students can be accommodated in college housing. College-sponsored living facilities include single-sex dormitories and married-student housing. On-campus housing is guaranteed for all 4 years. Alcohol is not permitted. All students may keep cars on campus.

Activities: About 19% of men belong to 6 national fraternities; about 12% of women belong to 3 national sororities. There are 66 groups on campus, including cheerleading, computers, drill team, honors, jazz band, literary magazine, marching band, newspaper, orchestra, radio and TV, religious, student government, and yearbook. Popular campus events include Global Fest, Greek Week, Parents Day, and Homecoming.

Sports: There are 5 intercollegiate sports for men and 2 for women, and 3 intramural sports for men and 2 for women. Athletic and recreation facilities include a coliseum, fields, an Olympic-size indoor pool, racquetball courts, and a 10,000-seat stadium. The Student Activities Building is the hub of indoor recreational activities.

Disabled Students: Eighty percent of the campus is accessible to disabled students. The following facilities are available: wheelchair ramps, elevators, special parking, and specially equipped rest rooms.

Services: In addition to many counseling and information services, tutoring is available in most subjects.

Campus Safety and Security: Campus safety and security measures include 24-hour foot and vehicle patrol.

Programs of Study: ATU awards the B.A., B.S., and B.F.A. degrees. Associate and master's degrees also are awarded. Bachelor's degrees are awarded in AGRICULTURE (agricultural business management), BIOLOGICAL SCIENCE (biology/biological science), BUSINESS (accounting, business administration and management, hotel/motel and restaurant management, office supervision and management, and recreation and leisure services), COMMUNICATIONS AND THE ARTS (creative writing, English, journalism, music, and speech/debate/rhetoric), COMPUTER AND PHYSICAL SCIENCE (chemistry, computer science, geology, mathematics, natural sciences, and physical sciences), EDUCATION (art, business, elementary, health, music, and secondary), ENGINEERING AND ENVIRONMENTAL DESIGN (engineering), HEALTH PROFESSIONS (medical laboratory technology and nursing), SOCIAL SCIENCE (economics, parks and recreation management, psychology, and sociology). Accounting, business administration, computer science, elementary education, engineering, and health and physical education have the largest enrollments.

Required: Students must complete at least 124 semester hours, including 40 hours of upper-level courses to fulfill a major, and maintain a minimum GPA of 2.0. General education requirements include 8 to 12 semester hours of science, 6 each of communications, social studies, and American studies, 3 each of mathematics, fine arts, and the humanities, and 2 of physical education or military science. Activity credits are limited to 8 semester hours.

Special: Special academic programs include internships, and work-study programs. Independent study is available to seniors. Off-campus courses are also offered. There is a freshman honors program on campus, as well as 4 national honor societies.

Faculty/Classroom: Sixty-eight percent of faculty are male; 32%, female. Ninety-nine percent teach undergraduates, 1% do research, and 28% do both. No introductory courses are taught by graduate students. The average class size in an introductory lecture is 48; in a laboratory, 23; and in a regular course offering, 40.

Admissions: All of the 1993–94 applicants were accepted. The ACT scores for the 1993–94 freshman class were as follows: 53% below 21, 24% between 21 and 23, 18% between 24 and 26, 3% between 27 and 28, and 2% above 28.

Requirements: A minimum GPA of 2.5 is required. The SAT I or ACT is required. Applicants must be graduates of a secondary school. In addition, academic ability must be demonstrated by one of the following: a high school GPA of at least 2.5 on a 4.0 scale; attainment of freshman placement test score standards; or completion of 6 semester hours with a cumulative average of C or better in summer sessions or as a part-time student in regular sessions, with at least 3 of

the hours being in English, mathematics, social studies, or science. AP and CLEP credits are accepted. Important factors used in the admissions decision are advanced placement or honor courses, evidence of special talent, leadership record, extracurricular activities record, and recommendations by school officials.

Procedure: Freshmen are admitted to all sessions. Application deadlines are open. The college accepts all applicants. Notification is sent on a rolling basis. There are early decision, early admissions, and deferred admissions plans.

Transfer: About 260 transfer students enrolled in 1993–94. Transfers are accepted for second-semester freshmen, sophomore, and junior classes. A C average is required. A total of 30 credits out of 124 must be completed at ATU.

Visiting: There are guides for informal visits. To arrange for a visit, contact the Admissions Office at (501) 968–0343.

Financial Aid: Ten percent of undergraduate students work part-time. Average earnings from campus work for the school year are $1150. The average financial indebtedness of recent year graduates was $4500. The college's own financial statement and federal application are required. The deadline for financial aid applications is May 1.

International Students: There are currently 37 international students enrolled. The school actively recruits these students. They must take the TOEFL and achieve a minimum score of 500. The student must also take the SAT I, ACT, or the college's own entrance exam.

Computers: The college provides computer facilities for student use. The mainframe is an IBM 4381, which can be accessed by 120 terminals campuswide. All students may access the system. There are no time limits on using the system and no fees.

Graduates: In 1992–93, 586 bachelor's degrees were awarded. The most popular majors among graduates were elementary education (22%), business administration (13%), and history and political science (5%). Some 72 companies recruited on campus in 1992–93. In the 1992 graduating class, 60% of the men and 75% of the women had found employment within 6 months of graduation.

Admissions Contact: Harold L. Cornett, Director of Admissions and School Relations.

HARDING UNIVERSITY

C-2

Searcy, AR 72143   (501) 279–4407; (800) 477–4407 (out-of-state)

Full-time: 1470 men, 1630 women	Faculty: 170; IIB, -$
Part-time: 77 men, 86 women	Ph.D.s: 70%
Graduate: 93 men, 122 women	Student/Faculty: 18 to 1
Year: semesters, summer session	Tuition: $5750
Application Deadline: May 1	Room & Board: $3300
Freshman Class: 1462 applied, 841 accepted, 775 enrolled	
ACT: 24	**VERY COMPETITIVE**

Harding University, founded in 1924, is a private, coeducational Christian institution comprised of the colleges of Arts and Sciences and Bible and Religion and the schools of Business, Education, and Nursing. There are 5 undergraduate and 2 graduate schools. In addition to regional accreditation, Harding has baccalaureate program accreditation with CSWE, NASM, NCATE, and NLN. The library contains 345,000 volumes, 95,598 microform items, and 1372 audiovisual forms, and subscribes to 1319 periodicals. Computerized library sources and services include the card catalog, interlibrary loans, and database searching. Special learning facilities include a learning resource center, art gallery, natural history museum, radio station, and TV station. The 200-acre campus is in a small town 50 miles northeast of Little Rock. Including residence halls, there are 48 buildings on campus.

Student Life: About 72% of undergraduates are from out-of-state, mostly the Southwest. Students come from 50 states, 36 foreign countries, and Canada. Seventy percent are from public schools; 30% from private. Ninety-three percent are white. Most are Protestant. The average age of freshmen is 18; all undergraduates, 21. Twenty-two percent drop out by the end of their first year; 60% remain to graduate.

Housing: A total of 2400 students can be accommodated in college housing. College-sponsored living facilities include single-sex dormitories, on-campus apartments, off-campus apartments, and married-student housing. On-campus housing is guaranteed for all 4 years. Seventy-five percent of students live on campus; of those, 85% remain on campus on weekends. Alcohol is not permitted. All students may keep cars on campus.

Activities: There are 15 local fraternities and local sororities. There are 40 groups on campus, including art, band, cheerleading, choir, chorale, chorus, computers, drama, drill team, ethnic, film, honors, international, jazz band, literary magazine, marching band, musical theater, newspaper, orchestra, pep band, photography, political, professional, radio and TV, religious, social, social service, student government, symphony, and yearbook. Popular campus events include Homecoming, Spring Sing, Parents Weekend, Youth Forum, and May Fete.

Sports: There are 7 intercollegiate sports for men and 5 for women, and 10 intramural sports for men and 10 for women. Athletic and recreation facilities include baseball and softball fields, racquetball, handball, and tennis courts, a football stadium, an indoor and outdoor track, a golf and practice range, a gymnastics and weight room, 2 Olympic-size swimming pools, and 2 gymnasiums.

Disabled Students: Ninety-five percent of the campus is accessible to disabled students. The following facilities are available: wheelchair ramps, elevators, special parking, specially equipped rest rooms, special class scheduling, lowered drinking fountains, and lowered telephones.

Services: In addition to many counseling and information services, tutoring is available in every subject. In addition, there is a reader service for the blind, and remedial math, reading, and writing.

Campus Safety and Security: Campus safety and security measures include 24-hour foot and vehicle patrol, self defense education, informal discussions, and pamphlets, posters, and films. In addition, there are lighted pathways and sidewalks.

Programs of Study: Harding awards the B.A., B.S., B.B.A., B.S.W., B.F.A, B.Mus., B.M.E., and B.S.N. degrees. Master's degrees also are awarded. Bachelor's degrees are awarded in BIOLOGICAL SCIENCE (biology/biological science), BUSINESS (accounting, business administration and management, business economics, international business management, and marketing/retailing/merchandising), COMMUNICATIONS AND THE ARTS (advertising, broadcasting, communications, design, dramatic arts, English, fine arts, French, music, and Spanish), COMPUTER AND PHYSICAL SCIENCE (chemistry, computer programming, computer science, mathematics, and physics), EDUCATION (art, early childhood, elementary, foreign languages, home economics, music, science, and secondary), ENGINEERING AND ENVIRONMENTAL DESIGN (interior design), HEALTH PROFESSIONS (nursing, predentistry, premedicine, and speech pathology/audiology), SOCIAL SCIENCE (dietetics, economics, history, international studies, liberal arts/general studies, ministries, political science/government, prelaw, psychology, religion, social science, social work, and sociology). Business, premedicine, and sciences are the strongest academically. Business and education have the largest enrollments.

Required: All students must complete 52 hours of general education courses, including religion, English composition, history, speech communications, social sciences, biology, physical science, mathematics, Western literature, music and art appreciation, and physical education. A total of 128 semester hours, with a minimum GPA of 2.0, is required in order to graduate.

Special: The Harding campus in Florence, Italy and a program in Athens, Greece offer international studies. Co-op programs in all majors, internships in social work, teaching, nursing, and international missions, work-study programs, dual majors, a general studies degree, and pass/fail options are available. A 3–2 engineering degree is offered with the University of Missouri, Georgia Institute of Technology, and the University of Southern California. Nondegree study is possible. There is a freshman honors program on campus, as well as one national honor society. Thirteen departments have honors programs.

Faculty/Classroom: Eighty percent of faculty are male; 20%, female. All teach undergraduates and 20% also do research. No introductory courses are taught by graduate students. The average class size in an introductory lecture is 60; in a laboratory, 15; and in a regular course offering, 20.

Admissions: About 58% of the 1993–94 applicants were accepted. The ACT scores for the 1993–94 freshman class were as follows: 15% below 21, 20% between 21 and 23, 30% between 24 and 26, 20% between 27 and 28, and 15% above 28. About 50% of the current freshmen were in the top fifth of their class; 85% were in the top two fifths. There were 15 National Merit finalists and 20 semifinalists. Forty-three freshmen graduated first in their class.

Requirements: Harding requires applicants to be in the upper 50% of their class. A minimum GPA of 3.0 is required. The SAT I or ACT is required. Applicants should be graduates of an accredited secondary school, having completed 19 high school hours, including 4 each in English, and mathematics, 3 each in science and social studies, 2 in foreign language, and 3 in art, history, or music. An interview is highly recommended. AP and CLEP credits are accepted. Important factors used in the admissions decision are leadership record, advanced placement or honor courses, evidence of special talent, personality, intangible qualities, and parents or siblings attending the school.

Procedure: Freshmen are admitted to all sessions. Entrance exams should be taken prior to application in the junior year. Early decision applications should be filed by January 1; regular applications, by May 1 for fall entry, along with an application fee of $35. Notification is sent on a rolling basis. There are early decision, early admissions, and deferred admissions plans. About 20 early decision candidates were accepted for the 1993–94 class. A waiting list is an active part of the admissions procedure, with about 20% of applicants on the list.

Transfer: About 175 transfer students enrolled in 1993–94. Transfer applicants with a minimum GPA of 2.0 and at least 14 semester hours earned are considred for admission. An interview is highly recommended. A total of 32 credits out of 128 must be completed at Harding.

Visiting: There are regularly scheduled orientations for prospective students, held in major U.S. cities. There are guides for informal visits and visitors may sit in on classes and stay overnight at the school. To arrange for a visit, contact the Admissions Office at (800) 477–4407.

Financial Aid: In 1993–94, 75% of all current freshmen and 82% of continuing students received some form of financial aid. About 50% of freshmen and 55% of continuing students received need-based aid. The average freshman award was $1500. Of that total, scholarships or need-based grants averaged $1250 ($10,000 maximum); loans averaged $2000 ($4500 maximum); and work contracts averaged $1000 ($2280 maximum). Fifty-five percent of undergraduate students work part-time. Average earnings from campus work for the school year are $1000. The average financial indebtedness of the 1992–93 graduate was $6000. Harding is a member of CSS. The FAF or FFS is required. The deadline for financial aid applications is May 1.

International Students: There are currently 141 international students enrolled. The school actively recruits these students. They must take the TOEFL and achieve a minimum score of 500. The SAT I or ACT is recommended for English-speaking foreign students.

Computers: The college provides computer facilities for student use. The mainframe is a DEC VAX 3600. There are numerous terminals for accessing the mainframe and 200 microcomputers available for student use. Many students have their own computer. All students may access the system. There are no time limits on using the system and no fees.

Graduates: In 1992–93, 565 bachelor's degrees were awarded. The most popular majors among graduates were business management (7%), preprofessional dental, medical, or veterinary science (5%), and elementary education (4%). Within an average freshman class, 10% graduate in 3 years, 50% in 4 years, 10% in 5 years, and 10% in 6 years. Some 114 companies recruited on campus in 1992–93. In the 1992 graduating class, 15% of the men and 14% of the women were enrolled in graduate school within 6 months of graduation; 98% of the men and 98% of the women had found employment.

Admissions Contact: Admissions Services.

HENDERSON STATE UNIVERSITY
B-4

Arkadelphia, AR 71999–0001   (501) 246–5511

Full-time: 1357 men, 1608 women	Faculty: 150; IIB, -$
Part-time: 180 men, 300 women	Ph.D.s: 75%
Graduate: 106 men, 281 women	Student/Faculty: 20 to 1
Year: semesters, summer session	Tuition: $1660 ($3220)
Application Deadline: open	Room & Board: $2200
Freshman Class: 1220 applied, 1100 accepted, 733 enrolled	
ACT: 21	COMPETITIVE

Henderson State University began in 1890 as Arkadelphia Methodist College, an affiliate of the Methodist Church. In 1929, it became a state institution offering liberal arts courses. There are 3 undergraduate schools and one graduate school. In addition to regional accreditation, the university has baccalaureate program accreditation with AACSB, NASM, NCATE, and NLN. The library contains 200,000 volumes and 34,700 microform items, and subscribes to 1564 periodicals. Computerized library sources and services include the card catalog, interlibrary loans, and database searching. Special learning facilities include a natural history museum and radio station. The 125-acre campus is in a small town 60 miles southwest of Little Rock. Including residence halls, there are 32 buildings on campus.

Student Life: About 94% of undergraduates are from Arkansas. Students come from 28 states, 7 foreign countries, and Canada. Eighty-seven percent are white; 13% African American.

Housing: A total of 1300 students can be accommodated in college housing. College-sponsored living facilities include single-sex dormitories and married-student housing. On-campus housing is available on a first-come, first-served basis. Fifty-five percent of students commute. Alcohol is not permitted. All students may keep cars on campus.

Activities: There are 62 groups on campus, including band, cheerleading, choir, chorale, chorus, dance, drama, ethnic, honors, international, jazz band, marching band, musical theater, newspaper, pep band, political, professional, radio and TV, religious, social, social service, student government, and yearbook.

Sports: There are intercollegiate and intramural sports programs for men and women.

Disabled Students: All of the campus is accessible to disabled students. The following facilities are available: wheelchair ramps, elevators, special parking, specially equipped rest rooms, special class scheduling, lowered drinking fountains, and lowered telephones.

Services: There is a remedial reading program.

Campus Safety and Security: Campus safety and security measures include 24-hour foot and vehicle patrol and lighted pathways and sidewalks.

Programs of Study: The university awards the B.A., B.S., B.F.A., B.M., B.M.E., B.S.E., and B.S.N. degrees. Associate and master's degrees also are awarded. Bachelor's degrees are awarded in BIOLOGICAL SCIENCE (biology/biological science), BUSINESS (accounting and business administration and management), COMMUNICATIONS AND THE ARTS (communications, English, fine arts, journalism, music, Spanish, and speech/debate/rhetoric), COMPUTER AND PHYSICAL SCIENCE (chemistry, computer science, mathematics, and physics), EDUCATION (business, elementary, home economics, music, physical, recreation, and secondary), ENGINEERING AND ENVIRONMENTAL DESIGN (preengineering), HEALTH PROFESSIONS (medical laboratory technology, pharmacy, predentistry, premedicine, and speech pathology/audiology), SOCIAL SCIENCE (history, human services, political science/government, prelaw, psychology, and sociology). Elementary education has the largest enrollment.

Required: All students must complete a total of 124 credit hours, including 30 in the major, with a minimum GPA of 2.0. Core requirements include 12 semester hours in social science, 11 in natural science, 9 in English, 6 in humanities, 3 each in mathematics and oral communication, and 2 in physical education or military science.

Special: The university offers co-op programs and cross-registration with Ouachita Baptist University, internships in business and public administration, work-study programs, credit for military experience, nondegree study, and pass/fail options. There is a freshman honors program on campus

Admissions: About 90% of the 1993–94 applicants were accepted. The ACT scores for the 1993–94 freshman class were as follows: 63% below 21, 21% between 21 and 23, 11% between 24 and 26, 3% between 27 and 28, and 2% above 28. About 19% of the current freshmen were in the top fifth of their class; 40% were in the top two fifths.

Requirements: A minimum GPA of 2.5 is required. The ACT is recommended. Applicants need at least 15 academic credits or 15 Carnegie units. Students with a predicted GPA of 1.5 or below will be admitted conditionally. Four units of English, 3 of history, civics, or American government, 2 each of natural science, mathematics, and foreign language, and a half unit of computer science are recommended. AP and CLEP credits are accepted.

Procedure: Freshmen are admitted to all sessions. Entrance exams should be taken during the senior year. Application deadlines are open. Notification is sent on a rolling basis.

Transfer: Transfer applicants with a cumulative GPA below 2.0 will be admitted conditionally. The entire academic record is considered. A total of 30 credits out of 124 must be completed at the university.

Visiting: There are regularly scheduled orientations for prospective students. There are guides for informal visits and visitors may stay overnight at the school. To arrange for a visit, contact Dr. Don Pennington at (501) 246–5511, ext. 3235.

Financial Aid: In 1993–94, 55% of all current freshmen and 68% of continuing students received some form of financial aid. About 49% of freshmen and 55% of continuing students received need-based aid. The average freshman award was $3500. Of that total, scholarships or need-based grants averaged $500 ($3120 maximum); loans averaged $1000 ($2625 maximum); and work contracts averaged $1000 ($2040 maximum). Ten percent of undergraduate students work part-time. The average financial indebtedness of the 1992–93 graduate was $6500. The FFS is required. The deadline for financial aid applications is March 1.

International Students: There are currently 9 international students enrolled. They must take the TOEFL or the University of Michigan Language Test and achieve a minimum score on the TOEFL of 500. The student must also take SAT I or the ACT.

Computers: The college provides computer facilities for student use. All students may access the system. There are no fees.

Graduates: In 1992–93, 510 bachelor's degrees were awarded.

Admissions Contact: Tom Gattin, Registrar and Director of Admissions.

HENDRIX COLLEGE
C-3

Conway, AR 72032   (501) 450–1362; (800) 277–9017 (in-state)

Full-time: 413 men, 535 women	Faculty: 68; IIB, av$
Part-time: 2 men, 4 women	Ph.D.s: 97%
Graduate: none	Student/Faculty: 14 to 1
Year: trimesters	Tuition: $8610
Application Deadline: open	Room & Board: $3060
Freshman Class: 823 applied, 723 accepted, 274 enrolled	
SAT I or ACT: required	COMPETITIVE

Hendrix College, founded in 1876, is a private, coeducational liberal arts college affiliated with the United Methodist Church. In addition to regional accreditation, Hendrix has baccalaureate program accreditation with NASM and NCATE. The library contains 185,517

volumes and 98,495 microform items, and subscribes to 635 periodicals. Special learning facilities include an art gallery and radio station. The 65-acre campus is in a suburban area 25 miles northwest of Little Rock. Including residence halls, there are 25 buildings on campus.

Student Life: About 82% of undergraduates are from Arkansas. Students come from 24 states and 12 foreign countries. Seventy-four percent are from public schools; 26% from private. Ninety-two percent are white. Sixty-seven percent are Protestant; 10% Catholic. The average age of freshmen is 18; all undergraduates, 20. Ten percent drop out by the end of their first year; 60% remain to graduate.

Housing: A total of 825 students can be accommodated in college housing. College-sponsored living facilities include single-sex and coed dormitories and off-campus apartments. In addition there are language houses. On-campus housing is guaranteed for the freshman year only, is available on a first-come, first-served basis, and is available on a lottery system for upperclassmen. Eighty-five percent of students live on campus; of those, 80% remain on campus on weekends. All students may keep cars on campus.

Activities: There are no fraternities or sororities on campus. There are 47 groups on campus, including art, band, cheerleading, chess, choir, chorus, computers, drama, ethnic, gay, honors, international, jazz band, literary magazine, musical theater, newspaper, opera, orchestra, pep band, photography, political, professional, radio and TV, religious, social, social service, student government, and yearbook. Popular campus events include Shirttail Serenade, Candlelight Carol Service, Basketball Homecoming, Kampus Kitty Week, and language house programs.

Sports: There are 9 intercollegiate sports for men and 7 for women, and 28 intramural sports for men and 28 for women. Athletic and recreation facilities include a 1600-seat gymnasium, an indoor activity center, intramural football and softball fields, and a nature fitness trail.

Disabled Students: Ninety-five percent of the campus is accessible to disabled students. The following facilities are available: wheelchair ramps, elevators, special parking, and specially equipped rest rooms.

Services: In addition to many counseling and information services, tutoring is available in some subjects.

Campus Safety and Security: Campus safety and security measures include 24-hour foot and vehicle patrol, escort service, informal discussions, and pamphlets, posters, and films. In addition, there are lighted pathways and sidewalks.

Programs of Study: Hendrix awards the B.A. degree. Bachelor's degrees are awarded in BIOLOGICAL SCIENCE (biology/ biological science), BUSINESS (accounting and business economics), COMMUNICATIONS AND THE ARTS (dramatic arts, English, fine arts, French, German, music, and Spanish), COMPUTER AND PHYSICAL SCIENCE (chemistry, mathematics, and physics), EDUCATION (art, elementary, music, and science), ENGINEERING AND ENVIRONMENTAL DESIGN (preengineering), HEALTH PROFESSIONS (predentistry, premedicine, and prepharmacy), SOCIAL SCIENCE (economics, history, international relations, philosophy, political science/government, prelaw, psychology, religion, social science, and sociology). Chemistry, mathematics, English, economics, business, political science, and biology are the strongest academically. Biology, economics, and business have the largest enrollments.

Required: Students must complete a total of 36 credits with a 2.0 GPA and a departmental comprehensive examination to graduate. Core requirements include a 2-term sequence in Western traditions and 2 terms of other cultural or linguistic traditions, as well as 3 courses each in humanities, natural sciences, and social sciences. English composition or literature is also required.

Special: Internships and work-study may be arranged in business, health care, and communications. The college offers 3–2 engineering programs with Columbia, Vanderbilt, and Washington universities. A Washington semester, study abroad, student-designed integrative majors, and a general studies degree are available. There are 3 national honor societies on campus. All departments have honors programs.

Faculty/Classroom: Seventy-seven percent of faculty are male; 23%, female. All teach undergraduates. The average class size in an introductory lecture is 18; in a laboratory, 18; and in a regular course offering, 18.

Admissions: About 88% of the 1993–94 applicants were accepted. About 66% of the current freshmen were in the top fifth of their class; 79% were in the top two fifths. There were 10 National Merit finalists and 17 semifinalists.

Requirements: The SAT I or ACT is required. In addition, Hendrix recommends that applicants have completed 4 high school units in English, 3 each in mathematics and social studies, 2 in science, and 1 in a foreign language. The GED is accepted. AP and CLEP credits are accepted. Important factors used in the admissions decision are extracurricular activities record, leadership record, evidence of special talent, personality, intangible qualities, and advanced placement or honor courses.

Procedure: Freshmen are admitted to all sessions. Entrance exams should be taken during the junior year. Application deadlines are open. Application fee is $15. Notification is sent on a rolling basis. There are early admissions and deferred admissions plans. A waiting list is an active part of the admissions procedure.

Transfer: About 20 transfer students enrolled in 1993–94. The SAT I or ACT is required, and an official transcript from all colleges previously attended must be submitted. An interview is recommended. A total of 18 course credits out of 36 must be completed at Hendrix.

Visiting: There are regularly scheduled orientations for prospective students, including attendance at a class, visits with students and faculty, and a campus tour. There are guides for informal visits and visitors may sit in on classes and stay overnight at the school. To arrange for a visit, contact the Office of Admissions at (501) 450–1362 or (800) 277–9017 (in state).

Financial Aid: In 1993–94, 74% of all current freshmen and 73% of continuing students received some form of financial aid. About 50% students received need-based aid. The average freshman award was $9298. Of that total, scholarships or need-based grants averaged $3325; loans averaged $2100 ($2659 maximum); and work contracts averaged $1453. Forty-five percent of undergraduate students work part-time. Average earnings from campus work for the school year are $1453. Hendrix is a member of CSS. The FAFSA financial statement is required. The deadline for financial aid applications is April 1.

International Students: There are currently 20 international students enrolled. The school actively recruits these students. They must take the TOEFL and achieve a minimum score of 600. The student must also take the SAT I or the ACT.

Computers: The college provides computer facilities for student use. The mainframe is a DEC VAX 6240 time-sharing system. There are computer laboratories utilizing 40 Apple, Macintosh, and IBM PC-compatible microcomputers. All students may access the system to at least midnight, 7 days a week. There are no time limits on using the system and no fees.

Graduates: In a recent year, 215 bachelor's degrees were awarded. The most popular majors among graduates were economics/ business/accounting (18%), biology (16%), and psychology (13%). Within an average freshman class, 60% graduate in 4 years. Some 75 companies recruited on campus in a recent year. In the 1992 graduating class, 45% of the men and women were enrolled in graduate school within 6 months of graduation.

Admissions Contact: Caroline Kelsey, Vice President for Enrollment.

JOHN BROWN UNIVERSITY
A-1
Siloam Springs, AR 72761

(501) 524-3131
(800) 634-6969, ext. 150 (out-of-state)

Full-time, part-time: 1061 men and women	**Faculty:** 65; IIB, --$
	Ph.D.s: 70%
Graduate: none	**Student/Faculty:** 14 to 1
Year: semesters	**Tuition:** $6520
Application Deadline: open	**Room & Board:** $3360
Freshman Class: 1061 enrolled	
SAT I Verbal/Math: 1020 composite	**ACT:** 23 **VERY COMPETITIVE**

John Brown University, founded in 1919, is a private, nondenominational Christian institution offering undergraduate programs in arts and literature, Bible studies, business, communication, engineering and technology, general studies, health promotion and human performance, natural science, social studies, and teacher education. In addition to regional accreditation, the university has baccalaureate program accreditation with NCATE. The library contains 95,000 volumes, 30,000 microform items, and 3000 audiovisual forms, and subscribes to 450 periodicals. Computerized library sources and services include interlibrary loans and database searching. Special learning facilities include a learning resource center, radio station, TV station, and a wellness assessment laboratory. The 200-acre campus is in a small town 80 miles east of Tulsa, Oklahoma. Including residence halls, there are 15 buildings on campus.

Student Life: About 58% of undergraduates are from out-of-state, mostly the Southwest. Students come from 44 states, 35 foreign countries, and Canada. About 88% are white; 10% foreign nationals; most are Protestant. The average age of freshmen is 19; all undergraduates, 21. Twenty-four percent drop out by the end of their first year; 45% remain to graduate.

Housing: A total of 750 students can be accommodated in college housing. College-sponsored living facilities include single-sex dormitories, on-campus apartments, off-campus apartments, and married-student housing. On-campus housing is guaranteed for the freshman year only. Seventy-five percent of students live on campus; of those, 80% remain on campus on weekends. Alcohol is not permitted. All students may keep cars on campus.

Activities: There are no fraternities or sororities on campus. There are many groups and organizations on campus, including band, cheerleading, choir, chorale, chorus, drama, ethnic, honors, newspaper, pep band, photography, radio and TV, religious, student government, and yearbook. Popular campus events include Christmas Candlelight Service, Spiritual Emphasis Week, Welcome banquet, Homecoming, and Marriage and Family Emphasis Week.

Sports: Athletic and recreation facilities include a 1500-seat gymnasium, soccer and softball fields, a baseball diamond, a training room, and a swimming pool. The Lifetime Health Complex includes an indoor track, 4 racquetball courts, a Nautilus fitness center, an aerobic room, and a 3-court recreation center.

Disabled Students: Seventy percent of the campus is accessible to disabled students. The following facilities are available: wheelchair ramps, elevators, special parking, specially equipped rest rooms, special class scheduling, and lowered drinking fountains and telephones.

Services: In addition to many counseling and information services, tutoring is available in most subjects and there is remedial math, reading, and writing.

Campus Safety and Security: Campus safety and security measures include escort service, informal discussions, and lighted pathways and sidewalks.

Programs of Study: The university awards the B.A., B.S., B.S.E., B.Mus.Ed., and B.Mus. degrees. Associate degrees also are awarded. Bachelor's degrees are awarded in BIOLOGICAL SCIENCE (biochemistry and biology/biological science), BUSINESS (accounting, business administration and management, and office supervision and management), COMMUNICATIONS AND THE ARTS (art, broadcasting, design, English, journalism, music, and public relations), COMPUTER AND PHYSICAL SCIENCE (chemistry, mathematics, and science), EDUCATION (business, early childhood, elementary, music, physical, science, and secondary), ENGINEERING AND ENVIRONMENTAL DESIGN (construction management, electrical/electronics engineering, and engineering), HEALTH PROFESSIONS (community health work, medical laboratory technology, and sports medicine), SOCIAL SCIENCE (biblical studies, crosscultural studies, family and community services, history, interdisciplinary studies, international studies, ministries, pastoral studies, prelaw, psychology, social studies, theological studies, and youth ministry). Engineering and teacher education are the strongest academically. Business, broadcasting, and psychology have the largest enrollments.

Required: All students must complete general education courses, including 12 hours in Bible studies, 9 in general education, 6 each in English and science, and 3 each in American history and humanities. Competencies in communication and quantitative skills, physical fitness concepts, and health and hygiene courses are also required. A total of 124 semester hours, with a minimum GPA of 2.0 (2.25 in teacher education and engineering), is required in order to graduate.

Special: Internships or field experiences are available in most majors. Study abroad in 3 countries, a Washington semester, and pass/fail options are offered. There is a freshman honors program on campus, as well as one national honor society.

Faculty/Classroom: Seventy percent of faculty are male; 30%, female and all teach undergraduates. The average class size in an introductory lecture is 40; in a laboratory, 25; and in a regular course offering, 30.

Admissions: There were 2 National Merit finalists and 2 semifinalists. About 11 freshmen graduated first in their class.

Requirements: The university requires applicants to be in the upper 50% of their class. A minimum GPA of 2.5 is required, as well as the SAT I or ACT. Applicants should have completed 14 high school units, including 4 in English, 3 in mathematics, 2 each in science, history, and foreign language, and 1 in social studies. Two references are required: one from a high school counselor or teacher, the other from a pastor or church leader. An essay and an interview are recommended. AP and CLEP credits are accepted. Important factors used in the admissions decision are advanced placement or honor courses, leadership record, evidence of special talent, parents or siblings attending the school, and recommendations by alumni.

Procedure: Freshmen are admitted fall and spring. Entrance exams should be taken during spring of the junior year or fall of the senior year. Application deadlines are open. Application fee is $25. Notification is sent on a rolling basis. There is an early admissions plan. A waiting list is an active part of the admissions procedure.

Transfer: About 92 transfer students enrolled in 1993–94. Transfer applicants must have completed at least 12 units of college work, with at least 9 transferable, and a minimum 2.0 GPA. A total of 36 credits out of 124 must be completed at the university.

Visiting: There are regularly scheduled orientations for prospective students, including campus tours, consultations with faculty and coaches, and examination of financial aid opportunities. There are guides for informal visits and visitors may sit in on classes and stay overnight at the school. To arrange for a visit, contact the Admissions Office at (800) 634-6969.

Financial Aid: Recently, 78% of all current freshmen and 81% of continuing students received some form of financial aid. About 70% of freshmen and 72% of continuing students received need-based aid. The average freshman award was $5100. Of that total, scholarships or need-based grants averaged $1500 ($5300 maximum); loans averaged $1970 ($2625 maximum); and work contracts averaged $1300. Forty-five percent of undergraduate students work part-time. Average earnings from campus work for the school year are $1300. The average financial indebtedness of the 1992–93 graduate was $4500. the university is a member of CSS. The FAF or FFS is required. The deadline for financial aid applications is April 15.

International Students: There are currently 111 international students enrolled. They must take the TOEFL and achieve a minimum score of 500.

Computers: The college provides computer facilities for student use. There are 80 IBM PCs and 20 Macintoshes in 4 computer rooms, and local area networks are available. All students may access the system. It may be used from 7:30 A.M. to 10:30 P.M. daily. There are no time limits on using the system. The fees are $15 per semester.

Graduates: In a recent year, 175 bachelor's degrees were awarded. The most popular majors among graduates were business (28%), Communications (14%), and education (14%). Within an average freshman class, 41% graduate in 4 years. Some 20 companies recruited on campus in 1992–93.

Admissions Contact: Don Crandall, Vice-President of Enrollment Management.

OUACHITA BAPTIST UNIVERSITY
B-4
Arkadelphia, AR 71923

(501) 246-4531, ext. 110
(800) 342-5628 (out-of-state)

Full-time: 648 men, 662 women	Faculty: 85; IIB, -$
Part-time: 29 men, 32 women	Ph.D.s: 65%
Graduate: none	Student/Faculty: 15 to 1
Year: semesters, summer session	Tuition: $6180
Application Deadline: open	Room & Board: $2760
Freshman Class: 910 applied, 700 accepted, 450 enrolled	
ACT: 23	COMPETITIVE

Ouachita Baptist University, founded in 1886, is a private coeducational liberal arts institution affiliated with the Arkansas Baptist State Convention. There are 3 undergraduate schools. In addition to regional accreditation, Ouachita has baccalaureate program accreditation with NASM and NCATE. The 2 libraries contain 130,000 volumes and 350,000 microform items, and subscribe to 1100 periodicals. Computerized library sources and services include the card catalog, interlibrary loans, and database searching. Special learning facilities include a learning resource center, art gallery, and planetarium. The 60-acre campus is in a small town 65 miles west of Little Rock. Including residence halls, there are 32 buildings on campus.

Student Life: About 80% of undergraduates are from Arkansas. Students come from 32 states and 25 foreign countries. Ninety-two percent are from public schools; 8% from private. Ninety-three percent are white. Most are Protestant. The average age of freshmen is 18; all undergraduates, 21. Twenty-four percent drop out by the end of their first year; 50% remain to graduate.

Housing: A total of 1100 students can be accommodated in college housing. College-sponsored living facilities include single-sex dormitories, on-campus apartments, off-campus apartments, and married-student housing. On-campus housing is guaranteed for the freshman year only and is available on a first-come, first-served basis. Eighty-two percent of students live on campus; of those, 60% remain on campus on weekends. Alcohol is not permitted. All students may keep cars on campus.

Activities: About 30% of men belong to 4 local fraternities; about 30% of women belong to 4 local sororities. There are 30 groups on campus, including band, cheerleading, choir, chorale, chorus, computers, drama, drill team, ethnic, film, honors, international, jazz band, marching band, musical theater, newspaper, opera, orchestra, pep band, photography, political, professional, religious, social, social service, student government, and yearbook. Popular campus events include Homecoming, International Student Fair, Tiger Tunes, and Tiger Traks.

Sports: There are 8 intercollegiate sports for men and 3 for women, and 5 intramural sports for men and 5 for women. Athletic and recreation facilities include a 6000-seat football stadium, an athletic complex featuring a 2500-seat basketball arena, volleyball and racquetball courts, a swimming pool, and a weight room.

Disabled Students: One percent of the campus is accessible to disabled students. The following facilities are available: wheelchair ramps, elevators, special parking, and special class scheduling.

Services: In addition to many counseling and information services, tutoring is available in most subjects. There is also a reader service for the blind and remedial math, reading, and writing.

Campus Safety and Security: Campus safety and security measures include 24-hour foot and vehicle patrol, informal discussions, pamphlets, posters, and films, and emergency telephones. In addition, there are lighted pathways and sidewalks.

Programs of Study: Ouachita awards the B.A., B.S., B.M., B.M.E., and B.S.E. degrees. Bachelor's degrees are awarded in BIOLOGICAL SCIENCE (biology/biological science), BUSINESS (accounting, banking and finance, business administration and management, business economics, marketing and distribution, and office supervision and management), COMMUNICATIONS AND THE ARTS (communications, English, fine arts, French, music, photography, Spanish, and speech/debate/rhetoric), COMPUTER AND PHYSICAL SCIENCE (chemistry, computer science, mathematics, and physics), EDUCATION (art, business, early childhood, elementary, foreign languages, health, home economics, middle school, music, science, and secondary), HEALTH PROFESSIONS (medical laboratory technology, predentistry, premedicine, and speech pathology/audiology), SOCIAL SCIENCE (dietetics, economics, history, philosophy, political science/government, prelaw, psychology, religion, and sociology). Business, music, and education are the strongest academically. Education and business have the largest enrollments.

Required: All students must fulfill 44 semester hours of general education courses, including 2 semesters of 1 foreign language, 7 chapel credits, and 4 semester hours of physical education. A passing grade must be received in the sophomore composition exam. A total of 128 semester hours, with a minimum GPA of 2.0, is required in order to graduate.

Special: Cross-registration is offered with Henderson State University. A Washington semester for political science majors, internships and co-op programs for business majors, B.A.-B.S. degrees, dual majors, and pass/fail options are available. Nondegree study is possible. Numerous study abroad opportunities are available in summer and there are exchange programs (one semester or more) with Germany, England, Russia, Japan, China, and Kazakhstan. There is a freshman honors program on campus

Faculty/Classroom: Sixty-five percent of faculty are male; 35%, female. All teach undergraduates. The average class size in an introductory lecture is 30; in a laboratory, 20; and in a regular course offering, 20.

Admissions: About 77% of the 1993–94 applicants were accepted. The ACT scores for the 1993–94 freshman class were as follows: 31% below 21, 25% between 21 and 23, 24% between 24 and 26, 8% between 27 and 28, and 12% above 28. There were 8 National Merit finalists and 25 semifinalists. About 36 freshmen graduated first in their class.

Requirements: Ouachita requires applicants to be in the upper 50% of their class. A minimum GPA of 2.5 is required. The SAT I or ACT is required. Applicants should have completed 19 high school units, including 4 in English, 2 each in science and history, and 1 each in mathematics, social studies, and foreign language. AP and CLEP credits are accepted. Important factors used in the admissions decision are personality, intangible qualities, leadership record, advanced placement or honor courses, geographic diversity, and extracurricular activities record.

Procedure: Freshmen are admitted to all sessions. Entrance exams should be taken in the junior year of high school. Application deadlines are open. Notification is sent on a rolling basis. There are early decision, early admissions, and deferred admissions plans. The application fee is $30. About 10 early decision candidates were accepted for the 1993–94 class.

Transfer: About 110 transfer students enrolled in 1993–94. Transfer applicants must be eligible to return to their previous school. A total of 30 credits out of 128 must be completed at Ouachita.

Visiting: There are regularly scheduled orientations for prospective students, including a campus tour and a question-and-answer session, and meetings with professors and students. There are guides for informal visits and visitors may sit in on classes and stay overnight at the school. To arrange for a visit, contact the Admissions Counseling Office at (800) 342-5628.

Financial Aid: In 1993–94, 50% of all current freshmen and 75% of continuing students received some form of financial aid. About 50% of freshmen and 50% of continuing students received need-based aid. The average freshman award was $4900. Fifty percent of undergraduate students work part-time. Average earnings from campus work for the school year are $1400. The FAF, FFS or SFS is required. The deadline for financial aid applications is May 1.

International Students: There are currently 50 international students enrolled. The school actively recruits these students. They must take the TOEFL and achieve a minimum score of 550. The student must also take the SAT I or the ACT.

Computers: The college provides computer facilities for student use. The mainframe is a Digital. There are 5 computer laboratories available to students. All academic departments have microcomputers. All students may access the system. There are no fees.

Graduates: In 1992–93, 225 bachelor's degrees were awarded. The most popular majors among graduates were education (24%), business related (20%), and religion (11%). Within an average freshman class, 50% graduate in 4 years. Some 30 companies recruited on campus in 1992–93. In the 1992 graduating class, 16% of the students were enrolled in graduate school within 6 months of graduation.

Admissions Contact: Randy Garner, Director of Admissions Counseling.

PHILANDER SMITH COLLEGE
Little Rock, AR 72202

C-3
(501) 370-5219

Full-time: 326 men, 393 women	Faculty: 34
Part-time: 86 men, 110 women	Ph.D.s: n/av
Graduate: none	Student/Faculty: 21 to 1
Year: semesters, summer session	Tuition: $2958
Application Deadline: June 15	Room & Board: $2476
Freshman Class: n/av	
ACT: 18	**NONCOMPETITIVE**

Philander Smith College, founded in 1877, is affiliated with the United Methodist Church. The college offers undergraduate degrees in education, humanities, natural and physical sciences, business, and social science. The library contains 83,000 volumes, 171 microform items, and 56 audiovisual forms, and subscribes to 365 periodicals. Computerized library sources and services include interlibrary loans. The 25-acre campus is in an urban area in Little Rock. Including residence halls, there are 14 buildings on campus.

Student Life: About 82% of undergraduates are from Arkansas. Thirty-eight percent drop out by the end of their first year; 31% remain to graduate.

Housing: A total of 220 students can be accommodated in college housing. In addition, there are apartments available for married students. Alcohol is not permitted.

Activities: There are 16 groups on campus, including art, drama, newspaper, pep band, religious, student government, and yearbook. Popular campus events include Religious Emphasis Week Observance.

Sports: Athletic and recreation facilities include a gymnasium with a basketball court, an athletic field, a student union, and activity rooms.

Services: In addition, there is remedial math, reading, and writing. Mini-workshops are offered for test-taking, problem solving, and term paper preparation.

Programs of Study: Philander Smith awards the B.A., B.S., and B.A.M. degrees. Bachelor's degrees are awarded in BIOLOGICAL SCIENCE (biology/biological science), BUSINESS (business administration and management, business economics, and office supervision and management), COMMUNICATIONS AND THE ARTS (English and music), COMPUTER AND PHYSICAL SCIENCE (chemistry and mathematics), EDUCATION (Christian Education, elementary, health, and special), SOCIAL SCIENCE (economics, home economics, philosophy, political science/government, psychology, social work, and sociology).

Required: In order to graduate, all students must complete at least 124 credit hours with a minimum 2.0 GPA and satisfy general education requirements. Students must pass an English proficiency test in usage, speech, and writing, and take the Graduate Record Examination during their senior year. Other requirements apply.

Special: There are 2 national honor societies on campus.

Admissions: The ACT scores for the 1993–94 freshman class were as follows: 99% below 21. About 10% of the current freshmen were in the top fifth of their class; 25% were in the top two fifths.

Requirements: A minimum GPA of 2.0 is required. The ACT is required. Applicants must be graduates of an accredited secondary school or have a GED certificate. Students should have completed 16 academic credits, including 4 units of English, 2 of mathematics, and 2 from 2 of the following: foreign language, science, or social studies. AP and CLEP credits are accepted.

Procedure: Applications should be filed by June 15 for fall entry, October 15 for spring entry, and May 15 for summer entry. The application fee is $5. The college accepts all in-state residents who apply. Notification is sent on a rolling basis. There is an early admissions plan.

Visiting: To arrange for a visit, contact the Admissions Office.

Financial Aid: In an earlier year, 60% of continuing students received some form of financial aid. Philander Smith is a member of CSS. The FFS is required.

International Students: They must take the TOEFL. The student must also take the ACT.

Graduates: In 1992–93, 65 bachelor's degrees were awarded.

Admissions Contact: Picola P. Smith, Director of Admissions.

SOUTHERN ARKANSAS UNIVERSITY

B-5

Magnolia, AR 71753 (501) 235-4040

Full-time: 1026 men, 1238 women	Faculty: 128; IIB, -$
Part-time: 95 men, 289 women	Ph.D.s: 51%
Graduate: 33 men, 104 women	Student/Faculty: 18 to 1
Year: semesters, summer session	Tuition: $1232 ($1940)
Application Deadline: open	Room & Board: $2200
Freshman Class: 792 applied, 792 accepted, 532 enrolled	
ACT: required	NONCOMPETITIVE

Southern Arkansas University, founded in 1909, is a state-supported coeducational liberal arts institution offering undergraduate and graduate degrees in business administration, education, liberal and performing arts, and science and technology. There are 4 undergraduate schools and one graduate school. In addition to regional accreditation, SAU has baccalaureate program accreditation with NASAD, NASM, and NCATE. The library contains 152,198 volumes, 93,059 microform items, and 5980 audiovisual forms, and subscribes to 906 periodicals. Computerized library sources and services include the card catalog, interlibrary loans, and database searching. Special learning facilities include a learning resource center and radio station. The 781-acre campus is in a small town 2 miles north of Magnolia. Including residence halls, there are 27 buildings on campus.

Student Life: About 78% of undergraduates are from Arkansas. Students come from 41 states, 17 foreign countries, and Canada. Ninety-nine percent are from public schools; 1% from private. Seventy-seven percent are white; 20% African American. The average age of freshmen is 19; all undergraduates, 27. Forty percent drop out by the end of their first year; 30% remain to graduate.

Housing: A total of 1068 students can be accommodated in college housing. College-sponsored living facilities include single-sex dormitories and married-student housing. On-campus housing is guaranteed for all 4 years. Fifty-five percent of students commute. Alcohol is not permitted. All students may keep cars on campus.

Activities: About 10% of men belong to 7 national fraternities; about 10% of women belong to 7 national sororities. There are 50 groups on campus, including art, band, cheerleading, choir, chorale, computers, drama, drill team, honors, international, jazz band, marching band, musical theater, newspaper, pep band, photography, political, professional, religious, social, student government, and yearbook. Popular campus events include Spring Fling and Celebration of Lights (Christmas).

Sports: There are 5 intercollegiate sports for men and 5 for women, and 15 intramural sports for men and 15 for women. Athletic and recreation facilities include a 6500-seat stadium, and a 2500-seat gymnasium.

Disabled Students: Forty percent of the campus is accessible to disabled students. The following facilities are available: wheelchair ramps, elevators, special parking, specially equipped rest rooms, special class scheduling, lowered drinking fountains, and lowered telephones.

Services: In addition to many counseling and information services, tutoring is available in most subjects. In addition, there is remedial math, reading, and writing.

Campus Safety and Security: Campus safety and security measures include 24-hour foot and vehicle patrol, informal discussions, pamphlets, posters, and films, and emergency telephones. In addition, there are lighted pathways and sidewalks.

Programs of Study: SAU awards the B.A., B.S., B.M.E., B.B.A. and B.S.E. degrees. Associate and master's degrees also are awarded. Bachelor's degrees are awarded in BIOLOGICAL SCIENCE (biology/biological science), BUSINESS (accounting, banking and finance, business administration and management, business economics, business law, marketing/retailing/merchandising, and personnel management), COMMUNICATIONS AND THE ARTS (advertising, broadcasting, communications, English, French, journalism, music, Spanish, and speech/debate/rhetoric), COMPUTER AND PHYSICAL SCIENCE (chemistry, computer programming, computer science, earth science, and mathematics), EDUCATION (business, early childhood, elementary, guidance, health, middle school, music, science, secondary, and teaching English as a second language/foreign language), HEALTH PROFESSIONS (medical laboratory technology, nursing, predentistry, and premedicine), SOCIAL SCIENCE (community services, economics, geography, and history). Business and nursing are the strongest academically.

Required: All students must complete 43 semester hours of general education courses, including humanities, social sciences, mathematics, natural science, and physical and health education. A total of 124 semester hours, with a minimum GPA of 2.0, is required in order to graduate.

Special: Work-study programs at SAU and a general studies degree are offered. There is a freshman honors program on campus, as well as 1 national honor society, Phi Beta Kappa.

Faculty/Classroom: Fifty-one percent of faculty are male; 49%, female. Ninety percent teach undergraduates, and 10% also do research. No introductory courses are taught by graduate students. The average class size in an introductory lecture is 35; in a laboratory, 50; and in a regular course offering, 35.

Admissions: About 37% of the 1993–94 applicants were accepted. The ACT scores for the 1993–94 freshman class were as follows: 71% below 21, 18% between 21 and 23, 9% between 24 and 26, and 1% between 27 and 28. About 20% of the current freshmen were in the top fifth of their class; 42% were in the top two fifths. There were 4 National Merit semifinalists. Six freshmen graduated first in their class.

Requirements: The ACT is required. Applicants should have completed 4 high school units in English, 3 each in mathematics, science and history, and 2 in social studies. AP and CLEP credits are accepted. Important factors used in the admissions decision are recommendations by school officials, leadership record, personality, intangible qualities, advanced placement or honor courses, and evidence of special talent.

Procedure: Freshmen are admitted to all sessions. Entrance exams should be taken in the fall prior to enrollment. Application deadlines are open. The university accepts all applicants. Notification is sent on a rolling basis. There is an early admissions plan.

Transfer: About 170 transfer students enrolled in 1993–94. Applicants must be eligible to return to the school from which they are transferring. A total of 30 credits out of 124 must be completed at SAU.

Visiting: There are regularly scheduled orientations for prospective students. There are guides for informal visits and visitors may sit in on classes. To arrange for a visit, contact the admissions office at (501) 235-4040.

Financial Aid: In 1993–94, 58% of all current freshmen and 62% of continuing students received some form of financial aid. About 48% of freshmen and 53% of continuing students received need-based aid. The average freshman award was $1200. Of that total, scholarships or need-based grants averaged $1050. Most undergraduate students work part-time. Average earnings from campus work for the school year are $1800. The FFS is required. The deadline for financial aid applications is August 1.

International Students: There are currently 47 international students enrolled. The school actively recruits these students. They must take the TOEFL and achieve a minimum score of 500. The student must also take the SAT I or the ACT.

Computers: The university provides computer facilities for student use. The mainframe is a DEC 1500. All students may access the system in the afternoon or early morning. There are no time limits on using the system and no fees.

Graduates: In 1992–93, 262 bachelor's degrees were awarded. The most popular majors among graduates were nursing (30%), elementary education (10%), and accounting (6%). Some 60 companies recruited on campus in 1992–93.

Admissions Contact: James E. Whittington, Jr. Director of Undergraduate Admissions.

UNIVERSITY OF ARKANSAS SYSTEM

The University of Arkansas system, established in 1871, is a system in Arkansas. It is governed by a board of trustees, whose chief administrator is president. The primary goals of the system are teaching, research, and public service. The total enrollment of all 5 campuses usually exceeds 32,000, with more than 2300 faculty members. Altogether there are 236 baccalaureate, 112 master's, and 30 doctoral programs offered in the system. Profiles of the 4-year campuses, located at Fayetteville, Little Rock, Pine Bluff, and Monticello, are included in this chapter.

UNIVERSITY OF ARKANSAS AT FAYETTEVILLE

A-1

Fayetteville, AR 72701 (501) 575-5346; (800) 632-0035 (in-state)

Full-time: 5466 men, 4512 women	Faculty: 732; I, --$
Part-time: 722 men, 808 women	Ph.D.s: 79%
Graduate: 1360 men, 1052 women	Student/Faculty: 14 to 1
Year: semesters, summer session	Tuition: $1946 ($4970)
Application Deadline: August 15	Room & Board: $3100
Freshman Class: 3700 applied, 3500 accepted, 2350 enrolled	
SAT I or ACT: required	COMPETITIVE

The University of Arkansas, founded in 1871, is a land-grant institution and part of the University of Arkansas System. It offers undergraduate and graduate programs in liberal arts and sciences, agriculture, home economics, business administration, engineering, architecture, and education. There are 6 undergraduate schools and one graduate school. In addition to regional accreditation, the university has baccalaureate program accreditation with AACSB, ABET, ACEJMC, ADA, AHEA, ASLA, CSWE, NAAB, NASM, NCATE, and NLN. The 6 libraries contain 123,782 volumes, 1,342,017 microform

items, and 11,805 audiovisual forms, and subscribe to 16,088 periodicals. Computerized library sources and services include the card catalog, interlibrary loans, and database searching. Special learning facilities include a learning resource center, art gallery, natural history museum, planetarium, radio station, and numerous research centers. The 329-acre campus is in an urban area in a small city 180 miles northwest of Little Rock. Including residence halls, there are 167 buildings on campus.

Student Life: About 84% of undergraduates are from Arkansas. Students come from 45 states and 51 foreign countries. Eighty-two percent are from public schools; 5% from private. Eighty-nine percent are white. The average age of freshmen is 19; all undergraduates, 21. About 32% of freshmen remain to graduate.

Housing: A total of 4300 students can be accommodated in college housing. College-sponsored living facilities include single-sex and coed dormitories, on-campus apartments, and married-student housing. In addition there are honors and special interest floors. On-campus housing is guaranteed for all 4 years. Seventy-eight percent of students commute. Alcohol is not permitted. All students may keep cars on campus.

Activities: About 23% of men belong to 21 national fraternities; about 23% of women belong to 12 national sororities. There are 200 groups on campus, including art, band, cheerleading, chess, choir, chorale, chorus, computers, dance, drama, drill team, ethnic, film, gay, honors, international, marching band, newspaper, opera, orchestra, pep band, photography, political, professional, radio and TV, religious, social, social service, student government, symphony, and yearbook. Popular campus events include Homecoming and Academic Festival.

Sports: Athletic and recreation facilities include a 51,500-seat stadium, 4 gymnasiums, indoor and outdoor jogging tracks, 2 dance studios, 10 racquetball courts, a fitness and weight training center, 2 swimming pools, an outdoor recreation center, 18 tennis courts, and 10 multipurpose playing fields.

Disabled Students: The entire campus is accessible to disabled students. The following facilities are available: wheelchair ramps, elevators, special parking, special class scheduling, lowered drinking fountains, and lowered telephones.

Services: In addition to many counseling and information services, tutoring is available in some subjects. In addition, there is a reader service for the blind, and remedial math, reading, and writing. Tutoring also is offered through the Learning Laboratory and the Model Student Program.

Campus Safety and Security: Campus safety and security measures include escort service and foot and vehicle patrol, crime prevention lectures, property engraving, and key checks in residence halls.

Programs of Study: The university awards the B.A., B.S., B.S.Ag., B.Arch., B.F.A., B.M., B.S.Ag.E., B.S.Bus.Adm., B.S.Ch.E., B.S.C.I.E., B.S.Comp.E., B.S.E., B.S.E.E., B.S.H.E., B.S.I.E., B.S.I.M., B.S.M.E., and B.S.P.A. degrees. Associate, master's, and doctoral degrees also are awarded. Bachelor's degrees are awarded in AGRICULTURE (agricultural business management, agricultural economics, agricultural mechanics, agriculture, animal science, dairy science, horticulture, plant protection (pest management), and poultry science), BIOLOGICAL SCIENCE (botany, microbiology, and zoology), BUSINESS (accounting, banking and finance, business administration and management, business economics, fashion merchandising, international business management, marketing management, marketing/retailing/merchandising, personnel management, and retailing), COMMUNICATIONS AND THE ARTS (classics, communications, dance, dramatic arts, English, fine arts, French, German, journalism, music, Spanish, and speech/debate/rhetoric), COMPUTER AND PHYSICAL SCIENCE (chemistry, computer science, earth science, geology, mathematics, natural sciences, and physics), EDUCATION (agricultural, art, business, early childhood, elementary, health, home economics, industrial arts, music, physical, recreation, secondary, special, and vocational), ENGINEERING AND ENVIRONMENTAL DESIGN (agricultural engineering, architectural engineering, chemical engineering, civil engineering, computer engineering, electrical/electronics engineering, industrial administration/management, industrial engineering, interior design, landscape architecture/design, mechanical engineering, transportation engineering, and urban design), HEALTH PROFESSIONS (speech pathology/audiology), SOCIAL SCIENCE (anthropology, clothing and textiles management/production/services, criminal justice, dietetics, economics, fashion design and technology, food science, geography, history, home economics, human development, philosophy, political science/government, psychology, public administration, social work, and sociology). Accounting has the largest enrollment.

Required: To graduate, all students must complete at least 124 credit hours, including 6 in freshman English and 3 in American history or government, and maintain a GPA of at least 2.0. No more than 25 percent of grades may be D or below.

Special: Co-op programs and internships are available. Students may study abroad in Japan, Costa Rica, Italy, and other countries. B.A.-B.S. degrees in natural sciences and mathematics, a 3–2 engineering degree, dual majors, and nondegree study also are possible. The university offers a unique graduate program in agricultural law at the National Center for Agricultural Law Research and Information. There is a freshman honors program on campus, as well as 18 national honor societies, including Phi Beta Kappa.

Faculty/Classroom: Eighty-one percent of faculty are male; 19%, female. The average class size in an introductory lecture is 75; in a laboratory, 15; and in a regular course offering, 35.

Admissions: About 95% of the 1993–94 applicants were accepted. About 55% of the current freshmen were in the top fifth of their class; 80% were in the top two fifths. There were 62 National Merit finalists.

Requirements: A minimum GPA of 2.0 is required. The SAT I or ACT is required. In addition, applicants must be graduates of an accredited secondary school with 4 units of English and 3 each of natural science, social studies, and mathematics (including algebra), plus 3 additional years of courses from these areas, a foreign language, or oral communication. The GED is accepted under some circumstances. Students meeting these requirements and presenting a GPA of 2.75 will be admitted unconditionally. Those with a GPA of at least 2.25 may be granted admission under a transitional status. AP and CLEP credits are accepted.

Procedure: Freshmen are admitted fall and spring. Entrance exams should be taken in October or December of the senior year. Applications should be filed by August 15 for fall entry and January 1 for spring entry, along with an application fee of $15. Notification is sent on a rolling basis. There is an early admissions plan.

Transfer: A total of 982 transfer students enrolled in 1993–94. Transfer applicants must present a GPA of 2.0 in all college course work attempted. Those with fewer than 24 transferrable semester credits must meet the requirements of entering freshmen. A total of 30 credits out of 124 must be completed at the university.

Visiting: There are regularly scheduled orientations for prospective students. There are guides for informal visits and visitors may sit in on classes and stay overnight at the school. To arrange for a visit, contact the Admissions Office.

Financial Aid: In a recent year, 32% of all current freshmen and 68% of continuing students received some form of financial aid. Scholarships or need-based grants averaged $650 ($12,000 maximum); and work contracts averaged $67 ($134 maximum). The university is a member of CSS. The FAF, the college's own financial statement, and the Arkansas scholarship application (AAFSSA) are required. The deadline for financial aid applications is April 1.

International Students: There are currently 421 international students enrolled. The school actively recruits these students. They must take the TOEFL and achieve a minimum score of 550. The student must also take the SAT I or ACT. Electrical engineering and computer science engineering plans require a composite score of 1000 on the SAT I or 25 on the ACT, and a Test of Spoken English (TSE) score of 220.

Computers: The university provides computer facilities for student use. The mainframes are an IBM 4381/R14 and an HP 9000/835. More than 350 Apple Macintosh, Zenith, and IBM or IBM-compatible microcomputers are available for academic use in student laboratories and in the computer center. All students may access the system 24 hours daily. There are some time limits, and fees vary by department.

Graduates: In a recent year, 1699 bachelor's degrees were awarded. Some 225 companies recruited on campus.

Admissions Contact: Office of Admissions.

UNIVERSITY OF ARKANSAS AT LITTLE ROCK   C-3
Little Rock, AR 72204   (501) 569–3127

Full-time: 2660 men, 3219 women	Faculty: 481; IIA, -$
Part-time: 1686 men, 2426 women	Ph.D.s: 46%
Graduate: 734 men, 1345 women	Student/Faculty: 12 to 1
Year: semesters, summer session	Tuition: $2054 ($5090)
Application Deadline: August 1	Room: $2365
Freshman Class: 1774 applied, 1330 accepted, 1202 enrolled	
ACT: 19	COMPETITIVE

The University of Arkansas at Little Rock began in 1927 as Little Rock Junior College, took the name of Little Rock University in 1957, and joined the University of Arkansas system in 1969. There are 5 undergraduate and 2 graduate schools. In addition to regional accreditation, UALR has baccalaureate program accreditation with AACSB, ABET, ACEJMC, ASLA, CSWE, NASAD, NASM, NCATE, and NLN. The library contains 367,648 volumes, 691,612 microform items, and 6403 audiovisual forms, and subscribes to 2322 periodicals. Computerized library sources and services include the card catalog, interlibrary loans, and database searching. Special learning facilities include a learning resource center, art gallery, planetarium, radio station, TV station, and a speech and hearing clinic. The 150-acre

campus is in an urban area in Little Rock. Including residence halls, there are 38 buildings on campus.

Student Life: About 94% of undergraduates are from Arkansas. Students come from 44 states, 65 foreign countries, and Canada. Eighty percent are white; 15% African American. The average age of freshmen is 19.6; all undergraduates, 25.7. Forty-one percent drop out by the end of their first year.

Housing: A total of 354 students can be accommodated in college housing. College-sponsored living facilities include coed dormitories and on-campus apartments. In addition there are university-owned rental houses. On-campus housing is available on a first-come, first-served basis. Ninety-seven percent of students commute. Alcohol is not permitted. All students may keep cars on campus.

Activities: About 5% of men belong to 6 national fraternities; about 3% of women belong to 5 national sororities. There are 50 groups on campus, including cheerleading, chess, chorale, dance, drama, honors, jazz band, literary magazine, musical theater, newspaper, opera, pep band, political, professional, radio and TV, religious, social service, and student government. Popular campus events include International Week, Sunshine Days, and Art Spree.

Sports: There are 8 intercollegiate sports for men and 8 for women, and 18 intramural sports for men and 18 for women. Athletic and recreation facilities include a 2000-seat gymnasium, a swimming pool, tennis courts, baseball and intramural fields, a horseshoe pit, a bowling alley, a fitness and weight room, an indoor jogging track, a steam room, a sauna, and basketball, volleyball, and racquetball courts.

Disabled Students: Eighty-five percent of the campus is accessible to disabled students. The following facilities are available: wheelchair ramps, elevators, special parking, specially equipped rest rooms, special class scheduling, lowered drinking fountains, and study rooms.

Services: In addition to many counseling and information services, tutoring is available in every subject. There is also a reader service for the blind, and remedial math, reading, and writing. Also available are a Braille dictionary, typewriter, reading machine, and interpreters.

Campus Safety and Security: Campus safety and security measures include 24-hour foot and vehicle patrol, self defense education, escort service, and informal discussions. In addition, there are emergency telephones, lighted pathways and sidewalks, and a student patrol crime prevention unit.

Programs of Study: UALR awards the B.A., B.S., B.B.A., B.S.E., and B.M. degrees. Associate, master's, and doctoral degrees also are awarded. Bachelor's degrees are awarded in BIOLOGICAL SCIENCE (biology/biological science), BUSINESS (accounting, banking and finance, business administration and management, management science, and marketing/retailing/merchandising), COMMUNICATIONS AND THE ARTS (advertising, art, art history and appreciation, dramatic arts, English, French, journalism, music, radio/television technology, Spanish, technical and business writing, and visual and performing arts), COMPUTER AND PHYSICAL SCIENCE (chemistry, computer science, geology, information sciences and systems, mathematics, and physics), EDUCATION (early childhood, education of the deaf and hearing impaired, elementary, and health), ENGINEERING AND ENVIRONMENTAL DESIGN (computer technology, construction technology, electrical/electronics engineering technology, manufacturing engineering, mechanical engineering technology, and surveying engineering), HEALTH PROFESSIONS (environmental health science, health science, and speech pathology/audiology), SOCIAL SCIENCE (criminal justice, economics, history, international studies, liberal arts/general studies, philosophy, political science/government, psychology, and sociology). Nursing, accounting, and psychology have the largest enrollments.

Required: All students must complete a minimum of 124 credit hours including 45 at the upper level while maintaining a GPA of 2.0. A minimum 44-hour core curriculum must be completed, and distribution requirements include freshman composition, speech and history, 3 hours of mathematics, and 2 hours of leisure science. Each student must complete a major and a minor or a double major. There also is an examination in written English. Language proficiency is required for the B.A., B.M., and B.S.E. degrees.

Special: Study abroad in Mexico, France, Spain, and Austria is available; UALR has exchange relationships with more than 30 countries. In addition, internships, work-study programs with the university, cross-registration with the University of Arkansas Medical School, B.A.-B.S. degrees, a general studies degree, student-designed majors, nondegree study, and pass/fail options are offered. There is a freshman honors program on campus, as well as 3 national honor societies, including Phi Beta Kappa. Six departments have honors programs.

Faculty/Classroom: Fifty-eight percent of faculty are male; 42%, female.

Admissions: About 75% of the 1993–94 applicants were accepted. The ACT scores for the 1993–94 freshman class were as follows: 65% below 21, 18% between 21 and 23, 12% between 24 and 26, 3% between 27 and 28, and 1% above 28.

Requirements: A minimum GPA of 2.0 is required. The SAT I or ACT is required, with minimum composite scores of 750 and 19, respectively. Scores below these or a GPA below 2.0 assigns a student to conditional status, in which the student is limited to 13 hours per semester and developmental courses are required. The GED is accepted. AP and CLEP credits are accepted.

Procedure: Freshmen are admitted to all sessions. Entrance exams should be taken during the fall of the senior year. Applications should be filed by August 1 for fall entry, December 1 for spring entry, and May 1 for summer entry, along with an application fee of $15. Notification is sent on a rolling basis. There are early admissions and deferred admissions plans.

Transfer: About 1050 transfer students enrolled in 1993–94. Transfer applicants must have a minimum college GPA of 2.0. Those students with fewer than 9 college credits must submit minimum composite scores of 750 on the SAT I or 19 on the ACT for unconditional admission. A total of 30 credits out of 124 must be completed at UALR.

Visiting: There are regularly scheduled orientations for prospective students, that take place before each semester and at which attendance is required. There are guides for informal visits and visitors may sit in on classes. To arrange for a visit, contact the Admissions Office at (501) 569–3127.

Financial Aid: In 1993–94, 31% of all current freshmen and 46% of continuing students received some form of financial aid. About 26% of freshmen and 38% of continuing students received need-based aid. Scholarships or need-based grants averaged $1996 (maximum); loans averaged $1300 ($5520 maximum); and work contracts averaged $1500 ($2790 maximum). Four percent of undergraduate students work part-time. Average earnings from campus work for the school year are $1400. The average financial indebtedness of the 1992–93 graduate was $1679. The FFS is required. The deadline for financial aid applications is May 1.

International Students: There are currently 435 international students enrolled. They must take the TOEFL with a minimum score of 500, the University of Michigan Language Test, or the college's own test.

Computers: The college provides computer facilities for student use. The mainframe is a DEC VAX 11/780. There are 3 computing laboratories providing access to the central VAX system and to about 80 terminals and microcomputers. Additionally, there are some 450 terminals and microcomputers in departmental laboratories. Students use the mainframe to access programming languages, electronic mail, and statistical packages. The microcomputers provide word processing, desktop publishing, and CAD/CAM capabilities. All students may access the system. It may be used 24 hours daily. There are no time limits and no fees.

Graduates: In 1992–93 1466 bachelor's degrees were awarded. The most popular majors among graduates were law (7%), psychology (5%), and nursing (5%). Within an average freshman class, 19% graduate in 6 years. Some 80 companies recruited on campus in 1992–93. Twenty-four percent of all 1992 students enrolled in graduate school within 6 months of graduation; 93% had found employment.

Admissions Contact: D. Sue Pine, Director, Office of Admissions.

UNIVERSITY OF ARKANSAS AT MONTICELLO   C-4

Monticello, AR 71655   (501) 460–1026; (800) 844–1826 (in-state)

Full-time: 1013 men, 1112 women	Faculty: 106; IIB, -$
Part-time: 100 men, 225 women	Ph.D.s: 56%
Graduate: 7 men, 55 women	Student/Faculty: 20 to 1
Year: semesters, summer session	Tuition: $1572 ($3492)
Application Deadline: August 15	Room & Board: $2260
Freshman Class: 589 applied, 589 accepted, 524 enrolled	
ACT: 18	NONCOMPETITIVE

The University of Arkansas at Monticello was established in 1909 as the Fourth District Agricultural School. Made part of the public University of Arkansas System in 1971, it provides liberal arts undergraduate courses to a coeducational student body. In addition to regional accreditation, UAM has baccalaureate program accreditation with NASM, NCATE, NLN, and SAF. The library contains 126,229 volumes, 452 microform items, and 957 audiovisual forms, and subscribes to 862 periodicals. Computerized library sources and services include the card catalog, interlibrary loans, and database searching. Special learning facilities include a learning resource center, natural history museum, planetarium, and a university forest and farm. The campus is in a small town 90 miles south of Little Rock. Including residence halls, there are 33 buildings on campus.

Student Life: About 91% of undergraduates are from Arkansas. Students come from 15 states and 3 foreign countries. Almost all are from public schools; 1% from private. Eighty-four percent are white; 14% African American. The average age of freshmen is 19; all undergraduates, 24. Twenty-eight percent drop out by the end of their first year; 26% remain to graduate.

Housing: A total of 532 students can be accommodated in college housing. College-sponsored living facilities include single-sex dormitories and married-student housing. On-campus housing is guaranteed for all 4 years. Sixty-nine percent of students commute. Alcohol is not permitted. All students may keep cars on campus.

Activities: There are 2 local and 5 national fraternities and 1 local and 3 national sororities. There are 56 groups on campus, including band, cheerleading, choir, chorus, honors, marching band, newspaper, orchestra, religious, social, social service, student government, and yearbook. Popular campus events include Forestry Festival, Homecoming, Miss UAM Pageant, Science Fair, Special Olympics, and the All-Campus Talent Show.

Sports: There are 5 intercollegiate sports for men and 4 for women, and 6 intramural sports each for men and women. Athletic and recreation facilities include a 4000-seat stadium, a 2500-seat gymnasium, a swimming pool, tennis and racquetball courts, and facilities for numerous intramural sports.

Disabled Students: Seventy percent of the campus is accessible to disabled students. The following facilities are available: wheelchair ramps, special parking, specially equipped rest rooms, and lowered drinking fountains.

Services: In addition to many counseling and information services, tutoring is available in some subjects. There is also remedial math, reading, and writing.

Campus Safety and Security: Campus safety and security measures include vehicle patrol.

Programs of Study: UAM awards the B.A., B.S., and B.M.Ed. degrees. Associate and master's degrees also are awarded. Bachelor's degrees are awarded in AGRICULTURE (agriculture and forestry and related sciences), BIOLOGICAL SCIENCE (biology/biological science), BUSINESS (accounting, business administration and management, and marketing/retailing/merchandising), COMMUNICATIONS AND THE ARTS (English, fine arts, and music), COMPUTER AND PHYSICAL SCIENCE (chemistry, computer programming, computer science, and mathematics), EDUCATION (business, elementary, music, physical, and special), HEALTH PROFESSIONS (premedicine), SOCIAL SCIENCE (history, political science/government, prelaw, psychology, and social science). Business and forestry are the strongest programs academically. Elementary education has the largest enrollment.

Required: All students are required to complete 124 total semester hours, 30 within their major, and maintain a minimum GPA of 2.0. Distribution requirements include 9 hours in basic sciences, 6 hours each in composition and humanities, and 3 hours each in fine arts, speech, U.S. history or government, psychology or sociology, social science, and mathematics.

Special: Work-study, a general studies degree, credit for military experience, and nondegree study are available. There is one national honor society on campus.

Faculty/Classroom: Seventy-one percent of faculty are male; 29%, female. No introductory courses are taught by graduate students. The average class size in an introductory lecture is 45; in a laboratory, 15; and in a regular course offering, 25.

Admissions: All of the 1993–94 applicants were accepted.

Requirements: The ACT is required. In addition, applicants must have earned 20 academic credits, including 3 in English and 2 in mathematics. The GED is accepted. AP and CLEP credits are accepted.

Procedure: Freshmen are admitted to all sessions. Applications should be filed by August 15 for fall entry, January 2 for spring entry, and May 23 and July 1 for summer entry. The college accepts all applicants.

Transfer: About 228 transfer students enrolled in a recent year. Transfer applicants must have earned a GPA of 1.5 if they have 29 or fewer credit hours, 1.8 for 30 to 59 credits, and 2.0 for 60 or more hours. The ACT or SAT I is also required.

Visiting: There are regularly scheduled orientations for prospective students. There are guides for informal visits, and visitors may sit in on classes and stay overnight at the school. To arrange for a visit, contact the Director of Admissions.

Financial Aid: In a recent year, 56% of all current freshmen and 39% of continuing students received some form of financial aid. Scholarships or need-based grants averaged $2940 ($3524 maximum); loans averaged $1796 ($6000 maximum); and work contracts averaged $1024 ($2890 maximum). The average financial indebtedness of a recent graduate was $2200. UAM is a member of CSS. The FFS is required. The deadline for financial aid applications is July 1.

International Students: There are currently 3 international students enrolled. They must take the TOEFL and achieve a minimum score of 500.

Computers: The college provides computer facilities for student use. The mainframe is a DEC VAX 11/750. There are also 150 Zenith and Macintosh microcomputers available in the computer laboratory and in offices. All students may access the system. There are no time limits and no fees.

Graduates: In a recent year, 246 bachelor's degrees were awarded.

Admissions Contact: JoBeth Johnson, Director of Admissions.

UNIVERSITY OF ARKANSAS AT PINE BLUFF　C-4
Pine Bluff, AR 71601–2799　(501) 543–8000

Full-time: 1263 men, 1731 women	Faculty: 165; IIB, --$
Part-time: 505 men, 516 women	Ph.D.s: 54%
Graduate: 14 men, 46 women	Student/Faculty: 18 to 1
Year: semesters, summer session	Tuition: $1570 ($3394)
Application Deadline: open	Room & Board: $2408
Freshman Class: 2000 applied, 1500 accepted, 900 enrolled	
ACT: required	LESS COMPETITIVE

The University of Arkansas at Pine Bluff, established in 1873 for the well-being of the poorer classes, is an historically black land-grant institution providing a liberal arts education as part of the public University of Arkansas system. There are 5 undergraduate schools and one graduate school. In addition to regional accreditation, the university has baccalaureate program accreditation with AHEA, CSWE, NASM, NCATE, and NLN. The library contains 203,793 volumes and 500 audiovisual forms, and subscribes to 810 periodicals. Computerized library sources and services include interlibrary loans and database searching. Special learning facilities include a learning resource center, art gallery, radio station, and TV station. The 300-acre campus is in a small town 38 miles south of Little Rock. Including residence halls, there are 49 buildings on campus.

Student Life: About 88% of undergraduates are from Arkansas. Eighty-one percent are African American; 17% white. About 28% of freshmen remain to graduate.

Housing: A total of 1226 students can be accommodated in college housing. College-sponsored living facilities include single-sex dormitories. In addition there are honors clusters in the dorms. On-campus housing is guaranteed for all 4 years. Seventy-one percent of students commute. Alcohol is not permitted. All students may keep cars on campus.

Activities: There are 4 local and 4 national fraternities and 4 local and 4 national sororities. There are 65 groups on campus, including art, band, cheerleading, choir, computers, drama, drill team, honors, jazz band, marching band, newspaper, orchestra, political, professional, radio and TV, religious, social, social service, student government, and yearbook. Popular campus events include Homecoming, Founders Day, Spring Emphasis, and Black History Month.

Sports: There are 5 intercollegiate sports for men and 2 for women, and 20 intramural sports for men and 19 for women. Athletic and recreation facilities include a physical education complex that provides activities such as flag football, basketball, volleyball, softball, tennis, handball, racquetball, track and field, and badminton. There also is a swimming pool and a 6,000-seat football stadium.

Disabled Students: The entire campus is accessible to disabled students. The following facilities are available: wheelchair ramps, elevators, special parking, specially equipped rest rooms, and lowered drinking fountains.

Services: In addition to many counseling and information services, tutoring is available in most subjects. In addition, there is remedial math, reading, and writing.

Campus Safety and Security: Campus safety and security measures include 24-hour foot and vehicle patrol, self defense education, escort service, and informal discussions. In addition, there are pamphlets, posters, films, emergency telephones, and lighted pathways and sidewalks. There is a Department of Public Safety and Security on campus.

Programs of Study: The university awards the B.A. and B.S. degrees. Associate and master's degrees also are awarded. Bachelor's degrees are awarded in AGRICULTURE (agricultural economics, agriculture, animal science, and fishing and fisheries), BIOLOGICAL SCIENCE (biology/biological science), BUSINESS (accounting, business administration and management, business economics, fashion merchandising, hotel/motel and restaurant management, and recreation and leisure services), COMMUNICATIONS AND THE ARTS (applied art, English, music, and speech/debate/rhetoric), COMPUTER AND PHYSICAL SCIENCE (chemistry, computer science, mathematics, and physics), EDUCATION (agricultural, art, business, early childhood, elementary, English, home economics, industrial arts, mathematics, music, physical, science, social science, special, and vocational), ENGINEERING AND ENVIRONMENTAL DESIGN (industrial engineering technology, occupational safety and health, and preengineering), HEALTH PROFESSIONS (nursing, predentistry, premedicine, and prepharmacy), SOCIAL SCIENCE (child care/child and family studies, criminal justice, dietetics, food science, gerontology, history, parks and recreation management, political science/government, psychology, social work, and sociology). Business administration is the strongest academically. Accounting and computer science have the largest enrollments.

Required: All students must complete at least 124 hours of credit, including 24 to 30 hours in their major, while earning an overall 2.0 GPA and a C or better in all major courses. Distribution requirements include English, mathematics, social and natural science, and physical education courses. Students must pass a comprehensive examination in their major.

Special: The university offers formal co-op education and work-study programs, concurrent registration with members of the University of Arkansas system, internships, B.A.-B.S. degrees, and dual and student-designed majors. Also available are credit for military experience, nondegree study, individualized programs of study for honors college students, and study abroad. There is a freshman honors program on campus

Faculty/Classroom: Sixty percent of faculty are male; 40%, female. The average class size in an introductory lecture, a laboratory, and in a regular course offering is 18.

Admissions: About 75% of the 1993–94 applicants were accepted.

Requirements: A minimum GPA of 2.0 is required. The SAT I or ACT is required. The ACT, with a minimum composite score of 15, is preferred. Applicants must have earned 15 credits, including 4 units of English and 3 each in social studies, mathematics, and science. The GED is accepted. Students not meeting these requirements may apply for conditional admission. CLEP credit is accepted.

Procedure: Entrance exams should be taken during the junior or senior year. Applications should be filed at least 1 month before registration. Notification is sent on a rolling basis. There is an early admissions plan.

Transfer: A total of 124 transfer students enrolled in 1993–94. Transfer students must have a minimum GPA of 2.0. Applicants with fewer than 60 semester hours of college credit must submit an application, ACT or SAT I scores, and all college transcripts. A total of 30 credits out of 124 must be completed at the university.

Visiting: There are regularly scheduled orientations for prospective students. There are guides for informal visits and visitors may sit in on classes and stay overnight at the school. To arrange for a visit, contact the Recruitment Coordinator.

Financial Aid: In a recent year, 91% of all current freshmen and 93% of continuing students received some form of financial aid. Scholarships or need-based grants averaged $1400 ($4000 maximum); loans averaged $3000 ($4000 maximum); and work contracts averaged $700 ($2400 maximum). All undergraduate students work part-time. The average financial indebtedness of a recent graduate was $7000. The FFS is required. The deadline for financial aid applications is April 15.

International Students: International students must take the TOEFL and achieve a minimum score of 550. The student must also take the SAT I or ACT. The ACT, with a minimum score of 15, is preferred.

Computers: The university provides computer facilities for student use. The mainframe is an IBM 4361. The academic computer center in Caldwell Hall is networked to the mainframe with a capacity for 30 microcomputers. All students may access the system 7 A.M. to 11 P.M. Monday through Friday, and during special weekend hours. There are no time limits on using the system and no fees.

Graduates: In 1992–93, 314 bachelor's degrees were awarded.

Admissions Contact: Acting Director of Admission and Academic Records.

UNIVERSITY OF CENTRAL ARKANSAS
Conway, AR 72035–0001

C-3

(501) 450–3128
(800) 243–8245 (in-state)

Full-time: 3333 men, 4074 women	Faculty: 345; IIA, --$
Part-time: 503 men, 616 women	Ph.D.s: 67%
Graduate: 280 men, 761 women	Student/Faculty: 21 to 1
Year: semesters, summer session	Tuition: $1700 ($3274)
Application Deadline: open	Room & Board: $2500
Freshman Class: 3236 applied	
ACT: 20	

LESS COMPETITIVE

The University of Central Arkansas, established in 1907 as the Arkansas State Normal School, is a public liberal arts institution. There are 5 undergraduate schools. In addition to regional accreditation, UCA has baccalaureate program accreditation with AACSB, APTA, CAHEA, NASM, NCATE, and NLN. The library contains 505,773 volumes and 546,487 microform items, and subscribes to 2564 periodicals. Computerized library sources and services include interlibrary loans and database searching. Special learning facilities include a learning resource center, art gallery, planetarium, radio station, and TV station. The 256-acre campus is in a small town 29 miles north of Little Rock. Including residence halls, there are 40 buildings on campus.

Student Life: About 98% of undergraduates are from Arkansas. Students come from 36 states. Ninety-six percent are from public schools; 4% from private. Eighty-five percent are white; 13% African American. The average age of all undergraduates is 21. Thirty-eight percent drop out by the end of their first year; 30% remain to graduate.

Housing: A total of 2200 students can be accommodated in college housing. College-sponsored living facilities include single-sex and coed dormitories and married-student housing. In addition there are honors houses and an international students residence hall. On-campus housing is available on a first-come, first-served basis. Seventy-five percent of students commute. Alcohol is not permitted. All students may keep cars on campus.

Activities: About 30% of men belong to 10 national fraternities; about 20% of women belong to 8 national sororities. There are 98 groups on campus, including art, band, cheerleading, choir, chorale, chorus, drama, ethnic, gay, honors, international, jazz band, literary magazine, marching band, newspaper, orchestra, photography, political, professional, radio and TV, religious, social, student government, symphony, and yearbook.

Sports: There are 6 intercollegiate sports for men and 4 for women, and 26 intramural sports for men and 26 for women. Athletic and recreation facilities include a gymnasium, a swimming pool, a fitness center, racquetball and tennis courts, a track, and a fitness trail.

Disabled Students: Ninety-eight percent of the campus is accessible to disabled students. The following facilities are available: wheelchair ramps, elevators, special parking, specially equipped rest rooms, special class scheduling, lowered drinking fountains and telephones, and special dormitory rooms.

Services: In addition to many counseling and information services, tutoring is available in most subjects. There is remedial math, reading, and writing.

Campus Safety and Security: Campus safety and security measures include 24-hour foot and vehicle patrol, informal discussions, pamphlets, posters, and films, and emergency telephones. In addition, there are lighted pathways and sidewalks and security checkpoints.

Programs of Study: UCA awards the B.A., B.S., B.B.A., B.M., B.M.E., and B.S.E. degrees. Associate and master's degrees also are awarded. Bachelor's degrees are awarded in BIOLOGICAL SCIENCE (biology/biological science), BUSINESS (accounting, business administration and management, business economics, and marketing/retailing/merchandising), COMMUNICATIONS AND THE ARTS (communications, dramatic arts, English, French, journalism, music, Spanish, and speech/debate/rhetoric), COMPUTER AND PHYSICAL SCIENCE (chemistry, computer science, information sciences and systems, mathematics, physics, and quantitative methods), EDUCATION (art, early childhood, education of the exceptional child, elementary, foreign languages, guidance, health, home economics, industrial arts, library science, middle school, music, physical, science, secondary, and special), ENGINEERING AND ENVIRONMENTAL DESIGN (military science and preengineering), HEALTH PROFESSIONS (medical laboratory technology, nursing, occupational therapy, physical therapy, predentistry, radiological science, respiratory therapy, and speech pathology/audiology), SOCIAL SCIENCE (economics, geography, history, philosophy, political science/government, psychology, public administration, and sociology). Business, the health-related sciences, and education are the strongest academically. Business and the health-related sciences have the largest enrollments.

Required: All students must earn a minimum of 124 semester hours, including 30 in the major. Distribution requirements include 6 hours each in the humanities and social sciences and 7 in science. A minimum GPA of 2.25 is needed for the B.B.A., 2.5 for most education programs. Minimum requirements also include 2 semester hours in physical education.

Special: Study abroad, work-study programs, a B.S.-B.A. degree, a 3–2 engineering degree with Arkansas State University, dual majors, nondegree study, and pass/fail options are available. There is a freshman honors program on campus, as well as 4 national honor societies.

Faculty/Classroom: Sixty-three percent of faculty are male; 37%, female. No introductory courses are taught by graduate students.

Admissions: There were 2 National Merit finalists and 4 semifinalists.

Requirements: UCA requires applicants to be in the upper 50% of their class. A minimum GPA of 2.5 is required. The SAT I or ACT is required, with a minimum ACT score of 19. Applicants must submit their high school rank and GPA. The GED is accepted. AP and CLEP credits are accepted. Important factors used in the admissions decision are advanced placement or honor courses, evidence of special talent, recommendations by school officials, extracurricular activities record, and leadership record.

Procedure: Freshmen are admitted to all sessions. Application deadlines are open. Notification is sent on a rolling basis.

Transfer: Transfer applicants need, on UCA's scale, a minimum cumulative GPA of 2.0. A total of 24 credits out of 124 must be completed at UCA.

Visiting: There are regularly scheduled orientations for prospective students, including tours at 11 A.M. and 2 P.M.; departments and dormitories may be visited. There are also special visitation days that include a campus tour, departmental session, lunch, parents' session,

optional residence hall tour, and classroom visit or planetarium show. To arrange for a visit, contact the Admissions Office at (501) 450–3128.

Financial Aid: In an earlier year, 64% of all current freshmen received some form of financial aid. Twelve percent of undergraduate students work part-time. The FFS is required.

International Students: The school actively recruits these students. They must take the TOEFL and achieve a minimum score of 500.

Computers: The college provides computer facilities for student use. The mainframe is an IBM 4381. There are also 110 IBM and Apple microcomputers available in academic buildings, the library, and dormitories. All students may access the system. There are no time limits on using the system and no fees.

Graduates: In 1992–93, 829 bachelor's degrees were awarded.

Admissions Contact: Director of Admissions.

UNIVERSITY OF THE OZARKS
B-2
Clarksville, AR 72830
(501) 754–3839
(800) 264–8636 (out-of-state)

Full-time: 250 men, 270 women	**Faculty:** 41; IIB, --$
Part-time: 20 men, 23 women	**Ph.D.s:** 52%
Graduate: 4 men, 6 women	**Student/Faculty:** 13 to 1
Year: semesters, summer session	**Tuition:** $4920
Application Deadline: July 1	**Room & Board:** $2850
Freshman Class: 274 applied, 233 accepted, 167 enrolled	
ACT: 23	**COMPETITIVE**

The University of the Ozarks, founded in 1834, is a private, coeducational liberal arts institution affiliated with the United Presbyterian Church. In addition to regional accreditation, U of O has baccalaureate program accreditation with NCATE. The library contains 69,960 volumes, 6927 microform items, and 2955 audiovisual forms, and subscribes to 611 periodicals. Special learning facilities include an art gallery, radio station, and TV station. The 35-acre campus is in a small town 100 miles northwest of Little Rock. Including residence halls, there are 12 buildings on campus.

Student Life: About 70% of undergraduates are from Arkansas. Students come from 26 states and 11 foreign countries. Eighty-two percent are white; 14% foreign nationals. Sixty percent are Protestant; 28% claim no religious affiliation; 11% Catholic. Forty-three percent drop out by the end of their first year.

Housing: A total of 365 students can be accommodated in college housing. On-campus housing is guaranteed for the freshman year only. Priority is given to out-of-town students. Sixty-five percent of students commute. Alcohol is not permitted. All students may keep cars on campus.

Activities: There are no fraternities or sororities. There are many groups and organizations on campus, including art, band, cheerleading, choir, chorale, computers, drama, film, honors, international, jazz band, newspaper, orchestra, photography, political, professional, radio and TV, religious, social, student government, symphony, and yearbook. Popular campus events include homecoming and the International Fair and Banquet.

Sports: Athletic and recreation facilities include a sports complex housing handball courts, a pool, and a 2200-seat basketball court. In addition, there are football, softball, and baseball fields, a quarter-mile track, tennis courts, and a 2000-seat stadium.

Disabled Students: The following facilities are available: elevators, special parking, specially equipped rest rooms, and lowered drinking fountains.

Services: In addition to many counseling and information services, tutoring is available in every subject.

Programs of Study: U of O awards the B.A., B.S., B.G.S. and B.M.E. degrees. Associate and master's degrees also are awarded. Bachelor's degrees are awarded in BIOLOGICAL SCIENCE (biology/biological science), BUSINESS (accounting, business administration and management, and marketing/retailing/merchandising), COMMUNICATIONS AND THE ARTS (communications, English, fine arts, and music), COMPUTER AND PHYSICAL SCIENCE (mathematics and physical sciences), EDUCATION (business, elementary, music, and physical), HEALTH PROFESSIONS (medical laboratory technology, radiograph medical technology, and respiratory therapy), SOCIAL SCIENCE (history, liberal arts/general studies, philosophy, political science/government, public administration, and sociology). Business is the strongest program academically and has the largest enrollment.

Required: Students are required to earn 128 hours, with 30 to 42 in the major, and maintain a minimum GPA of 2.0. Distribution requirements include 6 hours each in the humanities and fine arts, social science, or business, and 6 each in science and mathematics. Students must also take 4 hours in physical education or military science and 3 hours each of composition, mathematics for business majors, and an introduction to computers. In addition, 6 hours of foreign language are required for the B.A. and B.M.E.

Special: Internships, study abroad in Japan, and numerous work-study programs are available. Dual majors, a general studies degree, student-designed majors, a 3–2 engineering degree with the University of Arkansas, and pass/fail options are also offered.

Faculty/Classroom: The average class size in an introductory lecture is 35; in a laboratory, 24; and in a regular course offering, 25.

Admissions: About 85% of the 1993–94 applicants were accepted. The ACT scores for the freshman class were as follows: 30% below 21, 27% between 21 and 23, 25% between 24 and 26, 13% between 27 and 28, and 5% above 28. About 41% of the current freshmen were in the top fifth of their class; 87% were in the top two fifths.

Requirements: U of O requires applicants to be in the upper 50% of their class. A minimum GPA of 2.5 is required. The SAT I, with a minimum composite score of 800, or the ACT, with a minimum score of 18, is required. An interview is recommended. The GED is accepted. AP and CLEP credits are accepted. Important factors used in the admissions decision are advanced placement or honor courses, evidence of special talent, leadership record, recommendations by school officials, personality, and intangible qualities.

Procedure: Applications should be filed by July 1 for fall entry and December 1 for winter entry. Notification is sent on a rolling basis. There is a deferred admissions plan.

Transfer: About 65 transfer students enrolled in an earlier year. Transfer students with a GPA of less than 2.0 or fewer than 30 hours of college work must furnish high school transcripts. A total of 30 credits out of 128 must be completed at U of O.

Visiting: There are guides for informal visits, and visitors may sit in on classes and stay overnight at the school. To arrange for a visit, contact the Admissions Office at (501) 754–3839.

Financial Aid: In a recent year, 63% of all current freshmen and 79% of continuing students received some form of financial aid. About 42% of freshmen and 54% of continuing students received need-based aid. The average freshman award was $2000. Of that total, scholarships or need-based grants averaged $1000 ($7600 maximum); loans averaged $2000 ($2625 maximum); and work contracts averaged $1445 ($2890 maximum). Thirty percent of undergraduate students work part-time. Average earnings from campus work for the school year are $1445. The average financial indebtedness of a recent graduate was $5000. U of O is a member of CSS. The FFS is required. The deadline for financial aid applications is July 1.

International Students: There are currently 107 international students enrolled. The school actively recruits these students. They must take the TOEFL with a minimum score of 500.

Computers: U of O provides computer facilities and microcomputers for student use.

Graduates: In a recent year, 132 bachelor's degrees were awarded. The most popular majors among graduates are business administration (19%), elementary education (15%), and physical education (8%). About 50 companies usually recruit on campus. In a recent graduating class, 6% of the men and 13% of the women were enrolled in graduate school within 6 months of graduation; 76% of the men and 71% of the women had found employment.

Admissions Contact: Michael G. Heater, Director of Admissions.

WILLIAMS BAPTIST COLLEGE
D-1
Walnut Ridge, AR 72476
(501) 886–6741, ext. 127
(800) 722–4434 (out-of-state)

Full-time: 186 men, 261 women	**Faculty:** 26; IIB, --$
Part-time: 65 men, 92 women	**Ph.D.s:** 50%
Graduate: none	**Student/Faculty:** 17 to 1
Year: semesters, summer session	**Tuition:** $3592
Application Deadline: open	**Room & Board:** $2242
Freshman Class: 220 applied, 203 accepted, 131 enrolled	
ACT: 19	**LESS COMPETITIVE**

Williams Baptist College, founded in 1941, is a liberal arts institution providing undergraduate education in business, education, humanities, natural sciences, religion, and social sciences. The college is affiliated with the Southern Baptist Church and is sponsored by the Arkansas Baptist Convention. The library contains 76,816 volumes and 40,002 microform items and subscribes to 366 periodicals. Computerized library sources and services include interlibrary loans. Special learning facilities include a learning resource center, art gallery, and education curriculum laboratory. The 175-acre campus is in a small town 100 miles northwest of Memphis, Tennessee, and 125 miles north of Little Rock. Including residence halls, there are 40 buildings on campus.

Student Life: About 77% of undergraduates are from Arkansas. Students come from 12 states and 11 foreign countries. Ninety-five percent are from public schools; 5% from private. Ninety-one percent are white. Most are Protestant. The average age of freshmen is 19; all undergraduates, 24. Ten percent drop out by the end of their first year; 50% remain to graduate.

Housing: A total of 260 students can be accommodated in college housing. College-sponsored living facilities include single-sex dormitories, on-campus apartments, and married-student housing. In addition there are honors houses. On-campus housing is guaranteed for the freshman year only and is available on a first-come, first-served basis. Fifty-eight percent of students commute. Alcohol is not permitted. All students may keep cars on campus.

Activities: There are no fraternities or sororities. There are 27 groups on campus, including art, cheerleading, choir, chorale, chorus, drama, honors, international, newspaper, professional, religious, social, social service, student government, and yearbook. Popular campus events include Homecoming, Founder/Friends Day, lectures, and concerts.

Sports: There are 2 intercollegiate sports for men and 2 for women, and 7 intramural sports for men and 7 for women. Athletic and recreation facilities include a gymnasium, a weight room, racquetball courts, a jogging track, and whirlpools.

Disabled Students: Ninety percent of the campus is accessible to disabled students. The following facilities are available: wheelchair ramps, special parking, specially equipped rest rooms, and special class scheduling.

Services: In addition to many counseling and information services, tutoring is available in most subjects. In addition, there is a reader service for the blind and remedial math.

Campus Safety and Security: Campus safety and security measures include lighted pathways and sidewalks and vehicle and foot patrol.

Programs of Study: WBC awards the B.A.,B.S.,B.S.B.A., and B.S.Ed. degrees. Associate degrees also are awarded. Bachelor's degrees are awarded in BUSINESS (business administration and management), COMMUNICATIONS AND THE ARTS (music), EDUCATION (education), SOCIAL SCIENCE (psychology and religion). Education, psychology, and religion are the strongest academically. Education has the largest enrollment.

Required: In order to graduate, all students must follow a core curriculum including humanities, social science/religion, natural science/mathematics, and physical activity. Chapel attendance is mandatory. A total of 128 credits, with 36 to 64 hours in the major, and a minimum GPA of 2.0 are required to graduate.

Special: Internships are offered in business administration and psychology. There are 4 national honor societies on campus. One department has an honors program.

Faculty/Classroom: Forty percent of faculty are male; 60%, female. All faculty teach and also do research. The average class size in an introductory lecture is 26; in a laboratory, 24; and in a regular course offering, 18.

Admissions: About 92% of the 1993–94 applicants were accepted. The ACT scores for the 1993–94 freshman class were as follows: 64% below 21, 18% between 21 and 23, 17% between 24 and 26, and 1% between 27 and 28. About 29% of the current freshmen were in the top fifth of their class; 56% were in the top two fifths. One freshman graduated at the top of the senior class.

Requirements: A minimum GPA of 2.0 is required. The ACT is required. Applicants must be graduates of an accredited secondary school. A minimum of 16 academic credits is required and should include at least 12 in the areas of English, mathematics, social science, and natural science. AP and CLEP credits are accepted.

Procedure: Freshmen are admitted to all sessions. Application deadlines are open. The application fee is $15. There is an early admissions plan.

Transfer: About 40 transfer students enrolled in 1993–94. Transfer students must have a GPA of 2.0 for unconditional admission. A total of 32 credits out of 128 must be completed at WBC.

Visiting: There are guides for informal visits and visitors may sit in on classes and stay overnight at the school. To arrange for a visit, contact the Director of Admissions at (501) 886–6741, ext. 127.

Financial Aid: In a recent year, 88% of all current freshmen and 68% of continuing students received some form of financial aid. About 50% of freshmen and 47% of continuing students received need-based aid. The average freshman award was $4038. Of that total, scholarships or need-based grants averaged $2059 ($2400 maximum); loans averaged $1306 ($2624 maximum); and work contracts averaged $673 ($1088 maximum). Thirty-seven percent of undergraduate students work part-time. Average earnings from campus work for the school year are $1088. The average financial indebtedness of the 1992–93 graduate was $1942. WBC is a member of CSS. The FFS is required. The deadline for financial aid applications is May 1.

International Students: There are currently 33 international students enrolled. They must take the TOEFL and achieve a minimum score of 450. The student must also take the ACT and the college's own interest inventory test.

Computers: The college provides computer facilities for student use. WBC uses microcomputers for all computing and a computer laboratory is available to students. All students may access the system. There are no time limits on using the system and no fees.

Graduates: In 1992–93, 44 bachelor's degrees were awarded. The most popular majors among graduates were elementary education (55%), psychology (20%), and business administration (16%).

Admissions Contact: Scott Wright, Director of Admissions.

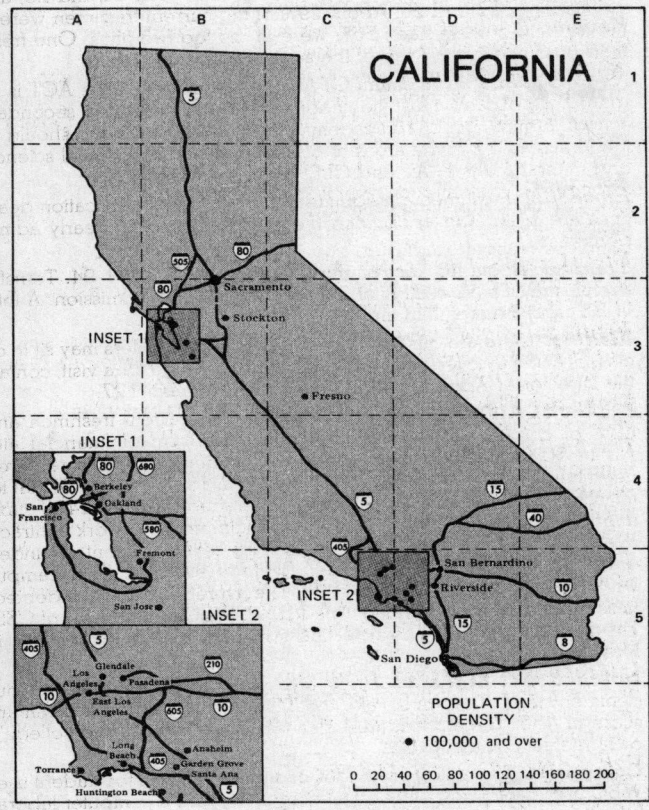

CALIFORNIA

POPULATION DENSITY
● 100,000 and over

0 20 40 60 80 100 120 140 160 180 200

ART CENTER COLLEGE OF DESIGN

C-5

Pasadena, CA 91103
(818) 396-2373

Full-time: 752 men, 502 women	Faculty: 56
Part-time: none	Ph.D.s: 10%
Graduate: 41 men, 28 women	Student/Faculty: 22 to 1
Year: semesters, summer session	Tuition: $13,550
Application Deadline: open	Room & Board: n/app
Freshman Class: 620 applied, 260 accepted, 220 enrolled	
SAT I or ACT: required	SPECIAL

Art Center College of Design, founded in 1930, is a private, nonprofit institution offering programs in the fine arts and design. There is one graduate school. In addition to regional accreditation, Art Center has baccalaureate program accreditation with NASAD. The library contains 32,000 volumes, 60,000 microform items, and 200 audiovisual forms, and subscribes to 400 periodicals. Computerized library sources and services include the card catalog and database searching. The 175-acre campus is in a suburban area 10 miles northwest of Los Angeles. All facilities, including 2 art galleries, are housed in a single building.

Student Life: About 51% of undergraduates are from California. Students come from 30 states, 30 foreign countries, and Canada. Sixty-two percent are white; 14% Asian American; 14% Hispanic. The average age of freshmen is 24. Five percent drop out by the end of their first year; 60% remain to graduate.

Housing: There are no residence halls. All students commute. Alcohol is not permitted. All students may keep cars on campus.

Activities: There are no fraternities or sororities on campus. Groups and organizations on campus include gay, international, literary magazine, religious, and student government. Popular campus events include Day Without Art.

Sports: There is no sports program at Art Center. Students have access to athletic facilities at Occidental College and California Institute of Technology.

Disabled Students: The entire campus is accessible to disabled students. The following facilities are available: wheelchair ramps, elevators, special parking, specially equipped rest rooms, lowered drinking fountains, and lowered telephones.

Services: In addition to many counseling and information services, tutoring is available in some subjects, including sketching for industrial design.

Campus Safety and Security: Campus safety and security measures include 24-hour foot and vehicle patrol and lighted pathways and sidewalks.

Programs of Study: Art Center awards the B.F.A. and B.S. degrees. Master's degrees also are awarded. Bachelor's degrees are awarded in COMMUNICATIONS AND THE ARTS (advertising, design, film arts, fine arts, graphic design, illustration, industrial design, and photography), ENGINEERING AND ENVIRONMENTAL DESIGN (environmental design). Illustration, photography, and graphic/packaging design have the largest enrollments.

Required: To graduate, students must complete 45 units of liberal arts and sciences. Course requirements, total number of credit hours, and total number of hours in the major vary by major. A minimum GPA of 2.5 and a core curriculum of English Composition, Introduction to Modernism, and Psychology of Success are also required.

Special: The college offers cross-registration with Occidental College and the California Institute of Technology, internships, study abroad, and nondegree study.

Faculty/Classroom: Seventy-nine percent of faculty are male; 21%, female. All teach undergraduates. The average class size in an introductory lecture is 25 and in a regular course offering, 30.

Admissions: About 42% of the 1993–94 applicants were accepted.

Requirements: The SAT I or ACT is required for high school students. In addition, applicants must be graduates of an accredited secondary school or have a GED. Official transcripts and a portfolio must be submitted. An interview is recommended. AP credits are accepted. Important factors used in the admissions decision are evidence of special talent, advanced placement or honor courses, personality, intangible qualities, recommendations by alumni, and recommendations by school officials.

Procedure: Freshmen are admitted to all sessions. Entrance exams should be taken in the senior year of high school. Application deadlines are open. Application fee is $35. Notification is sent on a rolling basis.

Transfer: About 220 transfer students enrolled in 1993–94. Transfer applicants must have a minimum 2.5 GPA and provide official transcripts from all colleges attended. Up to 60 units of liberal arts and studio credits may be transferred. Portfolios are required, and interviews are recommended. A maximum 32 of the 45 liberal arts and science units required for graduation may be transferred. There is a 4-semester residency requirement.

Visiting: There are regularly scheduled orientations for prospective students. There are guides for informal visits. To arrange for a visit, contact Admissions at (818) 396-2373.

Financial Aid: In an earlier year, 70% of freshmen and 85% of continuing students received some form of financial aid. Forty percent of undergraduate students work part-time. Art Center is a member of CSS. The FAF is required. The deadline for financial aid applications is March 1.

International Students: There are currently 180 international students enrolled. They must take the TOEFL and achieve a minimum score of 550.

Computers: The college provides computer facilities for student use. Many personal and graphics computers are available. There are no time limits on using the system and no fees.

Graduates: In a recent year, 371 bachelor's degrees were awarded. The most popular majors among graduates were graphics/packaging (23%), illustration (21%), and industrial design (19%). Some 50 companies recruited on campus in a recent year.

Admissions Contact: Kit Baron, Vice President of Student Services.

ART INSTITUTE OF SOUTHERN CALIFORNIA

D-5

Laguna Beach, CA 92651
Recognized candidate for accreditation
(714) 497-3309
(800) 255-0762 (out-of-state)

Full-time: 65 men, 60 women	Faculty: 8
Part-time: 15 men, 10 women	Ph.D.s: 10%
Graduate: none	Student/Faculty: 16 to 1
Year: semesters, summer session	Tuition: $8850
Application Deadline: n/av	Room & Board: $7650
Freshman Class: 108 applied, 108 accepted, 51 enrolled	
ACT: required	SPECIAL

The Art Institute of Southern California, founded in 1961, is a nonprofit, independent, coeducational institution offering full and part-time undergraduate art programs leading to the Bachelor of Fine Arts. In addition to regional accreditation, AISC has baccalaureate program accreditation with NASAD. The library contains 13,000 volumes, and subscribes to 90 periodicals. Computerized library sources

and services include the card catalog and interlibrary loans. Special learning facilities include a learning resource center and art gallery. The 5-acre campus is in a small town 20 miles southeast of Los Angeles. There are 11 buildings on campus.

Student Life: About 60% of undergraduates are from California. Students come from 10 states, 5 foreign countries, and Canada. Eighty-five percent are from public schools; 15% from private. Eighty percent are white; 10% Asian American. The average age of freshmen is 19; all undergraduates, 23. Fifteen percent drop out by the end of their first year; 40% remain to graduate.

Housing: There are no residence halls; all students commute. The institute will assist in the location of off-campus housing. Alcohol is not permitted. All students may keep cars on campus.

Activities: There are no fraternities or sororities on campus. There are some groups and organizations on campus, including art and student government.

Sports: There is no sports program at AISC.

Disabled Students: Ninety percent of the campus is accessible to disabled students. The following facilities are available: special parking, specially equipped rest rooms, special class scheduling, and lowered drinking fountains.

Services: In addition, there is remedial reading and writing.

Campus Safety and Security: Campus safety and security measures include an escort service and night security.

Programs of Study: AISC awards the B.F.A. degree. Bachelor's degrees are awarded in COMMUNICATIONS AND THE ARTS (drawing, graphic design, illustration, and painting).

Required: All students must complete 123 semester units, including 40 to 45 in a major. This program includes 45 units of liberal arts, a comprehensive mandatory freshman foundations program exploring all artistic mediums, 75 to 78 total semester units of studio art, and 15 to 18 units of art history. A minimum GPA of 2.0 must be maintained.

Special: Internships are possible, and work-study is available on campus. Students may petition the registrar if they wish to attempt more than 15 semester units.

Faculty/Classroom: Sixty-five percent of faculty are male; 35%, female. All teach undergraduates.

Admissions: All of the 1993–94 applicants were accepted.

Requirements: A minimum GPA of 2.0 is required. The ACT is required. Students must be a high school graduate with a 2.0 minimum GPA, or hold an equivalent GED. A personal essay and letter of recommendation are required, as is a personal or telephone interview. AP credits are accepted.

Procedure: Freshmen are admitted to all sessions. The application fee is $35. The college accepts all applicants. Notification is sent on a rolling basis.

Transfer: In addition to freshman requirements, transfer students must submit all prior college transcripts and a portfolio. A total of 45 credits out of 123 must be completed at AISC.

Visiting: To arrange for a visit, contact the Admissions Office at (714) 497–3309 or (800) 255–0762 (out-of-state).

Financial Aid: Scholarships or need-based grants averaged $200 ($5250 maximum). AISC is a member of CSS. The FAF or FFS, AFSA, FAFSA and SAAC for California Grants are required. The deadline for financial aid applications is April 20.

International Students: They must take the TOEFL and achieve a minimum score of 525.

Computers: The college provides computer facilities for student use. There are 11 Macintosh computers available in a network for student use, with all necessary software for desktop publishing and full color computer animation. All students may access the system. There are no time limits and no fees.

Admissions Contact: John R. Walker, Admissions Director.

AZUSA PACIFIC UNIVERSITY
D-5

Azusa, CA 91702   (818) 812–3016; (800) TALK-APU (out-of-state)

Full-time: 2126 men and women	Faculty: 90; IIA, --$
Part-time: 142 men and women	Ph.D.s: 50%
Graduate: 1678 men and women	Student/Faculty: 24 to 1
Year: semesters, summer session	Tuition: $11,084
Application Deadline: open	Room & Board: $3950
Freshman Class: 1080 applied, 948 accepted, 482 enrolled	
SAT I Verbal/Math: 428/474	ACT: 18 COMPETITIVE

Azusa Pacific University, founded in 1899, is a private, nondenominational Christian institution offering undergraduate and graduate programs in the liberal arts and emphasizing spiritual growth. There are 6 undergraduate and 6 graduate schools. In addition to regional accreditation, APU has baccalaureate program accreditation with CSWE and NLN. The library contains 500,000 volumes, 405,000 microform items, and 5000 audiovisual forms, and subscribes to 950 periodicals. Special learning facilities include an art gallery. The 52-acre campus is in a small town 26 miles east of Los Angeles. Including residence halls, there are 67 buildings on campus.

Student Life: About 79% of undergraduates are from California. Students come from 28 states, 24 foreign countries, and Canada. Eighty-one percent are white. Most are Protestant. The average age of freshmen is 18; all undergraduates, 22.

Housing: A total of 1120 students can be accommodated in college housing. College-sponsored living facilities include single-sex dormitories, on-campus apartments, and off-campus apartments. On campus housing is available on a lottery system for upperclassmen. Sixty-two percent of students live on campus; of those, 50% remain on campus on weekends. Alcohol is not permitted. All students may keep cars on campus.

Activities: There are no fraternities or sororities on campus. There are 100 groups on campus, including art, band, cheerleading, choir, chorale, chorus, computers, drama, ethnic, honors, international, jazz band, newspaper, orchestra, pep band, photography, political, religious, social, student government, and yearbook. Popular campus events include Homecoming Week, Missions Week, International Week, and Black Culture Week.

Sports: There are 7 intercollegiate sports for men and 7 for women, and 6 intramural sports for men and 4 for women. Athletic and recreation facilities include an all-weather track, a 3000-seat football stadium, a baseball field, a 1200-seat gymnasium, a residence hall lounge, and a recreation room.

Disabled Students: The following facilities are available: wheelchair ramps, elevators, special parking, and specially equipped rest rooms.

Services: In addition to many counseling and information services, tutoring is available in most subjects. There is remedial math, reading, and writing.

Campus Safety and Security: Campus safety and security measures include 24-hour foot and vehicle patrol, escort service, informal discussions, and lighted pathways and sidewalks.

Programs of Study: APU awards the B.A., and B.S. degrees. A master's degree is also conferred. Bachelor's degrees are awarded in BIOLOGICAL SCIENCE (biochemistry, biology/biological science, and life science), BUSINESS (accounting, business administration and management, and marketing/retailing/merchandising), COMMUNICATIONS AND THE ARTS (communications, English, and music), COMPUTER AND PHYSICAL SCIENCE (chemistry, computer science, information sciences and systems, mathematics, and physics), EDUCATION (art, music, and physical), HEALTH PROFESSIONS (health, nursing, predentistry, and premedicine), SOCIAL SCIENCE (biblical studies, crosscultural studies, history, international studies, liberal arts/general studies, ministries, philosophy, political science/government, psychology, religion, social science, social work, and sociology). Nursing, education, and religion are the strongest academically. Business administration has the largest enrollment.

Required: All students must take 126 semester units, including 70 in their major, and earn a minimum GPA of 2.0. Three units of community ministry, 15 units of Bible study, and 2 units of health are also required. General education requirements include courses in communication, fine arts, religion and philosophy, social science, science and mathematics, and physical education.

Special: Internships in ministerial and American studies, study abroad in Japan, Latin America, and Taiwan, and a Washington semester are available. In addition, work-study with the university, a B.A.-B.S. degree and dual majors in all programs, and a 3–2 engineering degree are offered. APU awards credit for life experience and allows nondegree study. There is a freshman honors program on campus, as well as 2 national honor societies.

Faculty/Classroom: The average class size in an introductory lecture is 40 and in a regular course offering, 35.

Admissions: About 88% of the 1993–94 applicants were accepted. The SAT scores for the 1993–94 freshman class were as follows: Verbal—59% below 500, 28% between 500 and 599, 11% between 600 and 700, and 3% above 700; Math—77% below 500, 18% between 500 and 599, and 4% between 600 and 700. The ACT scores were 36% below 21, 32% between 21 and 23, 23% between 24 and 26, 7% between 27 and 28, and 2% above 28.

Requirements: A minimum GPA of 2.5 is required. The SAT I is required, but no minimum score is necessary. An essay is required. A portfolio and interview are recommended for certain programs. The GED is accepted. AP and CLEP credits are accepted. Important factors used in the admissions decision are personality, intangible qualities, evidence of special talent, advanced placement or honor courses, leadership record, and extracurricular activities record.

Procedure: Freshmen are admitted to all sessions. Entrance exams should be taken prior to enrollment. Application deadlines are open. The application fee is $40. Notification is sent on a rolling basis.

Transfer: About 265 transfer students enrolled in a recent year. Transfer applicants must have a minimum GPA of 2.0 on previous college work. The SAT I or ACT is not required if 30 or more semester units have been completed. An associate degree and an interview are recommended. A total of 30 credits out of 126 must be completed at APU.

Visiting: There are regularly scheduled orientations for prospective students, including Seniors Only Day in November, and a Brother/Sister Weekend in February that is open to both juniors and seniors. There are guides for informal visits and visitors may sit in on classes and stay overnight at the school. To arrange for a visit, contact the Admissions Office at (818) 812-3016.

Financial Aid: In an earlier year, 80% of all students received some form of financial aid. The average freshman award was $7000. Of that total, scholarships or need-based grants averaged $1250 ($3950 maximum); loans averaged $2700 ($4875 maximum); and work contracts averaged $1500 ($2000 maximum). Sixty-five percent of undergraduate students work part-time. Average earnings from campus work for the school year are $1440. The average financial indebtedness of the 1992-93 graduate was $10,000. APU is a member of CSS. The FAF is required. The deadline for financial aid applications is January 1.

International Students: There are currently 323 international students enrolled. The school actively recruits these students. They must take the TOEFL and achieve a minimum score of 500.

Computers: The college provides computer facilities for student use. The mainframes are a Novell network, an Apple network, and a VAX Network. The computer center has 56 terminals. All students may access the system. It may be used Monday through Friday 8 A.M. to 11 P.M., Saturday 8:30 A.M. to 8 P.M., and Sunday 1 P.M. to 6 P.M. There are no time limits on using the system and no fees.

Graduates: Some 36 companies recruited on campus in an earlier year.

Admissions Contact: Deana Porterfield, Director of Admissions.

BIOLA UNIVERSITY
La Mirada, CA 90639-0001

D-5

(310) 903-4752

Full-time: 729 men, 1161 women	Faculty: 126; IIA, --$
Part-time: 60 men, 51 women	Ph.D.s: 65%
Graduate: 579 men, 285 women	Student/Faculty: 15 to 1
Year: 4-1-4, summer session	Tuition: $11,388
Application Deadline: June 1	Room & Board: $4736
Freshman Class: 1118 applied, 896 accepted, 459 enrolled	
SAT I Verbal/Math: 440/500	ACT: 22	COMPETITIVE

Biola University, founded in 1908, is a private, interdenominational Christian institution offering undergraduate and graduate degrees in arts and sciences, psychology, theology, and intercultural studies. There are 4 undergraduate and 4 graduate schools. In addition to regional accreditation, Biola has baccalaureate program accreditation with NASM and NLN. The library contains 257,000 volumes, 328,604 microform items, and 7500 audiovisual forms, and subscribes to 1000 periodicals. Special learning facilities include a learning resource center, an art gallery, and a radio station. The 95-acre campus is in a suburban area 22 miles southeast of Los Angeles. Including residence halls, there are 37 buildings on campus.

Student Life: About 70% of undergraduates are from California. Students come from 16 foreign countries and Canada. Sixty percent are from public schools; 40% from private. Seventy-two percent are white; 14% Asian American. The average age of freshmen is 18; all undergraduates, 21. Twenty-two percent drop out by the end of their first year; 77% remain to graduate.

Housing: A total of 1450 students can be accommodated in college housing. College-sponsored living facilities include single-sex dormitories, on-campus apartments, and married-student housing. On-campus housing is guaranteed for all 4 years. Sixty-five percent of students live on campus; of those, 55% remain on campus on weekends. Alcohol is not permitted. All students may keep cars on campus.

Activities: There are no fraternities or sororities on campus. There are 25 groups on campus, including art, band, cheerleading, chorale, computers, drama, ethnic, film, international, jazz band, musical theater, newspaper, orchestra, political, professional, radio and tv, religious, social, social service, student government, and yearbook. Popular campus events include Beach Bash, Multicultural Week, Christmas Celebration-Celebrate the Son, and dramatic arts productions in the spring.

Sports: There are 6 intercollegiate sports for men and 7 for women, and 10 intramural sports for men and 8 for women. Athletic and recreation facilities include a gymnasium-swimming complex, a 450-seat auditorium, athletic fields, including one for soccer, a quarter-mile track, a baseball diamond, an archery range, and tennis courts.

Disabled Students: Seventy percent of the campus is accessible to disabled students. The following facilities are available: wheelchair ramps, elevators, special parking, specially equipped rest rooms, special class scheduling, and lowered drinking fountains.

Services: In addition to many counseling and information services, tutoring is available in every subject. There is a reader service for the blind, and remedial math, reading, and writing.

Campus Safety and Security: Campus safety and security measures include 24-hour foot and vehicle patrol, self-defense education, escort service, and informal discussions. In addition, there are pamphlets, posters, and films, emergency telephones, and lighted pathways and sidewalks.

Programs of Study: Biola awards the B.A., B.S., B.M., and B.S.N. degrees. Master's and doctoral degrees also are awarded. Bachelor's degrees are awarded in BIOLOGICAL SCIENCE (biochemistry and biology/biological science), BUSINESS (business administration and management), COMMUNICATIONS AND THE ARTS (communications, English, fine arts, music, music performance, and music theory and composition), COMPUTER AND PHYSICAL SCIENCE (chemistry, computer science, and mathematics), EDUCATION (art, Christian Education, elementary, music, and secondary), HEALTH PROFESSIONS (nursing), SOCIAL SCIENCE (biblical studies, crosscultural studies, history, humanities, philosophy, psychology, religious education, social science, and sociology). Biology, biochemistry, nursing, and communications are the strongest academically. Business, communications, psychology, and education have the largest enrollments.

Required: To graduate, students must pass a writing competency examination, complete 30 units of biblical studies and theology, and fulfill the general education and physical education requirements. At least 130 semester hours must be completed, with 30 hours in the major and 24 of these in upper-division work. Other requirements vary by major. A minimum 2.0 GPA is required.

Special: Cross-registration with the Au Sable Institute of Environmental Studies is possible. Biola offers internships, summer travel tours, study abroad, and an American studies program in Washington D.C., sponsored by the Christian College Coalition. L.A. film studies and Biola Baja, programs offering a semester in Hollywood working in the film industry and 3 weeks at Vermillion Sea Field, Baja, respectively, are available. Also available are on- and off-campus work study programs, a B.A.-B.S. degree, a 3-2 engineering degree with the University of Southern California, dual and student-designed majors, and nondegree study. There is one national honor society on campus.

Faculty/Classroom: No introductory courses are taught by graduate students. The average class size in an introductory lecture is 100; in a laboratory, 15; and in a regular course offering, 25.

Admissions: About 80% of the 1993-94 applicants were accepted.

Requirements: A minimum GPA of 2.8 is required. The SAT I or ACT is required. Applicants need not be graduates of an accredited secondary school. The GED is accepted. Students should have completed 16 academic credits, including 3 years of English, 2 each of mathematics, foreign language, and social studies, and 1 of science. All students must be evangelical Christians who can demonstrate Christian character, leadership ability, and the aptitude for probable success in college. Applicants must submit 2 personal references: 1 from their pastor or someone on the pastoral staff, and 1 from the school last attended, or from an employer if they have been out of school for a year and have been working. An essay and interview are required. AP and CLEP credits are accepted. Important factors used in the admissions decision are advanced placement or honor courses, leadership record, personality, intangible qualities, evidence of special talent, and extracurricular activities record.

Procedure: Freshmen are admitted to all sessions. Entrance exams should be taken before February 1. Applications should be filed by June 1 for fall entry and January 1 for spring entry, along with an application fee of $35. Notification is sent on a rolling basis. There are early decision, early admissions, and deferred admissions plans.

Transfer: About 190 transfer students enrolled in 1993-94. Transfer students with fewer than 27 credit hours must submit both college transcripts and SAT I scores. All students must provide high school transcripts. A minimum 2.0 GPA and an interview are required. A total of 30 credits out of 130 must be completed at Biola.

Visiting: There are regularly scheduled orientations for prospective students, including class visits; orientation with the departments of admissions, financial aid, and student affairs; chapel; a sporting event; and Disneyland or Knott's Berry Farm visit. There are guides for informal visits and visitors may sit in on classes and stay overnight at the school. To arrange for a visit, contact the Admissions Office at (310) 903-4752.

Financial Aid: In 1993-94, 80% of all students received some form of financial aid. The average freshman award was $3000. Of that total, scholarships or need-based grants averaged $2895 ($14,232 maximum); loans averaged $3000 ($4000 maximum); and work contracts averaged $2000. Thirty-two percent of undergraduate students work part-time. Average earnings from campus work for the school year are $2000. Biola is a member of CSS. The FAF is required, and California residents should submit the SAAC. The deadline for financial aid applications is March 2.

International Students: The school actively recruits these students. They must take the TOEFL or the college's own test and achieve a minimum score on the TOEFL of 500. The student must also take the SAT I or the ACT.

Computers: The college provides computer facilities for student use. The mainframes are an HP 9000/Series 300, a DEC VAX 3100, and a DEC VAX 2100. There is 1 main computer center for the HP and VAX terminals. In addition, Apple Macintosh laboratories are located

throughout the campus, as well as Intel-based PC (IBM/IBM-compatible) laboratories. All students may access the system. There are no time limits on using the system. The fees are $25 per semester.
Graduates: In a recent year, 260 bachelor's degrees were awarded. The most popular majors among graduates were business administration (15%), communication (12%), and psychology (10%). Within an average freshman class, 51% graduate in 4 years and 77% in 5 years. In the 1992 graduating class, 20% of all graduates were enrolled in graduate school within 6 months of graduation; 65% had found employment.
Admissions Contact: Gregory G. Vaughan, Director of Enrollment Management.

CALIFORNIA BAPTIST COLLEGE
Riverside, CA 92504   **D-5**

(714) 689–5771, ext. 212
(800) 782–3382 (in-state)

Full-time: 702 men and women	Faculty: 46
Part-time: 161 men and women	Ph.D.s: 72%
Graduate: 53 men and women	Student/Faculty: 15 to 1
Year: 4–1-4, summer session	Tuition: $7338
Application Deadline: open	Room & Board: $3956
Freshman Class: n/av	
SAT I or ACT: required	**COMPETITIVE**

California Baptist College, founded in 1950, is a private institution supported by the California Southern Baptist Convention. There is one graduate school. In addition to regional accreditation, Cal Baptist has baccalaureate program accreditation with NASM. The library contains 110,000 volumes and 8200 microform items, and subscribes to 400 periodicals. Computerized library sources and services include interlibrary loans. The 60-acre campus is in a suburban area 60 miles east of Los Angeles. Including residence halls, there are 12 buildings on campus.
Student Life: About 69% of undergraduates are from California. Students come from 30 states, 21 foreign countries, and Canada. Eighty-five percent are white. Most are Protestant.
Housing: A total of 512 students can be accommodated in college housing. College-sponsored living facilities include single-sex dormitories and on-campus apartments. On-campus housing is guaranteed for all 4 years. Seventy-five percent of students live on campus. Alcohol is not permitted. All students may keep cars on campus.
Activities: There are no fraternities or sororities on campus. There are many groups and organizations on campus, including art, cheerleading, choir, chorale, chorus, computers, drama, ethnic, honors, international, newspaper, political, professional, religious, student government, and yearbook. Popular campus events include Campus Day, College Preview Days/Homecoming, Twirp Week, lighting of the Christmas tree, and Christmas Yule.
Sports: There are 5 intercollegiate sports for men and 4 for women, and 10 intramural sports for men and 10 for women. Athletic and recreation facilities include a 950-seat gymnasium; baseball, soccer, and softball fields; and tennis and sand volleyball courts.
Disabled Students: Ninety-five percent of the campus is accessible to disabled students. The following facilities are available: wheelchair ramps, elevators, and special parking.
Services: There is remedial math, reading, and writing.
Campus Safety and Security: Campus safety and security measures include 24-hour foot and vehicle patrol, escort service, informal discussions, and pamphlets, posters, and films. In addition, there are emergency telephones and lighted pathways and sidewalks.
Programs of Study: Cal Baptist awards the B.A., B.S., and B.M. degrees. Master's degrees also are awarded. Bachelor's degrees are awarded in BIOLOGICAL SCIENCE (biology/biological science), BUSINESS (business administration and management), COMMUNICATIONS AND THE ARTS (art, communications, English, fine arts, music, and Spanish), COMPUTER AND PHYSICAL SCIENCE (physical sciences), EDUCATION (elementary, physical, and secondary), SOCIAL SCIENCE (behavioral science, history, liberal arts/general studies, political science/government, psychology, public administration, religion, social science, and sociology). Education and behavioral science are the strongest academically. Business administration has the largest enrollment.
Required: All students must complete courses in fine arts, humanities, natural sciences, religion, social sciences, and physical education. A total of 124 units, with a minimum GPA of 2.0, is required in order to graduate.
Special: Cal Baptist offers an accelerated program in business administration. Study abroad, internships, work-study programs, a Washington semester, B.A.-B.S. degrees, and credit for military/work experience are available. There are 2 national honor societies on campus. One department has an honors program.
Faculty/Classroom: Sixty percent of faculty are male; 40%, female. No introductory courses are taught by graduate students. The average class size in an introductory lecture is 30; in a laboratory, 10; and in a regular course offering, 20.

Requirements: A minimum GPA of 2.0 and either the SAT I or ACT are required. Applicants should be graduates of an accredited high school or have a GED. An essay and interview are recommended and 2 references, preferably from a church leader and an official of an academic institution, are required. AP and CLEP credits are accepted. Important factors used in the admissions decision are recommendations by school officials, advanced placement or honors courses, ability to finance college education, extracurricular activities record, and leadership record.
Procedure: Freshmen are admitted to all sessions. Entrance exams should be taken during the junior year. Application deadlines are open. The application fee is $30. Notification is sent on a rolling basis. There are early decision and early admissions plans.
Transfer: About 80 transfer students enrolled in 1993–94. Applicants must have a minimum GPA of 2.0. Students who have completed fewer than 30 transferable semester units must submit SAT I or ACT scores. A total of 24 credits out of 124 must be completed at Cal Baptist.
Visiting: There are regularly scheduled orientations for prospective students. There are guides for informal visits and visitors may sit in on classes and stay overnight at the school. To arrange for a visit, contact the Admissions Office at (714) 689–5771, ext. 212, or (800) 782–3382 (in-state).
Financial Aid: In an earlier year, 90% of all current freshmen and 88% of continuing students received some form of financial aid. Scholarships or need-based grants averaged $2405 ($4810 maximum); loans averaged $1800 ($2625 maximum); and work contracts averaged $1000 ($1300 maximum). The average financial indebtedness of an earlier graduate was $7000. Cal Baptist is a member of CSS. The FAF, the college's own financial statement, and the FAFSA are required. The deadline for financial aid applications is April 15.
International Students: There are currently 58 international students enrolled. The school actively recruits these students. They must take the TOEFL and achieve a minimum score of 500.
Computers: The college provides computer facilities for student use. The mainframe is an HP 9000/Series 836. Academic computer laboratories house 43 Apple IIe, IBM PC, and Apple Macintosh II microcomputers. There are no time limits on using the system and no fees.
Graduates: In a recent year, 105 bachelor's degrees were awarded. The most popular majors among graduates were business administration, liberal arts, and psychology/sociology. Some 25 companies recruited on campus.
Admissions Contact: L. Kent Dacus, Director of Admissions.

CALIFORNIA COLLEGE OF ARTS AND CRAFTS
       B-3

Oakland, CA 94618   (510) 653–6522; (800) 447–1ART (out-of-state)

Full-time: 395 men, 495 women	Faculty: 34
Part-time: 79 men, 102 women	Ph.D.s: n/av
Graduate: 19 men, 56 women	Student/Faculty: 26 to 1
Year: semesters, summer session	Tuition: $13,080
Application Deadline: open	Room & Board: $4298
Freshman Class: 247 applied, 148 accepted, 59 enrolled	
SAT I or ACT: recommended	**SPECIAL**

California College of Arts and Crafts, established in 1907, is a private professional arts institution offering programs in fine arts, design, and architecture studies. There are 4 undergraduate schools and one graduate school. In addition to regional accreditation, CCAC has baccalaureate program accreditation with FIDER, NAAB, and NASAD. The 2 libraries contain 31,400 volumes, 400 microform items, and 6000 audiovisual forms, and subscribe to 12,700 periodicals. Computerized library sources and services include the card catalog and database searching. Special learning facilities include a learning resource center and art gallery. The 5-acre campus is in an urban area in Oakland. Including residence halls, there are 16 buildings on campus.
Student Life: About 70% of undergraduates are from California. Students come from 25 states, 27 foreign countries, and Canada. Sixty-eight percent are white; 12% foreign nationals; 11% Asian American. The average age of all undergraduates is 22. Twenty-four percent drop out by the end of their first year; 30% remain to graduate.
Housing: A total of 60 students can be accommodated in college housing. College-sponsored living facilities include coed dormitories, on-campus apartments, and off-campus apartments. On-campus housing is available on a first-come, first-served basis. Priority is given to out-of-town students. Ninety-five percent of students commute. Alcohol is not permitted.
Activities: There are no fraternities or sororities on campus. There are 15 groups on campus, including art, ethnic, gay, honors, international, newspaper, professional, and student government. Popular campus events include All-College Honors and Spring Fair.
Sports: There is no sports program at CCAC.

Disabled Students: Eighty percent of the campus is accessible to disabled students. The following facilities are available: wheelchair ramps, elevators, special parking, and specially equipped rest rooms.

Services: In addition to many counseling and information services, tutoring is available in some subjects, including humanities and sciences.

Campus Safety and Security: Campus safety and security measures include an escort service.

Programs of Study: CCAC awards the B.Arch. and B.F.A. degrees. A master's degree also is awarded. Bachelor's degrees are awarded in COMMUNICATIONS AND THE ARTS (design, film arts, fine arts, and photography), ENGINEERING AND ENVIRONMENTAL DESIGN (architecture).

Required: Students must successfully complete 126 credits for the B.F.A., with 54 in the major, and 156 for the B.Arch., with 84 in the major. Distribution requirements are 51 credits in humanities and science plus 75 in studio work for fine arts majors and 105 in studio work for architecture majors. All students must complete the core curriculum and maintain a minimum GPA of 2.0.

Special: Cross-registration is permitted with Mills College and Holy Names College in Oakland. Opportunities are provided for internships, student-designed majors, and nondegree study.

Faculty/Classroom: Sixty-five percent of faculty are male; 35%, female. The average class size in an introductory lecture is 40 and in a regular course offering, 16.

Admissions: About 60% of the 1993-94 applicants were accepted. The SAT scores for the 1993-94 freshman class were as follows: Verbal—67% below 500, 26% between 500 and 599, 4% between 600 and 700, and 3% above 700; Math—48% below 500, 30% between 500 and 599, 15% between 600 and 700, and 7% above 700.

Requirements: A minimum GPA of 2.0 is required. The SAT I or ACT is recommended. Graduation from an accredited secondary school is required; a GED will be accepted. An essay, portfolio, and letters of recommendation are required. An interview is strongly recommended. AP credits are accepted. Important factors used in the admissions decision are evidence of special talent, advanced placement or honor courses, leadership record, personality, intangible qualities, and recommendations by alumni.

Procedure: Freshmen are admitted fall and spring. Application deadlines are open. The application fee is $30. Notification is sent on a rolling basis.

Transfer: About 200 transfer students enrolled in 1993-94. Applicants must submit a portfolio. A total of 51 credits out of 126 must be completed at CCAC.

Visiting: There are guides for informal visits and visitors may sit in on classes. To arrange for a visit, contact the Office of Enrollment Services, at (510) 653-6522.

Financial Aid: In 1993-94, 77% of all current freshmen and 53% of continuing students received some form of financial aid. About 70% of freshmen and 49% of continuing students received need-based aid. The average freshman award was $9722. Of that total, scholarships or need-based grants averaged $4971 ($8750 maximum); loans averaged $2951 ($3825 maximum); and work contracts averaged $1800 ($2000 maximum). Ninety percent of undergraduate students work part-time. Average earnings from campus work for the school year are $1250. The average financial indebtedness of the 1992-93 graduate was $7000. CCAC is a member of CSS. The college's own financial statement and FAFSA are required. The deadline for financial aid applications is March 1.

International Students: There are currently 134 international students enrolled. They must take the TOEFL or the Comprehensive English Language Test and achieve a minimum score on the TOEFL of 500.

Computers: The college provides computer facilities for student use. An IBM and Apple Macintosh are available on the San Francisco campus. The learning center, with word processing capabilities on IBM and Macintosh computers, is available on the Oakland Campus. Students enrolled in computer courses may access the system.

Graduates: In a recent year, 165 bachelor's degrees were awarded. Within an average freshman class, 30% graduate in 4 years and 32% in 5 years.

Admissions Contact: Sheri Sivin McKenzie, Enrollment Services.

CALIFORNIA INSTITUTE OF TECHNOLOGY   C-5

Pasadena, CA 91125   (818) 395-6341; (800) LOV-TECH

Full-time: 670 men, 214 women	Faculty: 268; I, + +$
Part-time: none	Ph.D.s: 100%
Graduate: 858 men, 239 women	Student/Faculty: 3 to 1
Year: quarters	Tuition: $15,910
Application Deadline: January 1	Room & Board: $4873
Freshman Class: 1916 applied, 466 accepted, 210 enrolled	
SAT: required	**MOST COMPETITIVE**

California Institute of Technology, founded in 1891, is a private institution offering programs in engineering, science, and mathematics.

There are 6 graduate schools. In addition to regional accreditation, Caltech has baccalaureate program accreditation with ABET. The 16 libraries contain 487,000 volumes, and subscribe to 4500 periodicals. Computerized library sources and services include the card catalog, interlibrary loans, and database searching. Special learning facilities include a learning resource center. The 124-acre campus is in a suburban area 12 miles northeast of Los Angeles. Including residence halls, there are 59 buildings on campus.

Student Life: About 70% of undergraduates are from out-of-state, mostly the West. Students come from 52 states, 15 foreign countries, and Canada. Eighty-two percent are from public schools; 18% from private. Fifty-six percent are white; 25% Asian American; 10% foreign nationals. The average age of freshmen is 18; all undergraduates, 20. Two percent drop out by the end of their first year; 72% remain to graduate.

Housing: All students can be accomodated in college housing. College-sponsored living facilities include coed dormitories, off-campus apartments, and married-student housing. Seventy-eight percent of students live on campus. Alcohol is not permitted. All students may keep cars on campus.

Activities: There are no fraternities or sororities on campus. There are 70 groups on campus, including art, band, cheerleading, chess, choir, chorale, chorus, computers, dance, drama, ethnic, film, gay, honors, international, jazz band, literary magazine, musical theater, newspaper, orchestra, photography, political, professional, religious, social, social service, student government, symphony, and yearbook. Popular campus events include Ditch Day.

Sports: There are 12 intercollegiate sports for men and 6 for women, and 10 intramural sports for men and 10 for women. Athletic and recreation facilities include 2 Olympic-size swimming pools, a 300-seat gymnasium, a 440-meter track, a football field, 4 baseball fields, and 8 tennis courts. A new athletic facility includes another gymnasium, a 4000-square foot exercise room with equipment, and racquetball courts.

Disabled Students: Ninety-eight percent of the campus is accessible to disabled students. The following facilities are available: wheelchair ramps, elevators, special parking, specially equipped rest rooms, and lowered telephones.

Services: In addition to many counseling and information services, tutoring is available in every subject.

Campus Safety and Security: Campus safety and security measures include 24-hour foot and vehicle patrol, self defense education, escort service, and informal discussions. In addition, there are pamphlets, posters, films, emergency telephones, and lighted pathways and sidewalks.

Programs of Study: Caltech awards the B.S. degree. Master's and doctoral degrees also are awarded. Bachelor's degrees are awarded in BIOLOGICAL SCIENCE (biology/biological science), COMMUNICATIONS AND THE ARTS (literature), COMPUTER AND PHYSICAL SCIENCE (astronomy, chemistry, geochemistry, geology, geophysics and seismology, mathematics, physics, and planetary and space science), ENGINEERING AND ENVIRONMENTAL DESIGN (aeronautical engineering, chemical engineering, civil engineering, electrical/electronics engineering, engineering, engineering and applied science, and mechanical engineering), SOCIAL SCIENCE (economics, history, political science/government, and social science). Engineering, applied science, and electrical engineering have the largest enrollments.

Required: All students must complete 108 units in humanities and social science, 54 each in mathematics and physics, 30 in chemistry, and 3 terms of physical education. A total of 780 quarter units, including 516 in the major, and a minimum GPA of 1.9 are required in order to graduate.

Special: Caltech offers cross-registration with Scripps College, Occidental College, and Art Center College of Design, various work-study programs including those with NASA's Jet Propulsion Laboratory, B.A.-B.S. degrees, dual majors, and independent studies degrees with faculty-approved student-designed majors. A 3-2 engineering degree is possible with Bowdoin, Grinnell, Occidental, Pomona, Reed, and Whitman colleges, and Ohio Wesleyan and Wesleyan universities. Pass/fail options are available for freshmen. A summer undergraduate research fellowship program is offered.

Faculty/Classroom: Ninety percent of faculty are male; 10%, female. Twenty-seven percent teach undergraduates and 37% do research. No introductory courses are taught by graduate students. The average class size in an introductory lecture is 150 and in a regular course offering, 12.

Admissions: About 24% of the 1993-94 applicants were accepted. The SAT scores for the 1993-94 freshman class were as follows: Verbal—16% between 500 and 599, 63% between 600 and 700, and 21% above 700; Math—7% between 600 and 700 and 93% above 700. All of the current freshmen were in the top fifth of their class. There were 30 National Merit semifinalists.

Requirements: The SAT I is required. SAT II: Subject tests in writing, mathematics level II, and one in physics, biology, or chemistry, are also needed. Applicants should have completed 4 years of high school mathematics, 3 of English, 1 each of chemistry and history, and 5 units from other concentrations. Important factors used in the admissions decision are advanced placement or honor courses, recommendations by school officials, evidence of special talent, personality, intangible qualities, and extracurricular activities record.

Procedure: Freshmen are admitted in the fall. Entrance exams should be taken through December of the senior year. Early decision applications should be filed by October 15; regular applications, by January 1 for fall entry, along with an application fee of $40. Notification of early decision is sent December 15; regular decision, March 15. There are early decision and deferred admissions plans. About 17 early decision candidates were accepted for the 1993–94 class. A waiting list is an active part of the admissions procedure, with about 5% of applicants on the list.

Transfer: Twelve transfer students enrolled in a recent year. Transfers, admitted only into sophomore and junior classes, need a minimum GPA of 3.0. Applicants must have completed 1 year (2 years for juniors) of calculus and calculus-based physics, and must take Caltech's entrance examinations in mathematics and physics. Chemistry or chemical engineering majors also should have completed 1 year of chemistry and must take an additional entrance examination.

Visiting: There are regularly scheduled orientations for prospective students, including a campus tour leaving every day at 2 P.M. from Public Relations, followed by an Admissions Office information session. There are guides for informal visits and visitors may sit in on classes. To arrange for a visit, contact the Admissions Office at (800) LOV-TECH or (813) 395-6341.

Financial Aid: In 1993–94, 73% of all students received some form of financial aid; 66% received need-based aid. The average freshman award was $16,090. Of that total, scholarships or need-based grants averaged $12,241 ($24,295 maximum); loans averaged $3000 ($7000 maximum); and work contracts averaged $849 ($2000 maximum). Sixty percent of undergraduate students work part-time. Average earnings from campus work for the school year are $1500. The average financial indebtedness of the 1992–93 graduate was $7095. Caltech is a member of CSS. The FAF is required. The deadline for financial aid applications is February 1.

International Students: There are currently 194 international students enrolled. The student must take the SAT I. Students must also take SAT II: Subject tests in mathematics level II, writing, and one in either chemistry, physics, or biology.

Computers: The college provides computer facilities for student use. The mainframe is a SUN/UNIX cluster. Terminals are located in all buildings, including student housing. The mainframe computer can also be accessed from student-owned PCs. All students may access the system. It may be used anytime. There are no time limits on using the system and no fees.

Graduates: In 1992–93, 220 bachelor's degrees were awarded. The most popular majors among graduates were engineering and applied science (33%), biology (15%), and electrical engineering (14%). Within an average freshman class, 75% graduate in 4 years and 80% in 5 years. Some 130 companies recruited on campus in 1992–93.

Admissions Contact: Admissions Office.

CALIFORNIA INSTITUTE OF THE ARTS
C-5

Valencia, CA 91355
(805) 255–1050, ext. 2185
(800) 545-ARTS (out-of-state)

Full-time: 438 men, 233 women	Faculty: 88; IIA, --$
Part-time: 4 men, 4 women	Ph.D.s: n/av
Graduate: 176 men, 195 women	Student/Faculty: 8 to 1
Year: semesters	Tuition: $13,900
Application Deadline: February 1	Room & Board: $2500
Freshman Class: 1050 enrolled	
SAT I or ACT: not required	SPECIAL

California Institute of the Arts, founded in 1961, is a private, nonprofit institution offering undergraduate and graduate programs in art, dance, film and video, music, and theater. In addition to regional accreditation, Cal Arts has baccalaureate program accreditation with NASAD and NASM. The library contains 74,000 volumes, 7500 microform items, and 15,000 audiovisual forms, and subscribes to 650 periodicals. Computerized library sources and services include the card catalog, interlibrary loans, and database searching. Special learning facilities include an art gallery, radio station, TV station, and a movie theater. The 60-acre campus is in a suburban area 30 miles north of Los Angeles. Including residence halls, there are 3 buildings on campus.

Student Life: About 60% of undergraduates are from out-of-state. Students come from 41 states and 32 foreign countries. Seventy-eight percent are white. The average age of all undergraduates is 22.

Housing: A total of 450 students can be accommodated in college housing. College-sponsored living facilities include dormitories and on-campus apartments. On-campus housing is available on a first come, first-served basis and on a lottery system for upperclassmen. Priority is given to out-of-town students. Fifty-three percent of students live on campus. All students may keep cars on campus.

Activities: There are no fraternities or sororities on campus. There are some groups and organizations on campus, including newspaper, radio and TV, and student government. Popular campus events include music festivals, theater productions, and poetry readings.

Sports: There is no sports program at Cal Arts. Athletic and recreation facilities include tennis courts and a swimming pool.

Disabled Students: Ninety percent of the campus is accessible to disabled students. The following facilities are available: wheelchair ramps, elevators, special parking, and specially equipped rest rooms.

Services: Tutoring is available in all computerized media systems used in the 5 major departments.

Programs of Study: Cal Arts awards the B.F.A. degree. Master's degrees also are awarded. Bachelor's degrees are awarded in COMMUNICATIONS AND THE ARTS (dance, dramatic arts, film arts, fine arts, and music). Film, video, and art have the largest enrollments.

Required: To graduate, all students must complete the curriculum and degree requirements of the particular school, as well as 32 units in the liberal arts core.

Special: The institute offers internships with local and national companies, interdisciplinary studies, and a cooperative education program.

Faculty/Classroom: Sixty-three percent of the faculty are male, 37%, female.

Requirements: The SAT I or ACT is not required. Applicants must be graduates of an accredited secondary school or have a GED certificate. They must submit an official transcript and an essay. Portfolios and auditions are required and an interview is recommended. Evidence of special talent is an important factor used in the admission decision.

Procedure: Freshmen are admitted in the fall and spring. Applications should be filed by February 1 for fall entry and November 15 for spring entry, along with an application fee of $50. Notification is sent on a rolling basis. There is a deferred admissions plan.

Transfer: Transfer students must submit official college transcripts. An audition or a portfolio is required. Depending on the program, at least 1 or 2 years, including the final semester, must be completed in residence.

Visiting: There are regularly scheduled orientations for prospective students, including tours held Monday through Friday at 1 P.M. throughout the academic year. Visitors may sit in on classes. To arrange for a visit, contact the Office of Admissions.

Financial Aid: In 1993–94, 65% of all current freshmen and 78% of continuing students received some form of financial aid. Scholarships or need-based grants averaged $500 ($11,200 maximum); loans averaged $2625 ($3625 maximum); and work contracts averaged $1000 ($1800 maximum). Sixty-five percent of undergraduate students work part-time. The average financial indebtedness of a graduate was $13,250. Cal Arts is a member of CSS. The FAF or SAAC, and the FAFSA are required. The deadline for financial aid applications is March 1.

International Students: There are currently 79 international students enrolled. They must take the TOEFL and achieve a minimum score of 550.

Computers: The college provides computer facilities for student use. In addition to the library's computer center, the graphic design school has a Macintosh computer-imaging, text, and visual motion laboratory. The film and video school offers computer animation laboratories and editing equipment. The theater and dance schools feature computerized lighting facilities, and the music school has computerized composition and digital synthesis systems.

Graduates: In 1992–93, 132 bachelor's degrees were awarded.

Admissions Contact: Admissions Counselors.

CALIFORNIA LUTHERAN UNIVERSITY
C-5

Thousand Oaks, CA 91360
(805) 493-3135
(800) 252-5884 (western U.S. only)

Full-time: 649 men, 778 women	Faculty: 108; IIB, av$
Part-time: 201 men, 231 women	Ph.D.s: 72%
Graduate: 368 men, 551 women	Student/Faculty: 13 to 1
Year: semesters, summer session	Tuition: $12,040
Application Deadline: open	Room & Board: $5200
Freshman Class: 637 applied, 572 accepted, 273 enrolled	
SAT I Verbal/Math: 436/495	COMPETITIVE

California Lutheran University, founded in 1959, is a private, nonprofit liberal arts institution affiliated with the Evangelical Lutheran Church of America. The comprehensive, coeducational university offers undergraduate programs in arts and sciences and education. There are 3 undergraduate and 4 graduate schools. The library con-

ains 110,416 volumes, 14,559 microform items, and 2475 audiovi-ual forms, and subscribes to 644 periodicals. Computerized library ources and services include the card catalog and interlibrary loans. Special learning facilities include a learning resource center, radio tation, and TV station. The 285-acre campus is in an urban area 45 miles north of Los Angeles. Including residence halls, there are 34 buildings on campus.

Student Life: About 82% of undergraduates are from California. Students come from 28 states, 40 foreign countries, and Canada. Eighty-five percent are from public schools; 15% from private. Eighty-one percent are white; 11% Hispanic. Forty-eight percent are Protestant; 21% Catholic; 27% claim no religious affiliation. The average age of freshmen is 18; all undergraduates, 20. Twenty percent drop out by the end of their first year; 55% remain to graduate.

Housing: A total of 900 students can be accommodated in college housing. College-sponsored living facilities include coed dormitories. On-campus housing is guaranteed for all 4 years. Sixty-three percent of students live on campus; of those, 75% remain on campus on weekends. Alcohol is not permitted. All students may keep cars on campus.

Activities: There are no fraternities or sororities on campus. There are 26 groups on campus, including art, band, cheerleading, choir, chorale, chorus, computers, dance, drama, ethnic, honors, international, jazz band, literary magazine, musical theater, newspaper, orchestra, pep band, photography, political, professional, radio and TV, religious, social, social service, student government, symphony, and yearbook. Popular campus events include Homecoming, Santa Lucia, Black History Month, Scandinavian Day, Encuentros, and the Pulitzer Prize Symposium.

Sports: There are 8 intercollegiate sports for men and 7 for women, and 5 intramural sports for men and 5 for women. Athletic and recreation facilities include a 400-seat gymnasium, 2 fields, a swimming pool, tennis courts, and a 4500-seat stadium.

Disabled Students: Ninety percent of the campus is accessible to disabled students. The following facilities are available: wheelchair ramps, elevators, special parking, and specially equipped rest rooms.

Services: In addition to many counseling and information services, tutoring is available in every subject. The learning assistance and writing centers offer help with study and writing skills. In addition, there is remedial math. A student support services program helps low-income first-generation students adapt to the academic and social life of the campus.

Campus Safety and Security: Campus safety and security measures include 24-hour foot and vehicle patrol, escort service, informal discussions, pamphlets, posters, and films. In addition, there are emergency telephones, lighted pathways and sidewalks, and all residence halls are equipped with security systems.

Programs of Study: CAL Lu awards the B.A. and B.S. degrees. Master's degrees also are awarded. Bachelor's degrees are awarded in BIOLOGICAL SCIENCE (biochemistry and biology/biological science), BUSINESS (accounting, business administration and management, business economics, international business management, and marketing/retailing/merchandising), COMMUNICATIONS AND THE ARTS (advertising, communications, dramatic arts, English, fine arts, French, German, music, Spanish, and speech/debate/rhetoric), COMPUTER AND PHYSICAL SCIENCE (chemistry, computer science, geology, information sciences and systems, mathematics, and physics), EDUCATION (art, early childhood, elementary, foreign languages, guidance, health, middle school, music, physical, science, secondary, and special), HEALTH PROFESSIONS (predentistry and premedicine), SOCIAL SCIENCE (criminal justice, history, philosophy, political science/government, prelaw, psychology, religion, social science, and sociology). Biology, accounting, education, and humanities are the strongest academically. Business, psychology, education, and communication arts have the largest enrollments.

Required: To graduate, all students must complete a core curriculum including 14 units in social science, 9 in religion, 8 each in foreign language and science, 7 in English, 6 in creative arts, 4 in mathematics, and 3 in physical education. Students must also take 2 writing-intensive courses, global studies, gender and ethnic studies, and a senior level capstone course. Also needed are a total of 124 units, 40 of which must be upper division with 32 hours in the major for a B.A. and 40 hours for a B.S. Students must have a minimum 2.0 GPA, with 2.25 in the major.

Special: Cal Lu offers co-op programs, cross-registration with Wagner College, internships, and study abroad. Also available are work-study, accelerated degrees in business, computer science, and accounting, a general studies degree, and dual and student-designed interdisciplinary degree majors. A 3–2 engineering degree with Washington University of St. Louis, credit for experimental learning, special student status for nondegree study, pass/fail options, and an adult degree evening program are also offered. There is a freshman honors program on campus, as well as one national honor society.

Faculty/Classroom: Sixty-six percent of faculty are male; 34%, female. All teach undergraduates. No introductory courses are taught by graduate students. The average class size in an introductory lecture is 35; in a laboratory, 17; and in a regular course offering, 22.

Admissions: About 90% of the 1993–94 applicants were accepted. The SAT scores for the 1993–94 freshman class were as follows: Verbal—76% below 500, 19% between 500 and 599, and 4% between 600 and 700; Math—47% below 500, 37% between 500 and 599, 14% between 600 and 700, and 2% above 700. About 23% of the current freshmen were in the top fifth of their class; 58% were in the top two fifths.

Requirements: A minimum GPA of 2.5 is required. The SAT I or ACT is required. Minimum composite scores are 800 for the SAT I (400 verbal) and 19 for the ACT. Applicants must be graduates of an accredited secondary school or have a GED and have completed 4 years of English, 3 years of mathematics, and 2 years each of art, foreign language, history, science, and social studies. An essay is required and an interview is recommended. AP and CLEP credits are accepted. Important factors used in the admissions decision are advanced placement or honor courses, recommendations by school officials, evidence of special talent, leadership record, and personality.

Procedure: Freshmen are admitted fall and spring. Entrance exams should be taken in the fall. Application deadlines are open. The application fee is $35. Notification is sent on a rolling basis. There is a deferred admissions plan.

Transfer: About 220 transfer students enrolled in 1993–94. Transfers must have a minimum 2.25 GPA and at least 24 credit hours earned. An application is required. An interview is recommended. A total of 30 credits out of 124 must be completed at Cal Lu.

Visiting: There are regularly scheduled orientations for prospective students, including an admission and financial aid interview, a tour, visits with faculty or coaches, and lunch. There are guides for informal visits and visitors may sit in on classes and stay overnight at the school. To arrange for a visit, contact the Admission Office at (805) 493–3135.

Financial Aid: In 1993–94, 82% of all current freshmen and 87% of continuing students received some form of financial aid. About 78% of freshmen and 80% of continuing students received need-based aid. The average freshman award was $9772. Of that total, scholarships or need-based grants averaged $4900 ($6000 maximum); loans averaged $2526 ($4100 maximum); and work contracts averaged $1000 ($1500 maximum). Forty-five percent of undergraduate students work part-time. Average earnings from campus work for the school year are $1000. The average financial indebtedness of the 1992–93 graduate was $9000. The FAF is required. The deadline for financial aid applications is March 1.

International Students: There are currently 180 international students enrolled. The school actively recruits these students. They must take the TOEFL and achieve a minimum score of 530 or the SAT I, if unable to take the TOEFL.

Computers: The college provides computer facilities for student use. The mainframes are an HP 9000–825, a DEC VAX 11/750, and an IBM System/38. Students may access the mainframe through 26 terminals in the library. Apple and IBM-compatible laboratories are in the Computer Science Building. The Ahmanson Science Center has a hypermedia laboratory with 14 Apple Macintoshes. Six halls contain 3 Macintoshes with a printer. All students may access the system. It may be used anytime. There are no time limits on using the system and no fees.

Graduates: In 1992–93, 450 bachelor's degrees were awarded. The most popular majors among graduates were business (35%), education (12%), and communications (7%). Within an average freshman class, 50% graduate in 4 years and 60% in 5 years. Some 75 companies recruited on campus in 1992–93. In the 1992 graduating class, 36% of all graduates were enrolled in graduate school within 6 months of graduation; 50% had found employment.

Admissions Contact: Office of Admission.

CALIFORNIA MARITIME ACADEMY   B-3
Vallejo, CA 94590   (707) 648–4222

Full-time: 430 men, 57 women	Faculty: 27; IIB, +$
Part-time: none	Ph.Ds: 22%
Graduate: none	Student/Faculty: 18 to 1
Year: semesters	Tuition: $2548 ($8138)
Application Deadline: March 15	Room & Board: $4770
Freshman Class: 321 applied, 199 accepted, 117 enrolled	
SAT I or ACT: required	COMPETITIVE

California Maritime Academy, founded in 1929, is a public coeducational college that awards degrees in marine transportation, business administration, marine engineering technology, and mechanical engineering. In addition to regional accreditation, CMA has baccalaureate program accreditation with ABET. The library contains 22,000 volumes and 15,000 microform items and subscribes to 225 periodicals. Computerized library sources and services include interlibrary

loans. The 67-acre campus is in a suburban area 30 miles northeast of San Francisco. Including residence halls, there are 12 buildings on campus.

Student Life: About 88% of undergraduates are from California. Students come from 8 states and 4 foreign countries. Eighty percent are from public schools; 20% from private. Seventy-two percent are white; 13% Asian American. The average age of freshmen is 22; all undergraduates, 22. Ten percent drop out by the end of their first year; 73% remain to graduate.

Housing: A total of 460 students can be accommodated in college housing. College-sponsored living facilities include single-sex and coed dormitories. On-campus housing is guaranteed for all 4 years. Eighty-five percent of students live on campus; of those, 30% remain on campus on weekends. Alcohol is not permitted. All students may keep cars on campus.

Activities: There are no fraternities or sororities on campus. There are 16 groups on campus, including drill team, jazz band, newspaper, photography, professional, religious, student government, and yearbook.

Sports: There are 7 intercollegiate sports for men and 7 for women, and 10 intramural sports for men and 8 for women. Athletic and recreation facilities include a gymnasium, a weight room, physical therapy and exercise rooms, and a 25-meter pool.

Disabled Students: Seventy percent of the campus is accessible to disabled students. The following facilities are available: wheelchair ramps, special parking, specially equipped rest rooms, and lowered drinking fountains.

Services: In addition to many counseling and information services, tutoring is available in some subjects, including mathematics, English, engineering, and science. There is also remedial math, reading, and writing.

Campus Safety and Security: Campus safety and security measures include pamphlets, posters, films and lighted pathways and sidewalks.

Programs of Study: CMA awards the B.S degree. Bachelor's degrees are awarded in BUSINESS (business administration and management and transportation management), ENGINEERING AND ENVIRONMENTAL DESIGN (marine engineering and mechanical engineering). Mechanical engineering is the strongest academically and has the largest enrollment.

Required: Graduation requirements for all students include a minimum 2.0 GPA and completion of English composition, American government, U.S. history, algebra and trigonometry, computer science, and survival swimming courses. A total of 160 to 175 credits is required for graduation.

Special: The academy has simulator training and requires a 2-month session aboard the academy's ship. Laboratory time is a major part of each program.

Faculty/Classroom: Eighty-nine percent of faculty are male; 11%, female. All teach undergraduates. The average class size in an introductory lecture is 25; in a laboratory, 12; and in a regular course offering, 25.

Admissions: About 62% of the 1993–94 applicants were accepted. The SAT scores for the 1993–94 freshman class were as follows: Verbal—61% below 500, 29% between 500 and 599, 7% between 600 and 700, and 2% above 700; Math—47% below 500, 37% between 500 and 599, 14% between 600 and 700, and 1% above 700. About 42% of the current freshmen were in the top fifth of their class; 72% were in the top two fifths.

Requirements: A minimum GPA of 2.0 is required. The SAT I or the ACT is required. Applicant must be a graduate of an accredited secondary school or have a GED certificate. Secondary school courses must include 4 years of English, 3 years of mathematics, and 1 year of laboratory science. An essay is required. Interviews are recommended. CLEP credit is accepted. Important factors used in the admissions decision are leadership record, advanced placement or honor courses, evidence of special talent, personality, intangible qualities, and recommendations by school officials.

Procedure: Freshmen are admitted in the fall. Entrance exams should be taken by January. Applications should be filed by March 15 for fall entry, along with an application fee of $40. Notification is sent on a rolling basis.

Transfer: About 23 transfer students enrolled in 1993–94. Applicants must have a 2.0 GPA and must provide SAT I or ACT scores.

Visiting: There are regularly scheduled orientations for prospective students, consisting of a mandatory orientation for all new students, a week before classes start. There are guides for informal visits and visitors may sit in on classes. To arrange for a visit, contact the Admissions Office at (707) 648-4222.

Financial Aid: In 1993–94 45% of all current freshmen and 55% of continuing students received some form of financial aid. About 95% of freshmen and 85% of continuing students received need-based aid. The average freshman award was $4800. Of that total, scholarships or need-based grants averaged $1000 ($2000 maximum); and loans averaged $2000 ($2500 maximum). Seventy percent of under-

graduate students work part-time. Average earnings from campus work for the school year are $700. The average financial indebtedness of the 1992–93 graduate was $8000. The FAF, FFS, or SFS is required. The deadline for financial aid applications is March 2.

International Students: There are currently 12 international students enrolled. They must take the TOEFL and achieve a minimum score of 550.

Computers: The college provides computer facilities for student use. There are 22 self-contained microcomputers in the computer center and 4 microcomputers in the library. There are no time limits on using the system and no fees.

Graduates: In 1992–93 71 bachelor's degrees were awarded. The most popular majors among graduates were marine transportation (35%), business administration (20%), and marine engineering (19%). Within an average freshman class, 77% graduate in 4 years and 23% in 5 years. Some 15 companies recruited on campus in 1992–93. In the 1992 graduating class, 1% of the men were enrolled in graduate school within 6 months of graduation; all of the men and women had found employment.

Admissions Contact: Albert T. Perkins, Admissions Office.

CALIFORNIA POLYTECHNIC STATE UNIVERSITY

San Luis Obispo, CA 93407

B-4

(805) 756-2311

Full-time: 7971 men, 5593 women	Faculty: 622; IIA, + +$
Part-time: 305 men, 235 women	Ph.D.s: 63%
Graduate: 399 men, 471 women	Student/Faculty: 22 to 1
Year: quarters, summer session	Tuition: $2217 ($9597)
Application Deadline: November 30	Room & Board: $4763
Freshman Class: 9231 applied, 3264 accepted, 2652 enrolled	
SAT I Verbal/Math: 451/553	VERY COMPETITIVE +

California Polytechnic State University, founded in 1901, is a public institution that is part of the California State University system. It offers programs in agriculture, architecture and environmental design, business, education, engineering, liberal arts, sciences and mathematics, and preprofessional studies. There are 6 undergraduate and 19 graduate schools. In addition to regional accreditation, Cal Poly has baccalaureate program accreditation with AACSB, ABET, ACCE, ADA, AHEA, ASLA, and NAAB. The library contains 731,615 volumes and 2,869,965 microform items, and subscribes to 2983 periodicals. Computerized library sources and services include interlibrary loans. Special learning facilities include a learning resource center and radio station. The 400-acre campus is in a suburban area 200 miles from both San Francisco and Los Angeles. Including residence halls, there are 130 buildings on campus.

Student Life: About 91% of undergraduates are from California. Students come from 39 states, 92 foreign countries, and Canada. Ninety-two percent are from public schools; 8% from private. Sixty-two percent are white; 14% Hispanic. The average age of freshmen is 19.4; all undergraduates, 23.3. Eleven percent drop out by the end of their first year; 59% remain to graduate.

Housing: A total of 2800 students can be accommodated in college housing. College-sponsored living facilities include coed dormitories. In addition there are special interest houses and living/learning centers with an academic theme. On-campus housing is available on a first-come, first-served basis. Seventy-seven percent of students commute. Alcohol is not permitted. All students may keep cars on campus.

Activities: There is 1 local and 26 national fraternities and 8 national sororities. There are 400 groups on campus, including art, band, choir, chorale, chorus, computers, dance, drama, ethnic, film, honors, international, newspaper, orchestra, photography, political, professional, radio, social, social service, and student government. Popular campus events include Rose Float, Week of Welcome (WOW), and Civil Rights Awareness Week.

Sports: There are 9 intercollegiate sports for men and 8 for women, and 19 intramural sports for men and 19 for women. Athletic and recreation facilities include an indoor/outdoor swimming pool, volleyball, tennis, basketball, and racquetball courts, weight rooms, playing fields, and a track.

Disabled Students: Ninety-five percent of the campus is accessible to disabled students. The following facilities are available: wheelchair ramps, elevators, special parking, specially equipped rest rooms, and lowered telephones.

Services: In addition to many counseling and information services, tutoring is available in most subjects. There is a writing skills laboratory, and a test office. There is also a reader service for the blind.

Campus Safety and Security: Campus safety and security measures include 24-hour foot and vehicle patrol, escort service, pamphlets, posters, and films, and emergency telephones. In addition, there are lighted pathways and sidewalks.

Programs of Study: Cal Poly awards the B.A., B.S., and B.Arch. degrees. A master's degree also is awarded. Bachelor's degrees are awarded in AGRICULTURE (agricultural business management, agriculture, dairy science, horticulture, natural resource management, and soil science), BIOLOGICAL SCIENCE (biochemistry, biology/biological science, and microbiology), BUSINESS (business administration and management and recreation and leisure services), COMMUNICATIONS AND THE ARTS (English, graphic design, and journalism), COMPUTER AND PHYSICAL SCIENCE (chemistry, computer science, mathematics, physics, and statistics), EDUCATION (industrial arts, physical, and vocational), ENGINEERING AND ENVIRONMENTAL DESIGN (aeronautical engineering, agricultural engineering, architectural engineering, architecture, city/community/regional planning, civil engineering, computer engineering, construction management, electrical/electronics engineering, engineering, environmental engineering, industrial engineering, landscape architecture/design, mechanical engineering, and metallurgical engineering), SOCIAL SCIENCE (economics, food science, history, political science/government, and social science). Agricultural management, architecture, and business administration have the largest enrollments.

Required: Students must have a minimum 2.0 GPA and complete general education and breadth requirements including the following: 18 units each of physical and life sciences, social sciences, and literature and the arts; 14 units of English; and 5 units of psychology and health. Mathematics and computer literacy courses and completion of a senior project are required. A total of 186 to 263 quarter units is required to graduate.

Special: The college offers work-study programs, co-op programs in numerous majors, extensive study abroad in 9 countries, dual majors, and internships in many majors. Credit for military experience and pass/fail options are available.

Faculty/Classroom: Seventy-eight percent of faculty are male; 22%, female. Ninety-three percent teach undergraduates. The average class size in a regular course offering is 40.

Admissions: About 35% of the 1993-94 applicants were accepted.

Requirements: A minimum GPA of 2.0 is required. The SAT I is required. Applicant must be a graduate from an accredited high school or have a GED. Fifteen academic credits are required, including 4 years of English, 3 of mathematics, 2 of a foreign language, and one each of history, science, and visual or performing arts, and 3 college preparation electives. AP and CLEP credits are accepted.

Procedure: Freshmen are admitted fall and summer. Applications should be filed by November 30 for fall entry, June 30 for winter entry, August 31 for spring entry, and February 28 for summer entry, along with an application fee of $55. Notification is sent May 1.

Transfer: About 1130 transfer students enrolled in 1992-93. Applicants must have completed 56 semester or 84 quarter units with a minimum GPA of 2.0. A total of 50 quarter units out of 186 to 263 must be completed at Cal Poly.

Visiting: There are regularly scheduled orientations for prospective students, consisting of Mondays and Wednesdays at 10 A.M. and 2 P.M. Visitors may stay overnight at the school. To arrange for a visit, contact the Admissions Office at (805) 756-2311 or (805) 756-2792.

Financial Aid: In 1993-94, 31% of all current freshmen received some form of financial aid. About 30% of freshmen and 34% of continuing students received need-based aid. The average freshman award was $4242. Of that total, scholarships or need-based grants averaged $3055 ($10,796 maximum); and loans averaged $2000 ($2625 maximum). Two percent of undergraduate students work part-time. Average earnings from campus work for the school year are $1500. The college's own financial statement and FAFSA are required. The deadline for financial aid applications is March 1.

International Students: There are currently 1071 international students enrolled. They must take the TOEFL and achieve a minimum score of 550.

Computers: The college provides computer facilities for student use. The mainframe is an IBM ES/9000 Model 732. There are also 1006 IBM PC, Apple Macintosh, HP and DEC microcomputers available throughout campus. All students may access the system. There are no time limits on using the system and no fees.

Graduates: In 1992-93, 3352 bachelor's degrees were awarded. The most popular majors among graduates were business (13%), agribusiness (5%), and architecture (4%). Within an average freshman class, 5% graduate in 4 years, 13% in 5 years, and 39% in 6 years. Some 104 companies recruited on campus in 1992-93.

Admissions Contact: Admissions Office.

CALIFORNIA STATE POLYTECHNIC UNIVERSITY POMONA

D-5

Pomona, CA 91768-4019   (909) 869-2000

Full-time: 6666 men, 4556 women	Faculty: 638; IIA, +$
Part-time: 2500 men, 1626 women	Ph.D.s: 76%
Graduate: 733 men, 969 women	Student/Faculty: 18 to 1
Year: quarters, summer quarter	Tuition: $1576 ($7480)
Application Deadline: November 1	Room & Board: $4862

Freshman Class: 6008 applied, 3931 accepted, 1566 enrolled

SAT I Verbal/Math: 380/510   ACT: 20   **LESS COMPETITIVE**

California State Polytechnic University/Pomona, a coeducational, occupationally oriented institution founded in 1938, is part of the state-supported university system. It offers graduate and undergraduate programs in agriculture, liberal arts and sciences, business, engineering, and technical and professional training. There are 7 undergraduate schools and one graduate school. In addition to regional accreditation, Cal Poly has baccalaureate program accreditation with ABET, ADA, ASLA, NAAB, and NRPA. The library contains 577,687 volumes, 1,955,043 microform items, and 4513 audiovisual forms, and subscribes to 2919 periodicals. Computerized library sources and services include the card catalog, interlibrary loans, and database searching. Special learning facilities include a learning resource center, art gallery, TV station, and an interactive TV studio. The 1437-acre campus is in a suburban area 30 miles east of Los Angeles. Including residence halls, there are 60 buildings on campus.

Student Life: About 75% of undergraduates are from California. Students come from 39 states, 112 foreign countries, and Canada. Eighty-three percent are from public schools; 9% from private. Forty-two percent are white; 29% Asian American; 18% Hispanic. The average age of freshmen is 18; all undergraduates, 23. Twenty-three percent drop out by the end of their first year; 43% remain to graduate.

Housing: A total of 2025 students can be accommodated in college housing. College-sponsored living facilities include coed dormitories and on-campus apartments. In addition, there are special interest houses and a center for regenerative studies. On-campus housing is guaranteed for the freshman year only and is available on a first-come, first-served basis. Priority is given to out-of-town students. Eighty-eight percent of students commute. All students may keep cars on campus.

Activities: About 2% of men belong to 11 national fraternities; about 1% of women belong to 4 national sororities. There are 123 groups on campus, including art, band, cheerleading, chess, choir, chorale, chorus, computers, dance, drama, ethnic, film, gay, honors, international, jazz band, literary magazine, musical theater, newspaper, opera, pep band, photography, political, professional, religious, social, social service, student government, and yearbook. Popular campus events include Rose Float, Back-to-School parties, and the Performing Arts Series.

Sports: Athletic and recreation facilities include a 5000-seat stadium, tennis and racquetball courts, basketball and volleyball courts, a track, soccer, baseball and softball fields, a swimming pool, gymnastics and weight rooms, a horse arena, and dance studios.

Disabled Students: Ninety percent of the campus is accessible to disabled students. The following facilities are available: wheelchair ramps, elevators, special parking, specially equipped rest rooms, special class scheduling, and lowered telephones.

Services: In addition to many counseling and information services, tutoring is available in most subjects. There is also a reader service for the blind and remedial math and writing.

Campus Safety and Security: Campus safety and security measures include 24-hour foot and vehicle patrol, self defense education, escort service, and shuttle buses. In addition, there are informal discussions, pamphlets, posters, films, emergency telephones, and lighted pathways and sidewalks.

Programs of Study: Cal Poly awards the B.A. and B.S. degrees. Master's degrees also are awarded. Bachelor's degrees are awarded in AGRICULTURE (agricultural business management, agriculture, animal science, horticulture, international agriculture, and soil science), BIOLOGICAL SCIENCE (biology/biological science, biotechnology, botany, microbiology, and zoology), BUSINESS (accounting, banking and finance, business administration and management, hotel/motel and restaurant management, human resources, marketing/retailing/merchandising, and real estate), COMMUNICATIONS AND THE ARTS (communications, dramatic arts, English, fine arts, and music), COMPUTER AND PHYSICAL SCIENCE (chemistry, computer science, earth science, geology, information sciences and systems, mathematics, and physics), EDUCATION (physical), ENGINEERING AND ENVIRONMENTAL DESIGN (aeronautical engineering, agricultural engineering, architecture, chemical engineering, civil engineering, electrical/electronics engineering, engineering technology, industrial engineering, landscape architecture/design, manufacturing engineering, and mechanical engineering), SOCIAL

SCIENCE (American studies, anthropology, behavioral science, economics, food science, geography, history, humanities, parks and recreation management, philosophy, political science/government, psychology, social science, sociology, and urban studies). Electrical engineering, accounting, and marketing management have the largest enrollments.

Required: All students must complete general education requirements, including courses in written and oral communications, critical thinking, mathematics, humanities, natural sciences, and social sciences, and must pass a graduate writing test. A total of 186 to 250 quarter units with a minimum GPA of 2.0 is required in order to graduate.

Special: Cross-registration is possible with any California State University school. Internships and co-op programs are available in agriculture, business, environmental design, engineering, science, political science, behavioral science, and physical education. An international study program in 17 countries, work-study programs, B.A.-B.S. degrees, dual majors, a liberal studies degree, credit for military experience, an external degree program, and credit/no credit options are offered. Nondegree study is possible. There are 30 national honor societies on campus. Twenty-two departments have honors programs.

Faculty/Classroom: Seventy-two percent of faculty are male; 28%, female. Graduate students teach 3% of introductory courses. The average class size in an introductory lecture is 40; in a laboratory, 18; and in a regular course offering, 22.

Admissions: About 65% of the 1993–94 applicants were accepted. The SAT scores for the 1993–94 freshman class were as follows: Verbal—86% below 500, 11% between 500 and 599, 2% between 600 and 700, and 1% above 700; Math—44% below 500, 35% between 500 and 599, 17% between 600 and 700, and 4% above 700. The ACT scores were 49% below 21, 27% between 21 and 23, 13% between 24 and 26, 9% between 27 and 28, and 2% above 28. There were 3 National Merit finalists.

Requirements: The SAT I is required. Applicant must be a graduate of an accredited secondary school or have a GED equivalent. Secondary school courses must include 4 years of high school English, 3 each of mathematics and electives, 2 of foreign language, and 1 each of science, history, and art. AP and CLEP credits are accepted.

Procedure: Entrance exams should be taken during the fall of the senior year. Applications should be filed by November 1 for fall entry, June 1 for winter entry, August 1 for spring entry, and February 1 for summer entry, along with an application fee of $55. Notification is sent on a rolling basis. There are early decision, early admissions, and deferred admissions plans.

Transfer: About 1650 transfer students enrolled in 1993–94. Applicants must have completed 56 semester or 84 quarter units including college preparatory subjects. A 2.0 GPA (2.5 for nonresidents) is required. A total of 50 quarter units out of 182 to 250 must be completed at Cal Poly.

Visiting: There are regularly scheduled orientations for prospective students. There are guides for informal visits and visitors may sit in on classes and stay overnight at the school. To arrange for a visit, contact Student Outreach and Recruitment at (909) 869–3210 or (909) 869–3258.

Financial Aid: In 1993–94 26% of all current freshmen and 74% of continuing students received some form of financial aid. The average freshman award was $1626. Of that total, scholarships or need-based grants averaged $630 ($3000 maximum); loans averaged $1211 ($4000 maximum); and work contracts averaged $1200 ($3000 maximum). Two percent of undergraduate students work part-time. Averrage earnings from campus work for the school year are $1070. The average financial indebtedness of the 1992–93 graduate was $9000. Cal Poly is a member of CSS. The FAF and the SAC are required. The deadline for financial aid applications is March 2.

International Students: There are currently 482 international students enrolled. The school actively recruits these students. They must take the TOEFL and achieve a minimum score of 525.

Computers: The college provides computer facilities for student use. The mainframes are a DEC VAX 9000 and 6440, an AT&T 3B15, a Digital 6000–430, and a Digital 6000–440. Personal computer clusters are available in laboratories on campus. All students may access the system. It may be used 24 hours per day. There are no time limits on using the system and no fees.

Graduates: In 1992–93, 2718 bachelor's degrees were awarded. The most popular majors among graduates were finance, real estate, and law (7%), electrical engineering (6%), and marketing (5%). Within an average freshman class, 22% graduate in 5 years. Some 600 companies recruited on campus in 1992–93.

Admissions Contact: Joseph Marshall, Acting Admissions Officer.

CALIFORNIA STATE UNIVERSITY SYSTEM

The California State University system, established in 1961, is California's comprehensive public university system offering bachelor's, master's, and joint doctoral degrees. It is governed by a 24-member board of trustees, and its chief administrator is the chancellor. CSU' main priorities are to emphasize quality in instruction; to provide an environment in which scholarship, research, creative, artistic, and professional activity are valued and supported; and to stress the importance of the liberal arts and sciences. Total enrollment in fall 1993 of all 20 campuses was 326,000; there were more than 16,000 faculty members. The California State University System offers more than 900 baccalaureate, 600 master's, and 12 joint doctoral programs. CSU campuses are located in Bakersfield, Chico, Dominguez Hills (in Carson), Fresno, Fullerton, Hayward, Humboldt (in Arcata), Long Beach, Los Angeles, Northridge, Pomona, Sacramento, San Bernardino, San Diego, San Francisco, San Jose, San Luis Obispo, Sonoma (in Rohnert Park), and Stanislaus (in Turlock). Profiles of the 4-year campuses are included in this chapter in alphabetical order with other California schools.

CALIFORNIA STATE UNIVERSITY BAKERSFIELD
Bakersfield, CA 93311–1099 C-4

(805) 664–3380
(800) 788–2782 (in-state)

Full-time: 1157 men, 1767 women	**Faculty:** 224; IIA, +$
Part-time: 411 men, 626 women	**Ph.D.s:** 87%
Graduate: 439 men, 843 women	**Student/Faculty:** 13 to 1
Year: quarters, summer session	**Tuition:** $1692 ($9072)
Application Deadline: September 14	**Room & Board:** $3710
Freshman Class: 944 applied, 616 accepted, 376 enrolled	
SAT I Verbal/Math: 404/433	**ACT:** 21 COMPETITIVE

California State University/Bakersfield, founded in 1965, is part of the California State University System. The school offers graduate and undergraduate programs in liberal arts and sciences, business, public administration, education, health fields, preengineering, and pre-professional training. There are 3 undergraduate and 11 graduate schools. In addition to regional accreditation, Cal State Bakersfield has baccalaureate program accreditation with AACSB, NCATE, and NLN. The library contains 315,000 volumes and 453,448 microform items, and subscribes to 2700 periodicals. Computerized library sources and services include the card catalog, interlibrary loans, and database searching. Special learning facilities include a learning resource center, an art gallery, a natural history museum, a radio station, a TV station, a geological data sample repository, an archaelogical information center, an applied research center, and an animal care and treatment facility. The 375-acre campus is in an urban area 5 miles west of Bakersfield.

Student Life: About 97% of undergraduates are from California. Students come from 17 states, 58 foreign countries, and Canada. Ninety-eight percent are from public schools; 2% from private. Fifty-two percent are white; 22% Hispanic. The average age of freshmen is 19; all undergraduates, 26. Fifteen percent drop out by the end of their first year.

Housing: A total of 295 students can be accommodated in college housing. College-sponsored living facilities include single-sex and coed dormitories. On-campus housing is guaranteed for all 4 years and is available on a first-come, first-served basis. Priority is given to out-of-town students. Ninety-eight percent of students commute. Alcohol is not permitted. All students may keep cars on campus.

Activities: About 2% of men belong to 3 national fraternities; about 2% of women belong to 4 national sororities. There are 70 groups on campus, including art, band, cheerleading, chess, choir, chorale, computers, dance, drama, ethnic, film, gay, honors, international, jazz band, literary magazine, musical theater, newspaper, opera, orchestra, pep band, photography, political, professional, radio and TV, religious, social, social service, student government, and symphony. Popular campus events include Cinco de Mayo, Open Campus, and Jazz Festival.

Sports: There are 7 intercollegiate sports for men and 6 for women, and 12 intramural sports for men and 12 for women. Athletic and recreation facilities include a new 4000-seat gymnasium, a wrestling sport center, an aquatic center, tennis and racquetball courts, and softball and soccer fields.

Disabled Students: All of the campus is accessible to disabled students. The following facilities are available: wheelchair ramps, elevators, special parking, specially equipped rest rooms, special class scheduling, lowered drinking fountains, and lowered telephones.

Services: In addition to many counseling and information services, tutoring is available in most subjects. In addition, there is a reader service for the blind, and remedial math, reading, and writing.

Campus Safety and Security: Campus safety and security measures include 24-hour foot and vehicle patrol, self-defense education, escort service, and informal discussions. In addition, there are pamphlets, posters, and films, emergency telephones, and lighted pathways and sidewalks.

Programs of Study: Cal State Bakersfield awards the B.A. and B.S. degrees. Master's degrees also are awarded. Bachelor's degrees are awarded in BIOLOGICAL SCIENCE (biology/biological science), BUSINESS (banking and finance and business administration and

management), COMMUNICATIONS AND THE ARTS (communications, English, fine arts, and Spanish), COMPUTER AND PHYSICAL SCIENCE (chemistry, computer science, geology, mathematics, and physics), EDUCATION (early childhood), ENGINEERING AND ENVIRONMENTAL DESIGN (environmental science, land use management and reclamation, petroleum/natural gas engineering, and preengineering), HEALTH PROFESSIONS (clinical science, medical technology, nursing, predentistry, premedicine, prepharmacy, preveterinary science, and public health), SOCIAL SCIENCE (anthropology, criminal justice, economics, history, philosophy, political science/government, prelaw, psychology, public administration, religion, and sociology). Business, education, public administration, and nursing are the strongest academically. Business has the largest enrollment.

Required: All students must complete 72 quarter units of general education requirements and a senior seminar. They must also take a comprehensive writing examination or complete an upper-division writing course with a grade of C or better. A total of 186 quarter units with a minimum GPA of 2.0 is required in order to graduate.

Special: Cal State Bakersfield offers co-op programs in education and business administration, cross-registration through the National Student Exchange Program, and study abroad at 36 universities in 16 countries. A 3–2 engineering degree is offered with California Polytechnic State University/San Luis Obispo, and student-designed majors are possible. Credit for life experience, pass/fail options, and nondegree study are available. There is a freshman honors program on campus.

Faculty/Classroom: Sixty-two percent of faculty are male; 38%, female. All teach undergraduates and 100% do research. No introductory courses are taught by graduate students. The average class size in an introductory lecture is 40; in a laboratory, 24; and in a regular course offering, 30.

Admissions: About 65% of the 1993–94 applicants were accepted.

Requirements: Cal State Bakersfield requires applicants to be in the upper 33% of their class. A minimum GPA of 2.0 is required. The SAT I or ACT is required if the GPA is below 3.0. In addition, applicants must be graduates of an accredited secondary school or GED equivalent, and have a total of 15 units, including 4 years of high school English, 3 each of mathematics and electives, 2 of foreign language, and 1 each of laboratory science, history/government, and visual and performing arts. AP and CLEP credits are accepted.

Procedure: Freshmen are admitted fall, winter, and spring. Entrance exams should be taken by December of the senior year. Applications should be filed by September 14 for fall entry, January 4 for winter entry, and March 29 for spring entry, along with an application fee of $55. Notification is sent on a rolling basis. There are early decision, early admissions, and deferred admissions plans.

Transfer: About 620 transfer students enrolled in 1993–94. A 2.0 GPA (2.4 for nonresidents) is required in a minimum of 56 quarter units earned, including English and mathematics. A total of 45 quarter credits out of 186 must be completed at Cal State Bakersfield.

Visiting: There are regularly scheduled orientations for prospective students, consisting of a day-long orientation that includes meetings with faculty advisors and school deans. There are guides for informal visits and visitors may sit in on classes. To arrange for a visit, contact the Outreach Office at (805) 664-3181.

Financial Aid: In 1993–94, 46% of all current freshmen and 33% of continuing students received some form of financial aid. The average freshman award was $3500. Of that total, scholarships or need-based grants averaged $938 ($2070 maximum); loans averaged $1847 ($2625 maximum); and work contracts averaged $1295 ($2000 maximum). Nine percent of undergraduate students work part-time. Cal State Bakersfield is a member of CSS. The FAF, FFS, or SFS and the SAAC are required. The deadline for financial aid applications is March 2.

International Students: There are currently 121 international students enrolled. The school actively recruits these students. They must take the TOEFL and achieve a minimum score of 500. The SAT I or ACT is required if the GPA is below 3.0.

Computers: The college provides computer facilities for student use. The mainframe is a CDC CYBER 830 and a DEC VAX 8350. There are about 300 microcomputers available for student use in student laboratories located throughout the campus. All students may access the system. There are no time limits on using the system and no fees.

Graduates: In 1992–93, 800 bachelor's degrees were awarded. The most popular majors among graduates were education (16%), business (13%), and public administration (4%). Within an average freshman class, 28% graduate in 5 years. Some 80 companies recruited on campus in 1992–93.

Admissions Contact: Admissions Officer.

CALIFORNIA STATE UNIVERSITY
CHICO
B-2

Chico, CA 95929   (916) 898–6323

Full-time: 5914 men, 5914 women	Faculty: 631; IIA, +$
Part-time: 683 men, 660 women	Ph.D.s: 66%
Graduate: 645 men, 890 women	Student/Faculty: 19 to 1
Year: semesters, summer session	Tuition: $1782 ($9162)
Application Deadline: open	Room & Board: $4364
Freshman Class: 4816 applied, 3922 accepted, 1278 enrolled	
SAT I Verbal/Math: 420/480	ACT: 20 COMPETITIVE

California State University/Chico, founded in 1887, is a public coeducational institution offering undergraduate programs in behavioral and social sciences, business, communication and education, engineering, computer science and technology, humanities and fine arts, natural sciences, agriculture, and nursing. The university offers microwave television classes to receiving classrooms in northern California and satelite television to computer manufacturers. There are 9 undergraduate schools and one graduate school. In addition to regional accreditation, CSU, Chico has baccalaureate program accreditation with AACSB, ABET, ACCE, ADA, CSWE, NASAD, NASM, NLN, and NRPA. The library contains 1,315,481 volumes, 927,111 microform items, and 4414 audiovisual forms, and subscribes to 3698 periodicals. Computerized library sources and services include the card catalog, interlibrary loans, and database searching. Special learning facilities include a learning resource center, an art gallery, a planetarium, and a radio station. The 130-acre campus is in a small town 100 miles north of Sacramento. Including residence halls, there are 70 buildings on campus.

Student Life: About 98% of undergraduates are from California. Students come from 36 states, 70 foreign countries, and Canada. Eighty-nine percent are from public schools; 11% from private. Seventy-six percent are white. The average age of freshmen is 19; all undergraduates, 23. Nineteen percent drop out by the end of their first year.

Housing: A total of 1480 students can be accommodated in college housing. College-sponsored living facilities include coed dormitories, on-campus apartments, off-campus apartments, fraternity houses, and sorority houses. In addition there are honors houses, language houses, and special interest houses. On-campus housing is available on a first-come, first-served basis. Alcohol is not permitted. All students may keep cars on campus.

Activities: About 12% of men belong to 5 local and 14 national fraternities; about 12% of women belong to 7 local and 9 national sororities. There are 190 groups on campus, including art, band, cheerleading, chess, choir, chorale, chorus, computers, drama, drill team, ethnic, gay, honors, international, jazz band, literary magazine, musical theater, newspaper, opera, orchestra, political, professional, radio and TV, religious, social, social service, student government, symphony, and yearbook. Popular campus events include International Festival, Homecoming/Parents Weekend, Multicultural Night, Greek Week, and Fun Without Alcohol Fair.

Sports: There are 6 intercollegiate sports for men and 6 for women, and 12 intramural sports for men and 12 for women. Athletic and recreation facilities include 2 gymnasiums, weight rooms, a dance studio, swimming and diving pools, putting greens, tennis and handball/racquetball courts, baseball/softball fields, an all-weather track, a par course, a soccer stadium, a 7500-seat football stadium, and a dormitory sports center.

Disabled Students: Ninety-eight percent of the campus is accessible to disabled students. The following facilities are available: wheelchair ramps, elevators, special parking, specially equipped rest rooms, special class scheduling, lowered drinking fountains, lowered telephones, and sign language interpreters, on-campus transportation, books on tape, and a hi-tech center with adaptive computer equipment.

Services: In addition to many counseling and information services, tutoring is available in every subject. In addition, there is a reader service for the blind, and remedial math, reading, and writing. A student learning center offers a tutorial program, study skills development, and learning assistance workshops.

Campus Safety and Security: Campus safety and security measures include 24-hour foot and vehicle patrol, self-defense education, escort service, and shuttle buses. In addition, there are informal discussions, pamphlets, posters, and films, emergency telephones, lighted pathways and sidewalks, and a victim awareness program.

Programs of Study: CSU, Chico awards the B.A., B.S., B.F.A., and B.V.E. degrees. Master's degrees also are awarded. Bachelor's degrees are awarded in AGRICULTURE (agricultural business management, agriculture, and horticulture), BIOLOGICAL SCIENCE (biology/biological science and microbiology), BUSINESS (business administration and management and management engineering), COMMUNICATIONS AND THE ARTS (communications, English, fine arts, French, German, journalism, music, Spanish, speech/

debate/rhetoric, and telecommunications), COMPUTER AND PHYSICAL SCIENCE (chemistry, computer programming, computer science, geology, mathematics, and physics), EDUCATION (art, elementary, foreign languages, guidance, health, music, science, secondary, and special), ENGINEERING AND ENVIRONMENTAL DESIGN (civil engineering, computer engineering, electrical/electronics engineering, industrial engineering technology, and mechanical engineering), HEALTH PROFESSIONS (nursing, predentistry, premedicine, and speech pathology/audiology), SOCIAL SCIENCE (American studies, anthropology, community services, dietetics, economics, ethnic studies, geography, history, humanities, international relations, parks and recreation management, philosophy, political science/government, prelaw, psychology, public administration, religion, social science, social work, and sociology). Business administration, liberal studies, communications, and psychology have the largest enrollments.

Required: Graduation requirements for all students include the completion of mathematics, English literacy, ethnic studies, non-Western studies, U.S. history, U.S. Constitution, and U.S./California government courses. Also required are a 48-unit general education program, a 2.0 minimum GPA, 124 to 132 total credit hours, and 24 to 115 hours in the major.

Special: The university offers co-op programs and cross-registration as part of the National Student Exchange. Internships, study abroad, work-study, a general studies degree in liberal studies, student-designed majors, credit for experience, nondegree study, and pass/fail options are available. There is a freshman honors program on campus, as well as 2 national honor societies, including Phi Beta Kappa. Twenty-six departments have honors programs.

Faculty/Classroom: Sixty-six percent of faculty are male; 34%, female. All teach undergraduates. Graduate students teach 2% of introductory courses. The average class size in a regular course offering is 23.

Admissions: About 81% of the 1993–94 applicants were accepted. The SAT scores for the 1993–94 freshman class were as follows: Verbal—83% below 500, 15% between 500 and 599, and 2% between 600 and 700; Math—55% below 500, 34% between 500 and 599, 10% between 600 and 700, and 1% above 700. The ACT scores were 51% below 21, 30% between 21 and 23, 15% between 24 and 26, 2% between 27 and 28, and 2% above 28.

Requirements: A minimum GPA of 2.0 is required. The SAT I is required. Depending on the applicant's high school GPA, an index combining GPA and test scores is used to determine eligibility for admission. Applicants must be graduates of an accredited secondary school or have a GED and have completed 4 years of English, 3 years each of mathematics and college preparatory electives, 2 years of a foreign language, and 1 year each of history, science, art, and/or music. AP and CLEP credits are accepted.

Procedure: Freshmen are admitted fall and spring. Entrance exams should be taken in the fall of the senior year. Application deadlines are open. Priority filing for fall entry is November 1 to 30, and for spring entry is August 1 to 31. Application fee is $55. Notification is sent on a rolling basis. There is a deferred admissions plan.

Transfer: About 1830 transfer students enrolled in 1993–94. Transfer students who are California residents must have a minimum 2.0 GPA, and nonresidents need 2.4. A minimum of 56 transferable credit hours are needed, and students must have made up any missing college preparatory subjects. A total of 30 credits out of 124 must be completed at CSU, Chico.

Visiting: There are regularly scheduled orientations for prospective students. On Mondays, Wednesdays, and Fridays, a 1-hour tour is given at 11:30. Tours are also arranged on Saturdays by appointment. There are guides for informal visits and visitors may sit in on classes. To arrange for a visit, contact University Outreach at (916) 898-4428.

Financial Aid: CSU, Chico is a member of CSS. The FAFSA financial statement is required. The deadline for financial aid applications is March 1.

International Students: There are currently 206 international students enrolled. The school actively recruits these students. They must take the TOEFL and achieve a minimum score of 500.

Computers: The college provides computer facilities for student use. The mainframes are a CDC Cyber 180/830, IBM 4381, a VAX 6000–310, and an IBM 3090. There are 1,000 microcomputers available, with about 200 networked. There are also more than 50 'dumb' terminals. In addition, there are large department-based central computers. All students may access the system. There are no time limits on using the system and no fees.

Graduates: In 1992–93 3026 bachelor's degrees were awarded. The most popular majors among graduates were business administration (19%), liberal studies (9%), and information and communication studies (6%). Within an average freshman class, 10% graduate in 4 years, 33% in 5 years, and 13% in 6 years. Some 280 companies recruited on campus in 1992–93. In the 1992 graduating class, 55% of the students had found full-time employment within 6 months of graduation.

Admissions Contact: Ken Edson, Director of Admissions and Records.

CALIFORNIA STATE UNIVERSITY DOMINGUEZ HILLS

C-5

Carson, CA 90747–9960 (310) 516–361?

Full-time: 1624 men, 2788 women	Faculty: 259; IIA, +$
Part-time: 1049 men, 3026 women	Ph.D.s: 90%
Graduate: 966 men, 2316 women	Student/Faculty: 17 to 1
Year: semesters, summer session	Tuition: $1027 ($8407)
Application Deadline: June 1	Room & Board: $1830
Freshman Class: 1493 applied, 1158 accepted, 430 enrolled	
SAT I Verbal/Math: 360/430	LESS COMPETITIVE

California State University/Dominguez Hills, founded in 1960 as part of the state-supported university system, offers graduate and undergraduate programs in liberal arts and sciences, business, fine arts, health sciences, and technology to a primarily commuter student body. There are 4 undergraduate and 4 graduate schools. In addition to regional accreditation, CSU/Dominguez Hills has baccalaureate program accreditation with CAHEA, NASAD, NASM, NCATE, and NLN. The library contains 396,516 volumes, 569,634 microform items, and 17,129 audiovisual forms, and subscribes to 4739 periodicals. Computerized library sources and services include the card catalog and database searching. Special learning facilities include a learning resource center, art gallery, planetarium, and TV station. The 350-acre campus is in an urban area 10 miles south of Los Angeles. There are 40 buildings on campus.

Student Life: About 85% of undergraduates are from California. Students come from 23 states, 84 foreign countries, and Canada. Eighty-seven percent are from public schools; 13% from private. Forty-two percent are white; 25% African American; 20% Hispanic; 12% Asian American. The average age of freshmen is 18; all undergraduates, 28. Twenty-nine percent drop out by the end of their first year; 40% remain to graduate.

Housing: A total of 700 students can be accommodated in single-sex and coed on-campus apartments. Housing is available on a first-come, first-served basis. Priority is given to out-of-town students. Ninety-four percent of students commute. All students may keep cars on campus.

Activities: There are 4 national fraternities and 1 local and 2 national sororities. There are 69 groups on campus, including art, band, cheerleading, choir, chorale, computers, dance, drama, drill team, ethnic, gay, honors, international, jazz band, literary magazine, musical theater, newspaper, orchestra, photography, political, professional, radio and TV, religious, social, social service, student government, symphony, and yearbook.

Sports: Athletic and recreation facilities include the Olympic Velodrome (bicycle racing stadium), a gymnasium, tennis courts, baseball and soccer fields, a track, a weight room, and a swimming pool.

Disabled Students: The entire campus is accessible to disabled students. The following facilities are available: wheelchair ramps, elevators, special parking, specially equipped rest rooms, lowered drinking fountains, and lowered telephones.

Services: In addition to many counseling and information services, tutoring is available in most subjects. There is also a reader service for the blind, and remedial math, reading, and writing.

Campus Safety and Security: Campus safety and security measures include 24-hour foot and vehicle patrol, escort service, informal discussions, and pamphlets, posters, and films. In addition, there are emergency telephones and lighted pathways and sidewalks.

Programs of Study: CSU/Dominguez Hills awards the B.A. and B.S. degrees. Master's degrees are also awarded. Bachelor's degrees are awarded in BIOLOGICAL SCIENCE (biology/biological science), BUSINESS (business administration and management and labor studies), COMMUNICATIONS AND THE ARTS (communications, dramatic arts, English, fine arts, French, music, and Spanish), COMPUTER AND PHYSICAL SCIENCE (chemistry, computer science, geology, mathematics, and physics), EDUCATION (physical), HEALTH PROFESSIONS (clinical science, health science, and nursing), SOCIAL SCIENCE (anthropology, behavioral science, economics, geography, history, human services, interdisciplinary studies, liberal arts/general studies, Mexican-American/Chicano studies, philosophy, political science/government, psychology, public administration, and sociology). Liberal studies is the strongest academically. Business administration has the largest enrollment.

Required: To graduate, students must complete 124 to 132 semester units, including 52 to 59 units in general studies, 40 units in upper-division courses, and specific courses or proficiency tests in U.S. history and politics, mathematics, and writing. A minimum GPA of 2.0 must be maintained.

Special: Cross-registration is offered with 7 other California State University schools. Study abroad in 15 countries, co-op programs in all majors, on-campus work-study, internships, B.A.-B.S. degrees, dual and student-designed majors, credit for life experience, and pass/fail options are available. A B.A. in interdisciplinary studies, in which an

accelerated degree is possible, and a B.A. in liberal studies are offered. Many majors have evening programs. There is a freshman honors program on campus, as well as 2 national honor societies. Thirteen departments have honors programs.

Faculty/Classroom: Fifty-nine percent of faculty are male; 41%, female. Ninety-one percent teach undergraduates. The average class size in an introductory lecture is 45; in a laboratory, 20; and in a regular course offering, 35.

Admissions: About 78% of the 1993–94 applicants were accepted. The SAT scores for the 1993–94 freshman class were as follows: Verbal—89% below 500, 7% between 500 and 599, and 4% between 600 and 700; Math—82% below 500, 15% between 500 and 599, and 2% between 600 and 700.

Requirements: CSU/Dominguez Hills requires applicants to be in the upper 33% of their class. A minimum GPA of 2.0 is required. The SAT I or ACT is required, except of those with a GPA of at least 3.0 (3.6 for nonresidents). Students must be high school graduates with a GPA of at least 2.0 and 15 academic units, including 4 in English, 3 in mathematics, 2 in foreign language, and 1 each in U.S. history, laboratory science, and visual and performing arts. The GED is accepted. AP and CLEP credits are accepted.

Procedure: Freshmen are admitted in the fall and spring. Entrance exams should be taken prior to submitting an application. Applications should be filed by June 1 for fall entry and November 1 for spring entry, along with an application fee of $55. Notification is sent on a rolling basis. There are early decision and early admissions plans.

Transfer: About 1371 transfer students enrolled in 1993–94. Applicants should have a college GPA of at least 2.0 (2.4 for nonresidents) and submit SAT I or ACT scores if transferring fewer than 56 semester or 84 quarter units. A total of 30 credits out of 124 to 132 must be completed at CSU/Dominguez Hills.

Visiting: There are regularly scheduled orientations for prospective students. There are guides for informal visits and visitors may sit in on classes. To arrange for a group visit, contact the Outreach Office at (310) 516–3699; for individual visits, contact the Information Center at (310) 516–3696.

Financial Aid: In an earlier year, 10% of all current freshmen and 24% of continuing students received some form of financial aid. Scholarships or need-based grants averaged $1000 ($6000 maximum); loans averaged $100 ($3000 maximum); and work contracts averaged $3000. The FAF, or the SAAC for California residents, is required. The deadline for financial aid applications is April 15.

International Students: There are currently 227 international students enrolled. The school actively recruits these students. They must take the TOEFL and achieve a minimum score of 550. The student must also take the SAT I or the ACT.

Computers: The college provides computer facilities for student use. The mainframes are a CDC CYBER 960 and a DEC VAX 6500. About 450 Apple Macintosh, IBM, and IBM-compatible microcomputers are available in the library, student laboratories, and individual departments. All students may access the system. There are no time limits on using the system and no fees.

Graduates: In 1992–93, 1471 bachelor's degrees were awarded. The most popular majors among graduates were business administration (16%), nursing (15%), and interdisciplinary studies (6%). Within an average freshman class, 2% graduate in 4 years, 15% in 5 years, and 31% in 6 years. Some 180 companies recruited on campus in 1992–93.

Admissions Contact: Anita Gash, Director of Admissions.

CALIFORNIA STATE UNIVERSITY FRESNO

C-3

Fresno, CA 93740 (209) 278–2191

Full-time: 6654 men, 7403 women	Faculty: 816; IIA, +$
Part-time: 554 men, 668 women	Ph.D.s: 87%
Graduate: 1392 men, 2231 women	Student/Faculty: 17 to 1
Year: semesters, summer session	Tuition: $1446 ($8826)
Application Deadline: May 15	Room & Board: $4301
Freshman Class: 3839 applied, 2155 accepted, 1580 enrolled	
ACT: 19	COMPETITIVE

California State University/Fresno, founded in 1911, is part of the state-supported university system. The school offers undergraduate and graduate programs in agriculture and technology, liberal arts and sciences, business administration, education, engineering, health fields, and preprofessional training. There are 8 undergraduate and 8 graduate schools. In addition to regional accreditation, Fresno State University has baccalaureate program accreditation with AACSB, ABET, ACEJMC, ADA, AHEA, APTA, ASLA, CSWE, FIDER, NASM, NCATE, NLN, and NRPA. The library contains 852,607 volumes, 1,128,691 microform items, and 55,944 audiovisual forms, and subscribes to 2975 periodicals. Computerized library sources and services include the card catalog, interlibrary loans, and database searching. Special learning facilities include a learning resource center, art gallery, radio station, TV station, and various farm laboratory units. The 327-acre campus is in a suburban area 300 miles southeast of San Francisco. Including residence halls, there are 47 buildings on campus.

Student Life: About 95% of undergraduates are from California. Students come from 80 foreign countries and Canada. Ninety-nine percent are from public schools; 1% from private. Sixty-three percent are white; 22% Hispanic; 10% Asian American. The average age of freshmen is 18; all undergraduates, 21.5. Twenty percent drop out by the end of their first year; 56% remain to graduate.

Housing: A total of 1242 students can be accommodated in college housing. College-sponsored living facilities include single-sex and coed dormitories. In addition there are special interest houses. On-campus housing is available on a first-come, first-served basis. Ninety-three percent of students commute. Alcohol is not permitted. All students may keep cars on campus.

Activities: About 6% of men belong to 2 local and 11 national fraternities; about 5% of women belong to 3 local and 9 national sororities. There are 290 groups on campus, including art, band, cheerleading, chess, choir, chorale, chorus, computers, dance, drama, drill team, ethnic, film, gay, honors, international, jazz band, marching band, musical theater, newspaper, orchestra, pep band, photography, political, professional, radio and TV, religious, social, social service, and student government. Popular campus events include Vintage Days, International Week, Black History Month, Semana de La Raza, Women's Herstory Week, University lecture series, AmerAsia Week, and Cinco de Mayo Celebration.

Sports: There are 10 intercollegiate sports for men and 7 for women, and 10 intramural sports for men and 10 for women. Athletic and recreation facilities include 2 gymnasiums, an indoor/outdoor swimming pool, 12 tennis courts, 6 indoor handball/racquetball courts, and 2 putting greens and driving areas. There are sports clubs in cycling, fencing, judo, karate, rodeo, and rugby. The campus stadium seats 41,031 and the baseball stadium seats 4,575.

Disabled Students: All of the campus is accessible to disabled students. The following facilities are available: wheelchair ramps, elevators, special parking, specially equipped rest rooms, special class scheduling, lowered drinking fountains, and lowered telephones.

Services: In addition to many counseling and information services, tutoring is available in most subjects. There is also a reader service for the blind, and remedial math, reading, and writing.

Campus Safety and Security: Campus safety and security measures include 24-hour foot and vehicle patrol, self defense education, escort service, and informal discussions. In addition, there are pamphlets, posters, films, emergency telephones, and lighted pathways and sidewalks.

Programs of Study: Fresno State University awards the B.A., B.S., and B.V.E.D. degrees. Master's and doctoral degrees also are awarded. Bachelor's degrees are awarded in AGRICULTURE (agricultural business management, agriculture, animal science, and plant science), BIOLOGICAL SCIENCE (biology/biological science, botany, environmental biology, microbiology, and zoology), BUSINESS (accounting, banking and finance, business administration and management, business law, international business management, marketing/retailing/merchandising, and personnel management), COMMUNICATIONS AND THE ARTS (advertising, communications, dance, dramatic arts, English, fine arts, French, German, graphic design, journalism, music, photography, Russian, Spanish, speech/debate/rhetoric, and telecommunications), COMPUTER AND PHYSICAL SCIENCE (chemistry, computer science, geology, mathematics, and physics), EDUCATION (agricultural, art, business, early childhood, elementary, foreign languages, health, home economics, industrial arts, music, science, secondary, special, and teaching English as a second language/foreign language), ENGINEERING AND ENVIRONMENTAL DESIGN (civil engineering, computer engineering, construction engineering, electrical/electronics engineering, industrial engineering, interior design, mechanical engineering, and surveying engineering), HEALTH PROFESSIONS (nursing, physical therapy, predentistry, premedicine, prepharmacy, preveterinary science, public health, and speech pathology/audiology), SOCIAL SCIENCE (anthropology, criminology, dietetics, economics, food science, geography, history, parks and recreation management, philosophy, political science/government, prelaw, psychology, public administration, religion, social science, social work, sociology, and urban studies). Business and liberal arts have the largest enrollments.

Required: All students must complete general education requirements. A minimum of 124 to 137 semester units, with a minimum GPA of 2.0, is required in order to graduate.

Special: Study abroad in London, China, and the South Pacific, co-op programs, internships, work-study programs, B.A.-B.S. degrees, dual majors, and student-designed majors are offered. A liberal studies major, credit for military experience, pass/fail options and nondegree study are available. There are 21 national honor societies on campus.

Faculty/Classroom: Sixty-nine percent of faculty are male; 31%, female. All teach undergraduates and 30% do research. The average class size in an introductory lecture is 50; in a laboratory, 15; and in a regular course offering, 35.

Admissions: About 56% of the 1993–94 applicants were accepted.

Requirements: A minimum GPA of 2.0 is required. Only students with a GPA below 3.0 are required to submit SAT I or ACT scores. Applicant must be a graduate of an accredited secondary school or have a GED equivalent. Secondary school courses must include 15 academic credits, including 4 years of high school English, 3 each of mathematics and electives, 2 of a foreign language, and 1 each of science, history/government, and visual/performing arts. AP and CLEP credits are accepted.

Procedure: Freshmen are admitted fall and spring. Entrance exams should be taken as early as possible, by the first semester of the senior year. Applications should be filed by May 15 for fall entry and October 15 for spring entry, along with an application fee of $55. Notification is sent on a rolling basis.

Transfer: About 2770 transfer students enrolled in 1993–94. Transfer applicants must have a minimum GPA of 2.0 and 56 transferable semester units earned, including English and mathematics. A total of 30 credits out of 124 to 137 must be completed at Fresno State University.

Visiting: There are regularly scheduled orientations for prospective students, including 1- and 2-day overnight programs for entering students. There are guides for informal visits and visitors may stay overnight at the school. To arrange for a visit, contact Orientation and Transition Services or University Outreach Services at (209) 278-7533 or (209) 278-2048.

Financial Aid: In 1993–94, 47% of all current freshmen and 27% of continuing students received some form of financial aid. About 47% of freshmen received need-based aid. The average freshman award was $4360. Of that total, scholarships or need-based grants averaged $500 ($2000 maximum); loans averaged $1800 ($2625 maximum); and work contracts averaged $1700 ($4000 maximum). The average financial indebtedness of the 1992–93 graduate was $4300. Fresno State University is a member of CSS. The SAAC financial statement is required. The deadline for financial aid applications is March 2.

International Students: There are currently 809 international students enrolled. The school actively recruits these students. They must take the TOEFL and achieve a minimum score of 500. The student must also take SAT I or the ACT.

Computers: The college provides computer facilities for student use. The mainframe is an IBM 3090. There are 1500 IBM PCs and compatibles and Apple Macintoshes available for student use. All students may access the system. It may be used anytime. There are no time limits on using the system and no fees.

Graduates: In 1992–93, 3140 bachelor's degrees were awarded. The most popular majors among graduates were counseling and special education (16%), social work education (12%), and management (10%). Within an average freshman class, 35% graduate in 5 years and 51% in 6 years. Some 259 companies recruited on campus in 1992–93.

Admissions Contact: Carroll C. Cotten, Assistant Director of Admissions.

CALIFORNIA STATE UNIVERSITY FULLERTON

Fullerton, CA 92634   **D-5**

        (714) 773-2370

Full-time: 5837 men, 7135 women	Faculty: 758; IIA, +$
Part-time: 3307 men, 4034 women	Ph.D.s: 79%
Graduate: 1599 men, 2461 women	Student/Faculty: 17 to 1
Year: semesters, summer session	Tuition: $1650 ($9030)
Application Deadline: open	Room & Board: $3200
Freshman Class: 5546 applied, 4725 accepted, 1895 enrolled	
SAT I Verbal/Math: 390/460	ACT: 19 **LESS COMPETITIVE**

California State University/Fullerton, founded in 1957, is part of the California State University system. The school offers programs in the arts, business and economics, communications, engineering and computer science, human development and community services, humanities and social science, and natural science and mathematics. There are 7 undergraduate and 7 graduate schools. In addition to regional accreditation, Cal State Fullerton has baccalaureate program accreditation with AACSB, ABET, ACEJMC, NASAD, NASM, NCATE, and NLN. The library contains 697,785 volumes, 838,165 microform items, and 15,653 audiovisual forms, and subscribes to 4497 periodicals. Computerized library sources and services include the card catalog and database searching. Special learning facilities include a learning resource center and art gallery. The 225-acre campus is in a suburban area 30 miles east of Los Angeles. Including residence halls, there are 22 buildings on campus.

Student Life: About 83% of undergraduates are from California. Students come from 21 states, 41 foreign countries, and Canada. Fifty-six percent are white; 14% Asian American; 13% Hispanic. The average age of freshmen is 18.5; all undergraduates, 23.7. Twenty-three percent drop out by the end of their first year; 61% remain to graduate.

Housing: A total of 396 students can be accommodated in college housing. College-sponsored living facilities include coed on-campus apartments, fraternity houses, and sorority houses. On-campus housing is available on a first-come, first-served basis. Ninety-eight percent of students commute. All students may keep cars on campus.

Activities: There are 15 national fraternities and 7 national sororities. There are 200 groups on campus, including art, band, cheerleading, choir, chorus, computers, dance, drama, ethnic, gay, honors, international, jazz band, literary magazine, musical theater, newspaper, orchestra, pep band, photography, political, professional, religious, social, social service, student government, and yearbook. Popular campus events include Homecoming.

Sports: There are 8 intercollegiate sports for men and 7 for women. Athletic and recreation facilities include a gymnasium, a swimming pool, tennis and racquetball courts, baseball/softball, track, and soccer fields; a bowling alley, and a stadium.

Disabled Students: The entire campus is accessible to disabled students. The following facilities are available: wheelchair ramps, elevators, special parking, specially equipped rest rooms, lowered drinking fountains, and lowered telephones.

Services: In addition to many counseling and information services, tutoring is available in some subjects. There is also a reader service for the blind, and remedial math, reading, and writing available.

Campus Safety and Security: Campus safety and security measures include 24-hour foot and vehicle patrol, self defense education, escort service, and shuttle buses. In addition, there are pamphlets, posters, films, emergency telephones, and lighted pathways and sidewalks.

Programs of Study: Cal State Fullerton awards the B.A., B.S., B.F.A., and B.M. degrees. Master's degrees also are awarded. Bachelor's degrees are awarded in BIOLOGICAL SCIENCE (biology/biological science, botany, cell biology, ecology, genetics, marine biology, microbiology, and zoology), BUSINESS (accounting, banking and finance, business administration and management, business economics, international business management, management information systems, management science, and marketing/retailing/merchandising), COMMUNICATIONS AND THE ARTS (advertising, broadcasting, communications, comparative literature, dance, design, dramatic arts, English, film arts, fine arts, French, German, journalism, linguistics, music, photography, Spanish, and speech/debate/rhetoric), COMPUTER AND PHYSICAL SCIENCE (chemistry, computer science, geology, mathematics, physics, and statistics), EDUCATION (art, early childhood, and music), ENGINEERING AND ENVIRONMENTAL DESIGN (civil engineering, electrical/electronics engineering, and mechanical engineering), HEALTH PROFESSIONS (nursing and speech pathology/audiology), SOCIAL SCIENCE (African American studies, anthropology, criminal justice, economics, geography, history, Latin American studies, liberal arts/general studies, Mexican-American/Chicano studies, philosophy, political science/government, psychology, religion, Russian and Slavic studies, and sociology). Business administration, communications, and psychology have the largest enrollments.

Required: Graduation requirements for all students include the completion of a minimum of 51 units of general education courses, a 2.0 GPA, and an upper-division writing course designated by the major department. The total credit hours to be completed is 124.

Special: The university offers cross-registration with other schools in the California State University system, internships, study abroad, and work-study programs. A B.A.-B.S. degree in chemistry, dual and student-designed majors, and pass/fail options are available. There is a freshman honors program on campus, as well as 11 national honor societies. Eight departments have honors programs.

Faculty/Classroom: Seventy-six percent of faculty are male; 24%, female. The average class size in an introductory lecture is 50; in a laboratory, 24; and in a regular course offering, 25.

Admissions: About 85% of the 1993–94 applicants were accepted. The SAT scores for the 1993–94 freshman class were as follows: Verbal—87% below 500, 11% between 500 and 599, and 2% between 600 and 700; Math—60% below 500, 29% between 500 and 599, 10% between 600 and 700, and 1% above 700. The ACT scores were 58% below 21, 25% between 21 and 23, 12% between 24 and 26, 2% between 27 and 28, and 3% above 28.

Requirements: A minimum GPA of 2.0 is required. The SAT I or ACT is required. Applicant must be a graduate of an accredited secondary school or have a GED certificate. Secondary school courses must include 4 years of English, 3 years each of approved electives and mathematics, 2 years of a foreign language, and 1 year each of science, history, and visual or performing arts. Admission is based on the Qualifiable Eligibility Index, a combination of the high school

GPA and either the SAT I or ACT score. Auditions are required for music majors. AP and CLEP credits are accepted.

Procedure: Freshmen are admitted fall and spring. Entrance exams should be taken during the senior year of high school. Application deadlines are open. Notification is sent on a rolling basis 2 weeks after receipt of application. The application fee is $55. There is an early admissions plan.

Transfer: About 2703 transfer students enrolled in a recent year. Applicants must have a minimum 2.0 GPA. The SAT I or ACT is required for students with fewer than 56 transferable units earned. A total of 30 credits out of 124 must be completed at Cal State Fullerton.

Visiting: There are regularly scheduled orientations for prospective students. There are guides for informal visits. To arrange for a visit, contact the University Activities Center at (714) 773–3120.

Financial Aid: In an earlier year, 22% of all current freshmen and 19% of continuing students received some form of financial aid. Sixteen percent of undergraduate students work part-time. The average financial indebtedness of an earlier year's graduate was $3289. Cal State Fullerton is a member of CSS. The SAAC (Student Aid Application for California) is required. The deadline for financial aid applications is March 2.

International Students: There are currently 1011 international students enrolled. They must take the TOEFL and achieve a minimum score of 500.

Computers: The college provides computer facilities for student use. The mainframes are a DEC VAX 8550 and an IBM 3090/150E. Students may access mainframe via school-based and computer center laboratories. All students may access the system. It may be used 24 hours a day. There are no time limits and no fees.

Graduates: In a recent year, 3990 bachelor's degrees were awarded. The most popular majors among graduates were communication (12%), finance (10%), and accounting (7%). Within an average freshman class, 8% graduate in 4 years, 23% in 5 years, and 13% in 6 years.

Admissions Contact: Associate Director, Admissions and Records.

CALIFORNIA STATE UNIVERSITY HAYWARD

B-3

Hayward, CA 94542   (510) 881–3811

Full-time: 2667 men, 4357 women	Faculty: 408; IIA, +$
Part-time: 1083 men, 1642 women	Ph.D.s: n/av
Graduate: 1046 men, 1788 women	Student/Faculty: 17 to 1
Year: quarters	Tuition: $1630 ($9010)
Application Deadline: May 1	Room & Board: $3865
Freshman Class: 1195 applied, 720 accepted, 648 enrolled	
SAT I or ACT: required	COMPETITIVE

California State University/Hayward, founded in 1957, is part of the California State University system. The coeducational institution offers degree programs in the arts, sciences, business and economics, and education to a primarily commuter student body. There are 4 undergraduate and 4 graduate schools. In addition to regional accreditation, CSUH has baccalaureate program accreditation with AACSB, NASAD, NASM, NCATE, and NLN. The library contains 800,000 volumes, 670,000 microform items, and 18,000 audiovisual forms, and subscribes to 2509 periodicals. Computerized library sources and services include the card catalog, interlibrary loans, and database searching. Special learning facilities include a learning resource center, art gallery, natural history museum, radio station, TV station, marine biology laboratory, and a geology summer field camp. The 342-acre campus is in a suburban area 20 miles southeast of San Francisco in the Hayward Hills. Including residence halls, there are 17 buildings on campus.

Student Life: About 90% of undergraduates are from California. Students come from 25 states, 51 foreign countries, and Canada. Eighty-five percent are from public schools. Forty-nine percent are white; 25% Asian American; 12% African American; 10% Hispanic. The average age of freshmen is 20; all undergraduates, 25. Fifteen percent drop out by the end of their first year; 57% remain to graduate.

Housing: A total of 400 students can be accommodated in college housing. College-sponsored living facilities include coed on-campus apartments. On-campus housing is guaranteed for the freshman year only and is available on a first-come, first-served basis. Ninety-four percent of students commute. All students may keep cars on campus.

Activities: About 1% of men belong to 4 national fraternities; about 1% of women belong to 3 national sororities. There are 90 groups on campus, including art, cheerleading, chorale, chorus, computers, dance, drama, ethnic, film, gay, honors, international, jazz band, literary magazine, musical theater, newspaper, opera, orchestra, pep band, photography, political, professional, radio and TV, religious, social, social service, student government, symphony, and yearbook. Popular campus events include Homecoming, Science Fair, Al Fres-

co, African American Youth Leadership, Chicano/Latino Youth Leadership, and Asian Pacific American Youth Leadership.

Sports: Athletic and recreation facilities include tennis and racquetball courts, 2 swimming pools, a track, a football field, a martial arts facility, a gymnastics center, a dance studio, baseball and softball diamonds, a 9000-seat stadium, a 5000-seat gymnasium, and a 500-seat theater.

Disabled Students: Ninety percent of the campus is accessible to disabled students. The following facilities are available: wheelchair ramps, elevators, special parking, specially equipped rest rooms, lowered drinking fountains, and lowered telephones. The Disabled Student Services Center provides tutorial, scribe, interpretive, and translation services.

Services: In addition to many counseling and information services, tutoring is available in most subjects. There is also a reader service for the blind, and remedial math, reading, and writing.

Campus Safety and Security: Campus safety and security measures include 24-hour foot and vehicle patrol, self-defense education, escort service, and shuttle buses. In addition, there are informal discussions, pamphlets, posters, films, emergency telephones, and lighted pathways and sidewalks.

Programs of Study: CSUH awards the B.A. and B.S. degrees. Master's degrees also are awarded. Bachelor's degrees are awarded in BIOLOGICAL SCIENCE (biology/biological science and ecology), BUSINESS (business administration and management and recreation and leisure services), COMMUNICATIONS AND THE ARTS (art, communications, dramatic arts, English, French, German, music, Spanish, and speech/debate/rhetoric), COMPUTER AND PHYSICAL SCIENCE (chemistry, computer science, geology, mathematics, physical sciences, physics, and statistics), EDUCATION (physical), ENGINEERING AND ENVIRONMENTAL DESIGN (environmental science), HEALTH PROFESSIONS (health science, nursing, and speech pathology/audiology), SOCIAL SCIENCE (anthropology, criminal justice, economics, ethnic studies, geography, history, human development, Latin American studies, liberal arts/general studies, philosophy, political science/government, psychology, and sociology). Business administration, liberal studies, computer science, biology, criminal justice, nursing, and mass communication are the strongest academically. Business administration and liberal studies have the largest enrollments.

Required: In order to graduate, students must fulfill the University Writing Skills Requirement, have a 2.0 minimum GPA, and complete 186 quarter units, including 72 in distribution requirements. The number of hours in the major varies by program from 56 to 153 quarter units.

Special: CSUH offers cross-registration with local community colleges, other CSU campuses, and the University of California/Berkeley. Internships, study abroad in 15 countries, work-study programs, and student-designed majors are also available. The PACE program provides degree opportunities in liberal studies and in human development to working adults. There is one national honor society on campus. One department has an honors program.

Admissions: About 60% of the 1993–94 applicants were accepted.

Requirements: The SAT I or ACT is required. All students must meet the Qualifiable Eligibility Index, a combination of the high school GPA and SAT I or ACT scores. Applicants must be graduates of an accredited secondary school or have a GED certificate. Secondary school courses must include 4 years of English, 3 each of mathematics and electives, 2 of foreign language, and 1 each of history, science, and art, dance, drama/theater, or music. AP and CLEP credits are accepted. Important factors used in the admissions decision are advanced placement or honor courses, recommendations by school officials, recommendations by alumni, personality, intangible qualities, and parents or siblings attending the school.

Procedure: Freshmen are admitted to all sessions. Applications should be filed by May 1 for fall entry, October 1 for winter entry, January 1 for spring entry, and April 1 for summer entry, along with an application fee of $55. Notification of early decision is sent immediately; regular decision, within 2 to 4 weeks of filing an application. There are early decision, early admissions, and deferred admissions plans.

Transfer: About 2200 transfer students enrolled in 1993–94. Applicants must have a minimum 2.0 GPA (2.4 for nonresidents), be in good standing at the last college attended, and either meet freshman admission requirements or have completed at least 56 transferable semester (84 quarter) units. At least 45 quarter credits out of 186 must be completed at CSUH.

Visiting: There are regularly scheduled orientations for prospective students. There are guides for informal visits. To arrange for a visit, contact the Outreach Office at (510) 881–4226.

Financial Aid: In a recent year, 39% of all current freshmen received some form of financial aid. Loans averaged $1500. One-hundred percent of undergraduate students work part-time. CSUH is a member of CSS. The SAAC financial statement is required. The deadline for financial aid applications is March 2.

International Students: There are currently 320 international students enrolled. They must take the TOEFL and achieve a minimum score of 525. Graduates of a U.S. high school must also take the SAT I or ACT.

Computers: The college provides computer facilities for student use. The mainframes are an E/XSI and an IBM 9370. There are 300 IBM, AT&T, and Apple Macintosh microcomputers available throughout campus. All students may access the system. It may be used on a 24-hour basis from home and 16 hours per day on campus. There are no time limits on using the system and no fees.

Graduates: In 1992–93, 2596 bachelor's degrees were awarded. The most popular majors among graduates were business administration (25%), computer science, and liberal studies. Some 247 companies recruited on campus in 1992–93.

Admissions Contact: Admissions Information.

CALIFORNIA STATE UNIVERSITY LONG BEACH
D-5

Long Beach, CA 90840   (310) 985-5471

Full-time: 6804 men, 8065 women	Faculty: 898; IIA, +$
Part-time: 3163 men, 3392 women	Ph.D.s: 85%
Graduate: 2462 men, 3187 women	Student/Faculty: 17 to 1
Year: semesters, summer session	Tuition: $1557 ($8805)
Application Deadline: November 30	Room & Board: $4500
Freshman Class: 6839 applied, 6237 accepted, 2105 enrolled	
SAT I Verbal/Math: 362/438	**LESS COMPETITIVE**

California State University/Long Beach, founded in 1949, is a nonprofit institution that is part of the California State University system. The commuter university offers undergraduate programs in health and human services, humanities, natural sciences, social and behavioral sciences, business administration, engineering, and the arts. There are 6 undergraduate and 7 graduate schools. In addition to regional accreditation, CSULB has baccalaureate program accreditation with AACSB, ABET, ACEJMC, AHEA, APTA, CSWE, FIDER, NASAD, NASM, NLN, and NRPA. The 2 libraries contain 1,059,754 volumes, 1,522,962 microform items, and 36,688 audiovisual forms, and subscribe to 5854 periodicals. Computerized library sources and services include the card catalog and database searching. Special learning facilities include a learning resource center, art gallery, radio station, and TV station. The 322-acre campus is in a suburban area 25 miles southeast of Los Angeles. Including residence halls, there are 80 buildings on campus.

Student Life: About 98% of undergraduates are from California. Students come from 46 states, 113 foreign countries, and Canada. Ninety-two percent are from public schools; 8% from private. Forty-seven percent are white; 21% Asian American; 14% Hispanic. The average age of freshmen is 18; all undergraduates, 22. Twenty-five percent drop out by the end of their first year; 30% remain to graduate.

Housing: A total of 1844 students can be accommodated in college housing. College-sponsored living facilities include dormitories. In addition, there is an international house. On-campus housing is available on a first-come, first-served basis. Ninety-four percent of students commute. All students may keep cars on campus.

Activities: About 6% of men belong to 15 national fraternities; about 5% of women belong to 11 national sororities. There are 150 groups on campus, including art, band, cheerleading, choir, chorale, chorus, computers, dance, drama, drill team, ethnic, film, gay, honors, international, jazz band, literary magazine, marching band, musical theater, newspaper, opera, orchestra, pep band, photography, political, professional, radio and TV, religious, social, social service, student government, symphony, and yearbook. Popular campus events include the Kaleidoscope Spring Festival.

Sports: There are 10 intercollegiate sports for men and 9 for women, and 14 intramural sports for men and 12 for women. Athletic and recreation facilities include Long Beach Arena (seats 11,500 for basketball), a baseball field (seats 1500), and an indoor gymnasium (seats 2000). The largest auditorium seats 385.

Disabled Students: Ninety-five percent of the campus is accessible to disabled students. The following facilities are available: wheelchair ramps, elevators, special parking, specially equipped rest rooms, special class scheduling, lowered drinking fountains, and lowered telephones. The university also offers registration and mobility assistance, adaptive equipment, counseling, community referrals, and services to the learning-disabled.

Services: In addition to many counseling and information services, tutoring is available in most subjects. In addition, there is a reader service for the blind, and remedial math, reading, and writing.

Campus Safety and Security: Campus safety and security measures include 24-hour foot and vehicle patrol, escort service, shuttle buses, and pamphlets, posters, and films. In addition, there are emergency telephones and lighted pathways and sidewalks.

Programs of Study: CSULB awards the B.A., B.F.A., B.M., and B.Voc.Ed. degrees. Doctoral degrees also are awarded. Bachelor's degrees are awarded in BIOLOGICAL SCIENCE (biochemistry, biology/biological science, botany, microbiology, and zoology), BUSINESS (accounting, banking and finance, business administration and management, business data processing, marketing/retailing/merchandising, and personnel management), COMMUNICATIONS AND THE ARTS (broadcasting, comparative literature, dance, design, dramatic arts, English, film arts, French, journalism, music, photography, Spanish, and speech/debate/rhetoric), COMPUTER AND PHYSICAL SCIENCE (chemistry, computer science, earth science, geology, mathematics, and physics), EDUCATION (health, industrial arts, and vocational), ENGINEERING AND ENVIRONMENTAL DESIGN (chemical engineering, civil engineering, computer engineering, electrical/electronics engineering, engineering, and mechanical engineering), HEALTH PROFESSIONS (nursing, physical therapy, and speech pathology/audiology), SOCIAL SCIENCE (anthropology, criminal justice, dietetics, economics, geography, history, interdisciplinary studies, parks and recreation management, philosophy, political science/government, psychology, religion, social work, and sociology). Arts and most of the natural and social sciences are the strongest academically. Business administration and engineering have the largest enrollments.

Required: Graduation requirements for all students include the completion of 51 units in general education (45 for engineering majors), 40 units of upper-division coursework, and 30 units in residence at the university. Students must have a minimum 2.0 GPA and a total of 124 to 140 credit hours, depending on major. Required courses include University 100 and The University in Your Future.

Special: The university offers cross-registration with California State University/Dominguez Hills for courses not offered at CSULB. Internships, study abroad in 22 countries, dual majors in engineering, a 3–2 engineering degree, student-designed majors, and pass/fail options are also available. There is a freshman honors program on campus, as well as 23 national honor societies, including Phi Beta Kappa.

Faculty/Classroom: Sixty-seven percent of faculty are male; 33%, female. Graduate students teach 3% of introductory courses. The average class size in an introductory lecture is 42; in a laboratory, 23; and in a regular course offering, 33.

Admissions: About 91% of the 1993–94 applicants were accepted. The SAT scores for the 1993–94 freshman class were as follows: Verbal—93% below 500 and 7% between 500 and 599; Math—73% below 500, 22% between 500 and 599, and 5% between 600 and 700.

Requirements: CSULB requires applicants to be in the upper 33% of their class. The SAT I or ACT is recommended. Applicant must be a graduate of an accredited secondary school and have completed 4 years of English, 3 years each of mathematics and electives, 2 years of foreign language, and 1 year each of science with laboratory, U.S. history or U.S. history and government, and 1 year of visual and performing arts. Students are admitted on the basis of the Eligibility Index, which is computed from the secondary school GPA and SAT I or ACT scores. California residents with a minimum 3.0 GPA are automatically admissible. A portfolio is required for art and design students. An audition is required for dance, music, and theater students. AP and CLEP credits are accepted.

Procedure: Freshmen are admitted fall and spring. Entrance exams should be taken during the fall semester of the senior year. Applications should be filed by November 30 for fall entry and August 31 for spring entry, along with an application fee of $55. Notification is sent on a rolling basis.

Transfer: About 2500 transfer students enrolled in 1993–94. Applicants must be upper-division students who have completed a minimum of 60 semester units, and have a minimum 2.0 GPA. An associate degree is recommended. A total of 30 credits out of 124 to 140 must be completed at CSULB.

Visiting: There are regularly scheduled orientations for prospective students, scheduled through SOAR (Student Orientation and Assisted Registration). There are guides for informal visits. To arrange for a visit, contact Office of School Relations at (310) 985-5358.

Financial Aid: In 1993–94, 10% of all current freshmen and 8% of continuing students received some form of financial aid. Scholarships or need-based grants averaged $500; loans averaged $1862 ($1000 maximum); and work contracts averaged $2419 ($3000 maximum). Four percent of undergraduate students work part-time. The average financial indebtedness of the 1992–93 graduate was $3939. CSULB is a member of CSS. The FAF and SAAC are required. The deadline for financial aid applications is May 10.

International Students: There are currently 372 international students enrolled. The school actively recruits these students. They must take the TOEFL and achieve a minimum score of 500. The student must also take the SAT I or the ACT.

Computers: The college provides computer facilities for student use. The mainframes are a DEC VAX 6320, a Prime 9755, and a Prime 9955-II. There are also 888 PCs in 19 laboratories on campus. All stu-

dents may access the system. There are no time limits on using the system and no fees.

Graduates: In 1992–93, 4607 bachelor's degrees were awarded. The most popular majors among graduates were liberal studies (10%), psychology (8%), and finance (5%). Some 400 companies recruited on campus in 1992–93.

Admissions Contact: Office of Enrollment Services.

CALIFORNIA STATE UNIVERSITY
LOS ANGELES
C-5

Los Angeles, CA 90032
Full-time: 3768 men, 5089 women
Part-time: 1992 men, 2660 women
Graduate: 1668 men, 2611 women
Year: quarters, summer session
Application Deadline: August 7
Freshman Class: 5408 applied, 2773 accepted, 1218 enrolled
SAT I or ACT: required

(213) 343–2752/(213) 343–3901
Faculty: 536; IIA, +$
Ph.D.s: 95%
Student/Faculty: 18 to 1
Tuition: $2040 ($7944)
Room: $2900

VERY COMPETITIVE

California State University/Los Angeles, founded in 1947 as part of the state system, offers undergraduate and graduate programs in liberal arts and sciences, business education, engineering, health science, and professional training. There are 6 undergraduate schools. In addition to regional accreditation, CSU/LA has baccalaureate program accreditation with AACSB, ABET, ADA, AHEA, CSWE, NASAD, NASM, NCATE, and NLN. The library contains 1,091,496 volumes and 719,167 microform items, and subscribes to 3190 periodicals. Computerized library sources and services include the card catalog, interlibrary loans, and database searching. Special learning facilities include a learning resource center, art gallery, and TV station. The 173-acre campus is in an urban area 5 miles east of downtown Los Angeles. Including residence halls, there are 17 buildings on campus.

Student Life: About 94% of undergraduates are from California. Students come from 28 states, 125 foreign countries, and Canada. Eighty-nine percent are from public schools; 11% from private. Forty-one percent are Hispanic; 28% Asian American; 21% white; 10% African American. The average age of freshmen is 18; all undergraduates, 25. Twenty-three percent drop out by the end of their first year.

Housing: A total of 1006 students can be accommodated in college housing. College-sponsored living facilities include single-sex and coed on-campus apartments. In addition, there are special interest houses and an international house. On-campus housing is available on a first-come, first-served basis. Ninety-seven percent of students commute. All students may keep cars on campus.

Activities: Less than 1% of the students belong to 4 national fraternities and 2 local and 3 national sororities. There are 115 groups on campus, including band, choir, chorale, chorus, computers, dance, drama, ethnic, gay, honors, international, jazz band, literary magazine, musical theater, newspaper, opera, orchestra, political, professional, radio and TV, religious, social, social service, student government, symphony, and yearbook. Popular campus events include Christmas Toy and Food Drive, Earth Week, Career Day Homecoming, Honors Convocation, Cinco de Mayo, Black History Month, Women's History Month, and Chinese New Year.

Sports: There are 8 intercollegiate sports for men and 6 for women, and 9 intramural sports for men and 7 for women. Athletic and recreation facilities include a 4800-seat stadium, a 5500-seat gymnasium, a swimming pool, tennis and raquetball courts, a track, and athletic fields.

Disabled Students: All of the campus is accessible to disabled students. The following facilities are available: wheelchair ramps, elevators, special parking, specially equipped rest rooms, and lowered telephones.

Services: In addition to many counseling and information services, tutoring is available in most subjects. There is a reader service for the blind and remedial math, reading, and writing.

Campus Safety and Security: Campus safety and security measures include escort service, shuttle buses, emergency telephones, and lighted pathways and sidewalks.

Programs of Study: CSU/LA awards the B.A., B.S., B.M., and B.Voc.Ed degrees. Master's and doctoral degrees also are awarded. Bachelor's degrees are awarded in BIOLOGICAL SCIENCE (biochemistry, biology/biological science, microbiology, and nutrition), BUSINESS (accounting, banking and finance, business administration and management, business economics, human resources, international business management, labor studies, marketing/retailing/merchandising, real estate, retailing, and transportation management), COMMUNICATIONS AND THE ARTS (art history and appreciation, broadcasting, dance, dramatic arts, English, fine arts, French, Japanese, journalism, music, performing arts, Spanish, speech/debate/rhetoric, studio art, and telecommunications), COMPUTER AND PHYSICAL SCIENCE (chemistry, computer science, earth science, geology, information sciences and systems, mathematics, physi-

cal sciences, and physics), EDUCATION (art, business, health, industrial arts, music, physical, and vocational), ENGINEERING AND ENVIRONMENTAL DESIGN (aviation administration/management, civil engineering, electrical/electronics engineering, industrial engineering technology, and mechanical engineering), HEALTH PROFESSIONS (medical laboratory technology, nursing, rehabilitation therapy, and speech pathology/audiology), SOCIAL SCIENCE (African American studies, anthropology, child psychology/development, criminal justice, dietetics, economics, fire protection, geography, history, Latin American studies, liberal arts/general studies, Mexican-American/Chicano studies, philosophy, political science/government, prelaw, psychology, public administration, social science, social work, and sociology). Business administration, child development, nursing, electrical engineering, and psychology. have the largest enrollments.

Required: In order to graduate, students must complete 186 to 203 quarter units, with a minimum 2.0 GPA, and must demonstrate skills in mathematics and oral and written communications. General education requirements include 72 quarter units in the social sciences, natural sciences, and humanities.

Special: Cross-registration is offered with other California State University schools. Students may design their own majors. Internships, study-abroad opportunities, work-study programs, B.A.-B.S. degrees, dual majors, pass/fail options, and credit for life experience are available. An accelerated degree program in nursing is offered. There is a freshman honors program on campus, as well as 21 national honor societies, including Phi Beta Kappa. Five departments have honors programs.

Faculty/Classroom: Seventy percent of faculty are male; 30%, female. All teach and do research. No introductory courses are taught by graduate students. The average class size in an introductory lecture is 40; in a laboratory, 8; and in a regular course offering, 40.

Admissions: About 51% of the 1993–94 applicants were accepted.

Requirements: CSU/LA requires applicants to be in the upper 33% of their class. A minimum GPA of 2.0 is required. The SAT I or ACT is required. Applicant should be a graduate of an accredited secondary school or have a GED equivalent. Fifteen academic credits are required, including 4 years of English, 3 each of mathematics and electives, 2 of a foreign language, and 1 each of science, history, and the visual and performing arts. AP and CLEP credits are accepted.

Procedure: Freshmen are admitted to all sessions. Entrance exams should be taken during the senior year. Applications should be filed by August 7 for fall entry, November 15 for winter entry, February 15 for spring entry, and May 15 for summer entry, along with an application fee of $55. Notification is sent on a rolling basis. There is an early admissions plan.

Transfer: About 1188 transfer students enrolled in 1993–94. Applicants must have 56 semester units (84 quarter units) and a 2.0 GPA (2.4 GPA for nonresidents) or meet freshman admission requirements. A total of 45 quarter units out of 186 to 203 must be completed at CSU/LA.

Visiting: There are guides for informal visits and visitors may sit in on classes. To arrange for a visit, contact the Coordinator of College and School Relations at (213) 343–2752.

Financial Aid: In an earlier year, 46% of all current freshmen received some form of financial aid. Scholarships or need-based grants averaged $1000; and loans averaged $4000. Thirty-three percent of undergraduate students work part-time. CSU/LA is a member of CSS. The FAF or FFS and the SAAC (in-state) are required. The deadline for financial aid applications is March 2.

International Students: There are currently 1241 international students enrolled. They must take the TOEFL (and achieve a minimum score of 550) and the SAT I or the ACT.

Computers: The college provides computer facilities for student use. The academic computer is a 26-server network of AT&T 382s, Sun servers, and an Alliant FX 2800. Students use the network system through both general access computing laboratories and electronic classrooms, and remote access via modems. Currently, there are 767 workstations available to students, including PCs, Sun high-end workstations and Next computers. All students may access the system which may be used 24 hours a day. There is a 2-hour limit in the open access laboratories during peak demand periods. There are no fees.

Graduates: Some 221 companies recruited on campus in 1992–93.

Admissions Contact: George Bachmann, Associate Director, Admissions and University Outreach.

CALIFORNIA STATE UNIVERSITY NORTHRIDGE

C-5

Northridge, CA 91330

(818) 885-3700

Full-time: 6762 men, 8094 women	Faculty: 846; IIA, +$
Part-time: 2956 men, 3869 women	Ph.D.s: 83%
Graduate: 1992 men, 3609 women	Student/Faculty: 18 to 1
Year: semesters, summer session	Tuition: $1712 ($7616)
Application Deadline: November 30	Room & Board: $5410

Freshman Class: 7796 applied, 6198 accepted, 2157 enrolled

SAT I Verbal/Math: 365/444 **LESS COMPETITIVE**

California State University/Northridge, founded in 1958, is part of the state-supported university system offering degree programs in the liberal arts and sciences, business administration, education, engineering, music, health fields, and fine arts. There are 8 undergraduate schools and one graduate school. In addition to regional accreditation, CSUN has baccalaureate program accreditation with AACSB, ABET, ACEJMC, AHEA, APTA, CAHEA, and NASM. The 3 libraries contain 1 million volumes and 2.5 million microform items, and subscribe to 3700 periodicals. Computerized library sources and services include the card catalog, interlibrary loans, and database searching. Special learning facilities include a learning resource center, an art gallery, planetarium, radio station, TV station, observatory, anthropological museum, botanical gardens, urban archives center, the Natural Center on Deafness, and the Center for the Study of Cancer and Development Biology. The 353-acre campus is in a suburban area 25 miles north of Los Angeles. Including residence halls, there are 47 buildings on campus.

Student Life: About 84% of undergraduates are from California. Students come from 47 states, 101 foreign countries, and Canada. Ninety-six percent are from public schools; 4% from private. Fifty-three percent are white; 14% Hispanic; 11% Asian American. The average age of freshmen is 19; all undergraduates, 24.2. Thirty percent drop out by the end of their first year; 41% remain to graduate.

Housing: A total of 2400 students can be accommodated in college housing. College-sponsored living facilities include coed on-campus apartments. In addition, there is an international house. On-campus housing is available on a first-come, first-served basis. Ninety percent of students commute. All students may keep cars on campus.

Activities: About 6% of men belong to 23 national fraternities; about 4% of women belong to 13 national sororities. There are 210 groups on campus, including art, band, cheerleading, choir, chorale, chorus, computers, dance, drama, ethnic, film, gay, honors, international, jazz band, literary magazine, marching band, musical theater, newspaper, opera, orchestra, political, professional, radio and TV, religious, social, social service, student government, symphony, and yearbook. Popular campus events include Homecoming, International Student Days, and Campus Community Day.

Sports: There are 9 intercollegiate sports for men and 7 for women, and 12 intramural sports for men and 12 for women. Athletic and recreation facilities include 3 gymnasiums, 2 swimming pools, a 6000-seat football stadium, softball and soccer fields, and handball, racquetball, and tennis courts.

Disabled Students: Ninety-eight percent of the campus is accessible to disabled students. The following facilities are available: wheelchair ramps, elevators, special parking, specially equipped rest rooms, special class scheduling, lowered drinking fountains, lowered telephones, and electric doors.

Services: In addition to many counseling and information services, tutoring is available in some subjects, including English and mathematics. There is also a reader service for the blind, and remedial math, reading, and writing.

Campus Safety and Security: Campus safety and security measures include 24-hour foot and vehicle patrol, escort service, informal discussions, pamphlets, posters, and films. In addition, there are emergency telephones and lighted pathways and sidewalks.

Programs of Study: CSUN awards the B.A., B.S., and B.M. degrees. Master's degrees also are awarded. Bachelor's degrees are awarded in BIOLOGICAL SCIENCE (biochemistry, biology/biological science, cell biology, environmental biology, and microbiology), BUSINESS (accounting, banking and finance, business administration and management, management information systems, marketing/retailing/merchandising, real estate, and recreation and leisure services), COMMUNICATIONS AND THE ARTS (art history and appreciation, broadcasting, dance, design, dramatic arts, English, film arts, fine arts, French, German, journalism, linguistics, music, Spanish, and speech/debate/rhetoric), COMPUTER AND PHYSICAL SCIENCE (astrophysics, chemistry, computer mathematics, computer science, earth science, geology, geophysics and seismology, mathematics, physics, and radiological technology), EDUCATION (art, business, home economics, music, and physical), ENGINEERING AND ENVIRONMENTAL DESIGN (engineering), HEALTH PROFESSIONS (health, health care administration, medical laboratory technology, nursing, physical therapy, recreation therapy, and speech pathology/audiology), SO-

CIAL SCIENCE (African American studies, anthropology, child psychology/development, criminology, dietetics, economics, geography, history, liberal arts/general studies, Mexican-American/Chicano studies, philosophy, political science/government, psychology, religion, social work, sociology, and urban studies). Liberal studies is the strongest academically. Business administration and economics, psychology, and liberal studies have the largest enrollments.

Required: All students must complete 52 units of general education requirements in 6 areas, including courses in American history, U.S. Constitution, state and local government, English, mathematics, logic, and oral and written communication. A total of 124 semester units for the B.A., 128 to 132 for the B.S., and 132 for the B.M., with a minimum GPA of 2.0, is required in order to graduate. At least 30 semester units must be completed in residence.

Special: Cross-registration is offered through the Intra System Visitor Program. Study abroad in 16 countries, a London semester, internships, university work-study programs, dual majors, student-designed majors, credit for military experience, and pass/fail options for elective courses are offered. There is a freshman honors program on campus, as well as 4 national honor societies. Eight departments have honors programs.

Faculty/Classroom: Sixty-eight percent of faculty are male; 32%, female. The average class size in an introductory lecture is 35; in a laboratory, 24; and in a regular course offering, 30.

Admissions: About 80% of the 1993-94 applicants were accepted. SAT scores for the 1993-94 freshman class were as follows: Verbal—92% below 500, 7% between 500 and 599, 1% between 600 and 700, and fewer than 1% above 700; Math—70% below 500, 23% between 500 and 599, 6% between 600 and 700, and 1% above 700.

Requirements: CSUN requires applicants to be in the upper 33% of their class. A minimum GPA of 2.0 is required. The SAT I or ACT is required for students with a GPA below 3.0 (3.6 for nonresidents). Applicants should have completed 4 years of high school English, 3 each of mathematics and academic electives, 2 of foreign language, and 1 each of laboratory science, U.S. history/government, and visual/performing arts. AP and CLEP credits are accepted. Important factors used in the admissions decision are recommendations by school officials, evidence of special talent, leadership record, personality, intangible qualities, and parents or siblings attending the school.

Procedure: Freshmen are admitted fall and spring. Entrance exams should be taken by December of the senior year. Applications should be filed by November 30 for fall entry and August 31 for spring entry, along with an application fee of $55. Notification is sent on a rolling basis. There is an early decision plan.

Transfer: About 3050 transfer students enrolled in 1993-94. A GPA of 2.0 (2.4 for nonresidents) is required in a minimum of 56 transferable semester units. The last 30 credits out of a total of 124 to 132 must be completed at CSUN.

Visiting: There are regularly scheduled orientations for prospective students, held in June-July for fall entrance and in November for spring entrance. There are guides for informal visits and visitors may sit in on classes and stay overnight at the school. To arrange for a visit, contact Institutional Relations at (818) 885-2879.

Financial Aid: In 1993-94, 25% of continuing students received some form of financial aid. About 12% of freshmen and 16% of continuing students received need-based aid. The average freshman award was $3860. Of that total, scholarships or need-based grants averaged $2465 ($9500 maximum); loans averaged $3341 ($11,500 maximum); and work contracts averaged $1746 ($4366 maximum). CSUN is a member of CSS. The SAAC financial statement is required. The deadline for financial aid applications is March 2.

International Students: There are currently 450 international students enrolled. They must take the TOEFL and achieve a minimum score of 500.

Computers: The college provides computer facilities for student use. The mainframe is an IBM 4381. There are 1700 microcomputers on campus; 300 are networked by DOS and UNIX. All students may access the system. It may be used 24 hours a day, 7 days a week. There are no time limits on using the system and no fees.

Graduates: In 1992-93, 4095 bachelor's degrees were awarded. The most popular majors among graduates were business administration (21%), social services (12%), and home economics (9%). Within an average freshman class, 3% graduate in 4 years, 16% in 5 years, and 32% in 6 years. Some 400 companies recruited on campus in 1992-93.

Admissions Contact: Mary Baxton, Associate Director of Admissions and Records.

CALIFORNIA STATE UNIVERSITY
SACRAMENTO
B-3
Sacramento, CA 95819-6048

(916) 278-3901
(800) 722-4748 (in-state)

Full-time: 6628 men, 7454 women
Part-time: 2347 men, 2977 women
Graduate: 1892 men, 3170 women
Year: semesters, summer session
Application Deadline: November 30
Freshman Class: 4346 applied, 2578 accepted, 985 enrolled
SAT I Verbal/Math: 408/476

Faculty: 880; IIA, +$
Ph.D.s: 76%
Student/Faculty: 16 to 1
Tuition: $1674 ($9054)
Room & Board: $4713

COMPETITIVE

California State University/Sacramento, founded in 1947, is part of the state-supported university system. The school offers graduate and undergraduate programs in the liberal arts and sciences, business administration, education, engineering, music, and health and human service fields. There are 5 undergraduate and 5 graduate schools. In addition to regional accreditation, CSUS has baccalaureate program accreditation with AACSB, ABET, AHEA, CSWE, NASAD, NASM, NLN, and NRPA. The library contains 900,000 volumes and 254,382 microform items, and subscribes to 5734 periodicals. Computerized library sources and services include the card catalog, interlibrary loans, and database searching. Special learning facilities include a learning resource center, art gallery, planetarium, radio station, TV station, and an aquatic center. The 282-acre campus is in an urban area 90 miles northeast of San Francisco. Including residence halls, there are 51 buildings on campus.

Student Life: About 97% of undergraduates are from California. Students come from 40 states, 100 foreign countries, and Canada. Ninety percent are from public schools; 10% from private. Sixty-four percent are white. The average age of freshmen is 19; all undergraduates, 24. Twenty percent drop out by the end of their first year; 52% remain to graduate.

Housing: A total of 1299 students can be accommodated in college housing. College-sponsored living facilities include single-sex and coed dormitories. On-campus housing is available on a first-come, first-served basis. Ninety-five percent of students commute. All students may keep cars on campus.

Activities: About 8% of men belong to 1 local and 18 national fraternities; about 4% of women belong to 2 local and 8 national sororities. There are 200 groups on campus, including art, band, cheerleading, choir, chorale, chorus, computers, dance, drama, ethnic, film, gay, honors, international, jazz band, marching band, musical theater, newspaper, opera, orchestra, pep band, photography, political, professional, radio and TV, religious, social, social service, student government, and symphony. Popular campus events include Greek Week, Festival of New American Music, and River City Days.

Sports: There are 9 intercollegiate sports for men and 8 for women, and 13 intramural sports for men and 13 for women. Athletic and recreation facilities include a 7500-seat stadium, 2 gymnasiums, 2 swimming pools, and baseball, softball, and soccer fields.

Disabled Students: Ninety percent of the campus is accessible to disabled students. The following facilities are available: wheelchair ramps, elevators, special parking, specially equipped rest rooms, special class scheduling, and lowered drinking fountains.

Services: In addition to many counseling and information services, tutoring is available in most subjects. There is also a reader service for the blind, and remedial math, reading, and writing.

Campus Safety and Security: Campus safety and security measures include self defense education, escort service, shuttle buses, and informal discussions. In addition, there are pamphlets, posters, films, emergency telephones, and lighted pathways and sidewalks.

Programs of Study: CSUS awards the B.A., B.S., and B.M. degrees. Master's degrees are also awarded. Bachelor's degrees are awarded in BIOLOGICAL SCIENCE (biology/biological science and microbiology), BUSINESS (accounting, banking and finance, business administration and management, insurance, international business management, management information systems, marketing/retailing/merchandising, and real estate), COMMUNICATIONS AND THE ARTS (communications, dramatic arts, English, French, German, journalism, music, and Spanish), COMPUTER AND PHYSICAL SCIENCE (chemistry, computer science, geology, mathematics, physical sciences, and physics), EDUCATION (business, early childhood, and health), ENGINEERING AND ENVIRONMENTAL DESIGN (civil engineering, computer engineering, electrical/electronics engineering, engineering technology, and mechanical engineering), HEALTH PROFESSIONS (environmental health science, medical laboratory technology, nursing, and speech pathology/audiology), SOCIAL SCIENCE (anthropology, criminal justice, economics, geography, history, international relations, parks and recreation management, philosophy, psychology, public administration, social science, social work, and sociology). Nursing, criminal justice, business administration, and accounting are the strongest academically. Business admin-

istration, communications, criminal justice, and liberal studies have the largest enrollments.

Required: In order to graduate, students must complete a minimum of 124 semester hours, including 30 to 86 hours in the major, with a minimum 2.0 GPA. Students must complete 51 units in general education requirements and take proficiency examinations in writing and a foreign language. A course in race and ethnicity in American society is required.

Special: The university offers cross-registration with other California State University schools, co-op programs in engineering and computer science, internships, study abroad in 12 countries, and dual and student-designed majors. There are 12 national honor societies on campus, including Phi Beta Kappa.

Faculty/Classroom: Sixty-five percent of faculty are male; 35%, female.

Admissions: About 59% of the 1993-94 applicants were accepted. The SAT scores for the 1993-94 freshman class were as follows: Verbal—82% below 500, 15% between 500 and 599, and 3% between 600 and 700; Math—55% below 500, 33% between 500 and 599, 11% between 600 and 700, and 1% above 700.

Requirements: A minimum GPA of 2.0 is required. The SAT I or ACT is required of applicants with a GPA below 3.0. Applicants should have completed 4 years of high school English, 3 years of mathematics, 2 years of a foreign language, 1 each of laboratory science, history, and visual/performing arts and 3 years of college preparatory electives. AP and CLEP credits are accepted.

Procedure: Freshmen are admitted fall and spring. Entrance exams should be taken before December of the senior year. Applications should be filed by November 30 for fall entry and August 31 for spring entry, along with an application fee of $55. Notification is sent on a rolling basis.

Transfer: About 4100 transfer students enrolled in 1993-94. Applicants must have a 2.0 GPA and 56 transferable semester units, including 30 units of specific general education courses to include oral and written communication, critical thinking, and quantitative reasoning. A total of 30 credits out of 124 to 132 must be completed at CSUS.

Visiting: There are regularly scheduled orientations for prospective students. There are guides for informal visits and visitors may sit in on classes. To arrange for a visit, contact the University Outreach Services Office at (916) 278-7362.

Financial Aid: CSUS is a member of CSS. The SAAC financial statement is required. The deadline for financial aid applications is March 2.

International Students: There are currently 709 international students enrolled. They must take the TOEFL and achieve a minimum score of 510. The student must also take the SAT I or the ACT.

Computers: The college provides computer facilities for student use. The mainframes are an IBM 4381, an IBM 3090/150E, a DEC VAX 880, and a CDC CYBER 830. There are 400 terminals or microcomputer workstations located in 10 computer laboratories. Students must obtain account numbers and passwords to access specific computers based on sponsorship by the course faculty member. Only students who have requested accounts may access the systems. There are no time limits on using the system and no fees.

Graduates: In 1992-93, 3691 bachelor's degrees were awarded. The most popular majors among graduates were criminal justice (6%), liberal studies (6%), and communication studies (6%). Within an average freshman class, 15% graduate in 4 years, 40% in 5 years, and 3% in 6 years.

Admissions Contact: Larry D. Giasmire, Director of Admissions/Records.

CALIFORNIA STATE UNIVERSITY
SAN BERNARDINO
D-5
San Bernardino, CA 92407-2397

(909) 880-5190

Full-time: 2799 men, 4137 women
Part-time: 880 men, 1382 women
Graduate: 1230 men, 2057 women
Year: quarters, summer session
Application Deadline: see profile
Freshman Class: 2347 applied, 1619 accepted, 786 enrolled
SAT I or ACT: required

Faculty: 388; IIA, +$
Ph.D.s: 92%
Student/Faculty: 18 to 1
Tuition: $1598 ($7502)
Room & Board: $4457

LESS COMPETITIVE

California State University/San Bernardino, founded in 1965, is a public, commuter institute offering programs in business and public administration, natural sciences, education, humanities, and social and behavioral sciences. There are 5 undergraduate and 18 graduate schools. In addition to regional accreditation, CSU/San Bernardino has baccalaureate program accreditation with ADA, NASAD, and NLN. The library contains 489,000 volumes, 548,389 microform items, and 7600 audiovisual forms, and subscribes to 2348 periodicals. Computerized library sources and services include the card catalog, interlibrary loans, and database searching. Special learning fa-

cilities include a learning resource center, an art gallery, radio station, and TV station. The 430-acre campus is in a suburban area 60 miles east of Los Angeles. Including residence halls, there are 28 buildings on campus.

Student Life: About 96% of undergraduates are from California. Students come from 49 states, 52 foreign countries, and Canada. Ninety-six percent are from public schools; 4% from private. Sixty-two percent are white; 17% Hispanic. The average age of freshmen is 19.7; all undergraduates, 25.9. Thirty percent drop out by the end of their first year; 40% remain to graduate.

Housing: A total of 409 students can be accommodated in college housing. College-sponsored living facilities include single-sex and coed dormitories. On-campus housing is available on a first-come, first-served basis. Ninety-seven percent of students commute. All students may keep cars on campus.

Activities: About 6% of men belong to 6 national fraternities; about 3% of women belong to 4 national sororities. There are 100 groups on campus, including art, band, cheerleading, choir, chorale, chorus, computers, dance, drama, ethnic, film, gay, honors, international, jazz band, literary magazine, musical theater, newspaper, opera, orchestra, pep band, political, professional, radio and TV, religious, social, social service, and student government. Popular campus events include Homecoming, Black History Month, Cinco de Mayo, Fall Fest, and Spring Fest.

Sports: Athletic and recreation facilities include a gymnasium, basketball, volleyball, tennis and racquetball courts, a weight room, a swimming pool, softball and soccer fields, and a track.

Disabled Students: Ninety-eight percent of the campus is accessible to disabled students. The following facilities are available: wheelchair ramps, elevators, special parking, specially equipped rest rooms, student assistants, cart service, and special equipment such as TSS, phonic ear, and VisualTek.

Services: In addition to many counseling and information services, tutoring is available in most subjects. There is also a reader service for the blind and remedial math and writing.

Campus Safety and Security: Campus safety and security measures include 24-hour foot and vehicle patrol, self defense education, escort service, and emergency telephones. In addition, there are lighted pathways and sidewalks.

Programs of Study: CSU/San Bernardino awards the B.A. and B.S. degrees. Master's degrees are also awarded. Bachelor's degrees are awarded in BIOLOGICAL SCIENCE (biochemistry and biology/biological science), BUSINESS (accounting, banking and finance, business administration and management, business economics, international business management, and marketing/retailing/merchandising), COMMUNICATIONS AND THE ARTS (communications, design, dramatic arts, English, French, music, and Spanish), COMPUTER AND PHYSICAL SCIENCE (chemistry, computer science, geology, information sciences and systems, mathematics, and physics), EDUCATION (art, bilingual/bicultural, health, music, and physical), HEALTH PROFESSIONS (environmental health science and nursing), SOCIAL SCIENCE (anthropology, criminal justice, economics, food science, geography, history, human services, philosophy, political science/government, psychology, public administration, social science, social work, and sociology). Psychology and business have the largest enrollments.

Required: To graduate, students must complete 186 quarter hours, including 86 in the general education program, with a minimum GPA of 2.0.

Special: The university offers cross-registration with other CSU campuses and with Loma Linda University, and study abroad through the National and International Student Exchange. Also available are internships, campus and community work-study programs, B.A.-B.S. degrees, dual and student-designed majors, credit for vocational education and military experience, and nondegree study. There is a freshman honors program on campus.

Faculty/Classroom: The average class size in an introductory lecture is 200; in a laboratory, 30; and in a regular course offering, 30.

Admissions: About 69% of the 1993–94 applicants were accepted.

Requirements: A minimum GPA of 2.0 is required. The SAT I or ACT is required. Applicants must be graduates of an accredited secondary school. Preparatory work should include 4 years of English, 3 each of mathematics and electives, 2 of foreign language, and 1 each of U.S. history/government, laboratory science, and visual and performing arts. Admission is based on an eligibility index that weights the high school GPA and the SAT I or ACT score. Students with GPAs of 3.0 or better (3.6 for nonresidents) are exempt from test-score requirements. AP and CLEP credits are accepted.

Procedure: Freshmen are admitted fall, winter, and spring. Entrance exams should be taken prior to applying. Applications are accepted until programs are filled. Notification is sent on a rolling basis, 2 to 4 weeks after the completed application is received. The application fee is $55. There is an early admissions plan.

Transfer: About 1500 transfer students enrolled in 1993–94. Transfer applicants must have a minimum college GPA of 2.0 (2.4 for nonresidents) and be in good standing at the previously-attended institution. Those with fewer than 56 transferable semester units must meet freshmen entrance requirements. A total of 45 quarter hours out of 186 must be completed at CSU/San Bernardino.

Visiting: There are regularly scheduled orientations for prospective students. There are guides for informal visits and visitors may sit in on classes and stay overnight at the school. To arrange for a visit, contact Precollege Outreach/Campus Tours at (909) 880–5195.

Financial Aid: In 1993–94, 29% of all current freshmen and 29% of continuing students received some form of financial aid. About 26% of freshmen and 26% of continuing students received need-based aid. Scholarships or need-based grants averaged $757; and loans averaged $3535. Ninety percent of undergraduate students work part-time. The average financial indebtedness of an earlier year's graduate was $6200. CSU/San Bernardino is a member of CSS. The SAAC for California residents financial statement is required. The deadline for financial aid applications is March 1.

International Students: There are currently 275 international students enrolled. The school actively recruits these students. They must take the TOEFL and achieve a minimum score of 550.

Computers: The college provides computer facilities for student use. The mainframes are an IBM 4381 and a DEC VAX 3500. Apple Macintosh and IBM-compatible microcomputers are available for student use. All students may access the system. It may be used 14 hours a day, 7 days a week. There are no fees.

Graduates: In 1992–93, 1712 bachelor's degrees were awarded. The most popular majors among graduates were business (34%), liberal studies (20%), and psychology (8%). Within an average freshman class, 25% graduate in 5 years and 34% in 6 years. In an earlier graduating class, 8% of the men and 13% of the women were enrolled in graduate school within 6 months of graduation; 85% of the men and 80% of the women had found employment.

Admissions Contact: Enrollment Services.

CALIFORNIA STATE UNIVERSITY STANISLAUS
B-3
Turlock, CA 95382   (209) 667-3256

Full-time: 1750 men, 2593 women	**Faculty:** 200; IIA, +$
Part-time: 100 men, 136 women	**Ph.D.s:** 87%
Graduate: 428 men, 850 women	**Student/Faculty:** 22 to 1
Year: 4–1–4, summer session	**Tuition:** $1780 ($8322)
Application Deadline: December 1	**Room & Board:** $5019
Freshman Class: 1042 applied, 830 accepted, 461 enrolled	
SAT I Verbal/Math: 400/449	**COMPETITIVE**

California State University/Stanislaus, founded in 1957, is a state-supported, coeducational institution offering undergraduate and graduate programs in liberal and fine arts, business, health science, and teacher preparation. In addition to regional accreditation, CSU/Stanislaus has baccalaureate program accreditation with NASAD, NASM, and NLN. The library contains 290,000 volumes, and subscribes to 4000 periodicals. Computerized library sources and services include the card catalog, interlibrary loans, and database searching. Special learning facilities include a learning resource center, an art gallery, a planetarium, a theater, an animal care facility, and a laser laboratory. The 230-acre campus is in a rural area in the San Joaquin Valley, about 100 miles from San Francisco. Including residence halls, there are 14 buildings on campus.

Student Life: Most undergraduates are from California. The average age of freshmen is 18; all undergraduates, 28.

Housing: College-sponsored living facilities include coed dormitories and off-campus apartments.

Activities: There are some groups and organizations on campus, including drama, radio and TV, and student government.

Sports: Athletic and recreation facilities include a field house, a 2300-seat gymnasium, softball and baseball diamonds, a soccer field, tennis courts, an all-weather track, and a swimming pool.

Disabled Students: The following facilities are available: special parking, tutors, and notetakers.

Services: Tutoring is available.

Campus Safety and Security: Campus safety and security measures include escort service, emergency telephones, 24-hour security officers, safety awareness programs, motorist assistance, and CPR and first-aid training.

Programs of Study: CSU/Stanislaus awards the B.A. and B.S. degrees. Master's degrees also are awarded. Bachelor's degrees are awarded in BIOLOGICAL SCIENCE (biology/biological science and marine science), BUSINESS (business administration and management), COMMUNICATIONS AND THE ARTS (communications, dramatic arts, English, fine arts, French, German, music, Spanish, speech/debate/rhetoric, and studio art), COMPUTER AND PHYSICAL SCIENCE (chemistry, computer management, computer sci-

ence, earth science, geology, information sciences and systems, mathematics, physical sciences, and physics), EDUCATION (physical, secondary, and vocational), HEALTH PROFESSIONS (nursing), SOCIAL SCIENCE (anthropology, child psychology/development, cognitive science, criminal justice, economics, geography, history, liberal arts/general studies, philosophy, psychology, public administration, social science, and sociology).

Required: To graduate, students must complete at least 124 semester units, including 51 in the general education program and 40 in upper-division courses, with a minimum GPA of 2.0. Distribution requirements consist of 12 units of social science, 9 each of communication skills, natural science and mathematics, and humanities, and 3 of computer study or health.

Special: Numerous co-op programs and internships are offered. Cross-registration with the Higher Education Consortium of Central California, study abroad, work-study programs, nondegree study, and pass/fail options are also available. There is a freshman honors program on campus.

Admissions: About 80% of the 1993–94 applicants were accepted. About 35% of the current freshmen were in the top fifth of their class; 65% were in the top two fifths.

Requirements: A minimum GPA of 2.0 is required. The SAT I or ACT is required. Applicants should be graduates of an accredited secondary school with a GPA of 2.0. Applicants with a GPA of 3.0 (3.4 for nonresidents) are exempt for test score requirements. Preparatory course work should include 4 years of English, 3 of mathematics, 2 of foreign language, and 1 each of history, laboratory science, and visual and performing arts. Admission is based on an eligibility index that weights GPA and SAT I or ACT scores. AP and CLEP credits are accepted.

Procedure: Early decision applications should be filed by December 1; regular applications, by December 1 for fall entry, July 1 for winter entry, and August 1 for spring entry, along with an application fee of $55.

Transfer: Applicants must have a college GPA of 2.0 (2.4 for nonresidents). Those with fewer than 56 transferable semester credits must meet freshman entrance requirements. A total of 30 credits out of 124 must be completed at CSU/Stanislaus.

Visiting: There are guides for informal visits, and visitors may sit in on classes.

Financial Aid: The SAAC is required for California residents.

International Students: They must take the TOEFL and achieve a minimum score of 500.

Admissions Contact: Director, Admissions and Records.

CHAPMAN UNIVERSITY
D-5

Orange, CA 92666   (714) 997-6711

Full-time: 720 men, 942 women	Faculty: 105; IIA, av$
Part-time: 88 men, 121 women	Ph.D.s: 81%
Graduate: 331 men, 728 women	Student/Faculty: 16 to 1
Year: 4–1–4, summer session	Tuition: $16,228
Application Deadline: March 1	Room & Board: $5614
Freshman Class: 908 applied, 739 accepted, 351 enrolled	
SAT I: 440/485	ACT: 21 COMPETITIVE

Chapman University, founded in 1861, is a private coeducational institution affiliated with the Disciples of Christ Christian Church, offering degree programs in liberal and fine arts, business, education, and the health sciences. There are 4 undergraduate and 5 graduate schools. The library contains 155,000 volumes, 300 microform items, and 2595 audiovisual forms, and subscribes to 1200 periodicals. Computerized library sources and services include the card catalog, interlibrary loans, and database searching. Special learning facilities include a learning resource center, art gallery, radio station, and TV station. The 40-acre campus is in a suburban area 35 miles southeast of Los Angeles. Including residence halls, there are 23 buildings on campus.

Student Life: Students come from 33 foreign countries and Canada. Seventy-four percent are from public schools; 26% from private. Seventy-one percent are white; 10% Hispanic. Sixty-two percent claim no religious affiliation; 20% Catholic; 16% Protestant. The average age of freshmen is 19; all undergraduates, 22. Thirty-two percent drop out by the end of their first year; 39% remain to graduate.

Housing: A total of 937 students can be accommodated in college housing. College-sponsored living facilities include single-sex and coed dormitories and on-campus apartments. In addition there are houses for special interests, wellness, international living, and discovering southern California, as well as community houses. On-campus housing is guaranteed for the freshman year only, is available on a first-come, first-served basis, and is available on a lottery system for upperclassmen. Priority is given to out-of-town students. Fifty-nine percent of students commute. All students may keep cars on campus.

Activities: About 21% of men and 1% of women belong to 1 local and 4 national fraternities; about 16% of women belong to 4 national sororities. There are 50 groups on campus, including cheerleading,

choir, dance, drama, ethnic, film, gay, honors, international, literary magazine, newspaper, orchestra, photography, political, professional, radio and TV, religious, social, social service, student government, symphony, and yearbook. Popular campus events include lunchtime concerts, Black History Month, Harvest Hoedown, homecoming, All School Formal, midnight breakfast during finals, Haunted Crypt, Alcohol Awareness Week, Greek Week, Latino Heritage Month, and Family Weekend.

Sports: There are 8 intercollegiate sports for men and 8 for women, and 13 intramural sports for men and 13 for women. Athletic and recreation facilities include a gymnasium, a weight room, 3 practice fields, and 4 tennis courts. Baseball and softball fields, a track, and a pool are available for student use in the city of Orange.

Disabled Students: Thirty percent of the campus is accessible to disabled students. The following facilities are available: wheelchair ramps, elevators, special parking, specially equipped rest rooms, special class scheduling, and designated rooms in the residence halls.

Services: In addition to many counseling and information services, tutoring is available in most subjects, including mathematics, sciences, business, and English. There is a reader service for the blind, and remedial math, reading, and writing. In addition there are note takers, readers, and tapes for deaf, blind, and international students; special study skills workshops; and help for the learning disabled.

Campus Safety and Security: Campus safety and security measures include 24-hour foot and vehicle patrol, self-defense education, escort service, and shuttle buses. In addition, there are pamphlets, posters, films, emergency telephones, lighted pathways and sidewalks, and a 24-hour bicycle patrol.

Programs of Study: Chapman awards the B.A., B.S., B.F.A., B.M., and B.S.B.A. degrees. Master's degrees also are awarded. Bachelor's degrees are awarded in BIOLOGICAL SCIENCE (biology/biological science), BUSINESS (accounting and business administration and management), COMMUNICATIONS AND THE ARTS (communications, English, film arts, fine arts, French, music, and Spanish), COMPUTER AND PHYSICAL SCIENCE (chemistry, computer science, and mathematics), EDUCATION (physical), SOCIAL SCIENCE (criminal justice, economics, food science, history, liberal arts/general studies, philosophy, political science/government, psychology, social science, and sociology). Business, communications, liberal studies, and psychology have the largest enrollments.

Required: Students in the B.A., B.F.A., B.S., and B.S.B.A. programs must complete a total of 124 credits with at least a 2.0 GPA. In addition, students must meet requirements in basic subjects such as writing, oral communication, freshman seminar, mathematics, and physical education through course work, advanced credit, or examination. General education requirements include 9 credits in humanities, 10 in natural sciences, and 9 in social courses. Also required are 6 of cultural heritage/human diversity, 6 credits of foreign language, and a junior writing proficiency examination.

Special: Cooperative and internship programs are available. Students may study abroad for a semester or spend a semester in Washington, D.C. Dual and student-designed majors are possible. A general studies degree, a B.A.-B.S. degree, nondegree study options, and pass/fail options are also permitted. There is a freshman honors program on campus, as well as one national honor society.

Faculty/Classroom: Sixty-six percent of faculty are male; 34%, female. Ninety-one percent teach undergraduates. No introductory courses are taught by graduate students. The average class size in an introductory lecture is 21; in a laboratory, 17; and in a regular course offering, 19.

Admissions: About 81% of the 1993–94 applicants were accepted. The SAT scores for the 1993–94 freshman class were as follows: Verbal—73% below 500, 22% between 500 and 599, and 5% between 600 and 700; Math—53% below 500, 33% between 500 and 599, 11% between 600 and 700, and 3% above 700. The ACT scores were 43% below 21, 27% between 21 and 23, 18% between 24 and 26, 6% between 27 and 28, and 6% above 28. About 39% of the current freshmen were in the top fifth of their class; 66% were in the top two fifths. There was 1 National Merit finalist. Four freshmen graduated first in their class.

Requirements: A minimum GPA of 2.5 is required. The SAT I or ACT is required. Applicants should be graduates of accredited high schools or have earned the GED. Secondary preparation should include 3 years of social science or electives, 2 each of composition and/or literature, science, and a foreign language, and 1 year each of algebra and geometry. Prospective art or music majors should show some preparation in those fields. A personal essay is required. The college recommends that applicants also submit SAT II: Subject test scores in writing, and that they seek an interview. AP and CLEP credits are accepted. Important factors used in the admissions decision are advanced placement or honor courses, evidence of special talent, leadership record, extracurricular activities record, and recommendations by alumni.

Procedure: Freshmen are admitted to all sessions. Entrance exams should be taken by the fall of the senior year. Applications should be filed by March 1 for fall entry, December 15 for spring entry, and June 1 for summer entry, along with an application fee of $30. Notification is sent on a rolling basis. There is an early admissions plan.

Transfer: About 350 transfer students enrolled in 1993–94. Transfer applicants should have completed at least 15 credits of college work with a 2.0 minimum GPA and should submit SAT I scores. A minimum composite score of 850 on the SAT I is recommended. A total of 24 credits out of 124 must be completed at Chapman.

Visiting: There are regularly scheduled orientations for prospective students. There are guides for informal visits, and visitors may sit in on classes and stay overnight at the school. To arrange for a visit, contact the Office of Admissions at (714) 997–6711.

Financial Aid: In 1993–94, 51% of all current freshmen and 73% of continuing students received some form of financial aid. About 43% of freshmen and 63% of continuing students received need-based aid. The average freshman award was $15,470. Of that total, scholarships or need-based grants averaged $10,570; loans averaged $3000; and work contracts averaged $1900. Ninety-five percent of undergraduate students work part-time. Average earnings from campus work for the school year are $2000. The average financial indebtedness of the 1992–93 graduate was $16,000. Chapman is a member of CSS. The FAF is required. The deadline for financial aid applications is March 2.

International Students: There are currently 119 international students enrolled. The school actively recruits these students. They must take the TOEFL and achieve a minimum score of 500. The student must also take the SAT I or the ACT.

Computers: The college provides computer facilities for student use. The mainframe is an HP 3000. There are 25 Apple Macintosh IIsi, 30 Apple Macintosh Se, 50 IBM, AST, and other compatible microcomputers, 3 DEC Micro VAX II Unix-based minicomputers, 2 NCR Unix-based minicomputers, and 2 DEC workstations that are networked and have access to Internet. All students may access the system. It may be used 8 A.M. to 11 P.M. There are no time limits on using the system and no fees.

Graduates: In 1992–93, 306 bachelor's degrees were awarded. The most popular majors among graduates were business administration (22%), communications (21%), and liberal studies (10%). Within an average freshman class, 1% graduate in 3 years, 26% in 4 years, 37% in 5 years, and 39% in 6 years. Some 59 companies recruited on campus in 1992–93.

Admissions Contact: Mike Drummy, Director of Admissions.

CHRIST COLLEGE IRVINE
(See Concordia University)

CHRISTIAN HERITAGE COLLEGE
D-5

El Cajon, CA 92019   (619) 441–2200; (800) 676–2242 (out-of-state)

Full-time: 153 men, 170 women	Faculty: 26
Part-time: 10 men, 17 women	Ph.D.s: 50%
Graduate: none	Student/Faculty: 12 to 1
Year: semesters, summer session	Tuition: $7856
Application Deadline: open	Room & Board: $3900
Freshman Class: 218 applied, 173 accepted, 85 enrolled	
SAT I: 443/456	ACT: 20 COMPETITIVE

Christian Heritage College is a small, private institution founded in 1970 by the Scott Memorial Baptist Church of San Diego, with which it is still affiliated. It offers programs in the liberal arts, business, and education. The library contains 70,000 volumes and 3000 audiovisual forms and subscribes to 350 periodicals. Special learning facilities include the nearby Institute for Creation Research. The 30-acre campus is in a suburban area 15 miles east of San Diego. Including residence halls, there are 14 buildings on campus.

Student Life: About 65% of undergraduates are from California. Students come from 25 states and 5 foreign countries. Seventy-five percent are from public schools; 25% from private. Seventy-eight percent are white. Most are Protestant. The average age of freshmen is 18; all undergraduates, 21. Forty percent drop out by the end of their first year; 25% remain to graduate.

Housing: A total of 200 students can be accommodated in college housing. College-sponsored living facilities include single-sex dormitories. On-campus housing is guaranteed for all 4 years. Fifty percent of students live on campus; of those, 30% remain on campus on weekends. Alcohol is not permitted. All students may keep cars on campus.

Activities: There are no fraternities or sororities on campus. There are 14 groups on campus, including art, choir, chorale, chorus, computers, drama, honors, international, newspaper, pep band, photography, political, radio and TV, religious, social, student government, and yearbook. Popular campus events include spring, winter, and

Valentine's Day banquets, Homecoming, and the Missions Conference.

Sports: There are 2 intercollegiate sports for men and 1 for women, and 5 intramural sports for men and 4 for women. Athletic and recreation facilities include a swimming pool, a gymnasium, outdoor courts for tennis, volleyball, and basketball, and soccer and softball fields.

Disabled Students: Ninety percent of the campus is accessible to disabled students. The following facilities are available: wheelchair ramps, elevators, and special parking.

Services: In addition to many counseling and information services, tutoring is available in some subjects.

Campus Safety and Security: Campus safety and security measures include 24-hour foot and vehicle patrol, lighted pathways and sidewalks, and a fenced campus.

Programs of Study: Christian Heritage College awards the B.A. and B.S. degrees. Associate degrees also are awarded. Bachelor's degrees are awarded in BUSINESS (business administration and management and international business management), COMMUNICATIONS AND THE ARTS (English and music), COMPUTER AND PHYSICAL SCIENCE (physics), EDUCATION (early childhood, education, elementary, English, home economics, music, physical, science, and secondary), SOCIAL SCIENCE (biblical studies, counseling psychology, family/consumer studies, history, and religious education). Counseling psychology, education, and music are the strongest academically.

Required: The required credits for graduation vary by degree program and major. All students must take 45 to 60 credits in sciences and mathematics, social science, and humanities; 25 to 27 credits in personal Christian development, creationism, and evangelism; and the balance in major field requirements and electives. A 2.0 GPA is required for graduation.

Special: Students attend chapel three times each week, participate in an annual Bible Conference, and complete a student ministry assignment each semester. Independent study for 1 to 3 credits can be arranged. There are internships in psychology, pastoral studies, and education.

Faculty/Classroom: Ninety percent of faculty are male; 10%, female. The average class size in an introductory lecture is 80; in a laboratory, 15; and in a regular course offering, 10.

Admissions: About 79% of the 1993–94 applicants were accepted. The SAT scores for the 1993–94 freshman class were as follows: Verbal—97% below 500, 2% between 500 and 599, and 1% between 600 and 700; Math—95% below 500, 3% between 500 and 599, and 1% between 600 and 700. The ACT scores were 90% below 21, 7% between 21 and 23, 2% between 24 and 26, and 1% between 27 and 28. About 25% of the current freshmen were in the top fifth of their class; 80% were in the top two fifths.

Requirements: Christian Heritage College requires applicants to be in the upper 50% of their class. A minimum GPA of 2.0 is required. The SAT I or ACT is required. Applicants must have a high school diploma or the GED, or have successfully completed the California State High School Proficiency Examination. Secondary preparation must include 4 units of English, 3 units each of mathematics, natural science, and social studies, and 2 units of a single foreign language. A personal essay is also required. In addition, applicants must meet certain spiritual requirements. Important factors used in the admissions decision are recommendations by school officials, leadership record, extracurricular activities record, evidence of special talent, and advanced placement or honor courses.

Procedure: Entrance exams should be taken during the junior year. Application deadlines are open. The application fee is $25. Notification is sent on a rolling basis.

Transfer: About 90 transfer students enrolled in 1993–94. A total of 30 credits out of 124 must be completed at Christian Heritage College.

Visiting: There are regularly scheduled orientations for prospective students. There are guides for informal visits and visitors may sit in on classes and stay overnight at the school. To arrange for a visit, contact the Admissions Office at (619) 588–7747 or (800) 676–2242.

Financial Aid: In 1993–94 90% of all students received some form of financial aid, including received need-based aid. The average freshman award was $2000. Sixty percent of undergraduate students work part-time. Average earnings from campus work for the school year are $1000. Christian Heritage College is a member of CSS. The FAF and SAAC are required. The deadline for financial aid applications is June 15.

International Students: There are currently 6 international students enrolled. The school actively recruits these students. They must take the TOEFL and achieve a minimum score of 500.

Computers: The college provides computer facilities for student use. There are no time limits on using the system and no fees.

Graduates: In a recent year, 68 bachelor's degrees were awarded.

Admissions Contact: Deanna Weyman, Director of Admissions.

CLAREMONT MCKENNA COLLEGE
Claremont, CA 91711

D-5

(909) 621-8088

Full-time: 522 men, 365 women	Faculty: 92; IIB, +$
Part-time: 1 woman	Ph.D.s: 100%
Graduate: none	Student/Faculty: 10 to 1
Year: semesters	Tuition: $16,400
Application Deadline: February 1	Room & Board: $5750
Freshman Class: 1860 applied, 767 accepted, 227 enrolled	
SAT I Verbal/Math: 600/670	ACT: 28 **MOST COMPETITIVE**

Claremont McKenna College, founded in 1946, is a small liberal arts college with a curricular emphasis on economics, government, international relations, and public affairs. The 5 libraries contain 1.8 million volumes, and subscribe to 6238 periodicals. Computerized library sources and services include the card catalog, interlibrary loans, and database searching. Special learning facilities include a learning resource center, art gallery, radio station, and 8 research institutes. The 50-acre campus is in a small town 35 miles east of downtown Los Angeles. Including residence halls, there are 29 buildings on campus.

Student Life: About 63% of undergraduates are from California. Students come from 38 states and 20 foreign countries. Sixty-two percent are from public schools; 38% from private. Sixty-one percent are white; 18% Asian American; 11% Hispanic. The average age of all undergraduates is 19.6. Five percent drop out by the end of their first year; 84% remain to graduate.

Housing: A total of 821 students can be accommodated in college housing. College-sponsored living facilities include coed dormitories and on-campus apartments. On-campus housing is guaranteed for all 4 years. Ninety-six percent of students live on campus; of those, 95% remain on campus on weekends. All students may keep cars on campus.

Activities: There are no fraternities or sororities on campus. There are 185 groups on campus, including art, band, choir, computers, dance, drama, ethnic, film, gay, honors, international, jazz band, literary magazine, newspaper, orchestra, pep band, photography, political, professional, radio, religious, social, social service, student government, and yearbook. Popular campus events include Homecoming, International Festival, madrigal dinners, and Monte Carlo Night.

Sports: There are 10 intercollegiate sports for men and 10 for women, and 13 intramural sports for men and 12 for women. Athletic and recreation facilities include gymnasium facilities, a weight room, a swimming pool, courts for squash, tennis, and volleyball, and various playing fields.

Disabled Students: The following facilities are available: wheelchair ramps, elevators, special parking, specially equipped rest rooms, special class scheduling, and lowered drinking fountains.

Services: In addition to many counseling and information services, tutoring is available in most subjects. The English Resources Center offers writing help and specialized workshops.

Campus Safety and Security: Campus safety and security measures include 24-hour foot and vehicle patrol, escort service, informal discussions, and pamphlets, posters, and films. In addition, there are lighted pathways and sidewalks.

Programs of Study: CMC awards the B.A. degree. Bachelor's degrees are awarded in BIOLOGICAL SCIENCE (biology/biological science), BUSINESS (accounting, business economics, and management engineering), COMMUNICATIONS AND THE ARTS (classics, dramatic arts, English literature, film arts, French, German, literature, and Spanish), COMPUTER AND PHYSICAL SCIENCE (chemistry, information sciences and systems, mathematics, physics, science, and science and management), ENGINEERING AND ENVIRONMENTAL DESIGN (engineering management and environmental science), HEALTH PROFESSIONS (premedicine), SOCIAL SCIENCE (African American studies, American studies, Asian/Oriental studies, economics, European studies, history, international relations, law, Mexican-American/Chicano studies, philosophy, political science/government, psychology, religion, and women's studies). Economics, government, international relations, psychology and history are the strongest academically. Economics, government, and international relations have the largest enrollments.

Required: All students must complete 32 courses with a C average. Required courses include 1 semester each of English, calculus and a foreign language or civilization; 2 each of sciences and humanities; and 3 each of social science and physical education. A thesis is required of all students.

Special: CMC students may cross-register at any of the Claremont Colleges, and may participate in exchange programs with Haverford, Spelman, or Colby Colleges. Students may study abroad in 32 countries or spend a semester in Washington, D.C. Many part-time academic year internships and full-time summer internships are available. There are 3–2 programs in management-engineering with Stanford University, Harvey Mudd College, and others, and a 3–3 program

with Columbia Law School. A multidisciplinary program in leadership studies and an interdisciplinary program in legal studies are offered. Dual majors are common and students may design their own majors. There are limited pass/fail options. There is a freshman honors program on campus, as well as 4 national honor societies, including Phi Beta Kappa.

Faculty/Classroom: Seventy-seven percent of faculty are male; 23%, female. All teach undergraduates, 85% do research, and 85% do both. The average class size in an introductory lecture is 25; in a laboratory, 16; and in a regular course offering, 21.

Admissions: About 41% of the 1993–94 applicants were accepted. The SAT scores for the 1993–94 freshman class were as follows: Verbal—6% below 500, 38% between 500 and 590, 52% between 600 and 690, and 4% above 700; Math—2% below 500, 16% between 500 and 590, 45% between 600 and 690, and 37% above 700. The ACT scores were 9% between 21 and 23, 25% between 24 and 26, 25% between 27 and 28, and 41% above 28. About 89% of the current freshmen were in the top fifth of their class; 100% were in the top two fifths. There were 16 National Merit finalists and 16 semifinalists. About 14 freshmen graduated first in their class.

Requirements: The SAT I or ACT is required. Applicant must be a graduate of an accredited high school or have earned the GED. Secondary preparation must include 4 years of English, 3 years (preferably 4) of mathematics, at least 2 years of a foreign language and science, and 1 year of history. A personal essay is required and an interview is recommended. AP credits are accepted. Important factors used in the admissions decision are advanced placement or honor courses, leadership record, recommendations by school officials, extracurricular activities record, and evidence of special talent.

Procedure: Freshmen are admitted fall and spring. Entrance exams should be taken during the junior year or between October and January of the senior year. Early decision applications should be filed by December 1; regular applications, by February 1 for fall entry and November 1 for spring entry, along with an application fee of $40. Notification is sent April 1. There are early decision, early admissions, and deferred admissions plans. About 28 early decision candidates were accepted for the 1993–94 class. A waiting list is an active part of the admissions procedure, with about 15% of applicants on the list.

Transfer: About 40 transfer students enrolled in 1993–94. Applicants must submit SAT I or ACT scores, high school and college transcripts, essays, a college report form, mid-semester grades, and recommendations from a college professor or counselor. A total of 16 courses (2 years) out of 32 must be completed at CMC.

Visiting: There are regularly scheduled orientations for prospective students, a campus tour, faculty presentations, student discussions and admission and financial aid workshops. There are guides for informal visits and visitors may sit in on classes and stay overnight at the school. To arrange for a visit, contact the Admissions Office at (909) 621-8088.

Financial Aid: In 1993–94, 53% of all current freshmen and 45% of continuing students received some form of financial aid. About 46% of freshmen and 41% of continuing students received need-based aid. The average freshman award was $14,071. Of that total, scholarships or need-based grants averaged $9771 ($18,241 maximum); loans averaged $3000 (maximum); and work contracts averaged $1300 (maximum). Fifty-one percent of undergraduate students work part-time. Average earnings from campus work for the school year are $967. The average financial indebtedness of the 1992–93 graduate was $12,047. CMC is a member of CSS. The FAF and the FAFSA are required. The deadline for financial aid applications is February 1.

International Students: There are currently 38 international students enrolled. The school actively recruits these students. They must take the TOEFL and achieve a minimum score of 550. The student must also take the SAT I or the ACT.

Computers: The college provides computer facilities for student use. The mainframes are 2 DEC VAXs and an HP 1000 mini. Students have access to the VAXs through laboratory terminals. In addition, Apple Macintosh and IBM PS/2 microcomputers, with an extensive software library, are available. All students may access the system. There are no time limits on using the system and no fees.

Graduates: In 1992–93, 207 bachelor's degrees were awarded. The most popular majors among graduates were economics (30%), government (20%), and international relations (12%). Within an average freshman class, 79% graduate in 4 years and 84% in 5 years. Some 84 companies recruited on campus in 1992–93.

Admissions Contact: Richard C. Vos, Vice President and Dean of Admission and Financial Aid.

COGSWELL POLYTECHNICAL COLLEGE   B-3
Cupertino, CA 95014   (408) 252-5550; (800) 264-7955 (out-of-state)

Full-time: 145 men, 20 women	Faculty: 12
Part-time: 179 men, 24 women	Ph.D.s: 35%
Graduate: none	Student/Faculty: 14 to 1
Year: trimesters, summer session	Tuition: $6600
Application Deadline: August 25	Room Only: $1400
Freshman Class: 50 applied, 40 accepted, 35 enrolled	
SAT I or ACT: not required	**NONCOMPETITIVE**

Cogswell Polytechnical College, founded in 1887, is a small, independent engineering and arts college. In addition to regional accreditation, Cogswell has baccalaureate program accreditation with ABET. The library contains 13,000 volumes, 250 microform items, and 200 audiovisual forms, and subscribes to 125 periodicals. Computerized library sources and services include the card catalog and database searching. Special learning facilities include a commercial studio and a video post-production company. The 4-acre campus is in a suburban area 40 miles south of San Francisco. The campus consists of one building.

Student Life: About 70% of undergraduates are from California. Students come from 10 states, 6 foreign countries, and Canada. Sixty-five percent are from public schools; 35% from private. The average age of freshmen is 19; all undergraduates, 28. Six percent drop out by the end of their first year; 65% remain to graduate.

Housing: There are no residence halls. Arrangements can be made to accommodate students in private houses or at nearby corporate apartments. All students commute. Alcohol is not permitted. All students may keep cars on campus.

Activities: There are no fraternities or sororities on campus. There are 4 groups on campus, including art, computers, honors, international, professional, and student government. Popular campus events include Founders Day, ASB picnic, club competitions, and the Integrated Media Expo.

Sports: There is no sports program at Cogswell. Athletic and recreation facilities include a game room, a student lounge, and access to community athletic facilities.

Disabled Students: The entire campus is accessible to disabled students. The following facilities are available: wheelchair ramps, elevators, special parking, specially equipped rest rooms, special class scheduling, lowered drinking fountains, and lowered telephones.

Services: In addition to many counseling and information services, tutoring is available in every subject. There is remedial writing.

Programs of Study: Cogswell awards the B.S.E.E., B.S.E.T., B.S.F.A., B.S.F.P.T. and B.S.S.W.E., and B.A.C.V.I. degrees. Associate degrees also are awarded. Bachelor's degrees are awarded in COMPUTER AND PHYSICAL SCIENCE (computer programming), ENGINEERING AND ENVIRONMENTAL DESIGN (computer engineering, computer graphics, electrical/electronics engineering, engineering, and mechanical engineering), SOCIAL SCIENCE (fire control and safety technology and fire protection). Electronics, engineering, and technology are the strongest academically. Music, engineering, and technology have the largest enrollments.

Required: In order to graduate, students must complete a total of 120 to 130 credits and have a 2.0 GPA., with 18 to 27 in the major. Required courses vary by degree program.

Special: Cogswell offers various internships and work-study programs. The college administers the Open Learning for the Fire Service (OLFS) program for Arizona, California, and Nevada, through which nonresident students can earn a B.S. in fire administration or fire prevention technology. Nondegree study and pass/fail options are possible. There is a freshman honors program on campus and eight departments have honors programs.

Faculty/Classroom: Sixty-five percent of faculty are male; 35%, female. All teach undergraduates. The average class size in an introductory lecture is 15; in a laboratory, 8; and in a regular course offering, 25.

Admissions: About 80% of the 1993-94 applicants were accepted.

Requirements: A minimum GPA of 2.5 is required. Applicants must be high school graduates or have the GED. Secondary preparation must include 3 years each of English; mathematics, including algebra, geometry, and trigonometry; and 2 years of science. Cogswell requires a personal essay and recommends a personal interview. AP and CLEP credits are accepted. Important factors used in the admissions decision are advanced placement or honor courses, recommendations by school officials, ability to finance college education, personality, intangible qualities, and recommendations by alumni.

Procedure: Freshmen are admitted to all sessions. Applications should be filed by August 25 for fall entry, December 1 for spring entry, and April 1 for summer entry, along with an application fee of $30. The college accepts all applicants. Notification is sent on a rolling basis. There are early decision and early admissions plans.

Transfer: About 40 transfer students enrolled in 1993-94. Applicants must have completed at least 12 college credits with a 2.2 GPA. An interview is recommended. A total of 27 to 36 credits out of 120 to 130 must be completed at Cogswell.

Visiting: There are regularly scheduled orientations for prospective students. Visitors may sit in on classes. To arrange for a visit, contact Paul Schreivogel at (408) 252-5550.

Financial Aid: In an earlier year, 40% of all current freshmen and 30% of continuing students received some form of financial aid. Scholarships or need-based grants averaged $5590; loans averaged $5090; and work contracts averaged $1290. Two percent of undergraduate students work part-time. The average financial indebtedness of the 1992-93 graduate was $1500. Cogswell is a member of CSS. The FAF or SFS and the college's own financial statement is required. The deadline for financial aid applications is July 1.

International Students: There are currently 13 international students enrolled. The school actively recruits these students. They must take the TOEFL and achieve a minimum score of 550.

Computers: The college provides computer facilities for student use. The mainframe is a DEC VAX 11/780. There are also 35 IBM PC-PS2 microcomputers available in computer laboratories and the library. All students may access the system. It may be used during school hours. There are no time limits on using the system and no fees.

Graduates: In 1992-93, 64 bachelor's degrees were awarded. The most popular majors among graduates were engineering technology (82%), electrical engineering (10%), and liberal science (8%). Five companies recruited on campus in 1992-93. In the 1992 graduating class, all of the students had found employment within 6 months of graduation.

Admissions Contact: Paul Schreivogel, Dean of Student Services.

COLLEGE OF NOTRE DAME   B-3
Belmont, CA 94002   (415) 508-3607

Full-time: 151 men, 349 women	Faculty: 56; IIB, av$
Part-time: 85 men, 246 women	Ph.D.s: 81%
Graduate: 363 men, 453 women	Student/Faculty: 9 to 1
Year: semesters, summer session	Tuition: $10,980
Application Deadline: June 1	Room & Board: $5500
Freshman Class: 344 applied, 287 accepted, 97 enrolled	
SAT I or ACT: required	**COMPETITIVE**

The College of Notre Dame, founded in 1851, is an independent, coeducational liberal arts institution affiliated with the Roman Catholic Church. There is one graduate school. In addition to regional accreditation, CND has baccalaureate program accreditation with NASM and NCATE. The library contains 97,471 volumes, 16,487 microform items, and 7550 audiovisual forms, and subscribes to 650 periodicals. Computerized library sources and services include interlibrary loans and database searching. Special learning facilities include an art gallery and the Archives of Modern Christian Art. The 80-acre campus is in a suburban area 25 miles south of San Francisco. Including residence halls, there are 23 buildings on campus.

Student Life: About 80% of undergraduates are from California. Students come from 23 states, 18 foreign countries, and Canada. Seventy percent are from public schools; 30% from private. Thirty-eight percent are white; 25% Asian American; 17% foreign nationals; 13% Hispanic. Fifty-five percent are Catholic; 30% claim no religious affiliation. The average age of freshmen is 18; all undergraduates, 24. Thirty-one percent drop out by the end of their first year; 40% remain to graduate.

Housing: A total of 300 students can be accommodated in college housing. College-sponsored living facilities include coed dormitories and on-campus apartments. On-campus housing is guaranteed for all 4 years. Sixty-three percent of students commute. All students may keep cars on campus.

Activities: There are no fraternities or sororities on campus. There are more than 20 groups on campus, including cheerleading, choir, chorale, chorus, computers, drama, ethnic, honors, international, jazz band, literary magazine, musical theater, newspaper, orchestra, religious, social, social service, student government, and symphony. Popular campus events include Honors Day, Ralston Concert Series, Homecoming, International Reception, and Hawaiian Luau.

Sports: There are 5 intercollegiate sports for men and 6 for women, and 2 intramural sports for men and 2 for women. Athletic and recreation facilities include a gymnasium, a recreation center, tennis courts, a soccer field, a weight room, a swimming pool, a par course, an arcade, and pool and ping pong tables.

Disabled Students: Ninety percent of the campus is accessible to disabled students. The following facilities are available: wheelchair ramps, special parking, specially equipped rest rooms, and special class scheduling.

Services: In addition to many counseling and information services, tutoring is available in every subject. There is remedial math, reading, and writing.

Campus Safety and Security: Campus safety and security measures include 24-hour foot and vehicle patrol, escort service, informal discussions, pamphlets, posters, and films. In addition, there are lighted pathways and sidewalks.

Programs of Study: CND awards the B.A., B.S., B.F.A., and B.Mus. degrees. Associate and master's degrees also are awarded. Bachelor's degrees are awarded in BIOLOGICAL SCIENCE (biochemistry and biology/biological science), BUSINESS (accounting, banking and finance, business administration and management, business economics, international business management, and marketing/retailing/merchandising), COMMUNICATIONS AND THE ARTS (communications, dramatic arts, English, fine arts, French, graphic design, music, and studio art), COMPUTER AND PHYSICAL SCIENCE (computer science), ENGINEERING AND ENVIRONMENTAL DESIGN (interior design), HEALTH PROFESSIONS (predentistry, premedicine, prepharmacy, and preveterinary science), SOCIAL SCIENCE (behavioral science, history, humanities, Latin American studies, liberal arts/general studies, philosophy, political science/government, prelaw, psychology, religion, social science, and sociology). Biology, premedicine, English, and music are the strongest academically. Business administration, liberal studies, and psychology have the largest enrollments.

Required: All students must complete general education requirements and 3 units of career development. An American history requirement is necessary for those students who have not completed this course in an American high school. A total of 124 semester units with an overall GPA of 2.0 is required in order to graduate.

Special: The college offers a Washington semester through an exchange program with Trinity College as well as an exchange program with Emmanuel College in Boston. Internships, accelerated degree programs in business administration and human service, B.A.-B.S. degrees in biology and biochemistry, a 3–2 engineering degree with Boston University, dual and student-designed majors, a general studies degree, credit for military experience, and pass/fail options are offered. Study abroad is available in Great Britain, France, Greece, Japan, and Spain. Nondegree study is possible. There is a freshman honors program on campus, as well as 3 national honor societies.

Faculty/Classroom: Forty-six percent of faculty are male; 54%, female. Eighty-four percent teach undergraduates. No introductory courses are taught by graduate students. The average class size in an introductory lecture is 25; in a laboratory, 10; and in a regular course offering, 15.

Admissions: About 83% of the 1993–94 applicants were accepted. About 31% of the current freshmen were in the top fifth of their class; 69% were in the top two fifths. One freshman graduated first in class.

Requirements: The SAT I or ACT is required. In addition, applicants should have completed 13 Carnegie units, including 4 years of high school English, 2 each of mathematics, history/social studies, foreign language, and college preparatory electives, and 1 of laboratory science. An essay is required. An audition is required for music majors. AP and CLEP credits are accepted. Important factors used in the admissions decision are advanced placement or honor courses, evidence of special talent, leadership record, recommendations by school officials, and extracurricular activities record.

Procedure: Freshmen are admitted fall and spring. Entrance exams should be taken by the December test date of the senior year. Applications should be filed by June 1 for fall entry and December 1 for spring entry, along with an application fee of $35. Notification is sent on a rolling basis. There is a deferred admissions plan.

Transfer: About 160 transfer students enrolled in 1993–94. Transfer applicants must have a 2.0 GPA to be considered for admission. A total of 24 credits out of 124 must be completed at CND.

Visiting: There are regularly scheduled orientations for prospective students, consisting of tours and information on student life, financial aid, and academics. There are guides for informal visits and visitors may sit in on classes and stay overnight at the school. To arrange for a visit, contact the Admission Office at (415) 508–3607.

Financial Aid: In 1993–94, 67% of all current freshmen received some form of financial aid. About 55% of freshmen and 52% of continuing students received need-based aid. The average freshman award was $10,216. Of that total, scholarships or need-based grants averaged $9150 ($18,000 maximum); loans averaged $2938 ($4000 maximum); and work contracts averaged $1378 ($2000 maximum). Fifteen percent of undergraduate students work part-time. Average earnings from campus work for the school year are $1500. The average financial indebtedness of the 1992–93 graduate was $12,000. CND is a member of CSS. The FAF, FFS, or SFS and FAFSA are required. The deadline for financial aid applications is March 2.

International Students: There are currently 93 international students enrolled. The school actively recruits these students. They must take the TOEFL and achieve a minimum score of 450.

Computers: The college provides computer facilities for student use. The mainframe is an IBM AS/400. Two computer laboratories are available with Apple Macintosh microcomputers. All students may access the system 7 days a week. There are no time limits on using the system and no fees.

Graduates: In 1992–93, 130 bachelor's degrees were awarded. The most popular majors among graduates were business administration (35%), communication (7%), and liberal studies (7%). Within an average freshman class, 53% graduate in 5 years. Five companies recruited on campus in 1992–93.

Admissions Contact: Dr. Gregory Smith, Admission.

CONCORDIA UNIVERSITY   D-5
(Formerly Christ College Irvine)

Irvine, CA 92715	(714) 854–8002; (800) 229–1200
Full-time: 252 men, 389 women	Faculty: 32; IIB, --$
Part-time: 26 men, 75 women	Ph.D.s: 65%
Graduate: 17 men, 24 women	Student/Faculty: 20 to 1
Year: quarters, summer session	Tuition: $10,445
Application Deadline: July 1	Room & Board: $4230
Freshman Class: 564 applied, 497 accepted, 144 enrolled	
SAT I: 420/485	ACT: 22 COMPETITIVE

Concordia University, founded in 1972, is a private coeducational liberal arts institution affiliated with the Lutheran Church-Missouri Synod. There are 3 undergraduate schools and one graduate school. The library contains 82,540 volumes, 17,892 microform items, and 3953 audiovisual forms, and subscribes to 603 periodicals. Computerized library sources and services include the card catalog and database searching. Special learning facilities include a learning resource center and radio station. The 70-acre campus is in a suburban area 40 miles south of Los Angeles. Including residence halls, there are 18 buildings on campus.

Student Life: About 78% of undergraduates are from California. Students come from 26 states and 12 foreign countries. Sixty-five percent are from public schools; 35% from private. Seventy-three percent are white; 10% foreign nationals. Seventy-nine percent are Protestant; 11% claim no religious affiliation. The average age of freshmen is 18; all undergraduates, 21. Twenty percent drop out by the end of their first year; 55% remain to graduate.

Housing: A total of 500 students can be accommodated in college housing. College-sponsored living facilities include single-sex on-campus apartments. Sixty-seven percent of students live on campus. All students may keep cars on campus.

Activities: There are no fraternities or sororities on campus. There are 18 groups on campus, including art, cheerleading, choir, chorale, chorus, drama, ethnic, international, newspaper, pep band, professional, religious, student government, and yearbook. Popular campus events include Homecoming, Closing Banquet, Christmas Dance, Oktoberfest, Superteams, Cross-cultural Food Festival, and Black History Month.

Sports: There are 4 intercollegiate sports for men and 4 for women, and 6 intramural sports for men and 6 for women. Athletic and recreation facilities include a 1500-seat gymnasium, a soccer field, a baseball/softball diamond, and volleyball, tennis, and racquetball courts.

Disabled Students: Forty-five percent of the campus is accessible to disabled students. The following facilities are available: wheelchair ramps, special parking, specially equipped rest rooms, and lowered drinking fountains.

Services: In addition to many counseling and information services, tutoring is available in most subjects. There is also remedial math and writing.

Campus Safety and Security: Campus safety and security measures include 24-hour foot and vehicle patrol, self-defense education, escort service, and informal discussions. In addition, there are pamphlets, posters, films, emergency telephones, and lighted pathways and sidewalks.

Programs of Study: Concordia University awards the B.A. degree. Master's degrees also are awarded. Bachelor's degrees are awarded in BIOLOGICAL SCIENCE (biology/biological science), BUSINESS (business administration and management), COMMUNICATIONS AND THE ARTS (English and music), COMPUTER AND PHYSICAL SCIENCE (mathematics), EDUCATION (early childhood and physical), SOCIAL SCIENCE (behavioral science, history, humanities, liberal arts/general studies, psychology, and religion). Education, social science, and business administration are the strongest academically and have the largest enrollments.

Required: All students must complete 72 quarter hours of general education requirements, including courses in humanities, natural science, social science, religion, computer competency, and physical education. A total of 192 quarter credits, including 48 to 60 in the major, is required in order to graduate. A minimum GPA of 2.0 overall and 2.5 in the major must be maintained.

Special: Cross-registration is possible with University of California/ Irvine. Internships are available in the Director of Christian Education (DCE) program. Study abroad is offered in Mexico and Japan.

Faculty/Classroom: Seventy-six percent of faculty are male; 24%, female. Ninety percent teach undergraduates. No introductory courses are taught by graduate students. The average class size in an introductory lecture is 35 and in a regular course offering, 24.

Admissions: About 88% of the 1993–94 applicants were accepted. The SAT scores for the 1993–94 freshman class were as follows: Verbal—75% below 500, 22% between 500 and 599, and 3% between 600 and 700; Math—51% below 500, 33% between 500 and 599, 14% between 600 and 700, and 2% above 700. About 37% of the current freshmen were in the top fifth of their class; 75% were in the top two fifths.

Requirements: Concordia University requires applicants to be in the upper 50% of their class. A minimum GPA of 2.6 is required. The SAT I or ACT is required. Applicants should be high school graduates with 4 years of English, 3 each of mathematics and science, and 2 of social studies; 2 years of a foreign language are recommended. The GED is accepted. A school reference is also required. AP and CLEP credits are accepted. Important factors used in the admissions decision are leadership record, advanced placement or honor courses, recommendations by school officials, evidence of special talent, and extracurricular activities record.

Procedure: Freshmen are admitted to all sessions. Entrance exams should be taken by the fall of the senior year. Applications should be filed by July 1 for fall entry, November 1 for winter entry, February 1 for spring entry, and May 1 for summer entry, along with an application fee of $25. Notification is sent on a rolling basis. There are early decision, early admissions, and deferred admissions plans.

Transfer: About 100 transfer students enrolled in 1993–94. A minimum GPA of 2.5 is required in a minimum of 16 college credits earned. An academic reference is necessary. At least 48 quarter hours out of 192 must be completed at Concordia University.

Visiting: There are regularly scheduled orientations for prospective students. There are guides for informal visits, and visitors may sit in on classes and stay overnight at the school. To arrange for a visit, contact Jon Endicott at (714) 854-8002.

Financial Aid: In 1993–94, 80% of all current freshmen and 75% of continuing students received some form of financial aid. About 70% of all students received need-based aid. Scholarships or need-based grants averaged $3500 ($9995 maximum); loans averaged $2000 ($2625 maximum); and work contracts averaged $1950. Thirty-five percent of undergraduate students work part-time. Average earnings from campus work for the school year are $1950. Concordia University is a member of CSS. The FAF and SAAC are required. The deadline for financial aid applications is March 1.

International Students: There are currently 73 international students enrolled. The school actively recruits these students. They must take the TOEFL and achieve a minimum score of 525.

Computers: The college provides computer facilities for student use. There are no time limits on using the system and no fees.

Graduates: In a recent year, 99 bachelor's degrees were awarded. Within an average freshman class, 42% graduate in 4 years, 45% in 5 years, and 48% in 6 years. Some 20 companies recruited on campus in a recent year. In a recent graduating class, 10% of the men and 18% of the women were enrolled in graduate school within 6 months of graduation; 19% of the men and 45% of the women had found employment.

Admissions Contact: Stan Meyer, Dean of Enrollment Services.

DEVRY INSTITUTE OF TECHNOLOGY
LOS ANGELES
Pomona, CA 91768-2642

D-5

(310) 692-0551
(800) 882-7536 (out-of-state)

Full-time: 1721 men, 441 women	Faculty: 49
Part-time: 364 men, 94 women	Ph.D.s: n/av
Graduate: none	Student/Faculty: 44 to 1
Year: trimesters, summer session	Tuition: $5609
Application Deadline: open	Room & Board: n/app
Freshman Class: 1377 applied, 1264 accepted, 800 enrolled	
SAT I or ACT: required	**LESS COMPETITIVE**

DeVry Institute of Technology/Los Angeles (Pomona) is 1 of 11 DeVry Institutes in the United States and Canada. The school offers programs in accounting, business operations, computer information systems, electronics, and telecommunications management. In addition to regional accreditation, DeVry has baccalaureate program accreditation with ABET. The library contains 6000 volumes, 71 microform items, and 24 audiovisual forms, and subscribes to 157 periodicals. Computerized library sources and services include the card catalog, interlibrary loans, and database searching. Special learning facilities include a learning resource center and electronics and other labora-

tories. The 11-acre campus is in a suburban area 30 miles east of Los Angeles. The campus consists of one building.

Student Life: About 95% of undergraduates are from California. Students come from 26 foreign countries. Thirty-seven percent are white; 30% Hispanic; 19% Asian American; 12% African American. The average age of all undergraduates is 25. Fifty-two percent drop out by the end of their first year; 40% remain to graduate.

Housing: There are no residence halls. College-sponsored living facilities include off-campus apartments. All students commute. Alcohol is not permitted. All students may keep cars on campus.

Activities: There are no fraternities or sororities on campus. There are 10 groups on campus, including computers, ethnic, honors, newspaper, professional, and religious. Popular campus events include career fairs.

Sports: There are 5 intramural sports for men and 5 for women.

Disabled Students: Ninety percent of the campus is accessible to disabled students. The following facilities are available: wheelchair ramps, elevators, special parking, specially equipped rest rooms, lowered drinking fountains, and lowered telephones.

Services: In addition to many counseling and information services, tutoring is available in every subject.

Campus Safety and Security: Campus safety and security measures include informal discussions, pamphlets, posters, films, emergency telephones, and lighted pathways and sidewalks. In addition, a DeVry employee patrols the building from 4 P.M. to midnight; a guard service patrols the lot from 7 A.M. to midnight.

Programs of Study: DeVry awards the B.S. degree. Associate degrees also are awarded. Bachelor's degrees are awarded in BUSINESS (accounting and business administration and management), COMMUNICATIONS AND THE ARTS (telecommunications), COMPUTER AND PHYSICAL SCIENCE (computer programming and information sciences and systems), ENGINEERING AND ENVIRONMENTAL DESIGN (electrical/electronics engineering technology). Electronics engineering technology is the strongest academically and has the largest enrollment.

Required: In order to graduate, students must complete between 132 and 157 credit hours with a 2.0 minimum GPA. Course requirements vary according to program. All first-semester students take courses in business organization, computer applications, algebra, psychology, and student success strategies.

Special: Evening classes and nondegree study are possible. There is 1 national honor society on campus. One department has an honors program.

Faculty/Classroom: Ninety-one percent of faculty are male; 9%, female. All teach undergraduates. The average class size in an introductory lecture, in a laboratory, and in a regular course offering, is 30.

Admissions: About 92% of the 1993–94 applicants were accepted.

Requirements: Admissions requirements include graduation from a secondary school; the GED is also accepted. Applicants from accredited postsecondary institutions must pass the DeVry entrance exam or present satisfactory ACT, SAT I, or WPCT scores. CLEP credit is accepted.

Procedure: Freshmen are admitted to all sessions. Application deadlines are open. Application fee is $25. Notification is sent on a rolling basis. There are early decision and deferred admissions plans.

Transfer: Half the total credits must be completed at DeVry.

Visiting: There are regularly scheduled orientations for prospective students. There are guides for informal visits and visitors may sit in on classes. To arrange for a visit, contact Christopher Clifton, New Student Coordinator at (310) 692-0855.

Financial Aid: In 1993–94, 79% of all students received some form of financial aid, including need-based aid. DeVry is a member of CSS. The FAFSA financial statement is required.

International Students: International students must take the TOEFL and achieve a minimum score of 550. The student must also take the college's own entrance exam. ACT, SAT I, or WPCT may be accepted in lieu of the DeVry entrance exam.

Computers: The college provides computer facilities for student use. The mainframe is an IBM. Laboratory facilities include IBM-compatible PCs in stand-alone and network configurations with access to the mainframe. LANs provide access to a wide range of applications software. Hard copy from the mainframe is provided through a local minicomputer and medium- and high-speed printers. Computer information systems students may access the system. It may be used during published laboratory hours. There are no time limits on using the system and no fees.

Graduates: In 1992–93, 296 bachelor's degrees were awarded. The most popular majors among graduates were electronics technology (50%), business administration and management (21%), and telecommunications management (17%). Within an average freshman class, 40% graduate in 5 years. Some 73 companies recruited on campus in 1992–93. In the 1992 graduating class, 91% of the graduates had found employment within 6 months of graduation.

Admissions Contact: Keith Paridy, Director of Admissions.

DOMINICAN COLLEGE OF SAN RAFAEL

B-3

San Rafael, CA 94901-8008

(415) 485-3204
(800) 788-3522 (out-of-state)

Full-time: 150 men, 498 women	**Faculty:** 37
Part-time: 20 men, 130 women	**Ph.D.s:** 59%
Graduate: 80 men, 220 women	**Student/Faculty:** 18 to 1
Year: semesters, summer session	**Tuition:** $12,180
Application Deadline: open	**Room & Board:** $5680
Freshman Class: 213 applied, 173 accepted, 75 enrolled	
SAT I Verbal/Math: 432/452	**COMPETITIVE**

Dominican College of San Rafael, founded in 1890, is a coeducational Roman Catholic liberal arts college. There is one graduate school. In addition to regional accreditation, Dominican has baccalaureate program accreditation with NLN. The library contains 92,088 volumes, 2284 microform items, and 1437 audiovisual forms, and subscribes to 295 periodicals. Computerized library sources and services include database searching. Special learning facilities include an art gallery, natural history museum, radio station, and a music library, and an art history slide and print collection. The 80-acre campus is in a suburban area 17 miles north of San Francisco. Including residence halls, there are 16 buildings on campus.

Student Life: About 92% of undergraduates are from California. Students come from 25 states, 11 foreign countries, and Canada. Eighty percent are from public schools. Seventy-one percent are white; 10% Asian American; 10% Hispanic. The average age of freshmen is 18; all undergraduates, 25. Twenty-nine percent drop out by the end of their first year; 45% remain to graduate.

Housing: A total of 200 students can be accommodated in college housing. College-sponsored living facilities include coed dormitories. On-campus housing is available on a first-come, first-served basis. Seventy-five percent of students commute. All students may keep cars on campus.

Activities: There are no fraternities or sororities on campus. Groups on campus include Amnesty International, art, cheerleading, chorus, computers, drama, honors, literary magazine, newspaper, Nexus (international relations club), orchestra, psychology club, religious, science club, social service, student government, and yearbook. Popular campus events include an ecumenical Thanksgiving dinner, boat dance, and Shield Day (welcoming freshman class).

Sports: There are 4 intercollegiate sports for men and 4 for women. Athletic and recreation facilities include a gymnasium, a swimming pool, tennis courts, and a soccer field.

Disabled Students: Sixty percent of the campus is accessible to disabled students. The following facilities are available: wheelchair ramps, special parking, specially equipped rest rooms, special class scheduling, and lowered drinking fountains.

Services: In addition to many counseling and information services, tutoring is available in most subjects, including writing, mathematics, and chemistry. There is also remedial math and writing, time management and study skills available.

Campus Safety and Security: Campus safety and security measures include escort service, informal discussions, lighted pathways and sidewalks, and 24-hour weekend foot patrol (5 P.M. to 9 A.M. Monday through Friday).

Programs of Study: Dominican awards the B.A., B.S., B.F.A., and B.M. degrees. Master's degrees also are awarded. Bachelor's degrees are awarded in BIOLOGICAL SCIENCE (biology/biological science), BUSINESS (accounting, business administration and management, and international business management), COMMUNICATIONS AND THE ARTS (art history and appreciation, creative writing, English literature, fine arts, and music), COMPUTER AND PHYSICAL SCIENCE (mathematics), HEALTH PROFESSIONS (nursing, predentistry, and premedicine), SOCIAL SCIENCE (history, humanities, international studies, political science/government, psychology, and religion). Biology, business administration and international business, English literature, international studies, psychology, and nursing are the strongest academically. Business administration and international business, international studies, and nursing have the largest enrollments.

Required: All students must complete 124 credit hours with a minimum 2.0 GPA. Core requirements include a cultural heritage colloquium of 12 units; 6 units in religious heritage; 3 units each in human nature, verbal expression, quantitative reasoning, cross-cultural perspectives, human relationships, and creativity in the arts; and 3 to 4 units in the natural world. A senior thesis, project, or comprehensive examination is required.

Special: Students may cross-register with the University of California, Berkeley. There is a semester interchange program with colleges in Michigan, Florida, or New York. Dual majors, student-designed majors, and internships are offered. There are pass/fail options outside of major and general education courses. The school offers an evening bachelor's degree program. There is a freshman honors program on campus

Faculty/Classroom: Forty-four percent of faculty are male; 56%, female. Ninety percent teach undergraduates. No introductory courses are taught by graduate students. The average class size in a laboratory is 15 and in a regular course offering, 15.

Admissions: About 81% of the 1993–94 applicants were accepted. The SAT scores for the 1993–94 freshman class were as follows: Verbal—79% below 500, 17% between 500 and 599, and 4% between 600 and 700; Math—68% below 500, 27% between 500 and 599, and 5% between 600 and 700.

Requirements: A minimum GPA of 2.5 is required. The SAT I or ACT is required. Applicants must be graduates of an accredited high school or have earned the GED. Secondary preparation must include 4 years of English, 2 years each of mathematics and a foreign language, and 1 year each of science and history. An essay and two recommendations are required. An interview and visit to the campus are highly recommended. Prospective music majors are encouraged to schedule an audition. AP and CLEP credits are accepted. Important factors used in the admissions decision are leadership record, personality, intangible qualities, advanced placement or honor courses, evidence of special talents, and extracurricular activities record.

Procedure: Freshmen are admitted fall and spring. Entrance exams should be taken in late fall or early spring of the senior year. Application deadlines are open. The application fee is $25. Notification is sent on a rolling basis about 2 weeks after all materials have been submitted. There are early admissions and deferred admissions plans.

Transfer: About 130 transfer students enrolled in 1993–94. Applicants must have 2.0 GPA at an accredited college. They must also submit official high school or college transcripts and 2 recommendations, one of which must be from a professor, academic dean, or counselor. A total of 30 credits out of 124 to 128 credits must be completed at Dominican.

Visiting: There are regularly scheduled orientations for prospective students, including financial aid information/conferences, mathematics and writing placement testing, and a meeting with prospective academic adviser. There are guides for informal visits and visitors may sit in on classes and stay overnight at the school. To arrange for a visit, contact Michelle Hanson, the Admissions Office at (415) 485-3204 or (800) 788-3522.

Financial Aid: In a recent year, about 76% of all students received some form of financial aid, most of which was need-based. The average freshman award was $10,881. Of that total, scholarships or need-based grants averaged $5940 ($10,730 maximum); loans averaged $2287 ($2625 maximum); and work contracts averaged $1468 ($1800 maximum). Twenty-five percent of undergraduate students work part-time. Average earnings from campus work for the school year are $1425. Dominican is a member of CSS. The FAFSA is required. The deadline for financial aid applications is March 2.

International Students: There are currently 23 international students enrolled. They must take the TOEFL and achieve a minimum score of 550.

Computers: The college provides computer facilities for student use. The mainframe is an IBM RF 6000 Model 530 H. Students have access to 10 terminals, 3 graphics workstations, and 2 laser printers. They also have access to IBM PCs in the computer center. All students may access the system. It may be used Monday through Friday, 8 A.M. to 10 P.M. There are no time limits and no fees.

Graduates: In 1992–93 96 bachelor's degrees were awarded. The most popular majors among graduates were nursing (20%), psychology (11%), and international studies (8%). Within an average freshman class, 40% graduate in 4 years, 42% in 5 years, and 46% in 6 years. Some 40 companies recruited on campus in 1992–93.

Admissions Contact: Lydia Hull, Admissions Office.

FRESNO PACIFIC COLLEGE

C-3

Fresno, CA 93702

(209) 453-2039

Full-time: 306 men, 468 women	**Faculty:** 40; IIB, -$
Part-time: 65 men, 70 women	**Ph.D.s:** 55%
Graduate: 178 men, 530 women	**Student/Faculty:** 19 to 1
Year: semesters, summer session	**Tuition:** $9300
Application Deadline: July 31	**Room & Board:** $3720
Freshman Class: 346 applied, 274 accepted, 146 enrolled	
SAT I Verbal/Math: 477/532	**ACT:** 20	**COMPETITIVE**

Fresno Pacific College, founded in 1944, is a small private Christian liberal arts college affiliated with the Mennonite Brethren. The library contains 136,000 volumes and 4000 audiovisual forms, and subscribes to 920 periodicals. Special learning facilities include the Center for Mennonite Brethren Studies, the Center for Conflict Studies and Peacemaking, and the Center for Degree Completion. The 42-acre campus is in a suburban area 200 miles southeast of San Francisco. Including residence halls, there are 14 buildings on campus.

Student Life: About 90% of undergraduates are from California. Students come from 14 foreign countries and Canada. Seventy-four percent are white; 13% Hispanic. Seventy-nine percent are Protes-

tant; 10% Catholic. Thirty percent drop out by the end of their first year; 27% remain to graduate.

Housing: A total of 382 students can be accommodated in college housing. College-sponsored living facilities include single-sex dormitories, on-campus apartments, and married-student housing. In addition there are honors houses and special interest houses. Sixty-three percent of students commute. Alcohol is not permitted. All students may keep cars on campus.

Activities: There are no fraternities or sororities on campus. There are 15 groups on campus, including choir, chorale, drama, ethnic, honors, international, jazz band, newspaper, pep band, photography, professional, religious, social, social service, student government, and yearbook. Popular campus events include Homecoming and Mennonite Central Committee Relief Sale.

Sports: Athletic and recreation facilities include are housed in the gymnasium at the Special Events Center. There are tennis courts, a soccer field, a swimming pool, and a sand volleyball area.

Disabled Students: All of the campus is accessible to disabled students. The following facilities are available: wheelchair ramps, elevators, special parking, specially equipped rest rooms, lowered drinking fountains, and lowered telephones.

Services: In addition to many counseling and information services, tutoring is available in most subjects. There is remedial math, reading, and writing.

Campus Safety and Security: Campus safety and security measures include 24-hour foot and vehicle patrol, escort service, emergency telephones, and lighted pathways and sidewalks.

Programs of Study: Fresno Pacific awards the B.A. degree. Associate and master's degrees also are awarded. Bachelor's degrees are awarded in BUSINESS (accounting), COMMUNICATIONS AND THE ARTS (English, music, and Spanish), COMPUTER AND PHYSICAL SCIENCE (mathematics and natural sciences), EDUCATION (business, English, mathematics, music, physical, science, and social science), HEALTH PROFESSIONS (premedicine), SOCIAL SCIENCE (ministries, missions, prelaw, psychology, religion, social science, and social work).

Required: Students must complete 124 semester units, 45 of which are in upper division courses, with at least a 2.0 GPA. General education requirements include 4 courses each in Biblical and religious studies, humanities, social science, and physical education, and 3 courses in natural science and mathematics. Students are required to attend College Hour, a twice-weekly program of lectures, films, and concerts. Students are encouraged to volunteer 2 hours of community service per week. Several majors require practical internships.

Special: Internships are available, as is a one-semester cooperative program with the University of California, Davis. Other off-campus learning opportunities include programs in American studies in Washington, D.C., urban studies in Chicago, and study abroad in Israel, Japan, Costa Rica, and Brethren Colleges in England, Spain, France, Germany, or China. A summer semester in Mexico is offered. There is a freshman honors program on campus, as well as one national honor society. Five departments have honors programs.

Faculty/Classroom: Seventy-five percent of faculty are male; 25%, female. All teach undergraduates. The average class size in an introductory lecture is 25; in a laboratory, 20; and in a regular course offering, 17.

Admissions: About 79% of the 1993–94 applicants were accepted. The SAT scores for the 1993–94 freshman class were as follows: Verbal—60% below 500, 32% between 500 and 599, and 8% between 600 and 700; Math—34% below 500, 42% between 500 and 599, 19% between 600 and 700, and 4% above 700. The ACT scores were 57% below 21, 20% between 21 and 23, 17% between 24 and 26, and 6% between 27 and 28.

Requirements: A minimum GPA of 3.1 is required. The SAT I or ACT is required. Applicant should be a graduate of an accredited high school or have the GED. Required secondary preparation includes 4 years of English, 2 years of social studies, 1 year each of algebra and geometry, and at least 1 year of a laboratory science. The college recommends that applicants also take courses in art, music, and a foreign language. An essay is required, and an audition is recommended for prospective music majors. AP and CLEP credits are accepted. Important factors used in the admissions decision are recommendations by school officials, advanced placement or honor courses, extracurricular activities record, leadership record, and recommendations by alumni.

Procedure: Freshmen are admitted fall and spring. Entrance exams should be taken during the fall of the senior year. Applications should be filed by July 31 for fall entry and December 4 for spring entry, along with an application fee of $30. Notification is sent on a rolling basis. There is an early admissions plan. One early decision candidate was accepted for the 1993–94 class.

Transfer: About 100 transfer students enrolled in 1993–94. Applicants should have completed at least 24 transferable units of college work with a 2.4 GPA. Those with fewer credits must meet freshman

admission requirements. SAT I or ACT scores are recommended. A total of 30 credits out of 124 must be completed at Fresno Pacific.

Visiting: There are regularly scheduled orientations for prospective students. There are guides for informal visits and visitors may sit in on classes and stay overnight at the school. To arrange for a visit, contact Cary Templeton, Director of Admissions at (209) 453–2039.

Financial Aid: In 1993–94, 92% of all current freshmen and 90% of continuing students received some form of financial aid. About 71% of freshmen and 70% of continuing students received need-based aid. The average freshman award was $7900. Of that total, scholarships or need-based grants averaged $5079 ($6068 maximum); loans averaged $11,031 ($12,500 maximum); and work contracts averaged $750 (maximum). Eighty-four percent of undergraduate students work part-time. Average earnings from campus work for the school year are $1072. Fresno Pacific is a member of CSS. The college's own financial statement and FAFSA are required. The deadline for financial aid applications is March 2.

International Students: There are currently 48 international students enrolled. The school actively recruits these students. They must take the TOEFL and achieve a minimum score of 500.

Computers: The college provides computer facilities for student use. The college provides 12 microcomputers for academic use in the library. There is also a Macintosh laboratory, an IBM laboratory, and an Apple Macintosh laboratory. All students may access the system. There are no time limits on using the system and no fees.

Graduates: In a recent year, 103 bachelor's degrees were awarded. The most popular majors among graduates were liberal studies (29%), English (14%), and Bible (12%).

Admissions Contact: Cary Templeton, Director of Admissions.

GOLDEN GATE UNIVERSITY
San Francisco, CA 94105

B-3

(415) 442-7800
(800) 448-4968 (in-state)

Full-time: 249 men, 289 women	**Faculty:** 60
Part-time: 711 men, 817 women	**Ph.D.s:** 49%
Graduate: 2108 men, 1852 women	**Student/Faculty:** 9 to 1
Year: trimesters, summer session	**Tuition:** $5623
Application Deadline: July 1	**Room & Board:** n/app
Freshman Class: 271 applied, 208 accepted, 126 enrolled	
SAT I or ACT: not required	**VERY COMPETITIVE**

Golden Gate University, founded in 1853, is a private, nonprofit, independent institution offering undergraduate and graduate degrees in business administration, accounting, human and social sciences, and special progress. There are 5 undergraduate and 6 graduate schools. The 2 libraries contain 300,000 volumes and subscribe to 2500 periodicals. Special learning facilities include a learning resource center and an English as a second language center. The campus is in an urban area in the financial district of San Francisco. There is one building on campus.

Student Life: About 80% of undergraduates are from California. Students come from 10 states, 66 foreign countries, and Canada. Sixty-nine percent are white; 16% Asian American; 12% foreign nationals. The average age of freshmen is 19; all undergraduates, 25. Twelve percent drop out by the end of their first year; 35% remain to graduate.

Housing: There are no residence halls, all students commute. Alcohol is not permitted.

Activities: There are no fraternities or sororities on campus. There are some groups and organizations on campus, including ethnic, international, newspaper, professional, and social. Popular campus events include Commencement Ball and other social functions.

Sports: There is no sports program at Golden Gate.

Disabled Students: All of the campus is accessible to disabled students. The following facilities are available: wheelchair ramps, elevators, special parking, and specially equipped rest rooms.

Services: In addition to many counseling and information services, tutoring is available in some subjects. There is remedial math, reading, and writing.

Campus Safety and Security: Campus safety and security measures include escort service, informal discussions, and pamphlets, posters, and films.

Programs of Study: Golden Gate awards the B.A. and B.S. degrees. Associate, master's, and doctoral degrees also are awarded. Bachelor's degrees are awarded in BUSINESS (accounting, banking and finance, business economics, hotel/motel and restaurant management, international business management, management science, marketing management, and personnel management), COMMUNICATIONS AND THE ARTS (telecommunications), COMPUTER AND PHYSICAL SCIENCE (information sciences and systems), SOCIAL SCIENCE (political science/government and prelaw). Accounting, finance, and information systems are the strongest academically. Finance, accounting, management, and hotel, restaurant, and tourism management have the largest enrollments.

Required: A total of 123 semester hours, with 21 to 33 in the major, are required to graduate. A minimum GPA of 3.0 is also required.

Special: The university offers cooperative programs, cross-registration with the San Francisco Consortium, internships, B.A.-B.S. degrees, an accelerated degree program, dual majors, credit for military experience, nondegree study, and credit/no credit options. Also available are weekend classes and 12-week semesters.

Faculty/Classroom: Seventy-nine percent of faculty are male; 21%, female. No introductory courses are taught by graduate students. The average class size in an introductory lecture is 24 and in a regular course offering, 21.

Requirements: Applicants must be graduates of an accredited secondary school or have a GED certificate, and should have completed 3 years of English, 2 of mathematics, and 1 of history. A minimum 3.0 GPA, 3.2 for accounting and tax accounting majors, is required. AP and CLEP credits are accepted. Important factors used in the admissions decision are advanced placement or honor courses, recommendations by school officials, evidence of special talent, leadership record, and extracurricular activities record.

Procedure: Freshmen are admitted to all sessions. Applications should be filed by July 1 for fall entry, November 1 for spring entry, and March 1 for summer entry, along with an application fee of $40. Notification is sent on a rolling basis. There are early decision, early admissions, and deferred admissions plans. One early decision candidate was accepted for the 1993–94 class.

Transfer: About 240 transfer students enrolled in a recent year. At least 24 transferable units and a 2.0 overall GPA are required. A minimum of 24 units out of 123, including 21 in the major, must be completed at GGU.

Visiting: There are regularly scheduled orientations for prospective students. There are guides for informal visits and visitors may sit in on classes. To arrange for a visit, contact the Office of Marketing and Prospective Student Services at (415) 442–7800 or (800) 448–4968.

Financial Aid: In 1993–94, 32% of all students received some form of financial aid; 23% received need-based aid. The average freshman award was $5000. Of that total, scholarships or need-based grants averaged $1960 ($6810 maximum); loans averaged $3383 ($7825 maximum). Ninety-six percent of undergraduate students work part-time. Average earnings from campus work for the school year are $3200. The average financial indebtedness of the 1992–93 graduate was $11,600. Golden Gate is a member of CSS. The college's own financial statement and the FAFSA are required. The deadline for financial aid applications is March 1.

International Students: There are currently 361 international students enrolled. The school actively recruits these students. They must take the TOEFL or the Comprehensive English Language Test and achieve a minimum score on the TOEFL of 525. The student must also submit an essay.

Computers: The college provides computer facilities for student use. The mainframe is an HP 3000/Series 64. Microcomputers are available in the computer center. All students may access the system. It may be used at designated hours. There are no time limits on using the system. The fees are $30.

Graduates: In a recent year, 322 bachelor's degrees were awarded. The most popular majors among graduates were management (25%), accounting (13%), and human relations (11%). Within an average freshman class, 60% graduate in 5 years.

Admissions Contact: Office of Marketing and Prospective Student Services.

HARVEY MUDD COLLEGE   D-5
Claremont, CA 91711   (909) 621–8011

Full-time: 505 men, 149 women	Faculty: 68; IIB, +$
Part-time: 4 men, 1 woman	Ph.D.s: 100%
Graduate: 20 men, 4 women	Student/Faculty: 10 to 1
Year: semesters	Tuition: $16,876
Application Deadline: February 1	Room & Board: $6440
Freshman Class: 1377 applied, 572 accepted, 178 enrolled	
SAT I: required	**MOST COMPETITIVE**

Harvey Mudd College, founded in 1955, is one of the Claremont Colleges. It is an independent coeducational college specializing in engineering and physical science education within a liberal arts tradition. There are 5 undergraduate schools and one graduate school. In addition to regional accreditation, Harvey Mudd has baccalaureate program accreditation with ABET. The library contains 1.9 million volumes, and subscribes to 6800 periodicals. Computerized library sources and services include the card catalog, interlibrary loans, and database searching. Special learning facilities include an art gallery, planetarium, and radio station. The 30-acre campus is in a suburban area 35 miles east of Los Angeles. Including residence halls, there are 18 buildings on campus.

Student Life: About 51% of undergraduates are from out-of-state, mostly the West. Students come from 41 states, 11 foreign countries, and Canada. Eighty percent are from public schools; 20% from pri-

vate. Seventy-four percent are white; 22% Asian American. The average age of freshmen is 18; all undergraduates, 20. Ten percent drop out by the end of their first year; 76% remain to graduate.

Housing: A total of 632 students can be accommodated in college housing. College-sponsored living facilities include coed dormitories and on-campus apartments. On-campus housing is guaranteed for all 4 years. Ninety-five percent of students live on campus; of those, 94% remain on campus on weekends. All students may keep cars on campus.

Activities: There are no fraternities or sororities on campus. There are 23 groups on campus, including art, band, chess, choir, chorale, chorus, computers, dance, drama, ethnic, gay, international, jazz band, literary magazine, marching band, newspaper, orchestra, pep band, photography, political, professional, radio and TV, religious, social, social service, student government, symphony, and yearbook. Popular campus events include 5-class competition relay races.

Sports: There are 9 intercollegiate sports for men and 7 for women, and 6 intramural sports for men and 6 for women. Athletic and recreation facilities include a gymnasium housing 2 gymnasium floors, a weight room, and a boxing ring, a 400-meter track, 3 swimming pools, 16 tennis courts, volleyball courts, a 3.5 mile fitness course, and fields for intramural sports, football, baseball, and soccer.

Disabled Students: Ninety-nine percent of the campus is accessible to disabled students. The following facilities are available: wheelchair ramps, elevators, special parking, specially equipped rest rooms, and special class scheduling.

Services: In addition to many counseling and information services, tutoring is available in some subjects, on a need basis.

Campus Safety and Security: Campus safety and security measures include 24-hour foot and vehicle patrol, self defense education, escort service, and emergency telephones. In addition, there are lighted pathways and sidewalks.

Programs of Study: Harvey Mudd awards the B.S. degree. Bachelor's degrees are awarded in BIOLOGICAL SCIENCE (biology/biological science), COMPUTER AND PHYSICAL SCIENCE (chemistry, computer science, mathematics, and physics), ENGINEERING AND ENVIRONMENTAL DESIGN (engineering). Engineering has the largest enrollment.

Required: In order to graduate, all students must have a 2.0 GPA and complete a total of 128 hours, including 45 hours in a common core. This consists of 4 semesters of mathematics, 3 semesters of physics, 2 semesters of chemistry, and courses in biology programming, and system engineering, plus 2 electives chosen from core offerings. Another 37 hours are required in humanities and social sciences, including literature, psychology, philosophy, history, and institutions, and 46 in major and electives. All students take a computer science class and 3 semesters of noncredit physical education courses, and must pass a swimming test. A senior research or corporate clinic project is required.

Special: Students may cross-register at any of the other Claremont colleges. Internships are available for engineering and mathematics majors. Study abroad, a Washington semester, work-study, and student-designed majors are available. A 3–2 engineering degree with Claremont McKenna College is possible. Some courses may be audited. The first semester for freshmen is taken on a pass/fail basis; thereafter, only one noncore or nonmajor course per semester may be taken on that basis.

Faculty/Classroom: Eighty-two percent of faculty are male; 18%, female. All teach undergraduates, and also do research. Graduate students teach 1% of introductory courses. The average class size in an introductory lecture is 80; in a laboratory, 10; and in a regular course offering, 15.

Admissions: About 42% of the 1993–94 applicants were accepted. The SAT scores for the 1993–94 freshman class were as follows: Verbal—3% below 500, 23% between 500 and 599, 58% between 600 and 700, and 16% above 700; Math—20% between 600 and 700 and 80% above 700. About 97% of the current freshmen were in the top fifth of their class; 100% were in the top two fifths. There were 66 National Merit finalists and 66 semifinalists. About 33 freshmen graduated first in their class.

Requirements: Harvey Mudd requires applicants to be in the upper 10% of their class. The SAT I is required. Applicant must be a graduate of an accredited secondary school and have completed 4 years each of English and mathematics (including algebra, demonstrative and analytic geometry, trigonometry, and calculus), and 1 year each of physics and chemistry. The college strongly recommends that applicants take 2 years of a foreign language and 1 year each of history and biology. SAT II: Subject tests in mathematics II and writing and 1 other subject are required. Applicants must submit a personal essay and are encouraged to seek an interview. AP credits are accepted. Important factors used in the admissions decision are advanced placement or honor courses, recommendations by school officials, leadership record, extracurricular activities record, and evidence of special talent.

Procedure: Freshmen are admitted in the fall. Entrance exams should be taken by January of the senior year. Early decision applications should be filed by December 1; regular applications, by February 1 for fall entry, along with an application fee of $40. Notification of early decision is sent January 15; regular decision, April 1. There are early decision and deferred admissions plans. About 44 early decision candidates were accepted for the 1993–94 class. A waiting list is an active part of the admissions procedure, with about 10% of applicants on the list.

Transfer: Seven transfer students enrolled in 1993–94. Applicants must submit SAT II: Subject tests scores, transcripts, course descriptions, and references from a college mathematics, science, or engineering teacher or from a counselor. An interview is recommended. Students must have completed courses in calculus, physics, chemistry, and English composition. A total of 80 credits out of 128 must be completed at Harvey Mudd.

Visiting: There are regularly scheduled orientations for prospective students, including tours and interviews conducted Monday through Friday and Saturday mornings in the fall. There are guides for informal visits and visitors may sit in on classes and stay overnight at the school. To arrange for a visit, contact the Admission Office at (909) 621–8011.

Financial Aid: In 1993–94, 81% of all current freshmen and 70% of continuing students received some form of financial aid. About 50% of freshmen and 53% of continuing students received need-based aid. The average freshman award was $14,846. Of that total, scholarships or need-based grants averaged $11,780 ($20,726 maximum); loans averaged $2459 ($3500 maximum); and work contracts averaged $606 ($1250 maximum). Thirty percent of undergraduate students work part-time. Average earnings from campus work for the school year are $500. The average financial indebtedness of the 1992–93 graduate was $10,500. Harvey Mudd is a member of CSS. The FAF and FAFSA and the college's own financial statement are required. The deadline for financial aid applications is February 1.

International Students: There are currently 12 international students enrolled. The student must take the SAT I. Students must take SAT II: Subject tests in mathematics, writing, and in 1 other subject.

Computers: The college provides computer facilities for student use. The mainframe is a VAX Cluster. An optical fiber network connects all dormitory rooms, academic offices, and laboratories. There are 8 central processors with the Sequent Balance parallel processing machine, 8 Digital computers, two MicroVAX, 10 HP Apollo workstations and 30 other workstations and high-performance graphics terminals. All students may access the system. It may be used 24 hours a day. There are no time limits on using the system and no fees.

Graduates: In 1992–93, 115 bachelor's degrees were awarded. The most popular majors among graduates were engineering (58%) and physics (19%). Within an average freshman class, 68% graduate in 4 years, 75% in 5 years, and 76% in 6 years. Some 50 companies recruited on campus in 1992–93. In the 1992 graduating class, 65% of the students were enrolled in graduate school within 6 months of graduation; 27% of the students had found employment.

Admissions Contact: Patricia Coleman, Dean of Admissions and Financial Aid.

HOLY NAMES COLLEGE

Oakland, CA 94619

B-3

(510) 436-1321

Full-time: 95 men, 178 women	**Faculty:** 39
Part-time: 46 men, 271 women	**Ph.D.s:** 75%
Graduate: 90 men, 286 women	**Student/Faculty:** 7 to 1
Year: semesters	**Tuition:** $10,784
Application Deadline: August 1	**Room & Board:** $4876

Freshman Class: 258 applied, 157 accepted, 43 enrolled

SAT I Verbal/Math: 448/450

COMPETITIVE

Holy Names College, founded in 1868, is a small, independent liberal arts and teacher preparation college affiliated with the Roman Catholic Church. There is 1 graduate school. In addition to regional accreditation, Holy Names has baccalaureate program accreditation with NASM and NLN. The library contains 108,575 volumes, 44,500 microform items, and 4299 audiovisual forms and subscribes to 634 periodicals. Special learning facilities include a learning resource center and art gallery. The 60-acre campus is in an urban area 20 miles east of San Francisco. Including residence halls, there are 13 buildings on campus.

Student Life: About 90% of undergraduates are from California. Students come from 6 states and 10 foreign countries. Seventy-four percent are from public schools; 26% from private. Forty percent are white; 22% African American; 13% foreign nationals. The average age of freshmen is 19; all undergraduates, 23. Thirty percent drop out by the end of their first year; 40% remain to graduate.

Housing: A total of 250 students can be accommodated in college housing. College-sponsored living facilities include coed dormitories. On-campus housing is available on a first-come, first-served basis.

Sixty-six percent of students commute. Alcohol is not permitted. All students may keep cars on campus.

Activities: There are no fraternities or sororities on campus. There are many groups and organizations on campus, including choir, chorale, computers, drama, ethnic, honors, international, newspaper, orchestra, religious, social service, and student government. Popular campus events include Humanistic Studies Days and Founders Day.

Sports: There are 2 intercollegiate sports for men and 2 for women, and 5 intramural sports for men and 5 for women. Athletic and recreation facilities include a gymnasium, pool, fitness center, and outdoor fitness course.

Disabled Students: Ninety percent of the campus is accessible to disabled students. The following facilities are available: wheelchair ramps, elevators, special parking, and specially equipped rest rooms.

Services: In addition to many counseling and information services, tutoring is available in some subjects, including English and mathematics.

Campus Safety and Security: Campus safety and security measures include escort service, informal discussions, lighted pathways and sidewalks, 24-hour manned entrance gate, and nighttime foot patrol.

Programs of Study: Holy Names awards the B.A., B.S., B.Mus., and B.S.N. degrees. Master's degree also are awarded. Bachelor's degrees are awarded in BIOLOGICAL SCIENCE (biology/biological science), BUSINESS (business administration and management and business economics), COMMUNICATIONS AND THE ARTS (English, English studies for internationals, music, and Spanish), COMPUTER AND PHYSICAL SCIENCE (mathematics), HEALTH PROFESSIONS (nursing), SOCIAL SCIENCE (history, human services, humanities, international relations, liberal arts/general studies, philosophy, psychology, religion, and sociology). Business administration, nursing, music, psychology, and liberal studies have the largest enrollments.

Required: Students must have a 2.0 GPA and complete at least 120 hours, including at least 20 upper-level hours outside of the major field. Students must demonstrate proficiency in writing, oral communication, foreign language or linguistics, mathematics, computer competency, critical thinking, and knowledge of American institutions and democratic process. In some cases, these requirements may be satisfied by secondary record, advanced placement, or challenge test. All students must take multidisciplinary courses in humanistic studies, a senior colloquium, and health and/or physical education.

Special: Students may cross-register for 1 course per semester at any of 9 members of the Regional Association of East Bay Colleges and Universities. Internships, study abroad, and cooperative exchange programs with Central College in Iowa, Anna Maria College in Massachusetts, the Center for Bilingual Multicultural Studies in Mexico, and Kansai University of Foreign Studies in Japan are available. Double, interdisciplinary (including business administration and communication, business administration and philosophy, mathematics and engineering, and science and engineering), and student-designed majors are possible. A 3–2 engineering program is offered with the University of California, Berkeley. A weekend college for adults, limited nondegree study, and pass/fail options are available. There are 6 national honor societies on campus. One department has an honors program.

Faculty/Classroom: Thirty-seven percent of faculty are male; 63%, female. Seventy-four percent teach undergraduates. No introductory courses are taught by graduate students. The average class size in an introductory lecture is 20 and in a laboratory, 7.

Admissions: About 61% of the 1993–94 applicants were accepted. The SAT scores for the 1993–94 freshman class were as follows: Verbal—92% below 500 and 8% between 500 and 599; Math—67% below 500 and 33% between 500 and 599.

Requirements: A minimum GPA of 2.8 is required. The SAT I or ACT is required. Applicant must be a graduate of an accredited secondary school or have earned the GED. Secondary preparation should include at least 4 years of English, 3 years of mathematics, 2 years of 1 foreign language, 1 year each of laboratory science and U.S. history, 1 additional year of advanced courses in mathematics, laboratory science, or foreign language, and 3 other 1-year electives. SAT II: Subject tests are recommended but not required. In addition, the college requires a personal essay. Music auditions are required for scholarship applicants and recommended for others, and interviews are recommended for all. AP and CLEP credits are accepted. Important factors used in the admissions decision are recommendations by school officials, advanced placement or honor courses, leadership record, extracurricular activities record, and evidence of special talent.

Procedure: Freshmen are admitted in the fall and spring. Entrance exams should be taken during the fall of the senior year. Applications should be filed by August 1 for fall entry and January 1 for spring entry, along with an application fee of $35. Notification is sent on a rolling basis. There is a deferred admissions plan.

Transfer: About 31 transfer students enrolled in 1993–94. Applicants must have at least a 2.2 GPA in 12 to 30 credits of college work, or 2.1 for more than 30 credits. They must submit secondary and college records, SAT I or ACT scores, letters of recommendation from college teachers or counselors, and a personal statement of their educational goals. A total of 24 credits out of 120 must be completed at Holy Names.

Visiting: There are guides for informal visits and visitors may sit in on classes and stay overnight at the school. To arrange for a visit, contact the Admissions Office at (510) 436–1321.

Financial Aid: In 1993–94 66% of all current freshmen and 71% of continuing students received some form of financial aid. About 34% of freshmen and 60% of continuing students received need-based aid. The average freshman award was $8140. Of that total, scholarships or need-based grants averaged $3700 ($10,534 maximum); loans averaged $2500 ($2625 maximum); and work contracts averaged $1500 ($1800 maximum). Thirty percent of undergraduate students work part-time. Average earnings from campus work for the school year are $1500. The average financial indebtedness of the 1992–93 graduate was $10,000. Holy Names is a member of CSS. The college's own financial statement and FAFSA are required. The deadline for financial aid applications is March 2.

International Students: There are currently 90 international students enrolled. The school actively recruits these students. They must take the TOEFL or the University of Michigan Language Test and achieve a minimum score on the TOEFL of 500.

Computers: The college provides computer facilities for student use. The mainframe is not available for student use. IBM PCs and Apple Macintoshes are available in 2 large computer laboratories, open to all students. Additional computers are located in the accounting laboratory, the music resource laboratory, the library, and the residence halls. All students may access the system from 8 A.M. to 10 P.M. daily. There are no time limits on using the system and no fees.

Graduates: In 1992–93 113 bachelor's degrees were awarded. The most popular majors among graduates were business administration (21%), social sciences (19%), and nursing (9%). Within an average freshman class, 40% graduate in 4 years.

Admissions Contact: Joseph McDevitt, Senior Associate Director of Admissions.

HUMBOLDT STATE UNIVERSITY
A-1
Arcata, CA 95521 (707) 826–4402

Full-time: 2890 men, 2747 women	Faculty: 326; IIA, +$
Part-time: 348 men, 330 women	Ph.D.s: 80%
Graduate: 388 men, 419 women	Student/Faculty: 17 to 1
Year: semesters	Tuition: $1676 ($9000)
Application Deadline: see profile	Room & Board: $4000
Freshman Class: 3467 applied, 2190 accepted, 565 enrolled	
SAT I Verbal/Math: 460/510	ACT: 21 COMPETITIVE

Humboldt State University, founded in 1913, is primarily a commuter liberal arts institution and the northernmost campus of the California State University system. There are 4 undergraduate schools. In addition to regional accreditation, HSU has baccalaureate program accreditation with ABET, ACEJMC, NASAD, NASM, NLN, and SAF. The library contains 500,000 volumes, 531,000 microform items, and 15,229 audiovisual forms, and subscribes to 2000 periodicals. Computerized library sources and services include the card catalog, interlibrary loans, and database searching. Special learning facilities include an art gallery, a natural history museum, a radio station, an observatory, a greenhouse, a solar hydrogen project, wildlife sanctuaries, and the Center for Appropriate Technology. The 145-acre campus is in a small town 270 miles north of San Francisco. Including residence halls, there are 77 buildings on campus.

Student Life: About 98% of undergraduates are from California. Students come from 46 states, 43 foreign countries, and Canada. Eighty-nine percent are from public schools. Seventy-three percent are white. The average age of freshmen is 18.5; all undergraduates, 22. Twenty-one percent drop out by the end of their first year; 54% remain to graduate.

Housing: A total of 1353 students can be accommodated in college housing. College-sponsored living facilities include single-sex and coed dormitories and on-campus apartments. In addition, there are special interest houses. On-campus housing is available on a first-come, first-served basis. Eighty-five percent of students commute. All students may keep cars on campus.

Activities: About 2% of men belong to 3 national fraternities; about 2% of women belong to 1 national and 2 local sororities. There are 124 groups on campus, including art, band, cheerleading, chorale, chorus, computers, dance, drama, ethnic, film, gay, honors, international, jazz band, literary magazine, musical theater, newspaper, opera, orchestra, pep band, photography, political, professional, radio and TV, religious, social, social service, student government, and symphony. Popular campus events include Lumberjack Days, Native American Motivation Day, Cinco de Mayo, Alcohol Awareness Week, Women's Week, and Black History Month.

Sports: There are 5 intercollegiate sports for men and 5 for women, and 13 intramural sports for men and 12 for women. Athletic and recreation facilities include a 7000-seat stadium, an all-weather track, a swimming pool, a field house, tennis and racquetball courts, playing fields, 2 gymnasiums, a weight room, and a rock-climbing wall.

Disabled Students: Ninety percent of the campus is accessible to disabled students. The following facilities are available: wheelchair ramps, elevators, special parking, specially equipped rest rooms, special class scheduling, lowered drinking fountains and telephones, and wheelchair-accessible transportation.

Services: In addition to many counseling and information services, tutoring is available in most subjects, including mathematics, science, English, and foreign language. Additionally, there is a reader service for the blind, and remedial math, reading, and writing.

Campus Safety and Security: Campus safety and security measures include 24-hour foot and vehicle patrol, escort service, informal discussions, and pamphlets, posters, and films. In addition, there are emergency telephones, lighted pathways and sidewalks, and escort and emergency transportation services.

Programs of Study: HSU awards the B.A., B.S., and B.F.A. degrees. Master's degrees are also awarded. Bachelor's degrees are awarded in AGRICULTURE (fishing and fisheries, forestry and related sciences, natural resource management, and range/farm management), BIOLOGICAL SCIENCE (biology/biological science, botany, wildlife biology, and zoology), BUSINESS (business administration and management and business economics), COMMUNICATIONS AND THE ARTS (communications, dramatic arts, English, fine arts, French, German, journalism, music, Spanish, and speech/debate/rhetoric), COMPUTER AND PHYSICAL SCIENCE (chemistry, computer programming, geology, information sciences and systems, mathematics, oceanography, and physics), EDUCATION (art, business, early childhood, elementary, English, industrial arts, mathematics, middle school, music, physical, science, secondary, and social science), ENGINEERING AND ENVIRONMENTAL DESIGN (environmental engineering, environmental engineering technology, and industrial engineering technology), HEALTH PROFESSIONS (nursing, predentistry, and premedicine), SOCIAL SCIENCE (anthropology, geography, history, liberal arts/general studies, Native American studies, philosophy, political science/government, prelaw, psychology, religion, social science, social work, and sociology). Environmental resources engineering, natural resources, and performing arts are the strongest academically. The biological sciences have the largest enrollment.

Required: To graduate, students must complete 124 to 132 semester credits, including 48 in general education courses and at least 24 to 36 in the major, with a minimum overall GPA of 2.0. Requirements in freshman reading and composition, American institutions, U.S. history and the Constitution, and California governement may be met through course work or examinations.

Special: HSU offers campus work-study programs, co-op programs with a variety of public and private agencies, internships, and study abroad in 16 countries, with semesters in London, China, and Greece. Dual majors and degrees, student-designed majors, a general studies degree, credit for life and military experience and community service, and credit/no credit grading options are also available. There are 4 national honor societies on campus. Six departments have honors programs.

Faculty/Classroom: Seventy percent of faculty are male; 30%, female. The average class size in an introductory lecture is 34; in a laboratory, 22; and in a regular course offering, 30.

Admissions: About 63% of the 1993–94 applicants were accepted.

Requirements: A minimum GPA of 2.0 is required. The SAT I or ACT is required. Applicants must be high school graduates with a minimum GPA of 2.0 and 15 academic credits, including 4 in English, 3 each in mathematics and electives, 2 in foreign language, and 1 each in history/government, science, laboratory, and the visual and performing arts. The GED is accepted. HSU uses an eligibility index that combines GPA and ACT or SAT I scores for admission. Requirements are higher for out-of-state applicants. AP credits are accepted.

Procedure: Freshmen are admitted fall and spring. The priority months of application are November for fall entry and August for spring entry. The application fee is $55. Notification is sent on a rolling basis.

Transfer: About 760 transfer students enrolled in 1993–94. Applicants must have a minimum college GPA of 2.0 (2.4 for nonresidents). Students with fewer than 56 transferable semester units must meet freshman requirements. A total of 30 credits out of 124 to 132 must be completed at HSU.

Visiting: There are regularly scheduled orientations for prospective students, including Preview Day in the spring and mandatory summer orientation for new students, which provides peer and academic counseling, registration, and a variety of social activities. There are guides for informal visits and visitors may sit in on classes and stay

overnight at the school. To arrange for a visit, contact the Office of Admissions and School Relations at (707) 826–4402.

Financial Aid: In 1993–94, 51% of all current freshmen and 47% of continuing students received some form of financial aid. About 91% of all students received need-based aid. The average freshman award was $4742. Of that total, scholarships or need-based grants averaged $1024 ($2300 maximum); loans averaged $1308 ($2625 maximum); and work contracts averaged $1051 ($4000 maximum). Forty-seven percent of undergraduate students work part-time. The average financial indebtedness of the 1992–93 graduate was $5700. HSU is a member of CSS. The FAFSA financial statement is required. The deadline for financial aid applications is February 1.

International Students: There are currently 32 international students enrolled. They must take the TOEFL and achieve a minimum score of 550.

Computers: The college provides computer facilities for student use. The mainframe is a DEC VAX 8350. More than 200 Apple and IBM/IBM-compatible microcomputers are available in numerous locations. Students also have access to Internet, academic specialty centers, and specialized software programs. All students may access the system. It may be used 24 hours a day. There are no time limits on using the system and no fees.

Graduates: In 1992–93, 1151 bachelor's degrees were awarded. The most popular majors among graduates were psychology (7%), liberal studies (6%), and art (5%). Within an average freshman class, 54% graduate in 6 years. Some 64 companies recruited on campus in 1992–93.

Admissions Contact: Office of Admissions and School Relations.

HUMPHREYS COLLEGE
B-3
Stockton, CA 95207–3896   (209) 478–0800

Full-time: 45 men, 308 women	Faculty: 18
Part-time: 39 men, 260 women	Ph.Ds: 46%
Graduate: 45 men, 48 women	Student/Faculty: 20 to 1
Year: quarters, summer session	Tuition: $4704
Application Deadline: September 27	Room & Board: $5010
Freshman Class: 84 applied, 84 accepted, 73 enrolled	
SAT I Verbal/Math: 360/380	**NONCOMPETITIVE**

Humphreys College, founded in 1896, is an independent institution offering undergraduate degrees in business management, accounting, paralegal studies, computer management, and liberal arts to a primarily commuter student body. There is one graduate school. The library contains 21,000 volumes and 1000 audiovisual forms, and subscribes to 109 periodicals. The 8-acre campus is in a suburban area 40 miles south of Sacramento and 90 miles east of San Francisco. There are 9 buildings on campus.

Student Life: About 96% of undergraduates are from California. Ninety-seven percent are from public schools; 3% from private. Sixty-four percent are white; 11% Hispanic; 10% Asian American. The average age of freshmen is 23; all undergraduates, 25. Twenty percent drop out by the end of their first year; 50% remain to graduate.

Housing: A total of 64 students can be accommodated in college housing. College-sponsored living facilities include coed on-campus apartments and married-student housing. On-campus housing is available on a first-come, first-served basis. Priority is given to out-of-town students. Ninety percent of students commute. Alcohol is not permitted. All students may keep cars on campus.

Activities: There are no fraternities or sororities on campus. There are 4 groups on campus, including professional and student government. Popular campus events include Halloween party, Christmas dinner, and the quarterly Hot Dog Day barbecue.

Sports: There is no sports program at Humphreys. Athletic and recreation facilities include a swimming pool, a basketball court, a tennis court, and sports fields.

Disabled Students: All of the campus is accessible to disabled students. The following facilities are available: wheelchair ramps, special parking, specially equipped rest rooms, special class scheduling, lowered drinking fountains, and lowered telephones.

Services: In addition to many counseling and information services, tutoring is available in most subjects. There is remedial math and writing.

Campus Safety and Security: Campus safety and security measures include escort service, lighted pathways and sidewalks, and a 24-hour foot patrol.

Programs of Study: Humphreys awards the B.S. degree. Associate and doctoral degrees also are awarded. Bachelor's degrees are awarded in BUSINESS (accounting and business administration and management), COMPUTER AND PHYSICAL SCIENCE (computer science), SOCIAL SCIENCE (paralegal studies). Paralegal studies has the largest enrollment.

Required: To graduate, students must complete a total of 180 quarter units, including 56 in the major and 72 in general education courses, with a minimum overall GPA of 2.0.

Special: Local internship positions are available for students of paralegal studies and business administration.

Faculty/Classroom: Fifty-seven percent of faculty are male; 43%, female. All teach undergraduates. No introductory courses are taught by graduate students. The average class size in an introductory lecture is 17.

Admissions: All of the 1993–94 applicants were accepted. The SAT scores for the 1993–94 freshman class were as follows: Verbal—90% below 500 and 10% between 500 and 599; Math—87% below 500 and 13% between 500 and 599.

Requirements: A minimum GPA of 2.0 is required. The SAT I or ACT is recommended. Applicants must be graduates of an accredited secondary school or have earned a GED. AP and CLEP credits are accepted.

Procedure: Freshmen are admitted to all sessions. Applications should be filed by September 27 for fall entry, January 4 for winter entry, April 5 for spring entry, and July 3 for summer entry, along with an application fee of $20. The college accepts all applicants. Notification is sent on a rolling basis. There are early admissions and deferred admissions plans.

Transfer: Ninety-seven transfer students enrolled in 1993–94. Applicants must submit official transcripts and have a GPA of at least 2.0. A total of 36 credits out of 180 must be completed at Humphreys.

Visiting: There are regularly scheduled orientations for prospective students, including a tour of the campus, classroom visits, and meetings with admissions, financial aid, and academic advisers. There are guides for informal visits and visitors may sit in on classes. To arrange for a visit, contact Pam Knapp or John Seabreeze at (209) 478–0800.

Financial Aid: In 1993–94, 70% of all students received some form of financial aid, including need-based aid. The average freshman award was $6125. Of that total, scholarships or need-based grants averaged $3500 ($6533 maximum); and loans averaged $2625 ($4000 maximum). Sixty-four percent of undergraduate students work part-time. Average earnings from campus work for the school year are $1200. Humphreys is a member of CSS. The FAFSA financial statement is required.

International Students: There are currently 6 international students enrolled. They must take the TOEFL and achieve a minimum score of 450.

Computers: The college provides computer facilities for student use. The mainframes are an IBM 34/1540 and an IBM AS400. There are 25 microcomputers available. All students may access the system. It may be used when a laboratory aide or instructor is present or with an instructor's permission. There are no time limits on using the system and no fees.

Graduates: In 1992–93, 15 bachelor's degrees were awarded. The most popular majors among graduates were paralegal studies (50%), business management (35%), and accounting (10%). Within an average freshman class, 20% graduate in 3 years, 95% in 4 years, and 100% in 5 years.

Admissions Contact: Pam Knapp or John Seabreeze, Admissions Counselors.

LA SIERRA UNIVERSITY
D-5
Riverside, CA 92515–8247   (909) 785–2176
(800) 874–5587 (out-of-state)

Full-time: 538 men, 580 women	Faculty: 97
Part-time: 63 men, 61 women	Ph.Ds: 71%
Graduate: 140 men, 140 women	Student/Faculty: 12 to 1
Year: quarters, summer session	Tuition: $11,692
Application Deadline: August 15	Room & Board: $3780
Freshman Class: 659 applied, 530 accepted, 315 enrolled	
SAT I or ACT: required	**COMPETITIVE**

La Sierra University, founded originally as La Sierra Academy in 1922, is a Seventh-day Adventist, private coeducational university, offering undergraduate and graduate programs in applied and liberal arts and sciences, business and management, religion, and education. There are 5 undergraduate and 4 graduate schools. In addition to regional accreditation, La Sierra has baccalaureate program accreditation with ABET. The library contains 230,000 volumes, and subscribes to 1500 periodicals. Computerized library sources and services include the card catalog, interlibrary loans, and database searching. Special learning facilities include a learning resource center, an art gallery, a natural history museum, a radio station, an observatory, an equestrian center, a missionary museum, and an arboretum. The 300-acre campus is in a suburban area 40 miles east of Los Angeles. Including residence halls, there are 48 buildings on campus.

Student Life: About 70% of undergraduates are from California. Students come from 30 states, 68 foreign countries, and Canada. Forty percent are from public schools; 55% from private. Forty-five percent are white; 31% Asian American; 15% Hispanic. Ten percent are Protestant. The average age of freshmen is 18.5; all undergraduates, 21.6.

Housing: A total of 650 students can be accommodated in college housing. College-sponsored living facilities include single-sex dormitories, on-campus apartments, and married-student housing. In addition, there are honors houses. Fifty-two percent of students commute. Alcohol is not permitted. All students may keep cars on campus.

Activities: There are no fraternities or sororities on campus. There are 30 groups on campus, including band, choir, computers, drama, ethnic, international, newspaper, photography, professional, radio and TV, religious, social service, student government, and yearbook. Popular campus events include University Experience, Alumni Homecoming, Academic Expo, and Community Service Day.

Sports: There are 2 intercollegiate sports each for men and women, and 9 intramural sports each. Athletic and recreation facilities include a gymnasium, soccer and flag football fields, a running track, a swimming pool, and a gymnastics room.

Disabled Students: Almost all of the campus is accessible to disabled students. The following facilities are available: wheelchair ramps, elevators, special parking, and specially equipped rest rooms.

Services: In addition to many counseling and information services, tutoring is available in most subjects. There is also a reader service for the blind, remedial math, reading, and writing and a learning support center.

Campus Safety and Security: Campus safety and security measures include 24-hour foot and vehicle patrol, escort service, informal discussions, and lighted pathways and sidewalks.

Programs of Study: La Sierra awards the B.A., B.S., B.B.A., B.F.A., B.Mus., and B.S.W. degrees. Associate, master's, and doctoral degrees also are awarded. Bachelor's degrees are awarded in BIOLOGICAL SCIENCE (biochemistry, biometrics and biostatistics, and biophysics), BUSINESS (accounting, business administration and management, management information systems, management science, marketing management, and office supervision and management), COMMUNICATIONS AND THE ARTS (art, communications, English, English as a second/foreign language, French, journalism, music, music performance, radio/television technology, and studio art), COMPUTER AND PHYSICAL SCIENCE (chemistry, computer science, information sciences and systems, mathematics, physical sciences, and physics), EDUCATION (business, music, and physical), HEALTH PROFESSIONS (health science), SOCIAL SCIENCE (anthropology, behavioral science, child psychology/development, clinical psychology, developmental psychology, history, industrial and organizational psychology, liberal arts/general studies, ministries, psychobiology, psychology, religion, religious music, social work, and sociology). Biology, psychology, business, and education have the largest enrollments.

Required: To graduate, students must complete 190 units, at least 60 of which must be upper-division, with a GPA of 2.0. All students must complete a general education curriculum consisting of 20 to 24 units in humanities, 13 in communications, 20 in religious studies, 12 in social sciences, 16 each in natural science, mathematics, and health, and 2 1/2 in physical education.

Special: Cross-registration with Walla Walla College is necessary for engineering students. Internships are available in communications fields, as is study abroad in 3 countries through the Adventist Colleges Abroad Consortium. Liberal studies students work with an advisor to design their own major. Work-study is available on and off campus. There is a freshman honors program on campus.

Faculty/Classroom: Seventy-four percent of faculty are male; 26%, female. All teach undergraduates.

Admissions: About 80% of the 1993–94 applicants were accepted. The SAT scores for the freshman class were as follows: Verbal—72% below 500, 20% between 500 and 599, 5% between 600 and 700, and 3% above 700; Math—78% below 500, 14% between 500 and 599, 6% between 600 and 700, and 2% above 700.

Requirements: A minimum GPA of 2.5 is required. The SAT I or ACT is required. Prospective students should have a high school diploma or equivalent with a minimum GPA of 2.5. Test scores above the 50th percentile and a personal interview are recommended. Provisional acceptance may be considered with lesser credentials, following a more exhaustive examination. AP and CLEP credits are accepted.

Procedure: Freshmen are admitted to all sessions. Entrance exams should be taken during the senior year. Applications should be filed by August 15 for fall entry, December 1 for winter entry, March 1 for spring entry, and May 1 for summer entry, along with an application fee of $30. Notification is sent on a rolling basis.

Transfer: Transcripts from all previous colleges are required. A total of 36 credits out of 190 must be completed at La Sierra.

Visiting: There are regularly scheduled orientations for prospective students, including a tour and meetings with faculty and administrators. Visitors may sit in on classes. To arrange for a visit, contact Recruitment/Admissions at (909) 785-2176.

Financial Aid: Scholarships or need-based grants averaged $200 ($5250 maximum). La Sierra is a member of CSS. The FAF, SAAC and the FAFSA are required. The deadline for financial aid applications is March 1.

International Students: They must take the TOEFL or the University of Michigan Language Test.

Computers: The college provides computer facilities for student use. The mainframes are a DEC MicroVAX 3100 and 3900 and a Sequent SAM 2000/700. Terminals accessing the mainframes are available in every building on campus, and Apple Macintosh, AT&T, and IBM PCs are available in the microcomputer laboratory. All systems are connected to an Ethernet network and a Micom Dataswitch. All students may access the system 24 hours a day. There are no time limits and no fees.

Graduates: In 1992–93, 175 bachelor's degrees were awarded. The most popular majors among graduates were biology (22%), liberal arts/education (11%), and business administration (8%).

Admissions Contact: Myrna Costa-Casado, Director, Admissions.

LEE COLLEGE AT THE UNIVERSITY OF JUDAISM

Los Angeles, CA 90077   (310) 476-9777; (310) 476-0236 (collect)

C-5

Full-time: 44 men, 47 women	Faculty: 17
Part-time: 2 men, 7 women	Ph.D.s: 88%
Graduate: 49 men, 53 women	Student/Faculty: 5 to 1
Year: semesters	Tuition: $9710
Application Deadline: January 31	Room & Board: $5890
Freshman Class: 51 applied, 38 accepted, 18 enrolled	
SAT I Verbal/Math: 565/565	VERY COMPETITIVE

Lee College at the University of Judaism, founded in 1982, is an independent Jewish institution offering majors in bioethics, business, Judaic studies, literature, psychology, political science, and interdisciplinary studies. There are 4 graduate schools. The library contains 105,000 volumes and subscribes to 400 periodicals. Computerized library sources and services include the card catalog and interlibrary loans. Special learning facilities include a learning resource center, art gallery, and radio station. The 28-acre campus is in a suburban area 3 miles south of San Fernando Valley. Including residence halls, there are 9 buildings on campus.

Student Life: About 65% of undergraduates are from out-of-state, mostly the West. Students come from 13 states, 7 foreign countries, and Canada. Eighty percent are from public schools; 20% from private. Ninety-five percent are white. Most are Jewish. The average age of freshmen is 18; all undergraduates, 23. Eight percent drop out by the end of their first year; 65% remain to graduate.

Housing: A total of 192 students can be accommodated in college housing. College-sponsored living facilities include coed dormitories, on-campus apartments, and married-student housing. On-campus housing is guaranteed for all 4 years. Fifty-five percent of students live on campus; of those, 90% remain on campus on weekends. Alcohol is not permitted. All students may keep cars on campus.

Activities: There are no fraternities or sororities on campus. There are many groups and organizations on campus, including art, chorus, dance, drama, literary magazine, political, radio and TV, religious, social, social service, student government, and yearbook.

Disabled Students: All of the campus is accessible to disabled students. The following facilities are available: elevators, special parking, specially equipped rest rooms, lowered drinking fountains, and lowered telephones.

Services: In addition to many counseling and information services, tutoring is available in most subjects. In addition, there is remedial math and writing. There is also a living/learning series in residence halls.

Campus Safety and Security: Campus safety and security measures include 24-hour foot and vehicle patrol, self-defense education, informal discussions, and pamphlets, posters, and films. In addition, there are lighted pathways and sidewalks.

Programs of Study: Lee College at the University of Judaism awards the B.A. degree. Master's degrees also are awarded. Bachelor's degrees are awarded in BUSINESS (business economics), COMMUNICATIONS AND THE ARTS (literature), HEALTH PROFESSIONS (premedicine), SOCIAL SCIENCE (Judaic studies, political science/government, and psychology). Judaic studies, psychology, business, and political science are the strongest academically. Judaic studies, psychology, and business have the largest enrollments.

Required: All students must complete a core curriculum combining the study of Jewish and Western civilizations, as well as courses in communications and foreign language, and 1 in computer science. There are distribution requirements in mathematics, natural and behavioral sciences, and fine arts. Other requirements vary according to the major, with at least 32 to 36 upper-division credits needed. A total of 127 semester units, with a minimum GPA of 2.0, is required to graduate.

Special: Cross-registration and a joint bioethics major are offered with Mount Saint Mary's College in California. There is also a 5-year joint business program at the Lieber School of Graduate Studies. Student-designed majors and dual majors are available. Internships in all available majors, study abroad, work-study programs, accelerated degree programs, and pass/fail options are offered. Students may apply for independent study projects.

Faculty/Classroom: Seventy-five percent of faculty are male; 25%, female. All both teach and do research. No introductory courses are taught by graduate students. The average class size in an introductory lecture is 15; in a laboratory, 6; and in a regular course offering, 10.

Admissions: About 75% of the 1993–94 applicants were accepted. The SAT scores for the 1993–94 freshman class were as follows: Verbal—28% below 500, 36% between 500 and 599, and 36% between 600 and 700; Math—21% below 500, 43% between 500 and 599, 29% between 600 and 700, and 7% above 700. About 40% of the current freshmen were in the top fifth of their class; 80% were in the top two fifths.

Requirements: A minimum GPA of 3.2 is required. The SAT I or ACT is required. Scores of at least 1100 on the SAT I or 23 on the ACT are preferred. Applicants must be graduates of an accredited secondary school or have the GED. A visit and an interview are recommended for all students. Two recommendations from teachers, an autobiographical essay, and a secondary school report/recommendation from an academic counselor also are required. Students scoring below 500 on the verbal SAT I or earning below a 3.2 GPA are occasionally admitted if essay, recommendations, grades in English, and other humanities courses are exceptionally strong. AP credits are accepted. Important factors used in the admissions decision are recommendations by school officials, leadership record, advanced placement or honor courses, extracurricular activities record, and evidence of special talent.

Procedure: Freshmen are admitted fall and spring. Entrance exams should be taken no later than November of the year prior to enrollment. Early decision applications should be filed by November 15; regular applications, by January 31 for fall entry and November 1 for spring entry, along with an application fee of $25. Notification of early decision is sent December 1; regular decision, on a rolling basis. There are early decision and deferred admissions plans.

Transfer: Eighteen transfer students enrolled in 1993–94. Transfer students with fewer than 60 college units must have a minimum 3.0 high school GPA, at least 1100 on the SAT I or 23 on the ACT, 2 recommendations, and an autobiographical essay. The SAT I or ACT requirement is waived if the applicant has 60 or more units. A visit and an interview are recommended. A total of 34 credits out of 127 must be completed at Lee College at the University of Judaism.

Visiting: There are regularly scheduled orientations for prospective students consisting of a meeting with an admissions representative; campus tours, including dormitories; a meeting with a financial aid officer (by request); meals with students; sitting in on classes; and a meeting with an academic department chairman (by request). All visits are arranged on an individual basis. There are guides for informal visits and visitors may stay overnight at the school. To arrange for a visit, contact Tamara Greenebaum, Dean of Admissions, at (310) 476-9777 or (310) 476-0236.

Financial Aid: In 1993–94, 90% of all current freshmen and 74% of continuing students received some form of financial aid. About 84% of freshmen and 70% of continuing students received need-based aid. The average freshman award was $10,715. Of that total, scholarships or need-based grants averaged $9293 ($13,360 maximum); loans averaged $2625; and work contracts averaged $2000. Thirty percent of undergraduate students work part-time. Average earnings from campus work for the school year are $1104. The average financial indebtedness of the 1992–93 graduate was $9087. Lee College at the University of Judaism is a member of CSS. The college's own financial statement and the FAFSA are required. The deadline for financial aid applications is March 2.

International Students: There are currently 15 international students enrolled. They must take the TOEFL and achieve a minimum score of 550. The student must also take the SAT I or the ACT. A composite score of 1100 on the SAT I is preferred.

Computers: The college provides computer facilities for student use. There is a computer room with 15 IBM and Macintosh microcomputers and several printers available. All students may access the system. There are no time limits on using the system and no fees.

Graduates: In 1992–93, 16 bachelor's degrees were awarded. The most popular majors among graduates were psychology (46%), literature (23%), and Judaic studies (15%). Within an average freshman class, 60% graduate in 4 years and 40% in 5 years. In the 1992 graduating class, 85% of all graduates were enrolled in graduate school within 6 months of graduation; 100% had found employment.

Admissions Contact: Tamara Greenebaum, Dean of Admissions.

LINCOLN UNIVERSITY
B-3
San Francisco, CA 94118
Recognized candidate for accreditation (415) 221-1212

Full-time: 135 men, 53 women	Faculty: 6
Part-time: none	Ph.D.s: 88%
Graduate: 108 men, 73 women	Student/Faculty: 31 to 1
Year: semesters, summer session	Tuition: $4400
Application Deadline: open	Room & Board: n/app
Freshman Class: 181 applied, 157 accepted, 43 enrolled	
SAT I or ACT: not required	LESS COMPETITIVE

Lincoln University, founded in 1919, is a private institution with an international emphasis. The university offers undergraduate degree programs in business administration and computer science and is authorized to admit nonimmigrant alien students. There is one graduate school. Computerized library sources and services include database searching. Special learning facilities include a language laboratory. The 2-acre campus is in San Francisco. There is one building on campus.

Student Life: Students come from 47 foreign countries. Ninety-six percent are foreign nationals. The average age of freshmen is 25.

Housing: There are no residence halls; all students commute. Alcohol is not permitted.

Activities: There are no fraternities or sororities on campus. Extracurricular groups include ethnic, newspaper, and student government. Popular campus events include films and field trips.

Sports: There is no sports program at Lincoln.

Disabled Students: The campus is totally accessible to disabled students. The following facilities are available: wheelchair ramps and elevators.

Campus Safety and Security: Campus safety and security measures include informal discussions and lighted pathways and sidewalks.

Programs of Study: Lincoln awards the B.A. and B.S. degrees. Master's degrees are also awarded. Bachelor's degrees are awarded in BUSINESS (business administration and management), COMPUTER AND PHYSICAL SCIENCE (computer science), EDUCATION (teaching English as a second language/foreign language). Business administration has the largest enrollment.

Required: In order to graduate, all students must complete 124 credit hours, a general education (core) program, and the course requirements for their major. Certification of English proficiency is required.

Special: The American Language Program for Speakers of Other Languages (ALP-SOL) prepares students for the college environment, strengthens their communication skills, and offers a general introduction to social and cultural institutions. The program, required for all students, is offered at the beginner, intermediate, and advanced levels.

Faculty/Classroom: Seventy-four percent of faculty are male; 26%, female. The average class size in an introductory lecture is 25; in a laboratory, 10; and in a regular course offering, 15.

Admissions: About 87% of the 1993–94 applicants were accepted.

Requirements: A minimum GPA of 2.0 is required. The SAT I or ACT is not required. Applicant must be a graduate of an accredited secondary school. The GED is accepted. A total of 16 high school academic credits are required, including 4 credits of English, 3 each of mathematics, social science, and science (including 2 laboratory sciences), 2 of foreign language, 1 of fine and/or performing arts, and 1 of physical education/health. AP and CLEP credits are accepted. Important factors in the admissions decision are advanced placement or honor courses, recommendations by school officials, leadership record, parents or siblings attending the school, and extracurricular activities record.

Procedure: Freshmen are admitted to all sessions. Application deadlines are open and the fee is $50. Notification is sent on a rolling basis.

Transfer: About 85 transfer students enrolled in 1993–94. Applicants for transfer must meet the same criteria as entering freshmen. A total of 40 credits out of 124 must be completed at Lincoln.

Visiting: There are regularly scheduled orientations for prospective students. There are guides for informal visits and visitors may sit in on classes. To arrange for a visit, contact the Director of Admissions at (415) 221-1212.

Financial Aid: Scholarships or need-based grants averaged $1450. Lincoln is a member of CSS. The deadline for financial aid applications is March 1.

International Students: There are currently 342 international students enrolled. The school actively recruits these students. They must take the University of Michigan Language Test or the Comprehensive English Language Test.

Computers: The college provides computer facilities for student use. There are IBM PCs available for all students use.

Graduates: In 1992–93, 36 bachelor's degrees were awarded.

Admissions Contact: Director of Admissions.

LOYOLA MARYMOUNT UNIVERSITY
Los Angeles, CA 90045-2699

C-5

(310) 338-2750
(800) LMU-INFO (out-of-state)

Full-time: 1571 men, 1974 women
Part-time: 117 men, 162 women
Graduate: 476 men, 622 women
Year: semesters, summer session
Application Deadline: February 1
Freshman Class: 3595 applied, 2662 accepted, 753 enrolled
SAT I Verbal/Math: 473/535

Faculty: 241; IIA, +$
Ph.D.s: 81%
Student/Faculty: 15 to 1
Tuition: $13,060
Room & Board: $5500

COMPETITIVE

Loyola Marymount University is a private institution affiliated with the Roman Catholic Church, offering programs in liberal arts, business administration, fine arts, science, and engineering. There are 4 undergraduate schools and one graduate school. In addition to regional accreditation, LMU has baccalaureate program accreditation with AACSB, ABET, and NASAD. The 2 libraries contain 431,469 volumes, 253,471 microform items, and 11,826 audiovisual forms and subscribe to 8362 periodicals. Computerized library sources and services include the card catalog, interlibrary loans, and database searching. Special learning facilities include a learning resource center, art gallery, radio station, fine arts center, and the Little Theater. The 100-acre campus is in a suburban area 15 miles southwest of downtown Los Angeles on a mesa overlooking Marina del Rey and the Pacific Ocean. Including residence halls, there are 34 buildings on campus.

Student Life: About 81% of undergraduates are from California. Students come from 44 states, 55 foreign countries, and Canada. Forty-nine percent are from public schools; 51% from private. Fifty-four percent are white; 19% Hispanic; 15% Asian American. Sixty-two percent are Catholic; 21% claim no religious affiliation; 11% Protestant. The average age of freshmen is 18; all undergraduates, 20. Ten percent drop out by the end of their first year; 68% remain to graduate.

Housing: A total of 1869 students can be accommodated in college housing. College-sponsored living facilities include single-sex and coed dormitories, on-campus apartments, and off-campus apartments. On-campus housing is available on a lottery system for upperclassmen. Fifty-two percent of students commute. All students may keep cars on campus.

Activities: About 13% of men belong to 6 national fraternities; about 11% of women belong to 4 national sororities. There are 109 groups on campus, including art, cheerleading, chess, choir, chorale, chorus, computers, dance, drama, ethnic, film, honors, international, literary magazine, newspaper, orchestra, pep band, political, professional, radio and TV, religious, social, social service, student government, and yearbook. Popular campus events include Cinco de Mayo, Special Games (handicapped children), and the ASLMU Formal Dance.

Sports: There are 9 intercollegiate sports for men and 8 for women, and 11 intramural sports for men and 10 for women. Athletic and recreation facilities include an athletic pavilion, a 4166-seat gymnasium, swimming pools, tennis and handball courts, a baseball stadium, a floating crew shell house, and soccer, rugby, and football fields.

Disabled Students: Ninety percent of the campus is accessible to disabled students. The following facilities are available: wheelchair ramps, elevators, special parking, specially equipped rest rooms, special class scheduling, and lowered drinking fountains. Special arrangements are possible for placement tests and registration.

Services: In addition to many counseling and information services, tutoring is available in every subject. In addition, there is a reader service for the blind. There is an extensive learning resource center with full-time specialists in reading, writing, and study skills as well as a peer tutoring staff and computer-aided instruction. Note takers and special equipment and materials are available.

Campus Safety and Security: Campus safety and security measures include 24-hour foot and vehicle patrol, escort service, informal discussions, and emergency telephones. In addition, there are lighted pathways and sidewalks.

Programs of Study: LMU awards the B.A., B.S., B.B.A., B.S.A., and B.S.E. degrees. Master's and doctoral degrees also are awarded. Bachelor's degrees are awarded in BIOLOGICAL SCIENCE (biochemistry and biology/biological science), BUSINESS (accounting and business administration and management), COMMUNICATIONS AND THE ARTS (art history and appreciation, communications, dance, dramatic arts, English, French, Greek, Latin, music, Spanish, and studio art), COMPUTER AND PHYSICAL SCIENCE (computer science, mathematics, and physics), ENGINEERING AND ENVIRONMENTAL DESIGN (civil engineering, electrical/electronics engineering, and mechanical engineering), SOCIAL SCIENCE (African American studies, Chicano studies, classical/ancient civilization, economics, European studies, history, humanities, liberal arts/general studies, philosophy, political science/government, psychology, sociology, theological studies, and urban studies). Communication arts,

accounting, and psychology are the strongest academically. Liberal arts and business administration have the largest enrollments.

Required: The core curriculum required for all students in the liberal arts college includes 6 hours each of communication skills, history, science/technology, philosophy, and theology, and 3 hours of fine arts, literature/psychology, and social studies. A minimum 2.0 GPA is required, as are at least 120 semester credits, with at least 40 hours in the major. The last 30 semester hours of academic work and at least 12 hours of the major must be completed at LMU.

Special: LMU offers internships and volunteer work experience with local firms, study abroad in Europe, Mexico, and Japan, a Washington semester, student-designed majors, accelerated degree programs in all majors, a general studies degree, nondegree study, and pass/fail options for electives. There is a freshman honors program on campus, as well as 2 national honor societies. There is an interdisciplinary honors program; all departments may participate.

Faculty/Classroom: Seventy-four percent of faculty are male; 26%, female. All do research and 93% also teach undergraduates. No introductory courses are taught by graduate students. The average class size in a regular course offering is 24.

Admissions: About 74% of the 1993–94 applicants were accepted. The SAT scores for the 1993–94 freshman class were as follows: Verbal—63% below 500, 29% between 500 and 599, 8% between 600 and 700, and 1% above 700; Math—32% below 500, 46% between 500 and 599, 18% between 600 and 700, and 4% above 700.

Requirements: The SAT I or ACT is required. In addition, prospective students must be graduates of an accredited secondary school and have completed 4 years of English, 3 years each of a foreign language, mathematics, and social studies, 2 years of science, and 1 year of an academic elective. An essay and a recommendation from an official of the previous school are required. An interview is recommended. AP credits are accepted. Important factors used in the admissions decision are advanced placement or honor courses, recommendations by school officials, evidence of special talent, personality, intangible qualities, and leadership record.

Procedure: Freshmen are admitted in the fall and spring. Entrance exams should be taken during spring of the junior year or fall of the senior year. Applications should be filed by February 1 for fall entry and December 1 for spring entry, along with an application fee of $35. Notification is sent on a rolling basis. There are early admissions and deferred admissions plans. A waiting list is an active part of the admissions procedure, with about 10% of applicants on the list.

Transfer: About 379 transfer students enrolled in 1993–94. Applicants must have a minimum 2.5 GPA and at least 30 credit hours earned. No minimum credit hours are necessary for students who would have been accepted at the university as freshmen. The SAT I and an interview are recommended. A total of 30 credits out of 120 must be completed at LMU.

Visiting: There are regularly scheduled orientations for prospective students, consisting of an open house in the fall and a preview day in the spring. There are guides for informal visits and visitors may sit in on classes and stay overnight at the school. To arrange for a visit, contact the Admissions Office at (310) 338-2750.

Financial Aid: In 1993–94 76% of all current freshmen and 62% of continuing students received some form of financial aid. About 64% of freshmen and 51% of continuing students received need-based aid. The average freshman award was $12,628. Of that total, scholarships or need-based grants averaged $8287 ($18,852 maximum); loans averaged $2126 ($4000 maximum); and work contracts averaged $2215 ($2400 maximum). Forty-six percent of undergraduate students work part-time. Average earnings from campus work for the school year are $1450. The average financial indebtedness of the 1992–93 graduate was $5000. LMU is a member of CSS. The FAF or FFS is required. The deadline for financial aid applications is February 15.

International Students: There are currently 184 international students enrolled. They must take the TOEFL and achieve a minimum score of 550. The student must also take the SAT I or the ACT.

Computers: The college provides computer facilities for student use. The mainframe is an IBM 4381. There are 40 microcomputers in a student laboratory networked through the school's mainframe plus an additional number with dial-in capability. The library houses 20 microcomputers for stand-alone use. Residence halls are wired for access to a campuswide network through students' personal computers. All students may access the system through a 24-hour dial-in; laboratory hours are 8 A.M. to 2 A.M. There are no time limits on using the system and no fees.

Graduates: In 1992–93 982 bachelor's degrees were awarded. The most popular majors among graduates were business and management (33%), communications (16%), and social sciences (15%). Within an average freshman class, 53% graduate in 4 years, 66% in 5 years, and 68% in 6 years. Some 112 companies recruited on campus in 1992–93.

Admissions Contact: Matthew X. Fissinger, Director of Undergraduate Admissions.

MASTER'S COLLEGE
C-5

Santa Clarita, CA 91321

(805) 259-3540

(800) 568-6248 (out-of-state)

Full-time: 330 men, 371 women	Faculty: 46
Part-time: 31 men, 41 women	Ph.D.s: 34%
Graduate: none	Student/Faculty: 15 to 1
Year: semesters, summer session	Tuition: $8344
Application Deadline: August 1	Room & Board: $4472
Freshman Class: 339 applied, 298 accepted, 160 enrolled	
SAT I Verbal/Math: 449/474	ACT: 21 COMPETITIVE

Master's College, founded in 1927, is a private, coeducational, non-denominational Christian liberal arts college. The library contains 150,000 volumes, 1500 microform items, and 3000 audiovisual forms, and subscribes to 452 periodicals. Special learning facilities include a learning resource center. The 110-acre campus is in a rural area 35 miles north of Los Angeles. Including residence halls, there are 26 buildings on campus.

Student Life: About 70% of undergraduates are from California. Students come from 37 states, 11 foreign countries, and Canada. Sixty-nine percent are from public schools; 31% from private. Ninety percent are white. All are Protestant. The average age of freshmen is 18; all undergraduates, 22. Fifteen percent drop out by the end of their first year; 32% remain to graduate.

Housing: A total of 548 students can be accommodated in college housing. College-sponsored living facilities include single-sex dormitories and off-campus apartments. On-campus housing is guaranteed for the freshman year only and is available on a first-come, first-served basis. Seventy percent of students live on campus; of those, 95% remain on campus on weekends. Alcohol is not permitted. All students may keep cars on campus.

Activities: There are no fraternities or sororities on campus. There are some groups on campus, including cheerleading, choir, chorale, drama, pep band, religious, student government, and yearbook. Popular campus events include homecoming, College View Weekend, Community Day, and Mission Conference.

Sports: There are 3 intercollegiate sports for men and 2 for women, and 9 intramural sports each for men and women. Athletic and recreation facilities include a gymnasium, a sports field, tennis and volleyball courts, a swimming pool, and a fitness center.

Disabled Students: All of the campus is accessible to disabled students. The following facilities are available: wheelchair ramps, special parking, specially equipped rest rooms, and lowered drinking fountains and telephones.

Services: In addition to many counseling and information services, tutoring is available in most subjects.

Campus Safety and Security: Campus safety and security measures include 24-hour foot and vehicle patrol and lighted pathways and sidewalks.

Programs of Study: TMC awards the B.A. and B.S. degrees. Bachelor's degrees are awarded in BIOLOGICAL SCIENCE (biology/biological science), BUSINESS (business administration and management), COMMUNICATIONS AND THE ARTS (communications), COMPUTER AND PHYSICAL SCIENCE (mathematics), EDUCATION (elementary and secondary), SOCIAL SCIENCE (history and political science/government). Biological sciences, biblical studies, and business administration are the strongest programs academically. Biblical studies, education, and business administration have the largest enrollments.

Required: Students must complete at least 122 semester hours, including 85 distributed as follows: 27 hours in Bible studies, 20 in social sciences, 9 each in English and natural science, 8 in foreign languages, 3 each in communication and logical reasoning, and 2 in fine arts. Students must complete at least 40 semester hours in upper division courses and in the major and must maintain a minimum GPA of 2.0.

Special: Students may participate in a co-op program with the College of the Canyon and in internships with local churches, radio stations, and newspapers. A general studies degree is available. A one-year certificate Bible program called the Master's Institute is offered.

Faculty/Classroom: Eighty-three percent of faculty are male; 17%, female. All teach undergraduates. The average class size in an introductory lecture is 75; in a laboratory, 20; and in a regular course offering, 20.

Admissions: About 90% of the 1993-94 applicants were accepted. The SAT scores for the freshman class were as follows: Verbal—68% below 500, 23% between 500 and 599, and 9% between 600 and 700; Math—59% below 500, 30% between 500 and 599, 10% between 600 and 700, and 1% above 700. The ACT scores were 25% below 21, 28% between 21 and 23, 27% between 24 and 26, 15% between 27 and 28, and 5% above 28. About 45% of the current freshmen were in the top fifth of their class; 70% were in the top two fifths. There was 1 National Merit finalist. One freshman graduated first in their class.

Requirements: TMC requires applicants to be in the upper 25% of their class. A minimum GPA of 2.5 is required. The SAT I or ACT is required. Applicants must have completed 3 years each in English and mathematics, 2 years each of a foreign language, history, and science, and 8 units of electives. AP and CLEP credits are accepted. Important factors used in the admissions decision are personality, intangible qualities, recommendations by school officials, recommendations by alumni, ability to finance college education, and leadership record.

Procedure: Freshmen are admitted fall and spring. Entrance exams should be taken in the fall. Applications should be filed by August 1 for fall entry and January 2 for spring entry, along with an application fee of $25. Notification is sent on a rolling basis. There is a deferred admissions plan.

Transfer: About 107 transfer students enrolled in a recent year. Applicants must meet freshman requirements. A maximum of 70 units can be transferred. A total of 24 credits out of 122 must be completed at TMC.

Visiting: There are regularly scheduled orientations for prospective students. There are guides for informal visits, and visitors may sit in on classes and stay overnight at the school. To arrange for a visit, contact the Admissions Office at (800) 568-6248.

Financial Aid: In a recent year, 44% of all current freshmen and 91% of continuing students received some form of financial aid. About 35% of freshmen and 55% of continuing students received need-based aid. The average freshman award was $4852. Of that total, scholarships or need-based grants averaged $3300 ($6760 maximum); and loans averaged $1552 ($4125 maximum). Twenty-four percent of undergraduate students work part-time. Average earnings from campus work for the school year are $1050. The average financial indebtedness of an earlier graduate was $4500. TMC is a member of CSS. The FAF, the college's own financial statement, the SAAC, and the FAFSA are required. The deadline for financial aid applications is August 1.

International Students: There are currently 19 international students enrolled. The school actively recruits these students. They must take the TOEFL and achieve a minimum score of 475.

Computers: The college provides computer facilities for student use. Computer access is available in the library, business center, and mathematics laboratory. All students may access the system during specified times. There are no time limits on using the system. The fees are $20 per semester.

Graduates: In a recent year, 157 bachelor's degrees were awarded. The most popular majors among graduates were Biblical studies (24%), liberal studies (education) (17%), and business administration (11%). Within an average freshman class, 1% graduate in 3 years and 32% in 4 years. Some 20 companies recruited on campus.

Admissions Contact: Don Gilmore, Director of Admissions.

MENLO COLLEGE
B-3

Atherton, CA 94025

(415) 688-3753; (800) 556-3656 (in-state)

Full-time: 354 men, 204 women	Faculty: 33; IIB, +$
Part-time: 4 men, 6 women	Ph.D.s: 53%
Graduate: none	Student/Faculty: 17 to 1
Year: semesters, summer session	Tuition: $14,175
Application Deadline: August 1	Room & Board: $6200
Freshman Class: 315 applied, 275 accepted, 115 enrolled	
SAT I Verbal/Math: 450/380	ACT: 19 LESS COMPETITIVE

Menlo College, founded in 1927, is a private college offering pre-professional programs in the liberal arts. The library contains 60,400 volumes, 674 microform items, and 325 audiovisual forms, and subscribes to 742 periodicals. Special learning facilities include a learning resource center, radio station, TV station, a photo laboratory, a newspaper production facility, and an observation room for the psychology program. The 62-acre campus is in a suburban area 30 miles south of San Francisco. Including residence halls, there are 16 buildings on campus.

Student Life: About 63% of undergraduates are from California. Students come from 21 states, 29 foreign countries, and Canada. Sixty percent are from public schools; 40% from private. Seventy-four percent are white; 15% are foreign nationals. The average age of freshmen is 19; all undergraduates, 20. Twenty-five percent drop out by the end of their first year; 66% remain to graduate.

Housing: A total of 400 students can be accommodated in college housing. College-sponsored living facilities include single-sex and coed dormitories and on-campus apartments. On-campus housing is guaranteed for all 4 years. Sixty-two percent of students live on campus; of those, 55% remain on campus on weekends. All students may keep cars on campus.

Activities: About 5% of men belong to 2 local fraternities. There are no sororities on campus. There are 40 groups on campus, including computers, drama, ethnic, honors, international, newspaper, professional, radio and TV, social, social service, student government, and yearbook. Popular campus events include Spring Fest, SBA Day,

Communication Career Day, Homecoming, Leadership Symposium, and Alumni Reception.

Sports: There are 9 intercollegiate sports for men and 5 for women, and 4 intramural sports for men and 4 for women. Athletic and recreation facilities include 2 swimming pools, a soccer field, tennis courts, a track, and a 600-seat gymnasium. The campus stadium seats 1000, the largest auditorium/arena, 220.

Disabled Students: Ninety-five percent of the campus is accessible to disabled students. The following facilities are available: wheelchair ramps, elevators, special parking, specially equipped rest rooms, lowered drinking fountains, and lowered telephones.

Services: In addition to many counseling and information services, tutoring is available in every subject. There is also a reader service for the blind.

Campus Safety and Security: Campus safety and security measures include 24-hour foot and vehicle patrol, informal discussions, and lighted pathways and sidewalks.

Programs of Study: Menlo awards the B.A. and B.S. degrees. Associate degrees also are awarded. Bachelor's degrees are awarded in BIOLOGICAL SCIENCE (biology/biological science and biotechnology), BUSINESS (banking and finance, business administration and management, human resource management, international business management, and marketing management), COMMUNICATIONS AND THE ARTS (advertising, broadcasting, mass communications, journalism, and media arts), COMPUTER AND PHYSICAL SCIENCE (computer programming and computer science), HEALTH PROFESSIONS (premedicine), SOCIAL SCIENCE (history, humanities, philosophy, and psychology). Biotechnology management, business administration, mass communications, computer science, psychology, and human resource management are the strongest academically. Business administration and mass communications have the largest enrollments.

Required: All students must complete 55 to 57 units in the core curriculum, including 12 to 14 of humanities, 8 each of laboratory science and Western culture, 6 to 11 of English, 4 of quantitative skills, 3 to 4 of critical thinking and problem-solving, 3 each of American institutions and computer competency, and 2 of physical education. A total of 124 units, including 30 in the major, and a minimum 2.0 GPA are required to graduate.

Special: Students may earn 3 to 15 credits through internships. Students may study abroad in India, France, Morocco, Egypt, South America, Italy, Greece, and Germany. The college also offers dual majors, B.A.-B.S. degrees, and pass/fail options. There are 2 national honor societies on campus.

Faculty/Classroom: Sixty-five percent of faculty are male; 35%, female. All teach undergraduates. The average class size in an introductory lecture is 23; in a laboratory, 27; and in a regular course offering, 16.

Admissions: About 87% of the 1993-94 applicants were accepted. The SAT scores for the 1993-94 freshman class were as follows: Verbal—70% below 500, 24% between 500 and 599, 3% between 600 and 700, and 3% above 700; Math—77% below 500, 18% between 500 and 599, 4% between 600 and 700, and 1% above 700. The ACT scores were 93% below 21, 4% between 21 and 23, 2% between 24 and 26, and 1% between 27 and 28. About 5% of the current freshmen were in the top fifth of their class; 35% were in the top two fifths.

Requirements: The SAT I or ACT is required. In addition, a personal essay and letter of recommendation should be submitted. The GED is accepted. AP and CLEP credits are accepted. Important factors used in the admissions decision are advanced placement or honor courses, evidence of special talent, leadership record, personality, intangible qualities, and recommendations by school officials.

Procedure: Freshmen are admitted to all sessions. Entrance exams should be taken during the junior or senior year. Applications should be filed by August 1 for fall entry and December 1 for spring entry, along with an application fee of $40. Notification is sent on a rolling basis. There are early admissions and deferred admissions plans.

Transfer: About 90 transfer students enrolled in 1993-94. Transfer applicants must show potential for success at the college level. Those with fewer than 24 credits must meet freshman requirements. A total of 30 credits out of 124 must be completed at Menlo.

Visiting: There are regularly scheduled orientations for prospective students, including a fall preview with an introduction to college life and college decision making. The Spring visit for accepted students provides an in-depth view of Menlo. There are guides for informal visits and visitors may sit in on classes and stay overnight at the school. To arrange for a visit, contact the Office of Admissions at (415) 688-3753 or (800) 556-3656 (in-state).

Financial Aid: In 1993-94, 47% of all current freshmen and 43% of continuing students received some form of financial aid. About 47% of freshmen and 43% of continuing students received need-based aid. The average freshman award was $12,500. Of that total, scholarships or need-based grants averaged $7800 ($10,972 maximum); loans averaged $2000 ($2625 maximum); and work contracts

averaged $1500. Forty percent of undergraduate students work part-time. Average earnings from campus work for the school year are $1000. The average financial indebtedness of the 1992-93 graduate was $9250. Menlo is a member of CSS. The FAF and the FAFSA are required. The deadline for financial aid applications is March 2.

International Students: There are currently 80 international students enrolled. The school actively recruits these students. They must take the TOEFL and achieve a minimum score of 550 or take ELS 109.

Computers: The college provides computer facilities for student use. The mainframes are an HP 3000/Series 44 and an HP 9000/Series 300. There are 56 HP PCs and 10 Apple Macintosh microcomputers located in academic buildings. All students may access the system. It may be used 8 A.M. to 11 P.M. daily. There are no time limits on using the system and no fees.

Graduates: In an earlier class, 116 bachelor's degrees were awarded and 50 companies recruited on campus.

Admissions Contact: Debra Sanborn, Director of Admission.

MILLS COLLEGE
Oakland, CA 94613

B-3

(510) 430-2135; (800) 876-4557

Full-time: 776 women	Faculty: 74; IIA, av$
Part-time: 52 women	Ph.D.s: 73%
Graduate: 55 men, 258 women	Student/Faculty: 10 to 1
Year: semesters	Tuition: $14,848
Application Deadline: February 1	Room & Board: $6000
Freshman Class: 830 applied, 724 accepted, 306 enrolled	
SAT I Verbal/Math: 540/530	ACT: 25 VERY COMPETITIVE

Mills College, founded in 1852, is a private women's college offering instruction in liberal and fine arts, sciences, and teacher preparation. There is one undergraduate and one graduate school. The library contains 206,555 volumes, 7657 microform items, and 5017 audiovisual forms, and subscribes to 683 periodicals. Computerized library sources and services include the card catalog, interlibrary loans, and database searching. Special learning facilities include an art gallery, a children's school, a small book press, an electronic/computer music studio, a botanical garden, and a computer learning studio. The 135-acre campus is in an urban area 12 miles east of San Francisco. Including residence halls, there are 84 buildings on campus.

Student Life: About 79% of undergraduates are from California. Students come from 39 states, 20 foreign countries, and Canada. Eighty percent are from public schools; 20% from private. Sixty-nine percent are white; 14% Asian American. The average age of freshmen is 18.8; all undergraduates, 22.4. Twenty percent drop out by the end of their first year; 60% remain to graduate.

Housing: A total of 780 students can be accommodated in college housing. College-sponsored living facilities include single-sex and coed dormitories, on-campus apartments, and married-student housing. In addition, there are language houses and special interest houses. Married-student housing is offered on an equal basis to domestic partners of lesbian and gay students, and a student co-op house is available for juniors and seniors. On-campus housing is guaranteed for all 4 years. Fifty-eight percent of students live on campus; of those, 75% remain on campus on weekends. All students may keep cars on campus.

Activities: There are no fraternities or sororities on campus. There are 40 groups on campus, including art, band, choir, chorale, chorus, dance, drama, ethnic, gay, honors, international, literary magazine, musical theater, newspaper, political, professional, religious, social, social service, student government, and yearbook. Popular campus events include Women's and Black History Months, Boat Dance, Black and White Ball, Springfest, Fine Arts Festival, Eucalyptus Festival, Family Weekend, and Powwow.

Sports: There are intercollegiate amd intramural sports. Athletic and recreation facilities include an 872-seat gymnasium, a weight room/fitness center, athletic fields, a pool, and 6 tennis courts.

Disabled Students: Ninety percent of the campus is accessible to disabled students. The following facilities are available: wheelchair ramps, elevators, special parking, specially equipped rest rooms, special class scheduling, lowered telephones, and dorm housing.

Services: In addition to many counseling and information services, tutoring is available in every subject. There is a reader service for the blind.

Campus Safety and Security: Campus safety and security measures include 24-hour foot and vehicle patrol, self defense education, escort service, and shuttle buses. In addition, there are informal discussions, pamphlets, posters, and films, emergency telephones, and lighted pathways and sidewalks.

Programs of Study: Mills awards the B.A. degree. Master's degrees also are awarded. Bachelor's degrees are awarded in BIOLOGICAL SCIENCE (biochemistry and biology/biological science), BUSINESS (business economics), COMMUNICATIONS AND THE ARTS (art history and appreciation, communications, comparative literature, creative writing, dance, dramatic arts, English, French, German, music,

and studio art), COMPUTER AND PHYSICAL SCIENCE (chemistry, computer science, and mathematics), EDUCATION (early childhood), SOCIAL SCIENCE (American studies, anthropology, child psychology/development, economics, ethnic studies, Hispanic American studies, history, international relations, philosophy, political science/government, prelaw, psychology, sociology, and women's studies). Art, biology, computer science, dance, and music are the strongest academically. Communications, political, legal, and economic analysis, English, and psychology have the largest enrollments.

Required: All students must fulfill an English writing requirement and a core curriculum of a first-year seminar, a 2-semester sophomore course, and a cross-cultural course. Distribution requirements include 2 courses in each of 4 curricular areas. A total of 34 semester course credits is required, with 10 to 17 of them in the major. The minimum GPA is 2.0.

Special: There is cross-registration with the University of California/Berkeley and California State University, among others. The college offers co-op programs, internships, study abroad, a Washington semester, work-study programs, dual, student-designed, and interdisciplinary majors, including political, legal, and economic analysis, an accelerated degree program, a general studies degree, a 3-2 engineering program, joint master's programs in computer science and statistics with Stanford University, credit by examination, and pass/fail options. There is a freshman honors program on campus, as well as a chapter of Phi Beta Kappa.

Faculty/Classroom: Thirty-seven percent of faculty are male; 63%, female. All both teach and do research. No introductory courses are taught by graduate students. The average class size in a regular course offering is 14.

Admissions: About 87% of the 1993-94 applicants were accepted. The SAT scores for the 1993-94 freshman class were as follows: Verbal—33% below 500, 38% between 500 and 599, 25% between 600 and 700, and 3% above 700; Math—31% below 500, 40% between 500 and 599, 23% between 600 and 700, and 6% above 700. The ACT scores were 11% below 21, 30% between 21 and 23, 21% between 24 and 26, 10% between 27 and 28, and 28% above 28. About 55% of the current freshmen were in the top fifth of their class; 75% were in the top two fifths.

Requirements: Mills requires applicants to be in the upper 50% of their class. A minimum GPA of 3.0 is required. The SAT I or ACT is required. SAT II: Subject tests are recommended. Applicants should graduate from an accredited secondary school or have a GED. An essay is required; an interview, recommended. AP credits are accepted. Important factors used in the admissions decision are advanced placement or honor courses, personality, intangible qualities, recommendations by school officials, extracurricular activities record, and parents or siblings attending the school.

Procedure: Freshmen are admitted to all sessions. Entrance exams should be taken no later than 1 month prior to application. Applications should be filed by February 1 for fall entry and November 1 for spring entry, along with an application fee of $35. Notification is sent on a rolling basis. There is an early admissions plan.

Transfer: About 174 transfer students enrolled in 1993-94. Transfer applicants with fewer than 12 credits should take the SAT I or ACT. A total of 12 semester course credits out of 34 must be completed at Mills.

Visiting: There are regularly scheduled orientations for prospective students, consisting of class visits, campus tours, lunch with faculty, financial aid workshops, admissions interview, and an overnight stay. There are guides for informal visits, and visitors may sit in on classes and stay overnight at the school. To arrange for a visit, contact the Admissions Office at (510) 430-2135 or (800) 876-4557.

Financial Aid: In 1993-94 72% of all current freshmen and 70% of continuing students received some form of financial aid. About 72% of freshmen and 69% of continuing students received need-based aid. The average freshman award was $13,789. Of that total, scholarships or need-based grants averaged $7543 ($14,900 maximum); loans averaged $2420 ($2925 maximum); and work contracts averaged $1515 ($2000 maximum). Sixty-five percent of undergraduate students work part-time. Average earnings from campus work for the school year are $1800. The average financial indebtedness of the 1992-93 graduate was $10,004. Mills is a member of CSS. The FAF and the college's own financial statement are required. The deadline for financial aid applications is February 15.

International Students: There are currently 57 international students enrolled. The school actively recruits these students. They must take the TOEFL and achieve a minimum score of 550. The student must also take the SAT I.

Computers: The college provides computer facilities for student use. The mainframe is a DEC VAX 11/780. The college has 80 microcomputers available to students, 85% of which are networked, in addition to 37 LAN terminals. These workstations include about 12 NeXT computers. Microcomputers or terminals are located in the library, several laboratories, dormitories, and student lounges. Internet WAN is used. All students may access the system. It may be used 24 hours a day,

year-round. There are no time limits on using the system and no fees. It is recommended that students in computer science and book arts have personal computers, preferably an Apple Macintosh.

Graduates: In 1992-93 213 bachelor's degrees were awarded. The most popular majors among graduates were political, legal, and economic analysis (14%), communication (10%), and psychology (8%). Within an average freshman class, 2% graduate in 3 years, 58% in 4 years, 62% in 5 years, and 64% in 6 years. Some 15 companies recruited on campus in 1992-93.

Admissions Contact: Gene Ann Flaherty, Dean of Admission.

MOUNT SAINT MARY'S COLLEGE C-5
Los Angeles, CA 90049 (310) 471-9516
(800) 999-9893 (out-of-state)

Full-time: 18 men, 940 women	**Faculty:** 50; IIB, av$
Part-time: 22 men, 176 women	**Ph.D.s:** 79%
Graduate: 102 men, 233 women	**Student/Faculty:** 19 to 1
Year: semesters	**Tuition:** $11,690
Application Deadline: March 1	**Room & Board:** $4700
Freshman Class: 366 applied, 257 accepted, 116 enrolled	
ACT: 21	**VERY COMPETITIVE**

Mount Saint Mary's College, founded in 1925 and affiliated with the Catholic Church, is a private, primarily women's institution that offers programs in the liberal arts and sciences. There is one graduate school. In addition to regional accreditation, the Mount has baccalaureate program accreditation with NASM and NLN. The library contains 132,000 volumes, 318 microform items, and 2522 audiovisual forms and subscribes to 690 periodicals. Special learning facilities include a learning resource center and art gallery. The 72-acre campus is in an urban area 10 miles west of Los Angeles. Including residence halls, there are 26 buildings on campus.

Student Life: About 86% of undergraduates are from California. Students come from 21 states and 5 foreign countries. Seventy-six percent are from public schools; 24% from private. Thirty-eight percent are white; 35% Hispanic; 16% Asian American. Sixty percent are Catholic; 27% claim no religious affiliation. The average age of freshmen is 18; all undergraduates, 21. Nineteen percent drop out by the end of their first year; 68% remain to graduate.

Housing: A total of 350 students can be accommodated in college housing. College-sponsored living facilities include single-sex dormitories. On-campus housing is guaranteed for all 4 years. Priority is given to out-of-town students. Fifty percent of students live on campus; of those, 50% remain on campus on weekends. All students may keep cars on campus.

Activities: About 6% of women belong to 1 local sorority. There are no fraternities on campus. There are 23 groups on campus, including choir, chorale, chorus, computers, dance, drama, ethnic, honors, musical theater, newspaper, political, professional, religious, social, social service, student government, and yearbook. Popular campus events include Mary's Day (honors and awards), Horizon's Day, Spring Sing, Athenian Day, and Siena Day.

Sports: There are 3 intercollegiate sports for women and 4 intramural sports for women. Athletic and recreation facilities include a pool, tennis courts, exercise and weight rooms, and cardiovascular equipment.

Disabled Students: Elevators and special parking are available.

Services: In addition to many counseling and information services, tutoring is available in most subjects, and a peer tutoring program is available.

Campus Safety and Security: Campus safety and security measures include 24-hour foot and vehicle patrol, self defense education, shuttle buses, and informal discussions. In addition, there are pamphlets, posters, films, and lighted pathways and sidewalks.

Programs of Study: The Mount awards the B.A., B.S., and B.A.M. degrees. Associate and master's degrees also are awarded. Bachelor's degrees are awarded in BIOLOGICAL SCIENCE (biochemistry and biology/biological science), BUSINESS (accounting, business administration and management, international business management, and marketing/retailing/merchandising), COMMUNICATIONS AND THE ARTS (English, French, music, and Spanish), COMPUTER AND PHYSICAL SCIENCE (chemistry and mathematics), EDUCATION (art, elementary, foreign languages, music, science, and secondary), HEALTH PROFESSIONS (health science, nursing, and premedicine), SOCIAL SCIENCE (American studies, history, philosophy, political science/government, prelaw, psychology, religion, and sociology). Premedicine is the strongest academically. Nursing and business have the largest enrollments.

Required: Requirements for graduation include completion of 59 units of distribution requirements and 124 total credit hours, with the number of hours in the major varying by department. English courses and a minimum 2.0 GPA are required.

Special: The Mount offers cross-registration with UCLA, internships within the Business Department, study abroad in Spain, England, and France, a Washington semester, the B.A.-B.S. degree in business,

dual and student-designed majors, credit for prior experience, and pass/fail options. There is a freshman honors program on campus, as well as 11 national honor societies. Nine departments have honors programs.

Faculty/Classroom: Twenty-five percent of faculty are male; 75%, female. All teach undergraduates. No introductory courses are taught by graduate students. The average class size in an introductory lecture is 20; in a laboratory, 20; and in a regular course offering, 19.

Admissions: About 70% of the 1993–94 applicants were accepted. The SAT scores for the 1993–94 freshman class were as follows: Verbal—64% below 500, 26% between 500 and 599, 9% between 600 and 700, and 1% above 700; Math—46% below 500, 39% between 500 and 599, 10% between 600 and 700, and 4% above 700. About 70% of the current freshmen were in the top fifth of their class; 90% were in the top two fifths.

Requirements: The SAT I or ACT is required. Applicants must be graduates of an accredited secondary school or have earned the GED, with 16 academic credits and 16 Carnegie units, including 4 years of English literature and composition, 2 or 3 years each of mathematics, science, and social studies, and 1 or 2 years of history. An essay is required, and an interview is recommended. AP and CLEP credits are accepted. Important factors used in the admissions decision are recommendations by school officials, recommendations by alumni, personality, intangible qualities, advanced placement or honor courses, and parents or siblings attending the school.

Procedure: Freshmen are admitted in the fall. Entrance exams should be taken at the end of junior year or the beginning of senior year. Applications should be filed by March 1 for fall entry, along with an application fee of $30. Notification is sent on a rolling basis.

Transfer: About 116 transfer students enrolled in 1993–94. Transfer students must have a minimum 2.25 GPA with at least 24 completed credit hours. A total of 30 credits out of 124 must be completed at the Mount.

Visiting: There are regularly scheduled orientations for prospective students, including workshops, student panels, tours, class visitations, and faculty presentations. There are guides for informal visits and visitors may sit in on classes. To arrange for a visit, contact the Admissions Office at (800) 999–9893.

Financial Aid: In 1993–94 86% of all current freshmen received some form of financial aid. About 80% of freshmen received need-based aid. The average freshman award was $13,000. Of that total, scholarships or need-based grants averaged $7456; and loans averaged $2625. Forty-five percent of undergraduate students work part-time. Average earnings from campus work for the school year are $1800. The average financial indebtedness of the 1992–93 graduate was $15,000. The Mount is a member of CSS. The FAF and the FAFSA are required. The deadline for financial aid applications is March 2.

International Students: There are currently 30 international students enrolled. They must take the TOEFL and achieve a minimum score of 500.

Computers: The college provides computer facilities for student use. The mainframe is a Sequent S27. There are 20 terminals available for WordPerfect word processing, database use, and computer programming, and 40 PCs are available in the library. All students may access the system during regular working hours, 4 nights per week, and from 3 P.M. to 11 P.M. on Sunday. There are no time limits on using the system and no fees.

Graduates: In 1992–93 208 bachelor's degrees were awarded. The most popular majors among graduates were nursing (20%), premedicine (19%), and business (18%). Within an average freshman class, 66% graduate in 5 years. In the 1992 graduating class, 65% of the women were enrolled in graduate school within 6 months of graduation; 92% of the women had found employment.

Admissions Contact: Katy Murphy, Executive Director of Admissions and Financial Aid.

NATIONAL UNIVERSITY

D-5

San Diego, CA 92108–4107   (619) 563–7100; (800) NAT-UNIV

Full-time: 861 men, 786 women	Faculty: 69; IIA, --$
Part-time: 1179 men, 1066 women	Ph.D.s: 79%
Graduate: 2257 men, 2942 women	Student/Faculty: 24 to 1
Year: see profile	Tuition: $6135
Application Deadline: open	Room & Board: n/app
Freshman Class: n/av	
SAT I or ACT: not required	COMPETITIVE

National University, founded in 1971, is a private, coeducational commuter institution offering curricula in liberal arts, business, engineering, education, and aviation. The various undergraduate programs, primarily for career-oriented working adults, are offered at several locations. In California, campuses are located in San Diego (the main campus), Vista, Irvine, Sacramento, Fresno, San Jose, Oakland, and Los Angeles. There is also a campus in San Jose, Costa Rica. There are 4 undergraduate and 5 graduate schools. The 2 libraries contain 162,413 volumes, 1,266,660 microform items, and 100 audiovisual forms, and subscribe to 5825 periodicals. Computerized library sources and services include the card catalog, interlibrary loans, and database searching. Special learning facilities include a learning resource center. The 15-acre campus is in an urban area 3 miles northeast of downtown San Diego. There are 8 buildings on campus.

Student Life: Students come from 64 foreign countries and Canada. Seventy percent are white. The average age of freshmen is 29; all undergraduates, 31. Forty-nine percent drop out by the end of their first year.

Housing: There are no residence halls; all students commute. Alcohol is not permitted. All students may keep cars on campus.

Activities: There is 1 national fraternity and no sororities on campus.

Sports: There is no sports program at National.

Disabled Students: Ninety-five percent of the campus is accessible to disabled students. The following facilities are available: wheelchair ramps, elevators, special parking, specially equipped rest rooms, special class scheduling, and lowered telephones.

Services: In addition to many counseling and information services, tutoring is available in most subjects, including social sciences, economics, finance, accounting, taxation, and natural sciences. There is remedial math, reading, and writing.

Campus Safety and Security: Campus safety and security measures include 24-hour foot and vehicle patrol and lighted pathways and sidewalks.

Programs of Study: National awards the B.A., B.S., B.A.I.S., B.B.A., B.S.L. and B.T.E. degrees. Associate, master's, and doctoral degrees are also awarded. Bachelor's degrees are awarded in BUSINESS (accounting, banking and finance, business administration and management, human resources, and marketing and distribution), COMPUTER AND PHYSICAL SCIENCE (computer science and mathematics), EDUCATION (technical and vocational), ENGINEERING AND ENVIRONMENTAL DESIGN (manufacturing engineering), SOCIAL SCIENCE (behavioral science, criminal justice, interdisciplinary studies, prelaw, psychology, safety and security technology, and safety management). Computer science, accounting, and law are the strongest academically. Business and computer science have the largest enrollments.

Required: To graduate, students must complete a total of 180 quarter hours with a minimum GPA of 2.0. A minimum of 45 hours in the major and 70 hours in general education is required.

Special: National offers students a 12-month academic year, during which courses lasting 1 month each meet 2 nights a week plus a full Saturday.

Faculty/Classroom: Sixty-seven percent of faculty are male; 33%, female. All teach undergraduates. No introductory courses are taught by graduate students. The average class size in an introductory lecture is 20 and in a regular course offering, 22.

Requirements: A minimum GPA of 2.0 is required. Graduation from an accredited secondary school or satisfactory scores on the GED are required for admission. Applicants are generally expected to have 5 or more years of successful work experience. National requires an interview and a writing sample. AP and CLEP credits are accepted. Important factors used in the admissions decision are leadership record, evidence of special talent, advanced placement or honor courses, and ability to finance college education.

Procedure: Freshmen are admitted to all sessions. Application deadlines are open. Application fee is $60. Notification is sent on a rolling basis. There is a deferred admissions plan.

Transfer: Transfer applicants must have a minimum GPA of 2.0. Transcripts from all previous institutions attended must be submitted. A total of 45 quarter hours out of 180 must be completed at National.

Visiting: There are guides for informal visits and visitors may sit in on classes. To arrange for a visit, contact the Assistant Director of Admissions at (619) 563–7100 or (800) NAT-UNIV.

Financial Aid: In an earlier year, 35% of all students received some form of financial aid. About 35% of freshmen and 40% of continuing students received need-based aid. The average freshman award was $8000. Of that total, scholarships or need-based grants averaged $1000 ($9400 maximum); loans averaged $5000 ($8000 maximum); and work contracts averaged $2000 ($10,000 maximum). Two percent of undergraduate students work part-time. Average earnings from campus work for the school year are $2000. The average financial indebtedness of the recent graduate was $4000. National is a member of CSS. The FAF is required.

International Students: Students must take the TOEFL (and achieve a minimum score of 525) or the University of Michigan Language Test.

Computers: The college provides computer facilities for student use. The mainframe is an IBM 3081-GX. Students have access to National's microcomputer laboratories. All students may access the system. It may be used Monday through Friday, 8 A.M. to 9 P.M., and Saturday, 8 A.M. to 2 P.M. There are no time limits on using the system and no fees.

Graduates: In a recent year, 1444 bachelor's degrees were awarded. The most popular majors among graduates were business and management (52%), computer and information science (15%), and psychology (9%). Some 120 companies recruited on campus that year.

Admissions Contact: Admissions Office.

NEW COLLEGE OF CALIFORNIA

B-3

San Francisco, CA 94110   (415) 626-0884

Full-time: 600 men and women	Faculty: 14
Part-time: 300 men and women	Ph.D.s: 50%
Graduate: none	Student/Faculty: 43 to 1
Year: semesters, summer session	Tuition: $6900
Application Deadline: September 1	Room & Board: n/app
Freshman Class: n/av	
SAT I or ACT: not required	NONCOMPETITIVE

New College of California, founded in 1971, is a private college offering a liberal arts program. There are 3 graduate schools. The library contains 30,000 volumes. Computerized library sources and services include the card catalog, interlibrary loans, and database searching. Special learning facilities include a learning resource center, a video-editing lab, and a theater. The 2-acre campus is in an urban area. There are 3 buildings on campus.

Student Life: About 70% of undergraduates are from California. Students come from 10 states, 5 foreign countries, and Canada. Eighty percent are from public schools; 20% from private. Sixty-one percent are white; 16% African American; 10% Hispanic. The average age of freshmen is 25; all undergraduates, 28. Thirty percent drop out by the end of their first year; 70% remain to graduate.

Housing: There are no residence halls; all students commute. Alcohol is not permitted.

Activities: There are no fraternities or sororities on campus. There are 10 groups on campus, including band, drama, ethnic, gay, literary magazine, newspaper, political, professional, social, social service, student government, and women's. Popular campus events include an arts and social change showcase.

Disabled Students: Sixty percent of the campus is accessible to disabled students. The following facilities are available: wheelchair ramps, specially equipped rest rooms, and special class scheduling.

Services: Remedial math, reading, and writing are available.

Campus Safety and Security: Campus safety and security measures include front desk security in all buildings.

Programs of Study: New College awards the B.A. degree. Master's degrees are also awarded. Bachelor's degrees are awarded in COMMUNICATIONS AND THE ARTS (dramatic arts, English, film arts, fine arts, music, and Spanish), SOCIAL SCIENCE (anthropology, political science/government, psychology, and social science). Humanities is the strongest academically Humanities and has the largest enrollment.

Required: To graduate, students must complete at least 120 credit hours, including 30 in the major. Requirements include 6 units of core humanities and 3 units each of arts, literature or writing, social sciences, scientific reasoning, quantitative reasoning, research methods, a practicum, and a senior project. A minimum GPA of 2.0 is required.

Special: Internships include a required 3-unit practicum on or off campus. New College offers work-study programs, independent study, study abroad in Mexico and Nepal, an accelerated degree program, student-designed majors, and pass/fail options. Students can earn up to 30 units of credit for prior life, military, and work experience.

Faculty/Classroom: Sixty percent of faculty are male; 40%, female. All teach undergraduates. The average class size in an introductory lecture is 12; in a laboratory, 10; and in a regular course offering, 12.

Requirements: The SAT I or ACT is not required. New College requires graduation from an accredited secondary school; the GED is also accepted. An essay is required. AP and CLEP credits are accepted. Personality and other intangible qualities are important factors used in the admission decision.

Procedure: Freshmen are admitted fall and spring. Applications should be filed by September 1 for fall entry, January 1 for winter entry, and May 1 for spring entry, along with an application fee of $25. The college accepts all applicants. Notification is sent on a rolling basis. There is a deferred admissions plan.

Transfer: About 75 transfer students enrolled in 1993-94. A total of 30 credits out of 120 must be completed at New College.

Visiting: There are regularly scheduled orientations for prospective students, consisting of monthly open houses. There are guides for informal visits and visitors may sit in on classes. To arrange for a visit, contact the Admissions Coordinator at (415) 626-0884.

Financial Aid: In an earlier year, 80% of all students received need-based aid. The average freshman award was $4500. Of that total, scholarships or need-based grants averaged $2300; loans averaged $2000; and work contracts averaged $1000. Eighty-five percent of undergraduate students work part-time. Average earnings from campus work for the school year are $3500. The average financial indebtedness of the 1992-93 graduate was $2000. New College is a member of CSS. The FAF, FFS or SFS and the college's own financial statement are required. The deadline for financial aid applications is September 1.

International Students: There are currently 10 international students enrolled. They must take the TOEFL and achieve a minimum score of 500.

Computers: The college provides computer facilities for student use. The mainframe is a Prime unit. Terminals are located in the library. IBM PCs and Apple Macintosh microcomputers are available for word processing and layout/design. All students may access the system. There are no time limits on using the system and no fees.

Graduates: In an earlier year, 50 bachelor's degrees were awarded. Some 25 companies recruited on campus that year.

Admissions Contact: Arlene Biala, Admissions Coordinator.

OCCIDENTAL COLLEGE

C-5

Los Angeles, CA 90041   (213) 259-2700
          (800) 825-5262 (out-of-state)

Full-time: 729 men, 857 women	Faculty: 125; IIB, +$
Part-time: 18 men, 17 women	Ph.D.s: 93%
Graduate: 20 men, 20 women	Student/Faculty: 13 to 1
Year: trimesters, summer session	Tuition: $16,182
Application Deadline: February 1	Room & Board: $5610
Freshman Class: 2324 applied, 1371 accepted, 627 enrolled	
SAT I or ACT: required	HIGHLY COMPETITIVE

Occidental College, founded in 1887, is a nonsectarian, coeducational school of liberal arts and sciences. The library contains 486,000 volumes, 175,000 microform items, and 10,770 audiovisual forms, and subscribes to 2000 periodicals. Computerized library sources and services include the card catalog, interlibrary loans, and database searching. Special learning facilities include a learning resource center, art gallery, radio station, and an ocean-going research vessel, and a small nuclear reactor. The 120-acre campus is in an urban area in Los Angeles. Including residence halls, there are 44 buildings on campus.

Student Life: About 54% of undergraduates are from California. Students come from 45 states and 28 foreign countries. Sixty-six percent are from public schools; 33% from private. Seventy-three percent are white; 12% Asian American. Fifty-five percent are Protestant; 20% Catholic; 10% claim no religious affiliation; 10% Jewish. The average age of freshmen is 18; all undergraduates, 21. Nine percent drop out by the end of their first year; 78% remain to graduate.

Housing: A total of 1250 students can be accommodated in college housing. College-sponsored living facilities include dormitories, fraternity houses, and sorority houses. In addition there are special interest and language floors. On-campus housing is guaranteed for the freshman year only and is available on a lottery system for upperclassmen. Seventy-four percent of students live on campus; of those, 85% remain on campus on weekends. All students may keep cars on campus.

Activities: About 7% of men belong to 4 national fraternities; about 5% of women belong to 3 local sororities. There are 86 groups on campus, including art, cheerleading, chess, choir, chorale, dance, drama, ethnic, film, gay, honors, international, jazz band, literary magazine, musical theater, newspaper, orchestra, pep band, photography, political, professional, radio and TV, religious, social, social service, student government, and yearbook. Popular campus events include Da Getaway, Oxy-Gras, Hawaiian Luau, Cinco de Mayo, and Asian Pacific Heritage Week.

Sports: Athletic and recreation facilities include playing fields, an all-weather track, tennis courts, an outdoor pool, a dance studio, a sports medicine center, gymnasium, and a weight room.

Disabled Students: Eighty percent of the campus is accessible to disabled students. The following facilities are available: wheelchair ramps, elevators, special parking, specially equipped rest rooms, lowered drinking fountains, and lowered telephones.

Services: In addition to many counseling and information services, tutoring is available in most subjects. There is a reader service for the blind and remedial math and writing.

Programs of Study: Occidental awards the B.A. degree, and master's degrees are also awarded. Bachelor's degrees are awarded in BIOLOGICAL SCIENCE (biochemistry and biology/biological science), COMMUNICATIONS AND THE ARTS (art history and appreciation, comparative literature, dramatic arts, French, German, languages, music, and Spanish), COMPUTER AND PHYSICAL SCIENCE (chemistry, geochemistry, geology, geophysics and seismology, mathematics, and physics), EDUCATION (early childhood, elementary, foreign languages, middle school, music, science, secondary, and teaching English as a second language/foreign language), ENGINEERING AND ENVIRONMENTAL DESIGN (electrical/electronics engineering and mechanical engineering), HEALTH PROFESSIONS (predentistry and premedicine), SOCIAL SCIENCE (American studies, anthropology, cognitive science, eco-

nomics, history, international relations, philosophy, physical fitness/movement, political science/government, psychology, religion, sociology, and urban studies). Social sciences, biology, and chemistry are the strongest academically. Social sciences, biology, and English have the largest enrollments.

Required: To graduate, students must complete 35 courses of 4 semester hours or 6 quarter units each, and must maintain a minimum GPA of 2.0. In addition, all students must fulfill core courses in science, mathematics, fine arts, language proficiency, and American, European and world cultures. Proficiency in English can be demonstrated by course work or testing.

Special: Cross-registration is permitted with California Institute of Technology and Art Center College of Design. Cooperative programs are available with Columbia University. Students may study abroad in Europe, Asia, and Latin America. Opportunities are provided for internships, a Washington semester, work-study programs, B.A.-B.S. degrees, dual and student-designed majors, a 3–2 engineering degree, credit by examination, nondegree study, and pass/fail options. There are 9 national honor societies on campus, including Phi Beta Kappa.

Faculty/Classroom: Sixty-five percent of faculty are male; 35%, female. All teach undergraduates and do research. The average class size in a regular course offering is 23.

Admissions: About 59% of the 1993–94 applicants were accepted. The SAT scores for the 1993–94 freshman class were as follows: Verbal—42% below 500, 41% between 500 and 599, 16% between 600 and 700, and 1% above 700; Math—22% below 500, 38% between 500 and 599, 28% between 600 and 700, and 12% above 700. About 75% of the current freshmen were in the top fifth of their class; 92% were in the top two fifths. About 19 freshmen graduated first in their class.

Requirements: The SAT I or ACT is required. Applicants should be high school graduates of high academic standing with 5 years of English, 3 to 4 of mathematics, 3 each of foreign language and social studies, and 1 each of biological and physical science. The GED is accepted. An essay is required, and an interview is recommended. AP credits are accepted. Important factors used in the admissions decision are advanced placement or honor courses, recommendations by school officials, leadership record, extracurricular activities record, and personality, intangible qualities.

Procedure: Freshmen are admitted in the fall. Entrance exams should be taken no later than January of the senior year. Early decision applications should be filed by November 15; regular applications, by February 1 for fall entry, along with an application fee of $30. Notification is sent April 1. There are early decision, early admissions, and deferred admissions plans. About 63 early decision candidates were accepted for the 1993–94 class. A waiting list is an active part of the admissions procedure.

Transfer: About 67 transfer students enrolled in 1993–94. A minimum of a B average (3.0 GPA) is required for all courses submitted for transfer credit. The SAT I or ACT is required. The application deadline is April 15.

Visiting: There are regularly scheduled orientations for prospective students. There are guides for informal visits and visitors may sit in on classes and stay overnight at the school. To arrange for a visit, contact the Office of Admission at (800) 825–5262.

Financial Aid: In an earlier year, 78% of all current freshmen and 72% of continuing students received some form of financial aid. Scholarships or need-based grants averaged $10,509 ($19,059 maximum); loans averaged $1470 ($5125 maximum); and work contracts averaged $693 ($1350 maximum). The average financial indebtedness of a recent graduate was $5917. Occidental is a member of CSS. The FAF and SAAC for California residents is required. The deadline for financial aid applications is February 1.

International Students: There were 63 international students enrolled in an earlier year. The school actively recruits these students. They must take the TOEFL and achieve a minimum score of 600.

Computers: The college provides computer facilities for student use. The mainframe is a Prime 9955 and 6350. Apple and IBM PCs are available in the library's computer center. All students may access the system. It may be used at any time. There are no time limits on using the system and no fees.

Graduates: In an earlier year, 381 bachelor's degrees were awarded. The most popular majors among graduates were social sciences (51%), humanities (27%), and natural sciences (23%). Recently, some 69 companies recruited on campus. In an earlier graduating class, 25% of the men and 22% of the women were enrolled in graduate school within 6 months of graduation; 25% of the men and 28% of the women had found employment.

Admissions Contact: Charlene Liebau, Dean of Admission.

OTIS COLLEGE OF ART AND DESIGN
(Formerly Otis Parsons School of Art and Design)
Los Angeles, CA 90057

C-5

(213) 251–0501
(800) 527–6847 (out-of-state)

Full-time: 243 men, 391 women	**Faculty:** 26
Part-time: 22 men, 70 women	**Ph.D.s:** 98%
Graduate: 12 men, 8 women	**Student/Faculty:** 24 to 1
Year: semesters, summer session	**Tuition:** $12,286
Application Deadline: August 15	**Room & Board:** $4400
Freshman Class: 260 applied, 229 accepted, 156 enrolled	
SAT I Verbal/Math: 500/467	**SPECIAL**

Otis College of Art and Design, founded in 1918, is a private, coeducational college offering undergraduate and graduate programs in fine arts, ceramics, graphic design and illustration, environmental arts, fashion design, surface design, and photography. As part of their instruction, students work directly with professional artists, designers, critics, and writers. There are 2 undergraduate schools and one graduate school. In addition to regional accreditation, Otis has baccalaureate program accreditation with NASAD. The library contains 27,000 volumes, and subscribes to 180 periodicals. Computerized library sources and services include database searching. Special learning facilities include an art gallery and large multiuse studios, a ceramics building with multikiln firing capabilities, full foundry and casting facilities, a photographic darkroom, and a fully equipped printmaking studio. In addition, there is a fine book press room, a computer laboratory, and woodworking and metal working shops. The 3-acre campus is in an urban area half a mile west of Downtown Los Angeles. Including residence halls, there are 7 buildings on campus.

Student Life: About 61% of undergraduates are from California. Students come from 50 states, 31 foreign countries, and Canada. Seventy-five percent are from public schools; 25% from private. Thirty-eight percent are white; 25% Asian American; 19% foreign nationals; 11% Hispanic. The average age of freshmen is 20; all undergraduates, 23. Twelve percent drop out by the end of their first year; 80% remain to graduate.

Housing: A total of 175 students can be accommodated in college housing. College-sponsored living facilities include coed dormitories. On-campus housing is guaranteed for the freshman year only and is available on a first-come, first-served basis. Priority is given to out-of-town students. Seventy-three percent of students commute. Alcohol is not permitted. All students may keep cars on campus.

Activities: There are no fraternities or sororities on campus. There are some groups and organizations on campus, including art, computers, film, literary magazine, photography, student government, and yearbook. Popular campus events include gallery openings, a lecture/film series, an annual student art sale, and a yearly fashion design show.

Sports: There is no sports program at Otis.

Disabled Students: Ninety-five percent of the campus is accessible to disabled students. The following facilities are available: wheelchair ramps, elevators, special parking, specially equipped rest rooms, and lowered telephones.

Services: In addition to many counseling and information services, tutoring is available in most subjects, including drawing. There is remedial math and writing.

Campus Safety and Security: Campus safety and security measures include 24-hour foot and vehicle patrol, self defense education, escort service, and shuttle buses. In addition, there are informal discussions, pamphlets, posters, films, emergency telephones, and lighted pathways and sidewalks.

Programs of Study: Otis awards the B.F.A. degree. Associate and master's degrees also are awarded. Bachelor's degrees are awarded in COMMUNICATIONS AND THE ARTS (ceramic art and design, design, fine arts, graphic design, illustration, and photography), ENGINEERING AND ENVIRONMENTAL DESIGN (environmental design), SOCIAL SCIENCE (fashion design and technology). Graphic design and fine arts are the strongest academically. Fine arts, graphic design, illustration, and fashion design have the largest enrollments.

Required: Requirements for graduation include courses in liberal arts and sciences, art history, and studio arts. A senior thesis and a minimum of 134 total credit hours with a 2.0 minimum GPA are also required.

Special: Otis offers cross-registration with the Chicago Art Institute and a consortium of east coast art schools, and study abroad in London, Paris, and Stockholm.

Faculty/Classroom: Fifty-two percent of faculty are male; 48%, female. All teach undergraduates. The average class size in an introductory lecture is 25; in a laboratory, 10; and in a regular course offering, 18.

Admissions: About 88% of the 1993–94 applicants were accepted. The SAT scores for the 1993–94 freshman class were as follows: Verbal—47% below 500, 50% between 500 and 599, and 3% between

600 and 700; Math—65% below 500, 34% between 500 and 599, and 1% between 600 and 700. About 30% of the current freshmen were in the top fifth of their class; 75% were in the top two fifths. There was 1 National Merit finalist and 4 semifinalists. One freshman graduated first in his class.

Requirements: The SAT I or ACT is required. Applicants must be graduates of an accredited secondary school or have a GED certificate, and submit a portfolio. Seventy-five percent of the admissions decision is based on the portfolio. Interviews are required for students living within 200 miles of campus; essays are recommended. AP credits are accepted. Important factors used in the admissions decision are evidence of special talent, advanced placement or honor courses, recommendations by school officials, leadership record, and extracurricular activities record.

Procedure: Freshmen are admitted fall and spring. Entrance exams should be taken in the fall. Early decision applications should be filed by January 15; regular applications, by August 15 for fall entry, December 15 for spring entry, and August 15 for summer entry, along with an application fee of $40. Notification of early decision is sent January 31; regular decision, on a rolling basis. There are early decision, early admissions, and deferred admissions plans. Twenty-two early decision candidates were accepted for the 1993–94 class.

Transfer: About 60 transfer students enrolled in 1993–94. Transfer students must have a minimum 2.5 GPA and at least 18 credit hours earned. An interview is recommended. A total of 70 credits out of 134 must be completed at Otis.

Visiting: There are regularly scheduled orientations for prospective students, including a campus tour and departmental, portfolio, and financial aid presentations. There are guides for informal visits and visitors may sit in on classes and stay overnight at the school. To arrange for a visit, contact the Admissions Office at (213) 251–0501 or (800) 527-OTIS.

Financial Aid: In 1993–94, 80% of all current freshmen and 75% of continuing students received some form of financial aid. About 70% of freshmen and 63% of continuing students received need-based aid. Scholarships or need-based grants averaged $3200 ($11,500 maximum); loans averaged $2500 ($5000 maximum); and work contracts averaged $1500 ($2500 maximum). Eighty percent of undergraduate students work part-time. Average earnings from campus work for the school year are $2000. The average financial indebtedness of the 1992–93 graduate was $5000. Otis is a member of CSS. The FAF, the college's own financial statement, and the SAAC for California residents are required.

International Students: There are currently 127 international students enrolled. They must take the TOEFL and achieve a minimum score of 550.

Computers: The college provides computer facilities for student use. Otis provides 15 Macintosh IIXci and 5 Macintosh SE microcomputers. All students may access the system. There are no time limits on using the system and no fees.

Graduates: In a recent year, 110 bachelor's degrees were awarded. The most popular majors among graduates were fashion design (34%), fine arts (34%), and illustration (22%). Within an average freshman class, 80% graduate in 4 years, 15% in 5 years, and 5% in 6 years. Some 72 companies recruited on campus in 1992–93.

Admissions Contact: Joseph Suszynski, Director of Admissions.

OTIS PARSONS SCHOOL OF ART AND DESIGN

(See Otis College of Art and Design)

PACIFIC CHRISTIAN COLLEGE   D-5

Fullerton, CA 92631   (714) 879–3901; (800) 762–1294 (out-of-state)

Full-time: 461 men and women	Faculty: 23
Part-time: 138 men and women	Ph.D.s: 67%
Graduate: 69 men and women	Student/Faculty: 20 to 1
Year: 4–1–4, summer session	Tuition: $6710
Application Deadline: July 1	Room & Board: $5990
Freshman Class: 326 applied, 282 accepted, 195 enrolled	
SAT I Verbal/Math: 436/477	ACT: 22 COMPETITIVE

Pacific Christian College, founded in 1928, is a small, private, liberal arts institution affiliated with Christian Church/Churches of Christ. There is one graduate school. The library contains 55,000 volumes, 100 microform items, and 2700 audiovisual forms, and subscribes to 358 periodicals. Special learning facilities include a learning resource center and a 1000-seat theater. The 10-acre campus is in an urban area 45 miles southeast of Los Angeles. Including residence halls, there are 6 buildings on campus.

Student Life: About 58% of undergraduates are from California. Students come from 25 states and 16 foreign countries. About 40% of freshmen remain to graduate.

Housing: A total of 450 students can be accommodated in college housing. College-sponsored living facilities include single-sex dormitories and married-student housing. On-campus housing is guaranteed for all 4 years. Eighty percent of students live on campus. Alcohol is not permitted. All students may keep cars on campus.

Activities: There are no fraternities or sororities on campus. There are many groups and organizations on campus, including band, cheerleading, choir, chorale, chorus, drama, international, literary magazine, newspaper, orchestra, religious, social service, student government, and yearbook. Popular campus events include Sadie Hawkins, Spring Formal, PCC Preview, and Harvest.

Sports: There are 3 intercollegiate sports for men and 3 for women, and 10 intramural sports for men and 8 for women. Athletic and recreation facilities include a swimming pool and game rooms.

Disabled Students: Ninety-five percent of the campus is accessible to disabled students. The following facilities are available: elevators, special parking, specially equipped rest rooms, and priority is given to handicapped students for first floor housing.

Services: In addition to many counseling and information services, tutoring is available in most subjects. There is a reader service for the blind, and remedial math, reading, and writing.

Programs of Study: PCC awards the B.A. degree. Associate and master's degrees also are awarded. Bachelor's degrees are awarded in BUSINESS (business administration and management), COMMUNICATIONS AND THE ARTS (communications, English, fine arts, journalism, and music), COMPUTER AND PHYSICAL SCIENCE (computer science and mathematics), EDUCATION (early childhood, elementary, physical, and secondary), SOCIAL SCIENCE (biblical studies, child psychology/development, ministries, psychology, social science, and social work). Education, business, and religious studies have the largest enrollments.

Required: Regular attendance at convocation and Christian service is required. To graduate, students must complete at least 124 credit units and demonstrate 80% or better competency on the Pacific Placement Test. A minimum GPA of 2.0 must be maintained. Distribution requirements include 24 credits in biblical studies, 64 in general education courses, and approximately 36 in the major. One physical education course is required.

Special: PCC offers co-op programs and B.A.-B.S. degrees in conjunction with California State University at Fullerton. Internships, study abroad in England, work-study programs, dual and student-designed majors, nondegree study, pass/fail options, and credit for life, military, and work experience are also available. There is a freshman honors program on campus

Faculty/Classroom: Seventy-four percent of faculty are male; 26%, female.

Admissions: About 87% of the 1993–94 applicants were accepted. The SAT scores for the 1993–94 freshman class were as follows: Verbal—41% below 400, 33% between 400 and 499, 19% between 500 and 599, 4% 600–699, and 3% above 700; Math—20% below 400, 37% between 400 and 499, 30% between 500 and 599, 11% between 600 and 699, and 2% above 700. The ACT scores were 8% between 12 and 16, 22% between 17 and 20, 50% between 21 and 25, and 20% 26 and above.

Requirements: A minimum GPA of 2.5 is required. The SAT I or ACT is also required. Applicants must be high school graduates with a GPA of 2.0. The GED is accepted. A personal essay and references from a church leader and an academic counselor are required. AP and CLEP credits are accepted.

Procedure: Freshmen are admitted fall and spring. Entrance exams should be taken before enrolling. Applications should be filed by July 1 for fall entry and December 1 for spring entry, along with an application fee of $30. Notification is sent on a rolling basis. There are early admissions and deferred admissions plans.

Transfer: About 47 transfer students enrolled in 1993–94. Transfer students must submit copies of college transcripts and SAT I scores if fewer than 60 college units have been completed. A minimum GPA of 2.0 is required. A total of 30 credits out of 124 must be completed at PCC.

Visiting: There are regularly scheduled orientations for prospective students. There are guides for informal visits and visitors may sit in on classes and stay overnight at the school. To arrange for a visit, contact the Admissions Office.

Financial Aid: The FAF, SAAC, or AFSA should be submitted; financial statement is required. The deadline for financial aid applications is March 31.

International Students: There are currently 32 international students enrolled. They must take the TOEFL and achieve a minimum score of 525. The student must also take the college's own entrance exam.

Computers: The college provides computer facilities for student use. Microcomputer facilities are available for student use at the campus learning center.

Admissions Contact: Admissions Counselor.

PACIFIC UNION COLLEGE
B-2

Angwin, CA 94508   (707) 965-6336; (800) 358-9180 (out-of-state)

Full-time: 608 men, 708 women	Faculty: 90; IIB, --$
Part-time: 52 men, 87 women	Ph.D.s: 39%
Graduate: 12 men, 21 women	Student/Faculty: 15 to 1
Year: quarters, summer session	Tuition: $11,400
Application Deadline: open	Room & Board: $3675
Freshman Class: 740 applied, 668 accepted, 385 enrolled	
ACT: 22	COMPETITIVE

Pacific Union College, founded in 1888, is a private, coeducational college affiliated with the Seventh-day Adventist Church and offering programs in liberal arts, religion, business, health science, and teacher preparation. In addition to regional accreditation, PUC has baccalaureate program accreditation with ADA, CSWE, NASM, and NLN. The library contains 118,272 volumes, 15,544 microform items, and 6078 audiovisual forms, and subscribes to 8649 periodicals. Computerized library sources and services include the card catalog and interlibrary loans. Special learning facilities include a learning resource center, art gallery, natural history museum, and radio station. The 2000-acre campus is in a small town 70 miles north of San Francisco. Including residence halls, there are 57 buildings on campus.

Student Life: About 80% of undergraduates are from California. Students come from 31 states, 15 foreign countries, and Canada. Twenty-nine percent are from public schools; 71% from private. Fifty-nine percent are white; 30% Asian American; most are Protestant. The average age of freshmen is 19; all undergraduates, 22.

Housing: A total of 1344 students can be accommodated in college housing. College-sponsored living facilities include single-sex dormitories and married-student housing. On-campus housing is guaranteed for all 4 years. Eighty percent of students live on campus. Alcohol is not permitted. All students may keep cars on campus.

Activities: There are no fraternities or sororities on campus. There are 10 groups on campus, including art, band, choir, chorale, ethnic, newspaper, orchestra, religious, student government, and yearbook. Popular campus events include picnic and ski days.

Sports: There is no sports program at PUC. Athletic and recreation facilities include a gymnasium, a pool, a stadium, and 3 athletic fields.

Disabled Students: Ninety-five percent of the campus is accessible to disabled students. The following facilities are available: wheelchair ramps, elevators, and special parking.

Services: In addition to many counseling and information services, tutoring is available in some subjects, including mathematics and the sciences. There is a reader service for the blind, and remedial math, reading, and writing.

Campus Safety and Security: Campus safety and security measures include 24-hour foot and vehicle patrol, self defense education, escort service, and emergency telephones. In addition, there are lighted pathways and sidewalks.

Programs of Study: PUC awards the B.A., B.S., B.B.A., B.Mus., B.S.Med.Tech., and B.S.W. degrees. Associate and master's degrees also are awarded. Bachelor's degrees are awarded in BIOLOGICAL SCIENCE (biology/biological science and biophysics), BUSINESS (business administration and management, fashion merchandising, office supervision and management, and recreation and leisure services), COMMUNICATIONS AND THE ARTS (art history and appreciation, communications, design, English, fine arts, French, journalism, music, public relations, Spanish, and studio art), COMPUTER AND PHYSICAL SCIENCE (applied mathematics, chemistry, computer science, mathematics, physical sciences, and physics), EDUCATION (business, early childhood, physical, and trade and industrial), ENGINEERING AND ENVIRONMENTAL DESIGN (engineering technology, industrial engineering technology, and interior design), HEALTH PROFESSIONS (medical laboratory technology and nursing), SOCIAL SCIENCE (behavioral science, family/consumer studies, food science, history, interdisciplinary studies, liberal arts/general studies, psychology, religion, social studies, social work, sociology, and theological studies). Business administration has the largest enrollment.

Required: To graduate, a student must complete a minimum of 192 quarter hours, including 60 upper level course hours. The student must maintain a minimum GPA of 2.0 generally and 2.25 in the major. The required total hours in the major varies. The general education requirements also vary according to the major.

Special: Students may study abroad in 3 countries, earn B.A.-B.S. degrees, take dual majors, earn a general studies degree in liberal studies, and take a student-designed major in interdisciplinary studies. The college offers nondegree study and credit for life, and work experience. There is a freshman honors program on campus

Faculty/Classroom: Sixty-eight percent of faculty are male; 32%, female. The average class size in an introductory lecture is 19; in a laboratory, 18; and in a regular course offering, 17.

Admissions: About 90% of the 1993-94 applicants were accepted. The ACT scores for the 1993-94 freshman class were as follows: 37% below 21, 25% between 21 and 23, 21% between 24 and 26, 12% between 27 and 28, and 5% above 28. There was 1 National Merit semifinalist.

Requirements: A minimum GPA of 2.0 is required. The SAT I or ACT is not required. Scores are used only for advising purposes. Candidates for admission should have completed 4 years of English, 2 years of mathematics, and 1 year each of science and history. AP and CLEP credits are accepted. Important factors used in the admissions decision are recommendations by school officials, leadership record, advanced placement or honor courses, extracurricular activities record, and personality, intangible qualities.

Procedure: Entrance exams should be taken in the junior or senior year. Application deadlines are open. Application fee is $30. A waiting list is an active part of the admissions procedure.

Transfer: About 202 transfer students were recently enrolled. Requirements for transfer students are the same as for nontransfer students. A total of 36 quarter credits out of 192 must be completed at PUC.

Visiting: There are regularly scheduled orientations for prospective students. There are guides for informal visits and visitors may sit in on classes and stay overnight at the school. To arrange for a visit, contact the Admissions Office at (707) 965-6671.

Financial Aid: In an earlier year, 65% of all students received some form of financial aid. Scholarships or need-based grants averaged $1200 ($2300 maximum); loans averaged $2000 ($3350 maximum); and work contracts averaged $1500 ($2000 maximum). Fifty-five percent of undergraduate students work part-time. PUC is a member of CSS. The FAF is required. The deadline for financial aid applications is March 2.

International Students: There are currently 112 international students enrolled. The school actively recruits these students. They must take the University of Michigan Language Test.

Computers: The college provides computer facilities for student use. The mainframe is an HP 3000 and a Sequent. Students who have clearance may access the system. may access the system. It may be used anytime. There are no time limits on using the system and no fees.

Graduates: In a recent year, 204 bachelor's degrees were awarded.

Admissions Contact: Alvin K. Trace, Director of Enrollment Services.

PEPPERDINE UNIVERSITY
C-5

Malibu, CA 90265   (310) 456-4392

Full-time: 1089 men, 1443 women	Faculty: 153; IIA, +$
Part-time: 98 men, 129 women	Ph.D.s: 99%
Graduate: 164 men, 115 women	Student/Faculty: 17 to 1
Year: semesters, summer session	Tuition: $17,200
Application Deadline: February 1	Room & Board: $6530
Freshman Class: 3123 applied, 2037 accepted, 590 enrolled	
SAT I Verbal/Math: 514/582	ACT: 25 VERY COMPETITIVE

Pepperdine University, founded in 1937, is a private, coeducational liberal arts university affiliated with the Church of Christ. There are one undergraduate and 4 graduate schools. The 2 libraries contain 465,695 volumes, 438,896 microform items, and 8684 audiovisual forms, and subscribe to 3148 periodicals. Computerized library sources and services include the card catalog, interlibrary loans, and database searching. Special learning facilities include an art gallery, radio station, TV station, writing center, and a Japenese tea ceremony room. The 830-acre campus is in a suburban area 35 miles west of Los Angeles, overlooking the Pacific Ocean. Including residence halls, there are 76 buildings on campus.

Student Life: About 51% of undergraduates are from California. Students come from 51 states, 46 foreign countries, and Canada. Sixty-five percent are from public schools; 35% from private. Seventy-two percent are white; 11% foreign nationals. Sixty percent are Protestant; 21% Catholic. The average age of freshmen is 18.3; all undergraduates, 21.4. Fifteen percent drop out by the end of their first year; 74% remain to graduate.

Housing: A total of 1863 students can be accommodated in college housing. College-sponsored living facilities include single-sex dormitories and on-campus apartments. On-campus housing is guaranteed for the freshman and sophomore years and is available on a first-come, first-served basis. Sixty-five percent of students live on campus; of those, 55% remain on campus on weekends. Alcohol is not permitted. All students may keep cars on campus.

Activities: About 15% of men belong to 6 local fraternities; about 17% of women belong to 6 local sororities. There are 60 groups on campus, including art, band, cheerleading, chess, choir, chorale, chorus, computers, dance, drama, ethnic, honors, international, jazz band, literary magazine, musical theater, newspaper, opera, orchestra, pep band, photography, political, professional, radio and TV, religious, social, social service, student government, symphony, and

yearbook. Popular campus events include new student orientation, Songfest, coffeehouses, Moonlight Harvest Dance, Parents Weekend, and Homecoming.

Sports: There are 7 intercollegiate sports for men and 7 for women, and 25 intramural sports for men and 20 for women. Athletic and recreation facilities include a field house; a pool; a sauna; a weight room; basketball, raquetball, and tennis courts; playing fields; an all-weather track, and an aerobics room.

Disabled Students: The entire campus is accessible to disabled students. The following facilities are available: wheelchair ramps, elevators, special parking, specially equipped rest rooms, special class scheduling, lowered drinking fountains, and lowered telephones.

Services: In addition to many counseling and information services, tutoring is available in most subjects.

Campus Safety and Security: Campus safety and security measures include 24-hour foot and vehicle patrol, self defense education, escort service, and shuttle buses. In addition, there are informal discussions, pamphlets, posters, and films, emergency telephones, lighted pathways and sidewalks, guarded entrances to campus, security cameras, and a campus crimewatch program.

Programs of Study: Pepperdine awards the B.A., B.S., and B.S.M. degrees. Master's and doctoral degrees also are awarded. Bachelor's degrees are awarded in BIOLOGICAL SCIENCE (biology/biological science and nutrition), BUSINESS (accounting and business administration and management), COMMUNICATIONS AND THE ARTS (advertising, broadcasting, communications, dramatic arts, English, fine arts, French, German, Italian, Japanese, journalism, music, public relations, Spanish, speech/debate/rhetoric, and telecommunications), COMPUTER AND PHYSICAL SCIENCE (chemistry, computer science, and mathematics), EDUCATION (art, elementary, foreign languages, music, physical, science, and secondary), HEALTH PROFESSIONS (sports medicine), SOCIAL SCIENCE (economics, history, humanities, international studies, liberal arts/general studies, philosophy, political science/government, psychology, religion, social science, and sociology). Natural sciences (premedical), sports medicine, political science, international studies, liberal arts, and business are the strongest academically. Communication and business have the largest enrollments.

Required: To graduate, students must complete 128 credit hours, including 36 to 72 in the major. Two years of a broad liberal arts core curriculum are needed. Required courses include those in English, religion, Western heritage, non-Western heritage, American heritage, behavioral science, foreign language, laboratory science, mathematics, speech and rhetoric, a freshman seminar, and physical education. Students must take at least 40 upper-division units and complete a 28-unit residency requirement. Pepperdine requires a minimum GPA of 2.0 for graduation.

Special: Students may earn 1 to 4 units for an internship, available in most majors, participate in a Washington or a Sacramento semester, and study abroad in 8 countries. The school offers a 3–2 engineering degree with Washington University in St. Louis and the University of Southern California, dual majors in any discipline, student-designed contract majors, nondegree study, and pass/fail options. There is a freshman honors program on campus, as well as 12 national honor societies. Three departments have honors programs.

Faculty/Classroom: Eighty percent of faculty are male; 20%, female. All teach undergraduates. No introductory courses are taught by graduate students. The average class size in an introductory lecture is 18; in a laboratory, 15; and in a regular course offering, 18.

Admissions: About 65% of the 1993–94 applicants were accepted. The SAT scores for the 1993–94 freshman class were as follows: Verbal—29% below 500, 57% between 500 and 599, 12% between 600 and 700, and 2% above 700; Math—28% below 500, 50% between 500 and 599, 20% between 600 and 700, and 2% above 700. The ACT scores were 5% below 21, 21% between 21 and 23, 37% between 24 and 26, 20% between 27 and 28, and 17% above 28. About 80% of the current freshmen were in the top fifth of their class; 90% were in the top two fifths.

Requirements: The SAT I or ACT is required. It is strongly recommended that candidates for admission have completed a college preparatory program including 4 years of English and courses in speech communication, humanities, foreign language, mathematics, science, and social science. AP and CLEP credits are accepted. Important factors used in the admissions decision are advanced placement or honor courses, recommendations by school officials, leadership record, personality, intangible qualities, and parents or siblings attending the school.

Procedure: Freshmen are admitted fall and winter. Entrance exams should be taken in the fall. Early decision applications should be filed by November 15; regular applications, by February 1 for fall entry, October 15 for winter entry, February 15 for spring entry, and February 15 for summer entry, along with an application fee of $45. Notification of early decision is sent December 15; regular decision, April 1. There is an early decision plan. About 325 early decision candidates were accepted for the 1993–94 class. A waiting list is an active

part of the admissions procedure, with about 5% of applicants on the list.

Transfer: About 90 transfer students enrolled in 1993–94. Transfer applicants should have a minimum GPA of 2.7 from an accredited college. A total of 28 credits out of 128 must be completed at Pepperdine.

Visiting: There are regularly scheduled orientations for prospective students, including tours of the campus, meetings with faculty and current students, and sesions on admission and financial aid; interviews may be arranged on the hour with admission counselors. There are guides for informal visits and visitors may sit in on classes. Students who have applied for admission may stay 1 night on campus. To arrange for a visit, contact Armond Lawson at (310) 456–4392.

Financial Aid: In 1993–94, 70% of all current freshmen and 65% of continuing students received some form of financial aid. About 55% of students received need-based aid. The average freshman award was $17,000. Of that total, scholarships or need-based grants averaged $7500 ($12,000 maximum); loans averaged $3500 ($5000 maximum); and work contracts averaged $1000 ($1200 maximum). Ninety-seven percent of undergraduate students work part-time. Average earnings from campus work for the school year are $1000. The average financial indebtedness of the 1992–93 graduate was $5103. Pepperdine is a member of CSS. The FAF and the FAFSA, and the college's own financial statement are required. The deadline for financial aid applications is March 1.

International Students: There are currently 300 international students enrolled. The school actively recruits these students. They must take the TOEFL or the college's own test and achieve a minimum score on the TOEFL of 550. The student must also take the SAT I or the ACT.

Computers: The university provides computer facilities for student use. The mainframe is an IBM ES/9000 Model 210. There are terminals in each dormitory, in computer laboratories, and in the writing center. Access to minicomputer, mainframe, VAX, and the library system is available. Students may access the system with permission from the faculty. It may be used any time. Word-processing laboratories are open to all students. There are no time limits on using the system and no fees.

Graduates: In 1992–93, 555 bachelor's degrees were awarded. The most popular majors among graduates were business administration (20%), psychology (6%), and telecommunications (6%). Within an average freshman class, 4% graduate in 3 years, 54% in 4 years, 65% in 5 years, and 75% in 6 years. Some 100 companies recruited on campus in 1992–93. In the 1992 graduating class, 29% of the men and 27% of the women were enrolled in graduate school within 6 months of graduation; 71% of the men and 73% of the women had found employment.

Admissions Contact: Paul A. Long, Dean of Admission and Enrollment Management.

PITZER COLLEGE
D-5

Claremont, CA 91711   (909) 621–8129

Full-time: 355 men, 395 women	Faculty: 80; IIB, +$
Part-time: 4 men, 6 women	Ph.D.s: 100%
Graduate: none	Student/Faculty: 9 to 1
Year: semesters	Tuition: $18,198
Application Deadline: February 1	Room & Board: $5582
Freshman Class: 1155 applied, 610 accepted, 220 enrolled	
SAT I Verbal/Math: 560/580	ACT: 26 **HIGHLY COMPETITIVE**

Pitzer College, founded in 1963, is a private liberal arts college emphasizing the social and behavioral sciences. It is one of the Claremont Colleges. There are 5 undergraduate schools and one graduate school. The library contains 2 million volumes and 10,000 microform items, and subscribes to 1800 periodicals. Computerized library sources and services include the card catalog, interlibrary loans, and database searching. Special learning facilities include an art gallery, radio station, TV station, and a social science laboratory, and an arboretum. The 30-acre campus is in a suburban area 35 miles east of Los Angeles. Including residence halls, there are 13 buildings on campus.

Student Life: About 55% of undergraduates are from out-of-state, mostly the Northeast. Students come from 29 states, 22 foreign countries, and Canada. Fifty-five percent are from public schools; 45% from private. Sixty-eight percent are white; 12% Hispanic. Forty percent claim no religious affiliation; 30% Jewish; 15% Catholic; 15% Protestant. The average age of freshmen is 18; all undergraduates, 20. Nine percent drop out by the end of their first year; 75% remain to graduate.

Housing: A total of 600 students can be accommodated in college housing. College-sponsored living facilities include coed dormitories and off-campus apartments. On-campus housing is guaranteed for all 4 years. Ninety-two percent of students live on campus; of those, 70% remain on campus on weekends. Alcohol is not permitted. All students may keep cars on campus.

Activities: There are no fraternities or sororities on campus. There are 200 groups on campus, including art, choir, chorus, computers, dance, drama, ethnic, film, gay, honors, international, literary magazine, musical theater, newspaper, photography, political, radio and TV, religious, social, social service, student government, and yearbook. Popular campus events include the Kaneutck Festival and the Ritz of the Pitz dance.

Sports: Athletic and recreation facilities include some of those shared by all the Claremont Colleges, including 3 gymnasiums, 5 swimming pools, 20 tennis courts, numerous playing fields, and lighted volleyball courts. The campus stadium seats 1200.

Disabled Students: All of the campus is accessible to disabled students. The following facilities are available: wheelchair ramps, elevators, special parking, specially equipped rest rooms, lowered drinking fountains, and lowered telephones.

Services: In addition to many counseling and information services, tutoring is available in every subject. In addition, there is a reader service for the blind.

Campus Safety and Security: Campus safety and security measures include 24-hour foot and vehicle patrol, self defense education, escort service, and informal discussions. In addition, there are pamphlets, posters, and films, emergency telephones, and lighted pathways and sidewalks.

Programs of Study: Pitzer awards the B.A. degree. Bachelor's degrees are awarded in BIOLOGICAL SCIENCE (biology/biological science), BUSINESS (management engineering and organizational behavior), COMMUNICATIONS AND THE ARTS (classics, dramatic arts, English, film arts, fine arts, folklore and mythology, French, German, linguistics, and Spanish), COMPUTER AND PHYSICAL SCIENCE (chemistry, mathematics, physics, and science), ENGINEERING AND ENVIRONMENTAL DESIGN (environmental science), SOCIAL SCIENCE (anthropology, Asian/Oriental studies, economics, European studies, history, international relations, Latin American studies, Mexican-American/Chicano studies, philosophy, psychobiology, psychology, sociology, and women's studies). Social and behavioral sciences are the strongest academically. Social and behavioral sciences have the largest enrollments.

Required: Students must complete a total of 32 courses with a 2.0 GPA. Although requirements vary according to major, most students take introductory or preparatory courses in their first 2 years and courses in or related to their major in the last 2 years.

Special: Students may cross-register at any of the other Claremont Colleges, or study abroad in Africa, Asia, Europe, Latin America, North America, or Oceania. There is an extensive freshman seminar program, and interdisciplinary study is offered in areas such as science and technology, education, chemical dependency, and international or intercultural studies. Joint B.A.-M.S. degrees are offered in mathematics, business administration, and public policy. Dual concentrations are possible in most areas. There are independent study and limited pass/fail options.

Faculty/Classroom: Sixty percent of faculty are male; 40%, female. All teach undergraduates and 100% do research. The average class size in an introductory lecture is 35; in a laboratory, 50; and in a regular course offering, 15.

Admissions: About 53% of the 1993–94 applicants were accepted. The SAT scores for the 1993–94 freshman class were as follows: Verbal—14% below 500, 50% between 500 and 599, 27% between 600 and 700, and 9% above 700; Math—10% below 500, 51% between 500 and 599, 31% between 600 and 700, and 8% above 700. The ACT scores were 6% below 21, 17% between 21 and 23, 25% between 24 and 26, 39% between 27 and 28, and 13% above 28. About 71% of the current freshmen were in the top fifth of their class; 93% were in the top two fifths. About 10 freshmen graduated first in their class.

Requirements: The SAT I is required. Pitzer recommends that applicants submit SAT II: Subject test scores in mathematics I or II, and 1 other subject. Applicant must be a graduate of an accredited secondary school or have earned the GED. Secondary school courses must include 4 years of English courses requiring extensive writing, and 3 years each of social and behavioral sciences including history, laboratory science, foreign language, and mathematics. A personal essay is required, and a personal interview is recommended. AP credits are accepted. Important factors used in the admissions decision are advanced placement or honor courses, geographic diversity, recommendations by school officials, extracurricular activities record, and recommendations by alumni.

Procedure: Freshmen are admitted fall and spring. Applications should be filed by February 1 for fall entry and December 1 for spring entry, along with an application fee of $30. Notification of early decision is sent December 31; regular decision, April 1. There are early decision, early admissions, and deferred admissions plans. About 45 early decision candidates were accepted for the 1993–94 class. A waiting list is an active part of the admissions procedure, with about 10% of applicants on the list.

Transfer: About 40 transfer students enrolled in 1993–94. Applicants must have at least a 3.0 GPA in previous college work. No more than 2 years of previous credits may be transferred. A total of 16 credits out of 32 must be completed at Pitzer.

Visiting: There are regularly scheduled orientations for prospective students. There are guides for informal visits and visitors may sit in on classes and stay overnight at the school. To arrange for a visit, contact the Office of Admissions at (909) 621–8129.

Financial Aid: In 1993–94, 43% of all current freshmen and 50% of continuing students received some form of financial aid. The average freshman award was $16,900. Seventy-five percent of undergraduate students work part-time. Average earnings from campus work for the school year are $1500. The average financial indebtedness of the 1992–93 graduate was $12,000. Pitzer is a member of CSS. The FAF is required. The deadline for financial aid applications is February 1.

International Students: There are currently 58 international students enrolled. The school actively recruits these students. They must take the TOEFL and achieve a minimum score of 550.

Computers: The college provides computer facilities for student use. The mainframe is an IBM. Macintosh microcomputers are available in laboratories. All students may access the system. There are no time limits on using the system and no fees.

Graduates: In 1992–93, 191 bachelor's degrees were awarded. Within an average freshman class, 3% graduate in 3 years, 95% in 4 years, and 2% in 5 years. Some 100 companies recruited on campus in 1992–93. In the 1992 graduating class, 17% of the men and 15% of the women were enrolled in graduate school within 6 months of graduation; 41% of the men and 27% of the women had found employment.

Admissions Contact: Office of Admissions.

POINT LOMA NAZARENE COLLEGE D-5
San Diego, CA 92106–2899 (619) 221–2225

Full-time: 747 men, 1143 women	Faculty: 118; IIB, av$
Part-time: 75 men, 142 women	Ph.D.s: 63%
Graduate: 113 men, 264 women	Student/Faculty: 16 to 1
Year: semesters, summer session	Tuition: $9542
Application Deadline: open	Room & Board: $3990
Freshman Class: 809 applied, 687 accepted, 426 enrolled	
SAT I Verbal/Math: 425/472	ACT: 21 COMPETITIVE

Point Loma Nazarene College, founded in 1902, is a private, coeducational liberal arts college affiliated with the Church of the Nazarene. There is one graduate school. In addition to regional accreditation, PLNC has baccalaureate program accreditation with NLN. The library contains 155,904 volumes, 36,934 microform items, and 2499 audiovisual forms, and subscribes to 656 periodicals. Computerized library sources and services include interlibrary loans and database searching. Special learning facilities include a learning resource center, radio station, and a laboratory preschool. The 90-acre campus is in a suburban area 5 miles southwest of San Diego. Including residence halls, there are 42 buildings on campus.

Student Life: About 87% of undergraduates are from California. Students come from 34 states, 25 foreign countries, and Canada. Eighty-five percent are from public schools; 15% from private. Eighty percent are white. Eighty-one percent are Protestant; 12% Catholic. The average age of freshmen is 18; all undergraduates, 21.5. Twenty-five percent drop out by the end of their first year; 37% remain to graduate.

Housing: A total of 1350 students can be accommodated in college housing. College-sponsored living facilities include single-sex dormitories, on-campus apartments, off-campus apartments, and married-student housing. On-campus housing is guaranteed for all 4 years. Sixty-two percent of students live on campus. Alcohol is not permitted. All students may keep cars on campus.

Activities: About 8% of men belong to 3 local fraternities; about 5% of women belong to 2 local and 1 national sororities. There are 27 groups on campus, including art, band, cheerleading, choir, chorale, computers, drama, ethnic, honors, international, jazz band, literary magazine, newspaper, opera, orchestra, pep band, political, professional, radio and TV, religious, social, social service, student government, and yearbook. Popular campus events include Spiritual Emphasis Week and Homecoming.

Sports: There are 7 intercollegiate sports for men and 5 for women, and 17 intramural sports for men and 17 for women. Athletic and recreation facilities include a gymnasium, baseball and soccer fields, a track, tennis courts, dormitory lounges, and table tennis and pool tables.

Disabled Students: Seventy-five percent of the campus is accessible to disabled students. The following facilities are available: wheelchair ramps, elevators, special parking, specially equipped rest rooms, special class scheduling, lowered drinking fountains, and lowered telephones.

Services: In addition to many counseling and information services, tutoring is available in most subjects. There is also a reader service for the blind, and remedial math, reading, and writing available.

Campus Safety and Security: Campus safety and security measures include 24-hour foot and vehicle patrol, self defense education, escort service, and shuttle buses. In addition, there are informal discussions, pamphlets, posters, films, emergency telephones, and lighted pathways and sidewalks.

Programs of Study: PLNC awards the B.A. and B.S.N. degrees. Master's degrees also are awarded. Bachelor's degrees are awarded in BIOLOGICAL SCIENCE (biology/biological science), BUSINESS (accounting, business administration and management, and office supervision and management), COMMUNICATIONS AND THE ARTS (communications, dramatic arts, English, fine arts, graphic design, journalism, music, music theory and composition, piano/organ, Spanish, speech/debate/rhetoric, technical and business writing, and voice), COMPUTER AND PHYSICAL SCIENCE (chemistry, computer science, information sciences and systems, mathematics, and physics), EDUCATION (art, business, English, home economics, music, and physical), ENGINEERING AND ENVIRONMENTAL DESIGN (engineering physics), HEALTH PROFESSIONS (nursing, predentistry, premedicine, and speech pathology/audiology), SOCIAL SCIENCE (biblical studies, economics, history, ministries, philosophy, political science/government, prelaw, psychology, religion, religious education, sociology, and theological studies). Mathematics, physics, and philosophy are the strongest academically. Liberal studies and business courses have the largest enrollments.

Required: To graduate, students must complete a minimum of 128 semester units, 44 in upper-division courses. At least 24 upper-division semester units are needed for the major. A minimum GPA of 2.0 is required. Students must complete the general education requirements, though B.S.N. candidates need not take a foreign language. General education requirements include 9 courses in cultural studies, 5 in the sciences, 4 in cognitive studies, and 3 in religious studies. Students must demonstrate proficiency in writing and mathematics.

Special: Students may participate in church-related internships and a Washington semester through the Christian College Coalition and the American Studies Program. A general studies degree in liberal studies is available, as is credit for life, military, and work experience for nursing students. PLNC offers nondegree study and pass/fail options. There is a freshman honors program on campus, as well as one national honor society. One department has an honors program.

Faculty/Classroom: Seventy-five percent of faculty are male; 25%, female. Ninety-five percent teach undergraduates and 10% both teach and do research. No introductory courses are taught by graduate students. The average class size in an introductory lecture is 75; in a laboratory, 18; and in a regular course offering, 25.

Admissions: About 85% of the 1993–94 applicants were accepted. The SAT scores for the 1993–94 freshman class were as follows: Verbal—77% below 500, 19% between 500 and 599, 4% between 600 and 700, and 1% above 700; Math—59% below 500, 28% between 500 and 599, 11% between 600 and 700, and 2% above 700. The ACT scores were 52% below 21, 27% between 21 and 23, 13% between 24 and 26, 3% between 27 and 28, and 5% above 28. About 36% of the current freshmen were in the top fifth of their class; 58% were in the top two fifths. Eleven freshmen graduated first in their class.

Requirements: A minimum GPA of 2.5 is required. The SAT I or ACT is required. Candidates for admission should have completed 3 years of English, 2 years each of foreign language and mathematics, and 1 year each of history and science. AP and CLEP credits are accepted. Important factors used in the admissions decision are personality, intangible qualities, leadership record, advanced placement or honor courses, evidence of special talents, and extracurricular activities record.

Procedure: Freshmen are admitted to all sessions. Entrance exams should be taken in the junior year or early in the senior year. Application deadlines are open. The application fee is $20. Notification is sent on a rolling basis. There are early admissions and deferred admissions plans.

Transfer: About 281 transfer students enrolled in 1993–94. Transfer students must have a C average in all college work and present transcripts, including certificates of honorable dismissal. Credits submitted from nonaccredited schools will be evaluated individually. Advanced standing is provisional for at least one term, in which the student must maintain at least a C average. A total of 24 credits out of 128 must be completed at PLNC.

Visiting: There are regularly scheduled orientations for prospective students, including campus tours and appointments with major advisers. There are guides for informal visits and visitors may sit in on classes and stay overnight at the school. To arrange for a visit, contact Admissions at (619) 221-2273.

Financial Aid: In a recent year, 75% of all current freshmen and 72% of continuing students received some form of financial aid. About 60% of freshmen and 52% of continuing students received need-based aid. Fifty-five percent of undergraduate students work part-time. PLNC is a member of CSS. The FAF and the college's own financial statements are required. The deadline for financial aid applications is April 10.

International Students: There are currently 73 international students enrolled. They must take the TOEFL and achieve a minimum score of 550. The student must also take the SAT I.

Computers: The college provides computer facilities for student use. The mainframe is a Data General MV/10,000. Terminals are located in the computer center and the business and science areas. There are 30 PCs and 20 Apple IIes in computer laboratories available for classes and by students for general use. There are no time limits on using the system and no fees.

Graduates: In 1992–93 334 bachelor's degrees were awarded. The most popular majors among graduates were liberal studies (15%), business (15%), and nursing (8%). Within an average freshman class, 20% graduate in 4 years, 37% in 5 years, and 38% in 6 years. Some 140 companies recruited on campus in 1992–93.

Admissions Contact: Bill Young, Executive Director for Enrollment Services.

POMONA COLLEGE
D-5

Claremont, CA 91711   (909) 621-8134

Full-time: 721 men, 661 women	Faculty: 153; IIB, +$
Part-time: none	Ph.D.s: 100%
Graduate: none	Student/Faculty: 9 to 1
Year: semesters	Tuition: $16,900
Application Deadline: January 15	Room & Board: $6920
Freshman Class: 3037 applied, 1060 accepted, 390 enrolled	
SAT I Verbal/Math: 640/700	ACT: 31 **MOST COMPETITIVE**

Pomona College, the oldest and largest of the Claremont Colleges, is an independent, coeducational liberal arts and sciences institution founded in 1887. The 3 libraries contain 1.8 million volumes, and subscribe to 5800 periodicals. Computerized library sources and services include the card catalog and interlibrary loans. Special learning facilities include an art gallery, radio station, and an observatory, and a modern languages and international relations center. The 130-acre campus is in a suburban area 35 miles east of Los Angeles. Including residence halls, there are 31 buildings on campus.

Student Life: About 60% of undergraduates are from out-of-state, mostly the Northeast. Students come from 49 states, 29 foreign countries, and Canada. Seventy-two percent are from public schools; 24% from private. Fifty-four percent are white; 21% Asian American; 11% Hispanic. The average age of freshmen is 18; all undergraduates, 20. One percent drop out by the end of their first year; 94% remain to graduate.

Housing: A total of 1325 students can be accommodated in college housing. College-sponsored living facilities include coed dormitories and on-campus apartments. In addition there are language houses. On-campus housing is guaranteed for all 4 years. Ninety-six percent of students live on campus; of those, 95% remain on campus on weekends. All students may keep cars on campus.

Activities: About 10% of men and about 5% of women belong to 6 local fraternities. There are no sororities on campus. There are 280 groups on campus, including art, band, choir, chorus, dance, drama, ethnic, film, gay, honors, international, jazz band, literary magazine, musical theater, newspaper, orchestra, pep band, photography, political, professional, radio and TV, religious, social, social service, student government, symphony, and yearbook.

Sports: There are 11 intercollegiate sports for men and 7 for women, and 13 intramural sports for men and 13 for women. Athletic and recreation facilities include an all-weather track, 2 swimming pools, a weight room, a dance studio, various playing fields, and courts for tennis, squash, racquetball, and basketball.

Disabled Students: Sixty percent of the campus is accessible to disabled students. The following facilities are available: wheelchair ramps, elevators, special parking, specially equipped rest rooms, special class scheduling, lowered drinking fountains, and lowered telephones.

Services: In addition to many counseling and information services, tutoring is available in most subjects. In addition, there is a reader service for the blind.

Campus Safety and Security: Campus safety and security measures include 24-hour foot and vehicle patrol, self defense education, escort service, and informal discussions. In addition, there are pamphlets, posters, films, emergency telephones, and lighted pathways and sidewalks.

Programs of Study: Pomona awards the B.A. degree. Bachelor's degrees are awarded in BIOLOGICAL SCIENCE (biology/biological science and molecular biology), COMMUNICATIONS AND THE ARTS (Chinese, classics, dramatic arts, English, fine arts,

French, German, Japanese, languages, linguistics, literature, media arts, music, Russian, and Spanish), COMPUTER AND PHYSICAL SCIENCE (chemistry, computer science, geology, mathematics, physics, and science), ENGINEERING AND ENVIRONMENTAL DESIGN (technology and public affairs), SOCIAL SCIENCE (American studies, anthropology, Asian/Oriental studies, economics, history, international relations, philosophy, political science/government, psychology, public affairs, religion, sociology, and women's studies). Social sciences and sciences have the largest enrollments.

Required: All students are required to take a freshman seminar and to meet writing and foreign language requirements. In addition, 3 courses each in humanities and social sciences, 2 in natural sciences, and 1 in a quantitative area must be completed. In all, 32 semester courses must be completed with a 6.0 GPA on a 12.0 scale.

Special: Students may cross-register at any of the Claremont Colleges, study abroad in 30 countries, and spend a semester in Washington, D.C. Dual and student-designed majors and internships are possible. A 3–2 engineering program is offered with California Institute of Technology or Washington University in St. Louis. There are pass/fail options. There are 9 national honor societies on campus, including Phi Beta Kappa.

Faculty/Classroom: All teach undergraduates and do research. The average class size in an introductory lecture is 30; in a laboratory, 14; and in a regular course offering, 14.

Admissions: About 35% of the 1993–94 applicants were accepted. The SAT scores for the 1993–94 freshman class were as follows: Verbal—4% below 500, 22% between 500 and 599, 59% between 600 and 700, and 15% above 700; Math—2% below 500, 8% between 500 and 599, 39% between 600 and 700, and 51% above 700. About 92% of the current freshmen were in the top fifth of their class; 100% were in the top two fifths. There were 50 National Merit finalists. Thirty-eight freshmen graduated first in their class.

Requirements: The SAT I or ACT is required. Although applicants need not be graduates of accredited high schools (some may be admitted after the junior year), most are, or have earned the GED. Secondary preparation must include 4 years of English, 3 years each of mathematics and foreign languages, and 2 years each of laboratory and social sciences. An essay is required and an interview is strongly recommended. AP credits are accepted. Important factors used in the admissions decision are advanced placement or honor courses, leadership record, extracurricular activities record, geographic diversity, and evidence of special talent.

Procedure: Freshmen are admitted in the fall. Entrance exams should be taken before December of the senior year. There are early decision, early admissions, and deferred admissions plans. Early decision applications should be filed by November 15; regular applications, by January 15 for fall entry, along with an application fee of $45. Notification of early decision is sent December 15; regular decision, April 10. More than 80 early decision candidates were accepted for the 1993–94 class. A waiting list is an active part of the admissions procedure.

Transfer: About 20 transfer students enrolled in 1993–94. Applicants must have completed at least 1 year (24 semester hours) of college-level courses at time of enrollment. A total of 16 courses out of 32 must be completed at Pomona.

Visiting: There are regularly scheduled orientations for prospective students, including interviews, information sessions, and tours. There are guides for informal visits and visitors may sit in on classes and stay overnight at the school. To arrange for a visit, contact the Admissions Office at (909) 621–8134.

Financial Aid: In 1993–94, 60% of all current freshmen and 55% of continuing students received some form of financial aid. About 60% of freshmen and 55% of continuing students received need-based aid. The average freshman award was $18,300. Of that total, scholarships or need-based grants averaged $11,150 ($20,000 maximum); loans averaged $2500; and work contracts averaged $1500. Sixty-five percent of undergraduate students work part-time. Average earnings from campus work for the school year are $1500. The average financial indebtedness of the 1992–93 graduate was $12,000. Pomona is a member of CSS. The FAF or FFS and the college's own financial statement is required. The deadline for financial aid applications is February 11.

International Students: There are currently 124 international students enrolled. The school actively recruits these students. They must take the TOEFL and achieve a minimum score of 600. The student must also take the SAT I or the ACT.

Computers: The college provides computer facilities for student use. The mainframe is a DEC VAX. Students may access the mainframe computer at several public facilities and from dormitory rooms. Macintosh and IBM PS/2s are available in public work areas. All students may access the system. There are no time limits on using the system and no fees.

Graduates: In 1992–93, 364 bachelor's degrees were awarded. The most popular majors among graduates were politics (11%), international relations (9%), and biology/molecular biology (9%). Within an average freshman class, 90% graduate in 4 years and 94% in 5 years. Some 165 companies recruited on campus in 1992–93.

Admissions Contact: Bruce J. Poch, Dean of Admissions.

SAINT MARY'S COLLEGE OF CALIFORNIA   B-3
Moraga, CA 94575–9988   (510) 631–4224

Full-time: 1291 men, 1356 women	Faculty: 146; IIA, av$
Part-time: 79 men, 155 women	Ph.D.s: 91%
Graduate: 420 men, 520 women	Student/Faculty: 18 to 1
Year: 4–1–4	Tuition: $12,738
Application Deadline: March 1	Room & Board: $6110
Freshman Class: 2693 applied, 1598 accepted, 465 enrolled	
SAT I Verbal/Math: 493/539	VERY COMPETITIVE

Saint Mary's College of California, founded in 1863, is a private, independent, coeducational liberal arts college affiliated with the Roman Catholic Church. The school offers undergraduate and graduate programs in liberal arts, nursing, economics and business administration, education, and preprofessional studies. There are 5 undergraduate and 4 graduate schools. In addition to regional accreditation, The college has baccalaureate program accreditation with NLN. The library contains 170,938 volumes and 1000 audiovisual forms, and subscribes to 1014 periodicals. Computerized library sources and services include the card catalog and database searching. Special learning facilities include an art gallery, natural history museum, radio station, and TV station. The 420-acre campus is in a suburban area 20 miles east of San Francisco. Including residence halls, there are 31 buildings on campus.

Student Life: About 74% of undergraduates are from California. Students come from 35 states, 24 foreign countries, and Canada. Fifty-five percent are from public schools; 45% from private. Sixty-five percent are white; 13% Hispanic; 12% Asian American. Sixty-six percent are Catholic; 30% Protestant. The average age of freshmen is 18; all undergraduates, 20.2. Eight percent drop out by the end of their first year; 80% remain to graduate.

Housing: A total of 1400 students can be accommodated in college housing. College-sponsored living facilities include single-sex and coed dormitories and on-campus apartments. On-campus housing is guaranteed for the freshman year only and is available on a lottery system for upperclassmen. Priority is given to out-of-town students. Sixty-six percent of students live on campus; of those, 66% remain on campus on weekends. Alcohol is not permitted. All students may keep cars on campus.

Activities: There are no fraternities or sororities on campus. There are many groups and organizations on campus, including cheerleading, choir, communications, ethnic, gourmet, honors, international, language debate, literary magazine, musical theater, newspaper, pep band, political, professional, radio and TV, religious, social, social service, student government, and yearbook.

Sports: There are 7 intercollegiate sports for men and 7 for women, and 6 intramural sports for men and 5 for women. Athletic and recreation facilities include a gymnasium, football and baseball fields, a swimming pool, lighted tennis courts, a soccer field, and rugby pitch.

Disabled Students: The following facilities are available: wheelchair ramps, elevators, special parking, specially equipped rest rooms, special class scheduling, lowered drinking fountains, and lowered telephones.

Services: In addition to many counseling and information services, tutoring is available in most subjects, including 1-on-1 sessions and group workshops. Readers, notetakers, and other services are provided to learning or physically disabled students.

Campus Safety and Security: Campus safety and security measures include 24-hour foot and vehicle patrol and lighted pathways and sidewalks.

Programs of Study: The college awards the B.A., B.S., B.S.B.A., and B.S.N. degrees. Master's degrees are also awarded. Bachelor's degrees are awarded in BIOLOGICAL SCIENCE (biology/biological science), BUSINESS (accounting, banking and finance, business administration and management, and international business management), COMMUNICATIONS AND THE ARTS (communications, English, fine arts, French, Greek, Latin, and Spanish), COMPUTER AND PHYSICAL SCIENCE (chemistry and mathematics), EDUCATION (art, early childhood, elementary, and secondary), HEALTH PROFESSIONS (nursing, predentistry, and premedicine), SOCIAL SCIENCE (economics, history, philosophy, political science/government, prelaw, psychology, and religion).

Required: To graduate, students must complete 36 course credits, including 17 at the upper level, with a GPA of 2.0 overall and in the major. Specific requirements include a freshman seminar and 2 courses each in religious studies, humanities, mathematics/science, and social sciences. All students must demonstrate competence in written English.

Special: Saint Mary's College and Samuel Merritt College confer the B.S.N. degree to students completing the Intercollegiate Nursing Program. The college offers seminars in all fields, dual and student-

designed majors, study abroad in 8 countries, a Washington semester, and an integral liberal arts degree. There is a 3–2 engineering program with Washington University and the University of Southern California. Two departments have honors programs.

Faculty/Classroom: All teach undergraduates. No introductory courses are taught by graduate students. The average class size in an introductory lecture is 25; in a laboratory, 16; and in a regular course offering, 18.

Admissions: About 59% of the 1993–94 applicants were accepted. The SAT scores for the 1993–94 freshman class were as follows: Verbal—48% below 500, 39% between 500 and 599, 12% between 600 and 700, and 1% above 700; Math—35% below 500, 43% between 500 and 599, 19% between 600 and 700, and 3% above 700. About 63% of the current freshmen were in the top fifth of their class; 82% were in the top two fifths. There were 10 National Merit finalists and 23 semifinalists. About 32 freshmen graduated first in their class.

Requirements: The SAT I is required. Candidates should be graduates of an accredited secondary school, with 16 academic units, including 4 in English and 1 each in algebra, advanced algebra, geometry, and U.S. history. It is recommended that the remaining units be made up of foreign language, laboratory science, and additional academic electives in the student's areas of strength. The GED is accepted. An essay is required. AP and CLEP credits are accepted. Important factors used in the admissions decision are extracurricular activities record, evidence of special talents, recommendations by alumni, recommendations by school officials, and parents or siblings attending the school.

Procedure: Freshmen are admitted to all sessions. Entrance exams should be taken by December of the senior year. Applications should be filed by March 1 for fall entry and January 1 for spring entry, along with an application fee of $35. Notification is sent April 1. There is an early admissions plan. A waiting list is an active part of the admissions procedure, with about 15% of applicants on the list.

Transfer: About 194 transfer students enrolled in 1993–94. Applicants must have a GPA of 2.3 and a minimum of 23 transferable academic semester units. A total of 9 credits out of 36 course credits must be completed at the college.

Visiting: There are regularly scheduled orientations for prospective students. There are guides for informal visits and visitors may sit in on classes and stay overnight at the school. To arrange for a visit, contact the Admissions Office at (510) 631–4224.

Financial Aid: In 1993–94 53% of all current freshmen received some form of financial aid. About 51% of freshmen received need-based aid. The average freshman award was $9896. Twenty-seven percent of undergraduate students work part-time. The college is a member of CSS. The FAF and the FAFSA are required. The deadline for financial aid applications is March 1.

International Students: There are currently 126 international students enrolled. The school actively recruits these students. They must take the TOEFL and achieve a minimum score of 525. Non-native English speakers who submit a score of 525 or higher on the TOEFL may be admitted as full-time undergraduates. Others may be accepted conditionally and enrolled in the college's Intensive English Program.

Computers: The college provides computer facilities for student use. The mainframe is a Prime minicomputer networked to microcomputer systems at several campus locations. The central computer laboratory in the library is available to all students. There are no time limits and no fees.

Graduates: In 1992–93 476 bachelor's degrees were awarded. Within an average freshman class, 64% graduate in 4 years, 66% in 5 years, and 68% in 6 years.

Admissions Contact: Michael Beseda, Director of Admissions.

SAMUEL MERRITT COLLEGE
Oakland, CA 94609–9954

B-3
(510) 420–6076

Full-time: 19 men, 263 women	Faculty: 11
Part-time: 1 man, 18 women	Ph.D.s: 18%
Graduate: 56 men, 224 women	Student/Faculty: 26 to 1
Year: 4-1-4, summer session	Tuition: $11,930
Application Deadline: July 15	Room & Board: $5520
Freshman Class: 75 applied, 38 accepted, 14 enrolled	
SAT I Verbal/Math: 453/459	**COMPETITIVE**

Samuel Merritt College, founded in 1909, is a private, independent, coeducational college offering a nursing program in cooperation with St. Mary's College of California. There are 3 graduate schools. In addition to regional accreditation, Samuel Merritt College has baccalaureate program accreditation with NLN. The 2 libraries contain 6910 volumes, 108 microform items, and 290 audiovisual forms, and subscribe to 271 periodicals. Computerized library sources and services include the card catalog. Special learning facilities include a Health Education Center, and a television studio. The 1-acre campus is in an urban area 10 miles east of San Francisco. Including residence halls, there are 3 buildings on campus.

Student Life: Most of the undergraduates are from California. Students come from 9 foreign countries. The average age of all undergraduates is 23.

Housing: A total of 93 students can be accommodated in college housing. College-sponsored living facilities include coed dormitories. On-campus housing is guaranteed for all 4 years. Some 67% of students commute. Alcohol is not permitted. All students may keep cars on campus.

Activities: There are no fraternities or sororities on campus. There are 3 groups on campus, including international, professional, radio and TV, religious, social service, student government, and yearbook. Popular campus events include Career Fair, Beginning-of-the-Year Bar-B-Que, and Half-Way Dinner.

Sports: There is no sports program at Samuel Merritt College. Athletic and recreation facilities include a swimming pool and an exercise room.

Disabled Students: The entire campus is accessible to disabled students. The following facilities are available: wheelchair ramps, elevators, special parking, specially equipped rest rooms, and lowered drinking fountains.

Services: In addition to many counseling and information services, tutoring is available in every subject. In addition, there is remedial math, reading, and writing.

Programs of Study: Samuel Merritt College awards the B.S.N. degree. Bachelor's degrees are awarded in HEALTH PROFESSIONS (nursing).

Required: Students must take a basic core curriculum with a minimum of 128 total credit hours including 69 lower division and 60 upper-division courses. Students must take at least 60 hours in the major. A minimum GPA of 2.0 overall and in the nursing major is necessary.

Special: The college offers study abroad in Switzerland and work-study programs with the federal government. Students may take advantage of an accelerated degree program in nursing if they have a prior degree, and may declare a second major through St. Mary's College of California. The college offers nondegree study, pass/fail options, and credit for life, military, and work experience. There is a freshman honors program on campus, as well as 1 national honor society.

Faculty/Classroom: About 5% of faculty are male; 95%, female. The average class size in an introductory lecture is 30 and in a laboratory, 16.

Admissions: About 51% of the 1993–94 applicants were accepted. The SAT scores for the 1993–94 freshman class were as follows: Verbal—83% below 500 and 17% between 500 and 599; Math—83% below 500 and 17% between 500 and 599. About 20% of the current freshmen were in the top fifth of their class; 33% were in the top two fifths.

Requirements: A minimum GPA of 2.5 is required. The SAT I is required. Students must be high school graduates, or hold a GED. Candidates for admission should have completed 3 years of English, 2 years of mathematics, 2 years of science, and 2 years of social studies. AP and CLEP credits are accepted. Important factors used in the admissions decision are recommendations by school officials and advanced placement or honor courses.

Procedure: Freshmen are admitted in the fall, spring, and summer. Entrance exams should be taken within 3 to 4 months of admission. Applications should be filed by July 15 for fall entry, December 15 for spring entry, and July 1 for summer entry, along with an application fee of $35. Notification is sent on a rolling basis. There is a deferred admissions plan.

Transfer: A minimum college GPA of 2.5 for students with more than 30 prior credits is required. A total of 18 credits out of 128 must be completed at Samuel Merritt College.

Visiting: There are regularly scheduled orientations for prospective students, including a campus tour and meetings with students and faculty. There are guides for informal visits and visitors may sit in on classes and stay overnight at the school. To arrange for a visit, contact the Office of Admission at (510) 420–6076.

Financial Aid: In an earlier year, 80% of all current freshmen and 62% of continuing students received some form of financial aid. Scholarships or need-based grants averaged $7200 ($9000 maximum); loans averaged $2625 ($5125 maximum); and work contracts averaged $300. Some 90% of undergraduate students work part-time. The average financial indebtedness of the 1992–93 graduate was $20,100. Samuel Merritt College is a member of CSS. The FAF, FFS, SFS, or SAAC is required. The deadline for financial aid applications is March 2.

International Students: The school actively recruits these students. They must take the TOEFL and achieve a minimum score of 550. The student must also take the SAT I or the ACT.

Computers: The college provides computer facilities for student use. The academic computer laboratory at St. Mary's College is available to Samuel Merritt students. There are no time limits on using the system and no fees.

Graduates: In an earlier year, 52 bachelor's degrees were awarded. Some 55 companies recruited on campus in an earlier year.

Admissions Contact: Admissions Office.

SAN DIEGO STATE UNIVERSITY
D-5

San Diego, CA 92182   (619) 594-6871

Full-time: 7961 men, 8446 women	Faculty: 1199; IIA, +$
Part-time: 2697 men, 2853 women	Ph.D.s: n/av
Graduate: 2304 men, 3312 women	Student/Faculty: 18 to 1
Year: semesters	Tuition: $1742 ($7646)
Application Deadline: November 30	Room & Board: $4950
Freshman Class: 8187 applied, 7319 accepted, 2209 enrolled	
SAT I Verbal/Math: 390/460	ACT: 19 LESS COMPETITIVE

San Diego State University, founded in 1897, is a public, coeducational, liberal arts university that is part of the California State University system. There are 8 undergraduate schools. In addition to regional accreditation, SDSU has baccalaureate program accreditation with ACEJMC, ADA, ASLA, CSWE, FIDER, NASAD, NASM, NCATE, NLN, and NRPA. The library contains 1,062,800 volumes, 3,400,000 microform items, and 5300 audiovisual forms, and subscribes to 5132 periodicals. Computerized library sources and services include the card catalog. Special learning facilities include a learning resource center, art gallery, and radio station. The 279-acre campus is in an urban area 8 miles east of San Diego.

Student Life: Fifty-eight percent are white; 12% Hispanic.

Housing: College-sponsored living facilities include coed dormitories, fraternity houses, and sorority houses. On-campus housing is available on a first-come, first-served basis. All students may keep cars on campus.

Activities: There are 17 national fraternities and 12 national sororities. There are many groups and organizations on campus, including band, cheerleading, dance, drama, drill team, honors, international, jazz band, marching band, musical theater, newspaper, opera, pep band, radio and TV, and student government.

Sports: Intercollegiate athletic teams at SDSU complete in the Western Athletic Conference.

Disabled Students: Ninety percent of the campus is accessible to disabled students. The following facilities are available: wheelchair ramps, elevators, special parking, specially equipped rest rooms, and special class scheduling.

Campus Safety and Security: Campus safety and security measures include 24-hour foot and vehicle patrol, self defense education, escort service, and informal discussions. In addition, there are emergency telephones.

Programs of Study: SDSU awards the B.A. and B.S. degrees. Master's degrees also are awarded. Bachelor's degrees are awarded in BIOLOGICAL SCIENCE (biology/biological science), BUSINESS (accounting and business administration and management), COMMUNICATIONS AND THE ARTS (broadcasting, dance, dramatic arts, English, fine arts, journalism, and music), COMPUTER AND PHYSICAL SCIENCE (chemistry, computer programming, computer science, geology, mathematics, and physics), EDUCATION (home economics), ENGINEERING AND ENVIRONMENTAL DESIGN (aeronautical engineering, civil engineering, electrical/electronics engineering, and mechanical engineering), HEALTH PROFESSIONS (nursing and speech pathology/audiology), SOCIAL SCIENCE (anthropology, criminal justice, economics, geography, history, philosophy, political science/government, psychology, public administration, religion, social science, social work, sociology, and urban studies). Business administration is the strongest academically and has the largest enrollment.

Required: Students must complete 124 to 133 credit hours, including 49 general education units. The number of hours in the major varies by program. A 2.0 or higher GPA must be maintained, depending on the major.

Special: Students may study abroad in London and Paris and receive special credit for life, military, and work experience. There is a freshman honors program on campus, as well as 20 national honor societies, including Phi Beta Kappa.

Admissions: About 89% of the 1993–94 applicants were accepted. The SAT scores for the 1993–94 freshman class were as follows: Verbal—86% below 500, 12% between 500 and 599, and 2% between 600 and 700; Math—65% below 500, 26% between 500 and 599, 8% between 600 and 700, and 1% above 700. The ACT scores were 63% below 21, 24% between 21 and 23, 10% between 24 and 26, 1% between 27 and 28, and 2% above 28.

Requirements: A minimum GPA of 2.0 is required. The SAT I or ACT is required. Candidates for admission should have completed 4 years of English, 2 years of a foreign language, 3 years of mathematics, and 1 year each of science with laboratory, and visual and performing arts. Advanced placement or honor courses is an important factor used in the admission decision.

Procedure: Freshmen are admitted fall and spring. Entrance exams should be taken in high school. Applications should be filed by November 30 for fall entry and August 30 for spring entry, along with an application fee of $55. Notification is sent on a rolling basis.

Transfer: Transfer students must complete a total of 124 to 133 credit hours at SDSU.

Visiting: There are regularly scheduled orientations for prospective students, including tours that can be scheduled with SDSU ambassadors. Visitors may stay overnight at the school. To arrange for a visit, contact Housing and Residential Life at (619) 594–5742.

Financial Aid: In a recent year 38% of all current freshmen and 26% of continuing students received some form of financial aid. The FAF or FFS and SAAC are required.

International Students: They must take the TOEFL and achieve a minimum score of 550.

Computers: The college provides computer facilities for student use. The mainframe is an IBM. There are no time limits on using the system and no fees.

Admissions Contact: Admissions and Records Office.

SAN FRANCISCO ART INSTITUTE
B-3

San Francisco, CA 94133   (415) 749–4500
    (800) 345-SFAI (out-of-state)

Full-time: 229 men, 206 women	Faculty: 40
Part-time: 26 men, 44 women	Ph.D.s: 90%
Graduate: 58 men, 75 women	Student/Faculty: 11 to 1
Year: semesters, summer session	Tuition: $12,900
Application Deadline: open	Room & Board: n/app
Freshman Class: 196 applied, 146 accepted, 43 enrolled	SPECIAL

San Francisco Art Institute, founded in 1871, is a private, coeducational commuter college devoted solely to the fine arts. In addition to regional accreditation, SFAI has baccalaureate program accreditation with NASAD. The library contains 27,000 volumes and 810 audiovisual forms, and subscribes to 200 periodicals. Special learning facilities include a learning resource center and art gallery. The 3-acre campus is in an urban area. There is one building on campus. There are no residence halls.

Student Life: About 66% of undergraduates are from California. Students come from 24 states, 18 foreign countries, and Canada. Seventy-nine percent are white. The average age of freshmen is 20; all undergraduates, 26. Twelve percent drop out by the end of their first year; 27% remain to graduate.

Housing: There are no residence halls. All students commute. Alcohol is not permitted.

Activities: There are no fraternities or sororities on campus. There are 6 groups on campus, including art, ethnic, gay, international, newspaper, and student government. Popular campus events include visiting artist lectures, symposia, and annual Halloween and Mardi Gras parties.

Sports: There is no sports program at SFAI.

Disabled Students: Ten percent of the campus is accessible to disabled students. The following facilities are available: wheelchair ramps, special parking, specially equipped rest rooms, and special class scheduling.

Services: In addition to many counseling and information services, tutoring is available in most subjects. There is also remedial math, reading, and writing.

Campus Safety and Security: Campus safety and security measures include 24-hour foot and vehicle patrol and emergency telephones.

Programs of Study: SFAI awards the B.F.A. degree. Master's degrees also are awarded. Bachelor's degrees are awarded in COMMUNICATIONS AND THE ARTS (film arts, fine arts, painting, photography, printmaking, sculpture, and video). Painting and photography have the largest enrollments.

Required: Students are required to complete at least 120 credit hours, 36 of which must be in the major. Six liberal arts units, 24 studio units, and 15 art history units must be completed, as well as 33 units in the Letters and Science Program. SFAI requires a minimum GPA of 2.0.

Special: Students may cross-register with various other institutions and participate in off-campus internships for credit. There are study-abroad opportunities in 9 countries. The institute offers dual majors in all subjects, nondegree study, work-study with SFAI, and pass/fail options in the senior year.

Faculty/Classroom: Seventy percent of faculty are male; 30%, female. All teach undergraduates. No introductory courses are taught by graduate students. The average class size in an introductory lecture is 100; in a laboratory and in a regular course offering, 17.

Admissions: About 74% of a recent year's applicants were accepted.

Requirements: The SAT I or ACT is required, with a minimum required score of 20 on the ACT or 420 on the SAT I verbal. AP and CLEP credits are accepted. Important factors used in the admissions

decision are evidence of special talents, personality, intangible qualities, leadership record, extracurricular activities record, and ability to finance college education.

Procedure: Freshmen are admitted to all sessions. Application deadlines are open. The application fee is $50. Notification is sent on a rolling basis. There is a deferred admissions plan.

Transfer: About 162 transfer students enrolled in 1993–94. Transfer students must have satisfactory prior college performance and a portfolio appropriate to their level of experience. A total of 30 credits out of 120 must be completed at SFAI.

Visiting: There are guides for informal visits and visitors may sit in on classes. To arrange for a visit, contact the Office of Admissions at (800) 345-SFAI.

Financial Aid: In 1993–94 60% of all students received some form of financial aid, of which all was need-based. The average freshman award was $10,461. Of that total, scholarships or need-based grants averaged $4807 ($7000 maximum); loans averaged $2625 (maximum); work contracts averaged $1000 (maximum); and Pell grants averaged $1599 ($2300 maximum). Thirty-two percent of undergraduate students work part-time. Average earnings from campus work for the school year are $2500. The average financial indebtedness of the 1992–93 graduate was $10,000. The FAF, the college's own financial statement and the FAFSA are required. The priority deadline for financial aid applications is April 1.

International Students: There are currently 57 international students enrolled. They must take the TOEFL and achieve a minimum score of 500.

Computers: The college provides computer facilities for student use. The mainframe is a DEC MiniVAX. Students have access to 2 computer laboratories. Six Macintoshes are for learning-disabled students, and 6 Amigas can be used for video processing. There are no time limits and no fees.

Graduates: In 1992–93, 135 bachelor's degrees were awarded. Within an average freshman class, 27% graduate in 5 years.

Admissions Contact: Tim Robison, Director of Admissions.

SAN FRANCISCO CONSERVATORY OF MUSIC   B-3
San Francisco, CA 94122   (415) 759–3431

Full-time: 60 men, 84 women	Faculty: 23
Part-time: 10 men, 12 women	Ph.D.s: 29%
Graduate: 40 men, 68 women	Student/Faculty: 6 to 1
Year: semesters	Tuition: $12,250
Application Deadline: July 1	Room & Board: n/app
Freshman Class: 68 applied, 37 accepted, 23 enrolled	
SAT I Verbal/Math: 468/547	**SPECIAL**

San Francisco Conservatory of Music, founded in 1917, is a private, coeducational college, offering undergraduate, graduate, and non-degree programs in music. There is one graduate school. In addition to regional accreditation, SFCM has baccalaureate program accreditation with NASM. The library contains 33,500 volumes, 10,700 audiovisual forms, and subscribes to 73 periodicals. Computerized library sources and services include the card catalog, interlibrary loan, and database searching. The 5-acre campus is in an urban area in a residential neighborhood of San Francisco. There are 3 buildings on campus.

Student Life: About 48% of undergraduates are from California. Students come from 26 states, 15 foreign countries, and Canada. Ninety percent are from public schools; 10% from private. Fifty-three percent are white; 27% foreign nationals; 14% Asian American. The average age of freshmen is 18; all undergraduates, 21. Five percent drop out by the end of their first year; 45% remain to graduate.

Housing: There are no residence halls; all students commute. All students may keep cars on campus.

Activities: There are no fraternities or sororities on campus. There are some groups and organizations on campus, including chorus, opera, orchestra, student government, and symphony. Popular campus events include Musical Marathon and the nearly 300 recitals and concerts scheduled each year.

Sports: There is no sports program at SFCM.

Disabled Students: Ninety percent of the campus is accessible to disabled students. The following facilities are available: wheelchair ramps, elevators, special parking, and specially equipped rest rooms.

Campus Safety and Security: Campus safety and security measures include pamphlets, posters, and films, emergency telephones, and lighted pathways and sidewalks.

Programs of Study: SFCM awards the B.Mus. degree. Master's degrees also are awarded. Bachelor's degrees are awarded in COMMUNICATIONS AND THE ARTS (music). However, students may only specialize in specific fields such as guitar, composition, conducting, all orchestral instruments, all keyboard instruments, and voice. Voice, piano, violin, cello, and guitar have the largest enrollments.

Required: Students must complete 130 credit hours, 100 of which must be music-related, and the remainder in general education courses. Specific required courses and total number of hours in the

major vary by instrument. Students must also pass the senior recital and maintain a minimum GPA of 2.0.

Faculty/Classroom: Seventy-one percent of faculty are male; 29%, female. All teach undergraduates. No introductory courses are taught by graduate students. The average class size in an introductory lecture is 15 and in a regular course offering, 7.

Admissions: About 54% of the 1993–94 applicants were accepted. The SAT scores for the 1993–94 freshman class were as follows: Verbal—50% below 500, 25% between 500 and 599, 19% between 600 and 700, and 6% above 700; Math—43% below 500, 12% between 500 and 599, 39% between 600 and 700, and 6% above 700.

Requirements: A minimum GPA of 2.0 is required. The SAT I is required. No minimum score is necessary. All applicants must have reached a high level of musical proficiency. An audition is required. AP and CLEP credits are accepted. Important factors used in the admissions decision are evidence of special talents, recommendations by school officials, recommendations by alumni, personality, intangible qualities, and extracurricular activities record.

Procedure: Freshmen are admitted fall and spring. Applications should be filed by July 1 for fall entry and November 15 for spring entry, along with an application fee of $60. Notification is sent on a rolling basis. There are early admissions and deferred admissions plans. A waiting list is an active part of the admissions procedure, with about 15% of applicants on the list.

Transfer: About 36 transfer students enrolled in 1993–94. Transfer students must demonstrate a high level of musical proficiency and have a good academic record. An audition is required. A total of 30 credits out of 130 must be completed at SFCM.

Visiting: There are guides for informal visits and visitors may sit in on classes. To arrange for a visit, contact Kate Murdock, Admissions at (415) 759–3431.

Financial Aid: In 1993–94 43% of all current freshmen and 65% of continuing students received some form of financial aid. About 35% of freshmen and 60% of continuing students received need-based aid. The average freshman award was $6860. Of that total, scholarships or need-based grants averaged $3900 ($8000 maximum); loans averaged $3734 ($5625 maximum); and work contracts averaged $500 ($1200 maximum). Sixty percent of undergraduate students work part-time. Average earnings from campus work for the school year are $1100. The average financial indebtedness of graduates in a recent year was $8450. The FAF, the college's own financial statement, and the SAR are required. The deadline for financial aid applications is April 1.

International Students: There are currently 74 international students enrolled. They must take the TOEFL and achieve a minimum score of 500.

Computers: The college provides computer facilities for student use. Students have access to a computer laboratory equipped with Apple microcomputers, electronic keyboards, and a laser printer. Software includes class tutorials and a variety of commercially available music programs. All students may access the system. It may be used when the building is open. There are no time limits and no fees.

Graduates: In 1992–93 32 bachelor's degrees were awarded. The most popular majors among graduates were voice (34%), cello (12%), and violin and piano (9% each). Within an average freshman class, 38% graduate in 4 years, 43% in 5 years, and 52% in 6 years. In the 1992 graduating class, 60% of the men and 50% of the women were enrolled in graduate school within 6 months of graduation; 30% of the men and 40% of the women had found employment.

Admissions Contact: Kate Murdock, Admissions Office.

SAN FRANCISCO STATE UNIVERSITY   B-3
San Francisco, CA 94132   (415) 338–2017

Full-time: 5656 men, 7509 women	Faculty: 977
Part-time: 2567 men, 3370 women	Ph.D.s: n/av
Graduate: 2462 men, 4149 women	Student/Faculty: 13 to 1
Year: semesters, summer session	Tuition: $1792 ($9172)
Application Deadline: November 30	Room & Board: $5500
Freshman Class: 3989 applied, 3539 accepted, 1259 enrolled	
SAT I or ACT: required	**LESS COMPETITIVE**

San Francisco State University, founded in 1899, is a public liberal arts institution offering graduate and undergraduate programs as part of the California State University system. There are 8 undergraduate and 8 graduate schools. In addition to regional accreditation, SFSU has baccalaureate program accreditation with AACSB, ACEJMC, ADA, AHEA, NASM, and NLN. The library contains 636,369 volumes and 970,498 microform items, and subscribes to 559,000 periodicals. Computerized library sources and services include the card catalog. Special learning facilities include a learning resource center and a field campus and an anthropology museum. The 130-acre campus is in an urban area. Including residence halls, there are 23 buildings on campus.

Student Life: About 78% of undergraduates are from California. Students come from 17 states, 12 foreign countries, and Canada. Forty-eight percent are white; 31% Asian American; 10% Hispanic. The average age of all undergraduates is 23.7. Seventeen percent drop out by the end of their first year; 62% remain to graduate.

Housing: College-sponsored living facilities include coed dormitories. On-campus housing is available on a first-come, first-served basis. Ninety-five percent of students commute. Alcohol is not permitted. All students may keep cars on campus.

Activities: There are 12 national fraternities and 4 local and 8 national sororities. There are 200 groups on campus, including art, band, cheerleading, chorale, dance, drama, ethnic, film, gay, honors, jazz band, literary magazine, musical theater, newspaper, opera, orchestra, pep band, political, radio and TV, social service, student government, symphony, and yearbook. Popular campus events include Activities Fair and Crafts Festival.

Sports: There are 8 intercollegiate sports for men and 7 for women, and 10 intramural sports for men and 10 for women. Athletic and recreation facilities include a 6500-seat stadium, 2 gymnasiums, an indoor pool, a weight room, a training room, wrestling and gymnastics areas, an all-weather track, 14 tennis courts, softball and baseball fields, and auxiliary practice fields.

Disabled Students: The following facilities are available: wheelchair ramps, elevators, special parking, specially equipped rest rooms, lowered drinking fountains, lowered telephones, readers, interpreters, an equipment loan, on-campus transportation, and priority registration.

Services: In addition to many counseling and information services, tutoring is available in every subject.

Campus Safety and Security: Campus safety and security measures include escort service, shuttle buses, emergency telephones, and lighted pathways and sidewalks.

Programs of Study: SFSU awards the B.A., B.S., B.M., and B.Voc.Ed. degrees. Associate, master's, and doctoral degrees also are awarded. Bachelor's degrees are awarded in BIOLOGICAL SCIENCE (biochemistry, biology/biological science, botany, cell biology, ecology, marine biology, microbiology, physiology, and zoology), BUSINESS (accounting, banking and finance, business administration and management, international business management, labor studies, management science, marketing/retailing/merchandising, personnel management, real estate, and transportation management), COMMUNICATIONS AND THE ARTS (broadcasting, Chinese, classics, comparative literature, dance, dramatic arts, English, film arts, fine arts, French, German, Italian, Japanese, journalism, music, Russian, and speech/debate/rhetoric), COMPUTER AND PHYSICAL SCIENCE (applied mathematics, chemistry, computer science, geology, information sciences and systems, mathematics, physics, science, and statistics), EDUCATION (early childhood, elementary, home economics, industrial arts, physical, recreation, secondary, special, and vocational), ENGINEERING AND ENVIRONMENTAL DESIGN (civil engineering, electrical/electronics engineering, engineering, industrial administration/management, interior design, and mechanical engineering), HEALTH PROFESSIONS (allied health, clinical science, health science, medical laboratory technology, nursing, physical therapy, public health, and speech pathology/audiology), SOCIAL SCIENCE (African American studies, American studies, anthropology, clothing and textiles management/production/services, dietetics, economics, geography, history, humanities, interdisciplinary studies, international relations, liberal arts/general studies, philosophy, political science/government, psychology, social work, sociology, urban studies, and women's studies).

Required: To graduate, students must complete 124 to 132 credits with a minimum GPA of 2.0. The required general education core includes 27 credits in arts and sciences, 12 in basic skills subjects, and 9 in upper-division courses. English composition and U.S. history and government competency requirements may be fulfilled by either examination or course work.

Special: Students may cross-register with the California College of Podiatric Medicine, the City College of San Francisco, Cogswell College of Engineering, and several other area universities. Study abroad in numerous countries, a Washington semester, campus work-study, a general studies degree, dual and student-designed majors, credit for life experience, nondegree study, and pass/fail options are also offered. There is a chapter of Phi Beta Kappa on campus. Two departments have honors programs.

Faculty/Classroom: No introductory courses are taught by graduate students.

Admissions: About 89% of the 1993–94 applicants were accepted. The SAT scores for the 1993–94 freshman class were as follows: Verbal—87% below 500, 9% between 500 and 599, and 3% between 600 and 700; Math—66% below 500, 25% between 500 and 599, and 8% between 600 and 700. The ACT scores were 66% below 21, 19% between 21 and 23, 12% between 24 and 26, 1% between 27 and 28, and 2% above 28.

Requirements: A minimum GPA of 2.0 is required. The SAT I or ACT is required. Applicants should be graduates of an accredited secondary school with a minimum GPA of 2.0. The GED is accepted. High school courses should include 4 years of English, 3 of mathematics, 2 of foreign language, and 1 each of U.S. history or government, laboratory science, and visual and performing arts. AP and CLEP credits are accepted.

Procedure: Freshmen are admitted fall and spring. Applications should be filed by November 30 for fall entry and August 31 for spring entry, along with an application fee of $55. Notification is sent on a rolling basis beginning April 1.

Transfer: More than 2000 transfer students enrolled in an earlier year. Applicants must have a college GPA of 2.0 (2.4 for nonresidents). Those with fewer than 56 tranferable semester credits must meet freshman entrance requirements. A total of 30 credits out of 124 to 140 must be completed at SFSU.

Visiting: There are regularly scheduled orientations for prospective students. Visitors may sit in on classes. To arrange for a visit, contact Student Outreach Services.

Financial Aid: In an earlier year, 54% of all freshmen and 35% of continuing students received some form of financial aid. SFSU is a member of CSS. The FAF or FFS is required. The deadline for financial aid applications is March 2.

International Students: There are currently 1200 international students enrolled. They must take the TOEFL and achieve a minimum score of 500.

Computers: The college provides computer facilities for student use. The mainframe is a DEC VAX 6420 and an IBM 4381/R22. There are 46 dial-in modems, more than 100 networked terminals, and more than 1000 IBM, Apple, and other personal computers available for all students' use. It may be used 24 hours daily with no time limits on using the system and no fees.

Graduates: In 1992–93, 4095 bachelor's degrees were awarded. The most popular majors among graduates were business administration (28%), psychology (7%), and liberal studies (6%).

Admissions Contact: Patricia Wade, Admissions Officer.

SAN JOSE STATE UNIVERSITY B-3

San Jose, CA 95192 **(408) 924-2000**

Full-time: 7199 men, 7193 women	Faculty: 1053; IIA, +$
Part-time: 3678 men, 3585 women	Ph.D.s: 49%
Graduate: 2152 men, 3250 women	Student/Faculty: 14 to 1
Year: semesters, summer session	Tuition: $1724 ($7628)
Application Deadline: November 1	Room & Board: $4956
Freshman Class: 4615 applied, 4094 accepted, 1420 enrolled	
SAT I Verbal/Math: 360/460	ACT: 18 LESS COMPETITIVE

San Jose State University, founded in 1857 and part of the California State University system, is a public coeducational institution offering undergraduate and graduate programs in applied arts and science, social science, and social work to a primarily commuter student body. There are 8 undergraduate and 8 graduate schools. In addition to regional accreditation, SJSU has baccalaureate program accreditation with AACSB, ABET, ACEJMC, ADA, ASLA, NASAD, NASM, NCATE, and NLN. The 2 libraries contain 1,015,000 volumes, 1,365,000 microform items, and 38,000 audiovisual forms, and subscribe to 4400 periodicals. Computerized library sources and services include the card catalog, interlibrary loans, and database searching. Special learning facilities include a learning resource center, art gallery, radio station, and TV station. The 117-acre campus is in an urban area in the center of San Jose. Including residence halls, there are 55 buildings on campus.

Student Life: About 97% of undergraduates are from California; 2% are foreign. Students come from 41 states, 114 foreign countries, and Canada. Some 82% are from public schools; 13% from private. About 41% are white; 25% Asian American; 12% Hispanic. The average age of freshmen is 19.5; all undergraduates, 25.3. About 20% drop out by the end of their first year; 40% remain to graduate.

Housing: A total of 2014 students can be accommodated in college housing. College-sponsored living facilities include coed dormitories, on-campus apartments, and fraternity and sorority houses. In addition, there are special interest houses and and an international students' center. On-campus housing is available on a first-come, first-served basis. Alcohol is not permitted. All students may keep cars on campus.

Activities: About 8% of men belong to 2 local and 19 national fraternities; about 4% of women belong to 2 local and 10 national sororities. There are 200 groups on campus, including art, band, cheerleading, choir, chorale, chorus, dance, drama, ethnic, film, gay, international, jazz band, literary magazine, marching band, musical theater, newspaper, photography, political, radio and TV, social, student government, and symphony.

Sports: Athletic and recreation facilities include a gymnasium, pool, track, football field, and a recreation center with racquetball courts and a bowling alley.

Disabled Students: About 95% of the campus is accessible to disabled students. The following facilities are available: wheelchair ramps, elevators, special parking, specially equipped rest rooms, special class scheduling, lowered drinking fountains, lowered telephones, and preadmission assistance.

Services: In addition to many counseling and information services, tutoring is available in most subjects. There is also a reader service for the blind. There are also test accommodations, sign-language interpreters, liaisons to faculty, and note takers.

Campus Safety and Security: Campus safety and security measures include 24-hour foot and vehicle patrol, self defense education, escort service, and shuttle buses. In addition, there are informal discussions, pamphlets, posters, and films, emergency telephones, lighted pathways and sidewalks, and a canine patrol.

Programs of Study: SJSU awards the B.A., B.S., and B.F.A. degrees. Master's degrees are also awarded. Bachelor's degrees are awarded in BIOLOGICAL SCIENCE (biochemistry, biology/biological science, botany, microbiology, and zoology), BUSINESS (accounting, banking and finance, international business management, and marketing/retailing/merchandising), COMMUNICATIONS AND THE ARTS (advertising, broadcasting, dance, design, dramatic arts, English, film arts, fine arts, French, German, journalism, music, Spanish, and speech/debate/rhetoric), COMPUTER AND PHYSICAL SCIENCE (chemistry, computer science, geology, mathematics, physics, and statistics), EDUCATION (early childhood and teaching English as a second language/foreign language), ENGINEERING AND ENVIRONMENTAL DESIGN (aeronautical engineering, chemical engineering, civil engineering, computer engineering, electrical engineering, engineering, industrial engineering, materials engineering, and mechanical engineering), HEALTH PROFESSIONS (nursing, occupational therapy, and speech pathology/audiology), SOCIAL SCIENCE (anthropology, criminal justice, economics, food science, geography, history, philosophy, political science/government, psychology, religion, social science, social work, and sociology). Accounting is the strongest program academically. Accounting, electrical engineering, management, and art have the largest enrollments.

Required: Students must complete 39 units of core general education, including 12 units of upper-division courses in residence and 6 units of American history and institutions. A minimum of 124 credits, with at least 24 in the major, a minimum GPA of 2.0, and the successful completion of writing, English, and entry-level mathematics tests are required in order to graduate.

Special: SJSU has opportunities for cooperative programs in business, science, engineering, arts, and the humanities, work-study with many employers, internships (some required, some optional), study abroad in 16 countries, field experiences, and student teaching. An accelerated program is offered in nursing, and the B.A.-B.S. degree and dual majors are available in various areas of study. A general studies degree, student-designed majors, nondegree study, and credit/no-credit options are possible. There are 3 national honor societies on campus. Eighteen departments have honors programs.

Faculty/Classroom: About 70% of faculty are male; 30%, female. The average class size in an introductory lecture is 30; in a laboratory, 20; and in a regular course offering, 25.

Admissions: About 89% of the 1993-94 applicants were accepted. The SAT scores for the 1993-94 freshman class were as follows: Verbal—89% below 500, 9% between 500 and 599, and 1% between 600 and 700; Math—60% below 500, 28% between 500 and 599, 12% between 600 and 700, and 1% above 700. The ACT scores were 66% below 21, 18% between 21 and 23, 11% between 24 and 26, 4% between 27 and 28, and 1% above 28.

Requirements: A minimum GPA of 2.1 is required. The SAT I or ACT is required. Scores are used to calculate an eligibility index rating, which determines qualification for admission. Graduation from an accredited secondary school is required; the GED is accepted. Applicants must have completed 4 years of English, 2 of a foreign language, 1 each of history, science, and art, and 3 each of mathematics and electives. AP and CLEP credits are accepted. Important factors used in the admissions decision are recommendations by school officials, recommendations by alumni, personality, intangible qualities, parents or siblings attending the school, and leadership record.

Procedure: Freshmen are admitted in the fall and spring. Entrance exams should be taken prior to the fall semester. Applications should be filed by November 1 for fall entry, August 1 for spring entry, and February 1 for summer entry, along with an application fee of $55. Notification is sent on a rolling basis.

Transfer: About 3272 transfer students enrolled in a recent year. Transfer students must have a minimum GPA of 2.0. The student's rating in the eligibility index is also considered in determining qualification for transfer. A total of 30 credits out of at least 124 must be completed at SJSU.

Visiting: There are regularly scheduled orientations for prospective students. There are guides for informal visits and visitors may sit in on classes. To arrange for a visit, contact the Office of Relations with Schools at (408) 924-2564.

Financial Aid: In a recent year, 24% of all current freshmen and 39% of continuing students received some form of financial aid. The average freshman award was $3500. Of that total, scholarships or need-based grants averaged $965 ($3000 maximum); loans averaged $800 ($1500 maximum); and work contracts averaged $750 ($2500 maximum). The average financial indebtedness of a recent graduate was $4905. SJSU is a member of CSS. The FAF, FFS, SFS, or AFSA is required. The deadline for financial aid applications is March 1.

International Students: There are currently 385 international students enrolled. The school actively recruits these students. They must take the TOEFL and achieve a minimum score of 500. The student must also take the SAT I or the ACT.

Computers: The college provides computer facilities for student use. The mainframe is an IBM 3090. Approximately 50% of students use the 1597 microcomputers available, about 300 of which are networked. All students may access the system. It may be used 9 A.M. to 8 P.M. Monday through Friday and 9 A.M. to 5 P.M. Saturday. There are no time limits on using the system and no fees.

Graduates: In 1992-93, 4364 bachelor's degrees were awarded. The most popular majors among graduates were accounting (7%), marketing (5%), and psychology (4%). Within an average freshman class, 5% graduate in 4 years, 24% in 5 years, and 36% in 6 years. Some 949 companies recruited on campus in 1992-93.

Admissions Contact: Edgar Chambers, Admissions Office.

SANTA CLARA UNIVERSITY
B-3
Santa Clara, CA 95053
(408) 554-4700

Full-time: 1875 men, 2016 women
Part-time: 76 men, 52 women
Graduate: 2117 men, 1542 women
Year: quarters, summer session
Application Deadline: February 1
Freshman Class: 4019 applied, 2779 accepted, 888 enrolled
SAT I: required

Faculty: 300; IIA, +$
Ph.Ds: 91%
Student/Faculty: 13 to 1
Tuition: $12,879
Room & Board: $5904

VERY COMPETITIVE

Santa Clara University, founded in 1851 by Jesuit priests, is a private, coeducational institution offering undergraduate and graduate degrees in arts and sciences, engineering, and business. There are 3 undergraduate and 4 graduate schools. In addition to regional accreditation, SCU has baccalaureate program accreditation with AACSB, ABET, and NASM. The 3 libraries contain 567,386 volumes and 511,070 microform items, and subscribe to 5375 periodicals. Computerized library sources and services include the card catalog, interlibrary loans, and database searching. Special learning facilities include a learning resource center, art gallery, planetarium, radio station, and TV station. The 103-acre campus is in a suburban area 46 miles south of San Francisco. Including residence halls, there are 51 buildings on campus.

Student Life: About 66% of undergraduates are from California. Students come from 42 states, 71 foreign countries, and Canada. Fifty-six percent are from public schools; 44% from private. Fifty-nine percent are white; 16% Asian American; 13% Hispanic. Fifty-five percent are Catholic; 25% claim no religious affiliation; 14% Protestant. The average age of freshmen is 18; all undergraduates, 21. Nine percent drop out by the end of their first year; 80% remain to graduate.

Housing: A total of 1916 students can be accommodated in college housing. College-sponsored living facilities include coed dormitories and off-campus apartments. In addition there are language houses and special interest houses. On-campus housing is available on a lottery system for upperclassmen. Priority is given to out-of-town students. All students may keep cars on campus.

Activities: About 16% of men belong to 4 national fraternities; about 17% of women belong to 3 national sororities. There are 100 groups on campus, including art, cheerleading, chess, choir, chorale, chorus, computers, dance, drama, ethnic, gay, honors, international, jazz band, literary magazine, musical theater, newspaper, orchestra, pep band, photography, political, professional, radio and TV, religious, social, social service, student government, symphony, and yearbook. Popular campus events include Bronco Bust (Spirit Week), Special Olympics, Cinco de Mayo, Hawaiian Luau, and soccer and basketball games.

Sports: There are 13 intercollegiate sports for men and 9 for women, and 6 intramural sports for men and 6 for women. Athletic and recreation facilities include an activities center which has a pavilion for basketball, racquetball and volleyball courts, a swimming pool, a weight-training section, and a sauna. There also is a 10,000-seat stadium with practice fields nearby.

Disabled Students: Fifty percent of the campus is accessible to disabled students. The following facilities are available: wheelchair ramps, elevators, special parking, specially equipped rest rooms, spe-

cial class scheduling, lowered drinking fountains, and lowered telephones.

Services: In addition to many counseling and information services, tutoring is available in most subjects.

Campus Safety and Security: Campus safety and security measures include 24-hour foot and vehicle patrol, escort service, informal discussions, and pamphlets, posters, and films. In addition, there are emergency telephones and lighted pathways and sidewalks.

Programs of Study: SCU awards the B.A., B.S., B.M., and B.S.C. degrees. Master's and doctoral degrees also are awarded. Bachelor's degrees are awarded in BIOLOGICAL SCIENCE (biology/ biological science), BUSINESS (accounting, banking and finance, business economics, management information systems, marketing/ retailing/merchandising, and organizational behavior), COMMUNICATIONS AND THE ARTS (classics, communications, dramatic arts, English, fine arts, French, German, Italian, music, and Spanish), COMPUTER AND PHYSICAL SCIENCE (chemistry, computer science, information sciences and systems, mathematics, physics, and science), ENGINEERING AND ENVIRONMENTAL DESIGN (civil engineering, computer engineering, electrical/electronics engineering, engineering, engineering physics, and mechanical engineering), SOCIAL SCIENCE (anthropology, economics, history, interdisciplinary studies, philosophy, political science/government, psychology, religion, and sociology). Psychology, finance, English, political science, and economics have the largest enrollments.

Required: All students are required to maintain a GPA of at least 2.0 in both major and minor subjects. Students must take 175 quarter units for most bachelor's degrees, and distribution requirements include composition and literature, Western culture, foreign language, social studies, mathematics and natural sciences, ethics, religious studies, and fine arts.

Special: Study abroad, offered through the Institute of European Studies and in conjunction with other universities, is offered in 15 countries, including such cities as Rome, Tokyo, Paris, Madrid, and Hong Kong. A co-op program in engineering, dual majors, internships, a general studies degree, a Washington semester, student-designed majors, and pass/fail options also are available. Students can choose minors in environmental studies, international business, and retail studies. SCU periodically establishes temporary institutes for the study of themes such as war and conscience, the family, poverty and conscience, and technology and society. The programs involve traditional-style classes as well as public lectures, dramatic productions, films, and social events. There is a freshman honors program on campus, as well as 13 national honor societies, including Phi Beta Kappa.

Faculty/Classroom: Seventy-one percent of faculty are male; 29%, female. Seventy-nine percent teach undergraduates. No introductory courses are taught by graduate students. The average class size in an introductory lecture is 28; in a laboratory, 18; and in a regular course offering, 26.

Admissions: About 69% of the 1993–94 applicants were accepted. The SAT scores for the 1993–94 freshman class were as follows: Verbal—53% below 500, 36% between 500 and 599, 10% between 600 and 700, and 1% above 700; Math—16% below 500, 43% between 500 and 599, 33% between 600 and 700, and 8% above 700. About 64% of the current freshmen were in the top fifth of their class; 95% were in the top two fifths. There were 4 National Merit finalists and 9 semifinalists. About 45 freshmen graduated first in their class.

Requirements: The SAT I is required. Applicants are required to have 16 academic units, including 4 years of English, 3 each in mathematics and foreign language, 1 each in history and science, and 4 in electives (except for business and social science majors, 3 1/2, and natural science, mathematics and engineering majors, 2 1/2). An essay is required. An audition is recommended for theater arts majors. The GED is not accepted. AP credits are accepted. Important factors used in the admissions decision are advanced placement or honor courses, parents or siblings attending the school, leadership record, evidence of special talent, and extracurricular activities record.

Procedure: Freshmen are admitted fall, winter, and spring. Entrance exams should be taken by February 1. Applications should be filed by February 1 for fall entry, October 15 for winter entry, and January 15 for spring entry, along with an application fee of $35. Notification is sent on a rolling basis. A waiting list is an active part of the admissions procedure, with about 6% of applicants on the list.

Transfer: About 264 transfer students enrolled in 1993–94. Transfer students need a minimum GPA of 3.0. The SAT I is recommended. A total of 45 quarter units out of 175 must be completed at SCU.

Visiting: There are regularly scheduled orientations for prospective students, including an open house in October, with overviews of academic programs and student activities, and preview days in April for accepted students. There are guides for informal visits and visitors may sit in on classes and stay overnight at the school. Visits can be arranged anytime except during exams and vacations. To arrange for a visit, contact the Undergraduate Admissions Office at (408) 554-4700.

Financial Aid: In 1993–94, 66% of all current freshmen and 62% of continuing students received some form of financial aid. About 56% of freshmen and 56% of continuing students received need-based aid. The average freshman award was $11,251. Of that total, scholarships or need-based grants averaged $7200 ($17,000 maximum); loans averaged $3263 ($4125 maximum); and work contracts averaged $788 ($1800 maximum). Seventy percent of undergraduate students work part-time. Average earnings from campus work for the school year are $900. The average financial indebtedness of the 1992–93 graduate was $12,150. SCU is a member of CSS. The FAF and FAFSA are required. The deadline for financial aid applications is February 1.

International Students: There are currently 129 international students enrolled. They must take the TOEFL and achieve a minimum score of 550. The student must also take the SAT I or the ACT.

Computers: The college provides computer facilities for student use. The mainframes are an IBM 4381, a DEC VAX 8650, and a 750 DEC VAX. There are also IBM PCs available in computer laboratories. All students may access the system. There are no time limits and no fees.

Graduates: In 1992–93 1081 bachelor's degrees were awarded. The most popular majors among graduates were political science (10%), psychology (8%), and finance (8%). Within an average freshman class, 69% graduate in 4 years, 81% in 5 years, and 83% in 6 years. Some 300 companies recruited on campus in an earlier year.

Admissions Contact: Daniel J. Saracino, Dean of Admissions.

SCRIPPS COLLEGE
D-5
Claremont, CA 91711   (909) 621-8149

Full-time: 600 women	Faculty: 60; IIB, + +$
Part-time: 12 women	Ph.D.s: 98%
Graduate: none	Student/Faculty: 10 to 1
Year: semesters	Tuition: $16,550
Application Deadline: February 1	Room & Board: $7050
Freshman Class: 856 applied, 600 accepted, 139 enrolled	
SAT I Verbal/Math: 562/590	ACT: 26 HIGHLY COMPETITIVE

Scripps College, founded in 1926, is a private liberal arts institution for women. It is one of the Claremont Colleges. The 7 libraries contain 1.9 million volumes and subscribe to 1000 periodicals. Computerized library sources and services include the card catalog, interlibrary loans, and database searching. Special learning facilities include an art gallery, radio station, the Clark Humanities Museum, and the Mary B. Eyre preschool. The 28-acre campus is in a suburban area 35 miles east of Los Angeles. Including residence halls, there are 22 buildings on campus.

Student Life: About 51% of undergraduates are from California. Students come from 37 states, 18 foreign countries, and Canada. Sixty-five percent are from public schools; 35% from private. Seventy-two percent are white; 11% Asian American; 10% Hispanic. The average age of freshmen is 18; all undergraduates, 20.5. Thirteen percent drop out by the end of their first year; 76% remain to graduate.

Housing: A total of 537 students can be accommodated in college housing. College-sponsored living facilities include dormitories and on-campus apartments. In addition there are foreign language, science, honors, and political science corridors. On-campus housing is guaranteed for all 4 years. Ninety percent of students live on campus; of those, 85% remain on campus on weekends. All students may keep cars on campus.

Activities: There are no sororities on campus. There are 200 groups on campus, including art, band, choir, chorale, chorus, computers, dance, drama, ethnic, film, gay, honors, international, jazz band, literary magazine, musical theater, newspaper, opera, orchestra, photography, political, professional, radio and TV, religious, social, social service, student government, symphony, and yearbook. Popular campus events include Break Away Days, Annual Spring Experiential Program, monthly teas, Scripps Outdoor Adventure Program, Freshman Mugging, and Sophomore Candlelight Dinner.

Sports: Athletic and recreation facilities include a gymnasium, tennis courts, competition swimming pools, baseball and soccer fields, a climbing wall, and a workout room.

Disabled Students: Seventy percent of the campus is accessible to disabled students. The following facilities are available: wheelchair ramps, elevators, special parking, specially equipped rest rooms, special class scheduling, lowered drinking fountains, and specialized dormitory space.

Services: In addition to many counseling and information services, tutoring is available in every subject. There is a reader service for the blind.

Campus Safety and Security: Campus safety and security measures include 24-hour foot and vehicle patrol, self defense education, escort service, and informal discussions. In addition, there are pamphlets, posters, films, emergency telephones, and lighted pathways and sidewalks.

Programs of Study: Scripps awards the B.A. degree. Bachelor's degrees are awarded in BIOLOGICAL SCIENCE (biochemistry and biology/biological science), BUSINESS (accounting), COMMUNICATIONS AND THE ARTS (art, art history and appreciation, Chinese, classics, comparative literature, dance, dramatic arts, English, film arts, French, German, Germanic languages and literature, Greek, Hebrew, Italian, Japanese, Latin, linguistics, literature, music, photography, Russian, Spanish, and studio art), COMPUTER AND PHYSICAL SCIENCE (chemistry, computer science, geology, mathematics, and physics), ENGINEERING AND ENVIRONMENTAL DESIGN (engineering, environmental science, and preengineering), SOCIAL SCIENCE (African studies, American studies, anthropology, Asian/Oriental studies, economics, European studies, French studies, Hispanic American studies, history, international relations, Mexican-American/Chicano studies, philosophy, political science/government, prelaw, psychobiology, psychology, religion, social science, sociology, Spanish studies, and women's studies). Premed, art, and English are the strongest academically. Social science has the largest enrollment.

Required: In order to graduate, students must complete a total of 128 credits, or 32 courses. Core requirements include 2 courses each in fine arts, humanities, letters, natural sciences, and social sciences, and 1 course in mathematics. All students must also fulfill a language, a multicultural, and a thesis requirement.

Special: Students may cross register with any of the other Claremont Colleges. Internships, work-study programs, study abroad in 34 countries, and a Washington semester are available. A 3–2 engineering degree, student-designed, dual and interdisciplinary majors, including organizational studies and science, technology, and society, are possible. Most courses are offered as seminars. There are 3 national honor societies on campus, including Phi Beta Kappa. All departments have honors programs.

Faculty/Classroom: Forty percent of faculty are male; 60%, female. All teach undergraduates and do research. The average class size in an introductory lecture is 15; in a laboratory, 20; and in a regular course offering, 15.

Admissions: About 70% of the 1993–94 applicants were accepted. The SAT scores for the 1993–94 freshman class were as follows: Verbal—19% below 500, 45% between 500 and 599, 29% between 600 and 700, and 6% above 700; Math—9% below 500, 38% between 500 and 599, 42% between 600 and 700, and 10% above 700. The ACT scores were 25% between 21 and 23, 50% between 24 and 26, 12% between 27 and 28, and 13% above 28. About 81% of the current freshmen were in the top fifth of their class; 93% were in the top two fifths. There were 2 National Merit finalists and 20 semifinalists. Nine freshmen graduated first in their class.

Requirements: Scripps requires applicants to be in the upper 50% of their class. A minimum GPA of 3.0 is required. The SAT I or ACT is required. Applicants must have completed 4 units of high school English, 3 each of mathematics, science, and a foreign language, and 2 of history/social studies. SAT II: Subject tests are recommended. An essay and a graded English paper from the junior or senior year are required. An interview is recommended. AP credits are accepted. Important factors used in the admissions decision are advanced placement or honor courses, recommendations by school officials, leadership record, evidence of special talent, and personality, intangible qualities.

Procedure: Freshmen are admitted to all sessions. Entrance exams should be taken by December. Early decision applications should be filed by November 15; regular applications, by February 1 for fall entry and November 15 for spring entry, along with an application fee of $40. Notification of early decision is sent December 15; regular decision, April 1. There are early decision, early admissions, and deferred admissions plans. Eight early decision candidates were accepted for the 1993–94 class. A waiting list is an active part of the admissions procedure, with about 10% of applicants on the list.

Transfer: Thirty-four transfer students enrolled in 1993–94. A cumulative college GPA of 3.0 is required. A total of 64 credits out of 128 must be completed at Scripps.

Visiting: There are regularly scheduled orientations for prospective students, Individually tailored appointments can be arranged to meet a prospective student's interests. Visitors may sit in on classes and stay overnight at the school. To arrange for a visit, contact the Admissions Office at (909) 621-8149.

Financial Aid: In 1993–94, 58% of all current freshmen and 62% of continuing students received some form of financial aid. About 46% of freshmen and 52% of continuing students received need-based aid. The average freshman award was $17,664. Of that total, scholarships or need-based grants averaged $10,827 ($19,500 maximum); loans averaged $3278 ($3500 maximum); and work contracts averaged $1139 ($1400 maximum). All undergraduate students work part-time. Average earnings from campus work for the school year are $1400. The average financial indebtedness of the 1992–93 graduate was $14,000. Scripps is a member of CSS. The FAF and

FAFSA are required. The deadline for financial aid applications is February 1.

International Students: There are currently 26 international students enrolled. The school actively recruits these students. They must take the TOEFL and achieve a minimum score of 550. The student must also take the SAT I or the ACT.

Computers: The college provides computer facilities for student use. Harvey Mudd College houses the mainframe. IBM and Macintosh microcomputers are available. All students may access the system. There are no time limits on using the system and no fees.

Graduates: In 1992–93, 152 bachelor's degrees were awarded. The most popular majors among graduates were psychology (18%), English (15%), and studio art (12%). Within an average freshman class, 69% graduate in 4 years and 76% in 5 years. Some 150 companies recruited on campus in 1992–93. In the 1992 graduating class, 21% of the women were enrolled in graduate school within 6 months of graduation; 69% of the women had found employment.

Admissions Contact: Mimi Tung, Director of Admissions.

SIMPSON COLLEGE
B-3

Redding, CA 96003   (916) 224–5606; (800) 598–2493 (in-state)

Full-time: 187 men, 320 women	Faculty: 21
Part-time: 2 men, 9 women	Ph.D.s: 48%
Graduate: 40 men, 94 women	Student/Faculty: 24 to 1
Year: semesters, summer session	Tuition: $6938
Application Deadline: open	Room & Board: $3690
Freshman Class: 199 applied, 165 accepted, 81 enrolled	
SAT I Verbal/Math: 450/450	ACT: 21 COMPETITIVE

Simpson College, founded in 1921, is a small, private, coeducational, Christian liberal arts college affiliated with The Christian and Missionary Alliance. There is one graduate school. The library contains 53,390 volumes, 57,960 microform items, and 1853 audiovisual forms, and subscribes to 246 periodicals. Computerized library sources and services include database searching. The 60-acre campus is in a suburban area 3 miles northeast of Redding. Including residence halls, there are 4 buildings on campus.

Student Life: About 87% of undergraduates are from California. Students come from 13 states, 5 foreign countries, and Canada. Eighty-six percent are white. Most are Protestant. The average age of freshmen is 20; all undergraduates, 25.

Housing: A total of 192 students can be accommodated in college housing. College-sponsored living facilities include single-sex dormitories. On-campus housing is guaranteed for all 4 years. Priority is given to out-of-town students. Fifty-seven percent of students commute. Alcohol is not permitted. All students may keep cars on campus.

Activities: There are no fraternities or sororities on campus. There are some groups and organizations on campus, including choir, chorale, drama, pep band, professional, religious, social, social service, student government, and yearbook. Popular campus events include Thanksgiving, Christmas and Easter programs, Homecoming, Spring Banquet, Spiritual Emphasis Week, Missions Emphasis Week, and Multicultural Appreciation Day.

Sports: There are 3 intercollegiate sports for men and 2 for women, and 3 intramural sports for men and 3 for women. Athletic and recreation facilities include a new soccer field.

Disabled Students: Sixty-five percent of the campus is accessible to disabled students. The following facilities are available: wheelchair ramps, special parking, specially equipped rest rooms, lowered drinking fountains, lowered telephones, and specially equipped dormitory rooms.

Services: There are many counseling and information services and tutoring is available in some subjects. In addition, there is remedial math, reading, and writing, including English as a second language.

Campus Safety and Security: Campus safety and security measures include 24-hour foot and vehicle patrol, informal discussions, and lighted pathways and sidewalks.

Programs of Study: Simpson awards the B.A. degree. Associate and master's degrees also are awarded. Bachelor's degrees are awarded in BUSINESS (accounting, business administration and management, and human resources), COMMUNICATIONS AND THE ARTS (English and music), EDUCATION (Christian Education, elementary, music, and secondary), SOCIAL SCIENCE (biblical studies, crosscultural studies, history, liberal arts/general studies, ministries, missions, pastoral studies, psychology, religion, and social science). Psychology, education, and business have the largest enrollments.

Required: Students must complete at least 124 credits, with a minimum of 36 upper-division credits and at least 32 in the major. General education requirements include 12 credits each in natural sciences and mathematics, English and communication, and social sciences and history, 24 in humanities, and 2 in physical education. Students must maintain a minimum GPA of 2.0. All students must complete a biblical studies requirement of 24 credits.

Special: Students may take internships in Christian education, pastoral studies, and youth ministries or study abroad in London or the Middle East. There are a variety of options for dual majors, and student-designed majors are available. There is a 1-year, nondegree Bible certificate program. Working professionals may take the Degree Completion Program in monthly modules by meeting evenings. An accelerated degree program in business and human resources management, psychology, or liberal arts is possible for students with 60 college credits and 5 years of full-time work experience.

Faculty/Classroom: Seventy percent of faculty are male; 30%, female. Eighty-six percent teach undergraduates. No introductory courses are taught by graduate students. The average class size in an introductory lecture is 45; in a laboratory, 20; and in a regular course offering, 30.

Requirements: Simpson requires applicants to be in the upper 50% of their class. A minimum GPA of 2.0 is required. The SAT I or ACT is required. Applicant must be a graduate from an accredited high school or have a GED. It is recommended that applicants have completed 4 years of high school English, 2 of a foreign language, and 3 each of mathematics, science, and social studies/history. AP and CLEP credits are accepted. Important factors used in the admissions decision are recommendations by school officials, advanced placement or honor courses, leadership record, personality, intangible qualities, and extracurricular activities record.

Procedure: Freshmen are admitted to all sessions. Entrance exams should be taken prior to admission. Application deadlines are open. Notification is sent on a rolling basis. The application fee is $20. There is a deferred admissions plan.

Transfer: About 67 transfer students enrolled in 1993–94. Transfer applicants with at least 30 semester college credits need not submit SAT I or ACT scores. A total of 30 credits out of 124 must be completed at Simpson.

Visiting: There are regularly scheduled orientations for prospective students, consisting of College Days weekend offered each spring. There are guides for informal visits and visitors may sit in on classes and stay overnight at the school. To arrange for a visit, contact Beth Spencer, Administrative Assistant for Recruitment at (800) 598–2493.

Financial Aid: In 1993–94 65% of all current freshmen and 85% of continuing students received some form of financial aid. About 59% of freshmen and 79% of continuing students received need-based aid. The average freshman award was $13,166. Of that total, scholarships or need-based grants averaged $4200; loans averaged $7966; and work contracts averaged $1000. Average earnings from campus work for the school year are $700. The average financial indebtedness of the 1992–93 graduate was $6500. Simpson is a member of CSS. The FAF and the college's own financial statement are required. The deadline for financial aid applications is March 31.

International Students: There are currently 5 international students enrolled. The school actively recruits these students. They must take the TOEFL and achieve a minimum score of 500.

Computers: The college provides computer facilities for student use. The college provides personal computers for academic use. There are 15 IBM compatibles available in the computer laboratory. Only students enrolled in computer courses may access the system. Students may access the system only during work hours.

Graduates: In 1992–93, 128 bachelor's degrees were awarded.

Admissions Contact: Beth Spencer, Administrator Assistant to the Dean for Enrollment Management.

SONOMA STATE UNIVERSITY

Rohnert Park, CA 94928

B-3
(707) 664-2778

Full-time: 1676 men, 2563 women	Faculty: 257; IIA, +$
Part-time: 501 men, 758 women	Ph.D.s: 81%
Graduate: 279 men, 773 women	Student/Faculty: 16 to 1
Year: semesters	Tuition: $1746 ($9126)
Application Deadline: November	Room & Board: $5250
Freshman Class: 2726 applied, 982 accepted, 601 enrolled	
SAT I Verbal/Math: 486/482	ACT: 22 COMPETITIVE +

Sonoma State University, founded in 1960, is one of the liberal arts institutions in the California State University system, offering undergraduate programs in business and economics, natural sciences, social sciences, and arts and humanities, and a graduate program in education. There are 4 undergraduate schools and one graduate school. In addition to regional accreditation, Sonoma State has baccalaureate program accreditation with NASAD, NASM, and NLN. The library contains 468,307 volumes, 1,299,774 microform items, and 23,473 audiovisual forms, and subscribes to 2071 periodicals. Computerized library sources and services include the card catalog, interlibrary loans, and database searching. Special learning facilities include a learning resource center, art gallery, radio station, and an observatory. The 220-acre campus is in a suburban area 45 miles north of San Francisco. Including residence halls, there are 20 buildings on campus.

Student Life: About 93% of undergraduates are from California. Students come from 50 states, 40 foreign countries, and Canada. Ninety-five percent are from public schools; 5% from private. Seventy percent are white. The average age of freshmen is 19; all undergraduates, 29. Twenty-four percent drop out by the end of their first year.

Housing: A total of 900 students can be accommodated in college housing. College-sponsored living facilities include single-sex and coed dormitories and on-campus apartments. In addition there are special interest houses and women-in-science, substance-free, and intensive-study houses. On-campus housing is guaranteed for the freshman year only, is available on a first-come, first-served basis, and is available on a lottery system for upperclassmen. Seventy-seven percent of students commute. All students may keep cars on campus.

Activities: About 3% of men belong to 6 national fraternities; about 4% of women belong to 4 local and 5 national sororities. There are 90 groups on campus, including art, cheerleading, chess, choir, chorale, chorus, computers, dance, drama, ethnic, gay, honors, international, jazz band, literary magazine, musical theater, newspaper, orchestra, pep band, political, professional, radio and TV, religious, social, social service, and student government. Popular campus events include Science Night, Homecoming, Parents Day, and freshman orientation.

Sports: There are 4 intercollegiate sports for men and 4 for women, and 21 intramural sports for men and 15 for women. Athletic and recreation facilities include a 5000-seat stadium, a 3000-seat gymnasium, a field house, tennis courts, a pool, a 500-seat auditorium, and various playing fields.

Disabled Students: The entire campus is accessible to disabled students. The following facilities are available: wheelchair ramps, elevators, special parking, specially equipped rest rooms, special class scheduling, lowered drinking fountains, and lowered telephones. A reading machine, phonic listening devices, micro/mainframe computer access, and interpreters are also available.

Services: In addition to many counseling and information services, tutoring is available in most subjects. In addition, there is a reader service for the blind, learning disability assessment, and remedial math, reading, and writing.

Campus Safety and Security: Campus safety and security measures include 24-hour foot and vehicle patrol, escort service, pamphlets, posters, and films, and emergency telephones. In addition, there are lighted pathways and sidewalks.

Programs of Study: Sonoma State awards the B.A., B.S., and B.F.A. degrees. Master's degrees also are awarded. Bachelor's degrees are awarded in BIOLOGICAL SCIENCE (biology/biological science, botany, cell biology, marine biology, microbiology, and zoology), BUSINESS (accounting, banking and finance, business economics, international business management, marketing/retailing/merchandising, and personnel management), COMMUNICATIONS AND THE ARTS (art, communications, dance, dramatic arts, English, fine arts, French, German, music, and Spanish), COMPUTER AND PHYSICAL SCIENCE (chemistry, computer science, geology, mathematics, and physics), ENGINEERING AND ENVIRONMENTAL DESIGN (environmental science), HEALTH PROFESSIONS (nursing), SOCIAL SCIENCE (anthropology, criminal justice, economics, geography, history, philosophy, political science/government, psychology, and sociology). Liberal arts, physics, mathematics, and history are the strongest academically. Business, psychology, liberal studies, English, and biology have the largest enrollments.

Required: To graduate, students must complete at least 124 credits with a 2.5 GPA; the liberal studies program has slightly different requirements. All students take an ethnic course, a personal development course, and general education courses in oral and written communications, critical thinking, natural sciences and mathematics, arts and humanities, and social sciences.

Special: Students may cross-register at Mills college and the University of California/Berkeley, and study abroad in 16 countries. Internships, work-study programs, accelerated study, nondegree study, and pass/fail options, are available. Combined B.A.-B.S. degrees are offered in chemistry, geology, mathematics, and physics. The Hutchins School awards a B.A. in liberal studies, with special, student-designed majors. There are 3 national honor societies on campus. Three departments have honors programs.

Faculty/Classroom: Sixty-three percent of faculty are male; 37%, female. The average class size in an introductory lecture is 28; in a laboratory, 15; and in a regular course offering, 22.

Admissions: About 36% of the 1993–94 applicants were accepted. The SAT scores for the 1993–94 freshman class were as follows: Verbal—78% below 500, 18% between 500 and 599, 4% between 600 and 700, and 1% above 700; Math—52% below 500, 36% between 500 and 599, 11% between 600 and 700, and 1% above 700.

Requirements: A minimum GPA of 2.0 is required. The SAT I or ACT is required, unless the applicant has a 3.0 GPA. Applicants should be graduates of accredited high schools or have earned the GED. Secondary school preparation should include 4 years each of arts and humanities, 3 each of English, mathematics, social science,

and academic electives, and 1 each of music, history, and a laboratory science. AP and CLEP credits are accepted. Important factors used in the admissions decision are recommendations by school officials, recommendations by alumni, personality, intangible qualities, parents or siblings attending the school, and leadership record.

Procedure: Freshmen are admitted fall and spring. Applications should be filed by November for fall entry and August for spring entry, along with an application fee of $55. Notification is sent on a rolling basis.

Transfer: A total of 1117 transfer students enrolled in 1993–94. Applicants must have a minimum 2.0 GPA. The maximum number of transferable credits is 70. A total of 30 credits out of 124 must be completed at Sonoma State.

Visiting: There are regularly scheduled orientations for prospective students, consisting of programs in the spring and summer. There are guides for informal visits and visitors may sit in on classes. To arrange for a visit, contact the Admissions Development Office at (707) 664-3032.

Financial Aid: In 1993–94, 60% of all current freshmen and 57% of continuing students received some form of financial aid. About 60% of freshmen and 57% of continuing students received need-based aid. The average freshman award was $6925. Of that total, scholarships or need-based grants averaged $3300 ($5300 maximum); loans averaged $2625 ($6625 maximum); and work contracts averaged $1000 ($3000 maximum). The average financial indebtedness of the 1992–93 graduate was $8000. Sonoma State is a member of CSS. The SAAC financial statement is required. The deadline for financial aid applications is March 2.

International Students: There are currently 389 international students enrolled. The school actively recruits these students. They must take the TOEFL and achieve a minimum score of 500. The student must also take the SAT I or the ACT.

Computers: The university provides computer facilities for student use. The mainframes are a DEC VAX 6360, a MicroVAX 2000, and a MicroVAX II. Sonoma State provides 850 microcomputers, 800 of which are networked with Internet, CSUNSET, Next, or LAN systems, in laboratories, the library, and the computer center. All students may access the system. There are no time limits on using the system and no fees.

Graduates: In 1992–93, 1429 bachelor's degrees were awarded. The most popular majors among graduates were psychology (19%), management (18%), and liberal studies (9%). Within an average freshman class, 2% graduate in 3 years, 12% in 4 years, 26% in 5 years, and 26% in 6 years. Some 300 companies recruited on campus in 1992–93. In the 1992 graduating class, 25% of graduates were enrolled in graduate school within 6 months of graduation; 90% had found employment.

Admissions Contact: Marlene Ballaine, Admissions Office.

SOUTHERN CALIFORNIA COLLEGE D-5

Costa Mesa, CA 92626	(714) 556-3610; (800) 722-6279
Full-time: 343 men, 441 women	Faculty: 40; IIB, av$
Part-time: 62 men, 54 women	Ph.D.s: 67%
Graduate: 51 men, 14 women	Student/Faculty: 20 to 1
Year: semesters, summer session	Tuition: $8536
Application Deadline: July 31	Room & Board: $3820
Freshman Class: 502 applied, 444 accepted, 222 enrolled	
SAT I Verbal/Math: 410/460	ACT: 22 **COMPETITIVE**

Southern California College, founded in 1920, is a private, coeducational liberal arts college affiliated with the Assemblies of God, offering 26 majors in 6 comprehensive fields. There is one graduate school. The library contains 115,000 volumes, 8300 microform items, and 3600 audiovisual forms, and subscribes to 810 periodicals. Computerized library sources and services include the card catalog, interlibrary loans, and database searching. Special learning facilities include a learning resource center. The 38-acre campus is in a suburban area 40 miles southeast of Los Angeles and 5 miles north of Newport Beach. Including residence halls, there are 20 buildings on campus.

Student Life: About 75% of undergraduates are from California. Students come from 38 states, 14 foreign countries, and Canada. Sixty-nine percent are from public schools; 31% from private. Seventy-four percent are white; 12% Hispanic. Most are Protestant. The average age of freshmen is 18; all undergraduates, 20. Twenty-nine percent drop out by the end of their first year; 35% remain to graduate.

Housing: A total of 538 students can be accommodated in college housing. College-sponsored living facilities include single-sex dormitories, on-campus apartments, and married-student housing. On-campus housing is guaranteed for all 4 years. Fifty-two percent of students live on campus. Alcohol is not permitted. All students may keep cars on campus.

Activities: There are no fraternities or sororities on campus. There are many groups and organizations on campus, including art, cheerleading, choir, drama, ethnic, international, musical theater, newspaper, orchestra, pep band, political, student government, and yearbook.

Sports: There are 5 intercollegiate sports for men and 6 for women, and 15 intramural sports for men and 15 for women. Athletic and recreation facilities include an indoor gymnasium.

Disabled Students: The entire campus is accessible to disabled students. The following facilities are available: wheelchair ramps, elevators, special parking, and specially equipped rest rooms.

Services: In addition to many counseling and information services, tutoring is available in every subject.

Campus Safety and Security: Campus safety and security measures include 24-hour foot and vehicle patrol, self defense education, informal discussions, and lighted pathways and sidewalks.

Programs of Study: SCC awards the B.A. degree. Master's degrees also are awarded. Bachelor's degrees are awarded in BIOLOGICAL SCIENCE (biology/biological science), BUSINESS (accounting, banking and finance, business administration and management, marketing/retailing/merchandising, and personnel management), COMMUNICATIONS AND THE ARTS (broadcasting, communications, dramatic arts, English, fine arts, journalism, music, and radio/television technology), COMPUTER AND PHYSICAL SCIENCE (chemistry and mathematics), EDUCATION (business, education, elementary, English, music, physical, science, and secondary), HEALTH PROFESSIONS (premedicine), SOCIAL SCIENCE (anthropology, biblical studies, counseling psychology, experimental psychology, history, ministries, political science/government, prelaw, psychology, religious education, and sociology). Religion, history/political science, anthropology, and sociology are the strongest academically. Social sciences and business have the largest enrollments.

Required: Students must complete a minimum of 124 credits, with 40 to 70 in the major. General education requirements include 15 credits in humanities and fine arts, 10 in natural sciences and mathematics, 16 in religion, 12 in social science, and 2 in physical education. The college requires a minimum GPA of 2.0 and a writing competency examination.

Special: Study abroad in Israel and Costa Rica, internships, a Washington semester, dual majors, a general studies degree, an accelerated degree program, work-study, pass/fail options, and credit for life, military, and work experience are available. Three summer sessions are offered.

Faculty/Classroom: Seventy-seven percent of faculty are male; 23%, female. All teach undergraduates. No introductory courses are taught by graduate students. The average class size in an introductory lecture is 30; in a laboratory, 12; and in a regular course offering, 16.

Admissions: About 88% of the 1993–94 applicants were accepted. The SAT scores for the 1993–94 freshman class were as follows: Verbal—80% below 500, 15% between 500 and 599, 4% between 600 and 700, and 1% above 700; Math—66% below 500, 23% between 500 and 599, 10% between 600 and 700, and 1% above 700. The ACT scores were 47% below 21, 27% between 21 and 23, 15% between 24 and 26, 7% between 27 and 28, and 4% above 28. About 42% of the current freshmen were in the top fifth of their class. There was 1 National Merit finalist. Two freshmen graduated first in their class.

Requirements: A minimum GPA of 2.5 is required. The SAT I or ACT is required. High school courses should include 4 years of English, 2 of mathematics and science, and 3 of social studies. Applicants are required to write an application essay and submit references from a pastor/minister. AP and CLEP credits are accepted. Important factors used in the admissions decision are leadership record, evidence of special talent, advanced placement or honor courses, ability to finance college education, and extracurricular activities record.

Procedure: Freshmen are admitted fall and spring. Entrance exams should be taken in the junior year. Applications should be filed by July 31 for fall entry and November 30 for spring entry, along with an application fee of $30. Notification is sent on a rolling basis.

Transfer: About 120 transfer students enrolled in 1993–94. Transfer applicants must submit college transcripts and have a minimum college GPA of 2.0. A total of 24 credits out of a minimum of 124 must be completed at SCC.

Visiting: There is a regularly scheduled orientation for prospective students, consisting of College Preview on Veterans' Day each year. There are guides for informal visits and visitors may sit in on classes and stay overnight at the school. To arrange for a visit, contact Admissions at (800) 722-6279.

Financial Aid: In 1993–94, 80% of all students received some form of financial aid. About 75% of students received need-based aid. The average freshman award was $8000. Eighty percent of undergraduate students work part-time. Average earnings from campus work for the school year are $1200. The average financial indebtedness of the 1992–93 graduate was $10,000. SCC is a member of CSS. The col-

lege's own financial statement, FAFSA, and state (or province) scholarship/grant forms are required. The deadline for financial aid applications is March 2.

International Students: There are currently 19 international students enrolled. They must take the TOEFL and achieve a minimum score of 550.

Computers: The college provides computer facilities for student use. There are 50 academic IBM-compatible PCs in 4 locations on campus. All students may access the system. There are no time limits on using the system. The fees are $25 per semester.

Graduates: In 1992–93, 150 bachelor's degrees were awarded. Within an average freshman class, 19% graduate in 4 years and 30% in 5 years. Some 30 companies recruited on campus in 1992–93.

Admissions Contact: Rick Hardy, Dean for Enrollment Management.

STANFORD UNIVERSITY
B-3
Stanford, CA 94305 (415) 723-2091

Full-time: 3500 men, 3073 women	Faculty: I, ++$
Part-time: none	Ph.D.s: 99%
Graduate: 5115 men, 2314 women	Student/Faculty: n/av
Year: quarters, summer session	Tuition: $17,775
Application Deadline: December 15	Room & Board: $6535
Freshman Class: 13,608 applied, 2926 accepted, 1616 enrolled	
SAT I or ACT: required	**MOST COMPETITIVE**

Stanford University, founded in 1891, is a private, coeducational university offering a broad curriculum in liberal arts and professional training. There are 3 undergraduate and 7 graduate schools. In addition to regional accreditation, Stanford has baccalaureate program accreditation with AACSB and ABET. The 19 libraries contain 6.2 million volumes. Computerized library sources and services include the card catalog, interlibrary loans, and database searching. Special learning facilities include a learning resource center, art gallery, radio station, and TV station. The 8180-acre campus is in a suburban area 30 miles south of San Francisco.

Student Life: About 58% of undergraduates are from out-of-state, mostly the Middle Atlantic. Students come from 50 states, 56 foreign countries, and Canada. Seventy percent are from public schools; 30% from private. Fifty-three percent are white; 17% Asian American; 16% foreign nationals. Two percent drop out by the end of their first year; 93% remain to graduate.

Housing: A total of 8897 students can be accommodated in college housing. College-sponsored living facilities include single-sex and coed dormitories, on-campus apartments, married-student housing, and fraternity houses. In addition there are language houses, special interest houses, and ethnic theme houses. On-campus housing is guaranteed for the freshman year only and is available on a lottery system for upperclassmen. Ninety-two percent of students live on campus. All students may keep cars on campus.

Activities: About 10% of men belong to 19 national fraternities; about 10% of women belong to 8 national sororities. There are 300 groups on campus, including art, band, cheerleading, chess, choir, chorale, computers, dance, drama, ethnic, film, gay, honors, international, jazz band, literary magazine, marching band, musical theater, newspaper, orchestra, photography, political, professional, radio and TV, religious, social, social service, student government, symphony, and yearbook. Popular campus events include You Can Make a Difference public service conference, Annual Powwow, Holiday Faire, and big game activities (football).

Sports: There are 15 intercollegiate sports for men and 15 for women, and 35 intramural sports for men and 35 for women. Athletic and recreation facilities include athletic fields, a gymnasium, swimming pools, volleyball courts, lighted tennis courts, a dance studio, an 18-hole golf course, a sailing center, a rowing facility, and handball, racquetball, and squash courts.

Disabled Students: Eighty percent of the campus is accessible to disabled students. The following facilities are available: wheelchair ramps, elevators, special parking, specially equipped rest rooms, special class scheduling, lowered drinking fountains, and lowered telephones.

Services: In addition to many counseling and information services, tutoring is available in most subjects. In addition, there is a reader service for the blind.

Campus Safety and Security: Campus safety and security measures include 24-hour foot and vehicle patrol, self-defense education, escort service, and shuttle buses. In addition, there are informal discussions, pamphlets, posters, and films, emergency telephones, and lighted pathways and sidewalks.

Programs of Study: Stanford awards the A.B., B.S., and B.A.S. degrees. Master's and doctoral degrees also are awarded. Bachelor's degrees are awarded in BIOLOGICAL SCIENCE (biology/biological science and microbiology), COMMUNICATIONS AND THE ARTS (Chinese, classics, communications, comparative literature, dramatic arts, English, fine arts, French, Italian, Japanese, linguis-

tics, music, and Spanish), COMPUTER AND PHYSICAL SCIENCE (chemistry, computer science, earth science, geology, geoscience, mathematics, and physics), ENGINEERING AND ENVIRONMENTAL DESIGN (chemical engineering, civil engineering, electrical/electronics engineering, engineering, industrial engineering, materials science, mechanical engineering, and petroleum/natural gas engineering), SOCIAL SCIENCE (African American studies, American studies, anthropology, East Asian studies, economics, history, humanities, international relations, Latin American studies, philosophy, political science/government, psychology, public policy, religion, sociology, systems science, and urban studies). Economics, human biology, biology, and English have the largest enrollments.

Required: To graduate, students must take 180 quarter units including freshman English; 3 courses in culture, ideas, and values; and 1 course each in literature and arts; philosophical, social, and religious thought; human development, behavior, and language; social processes and institutions; mathematical sciences; natural sciences; and technology and applied sciences. Requirements for the major vary.

Special: Internships, study abroad, a Washington semester, student-designed majors, dual majors, a B.A.-B.S. degree, a 3–2 engineering degree, and pass/no credit options are offered. There is a chapter of Phi Beta Kappa on campus. All departments have honors programs.

Faculty/Classroom: Eighty-four percent of faculty are male; 16%, female. All do research.

Admissions: About 22% of the 1993–94 applicants were accepted. The SAT scores for the 1993–94 freshman class were as follows: Verbal—6% below 500, 22% between 500 and 599, 50% between 600 and 700, and 22% above 700; Math—1% below 500, 10% between 500 and 599, 30% between 600 and 700, and 59% above 700. About 95% of the current freshmen were in the top fifth of their class.

Requirements: The SAT I or ACT is required. The university recommends that applicants have strong preparation in high school English, mathematics, a foreign language, science, and social studies. Achievement tests are strongly recommended. AP credits are accepted. Important factors used in the admissions decision are advanced placement or honor courses, recommendations by school officials, personality, intangible qualities, leadership record, and extracurricular activities record.

Procedure: Freshmen are admitted in the fall. Entrance exams should be taken before December of the application year. Applications should be filed by December 15 for fall entry, along with an application fee of $50. Notification is sent the first week of April. There is a deferred admissions plan. A waiting list is an active part of the admissions procedure.

Transfer: About 120 transfer students enrolled in 1993–94. Transfer students must complete one full year of academic work prior to enrollment. There is only fall quarter enrollment for transfer students. The application deadline is March 15. A total of 90 quarter credits out of 180 must be completed at Stanford.

Visiting: There are regularly scheduled orientations for prospective students, including group information sessions and campus tours. There are guides for informal visits and visitors may sit in on classes. To arrange for a visit, contact the Undergraduate Admissions Office at (415) 723-2091.

Financial Aid: In 1993–94, 67% of all current freshmen and 67% of continuing students received some form of financial aid. About 45% of freshmen and 45% of continuing students received need-based aid. The average freshman award was $13,370. Stanford is a member of CSS. The FAF and the college's own financial statement are required. The deadline for financial aid applications is February 1.

International Students: There are currently 2208 international students enrolled. The school actively recruits these students. They must take the TOEFL. The student must also take the SAT I or the ACT.

Computers: The college provides computer facilities for student use. There are several kinds of mainframes. There are also microcomputers available in residences, libraries, and other campus clusters. All students may access the system.

Graduates: In 1992–93, 1837 bachelor's degrees were awarded. Within an average freshman class, 10% graduate in 3 years, 78% in 4 years, and 87% in 5 years. Some 500 companies recruited on campus in a recent year. In the 1992 graduating class, 50% of all graduates were enrolled in graduate school within 6 months of graduation.

Admissions Contact: Jim Montoya, Dean of Undergraduate Admissions.

THOMAS AQUINAS COLLEGE
C-5

Santa Paula, CA 93060   (805) 525-4417; (800) 634-9797 (in-state)

Full-time: 109 men, 99 women	Faculty: 19
Part-time: none	Ph.D.s: 65%
Graduate: none	Student/Faculty: 11 to 1
Year: semesters	Tuition: $12,790
Application Deadline: open	Room & Board: $5110

Freshman Class: 125 applied, 87 accepted, 67 enrolled

SAT I Verbal/Math: 580/570   ACT: 27   **HIGHLY COMPETITIVE**

Thomas Aquinas College, founded in 1969 and affiliated with the Roman Catholic Church, is a small, private, liberal arts college offering an integrated studies curriculum based on the Great Books. All classes are conducted as conversations directed by the teacher in the so-called Socratic method. The library contains 33,500 volumes and 2000 audiovisual forms and subscribes to 40 periodicals. The 170-acre campus is in a rural area 60 miles northwest of Los Angeles. Including residence halls, there are 15 buildings on campus.

Student Life: About 69% of undergraduates are from out-of-state, mostly the West. Students come from 33 states, 8 foreign countries, and Canada. Forty-five percent are from public schools; 55% from private. Eighty-seven percent are white. Most are Catholic. The average age of freshmen is 19.1; all undergraduates, 21. Fifteen percent drop out by the end of their first year; 70% remain to graduate.

Housing: A total of 216 students can be accommodated in college housing. College-sponsored living facilities include single-sex dormitories. On-campus housing is guaranteed for all 4 years. Ninety-nine percent of students live on campus; of those, 85% remain on campus on weekends. Alcohol is not permitted. All students may keep cars on campus.

Activities: There are no fraternities or sororities on campus. There are several groups and organizations on campus, including choir and religious. Popular campus events include St. Thomas Aquinas Day, President's Day, and Alumni Day.

Sports: There are 4 intramural sports for men and 2 for women. Athletic and recreation facilities include tennis, basketball, and volleyball courts, a soccer field, and a baseball field.

Disabled Students: All of the campus is accessible to disabled students. The following facilities are available: wheelchair ramps, specially equipped rest rooms, and lowered drinking fountains.

Services: All students may be tutored by the full-time teaching faculty.

Campus Safety and Security: Campus safety and security measures include lighted pathways and sidewalks.

Programs of Study: TAC awards the B.A. degree. Bachelor's degrees are awarded in SOCIAL SCIENCE (liberal arts/general studies).

Required: The entire curriculum is required of all students: 4 years of philosophy, theology, mathematics, and laboratory science; 2 years of language; 1 year of music; and 4 years of seminars in literature, history, and social sciences. A total of 148 semester hours, with a minimum GPA of 2.0, is required in order to graduate.

Special: There are no electives, majors, or minors. Students read original writings of Western civilization and discuss them in small seminar-style groups. Many examinations are oral.

Faculty/Classroom: Eighty-five percent of faculty are male; 15%, female. All teach undergraduates. The average class size in an introductory lecture is 17; in a laboratory, 17; and in a regular course offering, 17.

Admissions: About 70% of the 1993-94 applicants were accepted. The SAT scores for the 1993-94 freshman class were as follows: Verbal—20% below 500, 36% between 500 and 599, 30% between 600 and 700, and 14% above 700; Math—12% below 500, 42% between 500 and 599, 36% between 600 and 700, and 10% above 700. The ACT scores were 11% between 21 and 23, 28% between 24 and 26, 33% between 27 and 28, and 28% above 28. About 47% of the current freshmen were in the top fifth of their class; 83% were in the top two fifths. There was 1 National Merit finalist and 1 semifinalist. Two freshmen graduated first in their class.

Requirements: The SAT I or ACT is required. Candidates for admission should have completed 4 years of English, 2 years each of a foreign language, history, and science, and 3 years of mathematics. Important factors used in the admissions decision are personality, intangible qualities, advanced placement or honor courses, recommendations by alumni, recommendations by school officials, and extracurricular activities record.

Procedure: Freshmen are admitted in the fall. Entrance exams should be taken by December. Application deadlines are open. There is no application fee. Notification is sent on a rolling basis. There is a deferred admissions plan.

Transfer: Transfers are not accepted.

Visiting: There are regularly scheduled orientations for prospective students, including hosting of prospective students by current students; visits are for up to 1 week and consist of observing classes and attending lectures, concerts, and meals. There are guides for informal visits and visitors may sit in on classes and stay overnight at the school. To arrange for a visit, contact the Admissions Office at (800) 634-9797.

Financial Aid: In 1993-94, 84% of all current freshmen and 83% of continuing students received some form of financial aid. About 84% of freshmen and 80% of continuing students received need-based aid. The average freshman award was $11,570. Of that total, scholarships or need-based grants averaged $6478 ($12,850 maximum); loans averaged $2665 ($4000 maximum); and work contracts averaged $2600 (maximum). Seventy-four percent of undergraduate students work part-time. Average earnings from campus work for the school year are $2600. The average financial indebtedness of the 1992-93 graduate was $9991. TAC is a member of CSS. The FAF and the college's own financial statement are required. The deadline for financial aid applications is March 1.

International Students: There are currently 31 international students enrolled. They must take the TOEFL. The student must also take the SAT I.

Computers: The college provides computer facilities for student use. One personal computer is available to students in each of the 6 dormitory buildings. All students may access the system. There are no time limits on using the system and no fees.

Graduates: In 1992-93, 42 bachelor's degrees were awarded. Within an average freshman class, 67% graduate in 4 years. In the 1992 graduating class, 11% of the men were enrolled in graduate school within 6 months of graduation; 63% of the men and 67% of the women had found employment.

Admissions Contact: Thomas J. Susanka, Jr., Director of Admissions.

UNITED STATES INTERNATIONAL UNIVERSITY
D-5

San Diego, CA 92131-1799   (619) 693-4772

Full-time: 620 men, 545 women	Faculty: 141
Part-time: 140 men, 145 women	Ph.D.s: 78%
Graduate: 900 men, 1275 women	Student/Faculty: 8 to 1
Year: quarters, summer session	Tuition: $9810
Application Deadline: open	Room & Board: $4725

Freshman Class: n/av

SAT I or ACT: required   **LESS COMPETITIVE**

United States International University, established in 1952, is a private institution offering programs in education, business, and international studies. The university also has campuses in Nairobi and Mexico City. There are 4 undergraduate and 4 graduate schools. The library contains 186,000 volumes and 225,000 microform items, and subscribes to 1300 periodicals. Computerized library sources and services include database searching. The 200-acre campus is in a suburban area 15 miles north of San Diego. Including residence halls, there are 67 buildings on campus.

Student Life: About 55% of undergraduates are from California. Students come from 47 states and 69 foreign countries. Sixty-five percent are from public schools; 35% from private. Sixty-nine percent are white; 17% Asian American. The average age of freshmen is 18; all undergraduates, 22. Fifteen percent drop out by the end of their first year.

Housing: A total of 600 students can be accommodated in college housing. College-sponsored housing is single-sex and is guaranteed for all 4 years. Sixty-five percent of students commute. Alcohol is not permitted. All students may keep cars on campus.

Activities: There are no fraternities or sororities on campus. There are 17 groups on campus, including ethnic, gay, honors, international, newspaper, social, social service, student government, and yearbook. Popular campus events include cultural fashion shows, harbor cruises, beach parties, and an international friendship festival.

Sports: There are 7 intramural sports for men and 7 for women. Athletic and recreation facilities include weight and exercise rooms; tennis courts; softball, baseball, and soccer fields; 4 swimming pools; and an all-purpose playing field.

Disabled Students: Eighty percent of the campus is accessible to disabled students. The following facilities are available: wheelchair ramps, elevators, special parking, and specially equipped rest rooms.

Services: In addition to many counseling and information services, tutoring is available in most subjects. In addition, there is remedial math, reading, and writing.

Campus Safety and Security: Campus safety and security measures include 24-hour foot and vehicle patrol and pamphlets, posters, and films.

Programs of Study: USIU awards the B.A., B.S., and B.B.A. degrees. Master's and doctoral degrees also are awarded. Bachelor's degrees are awarded in BUSINESS (accounting, business administration and management, hotel/motel and restaurant management, and international business management), COMMUNICATIONS AND

THE ARTS (English), COMPUTER AND PHYSICAL SCIENCE (information sciences and systems), EDUCATION (elementary and secondary), SOCIAL SCIENCE (international relations, prelaw, psychology, and social science). International relations is the strongest academically. Business has the largest enrollment.

Required: To graduate, students must complete 180 quarter hours with a minimum GPA of 2.0. Required courses include English, mathematics, science, and international studies.

Special: USIU offers internships, study abroad at the university's international campuses, an accelerated degree program, a general studies degree, B.A.-B.S. degrees, nondegree study, and pass/fail options. There is 1 national honor society on campus. One department has an honors program.

Faculty/Classroom: Seventy-nine percent of faculty are male; 21%, female. The average class size in an introductory lecture is 35 and in a regular course offering, 12.

Requirements: The SAT I or ACT is required. In addition, applicants should be graduates of a regionally accredited secondary school and have a GPA of 2.5. High school preparation should include 4 years each of English, history, and mathematics, 3 of social studies, and 2 of science. An essay is required, along with a recommendation. AP and CLEP credits are accepted. Important factors used in the admissions decision are advanced placement or honor courses, leadership record, evidence of special talent, extracurricular activities record, and recommendations by school officials.

Procedure: Freshmen are admitted to all sessions. Entrance exams should be taken by the end of the senior year. Application deadlines are open. The application fee is $30. Notification is sent on a rolling basis. There is an early decision plan.

Transfer: About 140 transfer students enrolled in an earlier year. A college GPA of 2.5 is recommended. Applicants with fewer than 30 college credits must submit high school as well as college transcripts. A total of 45 quarter credits out of 180 must be completed at USIU.

Visiting: There are regularly scheduled orientations for prospective students. There are guides for informal visits and visitors may sit in on classes and stay overnight at the school. To arrange for a visit, contact the Admissions Office at (619) 693-4772.

Financial Aid: In 1993–94, 80% of continuing students received some form of financial aid. Maximum awards for scholarships or need-based grants were $5400; for loans, $4875; and for work contracts, $2400. Fifty percent of undergraduate students work part-time. USIU is a member of CSS. The FAF or FFS, the college's own financial statement, and the FAFSA are required. The deadline for financial aid applications is April 15.

International Students: There are currently more than 1000 international students enrolled. The school actively recruits these students. They must take the TOEFL, the Comprehensive English Language Test, or the college's own test and achieve a minimum score on the TOEFL of 550.

Computers: USIU provides computer facilities for student use. The mainframe is a BTI 8000. The computer laboratory has about 40 IBM-compatible microcomputers, linked through a network, in 2 classroom areas. They are available to all students during off-peak hours and on a first-come, first-served basis when computer classes are in session. The laboratory is open daily from 8 A.M. to 10 P.M. There are no time limits on using the system. The fees are $35 per quarter.

Graduates: In an earlier year, 206 bachelor's degrees were awarded.

Admissions Contact: Darla J. Wilson, Acting Director of Admissions.

UNIVERSITY OF CALIFORNIA

The University of California, established in 1868, is a public system in California. It is governed by a board of regents, whose chief administrator is the president. The primary goals of the system are teaching, research, and public service. The total enrollment of all 9 campuses is approximately 163,000, with more than 7000 faculty members. Altogether there are 565 baccalaureate, 250 master's, and 200 doctoral programs offered in University of California. Four-year campuses are located in Berkeley, Davis, Irvine, Los Angeles, Riverside, San Diego, Santa Barbara, and Santa Cruz. Profiles of those campuses are included in this chapter.

UNIVERSITY OF CALIFORNIA AT BERKELEY B-3
Berkeley, CA 94720 (510) 642-0200 or (510) 642-3175
Full-time: 11,512 men, 10,201 women Faculty: I, +$
Part-time: none Ph.D.s: n/av
Graduate: 8628 men and women Student/Faculty: n/av
Year: semesters, summer session Tuition: $3970 ($11,669)
Application Deadline: November 30 Room & Board: $5992
Freshman Class: 19,873 applied, 8252 accepted, 3206 enrolled
SAT I or ACT: required HIGHLY COMPETITIVE +

University of California at Berkeley, founded in 1868, is a large public institution offering a wide variety of programs in the liberal arts and professional fields. It is the oldest campus of the University of California system. There are 14 undergraduate and graduate colleges and schools. In addition to regional accreditation, University of California at Berkeley has baccalaureate program accreditation with AACSB, ABET, ADA, ASLA, CSWE, NAAB, and SAF. The 26 libraries contain 7.85 million volumes, 4.58 million microform items, and 60,000 audiovisual forms, and subscribe to 88,300 periodicals. Computerized library sources and services include the card catalog, interlibrary loans, and database searching. Special learning facilities include a learning resource center, art gallery, natural history museum, radio station, botanical garden, anthropology museum, and hall of science. The 1232-acre campus is in an urban area 10 miles east of San Francisco. Including residence halls, there are 100 buildings on campus.

Student Life: About 87% of undergraduates are from California. Students come from 50 states, 99 foreign countries, and Canada. Eighty-four percent are from public schools; 16% from private. Thirty-seven percent are Asian American; 35% white; 14% Hispanic. The average age of freshmen is 18; all undergraduates, 20.8. Seven percent drop out by the end of their first year; 77% remain to graduate.

Housing: A total of 5200 students can be accommodated in college housing. College-sponsored living facilities include single-sex and coed dormitories, married-student housing, fraternity houses, and sorority houses. In addition, there are language houses, special interest houses, an international house, and co-ops. On-campus housing is guaranteed for the freshman year only and is available on a lottery system for upperclassmen. All students may keep cars on campus.

Activities: About 13% of men belong to 42 fraternities; about 11% of women belong to 17 sororities. There are 300 groups on campus, including art, band, cheerleading, chess, choir, chorale, chorus, computers, dance, drama, ethnic, film, gay, honors, international, jazz band, literary magazine, marching band, musical theater, newspaper, orchestra, pep band, photography, political, professional, radio and TV, religious, social, social service, student government, symphony, and yearbook. Popular campus events include on-campus films, The Big Game, and Cal Performances.

Sports: There are 13 intercollegiate sports for men and 11 for women, and 30 intramural sports for men and 30 for women. Athletic and recreation facilities include football and track stadiums, a basketball pavilion, 4 gymnasiums, a martial-arts room, 7 swimming pools, 3 weight rooms, squash, racquetball, handball, volleyball, and tennis courts, and a baseball field.

Disabled Students: Ninety-five percent of the campus is accessible to disabled students. The following facilities are available: wheelchair ramps, elevators, special parking, specially equipped rest rooms, special class scheduling, lowered drinking fountains, and lowered telephones, and a program for disabled students.

Services: In addition to many counseling and information services, tutoring is available in most subjects. In addition, there is a reader service for the blind, remedial math, reading, and writing, a workshop in study strategy and note taking, special tutoring for student athletes, and cult-awareness counseling.

Campus Safety and Security: Campus safety and security measures include 24-hour foot and vehicle patrol, self defense education, escort service, and shuttle buses. In addition, there are informal discussions, pamphlets, posters, and films, emergency telephones, lighted pathways and sidewalks, a rape prevention peer education program, and an earthquake emergency preparedness program.

Programs of Study: University of California at Berkeley awards the A.B. and B.S. degrees. Master's and doctoral degrees also are awarded. Bachelor's degrees are awarded in AGRICULTURE (conservation and regulation, forestry and related sciences, forestry production and processing, natural resource management, plant science, and soil science), BIOLOGICAL SCIENCE (biology/biological science, entomology, molecular biology, and nutrition), BUSINESS (business administration and management), COMMUNICATIONS AND THE ARTS (applied art, art history and appreciation, classical languages, communications, comparative literature, dance, dramatic arts, Dutch, East Asian languages and literature, English, film arts, French, German, Greek, Italian, Latin, linguistics, music, Scandinavian languages, Slavic languages, Spanish, and speech/debate/rhetoric), COMPUTER AND PHYSICAL SCIENCE (applied mathematics, astrophysics, chemistry, computer science, earth science, geodetic sci-

ence, geology, geophysics and seismology, mathematics, physical sciences, physics, and statistics), EDUCATION (physical), ENGINEERING AND ENVIRONMENTAL DESIGN (architecture, bioengineering, chemical engineering, civil engineering, electrical/electronics engineering, engineering physics, environmental science, industrial engineering, landscape architecture/design, manufacturing engineering, materials engineering, mechanical engineering, mining and mineral engineering, naval architecture and marine engineering, nuclear engineering, and petroleum/natural gas engineering), HEALTH PROFESSIONS (optometry), SOCIAL SCIENCE (African American studies, American studies, anthropology, Asian/American studies, Asian/Oriental studies, Celtic studies, classical/ancient civilization, cognitive science, economics, ethnic studies, food science, geography, history, humanities, interdisciplinary studies, Latin American studies, Mexican-American/Chicano studies, Middle Eastern studies, Native American studies, Near Eastern studies, paralegal studies, peace studies, philosophy, political science/government, psychology, religion, social science, social work, sociology, South Asian studies, theological studies, and women's studies). Electrical engineering and computer science, English, and architecture have the largest enrollments.

Required: All undergraduate students are required to satisfy the general university requirements of English and writing proficiency, and integrative and comparative courses in American history, cultures, and institutions. Students must complete 120 units with a minimum GPA of 2.0.

Special: Co-op programs, internships, work-study programs, and study abroad in 33 countries are available. Interdisciplinary majors, including development studies, integrative biology, political economy of industrial societies, and rhetoric are also available. There are 6 national honor societies on campus, including Phi Beta Kappa.

Admissions: About 42% of the 1993–94 applicants were accepted. About 95% of the current freshmen were in the top fifth of their class.

Requirements: A minimum GPA of 3.3 is required for California residents and 3.4 for out-of-state applicants. The SAT I or ACT is required. Also required are 4 years of English, 3 of mathematics (4 recommended), 2 each of history/social sciences, laboratory science (3 recommended), foreign language (3 recommended), and college preparatory electives. AP credits are accepted. Important factors used in the admissions decision are personality, intangible qualities, leadership record, extracurricular activities record, evidence of special talent, and advanced placement or honor courses.

Procedure: Freshmen are admitted in the fall. Entrance exams should be taken by December of the senior year. Applications should be filed by November 30 for fall entry and July 31 for spring entry, along with an application fee of $40. Notification is sent March 15. There is a deferred admissions plan.

Transfer: About 1870 transfer students enrolled in 1993–94. A minimum GPA of 2.4 generally is required for in-state students and 2.8 for out-of-state students, but requirements may be higher. For graduation, 120 hours are required; 24 of the last 30 hours must be completed at University of California at Berkeley.

Visiting: There are regularly scheduled orientations for prospective students, consisting of tours by the Visitor Information Center and group advising from the Office of Undergraduate Admission. There are guides for informal visits, and visitors may sit in on classes. To arrange for a visit, contact the Visitor Information Center at (510) 642-5215.

Financial Aid: In a recent year, 50% of all current freshmen and 50% of continuing students received some form of financial aid. About 38% of freshmen and 38% of continuing students received need-based aid. The average freshman award was $4600. Of that total, scholarships or need-based grants averaged $1437 ($3000 maximum); loans averaged $2657 ($4000 maximum); and work contracts averaged $1787 ($3000 maximum). Thirty-four percent of undergraduate students work part-time. Average earnings from campus work for the school year are $2218. The average financial indebtedness of a recent year's graduate was $5037. University of California at Berkeley is a member of CSS. The SAAC financial statement is required. The deadline for financial aid applications is March 2.

International Students: There are currently 798 international students enrolled. They must take the TOEFL and achieve a minimum score of 550. The student must also take the SAT I or the ACT.

Computers: The college provides computer facilities for student use. The mainframes are an IBM 3090, a Cray X-MP/14, and a DEC VAX 86500 and 8800. There are also IBM PC, Apple Macintosh, DEC VAX station II, and Sun System 3 microcomputers available in numerous locations campuswide, including residence halls. All students may access the system all hours.

Graduates: In 1992–93 5829 bachelor's degrees were awarded. The most popular majors among graduates were English (8%), electrical engineering and computer science (8%), and political science (6%). Within an average freshman class, 70% graduate in 5 years and 77% in 6 years. Some 630 companies recruited on campus in a recent year.

Admissions Contact: Bob Laird, Director, Office of Undergraduate Admission and Relations with Schools.

UNIVERSITY OF CALIFORNIA AT DAVIS   B-2
Davis, CA 95616   (916) 752-2971

Full-time: 8169 men, 8559 women	**Faculty:** 1370; I, av$
Part-time: 250 men, 228 women	**Ph.D.s:** 98%
Graduate: 2941 men, 2339 women	**Student/Faculty:** 12 to 1
Year: quarters, summer session	**Tuition:** $3712 ($11,411)
Application Deadline: November 30	**Room & Board:** $5822
Freshman Class: 16,343 applied, 11,399 accepted, 3124 enrolled	
SAT I Verbal/Math: 490/590	**ACT:** 24 **VERY COMPETITIVE**

University of California at Davis, founded in 1905, is a public, comprehensive institution offering programs in arts and science, agricultural and environmental sciences, and engineering. There are 3 undergraduate and 5 graduate schools. In addition to regional accreditation, UCD has baccalaureate program accreditation with ABET and ASLA. The 5 libraries contain 2,659,270 volumes, 3,177,893 microform items, and 14,138 audiovisual forms, and subscribe to 50,298 periodicals. Computerized library sources and services include the card catalog and database searching. Special learning facilities include a learning resource center, an art gallery, a radio station, experimental farms, a 50-acre arboretum, a raptor center, an equestrian center, the California regional primate research center, and the Crocker nuclear laboratory. The 6024-acre campus is in a suburban area 15 miles west of Sacramento and 72 miles northeast of San Francisco. Including residence halls, there are 1076 buildings on campus.

Student Life: About 96% of undergraduates are from California. Students come from 45 states, 32 foreign countries, and Canada. Eighty-seven percent are from public schools; 13% from private. Fifty-one percent are white; 25% Asian American; 10% Hispanic. The average age of freshmen is 18.5; all undergraduates, 21.2. Seven percent drop out by the end of their first year; 75% remain to graduate.

Housing: A total of 3502 students can be accommodated in college housing. College-sponsored living facilities include single-sex and coed dormitories, on-campus apartments, off-campus apartments, and married-student housing. In addition there are honors houses, language houses, and special interest houses. Seventy-eight percent of students commute. Alcohol is not permitted. All students may keep cars on campus.

Activities: About 12% of men belong to 3 local and 28 national fraternities; about 9% of women belong to 6 local and 14 national sororities. There are 350 groups on campus, including art, band, cheerleading, chess, chorus, computers, dance, drama, ethnic, film, gay, honors, international, jazz band, literary magazine, marching band, musical theater, newspaper, orchestra, pep band, photography, political, professional, radio and TV, religious, social, social service, student government, symphony, and yearbook. Popular campus events include Picnic Day, Whole Earth Festival, Asian Pacific Cultural Week, Native American Cultural Week and Powwow, African American Continuum, and La Raza Cultural Days.

Sports: There are 11 intercollegiate sports for men and 9 for women, and 15 intramural sports for men and 15 for women. Athletic and recreation facilities include a football stadium, tennis and basketball courts, equestrian trails, a track field, baseball, soccer, and softball fields, a recreation hall, 2 gymnasiums, 2 swimming pools, bowling alleys, and weight-training facilities.

Disabled Students: Ninety-nine percent of the campus is accessible to disabled students. The following facilities are available: wheelchair ramps, elevators, special parking, specially equipped rest rooms, special class scheduling, lowered drinking fountains, and lowered telephones.

Services: In addition to many counseling and information services, tutoring is available in most subjects. In addition, there is a reader service for the blind and remedial math and writing.

Campus Safety and Security: Campus safety and security measures include 24-hour foot and vehicle patrol, self-defense education, escort service, and shuttle buses. In addition, there are informal discussions, pamphlets, posters, and films, emergency telephones, and lighted pathways and sidewalks.

Programs of Study: UCD awards the A.B., B.S., and B.A.S. degrees. Master's and doctoral degrees also are awarded. Bachelor's degrees are awarded in AGRICULTURE (agricultural business management, agricultural economics, animal science, international agriculture, plant science, range/farm management, and soil science), BIOLOGICAL SCIENCE (avian sciences, bacteriology, biochemistry, biology/biological science, botany, entomology, environmental biology, genetics, microbiology, nutrition, physiology, wildlife biology, and zoology), BUSINESS (organizational behavior), COMMUNICATIONS AND THE ARTS (art history and appreciation, Chinese, communications, comparative literature, design, dramatic arts, English, fine arts, French, German, Greek, Italian, Japanese, Latin, linguistics, music, Russian, Spanish, speech/debate/rhetoric, and studio art),

COMPUTER AND PHYSICAL SCIENCE (atmospheric sciences and meteorology, chemistry, computer science, geology, mathematics, physics, and statistics), EDUCATION (physical), ENGINEERING AND ENVIRONMENTAL DESIGN (aeronautical engineering, agricultural engineering, bioengineering, chemical engineering, civil engineering, computer engineering, electrical/electronics engineering, environmental science, landscape architecture/design, materials engineering, and mechanical engineering), HEALTH PROFESSIONS (community health work), SOCIAL SCIENCE (African American studies, American studies, anthropology, behavioral science, classical/ancient civilization, dietetics, East Asian studies, economics, food science, geography, history, human development, international relations, medieval studies, Native American studies, philosophy, political science/government, psychology, religion, social science, sociology, textiles and clothing, and women's studies). Art, biological sciences, entomology, agricultural sciences, and engineering are the strongest academically. Biological science, psychology, biochemistry, international relations, and political science have the largest enrollments.

Required: General education requirements vary by college. A minimum of 180 quarter units with a minimum GPA of 2.0 are required for graduation.

Special: There are credit and noncredit internship programs. Study abroad in over 32 countries and a Washington semester are offered. Students may participate in college work-study, federal work-study, and California work-study programs. Several A.B.-B.S. degrees are offered. Students may design their own majors, take dual majors, and elect pass/fail options. Interdisciplinary majors offered include agricultural systems and environment, chemical engineering/materials science and engineering, Chicana/Chicano studies, civil engineering/materials science and engineering, computer science and engineering, electrical engineering/materials science and engineering, fermentation science, fiber and polymer science, and mechanical engineering/materials science and engineering. There is a freshman honors program on campus, as well as 24 national honor societies, including Phi Beta Kappa. Three departments have honors programs.

Faculty/Classroom: Eighty-two percent of faculty are male; 18%, female. The average class size in an introductory lecture is 60; in a laboratory, 41; and in a regular course offering, 49.

Admissions: About 70% of the 1993–94 applicants were accepted. The SAT scores for the 1993–94 freshman class were as follows: Verbal—51% below 500, 36% between 500 and 599, 12% between 600 and 700, and 1% above 700; Math—16% below 500, 34% between 500 and 599, 37% between 600 and 700, and 13% above 700. About 95% of the current freshmen were in the top fifth of their class; 100% were in the top two fifths. There were 22 National Merit finalists.

Requirements: UCD requires applicants to be in the upper 12% of their class. The SAT I or the ACT is required. Candidates for admission should have completed 4 units of English, 3 of mathematics, and 2 each of foreign language, history, and laboratory science. SAT II: Subject tests are required in writing, mathematics, and 1 other subject of the student's choice. AP credits are accepted. Important factors used in the admissions decision are advanced placement or honor courses, leadership record, evidence of special talent, extracurricular activities record, and personality and intangible qualities.

Procedure: Freshmen are admitted fall, winter, and spring. Entrance exams should be taken no later than December of the senior year. Applications should be filed by November 30 for fall entry, July 31 for winter entry, October 31 for spring entry, and March for summer entry, along with an application fee of $40. Notification is sent March 15. There is a deferred admissions plan.

Transfer: About 1450 transfer students enrolled in 1993–94. Junior-level transfers have priority. Requirements vary by college, discipline, and major.

Visiting: There are regularly scheduled orientations for prospective students, including drop-in visits to the Admissions Officer and campus tours. The campus also offers a one-day preview for prospective students and their families. There are guides for informal visits and visitors may sit in on classes (with permission from the instructor) and stay overnight at the school during the summer. To arrange for a visit, contact Rich Donnell, Information Services Coordinator at (916) 752-8111.

Financial Aid: The average freshman award was $9329. Forty-four percent of undergraduate students work part-time. The average financial indebtedness of the 1992–93 graduate was $8000. UCD is a member of CSS. The FAF or FFS is required. The deadline for financial aid applications is March 2.

International Students: There are currently 217 international students enrolled. They must take the TOEFL and achieve a minimum score of 500. The student must also take the SAT I or the ACT.

Computers: The college provides computer facilities for student use. Students have access to several campus microcomputers. There are hundreds of microcomputers and terminals located in numerous computer laboratories and classrooms throughout the campus. In addi-

tion, many microcomputers are provided for student use in the residence halls. All students may access the system. There are no fees.

Graduates: In 1992–93, 4355 bachelor's degrees were awarded. The most popular majors among graduates were international relations (6%), biological sciences (6%), and psychology (6%). Within an average freshman class, 1% graduate in 3 years, 29% in 4 years, 70% in 5 years, and 75% in 6 years. Some 252 companies recruited on campus in 1992–93. In an earlier graduating class, 43% of the students were enrolled in graduate school within 6 months of graduation; 93% had found employment.

Admissions Contact: Gary Tudor, Director of Undergraduate Admissions.

UNIVERSITY OF CALIFORNIA AT LOS ANGELES
C-5
Los Angeles, CA 90024
(213) 825–3101

Full-time: 11,525 men, 11,367 women	Faculty: I, +$
Part-time: none	Ph.D.s: 100%
Graduate: 6406 men, 5149 women	Student/Faculty: 14 to 1
Year: quarters, summer session	Tuition: $3549 ($11,248)
Application Deadline: November 30	Room & Board: $5410
Freshman Class: 22,165 applied, 10,096 accepted, 3391 enrolled	
SAT I or ACT: required	HIGHLY COMPETITIVE

University of California at Los Angeles (UCLA), founded in 1919, is a public, coeducational institution offering undergraduate and graduate degrees in arts and sciences, engineering, applied science, nursing, and theater, film, and television. There are 5 undergraduate and 14 graduate schools. In addition to regional accreditation, UCLA has baccalaureate program accreditation with AACSB, ABET, ADA, CSWE, NAAB, and NLN. The 13 libraries contain 6,390,409 volumes, 5,432,043 microform items, and 150,603 audiovisual forms, and subscribe to 94,612 periodicals. Special learning facilities include a learning resource center, an art gallery, a natural history museum, and a radio station. The 419-acre campus is in an urban area. Including residence halls, there are 230 buildings on campus.

Student Life: About 94% of undergraduates are from California. Students come from 47 states, 100 foreign countries, and Canada. Eighty-three percent are from public schools; 17% from private. Forty-six percent are white; 28% Asian American; 15% Hispanic. The average age of freshmen is 18; all undergraduates, 21. Six percent drop out by the end of their first year; 70% remain to graduate.

Housing: A total of 5750 students can be accommodated in college housing. College-sponsored living facilities include coed dormitories, off-campus apartments, and married-student housing. On-campus housing is guaranteed for the freshman year only and is available on a lottery system for upperclassmen. Seventy-five percent of students commute. Alcohol is not permitted.

Activities: About 13% of men belong to 2 local and 32 national fraternities; about 12% of women belong to 2 local and 17 national sororities. There are 700 groups on campus, including band, cheerleading, choir, chorale, chorus, computers, dance, drama, ethnic, film, gay, honors, international, literary magazine, marching band, newspaper, photography, political, professional, radio and TV, religious, social, social service, student government, and yearbook.

Sports: There are 10 intercollegiate sports for men and 8 for women, and 21 intramural sports for men and 17 for women. Athletic and recreation facilities include a pavilion, a stadium, a tennis center, and a recreation and sports center.

Disabled Students: The following facilities are available: wheelchair ramps, elevators, special parking, specially equipped rest rooms, special class scheduling, lowered drinking fountains, and lowered telephones.

Services: In addition to many counseling and information services, tutoring is available in most subjects. In addition, there is a reader service for the blind, and remedial math, reading, and writing.

Campus Safety and Security: Campus safety and security measures include escort service, shuttle buses, informal discussions, and pamphlets, posters, and films. In addition, there are lighted pathways and sidewalks.

Programs of Study: UCLA awards the B.A. and B.S. degrees. Master's and doctoral degrees also are awarded. Bachelor's degrees are awarded in BIOLOGICAL SCIENCE (biochemistry, biology/biological science, microbiology, neurosciences, and physiology), BUSINESS (international economics, labor studies, and organizational behavior), COMMUNICATIONS AND THE ARTS (African languages, Arabic, art, art history and appreciation, broadcasting, Chinese, classics, communications, dance, design, dramatic arts, English, film arts, fine arts, French, German, Greek, Hebrew, Italian, Japanese, Latin, linguistics, music, Portuguese, Scandinavian languages, Slavic languages, Spanish, and video), COMPUTER AND PHYSICAL SCIENCE (applied mathematics, astrophysics, atmospheric sciences and meteorology, chemistry, computer science, cybernetics, earth science, geology, geophysics and seismology, mathematics, paleontolo-

gy, and physics), ENGINEERING AND ENVIRONMENTAL DESIGN (aeronautical engineering, Aerospace Studies, chemical engineering, civil engineering, computer engineering, electrical/electronics engineering, engineering, materials engineering, materials science, and mechanical engineering), HEALTH PROFESSIONS (nursing), SOCIAL SCIENCE (African American studies, anthropology, classical/ancient civilization, cognitive science, crosscultural studies, developmental psychology, East Asian studies, economics, geography, history, human development, international relations, Judaic studies, Latin American studies, Mexican-American/Chicano studies, Near Eastern studies, philosophy, political science/government, psychobiology, psychology, religion, Russian and Slavic studies, social studies, sociology, urban studies, and women's studies). Economics, psychology, political science, and engineering have the largest enrollments.

Required: Students must complete a minimum of 180 quarter units and maintain a minimum GPA of 2.0 in all courses. All students must demonstrate a proficiency in English composition, or take specific courses to achieve this proficiency, and must also meet course requirements in American history and institutions. Other requirements vary by major and college or school.

Special: Opportunities are provided for internships, work-study programs, study abroad in 33 countries, B.A.-B.S. degrees, student-designed majors, dual majors, and interdisciplinary majors, including chemistry/materials science, Chicana and Chicano studies, engineering geology, economics/systems science, ethnomusicology, and computer science and engineering. There is a Washington, D.C. program for 20 to 30 students selected each fall and spring. There is a freshman honors program on campus, as well as 4 national honor societies, including Phi Beta Kappa.

Faculty/Classroom: Eighty percent of faculty are male; 20%, female.

Admissions: About 46% of the 1993–94 applicants were accepted. The SAT scores for the 1993–94 freshman class were as follows: Verbal—38% below 500, 39% between 500 and 599, 21% between 600 and 700, and 2% above 700; Math—12% below 500, 24% between 500 and 599, 38% between 600 and 700, and 26% above 700. There were 74 National Merit finalists.

Requirements: UCLA requires applicants to be in the upper 12 1/2% of their class. The SAT I or ACT is required. Graduation from an accredited secondary school is required; a GED will be accepted. Applicants must submit a minimum of 15 Carnegie units, distributed as follows: 4 years of English, 3 of mathematics, 2 each of a foreign language and science, 1 of history, and the remainder from other academic electives. SAT II: Subject tests in writing, mathematics, and 1 subject of the student's choice are required. An essay is required, and a portfolio and audition are required for all majors in arts and theater and film and television. AP credits are accepted. Important factors used in the admissions decision are advanced placement or honor courses, evidence of special talent, leadership record, recommendations by school officials, and recommendations by alumni.

Procedure: Freshmen are admitted in the fall. Entrance exams should be taken preferably in the junior year, but no later than December of the senior year. Applications should be filed by November 30 for fall entry, along with an application fee of $40. Notification is sent March 15.

Transfer: About 1800 transfer students were enrolled in an earlier year. Transfer students must have earned a minimum of 84 quarter units at the previous college and have maintained a minimum GPA of 2.4. Most students selected present a GPA of 3.0 or better. A total of 68 quarter units out of 180 must be completed at UCLA.

Visiting: There are regularly scheduled orientations for prospective students, including campus tours led by current UCLA students offered weekdays at 10:15 and 2:15. Reservations are required. Visitors may sit in on classes. To arrange for a visit, contact Tours in Undergraduate Admissions at (310) 825–8764.

Financial Aid: In a recent year, 82% of all current freshmen and 80% of continuing students received some form of financial aid. About 72% of freshmen and 60% of continuing students received need-based aid. The average freshman award was $3200. Of that total, scholarships or need-based grants averaged $758 ($4000 maximum); loans averaged $939 ($4300 maximum); and work contracts averaged $1503 ($3000 maximum). Thirty-five percent of undergraduate students work part-time. Average earnings from campus work for the school year are $2000. The average financial indebtedness of the 1992–93 graduate was $2200. UCLA is a member of CSS. The FAF, the college's own financial statement, and the FAFSA are required. The deadline for financial aid applications is March 2.

International Students: There are currently 1730 international students enrolled. Students must take the SAT I or the ACT and SAT II: Subject tests in writing, mathematics, and their choice of literature, foreign language, science, or social science.

Computers: The college provides computer facilities for student use. The mainframe is an IBM 3090 Model 600S. There are also IBM, HP, Zenith, and DEC VAX PCs available throughout the campus. All students may access the system. It may be used 24 hours a day, 7 days a week, with the limit on the amount of time each student may access the system varying by individual department. There are no fees.

Graduates: In 1992–93, 5911 bachelor's degrees were awarded. The most popular majors among graduates were political science (17%), psychology (12%), and economics (11%). Within an average freshman class, 70% graduate in 5 years and 71% in 6 years. Some 396 companies recruited on campus in 1992–93.

Admissions Contact: Director, Undergraduate Admissions and Relations with Schools.

UNIVERSITY OF CALIFORNIA AT SANTA BARBARA
C-5

Santa Barbara, CA 93106   (805) 893–2485

Full-time: 7660 men, 7941 women	Faculty: 746; I, +$
Part-time: 397 men, 279 women	Ph.D.s: 95%
Graduate: 1463 men, 915 women	Student/Faculty: 21 to 1
Year: quarters, summer session	Tuition: $3617 ($11,315)
Application Deadline: November 30	Room & Board: $5843
Freshman Class: 16,662 applied, 14,141 accepted, 3230 enrolled	
SAT I Verbal/Math: 459/547	**COMPETITIVE**

The University of California at Santa Barbara, founded in 1909, is a public, coeducational liberal arts institution offering programs in creative studies, engineering, and letters and science. There are 3 undergraduate schools and one graduate school. In addition to regional accreditation, UCSB has baccalaureate program accreditation with ABET. The library contains 2,126,000 volumes, 3,757,000 microform items, and 93,000 audiovisual forms, and subscribes to 24,325 periodicals. Computerized library sources and services include the card catalog, interlibrary loans, and database searching. Special learning facilities include a learning resource center, art gallery, radio station, and a language and learning laboratory. The 813-acre campus is in a suburban area 10 miles west of Santa Barbara. Including residence halls, there are 300 buildings on campus.

Student Life: About 94% of undergraduates are from California. Students come from 48 states, 45 foreign countries, and Canada. Eighty-six percent are from public schools; 14% from private. Sixty-eight percent are white; 13% Asian American; 10% Hispanic. The average age of freshmen is 18; all undergraduates, 21. Twelve percent drop out by the end of their first year; 67% remain to graduate.

Housing: A total of 4069 students can be accommodated in college housing. College-sponsored living facilities include coed dormitories, on-campus apartments, off-campus apartments, and married-student housing. In addition, there are special interest floors. On-campus housing is available on a first-come, first-served basis. All students may keep cars on campus.

Activities: About 15% of men belong to 2 local and 20 national fraternities; about 16% of women belong to 4 local and 14 national sororities. There are 300 groups on campus, including cheerleading, chess, choir, chorus, computers, dance, drama, ethnic, film, gay, honors, international, literary magazine, newspaper, pep band, photography, political, professional, radio and TV, religious, social, social service, student government, and yearbook. Popular campus events include Club Day, Activities Fair, UCEN Cultural Festival, Martin Luther King Week celebration, Open House, and Extravaganza.

Sports: There are 11 intercollegiate sports for men and 9 for women, and 18 intramural sports for men and 18 for women. Athletic and recreation facilities include a football stadium, a track, tennis courts, a swimming pool, 2 gymnasiums, a gymnastics area, a weight room, a Nautilus facility, a wellness institute, an aerobics studio, outdoor basketball courts, softball and baseball fields, a ropes course and climbing wall, and a sailing center.

Disabled Students: Nearly all of the campus is accessible to disabled students. The following facilities are available: wheelchair ramps, elevators, special parking, specially equipped rest rooms, special class scheduling, lowered drinking fountains, and lowered telephones.

Services: In addition to many counseling and information services, tutoring is available in most subjects. There is also a reader service for the blind and remedial reading and writing.

Campus Safety and Security: Campus safety and security measures include 24-hour foot and vehicle patrol, self defense education, escort service, and emergency telephones. In addition, there are lighted pathways and sidewalks.

Programs of Study: UCSB awards the B.A., B.S., B.F.A., and B.Mus. degrees. Master's and doctoral degrees also are awarded. Bachelor's degrees are awarded in BIOLOGICAL SCIENCE (biochemistry, biology/biological science, botany, cell biology, evolutionary biology, microbiology, and zoology), BUSINESS (business economics), COMMUNICATIONS AND THE ARTS (art history and appreciation, Chinese, classics, communications, dance, dramatic arts, English, film arts, fine arts, French, German, Greek, Italian, Japanese, Latin, linguistics, music, Portuguese, Slavic languages, and Spanish), COMPUTER AND PHYSICAL SCIENCE (chemistry, computer science, ge-

ology, geophysics and seismology, mathematics, physics, and statistics), ENGINEERING AND ENVIRONMENTAL DESIGN (chemical engineering, computer engineering, electrical/electronics engineering, environmental science, mechanical engineering, and nuclear engineering), HEALTH PROFESSIONS (pharmacy), SOCIAL SCIENCE (African American studies, anthropology, archeology, Asian/Oriental studies, classical/ancient civilization, criminal justice, economics, geography, history, Latin American studies, law, medieval studies, Mexican-American/Chicano studies, philosophy, political science/government, psychobiology, psychology, religion, sociology, and women's studies). Business economics, political science, and biological science have the largest enrollments.

Required: Graduation requirements vary by college. Generally, students will take one third of their distribution in the major subject, one third in general education courses, and one third in elective courses. They must earn at least 180 quarter units, with a minimum GPA of 2.0, and have completed the American History and Institutions requirement.

Special: A Washington semester, internships, study abroad in 32 countries, work-study programs, student-designed majors, an accelerated degree program in electrial engineering, and the B.A.-B.S. degree are offered. There is a freshman honors program on campus, as well as 6 national honor societies, including Phi Beta Kappa.

Faculty/Classroom: Eighty percent of faculty are male; 20%, female. All teach undergraduates and do research. The average class size in an introductory lecture is 60; in a laboratory, 24; and in a regular course offering, 30.

Admissions: About 85% of the 1993–94 applicants were accepted. The SAT scores for the 1993–94 freshman class were as follows: Verbal—65% below 500, 29% between 500 and 599, and 6% between 600 and 700; Math—26% below 500, 44% between 500 and 599, 25% between 600 and 700, and 6% above 700. There were 8 National Merit finalists.

Requirements: UCSB requires applicants to be in the upper 13% of their class. The SAT I is required, along with 3 SAT II: Subject tests in writing, mathematics I or II, and 1 other choice. Candidates for admission must have completed 4 years each of English and college preparatory electives, 3 of mathematics, 2 of foreign language, and 1 each of history and science for a total of 15 units. An additional year each in foreign language, mathematics, and science is recommended. AP and CLEP credits are accepted.

Procedure: Freshmen are admitted in the fall. Entrance exams should be taken by December of the senior year. Applications should be filed by November 30 for fall entry and October 31 for winter entry, along with an application fee of $40. Notification is sent March 1.

Transfer: About 1840 transfer students enrolled in 1993–94. California residents should have a minimum 2.0 GPA in transferable course work; nonresidents, a 2.8 GPA. A total of 35 of the final 45 quarter units out of 180 must be completed at UCSB.

Visiting: There are regularly scheduled orientations for prospective students, consisting of a campus film, an information session, and a walking tour of the campus led by a student guide. There are guides for informal visits and visitors may sit in on classes and stay overnight at the school. To arrange for a visit, contact the Office of Relations with Schools at (805) 893-2485.

Financial Aid: In 1993–94 39% of all current freshmen and 37% of continuing students received some form of financial aid. About 32% of freshmen and 34% of continuing students received need-based aid. The average freshman award was $3924. Of that total, scholarships or need-based grants averaged $3126 ($4200 maximum); loans averaged $613 ($2000 maximum); and work contracts averaged $922 ($2000 maximum). Seventeen percent of undergraduate students work part-time. UCSB is a member of CSS. The FAF, FFS or SFS, and the SAAC are required. The deadline for financial aid applications is March 2.

International Students: There are currently 536 international students enrolled. They must take the TOEFL and achieve a minimum score of 500. The student must also take SAT I or the ACT.

Computers: The college provides computer facilities for student use. They are accessed via numerous systems and networks on campus. There are several hundred microcomputers available in microcomputer laboratories and department laboratories. All students may access the system. It may be used at any time, if students have their own computer and modem.

Graduates: Within an average freshman class, 36% graduate in 4 years, 61% in 5 years, and 67% in 6 years. Some 193 companies recruited on campus in 1992–93.

Admissions Contact: The Office of Relations with Schools.

UNIVERSITY OF CALIFORNIA AT SANTA CRUZ
B-3

Santa Cruz, CA 95064 (408) 459–4008

Full-time: 3912 men, 5310 women	Faculty: 400; I, av$
Part-time: 244 men and women	Ph.D.s: 100%
Graduate: 530 men, 442 women	Student/Faculty: 23 to 1
Year: quarters, summer session	Tuition: $3129 ($10,828)
Application Deadline: November 30	Room & Board: $5931
Freshman Class: 10,758 applied, 8559 accepted, 1717 enrolled	
SAT I Verbal/Math: 515/560	VERY COMPETITIVE

University of California at Santa Cruz, opened in 1965, is a public institution offering programs in the arts, humanities, natural sciences, and social sciences. There are 24 graduate schools. In addition to regional accreditation, UCSC has baccalaureate program accreditation with ABET. The 10 libraries contain 1,065,529 volumes, and subscribe to 10,004 periodicals. Computerized library sources and services include the card catalog, interlibrary loans, and database searching. Special learning facilities include a learning resource center, an art gallery, a radio station, an agroecology program farm, and an arboretum. The 2000-acre campus is in a small town 50 miles north of Monterey and 75 miles south of San Francisco. Including residence halls, there are 467 buildings on campus.

Student Life: About 90% of undergraduates are from California. Students come from 50 states, 22 foreign countries, and Canada. Eighty percent are from public schools; 20% from private. Sixty-seven percent are white; 14% Hispanic; 13% Asian American. The average age of freshmen is 18; all undergraduates, 21. Seventeen percent drop out by the end of their first year; 83% remain to graduate.

Housing: A total of 4050 students can be accommodated in college housing. College-sponsored living facilities include single-sex and coed dormitories, on-campus apartments, and married-student housing. In addition, there are language houses, special interest houses, and multicultural residence halls. On-campus housing is guaranteed for the freshman year only and is available on a lottery system for upperclassmen. Alcohol is not permitted. All students may keep cars on campus.

Activities: There are no fraternities or sororities on campus. There are 100 groups on campus, including art, choir, chorale, chorus, computers, dance, drama, ethnic, film, gay, international, jazz band, literary magazine, newspaper, orchestra, photography, political, radio and TV, religious, social, social service, student government, and symphony. Popular campus events include Fall Preview Day, Multicultural Festival, Spring Open House, Community Day, and Martin Luther King Convocation.

Sports: There are 6 intercollegiate sports each for men and women, and 17 intramural sports each for men and women. Athletic and recreation facilities include a 50-meter pool, 2 playing fields, a weight room, an all-weather jogging track, fully equipped gymnasiums, a fitness course, and racquetball, tennis, and basketball courts.

Disabled Students: Ninety-nine percent of the campus is accessible to disabled students. The following facilities are available: wheelchair ramps, elevators, special parking, specially equipped rest rooms, special class scheduling, lowered drinking fountains, lowered telephones, and wheelchair lift-equipped transportation.

Services: There is a reader service for the blind. A learning center helps SAA/EOP students with math and writing skills.

Campus Safety and Security: Campus safety and security measures include 24-hour foot and vehicle patrol, self-defense education, escort service, and shuttle buses. In addition, there are informal discussions, pamphlets, posters, films, emergency telephones, lighted pathways and sidewalks, a rape prevention program, and seminars for residential staff.

Programs of Study: UCSC awards the B.A. and B.S. degrees. Master's and doctoral degrees are also awarded. Bachelor's degrees are awarded in BIOLOGICAL SCIENCE (biochemistry, biology/biological science, and marine biology), BUSINESS (business economics), COMMUNICATIONS AND THE ARTS (dramatic arts, English, film arts, fine arts, French, German, Italian, Japanese, linguistics, music, photography, Russian, and Spanish), COMPUTER AND PHYSICAL SCIENCE (chemistry, earth science, geology, information sciences and systems, mathematics, and physics), ENGINEERING AND ENVIRONMENTAL DESIGN (computer engineering), SOCIAL SCIENCE (American studies, anthropology, economics, history, Latin American studies, philosophy, political science/government, psychobiology, psychology, religion, sociology, and western civilization/culture). Marine sciences and biology are the strongest academically. Biology, psychology, and literature have the largest enrollments.

Required: In order to graduate, all students must complete 36 full-credit courses (180 quarter units). They must satisfy university requirements in American history and institutions and in English composition, the senior residence, core courses, and a comprehensive examination or senior thesis. Particular college requirements and those of an approved major vary.

Special: Cross-registration is possible with other University of California campuses, Hampshire College, the University of New Hampshire, and the University of New Mexico. UCSC also offers internships in business and government, study abroad in 32 countries, student-designed majors, a 3-2 engineering degree with the University of California at Berkeley, and a B.A.-B.S. degree in earth sciences, chemistry and biochemistry, computer engineering, and physics. Students receive a written narrative evaluation of their academic performance. Grades are optional. There is a chapter of Phi Beta Kappa on campus.

Faculty/Classroom: Seventy-two percent of faculty are male; 28%, female. Ninety-eight percent teach undergraduates, 100% do research, and 98% do both. Graduate students teach 1% of introductory courses.

Admissions: About 80% of the 1993-94 applicants were accepted. The SAT scores for the 1993-94 freshman class were as follows: Verbal—43% below 500, 36% between 500 and 599, 16% between 600 and 700, and 3% above 700; Math—25% below 500, 39% between 500 and 599, 27% between 600 and 700, and 7% above 700. About 94% of the current freshmen were in the top fifth of their class; 100% were in the top two fifths.

Requirements: The SAT I is required. SAT II: Subject tests are required in writing, mathematics, and either English literature, social science, foreign language, or science. Applicants must be graduates of an accredited secondary school or have a GED certificate. They should have completed 15 academic credits, including 4 years of English, 3 of mathematics, and 2 each of foreign language, history, laboratory science, and college preparatory electives. Auditions are required for music majors, and portfolios are recommended for art majors. All students must submit an essay. Nonresidents must meet additional requirements. AP credits are accepted. Important factors used in the admissions decision are advanced placement or honor courses, recommendations by school officials, evidence of special talent, leadership record, and extracurricular activities record.

Procedure: Freshmen are admitted fall, winter, and spring. Entrance exams should be taken by December of the senior year. Applications should be filed by November 30 for fall entry, July 31 for winter entry, and October 31 for spring entry, along with an application fee of $40. Notification is sent March 1.

Transfer: About 980 transfer students enrolled in 1993-94. Applicants should have completed 84 quarter credits, with a GPA of 2.4 required for California residents and 2.8 for nonresidents. A total of 7 courses out of 36 must be completed at UCSC.

Visiting: There are regularly scheduled orientations for prospective students, including programs at 10:30 A.M. and 1:30 P.M. on weekdays and some Saturdays; reservations are required. There are guides for informal visits and visitors may sit in on classes. To arrange for a visit, contact the Office of Admissions at (408) 459-4008.

Financial Aid: In 1993-94, 40% of all current freshmen and 45% of continuing students received some form of financial aid. The average freshman award was $7160. UCSC is a member of CSS. The FAFSA financial statement is required. The deadline for financial aid applications is March 2.

International Students: There are currently 100 international students enrolled. They must take the TOEFL and achieve a minimum score of 550. The student must also take the SAT I or the ACT.

Computers: The college provides computer facilities for student use. The mainframe is a SUN SPARC Station 10. There are also 150 Apple Macintosh and IBM PCs available throughout the campus, providing E-mail and Internet access. All students may access the system. There are no time limits on using the system and no fees.

Graduates: In 1992-93, 2363 bachelor's degrees were awarded. The most popular majors among graduates were literature (11%), biology (11%), and psychology (10%). Within an average freshman class, 1% graduate in 3 years, 42% in 4 years, 57% in 5 years, and 59% in 6 years.

Admissions Contact: Office of Admissions.

UNIVERSITY OF CALIFORNIA, RIVERSIDE   D-5
Riverside, CA 92521   (909) 787-4531

Full-time: 3293 men, 3629 women	Faculty: 500; I, av$
Part-time: 131 men, 134 women	Ph.D.s: 96%
Graduate: 769 men, 721 women	Student/Faculty: 14 to 1
Year: quarters, summer session	Tuition: $3748 ($11,447)
Application Deadline: November 30	Room & Board: $5430
Freshman Class: 9798 applied, 7566 accepted, 1470 enrolled	
SAT I Verbal/Math: 440/541	**COMPETITIVE**

University of California, Riverside, founded in 1954, is a public liberal arts institution with undergraduate programs in engineering, humanities and social sciences, and natural and agricultural sciences. There are 3 undergraduate and 3 graduate schools. The 5 libraries contain 1,561,000 volumes, 1,365,000 microform items, and 14,150 audiovisual forms, and subscribe to 12,900 periodicals. Computerized library sources and services include the card catalog, interlibrary loans, and database searching. Special learning facilities include a learning resource center, art gallery, radio station, a museum of photography, and botanical gardens. The 1200-acre campus is in a suburban area 50 miles east of Los Angeles. Including residence halls, there are more than 60 buildings on campus.

Student Life: About 98% of undergraduates are from California. Students come from 24 states and 12 foreign countries. Eighty-eight percent are from public schools; 12% from private. Forty-four percent are white; 37% Asian American; 14% Hispanic. The average age of freshmen is 18.4; all undergraduates, 20. Eleven percent drop out by the end of their first year; 62% remain to graduate.

Housing: A total of 2400 students can be accommodated in college housing. College-sponsored living facilities include coed dormitories, on-campus apartments, and married-student housing. On-campus housing is guaranteed for all 4 years. Sixty percent of students commute. All students may keep cars on campus.

Activities: About 10% of men belong to 3 local and 11 national fraternities; about 14% of women belong to 3 local and 9 national sororities. There are 136 groups on campus, including art, band, cheerleading, chess, computers, dance, drama, ethnic, honors, international, jazz band, literary magazine, marching band, newspaper, pep band, political, professional, radio and TV, religious, social, social service, student government, and yearbook. Popular campus events include Highlander Days, Oktoberfest, Winter Arts Festival, Wednesday Noon Music, Scots Week, Chancellor's Ball, Homecoming, Open House, Music-on-the-Patio, Barn Folk Concerts, Founders Day, Market Day, and Activities Faire.

Sports: There are 7 intercollegiate sports for men and 7 for women, and 14 intramural sports for men and 14 for women. Athletic and recreation facilities include a heated Olympic-size pool, weight rooms, a track, a vita course, racquetball and tennis courts, basketball and volleyball courts, a gymnasium, an aerobics room, and a new student recreation center.

Disabled Students: Ninety percent of the campus is accessible to disabled students. The following facilities are available: wheelchair ramps, elevators, special parking, specially equipped rest rooms, lowered drinking fountains, lowered telephones, and automatic doors.

Services: In addition to many counseling and information services, individual and group tutoring are both available. In addition, there is a reader service for the blind, and remedial math, reading, and writing. There are also study skills classes, preparation sessions for graduate entrance exams, study groups, individual counseling and laboratory work, speed-reading classes, and English as a Second Language classes.

Campus Safety and Security: Campus safety and security measures include 24-hour foot and vehicle patrol, self defense education, escort service, and informal discussions. In addition, there are pamphlets, posters, and films, emergency telephones, lighted pathways and sidewalks, and a ride-along program.

Programs of Study: UCR awards the B.A. and B.S. degrees. Master's and doctoral degrees also are awarded. Bachelor's degrees are awarded in AGRICULTURE (soil science), BIOLOGICAL SCIENCE (biochemistry, biology/biological science, botany, and entomology), BUSINESS (business administration and management and business economics), COMMUNICATIONS AND THE ARTS (art history and appreciation, classics, comparative literature, creative writing, dance, dramatic arts, English, fine arts, French, German, languages, linguistics, music, Russian, and Spanish), COMPUTER AND PHYSICAL SCIENCE (chemistry, computer science, geology, geophysics and seismology, mathematics, physical sciences, physics, and statistics), ENGINEERING AND ENVIRONMENTAL DESIGN (chemical engineering, electrical/electronics engineering, environmental engineering, and environmental science), HEALTH PROFESSIONS (premedicine), SOCIAL SCIENCE (anthropology, Asian/Oriental studies, community services, economics, ethnic studies, geography, history, human development, humanities, Latin American studies, liberal arts/general studies, philosophy, political science/government, psychobiology, psychology, religion, social science, sociology, and women's studies). Biomedical sciences is the strongest academically. Business administration has the largest enrollment.

Required: Students must demonstrate proficiency in English and a knowledge of American history and institutions and complete a maximum of 6 physical education units. A total of 180 quarter credit hours with a minimum GPA of 2.0 is required in order to graduate. The number of hours in the major varies. All students must complete a 1-year sequence in English composition, 1 course in computers, mathematics, or statistics, and 1 course in the concepts/issues of ethnicity. There are breadth requirements in humanities, social sciences, and natural sciences/mathematics for all students; the number of units/courses in each group depends on the student's college and major. A thesis is required for honors program students.

Special: Internships and work-study programs are offered with various agencies and employers on and off campus. Study abroad in 29 countries, and a semester in Washington in conjunction with the College of William and Mary are available. An accelerated degree in

biomedical science is available in conjunction with UCLA. Student-designed majors, dual majors, and opportunities for undergraduate research are possible. Pass/fail options are available in elective subjects only. Grants are available for research, fieldwork, or other creative activity. Co-op programs are available for students maajoring in Law and Society and Administrative Studies. There is a freshman honors program on campus, as well as 3 national honor societies, including Phi Beta Kappa. Most departments have honors programs.

Faculty/Classroom: The average class size in an introductory lecture is 21; in a laboratory, 20; and in a regular course offering, 20. Most faculty both teach undergraduates and do research.

Admissions: About 77% of the 1993–94 applicants were accepted. The SAT scores for the 1993–94 freshman class were as follows: Verbal—69% below 500, 23% between 500 and 599, 7% between 600 and 700, and 1% above 700; Math—33% below 500, 36% between 500 and 599, 22% between 600 and 700, and 9% above 700. About 95% of the current freshmen were in the top fifth of their class; all were in the top two fifths.

Requirements: UCR requires applicants to be in the upper 15% of their class. The SAT I or the ACT is required. Minimum GPA required varies from 2.8 to 3.3, depending on SAT I or ACT scores. Candidates for admission should have completed 4 years of English, 2 years of foreign language, 2 of history, 3 of mathematics, 2 of science, and 2 of electives. College Board SAT II: Subject tests are required in writing, mathematics, and 1 subject of the student's choice. AP credits are accepted. Important factors used in the admissions decision are advanced placement or honor courses, evidence of special talent, extracurricular activities record, leadership record, and geographic diversity.

Procedure: Freshmen are admitted fall, winter, and spring. Entrance exams should be taken in October or November of the senior year. Applications should be filed by November 30 for fall entry, July 31 for winter entry, and October 31 for spring entry, along with an application fee of $40. Notification is sent by March 15.

Transfer: A total of 614 transfer students enrolled in 1993–94. Transfers need a minimum college GPA of 2.4. A total of 45 quarter hours out of 180 must be completed at UCR.

Visiting: There are regularly scheduled orientations for prospective students, Tours are available throughout the year. Through the Host program, prospective students may attend classes and stay overnight in a residence hall. There is also University Preview Day in October and Open House in April. There are guides for informal visits. To arrange for a visit, contact the Office of Undergraduate Admission at (909) 787–3411 or 787–4531.

Financial Aid: In 1993–94, 50% of all students received some form of financial aid. About 50% of students received need-based aid. Twenty percent of undergraduate students work part-time. UCR is a member of CSS. The FAFSA financial statement is required. It is recommended that financial aid applications be filed by March 2.

International Students: There are currently 62 international students enrolled. They must take the TOEFL and achieve a minimum score of 550.

Computers: The university provides computer facilities for student use. The mainframes are a DEC VAX cluster (VAX 8820 and VAX 6310) and an IBM 9121–210. There are over 170 terminals and microcomputers, including Next, Apple II, Macintosh, PS/2, and PC-compatible microcomputers, plus over 60 printers. They are located in the main library, branch libraries, dormitories, a computer laboratory, the student center, and other campus buildings. All students may access the system. There are no time limits on using the system and no fees. A computer purchase plan is available to students.

Graduates: In 1992–93, 1712 bachelor's degrees were awarded. The most popular majors among recent graduates were business administration (22%), psychology (9%), and biology (9%). Within an average freshman class, 46% graduate in 4 years, 60% in 5 years, and 62% in 6 years. Some 51 companies recruited on campus in 1992–93. In the 1992 graduating class, 47% of the graduates were enrolled in graduate school within 6 months of graduation; 50% had found employment.

Admissions Contact: Laurie Nelson, Assistant Director, Office of Undergraduate Admission.

UNIVERSITY OF CALIFORNIA, SAN DIEGO D-5
La Jolla, CA 92093 (619) 534–4831

Full-time, Part-time: 7352 men, 7008 women	Faculty: 1146; I, +$
	Ph.D.s: 97%
Graduate: 3510 men and women	Student/Faculty: 13 to 1
Year: quarters, summer session	Tuition: $3613 ($11,312)
Application Deadline: November 30	Room & Board: $6415
Freshman Class: 19,431 applied, 11,535 accepted, 2481 enrolled	
SAT I Verbal/Math: 515/616	**VERY COMPETITIVE +**

University of California, San Diego, founded in 1959, is a public, coeducational liberal arts institution. There are 5 undergraduate and 5 graduate schools. In addition to regional accreditation, UCSD has baccalaureate program accreditation with ABET. The 6 libraries contain 2,055,113 volumes, 2,019,174 microform items, and 60,821 audiovisual forms, and subscribe to 23,784 periodicals. Computerized library sources and services include the card catalog, interlibrary loans, and database searching. Special learning facilities include an art gallery, radio station, and a TV station, and an aquarium-museum. The 1200-acre campus is in a suburban area 12 miles north of downtown San Diego. Including residence halls, there are 501 buildings on campus.

Student Life: About 92% of undergraduates are from California. Students come from 56 foreign countries and Canada. Ninety percent are from public schools; 10% from private. Fifty-eight percent are white; 21% Asian American; 10% Hispanic. The average age of freshmen is 18; all undergraduates, 21. Eight percent drop out by the end of their first year; 60% remain to graduate.

Housing: A total of 6214 students can be accommodated in college housing. College-sponsored living facilities include coed dormitories, on-campus apartments, off-campus apartments, and married-student housing. In addition there are language houses and special interest houses. On-campus housing is available on a lottery system for upperclassmen. Sixty-seven percent of students commute. All students may keep cars on campus.

Activities: About 12% of men belong to 14 national fraternities; about 8% of women belong to 8 national sororities. There are 250 groups on campus, including art, band, cheerleading, chess, choir, chorus, computers, dance, drama, ethnic, film, gay, honors, international, jazz band, literary magazine, newspaper, orchestra, pep band, political, professional, radio and TV, religious, social, social service, student government, symphony, and yearbook. Popular campus events include Fall Festival on the Green, Spring Sun God Festival, Asian Pacific Awareness Week, Jazz Festival, and cultural celebration.

Sports: There are 12 intercollegiate sports for men and 12 for women, and 27 intramural sports for men and 23 for women. Athletic and recreation facilities include a 9-lane, all-weather track, soccer and softball fields, an athletic training facility, a recreation center, 2 pools, a spa, a weight room, tennis courts, playing fields, and a golf driving range.

Disabled Students: The whole campus is accessible to disabled students. The following facilities are available: wheelchair ramps, elevators, special parking, specially equipped rest rooms, special class scheduling, lowered drinking fountains and telephones, special accommodations, and administrative support services.

Services: In addition to many counseling and information services, tutoring is available in most subjects. In addition, there is a reader service for the blind.

Campus Safety and Security: Campus safety and security measures include 24-hour foot and vehicle patrol, self defense education, escort service, and shuttle buses. In addition, there are informal discussions, pamphlets, posters, and films, emergency telephones, lighted pathways and sidewalks, and, a student safety awareness program, peer educators, and an on-campus police department.

Programs of Study: UCSD awards the B.A. and B.S. degrees. Master's and doctoral degrees also are awarded. Bachelor's degrees are awarded in BIOLOGICAL SCIENCE (biochemistry, biology/biological science, biophysics, ecology, microbiology, molecular biology, and physiology), COMMUNICATIONS AND THE ARTS (art history and appreciation, Chinese, classical languages, communications, dramatic arts, English, French, German, Italian, linguistics, literature, music, Russian, Spanish, studio art, and visual and performing arts), COMPUTER AND PHYSICAL SCIENCE (applied mathematics, chemistry, computer science, earth science, information sciences and systems, mathematics, physics, and quantitative methods), ENGINEERING AND ENVIRONMENTAL DESIGN (aeronautical engineering, bioengineering, chemical engineering, computer engineering, construction engineering, electrical/electronics engineering, engineering, engineering physics, mechanical engineering, and systems engineering), SOCIAL SCIENCE (anthropology, cognitive science, crosscultural studies, economics, ethnic studies, history, Judaic studies, Mexican-American/Chicano studies, philosophy, political science/government, psychology, sociology, and urban studies). The sciences, the arts, and social sciences are the strongest academically. Biology, engineering, psychology, and political science have the largest enrollments.

Required: Graduation requirements vary by college but students must complete 180 to 184 total quarter units or 45 to 46 courses, with a minimum of 60 credit hours or 12 to 22 courses in the major. Students must maintain a minimum GPA of 2.0.

Special: Internships, work-study, study abroad, and a Washington semester are offered. B.A.-B.S. degrees, an accelerated degree, dual majors, and student-designed majors are available. Nondegree study, credit for military experience, and pass/fail options are possible. There is a freshman honors program on campus, as well as 2 national honor societies, including Phi Beta Kappa. Fourteen departments have honors programs.

Faculty/Classroom: Eighty-five percent of faculty are male; 15%, female. All teach undergraduates and 100% do research. The average class size in an introductory lecture is 300; in a laboratory, 40; and in a regular course offering, 100.

Admissions: About 59% of the 1993–94 applicants were accepted. The SAT scores for the 1993–94 freshman class were as follows: Verbal—11% below 400, 35% between 401 and 500, 39% between 501 and 600, and 16% above 600; Math—1% below 400, 9% between 401 and 500, 33% between 501 and 600, and 57% above 600. There were 58 National Merit finalists.

Requirements: The SAT I or ACT and 3 SAT II: Subject tests, including writing, mathematics I or II, and a choice of English literature, foreign language, science, or social studies, are required. Candidates for admission should have completed 8 courses each in English and college preparatory electives, 6 in advanced mathematics, 4 in a foreign language, and 2 each in laboratory science and history. AP credits are accepted. Important factors used in the admissions decision are advanced placement or honor courses, evidence of special talent, leadership record, recommendations by school officials, and personality and other intangible qualities.

Procedure: Freshmen are admitted in the fall. Entrance exams should be taken by December of the senior year. Applications should be filed by November 30 for fall entry, along with an application fee of $40. Notification is sent on a rolling basis. There is an early admissions plan.

Transfer: About 992 transfer students enrolled in a recent year. California residents should have a 2.4 GPA; nonresidents, a 2.8 GPA. Transfers should have completed 84 quarter units. Preference is given to applicants from state community colleges. A total of 36 quarter credits out of 180 to 184 must be completed at UCSD.

Visiting: There are regularly scheduled orientations for prospective students. There are guides for informal visits and visitors may sit in on classes. To arrange for a visit, contact Tim Johnston, Tour Coodinator, Student Outreach and Recruitment at (619) 534-4831.

Financial Aid: Recently, 39% of all current freshmen and 36% of continuing students received some form of financial aid. The average freshman award was $8000. Of that total, scholarships or need-based grants averaged $500 ($15,465 maximum); loans averaged $1172 ($4500 maximum); and work contracts averaged $1325 ($3000 maximum). Seventy-five percent of undergraduate students work part-time. Average earnings from campus work for the school year are $1325. The average financial indebtedness of recent graduate was $8900. UCSD is a member of CSS. The FAF and the SAAC is required. The deadline for financial aid applications is May 1.

International Students: There are currently 837 international students enrolled. They must take the TOEFL and achieve a minimum score of 550. The student must also take the SAT I or the ACT.

Computers: The college provides computer facilities for student use. A wide variety of minicomputers are available with access to about 350 computer terminals. There are also hundreds of MS-DOS and Macintosh PCs. An on-campus computer center also provides Apple and Zenith microcomputers. All students may access the system. It may be used 24 hours every day. There are no fees.

Graduates: In an earlier year 3024 bachelor's degrees were awarded. The most popular majors among graduates were biology (16%), economics (12%), and political science (8%). Recently some 247 companies recruited on campus.

Admissions Contact: Victoria Valle, Director, Student Outreach and Recruitment.

UNIVERSITY OF CALIFORNIA
IRVINE

Irvine, CA 92717

D-5

(714) 856-6703

Full-time: 6390 men, 7151 women	Faculty: 998; I, +$
Part-time: none	Ph.D.s: 96%
Graduate: 3232 men and women	Student/Faculty: 14 to 1
Year: quarters, summer session	Tuition: $4070 ($11,769)
Application Deadline: November 30	Room & Board: $8610
Freshman Class: 15,698 applied, 10,775 accepted, 2479 enrolled	
SAT I Verbal/Math: 450/580	**VERY COMPETITIVE**

The University of California, Irvine, founded in 1965, is a public research university and part of the University of California System. There are 6 undergraduate and 4 graduate schools. In addition to regional accreditation, UCI has baccalaureate program accreditation with AACSB and ABET. The 5 libraries contain 1.5 million volumes, 1,825,445 microform items, and 47,195 audiovisual forms, and subscribe to 19,522 periodicals. Computerized library sources and services include the card catalog, interlibrary loans, and database searching. Special learning facilities include a learning resource center, art gallery, planetarium, radio station, the San Joaquin Freshwater Marsh Reserve, the Beckman Laser Institute, and an arboretum. The 1489-acre campus is in a suburban area 40 miles south of Los Angeles.

Student Life: About 97% of undergraduates are from California. Students come from 50 states, 59 foreign countries, and Canada. Fifty-three percent are from public schools; 8% from private. Forty-seven percent are Asian American; 32% white; 12% Hispanic. The average age of freshmen is 18; all undergraduates, 21.3. Fifteen percent drop out by the end of their first year; 50% remain to graduate.

Housing: A total of 4645 students can be accommodated in college housing. College-sponsored living facilities include single-sex and coed dormitories, on-campus apartments, and married-student housing. On-campus housing is available on a first-come, first-served basis and is available on a lottery system for upperclassmen. Priority is given to out-of-town students. Seventy percent of students commute. Alcohol is not permitted. All students may keep cars on campus.

Activities: About 11% of men belong to 2 local and 11 national fraternities; about 14% of women belong to 1 local sorority and 11 national sororities. There are 187 groups on campus, including art, band, cheerleading, choir, computers, dance, drama, ethnic, film, gay, honors, international, jazz band, literary magazine, musical theater, newspaper, political, professional, radio and TV, religious, social, social service, student government, and yearbook. Popular campus events include Celebrate UCI, Rainbow Festival, Orientation Week, Oktoberfest, St. Patrick's Day Festival, Asian Week, Greek Week, and Engineering Week.

Sports: There are 12 intercollegiate sports for men and 8 for women, and 23 intramural sports for men and 20 for women. Athletic and recreation facilities include a stadium seating 2,500, a gymnasium seating 2,500, basketball and volleyball courts, baseball fields, an outdoor track, a tennis stadium, a swimming pool, and indoor handball, racquetball, and squash courts.

Disabled Students: Ninety-nine percent of the campus is accessible to disabled students. The following facilities are available: wheelchair ramps, elevators, special parking, specially equipped rest rooms, special class scheduling, lowered drinking fountains, lowered telephones, automatic doors, and transportation on and off campus.

Services: In addition to many counseling and information services, tutoring is available in most subjects. In addition, there is a reader service for the blind, and remedial math, reading, and writing.

Campus Safety and Security: Campus safety and security measures include 24-hour foot and vehicle patrol, self defense education, escort service, and shuttle buses. In addition, there are informal discussions, pamphlets, posters, and films, emergency telephones, and lighted pathways and sidewalks.

Programs of Study: UCI awards the B.A., B.S., B. Mus. degrees. Master's and doctoral degrees also are awarded. Bachelor's degrees are awarded in BIOLOGICAL SCIENCE (biology/biological science), COMMUNICATIONS AND THE ARTS (art history and appreciation, classics, comparative literature, dance, dramatic arts, English, film arts, fine arts, French, German, linguistics, music, Russian, Spanish, and studio art), COMPUTER AND PHYSICAL SCIENCE (chemistry, information sciences and systems, mathematics, and physics), ENGINEERING AND ENVIRONMENTAL DESIGN (civil engineering, electrical/electronics engineering, engineering, environmental science, and mechanical engineering), SOCIAL SCIENCE (anthropology, classical/ancient civilization, economics, history, humanities, philosophy, political science/government, psychology, social science, and sociology). Biological sciences, political science, economics, and humanities are the strongest academically. Biological sciences, social ecology, economics, psychology, political science, and English have the largest enrollments.

Required: All students must maintain a GPA of at least 2.0 and earn 180 quarter units. Under distribution requirements, 12 units must be earned in each of the following areas: writing, natural sciences, social and behavioral sciences, humanistic inquiry, foreign language, linguistics, logic, and mathematics or computer science. In addition, 2 writing courses are necessary.

Special: Internships, study abroad in Spain, England, India, Kenya, Sweden and Egypt, a Washington semester, and work-study program with the university are available. B.A.-B.S. degrees, dual majors, and a 3–2 engineering degree are possible. In addition, there are pass/fail options. There is a freshman honors program on campus, as well as 3 national honor societies, including Phi Beta Kappa. Six departments have honors programs.

Faculty/Classroom: Eighty-one percent of faculty are male; 19%, female. All teach undergraduates and do research.

Admissions: About 69% of the 1993–94 applicants were accepted. All of the current freshmen were in the top fifth of their class.

Requirements: The SAT I or ACT is required. Required minimum scores are determined by an eligibility index. Applicants need 16 academic credits, including 4 years of English, 3 in mathematics (4 recommended), 2 each in foreign language (3 recommended) and history/social studies, 1 in laboratory science (3 recommended), and 4 electives. In addition, SAT II: Subject tests in writing, mathematics, and a third chosen from science, social science, foreign language, or English literature are required. An essay also is needed. The GED is accepted. AP credits are accepted. Important factors used in the ad-

missions decision are advanced placement or honor courses, leadership record, geographic diversity, evidence of special talent, and extracurricular activities record.

Procedure: Freshmen are admitted in the fall. Entrance exams should be taken no later than December of the senior year. Applications should be filed by November 30 for fall entry, July 1 for winter entry, and October 1 for spring entry, along with an application fee of $40. Notification is sent March 1 to March 15.

Transfer: A total of 1083 transfer students enrolled in 1993–94. Transfer applicant's minimum GPA and scores on the SAT I or ACT are determined by the university's eligibility index. The index requirements also vary with the number of credits previously earned in colleges. The last 36 quarter credits out of 180 must be completed at UCI.

Visiting: There are regularly scheduled orientations for prospective students. There are guides for informal visits and visitors may sit in on classes and stay overnight at the school. To arrange for a visit, contact the Office of Relations with Schools and Colleges at (714) 856–5518.

Financial Aid: In 1993–94, 46% of all current freshmen and 49% of continuing students received some form of financial aid. About 97% of freshmen and 81% of continuing students received need-based aid. The average freshman award was $7237. UCI is a member of CSS. The SAAC financial statement is required. The deadline for financial aid applications is March 2.

International Students: There are currently 748 international students enrolled. They must take the TOEFL and achieve a minimum score of 550. Students must take SAT II: Subject tests.

Computers: The university provides computer facilities for student use. The mainframes are a Convex C240; a DEC VAX 8350 and 6330; a Sequent, Symmetry 581 multiprocessor, and a SUN. There are approximately 500 computer terminals/PCs available for student use located in the computer center, the student center, the library, and departmental computer laboratories. All students may access the system for 2-hour sessions. There are no fees.

Graduates: In 1992–93, 3220 bachelor's degrees were awarded. Within an average freshman class, 32% graduate in 4 years, 59% in 5 years, and 65% in 6 years. Some 266 companies recruited on campus in 1992–93.

Admissions Contact: Admissions Office Undergraduate.

UNIVERSITY OF LA VERNE
La Verne, CA 91750–4443

D-5

(909) 593–3511, ext. 4026
(800) 876–4858 (in-state)

Full-time: 475 men, 598 women	Faculty: 130; IIA, --$
Part-time: 120 men, 154 women	Ph.D.s: 70%
Graduate: 567 men, 783 women	Student/Faculty: 8 to 1
Year: 4–1–4, summer session	Tuition: $12,900
Application Deadline: March 1	Room & Board: $4500
Freshman Class: 1500 applied, 852 accepted, 291 enrolled	
SAT I Verbal/Math: 420/460	COMPETITIVE

The University of La Verne, founded in 1891, is an independent, coeducational institution with historical ties to the Church of the Brethren. There are 3 undergraduate and 4 graduate schools. The 12 libraries contain 150,000 volumes, 150 microform items, and 2400 audiovisual forms, and subscribe to 1080 periodicals. Computerized library sources and services include the card catalog, interlibrary loans, and database searching. Special learning facilities include a learning resource center, art gallery, natural history museum, radio station, TV station, and a theater house. The 26-acre campus is in a suburban area 35 miles east of Los Angeles. Including residence halls, there are 16 buildings on campus.

Student Life: Students come from 16 states and 15 foreign countries. Forty-six percent are white; 30% Hispanic; 11% Asian American; 10% African American. Thirty-five percent are Catholic; 29% claim no religious affiliation; 24% Protestant. The average age of freshmen is 18; all undergraduates, 21. Thirty percent drop out by the end of their first year; 31% remain to graduate.

Housing: A total of 423 students can be accommodated in college housing. College-sponsored living facilities include single-sex and coed dormitories. On-campus housing is available on a first-come, first-served basis. Priority is given to out-of-town students. Fifty-two percent of students commute. Alcohol is not permitted. All students may keep cars on campus.

Activities: About 10% of men belong to 1 local and 2 national fraternities; about 12% of women belong to 1 local and 2 national sororities. There are 20 groups on campus, including art, cheerleading, choir, chorale, chorus, computers, dance, drama, ethnic, honors, international, jazz band, literary magazine, newspaper, photography, political, professional, radio and TV, religious, social, social service, student government, and yearbook. Popular campus events include Build La Verne, 'L' Day, Homecoming, and Senior Retreat.

Sports: There are 9 intercollegiate sports for men and 7 for women, and 5 intramural sports for men and 5 for women. Athletic and recreation facilities include a football stadium, 2 gymnasiums, a weight and fitness center, tennis courts, an outdoor track, and playing fields.

Disabled Students: All of the campus is accessible to disabled students. The following facilities are available: wheelchair ramps, elevators, special parking, specially equipped rest rooms, and lowered telephones.

Services: In addition to many counseling and information services, tutoring is available in most subjects. In addition, there is a reader service for the blind, and remedial math, reading, and writing. Students may use the computerized Learning Enhancement Center free of charge.

Campus Safety and Security: Campus safety and security measures include informal discussions and lighted pathways and sidewalks.

Programs of Study: ULV awards the B.A. and B.S. degrees. Master's and doctoral degrees also are awarded. Bachelor's degrees are awarded in BIOLOGICAL SCIENCE (biology/biological science), BUSINESS (accounting, business administration and management, business economics, and international business management), COMMUNICATIONS AND THE ARTS (broadcasting, communications, dramatic arts, English, fine arts, French, German, Indic languages, journalism, music, and Spanish), COMPUTER AND PHYSICAL SCIENCE (chemistry, computer science, mathematics, natural sciences, and physics), EDUCATION (art, business, early childhood, elementary, foreign languages, music, and secondary), ENGINEERING AND ENVIRONMENTAL DESIGN (computer engineering, electrical/electronics engineering, environmental science, and optical engineering), HEALTH PROFESSIONS (nursing, predentistry, and premedicine), SOCIAL SCIENCE (criminal justice, economics, history, international relations, philosophy, political science/government, prelaw, psychology, public administration, religion, social science, and sociology). Natural science and education are the strongest academically. Business has the largest enrollment.

Required: To graduate, students must complete a minimum of 128 credit hours, including 32 hours in the major, with a GPA of 2.0.

Special: ULV offers a co-op program with the College of Osteopathic Medicine of the Pacific, internships, study abroad, work-study programs, B.A.-B.S. degrees, dual majors, and nondegree study. Pass/fail options and credit for life, military, and work experience are also available. There is a freshman honors program on campus. There is one honors program for all departments.

Faculty/Classroom: Sixty-eight percent of faculty are male; 32%, female. All teach undergraduates, 40% do research, and 40% do both. The average class size in an introductory lecture is 26; in a laboratory, 20; and in a regular course offering, 21.

Admissions: About 57% of the 1993–94 applicants were accepted. The SAT scores for the 1993–94 freshman class were as follows: Verbal—64% below 500, 31% between 500 and 599, 4% between 600 and 700, and 1% above 700; Math—58% below 500, 37% between 500 and 599, 4% between 600 and 700, and 1% above 700. The ACT scores were 53% below 21, 32% between 21 and 23, 12% between 24 and 26, 2% between 27 and 28, and 1% above 28. About 61% of the current freshmen were in the top fifth of their class; 85% were in the top two fifths.

Requirements: ULV requires applicants to be in the upper 60% of their class. A minimum GPA of 2.4 is required. The SAT I is required. Applicants must be graduates of an accredited secondary school. The GED is not accepted. An essay is required and an interview is recommended. AP and CLEP credits are accepted. Important factors used in the admissions decision are advanced placement or honor courses, evidence of special talent, personality, intangible qualities, extracurricular activities record, and recommendations by school officials.

Procedure: Freshmen are admitted fall and spring. Entrance exams should be taken in the junior or senior year. Applications should be filed by March 1 for fall entry and December 1 for spring entry, along with an application fee of $20. Notification is sent on a rolling basis. There is a deferred admissions plan.

Transfer: About 80 transfer students enrolled in a recent year. Applicants must have a GPA of 2.0 and be in good standing at all previous colleges attended. Students with fewer than 30 transferable semester credits must submit SAT I or ACT scores. A total of 32 credits out of 128 must be completed at ULV.

Visiting: There are regularly scheduled orientations for prospective students. There are guides for informal visits and visitors may sit in on classes and stay overnight at the school. To arrange for a visit, contact Admissions Office at (800) 876–4858.

Financial Aid: In a recent year, 75% of all current freshmen and 90% of continuing students received some form of financial aid. The average financial indebtedness of the 1992–93 graduate was $7500. ULV is a member of CSS. The FAF, the college's own financial statement, or the SAAC is required. The deadline for financial aid applications is April 15.

International Students: There are currently 139 international students enrolled. The school actively recruits these students.

Computers: The college provides computer facilities for student use. The mainframe is a DEC VAX 3500. Several PC laboratories on campus offer a variety of hardware, software, and classes. All students may access the system. It may be used 24 hours, 7 days a week. There are no time limits on using the system and no fees.

Graduates: In 1992–93, 889 bachelor's degrees were awarded. The most popular majors among graduates were business/economics (28%), behavioral sciences (16%), and education (11%). Within an average freshman class, 1% graduate in 3 years, 25% in 4 years, 5% in 5 years, and 1% in 6 years. Some 22 companies recruited on campus in 1992–93.

Admissions Contact: Doug Wible, Associate Director of Admissions.

UNIVERSITY OF REDLANDS   D-5
Redlands, CA 92373–0999   (714) 335–4074

Full-time, part-time: 1500 men and women	Faculty: 92; IIA, av$
	Ph.D.s: 89%
Graduate: 99 men and women	Student/Faculty: 16 to 1
Year: 4–1–4	Tuition: $16,060
Application Deadline: March 1	Room & Board: $5999
Freshman Class: 1821 applied, 1150 accepted, 470 enrolled	
SAT I Verbal/Math: 510/540	**VERY COMPETITIVE**

The University of Redlands, founded in 1907, is an independent institution that offers programs in liberal and fine arts, business, health science, and teacher preparation. There are 2 undergraduate and 4 graduate schools. The library contains 277,000 volumes, and subscribes to 1027 periodicals. Computerized library sources and services include the card catalog, interlibrary loans, and database searching. Special learning facilities include an art gallery, radio station, archaeology laboratory, and a recording studio. The 130-acre campus is in a small town 60 miles east of Los Angeles. Including residence halls, there are 40 buildings on campus.

Student Life: About 52% of undergraduates are from California. Students come from 42 states, 35 foreign countries, and Canada. Fifty percent are Protestant; 40% claim no religious affiliation. The average age of freshmen is 18; all undergraduates, 20. About 75% of freshmen remain to graduate.

Housing: A total of 95 students can be accommodated in college housing. College-sponsored living facilities include coed dormitories, on-campus apartments, married-student housing, fraternity houses, and sorority houses. In addition there are honors houses. On-campus housing is guaranteed for 4 years. Ninety-three percent of students live on campus and all students may keep cars on campus.

Activities: About 18% of men belong to 5 local fraternities; about 20% of women belong to 4 local sororities. There are many groups and organizations on campus, including art, band, cheerleading, choir, chorale, chorus, dance, drama, ethnic, honors, international, jazz band, literary magazine, musical theater, newspaper, opera, orchestra, pep band, photography, political, professional, radio and TV, religious, social, social service, student government, symphony, and yearbook. Popular campus events include Mayfest, Casino Night, Spree Annual Formal, convocations, Fallfest, Octoberfest, Mud Fest, Greek Week, and Homecoming.

Sports: Athletic and recreation facilities include a gymnasium, a weight room, and a fitness center.

Disabled Students: The following facilities are available: wheelchair ramps, special parking, and special class scheduling.

Services: In addition to many counseling and information services, tutoring is available in most subjects. There are mathematics and writing laboratories.

Campus Safety and Security: Campus safety and security measures include 24-hour foot and vehicle patrol, escort service, shuttle buses, and informal discussions. In addition, there are pamphlets, posters, and films and lighted pathways and sidewalks.

Programs of Study: Redlands awards the B.A., B.S., and B.Mus. degrees. Master's degrees also are awarded. Bachelor's degrees are awarded in BIOLOGICAL SCIENCE (biology/biological science), BUSINESS (accounting and business administration and management), COMMUNICATIONS AND THE ARTS (art, English, French, German, music, and Spanish), COMPUTER AND PHYSICAL SCIENCE (chemistry, computer science, mathematics, and physics), EDUCATION (elementary and secondary), ENGINEERING AND ENVIRONMENTAL DESIGN (engineering), HEALTH PROFESSIONS (speech pathology/audiology), SOCIAL SCIENCE (anthropology, Asian/Oriental studies, economics, history, humanities, international relations, philosophy, political science/government, psychology, religion, and sociology). Liberal arts is the strongest academically. Business has the largest enrollment.

Required: Requirements for graduation vary according to the degree and major. Students must complete at least 120 units and maintain a minimum GPA of 2.0.

Special: Cross-registration with sister colleges, various internships and study abroad in 50 countries are offered. A Washington semester, a co-op program in engineering, various work-study programs B.A.-B.S. degrees, a general studies degree, dual majors, and accelerated degree programs are available. Students may pursue nondegree study, take advantage of pass/fail options, and receive credit for life or work experience. At the Johnson Center for Individual Learning, students design their own majors and courses of study. There is a freshman honors program on campus

Faculty/Classroom: All teach undergraduates. The average class size in an introductory lecture is 35; in a laboratory, 10; and in a regular course offering, 16.

Admissions: About 63% of the 1993–94 applicants were accepted. There were 15 National Merit finalists.

Requirements: The SAT I or the ACT is required. Redlands recommends that applicants have completed a minimum of 16 units in solid academic areas. The student should have completed at least 4 years of high school English, 2 to 3 years each of mathematics, laboratory sciences, and social science, and 2 years of a foreign language. AP credits are accepted. Important factors used in the admissions decision are advanced placement or honor courses, extracurricular activities record, leadership record, evidence of special talent, and personality, intangible qualities.

Procedure: Freshmen are admitted to all sessions. Entrance exams should be taken prior to application. Applications should be filed by March 1 for fall entry, (January 1 for merit scholarship) along with an application fee of $40. Notification is sent on a rolling basis. There is a deferred admissions plan.

Transfer: About 110 transfer students enrolled in an earlier year. The SAT I or the ACT may be required of transfer applicants, depending on how many units are accepted. A total of 60 credits out of 120 must be completed at Redlands.

Visiting: There are regularly scheduled orientations for prospective students. There are guides for informal visits and visitors may sit in on classes and stay overnight at the school. To arrange for a visit, contact Marliyn Crampton, Visit Coordinator at (714) 335–4073.

Financial Aid: Recently, 80% of all current freshmen and 75% of continuing students received some form of financial aid. Sixty-five percent of undergraduate students work part-time. Redlands is a member of CSS. The FAF, the college's own financial statement, and the SAAC for California residents are required. The deadline for financial aid applications is March 1.

International Students: There are currently 108 international students enrolled. The school actively recruits these students. They must take the TOEFL and achieve a minimum score of 550.

Computers: The college provides computer facilities for student use. The mainframe is a DEC VAX 11/750. To support the various laboratories, the computer center has more than 100 different software packages, as well as scanners, file exchange capabilities, laser printing, and desktop publishing software. All students may access the system. There are no time limits on using the system and no fees.

Admissions Contact: Paul M. Driscoll, Dean of Admission.

UNIVERSITY OF SAN DIEGO   D-5
San Diego, CA 92110   (619) 260–4506

Full-time: 1268 men, 1647 women	Faculty: 212; IIA, +$
Part-time: 427 men, 573 women	Ph.D.s: 97%
Graduate: 452 men, 763 women	Student/Faculty: 14 to 1
Year: 4–1–4, summer session	Tuition: $12,970
Application Deadline: January 15	Room & Board: $6000
Freshman Class: 3393 applied, 2735 accepted, 886 enrolled	
SAT I Verbal/Math: 506/548	**VERY COMPETITIVE**

The University of San Diego, founded in 1949, is an independent, Catholic liberal arts university. There are 4 undergraduate and 5 graduate schools. In addition to regional accreditation, USD has baccalaureate program accreditation with AACSB and NLN. The 2 libraries contain 475,000 volumes and 130,000 microform items, and subscribe to 1500 periodicals. Computerized library sources and services include the card catalog, interlibrary loans, and database searching. Special learning facilities include a learning resource center, an art gallery, a media center, and a child development center. The 180-acre campus is in an urban area 10 miles north of downtown San Diego. Including residence halls, there are 21 buildings on campus.

Student Life: About 63% of undergraduates are from California. Students come from 50 states, 50 foreign countries, and Canada. Sixty-seven percent are from public schools; 33% from private. Sixty-eight percent are white; 13% Hispanic; 10% Asian American. Sixty-two percent are Catholic; 19% Protestant. The average age of freshman is 18; all undergraduates, 20. Ten percent drop out by the end of their first year; 65% remain to graduate.

Housing: A total of 1900 students can be accommodated in college housing. College-sponsored living facilities include single-sex and coed dormitories and on-campus apartments. In addition there are

special interest houses. On-campus housing is guaranteed for all 4 years. Fifty percent of students live on campus; of those, 70% remain on campus on weekends. All students may keep cars on campus.

Activities: About 20% of men belong to 4 national fraternities; about 20% of women belong to 4 national sororities. There are 50 groups on campus, including art, cheerleading, choir, dance, drama, ethnic, honors, international, newspaper, opera, orchestra, political, professional, religious, social, social service, student government, and yearbook. Popular campus events include Homecoming, the Annual Bike Race, and Hunger Awareness Week.

Sports: There are 8 intercollegiate sports for men and 8 for women, and 15 intramural sports for men and 15 for women. Athletic and recreation facilities include the sports center, a stadium, tennis courts, a golf course, a swimming pool, soccer, baseball, and softball fields, and the Mission Bay Aquatic Center.

Disabled Students: Eighty percent of the campus is accessible to disabled students. The following facilities are available: wheelchair ramps, elevators, special parking, and specially equipped rest rooms.

Services: In addition to many counseling and information services, tutoring is available in every subject.

Campus Safety and Security: Campus safety and security measures include 24-hour foot and vehicle patrol, self defense education, escort service, and shuttle buses. In addition, there are informal discussions, pamphlets, posters, films, emergency telephones, and lighted pathways and sidewalks.

Programs of Study: USD awards the B.A., B.S., B.B.A., B.S.N., and B. Acc. degrees. Master's and doctoral degrees also are awarded. Bachelor's degrees are awarded in BIOLOGICAL SCIENCE (biology/biological science and marine science), BUSINESS (accounting, business administration and management, and business economics), COMMUNICATIONS AND THE ARTS (communications, English, fine arts, French, music, and Spanish), COMPUTER AND PHYSICAL SCIENCE (chemistry, computer science, mathematics, oceanography, and physics), EDUCATION (elementary and secondary), ENGINEERING AND ENVIRONMENTAL DESIGN (electrical/electronics engineering), HEALTH PROFESSIONS (nursing), SOCIAL SCIENCE (anthropology, economics, history, humanities, international relations, liberal arts/general studies, philosophy, political science/government, psychology, religion, and sociology). Business administration has the largest enrollment.

Required: All students must take 124 credit hours including 36 to 72 in their major, while maintaining a minimum GPA of 2.0. Distribution requirements include 3 units of composition and literature, 3 or 4 of mathematics, 9 each of religious studies, humanities, and fine arts, 6 each of philosophy, natural sciences, and social sciences, as well as 3 semesters of foreign language.

Special: A co-op program and a B.A.-B.S. degree are offered in electrical engineering. Internships in all disciplines, study abroad in 6 countries, work-study programs on campus, dual majors in marine science and ocean studies, nondegree study through the lawyer assistance program, and pass/fail options are available. There is a freshman honors program on campus, as well as 15 national honor societies.

Faculty/Classroom: Sixty-two percent of faculty are male; 38%, female. Eighty percent teach undergraduates. No introductory courses are taught by graduate students. The average class size in an introductory lecture is 30; in a laboratory, 15; and in a regular course offering, 22.

Admissions: About 81% of the 1993–94 applicants were accepted. The SAT scores for the 1993–94 freshman class were as follows: Verbal—56% below 500, 31% between 500 and 599, 12% between 600 and 700, and 1% above 700; Math—30% below 500, 44% between 500 and 599, 23% between 600 and 700, and 3% above 700. About 52% of the current freshmen were in the top fifth of their class; 81% were in the top two fifths. About 11 freshmen graduated first in their class.

Requirements: The SAT I is required, with a recommended score of 500 verbal and 500 mathematics. In addition, the university recommends that applicants have 4 units each of high school English, and mathematics, 3 or 4 in foreign language, 2 or 3 in science, and 2 each in history and social studies. An essay also is necessary. The GED is accepted. AP and CLEP credits are accepted. Important factors used in the admissions decision are advanced placement or honor courses, extracurricular activities record, recommendations by school officials, leadership record, and parents or siblings attending the school.

Procedure: Freshmen are admitted fall, spring, and summer. Entrance exams should be taken before December 30. Applications should be filed by January 15 for fall entry and November 1 for spring entry, along with an application fee of $45. Notification is sent April 15. There is an early admissions plan. A waiting list is an active part of the admissions procedure, with about 6% of applicants on the list.

Transfer: About 317 transfer students enrolled in a recent year. Transfer students must have a minimum GPA of 2.7 and have earned 24 credit hours. A total of 30 credits out of 124 must be completed at USD.

Visiting: There are regularly scheduled orientations for prospective students. There are guides for informal visits and visitors may sit in on classes. To arrange for a visit, contact the Admissions Office at (619) 260–4506.

Financial Aid: In 1993–94 67% of all current freshmen and 56% of continuing students received some form of financial aid. About 49% of freshmen and 45% of continuing students received need-based aid. The average freshman award was $12,000. Of that total, scholarships or need-based grants averaged $8500; loans averaged $3200; and work contracts averaged $1900. Thirty-five percent of undergraduate students work part-time. Average earnings from campus work for the school year are $1600. USD is a member of CSS. The FAF and FAFSA are required. The deadline for financial aid applications is February 20.

International Students: There are currently 109 international students enrolled. They must take the TOEFL and achieve a minimum score of 550. The student must also take the SAT I or the ACT.

Computers: The college provides computer facilities for student use. The mainframe is a DEC VAX. There are 300 Apple II, IBM, and Rainbow microcomputers located in buildings across campus. All students may access the system. There are no time limits and no fees.

Graduates: In 1992–93 937 bachelor's degrees were awarded. The most popular majors among graduates were business administration (30%), communication (9%), international relations and psychology (7%). Some 110 companies recruited on campus in 1992–93.

Admissions Contact: Warren Muller, Director of Undergraduate Admissions.

UNIVERSITY OF SAN FRANCISCO
B-3
San Francisco, CA 94117–1080   (415) 666–6563
(800) CALL-USF (out-of-state)

Full-time: 1201 men, 1918 women	Faculty: 214
Part-time: 80 men, 116 women	Ph.D.s: 86%
Graduate: 1171 men, 1507 women	Student/Faculty: 15 to 1
Year: 4–1–4, summer session	Tuition: $12,578
Application Deadline: March 2	Room & Board: $5830
Freshman Class: 2307 applied, 1733 accepted, 537 enrolled	
SAT I Verbal/Math: 450/500	ACT: 21 COMPETITIVE

The University of San Francisco, founded in 1855, is a private Roman Catholic institution run by the Jesuit Fathers and offering degree programs in the arts and sciences, business, education, and nursing. There are 4 undergraduate and 6 graduate schools. In addition to regional accreditation, USF has baccalaureate program accreditation with AACSB and NLN. The 2 libraries contain 695,312 volumes, 724,716 microform items, and 502 audiovisual forms, and subscribe to 2689 periodicals. Computerized library sources and services include the card catalog, interlibrary loans, and database searching. Special learning facilities include a learning resource center, radio station, rare book room, the Institute for Chinese-Western Cultural History, and the Center for Pacific Rim Studies. The 52-acre campus is the heart of the city. Including residence halls, there are 16 buildings on campus.

Student Life: About 65% of undergraduates are from California. Students come from 50 states, 80 foreign countries, and Canada. Forty-five percent are from public schools; 55% from private. Forty-seven percent are white; 18% Asian American; 11% foreign nationals. Forty-seven percent are Catholic; 13% Protestant. The average age of freshmen is 18; all undergraduates, 21. Twelve percent drop out by the end of their first year; 59% remain to graduate.

Housing: A total of 1353 students can be accommodated in college housing. College-sponsored living facilities include single-sex and coed dormitories. In addition, there are special interest houses, a multicultural floor, and an academic interest floor. On-campus housing is guaranteed for all 4 years. Fifty-five percent of students commute. Alcohol is not permitted. All students may keep cars on campus.

Activities: About 2% of men belong to 4 national fraternities; about 1% of women belong to 2 national sororities. There are 50 groups on campus, including cheerleading, chorus, computers, drama, ethnic, honors, international, literary magazine, musical theater, newspaper, pep band, political, professional, radio and TV, religious, social, social service, student government, and yearbook. Popular campus events include Founders Day and International Week.

Sports: There are 8 intercollegiate sports for men and 7 for women, and 18 intramural sports for men and 15 for women. Athletic and recreation facilities include a 600-seat soccer stadium, a recreation center with a 50-meter swimming pool, a multipurpose gymnasium, a weight room, a dance and aerobics room, a martial arts room, and 5 racquetball/handball courts.

Disabled Students: All of the campus is accessible to disabled students. The following facilities are available: wheelchair ramps, elevators, special parking, specially equipped rest rooms, and lowered drinking fountains.

Services: In addition to many counseling and information services, tutoring is available in every subject. There also is a reader service for the blind and a full-time counselor for learning-disabled students.

Campus Safety and Security: Campus safety and security measures include 24-hour foot and vehicle patrol, self defense education, escort service, and shuttle buses. In addition, there are informal discussions, pamphlets, posters, and films, emergency telephones, and lighted pathways and sidewalks.

Programs of Study: USF awards the B.A., B.S., B.F.A., B.P.A., and B.S.B.A. degrees. Master's and doctoral degrees also are awarded. Bachelor's degrees are awarded in BIOLOGICAL SCIENCE (biology/biological science), BUSINESS (accounting, banking and finance, business administration and management, hospitality management services, international business management, management information systems, management science, and marketing/retailing/merchandising), COMMUNICATIONS AND THE ARTS (communications, design, English, fine arts, French, illustration, photography, and Spanish), COMPUTER AND PHYSICAL SCIENCE (chemistry, computer science, electron physics, information sciences and systems, mathematics, and physics), EDUCATION (elementary, middle school, physical, and secondary), ENGINEERING AND ENVIRONMENTAL DESIGN (environmental science and interior design), HEALTH PROFESSIONS (nursing), SOCIAL SCIENCE (economics, fashion design and technology, history, philosophy, political science/government, psychology, public administration, religion, sociology, and theological studies). Sciences and business are the strongest academically. Communications, nursing, psychology, and biology have the largest enrollments.

Required: All students must maintain a GPA of at least 2.0 and take 128 credit hours, including 58 in upper-division courses. The current general education requirements include 9 units each of basic skills and history/social science, 3 of ethics, and 6 each of philosophy, religious studies, cultural perspectives, natural science, and literature and fine arts.

Special: USF offers a cooperative program with the San Francisco Academy of Art, cross-registration with the San Francisco Consortium, and internships with local business, social services, and research opportunities. Study abroad in Europe and Japan, work-study programs both on and off campus, dual majors in religion and psychology, a general studies degree, student-designed majors, nondegree study, and limited pass/fail options are also available. The College of Professional Studies is a degree completion program for working adults. There is a freshman honors program on campus, as well as 4 national honor societies. One department has an honors program.

Faculty/Classroom: Sixty-five percent of faculty are male; 35%, female. Ninety percent teach undergraduates, 75% do research, and 90% do both. No introductory courses are taught by graduate students. The average class size in an introductory lecture is 26; in a laboratory, 13; and in a regular course offering, 17.

Admissions: About 75% of the 1993–94 applicants were accepted. The SAT scores for the 1993–94 freshman class were as follows: Verbal—64% below 500, 24% between 500 and 599, 11% between 600 and 700, and 1% above 700; Math—46% below 500, 31% between 500 and 599, 18% between 600 and 700, and 5% above 700. The ACT scores were 42% below 21, 28% between 21 and 23, 22% between 24 and 26, 2% between 27 and 28, and 6% above 28. About 45% of the current freshmen were in the top fifth of their class; 77% were in the top two fifths.

Requirements: The SAT I or ACT is required. In addition, applicants are required to have 20 academic units, based on 4 years of high school English, 3 each of mathematics and social studies, 2 each of foreign language and science, and 6 of electives. An essay is required. The GED is accepted. AP and CLEP credits are accepted. Important factors used in the admissions decision are advanced placement or honor courses, recommendations by school officials, leadership record, parents or siblings attending the school, and evidence of special talent.

Procedure: Freshmen are admitted fall and spring. Entrance exams should be taken during the first half of the senior year. Applications should be filed by March 2 for fall entry and December 15 for spring entry, along with an application fee of $35. Notification is sent on a rolling basis after December 1. There are early admissions and deferred admissions plans.

Transfer: A total of 546 transfer students enrolled in 1993–94. Applicants need a minimum GPA of 2.0, or 2.5 if they have earned fewer than 24 semester units. A total of 30 credits out of 128 must be completed at USF.

Visiting: There are regularly scheduled orientations for prospective students. There are guides for informal visits and visitors may sit in on classes and stay overnight at the school. To arrange for a visit, contact the Office of Admissions at (415) 666–6563 or (800) CALL-USF (out of-state).

Financial Aid: In 1993–94, 64% of all current freshmen and 53% of continuing students received some form of financial aid. About 61% of freshmen and 52% of continuing students received need based aid. The average freshman award was $11,736. Of that total scholarships or need-based grants averaged $7310 ($21,804 maximum); loans averaged $5447 ($21,877 maximum); and work contracts averaged $1614 ($2500 maximum). Fourteen percent of undergraduate students work part-time. Average earnings from campus work for the school year are $1788. The average financial indebtedness of the 1992–93 graduate was $13,804. USF is a member of CSS. The FAF is required. The deadline for financial aid applications is March 2.

International Students: There are currently 487 international students enrolled. The school actively recruits these students. They must take the TOEFL and achieve a minimum score of 550.

Computers: USF provides computer facilities for student use. There are 162 microcomputers available in 7 locations and operating on a LAN system. All students may access the system. There are no time limits on using the system and no fees.

Graduates: In 1992–93, 681 bachelor's degrees were awarded. The most popular majors among graduates were nursing (21%), communication (7%), and accounting (6%). Within an average freshman class, 2% graduate in 3 years, 35% in 4 years, 55% in 5 years, and 59% in 6 years. Some 114 companies recruited on campus in 1992–93.

Admissions Contact: William A. Henley, Director of Admissions.

UNIVERSITY OF SOUTHERN CALIFORNIA   C-5
Los Angeles, CA 90089   (213) 740-1111

Full-time: 14,577 men and women	**Faculty:** 1643; I, +$
Part-time: 1270 men and women	**Ph.D.s:** 94%
Graduate: 17,651 men and women	**Student/Faculty:** 9 to 1
Year: semesters, summer session	**Tuition:** $16,810
Application Deadline: February 1	**Room & Board:** $6196
Freshman Class: 12,229 applied, 8498 accepted, 2474 enrolled	
SAT I Verbal/Math: 480/580	**ACT:** 25 **VERY COMPETITIVE**

The University of Southern California, founded in 1880, is a private institution offering undergraduate and graduate programs in liberal arts, fine arts, education, business, law, dentistry, and engineering. There are 16 undergraduate and 23 graduate schools. In addition to regional accreditation, USC has baccalaureate program accreditation with AACSB, ABET, ACEJMC, ACPE, ADA, APTA, CSWE, NAAB, NASM, and NCATE. The 18 libraries contain 3,168,668 volumes and 1.5 million microform items, and subscribe to 16,000 periodicals. Computerized library sources and services include the card catalog, interlibrary loans, and database searching. Special learning facilities include a learning resource center, art gallery, natural history museum, and radio station. The 150-acre campus is in an urban area 2 miles south of downtown Los Angeles. Including residence halls, there are 130 buildings on campus.

Student Life: About 74% of undergraduates are from California. Students come from 50 states, 110 foreign countries, and Canada. Sixty-five percent are from public schools; 20% from private. Fifty-one percent are white; 23% Asian American; 14% Hispanic. Forty-two percent are Protestant; 40% Catholic. The average age of freshmen is 19; all undergraduates, 21. Ten percent drop out by the end of their first year; 68% remain to graduate.

Housing: A total of 6700 students can be accommodated in college housing. College-sponsored living facilities include single-sex and coed dormitories, on-campus apartments, off-campus apartments, married-student housing, fraternity houses, and sorority houses. In addition there are honors houses, language houses, special interest houses, a Latino floor, business floors, Greek honors house, and a cinema floor. On-campus housing is guaranteed for the freshman year only, is available on a first-come, first-served basis, and is available on a lottery system for upperclassmen. Sixty-five percent of students live on campus; of those, 55% remain on campus on weekends. Alcohol is not permitted. All students may keep cars on campus.

Activities: About 18% of men belong to 26 national fraternities; about 18% of women belong to 12 national sororities. There are 450 groups on campus, including art, band, cheerleading, chess, choir, chorale, chorus, computers, dance, drama, drill team, ethnic, film, gay, honors, international, jazz band, marching band, musical theater, newspaper, opera, orchestra, photography, political, professional, radio and TV, religious, social, social service, student government, symphony, and yearbook. Popular campus events include appearances by presidential candidates, Springfest, noontime concerts, International Film Festival, and International Cultural Week.

Sports: There are 12 intercollegiate sports for men and 9 for women, and 37 intramural sports for men and 33 for women. Athletic and recreation facilities include a student athletic center, tennis, swimming, and baseball stadiums, a track, a gymnasium, and 2 Olympic pools.

Disabled Students: Ninety-five percent of the campus is accessible to disabled students. The following facilities are available: wheelchair ramps, elevators, special parking, specially equipped rest rooms, special class scheduling, lowered drinking fountains, and lowered telephones.

Services: In addition to many counseling and information services, tutoring is available in every subject. In addition, there is a reader service for the blind, and remedial math, reading, and writing.

Campus Safety and Security: Campus safety and security measures include 24-hour foot and vehicle patrol, self-defense education, escort service, and shuttle buses. In addition, there are informal discussions, pamphlets, posters, and films, emergency telephones, lighted pathways and sidewalks, and the safety department patrols an area 5 times the area of the campus.

Programs of Study: USC awards the B.A., B.S., B.Arch., B.F.A., and B.M. degrees. Master's and doctoral degrees also are awarded. Bachelor's degrees are awarded in BUSINESS (accounting and business administration and management), COMMUNICATIONS AND THE ARTS (broadcasting, communications, dramatic arts, English, film arts, fine arts, journalism, languages, music, and photography), COMPUTER AND PHYSICAL SCIENCE (chemistry, computer science, geology, mathematics, and physics), EDUCATION (elementary), ENGINEERING AND ENVIRONMENTAL DESIGN (aeronautical engineering, architecture, chemical engineering, civil engineering, computer engineering, electrical/electronics engineering, industrial engineering technology, and mechanical engineering), HEALTH PROFESSIONS (nursing, occupational therapy, and predentistry), SOCIAL SCIENCE (anthropology, economics, geography, history, international relations, philosophy, political science/government, psychology, public administration, religion, social science, and sociology). Engineering, science, business, and cinema-TV are the strongest academically. Business, engineering, and arts and sciences have the largest enrollments.

Required: All students must satisfy requirements in freshman writing and general education. Graduation requirements include a minimum of 128 credit hours, with 48 or more in the major, and a minimum GPA of 2.0.

Special: Cross-registration is permitted with Hebrew Union College and Howard University. Cooperative programs in engineering, internships in various majors, a Washington semester, study abroad in 14 countries, and work-study programs are offered. B.A.-B.S. degrees, dual majors, a general studies degree, student-designed majors, a 3–2 engineering degree, and pass/fail options are available. There is a freshman honors program on campus, as well as 39 national honor societies, including Phi Beta Kappa.

Faculty/Classroom: Seventy-nine percent of faculty are male; 21%, female. Eighty-five percent teach undergraduates, 80% do research, and 75% do both. No introductory courses are taught by graduate students. The average class size in an introductory lecture is 32; in a laboratory, 28; and in a regular course offering, 28.

Admissions: About 69% of the 1993–94 applicants were accepted. The SAT scores for the 1993–94 freshman class were as follows: Verbal—50% below 500, 32% between 500 and 599, 16% between 600 and 700, and 2% above 700; Math—15% below 500, 37% between 500 and 599, 35% between 600 and 700, and 13% above 700. The ACT scores were 15% below 21, 24% between 21 and 23, 23% between 24 and 26, 13% between 27 and 28, and 25% above 28. About 64% of the current freshmen were in the top fifth of their class; 87% were in the top two fifths. There were 109 National Merit finalists. About 120 freshmen graduated first in their class.

Requirements: USC requires applicants to be in the upper 50% of their class. A minimum GPA of 2.8 is required. The SAT I or ACT is required, with a composite SAT I score of 1000 or ACT score of 24 recommended. Graduation from an accredited secondary school is required. Applicants must have completed 16 high school courses, including 4 years of English, 3 of mathematics, 2 each of a foreign language, science, and social studies, plus 3 academic electives. An essay is required, and an interview is recommended. AP credits are accepted. Important factors used in the admissions decision are advanced placement or honor courses, recommendations by school officials, evidence of special talent, leadership record, and extracurricular activities record.

Procedure: Freshmen are admitted fall and spring. Entrance exams should be taken by October of the senior year. Applications should be filed by February 1 for fall entry and November 1 for spring entry, along with an application fee of $50. Notification is sent by April. There is a deferred admissions plan.

Transfer: About 1550 transfer students enrolled in 1993–94. Transfer applicants must submit 30 units of transferable work with a B average. A total of 48 credits out of 128 must be completed at USC.

Visiting: There are regularly scheduled orientations for prospective students. There are guides for informal visits and visitors may sit in on classes and stay overnight at the school. To arrange for a visit, contact the Admission Office at (213) 740-6616.

Financial Aid: In 1993–94, 74% of all current freshmen and 65% of continuing students received some form of financial aid. About 57% of freshmen and 47% of continuing students received need-based aid. The average freshman award was $17,748. Of that total, scholarships or need-based grants averaged $10,710 ($15,609 maximum); loans averaged $4774 ($6850 maximum); and work contracts averaged $2264 ($2500 maximum). Average earnings from campus work for the school year are $1500. The average financial indebtedness of the 1992–93 graduate was $3208. USC is a member of CSS. The FAF and FAFSA are required. The deadline for financial aid applications is February 15.

International Students: There are currently 1272 international students enrolled. The school actively recruits these students. They must take the college's own test.

Computers: The college provides computer facilities for student use. There are various microcomputers available on campus. All students may access the system. There are no time limits on using the system. The fees vary.

Graduates: In a recent year, 3358 bachelor's degrees were awarded. The most popular majors among graduates were business (31%), social sciences (28%), and engineering (10%). Within an average freshman class, 1% graduate in 3 years, 45% in 4 years, 62% in 5 years, and 66% in 6 years. Some 250 companies recruited on campus in a recent year.

Admissions Contact: Duncan Murdoch, Associate Dean/Director.

UNIVERSITY OF THE PACIFIC

B-3

Stockton, CA 95211 (209) 946-2211; (800) 959-UOP (in-state)

Full-time: 1482 men, 1845 women	Faculty: 247; IIA, av$
Part-time: 105 men, 126 women	Ph.D.s: 84%
Graduate: 199 men, 383 women	Student/Faculty: 14 to 1
Year: semesters, summer session	Tuition: $15,800
Application Deadline: March 1	Room & Board: $5300
Freshman Class: 2459 applied, 1997 accepted, 582 enrolled	
SAT I Verbal/Math: 440/530	COMPETITIVE

The University of the Pacific, founded in 1851, is an independent coeducational institution affiliated with the Methodist faith. It offers undergraduate and graduate programs in arts and sciences and in the professions. There are 8 undergraduate schools and one graduate school. In addition to regional accreditation, UOP has baccalaureate program accreditation with AACSB, ABET, ACPE, NASAD, NASM, and NCATE. The 2 libraries contain 432,661 volumes, 502,888 microform items, and 6078 audiovisual forms, and subscribe to 2304 periodicals. Computerized library sources and services include the card catalog, interlibrary loans, and database searching. Special learning facilities include a learning resource center, art gallery, and radio station. The 175-acre campus is in a suburban area 80 miles east of San Francisco and 40 miles south of Sacramento. Including residence halls, there are 98 buildings on campus.

Student Life: About 70% of undergraduates are from California. Students come from 45 states, 50 foreign countries, and Canada. Eighty percent are from public schools; 20% from private. Fifty-nine percent are white; 23% Asian American. The average age of freshmen is 18; all undergraduates, 20. Sixteen percent drop out by the end of their first year; 63% remain to graduate.

Housing: A total of 2400 students can be accommodated in college housing. College-sponsored living facilities include single-sex and coed dormitories, on-campus apartments, married-student housing, fraternity houses, and sorority houses. In addition there are honors houses, language houses, special interest houses, an international house, and wellness and quiet houses. On-campus housing is guaranteed for all 4 years. Fifty percent of students live on campus. All students may keep cars on campus.

Activities: About 17% of men belong to 2 local and 3 national fraternities; about 18% of women belong to 4 national sororities. There are 120 groups on campus, including art, band, cheerleading, choir, chorale, chorus, computers, dance, drama, ethnic, gay, honors, international, jazz band, literary magazine, musical theater, newspaper, opera, orchestra, pep band, photography, political, professional, radio and TV, religious, social, social service, student government, symphony, and yearbook. Popular campus events include a variety show called Band Frolic, women's volleyball games, Pacific Boardwalk Carnival, Homecoming, and Cultural Diversity Week.

Sports: There are 8 intercollegiate sports for men and 8 for women, and 20 intramural sports for men and 20 for women. Athletic and recreation facilities include a 30,000-seat stadium, a 6,000-seat gymnasium, an Olympic-size pool, tennis courts, a new softball field, and a new fitness center.

Disabled Students: Ninety percent of the campus is accessible to disabled students. The following facilities are available: wheelchair ramps, elevators, special parking, specially equipped rest rooms, special class scheduling, lowered drinking fountains, and lowered telephones.

Services: In addition to many counseling and information services, tutoring is available in every subject. There is a reader service for the blind, and remedial math, reading, and writing.

Campus Safety and Security: Campus safety and security measures include 24-hour foot and vehicle patrol, escort service, informal discussions, pamphlets, posters, and films. In addition, there are emergency telephones and lighted pathways and sidewalks.

Programs of Study: UOP awards the B.A., B.S., B.F.A., B.M., and B.S. in Eng. degrees. Master's and doctoral degrees also are awarded. Bachelor's degrees are awarded in BIOLOGICAL SCIENCE (biochemistry and biology/biological science), BUSINESS (business administration and management, business economics, international business management, and sports management), COMMUNICATIONS AND THE ARTS (art history and appreciation, arts administration/management, classics, communications, dramatic arts, English, French, German, graphic design, Greek, Japanese, Latin, linguistics, music, music business management, music performance, Spanish, and studio art), COMPUTER AND PHYSICAL SCIENCE (applied mathematics, chemistry, computer science, geology, geophysics and seismology, information sciences and systems, mathematics, physical sciences, and physics), EDUCATION (art, elementary, foreign languages, middle school, music, physical, recreation, science, secondary, special, and teaching English as a second language/foreign language), ENGINEERING AND ENVIRONMENTAL DESIGN (civil engineering, computer engineering, electrical/electronics engineering, engineering management, engineering physics, and mechanical engineering), HEALTH PROFESSIONS (music therapy, pharmacy, predentistry, speech pathology/audiology, and sports medicine), SOCIAL SCIENCE (African American studies, anthropology, crosscultural studies, economics, history, human development, international relations, international studies, ministries, philosophy, political science/government, prelaw, psychology, public administration, religion, social science, sociology, and urban studies). Natural sciences and the professions are the strongest academically. Arts/sciences, pharmacy, business, and engineering have the largest enrollments.

Required: Students must complete at least 124 credit hours to graduate. The required general education program consists of 3 mentor seminars and 6 to 9 courses chosen from categories such as the Individual and Society, Human Heritage, and Natural World and Formal Systems of Thought.

Special: The engineering school offers a co-op program for specialized training in the field. Internships for credit/pay in all majors, more than 200 study-abroad programs in more than 60 countries, a Washington semester, and more than 20 work-study programs also are available. An accelerated degree in dentistry and pharmacy, a general studies degree, student-designed majors, dual majors in most disciplines, credit for life experience, and pass/fail options are possible. There is a freshman honors program on campus, as well as 13 national honor societies.

Faculty/Classroom: Seventy-five percent of faculty are male; 25%, female. All teach undergraduates. No introductory courses are taught by graduate students. The average class size in an introductory lecture is 33; in a laboratory, 15; and in a regular course offering, 20.

Admissions: About 81% of the 1993–94 applicants were accepted. About 50% of the current freshmen were in the top fifth of their class; 76% were in the top two fifths.

Requirements: A minimum GPA of 2.0 is required. The SAT I or ACT is required. Applicants must have 16 academic credits, including a recommended 4 years of high school English, 3 of mathematics, 2 in a foreign language, 1 each of laboratory science and U.S history or government, and additional academic courses. An essay is required; an interview is recommended. An audition is needed for music students. The GED is accepted. AP and CLEP credits are accepted. Important factors used in the admissions decision are advanced placement or honor courses, recommendations by school officials, leadership record, evidence of special talent, and recommendations by alumni.

Procedure: Freshmen are admitted fall and spring. Entrance exams should be taken in spring of the junior year or fall of the senior year. Early action applications should be filed by December 15; regular applications, by March 1 for fall entry and December 15 for spring entry, along with an application fee of $50. Notification of early decision is sent in January; regular decision, on a rolling basis. There are early action, early admissions, and deferred admissions plans.

Transfer: About 496 transfer students enrolled in 1993–94. Transfer applicants should have a minimum GPA of 2.3 and at least 16 credit hours. The SAT I or ACT is required if there is less than 1 year of college work completed. A total of 32 credits out of 124 must be completed at UOP.

Visiting: There are regularly scheduled orientations for prospective students, consisting of 3 summer options for a 3-day comprehensive academic and social orientation. Visits may also include a tour and appointments with faculty and admissions and financial aid and personnel. Student-led tours are available twice on weekdays and on selected Saturdays. There are guides for informal visits and visitors may sit in on classes and stay overnight at the school. To arrange for a visit contact Admissions at (209) 946–2211 or (800) 959–2UOP.

Financial Aid: In 1993–94, 65% of all students received some form of financial aid and need-based aid. The average freshman award was $16,000. Of that total, scholarships or need-based grants averaged $11,400; loans averaged $3000; and work contracts averaged $1600. Thirty-three percent of undergraduate students work part time. Average earnings from campus work for the school year are $1000. UOP is a member of CSS. The FFS or the FAFSA is required. The deadline for financial aid applications is March 2.

International Students: There are currently 251 international students enrolled. The school actively recruits these students. They must take the TOEFL and achieve a minimum score of 475. The SAT I or ACT is required if the student has attended a V.S.-style high school.

Computers: The college provides computer facilities for student use. The mainframe is a DEC VAX 11/785. More than 100 PCs, primarily IBMs and Apple Macintoshes, are available for student use in residence halls and computer laboratories. All students may access the system. There are no time limits on using the system and no fees.

Graduates: In 1992–93 771 bachelor's degrees were awarded. The most popular majors among graduates were pharmacy (22%), business (13%), and communications (9%). Within an average freshman class, 62% graduate in 5 years. Some 100 companies recruited on campus in 1992–93.

Admissions Contact: Edward Schoenberg, Dean of Admissions.

WEST COAST UNIVERSITY
C-5
Los Angeles, CA 90020   (213) 487–4433; (800) 2484-WCU (in-state)

Full-time: none	Faculty: 10
Part-time: 300 men, 200 women	Ph.D.s: 25%
Graduate: 500 men, 300 women	Student/Faculty: 50 to 1
Year: see profile	Tuition: $9120
Application Deadline: open	Room & Board: n/app
Freshman Class: n/av	
SAT I or ACT: not required	NONCOMPETITIVE

West Coast University, founded in 1909, is a private, coeducational institution for commuter students. The multicampus university offers evening programs in business and management, computer science, engineering, and health science. There are 6 8-week terms per year. There are 3 undergraduate and 3 graduate schools. The library contains 15,000 volumes, 1000 microform items, and 10 audiovisual forms, and subscribes to 100 periodicals. Computerized library sources and services include the card catalog and interlibrary loans. The 1-acre campus is in an urban area. There is one building on campus.

Student Life: About 70% of undergraduates are from California. Students come from 15 foreign countries and Canada. Seventy-five percent are white; 10% Hispanic; 10% African American. The average age of all undergraduates is 32. About 35% of freshmen remain to graduate.

Housing: There are no residence halls. All students commute. Alcohol is not permitted.

Activities: There are no fraternities or sororities on campus.

Sports: There is no sports program at WCU.

Services: In addition to many counseling and information services, tutoring is available in most subjects.

Programs of Study: WCU awards the B.S. degree. Associate and master's degrees also are awarded. Bachelor's degrees are awarded in BUSINESS (accounting and business administration and management), COMPUTER AND PHYSICAL SCIENCE (computer programming, computer science, and information sciences and systems), ENGINEERING AND ENVIRONMENTAL DESIGN (electrical/electronics engineering, industrial engineering, industrial engineering technology, and mechanical engineering). Business and engineering are the strongest academically. Business has the largest enrollment.

Required: To graduate, students must complete 12 units in communications and 9 each in mathematics, humanities, social sciences, and natural sciences. Students must maintain a minimum 2.0 GPA and complete at least 124 semester units, with 24 in the major, 1 in computer science, and physical education credit. Additional requirements vary.

Special: WCU offers credit for military experience and nondegree study.

Faculty/Classroom: Seventy-five percent of faculty are male; 25%, female. All teach undergraduates.

Requirements: Applicants must be graduates of an accredited secondary school or have a GED certificate.

Procedure: Freshmen are admitted to all sessions. Application deadlines are open. The application fee is $35. Notification is sent on a rolling basis.

Transfer: A total of 75 transfer students enrolled in a recent year. Applicants need a minimum GPA of 2.0 and 30 to 60 semester credit hours earned. A total of 30 credits out of 124 must be completed at WCU.

Visiting: Visitors may sit in on classes. To arrange for a visit, contact the counseling office.

Financial Aid: In a recent year, 25% of all students received some form of financial aid.

International Students: There are currently 275 international students enrolled. They must take the TOEFL, the University of Michigan Language Test, or the college's own test and achieve a minimum score on the TOEFL of 450.

Computers: WCU provides computer facilities for student use. The mainframe is a DEC VAX 11/750. Apple Macintosh microcomputers are available in the computer laboratory. All students may access the system. There are no time limits on using the system and no fees.

Graduates: In 1992–93, 105 bachelor's degrees were awarded. Within an average freshman class, 15% graduate in 3 years, 25% in 4 years, 35% in 5 years, and 25% in 6 years.

Admissions Contact: Roger A. Miller, Dean of Admissions and Registrar.

WESTMONT COLLEGE
Santa Barbara, CA 93108

C-5

(805) 565-6200
(800) 777-9011 (out-of-state)

Full-time: 505 men, 771 women	Faculty: 79; IIB, av$
Part-time: 3 men, 6 women	Ph.D.s: 81%
Graduate: none	Student/Faculty: 16 to 1
Year: semesters, summer session	Tuition: $13,660
Application Deadline: February 15	Room & Board: $5072
Freshman Class: 950 applied, 713 accepted, 351 enrolled	
SAT I Verbal/Math: 501/550	ACT: 24 COMPETITIVE

Westmont College, founded in 1940, is a private, interdenominational, coeducational Christian institution offering a liberal arts and sciences education. The library contains 150,000 volumes, 20,687 microform items, and 5303 audiovisual forms and subscribes to 710 periodicals. Computerized library sources and services include the card catalog, interlibrary loans, and database searching. Special learning facilities include a learning resource center, art gallery, radio station, observatory, and science center with state-of-the-art premedical center. The 133-acre campus is in a suburban area 90 miles north of Los Angeles. Including residence halls, there are 30 buildings on campus.

Student Life: About 75% of undergraduates are from California. Students come from 37 states, 11 foreign countries, and Canada. Seventy-eight percent are from public schools; 22% from private. Eighty-eight percent are white. Most are Protestant. The average age of freshmen is 18; all undergraduates, 20. Nineteen percent drop out by the end of their first year.

Housing: A total of 1145 students can be accommodated in college housing. College-sponsored living facilities include dormitories, off-campus apartments, and married-student housing. On-campus housing is guaranteed for all 4 years. Eighty-two percent of students live on campus; of those, 80% remain on campus on weekends. Alcohol is not permitted. Upperclassmen may keep cars on campus.

Activities: There are no fraternities or sororities on campus. There are 40 groups on campus, including art, band, cheerleading, chess, choir, chorale, chorus, computers, dance, departmental, drama, ethnic, honors, international, jazz band, leadership, literary magazine, musical theater, newspaper, orchestra, pep band, political, professional, radio, religious, social, social service, student government, and yearbook. Popular campus events include college visit days for prospective students, Community Service Day, chapel, Homecoming, Fall Follies, and Spring Sing.

Sports: There are 6 intercollegiate sports for men and 5 for women, and 17 intramural sports for men, 15 for women, and 11 for both men and women. Athletic and recreation facilities include a 2200-seat gymnasium, volleyball, tennis, basketball, and racquetball courts, a soccer/baseball field, swimming pool, weight room, dance studio, and a track.

Disabled Students: Seventy percent of the campus is accessible to disabled students. The following facilities are available: wheelchair ramps, elevators, special parking, specially equipped rest rooms, special class scheduling, lowered drinking fountains, and lowered telephones.

Services: In addition to many counseling and information services, tutoring is available in every subject. In addition, there is a reader service for the blind and remedial math and writing.

Campus Safety and Security: Campus safety and security measures include 24-hour foot and vehicle patrol, self defense education, escort service, and shuttle buses. In addition, there are informal discussions, pamphlets, posters, and films, emergency telephones, and lighted pathways and sidewalks.

Programs of Study: Westmont awards the B.A. and B.S. degrees. Bachelor's degrees are awarded in BIOLOGICAL SCIENCE (biology/biological science), BUSINESS (business economics), COMMUNICATIONS AND THE ARTS (communications, dramatic arts, English, fine arts, French, modern language, and Spanish), COMPUTER AND PHYSICAL SCIENCE (chemistry, computer science, mathematics, natural sciences, and physics), EDUCATION (art, elementary, music, physical, science, and secondary), ENGINEERING AND ENVIRONMENTAL DESIGN (engineering physics), SOCIAL SCIENCE (history, international studies, kinesiology, liberal arts/general studies, philosophy, political science/government, psychology, religion, social science, and sociology). Economics/business, English, and communication studies have the largest enrollments.

Required: All students must earn a minimum GPA of 2.0 while taking at least 124 credit hours, including 36 to 66 in the major. A total of 60 units in general education courses is required, with 16 units in religious studies and 4 units in physical education. Also required are courses in the history of Western civilization and Fitness for Life.

Special: Westmont offers cross-registration with 13 Christian colleges, internships in local businesses and social agencies, study abroad in 11 countries, and semesters in Washington D.C., San Francisco, and Los Angeles. B.A. and B.S. degrees, student-designed majors, work-study programs, a 3–2 engineering program with several California universities, and pass/fail options also are available. There are also preprofessional programs in dentistry, law, medicine, ministry/missions, optometry, pharmacology, physical therapy, and veterinary medicine. There is a freshman honors program on campus, as well as 3 national honor societies. Nine departments have honors programs.

Faculty/Classroom: Sixty-three percent of faculty are male; 37%, female. All teach undergraduates and do research. The average class size in an introductory lecture is 25; in a laboratory, 18; and in a regular course offering, 22.

Admissions: About 75% of the 1993–94 applicants were accepted. The SAT scores for the 1993–94 freshman class were as follows: Verbal—44% below 500, 43% between 500 and 599, 12% between 600 and 700, and 1% above 700; Math—29% below 500, 40% between 500 and 599, 25% between 600 and 700, and 7% above 700. The ACT scores were 10% below 21, 34% between 21 and 23, 33% between 24 and 26, 9% between 27 and 28, and 13% above 28. About 64% of the current freshmen were in the top fifth of their class; 85% were in the top two fifths. There were 2 National Merit finalists and 1 semifinalist. About 15 freshmen graduated first in their class.

Requirements: The SAT I or the ACT is required. SAT I scores of 450 verbal and 450 math or an ACT composite score of 24 are recommended. Applicants are required to have 16 academic credits, including 4 years of high school English, 3 of mathematics, and 2 each of a foreign language, physical science, history, social science, and biological science. Interviews are recommended. Essays are required. The GED is accepted. AP and CLEP credits are accepted. Important factors used in the admissions decision are advanced placement or honor courses, leadership record, extracurricular activities record, personality, intangible qualities, and evidence of special talent.

Procedure: Freshmen are admitted in the fall and spring. Entrance exams should be taken during the spring of the junior year or the beginning of the senior year. Applications should be filed by February 15 for fall entry and November 1 for spring entry, along with an application fee of $30. Notification is sent March 15. There is a deferred admissions plan.

Transfer: About 112 transfer students enrolled in 1993–94. Transfer students from 2-year colleges must have a GPA between 2.5 and 2.8, and those students from 4-year schools, a 2.0. The college will not accept more than 64 transferable units from a community college. There is no maximum number of transferable units from a 4-year college. High school transcript and test scores are required if the student has fewer than 24 transferable units. At least half of the upper-division units for the major as well as the 2 final full-time semesters must be completed at Westmont.

Visiting: There are regularly scheduled orientations for prospective students, consisting of meeting faculty and administrators and attending classes, academic seminars, student/parent panels, academic open houses, and admission and financial aid sessions. There are guides for informal visits and visitors may sit in on classes and stay overnight at the school. To arrange for a visit, contact Admissions at (805) 565-6200.

Financial Aid: In 1993–94 80% of all current freshmen and 80% of continuing students received some form of financial aid. About 74% of freshmen and 73% of continuing students received need-based aid. The average freshman award was $9125. Of that total, scholarships or need-based grants averaged $5000 ($12,000 maximum); loans averaged $2625 ($4625 maximum); and work contracts averaged $1000 ($2000 maximum). All undergraduate students work part-time. Average earnings from campus work for the school year are $1200. The average financial indebtedness of the 1992–93 graduate was $15,000. Westmont is a member of CSS. The FAF and FAFSA are required. The deadline for financial aid applications is March 2.

International Students: There are currently 13 international students enrolled. The school actively recruits these students. They must take the TOEFL and achieve a minimum score of 560.

Computers: The college provides computer facilities for student use. The mainframe is an IBM RS-6000. There are 7 IBM-compatible and 17 Macintosh microcomputers available in the library. There are also 15 terminals available in the library. Students may use them to access the main computer and, through the main computer, the Internet. All students may access the system with no time limits and no fees.

Graduates: In 1992–93 311 bachelor's degrees were awarded. The most popular majors among graduates were economics and business (20%), English (10%), and education (9%). Some 34 companies recruited on campus in 1992–93.

Admissions Contact: David A. Morley, Director of Admissions and Financial Aid.

WHITTIER COLLEGE
Whittier, CA 90608   **D-5**
(310) 907–4238

Full-time: 562 men, 668 women	Faculty: 82; IIA, +$
Part-time: 13 men, 18 women	Ph.D.s: 89%
Graduate: 398 men, 263 women	Student/Faculty: 15 to 1
Year: 4–1–4, summer session	Tuition: $16,181
Application Deadline: February 15	Room & Board: $5480
Freshman Class: 1681 applied, 1069 accepted, 345 enrolled	
SAT I Verbal/Math: 450/510	**COMPETITIVE**

Whittier College, founded in 1887 by the Society of Friends, is an independent, liberal arts institution with no religious affiliation. There are 2 graduate schools. In addition to regional accreditation, Whittier has baccalaureate program accreditation with CSWE. The 2 libraries contain 416,005 volumes, 137,025 microform items, and 4480 audiovisual forms, and subscribe to 1357 periodicals. Computerized library sources and services include the card catalog, interlibrary loans, and database searching. Special learning facilities include a learning resource center, art gallery, radio station, the Fairchild Aerial Photography Collection, a performing arts center, and a writing center. The 95-acre campus is in a suburban area 18 miles southeast of Los Angeles, in the foothills of the San Gabriel Mountains. Including residence halls, there are 50 buildings on campus.

Student Life: About 67% of undergraduates are from California. Students come from 15 states, 18 foreign countries, and Canada. Seventy-three percent are from public schools; 27% from private. Fifty-nine percent are white; 23% Hispanic. The average age of freshmen is 18; all undergraduates, 20. Twenty percent drop out by the end of their first year; 51% remain to graduate.

Housing: A total of 813 students can be accommodated in college housing. College-sponsored living facilities include coed residence halls. In addition there are special interest houses, a multicultural community residence hall, and a substance-free living environment residence hall. On-campus housing is guaranteed for all 4 years. Sixty percent of students live on campus; of those, 85% remain on campus on weekends. All students may keep cars on campus.

Activities: About 17% of men belong to 4 local fraternities; about 24% of women belong to 5 local sororities. There are 45 groups on campus, including art, band, cheerleading, choir, chorale, chorus, computers, dance, drama, ethnic, film, gay, honors, international, literary magazine, musical theater, newspaper, orchestra, photography, political, professional, radio and TV, religious, social, social service, student government, and yearbook. Popular campus events include Homecoming, the Spring Sing (annual talent show), the Reggae Concert, SportsFest, and Volunteer Day.

Sports: There are 11 intercollegiate sports for men and 9 for women, and 10 intramural sports for men and 10 for women. Athletic and recreation facilities include a 7500-seat stadium, a 2000-seat gymnasium, 3 playing fields, an activities center, an aquatics center, and tennis courts.

Disabled Students: Seventy-five percent of the campus is accessible to disabled students. The following facilities are available: wheelchair ramps, elevators, special parking, specially equipped rest rooms, special class scheduling, lowered drinking fountains, and lowered telephones.

Services: In addition to many counseling and information services, tutoring is available in every subject.

Campus Safety and Security: Campus safety and security measures include 24-hour foot and vehicle patrol, self defense education, escort service, and informal discussions. In addition, there are pamphlets, posters, films, emergency telephones, and lighted pathways and sidewalks.

Programs of Study: Whittier awards the B.A. degree. Master's and doctoral degrees also are awarded. Bachelor's degrees are awarded in BIOLOGICAL SCIENCE (biochemistry and biology/biological science), BUSINESS (business administration and management and business economics), COMMUNICATIONS AND THE ARTS (dramatic arts, English, fine arts, French, music, and Spanish), COMPUTER AND PHYSICAL SCIENCE (chemistry, earth science, geology, math-

ematics, and physics), EDUCATION (physical), HEALTH PROFESSIONS (speech pathology/audiology), SOCIAL SCIENCE (anthropology, child psychology/development, economics, history, international studies, Latin American studies, philosophy, political science/government, psychology, religion, social work, sociology, and urban studies). Business administration, political science, and English have the largest enrollments.

Required: All students must take a total of 120 credits including at least 30 in the major field, with a minimum GPA of 2.0. Distribution requirements include 3 credits in college writing, 6 in paired courses from European and North American civilizations, Asian, African, and Latin American civilizations, or contemporary society and the individual, 8 in natural sciences, and 3 each in humanities, mathematics, and fine arts.

Special: Internships are possible in business, counseling, teaching, and other areas. Study abroad is offered in 5 countries, with additional opportunities with 36 universities overseas through the University of Miami consortium. A Washington semester in January is optional. The Whittier Scholars Program offers self-designed interdisciplinary curricula. Nondegree study and pass/fail options are available. Whittier offers a 3–2 engineering program with University of Southern California, Dartmouth College, and Columbia, Washington, Case Western Reserve, or Colorado State universities. There are 10 national honor societies on campus.

Faculty/Classroom: Sixty-three percent of faculty are male; 37%, female. All teach undergraduates and do research. No introductory courses are taught by graduate students. The average class size in an introductory lecture is 35; in a laboratory, 25; and in a regular course offering, 20.

Admissions: About 64% of the 1993–94 applicants were accepted. The SAT scores for the 1993–94 freshman class were as follows: Verbal—70% below 500, 23% between 500 and 599, 6% between 600 and 700, and 1% above 700; Math—44% below 500, 37% between 500 and 599, 17% between 600 and 700, and 3% above 700. About 56% of the current freshmen were in the top fifth of their class; 78% were in the top two fifths. About 10 freshmen graduated first in their class.

Requirements: The SAT I or ACT is required. The college recommends that applicants have 4 years of high school English, 3 years each of history, mathematics, and science, and 2 years of a foreign language. An essay is required and an interview is recommended. AP credits are accepted. Important factors used in the admissions decision are advanced placement or honor courses, recommendations by school officials, leadership record, recommendations by alumni, and evidence of special talent.

Procedure: Freshmen are admitted fall and spring. Entrance exams should be taken during the junior year. Early decision applications should be filed by December 10; regular applications, by February 15 for fall entry and December 20 for spring entry, along with an application fee of $35. Notification of early decision is sent December 30; regular decision, on a rolling basis beginning in March. There are early decision and deferred admissions plans. About 57 early decision candidates were accepted for the 1993–94 class.

Transfer: About 99 transfer students enrolled in 1993–94. Transfer applicants are considered on a case-by-case basis, but a minimum GPA of 2.5 is recommended in academic course work. The SAT I or the ACT is required for students with fewer than 30 academic units. The GED is accepted for transfer applicants with at least 30 academic units. A total of 30 credits out of 120 must be completed at Whittier.

Visiting: There are regularly scheduled orientations for prospective students, consisting of an admission interview and a campus tour. A presentation about academic programs and opportunities, and interactions with faculty may be scheduled. There are guides for informal visits and visitors may sit in on classes and stay overnight at the school. To arrange for a visit, contact the Office of Admissions at (310) 907–4238.

Financial Aid: In 1993–94 79% of all current freshmen and 74% of continuing students received some form of financial aid. About 75% of freshmen and 60% of continuing students received need-based aid. The average freshman award was $17,006. Of that total, scholarships or need-based grants averaged $10,635 ($19,250 maximum); loans averaged $4569 ($6625 maximum); and work contracts averaged $1780 ($2500 maximum). Eighty-one percent of undergraduate students work part-time. Average earnings from campus work for the school year are $1205. The average financial indebtedness of the 1992–93 graduate was $13,390. Whittier is a member of CSS. The FAF and FAFSA are required. The deadline for financial aid applications is February 15.

International Students: There are currently 38 international students enrolled. The school actively recruits these students. They must take the TOEFL and achieve a minimum score of 550. The student must also take the SAT I or the ACT.

Computers: The college provides computer facilities for student use. The mainframe is a DEC VAX 3100 cluster. There is a computer center and a microcomputing laboratory. The college has 2 Micro VAX

3100 computers, Internet access, and a file server to a Macintosh Appletalk network accessible across campus in laboratories and residence halls. Printing is available at most locations. All students may access the system. It may be used 24 hours daily. There are no time limits and no fees.

Graduates: In 1992–93 232 bachelor's degrees were awarded. The most popular majors among graduates were business (19%), political science (14%), and English (12%). Within an average freshman class, 3% graduate in 3 years, 38% in 4 years, 9% in 5 years, and 1% in 6 years. Some 17 companies recruited on campus in 1992–93. In the 1992 graduating class, 11% of the men and 21% of the women were enrolled in graduate school within 6 months of graduation; 15% of the men and 27% of the women had found employment.

Admissions Contact: Doug Locker, Director School Relations.

WOODBURY UNIVERSITY
Burbank, CA 91510–7846

C-5

(818) 767–0888, ext. 221
(800) 784-WOOD (out-of-state)

Full-time: 358 men, 407 women	Faculty: 23; IIA, --$
Part-time: 66 men, 125 women	Ph.Ds: 39%
Graduate: 73 men, 60 women	Student/Faculty: 33 to 1
Year: quarters, summer session	Tuition: $12,120
Application Deadline: open	Room & Board: $5500
Freshman Class: 349 applied, 313 accepted, 111 enrolled	
SAT I Verbal/Math: 381/441	ACT: 20 **LESS COMPETITIVE**

Woodbury University, founded in 1884, is a private, nonsectarian institution that emphasizes business and professional design education. There is one undergraduate and one graduate school. In addition to regional accreditation, Woodbury has baccalaureate program accreditation with FIDER. The library contains 57,000 volumes, 55,000 microform items, and 6300 audiovisual forms, and subscribes to 500 periodicals. Computerized library sources and services include interlibrary loans and database searching. Special learning facilities include a learning resource center and a historical costume collection. The 23-acre campus is in a suburban area 20 miles north of Los Angeles. Including residence halls, there are 11 buildings on campus.

Student Life: About 75% of undergraduates are from California. Students come from 25 states, 34 foreign countries, and Canada. Eighty-five percent are from public schools; 15% from private. Forty-five percent are white; 19% Hispanic; 15% foreign nationals; 13% Asian American. The average age of all undergraduates is 21.

Housing: A total of 188 students can be accommodated in college housing. College-sponsored living facilities include single-sex and coed dormitories. On-campus housing is available on a first-come, first-served basis. Priority is given to out-of-town students. Eighty percent of students commute. Alcohol is not permitted. All students may keep cars on campus.

Activities: About 20% of men and about 1% of women belong to 1 national and 2 local fraternities; about 20% of women belong to 1 national and 2 local sororities. There are 20 groups on campus, including choir, computers, drama, ethnic, international, literary magazine, newspaper, photography, professional, religious, social, student government, and yearbook. Popular campus events include Chinese New Year, Black History Dinner, Winter Formal, Showboat, Cinco De Mayo, a ski trip, and annual fashion shows.

Sports: There are 5 intramural sports for men and 4 for women. Athletic and recreation facilities include a gymnasium, basketball and volleyball courts, weight training and aerobics rooms, an outdoor swimming pool, a quarter-mile track, and a field for soccer and other sports.

Disabled Students: The entire campus is accessible to disabled students. The following facilities are available: wheelchair ramps, elevators, special parking, and specially equipped rest rooms.

Services: In addition to many counseling and information services, tutoring is available in most subjects.

Campus Safety and Security: Campus safety and security measures include escort service, informal discussions, pamphlets, posters, and films, and lighted pathways and sidewalks.

Programs of Study: Woodbury awards the B.S. and B.Arch. degrees. Master's degrees also are awarded. Bachelor's degrees are awarded in BUSINESS (accounting, banking and finance, business administration and management, fashion merchandising, international business management, management science, marketing/retailing/merchandising, and personnel management), COMMUNICATIONS AND THE ARTS (design, graphic design, and telecommunications), COMPUTER AND PHYSICAL SCIENCE (computer programming), ENGINEERING AND ENVIRONMENTAL DESIGN (architecture and interior design), SOCIAL SCIENCE (fashion design and technology). Business and architecture are the strongest programs academically and have the largest enrollments.

Required: To graduate with a B.S., students must complete 188 quarter hours, including 68 in the major; with a B.Arch., 240 quarter hours, including 148 in the major. All students must maintain a minimum GPA of 2.0 and take computer literacy and public speaking courses.

Special: Internships are required for fashion design and fashion marketing majors and encouraged for all others. Concurrent registration with area institutions, work-study programs, dual majors, and pass/fail options also are offered.

Faculty/Classroom: Fifty-nine percent of faculty are male; 41%, female. Eighty-five percent teach undergraduates and 7% both teach and do research. No introductory courses are taught by graduate students. The average class size in an introductory lecture is 30; in a laboratory, 15; and in a regular course offering, 18.

Admissions: About 90% of the 1993–94 applicants were accepted. The SAT scores for the 1993–94 freshman class were as follows: Verbal—89% below 500, 9% between 500 and 599, and 2% between 600 and 700; Math—70% below 500, 22% between 500 and 599, and 8% between 600 and 700. The ACT scores were 60% below 21, 30% between 21 and 23, and 10% between 24 and 26.

Requirements: The SAT I or ACT is required. Test scores are used for placement purposes only. An essay is required. AP and CLEP credits are accepted.

Procedure: Freshmen are admitted to all sessions. Entrance exams should be taken prior to or upon registration. Application deadlines are open. Application fee is $30; $50 for international applicants. Notification is sent on a rolling basis. There is a deferred admissions plan.

Transfer: About 100 transfer students enrolled in a recent year. Applicants are required to have maintained a minimum GPA of 2.0 and to take the SAT I or ACT if they have completed fewer than 45 quarter hours. The priority application deadline for fall entry is April 15. A total of 68 quarter hours out of 188 to 240 must be completed at Woodbury.

Visiting: There are regularly scheduled orientations for prospective students. There are guides for informal visits and visitors may sit in on classes and stay overnight at the school. To arrange for a visit, contact the Admissions Office at (818) 767–0888, ext. 221.

Financial Aid: In a recent year, 65% of all freshmen and 65% of continuing students received some form of financial aid. About 75% of freshmen and 65% of continuing students received need-based aid. The average freshman award in a recent year was $10,500. Of that total, scholarships or need-based grants averaged $3656 ($4875 maximum); loans averaged $2508 ($2625 maximum); and work contracts averaged $1440 ($1500 maximum). Twelve percent of undergraduate students work part-time. Average earnings from campus work for the school year are $1146. The average financial indebtedness of a recent year's graduate was $6000. Woodbury is a member of CSS. The FAF, the college's own financial statement, and the SAAC are required.

International Students: There are currently 165 international students enrolled. The school actively recruits these students. They must take the TOEFL and achieve a minimum score of 500. The student must also take the SAT I or the ACT.

Computers: The college provides computer facilities for student use. The mainframe is a DEC VAX 11/750. There are 15 VAX terminals in the VAX laboratory, with dial-up connection available to students with modems. Other peripherals include 20 Apple Macintosh IIs and 28 IBM-compatible PCs, laser printers, a scanner, a plotter, and support software. All students may access the system. The VAX terminals may be used 24 hours per day; the other microcomputers, 15 hours per day. There are no time limits on using the system and no fees.

Graduates: In a recent year, 174 bachelor's degrees were awarded. The most popular majors among graduates were business administration (37%), fashion marketing (16%), and architecture (10%). Some 33 companies recruited on campus in a recent year.

Admissions Contact: Patrick N. Contrades, Director of Admission.

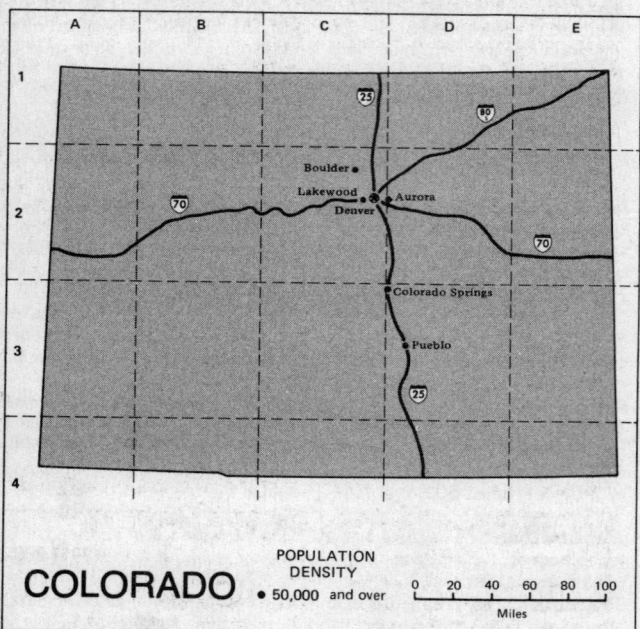

COLORADO

POPULATION
DENSITY

● 50,000 and over

0 20 40 60 80 100

Miles

ADAMS STATE COLLEGE
C-4

Alamosa, CO 81102   (719) 589–7712; (800) 824–6494 (in-state)

Full-time: 874 men, 941 women   Faculty: 100; IIA, --$
Part-time: 53 men, 149 women   Ph.D.s: 66%
Graduate: 90 men, 246 women   Student/Faculty: 18 to 1
Year: semesters, summer session   Tuition: $1650 ($4808)
Application Deadline: August 1   Room & Board: $3260
Freshman Class: 1346 applied, 1212 accepted, 501 enrolled
SAT I Verbal/Math: 442/478   ACT: 21   **COMPETITIVE**

Adams State College, founded in 1921, is a public liberal arts school with business and teacher preparation courses emphasized. There are 4 undergraduate schools and one graduate school. In addition to regional accreditation, Adams State has baccalaureate program accreditation with NCATE. The library contains 208,695 volumes, 650,000 microform items, and 9340 audiovisual forms, and subscribes to 972 periodicals. Computerized library sources and services include interlibrary loans and database searching. Special learning facilities include a learning resource center, art gallery, planetarium, and radio station. The 90-acre campus is in a small town 220 miles south of Denver. Including residence halls, there are 52 buildings on campus.

Student Life: About 80% of undergraduates are from Colorado. Students come from 38 states, 10 foreign countries, and Canada. About 95% are from public schools; 5% from private. Some 70% are white; 24% Hispanic. The average age of all undergraduates is 23. About 35% drop out by the end of their first year; 40% remain to graduate.

Housing: A total of 1052 students can be accommodated in college housing. College-sponsored living facilities include single-sex and coed dormitories, on-campus apartments, and married-student housing. In addition, there are honors houses. On-campus housing, guaranteed for the freshman year only, is available on a first-come, first-served basis and on a lottery system for upperclassmen. About half of the students commute. Alcohol is not permitted. All students may keep cars on campus.

Activities: There are no fraternities or sororities. There are many groups and organizations on campus, including band, cheerleading, chess, choir, chorale, computers, drama, ethnic, honors, international, jazz band, marching band, musical theater, newspaper, pep band, political, social service, student government, and yearbook. Popular campus events include the Appreciation Breakfast, Homecoming, Spud Bowl, Snow Daze, and Springfest.

Sports: There are 6 intercollegiate sports for men and 5 for women, and 5 intramural sports for men and 5 for women. Athletic and recreation facilities include swimming pools; handball, racquetball, and tennis courts; horseshoe pits; indoor and outdoor tracks; weight room; and game facilities.

Disabled Students: About 90% of the campus is accessible to disabled students. The following facilities are available: wheelchair ramps, elevators, special parking, and specially equipped rest rooms.

Services: In addition to many counseling and information services, tutoring is available in every subject. There is also remedial math, reading, and writing.

Campus Safety and Security: Campus safety and security measures include escort service, informal discussions, pamphlets, posters, and films, and emergency telephones. In addition, there are lighted pathways and sidewalks, a 20-hour foot and vehicle patrol, and formal safety seminars.

Programs of Study: Adams State awards the B.A. and B.S. degrees. Associate and master's degrees also are awarded. Bachelor's degrees are awarded in BIOLOGICAL SCIENCE (biology/biological science), BUSINESS (accounting, business administration and management, and marketing/retailing/merchandising), COMMUNICATIONS AND THE ARTS (advertising, English, fine arts, journalism, and music), COMPUTER AND PHYSICAL SCIENCE (chemistry, geology, mathematics, and physics), EDUCATION (art, business, elementary, foreign languages, music, science, and secondary), HEALTH PROFESSIONS (medical laboratory technology), SOCIAL SCIENCE (Hispanic American studies, history, physical fitness/movement, psychology, and sociology). Business and education have the largest enrollments.

Required: All students must maintain a GPA of at least 2.0 and complete 124 credit hours, including 24 in the major. General education requirements total 35 semester hours, with 6 in communication arts, 2 in wellness courses, and 1 in physical education. Courses in history, government, philosophy, music, literature, psychology, sociology, and natural science are required.

Special: Cross-registration through the State Colleges of Colorado consortium is available. Work-study programs with the college, dual majors, a general studies degree, nondegree study, and student-designed majors are possible.

Faculty/Classroom: Some 66% of faculty are male; 34%, female. All teach undergraduates and 10% do research. The average class size in an introductory lecture is 40; in a laboratory, 30; and in a regular course offering, 30.

Admissions: About 90% of the 1993–94 applicants were accepted. The ACT scores for the 1993–94 freshman class were as follows: 40% below 21, 40% between 21 and 23, 14% between 24 and 26, 4% between 27 and 28, and 2% above 28. About 33% of the current freshmen were in the top fifth of their class; 68% were in the top two fifths.

Requirements: Adams State requires applicants to be in the upper 50% of their class. A minimum GPA of 2.5 is required, as is the ACT with a minimum score of 19. Applicants are required to have 15 academic credits, including 3 in high school English, 2 each in history, mathematics and science, and 1 in a foreign language. The GED is accepted. AP and CLEP credits are accepted. Important factors used in the admissions decision are advanced placement or honor courses, leadership record, recommendations by school officials, evidence of special talent, and extracurricular activities record.

Procedure: Freshmen are admitted in the fall, spring, and summer. Entrance exams should be taken during the junior year. Applications should be filed by August 1 for fall entry and December 1 for spring entry, along with an application fee of $15. Notification is sent on a rolling basis. There are early admissions and deferred admissions plans.

Transfer: About 129 transfer students enrolled in 1993–94. Transfer students must have a minimum GPA of 2.0. If they have fewer than 12 credits, the SAT I or ACT also is required. A total of 64 credits out of 124 must be completed at Adams State.

Visiting: There are regularly scheduled orientations for prospective students, including meeting with the academic faculty, a campus tour, information on the availability of financial aid and housing, and a free ticket to an athletic event. There are guides for informal visits and visitors may sit in on classes and stay overnight at the school. To arrange for a visit, contact the Admissions Office at (800) 824–6494.

Financial Aid: In 1993–94, 84% of all current freshmen and 82% of continuing students received some form of financial aid. About 69% of freshmen and 67% of continuing students received need-based aid. The average freshman award was $4138. Of that total, scholarships or need-based grants averaged $1824 ($4000 maximum); loans averaged $2576 ($4125 maximum); and work contracts averaged $1598 ($1914 maximum). Nearly half of the undergraduate students work part-time. Average earnings from campus work for the school year are $1100. The average financial indebtedness of the 1992–93 graduate was $6900. The FAF or FFS is required. The deadline for financial aid applications is April 15.

International Students: There are currently 6 international students enrolled. The school actively recruits these students. They must take the TOEFL and achieve a minimum score of 550.

Computers: The college provides computer facilities for student use. The mainframe is a network of 10 AT&T computers. There are 25 stand-alone XT class PCs and 75 networked XT 1286/386 computers located in 7 laboratories scattered throughout the campus and sup-

ported by 13 file servers. There are no time limits on using the system and no fees.

Graduates: In 1992–93, 279 bachelor's degrees were awarded. The most popular majors among graduates were business (32%), education (29%), and psychology/sociology (12%). Within an average freshman class, 2% graduate in 3 years, 18% in 4 years, 35% in 5 years, and 40% in 6 years. Some 80 companies usually recruit on campus. In a recent graduating class, 7% of the men and 12% of the women were enrolled in graduate school within 6 months of graduation; 55% of the men and 53% of the women had found employment.

Admissions Contact: Cheryl Billingsley, Director of Admissions.

BETH-EL COLLEGE OF NURSING

D-3

Colorado Springs, CO 80917–5338   **(719) 475–5170**

Full-time: 49 men, 300 women	Faculty: 13
Part-time: 6 women	Ph.D.s: 5%
Graduate: 2 women	Student/Faculty: 27 to 1
Year: semesters, summer session	Tuition: $4660
Application Deadline: April 15	Room & Board: n/app
Freshman Class: 80 applied, 75 accepted, 69 enrolled	
ACT: 22	**VERY COMPETITIVE**

Beth-El College of Nursing, founded in 1904, is a public, coeducational commuter institution offering degree programs in nursing with a liberal arts foundation. In addition to regional accreditation, Beth-El has baccalaureate program accreditation with NLN. The 1-acre campus is in an urban area 60 miles south of Denver. One building houses all academic facilities.

Student Life: About 86% of undergraduates are from Colorado. Students come from 16 states. Ninety-seven percent are from public schools; 3% from private. Eighty-four percent are white. The average age of freshmen is 29.9; all undergraduates, 32.1. Fifteen percent drop out by the end of their first year; 56% remain to graduate.

Housing: There are no residence halls. All students commute and may keep cars on campus. Alcohol is not permitted.

Activities: There are no fraternities or sororities on campus. There are 5 groups on campus, including honors, newspaper, professional, student government, and yearbook. Popular campus events include Christmas Party, Senior Luncheon, Spring Banquet, and Orientation Picnic.

Sports: Although there is no sports program at Beth-El, students may participate in intramural sports at the University of Colorado at Colorado Springs. Athletic and recreation activities center around the school's proximity to Pikes Peak and other facilities in Colorado Springs.

Disabled Students: Fifty percent of the campus is accessible to disabled students. Wheelchair ramps and special parking are available.

Services: In addition to many counseling and information services, tutoring is available in most subjects, including clinical nursing and pharmacology.

Campus Safety and Security: Campus safety and security measures include escort service, informal discussions, pamphlets, posters, and films, and emergency telephones. In addition, there are lighted pathways and sidewalks.

Programs of Study: Beth-El awards the B.S.N. degree. Master's degrees also are awarded. Bachelor's degrees are awarded in HEALTH PROFESSIONS (nursing).

Required: All students must earn a 2.0 GPA in a total of 129 credit hours, including 73 in nursing. Distribution requirements include such courses as health communication, nursing theory, pharmacology, personnel management, and nursing electives.

Special: General education courses for freshmen are offered through cross-registration with the University of Colorado at Colorado Springs, or may be completed at another area college. Beth-El offers challenge-for-credit exams and work-study programs.

Faculty/Classroom: Ten percent of faculty are male; 90%, female. All both teach and do research. No introductory courses are taught by graduate students. The average class size in an introductory lecture is 60 and in a laboratory, 10.

Admissions: About 94% of the 1993–94 applicants were accepted. The ACT scores for the 1993–94 freshman class were as follows: 100% between 21 and 23. All of the current freshmen were in the top two fifths of their class.

Requirements: Beth-El requires applicants to be in the upper 40% of their class. A minimum GPA of 2.8 is required. The ACT is recommended, with a minimum composite score of 23. Applicants must have completed 4 years of high school English, 3 each of mathematics and science, 2 each of foreign language and social sciences, and 1 of an elective. The college also recommends completion of 2 terms of psychology, 2 of physics, and 1 each of typing and speech. An essay is required and an interview is recommended. The GED is accepted. CLEP credit is accepted. Important factors used in the admissions decision are personality, intangible qualities, advanced placement or honor courses, evidence of special talent, leadership record, and recommendations by alumni.

Procedure: Freshmen are admitted in the fall and spring. Applications should be filed by April 15 for fall entry and October 15 for spring entry, along with an application fee of $30. Notification is sent on a rolling basis, within a week of the admissions committee decision. There is a deferred admissions plan.

Transfer: About 35 transfer students enrolled in 1993–94. Transfer students must have a minimum GPA of 2.0 and be in good standing at all institutions previously attended. A total of 24 credits out of 129 must be completed at Beth-El.

Visiting: There are guides for informal visits and visitors may sit in on classes. To arrange for a visit, contact Marilyn J. Atwood, Director of Student Affairs, at (719) 475–5170.

Financial Aid: In 1992–93, 45% of continuing students received some form of financial aid. Scholarships or need-based grants averaged $750 ($1000 maximum); loans averaged $1500 ($2400 maximum); and work contracts averaged $750 ($2500 maximum). Eighty-nine percent of undergraduate students work part-time. Average earnings from campus work for the school year are $1000. The average financial indebtedness of the 1992–93 graduate was $4500. The FFS is required. The deadline for financial aid applications is May 1 for priority consideration.

International Students: International students may be required to take Spoken English-ETS or the TOEFL with a minimum score of 500.

Computers: The college provides 4 IBM PCs for academic use. There are no time limits on using the system and no fees.

Graduates: In a recent year, 52 bachelor's degrees were awarded. Some 15 companies usually recruit on campus. All of the members of a recent graduating class had found employment within 6 months of graduation.

Admissions Contact: Marilyn J. Atwood, Director of Student Affairs.

COLORADO CHRISTIAN UNIVERSITY

C-2

Lakewood, CO 80226   **(303) 238–5386**

Full-time: 461 men, 540 women	Faculty: 24
Part-time: 24 men, 41 women	Ph.D.s: 35%
Graduate: 48 men, 52 women	Student/Faculty: 42 to 1
Year: semesters, summer session	Tuition: $6350
Application Deadline: open	Room & Board: $3400
Freshman Class: 175 enrolled	
SAT I Verbal/Math: 422/445	ACT: 21 **LESS COMPETITIVE**

Colorado Christian University, founded in 1914, is a private, coeducational, interdenominational institution offering undergraduate and graduate programs in the arts and sciences, biblical studies, and music education. There are 3 undergraduate schools and one graduate school. Special learning facilities include a radio station and TV station. The 24-acre campus is in a suburban area 9 miles west of Denver. Including residence halls, there are 10 buildings on campus.

Student Life: About 61% of undergraduates are from Colorado. Students come from 26 states. The average age of freshmen is 18.

Housing: A total of 280 students can be accommodated in college housing. College-sponsored living facilities include single-sex on-campus apartments. On-campus housing is guaranteed for the freshman year only, is available on a first-come, first-served basis, and is available on a lottery system for upperclassmen. Priority is given to out-of-town students. Alcohol is not permitted. All students may keep cars on campus.

Activities: There is 1 national fraternity. There are no sororities on campus. There are 20 groups on campus, including band, cheerleading, choir, chorus, computers, drama, ethnic, honors, international, jazz band, literary magazine, missions, newspaper, orchestra, pep band, photography, professional, radio and TV, religious, social, social service, student government, and yearbook. Popular campus events include Festival, Homecoming, Campus Days, and Campus Retreat.

Sports: Athletic and recreation facilities include a gymnasium and soccer and practice fields.

Disabled Students: The following facilities are available: special parking, specially equipped rest rooms, and special class scheduling.

Campus Safety and Security: Campus safety and security measures include 24-hour foot and vehicle patrol, emergency telephones, and lighted pathways and sidewalks.

Programs of Study: CCU awards the B.A., B.S., B.C.M., and B.M.E. degrees. Associate and master's degrees also are awarded. Bachelor's degrees are awarded in BIOLOGICAL SCIENCE (biology/biological science), BUSINESS (accounting, business administration and management, human resources, management information systems, management science, and marketing management), COMMUNICATIONS AND THE ARTS (art, broadcasting, communications, dramatic arts, English, fine arts, music, and music performance), COMPUTER AND PHYSICAL SCIENCE (computer management, mathematics, and science), EDUCATION (elementary, music, and secondary), HEALTH PROFESSIONS (premedicine), SOCIAL SCIENCE (biblical studies, history, liberal arts/general studies, missions, political science/government, prelaw, psychology, religion, social science, social studies, and youth ministry). Elementary education has the largest enrollment.

Required: To graduate, students must complete at least 128 semester hours, including the 44-hour general education requirement and courses specified for the major, with a minimum cumulative GPA of 2.0; 2.5 in the major. The university requires 4 semesters of Christian

service and regular chapel attendance. All students must minor in biblical studies.

Special: The school offers co-op programs with Colorado Art Institute and Metro State College, internships, mission work abroad, and a Washington semester. Accelerated degree programs, dual and student-designed majors, nondegree study, pass/fail options, and credit for life, military, and work experience are also available. There is a freshman honors program on campus.

Faculty/Classroom: Seventy percent of faculty are male; 30%, female. The average class size in an introductory lecture is 45; in a laboratory, 20; and in a regular course offering, 198.

Admissions: Six freshmen graduated first in their class.

Requirements: A minimum GPA of 2.0 is required. The SAT I or ACT is required, with a minimum composite score of 800 on the SAT I or 18 on the ACT. Applicants must be graduates of an accredited secondary school. The GED is accepted. An essay is required. AP and CLEP credits are accepted.

Procedure: Freshmen are admitted to all sessions. Application deadlines are open. The application fee is $20. Notification is sent on a rolling basis. There is a deferred admissions plan.

Transfer: About 86 transfer students enrolled in 1993–94. Applicants for transfer should have completed 12 college credits with a minimum GPA of 2.0. A total of 30 credits out of 128 must be completed at CCU.

Visiting: There are guides for informal visits and visitors may sit in on classes and stay overnight at the school. To arrange for a visit, contact the Office of Admissions at (303) 238–5386.

Financial Aid: In an earlier year, 91% of all current freshmen and 85% of continuing students received some form of financial aid. Scholarships or need-based grants averaged $1500 (maximum); loans averaged $2500 ($2625 maximum); and work contracts averaged $1600 (maximum). The average financial indebtedness of an earlier year's graduate was $5000. CCU is a member of CSS. The FAF, FFS, or SFS and FAFSA are required. The deadline for financial aid applications is April 1.

International Students: There are currently 12 international students enrolled. They must take the TOEFL and achieve a minimum score of 500.

Computers: The college provides computer facilities for student use. The mainframe is a Northstar. IBM-compatible, Apple Macintosh, and Apple IIgs microcomputers are available in the computer laboratory. Those taking computer classes may access the system. It may be used 8 A.M. to 8 P.M., Monday through Friday. There are no time limits on using the system. The fees are $50 per semester.

Graduates: In 1992–93 381 bachelor's degrees were awarded. The most popular majors among graduates were management of human resourses (75%), psychology (4%), and biblical studies (3%).

Admissions Contact: Anna DiTorrice, Director of Admissions.

COLORADO COLLEGE
Colorado Springs, CO 80903　　　　　　　　　　　　　　　**D-3**

(719) 389-6344
(800) 542-7214 (out-of-state)

Full-time: 922 men, 965 women	**Faculty:** 152; IIB, +$
Part-time: 3 men, 7 women	**Ph.D.s:** 95%
Graduate: 7 men, 23 women	**Student/Faculty:** 12 to 1
Year: see profile	**Tuition:** $15,942
Application Deadline: January 15	**Room & Board:** $4096
Freshman Class: 3207 applied, 1577 accepted, 490 enrolled	
SAT I or ACT: required	**HIGHLY COMPETITIVE**

Colorado College, founded in 1874, is an independent, coeducational liberal arts institution. The academic year is based on the block plan, under which students take only 1 course during each of the eight 3 1/2 week-long blocks of study; there is also a 9-week summer session. In addition to regional accreditation, CC has baccalaureate program accreditation with NASM. The library contains 664,082 volumes, 36,337 microform items, and 9600 audiovisual forms and subscribes to 1527 periodicals. Computerized library sources and services include the card catalog and interlibrary loans. Special learning facilities include an art gallery, radio station, electronic music studio, writer's workbench, telescope dome, and foreign language video laboratory. The 90-acre campus is in a suburban area 70 miles south of Denver. Including residence halls, there are 52 buildings on campus.

Student Life: About 71% of undergraduates are from out-of-state, mostly the Midwest. Students come from 50 states, 29 foreign countries, and Canada. Seventy-four percent are from public schools; 26% from private. Seventy-five percent are white. The average age of freshmen is 18; all undergraduates, 21. Eight percent drop out by the end of their first year; 80% remain to graduate.

Housing: A total of 1309 students can be accommodated in college housing. College-sponsored living facilities include single-sex and coed dormitories, married-student housing, and fraternity houses. In addition there are language houses, special interest houses, and theme houses. On-campus housing is guaranteed for all 4 years. Seventy percent of students live on campus. All students may keep cars on campus.

Activities: About 20% of men belong to 4 national fraternities; about 20% of women belong to 4 national sororities. There are 70 groups on campus, including art, band, cheerleading, chess, choir, chorale, chorus, computers, concert band, dance, debate, drama, ethnic, film, gay, honors, international, jazz band, literary magazine, musical theater, newspaper, opera, orchestra, outdoor recreation, photography, political, professional, radio, religious, social, social service, student government, and yearbook. Popular campus events include Symposium Week and the Great Performances and Ideas program.

Sports: There are 20 intercollegiate sports for men and 16 for women, and 13 intramural sports for men and 13 for women. Athletic and recreation facilities include a sports center with a gymnasium, weight and exercise rooms, squash, tennis, and racquetball courts, a pool, an ice rink, and playing fields.

Disabled Students: Eighty percent of the campus is accessible to disabled students. The following facilities are available: wheelchair ramps, elevators, special parking, specially equipped rest rooms, lowered drinking fountains, and lowered telephones.

Services: In addition to many counseling and information services, tutoring is available in some subjects. A writing center is available.

Campus Safety and Security: Campus safety and security measures include 24-hour foot and vehicle patrol, self defense education, escort service, and informal discussions. In addition, there are pamphlets, posters, and films, emergency telephones, and lighted pathways and sidewalks.

Programs of Study: CC awards the B.A. degree. Master's degrees also are awarded. Bachelor's degrees are awarded in BIOLOGICAL SCIENCE (biochemistry and biology/biological science), COMMUNICATIONS AND THE ARTS (classics, comparative literature, dance, dramatic arts, English, fine arts, French, German, music, and Spanish), COMPUTER AND PHYSICAL SCIENCE (chemistry, geology, mathematics, and physics), ENGINEERING AND ENVIRONMENTAL DESIGN (environmental geology), HEALTH PROFESSIONS (medical laboratory technology), SOCIAL SCIENCE (anthropology, economics, history, liberal arts/general studies, philosophy, political science/government, psychology, religion, and sociology). English, political science, and biology have the largest enrollments.

Required: Students must complete 32 units, with at least 9 units outside the division of the major, and 4 in Alternative Perspectives. At least 3 courses in each division are required.

Special: In addition to its modular schedule, CC offers co-op programs with Columbia University Law School, Rush University for nursing, Duke University for forestry, the Universities of Regensburg and Gottingen in West Germany, and the Kansai Gaidai in Japan. Internships, study abroad in 13 countries, a Washington semester, student-designed majors, a general studies degree, and pass/fail options are offered. A 3–2 engineering degree is offered with Columbia University, Rennsselaer Polytechnic, Washington University, and the University of Southern California. There are 3 national honor societies on campus, including Phi Beta Kappa.

Faculty/Classroom: Sixty-seven percent of faculty are male; 33%, female. All teach and also do research. No introductory courses are taught by graduate students. The average class size in an introductory lecture is 15; in a laboratory, 15; and in a regular course offering, 15.

Admissions: About 49% of the 1993–94 applicants were accepted. The SAT scores for the 1993–94 freshman class were as follows: Verbal—19% below 500, 46% between 500 and 599, 31% between 600 and 700, and 4% above 700; Math—8% below 500, 33% between 500 and 599, 45% between 600 and 700, and 14% above 700. The ACT scores were 5% below 21, 9% between 21 and 23, 26% between 24 and 26, 23% between 27 and 28, and 37% above 28. About 78% of the current freshmen were in the top fifth of their class; 97% were in the top two fifths. There were 19 National Merit finalists. Thirty-three freshmen graduated first in their class.

Requirements: The SAT I or ACT is required. Applicants should have completed at least 16 high school academic credits. The GED is accepted. An essay is required. AP credits are accepted. Important factors used in the admissions decision are advanced placement or honor courses, extracurricular activities record, personality, intangible qualities, evidence of special talent, and recommendations by school officials.

Procedure: Freshmen are admitted in the fall. Entrance exams should be taken by fall of the senior year. Applications should be filed by January 15 for fall entry, along with an application fee of $40. Notification is sent April 15. There are early admissions and deferred admissions plans. A waiting list is an active part of the admissions procedure.

Transfer: About 68 transfer students enrolled in 1993–94. Transfer candidates who have not completed 1 full year of college work must submit their high school record. A letter of recommendation from a professor or teacher and a dean's form are required. A total of 8 units out of 32 must be completed at CC.

Visiting: There are regularly scheduled orientations for prospective students, including a class visit, an information session with an admissions director, and a student-led tour. Visitors may sit in on classes and stay overnight at the school. To arrange for a visit, contact the Admission Office at (800) 542-7214.

Financial Aid: In 1993–94 57% of all current freshmen and 54% of continuing students received some form of financial aid. About 52% of freshmen and 50% of continuing students received need-based aid. The average freshman award was $12,805. Of that total, scholarships or need-based grants averaged $9824 ($15,000 maximum); loans averaged $2789 ($4000 maximum); and work contracts averaged $1263 ($1400 maximum). Thirty-eight percent of undergraduate students work part-time. Average earnings from campus work for the school year are $800. The average financial indebtedness of the 1992–93 graduate was $8500. CC is a member of CSS. The FAF is required. The deadline for financial aid applications is February 15.

International Students: There are currently 49 international students enrolled. They must take the TOEFL and achieve a minimum score of 550.

Computers: The college provides computer facilities for student use. The mainframes are a DEC VAX 11/750, a Prime 2655, and an AT&T 3B/2300. There are about 190 microcomputers available across the campus. All students may access the system. There are no time limits on using the system and no fees.

Graduates: In 1992–93 512 bachelor's degrees were awarded. The most popular majors among graduates were biology (13%), English (10%), and political science (9%). Within an average freshman class, 1% graduate in 3 years, 70% in 4 years, 10% in 5 years, and 1% in 6 years. Some 40 companies recruited on campus in 1992–93.

Admissions Contact: Terrance K. Swenson, Dean of Admission and Financial Aid.

COLORADO SCHOOL OF MINES
Golden, CO 80401–9952

C-2

(303) 273-3220

(800) 446-9488 (out-of-state)

Full-time: 1585 men, 483 women
Part-time: 41 men, 13 women
Graduate: 774 men, 197 women
Year: semesters, summer session
Application Deadline: May 1
Freshman Class: 1494 applied, 1210 accepted, 495 enrolled
SAT I Verbal/Math: 550/650

Faculty: 175; IIA, +$
Ph.Ds: 90%
Student/Faculty: 12 to 1
Tuition: $4386 ($11,982)
Room & Board: $4050

ACT: 28 HIGHLY COMPETITIVE +

The Colorado School of Mines, founded in 1874, is a public, coeducational institution, offering engineering, science, and technical programs. There is one graduate school. In addition to regional accreditation, CSM has baccalaureate program accreditation with ABET. The library contains 395,000 volumes and 2000 microform items, and subscribes to 2150 periodicals. Computerized library sources and services include the card catalog, interlibrary loans, and database searching. Special learning facilities include a geology museum. The 307-acre campus is in a small town 15 miles west of Denver. Including residence halls, there are 24 buildings on campus.

Student Life: About 69% of undergraduates are from Colorado. Students come from 50 states, 67 foreign countries, and Canada. Eighty-five percent are from public schools; 15% from private. Seventy-six percent are white; 14% foreign nationals. Fifty-two percent are Protestant; 21% Catholic; 20% claim no religious affiliation. The average age of freshmen is 18; all undergraduates, 20. Fifteen percent drop out by the end of their first year; 65% remain to graduate.

Housing: A total of 507 students can be accommodated in college housing. College-sponsored living facilities include single-sex and coed dormitories and married-student housing. On-campus housing is guaranteed for the freshman year only and is available on a first-come, first-served basis. All students may keep cars on campus.

Activities: About 19% of men belong to 7 national fraternities; about 20% of women belong to 2 national sororities. There are 35 groups on campus, including band, cheerleading, choir, chorus, computers, drama, ethnic, honors, international, literary magazine, marching band, musical theater, newspaper, political, professional, religious, social, social service, student government, and yearbook. Popular campus events include Homecoming, International Day, E-Day, Winter Carnival, Parents Day, The Big Event, and Casino Night.

Sports: There are 11 intercollegiate sports for men and 6 for women, and 20 intramural sports for men and 10 for women. Athletic and recreation facilities include a 10,000-seat stadium, a gymnasium, numerous intramural fields, tennis courts, and a field house.

Disabled Students: Fifteen percent of the campus is accessible to disabled students. The following facilities are available: wheelchair ramps, elevators, special parking, specially equipped rest rooms, and special class scheduling.

Services: In addition to many counseling and information services, tutoring is available in most subjects. There is also remedial math and writing.

Campus Safety and Security: Campus safety and security measures include 24-hour foot and vehicle patrol, informal discussions, and lighted pathways and sidewalks.

Programs of Study: CSM awards the B.S. degree. Master's and doctoral degrees also are awarded. Bachelor's degrees are awarded in COMPUTER AND PHYSICAL SCIENCE (chemistry, mathematics, and physics), ENGINEERING AND ENVIRONMENTAL DESIGN (chemical engineering, engineering, geological engineering, geophysical engineering, metallurgical engineering, mining and mineral

engineering, and petroleum/natural gas engineering). Chemical engineering, physics, mining engineering, geological engineering, geophysical engineering, metallurgical and materials engineering, and petroleum engineering are the strongest academically. General engineering, chemical engineering, and petroleum engineering have the largest enrollments.

Required: Students must complete 138 to 148 credit hours, with 35 to 40 hours in the major and a GPA of 2.0. Required courses include humanities, calculus, physics, computer science, chemistry, and physical education.

Special: Co-op programs, internship in the McBride Honors Program in the humanities, study abroad, accelerated degree programs in all majors, dual majors, and nondegree study are offered. There is a freshman honors program on campus, as well as one national honor society. Three departments have honors programs.

Faculty/Classroom: Ninety-one percent of faculty are male; 9%, female. Eighty-five percent teach undergraduates and 50% also do research. No introductory courses are taught by graduate students. The average class size in an introductory lecture is 75; in a laboratory, 22; and in a regular course offering, 35.

Admissions: About 81% of the 1993–94 applicants were accepted. The SAT scores for the 1993–94 freshman class were as follows: Verbal—23% below 500, 65% between 500 and 599, 11% between 600 and 700, and 1% above 700; Math—20% between 500 and 599, 70% between 600 and 700, and 10% above 700. The ACT scores were 5% between 21 and 23, 25% between 24 and 26, 40% between 27 and 28, and 30% above 29. About 88% of the current freshmen were in the top fifth of their class; 100% were in the top two fifths. About 40 freshmen graduated first in their class.

Requirements: CSM requires applicants to be in the upper 33% of their class. The SAT I or ACT is required. Applicants must be graduates of an accredited secondary school. The GED is accepted. Students should have completed 16 high school academic credits, including 4 credits each of English and mathematics, 3 of science, 2 of social studies, and 3 academic electives. AP credits are accepted. Important factors used in the admissions decision are advanced placement or honor courses, recommendations by school officials, extracurricular activities record, leadership record, and evidence of special talents.

Procedure: Freshmen are admitted to all sessions. Entrance exams should be taken late in the junior year or early in the senior year. Applications should be filed by May 1 for fall entry, December 1 for spring, and June 10 for summer, along with an application fee of $25. Notification is sent on a rolling basis. There is a deferred admissions plan.

Transfer: About 110 transfer students enrolled in 1993–94. Transfer applicants must have a minimum GPA of 2.5. A total of 30 credit hours out of 138 to 148 must be completed at CSM.

Visiting: There are regularly scheduled orientations for prospective students, including a day-long visitation program once each fall where students may visit departments and talk with faculty. Sessions in admissions and financial aid also are given. There are guides for informal visits and visitors may sit in on classes and stay overnight at the school. To arrange for a visit, contact Carmen Brener or Mary Vigil at (303) 273–3220/(800) 245–1060 (in-state) or (800) 446–9488.

Financial Aid: In 1993–94 85% of all students received some form of financial aid; 70% of all students received need-based aid. The average freshman award was $7680. Of that total, scholarships or need-based grants averaged $3455 ($11,600 maximum); loans averaged $3500 ($5500 maximum); and work contracts averaged $725 ($1500 maximum). Forty-five percent of undergraduate students work part-time. Average earnings from campus work for the school year are $725. The average financial indebtedness of the 1992–93 graduate was $20,000. CSM is a member of CSS. The college's own financial statement, the FAF, and the FAFSA are required. The deadline for financial aid applications is March 1.

International Students: There are currently 429 international students enrolled. The school actively recruits these students. They must take the TOEFL and achieve a minimum score of 550.

Computers: The college provides computer facilities for student use. The mainframes are a DEC VAX 4500 and an IBM RS 600/930. There are about 250 IBM, IBM-compatible, Apple Macintosh, and NXT microcomputers, and RS 6000 workstations of which 175 are networked. They are located in residence halls, classroom buildings, and elsewhere on campus. All students may access the system. It may be used on weekends and from 7 A.M. to 12 P.M., Monday through Friday. There are no time limits and no fees.

Graduates: In 1992–93 262 bachelor's degrees were awarded. The most popular majors among graduates were engineering (40%), chemical engineering (19%), and metallurgical and materials engineering (9%). Within an average freshman class, 1% graduate in 3 years, 33% in 4 years, and 65% in 5 years. Some 174 companies recruited on campus in a recent year. In a recent graduating class, 10% were enrolled in graduate school and 80% had found employment within 6 months of graduation.

Admissions Contact: Bill Young, Director of Enrollment Management.

COLORADO STATE UNIVERSITY
Fort Collins, CO 80523

C-1
(303) 491-6909

Full-time: 8047 men, 7599 women
Part-time: 946 men, 883 women
Graduate: 1961 men, 1674 women
Year: semesters, summer session
Application Deadline: July 1
Freshman Class: 6312 accepted, 2194 enrolled
SAT I Verbal/Math: 470/540

Faculty: 1006; I, -$
Ph.D.s: 88%
Student/Faculty: 16 to 1
Tuition: $2566 ($8192)
Room & Board: $4000

ACT: 24   **VERY COMPETITIVE**

Colorado State University, founded in 1870 and part of the Colorado State University system, is a public, land-grant, coeducational institution, offering 74 undergraduate majors in 56 departments within 8 colleges. In addition to regional accreditation, Colorado State has baccalaureate program accreditation with AACSB, ABET, ACCE, ACEJMC, ASLA, CSWE, FIDER, NASM, NCATE, and SAF. The 4 libraries contain 1,825,000 volumes, 1,832,000 microform items, and 6625 audiovisual forms, and subscribe to 20,500 periodicals. Computerized library sources and services include the card catalog, interlibrary loans, and database searching. Special learning facilities include a learning resource center, art gallery, radio station, and TV station. The 666-acre campus is in a suburban area in Fort Collins, 65 miles north of Denver. Including residence halls, there are 100 buildings on campus.

Student Life: About 78% of undergraduates are from Colorado. Students come from 50 states, 95 foreign countries, and Canada. Eighty-five percent are white. The average age of freshmen is 18; all undergraduates, 22. Fifteen percent drop out by the end of their first year; 57% remain to graduate.

Housing: A total of 4600 students can be accommodated in college housing. College-sponsored living facilities include coed dormitories, on-campus apartments, married-student housing, fraternity houses, and sorority houses. In addition there are honors floors and 24 other special interest floors. On-campus housing is guaranteed for the freshman year only and is available on a first-come, first-served basis. All students may keep cars on campus.

Activities: About 14% of men belong to 20 national fraternities; about 14% of women belong to 14 national sororities. There are 300 groups on campus, including art, band, cheerleading, chess, choir, chorale, chorus, computers, dance, drama, drill team, ethnic, film, gay, honors, international, jazz band, literary magazine, marching band, musical theater, newspaper, orchestra, pep band, photography, political, professional, radio and TV, religious, social, social service, student government, and yearbook. Popular campus events include Family Homecoming, International Week, Cinco de Mayo Celebration, Hawaiian Luau, Native American Powwow, Black Awareness Month, Centertainment, International Poster Exhibition, Fine Arts Series, American West Series, and Summer Outdoor Theater.

Sports: There are 7 intercollegiate sports for men and 9 for women, and 15 intramural sports for men and 15 for women. Athletic and recreation facilities include a 9000-seat arena, indoor and outdoor tracks, a football stadium, a baseball diamond, indoor swimming pools, a student recreation center, and an experimental obstacle course for personal development.

Disabled Students: Ninety percent of the campus is accessible to disabled students. The following facilities are available: wheelchair ramps, elevators, special parking, specially equipped rest rooms, special class scheduling, lowered drinking fountains, lowered telephones, an advocacy office for disabled students, telecommunication devices for the deaf, and special transportation.

Services: In addition to many counseling and information services, tutoring is available in most subjects. There are also reader services for the blind along with interpreters and note takers.

Campus Safety and Security: Campus safety and security measures include 24-hour foot and vehicle patrol, self defense education, escort service, and shuttle buses. In addition, there are informal discussions, pamphlets, posters, films, emergency telephones, lighted pathways and sidewalks, lectures by campus police on a variety of safety issues, crime victim support unit, and bike patrol.

Programs of Study: Colorado State awards the B.A., B.S., B.F.A., and B.M. degrees. Master's and doctoral degrees also are awarded. Bachelor's degrees are awarded in AGRICULTURE (agricultural business management, agricultural economics, animal science, equestrian science, fishing and fisheries, forestry and related sciences, horticulture, natural resource management, and range/farm management), BIOLOGICAL SCIENCE (biochemistry, biology/biological science, botany, ecology, microbiology, nutrition, wildlife biology, and zoology), BUSINESS (accounting, apparel and accessories marketing, banking and finance, business administration and management, finance/real estate, hotel/motel and restaurant management, marketing/retailing/merchandising, and recreational facilities management), COMMUNICATIONS AND THE ARTS (art, English, fine arts, French, German, journalism, music, performing arts, Spanish, speech/debate/rhetoric, and technical and business writing), COMPUTER AND PHYSICAL SCIENCE (chemistry, computer science, geology, information sciences and systems, mathematics, physical sciences, physics, and statistics), EDUCATION (agricultural,

home economics, and physical), ENGINEERING AND ENVIRONMENTAL DESIGN (agricultural engineering, chemical engineering, civil engineering, construction management, electrical/electronics engineering, engineering and applied science, industrial engineering technology, interior design, landscape architecture/design, and mechanical engineering), HEALTH PROFESSIONS (environmental health science and occupational therapy), SOCIAL SCIENCE (anthropology, economics, food science, history, home economics, human development, humanities, philosophy, political science/government, psychology, social science, social work, and sociology). Agricultural sciences, biochemistry, business, biological sciences, forestry and natural resources, engineering, interior design, microbiology, technical journalism, occupational therapy, veterinary medicine, graphic arts, and chemistry are the strongest academically. Psychology, biological sciences, art, exercise and sport science, engineering, and business have the largest enrollments.

Required: To graduate, students must complete at least 128 credit hours with a minimum GPA of 2.0. Students must complete the University Studies Program, consisting of a minimum of 37 credits in communication and reasoning, natural sciences, arts, humanities, behavioral and social sciences, physical education/wellness, and cross-cultural studies.

Special: Colorado State offers co-op programs with Metropolitan State College and Universidad Autonoma in Mexico. Participation in the National Student Exchange and cross-registration with AIMS Community College and Front Range Community College are possible. Study abroad in more than 30 countries, a semester at sea, work-study programs, B.A.-B.S. degrees, and pass/fail options are available. Teaching certification students receive a bachelor's degree in their chosen subject and also complete a certification sequence through the School of Occupational and Educational Studies. There is a freshman honors program on campus and a university-wide honors program, as well as 41 national honor societies including Phi Beta Kappa.

Faculty/Classroom: Eighty-two percent of faculty are male; 18%, female. The average class size in an introductory lecture is 58 and in a laboratory, 24.

Admissions: The SAT scores for the 1993–94 freshman class were as follows: Verbal—59% below 500, 33% between 500 and 599, 6% between 600 and 700, and 2% above 700; Math—27% below 500, 43% between 500 and 599, 16% between 600 and 700, and 13% above 700. The ACT scores were 9% below 21, 30% between 21 and 23, 35% between 24 and 26, 14% between 27 and 28, and 12% above 28. Nearly 55% of the current freshmen were in the top fifth of their class; 87% were in the top two fifths. About 83 freshmen graduated first in their class.

Requirements: The SAT I or the ACT is required. The average freshman has a composite SAT I score of 1014 and an ACT composite of 24. Graduation from secondary school is required. The GED is accepted. Students should have completed 18 high school credits, 15 of which are academic credits, including 4 years of English, 3 of mathematics, 2 of natural science, 2 of social science, and 1 additional year of natural or social science. An essay is strongly recommended. AP and CLEP credits are accepted. Important factors used in the admissions decision are advanced placement or honor courses, extracurricular activities record, geographic diversity, recommendations by school officials, and leadership record.

Procedure: Freshmen are admitted to all sessions. Entrance exams are recommended during the junior year or early fall of the senior year. Applications should be filed by July 1 for fall entry and December 15 for spring entry, along with an application fee of $30. Notification is sent on a rolling basis. There is an early admissions plan.

Transfer: About 2073 transfer students enrolled in 1993–94. Transfer applicants should have at least 12 semester credits of academic classes (not remedial, technical, or applied) completed at accredited institutions and should submit transcripts from all universities and colleges attended. Applicants with fewer than 12 credits must also submit high school transcripts and ACT or SAT I scores. A minimum cumulative 2.0 GPA is required for admission. However, applicants with fewer than 30 credits should have at least a 2.5 GPA to be considered a strong candidate for admission. A total of 32 credits out of 128 must be completed at Colorado State.

Visiting: There are regularly scheduled orientations for prospective students, consisting of day-and-a-half sessions held during the summer that include meeting with an academic adviser to register for the fall semester, taking the required placement exams, and receiving information about student services, campus life, residence hall life and financial concerns. There are guides for informal visits and visitors may sit in on classes. To arrange for a visit, contact Barb Formby in the Office of Admissions at (303) 491-7044.

Financial Aid: In a recent year 71% of all freshmen and 65% of continuing students received some form of financial aid. About 30% of freshmen and 40% of continuing students received need-based aid. The average freshman award was $3300. Of that total, scholarships or need-based grants averaged $1000; loans averaged $2625 (maximum); and work contracts averaged $1600 (maximum). Sixty-five percent of undergraduate students work part-time. Average earnings from campus work for the school year are $1850. The average financial indebtedness of the 1992–93 graduate was $13,500. Colorado State is a member of CSS. The FAFSA is preferred; the FFS, FAF, and

AFSA are accepted. The deadline for financial aid applications is March 1 for priority consideration.

International Students: There are currently 716 international students enrolled. They must take the TOEFL and achieve a minimum score of 525. The student must also take the SAT I or the ACT.

Computers: The college provides computer facilities for student use. The mainframe consists of 3 IBM RISC System/6000 servers; the primary server is an IBM RS/6000 Model 970. There are numerous student computer laboratories on campus and some in residence halls. Those students who are given an account number from a course instructor may access the system. It may be used 24 hours a day. There are no time limits and no fees.

Graduates: In 1992–93 3482 bachelor's degrees were awarded. The most popular majors among graduates were business (15%), social sciences (6%), and human development and family studies (5%). Within an average freshman class, 23% graduate in 4 years and 27% in 5 years. Some 200 companies recruited on campus in 1992–93.

Admissions Contact: Admissions Counselors.

COLORADO TECHNICAL COLLEGE
D-3

Colorado Springs, CO 80907–3896   (719) 598–0200

Full-time: 355 men, 62 women	Faculty: 28
Part-time: 608 men, 145 women	Ph.D.s: 38%
Graduate: 189 men, 43 women	Student/Faculty: 15 to 1
Year: quarters, summer session	Tuition: $6005
Application Deadline: October 1	Room & Board: n/app

Freshman Class: 421 applied, 364 accepted, 326 enrolled

SAT I or ACT: recommended   **LESS COMPETITIVE**

Colorado Technical College, founded in 1965, is a private, commuter institution offering science programs with extensive laboratory emphasis in electronic engineering technology, logistic systems management, computer engineering, and electrical engineering. Most of the students are working adults who have transferred from other colleges. There are 4 undergraduate and 3 graduate schools. In addition to regional accreditation, Colorado Tech has baccalaureate program regional accreditation with ABET. The library contains 10,000 volumes, 15,000 microform items, and 350 audiovisual forms, and subscribes to 350 periodicals. Computerized library sources and services include database searching. Special learning facilities include a learning resource center. The 5-acre campus is in a suburban area of Colorado Springs. There are 2 buildings on campus. There are no residence halls.

Student Life: About 95% of undergraduates are from Colorado. Students come from 14 foreign countries. Seventy-seven percent are white. The average age of freshmen is 22.8; all undergraduates, 26. Thirty percent drop out by the end of their first year.

Housing: There are no residence halls. All students commute. Alcohol is not permitted.

Activities: There are no fraternities or sororities on campus. There are 6 groups on campus, including honors, professional, and student government. Popular campus events include ski activities, a summer picnic, and Artsfest.

Sports: There are 4 intramural sports for men and 4 for women. Athletic and recreation facilities include a high-tech workout facility.

Disabled Students: The entire campus is accessible to disabled students. The following facilities are available: wheelchair ramps, special parking, specially equipped rest rooms, and lowered drinking fountains.

Services: In addition to many counseling and information services, tutoring is available in most subjects, including mathematics and computer science. Taped tutorials are also offered and there is remedial math. Upon entry to Colorado Tech, students are assigned a counselor/mentor who can assist them throughout their academic career.

Campus Safety and Security: Campus safety and security measures include informal discussions, pamphlets, posters, films, emergency telephones, and lighted pathways and sidewalks.

Programs of Study: Colorado Tech awards the B.S. degree. Associate and master's degrees also are awarded. Bachelor's degrees are awarded in BUSINESS (management information systems), COMPUTER AND PHYSICAL SCIENCE (computer science), ENGINEERING AND ENVIRONMENTAL DESIGN (computer engineering, electrical/electronics engineering, electrical/electronics engineering technology, engineering technology, and telecommunication electronics technology), SOCIAL SCIENCE (logistic systems management and systems science). Engineering, computer science, and engineering technology are the strongest academically. Engineering technology, computer science, and engineering have the largest enrollments.

Required: All students must complete 90 quarter hours in core curriculum courses, including mathematics, basic science, humanities, English, social science, computer foundations and engineering science. An average of 200 quarter hours, with a cummulative GPA of 2.0 is required to graduate, as is a course in career development.

Special: A co-op program in logistics is offered. Work-study programs are available with social services, the public library, the Space Foundation, and the college. Nondegree study and credit for life, military, and work experience are possible. There is one national honor society on campus.

Faculty/Classroom: Eighty-eight percent of faculty are male; 12%, female. All teach undergraduates and all do research. No introductory courses are taught by graduate students. The average class size in an introductory lecture is 30; in a laboratory, 24; and in a regular course offering, 20.

Admissions: About 86% of the 1993–94 applicants were accepted. The SAT scores for the 1993–94 freshman class were as follows: Verbal—100% below 500; Math—25% between 500 and 599 and 75% between 600 and 700.

Requirements: The SAT I or ACT is recommended, with minimum composite scores of 1050 (550 math) on SAT I or 24 on the ACT. Applicants should be graduates of an accredited high school. The GED is accepted. An essay is required for scholarships. An interview is recommended. Students without transfer of credit or an ACT or SAT I test report must pass the ACT Asset tests in mathematics and English. AP and CLEP credits are accepted. Important factors used in the admissions decision are ability to finance college education, personality, intangible qualities, recommendations by school officials, recommendations by alumni, and leadership record.

Procedure: Freshmen are admitted to all sessions. Entrance exams should be taken prior to the student's desired entry date. Applications should be filed by October 1 for fall entry, January 1 for winter entry, April 1 for spring entry, and July 1 for summer entry, along with an application fee of $50. Notification is sent on a rolling basis. There are early admissions and deferred admissions plans.

Transfer: About 174 transfer students enrolled in a recent class. Most new students are transfers. They must meet the same criteria as entering freshmen. The college uses the ACT Asset Placement Evaluation in mathematics and English for acceptance and placement. A total of 60 quarter hours out of an average of 200 quarter hours must be completed at Colorado Tech.

Visiting: There are regularly scheduled orientations for prospective students, consisting of a tour and admissions overview program. There are guides for informal visits and visitors may sit in on classes. To arrange for a visit, contact the Admissions Director at (719) 598–0200.

Financial Aid: In 1993–94 45% of all current freshmen and 49% of continuing students received some form of financial aid. About 35% of freshmen and 33% of continuing students received need-based aid. The average freshman award was $6250. Of that total, scholarships or need-based grants averaged $2137 ($6333 maximum); and loans averaged $2625 ($6625 maximum). Two percent of undergraduate students work part-time. Average earnings from campus work for the school year are $3060. The average financial indebtedness of the 1992–93 graduate was $15,000. Colorado Tech is a member of CSS. The FAF and the college's own financial statement are required.

International Students: There are currently 36 international students enrolled. They must take the TOEFL and achieve a minimum score of 550, the college's own test, or the ELS. The student must also take the SAT I, ACT, and the ACT Asset and Placement Evaluation for placement, and achieve a minimum score on SAT I of 1050 (550 mathematics), and a minimum score of 24 on the ACT.

Computers: The college provides computer facilities for student use. Five laboratories with 20 to 24 computers each are available for student use in structured course laboratories with professors, and unstructured use any other time. One laboratory has 20 DEC 5000 networked workstations, another 3 contain the remaining DEC Alpha Servers for 24 PCs and 72 PCs. Printers and plotters are available. All students may access the system. It may be used 8 A.M. to 11 P.M. Monday through Friday and 8 A.M. to 5 P.M. Saturday. There are no time limits on using the system. The fees are $50 for courses with laboratories. There is no charge for other purposes.

Graduates: In 1992–93 156 bachelor's degrees were awarded. The most popular majors among graduates were logistics systems management (19%), electrical engineering (19%), and computer science (16%). Some 40 companies recruited on campus in 1992–93. In the 1992 graduating class, 96% of the men and 96% of the women had found employment within 6 months of graduation.

Admissions Contact: Admissions Director.

FORT LEWIS COLLEGE
B-4

Durango, CO 81301   (303) 247–7184; (800) 233–6731 (out-of-state)

Full-time: 2082 men, 1711 women	Faculty: 180; IIB, av$
Part-time: 231 men, 255 women	Ph.D.s: 87%
Graduate: none	Student/Faculty: 21 to 1
Year: trimesters, summer session	Tuition: $1777 ($6525)
Application Deadline: August 1	Room & Board: $3320

Freshman Class: 2872 applied, 1986 accepted, 1123 enrolled

ACT: 21   **COMPETITIVE**

Fort Lewis College, founded in 1911, is a public institution with undergraduate programs in arts and sciences, business, and education. There are 3 undergraduate schools. In addition to regional accreditation, Fort Lewis College has baccalaureate program accreditation with AACSB and NASM. The library contains 185,000 volumes and 200 microform items, and subscribes to 1200 periodicals. Computerized library sources and services include the card catalog, interlibrary loans, and database searching. Special learning facilities include a

learning resource center, art gallery, radio station, and a center for Southwest studies. The 600-acre campus is in a small town 350 miles southwest of Denver. Including residence halls, there are 43 buildings on campus.

Student Life: About 70% of undergraduates are from Colorado. Students come from 45 states, 14 foreign countries, and Canada. Eighty-five percent are from public schools; 15% from private. Seventy-eight percent are white; 11% Native American/Eskimo. The average age of freshmen is 18.5; all undergraduates, 23. Thirty-five percent drop out by the end of their first year; 50% remain to graduate.

Housing: A total of 1540 students can be accommodated in college housing. College-sponsored living facilities include single-sex and coed dormitories, on-campus apartments, and married-student housing. On-campus housing is guaranteed for the freshman year only and is available on a first-come, first-served basis. All students may keep cars on campus.

Activities: There are no fraternities or sororities on campus. There are 50 groups on campus, including art, cheerleading, choir, chorale, chorus, concert band, dance, drama, ethnic, honors, jazz band, literary magazine, marching band, newspaper, orchestra, political, professional, radio and TV, religious, social, social service, student government, and symphony. Popular campus events include Weekend Wipeout, Snowdown, and Homecoming.

Sports: There are 6 intercollegiate sports for men and 4 for women, and 35 intramural sports for men and 35 for women. Athletic and recreation facilities include a field house, outdoor sports complex, indoor swimming pool, and weight room.

Disabled Students: Ninety-five percent of the campus is accessible to disabled students. The following facilities are available: wheelchair ramps, elevators, special parking, specially equipped rest rooms, lowered drinking fountains, lowered telephones, and workstations modified for individual needs.

Services: In addition to many counseling and information services, tutoring is available in most subjects. There is also a reader service for the blind and remedial math and writing.

Campus Safety and Security: Campus safety and security measures include 24-hour foot and vehicle patrol, escort service, informal discussions, and lighted pathways and sidewalks.

Programs of Study: Fort Lewis College awards the B.A. and B.S. degrees. Associate degrees also are awarded. Bachelor's degrees are awarded in BIOLOGICAL SCIENCE (biology/biological science), BUSINESS (accounting, business administration and management, marketing/retailing/merchandising, and tourism), COMMUNICATIONS AND THE ARTS (English, fine arts, music, and Spanish), COMPUTER AND PHYSICAL SCIENCE (chemistry, geology, information sciences and systems, mathematics, physics, and science), EDUCATION (secondary), SOCIAL SCIENCE (anthropology, economics, history, humanities, international studies, philosophy, physical fitness/movement, political science/government, psychology, sociology, and Southwest studies). Business, chemistry, and geology are the strongest academically. Business has the largest enrollment.

Required: For graduation, students must complete 128 semester hours with 30 to 44 hours in the major and a minimum GPA of 2.0 overall and within the major. A total of 44 hours in general distribution courses is required, including 3 courses each in language and natural or quantitative science, 2 each in composition, foundation of culture, behavioral science, physical education, and 1 in non-Western studies.

Special: The college offers cooperative programs in most majors, numerous internships, a Washington semester for political science majors, study abroad, student-designed majors, a general studies degree, nondegree study, pass/fail options, B.A.-B.S. degrees, and credit for life, military, and work experience are available. There are 3-2 engineering degrees and an opportunity to earn a preforestry degree in association with Colorado State and Northern Arizona Universities. There is a freshman honors program on campus, as well as 12 national honor societies.

Faculty/Classroom: Sixty-seven percent of faculty are male; 33%, female. All teach undergraduates. The average class size in an introductory lecture is 80; in a laboratory, 25; and in a regular course offering, 30.

Admissions: About 69% of the 1993-94 applicants were accepted. The ACT scores for the 1993-94 freshman class were as follows: 38% below 21, 24% between 21 and 23, 23% between 24 and 26, 10% between 27 and 28, and 5% above 28. About 20% of the current freshmen were in the top fifth of their class; 65% were in the top two fifths. There were 6 National Merit semifinalists. About 9 freshmen graduated first in their class.

Requirements: Fort Lewis College requires applicants to be in the upper 50% of their class. A minimum GPA of 2.0 is required. The SAT I or ACT is required with recommended minimum composite scores of 800 and 17 (20 enhanced) respectively. Applicants must be graduates of an accredited secondary school or have a GED certificate. An interview is recommended. AP and CLEP credits are accepted.

Procedure: Freshmen are admitted to all sessions. Applications should be filed by August 1 for fall entry (however, to qualify for on-campus housing, students must have applications and all documents in by June 30), December 1 for winter entry, and April 1 for summer

entry, along with an application fee of $20. Notification is sent on a rolling basis. There are early decision, early admissions, and deferred admissions plans.

Transfer: About 360 transfer students enrolled in 1993-94. Applicants for transfer should have a minimum of 12 credit hours and have a GPA of 2.0. An interview is recommended. A total of 28 credits out of 128 must be completed at Fort Lewis College.

Visiting: There are guides for informal visits and visitors may sit in on classes and stay overnight at the school. To arrange for a visit, contact the Office of Admission at (303) 247-7184.

Financial Aid: In 1993-94 78% of all current freshmen and 69% of continuing students received some form of financial aid. About 59% of freshmen and 62% of continuing students received need-based aid. The average freshman award was $2250. Of that total, scholarships or need-based grants averaged $500 ($3000 maximum); loans averaged $1200 ($6650 maximum); and work contracts averaged $550 ($1700 maximum). Eighty-five percent of undergraduate students work part-time. Average earnings from campus work for the school year are $1500. The average financial indebtedness of the 1992-93 graduate was $4900. Fort Lewis College is a member of CSS. The FAFSA financial statement is required. The deadline for financial aid applications is February 15.

International Students: There are currently 73 international students enrolled. They must take the TOEFL and achieve a minimum score of 500.

Computers: The college provides computer facilities for student use. The mainframes are a DEC VAX 11/750 and an AT&T 3B2/500. There are also some 175 Macintosh and AT&T microcomputers available with software provided. All students may access the system. It may be used Monday through Friday, 7 A.M. to 11 P.M. and Saturday and Sunday, noon to 10 P.M. There are no time limits and no fees.

Graduates: In 1992-93 600 bachelor's degrees were awarded. The most popular majors among graduates were business administration (25%), English (12%), and humanities (10%). Within an average freshman class, 40% graduate in 4 years and 80% in 5 years. Some 60 companies recruited on campus in 1992-93. In a graduating class in an earlier year, 30% of the students were enrolled in graduate school within 6 months of graduation.

Admissions Contact: Dean Garland, Director of Admission.

MESA STATE COLLEGE
A-2

Grand Junction, CO 81502

(303) 248-1875
(800) 982-MESA (in-state)

Full-time: 1585 men, 1869 women	Faculty: 154; IIB, -$
Part-time: 414 men, 732 women	Ph.D.s: 50%
Graduate: none	Student/Faculty: 22 to 1
Year: semesters, summer session	Tuition: $1754 ($4946)
Application Deadline: August 1	Room & Board: $3373
Freshman Class: 1900 applied, 1900 accepted, 1125 enrolled	
SAT I Verbal/Math: 407/439	ACT: 19 NONCOMPETITIVE

Mesa State College, founded in 1925, is a public, coeducational institution offering undergraduate programs in liberal arts, sciences, business, and professional areas. There are 3 undergraduate schools. In addition to regional accreditation, Mesa State has baccalaureate program accreditation with CAHEA and NLN. The library contains 168,593 volumes, 510,728 microform items, 24,570 audiovisual forms, and subscribes to 1204 periodicals. Computerized library sources and services include the card catalog, interlibrary loans, and database searching. Special learning facilities include a learning resource center, art gallery, radio station, and a TV studio. The 42-acre campus is in a small town 250 miles west of Denver. Including residence halls, there are 25 buildings on campus.

Student Life: About 92% of undergraduates are from Colorado. Students come from 20 states, 30 foreign countries, and Canada. Eighty-five percent are white. The average age of freshmen is 21; all undergraduates, 26.

Housing: A total of 722 students can be accommodated in college housing. College-sponsored living facilities include coed dormitories and on-campus apartments. On-campus housing is available on a first-come, first-served basis. Eighty-four percent of students commute. Alcohol is not permitted. All students may keep cars on campus.

Activities: There are no fraternities or sororities on campus. There are 50 groups on campus, including art, cheerleading, choir, chorus, computers, dance, ethnic, honors, international, jazz band, literary magazine, musical theater, newspaper, political, professional, radio and TV, religious, social, social service, and student government.

Sports: There are 4 intercollegiate sports for men and 5 for women, and 14 intramural sports for men and 14 for women. Athletic and recreation facilities include a weight room, tennis courts, and a swimming pool.

Disabled Students: Ninety-five percent of the campus is accessible to disabled students. The following facilities are available: wheelchair ramps, elevators, special parking, specially equipped rest rooms, special class scheduling, lowered drinking fountains, and lowered telephones.

Services: In addition to many counseling and information services, tutoring is available in every subject except accounting. There is also a reader service for the blind, and remedial math, reading, and writing.

Campus Safety and Security: Campus safety and security measures include 24-hour foot and vehicle patrol, self-defense education, escort service, and informal discussions. In addition, there are pamphlets, posters, films, lighted pathways, and sidewalks, a crime watch program, an emergency contact service, and first-aid and CPR courses.

Programs of Study: Mesa State awards the B.A., B.S., B.B.A., and B.S.N. degrees. Associate degrees also are awarded. Bachelor's degrees are awarded in BIOLOGICAL SCIENCE (biology/biological science), BUSINESS (accounting, banking and finance, business administration and management, business economics, management information systems, marketing/retailing/merchandising, personnel management, and recreation and leisure services), COMMUNICATIONS AND THE ARTS (communications, dramatic arts, English, fine arts, mass communications, and music), COMPUTER AND PHYSICAL SCIENCE (computer science, geology, mathematics, and physics), EDUCATION (science and secondary), ENGINEERING AND ENVIRONMENTAL DESIGN (environmental engineering technology and environmental management/waste management), HEALTH PROFESSIONS (nursing), SOCIAL SCIENCE (anthropology, economics, history, human services, liberal arts/general studies, parks and recreation management, political science/government, psychology, social science, and sociology). Nursing and allied health, and natural science and mathematics are the strongest academically. Business, natural science, and mathematics have the largest enrollments.

Required: To graduate, students must complete a minimum of 124 credits, with 40 hours in upper-level courses in the emphasis area and a minimum GPA of 2.0. All students must take English 111 and 112 as well as 40 to 44 hours of general education courses and 4 hours of physical education. A comprehensive exam is required.

Special: Mesa State offers internships in many of its programs, including one in the state legislature, a Washington semester, work-study programs, student-designed majors in selected studies, and the B.A.-B.S. degree in several majors. Nondegree study for students over 20 years of age and credit for life, military, and work experience are available. There is a freshman honors program on campus, as well as 8 national honor societies. Seven departments have honors programs.

Faculty/Classroom: Seventy-nine percent of faculty are male; 21%, female. All teach undergraduates. The average class size in an introductory lecture is 30; in a laboratory, 20; and in a regular course offering, 30.

Admissions: All of the 1993–94 applicants were accepted.

Requirements: Mesa State requires applicants to be in the upper 75% of their class. A minimum GPA of 2.5 is required. The SAT I or ACT is required with a minimum composite score of 810 on the SAT I or 19 on the ACT. Applicants must be graduates of an accredited secondary school or hold the GED. The college prefers that students complete 4 years of high school English, 3 each of mathematics, science, and social studies, 2 of foreign language and 1 of history. An essay, an interview, and an audition for some classes are recommended. AP and CLEP credits are accepted. Important factors used in the admissions decision are recommendations by school officials, personality, intangible qualities, evidence of special talents, parents or siblings attending the school, and leadership record.

Procedure: Freshmen are admitted to all sessions. Entrance exams should be taken late in the junior year or early in the senior year. Applications should be filed by August 1 for fall entry and December 1 for spring entry, along with an application fee of $20. The college accepts all applicants. Notification is sent on a rolling basis within 2 weeks after receipt of application. There is a deffered admissions plan.

Transfer: About 690 transfer students enrolled in 1993–94. Applicants for transfer must have a minimum GPA of 2.0 with 30 semester hours; otherwise, they must meet the criteria for entering freshmen. A total of 28 credits out of 124 must be completed at Mesa State.

Visiting: There are regularly scheduled orientations for prospective students, including advising sessions. There are guides for informal visits and visitors may sit in on classes and stay overnight at the school. To arrange for a visit, contact the Admissions Office at (800) 982-MESA (in-state) or (303) 248–1875 (out-of-state).

Financial Aid: In an earlier year 65% of all current freshmen and 72% of continuing students received some form of financial aid. Scholarships or need-based grants averaged $700 ($1326 maximum); loans averaged $2000 ($2625 maximum); and work contracts averaged $1200 (maximum). The FFS is required. The deadline for financial aid applications is May 1.

International Students: There are currently 84 international students enrolled. They must take the TOEFL, and achieve a minimum score of 525, the University of Michigan Language Test, or the Comprehensive English Language Test. The student must also take the SAT I and achieve a minimum score of 810 or the ACT with a composite score of 19.

Computers: The college provides computer facilities for student use. The mainframe is a DEC VAX. All students may access the system. There are no time limits on using the system. The fees are $13 a semester.

Graduates: In a recent year 379 bachelor's degrees were awarded. The most popular majors among graduates were business and management (28%), public affairs and services (10%), and health professions (10%).

Admissions Contact: Director of Admissions.

METROPOLITAN STATE COLLEGE OF DENVER

Denver, CO 80217–3362
C-2
(303) 556–3058

Full-time: 4608 men, 4877 women	Faculty: 394; IIB, av$
Part-time: 3616 men, 4419 women	Ph.Ds: 75%
Graduate: none	Student/Faculty: 24 to 1
Year: semesters, summer session	Tuition: $1751 ($6047)
Application Deadline: August 1	Room & Board: n/app
Freshman Class: 4919 applied, 4242 accepted, 2359 enrolled	
SAT I: 404/439	ACT: 19 NONCOMPETITIVE

Metropolitan State College, founded in 1963, is a public, nonresidential institution, offering degree programs in the liberal arts and sciences, business, and professional studies. There are 3 undergraduate schools. In addition to regional accreditation, Metro State has baccalaureate program accreditation with ABET, AUPHA, NASM, NCATE, NLN, and NRPA. The library contains 699,976 volumes, 644,956 microform items, and 16,460 audiovisual forms, and subscribes to 3349 periodicals. Computerized library sources and services include the card catalog, interlibrary loans, and database searching. Special learning facilities include a learning resource center, art gallery, and flight simulator. The 169-acre campus is in an urban area in Denver. There are 38 buildings on campus.

Student Life: About 98% of undergraduates are from Colorado. Students come from 25 states, 80 foreign countries, and Canada. Ninety-eight percent are from public schools; 2% from private. Seventy-seven percent are white; 10% African American. The average age of freshmen is 23.6; all undergraduates, 27.4. Forty-one percent drop out by the end of their first year.

Housing: There are no residence halls. All students may keep cars on campus.

Activities: There are no fraternities or sororities on campus. There are 80 groups on campus, including art, band, cheerleading, chess, choir, chorus, computers, drama, ethnic, gay, honors, international, jazz band, literary magazine, newspaper, political, professional, radio and TV, religious, social, social service, student government, and symphony. Popular campus events include Club Day, World Friendship Festival, and Family Night.

Sports: There are 5 intercollegiate sports for men and 5 for women, and 22 intramural sports for men and 22 for women. Athletic and recreation facilities include playing fields, volleyball, basketball, badminton, racquetball, handball, squash, and tennis courts, a swimming pool, a dance studio, a weight room, a fitness center and green room, a 3500-seat events center, an auxiliary gymnasium, and a 400-meter track.

Disabled Students: The entire campus is accessible to disabled students. The following facilities are available: wheelchair ramps, elevators, special parking, specially equipped rest rooms, special class scheduling, and lowered drinking fountains and telephones, as well as telephones, tapes, and classroom aids for the hearing impaired.

Services: In addition to many counseling and information services, tutoring is available in most subjects. There is a reader service for the blind. ESL services and an adult learning services office are available.

Campus Safety and Security: Campus safety and security measures include 24-hour foot and vehicle patrol, self defense education, escort service, and shuttle buses. In addition, there are informal discussions, pamphlets, posters, films, emergency telephones, and lighted pathways and sidewalks.

Programs of Study: Metro State awards the B.A., B.S., and B.F.A. degrees. Bachelor's degrees are awarded in BIOLOGICAL SCIENCE (biology/biological science), BUSINESS (accounting, banking and finance, hospitality management services, management science, marketing/retailing/merchandising, and recreation and leisure services), COMMUNICATIONS AND THE ARTS (art, communications, English, fine arts, industrial design, journalism, modern language, music performance, and Spanish), COMPUTER AND PHYSICAL SCIENCE (atmospheric sciences and meteorology, chemistry, computer management, computer science, information sciences and systems, mathematics, and physics), EDUCATION (music and physical), ENGINEERING AND ENVIRONMENTAL DESIGN (airline piloting and navigation, aviation management, aviation technology, civil engineering technology, electrical/electronics engineering technology, industrial administration/management, industrial engineering technology, land use management and reclamation, mechanical engineering technology, and surveying engineering), HEALTH PROFESSIONS (health care administration and nursing), SOCIAL SCIENCE (African American studies, anthropology, behavioral science, criminal justice, eco-

nomics, history, human services, Mexican-American/Chicano studies, philosophy, political science/government, psychology, social work, sociology, and urban studies). Accounting, management, and psychology have the largest enrollments.

Required: To graduate, students must complete at least 120 credit hours, 40 of which must be upper division, and 30 in the major, with a minimum overall GPA of 2.0. There are 3 levels of general education requirements, totaling 36 hours and including a multicultural requirement.

Special: The university offers co-op programs with a consortium of state colleges and the University of Colorado at Denver. Internships, study abroad, work-study programs, B.A.-B.S. degrees, dual and student-designed majors, nondegree study, and pass/fail options are available. There is a freshman honors program on campus, as well as 12 national honor societies.

Faculty/Classroom: Sixty percent of faculty are male; 40%, female. All teach undergraduates. The average class size in a laboratory is 12.

Admissions: About 86% of the 1993–94 applicants were accepted. The SAT scores for the 1993–94 freshman class were as follows: Verbal—84% below 500, 13% between 500 and 599, and 2% between 600 and 700; Math—70% below 500, 21% between 500 and 599, 8% between 600 and 700, and 1% above 700. The ACT scores were 67% below 21, 21% between 21 and 23, 9% between 24 and 26, 2% between 27 and 28, and 1% above 28. About 21% of the current freshmen were in the top fifth of their class; 20% were in the top two fifths.

Requirements: The SAT I or the ACT (preferred) is required. Applicants should be graduates of an accredited secondary school or have a GED certificate. They should have completed 15 Carnegie units. AP and CLEP credits are accepted. Important factors used in the admissions decision are recommendations by school officials, extracurricular activities record, evidence of special talent, advanced placement or honor courses, and ability to finance college education.

Procedure: Freshmen are admitted to all sessions. Entrance exams should be taken prior to application. Applications should be filed by August 1 for fall entry, December 1 for spring entry, and May 1 for summer entry, along with an application fee of $25. The college has a modified open admissions policy. Notification is sent on a rolling basis. There is an early admissions plan.

Transfer: About 2061 transfer students enrolled in 1993–94. Applicants for transfer must have a 2.0 GPA and be in good standing in their previous school. Some probationary transfers are considered. A total of 30 credits out of 120 must be completed at Metro State.

Visiting: There are regularly scheduled orientations for prospective students. There are guides for informal visits, and visitors may sit in on classes. To arrange for a visit, contact Paul Cesare, Office of Admissions and Records, at (303) 556–3994.

Financial Aid: Six percent of undergraduate students work part-time. Metro State is a member of CSS. The Singlefile Form is preferred, but the FAF is accepted. The deadline for financial aid applications is March 1.

International Students: There are currently 156 international students enrolled. They must take the TOEFL and achieve a minimum score of 500.

Computers: The college provides computer facilities for student use. A VAX and an HP minicomputer are available. There are 12 student laboratories located in 5 buildings on campus and 2 at off-campus locations; most on-campus laboratories are on a LAN system. There are 25 terminals, 150 DOS machines, about 80 Apple Macintoshes, and 22 NEXT (UNIX-based) computers. All students may access the system. Laboratories are open 75 hours a week, and call-up lines are available 24 hours a day. Students may access the system 1.5 hours per session on terminals (VAX/HP access), with unlimited access to PCs unless other students are waiting (then there is a 1-hour limit). The fees are $16 per semester.

Graduates: In 1992–93 1962 bachelor's degrees were awarded. The most popular majors among graduates were accounting (7%), psychology (6%), and management (6%). Within an average freshman class, 4% graduate in 4 years, 11% in 5 years, and 16% in 6 years. Some 60 to 80 companies recruited on campus in 1992–93.

Admissions Contact: Office of Admissions and Records.

REGIS COLLEGE OF REGIS UNIVERSITY
(See Regis University)

REGIS UNIVERSITY
(Formerly Regis College of Regis University)
Denver, CO 80221–1099

C-2

(303) 458–4900; (800) 388–2366

Full-time: 473 men, 669 women	Faculty: 70; IIB, av$
Part-time: 10 men, 17 women	Ph.D.s: 90%
Graduate: n/av	Student/Faculty: 16 to 1
Year: semesters, summer session	Tuition: $11,840
Application Deadline: open	Room & Board: $5500
Freshman Class: 950 applied, 904 accepted, 307 enrolled	
SAT I: 480/425	ACT: 21

COMPETITIVE

Regis University, founded in 1877, is a coeducational, private, Roman Catholic liberal arts institution operated by the Jesuits. There is one graduate school. In addition to regional accreditation, Regis has baccalaureate program accreditation with CAHEA, NCATE, and NLN. The library contains 246,839 volumes, 86,273 microform items, and 112,240 audiovisual forms, and subscribes to 2232 periodicals. Computerized library sources and services include the card catalog, interlibrary loans, and database searching. Special learning facilities include a learning resource center and radio station. The 90-acre campus is in a suburban area of Denver. Including residence halls, there are 12 buildings on campus.

Student Life: About 59% of undergraduates are from Colorado. Students come from 43 states and 11 foreign countries. Sixty-one percent are from public schools; 39% from private. Eighty-four percent are white. Fifty-four percent are Catholic; 31% Buddhist, Greek Orthodox, Islamic, and unknown; 13% Protestant. The average age of freshmen is 18; all undergraduates, 20. Thirty-eight percent drop out by the end of their first year; 22% remain to graduate.

Housing: A total of 600 students can be accommodated in college housing. College-sponsored living facilities include single-sex and coed dormitories. In addition, there are special interest houses. On-campus housing is guaranteed for all 4 years. Fifty percent of students live on campus; of those, 50% remain on campus on weekends. Alcohol is not permitted. All students may keep cars on campus.

Activities: There are no fraternities or sororities on campus. There are many groups on campus, including band, cheerleading, choir, chorus, computers, dance, drama, drill team, ethnic, honors, international, literary magazine, newspaper, photography, political, professional, radio and TV, religious, social, social service, student government, and yearbook. Popular campus events include Fall Frolic, Ranger Week, Hall Olympics, spring break trip, Thanksgiving ski trip, and Wake-up Week.

Sports: There are 5 intercollegiate sports for men and 5 for women, and 5 intramural sports for men and 5 for women. Athletic and recreation facilities include a 2800-seat gymnasium, a pool, tennis courts, and playing fields.

Disabled Students: Forty percent of the campus is accessible to disabled students. The following facilities are available: wheelchair ramps, elevators, special parking, specially equipped rest rooms, special class scheduling, lowered drinking fountains, and lowered telephones.

Services: In addition to many counseling and information services, tutoring is available in every subject.

Campus Safety and Security: Campus safety and security measures include 24-hour foot and vehicle patrol, self defense education, escort service, and pamphlets, posters, and films. In addition, there are lighted pathways and sidewalks.

Programs of Study: Regis awards the B.A., B.S., and B.S.N. degrees. Master's degrees also are awarded. Bachelor's degrees are awarded in BIOLOGICAL SCIENCE (biology/biological science), BUSINESS (accounting, business administration and management, business economics, international business management, and marketing/retailing/merchandising), COMMUNICATIONS AND THE ARTS (communications, English, French, and Spanish), COMPUTER AND PHYSICAL SCIENCE (chemistry, computer science, and mathematics), ENGINEERING AND ENVIRONMENTAL DESIGN (engineering), HEALTH PROFESSIONS (medical records administration/services and nursing), SOCIAL SCIENCE (economics, history, philosophy, political science/government, prelaw, psychology, religion, and sociology). Business has the largest enrollment.

Required: Students must complete 128 credit hours with a minimum GPA of 2.0. Required courses include 12 hours of college core seminars, 7 to 8 of mathematics and natural science, 6 of literature/humanities, social science, religious studies, and philosophy, and 3 each of economics, communication arts, and fine arts.

Special: Cross-registration is possible with Denver University and Metropolitan State. Internships, study abroad, and work-study programs with Regis are available. The college offers B.A.-B.S. degrees, dual and student-designed majors, a 3–2 engineering degree with Washington University, and pass/fail options. There is a freshman honors program on campus, as well as 1 national honor society.

Faculty/Classroom: Sixty-three percent of faculty are male; 37%, female. All faculty both teach and do research. The average class size in an introductory lecture is 30; in a laboratory, 15; and in a regular course offering, 30.

Admissions: About 95% of the 1993–94 applicants were accepted. The SAT scores for the 1993–94 freshman class were as follows: Verbal—76% below 500, 16% between 500 and 599, 6% between 600 and 700, and 2% above 700; Math—56% below 500, 31% between 500 and 599, 11% between 600 and 700, and 3% above 700. The ACT scores were 40% below 21, 29% between 21 and 23, 19% between 24 and 26, 7% between 27 and 28, and 4% above 28.

Requirements: A minimum GPA of 2.0 is required. The SAT I or ACT is required. Applicants should be graduates of an accredited secondary school. The GED is accepted. Students should have completed 16 high school academic credits, including 4 years of English, 3 each of mathematics, science, and history, 2 of a foreign language, and 1 to 2 of social studies. A recommendation from the high school counselor and an essay are required. An interview is recommended. AP and CLEP credits are accepted. Important factors used in the admissions decision are advanced placement or honor courses, leadership record, recommendations by school officials, extracurricular activities record, and personality, intangible qualities.

Procedure: Freshmen are admitted fall and spring. Entrance exams should be taken in the fall. Application deadlines are open. The fee is $35. Notification is sent on a rolling basis. There is a deferred admissions plan. A waiting list is an active part of the admissions procedure, with about 3% of applicants on the list.

Transfer: About 139 transfer students enrolled in 1993–94. Transfer applicants must have a GPA of 2.5. All previous college work is considered. The college reviews each applicant individually. A total of 30 credits out of 128 must be completed at Regis.

Visiting: There are guides for informal visits, and visitors may sit in on classes and stay overnight at the school. To arrange for a visit, contact the Admissions Office at (800) 388–2366 or (303) 458–4900.

Financial Aid: In a recent year, 68% of all current freshmen and 73% of continuing students received some form of financial aid. About 51% of freshmen and 43% of continuing students received need-based aid. The average freshman award was $8445. Of that total, scholarships or need-based grants averaged $3500 ($8000 maximum); loans averaged $2945 ($6000 maximum); and work contracts averaged $2000 ($2400 maximum). Forty percent of undergraduate students work part-time. Average earnings from campus work for the school year are $1500. The average financial indebtedness of the a recent year's graduate was $14,980. Regis is a member of CSS. The FAF or FFS and the college's own financial statement are required. The deadline for financial aid applications is March 15.

International Students: International students must take the TOEFL or the University of Michigan Language Test and achieve a minimum score on the TOEFL of 550.

Computers: The college provides computer facilities for student use. The mainframe is a DEC VAX 11/785. The mainframe and networked microcomputer systems are available 24 hours a day in the computer laboratories in Carroll Hall. All students may access the system. There are no time limits on using the system and no fees.

Graduates: In a recent year, 244 bachelor's degrees were awarded. The most popular majors among graduates were business administration (23%), communications (11%), and mathematics (9%). Some 45 companies recruited on campus in a recent year.

Admissions Contact: Robert G. Blust, Director of Admissions.

UNITED STATES AIR FORCE ACADEMY D-3
USAFA, CO 80840–5025 (719) 472–2520

Full-time: 3687 men, 549 women	Faculty: 517
Part-time: none	Ph.D.s: 40%
Graduate: none	Student/Faculty: 8 to 1
Year: semesters, summer session	Room & Board: n/app
Application Deadline: January 31	

Freshman Class: 9500 applied, 1605 accepted, 1160 enrolled
SAT I: 569/663 ACT: 27 **MOST COMPETITIVE**

The United States Air Force Academy, the newest of the United States service academies, was founded in 1954 and is a public, coeducational undergraduate institution. Graduates receive the B.S. degree and a second lieutenant's commission in the regular Air Force. In addition to regional accreditation, USAFA has baccalaureate program accreditation with ABET. The 3 libraries contain 601,000 volumes, 495,000 microform items, and 5200 audiovisual forms, and subscribe to 3900 periodicals. Computerized library sources and services include the card catalog, interlibrary loans, and database searching. Special learning facilities include a learning resource center, art gallery, planetarium, radio station, and TV station. The 18,000-acre campus is in a suburban area 50 miles south of Denver and 10 miles North of Colorado Springs. Including residence halls, there are 14 buildings on campus.

Student Life: About 4% of undergraduates are from Colorado. Students come from 50 states. Seventy percent are from public schools. Eighty-three percent are white. Fifty-six percent are Protestant; 40% Catholic. The average age of freshmen is 18.5; all undergraduates, 20.5. Fifteen percent drop out by the end of their first year; 70% remain to graduate.

Housing: A total of 4400 students can be accommodated in college housing. College-sponsored living facilities include coed dormitories. On-campus housing is guaranteed for all 4 years. All students live on campus and remain on weekends. Alcohol is not permitted. Upperclassmen may keep cars on campus.

Activities: There are no fraternities or sororities on campus. There are many groups and organizations on campus, including cheerleading, chorale, chorus, drama, drill team, drum and bugle corps, ethnic, marching band, musical theater, newspaper, professional, radio and TV, religious, student government, and yearbook.

Sports: There are 16 intercollegiate sports for men and 10 for women, and 16 intramural sports for men and 13 for women. Athletic and recreation facilities include a 47,000-seat stadium, a cadet gymnasium, a field house, and 143 acres of athletic facilities and recreational areas.

Services: In addition to many counseling and information services, tutoring is available in every subject, including studying techniques and English as a second language. There is remedial math, reading, and writing.

Campus Safety and Security: Campus safety and security measures include 24-hour foot and vehicle patrol, self defense education, informal discussions, and pamphlets, posters, and films. In addition, there are emergency telephones and lighted pathways and sidewalks.

Programs of Study: USAFA awards the B.S. degree. Bachelor's degrees are awarded in BIOLOGICAL SCIENCE (biology/biological science), BUSINESS (management science and operations research), COMMUNICATIONS AND THE ARTS (English), COMPUTER AND PHYSICAL SCIENCE (chemistry, computer science, mathematics, physics, and science), ENGINEERING AND ENVIRONMENTAL DESIGN (aeronautical engineering, civil engineering, computer engineering, electrical/electronics engineering, and engineering and applied science), SOCIAL SCIENCE (behavioral science, economics, geography, history, humanities, political science/government, psychology, and social science).

Required: Cadets must complete the requirements for the core curriculum and for an academic major or the bachelor of science program. They must be proficient in physical education and military training, and demonstrate an aptitude for commissioned service and leadership. A total of 173 semester hours are required, with a minimum GPA of 2.0, to graduate.

Special: All cadets receive orientation flights in Air Force aircraft and take aviation science courses. A semester exchange program is available with the French Air Force Academy and U.S. Army, Naval, and Coast Guard Academies. Freshman classes start in June, and basic cadet training must be completed before academics begin in August.

Faculty/Classroom: All teach undergraduates.

Admissions: About 17% of the 1993–94 applicants were accepted. The SAT I scores for the 1993–94 freshman class were as follows: Verbal—7% below 500, 61% between 500 and 599, 31% between 600 and 700, and 1% above 700; Math—15% between 500 and 599, 61% between 600 and 700, and 24% above 700. The ACT scores were 2% below 21, 4% between 21 and 23, 34% between 24 and 26, 27% between 27 and 28, and 33% above 28. About 90% of the current freshmen were in the top fifth of their class; all were in the top two fifths. There were 43 National Merit finalists and 23 semifinalists. Nearly 120 freshmen graduated first in their class.

Requirements: USAFA requires applicants to be in the upper 10% of their class. A minimum GPA of 3.8 is required. The SAT, with a score of 500 verbal and 550 mathematics, or the ACT, with a score of 24 each in English and reading and 25 each in science and mathematics, is required. Candidates must be American citizens in good physical condition, unmarried and with no dependents, and between 17 and 22 years of age. Nomination from a legal source is required. Students should have completed 4 years each of high school English, mathematics and science, and 2 of a foreign language. An essay, an interview, a physical fitness test, and a medical exam are required. AP credits are accepted. Important factors used in the admissions decision are leadership record, advanced placement or honor courses, extracurricular activities record, and evidence of special talent.

Procedure: Freshmen are admitted in the fall. Entrance exams should be taken in the junior year. Applications should be filed by January 31 for fall entry. Notification is sent on a rolling basis.

Transfer: About 120 transfer students enrolled in 1993–94. All students must enter as freshmen and attend 4 years. A total of 173 credits out of 173 must be completed at USAFA.

Visiting: There are regularly scheduled orientations for prospective students, consisting of 2-day orientations held in March and April. Students are given briefings by the superintendent, commandant of cadets, dean of cadets, and director of athletics. Students stay overnight in the dormitories and shadow their escort cadets the second day, attending classes, training, and meals. There are guides for informal visits. To arrange for a visit, contact the Special Projects Office at (719) 472–2233.

International Students: There are currently 40 international students enrolled. They must take the SAT I or the ACT.

Computers: The college provides computer facilities for student use. The mainframe is a Gould, a DEC VAX, and a UNIVAC. All cadets reimburse the academy for an IBM-compatible microcomputer upon entry. These microcomputers are all networked to the mainframe and to laser printers. All students may access the system. It may be used from 7:30 A.M. to 11 P.M. There are no time limits on using the system and no fees.

Graduates: In 1992–93 960 bachelor's degrees were awarded. The most popular majors among graduates were engineering (24%), social science (23%), and physical science (13%). Within an average freshman class, 75% graduate in 4 years. In the 1992 graduating class, 4% of the men and 1% of the women were enrolled in graduate school within 6 months of graduation.

Admissions Contact: Lt Col Danny L. Moore, Director of Admissions/Selections.

UNIVERSITY OF COLORADO

The University of Colorado, established in 1876, is a public system in Colorado. It is governed by a board of regents, whose chief administrator is the president. The primary goal of the system is comprehensive research. The main priorities are research, teaching, and public service. The total enrollment of all campuses is usually about 41,000, with 4500 faculty members. Profiles of the 4-year campuses in Boulder, Colorado Springs, and Denver are included in this chapter.

UNIVERSITY OF COLORADO AT BOULDER   C-2
Boulder, CO 80309–0030   (303) 492-6301

Full-time: 9842 men, 8623 women	Faculty: 898; I, av$
Part-time: 796 men, 745 women	Ph.D.s: 91%
Graduate: 2938 men, 2069 women	Student/Faculty: 21 to 1
Year: semesters, summer session	Tuition: $2580 ($12,086)
Application Deadline: February 15	Room & Board: $3830
Freshman Class: 14,063 applied, 9320 accepted, 3436 enrolled	
SAT I or ACT: required	**VERY COMPETITIVE**

The University of Colorado at Boulder, established in 1876, is a public institution offering programs in arts and sciences, business, engineering, architecture and planning, music, education, and journalism. There are 7 undergraduate and 3 graduate schools. In addition to regional accreditation, CU-Boulder has baccalaureate program accreditation with AACSB, ABET, ACEJMC, NASM, and NCATE. The 7 libraries contain 2,504,405 volumes, 4,864,772 microform items, and 50,000 audiovisual forms, and subscribe to 27,727 periodicals. Computerized library sources and services include the card catalog, interlibrary loans, and database searching. Special learning facilities include a learning resource center, art gallery, natural history museum, planetarium, radio station, and TV station. The 600-acre campus is in a suburban area 30 miles northwest of Denver. Including residence halls, there are 150 buildings on campus.

Student Life: About 67% of undergraduates are from Colorado. Students come from 52 states, 90 foreign countries, and Canada. Eighty-one percent are white. The average age of freshmen is 18; all undergraduates, 21.2. Twenty percent drop out by the end of their first year; 59% remain to graduate.

Housing: A total of 6100 students can be accommodated in college housing. College-sponsored living facilities include coed dormitories, on-campus apartments, and married-student housing. In addition there are honors houses, special interest houses, and a residential program that includes housing. On-campus housing is available on a first-come, first-served basis and is available on a lottery system for upperclassmen. All students may keep cars on campus.

Activities: About 15% of men belong to 26 national fraternities; about 16% of women belong to 14 national sororities. There are 351 groups on campus, including art, band, cheerleading, chess, choir, chorale, chorus, computers, dance, drama, drill team, ethnic, film, gay, honors, international, jazz band, literary magazine, marching band, musical theater, newspaper, opera, orchestra, pep band, photography, political, professional, radio and TV, religious, social, social service, student government, symphony, and yearbook. Popular campus events include World Affairs Conference, International Women's Week, Black History Month, Native American Week, Cinco de Mayo, Trivia Bowl, and the University's Artists Series.

Sports: There are 7 intercollegiate sports for men and 6 for women, and 20 intramural sports for men and 20 for women. Athletic and recreation facilities include a 52,000-seat stadium and an 8700-seat events center, a recreation center that includes an 8-lane swimming pool, diving pool, ice rink, handball and racquetball courts, basketball and squash courts, outdoor tennis courts, weight-training rooms, and an indoor running track.

Disabled Students: Eighty-five percent of the campus is accessible to disabled students. The following facilities are available: wheelchair ramps, elevators, special parking, specially equipped rest rooms, special class scheduling, and lowered drinking fountains. There are also assisted classroom listening devices, and TTY, TDD, TT phone support systems.

Services: In addition to many counseling and information services, tutoring is available in most subjects. There is a learning disabilities program and an interpreter for the deaf (curricular and non-

curricular). In addition, there is a reader service for the blind, and remedial math, reading, and writing. There is also a Multicultural Center for Counseling.

Campus Safety and Security: Campus safety and security measures include 24-hour foot and vehicle patrol, self defense education, escort service, and shuttle buses. In addition, there are informal discussions, pamphlets, posters, and films, emergency telephones, and lighted pathways and sidewalks. Campus police are academy-trained and commissioned officers of the Boulder police force.

Programs of Study: CU-Boulder awards the B.A., B.S., B.Env.D., B.F.A., B.Mus., and B.Mus.Ed. degrees. Master's and doctoral degrees also are awarded. Bachelor's degrees are awarded in BIOLOGICAL SCIENCE (biochemistry, cell biology, environmental biology, and molecular biology), BUSINESS (business administration and management and personnel management), COMMUNICATIONS AND THE ARTS (advertising, art history and appreciation, broadcasting, Chinese, classics, communications, dance, dramatic arts, English, film arts, fine arts, French, German, Italian, Japanese, journalism, linguistics, music, Russian, Spanish, and studio art), COMPUTER AND PHYSICAL SCIENCE (applied mathematics, chemistry, computer science, geology, mathematics, and physics), EDUCATION (art, foreign languages, middle school, and music), ENGINEERING AND ENVIRONMENTAL DESIGN (aeronautical engineering, architectural engineering, chemical engineering, civil engineering, computer engineering, electrical/electronics engineering, engineering, engineering physics, environmental design, environmental science, and mechanical engineering), HEALTH PROFESSIONS (pharmacy and speech pathology/audiology), SOCIAL SCIENCE (African American studies, American studies, anthropology, Asian/Oriental studies, Eastern European studies, economics, geography, history, humanities, interdisciplinary studies, international relations, Latin American studies, philosophy, physical fitness/movement, political science/government, psychology, religion, sociology, and women's studies). Engineering, biological sciences, chemistry, biochemistry, astrophysics, music, and space sciences are the strongest academically. Psychology; environmental, population, and organismic biology; English; kinesiology; and molecular, cellular, and developmental biology have the largest enrollments.

Required: For graduation, students must complete at least 120 credits, including a minimum of 30 in the major. A GPA of at least 2.0 is required. Other requirements vary by undergraduate college.

Special: The summer session includes a creative arts festival. The Sewall and the Farrand residential programs for freshmen and sophomores both offer a small liberal arts college atmosphere, while taking advantage of the resources of a major university. A new residential program in Williams Village offers courses in the environmental sciences. Student-designed and dual majors, study abroad in 43 countries, internships, a Washington semester, 5-year B.A.-B.S. degrees, and cooperative programs in engineering are available. Concurrent registration with other University of Colorado campuses is available. There is a freshman honors program on campus, as well as 19 national honor societies, including Phi Beta Kappa. Eleven departments have honors programs.

Faculty/Classroom: Seventy-four percent of faculty are male; 26%, female. Graduate students teach 19% of introductory courses. The average class size in an introductory lecture is 40; in a laboratory, 18; and in a regular course offering, 35.

Admissions: About 66% of the 1993–94 applicants were accepted. The SAT scores for the 1993–94 freshman class were as follows: Verbal—48% below 500, 40% between 500 and 599, and 11% between 600 and 700; Math—19% below 500, 38% between 500 and 599, 33% between 600 and 700, and 9% above 700. The ACT scores were 11% below 21, 24% between 21 and 23, 32% between 24 and 26, 18% between 27 and 28, and 16% above 28. About 54% of the current freshmen were in the top fifth of their class; 87% were in the top two fifths. A total of 83 freshmen graduated first in their class.

Requirements: The SAT I or ACT is required. Applicants must have completed 16 credits of high school work as identified by the University of Colorado Minimum Academic Preparation Standards. Students are asked to write a personal statement. Interviews are not used in the decision-making process. Auditions are required for consideration to the College of Music. Portfolios are discouraged. Students with a GED are considered on an individual basis. AP and CLEP credits are accepted. Important factors used in the admissions decision are advanced placement or honor courses, leadership record, geographic diversity, recommendations by school officials, and personality, intangible qualities.

Procedure: Freshmen are admitted to all sessions. Entrance exams should be taken no later than December of the senior year. Applications should be filed by February 15 for fall entry, November 1 for spring entry, and February 15 for summer entry, along with an application fee of $40. Notification is sent on a rolling basis beginning November 1. There is a deferred admissions plan. A waiting list is an active part of the admissions procedure.

Transfer: A total of 1756 transfer students enrolled in 1993–94. All applicants must submit a high school transcript. Students who have completed fewer than 30 semester hours must also submit SAT I or ACT results. A total of 30 credits out of 120 to 128 must be completed at CU-Boulder.

Visiting: There are regularly scheduled orientations for prospective students, including advising, placement testing, registration, social and campus orientation, and meetings with college deans and faculty. Parents are invited also. There are guides for informal visits and visitors may sit in on classes. To arrange for a visit, contact Admissions/Campus Visit Programs at (303) 492–6301.

Financial Aid: In 1993–94, 50% of all current freshmen and 41% of continuing students received some form of financial aid. About 32% of freshmen and 29% of continuing students received need-based aid. The average freshman award was $8602. Of that total, scholarships or need-based grants averaged $2404 ($6300 maximum); loans averaged $4476 ($6620 maximum); and work contracts averaged $1727 ($2500 maximum). Average earnings from campus work for the school year are $1827. The average financial indebtedness of the 1992–93 graduate was $14,310. CU-Boulder is a member of CSS. The FAFSA financial statement is required. The priority deadline for financial aid applications is April 1.

International Students: There are currently 1054 international students enrolled. They must take the TOEFL or the University of Michigan Language Test and achieve a minimum score on the TOEFL of 500. The student must also take the SAT I or the ACT.

Computers: The university provides computer facilities for student use. The mainframes are a DEC station 5000/2405, an IBM RS/6000, a Powerserver 370 and 550, and a DEC VAX cluster including Model 6430 and 6510 computers. More than 820 public access terminal/microcomputers are available in the computer laboratory, classroom buildings, dormitories, and libraries. All student rooms have a port to connect to the INS wide area network. The university also has Internet access. All students may access the system 24 hours per day. There are no time limits on using the system. There is a computing fee of $10 per semester.

Graduates: In 1992–93, 4387 bachelor's degrees were awarded. The most popular majors among graduates were business (17%), psychology (8%), and English (7%). Within an average freshman class, 33% graduate in 4 years, 60% in 5 years, and 66% in 6 years. Some 296 companies recruited on campus in 1992–93.

Admissions Contact: Admissions Office.

UNIVERSITY OF COLORADO AT COLORADO SPRINGS

D-3

Colorado Springs, CO 80933–7150   (719) 593–3383

Full-time: 1112 men, 1458 women	Faculty: 193; IIA, av$
Part-time: 631 men, 938 women	Ph.D.s: 90%
Graduate: 805 men, 780 women	Student/Faculty: 13 to 1
Year: semesters, summer session	Tuition: $2269 ($7369)
Application Deadline: July 1	Room & Board: n/app
Freshman Class: 826 applied, 620 accepted, 373 enrolled	
SAT I Verbal/Math: 448/510	ACT: 23 **COMPETITIVE**

The University of Colorado at Colorado Springs, established in 1965, is a public, coeducational, commuter institution, with programs in liberal arts, business, engineering, and education. There are 4 undergraduate and 3 graduate schools. In addition to regional accreditation, the university has baccalaureate program accreditation with AACSB, ABET, and NCATE. The library contains 453,570 volumes, 277,921 microform items, and 3846 audiovisual forms, and subscribes to 2440 periodicals. Computerized library sources and services include the card catalog, interlibrary loans, and database searching. Special learning facilities include a learning resource center and art gallery. The 400-acre campus is in an urban area 70 miles south of Denver. There are 7 buildings on campus. There are no residence halls.

Student Life: About 87% of undergraduates are from Colorado. Eighty-five percent are white. The average age of freshmen is 22; all undergraduates, 27. Thirty-nine percent drop out by the end of their first year; 62% remain to graduate.

Housing: There are no residence halls; all students commute and may keep cars on campus. Alcohol is not permitted.

Activities: There are no fraternities or sororities on campus. There are 50 groups on campus, including art, choir, computers, dance, drama, ethnic, film, gay, honors, international, literary magazine, newspaper, photography, political, professional, religious, social, and student government. Popular campus events include Welcome Back Week, Halloween, Winter Holiday Festival, May Day Mixer, Cinco de Mayo, and Black History Month.

Sports: There are 4 intercollegiate sports for men and 4 for women, and 13 intramural sports for men and 12 for women. Athletic and recreation facilities include a gymnasium, softball and soccer fields, a multipurpose field, tennis and volleyball courts, and a fitness center.

Disabled Students: Ninety-five percent of the campus is accessible to disabled students. The following facilities are available: wheelchair ramps, elevators, special parking, specially equipped rest rooms, lowered drinking fountains, and lowered telephones.

Services: In addition to many counseling and information services, tutoring is available in most subjects, including writing, oral communication, mathematics, science, and cross-cultural areas. In addition, there is a reader service for the blind.

Campus Safety and Security: Campus safety and security measures include 24-hour foot and vehicle patrol, self defense education, escort service, and informal discussions. In addition, there are pamphlets, posters, films, and lighted pathways and sidewalks.

Programs of Study: The university awards the B.A. and B.S. degrees. Master's and doctoral degrees also are awarded. Bachelor's degrees are awarded in BIOLOGICAL SCIENCE (biology/biological science), BUSINESS (business administration and management), COMMUNICATIONS AND THE ARTS (communications, English, fine arts, and Spanish), COMPUTER AND PHYSICAL SCIENCE (chemistry, computer science, mathematics, and physics), ENGINEERING AND ENVIRONMENTAL DESIGN (electrical/electronics engineering), SOCIAL SCIENCE (anthropology, economics, geography, history, philosophy, political science/government, psychology, and sociology). Business, engineering, psychology, biology, and communications are the strongest academically and have the largest enrollments.

Required: In order to graduate, students must complete 124 credit hours, 30 of them in the major, with a minimum GPA of 2.0. All students must take English 131, and a computer literacy course. Other requirements vary with the program.

Special: The university offers dual majors, nondegree study, and pass/fail options. There are 3 national honor societies on campus, including Phi Beta Kappa.

Faculty/Classroom: Seventy-five percent of faculty are male; 25%, female.

Admissions: About 75% of the 1993–94 applicants were accepted. About 31% of the current freshmen were in the top fifth of their class; 72% were in the top two fifths.

Requirements: The university requires applicants to be in the upper 50% of their class. A minimum GPA of 2.8 is required. The SAT I or ACT is required, with recommended minimum composite scores of 810 and 18 respectively. Applicant must be a graduate of an accredited secondary school. The GED is accepted. Secondary school courses must include 15 high school credits, including 4 years of English, 3 years each of mathematics and science, 2 years each of foreign language and social studies, and 1 academic elective. AP and CLEP credits are accepted. Important factors used in the admissions decision are advanced placement or honor courses, evidence of special talent, recommendations by school officials, leadership record, and recommendations by alumni.

Procedure: Freshmen are admitted to all sessions. Entrance exams should be taken during the senior year. Applications should be filed by July 1 for fall entry, December 1 for spring entry, and May 1 for summer entry, along with an application fee of $30. Notification is sent on a rolling basis.

Transfer: About 450 transfer students enrolled in 1993–94. Applicants must have a minimum GPA of 2.5 and a minimum of 12 credit hours earned. The school recommends minimum composite scores of 810 on the SAT I or 18 on the ACT. A total of 30 credits out of 124 must be completed at the university.

Visiting: There are guides for informal visits and visitors may sit in on classes. Campus tours can generally be arranged with 48 hours advance notice. To arrange for a visit, contact the Office of Student Life at (719) 593–3264.

Financial Aid: In 1993–94 39% of all current freshmen and 33% of continuing students received some form of financial aid. About 32% of freshmen and 29% of continuing students received need-based aid. The average freshman award was $3291. Of that total, scholarships or need-based grants averaged $1271 ($2924 maximum); loans averaged $973 ($7500 maximum); and work contracts averaged $1047 ($4000 maximum). Eleven percent of undergraduate students work part-time. Average earnings from campus work for the school year are $2609. The average financial indebtedness of the 1992–93 graduate was $8000 with Federal Stafford Loan and Federal Perkins Loan plans. The FFS and FAFSA are required. The deadline for financial aid applications is April 1.

International Students: There are currently 60 international students enrolled. They must take the TOEFL and achieve a minimum score of 550. The student must also take the SAT I or the ACT.

Computers: The college provides computer facilities for student use. The mainframes are a DEC VAX 8600, a DEC VAX 11/780, a DEC VAX 4000, and a DEC VAX Station 3100. There are laboratories with 50 VAX Terminals, and 60 microcomputers. All students may access the system. It may be used 24 hours a day. There are no time limits and no fees.

Graduates: In 1992–93 597 bachelor's degrees were awarded. The most popular majors among graduates were business (21%), communications (12%), and psychology (10%).

Admissions Contact: Admissions Office.

UNIVERSITY OF COLORADO AT DENVER
C-2
Denver, CO 80202
(303) 556-2873

Full-time: 1746 men, 1955 women | Faculty: 300; IIA, av$
Part-time: 1153 men, 1200 women | Ph.D.s: 96%
Graduate: 2091 men, 2532 women | Student/Faculty: 12 to 1
Year: semesters, summer session | Tuition: $1955 ($8619)
Application Deadline: July 22 | Room & Board: n/app
Freshman Class: 1199 applied, 562 accepted, 261 enrolled
SAT I or ACT: required | **VERY COMPETITIVE**

The University of Colorado at Denver, established in 1957, is a public, commuter institution with programs in the liberal arts and sciences, business, engineering and applied sciences, and music. There are 3 undergraduate and 6 graduate schools. In addition to regional accreditation, the university has baccalaureate program accreditation with AACSB, ABET, ASLA, NAAB, NASM, and NCATE. The library contains 507,914 volumes, 644,956 microform items, and 14,248 audiovisual forms, and subscribes to 3332 periodicals. Computerized library sources and services include the card catalog, interlibrary loans, and database searching. Special learning facilities include a learning resource center, art gallery, and writing center. The 171-acre campus is in an urban area. There are 30 buildings on campus.
Student Life: About 96% of undergraduates are from Colorado. Eighty percent are white. The average age of freshmen is 19; all undergraduates, 27. Twenty percent drop out by the end of their first year; 24% remain to graduate.
Housing: There are no residence halls. College-sponsored living facilities include off-campus apartments. All students commute. Alcohol is not permitted. All students may keep cars on campus.
Activities: There are no fraternities or sororities on campus. There are 40 groups on campus, including art, computers, drama, ethnic, honors, newspaper, religious, social, and student government. Popular campus events include World Friendship Festival, Madrigal Fest, Family Night, and Springfest.
Sports: There are 20 intramural sports for men and 20 for women. Athletic and recreation facilities include a physical education building with a pool, a weight room, a dance room, and racquetball, tennis, and basketball courts.
Disabled Students: The entire campus is accessible to disabled students. The following facilities are available: wheelchair ramps, elevators, special parking, specially equipped rest rooms, special class scheduling, lowered drinking fountains, lowered telephones, and a transit system.
Services: In addition to many counseling and information services, tutoring is available in some subjects. In addition, there is a reader service for the blind.
Campus Safety and Security: Campus safety and security measures include 24-hour foot and vehicle patrol, self defense education, escort service, and shuttle buses. In addition, there are informal discussions, pamphlets, posters, and films, emergency telephones, and lighted pathways and sidewalks.
Programs of Study: The university awards the B.A., B.S., and B.F.A degrees. Master's and doctoral degrees also are awarded. Bachelor's degrees are awarded in BIOLOGICAL SCIENCE (biology/biological science), BUSINESS (accounting, banking and finance, business administration and management, international business management, and marketing/retailing/merchandising), COMMUNICATIONS AND THE ARTS (communications, English, fine arts, French, German, music, and Spanish), COMPUTER AND PHYSICAL SCIENCE (chemistry, computer science, geology, mathematics, and physics), ENGINEERING AND ENVIRONMENTAL DESIGN (civil engineering, electrical/electronics engineering, and mechanical engineering), SOCIAL SCIENCE (anthropology, economics, geography, history, philosophy, political science/government, psychology, and sociology). Business is the strongest academically. Psychology has the largest enrollment.
Required: To graduate, students must complete 120 credit hours with a minimum GPA of 2.0. All students must complete the core curriculum courses in addition to the requirements for the major.
Special: Cross-registration is possible with Metropolitan State College. Cooperative programs, internships, study abroad, work-study programs, an accelerated degree program in business, and B.A.-B.S. degrees are available. The university offers dual and student-designed majors, a general studies degree, nondegree study, and pass/fail options. There are small individualized classes, peer advocates, and workshops. There are 8 national honor societies on campus, including Phi Beta Kappa. Most departments have honors programs.
Faculty/Classroom: Seventy percent of faculty are male; 30%, female. The average class size in an introductory lecture is 30; in a laboratory, 23; and in a regular course offering, 40.
Admissions: About 47% of the 1993-94 applicants were accepted. The SAT scores for the 1993-94 freshman class were as follows: Verbal—59% below 500, 26% between 500 and 599, 12% between 600 and 700, and 3% above 700; Math—40% below 500, 35% between 500 and 599, 22% between 600 and 700, and 3% above 700. About 47% of the current freshmen were in the top fifth of their class; 81% were in the top two fifths.

Requirements: A minimum GPA of 3.2 is required. The SAT I or ACT is required. Preference for admission is given to applicants who rank in the top 30% of their high school graduating class and present a composite score of 26 or higher on the ACT or a combined score of 1070 or higher on the SAT I. AP and CLEP credits are accepted. Important factors used in the admissions decision are advanced placement or honor courses, evidence of special talent, extracurricular activities record, recommendations by school officials, and recommendations by alumni.
Procedure: Freshmen are admitted to all sessions. Entrance exams should be taken in the junior or senior year of high school. Early decision applications should be filed by March 1; regular applications, by July 22 for fall entry, December 1 for spring entry, and May 3 for summer entry, along with an application fee of $30. Notification is sent on a rolling basis. There are early decision, early admissions, and deferred admissions plans.
Transfer: A total of 1110 transfer students enrolled in 1993-94. Applicants for transfer must have earned at least 12 credit hours for admission to liberal arts and sciences and music programs, and 24 credit hours for admission to business and engineering. A minimum GPA of 2.0 is required. A total of 30 credits out of 120 must be completed at the university.
Visiting: There are regularly scheduled orientations for prospective students, including a mini-lecture, tour of campus, and financial aid and academic advising. There are guides for informal visits and visitors may sit in on classes. To arrange for a visit, contact the Office of Admissions at (303) 556-3287.
Financial Aid: In 1993-94, 34% of all current freshmen and 42% of continuing students received some form of financial aid. About 25% of freshmen and 36% of continuing students received need-based aid. The average freshman award was $3242. Of that total, scholarships or need-based grants averaged $933 ($4000 maximum); loans averaged $1530 ($6625 maximum); and work contracts averaged $779 ($3400 maximum). Eighty-nine percent of undergraduate students work part-time. Average earnings from campus work for the school year are $2134. The average financial indebtedness of the 1992-93 graduate was $11,729. The university is a member of CSS. The school's own financial statement and tax returns and the FAFSA are required. The deadline for financial aid applications is March 31.
International Students: There are currently 272 international students enrolled. The school actively recruits these students. They must take the TOEFL and achieve a minimum score of 525.
Computers: The university provides computer facilities for student use. The mainframes are a DEC Station 5000/240, a VAX 8800, a microVAX 3100, a DEC Alpha, and a SPARC Station 10/30. There are computer laboratories available. Sequent PCs are located in the main machine room. Students can connect with the laboratories from home. All students may access the system anytime. There are no time limits on using the system. The fees are $10 per semester.
Graduates: In 1992-93, 941 bachelor's degrees were awarded. The most popular majors among graduates were business (29%), engineering (15%), and psychology (11%). Some 138 companies recruited on campus in 1992-93.
Admissions Contact: Sharon Simmons, Admissions Counselor.

UNIVERSITY OF DENVER
C-2
Denver, CO 80208
(303) 871-3377; (800) 525-9495 (out-of-state)

Full-time: 1296 men, 1379 women | Faculty: 374; I, -$
Part-time: 101 men, 431 women | Ph.D.s: 89%
Graduate: 2467 men, 2528 women | Student/Faculty: 7 to 1
Year: quarters, summer session | Tuition: $14,502
Application Deadline: March 1 | Room & Board: $4788
Freshman Class: 2703 applied, 1807 accepted, 562 enrolled
SAT I Verbal/Math: 500/510 | ACT: 24 | **COMPETITIVE +**

The University of Denver, established in 1864 and affiliated with the Methodist Church, is a private, coeducational institution offering degrees in arts and sciences, fine arts, music, business, engineering, and education. There are 7 undergraduate and 6 graduate schools. In addition to regional accreditation, DU has baccalaureate program accreditation with AACSB, ABET, CSWE, NASAD, NASM, and NCATE. The 2 libraries contain 2,900,000 volumes and 1,079,862 microform items, and subscribe to 5316 periodicals. Computerized library sources and services include the card catalog, interlibrary loans, and database searching. Special learning facilities include an art gallery and a program for learning-disabled students. The 123-acre campus is in a suburban area 8 miles southeast of the Denver business district. Including residence halls, there are 90 buildings on campus.
Student Life: About 68% of undergraduates are from out-of-state. Students come from 50 states, 80 foreign countries, and Canada. Eighty-five percent are from public schools; 15% from private. Eighty percent are white. The average age of freshmen is 18; all undergraduates, 20. Twenty percent drop out by the end of their first year; 66% remain to graduate.
Housing: A total of 1370 students can be accommodated in college housing. College-sponsored living facilities include single-sex and coed dormitories, on-campus apartments, married-student housing,

fraternity houses, and sorority houses. In addition there are honors and special interest floors. On-campus housing is guaranteed for all 4 years. All students may keep cars on campus.

Activities: About 51% of men belong to 10 national fraternities; about 42% of women belong to 6 national sororities. There are 120 groups on campus, including art, band, cheerleading, chess, choir, chorale, chorus, computers, drama, ethnic, film, gay, honors, international, jazz band, literary magazine, musical theater, newspaper, opera, orchestra, pep band, photography, political, professional, radio and TV, religious, social, social service, student government, symphony, and yearbook. Popular campus events include Winter Carnival, Homecoming, Martin Luther King Day, Cinco de Mayo Day, Festival of Nations Celebration, 'Pioneers in the Rockies' Freshman Camp, and 'Celebrating Our Own' Women's Celebration Week.

Sports: There are 8 intercollegiate sports for men and 6 for women, and 33 intramural sports for men and 32 for women. Athletic and recreation facilities include a hockey arena, a field house, a swimming pool, tennis courts, and playing fields.

Disabled Students: Fifty percent of the campus is accessible to disabled students. The following facilities are available: wheelchair ramps, elevators, special parking, specially equipped rest rooms, special class scheduling, lowered drinking fountains, and lowered telephones.

Services: In addition to many counseling and information services, tutoring is available in most subjects. There is also a reader service for the blind and remedial math and writing.

Campus Safety and Security: Campus safety and security measures include 24-hour foot and vehicle patrol, escort service, shuttle buses, and informal discussions. In addition, there are pamphlets, posters, films, emergency telephones, lighted pathways and sidewalks, and a bicycle patrol.

Programs of Study: DU awards the B.A., B.S., B.B.A., B.F.A., B.M., B.M.E., B.Mus., B.S.Acc., B.S.A.T., B.S.B.A., B.S.Chem., B.S.E.E., and B.S.M.E. degrees. Master's and doctoral degrees also are awarded. Bachelor's degrees are awarded in AGRICULTURE (animal science), BIOLOGICAL SCIENCE (biochemistry, biology/biological science, and botany), BUSINESS (accounting, banking and finance, business economics, business law, hospitality management services, international business management, marketing/retailing/merchandising, and real estate), COMMUNICATIONS AND THE ARTS (applied art, art, communications, comparative literature, dramatic arts, English, French, German, languages, music, Spanish, and speech/debate/rhetoric), COMPUTER AND PHYSICAL SCIENCE (chemistry, computer science, mathematics, physics, science, and statistics), EDUCATION (education, foreign languages, music, and science), ENGINEERING AND ENVIRONMENTAL DESIGN (construction management, electrical/electronics engineering, environmental science, and mechanical engineering), HEALTH PROFESSIONS (predentistry, premedicine, and preveterinary science), SOCIAL SCIENCE (anthropology, economics, geography, history, international relations, Latin American studies, philosophy, political science/government, prelaw, psychology, public affairs, religion, Russian and Slavic studies, social science, sociology, and women's studies). Communications, psychology, business, chemistry, biology, accounting, international relations, English, music, and hospitality management and tourism are the strongest academically. Communications, accounting, political science, psychology, international studies, music, biology, and hospitality management and tourism have the largest enrollments.

Required: For graduation, students must complete 183 to 204 quarter hours, including 42 to 135 in the major, with a minimum GPA of 2.0. All students must take 12 quarter hours each of English, natural sciences, arts and humanities, and social sciences, 8 of mathematics and computer science, and 4 of oral communication.

Special: DU offers co-op programs, study abroad, internships, a Washington quarter, and work-study programs. Dual majors, 3–2 engineering and B.A.-B.S. programs, nondegree study, and pass/fail options are also available. There is a freshman honors program on campus, as well as 13 national honor societies, including Phi Beta Kappa. Thirteen departments have honors programs.

Faculty/Classroom: Seventy-two percent of faculty are male; 28%, female. Eighty percent teach undergraduates; all do research. Graduate students teach 5% of introductory courses. The average class size in an introductory lecture is 40; in a laboratory, 17; and in a regular course offering, 20.

Admissions: About 67% of the 1993–94 applicants were accepted. The SAT scores for the 1993–94 freshman class were as follows: Verbal—63% below 500, 28% between 500 and 599, 8% between 600 and 700, and 1% above 700; Math—36% below 500, 43% between 500 and 599, 19% between 600 and 700, and 2% above 700. The ACT scores were 24% below 21, 23% between 21 and 23, 23% between 24 and 26, 16% between 27 and 28, and 14% above 28. About 73% of the current freshmen were in the top two fifths of their class. Twenty-seven freshmen graduated first in their class.

Requirements: A minimum GPA of 2.0 is required. The SAT I or ACT is required. In addition, applicants must be graduates of an accredited secondary school. The GED is accepted. The university recommends that applicants have 15 to 20 high school academic credits, including 4 in English, 3 to 4 each in mathematics and science, 2

to 4 in foreign language, 2 in history, and 1 to 2 in social studies. Course work in the arts is encouraged. An essay is required of all students, and an interview is recommended. An audition is required for music applicants and a portfolio is recommended for art students. AP and CLEP credits are accepted. Important factors used in the admissions decision are advanced placement or honor courses, recommendations by school officials, evidence of special talent, leadership record, and extracurricular activities record.

Procedure: Freshmen are admitted to all sessions. Entrance exams should be taken by February of the senior year. Early action applications should be filed by December 20; regular applications, by March 1 for fall entry, December 1 for winter entry, February 15 for spring entry, and May 15 for summer entry, along with an application fee of $35. Notification of early action is sent February 1; regular decision, on a rolling basis. There are early decision, early admissions, and deferred admissions plans.

Transfer: About 257 transfer students enrolled in 1993–94. Transfer applicants must submit a transcript from all colleges attended. Those with fewer than 30 hours of college credit must submit a high school record as well. A total of 45 quarter hours out of 183 to 204 quarter hours must be completed at DU.

Visiting: There are regularly scheduled orientations for prospective students, including an interview and a tour. There are guides for informal visits and visitors may sit in on classes and stay overnight at the school. To arrange for a visit, contact Jean Sanderson in Undergraduate Admission at (303) 871–3377 or (800) 525–9495.

Financial Aid: In 1993–94 57% of all current freshmen and 49% of continuing students received some form of financial aid. About 54% of freshmen and 48% of continuing students received need-based aid. The average freshman award was $14,000. Of that total, scholarships or need-based grants averaged $8905 ($13,572 maximum); loans averaged $3295 ($4125 maximum); and work contracts averaged $1500 ($1800 maximum). Twenty-four percent of undergraduate students work part-time. Average earnings from campus work for the school year are $1200. The average financial indebtedness of a recent year's graduate was $9700. DU is a member of CSS. The FAFSA is required. The deadline for financial aid applications is March 1.

International Students: There are currently 614 international students enrolled. The school actively recruits these students. They must take the TOEFL and achieve a minimum score of 500.

Computers: The college provides computer facilities for student use. The mainframe is a DEC VAX. There are 250 microcomputers available in dormitories, computer laboratories, the library, and most classrooms. All students may access the system, 24 hours daily. There are no time limits and no fees.

Graduates: In a recent year, 654 bachelor's degrees were awarded. The most popular majors among graduates were general business (10%), hospitality management and tourism (7%), and mass communications (5%). Within an average freshman class, 1% graduate in 3 years, 5% in 4 years, 63% in 5 years, and 64% in 6 years. Some 165 companies recruited on campus in a recent year. Twenty-seven percent of all 1992 graduates enrolled in graduate school within 6 months of graduation; 51% found employment within 6 months.

Admissions Contact: Office of Admission.

UNIVERSITY OF NORTHERN COLORADO   D-1
Greeley, CO 80639   (303) 351-2881

Full-time: 3374 men, 4651 women	Faculty: 426; I, --$
Part-time: 325 men, 436 women	Ph.D.s: 75%
Graduate: 586 men, 1011 women	Student/Faculty: 19 to 1
Year: semesters, summer session	Tuition: $2114 ($7400)
Application Deadline: August 1	Room & Board: $3894
Freshman Class: 5530 applied, 4007 accepted, 1721 enrolled	
SAT I Verbal/Math: 430/480	ACT: 22 COMPETITIVE

The University of Northern Colorado, founded in 1890, is a state-supported institution offering undergraduate and graduate programs in liberal arts and sciences, business, education, health and human sciences, and performing and visual arts. There are 5 undergraduate schools and one graduate school. In addition to regional accreditation, UNC has baccalaureate program accreditation with AACSB, NASM, NCATE, and NLN. The 3 libraries contain 901,042 volumes, 859,964 microform items, and 92,634 audiovisual forms, and subscribe to 4250 periodicals. Computerized library sources and services include the card catalog, interlibrary loans, and database searching. Special learning facilities include a learning resource center, art gallery, radio station, TV station, and a laboratory school. The 240-acre campus is in a suburban area 50 miles north of Denver. Including residence halls, there are 46 buildings on campus.

Student Life: About 89% of undergraduates are from Colorado. Students come from 49 states, 49 foreign countries, and Canada. Ninety-five percent are from public schools; 5% from private. Eighty-five percent are white. The average age of freshmen is 18.1; all undergraduates, 21.8. Thirty-five percent drop out by the end of their first year; 41% remain to graduate.

Housing: A total of 2962 students can be accommodated in college housing. College-sponsored living facilities include single-sex and coed dormitories, on-campus apartments, off-campus apartments,

married-student housing, fraternity houses, and sorority houses. In addition there are off-campus houses, graduate women's houses, and special interest floors. On-campus housing is guaranteed for the freshman year only, is available on a first-come, first-served basis, and is available on a lottery system for upperclassmen. Seventy percent of students commute. All students may keep cars on campus.

Activities: About 9% of men belong to 9 national fraternities; about 6% of women belong to 5 national sororities. There are 72 groups on campus, including art, band, cheerleading, chess, choir, computers, dance, drama, drill team, ethnic, film, gay, honors, international, jazz band, literary magazine, marching band, musical theater, newspaper, pep band, photography, political, professional, radio and TV, religious, social, social service, and student government. Popular campus events include Homecoming.

Sports: There are 7 intercollegiate sports for men and 6 for women, and 12 intramural sports for men and 10 for women. Athletic and recreation facilities include several gymnasiums, playing fields, tennis courts, a swimming pool, and a weight room.

Disabled Students: The entire campus is accessible to disabled students. The following facilities are available: wheelchair ramps, elevators, special parking, specially equipped rest rooms, special class scheduling, lowered drinking fountains, and lowered telephones. Also offered are academic support services such as note taking, transportation, interpreters, adaptive computer instruction, and library assistance.

Services: In addition to many counseling and information services, tutoring is available in most subjects. In addition, there is a reader service for the blind, and remedial math, reading, and writing.

Campus Safety and Security: Campus safety and security measures include 24-hour foot and vehicle patrol, escort service, shuttle buses, and pamphlets, posters, and films. In addition, there are emergency telephones and lighted pathways and sidewalks.

Programs of Study: UNC awards the B.A., B.S., B.Mus., and B.Mus.Ed. degrees. Master's and doctoral degrees also are awarded. Bachelor's degrees are awarded in BIOLOGICAL SCIENCE (biochemistry and biology/biological science), BUSINESS (accounting, business administration and management, management science, and marketing/retailing/merchandising), COMMUNICATIONS AND THE ARTS (advertising, art, communications, dance, dramatic arts, English, fine arts, French, German, graphic design, journalism, music, public relations, Spanish, and telecommunications), COMPUTER AND PHYSICAL SCIENCE (actuarial science, atmospheric sciences and meteorology, chemistry, computer science, earth science, geology, information sciences and systems, mathematics, physics, and statistics), EDUCATION (physical and science), HEALTH PROFESSIONS (community health work, health care administration, medical laboratory technology, nursing, rehabilitation therapy, and speech pathology/audiology), SOCIAL SCIENCE (African American studies, criminal justice, dietetics, economics, geography, gerontology, Hispanic American studies, history, interdisciplinary studies, international relations, philosophy, physical fitness/movement, political science/government, psychology, social science, social work, and sociology). Music and nursing are the strongest academically. Business has the largest enrollment.

Required: Students must earn a minimum of 120 semester hours (some majors require additional hours) with a minimum GPA of 2.0. All students must complete 40 semester hours in required general education courses, meet all degree requirements in the major, and pass an English essay examination.

Special: The university offers internships and co-op programs in many majors and study abroad in England, Spain, France, and Germany. Dual majors, student-designed majors, credit by examination, and pass/fail options are also available. Cross-registration is available with Aims Community College, and there is an accelerated degree program in nursing. There is a freshman honors program on campus, as well as one national honor society.

Faculty/Classroom: Sixty-two percent of faculty are male; 38%, female. Ninety-seven percent teach undergraduates and 67% do research. Graduate students teach 10% of introductory courses. The average class size in an introductory lecture is 36 and in a laboratory, 20.

Admissions: About 72% of the 1993–94 applicants were accepted. The SAT scores for the 1993–94 freshman class were as follows: Verbal—78% below 500, 18% between 500 and 599, and 4% between 600 and 700; Math—55% below 500, 35% between 500 and 599, 8% between 600 and 700, and 2% above 700. The ACT scores were 37% below 21, 31% between 21 and 23, 23% between 24 and 26, 7% between 27 and 28, and 2% above 28. About 29% of the current freshmen were in the top fifth of their class; 63% were in the top two fifths. Seventeen freshmen graduated first in their class.

Requirements: UNC requires applicants to be in the upper 40% of their class. The SAT I or ACT is required. Admission standards are set by the Colorado Commission on Higher Education, but each applicant is evaluated on an individual basis. In general, an ACT score of 22 or an 890 on the SAT I, and a cumulative GPA of 2.8 are required. Graduation from an accredited high school is required. AP and CLEP credits are accepted. Important factors used in the admissions decision are recommendations by school officials, evidence of special tal-

ent, advanced placement or honor courses, personality, intangible qualities, and geographic diversity.

Procedure: Freshmen are admitted to all sessions. Entrance exams should be taken as early as possible. Applications should be filed by August 1 for fall entry, December 20 for spring entry, and May 1 for summer entry, along with an application fee of $30. Notification is sent on a rolling basis. There is an early admissions plan.

Transfer: About 1000 transfer students enrolled in 1993–94. Applicants for transfer with 30 or more credit hours must have a minimum college GPA of 2.0. Transfer students who have completed less than 12 credit hours of college must meet the same criteria for admission as entering freshmen. A total of 30 credits out of 120 must be completed at UNC.

Visiting: There are regularly scheduled orientations for prospective students, including academic advising, registration, tours, and special activities. There are guides for informal visits and visitors may sit in on classes. To arrange for a visit, contact UNC Visitors Center at (303) 351–2097.

Financial Aid: In 1993–94, 74% of all current freshmen and 62% of continuing students received some form of financial aid. About 59% of freshmen and 55% of continuing students received need-based aid. The average freshman award was $3448. Of that total, scholarships or need-based grants averaged $1474 ($11,627 maximum); loans averaged $1618 ($8461 maximum); and work contracts averaged $356 ($4163 maximum). Twenty-eight percent of undergraduate students work part-time. Average earnings from campus work for the school year are $1398. The FAFSA financial statement is required. The deadline for financial aid applications is March 1.

International Students: There are currently 151 international students enrolled. They must take the TOEFL or the University of Michigan Language Test and achieve a minimum score on the TOEFL of 520.

Computers: The university provides computer facilities for student use. The mainframe is an IBM 3081. Students may access the mainframe from a variety of computer laboratories, including those in academic buildings, the library, the student center, and residence halls. The university's 15 computer laboratories (most with access to networks) include terminals and Apple and IBM or IBM-compatible microcomputers. All students may access the system. There are no time limits on using the system and no fees.

Graduates: In 1992–93, 1613 bachelor's degrees were awarded. The most popular majors among graduates were social sciences (17%), business and management (16%), and health sciences (12%). Within an average freshman class, 1% graduate in 3 years, 16% in 4 years, 30% in 5 years, and 41% in 6 years. Some 349 companies recruited on campus in 1992–93. In the 1992 graduating class, 9% of the graduates were enrolled in graduate school within 6 months of graduation; 85% had found employment.

Admissions Contact: Director of Admissions.

UNIVERSITY OF SOUTHERN COLORADO D-3
Pueblo, CO 81001   (719) 549–2461; (800) 872–4769 **(out-of-state)**

Full-time: 1655 men, 1810 women	Faculty: 171; IIA, --$
Part-time: 320 men, 360 women	Ph.D.s: 85%
Graduate: 60 men, 55 women	Student/Faculty: 20 to 1
Year: semesters, summer session	Tuition: $1878 ($6768)
Application Deadline: July 21	Room & Board: $3472
Freshman Class: 1780 applied, 1539 accepted, 719 enrolled	
SAT I or ACT: required	**LESS COMPETITIVE**

The University of Southern Colorado, founded in 1933, is part of the Colorado State University system and offers undergraduate programs in liberal arts, business administration, nursing, applied science, technology, industrial engineering, and social sciences. There are 5 undergraduate and 3 graduate schools. In addition to regional accreditation, USC has baccalaureate program accreditation with ABET, ACS, CSWE, NASM, NCATE, and NLN. The library contains 180,000 volumes, 6450 microform items, and 10,000 audiovisual forms, and subscribes to 1312 periodicals. Computerized library sources and services include the card catalog, interlibrary loans, and database searching. Special learning facilities include a learning resource center, art gallery, radio station, and TV station. The 275-acre campus is in an urban area 100 miles south of Denver. Including residence halls, there are 14 buildings on campus.

Student Life: About 93% of undergraduates are from Colorado. Students come from 41 states, 32 foreign countries, and Canada. Sixty-nine percent are white; 24% Hispanic. The average age of freshmen is 19; all undergraduates, 26. Thirty-nine percent drop out by the end of their first year; 27% remain to graduate.

Housing: A total of 500 students can be accommodated in college housing. College-sponsored living facilities include coed dormitories. On-campus housing is guaranteed for the freshman year only and is available on a first-come, first-served basis. Ninety-one percent of students commute. Alcohol is not permitted. All students may keep cars on campus.

Activities: There are no fraternities or sororities on campus. There are 65 groups on campus, including cheerleading, chorale, drama, ethnic, honors, jazz band, musical theater, newspaper, pep band, political, professional, radio and TV, religious, social, social service, stu-

dent government, and symphony. Popular campus events include the Town and Gown Series, Parti-Gras, Teacher Career Fair, Departmental Lecture Series, and Cinco de Mayo Fiesta.

Sports: There are 6 intercollegiate sports for men and 5 for women, and 5 intramural sports for men and 3 for women. Athletic and recreation facilities include a swimming pool; a weight room; racquetball, basketball, volleyball, and tennis courts; bike trails; and a nature center.

Disabled Students: The entire campus is accessible to disabled students. The following facilities are available: wheelchair ramps, elevators, special parking, specially equipped rest rooms, special class scheduling, lowered drinking fountains, and lowered telephones.

Services: In addition to many counseling and information services, tutoring is available in most subjects.

Campus Safety and Security: Campus safety and security measures include 24-hour foot and vehicle patrol, self defense education, escort service, and informal discussions. In addition, there are pamphlets, posters, and films, emergency telephones, and lighted pathways and sidewalks.

Programs of Study: USC awards the B.A., B.S., B.S.B.A., B.S.C.E.T., B.S.E.E.T., B.S.Met.E., B.S.N., and B.S.W. degrees. Master's degrees also are awarded. Bachelor's degrees are awarded in BIOLOGICAL SCIENCE (biology/biological science), BUSINESS (accounting, business administration and management, and business economics), COMMUNICATIONS AND THE ARTS (broadcasting, communications, English, fine arts, journalism, languages, music, and speech/debate/rhetoric), COMPUTER AND PHYSICAL SCIENCE (chemistry, computer science, mathematics, and physics), ENGINEERING AND ENVIRONMENTAL DESIGN (engineering technology and industrial engineering), HEALTH PROFESSIONS (nursing, predentistry, premedicine, and sports medicine), SOCIAL SCIENCE (criminal justice, history, political science/government, prelaw, psychology, social science, social work, and sociology). Business, engineering, technologies, nursing, mass communications, and teacher certification are the strongest academically. Accounting, biology, management, mass communications, psychology, and nursing have the largest enrollments.

Required: To graduate, all students must complete at least 128 to 135 semester hours, including 40 in upper-division courses and 30 to 48 in the major, with a minimum GPA of 2.0. The general education requirements are courses in speech communication, writing, computer literacy, and mathematics. Other requirements vary with the major.

Special: USC offers co-op programs, internships, study abroad, on-campus work-study programs, 5-year combined B.A-B.S degrees, a 3–2 engineering degree with Colorado State University, a dual major in biology and chemistry, nondegree study, and is a member of the National Student Exchange. There is a freshman honors program on campus, as well as 2 national honor societies.

Faculty/Classroom: Seventy-eight percent of faculty are male; 22%, female. Ninety-eight percent teach undergraduates and 2% both teach and do research. No introductory courses are taught by graduate students. The average class size in an introductory lecture is 70; in a laboratory, 24; and in a regular course offering, 22.

Admissions: About 86% of the 1993–94 applicants were accepted. Two freshmen graduated first in their class.

Requirements: The SAT I or ACT is required. In addition, applicants must be graduates of an accredited secondary school or have a GED certificate. A portfolio or audition is recommended. The university computes a CCHE admissions index, comprised of the high school GPA and SAT I or ACT scores. Students scoring below 79 will still be considered by an admissions committee. AP and CLEP credits are accepted. Important factors used in the admissions decision are advanced placement or honor courses, evidence of special talent, recommendations by school officials, extracurricular activities record, and leadership record.

Procedure: Freshmen are admitted to all sessions. Entrance exams should be taken prior to application. Applications should be filed by July 21 for fall entry, November 30 for spring entry, and April 28 for summer entry, along with an application fee of $15. Notification is sent on a rolling basis. There are early admissions and deferred admissions plans.

Transfer: A total of 417 transfer students enrolled in a recent year. Applicants with fewer than 12 credit hours must submit ACT or SAT I scores and high school transcripts. A minimum GPA of 2.0 and official transcripts of previous college work are required. A total of 36 credits out of 128 must be completed at USC.

Visiting: There are regularly scheduled orientations for prospective students. There are guides for informal visits and visitors may sit in on classes and stay overnight at the school. To arrange for a visit, contact Patricia Skehan in Admissions.

Financial Aid: In a recent year, 59% of all current freshmen and 76% of continuing students received some form of financial aid. About 49% of freshmen and 57% of continuing students received need-based aid. The average freshman award was $2500. Of that total, scholarships or need-based grants averaged $1200 ($4000 maximum); loans averaged $800 ($2625 maximum); and work contracts averaged $800 ($2000 maximum). Twenty-five percent of undergraduate students work part-time. Average earnings from campus

work for the school year are $1740. The average financial indebtedness of a recent graduate was $6000. USC is a member of CSS. The SFS and the college's own financial statement are required. The deadline for financial aid applications is March 1.

International Students: There are currently 160 international students enrolled. The school actively recruits these students. They must take the TOEFL or the University of Michigan Language Test and achieve a minimum score on the TOEFL of 500.

Computers: USC provides computer facilities for student use. The mainframe is a Prime 850 with a DOS-based local area network and 12 macrocomputers. There are 100 IBM or IBM-compatible microcomputers and 36 Apple microcomputers available for student use in the library, the administration and technology buildings, and several departments. All students may access the system 14 hours a day. There are no time limits on using the system and no fees.

Graduates: In a recent year, 500 bachelor's degrees were awarded. The most popular majors among graduates were business management (10%), mass communications (6%), and biology (5%). Within an average freshman class, 9% graduate in 4 years and 26% in 5 years. Some 130 companies recruited on campus in a recent year.

Admissions Contact: Frederick L. Kidd, Dean of Admissions and Enrollment Management.

WESTERN STATE COLLEGE OF COLORADO   B-3

Gunnison, CO 81231   (303) 943–2119; (800) 876–5309 (out-of-state)

Full-time: 1374 men, 941 women	Faculty: 112; IIB, av$
Part-time: 60 men, 80 women	Ph.D.s: 63%
Graduate: none	Student/Faculty: 21 to 1
Year: see profile	Tuition: $1819 ($5918)
Application Deadline: none	Room & Board: $3741
Freshman Class: 2086 applied, 1609 accepted, 604 enrolled	
SAT I Verbal/Math: 420/470	ACT: 21 COMPETITIVE

Western State College of Colorado, founded in 1911, is a public institution offering programs in liberal arts and sciences. The academic year consists of 4 terms: Fall (12 weeks), Winter (8 weeks), Spring (12 weeks), and Summer (8 weeks). There are 10 undergraduate schools. In addition to regional accreditation, Western has baccalaureate program accreditation with NASM. The library contains 110,000 volumes, 661,000 microform items, and 4000 audiovisual forms, and subscribes to 630 periodicals. Computerized library sources and services include the card catalog and interlibrary loans. Special learning facilities include a learning resource center, art gallery, radio station, TV station, and botanical gardens. The 228-acre campus is in a rural area 210 miles southwest of Denver. Including residence halls, there are 30 buildings on campus.

Student Life: About 65% of undergraduates are from Colorado. Students come from 50 states, 12 foreign countries, and Canada. Eighty-five percent are from public schools; 15% from private. Eighty-five percent are white. Eleven percent are Protestant; 10% Catholic. The average age of freshmen is 18; all undergraduates, 21. Forty-seven percent drop out by the end of their first year.

Housing: A total of 1350 students can be accommodated in college housing. College-sponsored living facilities include single-sex and coed dormitories, on-campus apartments, and married-student housing. On-campus housing is guaranteed for the freshman year only and is available on a first-come, first-served basis. Fifty-five percent of students commute. Alcohol is not permitted. All students may keep cars on campus.

Activities: About 3% of men belong to fraternities; about 2% of women belong to 3 local sororities. There are 60 groups on campus, including art, band, cheerleading, choir, chorale, chorus, dance, drama, ethnic, gay, honors, international, jazz band, literary magazine, marching band, musical theater, newspaper, opera, orchestra, pep band, photography, political, professional, radio and TV, religious, social, social service, student government, and yearbook. Popular campus events include Parents Weekend, Homecoming, Winter Carnival, Cinderella Ball, Senior Days, and Chilly Willy Luau.

Sports: There are 6 intercollegiate sports for men and 5 for women, and 15 intramural sports for men and 13 for women. Athletic and recreation facilities include a fitness center; 2 gymnasiums; a 5000-seat football stadium; an all-weather track; baseball and playing fields; a weight room; an indoor swimming pool; a par course; racquetball, tennis, and volleyball courts; and a games/pool area with a bowling alley.

Disabled Students: The following facilities are available: wheelchair ramps, elevators, special parking, specially equipped rest rooms, and lowered drinking fountains.

Services: In addition to many counseling and information services, tutoring is available in most subjects. In addition, there is a reader service for the blind and remedial math and writing.

Campus Safety and Security: Campus safety and security measures include informal discussions, pamphlets, posters, and films, and lighted pathways and sidewalks.

Programs of Study: Western awards the B.A. degree in BIOLOGICAL SCIENCE (biology/biological science), BUSINESS (accounting, business administration and management, and recreation and leisure services), COMMUNICATIONS AND THE ARTS (communications, dramatic arts, English, fine arts, French, music, and Spanish), COM-

PUTER AND PHYSICAL SCIENCE (chemistry, geology, mathematics, and physics), EDUCATION (art, business, elementary, foreign languages, industrial arts, music, science, and secondary), ENGINEERING AND ENVIRONMENTAL DESIGN (preengineering and technological management), HEALTH PROFESSIONS (physical therapy and predentistry), SOCIAL SCIENCE (economics, history, physical fitness/movement, political science/government, prelaw, psychology, and sociology). Education, business, biological sciences, and communications are the strongest academically. Business, biology, and communications have the largest enrollments.

Required: For graduation, students must complete 120 credit hours with a minimum GPA of 2.0. There are liberal arts requirements of 30 credits in human relationships, natural sciences, and creative arts, as well as competencies in written expression, oral communication, and mathematics.

Special: The Department of Business and Accounting offers a co-op program. Students may cross-register with Mesa, Adams, and Metro State colleges. Internships, study abroad, a 3–2 engineering program with Colorado State University, work-study programs, dual and student-designed majors, and credit for military and work experience are available. There is a freshman honors program on campus, as well as 9 national honor societies. Two departments have honors programs.

Faculty/Classroom: Seventy-two percent of faculty are male; 28%, female. All teach undergraduates and 10% also do research. The average class size in an introductory lecture is 35; in a laboratory, 15; and in a regular course offering, 20.

Admissions: About 77% of the 1993–94 applicants were accepted. The SAT scores for the 1993–94 freshman class were as follows: Verbal—82% below 500, 15% between 500 and 599, 2% between 600 and 700, and 1% above 700; Math—65% below 500, 29% between 500 and 599, and 6% between 600 and 700. The ACT scores were 53% below 21, 29% between 21 and 23, 13% between 24 and 26, 4% between 27 and 28, and 1% above 28. About 15% of the current freshmen were in the top fifth of their class; 36% were in the top two fifths.

Requirements: Western requires applicants to be in the upper 67% of their class. A minimum GPA of 2.5 is required. The SAT I or ACT is required, with a minimum composite SAT I score of 820 or ACT score of 20 recommended. An essay and an interview also are recommended. Applicants must be graduates of an accredited secondary school. The GED is accepted with an overall score of 50 or above and a minimum score of 35 in each area. The college recommends that students complete 4 years of English, 3 of mathematics, 2 each of natural and social science, and course work in a foreign language and computer science. AP and CLEP credits are accepted. Important factors used in the admissions decision are evidence of special talent, advanced placement or honor courses, leadership record, recommendations by school officials, and extracurricular activities record.

Procedure: Freshmen are admitted to all sessions. Application deadlines are open. The application fee is $25. Notification is sent on a rolling basis. There are early decision, early admissions, and deferred admissions plans.

Transfer: A total of 246 transfer students enrolled in 1993–94. Applicants for transfer must have a minimum GPA of 2.0 and either a minimum composite SAT I score of 820 or a minimum composite ACT score of 20. A total of 30 credits out of 120 must be completed at Western.

Visiting: There are regularly scheduled orientations for prospective students. There are guides for informal visits and visitors may sit in on classes and stay overnight at the school. To arrange for a visit, contact the Admissions Office at (303) 943–2119 or (800) 876–5309.

Financial Aid: In 1993–94, 60% of all current freshmen and 70% of continuing students received some form of financial aid. About 60% of all students received need-based aid. The average freshman award was $5200. Of that total, scholarships or need-based grants averaged $1700 ($2300 maximum); loans averaged $2600 ($2625 maximum); and work contracts averaged $900 ($2500 maximum). Thirty-five percent of undergraduate students work part-time. Average earnings from campus work for the school year are $900. The average financial indebtedness of the 1992–93 graduate was $9000. Western is a member of CSS. The FAFSA is required. The deadline for financial aid applications is April 1.

International Students: There are currently 29 international students enrolled. They must take the TOEFL and achieve a minimum score of 525.

Computers: The college provides computer facilities for student use. The mainframe is a DEC VAX 8530. Students have access to WordPerfect, Lotus 1–2–3, and dBase software with free printing. An Apple Macintosh laboratory and several other computer laboratories are located on campus. All students may access the system at all times. There are no time limits on using the system. The fees are $25 per year.

Graduates: In 1992–93, 391 bachelor's degrees were awarded. The most popular majors among graduates were business/accounting (33%), social sciences (19%), and communications (10%). Some 15 companies recruited on campus in 1992–93. In the 1992 graduating class, 98% of all students had found employment within 6 months of graduation.

Admissions Contact: Monica Bruning, Director of Admissions.

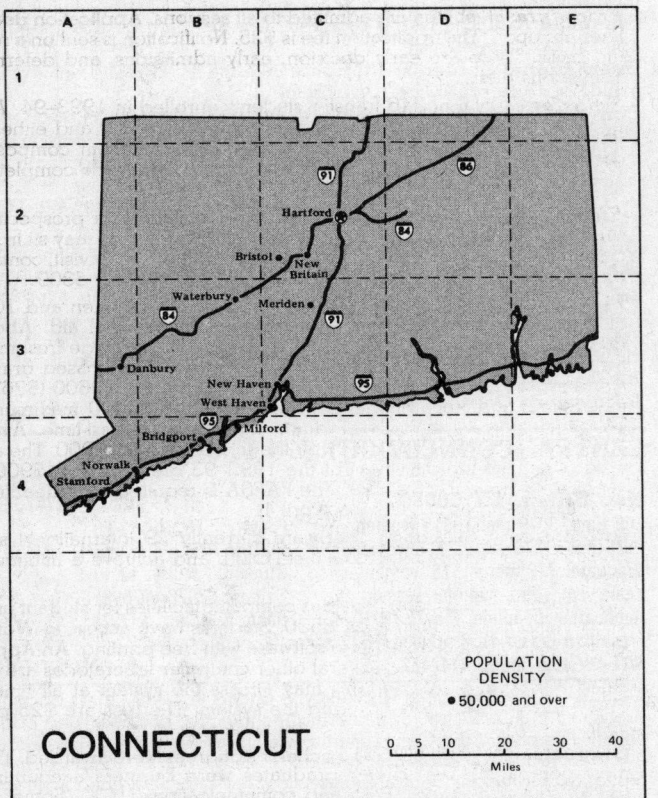

CONNECTICUT

POPULATION
DENSITY
● 50,000 and over

0   5 10   20   30   40
Miles

ALBERTUS MAGNUS COLLEGE

C-3

New Haven, CT 06511-1189   (203) 773-8501

Full-time: 200 men, 250 women	Faculty: 36; IIB, -$
Part-time: none	Ph.D.s: 70%
Graduate: none	Student/Faculty: 13 to 1
Year: trimesters, summer session	Tuition: $11,560
Application Deadline: open	Room & Board: $4720
Freshman Class: n/av	
SAT I: required	**LESS COMPETITIVE**

Albertus Magnus College, founded in 1925, is affiliated with the Roman Catholic Church and operated by the Dominican Sisters of Saint Mary of the Springs. The college offers undergraduate and graduate degrees in the liberal arts and sciences. There is one graduate school. The library contains 99,000 volumes and 5000 microform items, and subscribes to 410 periodicals. Computerized library sources and services include the card catalog, interlibrary loans, and database searching. Special learning facilities include a learning resource center and a theater. The 55-acre campus is in a suburban area in a residential section of New Haven. Including residence halls, there are 17 buildings on campus.

Student Life: About 60% of undergraduates are from Connecticut. Students come from 15 states and 8 foreign countries. Fifty percent are from public schools; 50% from private. Eighty-one percent are white. The average age of freshmen is 19; all undergraduates, 22. Twelve percent drop out by the end of their first year; 60% remain to graduate.

Housing: A total of 500 students can be accommodated in college housing. College-sponsored living facilities include single-sex and coed dormitories. Residence halls are old mansions that have been converted into student housing. Each building houses 15 to 65 students. On-campus housing is guaranteed for all 4 years. Seventy percent of students live on campus; of those, 60% remain on campus on weekends. All students may keep cars on campus.

Activities: There are no fraternities or sororities on campus. There are 20 groups on campus, including art, choir, chorale, chorus, computers, dance, drama, ethnic, honors, international, literary magazine, musical theater, newspaper, orchestra, photography, political, professional, religious, social, social service, student government, and yearbook.

Sports: There are 7 intercollegiate sports for men and 7 for women, and 10 intramural sports for men and 10 for women. Athletic and recreation facilities include an Olympic-size pool, a gymnasium, indoor and outdoor tracks, racquetball and volleyball courts, weight and dance rooms, soccer and softball fields, 4 tennis courts, and a game room.

Disabled Students: Fifty percent of the campus is accessible to disabled students. The following facilities are available: wheelchair ramps, elevators, special parking, specially equipped rest rooms, and special class scheduling.

Services: In addition to many counseling and information services, tutoring is available in every subject. There is also remedial math and reading.

Campus Safety and Security: Campus safety and security measures include 24-hour foot and vehicle patrol, shuttle buses, informal discussions, pamphlets, posters, and films. In addition, there are lighted pathways and sidewalks.

Programs of Study: Albertus Magnus awards the B.A. and B.F.A. degrees. Associate and master's degrees also are awarded. Bachelor's degrees are awarded in BIOLOGICAL SCIENCE (biology/biological science), BUSINESS (accounting and business economics), COMMUNICATIONS AND THE ARTS (classics, communications, dramatic arts, English, fine arts, French, Italian, romance languages, and Spanish), COMPUTER AND PHYSICAL SCIENCE (mathematics and physical sciences), ENGINEERING AND ENVIRONMENTAL DESIGN (industrial engineering), HEALTH PROFESSIONS (health care administration, predentistry, premedicine, and preveterinary science), SOCIAL SCIENCE (community psychology, criminology, economics, history, human services, humanities, industrial and organizational psychology, liberal arts/general studies, philosophy, political science/government, prelaw, psychology, religion, sociology, and urban studies). Liberal arts is the strongest academically. Business/economics, English, and psychology have the largest enrollments.

Required: To graduate, all students must complete at least 120 credit hours, including 60 outside the major and 30 in the major. General education requirements, including 6 credits each in foreign language and mathematics/science must be fulfilled. A minimum 2.0 GPA is required.

Special: The college offers cross-registration with Quinnipiac College and the University of New Haven, junior- and senior-year internships allowing up to 15 credits, study abroad, a Washington semester, work-study programs, and accelerated degree programs in business and economics, communications, English, humanities, and general studies. Also available are dual and student-designed majors, nondegree study, pass/fail options, independent study, and preprofessional programs. Students may take evening or weekend courses. A summer theater workshop is offered. There is a freshman honors program on campus. All departments have honors programs.

Faculty/Classroom: The average class size in an introductory lecture is 20; in a laboratory, 10; and in a regular course offering, 15.

Requirements: The SAT I is required, with a minimum recommended composite score of 800. Applicants must be graduates of an accredited secondary school or have a GED certificate and have completed 16 academic credits, including 4 years of English, 2 or 3 years each of foreign language, mathematics, and science, 2 years of history, and 1 year of social studies. High school transcripts, rank, and 2 letters of recommendation are required. The SAT II: Subject test in writing and an interview are recommended. AP and CLEP credits are accepted. Important factors used in the admissions decision are advanced placement or honor courses, recommendations by school officials, leadership record, extracurricular activities record, and parents or siblings attending the school.

Procedure: Freshmen are admitted fall, winter, and spring. Entrance exams should be taken between April of the junior year and November of the senior year. Application deadlines are open. Application fee is $30. There are early decision and deferred admissions plans. Notification of early decision is sent November 15; regular decision, beginning December 15.

Transfer: About 35 transfer students enrolled in a recent year. Transfer students must present a minimum 2.0 GPA. At least 45 credits out of 120 must be completed at Albertus Magnus.

Visiting: There are regularly scheduled orientations for prospective students, consisting of a general introduction, a financial aid/major introduction, lunch, a campus tour, and an interview. Visitors may sit in on classes and stay overnight at the school. To arrange for a visit, contact the Admissions Office at (203) 773-8501.

Financial Aid: In 1993–94, 75% of all current freshmen and 70% of continuing students received some form of financial aid. About 75% of freshmen and 70% of continuing students received need-

based aid. The average freshman award was $5568. Of that total, scholarships or need-based grants averaged $1027; loans averaged $2504; and work contracts averaged $600. Three percent of undergraduate students work part-time. Average earnings from campus work for the school year are $600. Albertus Magnus is a member of CSS. The FAF and the college's own financial statement are required. The deadline for financial aid applications is February 15.

International Students: There are currently 33 international students enrolled. They must take the TOEFL and achieve a minimum score of 500 and must also take the SAT I or the ACT.

Computers: The college provides computer facilities for student use. The mainframe is a Prime 2450. There are also 25 terminals and 10 personal computers available for student use in the computer center and the library. All students may access the system from 9 A.M. to 5 P.M. There are no time limits on using the system and no fees.

Graduates: In a recent year, 123 bachelor's degrees were awarded. The most popular majors among graduates were business/economics (35%), English (17%), and communications (17%). Within an average freshman class, 80% graduate in 4 years and 50% in 5 years.

Admissions Contact: Richard Lolatte, Dean of Admissions and Enrollment Management.

BRIDGEPORT ENGINEERING INSTITUTE

B-4

Fairfield, CT 06430   (203) 259–5717; (800) 245–4234 (in-state)

Full-time: 11 men, 1 women	Faculty: 85
Part-time: 289 men, 26 women	Ph.D.s: 20%
Graduate: none	Student/Faculty: 4 to 1
Year: trimesters, summer session	Tuition: $6135
Application Deadline: open	Room & Board: n/app
Freshman Class: n/av	
ACT: not required	**NONCOMPETITIVE**

Bridgeport Engineering Institute, founded in 1924, is an evening commuter engineering college whose students and faculty meet primarily on a part-time basis. The library contains 100,000 volumes. Computerized library sources and services include the card catalog. The 10-acre campus is in a small town 5 miles from Bridgeport.

Student Life: About 99% of undergraduates are from Connecticut. Ninety-three percent are white. The average age of all undergraduates is 27. Twenty percent drop out by the end of their first year; 50% remain to graduate.

Housing: There are no residence halls. One-hundred percent of students commute.

Sports: There is no sports program at BEI.

Disabled Students: The entire campus is accessible to disabled students. The following facilities are available: wheelchair ramps, elevators, special parking, lowered drinking fountains, and lowered telephones.

Services: In addition to many counseling and information services, tutoring is available in most subjects, including mathematics. There is also remedial math, reading, and writing.

Campus Safety and Security: Campus safety and security measures include pamphlets, posters, films, and lighted pathways and sidewalks.

Programs of Study: BEI awards the B.S.E.E. and B.S.M.E. degrees. Associate degrees are also awarded. Bachelor's degrees are awarded in ENGINEERING AND ENVIRONMENTAL DESIGN (electrical/electronics engineering, mechanical engineering, and systems engineering).

Required: To graduate, students must complete a minimum of 139 credit hours, including courses in mathematics, computer science, physical sciences, engineering science, humanities and social science, industrial management, and engineering economy. At least 44 credit hours are needed in the major. A 70% or better grade average is required in all courses.

Special: There is a manufacturing engineering option in the mechanical engineering major. Nondegree study is available.

Faculty/Classroom: Eighty-five percent of faculty are male; 15%, female.

Requirements: Students should be graduates of an accredited secondary school, have passed the State High School Equivalency examination, or received the GED. SAT I or the ACT is not required. Students should have completed at least 4 units of English and 3 units of mathematics, including algebra, geometry, and trigonometry. A working knowledge of the computer language BASIC is required. Preparation in physics and chemistry is strongly recommended. CLEP credit is accepted.

Procedure: Application deadlines are open. The application fee is $50. The college accepts all applicants.

Transfer: About 38 transfer students enrolled in an earlier year. Applicants must provide transcripts and course description catalogs for all schools previously attended, including high school. A total of 36 credits out of 139 must be completed at BEI.

Visiting: There are regularly scheduled orientations for prospective students. There are guides for informal visits and visitors may sit in on classes. To arrange for a visit, contact Patricia Meehan, Registrar, at (203) 259–5717.

Financial Aid: The FAF is required. The deadline for financial aid applications is open.

International Students: They must take the TOEFL and achieve a minimum score of 500 or 1087 on the ELS.

Computers: The college provides computer facilities for student use. The mainframe is an IBM. Available software includes computer-aided drafting, word processing, Lotus, Pascal, and design with C language. All students may access the system. It may be used 9 A.M. to 9 P.M. Monday through Friday and 9 A.M. to 12 P.M. Saturday. There are no fees.

Graduates: In a recent year, 45 bachelor's degrees were awarded. The most popular majors among graduates were electrical engineering (53%) and mechanical engineering (47%). Within an average freshman class, 40% graduate in 4 years, 45% in 5 years, and 15% in 6 years. Five companies recruited on campus in a recent year. In the 1992 graduating class, 5% of the men and 2% of the women enrolled in graduate school within 6 months of graduation.

Admissions Contact: Anthony Guglielmo, Dean of Admissions.

CENTRAL CONNECTICUT STATE UNIVERSITY

C-2

New Britain, CT 06050   (203) 827–7543

Full-time: 3079 men, 3315 women	Faculty: 376; IIA, +$
Part-time: 1870 men, 2011 women	Ph.D.s: 70%
Graduate: 772 men, 1618 women	Student/Faculty: 17 to 1
Year: semesters, summer session	Tuition: $2976 ($7688)
Application Deadline: May 1	Room & Board: $4132
Freshman Class: 4158 applied, 2532 accepted, 902 enrolled	
SAT I Verbal/Math: 414/457	**COMPETITIVE**

Central Connecticut State University, founded in 1849, offers degree programs in liberal arts, engineering technology, business, and education. It is part of the Connecticut State University system. There are 4 undergraduate schools and one graduate school. In addition to regional accreditation, Central Connecticut has baccalaureate program accreditation with ABET, NCATE, and NLN. The library contains 455,551 volumes, 60,875 microform items, and 6221 audiovisual forms, and subscribes to 2941 periodicals. Computerized library sources and services include the card catalog, interlibrary loans, and database searching. Special learning facilities include a learning resource center, art gallery, planetarium, radio station, a writing center, and a mathematics center. The 152-acre campus is in a suburban area 10 miles west of Hartford. Including residence halls, there are 29 buildings on campus.

Student Life: About 94% of undergraduates are from Connecticut. Students come from 25 states, 40 foreign countries, and Canada. Eighty-seven percent are white. Forty-three percent are Catholic; 41% claim no religious affiliation; 10% Protestant. The average age of freshmen is 19; all undergraduates, 22. Twenty-seven percent drop out by the end of their first year; 45% remain to graduate.

Housing: A total of 1623 students can be accommodated in college housing. College-sponsored living facilities include single-sex and coed dormitories. In addition, there are honors houses and special interest houses. On-campus housing is guaranteed for all 4 years. Seventy-five percent of students commute. Alcohol is not permitted. All students may keep cars on campus.

Activities: About 1% of all students belong to 1 national fraternity; about 1% of women belong to 1 local and 1 national sorority. There are more than 100 groups on campus, including art, band, cheerleading, choir, chorale, chorus, computers, dance, drama, ethnic, gay, honors, international, literary magazine, marching band, newspaper, orchestra, pep band, photography, political, professional, radio and TV, religious, social, social service, student government, and yearbook. Popular campus events include Winter and Spring weekends, First Week, Vance Lectures, International Festival, and planetarium shows.

Sports: There are 11 intercollegiate sports for men and 8 for women, and 11 intramural sports for men and 11 for women. Athletic and recreation facilities include a 4500-seat gymnasium, 8 tennis courts, a 6000-seat football stadium, several softball fields, a track-and-field facility, and a 3700-square-foot air-supported recreation facility.

Disabled Students: Ninety percent of the campus is accessible to disabled students. The following facilities are available: wheelchair ramps, elevators, special parking, specially equipped rest rooms, special class scheduling, lowered drinking fountains, and lowered telephones. Personal care attendants serve as roommates for physically disabled dormitory students.

Services: In addition to many counseling and information services, tutoring is available in some subjects. There is also a reader service for the blind, and remedial math, reading, and writing.

Campus Safety and Security: Campus safety and security measures include 24-hour foot and vehicle patrol, self defense education, escort service, and informal discussions. In addition, there are pamphlets, posters, films, emergency telephones, and lighted pathways and sidewalks.

Programs of Study: Central Connecticut awards the B.A., B.S., B.F.A., B.S.ED., B.S.E.T., B.S.I.T., and B.S.N. degrees. Master's degrees also are awarded. Bachelor's degrees are awarded in BIOLOGICAL SCIENCE (biology/biological science), BUSINESS (accounting, banking and finance, business administration and management, international business management, management information systems, marketing/retailing/merchandising, and office supervision and management), COMMUNICATIONS AND THE ARTS (art, communications, dramatic arts, English, French, German, Italian, music, and Spanish), COMPUTER AND PHYSICAL SCIENCE (actuarial science, chemistry, computer science, earth science, mathematics, physical sciences, physics, and science), EDUCATION (art, business, early childhood, elementary, marketing and distribution, music, physical, special, technical, and vocational), ENGINEERING AND ENVIRONMENTAL DESIGN (construction technology, industrial engineering technology, manufacturing technology, and mechanical engineering technology), HEALTH PROFESSIONS (nursing), SOCIAL SCIENCE (anthropology, East Asian studies, economics, geography, history, philosophy, political science/government, psychology, social science, social work, and sociology). Business and education have the largest enrollments.

Required: To graduate, all students must complete at least 122 credit hours, including 62 hours in the general education program, with a minimum GPA of 2.0.

Special: There is a freshman honors program on campus, as well as 7 national honor societies. One department has an honors program.

Faculty/Classroom: Sixty-seven percent of faculty are male; 33%, female. All teach undergraduates. No introductory courses are taught by graduate students. The average class size in an introductory lecture is 35; in a laboratory, 20; and in a regular course offering, 25.

Admissions: About 61% of the 1993–94 applicants were accepted. The SAT scores for the 1993–94 freshman class were as follows: Verbal—86% below 500, 13% between 500 and 599, and 1% between 600 and 700; Math—67% below 500, 26% between 500 and 599, 6% between 600 and 700, and 1% above 700. About 18% of the current freshmen were in the top fifth of their class; 48% were in the top two fifths.

Requirements: Central Connecticut requires applicants to be in the upper 50% of their class. A minimum GPA of 2.0 is required. The SAT I is required, with recommended minimum scores of 400 verbal and 400 mathematics. An interview is also recommended. Central Connecticut recommends that applicants have 13 academic credits: 4 in English, 3 in mathematics, and 2 each in foreign language, science, and social studies. An interview is encouraged. The GED is accepted. AP and CLEP credits are accepted.

Procedure: Freshmen are admitted fall and spring. Entrance exams should be taken in May of the junior year. Applications should be filed by May 1 for fall entry and November 1 for spring entry, along with an application fee of $20. Notification is sent on a rolling basis. There are early admissions and deferred admissions plans.

Transfer: About 689 transfer students enrolled in 1993–94. Transfer applicants must have a minimum of 12 credits and a GPA of 2.0. The SAT I and an interview are recommended if an applicant's GPA is less than 2.0. A total of 45 credits out of 122 must be completed at Central Connecticut.

Visiting: Visitors may sit in on classes. To arrange for a visit, contact the Admissions Office at (203) 827–7543.

Financial Aid: In a recent year, 37% of all current freshmen and 27% of continuing students received some form of financial aid. About 21% of freshmen and 14% of continuing students received need-based aid. The average freshman award was $3900. Of the 1993–1994 total package, scholarships or need-based grants averaged $2200 ($10,500 maximum); loans averaged $1500 ($5625 maximum); and work contracts averaged $1000 (maximum). Forty percent of undergraduate students work part-time. Average earnings from campus work for the school year are $1200. Central Connecticut is a member of CSS. The FAFSA financial statement is required. The deadline for financial aid applications is March 15.

International Students: There are currently 131 international students enrolled. They must take the TOEFL and achieve a minimum score of 500.

Computers: The college provides computer facilities for student use. The mainframe is a DEC VAX 7000/640. The microcomputer laboratory provides numerous networked microcomputers as well as terminals connected to the mainframe. Additional terminals are located in other buildings. Another laboratory provides a variety of Apple and Macintosh microcomputers for general student use. All students may access the system. It may be used 8:30 A.M. to 12 P.M., Monday to Thursday; 8:30 A.M. to 6 P.M., Friday; 9 A.M. to 6 P.M., Saturday; and 1 P.M. to 10 P.M., Sunday. There are no time limits and no fees.

Graduates: In 1992–93, 1404 bachelor's degrees were awarded. The most popular majors among graduates were accounting (10%), business administration and management (9%), and business management and organization (8%). Within an average freshman class, 15% graduate in 4 years, 40% in 5 years, and 45% in 6 years. Some 63 companies recruited on campus in 1992–93. Nineteen percent of all 1992 graduates were enrolled in graduate school within 6 months of graduation; 85% had found employment.

Admissions Contact: Admissions Office.

CHARTER OAK COLLEGE
(See Charter Oak State College)

CHARTER OAK STATE COLLEGE   C-2
(Formerly Charter Oak College)
Farmington, CT 06032–1934   (203) 677–0076

Full-time: none	Faculty: 59 part-time
Part-time: 561 men, 583 women	Ph.D.s: 83%
Graduate: none	Student/Faculty: 19 to 1
Year: n/app	Tuition: $314 ($451)
Application Deadline: open	Room & Board: n/app
Freshman Class: n/av	
SAT I or ACT: not required	**NONCOMPETITIVE**

Charter Oak State College, founded in 1973, is a public, coeducational liberal arts college offering an external degree program for adult students who cannot complete a college degree by conventional means because of family, job, or financial considerations. Credits may be earned by transfer, testing, and portfolio review. The campus is in a suburban area 10 miles west of Hartford.

Student Life: About 90% of undergraduates are from Connecticut. Students come from 30 states. Ninety percent are white.

Housing: There are no residence halls.

Disabled Students: The entire campus is accessible to disabled students. The following facilities are available: wheelchair ramps, elevators, special parking, specially equipped rest rooms, and lowered drinking fountains.

Programs of Study: Charter Oak awards the B.A. and B.S. degrees. Associate degrees also are awarded. Bachelor's degrees are awarded in BIOLOGICAL SCIENCE (biology/biological science), BUSINESS (business administration and management), COMMUNICATIONS AND THE ARTS (applied art, art history and appreciation, communications, languages, literature, and music), COMPUTER AND PHYSICAL SCIENCE (chemistry, computer science, geology, mathematics, natural sciences, physics, and science technology), ENGINEERING AND ENVIRONMENTAL DESIGN (technological management), SOCIAL SCIENCE (economics, fire control and safety technology, geography, history, human services, humanities, interdisciplinary studies, philosophy, political science/government, psychology, social science, and sociology). Business, human services and interdisciplinary studies have the largest enrollments.

Required: All students must complete 120 total credits, 60 of which should be in liberal arts and 36 in the field of concentration. Distribution should include 12 credits in humanities, 9 in social science, 3 in mathematics and 4 to 6 in sciences. Students also need to maintain a minimum GPA of 2.0 and earn credits in English composition and history or political science.

Faculty/Classroom: Fifty-six percent of faculty are male; 44%, female.

Requirements: Charter Oaks State College requires applicants to have either a high school diploma or an equivalency certificate and to have earned at least 9 credits from an accredited college or university. The SAT I or ACT is not required. An interview is recommended. AP and CLEP credits are accepted.

Procedure: Application deadlines are open. Application fee is $25. Notification is sent on a rolling basis.

Transfer: About 451 transfer students enrolled in 1993–94. Most students who enroll in Charter Oak State College have attended college previously.

Financial Aid: One or more fees may be waived to help students who demonstrate financial need.

Graduates: In 1992–93 287 bachelor's degrees were awarded. The most popular majors among graduates were business (18%), human services: health studies (14%), and interdisciplinary studies: social science (10%). In the 1992 graduating class, 29% of the men and 20% of the women were enrolled in graduate school within 6 months of graduation.

Admissions Contact: Ruth Budlong, Director of Student Services and Public Information.

CONNECTICUT COLLEGE

E-3

New London, CT 06320-4195 (203) 439-2200

Full-time: 699 men, 931 women	Faculty: 175; IIB, +$
Part-time: 91 men, 141 women	Ph.D.s: 94%
Graduate: 14 men, 71 women	Student/Faculty: 10 to 1
Year: semesters	Tuition: $18,130
Application Deadline: January 15	Room & Board: $6030
Freshman Class: 3035 applied, 1546 accepted, 438 enrolled	
SAT I Verbal/Math: 600/620	ACT: 27 HIGHLY COMPETITIVE

Connecticut College, founded in 1911, is a private coeducational institution offering degree programs in the liberal arts and sciences. The library contains 464,894 volumes, 252,764 microform items, and 17,247 audiovisual forms, and subscribes to 1723 periodicals. Computerized library sources and services include the card catalog, interlibrary loans, and database searching. Special learning facilities include a radio station and an arboretum. The 702-acre campus is in a small town midway between Boston and New York City. Including residence halls, there are 41 buildings on campus.

Student Life: About 65% of undergraduates are from out-of-state, mostly the Northeast. Students come from 45 states and 42 foreign countries. Fifty-four percent are from public schools. Eighty-one percent are white. Thirty percent are Protestant; 29% claim no religious affiliation; 26% Catholic; 10% Jewish. The average age of freshmen is 18; all undergraduates, 19.4. Six percent drop out by the end of their first year; 92% remain to graduate.

Housing: A total of 1689 students can be accommodated in college housing. College-sponsored living facilities include coed dormitories. In addition, there are language houses and special interest houses. On-campus housing is guaranteed for all 4 years and is available on a lottery system for upperclassmen. Ninety-eight percent of students live on campus; of those, 85% remain on campus on weekends. All students may keep cars on campus.

Activities: There are no fraternities or sororities on campus. There are 75 groups on campus, including art, chess, choir, chorale, computers, dance, drama, ethnic, film, gay, honors, international, jazz band, literary magazine, musical theater, newspaper, orchestra, photography, political, radio and TV, religious, social, social service, student government, symphony, and yearbook. Popular campus events include Eclipse Weekend, Harvestfest and Floralia.

Sports: There are 11 intercollegiate sports for men and 12 for women, and 17 intramural sports for men and 17 for women. Athletic and recreation facilities include an 800-seat gymnasium, playing fields, an ice rink, a boat house, a weight training room, an indoor pool, a dance studio, 12 tennis courts, and courts for squash, racquetball, badminton, basketball, and volleyball.

Disabled Students: Twenty-five percent of the campus is accessible to disabled students. The following facilities are available: wheelchair ramps, elevators, special parking, specially equipped rest rooms, special class scheduling, lowered drinking fountains, and lowered telephones.

Services: In addition to many counseling and information services, tutoring is available in most subjects.

Campus Safety and Security: Campus safety and security measures include 24-hour foot and vehicle patrol, escort service, informal discussions, and pamphlets, posters, and films. In addition, there are emergency telephones, lighted pathways and sidewalks, and an electronic access system in the student residence.

Programs of Study: Connecticut College awards the B.A. degree. Master's degrees also are awarded. Bachelor's degrees are awarded in BIOLOGICAL SCIENCE (biochemistry, biology/biological science, botany, and zoology), COMMUNICATIONS AND THE ARTS (art history and appreciation, Chinese, classics, dance, dramatic arts, English, French, German, Japanese, languages, music, and studio art), COMPUTER AND PHYSICAL SCIENCE (chemistry, mathematics, and physics), SOCIAL SCIENCE (anthropology, Asian/Oriental studies, child psychology/development, economics, Hispanic American studies, history, international relations, philosophy, political science/government, psychology, religion, sociology, and urban studies). Government, history, economics, psychology, and English have the largest enrollments.

Required: To graduate, students must complete at least 128 credit hours with a minimum GPA of 2.0. Distribution requirements cover 9 courses from 8 academic areas, including a foreign language.

Special: Cross-registration with area colleges, professional internships, a Washington semester at American University, dual majors, student-designed majors, a 3-2 engineering degree with Washington University in St. Louis, nondegree study, and pass/fail options are available. One-third of the junior class studies abroad. An international studies certificate program is available, which combines competency in a foreign language and an internship, and study abroad. There are 2 national honor societies on campus, including Phi Beta Kappa. All departments have honor programs.

Faculty/Classroom: Fifty-eight percent of faculty are male; 42%, female. All teach undergraduates. No introductory courses are taught by graduate students. The average class size in an introductory lecture is 27; in a laboratory, 17; and in a regular course offering, 20.

Admissions: About 51% of the 1993-94 applicants were accepted. The SAT scores for the 1993-94 freshman class were as follows: Verbal—11% below 500, 40% between 500 and 599, 45% between 600 and 700, and 5% above 700; Math—6% below 500, 28% between 500 and 599, 52% between 600 and 700, and 15% above 700. About 77% of the current freshmen were in the top fifth of their class; 96% were in the top two fifths. There were 2 National Merit finalists and 8 semifinalists. About 7 freshmen graduated first in their class.

Requirements: The SAT I or the ACT is required, along with SAT II: Subject tests in writing and 2 other subjects. In addition, applicants must be graduates of an accredited secondary school. An essay is required and an interview is recommended. AP credits are accepted. Important factors used in the admissions decision are advanced placement or honor courses, evidence of special talents, leadership record, personality, intangible qualities, and extracurricular activities record.

Procedure: Freshmen are admitted fall and spring. Early decision applications should be filed by November 15 for the first round and by January 15 for the second round; regular applications, by January 15 for fall entry and December 1 for spring entry, along with an application fee of $45. Notification of early decision is sent December 15 for the first round and by February 15 for the second round; regular decision, March 30. There are early decision, early admissions, and deferred admissions plans. About 110 early decision candidates were accepted for the 1993-94 class. A waiting list is an active part of the admissions procedure, with about 11% of applicants on the list.

Transfer: About 36 transfer students enrolled in 1993-94. Transfer applicants must have a minimum college GPA of 3.0 and should submit SAT I or ACT scores. An interview is recommended. A total of 64 credits out of 128 must be completed at Connecticut College.

Visiting: There are regularly scheduled orientations for prospective students, including introduction to the college, student perspectives, academic programs, a luncheon for parents and students, tours, interviews, and a reception. There are guides for informal visits and visitors may sit in on classes and stay overnight at the school. To arrange for a visit, contact the Admissions Office at (203) 439-2200.

Financial Aid: In 1993-94 51% of all current freshmen and 54% of continuing students received some form of financial aid. About 51% of freshmen and 54% of continuing students received need-based aid. The average freshman award was $15,012. Of that total, scholarships or need-based grants averaged $13,011 ($24,660 maximum); loans averaged $2125 ($2625 maximum); and work contracts averaged $1000 ($1000 maximum). Fifty-two percent of undergraduate students work part-time. Average earnings from campus work for the school year are $646. The average financial indebtedness of the 1992-93 graduate was $7831. The college's own financial statement and parent and student tax forms are required. The deadline for financial aid applications is February 15.

International Students: There are currently 131 international students enrolled. The school actively recruits these students. They must take the TOEFL and achieve a minimum score of 590. The student must also take the SAT I. Students must take the SAT II: Writing test.

Computers: The college provides computer facilities for student use. The mainframe is a DEC VAX 3900 operating under an ULTRIX System. There are 3 public terminal rooms for the mainframe system. Macintoshes and IBM PCs are available for student use in computer laboratories and individual departments. Laser printers, plotters, and scanners are also available. A campuswide network links computer cluster, classroom, laboratory, dormitory rooms, and the library with voice data and video transmission capabilities. BITNET and Internet are also available. All students may access the system. It may be used 8 a.m to midnight. There are no time limits and no fees.

Graduates: In 1992-93, 448 bachelor's degrees were awarded. The most popular majors among graduates were government (15%), history (15%), and English (13%). Within an average freshman class, 1% graduate in 3 years, 84% in 4 years, and 92% in 5 years. Some 70 companies recruited on campus in a recent year.

Admissions Contact: Claire K. Matthews, Dean of Admissions.

CONNECTICUT STATE UNIVERSITY

The Connecticut State University, established in 1983, is a public system in Connecticut. It is governed by a board of trustees, whose chief administrator is president. The primary goal of the system is teaching. The main priorities are access, with emphasis on a multi-cultural experience; quality, within a context of curriculum diversity and a range of delivery systems; and public service, including linkages with schools, state government, and private enterprise. The total enrollment in a recent year of all 4 campuses was 36,429; there were 2143 faculty members. Altogether there are 70 baccalaureate and 60 master's

programs offered at Connecticut State University. Profiles of the 4-year campuses are included in this chapter in alphabetical order with other Connecticut schools.

EASTERN CONNECTICUT STATE UNIVERSITY D-2
Willimantic, CT 06226 (203) 456-5286

Full-time: 1269 men, 1497 women	Faculty: 127; IIA, +$
Part-time: 518 men, 1001 women	Ph.D.s: n/av
Graduate: 45 men, 234 women	Student/Faculty: 22 to 1
Year: semesters, summer session	Tuition: $2946 ($7658)
Application Deadline: May 1	Room & Board: $4020
Freshman Class: 2172 applied, 1493 accepted, 564 enrolled	
SAT I Verbal/Math: 430/460	**COMPETITIVE**

Eastern Connecticut State University, founded in 1889, is a public, coeducational institution offering undergraduate programs in liberal arts and sciences, business, and education. There are 3 undergraduate schools and one graduate school. The library contains 212,500 volumes and 350,000 microform items, and subscribes to 1850 periodicals. Computerized library sources and services include the card catalog, interlibrary loans, and database searching. Special learning facilities include a learning resource center, art gallery, planetarium, radio station, and TV station. The 174-acre campus is in a suburban area 29 miles east of Hartford, and 90 miles from Boston, Massachusetts. Including residence halls, there are 29 buildings on campus.

Student Life: About 90% of undergraduates are from Connecticut. Students come from 16 states, 31 foreign countries, and Canada. Eighty-eight percent are from public schools; 12% from private. Eighty-three percent are white. The average age of freshmen is 18; all undergraduates, 23. Twelve percent drop out by the end of their first year; 50% remain to graduate.

Housing: A total of 1520 students can be accommodated in college housing. College-sponsored living facilities include single-sex and coed dormitories and on-campus apartments. On-campus housing is guaranteed for all 4 years. Sixty percent of students live on campus. Alcohol is not permitted. Upperclassmen may keep cars on campus.

Activities: There are no fraternities or sororities on campus. There are 48 groups on campus, including art, band, cheerleading, choir, chorus, computers, dance, drama, ethnic, gay, honors, international, jazz band, literary magazine, musical theater, newspaper, orchestra, photography, political, professional, radio and TV, religious, social, social service, student government, and yearbook. Popular campus events include Homecoming, Spring Weekend, and Parents Day.

Sports: There are 5 intercollegiate sports for men and 6 for women, and 17 intramural sports for men and 14 for women. Athletic and recreation facilities include a 2800-seat field house, a 6-lane swimming pool, a soccer field, baseball and softball stadiums, and tennis, basketball, racquetball, and squash courts.

Disabled Students: Seventy-five percent of the campus is accessible to disabled students. The following facilities are available: wheelchair ramps, elevators, special parking, specially equipped rest rooms, special class scheduling, lowered drinking fountains, and lowered telephones.

Services: In addition to many counseling and information services, tutoring is available in most subjects. In addition, there is a reader service for the blind, and remedial math, reading, and writing.

Campus Safety and Security: Campus safety and security measures include 24-hour foot and vehicle patrol, self-defense education, escort service, and shuttle buses. In addition, there are informal discussions, pamphlets, posters, and films, emergency telephones, and lighted pathways and sidewalks.

Programs of Study: ECSU awards the B.A., B.S., and B.G.S. degrees. Associate and master's degrees also are awarded. Bachelor's degrees are awarded in BIOLOGICAL SCIENCE (biology/biological science), BUSINESS (accounting and business administration and management), COMMUNICATIONS AND THE ARTS (communications, English, and Spanish), COMPUTER AND PHYSICAL SCIENCE (computer science and mathematics), EDUCATION (early childhood, elementary, middle school, physical, and secondary), SOCIAL SCIENCE (economics, history, political science/government, prelaw, psychology, and sociology). Liberal arts and sciences, business, and education are the strongest academically. Business administration, education, psychology, sociology, and communications have the largest enrollments.

Required: To graduate, students must complete 120 credit hours, including 30 to 48 hours in the major, with a GPA of 2.0. The general education requirement of 42 credits includes courses in interdisciplinary studies, humanities, science and mathematics, and social sciences.

Special: Co-op programs are available in all majors, and students may cross-register with the University of Connecticut. The university also offers internships, study abroad, a Washington semester, work-study programs, accelerated degree programs, dual majors, a general studies degree, nondegree study, pass/fail options, and credit for military experience. There is a freshman honors program on campus,

as well as 5 national honor societies. Four departments have honors programs.

Faculty/Classroom: All teach undergraduates. No introductory courses are taught by graduate students. The average class size in an introductory lecture is 35; in a laboratory, 18; and in a regular course offering, 35.

Admissions: About 69% of the 1993-94 applicants were accepted. The SAT scores for the 1993-94 freshman class were as follows: Verbal—80% below 500, 16% between 500 and 599, 3% between 600 and 700, and 1% above 700; Math—67% below 500, 27% between 500 and 599, 5% between 600 and 700, and 1% above 700. About 27% of the current freshmen were in the top fifth of their class; 82% were in the top two fifths.

Requirements: ECSU requires applicants to be in the upper 50% of their class. The SAT I is required. Applicants must be graduates of an accredited secondary school with a minimum GPA of 2.5 or have a GED. They should have completed 13 high school academic credits, including 4 years of English, 3 years of mathematics, and 2 years each of foreign language, social studies, and science (including 1 year of laboratory science). An interview is recommended. AP and CLEP credits are accepted. Important factors used in the admissions decision are recommendations by school officials, advanced placement or honor courses, leadership record, personality, intangible qualities, and extracurricular activities record.

Procedure: Freshmen are admitted fall and spring. Entrance exams should be taken in November or December of the senior year. Applications should be filed by May 1 for fall entry and November 15 for spring entry, along with an application fee of $20. Notification is sent on a rolling basis. There is a deferred admissions plan. A waiting list is an active part of the admissions procedure, with about 10% of applicants on the list.

Transfer: About 530 transfer students enrolled in 1993-94. Applicants for transfer should have completed a minimum of 12 credit hours with a GPA of 2.5. An associate degree and an interview are recommended. A total of 30 credits out of 120 must be completed at ECSU.

Visiting: There are regularly scheduled orientations for prospective students, including small group discussions, a tour of the campus, and a personal interview. There are guides for informal visits, and visitors may sit in on classes. To arrange for a visit, contact the Admissions Office at (203) 456-5286.

Financial Aid: In 1993-94, 60% of all current freshmen and 60% of continuing students received some form of financial aid. About 60% of freshmen and 60% of continuing students received need-based aid. The average freshman award was $5700. Of that total, scholarships or need-based grants averaged $4000 ($9900 maximum); loans averaged $850 ($2100 maximum); and work contracts averaged $850 ($2100 maximum). Fifty percent of undergraduate students work part-time. Average earnings from campus work for the school year are $1300. ECSU is a member of CSS. The FAFSA financial statement is required. The deadline for financial aid applications is March 15.

International Students: There are currently 103 international students enrolled. The school actively recruits these students. They must take the TOEFL and achieve a minimum score of 550.

Computers: The college provides computer facilities for student use. The mainframe is a DEC VAX 6420 minicomputer. The main laboratory houses approximately 100 microcomputer stations, consisting of IBM, Apple, and Zenith equipment. Other computer laboratories are located in the Media Building and in the Learning Center. All systems are connected to the campus Ethernet network. All students may access the system. There are no time limits on using the system and no fees.

Graduates: In 1992-93, 733 bachelor's degrees were awarded. The most popular majors among graduates were business administration (32%), education (16%), and psychology (10%). Within an average freshman class, 40% graduate in 4 years and 50% in 5 years. Some 200 companies recruited on campus in 1992-93. Of the 1992 graduating class, 32% of all graduates were enrolled in graduate school within 6 months of graduation; 82% had found employment.

Admissions Contact: Director of Admissions and Enrollment Planning.

FAIRFIELD UNIVERSITY B-4
Fairfield, CT 06430-7524 (203) 254-4100

Full-time: 1310 men, 1607 women	Faculty: 192; IIA, +$
Part-time: 382 men, 722 women	Ph.D.s: 90%
Graduate: 161 men, 595 women	Student/Faculty: 15 to 1
Year: semesters, summer session	Tuition: $14,560
Application Deadline: March 1	Room & Board: $5900
Freshman Class: 4784 applied, 3346 accepted, 773 enrolled	
SAT I Verbal/Math: 498/560	**VERY COMPETITIVE**

Fairfield University, founded by the Jesuits in 1942, is an independent, Roman Catholic coeducational institution. There are 3 under-

graduate and 2 graduate schools. In addition to regional accreditation, Fairfield has baccalaureate program accreditation with NLN. The library contains 298,221 volumes, 410,125 microform items, and 6229 audiovisual forms, and subscribes to 1798 periodicals. Computerized library sources and services include interlibrary loans and database searching. Special learning facilities include an art gallery, radio station, TV station, a media center, and a 750-seat concert hall/theater. The 200-acre campus is in a suburban area 60 miles northeast of New York City. Including residence halls, there are 30 buildings on campus.

Student Life: About 68% of undergraduates are from out-of-state, mostly the Northeast. Students come from 38 states, 17 foreign countries, and Canada. Fifty percent are from public schools; 50% from private. Eighty-eight percent are white. Most are Catholic. The average age of freshmen is 18; all undergraduates, 21. Ten percent drop out by the end of their first year; 84% remain to graduate.

Housing: College-sponsored living facilities include coed dormitories and on-campus apartments. In addition there are special interest houses, a wellness floor, and a service floor. On-campus housing is guaranteed for all 4 years. Eighty percent of students live on campus; of those, 80% remain on campus on weekends. Upperclassmen may keep cars on campus.

Activities: There are no fraternities or sororities on campus. There are 100 groups on campus, including art, band, cheerleading, chorale, computers, dance, drama, ethnic, film, honors, international, jazz band, literary magazine, musical theater, newspaper, orchestra, pep band, photography, political, professional, radio and TV, religious, social, social service, student government, and yearbook. Popular campus events include Dogwood Festival, Martin Luther King Week, Luck of the Roommate Dance, May Day, and major concerts.

Sports: There are 9 intercollegiate sports for men and 8 for women, and 8 intramural sports for men and 8 for women. Athletic and recreation facilities include a gymnasium, a 25-meter swimming pool, weight rooms, indoor and outdoor tennis courts, racquetball and volleyball courts, indoor and outdoor tracks, and a sauna and whirlpool.

Disabled Students: The entire campus is accessible to disabled students. The following facilities are available: wheelchair ramps, elevators, special parking, specially equipped rest rooms, special class scheduling, lowered drinking fountains, and lowered telephones. In addition, single rooms are available for disabled students, and seeing-eye dogs can be accommodated.

Services: In addition to many counseling and information services, tutoring is available in every subject. There is also a reader service for the blind.

Campus Safety and Security: Campus safety and security measures include 24-hour foot and vehicle patrol, self defense education, escort service, and shuttle buses. In addition, there are informal discussions, pamphlets, posters, films, emergency telephones, lighted pathways and sidewalks, EMT security officers, and bike patrol.

Programs of Study: Fairfield awards the B.S. and B.A. degrees. Master's degrees also are awarded. Bachelor's degrees are awarded in BIOLOGICAL SCIENCE (biology/biological science), BUSINESS (accounting, banking and finance, business administration and management, international business management, and marketing/retailing/merchandising), COMMUNICATIONS AND THE ARTS (communications, English, fine arts, French, German, Italian, and Spanish), COMPUTER AND PHYSICAL SCIENCE (chemistry, computer science, information sciences and systems, mathematics, and physics), HEALTH PROFESSIONS (nursing), SOCIAL SCIENCE (economics, history, philosophy, political science/government, psychology, religion, and sociology). Economics, politics, prelaw and premedicine, and accounting are the strongest academically. English, biology, accounting, and social sciences have the largest enrollments.

Required: In order to graduate, students must complete 120 credits, 60 of them in general education core requirements, with a minimum GPA of 2.0. Distribution requirements include 12 credits in mathematics and natural sciences, 12 credits in history and social sciences, 15 credits in philosophy, religious studies, and ethics, 15 credits in English and fine arts, and 6 credits in foreign languages.

Special: Cross-registration with Sacred Heart College and the University of Bridgeport is possible. Fairfield offers study abroad, a Washington semester, federal work-study program, B.A.-B.S. degrees, and dual majors. A 3–2 engineering degree is offered with the University of Connecticut, Rensselaer Polytechnic Institute, and Columbia University. A general studies degree and credit for life, military, and work experience are available through the School of Continuing Education. Internships are offered at area corporations, publications, banks, and other businesses. There is a minor available in women's studies. There is a freshman honors program on campus, as well as 7 national honor societies. In addition, there is an interdisciplinary honors program in humanities.

Faculty/Classroom: Sixty-four percent of faculty are male; 36%, female. All faculty teach and do research. No introductory courses are taught by graduate students. The average class size in an introductory lecture is 35; in a laboratory, 20; and in a regular course offering, 24.

Admissions: About 70% of the 1993–94 applicants were accepted. The SAT scores for the 1993–94 freshman class were as follows: Verbal—47% below 500, 45% between 500 and 599, 7% between 600 and 700, and 1% above 700; Math—18% below 500, 49% between 500 and 599, 29% between 600 and 700, and 4% above 700. About 57% of the current freshmen were in the top fifth of their class; 90% were in the top two fifths. There was 1 National Merit semifinalist. Six freshmen graduated first in their class.

Requirements: Fairfield requires applicants to be in the upper 40% of their class. A minimum GPA of 3.0 is required. The SAT I is required. Applicants must be graduates of an accredited secondary school. The GED is accepted. A B average is required. Students should have completed 16 academic credits, including 4 credits of English, 3 credits each of history and mathematics, and 2 credits each of a foreign language, science, and social studies. The school recommends SAT II: Subject tests in writing and mathematics, and, for nursing and science majors, in the sciences. An interview is recommended. AP and CLEP credits are accepted. Important factors used in the admissions decision are advanced placement or honor courses, leadership record, evidence of special talents, geographic diversity, and recommendations by alumni.

Procedure: Freshmen are admitted in the fall. Entrance exams should be taken in spring of the junior year or fall of the senior year. Early decision applications should be filed by December 1; regular applications, by March 1 for fall entry, along with an application fee of $35. Notification of early decision is sent January 1; regular decision, May 1. There are early decision and deferred admissions plans. About 107 early decision candidates were accepted for the 1993–94 class. A waiting list is an active part of the admissions procedure, with about 4% of applicants on the list.

Transfer: About 36 transfer students enrolled in a recent year. The SAT I and a college GPA of 2.5 are required. A total of 60 credits out of 120 must be completed at Fairfield.

Visiting: There are regularly scheduled orientations for prospective students. There are guides for informal visits and visitors may sit in on classes.

Financial Aid: In 1993–94 69% of all current freshmen and 61% of continuing students received some form of financial aid. About 43% of freshmen and 39% of continuing students received need-based aid. The average freshman award was $8066. Of that total, scholarships or need-based grants averaged $7225 ($17,600 maximum); loans averaged $2570 ($4625 maximum); and work contracts averaged $1500 ($1500 maximum). Ten percent of undergraduate students work part-time. Average earnings from campus work for the school year are $950. Fairfield is a member of CSS. The FAF, parent and student tax returns, and a verification statement are required. The deadline for financial aid applications is February 1.

International Students: There are currently 23 international students enrolled. They must take the TOEFL.

Computers: The college provides computer facilities for student use. The mainframe is a VAX 6430. Staffed computer laboratories are maintained in all academic buildings. Macintosh, IBM PS/2, and Apple II microcomputers are available. The VAX 6430 mainframe is accessible through 20 terminals. All students may access the system. It may be used daily until midnight. There are no time limits on using the system. The fees are $45.

Graduates: In 1992–93 821 bachelor's degrees were awarded. The most popular majors among graduates were English (11%), marketing (9%), and accounting (9%). Within an average freshman class, 84% graduate in 4 years, 2% in 5 years, and 1% in 6 years. Some 99 companies recruited on campus in 1992–93.

Admissions Contact: Dave Flynn, Dean of Admissions.

PAIER COLLEGE OF ART

C-3

Hamden, CT 06514

Recognized candidate for accreditation (203) 287-3030

Full-time: 80 men, 72 women	Faculty: 10
Part-time: 36 men, 65 women	Ph.D.s: 1%
Graduate: none	Student/Faculty: 15 to 1
Year: semesters, summer session	Tuition: $10,120
Application Deadline: August 20	Room & Board: n/app
Freshman Class: 116 applied, 68 accepted, 67 enrolled	
SAT I Verbal/Math: 410/410	SPECIAL

Paier College of Art, founded in 1946, is an independent college emphasizing academic studies, fine arts, graphic and interior design, illustration, and photography. The library contains 12,000 volumes and 50,000 audiovisual forms, and subscribes to 90 periodicals. The 3-acre campus is in an urban area 2 miles west of New Haven. There are 5 buildings on campus. There are no residence halls.

Student Life: About 96% of undergraduates are from Connecticut. Students come from 3 states and 4 foreign countries. Ninety-five percent are from public schools; 5% from private. Ninety-eight percent are white. The average age of freshmen is 24. Twenty percent drop out by the end of their first year; 58% remain to graduate.

Housing: There are no residence halls. In addition there are a list of rooms in nearby private houses and apartments is available. One-hundred percent of students commute. Alcohol is not permitted. All students may keep cars on campus.

Activities: There are no fraternities or sororities on campus. There are some groups and organizations on campus, including newspaper and yearbook. Popular campus events include Christmas and spring student art shows, Halloween Dance, Winter Dinner Dance, Spring Outing and Picnic, fall get-together, faculty and visiting artist exhibitions, art films, and lectures.

Sports: There is no sports program at Paier.

Disabled Students: Sixty percent of the campus is accessible to disabled students. The following facilities are available: special parking, specially equipped rest rooms, lowered drinking fountains, and telephones.

Programs of Study: Paier awards the B.F.A. degree and Associate degrees are also awarded. Bachelor's degrees are awarded in COMMUNICATIONS AND THE ARTS (design, fine arts, graphic design, and illustration), ENGINEERING AND ENVIRONMENTAL DESIGN (interior design).

Required: All students are required to take electives in psychology, philosophy, mathematics, and biology. Other electives must include 3 semester hours of humanities, 6 of social studies, and 3 of science or mathematics. Students also must maintain a minimum GPA of 2.0 and take 130 total credit hours, including 88 within their major field.

Special: Paier offers a co-op program with Albertus Magnus College for academic studies, in addition to pass/fail options, nondegree studies, and a B.A.-B.S. degrees.

Faculty/Classroom: Sixty-nine percent of faculty are male; 31%, female. The average class size in an introductory lecture is 20; in a laboratory, 10; and in a regular course offering, 20.

Admissions: About 59% of the 1993–94 applicants were accepted. About 5% of the current freshmen were in the top fifth of their class; 9% were in the top two fifths.

Requirements: The SAT I or ACT is required. Applicants must be graduates of an accredited secondary school. The GED is accepted. A portfolio of recent artwork is a vital part of the admissions process. An interview, during which the portfolio is presented, is necessary. Paier also considers artistic talent, recommendations, and intangibles for admission. AP and CLEP credits are accepted. Important factors used in the admissions decision are evidence of special talent, personality, intangible qualities, parents or siblings attending the school, leadership record, and advanced placement or honor courses.

Procedure: Freshmen are admitted fall and spring. Applications should be filed by August 20 for fall entry, January 8 for spring entry, and July 1 for summer entry, along with an application fee of $25. Notification is sent on a rolling basis.

Transfer: About 30 transfer students enrolled in an earlier year. Transfer applicants are required to have a minimum GPA of 2.0 and meet the same qualifications as other students, including the SAT I or ACT, an interview, and a portfolio. A total of 65 credits out of 130 must be completed at Paier.

Visiting: There are regularly scheduled orientations for prospective students. There are guides for informal visits and visitors may sit in on classes. To arrange for a visit, contact the Admissions Office at (203) 287–7319.

Financial Aid: Recently, 41% of all current freshmen and 28% of continuing students received some form of financial aid. Paier is a member of CSS. The FAF and SAR, parent and student income tax forms, and FATs from previously attended schools are required.

International Students: They must take the TOEFL. The student must also take the SAT I or the ACT.

Graduates: In an earlier year, 29 bachelor's degrees were awarded. Recently, some 4 companies recruited on campus. In an earlier graduating class, 10% of the women were enrolled in graduate school within 6 months of graduation; 16% of the men and 45% of the women had found employment.

Admissions Contact: Daniel Paier, Assistant Dean.

QUINNIPIAC COLLEGE
Hamden, CT 06518   (203) 281-8600; (800) 462-1944 (out-of-state)   C-3

Full-time: 1219 men, 1488 women	Faculty: 208; IIB, +$
Part-time: 207 men, 491 women	Ph.D.s: 70%
Graduate: 607 men, 615 women	Student/Faculty: 13 to 1
Year: semesters, summer session	Tuition: $11,810
Application Deadline: March 1	Room & Board: $5790
Freshman Class: 3712 applied, 2153 accepted, 672 enrolled	
SAT I Verbal/Math: 510/535	COMPETITIVE +

Quinnipiac College, founded in 1929, is a private, coeducational institution offering undergraduate and graduate degrees in allied health and natural sciences, business, communications, and liberal arts. There are 3 undergraduate and 2 graduate schools. In addition to regional accreditation, Quinnipiac has baccalaureate program accreditation with APTA, CAHEA, and NLN. The library contains 150,000 volumes, 9100 microform items, and 1890 audiovisual forms, and subscribes to 860 periodicals. Computerized library sources and services include interlibrary loans and database searching. Special learning facilities include a learning resource center and radio station. The 180-acre campus is in a suburban area 10 miles north of New Haven and 35 miles south of Hartford. Including residence halls, there are 34 buildings on campus.

Student Life: About 55% of undergraduates are from out-of-state, mostly the Northeast. Students come from 22 states, 10 foreign countries, and Canada. Sixty percent are from public schools; 40% from private. Eighty-nine percent are white. Sixty-five percent are Catholic; 20% Protestant; 12% Jewish. The average age of freshmen is 19; all undergraduates, 21. Sixteen percent drop out by the end of their first year; 70% remain to graduate.

Housing: A total of 1770 students can be accommodated in college housing. College-sponsored living facilities include single-sex and coed dormitories and on-campus apartments. In addition there are quiet houses, and wellness houses. On-campus housing is guaranteed for all 4 years. Seventy-five percent of students live on campus; of those, 70% remain on campus on weekends. All students may keep cars on campus.

Activities: About 3% of men belong to 1 local and 3 national fraternities; about 3% of women belong to 1 local and 2 national sororities. There are 65 groups on campus, including cheerleading, dance, drama, ethnic, film, honors, international, jazz band, literary magazine, musical theater, newspaper, photography, political, professional, radio and TV, religious, social, social service, student government, and yearbook. Popular campus events include May Weekend, Halloween Mixer, Lip Sync Contest, Oktoberfest, Holiday Dinner, NICHE Conference, Alumni-Endowed Lecture, Thursdays at Quinnipiac, Presidential Lecture Series, Admitted Student Days, jazz concerts, and special athletic events.

Sports: There are 7 intercollegiate sports for men and 7 for women, and 9 intramural sports for men and 9 for women. Athletic and recreation facilities include over 20 acres of playing fields, a 1500-seat gymnasium, 2 basketball courts, a weight training room, a steam room, aerobic rooms with sauna, and a state-of-the-art fitness facility with a large multipurpose room for indoor tennis, basketball, volleyball, and track.

Disabled Students: The entire campus is accessible to disabled students. The following facilities are available: wheelchair ramps, elevators, special parking, specially equipped rest rooms, special class scheduling, lowered drinking fountains, lowered telephones, and residence rooms designed for wheelchair students.

Services: In addition to many counseling and information services, tutoring is available in most subjects, including all freshmen-level courses and for others by request, and special workshops on study skills, time management, and notetaking are offered. There is also a reader service for the blind, and remedial math, reading, and writing.

Campus Safety and Security: Campus safety and security measures include 24-hour foot and vehicle patrol, self defense education, escort service, and informal discussions. In addition, there are pamphlets, posters, and films, lighted pathways and sidewalks, and staffed guard shacks. There is perimeter security in the form of contract guards at all entrances, vehicle and pedestrian check-in identification, and police attendance at all major college functions.

Programs of Study: Quinnipiac awards the B.A., B.S., and B.H.S. degrees. A master's degrees also are awarded. Bachelor's degrees are awarded in BIOLOGICAL SCIENCE (biochemistry, biology/biological science, biotechnology, and microbiology), BUSINESS (accounting, banking and finance, business administration and management, business economics, international business management, management science, and marketing/retailing/merchandising), COMMUNICATIONS AND THE ARTS (communications and English), COMPUTER AND PHYSICAL SCIENCE (chemistry, computer science, and mathematics), HEALTH PROFESSIONS (health care administration, medical laboratory science, medical laboratory technology, nursing, occupational therapy, physical therapy, predentistry, premedicine, and radiological science), SOCIAL SCIENCE (economics, gerontology, history, political science/government, prelaw, psychobiology, psychology, social science, and sociology). Psychology, mass communications, physical therapy, occupational therapy, psychobiology, biology, computer science, English, and accounting are the strongest academically. Physical therapy, mass communications, accounting, occupational therapy, psychology, and nursing have the largest enrollments.

Required: All students must complete 50 semester hours of the core curriculum, which includes competency in English, mathematics, foreign languages, oral communications, and computer information systems. Courses in arts, behavioral and social sciences, humanities, physical and biological sciences, economics, and management are also part of the core. One hour of physical education and completion of a computer skills workshop are required. To graduate, students must maintain a minimum GPA of 2.0 over 120 total semester hours.

Special: Quinnipiac offers cross-registration with the University of New Haven and Albertus Magnus College, internships in most majors, study abroad in more than 14 countries, a Washington semester with American University, work-study programs, dual majors, student-designed majors, a co-op program with the IRS in accounting, credit for life experience, and nondegree study. There is a freshman honors program on campus, as well as 8 national honor societies. Nine departments have honors programs.

Faculty/Classroom: Sixty-eight percent of faculty are male; 32%, female. All teach undergraduates and 1% also do research. No introductory courses are taught by graduate students. The average class size in an introductory lecture is 23; in a laboratory, 15; and in a regular course offering, 20.

Admissions: About 58% of the 1993–94 applicants were accepted. The SAT scores for the 1993–94 freshman class were as follows: Verbal—48% below 500, 34% between 500 and 599, 14% between 600 and 700, and 4% above 700; Math—35% below 500, 45% between 500 and 599, 14% between 600 and 700, and 6% above 700. About 40% of the current freshmen were in the top fifth of their class; 75% were in the top two fifths. Eight freshmen graduated first in their class.

Requirements: Quinnipiac requires applicants to be in the upper 50% of their class. A minimum GPA of 2.5 is required. The SAT I or ACT is required, with a recommended minimum composite score of 950 on the SAT I or 20 on the ACT. All students must have completeted 16 academic credits, including 4 in English, 3 in mathematics, 2 each in science and social studies, and 5 in electives. The GED is accepted. An interview is recommended and an essay is required. AP and CLEP credits are accepted. Important factors used in the admissions decision are advanced placement or honor courses, recommendations by school officials, leadership record, personality, intangible qualities, and evidence of special talent.

Procedure: Freshmen are admitted fall and spring. Entrance exams should be taken in the junior year and early in the senior year. Applications should be filed by March 1 for fall entry and December 15 for spring entry, along with an application fee of $40. Notification is sent on a rolling basis. There are early admissions and deferred admissions plans. A waiting list is an active part of the admissions procedure, with about 3% of applicants on the list.

Transfer: About 190 transfer students enrolled in 1993–94. Transfer students must have a minimum college GPA of 2.0, and must submit SAT I scores and high school or college transcripts. An interview is recommended. A total of 45 credits out of 120 must be completed at Quinnipiac.

Visiting: There are regularly scheduled orientations for prospective students, consisting of interviews, a group information session, student-guided tours, financial aid sessions, an opportunity to speak with faculty, and open houses. There are guides for informal visits and visitors may sit in on classes and stay overnight at the school. To arrange for a visit, contact the Admissions Office at (203) 281–8600 or (800) 462–1944.

Financial Aid: In 1993–94, 66% of all current freshmen and 65% of continuing students received some form of financial aid. About 44% of freshmen and 45% of continuing students received need-based aid. The average freshman award was $6599. Of that total, scholarships or need-based grants averaged $3096 ($11,250 maximum); loans averaged $2625; and work contracts averaged $1500 ($2000 maximum). Seventeen percent of undergraduate students work part-time. Average earnings from campus work for the school year are $1000. The average financial indebtedness of the 1992–93 graduate was $8250. Quinnipiac is a member of CSS. The college's own financial statement and FAFSA are required. The deadline for financial aid applications is March 1.

International Students: There are currently 54 international students enrolled. The school actively recruits these students. They must take the TOEFL and achieve a minimum score of 550. The student must also take the SAT I or the ACT.

Computers: The college provides computer facilities for student use. The mainframe is a DEC 5500. Every freshman is required to take a 5-week workshop on word processing and spreadsheets in the computer center's 22-station teaching laboratory. The center, which is open 7 days a week, has 45 IBM PCs and compatibles connected to an HP 3000/Series 68 minicomputer. The instructional classroom consists of 20 IBM PS/2 Model 55s operating on an IBM 05/2 LAN Server Network. All students may access the system. It may be used 8 A.M. to midnight, 7 days a week. There are no time limits on using the system and no fees.

Graduates: In 1992–93, 461 bachelor's degrees were awarded. The most popular majors among graduates were marketing (12%), physical therapy (11%), and occupational therapy (11%). Within an average freshman class, 66% graduate in 5 years and 70% in 6 years. Some 75 companies recruited on campus in 1992–93. In the 1992 graduating class, 15% of the men and 25% of the women were enrolled in graduate school within 6 months of graduation; 80% of the

men and 85% of the women had found employment.

Admissions Contact: Joan Isaac Mohr, Dean of Admissions.

SACRED HEART UNIVERSITY   B-4
Fairfield, CT 06432–1000   (203) 371–7880

Full-time: 814 men, 893 women	**Faculty:** 111; IIB, av$
Part-time: 583 men, 1306 women	**Ph.D.s:** 81%
Graduate: 552 men, 970 women	**Student/Faculty:** 15 to 1
Year: semesters, summer session	**Tuition:** $10,550
Application Deadline: open	**Room & Board:** $5800
Freshman Class: 2307 applied, 1896 accepted, 509 enrolled	
SAT I Verbal/Math: 420/480	**COMPETITIVE**

Sacred Heart University, founded in 1963, is a private Catholic institution that offers majors within health sciences, liberal arts and sciences, and business. In addition to regional accreditation, SHU has baccalaureate program accreditation with CSWE. The library contains 153,000 volumes, 52,400 microform items, and 10,900 audiovisual forms, and subscribes to 717 periodicals. Computerized library sources and services include interlibrary loans and database searching. Special learning facilities include a learning resource center, an art gallery, a radio station, a TV station, and a theater. The 56-acre campus is in a suburban area in southwestern Connecticut, 55 miles northeast of New York City. Including residence halls, there are 10 buildings on campus.

Student Life: About 70% of undergraduates are from Connecticut. Students come from 18 states, 42 foreign countries, and Canada. Sixty percent are from public schools; 40% from private. Seventy-seven percent are white. The average age of freshmen is 18; all undergraduates, 20. Fifteen percent drop out by the end of their first year; 75% remain to graduate.

Housing: A total of 900 students can be accommodated in college housing. College-sponsored living facilities include coed dormitories, on-campus apartments, and off-campus apartments. On-campus housing is guaranteed for all 4 years. Fifty percent of students live on campus; of those, 75% remain on campus on weekends. Upperclassmen may keep cars on campus.

Activities: About 2% of men belong to 1 local fraternity; about 5% of women belong to 3 local sororities. There are 70 groups on campus, including art, cheerleading, choir, chorale, chorus, computers, dance, drama, ethnic, film, honors, international, jazz band, literary magazine, marching band, musical theater, newspaper, orchestra, pep band, photography, political, professional, radio and TV, religious, social, social service, student government, and yearbook. Popular campus events include Harvest Weekend, Pioneer Weekend, International Festival, and Springfest.

Sports: There are 11 intercollegiate sports for men and 10 for women, and 6 intramural sports for men and 3 for women. Athletic and recreation facilities include 6 championship tennis courts, an artificial turf field and track, an 1100-seat gymnasium, and soccer, softball, and baseball fields.

Disabled Students: All of the campus is accessible to disabled students. The following facilities are available: wheelchair ramps, elevators, special parking, specially equipped rest rooms, special class scheduling, and lowered drinking fountains.

Services: In addition to many counseling and information services, tutoring is available in most subjects. There is also remedial math, reading, and writing.

Campus Safety and Security: Campus safety and security measures include 24-hour foot and vehicle patrol, self-defense education, escort service, and shuttle buses. In addition, there are informal discussions, pamphlets, posters, films, emergency telephones, and lighted pathways and sidewalks.

Programs of Study: SHU awards the B.A. and B.S. degrees. Associate and master's degrees are also awarded. Bachelor's degrees are awarded in BIOLOGICAL SCIENCE (biology/biological science), BUSINESS (accounting, banking and finance, business administration and management, business economics, international business management, and marketing/retailing/merchandising), COMMUNICATIONS AND THE ARTS (communications, English, film arts, fine arts, graphic design, illustration, painting, and Spanish), COMPUTER AND PHYSICAL SCIENCE (chemistry, computer science, and mathematics), EDUCATION (business, early childhood, elementary, middle school, science, and secondary), HEALTH PROFESSIONS (medical laboratory technology, nursing, predentistry, premedicine, prepharmacy, and preveterinary science), SOCIAL SCIENCE (criminal justice, economics, history, international relations, law, paralegal studies, philosophy, political science/government, prelaw, psychology, religion, social work, and sociology). Business, biology, psychology, and paralegal studies are the strongest academically. Business, accounting, psychology, and education have the largest enrollments.

Required: All students must complete 120 credit hours, including 30 to 58 in the major, while maintaining a minimum 2.0 GPA. Distribution requirements include freshman writing, college mathematics, and oral communications; 3 hours each in literature and civilization; 6

each in humanities, mathematics, and foreign language (for a B.A.); and 9 each in social science and philosophy and religious studies. B.S. candidates need an additional hour each of mathematics and science.

Special: SHU offers co-op programs in all majors, cross-registration with Fairfield University and the University of Bridgeport, paid and unpaid internships at area corporations, including Fortune 500 companies, hospitals, newspapers, and social service agencies, study abroad worldwide through International Education partnerships, a Washington semester, and on-campus work-study. There is a 5-year B.A./B.S.-M.B.A. program and a combined undergraduate and graduate program in physical therapy, with a comparable program in occupational therapy slated for 1995. There is a freshman honors program on campus, as well as 7 national honor societies, including Phi Beta Kappa.

Faculty/Classroom: Fifty-eight percent of faculty are male; 42%, female. All teach undergraduates. No introductory courses are taught by graduate students. The average class size in an introductory lecture is 30; in a laboratory, 10; and in a regular course offering, 19.

Admissions: About 82% of the 1993–94 applicants were accepted. The SAT scores for the 1993–94 freshman class were as follows: Verbal—78% below 500, 19% between 500 and 599, and 3% between 600 and 700; Math—54% below 500, 35% between 500 and 599, 10% between 600 and 700, and 1% above 700. About 39% of the current freshmen were in the top fifth of their class; 70% were in the top two fifths. There were 3 National Merit semifinalists. Eight freshmen graduated first in their class.

Requirements: SHU requires applicants to be in the upper 40% of their class. A minimum GPA of 3.0 is required. The SAT I is required, with a recommended minimum composite score of 900, 450 verbal and 450 math; SAT II: Subject tests in writing, mathematics, and language are advised. In addition, applicants must have 16 academic credits and 16 Carnegie units, including 4 years in English, 3 each in mathematics and science, 2 each in foreign language and social studies, and 1 in history. An essay is required and an interview recommended. AP and CLEP credits are accepted. Important factors used in the admissions decision are advanced placement or honor courses, leadership record, recommendations by school officials, extracurricular activities record, and personality and other intangible qualities.

Procedure: Freshmen are admitted fall and spring. Entrance exams should be taken in May of the junior year or November of the senior year. Early decision applications should be filed by December 7, along with an application fee of $30. Notification of early decision is sent December 21; regular decision, on a rolling basis. There are early decision, early admissions, and deferred admissions plans. About 70 early decision candidates were accepted for the 1993–94 class.

Transfer: About 160 transfer students enrolled in 1993–94. Applicants must submit 2 letters of recommendation and high school and college transcripts. A total of 30 credits out of 120 must be completed at SHU.

Visiting: There are regularly scheduled orientations for prospective students, including open houses on weekends and daily tours. There are guides for informal visits and visitors may sit in on classes and stay overnight at the school. To arrange for a visit, contact the Admissions Office at (203) 371-7880.

Financial Aid: In 1993–94, 82% of all current freshmen and 84% of continuing students received some form of financial aid. About 77% of freshmen and 72% of continuing students received need-based aid. The average freshman award was $7546. Of that total, scholarships or need-based grants averaged $3989 ($8550 maximum); loans averaged $2485 ($2625 maximum); and work contracts averaged $930 ($1500 maximum). Twenty-three percent of undergraduate students work part-time. Average earnings from campus work for the school year are $1015. The average financial indebtedness of the 1992–93 graduate was $13,250. SHU is a member of CSS. The FAF and the FAFSA are required. The deadline for financial aid applications is March 1.

International Students: There are currently 68 international students enrolled. The school actively recruits these students. They must take the TOEFL, the University of Michigan Language Test, the Comprehensive English Language Test, or the college's own test. The student must also take the SAT I or the ACT.

Computers: The college provides computer facilities for student use. The mainframes are a DEC VAX 11/750 and an MIPS M120. There are nearly 150 computer terminals and microcomputers, including DEC, IBM-compatible, and Apple models. The campuswide DEC fiber-optic network and academic computing technology serves the entire university, with every residence hall room wired to a port for the network. All students may access the system. It may be used 7 days per week. There are no time limits on using the system and no fees.

Graduates: In 1992–93, 333 bachelor's degrees were awarded. The most popular majors among graduates were business (36%), accounting (13%), and psychology (9%). Within an average freshman class,

70% graduate in 4 years and 73% in 5 years. Some 47 companies recruited on campus in 1992–93. In a recent graduating class, 5% of all graduates were enrolled in graduate school within 6 months of graduation; 45% had found employment.

Admissions Contact: Karen N. Pagliuco, Associate Director of Admissions.

SAINT JOSEPH COLLEGE

C-2

West Hartford, CT 06117   (203) 232–4571, ext. 216

Full-time: 543 women	**Faculty:** 68; IIA, -$
Part-time: 61 men, 651 women	**Ph.D.s:** 68%
Graduate: 93 men, 674 women	**Student/Faculty:** 8 to 1
Year: semesters, summer session	**Tuition:** $11,600
Application Deadline: May 1	**Room & Board:** $4625
Freshman Class: 322 applied, 241 accepted, 96 enrolled	
SAT I Verbal/Math: 420/450	**COMPETITIVE**

Saint Joseph College, founded in 1932 and affiliated with the Roman Catholic Church, is a private women's college offering a liberal arts education with preprofessional programs in nursing, education, and business at the undergraduate level. The Weekend College and graduate school offer coeducational studies. There are 2 undergraduate schools and 1 graduate school. In addition to regional accreditation, the college has baccalaureate program accreditation with ADA and NLN. The library contains 120,000 volumes and 10,200 microform items and subscribes to 637 periodicals. Computerized library sources and services include the card catalog, interlibrary loans, and database searching. Special learning facilities include a learning resource center, art gallery, academic resources center, and 2 laboratory schools: the Gengras Center for Exceptional Children and the School for Young Children. The 84-acre campus is in a suburban area 3 miles west of Hartford. Including residence halls, there are 13 buildings on campus.

Student Life: About 97% of undergraduates are from Connecticut. Students come from 10 states and 3 foreign countries. Seventy-six percent are from public schools; 24% from private. Ninety-one percent are white. The average age of freshmen is 19; all undergraduates, 23. Twelve percent drop out by the end of their first year; 88% remain to graduate.

Housing: A total of 333 students can be accommodated in college housing. College-sponsored living facilities include dormitories. On-campus housing is guaranteed for all 4 years. Fifty-eight percent of students commute. All students may keep cars on campus.

Activities: There are no sororities on campus. There are 26 groups on campus, including choir, chorale, chorus, dance, drama, ethnic, honors, international, literary magazine, musical theater, political, professional, religious, social, social service, student government, and yearbook. Popular campus events include October Fest, Cultural Awareness Day, Halloween Hayride, Thanksgiving Dinner, Winter Weekend, Festival of Lights, Tree Trim, Ring Ceremony, Spring Weekend, and May Day.

Sports: There are 4 intercollegiate and 6 intramural sports. Athletic and recreation facilities include an all-weather track, a gymnasium, an exercise room, tennis and platform tennis courts, a dance studio, and a pool.

Disabled Students: Seventy percent of the campus is accessible to disabled students. The following facilities are available: wheelchair ramps, elevators, special parking, specially equipped rest rooms, special class scheduling, and lowered telephones. Other needs are met on a case-by-case basis.

Services: In addition to many counseling and information services, tutoring is available in most subjects. There is also remedial math, reading, and writing. Other services are arranged as needed through the Academic Resource Center.

Campus Safety and Security: Campus safety and security measures include 24-hour foot and vehicle patrol, self defense education, informal discussions, and emergency telephones. In addition, there are lighted pathways and sidewalks and an escort service by request.

Programs of Study: The college awards the B.A., B.S., and B.S.N. degrees. Master's degrees also are awarded. Bachelor's degrees are awarded in BIOLOGICAL SCIENCE (biochemistry, biology/biological science, and nutrition), BUSINESS (business administration and management), COMMUNICATIONS AND THE ARTS (art history and appreciation, English, French, and Spanish), COMPUTER AND PHYSICAL SCIENCE (chemistry, mathematics, and natural sciences), EDUCATION (early childhood, home economics, and special), HEALTH PROFESSIONS (nursing and premedicine), SOCIAL SCIENCE (American studies, dietetics, family studies, history, humanities, philosophy, political science/government, prelaw, psychology, religion, social science, social work, and sociology). Nursing, sciences, education, and business are the strongest academically. Nursing, education, business, and psychology have the largest enrollments.

Required: All students must maintain a minimum GPA of 2.0, pass a written or oral comprehensive examination, and take 120 total credit hours including a minimum of 30 in the major and liberal arts re-

quirements of 12 credits in 4 core areas, plus 6 credits in religion, 9 in humanities, 9 in social studies, 7 to 8 in natural science/mathematics, and 1 in physical education.

Special: The college offers cross-registration through the Hartford and Wesleyan consortiums, numerous internships, study abroad in Great Britain, Europe, Japan, and Spain, accelerated degree programs, interdisciplinary majors, student-designed majors, a 3–2 engineering degree with George Washington University, and a dual major in biology-chemistry. Credit for life experience, nondegree study, and pass/fail options are available. There is a freshman honors program on campus, as well as 1 national honor society.

Faculty/Classroom: Thirty-five percent of faculty are male; 65%, female. Most both teach and do research. The average class size in an introductory lecture is 30; in a laboratory, 20; and in a regular course offering, 20.

Admissions: About 75% of the 1993–94 applicants were accepted. The SAT scores for the 1993–94 freshman class were as follows: Verbal—75% below 500, 23% between 500 and 599, and 2% between 600 and 700; Math—66% below 500, 29% between 500 and 599, 4% between 600 and 700, and 1% above 700. About 46% of the current freshmen were in the top fifth of their class; 73% were in the top two fifths.

Requirements: The college requires applicants to be in the upper 33 to 50% of their class. A minimum GPA of 3.0 is required. The SAT I is required. Applicants need 16 academic credits distributed among English, foreign language, history, mathematics, science, and social studies. The GED is accepted, and an interview is recommended. AP and CLEP credits are accepted. Important factors used in the admissions decision are advanced placement or honor courses, recommendations by school officials, recommendations by alumni, evidence of special talent, and parents or siblings attending the school.

Procedure: Freshmen are admitted in the fall and spring. Applications should be filed by May 1 for fall entry and December 1 for spring entry, along with an application fee of $25. Notification is sent on a rolling basis. There is a deferred admissions plan.

Transfer: About 104 transfer students enrolled in a recent year. Saint Joseph accepts transfers up to the beginning of the junior year. Applicants need a minimum college GPA of 2.7 in addition to an interview. Nursing applicants are required to take the SAT I. A total of 60 credits out of 120 must be completed at the college.

Visiting: There are regularly scheduled orientations for prospective students. There are guides for informal visits and visitors may sit in on classes and stay overnight at the school. To arrange for a visit, contact Mary C. Demo, Director of Admissions, at (203) 232–4571, ext. 216.

Financial Aid: In 1993–94, 98% of all current freshmen and 53% of continuing students received some form of financial aid. About 90% of freshmen and 64% of continuing students received need-based aid. The average freshman award was $8980. Of that total, scholarships or need-based grants averaged $5574 ($11,600 maximum); loans averaged $4234; and work contracts averaged $1150 (maximum). Fifteen percent of undergraduate students work part-time. Average earnings from campus work for the school year are $850. The average financial indebtedness of the 1992–93 graduate was $5360. The college is a member of CSS. The FAF, the college's own financial statement, and parent tax returns and W-2 statements are required. The deadline for financial aid applications is February 1.

International Students: There are currently 3 international students enrolled. They must take the TOEFL and the SAT I or ACT and achieve a minimum score on the TOEFL of 530.

Computers: The college provides computer facilities for student use. The mainframe is a DEC VAX 3400. The VAX laboratory is open to all students daily until 9 P.M. The IBM token ring laboratory (LAN) is used by many classes both formally and informally. The IBM and Macintosh microcomputer laboratory is open during library hours for general student use. All students may access the system during scheduled laboratory hours. There are no time limits on using the system and no fees.

Graduates: In 1992–93, 211 bachelor's degrees were awarded. The most popular majors among graduates were child study (20%), nursing (19%), and business administration (10%). Within an average freshman class, 67% graduate in 6 years. In the 1992 graduating class, 7% of the women were enrolled in graduate school within 6 months of graduation; 84% of the women had found employment.

Admissions Contact: Mary C. Demo, Director of Admissions.

SOUTHERN CONNECTICUT STATE UNIVERSITY

C-3

New Haven, CT 06515　　　　　　　　　(203) 397–4450

Full-time: 2642 men, 3250 women	Faculty: 378; IIA, +$
Part-time: 1113 men, 1365 women	Ph.D.s: 68%
Graduate: 969 men, 2805 women	Student/Faculty: 16 to 1
Year: semesters, summer session	Tuition: $3080 ($7792)
Application Deadline: May 1	Room & Board: $4452

Freshman Class: 3860 applied, 2654 accepted, 1082 enrolled
SAT I Verbal/Math: 427/462　　　　　　　　　　**COMPETITIVE**

Southern Connecticut State University, founded in 1893, provides undergraduate and graduate liberal arts programs emphasizing business and education. It is part of the Connecticut State University system. There are 5 undergraduate and 6 graduate schools. In addition to regional accreditation, SCSU has baccalaureate program accreditation with CSWE and NLN. The library contains 369,838 volumes, 671,485 microform items, and 3549 audiovisual forms, and subscribes to 3146 periodicals. Special learning facilities include a learning resource center, art gallery, planetarium, radio station, and TV station. The 168-acre campus is in an urban area 35 miles south of Hartford and 90 miles from New York City. Including residence halls, there are 28 buildings on campus.

Student Life: About 90% of undergraduates are from Connecticut. Students come from 43 states and 26 foreign countries. Eighty-one percent are white. Sixty-four percent are Catholic; 18% Protestant. The average age of freshmen is 19; all undergraduates, 21. Eleven percent drop out by the end of their first year.

Housing: A total of 2400 students can be accommodated in college housing. College-sponsored living facilities include single-sex dormitories and on-campus apartments. On-campus housing is guaranteed for all 4 years. Sixty-five percent of students commute. Upperclassmen may keep cars on campus.

Activities: About 1% of men belong to 3 local and 3 national fraternities; about 1% of women belong to 1 local and 2 national sororities. There are 70 groups on campus, including art, band, cheerleading, choir, chorale, chorus, computers, dance, drama, drill team, ethnic, gay, honors, international, jazz band, literary magazine, marching band, musical theater, newspaper, pep band, photography, political, professional, radio and TV, religious, social, social service, student government, and yearbook. Popular campus events include Homecoming, Springfest, Parents Day, and Oktoberfest.

Sports: Athletic and recreation facilities include a 6,000-seat artificial-surface playing complex for football, soccer, field hockey, and track; field house and gymnasium facilities for basketball, gymnastics, badminton, tennis, track and field, volleyball, and indoor baseball; and an 8-lane swimming pool.

Disabled Students: Eighty percent of the campus is accessible to disabled students. The following facilities are available: wheelchair ramps, elevators, special parking, specially equipped rest rooms, special class scheduling, lowered drinking fountains, lowered telephones, and special computer facilities.

Services: In addition to many counseling and information services, tutoring is available in every subject. In addition, there is a reader service for the blind, and remedial math, reading, and writing.

Campus Safety and Security: Campus safety and security measures include 24-hour foot and vehicle patrol, self-defense education, escort service, and shuttle buses. In addition, there are informal discussions, pamphlets, posters, films, emergency telephones, lighted pathways and sidewalks, and security provided by the State Police of Connecticut.

Programs of Study: SCSU awards the B.A. and B.S. degrees. Associate and master's degrees also are awarded. Bachelor's degrees are awarded in BIOLOGICAL SCIENCE (biochemistry and biology/biological science), BUSINESS (accounting, banking and finance, business administration and management, business economics, marketing/retailing/merchandising, and recreation and leisure services), COMMUNICATIONS AND THE ARTS (art history and appreciation, communications, dramatic arts, English, fine arts, French, German, Italian, journalism, Spanish, and studio art), COMPUTER AND PHYSICAL SCIENCE (chemistry, computer science, earth science, mathematics, and physics), EDUCATION (art, early childhood, elementary, foreign languages, health, library science, physical, science, secondary, and special), HEALTH PROFESSIONS (nursing and public health), SOCIAL SCIENCE (economics, geography, history, philosophy, political science/government, psychology, social work, and sociology). Business and economics, education, communications, and nursing have the largest enrollments.

Required: All students must complete distribution requirements that include 3 credits each in American politics, fine arts, foreign languages, mathematics, literature, philosophy, and Western civilization, 6 credits each in English composition and speech, natural sciences, and social sciences, and 1 credit each in physical education and

health. Students must take 122 total credits, with a minimum of 30 hours in the major field, and maintain a minimum GPA of 2.0.

Special: SCSU offer co-op programs in all academic majors, internships in many departments, study abroad in a variety of countries, a combined B.A.-B.S. degree, dual majors, a general studies degree, student-designed majors in liberal studies, and pass/fail options. There is a freshman honors program on campus, as well as 2 national honor societies. One department has an honors program.

Faculty/Classroom: No introductory courses are taught by graduate students. The average class size in an introductory lecture is 35; in a laboratory, 21; and in a regular course offering, 40.

Admissions: About 69% of the 1993–94 applicants were accepted. About 11% of the current freshmen were in the top fifth of their class; 42% were in the top two fifths.

Requirements: SCSU requires applicants to be in the upper 50% of their class. A minimum GPA of 2.5 is required. The SAT I or ACT is required. A minimum composite score of 800 on the SAT I, with at least 400 each in verbal and mathematics, or a composite score of 15 on the ACT, is needed. In addition, applicants should graduate with 4 years in English, 3 in mathematics, and 2 each in natural sciences and social sciences, including American history. The GED is accepted. Two years of foreign language are recommended. An essay also is needed. AP and CLEP credits are accepted. Important factors used in the admissions decision are advanced placement or honor courses, recommendations by school officials, leadership record, parents or siblings attending the school, and extracurricular activities record.

Procedure: Freshmen are admitted fall and spring. Applications should be filed by May 1 for fall entry and December 1 for spring entry, along with an application fee of $20. Notification is sent on a rolling basis.

Transfer: About 780 transfer students enrolled in 1993–94. Transfer applicants must have a minimum of 6 college credits with a grade of C or better and a minimum GPA of 2.0. The SAT I is required for applicants with fewer than 24 college credits. At least 30 credits out of 122 must be completed at SCSU.

Visiting: There are regularly scheduled orientations for prospective students. Visitors may sit in on classes. To arrange for a visit, contact the Student Affairs Office at (203) 397–4281.

Financial Aid: In a recent year, 30% of all current freshmen and 38% of continuing students received some form of financial aid. Scholarships or need-based grants averaged $2100 ($4000 maximum); and loans averaged $1000 ($4500 maximum). Fifteen percent of undergraduate students work part-time. Average earnings from campus work for the school year are $1500. The average financial indebtedness of a recent graduate was $2800. SCSU is a member of CSS. The college's own financial statement and the FAFSA are required. The deadline for financial aid applications is March 16.

International Students: There are currently 90 international students enrolled. They must take the TOEFL and achieve a minimum score of 525 and must also take the SAT I or the ACT.

Computers: The college provides computer facilities for student use. The mainframe is a DEC VAX 8650. More than 200 microcomputers are available for student use in various campus locations. All students may access the system 24 hours a day. There are no time limits on using the system and no fees.

Graduates: In 1992–93, 1506 bachelor's degrees were awarded. Some 150 companies recruited on campus in a recent year.

Admissions Contact: Sharon Brennan, Director of Admissions.

TEIKYO POST UNIVERSITY
Waterbury, CT 06723

B-3

(203) 596–4520
(800) 345–2562 (out-of-state)

Full-time: 570, men and women	Faculty: 27; IIB, +$
Part-time: 1273, men and women	Ph.D.s: 92%
Graduate: none	Student/Faculty: 21 to 1
Year: semesters, summer session	Tuition: $11,110
Application Deadline: open	Room & Board: $5250
Freshman Class: 487 applied, 410 accepted, 141 enrolled	
SAT I: required	LESS COMPETITIVE

Teikyo Post University, founded in 1890, is a private coeducational institution offering liberal arts and business programs with an international focus. There are 2 undergraduate schools. The library contains 45,000 volumes, 4200 microform items, and 700 audiovisual forms, and subscribes to 525 periodicals. Computerized library sources and services include the card catalog, interlibrary loans, and database searching. Special learning facilities include a learning resource center and a tutorial center. The 70-acre campus is in a suburban area 1 mile west of Waterbury. Including residence halls, there are 12 buildings on campus.

Student Life: About 82% of undergraduates are from Connecticut. Students come from 17 states, 32 foreign countries, and Canada. Seventy percent are from public schools; 30% from private. Eighty-two percent are white. The average age of freshmen is 20; all undergraduates, 24.

Housing: A total of 330 students can be accommodated in college housing. College-sponsored living facilities include single-sex and coed dormitories and off-campus apartments. In addition there are honors houses. On-campus housing is guaranteed for all 4 years. Fifty-seven percent of students live on campus; of those, 40% remain on campus on weekends. All students may keep cars on campus.

Activities: There are no fraternities or sororities on campus. There are 26 groups on campus, including cheerleading, chorale, chorus, drama, ethnic, honors, international, social, social service, student government, and yearbook. Popular campus events include Homecoming Dance, Peer Guide Program, Spring Week, Career Fair, and Karaoke Nights.

Sports: There are 2 intercollegiate sports for men and 2 for women, and 15 intramural sports for men and 15 for women. Athletic and recreation facilities include a gymnasium, a soccer/football field, a fitness center, a health club, a swimming pool, and handball and tennis courts.

Disabled Students: Seventy percent of the campus is accessible to disabled students. The following facilities are available: wheelchair ramps, elevators, special parking, and specially equipped rest rooms.

Services: In addition to many counseling and information services, tutoring is available in some subjects, including English and mathematics. There is also a reader service for the blind, and remedial math, reading, and writing.

Campus Safety and Security: Campus safety and security measures include 24-hour foot and vehicle patrol, self defense education, escort service, and informal discussions. In addition, there are pamphlets, posters, and films and lighted pathways and sidewalks.

Programs of Study: Teikyo Post awards the B.A. and B.S. degrees. Associate degrees are also awarded. Bachelor's degrees are awarded in BUSINESS (accounting, banking and finance, business administration and management, management science, and marketing/retailing/merchandising), COMMUNICATIONS AND THE ARTS (English), SOCIAL SCIENCE (history, liberal arts/general studies, psychology, and sociology). Business and general studies are the strongest academically. Management and general studies have the largest enrollments.

Required: To graduate, all students must maintain a minimum GPA of 2.0 and earn a total of 120 credits for a B.S degree or 122 for a B.A degree.

Special: Co-op programs in all majors with the universities of Hartford and Bridgeport, cross-registration with Mattatuck Community College, study abroad in England, the Netherlands, Poland, and Japan, internships with area businesses, B.A.-B.S. degrees, general studies degrees, student-designed majors, and credit for life experience are available. There are 2 national honor societies on campus. One department has an honors program.

Faculty/Classroom: Fifty-three percent of faculty are male; 47%, female. All teach undergraduates. The average class size in an introductory lecture is 30; in a laboratory, 16; and in a regular course offering, 21.

Admissions: About 84% of the 1993–94 applicants were accepted. About 15% of the current freshmen were in the top fifth of their class; 35% were in the top two fifths. There were 3 National Merit semifinalists. One freshman graduated first in his class.

Requirements: A minimum GPA of 2.0 is required. The SAT I is required. Applicants must be graduates of an accredited secondary school, with 4 years of English and at least 16 total academic credits. The GED is accepted. A high school GPA of 2.0 is required. AP and CLEP credits are accepted. Important factors used in the admissions decision are advanced placement or honor courses, recommendations by school officials, personality, intangible qualities, leadership record, and evidence of special talent.

Procedure: Freshmen are admitted to all sessions. Entrance exams should be taken as early as possible. Application deadlines are open. Application fee is $40. Notification is sent on a rolling basis. There are early decision, early admissions, and deferred admissions plans.

Transfer: About 70 transfer students enrolled in a recent year. Transfer applicants must have a minimum college GPA of 2.0. The SAT I is recommended. A total of 30 credits out of 120 to 122 must be completed at Teikyo Post.

Visiting: There are regularly scheduled orientations for prospective students, including tours, interviews with admissions counselors, and meetings with faculty and students. There are guides for informal visits and visitors may sit in on classes and stay overnight at the school. To arrange for a visit, contact the Admissions Office at (203) 596–4520 or (800) 345–2562.

Financial Aid: In 1993–94, 85% of all current freshmen and 70% of continuing students received some form of financial aid. The average freshman award in a recent year was $6629. Of that total, scholarships or need-based grants averaged $5838 ($10,219 maximum); loans averaged $2625 ($4000 maximum); and work contracts averaged $1400 ($1400 maximum). The average financial indebtedness of a recent graduate was $11,250. Teikyo Post is a member of CSS. The FAF, the college's own financial statement, and the parent and

student federal tax returns are required. The deadline for financial aid applications is March 15.

International Students: There are currently 45 international students enrolled. The school actively recruits these students. They must take the TOEFL and achieve a minimum score of 550. The student must also take the SAT I or the college's own entrance exam.

Computers: The college provides computer facilities for student use. The mainframe is a DEC. IBM and Apple Macintosh microcomputers are available for student use in the computer laboratory, the library, and the tutorial center. All students may access the system. There are no time limits on using the system and no fees.

Graduates: In a recent year, 214 bachelor's degrees were awarded. The most popular majors among graduates were business and management (83%), area studies (13%), and psychology (2%). Some 21 companies recruited on campus in a recent year.

Admissions Contact: Vincent C. Schaff, Associate Director of Admissions.

TRINITY COLLEGE
C-2

Hartford, CT 06106   (203) 297-2180

Full-time: 881 men, 856 women	Faculty: 155; IIB, +$
Part-time: 73 men, 136 women	Ph.D.s: 98%
Graduate: 104 men, 86 women	Student/Faculty: 11 to 1
Year: semesters	Tuition: $18,700
Application Deadline: January 15	Room & Board: $5420

Freshman Class: 3058 applied, 1798 accepted, 478 enrolled
SAT I or ACT: required   **HIGHLY COMPETITIVE**

Trinity College, founded in 1823, is an independent, nonsectarian liberal arts college emphasizing interdisciplinary study and interaction with Hartford. There is one graduate school. The library contains 860,093 volumes, 266,492 microform items, and 183,146 audiovisual forms, and subscribes to 2215 periodicals. Special learning facilities include an art gallery and a radio station. The 96-acre campus is in an urban area southwest of downtown Hartford. Including residence halls, there are 50 buildings on campus.

Student Life: About 78% of undergraduates are from out-of-state, mostly the Northeast. Students come from 45 states and 20 foreign countries. Fifty-two percent are from public schools; 48% from private. Eighty-two percent are white. The average age of freshmen is 18; all undergraduates, 20. Three percent drop out by the end of their first year; 88% remain to graduate.

Housing: A total of 1600 students can be accommodated in college housing. College-sponsored living facilities include coed dormitories, on-campus apartments, fraternity houses, and sorority houses. In addition, there are special interest houses. On-campus housing is guaranteed for all 4 years. Ninety-six percent of students live on campus; of those, 70% remain on campus on weekends. Upperclassmen may keep cars on campus.

Activities: About 33% of men and about 2% of women belong to 9 local fraternities; about 11% of women belong to 2 local sororities. There are 70 groups on campus, including art, cheerleading, chess, choir, chorale, dance, drama, ethnic, film, gay, international, jazz band, literary magazine, musical theater, newspaper, photography, political, radio and TV, religious, social, social service, student government, and yearbook.

Sports: There are 15 intercollegiate sports for men and 13 for women, and 7 intramural sports for men and 3 for women. Athletic and recreation facilities include a pool; outdoor and indoor tracks; tennis, squash, and basketball courts; playing fields; a weight room; and a fitness center.

Disabled Students: Sixty percent of the campus is accessible to disabled students. The following facilities are available: wheelchair ramps, elevators, special parking, specially equipped rest rooms, special class scheduling, lowered drinking fountains, and lowered telephones.

Services: In addition to many counseling and information services, tutoring is available in every subject. There is also a reader service for the blind.

Campus Safety and Security: Campus safety and security measures include 24-hour foot and vehicle patrol, self-defense education, escort service, and shuttle buses. In addition, there are informal discussions, pamphlets, posters, films, emergency telephones, and lighted pathways and sidewalks.

Programs of Study: Trinity awards the B.A. and B.S. degrees. Master's degrees also are awarded. Bachelor's degrees are awarded in BIOLOGICAL SCIENCE (biochemistry, biology/biological science, and neurosciences), COMMUNICATIONS AND THE ARTS (classics, dance, dramatic arts, English, fine arts, French, German, Italian, modern language, music, Russian, and Spanish), COMPUTER AND PHYSICAL SCIENCE (chemistry, computer science, mathematics, and physics), ENGINEERING AND ENVIRONMENTAL DESIGN (engineering), SOCIAL SCIENCE (area studies, economics, history, philosophy, political science/government, psychology, public affairs, re-

ligion, and sociology). English, history, and economics have the largest enrollments.

Required: All students must complete 36 course credits, including 10 to 15 in the major and 1 from each of 5 distribution areas: arts, humanities, natural sciences, numerical and symbolic reasoning, and social sciences. There is also an integration of knowledge requirement (usually 5 to 6 courses). Students must maintain at least a C- grade average.

Special: Trinity offers special freshman programs for exceptional students, including interdisciplinary programs in the sciences and the humanities. There is an intensive study program under which students can devote a semester to 1 subject. Cross-registration through such programs as the Hartford Consortium and the Twelve-College Exchange Program, hundreds of internships, study abroad virtually worldwide, a Washington semester, dual and student-designed majors, nondegree study, and pass/fail options also are offered. There are 4 national honor societies on campus, including Phi Beta Kappa.

Faculty/Classroom: Sixty percent of faculty are male; 40%, female. All both teach and do research. No introductory courses are taught by graduate students. The average class size in an introductory lecture is 35; in a laboratory, 20; and in a regular course offering, 18.

Admissions: About 59% of the 1993–94 applicants were accepted. The SAT scores for the 1993–94 freshman class were as follows: Verbal—19% below 500, 54% between 500 and 599, 25% between 600 and 700, and 2% above 700; Math—7% below 500, 36% between 500 and 599, 46% between 600 and 700, and 11% above 700. The ACT scores were 2% below 21, 22% between 21 and 23, 44% between 24 and 26, 23% between 27 and 28, and 9% above 28.

Requirements: The SAT I or ACT is required. The SAT II: Subject test in writing also is required. Trinity strongly emphasizes individual character and personal qualities in admission. Consequently, an interview and essay are recommended. The college requires 4 years of English, 2 years each in foreign language and algebra, and 1 year each in geometry, history, and laboratory science. AP credits are accepted. Important factors used in the admissions decision are advanced placement or honor courses, recommendations by school officials, extracurricular activities record, evidence of special talent, and leadership record.

Procedure: Freshmen are admitted in the fall. Entrance exams should be taken in the fall of the senior year. There are early decision, early admissions, and deferred admissions plans. Early decision applications should be filed by December 1; regular applications, by January 15 for fall entry, along with an application fee of $50. Notification of early decision is sent December 31; regular decision, early April. About 95 early decision candidates were accepted for the 1993–94 class. A waiting list is an active part of the admissions procedure, with about 8% of applicants on the list.

Transfer: About 25 transfer students enrolled in 1993–94. Transfer applicants must take the SAT I or ACT. A minimum GPA of 3.2 and an interview are recommended. At least 16 course credits out of 36 must be completed at Trinity.

Visiting: There are regularly scheduled orientations for prospective students. There are guides for informal visits, and visitors may sit in on classes and stay overnight at the school. To arrange for a visit, contact the Admissions Office at (203) 297-2180.

Financial Aid: In 1993–94, 45% of all current freshmen and 42% of continuing students received some form of financial aid. About 45% of freshmen and 42% of continuing students received need-based aid. The average freshman award was $17,600. Of that total, scholarships or need-based grants averaged $13,600 ($22,000 maximum); loans averaged $2625 ($3625 maximum); and work contracts averaged $1350 (maximum). Fifty-five percent of undergraduate students work part-time. Average earnings from campus work for the school year are $1300. The average financial indebtedness of the 1992–93 graduate was $12,750. Trinity is a member of CSS. The FAF and the college's own financial statement are required. The deadline for financial aid applications is February 1.

International Students: There are currently 30 international students enrolled. They must take the TOEFL and achieve a minimum score of 550 and must also take the SAT I or the ACT.

Computers: The college provides computer facilities for student use. The mainframe is a Sun SPARC network. More than 100 Apple Macintosh and other microcomputers are networked and available for student use. Each can access the Sun or other Internet hosts. A wide variety of applications are available. Student-owned Apple Macintoshes in the residence halls are directly connected to the campus network. All students may access the system 24 hours a day. There are no time limits on using the system and no fees.

Graduates: In 1992–93, 493 bachelor's degrees were awarded. Within an average freshman class, 88% graduate in 4 years.

Admissions Contact: David M. Borus, Dean of Admission and Financial Aid.

UNITED STATES COAST GUARD ACADEMY   E-3
New London, CT 06320-4195   (203) 444-8500

Full-time: 761 men, 169 women   **Faculty:** 112
Part-time: none   **Ph.D:s:** 30%
Graduate: none   **Student/Faculty:** 8 to 1
Year: semesters, summer session   **Tuition:** See profile
Application Deadline: December 15   **Room & Board:** See profile
Freshman Class: 2591 applied, 466 accepted, 277 enrolled
SAT I Verbal/Math: 542/643   **MOST COMPETITIVE**

The U.S. Coast Guard Academy, founded in 1876, is an Armed Forces Service Academy for men and women. Appointments are made solely on the basis of an annual nationwide competition. Except for an entrance fee of $1500, the federal government covers all cadet expenses by providing a monthly allowance of $525 plus a daily food allowance. In addition to regional accreditation, the academy has baccalaureate program accreditation with ABET. The library contains 150,000 volumes, 60,000 microform items, and 1500 audiovisual forms, and subscribes to 850 periodicals. Computerized library sources and services include the card catalog. Special learning facilities include the Coast Guard Museum and a $5-million bridge simulator. The 110-acre campus is in a suburban area 45 miles southeast of Hartford. Including residence halls, there are 25 buildings on campus.

Student Life: About 93% of undergraduates are from out-of-state, mostly the Middle Atlantic. Students come from 50 states and 11 foreign countries. Eighty-three percent are from public schools; 17% from private. Eighty percent are white. The average age of freshmen is 18.5; all undergraduates, 21. Twenty-one percent drop out by the end of their first year; 66% remain to graduate.

Housing: A total of 900 students can be accommodated in college housing. College-sponsored living facilities include dormitories. On-campus housing is guaranteed for all 4 years. One-hundred percent of students live on campus and remain on campus on weekends. Alcohol is not permitted. Upperclassmen may keep cars on campus.

Activities: There are no fraternities or sororities on campus. There are many groups and organizations on campus, including band, choir, chorale, chorus, drill team, drum and bugle corps, ethnic, jazz band, literary magazine, marching band, musical theater, newspaper, pep band, political, professional, religious, social service, student government, and yearbook. Popular campus events include Homecoming, Parents Weekend, Graduation, Coast Guard Day, and Hispanic Heritage and Black History months.

Sports: There are 14 intercollegiate sports for men and 7 for women, and 13 intramural sports for men and 10 for women. Athletic and recreation facilities include a field house with 3 basketball courts, a 6-lane swimming pool, 5 racquetball courts, and facilities for track meets, tennis matches, and baseball and softball games; an additional athletic facility with a wrestling room, weight room, basketball courts, gymnastics areas, swimming pool, and saunas; a 4500-seat stadium; and practice and playing fields, outdoor tennis courts, and seamanship-sailing centers.

Disabled Students: Twenty-four percent of the campus is accessible to disabled students. The following facilities are available: wheelchair ramps, elevators, special parking, and specially equipped rest rooms.

Services: In addition to many counseling and information services, tutoring is available in every subject.

Campus Safety and Security: Campus safety and security measures include 24-hour foot and vehicle patrol, self-defense education, and lighted pathways and sidewalks.

Programs of Study: The academy awards the B.S. degree. Bachelor's degrees are awarded in BIOLOGICAL SCIENCE (marine science), BUSINESS (management science), COMPUTER AND PHYSICAL SCIENCE (computer mathematics), ENGINEERING AND ENVIRONMENTAL DESIGN (civil engineering, electrical/electronics engineering, mechanical engineering, and naval architecture and marine engineering), SOCIAL SCIENCE (political science/government). Electrical engineering is the strongest academically.

Required: To graduate, cadets must pass at least 37 courses, of which 25 are core; accumulate a minimum of 126 credit hours, with at least 90 credits of C or better, exclusive of physical education; complete the academic requirements for one of the approved majors and attain a minimum GPA of 2.0 in all required upper-division courses in the major; successfully complete all professional development and physical education requirements; and maintain a high sense of integrity.

Special: Cross-registration with Connecticut College, summer cruises to foreign ports, 6-week internships with various government agencies, and a 1 semester exchange program with the 3 other military academies are available. All graduates are commissioned in the U.S. Coast Guard. There is a freshman honors program on campus, as well as 2 national honor societies. Three departments have honors programs.

Faculty/Classroom: Ninety percent of faculty are male; 10%, female. The average class size in an introductory lecture is 28; in a laboratory, 18; and in a regular course offering, 20.

Admissions: About 18% of the 1993-94 applicants were accepted. The SAT scores for the 1993-94 freshman class were as follows: Verbal—25% below 500, 50% between 500 and 599, 23% between 600 and 700, and 2% above 700; Math—24% between 500 and 599, 49% between 600 and 700, and 27% above 700. About 93% of the current freshmen were in the top fifth of their class; 100% were in the top two fifths. Thirteen freshmen graduated first in their class.

Requirements: The SAT I or ACT is required. Applicants must have reached the age of 17 but not the age of 22 by July 1 of the year of admission, be citizens of the United States, be single at the time of appointment and remain single while attending the academy, and satisfy the commandant concerning moral character. Required secondary school courses include 3 years of English and 3 of mathematics. The minimum SAT I composite score is 950, with 500 in mathematics. The minimum ACT composite score is 40, with 21 in mathematics. AP credits are accepted. Important factors used in the admissions decision are leadership record, extracurricular activities record, advanced placement or honor courses, recommendations by school officials, and evidence of special talent.

Procedure: Freshmen are admitted in the summer. Entrance exams should be taken by December 15. Applications should be filed by December 15 for summer entry. Notification is sent on a rolling basis. A waiting list is an active part of the admissions procedure, with about 7% of applicants on the list.

Transfer: All transfer students must meet the same standards as incoming freshmen and must begin as freshmen no matter how many semesters or years of college they have completed. A total of 126 credits must be completed at the academy.

Visiting: There are regularly scheduled orientations for prospective students, including an admissions briefing and tour of the academy every Friday.

International Students: There are currently 23 international students enrolled. The academy actively recruits these students. They must take the TOEFL. The student must also take the SAT I or the ACT.

Computers: The college provides computer facilities for student use. Computer rooms in the dormitories and academic building are available. Access to Sun Model 10 main server is also available. All students may access the system. It may be used 24 hours a day. There are no time limits on using the system and no fees. It is recommended that students in all programs have personal computers. Apple Macintosh is recommended.

Graduates: In 1992-93, 185 bachelor's degrees were awarded. The most popular majors among graduates were government (23%), civil engineering (20%), and marine science (18%). Within an average freshman class, 66% graduate in 4 years and 1% in 5 years.

Admissions Contact: Robert W. Thorne, Director of Admissions.

UNIVERSITY OF BRIDGEPORT   B-4
Bridgeport, CT 06602   (203) 576-4552
(800) 243-9496 (out-of-state)

Full-time: 258 men, 269 women   **Faculty:** 92; IIA, -$
Part-time: 126 men, 186 women   **Ph.D:s:** 82%
Graduate: 381 men, 385 women   **Student/Faculty:** 6 to 1
Year: semesters, summer session   **Tuition:** $12,445
Application Deadline: April 1   **Room & Board:** $6540
Freshman Class: 598 applied, 441 accepted, 153 enrolled
SAT I Verbal/Math: 420/510   **COMPETITIVE**

The University of Bridgeport, founded in 1927, is a private, independent university offering programs in the arts and sciences, business, engineering, human services, dental hygiene, and teacher preparation. There are 6 undergraduate and 5 graduate schools. In addition to regional accreditation, UB has baccalaureate program accreditation with AACSB, ABET, ADA, and NASAD. The library contains 208,000 volumes, 943,000 microform items, and 1200 audiovisual forms, and subscribes to 1000 periodicals. Computerized library sources and services include interlibrary loans and database searching. Special learning facilities include a learning resource center and an art gallery. The 86-acre campus is in an urban area 60 miles northeast of New York City. Including residence halls, there are 30 buildings on campus.

Student Life: About 58% of undergraduates are from Connecticut. Students come from 16 states and 39 foreign countries. Ninety-three percent are from public schools; 7% from private. Forty-three percent are white; 17% African American; and 27% foreign nationals. Eighteen percent are Catholic. The average age of freshmen is 20; all undergraduates, 23. Thirty percent drop out by the end of their first year; 50% remain to graduate.

Housing: A total of 500 students can be accommodated in college housing. College-sponsored living facilities include single-sex and coed dormitories. In addition there are alcohol- and tobacco-free

floors. On-campus housing is guaranteed for all 4 years. Sixty-two percent of students live on campus; of those, 75% remain on campus on weekends. All students may keep cars on campus.

Activities: About 5% of men belong to 3 local fraternities; about 5% of women belong to 2 local and 1 national sororities. There are 30 groups on campus, including art, band, cheerleading, choir, chorale, chorus, computers, drama, ethnic, honors, international, jazz band, literary magazine, musical theater, newspaper, photography, political, professional, religious, social, social service, student government, symphony, and yearbook. Popular campus events include Homecoming/Parents Weekend, Spring Week, Dance Marathon, International Festival, Winter Weekend, Mad Hatter's Ball, Wisteria Ball, and local trips and travel.

Sports: There are 5 intercollegiate sports for men and 5 for women, and 8 intramural sports for men and 8 for women. Athletic and recreation facilities include a gymnasium, athletic fields, tennis and racquetball courts, and a recreation center with an indoor pool.

Disabled Students: Sixty percent of the campus is accessible to disabled students. The following facilities are available: wheelchair ramps, elevators, special parking, specially equipped rest rooms, and special class scheduling.

Services: In addition to many counseling and information services, tutoring is available in every subject. In addition, there is a reader service for the blind, and remedial math, reading, and writing.

Campus Safety and Security: Campus safety and security measures include 24-hour foot and vehicle patrol, escort service, informal discussions, and pamphlets, posters, and films. In addition, there are emergency telephones and lighted pathways and sidewalks.

Programs of Study: UB awards the B.A., B.S., B.E.S., B.F.A., and B.M. degrees. Associate, master's, and doctoral degrees also are awarded. Bachelor's degrees are awarded in BIOLOGICAL SCIENCE (biology/biological science), BUSINESS (accounting, banking and finance, business administration and management, business economics, fashion merchandising, international business management, and marketing/retailing/merchandising), COMMUNICATIONS AND THE ARTS (advertising, communications, design, English, film arts, fine arts, industrial design, journalism, music, and photography), COMPUTER AND PHYSICAL SCIENCE (chemistry, computer programming, computer science, mathematics, and physics), EDUCATION (art and music), ENGINEERING AND ENVIRONMENTAL DESIGN (computer engineering, electrical/electronics engineering, engineering, interior design, and mechanical engineering), HEALTH PROFESSIONS (chiropractic, dental hygiene, medical laboratory technology, predentistry, premedicine, and respiratory therapy), SOCIAL SCIENCE (economics, history, human services, political science/government, prelaw, and psychology). Engineering, business, and dental hygiene are the strongest academically. Dental hygiene, business administration, computer science/engineering, electrical engineering, and human services have the largest enrollments.

Required: All students are required to complete at least 120 credit hours including at least 30 in the major field. A minimum GPA of 2.0 is necessary. Distribution requirements cover 36 core credits and consist of skills, heritage, and capstone sections, including 6 hours in English composition, 3 each in oral communication and quantitative skills, and 21 semester hours from fine arts, humanities, natural science, and social science courses.

Special: The university offers co-op programs with several local institutions, cross-registration with Sacred Heart and Fairfield Universities, internships in many degree programs, study abroad in England, Switzerland, or Spain, a Washington semester, and work-study programs. In addition, an elective studies accelerated degree program, dual majors, and student-designed majors are available. Credit for life experience, nondegree study, and pass/fail options are offered. There are 14 national honor societies on campus. One department has an honors program.

Faculty/Classroom: Eighty-four percent of faculty are male; 16%, female. All both teach and do research. No introductory courses are taught by graduate students. The average class size in an introductory lecture is 15; in a laboratory, 10; and in a regular course offering, 11.

Admissions: About 74% of the 1993–94 applicants were accepted. About 30% of the current freshmen were in the top fifth of their class; 60% were in the top two fifths. One freshman graduated first in her class.

Requirements: The SAT I or ACT is required. In addition, applicants are required to have 16 academic credits or Carnegie units, including 4 units of English, 3 of mathematics, 2 of history, and 1 each in social studies and a laboratory science. A portfolio is required for B.F.A. students and an audition for B.M. candidates. AP and CLEP credits are accepted. Important factors used in the admissions decision are advanced placement or honor courses, leadership record, evidence of special talent, and extracurricular activities.

Procedure: Freshmen are admitted fall and spring. Entrance exams should be taken during the senior year. Applications should be filed by April 1 for fall entry and December 1 for spring entry, along with

an application fee of $35. Notification is sent on a rolling basis. There are early decision, early admissions, and deferred admissions plans.

Transfer: About 110 transfer students enrolled in 1993–94. Transfer applicants need a minimum GPA of 2.5 and at least 12 earned credit hours. The SAT I or ACT and an interview are recommended. A total of 30 credits out of 120 must be completed at UB.

Visiting: There are regularly scheduled orientations for prospective students. There are guides for informal visits, and visitors may sit in on classes and stay overnight at the school. To arrange for a visit, contact the Admissions Office at (203) 576–4552 or (800) 243–9496 (out-of-state).

Financial Aid: In 1993–94, 80% of all current freshmen and 58% of continuing students received some form of financial aid. About 47% of freshmen and 79% of continuing students received need-based aid. The average freshman award was $17,700. Of that total, scholarships or need-based grants averaged $13,875 ($21,274 maximum); loans averaged $3825 ($8500 maximum); and work contracts averaged $1200 ($2000 maximum). Forty-five percent of undergraduate students work part-time. Average earnings from campus work for the school year are $1200. The average financial indebtedness of the 1992–93 graduate was $15,300. UB is a member of CSS. The FAF and the college's own financial statement are required. The deadline for financial aid applications is April 15.

International Students: There are currently 352 international students enrolled. The school actively recruits these students. They must take the TOEFL and achieve a minimum score of 500.

Computers: The college provides computer facilities for student use. The mainframe is a Prime 6350. Computer systems available to students throughout campus include SUN Microsystems workstations, Apollo workstations, a DEC VAX ll/785, 7 all-purpose PC laboratories, and a specialized microprocessor laboratory. All students may access the system. It may be used 8 a.m to 11 p.m daily. There are no time limits on using the system and no fees.

Graduates: In 1992–93, 240 bachelor's degrees were awarded. The most popular majors among graduates were engineering (30%), social sciences (19%), and business (15%). Within an average freshman class, 40% graduate in 4 years, 45% in 5 years, and 50% in 6 years. Some 50 companies recruited on campus in 1992–93.

Admissions Contact: Andrew G. Nelson, Dean of Admissions and Financial Aid.

UNIVERSITY OF CONNECTICUT D-2
Storrs, CT 06269 (203) 486-3137

Full-time: 5569 men, 5697 women	Faculty: 1211; I, +$
Part-time: 420 men, 373 women	Ph.Ds: 90%
Graduate: 1941 men, 1966 women	Student/Faculty: 9 to 1
Year: semesters, summer session	Tuition: $4290 ($11,410)
Application Deadline: April 1	Room & Board: $4878
Freshman Class: 9735 applied, 7187 accepted, 2064 enrolled	
SAT I Verbal/Math: 480/500	COMPETITIVE

The University of Connecticut, founded in 1881, is a public, land-grant, multicampus, coeducational institution offering degree programs in liberal arts and sciences and professional studies. There are 10 undergraduate schools and one graduate school. In addition to regional accreditation, UConn has baccalaureate program accreditation with AACSB, ABET, ACPE, APTA, ASLA, NASAD, NASM, NCATE, and NLN. The library contains 1,900,000 volumes, 2,600,000 microform items, and 15,013 audiovisual forms, and subscribes to 9000 periodicals. Computerized library sources and services include the card catalog and database searching. Special learning facilities include a learning resource center, art gallery, natural history museum, and radio station. The 3100-acre campus is in a rural area 25 miles east of Hartford. Including residence halls, there are 150 buildings on campus.

Student Life: About 85% of undergraduates are from Connecticut. Eighty-five percent are white. The average age of freshmen is 19; all undergraduates, 21. Thirteen percent drop out by the end of their first year; 71% remain to graduate.

Housing: A total of 8633 students can be accommodated in college housing. College-sponsored living facilities include single-sex and coed dormitories. In addition, there are language houses, special interest houses, a floor for older students, and a living/learning center. On-campus housing is guaranteed for the freshman year only. Sixty-five percent of students live on campus; of those, 70% remain on campus on weekends. Upperclassmen may keep cars on campus.

Activities: About 10% of men belong to 16 national fraternities; about 10% of women belong to 9 national sororities. There are 200 groups on campus, including art, cheerleading, chess, chorus, drama, ethnic, gay, honors, international, literary magazine, marching band, newspaper, political, professional, radio and TV, religious, social, social service, student government, and yearbook. Popular campus events include Homecoming, Spring Weekend, and 'UConn Do It' campus clean-up day.

Sports: There are 11 intercollegiate sports for men and 10 for women, and 20 intramural sports for men and 20 for women. Athletic and recreation facilities include a sports center, a field house, and a 16,000-seat stadium.

Disabled Students: Seventy-five percent of the campus is accessible to disabled students. The following facilities are available: wheelchair ramps, elevators, special parking, specially equipped rest rooms, special class scheduling, lowered drinking fountains, and lowered telephones.

Services: In addition to many counseling and information services, tutoring is available in most subjects. Also available are a Braille printer, a Kurzweil reading machine, an Apple computer with voice synthesizer, a machine to enlarge printed material, a talking calculator, and a TDD. In addition, there is a reader service for the blind.

Campus Safety and Security: Campus safety and security measures include 24-hour foot and vehicle patrol, escort service, shuttle buses, and informal discussions. In addition, there are pamphlets, posters, films, emergency telephones, and lighted pathways and sidewalks.

Programs of Study: UConn awards the B.A., B.S., B.F.A., B.Mus., B.Pharm., B.S.E., and B.G.S. degrees. Master's and doctoral degrees also are awarded. Bachelor's degrees are awarded in AGRICULTURE (agricultural economics, agriculture, animal science, horticulture, and natural resource management), BIOLOGICAL SCIENCE (biology/biological science, biophysics, molecular biology, nutrition, and physiology), BUSINESS (accounting, banking and finance, business administration and management, insurance and risk management, management information systems, marketing/retailing/merchandising, real estate, and sports management), COMMUNICATIONS AND THE ARTS (art, art history and appreciation, classics, communications, design, dramatic arts, English, fine arts, French, German, graphic design, Italian, journalism, linguistics, music, music history and appreciation, music theory and composition, painting, photography, Portuguese, printmaking, sculpture, Spanish, and theater design), COMPUTER AND PHYSICAL SCIENCE (actuarial science, chemistry, geology, information sciences and systems, mathematics, physics, and statistics), EDUCATION (agricultural, elementary, English, foreign languages, mathematics, music, physical, recreation, and special), ENGINEERING AND ENVIRONMENTAL DESIGN (ceramic science, chemical engineering, civil engineering, computer engineering, electrical/electronics engineering, landscape architecture/design, and mechanical engineering), HEALTH PROFESSIONS (cytotechnology, medical laboratory technology, nursing, pharmacy, and physical therapy), SOCIAL SCIENCE (anthropology, dietetics, Eastern European studies, economics, geography, history, human development, Latin American studies, Middle Eastern studies, philosophy, political science/government, psychology, Russian and Slavic studies, sociology, urban studies, and women's studies). English, economics, psychology, and political science have the largest enrollments.

Required: To graduate, students must complete 120 credits with a minimum GPA of 2.0. There are general education requirements in foreign language, expository writing, mathematics, literature and the arts, culture and modern society, philosophical and ethical analysis, social scientific and comparative analysis, and science and technology.

Special: The university offers co-op programs in most majors, internships, study abroad in more than 25 countries, dual majors, general studies degrees, student-designed majors, work-study programs, nondegree study, and pass/fail options. There is a freshman honors program on campus, as well as 24 national honor societies, including Phi Beta Kappa. Eighty-three departments have honors programs.

Faculty/Classroom: Seventy-six percent of faculty are male; 24% female. Ninety-five percent both teach and do research. The average class size in an introductory lecture is 38 and in a regular course offering, 30.

Admissions: About 74% of the 1993–94 applicants were accepted. The SAT scores for the 1993–94 freshman class were as follows: Verbal—58% below 500, 34% between 500 and 599, 7% between 600 and 700, and 1% above 700; Math—26% below 500, 42% between 500 and 599, 25% between 600 and 700, and 7% above 700. About 48% of the current freshmen were in the top fifth of their class; 86% were in the top two fifths. There were 22 National Merit semifinalists. A total of 22 freshmen graduated first in their class.

Requirements: The SAT I (preferred) or ACT is required. Applicants must be graduates of an accredited secondary school and rank in the upper 50% of their class. The GED is accepted. Students should have completed 15 high school academic units, including 4 years of English, 3 years of mathematics, and 2 years each of foreign language, science, social studies, and electives. An essay is recommended. An audition is required for music students and a portfolio for art students. AP credits are accepted. Important factors used in the admissions decision are evidence of special talent, advanced placement or honor courses, leadership record, extracurricular activities record, and recommendations by school officials.

Procedure: Freshmen are admitted fall and spring. Applications should be filed by April 1 for fall entry and October 1 for spring entry, along with an application fee of $40. Notification is sent on a rolling basis. There are deferred and early admission plans.

Transfer: About 600 transfer students enrolled in a recent year. Applicants for transfer should have a minimum GPA of 2.5. The school recommends that transfer applicants have an associate degree or a minimum of 54 credit hours. At least 30 credits out of 120 must be completed at UConn.

Visiting: There are regularly scheduled orientations for prospective students, including daily tours and information sessions. There are guides for informal visits, and visitors may sit in on classes and stay overnight at the school. To arrange for a visit, contact Barry Wilson at (203) 486–3137 for overnight reservation or (203) 486–4866 for tour reservation.

Financial Aid: In 1993–94, 35% of all current freshmen and 65% of continuing students received some form of financial aid. Scholarships or need-based grants averaged $985; loans averaged $2400 ($3800 maximum); and work contracts averaged $1300 ($1500 maximum). The average financial indebtedness of the 1992–93 graduate was $6900. UConn is a member of CSS. The FAF and the college's own financial statement and the FAFSA are required. The deadline for financial aid applications is February 15.

International Students: There are currently 99 international students enrolled. They must take the TOEFL or the college's own test and achieve a minimum score on the TOEFL of 550. They must also take the SAT I.

Computers: The college provides computer facilities for student use. The mainframes are an IBM 3090, Models 150E and 180E. There are more than 1800 terminals on campus, located in the computer center, the library, the various schools and colleges, and some residence halls. All students may access the system 24 hours a day weekdays, and 8 A.M. to 12 P.M. weekends. There are no time limits on using the system and no fees.

Graduates: In a recent year, 3470 bachelor's degrees were awarded. The most popular majors among graduates were economics (8%), English (8%), and psychology (6%). Within an average freshman class, 33% graduate in 4 years, 66% in 5 years, and 71% in 6 years. Some 310 companies recruited on campus in 1992–93.

Admissions Contact: Dr. Ann Huckenbeck, Director of Admissions.

UNIVERSITY OF HARTFORD

West Hartford, CT 06117

C-2

(203) 243-4296

Full-time: 1933 men, 1835 women	Faculty: 333; IIA, av$
Part-time: 748 men, 938 women	Ph.D.s: 77%
Graduate: 956 men, 1119 women	Student/Faculty: 11 to 1
Year: semesters, summer session	Tuition: $14,260
Application Deadline: open	Room & Board: $5598
Freshman Class: 5117 applied, 4033 accepted, 1200 enrolled	
SAT I Verbal/Math: 450/500	**LESS COMPETITIVE**

The University of Hartford, founded in 1877, is an independent, nonsectarian, coeducational institution offering extensive undergraduate and graduate programs ranging from liberal arts to business. There are 9 undergraduate and 7 graduate schools. In addition to regional accreditation, the university has baccalaureate program accreditation with ABET, CAHEA, NASAD, NASM, and NCATE. The 3 libraries contain 389,487 volumes, 220,000 microform items, and 25,697 audiovisual forms, and subscribe to 2450 periodicals. Computerized library sources and services include the card catalog, interlibrary loans, and database searching. Special learning facilities include a learning resource center, art gallery, radio station, and the Museum of American Political Life. The 320-acre campus is in a suburban area 4 miles northwest of Hartford. Including residence halls, there are 35 buildings on campus.

Student Life: About 67% of undergraduates are from out-of-state, mostly the Northeast. Students come from 39 states, 42 foreign countries, and Canada. Seventy-four percent are from public schools; 26% from private. Eighty-one percent are white. Forty percent are Catholic; 30% Protestant; 25% Jewish. The average age of freshmen is 18.

Housing: A total of 3495 students can be accommodated in college housing. College-sponsored living facilities include coed dormitories and on-campus apartments. In addition there are honors houses, special interest houses, and the Residential College for the Arts. On-campus housing is guaranteed for all 4 years and is available on a first-come, first-served basis. Seventy-two percent of students live on campus; of those, 85% remain on campus on weekends. All students may keep cars on campus.

Activities: About 12% of men belong to 8 national fraternities; about 12% of women belong to 5 national sororities. There are more than 100 groups and organizations on campus, including art, band, cheerleading, choir, chorale, chorus, computers, drama, ethnic, gay, honors, international, jazz band, literary magazine, musical theater, newspaper, opera, orchestra, pep band, political, professional, radio and TV, religious, social, social service, student government, symphony,

and yearbook. Popular campus events include Welcome Weekend, Spring Weekend, Winter Carnival, University Players Productions, Hart School of Music performances, and Homecoming.

Sports: There are 9 intercollegiate sports for men and 9 for women, and 16 intramural sports for men and 16 for women. Athletic and recreation facilities include playing fields, a 25-meter outdoor pool, tennis courts, golf practice cages, a fitness trail, and a sports center with a 4600-seat multipurpose court, an 8-lane swimming pool, a weight room, racquetball courts, a squash court, and saunas.

Disabled Students: All of the campus is accessible to disabled students. The following facilities are available: wheelchair ramps, elevators, special parking, specially equipped rest rooms, lowered drinking fountains, and lowered telephones.

Services: In addition to many counseling and information services, tutoring is available in most subjects. In addition, there is a reader service for the blind, and remedial math, reading, and writing. The health education office offers peer counseling and workshops on health-related topics. Professional counseling is available.

Campus Safety and Security: Campus safety and security measures include 24-hour foot and vehicle patrol, self-defense education, escort service, and shuttle buses. In addition, there are informal discussions, pamphlets, posters, and films, emergency telephones, lighted pathways and sidewalks, and bicycle patrol.

Programs of Study: The university awards the B.A., B.F.A., B.Mus., B.S.N., B.S.B.A., B.S.A.E.T., B.S.Ed., B.S.E.E., B.S.M.E., B.S.C.E., B.S.Comp.E., and B.S.E.E.T. degrees. Associate, master's, and doctoral degrees also are awarded. Bachelor's degrees are awarded in BIOLOGICAL SCIENCE (biology/biological science), BUSINESS (accounting, insurance, management information systems, management science, and marketing/retailing/merchandising), COMMUNICATIONS AND THE ARTS (art history and appreciation, audio technology, communications, dance, design, dramatic arts, drawing, English, film arts, fine arts, illustration, languages, music, painting, photography, printmaking, sculpture, and video), COMPUTER AND PHYSICAL SCIENCE (actuarial science, chemistry, computer science, mathematics, physics, and radiological technology), EDUCATION (early childhood, elementary, music, secondary, and special), ENGINEERING AND ENVIRONMENTAL DESIGN (architectural technology, ceramic science, civil engineering, computer engineering, electrical/electronics engineering, electrical/electronics engineering technology, engineering, mechanical engineering, and mechanical engineering technology), HEALTH PROFESSIONS (medical laboratory technology, nursing, occupational therapy, optometry, and respiratory therapy), SOCIAL SCIENCE (criminal justice, economics, history, human services, philosophy, political science/government, psychology, and sociology). Computer science, engineering, music, art, and actuarial science are the strongest academically. Communication, psychology, and marketing have the largest enrollments.

Required: To graduate, students must complete at least 120 credit hours, fulfill the university's core curriculum requirements, and maintain an overall GPA of 2.0. Specific core and course requirements vary with the major.

Special: Cross-registration with the Greater Hartford Consortium, internships in all majors, study abroad, a Washington semester, work-study programs, credit for life experience, nondegree study, and pass/fail options are available. In addition, students may pursue accelerated degrees, B.A.-B.S. degrees, dual majors, or their own individually designed majors. There is a freshman honors program on campus, as well as 7 national honor societies. Nine departments have honors programs.

Faculty/Classroom: Seventy-one percent of faculty are male; 29%, female. Ninety-six percent teach undergraduates, 100% do research, and 96% do both. No introductory courses are taught by graduate students. The average class size in an introductory lecture is 40; in a laboratory, 20; and in a regular course offering, 30.

Admissions: About 79% of the 1993–94 applicants were accepted. The SAT scores for the 1993–94 freshman class were as follows: Verbal—73% below 500, 22% between 500 and 599, and 5% between 600 and 700; Math—49% below 500, 35% between 500 and 599, and 15% between 600 and 700. About 31% of the current freshmen were in the top fifth of their class; 50% were in the top two fifths.

Requirements: The SAT I is required. Applicants should have 16 academic high school credits and 16 Carnegie units, including 4 units in English, 3 in mathematics (3 1/2 for B.S. candidates), and 2 each in foreign language, science, and social studies. A portfolio and an audition are required for B.F.A. and B.Mus. candidates, respectively. A personal statement is required and an interview is recommended for all students. AP and CLEP credits are accepted. Important factors used in the admissions decision are advanced placement or honor courses, recommendations by school officials, leadership record, evidence of special talent, and extracurricular activities record.

Procedure: Freshmen are admitted fall and spring. Entrance exams should be taken in the spring of the junior year or the fall of the senior year. Application deadlines are open. The application fee is $35. No-

tification is sent on a rolling basis. There are early admissions and deferred admissions plans.

Transfer: About 380 transfer students enrolled in 1993–94. Transfer students must have a minimum college GPA of 2.0, with 2.5 recommended, and must submit SAT I or ACT scores if they have fewer than 30 transferable college-level credits. An interview is also recommended. A total of 30 credits out of 120 must be completed at the university.

Visiting: There are regularly scheduled orientations for prospective students. There are guides for informal visits and visitors may sit in on classes and stay overnight at the school. To arrange for a visit, contact the Office of Admissions at (203) 768–4296.

Financial Aid: In 1993–94, 84% of all current freshmen and 64% of continuing students received some form of financial aid. About 55% of freshmen and 67% of continuing students received need-based aid. The average freshman award was $11,018. Of that total, scholarships or need-based grants averaged $9300 ($15,900 maximum); loans averaged $2800 ($4000 maximum); and work contracts averaged $1000 ($1200 maximum). Twenty-five percent of undergraduate students work part-time. Average earnings from campus work for the school year are $1000. The average financial indebtedness of the 1992–93 graduate was $9800. The university is a member of CSS. The FAFSA financial statement is required. The deadline for financial aid applications is February 1.

International Students: There are currently 440 international students enrolled. The school actively recruits these students. They must take the TOEFL and achieve a minimum score of 550. The SAT I or ACT is recommended.

Computers: The college provides computer facilities for student use. The mainframe is a DEC VAX 6320. Approximately 400 personal computers, terminals, and workstations are available for student use in a variety of university locations, some of which are open 24 hours a day. All students may access the system. There are no time limits on using the system and no fees.

Graduates: In 1992–93, 958 bachelor's degrees were awarded. The most popular majors among graduates were communication (13%), marketing (5%), and mechanical engineering (3%). Within an average freshman class, 47% graduate in 4 years, 56% in 5 years, and 57% in 6 years. Some 63 companies recruited on campus in 1992–93. In the 1992 graduating class, 85% of the men and 85% of the women had found employment within 6 months of graduation.

Admissions Contact: Richard A. Zeiser, Director of Admissions.

UNIVERSITY OF NEW HAVEN   C-3
West Haven, CT 06516   (203) 932-7319
(800) DIAL-UNH (out-of-state)

Full-time: 979 men, 430 women	Faculty: 151; IIA, av$
Part-time: 1128 men, 573 women	Ph.D.s: 90%
Graduate: 1504 men, 1083 women	Student/Faculty: 9 to 1
Year: 4–1–4, summer session	Tuition: $10,180
Application Deadline: September 1	Room & Board: $4800
Freshman Class: 1651 applied, 1412 accepted, 336 enrolled	
SAT I Verbal/Math: 434/495	COMPETITIVE

The University of New Haven, founded in 1920, is an independent institution offering programs in arts and sciences, business, engineering, public safety and professional studies, and hotel, restaurant, and tourism administration. There are 5 undergraduate schools and one graduate school. In addition to regional accreditation, UNH has baccalaureate program accreditation with ABET. The library contains 368,069 volumes, 48,447 microform items, and 10,200 audiovisual forms, and subscribes to 1673 periodicals. Computerized library sources and services include interlibrary loans and database searching. Special learning facilities include a learning resource center, art gallery, and radio station. The 73-acre campus is in a suburban area 5 miles west of New Haven. Including residence halls, there are 22 buildings on campus.

Student Life: About 65% of undergraduates are from Connecticut. Students come from 25 states, 51 foreign countries, and Canada. Seventy-nine percent are from public schools; 21% from private. Seventy-five percent are white; 12% African American. The average age of all undergraduates is 20. Twenty-five percent drop out by the end of their first year; 40% remain to graduate.

Housing: A total of 733 students can be accommodated in college housing. College-sponsored living facilities include coed dormitories and on-campus apartments. On-campus housing is guaranteed for the freshman year only, is available on a first-come, first-served basis, and is available on a lottery system for upperclassmen. Sixty-eight percent of students commute. All students may keep cars on campus.

Activities: About 8% of men belong to 4 local and 1 national fraternities; about 8% of women belong to 3 local sororities. There are 40 groups on campus, including cheerleading, chorus, drama, ethnic, honors, international, jazz band, literary magazine, newspaper, photography, political, professional, radio and TV, religious, social, social service, student government, and yearbook. Popular campus events

include Homecoming, Parents Weekend, AIDS Awareness Week, Alcohol Awareness Week, May Day, and International Festival.

Sports: There are 8 intercollegiate sports for men and 5 for women, and 10 intramural sports for men and 6 for women. Athletic and recreation facilities include playing fields, tennis courts, and a gymnasium with a basketball court, weight training room, racquetball court, and gymnastics area.

Disabled Students: Sixty percent of the campus is accessible to disabled students. The following facilities are available: wheelchair ramps, elevators, special parking, specially equipped rest rooms, special class scheduling, lowered drinking fountains, lowered telephones, and special door handles.

Services: In addition to many counseling and information services, tutoring is available in most subjects. In addition, there is remedial math, reading, and writing.

Campus Safety and Security: Campus safety and security measures include 24-hour foot and vehicle patrol, informal discussions, pamphlets, posters, and films, and required programs during orientation for new students.

Programs of Study: UNH awards the B.A. and B.S. degrees. Associate, master's, and doctoral degrees also are awarded. Bachelor's degrees are awarded in BIOLOGICAL SCIENCE (biology/biological science), BUSINESS (accounting, banking and finance, business administration and management, business economics, hotel/motel and restaurant management, human resources, international business management, management information systems, marketing/retailing/merchandising, sports management, and tourism), COMMUNICATIONS AND THE ARTS (art, audio technology, communications, creative writing, English, fine arts, graphic design, music, and public relations), COMPUTER AND PHYSICAL SCIENCE (applied mathematics, chemistry, computer science, mathematics, natural sciences, and statistics), ENGINEERING AND ENVIRONMENTAL DESIGN (aviation administration/management, chemical engineering, civil engineering, electrical/electronics engineering, environmental science, fire protection engineering, industrial engineering, interior design, mechanical engineering, and occupational safety and health), HEALTH PROFESSIONS (health care administration, medical technology, predentistry, premedicine, and preveterinary science), SOCIAL SCIENCE (clinical psychology, community psychology, criminal justice, criminology, dietetics, economics, fire science, forensic studies, history, industrial and organizational psychology, liberal arts/general studies, political science/government, psychology, and public administration). Engineering, criminal justice, and forensic science are the strongest academically. Business, engineering, and arts and sciences have the largest enrollments.

Required: All students must maintain a GPA of 2.0 and complete a total of 121 to 134 credits, depending on the major. Students must take 34 credits from the university core curriculum, which includes English composition, literature, mathematics or computer science, the scientific method, laboratory science, history, social science, and fine arts or theater.

Special: Co-op programs in most majors, internships, work-study programs, student-designed majors in the school of professional studies, interdisciplinary majors including biomedical computing, and nondegree study are possible. There is a freshman honors program on campus, as well as 5 national honor societies.

Faculty/Classroom: Eighty-eight percent of faculty are male; 12%, female. All teach undergraduates. No introductory courses are taught by graduate students. The average class size in a regular course offering is 19.

Admissions: About 86% of the 1993–94 applicants were accepted. The SAT scores for the 1993–94 freshman class were as follows: Verbal—91% below 500, 6% between 500 and 599, and 3% between 600 and 700; Math—48% below 500, 50% between 500 and 599, and 2% between 600 and 700. About 13% of the current freshmen were in the top fifth of their class; 31% were in the top two fifths.

Requirements: UNH requires applicants to be in the upper 60% of their class. A minimum GPA of 2.0 is required. The SAT I or ACT is required, with the SAT I preferred. In addition, applicants should be graduates of an accredited secondary school and have 16 academic credits or Carnegie units, including 4 in English, 3 each in mathematics and electives, and 2 each in science and history, with an additional 2 credits in foreign language advised. An interview is recommended. The GED is accepted. AP and CLEP credits are accepted. Important factors used in the admissions decision are advanced placement or honor courses, evidence of special talent, extracurricular activities record, leadership record, and parents or siblings attending the school.

Procedure: Freshmen are admitted fall and spring. Entrance exams should be taken in the fall or winter of the senior year. Applications should be filed by September 1 for fall entry and January 10 for spring entry, along with an application fee of $25. Notification is sent on a rolling basis. There is a deferred admissions plan.

Transfer: A total of 248 transfer students enrolled in 1993–94. Applicants should have a minimum college GPA of 2.0 and should submit all official transcripts. An interview is recommended, and the SAT I is required for students with fewer than 30 college credits. A total of 30 credits out of 121 to 134 must be completed at UNH.

Visiting: There are regularly scheduled orientations for prospective students, including 2 open houses in the fall, and in March each undergraduate school of the university hosts a special day for accepted students. There are guides for informal visits and visitors may sit in on classes and stay overnight at the school. To arrange for a visit, contact the Admissions Office at (203) 932-7319 or (800) DIAL-UNH.

Financial Aid: In 1993–94, 70% of all students received some form of financial aid, including need-based aid. The average freshman award was $9699. Of that total, scholarships or need-based grants averaged $5067 ($15,250 maximum); loans averaged $3340 ($4425 maximum); and work contracts averaged $4292. Fifty-five percent of undergraduate students work part-time. Average earnings from campus work for the school year are $882. UNH is a member of CSS. The FAF, the college's own financial statement, the FAFSA, and the 1040 tax form are required. The deadline for financial aid applications is March 15.

International Students: There are currently about 500 international students enrolled. The school actively recruits these students. They must take the TOEFL and achieve a minimum score of 500. English-speaking students must also take the SAT I.

Computers: UNH provides computer facilities for student use. The mainframes are a DEC VAX 6220, a Prime 9955, and a Data General MV/800. There are 140 microcomputers located in the computer center, the library, and academic and administrative buildings. All students may access the system 24 hours a day. There are no time limits on using the system and no fees.

Graduates: In an earlier class, 434 bachelor's degrees were awarded. Some 104 companies recruited on campus in 1992–93. In the 1992 graduating class, 15% of all students were enrolled in graduate school within 6 months of graduation; 93% of all students had found employment.

Admissions Contact: Steven T. Briggs, Dean of Undergraduate Admissions and Financial Aid.

WESLEYAN UNIVERSITY
C-3
Middletown, CT 06457 (203) 344-7900

Full-time: 1323 men, 1391 women	Faculty: 280; IIA, + +$
Part-time: 9 men, 18 women	Ph.D.s: 90%
Graduate: 228 men, 335 women	Student/Faculty: 10 to 1
Year: semesters	Tuition: $18,780
Application Deadline: January 15	Room & Board: $4990
Freshman Class: 4772 applied, 2029 accepted, 724 enrolled	
SAT I Verbal/Math: 630/660	ACT: 30 **MOST COMPETITIVE**

Wesleyan University, founded in 1831, is an independent liberal arts institution. There is one graduate school. The 5 libraries contain 1 million volumes and 190,000 microform items, and subscribe to 3358 periodicals. Computerized library sources and services include the card catalog, interlibrary loans, and database searching. Special learning facilities include a learning resource center, art gallery, radio station, and and an observatory. The 120-acre campus is located 15 miles south of Hartford. Including residence halls, there are 90 buildings on campus.

Student Life: About 90% of undergraduates are from out-of-state, mostly the Northeast. Students come from 48 states, 21 foreign countries, and Canada. Sixty-three percent are from public schools; 31% from private. Sixty-seven percent are white; 12% Asian American; 11% African American. Twenty-five percent are Jewish; 22% Protestant; 16% Catholic. The average age of freshmen is 18; all undergraduates, 20. Two percent drop out by the end of their first year; 91% remain to graduate.

Housing: A total of 2400 students can be accommodated in college housing. College-sponsored living facilities include single-sex and coed dormitories, on-campus apartments, off-campus apartments, married-student housing, fraternity houses, and sorority houses. In addition, there are language houses and special interest houses. On-campus housing is guaranteed for all 4 years. Ninety percent of students live on campus; of those, 95% remain on campus on weekends. All students may keep cars on campus.

Activities: About 10% of men and 3% of women belong to 2 local and 5 national fraternities; about 5% of women belong to 2 local sororities. There are 150 groups on campus, including art, bagpipe band, band, cheerleading, chess, choir, chorale, chorus, computers, dance, drama, ethnic, film, gay, honors, international, jazz band, literary magazine, musical theater, newspaper, opera, orchestra, pep band, photography, political, professional, radio and TV, religious, social, social service, student government, symphony, and yearbook. Popular campus events include Fall Ball and Spring Fling.

Sports: There are 15 intercollegiate sports for men and 14 for women, and 10 intramural sports for men and 10 for women. Athletic and recreation facilities include a 5000-seat stadium, a 3000-seat gymnasium, a 50-meter Olympic pool, a 400-meter outdoor track, a 200-meter indoor track, a hockey arena, a strength and fitness center, 16 tennis courts, 14 squash courts, 4 soccer fields, 2 football practice fields, 2 rugby pitches, a boathouse, and field hockey, ultimate frisbee, baseball, and softball fields.

Disabled Students: Twenty-five percent of the campus is accessible to disabled students. The following facilities are available: wheelchair ramps, elevators, special parking, specially equipped rest rooms, special class scheduling, lowered drinking fountains, and lowered telephones.

Services: In addition to many counseling and information services, tutoring is available in most subjects. There also is remedial math, reading, and writing.

Campus Safety and Security: Campus safety and security measures include 24-hour foot and vehicle patrol, self defense education, escort service, and shuttle buses. In addition, there are informal discussions, pamphlets, posters, films, emergency telephones, and lighted pathways and sidewalks.

Programs of Study: Wesleyan awards the B.A. degree. Master's and doctoral degrees also are awarded. Bachelor's degrees are awarded in BIOLOGICAL SCIENCE (biochemistry and biology/biological science), COMMUNICATIONS AND THE ARTS (Chinese, dance, dramatic arts, English, film arts, fine arts, French, German, Greek, Hebrew, Italian, Japanese, Latin, music, photography, Russian, and Spanish), COMPUTER AND PHYSICAL SCIENCE (astronomy, chemistry, computer science, earth science, geology, mathematics, and physics), ENGINEERING AND ENVIRONMENTAL DESIGN (environmental science), SOCIAL SCIENCE (African studies, American studies, anthropology, Asian/Oriental studies, economics, history, international relations, philosophy, political science/government, public administration, social science, sociology, urban studies, and women's studies). Sciences, economics, history, and government are the strongest academically. English, history, and biology have the largest enrollments.

Required: To graduate, all students must complete 119 credit hours, including 35 in the major. Distribution requirements include 3 courses in humanities and arts, 3 in social and behavioral sciences, and 3 in natural science and mathematics. A minimum academic average of 70 must be maintained.

Special: Wesleyan offers cross-registration with 11 area colleges, internships, study abroad in 10 countries, a Washington semester, work-study programs, and pass/fail options. Accelerated degree programs in all majors, dual and student-designed majors, and 3–2 engineering programs with Caltech and Columbia University are also available. There are 2 national honor societies on campus, including Phi Beta Kappa. Forty departments have honors programs.

Faculty/Classroom: Sixty-nine percent of faculty are male; 31%, female. Ninety-eight percent teach undergraduates, 100% do research, and 98% do both. No introductory courses are taught by graduate students. The average class size in an introductory lecture is 50; in a laboratory, 15; and in a regular course offering, 23.

Admissions: About 43% of the 1993–94 applicants were accepted. The SAT scores for the 1993–94 freshman class were as follows: Verbal—10% below 500, 25% between 500 and 599, 50% between 600 and 700, and 12% above 700; Math—4% below 500, 17% between 500 and 599, 48% between 600 and 700, and 32% above 700. About 89% of the current freshmen were in the top fifth of their class; 99% were in the top two fifths. There were 18 National Merit finalists and 56 semifinalists. A total of 31 freshmen graduated first in their class.

Requirements: The SAT I or ACT is required, as are SAT II: Subject tests in writing and 2 other subjects. In addition, applicants should have 20 academic credits, including 4 years each of English, foreign language, mathematics, science, and social studies. An essay is necessary. AP credits are accepted. Important factors used in the admissions decision are advanced placement or honor courses, recommendations by school officials, leadership record, extracurricular activities record, and evidence of special talent.

Procedure: Freshmen are admitted to all sessions. Entrance exams should be taken in the spring of the junior year or the fall of the senior year. Early decision applications should be filed by November 15; regular applications, by January 15 for fall entry and October 1 for spring entry. The application fee is $50. Notification of early decision is sent December 15; regular decision, April 7. There are early decision and deferred admissions plans. A total of 195 early decision candidates were accepted for a recent class. A waiting list is an active part of the admissions procedure, with about 10% of applicants on the list.

Transfer: A total of 66 transfer students enrolled in a recent year. Applicants need an exceptional academic record and SAT I or ACT scores. An interview is recommended.

Visiting: There are regularly scheduled orientations for prospective students. There are guides for informal visits and visitors may sit in on classes and stay overnight at the school. To arrange for a visit, contact the Admissions Office at (203) 344-7900.

Financial Aid: In 1993–94, 48% of all current freshmen and 47% of continuing students received some form of financial aid, including need-based aid. Scholarships or need-based grants averaged $12,000 ($16,100 maximum); loans averaged $2000 ($2450 maximum); and work contracts averaged $1200 ($1250 maximum). Seventy-five percent of undergraduate students work part-time. The average financial indebtedness of the 1992–93 graduate was $3300. Wesleyan is a member of CSS. The FAF and the college's own financial statement are required. The deadline for financial aid applications is February 1.

International Students: There are currently 58 international students enrolled. The school actively recruits these students. They must take the TOEFL and achieve a minimum score of 600. The student must also take the SAT I or the ACT, as well as the SAT II: Subject test in writing.

Computers: Wesleyan provides computer facilities for student use. The mainframe is a DEC VAX 8550. There are more than 200 terminals connected to the mainframe at various campus locations. Software for word processing and statistical analysis is also available. All students may access the system. There are no time limits on using the system and no fees.

Graduates: In an earlier year, 690 bachelor's degrees were awarded. Within an average freshman class, 85% graduate in 4 years, 92% in 5 years, and 93% in 6 years.

Admissions Contact: Barbara-Jan Wilson, Dean of Admissions.

WESTERN CONNECTICUT STATE UNIVERSITY

Danbury, CT 06810-9972	**A-3** **(203) 837-9000**
Full-time: 1376 men, 1442 women	**Faculty:** 176
Part-time: 741 men, 1120 women	**Ph.D s:** 69%
Graduate: 346 men, 701 women	**Student/Faculty:** 16 to 1
Year: semesters, summer session	**Tuition:** $2900 ($7612)
Application Deadline: April 1	**Room & Board:** $3722
Freshman Class: 2486 applied, 1503 accepted, 528 enrolled	
SAT I Verbal/Math: 424/470	**COMPETITIVE**

Western Connecticut State University, founded in 1903, is a public, coeducational institution offering programs in business, arts and sciences, and professional studies. It is part of the Connecticut State University system. There are 3 undergraduate schools and one graduate school. In addition to regional accreditation, WestConn has baccalaureate program accreditation with CSWE and NLN. The 2 libraries contain 154,503 volumes, 50,268 microform items, and 4080 audiovisual forms, and subscribe to 1669 periodicals. Special learning facilities include an art gallery, radio station, and an observatory, an electron microscope, and a photography studio. The 346-acre campus is in a suburban area 65 miles north of New York City. Including residence halls, there are 14 buildings on campus.

Student Life: About 87% of undergraduates are from Connecticut. Ninety-eight percent are from public schools. Ninety percent are white. The average age of all undergraduates is 20. Thirty-three percent drop out by the end of their first year; 32% remain to graduate.

Housing: A total of 896 students can be accommodated in college housing. College-sponsored living facilities include single-sex and coed dormitories and on-campus apartments. On-campus housing is guaranteed for all 4 years. Sixty-six percent of students commute. Alcohol is not permitted. All students may keep cars on campus.

Activities: About 7% of men belong to 5 national fraternities; about 6% of women belong to 1 local and 3 national sororities. There are 42 groups on campus, including art, band, cheerleading, chess, chorale, computers, dance, drama, ethnic, film, gay, honors, international, jazz band, literary magazine, marching band, musical theater, newspaper, orchestra, photography, political, professional, radio and TV, religious, social, social service, student government, and yearbook.

Sports: There are 6 intercollegiate sports for men and 5 for women, and 7 intramural sports each for men and women. Athletic and recreation facilities include a gymnasium, a weight training area, 4 tennis courts, and 2 playing fields.

Disabled Students: Ninety-five percent of the campus is accessible to disabled students. The following facilities are available: wheelchair ramps, elevators, special parking, specially equipped rest rooms, special class scheduling, lowered drinking fountains, and lowered telephones.

Services: In addition to many counseling and information services, tutoring is available in some subjects. There is a reader service for the blind, and remedial math, reading, and writing.

Campus Safety and Security: Campus safety and security measures include 24-hour foot and vehicle patrol, escort service, shuttle buses, and informal discussions. In addition, there are pamphlets, posters, and films, emergency telephones, and lighted pathways and sidewalks.

Programs of Study: WestConn awards the B.A., B.S., B.B.A., and B.Mus. degrees. Associate and master's degrees are also awarded. Bachelor's degrees are awarded in BIOLOGICAL SCIENCE (biology/biological science), BUSINESS (accounting, banking and finance, business administration and management, management information systems, and marketing/retailing/merchandising), COMMUNICATIONS AND THE ARTS (art, communications, dramatic arts, English, fine arts, graphic design, illustration, music, music performance, photography, Spanish, and studio art), COMPUTER AND PHYSICAL SCIENCE (atmospheric sciences and meteorology, chemistry, computer mathematics, computer science, earth science, and mathematics), EDUCATION (elementary, health, music, and secondary), ENGINEERING AND ENVIRONMENTAL DESIGN (environmental science), HEALTH PROFESSIONS (medical laboratory technology and nursing), SOCIAL SCIENCE (American studies, economics, history, law enforcement and corrections, political science/government, psychology, social science, social work, and sociology). Social science is the strongest academically. Business has the largest enrollment.

Required: To graduate, students must complete 122 credit hours, with a minimum GPA of 2.0. A common core of courses is required, along with physical education. All students must also fulfill the foreign language requirement.

Special: The university offers co-op programs with local corporations, and cross-registration with the New England Regional Student Program. A B.A.-B.S. degree, dual and student-developed majors, and pass/fail options are available. Credit for military service is accepted. Nondegree study is offered at the Center for Lifelong Learning. There is a freshman honors program on campus.

Faculty/Classroom: Sixty-five percent of faculty are male; 35%, female. All teach undergraduates and 25% do research.

Admissions: About 60% of the 1993–94 applicants were accepted. The SAT scores for the 1993–94 freshman class were as follows: Verbal—82% below 500, 15% between 500 and 599, and 3% between 600 and 700; Math—64% below 500, 28% between 500 and 599, and 8% between 600 and 700. About 17% of the current freshmen were in the top fifth of their class; 44% were in the top two fifths.

Requirements: WestConn requires applicants to be in the upper 50% of their class. A minimum GPA of 2.5 is required. The SAT I or ACT is required. Applicants must be graduates of an accredited secondary school. The GED is accepted. Students should have completed 16 high school academic credits, including 4 in English, 3 in mathematics, 2 to 3 in foreign language, 2 in science, and one each in history and social studies. Additional credits in art, music, and computer science are highly recommended. An essay and an interview are recommended. AP and CLEP credits are accepted. Important factors used in the admissions decision are advanced placement or honor courses, evidence of special talent, recommendations by school officials, recommendations by alumni, and parents or siblings attending the school.

Procedure: Freshmen are admitted fall and spring. Entrance exams should be taken by December of the senior year. Applications should be filed by April 1 for fall entry and January 1 for spring entry, along with an application fee of $20. Notification is sent on a rolling basis, beginning December 1. There are early admissions and deferred admissions plans. A waiting list is an active part of the admissions procedure, with about 1% of applicants on the list.

Transfer: Transfer students must have a minimum of 7 college credits. Applicants must have a minimum GPA of 2.5 for all college course work. A total of 30 credits out of 122 must be completed at West-Conn.

Visiting: There are regularly scheduled orientations for prospective students. There are guides for informal visits and visitors may sit in on classes. To arrange for a visit, contact the Office of Admissions at (203) 837–4298.

Financial Aid: In a recent year, 38% of all current freshmen and 28% of continuing students received some need-based financial aid. The average freshman award was $2800. Of that total, need-based grants averaged $1000 ($3500 maximum); loans averaged $1500 ($3500 maximum); and work contracts averaged $1000 ($2000 maximum). Ninety percent of undergraduate students work part-time. Average earnings from campus work for the school year are $800. The average financial indebtedness of a recent graduate was $8000. WestConn is a member of CSS. The college's own financial statement and the FAFSA are required. The deadline for financial aid applications is March 15.

International Students: Students must take the TOEFL and achieve a minimum score of 550.

Computers: The college provides computer facilities for student use. IBM and Apple microcomputers are available for student use in various campus locations. All students may access the system at any time. There are no time limits and no fees.

Graduates: In an earlier year, 610 bachelor's degrees were awarded. The most popular majors among graduates were business administration (31%), visual and performing arts (11%), and education (11%). Some 60 companies recruited on campus that year. In an earlier year's graduating class, 12% of the men and 20% of the women were enrolled in graduate school within 6 months of graduation; 42% of the men and 28% of the women had found employment.

Admissions Contact: Delmore Kinney, Director of Admissions.

YALE UNIVERSITY

C-3

New Haven, CT 06520
(203) 432–1900

Full-time: 2841 men, 2353 women	Faculty: 2287; I, +$
Part-time: 35 men, 58 women	Ph.D.s: 96%
Graduate: 3126 men, 2536 women	Student/Faculty: n/av
Year: semesters, summer session	Tuition: $18,630
Application Deadline: December 31	Room & Board: $6480
Freshman Class: 10,705 applied, 2453 accepted, 1333 enrolled	
SAT I or ACT: required	**MOST COMPETITIVE**

Yale University, founded in 1701, is a private liberal arts institution. There is one undergraduate and 11 graduate schools. In addition to regional accreditation, Yale has baccalaureate program accreditation with ABET, CAHEA, NAAB, NASM, NLN, and SAF. The 43 libraries contain 10.2 million volumes, 4 million microform items, and 168,000 audiovisual forms, and subscribe to 54,601 periodicals. Computerized library sources and services include the card catalog, interlibrary loans, and database searching. Special learning facilities include an art gallery, natural history museum, planetarium, radio station, and the Beinecke Rare Books and Manuscript Library, the Marsh Botanical Gardens and Yale Natural Preserves, and several research centers. The 170-acre campus is in an urban area 75 miles northeast of New York City. Including residence halls, there are 200 buildings on campus.

Student Life: About 84% of undergraduates are from out-of-state, mostly the Middle Atlantic. Students come from 50 states, 51 foreign countries, and Canada. Sixty percent are from public schools; 40% from private. Seventy percent are white; 14% Asian American. The average age of freshmen is 18; all undergraduates, 20. Two percent drop out by the end of their first year; 93% remain to graduate.

Housing: A total of 4628 students can be accommodated in college housing. College-sponsored living facilities include coed dormitories and on-campus apartments. On-campus housing is guaranteed for the freshman year only and is available on a lottery system for upperclassmen. Ninety percent of students live on campus. All students may keep cars on campus.

Activities: There are many groups and organizations on campus, including art, band, cheerleading, chess, choir, chorale, chorus, computers, dance, drama, ethnic, film, gay, honors, international, jazz band, literary magazine, marching band, musical theater, newspaper, opera, orchestra, pep band, photography, political, professional, radio and TV, religious, social, social service, student government, symphony, and yearbook. Popular campus events include Communiversity Day, fall and spring concerts, and the East/West Film Festival.

Sports: There are 15 intercollegiate sports for men and 17 for women, and 25 intramural sports for men and 21 for women. Athletic and recreation facilities include the 71,000 seat Yale Bowl, a sports complex, gymnasium, swimming pool, skating rink, sailing center, equestrian center, and golf courses.

Disabled Students: The following facilities are available: wheelchair ramps, elevators, special parking, specially equipped rest rooms, special class scheduling, lowered drinking fountains, lowered telephones, and door to door lift-van service.

Services: In addition to many counseling and information services, tutoring is available in every subject. In addition, there is a reader service for the blind.

Campus Safety and Security: Campus safety and security measures include 24-hour foot and vehicle patrol, self defense education, escort service, and shuttle buses. In addition, there are informal discussions, pamphlets, posters, and films, emergency telephones, and lighted pathways and sidewalks.

Programs of Study: Yale awards the B.A., B.S., and B.L.S. degrees. Master's and doctoral degrees also are awarded. Bachelor's degrees are awarded in BIOLOGICAL SCIENCE (biology/biological science), COMMUNICATIONS AND THE ARTS (art, Chinese, classics, comparative literature, dramatic arts, English, film arts, French, German, Italian, Japanese, linguistics, literature, music, Russian, and Spanish), COMPUTER AND PHYSICAL SCIENCE (applied mathematics, astronomy, chemistry, computer science, mathematics, and physics), ENGINEERING AND ENVIRONMENTAL DESIGN (architecture, chemical engineering, electrical/electronics engineering, engineering, and mechanical engineering), SOCIAL SCIENCE (African

American studies, American studies, anthropology, archeology, classical/ancient civilization, East Asian studies, Eastern European studies, economics, history, history of science, humanities, Judaic studies, Latin American studies, Near Eastern studies, philosophy, political science/government, psychology, religion, sociology, and women's studies).

Required: To graduate, students must complete 36 semester courses, including at least 3 courses in each of 4 distributional groups, and at least 12 courses from outside the distributional group that includes their major. Foreign language proficiency must be demonstrated.

Special: The university offers study abroad, an accelerated degree program, B.A.-B.S. degrees, dual majors, and student-designed majors. Directed Studies, a special freshman program in the humanities, offers outstanding students the opportunity to survey the Western cultural tradition. Programs in the residential colleges allow students with special interests to pursue them in a more informal atmosphere. There is a chapter of Phi Beta Kappa on campus.

Faculty/Classroom: Seventy-two percent of faculty are male; 28%, female.

Admissions: About 23% of the 1993–94 applicants were accepted. The SAT scores for the 1993–94 freshman class were as follows: Verbal—3% below 500, 17% between 500 and 599, 44% between 600 and 700, and 36% above 700; Math—1% below 500, 8% between 500 and 599, 35% between 600 and 700, and 57% above 700. About 98% of the current freshmen were in the top fifth of their class.

Requirements: The SAT I or the ACT is required. Only those applicants submitting SAT I scores must also take any 3 SAT II: Subject tests. Most successful applicants rank in the top 10% of their high school class. All students must have completed a rigorous high school program encompassing all academic disciplines. An essay is required and an interview is recommended. AP credits are accepted. Important factors used in the admissions decision are advanced placement or honor courses, recommendations by school officials, personality, intangible qualities, leadership record, and extracurricular activities record.

Procedure: Freshmen are admitted in the fall. Entrance exams should be taken anytime up to and including the January test date in the year of application. Early decision applications should be filed by November 1; regular applications, by December 31 for fall entry, along with an application fee of $60. Notification of early decision is sent mid-December; regular decision, mid-April. There are early decision, early admissions, and deferred admissions plans. A waiting list is an active part of the admissions procedure, with about 6% of applicants on the list.

Transfer: Twenty-four transfer students enrolled in 1993–94. Applicants must take either the SAT I or ACT and have 1 full year of credit. An essay and 3 letters of recommendation are required. A total of 18 semester courses out of 36 must be completed at Yale.

Visiting: There are regularly scheduled orientations for prospective students. There are guides for informal visits and visitors may sit in on classes and stay overnight at the school. To arrange for a visit, contact the Admissions Office at (203) 432–1900.

Financial Aid: In 1993–94, 68% of all current freshmen and 48% of continuing students received some form of financial aid. About 46% of freshmen and 42% of continuing students received need-based aid. The average freshman award was $19,900. Of that total, scholarships or need-based grants averaged $14,980; loans averaged $3320; and work contracts averaged $1600. Fifty-two percent of undergraduate students work part-time. Average earnings from campus work for the school year are $1400. The average financial indebtedness of the 1992–93 graduate was $11,800. Yale is a member of CSS. The FAF, FAFSA, and the university's own financial statement and student and parent tax returns, as well as the CSS Divorced/Separated Parents Statement and Business/Farm Supplement, if applicable, are required. The deadline for financial aid applications is February 1.

International Students: There are currently 223 international students enrolled. The school actively recruits these students. They must take the TOEFL and achieve a minimum score of 600. The student must also take the SAT I and 3 SAT II: Subject tests, or the ACT.

Computers: The college provides computer facilities for student use. The mainframes are 2 IBM 4341s, 5 DEC 11/750s, and a DEC VAX 8600. There are also IBM and Apple Macintosh microcomputers available in dormitories, libraries, classrooms, and the computer center. All students may access the system. It may be used 24 hours a day. There are no time limits on using the system and no fees.

Graduates: In 1992–93, 1260 bachelor's degrees were awarded. The most popular majors among graduates were history (17%), English (10%), and biology (8%). Within an average freshman class, 93% graduate in 5 years and 95% in 6 years. Some 300 companies recruited on campus in 1992–93. In the 1992 graduating class, 32% of the men and 34% of the women were enrolled in graduate school within 6 months of graduation; 63% of the men and 59% of the women had found employment.

Admissions Contact: Dean of Undergraduate Admissions.

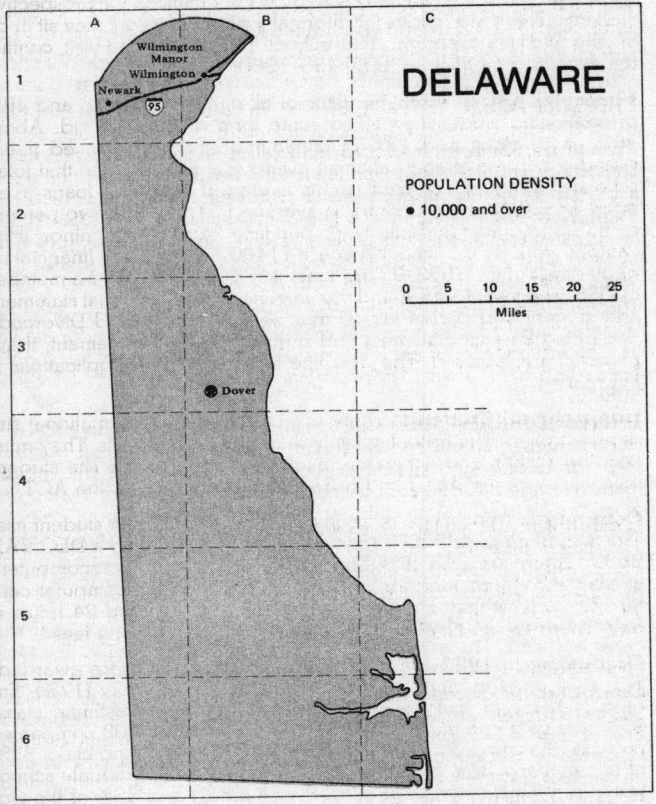

DELAWARE

POPULATION DENSITY

● 10,000 and over

0   5   10   15   20   25
Miles

DELAWARE STATE COLLEGE

B-3

Dover, Delaware 19901

(302) 739-4917

Full-time: 1070 men, 1341 women
Part-time: 236 men, 404 women
Graduate: 89 men, 161 women
Year: semesters, summer session
Application Deadline: June 1
Freshman Class: 2325 applied, 1709 accepted, 724 enrolled
SAT I or ACT: required

Faculty: 158; IIA, --$
Ph.D.s: 57%
Student/Faculty: 15 to 1
Tuition: $1846 ($4878)
Room & Board: $3810

COMPETITIVE

Delaware State College, founded in 1891, is a public institution offering programs in agricultural and technical fields, business, engineering, liberal and fine arts, health science, professional training, and teacher preparation. There are 2 undergraduate schools and one graduate school. The 2 libraries contain 156,605 volumes, 353,222 microform items, and 5369 audiovisual forms, and subscribe to 1111 periodicals. Computerized library sources and services include the card catalog, interlibrary loans, and database searching. Special learning facilities include a learning resource center, art gallery, planetarium, and radio station. The 400-acre campus is in a suburban area 45 miles south of Wilmington. Including residence halls, there are 21 buildings on campus.

Student Life: About 64% of undergraduates are from Delaware. Students come from 26 foreign countries. Ninety percent are from public schools; 10% from private. Sixty-four percent are African American; 32% white. The average age of freshmen is 19; all undergraduates, 19.

Housing: A total of 1002 students can be accommodated in college housing. College-sponsored living facilities include single-sex dormitories. On-campus housing is available on a first-come, first-served basis. Sixty-six percent of students commute. Alcohol is not permitted. All students may keep cars on campus.

Activities: About 50% of men and about 50% of women belong to 4 national fraternities; about 50% of women belong to 4 national sororities. There are 53 groups on campus, including cheerleading, choir, drama, ethnic, honors, international, jazz band, marching band, newspaper, pep band, radio and TV, religious, social service, student government, and yearbook. Popular campus events include Parents Day, Homecoming, and Annual Career Fair.

Sports: There are 7 intercollegiate sports for men and 6 for women, and 20 intramural sports for men and 20 for women. Athletic and recreation facilities include an indoor swimming pool, a gymnasium, a dance studio, and racquetball and handball courts.

Disabled Students: The following facilities are available: wheelchair ramps, elevators, special parking, and specially equipped rest rooms.

Services: In addition to many counseling and information services, tutoring is available in every subject. There is also remedial reading and writing.

Campus Safety and Security: Campus safety and security measures include 24-hour foot and vehicle patrol, shuttle buses, informal discussions, and pamphlets, posters, and films. In addition, there are lighted pathways and sidewalks.

Programs of Study: Delstate awards the B.A., B.S., B.Tech and master's degrees. Bachelor's degrees are awarded in AGRICULTURE (agricultural business management, fish and game management, and natural resource management), BIOLOGICAL SCIENCE (biology/biological science and botany), BUSINESS (accounting, business administration and management, fashion merchandising, hotel/motel and restaurant management, and marketing/retailing/merchandising), COMMUNICATIONS AND THE ARTS (English, French, journalism, music, and Spanish), COMPUTER AND PHYSICAL SCIENCE (chemistry, computer science, mathematics, and physics), EDUCATION (agricultural, art, business, early childhood, elementary, health, home economics, music, physical, science, and special), ENGINEERING AND ENVIRONMENTAL DESIGN (chemical engineering, civil engineering, electrical/electronics engineering, and mechanical engineering), HEALTH PROFESSIONS (community health work, environmental health science, and nursing), SOCIAL SCIENCE (economics, history, parks and recreation management, political science/government, psychology, social work, and sociology). Education is the strongest academically. Marketing and business administration have the largest enrollments.

Required: Forty-two credits of general education requirements include 12 hours of humanities, 11 of basic intellectual skills, 7 of social science, and 6 each of mathematics and natural science. Two semesters of physical education are also required. A total of 121 credit hours and a minimum GPA of 2.0 is required.

Special: The college offers accelerated degrees, combined B.A.-B.S. degrees, student-designed majors, and a 3–2 engineering program with the University of Delaware. Work-study is available on campus. There are assisted internships in airway science and nursing, and co-op programs in business, education, home economics, social work, and agriculture. There is a freshman honors program on campus, as well as 6 national honor societies, including Phi Beta Kappa.

Faculty/Classroom: Sixty-two percent of faculty are male; 38%, female. No introductory courses are taught by graduate students.

Admissions: About 74% of the 1993–94 applicants were accepted.

Requirements: The SAT I or ACT is required. Applicants should graduate from an accredited secondary school or have a GED. Fifteen academic credits are required, including 4 units of English, and 2 each of mathematics, science, and social studies. CLEP credit is accepted. Important factors used in the admissions decision are extracurricular activities record, advanced placement or honor courses, recommendations by school officials, personality, intangible qualities, and leadership record.

Procedure: Freshmen are admitted fall and spring. Entrance exams should be taken in December or January of the senior year. Applications should be filed by June 1 for fall entry and December 30 for spring entry, along with an application fee of $10. Notification is sent on a rolling basis. There is an early admissions plan.

Transfer: About 180 transfer students enrolled recently. Transfer applicants must submit a statement of honorable withdrawal and high school and college transcripts. A total of 30 credits out of 121 must be completed at Delstate.

Visiting: There are regularly scheduled orientations for prospective students, including a High School Day Program. There are guides for informal visits. To arrange for a visit, contact Jethro Williams at (302) 739-3559.

Financial Aid: In a recent year, 60% of all current freshmen received some form of financial aid. About 60% of freshmen received need-based aid. The average freshman award was $2500. Ninety percent of undergraduate students work part-time. Average earnings from campus work for the school year are $5000. Delstate is a member of CSS. The FAF or FFS is required. The deadline for financial aid applications is February 28.

International Students: They must take the TOEFL and achieve a minimum score of 500. The student must also take the SAT I or the ACT.

Computers: The college provides computer facilities for student use. The mainframe is an IBM. There is a computer laboratory specifically for students. Students may also use terminals in the library. All students may access the system. It may be used 8:30 A.M. to 4:30 A.M. There are no fees.

Graduates: In an earlier year, 270 bachelor's degrees were awarded. Within an average freshman class, 28% graduate in 5 years. Recently, some 276 companies recruited on campus.

Admissions Contact: Jethro C. Williams, Admissions Director.

GOLDEY-BEACOM COLLEGE
B-1
Wilmington, Delaware 19808
(302) 998–8814
(800) 833–4877 (out-of-state)

Full-time: 315 men, 508 women	Faculty: 24; IIB, av$
Part-time: 292 men, 680 women	Ph.D.s: 25%
Graduate: 26 men, 25 women	Student/Faculty: 34 to 1
Year: semesters, summer session	Tuition: $5250
Application Deadline: open	Room & Board: $2589
Freshman Class: 633 applied, 468 accepted, 284 enrolled	
SAT I Verbal/Math: 425/486	**COMPETITIVE**

Goldey-Beacom College, founded in 1886, is a private, coeducational business college that provides undergraduate training and education for careers in business, industry, and government. There are 2 undergraduate schools and one graduate school. The library contains 27,900 volumes, 27,283 microform items, and 693 audiovisual forms, and subscribes to 394 periodicals. Computerized library sources and services include interlibrary loans and database searching. Special learning facilities include a learning resource center. The 28-acre campus is in a suburban area 10 miles west of Wilmington. Including residence halls, there are 6 buildings on campus.

Student Life: About 60% of undergraduates are from Delaware. Students come from 10 states and 26 foreign countries. Seventy-five percent are from public schools; 25% from private. Eighty-one percent are white; 10% African American. The average age of freshmen is 19; all undergraduates, 21. Thirty percent drop out by the end of their first year; 70% remain to graduate.

Housing: A total of 300 students can be accommodated in college housing. College-sponsored living facilities include coed on-campus apartments. In addition there are special interest houses. On-campus housing is available on a first-come, first-served basis. Eighty-four percent of students commute. All students may keep cars on campus.

Activities: About 10% of men belong to 2 national fraternities; about 10% of women belong to 2 national sororities. There are 15 groups on campus, including chorus, computers, ethnic, honors, international, literary magazine, newspaper, professional, religious, social service, and student government. Popular campus events include Goldey-Beacom Follies.

Sports: There is 1 intercollegiate sport for men and 1 for women, and 7 intramural sports for men and 5 for women. Athletic and recreation facilities include soccer and softball fields, and tennis, basketball, and handball courts.

Disabled Students: All of the campus is accessible to disabled students. The following facilities are available: wheelchair ramps, elevators, special parking, specially equipped rest rooms, lowered drinking fountains, and lowered telephones.

Services: In addition to many counseling and information services, tutoring is available in most subjects. In addition, there is a reader service for the blind; remedial math, reading, and writing; and computer-based tutorials.

Campus Safety and Security: Campus safety and security measures include 24-hour foot and vehicle patrol, self-defense education, informal discussions, and pamphlets, posters, and films. In addition, there are lighted pathways and sidewalks and security from 6 P.M. to 6 A.M. on the small campus.

Programs of Study: Goldey-Beacom College awards the B.S. degree. Associate and master's degrees also are awarded. Bachelor's degrees are awarded in BUSINESS (accounting, banking and finance, international business management, marketing/retailing/merchandising, and office supervision and management), COMMUNICATIONS AND THE ARTS (communications), COMPUTER AND PHYSICAL SCIENCE (computer programming). Accounting and computer science are the strongest academically. Accounting and management have the largest enrollments.

Required: To graduate, students must complete a minimum of 126 credit hours with an overall GPA of 2.0. Students must also fulfill the college's core requirements in English and mathematics.

Special: Co-op programs in all majors, internships, study abroad, and work-study programs are available. There is a freshman honors program on campus, as well as one national honor society. Three departments have honors programs.

Faculty/Classroom: Sixty-six percent of faculty are male; 34%, female. All teach undergraduates. No introductory courses are taught by graduate students. The average class size in an introductory lecture is 35 and in a regular course offering, 25.

Admissions: About 74% of the 1993–94 applicants were accepted. The SAT scores for the 1993–94 freshman class were as follows: Verbal—92% below 500, 7% between 500 and 599, and 1% between 600 and 700; Math—60% below 500, 32% between 500 and 599, and 8% between 600 and 700. About 16% of the current freshmen were in the top fifth of their class; 45% were in the top two fifths.

Requirements: Goldey-Beacom College requires applicants to be in the upper 80% of their class. A minimum GPA of 2.0 is required. The SAT I is required. In addition, applicants must be high school graduates or have a GED. AP and CLEP credits are accepted. Important factors used in the admissions decision are evidence of special talent, advanced placement or honor courses, parents or siblings attending the school, recommendations by school officials, and leadership record.

Procedure: Freshmen are admitted to all sessions. Application deadlines are open. The application fee is $30. Notification is sent on a rolling basis. There are early admissions and deferred admissions plans.

Transfer: Seventy-five transfer students enrolled in 1993–94. Transfer applicants must submit high school and college transcripts. A total of 50 credits out of 126 must be completed at Goldey-Beacom College.

Visiting: There are regularly scheduled orientations for prospective students, including an open house. There are guides for informal visits, and visitors may sit in on classes and stay overnight at the school. To arrange for a visit, contact the Admissions Office at (302) 998-8814.

Financial Aid: In 1993–94, 89% of all current freshmen and 57% of continuing students received some form of financial aid. Scholarships or need-based grants averaged $1171 ($2300 maximum); loans averaged $2850 ($5500 maximum); and work contracts averaged $1200 ($6700 maximum). Average earnings from campus work for the school year are $1200. The average financial indebtedness of the 1992–93 graduate was $6012. Goldey-Beacom College is a member of CSS. The FAFSA financial statement is required. The deadline for financial aid applications is February 15.

International Students: There are currently 81 international students enrolled. The school actively recruits these students. Students must take the TOEFL and achieve a minimum score of 500.

Computers: The college provides computer facilities for student use. The mainframes are an IBM Series 4361 and a VM/SP Release 5. The college's 4 computer laboratories contain more than 160 IBM PS/2 Model 50 terminals. Modems may access the mainframe from off campus 24 hours a day. There are no fees.

Graduates: In 1992–93, 174 bachelor's degrees were awarded. The most popular majors among graduates were management (33%), office technology (26%), and accounting (17%). Within an average freshman class, 30% graduate in 3 years, 40% in 4 years, 20% in 5 years, and 10% in 6 years. In the 1992 graduating class, 1% of all graduates were enrolled in graduate school within 6 months of graduation.

Admissions Contact: Patricia M. Buhler, Acting Director of Admissions.

UNIVERSITY OF DELAWARE
A-1
Newark, Delaware 19716
(302) 831-8123

Full-time: 5824 men, 7663 women	Faculty: 954; I, -$
Part-time: 633 men, 812 women	Ph.D.s: 83%
Graduate: 1624 men, 1459 women	Student/Faculty: 14 to 1
Year: 4–1–4, summer session	Tuition: $3983 ($10,083)
Application Deadline: March 1	Room & Board: $4030
Freshman Class: 14,446 applied, 10,516 accepted, 3252 enrolled	
SAT I or ACT: required	**VERY COMPETITIVE**

The University of Delaware, founded in 1743 and chartered in 1833, is a privately-controlled, state-assisted, coeducational institution, offering programs in agriculture sciences, arts and science, business and economics, education, engineering, human resources, nursing, and physical education. There are 8 undergraduate and 2 graduate schools. In addition to regional accreditation, the university has baccalaureate program accreditation with AACSB, ABET, ADA, APTA, CAHEA, NASM, and NLN. The 4 libraries contain 2,000,000 volumes, 2,300,000 microform items, and 5100 audiovisual forms, and subscribe to 21,000 periodicals. Computerized library sources and services include the card catalog, interlibrary loans, and database searching. Special learning facilities include a learning resource center, art gallery, radio station, TV station, and a preschool laboratory. The 1100-acre campus is in a small town 12 miles southwest of Wilmington. Including residence halls, there are more than 400 buildings on campus.

Student Life: About 58% of undergraduates are from out-of-state, mostly the Middle Atlantic. Students come from 46 states, 85 foreign countries, and Canada. Seventy-seven percent are from public schools; 23% from private. Ninety-seven percent are white. Forty-two percent are Catholic; 30% Protestant; 14% claim no religious affiliation; 11% Jewish. The average age of freshmen is 18; all undergraduates, 20.5. Fourteen percent drop out by the end of their first year; 71% remain to graduate.

Housing: A total of 7319 students can be accommodated in college housing. College-sponsored living facilities include single-sex and coed dormitories, on-campus apartments, and married-student housing. In addition there are honors houses, language houses, special interest houses, and substance-free residence halls. On-campus housing is guaranteed for all 4 years. Fifty-two percent of students live on campus; of those, more than 50% remain on campus on weekends. Alcohol is not permitted.

Activities: About 10% of men belong to 24 national fraternities; about 14% of women belong to 14 national sororities. There are 150 groups on campus, including cheerleading, chess, chorale, dance, drama, ethnic, gay, honors, international, jazz band, literary magazine, marching band, musical theater, newspaper, political, professional, radio and TV, religious, social, social service, student government, symphony, and yearbook. Popular campus events include Homecoming, Delaware Day, Greek Week, Convocation, Graduation, and Parents Day.

Sports: There are 11 intercollegiate sports for men and 11 for women, and 23 intramural sports for men and 21 for women. Athletic and recreation facilities include a football stadium, 3 multipurpose gymnasiums, 6 outdoor multipurpose fields, 8 outdoor basketball courts, 2 squash courts, 15 racquetball courts, 22 outdoor tennis courts; indoor and outdoor pools, a universal weight room, a 6000-seat basketball arena, a climbing wall, a high-ropes challenge course; 2 student fitness centers, a strength and conditioning room with free weights, outdoor and indoor tracks, softball, baseball, lacrosse, and soccer fields, and 2 ice arenas.

Disabled Students: Ninety percent of the campus is accessible to disabled students. The following facilities are available: wheelchair ramps, elevators, special parking, specially equipped rest rooms, special class scheduling, lowered drinking fountains, and lowered telephones.

Services: In addition to many counseling and information services, tutoring is available in every subject. A reader service for the blind, and remedial math, reading, and writing are available. Other services include a writing center, a mathematics center, and an academic services center for assistance with academic self-management development, critical thinking, and problem solving.

Campus Safety and Security: Campus safety and security measures include 24-hour foot and vehicle patrol, escort service, shuttle buses, and informal discussions. In addition, there are pamphlets, posters, films, emergency telephones, and lighted pathways and sidewalks. Ongoing student-awareness programs are conducted within the residence halls.

Programs of Study: The university awards the B.A., B.S., B.A. Liberal Arts, B.C.E., B.Ch.E., B.E.E., B.F.A., B.M.E., B.Mus., B.S.Acc., B.S.Ag., B.S.B.A., B.S.Ed., B.S.N., and B.S.P.E. degrees. Associate, master's, and doctoral degrees also are awarded. Bachelor's degrees are awarded in AGRICULTURE (agricultural business management, agricultural economics, agriculture, animal science, and plant science), BIOLOGICAL SCIENCE (biochemistry, biology/biological science, entomology, and nutrition), BUSINESS (accounting, business administration and management, hotel/motel and restaurant management, and marketing/retailing/merchandising), COMMUNICATIONS AND THE ARTS (art, art history and appreciation, classics, communications, comparative literature, English, fine arts, French, German, historic preservation, Italian, journalism, Latin, music, music theory and composition, Russian, Spanish, and theater management), COMPUTER AND PHYSICAL SCIENCE (astronomy, chemistry, computer science, geology, geophysics and seismology, information sciences and systems, mathematics, physics, and statistics), EDUCATION (agricultural, early childhood, education, elementary, English, foreign languages, home economics, mathematics, music, physical, psychology, science, secondary, and special), ENGINEERING AND ENVIRONMENTAL DESIGN (agricultural engineering technology, chemical engineering, civil engineering, electrical/electronics engineering, environmental science, mechanical engineering, and textile engineering), HEALTH PROFESSIONS (medical laboratory technology and nursing), SOCIAL SCIENCE (anthropology, community services, criminal justice, dietetics, economics, fashion design and technology, food science, geography, history, human development, international relations, Latin American studies, parks and recreation management, philosophy, political science/government, psychology, sociology, textiles and clothing, and women's studies). Engineering, all sciences, and accounting are the strongest academically. Elementary teacher education, biological sciences, psychology, business administration, nursing, and accounting have the largest enrollments.

Required: For graduation, students must complete at least 124 credits with a minimum GPA of 2.0. All students must take freshman English and 3 credits of course work with multicultural or multiethnic content. Some majors require more than 124 credits. Most degree programs require that half of the courses be in the major field of study.

Special: Students may participate in cooperative programs, internships, and study abroad in 16 countries. A Washington semester and work-study programs are available. The college offers accelerated degree programs, B.A.-B.S. degrees, dual majors, student-designed majors (Bachelor of Arts in Liberal Studies), and pass/fail options. Nondegree study is available through the Division of Continuing Education. There is an extensive undergraduate research program. There is a freshman honors program on campus, as well as 36 national honor societies, including Phi Beta Kappa. All departments have honors programs.

Faculty/Classroom: Sixty-nine percent of faculty are male; 31%, female. Ninety percent both teach and do research. Graduate students teach 5% of introductory courses. The average class size in a laboratory is 18 and in a regular course offering, 35.

Admissions: About 73% of the 1993–94 applicants were accepted. About 47% of the current freshmen were in the top fifth of their class; 83% were in the top two fifths. There were 26 National Merit finalists. Thirty-four freshmen graduated first in their class.

Requirements: The SAT I or ACT is required. Applicants should be graduates of an accredited secondary school. The GED is accepted. Students should have completed 16 high school academic credits, including 4 years of English, 2 years each of mathematics, science, foreign language, and history, 1 year of social studies, and 3 years of academic course electives. SAT II: Subject tests are recommended, especially for honors consideration. A writing sample is required for honors consideration. AP credits are accepted. Important factors used in the admissions decision are advanced placement or honor courses, parents or siblings attending the school, recommendations by school officials, leadership record, and recommendations by alumni.

Procedure: Freshmen are admitted fall and spring. Entrance exams should be taken at the end of the junior year or the beginning of the senior year. Early decision applications should be filed by November 15; regular applications, by March 1 for fall entry and November 15 for spring entry, along with an application fee of $40. Notification of early decision is sent December 15; regular decision on a rolling basis from January through April. There are early decision, early admissions, and deferred admissions plans.

Transfer: About 700 transfer students enrolled in 1993–94. Applicants for transfer usually should have completed at least 24 credits with a minimum GPA of 2.5 for most majors; some majors require a GPA of 3.0 or better. A total of the last 30 credits or first 90 out of a minimum of 124 must be completed at the university.

Visiting: There are regularly scheduled orientations for prospective students. There are guides for informal visits and visitors may sit in on classes. To arrange for a visit, contact the Admissions Office at (302) 831–8123.

Financial Aid: In 1993–94, 60% of all current freshmen and 45% of continuing students received some form of financial aid. About 52% of freshmen and 43% of continuing students received need-based aid. The average freshman award was $3200. Of that total, scholarships or need-based grants averaged $1900 ($14,000 maximum); loans averaged $2000 ($3665 maximum); and work contracts averaged $1000 ($2000 maximum). Fifty percent of undergraduate students work part-time. Average earnings from campus work for the school year are $1000. The average financial indebtedness of an earlier year's graduate was $8700. The university is a member of CSS. The FAFSA financial statement is required. The deadline for financial aid applications is May 1.

International Students: There are currently 148 international students enrolled. The school actively recruits these students. They must take the TOEFL and achieve a minimum score of 550.

Computers: The college provides computer facilities for student use. The mainframes are an IBM 3090–400E/2VF, 2 IBM RS/6000–98E systems, a Sun Microsystems SPARCenter 2000, and 3 SPARCserver 690MP-41 systems. More than 30 computing sites are available to students, offering ample numbers of terminals, IBMs, IBM-compatibles, and Macintosh PCs. All residence hall rooms are equipped with data outlets for PCs. Those registered in computer courses or doing research that requires it may access the system. It may be used 24 hours a day. There are no time limits and no fees.

Graduates: In 1992–93, 3200 bachelor's degrees were awarded. The most popular majors among graduates were psychology (7%), English (7%), and elementary teacher education (6%). Within an average freshman class, 48% graduate in 4 years, 68% in 5 years, and 71% in 6 years. Some 207 companies recruited on campus in 1992–93. In the 1992 graduating class, 22% of the men and 15% of the women were enrolled in graduate school within 6 months of graduation; 66% of the men and 78% of the women had found employment.

Admissions Contact: Bruce Walker, Associate Provost, Admissions and Student Financial Aid.

WESLEY COLLEGE
B-3

Dover, Delaware 19901

Full-time: 412 men, 460 women
Part-time: 220 men, 228 women
Graduate: none
Year: semesters, summer session
Application Deadline: See profile
Freshman Class: 839 applied, 807 accepted, 350 enrolled
SAT I Verbal/Math: 380/410

(302) 736-2400; (800) WESLEYU

Faculty: 55; IIB, -$
Ph.D.s: 54%
Student/Faculty: 16 to 1
Tuition: $9645
Room & Board: $4100

LESS COMPETITIVE

Wesley College, founded in 1873, is a private, coeducational, liberal arts institution affiliated with the United Methodist Church. In addition to regional accreditation, Wesley College has baccalaureate program accreditation with NLN. The library contains 60,000 volumes, 2118 microform items, and 1594 audiovisual forms, and subscribes to 375 periodicals. Computerized library sources and services include interlibrary loans and database searching. Special learning facilities include a learning resource center, radio station, and TV station. The 20-acre campus is in a small town 60 miles south of Philadelphia. Including residence halls, there are 20 buildings on campus.

Student Life: About 55% of undergraduates are from Delaware. Students come from 20 states. Eighty-five percent are from public schools; 15% from private. Eighty-six percent are white; 11% African American. Fifty-three percent are Protestant; 41% Catholic. The average age of freshmen is 18; all undergraduates, 20. Twenty percent drop out by the end of their first year; 68% remain to graduate.

Housing: A total of 680 students can be accommodated in college housing. College-sponsored living facilities include single-sex dormitories. On-campus housing is guaranteed for all 4 years. Eighty-five percent of students live on campus; of those, 75% remain on campus on weekends. Alcohol is not permitted. All students may keep cars on campus.

Activities: About 15% of men belong to 2 national fraternities; about 15% of women belong to 2 local sororities. There are 25 groups on campus, including band, cheerleading, choir, chorus, computers, drama, ethnic, film, honors, international, jazz band, literary magazine, newspaper, photography, political, professional, radio and TV, religious, social, social service, student government, and yearbook. Popular campus events include Family Day, Homecoming, International Fair, and Spring Fling.

Sports: There are 8 intercollegiate sports for men and 4 for women, and 4 intramural sports for men and 4 for women. Athletic and recreation facilities include a pool, tennis courts, a football stadium, athletic fields, a gymnasium, a game room, and an exercise room.

Disabled Students: All of the campus is accessible to disabled students. The following facilities are available: wheelchair ramps, elevators, special parking, specially equipped rest rooms, special class scheduling, lowered drinking fountains, and lowered telephones.

Services: In addition to many counseling and information services, tutoring is available in every subject. In addition, there is remedial math, reading, and writing.

Campus Safety and Security: Campus safety and security measures include 24-hour foot and vehicle patrol, escort service, informal discussions, and pamphlets, posters, and films. In addition, there are emergency telephones and lighted pathways and sidewalks.

Programs of Study: Wesley College awards the B.A. and B.S. degrees. Associate and master's degrees also are awarded. Bachelor's degrees are awarded in BIOLOGICAL SCIENCE (biology/biological science), BUSINESS (accounting, business administration and management, management science, and marketing/retailing/merchandising), COMMUNICATIONS AND THE ARTS (communications), COMPUTER AND PHYSICAL SCIENCE (computer science and information sciences and systems), EDUCATION (elementary, physical, and secondary), ENGINEERING AND ENVIRONMENTAL DESIGN (environmental science), HEALTH PROFESSIONS (medical laboratory technology and nursing), SOCIAL SCIENCE (economics, history, political science/government, and psychology). Biological science is the strongest academically. Management science has the largest enrollment.

Required: For graduation, students must complete 128 credit hours, with at least 30 hours in the major and a minimum GPA of 2.0. Fifty hours of core courses, including English, orientation, religion, and physical education, are required.

Special: The college offers internships in business and industry, nursing, environmental science, study abroad in 5 countries, work-study programs, pass/fail options, and credit for life, military, and work experience. There are 2 national honor societies on campus.

Faculty/Classroom: Fifty-eight percent of faculty are male; 42%, female. All teach undergraduates. The average class size in an introductory lecture is 30; in a laboratory, 20; and in a regular course offering, 16.

Admissions: About 96% of the 1993-94 applicants were accepted. The SAT scores for the 1993-94 freshman class were as follows: Verbal—96% below 500 and 1% between 600 and 700; Math—85% below 500, 12% between 500 and 599, and 3% between 600 and 700. About 9% of the current freshmen were in the top fifth of their class; 26% were in the top two fifths. Five freshmen graduated first in their class.

Requirements: Wesley College requires applicants to be in the upper 80% of their class. A minimum GPA of 2.0 is required. The SAT I is required. Applicants must be graduates of an accredited secondary school with a minimum GPA of 2.0. The GED is accepted. Students should have completed 12 academic credits of 16 Carnegie units, including 4 units of English and 2 units each of mathematics, history, science, and social studies. An interview is recommended. AP and CLEP credits are accepted. Important factors used in the admissions decision are recommendations by school officials, personality, intangible qualities, leadership record, extracurricular activities record, and parents or siblings attending the school.

Procedure: Freshmen are admitted fall and winter. Entrance exams should be taken in the junior year. Application deadlines are open except for an early decision deadline of November 15. Application fee is $15. Notification of early decision is sent November 30; regular decision, on a rolling basis. There are early decision, early admissions, and deferred admissions plans. About 20 early decision candidates were accepted for the 1993-94 class. A waiting list is an active part of the admissions procedure, with about 10% of applicants on the list.

Transfer: About 30 transfer students enrolled in 1993-94. Applicants must have a minimum GPA of 2.0 and a minimum composite SAT I score of 800. A total of 32 credits out of 128 must be completed at Wesley College.

Visiting: There are regularly scheduled orientations for prospective students. There are guides for informal visits and visitors may sit in on classes and stay overnight at the school. To arrange for a visit, contact Admissions at (800) WESLEYU.

Financial Aid: In 1993-94, 72% of all current freshmen and 77% of continuing students received some form of financial aid. About 68% of freshmen and 73% of continuing students received need-based aid. The average freshman award was $6695. Of that total, scholarships or need-based grants averaged $3070 ($4000 maximum); loans averaged $2625 ($3125 maximum); and work contracts averaged $1000 (maximum). Twenty-four percent of undergraduate students work part-time. Average earnings from campus work for the school year are $1000. The average financial indebtedness of the 1992-93 graduate was $10,000. Wesley College is a member of CSS. The SFS is required. The deadline for financial aid applications is April 15.

International Students: There are currently 30 international students enrolled. The school actively recruits these students. They must take the TOEFL and achieve a minimum score of 500.

Computers: The college provides computer facilities for student use. The mainframe is a DEC MicroVAX 3400. It may be accessed from 16 terminals across campus for use in word processing, programming, accounting, and statistics. Microcomputers are available for student use in the writing center, computer center, and accounting laboratory. All students may access the system. It may be used 24 hours a day, 7 days a week. There are no time limits on using the system. The fees are $30 per course.

Graduates: In 1992-93, 104 bachelor's degrees were awarded. The most popular majors among graduates were management (18%), elementary education (13%), and nursing (9%). Within an average freshman class, 14% graduate in 3 years, 22% in 4 years, 35% in 5 years, and 44% in 6 years. Of the 1992 graduating class, 3% were enrolled in graduate school within 6 months of graduation, and 87% had found employment.

Admissions Contact: Dean of Admissions.

WILMINGTON COLLEGE
B-1

New Castle, Delaware 19720

Full-time/part-time men: 851
Full-time/part-time women: 1535
Graduate: 477 men, 650 women
Year: trimesters, summer session
Application Deadline: open
Freshman Class: n/av
SAT I or ACT: not required

(302) 328-9407

Faculty: 29
Ph.D.s: 38%
Student/Faculty: n/av
Tuition: $5200
Room & Board: n/app

NONCOMPETITIVE

Wilmington College, founded in 1967, is a private, liberal arts commuter college. In addition to regional accreditation, Wilmington has baccalaureate program accreditation with NLN. The library contains 75,000 volumes, 6248 microform items, and 4258 audiovisual forms, and subscribes to 325 periodicals. The 15-acre campus is 7 miles south of Wilmington. There are 16 buildings on campus.

Student Life: About 90% of undergraduates are from Delaware. Students come from 7 states. Some 98% are from public schools; 2% from private. About 80% are white; 16% African American. The average age of freshmen is 23; all undergraduates, 27.

Housing: There are no residence halls. The college provides a list of housing accommodations in the community. Alcohol is not permitted. All students commute and may keep cars on campus.

Activities: There are 2 local fraternities. There are 9 groups on campus, including film, honors, newspaper, photography, radio and TV, student government, and yearbook. Popular campus events include the Honors Convocation and cultural and social affairs.

Sports: Athletic and recreation facilities include a 1000-seat gymnasium and a recreation room.

Disabled Students: The entire campus is accessible to disabled students. The following facilities are available: wheelchair ramps, specially equipped rest rooms, and lowered drinking fountains.

Services: In addition to many counseling and information services, tutoring is available in most subjects. In addition, there is remedial math, reading, and writing. Staff members also are available to assist students with study skills such as test taking, reading, concentration development, and time management.

Campus Safety and Security: Campus safety and security measures include lighted pathways and sidewalks.

Programs of Study: Wilmington awards the B.A., B.S., and B.S.N. degrees. Associate, master's, and doctoral degrees also are awarded. Bachelor's degrees are awarded in BUSINESS (accounting, banking and finance, business administration and management, and personnel management), COMMUNICATIONS AND THE ARTS (communications), EDUCATION (early childhood and elementary), HEALTH PROFESSIONS (nursing), SOCIAL SCIENCE (behavioral science and criminal justice). Business, nursing, and elementary education are the strongest programs academically. Business, nursing, and elementary education have the largest enrollments.

Required: To graduate, students must complete a total of 120 hours with a minimum GPA of 2.0. A total of 54 hours are required in the major. The 36-hour general studies core requirement includes 12 hours of social science, 9 each of English and humanities, and 3 each of mathematics and science. At least 45 credit hours of upper-division course work are required, as is demonstrated competence in verbal and written communication and in computational skills. Nursing students must also submit official transcripts verifying graduation from a diploma or associate degree nursing program.

Special: The school offers practicums for education students, internships, a general studies degree, dual degrees, pass/fail options, credit for life experience, and by-challenge exam.

Faculty/Classroom: Some 70% of faculty are male; 30%, female. The average class size in an introductory lecture is 25; in a laboratory, 10; and in a regular course offering, 17.

Admissions: In a recent year, about 97% of the applicants were accepted.

Requirements: Graduation from an accredited secondary school or satisfactory scores on the GED are required for admission. An interview may be required of some students and an essay is recommended. AP and CLEP credits are accepted. Important factors used in the admissions decision are recommendations by school officials, advanced placement or honor courses, ability to finance college education, recommendations by alumni, and leadership record.

Procedure: Application deadlines are open. Notification is sent on a rolling basis. The application fee is $25. There are early admissions and deferred admissions plans.

Transfer: About 375 transfer students enrolled in 1993–94. Transfer applicants must have a 2.0 GPA; those with a lower GPA must have an interview. Some applicants may be required to submit SAT I or ACT scores. Those with fewer than 15 semester credits must submit high school transcripts. No more than 75 semester credits will be accepted for transfer credit. A total of 45 credits out of 120 must be completed at Wilmington.

Visiting: There are guides for informal visits and visitors may sit in on classes. To arrange for a visit, contact the Dean of Admissions, Financial Aid, and Marketing at (302) 328-9407.

Financial Aid: In an earlier year, 42% of all current freshmen and 39% of continuing students received some form of financial aid. Scholarships or need-based grants averaged $350 ($500 maximum); loans averaged $2625 ($6625 maximum); and work contracts averaged $600 ($1700 maximum). Only 2% of undergraduate students work part-time. The average financial indebtedness of a recent graduate was $10,500. Wilmington is a member of CSS. The FAF or FFS is required.

International Students: They must take the TOEFL and achieve a minimum score of 500, or they may submit a transcript indicating successful completion of at least 12 credit hours at an American institution of higher education.

Computers: The college provides computer facilities for student use. The mainframe is a DEC MicroVAX 3300. IBM models 25, PC, XT, and AT are available in the library and in the faculty study. There are no time limits on using the system and no fees.

Graduates: In an earlier year, 193 bachelor's degrees were awarded. Some 13 companies recruited on campus that year.

Admissions Contact: Ms. JoAnn Ciofettelli, Admissions Associate.

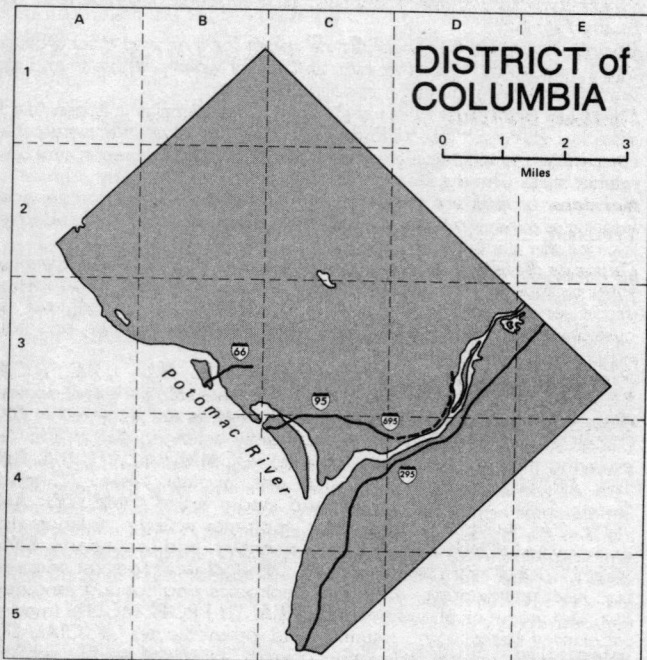

DISTRICT of COLUMBIA

0   1   2   3
Miles

Potomac River

AMERICAN UNIVERSITY
A-2
Washington, DC 20016
(202) 885–6000

Full-time: 1835 men, 2642 women
Faculty: 452; I, av$

Part-time: 220 men, 302 women
Ph.D.s: 92%

Graduate: 1673 men, 2022 women
Student/Faculty: 10 to 1

Year: semesters, summer session
Tuition: $15,130

Application Deadline: February 15
Room & Board: $6100

Freshman Class: 4570 applied, 3584 accepted, 1094 enrolled

SAT I Verbal/Math: 540/580
ACT: 26
VERY COMPETITIVE

American University, founded in 1893, is an independent liberal arts institution affiliated with the Methodist Church. There are 5 undergraduate and 6 graduate schools. In addition to regional accreditation, American University has baccalaureate program accreditation with AACSB, ACEJMC, and NCATE. The 2 libraries contain 530,000 volumes, 579,140 microform items, and 10,880 audiovisual forms, and subscribe to 4110 periodicals. Computerized library sources and services include the card catalog, interlibrary loans, and database searching. Special learning facilities include an art gallery, radio station, TV station, and a body-composition laboratory. The 78-acre campus is in a suburban area. Including residence halls, there are 37 buildings on campus.

Student Life: About 98% of undergraduates are from out-of-state, mostly the Middle Atlantic. Students come from 50 states, 130 foreign countries, and Canada. Seventy-eight percent are from public schools; 22% from private. Seventy-two percent are white; 12% foreign nationals. The average age of freshmen is 18; all undergraduates, 21. Fourteen percent drop out by the end of their first year; 59% remain to graduate.

Housing: A total of 3500 students can be accommodated in college housing. College-sponsored living facilities include single-sex and coed dormitories, off-campus apartments, fraternity houses, and sorority houses. In addition there are language houses, special interest houses, and honors floors, nonsmoking floors, and one nonsmoking dorm. On-campus housing is guaranteed for the freshman year only and is available on a first-come, first-served basis. Sixty-five percent of students live on campus; of those, 80% remain on campus on weekends. Alcohol is not permitted. Upperclassmen may keep cars on campus.

Activities: About 20% of men belong to 8 national fraternities; about 20% of women belong to 8 national sororities. There are 150 groups on campus, including art, band, cheerleading, chess, chorale, computers, dance, drama, ethnic, film, gay, honors, international, jazz band, literary magazine, musical theater, newspaper, orchestra, pep band, photography, political, professional, radio and TV, religious, social, social service, student government, symphony, and yearbook. Popular campus events include International Week and Spring Concert.

Sports: There are 6 intercollegiate sports for men and 6 for women, and 11 intramural sports for men and 8 for women. Athletic and recreation facilities include a 6000-seat gymnasium, 2 swimming pools, a hockey field, a softball diamond, an all-purpose field, weight rooms, and courts for tennis, racquetball, squash, badminton, basketball, and volleyball.

Disabled Students: Sixty percent of the campus is accessible to disabled students. The following facilities are available: wheelchair ramps, elevators, special parking, specially equipped rest rooms, special class scheduling, lowered drinking fountains, and a university shuttle is equipped to accommodate students in wheelchairs.

Services: In addition to many counseling and information services, tutoring is available in every subject. In addition, there is a reader service for the blind, and remedial math, reading, and writing.

Campus Safety and Security: Campus safety and security measures include 24-hour foot and vehicle patrol, escort service, shuttle buses, and informal discussions. In addition, there are pamphlets, posters, and films, emergency telephones, lighted pathways and sidewalks, and safety orientation programs.

Programs of Study: American University awards the B.A. and B.S. degrees. Master's and doctoral degrees also are awarded. Bachelor's degrees are awarded in BIOLOGICAL SCIENCE (biology/biological science), BUSINESS (accounting, banking and finance, business administration and management, international business management, management information systems, and marketing/retailing/merchandising), COMMUNICATIONS AND THE ARTS (art history and appreciation, audio technology, communications, design, dramatic arts, English, film arts, fine arts, French, German, journalism, languages, music, Russian, Spanish, and studio art), COMPUTER AND PHYSICAL SCIENCE (chemistry, computer science, information sciences and systems, mathematics, physics, and statistics), EDUCATION (elementary), SOCIAL SCIENCE (American studies, anthropology, criminal justice, economics, history, international studies, Judaic studies, philosophy, political science/government, psychology, religion, and sociology). Political science, international studies, communications, and business are the strongest academically. International studies and communications have the largest enrollments.

Required: To graduate, students must complete 120 credit hours with a minimum GPA of 2.0. In addition, students must complete 30 credit hours of general education requirements in 5 curricular areas and fulfill the school's competency requirements in English composition and mathematics by either passing an exam or taking a course in each area.

Special: The school offers co-op programs and internships in all majors, study abroad in 10 countries, work-study programs, dual majors, a general studies degree, an interdisciplinary program in environmental studies, student-designed majors, and B.A.-B.S. degrees. Cross-registration may be arranged through the Consortium of Universities of the Washington Metropolitan Area. Credit for life experience, nondegree study, and pass/fail options are available. There is a freshman honors program on campus, as well as 22 national honor societies.

Faculty/Classroom: Seventy-five percent of faculty are male; 25%, female. Ninety-four percent teach undergraduates. No introductory courses are taught by graduate students. The average class size in an introductory lecture is 26 and in a regular course offering, 22.

Admissions: About 78% of the 1993–94 applicants were accepted. The SAT scores for the 1993–94 freshman class were as follows: Verbal—25% below 500, 47% between 500 and 599, 26% between 600 and 700, and 2% above 700; Math—11% below 500, 47% between 500 and 599, 35% between 600 and 700, and 7% above 700. The ACT scores were 7% below 21, 16% between 21 and 23, 26% between 24 and 26, 29% between 27 and 28, and 22% above 28. About 61% of the current freshmen were in the top fifth of their class; 88% were in the top two fifths. There were 26 National Merit finalists.

Requirements: The SAT I or ACT is required. Graduation from an accredited secondary school or satisfactory scores on the GED are required for admission. Sixteen Carnegie units are required. High school courses must include 4 years of English, 3 years each of mathematics, science, and academic electives, 2 years each of history and foreign language, and 1 year of social studies. Students must submit an essay. AP and CLEP credits are accepted. Important factors used in the admissions decision are advanced placement or honor courses, recommendations by school officials, leadership record, evidence of special talent, and extracurricular activities record.

Procedure: Freshmen are admitted to all sessions. Entrance exams should be taken In the spring of the junior year. Early decision applications should be filed by November 15; regular applications, by February 15 for fall entry, along with an application fee of $45. Notification of early decision is sent December 15; regular decision, March 30. There are early decision, early admissions, and deferred admis-

sions plans. About 200 early decision candidates were accepted for the 1993–94 class.

Transfer: About 350 transfer students enrolled in 1993–94. Transfer applicants must have a minimum college GPA of 2.0. A total of 45 credits out of 120 must be completed at American University.

Visiting: There are regularly scheduled orientations for prospective students, including tours and information sessions. There are guides for informal visits and visitors may sit in on classes and stay overnight at the school. To arrange for a visit, contact the Assistant Director for On-Campus Programs at (202) 885–6000.

Financial Aid: In 1993–94, 60% of all current freshmen and 60% of continuing students received some form of financial aid. About 40% of freshmen and 38% of continuing students received need-based aid. The average freshman award was $13,200. Of that total, scholarships or need-based grants averaged $8000; loans averaged $3700; and work contracts averaged $1500. Sixty percent of undergraduate students work part-time. Average earnings from campus work for the school year are $1500. The average financial indebtedness of the 1992–93 graduate was $10,500. American University is a member of CSS. The FAF is required. The deadline for financial aid applications is March 1.

International Students: There are currently 500 international students enrolled. The school actively recruits these students. They must take the TOEFL or the college's own test. The SAT I or ACT is required only if the applicant attends a school with a U.S.-patterned system.

Computers: The college provides computer facilities for student use. The mainframe is an IBM 3090. Over 200 IBM, Apple Macintosh, and other microcomputers are available for student use in various campus locations. All students may access the system. There are no time limits on using the system and no fees.

Graduates: In a recent year, 1348 bachelor's degrees were awarded. The most popular majors among graduates were international studies (15%), communications (13%), and government (7%). Within an average freshman class, 68% graduate in 4 years and 82% in 5 years. Some 125 companies recruited on campus in a recent year. In the 1992 graduating class, 34% of the students were enrolled in graduate school within 6 months of graduation and 60% had found employment.

Admissions Contact: Director of Admissions.

CATHOLIC UNIVERSITY OF AMERICA
C-2

Washington, DC 20064

Full-time: 979 men, 1180 women
Part-time: 82 men, 129 women
Graduate: 1851 men, 1926 women
Year: semesters, summer session
Application Deadline: February 15
Freshman Class: 1754 applied, 1465 accepted, 517 enrolled
SAT I: required

(202) 635–5305; (800) 673–2772

Faculty: 302; I, --$
Ph.D.s: 95%
Student/Faculty: 7 to 1
Tuition: $12,986
Room & Board: $5870

COMPETITIVE

Catholic University of America, founded in 1887 and affiliated with the Roman Catholic Church, offers undergraduate programs through the schools of arts and sciences, engineering, architecture, nursing, philosophy, and music. There are 6 undergraduate and 10 graduate schools. In addition to regional accreditation, CUA has baccalaureate program accreditation with ABET, CAHEA, NAAB, NCATE, and NLN. The 8 libraries contain 1,321,879 volumes, 1,048,446 microform items, and 34,659 audiovisual forms, and subscribe to 8961 periodicals. Computerized library sources and services include the card catalog, interlibrary loans, and database searching. Special learning facilities include an art gallery, radio and TV stations, an archaeology laboratory, and a rare book collection. The 154-acre campus is in an urban area in Washington, D.C. Including residence halls, there are 57 buildings on campus.

Student Life: About 96% of undergraduates are from outside Washington, D.C., mostly the Middle Atlantic. Students come from 50 states, 100 foreign countries, and Canada. Twenty-five percent are from public schools; 75% from private. Eighty-six percent are white; 10% foreign nationals. Most are Catholic. The average age of freshmen is 18; all undergraduates, 20. Fifteen percent drop out by the end of their first year; 74% remain to graduate.

Housing: A total of 1582 students can be accommodated in college housing. College-sponsored living facilities include single-sex and coed dormitories. In addition, there are special interest houses. On-campus housing is guaranteed for the freshman year only, is available on a first-come, first-served basis, and is available on a lottery system for upperclassmen. Priority is given to out-of-town students. Fifty-one percent of students live on campus; of those, 90% remain on campus on weekends. Upperclassmen may keep cars on campus.

Activities: About 1% of men belong to 1 local fraternity; about 1% of women belong to 1 local sorority. There are 130 groups on campus, including art, cheerleading, choir, chorus, computers, dance, drama, ethnic, honors, international, jazz band, literary magazine, musical theater, newspaper, opera, orchestra, pep band, photography,

political, professional, radio and TV, religious, social, social service, student government, symphony, and yearbook. Popular campus events include Parents Weekend, Homecoming, Oktoberfest, and Beaux Arts Ball.

Sports: There are 8 intercollegiate sports for men and 8 for women, and 12 intramural sports for men and 11 for women. Athletic and recreation facilities include an athletic center.

Disabled Students: Seventy percent of the campus is accessible to disabled students. The following facilities are available: wheelchair ramps, elevators, special parking, specially equipped rest rooms, and special class scheduling.

Services: In addition to many counseling and information services, tutoring is available in most subjects. In addition, there is a reader service for the blind.

Campus Safety and Security: Campus safety and security measures include 24-hour foot and vehicle patrol, self-defense education, escort service, and shuttle buses. In addition, there are informal discussions, pamphlets, posters, films, emergency telephones, and lighted pathways and sidewalks.

Programs of Study: CUA awards the B.A., B.S., B.B.E., B.C.E., B.E.E., B.M., B.M.E., B.Ph., and B.S.N. degrees. Master's and doctoral degrees also are awarded. Bachelor's degrees are awarded in BIOLOGICAL SCIENCE (biology/biological science), BUSINESS (accounting and management science), COMMUNICATIONS AND THE ARTS (art, classics, dramatic arts, English, French, German, Greek, Latin, music, Spanish, and studio art), COMPUTER AND PHYSICAL SCIENCE (chemistry, computer science, mathematics, and physics), EDUCATION (art, elementary, and secondary), ENGINEERING AND ENVIRONMENTAL DESIGN (architectural engineering, civil engineering, electrical/electronics engineering, engineering, and mechanical engineering), HEALTH PROFESSIONS (medical laboratory technology, nursing, and premedicine), SOCIAL SCIENCE (anthropology, economics, history, medieval studies, philosophy, political science/government, prelaw, psychology, religion, social science, social work, and sociology). Politics is the strongest academically. Politics and business have the largest enrollments.

Required: To graduate, students must complete 120 credit hours, including 42 hours in the major, with a minimum GPA of 2.0. Distribution requirements include philosophy, religion, language, humanities, natural sciences, and social sciences. A comprehensive exam is required in most majors.

Special: Cross-registration is available with the Consortium of Universities of the Washington Metropolitan Area. Opportunities are also provided for internships, accelerated degree programs, dual majors, B.A.-B.S. degrees, student-designed majors, pass/fail options, and study abroad in 5 countries. There is a freshman honors program on campus, as well as 13 national honor societies, including Phi Beta Kappa.

Faculty/Classroom: Seventy percent of faculty are male; 30%, female. All teach undergraduates. Graduate students teach 7% of introductory courses. The average class size in an introductory lecture is 50; in a laboratory, 12; in a regular course offering, 25.

Admissions: About 84% of the 1993–94 applicants were accepted. The SAT scores for the 1993–94 freshman class were as follows: Verbal—45% below 500, 38% between 500 and 599, 15% between 600 and 700, and 2% above 700; Math—25% below 500, 44% between 500 and 599, 25% between 600 and 700, and 6% above 700. About 41% of the current freshmen were in the top fifth of their class; 66% were in the top two fifths.

Requirements: The SAT I is required, with a recommended minimum composite score of 1000 (500 verbal and 500 mathematics). SAT II: Subject tests in writing, mathematics, and language must also be submitted. Applicants must be graduates of an accredited secondary school. The GED is accepted. Students must present 16 academic credits, including 4 in English, 3 each in mathematics and science, and 2 each in social studies, history, and foreign languages. An essay is required. An audition is recommended for music applicants and a portfolio for architecture applicants. AP and CLEP credits are accepted. Important factors used in the admissions decision are advanced placement or honor courses, evidence of special talent, personality, intangible qualities, leadership record, and parents or siblings attending the school.

Procedure: Freshmen are admitted fall and spring. Entrance exams should be taken by December of the senior year of high school. Applications should be filed by February 15 for fall entry and November 15 for spring entry, along with an application fee of $20. Notification is sent March 15. There are early decision and deferred admissions plans. About 95 early decision candidates were accepted for the 1993–94 class. A waiting list is an active part of the admissions procedure, with about 8% of applicants on the list.

Transfer: About 160 transfer students enrolled in 1993–94. Applicants must submit a high school transcript showing a B average and a college transcript showing at least 24 credit hours earned with a minimum GPA of 3.0. A minimum composite SAT I score of 1000 is required. A letter of recommendation and an essay are required, and

an interview is recommended. At least 30 credits out of 120 must be completed at CUA.

Visiting: There are regularly scheduled orientations for prospective students. There are guides for informal visits, and visitors may sit in on classes and stay overnight at the school. To arrange for a visit, contact the Admissions Office at (202) 319-5305 or (800) 673-2722.

Financial Aid: In 1993-94, 76% of all current freshmen and 69% of continuing students received some form of financial aid. About 60% of freshmen and 61% of continuing students received need-based aid. The average freshman award was $9967. Of that total, scholarships or need-based grants averaged $6434 ($13,298 maximum); loans averaged $3083 ($21,944 maximum); and work contracts averaged $1640 ($6310 maximum). Thirty-two percent of undergraduate students work part-time. Average earnings from campus work for the school year are $1400. The average financial indebtedness of the 1992-93 graduate was $15,000. CUA is a member of CSS. The FAF is required. The deadline for financial aid applications is February 28.

International Students: There are currently 613 international students enrolled. The school actively recruits these students. They must take the TOEFL and achieve a minimum score of 500.

Computers: The college provides computer facilities for student use. The mainframe is a DEC VAX 4000. There are 200 terminals and 150 Macintosh, IBM, and IBM-compatible microcomputers available for student use in the computer center and in residence halls. All students may access the system more than 90 hours a week. There is also dial-up access 24 hours a day. Computers may be used freely but students are limited to 1 to 2 hours when demand is high. There are no fees.

Graduates: In a recent year, 745 bachelor's degrees were awarded. The most popular majors among graduates were politics (15%), economics (14%), and nursing (9%). Within an average freshman class, 4% graduate in 3 years, 58% in 4 years, 63% in 5 years, and 67% in 6 years. Some 80 companies recruited on campus in a recent year. In an earlier graduating class, 9% of the men and 11% of the women were enrolled in graduate school within 6 months of graduation.

Admissions Contact: David R. Gibson, Dean of Admissions.

CORCORAN SCHOOL OF ART
Washington, DC 20006

C-3
(202) 628-9484

Full-time: 138 men, 158 women	Faculty: 45
Part-time: none	Ph.D.s: 90%
Graduate: none	Student/Faculty: 7 to 1
Year: semesters	Tuition: $10,480
Application Deadline: open	Room & Board: $4000
Freshman Class: 275 applied, 225 accepted, 92 enrolled	
SAT I: 460	ACT: 22	SPECIAL

Established in 1890, the Corcoran School of Art is a private professional art college offering undergraduate programs in fine art and design, and photography. In addition to regional accreditation, Corcoran has baccalaureate program accreditation with NASAD. The library contains 13,300 volumes, and subscribes to 111 periodicals. Computerized library sources and services include the card catalog. Special learning facilities include a learning resource center and art gallery. The 7-acre campus is in an urban area. Including residence halls, there are 3 buildings on campus.

Student Life: About 64% of undergraduates are from District of Columbia. Students come from 28 states and 9 foreign countries. Seventy-five percent are from public schools; 25% from private. Seventy percent are white; 10% foreign nationals. The average age of freshmen is 19; all undergraduates, 23. Seven percent drop out by the end of their first year; 60% remain to graduate.

Housing: A total of 23 students can be accommodated in college housing. College-sponsored living facilities include coed dormitories. On-campus housing is guaranteed for the freshman year only and is available on a first-come, first-served basis. Priority is given to out-of-town students. Ninety-two percent of students commute. Alcohol is not permitted.

Activities: There are no fraternities or sororities on campus. There are some groups and organizations on campus, including art, literary magazine, and newspaper. Popular campus events include student art openings, museum and gallery openings, and visiting artists' lectures.

Sports: There is no sports program at Corcoran.

Disabled Students: Seventy percent of the campus is accessible to disabled students. The following facilities are available: wheelchair ramps, elevators, specially equipped rest rooms, and lowered telephones.

Campus Safety and Security: Campus safety and security measures include 24-hour foot and vehicle patrol.

Programs of Study: Corcoran awards the B.F.A. degree. Bachelor's degrees are awarded in COMMUNICATIONS AND THE ARTS (fine arts, graphic design, and photography). Fine arts has the largest enrollment.

Required: Students must complete 126 credits, with 65 to 70 of these in the major, and 23 in the core curriculum, and must maintain a minimum GPA of 2.0. Course distribution must involve the disciplines of art history, humanities, liberal arts, and writing. Curricula will include courses in drawing, design, idea resources, and media.

Special: Cooperative programs are permitted with the ACE and AICA art college consortiums. Opportunities are provided for internships in graphic design and photography, credit by examination, work-study programs with the Corcoran Gallery of Art, and nondegree study.

Faculty/Classroom: Fifty percent of faculty are male; 50%, female. All teach undergraduates. The average class size in an introductory lecture is 23; in a laboratory, 10; and in a regular course offering, 10.

Admissions: About 82% of the 1993-94 applicants were accepted. The SAT scores for the 1993-94 freshman class were as follows: Verbal—60% below 500, 29% between 500 and 599, 10% between 600 and 700, and 1% above 700.

Requirements: A minimum GPA of 2.0 is required. The SAT I or ACT is required. Applicants must have graduated from an approved secondary school; a GED will be accepted. A portfolio is required, and an interview is recommended. AP credits are accepted. Important factors used in the admissions decision are evidence of special talent, personality, intangible qualities, recommendations by alumni, advanced placement or honor courses, and ability to finance college education.

Procedure: Freshmen are admitted fall and spring. Application deadlines are open. Application fee is $30. Notification is sent on a rolling basis. There is a deferred admissions plan. A waiting list is an active part of the admissions procedure, with about 5% of applicants on the list.

Transfer: About 28 transfer students enrolled in a recent year. A review of studio art transcripts will be considered for the level of entry of transfer students. A portfolio review will be the final determining factor. A total of 63 credits out of 126 must be completed at Corcoran.

Visiting: There are regularly scheduled orientations for prospective students. There are guides for informal visits and visitors may sit in on classes. To arrange for a visit, contact the Admissions Department at (202) 628-9484.

Financial Aid: Recently, 61% of all current freshmen and 60% of continuing students received some form of financial aid. About 50% of freshmen and 50% of continuing students received need-based aid. The average freshman award was $4500. Of that total, scholarships or need-based grants averaged $1711 ($3000 maximum); loans averaged $3295 ($4500 maximum); and work contracts averaged $2000. Seven percent of undergraduate students work part-time. Average earnings from campus work for the school year are $2000. Corcoran is a member of CSS. The FAF and the college's own financial statement is required. The deadline for financial aid applications is March 15.

International Students: There are currently 18 international students enrolled. The school actively recruits these students. They must take the TOEFL and achieve a minimum score of 525. The student must also take the SAT I.

Computers: The college provides computer facilities for student use. There are 17 Apple Macintosh Plus SE microcomputers available in the Graphic Design Department and the computer laboratory. All students may access the system and there are no fees.

Graduates: In a recent year, 59 bachelor's degrees were awarded. The most popular majors among graduates were fine arts (48%), graphic design (34%), and photography (19%). Within an average freshman class, 60% graduate in 4 years.

Admissions Contact: Mark Sistek, Director of Admissions.

GALLAUDET UNIVERSITY
Washington, DC 20002

C-3
(202) 651-5114
(800) 995-0550 (out-of-state)

Full-time: 729 men, 812 women	Faculty: 300; IIA, av$
Part-time: 52 men, 67 women	Ph.D.s: 66%
Graduate: 68 men, 303 women	Student/Faculty: 5 to 1
Year: semesters, summer session	Tuition: $4740
Application Deadline: May 15	Room & Board: $5110
Freshman Class: n/av	
SAT I or ACT: not required	SPECIAL

Gallaudet University, founded in 1864 as a university designed exclusively for deaf and hard of hearing students, offers programs in liberal and fine arts, teacher preparation, and professional training. There are 4 undergraduate and 4 graduate schools. In addition to regional accreditation, Gallaudet has baccalaureate program accreditation with CSWE and NCATE. The library contains 195,000 volumes, 345,000 microform items, and 4400 audiovisual forms, and subscribes to 1415 periodicals. Computerized library sources and services include the card catalog, interlibrary loans, and database searching. Special learning facilities include a learning resource cen-

ter and TV station. The 99-acre campus is in an urban area. Including residence halls, there are 30 buildings on campus.

Student Life: About 95% of undergraduates are from out-of-state, mostly the Northeast. Students come from 50 states and Canada. Seventy-four percent are white; 14% foreign nationals.

Housing: College-sponsored living facilities include single-sex and coed dormitories. On-campus housing is guaranteed for the freshman year only and is available on a first-come, first-served basis. Fifty-one percent of students live on campus; of those, 51% remain on campus on weekends. Alcohol is not permitted. All students may keep cars on campus.

Activities: About 15% of men belong to 1 local and 3 national fraternities; about 20% of women belong to 2 local and 3 national sororities. There are 32 groups on campus, including art, cheerleading, computers, dance, drama, ethnic, gay, honors, international, literary magazine, newspaper, political, religious, social, social service, student government, and yearbook. Popular campus events include Homecoming, rock festival, drama productions, and lecture series.

Sports: There are 9 intercollegiate sports for men and 9 for women, and 12 intramural sports for men and 12 for women. Athletic and recreation facilities include a field house, gymnasium, swimming pool, tennis and racquetball courts, weight training rooms, playing fields, and bowling alleys.

Disabled Students: The following facilities are available: wheelchair ramps, elevators, special parking, specially equipped rest rooms, special class scheduling, lowered drinking fountains, lowered telephones, and phones with HY. Sign language skills are required of all faculty and professional staff.

Services: In addition to many counseling and information services, tutoring is available in most subjects. In addition, there is remedial math, reading, and writing. An information-on-deafness center is also available.

Campus Safety and Security: Campus safety and security measures include 24-hour foot and vehicle patrol, escort service, shuttle buses, and informal discussions. In addition, there are pamphlets, posters, and films and lighted pathways and sidewalks.

Programs of Study: Gallaudet awards the B.A. and B.S. degrees. Associate, master's, and doctoral degrees also are awarded. Bachelor's degrees are awarded in BIOLOGICAL SCIENCE (biochemistry and biology/biological science), BUSINESS (accounting, business administration and management, and recreation and leisure services), COMMUNICATIONS AND THE ARTS (art history and appreciation, communications, English, French, German, Russian, and Spanish), COMPUTER AND PHYSICAL SCIENCE (chemistry, computer science, mathematics, and physics), EDUCATION (early childhood, elementary, home economics, physical, and secondary), ENGINEERING AND ENVIRONMENTAL DESIGN (engineering technology), SOCIAL SCIENCE (economics, history, international studies, interpreter for the deaf, philosophy, political science/government, religion, and social work).

Required: The core curriculum requires 12 each hours of social science, English, and foreign language, 8 of a laboratory science, 6 of literature, 5 of communication arts, and 2 of philosophy. A total of 124 credits, 30 to 60 in the major, and a minimum 2.0 GPA are required.

Special: Gallaudet offers co-op programs with Oberlin College in Ohio and Western Maryland College, cross-registration with the Consortium of Universities of the Washington Metropolis area, and a 3–2 engineering degree with George Washington University. Internships, study abroad, dual majors, work-study programs, and B.A.-B.S. degrees are available. There is a freshman honors program on campus.

Faculty/Classroom: No introductory courses are taught by graduate students.

Admissions: About 67% of the 1993–94 applicants were accepted.

Requirements: Applicants must submit a recent audiogram and results of the 8th edition of the Stanford Achievement Test. High school transcripts, letters of recommendation, and writing samples are also required. The GED is accepted. AP and CLEP credits are accepted. Important factors used in the admissions decision are recommendations by school officials, leadership record, extracurricular activities record, and advanced placement or honor courses.

Procedure: Freshmen are admitted fall and spring. Entrance exams should be taken in October or November. Applications should be filed by May 15 for fall entry and November 15 for spring entry, along with an application fee of $35. Notification is sent on a rolling basis. There is a deferred admissions plan.

Transfer: About 100 transfer students enrolled in 1993–94. Deaf and hard of hearing transfer applicants should have completed 12 or more credit hours with at least a 2.0 GPA. At least half of major program credits must be completed at Gallaudet. One-hundred and twenty-four credits are required for the bachelor's degree.

Visiting: There are regularly scheduled orientations for prospective students, including a tour of campus, class observations, and interviews with selected offices and programs. There are guides for informal visits and visitors may sit in on classes. To arrange for a visit, contact the Gallaudet University Visitor's Center at (202) 651-5050.

Financial Aid: In 1993–94, 69% of all current freshmen and 54% of continuing students received some form of financial aid. About 59% of freshmen and 46% of continuing students received need-based aid. The average freshman award was $6841. Of that total, scholarships or need-based grants averaged $2244 ($5000 maximum); loans averaged $302 ($2625 maximum); and work contracts averaged $10 ($1400 maximum). The average financial indebtedness of the 1992–93 graduate was $4143. The college's own financial statement and FAFSA are required. The deadline for priority financial aid applications is June 15.

International Students: There are currently 254 international students enrolled. They must take the TOEFL, the University of Michigan Language Test, the Comprehensive English Language Test, or the college's own test. The student must also take the SAT I, ACT, the college's own entrance exam, or the 8th edition of the Stanford Achievement Test.

Computers: The college provides computer facilities for student use. The mainframes are a DEC VAX 6000, an 11/750, and an 11/785. There are microcomputers for student use in 4 student laboratories, a dormitory, a computer center, and a learning center. All students may access the system. There are no fees.

Graduates: In a recent year, 204 bachelor's degrees were awarded. Within an average freshman class, 15% graduate in 3 years, 21% in 4 years, 28% in 5 years, and 50% in 6 years. Some 30 companies recruited on campus in 1992–93.

Admissions Contact: Deborah DeStefano, Director.

GEORGE WASHINGTON UNIVERSITY
Washington, DC 20052

B-3
(202) 994-6040
(800) 447-3765 (out-of-state)

Full-time: 2528 men, 2782 women	Faculty: 605; I, +$
Part-time: 298 men, 292 women	Ph.D.s: 93%
Graduate: 4872 men, 4081 women	Student/Faculty: 9 to 1
Year: semesters, summer session	Tuition: $16,988
Application Deadline: See profile	Room & Board: $5482
Freshman Class: 7875 applied, 5062 accepted, 1531 enrolled	
SAT I or ACT: required	HIGHLY COMPETITIVE

George Washington University, founded in 1821, is a private, non-sectarian, coeducational institution providing degree programs in arts and sciences, business, engineering, international affairs, and health sciences. There are 6 undergraduate and 7 graduate schools. In addition to regional accreditation, GW has baccalaureate program accreditation with AACSB, ABET, NASAD, and NASM. The 3 libraries contain 1,690,644 volumes, 1,923,935 microform items, and 9857 audiovisual forms, and subscribe to 13,496 periodicals. Computerized library sources and services include the card catalog and interlibrary loans. Special learning facilities include a learning resource center, art gallery, radio station, and TV station. The 37-acre campus is in an urban area. Including residence halls, there are 90 buildings on campus.

Student Life: About 87% of undergraduates are from out-of-state, mostly the Middle Atlantic. Students come from 50 states, 99 foreign countries, and Canada. Eighty percent are from public schools; 20% from private. Sixty-five percent are white; 11% foreign nationals; 11% Asian American. Forty-five percent claim no religious affiliation; 20% Catholic; 14% Mormon, Islamic, and Eastern Orthodox; 11% Protestant; 10% Jewish. The average age of freshmen is 18; all undergraduates, 21. Thirteen percent drop out by the end of their first year; 71% remain to graduate.

Housing: A total of 2978 students can be accommodated in college housing. College-sponsored living facilities include single-sex and coed dormitories, on-campus apartments, and fraternity houses. In addition there are special interest houses. On-campus housing is available on a lottery system for upperclassmen. Fifty-four percent of students live on campus. Alcohol is not permitted. All students may keep cars on campus.

Activities: About 15% of men belong to 12 national fraternities; about 14% of women belong to 8 national sororities. There are 230 groups on campus, including art, band, cheerleading, choir, chorale, chorus, dance, drama, ethnic, gay, honors, international, jazz band, literary magazine, musical theater, newspaper, pep band, photography, political, professional, radio and TV, religious, social, social service, student government, and yearbook. Popular campus events include a yearly benefit auction, Spring Fling, Fall Fest, Honors Convocation, and Fall Family Weekend.

Sports: There are 9 intercollegiate sports for men and 8 for women, and 33 intramural sports combined for men and women. About 63% of men and 14% of women participate in sports. Athletic and recreation facilities include a 5000-seat gymnasium with 3 auxiliary gymnasiums, an AAU swimming pool, weight rooms, a jogging track, squash and racquetball courts, and soccer and baseball fields.

Disabled Students: Ninety percent of the campus is accessible to disabled students. The following facilities are available: wheelchair ramps, elevators, special parking, specially equipped rest rooms, special class scheduling, lowered drinking fountains, and lowered telephones.

Services: In addition to many counseling and information services, tutoring is available in every subject. In addition, there is a reader service for the blind.

Campus Safety and Security: Campus safety and security measures include 24-hour foot and vehicle patrol, self defense education, escort service, and informal discussions. In addition, there are pamphlets, posters, and films, emergency telephones, lighted pathways and sidewalks, and a bike patrol.

Programs of Study: GW awards the B.A., B.S., B.Accy., B.B.A., B.Mus., B.S.C.E., B.S.C.Eng., B.S.C.S., B.S.E.E., B.S.M.E., and B.S.S.A. degrees. Associate, master's, and doctoral degrees also are awarded. Bachelor's degrees are awarded in BIOLOGICAL SCIENCE (biology/biological science), BUSINESS (accounting, banking and finance, business administration and management, business economics, international business management, marketing/retailing/merchandising, and personnel management), COMMUNICATIONS AND THE ARTS (broadcasting, Chinese, classics, communications, dance, dramatic arts, English, fine arts, French, German, journalism, music, photography, Russian, Spanish, and speech/debate/rhetoric), COMPUTER AND PHYSICAL SCIENCE (chemistry, computer science, geology, information sciences and systems, mathematics, physics, statistics, and systems analysis), ENGINEERING AND ENVIRONMENTAL DESIGN (civil engineering, computer engineering, electrical/electronics engineering, engineering, environmental science, and mechanical engineering), HEALTH PROFESSIONS (medical laboratory technology, physician's assistant, and radiological science), SOCIAL SCIENCE (anthropology, criminal justice, economics, geography, history, human services, international relations, Judaic studies, philosophy, physical fitness/movement, political science/government, psychology, religion, and sociology). Political communication, international affairs, psychology, and electrical engineering are the strongest academically. Psychology, political science, international affairs, international business, and finance have the largest enrollments.

Required: Students must complete 120 semester hours with a minimum GPA of 2.0 for most majors. Arts and sciences majors must meet general curriculum requirements that include literacy, quantitative and logical reasoning, natural sciences, social and behavioral sciences, creative and performing arts, literature, Western civilization, and foreign languages or culture. Other specific course requirements vary with the different divisions of the university.

Special: Cross-registration is available with the Consortium of Universities in the Washington Metropolitan Area. Opportunities are provided for internships, study abroad, dual majors, secondary fields of study, co-op programs, work-study programs, student-designed majors, and a 3–2 engineering degree program with 8 colleges. Nondegree study, a general studies degree, credit by examination, and pass/fail options are possible. There is a freshman honors program on campus, as well as 22 national honor societies, including Phi Beta Kappa. Twenty-one departments have honors programs.

Faculty/Classroom: Seventy-two percent of faculty are male; 28%, female. Graduate students teach 4% of introductory courses. The average class size in an introductory lecture is 129; in a laboratory, 15; and in a regular course offering, 26.

Admissions: About 64% of the 1993–94 applicants were accepted. The SAT scores for the 1993–94 freshman class were as follows: Verbal—27% below 500, 45% between 500 and 599, 25% between 600 and 700, and 3% above 700; Math—10% below 500, 40% between 500 and 599, 39% between 600 and 700, and 11% above 700. The ACT scores were 5% below 21, 17% between 21 and 23, 27% between 24 and 26, 23% between 27 and 28, and 28% above 28. About 61% of the current freshmen were in the top fifth of their class; 89% were in the top two fifths. There were 70 National Merit finalists and 10 semifinalists. About 43 freshmen graduated first in their class.

Requirements: The SAT I or ACT is required. Graduation from an accredited secondary school is required. Students must have successfully completed 15 academic credits including 4 in English, 2 each in a foreign language, mathematics (4 for engineering majors), science, social studies, 1 in American history, and general electives. Three SAT II: Subject tests are required: writing, mathematics I or II, and a third test of student's choice. An essay also is required. AP and CLEP credits are accepted. Important factors used in the admissions decision are recommendations by school officials, advanced placement or honor courses, leadership record, evidence of special talent, and extracurricular activities record.

Procedure: Freshmen are admitted to all sessions. Entrance exams should be taken in the junior year and the fall semester of the senior year. Early decision applications should be filed by November 1 for Part 1, and December 1 for Part 2; regular applications, by December ber 1 for Part 1 and February 1 for Part 2 fall entry, November 1 for Part 1, and December 1 for Part 2 spring entry, and December 1 for Part 1 and February 1 for Part 2 summer entry, along with an application fee of $45. Notification of early decision is sent December 15; regular decision, March 1. There are early decision, early admissions, and deferred admissions plans. About 150 early decision candidates were accepted for the 1993–94 class. A waiting list is an active part of the admissions procedure, with about 1% of applicants on the list.

Transfer: About 345 transfer students enrolled in 1993–94. In addition to a record of high marks and examination scores, applicants must submit official transcripts of all postsecondary work. Minimum GPA requirements vary from 2.5 to 3.0, depending on the major. The SAT I or ACT is required, and an interview is encouraged. A total of 30 credits out of 120 must be completed at GW.

Visiting: There are regularly scheduled orientations for prospective students, including group information sessions, and campus tours. Class visitation, lunch with current students, and other activities can be arranged, if requested in advance. There are guides for informal visits and visitors may sit in on classes. To arrange for a visit, contact the University Visitor Center at (202) 994-6602.

Financial Aid: In 1993–94, 72% of all current freshmen and 67% of continuing students received some form of financial aid. About 47% of freshmen and 45% of continuing students received need-based aid. The average freshman award was $13,487. Of that total, scholarships or need-based grants averaged $10,460 ($16,398 maximum); loans averaged $3392 ($4625 maximum); and work contracts averaged $1870 ($2000 maximum). Average earnings from campus work for the school year are $1510. GW is a member of CSS. The FAF, the FAFSA and the college's own financial statement are required. The deadline for financial aid applications is February 1.

International Students: There are currently 509 international students enrolled. The school actively recruits these students. They must take the TOEFL or the college's own test and achieve a minimum score on the TOEFL of 550. The student must also take the SAT I or the ACT.

Computers: The college provides computer facilities for student use. The mainframes are an IBM 4381 and R14. All residence halls have computer rooms, and the campus computer center is open 24 hours a day. In addition, 7 computer classrooms are available as walk-in laboratories when classes are not scheduled. All students may access the system. There are no time limits on using the system and no fees.

Graduates: In 1992–93, 1619 bachelor's degrees were awarded. The most popular majors among graduates were international affairs (14%), psychology (8%), and political science (7%). Within an average freshman class, 2% graduate in 3 years, 64% in 4 years, 69% in 5 years, and 71% in 6 years. Some 100 companies recruited on campus in 1992–93.

Admissions Contact: Frederic Siegel, Director of Admissions.

GEORGETOWN UNIVERSITY B-3
Washington, DC 20057 (202) 687-3600

Full-time: 2841 men, 3040 women	Faculty: 470; I, +$
Part-time: 130 men, 276 women	Ph.Ds: 92%
Graduate: 3275 men, 2759 women	Student/Faculty: 13 to 1
Year: semesters, summer session	Tuition: $17,586
Application Deadline: January 10	Room & Board: $6824
Freshman Class: 11,113 applied, 2881 accepted, 1385 enrolled	
SAT I or ACT: required	**MOST COMPETITIVE**

Georgetown University, founded in 1789, is a private coeducational institution, affiliated with the Roman Catholic Church, offering programs in arts and sciences, business administration, foreign service, languages and linguistics, and nursing. There are 5 undergraduate and 3 graduate schools. In addition to regional accreditation, Georgetown has baccalaureate program accreditation with AACSB and NLN. The 2 libraries contain 1,422,322 volumes, 792,644 microform items, and 51,576 audiovisual forms, and subscribe to 12,560 periodicals. Computerized library sources and services include the card catalog, interlibrary loans, and database searching. Special learning facilities include a learning resource center, art gallery, planetarium, and radio station. The 110-acre campus is in an urban area 1.5 miles northwest of downtown Washington D.C. Including residence halls, there are 60 buildings on campus.

Student Life: About 97% of undergraduates are from out-of-state, mostly the Middle Atlantic. Students come from 50 states, 103 foreign countries, and Canada. Forty-two percent are from public schools; 58% from private. Sixty-eight percent are white; 10% foreign nationals. Fifty-four percent are Catholic; 24% Protestant; 14% claim no religious affiliation. The average age of freshmen is 18; all undergraduates, 20. Four percent drop out by the end of their first year; 91% remain to graduate.

Housing: A total of 3900 students can be accommodated in college housing. College-sponsored living facilities include coed dormitories, on-campus apartments, and off-campus apartments. In addition there are language houses, special interest houses, and handicapped hous-

ing. On-campus housing is available on a lottery system for upperclassmen. Seventy-five percent of students live on campus. Alcohol is not permitted. Upperclassmen may keep cars on campus.

Activities: There are no fraternities or sororities on campus. There are 100 groups on campus, including art, band, cheerleading, chess, choir, chorale, chorus, computers, dance, drama, ethnic, gay, honors, international, literary magazine, musical theater, newspaper, orchestra, pep band, political, professional, religious, social, social service, student government, symphony, and yearbook. Popular campus events include Founders Day, Spring Fest, a folk festival, Career Week, and new student orientation.

Sports: There are 12 intercollegiate sports for men and 10 for women, and 13 intramural sports for men and 13 for women. Athletic and recreation facilities include a field house, a 150,000-square-foot underground facility with swimming pool, handball/racquetball ball/squash courts, jogging track, and weight training equipment, and multipurpose courts for basketball, volleyball, and tennis.

Disabled Students: Ninety percent of the campus is accessible to disabled students. The following facilities are available: wheelchair ramps, elevators, special parking, specially equipped rest rooms, special class scheduling, lowered drinking fountains, lowered telephones, a special map of the campus with accessibility routes, a tactile map of the campus for visually disabled students, and a paratransit vehicle for mobility on the main campus.

Services: In addition to many counseling and information services, tutoring is available in every subject. In addition, there is a reader service for the blind.

Campus Safety and Security: Campus safety and security measures include escort service, shuttle buses, informal discussions, and pamphlets, posters, and films. In addition, there are emergency telephones and lighted pathways and sidewalks.

Programs of Study: Georgetown awards the B.A., B.S., B.S.B.A., and B.S.N. degrees. Master's and doctoral degrees also are awarded. Bachelor's degrees are awarded in BIOLOGICAL SCIENCE (biology/biological science), BUSINESS (accounting, banking and finance, business administration and management, international business management, and marketing/retailing/merchandising), COMMUNICATIONS AND THE ARTS (Arabic, Chinese, English, fine arts, French, German, Italian, Japanese, languages, linguistics, Portuguese, Russian, and Spanish), COMPUTER AND PHYSICAL SCIENCE (chemistry, computer science, mathematics, and physics), EDUCATION (foreign languages), ENGINEERING AND ENVIRONMENTAL DESIGN (engineering), HEALTH PROFESSIONS (nursing, predentistry, and premedicine), SOCIAL SCIENCE (economics, history, international public service, international relations, philosophy, political science/government, prelaw, psychology, religion, and sociology). Biology, economics, English, government, history, philosophy, psychology, and theology are the strongest academically. Government has the largest enrollment.

Required: Students must complete 120 credits and maintain a minimum GPA of 2.0. A core of liberal arts courses is required, consisting of 2 courses each in literature, philosophy, theology, history, social science, and mathematics/science. Computer science is required of students majoring in business, mathematics, science, and computer science.

Special: Cross-registration is available with a consortium of universities in the Washington metropolitian area, and a 3–2 engineering degree is available with Catholic University of America. Opportunities are provided for internships, study abroad in 24 countries, work-study programs, student-designed majors, and dual majors. A general studies degree, B.A.-B.S. degrees, nondegree study, credit by examination, and pass/fail options are also offered. There is a freshman honors program on campus, as well as 13 national honor societies, including Phi Beta Kappa. Four departments have honors programs.

Faculty/Classroom: Sixty-nine percent of faculty are male; 31%, female. Ninety-four percent teach undergraduates, 100% do research, and 94% do both. No introductory courses are taught by graduate students. The average class size in an introductory lecture is 33 and in a regular course offering, 22.

Admissions: About 26% of the 1993–94 applicants were accepted. The SAT scores for the 1993–94 freshman class were as follows: Verbal—13% below 500, 34% between 500 and 599, 45% between 600 and 700, and 8% above 700; Math—4% below 500, 20% between 500 and 599, 51% between 600 and 700, and 25% above 700. The ACT scores were 1% below 21, 6% between 21 and 23, 14% between 24 and 26, 15% between 27 and 28, and 64% above 28. About 81% of the current freshmen were in the top fifth of their class; 94% were in the top two fifths. There were 40 National Merit finalists and 122 semifinalists. About 190 freshmen graduated first in their class.

Requirements: The SAT I or ACT is required. In addition, graduation from an accredited secondary school is required, including 4 years of English, a minimum of 2 each of a foreign language, mathematics, and social studies, and 1 of natural science. An additional 2 years each of mathematics and science is required for students in-

tending to major in mathematics, science, nursing, or business. SAT II: Subject tests are strongly recommended. Applicants to the Walsh School of Foreign Service and the School of Languages and Linguistics are required to submit results of a modern foreign language SAT II: Subject test. AP credits are accepted. Important factors used in the admissions decision are advanced placement or honor courses, leadership record, evidence of special talent, recommendations by school officials, and extracurricular activities record.

Procedure: Freshmen are admitted in the fall. Entrance exams should be taken in the junior year and again at the beginning of the senior year. Early action applications should be filed by November 1; regular applications, by January 10 for fall entry, along with an application fee of $45. Notification of early action is sent December 15; regular decision, April 1. There are early action and deferred action plans. About 630 early decision candidates were accepted for the 1993–94 class. A waiting list is an active part of the admissions procedure, with about 10% of applicants on the list.

Transfer: About 320 transfer students enrolled in 1993–94. Transfer students must have succesfully completed a minimum of 12 credit hours with a minimum GPA of 3.0. Either the SAT I or the ACT is required. An interview is recommended. Transfers must complete their last 2 years at Georgetown. A total of 60 credits out of 120 must be completed at Georgetown.

Visiting: There are regularly scheduled orientations for prospective students. There are guides for informal visits and visitors may sit in on classes. To arrange for a visit, contact the Office of Undergraduate Admissions at (202) 687–3600.

Financial Aid: In 1993–94, 55% of all current freshmen and 52% of continuing students received some form of financial aid. About 43% of freshmen and 45% of continuing students received need-based aid. The average freshman award was $16,176. Of that total, scholarships or need-based grants averaged $11,351 (maximum); loans averaged $2625 (maximum); and work contracts averaged $2200 (maximum). Fifty-five percent of undergraduate students work part-time. Average earnings from campus work for the school year are $2500. The average financial indebtedness of the 1992–93 graduate was $12,250. Georgetown is a member of CSS. The FAF and the FAFSA are required. The deadline for financial aid applications is February 1.

International Students: There are currently 1176 international students enrolled. The school actively recruits these students. They must take the TOEFL and achieve a minimum score of 550. The student must also take the SAT I or the ACT.

Computers: The college provides computer facilities for student use. The mainframes are an IBM ES/9000–320; and a DEC VAX 4000–200, 4000–300, and 8700. In addition, there are more than 200 terminals and PCs in the library, computer laboratories, and the School of Business Administration. All students may access the system. There are no time limits on using the system. The fees are $40.

Graduates: In 1992–93, 1468 bachelor's degrees were awarded. The most popular majors among graduates were international affairs (19%), government (11%), and English (9%). Within an average freshman class, 1% graduate in 3 years, 85% in 4 years, 3% in 5 years, and 1% in 6 years. Some 140 companies recruited on campus in 1992–93.

Admissions Contact: Charles A. Deacon, Dean of Admissions.

HOWARD UNIVERSITY
C-3

Washington, DC 20059

(202) 806–2700; (800) 822–6363

Full-time: 2567 men, 4138 women

Part-time: 370 men, 504 women

Graduate: 1289 men, 1670 women

Year: semesters, summer session

Application Deadline: April 1

Freshman Class: 9005 applied, 5071 accepted, 1574 enrolled

SAT I or ACT: required

Faculty: 1195

Ph.Ds: 82%

Student/Faculty: 6 to 1

Tuition: $7535

Room & Board: $4145

COMPETITIVE

Howard University, founded in 1867, is a private, nonsectarian, coeducational institution, and the largest predominantly black university in the United States. There are 10 undergraduate and 13 graduate schools. In addition to regional accreditation, Howard has baccalaureate program accreditation with AACSB, ABET, ACEJMC, ACPE, ADA, AHEA, APTA, ASLA, CSWE, NAAB, NASAD, NASM, NCATE, and NLN. The 7 libraries contain 1.8 million volumes and 3,335,000 microform items, and subscribe to 26,280 periodicals. Computerized library sources and services include the card catalog, interlibrary loans, and database searching. Special learning facilities include a learning resource center, an art gallery, a radio station, a TV station, and a history and culture research center. The 260-acre campus is in an urban area in Washington, D.C. Including residence halls, there are 65 buildings on campus.

Student Life: About 88% of undergraduates are from out-of-state, mostly the Middle Atlantic. Students come from 48 states, 90 foreign countries, and Canada. Seventy-five percent are from public schools; 25% from private. Eighty percent are African American; 15% Native

American/Eskimo. The average age of freshmen is 18; all undergraduates, 21. Twenty percent drop out by the end of their first year; 45% remain to graduate.

Housing: A total of 5000 students can be accommodated in college housing. College-sponsored living facilities include single-sex and coed dormitories, on-campus apartments, off-campus apartments, and married-student housing. On-campus housing is guaranteed for the freshman year only, is available on a first-come, first-served basis, and is available on a lottery system for upperclassmen. Priority is given to out-of-town students. Fifty-seven percent of students commute. All students may keep cars on campus.

Activities: About 3% of men and about 1% of women belong to 4 national fraternities; about 3% of women belong to 4 national sororities. There are more than 150 groups on campus, including bagpipe band, band, cheerleading, chess, choir, chorale, chorus, computers, dance, drama, drill team, drum and bugle corps, honors, international, jazz band, literary magazine, marching band, newspaper, orchestra, political, professional, radio and TV, religious, social, social service, student government, and yearbook. Popular campus events include an arts festival and Homecoming.

Sports: There are 15 intercollegiate sports each for men and women, and 5 intramural sports each for men and women. Athletic and recreation facilities include a sports center, a gymnasium, and practice fields.

Disabled Students: Nearly all of the campus is accessible to disabled students. The following facilities are available: wheelchair ramps, elevators, special parking, specially equipped rest rooms, special class scheduling, and lowered drinking fountains and telephones.

Services: In addition to many counseling and information services, tutoring is available in most subjects. There is a reader service for the blind, and remedial math, reading, and writing.

Campus Safety and Security: Campus safety and security measures include 24-hour foot and vehicle patrol, escort service, shuttle buses, and informal discussions. In addition, there are lighted pathways and sidewalks.

Programs of Study: Howard awards the B.A., B.S., B.Arch., B.B.A., B.F.A., and B.S.W. degrees. Master's and doctoral degrees also are awarded. Bachelor's degrees are awarded in BIOLOGICAL SCIENCE (botany, microbiology, and zoology), BUSINESS (accounting, banking and finance, business administration and management, hotel/motel and restaurant management, insurance, international business management, and marketing/retailing/merchandising), COMMUNICATIONS AND THE ARTS (Arabic, broadcasting, communications, dance, design, dramatic arts, English, film arts, fine arts, French, German, Greek, journalism, Latin, music, photography, Russian, and Spanish), COMPUTER AND PHYSICAL SCIENCE (actuarial science, chemistry, computer programming, computer science, information sciences and systems, mathematics, and physics), EDUCATION (art, early childhood, elementary, and music), ENGINEERING AND ENVIRONMENTAL DESIGN (architecture, chemical engineering, civil engineering, computer engineering, electrical/electronics engineering, and mechanical engineering), HEALTH PROFESSIONS (medical laboratory technology, nursing, occupational therapy, pharmacy, physical therapy, physician's assistant, predentistry, premedicine, radiograph medical technology, and speech pathology/audiology), SOCIAL SCIENCE (anthropology, criminal justice, dietetics, economics, history, international relations, philosophy, political science/government, psychology, and sociology). Business and engineering are the strongest programs academically. Accounting, finance, and electrical engineering have the largest enrollments.

Required: To graduate, students must complete a at least 124 credit hours with a minimum GPA of 2.0. Four units of physical education are required, along with at least 1 year of precalculus mathematics in most majors and at least 1 course in African-American studies.

Special: Cross-registration is available with the Consortium of Universities in the Washington Metropolitan Area. Opportunities are also provided for internships, work-study and co-op programs, study abroad in Europe and Africa, B.A.-B.S. degrees in engineering and business, pass/fail options, and accelerated degree programs in medicine and dentistry. There is a freshman honors program and a university-wide honors program on campus.

Faculty/Classroom: Seventy-one percent of faculty are male; 29%, female. The average class size in an introductory lecture is 40; in a laboratory and regular course offering, 20.

Admissions: About 56% of the 1993-94 applicants were accepted.

Requirements: Howard requires applicants to be in the upper 50% of their class. A minimum GPA of 2.0 is required. The SAT I or ACT is required, with a minimum composite score of 800 on the SAT I (400 verbal, 400 mathematics) or 21 on the ACT. Graduation from an accredited secondary school is required. The GED is accepted. Students must have a minimum of 16 academic credits, distributed as follows: 4 in English and other electives and 2 each in foreign language, mathematics, science, and either history or social studies. Other requirements vary by college. Engineering majors take the SAT II: Sub-

ject test in mathematics I. Art majors must submit a portfolio, and an audition is required for music and majors. AP credits are accepted. Important factors used in the admissions decision are recommendations by school officials, advanced placement or honor courses, recommendations by alumni, personality, intangible qualities, and parents or siblings attending the school.

Procedure: Freshmen are admitted to all sessions. Entrance exams should be taken in the fall. Applications should be filed by April 1 for fall entry, November 1 for spring entry, and March 15 for summer entry, along with an application fee of $25. Notification is sent on a rolling basis. There are early admissions and deferred admissions plans. Three early decision candidates were accepted for a recent class.

Transfer: About 600 transfer students enrolled in a recent year. Students transferring to the School of Business must have successfully completed 18 semester hours or 23 quarter hours of courses, with a minimum GPA of 2.5. For many other majors, the requirement is 12 semester hours or 18 quarter hours, with a minimum GPA of 2.0. A total of 30 credits out of at least 124 must be completed at Howard.

Visiting: There are regularly scheduled orientations for prospective students. There are guides for informal visits and visitors may sit in on classes and stay overnight at the school. To arrange for a visit, contact the Office of Student Recruitment at (202) 806-2900.

Financial Aid: In a recent year, 67% of all current freshmen and 69% of continuing students received some form of financial aid. About 49% of freshmen and 50% of continuing students received need-based aid. The average freshman award was $5000. Of that total, scholarships or need-based grants averaged $3000 ($10,978 maximum); loans averaged $2200 ($2625 maximum); and work contracts averaged $1600 ($3200 maximum). Nine percent of undergraduate students work part-time. Average earnings from campus work for the school year are $3500. Howard is a member of CSS. The FAF is required. The deadline for financial aid applications is April 1.

International Students: There are currently 1200 international students enrolled. They must take the TOEFL and achieve a minimum score of 500. Students must also take the SAT I or the ACT, and SAT II: Subject test in mathematics I.

Computers: The university provides computer facilities for student use. The mainframe is an IBM 3033. Microcomputer laboratories are available across campus for academic use. Computer science and research students may access the system 8 a.m to 12 P.M. Monday through Thursday and 8 A.M. to 5 P.M. Friday and Saturday. There are no time limits on using the system and no fees.

Graduates: In an earlier class, 1206 bachelor's degrees were awarded. Some 120 companies recruited on campus.

Admissions Contact: Emmett R. Griffin Jr., Director of Admissions.

MOUNT VERNON COLLEGE
Washington, D. C. 20007

B-3

(202) 625-4682
(800) 682-4636 (out-of-state)

Full-time: 218 women	Faculty: 33; IIB, -$
Part-time: 27 women	Ph.D.s: 50%
Graduate: 32 women	Student/Faculty: 7 to 1
Year: semesters, summer session	Tuition: $13,750
Application Deadline: open	Room & Board: $6918
Freshman Class: 629 applied, 541 accepted, 213 enrolled	
ACT: 21	COMPETITIVE

Mount Vernon College, founded in 1875, is an independent liberal arts college for women offering undergraduate and graduate programs. In addition to regional accreditation, Mount Vernon has baccalaureate program accreditation with FIDER. The library contains 104,000 volumes and 2920 microform items and subscribes to 275 periodicals. Computerized library sources and services include database searching. Special learning facilities include an art gallery, radio station, and TV station. The 26-acre campus is in a suburban area in the northwest residential area of Georgetown. Including residence halls, there are 17 buildings on campus.

Student Life: Students come from 50 states and 35 foreign countries. Seventy percent are from public schools; 30% from private. Twenty-three percent are foreign nationals.

Housing: More than 300 students can be accommodated in college housing. College-sponsored living facilities include dormitories. On-campus housing is available on a first-come, first-served basis and is available on a lottery system for upperclassmen. Fifty percent of students live on campus. Alcohol is not permitted. Upperclassmen may keep cars on campus.

Activities: There are no sororities on campus. There are some groups and organizations on campus, including honors, newspaper, student government, and yearbook. Popular campus events include Founders Day, Winter and Spring Weekends, Winter and Spring Follies, the Performing Arts Series at Mount Vernon, Family Weekend, and International Day fests.

Sports: There are 3 intercollegiate and 2 intramural sports. Athletic and recreation facilities include a pool, tennis courts, a weight room, a gymnasium, basketball, badminton, and volleyball courts, lacrosse and field hockey fields, and a dance studio.

Disabled Students: The following facilities are available: wheelchair ramps, special parking, specially equipped rest rooms, special class scheduling, and accessible dining room and residence facilities.

Services: In addition to many counseling and information services, there is remedial math and writing.

Campus Safety and Security: Campus safety and security measures include 24-hour foot and vehicle patrol, shuttle buses, and informal discussions.

Programs of Study: Mount Vernon awards the B.A. degree. Associate and master's degrees also are awarded. Bachelor's degrees are awarded in BUSINESS (business administration and management), COMMUNICATIONS AND THE ARTS (communications), COMPUTER AND PHYSICAL SCIENCE (information sciences and systems), EDUCATION (early childhood), ENGINEERING AND ENVIRONMENTAL DESIGN (interior design), HEALTH PROFESSIONS (health science), SOCIAL SCIENCE (human development, humanities, interdisciplinary studies, international studies, political science/government, and urban studies).

Required: Students must complete 120 credit hours, with at least 24 in upper-level courses in the student's major, and must maintain a minimum GPA of 2.0. All students must meet a 48-credit liberal arts core requirement, which includes courses in social science, humanities, fine arts, and natural sciences.

Special: Cross-registration is permitted with 11 other schools in the Consortium of Universities of the Washington Metropolitan Area. Opportunities are also provided for internships, work-study programs, study abroad in London and Paris, student-designed majors, credit by examination, nondegree study, and credit for life and work experience. There is 1 national honor society on campus.

Faculty/Classroom: Thirty-two percent of faculty are male; 68%, female. All both teach and do research. No introductory courses are taught by graduate students. The average class size in an introductory lecture is 11; in a laboratory, 10; and in a regular course offering, 10.

Admissions: About 86% of the 1993–94 applicants were accepted. The SAT scores for the 1993–94 freshman class were as follows: Verbal—20% below 500, 75% between 500 and 599, and 5% between 600 and 700; Math—20% below 500, 75% between 500 and 599, and 5% between 600 and 700. The ACT scores were 20% below 21, 75% between 21 and 23, and 5% between 24 and 26. About 40% of the current freshmen were in the top two fifths of their class.

Requirements: The SAT I or ACT is required. Graduation from an accredited secondary school is required; a GED will be accepted. Applicants should submit 16 academic credits, including 4 units in English, 2 in mathematics, 2 in a foreign language, 1 each in a laboratory science and in social science, and 6 in other academic electives. An essay and a recommendation from a high school counselor or teacher are required. AP and CLEP credits are accepted. Important factors used in the admissions decision are parents or siblings attending the school, evidence of special talent, advanced placement or honor courses, leadership record, and recommendations by school officials.

Procedure: Freshmen are admitted in the fall and spring. Entrance exams should be taken at least 1 month prior to the semester of enrollment. Application deadlines are open. The application fee is $25. Notification is sent on a rolling basis. There is an early admissions plan.

Transfer: Students applying for transfer should submit an essay, an official transcript from each college previously attended, showing a minimum GPA of 2.0, and a recommendation from an academic adviser or teacher. If the student has not completed more than 1 year of college, an official high school transcript and SAT I or ACT scores are required.

Visiting: There are regularly scheduled orientations for prospective students, consisting of meetings with administrators, faculty, and students, visits to classes, and participation in campus social life. There are guides for informal visits and visitors may sit in on classes and stay overnight at the school. To arrange for a visit, contact the Admissions Office at (202) 625–4682.

Financial Aid: In 1993–94 60% of all current freshmen and 48% of continuing students received some form of financial aid. About 60% of freshmen and 45% of continuing students received need-based aid. The average freshman award was $12,455. Of that total, scholarships or need-based grants averaged $6290 ($10,000 maximum); loans averaged $2625 (maximum); and work contracts averaged $1400 ($1500 maximum). Twenty-four percent of undergraduate students work part-time. Average earnings from campus work for the school year are $850. The average financial indebtedness of the 1992–93 graduate was $13,250. The FAF and the FAFSA financial statement are required. The deadline for financial aid applications is March 1.

International Students: There are currently 57 international students enrolled. The school actively recruits these students. They must take the TOEFL or the Comprehensive English Language Test and achieve a minimum score on the TOEFL of 500. The student must also take the SAT I or the ACT.

Computers: The college provides computer facilities for student use. There is a microcomputer laboratory providing IBM-compatible hardware for students and a word-processing center in the library. All students may access the system Monday through Friday until midnight, and daytime hours on weekends. There are no time limits on using the system and no fees.

Admissions Contact: Joseph Yung, Director of Enrollment Management.

SOUTHEASTERN UNIVERSITY

D-4

Washington, DC 20024 — (202) 488–8162

Full-time: 207 men, 103 women — Faculty: 24
Part-time: 140 men, 200 women — Ph.D.s: n/av
Graduate: 180 men, 170 women — Student/Faculty: 13 to 1
Year: four 12-week terms, summer session — Tuition: $6625 — Room & Board: n/app
Application Deadline: open
Freshman Class: 300 applied, 250 accepted, 160 enrolled
SAT I or ACT: recommended — COMPETITIVE

Southeastern University, founded as Washington School for Accountancy in 1879, is a private, nonsectarian, commuter college offering programs in business administration, accounting, computer information systems, finance, banking, and marketing to a student body composed primarily of working adults. There are 4 graduate schools. In addition to regional accreditation, Southeastern has baccalaureate program accreditation with AACSB. The library contains 40,000 volumes and subscribes to 1200 periodicals. Special learning facilities include a learning resource center. The campus is in a residential part of southwest Washington, D.C. There is one building on campus. There are no residence halls.

Student Life: About 90% of undergraduates are from District of Columbia. Students come from 2 states and 65 foreign countries. The average age of freshmen is 26; all undergraduates, 32. Ten percent drop out by the end of their first year; 40% remain to graduate.

Housing: There are no residence halls. Referral listings of long- and short-term housing are available. Alcohol is not permitted on campus.

Activities: There is 1 local fraternity. There are no sororities on campus. There are some groups and organizations on campus, including chess, computers, newspaper, and student government. Popular campus events include Halloween, Christmas, graduation dances, the summer picnic, the Annual Awards Ceremony, the chess tournament, International Week, and Black History Month.

Sports: There is no sports program at Southeastern.

Disabled Students: The entire campus is accessible to disabled students. The following facilities are available: wheelchair ramps, special parking, specially equipped rest rooms, special class scheduling, and lowered telephones.

Services: In addition to many counseling and information services, tutoring is available in most subjects. In addition, there is remedial math, reading, and writing. There are also individualized learning programs for students in upper-level courses.

Campus Safety and Security: Campus safety and security measures include 24-hour foot and vehicle patrol and lighted pathways and sidewalks.

Programs of Study: Southeastern awards the B.S. degree. Associate and master's degrees also are awarded. Bachelor's degrees are awarded in BUSINESS (accounting, banking and finance, business administration and management, and marketing/retailing/merchandising), COMPUTER AND PHYSICAL SCIENCE (information sciences and systems), SOCIAL SCIENCE (law and public administration). Business is the strongest academically and has the largest enrollment.

Required: To graduate, students must complete 121 credit hours, including the general studies core curriculum, which consists of 31 hours in the fields of English, information systems, mathematics, humanities, social science, and accounting. Also required are 24 hours in the general studies electives, 27 hours of major requirements, 27 hours in the business/professional core, 6 hours of professional electives, and 6 hours of electives. All students must take an orientation course and a computer course.

Special: Southeastern offers extensive co-op programs, internships, dual majors, and credit by exam and for life/military/work experience. The Add-a-Degree program allows any student with a bachelor's degree to add a second area of expertise, or to add professional qualifications. There is one national honor society on campus.

Admissions: About 83% of the 1993–94 applicants were accepted.

Requirements: A minimum GPA of 2.0 is required. The SAT I or ACT is recommended. Students must be graduates of an accredited secondary school or have a GED and must pass Southeastern's placement test for regular admission. CLEP credit is accepted.

Procedure: Application deadlines are open. Application fee is $25.

Transfer: Transfer applicants must submit transcripts. At least 60 credits out of 121 must be completed at Southeastern.

Financial Aid: In a recent year, scholarships or need-based grants averaged $750 ($1000 maximum). The FAF is required. The deadline for financial aid applications is May 1.

International Students: They must take the TOEFL and achieve a minimum score of 500.

Computers: The college provides computer facilities for student use. Southeastern's computer center has a mainframe and microcomputers. Those students required to use computing in their major may access the system. There are no time limits on using the system and no fees.

Admissions Contact: Mahalia W. Rahman, Director of Retention Management and Alumni Affairs.

STRAYER COLLEGE

	C-3
Washington, DC 20005	(202) 408-2400 or (703) 892-5100
Full-time: 1190 men, 1168 women	**Faculty:** 60
Part-time: 1235 men, 1731 women	**Ph.D.s:** 40%
Graduate: 498 men, 417 women	**Student/Faculty:** 39 to 1
Year: quarters, summer session	**Tuition:** $5850
Application Deadline: open	**Room & Board:** n/app
Freshman Class: 781 enrolled	
SAT I or ACT: recommended	**LESS COMPETITIVE**

Strayer College, founded in 1892, is an independent coeducational business college with 8 campuses in the Washington, D.C., metropolitan area. All programs are computer- or business-related. There are 4 undergraduate and 3 graduate schools. The library contains 17,500 volumes and 2000 microform items, and subscribes to 310 periodicals. Computerized library sources and services include the card catalog and database searching. Special learning facilities include a learning resource center. Two of the campuses are located in Washington D.C., and 6 campuses are in suburban Virginia. There is 1 building on each campus. There are no residence halls.

Student Life: About 99% of undergraduates are from District of Columbia. Students come from 4 states and 80 foreign countries. Forty-five percent are white; 34% African American; 11% foreign nationals. The average age of all undergraduates is 31. About 59% of freshmen remain to graduate.

Housing: There are no residence halls. All students commute. Alcohol is not permitted on campus.

Activities: There are no fraternities or sororities on campus. There are some groups and organizations on campus, including honors, international, and professional.

Sports: There is no sports program at Strayer.

Disabled Students: The entire campus is accessible to disabled students. The following facilities are available: wheelchair ramps, elevators, special parking, and specially equipped rest rooms.

Campus Safety and Security: Campus safety and security measures include security guards at all the urban campuses.

Programs of Study: Strayer awards the B.S. degree. Associate and master's degrees also are awarded. Bachelor's degrees are awarded in BUSINESS (accounting and business administration and management), COMPUTER AND PHYSICAL SCIENCE (information sciences and systems), SOCIAL SCIENCE (economics). Computer information systems, business administration, and accounting are the strongest academically. Computer information systems and business administration have the largest enrollments.

Required: For the bachelor's degree, students must complete 180 quarter hours, with 54 in the major and a minimum GPA of 2.0. Introduction to computer information systems is a required course.

Special: The college offers cooperative programs, an accelerated diploma program in computer information systems, and gives credit for military and work experience. There is one national honor society on campus.

Faculty/Classroom: Seventy-five percent of faculty are male; 25%, female. All teach undergraduates. No introductory courses are taught by graduate students. The average class size in an introductory lecture is 30 and in a regular course offering, 25.

Requirements: The SAT I or the ACT is recommended. A GED is accepted. CLEP credit is accepted.

Procedure: Freshmen are admitted to all sessions. Application deadlines are open. Application fee is $25. Notification is sent on a rolling basis. There are early admissions and deferred admissions plans.

Transfer: About 230 transfer students enrolled in 1993-94. At least 54 quarter hours out of 180 must be completed at Strayer.

Visiting: There are guides for informal visits.

Financial Aid: In 1993-94, 45% of all current freshmen and 35% of continuing students received some form of financial aid. The average freshman award was $1170. The AFSA financial statement is required. The deadline for financial aid applications is May 1.

International Students: There are currently 347 international students enrolled. The school actively recruits these students. They must take the TOEFL and achieve a minimum score of 450.

Computers: The college provides computer facilities for student use. The mainframe is a Prime 4450. There are 350 microcomputers available for academic use. All students may access the system. There are no time limits on using the system and no fees.

Graduates: In 1992-93, 453 bachelor's degrees were awarded. The most popular majors among graduates were computer information systems (43%), business administration (38%), and accounting (18%). In the 1992 graduating class, 91% of all graduates had found employment within 6 months of graduation.

Admissions Contact: Admissions Office.

TRINITY COLLEGE

	C-2
Washington, DC 20017	(202) 939-5040; (800) 492-6882
Full-time: 309 women	**Faculty:** 48; IIB, --$
Part-time: 636 women	**Ph.D.s:** 88%
Graduate: 430 women	**Student/Faculty:** 6 to 1
Year: semesters	**Tuition:** $11,230
Application Deadline: open	**Room & Board:** $6430
Freshman Class: 253 applied, 217 accepted, 100 enrolled	
SAT I Verbal/Math: 500/510	**ACT:** 24 **COMPETITIVE**

Trinity College, founded in 1897, is a private, women's liberal arts college affiliated with the Roman Catholic Church. There are 2 graduate schools. In addition to regional accreditation, Trinity has baccalaureate program accreditation with NCATE. The library contains 178,232 volumes, 5392 microform items, and 2922 audiovisual forms, and subscribes to 620 periodicals. Computerized library sources and services include the card catalog and database searching. Special learning facilities include a learning resource center, art gallery, computer center, and writing center. The 26-acre campus is in an urban area 2 1/2 miles north of the United States Capitol. Including residence halls, there are 7 buildings on campus.

Student Life: About 89% of undergraduates are from outside Washington, D.C., mostly the Middle Atlantic. Students come from 35 states, 15 foreign countries, and Canada. Fifty percent are from public schools; 50% from private. Fifty-five percent are white; 28% African American. Most are Catholic. The average age of freshmen is 18; all undergraduates, 19.5. Eleven percent drop out by the end of their first year; 87% remain to graduate.

Housing: A total of 600 students can be accommodated in college housing. College-sponsored living facilities include dormitories. On-campus housing is guaranteed for all 4 years. Ninety-five percent of students live on campus; of those, 95% remain on campus on weekends. All students may keep cars on campus.

Activities: There are no sororities on campus. There are 28 groups on campus, including chorale, computers, dance, drama, ethnic, honors, international, jazz band, literary magazine, newspaper, orchestra, photography, political, professional, religious, social, social service, student government, and yearbook. Popular campus events include Founders Day, Class Days, Cap and Gown Sunday, Junior Ring Day, Christmas and spring formal, and Pub Night.

Sports: Athletic and recreation facilities include 2 athletic fields for soccer and field hockey, a fitness center, 6 tennis courts, and an outdoor sand volleyball court.

Disabled Students: The entire campus is accessible to disabled students. The following facilities are available: wheelchair ramps, elevators, special parking, specially equipped rest rooms, and lowered telephones.

Services: In addition to many counseling and information services, tutoring is available in every subject. In addition, there is a reader service for the blind, and remedial math, reading, and writing.

Campus Safety and Security: Campus safety and security measures include 24-hour foot and vehicle patrol, self-defense education, escort service, and shuttle buses. In addition, there are informal discussions, pamphlets, posters, films, emergency telephones, and lighted pathways and sidewalks.

Programs of Study: Trinity awards the B.A. and B.S. degrees. Master's degrees also are awarded. Bachelor's degrees are awarded in BIOLOGICAL SCIENCE (biochemistry and biology/biological science), BUSINESS (business administration and management), COMMUNICATIONS AND THE ARTS (communications, English, French, and Spanish), COMPUTER AND PHYSICAL SCIENCE (chemistry), EDUCATION (early childhood and elementary), ENGINEERING AND ENVIRONMENTAL DESIGN (environmental science), HEALTH PROFESSIONS (premedicine), SOCIAL SCIENCE (American studies, economics, history, international studies, political science/government, prelaw, and psychology). English, history, and political

science are the strongest academically. Business administration, political science, and psychology have the largest enrollments.

Required: To graduate, students must complete a total of 128 credit hours with a minimum GPA of 2.0. Between 42 and 50 hours are required in the major. All students must take the courses required in the core curriculum.

Special: Cross-registration and the Mentor Program are offered through the Consortium of Universities of the Washington Area. Trinity offers internships in all majors and minors, as well as work-study programs. Students may study in France, Italy, and various other countries by arrangement with their faculty advisor. B.A.-B.S. degrees, a 5-year accelerated degree in teaching, dual and student-designed majors, a general studies degree, credit for life experience, nondegree study, and pass/fail options are also available. There is a freshman honors program on campus, as well as 2 national honor societies, including Phi Beta Kappa.

Faculty/Classroom: Twenty-five percent of faculty are male; 75%, female. No introductory courses are taught by graduate students. The average class size in an introductory lecture is 20; in a laboratory, 10; and in a regular course offering, 8.

Admissions: About 86% of the 1993–94 applicants were accepted. About 42% of the current freshmen were in the top fifth of their class; 70% were in the top two fifths.

Requirements: Trinity requires applicants to be in the upper 50% of their class. A minimum GPA of 2.5 is required. The SAT I or ACT is required. In addition, graduation from an accredited secondary school or satisfactory scores on the GED are required for admission. A total of 16 academic credits is required, including 4 years of English and 3 to 4 years each of a foreign language, history, mathematics, and science. AP examinations and SAT II: Subject tests are recommended. An interview is recommended, and an essay is required. AP and CLEP credits are accepted. Important factors used in the admissions decision are personality, intangible qualities, advanced placement or honor courses, extracurricular activities record, recommendations by school officials, and recommendations by alumni.

Procedure: Freshmen are admitted fall and spring. It is recommended that students take entrance examinations in the junior year. Application deadlines are open. Application fee is $35. There are early decision, early admissions, and deferred admissions plans. Notification of early decision is sent December 15; regular decision, on a rolling basis. A total of 7 early decision candidates were accepted for the 1993–94 class.

Transfer: About 20 transfer students enrolled in 1993–94. Transfer applicants must have a minimum GPA of 2.0. An interview is recommended. At least 32 credits out of 128 must be completed at Trinity.

Visiting: There are regularly scheduled orientations for prospective students. There are guides for informal visits, and visitors may sit in on classes and stay overnight at the school. To arrange for a visit, contact the Office of Admissions at (202) 939–5040 or (800) 492–6882.

Financial Aid: In 1993–94, 81% of all current freshmen and 76% of continuing students received some form of financial aid. The average freshman award was $10,130. Of that total, scholarships or need-based grants averaged $6063 ($8000 maximum); loans averaged $2625; and work contracts averaged $1000 ($1200 maximum). Twenty percent of undergraduate students work part-time. Trinity is a member of CSS. The FAF is required. The deadline for financial aid applications is March 15.

International Students: There are currently 15 international students enrolled. The school actively recruits these students. They must take the TOEFL and achieve a minimum score of 500 and must also take the SAT I or the ACT.

Computers: The college provides computer facilities for student use. There are 31 IBM and 9 Apple microcomputers, located in the learning center and in residence halls. All have printer access. All students may access the system. There are no time limits on using the system and no fees.

Graduates: In 1992–93, 104 bachelor's degrees were awarded. Within an average freshman class, 75% graduate in 4 years and 9% in 5 years. Some 150 companies recruited on campus in 1992–93. In the 1992 graduating class, 50% of the women were enrolled in graduate school within 6 months of graduation.

Admissions Contact: Mary Agnes D. Evans, Director of Admissions.

UNIVERSITY OF THE DISTRICT OF COLUMBIA

C-2

Washington, DC 20008   (202) 282–2300

Full-time: 1664 men, 1994 women	**Faculty:** 343; IIA, av$
Part-time: 2641 men, 3686 women	**Ph.D.s:** 52%
Graduate: 268 men, 355 women	**Student/Faculty:** 11 to 1
Year: semesters, summer session	**Tuition:** $974 ($3566)
Application Deadline: June 15	**Room & Board:** n/app

Freshman Class: 3895 applied, 3866 accepted, 1717 enrolled
ACT: required   **NONCOMPETITIVE**

University of the District of Columbia, founded in 1977, is a publicly funded, land-grant commuter institution offering liberal arts, business, education, and technical programs. There are 5 undergraduate schools and one graduate school. In addition to regional accreditation, UDC has baccalaureate program accreditation with ABET, CAHEA, CSWE, and NLN. The 4 libraries contain 470,330 volumes, 623,991 microform items, and 21,207 audiovisual forms, and subscribes to 2787 periodicals. Computerized library sources and services include database searching. Special learning facilities include a learning resource center, art gallery, radio station, and TV station. The 22-acre campus is in a suburban area. There are 25 buildings on campus.

Student Life: About 87% of undergraduates are from the District of Columbia. Students come from 50 states and 55 foreign countries. Eighty-five percent are from public schools; 2% from private. Seventy-two percent are African American. The average age of freshmen is 18; all undergraduates, 27. Thirty-five percent drop out by the end of their first year; 65% remain to graduate.

Housing: There are no residence halls; all students commute. Alcohol is not permitted.

Activities: About 2% of men belong to 7 national fraternities; about 2% of women belong to 5 national sororities. There are 139 groups on campus, including art, band, cheerleading, chess, choir, chorale, computers, dance, drama, drum and bugle corps, ethnic, film, honors, international, jazz band, marching band, newspaper, orchestra, pep band, photography, political, professional, radio and TV, religious, social, social service, student government, and yearbook. Popular campus events include the Cross-Cultural Extended Family Program, International Multicultural Recognition Day, Homecoming, and International Day.

Sports: There are 6 intercollegiate sports for men and 6 for women, and 8 intramural sports for men and 6 for women. Athletic and recreation facilities include a 3000-seat gymnasium, a swimming pool, a weight room, a racquetball court, and tennis courts.

Disabled Students: All of the campus is accessible to disabled students. The following facilities are available: wheelchair ramps, elevators, special parking, specially equipped rest rooms, lowered drinking fountains, and lowered telephones.

Services: In addition to many counseling and information services, tutoring is available in every subject. In addition, there is a reader service for the blind and remedial math and reading.

Campus Safety and Security: Campus safety and security measures include 24-hour foot and vehicle patrol, emergency telephones, and lighted pathways and sidewalks.

Programs of Study: UDC awards the B.A. and B.S. degrees. Associate and master's degrees also are awarded. Bachelor's degrees are awarded in AGRICULTURE (horticulture), BIOLOGICAL SCIENCE (biology/biological science), BUSINESS (accounting, banking and finance, business administration and management, marketing/retailing/merchandising, and office supervision and management), COMMUNICATIONS AND THE ARTS (dramatic arts, English, fine arts, French, journalism, music, and Spanish), COMPUTER AND PHYSICAL SCIENCE (chemistry, computer science, geoscience, mathematics, and physics), EDUCATION (art, business, early childhood, elementary, home economics, library science, music, physical, special, and vocational), ENGINEERING AND ENVIRONMENTAL DESIGN (civil engineering, construction engineering, electrical/electronics engineering, electromechanical technology, environmental science, and mechanical engineering), HEALTH PROFESSIONS (medical laboratory technology, nursing, and speech pathology/audiology), SOCIAL SCIENCE (child care/child and family studies, clothing and textiles management/production/services, criminal justice, economics, fire science, food science, geography, history, philosophy, political science/government, psychology, public administration, social science, and sociology). Business is the strongest academically. Fine arts has the largest enrollment.

Required: To graduate, students must complete 120 to 130 semester hours with a minimum GPA of 2.0. All students must take 6 hours each of English composition, literature and advanced writing, social science, mathematics, and natural sciences, 3 hours each of philosophy and fine arts, and 4 hours of personal and community health. Some programs also require 6 hours of a foreign language.

Special: Cross-registration may be arranged through the Consortium of Universities of the Washington Metropolitan Area. Co-op programs with the federal government, internships, study abroad in 4 countries, work-study programs and B.A.-B.S. degrees in administration of justice, chemistry, and physics are offered. Nondegree study and credit for life experience are also available. There is a freshman honors program on campus, as well as 4 national honor societies.

Faculty/Classroom: Sixty-six percent of faculty are male; 34%, female. Eighty-nine percent teach undergraduates, 3% do research, and 20% do both. No introductory courses are taught by graduate students. The average class size in an introductory lecture is 23; in a laboratory, 23; and in a regular course offering, 23.

Admissions: About 99% of the 1993–94 applicants were accepted.

Requirements: The ACT is required. A high school diploma or GED is required for admission, along with an interview. High school courses must include 4 years of English and 2 years each of foreign language and social studies. AP and CLEP credits are accepted. Important factors used in the admissions decision are ability to finance college education, advanced placement or honor courses, recommendations by school officials, recommendations by alumni, and evidence of special talent.

Procedure: Freshmen are admitted to all sessions. Applications should be filed by June 15 for fall entry and November 1 for spring entry, along with an application fee of $20. The college accepts all applicants. Notification is sent within 30 days.

Transfer: About 428 transfer students enrolled in 1993–94. Transfer applicants must have a minimum GPA of 2.0. Those with fewer than 30 hours of college credit must submit a high school transcript along with college records. A total of 30 credits out of 120 must be completed at UDC.

Visiting: There are guides for informal visits and visitors may sit in on classes. To arrange for a visit, contact the Office of Student Recruitment at (202) 282–3350.

Financial Aid: In an earlier year 25% of all current freshmen and 25% of continuing students received some form of financial aid. About 19% of freshmen received need-based aid. Scholarships or need-based grants averaged $500 ($1000 maximum); loans averaged $500 ($2500 maximum); and work contracts averaged $600 ($1000 maximum). One percent of undergraduate students work part-time. UDC is a member of CSS. The FAF or FFS is required. The deadline for financial aid applications is March 15.

International Students: There are currently 950 international students enrolled. They must take the TOEFL and achieve a minimum score of 550. The student must also take the college's own English, mathematics, or reading tests.

Computers: The college provides computer facilities for student use. The mainframes are an IBM 4381 and a DEC VAX 8650. Microcomputers are also available. All students may access the system. It may be used 24 hours a day. There are no time limits on using the system and no fees.

Graduates: In 1992–93, 521 bachelor's degrees were awarded. Some 25 companies recruited on campus in 1992–93.

Admissions Contact: Sandra B. Dolphin, Director, Recruitment and Admissions.

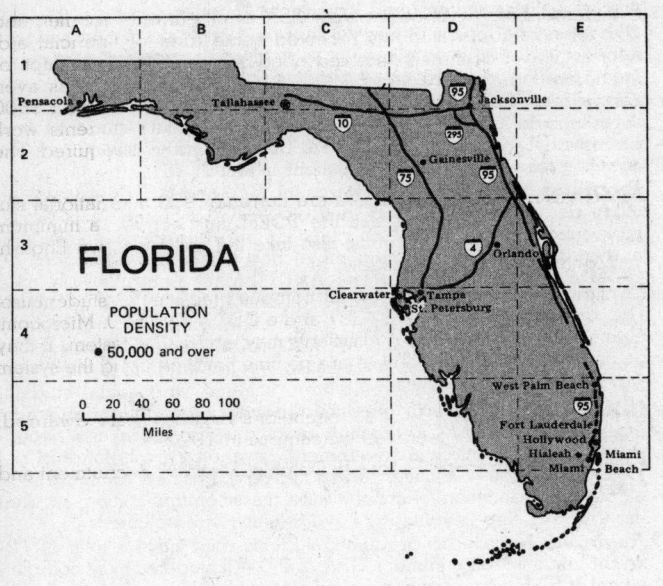

FLORIDA

POPULATION
DENSITY

● 50,000 and over

0 20 40 60 80 100
Miles

BARRY UNIVERSITY
Miami Shores, FL 33161

E-5

(305) 899–3129
(800) 695–2279 (in-state)

Full-time: 666 men, 1145 women	**Faculty:** 196; n/av
Part-time: 1087 men, 2057 women	**Ph.D.s:** 75%
Graduate: 580 men, 1315 women	**Student/Faculty:** 9 to 1
Year: semesters, summer session	**Tuition:** $10,850
Application Deadline: May 1	**Room & Board:** $5200
Freshman Class: 844 applied, 672 accepted, 250 enrolled	
SAT I Verbal/Math: 425/465	**ACT:** 20 **COMPETITIVE**

Barry University, founded in 1940, is a private liberal arts institution affiliated with the Roman Catholic Church. There are 6 undergraduate and 8 graduate schools. In addition to regional accreditation, Barry has baccalaureate program accreditation with NLN. The library contains 650,000 volumes and 400,000 microform items, and subscribes to 1200 periodicals. Computerized library sources and services include the card catalog, interlibrary loans, and database searching. Special learning facilities include a learning resource center, radio station, and TV station. The 90-acre campus is in a suburban area 12 miles north of Miami. Including residence halls, there are 26 buildings on campus.

Student Life: About 60% of undergraduates are from Florida. Students come from 46 states, 68 foreign countries, and Canada. Fifty percent are from public schools; 50% from private. Fifty percent are white; 20% Hispanic; 17% foreign nationals; 11% African American. Thirty-seven percent are Catholic. The average age of freshmen is 18; all undergraduates, 28. Thirty percent drop out by the end of their first year; 42% remain to graduate.

Housing: A total of 654 students can be accommodated in college housing. College-sponsored living facilities include single-sex and coed dormitories. On-campus housing is guaranteed for the freshman year only, and is available on a lottery system for upperclassmen. Priority is given to out-of-town students. Fifty-six percent of students commute. Alcohol is not permitted. All students may keep cars on campus.

Activities: About 50% of men belong to 4 national fraternities; about 25% of women belong to 1 national sorority. There are 43 groups on campus, including art, cheerleading, chorale, computers, dance, drama, ethnic, honors, international, jazz band, literary magazine, newspaper, political, professional, radio and TV, religious, social, social service, student government, and yearbook. Popular campus events include Founders Week, Fall Holiday, spring and winter formal, Halloween Dance, Winter Boat Parade on Biscayne Bay, and Barry Soccer Invitational.

Sports: There are 7 intercollegiate sports for men and 7 for women, and 13 intramural sports for men and 13 for women. Athletic and recreation facilities include baseball, softball, and soccer fields, a gymnasium, outdoor basketball courts, and racquetball and tennis courts.

Disabled Students: The entire campus is accessible to disabled students. The following facilities are available: wheelchair ramps, elevators, special parking, specially equipped rest rooms, special class scheduling, lowered drinking fountains, and lowered telephones.

Services: In addition to many counseling and information services, tutoring is available in every subject. There is also remedial math, reading, and writing.

Campus Safety and Security: Campus safety and security measures include 24-hour foot and vehicle patrol, escort service, informal discussions, pamphlets, posters, and films. In addition, there are emergency telephones and lighted pathways and sidewalks.

Programs of Study: Barry awards the B.A., B.S., B.F.A., B.L.S., B.P.S., B.S.N., and B.S.T. degrees. Master's and doctoral degrees also are awarded. Bachelor's degrees are awarded in BIOLOGICAL SCIENCE (biology/biological science), BUSINESS (accounting, banking and finance, international business management, management information systems, management science, marketing/retailing/merchandising, and sports management), COMMUNICATIONS AND THE ARTS (art, arts administration/management, broadcasting, communications, dramatic arts, English, fine arts, French, photography, public relations, Spanish, and theater management), COMPUTER AND PHYSICAL SCIENCE (chemistry, computer science, and mathematics), EDUCATION (early childhood and physical), ENGINEERING AND ENVIRONMENTAL DESIGN (preengineering), HEALTH PROFESSIONS (cytotechnology, medical laboratory technology, medical technology, nuclear medical technology, nursing, occupational therapy, predentistry, premedicine, prepharmacy, sports medicine, and ultrasound technology), SOCIAL SCIENCE (criminal justice, economics, history, international studies, philosophy, political science/government, prelaw, psychology, sociology, and theological studies). Biology, accounting, political science, and computer science are the strongest academically. Nursing, elementary and early childhood education, management, and psychology have the largest enrollments.

Required: To graduate, students must complete 120 credit hours, including at least 48 in upper-division courses, 30 to 40 in the major, 45 in distribution requirements, and 40 to 60 in the core curriculum of fine arts, humanities, mathematics, social sciences, behavioral sciences, and sciences. A minimum GPA of 2.0 must be maintained.

Special: Barry offers junior- or senior-year internships, a Washington semester for prelaw/political science students, on-campus work-study programs in all departments, dual majors, B.A.-B.S. degrees, a liberal studies degree, an accelerated degree program in nursing, nondegree study, and pass/fail options. Students may study in 5 European countries. A 3–2 engineering degree is possible with the University of Miami. The School of Adult and Continuing Education gives credit for life experience. Campus interchange programs exist with St. Thomas Aquinas, Dominican, and Aquinas colleges. There is a freshman honors program on campus as well as 16 national honor societies. Eleven departments have honors programs.

Faculty/Classroom: Fifty-three percent of faculty are male; 47%, female. All teach undergraduates. No introductory courses are taught by graduate students. The average class size in an introductory lecture is 25 and in a laboratory, 14.

Admissions: About 80% of the 1993–94 applicants were accepted. The SAT scores for the 1993–94 freshman class were as follows: Verbal—82% below 500, 15% between 500 and 599, and 4% between 600 and 700; Math—62% below 500, 30% between 500 and 599, 10% between 600 and 700, and 1% above 700. The ACT scores were 65% below 21, 17% between 21 and 23, 12% between 24 and 26, 5% between 27 and 28, and 1% above 28. Five freshmen graduated first in their class.

Requirements: Barry requires applicants to be in the upper 40% of their class. A minimum GPA of 2.0 is required. The SAT I or ACT is required. Graduation from an accredited secondary school or satisfactory scores on the GED are required for admission. An essay is required, and an interview is recommended. A portfolio is recommended for art students. AP and CLEP credits are accepted. Important factors used in the admissions decision are advanced placement or honor courses, leadership record, recommendations by school officials, evidence of special talent, and extracurricular activities record.

Procedure: Freshmen are admitted to all sessions. Entrance exams should be taken as early as possible, particularly if campus housing is desired; before March is recommended. Early decision applications should be filed by January 1; regular applications, by May 1 for fall entry, November 1 for spring entry, and May 1 for summer entry, along with an application fee of $30. Notification of early decision is

sent February 1; regular decision, on a rolling basis. There are early decision, early admissions, and deferred admissions plans.

Transfer: About 280 transfer students enrolled in 1993–94. Applicants must have at least 12 credit hours earned with a minimum GPA of 2.0. An associate degree is recommended, as is an interview. At least 30 credits out of 120 must be completed at Barry.

Visiting: There are regularly scheduled orientations for prospective students, including a tour, class visits, lunch, and a panel discussion. There are guides for informal visits, and visitors may sit in on classes and stay overnight at the school. To arrange for a visit, contact Louise Coulson Neppl, Director of Undergraduate Admissions, at (305) 899–3113.

Financial Aid: In a recent year, 60% of all current freshmen and 70% of continuing students received some form of financial aid. About 40% of freshmen and 50% of continuing students received need-based aid. The average freshman award was $7000. Of that total, scholarships or need-based grants averaged $3475 ($9250 maximum); loans averaged $2625 (maximum); and work contracts averaged $900 ($1800 maximum). Twenty percent of undergraduate students work part-time. Average earnings from campus work for the school year are $900. The average financial indebtedness of a recent graduate was $5750. Barry is a member of CSS. The FAF and the college's own financial statement are required. The deadline for financial aid applications is April 1.

International Students: There are currently 442 international students enrolled. The school actively recruits these students. They must take the TOEFL and achieve a minimum score of 550.

Computers: The college provides computer facilities for student use. The mainframe is a DEC VAX 6310. The system may be accessed via dial-up modems or networked microcomputers in laboratories. All students may access the system 24 hours a day. There are no time limits on using the system and no fees.

Graduates: In 1992–93, 961 bachelor's degrees were awarded. The most popular majors among graduates were nursing (45%), biology (40%), and education (22%). Within an average freshman class, 42% graduate in 4 years and 39% in 5 years. Some 91 companies recruited on campus in a recent year.

Admissions Contact: Robin Ray Roberts, Dean of Enrollment Services.

BETHUNE-COOKMAN COLLEGE

Daytona Beach, FL 32114–3099

D-2

(904) 255–1410, ext. 303/358
(800) 448–0228 (out-of-state)

Full-time: 868 men, 1260 women	Faculty: 125
Part-time: 31 men, 51 women	Ph.D.s: 48%
Graduate: none	Student/Faculty: 17 to 1
Year: semesters, summer session	Tuition: $5165
Application Deadline: July 30	Room & Board: $3210
Freshman Class: 1646 applied, 1150 accepted, 549 enrolled	
SAT I Verbal/Math: 367/408	ACT: 16 **LESS COMPETITIVE**

Bethune-Cookman College, founded in 1904, is a private liberal arts institution affiliated with the United Methodist Church. There are 5 undergraduate schools. In addition to regional accreditation, B-CC has baccalaureate program accreditation with CAHEA and NCATE. The library contains 145,864 volumes, 37,118 microform items, and 8009 audiovisual forms, and subscribes to 770 periodicals. Computerized library sources and services include the card catalog, interlibrary loans, and database searching. Special learning facilities include a learning resource center, art gallery, and radio station. The 52-acre campus is in an urban area 65 miles east of Orlando. Including residence halls, there are 33 buildings on campus.

Student Life: About 83% of undergraduates are from Florida. Students come from 32 states and 10 foreign countries. Ninety percent are from public schools; 10% from private. Ninety-six percent are African American. Most are Protestant. The average age of freshmen is 18; all undergraduates, 20. Twenty-four percent drop out by the end of their first year; 75% remain to graduate.

Housing: A total of 1536 students can be accommodated in college housing. College-sponsored living facilities include single-sex dormitories. In addition there are honor student dormitories, and dormitory wings for Greek letter organizations. On-campus housing is guaranteed for the freshman year only and is available on a first-come, first-served basis. Priority is given to out-of-town students. Sixty percent of students live on campus; of those, 88% remain on campus on weekends. Alcohol is not permitted. Upperclassmen may keep cars on campus.

Activities: About 10% of men belong to 4 national fraternities; about 15% of women belong to 4 national sororities. There are 42 groups on campus, including band, cheerleading, choir, chorale, computers, dance, drama, drill team, honors, international, marching band, newspaper, political, professional, radio and TV, religious, social, student government, and yearbook. Popular campus events include Religious Outreach, Career Day, Futurism Seminar, United Nations Week, Black History Month, Homecoming, and Founders Day.

Sports: There are 7 intercollegiate sports for men and 7 for women and 6 intramural sports for men and 6 for women. Athletic and recreation facilities include a gymnasium, a weight room, a practice field and tennis and racquetball courts.

Disabled Students: Ten percent of the campus is accessible to disabled students. The following facilities are available: wheelchair ramps, elevators, special parking, specially equipped rest rooms, lowered drinking fountains, and lowered telephones.

Services: In addition to many counseling and information services, tutoring is available in every subject. In addition, there is remedial math, reading, and writing.

Campus Safety and Security: Campus safety and security measures include 24-hour foot and vehicle patrol, escort service, informal discussions, and pamphlets, posters, and films. In addition, there are lighted pathways and sidewalks.

Programs of Study: B-CC awards the B.A. and B.S. degrees. Bachelor's degrees are awarded in BIOLOGICAL SCIENCE (biology/biological science), BUSINESS (accounting, business administration and management, and hotel/motel and restaurant management), COMMUNICATIONS AND THE ARTS (broadcasting, English, modern languages, and music), COMPUTER AND PHYSICAL SCIENCE (chemistry, computer science, information sciences and systems, mathematics, and physics), EDUCATION (business, education of the exceptional child, elementary, English, foreign languages, mathematics, music, physical and recreation, science, and social studies), HEALTH PROFESSIONS (medical laboratory technology and nursing), SOCIAL SCIENCE (criminal justice, history, liberal arts/general studies, political science/government, psychology, religion and philosophy, religious education, and sociology). Business administration, elementary education, criminal justice, mass communication, accounting, nursing, and psychology have the largest enrollments.

Required: In order to graduate, students must have a total of 124 credit hours with a minimum GPA of 2.0. All students must complete a total of 56 hours in the general education requirement, pass all parts of the college-level Academic Skills Test (CLAST), and pass at specified level 9 senior exit examinations that may include a standardized exam and/or senior area comprehensive exam. They must also complete a senior seminar and senior research paper.

Special: Students may take courses at other institutions with the approval of the area advisor or registrar. B-CC offers cooperative courses in all divisions, internships related to the student's major, work-study programs, a 3–2 engineering degree with the University of Florida, Tuskegee, Florida Agriculture and Mechanical, Florida State, and Florida Atlantic universities, and nondegree study. Study-abroad programs are available in Spain, France, and Germany. There is a freshman honors program on campus, as well as 6 national honor societies, including Phi Beta Kappa. Two departments have honors programs.

Faculty/Classroom: Fifty-eight percent of faculty are male; 42%, female. Ninety-five percent teach undergraduates and 5% do research. The average class size in an introductory lecture is 20; in a laboratory, 20; and in a regular course offering, 18.

Admissions: About 70% of the 1993–94 applicants were accepted. The SAT scores for the 1993–94 freshman class were as follows: Verbal—98% below 500 and 2% between 500 and 599; Math—93% below 500 and 7% between 500 and 599. The ACT scores were 92% below 21, 5% between 21 and 23, 2% between 24 and 26, and 1% between 27 and 28. About 25% of the current freshmen were in the top fifth of their class; 60% were in the top two fifths.

Requirements: A minimum GPA of 2.0 is required. The SAT I or the ACT is recommended. Graduation from an accredited secondary school or satisfactory scores on the GED are required for admission. High school courses must include 4 credits of English, 3 credits each of mathematics and science, 2 credits of history, 1 credit of social studies, 1/2 credit each of art, management skills, and physical education, and 9 credits of electives. Students must submit an essay. AP and CLEP credits are accepted. Important factors used in the admissions decision are ability to finance college education, advanced placement or honor courses, personality, intangible qualities, leadership record, and recommendations by school officials.

Procedure: Freshmen are admitted to all sessions. Entrance exams should be taken during the fall prior to application. Applications should be filed by July 30 for fall entry and November 30 for spring entry, along with an application fee of $25. Notification is sent on a rolling basis. There is a deferred admissions plan.

Transfer: About 32 transfer students enrolled in 1993–94. Transfer students must submit transcripts from previous institutions attended and a statement of good standing and eligibility to return. A minimum GPA of 2.0 is required. Applicants having fewer than 12 credit hours must meet the requirements for entering freshmen. A total of 30 credits out of 124 must be completed at B-CC.

Visiting: There are guides for informal visits and visitors may sit in on classes. To arrange for a visit, contact the Public Relations Office at (904) 255–1401, ext. 435/467.

Financial Aid: In 1993–94 97% of all current freshmen and 91% of continuing students received some form of financial aid. About 83% of freshmen and 83% of continuing students received need-based aid. The average freshman award was $5820. Of that total, scholarships or need-based grants averaged $2450 ($8760 maximum); loans averaged $2670 ($8560 maximum); and work contracts averaged $700 ($1620 maximum). Seventy-eight percent of undergraduate students work part-time. Average earnings from campus work for the school year are $1400. The average financial indebtedness of 1992–93 graduate was $11,600. B-CC is a member of CSS. The FAF, FFS or SFS is required. The deadline for financial aid applications is March 1.

International Students: There are currently 67 international students enrolled. The school actively recruits these students. They must take the TOEFL and achieve a minimum score of 500.

Computers: The college provides computer facilities for student use. The mainframe is a DEC VAX 11/750. Each academic building is equipped with computer facilities. More than 150 computer keyboards are available for student use. All students may access the system. There are no time limits on using the system. The fees are $20.

Graduates: In 1992–93 287 bachelor's degrees were awarded. The most popular majors among graduates were criminal justice (15%), business administration (15%), and elementary education (11%). Within an average freshman class, 3% graduate in 3 years, 15% in 4 years, 16% in 5 years, and 4% in 6 years. Some 141 companies recruited on campus in 1992–93. In the 1992 graduating class, 10% of the men and 13% of the women were enrolled in graduate school within 6 months of graduation; 22% of the men and 46% of the women had found employment.

Admissions Contact: Roberto Barragan, Director of Admissions.

CLEARWATER CHRISTIAN COLLEGE D-4
Clearwater, FL 34619–9997

(813) 726–1153, ext. 228
(800) 348–4463 (out-of-state)

Full-time: 185 men, 213 women
Part-time: 24 men, 19 women
Graduate: none
Year: semesters, summer session
Application Deadline: open
Freshman Class: 180 applied, 172 accepted, 154 enrolled
SAT I Verbal/Math: 433/442

Faculty: 35
Ph.D.s: n/av
Student/Faculty: 11 to 1
Tuition: $5300
Room & Board: $3200

ACT: 22   LESS COMPETITIVE

Clearwater Christian College is a private, fundamentalist, nonsectarian institution offering programs in Bible, liberal arts, business, and teacher preparation. The library contains 100,000 volumes, and subscribes to 500 periodicals. Special learning facilities include a learning resource center and a science museum. The 50-acre campus is in a small town 10 miles west of Tampa. Including residence halls, there are 7 buildings on campus.

Student Life: About 68% of undergraduates are from Florida. Ninety-four percent are white and most are Protestant. The average age of all undergraduates is 22.4.

Housing: A total of 220 students can be accommodated in college housing. College-sponsored living facilities include single-sex dormitories. On-campus housing is guaranteed for all 4 years. All students may keep cars on campus.

Activities: There are some groups and organizations on campus, including choir, drama, student government, and yearbook. Popular campus events include the Central Florida Youth Rally.

Sports: Athletic and recreation facilities include a gymnasium and a playing field.

Disabled Students: The following facilities are available: wheelchair ramps, special parking, lowered drinking fountains. The campus has limited access to physically handicapped students.

Services: Remedial math, reading, and writing are available.

Programs of Study: CCC awards the B.A., B.S. and associate degrees. Bachelor's degrees are awarded in BIOLOGICAL SCIENCE (biology/biological science), BUSINESS (business administration and management), COMMUNICATIONS AND THE ARTS (English), COMPUTER AND PHYSICAL SCIENCE (mathematics), EDUCATION (elementary, music, and secondary), SOCIAL SCIENCE (biblical studies, humanities, pastoral studies, psychology, and religious music).

Required: General education requirements include 12 hours of arts and communication, 24 of human adjustment, 10 of science and mathematics, and 9 each of social science and humanities. A total of 128 credit hours is required, as is a minimum GPA of 2.0. Students must have no grade lower than a C- in any major requirement, pass the College Level Academic Skills Test, complete the Graduate Record Exam, and maintain satisfactory Christian service involvement throughout the college career.

Special: On occasion, credit from an approved correspondence school may be accepted, or registration at another school for a course to complete degree requirements at CCC may be permitted. Work-study programs and nondegree study are possible.

Faculty/Classroom: Seventy-two percent of faculty are male; 28%, female.

Admissions: About 96% of the 1993–94 applicants were accepted.

Requirements: A minimum GPA of 2.0 is required. Applicants must take the SAT I or ACT for placement purposes. Applicants must have a high school diploma; a GED is accepted. AP and CLEP credits are accepted.

Procedure: Freshmen are admitted for fall and spring. Application deadlines are open and the fee is $25. Notification is sent on a rolling basis. There is a deferred admissions plan.

Transfer: Transfer applicants must submit transcripts from all post-secondary schools attended. Grades of C or better transfer. A total of 30 credits out of 128 must be completed at CCC.

Visiting: There are regularly scheduled orientations for prospective students. There are guides for informal visits and visitors may sit in on classes and stay overnight at the school. To arrange for a visit, contact the Admissions Office at (813) 726–1153.

Financial Aid: The FAF or FFS and FAFSA are required. The FFS is preferred. The deadline for financial aid applications is April 15.

International Students: They must take the TOEFL.

Computers: CCC provides Apple II and TRS 2000 microcomputers for academic use in the computer laboratory. All students may access the system.

Admissions Contact: Benjamin J. Puckett, Director of Admissions.

ECKERD COLLEGE D-4
St. Petersburg, FL 33711

(813) 864–8331
(800) 456–9009 (out-of-state)

Full-time: 677 men, 715 women
Part-time: 11 men, 15 women
Graduate: none
Year: 4–1–4, summer session
Application Deadline: open
Freshman Class: 1422 applied, 1109 accepted, 366 enrolled
SAT I Verbal/Math: 517/559

Faculty: 87; IIB, av$
Ph.D.s: 95%
Student/Faculty: 16 to 1
Tuition: $14,930
Room & Board: $3925

ACT: 25   VERY COMPETITIVE

Eckerd College, founded in 1958, is a private liberal arts institution affiliated with the Presbyterian Church, USA. Interdisciplinary programs are an important part of the school's curriculum. This is reflected in the organization of the faculty into 'collegia,' rather than into traditional departments. The library contains 110,000 volumes, 13,000 microform items, and 2000 audiovisual forms, and subscribes to 1000 periodicals. Computerized library sources and services include the card catalog, interlibrary loans, and database searching. Special learning facilities include an art gallery, radio station, TV station, and a sea mammal necropsy laboratory. The 267-acre campus is in a suburban area 5 miles south of St. Petersburg. Including residence halls, there are 66 buildings on campus.

Student Life: About 70% of undergraduates are from out-of-state, mostly the Middle Atlantic. Students come from 49 states, 60 foreign countries, and Canada. Seventy-five percent are from public schools; 25% from private. Ninety-one percent are white; 10% foreign nationals. Forty-five percent are Protestant; 30% Catholic; 15% claim no religious affiliation. The average age of freshmen is 18; all undergraduates, 21. Five percent drop out by the end of their first year; 70% remain to graduate.

Housing: A total of 1070 students can be accommodated in college housing. College-sponsored living facilities include single-sex and coed dormitories. In addition there are language houses. On-campus housing is guaranteed for all 4 years. Seventy-seven percent of students live on campus; of those, 95% remain on campus on weekends. All students may keep cars on campus.

Activities: There are no fraternities or sororities on campus. There are 50 groups on campus, including cheerleading, chess, choir, chorale, chorus, computers, drama, ethnic, film, gay, honors, international, literary magazine, musical theater, newspaper, photography, political, professional, radio and TV, religious, social, social service, student government, water search and rescue, and yearbook. Popular campus events include the Festival of Cultures, Kon-Tiki, and the Festival of Hope.

Sports: There are 9 intercollegiate sports for men and 8 for women, and 12 intramural sports for men and 12 for women. Athletic and recreation facilities include a gymnasium, baseball, softball, and soccer fields, tennis courts, a weight room, a swimming pool, and waterfront facilities.

Disabled Students: Ninety percent of the campus is accessible to disabled students. The following facilities are available: wheelchair ramps, elevators, special parking, specially equipped rest rooms, special class scheduling, and lowered drinking fountains.

Services: In addition to many counseling and information services, tutoring is available in some subjects, including mathematics, sciences, and foreign languages.

Campus Safety and Security: Campus safety and security measures include 24-hour foot and vehicle patrol, escort service, informal discussions, and pamphlets, posters, and films. In addition, there are

lighted pathways and sidewalks and a security gate at the entrance to the campus.

Programs of Study: Eckerd awards the B.A. and B.S. degrees. Bachelor's degrees are awarded in BIOLOGICAL SCIENCE (biology/biological science and marine science), BUSINESS (international business management and management science), COMMUNICATIONS AND THE ARTS (comparative literature, creative writing, dramatic arts, English, French, German, music, Russian, Spanish, and visual and performing arts), COMPUTER AND PHYSICAL SCIENCE (chemistry, computer science, mathematics, and physics), EDUCATION (elementary), ENGINEERING AND ENVIRONMENTAL DESIGN (environmental science), HEALTH PROFESSIONS (predentistry and premedicine), SOCIAL SCIENCE (American studies, anthropology, economics, history, human development, humanities, international relations, philosophy, political science/government, prelaw, psychology, religion, sociology, and women's studies). Biology, chemistry, creative writing, economics, psychology, and marine science are the strongest academically. Management, biology, psychology, and marine science have the largest enrollments.

Required: In order to graduate, students must complete a total of 126 semester hours (36 courses) with a minimum GPA of 2.0. Thirty-five semester hours are required in the major, and a writing portfolio must be submitted before the end of the sophomore year. All students must fulfill core requirements in Western civilization, aesthetics, cross cultural and environmental studies, and social relations. In addition, courses in mathematics, foreign languages, and the Judeo-Christian perspective on contemporary issues are required. All students must take a senior seminar.

Special: Eckerd offers internships in management, human development, and education. Work-study programs, dual majors in all subjects, interdisciplinary majors in comparative education studies and environmental studies, student-designed majors, nondegree study, and pass/fail options are also available. Study-abroad programs are available in a number of countries. Students may earn B.A.-B.S. degrees in biology, chemistry, and marine science. A 3–2 engineering degree is offered with 4 other universities. The program for Experienced Learners, for students 25 and older, offers independent study, weekend courses, and credit for experiential learning. There is a freshman honors program on campus, as well as 6 national honor societies. Thirty departments have honors programs.

Faculty/Classroom: Sixty-nine percent of faculty are male; 31%, female. All both teach and do research. The average class size in an introductory lecture is 35; in a laboratory, 15; and in a regular course offering, 20.

Admissions: About 78% of the 1993–94 applicants were accepted. The SAT scores for the 1993–94 freshman class were as follows: Verbal—43% below 500, 41% between 500 and 599, 15% between 600 and 700, and 1% above 700; Math—22% below 500, 47% between 500 and 599, 26% between 600 and 700, and 5% above 700. The ACT scores were 8% below 21, 28% between 21 and 23, 25% between 24 and 26, 19% between 27 and 28, and 20% above 28. About 58% of the current freshmen were in the top fifth of their class; 82% were in the top two fifths. There were 15 National Merit finalists and 9 semifinalists. About 15 freshmen graduated first in their class.

Requirements: The SAT I or ACT is required. Graduation from an accredited secondary school or satisfactory scores on the GED are required for admission. High school courses must include 4 years of English, 3 years each of mathematics and science, 2 years each of a foreign language and history, and 1 year of social studies. SAT II: Subject tests in writing and mathematics level II are recommended. An essay is required and an interview is recommended. AP and CLEP credits are accepted. Important factors used in the admissions decision are advanced placement or honor courses, leadership record, personality, intangible qualities, evidence of special talent, and extracurricular activities record.

Procedure: Freshmen are admitted fall, winter, and spring. Entrance exams should be taken in October, November, or December. Application deadlines are open. Notification is sent on a rolling basis after October 15. There are early admissions and deferred admissions plans. The application fee is $25. A waiting list is an active part of the admissions procedure, with about 5% of applicants on the list.

Transfer: About 76 transfer students enrolled in 1993–94. Transfer students must have a minimum GPA of 2.5. The SAT I or ACT is required. An interview is recommended. A faculty recommendation is also required. A total of 63 credits out of 126 must be completed at Eckerd.

Visiting: There are regularly scheduled orientations for prospective students, consisting of an interview and a tour. There are guides for informal visits and visitors may sit in on classes and stay overnight at the school. To arrange for a visit, contact the Admissions Office at (813) 864–8331 or (800) 456–9009.

Financial Aid: In 1993–94 82% of all students received some form of financial aid. About 72% of all students received need-based aid. The average freshman award was $12,800. Of that total, scholarships or need-based grants averaged $9000 ($16,800 maximum); loans averaged $2700 ($3625 maximum); and work contracts averaged $1100 ($1500 maximum). Eighty-five percent of undergraduate students work part-time. Average earnings from campus work for the school year are $1100. The average financial indebtedness of the 1992–93 graduate was $9500. Eckerd is a member of CSS. The FAFSA financial statement is required. The deadline for financial aid applications is March 15.

International Students: There are currently 146 international students enrolled. The school actively recruits these students. They must take the TOEFL and achieve a minimum score of 550.

Computers: The college provides computer facilities for student use. The mainframe is a Sun Sparkserver 10. There are 30 microcomputers in a Novell network in the computer laboratory and 20 microcomputers in the science laboratories through which students may access the mainframe. Students with their own personal computers may access the mainframe through modems from their dormitory rooms. All students may access the system. It may be used at any time. There are no time limits and no fees.

Graduates: In 1992–93 291 bachelor's degrees were awarded. The most popular majors among graduates were management (11%), international business (10%), and psychology (8%). Within an average freshman class, 3% graduate in 3 years, 60% in 4 years, 62% in 5 years, and 63% in 6 years. Some 150 companies recruited on campus in 1992–93. In the 1992 graduating class, 44% of the men and 41% of the women were enrolled in graduate school within 6 months of graduation; 56% of the men and 59% of the women had found employment.

Admissions Contact: Richard Hallin, Dean of Admissions.

EDWARD WATERS COLLEGE D-1
Jacksonville, FL 32209 (904) 366-2506

Full-time, part-time: 850 men and women	Faculty: n/av
	Ph.D.s: n/av
Graduate: none	Student/Faculty: n/av
Year: semesters, summer session	Tuition: $4000
Application Deadline: August 1	Room & Board: $4300
Freshman Class: n/av	
SAT I or ACT: recommended	NONCOMPETITIVE

Edward Waters College, founded in 1866, is the oldest independent institution of higher learning in Florida. Affiliated with the African Methodist Episcopal Church, the college offers undergraduate programs in the arts and sciences, business, and education. The library contains 132,000 volumes and 25,000 microform items, and subscribes to 231 periodicals. Special learning facilities include a radio station and an African American collection. The 21-acre campus is in an urban area in Jacksonville. Including residence halls, there are 9 buildings on campus.

Student Life: About 95% of undergraduates are from Florida.

Housing: A total of 200 students can be accommodated in college housing. College-sponsored living facilities include single-sex and coed dormitories. Alcohol is not permitted. All students may keep cars on campus.

Activities: There are 4 national fraternities and 4 national sororities. There are 20 groups on campus, including cheerleading, choir, honors, international, newspaper, pep band, professional, religious, and yearbook. Popular campus events include Fall and Spring Convocations, Religious Emphasis Week, Senior Breakfast, and African American History Celebration.

Sports: There are 5 intercollegiate sports for men and 5 for women, and 6 intramural sports for men and 6 for women.

Disabled Students: The following facilities are available: elevators and specially equipped rest rooms.

Services: In addition to many counseling and information services, tutoring is available in every subject. In addition, there is remedial math, reading, and writing. There is a student support services program for students who have potential but have an academically disadvantaged background.

Programs of Study: EWC awards the B.A., B.S., and B.B.A. degrees. Bachelor's degrees are awarded in BIOLOGICAL SCIENCE (biology/biological science), BUSINESS (accounting, business administration and management, and organizational behavior), COMMUNICATIONS AND THE ARTS (communications and English), COMPUTER AND PHYSICAL SCIENCE (chemistry, computer science, mathematics, and physics), EDUCATION (early childhood, elementary, and health), ENGINEERING AND ENVIRONMENTAL DESIGN (architecture and electrical/electronics engineering), SOCIAL SCIENCE (criminal justice, history, philosophy, political science/government, psychology, public administration, religion, social work, and sociology).

Required: In order to graduate, all students must complete at least 120 credit hours and a 30-credit major, with a minimum 2.0 GPA. Weekly chapel service attendance is required.

Special: Co-op programs and internships are available in some fields, and an engineering program is available in cooperation with the University of Miami. Dual and student-designed majors, and work-study are also available. There is a freshman honors program on campus.

Requirements: Applicants must be graduates of an accredited secondary school or have a GED certificate, and have taken the California Achievement Test. Advanced placement or honors courses, the ability to finance a college education, and recommendations are considered important. SAT I or ACT scores are necessary for unconditional admission. AP and CLEP credits are accepted.

Procedure: Freshmen are admitted fall and spring. Applications should be filed by August 1 for fall entry and December 30 for spring entry, along with an application fee of $15. The college accepts all applicants. Notification is sent on a rolling basis.

Transfer: At least 36 credits out of 120 must be completed at EWC.

Financial Aid: Fifteen percent of undergraduate students work part-time. EWC is a member of CSS. The FAF or FFS financial statement is required. The deadline for financial aid applications is April 1.

Computers: The college provides computer facilities for student use. There are computer laboratories in one academic building and in the library. There are no time limits on using the system and no fees.

Admissions Contact: Director of Admissions.

EMBRY-RIDDLE AERONAUTICAL UNIVERSITY

	D-2
Daytona Beach, FL 32114	(904) 226-6100
	(800) 222-ERAU (out-of-state)
Full-time: 3102 men, 401 women	**Faculty:** 218; IIA, --$
Part-time: 599 men, 76 women	**Ph.D.s:** 94%
Graduate: 152 men, 27 women	**Student/Faculty:** 16 to 1
Year: semesters, summer session	**Tuition:** $7370
Application Deadline: July 21	**Room & Board:** $3230
Freshman Class: 3042 applied, 2468 accepted, 1065 enrolled	
SAT I Verbal/Math: 450/530	**ACT:** 23 **COMPETITIVE**

Embry-Riddle Aeronautical University, founded in 1926, is a private institution offering undergraduate programs in aviation, engineering, and business on two campuses: one in Daytona Beach and the other, founded in 1978, in Prescott, Arizona. There are 2 undergraduate schools and one graduate school. In addition to regional accreditation, ERAU has baccalaureate program accreditation with ABET. The library contains 53,352 volumes, 159,484 microform items, and 2455 audiovisual forms, and subscribes to 1261 periodicals. Computerized library sources and services include the card catalog, interlibrary loans, and database searching. Special learning facilities include a learning resource center, radio station, and airway science simulation laboratory. The 113-acre campus is in an urban area 48 miles northeast of Orlando. Including residence halls, there are 36 buildings on campus.

Student Life: About 77% of undergraduates are from out-of-state, mostly the South. Students come from 52 states, 112 foreign countries, and Canada. Eighty percent are from public schools; 20% from private. Seventy-eight percent are white. The average age of freshmen is 18.2; all undergraduates, 22.

Housing: A total of 981 students can be accommodated in college housing. College-sponsored living facilities include coed dormitories and off-campus apartments. On-campus housing is available on a first-come, first-served basis. Seventy-seven percent of students commute. All students may keep cars on campus.

Activities: About 5% of men belong to 7 national fraternities; about 2% of women belong to 2 national sororities. There are 74 groups on campus, including cheerleading, chess, computers, dance, drama, drill team, ethnic, gay, honors, international, literary magazine, newspaper, pep band, photography, political, professional, radio, religious, social, social service, student government, and yearbook. Popular campus events include Homecoming, International Day, Skyfest, Movie Night, Attitude Adjustment, and Activities Fair.

Sports: There are 5 intercollegiate sports for men, and 20 intramural sports for men and 1 for women. Athletic and recreation facilities include softball and soccer fields, a swimming pool, a nautilus and weight room, courts for racquetball, tennis, and basketball, and a fitness trail.

Disabled Students: The following facilities are available: wheelchair ramps, elevators, special parking, specially equipped rest rooms, and lowered drinking fountains.

Services: In addition to many counseling and information services, tutoring is available in most subjects. In addition, there is remedial math, reading, and writing.

Campus Safety and Security: Campus safety and security measures include 24-hour foot and vehicle patrol, self defense education, escort service, and informal discussions. In addition, there are pamphlets, posters, and films, emergency telephones, lighted pathways and sidewalks, and 'Call A Ride And Live' (CARAL).

Programs of Study: ERAU awards the B.S. degree. Associate and master's degrees also are awarded. Bachelor's degrees are awarded in BUSINESS (business administration and management and transportation management), COMPUTER AND PHYSICAL SCIENCE (computer science and information sciences and systems), ENGINEERING AND ENVIRONMENTAL DESIGN (aeronautical engineering, aeronautical science, aeronautical technology, aerospace studies, electrical/electronics engineering, engineering physics, and engineering technology). Engineering is the strongest academically. Aeronautical science(flight) has the largest enrollment.

Required: In order to graduate, students must complete a total of 126 to 136 credit hours, including 60 in the major, with a minimum GPA of 2.0. All students must complete 36 credits of general education requirements, including courses in communication skills, technical report writing, humanities/social sciences, mathematics, physical science, economics, and computer science.

Special: ERAU offers co-op programs, internships, study abroad, work-study programs, credit for life experience, and nondegree study. There are 5 national honor societies on campus.

Faculty/Classroom: Ninety-two percent of faculty are male; 8%, female. All teach undergraduates and 8% also do research. Graduate students teach 2% of introductory courses. The average class size in a regular course offering is 18.

Admissions: The SAT I or ACT is required. About 81% of the 1993–94 applicants were accepted. The SAT scores for the 1993–94 freshman class were as follows: Verbal—72% below 500, 25% between 500 and 599, and 3% between 600 and 700; Math—33% below 500, 42% between 500 and 599, 23% between 600 and 700, and 2% above 700. The ACT scores were 27% below 21, 26% between 21 and 23, 27% between 24 and 26, 10% between 27 and 28, and 9% above 28. About 31% of the current freshmen were in the top fifth of their class; 59% were in the top two fifths. Four freshmen graduated first in their class.

Requirements: ERAU requires applicants to be in the upper 75% of their class. A minimum GPA of 2.0 is required. The SAT I or ACT is required. AP and CLEP credits are accepted. Important factors used in the admissions decision are recommendations by school officials, recommendations by alumni, personality, intangible qualities, parents or siblings attending the school, and leadership record.

Procedure: Freshmen are admitted to all sessions. Entrance exams should be taken during the spring of the junior year. Applications should be filed by July 21 for fall entry, along with an application fee of $30. Notification is sent on a rolling basis.

Transfer: About 300 transfer students enrolled in 1993–94. Applicants must have a minimum GPA of 2.0 in at least 12 credit hours. A total of 30 credits out of 126 must be completed at ERAU.

Visiting: There are regularly scheduled orientations for prospective students. There are guides for informal visits and visitors may sit in on classes. To arrange for a visit, contact the Admissions Office at (904) 226–6120 or (800) 222-ERAU.

Financial Aid: In 1993–94, 75% of all students received some form of financial aid. About 70% received need-based aid. The average freshman award was $9600. Of that total, scholarships or need-based grants averaged $1200 ($3600 maximum); loans averaged $8600 ($10,600 maximum); and work contracts averaged $2500 (maximum). Seventy-five percent of undergraduate students work part-time. Average earnings from campus work for the school year are $3200. The average financial indebtedness of the 1992–93 graduate was $15,000. ERAU is a member of CSS. The FAF, FFS or SFS is required. The deadline for financial aid applications is April 15.

International Students: There are currently 496 international students enrolled. The school actively recruits these students. They must take the TOEFL and achieve a minimum score of 500.

Computers: The college provides computer facilities for student use. The mainframe is an IBM 4361. The computer laboratory houses approximately 100 IBM microcomputers for student use. In addition, there are 6 IBM ATs and 20 terminals that are connected to the IBM 4361 mainframe. The Aerospace Engineering Department has a number of HP 2641 computers and a Prime 750 for use in the engineering program. There are also 27 Sun workstations available. All students may access the system. It may be used at any time. There are no time limits on using the system and no fees.

Graduates: In 1992–93 860 bachelor's degrees were awarded. The most popular majors among graduates were aeronautical science (24%), aviation business administration (10%), and aviation maintenance technology (10%). Some 39 companies recruited on campus in 1992–93.

Admissions Contact: Darryl Niemeyer, Director of Admissions.

FLAGLER COLLEGE
St. Augustine, FL 32085-1027

D-2

(904) 829-6481

Full-time: 545 men, 800 women	Faculty: 50
Part-time: 20 men, 24 women	Ph.Ds: 54%
Graduate: none	Student/Faculty: 27 to 1
Year: semesters, summer session	Tuition: $4920
Application Deadline: March 15	Room & Board: $3070
Freshman Class: 1415 applied, 714 accepted, 338 enrolled	
SAT I Verbal/Math: 470/510	ACT: 22 COMPETITIVE +

Flagler College, founded in 1968, is an independent coeducational, liberal arts college. The library contains 126,685 volumes, 30,780 microform items, and 1900 audiovisual forms, and subscribes to 525 periodicals. Special learning facilities include an art gallery, radio station, and TV station. The 35-acre campus is in a small town 35 miles south of Jacksonville. Including residence halls, there are 12 buildings on campus.

Student Life: About 56% of undergraduates are from Florida. Students come from 43 states, 20 foreign countries, and Canada. Some 75% are from public schools; 25% from private. About 88% are white. Some 55% are Protestant; 31% Catholic. The average age of freshmen is 18; all undergraduates, 20.5. Approximately 21% drop out by the end of their first year; 56% remain to graduate.

Housing: A total of 675 students can be accommodated in college housing. College-sponsored living facilities include single-sex dormitories. On-campus housing is guaranteed for the freshman year only and is available on a first-come, first-served basis. Some 60% of students live on campus; of those, 85% remain on campus on weekends. Alcohol is not permitted. All students may keep cars on campus.

Activities: There are no fraternities or sororities. There are 23 groups on campus, including art, cheerleading, choir, chorus, dance, drama, film, honors, international, literary magazine, newspaper, photography, professional, radio and TV, social service, student government, and yearbook. Popular campus events include Flagler Forum, Fall Weekend, Spring Weekend, Parents Weekend, Luau Weekend, and Flagler Follies.

Sports: There are 6 intercollegiate sports for men and 4 for women, and 6 intramural sports for men and 6 for women. Athletic and recreation facilities include a 17-acre complex for baseball, soccer, and softball, 10 tennis courts, a swimming pool, and a multipurpose gymnasium.

Disabled Students: About 80% of the campus is accessible to disabled students. The following facilities are available: wheelchair ramps, elevators, special parking, specially equipped rest rooms, lowered drinking fountains, lowered telephones, and specially equipped residence hall rooms.

Campus Safety and Security: Campus safety and security measures include 24-hour foot and vehicle patrol, informal discussions, pamphlets, posters, and films, and emergency telephones. In addition, there are lighted pathways and sidewalks.

Programs of Study: Flagler awards the B.A. degree. Bachelor's degrees are awarded in BUSINESS (accounting, business administration and management, and marketing/retailing/merchandising), COMMUNICATIONS AND THE ARTS (art, communications, dramatic arts, English, fine arts, languages, and Spanish), EDUCATION (art, education of the deaf and hearing impaired, elementary, middle school, physical, secondary, and special), SOCIAL SCIENCE (history, Latin American studies, philosophy, prelaw, psychology, religion, and social science). Business, education, and Latin American studies are the strongest programs academically. Business, education, communications, and psychology have the largest enrollments.

Required: In order to graduate, students must complete a minimum of 120 semester hours, including 30 to 90 hours in the major, with a minimum GPA of 2.0. All students must take 6 hours in English composition and in mathematics. In addition, students must take courses required by the General Education Program in humanities, social sciences, and mathematics/natural sciences.

Special: The school offers internships, student-designed majors, dual majors, and a Washington semester. Students may participate in study-abroad programs in almost any country. Students majoring in deaf education can work directly with students at the Florida State School for the Deaf. Students in the fashion buying, merchandising or design program participate in the visiting student program at the Fashion Institute of Technology in New York City. There is 1 national honor society on campus, and 1 department has an honors program.

Faculty/Classroom: Some 54% of faculty are male; 46%, female. All teach undergraduates. The average class size in an introductory lecture is 30; in a laboratory, 12; and in a regular course offering, 23.

Admissions: About 50% of the 1993-94 applicants were accepted. The SAT scores for the 1993-94 freshman class were as follows: Verbal—66% below 500, 29% between 500 and 599, 4% between 600 and 700, and 1% above 700; Math—43% below 500, 42% between 500 and 599, 13% between 600 and 700, and 2% above 700. The ACT scores were 31% below 21, 36% between 21 and 23, 22% between 24 and 26, 5% between 27 and 28, and 6% above 28. About 47% of the current freshmen were in the top fifth of their class; 77% were in the top two fifths. About 4 freshmen graduated first in their class.

Requirements: A minimum GPA of 2.0 is required. The SAT I or ACT is required. Graduation from an accredited secondary school or a satisfactory score on the GED is required for admission. Students must have a total of 19 academic credits. High school courses must include 4 credits of English, 2 credits of a foreign language, and 3 credits each of mathematics and science. An essay is required and an interview is recommended. AP and CLEP credits are accepted. Important factors used in the admissions decision are advanced placement or honor courses, leadership record, extracurricular activities record, geographic diversity, and recommendations by school officials.

Procedure: Freshmen are admitted in the fall and spring. Entrance exams should be taken during the fall of the senior year at the latest. Applications should be filed by March 15 for fall entry and November 30 for winter entry, along with an application fee of $20. Notification is sent January 1. There is a deferred admissions plan. A waiting list is an active part of the admissions procedure, with about 4% of applicants on the list.

Transfer: About 117 transfer students enrolled in 1993-94. Transfer students must have a minimum of 24 semester hours with a minimum GPA of 2.5. Transfers must also score at least 900 on the SAT I or 21 on the ACT. A total of 30 credits out of 120 must be completed at Flagler.

Visiting: There are guides for informal visits and visitors may sit in on classes and stay overnight at the school. To arrange for a visit, contact the Office of Admissions at (904) 829-6481.

Financial Aid: In 1993-94, 75% of all current freshmen and 82% of continuing students received some form of financial aid. About 45% of freshmen and 48% of continuing students received need-based aid. The average freshman award was $5300. Of that total, scholarships or need-based grants averaged $2400 ($7990 maximum); loans averaged $2100 ($2625 maximum); and work contracts averaged $800 ($1000 maximum). Some 63% of undergraduate students work part-time. Average earnings from campus work for the school year are $800. The average financial indebtedness of the 1992-93 graduate was $8500. Flagler is a member of CSS. The FAF, FFS or SFS and the college's own financial statement is required. The deadline for financial aid applications is April 1.

International Students: There are currently 38 international students enrolled. They must take the TOEFL and achieve a minimum score of 550.

Computers: The mainframe is a DEC PDP 11/34A. Those students enrolled in computer courses may access the system.

Graduates: In 1992-93, 304 bachelor's degrees were awarded. The most popular majors among graduates were business (29%), education (24%), and psychology/social sciences (10%). Within an average freshman class, 39% graduate in 4 years, 56% in 5 years, and 57% in 6 years. About 2 companies recruited on campus in 1992-93.

Admissions Contact: Marc G. Williar, Director of Admissions.

FLORIDA AGRICULTURAL AND MECHANICAL UNIVERSITY
Tallahassee, FL 32307

C-1

(904) 599-3796

Full-time: 3284 men, 4569 women	Faculty: 610; IIA, --$
Part-time: 450 men, 535 women	Ph.Ds: 51%
Graduate: 482 men, 298 women	Student/Faculty: 13 to 1
Year: semesters, summer session	Tuition: $1829 ($6731)
Application Deadline: June 1	Room & Board: $2822
Freshman Class: 4893 applied, 2948 accepted, 1395 enrolled	
SAT I: 439/489	ACT: 20 COMPETITIVE

Florida Agricultural and Mechanical University, founded in 1887, a public, coeducational institution within the State University system of Florida, offers undergraduate programs in agriculture, allied health science, architecture, the arts and sciences, business and industry, education, engineering, journalism, pharmacy and pharmaceutical sciences, upper-level nursing, and technology. There are 11 undergraduate schools and one graduate school. In addition to regional accreditation, Florida A & M has baccalaureate program accreditation with AACSB, ABET, ACEJMC, ACPE, APTA, CSWE, NAAB, NCATE, and NLN. The 8 libraries contain 485,985 volumes, 82,000 microform items, and 62,610 audiovisual forms, and subscribe to 3639 periodicals. Computerized library sources and services include the card catalog and database searching. Special learning facilities include a learning resource center, art gallery, radio station, black archives, and an observatory. The 419-acre campus is in an urban area 169 miles east of Jacksonville. Including residence halls, there are 111 buildings on campus.

Student Life: About 70% of undergraduates are from Florida. Students come from 45 states, 49 foreign countries, and Canada. Eighty-nine percent are African American. The average age of freshmen is 18; all undergraduates, 22. Twenty percent drop out by the end of their first year; 30% remain to graduate.

Housing: A total of 2500 students can be accommodated in college housing. College-sponsored living facilities include single-sex dormitories, on-campus apartments, and married-student housing. On-campus housing is guaranteed for the freshman year only and is available on a first-come, first-served basis. Priority is given to out-of-town students. Fifty-one percent of students commute. Alcohol is not permitted. All students may keep cars on campus.

Activities: There are 4 national fraternities and 4 national sororities. There are 126 groups on campus, including cheerleading, choir, chorus, dance, drama, drill team, ethnic, honors, international, jazz band, marching band, newspaper, orchestra, pep band, political, professional, radio and TV, religious, social, social service, student government, symphony, and yearbook. Popular campus events include Homecoming, FAMU Essen-Theater, FAMU Orchesis Dance Theater, Ebony Fashion Fair, and Harambee Arts Festival.

Sports: There are 9 intercollegiate sports for men and 8 for women, and 7 intramural sports for men and 5 for women. Athletic and recreation facilities include a 3300-seat gymnasium, a 1600-seat auditorium, a 25,559-seat football stadium, swimming pools, baseball diamonds, softball and track fields, tennis courts, a bowling alley, a pool hall, a student activities center, and a fitness center.

Disabled Students: Eighty percent of the campus is accessible to disabled students. The following facilities are available: wheelchair ramps, elevators, special parking, and specially equipped rest rooms.

Services: In addition to many counseling and information services, tutoring is available in some subjects, including mathematics, English, and reading. In addition, there is remedial math, reading, and writing.

Campus Safety and Security: Campus safety and security measures include 24-hour foot and vehicle patrol, self defense education, escort service, and informal discussions. In addition, there are pamphlets, posters, films, and lighted pathways and sidewalks.

Programs of Study: Florida A & M awards the B.A., B.S., B.Arch., B.C.J., B.S.Arch. and Constr.E.T., B.S.Arch.Studies, B.S.Arch.E.T., B.S.Ch.E., B.S.C.E., B.S.C.E.T., B.S.Constr.E.T., B.S.E.E., B.S.Elect.E.T., B.S.H.C.M., B.S.I.E., B.S.J., B.S.M.E., B.S.M.R.A., B.S.N., B.S.Pharm., B.S.P.T., B.S.R.T., B.S.T., and B.S.W. degrees. Associate, master's, and doctoral degrees also are awarded. Bachelor's degrees are awarded in AGRICULTURE (animal science and horticulture), BIOLOGICAL SCIENCE (biology/biological science), BUSINESS (accounting, banking and finance, business administration and management, and business economics), COMMUNICATIONS AND THE ARTS (dramatic arts, English, fine arts, journalism, and music), COMPUTER AND PHYSICAL SCIENCE (actuarial science, chemistry, computer science, mathematics, and physics), EDUCATION (art, business, early childhood, elementary, industrial arts, music, and science), ENGINEERING AND ENVIRONMENTAL DESIGN (chemical engineering, civil engineering, electrical/electronics engineering, engineering technology, industrial engineering, and mechanical engineering), HEALTH PROFESSIONS (nursing, occupational therapy, pharmacy, physical therapy, predentistry, and premedicine), SOCIAL SCIENCE (criminal justice, economics, history, political science/government, psychology, public administration, social science, social work, and sociology). Business, engineering, pharmacy, and architecture are the strongest academically. Business, pharmacy, arts and sciences, and engineering have the largest enrollments.

Required: General education requirements include a total of 36 credit hours in English, humanities, social science, natural science, American history, foreign language, and mathematics at the college algebra level or above. In order to graduate, students must complete at least 120 credit hours, including 30 in a major field, with a minimum GPA of 2.0.

Special: Cooperative programs and cross-registration are offered in conjunction with Florida State University. Internships are available either on or off campus. Florida A & M also offers a Washington semester for architecture majors, a B.A.-B.S. degree, credit for life experience, and pass/fail options. Nondegree study is possible. There is a freshman honors program on campus, as well as 10 national honor societies.

Faculty/Classroom: Fifty-seven percent of faculty are male; 42%, female. No introductory courses are taught by graduate students. The average class size in an introductory lecture is 40; in a laboratory, 15; and in a regular course offering, 40.

Admissions: About 60% of the 1993–94 applicants were accepted. The SAT scores for the 1993–94 freshman class were as follows: Verbal—78% below 500, 17% between 500 and 599, and 5% between 600 and 700; Math—59% below 500, 29% between 500 and 599, 11% between 600 and 700, and 1% above 700. The ACT scores were 71% below 21, 20% between 21 and 23, 6% between 24 and 26, 2% between 27 and 28, and 1% above 28. There were 2 National Merit finalists.

Requirements: A minimum GPA of 2.5 is required. The SAT I with a minimum composite score of 900, or 450 on each part, or the ACT, with a minimum composite score of 19 is required. Applicants must be graduates of accredited secondary schools or have earned a GED. The university requires 19 academic credits, including 2 in foreign language, 4 each in English and academic electives, and 3 each in mathematics, science, and social studies. AP and CLEP credits are accepted. Important factors used in the admissions decision are recommendations by school officials, extracurricular activities record, evidence of special talent, leadership record, and recommendations by alumni.

Procedure: Entrance exams should be taken by the fall of the senior year. Applications should be filed by June 1 for fall entry, November 15 for spring entry, and April 1 for summer entry, along with an application fee of $20. Notification is sent on a rolling basis. There are early admissions and deferred admissions plans.

Transfer: About 472 transfer students enrolled in 1993–94. Applicants must present a minimum GPA of 2.0 in at least 60 semester hours or 90 quarter hours earned. A total of 30 credits out of 120 must be completed at Florida A & M.

Visiting: There are regularly scheduled orientations for prospective students. There are guides for informal visits and visitors may sit in on classes. To arrange for a visit, contact Rosell R. Caswell at (904) 599–3869.

Financial Aid: In an earlier year 74% of all current freshmen and 51% of continuing students received some form of financial aid. Scholarships or need-based grants averaged $750 ($3500 maximum); loans averaged $1000 ($2625 maximum); and work contracts averaged $1050 ($4000 maximum). The average financial indebtedness of the 1992–93 graduate was $3619. The university prefers to receive the FFS but will accept the FAF. The deadline for financial aid applications is April 1.

International Students: There are currently 101 international students enrolled. They must take the TOEFL and achieve a minimum score of 500. The student must also take the SAT I or the ACT.

Computers: The college provides computer facilities for student use. The mainframe is an IBM 4381 Model 13. The school provides more than 100 Apple, Apple Macintosh, and IBM computers for academic use. All students may access the system. There are no time limits on using the system and no fees.

Graduates: In 1992–93 1468 bachelor's degrees were awarded. The most popular majors among graduates were business (15%) and education (12%). Some 525 companies recruited on campus in 1992–93.

Admissions Contact: Barbara Cox, Admissions Officer.

FLORIDA ATLANTIC UNIVERSITY

E-5

Boca Raton, FL 33431

(407) 367-3040
(800) 299-4FAU (out-of-state)

Full-time: 2707 men, 3207 women	Faculty: 528; IIA, av$
Part-time: 2269 men, 3507 women	Ph.Ds: 78%
Graduate: 1779 men, 2231 women	Student/Faculty: 11 to 1
Year: semesters, summer session	Tuition: $1550 ($5350)
Application Deadline: May 1	Room & Board: $3975
Freshman Class: 2977 applied, 1980 accepted, 819 enrolled	
SAT I: 462/528	ACT: 22 COMPETITIVE

Florida Atlantic University, founded in 1961, is a publicly funded institution in the state university system of Florida. There are 9 undergraduate and 8 graduate schools. In addition to regional accreditation, FAU has baccalaureate program accreditation with AACSB, ABET, CSWE, NASM, NCATE, and NLN. The 4 libraries contain 802,141 volumes, 2,515,820 microform items, and 13,486 audiovisual forms, and subscribe to 4571 periodicals. Computerized library sources and services include the card catalog, interlibrary loans, and database searching. Special learning facilities include a learning resource center, art gallery, radio station, TV station, engineering research laboratories, a marine sciences research center, Henderson University School, a nonnative fish research laboratory, and an environmental sciences center. The 700-acre campus is in a suburban area 17 miles north of Ft. Lauderdale and 45 miles north of Miami. Including residence halls, there are 42 buildings on campus.

Student Life: About 93% of undergraduates are from Florida. Students come from 35 states, 80 foreign countries, and Canada. Seventy-six percent are white. The average age of freshmen is 19; all undergraduates, 26. Nine percent drop out by the end of their first year; 84% remain to graduate.

Housing: A total of 1500 students can be accommodated in college housing. College-sponsored living facilities include single-sex and coed dormitories and on-campus apartments. In addition there are wellness and quiet floors, and 2 coeducational halls. On-campus housing is available on a first-come, first-served basis. Ninety-two percent of students commute. All students may keep cars on campus.

Activities: About 1% of men and about 1% of women belong to 1 local and 4 national fraternities; about 1% of women belong to 1 local and 2 national sororities. There are 113 groups on campus, including art, band, cheerleading, chess, choir, chorale, chorus, computers, dance, drama, ethnic, film, honors, international, jazz band, literary magazine, newspaper, opera, orchestra, pep band, political, professional, radio and TV, religious, social, social service, student government, and yearbook. Popular campus events include Luau, Homecoming Week, Freakers Ball, African American Festival, Earth Day, and Winter Carnival.

Sports: There are 7 intercollegiate sports for men and 7 for women, and 5 intramural sports for men and 5 for women. Athletic and recreation facilities include a gymnasium; a weight room; baseball and softball fields; a 25-meter swimming pool with 1- and 10-meter diving boards; lighted outdoor jai alai; 8 tennis, 5 racquetball, 2 basketball, 3 volleyball, and 4 badminton courts; and a dance area.

Disabled Students: Eighty percent of the campus is accessible to disabled students. The following facilities are available: wheelchair ramps, elevators, special parking, specially equipped rest rooms, lowered drinking fountains, and lowered telephones.

Services: In addition to many counseling and information services, tutoring is available in most subjects. There is also a reader service for the blind. Remedial work must be taken at the community college level.

Campus Safety and Security: Campus safety and security measures include 24-hour foot and vehicle patrol, escort service, shuttle buses, and informal discussions. In addition, there are pamphlets, posters, films, emergency telephones, and lighted pathways and sidewalks.

Programs of Study: FAU awards the B.A., B.S., B.A.E., B.B.A., B.F.A., B.H.S., B.P.A., B.S.E.E., B.S.M.E., B.S.N., B.S.O.E., and B.S.W. degrees. Associate, master's, and doctoral degrees also are awarded. Bachelor's degrees are awarded in BIOLOGICAL SCIENCE (biology/biological science, botany, marine biology, microbiology, and zoology), BUSINESS (accounting, banking and finance, business administration and management, international business management, marketing/retailing/merchandising, personnel management, real estate, and small business management), COMMUNICATIONS AND THE ARTS (communications, dramatic arts, English, fine arts, French, German, journalism, linguistics, music, and Spanish), COMPUTER AND PHYSICAL SCIENCE (chemistry, computer science, geology, information sciences and systems, mathematics, and physics), EDUCATION (art, early childhood, elementary, English, foreign languages, music, science, and special), ENGINEERING AND ENVIRONMENTAL DESIGN (computer engineering, electrical/electronics engineering, and ocean engineering), HEALTH PROFESSIONS (health care administration, health science, medical laboratory technology, and nursing), SOCIAL SCIENCE (anthropology, criminal justice, economics, geography, history, international relations, Latin American studies, philosophy, political science/government, prelaw, psychology, public administration, social science, sociology, and urban studies). Engineering, education, business, and nursing are the strongest academically. Business, social sciences, and education have the largest enrollments.

Required: All students must take the College Level Academic Skills Test (CLAST) required by the state. In order to graduate, students must complete a total of 120 credit hours with the last 30 in residence. A minimum GPA of 2.0 is required. All students must take the required courses in the core curriculum, including 6 credits each of English composition and mathematics, 12 credits of civilization, 3 credits each of art, the individual and society, social institutions, and a foreign language, 7 credits of science, and 8 credits of electives.

Special: FAU offers cooperative creative programs and internships in most majors. Work-study programs, dual and student-designed majors, a general studies degree, credit for military experience, nondegree study, and pass/fail options are available. The school offers study abroad through all state university system of Florida programs, and an exchange program in ocean engineering with the Polytechnic University of Madrid, Spain. Cross-registration is available with all Florida state universities, in science/engineering with Palm Beach and Broward Community colleges, and in military science with the University of Miami. Students may earn B.A.-B.A. degrees in a number of subjects. There is a freshman honors program on campus, as well as 15 national honor societies. Six departments have honors programs.

Faculty/Classroom: Sixty-nine percent of faculty are male; 31%, female. All both teach and do research. Graduate students teach 5% of introductory courses. The average class size in an introductory lecture is 50; in a laboratory, 20; and in a regular course offering, 32.

Admissions: About 67% of the 1993–94 applicants were accepted. The SAT scores for the 1993–94 freshman class were as follows: Verbal—68% below 500, 27% between 500 and 599, and 5% between 600 and 700; Math—35% below 500, 45% between 500 and 599, 18% between 600 and 700, and 2% above 700. There was 1 National Merit finalist and 2 semifinalists. Eight freshmen graduated first in their class.

Requirements: A minimum GPA of 2.0 is required. The SAT I or ACT is required, with minimum composite scores of 1000 on the SAT I and 23 on the ACT. In addition, graduation from an accredited secondary school or satisfactory scores on the GED are required for admission. Students must have 19 academic credits. High school courses must include 4 units of English, 2 units of a foreign language, and 3 units each of mathematics (algebra I and higher), science (including 2 units with substantial laboratory work), and social studies, and 4 units of electives in computer science, fine arts, or humanities. A portfolio or audition may be required by individual departments. An essay and an interview are required. AP and CLEP credits are accepted. Important factors used in the admissions decision are advanced placement or honor courses, evidence of special talent, recommendations by school officials, personality, intangible qualities, and leadership record.

Procedure: Freshmen are admitted fall and spring. Entrance exams should be taken by June. Applications should be filed by May 1 for fall entry, October 15 for spring entry, and March 15 for summer entry, along with an application fee of $20. Notification is sent on a rolling basis. There are early decision, early admissions, and deferred admissions plans.

Transfer: About 3700 transfer students enrolled in 1993–94. Transfer students must have completed 60 hours with a minimum GPA of 2.0 from an approved institution. Applicants from a community or junior college in Florida with an associate degree are automatically admitted. Students having fewer than 60 hours must meet the same criteria as entering freshmen. A total of 30 credits out of 120 must be completed at FAU.

Visiting: There are regularly scheduled orientations for prospective students, consisting of a group tour. There are guides for informal visits. To arrange for a visit, contact the Admissions Office at (407) 367-3040 or (800) 299-4FAU.

Financial Aid: In 1993–94, 51% of all current freshmen and 32% of continuing students received some form of financial aid. About 22% of freshmen received need-based aid. The average freshman award was $2170. Of that total, scholarships or need-based grants averaged $1200 ($2600 maximum); loans averaged $1500 ($2625 maximum); and work contracts averaged $1000 ($2500 maximum). Seventy-five percent of undergraduate students work part-time. Average earnings from campus work for the school year was $1500. The average financial indebtedness of the 1992–93 graduate was $10,000. FAU is a member of CSS. The FAF, FFS, or SFS and FAFSA are required. The deadline for financial aid applications is April 1.

International Students: There are currently 610 international students enrolled. They must take the TOEFL and achieve a minimum score of 550. The student must also take the SAT I, and achieve a minimum composite score of 740, or the ACT.

Computers: The college provides computer facilities for student use. The mainframe is a DEC VAX 6320. There are more than 250 on-campus personal computers available for student use. Also, students may access the mainframe at various sites on campus or via a modem. In addition, there is an on-campus network, including electronic mail, Bitnet, and common software. All students may access the system. Laboratories are open from 8 A.M. to 12 midnight; there is modem access 24 hours daily. There are no time limits on using the system and no fees.

Graduates: In 1992–93, 2165 bachelor's degrees were awarded. The most popular majors among graduates were elementary education (11%), accounting (7%), and management (6%). Within an average freshman class, 15% graduate in 3 years, 37% in 4 years, 73% in 5 years, and 85% in 6 years. Some 181 companies recruited on campus in 1992–93.

Admissions Contact: Brian Levin-Stankevich, Director of Admissions and Enrollment Management.

FLORIDA INSTITUTE OF TECHNOLOGY E-3
Melbourne, FL 32901-6988 (407) 768-8000, ext. 8030
(800) 888-4348

Full-time: 1342 men, 521 women	Faculty: 190
Part-time: 168 men, 65 women	Ph.D.s: 85%
Graduate: 1863 men, 1023 women	Student/Faculty: 10 to 1
Year: semesters, summer session	Tuition: $13,035
Application Deadline: April 1	Room & Board: $3900
Freshman Class: 1947 applied, 1580 accepted, 376 enrolled	
SAT I Verbal/Math: 500/596	VERY COMPETITIVE

Florida Institute of Technology, founded in 1958, offers undergraduate degrees in engineering and science, liberal arts, and the schools of management, psychology, and aeronautics. There are 5 undergraduate schools and one graduate school. In addition to regional accreditation, Florida Tech has baccalaureate program accreditation with ABET. The library contains 233,930 volumes, 187,605 microform items, and 3813 audiovisual forms, and subscribes to 1463 peri-

odicals. Special learning facilities include a learning resource center, planetarium, and radio station. The 175-acre campus is in a small town 70 miles east of Orlando. Including residence halls, there are 45 buildings on campus.

Student Life: About 62% of undergraduates are from out-of-state, mostly the Northeast. Students come from 50 states, 90 foreign countries, and Canada. Ninety percent are from public schools; 10% from private. Sixty-five percent are white; 21% foreign nationals. The average age of freshmen is 18; all undergraduates, 22. Twenty-five percent drop out by the end of their first year; 55% remain to graduate.

Housing: A total of 1200 students can be accommodated in college housing. College-sponsored living facilities include single-sex and coed dormitories and on-campus apartments. On-campus housing is guaranteed for all 4 years. Sixty-five percent of students commute. Alcohol is not permitted. All students may keep cars on campus.

Activities: About 15% of men belong to 8 national fraternities; about 10% of women belong to 3 national sororities. There are 70 groups on campus, including cheerleading, chess, drama, ethnic, international, newspaper, political, professional, radio and TV, religious, social, student government, and yearbook. Popular campus events include the Real Party and Engineering Week.

Sports: There are 6 intercollegiate sports for men and 5 for women, and 18 intramural sports for men and 6 for women. Athletic and recreation facilities include a 2000-seat gymnasium with basketball, volleyball, weight-training, and fencing facilities; swimming pools; soccer, baseball, and softball fields; a regulation putting green; and racquetball and tennis courts.

Disabled Students: Eighty-five percent of the campus is accessible to disabled students. The following facilities are available: wheelchair ramps, elevators, special parking, specially equipped rest rooms, special class scheduling, lowered drinking fountains, and lowered telephones.

Services: In addition to many counseling and information services, tutoring is available in every subject. In addition, there is a reader service for the blind, and remedial math, reading, and writing.

Campus Safety and Security: Campus safety and security measures include 24-hour foot and vehicle patrol, escort service, pamphlets, posters, and films, and emergency telephones. In addition, there are lighted pathways and sidewalks.

Programs of Study: Florida Tech awards the B.A. and B.S. degrees. Master's and doctoral degrees also are awarded. Bachelor's degrees are awarded in AGRICULTURE (fishing and fisheries), BIOLOGICAL SCIENCE (biochemistry, biology/biological science, marine biology, and microbiology), BUSINESS (accounting, business administration and management, business economics, hospitality management services, marketing/retailing/merchandising, and purchasing/inventory management), COMMUNICATIONS AND THE ARTS (communications, English as a second/foreign language, and technical and business writing), COMPUTER AND PHYSICAL SCIENCE (chemistry, computer science, mathematics, and physics), EDUCATION (science), ENGINEERING AND ENVIRONMENTAL DESIGN (aeronautical engineering, aeronautical science, Aerospace Studies, chemical engineering, civil engineering, computer engineering, electrical/electronics engineering, engineering, environmental engineering, environmental science, mechanical engineering, and ocean engineering), HEALTH PROFESSIONS (predentistry and premedicine), SOCIAL SCIENCE (humanities and psychology). Engineering and science are the strongest academically. Science, liberal arts, and aeronautics have the largest enrollments.

Required: To graduate, students must have a minimum 2.0 GPA and 120 credit hours. The required number of hours in the major varies. All students must take 4 courses in humanities and 3 in English composition. The core curriculum also requires 9 credit hours each in physical or life sciences and mathematics, and 3 hours in computer science.

Special: Florida Tech offers co-op program internships and dual programs in environmental engineering and chemical engineering, physics and space science, and mathematics and computer science. There are 3 national honor societies on campus.

Faculty/Classroom: Eighty-five percent of faculty are male; 15% female. Eighty percent teach undergraduates, 10% do research, and 20% do both. Graduate students teach 25% of introductory courses. The average class size in an introductory lecture is 50; in a laboratory, 25; and in a regular course offering, 20.

Admissions: About 81% of the 1993–94 applicants were accepted. The SAT scores for the 1993–94 freshman class were as follows: Verbal—47% below 500, 42% between 500 and 599, and 11% between 600 and 700; Math—13% below 500, 35% between 500 and 599, 39% between 600 and 700, and 14% above 700. About 68% of the current freshmen were in the top fifth of their class; 89% were in the top two fifths. There were 2 National Merit finalists and 5 semifinalists. About 16 freshmen graduated first in their class.

Requirements: Florida Tech requires applicants to be in the upper 50% of their class. A minimum GPA of 2.5 is required. The SAT I or ACT is required, with a minimum composite score of 1050 on the

SAT I and a minimum score of 26 recommended on the ACT. Applicants must be graduates of an accredited secondary school or have a GED certificate. At least 18 academic credits or Carnegie units are required, including 4 years each of English, mathematics, and science. An essay is required, and an interview is recommended. AP and CLEP credits are accepted. Important factors used in the admissions decision are recommendations by school officials, advanced placement or honor courses, leadership record, and extracurricular activities record.

Procedure: Freshmen are admitted to all sessions. Entrance exams should be taken during the junior year. Applications should be filed by April 1 for fall entry, March 9 for spring entry, and June 8 for summer entry, along with an application fee of $35. Notification is sent on a rolling basis. There is a deferred admissions plan.

Transfer: About 120 transfer students enrolled in 1993–94. Applicants must have a minimum 2.5 GPA and composite scores of 1050 on the SAT I or 25 on the ACT. An associate degree is recommended. Physics and calculus courses are required for engineering majors. A total of 30 credits out of 120 must be completed at Florida Tech.

Visiting: There are regularly scheduled orientations for prospective students, including tours and interviews with admissions staff, faculty, or department heads upon request. There are guides for informal visits, and visitors may sit in on classes and stay overnight at the school. To arrange for a visit, contact the Admissions Office at (407) 768-8000, ext. 8030 or (800) 888-7348.

Financial Aid: In an earlier class, 68% of all current freshmen and 60% of continuing students received some form of financial aid. About 60% of freshmen and 60% of continuing students received need-based aid in 1993–94. The average freshman award was $2500. Thirty percent of undergraduate students work part-time. Florida Tech is a member of CSS. The FAF is required. The deadline for financial aid applications is March 15.

International Students: There are currently 563 international students enrolled. The school actively recruits these students. They must take the TOEFL and achieve a minimum score of 550.

Computers: The college provides computer facilities for student use. The mainframe is a DEC VAX 8350. Students may access the system through 39 terminals located in a computer laboratory, through terminals in individual departments, and through 4 dial-up lines. The VAX system is also supplemented by a microlaboratory in the library. Microcomputers available for student use include IBM PCs, DEC Rainbows, Apple IIs, and Apple Macintoshes. All students may access the system. It may be used 18 hours per day. There are no time limits on using the system and no fees.

Graduates: In 1992–93 616 bachelor's degrees were awarded. The most popular majors among graduates were aviation management (21%), biological sciences (11%), and electrical engineering (8%). Within an average freshman class, 1% graduate in 3 years, 25% in 4 years, 47% in 5 years, and 58% in 6 years. Some 50 companies recruited on campus in 1992–93.

Admissions Contact: Louis T. Levy, Dean of Admissions.

FLORIDA INTERNATIONAL UNIVERSITY E-5
Miami, FL 33199 (305) 348-2363

Full-time: 4401 men, 5807 women	Faculty: 699; IIA, -$
Part-time: 3980 men, 5330 women	Ph.D.s: 96%
Graduate: 2014 men, 2789 women	Student/Faculty: 15 to 1
Year: semesters, summer session	Tuition: $1757 ($6659)
Application Deadline: June 1	Room: $2434
Freshman Class: 3306 applied, 2079 accepted, 1071 enrolled	
SAT I Verbal/Math: 470/542	ACT: 24 VERY COMPETITIVE

Florida International University, founded in 1965, is part of the State University System of Florida. Undergraduate degrees are offered through the colleges of arts and sciences, business administration, education, engineering and design, and health, and the schools of accounting, computer science, hospitality management, nursing, journalism and mass communication, and public affairs and services. The North and South campuses are in Miami, and there are 2 educational centers in Fort Lauderdale. In addition to regional accreditation, FIU has baccalaureate program accreditation with AACSB, ABET, ACCE, ACEJMC, ADA, APTA, CSWE, and NLN. The 2 libraries contain 1 million volumes, 284,126 microform items, and 82,704 audiovisual forms, and subscribe to 7025 periodicals. Computerized library sources and services include the card catalog, interlibrary loans, and database searching. Special learning facilities include a learning resource center, radio station, and an art museum. The 342-acre campus is in an urban area 10 miles west of downtown Miami. Including residence halls, there are 13 buildings on campus.

Student Life: About 91% of undergraduates are from Florida. Students come from 50 states, 94 foreign countries, and Canada. Sixty-one percent are from public schools; 39% from private. Forty-three percent are Hispanic; 39% white; 10% African American. The average age of freshmen is 19; all undergraduates, 26. Fourteen percent drop out by the end of their first year; 56% remain to graduate.

Housing: A total of 1193 students can be accommodated in college housing. College-sponsored living facilities include on-campus apartments and married-student housing. On-campus housing is guaranteed for all 4 years. Ninety-five percent of students commute. All students may keep cars on campus.

Activities: About 5% of men belong to 9 national fraternities; about 2% of women belong to 1 local and 4 national sororities. There are 100 groups on campus, including band, cheerleading, chorus, ethnic, gay, honors, international, newspaper, political, professional, radio and TV, religious, social, social service, student government, and yearbook.

Sports: There are 7 intercollegiate sports for men and 7 for women, and 14 intramural sports for men and 10 for women. Athletic and recreation facilities include a 5000-seat arena with basketball and racquetball courts, an aquatic center, baseball and soccer fields, a fitness center with Nautilus machines, and a racquet sports center with lighted tennis and racquetball courts.

Disabled Students: Most of the campus is accessible to disabled students. The following facilities are available: wheelchair ramps, elevators, special parking, specially equipped rest rooms, special class scheduling, and lowered drinking fountains and telephones. There is also accessible computer equipment for visually impaired students and talking and large-print computers as well as note-takers and readers.

Services: In addition to many counseling and information services, tutoring is available in most subjects. There is also a reader service for the blind, and remedial math, reading, and writing. Adapted testing and special registration may be arranged for disabled students.

Campus Safety and Security: Campus safety and security measures include 24-hour foot and vehicle patrol, escort service, informal discussions, and pamphlets, posters, and films. In addition, there are lighted pathways and sidewalks.

Programs of Study: FIU awards the B.A., B.S., B.Ac., B.B.A., B.F.A., B.H.S.A., B.M., B.P.A., and B.S.N. degrees. Associate, master's, and doctoral degrees also are awarded. Bachelor's degrees are awarded in BIOLOGICAL SCIENCE (biology/biological science), BUSINESS (accounting, banking and finance, business administration and management, hospitality management services, international business management, management information systems, management science, marketing/retailing/merchandising, and personnel management), COMMUNICATIONS AND THE ARTS (art, communications, dance, dramatic arts, English, French, German, music, Portuguese, and Spanish), COMPUTER AND PHYSICAL SCIENCE (chemistry, computer science, geology, mathematics, physics, and statistics), EDUCATION (art, elementary, English, environmental, foreign languages, health, history, home economics, mathematics, music, physical, science, social studies, special, specific learning disabilities, and vocational), ENGINEERING AND ENVIRONMENTAL DESIGN (architectural technology, civil engineering, computer engineering, construction management, electrical/electronics engineering, environmental science, industrial engineering, interior design, and mechanical engineering), HEALTH PROFESSIONS (health care administration, health information management, medical laboratory technology, nursing, occupational therapy, physical therapy, and rehabilitation therapy), and SOCIAL SCIENCE (criminal justice, dietetics, economics, history, humanities, international relations, liberal arts/general studies, parks and recreation management, philosophy, political science/government, psychology, public administration, religion, social work, and sociology). Accounting, engineering, biology, and hospitality management are the strongest academically. Accounting, hospitality management, elementary education, finance, management, marketing, computer science, nursing, biology, and electrical engineering have the largest enrollments.

Required: To graduate, students must complete between 120 and 152 hours with a 2.0 GPA. There are also general education and writing requirements. Students admitted with fewer than 48 hours must complete the core curriculum.

Special: The university offers co-op and work-study programs, study abroad, and cross-registration with the New World School of the Arts, a collaborative venture between Dade County Public Schools, Miami-Dade Community College, and FIU. Accelerated degree programs, nondegree study, dual majors, and B.A.-B.S. degrees may also be arranged. There is a freshman honors program on campus, as well as 10 national honor societies.

Faculty/Classroom: Sixty-nine percent of faculty are male; 31%, female. All both teach and do research. Graduate students teach 32% of introductory courses. The average class size in an introductory lecture is 41; in a laboratory, 15; and in a regular course offering, 23.

Admissions: About 63% of the 1993–94 applicants were accepted. The SAT scores for the 1993–94 freshman class were as follows: Verbal—63% below 500, 31% between 500 and 599, and 5% between 600 and 700; Math—30% below 500, 45% between 500 and 599, 21% between 600 and 700, and 4% above 700. The ACT scores were 15% below 21, 42% between 21 and 23, 24% between 24 and 26, 11% between 27 and 28, and 9% above 28. About 86% of the

current freshmen were in the top fifth of their class; 98% were in the top two fifths.

Requirements: The SAT I or ACT is required. In addition, the applicant must be a graduate of an accredited secondary school or have a GED certificate. The required academic courses include 4 units in English, 3 units each in mathematics, natural science, and social studies, 2 in a foreign language, and 4 in academic electives. The university's placement tests must be taken the semester before attending the university. An interview may be required. AP and CLEP credits are accepted. Important factors used in the admissions decision are advanced placement or honor courses, evidence of special talent, recommendations by school officials, leadership record, and extracurricular activities record.

Procedure: Freshmen are admitted to all sessions. Entrance exams should be taken during the spring of the junior year. Applications should be filed by June 1 for fall entry, October 1 for spring entry, and March 1 for summer entry, along with an application fee of $20. Notification is sent on a rolling basis. There are early admissions and deferred admissions plans.

Transfer: About 2150 transfer students enrolled in a recent year. Applicants with fewer than 60 semester credits must meet regular freshman admissions requirements. All students must pass the CLAST or take the pre-CLAST testing program during the first term of enrollment, fulfill core curriculum or general education requirements, and have a 2.0 GPA. A total of 30 credits out of 120 to 152 must be completed at FIU.

Visiting: There are regularly scheduled orientations for prospective students, including placement tests, advising, a tour, and student activities. There are guides for informal visits and visitors may sit in on classes. To arrange for a visit, contact the Office of Admissions at (305) 348-2363.

Financial Aid: In a recent year, 38% of all freshmen and 35% of continuing students received some form of financial aid. About 38% of freshmen and 35% of continuing students received need-based aid. The average freshman award was $4185. Of that total, scholarships or need-based grants averaged $834 ($2200 maximum); loans averaged $1769 ($4000 maximum); and work contracts averaged $1582 ($5400 maximum). Four percent of undergraduate students work part-time. Average earnings from campus work for a recent school year were $2000. FIU is a member of CSS. The FAFSA is required. The deadline for financial aid applications is April 1.

International Students: There are currently 1016 international students enrolled. The school actively recruits these students. They must take the TOEFL and achieve a minimum score of 500. The student must also take the SAT I or the ACT.

Computers: The college provides computer facilities for student use. The mainframes are a DEC VAX 8800 and a Sun 4/280. Students may access the campus Ethernet network through terminals and and personal computers, and through dial-up access from home. All students may access the system. It may be used 8 A.M. to 4 A.M. There are no time limits on using the system and no fees.

Graduates: In a recent year, 3077 bachelor's degrees were awarded. The most popular majors among graduates were hospitality management (10%), finance (6%), and marketing and psychology (5%). Within an average freshman class, 1% graduate in 3 years, 31% in 4 years, 39% in 5 years, and 68% in 6 years. Some 150 companies recruited on campus in a recent year.

Admissions Contact: Admissions Director.

FLORIDA MEMORIAL COLLEGE   E-5

Miami, FL 33054   (305) 626-3750; (800) 822-1362 (out-of-state)

Full-time: 553 men, 801 women	**Faculty:** 80
Part-time: 44 men, 65 women	**Ph.D.s:** 40%
Graduate: none	**Student/Faculty:** 18 to 1
Year: terms, summer session	**Tuition:** $4750
Application Deadline: open	**Room & Board:** $2850
Freshman Class: 3874 applied, 1548 accepted, 562 enrolled	
SAT I or ACT: required	**COMPETITIVE +**

Florida Memorial College, founded in 1879, is a private, coeducational, liberal arts institution affiliated with the American Baptist Church. There are 6 undergraduate schools. The library contains 88,000 volumes, and subscribes to 400 periodicals. Special learning facilities include an aviation center. The 77-acre campus is in an urban area in northwestern Miami. Including residence halls, there are 12 buildings on campus.

Student Life: All students are from public schools. Thirty-eight percent drop out by the end of their first year; 25% remain to graduate.

Housing: A total of 835 students can be accommodated in college housing. College-sponsored living facilities include single-sex dormitories and off-campus apartments. On-campus housing is guaranteed for all 4 years. Alcohol is not permitted.

Activities: There are 4 national fraternities and 4 national sororities. There are some groups and organizations on campus, including band, choir, jazz band, religious, and student government. Popular

campus events include concerts, lectures, movies, drama productions, and Sunday services.

Sports: There are 6 intercollegiate sports for men and 6 for women, and 7 intramural sports for men and 7 for women. Athletic and recreation facilities include a gymnasium, a pool, and a track.

Services: There is remedial math, reading, and writing.

Programs of Study: Florida Memorial awards the B.A., and B.S. degrees. Bachelor's degrees are awarded in BIOLOGICAL SCIENCE (biology/biological science), BUSINESS (accounting, business administration and management, and transportation management), COMMUNICATIONS AND THE ARTS (English, fine arts, and music), COMPUTER AND PHYSICAL SCIENCE (chemistry, computer science, and mathematics), EDUCATION (elementary, physical, and secondary), ENGINEERING AND ENVIRONMENTAL DESIGN (air traffic control, aviation administration/management, and aviation computer technology), SOCIAL SCIENCE (criminal justice, philosophy, political science/government, psychology, public administration, religion, and sociology).

Required: In order to graduate, all students must complete at least 124 credit hours, including 62 hours of general education requirements, with a minimum overall GPA of 2.0.

Special: Private sector and college internships, work-study, and a 3–2 engineering program with the University of Miami are available. Pass/fail credit and nondegree options are possible. There is a freshman honors program on campus.

Admissions: About 40% of the 1993–94 applicants were accepted.

Requirements: A minimum GPA of 2.0 is required. The SAT I or ACT is required. A minimum composite score of 840 is required on the SAT I or 17 on the ACT for education majors. Applicants must be graduates of an accredited secondary school or have a GED certificate. One faculty and 2 personal recommendations, an autobiography, and a health certificate are required. Up to 20% of a freshman class may be admitted for 1 semester on a conditional basis to demonstrate their abilities.

Procedure: Freshmen are admitted fall and spring. Application deadlines are open and the application fee is $15.

Transfer: Transcripts must be submitted for all previous college work, as well as high school transcripts for students with fewer than 3 credits. The SAT I or ACT is recommended. A total of 30 credits out of 124 must be completed at Florida Memorial.

Financial Aid: The FAF or FFS financial statement is required. The deadline for financial aid applications is March 15.

International Students: They must take the TOEFL.

Computers: The college provides computer facilities for student use. The mainframes are an IBM 9375/Model 60 and a DEC VAX 6210. There is an IBM PS/2 microcomputer laboratory in the aviation center and another computer laboratory in the classroom building. All students may access the system.

Admissions Contact: Peggy Kelly, Director of Admissions.

FLORIDA SOUTHERN COLLEGE
D-4
Lakeland,, FL 33801   (813) 680–4131; (800) 274–4131 (in-state)

Full-time: 649 men, 808 women	Faculty: 110; IIB, -$
Part-time: 363 men, 597 women	Ph.D.s: 66%
Graduate: 34 men, 19 women	Student/Faculty: 13 to 1
Year: semesters, summer session	Tuition: $7660
Application Deadline: August 1	Room & Board: $4600
Freshman Class: 1381 applied, 1040 accepted, 374 enrolled	
SAT I: 470/470	ACT: 22 COMPETITIVE

Florida Southern College, founded in 1885, is a private, coeducational institution affiliated with the United Methodist Church, offering undergraduate programs through the divisions of humanities, social sciences, and natural sciences. There are 68 undergraduate schools and one graduate school. The library contains 200,000 volumes, and subscribes to 1000 periodicals. Computerized library sources and services include the card catalog, interlibrary loans, and database searching. Special learning facilities include an art gallery, planetarium, radio station, and TV station. The 100-acre campus is in a suburban area 30 miles east of Tampa. Including residence halls, there are 55 buildings on campus.

Student Life: About 65% of undergraduates are from Florida. Students come from 25 states, 6 foreign countries, and Canada. Fifty-five percent are from public schools; 45% from private. Ninety-six percent are white. Forty percent are Protestant; 40% Catholic; 10% claim no religious affiliation. The average age of freshmen is 18; all undergraduates, 20. Nineteen percent drop out by the end of their first year; 46% remain to graduate.

Housing: A total of 1425 students can be accommodated in college housing. College-sponsored living facilities include single-sex dormitories, fraternity houses, and sorority houses. In addition there are honors houses and language houses. On-campus housing is guaranteed for all 4 years. Eighty-eight percent of students live on campus; of those, 75% remain on campus on weekends. Alcohol is not permitted. All students may keep cars on campus.

Activities: About 25% of men belong to 7 national fraternities; about 45% of women belong to 5 national sororities. There are 35 groups on campus, including art, band, cheerleading, choir, chorale, chorus, drama, ethnic, film, honors, international, jazz band, literary magazine, musical theater, newspaper, opera, orchestra, photography, political, professional, radio and TV, religious, social, student government, and yearbook. Popular campus events include outdoor movies, picnics, dances, theater productions, a jazz festival, and the Festival of Fine Art Series.

Sports: There are 5 intercollegiate sports for men and 5 for women, and 7 intramural sports for men and 7 for women. Athletic and recreation facilities include provisions for water sports, billiards, and table games, a 3600-seat field house, an 1800-seat auditorium, a gymnasium, and a pool.

Disabled Students: The following facilities are available: wheelchair ramps, elevators, special parking, specially equipped rest rooms, and lowered drinking fountains.

Services: In addition to many counseling and information services, tutoring is available in every subject.

Campus Safety and Security: Campus safety and security measures include 24-hour foot and vehicle patrol, self defense education, escort service, and informal discussions. In addition, there are pamphlets, posters, films, emergency telephones, and lighted pathways and sidewalks.

Programs of Study: Florida Southern awards the B.A. and B.S. degrees. Master's degrees also are awarded. Bachelor's degrees are awarded in AGRICULTURE (horticulture), BIOLOGICAL SCIENCE (biology/biological science), BUSINESS (accounting, banking and finance, business administration and management, business economics, hotel/motel and restaurant management, international business management, marketing/retailing/merchandising, and personnel management), COMMUNICATIONS AND THE ARTS (advertising, communications, dramatic arts, English, French, German, journalism, music, public relations, and Spanish), COMPUTER AND PHYSICAL SCIENCE (chemistry, information sciences and systems, mathematics, and physics), EDUCATION (art, early childhood, elementary, foreign languages, middle school, music, science, secondary, and special), ENGINEERING AND ENVIRONMENTAL DESIGN (environmental science), SOCIAL SCIENCE (criminal justice, economics, history, political science/government, psychology, religion, social science, and sociology). Humanities is the strongest academically. Business has the largest enrollment.

Required: In order to graduate, all students must have completed 124 semester hours of credit, with no more than 42 hours in the major for most programs and minimum 2.0 GPA. Required core courses include 9 hours of humanities, 8 of natural science, 6 each of English, humanities, and social studies, 3 each of history and fine arts, 2 of physical education, and attendance at faith and life convocation.

Special: Florida Southern offers study abroad in 8 countries, a Washington semester with American University, and the 3–2 engineering degree with Washington University/St. Louis and the universities of Florida and Miami. Students may choose the United Nations semester in cooperation with Drew University in New Jersey, the May Option Program, which combines study and travel in the United States and abroad, or the New York and Arizona snowmesters for course credit. Internships with corporations in Tampa, Lakeland, and Orlando are offered through most academic departments and are required by many. Credit for military experience, nondegree study, and pass/fail options also are available. There is a freshman honors program on campus, as well as 2 national honor societies. Thirteen departments have honors programs.

Faculty/Classroom: Seventy-two percent of faculty are male; 28%, female. All teach undergraduates. No introductory courses are taught by graduate students. The average class size in an introductory lecture is 30; in a laboratory, 15; and in a regular course offering, 25.

Admissions: About 75% of the 1993–94 applicants were accepted. The SAT scores for the 1993–94 freshman class were as follows: Verbal—75% below 500, 20% between 500 and 599, and 5% between 600 and 700; Math—80% below 500, 17% between 500 and 599, and 3% between 600 and 700. The ACT scores were 15% below 21, 75% between 21 and 23, 8% between 24 and 26, and 2% between 27 and 28. About 25% of the current freshmen were in the top fifth of their class; 75% were in the top two fifths. There were 10 National Merit finalists and 25 semifinalists. About 10 freshmen graduated first in their class.

Requirements: Florida Southern requires applicants to be in the upper 50% of their class. A minimum GPA of 2.5 is required. The SAT I with a minimum composite score of 900, or the ACT with a minimum composite score of 20 is required. Applicants must be graduates of an accredited secondary school or have a GED certificate. An essay is required and an interview is recommended. AP and CLEP credits are accepted. Important factors used in the admissions decision are advanced placement or honor courses, recommendations by school officials, personality, intangible qualities, evidence of special talent, and leadership record.

Procedure: Applications should be filed by August 1 for fall entry and December 1 for spring entry, along with an application fee of $20. Notification is sent on a rolling basis. There are early admissions and deferred admissions plans.

Transfer: About 191 transfer students enrolled in a recent year. Transfer students must have a minimum 2.0 GPA and must submit the SAT I or ACT scores. An associate degree and an interview are recommended. A total of 30 credits out of 124 must be completed at Florida Southern.

Visiting: There are regularly scheduled orientations for prospective students. There are guides for informal visits and visitors may sit in on classes and stay overnight at the school. To arrange for a visit, contact the Admissions Office at (800) 274-4131.

Financial Aid: In a recent year 80% of all current freshmen and 85% of continuing students received some form of financial aid. About 55% of freshmen and 60% of continuing students received need-based aid. The average freshman award was $5700. Of that total, scholarships or need-based grants averaged $4700 ($8900 maximum); and work contracts averaged $800 ($1100 maximum). Seventy-five percent of undergraduate students work part-time. Average earnings from campus work for the school year are $1100. Florida Southern is a member of CSS. The FAF, the college's own financial statement and the parents' and student's tax returns are required. The deadline for financial aid applications is April 15.

International Students: There are currently 24 international students enrolled. The school actively recruits these students. They must take the TOEFL and achieve a minimum score of 500.

Computers: The college provides computer facilities for student use. The mainframe is an IBM AS/400 ESO. There are also 15 IBM computers available in the library for students' academic and wordprocessing needs. In addition, there are specialized computer laboratories for the courses that require computer use. Those students enrolled in courses that offer a computer laboratory may access the system. It may be used during laboratory hours. Students may access the system for 2 hours a session. The fees are $50.

Graduates: In 1992–93 540 bachelor's degrees were awarded. The most popular majors among graduates were business (25%), science (15%), and education (12%). Within an average freshman class, 2% graduate in 3 years, 95% in 4 years, 2% in 5 years, and 1% in 6 years. Some 40 companies recruited on campus in 1992–93. In the 1992 graduating class, 2% were enrolled in graduate school within 6 months of graduation; 48% had found employment.

Admissions Contact: Bill Stephens, Director of Admissions.

FLORIDA STATE UNIVERSITY

C-1

Tallahassee, FL 32306

(904) 644-6200

Full-time: 8588 men, 10,281 women
Part-time: 1171 men, 1278 women
Graduate: 2767 men, 4013 women
Year: semesters, summer session
Application Deadline: March 1
Freshman Class: 11,651 applied, 8683 accepted, 3023 enrolled
SAT I or ACT: required

Faculty: 1028; I, --$
Ph.D.s: 90%
Student/Faculty: 18 to 1
Tuition: $1780 ($6682)
Room & Board: $4034

VERY COMPETITIVE

Florida State University, founded in 1857, is a large coeducational public institution with 14 undergraduate and 16 graduate schools. Its primary role is to serve as a center for advanced graduate and professional studies while emphasizing research in undergraduate programs. There are 14 undergraduate and 16 graduate schools. In addition to regional accreditation, FSU has baccalaureate program accreditation with AACSB, ABET, ADA, AHEA, ASLA, CSWE, FIDER, NASM, NCATE, NLN, and NRPA. The 6 libraries contain 2,028,509 volumes, 4,103,578 microform items, and 34,966 audiovisual forms, and subscribe to 18,420 periodicals. Computerized library sources and services include the card catalog, interlibrary loans, and database searching. Special learning facilities include a learning resource center, art gallery, planetarium, radio station, TV station, nuclear accelerator, and X-ray emission laboratory. The 418-acre campus is in a suburban area 163 miles west of Jacksonville. Including residence halls, there are 125 buildings on campus.

Student Life: About 85% of undergraduates are from Florida. Students come from 50 states, 121 foreign countries, and Canada. Eighty-five percent are from public schools; 15% from private. Eighty-one percent are white. The average age of freshmen is 18.5; all undergraduates, 21.7. Five percent drop out by the end of their first year; 54% remain to graduate.

Housing: A total of 4900 students can be accommodated in college housing. College-sponsored living facilities include single-sex and coed dormitories, on-campus apartments, married-student housing, fraternity houses, and sorority houses. In addition there are honors houses and special interest houses. On-campus housing is available on a first-come, first-served basis. All students may keep cars on campus.

Activities: About 20% of men belong to 25 national fraternities; about 20% of women belong to 20 national sororities. There are 300 groups on campus, including art, band, cheerleading, chess, choir, chorus, computers, dance, drama, drill team, ethnic, gay, honors, international, jazz band, literary magazine, marching band, musical theater, newspaper, opera, orchestra, pep band, political, professional, radio and TV, religious, social, social service, student government, symphony, and yearbook. Popular campus events include the Homecoming PowWow, the Twelve Days of Dance, Parents Weekend, Fall Convocation, and sports events.

Sports: There are 9 intercollegiate sports for men and 9 for women, and 22 intramural sports for men and 22 for women. Athletic and recreation facilities include a 60,000-seat stadium; an aquatic center with a heated outdoor pool; a gymnasium with an indoor pool; a golf course; a track; courts for basketball, tennis, squash, racquetball, and handball; an indoor Olympic-size pool; 2 Jacuzzis; a steam room; a sauna; a multipurpose gymnasium; a 3-lane jogging track; aerobic and weight rooms; and a lakefront recreation area for outdoor water sports.

Disabled Students: Fifty percent of the campus is accessible to disabled students. The following facilities are available: wheelchair ramps, elevators, special parking, specially equipped rest rooms, special class scheduling, and lowered drinking fountains and telephones.

Services: In addition to many counseling and information services, tutoring is available in most subjects. There is also a reader service for the blind, and remedial math, reading, and writing.

Campus Safety and Security: Campus safety and security measures include 24-hour foot and vehicle patrol, self-defense education, escort service, and shuttle buses. In addition, there are informal discussions, pamphlets, posters, films, emergency telephones, and lighted pathways and sidewalks.

Programs of Study: FSU awards the B.A., B.S., B.F.A, B.M., and B.M.Ed. degrees. Master's and doctoral degrees also are awarded. Bachelor's degrees are awarded in BIOLOGICAL SCIENCE (biochemistry, biology/biological science, and nutrition), BUSINESS (accounting, banking and finance, business administration and management, hotel/motel and restaurant management, insurance, international business management, management information systems, management science, marketing/retailing/merchandising, personnel management, real estate, and recreation and leisure services), COMMUNICATIONS AND THE ARTS (advertising, art history and appreciation, classics, communications, dance, dramatic arts, English, film arts, fine arts, French, German, Greek, Italian, Latin, literature, music, music history and appreciation, music performance, music theory and composition, Russian, Spanish, and speech/debate/rhetoric), COMPUTER AND PHYSICAL SCIENCE (atmospheric sciences and meteorology, chemistry, computer science, geology, mathematics, physics, and statistics), EDUCATION (art, early childhood, education of the mentally handicapped, education of the visually handicapped, elementary, home economics, music, physical, secondary, and specific learning disabilities), ENGINEERING AND ENVIRONMENTAL DESIGN (chemical engineering, civil engineering, electrical/electronics engineering, industrial engineering, interior design, and mechanical engineering), HEALTH PROFESSIONS (health science, music therapy, nursing, predentistry, prepharmacy, preveterinary science, rehabilitation therapy, and speech pathology/audiology), SOCIAL SCIENCE (American studies, anthropology, Asian/Oriental studies, child care/child and family studies, clothing and textiles management/production/services, criminology, Eastern European studies, economics, geography, history, home economics, humanities, international relations, Latin American studies, ministries, philosophy, political science/government, prelaw, psychology, religion, Russian and Slavic studies, social work, and sociology). Computer science and natural science are the strongest academically. Business, communication, and criminology have the largest enrollments.

Required: Most academic areas require at least 120 semester hours for graduation. Students must take the Florida College-level Academic Skills Test (CLAST). The required core curriculum includes 12 semester hours in communications, 10 in natural science, 9 each in humanities and social science, 6 in history, and 3 in fine and performing arts.

Special: Cross-registration with Florida Agricultural and Mechanical University and Tallahassee Community College is possible, as is study at FSU centers in London or Florence and in programs in Costa Rica, France, Panama, and Switzerland, among other countries. FSU offers cooperative programs in engineering, computer science, business, and communication; work-study programs; and general studies and combined B.A.-B.S. degrees. Internships are required in criminology, human science, and social work. There is a freshman honors program on campus, as well as 42 national honor societies, including Phi Beta Kappa. Forty-four departments have honors programs.

Faculty/Classroom: Seventy percent of faculty are male; 30%, female. Ninety-five percent both teach and do research. Graduate students teach 45% of introductory courses. The average class size in an

introductory lecture is 16; in a laboratory, 21; and in a regular course offering, 34.

Admissions: About 75% of the 1993–94 applicants were accepted. The SAT scores for the 1993–94 freshman class were as follows: Verbal—44% below 500, 42% between 500 and 599, 13% between 600 and 700, and 1% above 700; Math—19% below 500, 42% between 500 and 599, 32% between 600 and 700, and 7% above 700. There were 45 National Merit semifinalists and 3 finalists.

Requirements: The SAT I or ACT is required. Most in-state students accepted at FSU present at least a B average in all academic subjects (grades 9–12) and test scores of at least 24 (composite) on the ACT or 1000 (verbal plus math) on SAT I. Out-of-state applicants ordinarily must meet higher standards. Applicants should be graduates of accredited high schools or have the GED. Secondary preparation must include 4 units of English; 3 units each of mathematics (algebra I and above), natural science (at least 2 with laboratory), and social science; 2 units of the same foreign language; and 4 elective units, preferably from the above categories. AP and CLEP credits are accepted. Important factors used in the admissions decision are advanced placement or honor courses, evidence of special talent, leadership record, geographic diversity, and recommendations by school officials.

Procedure: Freshmen are admitted in the fall and summer. Entrance exams should be taken in the second semester of the junior year. Applications should be filed by March 1 for fall entry and March 1 for summer entry, along with an application fee of $20. Notification is sent on a rolling basis. There is an early admissions plan.

Transfer: A total of 2523 transfer students enrolled in 1993–94. Transfer applicants should present at least a 2.5 cumulative college GPA unless transferring from a Florida public institution with an associate degree, in which case the minimum college GPA needed varies according to major. GPA requirements for limited access programs vary. Applicants with fewer than 60 semester hours must also meet freshman admission requirements. Admission requirements vary yearly with enrollment limitations and the quantity and quality of applicants. The last 30 credits out of 120 must be completed at FSU.

Visiting: There are regularly scheduled orientations for prospective students, including special visitation days on most Mondays and Fridays throughout the year. The Visitor Information Center offers campus tours 3 times daily on weekdays and can be reached at (904) 644-3246. There are guides for informal visits, and visitors may sit in on classes. To arrange for a visit, contact the Office of Admissions at (904) 644-6200.

Financial Aid: In 1993–94, 42% of all current freshmen and 48% of continuing students received some form of financial aid. About 43% of freshmen and 47% of continuing students received need-based aid. The average freshman award was $7000. Of that total, scholarships or need-based grants averaged $1030 ($3300 maximum); loans averaged $1600 ($4000 maximum); and work contracts averaged $1000 ($1600 maximum). Ten percent of undergraduate students work part-time. Average earnings from campus work for the school year are $1600. The average financial indebtedness of the 1992–93 graduate was $9000. FSU is a member of CSS. The college's own financial statement and FAFSA are required. The deadline for financial aid applications is March 1.

International Students: There are currently 788 international students enrolled. The school actively recruits these students. They must take the TOEFL and achieve a minimum score of 550. Students whose native language is English must also take the SAT I or ACT; those scores are used for placement purposes.

Computers: The college provides computer facilities for student use. The mainframes are an IBM RS6000 and 9375, a Cray Y-MP, a CM-2, a CDC CYBER 850, and a DEC VAX 6210. There is also a supercomputer on campus. All students may access the system. There are no time limits on using the system and no fees. It is recommended that students in the College of Engineering have personal computers.

Graduates: In 1992–93, 5533 bachelor's degrees were awarded. The most popular majors among graduates were criminology (8%), communications (6%), and psychology (6%). Within an average freshman class, 1% graduate in 3 years, 29% in 4 years, 56% in 5 years, and 61% in 6 years.

Admissions Contact: Office of Admissions.

JACKSONVILLE UNIVERSITY
Jacksonville, FL 32211

D-1

(904) 745-7000
(800) 225-2027 (out-of-state)

Full-time: 841 men, 723 women
Part-time: 224 men, 285 women
Graduate: 155 men, 179 women
Year: semesters, summer session
Application Deadline: April 1
Freshman Class: 1347 applied, 1119 accepted, 305 enrolled
SAT I or ACT: required

Faculty: 110; IIB, -$
Ph.D.s: 64%
Student/Faculty: 14 to 1
Tuition: $9320
Room & Board: $4070

COMPETITIVE

Jacksonville University, founded in 1934, is an independent institution offering bachelor's degrees through the colleges of arts and sciences, fine arts, and business. There are 3 undergraduate and 2 graduate schools. In addition to regional accreditation, JU has baccalaureate program accreditation with NASM and NLN. The library contains 502,143 volumes, 97,395 microform items, and 31,734 audiovisual forms, and subscribes to 733 periodicals. Computerized library sources and services include the card catalog, interlibrary loans, and database searching. Special learning facilities include a learning resource center, art gallery, planetarium, and radio station. The 260-acre campus is in a suburban area near the Saint Johns River. Including residence halls, there are 33 buildings on campus.

Student Life: About 64% of undergraduates are from Florida. Students come from 44 states, 59 foreign countries, and Canada. Eighty-one percent are white. Forty-seven percent claim no religious affiliation; 18% Catholic. The average age of freshmen is 19; all undergraduates, 23. Twenty-nine percent drop out by the end of their first year; 39% remain to graduate.

Housing: A total of 1000 students can be accommodated in college housing. College-sponsored living facilities include single-sex dormitories and off-campus apartments. On-campus housing is guaranteed for all 4 years and is available on a first-come, first-served basis. Fifty-two percent of students commute. All students may keep cars on campus.

Activities: About 30% of men belong to 7 national fraternities; about 23% of women belong to 5 national sororities. There are 73 groups on campus, including art, band, cheerleading, choir, chorale, chorus, dance, drama, drill team, ethnic, film, honors, international, jazz band, literary magazine, musical theater, newspaper, opera, orchestra, pep band, photography, political, professional, radio and TV, religious, social, social service, student government, symphony, and yearbook. Popular campus events include Homecoming.

Sports: There are 8 intercollegiate sports for men and 6 for women, and 13 intramural sports for men and 13 for women. Athletic and recreation facilities include a 1500-seat stadium, a gymnasium, pool, a boat house, baseball and softball diamonds, a 9-hole golf course, a soccer field, and an archery range. There are also tennis, basketball, handball/racquetball, volleyball, and shuffleboard courts, an all-purpose playing field, a 440-yard track, a 540-seat auditorium, a 220-seat recital hall, and a dance pavilion.

Disabled Students: Ninety percent of the campus is accessible to disabled students. The following facilities are available: wheelchair ramps, elevators, special parking, specially equipped rest rooms, special class scheduling, and lowered drinking fountains.

Services: In addition to many counseling and information services, tutoring is available in most subjects. There is a reader service for the blind, remedial math, reading, and writing, and a writer service for note taking in class.

Campus Safety and Security: Campus safety and security measures include 24-hour foot and vehicle patrol, escort service, informal discussions, and pamphlets, posters, and films. In addition, there are emergency telephones and lighted pathways and sidewalks.

Programs of Study: JU awards the B.A., B.S., B.F.A., B.M., B.S.N., B.M.E., B.A.E., and B.G.S. degrees. Master's degrees also are awarded. Bachelor's degrees are awarded in BIOLOGICAL SCIENCE (biology/biological science and marine science), BUSINESS (accounting, banking and finance, business administration and management, business economics, entrepreneurial studies, international business management, management information systems, and marketing/retailing/merchandising), COMMUNICATIONS AND THE ARTS (art, art history and appreciation, communications, dance, design, dramatic arts, English, fine arts, languages, and music), COMPUTER AND PHYSICAL SCIENCE (chemistry, computer science, mathematics, and physics), EDUCATION (art, early childhood, education of the exceptional child, elementary, foreign languages, music, science, and secondary), ENGINEERING AND ENVIRONMENTAL DESIGN (commercial art, computer graphics, and environmental science), HEALTH PROFESSIONS (medical laboratory technology, nursing, predentistry, and premedicine), SOCIAL SCIENCE (economics, geography, history, international relations, philosophy, political science/government, psychology, public administration, and sociology). Science and mathematics are the strongest academically. Business programs have the largest enrollment.

Required: All students must complete a core curriculum, including English 111 and 112, 9 hours of humanities/fine arts, 7 hours of natural science, 6 hours each of English, mathematics, socio-political science, and Western civilization, 3 hours each of intensive writing, economics, and computer information systems, and 2 hours of physical education. A total of 128 hours, with a minimum GPA of 2.0 is needed to graduate.

Special: Internships and student-designed majors are available, as are an accelerated degree program in mechanical engineering and a dual major in music and business. There is a co-op program in art and a 3–2 engineering degree available with 7 major universities. Credit for military experience and study abroad are also possible. There is a freshman honors program on campus, as well as 12 national honor societies.

Faculty/Classroom: Sixty-seven percent of faculty are male; 33%, female. Eighty-three percent teach undergraduates. No introductory courses are taught by graduate students. The average class size in an introductory lecture is 15; in a laboratory, 13; and in a regular course offering, 15.

Admissions: About 83% of the 1993–94 applicants were accepted. About 27% of the current freshmen were in the top fifth of their class; 43% were in the top two fifths.

Requirements: The SAT I or ACT is required. Applicants must be graduates of an accredited secondary school or have a GED. At least 18 academic credits are required. Art students must submit a portfolio, and music and theater students must audition. AP and CLEP credits are accepted. Important factors used in the admissions decision are advanced placement or honor courses, recommendations by school officials, leadership record, evidence of special talent, and extracurricular activities record.

Procedure: Freshmen are admitted to all sessions. Entrance exams should be taken spring of the junior or senior year and/or fall of the senior year. Early decision applications should be filed by November 15; regular applications, by April 1 for fall entry and November 15 for spring entry, along with an application fee of $25. Notification of early decision is sent December 1; regular decision, on a rolling basis. There are early admissions and deferred admissions plans.

Transfer: About 269 transfer students enrolled in 1993–94. Transfer students must submit official transcripts from all colleges attended. Art students must submit a portfolio; music and dance students must audition. Transfer applicants must have completed at least one semester at an accredited university and be in good standing at the last institution attended. A total of 32 credits out of 128 must be completed at JU.

Visiting: There are regularly scheduled orientations for prospective students, consisting of an interview, campus tour, advisement, area presentations, registration, and parents program. There are guides for informal visits and visitors may sit in on classes and stay overnight at the school. To arrange for a visit, contact the Admissions office at (904) 745–7000 or (800) 225–2027.

Financial Aid: In 1993–94 82% of all current freshmen and 85% of continuing students received some form of financial aid. About 63% of freshmen and 46% of continuing students received need-based aid. The average freshman award was $10,678. Of that total, scholarships or need-based grants averaged $6342 ($16,000 maximum); and loans averaged $3000 ($5625 maximum). Sixteen percent of undergraduate students work part-time. Average earnings from campus work for the school year are $1000. JU is a member of CSS. The college's own financial statement and FAFSA are required. The deadline for financial aid applications is March 15.

International Students: There are currently 148 international students enrolled. The school actively recruits these students. They must take the TOEFL and achieve a minimum score of 500. The student must also take SAT I or the ACT.

Computers: The college provides computer facilities for student use. The mainframe is an HP 3000 Series 70. Seven laboratories are open for student use from 9 A.M. to 10 P.M. weekdays and noon to 10 P.M. on Sunday. One contains 20 terminals connected to the HP 3000, another is a network of 12 Macintosh SE's, and a third contains 10 terminals attached to a 3B2 computer. The remaining facilities have stand alone microcomputers with hard drives. There are also 44 PC-compatible machines available for student use in the laboratories. All students may access the system. It may be used during laboratory hours from 9 A.M. to 10 P.M. Monday through Thursday, 9 A.M. to 5 P.M. Friday, noon to 5 P.M. Saturday, and noon to 10 P.M. Sunday. There are no time limits on using the system and no fees.

Graduates: In 1992–93 457 bachelor's degrees were awarded. The most popular majors among graduates were communications (7%), business administration (7%), and marketing (6%). Within an average freshman class, 1% graduate in 3 years, 34% in 4 years, 46% in 5 years, and 47% in 6 years. Some 35 companies recruited on campus in 1992–93.

Admissions Contact: Frank J. Vastola, Director of Admissions.

LYNN UNIVERSITY
Boca Raton, FL 33431

E-5

(407) 994–0770

(800) 544–8035 (out-of-state)

Full-time: 670 men, 580 women	Faculty: 55
Part-time: 67 men, 152 women	Ph.D.s: 71%
Graduate: 25 men, 30 women	Student/Faculty: 23 to 1
Year: semesters, summer session	Tuition: $13,200
Application Deadline: open	Room & Board: $5100
Freshman Class: 1630 applied, 1206 accepted, 429 enrolled	
SAT I Verbal/Math: 440/470	ACT: 21 COMPETITIVE

Lynn University, formerly College of Boca Raton was founded in 1962, and is a private, nonsectarian, liberal arts college offering graduate and undergraduate programs in the arts and sciences, business, education, hospitality, and preprofessional studies. In addition to regional accreditation, LU has baccalaureate program accreditation with ABFSE. The library contains 75,000 volumes, 8600 microform items, and 1800 audiovisual forms, and subscribes to 630 periodicals. Computerized library sources and services include interlibrary loans and database searching. Special learning facilities include a learning resource center and art gallery. The 123-acre campus is in a suburban area midway between Fort Lauderdale and Palm Beach. Including residence halls, there are 15 buildings on campus.

Student Life: About 70% of undergraduates are from out-of-state, mostly the Northeast. Students come from 35 states, 40 foreign countries, and Canada. Thirty-four percent are from public schools; 66% from private. Thirty-eight percent are Protestant; 36% Catholic; 26% Jewish. The average age of freshmen is 19; all undergraduates, 20. Fifteen percent drop out by the end of their first year; 61% remain to graduate.

Housing: A total of 680 students can be accommodated in college housing. College-sponsored living facilities include single-sex and coed dormitories. On-campus housing is guaranteed for all 4 years. Sixty-five percent of students live on campus; of those, 74% remain on campus on weekends. All students may keep cars on campus.

Activities: There are 2 local fraternities. There are no sororities on campus. There are 26 groups on campus, including cheerleading, choir, ethnic, honors, international, newspaper, photography, political, religious, social, social service, student government, and yearbook. Popular campus events include Homecoming Weekend and Holiday Formal.

Sports: There are 5 intercollegiate sports for men and 4 for women, and 10 intramural sports for men and 6 for women. Athletic and recreation facilities include baseball and soccer fields, tennis courts, indoor and outdoor basketball courts, an outdoor pool, and a weight facility.

Disabled Students: Ninety percent of the campus is accessible to disabled students. The following facilities are available: wheelchair ramps, elevators, special parking, specially equipped rest rooms, special class scheduling, and lowered drinking fountains.

Services: In addition to many counseling and information services, tutoring is available in some subjects. There are services for learning disabled students. There is remedial math, reading, and writing.

Campus Safety and Security: Campus safety and security measures include self-defense education, escort service, informal discussions, and pamphlets, posters, and films. In addition, there are lighted pathways and sidewalks.

Programs of Study: LU awards the B.A. and B.S. degrees. Associate and master's degrees also are awarded. Bachelor's degrees are awarded in BUSINESS (accounting, business administration and management, fashion merchandising, hotel/motel and restaurant management, marketing/retailing/merchandising, recreational facilities management, sports management, and tourism), COMMUNICATIONS AND THE ARTS (communications, design, fine arts, and graphic design), EDUCATION (early childhood, education, elementary, and secondary), ENGINEERING AND ENVIRONMENTAL DESIGN (aviation administration/management), HEALTH PROFESSIONS (health care administration), SOCIAL SCIENCE (history, human services, humanities, political science/government, prelaw, psychology, and sociology). Accounting, international management, and education. are the strongest academically. Business administration and hotel restaurant management have the largest enrollments.

Required: Students are required to complete 122 to 128 credits, with 45 to 50 in the major, and must maintain a minimum GPA of 2.0. In addition, all students must complete a core curriculum of 38 semester hours.

Special: Opportunities are provided for internships, which are required in many majors. There is study abroad in Ireland and Sweden. Credit by examination, credit for life experience, and pass/fail options are available.

Faculty/Classroom: Sixty percent of faculty are male; 40%, female. No introductory courses are taught by graduate students. The average class size in an introductory lecture is 26; in a laboratory, 20; and in a regular course offering, 22.

Admissions: About 74% of the 1993–94 applicants were accepted. About 4 freshmen graduated first in their class.

Requirements: A minimum GPA of 2.0 is required. The SAT I or ACT is required. Graduation from an accredited secondary school is required; a GED will be accepted. Applicants must have a minimum high school GPA of 2.0. An essay and an interview are recommended. AP and CLEP credits are accepted. Important factors used in the admissions decision are recommendations by school officials, personality, intangible qualities, extracurricular activities record, leadership record, and evidence of special talent.

Procedure: Freshmen are admitted fall and spring. Entrance exams should be taken during the junior or senior year. Application deadlines are open. The application fee is $25. Notification is sent on a rolling basis. There are early admissions and deferred admissions plans.

Transfer: About 115 transfer students enrolled in 1993–94. Transfer students must submit an official transcript from each previous college attended, plus a recommendation from the dean of students. The student must have maintained a minimum GPA of 2.0. An interview is recommended. A total of 30 credits out of 122 must be completed at LU.

Visiting: There are guides for informal visits and visitors may sit in on classes. To arrange for a visit, contact the Office of Admissions at (407) 994-0770.

Financial Aid: In 1993–94 46% of all current freshmen and 49% of continuing students received some form of financial aid. Scholarships or need-based grants averaged $1000 ($14,000 maximum); loans averaged $2625 ($4000 maximum); and work contracts averaged $800 ($1200 maximum). The average financial indebtedness of the 1992–93 graduate was $5250. LU is a member of CSS. The FFS is required. The deadline for financial aid applications is February 15.

International Students: There are currently 220 international students enrolled. The school actively recruits these students. They must take the TOEFL and achieve a minimum score of 500.

Computers: The college provides computer facilities for student use. The mainframe is an AS400. Apple and IBM microcomputers are available in the library and computer classroom. All students may access the system. There are no time limits on using the system and no fees.

Graduates: In 1992–93 246 bachelor's degrees were awarded. Some 61 companies recruited on campus in 1992–93. In the 1992 graduating class, 92% of the men and 87% of the women had found employment within 6 months of graduation.

Admissions Contact: Chuck Somma, Director of Admissions.

NEW COLLEGE OF THE UNIVERSITY OF SOUTH FLORIDA

D-4

Sarasota, FL 34243–2197   (813) 359–4269

Full-time: 260 men, 276 women	Faculty: 51; I, --$
Part-time: none	Ph.D.s: 94%
Graduate: none	Student/Faculty: 11 to 1
Year: 4–1–4	Tuition: $2030 ($7913)
Application Deadline: May 1	Room & Board: $3667

Freshman Class: 803 applied, 283 accepted, 146 enrolled

SAT I or ACT: required   **MOST COMPETITIVE**

New College of the University of South Florida, established in 1960, is the honors college of the State University System of Florida. The library contains 228,000 volumes, 400,000 microform items, and 1300 audiovisual forms, and subscribes to 1196 periodicals. Computerized library sources and services include the card catalog, interlibrary loans, and database searching. Special learning facilities include a media and technology center. The 116-acre campus is in a suburban area 50 miles south of Tampa. Including residence halls, there are 31 buildings on campus.

Student Life: About 60% of undergraduates are from Florida. Students come from 40 states, 8 foreign countries, and Canada. Eighty percent are from public schools; 20% from private. Eighty-eight percent are white. The average age of freshmen is 18; all undergraduates, 23. Fifteen percent drop out by the end of their first year; 60% remain to graduate.

Housing: A total of 300 students can be accommodated in college housing. College-sponsored living facilities include single-sex and coed dormitories. On-campus housing is guaranteed for the freshman year only and is available on a lottery system for upperclassmen. Sixty percent of students live on campus; of those, 85% remain on campus on weekends. All students may keep cars on campus.

Activities: There are no fraternities or sororities on campus. Groups and organizations on campus include choir, dance, drama, ethnic, gay, international, literary magazine, political, religious, social, social service, and student government. Popular campus events include schoolwide Halloween and graduation parties, a student/faculty softball game, a semiformal dance, an AIDS benefit dance marathon, and open houses with the resident counselor and the college dean and warden.

Sports: Athletic and recreation facilities include outdoor racquetball, tennis, and basketball courts, a volleyball pit, a swimming pool, a fitness center with Nautilus equipment, and indoor facilities for racquetball, aerobics, and dance.

Disabled Students: Sixty percent of the campus is accessible to disabled students. The following facilities are available: wheelchair ramps, elevators, special parking, specially equipped rest rooms, lowered drinking fountains, and lowered telephones.

Services: In addition to many counseling and information services, tutoring is available in most subjects. There is a reader service for the blind and remedial writing.

Campus Safety and Security: Campus safety and security measures include 24-hour foot and vehicle patrol, self defense education, escort service, and informal discussions. In addition, there are pamphlets, posters, and films, emergency telephones, lighted pathways and sidewalks, 24-hour dispatch/information services, and fire/smoke alarm systems in all dormitories.

Programs of Study: New College awards the B.A. degree. Bachelor's degrees are awarded in BIOLOGICAL SCIENCE (biology/biological science), COMMUNICATIONS AND THE ARTS (art history and appreciation, classics, fine arts, French, German, languages, literature, music, Russian, and Spanish), COMPUTER AND PHYSICAL SCIENCE (chemistry, computer science, mathematics, natural sciences, and physics), ENGINEERING AND ENVIRONMENTAL DESIGN (environmental science), SOCIAL SCIENCE (anthropology, economics, history, humanities, international relations, philosophy, political science/government, psychology, religion, social science, and sociology). Biology, political science, physical sciences, and literature are the strongest academically. Psychology, biology, and literature have the largest enrollments.

Required: An academic credit system is not used. To qualify for graduation, students must complete 7 contracts, which are designed by the student in consultation with faculty; 3 independent study projects completed during January each year, between the fall and spring semesters; a senior thesis, which involves original research or creative work and includes working closely with a faculty committee of the student's choice; and an oral baccalaureate exam, which is primarily a defense of the senior thesis.

Faculty/Classroom: Seventy-five percent of faculty are male; 25%, female. All teach undergraduates and 95% also do research. The average class size in an introductory lecture is 35; in a laboratory, 15; and in a regular course offering, 15.

Admissions: About 35% of the 1993–94 applicants were accepted. The SAT scores for the 1993–94 freshman class were as follows: Verbal—3% below 500, 36% between 500 and 599, 46% between 600 and 700, and 15% above 700; Math—3% below 500, 23% between 500 and 599, 47% between 600 and 700, and 27% above 700. The ACT scores were 20% between 24 and 26, 22% between 27 and 28, and 57% above 28. About 89% of the current freshmen were in the top fifth of their class; 96% were in the top two fifths. There were 22 National Merit finalists.

Requirements: The SAT I or ACT is required. Graduation from an accredited secondary school (preferred) or GED is required; high school students should pursue at least 5 academic courses each year, at the most rigorous level available, with the minimum distribution of 4 years of English, 2 consecutive years of the same foreign language, and 3 years each of mathematics, sciences, and social sciences. A writing sample must be submitted as well as application essays. A formal interview is strongly recommended for all applicants and mandatory for students living within 100 miles of the campus. Important factors used in the admissions decision are advanced placement or honor courses, evidence of special talent, leadership record, personality, intangible qualities, and extracurricular activities record.

Procedure: Freshmen are admitted fall and spring. Entrance exams should be taken by the fall of the year prior to entrance. Applications should be filed by May 1 for fall entry and December 1 for spring entry, along with an application fee of $20. Notification is sent on a rolling basis. There are early admissions and deferred admissions plans.

Transfer: About 49 transfer students enrolled in 1993–94. Transfers must be in good academic and financial standing with their previous college(s). Transfers may receive credit for up to 3 semesters and 1 independent study project. While at New College, transfers receiving maximum credit must successfully complete at least 4 semesters, 2 independent study projects, and the senior thesis with baccalaureate exam.

Visiting: There are regularly scheduled orientations for prospective students, including a campus tour, information session, and/or class visit. Visitors may sit in on classes and stay overnight at the school. To arrange for a visit, contact the Office of Admissions at (813) 359–4269.

Financial Aid: In 1993–94, 60% of all current freshmen and 70% of continuing students received some form of financial aid. About 50% of all students received need-based aid. The average freshman award was $5900. Of that total, scholarships or need-based grants averaged $3700; loans averaged $1500 ($2625 maximum); and work contracts averaged $700 ($1800 maximum). Sixty-five percent of undergraduate students work part-time. Average earnings from campus work for the school year are $1800. The average financial indebtedness of the 1992–93 graduate was $9000. New College is a member of CSS. The FAF or FFS and FAFSA are required. The deadline for financial aid applications is March 1.

International Students: There are currently 20 international students enrolled. They must take the TOEFL and achieve a minimum score of 560. The student must also take the SAT I or ACT, if a native speaker of English.

Computers: The college provides computer facilities for student use. The mainframe is an IBM 3090. There are 16 IBM personal computers networked to the mainframe that are available for student use in a computer laboratory. There is also a student-operated Macintosh

laboratory, which has 12 microcomputers that are used mainly for word processing and are not connected to the mainframe. All students may access the system. It may be used 8 A.M. to 11 P.M. There are no time limits on using the system and no fees.

Graduates: In 1992–93, 106 bachelor's degrees were awarded. The most popular majors among graduates were biology (16%), psychology (8%), and literature (8%). Within an average freshman class, 15% graduate in 3 years, 48% in 4 years, 58% in 5 years, and 60% in 6 years. In the 1992 graduating class, 30% of the men and 30% of the women were enrolled in graduate school within 6 months of graduation.

Admissions Contact: David L. Anderson, Acting Director of Admissions.

NORTHWOOD INSTITUTE
(See Northwood University)

NORTHWOOD UNIVERSITY
(Formerly Northwood Institute)
West Palm Beach, FL 33409-9878

E-5

(407) 478-5500
(800) 458-8325 (out-of-state)

Full-time: 285 men, 205 women	Faculty: 12
Part-time: 20 men, 15 women	Ph.Ds: 54%
Graduate: none	Student/Faculty: 41 to 1
Year: quarters, summer session	Tuition: $9355
Application Deadline: August 1	Room & Board: $5214

Freshman Class: 494 applied, 359 accepted, 110 enrolled

SAT I or ACT: required

COMPETITIVE

Northwood University, founded in 1959, is an independent institution that offers an undergraduate program in business administration. The library contains 21,000 volumes and subscribes to 300 periodicals. Special learning facilities include an art gallery. The 90-acre campus is in a suburban area 70 miles north of Miami. Including residence halls, there are 4 buildings on campus.

Student Life: About 63% of undergraduates are from out-of-state, mostly the South. Students come from 27 states, 12 foreign countries, and Canada. Seventy-eight percent are from public schools; 22% from private. Seventy percent are white; 13% foreign nationals; 12% African American. The average age of freshmen is 18; all undergraduates, 20. Fifteen percent drop out by the end of their first year; 62% remain to graduate.

Housing: A total of 410 students can be accommodated in college housing. College-sponsored living facilities include single-sex on-campus apartments. On-campus housing is guaranteed for all 4 years. Fifty percent of students live on campus; of those, 65% remain on campus on weekends. Alcohol is not permitted. All students may keep cars on campus.

Activities: There are no fraternities or sororities on campus. There are 15 groups on campus, including art, computers, drama, ethnic, honors, international, newspaper, pep band, political, professional, social, social service, student government, and yearbook. Popular campus events include the Automotive Industry Show, Job Fair, speakers, and art showings.

Sports: There are 2 intercollegiate and 9 intramural sports each for men and women. Athletic and recreation facilities include playing fields, a student center, and a recreation center with an outdoor swimming pool and basketball, tennis, and handball/racquetball courts.

Disabled Students: Eighty percent of the campus is accessible to disabled students. The following facilities are available: wheelchair ramps, elevators, special parking, specially equipped rest rooms, and special class scheduling.

Services: In addition to many counseling and information services, tutoring is available in some subjects, including accounting, mathematics, English, and computers. There also is remedial math and writing.

Campus Safety and Security: Campus safety and security measures include 24-hour foot and vehicle patrol, informal discussions, pamphlets, posters, and films, and emergency telephones. In addition, there are lighted pathways and sidewalks.

Programs of Study: Northwood awards the B.B.A. degree. Associate degrees also are awarded. Bachelor's degrees are awarded in BUSINESS (accounting, banking and finance, business administration and management, and marketing management), COMPUTER AND PHYSICAL SCIENCE (computer science and information sciences and systems), ENGINEERING AND ENVIRONMENTAL DESIGN (industrial administration/management). Accounting and computer science are the strongest academically. Business management and automotive marketing have the largest enrollments.

Required: To graduate, all students must complete 194 to 200 quarter hours, including 44 to 52 in the major, with a minimum 2.0 GPA. Courses in computer science and executive fitness are required.

Special: Northwood offers cooperative programs and cross-registration with Georgian College in Canada; internships with various automotive and fashion marketing corporations; study in Great Britain, France, Greece, Italy, Germany, or several Eastern European nations; various work-study programs; an accelerated degree program in continuing education; dual majors, including automotive marketing/management; credit for military experience; and nondegree study. The External Plan of Study is a degree program offered through the extension center and located at military bases in Michigan, Louisiana, Washington, Texas, and Florida. There is a freshman honors program on campus

Faculty/Classroom: Sixty-one percent of faculty are male; 39%, female. All teach undergraduates. The average class size in an introductory lecture is 20; in a laboratory, 22; and in a regular course offering, 15.

Admissions: About 73% of the 1993–94 applicants were accepted. There were 2 National Merit semifinalists. Five freshmen graduated first in their class.

Requirements: A minimum GPA of 2.0 is required. The SAT I or ACT is required. In addition, applicants must be graduates of an accredited secondary school or have a GED certificate. An interview is recommended. AP and CLEP credits are accepted. Important factors used in the admissions decision are recommendations by school officials, personality, intangible qualities, extracurricular activities record, leadership record, and advanced placement or honor courses.

Procedure: Freshmen are admitted to all sessions. Entrance exams should be taken in the fall of the senior year. Applications should be filed by August 1 for fall entry, November 1 for winter entry, February 1 for spring entry, and May 1 for summer entry, along with an application fee of $15. Notification is sent on a rolling basis. There is a deferred admissions plan.

Transfer: A total of 95 transfer students enrolled in 1993–94. Applicants must have a minimum 2.0 GPA, with at least 15 credit hours earned. Good academic and social standing are required. An interview is recommended. A total of 45 quarter hours out of 194 to 200 must be completed at Northwood.

Visiting: There are regularly scheduled orientations for prospective students, including a fall and spring open house, campus tours, and meetings with students and financial aid and academic staff. There are guides for informal visits and visitors may sit in on classes, with prior permission. To arrange for a visit, contact Admissions at (800) 458-8325 (out-of-state) or (407) 478-5500.

Financial Aid: In a recent year, 79% of all current freshmen and 47% of continuing students received some form of financial aid. About 66% of freshmen and 36% of continuing students received need-based aid. The average freshman award was $10,275. Of that total, scholarships or need-based grants averaged $8165 ($10,250 maximum); loans averaged $2594 ($2625 maximum); and work contracts averaged $1800 (maximum). Ten percent of undergraduate students work part-time. Average earnings from campus work for the school year are $1250. The average financial indebtedness of a recent graduate was $6723. Northwood is a member of CSS. The FAF and the college's own financial statement are required. The deadline for financial aid applications is March 15.

International Students: There are currently 68 international students enrolled. The school actively recruits these students. They must take the TOEFL and achieve a minimum score of 500.

Computers: Northwood provides computer facilities for student use. There are 22 IBM or MS/DOS-compatible microcomputers in computer classrooms available to all students when classes are not in session; 6 in the student center, always available; 3 in the library for general use; and 13 tied to special automotive software for those academic majors. There are no time limits on using the system. The fees are $25 per academic year.

Graduates: In a recent year, 85 bachelor's degrees were awarded. The most popular majors among graduates were business management (27%), automotive marketing (24%), and management/marketing (21%). Within an average freshman class, 1% graduate in 3 years, 60% in 4 years, and 1% in 5 years. Some 47 companies recruited on campus in a recent year. In a recent graduating class, 3% of the men and 2% of the women were enrolled in graduate school within 6 months of graduation; 52% of the men and 39% of the women had found employment.

Admissions Contact: J. Bradford Sargent, Admissions Director.

NOVA SOUTHEASTERN UNIVERSITY
E-5

Fort Lauderdale, FL 33314

(305) 475-7360

(800) 541-6682 (out-of-state)

Full-time: 786 men, 1302 women	Faculty: 133
Part-time: 475 men, 946 women	Ph.D.s: 85%
Graduate: 3630 men, 5116 women	Student/Faculty: 16 to 1
Year: trimesters, summer session	Tuition: $8100
Application Deadline: open	Room & Board: $4742
Freshman Class: 1200 applied, 900 accepted, 360 enrolled	
SAT I Verbal/Math: 435/480	**LESS COMPETITIVE**

Nova University, founded in 1964, is a private, coeducational institution offering undergraduate and graduate programs in liberal arts, sciences, business, and education. In January 1994, Southeastern University of the Health Sciences merged with Nova University; the new Health Professions Division is the result of that merger. Information in this profile, however, relates only to the original institution. There are 3 undergraduate and 7 graduate schools. The 2 libraries contain 196,720 volumes, 73,654 microform items, and 1000 audiovisual forms and subscribe to 6355 periodicals. Computerized library sources and services include the card catalog, interlibrary loans, and database searching. Special learning facilities include a learning resource center and radio station. The 200-acre campus is in a suburban area 10 miles west of Fort Lauderdale. Including residence halls, there are 17 buildings on campus.

Student Life: About 86% of undergraduates are from Florida. Students come from 30 states, 20 foreign countries, and Canada. Seventy-five percent are from public schools; 25% from private. Fifty-nine percent are white; 18% Hispanic; 18% African American. The average age of freshmen is 20.9; all undergraduates, 32.4. Fifteen percent drop out by the end of their first year; 70% remain to graduate.

Housing: A total of 560 students can be accommodated in college housing. College-sponsored living facilities include a coed dormitory, on-campus apartments, and married-student housing. On-campus housing is available on a first-come, first-served basis. Ninety-three percent of students commute. Alcohol is not permitted. All students may keep cars on campus.

Activities: About 11% of men belong to 3 national fraternities; about 11% of women belong to 2 national sororities. There are 32 groups on campus, including chess, computers, dance, drama, ethnic, honors, international, literary magazine, musical theater, newspaper, political, professional, radio and TV, religious, social, student government, and yearbook. Popular campus events include Homecoming, Spring Fest, Cabaret, Raft Race, and Make-a-Difference Day (Karnival for Kids).

Sports: There are 4 intercollegiate sports for men and 3 for women, and 4 intramural sports for men and 4 for women. Athletic and recreation facilities include baseball and soccer fields and 3 swimming pools.

Disabled Students: All of the campus is accessible to disabled students. The following facilities are available: wheelchair ramps, elevators, special parking, specially equipped rest rooms, and lowered drinking fountains; some buildings have wheelchair lifts.

Services: In addition to many counseling and information services, tutoring is available in most subjects. There is remedial math, reading, and writing.

Campus Safety and Security: Campus safety and security measures include 24-hour foot and vehicle patrol, informal discussions, pamphlets, posters, and films, and emergency telephones. In addition, there are lighted pathways and sidewalks.

Programs of Study: Nova awards the B.S., B.A., and Ed.Spec. degrees. Master's and doctoral degrees also are awarded. Bachelor's degrees are awarded in BUSINESS (accounting and business administration and management), COMPUTER AND PHYSICAL SCIENCE (computer science and information sciences and systems), EDUCATION (education of the exceptional child, elementary, and secondary), ENGINEERING AND ENVIRONMENTAL DESIGN (computer engineering), HEALTH PROFESSIONS (premedicine), SOCIAL SCIENCE (international studies, liberal arts/general studies, and psychology). Ocean studies and computer sciences are the strongest academically. Business and education have the largest enrollments.

Required: In order to graduate, all students must complete at least 120 credit hours and courses in computer literacy and macroeconomics. A minimum 2.25 GPA is needed for courses in the major, and a 2.0 for all other courses.

Special: The college offers internships, study abroad, work-study and accelerated degree programs, dual majors, and the general studies degree. Credit for military experience and nondegree study also are available. There is 1 national honor society on campus.

Faculty/Classroom: Sixty-seven percent of faculty are male; 33% female. Seventy-eight percent teach undergraduates and 10% both teach and do research. No introductory courses are taught by graduate students. The average class size in an introductory lecture and in a regular course offering is 20.

Admissions: About 75% of the 1993-94 applicants were accepted. The SAT scores for the 1993-94 freshman class were as follows: Verbal—84% below 500, 12% between 500 and 599, and 4% between 600 and 700; Math—63% below 500, 30% between 500 and 599, and 7% between 600 and 700.

Requirements: The SAT I or ACT is required. Applicants must be graduates of an accredited secondary school or have a GED certificate and have completed at least 16 academic credits, including 4 years of English. An essay is required, and an interview is recommended. AP and CLEP credits are accepted. Important factors used in the admissions decision are recommendations by school officials, recommendations by alumni, extracurricular activities record, parents or siblings attending the school, and leadership record.

Procedure: Freshmen are admitted to all sessions. Entrance exams should be taken early in the senior year. Application deadlines are open. The application fee is $40. Notification is sent on a rolling basis. There is an early admissions plan.

Transfer: About 170 transfer students enrolled in 1993-94. Transfer students must have a minimum 2.3 GPA and at least 15 credit hours earned. An interview is recommended. A total of 30 credits out of 120 must be completed at Nova.

Visiting: There are regularly scheduled orientations for prospective students. There are guides for informal visits and visitors may sit in on classes. To arrange for a visit, contact the Admissions Office at (305) 475-7360.

Financial Aid: In a recent year, all freshman and 95% of continuing students received some form of financial aid. About 60% of freshmen received need-based aid. The average freshman award was $7959. Of that total, scholarships or need-based grants averaged $2000 ($4000 maximum); loans averaged $2625 (maximum); and work contracts averaged $1600 (maximum). The average financial indebtedness of a recent year's graduate was $10,000. Nova is a member of CSS. The FAF or FFS and the college's own financial statement are required. The deadline for financial aid applications is April 1.

International Students: There are currently 253 international students enrolled. The school actively recruits these students. They must take the TOEFL and achieve a minimum score of 500.

Computers: The college provides computer facilities for student use. The mainframe is a DEC 5910 RISC. There are several microcomputer laboratories available, including in the dormitories. All students may access the system. There are no time limits on using the system. The fees are $35.

Graduates: In 1992-93 1012 bachelor's degrees were awarded. The most popular majors among graduates were business (57%), education (31%), and psychology (6%). Within an average freshman class, 5% graduate in 4 years, 15% in 5 years, and 30% in 6 years. Some 50 companies recruited on campus in 1992-93.

Admissions Contact: Jean Lewis, Director of Undergraduate Admissions.

PALM BEACH ATLANTIC COLLEGE
E-5

West Palm Beach, FL 33416-4708

(407) 835-4309

(800) 238-3998 (out-of-state)

Full-time: 615 men, 814 women	Faculty: 68
Part-time: 153 men, 165 women	Ph.D.s: 73%
Graduate: 57 men, 44 women	Student/Faculty: 21 to 1
Year: semesters, summer session	Tuition: $7500
Application Deadline: open	Room & Board: $3220
Freshman Class: 700 applied, 625 accepted, 349 enrolled	
SAT I: 440/490	ACT: 21	**COMPETITIVE**

Palm Beach Atlantic College, founded in 1968 by Baptist church leaders, is a private, liberal arts institution with a Christian emphasis. The library contains more than 65,000 volumes and more than 600 audiovisual forms, and subscribes to more than 920 periodicals. Computerized library sources and services include interlibrary loans and database searching. Special learning facilities include a learning resource center. The 25-acre campus is in an urban area 60 miles north of Miami.

Student Life: About 63% of undergraduates are from Florida. Students come from 35 states, 23 foreign countries, and Canada. Eighty-four percent are white. Eighty-five percent are Protestant; 14% Catholic. The average age of freshmen is 18; all undergraduates, 20.

Housing: A total of 711 students can be accommodated in college housing. College-sponsored living facilities include single-sex dormitories, on-campus apartments, and married-student housing. On-campus housing is guaranteed for all 4 years. Priority is given to out-of-town students. Fifty-five percent of students live on campus. Alcohol is not permitted. All students may keep cars on campus.

Activities: There are no fraternities or sororities on campus. There are 30 groups on campus, including cheerleading, choir, chorale, chorus, computers, drama, honors, jazz band, musical theater, newspaper, orchestra, professional, religious, social, student government,

symphony, and yearbook. Popular campus events include American Free Enterprise Day and Christian Awareness Week.

Sports: There are 5 intercollegiate sports for men and 4 for women, and 18 intramural sports for men and 19 for women.

Disabled Students: Eighty percent of the campus is accessible to disabled students. The following facilities are available: wheelchair ramps, elevators, special parking, and specially equipped rest rooms.

Services: In addition to many counseling and information services, tutoring is available in most subjects. There is remedial math, reading, and writing.

Campus Safety and Security: Campus safety and security measures include 24-hour foot and vehicle patrol, escort service, emergency telephones, and lighted pathways and sidewalks.

Programs of Study: PBA awards the B.A., B.S., and B.H.R.M. degrees. Master's degrees also are awarded. Bachelor's degrees are awarded in BIOLOGICAL SCIENCE (biology/biological science), BUSINESS (accounting, banking and finance, business administration and management, business economics, human resources, international business management, and marketing/retailing/merchandising), COMMUNICATIONS AND THE ARTS (art, communications, dramatic arts, English, fine arts, music, speech/debate/rhetoric, and studio art), COMPUTER AND PHYSICAL SCIENCE (computer science and mathematics), EDUCATION (art, drama, elementary, and physical), SOCIAL SCIENCE (history, political science/government, psychology, and religion). Business, education, and psychology are the strongest academically and have the largest enrollments.

Required: In order to graduate, all students must complete basic core requirements and a minimum of 128 credit hours, with a minimum of 27 credit hours in the major. A minimum 2.0 GPA is required, as are courses in American Free Enterprise and the Old and New Testaments.

Special: PBA offers a London semester. There is a freshman honors program on campus.

Faculty/Classroom: Seventy-six percent of faculty are male; 24%, female. All teach and do research. No introductory courses are taught by graduate students. The average class size in an introductory lecture is 30; in a laboratory, 24; and in a regular course offering, 22.

Admissions: About 89% of the 1993–94 applicants were accepted. The SAT scores for the 1993–94 freshman class were as follows: Verbal—71% below 500, 23% between 500 and 599, and 6% between 600 and 700; Math—50% below 500, 34% between 500 and 599, 14% between 600 and 700, and 2% above 700. The ACT scores were 46% below 21, 24% between 21 and 23, 16% between 24 and 26, 7% between 27 and 28, and 7% above 28. About 21% of the current freshmen were in the top fifth of their class; 41% were in the top two fifths. About 2 freshmen graduated first in their class.

Requirements: A minimum GPA of 2.5 is required. Applicants must be graduates of an accredited secondary school or have a GED certificate, and have completed 18 academic credits. A minimum composite score of 920 on SAT I or 20 on the ACT, an essay, and an interview are required. A portfolio is recommended. AP and CLEP credits are accepted. Important factors used in the admissions decision are advanced placement or honor courses, leadership record, personality, intangible qualities, evidence of special talent, and extracurricular activities record.

Procedure: Freshmen are admitted to all sessions. Entrance exams should be taken in the junior year of high school. Notification is sent on a rolling basis. There are early admissions and deferred admissions plans. There is an application fee of $25. A waiting list is an active part of the admissions procedure, with about 8% of applicants on the list.

Transfer: About 226 transfer students enrolled in 1993–94. Transfer students must have a minimum 2.5 GPA, and an interview is encouraged. A total of 33 credits out of 128 must be completed at PBA.

Visiting: There are regularly scheduled orientations for prospective students, including a general open house and a school-0pecific open house during the year. There are guides for informal visits and visitors may sit in on classes and stay overnight at the school. To arrange for a visit, contact the Admissions Office at (407) 835-4309 or 800 238-3998.

Financial Aid: In an earlier year, 90% of all current freshmen and 85% of continuing students received some form of financial aid. Fifteen percent of undergraduate students work part-time. Average earnings from campus work for the school year are $1000. PBA is a member of CSS. The FAF or FFS is required. The deadline for financial aid applications is May 1.

International Students: There are currently 45 international students enrolled. The school actively recruits these students. They must take the TOEFL and achieve a minimum score of 500. The student must also take SAT I or the ACT.

Computers: The college provides computer facilities for student use. The mainframe is an IBM. No mainframe access is granted. Open-access computer laboratories are available to all students from 9 A.M. to 11 P.M. There are no fees.

Graduates: In an earlier class, 135 bachelor's degrees were awarded.

Admissions Contact: Rich Grimm, Dean of Admissions.

RINGLING SCHOOL OF ART AND DESIGN   D-4
Sarasota, FL 34234-5896   (813) 351-4614
(800) 255-7695 (out-of-state)

Full-time: 382 men, 238 women	Faculty: 80
Part-time: 10 men, 10 women	Ph.D.s: 70%
Graduate: none	Student/Faculty: 8 to 1
Year: semesters	Tuition: $10,350
Application Deadline: open	Room & Board: $5400
Freshman Class: 840 applied, 613 accepted, 240 enrolled	
SAT I or ACT: recommended	SPECIAL

Ringling School of Art and Design, founded in 1931, is a 4-year, private art college. In addition to regional accreditation, the college has baccalaureate program accreditation with FIDER and NASAD. The library contains 13,000 volumes, and subscribes to 200 periodicals. Computerized library sources and services include the card catalog, interlibrary loans, and database searching. Special learning facilities include an art gallery. The 30-acre campus is in an urban area 50 miles south of Tampa. Including residence halls, there are 12 buildings on campus.

Student Life: About 50% of undergraduates are from out-of-state, mostly the South. Students come from 38 states, 15 foreign countries, and Canada. Eighty-two percent are from public schools; 18% from private. Seventy-eight percent are white; 15% foreign nationals; 15% Hispanic. The average age of freshmen is 20; all undergraduates, 25. Sixteen percent drop out by the end of their first year; 80% remain to graduate.

Housing: A total of 166 students can be accommodated in college housing. College-sponsored living facilities include single-sex dormitories. On-campus housing is available on a first-come, first-served basis and is available on a lottery system for upperclassmen. Priority is given to out-of-town students. Sixty-seven percent of students commute. Alcohol is not permitted. All students may keep cars on campus.

Activities: There is 1 national fraternity. There are no sororities on campus. There are some groups and organizations on campus, including art, international, literary magazine, professional, social, social service, and student government. Popular campus events include Art in the Park, Founders Day, and Goombay Festival.

Sports: There are 3 intramural sports for men and 3 for women.

Disabled Students: Eighty percent of the campus is accessible to disabled students. The following facilities are available: wheelchair ramps, elevators, special parking, specially equipped rest rooms, special class scheduling, and lowered telephones.

Services: In addition to many counseling and information services, tutoring is available in some subjects, including English and mathematics. In addition, there is remedial math and writing.

Campus Safety and Security: Campus safety and security measures include 24-hour foot and vehicle patrol, escort service, informal discussions, and emergency telephones. In addition, there are lighted pathways and sidewalks.

Programs of Study: The college awards the B.F.A. degree. Bachelor's degrees are awarded in COMMUNICATIONS AND THE ARTS (fine arts, graphic design, and illustration), ENGINEERING AND ENVIRONMENTAL DESIGN (computer graphics and interior design). Illustration has the largest enrollment.

Required: In order to graduate, all students must complete 75 hours of studio art, 30 hours of liberal arts, and 18 hours of art history, with 75 hours in the major. A minimum 2.0 GPA and courses in drawing, 2-and 3-dimensional design, art history, American creativity, and written communication are required.

Faculty/Classroom: Sixty percent of faculty are male; 40%, female. The average class size in an introductory lecture is 30 and in a regular course offering, 20.

Admissions: About 73% of the 1993–94 applicants were accepted.

Requirements: A minimum GPA of 2.0 is required. The SAT I or ACT is recommended. Applicants must be graduates of an accredited secondary school or have a GED. Admission is based on a portfolio. An essay is required, and an interview is recommended. AP and CLEP credits are accepted. Important factors used in the admissions decision are evidence of special talent, advanced placement or honor courses, leadership record, extracurricular activities record, and recommendations by school officials.

Procedure: Freshmen are admitted in the fall. Application deadlines are open. Notification is sent on a rolling basis. There is an application fee of $30. A waiting list is an active part of the admissions procedure.

Transfer: Transfer students must meet the same criteria as freshmen and must also submit college transcripts. A total of 45 credits out of 123 must be completed at the college.

Visiting: There are guides for informal visits and visitors may sit in on classes. To arrange for a visit, contact the Admissions Office at (813) 351-4614.

Financial Aid: In 1993–94 80% of all current freshmen and 80% of continuing students received some form of financial aid. Scholarships or need-based grants averaged $1000 ($2500 maximum). The college is a member of CSS. The FAF and the college's own financial statement are required. The deadline for financial aid applications is March 15.

International Students: There are currently 28 international students enrolled. The school actively recruits these students. They must take the TOEFL and achieve a minimum score of 500.

Computers: The college provides computer facilities for student use. Microcomputers are available in the computer center. Those students enrolled in computer animation classes may access the system. There are no time limits on using the system and no fees.

Graduates: In a recent year, 78 bachelor's degrees were awarded.

Admissions Contact: James H. Dean, Director of Admissions.

ROLLINS COLLEGE

D-3

Winter Park, FL 32789

(407) 646–2161

Full-time: 621 men, 791 women

Part-time: 3 men, 4 women

Graduate: 297 men, 350 women

Year: 4–1–4

Application Deadline: February 15

Freshman Class: 1730 applied, 1125 accepted, 382 enrolled

SAT I or ACT: required

Faculty: 124; IIA, av$

Ph.Ds: 92%

Student/Faculty: 11 to 1

Tuition: $15,950

Room & Board: $4925

VERY COMPETITIVE

Rollins College, founded in 1885, is a private, liberal arts institution. There are 4 graduate schools. In addition to regional accreditation, Rollins has baccalaureate program accreditation with AACSB and NASM. The library contains 259,971 volumes, 32,635 microform items, and 3522 audiovisual forms, and subscribes to 1536 periodicals. Computerized library sources and services include the card catalog, interlibrary loans, and database searching. Special learning facilities include a learning resource center, art gallery, radio station, TV station, and art museum and theaters, a writing center, and a mathematics laboratory. The 65-acre campus is in a suburban area 5 miles north of Orlando. Including residence halls, there are 54 buildings on campus.

Student Life: About 65% of undergraduates are from out-of-state, mostly the Middle Atlantic. Students come from 45 states, 30 foreign countries, and Canada. Fifty-four percent are from public schools; 46% from private. Eighty-five percent are white. Forty-eight percent are Protestant; 28% Catholic; 12% Jewish. The average age of freshmen is 18; all undergraduates, 20. Twelve percent drop out by the end of their first year; 75% remain to graduate.

Housing: A total of 1100 students can be accommodated in college housing. College-sponsored living facilities include single-sex and coed dormitories, fraternity houses, and sorority houses. In addition there are honors houses and special interest houses. On-campus housing is guaranteed for all 4 years. Eighty percent of students live on campus; of those, 80% remain on campus on weekends. Upperclassmen may keep cars on campus.

Activities: About 35% of men belong to 1 local and 5 national fraternities; about 35% of women belong to 1 local and 5 national sororities. There are 75 groups on campus, including art, cheerleading, choir, chorale, chorus, computers, dance, drama, ethnic, film, gay, honors, international, jazz band, literary magazine, musical theater, newspaper, photography, political, professional, radio and TV, religious, social, social service, student government, and yearbook. Popular campus events include Rollins Autumn Art Festival, World Hunger Concert, the Bach Festival, Fox Day, Spring Thing, and Greek Week.

Sports: There are 9 intercollegiate sports for men and 10 for women, and 12 intramural sports for men and 12 for women. Athletic and recreation facilities include a 2500-seat auditorium, a 600-seat stadium, tennis courts, baseball and soccer fields, a field house with a gymnasium that seats 2500, a weight room, a new boat house, and a swimming pool.

Disabled Students: Fifty-five percent of the campus is accessible to disabled students. The following facilities are available: wheelchair ramps, elevators, special parking, specially equipped rest rooms, special class scheduling, lowered drinking fountains, and lowered telephones.

Services: In addition to many counseling and information services, tutoring is available in every subject, including mathematics, sciences, foreign languages, and others on request by peer tutors. In addition, there is a reader service for the blind, and remedial math, reading, and writing.

Campus Safety and Security: Campus safety and security measures include 24-hour foot and vehicle patrol, self defense education, escort service, and informal discussions. In addition, there are pam-

phlets, posters, films, emergency telephones, lighted pathways and sidewalks, and 24-hour locked residential units.

Programs of Study: Rollins awards the B.A. degree. Master's degrees also are awarded. Bachelor's degrees are awarded in BIOLOGICAL SCIENCE (biology/biological science), COMMUNICATIONS AND THE ARTS (art history and appreciation, dramatic arts, English, French, German, music history and appreciation, music performance, Spanish, studio art, and voice), COMPUTER AND PHYSICAL SCIENCE (chemistry, computer science, mathematics, and physics), EDUCATION (elementary), ENGINEERING AND ENVIRONMENTAL DESIGN (environmental science), SOCIAL SCIENCE (anthropology, classical/ancient civilization, economics, history, international relations, Latin American studies, philosophy, political science/government, psychology, religion, and sociology). English, biology, chemistry, physics, and theater arts are the strongest academically. Psychology, economics, English, politics, and environmental studies have the largest enrollments.

Required: All students must complete at least 6 skills, including at least 4 cognitive, and at least 2 affective courses, a values requirement, and 4 physical education courses. A minimum of 35 course units, with 12 to 16 in the course major, and a minimum GPA of 2.0 are required to graduate.

Special: Rollins offers cross-registration with the evening studies division, co-op programs with American University in Washington, D.C., and Paris and Duke University School of Forestry and Environmental Studies, departmental and professional internships, study abroad in 2 countries, and a Washington semester. Also available are work-study programs, an accelerated degree program in management, the B.A.-B.S. degree in preengineering, dual majors in any combination, and student-designed majors. A 3–2 engineering degree with Washington University in St. Louis, and Auburn, Georgia Institute of Technology, Case-Western Reserve, and Columbia Universities is offered. Nondegree study and pass/fail options are possible. There is a freshman honors program on campus, as well as 3 national honor societies.

Faculty/Classroom: Sixty-eight percent of faculty are male; 32%, female. One-hundred percent both teach and do research. No introductory courses are taught by graduate students. The average class size in an introductory lecture is 25; in a laboratory, 20; and in a regular course offering, 15.

Admissions: About 65% of the 1993–94 applicants were accepted. The SAT scores for the 1993–94 freshman class were as follows: Verbal—45% below 500, 43% between 500 and 599, 11% between 600 and 700, and 1% above 700; Math—20% below 500, 52% between 500 and 599, 23% between 600 and 700, and 5% above 700. The ACT scores were 23% below 21, 25% between 21 and 23, 22% between 24 and 26, 17% between 27 and 28, and 13% above 28. About 44% of the current freshmen were in the top fifth of their class; 68% were in the top two fifths. About 18 freshmen graduated first in their class.

Requirements: The SAT I or ACT is required. Applicants must be graduates of an accredited secondary school or have a GED certificate, and have completed 4 years of English, 3 years of mathematics, and 2 years each of foreign language, science, and social studies. An essay is required. SAT II: Subject tests in writing, mathematics, and foreign language and an interview are recommended. AP credits are accepted. Important factors used in the admissions decision are advanced placement or honor courses, evidence of special talent, extracurricular activities record, leadership record, and parents or siblings attending the school.

Procedure: Freshmen are admitted fall and spring. Entrance exams should be taken by the first semester of the senior year. Early decision applications should be filed by November 15 and January 15; regular applications, by February 15 for fall entry and December 1 for spring entry, along with an application fee of $35. Notification of early decision is sent December 15 and February 1; regular decision, April 1. There are early decision, early admissions, and deferred admissions plans. About 75 early decision candidates were accepted for the 1993–94 class. A waiting list is an active part of the admissions procedure, with about 10% of applicants on the list.

Transfer: About 90 transfer students enrolled in 1993–94. Transfer students must satisfy all regular admission requirements and submit official transcripts of college and high school work and SAT I or ACT scores. A recommended 2.5 GPA and a year's worth of credit hours earned are required. An interview is recommended. A total of 16 credits out of 35 must be completed at Rollins.

Visiting: There are regularly scheduled orientations for prospective students, including 2 all-campus previews in the fall. There are guides for informal visits and visitors may sit in on classes and stay overnight at the school. To arrange for a visit, contact the Office of Admissions at (407) 646–2161.

Financial Aid: In 1993–94, 59% of all current freshmen and 58% of continuing students received some form of financial aid. About 36% of freshmen and 33% of continuing students received need-based aid. The average freshman award was $16,720. Of that total,

scholarships or need-based grants averaged $12,363 ($20,000 maximum); loans averaged $3357 ($4625 maximum); and work contracts averaged $1000 ($1500 maximum). Fifteen percent of undergraduate students work part-time. Average earnings from campus work for the school year are $891. The average financial indebtedness of the 1992–93 graduate was $9460. Rollins is a member of CSS. The FAF, the college's own financial statement, and the FAFSA are required. The deadline for financial aid applications is March 1.

International Students: There are currently 60 international students enrolled. The school actively recruits these students. They must take the TOEFL and achieve a minimum score of 550. The student must also take the SAT I or the ACT.

Computers: The college provides computer facilities for student use. The mainframe is a MicroVAX 3100. The student computing center is open until midnight. More than 100 terminals and personal computers for student use are located in the writing center, residence halls, the library, and departmental lounges. Students may bring their own personal computer and, with a modem, access the mainframe 24 hours per day. All students may access the system. There are no time limits on using the system and no fees.

Graduates: In 1992–93 319 bachelor's degrees were awarded. The most popular majors among graduates were politics (11%), psychology (10%), and English (9%). Within an average freshman class, 72% graduate in 4 years and 75% in 5 years. Some 28 companies recruited on campus in 1992–93.

Admissions Contact: David G. Erdmann, Dean of Admission and Student Financial Planning.

SAINT LEO COLLEGE   D-3

Saint Leo, FL 33574   (904) 588-8283; (800) 247-6559 (out-of-state)

Full-time: 514 men, 456 women	Faculty: 62
Part-time: 24 men, 41 women	Ph.D.s: 64%
Graduate: none	Student/Faculty: 16 to 1
Year: semesters, summer session	Tuition: $9370
Application Deadline: August 1	Room & Board: $4200
Freshman Class: 1100 applied, 759 accepted, 340 enrolled	
SAT I Verbal/Math: 407/446	ACT: 21 COMPETITIVE

Saint Leo College, a private, coeducational institution founded in 1889, is affiliated with the Catholic Church. The nonprofit, liberal arts college offers undergraduate programs in the humanities, natural sciences, social sciences, and education. In addition to regional accreditation, Saint Leo has baccalaureate program accreditation with CSWE. The library contains 850,646 volumes, 8696 microform items, and 2846 audiovisual forms, and subscribes to 729 periodicals. Computerized library sources and services include the card catalog, interlibrary loans, and database searching. Special learning facilities include a learning resource center and TV station. The 170-acre campus is in a rural area 25 miles north of Tampa. Including residence halls, there are 20 buildings on campus.

Student Life: About 56% of undergraduates are from Florida. Students come from 34 states, 27 foreign countries, and Canada. Seventy percent are from public schools; 25% from private. Seventy-eight percent are white. Seventy-five percent are Catholic and 20% are Protestant. The average age of freshmen is 17; all undergraduates, 20. Twenty-three percent drop out by the end of their first year; 44% remain to graduate.

Housing: A total of 866 students can be accommodated in college housing. College-sponsored living facilities include single-sex dormitories. On-campus housing is guaranteed for all 4 years. Eighty-five percent of students live on campus; of those, 80% remain on campus on weekends. All students may keep cars on campus.

Activities: About 13% of men belong to 7 national fraternities; about 10% of women belong to 5 national sororities. There are 48 groups on campus, including art, band, cheerleading, choir, chorale, chorus, ethnic, honors, international, literary magazine, newspaper, professional, radio and TV, religious, social, social service, student government, and yearbook. Popular campus events include C.U.B. Day, Bovol Blow-Out, Humanities Day, and Parents Weekend.

Sports: There are 5 intercollegiate sports for men and 5 for women, and 17 intramural sports for men and 11 for women. Athletic and recreation facilities include a 1500-seat stadium; a 2750-seat indoor gymnasium; soccer, softball, baseball, and track fields; basketball, volleyball, lighted tennis, racquetball, and handball courts; a weight training room; and an outdoor swimming pool.

Disabled Students: Forty-five percent of the campus is accessible to disabled students. The following facilities are available: wheelchair ramps, elevators, and special parking.

Services: In addition to many counseling and information services, tutoring is available in some subjects, including mathematics and English. There is also remedial math, reading, and writing.

Campus Safety and Security: Campus safety and security measures include 24-hour foot and vehicle patrol, escort service, informal discussions and pamphlets, posters, and films. In addition, there are lighted pathways and sidewalks.

Programs of Study: Saint Leo awards the B.A., B.S., and B.S.W. degrees. Associate and master's degrees also are awarded. Bachelor's degrees are awarded in BIOLOGICAL SCIENCE (biology/biological science), BUSINESS (accounting, business administration and management, hotel/motel and restaurant management, management science, marketing/retailing/merchandising, personnel management, and sports management), COMMUNICATIONS AND THE ARTS (English, fine arts, and music), EDUCATION (art, elementary, physical, secondary, and special), HEALTH PROFESSIONS (medical laboratory technology, predentistry, premedicine, and preveterinary science), SOCIAL SCIENCE (criminology, history, international relations, political science/government, prelaw, psychology, public administration, religion, social work, and sociology). Biological science and English are the strongest academically. Hotel and restaurant management and education have the largest enrollments.

Required: In order to graduate, all students must complete a minimum 120 academic credits, with 36 to 69 hours in the major, all the requirements of their division and major, 45 hours in the Basic Studies Program, and 4 physical education courses. A minimum 2.0 GPA is required.

Special: There is a freshman honors program on campus, as well as one national honor society.

Faculty/Classroom: Sixty-eight percent of faculty are male; 32%, female. All teach undergraduates. The average class size in an introductory lecture is 25; in a laboratory, 10; and in a regular course offering, 16.

Admissions: About 69% of the 1993–94 applicants were accepted. The SAT scores for the 1993–94 freshman class were as follows: Verbal—84% below 500, 14% between 500 and 599, 1% between 600 and 700, and 1% above 700; Math—76% below 500, 22% between 500 and 599, 1% between 600 and 700, and 1% above 700. The ACT scores were 49% below 21, 20% between 21 and 23, 21% between 24 and 26, 5% between 27 and 28, and 5% above 28.

Requirements: A minimum GPA of 2.5 is required. The SAT I or ACT is required. Applicants must be graduates of an accredited secondary school or have a GED certificate, and have completed 4 credits each in English and electives, 3 credits each in mathematics and social studies, and 2 credits in science. AP and CLEP credits are accepted. Important factors used in the admissions decision are parents or siblings attending the school, recommendations by alumni, recommendations by school officials, leadership record, and geographic diversity.

Procedure: Freshmen are admitted fall and winter. Entrance exams should be taken in the fall of the senior year. Applications should be filed by August 1 for fall entry and December 1 for winter entry, along with an application fee of $35. Notification is sent on a rolling basis. There are early admissions and deferred admissions plans.

Transfer: About 124 transfer students enrolled in 1993–94. Transfer students must submit an official transcript from each previously attended college and a recommendation from the dean of students of the last institution attended. A minimum 2.5 GPA is required. A total of 30 credits out of 120 must be completed at Saint Leo.

Visiting: There are regularly scheduled orientations for prospective students, consisting of day-long open houses in the fall and spring. There are guides for informal visits and visitors may sit in on classes.

Financial Aid: In 1993–94 72% of all current freshmen and 70% of continuing students received some form of financial aid. About 49% of freshmen and 42% of continuing students received need-based aid. The average freshman award was $8500. Of that total, scholarships or need-based grants averaged $1000 ($12,000 maximum); loans averaged $2625 (maximum); and work contracts averaged $800 ($1100 maximum). Thirty-one percent of undergraduate students work part-time. Average earnings from campus work for the school year are $1100. The average financial indebtedness of the 1992–93 graduate was $7500. Saint Leo is a member of CSS. The college's own financial statement and FAFSA are required. The deadline for financial aid applications is April 1.

International Students: There are currently 60 international students enrolled. The school actively recruits these students. They must take the TOEFL and achieve a minimum score of 550.

Computers: The college provides computer facilities for student use. All students may use the 40 personal computers that are located in the library. There are no time limits on using the system and no fees.

Graduates: In 1992–93 190 bachelor's degrees were awarded. Some 23 companies recruited on campus in 1992–93.

Admissions Contact: Bonnie L. Black, Director of Admissions.

SAINT THOMAS UNIVERSITY
E-5

Miami, FL 33054   (305) 628-6546; (800) 367-9010 (out-of-state)

Full-time: 482 men, 643 women	Faculty: 73; IIB, +$
Part-time: 153 men, 329 women	Ph.D.s: 59%
Graduate: 695 men and women	Student/Faculty: 15 to 1
Year: semesters, summer session	Tuition: $9680
Application Deadline: open	Room & Board: $4600

Freshman Class: 849 applied, 649 accepted, 361 enrolled

SAT I: 390/440   ACT: 19   **LESS COMPETITIVE**

Saint Thomas University, founded in 1961, is a private, liberal arts university affiliated with the Roman Catholic Church and sponsored by the Archdiocese of Miami. There are 2 undergraduate and 2 graduate schools. The library contains 145,000 volumes and subscribes to 850 periodicals. Computerized library sources and services include the card catalog, interlibrary loans, and database searching. Special learning facilities include a learning resource center and a radio station. The 140-acre campus is in a suburban area 8 miles north of Miami. Including residence halls, there are 15 buildings on campus.

Student Life: About 74% of undergraduates are from Florida. Students come from 25 states, 47 foreign countries, and Canada. Forty percent are Hispanic; 23% white; 18% foreign nationals; 18% African American. Sixty-two percent are Catholic; 20% claim no religious affiliation.

Housing: A total of 424 students can be accommodated in college housing. College-sponsored living facilities include coed dormitories. In addition, there are special interest houses. On-campus housing is guaranteed for all 4 years. Fifty-five percent of students commute. All students may keep cars on campus.

Activities: About 2% of men belong to 1 local and 1 national fraternity; about 2% of women belong to 1 national sorority. There are 20 groups on campus, including art, cheerleading, choir, computers, drama, ethnic, honors, international, literary magazine, newspaper, political, professional, radio and TV, religious, social, social service, student government, and yearbook. Popular campus events include Senior Capping Ceremony, Freshman Investiture Ceremony, Land and Water Olympics, Halloween, and Christmas.

Sports: There are 3 intercollegiate sports for men and 3 for women, and 12 intramural sports for men and 12 for women. Athletic and recreation facilities include basketball and softball fields, tennis courts, a weight room, and a swimming pool.

Disabled Students: Ninety percent of the campus is accessible to disabled students. The following facilities are available: wheelchair ramps, elevators, special parking, specially equipped rest rooms, and special class scheduling.

Services: In addition to many counseling and information services, tutoring is available in most subjects. There is remedial math, reading, and writing. Computer-assisted instruction is available.

Campus Safety and Security: Campus safety and security measures include 24-hour foot and vehicle patrol, self defense education, escort service, and informal discussions. In addition, there are emergency telephones and lighted pathways and sidewalks.

Programs of Study: Saint Thomas awards the B.A. and B.B.A. degrees. Master's degrees also are awarded. Bachelor's degrees are awarded in BIOLOGICAL SCIENCE (biology/biological science), BUSINESS (accounting, banking and finance, business administration and management, hotel/motel and restaurant management, human resources, international business management, marketing/retailing/merchandising, and sports management), COMMUNICATIONS AND THE ARTS (communications, English, and Spanish), COMPUTER AND PHYSICAL SCIENCE (chemistry, computer programming, and computer science), EDUCATION (elementary, secondary, and social studies), HEALTH PROFESSIONS (predentistry and premedicine), SOCIAL SCIENCE (American studies, criminal justice, economics, history, international relations, political science/government, prelaw, psychology, public administration, religion, and sociology). Business management and accounting have the largest enrollments.

Required: All students must complete at least 120 semester credits, with 30 to 60 in the major, and specific courses, including 12 credits in English, 9 each in mathematics/physical science, philosophy, and religion, and 6 each in history, social science, and humanities. Students must maintain a 2.0 overall GPA and a 2.3 GPA in the major subject.

Special: Various internships, study abroad in Italy and Spain, and a general studies degree are available. The university grants credit for life, military, and work experience via the Life Experience Portfolio. There is a freshman honors program on campus, as well as 2 national honor societies.

Faculty/Classroom: Sixty-three percent of faculty are male; 37%, female. All teach undergraduates and 3% do research. The average class size in an introductory lecture is 25; in a laboratory, 12; and in a regular course offering, 17.

Admissions: About 76% of the 1993-94 applicants were accepted. The SAT I scores for the 1993-94 freshman class were as follows: Verbal—90% below 500, 8% between 500 and 599, and 2% between 600 and 700; Math—92% below 500, 6% between 500 and 599, 1% between 600 and 700, and 1% above 700. The ACT scores were 70% below 21, 19% between 21 and 23, 8% between 24 and 26, 2% between 27 and 28, and 1% above 28. About 30 freshmen graduated first in their class.

Requirements: The SAT I or ACT is required. Applicants should have completed 18 high school units, including 4 units in English, 3 each in mathematics and social science, and 2 in science. AP and CLEP credits are accepted. Important factors used in the admissions decision are recommendations by school officials, advanced placement or honor courses, evidence of special talent, personality, intangible qualities, and leadership record.

Procedure: Freshmen are admitted to all sessions. Entrance exams should be taken in December of the senior year. Application deadlines are open. The fee is $30. Notification is sent on a rolling basis. There is a deferred admissions plan.

Transfer: About 100 transfer students enrolled in a recent year. Maximum credit hours accepted are 60 from a junior college and 90 from a 4-year institution. No grade of D is acceptable in courses beyond the sophomore level or in the major. Students with fewer than 30 credits must submit a high school transcript and SAT I or ACT scores. A total of 30 credits out of 120 must be completed at Saint Thomas.

Visiting: There are guides for informal visits, and visitors may sit in on classes and stay overnight at the school. To arrange for a visit, contact the Admissions Office at (800) 367-9006 (in-state) or (800) 367-9010 (out of state).

Financial Aid: In 1993-94 90% of all current freshmen and 61% of continuing students received some form of financial aid. About 81% of freshmen and 73% of continuing students received need-based aid. The average freshman award was $8000. Of that total, scholarships or need-based grants averaged $1660 ($11,500 maximum); loans averaged $2360 ($3250 maximum); and work contracts averaged $1555 ($2400 maximum). Twenty-one percent of undergraduate students work part-time. The average financial indebtedness of the 1992-93 graduate was $9935. The FAF, the college's own financial statement, and the FAFSA are required.

International Students: There are currently 181 international students enrolled. The school actively recruits these students. They must take the TOEFL or the college's own test and achieve a minimum score on the TOEFL of 525. The student must also take the college's own entrance exam.

Computers: The college provides computer facilities for student use. The mainframe is a Prime 9755. There are also 30 IBM PS/2 Model 30-286 and 55SX personal computers available for academic use in the computer laboratory. All student workers and assistants may access the system. It may be used any time it is available. There are no time limits on using the system and no fees.

Graduates: In 1992-93 318 bachelor's degrees were awarded. The most popular majors among graduates were human resources (14%), business management (12%), and communication arts (12%). Some 75 to 100 companies recruited on campus in 1992-93.

Admissions Contact: John M. Letvinchuk, Director of Admissions.

SOUTHEASTERN COLLEGE OF THE ASSEMBLIES OF GOD
D-3

Lakeland, FL 33801   (813) 665-4404; (800) 854-7477 (out-of-state)

Full-time: 584 men, 573 women	Faculty: 49
Part-time: 38 men, 41 women	Ph.D.s: 37%
Graduate: none	Student/Faculty: 22 to 1
Year: semesters, summer session	Tuition: $3818
Application Deadline: August 1	Room & Board: $2800

Freshman Class: 290 applied, 282 accepted, 236 enrolled

SAT I or ACT: required   **NONCOMPETITIVE**

Southeastern College of the Assemblies of God, founded in 1935, is a private, coeducational, Protestant college offering programs in biblical studies, music, religion, and teacher preparation. The 2 libraries contain 80,713 volumes, 26,092 microform items, and 2006 audiovisual forms, and subscribe to 444 periodicals. Computerized library sources and services include interlibrary loans and database searching. Special learning facilities include a learning resource center and TV station. The 56-acre campus is in a small town 30 miles east of Tampa. Including residence halls, there are 32 buildings on campus.

Student Life: About 50% of undergraduates are from out-of-state, mostly the South. Students come from 43 states, 7 foreign countries, and Canada. Ninety-two percent are white. Most are Protestant. Twenty-five percent drop out by the end of their first year; 22% remain to graduate.

Housing: A total of 866 students can be accommodated in college housing. College-sponsored living facilities include single-sex dormitories, on-campus apartments, off-campus apartments, and married-

student housing. On-campus housing is guaranteed for all 4 years. Seventy-one percent of students live on campus. Alcohol is not permitted. All students may keep cars on campus.

Activities: There are no fraternities or sororities on campus. There are 48 groups on campus, including band, cheerleading, choir, chorale, chorus, computers, drama, honors, international, newspaper, radio and TV, religious, student government, and yearbook. Popular campus events include Homecoming, Missions Convention, Fall Festival, Valentine Banquet, Christmas Social, Junior-Senior Banquet, Spring Revival, Parents Weekend, Married Students Retreat, Education Day, District Superintendent Symposium, D-Caps, and Staley Lectures.

Sports: There are 4 intercollegiate sports for men and 2 for women, and 6 intramural sports for men and 6 for women. Athletic and recreation facilities include a gymnasium, a soccer field, tennis, racquetball, and beach volleyball courts, a weight room, and intramural fields.

Disabled Students: Seventy-five percent of the campus is accessible to disabled students. The following facilities are available: wheelchair ramps, elevators, special parking, specially equipped rest rooms, special class scheduling, and lowered drinking fountains.

Services: In addition to many counseling and information services, tutoring is available in some subjects. There is remedial math, reading, and writing.

Campus Safety and Security: Campus safety and security measures include informal discussions, pamphlets, posters, and films, lighted pathways and sidewalks, and 24 hour foot patrol and a main entrance security booth attendant.

Programs of Study: Southeastern awards the B.A. degree. Bachelor's degrees are awarded in COMMUNICATIONS AND THE ARTS (music), EDUCATION (early childhood, elementary, English, mathematics, middle school, music, science, secondary, and social studies), SOCIAL SCIENCE (ministries, psychology, and religion). Religion, education, and music are the strongest academically. Religion has the largest enrollment.

Required: Every degree student must complete at least 130 hours including 45 hours of general education and at least 24 hours of religion. Distribution requirements include 6 to 12 hours each in arts and communication, human adjustment, science and mathematics, social sciences, and humanities and fine arts. A minimum GPA of 2.0 must be maintained.

Special: Internships are available in education, ministry, psychology, pastoral studies, and Christian education. There is one national honor society on campus.

Faculty/Classroom: Sixty-nine percent of faculty are male; 31%, female. Ninety-six percent teach undergraduates. The average class size in an introductory lecture is 75.

Admissions: About 97% of the 1993–94 applicants were accepted.

Requirements: A minimum GPA of 2.0 is required. The SAT I or ACT is required. AP and CLEP credits are accepted.

Procedure: Freshmen are admitted to all sessions. Entrance exams should be taken prior to enrollment. Applications should be filed by August 1 for fall entry, December 1 for spring entry, and April 1 for summer entry, along with an application fee of $40. Notification is sent on a rolling basis. There is an early admissions plan.

Transfer: About 151 transfer students enrolled in 1993–94. Admission requirements for transfer students are the same as for first-time students. A total of 30 credits out of 130 must be completed at Southeastern.

Visiting: There are guides for informal visits and visitors may sit in on classes and stay overnight at the school. To arrange for a visit, contact Bonnie Yost at (813) 665-4404, ext. 207.

Financial Aid: In a recent year, 46% of all current freshmen and 51% of continuing students received some form of financial aid. The average freshman award was $3400. Of that total, scholarships or need-based grants averaged $2741 ($3100 maximum); loans averaged $3199 ($3825 maximum); and work contracts averaged $1350 ($1500 maximum). Average earnings from campus work for the school year are $1500. The average financial indebtedness of recent graduates was $8950. Southeastern is a member of CSS. The college's own financial statement and FAFSA are required. The deadline for financial aid applications is October 29.

International Students: There are currently 18 international students enrolled. The school actively recruits these students. They must take the TOEFL and achieve a minimum score of 500. The student must also take the SAT I or the ACT.

Computers: The college provides computer facilities for student use. The mainframe is a Data General MV 7800. Apple and Tandy personal computers are available for student use in the computer laboratory. All students may access the system. It may be used during designated laboratory hours. There are no time limits on using the system. The fees are $25 per semester.

Graduates: In 1992–93 195 bachelor's degrees were awarded. The most popular majors among graduates were biblical studies (25%), theological studies (25%), and elementary education (25%). Within an average freshman class, 25% graduate in 4 years.

Admissions Contact: Royce M. Shelton, Director of Admissions and Records.

STATE UNIVERSITY SYSTEM OF FLORIDA

The State University system of Florida, established in 1906, is a public system. It is governed by a board of regents, whose chief administrator is the chancellor. The primary goal of the system is teaching, research, and public service. The main priorities are to improve the quality of undergraduate education, to solve critical state problems, to forge public-private partnerships, and to increase the efficiency of the system. The total enrollment in a recent year of all 9 campuses was 181,889; there were 11,621 faculty members. Altogether there are 622 baccalaureate, 552 master's, and 204 doctoral programs offered in the State University System of Florida. Four-year campuses are located in Gainesville, Tallahassee, Tampa, Boca Raton, Pensacola, Orlando, Jacksonville, and Miami. Profiles of the 4-year campuses are included in this chapter in alphabetical order with other Florida schools.

STETSON UNIVERSITY   D-2

Deland, FL 32720   (904) 822–7100; (800) 688–0101

Full-time: 821 men, 1143 women	Faculty: 155; IIA, av$
Part-time: 34 men, 47 women	Ph.D.s: 88%
Graduate: 94 men, 169 women	Student/Faculty: 13 to 1
Year: 4–1–4, summer session	Tuition: $11,995
Application Deadline: March 1	Room & Board: $4440
Freshman Class: 1557 applied, 1227 accepted, 483 enrolled	
SAT I or ACT: required	**VERY COMPETITIVE**

Stetson University, founded in 1883, is a private institution offering undergraduate programs in liberal arts and sciences, music, and business administration. There are 3 undergraduate and 2 graduate schools. In addition to regional accreditation, Stetson has baccalaureate program accreditation with NASM. The 3 libraries contain 300,000 volumes, 250,000 microform items, and 12,500 audiovisual forms, and subscribe to 1300 periodicals. Computerized library sources and services include the card catalog, interlibrary loans, and database searching. Special learning facilities include an art gallery, radio station, and museum of minerals. The 150-acre campus is in a small town 35 miles north of Orlando. Including residence halls, there are 53 buildings on campus.

Student Life: About 80% of undergraduates are from Florida. Students come from 39 states, 32 foreign countries, and Canada. Seventy-two percent are from public schools; 28% from private. Eighty-seven percent are white. Sixty percent are Protestant; 26% Catholic; 12% claim no religious affiliation. The average age of freshmen is 18; all undergraduates, 20. Twenty percent drop out by the end of their first year; 60% remain to graduate.

Housing: A total of 1524 students can be accommodated in college housing. College-sponsored living facilities include single-sex and coed dormitories, fraternity houses, and sorority houses. In addition, there are honors houses, language houses, and special interest houses. On-campus housing is guaranteed for all 4 years. Seventy-five percent of students live on campus; of those, 60% remain on campus on weekends. Alcohol is not permitted. All students may keep cars on campus.

Activities: About 43% of men belong to 6 national fraternities; about 43% of women belong to 6 national sororities. There are 86 groups on campus, including band, cheerleading, chess, choir, chorale, chorus, computers, dance, drama, ethnic, gay, honors, international, jazz band, literary magazine, musical theater, newspaper, opera, orchestra, pep band, political, professional, radio and TV, religious, social, social service, student government, symphony, and yearbook. Popular campus events include Homecoming and Green Feather.

Sports: There are 7 intercollegiate sports for men and 8 for women, and 12 intramural sports for men and 11 for women. Athletic and recreation facilities include 11 tennis, 6 racquetball, and 8 volleyball courts, basketball courts, weight and training rooms, baseball and soccer fields, an Olympic pool with 1- and 3-meter diving boards, and a 5000-seat auditorium.

Disabled Students: Seventy-five percent of the campus is accessible to disabled students. The following facilities are available: wheelchair ramps, elevators, special parking, specially equipped rest rooms, and special class scheduling.

Services: In addition to many counseling and information services, tutoring is available in some subjects. There is a reader service for the blind.

Campus Safety and Security: Campus safety and security measures include 24-hour foot and vehicle patrol, self-defense education, escort service, and informal discussions. In addition, there are pamphlets, posters, films, emergency telephones, and lighted pathways and sidewalks.

Programs of Study: Stetson awards the B.A., B.S., B.B.A., B.M., and B.M.E. degrees. Master's degrees also are awarded. Bachelor's degrees are awarded in BIOLOGICAL SCIENCE (biology/biological science), BUSINESS (accounting, banking and finance, business administration and management, business economics, management science, and marketing/retailing/merchandising), COMMUNICATIONS AND THE ARTS (communications, dramatic arts, English, fine arts, French, German, music, Russian, Spanish, and speech/debate/rhetoric), COMPUTER AND PHYSICAL SCIENCE (chemistry, computer science, mathematics, and physics), EDUCATION (elementary, music, and secondary), HEALTH PROFESSIONS (medical laboratory technology), SOCIAL SCIENCE (American studies, economics, geography, history, Latin American studies, philosophy, physical fitness/movement, political science/government, prelaw, psychology, Russian and Slavic studies, social science, sociology, and urban studies). Business, psychology, political science, English, music, and education have the largest enrollments.

Required: In order to graduate, all students must complete 126 total credit hours, with 30 to 40 in the major. The minimum GPA is 2.0, and courses in English, religion, and philosophy are required.

Special: The university offers co-op programs with Washington University in St. Louis (preengineering) and Duke University (forestry and environmental studies), cross-registration during the winter terms, and study abroad in France, Germany, Spain, Russia, and England. Also available are a Washington semester at American University; the B.A.-B.S. degree in all natural sciences, economics, political science, psychology, sociology, and social science; dual majors; student-designed majors through the Honors Program; and pass/fail options. There are also the Leadership Development Program and the Roland George Investment Program, in which students manage an actual investment portfolio exceeding $1 million, and international 8-week programs in Egypt, Morocco, Guatemala, Jamaica, and Barbados. There is a freshman honors program on campus, as well as 4 national honor societies, including Phi Beta Kappa. Thirteen departments have honors programs.

Faculty/Classroom: Sixty-seven percent of faculty are male; 33%, female. All teach undergraduates and 50% both teach and do research. No introductory courses are taught by graduate students. The average class size in an introductory lecture is 25; in a laboratory, 20; and in a regular course offering, 20.

Admissions: About 79% of the 1993–94 applicants were accepted. The SAT scores for the 1993–94 freshman class were as follows: Verbal—57% below 500, 32% between 500 and 599, 10% between 600 and 700, and 1% above 700; Math—32% below 500, 40% between 500 and 599, 24% between 600 and 700, and 3% above 700. The ACT scores were 23% below 21, 28% between 21 and 23, 23% between 24 and 26, 13% between 27 and 28, and 13% above 28. About 59% of the current freshmen were in the top fifth of their class; 84% were in the top two fifths. There were 3 National Merit semifinalists, and 12 freshmen graduated first in their class.

Requirements: A minimum GPA of 2.0 is required. The SAT I or ACT is required. In addition, applicants must be graduates of an accredited secondary school or have a GED, and have completed 4 years of English, 3 of mathematics and science, and 2 each of foreign language, social studies, and electives. SAT II: Subject tests and an interview are recommended. Auditions are required for music students. AP and CLEP credits are accepted. Important factors used in the admissions decision are advanced placement or honor courses, leadership record, evidence of special talent, extracurricular activities record, and parents or siblings attending the school.

Procedure: Freshmen are admitted to all sessions. Entrance exams should be taken in the spring of the junior year or the fall of the senior year. Applications should be filed by March 1 for fall entry, January 1 for spring entry, and May 1 for summer entry, along with an application fee of $25. Notification is sent after March 1. There are early decision, early admissions, and deferred admissions plans. About 35 early decision candidates were accepted for the 1993–94 class.

Transfer: About 170 transfer students enrolled in 1993–94. Transfer students must have completed a semester of academic work in good standing at an accredited college with a minimum 2.0 GPA. A 2.5 GPA and an interview are recommended. At least 48 credits out of 126 must be completed at Stetson.

Visiting: There are regularly scheduled orientations for prospective students, consisting of a campus tour and orientation, interviews, class visits, and presentations. There are guides for informal visits and visitors may stay overnight at the school. To arrange for a visit, contact Linda Glover, Dean of Admissions, at (904) 822-7100 or (800) 688-0101.

Financial Aid: In 1993–94, 85% of all students received some form of financial aid. About 50% of all students received need-based aid. The average freshman award was $8500. Of that total, scholarships or need-based grants averaged $4000 ($10,000 maximum); loans averaged $2200 ($4800 maximum); and work contracts averaged $1300 ($1500 maximum). Average earnings from campus work for the school year are $1300. The average financial indebtedness of the

1992–93 graduate was $5500. Stetson is a member of CSS. The FAF or FFS is required. The deadline for financial aid applications is March 1.

International Students: There are currently 69 international students enrolled. The school actively recruits these students. They must take the TOEFL and achieve a minimum score of 550 and must also take the SAT I or the ACT.

Computers: The college provides computer facilities for student use. The mainframe is a DEC VAX 6210. There are 3 general-access computer laboratories, all of which have IBM PCs and Apple Macintosh microcomputers networked to one another and to the mainframe. All students may access the system. There are no time limits on using the system and no fees.

Graduates: In 1992–93, 493 bachelor's degrees were awarded. The most popular majors among graduates were business (40%), English (9%), and psychology (8%). Within an average freshman class, 50% graduate in 4 years, 60% in 5 years, and 63% in 6 years. Some 84 companies recruited on campus in an earlier year. In the 1992 graduating class, 39% of all students were enrolled in graduate school within 6 months of graduation; 53% had found employment.

Admissions Contact: Linda Glover, Dean of Admissions.

UNIVERSITY OF CENTRAL FLORIDA   D-3
Orlando, FL 32816   (407) 823–3000

Full-time: 5856 men, 6432 women	Faculty: 590; IIA, -$
Part-time: 3865 men, 4160 women	Ph.D.s: 80%
Graduate: 1544 men, 1476 women	Student/Faculty: 21 to 1
Year: semesters, summer session	Tuition: $1756 ($6753)
Application Deadline: March 15	Room & Board: $4305
Freshman Class: 6999 applied, 2962 accepted, 1903 enrolled	
SAT I Verbal/Math: 464/533	ACT: 23 COMPETITIVE +

The University of Central Florida, founded in 1963, is part of the State University System of Florida and offers programs in liberal and fine arts, business, engineering, health science, professional training, and teacher preparation. There are 5 undergraduate and 5 graduate schools. In addition to regional accreditation, UCF has baccalaureate program accreditation with AACSB, ABET, NASM, NCATE, and NLN. The library contains 955,903 volumes and 1,261,086 microform items. Computerized library sources and services include the card catalog, interlibrary loans, and database searching. Special learning facilities include a learning resource center, art gallery, and FM and AM radio stations. The 1227-acre campus is in an urban area 13 miles east of Orlando. Including residence halls, there are 50 buildings on campus.

Student Life: About 94% of undergraduates are from Florida. Students come from 42 states, 74 foreign countries, and Canada. Seventy-nine percent are white. The average age of freshmen is 18; all undergraduates, 24. Twenty-six percent drop out by the end of their first year.

Housing: A total of 899 students can be accommodated in college housing. College-sponsored living facilities include single-sex and coed dormitories, fraternity houses, and sorority houses. In addition, there are honors houses. On-campus housing is available on a first-come, first-served basis. Ninety-six percent of students commute. All students may keep cars on campus.

Activities: About 9% of men belong to 13 national fraternities; about 6% of women belong to 10 national sororities. There are 140 groups on campus, including art, band, cheerleading, choir, chorus, computers, drama, drill team, ethnic, film, gay, honors, international, jazz band, literary magazine, marching band, musical theater, newspaper, orchestra, photography, political, professional, radio and TV, religious, social, social service, student government, and yearbook. Popular campus events include Homecoming, Miss UCF, International Student Week, Black History Month, Hispanic Awareness Week, Student Showcase Week, and the Wellness Fair.

Sports: There are 8 intercollegiate sports for men and 7 for women, and 14 intramural sports for men and 14 for women. Athletic and recreation facilities include basketball, racquetball, tennis, disc golf, and badminton courts; a softball field; a swimming pool; a golf driving range; a 400-meter track; a dance/exercise studio; weight rooms; and a 92,000-square-foot arena.

Disabled Students: Ninety-five percent of the campus is accessible to disabled students. The following facilities are available: wheelchair ramps, elevators, special parking, specially equipped rest rooms, special class scheduling, lowered drinking fountains, and lowered telephones.

Services: In addition to many counseling and information services, tutoring is available in most subjects, including mathematics, English, reading, foreign languages, physics, and statistics. There is a reader service for the blind, and remedial math, reading, and writing. A re-

view program for the College-Level Academic Skills Test (CLAST) is also available.

Campus Safety and Security: Campus safety and security measures include 24-hour foot and vehicle patrol, self-defense education, escort service, and shuttle buses. In addition, there are informal discussions, pamphlets, posters, films, emergency telephones, and lighted pathways and sidewalks.

Programs of Study: UCF awards the B.A., B.S., B.F.A., B.S.As.E., B.S.B.A., B.S.C.E., B.S.Cp.E., B.S.E.E., B.S.Env.E., B.S.E.T., B.S.I.E., B.S.M.E., B.S.N., and B.S.W. degrees. Associate, master's, and doctoral degrees also are awarded. Bachelor's degrees are awarded in BIOLOGICAL SCIENCE (biology/biological science, botany, limnology, microbiology, and zoology), BUSINESS (accounting, banking and finance, business administration and management, hospitality management services, management science, and marketing/retailing/merchandising), COMMUNICATIONS AND THE ARTS (broadcasting, communications, dramatic arts, English, film arts, fine arts, French, journalism, languages, music, and Spanish), COMPUTER AND PHYSICAL SCIENCE (chemistry, computer science, mathematics, physics, and statistics), EDUCATION (art, business, early childhood, education of the exceptional child, elementary, English, foreign languages, mathematics, music, physical, science, social science, special, and technical), ENGINEERING AND ENVIRONMENTAL DESIGN (aeronautical engineering, civil engineering, computer engineering, drafting and design technology, electrical/electronics engineering, electrical/electronics engineering technology, engineering technology, environmental engineering, industrial engineering technology, and mechanical engineering), HEALTH PROFESSIONS (health care administration, health science, medical laboratory technology, medical records administration/services, medical science, nursing, physical therapy, radiological science, respiratory therapy, and speech pathology/audiology), SOCIAL SCIENCE (anthropology, criminal justice, economics, forensic studies, history, humanities, law, philosophy, political science/government, psychology, public administration, social science, social work, and sociology). Engineering, business administration, and computer science are the strongest academically. Business, education, and engineering have the largest enrollments.

Required: To graduate, students must complete at least 120 semester hours, with 40 hours in general education program courses including 9 each in communication foundations, cultural and historical foundations, and mathematics foundations, 3 in social foundations, and 7 in science foundations. Students must maintain a minimum GPA of 2.0.

Special: Students may participate in study abroad, internships, and co-op and work-study programs. Students may earn B.A.-B.S. degrees or a liberal studies degree, or pursue dual majors. Nondegree study and pass/fail options are available. There is a freshman honors program on campus, as well as 2 national honor societies, including Phi Beta Kappa.

Faculty/Classroom: Seventy-three percent of faculty are male; 27%, female.

Admissions: About 42% of the 1993–94 applicants were accepted. The SAT scores for the 1993–94 freshman class were as follows: Verbal—67% below 500, 23% between 500 and 599, 6% between 600 and 700, and 4% above 700; Math—36% below 500, 39% between 500 and 599, 17% between 600 and 700, and 8% above 700. The ACT scores were 32% below 21, 31% between 21 and 23, 20% between 24 and 26, 9% between 27 and 28, and 6% above 28.

Requirements: A minimum GPA of 2.0 is required. The SAT I or ACT is required. Applicants should have completed 4 units of English, 2 units of a foreign language, 3 units each of mathematics, science, and social studies, and 4 units of electives. AP and CLEP credits are accepted.

Procedure: Freshmen are admitted to all sessions. Entrance exams should be taken during the junior year or the first semester of the senior year. Applications should be filed by March 15 for fall entry, October 15 for spring entry, and February 15 for summer entry, along with an application fee of $20. Notification is sent on a rolling basis. There are early admissions and deferred admissions plans.

Transfer: About 3200 transfer students enrolled in 1993–94. The SAT I or the ACT is required of applicants with fewer than 60 credit hours. Other transfer requirements vary widely depending on credits already earned. At least 30 credits out of 120 must be completed at UCF.

Visiting: There are regularly scheduled orientations for prospective students, including tours Monday through Friday at 11 A.M. There are guides for informal visits, and visitors may sit in on classes. To arrange for a visit, contact the Student Center-Campus Tours at (407) 823-3000.

Financial Aid: In 1993–94, 82% of all current freshmen and 41% of continuing students received some form of financial aid. About 40% of freshmen and 38% of continuing students received need-based aid. The average freshman award was $5000. Of that total, scholarships or need-based grants averaged $2450 ($10,740 maximum); loans averaged $1150 ($2625 maximum); and work contracts averaged $2100 ($2400 maximum). Fifty percent of undergraduate students work part-time. Average earnings from campus work for the school year are $2500. The average financial indebtedness of the 1992–93 graduate was $10,000. UCF is a member of CSS. The FAF or FFS is required. The deadline for financial aid applications is March 1.

International Students: There are currently 373 international students enrolled. They must take the TOEFL and achieve a minimum score of 550.

Computers: The college provides computer facilities for student use. The mainframe is an IBM 4381. Five public-access computer laboratories are open 7 days a week, 24 hours a day. All students may access the system at all times. There are no time limits on using the system. For students not enrolled in a class that requires laboratory use, the fee is $26.50 per 50 hours of computer time.

Graduates: In 1992–93, 4189 bachelor's degrees were awarded. The most popular majors among graduates were elementary education (9%), management (6%), and general business administration (5%). Some 260 companies recruited on campus in a recent year.

Admissions Contact: Sue McKinnon, Director of Admissions.

UNIVERSITY OF FLORIDA   D-2
Gainesville, FL 32611   (904) 392–1365, ext. 7316

Full-time: 12,851 men, 11,235 women	Faculty: 1622; I, --$
Part-time: 1807 men, 1580 women	Ph.Ds: 93%
Graduate: 4905 men, 3600 women	Student/Faculty: 15 to 1
Year: semesters, summer session	Tuition: $1770 ($6890)
Application Deadline: February 1	Room & Board: $4080

Freshman Class: 12,445 applied, 8836 accepted, 3623 enrolled
SAT I or ACT: required   **HIGHLY COMPETITIVE**

The University of Florida, founded in 1853, is a coeducational land-grant liberal arts institution that is part of the state university system of Florida. There are 14 undergraduate and 17 graduate schools. In addition to regional accreditation, UF has baccalaureate program accreditation with AACSB, ABET, ACCE, ACEJMC, ACPE, ADA, AHEA, APTA, ASLA, FIDER, NAAB, NASAD, NASM, NCATE, NLN, and SAF. The 15 libraries contain 3,022,768 volumes, 5,282,887 microform items, and 30,545 audiovisual forms, and subscribe to 24,191 periodicals. Special learning facilities include a learning resource center, art gallery, natural history museum, radio station, TV station, a performing arts center, and a teaching hospital. The 2000-acre campus is in a suburban area 75 miles from Jacksonville. Including residence halls, there are 850 buildings on campus.

Student Life: About 92% of undergraduates are from Florida. Students come from 50 states, 114 foreign countries, and Canada. Seventy-seven percent are white. The average age of freshmen is 19; all undergraduates, 22. Twelve percent drop out by the end of their first year; 64% remain to graduate.

Housing: A total of 6363 students can be accommodated in college housing. College-sponsored living facilities include coed dormitories, on-campus apartments, off-campus apartments, married-student housing, fraternity houses, and sorority houses. In addition there are honors houses and special-interest houses. On-campus housing is available on a first-come, first-served basis and is available on a lottery system for upperclassmen. All students may keep cars on campus.

Activities: About 16% of men belong to 29 national fraternities; about 12% of women belong to 17 national sororities. There are 420 groups on campus, including art, band, cheerleading, chess, choir, chorale, chorus, computers, dance, drama, drill team, ethnic, film, gay, honors, international, jazz band, literary magazine, marching band, musical theater, newspaper, orchestra, pep band, photography, political, professional, radio and TV, religious, social, social service, student government, symphony, and yearbook. Popular campus events include Homecoming, Gator Growl, Madrigal dinners, and ongoing student-sponsored cultural programs. Gator Growl is the largest student-produced show in the country.

Sports: There are 8 intercollegiate sports for men and 8 for women, and 16 intramural sports for men and 13 for women. Athletic and recreation facilities include a 12,000-seat athletic center, tennis, volleyball, and basketball courts, an Olympic-size swimming pool, a running track, weight rooms, intramural fields, an 85,000-seat stadium, and lakefront facilities.

Disabled Students: Ninety-five percent of the campus is accessible to disabled students. The following facilities are available: wheelchair ramps, elevators, special parking, specially equipped rest rooms, special class scheduling, lowered drinking fountains, and lowered telephones. There is computer access for blind and visually impaired students.

Services: In addition to many counseling and information services, tutoring is available in every subject. There is also a reader service for the blind.

Campus Safety and Security: Campus safety and security measures include 24-hour foot and vehicle patrol, self-defense education, escort service, and shuttle buses. In addition, there are informal discussions, pamphlets, posters, and films, emergency telephones, and lighted pathways and sidewalks.

Programs of Study: UF awards the B.A., B.S., B.A.E., B.F.A., B.H.S., B.M.E., B.Mus., B.S.A., B.S.B.A., B.S.F., B.S.N., and B.S.P. degrees. Master's, doctoral, and professional degrees also are awarded. Bachelor's degrees are awarded in AGRICULTURE (agricultural business management, agronomy, animal science, dairy science, forestry and related sciences, horticulture, natural resource management, plant science, poultry science, and soil science), BIOLOGICAL SCIENCE (botany, entomology, microbiology, plant pathology, wildlife biology, and zoology), BUSINESS (accounting, banking and finance, insurance, management science, marketing/retailing/merchandising, real estate, and recreation and leisure services), COMMUNICATIONS AND THE ARTS (advertising, art, art history and appreciation, English, French, German, graphic design, journalism, linguistics, music, music history and appreciation, performing arts, photography, Portuguese, public relations, Russian, Spanish, speech/debate/rhetoric, telecommunications, and theater design), COMPUTER AND PHYSICAL SCIENCE (astronomy, chemistry, computer science, geology, mathematics, physics, and statistics), EDUCATION (agricultural, art, elementary, health, music, and special), ENGINEERING AND ENVIRONMENTAL DESIGN (aeronautical engineering, agricultural engineering, architecture, chemical engineering, civil engineering, computer engineering, construction engineering, electrical/electronics engineering, engineering and applied science, environmental engineering, industrial engineering technology, interior design, landscape architecture/design, materials engineering, mechanical engineering, nuclear engineering, nuclear engineering technology, and surveying engineering), HEALTH PROFESSIONS (allied health, nursing, occupational therapy, pharmacy, physical therapy, physician's assistant, and speech pathology/audiology), SOCIAL SCIENCE (American studies, anthropology, Asian/Oriental studies, classical/ancient civilization, criminal justice, East Asian studies, economics, food science, geography, history, home economics, interdisciplinary studies, Judaic studies, philosophy, physical fitness/movement, political science/government, psychology, religion, and sociology). Business, engineering, and liberal arts have the largest enrollments.

Required: Requirements for graduation vary depending on the major elected, but all students are required to maintain a minimum 2.0 GPA.

Special: UF offers many internships and dual majors, and study abroad in 32 countries. There is a freshman honors program on campus, as well as 53 national honor societies, including Phi Beta Kappa.

Faculty/Classroom: Eighty-two percent of faculty are male; 18%, female. Graduate students teach 10% of introductory courses.

Admissions: About 71% of the 1993–94 applicants were accepted. The SAT scores for the 1993–94 freshman class were as follows: Verbal—48% below 500, 37% between 500 and 599, 13% between 600 and 700, and 1% above 700; Math—17% below 500, 38% between 500 and 599, 37% between 600 and 700, and 8% above 700. The ACT scores were 12% below 21, 22% between 21 and 23, 28% between 24 and 26, 19% between 27 and 28, and 18% above 28. About 76% of the current freshmen were in the top fifth of their class; 96% were in the top two fifths. There were 135 National Merit finalists.

Requirements: The SAT I or ACT is required; the SAT I is preferred. Minimum composite scores required are 840 on the SAT I and 19 on the ACT. Candidates should have graduated from an accredited secondary school with at least a C average or have a GED, and have completed 4 years of English, 3 years each of mathematics, science, and social studies, 2 years of a foreign language, and 4 units of academic electives. AP and CLEP credits are accepted. Important factors used in the admissions decision are advanced placement or honor courses, parents or siblings attending the school, recommendations by school officials, recommendations by alumni, personality, and intangible qualities.

Procedure: Freshmen are admitted to all sessions. Entrance exams should be taken in the junior year. Early decision applications should be filed by October 1; regular applications, by February 1 for fall entry, November 1 for spring entry, and March 1 for summer entry, along with an application fee of $20. Notification of early decision is sent November 5; regular decision, March 25. There are early decision and early admissions plans. About 1200 early decision candidates were accepted for the 1993–94 class.

Transfer: About 2600 transfer students enrolled in 1993–94. Admission requirements for transfer students vary by college. The lower division is highly competitive; applicants are encouraged to apply at the upper-division level. The last 30 credits out of 128 must be completed at UF.

Visiting: There are regularly scheduled orientations for prospective students, consisting of general information sessions at 10 A.M. and 2 P.M., Monday through Friday (excluding holidays), and a student-guided walking tour of the central campus. There are guides for informal visits, and visitors may sit in on classes and stay overnight at the school. To arrange for a visit, contact the Admissions Office at (904) 392–1365.

Financial Aid: In 1993–94, 28% of all current freshmen and 64% of continuing students received some form of financial aid. About 22% of freshmen and 58% of continuing students received need-based aid. The average freshman award was $5800. Of that total, scholarships or need-based grants averaged $3900; loans averaged $1032; and work contracts averaged $800. Fourteen percent of undergraduate students work part-time. Average earnings from campus work for the school year are $1800. The average financial indebtedness of the 1992–93 graduate was $8000. UF is a member of CSS. The FAF or FFS, the college's own financial statement, and the FAFSA are required. The deadline for financial aid applications is April 15.

International Students: There are currently 1879 international students enrolled. They must take the TOEFL and achieve a minimum score of 550. Freshmen or lower-division transfers must take the SAT I or ACT.

Computers: The college provides computer facilities for student use. The mainframes are an IBM ES9000–740/3VF, a KSR1–96, and various 6000 and 8000 series DEC VAXes. There are also 353 IBM-compatible and 100 Macintosh microcomputers available for general student use. Upper-division teaching laboratories restricted to department majors add several hundred more. Terminal access is via 151 terminals for general student use. All students may access the system. There is a time limit on the IBM and KSR systems; no limit on the VAXes. There are no fees.

Graduates: In 1992–93, 5524 bachelor's degrees were awarded. The most popular majors among graduates were finance (7%), marketing (4%), and psychology (4%). Within an average freshman class, 1% graduate in 3 years, 31% in 4 years, 56% in 5 years, and 64% in 6 years. Some 347 companies recruited on campus in 1992–93.

Admissions Contact: Bill Kolb, Director of Admissions.

UNIVERSITY OF MIAMI
E-5
Coral Gables, FL 33124 (305) 284-4323

Full-time: 4017 men, 3625 women	Faculty: 623; I, -$
Part-time: 291 men, 419 women	Ph.D.s: 95%
Graduate: 2821 men, 2385 women	Student/Faculty: 12 to 1
Year: semesters, summer session	Tuition: $15,880
Application Deadline: March 1	Room & Board: $6227
Freshman Class: 7122 applied, 5386 accepted, 1643 enrolled	
SAT I or ACT: required	VERY COMPETITIVE

The University of Miami, founded in 1925, is a private, coeducational university that offers degrees in more than 125 majors and areas of study. There are 8 undergraduate and 6 graduate schools. In addition to regional accreditation, UM has baccalaureate program accreditation with AACSB, ABET, ACEJMC, APTA, NAAB, NASM, NCATE, and NLN. The 3 libraries contain 1,875,556 volumes, 3,192,822 microform items, and 56,450 audiovisual forms, and subscribe to 18,853 periodicals. Computerized library sources and services include the card catalog, interlibrary loans, and database searching. Special learning facilities include a learning resource center, art gallery, radio station, TV station, and a 600-seat acoustically perfect concert hall. The 260-acre campus is in a suburban area 6 miles south of Miami. Including residence halls, there are 100 buildings on campus.

Student Life: About 51% of undergraduates are from Florida. Students come from 50 states, 108 foreign countries, and Canada. Fifty-two percent are white; 24% Hispanic; 10% foreign nationals. Thirty-four percent are Catholic; 19% Protestant; 12% claim no religious affiliation; 11% Jewish. The average age of freshmen is 18; all undergraduates, 19.

Housing: A total of 4030 students can be accommodated in college housing. College-sponsored living facilities include coed dormitories, on-campus apartments, and fraternity houses. In addition, the International House offers a cross-cultural exchange in an intensive English environment. All freshmen living on campus live in residential colleges. On-campus housing is guaranteed for all 4 years. Fifty-seven percent of students commute. Alcohol is not permitted. All students may keep cars on campus.

Activities: About 16% of men belong to 15 national fraternities; about 18% of women belong to 11 national sororities. There are 150 groups on campus, including band, cheerleading, chess, choir, chorale, chorus, dance, drama, ethnic, film, gay, honors, international, jazz band, literary magazine, marching band, musical theater, newspaper, orchestra, pep band, photography, political, professional, radio and TV, religious, social service, student government, symphony, and yearbook. Popular campus events include International Week, Beaumont Cinema-Miami Film Festival, Gusman Concert Hall-Festivale Miami, Carni Gras, and Sports Fest.

Sports: There are 8 intercollegiate sports for men and 7 for women, and 21 intramural sports for men and 21 for women. Athletic and recreation facilities include a baseball stadium seating 6,000, a sports

complex, a tennis center, a track and field facility, an athletic center, lighted tennis courts, basketball/volleyball, racquetball, and squash courts, 4 sports fields, an Olympic-size swimming pool, weight-lifting and exercise rooms, and a sauna.

Disabled Students: More than ninety percent of the campus is accessible to disabled students. The following facilities are available: wheelchair ramps, elevators with lowered controls, special parking, specially equipped rest rooms, special class scheduling, lowered drinking fountains, and lowered telephones.

Services: In addition to many counseling and information services, tutoring is available in most subjects. There is also a reader service for the blind, and remedial math, reading, and writing.

Campus Safety and Security: Campus safety and security measures include 24-hour foot and vehicle patrol, self-defense education, escort service, and shuttle buses. In addition, there are informal discussions, pamphlets, posters, films, emergency telephones, and lighted pathways and sidewalks. There has been a comprehensive crime prevention program since 1981, including security card access to all residential colleges.

Programs of Study: UM awards the B.A., B.S., B.Arch., B.B.A., B.C.S., B.F.A., B.H.S., B.M., B.S.A.E., B.S.B.E., B.S.C., B.S.C.E., B.S.Cp.E., B.S.E.E., B.S.E.S., B.S.I.E., B.S.M.E., B.S.N., and B.G.S. degrees. Master's and doctoral degrees also are awarded. Bachelor's degrees are awarded in AGRICULTURE (wildlife management), BIOLOGICAL SCIENCE (biochemistry, biology/biological science, ecology, marine science, microbiology, and toxicology), BUSINESS (accounting, banking and finance, business administration and management, business economics, business law, entrepreneurial studies, human resources, international business management, marketing/retailing/merchandising, real estate, and sports management), COMMUNICATIONS AND THE ARTS (advertising, art, art history and appreciation, audio technology, broadcasting, ceramic art and design, communications, dramatic arts, English, fiber/textiles/weaving, film arts, fine arts, French, German, graphic design, jazz, journalism, music, music business management, music history and appreciation, music performance, music theory and composition, musical theater, painting, photography, printmaking, public relations, sculpture, Spanish, speech/debate/rhetoric, technical and business writing, telecommunications, and video), COMPUTER AND PHYSICAL SCIENCE (applied mathematics, chemistry, computer science, geology, information sciences and systems, mathematics, physics, and systems analysis), EDUCATION (elementary, music, secondary, and special), ENGINEERING AND ENVIRONMENTAL DESIGN (aeronautical engineering, architectural engineering, architecture, biomedical engineering, civil engineering, computer engineering, electrical/electronics engineering, engineering, engineering technology, environmental engineering technology, environmental science, industrial engineering, manufacturing engineering, mechanical engineering, and ocean engineering), HEALTH PROFESSIONS (cytotechnology, environmental health science, health science, medical laboratory technology, music therapy, nuclear medical technology, nursing, and ultrasound technology), SOCIAL SCIENCE (American studies, anthropology, Caribbean studies, criminal justice, economics, geography, history, human ecology, international relations, international studies, Judaic studies, Latin American studies, law, philosophy, political science/government, psychobiology, psychology, religion, and sociology). Marine science, international finance and marketing, and music are the strongest academically. Finance, accounting, biology, psychology, and business management and organization have the largest enrollments.

Required: All students must complete at least 120 credit hours. Most degree programs require courses in English composition, humanities, fine arts, history, social science, foreign language, and natural science. Students must complete 24 to 36 hours in the major and maintain a minimum GPA of 2.0.

Special: UM offers many opportunities for internships in communications, business, engineering, architecture, and science, work-study programs with local employers, and study abroad in 22 countries. There are special honors programs offered in medicine, law, marine and atmospheric science, engineering and medicine, and business. There is a freshman honors program on campus, as well as 42 national honor societies, including Phi Beta Kappa. Twenty departments have honors programs.

Faculty/Classroom: Seventy-one percent of faculty are male; 29%, female. Forty-four percent teach undergraduates. Graduate students teach 2% of introductory courses. The average class size in an introductory lecture is 28; in a laboratory, 28; and in a regular course offering, 18.

Admissions: About 76% of the 1993–94 applicants were accepted. The SAT scores for the 1993–94 freshman class were as follows: Verbal—54% below 500, 32% between 500 and 599, 12% between 600 and 700, and 2% above 700; Math—28% below 500, 34% between 500 and 599, 29% between 600 and 700, and 9% above 700. The ACT scores were 30% below 21, 23% between 22 and 24, 24% between 25 and 27, 17% between 28 and 30, and 6% above 31.

About 61% of the current freshmen were in the top fifth of their class; 83% were in the top two fifths. There were 28 National Merit finalists. Forty freshmen graduated first in their class.

Requirements: The SAT I or ACT is required. In addition, it is recommended that applicants have completed 4 years of English, 3 each of mathematics, science, and social sciences, and 2 of foreign language. Also considered in the admissions decision are a recommendation from a high school counselor and an essay. The GED is accepted. AP and CLEP credits are accepted. Important factors used in the admissions decision are advanced placement or honor courses, recommendations by school officials, evidence of special talent, extracurricular activities record, and leadership record.

Procedure: Freshmen are admitted to all sessions. Entrance exams should be taken in the fall of the senior year or earlier. There are early decision, early admissions, and deferred admissions plans. Early decision applications should be filed by November 15; regular applications, by March 1 for fall entry, November 1 for spring entry, and March 1 for summer entry, along with an application fee of $35. Notification is sent no later than April 15. About 645 early decision candidates were accepted for the 1993–94 class.

Transfer: About 620 transfer students enrolled in 1993–94. Transfer applicants must have a GPA of at least 2.0; higher admission standards are in effect for most programs. At least 45 credits out of 120 must be completed at UM.

Visiting: There are regularly scheduled orientations for prospective students, including the Miami Monday programs, during which prospective students who have made arrangements can meet with an admission officer, tour the campus, and attend a class. There are guides for informal visits, and visitors may sit in on classes and arrange in advance to stay overnight at the school. To arrange for a visit, contact Marilyn Rolfs, receptionist, at (305) 284-4323.

Financial Aid: In 1993–94, 81% of all current freshmen and 75% of continuing students received some form of financial aid. About 67% of freshmen and 62% of continuing students received need-based aid. The average freshman award was $13,000. Eighty percent of undergraduate students work part-time. Average earnings from campus work for the school year are $1700. The average financial indebtedness of the 1992–93 graduate was $11,500. UM is a member of CSS. The FAF, the college's own financial statement, and the FAFSA are required. The deadline for financial aid applications is March 1.

International Students: There are currently 826 international students enrolled. The school actively recruits these students. They must take the TOEFL and achieve a minimum score of 550.

Computers: The college provides computer facilities for student use. The mainframe is a DEC 4000 cluster. More than 1000 personal computers, workstations, and terminals are available to students. Each residential college has a computer laboratory with IBM PS/2 and Apple Macintosh systems, laser printers, and connections to the campuswide network. E-Mail access is available. All students may access the system 24 hours a day. There are no time limits on using the system and no fees.

Graduates: In 1992–93, 1810 bachelor's degrees were awarded. The most popular majors among graduates were psychology (8%), biology (7%), and accounting (5%). Some 112 companies recruited on campus in 1992–93.

Admissions Contact: Edward M. Gillis, Associate Dean of Enrollments and Director of Admissions.

UNIVERSITY OF NORTH FLORIDA
D-1
Jacksonville, FL 32224   (904) 646-2624

Full-time: 2280 men, 2374 women	**Faculty:** 232; IIB, av$
Part-time: 1511 men, 1704 women	**Ph.D.s:** 86%
Graduate: 685 men, 844 women	**Student/Faculty:** 20 to 1
Year: semesters, summer session	**Tuition:** $1722 ($6625)
Application Deadline: July 1	**Room & Board:** $3360
Freshman Class: 1837 applied, 1444 accepted, 569 enrolled	
SAT I or ACT: required	**COMPETITIVE**

The University of North Florida, founded in 1972, is a public university that is part of the state university system. There are 5 undergraduate and 5 graduate schools. In addition to regional accreditation, UNF has baccalaureate program accreditation with AACSB, ADA, NCATE, and NLN. The library contains 463,721 volumes, 701,076 microform items, and 37,380 audiovisual forms. Computerized library sources and services include the card catalog and database searching. Special learning facilities include a learning resource center and an art gallery. The 1000-acre campus is in an urban area 12 miles southeast of downtown Jacksonville. Including residence halls, there are 33 buildings on campus.

Student Life: About 93% of undergraduates are from Florida. Students come from 43 states, 75 foreign countries, and Canada. Ninety-two percent are from public schools; 8% from private. Eighty-three percent are white; 10% African American. The average age of fresh-

men is 18; all undergraduates, 25. Thirteen percent drop out by the end of their first year.

Housing: A total of 900 students can be accommodated in college housing. College-sponsored living facilities include coed dormitories and on-campus apartments. On-campus housing is available on a first-come, first-served basis and is available on a lottery system for upperclassmen. Priority is given to out-of-town students. Eighty-five percent of students commute. All students may keep cars on campus.

Activities: About 5% of men belong to fraternities; about 5% of women belong to sororities. There are 50 groups on campus, including art, band, cheerleading, choir, chorale, chorus, computers, drama, drill team, ethnic, honors, international, jazz band, literary magazine, musical theater, newspaper, orchestra, photography, political, professional, radio and TV, religious, social, social service, student government, and symphony. Popular campus events include Oktoberfest, Spring Musicfest, and Homecoming.

Sports: There are 7 intercollegiate sports for men and 5 for women, and 21 intramural sports for men and 19 for women. Athletic and recreation facilities include a baseball stadium, softball and multipurpose fields, an aquatic center, a fitness center, jogging trails, racquetball and tennis courts, and a new arena.

Disabled Students: The entire campus is accessible to disabled students. The following facilities are available: wheelchair ramps, elevators, special parking, specially equipped rest rooms, special class scheduling, lowered drinking fountains, and lowered telephones. The Disabled Students Services Office provides specialized assistance and equipment, including priority registration and an interpreter for the deaf.

Services: In addition to many counseling and information services, tutoring is available in every subject. In addition, there is a reader service for the blind. Tutoring in reading, writing, mathematics, business, accounting, and foreign languages is provided through the Academic Resource Center.

Campus Safety and Security: Campus safety and security measures include 24-hour foot and vehicle patrol, self-defense education, escort service, and shuttle service. In addition, there are informal discussions, pamphlets, posters, films, emergency telephones, and lighted pathways and sidewalks.

Programs of Study: UNF awards the B.A., B.S., B.B.A., B.F.A., B.S.N., and B.S.P.T. degrees. Master's and doctoral degrees also are awarded. Bachelor's degrees are awarded in BIOLOGICAL SCIENCE (biology/biological science), BUSINESS (accounting, banking and finance, business administration and management, business economics, insurance and risk management, marketing/retailing/merchandising, and transportation management), COMMUNICATIONS AND THE ARTS (art history and appreciation, communications, English, fine arts, literature, music, and Spanish), COMPUTER AND PHYSICAL SCIENCE (chemistry, computer science, information sciences and systems, mathematics, and statistics), EDUCATION (art, business, early childhood, elementary, health, mathematics, music, science, secondary, social science, and special), ENGINEERING AND ENVIRONMENTAL DESIGN (construction technology, electrical/electronics engineering, and engineering technology), HEALTH PROFESSIONS (nursing and physical therapy), SOCIAL SCIENCE (criminal justice, economics, history, political science/government, prelaw, psychology, and sociology). Computer science, business, and education are the strongest academically and have the largest enrollments.

Required: Students are required to take general education distribution requirements, including writing and mathematics courses. A minimum 2.0 GPA and 120 credit hours are needed for graduation.

Special: There are cooperative programs for preprofessional majors with the University of Florida and Florida State University, internships in most majors, and work-study programs with several Jacksonville businesses. Study abroad, dual majors in arts and sciences, and student-designed majors also are available. Credit is given for military experience. There is a freshman honors program on campus, as well as 2 national honor societies.

Faculty/Classroom: The average class size in an introductory lecture is 30; in a laboratory, 20; and in a regular course offering, 23.

Admissions: About 79% of the 1993–94 applicants were accepted. The SAT scores for the 1993–94 freshman class were as follows: Verbal—43% below 500, 43% between 500 and 599, and 14% between 600 and 700. About 30% of the current freshmen were in the top fifth of their class; 35% were in the top two fifths. There were 7 National Merit finalists and 5 semifinalists.

Requirements: A minimum GPA of 2.5 is required. The SAT I, with a minimum composite score of 900, or the ACT, with a minimum score of 19, is required. In addition, applicant must be a graduate of an accredited secondary school or have a GED. A total of 15 academic credits or 19 Carnegie units is required. Secondary school course work must include 4 years of English, 2 of foreign language, and 3 each of mathematics, science, and social studies. AP and CLEP credits are accepted. Important factors used in the admissions decision are advanced placement or honor courses, recommendations by

school officials, extracurricular activities record, leadership record, and geographic diversity.

Procedure: Freshmen are admitted to all sessions. Entrance exams should be taken during the fall of the senior year. Applications should be filed by July 1 for fall entry, November 20 for spring entry, and March 20 for summer entry, along with an application fee of $20. Notification is sent on a rolling basis. There are early admissions and deferred admissions plans.

Transfer: Transfer applicants with fewer than 60 credit hours must take the SAT I or the ACT. The minimum acceptable composite score on the SAT I is 900; the minimum acceptable ACT score is 19. The minimum GPA for transfers is 2.0 (2.5 for some programs). At least 30 credits out of 120 must be completed at UNF.

Visiting: There are regularly scheduled orientations for prospective students, consisting of a tour of the campus, a general information session, and a personal interview by request. There are guides for informal visits, and visitors may sit in on classes. To arrange for a visit, contact the Admissions Office at (904) 646–2624.

Financial Aid: In an earlier year, 25% of all students received some form of financial aid. UNF is a member of CSS. The FAF or FFS is required. The deadline for financial aid applications is April 1.

International Students: There are currently 150 international students enrolled. The school actively recruits these students. They must take the TOEFL and achieve a minimum score of 500 and must also take the SAT I or the ACT.

Computers: The college provides computer facilities for student use. The mainframes are IBM Models 3090, 4381, and 4341. There are also microcomputers available for student use in faculty offices. All students may access the system from 8 A.M. to 10 P.M. There are no time limits on using the system and no fees.

Graduates: In an earlier year, 852 bachelor's degrees were awarded. Within an average freshman class, 45% graduate in 6 years.

Admissions Contact: Mary S. Bolla, Director of Admissions.

UNIVERSITY OF SOUTH FLORIDA

D-1

Tampa, FL 33620   **(813) 974–2696**

Full-time: 13,235 men and women	**Faculty:** 1333; I, --$
Part-time: 8435 men and women	**Ph.D.s:** 70%
Graduate: 2538 men, 3426 women	**Student/Faculty:** 10 to 1
Year: semesters, summer session	**Tuition:** $1855 ($6755)
Application Deadline: June 1	**Room & Board:** $3620
Freshman Class: 7589 applied, 4676 accepted, 1878 enrolled	
SAT I: 492/553	**ACT:** 23 **COMPETITIVE +**

The University of South Florida, founded in 1956, is a comprehensive public coeducational institution, part of the state university system of Florida, offering programs in liberal and fine arts, business, engineering, health science, and teacher preparation. There are 7 undergraduate and 9 graduate schools. In addition to regional accreditation, USF has baccalaureate program accreditation with AACSB, ABET, ACEJMC, ASLA, CSWE, NASM, and NLN. The 2 libraries contain 716,970 volumes and 1,248,631 microform items. Computerized library sources and services include the card catalog and interlibrary loans. Special learning facilities include a learning resource center, art gallery, planetarium, radio station, and TV station. The 1600-acre campus is in a suburban area 10 miles northeast of Tampa. Including residence halls, there are 167 buildings on campus.

Student Life: About 89% of undergraduates are from Florida. Students come from 50 states and Canada. Eighty-four percent are white. The average age of freshmen is 19; all undergraduates, 25. Twelve percent drop out by the end of their first year.

Housing: A total of 3296 students can be accommodated in college housing. College-sponsored living facilities include single-sex and coed dormitories and on-campus apartments. In addition there are honors houses. On-campus housing is guaranteed for all 4 years. Eighty-five percent of students commute. All students may keep cars on campus.

Activities: There are 20 national fraternities and 10 national sororities. There are more than 200 groups on campus, including art, cheerleading, chess, choir, chorale, chorus, computers, dance, drama, drill team, ethnic, film, gay, honors, international, jazz band, literary magazine, musical theater, newspaper, opera, orchestra, pep band, photography, political, professional, radio and TV, religious, social, social service, student government, symphony, and yearbook. Popular campus events include Homecoming, Black Awareness Month, Women's Awareness Week, Founders Week, and Bull Blast.

Sports: Athletic and recreation facilities include 4 pools, tennis and racquetball courts, a track, and a jogging course.

Disabled Students: All of the campus is accessible to disabled students. The following facilities are available: wheelchair ramps, elevators, special parking, specially equipped rest rooms, special class scheduling, lowered drinking fountains, and lowered telephones.

Services: In addition to many counseling and information services, tutoring is available in most subjects. In addition, there is a reader service for the blind.

Campus Safety and Security: Campus safety and security measures include 24-hour foot and vehicle patrol, escort service, informal discussions, and pamphlets, posters, and films. In addition, there are emergency telephones and lighted pathways and sidewalks.

Programs of Study: USF awards the B.A., B.S., B.F.A., B.I.S., B.Mus., B.S.W., and several engineering degrees. Master's and doctoral degrees also are awarded. Bachelor's degrees are awarded in BIOLOGICAL SCIENCE (biology/biological science, botany, microbiology, and zoology), BUSINESS (accounting, business administration and management, business economics, marketing/retailing/merchandising, and personnel management), COMMUNICATIONS AND THE ARTS (advertising, broadcasting, communications, dance, dramatic arts, English, film arts, fine arts, French, German, Greek, Italian, journalism, Latin, music, photography, Russian, Spanish, and speech/debate/rhetoric), COMPUTER AND PHYSICAL SCIENCE (chemistry, computer programming, computer science, earth science, geology, information sciences and systems, mathematics, and physics), EDUCATION (art, business, early childhood, elementary, foreign languages, health, industrial arts, middle school, music, science, secondary, and teaching English as a second language/foreign language), ENGINEERING AND ENVIRONMENTAL DESIGN (chemical engineering, civil engineering, computer engineering, electrical/electronics engineering, engineering, engineering technology, industrial engineering technology, and mechanical engineering), HEALTH PROFESSIONS (medical laboratory technology, nursing, predentistry, premedicine, and speech pathology/audiology), SOCIAL SCIENCE (anthropology, community services, criminal justice, economics, geography, history, international relations, philosophy, political science/government, prelaw, psychology, religion, social science, social work, sociology, and urban studies). Education, fine arts, sciences, accounting, nursing, and psychology are the strongest academically. Business has the largest enrollment.

Required: All students are required to complete at least 120 credit hours including 45 distributed among English, mathematics, science, social science, fine arts, and humanities. The number of hours required for each major varies. Students must maintain a minimum GPA of 2.0.

Special: USF offers co-op programs, cross-registration, internships, study abroad, and work-study programs. An accelerated degree program in medicine is also offered. Students may take dual majors and design a few majors as well as earn a liberal arts degree. Nondegree study is available, as are pass/fail options for some courses. There is a freshman honors program on campus, as well as 6 national honor societies. Ten departments have honors programs.

Faculty/Classroom: Seventy-seven percent of faculty are male; 23%, female. The average class size in an introductory lecture is 150; in a laboratory, 20; and in a regular course offering, 50.

Admissions: About 62% of the 1993–94 applicants were accepted. The SAT scores for the 1993–94 freshman class were as follows: Verbal—53% below 500, 33% between 500 and 599, 12% between 600 and 700, and 2% above 700; Math—25% below 500, 43% between 500 and 599, 26% between 600 and 700, and 6% above 700. The ACT scores were 25% below 21, 30% between 21 and 23, 23% between 24 and 26, 10% between 27 and 28, and 12% above 28.

Requirements: A minimum GPA of 2.0 is required. The SAT I or ACT is required. Candidates for admission should have completed 4 units of English, 2 units of a foreign language, 3 units each of mathematics, science, and social studies, and 4 additional academic electives. The GED is accepted. Applicants who do not meet minimum requirements but have important attributes, special talents, or unique circumstances are considered for admission by an academic faculty committee. AP and CLEP credits are accepted. Important factors used in the admissions decision are evidence of special talent, advanced placement or honor courses, recommendations by school officials, leadership record, and extracurricular activities record.

Procedure: Freshmen are admitted to all sessions. Entrance exams should be taken at the end of the junior year or beginning of the senior year of high school. Applications should be filed by June 1 for fall entry, October 25 for spring entry, and March 1 for summer entry, along with an application fee of $20. Notification is sent on a rolling basis. There is an early admissions plan.

Transfer: About 3740 transfer students enrolled in 1993–94. Students with fewer than 60 transferable hours must meet freshmen requirements. Additionally, transfer applicants must have a cumulative college GPA of 2.0 and be in good standing at their last institution. A total of 30 credits out of 120 must be completed at USF.

Visiting: There are regularly scheduled orientations for prospective students, including a 2-day orientation program designed to introduce new students to the USF community. There are guides for informal visits and visitors may sit in on classes. To arrange for a visit, contact the Admissions Office at (813) 974–3350.

Financial Aid: In a recent year, 60% of all current freshmen and 68% of continuing students received some form of financial aid. Twenty-five percent of undergraduate students work part-time. Aver-

age earnings from campus work for the school year are $2500. USF is a member of CSS. The FAFSA financial statement is required.

International Students: There are currently 671 international students enrolled. The school actively recruits these students. They must take the TOEFL and achieve a minimum score of 550. The student must also take the SAT I or the ACT.

Computers: The college provides computer facilities for student use. The mainframe is an IBM. There are also Macintosh and IBM computers available in the Student Union. All students may access the system. There are no time limits on using the system and no fees.

Graduates: In a recent year, 6532 bachelor's degrees were awarded. Within an average freshman class, 47% graduate in 4 years.

Admissions Contact: Marc L. Harding, Associate Director of Admissions.

UNIVERSITY OF TAMPA
Tampa, FL 33606   **D-4**

Full-time: 1960 men and women	(813) 253–6228; (800) 733–4773
Part-time: 500 men and women	**Faculty:** 134; IIB, av$
Graduate: 350 men and women	**Ph.D.s:** 85%
Year: semesters, summer session	**Student/Faculty:** 15 to 1
Application Deadline: open	**Tuition:** $12,280
Freshman Class: 1608 applied, 1377 accepted, 305 enrolled	**Room & Board:** $4500
SAT I Verbal/Math: 420/471	**COMPETITIVE**

The University of Tampa, founded in 1931, is a private, coeducational institution offering programs in the arts and sciences, business, education, and nursing. There are 2 undergraduate schools and one graduate school. In addition to regional accreditation, UT has baccalaureate program accreditation with NASM and NLN. The library contains 225,425 volumes, 50,000 microform items, and 2223 audiovisual forms, and subscribes to 1883 periodicals. Computerized library sources and services include the card catalog, interlibrary loans, and database searching. Special learning facilities include a learning resource center, art gallery, natural history museum, radio station, TV station, a fully equipped research vessel for marine science studies, and a music facility. The 68-acre campus is in an urban area in Tampa. Including residence halls, there are 37 buildings on campus.

Student Life: About 36% of undergraduates are from Florida. Students come from 50 states, 42 foreign countries, and Canada. Sixty percent are from public schools; 40% from private. Seventy-nine percent are white. The average age of freshmen is 18; all undergraduates, 21. Thirty-three percent drop out by the end of their first year; 40% remain to graduate.

Housing: A total of 1050 students can be accommodated in college housing. College-sponsored living facilities include single-sex and coed dormitories and on-campus apartments. In addition, there is a special honors floor in one of the residence halls. On-campus housing is guaranteed for all 4 years. Fifty-five percent of students live on campus; of those, 80% remain on campus on weekends. All students may keep cars on campus.

Activities: About 7% of men belong to 5 national fraternities; about 7% of women belong to 3 national sororities. There are 56 groups on campus, including art, band, cheerleading, chorale, chorus, computers, dance, drama, drill team, ethnic, honors, international, jazz band, literary magazine, musical theater, newspaper, pep band, political, professional, radio and TV, religious, social, student government, and yearbook. Popular campus events include Parents Day, Oktoberfest, Bay Day, Gaspirilla, International Student Fest, Plant Park Art Festival, and Food Fest.

Sports: There are 8 intercollegiate sports for men and 7 for women, and 6 intramural sports for men and 6 for women. Athletic and recreation facilities include a sports center, a stadium, a playing field, a boat house, an Olympic-size pool, 6 lighted tennis courts, 2 racquetball courts, an activity center, a dance studio, and the student union.

Disabled Students: The entire campus is accessible to disabled students. The following facilities are available: wheelchair ramps, elevators, special parking, specially equipped rest rooms, and lowered drinking fountains.

Services: In addition to many counseling and information services, tutoring is available in every subject. In addition, there is a reader service for the blind, and remedial math, reading, and writing.

Campus Safety and Security: Campus safety and security measures include 24-hour foot and vehicle patrol, self-defense education, escort service, and shuttle buses. In addition, there are informal discussions, pamphlets, posters, films, emergency telephones, lighted pathways and sidewalks, and a full-service, on-campus police office with licensed deputies.

Programs of Study: UT awards the B.A., B.S., B.F.A., B.L.S., B.Mus., B.P.M., and B.S.N. degrees. Associate and master's degrees also are awarded. Bachelor's degrees are awarded in BIOLOGICAL SCIENCE (biochemistry, biology/biological science, and marine science), BUSINESS (accounting, banking and finance, business economics, international business management, and marketing/retailing/merchandising), COMMUNICATIONS AND THE ARTS

(communications, creative writing, English, fine arts, French, music, and Spanish), COMPUTER AND PHYSICAL SCIENCE (chemistry, information sciences and systems, and mathematics), EDUCATION (elementary, physical, and secondary), HEALTH PROFESSIONS (medical laboratory technology and nursing), SOCIAL SCIENCE (criminal justice, history, international studies, philosophy, political science/government, psychology, social science, social work, sociology, and urban studies). Management, accounting, communications, psychology, and marine biology have the largest enrollments.

Required: To graduate, students must maintain a minimum GPA of 2.0 in at least 124 credit hours, including 15 in academic skills, 6 in natural science, 11 in humanities/fine arts, 11 in social science, and 4 in interdisciplinary studies. Students must also complete Introduction to Computers. The requirements for individual majors vary.

Special: Students may participate in internships, work-study programs on campus, study abroad, and a Washington semester. The university also offers nondegree study, pass/fail options, and credit for life, military, and work experience. There is a freshman honors program on campus, as well as 16 national honor societies. Six departments have honors programs.

Faculty/Classroom: All faculty teach undergraduates. No introductory courses are taught by graduate students. The average class size in a regular course offering is 18.

Admissions: About 86% of the 1993–94 applicants were accepted.

Requirements: A minimum GPA of 2.2 is required. The SAT I or ACT is required, with minimum composite scores of 900 on the SAT I or 21 on the ACT. Candidates for admission should have completed 5 credits in electives, 4 in English, and 2 each in mathematics, science, and social studies. A portfolio or an audition is required for specific arts and music programs. AP and CLEP credits are accepted. Important factors used in the admissions decision are recommendations by school officials, personality, intangible qualities, advanced placement or honor courses, leadership record, and evidence of special talent.

Procedure: Freshmen are admitted to all sessions. Entrance exams should be taken by the end of the junior year. Application deadlines are open. Application fee is $50. Notification is sent on a rolling basis. There are early decision and early admissions plans.

Transfer: About 220 transfer students enrolled in 1993–94. Applicants should have earned 24 credits with a minimum GPA of 2.0. At least 31 credits out of 124 must be completed at UT.

Visiting: There are regularly scheduled orientations for prospective students, including a campus tour and interview with an admissions counselor. There are guides for informal visits, and visitors may sit in on classes and stay overnight at the school. To arrange for a visit, contact Audrey Ashley at (800) 733–4773.

Financial Aid: In 1993–94, 83% of all students received some form of financial aid. About 70% of students received need-based aid. The average freshman award was $8500. Of that total, scholarships or need-based grants averaged $2500 ($10,400 maximum); loans averaged $2625 (maximum); and work contracts averaged $1200 ($2000 maximum). Forty percent of undergraduate students work part-time. Average earnings from campus work for the school year are $1000. The average financial indebtedness of a recent graduate was $9000. UT is a member of CSS. The FAF is required.

International Students: There are currently 177 international students enrolled. The school actively recruits these students. They must take the TOEFL and achieve a minimum score of 550 and must take the SAT I or ACT to be eligible for scholarships or grants.

Computers: The college provides computer facilities for student use. The mainframe is a DEC VAX 8250. There are also 71 Apple Macintoshes available in the library, computer centers, and Plant Hall. All students may access the system. There are no time limits on using the system and no fees.

Graduates: In 1992–93, 294 bachelor's degrees were awarded. Some 135 companies recruited on campus in a recent year. In the 1992 graduating class, 93% of the men and 91% of the women had found employment within 6 months of graduation.

Admissions Contact: Admissions Representative.

UNIVERSITY OF WEST FLORIDA
A-1
Pensacola, FL 32514–5750   (904) 474–2230

Full-time: 1521 men, 2044 women	Faculty: 239; IIA, --$
Part-time: 769 men, 1132 women	Ph.D.s: 84%
Graduate: 524 men, 603 women	Student/Faculty: 15 to 1
Year: semesters, summer session	Tuition: $1556 ($6280)
Application Deadline: June 1	Room & Board: $3859
Freshman Class: 1717 applied, 1287 accepted, 500 enrolled	
SAT I or ACT: required	COMPETITIVE

The University of West Florida, founded in 1963, is a public, liberal arts institution that is part of the State University System of Florida. There are 4 undergraduate and 4 graduate schools. In addition to regional accreditation, UWF has baccalaureate program accreditation with ABET, NCATE, and NLN. The library contains 660,000 volumes and 980,000 microform items, and subscribes to 5013 periodicals. Computerized library sources and services include the card catalog. Special learning facilities include an art gallery and radio station. The 1000-acre campus is in a suburban area 10 miles north of Pensacola. Including residence halls, there are 71 buildings on campus.

Student Life: About 90% of undergraduates are from Florida. Eighty-five percent are white.

Housing: A total of 800 students can be accommodated in college housing. College-sponsored living facilities include coed dormitories. On-campus housing is guaranteed for all 4 years. Eighty-nine percent of students commute; all may keep cars on campus.

Activities: There are 6 national fraternities and 4 national sororities. There are 18 groups on campus, including art, band, cheerleading, chorale, chorus, drama, ethnic, film, honors, international, jazz band, literary magazine, newspaper, orchestra, political, professional, radio and TV, religious, social, and student government. Popular campus events include Homecoming.

Sports: Athletic and recreation facilities include facilities for baseball, track, tennis, racquetball, handball, softball, soccer, swimming, and diving.

Disabled Students: All of the campus is accessible to disabled students. The following facilities are available: wheelchair ramps, elevators, special parking, specially equipped rest rooms, and special class scheduling.

Services: In addition to many counseling and information services, tutoring is available in most subjects.

Campus Safety and Security: Campus safety and security measures include 24-hour foot and vehicle patrol, escort service, informal discussions, pamphlets, posters, and films. In addition, there are emergency telephones and lighted pathways and sidewalks.

Programs of Study: UWF awards the B.A., B.S., B.F.A. and B.S.N degrees. Associate and master's degrees are also awarded. Bachelor's degrees are awarded in BIOLOGICAL SCIENCE (biology/biological science), BUSINESS (accounting, banking and finance, business administration and management, business economics, and marketing/retailing/merchandising), COMMUNICATIONS AND THE ARTS (communications, English, French, music, and Spanish), COMPUTER AND PHYSICAL SCIENCE (chemistry, computer science, mathematics, physics, and statistics), EDUCATION (art, early childhood, elementary, health, middle school, music, and secondary), HEALTH PROFESSIONS (medical laboratory technology, nursing, predentistry, and premedicine), SOCIAL SCIENCE (criminal justice, history, philosophy, political science/government, prelaw, psychology, religion, social science, social work, and sociology). Accounting, management, marketing, and marine biology are the strongest academically. Accounting, management, and marketing have the largest enrollments.

Required: In order to graduate, students must maintain a 2.0 GPA and complete 120 semester hours with a minimum of 24 hours in the major and 24 hours in upper-division courses.

Special: Internships are arranged on an individual basis through a student's major department. The college offers pass/fail options and credit for life, military, and work experience. A 3–2 engineering degree is also offered. There is a freshman honors program on campus, as well as 5 national honor societies.

Faculty/Classroom: Seventy-two percent of faculty are male; 28%, female. The average class size in an introductory lecture is 26; in a laboratory, 20; and in a regular course offering, 26.

Admissions: About 75% of the 1993–94 applicants were accepted. Half of the current freshmen were in the top fifth of their class. There were 3 National Merit semifinalists.

Requirements: UWF requires applicants to be in the upper 50% of their class. A minimum GPA of 3.0 is required. The SAT I or ACT is required. Students must have completed 4 years of English, 3 each of mathematics, science, and social studies, and 2 of a foreign language. AP and CLEP credits are accepted. Important factors used in the admissions decision are advanced placement or honor courses, evidence of special talent, leadership record, parents or siblings attending the school, and extracurricular activities record.

Procedure: Freshmen are admitted to all sessions. Entrance exams should be taken by the fall of the senior year. Applications should be filed by June 1 for fall entry, December 1 for spring entry, and June 1 for summer entry, along with an application fee of $20. Notification is sent on a rolling basis. There is an early admissions plan.

Transfer: Nearly 1300 transfer students enrolled in an earlier year. Applicants must have a 2.0 GPA and 36 semester hours of general education courses. Transfer students with fewer than 60 semester hours of transferable credit must meet freshman admission requirements. A total of 30 credits out of 120 must be completed at UWF.

Visiting: There are regularly scheduled orientations for prospective students. There are guides for informal visits and visitors may sit in on classes and stay overnight at the school. To arrange for a visit, contact the Admissions Office at (904) 474–2230.

Financial Aid: The FAF and University of West Florida Request for Financial Aid Consideration form, SAR is required.

International Students: There are currently 192 international students enrolled. They must take the TOEFL, with a minimum score of 500 or the University of Michigan Language Test and the SAT I or the ACT.

Computers: The college provides computer facilities for student use. The mainframe is an IBM 4381. All students may access the system. There are no time limits on using the system and no fees.

Graduates: Nearly 1150 bachelor's degrees were awarded in an earlier year. About 120 companies recruited on campus that year.

Admissions Contact: Susie Neeley, Director of Admissions.

WEBBER COLLEGE
Babson Park, FL 33827

D-3

(813) 638-1431; (800) 741-1844

Full-time: 160 men, 167 women	**Faculty:** 19
Part-time: 54 men, 56 women	**Ph.D.s:** 37%
Graduate: none	**Student/Faculty:** 17 to 1
Year: semesters, summer session	**Tuition:** $5790
Application Deadline: open	**Room & Board:** $2920
Freshman Class: 280 applied, 191 accepted, 79 enrolled	
ACT: 18	COMPETITIVE

Webber College, a privately endowed, coeducational, nonprofit institution founded in 1927, offers undergraduate degrees in business. The library contains 35,000 volumes, 98 microform items, and 1500 audiovisual forms, and subscribes to 155 periodicals. Special learning facilities include a learning resource center and an Audubon Society museum. The 110-acre campus is in a small town 50 miles east of Tampa. Including residence halls, there are 10 buildings on campus.

Student Life: About 47% of undergraduates are from Florida. Students come from 11 states, 10 foreign countries, and Canada. Seventy-six percent are from public schools; 24% from private. Sixty-eight percent are white; 16% foreign nationals; 11% African American. The average age of freshmen is 20. Fourteen percent drop out by the end of their first year; 73% remain to graduate.

Housing: A total of 210 students can be accommodated in college housing. College-sponsored living facilities include single-sex dormitories. On-campus housing is guaranteed for the freshman year only and is available on a first-come, first-served basis. Fifty-two percent of students commute. Alcohol is not permitted. All students may keep cars on campus.

Activities: About 25% of men belong to 1 national fraternity. There are no sororities on campus. There are 11 groups on campus, including cheerleading, computers, drama, international, newspaper, professional, social service, student government, and yearbook. Popular campus events include Homecoming, Webber Weekend, and Christmas Party.

Sports: There are 7 intercollegiate sports for men and 6 for women, and 6 intramural sports for men and 6 for women. Athletic and recreation facilities include 2 gymnasiums, a lake, a weight room, tennis courts, a swimming pool, softball and soccer fields, and beach volleyball courts.

Disabled Students: Sixty-four percent of the campus is accessible to disabled students. The following facilities are available: wheelchair ramps, special parking, specially equipped rest rooms, special class scheduling, lowered drinking fountains, and lowered telephones.

Services: In addition to many counseling and information services, tutoring is available in most subjects. In addition, there is remedial math, reading, and writing.

Campus Safety and Security: Campus safety and security measures include escort service, informal discussions, pamphlets, posters, films, and lighted pathways and sidewalks. In addition, there is a security patrol overnight and all weekend.

Programs of Study: Webber awards the B.S. degree. Associate degrees also are awarded. Bachelor's degrees are awarded in BUSINESS (accounting, banking and finance, business administration and management, hotel/motel and restaurant management, international business management, management information systems, marketing/retailing/merchandising, recreational facilities management, and tourism). Business administration is the strongest academically and has the largest enrollment.

Required: To graduate, all students must complete 122 credit hours, including their major, a 41-credit general curriculum, and a 30-credit business core. A minimum GPA of 2.0 must be maintained. Students must pass the college's required English courses and meet its writing requirements. All students must take the GMAT before graduation.

Special: On-campus work-study programs and internships in the areas of fashion, travel and tourism, hotel and restaurant management, and club and recreation management, study abroad, and B.A.-B.S. degrees are offered.

Faculty/Classroom: Sixty-nine percent of faculty are male; 31%, female. All teach. The average class size in an introductory lecture is 30; in a laboratory, 10; and in a regular course offering, 18.

Admissions: About 68% of the 1993–94 applicants were accepted.

Requirements: Webber requires applicants to be in the upper 50% of their class. A minimum GPA of 2.0 is required. The SAT I or ACT is required, with a minimum composite score of 800 or 17, respectively. Applicants should be graduates of accredited secondary schools and have completed 3 years each of English, mathematics, and science and 2 years of social studies. An essay is also required. A GED is accepted. AP and CLEP credits are accepted. Important factors used in the admissions decision are personality, intangible qualities, advanced placement or honor courses, leadership record, evidence of special talent, and extracurricular activities record.

Procedure: Freshmen are admitted to all sessions. Entrance exams should be taken during the senior year. Application deadlines are open. Application fee is $25. Notification is sent on a rolling basis. There are early decision, early admissions, and deferred admissions plans.

Transfer: Applicants should have a minimum GPA of 2.0 with 24 credit hours, and must leave their previous institution in good academic standing. At least 30 credits out of 122 must be completed at Webber.

Visiting: There are guides for informal visits, and visitors may sit in on classes and stay overnight at the school. To arrange for a visit, contact the Director of Admissions at (813) 638-1431.

Financial Aid: In 1993–94, 80% of all current freshmen and 67% of continuing students received some form of financial aid. About 67% of freshmen received need-based aid. The average freshman award was $650. Of that total, scholarships or need-based grants averaged $650 ($2000 maximum); loans averaged $3292; and work contracts averaged $400 ($600 maximum). Thirty-five percent of undergraduate students work part-time. The average financial indebtedness of the 1992–93 graduate was $9200. Webber is a member of CSS. The FAF, FFS, or SFS is required; the FFS is preferred. The deadline for financial aid applications is August 1.

International Students: There are currently 70 international students enrolled. The school actively recruits these students. They must take the TOEFL and achieve a minimum score of 500.

Computers: The college provides computer facilities for student use. The mainframe is an IBM. There are 30 microcomputers located at the computer center and in the library. All students may access the system. There are no time limits on using the system and no fees.

Graduates: In 1992–93, 39 bachelor's degrees were awarded. Within an average freshman class, 74% graduate in 4 years, 10% in 5 years, and 2% in 6 years.

Admissions Contact: Director of Admissions.

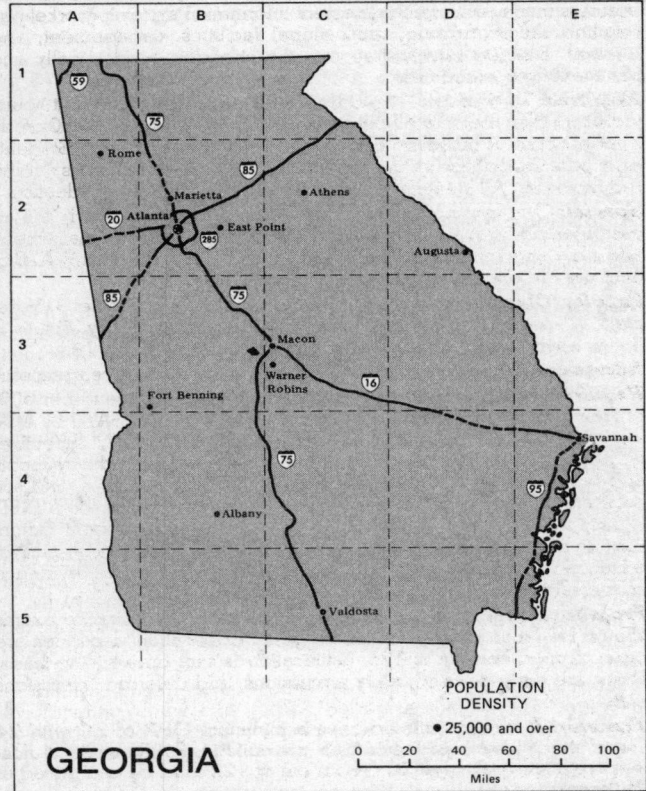

GEORGIA

POPULATION DENSITY

● 25,000 and over

0 20 40 60 80 100
Miles

AGNES SCOTT COLLEGE
B-2

Decatur, GA 30030   (404) 371-6285; (800) 868-8602 (out-of-state)

Full-time: 510 women
Part-time: 2 men, 61 women
Graduate: 3 men, 24 women
Year: semesters
Application Deadline: February 1
Freshman Class: 417 applied, 349 accepted, 137 enrolled
SAT I Verbal/Math: required

Faculty: 66; IIB, +$
Ph.D.s: 97%
Student/Faculty: 8 to 1
Tuition: $12,135
Room & Board: $5000

VERY COMPETITIVE

Agnes Scott College, founded in 1889, is an independent college, predominantly for women, affiliated with the Presbyterian Church. It offers programs in liberal arts and teacher preparation. There is one graduate school. The library contains 191,352 volumes, 23,997 microform items, and 6953 audiovisual forms, and subscribes to 816 periodicals. Computerized library sources and services include database searching. Special learning facilities include a learning resource center, art gallery, and planetarium. The 100-acre campus is in an urban area 6 miles from downtown Atlanta. Including residence halls, there are 21 buildings on campus.

Student Life: About 61% of undergraduates are from Georgia. Students come from 27 states and 13 foreign countries. Eighty-five percent are from public schools; 15% from private. Seventy-six percent are white; 12% African American. Forty-four percent are Protestant; 10% Catholic. The average age of freshmen is 18; all undergraduates, 21. Twenty-two percent drop out by the end of their first year; 60% remain to graduate.

Housing: A total of 600 students can be accommodated in college housing. College-sponsored living facilities include single-sex dormitories. In addition, there are language wings within residence halls for Spanish, French, and German. On-campus housing is guaranteed for all 4 years. Seventy-one percent of students live on campus; of those, 75% remain on campus on weekends. All students may keep cars on campus.

Activities: There are no fraternities or sororities on campus. There are 36 groups on campus, including art, choir, dance, drama, ethnic, gay, honors, international, literary magazine, newspaper, orchestra, political, religious, social, social service, student government, and yearbook. Popular campus events include Black-Cat—the culmination of orientation—with student productions, athletic competition, a bonfire, and a formal dance. Also popular are street dances, holiday parties, Senior Investiture, Sophomore Families Weekend, and commencement.

Sports: There are 5 intercollegiate and 5 intramural sports for women. Athletic and recreation facilities include a gymnasium with a regulation basketball court, an 8-lane indoor pool, a soccer field, tennis and racquetball courts, a weight room, a track, an aerobics room, dance studios, and ping-pong tables.

Disabled Students: All of the campus is accessible to disabled students. The following facilities are available: wheelchair ramps, elevators, special parking, specially equipped rest rooms, special class scheduling as needed, and lowered drinking fountains.

Services: In addition to many counseling and information services, tutoring is available in some subjects, including chemistry, classical languages, English, French, mathematics, and physics. A writing workshop and a collaborative learning center are also available.

Campus Safety and Security: Campus safety and security measures include 24-hour foot and vehicle patrol, self defense education, escort service, and informal discussions. In addition, there are pamphlets, posters, and films, emergency telephones, and lighted pathways and sidewalks. Taxi service for cross-registration students is provided and shuttle buses run on weekends.

Programs of Study: Agnes Scott awards the B.A. degree. Master's degrees also are awarded. Bachelor's degrees are awarded in BIOLOGICAL SCIENCE (biology/biological science), COMMUNICATIONS AND THE ARTS (classics, creative writing, dramatic arts, English, fine arts, French, German, Greek (classical), Latin, literature, music, and Spanish), COMPUTER AND PHYSICAL SCIENCE (astrophysics, chemistry, mathematics, and physics), SOCIAL SCIENCE (anthropology, biblical studies, economics, history, international relations, Latin American studies, philosophy, political science/government, psychobiology, psychology, and sociology). Psychology, international relations, and English have the largest enrollments.

Required: Requirements for graduation include courses in English composition and reading, foreign language, and physical education, as well as courses in humanities and fine arts, religious and philosophical thought, history, natural science, mathematics, and social science. Students must complete 124 credit hours, including 30 to 48 in the major, with a 2.0 GPA.

Special: There is cross-registration with the University Center in Georgia; internships; study abroad, including exchange programs in France, Germany, and Japan; a 3–2 engineering program with the Georgia Institute of Technology; dual, student-designed, and interdisciplinary majors, including anthropology/sociology and creative writing/English literature; and pass/fail options. A Global Awareness Program combines fall and spring semester class work with a January travel experience. Washington Semester, PLEN Public Policy Semester, Mills College Exchange, a 3–4 architecture degree with Washington University, and teacher certification programs are offered. B.A. degree requirements may be completed in 3 years. There are 4 national honor societies on campus, including Phi Beta Kappa.

Faculty/Classroom: Forty-one percent of faculty are male; 59%, female. All members both teach and do research. No introductory courses are taught by graduate students. The average class size in an introductory lecture is 17; in a laboratory, 13; and in a regular course offering, 12.

Admissions: About 84% of the 1993–94 applicants were accepted. About 81% of the current freshmen were in the top fifth of their class; 96% were in the top two fifths. There was 1 National Merit finalist. Nine freshmen graduated first in their class.

Requirements: Agnes Scott recommends that applicants be in the upper 30% of their class. The SAT I or ACT is required. Applicants (except early admission) must graduate from an accredited secondary school or have a GED. A total of 16 academic credits is recommended, including 4 years of English, 3 of mathematics, 2 of a foreign language, and 1 or more each of science and social studies. An essay is required and an interview is recommended. An audition is required for those seeking a music scholarship. AP credits are accepted. Important factors used in the admissions decision are advanced placement or honor courses, recommendations by school officials, leadership record, extracurricular activities record, and evidence of special talent.

Procedure: Freshmen are admitted to all sessions. Entrance exams should be taken late in the junior year or by January of the senior year. Early decision applications should be filed by November 15; regular applications, by February 1 for fall entry and November 1 for spring entry, along with an application fee of $35. Scholarship applicants should file applications in time to meet the January 15 deadline. Notification of early decision is sent December 15; regular decision, beginning of February. There are early decision, early admissions, and deferred admissions plans. Twenty early decision candidates were accepted for the 1993–94 class.

Transfer: Thirteen transfer students enrolled in 1993–94. A minimum GPA of 2.5 is recommended, as is an interview and a letter of recommendation from a professor. A total of 60 credits out of 124, in-

cluding the junior and senior years, must be completed at Agnes Scott.

Visiting: There are regularly scheduled orientations for prospective students, including classes, tours, interviews, residence hall experiences, and informational sessions. There are guides for informal visits and visitors may sit in on classes and stay overnight at the school. To arrange for a visit, contact the Office of Admission at (404) 371-6285.

Financial Aid: In 1993-94, 96% of all current freshmen and 88% of continuing students received some form of financial aid. About 64% of freshmen and 65% of continuing students received need-based aid. The average freshman award was $10,973. Of that total, scholarships or need-based grants averaged $7048 ($18,085 maximum); loans averaged $2625 ($6625 maximum); and work contracts averaged $1300 (maximum). Forty-six percent of undergraduate students work part-time. Average earnings from campus work for the school year was $1300. The average financial indebtedness of the 1992-93 graduate was $8000. Agnes Scott is a member of CSS. The FAF is required. The deadline for financial aid applications is May 1.

International Students: There are currently 17 international students enrolled. The school actively recruits these students. They must take the TOEFL; a minimum score of 600 is recommended. The student must also take the SAT I or the ACT.

Computers: The college provides computer facilities for student use. The mainframe is an IBM RS6000. There are 60 IBM and IBM-compatible 486 personal computers, located in 3 computer centers and in 3 satellite centers in the residence halls, and 8 Apple Macintosh microcomputers located in the fine arts building. All students may access the system. There are no time limits on using the system and no fees.

Graduates: In 1992-93, 127 bachelor's degrees were awarded. The most popular majors among graduates were English (14%), psychology (11%), and economics (9%). Within an average freshman class, 1% graduate in 3 years, 59% in 4 years, and 2% in 5 years. Some 27 companies recruited on campus in 1992-93.

Admissions Contact: Jenifer Cooper, Director of Admission.

ALBANY STATE COLLEGE
Albany, GA 31705-2796

B-4

(912) 430-4646
(800) 822-RAMS (out-of-state)

Full-time: 792 men, 1471 women	**Faculty:** 132
Part-time: 237 men, 439 women	**Ph.Ds:** 54%
Graduate: 103 men, 215 women	**Student/Faculty:** 17 to 1
Year: quarters, summer session	**Tuition:** $1772 ($4535)
Application Deadline: September 1	**Room & Board:** $2709
Freshman Class: 1340 applied, 1336 accepted, 701 enrolled	
SAT I or ACT: required	**LESS COMPETITIVE**

Albany State College, founded in 1903, is a state-supported coeducational liberal arts and teacher education college. There are 4 undergraduate schools and one graduate school. In addition to regional accreditation, Albany State has baccalaureate program accreditation with NCATE and NLN. The library contains 162,347 volumes and 471,000 microform items, and subscribes to 1066 periodicals. The 128-acre campus is in a small town 175 miles south of Atlanta. Including residence halls, there are 6 buildings on campus.

Student Life: About 94% of undergraduates are from Georgia. Students come from 8 states and 1 foreign country. Eighty-five percent are African American; 15% white.

Housing: College-sponsored living facilities include single-sex dormitories. Priority for on-campus housing is given to out-of-town students. Sixty percent of students commute. All students may keep cars on campus.

Activities: There are 4 national fraternities and 4 national sororities. There are many groups and organizations on campus, including cheerleading, choir, computers, drama, drill team, honors, jazz band, marching band, professional, social, social service, and student government.

Sports: There are 5 intercollegiate sports for men and 4 for women, and 7 intramural sports for men and 6 for women. Athletic and recreation facilities include tennis courts, baseball and softball fields, a swimming pool, a recreation room, and an all-weather track.

Services: Remedial math, reading, and writing is available.

Programs of Study: Albany State awards the B.A., B.S., B.S.N, and B.S.W. degrees. Associate and master's degrees are also awarded. Bachelor's degrees are awarded in BIOLOGICAL SCIENCE (biology/biological science), BUSINESS (accounting, management science, marketing/retailing/merchandising, and office supervision and management), COMMUNICATIONS AND THE ARTS (art, dramatic arts, English, fine arts, French, music, Spanish, and speech/debate/rhetoric), COMPUTER AND PHYSICAL SCIENCE (chemistry, computer science, and mathematics), EDUCATION (art, early childhood, health, middle school, music, physical, science, and special), HEALTH PROFESSIONS (allied health and nursing), SOCIAL SCIENCE (criminal justice, history, political science/government, psychology, social work, and sociology). Biology and chemistry are the strongest academically.

Required: All students must complete 186 quarter hours, including 20 hours each in humanities, mathematics and sciences, and social sciences, and 30 hours in the major. Health and physical education, and art and music appreciation are required. Students must take a Regents examination to assess English language skills competency, pass a comprehensive exam in their major, and score satisfactorily on the aptitude section of the GRE.

Special: The school offers co-op programs in all majors, 2+2 programs with Darton College, dual majors in social sciences, and 3-2 engineering degrees with the Georgia Institute of Technology. Several work-study programs and a gerontology training program are available. The school participates in the Georgian Intern Programs. All language majors are eligible to study abroad. There is a freshman honors program on campus, as well as 6 national honor societies.

Admissions: Nearly all of the 1993-94 applicants were accepted. The SAT scores for the 1993-94 freshman class were as follows: Verbal—94% below 500 and 6% between 500 and 599; Math—92% below 500 and 8% between 500 and 599.

Requirements: A minimum GPA of 1.8 is required. The SAT I or ACT is required. If the SAT I is selected, student must have a minimum verbal score of 250 and a mathematics score of 280. Students with SAT I scores below 350 on either section, or ACT scores below acceptable levels, may be admitted provisionally. Applicants must be graduates of an accredited secondary school, have a minimum GPA of 1.8, and have completed 4 years of English; 3 each of mathematics, science, and social studies; and 2 of a foreign language. A GED is accepted. AP and CLEP credits are accepted.

Procedure: Freshmen are admitted to all sessions. Entrance exams should be taken by December of the senior year. Applications should be filed by September 1 for fall entry, December 1 for winter entry, March 1 for spring entry, and June 1 for summer entry, along with an application fee of $10. Notification is sent on a rolling basis. There are early decision, early admissions, and deferred admissions plans.

Transfer: Students must provide transcripts of all previous college work. A total of 51 credits out of 186 must be completed at Albany State.

Financial Aid: In an earlier year, scholarships or need-based grants averaged $686; loans averaged $1525; and work contracts averaged $913. Albany State is a member of CSS. The FAF and the college's own financial statement is required. The deadline for financial aid applications is June 1.

International Students: Students must take the TOEFL. The student must also take the SAT I, ACT, or the college's own entrance exam.

Computers: The college provides computer facilities for student use. The mainframe is an NCR Tower. All students may access the system. It may be used from 8 A.M. to 5 P.M. and from 6 P.M. to 8 P.M.

Admissions Contact: Director of Admissions/Financial Aid.

AMERICAN COLLEGE FOR THE APPLIED ARTS

B-2

Atlanta, GA 30326   (404) 231-9000; (800) 255-6839 (out-of-state)

Full-time: 96 men, 386 women	**Faculty:** 12
Part-time: 20 men, 160 women	**Ph.Ds:** 89%
Graduate: none	**Student/Faculty:** 40 to 1
Year: quarters, summer session	**Tuition:** $8020
Application Deadline: open	**Room:** $3850
Freshman Class: 602 applied, 490 accepted, 330 enrolled	
SAT I or ACT: not required	**SPECIAL**

The American College for the Applied Arts, founded in 1977, is a private, coeducational college offering undergraduate programs in interior design, commercial art, fashion design, fashion merchandising, and business. In addition to regional accreditation, The college has baccalaureate program accreditation with FIDER. The library contains 21,000 volumes, 17 microform items, and 340 audiovisual forms, and subscribes to 225 periodicals. Special learning facilities include an art gallery. The 1-acre campus is in an urban area 1 mile north of Atlanta. There is 1 building on campus.

Student Life: About 60% of undergraduates are from out-of-state, mostly the South. Students come from 45 states, 70 foreign countries, and Canada. Forty-five percent are white; 25% foreign nationals; 25% African American. The average age of freshmen is 19; all undergraduates, 28.

Housing: College-sponsored living facilities include single-sex off-campus apartments. All students commute. Alcohol is not permitted. All students may keep cars on campus.

Activities: There are no fraternities or sororities on campus. There are 6 groups on campus, including newspaper, professional, social, and student government. Popular campus events include International Day, Health Fair Day, Career Days, and Fashion Association Bazaar.

Sports: There is no sports program at the college.

Disabled Students: The entire campus is accessible to disabled students. The following facilities are available: wheelchair ramps, elevators, special parking, specially equipped rest rooms, special class scheduling, and lowered telephones.

Services: Remedial math, reading, and writing are available.

Campus Safety and Security: Campus safety and security measures include 24-hour foot and vehicle patrol, escort service, informal discussions, and pamphlets, posters, and films. In addition, there are emergency telephones and lighted pathways and sidewalks.

Programs of Study: The college awards the B.A. degree. Associate degrees also are awarded. Bachelor's degrees are awarded in BUSINESS (business administration and management and fashion merchandising), ENGINEERING AND ENVIRONMENTAL DESIGN (commercial art and interior design), SOCIAL SCIENCE (fashion design and technology). Interior design is the strongest academically and has the largest enrollment.

Required: In addition to specific requirements for each individual program of study, all students must complete 25 credit hours each in humanities and social sciences and 5 credit hours in mathematics. Students may substitute 10 hours of a foreign language for 10 hours of social science. The total number of quarter credit hours required is 190, with 140 in the major. Students must maintain a minimum GPA of 2.0.

Special: Students may earn up to 20 credit hours in internships. Study abroad in London is offered. All 5 majors offer accelerated degree opportunities. A dual major in fashion merchandising and design is available.

Faculty/Classroom: Thirty-two percent of faculty are male; 68%, female. All teach undergraduates. The average class size in an introductory lecture is 25; in a laboratory, 16; and in a regular course offering, 18.

Admissions: About 81% of the 1993–94 applicants were accepted.

Requirements: A minimum GPA of 2.0 is required. Applicants should be graduates of a secondary school and should submit 2 personal references. The GED is accepted. Important factors used in the admissions decision are personality, intangible qualities, leadership record, evidence of special talent, advanced placement or honor courses, and ability to finance college education.

Procedure: Freshmen are admitted to all sessions. Application deadlines are open. The college accepts all applicants. The application fee is $35. There is an early admissions plan.

Transfer: Transfer students must have a minimum GPA of 2.0. Two personal references must be submitted. A total of 60 credits out of 190 must be completed at the college.

Visiting: There are regularly scheduled orientations for prospective students, Monday through Saturday, 9 A.M. to 8 P.M. There are guides for informal visits and visitors may sit in on classes. To arrange for a visit, contact Suzanne McBride at (404) 231–9000.

Financial Aid: In 1993–94 45% of all students received some form of financial aid. About 80% of all students received need-based aid. The average freshman award was $8000. Of that total, scholarships or need-based grants averaged $500 (maximum); loans averaged $2625 (maximum); and work contracts averaged $1200 ($3000 maximum). Seventy-six percent of undergraduate students work part-time. Average earnings from campus work for the school year are $900. The average financial indebtedness of the 1992–93 graduate was $15,000. The college is a member of CSS. The FAF, the college's own financial statement, and the FAFSA are required.

International Students: There are currently 120 international students enrolled. The school actively recruits these students. They must take the TOEFL or the college's own test and achieve a minimum score of 500 on the TOEFL.

Computers: The college provides computer facilities for student use. There are 52 PCs available to students, 40 in a classroom setting, 12 in a computer laboratory. All students may access the system. There are no time limits on using the system and no fees.

Graduates: In 1992–93 205 bachelor's degrees were awarded. The most popular majors among graduates were fashion merchandising (40%), interior design (40%), and fashion design (20%). Some 20 companies recruited on campus in 1992–93. In the 1992 graduating class, 80% of the men and 84% of the women had found employment within 6 months of graduation.

Admissions Contact: Suzanne McBride, Director of Admissions.

ARMSTRONG STATE COLLEGE   E-4
Savannah, GA 31419–1997   (912) 927–5277; (800) 633–2349

Full-time: 2796 men and women	Faculty: 50; IIB, –$
Part-time: 2391 men and women	Ph.D.s: n/av
Graduate: none	Student/Faculty: 56 to 1
Year: quarters, summer session	Tuition: $1568 ($4331)
Application Deadline: August 1	Room & Board: $3306
Freshman Class: n/av	
SAT I or ACT: required	LESS COMPETITIVE

Armstrong State College, founded in 1935, is a public institution within the University System of Georgia, offering programs in the arts and sciences, education, and health professions. There are 4 undergraduate schools and one graduate school. In addition to regional accreditation, Armstrong State College has baccalaureate program accreditation with CAHEA, NASM, NCATE, and NLN. The library contains 162,000 volumes, 525,000 microform items, and 35,000 audiovisual forms, and subscribes to 1120 periodicals. Computerized library sources and services include the card catalog, interlibrary loans, and database searching. The 250-acre campus is in an urban area.

Student Life: About 90% of undergraduates are from Georgia. Students come from 33 states, 12 foreign countries, and Canada. Eighty-four percent are white; 14% African American.

Housing: A total of 192 students can be accommodated in college housing. College-sponsored living facilities include on-campus apartments. Alcohol is not permitted. All students may keep cars on campus.

Activities: There are no fraternities on campus. There are many groups and organizations on campus, including band, cheerleading, choir, chorus, ethnic, international, literary magazine, newspaper, political, professional, religious, student government, and yearbook.

Sports: There are 4 intercollegiate sports each for men and women. Athletic and recreation facilities include an indoor pool, a gymnasium, a weight room, tennis courts, and playing fields.

Disabled Students: Specially equipped living facilities are available.

Services: Remedial math, reading, and writing is available.

Programs of Study: Armstrong State College awards the B.A., B.S., B.S.D.H., B.S.Ed., B.Health Science, B.S.M.T., B.Mus.Ed., B.S.N., and B.G.S. degrees. Associate and master's degrees are also awarded. Bachelor's degrees are awarded in BIOLOGICAL SCIENCE (biology/biological science), COMMUNICATIONS AND THE ARTS (art, dramatic arts, English, music, and speech/debate/rhetoric), COMPUTER AND PHYSICAL SCIENCE (chemistry, computer science, mathematics, and physical sciences), EDUCATION (art, business, elementary, middle school, music, physical, secondary, and social science), HEALTH PROFESSIONS (dental hygiene, medical laboratory technology, and nursing), SOCIAL SCIENCE (criminal justice, history, political science/government, and psychology).

Required: The core curriculum consists of 20 hours each in humanities, mathematics, natural sciences, and social sciences, and 6 in physical education. A minimum GPA of 2.0 overall and a grade of C or better in each major course is required. Each student must complete 191 quarter hours, with 40 hours in the major, and must take a comprehensive exam.

Special: The college offers co-op programs and many dual-degree programs, including a 3–2 degree in forestry and environmental science with Duke University, and 3–2 engineering programs with several colleges. A general studies degree, cross-registration, and credit for military experience are also offered.

Requirements: A minimum GPA of 2.0 is required. The SAT I or ACT is required. The minimum score on the SAT I is 380 on each section. Art students must submit a portfolio. Applicants should graduate from an accredited secondary school. A GED may be accepted. College preparatory work should include 4 units of English, 3 each of mathematics, science, and social studies, and 2 of foreign language. AP and CLEP credits are accepted.

Procedure: Freshmen are admitted to all sessions. Applications should be filed by August 1 for fall entry, December 1 for winter entry, February 1 for spring entry, and June 1 for summer entry, along with an application fee of $10. There is an early admissions plan.

Transfer: Transfer applicants must submit all transcripts and must be in good standing at last college attended.

Financial Aid: The college's own financial statement and the FAFSA are required. The deadline for financial aid applications is May 1.

International Students: Students must take the TOEFL and achieve a minimum score of 500. The student must also take the SAT I or the ACT.

Computers: The mainframe is a DEC VAX 4/750. There are also AT&T, Zenith, and Apple Macintosh microcomputers for student use. Those students enrolled in computer courses may access the system. There are no time limits on using the system and no fees.

Graduates: In a recent year, 311 bachelor's degrees were awarded.

Admissions Contact: Admissions Officer.

ATLANTA COLLEGE OF ART   B-2
Atlanta, GA 30309   (404) 898–1163; (800) 832–2104 (out-of-state)

Full-time: 229 men, 206 women	Faculty: 24
Part-time: none	Ph.D.s: 20%
Graduate: none	Student/Faculty: 18 to 1
Year: semesters, summer session	Tuition: $9495
Application Deadline: open	Room & Board: $3000
Freshman Class: 450 applied, 273 accepted, 137 enrolled	
SAT I or ACT: required	SPECIAL

The Atlanta College of Art, founded in 1928, is a private professional school offering programs in the visual, fine, and applied arts. In addition to regional accreditation, the college has baccalaureate program accreditation with NASAD. The library contains 27,000 volumes and 50,000 microform items, and subscribes to 250 periodicals. Special learning facilities include an art gallery. The 6-acre campus is in an urban area. Including residence halls, there are 3 buildings on campus.

Student Life: About 60% of undergraduates are from out-of-state, mostly the South. Students come from 21 states and 6 foreign countries. Eighty percent are from public schools; 20% from private.

Seventy-eight percent are white; 13% African American. The average age of freshmen is 18; all undergraduates, 21.

Housing: A total of 100 students can be accommodated in college housing. College-sponsored living facilities include on-campus apartments. On-campus housing is guaranteed for the freshman year only and is available on a first-come, first-served basis. Seventy-three percent of students commute. Alcohol is not permitted. All students may keep cars on campus.

Activities: There are no fraternities or sororities on campus. There are a number of groups on campus, including art, band, ethnic, film, honors, literary magazine, newspaper, photography, social, social service, and student government. Popular campus events include Halloween Party, Spring Picnic, student gallery openings, and gallery receptions.

Sports: There is no sports program at the college.

Disabled Students: Ninety-five percent of the campus is accessible to disabled students. The following facilities are available: wheelchair ramps, elevators, special parking, specially equipped rest rooms, and lowered drinking fountains.

Services: In addition to many counseling and information services, tutoring is available in some subjects, including liberal arts.

Campus Safety and Security: Campus safety and security measures include 24-hour foot and vehicle patrol, informal discussions, pamphlets, posters, films, and emergency telephones. In addition, there are lighted pathways and sidewalks.

Programs of Study: The college awards the B.F.A. degree. Bachelor's degrees are awarded in COMMUNICATIONS AND THE ARTS (design, drawing, fine arts, graphic design, illustration, painting, photography, printmaking, sculpture, and video), ENGINEERING AND ENVIRONMENTAL DESIGN (computer graphics and interior design). Communication design and electronic arts have the largest enrollments.

Required: To graduate, the student must complete a total of 120 credit hours, including 78 in studio art, 42 in liberal arts/humanities, and 30 to 36 in the major. The student must also complete the modern studies course, art history survey I, II, and III, and maintain a GPA of 2.0. A senior review is required.

Special: Students may design their own majors, combining 2 or 3 areas of the arts. Special academic programs include cross-registration with the colleges of the University Center in Georgia, as well as highly supervised internships. The college is a member of the East Coast Consortium of Art Colleges and the Art College Exchange. There is a freshman honors program on campus

Faculty/Classroom: All teach undergraduates. The average class size in a regular course offering is 12.

Admissions: About 61% of the 1993–94 applicants were accepted.

Requirements: The SAT I or ACT is required. Applicants must have graduated from an accredited secondary school and must submit an essay and portfolio; an interview is recommended. The GED is accepted. AP credit is accepted. Important factors used in the admissions decision are evidence of special talent, advanced placement or honor courses, extracurricular activities record, personality, intangible qualities, and leadership record.

Procedure: Freshmen are admitted fall and spring. Entrance exams should be taken during the senior year. Application deadlines are open. The application fee is $25 ($50 for international students). Notification is sent on a rolling basis. There are early admissions and deferred admissions plans.

Transfer: About 50 transfer students enrolled in a recent year. Transfer students must have a GPA of at least 2.0 and must submit a portfolio. A total of 39 credits out of 120 must be completed at the college.

Visiting: There are regularly scheduled orientations for prospective students. There are guides for informal visits and visitors may sit in on classes. To arrange for a visit, contact the Admissions Office at (404) 898-1163.

Financial Aid: In a recent year, 73% of all current freshmen and 79% of continuing students received some form of financial aid. About 44% of freshmen and 56% of continuing students received need-based aid. The average freshman award that year was $5821. Of that total, scholarships or need-based grants averaged $2339 ($3969 maximum); loans averaged $2618 ($2625 maximum); and work contracts averaged $1400. Sixty-two percent of undergraduate students work part-time. Average earnings from campus work for the school year are $1400 (maximum). The average financial indebtedness of a recent graduate was $14,028. The college is a member of CSS. The FAF and the college's own financial statement are required. The deadline for financial aid applications is March 15.

International Students: There are currently 15 international students enrolled. The school actively recruits these students. They must take the TOEFL and achieve a minimum score of 500.

Computers: The college provides computer facilities for student use. There are 24 computers in the computer center and the electronic arts studio. All students may access the system during scheduled hours. There are no time limits on using the system and no fees.

Graduates: In an earlier year, 50 bachelor's degrees were awarded.

Admissions Contact: John A. Farkas, Director of Enrollment Management.

AUGUSTA COLLEGE
D-2

Augusta, GA 30904–2200 (706) 737-1632

Full-time: 1210 men, 1693 women	Faculty: 184; IIA, --$
Part-time: 604 men, 1253 women	Ph.D.s: 73%
Graduate: 280 men, 584 women	Student/Faculty: 16 to 1
Year: quarters, summer session	Tuition: $1452 ($4215)
Application Deadline: August 18	Room & Board: n/app
Freshman Class: 1428 applied, 1148 accepted, 863 enrolled	
SAT I or ACT: required	LESS COMPETITIVE

Augusta College, founded in 1925, is a liberal arts commuter institution within the university system of Georgia. There are 3 undergraduate and 3 graduate schools. In addition to regional accreditation, Augusta has baccalaureate program accreditation with NASM, NCATE, and NLN. The library contains 453,825 volumes and 8800 microform items, and subscribes to 1468 periodicals. Computerized library sources and services include the card catalog, interlibrary loans, and database searching. Special learning facilities include a learning resource center, an art gallery, and a radio station. The 72-acre campus is in an urban area 140 miles east of Atlanta. There are 35 buildings on campus.

Student Life: About 88% of undergraduates are from Georgia. Students come from 25 foreign countries and Canada. Seventy-six percent are white; 19% African American. The average age of freshmen is 20; all undergraduates, 24.9. Thirty-seven percent drop out by the end of their first year; 33% remain to graduate.

Housing: There are no residence halls; all students commute. Alcohol is not permitted. All students may keep cars on campus.

Activities: About 7% of men belong to 2 national fraternities; about 4% of women belong to 1 local and 2 national sororities. There are 45 groups on campus, including art, band, cheerleading, choir, chorus, drama, ethnic, honors, international, jazz band, literary magazine, newspaper, orchestra, pep band, photography, political, professional, religious, social, social service, student government, and yearbook. Popular campus events include Homecoming, Octoberfest, and Spring Fling.

Sports: There are 6 intercollegiate sports each for men and women, and 5 intramural sports for men and 3 for women. Athletic and recreation facilities include a 2000-seat gymnasium, baseball and soccer fields, a tennis center, and an 18-hole golf course.

Disabled Students: Ninety percent of the campus is accessible to disabled students. The following facilities are available: wheelchair ramps, elevators, special parking, specially equipped rest rooms, special class scheduling, and lowered drinking fountains.

Services: In addition to many counseling and information services, tutoring is available in most subjects. In addition, there is a reader service for the blind, and remedial math, reading, and writing.

Campus Safety and Security: Campus safety and security measures include 24-hour foot and vehicle patrol, escort service, informal discussions, and pamphlets, posters, and films.

Programs of Study: Augusta awards the B.A., B.S., B.B.A., B.F.A., B.M., and B.S.Ed. degrees. Associate and master's degrees are also awarded. Bachelor's degrees are awarded in BIOLOGICAL SCIENCE (biology/biological science), BUSINESS (accounting, banking and finance, business administration and management, business economics, and marketing/retailing/merchandising), COMMUNICATIONS AND THE ARTS (communications, English, fine arts, journalism, languages, and music), COMPUTER AND PHYSICAL SCIENCE (chemistry, computer science, mathematics, and physics), EDUCATION (early childhood, elementary, health, middle school, and secondary), HEALTH PROFESSIONS (nursing), SOCIAL SCIENCE (history, political science/government, psychology, and sociology). Biology has the largest enrollment.

Required: In order to graduate, all students must complete 180 credit hours, including 75 in the major, with a minimum GPA of 2.0. All students are required to take 6 courses in physical education; pass the Regents test in reading and composition; and demonstrate, through course completion or examination, a knowledge of U.S. and Georgia history and their constitutions.

Special: A Washington semester and study abroad may be arranged. The school offers co-op programs with area companies, internships, work-study programs, dual majors, nondegree study, and cross-registration with Paine College, the Medical College of Georgia, and Augusta Technical Institute. There is a freshman honors program on campus, as well as 3 national honor societies. Two departments have honors programs.

Faculty/Classroom: Fifty-five percent of faculty are male; 45%, female. All teach undergraduates. No introductory courses are taught by graduate students. The average class size in an introductory lecture is 30 and in a regular course offering, 27.

Admissions: About 80% of the 1993–94 applicants were accepted.

Requirements: A minimum GPA of 2.0 is required. The SAT I or ACT is required, with a minimum score of 350 on both sections of the SAT I and a composite score of 14 on the ACT. Applicants must be graduates of an accredited secondary school. The GED is accepted. Secondary school courses must include 4 units of English, 2 each of a foreign language and history, 3 each of mathematics and science,

and 1 of social studies. An essay is not required. AP and CLEP credits are accepted.

Procedure: Freshmen are admitted to all sessions. Entrance exams should be taken as early as possible. Applications should be filed by August 18 for fall entry, December 4 for winter entry, February 16 for spring entry, and May 14 for summer entry, along with an application fee of $10. Notification is sent on a rolling basis. There is a deferred admissions plan.

Transfer: About 680 transfer students enrolled in an earlier year. Applicants must have completed 30 credit hours with a minimum GPA of 2.0. If fewer than 30 hours have been completed, a high school transcript and SAT I or ACT scores are required. A total of 45 credits out of 180 must be completed at Augusta.

Visiting: There are regularly scheduled orientations for prospective students. There are guides for informal visits and visitors may sit in on classes. To arrange for a visit, contact the Admissions Office at (706) 737–1632.

Financial Aid: In 1993–94, 8% of all current freshmen and 20% of continuing students received some form of financial aid. About 59% of freshmen received need-based aid. Augusta is a member of CSS. The FAF and the college's own financial statement are required. There is no deadline for financial aid applications.

International Students: There are currently 60 international students enrolled. They must take the TOEFL and achieve a minimum score of 540. The student must also take the SAT I and achieve a minimum score of 350 in each section.

Computers: The college provides computer facilities for student use. The mainframe is a DEC VAX 4200. There is access to Telnet from any LAN workstation, with 18 dial-up ports available. All students may access the system. There are no time limits on using the system and no fees.

Graduates: In 1992–93, 434 bachelor's degrees were awarded. The most popular majors among graduates were management (12%), accounting (9%), and psychology (7%). Within an average freshman class, 10% graduate in 4 years, 29% in 5 years, and 37% in 6 years. Some 100 companies recruited on campus in 1992–93.

Admissions Contact: Sam McNair, Acting Director of Admissions.

BERRY COLLEGE

A-2
Rome, GA 30149

(706) 236–2215; (800) BERRYGA

Full-time: 627 men, 994 women	Faculty: 87; IIB, av$
Part-time: 22 men, 32 women	Ph.D.s: 81%
Graduate: 21 men, 92 women	Student/Faculty: 19 to 1
Year: semesters, summer session	Tuition: $8050
Application Deadline: February 1	Room & Board: $3940
Freshman Class: 1657 applied, 1221 accepted, 480 enrolled	
SAT I or ACT: required	**VERY COMPETITIVE**

Berry College, founded in 1902, is a private nonsectarian Christian college offering programs in fine and liberal arts, agriculture, business, teacher preparation, and religion. There are 4 undergraduate schools and one graduate school. In addition to regional accreditation, Berry has baccalaureate program accreditation with NCATE. The library contains 455,660 volumes, and subscribes to 1336 periodicals. Special learning facilities include an art gallery, radio station, equine center, forestry center, and beef- and dairy-cattle operations. The 26,500-acre campus is in a rural area 65 miles northwest of Atlanta. Including residence halls, there are 37 buildings on campus.

Student Life: About 82% of undergraduates are from Georgia. Students come from 29 states and 29 foreign countries. Ninety-one percent are from public schools; 9% from private. Ninety-five percent are white. The average age of all undergraduates is 22. Twenty-two percent drop out by the end of their first year; 57% remain to graduate.

Housing: A total of 1300 students can be accommodated in college housing. College-sponsored living facilities include single-sex dormitories and on-campus apartments. Eighty percent of students live on campus; of those, 57% remain on campus on weekends. Alcohol is not permitted. All students may keep cars on campus.

Activities: There are no fraternities or sororities on campus. There are 60 groups on campus, including cheerleading, choir, computers, drama, ethnic, honors, international, newspaper, orchestra, pep band, political, professional, radio and TV, religious, social, social service, student government, and yearbook. Popular campus events include Mountain Day, Homecoming, and Founders Day.

Sports: There are 7 intercollegiate sports for men and 5 for women, and 13 intramural sports for men and 13 for women. Athletic and recreation facilities include running and biking trails, 10 tennis courts, intramural fields, 3 gymnasiums, a weight-training room, and an indoor swimming pool.

Disabled Students: The following facilities are available: wheelchair ramps, elevators, special parking, and specially equipped rest rooms.

Services: In addition to many counseling and information services, tutoring is available in most subjects. In addition, there is a reader service for the blind.

Campus Safety and Security: Campus safety and security measures include 24-hour foot and vehicle patrol, shuttle buses, and lighted pathways and sidewalks.

Programs of Study: Berry awards the B.A., B.S., and B.Mu. degrees. Master's degrees also are awarded. Bachelor's degrees are awarded in AGRICULTURE (animal science and horticulture), BIOLOGICAL SCIENCE (biochemistry and biology/biological science), BUSINESS (accounting, banking and finance, business administration and management, fashion merchandising, hotel/motel and restaurant management, and marketing/retailing/merchandising), COMMUNICATIONS AND THE ARTS (communications, dramatic arts, English, French, German, languages, music, music performance, Spanish, and studio art), COMPUTER AND PHYSICAL SCIENCE (chemistry, computer science, mathematics, and physics), EDUCATION (art, early childhood, home economics, mathematics, middle school, music, and physical), ENGINEERING AND ENVIRONMENTAL DESIGN (preengineering), HEALTH PROFESSIONS (optometry, predentistry, premedicine, prepharmacy, and preveterinary science), SOCIAL SCIENCE (economics, family/consumer studies, food production/management/services, history, interdisciplinary studies, international studies, philosophy, political science/government, prelaw, psychology, religion, social science, sociology, and theological studies). Business and education have the largest enrollments.

Required: All students must take courses in English, speech, and health and physical education. Core requirements include 5 courses in the humanities, and 3 each in behavioral science, mathematics, and natural sciences. A 2.0 minimum GPA and a total of 124 credits, including at least 30 hours in the major, are required for graduation. All students are also required to attend at least 3 approved cultural events per semester.

Special: The college offers internships, a Washington semester, study abroad in 6 countries, work-study programs, credit by exam, and nondegree study. There are 3–2 engineering degrees and dual degree programs in several fields with the Georgia Institute of Technology. There is also a dual degree program in nursing with Emory University. An interdepartmental major is offered in decision science, including course work in business and economics, mathematics, and computer science. There is a freshman honors program on campus, as well as 15 national honor societies. One department has an honors program.

Faculty/Classroom: Seventy-one percent of faculty are male; 29%, female. Ninety-nine percent teach undergraduates, 33% do research, and 33% do both. No introductory courses are taught by graduate students. The average class size in an introductory lecture is 29; in a laboratory, 22; and in a regular course offering, 21.

Admissions: About 74% of the 1993–94 applicants were accepted. The SAT scores for the 1993–94 freshman class were as follows: Verbal—54% below 500, 33% between 500 and 599, 13% between 600 and 700, and 1% above 700; Math—31% below 500, 41% between 500 and 599, 24% between 600 and 700, and 4% above 700. The ACT scores were 18% below 21, 25% between 21 and 23, 27% between 24 and 26, 17% between 27 and 28, and 13% above 28. About 60% of the current freshmen were in the top fifth of their class; 87% were in the top two fifths.

Requirements: The SAT I or ACT is required. Applicant should be a graduate of an accredited high school or have a GED. Twenty academic credits are required, including 4 units of English, 3 units each of mathematics (to include Algebra I, Algebra II, and either geometry or trigonometry), science, social studies, and 2 units of a foreign language. AP and CLEP credits are accepted. Important factors used in the admissions decision are advanced placement or honor courses, leadership record, recommendations by school officials, recommendations by alumni, and parents or siblings attending the school.

Procedure: Freshmen are admitted to all sessions. Entrance exams should be taken by the fall of the senior year. Applications should be filed 30 days prior to the beginning of the semester; February 1 is the priority date for fall entry. The application fee is $20. Notification is sent on a rolling basis. There are early decision and early admissions plans.

Transfer: About 105 transfer students enrolled in 1993–94. Applicants must submit official transcripts from all colleges previously attended and have a minimum GPA of 2.2. At least 30 credits out of 124 must be completed at Berry.

Visiting: There are regularly scheduled orientations for prospective students, Monday through Friday from 8 A.M. to 5 P.M. and on Saturday mornings from 9 A.M. to noon. Students should schedule their campus visit in advance. There are guides for informal visits, and visitors may sit in on classes and stay overnight at the school. To arrange for a visit, contact the Admissions Office at (706) 236–2215.

Financial Aid: Average earnings from campus work for the school year are $1305. Berry is a member of CSS. The FAF, FFS, or SFS is required. The deadline for financial aid applications is April 1.

International Students: The school actively recruits these students. They must take the TOEFL and achieve a minimum score of 550 and must also take the SAT I or ACT if from an English-speaking country.

Computers: The college provides computer facilities for student use. The mainframe is a Digital PDP 11/44. IBM and Apple microcomputers are located in the computer laboratory. All students may access the system. There are no time limits on using the system and no fees.

Admissions Contact: Admissions Office.

BRENAU WOMEN'S COLLEGE
(See Women's College of Brenau University)

BREWTON-PARKER COLLEGE
C-4
Mt. Vernon, GA 30445-0197

(912) 583-2241
(800) 342-1087 (in-state)

Full-time: 1320 men and women	Faculty: 41
Part-time: 822 men and women	Ph.D.s: 62%
Graduate: none	Student/Faculty: 32 to 1
Year: quarters, summer session	Tuition: $4521
Application Deadline: open	Room & Board: $2307
Freshman Class: n/av	
SAT I or ACT: recommended	NONCOMPETITIVE

Brewton-Parker College, founded in 1904, is a private institution offering instruction in liberal arts and religion. It is affiliated with the Baptist Church. The library contains 52,000 volumes, 1307 microform items, and 36,589 audiovisual forms, and subscribes to 411 periodicals. Computerized library sources and services include the card catalog, interlibrary loans, and database searching. Special learning facilities include a learning resource center and art gallery. The 240-acre campus is in a rural area 90 miles west of Savannah. Including residence halls, there are 29 buildings on campus.

Student Life: About 95% of undergraduates are from Georgia. Students come from 8 states, 16 foreign countries, and Canada. More than 90% are from public schools; 8% from private. Eighty percent are white; 18% African American. Most are Protestant. The average age of freshmen is 19; all undergraduates, 23. Eleven percent drop out by the end of their first year; 42% remain to graduate.

Housing: A total of 529 students can be accommodated in college housing. College-sponsored living facilities include single-sex dormitories. On-campus housing is guaranteed for all 4 years. Alcohol is not permitted. All students may keep cars on campus.

Activities: About 21% of men belong to 4 local fraternities; 24% of women belong to 4 local sororities. There are 17 groups on campus, including band, cheerleading, choir, chorus, drama, ethnic, honors, international, jazz band, newspaper, pep band, professional, religious, social service, student government, and yearbook. Popular campus events include Visitation Days, Homecoming Week, Intramural Program, Sadie Hawkins Dance, Road Rally, Fun Flicks, Alumni Day, and the Fine Arts Series.

Sports: There are 5 intercollegiate sports each for men and women, and 14 intramural sports each for men and women. Athletic and recreation facilities include a track; softball, baseball, and soccer fields; an outdoor volleyball and tennis courts; a gymnasium and a physical fitness building; and a swimming pool and a campus lake.

Disabled Students: The following facilities are available: wheelchair ramps, special parking, specially equipped rest rooms, and lowered drinking fountains.

Services: There is remedial math, reading, and writing.

Campus Safety and Security: Campus safety and security measures include 24-hour foot and vehicle patrol, self-defense education, informal discussions, pamphlets, posters, and films. There are also lighted pathways and sidewalks.

Programs of Study: BPC awards the B.A., B.S., B.Min., and B.Mu. degrees. Associate degrees are also awarded. Bachelor's degrees are awarded in BUSINESS (business administration and management), COMMUNICATIONS AND THE ARTS (music), EDUCATION (early childhood, health, middle school, and physical), SOCIAL SCIENCE (liberal arts/general studies and religion).

Required: The required core curriculum consists of humanities, mathematics and natural science, social science, physical education, and foreign language. Students must maintain a minimum 2.0 GPA and must complete 187 hours, with 50 in the major.

Special: The college offers internships, study abroad in several countries, work-study programs, a general studies degree, and nondegree study. There is a freshman honors program on campus, as well as 2 national honor societies.

Faculty/Classroom: The average class size in an introductory lecture is 15; in a laboratory, 17; and in a regular course offering, 16.

Admissions: Three freshmen graduated first in their class.

Requirements: The SAT I or ACT is recommended. The SAT I or ACT is recommended for placement purposes. The college follows an open admissions policy. A GED is accepted. Students should prepare with 4 years of English, 3 of social studies, and 2 each of foreign language, mathematics, and science. AP credits are accepted. Important factors used in the admissions decision are ability to finance college education, personality, intangible qualities, advanced placement or honor courses, leadership record, and evidence of special talent.

Procedure: Freshmen are admitted to all sessions. Entrance exams should be taken during senior year of high school. Application deadlines are open; the fee is $15. The college accepts all applicants; notification is sent within 1 to 2 weeks. There are early decision and early admissions plans. About 5 early decision candidates were accepted for the 1993-94 class.

Transfer: More than 120 transfer students enrolled in a recent year. Transfer applicants must submit transcripts from previously attended institutions, along with high school transcripts if they have completed fewer than 15 quarter units. A total of 45 quarter hours out of 187 must be completed at BPC.

Visiting: There are regularly scheduled orientations for prospective students, consisting of a campus tour and academic and financial aid sessions. There are guides for informal visits and visitors may sit in on classes and stay overnight at the school. To arrange for a visit, contact Jill O'Neal, Director of Admissions at (912) 583-2241.

Financial Aid: In a recent year, 90% of all current freshmen and 88% of continuing students received some form of financial aid. About 75% of freshmen and 73% of continuing students received need-based aid. The average freshman award was $2800. Of that total, scholarships or need-based grants averaged $1500; loans averaged $1300. Sixty percent of undergraduate students work part-time. Average earnings from campus work for the school year are $1200. The average financial indebtedness of the 1992-93 graduate was $8000. BPC is a member of CSS. The college's own financial statement and the FAFSA are required.

International Students: There are currently 23 international students enrolled. The school actively recruits these students. They must take the TOEFL or the University of Michigan Language Test and achieve a minimum score on the TOEFL of 500.

Computers: The college provides computer facilities for student use. PCs are available in computer laboratories. All students may access the system. There are no time limits on using the system and no fees.

Graduates: About 120 bachelor's degrees were awarded in 1992-93; 30 companies recruited on campus. In the 1992 graduating class, 8% of the men and 4% of the women were enrolled in graduate school within 6 months of graduation; 21% of the men and 28% of the women had found employment.

Admissions Contact: Jill O'Neal, Director of Admissions.

CLARK ATLANTA UNIVERSITY
B-2
Atlanta, GA 30314   (404) 880-8784; (800) 668-3228 (out-of-state)

Full-time: 4100 men and women	Faculty: 246
Part-time: none	Ph.D.s: 61%
Graduate: 1000 men and women	Student/Faculty: 11 to 1
Year: semesters, summer session	Tuition: $7460
Application Deadline: August 30	Room & Board: $4386
Freshman Class: 8000 applied, 5048 accepted, 1578 enrolled	
SAT I Verbal/Math: 460/420	ACT: 20 COMPETITIVE

Clark Atlanta University was founded in 1988 from the union of Clark College and Atlanta University. It is a private, coeducational, predominantly black college affiliated with the United Methodist Church, and it offers programs in arts and sciences, business administration, education, and social work. In addition to regional accreditation, CAU has baccalaureate program accreditation with CAHEA. The library contains 545,118 volumes and 282,994 microform items, and subscribes to 47,786 periodicals. Computerized library sources and services include interlibrary loans and database searching. Special learning facilities include a learning resource center, art gallery, radio station, and TV station. The 67-acre campus is in an urban area 3 miles southwest of Atlanta. Including residence halls, there are 25 buildings on campus.

Student Life: About 50% of undergraduates are from out-of-state, mostly the South. Students come from 46 states and 50 foreign countries. Eighty-three percent are African American. The average age of freshmen is 18; all undergraduates, 20. Twenty-four percent drop out by the end of their first year; 44% remain to graduate.

Housing: A total of 1600 students can be accommodated in college housing. College-sponsored living facilities include single-sex and coed dormitories and off-campus apartments. On-campus housing is available on a first-come, first-served basis. Alcohol is not permitted. All students may keep cars on campus.

Activities: There are 5 national fraternities and 4 national sororities. There are 60 groups on campus, including art, band, cheerleading, choir, chorale, chorus, dance, drama, drill team, ethnic, film, honors, international, jazz band, marching band, musical theater, newspaper, orchestra, pep band, photography, professional, radio and TV, religious, social, social service, student government, symphony, and yearbook. Popular campus events include Homecoming, commencement, and Alumni Weekend.

Sports: There are 4 intercollegiate sports for men and 4 for women, and 6 intramural sports for men and 6 for women.

Disabled Students: The following facilities are available: wheelchair ramps, special parking, and specially equipped rest rooms.

Services: In addition to many counseling and information services, tutoring is available in every subject. In addition, there is remedial math, reading, and writing.

Campus Safety and Security: Campus safety and security measures include 24-hour foot and vehicle patrol, escort service, shuttle buses, and informal discussions. In addition, there are emergency telephones and lighted pathways and sidewalks.

Programs of Study: CAU awards the B.A. and B.S. degrees. Master's and doctoral degrees also are awarded. Bachelor's degrees are awarded in BIOLOGICAL SCIENCE (biology/biological science), BUSINESS (accounting and business administration and management), COMMUNICATIONS AND THE ARTS (communications, English, fine arts, languages, music, and speech/debate/rhetoric), COMPUTER AND PHYSICAL SCIENCE (chemistry, mathematics, and physics), EDUCATION (business), HEALTH PROFESSIONS (allied health and medical records administration/services), SOCIAL SCIENCE (economics, history, philosophy, political science/government, psychology, religion, social work, and sociology).

Required: To graduate, students must complete a minimum of 122 hours of course work with a minimum 2.0 GPA, and must complete a prescribed major sequence. Beyond the general education core requirements, at least 60% of courses must represent work at or above the 300 level.

Special: CAU offers cross-registration with Atlanta University Center, Georgia Institute of Technology, and Georgia State University. B.A.-B.S. degrees may be obtained in business and management, education, and social and natural sciences. Dual majors in allied health and engineering and a 3–2 engineering degree with 6 universities are also available. There is a freshman honors program on campus, as well as 10 national honor societies. Eight departments have honors programs.

Faculty/Classroom: Sixty-two percent of faculty are male; 38%, female. All teach undergraduates. The average class size in a regular course offering is 19.

Admissions: About 63% of the 1993–94 applicants were accepted. The SAT scores for the 1993–94 freshman class were as follows: Verbal—85% below 500 and 15% between 500 and 599; Math—85% below 500 and 15% between 500 and 599. Five freshmen graduated first in their class.

Requirements: A minimum GPA of 2.5 is required. Applicants must submit ACT or SAT I scores. AP credit is accepted.

Procedure: Freshmen are admitted to all sessions. Entrance exams should be taken by January. Applications should be filed by August 30 for fall entry, January 5 for spring entry, and June 6 for summer entry, along with an application fee of $20. Notification is sent on a rolling basis. There is an early admissions plan.

Transfer: About 273 transfer students enrolled in a recent year. A total of 30 credits out of 122 must be completed at CAU.

Visiting: There are regularly scheduled orientations for prospective students. There are guides for informal visits and visitors may sit in on classes. To arrange for a visit, contact Clyde Gaylord, Admissions Counselor, at (404) 880–8783.

Financial Aid: In a recent year, 90% of all freshmen and 80% of continuing students received some form of financial aid. About 70% of freshmen and 70% of continuing students received need-based aid. The average freshman award in a recent year was $7025. Of that total, scholarships or need-based grants averaged $2000 ($3400 maximum); loans were $2625 (maximum); and work contracts averaged $1200 ($1500 maximum). Three percent of undergraduate students work part-time. Average earnings from campus work for the school year are $2000. CAU is a member of CSS. The FAF is required. The deadline for financial aid applications is April 30.

International Students: There are currently 126 international students enrolled. The school actively recruits these students. They must take the TOEFL and achieve a minimum score of 500.

Computers: The college provides computer facilities for student use. The mainframe is a DEC VAX 8550. Students may access the mainframe through the academic student computer laboratory. Those students with assigned user identification codes may access the system. It may be used during assigned scheduled times. There are no time limits on using the system and no fees.

Graduates: In a recent year, 246 bachelor's degrees were awarded. The most popular majors among graduates were business and management (31%), education (17%), and social sciences (13%).

Admissions Contact: Cliff Rawles, Director of Admissions.

CLAYTON STATE COLLEGE
Morrow, GA 30260

B-2
(404) 961–3500

Full-time: 768 men, 998 women
Part-time: 1053 men, 1941 women
Graduate: none
Year: quarters, summer session
Application Deadline: September 1
Freshman Class: 1287 applied, 883 accepted, 780 enrolled
SAT I or ACT: required

Faculty: 108
Ph.D.s: 57%
Student/Faculty: 16 to 1
Tuition: $1496 ($4259)
Room & Board: n/app

LESS COMPETITIVE

Clayton State College, founded in 1969 as a public junior college, has been a 4-year undergraduate college in the University System of Georgia since 1989, when its first baccalaureate degrees were awarded. There are 4 undergraduate schools. In addition to regional accreditation, Clayton State has baccalaureate program accreditation with ADA and NLN. The library contains 75,000 volumes, 77,000 microform items, and 26,000 audiovisual forms, and subscribes to 685 periodicals. Computerized library sources and services include the card catalog, interlibrary loans, and database searching. Special

learning facilities include a learning resource center. The 160-acre campus is in a suburban area 17 miles south of Atlanta. There are 10 buildings on campus.

Student Life: About 98% of undergraduates are from Georgia. Eighty percent are white; 18% African American. The average age of all undergraduates is 27. Ten percent drop out by the end of their first year; 64% remain to graduate.

Housing: There are no residence halls. All students commute. Alcohol is not permitted. All students may keep cars on campus.

Activities: There are no fraternities or sororities on campus. There are many groups and organizations on campus, including art, band, cheerleading, choir, chorale, computers, drama, ethnic, honors, international, jazz band, literary magazine, musical theater, newspaper, professional, religious, social service, and student government.

Sports: There are 4 intercollegiate sports for men and 4 for women, and 6 intramural sports for men and 4 for women. Athletic and recreation facilities include a gymnasium, jogging trails, tennis, badminton, volleyball, and basketball courts, and a weight room.

Disabled Students: The entire campus is accessible to disabled students. The following facilities are available: wheelchair ramps, elevators, special parking, specially equipped rest rooms, and special class scheduling.

Services: In addition to many counseling and information services, tutoring is available in most subjects. In addition, there is remedial math, reading, and writing.

Campus Safety and Security: Campus safety and security measures include 24-hour foot and vehicle patrol, self-defense education, shuttle buses, and lighted pathways and sidewalks.

Programs of Study: Clayton State awards the B.A., B.B.A., B.M., and B.S.N. degrees. Associate degrees also are awarded. Bachelor's degrees are awarded in BUSINESS (accounting and business administration and management), COMMUNICATIONS AND THE ARTS (music, music performance, and music theory and composition), COMPUTER AND PHYSICAL SCIENCE (information sciences and systems), EDUCATION (middle school), HEALTH PROFESSIONS (nursing). Management has the largest enrollment.

Required: All students must complete 180 quarter hours, 90 of which must be in the major, including 20 quarter hours each in English and humanities, mathematics or sciences, and social sciences. A 2.0 minimum GPA is required for graduation. All students must complete a physical education requirement.

Special: Students may study abroad in various 9-week programs conducted by University System of Georgia faculty. Cooperative programs with Georgia State University and Atlanta Area Technical College are available, as is a work-study program. The general studies program emphasizes writing and communications skills. Nondegree study and credit by correspondence are possible. There is a freshman honors program on campus, as well as one national honor society.

Faculty/Classroom: All faculty teach. The average class size in an introductory lecture is 28; in a laboratory, 20; and in a regular course offering, 28.

Admissions: About 69% of the 1993–94 applicants were accepted.

Requirements: A minimum GPA of 1.8 is required. The SAT I or ACT is required, with minimum SAT I scores of 250 verbal and 280 mathematics, or a minimum composite ACT score of 9 required. Applicants should be graduates of accredited secondary schools or have the GED. High school preparation should include 4 English courses, 3 each in mathematics, natural sciences, and social sciences, and 2 in a foreign language. AP and CLEP credits are accepted. Students may also be admitted on the strength of their high school academic records.

Procedure: Freshmen are admitted to all sessions. Applications should be filed by September 1 for fall entry, December 1 for winter entry, March 1 for spring entry, and June 1 for summer entry. Notification is sent on a rolling basis. There are early admissions and deferred admissions plans.

Transfer: About 285 transfer students enrolled in an earlier year. Transfer applicants with fewer than 20 quarter credits must meet the same criteria as entering freshmen. At least 45 quarter hours out of 180 must be completed at Clayton State.

Visiting: There are guides for informal visits. To arrange for a visit, contact the Office of Admissions at (404) 961–3500.

Financial Aid: Seventy-one percent of undergraduate students work part-time. Clayton State is a member of CSS. The college's own financial statement and the FAFSA are required. The deadline for financial aid applications is July 1.

International Students: They must take the TOEFL and achieve a minimum score of 550 and must also take the SAT I or the ACT.

Computers: The college provides computer facilities for student use. The mainframe is a TI 990. Microcomputers are available in the learning resource center, academic departments, and offices. All students may access the system during library hours. There are no time limits on using the system and no fees.

Graduates: In 1992–93, 125 bachelor's degrees were awarded. Some 120 companies recruited on campus in an earlier year.

Admissions Contact: Tonya R. Hobson, Director of Admissions and Registrar.

COLUMBUS COLLEGE
A-3

Columbus, GA 31907-5645   **(706) 568-2035**

Full-time: 1051 men, 1749 women	**Faculty:** 180; IIA, --$
Part-time: 627 men, 1027 women	**Ph.D.s:** 64%
Graduate: 202 men, 353 women	**Student/Faculty:** 16 to 1
Year: quarters, summer session	**Tuition:** $1601 ($4364)
Application Deadline: August 27	**Room & Board:** $3291
Freshman Class: 1196 enrolled	
SAT I Verbal/Math: 420/464	**LESS COMPETITIVE**

Columbus College, established in 1958, is a public liberal arts institution within the University System of Georgia, primarily serving local commuters. There are 4 undergraduate schools and 1 graduate school. In addition to regional accreditation, Columbus has baccalaureate program accreditation with NCATE and NLN. The library contains 235,000 volumes, 742,043 microform items, and 8308 audiovisual forms and subscribes to 1389 periodicals. The 132-acre campus is in a suburban area 100 miles south of Atlanta. Including residence halls, there are 21 buildings on campus.

Student Life: About 82% of undergraduates are from Georgia. Students come from 30 states and 29 foreign countries. Ninety-seven percent are from public schools; 3% from private. Seventy-three percent are white; 21% African American. The average age of freshmen is 19; all undergraduates, 23.

Housing: A total of 232 students can be accommodated in college housing. College-sponsored living facilities include single-sex on-campus apartments, fraternity houses, and sorority houses. In addition, special interest, music student, and athletic student housing is available. On-campus housing is available on a first-come, first-served basis. Ninety-five percent of students commute. Alcohol is not permitted. All students may keep cars on campus.

Activities: About 4% of men belong to 2 local and 3 national fraternities; about 5% of women belong to 1 local and 3 national sororities. There are 50 groups on campus, including art, band, cheerleading, chess, choir, chorale, chorus, drama, ethnic, honors, international, jazz band, musical theater, newspaper, opera, orchestra, pep band, photography, political, professional, religious, social, student government, symphony, and yearbook. Popular campus events include Homecoming, Black History Month, Halloween, Greek Week, and Indian Cultural Festival.

Sports: There are 6 intercollegiate sports for men and 4 for women, and 16 intramural sports for men and 16 for women. Athletic and recreation facilities include a gymnasium, a weight room, a swimming pool, tennis and outdoor basketball courts, baseball, soccer, softball, and intramural multipurpose fields, an archery range, and a walking trail.

Disabled Students: All of the campus is accessible to disabled students. The following facilities are available: wheelchair ramps, elevators, special parking, specially equipped rest rooms, lowered drinking fountains, lowered telephones, and specially equipped electronic doors.

Services: In addition to many counseling and information services, tutoring is available in every subject. In addition, there is remedial math, reading, and writing.

Campus Safety and Security: Campus safety and security measures include 24-hour foot and vehicle patrol, escort service, informal discussions, and pamphlets, posters, and films. In addition, there are lighted pathways and sidewalks.

Programs of Study: Columbus awards the B.A., B.S., B.B.A., B.M., B.S.E., and B.S.N. degrees. Associate and master's degrees also are awarded. Bachelor's degrees are awarded in BIOLOGICAL SCIENCE (biology/biological science), BUSINESS (accounting, business administration and management, and marketing/retailing/merchandising), COMMUNICATIONS AND THE ARTS (dramatic arts, English, fine arts, music, and speech/debate/rhetoric), COMPUTER AND PHYSICAL SCIENCE (chemistry, computer science, geology, and mathematics), EDUCATION (art, early childhood, middle school, music, secondary, and special), HEALTH PROFESSIONS (health science, medical laboratory technology, and nursing), SOCIAL SCIENCE (criminal justice, history, parks and recreation management, political science/government, prelaw, psychology, public administration, and sociology). Premedicine and education are the strongest academically. Business, education, nursing, and allied health have the largest enrollments.

Required: To graduate, all students must maintain a 2.0 GPA and complete a minimum of 180 quarter hours, 90 of them in a core curriculum. Three quarter hours each of physical education and speech are required. All students must pass the Georgia Regents Test for competency in reading and writing, complete English 101 and 102 with a C or better, and satisfy the Georgia history and constitution requirement by taking specified courses at a University System of Georgia institution or, for transfers from outside the system, by passing an exemption test.

Special: Cooperative programs in computer programming, electronics, and engineering, cross-registration with Georgia Institute of Technology and Columbus Technological Institute, internships, and study abroad in Asia, Africa, Europe, and the Americas are possible. A 3-2 engineering degree with the Georgia Institute of Technology, an ac-

celerated degree program in computers, and a B.A.-B.S. degree in political science, biology, chemistry, mathematics, and psychology are also available.

Faculty/Classroom: Sixty-five percent of faculty are male; 35%, female. Graduate students teach 1% of introductory courses. The average class size in an introductory lecture is 25; in a laboratory, 17; and in a regular course offering, 20.

Admissions: The SAT scores for the 1993-94 freshman class were as follows: Verbal—87% below 500, 11% between 500 and 599, and 2% between 600 and 700; Math—70% below 500, 24% between 500 and 599, and 6% between 600 and 700.

Requirements: A minimum GPA of 1.8 is required. The SAT I or ACT is required. The SAT I is preferred, with minimum verbal and mathematics scores of 350 each. A minimum composite ACT of 27 is accepted. Applicants must be graduates of accredited secondary schools or have earned the GED certificate. Fifteen academic credits are required, including 4 in English, 3 each in mathematics, science, and social studies, and 2 in a foreign language. AP and CLEP credits are accepted.

Procedure: Freshmen are admitted to all sessions. Entrance exams should be taken in the fall of the senior year. Early decision applications should be filed by July 9; regular applications, by August 27 for fall entry, December 7 for winter entry, March 11 for spring entry, and June 7 for summer entry, along with an application fee of $10. Notification is sent on a rolling basis. There is an early admissions plan.

Transfer: About 402 transfer students enrolled in 1993-94. Transfer students with fewer than 20 hours of credit must meet the same requirements as entering freshmen. Those with fewer than 45 hours of credit or with a GPA below 2.0 must submit their high school transcripts. A total of 45 quarter hours out of 180 must be completed at Columbus.

Visiting: There are regularly scheduled orientations for prospective students, consisting of a college visitation program during the fall quarter. Prospective students may arrange a tour on any weekday. There are guides for informal visits and visitors may stay overnight at the school. To arrange for a visit, contact the Admissions Office at (706) 568-2035.

Financial Aid: In a recent year 52% of all freshmen and 39% of continuing students received some form of financial aid. About 31% of freshmen and 21% of continuing students received need-based aid. The average freshman award was $2380. Of that total, scholarships or need-based grants averaged $825 ($2400 maximum); loans averaged $900 ($2625 maximum); and work contracts averaged $655 ($2400 maximum). Two percent of undergraduate students work part-time. Average earnings from campus work for the school year are $1854. The average financial indebtedness of a recent graduate was $5175. Columbus is a member of CSS. The FAF is required.

International Students: There are currently 74 international students enrolled. They must take the TOEFL or the University of Michigan Language Test and achieve a minimum score on the TOEFL of 500. The student must also take the SAT I or the ACT, and achieve a minimum composite score on the SAT I of 700.

Computers: The college provides computer facilities for student use. The mainframe is an IBM 4361. Computers are available in the computer center, library, business department, and education department. All students may access the system. There are no time limits on using the system and no fees.

Graduates: In a recent year 388 bachelor's degrees were awarded. The most popular majors among graduates were general studies (8%), criminal justice (6%), and elementary education (5%).

Admissions Contact: Patty Ross, Admissions Office.

COVENANT COLLEGE
D-4

Lookout Mountain, GA 30750   **(706) 820-1560**

Full-time: 273 men, 332 women	**Faculty:** 40; IIB, av$
Part-time: 18 men, 16 women	**Ph.D.s:** 70%
Graduate: 20 men, 21 women	**Student/Faculty:** 15 to 1
Year: semesters, summer session	**Tuition:** $9310
Application Deadline: May 1	**Room & Board:** $3744
Freshman Class: 407 applied, 318 accepted, 169 enrolled	
SAT I Verbal/Math: 500/540	**ACT:** 25 **VERY COMPETITIVE**

Covenant College, founded in 1955, is a private, coeducational liberal arts college affiliated with the Presbyterian Church in America. The library contains 67,944 volumes, 26,850 microform items, and 6615 audiovisual forms, and subscribes to 474 periodicals. Computerized library sources and services include interlibrary loans. The 250-acre campus is in a suburban area 12 miles southwest of Chattanooga, Tennessee. Including residence halls, there are 7 buildings on campus.

Student Life: About 76% of undergraduates are from out-of-state, mostly the South. Students come from 40 states, 14 foreign countries, and Canada. Ninety-three percent are white. Most are Protestant. The average age of freshmen is 18; all undergraduates, 20. Twenty-six percent drop out by the end of their first year; 41% remain to graduate.

Housing: A total of 540 students can be accommodated in college housing. College-sponsored living facilities include single-sex dormitories and on-campus apartments. On-campus housing is guaranteed for all 4 years. Eighty-one percent of students live on campus; of those, 99% remain on campus on weekends. Alcohol is not permitted. All students may keep cars on campus.

Activities: There are no fraternities or sororities on campus. There are 16 groups on campus, including cheerleading, choir, chorale, dance, drama, international, literary magazine, newspaper, orchestra, professional, religious, social, social service, student government, symphony, and yearbook.

Sports: There are 3 intercollegiate sports for men and 3 for women, and 4 intramural sports for men and 3 for women. Athletic and recreation facilities include a gymnasium, a weight room, a judo room, a swimming pool, tennis courts, and 3 soccer fields.

Disabled Students: Eighty percent of the campus is accessible to disabled students. The following facilities are available: wheelchair ramps, elevators, special parking, and specially equipped rest rooms.

Services: In addition to many counseling and information services, tutoring is available in some subjects. In addition, there is remedial writing.

Campus Safety and Security: Campus safety and security measures include lighted pathways and sidewalks and a night watchman who maintains campus security at night.

Programs of Study: Covenant awards the B.A., B.S., and B.Mus. degrees. Associate and master's degrees also are awarded. Bachelor's degrees are awarded in BIOLOGICAL SCIENCE (biology/biological science), BUSINESS (business administration and management and organizational behavior), COMMUNICATIONS AND THE ARTS (applied music, English, and music), COMPUTER AND PHYSICAL SCIENCE (chemistry, computer science, and natural sciences), EDUCATION (elementary, middle school, and music), SOCIAL SCIENCE (biblical studies, history, interdisciplinary studies, psychology, and sociology). Education is the strongest academically. Business and management, English, and education have the largest enrollments.

Required: All students must complete core and distribution requirements totaling 55 to 63 hours. A minimum total of 126 credits and a GPA of 2.0 are required for graduation. All students must also complete a senior integration project, in which they explore and analyze a problem in their major field in light of Christian philosophy.

Special: Study abroad in 7 countries and a Washington semester are available. There is a 3–2 engineering program with the Georgia Institute of Technology. Juniors and seniors may take classes on a pass/fail basis. Also, there is a 13-month degree-completion program for students with 2 years of previous college experience. There is a freshman honors program on campus

Faculty/Classroom: Ninety-six percent of faculty are male; 4%, female. All teach undergraduates. No introductory courses are taught by graduate students. The average class size in a laboratory is 12 and in a regular course offering, 19.

Admissions: About 78% of the 1993–94 applicants were accepted. The SAT scores for the 1993–94 freshman class were as follows: Verbal—48% below 500, 28% between 500 and 599, 21% between 600 and 700, and 3% above 700; Math—28% below 500, 41% between 500 and 599, 23% between 600 and 700, and 8% above 700. The ACT scores were 12% below 21, 26% between 21 and 23, 27% between 24 and 26, 16% between 27 and 28, and 19% above 28. About 38% of the current freshmen were in the top fifth of their class; 71% were in the top two fifths. About 6 freshmen graduated first in their class.

Requirements: A minimum GPA of 2.5 is required. Applicants must graduate from an accredited high school or have a GED. A minimum GPA of 2.5 is required. Applicants should have 4 years of high school English, 3 years of mathematics, and 2 years each of foreign language, history, science, and social studies. The SAT I or ACT is required. The minimum composite score on the SAT I is 900 and on the ACT, 21. An essay and an interview are required. AP and CLEP credits are accepted. Important factors used in the admissions decision are leadership record, extracurricular activities record, advanced placement or honor courses, evidence of special talent, and recommendations by school officials.

Procedure: Freshmen are admitted fall and spring. Entrance exams should be taken by January of the senior year. Applications should be filed by May 1 for fall entry and November 1 for spring entry, along with an application fee of $20. Notification is sent on a rolling basis. There is an early admissions plan.

Transfer: About 46 transfer students enrolled in 1993–94. Transfer applicants must take either the SAT I or the ACT. The minimum composite score required on the SAT I is 900; on the ACT, 21. Transfer courses with a grade of C or better that apply toward the selected Covenant program will receive transfer credit. A total of 30 credits out of 126 must be completed at Covenant.

Visiting: There are regularly scheduled orientations for prospective students, consisting of a campus preview weekend during which high school students stay in dormitories and attend classes, seminars, and other college activities. There are guides for informal visits and visitors may sit in on classes and stay overnight at the school. To arrange for a visit, contact the Events Coordinator at (706) 820-1560.

Financial Aid: In 1993–94 96% of all current freshmen and 90% of continuing students received some form of financial aid. About 75% of freshmen and 68% of continuing students received need-based aid. The average freshman award was $5532. Of that total, scholarships or need-based grants averaged $4163 ($9050 maximum); loans averaged $1773 ($4875 maximum); and work contracts averaged $896 ($1560 maximum). Forty-three percent of undergraduate students work part-time. Average earnings from campus work for the school year are $1360. The average financial indebtedness of the 1992–93 graduate was $6850. Covenant is a member of CSS. The FAF is required. The deadline for financial aid applications is March 15.

International Students: There are currently 26 international students enrolled. The school actively recruits these students. They must take the TOEFL and achieve a minimum score of 500.

Computers: The college provides computer facilities for student use. The mainframe is a DEC MicroVAX 3900. There are also 54 microcomputers available for student use in the computer center and the library. All students may access the system. It may be used 8 A.M. to 12 A.M., Monday through Saturday. There are no time limits on using the system. The fees are $30 per semester.

Graduates: In 1992–93 125 bachelor's degrees were awarded. The most popular majors among graduates were business and management (16%), elementary education (14%), and interdisciplinary studies (10%). Within an average freshman class, 1% graduate in 3 years, 35% in 4 years, 2% in 5 years, and 1% in 6 years.

Admissions Contact: Gretta Erickson, Information Services.

DEVRY INSTITUTE OF TECHNOLOGY
ATLANTA
B-2
Decatur, GA 30030–2198

(404) 292-2645
(800) 221-4771 (out-of-state)

Full-time: 1692 men, 608 women	Faculty: 72
Part-time: 334 men, 191 women	Ph.D.s: n/av
Graduate: none	Student/Faculty: 32 to 1
Year: trimesters, summer session	Tuition: $5609
Application Deadline: open	Room & Board: n/app
Freshman Class: 1956 applied, 1741 accepted, 826 enrolled	
SAT I or ACT: see profile	**LESS COMPETITIVE**

The DeVry Institute of Technology/Atlanta, a private coeducational institution, was established in 1969; there are 10 other DeVry Institutes in the United States and Canada owned by Keller Graduate School of Management. The school offers technology-based undergraduate programs in accounting, business operations, electronics, and computer information systems. In addition to regional accreditation, DeVry has baccalaureate program accreditation with ABET. The library contains 13,324 volumes, 194 microform items, and 165 audiovisual forms, and subscribes to 170 periodicals. Computerized library sources and services include the card catalog, interlibrary loans, and database searching. Special learning facilities include a learning resource center and electronics and other laboratories. The 21-acre campus is in a suburban area 15 miles east of Atlanta. There is one building on campus.

Student Life: About 51% of undergraduates are from out-of-state, mostly the South. Students come from 41 states and 16 foreign countries. Sixty-one percent are African American; 32% white. The average age of all undergraduates is 25. Sixty-seven percent drop out by the end of their first year; 34% remain to graduate.

Housing: There are no residence halls. College-sponsored living facilities include off-campus apartments. All students commute. Alcohol is not permitted. All students may keep cars on campus.

Activities: There are no fraternities or sororities on campus. There are 20 groups on campus, including chess, choir, computers, film, honors, international, newspaper, professional, religious, and social service.

Disabled Students: Ninety percent of the campus is accessible to disabled students. The following facilities are available: wheelchair ramps, elevators, special parking, specially equipped rest rooms, and lowered drinking fountains.

Services: In addition to many counseling and information services, tutoring is available in every subject.

Campus Safety and Security: Campus safety and security measures include informal discussions, pamphlets, posters, films, emergency telephones, and lighted pathways and sidewalks. In addition, the campus is patrolled by county police 9 A.M. to 8 P.M. Monday through Friday and by DeVry security 6:30 A.M. to 11 P.M. Monday through Friday and 8 A.M. to 5 P.M. Saturday.

Programs of Study: DeVry awards the B.S. degree. Associate degrees also are awarded. Bachelor's degrees are awarded in BUSINESS (accounting and business administration and management), COMPUTER AND PHYSICAL SCIENCE (information sciences and systems), ENGINEERING AND ENVIRONMENTAL DESIGN (electrical/electronics engineering technology). Electronics has the largest enrollment.

Required: In order to graduate, students must complete between 143 and 158 credit hours with a 2.0 minimum GPA. Course requirements vary according to program. All first-semester students take

courses in business organization, computer applications, algebra, psychology, and student success strategies.

Special: Evening classes and nondegree study are possible. There are 3 national honor societies on campus. Three departments have honors programs.

Faculty/Classroom: Seventy-eight percent of faculty are male; 22%, female. All teach. The average class size in an introductory lecture is 30; in a laboratory, 30; and in a regular course offering, 30.

Admissions: About 89% of the 1993–94 applicants were accepted.

Requirements: Admissions requirements include graduation from a secondary school; the GED is also accepted. Applicants must pass the DeVry entrance exam, although this requirement may be waived if satisfactory ACT, SAT I, or WPCT scores are presented. CLEP credit is accepted.

Procedure: Freshmen are admitted to all sessions. Application deadlines are open. Application fee is $25. Notification is sent on a rolling basis. There are early decision and deferred admissions plans.

Transfer: Transfer students must take the DeVry entrance exam. It is recommended that transfers have math scores of at least 23 on the ACT or 480 on the SAT I. At least 35% of total credits must be completed at DeVry.

Visiting: There are regularly scheduled orientations for prospective students. There are guides for informal visits, and visitors may sit in on classes. To arrange for a visit, contact Olga Macy, New Student Coordinator at (404) 292-2621.

Financial Aid: In 1993–94, 74% of all students received some form of financial aid, including need-based aid. The FAFSA is required.

International Students: They must take the TOEFL and achieve a minimum score of 550 and must also take the college's own entrance exam. The ACT, SAT I, or WPCT may be accepted in lieu of the DeVry entrance exam.

Computers: The college provides computer facilities for student use. The mainframe is an IBM 3081K. Laboratory facilities include IBM and IBM-compatible PCs in stand-alone and network configurations, with access to the mainframe. LANs provide access to a wide range of applications software. Hard copy from mainframe is provided through a local minicomputer and medium- and high-speed printers. Students in the computer information systems program may access the system during published laboratory hours. There are no fees.

Graduates: In 1992–93, 309 bachelor's degrees were awarded. The most popular majors among graduates were electronics technology (58%), business administration and management (24%), and computer information systems and sciences (18%). Within an average freshman class, 34% graduate in 5 years. Some 106 companies recruited on campus in 1992–93. In the 1992 graduating class, 77% of all graduates had found employment within 6 months of graduation.

Admissions Contact: Susann Hirst, Director of Admissions.

EMORY UNIVERSITY
Atlanta, GA 30322   **B-2**

                                   (800) 727-6036

Full-time: 2168 men, 2669 women	**Faculty:** 519; I, +$
Part-time: none	**Ph.D.s:** 96%
Graduate: 2305 men, 2326 women	**Student/Faculty:** 9 to 1
Year: semesters, summer session	**Tuition:** $16,820
Application Deadline: February 1	**Room & Board:** $5110
Freshman Class: 8500 applied, 4165 accepted, 1166 enrolled	
SAT I Verbal/Math: 570/650	**ACT:** 28 **HIGHLY COMPETITIVE**

Emory University, founded in 1836, is a private, coeducational institution affiliated with the United Methodist Church. There are 4 undergraduate and 6 graduate schools. The 7 libraries contain 2,200,000 volumes, 2,400,000 microform items, and more than 3000 audiovisual forms, and subscribe to 18,842 periodicals. Computerized library sources and services include the card catalog, interlibrary loans, and database searching. Special learning facilities include a learning resource center, art gallery, radio station, museum, the Carter Center, and facilities for direct monitoring of former Soviet domestic television. The 631-acre campus is in a suburban area 5 miles northeast of Atlanta. Including residence halls, there are 112 buildings on campus.

Student Life: About 80% of undergraduates are from out-of-state, mostly the South. Students come from 47 states, 51 foreign countries, and Canada. Sixty-five percent are from public schools; 35% from private. Seventy-seven percent are white; 10% Asian American. Thirty-five percent are Protestant; 30% Jewish; 15% claim no religious affiliation; 14% Catholic. The average age of freshmen is 18; all undergraduates, 20. Eight percent drop out by the end of their first year; 80% remain to graduate.

Housing: A total of 3440 students can be accommodated in college housing. College-sponsored living facilities include single-sex and coed dormitories, on-campus apartments, married-student housing, fraternity houses, and sorority houses. In addition, there are honors houses, language houses, and special interest houses. On-campus housing is guaranteed for the freshman year only and is available on a lottery system for upperclassmen. Seventy percent of students live on campus; of those, 95% remain on campus on weekends. All students may keep cars on campus.

Activities: About 35% of men belong to 15 national fraternities; about 35% of women belong to 10 national sororities. There are 200 groups on campus, including art, bagpipe band, band, cheerleading, chess, choir, chorale, chorus, computers, dance, drama, ethnic, film, gay, honors, international, jazz band, literary magazine, musical theater, newspaper, orchestra, pep band, photography, political, professional, radio and TV, religious, social, social service, student government, symphony, and yearbook. Popular campus events include Homecoming, Heritage Ball, Lullwater Day, Dooleys Week, Festival of Nine Lessons, Martin Luther King Week, and caroling.

Sports: There are 9 intercollegiate sports for men and 8 for women, and 50 intramural sports for men and 50 for women. Athletic and recreation facilities include a physical education center that contains a 3000-seat gymnasium with 4 basketball courts, an Olympic-size swimming pool, 2 Nautilus weight rooms, and tennis, racquetball, and squash courts. In addition, there is a soccer field and a 400-meter track, with seating for 2000 spectators.

Disabled Students: Seventy percent of the campus is accessible to disabled students. The following facilities are available: wheelchair ramps, elevators, special parking, specially equipped rest rooms, special class scheduling, lowered drinking fountains, and lowered telephones.

Services: In addition to many counseling and information services, tutoring is available in most subjects. In addition, there is a reader service for the blind.

Campus Safety and Security: Campus safety and security measures include 24-hour foot and vehicle patrol, self-defense education, escort service, and shuttle buses. In addition, there are informal discussions, pamphlets, posters, films, emergency telephones, and lighted pathways and sidewalks. The campus patrol is a fully accredited police department.

Programs of Study: Emory awards the B.A., B.S., B.B.A., B. Med.Sc., and B.S.N. degrees. Master's and doctoral degrees also are awarded. Bachelor's degrees are awarded in BIOLOGICAL SCIENCE (biology/biological science), BUSINESS (accounting, banking and finance, business administration and management, business economics, and marketing/retailing/merchandising), COMMUNICATIONS AND THE ARTS (art history and appreciation, classics, creative writing, dramatic arts, English, fine arts, French, German, Greek, Latin, literature, modern language, music, Russian, and Spanish), COMPUTER AND PHYSICAL SCIENCE (chemistry, computer science, geology, mathematics, physics, and radiological technology), EDUCATION (early childhood, education, elementary, and secondary), HEALTH PROFESSIONS (nursing), SOCIAL SCIENCE (African studies, anthropology, classical/ancient civilization, economics, European studies, history, international studies, Judaic studies, Latin American studies, medieval studies, philosophy, political science/government, psychology, religion, sociology, and women's studies). Sciences, English, psychology, philosophy, history, and political science are the strongest academically. Biology, English, psychology, and political science have the largest enrollments.

Required: To graduate, students must complete 132 semester hours, including courses during the first 2 years in English, science, mathematics, history, the social sciences, health, and physical education. Students must have a minimum GPA of 1.9 for the first 3 years and 2.0 in the senior year. The number of hours required for the major varies by department.

Special: Special academic programs include cross-registration with the 18 colleges and universities of the University Center in Georgia, departmental internships, work-study programs, dual majors, 3–2 engineering degrees, and pass/fail options. Students may study abroad at Oxford and Cambridge universities, as well as at schools in Scotland, Japan, Austria, and other countries. There are accelerated degree programs offered in biology, chemistry, mathematics, physics, English, history, philosophy, political science, sociology, and computer science. There are 25 national honor societies on campus, including Phi Beta Kappa. All departments have honors programs.

Faculty/Classroom: Seventy-five percent of faculty are male; 25%, female. All both teach and do research. Graduate students teach 10% of introductory courses. The average class size in an introductory lecture is 35.

Admissions: About 49% of the 1993–94 applicants were accepted. The SAT scores for the 1993–94 freshman class were as follows: Verbal—8% below 500, 55% between 500 and 599, 33% between 600 and 700, and 4% above 700; Math—23% between 500 and 599, 56% between 600 and 700, and 21% above 700. The ACT scores were 5% between 21 and 23, 30% between 24 and 26, 26% between 27 and 28, and 39% above 28. There were 56 National Merit finalists.

Requirements: Emory requires applicants to be in the upper 50% of their class. The SAT I or the ACT is required, and an SAT II: Subject test is recommended. The student must have acquired 16 academic credits in secondary school, including 2 years each of history and science, 3 of mathematics, and 4 of English. The university requires the student to submit an essay. AP credits are accepted. Important factors used in the admissions decision are advanced placement or honor courses, recommendations by school officials, extracurricular activities record, personality, intangible qualities, and leadership record.

Procedure: Freshmen are admitted in the fall. Entrance exams should be taken prior to applying. There are early decision, early admissions, and deferred admissions plans. Early decision applications should be filed by November 1; regular applications, by February 1 for fall entry, along with an application fee of $35. Notification of early decision is sent December 15; regular decision, April 1. About 320 early decision candidates were accepted for the 1993–94 class. A waiting list is an active part of the admissions procedure, with about 4% of applicants on the list.

Transfer: About 110 transfer students enrolled in 1993–94. Applicants must have taken the SAT I or ACT and completed at least 1 year of college, with a minimum GPA of 3.0. At least 64 credits out of 132 must be completed at Emory.

Visiting: There are regularly scheduled orientations for prospective students, including a group information session and a campus tour. There are guides for informal visits, and visitors may sit in on classes and stay overnight at the school. To arrange for a visit, contact the Admissions Office at (800) 727-6036.

Financial Aid: In 1993–94, 57% of all current freshmen and 61% of continuing students received some form of financial aid. About 33% of all students received need-based aid. The average freshman award was $13,745. Of that total, scholarships or need-based grants averaged $9271 ($21,930 maximum); loans averaged $3099 ($5625 maximum); and work contracts averaged $1375. Seventy percent of undergraduate students work part-time. Average earnings from campus work for the school year are $1400. The average financial indebtedness of the 1992–93 graduate was $12,000. Emory is a member of CSS. The FAF and the FAFSA are required. The deadline for financial aid applications is February 15.

International Students: There are currently 80 international students enrolled. They must take the TOEFL and must also take the SAT I or the ACT.

Computers: The college provides computer facilities for student use. The mainframes are an IBM 3090 and a DEC VAX 11/780. There are about 500 terminals located in the library, dormitories, computing centers, and some academic departments. All students may access the system. There are no time limits on using the system and no fees.

Graduates: In 1992–93, 1438 bachelor's degrees were awarded. The most popular majors among graduates were psychology (14%), biology (10%), and political science (10%). Within an average freshman class, 80% graduate in 4 years and 85% in 5 years. Some 138 companies recruited on campus in 1992–93. In the 1992 graduating class, 60% of all graduates were enrolled in graduate school within 6 months of graduation.

Admissions Contact: Daniel C. Walls, Dean of Admissions.

FORT VALLEY STATE COLLEGE
B-3

Fort Valley, GA 31030-3298

Full-time: 962 men, 1226 women	(912) 825-6307; (800) 248-7343
Part-time: 83 men, 86 women	Faculty: 146; IIB, -$
Graduate: 87 men, 299 women	Ph.D.s: 55%
Year: quarters, summer session	Student/Faculty: 15 to 1
Application Deadline: August 27	Tuition: $1514 ($2896)
	Room & Board: $2460

Freshman Class: 2188 applied, 1506 accepted, 727 enrolled
SAT I or ACT: required **LESS COMPETITIVE**

Fort Valley State College, founded in 1895, is a coeducational, public, land-grant member of the University System of Georgia. The college offers undergraduate programs in the arts and sciences, business, education, agriculture, engineering, and other vocational and technical fields. There are 3 undergraduate schools and one graduate school. In addition to regional accreditation, FVSC has baccalaureate program accreditation with NCATE. The library contains 250,000 volumes and 172,000 microform items, and subscribes to 1168 periodicals. Computerized library sources and services include the card catalog, interlibrary loans, and database searching. Special learning facilities include experimental agricultural plots, animal research centers, and a greenhouse complex. The 1375-acre campus is in a small town 30 miles southwest of Macon. Including residence halls, there are 35 buildings on campus.

Student Life: Sixty-four percent drop out by the end of their first year; 20% remain to graduate.

Housing: A total of 982 students can be accommodated in college housing. College-sponsored living facilities include single-sex dormitories. Sixty-five percent of students live on campus.

Activities: There are 73 groups on campus, including choir, chorus, dance, drama, honors, jazz band, marching band, newspaper, opera, orchestra, political, religious, social service, student government, and yearbook.

Sports: Athletic and recreation facilities include a stadium, a gymnasium, a baseball field, lighted tennis courts, an indoor swimming pool, indoor and outdoor tracks, and shuffleboard courts.

Services: In addition to many counseling and information services, tutoring is available in most subjects.

Programs of Study: FVSC awards the B.A., B.S., B.B.A., and B.S.W. degrees. Associate and master's degrees are also awarded. Bachelor's degrees are awarded in AGRICULTURE (agricultural economics, animal science, horticulture, and plant science), BIOLOGICAL

SCIENCE (biology/biological science, nutrition, and zoology), BUSINESS (accounting, business administration and management, marketing/retailing/merchandising, and office supervision and management), COMMUNICATIONS AND THE ARTS (communications and English), COMPUTER AND PHYSICAL SCIENCE (chemistry, computer science, information sciences and systems, and mathematics), EDUCATION (agricultural, early childhood, home economics, mathematics, middle school, physical, and secondary), ENGINEERING AND ENVIRONMENTAL DESIGN (agricultural engineering technology, commercial art, and electrical/electronics engineering technology), HEALTH PROFESSIONS (veterinary science), SOCIAL SCIENCE (child psychology/development, criminal justice, economics, political science/government, psychology, social work, and sociology).

Required: Students must complete 90 quarter hours of general education requirements, including 20 hours each of humanities, social science, and mathematics/science, and 30 hours of courses in the major. The bachelor's degree requires completion of at least 180 quarter hours with a minimum GPA of 2.0 and no grade below C in the major.

Special: Students may participate in cooperative work-study programs with local industries, cross-register for courses at Robins Residence Center, and study abroad. FVSC also offers a 3–2 dual degree program in chemistry, mathematics, or physics at FVSC, and engineering or other technical fields with Georgia Tech. There are 5 national honor societies on campus.

Faculty/Classroom: The average class size in a regular course offering is 25.

Admissions: About 70% of the 1993–94 applicants were accepted.

Requirements: A minimum GPA of 1.8 is required. The SAT I or ACT is required. Applicants must be graduates of an accredited secondary school or have earned a GED. The college requires at least 17 academic units of study, including 4 in English, 3 in social science, 3 each in mathematics and science, and 2 of foreign language. AP and CLEP credits are accepted.

Procedure: Applications should be filed by August 27 for fall entry, December 8 for winter entry, March 11 for spring entry, and May 27 for summer entry. Notification is sent on a rolling basis. There is an early admissions plan.

Transfer: In addition to meeting standard admission requirements, transfers must submit transcripts from all colleges previously attended. Transfer credit is accepted based on a 2.0 minimum GPA, and only courses with a C or better will be accepted. A total of 45 quarter hours out of 180 must be completed at FVSC.

Visiting: Visitors may sit in on classes. To arrange for a visit, contact the Office of Recruitment at (912) 825-6227.

Financial Aid: The FAF is required. The deadline for financial aid applications is April 15.

International Students: The student must take the SAT I or the ACT.

Computers: The college provides computer facilities for student use.

Admissions Contact: Delia Taylor, Director of Admissions.

GEORGIA COLLEGE
C-3

Milledgeville, GA 31061 (912) 453-5004; (800) 342-0471 (in-state)

Full-time: 1273 men, 2194 women	Faculty: 184; IIA, --$
Part-time: 486 men, 681 women	Ph.D.s: 70%
Graduate: 393 men, 641 women	Student/Faculty: 19 to 1
Year: quarters, summer session	Tuition: $1694 ($4466)
Application Deadline: August 31	Room & Board: $2616

Freshman Class: 2747 applied, 2667 accepted, 1341 enrolled
SAT I Verbal/Math: 460/480 **ACT:** 19 **LESS COMPETITIVE**

Georgia College, founded in 1889, is a public, coeducational institution and a senior college of the University System of Georgia. There are 4 undergraduate schools and one graduate school. In addition to regional accreditation, the college has baccalaureate program accreditation with NASM, NCATE, and NLN. The library contains 161,877 volumes, 441,638 microform items, and 2695 audiovisual forms, and subscribes to 1138 periodicals. Computerized library sources and services include the card catalog, interlibrary loans, and database searching. Special learning facilities include a learning resource center, art gallery, radio station, TV station, and a museum. The 696-acre campus is in an urban area 30 miles from Macon. Including residence halls, there are 40 buildings on campus.

Student Life: About 95% of undergraduates are from Georgia. Students come from 34 states, 31 foreign countries, and Canada. Some 85% are from public schools. About 80% are white; 17% African American. The average age of freshmen is 18; all undergraduates, 23. Approximately 17% drop out by the end of their first year; 58% remain to graduate.

Housing: A total of 1400 students can be accommodated in college housing. College-sponsored living facilities include single-sex dormitories. In addition, there are honors houses. On-campus housing is guaranteed for all 4 years. About 74% of students commute. Alcohol is not permitted. All students may keep cars on campus.

Activities: About 20% of men belong to 8 national fraternities and 20% of women belong to 6 national sororities. There are 87 groups on campus, including art, band, cheerleading, choir, chorale, chorus, dance, drama, ethnic, film, honors, international, jazz band, literary magazine, musical theater, newspaper, orchestra, pep band, photography, political, professional, radio and TV, religious, social, social service, student government, symphony, and yearbook. Popular campus events include Cruisin, Homecoming, Parents Day, Progressive Dinner, International Week, Greek Week, Black History Month, Spring Carnival, Beach Week, Formals, and Kwanzaa.

Sports: There are 5 intercollegiate sports for men and 5 for women, and 3 intramural sports for men and 3 for women. Athletic and recreation facilities include a 4300-seat basketball arena, a track, racquetball and tennis courts, a weight room, training facilities and classrooms, a 70-acre physical education complex, a soccer field, a ball park, a gymnasium, a golf course, a private bowling alley, indoor and outdoor pools, and nearby lakes.

Disabled Students: The entire campus is accessible to disabled students. The following facilities are available: wheelchair ramps, elevators, special parking, specially equipped rest rooms, special class scheduling, lowered drinking fountains, lowered telephones, and disabled student housing.

Services: In addition to many counseling and information services, tutoring is available in most subjects. In addition, there is a reader service for the blind, and remedial math, reading, and writing.

Campus Safety and Security: Campus safety and security measures include 24-hour foot and vehicle patrol, self defense education, escort service, and informal discussions. In addition, there are pamphlets, posters, films, and lighted pathways and sidewalks.

Programs of Study: The college awards the B.A., B.S., B.B.A., B.Gen.Stud., B.M., B.Mus.Ed., B.Mus.Ther., B.S.Ed., B.S.H.E., and B.S.N. degrees. Master's degrees also are awarded. Bachelor's degrees are awarded in BIOLOGICAL SCIENCE (biology/biological science), BUSINESS (accounting, business administration and management, management information systems, marketing/retailing/merchandising, and office supervision and management), COMMUNICATIONS AND THE ARTS (arts administration/management, English, fine arts, French, journalism, music, Spanish, and voice), COMPUTER AND PHYSICAL SCIENCE (chemistry, computer science, and mathematics), EDUCATION (art, early childhood, health, middle school, music, physical, and special), HEALTH PROFESSIONS (music therapy and nursing), SOCIAL SCIENCE (economics, history, paralegal studies, political science/government, psychology, public administration, social science, and sociology). Education is the strongest program academically. Arts and sciences have the largest enrollments.

Required: To graduate, students must complete 186 quarter hours, with 96 in the major, and must maintain a minimum GPA of 2.0. All B.A. candidates and some B.S. candidates must take foreign language. There are requirements for all students in English literature, English composition, mathematics, science, social studies, Western civilization, fine arts, and physical education. All students must take a comprehensive exam.

Special: The college offers cross-registration with University of Valladolid (Spain) and Demontfort University (England), co-op programs, internships, study abroad, work-study programs, the B.A.-B.S. degrees, dual majors, independent study, and student-designed majors. There is a 2–2 and 2–3 engineering degree program with the Georgia Institute of Technology. There is a freshman honors program on campus, as well as 10 national honor societies. All departments have honors programs.

Faculty/Classroom: Some 60% of faculty are male; 40%, female. Nearly all teach undergraduates and 24% do research. No introductory courses are taught by graduate students. The average class size in an introductory lecture is 30; in a laboratory, 13; and in a regular course offering, 24.

Admissions: About 97% of the 1993–94 applicants were accepted. The SAT scores for the 1993–94 freshman class were as follows: Verbal—83% below 500, 14% between 500 and 599, and 3% between 600 and 700; Math—55% below 500, 35% between 500 and 599, and 10% between 600 and 700. The ACT scores were 80% below 21, 12% between 21 and 23, 4% between 24 and 26, and 4% between 27 and 28.

Requirements: The SAT I, with a minimum required composite score of 740 (360 verbal and 380 math), or the ACT is required. Applicants must be graduates of an accredited secondary school and must complete the Georgia college preparatory curriculum requirements, including 4 years of English, 3 each of laboratory science and college preparatory mathematics, 2 of the same foreign language, and 1 each of U.S. history, world history, and economics/government. AP and CLEP credits are accepted.

Procedure: Freshmen are admitted to all sessions. Entrance exams should be taken by January of the senior year. Applications should be filed by August 31 for fall entry, December 1 for winter entry, March 1 for spring entry, and June 1 for summer entry, along with an application fee of $10. Notification is sent as soon as the file is complete and evaluated. There is an early admissions plan.

Transfer: About 579 transfer students enrolled in 1993–94. Applicants for transfer must have at least a C average and be eligible to return to their previous institution. Applicants who have completed fewer than 20 quarter hours must complete all the requirements for freshman admissions. A total of 60 quarter hours out of 186 must be completed at the college.

Visiting: There are regularly scheduled orientations for prospective students, including activities, dinner, receptions, tours, school meetings, information sessions, co-curricular advising and registration, and academic advising and registration. There are guides for informal visits and visitors may sit in on classes. To arrange for a visit, contact the Office of Admissions at (912) 453–5004 or (800) 342–0471 (in-state).

Financial Aid: In 1993–94, 62% of all current freshmen and 66% of continuing students received some form of financial aid. About 40% of freshmen and 43% of continuing students received need-based aid. The average freshman award was $2600. Of that total, scholarships or need-based grants averaged $350 ($2400 maximum); loans averaged $1500 ($2625 maximum); and work contracts averaged $750 ($1800 maximum). Some 15% of undergraduate students work part-time. Average earnings from campus work for the school year are $1500. The FAF and the Georgia State Financial Aid Application are required. The deadline for financial aid applications is April 15.

International Students: There are currently 80 international students enrolled. The school actively recruits these students. They must take the TOEFL and achieve a minimum score of 500. The student must also take the college's own entrance exam.

Computers: The college provides computer facilities for student use. The mainframe is a TI 1500. A VAX minicomputer with Peachnet, Telnet, and LAN access and access to a CYBER mainframe are available for student use. There are also microcomputers available for student use. All students may access the system. It may be used 8 A.M. to 11 P.M. There are no time limits on using the system and no fees.

Graduates: In 1992–93, 850 bachelor's degrees were awarded. The most popular majors among graduates were early childhood education (12%), nursing (11%), and management (9%). Within an average freshman class, 14% graduate in 4 years, 45% in 5 years, and 56% in 6 years. Some 60 companies recruited on campus in 1992–93.

Admissions Contact: Admissions Officer.

GEORGIA INSTITUTE OF TECHNOLOGY   B-2
Atlanta, GA 30332   **(404) 894-4154**

Full-time: 6334 men, 2194 women	Faculty: 615; I, av$
Part-time: 488 men, 166 women	Ph.D.s: 91%
Graduate: 2870 men, 794 women	Student/Faculty: 14 to 1
Year: quarters, summer session	Tuition: $2265 ($6765)
Application Deadline: February 1	Room & Board: $4404
Freshman Class: 7947 applied, 4536 accepted, 1771 enrolled	
SAT I Verbal/Math: 559/673	**HIGHLY COMPETITIVE +**

Georgia Institute of Technology, founded in 1885, is a public, technological institution offering programs in architecture, management, engineering, computing, and science. There are 5 undergraduate and 5 graduate schools. In addition to regional accreditation, Georgia Tech has baccalaureate program accreditation with AACSB, ABET, and NAAB. The library contains 2 million volumes, 3 million microform items, and 2000 audiovisual forms, and subscribes to 22,000 periodicals. Computerized library sources and services include the card catalog, interlibrary loans, and database searching. Special learning facilities include a learning resource center, art gallery, and radio station. The 330-acre campus is in an urban area in Atlanta. Including residence halls, there are 124 buildings on campus.

Student Life: About 66% of undergraduates are from Georgia. Students come from 50 states, 82 foreign countries, and Canada. Seventy-eight percent are white. The average age of freshmen is 18; all undergraduates, 20. Seventeen percent drop out by the end of their first year; 30% remain to graduate.

Housing: A total of 5532 students can be accommodated in college housing. College-sponsored living facilities include single-sex dormitories, on-campus apartments, married-student housing, fraternity houses, and sorority houses. In addition there are language houses. On-campus housing is guaranteed for the freshman year only and is available on a lottery system for upperclassmen. Alcohol is not permitted. All students may keep cars on campus.

Activities: About 30% of men belong to 31 national fraternities; about 24% of women belong to 8 national sororities. There are 250 groups on campus, including band, cheerleading, chess, chorale, chorus, computers, dance, drama, drill team, ethnic, gay, honors, international, jazz band, literary magazine, marching band, newspaper, orchestra, pep band, political, professional, radio and TV, religious, social, social service, student government, symphony, and yearbook. Popular campus events include Homecoming and Greek Week.

Sports: There are 9 intercollegiate sports for men and 7 for women, and 45 intramural sports for men and 45 for women. Athletic and recreation facilities include indoor and outdoor tennis, swimming, track, a baseball field, and a 45,000-seat football stadium.

Disabled Students: Thirty-five percent of the campus is accessible to disabled students. The following facilities are available: wheelchair ramps, elevators, special parking, specially equipped rest rooms, spe-

cial class scheduling, lowered drinking fountains, lowered telephones, visual alarms in housing, listening devices, adapted furniture in computer laboratories, and adaptable living space.

Services: In addition to many counseling and information services, tutoring is available in most subjects.

Campus Safety and Security: Campus safety and security measures include 24-hour foot and vehicle patrol, self-defense education, escort service, and shuttle buses. In addition, there are informal discussions, pamphlets, posters, and films, emergency telephones, and lighted pathways and sidewalks.

Programs of Study: Georgia Tech awards the B.S. and many specialized bachelor's degrees in the science, engineering, and computing fields. Master's and doctoral degrees also are awarded. Bachelor's degrees are awarded in BIOLOGICAL SCIENCE (biology/biological science), BUSINESS (management and management science), COMMUNICATIONS AND THE ARTS (industrial design), COMPUTER AND PHYSICAL SCIENCE (chemistry, computer science, mathematics, physics, and polymer science), ENGINEERING AND ENVIRONMENTAL DESIGN (aeronautical engineering, architecture, ceramic engineering, chemical engineering, civil engineering, computer engineering, construction management, electrical/electronics engineering, engineering and applied science, industrial engineering, materials engineering, mechanical engineering, nuclear engineering, and textile engineering), SOCIAL SCIENCE (economics, international relations, psychology, and textiles and clothing). Various engineering programs are the strongest academically. Electrical engineering, mechanical engineering, and management have the largest enrollments.

Required: All freshmen must take English, calculus, computer science, social science, and a physical education course selected from 2 options. Distribution requirements include 18 hours of social science, including specific course work in U.S. and Georgia history and government, 15 of mathematics, 10 to 12 of science, and 8 of humanities. Students must maintain a 2.0 GPA in approximately 200 quarter hours, and must pass a reading and writing competency examination.

Special: Co-op programs, cross-registration with other Atlanta area colleges, and internships are available. Study abroad in numerous countries is possible, and more han 500 companies participate in work-study programs. A 3–2 engineering degree is offered within the university system, and a joint liberal arts-engineering degree program serves area colleges and institutions nationwide. A dual degree program is offered. Pass/fail options, summer internships, and dual majors are available. There is a freshman honors program on campus, as well as 21 national honor societies. Eleven departments have honors programs.

Faculty/Classroom: Eighty-nine percent of faculty are male; 11%, female. The average class size in a regular course offering is 28.

Admissions: About 57% of the 1993–94 applicants were accepted. About 89% of the current freshmen were in the top fifth of their class; 99% were in the top two fifths. There were 92 National Merit finalists.

Requirements: The SAT I is required and the ACT is recommended. Candidates for admission must have completed 4 years each of English and mathematics, 3 of science, 2 each of history and a foreign language, and 1 of social studies. AP credits are accepted. Important factors used in the admissions decision are advanced placement or honor courses, parents or siblings attending the school, leadership record, recommendations by school officials, and recommendations by alumni.

Procedure: Freshmen are admitted to all sessions. Entrance exams should be taken by the end of the junior year. Applications should be filed by February 1 for fall entry, October 1 for winter entry, January 1 for spring entry, and February 1 for summer entry, along with an application fee of $25. Notification is sent on a rolling basis.

Transfer: About 358 transfer students enrolled in 1993–94. Transfer applicants must have completed a minimum of 45 quarter hours or 30 semester hours of course work with a minimum GPA of 2.7 for in-state applicants and 3.0 for out-of-state applicants. Grades and academic standing must be satisfactory for the last term of enrollment at the prior college. A total of 50 quarter hours out of 200 must be completed at Georgia Tech.

Visiting: There are regularly scheduled orientations for prospective students. There are guides for informal visits, and visitors may sit in on classes. To arrange for a visit, contact Deborah Smith, Undergraduate Recruiting, at (404) 894–4154.

Financial Aid: In 1993–94, 69% of continuing students received some form of financial aid. Georgia Tech is a member of CSS. The college's own financial statement and the Single File Form are required. The deadline for financial aid applications is March 1.

International Students: There are currently 1102 international students enrolled. They must take the TOEFL and achieve a minimum score of 550. The student must also take the SAT I or the ACT.

Computers: The college provides computer facilities for student use. The mainframes are a CDC CYBER, a CRAY, an IBM, a Sequent, a DEC VAX, and a SUN. Hundreds of microcomputers and workstations are available throughout the campus, in dormitories, academic buildings, and the computer center. Sophisticated networking covers the entire campus. All students may access the system. There are no time limits on using the system and no fees.

Graduates: In 1992–93, 1975 bachelor's degrees were awarded. The most popular majors among graduates were electrical engineering (17%), management (15%), and mechanical engineering (14%). Within an average freshman class, 30% graduate in 4 years, 61% in 5 years, and 69% in 6 years. Some 700 companies recruited on campus in an earlier year.

Admissions Contact: Deborah Smith, Director of Admissions.

GEORGIA SOUTHERN UNIVERSITY
D-3
Statesboro, GA 30460 (912) 681-5531

Full-time: 11,405 men and women	Faculty: 549; IIA, --$
Part-time: 1006 men and women	Ph.D.s: 65%
Graduate: 1780 men and women	Student/Faculty: 21 to 1
Year: quarters, summer session	Tuition: $1808 ($4571)
Application Deadline: September 1	Room & Board: $3180
Freshman Class: n/av	
SAT I: required	LESS COMPETITIVE

Georgia Southern University, founded in 1906, is a member of the public University System of Georgia and offers undergraduate degree programs in the arts and sciences, education, business, health science, and music. There are 5 undergraduate schools and one graduate school. In addition to regional accreditation, GSU has baccalaureate program accreditation with AACSB, ABET, ADA, AHEA, NASM, NCATE, NLN, and NRPA. The library contains 401,741 volumes, 646,331 microform items, and 8390 audiovisual forms, and subscribes to 3333 periodicals. Computerized library sources and services include the card catalog, interlibrary loans, and database searching. Special learning facilities include a learning resource center, art gallery, natural history museum, planetarium, and radio station. The 600-acre campus is in a small town 50 miles northwest of Savannah. Including residence halls, there are 88 buildings on campus.

Student Life: About 88% of undergraduates are from Georgia. Students come from 47 states, 67 foreign countries, and Canada. Ninety-five percent are from public schools; 5% from private. Eighty-four percent are white; 13% African American. The average age of freshmen is 19; all undergraduates, 20. Twenty-six percent drop out by the end of their first year; 40% remain to graduate.

Housing: A total of 3200 students can be accommodated in college housing. College-sponsored living facilities include single-sex and coed dormitories, on-campus apartments, fraternity houses, and sorority houses. On-campus housing is available on a first-come, first-served basis and is available on a lottery system for upperclassmen. Seventy-five percent of students commute. Alcohol is not permitted. All students may keep cars on campus.

Activities: About 27% of men belong to 13 national fraternities; about 23% of women belong to 11 national sororities. There are 150 groups on campus, including art, band, cheerleading, choir, chorus, dance, drama, honors, international, jazz band, literary magazine, marching band, musical theater, newspaper, opera, orchestra, pep band, photography, political, professional, radio and TV, religious, social, student government, symphony, and yearbook. Popular campus events include Back to School Dance, Homecoming, Alcohol Awareness Week, the Union Birthday, and Spring Fling.

Sports: There are 8 intercollegiate sports for men and 7 for women, and 36 intramural sports for men and 36 for women. Athletic and recreation facilities include an 18,000-seat football stadium, a baseball stadium, 15 tennis courts, 6 racquetball courts, 4 beach volleyball courts, 2 outdoor basketball courts, an 8-lane pool, a training room, and 2 gymnasiums, one of which seats 5500.

Disabled Students: Ninety-nine percent of the campus is accessible to disabled students. The following facilities are available: wheelchair ramps, elevators, special parking, specially equipped rest rooms, and special class scheduling.

Services: In addition to many counseling and information services, tutoring is available in most subjects. There also is a reader service for the blind, and remedial math, reading, and writing.

Campus Safety and Security: Campus safety and security measures include 24-hour foot and vehicle patrol, self-defense education, escort service, and informal discussions. In addition, there are pamphlets, posters, and films, emergency telephones, and lighted pathways and sidewalks.

Programs of Study: GSU awards the B.A., B.S., B.B.A., and B.M. degrees. Associate, master's, and doctoral degrees also are awarded. Bachelor's degrees are awarded in BIOLOGICAL SCIENCE (biology/biological science), BUSINESS (accounting, banking and finance, business administration and management, business economics, fashion merchandising, hotel/motel and restaurant management, insurance, marketing/retailing/merchandising, recreation and leisure services, and sports management), COMMUNICATIONS AND THE ARTS (art, communications, English, French, German, journalism, music performance, music theory and composition, performing arts, and Spanish), COMPUTER AND PHYSICAL SCIENCE (chemistry, computer science, geology, information sciences and systems, mathematics, and physics), EDUCATION (art, early childhood, health, middle school, music, physical, secondary, and special), ENGINEERING AND ENVIRONMENTAL DESIGN (civil engineering technology, construction management, electrical/electronics engineering technology, industrial engineering technology, interior design, and mechanical

engineering technology), HEALTH PROFESSIONS (medical technology and nursing), SOCIAL SCIENCE (anthropology, child care/child and family studies, criminal justice, economics, family/consumer studies, fashion design and technology, food production/management/services, history, political science/government, psychology, and sociology). Business and education are the strongest academically and have the largest enrollments.

Required: All students must complete a total of 190 credit hours, including at least 30 in the major, with a minimum GPA of 2.0. Specific courses must be completed in English, college algebra, and physical education.

Special: GSU offers opportunities for study abroad in Europe, internships, work-study programs, B.A.-B.S. degrees, cooperative programs, a general studies degree, a 3–2 engineering degree with Georgia Institute of Technology, pass/fail options, credit for military service, and nondegree study. There is a freshman honors program on campus, as well as 2 national honor societies, including Phi Beta Kappa.

Faculty/Classroom: Sixty-two percent of faculty are male; 37%, female. No introductory courses are taught by graduate students. The average class size in an introductory lecture is 150; in a laboratory, 22; and in a regular course offering, 30.

Requirements: A minimum GPA of 2.0 is required. The SAT I is required, with minimum scores of 370 verbal and 380 mathematics. Students must be graduates of an accredited secondary school or have a GED certificate. A minimum of 15 credits in college preparatory courses should include 4 in English, 2 in a foreign language, and 3 each in history, mathematics, and science. An interview is recommended. AP and CLEP credits are accepted.

Procedure: Freshmen are admitted to all sessions. Entrance exams should be taken during the junior year. Applications should be filed by September 1 for fall entry, December 1 for winter entry, and March 1 for spring entry, along with an application fee of $10. Notification is sent within 1 week after receipt of the completed application. There is an early admissions plan.

Transfer: A total of 758 transfer students enrolled in a recent year. Applicants must have completed at least 30 quarter credit hours of college courses with a minimum GPA of 2.0. Those with fewer than 30 hours must meet freshman requirements. Students transferring with an associate degree must have completed 101 credit hours. A total of 45 credits out of 190 must be completed at GSU.

Visiting: There are regularly scheduled orientations for prospective students. There are guides for informal visits and visitors may sit in on classes and stay overnight at the school. To arrange for a visit, contact Sally Waters at (912) 681–5531.

Financial Aid: In 1993–94, 78% of all current freshmen received some form of financial aid. Thirty percent of undergraduate students work part-time. The FAF and the college's own financial statement are required. The deadline for financial aid applications is April 15.

International Students: There are currently 300 international students enrolled. They must take the University of Michigan Language Test after admission.

Computers: GSU provides computer facilities for student use. The mainframes are IBM, DEC VAX, and HP units. There are 200 IBM PS/2 Model 30, Zenith, Apple, and Apple Macintosh microcomputers available in the learning resource center and various laboratories. Students can obtain VAX and Internet accounts to access the mainframe computers 24 hours a day. There are no time limits on using the system and no fees.

Graduates: In a recent year, 1091 bachelor's degrees were awarded. The most popular majors were arts and sciences, business, and education. Some 95 companies recruited on campus.

Admissions Contact: Dale Wasson, Director of Admissions.

GEORGIA SOUTHWESTERN COLLEGE

B-4

Americus, GA 31709 (912) 928–1273; (800) 338–0082 (out-of-state)

Full-time, part-time: 2176 men and women	Faculty: 118
	Ph.D.s: 60%
Graduate: 381 men and women	Student/Faculty: 15 to 1
Year: quarters, summer session	Tuition: $1728 ($4491)
Application Deadline: see profile	Room & Board: $2610
Freshman Class: 851 applied, 825 accepted, 389 enrolled	
SAT I Verbal/Math: 404/446	**LESS COMPETITIVE**

Georgia Southwestern College, founded in 1906, is a coeducational liberal arts and teachers college that is part of the public University System of Georgia. There are 2 graduate schools. In addition to regional accreditation, GSW has baccalaureate program accreditation with NCATE and NLN. The library contains 156,457 volumes, 469,857 microform items, and 1849 audiovisual forms, and subscribes to 845 periodicals. Computerized library sources and services include the card catalog, interlibrary loans, and database searching. Special learning facilities include a learning resource center and art gallery. The 187-acre campus is in a small town 38 miles north of Albany. Including residence halls, there are 30 buildings on campus.

Student Life: About 95% of undergraduates are from Georgia. Students come from 16 states, 17 foreign countries, and Canada. Seventy percent are from public schools; 30% from private. Eighty percent

are white; 17% African American. The average age of freshmen is 20.2; all undergraduates, 23. Thirty-four percent drop out by the end of their first year; 25% remain to graduate.

Housing: A total of 941 students can be accommodated in college housing. College-sponsored living facilities include single-sex dormitories. In addition, there are independent fraternity houses. On-campus housing is guaranteed for all 4 years. Sixty percent of students live on campus. All students may keep cars on campus.

Activities: About 10% of men belong to 7 national fraternities; about 10% of women belong to 6 national sororities. There are 60 groups on campus, including art, band, cheerleading, choir, chorale, chorus, drama, ethnic, honors, international, jazz band, literary magazine, musical theater, newspaper, orchestra, photography, political, religious, social, and student government.

Sports: There are 4 intercollegiate sports for men and 2 for women, and 9 intramural sports for men and 7 for women. Athletic and recreation facilities include 2 gymnasiums, tennis courts, an indoor/outdoor pool, a lake for canoeing, and playing fields for baseball, football, and soccer. The larger gymnasium seats 3000; the auditorium, 500.

Disabled Students: Seventy-five percent of the campus is accessible to disabled students. The following facilities are available: wheelchair ramps, elevators, special parking, specially equipped rest rooms, special class scheduling, lowered drinking fountains, and accessible dormitories.

Services: In addition to many counseling and information services, tutoring is available in most subjects. In addition, there is a reader service for the blind, and remedial math, reading, and writing.

Campus Safety and Security: Campus safety and security measures include 24-hour foot and vehicle patrol, informal discussions, pamphlets, posters, and films, and lighted pathways and sidewalks.

Programs of Study: GSW awards the B.A., B.S., B.B.A., B.F.A., B.S.Ed., and B.S.N. degrees. Associate and master's degrees also are awarded. Bachelor's degrees are awarded in BIOLOGICAL SCIENCE (biology/biological science), BUSINESS (accounting, business administration and management, and marketing/retailing/merchandising), COMMUNICATIONS AND THE ARTS (dramatic arts, English, fine arts, and music), COMPUTER AND PHYSICAL SCIENCE (chemistry, computer programming, computer science, geology, and mathematics), EDUCATION (art, business, early childhood, elementary, English, foreign languages, mathematics, middle school, music, recreation, science, social science, and special), ENGINEERING AND ENVIRONMENTAL DESIGN (computer technology), HEALTH PROFESSIONS (nursing), SOCIAL SCIENCE (history, political science/government, psychology, and sociology). The sciences, geology, preprofessional health and nursing, and education are the strongest programs academically. Business, education, and nursing have the largest enrollments.

Required: To graduate, the student must complete 180 credit hours, including 30 in the major, with a minimum GPA of 2.0. The core curriculum consists of 20 hours each in English and the humanities, science, mathematics, and social science. The student must also complete 4 courses in health and physical education, including swimming, and pass tests in reading, writing, and geography.

Special: The college offers a 3–2 engineering degree with the Georgia Institute of Technology, cooperative programs with the South Georgia Technical School, a 2–2 degree program in nursing, internships through the Governor's Intern Program, study abroad, and credit for military physical education and training. There is a freshman honors program on campus, as well as 14 national honor societies. One department has an honors program.

Faculty/Classroom: Sixty-six percent of faculty are male; 34%, female. All teach undergraduates, 25% do research, and 25% do both. No introductory courses are taught by graduate students.

Admissions: About 97% of the 1993–94 applicants were accepted.

Requirements: The SAT I or the ACT is required; the SAT I is preferred. Students must score at least 350 on each part of the SAT I, and no lower than 18 on the verbal part and 16 on the mathematics part of the ACT; those with lower scores may gain acceptance through the Developmental Studies Program. Students must be graduates of an accredited secondary school or have a GED certificate. The college requires 15 academic credits and 21 Carnegie units, based on 4 years of English, 3 each of science and mathematics, 2 each of history and a foreign language, and 1 of social studies. An art portfolio and a music audition are recommended. AP and CLEP credits are accepted.

Procedure: Freshmen are admitted to all sessions. Entrance exams should be taken before the end of the senior year. Application deadlines are 20 days prior to each quarter. Application fee is $10. Notification is sent on a rolling basis. There is an early admissions plan.

Transfer: About 165 transfer students enrolled in a recent year. Applicants should be in good standing at their former institutions. Those with fewer than 20 hours of transfer credit must meet freshman requirements. A total of 45 quarter hours out of 180 must be completed at GSW.

Visiting: There are regularly scheduled orientations for prospective students. There are guides for informal visits and visitors may sit in on classes and stay overnight at the school. To arrange for a visit, contact the Admissions Office at (800) 338–0082 or (912) 928–1273.

Financial Aid: In a recent year 50% of all freshmen and 50% of continuing students received some form of financial aid. About 28% of freshmen and 14% of continuing students received need-based aid. The average freshman award is a recent year was $5319. Of that total, scholarships or need-based grants averaged $1334 ($2400 maximum); loans averaged $2625 (maximum); and work contracts averaged $1350 ($2025 maximum). Average earnings from campus work for the school year are $1350. The average financial indebtedness of a recent year's graduate was $3047. GSW is a member of CSS. The FAF and the college's own financial statement are required. The deadline for financial aid applications is May 1.

International Students: There are currently 56 international students enrolled. The school actively recruits these students. They must take the TOEFL and achieve a minimum score of 500.

Computers: The college provides computer facilities for student use. The mainframe is an IBM 9375. Two computer laboratories are equipped with IBM microcomputers, which are connected to the main computer by a token ring network. All students may access the system. It may be used from 8 A.M. to 12 midnight Monday through Friday and selected hours on weekends. There are no time limits on using the system and no fees.

Graduates: In a recent year 315 bachelor's degrees were awarded. The most popular majors among graduates were education (32%), business (23%), and nursing (11%). Within an average freshman class, 24% graduate in 4 years. Some 100 companies recruited on campus in a recent year.

Admissions Contact: Tim Buchanan, Director of Admissions.

GEORGIA STATE UNIVERSITY
B-2
Atlanta, GA 30303-3083
(404) 651-2365

Full-time: 3298 men, 4434 women	Faculty: 746; I, -$
Part-time: 3816 men, 5238 women	Ph.D.s: 83%
Graduate: 2819 men, 4046 women	Student/Faculty: 10 to 1
Year: quarters, summer session	Tuition: $2019 ($6452)
Application Deadline: August 10	Room & Board: n/app
Freshman Class: 3792 applied, 2341 accepted, 1237 enrolled	
SAT I Verbal/Math: 424/468	ACT: 20 COMPETITIVE

Georgia State University, founded in 1913, is part of the University System of Georgia and is a public commuter university offering programs in liberal arts and sciences, business administration, education, health sciences, and public and urban affairs. There are 5 undergraduate and 6 graduate schools. In addition to regional AACSB, GSU has baccalaureate program accreditation with AACSB, ADA, APTA, CAHEA, CSWE, NASAD, NASM, NCATE, and NLN. The 2 libraries contain 1,500,000 volumes, 1,600,000 microform items, and 60,000 audiovisual forms, and subscribe to 14,388 periodicals. Special learning facilities include a learning resource center, art gallery, radio station, and TV station. The 57-acre campus is in an urban area. There are 20 buildings on campus.

Student Life: About 93% of undergraduates are from Georgia. Students come from 49 states and 94 foreign countries. Sixty-four percent are white; 27% African American. The average age of freshmen is 19; all undergraduates, 25.

Housing: There are no residence halls. All students commute. Alcohol is not permitted. All students may keep cars on campus.

Activities: About 8% of men belong to 12 national fraternities; about 6% of women belong to 9 national sororities. There are 104 groups on campus, including art, band, cheerleading, chess, chorale, computers, dance, drama, ethnic, film, gay, honors, international, jazz band, literary magazine, musical theater, newspaper, orchestra, pep band, photography, political, professional, radio and TV, religious, social, social service, student government, and yearbook. Popular campus events include International Student Festival, Homecoming, Honors Day, and Greek Week.

Sports: There are 6 intercollegiate sports for men and 6 for women, and 25 intramural sports for men and 25 for women. Athletic and recreation facilities include a physical education complex with 3 gymnasiums, a pool, a diving well, a weight room, indoor and outdoor tennis courts, a climbing wall, a jogging track, exercise rooms, a dance studio, and racquetball courts; a recreation area with a pool, 3 tennis courts, picnic facilities, regular and sand volleyball, basketball courts, and a rope challenge course; and athletic fields.

Disabled Students: The entire campus is accessible to disabled students. The following facilities are available: wheelchair ramps, elevators, special parking, specially equipped rest rooms, special class scheduling, lowered drinking fountains, and lowered telephones.

Services: In addition to many counseling and information services, tutoring is available in most subjects. In addition, there is a reader service for the blind, and remedial math, reading, and writing. Programs are available in effective studying, reading comprehension, speedreading, test and note taking, overcoming test anxiety and fear of public speaking, and organization and planning.

Programs of Study: GSU awards the B.A., B.S., B.B.A., B.F.A., B.I.S., B.M., B.S.Ed., and B.S.W. degrees. Associate, master's, and doctoral degrees also are awarded. Bachelor's degrees are awarded in AGRICULTURE (forestry and related sciences), BIOLOGICAL SCIENCE (biology/biological science), BUSINESS (accounting, banking and finance, business administration and management, business economics, and marketing/retailing/merchandising), COMMUNICATIONS AND THE ARTS (communications, English, fine arts, French, journalism, music, music performance, and Spanish), COMPUTER AND PHYSICAL SCIENCE (chemistry, computer science, elementary particle physics, information sciences and systems, and mathematics), EDUCATION (art, business, elementary, English, foreign languages, health, mathematics, middle school, music, science, secondary, and social studies), ENGINEERING AND ENVIRONMENTAL DESIGN (preengineering), HEALTH PROFESSIONS (nursing, predentistry, premedicine, prepharmacy, and preveterinary science), SOCIAL SCIENCE (history, international relations, political science/government, prelaw, psychology, and social work). Management, computer science, and psychology have the largest enrollments.

Required: Students must complete distribution requirements, including 20 quarter hours each in humanities, natural science and mathematics, and social science. A minimum of 180 quarter hours must be completed for graduation, with 30 to 40 in the major. A 2.0 minimum GPA is required for graduation.

Special: There is cross-registration with the University Center in Georgia. Internships with numerous employers and government agencies can be arranged. Study abroad is available in Western Europe, Mexico, Israel, the former Soviet Union, and Canada. Work-study, student-designed majors, and pass/fail options are available. The university is also a member of the National Student Exchange. There is a freshman honors program on campus, as well as 16 national honor societies. All departments have honors programs.

Faculty/Classroom: Sixty-nine percent of faculty are male; 31%, female.

Admissions: About 62% of the 1993-94 applicants were accepted.

Requirements: A minimum GPA of 2.0 is required. The SAT I or ACT is required, with minimum scores on the SAT I of 400 verbal, 400 mathematics; on the ACT, 21 English, 19 mathematics. Applicants should graduate from an accredited high school or have a GED. A total of 15 academic credits is required. Students should prepare with 4 years of high school English, 2 years of the same foreign language, and 3 years each of mathematics, science, and social science. AP and CLEP credits are accepted. Important factors used in the admissions decision are evidence of special talent, advanced placement or honor courses, extracurricular activities record, leadership record, personality, and intangible qualities.

Procedure: Freshmen are admitted to all sessions. Entrance exams should be taken during the first semester of the senior year. Applications should be filed by August 10 for fall entry, November 22 for winter entry, February 22 for spring entry, and May 10 for summer entry, along with an application fee of $10. Notification is sent on a rolling basis. There is an early admissions plan.

Transfer: About 4520 transfer students enrolled in 1993-94. Transfer applicants must submit official transcripts of all college-level work, have a minimum GPA of 2.0, have earned 30 quarter hours, and be in good academic standing. Those with fewer than 30 quarter hours earned must meet freshman requirements. At least 45 credits out of 180 must be completed at GSU.

Visiting: There are guides for informal visits, and visitors may sit in on classes. To arrange for a visit, contact Susan Goodroe, Welcome Center at (404) 651-3900.

Financial Aid: GSU is a member of CSS. The FAF and the college's own financial statement are required. The deadline for financial aid applications is April 15.

International Students: There are currently 1054 international students enrolled. The school actively recruits these students. They must take the TOEFL (minimum score 525) or the college's own test and the SAT I or the ACT.

Computers: The college provides computer facilities for student use. The mainframes are an Amdahl 5880 and a Unisys 1100/72. There are 160 microcomputer workstations in 3 microcomputer laboratories. Access to the mainframe is available through 1900 communication lines. Also available are a Xerox 8700 Electronic Printer-Plotter, a Tektronic 4662 plotter, a Tektronic terminal, a Calcomp Colormaster Plotter Printer, and a Xerox 9700 electronic page printer. All students may access the system 24 hours per day. There are no time limits on using the system and no fees.

Admissions Contact: Dr. Earnest W. Beals, Dean of Admissions.

KENNESAW STATE COLLEGE
B-2
Marietta, GA 30061
(404) 423-6300

Full-time: 2254 men, 3184 women	Faculty: 350; IIA, --$
Part-time: 1955 men, 3601 women	Ph.D.s: 71%
Graduate: 494 men, 771 women	Student/Faculty: 16 to 1
Year: quarters, summer session	Tuition: $1553 ($4316)
Application Deadline: September 1	Room & Board: n/app
Freshman Class: 2017 applied, 1824 accepted, 1223 enrolled	
SAT I Verbal/Math: 467/493	COMPETITIVE

Kennesaw State College, founded in 1963, is a 4-year public commuter college in the University System of Georgia. There are 4 undergraduate and 2 graduate schools. In addition to regional accreditation, Kennesaw State has baccalaureate program accreditation with NASM and NLN. The library contains 750,000 microform items and 7500 audiovisual forms, and subscribes to 3300 periodicals. Com-

puterized library sources and services include the card catalog, inter-library loans, and database searching. Special learning facilities include a learning resource center and art gallery. The 185-acre campus is in a suburban area 25 miles north of Atlanta. There are 17 buildings on campus.

Student Life: About 97% of undergraduates are from Georgia. Students come from 26 states, 87 foreign countries, and Canada. Ninety percent are white. The average age of freshmen is 21; all undergraduates, 27. Thirty percent drop out by the end of their first year; 26% remain to graduate.

Housing: There are no residence halls. Although all students commute, there are a number of apartments within walking distance of the college. Alcohol is not permitted. All students may keep cars on campus.

Activities: About 1% of men belong to 1 local and 1 national fraternity; about 10% of women belong to 1 local and 2 national sororities. There are 73 groups on campus, including cheerleading, choir, chorale, chorus, computers, drama, ethnic, gay, honors, international, literary magazine, newspaper, opera, pep band, political, professional, religious, social, social service, student government, and symphony. Popular campus events include KSC Day and Black History Month.

Sports: There are 3 intercollegiate sports for men and 2 for women, and 16 intramural sports for men and 16 for women. Athletic and recreation facilities include a gymnasium, a pool, tennis and racquetball courts, and baseball, softball, and soccer fields.

Disabled Students: Eighty percent of the campus is accessible to disabled students. The following facilities are available: wheelchair ramps, elevators, special parking, specially equipped rest rooms, special class scheduling, lowered drinking fountains, lowered telephones, marked crosswalks with curb cuts, adapted computer equipment with voice synthesizer, a voice-activated computer, screen-enlarging programs, a swimming pool lift, microfilm and microfiche facilities for wheelchair-bound and blind students, a brailler, and enlarged-print machines.

Services: In addition to many counseling and information services, tutoring is available in some subjects. There also is a reader service for the blind, and remedial math, reading, and writing.

Campus Safety and Security: Campus safety and security measures include 24-hour foot and vehicle patrol, self defense education, escort service, and informal discussions. In addition, there are pamphlets, posters, and films, emergency telephones, and lighted pathways and sidewalks.

Programs of Study: Kennesaw State awards the B.A., B.S., B.B.A., and B.M. degrees. Associate and master's degrees also are awarded. Bachelor's degrees are awarded in BIOLOGICAL SCIENCE (biology/biological science), BUSINESS (accounting, banking and finance, business economics, management science, and marketing/retailing/merchandising), COMMUNICATIONS AND THE ARTS (art, communications, English, French, journalism, music, music performance, and Spanish), COMPUTER AND PHYSICAL SCIENCE (chemistry, computer science, information sciences and systems, and mathematics), EDUCATION (art, business, elementary, English, foreign languages, health, mathematics, middle school, music, physical, science, secondary, and social studies), ENGINEERING AND ENVIRONMENTAL DESIGN (preengineering), HEALTH PROFESSIONS (nursing, predentistry, premedicine, prepharmacy, and preveterinary science), SOCIAL SCIENCE (history, political science/government, prelaw, and psychology). Business, psychology, education, and nursing are the strongest academically. Business and education have the largest enrollments.

Required: Requirements vary by degree program. Generally, all students must complete 186 to 219 quarter hour credits, including 95 in core curriculum courses, at least 90 in the major, and 6 in health or physical education, with a minimum GPA of 2.0 and grades of C or better in the major and in required English courses.

Special: Students may register for courses with any of the colleges in the University System of Georgia and may study abroad in 2 countries. Work-study programs and internships are available; some internships have pass/fail options. Dual majors and nondegree programs also are offered. There is a freshman honors program on campus, as well as 6 national honor societies. Seven departments have honors programs.

Faculty/Classroom: All teach undergraduates and 10% do research. No introductory courses are taught by graduate students. The average class size in an introductory lecture is 33; in a laboratory, 34; and in a regular course offering, 33.

Admissions: About 90% of the 1993–94 applicants were accepted. The SAT scores for the 1993–94 freshman class were as follows: Verbal—77% below 500, 20% between 500 and 599, and 3% between 600 and 700; Math—58% below 500, 31% between 500 and 599, 10% between 600 and 700, and 1% above 700.

Requirements: A minimum GPA of 2.0 and either the SAT I or ACT are required. Applicants should submit SAT I scores of 430 verbal and 430 mathematics or a 650 composite, and ACT scores of 17. Applicants should be graduates of accredited secondary schools or have the GED. Secondary preparation should include 4 courses in English, 2 each in algebra, laboratory sciences, and a foreign language, 1 each in geometry and physical science, and 3 in social sciences, including American history, world history, and economics

and government. AP and CLEP credits are accepted. Important factors used in the admissions decision are advanced placement or honor courses and ability to finance college education.

Procedure: Freshmen are admitted to all sessions. Entrance exams should be taken before June 1. Applications should be filed by September 1 for fall entry, December 8 for winter entry, March 1 for spring entry, and June 1 for summer entry, along with an application fee of $20. Notification is sent on a rolling basis.

Transfer: A total of 1071 transfer students enrolled in 1993–94. Applicants should have completed 45 quarter hour credits with a GPA of 2.0 or above; those with a lower GPA may be admitted on probation. Grades of D or better (C or better in English) may be transferred by those with a 2.0 cumulative GPA. A total of 45 quarter hour credits out of 186 to 219 must be completed at Kennesaw State.

Visiting: There are regularly scheduled orientations for prospective students, including Insight Sessions every Tuesday at 4 P.M. There are guides for informal visits. To arrange for a visit, contact the Admissions Office at (404) 423–6300.

Financial Aid: In 1993–94, 30% of all current freshmen and 20% of continuing students received some form of financial aid. About 19% of freshmen and 20% of continuing students received need-based aid. The average freshman award was $2000. Of that total, scholarships or need-based grants averaged $750 ($2000 maximum); loans averaged $2000 ($2625 maximum); and work contracts averaged $1000 ($2500 maximum). Sixty-five percent of undergraduate students work part-time. Average earnings from campus work for the school year are $2000. The average financial indebtedness of the 1992–93 graduate was $2670. Kennesaw State is a member of CSS. The FAF is required. The deadline for financial aid applications is April 15.

International Students: There are currently 480 international students enrolled. The school actively recruits these students. They must take the TOEFL and earn a minimum score of 500, the University of Michigan Language Test, the Comprehensive English Language Test, or the college's own test. The student must also take the SAT I or the ACT.

Computers: The college provides computer facilities for student use. The mainframe is a CDC CYBER 850. There are also 78 networked microcomputers in an open laboratory that can access mainframes available to all state institutions. Computers may be used for any work associated with instruction. Local software includes Lotus 1–2-3, dBASE III Plus, LOGO, PC-Write, and specific intructors' software. All students may access the system 24 hours per day. There are no time limits on using the system and no fees.

Graduates: In 1992–93, 1001 bachelor's degrees were awarded. The most popular majors among graduates were business and management (51%), education (13%), and psychology (8%). Within an average freshman class, 1% graduate in 3 years, 15% in 4 years, 17% in 5 years, and 21% in 6 years. A total of 187 companies recruited on campus in 1992–93.

Admissions Contact: David Balentine, Admissions Specialist.

LAGRANGE COLLEGE
LaGrange, GA 30240

A-3
(404) 882–2911

Full-time: 275 men, 325 women	**Faculty:** 66
Part-time: 128 men, 235 women	**Ph.D.s:** 82%
Graduate: 31 men, 29 women	**Student/Faculty:** 9 to 1
Year: quarters, summer session	**Tuition:** $7197
Application Deadline: August 1	**Room & Board:** $3405
Freshman Class: n/av	
SAT I Verbal/Math: 410/370	**COMPETITIVE**

LaGrange College, founded in 1831, is a private, coeducational, liberal arts institution affiliated with the United Methodist Church. Major undergraduate programs include business, art, education, biology, and psychology. There are 2 graduate schools. The library contains 102,614 volumes, 1955 microform items, and 66,808 audiovisual forms, and subscribes to 409 periodicals. Computerized library sources and services include the card catalog, interlibrary loans, and database searching. Special learning facilities include a learning resource center and art gallery. The 85-acre campus is in an urban area 70 miles southwest of Atlanta. Including residence halls, there are 22 buildings on campus.

Student Life: About 86% of undergraduates are from Georgia. Students come from 23 states and 13 foreign countries. Sixty percent are from public schools; 40% from private. Eighty-one percent are white; 11% African American. Seventy-four percent are Protestant; 16% claim no religious affiliation. The average age of freshmen is 20; all undergraduates, 24. Twelve percent drop out by the end of their first year; 68% remain to graduate.

Housing: A total of 480 students can be accommodated in college housing. College-sponsored living facilities include single-sex and coed dormitories. On-campus housing is guaranteed for all 4 years. Fifty-five percent of students live on campus; of those, 50% remain on campus on weekends. Alcohol is not permitted. All students may keep cars on campus.

Activities: About 25% of men belong to 3 national fraternities; about 25% of women belong to 3 national sororities. There are 48 groups on campus, including art, cheerleading, choir, chorale, computers,

drama, drill team, ethnic, honors, international, jazz band, literary magazine, musical theater, newspaper, orchestra, photography, political, professional, radio and TV, religious, social, social service, student government, symphony, and yearbook. Popular campus events include May Day, Homecoming, Greek Week, International Week, Quadrangle Dance, Ski Weekend, Community Week, art exhibit openings, and college plays.

Sports: There are 6 intercollegiate sports for men and 5 for women, and 7 intramural sports for men and 7 for women. Athletic and recreation facilities include an athletic center, West Point lake, and an auditorium.

Disabled Students: Forty-five percent of the campus is accessible to disabled students. The following facilities are available: wheelchair ramps, elevators, special parking, specially equipped rest rooms, special class scheduling, and lowered drinking fountains.

Services: In addition to many counseling and information services, tutoring is available in some subjects, including mathematics and English.

Campus Safety and Security: Campus safety and security measures include 24-hour foot and vehicle patrol, pamphlets, posters, and films, lighted pathways and sidewalks, and safety awareness seminars during freshman orientation.

Programs of Study: LaGrange awards the B.A., B.S., and B.B.A. degrees. Associate and master's degrees also are awarded. Bachelor's degrees are awarded in BUSINESS (business administration and management and business economics), COMMUNICATIONS AND THE ARTS (dramatic arts, English, fine arts, and Spanish), COMPUTER AND PHYSICAL SCIENCE (chemistry, computer science, mathematics, and physics), EDUCATION (art, early childhood, middle school, and secondary), HEALTH PROFESSIONS (predentistry and premedicine), SOCIAL SCIENCE (economics, history, political science/government, prelaw, psychology, religion, and social work). Business, art, education and psychology are the strongest academically. Business has the largest enrollment.

Required: To graduate, all students must complete 195 quarter hours, including 95 in a core curriculum and 60 in the major. The core curriculum includes freshman seminar, English grammar and composition, history, mathematics, computer science, religion, speech and physical education. All students must have a minimum GPA of 2.0.

Special: Internships are offered in business, social work, and political science, including positions in a congressional office in Washington. Students may study abroad in Israel. A 3–2 engineering degree is offered with Georgia Institute of Technology and Auburn University. There is a freshman honors program on campus, as well as one national honor society. Sixty departments have honors programs.

Faculty/Classroom: Sixty-six percent of faculty are male; 34%, female. All teach undergraduates and 30% both teach and do research. No introductory courses are taught by graduate students. The average class size in an introductory lecture is 25; in a laboratory, 10; and in a regular course offering, 15.

Admissions: The SAT scores for the 1993–94 freshman class were as follows: Verbal—90% below 500, 10% between 500 and 599, and 1% between 600 and 700; Math—75% below 500, 20% between 500 and 599, and 5% between 600 and 700. There was 1 National Merit semifinalist.

Requirements: A minimum GPA of 2.0 is required. The SAT I is required. Applicants should be graduates of accredited secondary schools or have a GED certificate. They should have completed 4 units of English, 3 of social studies, and 2 each of mathematics and science. AP credits are accepted. Important factors used in the admissions decision are extracurricular activities record, personality, intangible qualities, leadership record, evidence of special talent, and advanced placement or honor courses.

Procedure: Freshmen are admitted to all sessions. Applications should be filed by August 1 for fall entry, December 1 for winter entry, March 1 for spring entry, and May 1 for summer entry, along with an application fee of $20. Notification is sent on a rolling basis. There is an early admissions plan.

Transfer: About 105 transfer students enrolled in 1993–94. Transfer students must have a minimum 2.0 GPA and be in good standing with the previous college. A total of 65 credits out of 195 must be completed at LaGrange.

Visiting: There are regularly scheduled orientations for prospective students, including admissions workshops, a student panel, and a guided tour of the campus. There are guides for informal visits and visitors may sit in on classes and stay overnight at the school. To arrange for a visit, contact the Admission Office at (706) 882-2911.

Financial Aid: In 1993–94 78% of all current freshmen and 67% of continuing students received some form of financial aid. About 63% of freshmen and 54% of continuing students received need-based aid. The average freshman award was $6891. Of that total, scholarships or need-based grants averaged $2203 ($3500 maximum); loans averaged $2709 ($3000 maximum); and work contracts averaged $776 ($1148 maximum). Thirty-five percent of undergraduate students work part-time. Average earnings from campus work for the school year are $765. The average financial indebtedness of the 1992–93 graduate was $6987. LaGrange is a member of CSS. The

FAF and FAFSA are required. The deadline for financial aid applications is May 1.

International Students: There are currently 65 international students enrolled. The school actively recruits these students. They must take the TOEFL and achieve a minimum score of 500.

Computers: The college provides computer facilities for student use. The mainframe is an HCX-7 and Sun Microsystems models. Computers are networked via underground fiber optic cables to dormitory rooms and 5 computer laboratories, with more than 150 terminals available. All students may access the system. It may be used 24 hours a day. There are no time limits on using the system and no fees.

Graduates: In 1992–93 131 bachelor's degrees were awarded. The most popular majors among graduates were business (17%), education (11%), and art (7%). Some 40 companies recruited on campus in 1992–93. In the 1992 graduating class, 15% of the men and 20% of the women were enrolled in graduate school within 6 months of graduation.

Admissions Contact: Phil Dodson, Director of Admission.

MERCER UNIVERSITY

The Mercer University, established in 1833, is a private system in Georgia affiliated with Georgia Baptist Convention. It is governed by a board of trustees, whose chief administrator is president. The primary goal of the system is teaching, then research, and public service. The main priorities are to achieve excellence and scholarly discipline in the fields of liberal learning and professional knowledge. The university is guided by principles of religious and intellectual freedom, while affirming religious and moral values that arise from the Judaeo-Christian understanding of the world. The total enrollment in a recent year of the 2 campuses was 5856; there were 320 faculty members. Altogether there are approximately 50 baccalaureate, 20 master's, and 5 doctoral programs offered at Mercer University. Profiles of the 4-year campuses are included in this chapter in alphabetical order with other Georgia schools.

MERCER UNIVERSITY
C-3
Macon, GA 31207-0001

(912) 752-2650
(800) 637-2378 (out-of-state)

Full-time: 1309 men, 1634 women	Faculty: 170
Part-time: 685 men, 575 women	Ph.D.s: 93%
Graduate: 623 men, 810 women	Student/Faculty: 17 to 1
Year: quarters, summer session	Tuition: $11,160
Application Deadline: open	Room & Board: $3963
Freshman Class: 2297 applied, 1904 accepted, 571 enrolled	
SAT I Verbal/Math: 473/529	ACT: 24 COMPETITIVE

Mercer University, founded in 1833, is a private, coeducational institution affiliated with the Georgia Baptist Convention. The university offers degree programs in liberal arts, business and economics, engineering, and professional studies. Mercer also offers a Great Books program as an alternative to the traditional core curriculum. There are 3 undergraduate and 6 graduate schools. In addition to regional accreditation, Mercer has baccalaureate program accreditation with ABET, NASM, and NCATE. The 3 libraries contain 477,485 volumes, 42,693 microform items, and 8735 audiovisual forms, and subscribe to 5622 periodicals. Computerized library sources and services include the card catalog, interlibrary loans, and database searching. Special learning facilities include a learning resource center. The 130-acre campus is in a suburban area 85 miles south of Atlanta. Including residence halls, there are 36 buildings on campus.

Student Life: About 63% of undergraduates are from Georgia. Students come from 37 states, 24 foreign countries, and Canada. Some 81% are white; 13% African American. About 16% claim no religious affiliation; 13% are Catholic. The average age of freshmen is 18; all undergraduates, 21. Approximatley 19% drop out by the end of their first year; 71% remain to graduate.

Housing: A total of 1200 students can be accommodated in college housing. College-sponsored living facilities include single-sex and coed dormitories, on-campus apartments, married-student housing, and sorority houses. On-campus housing is guaranteed for all 4 years. About 61% of students live on campus; of those, 60% remain on weekends. Alcohol is not permitted. All students may keep cars on campus.

Activities: About 35% of men belong to 9 national fraternities; about 32% of women belong to 6 national sororities. There are 65 groups on campus, including band, cheerleading, choir, chorale, chorus, computers, dance, drama, ethnic, honors, international, jazz band, literary magazine, musical theater, newspaper, political, professional, religious, social service, student government, and yearbook. Popular campus events include Pilgrimage to Penfield, Spring Concert, Homecoming, the Miss Mercer Pageant, and Family Weekend.

Sports: There are 6 intercollegiate sports for men and 6 for women, and 10 intramural sports for men and 10 for women. Athletic and recreation facilities include 2 gymnasiums, 3 playing fields, a student center, a swimming pool, a 30-station fitness trail, a lighted intramural complex, and tennis, volleyball, and racquetball courts.

Disabled Students: About 85% of the campus is accessible to disabled students. The following facilities are available: wheelchair ramps, elevators, special parking, specially equipped rest rooms, special class scheduling, lowered drinking fountains, lowered telephones, and assistance with registration. There is also a reader service for the blind.

Services: In addition to many counseling and information services, tutoring is available in every subject, and there is remedial math, reading, and writing.

Campus Safety and Security: Campus safety and security measures include 24-hour foot and vehicle patrol, self defense education, escort service, and informal discussions. In addition, there are pamphlets, posters, and films, emergency telephones, and lighted pathways and sidewalks.

Programs of Study: Mercer awards the B.A., B.S., B.B.A., B.M., B.M.Ed., and B.S.E. degrees. Master's and doctoral degrees also are awarded. Bachelor's degrees are awarded in BIOLOGICAL SCIENCE (biology/biological science), BUSINESS (accounting, banking and finance, business administration and management, and marketing/retailing/merchandising), COMMUNICATIONS AND THE ARTS (English, French, German, Greek, Latin, music, and Spanish), COMPUTER AND PHYSICAL SCIENCE (chemistry, computer science, mathematics, natural sciences, and physics), EDUCATION (early childhood, elementary, music, secondary, and special), ENGINEERING AND ENVIRONMENTAL DESIGN (biomedical engineering, electrical/electronics engineering, environmental engineering, industrial engineering, and mechanical engineering), HEALTH PROFESSIONS (predentistry, premedicine, and prepharmacy), SOCIAL SCIENCE (economics, history, philosophy, political science/government, prelaw, psychology, religion, social science, and sociology). Business, chemistry, English, engineering, and psychology are the strongest programs academically. Business, English, communication, psychology, and education have the largest enrollments.

Required: In order to graduate, all students must complete at least 180 quarter hours with a minimum GPA of 2.0.

Special: Mercer offers co-op programs in all majors, a 3–2 program in forestry with Duke University, B.A.-B.S. degrees in various science and mathematics fields, internships, work-study programs, and satisfactory-unsatisfactory options for elective courses. Students may study abroad in Spain, France, Great Britain, and Italy. There are 2 national honor societies on campus.

Faculty/Classroom: Some 69% of faculty are male; 31%, female. All teach undergraduates. No introductory courses are taught by graduate students. The average class size in an introductory lecture is 30; in a laboratory, 15; and in a regular course offering, 23.

Admissions: About 83% of the 1993–94 applicants were accepted. The SAT scores for the 1993–94 freshman class were as follows: Verbal—60% below 500, 33% between 500 and 599, 7% between 600 and 700, and 1% above 700; Math—34% below 500, 43% between 500 and 599, 20% between 600 and 700, and 3% above 700. Ten freshmen graduated first in their class.

Requirements: Mercer requires applicants to be in the upper 50% of their class. A minimum GPA of 2.5 is required. The SAT I or ACT is required. Applicants must be graduates of an accredited secondary school and have completed 13 academic units. Students should submit their transcript and class rank, a recommendation from a guidance counselor, and a list of extracurricular activities, including employment. AP and CLEP credits are accepted. Important factors used in the admissions decision are advanced placement or honor courses, extracurricular activities record, evidence of special talent, leadership record, and recommendations by school officials.

Procedure: Freshmen are admitted to all sessions. Entrance exams should be taken in spring of the junior year or fall of the senior year. Application deadlines are open. Notification of early decision is sent December 15; regular decision, on a rolling basis. There are early decision, early admissions, and deferred admissions plans. About 42 early decision candidates were accepted for the 1993–94 class. There is an application fee of $25. A waiting list is an active part of the admissions procedure, with about 3% of applicants on the list.

Transfer: About 232 transfer students enrolled in 1993–94. A minimum GPA of 2.0 is required for all transfer students. Applicants with fewer than 15 quarter hours earned must meet freshman entrance requirements. Those with 15 to 30 hours must submit the high school transcript and SAT I or ACT scores. Those with more than 30 hours must submit transcripts from all colleges attended and be in good academic standing at their present school or present evidence of satisfactory work in a previously attended college. A total of 45 quarter hours out of 180 must be completed at Mercer.

Visiting: There are regularly scheduled orientations for prospective students, including 4 preorientation sessions during the summer and a 4-day orientation prior to the beginning of classes. There are guides for informal visits and visitors may sit in on classes and stay overnight at the school. To arrange for a visit, contact the Office of Admissions at (912) 752-2650.

Financial Aid: In 1993–94, 92% of all current freshmen and 93% of continuing students received some form of financial aid. About 65% of freshmen and 68% of continuing students received need-based aid. The average freshman award was $10,726. Of that total, scholarships or need-based grants averaged $7713 ($16,630 maxi-

mum); loans averaged $4213 ($16,625 maximum); and work contracts averaged $1186 ($2000 maximum). Some 55% of undergraduate students work part-time. Average earnings from campus work for the school year are $1000. The average financial indebtedness of the 1992–93 graduate was $10,000. Mercer is a member of CSS. The FAF, the college's own financial statement and the FAFSA are required. The deadline for financial aid applications is May 1.

International Students: There are currently 29 international students enrolled. They must take the TOEFL and achieve a minimum score of 525. The student must also take the SAT I and score 800, or the ACT with a score of 20.

Computers: The college provides computer facilities for student use. The mainframes are DEC VAX 6310, 8350, and 4000 models. Terminals are located in designated student computer laboratories. All students may access the system. It may be used 24 hours per day if the student has dial-in access. There are no time limits on using the system and no fees. It is recommended that students in engineering have personal computers.

Graduates: About 640 bachelor's degrees are awarded each year. The most popular majors among graduates have been business management (14%), elementary education (12%), and accounting (8%). Some 50 to 60 companies recruited on campus in 1992–93. Approximately 20% of the 1992 graduates were enrolled in graduate school within 6 months of graduation.

Admissions Contact: J. Thompson Biggers, Enrollment Management.

MOREHOUSE COLLEGE   B-2

Atlanta, GA 30314   (404) 215–2632; (800) 992–0642

Full-time: 2990 men	Faculty: 150
Part-time: 160 men	Ph.D.s: 74%
Graduate: none	Student/Faculty: 20 to 1
Year: semesters, summer session	Tuition: $8000
Application Deadline: February 15	Room & Board: $5224
Freshman Class: n/av	
SAT I or ACT: required	**LESS COMPETITIVE**

Morehouse College, founded in 1867, is a private men's liberal arts college offering undergraduate programs in the arts and humanities, natural sciences, mathematics, social sciences, and business. The library contains 550,000 volumes, 15,000 microform items, and 8000 audiovisual forms, and subscribes to 110 periodicals. Computerized library sources and services include the card catalog, interlibrary loans, and database searching. Special learning facilities include a learning resource center. The 47-acre campus is in an urban area 3 miles southwest of downtown Atlanta. Including residence halls, there are 26 buildings on campus.

Student Life: About 72% of undergraduates are from out-of-state, mostly the Northeast. Students come from 42 states and 14 foreign countries. Eighty percent are from public schools; 20% from private. Ninety-eight percent are African American. The average age of freshmen is 18; all undergraduates, 20. About 77% of freshmen remain to graduate.

Housing: A total of 1500 students can be accommodated in college housing. College-sponsored living facilities include dormitories and off-campus apartments. On-campus housing is guaranteed for the freshman year only and is available on a first-come, first-served basis. Priority is given to out-of-town students. Fifty-five percent of students live on campus; of those, all remain on campus on weekends. Alcohol is not permitted. Upperclassmen may keep cars on campus.

Activities: About 7% of men belong to 6 national fraternities. There are 60 groups on campus, including band, chess, choir, computers, dance, drama, drill team, ethnic, honors, international, jazz band, literary magazine, marching band, musical theater, newspaper, political, professional, religious, social, social service, student government, and yearbook. Popular campus events include Homecoming, Founders Day, Religious Emphasis Week, and Parents Weekend.

Sports: There are 5 intercollegiate and 10 intramural sports available. Athletic and recreation facilities include a comprehensive health and physical education center, a 9000-seat football stadium, and a track.

Disabled Students: Seventy percent of the campus is accessible to disabled students. The following facilities are available: wheelchair ramps, elevators, special parking, specially equipped rest rooms, lowered drinking fountains, and lowered telephones.

Services: In addition to many counseling and information services, tutoring is available in most subjects. There is also remedial math, reading, and writing.

Campus Safety and Security: Campus safety and security measures include 24-hour foot and vehicle patrol, shuttle buses, informal discussions, and pamphlets, posters, and films. In addition, there are lighted pathways and sidewalks.

Programs of Study: Morehouse awards the B.A. and B.S. degrees. Bachelor's degrees are awarded in BIOLOGICAL SCIENCE (biology/biological science), BUSINESS (accounting, banking and finance, business administration and management, business economics, and marketing/retailing/merchandising), COMMUNICATIONS AND THE ARTS (dramatic arts, English, fine arts, French, German, music, Spanish, and speech/debate/rhetoric), COMPUTER AND

PHYSICAL SCIENCE (actuarial science, chemistry, computer science, mathematics, and physics), EDUCATION (early childhood, elementary, middle school, physical, and secondary), ENGINEERING AND ENVIRONMENTAL DESIGN (engineering and preengineering), HEALTH PROFESSIONS (predentistry and premedicine), and SOCIAL SCIENCE (Caribbean studies, criminal justice, economics, history, international relations, philosophy, political science/government, prelaw, psychology, religion, social work, sociology, and urban studies). Engineering, business administration, English, and philosophy are the strongest academically. Biology has the largest enrollment.

Required: Students must complete a minimum of 124 semester hours, including 68 hours in general studies, plus 8 noncredit hours in Freshman Orientation and College Assembly. A 2.0 GPA is required, with no grade below C in the major.

Special: Morehouse is a member of the Atlanta University Center; students may register for courses and even complete a major in any of the 6 member institutions. In addition, students may study abroad in Europe or Africa. A dual-degree engineering program is offered with Georgia Institute of Technology and a dual-degree program in architecture is offered with the University of Michigan; students in these programs are offered summer internships. Work-study is also available. There is a freshman honors program on campus, as well as 6 national honor societies, including Phi Beta Kappa. Ten departments have honors programs.

Faculty/Classroom: Sixty percent of faculty are male; 40%, female. The average class size in an introductory lecture is 25; in a laboratory, 30; and in a regular course offering, 20.

Admissions: Fifteen freshmen graduated first in their class in an earlier year.

Requirements: Morehouse requires applicants to be in the upper 50% of their class. A minimum GPA of 2.0 is required. Minimum SAT I composite scores of 950 are required; the ACT is accepted. In addition, applicants should be graduates of accredited secondary schools or have the GED. Secondary preparation should include 4 units in English, 3 in mathematics, 2 each in natural and social sciences, and 5 in other disciplines. Applicants must write an essay and are urged to seek an interview. AP and CLEP credits are accepted. Important factors used in the admissions decision are advanced placement or honor courses, leadership record, recommendations by school officials, evidence of special talent, and extracurricular activities record.

Procedure: Freshmen are admitted to all sessions. Entrance exams should be taken by fall of the senior year. Early decision applications should be filed by February 15; regular applications, by February 15 for fall entry, October 15 for spring entry, and June 1 for summer entry, along with an application fee of $35. Notification is sent on a rolling basis. There are early decision, early admissions, and deferred admissions plans. Five hundred early decision candidates were accepted for an earlier class. A waiting list is an active part of the admissions procedure, with about 15% of applicants on the list.

Transfer: About 140 transfer students enrolled in a recent year. Transfer applicants must have at least a 2.5 GPA and have earned a minimum of 26 semester hours of credit. A total of 64 semester hours out of 124 must be completed at Morehouse.

Visiting: There are regularly scheduled orientations for prospective students. There are guides for informal visits and visitors may sit in on classes. To arrange for a visit, contact the Admissions Office at (404) 215-2632.

Financial Aid: In a recent year, 70% of all students received some form of financial aid. Scholarships or need-based grants averaged $4500 ($8500 maximum). Twenty-one percent of undergraduate students work part-time. Average earnings from campus work for the school year are $1500. The average financial indebtedness of an earlier graduate was $12,000. Morehouse is a member of CSS. The FAF and the college's own financial statement are required. The deadline for financial aid applications is April 1.

International Students: There are currently 75 international students enrolled. The school actively recruits these students. They must take the TOEFL and achieve a minimum score of 500. The student must also take the SAT I.

Computers: The college provides computer facilities for student use. The mainframe is a DEC VAX. Microcomputers are available for student use. All students may access the system. There are no fees.

Graduates: In a recent year, 327 bachelor's degrees were awarded. Some 360 companies recruited on campus. In an earlier graduating class, 38% of the men were enrolled in graduate school within 6 months of graduation; 49% of the men had found employment.

Admissions Contact: Sterling H. Hudson III, Director of Admissions.

MORRIS BROWN COLLEGE

B-2

Atlanta, GA 30314   (404) 220-0270, ext. 152/375

Full-time: 772 men, 1025 women	Faculty: 93
Part-time: 25 men, 36 women	Ph.D.s: 53%
Graduate: none	Student/Faculty: 19 to 1
Year: semesters	Tuition: $7796
Application Deadline: August 15	Room & Board: $4438
Freshman Class: 1877 enrolled	
SAT I or ACT: required	NONCOMPETITIVE

Morris Brown College, founded in 1881, is a private institution affiliated with the African Methodist Episcopal Church and offering degrees in the arts and sciences, engineering, health science, music, business administration, and education. There are 4 undergraduate and 2 graduate schools. In addition to regional accreditation, Morris Brown has baccalaureate program accreditation with NLN. The library contains 56,000 volumes. Computerized library sources and services include the card catalog and database searching. Special learning facilities include a learning resource center, an art gallery, and Herndon Home, a museum. The 18-acre campus is in an urban area 1 mile northwest of downtown Atlanta. Including residence halls, there are 13 buildings on campus.

Student Life: About 52% of undergraduates are from out-of-state, mostly the South. Students come from 38 states and 26 foreign countries. Ninety-five percent are from public schools; 5% from private. Seventy-nine percent are African American; 20% Asian American. Seventy percent are Protestant; 15% claim no religious affiliation; 15% are Catholic. The average age of freshmen is 17; all undergraduates, 20. About 29% of freshmen remain to graduate.

Housing: A total of 900 students can be accommodated in college housing. College-sponsored living facilities include single-sex dormitories and off-campus apartments. In addition, there are special interest houses. On-campus housing is guaranteed for the freshman year only and is available on a first-come, first-served basis. Fifty percent of students live on campus; of those, 95% remain on campus on weekends. Alcohol is not permitted. All students may keep cars on campus.

Activities: There are 4 local fraternities and 5 local and 3 national sororities. There are 20 groups on campus, including art, band, cheerleading, chess, choir, chorus, computers, dance, drama, ethnic, film, honors, international, jazz band, marching band, newspaper, photography, political, professional, radio and TV, religious, social, social service, student government, and yearbook. Popular campus events include Homecoming, Dr. Martin Luther King Jr.'s birthday, Honors Convocation, Black History Week, and Religious Emphasis Week.

Sports: There are 2 intercollegiate sports each for men and women, and 7 intramural sports for men and 6 for women. Athletic and recreation facilities include a weight room, a swimming pool, a gymnasium, and billiards tables, with use of YWCA facilities available.

Disabled Students: Ninety-five percent of the campus is accessible to disabled students. The following facilities are available: wheelchair ramps, elevators, and special parking.

Services: In addition to many counseling and information services, tutoring is available in some subjects, including mathematics and science. Reader equipment is available. There is also remedial math, reading, and writing.

Campus Safety and Security: Campus safety and security measures include 24-hour foot and vehicle patrol, escort service, shuttle buses, and pamphlets, posters, and films. In addition, there are emergency telephones and lighted pathways and sidewalks.

Programs of Study: Morris Brown awards the B.A. and B.S. degrees. Bachelor's degrees are awarded in BIOLOGICAL SCIENCE (biology/biological science), BUSINESS (business administration and management, business economics, and marketing/retailing/merchandising), COMMUNICATIONS AND THE ARTS (communications, English, fine arts, and music), COMPUTER AND PHYSICAL SCIENCE (chemistry, computer programming, computer science, mathematics, and physics), EDUCATION (art, business, early childhood, elementary, foreign languages, and music), ENGINEERING AND ENVIRONMENTAL DESIGN (architectural engineering, chemical engineering, civil engineering, computer engineering, electrical/electronics engineering, engineering, industrial engineering, and mechanical engineering), HEALTH PROFESSIONS (medical laboratory technology, nursing, and premedicine), SOCIAL SCIENCE (criminal justice, economics, history, philosophy, political science/government, prelaw, psychology, religion, social science, and sociology). Business administration, biology, education, and criminology are the strongest academically and have the largest enrollments.

Required: Students must complete at least 124 credit hours, including 24 or more in the major, with a minimum GPA of 2.0 and must pass the junior English qualifying writing exam. There are core requirements in English, foreign language, mathematics, natural science, and social sciences.

Special: Students may earn a 3-2 engineering degree with Georgia Institute of Technology. Internships, work-study programs, a general studies degree, dual majors in engineering and architecture, and a B.A.-B.S. degree program are available. Morris Brown is part of the Atlanta University Center, which also includes the Interdenomination-

al Theological Center, Clark Atlanta University, and Morehouse and Spelman colleges, making this the largest consortium of black colleges in the world. Cross-registration is offered with several of these institutions and with members of the University Center in Georgia. There is a freshman honors program on campus

Faculty/Classroom: Sixty-three percent of faculty are male; 37%, female.

Requirements: The SAT I or ACT is required. Graduation from an accredited secondary school is required; the GED is accepted. Students must have completed 21 Carnegie units, including 4 in English, 1 in a foreign language, at least 1 in art, and at least 2 each in mathematics, science, and social studies. An essay is recommended. AP and CLEP credits are accepted. Important factors used in the admissions decision are ability to finance college education, leadership record, parents or siblings attending the school, personality, intangible qualities, and evidence of special talent.

Procedure: Freshmen are admitted fall and spring. Entrance exams should be taken in November of the senior year. Applications should be filed by August 15 for fall entry and December 1 for spring entry, along with an application fee of $20. The college accepts all applicants. Notification is sent on a rolling basis. There is an early admissions plan.

Transfer: Transfer applicants must submit transcripts from high school and colleges attended, and have a composite score of 700 on the SAT I or 14 on the ACT and a minimum GPA of 2.0. A physical examination is also required.

Visiting: There are regularly scheduled orientations for prospective students. There are guides for informal visits and visitors may sit in on classes. To arrange for a visit, contact the Office of Admissions at (404) 220–0369.

Financial Aid: In an earlier year, 98% of all students received some form of financial aid. Eighteen percent of undergraduate students work part-time. Morris Brown is a member of CSS. The FAF, the college's own financial statement, and income tax information are required. The deadline for financial aid applications is May 15.

International Students: There are currently 245 international students enrolled. The school actively recruits these students. They must take the TOEFL, the University of Michigan Language Test, the Comprehensive English Language Test, or the college's own English test. The student must also take the college's entrance exam.

Computers: The college provides computer facilities for student use. The mainframe is an IBM. PCs are also available. All students may access the system. There are no time limits on using the system and no fees.

Graduates: In an earlier class, 101 bachelor's degrees were awarded.

Admissions Contact: Tyrone P. Fletcher, Director of Admissions.

NORTH GEORGIA COLLEGE

B-1

Dahlonega, GA 30597 (706) 864–1800

Full-time: 835 men, 1275 women	Faculty: IIA, --$
Part-time: 138 men, 291 women	Ph.D.s: 59%
Graduate: 74 men, 285 women	Student/Faculty: 14 to 1
Year: quarters	Tuition: $1381 ($4144)
Application Deadline: September 1	Room & Board: $2460
Freshman Class: 1824 applied, 1359 accepted, 482 enrolled	
SAT I Verbal/Math: 437/475	LESS COMPETITIVE

North Georgia College, founded in 1873 as a military college, is today a military, liberal arts, and teacher's college that is part of the public university system of Georgia. One of 4 colleges in the United States classified as military colleges by the Department of the Army, the school requires all male resident students to join its ROTC Program, called the Corps of Cadets; other students are given an option to join. There is one graduate school. In addition to regional accreditation, North Georgia has baccalaureate program accreditation with NCATE and NLN. The library contains 109,341 volumes, 419,412 microform items, and 1035 audiovisual forms, and subscribes to 853 periodicals. Computerized library sources and services include the card catalog and database searching. Special learning facilities include an art gallery, planetarium, and a mathematics laboratory. The 255-acre campus is in a small town 60 miles north of Atlanta. Including residence halls, there are 25 buildings on campus.

Student Life: About 96% of undergraduates are from Georgia. Students come from 13 states and 5 foreign countries. Some 97% are white. The average age of freshmen is 19; all undergraduates, 21. About 20% drop out by the end of their first year; 40% remain to graduate.

Housing: A total of 1200 students can be accommodated in college housing. College-sponsored living facilities include single-sex dormitories. On-campus housing is available on a first-come, first-served basis. About 52% of students live on campus; of those, 40% remain on campus on weekends. Alcohol is not permitted. All students may keep cars on campus.

Activities: About 20% of men belong to 2 local and 3 national fraternities; about 23% of women belong to 4 national sororities. There are 52 groups on campus, including band, cheerleading, choir, chorale, chorus, drama, drill team, ethnic, honors, marching band, newspa-

per, pep band, political, professional, religious, student government, and yearbook. Popular campus events include Spring Jam, frisbee golf, Gold Rush, and formal dances.

Sports: There are 5 intercollegiate sports for men and 6 for women, and 7 intramural sports for men and 7 for women. Athletic and recreation facilities include a pool, track, fully equipped exercise room, rappel tower, confidence course, picnic area, 2000-seat gymnasium and 250-seat arena.

Disabled Students: About 50% of the campus is accessible to disabled students. The following facilities are available: wheelchair ramps, elevators, special parking, and specially equipped rest rooms.

Services: In addition to many counseling and information services, tutoring is available in some subjects. There is also remedial math, reading, and writing.

Campus Safety and Security: Campus safety and security measures include 24-hour foot and vehicle patrol, escort service, and emergency telephones.

Programs of Study: North Georgia awards the B.A., B.S., B.B.A., and B.S.N. degrees. Associate and master's degrees also are awarded. Bachelor's degrees are awarded in BIOLOGICAL SCIENCE (biology/biological science), BUSINESS (accounting, banking and finance, business administration and management, business economics, and marketing/retailing/merchandising), COMMUNICATIONS AND THE ARTS (English, fine arts, and languages), COMPUTER AND PHYSICAL SCIENCE (chemistry, computer science, mathematics, and physics), EDUCATION (art, business, early childhood, elementary, foreign languages, middle school, music, science, secondary, and special), HEALTH PROFESSIONS (nursing, predentistry, and premedicine), SOCIAL SCIENCE (criminal justice, history, political science/government, prelaw, psychology, social work, and sociology). Premedicine and nursing are the strongest programs academically. Business and teacher education have the largest enrollments.

Required: To graduate, students must complete 185 quarter credit hours with a minimum GPA of 2.0. English, mathematics, laboratory sciences, social sciences, and physical education courses are required.

Special: Special academic programs include a co-op program in business, internships in business and criminal justice, a 3–2 engineering degree with Georgia Institute of Technology, and credit for life, military, or work experience. There is a chapter of Phi Beta Kappa on campus.

Faculty/Classroom: All teach undergraduates. Graduate students teach 5% of introductory courses. The average class size in an introductory lecture, a laboratory, and in a regular course offering, is 30.

Admissions: About 75% of the 1993–94 applicants were accepted.

Requirements: The SAT I is required. Students must have graduated from a secondary school with 4 years of English, 3 each of mathematics, science, and social studies, and 2 of a foreign language. The GED is accepted as are AP and CLEP credits. Important factors used in the admissions decision are leadership record, advanced placement or honor courses, and recommendations by school officials.

Procedure: Freshmen are admitted to all sessions. Entrance exams should be taken in the junior year. Applications should be filed by September 1 for fall entry, December 1 for winter entry, March 1 for spring entry, and June 1 for summer entry, along with an application fee of $10. Notification is sent on a rolling basis. There are early admissions and deferred admissions plans. A waiting list is an active part of the admissions procedure, with about 40% of applicants on the list.

Transfer: About 406 transfer students enrolled in an earlier year. Transfer students must have maintained a C average and a clear conduct record, and be in good academic standing. Those who have not completed 90 quarter hours of transferable credit must have completed the approved precollege curriculum; high school transcripts and SAT I or ACT results are required of such transfers. A total of 45 quarter credits out of 185 must be completed at North Georgia.

Visiting: There are regularly scheduled orientations for prospective students. There are guides for informal visits and visitors may sit in on classes and stay overnight at the school. To arrange for a visit, contact the Admissions Office at (706) 864–1800.

Financial Aid: In an earlier year, 65% of all current freshmen and 55% of continuing students received some form of financial aid. Scholarships or need-based grants averaged $2000 ($5000 maximum); loans averaged $1700 ($2625 maximum); and work contracts averaged $1500 ($1500 maximum). Some 20% of undergraduate students work part-time. The average financial indebtedness of an earlier graduate was $2000. North Georgia is a member of CSS. The FAF, the college's own financial statement, and tax returns are required.

International Students: There are currently 12 international students enrolled. They must take the TOEFL and achieve a minimum score of 500. The student must also take the SAT I or the ACT.

Computers: The college provides computer facilities for student use. There are 43 IBM PCs, XTs, or Model 25s available in the education building. Students enrolled in computer courses may access the system. There are no time limits on using the system and no fees.

Graduates: In an earlier year, 354 bachelor's degrees were awarded.

Admissions Contact: Bill Smith, Director of Student Recruiting.

OGLETHORPE UNIVERSITY
Atlanta, GA 30319-2797

B-2

(404) 364-8307
(800) 428-4484 (out-of-state)

Full-time: 314 men, 446 women
Part-time: 103 men, 285 women
Graduate: 5 men, 62 women
Year: semesters, summer session
Application Deadline: August 1
Freshman Class: 792 applied, 648 accepted, 186 enrolled
SAT I: 549/570

Faculty: 44; IIB, +$
Ph.D.s: 95%
Student/Faculty: 17 to 1
Tuition: $12,030
Room & Board: $4330

ACT: 27   **VERY COMPETITIVE**

Oglethorpe University, founded in 1835, is an independent, coeducational institution offering programs in the liberal arts, business, and teacher preparation. There is one graduate school. In addition to regional accreditation, Oglethorpe has baccalaureate program accreditation with NCATE. The library contains 101,000 volumes and 2200 audiovisual forms and subscribes to 760 periodicals. Computerized library sources and services include the card catalog and database searching. Special learning facilities include a learning resource center and art gallery. The 118-acre campus is in an urban area 10 miles northeast of downtown Atlanta. Including residence halls, there are 13 buildings on campus.

Student Life: About 62% of undergraduates are from Georgia. Students come from 27 states and 28 foreign countries. Eighty-two percent are from public schools; 18% from private. Eighty-one percent are white. Forty-three percent are Protestant; 26% claim no religious affiliation; 14% Catholic. The average age of freshmen is 18; all undergraduates, 21. Seventeen percent drop out by the end of their first year; 65% remain to graduate.

Housing: A total of 470 students can be accommodated in college housing. College-sponsored living facilities include single-sex and coed dormitories, fraternity houses, and sorority houses. On-campus housing is available on a first-come, first-served basis. Priority is given to out-of-town students. Sixty-six percent of students live on campus; of those, 50% remain on campus on weekends. All students may keep cars on campus.

Activities: About 41% of men belong to 4 national fraternities; about 22% of women belong to 2 national sororities. There are 60 groups on campus, including art, cheerleading, choir, chorale, chorus, computers, dance, drama, ethnic, gay, honors, international, literary magazine, newspaper, pep band, photography, political, professional, religious, social, social service, student government, and yearbook. Popular campus events include Boar's Head Ceremony, Oglethorpe Day, International Night, and Night of the Arts.

Sports: There are 6 intercollegiate sports for men and 6 for women, and 5 intramural sports for men and 5 for women. Athletic and recreation facilities include a field house, 8 tennis courts, soccer, baseball, and intramural fields, an all-weather track, and an outdoor pool.

Disabled Students: Ninety percent of the campus is accessible to disabled students. The following facilities are available: wheelchair ramps, elevators, special parking, specially equipped rest rooms, and special class scheduling.

Services: In addition to many counseling and information services, tutoring is available in some subjects, including English, accounting, and computer science. Additional tutoring is available through the Academic Resource Center in all core curriculum courses.

Campus Safety and Security: Campus safety and security measures include 24-hour foot and vehicle patrol, self defense education, informal discussions, and pamphlets, posters, and films. In addition, there are lighted pathways and sidewalks.

Programs of Study: Oglethorpe awards the B.A., B.S., and B.B.A degrees. Master's degrees also are awarded. Bachelor's degrees are awarded in BIOLOGICAL SCIENCE (biology/biological science), BUSINESS (accounting and business administration and management), COMMUNICATIONS AND THE ARTS (communications and English), COMPUTER AND PHYSICAL SCIENCE (chemistry, computer science, mathematics, and physics), EDUCATION (early childhood, middle school, and secondary), HEALTH PROFESSIONS (medical laboratory technology, predentistry, premedicine, and prepharmacy), SOCIAL SCIENCE (American studies, behavioral science, economics, history, international studies, philosophy, prelaw, psychology, social work, and sociology). Premedicine, accounting, writing, and biology are the strongest academically. Business administration, biology, education, accounting, English, and psychology have the largest enrollments.

Required: In order to graduate, students must complete at least 120 credit hours, maintain a minimum GPA of 2.0, and take a comprehensive exam. The core curriculum includes course work in writing, literature, Western civilization, mathematics or computer science, psychology, philosophy, interdisciplinary social sciences, music or art, physical science, biological science, and a freshman seminar.

Special: Oglethorpe offers co-op programs in all majors and cross-registration with the University Center in Georgia and Seigakuin University in Tokyo. Internships are available in all areas of study, and study abroad is possible in many countries. A Washington semester offers internships with Georgia senators and others. There is a dual-degree program with the Atlanta College of Art and a 3-2 engineering program with Georgia Institute of Technology, the University of Florida, the University of Southern California, and Auburn University. Accelerated degrees, dual majors, student-designed majors, federal work-study programs, and nondegree study are offered. There are 7 national honor societies on campus.

Faculty/Classroom: Seventy percent of faculty are male; 30%, female. All teach undergraduates. No introductory courses are taught by graduate students. The average class size in an introductory lecture is 23; in a laboratory, 20; and in a regular course offering, 17.

Admissions: About 82% of the 1993-94 applicants were accepted. The SAT scores for the 1993-94 freshman class were as follows: Verbal—28% below 500, 46% between 500 and 599, 25% between 600 and 700, and 1% above 700; Math—18% below 500, 44% between 500 and 599, 31% between 600 and 700, and 7% above 700. The ACT scores were 4% below 21, 16% between 21 and 23, 27% between 24 and 26, 19% between 27 and 28, and 34% above 28. About 77% of the current freshmen were in the top fifth of their class; 93% were in the top two fifths. There were 3 National Merit finalists and 8 semifinalists. Nine freshmen graduated first in their class.

Requirements: A minimum GPA of 2.8 is required. The SAT I, with a minimum recommended composite score of 950, or the ACT, with a minimum recommended composite score of 21, is required. Students should graduate from an accredited high school or have a GED certificate. They should have completed 4 courses in English, 3 each in science and social studies, and a mathematics sequence of algebra I and II and geometry. A counselor's recommendation is required, and an essay is required for a scholarship. An interview is recommended. AP and CLEP credits are accepted. Important factors used in the admissions decision are recommendations by school officials, extracurricular activities record, geographic diversity, evidence of special talent, and advanced placement or honor courses.

Procedure: Freshmen are admitted to all sessions. Entrance exams should be taken late in the junior year or early in the senior year. Early decision applications should be filed by December 1; regular applications, by August 1 for fall entry and January 7 for spring entry, along with an application fee of $25. Notification of early decision is sent December 13; regular decision, February 1. There are early decision, early admissions, and deferred admissions plans. About 51 early decision candidates were accepted for the 1993-94 class.

Transfer: About 57 transfer students enrolled in 1993-94. Applicants who have completed less than a full year of college work must take the SAT I or ACT. All transfers must be in good academic standing with a minimum GPA of 2.5. An interview is recommended. A total of 60 credits out of 120 must be completed at Oglethorpe.

Visiting: There are regularly scheduled orientations for prospective students, including placement tests, class registration, an activities fair, and group activities. There are guides for informal visits and visitors may sit in on classes and stay overnight at the school. To arrange for a visit, contact the Admissions Office at (404) 364-8307 or (800) 428-4484.

Financial Aid: In 1993-94 90% of all current freshmen and 83% of continuing students received some form of financial aid. About 65% of freshmen and 56% of continuing students received need-based aid. The average freshman award was $14,044. Of that total, scholarships or need-based grants averaged $8643 ($16,320 maximum); loans averaged $5842 ($10,847 maximum); and work contracts averaged $1188 ($1200 maximum). Forty-two percent of undergraduate students work part-time. Average earnings from campus work for the school year are $913. The average financial indebtedness of the 1992-93 graduate was $11,193. Oglethorpe is a member of CSS. The FAFSA financial statement is required. The deadline for financial aid applications is May 1.

International Students: There are currently 53 international students enrolled. The school actively recruits these students. They must take the TOEFL and achieve a minimum score of 500.

Computers: The college provides computer facilities for student use. There are 25 IBM-compatible PCs available in the computer laboratory. In addition, 20 PCs, a server machine, and a local area network (LAN) are available in the science area. All students may access the system. There are no time limits on using the system and no fees.

Graduates: In 1992-93 186 bachelor's degrees were awarded. The most popular majors among graduates were history (12%), accounting (11%), and early childhood education (8%). Within an average freshman class, 2% graduate in 3 years, 56% in 4 years, and 73% in 5 years. Some 20 companies recruited on campus in 1992-93. In the 1992 graduating class, 30% of the graduates were enrolled in graduate school within 6 months of graduation and 60% had found employment.

Admissions Contact: Dennis Mathews, Director of Admissions.

PAINE COLLEGE
D-2

Augusta, GA 30901-3182
(706) 821-8320
(800) 476-7703 (out-of-state)

Full-time: 186 men, 444 women	Faculty: 57; IIB, --$
Part-time: 38 men, 55 women	Ph.D.s: 47%
Graduate: none	Student/Faculty: 11 to 1
Year: semesters, summer session	Tuition: $5468
Application Deadline: July 15	Room & Board: $2739
Freshman Class: 1451 applied, 707 accepted, 232 enrolled	
SAT I Verbal/Math: 340/342	ACT: 17 LESS COMPETITIVE

Paine College, founded in 1882, is a largely black private institution affiliated with the Christian Methodist Episcopal Church and the United Methodist Church. It offers programs in liberal arts, business, and teacher preparation. The library contains 88,259 volumes, 10,172 microform items, and 1098 audiovisual forms, and subscribes to 460 periodicals. Computerized library sources and services include interlibrary loans and database searching. Special learning facilities include a learning resource center. The 54-acre campus is in an urban area. Including residence halls, there are 24 buildings on campus.

Student Life: About 78% of undergraduates are from Georgia. Students come from 21 states and 2 foreign countries. Ninety-nine percent are African American. Most are Protestant.

Housing: A total of 506 students can be accommodated in college housing. College-sponsored living facilities include single-sex dormitories. On-campus housing is guaranteed for all 4 years. Sixty-three percent of students live on campus; of those, 15% remain on campus on weekends. Alcohol is not permitted. All students may keep cars on campus.

Activities: About 10% of men belong to 4 national fraternities; about 10% of women belong to 5 national sororities. There are 15 groups on campus, including cheerleading, choir, chorus, computers, drama, ethnic, honors, international, newspaper, professional, religious, social, student government, and yearbook. Popular campus events include Homecoming, Miss Paine Coronation, Founders Day, and black history activities.

Sports: There are 4 intercollegiate sports for men and 5 for women, and 7 intramural sports each for men and women. Athletic and recreation facilities include a gymnasium, a tennis court, a track, and a baseball field.

Disabled Students: Sixty percent of the campus is accessible to disabled students. The following facilities are available: wheelchair ramps, elevators, special parking, specially equipped rest rooms, and lowered drinking fountains.

Services: In addition to many counseling and information services, tutoring is available in most subjects. There is also remedial math, reading, and writing.

Campus Safety and Security: Campus safety and security measures include 24-hour foot and vehicle patrol, informal discussions, pamphlets, posters, and lighted pathways and sidewalks.

Programs of Study: Paine awards the B.A. and B.S. degrees. Bachelor's degrees are awarded in BIOLOGICAL SCIENCE (biology/biological science), BUSINESS (business administration and management), COMMUNICATIONS AND THE ARTS (communications and English), COMPUTER AND PHYSICAL SCIENCE (chemistry and mathematics), EDUCATION (early childhood, middle school, and music), SOCIAL SCIENCE (history, philosophy, psychology, and sociology). Business has the largest enrollment.

Required: Common curriculum requirements include 18 hours in world citizenship/society, 14 in science/technology, 8 to 10 in fundamentals, 9 in spiritual and social values, and 6 in the aesthetic heritage. From 33 to 71 hours are required in the major. A minimum GPA of 2.0. in the major is needed. In order to graduate, at least 124 credits must be completed. A thesis in most programs and comprehensive exams in some programs may also be required.

Special: Paine has co-op programs in natural and social sciences and business administration, cross-registration with Augusta College, internships for business administration and sociology majors, and study abroad in France. A 3-2 engineering degree is offered with Georgia Institute of Technology and Florida Agricultural and Mechanical University. There are transfer programs with the Medical University of South Carolina at Charleston School of Nursing and Medical College of Georgia. There is a freshman honors program on campus, as well as one national honor society.

Faculty/Classroom: Fifty-three percent of faculty are male; 47%, female. All teach undergraduates. The average class size in an introductory lecture is 25; in a laboratory, 20; and in a regular course offering, 23.

Admissions: About 49% of the 1993-94 applicants were accepted. The SAT scores for the 1993-94 freshman class were as follows: Verbal—96% below 500, 3% between 500 and 599, and 1% between 600 and 700; Math—89% below 500, 9% between 500 and 599, and 2% between 600 and 700.

Requirements: A minimum GPA of 2.0 is required. The SAT I or ACT is required. Applicants should be graduates of an accredited secondary school or have a GED. A total of 15 academic credits is required, including 4 units of English, 2 each of mathematics and social studies, and 1 of science. AP and CLEP credits are accepted. Impor-

tant factors used in the admissions decision are recommendations by school officials, advanced placement or honor courses, evidence of special talent, extracurricular activities record, and leadership record.

Procedure: Freshmen are admitted to all sessions. Entrance exams should be taken during spring and summer testing sessions; they are also offered during each orientation period. Applications should be filed by July 15 for fall entry, December 1 for spring entry, and May 1 for summer entry, along with an application fee of $10. Notification is sent on a rolling basis. There are early admissions and deferred admissions plans.

Transfer: About 21 transfer students enrolled in 1993-94. Transfer applicants must meet freshmen criteria except for the SAT I requirement.

Visiting: There are regularly scheduled orientations for prospective students, including meetings with administrators, tours of the city and campus, and placement testing. There are guides for informal visits and visitors may sit in on classes and stay overnight at the school. To arrange for a visit, contact Mr. Terry McMullen, Director of Admission at (706) 821-8320.

Financial Aid: In a recent year, about 93% of all students received some form of financial aid and 48% of freshmen and 73% of continuing students received need-based aid. Average earnings from campus work for that year were $2000. Paine is a member of CSS. The FAF and the college's own financial statement are required. The deadline for financial aid applications is March 1.

International Students: There are currently 20 international students enrolled. The school actively recruits these students. They must take the TOEFL and achieve a minimum score of 500. The student must also take the SAT I or the ACT.

Computers: The college provides computer facilities for student use. There is a Compaq supermicrocomputer on a Novell network available for students use. There are 125 IBM PC or compatible Apple Macintosh and Apple IIe microcomputers in three main laboratories in the Learning Resource Center, one science laboratory, the Tutorial and Enrichment Center, and some faculty offices. All students may access the system. There are no time limits and no fees.

Graduates: In 1992-93, 50 bachelor's degrees were awarded. The most popular majors among graduates were biology (16%), English, business administration, and early childhood Education (14%), and sociology (12%).

Admissions Contact: Mr. Terry McMullen, Director of Admission.

PIEDMONT COLLEGE
C-1

Demorest, GA 30535 (706) 778-8500; (800) 277-7020 (out-of-state)

Full-time: 268 men, 373 women	Faculty: 43
Part-time: 21 men, 42 women	Ph.D.s: 79%
Graduate: none	Student/Faculty: 15 to 1
Year: semesters, summer session	Tuition: $4920
Application Deadline: July 1	Room & Board: $3620
Freshman Class: 663 applied, 562 accepted, 266 enrolled	
SAT I Verbal/Math: 452/499	LESS COMPETITIVE

Piedmont College, founded in 1897, is a private, coeducational, liberal arts institution affiliated with the Congregational Church. In addition to regional accreditation, Piedmont has baccalaureate program accreditation with NCATE. The library contains 105,000 volumes, 9000 microform items, and 368 audiovisual forms, and subscribes to 442 periodicals. Computerized library sources and services include interlibrary loans and database searching. Special learning facilities include an art gallery and radio station. The 300-acre campus is in a small town 75 miles northeast of Atlanta. Including residence halls, there are 16 buildings on campus.

Student Life: About 85% of undergraduates are from Georgia. Students come from 20 states and 9 foreign countries. Ninety-two percent are white. The average age of freshmen is 19; all undergraduates, 26.3. Forty-five percent drop out by the end of their first year; 24% remain to graduate.

Housing: A total of 320 students can be accommodated in college housing. College-sponsored living facilities include single-sex and coed dormitories, on-campus apartments, and married-student housing. On-campus housing is guaranteed for the freshman year only and is available on a first-come, first-served basis. Priority is given to out-of-town students. Seventy percent of students commute. Alcohol is not permitted. All students may keep cars on campus.

Activities: About 1% of men belong to 1 local fraternity; about 5% of women belong to 1 local sorority. There are 22 groups on campus, including art, cheerleading, chess, choir, chorale, chorus, computers, drama, honors, international, literary magazine, musical theater, newspaper, political, professional, radio and TV, religious, social, social service, student government, and yearbook. Popular campus events include Homecoming, Halloween Dance, Spring Formal Dinner, the Lyceum series, and theme nights.

Sports: There are 6 intercollegiate sports for men and 6 for women, and 8 intramural sports for men and 8 for women. Athletic and recreation facilities include a gymnasium, a golf course, tennis courts, playing fields, and a student center.

Disabled Students: Eighty percent of the campus is accessible to disabled students. The following facilities are available: wheelchair ramps, elevators, special parking, specially equipped rest rooms, special class scheduling, and lowered telephones.

Services: In addition to many counseling and information services, tutoring is available in every subject. In addition, there is remedial math, reading, and writing.

Campus Safety and Security: Campus safety and security measures include self defense education, informal discussions, lighted pathways and sidewalks, and campus patrol by the local police department.

Programs of Study: Piedmont awards the B.A. and B.S. degrees. Bachelor's degrees are awarded in BIOLOGICAL SCIENCE (biology/biological science), BUSINESS (accounting, business administration and management, and business economics), COMMUNICATIONS AND THE ARTS (art history and appreciation, English, fine arts, music, and Spanish), COMPUTER AND PHYSICAL SCIENCE (chemistry, information sciences and systems, and mathematics), EDUCATION (art, early childhood, foreign languages, middle school, music, and special), SOCIAL SCIENCE (economics, history, psychology, and sociology). Biology, education, and art are the strongest academically. Business administration has the largest enrollment.

Required: A minimum of 124 credit hours must be completed for graduation, with a minimum GPA of 2.0. In some majors the minimum GPA requirement is higher. Students must complete 27 to 36 credit hours in their major, 26 in humanities, 12 in social science, 14 to 15 in natural science, and a semester course in Piedmont Studies, as well as pass an English proficiency exam.

Special: Piedmont offers work-study programs and internships in business, psychology, and art management. There is a 3–2 nursing degree program with Emory University. Credit by exam is given for the foreign language requirement. There is a freshman honors program on campus, as well as 2 national honor societies. One department has an honors program.

Faculty/Classroom: Sixty-four percent of faculty are male; 36%, female. All teach undergraduates. The average class size in an introductory lecture is 20; in a laboratory, 16; and in a regular course offering, 15.

Admissions: About 85% of the 1993–94 applicants were accepted. The SAT scores for the 1993–94 freshman class were as follows: Verbal—81% below 500, 16% between 500 and 599, and 3% between 600 and 700; Math—71% below 500, 21% between 500 and 599, and 8% between 600 and 700.

Requirements: A minimum GPA of 2.0 is required. The SAT I (preferred) or ACT is required. Applicants must be graduates of an accredited secondary school or have a GED certificate. Students must have completed a minimum of 21 academic units. Piedmont Scholars are required to submit an essay. A portfolio is required for art scholarship applicants and an audition for music scholarship applicants. An interview is recommended for all students. AP and CLEP credits are accepted. Important factors used in the admissions decision are advanced placement or honor courses, evidence of special talent, recommendations by school officials, leadership record, and extracurricular activities record.

Procedure: Freshmen are admitted to all sessions. Applications should be filed by July 1 for fall entry and December 1 for spring entry, along with an application fee of $20. Notification is sent on a rolling basis. There is a deferred admissions plan.

Transfer: About 89 transfer students enrolled in 1993–94. Applicants must have a GPA of 2.0 at each institution attended. An interview is recommended. A total of 90 credits out of 124 must be completed at Piedmont.

Visiting: There are regularly scheduled orientations for prospective students, including student activities, academic assistance, and resident orientation. There are guides for informal visits and visitors may sit in on classes and stay overnight at the school. To arrange for a visit, contact the Admissions Office at (800) 277-7020.

Financial Aid: In 1993–94 95% of all students received some form of financial aid. About 62% of freshmen and 70% of continuing students received need-based aid. The average freshman award was $5275. Of that total, scholarships or need-based grants averaged $1250 ($1880 maximum); loans averaged $1400 ($2625 maximum); and work contracts averaged $1200 ($2000 maximum). Seventy-one percent of undergraduate students work part-time. Average earnings from campus work for the school year are $1200. The average financial indebtedness of the 1992–93 graduate was $6800. Piedmont is a member of CSS. The FAFSA financial statement is required. The deadline for financial aid applications is July 1.

International Students: There are currently 13 international students enrolled. The school actively recruits these students. They must take the TOEFL and achieve a minimum score of 500.

Computers: The college provides computer facilities for student use. In addition to PC and Macintosh laboratories, there are 4 computer terminals that can connect to the network system. All students may access the system. It may be used 8 A.M. to midnight, Monday through Thursday, 8 A.M. to 5 P.M. on Friday, 1 P.M. to 4 P.M. and 6 P.M. to 10 P.M. on Saturday, and 1 P.M. to midnight on Sunday. There are no time limits on using the system and no fees.

Graduates: In 1992–93 115 bachelor's degrees were awarded. The most popular majors among graduates were business administration (36%), education (26%), and history (13%). Within an average freshman class, 5% graduate in 3 years, 24% in 4 years, 29% in 5 years, and 28% in 6 years. Some 15 companies recruited on campus in 1992–93. In the 1992 graduating class, 90% of the men and 85% of the women had found employment within 6 months of graduation.

Admissions Contact: Penny L. Graber, Director of Admissions.

SAVANNAH COLLEGE OF ART AND DESIGN E-4
Savannah, GA 31401 (912) 238-2483

Full-time: 1058 men, 790 women	Faculty: 126
Part-time: 108 men, 100 women	Ph.Ds: 98%
Graduate: 105 men, 120 women	Student/Faculty: 15 to 1
Year: quarters, summer session	Tuition: $9180
Application Deadline: open	Room & Board: $5100
Freshman Class: 1199 applied, 623 accepted, 386 enrolled	
SAT I Verbal/Math: 470/492	ACT: 21 SPECIAL

Savannah College of Art and Design, founded in 1978, is a private, coeducational institution offering degrees in art, design, and architecture. There is one undergraduate and one graduate school. In addition to regional accreditation, SCAD has baccalaureate program accreditation with NAAB. The library contains 30,000 volumes and 600 audiovisual forms, and subscribes to 467 periodicals. Computerized library sources and services include interlibrary loans. Special learning facilities include an art gallery. The campus is in an urban area 150 miles north of Jacksonville, Florida. Including residence halls, there are 30 buildings on campus.

Student Life: About 87% of undergraduates are from out-of-state, mostly the South. Students come from 48 states, 59 foreign countries, and Canada. Seventy-eight percent are white; 10% foreign nationals. The average age of freshmen is 18; all undergraduates, 20. Thirty-five percent drop out by the end of their first year; 60% remain to graduate.

Housing: A total of 600 students can be accommodated in college housing. College-sponsored living facilities include single-sex and coed dormitories and on-campus apartments. On-campus housing is available on a first-come, first-served basis. Seventy-five percent of students commute. Alcohol is not permitted. All students may keep cars on campus.

Activities: There are no fraternities or sororities on campus. There are 27 groups on campus, including art, cheerleading, chess, computers, drama, ethnic, film, international, literary magazine, orchestra, photography, professional, radio and TV, religious, and social service. Popular campus events include Focus Week, Sidewalk Arts Festival, Fall Weekend, Beaux Arts Ball, and visitation weekends.

Sports: There are 8 intercollegiate sports each for men and women, and 8 intramural sports each for men and women.

Disabled Students: All of the campus is accessible to disabled students. The following facilities are available: Facilities vary by building, but individual situations are accommodated.

Services: In addition to many counseling and information services, tutoring is available in every subject.

Campus Safety and Security: Campus safety and security measures include 24-hour foot and vehicle patrol, self-defense education, escort service, and shuttle buses. In addition, there are informal discussions, pamphlets, posters, films, emergency telephones, lighted pathways and sidewalks, and video surveillance cameras.

Programs of Study: SCAD awards the B.Arch. and B.F.A. degrees. Master's degrees also are awarded. Bachelor's degrees are awarded in COMMUNICATIONS AND THE ARTS (art, art history and appreciation, fiber/textiles/weaving, graphic design, historic preservation, illustration, metal/jewelry, painting, photography, and video), ENGINEERING AND ENVIRONMENTAL DESIGN (architecture, computer graphics, furniture design, and interior design), SOCIAL SCIENCE (fashion design and technology). Graphic design, illustration, and architecture have the largest enrollments.

Required: For the B.Arch. degree, students need 35 quarter hours of foundation drawing/design, 60 of liberal arts, 90 in the major, and 40 in electives, for a total of 225 quarter hours. For the B.F.A. degree, students need 50 quarter hours of foundation drawing/design, 60 of liberal arts, 60 in the major, and 10 of electives, for a total of 180 quarter hours. All students must earn 10 quarter hours in computer courses. Students must maintain a 2.0 average overall and a 3.0 in the major.

Special: The college offers study abroad through 2 European programs each summer, on-campus work-study programs, dual majors in all disciplines, a B.A.-B.S. degree, sessions for credit in New York, and internships with artists, designers, museums, agencies, and architectural firms in the United States and abroad.

Faculty/Classroom: Fifty-eight percent of faculty are male; 42%, female. All teach undergraduates. No introductory courses are taught by graduate students. The average class size is 17.

Admissions: About 52% of the 1993–94 applicants were accepted. The SAT scores for the 1993–94 freshman class were as follows: Verbal—56% below 500, 29% between 500 and 599, 13% between 600 and 700, and 2% above 700; Math—47% below 500, 32% between 500 and 599, 19% between 600 and 700, and 2% above 700.

The ACT scores were 37% below 21, 22% between 21 and 23, 23% between 24 and 26, 15% between 27 and 28, and 3% above 28. About 60% of the current freshmen were in the top fifth of their class; 90% were in the top two fifths. Two freshmen graduated first in their class.

Requirements: SCAD requires applicants to be in the upper 50% of their class. A minimum GPA of 2.0 is required. The SAT I, with a recommended minimum composite score of 1000, or the ACT, with a recommended minimum composite score of 26, is required. A portfolio and an interview are recommended. Applicants must be graduates of an accredited secondary school or have a GED certificate. AP credits are accepted. Important factors used in the admissions decision are advanced placement or honor courses, evidence of special talent, leadership record, extracurricular activities record, and recommendations by school officials.

Procedure: Freshmen are admitted to all sessions. Entrance exams should be taken by November of the senior year. Application deadlines are open. Application fee is $50. Notification is sent on a rolling basis. There is an early admissions plan.

Transfer: About 220 transfer students enrolled in 1993–94. SCAD recommends that transfer applicants have a minimum GPA of 3.0, a minimum composite score of 1000 on the SAT I or 26 on the ACT, a portfolio, and an interview. A total of 90 quarter hours out of 180 to 225 must be completed at SCAD.

Visiting: There are regularly scheduled orientations for prospective students, including check-in, tours, visits with faculty from areas of interest, portfolio reviews, financial aid information, student life exhibits, workshops, and a dance. There are guides for informal visits and visitors may sit in on classes and stay overnight at the school. To arrange for a visit, contact the Director of Admissions at (912) 238–2483.

Financial Aid: In 1993–94, 60% of all current freshmen and 64% of continuing students received some form of financial aid. About 52% of freshmen and 71% of continuing students received need-based aid. The average freshman award was $1400. Of that total, scholarships or need-based grants averaged $1300 ($4000 maximum); loans averaged $2500 ($2600 maximum); and work contracts averaged $800 ($1500 maximum). Seventy-six percent of undergraduate students work part-time. Average earnings from campus work for the school year are $800. The average financial indebtedness of the 1992–93 graduate was $17,000. SCAD is a member of CSS. The FAF and a customized packet of materials are sent to each applicant interested in financial aid. The deadline for financial aid applications is July 15.

International Students: There are currently 225 international students enrolled. The school actively recruits these students. They must take the TOEFL and achieve a minimum score of 500. The student must also take the SAT I or the ACT.

Computers: The college provides computer facilities for student use. Approximately 49 Commodore Amiga, 104 Apple Macintosh, and 60 486/66 personal computers are available in computer laboratories. All students may access the system. Students may access the system at designated times. There are no fees.

Graduates: In 1992–93, 366 bachelor's degrees were awarded. The most popular majors among graduates were graphic design (28%), illustration (17%), and photography (12%). Within an average freshman class, 38% graduate in 4 years, 55% in 5 years, and 60% in 6 years. In the 1992 graduating class, 10% of all graduates were enrolled in graduate school within 6 months of graduation; 80% had found employment.

Admissions Contact: Director of Admissions.

SAVANNAH STATE COLLEGE
E-4

Savannah, GA 31404   (912) 356–2181; (800) 788–0478 (out-of-state)

Full-time: 1212 men, 1514 women	Faculty: 129
Part-time: 201 men, 271 women	Ph.D.s: 52%
Graduate: none	Student/Faculty: 21 to 1
Year: quarters, summer session	Tuition: $1742 ($4505)
Application Deadline: August 15	Room & Board: $2310
Freshman Class: 2252 applied, 1755 accepted, 871 enrolled	
SAT I or ACT: required	COMPETITIVE

Savannah State College, founded in 1890, is a liberal arts institution that is part of the University System of Georgia. Degrees are offered in business, humanities, social sciences, sciences and technology, and preprofessional programs. There are 3 undergraduate schools. In addition to regional accreditation, Savannah State has baccalaureate program accreditation with ABET, CSWE, and NCATE. The library contains 164,810 volumes and 416,050 microform items, and subscribes to 720 periodicals. Special learning facilities include a learning resource center, radio station, arts center, and laboratory nursery school and kindergarten. The 165-acre campus is in a suburban area of Savannah. Including residence halls, there are 38 buildings on campus.

Student Life: About 80% of undergraduates are from Georgia. Students come from 20 states and 18 foreign countries. Fifty percent are from public schools. Ninety-two percent are African American. The average age of freshmen is 18; all undergraduates, 22.

Housing: A total of 1260 students can be accommodated in college housing. College-sponsored living facilities include single-sex dormitories, on-campus apartments, and married-student housing. On-campus housing is available on a first-come, first-served basis. Fifty percent of students live on campus; of those, 70% remain on campus on weekends. Alcohol is not permitted. All students may keep cars on campus.

Activities: About 15% of men belong to 6 national fraternities; about 20% of women belong to 4 national sororities. There are 17 groups on campus, including band, cheerleading, choir, chorale, computers, dance, drama, ethnic, international, marching band, newspaper, professional, radio and TV, religious, student government, and yearbook. Popular campus events include drama presentations, musical programs, films, forums, a Fine Arts Festival, and Christmas and spring concerts.

Sports: There are 5 intercollegiate sports for men and 4 for women, and 1 intramural sport for men and 1 for women. Athletic and recreation facilities include a student center, a gymnasium complex, a swimming pool, a stadium, and a field house.

Disabled Students: Eighty percent of the campus is accessible to disabled students. The following facilities are available: wheelchair ramps, elevators, special parking, specially equipped rest rooms, and lowered drinking fountains.

Services: In addition to many counseling and information services, tutoring is available in every subject. There also is remedial math, reading, and writing.

Campus Safety and Security: Campus safety and security measures include 24-hour foot and vehicle patrol, informal discussions, pamphlets, posters, and films, and lighted pathways and sidewalks. The Campus Security Department is staffed with public safety officers, building attendants, security guards, safety inspectors, and telephone operators.

Programs of Study: Savannah State awards the B.A., B.S., B.B.A., and B.S.W. degrees. Associate and master's degrees also are awarded. Bachelor's degrees are awarded in BIOLOGICAL SCIENCE (biology/biological science and marine biology), BUSINESS (accounting, management information systems, and marketing/retailing/merchandising), COMMUNICATIONS AND THE ARTS (broadcasting, communications, English, and music), COMPUTER AND PHYSICAL SCIENCE (chemistry, computer science, mathematics, and physics), ENGINEERING AND ENVIRONMENTAL DESIGN (chemical engineering, civil engineering, engineering technology, environmental science, mechanical engineering, and petroleum/natural gas engineering), HEALTH PROFESSIONS (medical laboratory technology, predentistry, and premedicine). Biology, chemistry, accounting, and engineering are the strongest academically. Accounting, criminal justice, management, mass communications, social work, biology, electronic engineering technology, and computer science technology have the largest enrollments.

Required: To graduate, all students must fulfill the core curriculum requirements of 30 hours in courses appropriate to the major and 20 hours each of humanities, mathematics and science, and social science. Students must complete at least 185 quarter hours, with 45 in the major, and must maintain a minimum 2.0 GPA. Students must pass the University System of Georgia Language Skills Exam, 6 hours of physical education courses, and 3 to 5 hours of a freshman orientation course. Exit competency examinations and other requirements may apply.

Special: The college offers co-op programs, study abroad, a student exchange program with Armstrong State College, a dual degree program with Georgia Institute of Technology, the Georgia Legislative Internship Program, on- and off-campus work-study programs, correspondence study, credit for military experience, and nondegree study. There are 7 national honor societies on campus.

Faculty/Classroom: All faculty teach undergraduates. The average class size in an introductory lecture is 50 to 65; in a laboratory, 22; and in a regular course offering, 33 to 55.

Admissions: About 78% of the 1993–94 applicants were accepted. Five freshmen graduated first in their class.

Requirements: Savannah State requires applicants to be in the upper 40% of their class. A minimum GPA of 2.0 is required. The SAT I, minimum composite score 750, or the ACT, minimum composite score 19, is required. In addition, applicants must be graduates of an accredited secondary school or have a GED certificate. Students should have completed 4 units of English, 3 each of mathematics, science, and social science, and 2 of the same foreign language. AP and CLEP credits are accepted.

Procedure: Freshmen are admitted to all sessions. Entrance exams should be taken early in the senior year. Applications should be filed by August 15 for fall entry, November 15 for winter entry, February 15 for spring entry, and May 15 for summer entry, along with an application fee of $10. There are early admissions and deferred admissions plans.

Transfer: A total of 94 transfer students enrolled in 1993–94. Applicants with at least 45 hours of core curriculum credit do not need to submit high school transcripts. A total of 45 quarter hours out of 185 must be completed at Savannah State.

Visiting: Visitation Day, usually on a Saturday in April, allows students and parents to meet with the president, faculty, and admissions and financial aid staff, and to participate in workshops and campus tours. There are guides for informal visits and visitors may sit in on classes. To arrange for a visit, contact the Office of Admissions at (912) 356–2181 or (800) 788–0478.

Financial Aid: In 1993–94, 90% of all students received some form of financial aid. Grants, loans, and scholarships are available. Thirty percent of undergraduate students work part-time. The FAF, the college's own financial statement, and the Scholarship Application Form are required.

International Students: International students must take the TOEFL and achieve a minimum score of 500. The student must also take the SAT I, ACT, and the Collegiate Placement Exams.

Computers: The college provides computer facilities for student use. Students may access Prime minicomputer/mainframe systems located in the School of Business and Hubert Technical Sciences Center. All students may access the system. It may be used from 8 A.M. to 10 P.M. There are no time limits on using the system and no fees.

Graduates: In 1992–93, 249 bachelor's degrees were awarded. The most popular majors among graduates were management (21%), criminal justice (14%), and social work (7%). Ten companies recruited on campus in 1992–93.

Admissions Contact: Office of Admissions.

SHORTER COLLEGE
Rome, GA 30165–4298

A-2

(706) 291–2121, ext. 220
(800) 868–6980 (out-of-state)

Full-time: 405 men, 672 women	Faculty: 55; IIB, --$
Part-time: 58 men, 53 women	Ph.D.s: 62%
Graduate: 4 men, 13 women	Student/Faculty: 20 to 1
Year: semesters, summer session	Tuition: $6670
Application Deadline: open	Room & Board: $3600
Freshman Class: 540 applied, 445 accepted, 175 enrolled	
SAT I Math: 500	ACT: 22	COMPETITIVE

Shorter College, founded in 1873, is a private institution affiliated with the Baptist Church and offering undergraduate degree programs in communications, education, business, fine arts, humanities, social sciences, religion, and natural sciences. There is one graduate school. In addition to regional accreditation, Shorter has baccalaureate program accreditation with NASM. The library contains 122,818 volumes, 4354 microform items, and 10,069 audiovisual forms, and subscribes to 844 periodicals. Computerized library sources and services include the card catalog, interlibrary loans, and database searching. Special learning facilities include a learning resource center, art gallery, natural history museum, and radio station. The 150-acre campus is in a small town 70 miles northwest of Atlanta. Including residence halls, there are 18 buildings on campus.

Student Life: About 94% of undergraduates are from Georgia. Students come from 13 states, 13 foreign countries, and Canada. Ninety-six percent are from public schools; 4% from private. Eighty-one percent are white; 16% African American. Seventy-five percent are Protestant; 21% claim no religious affiliation. The average age of freshmen is 19; all undergraduates, 23. Thirty-one percent drop out by the end of their first year; 42% remain to graduate.

Housing: A total of 455 students can be accommodated in college housing. College-sponsored living facilities include single-sex dormitories, on-campus apartments, and married-student housing. On-campus housing is guaranteed for the freshman year only and is available on a first-come, first-served basis. Sixty-five percent of students commute. Alcohol is not permitted. All students may keep cars on campus.

Activities: About 35% of men belong to 4 local fraternities; about 32% of women belong to 3 local sororities. There are 41 groups on campus, including art, band, cheerleading, choir, chorale, chorus, drama, ethnic, honors, international, literary magazine, musical theater, newspaper, opera, professional, radio and TV, religious, social service, student government, and yearbook. Popular campus events include Homecoming, Football Homecoming, Founders Day, Christmas Dinners, Christian Focus Week, and Parents Day.

Sports: There are 6 intercollegiate sports for men and 4 for women, and 12 intramural sports for men and 12 for women. Athletic and recreation facilities include tennis courts, a pool, and a weight room.

Disabled Students: Fifty percent of the campus is accessible to disabled students. The following facilities are available: wheelchair ramps, elevators, special parking, and specially equipped rest rooms.

Services: In addition to many counseling and information services, tutoring is available in every subject. There also is a reader service for the blind; remedial math, reading, and writing; and computerized study skills assessment and training.

Campus Safety and Security: Campus safety and security measures include 24-hour foot and vehicle patrol, self defense education, escort service, and informal discussions. In addition, there are pamphlets, posters, and films, and lighted pathways and sidewalks. Campus access is controlled via a gate house from 5 P.M. to 6 A.M. evenings, all weekend, and during vacations.

Programs of Study: Shorter awards the B.A., B.S., B.B.A., B.C.M., B.F.A., B.M., B.M.Ed., and B.S.E. degrees. Master's degrees also are awarded. Bachelor's degrees are awarded in BIOLOGICAL SCIENCE (biology/biological science), BUSINESS (accounting, banking and finance, business administration and management, marketing/retailing/merchandising, and recreational facilities management), COMMUNICATIONS AND THE ARTS (art, broadcasting, communications, dramatic arts, English, French, journalism, music, music business management, musical theater, piano/organ, public relations, Spanish, speech/debate/rhetoric, and voice), COMPUTER AND PHYSICAL SCIENCE (chemistry, mathematics, and natural sciences), EDUCATION (art, early childhood, elementary, middle school, music, science, and secondary), HEALTH PROFESSIONS (medical laboratory technology), SOCIAL SCIENCE (economics, history, parks and recreation management, philosophy, political science/government, psychology, religion, religious music, social science, and sociology). Music and natural sciences are the strongest academically. Business, music, biology, and early childhood education have the largest enrollments.

Required: To graduate, students must maintain at least a 2.0 overall GPA (2.5 for education degrees) in 126 to 138 credits, with grades of C or better in the 27 to 96 credits required for a major. The core curriculum requires 42 to 43 hours in English, speech, literature, religion, social science, science, mathematics, physical education, and the arts. In addition, students must complete 42 hours in upper-level courses and pass an English writing examination.

Special: Shorter offers a cooperative program in medical technology, internships in most programs, and study abroad in England. Dual majors, student-designed majors, and pass/fail options are available. There is a freshman honors program on campus, as well as 5 national honor societies. Shorter's Honors Program is collegewide in traditional subjects.

Faculty/Classroom: Seventy-five percent of faculty are male; 25%, female. All teach undergraduates and 62% both teach and do research. No introductory courses are taught by graduate students. The average class size in an introductory lecture is 19; in a laboratory, 18; and in a regular course offering, 14.

Admissions: About 82% of the 1993–94 applicants were accepted. The SAT scores for the 1993–94 freshman class were as follows: Verbal—67% below 500, 28% between 500 and 599, and 6% between 600 and 700; Math—46% below 500, 37% between 500 and 599, and 16% between 600 and 700. The ACT scores were 38% below 21, 26% between 21 and 23, 26% between 24 and 26, 3% between 27 and 28, and 9% above 28. About 60% of the current freshmen were in the top fifth of their class. Four freshmen graduated first in their class.

Requirements: A minimum GPA of 2.0 and either the SAT I or ACT are required. Applicants should be graduates of accredited secondary schools or have a GED certificate. Secondary preparation should include 4 units in English, 3 in history or social sciences, 3 each in mathematics and natural sciences, and 2 in foreign language. Prospective music majors must audition and take a theory placement test; prospective theater majors must audition. AP and CLEP credits are accepted. Important factors used in the admissions decision are recommendations by school officials, evidence of special talent, personality, intangible qualities, recommendations by alumni, and leadership record.

Procedure: Freshmen are admitted to all sessions. Entrance exams should be taken no later than the fall of the senior year. Application deadlines are open. The application fee is $20. Notification is sent on a rolling basis. There is an early admissions plan.

Transfer: A total of 72 transfer students enrolled in 1993–94. Applicants must submit transcripts, a character reference, and catalogs from any out-of-state colleges attended. A minimum 2.0 GPA based on transferable credit is required. A total of 30 credits out of 126 to 138 must be completed at Shorter.

Visiting: There are regularly scheduled orientations for prospective students, consisting of entertainment, financial aid workshops, a student-administration panel discussion, faculty consultations, admissions consultations, and campus/residence hall tours. There are guides for informal visits and visitors may sit in on classes and stay overnight at the school. To arrange for a visit, contact John P. McElveen, Director of Admissions, at (800) 868–6980 or (706) 291–2121.

Financial Aid: In 1993–94, all students received some form of financial aid. About 43% of freshmen and 39% of continuing students received need-based aid. The average freshman award was $6206. Of that total, scholarships or need-based grants averaged $4885 ($10,580 maximum); loans averaged $1321 ($9124 maximum); and work contracts averaged $600. Fifty-nine percent of undergraduate students work part-time. Average earnings from campus work for the school year are $600. Shorter is a member of CSS. The FAF, FFS, or SFS and the college's own financial statement are required. The deadline for financial aid applications is April 1.

International Students: There are currently 21 international students enrolled. The school actively recruits these students. They must take the TOEFL and achieve a minimum score of 500.

Computers: The college provides computer facilities for student use. There are 67 MS-DOS and Apple Macintosh microcomputers distributed among 3 networked laboratories, the library, and the counseling

center. All students may access the system, but the business and communications laboratories are for majors only. There are no time limits on using the system. The fees are $25 for use of the business laboratory only.

Graduates: In 1992–93, 161 bachelor's degrees were awarded. The most popular majors among graduates were early childhood education (16%), business (10%), and psychology (9%). Within an average freshman class, 35% graduate in 4 years and 43% in 5 years. Some 20 companies recruited on campus in 1992–93. In the 1992 graduating class, 43% of the men and 14% of the women were enrolled in graduate school within 6 months of graduation; 57% of the men and 86% of the women had found employment.

Admissions Contact: John P. McElveen, Director of Admissions.

SOUTHERN COLLEGE OF TECHNOLOGY B-2

Marietta, GA 30060   (404) 528–7281; (800) 635–3204 (in-state)

Full-time: 1878 men, 352 women	**Faculty:** 142; IIB, av$
Part-time: 1094 men, 195 women	**Ph.D.s:** 45%
Graduate: 294 men, 147 women	**Student/Faculty:** 16 to 1
Year: quarters, summer session	**Tuition:** $3375
Application Deadline: August 31	**Room & Board:** $5024 ($7787)
Freshman Class: 652 applied, 503 accepted, 297 enrolled	
SAT I: 430/510	**ACT:** 22 **COMPETITIVE**

Southern College of Technology, founded in 1948, is a public institution that is part of the university system of Georgia. The coeducational college offers undergraduate programs in arts and sciences, management, technology, and architecture. There are 4 undergraduate schools. In addition to regional accreditation, Southern Tech has baccalaureate program accreditation with ABET and ACCE. The library contains 100,000 volumes, 32,000 microform items, and 8000 audiovisual forms, and subscribes to 1400 periodicals. Computerized library sources and services include the card catalog, interlibrary loans, and database searching. Special learning facilities include a learning resource center and radio station. The 200-acre campus is in a suburban area 15 miles northwest of Atlanta. Including residence halls, there are 23 buildings on campus.

Student Life: About 93% of undergraduates are from Georgia. Students come from 33 states, 52 foreign countries, and Canada. Ninety-five percent are from public schools; 5% from private. Seventy-four percent are white; 17% African American. The average age of freshmen is 19; all undergraduates, 25. Thirty-eight percent drop out by the end of their first year; 35% remain to graduate.

Housing: A total of 474 students can be accommodated in college housing. College-sponsored living facilities include single-sex and coed dormitories. On-campus housing is available on a first-come, first-served basis. Eighty-eight percent of students commute. All students may keep cars on campus.

Activities: About 7% of men belong to 6 national fraternities; about 8% of women belong to 2 national sororities. There are 52 groups on campus, including chess, computers, drama, ethnic, honors, international, jazz band, newspaper, political, professional, radio and TV, religious, student government, and yearbook. Popular campus events include Techfest.

Sports: There are 3 intercollegiate sports for men and 11 intramural sports for women. Athletic and recreation facilities include a 1000-seat gymnasium, a baseball field, tennis courts, a weight room, a 500-seat auditorium, and areas for badminton, volleyball, and horseshoes.

Disabled Students: Eighty percent of the campus is accessible to disabled students. The following facilities are available: wheelchair ramps, elevators, special parking, specially equipped rest rooms, special class scheduling, and lowered drinking fountains.

Services: In addition to many counseling and information services, tutoring is available in some subjects, including English, mathematics, and physics. In addition, there is a reader service for the blind, and remedial math, reading, and writing.

Campus Safety and Security: Campus safety and security measures include 24-hour foot and vehicle patrol, escort service, informal discussions, and pamphlets, posters, and films. In addition, there are lighted pathways and sidewalks.

Programs of Study: Southern Tech awards the B.S. and B.Arch degrees. Associate and master's degrees also are awarded. Bachelor's degrees are awarded in COMMUNICATIONS AND THE ARTS (technical and business writing), COMPUTER AND PHYSICAL SCIENCE (computer science, mathematics, and physics), ENGINEERING AND ENVIRONMENTAL DESIGN (architecture, civil engineering technology, computer technology, construction engineering, electrical/electronics engineering technology, environmental design, industrial administration/management, industrial engineering technology, manufacturing engineering, mechanical engineering technology, and technological management). Electrical engineering technology and mechanical engineering technology are the strongest academically and also have the largest enrollments.

Required: In order to graduate, all students must take a computer programming course and complete 20 hours each of humanities, mathematics and natural sciences, and social sciences. Students must also maintain a minimum 2.0 GPA in 205 quarter credit hours.

Special: Southern Tech offers cross-registration with the University Center in Georgia, cooperative programs in all majors, dual majors in all disciplines, and study abroad in England and China. Credit is given for life experience and by exam. There is one national honor society on campus.

Faculty/Classroom: Eighty-three percent of faculty are male; 17%, female. All teach undergraduates. Graduate students teach 1% of introductory courses. The average class size in an introductory lecture is 30; in a laboratory, 20; and in a regular course offering, 25.

Admissions: About 77% of the 1993–94 applicants were accepted. The SAT scores for the 1993–94 freshman class were as follows: Verbal—86% below 500, 12% between 500 and 599, and 2% between 600 and 700; Math—40% below 500, 46% between 500 and 599, 13% between 600 and 700, and 2% above 700. The ACT scores were 17% below 21, 67% between 21 and 23, and 17% between 24 and 26.

Requirements: A minimum GPA of 2.0 is required. The SAT I or ACT is required. Applicants must be graduates of an accredited secondary school or have a GED certificate. Students should have completed 21 academic credits, including 4 years of English, 2 of a foreign language, and 3 each of mathematics, science, and social studies. AP and CLEP credits are accepted.

Procedure: Freshmen are admitted to all sessions. Entrance exams should be taken at the end of the junior year. Applications should be filed by August 31 for fall entry, December 5 for winter entry, March 10 for spring entry, and June 1 for summer entry. Notification is sent on a rolling basis. There are early admissions and deferred admissions plans.

Transfer: About 408 transfer students enrolled in 1993–94. Applicants must have a GPA of 2.0. Minimum SAT I or ACT scores may be required for some students. A total of 45 credits out of 205 must be completed at Southern Tech.

Visiting: There are guides for informal visits. To arrange for a visit, contact the Director of Admissions at (404) 528–7281.

Financial Aid: In a recent year 38% of all current freshmen and 33% of continuing students received some form of financial aid. About 33% of freshmen and 30% of continuing students received need-based aid. The average freshman award was $1500. Of that total, scholarships or need-based grants averaged $1500 ($2500 maximum); and loans averaged $1850 ($2625 maximum). Seventy percent of undergraduate students work part-time. Average earnings from campus work for the school year are $1000. The average financial indebtedness of a recent graduate was $9000. Southern Tech is a member of CSS. The FAF, FFS, or SFS is required. The deadline for financial aid applications is March 15.

International Students: There are currently 105 international students enrolled. The school actively recruits these students. They must take the TOEFL and achieve a minimum score of 50 on each part.

Computers: The college provides computer facilities for student use. The mainframe is an IBM RS/6000 Model 550. There are 120 IBM and Apple Macintosh microcomputers available in the central computing laboratories. All students may access the system. There are no time limits on using the system and no fees.

Graduates: In 1992–93 423 bachelor's degrees were awarded. The most popular majors among graduates were electrical engineering technology (22%), industrial engineering technology (18%), and mechanical engineering technology (15%). Within an average freshman class, 1% graduate in 3 years, 5% in 4 years, 15% in 5 years, and 25% in 6 years. Some 150 companies recruited on campus in 1992–93. In the 1992 graduating class, 3% of the men and 3% of the women were enrolled in graduate school within 6 months of graduation; 95% of the men and 95% of the women had found employment.

Admissions Contact: Director of Admissions.

SPELMAN COLLEGE B-2

Atlanta, GA 30314   (404) 681–3643; (800) 241–3421 (in-state)

Full-time: 1984 women	**Faculty:** 116
Part-time: 91 women	**Ph.D.s:** 87%
Graduate: none	**Student/Faculty:** 17 to 1
Year: semesters	**Tuition:** $7692
Application Deadline: February 1	**Room & Board:** $5250
Freshman Class: 3711 applied, 1237 accepted, 443 enrolled	
SAT I Verbal/Math: 490/520	**ACT:** 23 **VERY COMPETITIVE**

Spelman College, founded in 1881, is a private, nonsectarian, liberal arts college for black women. In addition to regional accreditation, Spelman has baccalaureate program accreditation with NASM and NCATE. The library contains 379,912 volumes and 385,538 microform items, and subscribes to 1439 periodicals. Special learning facilities include an art gallery. The 32-acre campus is in an urban area 3 miles southwest of Atlanta. Including residence halls, there are 25 buildings on campus.

Student Life: About 79% of undergraduates are from out-of-state. Students come from 41 states and 20 foreign countries. Eighty-six percent are from public schools; 14% from private. Ninety-nine percent are African American. The average age of freshmen is 18; all undergraduates, 20. Ten percent drop out by the end of their first year; 72% remain to graduate.

Housing: A total of 1174 students can be accommodated in college housing. College-sponsored living facilities include dormitories. In addition there are honors houses. On-campus housing is guaranteed for the freshman year only, is available on a first-come, first-served basis, and is available on a lottery system for upperclassmen. Priority is given to out-of-town students. Fifty-eight percent of students live on campus; of those, 67% remain on campus on weekends. Alcohol is not permitted. Upperclassmen may keep cars on campus.

Activities: About 8% of women belong to 2 local and 2 national sororities. There are 46 groups on campus, including art, band, cheerleading, chorus, dance, drama, honors, international, jazz band, literary magazine, musical theater, newspaper, religious, social, student government, and yearbook. Popular campus events include Homecoming celebrated with Morehouse College, Founders Day, and Martin Luther King's Birthday.

Sports: Athletic and recreation facilities include a gymnasium, tennis courts, and a swimming pool.

Disabled Students: Twenty-five percent of the campus is accessible to disabled students. The following facilities are available: wheelchair ramps, elevators, special parking, and specially equipped rest rooms.

Services: In addition to many counseling and information services, tutoring is available in every subject.

Campus Safety and Security: Campus safety and security measures include 24-hour foot and vehicle patrol, escort service, shuttle buses, and informal discussions. In addition, there are lighted pathways and sidewalks.

Programs of Study: Spelman awards the B.A. and B.S. degrees. Bachelor's degrees are awarded in BIOLOGICAL SCIENCE (biochemistry and biology/biological science), COMMUNICATIONS AND THE ARTS (dramatic arts, English, fine arts, French, music, and Spanish), COMPUTER AND PHYSICAL SCIENCE (chemistry, computer science, mathematics, natural sciences, and physics), EDUCATION (art), SOCIAL SCIENCE (child psychology/development, economics, history, philosophy, political science/government, psychology, religion, and sociology). Biology, engineering, and natural sciences are the strongest academically. Biology, psychology, economics, and English have the largest enrollments.

Required: To graduate, the student must complete 120 semester hours, including at least 30 or more in the major. She must complete the college's general and divisional requirements, including 12 hours of social science, 9 of humanities, 6 to 8 of natural science, 6 of fine arts, 4 each of mathematics and computer science, 2 of physical education, up to 16 of a foreign language, and up to 4 of English. A reading course may be required, based on the student's scores on placement tests.

Special: Students may cross-register with Atlanta University Center member institutions. Spelman offers internships, study abroad in several countries, student-designed majors, work-study programs at the school, B.A.-B.S. degrees, and dual majors, as well as a 3–2 engineering degree with Georgia Tech, Rochester Institute of Technology, University of Alabama at Huntsville, and Auburn, Boston and North Carolina Agricultural and Technical State universities. The college grants credit for life experience and permits nondegree study. There is a freshman honors program on campus, as well as 9 national honor societies.

Faculty/Classroom: Thirty-nine percent of faculty are male; 61%, female.

Admissions: About 33% of the 1993–94 applicants were accepted. There were 16 National Merit finalists. Eighteen freshmen graduated first in their class.

Requirements: A minimum GPA of 2.0 is required. The SAT I or ACT is required. Applicants should be high school graduates or have a GED certificate. Students should have earned at least 15 academic credits, including 4 in English, 1 in laboratory science, and 2 each in mathematics, history, and science; the rest may be in language, literature, science, and social science. The college requires submission of an essay and recommends a portfolio for art students or an audition for music students. AP and CLEP credits are accepted. Important factors used in the admissions decision are leadership record, extracurricular activities record, advanced placement or honor courses, parents or siblings attending the school, and geographic diversity.

Procedure: Freshmen are admitted in the fall and spring. Entrance exams should be taken by December of the senior year. Early decision applications should be filed by November 15; regular applications, by February 1 for fall entry and November 1 for spring entry, along with an application fee of $35. Notification of early decision is sent December 31; regular decision, March 15. There are early decision and early admissions plans. About 165 early decision candidates were accepted for the 1993–94 class. A waiting list is an active part of the admissions procedure.

Transfer: Thirty-three transfer students enrolled in 1993–94. A 3.0 GPA is recommended, with a minimum 2.0 required. Applicants must submit a recommendation from a school official. A total of 32 credits out of 120 must be completed at Spelman.

Visiting: There are regularly scheduled orientations for prospective students, including a general information session and a campus tour. There are also high school senior days and junior days. There are guides for informal visits, and visitors may sit in on classes. To arrange a visit, contact the Admissions Office at (404) 681-3643, ext. 2188.

Financial Aid: In 1993–94, 87% of all current freshmen received some form of financial aid. About 69% of freshmen and 87% of continuing students received need-based aid. The average freshman award was $6725. Of that total, scholarships or need-based grants averaged $1100 ($2000 maximum); loans averaged $2000 ($2625 maximum); and work contracts averaged $900 ($1200 maximum). Twenty percent of undergraduate students work part-time. Average earnings from campus work for the school year are $900. Spelman is a member of CSS. The FAF, the college's own financial statement, and the FAFSA are required. The deadline for financial aid applications is April 1.

International Students: There are currently 37 international students enrolled. The school actively recruits these students. They must take the TOEFL and achieve a minimum score of 450. The student must also take the SAT I or the ACT.

Computers: The college provides computer facilities for student use. The mainframe is a DEC VAX 11/780. There are also 120 IBM PC and PS/2 Model 30, Commodore Amiga, Apple IIe and Macintosh Plus, and Zenith 100 microcomputers available throughout the campus. All students may access the system. It may be used 24 hours per day. There are no time limits on using the system. The fees are $40 per semester, included in the total student fees.

Graduates: In 1992–93, 412 bachelor's degrees were awarded. The most popular majors among graduates were psychology (21%), English (16%), and biology (9%). Within an average freshman class, 83% graduate in 4 years. Some 320 companies recruited on campus in 1992–93.

Admissions Contact: Aline Rivers-Jones, Executive Director of Enrollment Management.

THOMAS COLLEGE
B-5
Thomasville, GA 31792–7499
(912) 226-1621

Full-time: 164 men, 278 women	Faculty: 16; IIB, --$
Part-time: 62 men, 97 women	Ph.D.s: 27%
Graduate: none	Student/Faculty: 28 to 1
Year: quarters, summer session	Tuition: $3123
Application Deadline: open	Room & Board: n/app
Freshman Class: 174 applied, 174 accepted, 130 enrolled	
SAT I Verbal/Math: 360/390	NONCOMPETITIVE

Thomas College, founded in 1950, is a private liberal arts institution offering an undergraduate program in business administration and management. The library contains 33,628 volumes, 902 microform items, and 774 audiovisual forms, and subscribes to 289 periodicals. Computerized library sources and services include the card catalog. Special learning facilities include a learning resource center. The 27-acre campus is in a suburban area 28 miles north of Tallahassee, Florida. There are 7 buildings on campus.

Student Life: About 97% of undergraduates are from Georgia. Students come from 4 states and 2 foreign countries. Ninety-nine percent are from public schools; 1% from private. Sixty-nine percent are white; 28% African American. The average age of freshmen is 25; all undergraduates, 27. Sixty-three percent drop out by the end of their first year; 37% remain to graduate.

Housing: There are no residence halls. All students commute. Alcohol is not permitted. All students may keep cars on campus.

Activities: There are no fraternities or sororities on campus. There are some groups on campus, including chorus, jazz band, newspaper, and student government. Popular campus events include Day on the Green.

Disabled Students: Ninety-five percent of the campus is accessible to disabled students. The following facilities are available: wheelchair ramps, special parking, and specially equipped rest rooms.

Services: In addition to many counseling and information services, tutoring is available in some subjects, including mathematics, biology, and English. There is also remedial math, reading, and writing.

Campus Safety and Security: Campus safety and security measures include informal discussions, pamphlets, posters, films, lighted pathways and sidewalks, and evening vehicle patrol.

Programs of Study: Thomas College awards the B.A., B.S., and B.S.Ed. degrees. Associate degrees also are awarded. Bachelor's degrees are awarded in BUSINESS (business administration and management), EDUCATION (early childhood), SOCIAL SCIENCE (liberal arts/general studies). Business administration is the strongest academically. Business administration and early childhood education have the largest enrollments.

Required: To graduate, students must complete 183 quarter hours, including 80 in the major, with a minimum GPA of 2.0. Core requirements include 45 quarter hours in English composition, history, biology, mathematics, political science, music or art, and computer science. All students must pass a comprehensive English exam.

Special: A B.A.-B.S. degree is available in all majors.

Faculty/Classroom: Seventy-nine percent of faculty are male; 21%, female. All teach undergraduates. The average class size in an introductory lecture is 24 and in a laboratory, 20.

Admissions: All of the 1993–94 applicants were accepted. The SAT scores for the 1993–94 freshman class were as follows: Verbal—89% below 500 and 11% between 500 and 599; Math—85% below 500 and 15% between 500 and 599.

Requirements: The SAT I or ACT is recommended. Students should be graduates of an accredited high school or its equivalent. AP and CLEP credits are accepted.

Procedure: Freshmen are admitted to all sessions. Application deadlines are open. Application fee is $25. The college accepts all applicants. Notification is sent on a rolling basis.

Transfer: About 80 transfer students enrolled in 1993–94. Applicants should have a minimum college GPA of 2.0 and be in good standing at their current or previous institution. At least 90 quarter hours out of 183 must be completed at Thomas College.

Financial Aid: In 1993–94, 85% of all current freshmen and 56% of continuing students received some form of financial aid. About 41% of freshmen and 56% of continuing students received need-based aid. The average freshman award was $644. Of that total, scholarships or need-based grants averaged $500 ($2300 maximum); and loans averaged $2000 ($2625 maximum). One percent of undergraduate students work part-time. Average earnings from campus work for the school year are $750. Thomas College is a member of CSS. The FAF, FFS, or SFS is required.

International Students: There are currently 6 international students enrolled. They must take the TOEFL and achieve a minimum score of 550. They must also take MAPS (Multiple Assessment Program or Services).

Computers: The college provides computer facilities for student use. There are 25 IBM microcomputers in 2 campus laboratories. There are no time limits on using the system and no fees.

Graduates: In 1992–93, 11 bachelor's degrees were awarded. The most popular major among graduates was business administration (30%). Some 12 companies recruited on campus in 1992–93.

Admissions Contact: Robert Bohman, Dean of Student Services.

TOCCOA FALLS COLLEGE
Toccoa Falls, GA 30598
C-1

(404) 886–6831, ext. 245
(800) 868–3257 (out-of-state)

Full-time: 397 men, 384 women	Faculty: 39
Part-time: 31 men, 61 women	Ph.D.s: 36%
Graduate: none	Student/Faculty: 20 to 1
Year: 4–1–4, summer session	Tuition: $5784
Application Deadline: open	Room & Board: $3566
Freshman Class: 1002 applied, 825 accepted, 389 enrolled	
SAT I Verbal/Math: 433/450	ACT: 21 **COMPETITIVE**

Toccoa Falls College is an independent, interdenominational Christian college founded in 1907 and offering programs in Bible studies, Christian counseling, Christian education, communications, missions, education, theology, and music. In addition to regional accreditation, TFC has baccalaureate program accreditation with NASM. The library contains 88,648 volumes, 6647 microform items, and 7684 audiovisual forms, and subscribes to 590 periodicals. Computerized library sources and services include interlibrary loans and database searching. Special learning facilities include a learning resource center, and a 100,000-watt radio station on campus offering programs 24 hours a day. The 1100-acre campus is in a small town 80 miles northeast of Atlanta. Including residence halls, there are 45 buildings on campus.

Student Life: About 73% of undergraduates are from out-of-state, mostly the South. Students come from 43 states, 27 foreign countries, and Canada. Ninety percent are white. Most are Protestant. The average age of freshmen is 19; all undergraduates, 22. Forty-two percent drop out or transfer by the end of their first year; 52% remain to graduate.

Housing: A total of 693 students can be accommodated in college housing. College-sponsored living facilities include single-sex dormitories, on-campus apartments, and married-student housing. On-campus housing is guaranteed for all 4 years. Eighty percent of students live on campus; of those, 80% remain on campus on weekends. Alcohol is not permitted. All students may keep cars on campus.

Activities: There are no fraternities or sororities on campus. There are many groups and organizations on campus, including art, band, cheerleading, choir, chorale, chorus, computers, drama, ethnic, honors, international, jazz band, newspaper, orchestra, pep band, photography, political, radio and TV, religious, social, social service, student government, and yearbook. Popular campus events include Artist Series, Staley Lectures, Spiritual Emphasis Week, Campus Preview, Homecoming, Graduation, and the Woerner Missionary Lecture Series.

Sports: There are 4 intercollegiate sports for men and 4 for women, and 10 intramural sports for men and 10 for women. Athletic and recreation facilities include a gymnatorium with racquetball courts and a weight room, tennis courts, and soccer and baseball fields.

Disabled Students: Seventy percent of the campus is accessible to disabled students. The following facilities are available: wheelchair ramps, special parking, specially equipped rest rooms, special class scheduling, lowered drinking fountains, and lowered telephones.

Services: In addition to many counseling and information services, tutoring is available in most subjects. There is also remedial math, reading, and writing.

Campus Safety and Security: Campus safety and security measures include 24-hour foot and vehicle patrol, escort service, informal discussions, and lighted pathways and sidewalks. In addition, the campus is locked at night and the entrance is guard gated.

Programs of Study: TFC awards the B.A., B.S., and B.Th. degrees. Associate degrees are also awarded. Bachelor's degrees are awarded in COMMUNICATIONS AND THE ARTS (broadcasting, communications, English, journalism, music, music performance, music theory and composition, and public relations), EDUCATION (Christian education, early childhood, elementary, middle school, music, secondary, and teaching English as a second language/foreign language), SOCIAL SCIENCE (biblical languages, biblical studies, counseling psychology, interdisciplinary studies, ministries, missions, pastoral studies, philosophy, religion, religious education, and theological studies). Missions and teaching are the strongest academically. Teacher education and Christian counseling psychology have the largest enrollments.

Required: Students must successfully complete 130 semester hours with 34 to 70 in their major, to earn a bachelor's degree. All students must also complete a core curriculum, which includes 30 hours of Bible studies, an English sequence, physical education, and mathematics, for a total of 66 hours. A GPA of 2.0 to 2.5 must be maintained. Additional requirements for graduation are a senior oral comprehensive examination or a thesis and performance of a student ministry.

Special: The college offers many dual majors, and B.A.-B.S. degrees are available. An on-campus work-study program and internships for ministry, teaching, or counseling majors are also provided. The interdisciplinary studies major is student designed. There are 2 national honor societies on campus. Eight departments have honors programs.

Faculty/Classroom: Seventy-one percent of faculty are male; 29%, female. All teach undergraduates. The average class size in an introductory lecture is 30; in a laboratory, 17; and in a regular course offering, 20.

Admissions: About 82% of the 1993–94 applicants were accepted. The SAT scores for the 1993–94 freshman class were as follows: Verbal—71% below 500, 24% between 500 and 599, and 5% between 600 and 700; Math—70% below 500, 22% between 500 and 599, and 8% between 600 and 700. The ACT scores were 49% below 21, 27% between 21 and 23, 12% between 24 and 26, 9% between 27 and 28, and 3% above 28. About 30% of the current freshmen were in the top fifth of their class; 54% were in the top two fifths. Four freshmen graduated first in their class.

Requirements: A minimum GPA of 2.0 is required. Students may submit either SAT I or ACT results, with minimum composite scores of 800 on the SAT I or 18 on the ACT recommended. High school graduation or a GED certificate is required. Three personal references, one of which should be a reference from the student's pastor, are required. An essay submitted with the student's application is recommended. AP and CLEP credits are accepted. Important factors used in the admissions decision are personality, intangible qualities, extracurricular activities record, leadership record, advanced placement or honor courses, and recommendations by school officials.

Procedure: Freshmen are admitted to all sessions. Entrance exams should be taken early in the senior year. Application deadlines are open. Notification is sent on a rolling basis. The application fee is $20. There are early decision and early admissions plans.

Transfer: About 70 transfer students enrolled in 1993–94. Transfer students must have successfully completed 12 semester hours of college credit courses and have maintained a minimum GPA of 2.0. Students must also provide 3 references. At least the final 30 credits must be completed at TFC.

Visiting: There are regularly scheduled orientations for prospective students, including visits to the admissions counselor, school directors, and the financial aid office arranged 2 weeks in advance. There are guides for informal visits, and visitors may sit in on classes and stay overnight at the school. To arrange for a visit, contact Chris Taylor, Office of Admissions, at (800) 868–3257.

Financial Aid: Scholarships or need-based grants averaged $3000 ($3975 maximum); loans averaged $2625 (maximum); and work contracts averaged $1000 (maximum). Fifty percent of undergraduate students work part-time. TFC is a member of CSS. The FAF and the college's own financial statement are required. The deadline for financial aid applications is May 30.

International Students: There are currently 48 international students enrolled. They must take the TOEFL and achieve a minimum score of 500. The applicant must also take SAT I.

Computers: The college provides computer facilities for student use. All students may access the system but must sign up for computer time, which varies according to need. The fees are $100 for computer classes, $10 per semester for other students.

Graduates: In 1992–93, 134 bachelor's degrees were awarded. The most popular majors among graduates were early childhood education (13%), pastoral ministries (11%), and interpersonal and organizational communication (10%). Within an average freshman class, 45% graduate in 4 years. Some 120 companies recruited on campus in

1992–93.

Admissions Contact: Matthew L. King, Director of Admissions.

UNIVERSITY OF GEORGIA
Athens, GA 30602

C-2

(404) 542–8776

Full-time: 9184 men, 10,369 women	Faculty: 1712; I, --$
Part-time: 1464 men, 1284 women	Ph.D.s: 94%
Graduate: 2930 men, 3522 women	Student/Faculty: 11 to 1
Year: quarters, summer session	Tuition: $2250 ($5940)
Application Deadline: August 1	Room & Board: $3405

Freshman Class: 11,220 applied, 7871 accepted, 3320 enrolled
SAT I Verbal/Math: 540/570 **VERY COMPETITIVE**

The University of Georgia, chartered in 1785 and part of the University System of Georgia, offers degree programs in the arts and sciences, marine studies, music, business, agricultural and environmental sciences, education, family and consumer sciences, and preprofessional studies. There are 12 undergraduate schools and one graduate school. In addition to regional accreditation, UGA has baccalaureate program accreditation with AACSB, ABET, ACEJMC, ACPE, ADA, AHEA, ASLA, CSWE, FIDER, NASAD, NASM, NCATE, and SAF. The 3 libraries contain 3,131,402 volumes, 5,039,725 microform items, and 61,285 audiovisual forms, and subscribe to 47,993 periodicals. Computerized library sources and services include the card catalog, interlibrary loans, and database searching. Special learning facilities include a learning resource center, an art gallery, a natural history museum, a radio station, a TV station, a bioscience learning center, a rare book and manuscript library, and the State Botanical Garden of Georgia. The 605-acre campus is in a small city 80 miles east of Atlanta. Including residence halls, there are 306 buildings on campus.

Student Life: About 84% of undergraduates are from Georgia. Students come from 50 states, 115 foreign countries, and Canada. Eighty-seven percent are from public schools; 9% from private. Eighty-seven percent are white. The average age of freshmen is 19; all undergraduates, 21. Fourteen percent drop out by the end of their first year; 61% remain to graduate.

Housing: A total of 6417 students can be accommodated in college housing. College-sponsored living facilities include single-sex and coed dormitories and married-student housing. On-campus housing is available on a first-come, first-served basis. Alcohol is not permitted. All students may keep cars on campus.

Activities: About 19% of men belong to 24 national fraternities; about 23% of women belong to 22 national sororities. There are 250 groups on campus, including art, band, cheerleading, chess, chorus, computers, dance, drama, drill team, ethnic, film, honors, international, jazz band, literary magazine, marching band, musical theater, newspaper, orchestra, pep band, photography, political, professional, radio and TV, religious, social, social service, student government, and yearbook. Popular campus events include Homecoming, UGA Health Fair, and sports events.

Sports: There are 8 intercollegiate sports each for men and women, and 18 intramural sports for men and 14 for women. Athletic and recreation facilities include an 82,122-seat coliseum; a 12,000-seat basketball arena; a 4500-seat tennis stadium; a sports complex with a lake, a beach, playing fields, and trails; 4 indoor tennis courts; and complete football-training facilities.

Disabled Students: Fifty percent of the campus is accessible to disabled students. The following facilities are available: wheelchair ramps, elevators, special parking, specially equipped rest rooms, special class scheduling, lowered drinking fountains, lowered telephones, wheelchair vans, and auxiliary aides.

Services: In addition to many counseling and information services, tutoring is available in every subject. There is also a reader service for the blind, remedial math, reading, and writing, recorded textbooks, early registration, note-takers, modifications for tests and assignments, and counseling and advisement from learning-disability specialists for students diagnosed as learning disabled.

Campus Safety and Security: Campus safety and security measures include 24-hour foot and vehicle patrol, self-defense education, escort service, and shuttle buses. In addition, there are informal discussions, pamphlets, posters, and films, emergency telephones, and lighted pathways and sidewalks.

Programs of Study: UGA awards the B.A., B.S., B.B.A., B.F.A., B.L.A., B.Mus., B.S.A., B.S.A.E., B.S.Chem., B.S.Ed., B.S.E.H., B.S.F.R., B.S.H.E., B.S.P.A., B.S.Pcs., B.S.Phr., and B.S.W. degrees. Associate, master's, and doctoral degrees are also awarded. Bachelor's degrees are awarded in AGRICULTURE (agriculture, animal science, dairy science, forestry and related sciences, horticulture, plant protection (pest management), and poultry science), BIOLOGICAL SCIENCE (biochemistry, biology/biological science, botany, genetics, microbiology, plant pathology, and zoology), BUSINESS (accounting, banking and finance, business administration and management, business economics, hotel/motel and restaurant management, international business management, management information systems, marketing/retailing/merchandising, and organizational behavior), COMMUNICATIONS AND THE ARTS (advertising, broadcasting, communications, design, dramatic arts, English, film arts, fine arts, Italian, journalism, Latin, music, photography, romance languages, Slavic languages, speech/debate/rhetoric, and telecommunications),

COMPUTER AND PHYSICAL SCIENCE (actuarial science, chemistry, computer science, geology, mathematics, physics, and statistics), EDUCATION (agricultural, art, business, early childhood, education of the mentally handicapped, elementary, foreign languages, health, home economics, industrial arts, marketing and distribution, middle school, music, science, secondary, and trade and industrial), ENGINEERING AND ENVIRONMENTAL DESIGN (agricultural engineering), HEALTH PROFESSIONS (music therapy, pharmacy, predentistry, premedicine, rehabilitation therapy, and speech pathology/audiology), SOCIAL SCIENCE (anthropology, criminal justice, dietetics, economics, food science, geography, history, Pacific area studies, parks and recreation management, philosophy, political science/government, psychology, religion, social work, and sociology). Business, law, veterinary medicine, social work, education, genetics, forest resources, journalism, botany, and child and family development are the strongest academically. General business, prejournalism, accounting, psychology, and political science have the largest enrollments.

Required: Students must have a 2.0 GPA to graduate and must complete a maximum of 192 quarter credit hours, with at least 30 in the major and 20 each in humanities/fine arts, mathematics/natural science, and social science. Required specific disciplines are grammar, composition, literature, mathematics, biological sciences, history, and American government; specific courses include basic physical education and English 101 and 102. UGA also requires all students to pass the Regents Exit Examination, as well as examinations on the federal and state constitutions.

Special: UGA offers co-op programs with the Medical College of Georgia and the Georgia Institute of Technology, as well as cross-registration with University Center institutions in urban Atlanta. With the Governor's Intern Program, students may serve a full-time 10-week internship in a state government agency; many other internships are available within the departments, as well as work-study programs within the university and with many area businesses. Students may study abroad in 13 countries. A Washington semester, an accelerated degree program in business, general studies and 3–2 engineering degrees, student-designed majors, and nondegree study are available. There is a freshman honors program on campus, as well as 48 national honor societies, including Phi Beta Kappa. Fifty departments have honors programs.

Faculty/Classroom: Seventy-five percent of faculty are male; 25%, female. Eighty-one percent teach undergraduates. Graduate students teach 35% of introductory courses. The average class size in an introductory lecture is 75; in a laboratory, 21; and in a regular course offering, 26.

Admissions: About 70% of the 1993–94 applicants were accepted. The SAT scores for the 1993–94 freshman class were as follows: Verbal—45% below 500, 39% between 500 and 599, 14% between 600 and 700, and 2% above 700; Math—16% below 500, 47% between 500 and 599, 29% between 600 and 700, and 8% above 700. About 80% of the current freshmen were in the top quarter of their class; 98% were in the top half. There were 29 National Merit finalists.

Requirements: A minimum GPA of 2.0 is required. The SAT I is required, with a minimum composite score of 900. Applicants should be high school graduates or present a GED certificate. Students should have taken 4 years of English, 3 each of mathematics, science, and social studies, and 2 of a foreign language. An audition is required for music majors. AP and CLEP credits are accepted.

Procedure: Freshmen are admitted to all sessions. Entrance exams should be taken in January of the senior year. Applications should be filed by February 1 for fall entry, December 1 for winter entry, March 1 for spring entry, and May 1 for summer entry, along with an application fee of $25. Notification is sent on a rolling basis. There are early admissions and deferred admissions plans.

Transfer: About 1930 transfer students enrolled in 1993–94. Applicants must have a GPA of 2.2. Those with fewer than 45 hours of college credit must enter as freshmen. A total of 90 quarter credit hours out of a maximum of 192 must be completed at UGA.

Visiting: There are regularly scheduled orientations for prospective students, consisting of campus tours and meetings with faculty, staff, and students. There are guides for informal visits and visitors may sit in on classes and stay overnight at the school. To arrange for a visit, contact the Admissions Office at (404) 542-2112.

Financial Aid: In 1993–94, 40% of all current freshmen and 50% of continuing students received some form of financial aid. About 30% received need-based aid. The average freshman award was $2500. Of that total, scholarships or need-based grants averaged $900 ($1500 maximum); loans averaged $500 ($3500 maximum); and work contracts averaged $900 ($2700 maximum). Twenty-five percent of undergraduate students work part-time. Average earnings from campus work for the school year were $2500. The average financial indebtedness of the 1992–93 graduate was $3000. UGA is a member of CSS. The college's own financial statement and the SAR from any processor are required. The deadline for financial aid applications is March 1.

International Students: There are currently 1213 international students enrolled. They must take the TOEFL and achieve a minimum score of 520. The student must also take the SAT I or the ACT. The required minimum composite score on the SAT I is 900.

Computers: The college provides computer facilities for student use. The mainframes are an IBM 3090 Model 400; a CDC CYBER 180/850, a 180/845, and a 205; and a DEC VAX 11/780. Computers for student use are located at various points across campus, including the library, residence halls, the computer center, academic departments, and computer laboratories. All students may access the system. It may be used at designated times for the various locations. There are no time limits on using the system and no fees.

Graduates: In 1992–93, 4777 bachelor's degrees were awarded. The most popular majors among graduates were English (5%), political science (4%), and accounting (4%). Within an average freshman class, 1% graduate in 3 years, 36% in 4 years, 57% in 5 years, and 61% in 6 years. Some 731 companies recruited on campus in 1992–93.

Admissions Contact: Director of Admissions.

UNIVERSITY SYSTEM OF GEORGIA

The University System of Georgia, established in 1932, is a public system in Georgia. It is governed by a 16-member board of regents, whose chief administrator is the chancellor. The primary goals of the system are teaching, research, and public service. The main priorities are to provide broad access to undergraduate education at a high level of excellence, to provide sound programs of graduate education and research addressing state and national problems and advancing the frontiers of knowledge, and to work cooperatively with all levels and sectors of education to improve the social, cultural, and economic welfare of the state's citizens. The total enrollment in fall 1993 of all 34 campuses was more than 203,000; there were 8000 faculty members. Altogether there are more than 1,000 baccalaureate, 600 master's, and 175 doctoral programs offered in the University System of Georgia. A profile of the 4-year campus in Albany is included in this chapter in alphabetical order with other Georgia schools.

VALDOSTA STATE COLLEGE
(See Valdosta State University)

VALDOSTA STATE UNIVERSITY
(Formerly Valdosta State College)   **C-5**

Valdosta, GA 31698

Full-time: 2428 men, 3554 women	(912) 333-5791; (800) 618-1878
Part-time: 629 men, 789 women	Faculty: 300; IIA, --$
Graduate: 809 men, 1139 women	Ph.D.s: n/av
Year: quarters, summer session	Student/Faculty: 20 to 1
Application Deadline: open	Tuition: $1730 ($4494)
Freshman Class: 3674 applied, 2663 accepted, 1900 enrolled	Room & Board: $2940 ($2940)
SAT I Verbal/Math: 396/434	**LESS COMPETITIVE**

Valdosta State University, founded in 1906 and a unit of the University System of Georgia, is a public liberal arts institution offering degrees in arts and sciences, education, business administration, nursing, and fine arts. There are 5 undergraduate and 4 graduate schools. In addition to regional accreditation, VSU has baccalaureate program accreditation with AACSB, NASM, NCATE, and NLN. The library contains 367,718 volumes, 321,877 microform items, and 12,629 audiovisual forms, and subscribes to 2848 periodicals. Special learning facilities include a learning resource center, art gallery, planetarium, and radio station. The 168-acre campus is in a small town 180 miles south of Macon. Including residence halls, there are 25 buildings on campus.

Student Life: About 87% of undergraduates are from Georgia. Students come from 47 states, 41 foreign countries, and Canada. Seventy-nine percent are white; 19% African American. The average age of freshmen is 21.1; all undergraduates, 23.4. Sixteen percent drop out by the end of their first year.

Housing: A total of 2000 students can be accommodated in college housing. College-sponsored living facilities include single-sex and coed dormitories, on-campus apartments, off-campus apartments, and fraternity houses. In addition there is an honors wing. On-campus housing is guaranteed for the freshman year only and is available after that on a first-come, first-served basis. All students may keep cars on campus.

Activities: There are 8 national fraternities and 9 national sororities. There are 90 groups on campus, including band, cheerleading, choir, drama, drill team, international, jazz band, literary magazine, marching band, musical theater, newspaper, political, radio and TV, religious, social, social service, and student government. Popular campus events include dances, films, Slam Dunk Contest, Three-Point Shoot-Out, Free-Throw Contest, and Home Run Derby.

Sports: There are 6 intercollegiate sports for men and 4 for women, and 6 intramural sports each for men and women. Athletic and recreation facilities include a physical education complex with a 5500-seat basketball arena; a health fitness center with a weight training room and a human performance laboratory; and a gymnasium building with a weight room, a training room, a dance studio, and an auxiliary gymnasium.

Disabled Students: All of the campus is accessible to disabled students. The following facilities are available: wheelchair ramps, elevators, special parking, specially equipped rest rooms, and modified furnishings in dormitory rooms.

Services: In addition to many counseling and information services, tutoring is available in most subjects. There is remedial math, reading, and writing.

Campus Safety and Security: Campus safety and security measures include escort service, shuttle buses, and lighted pathways and sidewalks.

Programs of Study: VSU awards the B.A., B.S., B.B.A., B.F.A., B.M., B.S.C.J., B.S.Ed., and B.S.N. degrees. Associate and master's degrees are also awarded. Bachelor's degrees are awarded in BIOLOGICAL SCIENCE (biology/biological science), BUSINESS (accounting, banking and finance, business administration and management, business economics, management engineering, and marketing/retailing/merchandising), COMMUNICATIONS AND THE ARTS (broadcasting, communications, dramatic arts, English, fine arts, French, music, Spanish, speech/debate/rhetoric, and telecommunications), COMPUTER AND PHYSICAL SCIENCE (applied mathematics, astronomy, chemistry, computer management, computer science, mathematics, and physics), EDUCATION (art, business, early childhood, elementary, guidance, health, middle school, music, physical, science, secondary, and special), ENGINEERING AND ENVIRONMENTAL DESIGN (preengineering), HEALTH PROFESSIONS (nursing, speech pathology/audiology, and sports medicine), SOCIAL SCIENCE (anthropology, criminal justice, history, paralegal studies, philosophy, political science/government, prelaw, psychology, public administration, social science, and sociology). Sports medicine is the strongest academically. Education and business have the largest enrollments.

Required: To graduate, all students must complete a minimum of 183 quarter credit hours including 90 in the core curriculum, and 60 of senior-college rank including 30 in a major. A GPA of 2.0. must be maintained. Health education is required. Reasonable proficiency in written and spoken English is also required.

Special: The college offers more than 30 dual degrees with the Georgia Institute of Technology and has a co-op program with the Medical College of Georgia. Internships are available as are work-study programs and study abroad. A general studies degree is offered, and credit is given for life experience. There is a freshman honors program on campus, as well as 2 national honor societies, including Phi Beta Kappa.

Faculty/Classroom: The average class size in an introductory lecture is 40; in a laboratory, 30; and in a regular course offering, 35.

Admissions: About 72% of the 1993–94 applicants were accepted.

Requirements: Either the SAT I with a minimum verbal score of 300 and minimum mathematics score of 330, or the ACT, with a minimum score each of 15 English and 15 mathematics, is required. Applicants must be graduates of accredited high schools with a GPA of 2.0 and have completed 4 years of English, 3 each of mathematics, science, and social science, and 2 of the same foreign language. A GED is accepted. AP and CLEP credits are accepted.

Procedure: Freshmen are admitted to all sessions. Application deadlines are open. The fee is $10. Notification is sent as early as possible on a rolling basis.

Transfer: Applicants with fewer than 20 hours of transferable credit must meet the same qualifications as entering freshmen. Transcripts from all previously attended colleges must be submitted. A total of 45 quarter credit hours out of 183 must be completed at VSU.

Visiting: There are regularly scheduled orientations for prospective students. There are guides for informal visits and visitors may sit in on classes and stay overnight at the school. To arrange for a visit, contact the Admissions Office at (912) 333-5791.

Financial Aid: In an earlier year, 40% of all students received some form of financial aid. Scholarships or need-based grants that year averaged $100 ($1500 maximum); loans averaged $1200 ($2625 maximum); and work contracts averaged $1200 ($1650 maximum). About 45% of undergraduate students work part-time. The average financial indebtedness of a graduate has been $4093. VSU is a member of CSS. The FAF, FFS or SFS is required. The deadline for financial aid applications is April 1.

International Students: There are currently 113 international students enrolled. They must take the TOEFL and achieve a minimum score of 500.

Computers: The college provides computer facilities for student use. The mainframes are a UNISYS A 4FX, a Texas Instruments 1500, and a Prime 750. In addition to its own system, VSU also has access to the CDC CYBER 850, IBM 3090, and other computing facilities of the University System of Georgia. There are also microcomputer and terminal laboratories. All students may access the system. There are no time limits on using the system and no fees.

Admissions Contact: Director of Admissions.

WESLEYAN COLLEGE

Macon, GA 31297   (912) 477-1110; (800) 447-6610 (out-of-state)

Full-time: 387 women	Faculty: 41; IIB, --$
Part-time: 69 women	Ph.D.s: 73%
Graduate: none	Student/Faculty: 9 to 1
Year: semesters, summer session	Tuition: $11,195
Application Deadline: March 1	Room & Board: $4250
Freshman Class: 291 applied, 287 accepted, 109 enrolled	
SAT I Verbal/Math: 510/480	**COMPETITIVE**

Wesleyan College, founded in 1836, is a private, liberal arts women's college affiliated with the United Methodist Church. In addition to regional accreditation, Wesleyan has baccalaureate program accreditation with NASM. The library contains 134,484 volumes, 19,504 microform items, and 6229 audiovisual forms, and subscribes to 556 periodicals. Computerized library sources and services include interlibrary loans. Special learning facilities include an art gallery, a computerized teaching classroom, and language and mathematics laboratories. The 200-acre campus is in a suburban area 70 miles south of Atlanta. Including residence halls, there are 16 buildings on campus.

Student Life: About 58% of undergraduates are from Georgia. Students come from 19 states, 16 foreign countries, and Canada. Seventy-seven percent are from public schools; 23% from private. Seventy-eight percent are white; 11% are African American. Sixty-eight percent are Protestant; 16%, Catholic; 11% claim no religious affiliation. The average age of freshmen is 18; all undergraduates, 21. Thirty percent drop out by the end of their first year; 47% remain to graduate.

Housing: A total of 466 students can be accommodated in college housing. College-sponsored living facilities include dormitories. On-campus housing is guaranteed for all 4 years. Ninety percent of students live on campus; of those, 60% remain on campus on weekends. Alcohol is not permitted. All students may keep cars on campus.

Activities: There are no sororities. There are 40 groups on campus, including art, choir, chorus, computers, dance, drama, ethnic, honors, international, literary magazine, musical theater, newspaper, political, professional, religious, social, social service, student government, and yearbook. Popular campus events include Homecoming, Parents Weekend, Stunt, the Christmas banquet, and mixers.

Sports: Athletic and recreation facilities include a soccer field, golf course, equestrian arena, indoor pool, gymnasium, dance studio, weight room, lake for boating, and fitness trail.

Disabled Students: The following facilities are available: wheelchair ramps and special parking.

Services: In addition to many counseling and information services, tutoring is available in every subject. There is a writing laboratory, and a study skills workshop.

Campus Safety and Security: Campus safety and security measures include 24-hour foot and vehicle patrol, escort service, informal discussions, and emergency telephones. In addition, there are lighted pathways and sidewalks, and dormitories have combination locks on entry doors.

Programs of Study: Wesleyan awards the A.B. degree. Bachelor's degrees are awarded in BIOLOGICAL SCIENCE (biology/biological science), BUSINESS (business administration and management), COMMUNICATIONS AND THE ARTS (arts administration/management, communications, English, French, journalism, music, and Spanish), COMPUTER AND PHYSICAL SCIENCE (chemistry and mathematics), EDUCATION (early childhood, middle school, and secondary), SOCIAL SCIENCE (history, interdisciplinary studies, international relations, philosophy, political science/government, psychology, religion, and sociology). Education, business, and English are the strongest academically. Business and education have the largest enrollments.

Required: Students must complete 120 credit hours with a minimum GPA of 2.0 in order to graduate. General requirements include 8 hours of science and technology, first year seminar and 1 mathematics for a total of 6 hours, 6 hours each of literature, language, fine arts, history, and self and society, and 3 hours each of junior seminar and oral communication. All students must take a course in English composition. The total number of hours required in the major varies.

Special: Wesleyan offers a 3-2 engineering degree with Georgia Institute of Technology and Auburn and Mercer universities. More than 150 internships are available, as are interdisciplinary, student-designed, and dual majors, a Washington semester offered through Trinity College, study abroad, work-study programs, credit for life experience, nondegree study, and pass/fail options. There is a freshman honors program on campus, as well as 11 national honor societies. Five departments have honors programs.

Faculty/Classroom: Forty-six percent of faculty are male; 54%, female. All teach undergraduates. The average class size in an introductory lecture is 24; in a laboratory, 24; and in a regular course offering, 15.

Admissions: About 99% of the 1993-94 applicants were accepted. The SAT scores for the 1993-94 freshman class were as follows: Verbal—40% below 500, 28% between 500 and 599, 26% between 600 and 700, and 6% above 700; Math—56% below 500, 25% between 500 and 599, 18% between 600 and 700, and 1% above 700.

About 80% of the current freshmen were in the top fifth of their class; 100% were in the top two fifths. There was 1 National Merit semifinalist. One freshman graduated first in her class.

Requirements: The SAT I or ACT is required. The college uses a formula to evaluate the GPA and the standardized test scores for acceptance decisions. Applicants must be graduates of an accredited secondary school or have a GED certificate. They should have completed 16 Carnegie units, including 4 units each of English and electives, 3 units each of mathematics and social science, and 2 units in natural science. An essay is required and an interview is recommended. A portfolio or audition is required for art and music students. AP and CLEP credits are accepted. Important factors used in the admissions decision are advanced placement or honor courses, leadership record, evidence of special talent, extracurricular activities record, and geographic diversity.

Procedure: Freshmen are admitted in the fall and spring. Entrance exams should be taken in the fall of the senior year. Early decision applications should be filed by November 1; regular applications, by March 1 for fall entry, along with an application fee of $25. Notification of early decision is sent December 1; regular decision, no later than April 1. There are early decision, early admissions, and deferred admissions plans. Six early decision candidates were accepted for the 1993-94 class.

Transfer: Fifteen transfer students enrolled in 1993-94. Applicants should have earned at least 15 credit hours with a minimum GPA of 2.0. An interview is recommended. A total of 30 credits out of 120 must be completed at Wesleyan.

Visiting: There are regularly scheduled orientations for prospective students, including a tour of the campus, parent/student panels, class visitation, financial aid sessions, and meals in the dining hall. There are guides for informal visits, and visitors may sit in on classes and stay overnight at the school. To arrange for a visit, contact Carole Nichols at (912) 477-1110, ext. 206, or (800) 447-6610.

Financial Aid: In 1993-94, 97% of all current freshmen and 92% of continuing students received some form of financial aid. About 74% of freshmen and 80% of continuing students received need-based aid. The average freshman award was $12,746. Of that total, scholarships or need-based grants averaged $4429 ($15,445 maximum); loans averaged $2600 ($5625 maximum); and work contracts averaged $1000 ($1200 maximum). Eighty-five percent of undergraduate students work part-time. Average earnings from campus work for the school year are $1000. The average financial indebtedness of the 1992-93 graduate was $5912. Wesleyan is a member of CSS. The FFS and the college's own financial statement are required. The deadline for financial aid applications is April 1.

International Students: There are currently 16 international students enrolled. The school actively recruits these students. They must take the TOEFL and achieve a minimum score of 550.

Computers: The college provides computer facilities for student use. Entering first-year students receive an Apple Macintosh Classic as part of their tuition. There are also Apple Macintosh SEs and NCR 486 PCs available in the computer laboratory. All students may access the system. There are no time limits on using the system and no fees.

Graduates: In 1992-93, 82 bachelor's degrees were awarded. The most popular majors among graduates were business administration (18%), psychology (13%), and communication (12%). Some 35 companies recruited on campus in 1992-93. Of the 1992 graduating class, 40% were enrolled in graduate school within 6 months of graduation; 60% had found employment.

Admissions Contact: Director of Admissions.

WEST GEORGIA COLLEGE

Carrollton, GA 30118   (404) 836-6416

Full-time: 1850 men, 2688 women	Faculty: 251; IIA, --$
Part-time: 437 men, 752 women	Ph.D.s: 76%
Graduate: 457 men, 1766 women	Student/Faculty: 18 to 1
Year: quarters, summer session	Tuition: $1766 ($4528)
Application Deadline: September 1	Room & Board: $2490
Freshman Class: 3668 applied, 2690 accepted, 1331 enrolled	
SAT I Verbal/Math: 400/450	ACT: 20 **COMPETITIVE**

West Georgia College, founded in 1933 as part of the university system of Georgia, is a public coeducational institution offering degree programs in liberal arts, business, and teacher preparation. There are 3 undergraduate schools and one graduate school. In addition to regional accreditation, West Georgia College has baccalaureate program accreditation with AACSB, NASM, NCATE, and NLN. The library contains 295,260 volumes, 824,949 microform items, and 117 audiovisual forms, and subscribes to 1495 periodicals. Computerized library sources and services include the card catalog, interlibrary loans, and database searching. Special learning facilities include a learning resource center, art gallery, radio and TV stations, and an observatory, a state archeological office, and a performing arts center. The 394-acre campus is in a suburban area 50 miles southwest of Atlanta. Including residence halls, there are 60 buildings on campus.

Student Life: About 97% of undergraduates are from Georgia. Students come from 30 states, 30 foreign countries, and Canada. Ninety-five percent are from public schools; 5% from private. Eighty-two per-

cent are white; 16% African American. The average age of freshmen is 21.3; all undergraduates, 23.7. Forty percent drop out by the end of their first year; 30% remain to graduate.

Housing: A total of 2762 students can be accommodated in college housing. College-sponsored living facilities include single-sex and coed dormitories. In addition, there are special interest houses. On-campus housing is guaranteed for the freshman year only and is available on a first-come, first-served basis. Seventy-six percent of students commute. All students may keep cars on campus.

Activities: About 24% of men belong to 10 national fraternities; about 14% of women belong to 9 national sororities. There are 88 groups on campus, including band, cheerleading, choir, computers, dance, drama, drill team, ethnic, gay, honors, international, jazz band, literary magazine, marching band, newspaper, opera, pep band, political, professional, radio and TV, religious, social, social service, student government, and symphony. Popular campus events include Greek Week, Homecoming, Fine Arts Festival, Spring Fling, Honor Convocation, International Student Night, Black History Month, Sex in the 90s, Street Dance, and Welcome Back Blast.

Sports: There are 6 intercollegiate sports for men and 5 for women, and 26 intramural sports for men and 23 for women. Athletic and recreation facilities include 3 gymnasiums, an Olympic-size swimming pool, a weight room, and a 10,000-seat stadium.

Disabled Students: Sixty-five percent of the campus is accessible to disabled students. The following facilities are available: wheelchair ramps, elevators, special parking, specially equipped rest rooms, special class scheduling, and lowered drinking fountains and telephones.

Services: In addition to many counseling and information services, tutoring is available in some subjects, including most core subjects. There is also a reader service for the blind, and remedial math, reading, and writing. Braille equipment and a speak computer are available.

Campus Safety and Security: Campus safety and security measures include 24-hour foot and vehicle patrol, escort service, shuttle buses, and informal discussions. In addition, there are pamphlets, posters, films, emergency telephones, and lighted pathways and sidewalks.

Programs of Study: West Georgia College awards the B.A., B.S., B.B.A., B.F.A., B.M., B.S. Ed., B.S.E.S., B.S.N., and B.S.Rec. degrees. Associate and master's degrees also are awarded. Bachelor's degrees are awarded in BIOLOGICAL SCIENCE (biology/biological science), BUSINESS (accounting, banking and finance, business economics, management information systems, management science, and marketing/retailing/merchandising), COMMUNICATIONS AND THE ARTS (communications, English, fine arts, French, music, Spanish, and speech/debate/rhetoric), COMPUTER AND PHYSICAL SCIENCE (chemistry, computer science, earth science, geology, mathematics, and physics), EDUCATION (business, early childhood, middle school, physical, secondary, and special), HEALTH PROFESSIONS (nursing), SOCIAL SCIENCE (anthropology, economics, geography, history, liberal arts/general studies, parks and recreation management, philosophy, political science/government, psychology, sociology, and systems science). Early childhood education has the largest enrollment.

Required: In order to graduate, the student must have earned 190 quarter credit hours with a minimum GPA of 2.0. Distribution requirements include 35 hours in the major, 6 in physical education, and 20 each in the humanities, science, mathematics, and social sciences.

Special: The college has cooperative and work-study programs with state, regional, national, and international corporations, and offers short-term internships and supervised work experience, usually for credit. Cross-registration with the University of Georgia is available. The student may undertake an accelerated-degree program in any major, a dual major in physics/engineering, a 3–2 engineering degree program from Georgia Tech or Auburn University, or nondegree study for teacher certification. Students may study abroad in Europe, Canada, and Taiwan. There is a freshman honors program on campus, as well as 15 national honor societies, including Phi Beta Kappa. Eleven departments have honors programs.

Faculty/Classroom: Sixty-seven percent of faculty are male; 33%, female. Ninety percent teach undergraduates and 15% do research. No introductory courses are taught by graduate students. The average class size in an introductory lecture is 40; in a laboratory, 20; and in a regular course offering, 30.

Admissions: About 73% of the 1993–94 applicants were accepted. The SAT scores for the 1993–94 freshman class were as follows: Verbal—89% below 500, 9% between 500 and 599, and 2% between 600 and 700; Math—77% below 500, 17% between 500 and 599, and 5% between 600 and 700. The ACT scores were 62% below 21, 23% between 21 and 23, 11% between 24 and 26, 3% between 27 and 28, and 1% above 28.

Requirements: A minimum GPA of 2.5 is required. The SAT I or ACT is required, with a composite score of at least 680 on SAT I or 17 on the ACT. Students must be graduates of an accredited secondary school or have a GED certificate. They should have completed 2 years of a foreign language, 4 of English, and 3 each of mathematics, science, and social studies. An interview is recommended. AP and CLEP credits are accepted.

Procedure: Freshmen are admitted to all sessions. Entrance exams should be taken by December of the senior year. Applications should be filed by September 1 for fall entry, December 1 for winter entry, March 1 for spring entry, and June 1 for summer entry, along with an application fee of $10. Notification is sent on a rolling basis. There is an early admissions plan.

Transfer: About 461 transfer students enrolled in 1993–94. Applicants must have a minimum GPA of 1.6 to 2.0, determined by the number of quarter credits attempted at the previous college. A total of 50 quarter credit hours out of 190 must be completed at West Georgia College.

Visiting: There are regularly scheduled orientations for prospective students. There are guides for informal visits and visitors may sit in on classes. To arrange for a visit, contact Jennifer W. Payne, Director of Admissions at (404) 836–6416.

Financial Aid: In 1993–94, 51% of all current freshmen and 47% of continuing students received some form of financial aid. About 32% of freshmen and 34% of continuing students received need-based aid. The average freshman award was $2642. Of that total, scholarships or need-based grants averaged $926 (maximum); loans averaged $1599 ($2625 maximum); and work contracts averaged $628 ($1800 maximum). Thirty-nine percent of undergraduate students work part-time. Average earnings from campus work for the school year are $747. The average financial indebtedness of the 1992–93 graduate was $9300. West Georgia College is a member of CSS. The FAFSA financial statement is required. There is no deadline for financial aid applications.

International Students: There are currently 112 international students enrolled. The school actively recruits these students. They must take the TOEFL and achieve a minimum score of 550. The student must also take the SAT I or the ACT.

Computers: The college provides computer facilities for student use. The mainframe is an IBM 4341 Model II, a Sun 4280, and a TI 990–20, with access to the University of Georgia's CDC Cyber 180/850 and IBM 3090 facilities. Nearly 500 microcomputers support 3 computer laboratories as well as the business, arts and sciences, and education departments. All students may access the system. There are no time limits and no fees.

Graduates: In 1992–93, 807 bachelor's degrees were awarded. The most popular majors among graduates were early childhood education (15%), psychology (9%), and marketing (8%). Within an average freshman class, 9% graduate in 4 years, 19% in 5 years, and 24% in 6 years. Some 342 companies recruited on campus in an earlier year.

Admissions Contact: Jennifer W. Payne, Director of Admissions.

WOMEN'S COLLEGE OF BRENAU UNIVERSITY   B-2
(Formerly Brenau Women's College)
Gainesville, GA 30501

(404) 534–6100
(800) 252–5119 (out-of-state)

Full-time: 111 men, 806 women	Faculty: 90
Part-time: 162 men, 317 women	Ph.D.s: 80%
Graduate: 256 men, 468 women	Student/Faculty: 10 to 1
Year: quarters, summer session	Tuition: $8840
Application Deadline: open	Room & Board: $5894
Freshman Class: 380 applied, 284 accepted, 155 enrolled	
SAT I or ACT: required	COMPETITIVE

Women's College of Brenau University, founded in 1878, is a private undergraduate and graduate liberal arts institution primarily for women. Coeducational programs are offered as part of the university, in an evening and weekend format. In addition to regional accreditation, Brenau has baccalaureate program accreditation with FIDER and NLN. The library contains 80,000 volumes, 131,622 microform items, and 9102 audiovisual forms, and subscribes to 1000 periodicals. Computerized library sources and services include the card catalog, interlibrary loans, and database searching. Special learning facilities include a learning resource center, an art gallery, a radio station, and a TV studio. The 50-acre campus is in a small town 50 miles northeast of Atlanta. Including residence halls, there are 50 buildings on campus.

Student Life: About 79% of undergraduates are from Georgia. Students come from 47 states, 25 foreign countries, and Canada. Ninety percent are from public schools; 10% from private. Eighty-three percent are white; 16% African American. The average age of freshmen is 19; all undergraduates, 23. Thirty percent drop out by the end of their first year; 52% remain to graduate.

Housing: A total of 418 students can be accommodated in college housing. College-sponsored living facilities include single-sex dormitories, on-campus apartments, and sorority houses. On-campus housing is guaranteed for all 4 years. Sixty-four percent of students live on campus; of those, 90% remain on campus on weekends. All students may keep cars on campus.

Activities: About 60% of women belong to 8 local and 7 national sororities. There are no fraternities on campus. There are 40 groups on campus, including art, choir, chorale, chorus, computers, dance, drama, film, honors, international, literary magazine, musical theater, newspaper, opera, photography, professional, radio and TV, religious, social, student government, symphony, and yearbook. Popular

campus events include Rat Week, May Day, Spade Hunt, and Miss Brenau.

Sports: There are 2 intercollegiate sports for women and 6 intramural sports for women. Athletic and recreation facilities include a tennis center, a recreation field, a gymnasium, and a natatorium.

Disabled Students: Ninety percent of the campus is accessible to disabled students. The following facilities are available: wheelchair ramps, elevators, special parking, specially equipped rest rooms, and special class scheduling.

Services: In addition to counseling and information services, there is remedial math, reading, and writing.

Campus Safety and Security: Campus safety and security measures include 24-hour foot and vehicle patrol, self-defense education, escort service, and informal discussions. In addition, there are lighted pathways and sidewalks.

Programs of Study: Brenau awards the B.A., B.S., B.F.A., B.M., and B.S.N. degrees. Master's degrees also are awarded. Bachelor's degrees are awarded in BIOLOGICAL SCIENCE (biology/biological science), BUSINESS (accounting and business administration and management), COMMUNICATIONS AND THE ARTS (broadcasting, communications, dance, design, dramatic arts, English, fine arts, journalism, and music), EDUCATION (early childhood, middle school, and special), HEALTH PROFESSIONS (medical laboratory technology, nursing, predentistry, and premedicine), SOCIAL SCIENCE (criminal justice, history, political science/government, prelaw, psychology, and public administration). Nursing, business administration, and early childhood education have the largest enrollments.

Required: To graduate, all students must complete at least 200 quarter hours of work including 60 to 80 hours in the major. Requirements for each degree vary, but students must maintain a 2.0 GPA overall and a 2.5 GPA in course work required by the major. Most majors require or allow internships. In addition to specific requirements, students must take physical education courses and demonstrate computer proficiency.

Special: Students may study abroad in 6 foreign countries. Brenau offers B.A.-B.S. degrees, dual majors, internships, a general studies degree, and student-designed majors. Students may receive credit for life, military, and work experience. There is a freshman honors program on campus, as well as 11 national honor societies. Four departments have honors programs.

Faculty/Classroom: Fifty percent of faculty are male; 50%, female. Eighty-nine percent teach undergraduates. No introductory courses are taught by graduate students. The average class size in an introductory lecture is 18; in a laboratory, 18; and in a regular course offering, 13.

Admissions: About 75% of the 1993–94 applicants were accepted. **Requirements:** A minimum GPA of 2.2 is required. The SAT I or ACT is required. In addition, candidates for admission should have completed 4 units of English, 3 units of mathematics, 2 units of science, 2 to 3 units of social studies, and 7 to 9 units of electives. AP and CLEP credits are accepted. Important factors used in the admissions decision are advanced placement or honor courses, recommendations by school officials, personality, intangible qualities, leadership record, and evidence of special talent.

Procedure: Freshmen are admitted to all sessions. Entrance exams should be taken in the fall of the senior year. Application deadlines are open. The application fee is $25. Notification of early decision is sent November 15; regular decision, on a rolling basis. There are early decision, early admissions, and deferred admissions plans. Two early decision candidates were accepted for the 1993–94 class.

Transfer: About 340 transfer students enrolled in 1993–94. The last 45 quarter hours, including at least 35 in the major, must be taken at the college. Students must maintain a minimum GPA of 2.0. A total of 45 credits out of 200 must be completed at Brenau.

Visiting: There are regularly scheduled orientations for prospective students, consisting of a campus tour, an information session, and an interview. There are guides for informal visits, and visitors may sit in on classes and stay overnight at the school. To arrange for a visit, contact the Admissions Office.

Financial Aid: In a recent year, 70% of all current freshmen and 61% of continuing students received some form of financial aid. About 50% of freshmen and 40% of continuing students received need-based aid. Scholarships or need-based grants averaged $5314 ($12,500 maximum); loans averaged $1489 ($2625 maximum); and work contracts averaged $1015 ($2000 maximum). Average earnings from campus work for the school year are $1275. The average financial indebtedness of the 1992–93 graduate was $5705. Brenau is a member of CSS. The FAF and the college's own financial statement are required. The deadline for financial aid applications is June 1.

International Students: There are currently 29 international students enrolled. The school actively recruits these students. They must take the TOEFL and achieve a minimum score of 500.

Computers: The college provides computer facilities for student use. There are 90 microcomputers located in laboratories and residence halls around campus. The residence hall units have modems to interface with the library computer. All students may access the system. It may be used 24 hours per day. There are no time limits on using the system and no fees.

Graduates: In 1992–93, 400 bachelor's degrees were awarded. The most popular majors among graduates were business administration (20%), education (20%), and public administration (10%). Within an average freshman class, 52% graduate in 4 years and 3% in 5 years.

Admissions Contact: Dr. John D. Upchurch, Dean of Admissions.

GUAM

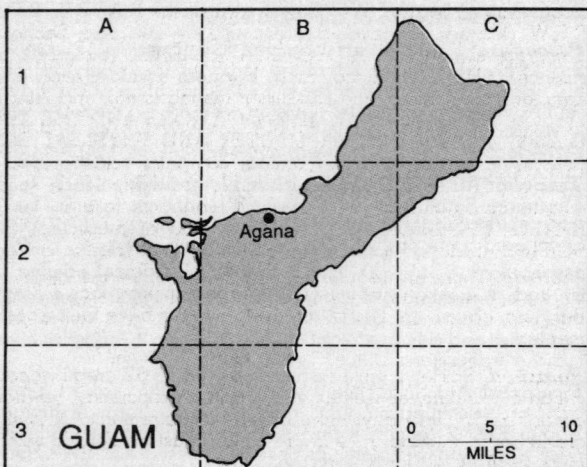

A   B   C

1

2   Agana

3   **GUAM**

0   5   10
MILES

UNIVERSITY OF GUAM
Mangilao, GU 96923   **(671) 734–3450**

Full-time: 908 men, 1462 women   **Faculty:** 191; IIB, + +$
Part-time: 424 men, 533 women   **Ph.D.s:** 57%
Graduate: 133 men, 193 women   **Student/Faculty:** 12 to 1
Year: semesters, summer session   **Tuition:** $1234 ($2194)
Application Deadline: August 4   **Room & Board:** $2905
Freshman Class: n/av
SAT I or ACT: not required   **NONCOMPETITIVE**

The University of Guam, founded in 1952, is a public liberal arts institution located on the island of Guam. There are 4 undergraduate schools and one graduate school. The library contains 300,000 volumes. The 100-acre campus is in a rural area. Including residence halls, there are 52 buildings on campus.

Student Life: About 80% of undergraduates are from Guam. Students come from 49 states, 37 foreign countries, and Canada. Eleven percent are white. The average age of freshmen is 19.

Housing: College-sponsored living facilities include coed dormitories. On-campus housing is available on a first-come, first-served basis. Ninety-three percent of students commute. Alcohol is not permitted. All students may keep cars on campus.

Activities: There are no fraternities or sororities on campus. There are 7 groups on campus, including art, dance, drama, newspaper, student government, and yearbook. Popular campus events include Charter Day.

Disabled Students: The following facilities are available: wheelchair ramps, special parking, and special class scheduling.

Programs of Study: University of Guam awards the B.A., B.S., B.B.A., and B.B.S. degrees. Associate and master's degrees are also awarded. Bachelor's degrees are awarded in BIOLOGICAL SCIENCE (biology/biological science), BUSINESS (accounting, business administration and management, and marketing/retailing/merchandising), COMMUNICATIONS AND THE ARTS (communications and fine arts), COMPUTER AND PHYSICAL SCIENCE (chemistry and mathematics), EDUCATION (art, early childhood, elementary, guidance, and secondary), HEALTH PROFESSIONS (nursing), SOCIAL SCIENCE (anthropology, criminal justice, history, political science/government, psychology, public administration, social science, social work, and sociology).

Required: To graduate, all students must have a 2.0 GPA and a minimum of 124 credit hours, including 40 upper-division credits. General requirements vary by major.

Procedure: Entrance exams should be taken at least 1 week before registration. Applications should be filed by August 4 for fall entry, along with an application fee of $10. The college accepts all applicants

Transfer: About 222 transfer students enrolled in a recent year. A total of 32 credits out of 124 must be completed at University of Guam.

Visiting: Visitors may sit in on classes. To arrange for a visit, contact the Director of Housing.

Financial Aid: In an earlier year, 31% of all current freshmen and 34% of continuing students received some form of financial aid. Scholarships or need-based grants averaged $3000; loans averaged $2625 ($5625 maximum); and work contracts averaged $1500 ($3000 maximum). Ten percent of undergraduate students work part-time. The average financial indebtedness of the 1992–93 graduate was $2346. University of Guam is a member of CSS. The FAF is required. The deadline for financial aid applications is November 24.

International Students: Students must take the TOEFL.

Computers: The college provides computer facilities for student use. The mainframe is an IBM 4300. There are no time limits on using the system and no fees.

Graduates: In a recent year, 203 bachelor's degrees were awarded.

Admissions Contact: Kathleen R. Owings, Admissions and Records Director.

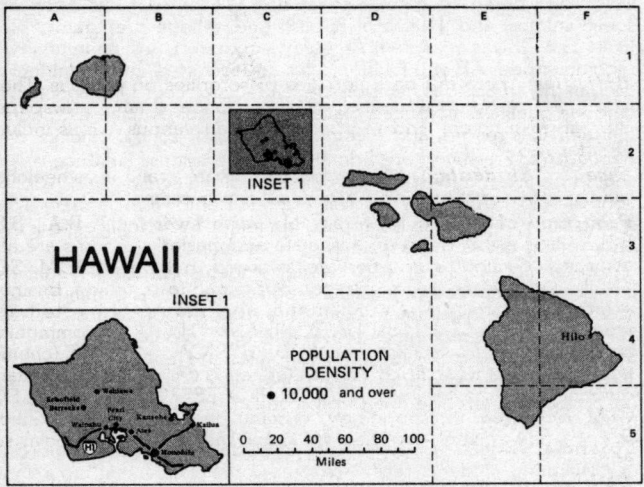

HAWAII

INSET 1

INSET 1

POPULATION
DENSITY
● 10,000 and over

0 20 40 60 80 100
Miles

BRIGHAM YOUNG UNIVERSITY
HAWAII
C-2
Oahu, HI 96762   (808) 293–3738

Full-time: 772 men, 1038 women   **Faculty:** 153
Part-time: 92 men, 126 women   **Ph.D.s:** 64%
Graduate: none   **Student/Faculty:** 12 to 1
Year: 4-4-2-2, summer session   **Tuition:** $2375
Application Deadline: March 31   **Room & Board:** $4375
Freshman Class: 835 applied, 589 accepted, 495 enrolled
ACT: 21   **VERY COMPETITIVE**

Brigham Young University/Hawaii, founded in 1955 by the Church of Latter-day Saints, is a private, coeducational institution offering programs in liberal arts, business, and education. There are 3 undergraduate schools. The library contains 160,000 volumes, 800,000 microform items, and 3500 audiovisual forms, and subscribes to 1050 periodicals. Computerized library sources and services include the card catalog, interlibrary loans, and database searching. Special learning facilities include a learning resource center and natural history museum. The 60-acre campus is in a small town 30 miles north of Honolulu. Including residence halls, there are 42 buildings on campus.

Student Life: About 29% of undergraduates are from Hawaii. Students come from 40 states, 56 foreign countries, and Canada. Some 33% are Asian American; 32% white; 31% foreign nationals.

Housing: A total of 1360 students can be accommodated in college housing. College-sponsored living facilities include single-sex dormitories, on-campus apartments, and married-student housing. On-campus housing is available on a first-come, first-served basis. Priority is given to out-of-town students. About 70% of students live on campus; of those, 100% remain on campus on weekends. Alcohol is not permitted. All students may keep cars on campus.

Activities: There are no fraternities or sororities on campus. There are 35 groups on campus, including band, cheerleading, choir, chorale, computers, dance, drama, ethnic, film, honors, international, jazz band, literary magazine, musical theater, newspaper, pep band, political, professional, religious, social, social service, and student government. Popular campus events include International Food Fest, International Cultural Night, Na Hoa Pono Pageant, and Talent Show.

Sports: There are 6 intercollegiate sports for men and 5 for women, and 10 intramural sports for men and 10 for women. Athletic and recreation facilities include 3 softball fields, 2 soccer fields and a rugby field; 10 tennis and 5 racquetball courts; a swimming pool; a weight room; a bowling alley; a dance studio; pool tables; a 5000-seat activity center; and 2 basketball gymnasiums, one of which seats 1500.

Disabled Students: About 95% of the campus is accessible to disabled students. The following facilities are available: wheelchair ramps, elevators, special parking, specially equipped rest rooms, and lowered drinking fountains.

Services: In addition to many counseling and information services, tutoring is available in most subjects. There is remedial math, reading, and writing.

Campus Safety and Security: Campus safety and security measures include 24-hour foot and vehicle patrol, escort service, informal discussions, and pamphlets, posters, and films. In addition, there are emergency telephones and lighted pathways and sidewalks.

Programs of Study: BYU/Hawaii awards the B.A., B.S., B.F.A., and B.S.W. degrees. Associate degrees also are awarded. Bachelor's degrees are awarded in BIOLOGICAL SCIENCE (biology/biological science), BUSINESS (accounting, business administration and management, hotel/motel and restaurant management, and international business management), COMMUNICATIONS AND THE ARTS (art, English, and fine arts), COMPUTER AND PHYSICAL SCIENCE (chemistry, computer programming, computer science, and mathematics), EDUCATION (art, business, elementary, science, secondary, and teaching English as a second language/foreign language), HEALTH PROFESSIONS (predentistry and premedicine), SOCIAL SCIENCE (history, Pacific area studies, political science/government, psychology, social work, and sociology). Biological science, chemistry, and information systems are the strongest programs academically. Business, education, and information systems have the largest enrollments.

Required: Students must complete the 44 to 62 credit general education curriculum, as well as meet English proficiency, religious education, health, and physical education requirements. A total of 128 credit hours, including 24 in the major, must be earned with a minimum GPA of 2.0 for graduation.

Special: BYU/Hawaii offers work-study programs within the community, cooperative programs in most majors, nondegree study, and pass/fail options. There is a freshman honors program on campus, as well as 5 national honor societies.

Faculty/Classroom: Some 69% of faculty are male; 31%, female. All teach undergraduates and 15% both teach and do research.

Admissions: About 71% of the 1993–94 applicants were accepted. The ACT scores for the 1993–94 freshman class were as follows: 13% below 21, 42% between 21 and 23, 32% between 24 and 26, 11% between 27 and 28, and 2% above 28.

Requirements: A minimum GPA of 2.5 is required, as is the ACT, with a minimum composite score of 20. The applicant should be a high school graduate; an interview is required. AP and CLEP credits are accepted. Important factors used in the admissions decision are recommendations by school officials, recommendations by alumni, evidence of special talent, advanced placement or honor courses, and parents or siblings attending the school.

Procedure: Freshmen are admitted in the fall, winter, and spring. Entrance exams should be taken prior to the application deadline. Applications should be filed by March 31 for fall entry, October 1 for winter entry, and February 1 for spring entry, along with an application fee of $10. Notification is sent within 14 days after receipt of the completed application. There is an early admissions plan. A waiting list is an active part of the admissions procedure.

Transfer: About 179 transfer students enrolled in 1993–94. Applicants must have 24 hours of college credit, with a minimum GPA of 2.5. A total of 30 credits out of 128 must be completed at BYU/Hawaii.

Visiting: There are regularly scheduled orientations for prospective students. There are guides for informal visits. To arrange for a visit, contact the University Relations Office at (808) 293–3660.

Financial Aid: In a recent year, 80% of all students received some form of financial aid. Some 60% of undergraduate students work part-time. Average earnings from campus work for the school year are $6000. BYU/Hawaii is a member of CSS. The FAF is required. The deadline for financial aid applications is April 30.

International Students: There are currently 882 international students enrolled. The school actively recruits these students. They must take the TOEFL or the University of Michigan Language Test and achieve a minimum score on the TOEFL of 475.

Computers: The college provides computer facilities for student use. The mainframe is a DEC MicroVAX. There are also 60 Apple IIe, Apple Macintosh, and IBM microcomputers available in the computer laboratories. All students may access the system, which may be used 18 hours per day. There are no time limits on using the system. The fees are $25.

Graduates: In 1992–93, 269 bachelor's degrees were awarded. The most popular majors among graduates were business management (12%), elementary education (10%), and accounting (10%). Some 85 companies recruited on campus in a recent year.

Admissions Contact: Clark E. Hirschi, Coordinator of Admissions.

CHAMINADE UNIVERSITY OF HONOLULU

C-2

Honolulu, HI 96816   (808) 735-4735; (800) 735-3733 (out-of-state)

Full-time: 766	Faculty: 50
Part-time: 1154	Ph.D.s: 40%
Graduate: 532 men and women	Student/Faculty: 15 to 1
Year: semesters, summer session	Tuition: $9990
Application Deadline: August 1	Room & Board: $4300
Freshman Class: 310 applied, 273 accepted, 119 enrolled	
SAT I Verbal/Math: 440/480	ACT: 19 COMPETITIVE

Chaminade University of Honolulu, founded in 1955, is a private, co-educational institution affiliated with the Roman Catholic Church. The university offers degree programs in business and the arts and sciences. There are 5 undergraduate and 5 graduate schools. The library contains 60,000 volumes, 10,000 microform items, and 985 audiovisual forms, and subscribes to 500 periodicals. Special learning facilities include a learning resource center and an audiovisual media center. The 62-acre campus is in a suburban area 4 miles east of downtown Honolulu. Including residence halls, there are 8 buildings on campus.

Student Life: About 45% of undergraduates are from Hawaii. Students come from 35 states, 30 foreign countries, and Canada. Forty-five percent are from public schools; 55%, from private. Forty-four percent are Asian American; 35%, white; 15%, foreign nationals. Forty-two percent are Catholic. The average age of freshmen is 18. Thirty percent drop out by the end of their first year.

Housing: A total of 270 students can be accommodated in college housing. College-sponsored living facilities include single-sex and coed dormitories and on-campus apartments. On-campus housing is available on a first-come, first-served basis. Sixty-six percent of students commute. All students may keep cars on campus.

Activities: There are no fraternities or sororities on campus. There are 30 groups on campus, including art, cheerleading, choir, computers, drama, ethnic, honors, international, literary magazine, newspaper, political, professional, religious, social, social service, student government, and yearbook. Popular campus events include Spring Serendipity, International Extravaganza, and Club Fest.

Sports: There are 4 intercollegiate sports for men and 4 for women, and 8 intramural sports for men and 8 for women. Athletic and recreation facilities include tennis courts and basketball courts.

Disabled Students: Five percent of the campus is accessible to disabled students. The following facilities are available: special parking and specially equipped rest rooms.

Services: In addition to many counseling and information services, tutoring is available in most subjects. There is remedial math, reading, and writing.

Campus Safety and Security: Campus safety and security measures include 24-hour foot and vehicle patrol, self-defense education, informal discussions, and pamphlets, posters, and films. In addition, there are emergency telephones and lighted pathways and sidewalks.

Programs of Study: Chaminade awards the B.A., B.S., B.B.A., and B.F.A. degrees. Associate and master's degrees also are awarded. Bachelor's degrees are awarded in BIOLOGICAL SCIENCE (biology/biological science), BUSINESS (accounting, business administration and management, business economics, and marketing/retailing/merchandising), COMMUNICATIONS AND THE ARTS (art, communications, and English), COMPUTER AND PHYSICAL SCIENCE (chemistry, computer science, and mathematics), EDUCATION (early childhood, elementary, and secondary), ENGINEERING AND ENVIRONMENTAL DESIGN (interior design), SOCIAL SCIENCE (American studies, behavioral science, criminal justice, history, humanities, international relations, philosophy, political science/government, psychology, religion, and social science). Education and communications are the strongest academically. Interior design, business, biology, and education have the largest enrollments.

Required: To graduate, students must maintain a minimum GPA of 2.0 in 124 credit hours, which include 61 in general education courses and at least 24 in the major at the upper division level.

Special: Dual majors are permitted in all programs, and cross-registration is available with 4 other colleges in Hawaii. There are 3-2 engineering degree programs with St. Mary's University in Texas and the University of Dayton. Internships with local companies, work-study programs, study abroad in Japan, and accelerated degree programs are available. Credit by examination, pass/fail options, and nondegree study are also offered. There is a freshman honors program on campus, as well as 4 national honor societies.

Faculty/Classroom: Sixty-five percent of faculty are male; 35%, female. All teach undergraduates, 5% do research, and 5% do both. No introductory courses are taught by graduate students. The average class size in an introductory lecture is 22; in a laboratory, 22; and in a regular course offering, 25.

Admissions: About 88% of the 1993-94 applicants were accepted.

Requirements: A minimum GPA of 2.0 is required. The SAT I or the ACT is required, with a minimum SAT I score of 400 on each part or a composite ACT score of 18. In addition, students must have earned 16 credits, based on 2 years of science, 3 each of mathematics and social studies, and 4 each of English and college preparatory electives. The GED is accepted. An essay is required, and an interview is recommended. AP and CLEP credits are accepted. Important factors used in the admissions decision are leadership record, personality, intangible qualities, advanced placement or honor courses, extracurricular activities record, and recommendations by school officials.

Procedure: Freshmen are admitted to all sessions. Entrance exams should be taken during the first semester of the senior year. Applications should be filed by August 1 for fall entry and January 1 for spring entry, along with an application fee of $45. Notification is sent on a rolling basis. There is an early admissions plan.

Transfer: In 1993-94, 168 transfer students enrolled. Applicants must have completed at least 12 credit hours with a minimum GPA of 2.0 or better. A minimum composite score of 800 on the SAT I or 18 on the ACT is recommended. A total of 30 credits out of 124 with at least 12 in the major must be completed at Chaminade.

Visiting: There are guides for informal visits, and visitors may sit in on classes. To arrange for a visit, contact the Admissions Office at (808) 735-4735.

Financial Aid: In 1993-94, 24% of all current freshmen and 64% of continuing students received some form of financial aid. About 70% of freshmen and 65% of continuing students received need-based aid. Scholarships or need-based grants averaged $1500 ($4000 maximum); loans averaged $2625 ($4000 maximum); and work contracts averaged $2000 ($2352 maximum). Thirteen percent of undergraduate students work part-time. The average financial indebtedness of the 1992-93 graduate was $3068. Chaminade is a member of CSS. The FAF, FFS, or SFS is required. The deadline for financial aid applications is March 15.

International Students: There are currently 182 international students enrolled. The school actively recruits these students. They must take the TOEFL and achieve a minimum score of 450. The SAT or ACT is recommended.

Computers: The college provides computer facilities for student use. The mainframe is a DEC PDP 11/24. There are 41 IBM-compatible microcomputers available in the computer science center and the writing laboratory. All students may access the system. There are no time limits on using the system and no fees.

Graduates: In 1992-93, 263 bachelor's degrees were awarded. The most popular majors among graduates were criminal justice (10%), management (8%), and behavioral science (6%). Some 35 companies recruited on campus in 1992-93.

Admissions Contact: Faye Conquest, Director of Admissions.

HAWAII PACIFIC UNIVERSITY

C-2

Honolulu, HI 96813   (808) 544-0238; (800) 669-4724 (out-of-state)

Full-time: 2319 men, 1797 women	Faculty: 140
Part-time: 1196 men, 828 women	Ph.D.s: 77%
Graduate: 497 men, 339 women	Student/Faculty: 29 to 1
Year: 4-1-4, summer session	Tuition: $5900
Application Deadline: open	Room & Board: $6400
Freshman Class: 2900 applied, 2266 accepted, 1799 enrolled	
SAT I Verbal/Math: 479/525	ACT: 23 COMPETITIVE

Hawaii Pacific University, founded in 1965, is a private, coeducational institution offering undergraduate and graduate programs in liberal arts, business, marine science, nursing, and travel industry management. There are 4 undergraduate schools and one graduate school. Hawaii Loa College, founded in 1963, merged with Hawaii Pacific in 1992. In addition to regional accreditation, HPU has baccalaureate program accreditation with NLN. The 2 libraries contain 115,000 volumes, 157,000 microform items, and 3000 audiovisual forms, and subscribe to 1750 periodicals. Computerized library sources and services include interlibrary loans and database searching. Special learning facilities include a learning resource center and art gallery. The 135-acre campus is in an urban area in downtown Honolulu. Including residence halls, there are 15 buildings on campus.

Student Life: About 52% of undergraduates are from out-of-state, mostly the West. Students come from 50 states, 70 foreign countries, and Canada. Seventy-five percent are from public schools; 25% from private. Forty percent are white; 25% foreign nationals; 20% Asian American; 10% African American. The average age of freshmen is 18.6; all undergraduates, 24. Twenty-eight percent drop out by the end of their first year; 60% remain to graduate.

Housing: A total of 300 students can be accommodated in college housing. College-sponsored living facilities include single-sex and coed dormitories and off-campus apartments. In addition, there is a homestay program. The housing office assists students in finding apartments and other living arrangements in Honolulu. On-campus housing is available on a first-come, first-served basis. Ninety-eight

percent of students commute. Alcohol is not permitted. All students may keep cars on campus.

Activities: There are no fraternities or sororities on campus. There are 32 groups on campus, including art, band, cheerleading, computers, drama, ethnic, honors, international, literary magazine, newspaper, pep band, political, professional, religious, social, social service, and student government. Popular campus events include Intercultural Day, Honors Banquet, Homecoming, Sweethearts Ball, Concert on the Green, a boat cruise, and the annual awards luau.

Sports: There are 7 intercollegiate sports for men and 6 for women, and 5 intramural sports for men and 5 for women. Athletic and recreation facilities include soccer and softball fields and tennis courts. HPU also uses local high school gymnasiums and YMCA facilities.

Disabled Students: Seventy-five percent of the campus is accessible to disabled students. The following facilities are available: wheelchair ramps, elevators, special parking, specially equipped rest rooms, special class scheduling, lowered drinking fountains, and lowered telephones.

Services: In addition to many counseling and information services, tutoring is available in most subjects. There is also remedial math, reading, and writing.

Campus Safety and Security: Campus safety and security measures include 24-hour foot and vehicle patrol, shuttle buses, pamphlets, posters, films, and emergency telephones. In addition, there are lighted pathways and sidewalks.

Programs of Study: HPU awards the B.A., B.S.B.A., and B.S. Comp. Sci. degrees. Associate and master's degrees also are awarded. Bachelor's degrees are awarded in BIOLOGICAL SCIENCE (marine science), BUSINESS (accounting, business administration and management, business economics, human resources, international business management, management science, marketing management, personnel management, small business management, and tourism), COMMUNICATIONS AND THE ARTS (communications, English, and literature), COMPUTER AND PHYSICAL SCIENCE (computer programming, computer science, and science), EDUCATION (teaching English as a second language/foreign language), HEALTH PROFESSIONS (nursing), SOCIAL SCIENCE (American studies, Asian/Oriental studies, criminal justice, economics, history, human services, humanities, international relations, international studies, Pacific area studies, political science/government, psychology, public administration, social science, and sociology). Accounting, computer science, management, nursing, marine science, and travel industry management are the strongest academically. Travel industry management, management, and accounting have the largest enrollments.

Required: To graduate, students must complete 124 semester hours, including 21 to 36 in the major, with a minimum GPA of 2.0. The core curriculum includes English, communications, quantitative skills, economics, humanities, history, and the behavioral and natural sciences; specific courses include an introduction to computers and a career seminar.

Special: Upperclassmen may participate in internships and work-study programs with numerous companies. HPU also offers accelerated degree and co-op programs in all majors, B.A.-B.S. degrees in mathematics and computer science, student-designed majors, dual majors in all business subjects, a 3–2 engineering degree with Washington University in St. Louis and the University of Southern California, credit for military experience, nondegree study, and pass/fail options. There is a freshman honors program on campus, as well as 5 national honor societies. All departments have honors programs.

Faculty/Classroom: Seventy-one percent of faculty are male; 29%, female. Ninety-two percent teach undergraduates and 92% both teach and do research. No introductory courses are taught by graduate students. The average class size in an introductory lecture is 25; in a laboratory, 15; in a regular course offering, 23.

Admissions: About 78% of the 1993–94 applicants were accepted. The SAT scores for the 1993–94 freshman class were as follows: Verbal—70% below 500, 20% between 500 and 599, and 10% between 600 and 700; Math—60% below 500, 35% between 500 and 599, and 5% between 600 and 700. About 48% of the current freshmen were in the top fifth of their class; 76% were in the top two fifths.

Requirements: A minimum GPA of 2.3 is required. The SAT I or ACT is recommended. Applicants must be high school graduates or have a GED certificate. The university prefers completion of 20 credits based on 4 years of English, 2 each of mathematics and social studies, and 1 each of history and science. An essay and an interview are recommended. Certain programs, for example, marine science and nursing, have more specific admission requirements. AP and CLEP credits are accepted. Important factors used in the admissions decision are recommendations by school officials, advanced placement or honor courses, evidence of special talent, leadership record, and personality, intangible qualities.

Procedure: Freshmen are admitted to all sessions. Application deadlines are open. The application fee is $50. Notification is sent on a rolling basis. There are early decision and deferred admissions plans.

About 60 early decision candidates were accepted for the 1993–94 class.

Transfer: About 599 transfer students enrolled in 1993–94. Applicants must have a GPA of 2.0 in a minimum of 24 credit hours. The SAT I or ACT and an interview are recommended. A total of 30 credits out of 124 must be completed at HPU.

Visiting: There are regularly scheduled orientations for prospective students. There are guides for informal visits and visitors may sit in on classes and stay overnight at the school. To arrange for a visit, contact Scott Stensrud, Admissions Office at (808) 544–0238 or (800) 669–4724.

Financial Aid: In 1993–94, 39% of all current freshmen and 32% of continuing students received some form of financial aid. About 30% of freshmen and 35% of continuing students received need-based aid. The average freshman award was $8500. Of that total, scholarships or need-based grants averaged $3000 ($3800 maximum); loans averaged $2625 ($3625 maximum); and work contracts averaged $2250 ($3000 maximum). Eighty-five percent of undergraduate students work part-time. Average earnings from campus work for the school year are $2500. The average financial indebtedness of the 1992–93 graduate was $10,500. HPU is a member of CSS. The college's own financial statement and FAFSA are required. The deadline for financial aid applications is March 15.

International Students: There are currently 1734 international students enrolled. The school actively recruits these students. They must take the TOEFL or the college's own test and achieve a minimum score on the TOEFL of 550.

Computers: The college provides computer facilities for student use. There are 200 IBM-compatible PCs located in the computer center and tutoring laboratories equipped with the UNIX system and CD-ROM. Those enrolled in computer courses and others who pay a fee may access the system. It may be used 7 days a week during day and evening hours. There are no time limits on using the system. The fee is $35 per 10 hours of use.

Graduates: In 1992–93 769 bachelor's degrees were awarded. The most popular majors among graduates were computer and information science (13%), travel industry management (12%), and business, general (10%). Some 75 companies recruited on campus in 1992–93. Fifty-five percent of all 1992 graduates enrolled in graduate school 6 months after graduation; 70% found employment.

Admissions Contact: Scott Stensrud, Director of Admissions.

UNIVERSITY OF HAWAII

The University of Hawaii, established in 1907, is a public system in Hawaii. It is governed by a board of regents, whose chief administrator is the president and the chancellor. The primary goal of the system is to provide all qualified people in Hawaii an equal opportunity for quality college and university education, to create knowledge and gain insights through research and scholarship, to preserve and contribute to the artistic and cultural heritage of the community, and to provide other public service through the dissemination of current and new ideas and techniques. The main priorities are serving the state of Hawaii, achieving program quality, establishing Pacific/Asian focus, and adapting to scientific change. The total enrollment in fall 1991 of all 10 campuses was 51,197; there were 3107 faculty members. Altogether there are 115 baccalaureate, 86 master's, and 49 doctoral programs offered in University of Hawaii. There is a four-year campus located in Hilo and Manoa. Profiles of the 4-year campuses are included in this chapter in alphabetical order with other Hawaii schools.

UNIVERSITY OF HAWAII AT HILO
Hilo, HI 96720

F-4
(808) 933–3414

Full-time: 833 men, 1249 women	Faculty: 148; IIB, +$
Part-time: 348 men, 523 women	Ph.D.s: 80%
Graduate: none	Student/Faculty: 14 to 1
Year: semesters, summer session	Tuition: $510 ($2850)
Application Deadline: May 15	Room & Board: $3631
Freshman Class: 976 applied, 568 accepted, 309 enrolled	
SAT I Verbal/Math: 401/473	COMPETITIVE

The University of Hawaii at Hilo, founded in 1970, is part of the public University of Hawaii, and offers degree programs through its colleges of agriculture, arts and sciences, education, and continuing education and community service. It has a branch campus at Kealakekua, West Hawaii. Major programs include marine science, volcanology, and astronomy. There are 3 undergraduate schools. The library contains 200,000 volumes and 11,000 microform items, and subscribes to 1600 periodicals. Computerized library sources and services include the card catalog, interlibrary loans, and database searching. Special learning facilities include a learning resource center, an art gallery, a space science center, a marine education center, and a small business development center. The 115-acre campus is in a small town 200 miles southeast of Honolulu. Including residence halls, there are 53 buildings on campus.

Student Life: About 85% of undergraduates are from Hawaii. Students come from Canada. Eighty percent are from public schools; 20% from private. Thirty-five percent are white; 34% Asian American; 18% Native American/Eskimo. Eleven percent are mixed nationality. The average age of all undergraduates is 27. Twenty-nine percent drop out by the end of their first year; 35% remain to graduate.

Housing: A total of 730 students can be accommodated in college housing. College-sponsored living facilities include coed dormitories, on-campus apartments, off-campus apartments, and married-student housing. In addition, there are honors houses, special interest houses, and educational/recreational enrichment hall. On-campus housing is available on a first-come, first-served basis. Priority is given to out-of-town students. Seventy-five percent of students commute. Alcohol is not permitted. All students may keep cars on campus.

Activities: There are no fraternities or sororities on campus. There are 40 groups on campus, including art, band, cheerleading, chess, choir, chorale, chorus, computers, dance, drama, ethnic, gay, honors, international, jazz band, literary magazine, musical theater, newspaper, pep band, political, professional, religious, social, social service, and student government. Popular campus events include Homecoming, International Night, May Day, dances, plays, noon-time performances, and a film festival.

Sports: Athletic and recreation facilities include a student activities center with billiards and a game room, an athletic complex with basketball courts and weight room, 8 tennis courts, and a baseball field.

Disabled Students: Eighty percent of the campus is accessible to disabled students. The following facilities are available: wheelchair ramps, elevators, special parking, specially equipped rest rooms, special class scheduling, lowered drinking fountains, lowered telephones, and specially designed dormitory rooms, cassette recorders, talking calculators, TDY terminal for the deaf, visual tech magnifier projector, large print typewriter, microcomputers, and taped textbooks for the blind.

Services: In addition to many counseling and information services, tutoring is available in most subjects. There is also remedial math, reading, and writing.

Campus Safety and Security: Campus safety and security measures include 24-hour foot and vehicle patrol, informal discussions, emergency telephones, lighted pathways and sidewalks, and educational programs.

Programs of Study: UHH awards the B.A., B.S., B.B.A., and B.S.N. degrees. Bachelor's degrees are awarded in AGRICULTURE (animal science and horticulture), BIOLOGICAL SCIENCE (biology/biological science and marine science), BUSINESS (accounting and business administration and management), COMMUNICATIONS AND THE ARTS (English, fine arts, Japanese, linguistics, music, and speech/debate/rhetoric), COMPUTER AND PHYSICAL SCIENCE (chemistry, computer science, geology, mathematics, natural sciences, and physics), EDUCATION (elementary), HEALTH PROFESSIONS (nursing), SOCIAL SCIENCE (anthropology, criminal justice, economics, geography, Hawaiian studies, history, philosophy, political science/government, psychology, and sociology). Business, computer science, and biology are the strongest academically. Business, psychology, and marine science have the largest enrollments.

Required: To graduate, students must earn a minimum of 120 semester hours, including at least 30 in the college from which a degree is sought, with a 2.0 GPA overall and in the major. Students also must complete general education requirements, including English 100 and at least 3 credits from courses related to Hawaii or in historical and cultural studies of Asia or the Pacific.

Special: UHH offers cross-registration with Hawaii Community College, a political science legislative internship, and many work-study programs. Students may study abroad through a variety of programs. The school permits a student-designed liberal studies major, dual degrees, a 3–2 engineering degree with the University of Hawaii at Manoa, nondegree study, pass/fail options, and credit for military experience. There is a freshman honors program on campus. One department has an honors program.

Faculty/Classroom: Sixty-five percent of faculty are male; 35%, female. All both teach and do research. The average class size in an introductory lecture is 20; in a laboratory, 25; and in a regular course offering, 17.

Admissions: About 58% of the 1993–94 applicants were accepted. The SAT scores for the 1993–94 freshman class were as follows: Verbal—85% below 500, 12% between 500 and 599, 3% between 600 and 700, and 1% above 700; Math—58% below 500, 29% between 500 and 599, 11% between 600 and 700, and 2% above 700. About 43% of the current freshmen were in the top fifth of their class; 71% were in the top two fifths.

Requirements: UHH requires applicants to be in the upper 50% of their class. A minimum GPA of 2.5 is required. The SAT I is required, with a minimum composite score of 800. Applicants should be high school graduates or present a GED certificate. Students should have earned 15 academic credits, including 4 units of English, 2 of algebra, 5 from among the natural and social sciences, mathematics beyond algebra, English beyond the 4-year minimum, and foreign language, and 5 from any other subject except ROTC and physical education. AP and CLEP credits are accepted. Important factors used in the admissions decision are advanced placement or honor courses, recommendations by school officials, evidence of special talent, extracurricular activities record, and personality, and other intangible qualities.

Procedure: Freshmen are admitted fall and spring. Entrance exams should be taken by November of the senior year. Applications should be filed by May 15 for fall entry and October 15 for spring entry, along with an application fee of $10. Notification is sent on a rolling basis.

Transfer: About 450 transfer students enrolled in 1993–94. Applicants must have a GPA of 2.0; those with fewer than 24 college credits must apply as freshmen. A total of 30 credits out of 120 must be completed at UHH.

Visiting: There are regularly scheduled orientations for prospective students, including a campus tour and a meeting with an admissions counselor. There are guides for informal visits and visitors may sit in on classes. To arrange for a visit, contact the Admissions Office at (808) 933-3714.

Financial Aid: In 1993–94, 30% of all current freshmen and 35% of continuing students received some form of financial aid. About 23% of freshmen and 31% of continuing students received need-based aid. The average freshman award was $3286. Of that total, scholarships or need-based grants averaged $1413 ($3286 maximum); loans averaged $1281 ($2625 maximum); and work contracts averaged $592 ($2699 maximum). Sixty-four percent of undergraduate students work part-time. Average earnings from campus work for the school year are $1253. The average financial indebtedness of the 1992–93 graduate was $9120. UHH is a member of CSS. The FAF is required. The deadline for financial aid applications is March 1.

International Students: There are currently 207 international students enrolled. The school actively recruits these students. They must take the TOEFL and achieve a minimum score of 500. The student must also take the SAT I (preferred), or the ACT.

Computers: The college provides computer facilities for student use. The mainframes are a DEC VAX 11/750, a VAX 8550, a VAX 8650, a MicroVAX II, and an IBM 3081D. There are 108 microcomputers and terminals in various locations on campus. Access to E-mail and Internet requires a password assignment from the computer center. All students may access the system 7:45 a.m to 10:30 P.M. in computer laboratories or anytime by modem. There are no time limits on using the system and no fees.

Graduates: In 1992–93, 342 bachelor's degrees were awarded. The most popular majors among graduates were business administration (19%), liberal studies (10%), and psychology (8%).

Admissions Contact: Admissions Office.

UNIVERSITY OF HAWAII AT MANOA
Honolulu, HI 96822

C-2
(808) 956-8975

Full-time: 4930 men, 5948 women	Faculty: 1249; I, av$
Part-time: 1139 men, 1209 women	Ph.D.s: 85%
Graduate: 3008 men, 3602 women	Student/Faculty: 9 to 1
Year: semesters, summer session	Tuition: $1497 ($4357)
Application Deadline: May 1	Room & Board: $4129
Freshman Class: 3435 applied, 2903 accepted, 1866 enrolled	
SAT I Verbal/Math: 440/540	COMPETITIVE

The University of Hawaii at Manoa, founded in 1907, is the major research institution in the University of Hawaii system. The undergraduate programs offered include liberal arts and sciences, business, education, engineering, health sciences, tropical agriculture, architecture, travel industry management, physical science, technology, and Hawaiian, Asian-Pacific studies. There are 13 undergraduate and 6 graduate schools. In addition to regional accreditation, UHM has baccalaureate program accreditation with AACSB, ABET, ACEJMC, ADA, CSWE, NAAB, NASM, and NLN. The 2 libraries contain 2,718,618 volumes, 3,366,035 microform items, and 23,694 audiovisual forms, and subscribe to 36,592 periodicals. Computerized library sources and services include the card catalog and database searching. Special learning facilities include a learning resource center, art gallery, radio station, and TV station. The 300-acre campus is in an urban area. Including residence halls, there are 119 buildings on campus.

Student Life: About 84% of undergraduates are from Hawaii. Students come from 50 states, 84 foreign countries, and Canada. Sixty-five percent are Asian American; 22%, white. The average age of freshmen is 18.3; all undergraduates, 22.5.

Housing: A total of 3202 students can be accommodated in college housing. College-sponsored living facilities include single-sex and coed dormitories, on-campus apartments, and married-student housing. Priority for on-campus housing is given to neighbor-island students. Eighty-four percent of students commute. Upperclassmen may keep cars on campus.

Activities: About 10% of men belong to 5 local and 3 national fraternities; about 10% of women belong to 6 local and 1 national sororities. There are 250 groups on campus, including art, band, cheerleading, chess, choir, chorale, chorus, dance, drama, drill team, ethnic, film, gay, honors, international, literary magazine, marching band, musical theater, newspaper, opera, pep band, photography, political, professional, radio and TV, religious, social, social service, student government, and symphony. Popular campus events include Kanikapila, a Hawaiian music festival, and international fairs.

Sports: There are 8 intercollegiate sports for men and 8 for women, and 20 intramural sports for men and 20 for women. Athletic and recreation facilities include a 10,000-seat basketball arena, 5000-seat baseball stadium, swimming facilities, 2 weight rooms, a turf field and rubberized track, 2 grass fields, 3 gymnasiums, and an off-campus football stadium.

Disabled Students: The following facilities are available: wheelchair ramps, elevators, special parking, specially equipped rest rooms, special class scheduling, lowered drinking fountains, lowered telephones. Disability access information is available on request, and auxiliary aids and program adjustments can be arranged on an individual basis.

Services: In addition to many counseling and information services, tutoring is available in most subjects. There is a reader service for the blind.

Campus Safety and Security: Campus safety and security measures include escort service, shuttle buses, emergency telephones, and lighted pathways and sidewalks.

Programs of Study: UHM awards the B.A., B.S., B.Arch., B.B.A., B.Ed., B.F.A, B.Mus., and B.S.W. degrees. Master's and doctoral degrees also are awarded. Bachelor's degrees are awarded in AGRICULTURE (agricultural economics, agriculture, animal science, and horticulture), BIOLOGICAL SCIENCE (biology/biological science, botany, entomology, microbiology, and zoology), BUSINESS (accounting, banking and finance, business administration and management, business economics, fashion merchandising, international business management, management information systems, management science, marketing/retailing/merchandising, real estate, and tourism), COMMUNICATIONS AND THE ARTS (Chinese, classics, communications, dance, English, fine arts, French, German, Hawaiian, Japanese, journalism, music, Russian, Spanish, speech/debate/rhetoric, and theater design), COMPUTER AND PHYSICAL SCIENCE (atmospheric sciences and meteorology, chemistry, computer science, geology, mathematics, and physics), EDUCATION (art, elementary, health, physical, recreation, secondary, and teaching English as a second language/foreign language), ENGINEERING AND ENVIRONMENTAL DESIGN (architecture, civil engineering, electrical/electronics engineering, and mechanical engineering), HEALTH PROFESSIONS (dental hygiene, medical laboratory technology, nursing, and speech pathology/audiology), SOCIAL SCIENCE (American studies, anthropology, Asian/Oriental studies, economics, family/consumer resource management, food science, geography, history, philosophy, political science/government, psychology, religion, social work, sociology, and women's studies). Elementary education, general business, psychology, civil engineering and art have the largest enrollments.

Required: In most disciplines, a minimum GPA of 2.0 and a total of 124 credit hours are required for graduation. The total number of hours required in the major varies according to discipline. All students must fulfill general education core requirements, including 1 semester each of expository writing and mathematics/logic, 2 semesters of world civilization, 3 semesters each of arts and humanities, natural sciences, and social sciences, and 4 semesters of a foreign language or Hawaiian. In addition, 5 of the core courses must be writing-intensive.

Special: Internships are available with the state legislature and through the honors and the environmental studies programs. Co-op and work-study programs, dual majors, nondegree study, and pass/fail options are available. The liberal studies program offers student-designed majors. Study abroad may be arranged in England, France, Germany, Japan, and Samoa. There is a freshman honors program on campus, as well as 27 national honor societies, including Phi Beta Kappa.

Faculty/Classroom: Seventy percent of faculty are male; 30%, female.

Admissions: About 85% of the 1993–94 applicants were accepted. The SAT scores for the 1993–94 freshman class were as follows: Verbal—75% below 500, 20% between 500 and 599, and 5% between 600 and 700; Math—34% below 500, 38% between 500 and 599, 24% between 600 and 700, and 4% above 700.

Requirements: UHM requires applicants to be in the upper 40% of their class. A minimum GPA of 3.2 is required. The SAT I with minimum scores on sections of 480, or the ACT with a composite score of 22, is required. Applicants must be graduates of an accredited secondary school. The GED is accepted. Twenty Carnegie units or 15 academic credits are required, including 4 units of English, and 2 units each of mathematics and science. Seven additional units of college preparatory courses and 5 electives are also required. AP and CLEP credits are accepted. Important factors used in the admissions decision are advanced placement or honor courses, personality, intangible qualities, leadership record, evidence of special talent, and extracurricular activities record.

Procedure: Freshmen are admitted to all sessions. Entrance exams should be taken by December of the senior year for fall admission. Applications should be filed by May 1 for fall entry and November 1 for spring entry, along with an application fee of $10. Notification is sent on a rolling basis. There is an early admissions plan.

Transfer: In 1993–94, 1759 transfer students enrolled. Transfer students must have a total of 24 semester credits with a minimum GPA of 2.5. A total of 30 credits out of 124 must be completed at UHM.

Visiting: There are regularly scheduled orientations for prospective students. There are guides for informal visits and visitors may sit in on classes. To arrange for a visit, contact the Campus Center at (808) 956-7235.

Financial Aid: In 1993–94, 9% of all current freshmen and 5% of continuing students received some form of financial aid. About 9% of freshmen and 15% of continuing students received need-based aid. The average freshman award was $3780. Of that total, scholarships or need-based grants averaged $1820 ($4300 maximum); loans averaged $1140 ($5000 maximum); and work contracts averaged $800 ($3200 maximum). All undergraduate students work part-time. Average earnings from campus work for the school year are $1570. The average financial indebtedness of the 1992–93 graduate was $5200. UHM is a member of CSS. The college's own financial statement is required. The deadline for financial aid applications is March 1.

International Students: There are currently 2102 international students enrolled. They must take the TOEFL and achieve a minimum score of 500. The student must also take the SAT I or the ACT.

Computers: The college provides computer facilities for student use. The mainframe are an IBM ES 9000, a DEC VAX 8650 and 8550, and a CDC CYBER 180/830. There are also IBM PC, XT, and PS/2 and Apple microcomputers available in laboratories, academic departments, and offices. There are no fees.

Graduates: In 1992–93, 2525 bachelor's degrees were awarded. The most popular majors among graduates were accounting (6%), marketing (5%), and psychology (5%). Within an average freshman class, 10% graduate in 4 years, 32% in 5 years, and 47% in 6 years. Some 95 companies recruited on campus in 1992–93.

Admissions Contact: Office of Admissions and Records.

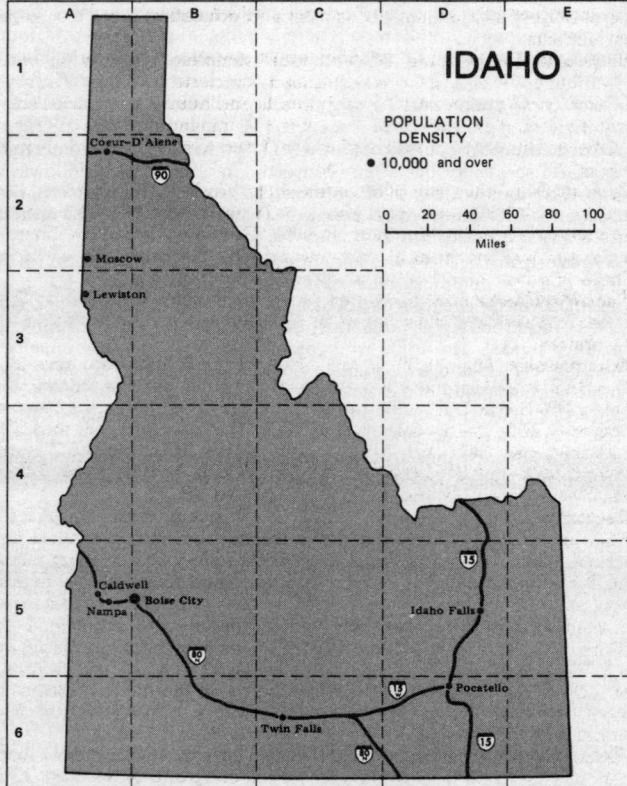

IDAHO

POPULATION
DENSITY

● 10,000 and over

0 20 40 60 80 100
Miles

ALBERTSON COLLEGE   A-5
Caldwell, ID 83605   (208) 459–5209; (800) 635–0434 (out-of-state)

Full-time: 330 men, 348 women   Faculty: 58; IIB, --$
Part-time: 21 men, 20 women   Ph.D.s: 71%
Graduate: 191 men and women   Student/Faculty: 12 to 1
Year: 4–1–4   Tuition: $12,942
Application Deadline: open   Room & Board: $3000
Freshman Class: 587 applied, 479 accepted, 158 enrolled
SAT I Verbal/Math: 487/524   ACT: 24   COMPETITIVE +

Albertson College, founded in 1891, is an independent, coeducational institution offering degree programs in the liberal arts and education. The 2 libraries contain 158,769 volumes and 45,925 microform items, and subscribe to 776 periodicals. Computerized library
sources and services include the card catalog, interlibrary loans, and
database searching. Special learning facilities include an art gallery,
natural history museum, planetarium, and and a rock and mineral collection. The 43-acre campus is in a small town 25 miles west of Boise.
Including residence halls, there are 20 buildings on campus.
Student Life: About 73% of undergraduates are from Idaho. Students come from 21 states, 11 foreign countries, and Canada. Some
95% are from public schools; 5% from private. About 84% are white.
The average age of freshmen is 18; all undergraduates, 20. Some
14% drop out by the end of their first year; 50% remain to graduate.
Housing: A total of 596 students can be accommodated in college
housing. College-sponsored living facilities include single-sex and
coed dormitories and fraternity houses. On-campus housing is guaranteed for the freshman year only and is available on a first-come,
first-served basis. About 54% of students commute. All students may
keep cars on campus.
Activities: About 20% of men belong to 2 local and 2 national fraternities; about 20% of women belong to national and 3 local sororities.
There are 40 groups on campus, including art, cheerleading, choir,
chorale, chorus, computers, dance, drama, honors, international, musical theater, newspaper, orchestra, political, religious, social, social
service, student government, and yearbook. Popular campus events
include the Fine Arts Series, Spring Symposium, Student-Alumni Career Forum, and fall convocations.
Sports: There are 4 intercollegiate sports for men and 4 for women,
and 5 intramural sports for men and 3 for women. Athletic and recreation facilities include an activities center with a 3,000-seat gymnasium, weight room, and swimming pool, as well as a 6,500-seat baseball stadium and softball and soccer fields.

Disabled Students: The following facilities are available: wheelchair
ramps, elevators, special parking, specially equipped rest rooms, lowered drinking fountains, and lowered telephones.
Services: In addition to many counseling and information services,
tutoring is available in most subjects. There is a reader service for the
blind, and remedial math, reading, and writing.
Campus Safety and Security: Campus safety and security measures include 24-hour foot and vehicle patrol, self defense education,
escort service, and informal discussions. In addition, there are lighted
pathways and sidewalks.
Programs of Study: Albertson awards the B.A. and B.S. degrees.
Master's degrees also are awarded. Bachelor's degrees are awarded
in BIOLOGICAL SCIENCE (biology/biological science), BUSINESS
(accounting, business administration and management, and sports
management), COMMUNICATIONS AND THE ARTS (art, English,
French, music, Spanish, and theater design), COMPUTER AND
PHYSICAL SCIENCE (chemistry, computer science, mathematics,
and physics), EDUCATION (elementary, English, mathematics, physical, and social studies), SOCIAL SCIENCE (anthropology, economics, history, philosophy, physical fitness/movement, political science/
government, psychology, religion, and sociology). Biology and history are the strongest programs academically. Business, biology, elementary education, psychology, and history have the largest enrollments.
Required: To graduate, the student must earn 124 credits, including
30 or more in the major, with a minimum GPA of 2.0. Required disciplines include religion, philosophy, Western civilization, English, social sciences, fine arts, literature, natural sciences, and physical education.
Special: The college offers cooperative programs and a 3–2 engineering degree with Washington University in St. Louis, as well as
cross-registration with Northwest Nazarene College. Internships with
major corporations, work-study programs on campus, study abroad,
some pass/fail options, physical education credit for military experience, and nondegree study are also available. The Gipson Scholar
Program allows freshmen with superior records to design their own
programs. There is a freshman honors program on campus, as well as
one national honor society.
Faculty/Classroom: Some 65% of faculty are male; 35%, female.
Almost 96% teach undergraduates. No introductory courses are
taught by graduate students.
Admissions: About 82% of the 1993–94 applicants were accepted.
The SAT scores for the 1993–94 freshman class were as follows: Verbal—56% below 500, 28% between 500 and 599, 15% between
600 and 700, and 1% above 700; Math—39% below 500, 38% between 500 and 599, 16% between 600 and 700, and 7% above 700.
The ACT scores were 27% below 21, 25% between 21 and 23, 19%
between 24 and 26, 14% between 27 and 28, and 14% above 28.
There were 8 National Merit finalists.
Requirements: The SAT I or ACT is required. Applicants must be
high school graduates or present a GED certificate. The college recommends that students have 4 years of English, 3 each of mathematics, history, and social studies, and 2 of science. An essay is required.
AP and CLEP credits are accepted. Important factors used in the admissions decision are recommendations by school officials, leadership record, extracurricular activities record, recommendations by
alumni, and parents or siblings attending the school.
Procedure: Freshmen are admitted to all sessions. Application deadlines are open. Notification is sent on a rolling basis. There is an application fee of $25. There is a deferred admissions plan.
Transfer: About 53 transfer students enrolled in 1993–94. Applicants must supply official transcripts and clearance reports from colleges attended, as well as an essay and 1 teacher recommendation.
They must also have at least 12 hours of college credit. A total of 30
credits out of 124 must be completed at Albertson.
Visiting: There are regularly scheduled orientations for prospective
students. There are guides for informal visits and visitors may sit in on
classes and stay overnight at the school. To arrange for a visit, contact
the Enrollment Services Office at (800) 635–0434 (out-of-state) or
(800) 841–8648 (in-state).
Financial Aid: In 1993–94, 93% of all current freshmen and 89%
of continuing students received some form of financial aid. About
55% of freshmen and continuing students received need-based aid.
The average freshman award was $8679. Of that total, work contracts
averaged $1500 ($2000 maximum). About 30% of undergraduate
students work part-time. Average earnings from campus work for the
school year are $1500. Albertson is a member of CSS. The FAF is re-
quired. The deadline for financial aid applications is February 15.
International Students: There are currently 37 international students enrolled. The school actively recruits these students. They must
take the TOEFL and achieve a minimum score of 500.

Computers: The college provides computer facilities for student use. The mainframe is an HP 9000. There are 8 computer laboratory clusters with 120 microcomputers. All students may access the system. It may be used at designated times. There are no time limits on using the system and no fees.

Graduates: In 1992–93, 100 bachelor's degrees were awarded. The most popular majors among graduates were business administration (25%), biology/zoology (16%), and elementary education (12%). Within an average freshman class, 50% graduate in 4 years and 50% in 5 years. Some 20 companies recruited on campus in 1992–93.

Admissions Contact: Director of Enrollment Services.

BOISE STATE UNIVERSITY

B-5

Boise, ID 83725	(208) 385–1177; (800) 824–7017 (out-of-state)
Full-time: 3797 men, 4322 women	Faculty: 580; IIA, --$
Part-time: 2008 men, 2870 women	Ph.D.s: 67%
Graduate: 489 men, 1094 women	Student/Faculty: 14 to 1
Year: semesters, summer session	Tuition: $1716 ($4766)
Application Deadline: July 27	Room & Board: $3193
Freshman Class: 3619 applied, 3080 accepted, 1888 enrolled	
SAT I Verbal/Math: 435/474	ACT: 21 LESS COMPETITIVE

Boise State University, founded in 1932, is part of the Idaho Higher Education System and offers degree programs in the arts and sciences, business, education, health science, public affairs, technology, and vocational technical education. There are 7 undergraduate schools and one graduate school. In addition to regional accreditation, BSU has baccalaureate program accreditation with AACSB, CAHEA, CSWE, NASM, NCATE, and NLN. The library contains 390,892 volumes, 988,100 microform items, and 54,289 audiovisual forms, and subscribes to 4700 periodicals. Computerized library sources and services include the card catalog, interlibrary loans, and database searching. Special learning facilities include a learning resource center, an art gallery, a radio station, and a technology center. The 110-acre campus is in an urban area. Including residence halls, there are 60 buildings on campus.

Student Life: About 92% of undergraduates are from Idaho. Students come from 46 states, 50 foreign countries, and Canada. Eighty-five percent are white. The average age of freshmen is 21; all undergraduates, 26.

Housing: A total of 929 students can be accommodated in college housing. College-sponsored living facilities include single-sex and coed dormitories, on-campus apartments, and married-student housing. On-campus housing is available on a first-come, first-served basis. Ninety-three percent of students commute. All students may keep cars on campus.

Activities: About 1% of men belong to 4 national fraternities; about 1% of women belong to 3 national sororities. There are 136 groups on campus, including art, band, cheerleading, chess, choir, chorale, dance, drama, drill team, ethnic, gay, honors, international, jazz band, literary magazine, marching band, newspaper, orchestra, pep band, political, professional, radio and TV, religious, social, social service, and student government. Popular campus events include Homecoming, Spring Fling, Leadership Quest, and Martin Luther King, Jr. Celebration.

Sports: Athletic and recreation facilities include a 21,000-seat stadium, a 12,000-seat indoor arena, a swimming pool, racquetball, indoor and outdoor tennis courts, indoor and outdoor tracks, and a weight room.

Disabled Students: Ninety-seven percent of the campus is accessible to disabled students. The following facilities are available: wheelchair ramps, elevators, special parking, specially equipped rest rooms, special class scheduling, lowered drinking fountains, lowered telephones, and electric doors.

Services: In addition to many counseling and information services, tutoring is available in most subjects. There is a reader service for the blind, and remedial math, reading, and writing.

Campus Safety and Security: Campus safety and security measures include 24-hour foot and vehicle patrol, shuttle buses, informal discussions, pamphlets, posters, and films. In addition, there are emergency telephones and lighted pathways and sidewalks.

Programs of Study: BSU awards the B.A., B.S., B.A.A.S., B.B.A., B.F.A., B.I.S., and B.Mus. degrees. Associate, master's, and doctoral degrees also are awarded. Bachelor's degrees are awarded in BIOLOGICAL SCIENCE (biology/biological science), BUSINESS (accounting, banking and finance, business administration and management, and marketing/retailing/merchandising), COMMUNICATIONS AND THE ARTS (art, communications, dramatic arts, English, fine arts, and music), COMPUTER AND PHYSICAL SCIENCE (chemistry, geology, geophysics and seismology, information sciences and systems, mathematics, physics, and radiological technology), EDUCATION (art, education, elementary, English, music, physical, and secondary), ENGINEERING AND ENVIRONMENTAL DESIGN (construction management), HEALTH PROFESSIONS (environmental health science, health science, medical laboratory

technology, nursing, predentistry, premedicine, and respiratory therapy), SOCIAL SCIENCE (anthropology, criminal justice, economics, history, interdisciplinary studies, philosophy, political science/government, psychology, social science, social work, and sociology). Business, art, theater arts, music, social sciences, and public affairs are the strongest academically. Business and education have the largest enrollments.

Required: To graduate, students must complete 128 credits with a minimum GPA of 2.0. Core requirements include 6 semester hours in English composition and 12 each in arts and humanities, social sciences, mathematics, and natural sciences. A minimum grade of C is required in all major courses and courses used to meet the core requirements.

Special: The university offers internships, work-study programs, dual majors, a general studies degree, nondegree study, pass/fail options, and study abroad in England, France, Germany, and Italy. There is a cooperative program in engineering with the University of Idaho. There is a freshman honors program on campus.

Faculty/Classroom: Sixty-nine percent of faculty are male; 31%, female. The average class size in an introductory lecture is 30 and in a laboratory, 21.

Admissions: About 85% of the 1993–94 applicants were accepted. The SAT scores for the 1993–94 freshman class were as follows: Verbal—77% below 500, 19% between 500 and 599, and 4% between 600 and 700; Math—60% below 500, 28% between 500 and 599, 11% between 600 and 700, and 1% above 700. The ACT scores were 52% below 21, 26% between 21 and 23, 14% between 24 and 26, 5% between 27 and 28, and 3% above 28.

Requirements: A minimum GPA of 2.0 is required. The SAT I or ACT is required. Students must graduate from an accredited high school and have a minimum high school GPA of 2.0 and a minimum ACT composite score of 17 or SAT I combined score of 700. In addition, students must have completed 4 years of English, 3 years each of mathematics (algebra I and higher) and natural science, 2 1/2 years of social science, 1 year of humanities or foreign language, and 1 1/2 in other college preparation classes, all with an average grade of 2.0. Students who have not completed all the above classes but meet the other admission requirements will be considered for provisional admission status. AP and CLEP credits are accepted.

Procedure: Freshmen are admitted fall, spring, and summer. Applications should be filed by July 27 for fall entry and November 23 for spring entry, along with an application fee of $15. Notification is sent on a rolling basis.

Transfer: About 1160 transfer students enrolled in 1993–94. A minimum GPA of 2.0 is required for students with at least 14 college credits. Those students with fewer credits must submit SAT I or ACT scores and a high school transcript. A total of 30 credits out of 128 must be completed at BSU.

Visiting: There are guides for informal visits, and visitors may sit in on classes. To arrange for a visit, contact the New Student Information Center at (208) 385–1820 or (800) 824–7017 (out-of-state).

Financial Aid: Scholarships or need-based grants averaged $545; loans averaged $750 ($1500 maximum); and work contracts averaged $2300 ($4000 maximum). The average financial indebtedness of recent graduates was $9764. BSU is a member of CSS. The FAF is required. The deadline for financial aid applications is March 1.

International Students: There are currently 160 international students enrolled. They must take the TOEFL and achieve a minimum score of 500.

Computers: The college provides computer facilities for student use. The mainframes are an IBM 4341–2 and an HP 3000. There are also 579 IBM, AT&T, and Apple microcomputers available in laboratories and faculty offices. All students may access the system. Students may access the system 2 hours at a time in the laboratories. The fees are $8 per semester.

Graduates: In 1992–93, 1149 bachelor's degrees were awarded. The most popular majors among graduates were elementary education (11%), accounting (7%), and nursing (5%). Some 54 companies recruited on campus in 1992–93.

Admissions Contact: Stephen E. Spafford, Dean of Admissions.

IDAHO STATE UNIVERSITY

D-6

Pocatello, ID 83209–0009	(208) 236–2475
	(800) 634–7918 (out-of-state)
Full-time: 3116 men, 3431 women	Faculty: 434; IIA, --$
Part-time: 1059 men, 1405 women	Ph.D.s: 88%
Graduate: 830 men, 938 women	Student/Faculty: 15 to 1
Year: semesters, summer session	Tuition: $1602 ($5216)
Application Deadline: open	Room & Board: $2840
Freshman Class: 2747 applied, 1996 accepted, 1424 enrolled	
ACT: 18	COMPETITIVE

Idaho State University, founded in 1901, is a public university offering programs in the liberal arts and sciences, business, education, engineering, and health professions. There are 7 undergraduate

schools and 1 graduate school. In addition to regional accreditation, ISU has baccalaureate program accreditation with AACSB, ABET, ACPE, CSWE, NASM, NCATE, and NLN. The library contains 350,000 volumes and 1.2 million microform items, and subscribes to 3100 periodicals. Computerized library sources and services include the card catalog, interlibrary loans, and database searching. Special learning facilities include a learning resource center, natural history museum, planetarium, and TV station. The 317-acre campus is in a small city. Including residence halls, there are 62 buildings on campus.

Student Life: About 92% of undergraduates are from Idaho. Students come from 45 states, 41 foreign countries, and Canada. Ninety-six percent are from public schools; 4% from private. Ninety-three percent are white. The average age of freshmen is 20.8; all undergraduates, 26.9. Thirty percent drop out by the end of their first year; 50% remain to graduate.

Housing: A total of 878 students can be accommodated in college housing. College-sponsored living facilities include single-sex dormitories, on-campus apartments, and married-student housing. On-campus housing is available on a first-come, first-served basis. Ninety-one percent of students commute. Alcohol is not permitted. All students may keep cars on campus.

Activities: There are 2 national fraternities and 1 national sorority. There are some groups and organizations on campus, including band, chorus, drama, jazz band, newspaper, pep band, professional, social, student government, and symphony. Popular campus events include movies, dances, Homecoming, concerts, art displays, games, tournaments, and speakers.

Sports: There are 5 intercollegiate sports for men and 5 for women, and 17 intramural sports for men and 15 for women. Athletic and recreation facilities include playing fields, a field house, a gymnasium, a recreation facility, tennis courts, an athletic arena, a fitness/wellness center, and facilities for bowling and billiards.

Disabled Students: The following facilities are available: wheelchair ramps, elevators, special parking, specially equipped rest rooms, lowered drinking fountains, lowered telephones, electric doors, and handrails.

Services: There is remedial math, reading, and writing.

Campus Safety and Security: Campus safety and security measures include 24-hour foot and vehicle patrol, escort service, shuttle buses, and informal discussions. In addition, there are pamphlets, posters, films, emergency telephones, and lighted pathways and sidewalks.

Programs of Study: ISU awards the B.A., B.S., B.A.G.S., B.A.T., B.B.A., B.F.A., B.Mu., B.Mu.Ed., and B.U.S. degrees. Associate, master's, and doctoral degrees also are awarded. Bachelor's degrees are awarded in BIOLOGICAL SCIENCE (biochemistry, biology/biological science, botany, ecology, microbiology, and zoology), BUSINESS (accounting, banking and finance, business administration and management, business systems analysis, hospitality management services, management science, marketing/retailing/merchandising, personnel management, and secretarial studies/office management), COMMUNICATIONS AND THE ARTS (art, communications, dramatic arts, English, fine arts, French, German, graphic design, music, music performance, Spanish, and speech/debate/rhetoric), COMPUTER AND PHYSICAL SCIENCE (chemistry, computer programming, computer science, geology, information sciences and systems, mathematics, physics, and radiological technology), EDUCATION (business, early childhood, education of the exceptional child, elementary, health, home economics, middle school, music, physical, secondary, special, and vocational), ENGINEERING AND ENVIRONMENTAL DESIGN (automotive technology, civil engineering technology, drafting and design technology, electrical/electronics engineering technology, electromechanical technology, engineering, engineering management, graphic arts technology, laser electro-optics technology, manufacturing technology, and transportation technology), HEALTH PROFESSIONS (dental hygiene, dental laboratory technology, health care administration, medical laboratory technology, medical records administration/services, nursing, pharmacy, physician's assistant, and speech pathology/audiology), SOCIAL SCIENCE (American studies, anthropology, clinical psychology, dietetics, economics, fire control and safety technology, history, home economics, international studies, liberal arts/general studies, philosophy, political science/government, psychology, social work, and sociology).

Required: Students must satisfy general education requirements in the areas of written and spoken English, mathematics, biological and physical sciences, fine arts, literature, philosophy, U.S. history, non-U.S. history, government/economics, foreign language, and psychology. A total of 128 credit hours is required, with 24 to 50 in the major. Minimum GPA is 2.0.

Special: ISU participates in the Idaho Dental Education Program and several other medical co-op programs. Students may cross-register through the Western Education Exchange. There is a work-study program. Credit is given by challenge examination or for life/military/work experience, and nondegree study and a general studies degree

are offered. As many as 16 credits of correspondence study may be applied toward the bachelor's degree at ISU.

Faculty/Classroom: Seventy-one percent of faculty are male; 29% female. The average class size in an introductory lecture is 25 and in a laboratory, 23.

Admissions: About 73% of the 1993-94 applicants were accepted. The ACT scores for the 1993-94 freshman class were as follows: 53% below 21, 25% between 21 and 23, 15% between 24 and 26, 5% between 27 and 28, and 2% above 28. About 39% of the current freshmen were in the top fifth of their class; 77% were in the top two fifths.

Requirements: A minimum GPA of 2.0 and either the SAT I, ACT, or WPCT are required. A GED is accepted. Applicants should prepare with 8 credits of English, 6 each of mathematics and science, 5 of social science, 3 of speech/fine arts, and 2 of foreign language/humanities. AP and CLEP credits are accepted.

Procedure: Freshmen are admitted to all sessions. Entrance exams should be taken early in the senior year. Application deadlines are open. The application fee is $10. Notification is sent on a rolling basis.

Transfer: A total of 1183 transfer students enrolled in 1993-94. Applicants must submit a final, official transcript from each college attended. At least 14 credit hours with a minimum GPA of 2.0 is required. Applicants with fewer than 25 credits must submit high school transcripts. Those with fewer than 14 credit hours must apply as freshmen. A total of 32 credits out of 128 must be completed at ISU.

Financial Aid: ISU is a member of CSS. The FAF is required. The deadline for financial aid applications is March 1.

International Students: There are currently 221 international students enrolled. Applicants must take the TOEFL and achieve a minimum score of 500.

Computers: ISU provides computer facilities for student use. The mainframe is an HP 3000. Apple and IBM microcomputers are also available to all students in academic buildings. There are no time limits on using the system and no fees.

Graduates: In 1992-93, 913 bachelor's degrees were awarded. The most popular majors among graduates were elementary education (13%), nursing (6%), and secondary education (5%).

Admissions Contact: Mike Echanis, Associate Director for Admissions and Enrollment Programs.

LEWIS-CLARK STATE COLLEGE
A-3
Lewiston, ID 83501-2698
(208) 799-2210
(800) 933-LCSC (in-state)

Full-time: 832 men, 1138 women	Faculty: 117; IIB, --$
Part-time: 409 men, 847 women	Ph.D.s: 80%
Graduate: none	Student/Faculty: 17 to 1
Year: semesters, summer session	Tuition: $1320 ($4240)
Application Deadline: open	Room & Board: $2720
Freshman Class: 700 applied, 692 accepted, 399 enrolled	
ACT: 20	NONCOMPETITIVE

Lewis-Clark State College, founded in 1893 and today part of the Idaho Higher Education System, offers programs in the arts and sciences, business, education, nursing, and preprofessional and technical training. It is named for the famed explorers, who once camped near what is now the campus. There are 3 undergraduate schools. In addition to regional accreditation, Lewis-Clark has baccalaureate program accreditation with NCATE and NLN. The library contains 167,000 volumes, 98,691 microform items, and 1797 audiovisual forms, and subscribes to 994 periodicals. Computerized library sources and services include the card catalog, interlibrary loans, and database searching. Special learning facilities include a learning resource center and an art gallery. The 40-acre campus is in an urban area 100 miles southeast of Spokane. Including residence halls, there are 20 buildings on campus.

Student Life: About 87% of undergraduates are from Idaho. Students come from 21 states, 29 foreign countries, and Canada. Ninety-four percent are white. The average age of freshmen is 22; all undergraduates, 30.

Housing: A total of 230 students can be accommodated in college housing. College-sponsored living facilities include single-sex and coed dormitories, off-campus apartments, and married-student housing. In addition there are honors houses and language houses. On-campus housing is available on a first-come, first-served basis. Ninety-three percent of students commute. Alcohol is not permitted. All students may keep cars on campus.

Activities: There are no fraternities or sororities. There are 37 groups on campus, including cheerleading, choir, chorale, chorus, drama, ethnic, honors, international, jazz band, newspaper, pep band, political, professional, religious, and student government. Popular campus events include the World Perspectives Lecture Series, International Exchange Conference, Artists Series, Dogwood Festival, Native American Awareness Week, Career Fair, and Japan Week.

Sports: There are 3 intercollegiate sports for men and 3 for women, and 9 intramural sports for men and 9 for women. Athletic and recreation facilities include a gymnasium, an athletic field, and indoor tennis courts.

Disabled Students: Nearly all of the campus is accessible to disabled students. The following facilities are available: wheelchair ramps, elevators, special parking, and specially equipped rest rooms.

Services: In addition to many counseling and information services, tutoring is available in most subjects. There is also a reader service for the blind, and remedial math, reading, and writing.

Campus Safety and Security: Campus safety and security measures include 24-hour foot and vehicle patrol, self-defense education, and shuttle buses.

Programs of Study: Lewis-Clark awards the B.A., B.S., B.Applied S., B. Applied Tech., B.S.N., and B.S.W. degrees. Associate degrees are also awarded. Bachelor's degrees are awarded in BIOLOGICAL SCIENCE (biology/biological science), BUSINESS (accounting, business administration and management, and personnel management), COMMUNICATIONS AND THE ARTS (communications and English), COMPUTER AND PHYSICAL SCIENCE (chemistry, earth science, geology, mathematics, and natural sciences), EDUCATION (elementary, secondary, and special), HEALTH PROFESSIONS (nursing), SOCIAL SCIENCE (criminal justice, history, liberal arts/general studies, social science, and social work). Education, business, and nursing are the strongest academically. Education, business, and nursing have the largest enrollments.

Required: Students must earn 128 credit hours including 43 to 50 in the core curriculum, with a minimum GPA of 2.0 to graduate.

Special: Lewis-Clark offers cooperative programs and cross-registration with 3 Idaho universities, on-campus internships, work-study programs, B.A.-B.S. or general studies degrees, student-designed majors, nondegree study, and pass/fail options. The college grants credit for life, military, and work experience through its Portfolio Program. The Individualized Study Center provides instructors and materials for about 50 nonscheduled courses so that students may work at their chosen times. There are also between-semester and weekend academic programs.

Faculty/Classroom: All faculty teach undergraduates.

Admissions: About 99% of the 1993–94 applicants were accepted. The ACT scores for the 1993–94 freshman class were as follows: 62% below 21, 21% between 21 and 23, 10% between 24 and 26, 5% between 27 and 28, and 2% above 28.

Requirements: A minimum GPA of 2.0 is required. The ACT is required if the applicant is under age 21 at the time of college entrance. Lewis-Clark has a liberal admissions policy, but students must be high school graduates or present a GED certificate. They must have fulfilled requirements in English, mathematics, social and natural sciences, fine arts, foreign language, humanities, and speech, with a minimum GPA of 2.0. CLEP credit is accepted.

Procedure: Freshmen are admitted to all sessions. Entrance exams should be taken before registration. Application deadlines are open. Notification is sent on a rolling basis. The application fee is $10. There is a deferred admissions plan.

Transfer: In 1993–94, 148 transfer students enrolled. Applicants who do not have a minimum GPA of 2.0 must submit standardized test scores. A total of 32 credits out of 128 must be completed at Lewis-Clark.

Visiting: There are guides for informal visits, and visitors may sit in on classes and stay overnight at the school. To arrange for a visit, contact the Admissions Office at (208) 799–2210.

Financial Aid: In an earlier year, 70% of all current freshmen received some form of financial aid. The FAF and the college's own financial statement are required. The deadline for financial aid applications is March 15.

International Students: There are currently 75 international students enrolled. The school actively recruits these students. They must take the TOEFL and achieve a minimum score of 500. The student must also take the SAT I or the ACT.

Computers: The college provides computer facilities for student use. There are 50 IBM and Apple microcomputers available in the library. All students may access the system. There are no time limits on using the system and no fees.

Graduates: In an earlier graduating class, 9% of the men and 9% of the women were enrolled in graduate school within 6 months of graduation and 79% of all graduates had found employment.

Admissions Contact: Steven J. Bussolini, Director of Enrollment Management.

NORTHWEST NAZARENE COLLEGE   A-5

Nampa, ID 83686   (208) 467–8496; (800) 622–4968

Full-time: 473 men, 668 women	Faculty: 89; IIB, --$
Part-time: 35 men, 53 women	Ph.D.s: n/av
Graduate: 517 men and women	Student/Faculty: 13 to 1
Year: quarters	Tuition: $9105
Application Deadline: September 15	Room & Board: $2645

Freshman Class: 541 applied, 448 accepted, 370 enrolled

ACT: required   **COMPETITIVE**

Northwest Nazarene College, founded in 1913, is a liberal arts college affiliated with the Church of the Nazarene. It offers programs in fine arts, language and literature, mathematics and natural science, philosophy and religion, professional studies, and social science. In addition to regional accreditation, NNC has baccalaureate program accreditation with CSWE, NASM, and NCATE. The library contains 124,000 volumes and 19,500 microform items, and subscribes to 478 periodicals. Computerized library sources and services include the card catalog and database searching. Special learning facilities include an educational media center and an arboretum. The 68-acre campus is in a small town 20 miles west of Boise. Including residence halls, there are 23 buildings on campus.

Housing: A total of 781 students can be accommodated in college housing. College-sponsored living facilities include dormitories, off-campus apartments, and married-student housing. On-campus housing is guaranteed for all 4 years. Sixty-five percent of students live on campus. Alcohol is not permitted. All students may keep cars on campus.

Activities: There are some groups and organizations on campus, including band, cheerleading, choir, computers, honors, international, jazz band, orchestra, professional, and social service.

Sports: Athletic and recreation facilities include basketball fields, basketball and tennis courts, a track, a park, and a field house.

Disabled Students: The following facilities are available: special class scheduling and alternate testing and evaluation methods.

Services: In addition to many counseling and information services, tutoring is available in every subject. There is also remedial math, reading, and writing.

Campus Safety and Security: Campus safety and security measures include a professional security company, student Lock Up/Unlock, and Walk Around Campus teams.

Programs of Study: NNC awards the B.A. and B.S. degrees. Associate and master's degrees are also awarded. Bachelor's degrees are awarded in BIOLOGICAL SCIENCE (biology/biological science), BUSINESS (accounting, banking and finance, business administration and management, fashion merchandising, and marketing/retailing/merchandising), COMMUNICATIONS AND THE ARTS (dramatic arts, English, fine arts, music, Spanish, and speech/debate/rhetoric), COMPUTER AND PHYSICAL SCIENCE (chemistry, computer science, mathematics, natural sciences, physical sciences, physics, and science technology), EDUCATION (curriculum and instruction, early childhood, elementary, health, home economics, physical, secondary, and special), ENGINEERING AND ENVIRONMENTAL DESIGN (engineering technology), HEALTH PROFESSIONS (nursing, optometry, physical therapy, predentistry, premedicine, preveterinary science, and speech pathology/audiology), SOCIAL SCIENCE (dietetics, history, human services, international studies, liberal arts/general studies, parks and recreation management, philosophy, physical fitness/movement, political science/government, prelaw, psychology, public affairs, religion, social science, social work, and sociology).

Required: All students must complete 20 credits each of humanities and social studies, 17 of mathematics and natural science, 12 each of biblical and religious studies and communications, and 4 of health and physical education. A total of 188 quarter units is required, with at least 64 in upper-level courses, as is a minimum 2.0 GPA. All students must demonstrate competency in English communication and language skills and must take comprehensive exams in the senior year covering general education requirements.

Special: The college offers a work-study program, a general studies degree, dual and student-designed majors, and credit for military experience. Study abroad is required of all international studies majors. There is one national honor society on campus.

Faculty/Classroom: Twenty-seven percent of faculty are male; 73%, female.

Admissions: About 83% of the 1993–94 applicants were accepted. The ACT scores for the 1993–94 freshman class were as follows: 24% below 21, 40% between 21 and 23, 25% between 24 and 26, and 11% between 27 and 28. About 46% of the current freshmen were in the top fifth of their class; 62% were in the top two fifths.

Requirements: NNC requires applicants to be in the upper 50% of their class. A minimum GPA of 2.0 is required. The ACT is required. Applicants should be graduates of an accredited secondary school; the GED may also be accepted. Applicants should prepare with 4

years of English, 3 each of mathematics, science, and social studies, and 2 of foreign language. AP and CLEP credits are accepted.

Procedure: Freshmen are admitted to all sessions. Entrance exams should be taken early in the senior year. Applications should be filed by September 15 for fall entry, along with an application fee of $10. Notification is sent on a rolling basis.

Transfer: Students who have earned at least 36 credit hours can be admitted as transfer students. Official transcripts from all colleges previously attended must be submitted. A total of 44 quarter credits out of 188 must be completed at NNC.

Visiting: Visitors may sit in on classes and stay overnight at the school. To arrange for a visit, contact the Admissions Office at (208) 467–8496 or (800) 662–4968.

Financial Aid: NNC is a member of CSS. The FAF is required. The deadline for financial aid applications is March 1.

International Students: They must take the TOEFL and achieve a minimum score of 500.

Computers: The mainframe is an HP/3000 Series 58. Interactive display terminals and a 600-lpm printer are connected to the mainframe. There are also microcomputers, including Apple. Computer programming languages available include APL, Assembly, BASIC, C + +, COBOL, FORTRAN, LOGO, MODSIM II, Paradox, Pascal, Powerhouse 4GL, and RPG. Word Perfect (word processing) and Quattro (spreadsheet) are installed in all microcomputers. All students may access the system.

Admissions Contact: Robbyn Lande, Director of Admissions.

UNIVERSITY OF IDAHO
A-2

Moscow, ID 83844   (208) 885–6326; (800) 422–6013 (in-state)

Full-time: 4298 men, 2944 women   Faculty: 627; I, --$
Part-time: 837 men, 594 women   Ph.D.s: 79%
Graduate: 1725 men, 1145 women   Student/Faculty: 12 to 1
Year: semesters, summer session   Tuition: $1426 ($5326)
Application Deadline: August 1   Room & Board: $3404
Freshman Class: 3133 applied, 2799 accepted, 1337 enrolled
SAT I Verbal/Math: 460/520   ACT: 23   **COMPETITIVE**

The University of Idaho, founded in 1889 as a land-grant institution, offers programs in art and architecture, agriculture, business and economics, education, engineering, letters and science, mines and earth resources, and forestry, wildlife, and range sciences. There are 8 undergraduate schools and 1 graduate school. In addition to regional accreditation, UI has baccalaureate program accreditation with ABET, ASLA, FIDER, NAAB, NASM, NCATE, and SAF. The 2 libraries contain 932,760 volumes, 1,289,222 microform items, and 3105 audiovisual forms and subscribe to 13,248 periodicals. Computerized library sources and services include interlibrary loans and database searching. Special learning facilities include a learning resource center, art gallery, radio station, and TV station. The 800-acre campus is in a small town 90 miles south of Spokane. Including residence halls, there are 106 buildings on campus.

Student Life: About 77% of undergraduates are from Idaho. Students come from 50 states, 74 foreign countries, and Canada. Ninety-eight percent are from public schools; 2% from private. Ninety-four percent are white. The average age of freshmen is 19; all undergraduates, 23. Twenty-six percent drop out by the end of their first year; 50% remain to graduate.

Housing: A total of 2850 students can be accommodated in college housing. College-sponsored living facilities include single-sex dormitories, on-campus apartments, off-campus apartments, married-student housing, fraternity houses, and sorority houses. On-campus housing is guaranteed for all 4 years. Sixty percent of students commute. Alcohol is not permitted. All students may keep cars on campus.

Activities: About 28% of men belong to 18 national fraternities; about 21% of women belong to 8 national sororities. There are 90 groups on campus, including art, band, cheerleading, chess, choir, chorale, chorus, computers, dance, drama, drill team, ethnic, film, honors, international, jazz band, literary magazine, marching band, musical theater, newspaper, opera, orchestra, pep band, photography, political, professional, radio and TV, religious, social, social service, student government, symphony, and yearbook. Popular campus events include Homecoming, Parents Weekend, Jazz Festival, and the Borah Symposium.

Sports: There are 7 intercollegiate sports for men and 7 for women, and 28 intramural sports for men and 27 for women. Athletic and recreation facilities include an activity center, a domed, 17,000-seat stadium for basketball and football games, indoor and outdoor tracks, a 2-pool swim center, 3 gymnasiums, a bowling alley, a 500-seat auditorium, an 18-hole championship golf course, and tennis, raquetball, and handball courts.

Disabled Students: Eighty-five percent of the campus is accessible to disabled students. The following facilities are available: wheelchair ramps, elevators, special parking, specially equipped rest rooms, special class scheduling, lowered drinking fountains, lowered telephones, and 2 motorized wheelchairs.

Services: In addition to many counseling and information services, tutoring is available in most subjects. There is a reader service for the blind, and remedial math, reading, and writing.

Campus Safety and Security: Campus safety and security measures include 24-hour foot and vehicle patrol, self defense education, informal discussions, and pamphlets, posters, and films. In addition there are emergency telephones and lighted pathways and sidewalks.

Programs of Study: UI awards the B.A., B.S., B.Appl.Phys., B.Arch., B.Dance, B.F.A., B.G.S., B.L.Arch., B.M., B.N.S., and B.Tech. degrees. Master's and doctoral degrees also are awarded. Bachelor's degrees are awarded in AGRICULTURE (agricultural mechanics, animal science, fishing and fisheries, forestry production and processing, horticulture, and wildlife management), BIOLOGICAL SCIENCE (bacteriology, biology/biological science, botany, entomology, and zoology), BUSINESS (accounting, banking and finance, business economics, management information systems, marketing/retailing/merchandising, personnel management, and sports management), COMMUNICATIONS AND THE ARTS (classics, communications, dance, design, dramatic arts, English, fine arts, French, German, journalism, Latin, music, photography, Spanish, and telecommunications), COMPUTER AND PHYSICAL SCIENCE (actuarial science, chemistry, computer science, geology, information sciences and systems, mathematics, and physics), EDUCATION (agricultural, art, business, early childhood, elementary, foreign languages, home economics, industrial arts, music, physical, recreation, science, secondary, and special), ENGINEERING AND ENVIRONMENTAL DESIGN (agricultural engineering, architectural engineering, cartography, chemical engineering, civil engineering, computer engineering, electrical/electronics engineering, geological engineering, mechanical engineering, metallurgical engineering, and mining and mineral engineering), HEALTH PROFESSIONS (medical laboratory technology and veterinary science), SOCIAL SCIENCE (American studies, anthropology, criminal justice, dietetics, economics, food science, geography, history, international relations, parks and recreation management, philosophy, political science/government, psychology, and sociology). Electrical engineering, forestry, and accounting are the strongest academically. Architecture, electrical engineering, communications, accounting, and mechanical engineering have the largest enrollments.

Required: To graduate, students must complete at least 128 credit hours, including 40 in the major, with a minimum GPA of 2.0. The core curriculum requires a total of 30 credits in communications, mathematics, natural sciences, humanities, and social sciences. A comprehensive exam is required.

Special: The university offers cooperative programs with Washington State University, cross-registration with Washington State University, internships, study abroad, work-study programs, B.A.-B.S. degrees, dual and student-designed majors, a general studies degree, credit for life and work experience, nondegree study, and pass/fail options. There is a freshman honors program on campus, as well as 23 national honor societies, including Phi Beta Kappa.

Faculty/Classroom: Eighty-four percent of faculty are male; 16%, female. Seventy percent teach undergraduates, 85% do research, and 65% do both. Graduate students teach 20% of introductory courses. The average class size in an introductory lecture is 50; in a laboratory, 20; and in a regular course offering, 40.

Admissions: About 89% of the 1993–94 applicants were accepted. The SAT scores for the 1993–94 freshman class were as follows: Verbal—66% below 500, 26% between 500 and 599, 7% between 600 and 700, and 1% above 700; Math—42% below 500, 33% between 500 and 599, 20% between 600 and 700, and 5% above 700. The ACT scores were 22% below 21, 34% between 21 and 23, 29% between 24 and 26, 11% between 27 and 28, and 5% above 28. About 42% of the current freshmen were in the top fifth of their class; 72% were in the top two fifths. About 64 freshmen graduated first in their class.

Requirements: A minimum GPA of 2.5 is required. The SAT I or ACT is required, with a minimum SAT I composite score of 830 or enhanced ACT score of 19. Applicants must be graduates of an accredited secondary school. GED certificates are accepted for special admissions only. Students must have completed 15 academic credits and 15 Carnegie units based on 4 years of English, 3 each of mathematics and science, 2 1/2 of history and government, 1 each of humanities and a foreign language, and 1 1/2 of other college preparatory courses. AP and CLEP credits are accepted.

Procedure: Freshmen are admitted to all sessions. Entrance exams should be taken during the junior or senior year. Applications should be filed by August 1 for fall entry, December 1 for spring entry, and May 1 for summer entry, along with an application fee of $25. Notification is sent on a rolling basis. There are early admissions and deferred admissions plans.

Transfer: About 728 transfer students enrolled in 1993–94. Applicants must have completed at least 14 credit hours with a minimum GPA of 2.0 or 2.8 for engineering. A total of 32 credits out of 128 must be completed at UI.

Visiting: There are regularly scheduled orientations for prospective students. There are guides for informal visits and visitors may sit in on classes and stay overnight at the school. To arrange for a visit, contact the Office of New Student Services at (208) 885–6163.

Financial Aid: In 1993–94 65% of all current freshmen and 58% of continuing students received some form of financial aid. About 40% of freshmen and 40% of continuing students received need-based aid. The average freshman award was $4200. Of that total, scholarships or need-based grants averaged $1722 ($8000 maximum); loans averaged $2310 ($3925 maximum); and work contracts averaged $168 ($1200 maximum). Eighty percent of undergraduate students work part-time. Average earnings from campus work for the school year are $1500. The average financial indebtedness of the 1992–93 graduate was $5500. UI is a member of CSS. The college's own financial statement and FAFSA are required. The deadline for financial aid applications is February 15.

International Students: There are currently 480 international students enrolled. The school actively recruits these students. They must take the TOEFL and achieve a minimum score of 550.

Computers: The college provides computer facilities for student use. The mainframe is an IBM 4381. There are 250 microcomputers available in cluster sites across campus and in the microcomputer laboratory. All students may access the system whenever required for a class project or research. Students may access the system according to individual time allocation. The fees vary.

Graduates: In a recent year 1040 bachelor's degrees were awarded. The most popular majors among graduates were communications (6%), accounting (5%), and secondary education (5%). Within an average freshman class, 1% graduate in 3 years, 11% in 4 years, 32% in 5 years, and 40% in 6 years. Some 173 companies recruited on campus in a recent year.

Admissions Contact: Peter T. Brown, Director of Admissions.

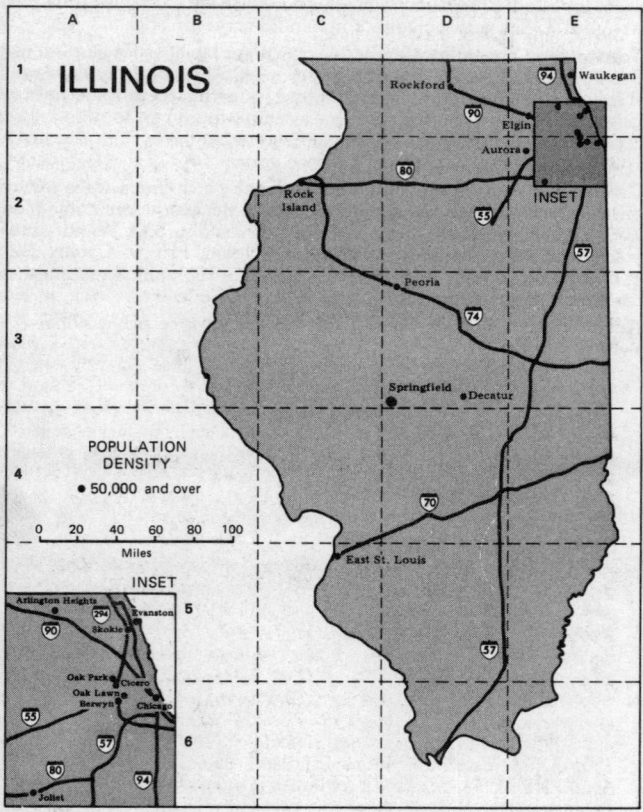

ILLINOIS

POPULATION DENSITY
• 50,000 and over

0 20 40 60 80 100
Miles

INSET

AUGUSTANA COLLEGE
Rock Island, IL 61201

C-2

(309) 794–7341
(800) 798–8100 (out-of-state)

Full-time: 911 men, 1135 women	**Faculty:** 142; IIB, av$
Part-time: 17 men, 17 women	**Ph.D.s:** 79%
Graduate: none	**Student/Faculty:** 14 to 1
Year: terms, summer session	**Tuition:** $12,942
Application Deadline: open	**Room & Board:** $4017

Freshman Class: 1879 applied, 1658 accepted, 508 enrolled
ACT: 25   **VERY COMPETITIVE**

Augustana College, founded in 1860, is a private, coeducational liberal arts institution affiliated with the Evangelical Lutheran Church in America. In addition to regional accreditation, Augustana has baccalaureate program accreditation with NASM and NCATE. The 3 libraries contain 235,834 volumes, 95,783 microform items, and 2615 audiovisual forms and subscribe to 1489 periodicals. Computerized library sources and services include the card catalog, interlibrary loans, and database searching. Special learning facilities include a learning resource center, art gallery, planetarium, radio station, preschool, center for communicative disorders, geology museum, observatory, map library, Swedish immigration research center, 420-acre environmental laboratory, and link-up with the National Center for Super Computing Applications. The 115-acre campus is in an urban area 165 miles west of Chicago. Including residence halls, there are 41 buildings on campus.

Student Life: About 80% of undergraduates are from Illinois. Students come from 37 states and 23 foreign countries. Eighty-eight percent are white. Fifty percent are Protestant; 26% Catholic; 11% claim no religious affiliation. The average age of freshmen is 18; all undergraduates, 20. Fourteen percent drop out by the end of their first year; 69% remain to graduate.

Housing: A total of 1309 students can be accommodated in college housing. College-sponsored living facilities include single-sex and coed dormitories, on-campus apartments, and off-campus apartments. On-campus housing is guaranteed for all 4 years. Sixty percent of students live on campus; of those, 80% remain on campus on weekends. Alcohol is not permitted. All students may keep cars on campus.

Activities: About 15% of men belong to 7 local fraternities; about 15% of women belong to 7 local sororities. There are 109 groups on campus, including alcohol responsibility, band, cheerleading, choir,

chorale, chorus, computers, dance, debate, drama, environmental, ethnic, gay, honors, international, jazz band, literary magazine, musical theater, newspaper, opera, orchestra, pep band, political, professional, radio and TV, religious, social, social service, student government, volunteer, and yearbook. Popular campus events include Homecoming, Messiah performances, Greek Olympics, and Santa Lucia Festival.

Sports: There are 11 intercollegiate sports for men and 8 for women, and 15 intramural sports for men and 13 for women. Athletic and recreation facilities include an all-weather track, lighted tennis courts, a physical education center, an exhibition basketball court, a swimming pool with space for 500 spectators, a college center, and playing fields. The campus stadium seats 3500.

Disabled Students: Seventy-five percent of the campus is accessible to disabled students. The following facilities are available: wheelchair ramps, elevators, special parking, specially equipped rest rooms, lowered telephones, and adapted college-owned housing.

Services: In addition to many counseling and information services, tutoring is available in every subject. In addition, there is a reader service for the blind.

Campus Safety and Security: Campus safety and security measures include 24-hour foot and vehicle patrol, self defense education, escort service, and shuttle buses. In addition, there are informal discussions, pamphlets, posters, films, lighted pathways and sidewalks, and security bulletin boards.

Programs of Study: Augustana awards the B.A., B.M., and B.M.E. degrees. Bachelor's degrees are awarded in BIOLOGICAL SCIENCE (biology/biological science), BUSINESS (accounting and business administration and management), COMMUNICATIONS AND THE ARTS (art history and appreciation, classics, dramatic arts, English, French, German, music, Scandinavian languages, Spanish, speech/debate/rhetoric, and studio art), COMPUTER AND PHYSICAL SCIENCE (chemistry, computer science, earth science, geology, mathematics, and physics), EDUCATION (art, elementary, music, physical, and secondary), ENGINEERING AND ENVIRONMENTAL DESIGN (engineering physics, environmental science, landscape architecture/design, and preengineering), HEALTH PROFESSIONS (clinical science, occupational therapy, predentistry, premedicine, and speech pathology/audiology), SOCIAL SCIENCE (economics, geography, history, humanities, international relations, philosophy, political science/government, psychology, public administration, religion, and sociology). Business administration, accounting, biology, premedicine, psychology, and English have the largest enrollments.

Required: A total of 123 credits with a minimum GPA of 2.0 is required to graduate. All students must complete a core curriculum, including 4 courses in foreign language, 3 each in religion, social sciences, and natural sciences, 2 in literature, and 1 each in English, speech communication, fine arts, and philosophy.

Special: Coordinated degree programs are offered in engineering, environmental management, forestry, landscape architecture, and occupational therapy with Duke, Iowa State, Northwestern, Purdue and Washington (St. Louis) universities, and the University of Illinois (Urbana-Champaign). Domestic and international internships are offered. Study abroad is possible in 17 countries, including China, Peru, Sweden, Germany, and France, as well as fall quarter study in East Asia, Europe, and Latin America. Interdisciplinary majors are offered in earth science, teaching, Asian studies, and public administration. A B.A.-B.S. degree in occupational therapy is offered, as well as 3–2 engineering programs with the University of Illinois, Purdue, and Washington and Iowa State universities. Work-study programs, double majors, physical education credits, and pass/fail options are available. There is a freshman honors program on campus, as well as 13 national honor societies, including Phi Beta Kappa. Twelve departments have honors programs.

Faculty/Classroom: Sixty-six percent of faculty are male; 34%, female. All teach undergraduates and do research. The average class size in an introductory lecture is 28; in a laboratory, 24; and in a regular course offering, 20.

Admissions: About 88% of the 1993–94 applicants were accepted. The ACT scores for the 1993–94 freshman class were as follows: 14% below 21, 27% between 21 and 23, 27% between 24 and 26, 15% between 27 and 28, and 17% above 28. About 58% of the current freshmen were in the top fifth of their class; 85% were in the top two fifths. About 21 freshmen graduated first in their class.

Requirements: Augustana requires applicants to be in the upper 50% of their class. The SAT I or ACT is required. Applicants should be graduates of an accredited secondary school or GED equivalent with 16 academic credits, including 4 in English, 3 in mathematics, 2 each in science and social studies, and 1 in foreign language, and

other science and mathematics courses for appropriate majors. An audition for music majors and an interview are recommended. AP credits are accepted. Important factors used in the admissions decision are advanced placement or honor courses, evidence of special talent, recommendations by school officials, leadership record, and extracurricular activities record.

Procedure: Freshmen are admitted in the fall, winter, and spring. Entrance exams should be taken by fall of the senior year. Application deadlines are open. The application fee is $200. Notification is sent on a rolling basis. There is a deferred admissions plan. A waiting list is an active part of the admissions procedure.

Transfer: About 84 transfer students enrolled in a recent year. A minimum GPA of 2.5 is required. SAT I or ACT scores and an interview are recommended. A total of 30 credits out of 123 must be completed at Augustana.

Visiting: There are regularly scheduled orientations for prospective students, including information sessions with speakers, exhibits, campus tours, meetings with faculty, counselors, and students, and social activities. There are guides for informal visits and visitors may sit in on classes and stay overnight at the school. To arrange for a visit, contact Martin Sauer, Director of Admissions, at (309) 794-7341 or (800) 798-8100.

Financial Aid: In 1993–94 91% of all current freshmen and 85% of continuing students received some form of financial aid. About 80% of freshmen and 66% of continuing students received need-based aid. The average freshman award was $10,437. Of that total, scholarships or need-based grants averaged $7010 ($12,852 maximum); loans averaged $2450 ($3625 maximum); and work contracts averaged $977 ($1120 maximum). Seventy-five percent of undergraduate students work part-time. Average earnings from campus work for the school year are $950. The average financial indebtedness of the 1992–93 graduate was $12,000. Augustana is a member of CSS. The FAF or FFS is required; the FAF is preferred. The deadline for financial aid applications is June 1.

International Students: There are currently 44 international students enrolled. The school actively recruits these students. They must take the TOEFL and achieve a minimum score of 500. The student must also take the SAT I or the ACT.

Computers: The college provides computer facilities for student use. The mainframes are a DEC MicroVax II, a DEC VAX 8200, and a DEC VAX 4000/200. There are more than 250 networked terminals and IBM-compatible and Apple Macintosh microcomputers located in the computer center, all residence halls, and classroom buildings. The network, 'AugieNet,' also connects with the mainframe equipment and to Internet. A link-up with the Center for Super Computing Applications at the University of Illinois is used by students and by faculty for research and classroom instruction. All students may access the system. There are no time limits on using the system and no fees.

Graduates: In 1992–93 509 bachelor's degrees were awarded. The most popular majors among graduates were business administration (23%), biology (13%), and English (10%). Within an average freshman class, 69% graduate in 4 years and 74% in 5 years. Some 51 companies recruited on campus in 1992–93. In the 1992 graduating class, 15% of the men and 15% of the women were enrolled in graduate school within 6 months of graduation; 33% of the men and 33% of the women had found employment.

Admissions Contact: Martin R. Sauer, Director of Admissions.

AURORA UNIVERSITY
Aurora, IL 60506

E-2
(708) 896-1975

Full-time: 354 men, 432 women	Faculty: 95; IIB, -$
Part-time: 304 men, 403 women	Ph.D.s: 43%
Graduate: 151 men, 288 women	Student/Faculty: 8 to 1
Year: trimesters, summer session	Tuition: $9700
Application Deadline: open	Room & Board: $3681
Freshman Class: 402 applied, 350 accepted, 129 enrolled	
ACT: 21	COMPETITIVE

Aurora University, founded in 1893, is a private institution that offers graduate and undergraduate degrees in arts and sciences, education, business and information science, nursing and health, and social work, and a professional/staff program. There are 5 undergraduate and 5 graduate schools. In addition to regional accreditation, AU has baccalaureate program accreditation with CSWE, NLN, and NRPA. The library contains 130,000 volumes, 67,000 microform items, and 7900 audiovisual forms, and subscribes to 700 periodicals. Computerized library sources and services include the card catalog, interlibrary loans, and database searching. Special learning facilities include a learning resource center, TV station, and an American Indian museum. The 26-acre campus is in a suburban area 40 miles west of Chicago. Including residence halls, there are 19 buildings on campus.

Student Life: About 96% of undergraduates are from Illinois. Students come from 12 states and 3 foreign countries. Seventy-eight percent are white; 12%, African American. Thirty-eight percent claim no religious affiliation; 31%, Protestant; 30%, Catholic. The average age of freshmen is 18; all undergraduates, 25. Seventeen percent drop out by the end of their first year.

Housing: A total of 420 students can be accommodated in college housing. College-sponsored living facilities include single-sex and coed dormitories. On-campus housing is available on a first-come, first-served basis. Eighty percent of students commute. Alcohol is not permitted. All students may keep cars on campus.

Activities: About 33% of men belong to 1 local and 3 national fraternities; about 34% of women belong to 2 local and 2 national sororities. There are 40 groups on campus, including cheerleading, choir, chorus, computers, dance, drama, ethnic, film, gay, honors, international, literary magazine, musical theater, newspaper, photography, political, professional, radio and TV, religious, social service, student government, and yearbook. Popular campus events include Homecoming, Black Awareness Week, Greekfest, and Spring Fling.

Sports: There are 6 intercollegiate sports for men and 4 for women, and 7 intramural sports for men and 6 for women. Athletic and recreation facilities include a fitness center, weight room, 3000-seat gymnasium, football and soccer field, and several racquetball courts.

Disabled Students: Fifty percent of the campus is accessible to disabled students. The following facilities are available: wheelchair ramps, elevators, special parking, and specially equipped rest rooms.

Services: In addition to many counseling and information services, tutoring is available in most subjects.

Campus Safety and Security: Campus safety and security measures include 24-hour foot and vehicle patrol, escort service, informal discussions, and pamphlets, posters, and films. In addition, there are emergency telephones and lighted pathways and sidewalks.

Programs of Study: AU awards the B.A., B.S., B.S.N., and B.S.W. degrees. Master's degrees are also awarded. Bachelor's degrees are awarded in BIOLOGICAL SCIENCE (biology/biological science), BUSINESS (accounting, banking and finance, business administration and management, business economics, management science, and marketing/retailing/merchandising), COMMUNICATIONS AND THE ARTS (communications, English, and literature), COMPUTER AND PHYSICAL SCIENCE (chemistry, computer programming, computer science, mathematics, and physics), EDUCATION (elementary and physical), ENGINEERING AND ENVIRONMENTAL DESIGN (engineering, environmental science, industrial administration/management, and preengineering), HEALTH PROFESSIONS (medical laboratory technology, nursing, predentistry, premedicine, and preveterinary science), SOCIAL SCIENCE (criminal justice, history, humanities, parks and recreation management, philosophy, political science/government, prelaw, psychology, religion, social work, and sociology). Science, education, nursing, and business are the strongest academically. Business has the largest enrollment.

Required: To graduate, students must complete 120 semester hours with a minimum GPA of 2.0. Distribution requirements include 2 courses in freshman English, 1 in communication, and 4 each in humanities, social/behavioral science, and natural science/mathematics, as well as senior colloquium.

Special: AU offers cross-registration with North Central and Illinois Benedictine colleges, field-related job experience, work-study programs, study abroad, and student-designed and dual majors. Nondegree study, a B.A.-B.S. degree, 3–2 engineering degree, pass/fail options, and credit for life, military, or work experience are possible. There is a freshman honors program on campus.

Faculty/Classroom: Fifty-one percent of faculty are male; 49%, female. All teach undergraduates. No introductory courses are taught by graduate students. The average class size in an introductory lecture is 25 and in a regular course offering, 15.

Admissions: About 87% of the 1993–94 applicants were accepted.

Requirements: AU requires applicants to be in the upper 50% of their class. A minimum GPA of 2.0 is required. The SAT I or ACT is required. AP and CLEP credits are accepted. Important factors used in the admissions decision are leadership record, advanced placement or honor courses, extracurricular activities record, evidence of special talent, and recommendations by school officials.

Procedure: Freshmen are admitted in the fall, winter, and spring. Entrance exams should be taken by late in the junior year or early in the senior year. Application deadlines are open. Notification is sent on a rolling basis.

Transfer: In 1993–94, 154 transfer students enrolled. Applicants are required to have a minimum GPA of 2.0 and must have completed at least 5 courses or 15 semesters hours. A total of 30 credits out of 120 must be completed at AU.

Visiting: There are regularly scheduled orientations for prospective students. There are guides for informal visits and visitors may sit in on classes and stay overnight at the school. To arrange for a visit, contact the Admissions Office at (708) 896-1975.

Financial Aid: In a recent year, 95% of all current freshmen and 90% of continuing students received some form of financial aid. Scholarships or need-based grants averaged $5500; loans averaged $2000 ($4000 maximum); and work contracts averaged $1000 ($2000 maximum). AU is a member of CSS. The FAF, FFS, or SFS is required. The deadline for financial aid applications is September 1.
International Students: There are currently 8 international students enrolled. They must take the TOEFL and achieve a minimum score of 550.
Computers: The college provides computer facilities for student use. The mainframe is a DEC VAX 6320. DEC, HP, IBM, and Apple terminals are available in 4 computer laboratories. All students may access the system. It may be used until midnight. There are no time limits and no fees.
Graduates: In a recent year, 320 bachelor's degrees were awarded. The most popular majors among graduates were nursing (17%), business (15%), and social work (7%). Some 72 companies recruited on campus in 1992–93. In the 1992 graduating class, 9% of the men and 86% of the women were enrolled in graduate school within 6 months of graduation.
Admissions Contact: Frank Johnson, Director of Admissions.

BARAT COLLEGE
Lake Forest, IL 60045　　　　　　　　　　　**E-1**
　　　　　　　　　　　　　　　　　　　　　(708) 295-4260

Full-time: 119 men, 306 women	Faculty: 41; IIB, -$
Part-time: 80 men, 205 women	Ph.D.s: 70%
Graduate: none	Student/Faculty: 10 to 1
Year: semesters, summer session	Tuition: $9690
Application Deadline: open	Room & Board: $4300
Freshman Class: 296 applied, 204 accepted, 92 enrolled	
SAT I Verbal/Math: 488/495	COMPETITIVE

Barat College, founded in 1858, is a private institution affiliated with the Catholic Church offering programs in the liberal and fine arts, business, education, and nursing. The library contains 100,000 volumes, 3217 microform items, and 1291 audiovisual forms, and subscribes to 350 periodicals. Computerized library sources and services include the card catalog, interlibrary loans, and database searching. Special learning facilities include an art gallery and radio station. The 30-acre campus is in a suburban area 29 miles north of Chicago. Including residence halls, there are 8 buildings on campus.
Student Life: About 85% of undergraduates are from Illinois. Students come from 22 states and 14 foreign countries. Seventy-nine percent are from public schools; 21% from private. Eighty-one percent are white; 10% African American. The average age of freshmen is 18; all undergraduates, 24. Fifteen percent drop out by the end of their first year; 73% remain to graduate.
Housing: A total of 540 students can be accommodated in college housing. College-sponsored living facilities include single-sex and coed dormitories. On-campus housing is guaranteed for all 4 years and is available on a first-come, first-served basis. Fifty-two percent of students live on campus; of those, 90% remain on campus on weekends. All students may keep cars on campus.
Activities: There are no fraternities or sororities on campus. There are 20 groups on campus, including art, cheerleading, choir, dance, drama, international, literary magazine, newspaper, photography, radio and TV, social, social service, student government, and yearbook. Popular campus events include Homecoming, the Christmas dance, and the spring formal.
Sports: There is 1 intercollegiate sport for men and women, and 7 intramural sports each for men and women. Athletic and recreation facilities include a 150-seat gymnasium and a weight room.
Disabled Students: All of the campus is accessible to disabled students. The following facilities are available: wheelchair ramps, elevators, special parking, specially equipped rest rooms, and special class scheduling.
Services: In addition to many counseling and information services, tutoring is available in most subjects. In addition, there is remedial math, reading, and writing.
Campus Safety and Security: Campus safety and security measures include 24-hour foot and vehicle patrol, self-defense education, escort service, and informal discussions. In addition, there are pamphlets, posters, films, emergency telephones, lighted pathways and sidewalks, a 24-hour secured residence hall, and key card entry systems in all residence halls.
Programs of Study: Barat awards the B.A., B.S., B.F.A., and B.S.N. degrees. Bachelor's degrees are awarded in BIOLOGICAL SCIENCE (biology/biological science), BUSINESS (business administration and management), COMMUNICATIONS AND THE ARTS (communications, dance, English, performing arts, and studio art), COMPUTER AND PHYSICAL SCIENCE (chemistry, computer programming, information sciences and systems, mathematics, and science), EDUCATION (psychology), HEALTH PROFESSIONS (art therapy, dance therapy, health science, and nursing), SOCIAL SCIENCE (economics, humanities, political science/government, psychology,

and sociology). Education and the performing arts are the strongest academically. Management and business have the largest enrollments.
Required: In order to graduate, all students must complete 120 credit hours, including 16 in humanities and 12 in social sciences. Also required are a minimum GPA of 2.0 and passing grades on English and mathematics personal skills tests.
Special: Barat offers cooperative programs with Chicago Medical School in medical technology, medical radiation physics, physical therapy, and B.S.N. completion. Cross-registration with Lake Forest College, internships for credit with local companies and corporations, study abroad in 20 countries, student-designed majors, and pass/fail options are also available. There is a freshman honors program on campus, as well as 2 national honor societies.
Faculty/Classroom: Forty-two percent of faculty are male; 58%, female. All teach undergraduates and 50% both teach and do research. The average class size in an introductory lecture is 30; in a laboratory, 6; and in a regular course offering, 18.
Admissions: About 69% of the 1993–94 applicants were accepted. The SAT scores for the 1993–94 freshman class were as follows: Verbal—70% below 500 and 30% between 500 and 599; Math—66% below 500 and 34% between 500 and 599. The ACT scores were 49% below 21, 25% between 21 and 23, 23% between 24 and 26, and 3% between 27 and 28. About 24% of the current freshmen were in the top fifth of their class; 48% were in the top two fifths.
Requirements: A minimum GPA of 2.5 is required. The SAT I or ACT is required, with a minimum SAT I composite of 900 or ACT composite of 20. Applicants must be graduates of an accredited secondary school or have a GED certificate. An essay is required and an interview is recommended for all applicants. An audition is required for dance majors and a portfolio is recommended for fine arts majors. AP and CLEP credits are accepted. Important factors used in the admissions decision are leadership record, evidence of special talent, advanced placement or honor courses, personality, intangible qualities, and extracurricular activities record.
Procedure: Freshmen are admitted to all sessions. Entrance exams should be taken no later than the July before entering. Application deadlines are open. Application fee is $20. Notification is sent on a rolling basis.
Transfer: About 165 transfer students enrolled in 1993–94. Applicants must have a minimum GPA of 2.0 and must submit all college transcripts. SAT I or ACT scores are required for students with fewer than 30 transferable credits. A total of 45 credits out of 120 must be completed at Barat.
Visiting: There are regularly scheduled orientations for prospective students, including a tour of campus and presentations by student, faculty, and staff. There are guides for informal visits and visitors may sit in on classes and stay overnight at the school. To arrange for a visit, contact the Admissions Office at (708) 295-4260.
Financial Aid: In 1993–94, 37% of all current freshmen and 63% of continuing students received some form of financial aid. About 35% of freshmen and 62% of continuing students received need-based aid. The average freshman award was $5400. Of that total, scholarships or need-based grants averaged $1500 ($4000 maximum); loans averaged $2625; and work contracts averaged $1600 ($2000 maximum). Sixty-three percent of undergraduate students work part-time. Average earnings from campus work for the school year are $1200. The average financial indebtedness of the 1992–93 graduate was $12,000. Barat is a member of CSS. The FAF, FFS or SFS and the college's own financial statement are required.
International Students: There are currently 18 international students enrolled. The school actively recruits these students. They must take the TOEFL or the University of Michigan Language Test and achieve a minimum score on the TOEFL of 550.
Computers: The college provides computer facilities for student use. Barat has a new Apple Macintosh/IBM computer center. There are also IBM-compatible PCs located in the library, computer laboratories, and language and writing centers. All students may access the system. There are no time limits on using the system and no fees.
Graduates: In 1992–93, 112 bachelor's degrees were awarded. The most popular majors among graduates were management and business (36%), psychology and education (22%), and English (6%). Within an average freshman class, 60% graduate in 4 years. Some 32 companies recruited on campus in 1992–93.
Admissions Contact: Director of Admissions.

BLACKBURN COLLEGE
C-4

Carlinville, IL 62626   (217) 854-3231; (800) 233-3550

Full-time: 219 men, 232 women	Faculty: 35; IIB, --$
Part-time: 17 men, 31 women	Ph.D.s: 80%
Graduate: none	Student/Faculty: 13 to 1
Year: semesters	Tuition: $8120
Application Deadline: August 20	Room & Board: $1000
Freshman Class: 478 applied, 395 accepted, 211 enrolled	
ACT: 21	COMPETITIVE

Blackburn College, founded in 1837, is a private liberal arts institution affiliated with the Presbyterian Church USA. The college is noted for its work program, which allows resident students to reduce their education costs and develop useful skills by managing and administering all essential campus services. The library contains 75,000 volumes, and subscribes to 400 periodicals. Computerized library sources and services include interlibrary loans and database searching. Special learning facilities include a learning resource center and art gallery. The 80-acre campus is in a rural area 60 miles north of St. Louis, Missouri. Including residence halls, there are 13 buildings on campus.

Student Life: About 80% of undergraduates are from Illinois. Students come from 20 states and 9 foreign countries. Ninety percent are from public schools; 10% from private. Eighty-two percent are white; 11% African American. The average age of freshmen is 18; all undergraduates, 19. Twenty-four percent drop out by the end of their first year; 47% remain to graduate.

Housing: A total of 441 students can be accommodated in college housing. College-sponsored living facilities include single-sex and coed dormitories. On-campus housing is guaranteed for all 4 years. Eighty-five percent of students live on campus; of those, 60% remain on campus on weekends. All students may keep cars on campus.

Activities: There are no fraternities or sororities on campus. There are many groups and organizations on campus, including band, cheerleading, choir, chorale, chorus, drama, ethnic, international, jazz band, literary magazine, newspaper, religious, social, student government, and yearbook.

Sports: There are 6 intercollegiate sports for men and 5 for women, and 9 intramural sports each for men and women. Athletic and recreation facilities include a gymnasium, a swimming pool, racquetball and tennis courts, weight and wrestling rooms, an outdoor track, and lighted playing fields.

Disabled Students: The following facilities are available: wheelchair ramps, special parking, specially equipped rest rooms, special class scheduling, lowered drinking fountains, and lowered telephones.

Services: In addition to many counseling and information services, tutoring is available in most subjects.

Campus Safety and Security: Campus safety and security measures include lighted pathways and sidewalks and student-run security through the work program.

Programs of Study: Blackburn awards the B.A. degree. Bachelor's degrees are awarded in BIOLOGICAL SCIENCE (biology/biological science), BUSINESS (accounting and business administration and management), COMMUNICATIONS AND THE ARTS (English literature, music business management, music performance, and Spanish), COMPUTER AND PHYSICAL SCIENCE (chemistry, computer science, and mathematics), EDUCATION (art, elementary, English, music, physical, secondary, and social science), HEALTH PROFESSIONS (medical laboratory technology), SOCIAL SCIENCE (history, political science/government, psychology, and public administration). The life sciences and physical sciences are the strongest academically. Business administration, psychology, elementary education, and English have the largest enrollments.

Required: To graduate, students must complete 122 semester hours with a minimum 2.0 GPA. Requirements include interdisciplinary courses, intercultural courses in foreign languages or English, and foundation courses in writing, mathematics, philosophy, religion, analysis, and physical education. Work program participation is required of resident students. All students must complete their last year in residence.

Special: The college offers supervised off-campus internships related to student majors, co-op programs, work-study, summer study in Europe, and a semester in Mexico or Washington, D.C. A 3-2 engineering degree with Washington University is offered. Students may design their own majors. There is one national honor society on campus.

Faculty/Classroom: Thirty-eight percent of faculty are male; 62%, female. All teach undergraduates. The average class size in an introductory lecture is 30; in a laboratory, 20; and in a regular course offering, 18.

Admissions: About 83% of the 1993-94 applicants were accepted. The ACT scores for the 1993-94 freshman class were as follows: 56% below 21, 20% between 21 and 23, 16% between 24 and 26, 5% between 27 and 28, and 3% above 28. About 29% of the current freshmen were in the top fifth of their class; 58% were in the top two fifths.

Requirements: Blackburn requires applicants to be in the upper 50% of their class. A minimum GPA of 2.0 is required. The SAT I or ACT is required. Applicants should be graduates of an accredited secondary school or have a GED certificate. Blackburn recommends completion of 4 years of English and 2 each of mathematics, natural sciences, social sciences, and foreign language. AP credits are accepted. Important factors used in the admissions decision are leadership record, personality, intangible qualities, and extracurricular activities record.

Procedure: Freshmen are admitted fall and spring. Entrance exams should be taken in the junior year. Applications should be filed by August 20 for fall entry and January 10 for spring entry. Notification is sent on a rolling basis. There is an early admissions plan.

Transfer: About 40 transfer students enrolled in a recent year. Applicants from accredited colleges may receive credit for grades of C or better; those with associate degrees may transfer some D grades. Credit for work at unaccredited institutions may be accepted provisionally. A total of 30 credits out of 122 must be completed at Blackburn.

Visiting: There are regularly scheduled orientations for prospective students, including a campus tour and meetings with an admissions representative, the financial aid director, and a department head. There are guides for informal visits and visitors may sit in on classes and stay overnight at the school. To arrange for a visit, contact the Admissions Office at (800) 233-3550.

Financial Aid: In a recent year, 95% of all current freshmen and 92% of continuing students received some form of financial aid. About 90% of students received need-based aid. The average freshman award was $6812. Of that total, scholarships or need-based grants averaged $2000 ($3500 maximum); and loans averaged $1500 ($2625 maximum). All undergraduate students work part-time. The average financial indebtedness of the 1992-93 graduate was $6543. Blackburn is a member of CSS. The FAF, FFS, or SFS and the FAFSA are required. The deadline for financial aid applications is April 1.

International Students: The school actively recruits international students. They must take the TOEFL and achieve a minimum score of 500. The student must also take the SAT I or the ACT.

Computers: The college provides computer facilities for student use. The mainframe is a DEC VAX 11/750. There are also 13 microcomputers, including IBM PC and Apple models, available in the computer center. All students may access the system every day during laboratory hours. There are no time limits on using the system and no fees.

Graduates: In a recent year, 78 bachelor's degrees were awarded. The most popular majors among graduates were business administration (24%), education (17%), and psychology (14%).

Admissions Contact: John C. Malin, Director of Admissions.

BRADLEY UNIVERSITY
D-3

Peoria, IL 61625   (309) 677-1000; (800) 447-6460

Full-time: 2285 men, 2246 women	Faculty: 300; IIA, av$
Part-time: 279 men, 364 women	Ph.D.s: 82%
Graduate: 447 men, 403 women	Student/Faculty: 15 to 1
Year: semesters, summer session	Tuition: $10,408
Application Deadline: open	Room & Board: $4310
Freshman Class: 3767 applied, 3414 accepted, 1061 enrolled	
SAT I Verbal/Math: 530/590	ACT: 25 COMPETITIVE +

Bradley University, founded in 1897, is a private, coeducational, independent university that offers programs in the liberal arts and sciences, communications and fine arts, engineering and technology, education and health sciences, and business administration. There are 5 undergraduate schools and one graduate school. In addition to regional accreditation, Bradley has baccalaureate program accreditation with AACSB, ABET, ACCE, ADA, NASAD, NASM, NCATE, and NLN. The library contains 600,000 volumes, 736,000 microform items, and 9000 audiovisual forms, and subscribes to 2407 periodicals. Computerized library sources and services include the card catalog, interlibrary loans, and database searching. Special learning facilities include a learning resource center, art gallery, radio station, and TV station. The 65-acre campus is in an urban area 160 miles southwest of Chicago. Including residence halls, there are 35 buildings on campus.

Student Life: About 75% of undergraduates are from Illinois. Students come from 45 states, 39 foreign countries, and Canada. Seventy-six percent are from public schools; 24% from private. Eighty-two percent are white. Thirty-six percent are Catholic; 20% Protestant; 11% Jewish. The average age of freshmen is 18; all undergraduates, 21. Twelve percent drop out by the end of their first year; 67% remain to graduate.

Housing: A total of 2155 students can be accommodated in college housing. College-sponsored living facilities include single-sex and coed dormitories, fraternity houses, and sorority houses. Wellness floors are available in residence halls. On-campus housing is guaranteed for all 4 years. Sixty-three percent of students live on campus; of

those, 99% remain on campus on weekends. Upperclassmen may keep cars on campus.

Activities: About 43% of men belong to 19 national fraternities; about 33% of women belong to 10 national sororities. There are 205 groups on campus, including art, band, cheerleading, chess, choir, chorale, chorus, computers, dance, drama, gay, honors, international, jazz band, literary magazine, musical theater, newspaper, orchestra, pep band, photography, political, professional, radio and TV, religious, social, social service, student government, symphony, and yearbook. Popular campus events include Founders Day, Greek Week, Garret week, Black History Month events, and International Night.

Sports: There are 7 intercollegiate sports for men and 7 for women, and 24 intramural sports for men and 24 for women. Athletic and recreation facilities include a civic center, playing fields, a golf course, a field house, and a 6,500-seat gymnasium.

Disabled Students: Eighty percent of the campus is accessible to disabled students. The following facilities are available: wheelchair ramps, elevators, special parking, specially equipped rest rooms, and lowered drinking fountains.

Services: In addition to many counseling and information services, tutoring is available in most subjects, including introductory subjects and selected higher level classes. In addition, there is remedial math and writing.

Campus Safety and Security: Campus safety and security measures include 24-hour foot and vehicle patrol, escort service, informal discussions, and pamphlets, posters, and films. In addition, there are emergency telephones, lighted pathways and sidewalks, engravers for marking personal property, and a medical escort service.

Programs of Study: Bradley awards the B.A., B.S., B.F.A., B.M.F., B.Mus., B.S.C., B.S.C.E., B.S.E.E., B.S.I.E., B.S.M.E., B.S.M.F.E., B.S.N., and B.S.P.T. degrees. Master's degrees also are awarded. Bachelor's degrees are awarded in BIOLOGICAL SCIENCE (biochemistry, biology/biological science, and biotechnology), BUSINESS (accounting, banking and finance, business administration and management, business economics, international business management, and marketing/retailing/merchandising), COMMUNICATIONS AND THE ARTS (art history and appreciation, communications, dramatic arts, English, French, German, graphic design, music, painting, photography, printmaking, sculpture, and Spanish), COMPUTER AND PHYSICAL SCIENCE (chemistry, computer science, geology, mathematics, and physics), EDUCATION (art, early childhood, elementary, foreign languages, home economics, music, secondary, and special), ENGINEERING AND ENVIRONMENTAL DESIGN (ceramic science, civil engineering, construction engineering, electrical/electronics engineering, engineering physics, environmental science, industrial engineering, manufacturing engineering, and mechanical engineering), HEALTH PROFESSIONS (medical laboratory technology and nursing), SOCIAL SCIENCE (criminal justice, economics, history, philosophy, political science/government, psychology, religion, social work, and sociology). Business, engineering, and natural sciences are the strongest academically. Business, engineering, and communication have the largest enrollments.

Required: To graduate, the student must complete the school's basic skills and general education curriculum. Overall, the college requires 124 total credit hours, with 32 hours in the major and a minimum GPA of 2.0.

Special: Special academic programs include co-op programs, internships, a Washington semester, work-study programs, study abroad in 12 countries, and dual majors. There is a freshman honors program on campus, as well as 31 national honor societies. Eight departments have honors programs.

Faculty/Classroom: Seventy percent of faculty are male; 30%, female. Ninety-eight percent teach undergraduates and do research. The average class size in a laboratory is 14 and in a regular course offering, 20.

Admissions: About 91% of the 1993–94 applicants were accepted. The SAT scores for the 1993–94 freshman class were as follows: Verbal—36% below 500, 38% between 500 and 599, 22% between 600 and 700, and 4% above 700; Math—13% below 500, 38% between 500 and 599, 34% between 600 and 700, and 15% above 700. The ACT scores were 15% below 21, 42% between 21 and 25, 36% between 26 and 30, and 7% above 31. About 50% of the current freshmen were in the top fifth of their class; 74% were in the top two fifths. There were 49 National Merit finalists. About 40 freshmen graduated first in their class.

Requirements: The SAT I or ACT is required, and the college recommends a minimum of 900 on the SAT I, or 18 on the ACT. Applicants must be high school graduates or submit a GED certificate. The student should have completed 8 Carnegie units, including 3 years of English, 2 each of mathematics and social studies, and one of science. AP and CLEP credits are accepted. Important factors used in the admissions decision are extracurricular activities record, geographic diversity, advanced placement or honor courses, evidence of special talent, and recommendations by alumni.

Procedure: Freshmen are admitted to all sessions. Entrance exams should be taken in spring of the junior year or fall of the senior year. Application deadlines are open. The application fee is $35. Notification is sent on a rolling basis. There is an early admissions plan.

Transfer: About 400 transfer students enrolled in 1993–94. Transfer students must have a minimum GPA of 2.0. Those with fewer than 15 hours of college credit must submit their ACT or SAT I scores and a high school transcript. A total of 30 credits out of 124 must be completed at Bradley.

Visiting: There are regularly scheduled orientations for prospective students, including class visits, campus tours, admissions information, financial assistance seminars, lunch, and student and parent meetings. There are guides for informal visits and visitors may stay overnight at the school. To arrange for a visit, contact the Office of Admissions at (309) 677-1000.

Financial Aid: In 1993–94, 82% of all current freshmen and 80% of continuing students received some form of financial aid. About 50% received need-based aid. The average freshman award was $7196. Of that total, scholarships or need-based grants averaged $4400 ($10,000 maximum); loans averaged $2200 ($4800 maximum); and work contracts averaged $600 ($1500 maximum). Six percent of undergraduate students work part-time. The average financial indebtedness of the 1992–93 graduate was $10,200. Bradley is a member of CSS. The FAFSA financial statement is required. The deadline for financial aid applications is March 1.

International Students: There are currently 79 international students enrolled. The school actively recruits these students. They must take the TOEFL and achieve a minimum score of 500.

Computers: The university provides computer facilities for student use. The mainframe is a Control Data CYBER 930. There are 390 AT&T, Zenith, IBM, and Apple Macintosh microcomputers available throughout the campus. All students may access the system 24 hours a day. There are no time limits and no fees.

Graduates: In 1992–93, 1062 bachelor's degrees were awarded. Within an average freshman class, 38% graduate in 4 years, 61% in 5 years, and 64% in 6 years. Some 93 companies recruited on campus in 1992–93. In the 1992 graduating class, 16% of the men and women were enrolled in graduate school within 6 months of graduation; 89% had found employment.

Admissions Contact: Gary R. Bergman, Executive Director, Enrollment Management.

CHICAGO STATE UNIVERSITY

E-2

Chicago, IL 60628 (312) 995-2513

Full-time/part-time men: 2259	Faculty: 370; IIA, --$
Full-time/part-time women: 4976	Ph.D.s: 62%
Graduate: 781 men, 1491 women	Student/Faculty: 15 to 1
Year: semesters, summer session	Tuition: $2198 ($5894)
Application Deadline: June 1	Room & Board: n/app
Freshman Class: 3553 applied, 1719 accepted, 802 enrolled	
ACT: 17	COMPETITIVE

Chicago State University, founded in 1867, is a public, coeducational commuter institution controlled by the State Board of Governors. It offers day and evening undergraduate programs through the colleges of Arts and Sciences, Allied Health, Business Administration, Education, and Nursing. There are 5 undergraduate and 2 graduate schools. In addition to regional accreditation, Chicago State has baccalaureate program accreditation with ADA, CAHEA, NCATE, and NLN. The library contains 26,000 volumes and 388,028 microform items, and subscribes to 1734 periodicals. Computerized library sources and services include the card catalog, interlibrary loans, and database searching. Special learning facilities include a learning resource center. The 161-acre campus is in an urban area 12 miles south of downtown Chicago. There are 9 buildings on campus.

Student Life: About 98% of undergraduates are from Illinois. Students come from 7 foreign countries. About 85% are from public schools; 15% from private. Some 84% are African American; 10% white. The average age of all undergraduates is 30.6.

Housing: There are no residence halls. All students commute. Alcohol is not permitted.

Activities: About 12% of men and about 15% of women belong to 4 national fraternities and 4 national sororities. There are 17 groups on campus, including cheerleading, choir, drama, drill team, honors, jazz band, literary magazine, musical theater, newspaper, photography, professional, radio and TV, religious, social, student government, and yearbook. Popular campus events include Homecoming Week activities, plays, open house, Welcome Week activities, art exhibits, Black History Month, and Black Writer's Conference.

Sports: There are 8 intercollegiate sports for men and 3 for women, and 4 intramural sports for men and 2 for women. Athletic and recreation facilities include tennis courts, indoor/outdoor tracks, an Olympic-size swimming pool, weight rooms, basketball courts, and a fitness center.

Disabled Students: The entire campus is accessible to disabled students. The following facilities are available: wheelchair ramps, elevators, special parking, specially equipped rest rooms, lowered drinking fountains, and lowered telephones.

Services: In addition to many counseling and information services, tutoring is available in some subjects, including mathematics, science, and accounting. In addition, there is remedial math, reading, and writing.

Campus Safety and Security: Campus safety and security measures include 24-hour foot and vehicle patrol, escort service, informal discussions, and pamphlets, posters, and films. In addition, there are emergency telephones and lighted pathways and sidewalks.

Programs of Study: Chicago State awards the B.A., B.S. and B.S. Ed. degrees. Master's degrees also are awarded. Bachelor's degrees are awarded in BIOLOGICAL SCIENCE (biochemistry and biology/biological science), BUSINESS (accounting, banking and finance, business administration and management, hotel/motel and restaurant management, and marketing/retailing/merchandising), COMMUNICATIONS AND THE ARTS (broadcasting, English, music, Spanish, and speech/debate/rhetoric), COMPUTER AND PHYSICAL SCIENCE (chemistry, computer science, data processing, information sciences and systems, mathematics, and physics), EDUCATION (art, business, early childhood, elementary, industrial arts, music, physical, secondary, special, and vocational), HEALTH PROFESSIONS (medical records administration/services, nursing, occupational therapy, predentistry, and premedicine), SOCIAL SCIENCE (criminal justice, dietetics, economics, geography, history, political science/government, prelaw, psychology, and sociology). Business administration, and computer science are the strongest programs academically. Business administration and computer science have the largest enrollments.

Required: All students must complete 120 credit hours and maintain a 2.0 GPA. They must complete a 39-hour core curriculum as well as examinations in English, mathematics, reading, and the U.S. Constitution.

Special: There is a freshman honors program on campus

Faculty/Classroom: Almost all faculty teach undergraduates. The average class size in an introductory lecture is 60; in a laboratory, 26; and in a regular course offering, 35.

Admissions: About 48% of the 1993–94 applicants were accepted. The ACT scores for the 1993–94 freshman class were as follows: 91% below 21, 8% between 21 and 23, and 1% between 24 and 26. About 29% of the current freshmen were in the top fifth of their class; 57% were in the top two fifths. One freshman graduated first in the class.

Requirements: Chicago State requires applicants to be in the upper 50% of their class. The SAT I or ACT is required, but scores need not be submitted if the applicant is over 23 years of age. Graduation from an accredited secondary school is required; a GED will be accepted. Minimum credits submitted should include 4 units of English, and 2 each of mathematics, science, and social sciences. AP and CLEP credits are accepted.

Procedure: Freshmen are admitted to all sessions. Entrance exams should be taken between April of the junior year and February of the senior year. Applications should be filed by June 1 for fall entry, November 1 for winter entry, February 1 for spring entry, and April 1 for summer entry. Notification is sent on a rolling basis.

Transfer: About 787 transfer students enrolled in 1993–94. Transfer students must have a minimum GPA of 2.0, and those with fewer than 30 hours must also meet freshman admission requirements. A total of 30 credits out of 120 must be completed at Chicago State.

Visiting: There are regularly scheduled orientations for prospective students. To arrange for a visit, contact the Office of Admissions at (312) 995–2513.

Financial Aid: In 1993–94, 85% of all current freshmen and 80% of continuing students received some form of financial aid. About 98% of freshmen and 78% of continuing students received need-based aid. The average freshman award was $4500. Of that total, scholarships or need-based grants averaged $1868 ($1880 maximum); loans averaged $4000; and work contracts averaged $1000 ($3000 maximum). Average earnings from campus work for the school year are $2700. The average financial indebtedness of the 1992–93 graduate was $8500. The FFS and the college's own financial statement are required. The deadline for financial aid applications is April 15.

International Students: There are currently 88 international students enrolled. They must take the TOEFL or the college's own test and achieve a minimum score on the TOEFL of 500.

Computers: The college provides computer facilities for student use. The mainframes are a CDC CYBER 180 Model 130A and an IBM 4341. There are 40 Zenith microcomputers available. All students may access the system. It may be used 8:30 A.M. to 10 P.M. Monday through Friday, 8:30 A.M. to 5 P.M. Saturday, and 1 p.m to 8 P.M. Sunday. There are no time limits on using the system. The fees are $5.

Graduates: In a recent year, 507 bachelor's degrees were awarded. The most popular majors among graduates were education (18%), psychology (10%), and business administration (10%).

Admissions Contact: Admissions Counselors.

COLLEGE OF SAINT FRANCIS E-2

Joliet, IL 60435 (815) 740–3400; (800) 735–7500 (in-state)

Full-time: 390 men, 427 women	Faculty: 47; IIB, av$
Part-time: 154 men, 102 women	Ph.D.s: 52%
Graduate: 370 men, 648 women	Student/Faculty: 17 to 1
Year: semesters, summer session	Tuition: $9100
Application Deadline: June 1	Room & Board: $3960
Freshman Class: 420 applied, 310 accepted, 160 enrolled	
ACT: 23	VERY COMPETITIVE

The College of Saint Francis, founded in 1920, is a private, coeducational liberal arts and professional college affiliated with the Roman Catholic Church. There is one graduate school. In addition to regional accreditation, CSF has baccalaureate program accreditation with CSWE and NRPA. The library contains 186,000 volumes, 185,384 microform items, and 1500 audiovisual forms, and subscribes to 525 periodicals. Computerized library sources and services include interlibrary loans and database searching. Special learning facilities include a radio station and TV station. The 17-acre campus is in a suburban area 35 miles southwest of Chicago. Including residence halls, there are 7 buildings on campus.

Student Life: About 90% of undergraduates are from Illinois. Students come from 15 states, 3 foreign countries, and Canada. Fifty-five percent are from public schools; 45%, from private. Ninety percent are white. Seventy percent are Catholic; 28%, Protestant. The average age of freshmen is 19; all undergraduates, 23. Nine percent drop out by the end of their first year; 63% remain to graduate.

Housing: A total of 450 students can be accommodated in college housing. College-sponsored living facilities include coed dormitories. On-campus housing is guaranteed for the freshman year only, is available on a first-come, first-served basis, and is available on a lottery system for upperclassmen. Priority is given to out-of-town students. Fifty percent of students live on campus; of those, 70% remain on campus on weekends. All students may keep cars on campus.

Activities: There are no fraternities or sororities on campus. There are 23 groups on campus, including cheerleading, chess, choir, chorale, chorus, computers, drama, ethnic, honors, literary magazine, musical theater, newspaper, pep band, photography, political, professional, radio and TV, religious, social, social service, and student government. Popular campus events include Octoberfest, Homecoming, Christmas Dance, and spring Olympics.

Sports: There are 6 intercollegiate sports for men and 5 for women, and 18 intramural sports for men and 17 for women. Athletic and recreation facilities include a 10,000-seat lighted football stadium, an indoor arena, a baseball field, a Nautilus center, and basketball, racquetball, volleyball, and badminton courts.

Disabled Students: Ninety percent of the campus is accessible to disabled students. The following facilities are available: wheelchair ramps, elevators, special parking, specially equipped rest rooms, special class scheduling, lowered drinking fountains, and lowered telephones.

Services: In addition to many counseling and information services, tutoring is available in most subjects. The writing center provides help with papers. A math center for tutorial assistance and numerous computerized tutorial programs for courses are also available.

Campus Safety and Security: Campus safety and security measures include 24-hour foot and vehicle patrol, self defense education, escort service, and informal discussions. In addition, there are pamphlets, posters, films, emergency telephones, and lighted pathways and sidewalks.

Programs of Study: CSF awards the B.A., B.S., and B.B.A. degrees. Master's degrees are also awarded. Bachelor's degrees are awarded in BIOLOGICAL SCIENCE (biology/biological science), BUSINESS (accounting, banking and finance, business administration and management, international business management, and marketing/retailing/merchandising), COMMUNICATIONS AND THE ARTS (advertising, broadcasting, communications, English, and journalism), COMPUTER AND PHYSICAL SCIENCE (computer programming, computer science, information sciences and systems, and mathematics), EDUCATION (secondary), ENGINEERING AND ENVIRONMENTAL DESIGN (environmental science), HEALTH PROFESSIONS (medical laboratory technology, predentistry, and premedicine), SOCIAL SCIENCE (history, parks and recreation management, political science/government, prelaw, psychology, religion, and social work). Journalism, computer science, business and sciences are the strongest academically. Business, computer science, and education have the largest enrollments.

Required: To graduate, students are required to complete 128 credit hours, including 3 hours each in literature, history, fine arts, science, computer science, and speech, and 6 hours each in social sciences,

philosophy, and religious studies. They must also take college writing 1 and 2 and college algebra or higher mathematics and maintain a GPA of 2.0. A core curriculum of 48 credit hours must be completed, and a thesis or senior experience is required.

Special: Internships with major corporations or agencies are available for most majors. The college also offers study abroad in a variety of European countries, a Washington semester, dual majors, and credit for life, military, and work experience. There are 10 national honor societies on campus.

Faculty/Classroom: Sixty percent of faculty are male; 40%, female. All teach undergraduates, 20% do research, and 20% do both. No introductory courses are taught by graduate students. The average class size in an introductory lecture is 30; in a laboratory, 20; and in a regular course offering, 20.

Admissions: About 74% of the 1993–94 applicants were accepted. The ACT scores for the 1993–94 freshman class were as follows: 31% below 21, 29% between 21 and 23, 24% between 24 and 26, 8% between 27 and 28, and 8% above 28. About 49% of the current freshmen were in the top fifth of their class; 78% were in the top two fifths. There were 12 National Merit semifinalists. Five freshmen graduated first in their class.

Requirements: CSF requires applicants to be in the upper 50% of their class. A minimum GPA of 2.5 is required. The SAT I or ACT is required. Admission requirements also include 4 years of English, 3 of mathematics, 2 each of science and social studies, and 3 of either art, music, theater, or computer science. AP and CLEP credits are accepted. Important factors used in the admissions decision are geographic diversity, advanced placement or honor courses, leadership record, recommendations by school officials, and extracurricular activities record.

Procedure: Freshmen are admitted in the fall and spring. Entrance exams should be taken in the spring of the junior year or the fall of the senior year. Applications should be filed by June 1 for fall entry and December 1 for spring entry, along with an application fee of $20. Notification is sent on a rolling basis.

Transfer: About 118 transfer students enrolled in 1993–94. Transfer students must have completed a minimum of 32 semester hours and earned a GPA of 2.0. A minimum of 20 on the ACT is recommended. Students must also have completed 1 course each in mathematics and writing. A total of 32 credits out of 128 must be completed at CSF.

Visiting: There are regularly scheduled orientations for prospective students, including meeting faculty, a tour, and student presentations. There are guides for informal visits, and visitors may sit in on classes and stay overnight at the school. To arrange for a visit, contact the Admissions Office at (815) 740–3400.

Financial Aid: In 1993–94, 84% of all current freshmen and 85% of continuing students received some form of financial aid. About 68% of freshmen and 64% of continuing students received need-based aid. The average freshman award was $7652. Of that total, scholarships or need-based grants averaged $3650 ($8000 maximum); loans averaged $2500 ($2500 maximum); and work contracts averaged $1500 (maximum). Forty-seven percent of undergraduate students work part-time. Average earnings from campus work for the school year are $1400. The average financial indebtedness of the 1992–93 graduate was $6900. CSF is a member of CSS. The FAF or FFS is required. The deadline for financial aid applications is May 1.

International Students: There are currently 5 international students enrolled. They must take the TOEFL and achieve a minimum score of 550. The student must also take SAT I or the ACT and achieve a minimum score of 850 on SAT I or 21 on the ACT.

Computers: The college provides computer facilities for student use. The mainframes are 2 Digital 6000s and a Digital 850. There are about 100 terminals or microcomputers in 3 student laboratories, and 24-hour telephone access to the computer network is available from off-campus or student rooms. All students may access the system 24 hours a day. The fee is $40 a year.

Graduates: In 1992–93, 191 bachelor's degrees were awarded. The most popular majors among graduates were elementary education (11%), accounting (10%), and computer science (9%). Within an average freshman class, 61% graduate in 4 years, 2% in 5 years, and 1% in 6 years. Some 42 companies recruited on campus in 1992–93. In the 1992 graduating class, 7% of the men and 8% of the women were enrolled in graduate school within 6 months of graduation and 89% had found employment.

Admissions Contact: Chuck Beutel, Dean of Enrollment Management.

COLUMBIA COLLEGE   E-2
Chicago, IL 60605   (312) 663–1600, ext. 129

Full-time: 2526 men, 2326 women	Faculty: 157; IIB, av$
Part-time: 956 men, 1035 women	Ph.D.s: n/av
Graduate: 161 men, 323 women	Student/Faculty: 31 to 1
Year: semesters, summer session	Tuition: $3529
Application Deadline: open	Room: $4350
Freshman Class: n/av	
SAT I or ACT: not required	**SPECIAL**

Columbia College, founded in 1890, is a private, liberal arts college with programs in the visual arts, performing arts, and media and commununication arts. The college seeks to educate students for creative occupations in the arts. There is one undergraduate school. The library contains 113,228 volumes, 225 microform items, and 2792 audiovisual forms, and subscribes to 1054 periodicals. Computerized library sources and services include interlibrary loans and database searching. Special learning facilities include an art gallery and a contemporary photography museum. The campus is in an urban area. There are 5 buildings on campus.

Student Life: About 90% of undergraduates are from Illinois. Students come from 31 states and 36 foreign countries. Sixty-two percent are white; 23% African American. The average age of freshmen is 18; all undergraduates, 24. Thirty-five percent drop out by the end of their first year.

Housing: There are no residence halls.

Activities: There are no fraternities or sororities on campus. There are 35 groups on campus, including art, chorus, computers, drama, film, gay, jazz band, literary magazine, musical theater, newspaper, photography, political, professional, radio and TV, and social service.

Sports: There is no sports program at the college.

Disabled Students: Ninety-five percent of the campus is accessible to disabled students. The following facilities are available: wheelchair ramps, elevators, specially equipped rest rooms, and special class scheduling.

Services: In addition to many counseling and information services, tutoring is available in some subjects. There is remedial math, reading, and writing.

Campus Safety and Security: Campus safety and security measures include informal discussions and emergency telephones.

Programs of Study: The college awards the B.A. degree. Master's degrees are also awarded. Bachelor's degrees are awarded in COMMUNICATIONS AND THE ARTS (art, arts administration/management, broadcasting, communications, creative writing, dance, dramatic arts, film arts, fine arts, journalism, and photography). Art, film/video, marketing communication, and radio have the largest enrollments.

Required: All students must complete 124 semester hours of study including 1 intensive writing course. General studies distribution consists of 6 hours each of English, history, and social science; 9 each of literature/humanities, science/mathematics, and 3 of computer applications and electives.

Special: The college offers study abroad, independent study, internships, work-study programs, student-designed majors, and a general studies degree.

Faculty/Classroom: All faculty teach undergraduates. No introductory courses are taught by graduate students. The average class size in an introductory lecture is 45; in a laboratory, 21; and in a regular course offering, 25.

Requirements: Applicants should be graduates of accredited secondary schools. The GED is also accepted. An interview is recommended. The SAT I and ACT are not required. AP and CLEP credits are accepted.

Procedure: Application deadlines are open. Application fee is $25. The college accepts all applicants. Notification is sent on a rolling basis. There is a deferred admissions plan.

Transfer: About 1275 transfer students enrolled in a recent year. A total of 36 credits out of 124 must be completed at The college.

Visiting: There are regularly scheduled orientations for prospective students. There are guides for informal visits and visitors may sit in on classes. To arrange for a visit, contact the Undergraduate Admissions Office at (312) 663–1600, ext. 129 or 130.

Financial Aid: In a recent year, 49% of all current freshmen and 45% of continuing students received some form of financial aid. The average freshman award was $6200. Of that total, scholarships or need-based grants averaged $4000 ($5900 maximum); and loans averaged $2200 ($2625 maximum). All undergraduate students work part-time. Average earnings from campus work for the school year are $1551. The average financial indebtedness of a recent year's graduate was $6000. The FAF, FFS, SFS, or Singlefile Form (preferred) is required.

International Students: There are currently 136 international students enrolled. They must take the TOEFL and achieve a minimum score of 500.

Computers: The college provides computer facilities for student use. Personal computers are available for student use in the college's computer laboratories.

Graduates: In a recent year, 760 bachelor's degrees were awarded. The most popular majors among graduates were marketing communication (14%), television (8%), and journalism (6%).

Admissions Contact: Judy Nelson, Director of Admissions.

CONCORDIA UNIVERSITY E-1

River Forest, IL 60305 (708) 209-3104; (800) 285-2668 (in-state)

Full-time: 387 men, 781 women	Faculty: 89; IIB, --$
Part-time: 31 men, 114 women	Ph.D.s: 61%
Graduate: 211 men, 934 women	Student/Faculty: 12 to 1
Year: quarters, summer session	Tuition: $8576
Application Deadline: open	Room & Board: $4035
Freshman Class: 528 applied, 403 accepted, 186 enrolled	
ACT: 23	**COMPETITIVE**

Concordia University, founded in 1864, is a private liberal arts institution affiliated with the Lutheran Church, Missouri Synod. There are 3 undergraduate schools and one graduate school. In addition to regional accreditation, Concordia has baccalaureate program accreditation with NCATE and NLN. The 2 libraries contain 150,409 volumes, 464,818 microform items, and 3787 audiovisual forms, and subscribe to 600 periodicals. Computerized library sources and services include interlibrary loans and database searching. Special learning facilities include a learning resource center, art gallery, natural history museum, TV station, early childhood resource center, human performance laboratory, language laboratory, computer center, and weather station. The 40-acre campus is in a suburban area 10 miles west of downtown Chicago. Including residence halls, there are 23 buildings on campus.

Student Life: About 67% of undergraduates are from Illinois. Students come from 28 states, 7 foreign countries, and Canada. Sixty-seven percent are from public schools; 33% from private. Seventy-eight percent are white; 16%, African American. Seventy-four percent are Protestant; 20%, Catholic. The average age of freshmen is 18; all undergraduates, 20. Twenty-five percent drop out by the end of their first year; 52% remain to graduate.

Housing: A total of 700 students can be accommodated in college housing. College-sponsored living facilities include single-sex and coed dormitories and married-student housing. On-campus housing is guaranteed for all 4 years. Sixty percent of students live on campus; of those, 80% remain on campus on weekends. Alcohol is not permitted. All students may keep cars on campus.

Activities: There are no fraternities or sororities on campus. There are 50 groups on campus, including art, band, cheerleading, choir, chorale, chorus, computers, dance, drama, international, jazz band, literary magazine, musical theater, newspaper, pep band, photography, professional, radio and TV, religious, social, social service, student government, symphony, and yearbook. Popular campus events include Orientation Week, Campus Awareness Day, Homecoming, Christmas Craft Show, Family Weekend, Winter Festival, and Spring Formal.

Sports: There are 7 intercollegiate sports for men and 6 for women, and 10 intramural sports for men and 10 for women. Athletic and recreation facilities include 2 gymnasiums, an indoor swimming pool, a weight training room, a football field, tennis courts, baseball and softball fields, a track, a wrestling room, a first aid training room, table tennis, billiards, table games, and video games.

Disabled Students: The following facilities are available: wheelchair ramps, elevators, special parking, specially equipped rest rooms, special class scheduling, lowered drinking fountains, and lowered telephones.

Services: In addition to many counseling and information services, tutoring is available in most subjects. There is remedial math, reading, and writing.

Campus Safety and Security: Campus safety and security measures include 24-hour foot and vehicle patrol, shuttle buses, and lighted pathways and sidewalks.

Programs of Study: Concordia awards the B.A., B.Mus., B.Mus.Ed., and B.S.N. degrees. Master's degrees are also awarded. Bachelor's degrees are awarded in BIOLOGICAL SCIENCE (biology/biological science), BUSINESS (business administration and management), COMMUNICATIONS AND THE ARTS (communications, English, and music), COMPUTER AND PHYSICAL SCIENCE (chemistry, computer programming, computer science, earth science, and mathematics), EDUCATION (computer, early childhood, elementary, middle school, music, science, and secondary), HEALTH PROFESSIONS (nursing, predentistry, and premedicine), SOCIAL SCIENCE (geography, history, philosophy, physical fitness/movement, political science/government, prelaw, psychology, religion, social science, and sociology). Teacher education, music, computer science, psychology, and nursing are the strongest academically. Teacher education, nursing, and business have the largest enrollments.

Required: All students are required to take 2 years of liberal arts, including humanities, English, science, religion, and social science, and 5 quarter hours of physical education. A 2.0-2.25 GPA and a total of 188 to 210 quarter hours are required.

Special: Cross-registration is possible with Rosany College and the Chicago Consortium of Colleges. Concordia also offers internships for liberal arts majors and pass/fail options. There are 3 national honor societies on campus, including Phi Beta Kappa.

Faculty/Classroom: Seventy-two percent of faculty are male; 28%, female. Ninety percent teach undergraduates and 24% also do research. No introductory courses are taught by graduate students. The average class size in an introductory lecture is 20; in a laboratory, 18; and in a regular course offering, 27.

Admissions: About 76% of the 1993-94 applicants were accepted. The ACT scores for the 1993-94 freshman class were as follows: 33% below 21, 23% between 21 and 23, 23% between 24 and 26, 12% between 27 and 28, and 9% above 28. About 44% of the current freshmen were in the top fifth of their class; 71% were in the top two fifths. Two freshmen graduated first in their class.

Requirements: Concordia requires applicants to be in the upper 50% of their class. A minimum GPA of 2.0 is required. Applicants should have 15 units of credit, with 11 units in college preparatory courses, including English, mathematics, laboratory science, and social studies. A letter of recommendation is required, as is a minimum GPA of 2.0 in the college preparatory subjects and a ranking in the top half of their graduating class. AP and CLEP credits are accepted. Important factors used in the admissions decision are advanced placement or honor courses, recommendations by school officials, leadership record, extracurricular activities record, and personality, intangible qualities.

Procedure: Freshmen are admitted to all sessions. Entrance exams should be taken in the spring of the junior year or the fall of the senior year. Application deadlines are open. Notification is sent on a rolling basis.

Transfer: In 1993-94, 151 transfer students enrolled. A total of 48 credits out of 188 to 210 must be completed at Concordia.

Visiting: There are regularly scheduled orientations for prospective students. There are guides for informal visits, and visitors may sit in on classes and stay overnight at the school. To arrange for a visit, contact the Office of Admission at (708) 209-3104 or (800) 285-2668 (in state).

Financial Aid: In a recent year, 76% of all current freshmen and 73% of continuing students received some form of financial aid. About 63% of freshmen and 40% of continuing students received need-based aid. The average freshman award was $6900. Of that total, scholarships or need-based grants averaged $1073 ($7500 maximum); loans averaged $1717 ($4000 maximum); and work contracts averaged $1165 ($1999 maximum). Thirty-one percent of undergraduate students work part-time. Average earnings from campus work for the school year are $750. The average financial indebtedness of the 1992-93 graduate was $5000. Concordia is a member of CSS. The FAF and student and parent 1040 federal tax forms are required. The deadline for financial aid applications is June 1.

International Students: There are currently 8 international students enrolled. They must take the TOEFL or the University of Michigan Language Test and achieve a minimum score on the TOEFL of 525. The student must also take the SAT I or the ACT.

Computers: The college provides computer facilities for student use. The mainframes are a DEC VAX 8650, 8700, and 11/785. There are 30 Apple II and IBM-compatible Zenith microcomputers available in the computer center and the library. All students may access the system. It may be used 7:30 A.M. to 11 P.M. Monday to Friday; 9 A.M. to 5 P.M. Saturday; 2 P.M. to 11 P.M. Sunday; and 7 days per week, 24 hours per day, through dial-up access. There are no time limits on using the system and no fees.

Graduates: In a recent year, 180 bachelor's degrees were awarded. The most popular majors among graduates were education (48%), nursing (11%), and business (8%).

Admissions Contact: Sara Dahms, Acting Director of Admissions.

DEPAUL UNIVERSITY E-2

Chicago, IL 60604 (312) 362-8300; (800) 4-DEPAUL (out-of-state)

Full-time: 2637 men, 3339 women	Faculty: 424; IIA, +$
Part-time: 1478 men, 2329 women	Ph.D.s: 88%
Graduate: 3619 men, 3097 women	Student/Faculty: 14 to 1
Year: quarters, summer session	Tuition: $10,590
Application Deadline: August 15	Room & Board: $4945
Freshman Class: 4913 applied, 3553 accepted, 1230 enrolled	
SAT I Verbal/Math: 520/560	ACT: 25 **VERY COMPETITIVE**

DePaul University, founded by the Vincentian Order in 1898, is a private, coeducational Catholic institution comprising 2 main campuses: the Lincoln Park Campus houses undergraduate programs in liberal arts and sciences, education, theater, and music; the Loop Campus offers programs in commerce, law, and computer science and infor-

mation systems. There are 7 undergraduate and 6 graduate schools. In addition to regional accreditation, DePaul has baccalaureate program accreditation with AACSB, NASM, NCATE, and NLN. The 3 libraries contain 615,019 volumes, 291,775 microform items, and 22,829 audiovisual forms, and subscribe to 16,088 periodicals. Computerized library sources and services include the card catalog, interlibrary loans, and database searching. Special learning facilities include an art gallery, radio station, performing arts center, recording studio, and marketing research center. The 32-acre campus is in an urban area. Including residence halls, there are 31 buildings on campus.

Student Life: About 73% of undergraduates are from Illinois. Students come from 50 states, 56 foreign countries, and Canada. Sixty-two percent are from public schools; 38%, from private. Seventy percent are white; 13%, Hispanic; 10%, African American. Fifty-five percent are Catholic; 10%, Jewish. The average age of freshmen is 18. Eighteen percent drop out by the end of their first year; 63% remain to graduate.

Housing: A total of 1426 students can be accommodated in college housing. College-sponsored living facilities include coed dormitories and on-campus apartments. In addition there are honors houses and limited off-campus apartments, and a recently acquired condominium complex for upperclassmen. On-campus housing is available on a first-come, first-served basis and is available on a lottery system for upperclassmen. Priority is given to out-of-town students. Seventy-five percent of students commute. All students may keep cars on campus.

Activities: About 6% of men belong to 1 local and 4 national fraternities; about 4% of women belong to 4 national sororities. There are 85 groups on campus, including band, cheerleading, choir, chorale, chorus, computers, drill team, ethnic, gay, honors, international, jazz band, literary magazine, newspaper, pep band, political, professional, radio and TV, religious, social, social service, student government, symphony, and yearbook. Popular campus events include the Fest, Organization Fest, World's Highest Block Party, Taste of DePaul Student Organizations, Homecoming, Hispanic Awareness Month, Women's History Month, Martin Luther King Day, and African American History Month.

Sports: There are 7 intercollegiate sports for men and 7 for women, and 10 intramural sports for men and 9 for women. Athletic and recreation facilities include 2 gymnasiums seating 5308, 4 racquetball courts, 6 tennis courts, a dance/aerobics room, a softball/soccer field, a weight room, and a swimming pool.

Disabled Students: Ninety percent of the campus is accessible to disabled students. The following facilities are available: wheelchair ramps, elevators, special parking, specially equipped rest rooms, lowered drinking fountains, lowered telephones, and a disabled student services department.

Services: In addition to many counseling and information services, tutoring is available in most subjects. There is a writing center, project learning strategies program, and student development center. In addition, there is a reader service for the blind, and remedial math, reading, and writing.

Campus Safety and Security: Campus safety and security measures include 24-hour foot and vehicle patrol, self defense education, escort service, and shuttle buses. In addition, there are informal discussions, pamphlets, posters and films, emergency telephones, lighted pathways and sidewalks, and a crime prevention office.

Programs of Study: DePaul awards the B.A., B.S., B.F.A., B.M., and B.S.C. degrees. Master's and doctoral degrees are also awarded. Bachelor's degrees are awarded in BIOLOGICAL SCIENCE (biology/biological science), BUSINESS (accounting, banking and finance, business administration and management, business economics, and marketing/retailing/merchandising), COMMUNICATIONS AND THE ARTS (applied music, art, communications, comparative literature, dramatic arts, English, fine arts, French, German, Italian, jazz, music, music business management, Spanish, and theater design), COMPUTER AND PHYSICAL SCIENCE (chemistry, computer science, information sciences and systems, mathematics, and physics), EDUCATION (early childhood, elementary, foreign languages, music, physical, and secondary), ENGINEERING AND ENVIRONMENTAL DESIGN (environmental science), HEALTH PROFESSIONS (medical laboratory technology), SOCIAL SCIENCE (American studies, economics, geography, history, international studies, Judaic studies, Latin American studies, philosophy, political science/government, psychology, religion, social science, social studies, sociology, urban studies, and women's studies). Computer science, preprofessional, psychology, and theater are the strongest academically. Accountancy, management, communication, and computer science have the largest enrollments.

Required: All students must complete general education requirements, including 4 courses in behavioral and social sciences, 3 each in natural sciences and mathematics, 2 each in English composition, world civilization, and philosophy and religion, and 1 each in art, music and literature. A total of 188 quarter hour credits, including a mini-

mum of 52 in the student's major, and a minimum GPA of 2.0 are required in order to graduate.

Special: A co-op program in Jewish studies is offered with Spertus College of Judaica. Numerous internships in communications, commerce, and social sciences are possible. Study abroad is offered in 11 countries, and in a West European Seminar in Comparative Business Practices. There are accelerated degree programs, dual majors, a certificate program in acting and costume construction, pass/fail options, and concentrations within the theater major including acting, costume design, general theater studies, lighting design, playwriting, production theater management, and theater technology. The School for New Learning provides evening and weekend degree programs for adult learners, with credit given for life and work experience. There is a freshman honors program on campus, as well as 5 national honor societies. Twenty-nine departments have honors programs.

Faculty/Classroom: Sixty-six percent of faculty are male; 34%, female. No introductory courses are taught by graduate students. The average class size in an introductory lecture is 28; in a laboratory, 13; and in a regular course offering, 23.

Admissions: About 72% of the 1993–94 applicants were accepted. The SAT scores for the 1993–94 freshman class were as follows: Verbal—49% below 500, 39% between 500 and 599, 10% between 600 and 700, and 1% above 700; Math—34% below 500, 37% between 500 and 599, 22% between 600 and 700, and 6% above 700. The ACT scores were 18% below 21, 32% between 21 and 23, 24% between 24 and 26, 12% between 27 and 28, and 14% above 28. About 32% of the current freshmen were in the top fifth of their class; 60% were in the top two fifths. There were 10 National Merit finalists and 10 semifinalists. Thirty-five freshmen graduated first in their class.

Requirements: DePaul requires applicants to be in the upper 40% of their class. A minimum GPA of 3.0 is required. The SAT I is required. Applicants should have completed 16 Carnegie units or submit the GED. A portfolio is required for theater majors, and an audition for acting and music majors. AP and CLEP credits are accepted. Important factors used in the admissions decision are advanced placement or honor courses, leadership record, extracurricular activities record, evidence of special talent, and personality, intangible qualities.

Procedure: Freshmen are admitted to all sessions. Entrance exams should be taken by the spring of the junior year. Early decision applications should be filed by November 15; regular applications, by August 15 for fall entry, December 3 for winter entry, February 24 for spring entry, and June 12 for summer entry, along with an application fee of $25. Notification of early decision is sent December 1; regular decision, on a rolling basis. There are early decision, early admissions, and deferred admissions plans.

Transfer: In 1993–94, 1090 transfer students enrolled. A 2.0 GPA is required for most programs, a 2.5 in commerce. Applicants with fewer than 30 semester hours or 44 quarter hours should submit high school transcripts and SAT I or ACT scores. An audition is required for music and theater majors. A total of 45 quarter hours out of 188 must be completed at DePaul.

Visiting: There are regularly scheduled orientations for prospective students, including a 2-day program offered throughout the summer that provides academic advising, assessment testing, and registration in addition to information on social activities and residence life. There are guides for informal visits, and visitors may sit in on classes and stay overnight at the school. To arrange for a visit, contact the Admissions Office at (312) 362-8300.

Financial Aid: In 1993–94, 65% of all current freshmen and 67% of continuing students received some form of financial aid, including need-based aid. The average freshman award was $9625. Of that total, scholarships or need-based grants averaged $5500 ($9340 maximum); loans averaged $2625 ($4625 maximum); and work contracts averaged $1500 ($2500 maximum). Eighty-eight percent of undergraduate students work part-time. Average earnings from campus work for the school year are $2000. The average financial indebtedness of the 1992–93 graduate was $15,250. DePaul is a member of CSS. The FAF is required. The deadline for financial aid applications is April 1.

International Students: There are currently 426 international students enrolled. They must take the TOEFL and achieve a minimum score of 550. The student must also take the SAT I or the ACT.

Computers: The college provides computer facilities for student use. The mainframes are a DEC 2 VAX 11/780, an IBM 4381, and a Harris HCX 9. There are also 200 mainframe terminals and more than 750 PCs available. All students may access the system. It may be used 14 hours each day or 24 hours a day by modem. There are no time limits on using the system and no fees.

Graduates: In 1992–93, 1633 bachelor's degrees were awarded. The most popular majors among graduates were accounting (17%), finance (10%), and marketing (9%). Within an average freshman class, 57% graduate in 5 years and 63% in 6 years. Some 250 companies recruited on campus in 1992–93.

Admissions Contact: Lucy Leusch, Director of Undergraduate Admissions.

DEVRY INSTITUTE OF TECHNOLOGY
ADDISON (DUPAGE COUNTY)   E-2
(Formerly DeVry Institute of Technology/Lombard)
Addison, IL 60101-6106   (708) 953-2000
                                                 (800) 346-5420 (out-of-state)

Full-time: 1504 men, 339 women	Faculty: 54
Part-time: 721 men, 215 women	Ph.Ds: n/av
Graduate: none	Student/Faculty: 34 to 1
Year: trimesters, summer session	Tuition: $5609
Application Deadline: open	Room & Board: n/app

Freshman Class: 1430 applied, 1317 accepted, 746 enrolled
SAT I or ACT: see profile   **LESS COMPETITIVE**

The DeVry Institute of Technology/Addison (DuPage County), a private coeducational institution, opened in 1982; there are 10 other DeVry institutes in the United States and Canada that are owned by Keller Graduate School of Management. The school offers hands-on technology-based programs in electronics, accounting, business operations, telecommunications management, and computer information systems. In addition to regional accreditation, DeVry has baccalaureate program accreditation with ABET. The library contains 7073 volumes, 127 microform items, and 343 audiovisual forms, and subscribes to 169 periodicals. Computerized library sources and services include the card catalog, interlibrary loans, and database searching. Special learning facilities include a learning resource center and electronics and other laboratories. The 15-acre campus is in a suburban area 20 miles west of Chicago. There is one building on campus.

Student Life: About 84% of undergraduates are from Illinois. Students come from 12 foreign countries. Seventy-eight percent are white; 11% African American. The average age of all undergraduates is 25. Fifty-three percent drop out by the end of their first year; 44% remain to graduate.

Housing: There are no residence halls. College-sponsored living facilities include off-campus apartments. All students commute. Alcohol is not permitted. All students may keep cars on campus.

Activities: There are no fraternities or sororities on campus. There are 16 groups on campus, including computers, drama, honors, newspaper, professional, social service, and student government. Popular campus events include theater trips, ski trips and other outdoor weekend excursions, and career-related lectures by professionals.

Sports: There are 4 intramural sports for men and 4 for women.

Disabled Students: Ninety percent of the campus is accessible to disabled students. The following facilities are available: wheelchair ramps, elevators, special parking, specially equipped rest rooms, lowered drinking fountains, and lowered telephones.

Services: In addition to many counseling and information services, tutoring is available in every subject.

Campus Safety and Security: Campus safety and security measures include escort service, informal discussions, pamphlets, posters, and films, and emergency telephones. In addition, there are lighted pathways and sidewalks. During business hours, the campus is patrolled by student assistants. An alarm system is in operation during other hours.

Programs of Study: DeVry awards the B.S. degree. Associate degrees also are awarded. Bachelor's degrees are awarded in BUSINESS (accounting and business administration and management), COMMUNICATIONS AND THE ARTS (telecommunications), COMPUTER AND PHYSICAL SCIENCE (information sciences and systems), ENGINEERING AND ENVIRONMENTAL DESIGN (electrical/electronics engineering technology). Electronics has the largest enrollment.

Required: In order to graduate, students must complete between 133 and 158 credit hours with a 2.0 minimum GPA. Course requirements vary according to program. All first-semester students take courses in business organization, computer applications, algebra, psychology, and student success strategies.

Special: Nondegree study and evening classes are available. There are 3 national honor societies on campus. Three departments have honors programs.

Faculty/Classroom: Seventy-six percent of faculty are male; 24%, female. All teach undergraduates. The average class size is 30.

Admissions: About 92% of the 1993–94 applicants were accepted.

Requirements: Admissions requirements include graduation from a secondary school; the GED is also accepted. Applicants from accredited postsecondary institutions must pass the DeVry entrance exam or present satisfactory ACT, SAT I, or WPCT scores. CLEP credit is accepted.

Procedure: Freshmen are admitted to all sessions. Application deadlines are open. The application fee is $25. Notification is sent on a rolling basis. There are early decision and deferred admissions plans.

Transfer: Transfer students must take the DeVry entrance exam. It is recommended that applicants have math scores of at least 23 on the ACT or 480 on SAT I. At least 35% of 133 to 158 credits must be completed at DeVry.

Visiting: There are regularly scheduled orientations for prospective students. There are guides for informal visits and visitors may sit in on classes. To arrange for a visit, contact Billy Bungert, New Student Coordinator, at (708) 953-0610.

Financial Aid: In 1993–94, 70% of all students received some form of financial aid, including need-based aid. DeVry is a member of CSS. The FAFSA is required.

International Students: International students must take the TOEFL (minimum score 550), the University of Michigan Language Test, or the Comprehensive English Language Test. The student may also take the college's own entrance exam, but the ACT, SAT I, or WPCT may be accepted in its place.

Computers: DeVry provides computer facilities for student use. The mainframe is an IBM 3081K. Laboratory facilities include IBM and IBM-compatible PCs in stand-alone and network configuration, with access to the mainframe. LANs provide access to a wide range of applications software. Hard copy from mainframe is provided through a local minicomputer and medium- and high-speed printers. It may be used during published laboratory hours. There are no time limits on using the system and no fees.

Graduates: In 1992–93, 323 bachelor's degrees were awarded. The most popular majors among graduates were electronics technology (59%), business administration and management (14%), and computer information systems and sciences (14%). Within an average freshman class, 44% graduate in 5 years. Some 75 companies recruited on campus in 1992–93. In the 1992 graduating class, 93% of all students had found employment within 6 months of graduation.

Admissions Contact: Milt Kobus, Director of Admissions.

DEVRY INSTITUTE OF TECHNOLOGY
CHICAGO   E-2
Chicago, IL 60618-5994   (312) 929-6550
                                                 (800) 383-3879 (out-of-state)

Full-time: 1510 men, 513 women	Faculty: 55
Part-time: 689 men, 313 women	Ph.Ds: n/av
Graduate: none	Student/Faculty: 37 to 1
Year: trimesters, summer session	Tuition: $5609
Application Deadline: open	Room & Board: n/app

Freshman Class: 1197 applied, 1049 accepted, 769 enrolled
SAT I or ACT: see profile   **LESS COMPETITIVE**

DeVry Institute of Technology/Chicago, founded in 1931, is a private institution offering hands-on programs in electronics, accounting, business operations, and computer information systems. The school is a part of Keller Graduate School of Management, an organization administering the 11 DeVry institutes throughout the United States and Canada. In addition to regional accreditation, DeVry has baccalaureate program accreditation with ABET. The library contains 10,000 volumes, 139 microform items, and 350 audiovisual forms, and subscribes to 200 periodicals. Computerized library sources and services include the card catalog, interlibrary loans, and database searching. Special learning facilities include a learning resource center and electronics and other laboratories. The 12-acre campus is in an urban area in northwest Chicago. There is one building on campus.

Student Life: About 95% of undergraduates are from Illinois. Students come from 30 foreign countries and Canada. Thirty-three percent are African American; 31% white; 22% Hispanic; 11% Asian American. The average age of all undergraduates is 25. Fifty-five percent drop out by the end of their first year; 38% remain to graduate.

Housing: There are no residence halls. Housing referrals may be obtained through the Student Housing Office. All students commute. Alcohol is not permitted. All students may keep cars on campus.

Activities: There are no fraternities or sororities on campus. There are 19 groups on campus, including drama, ethnic, honors, international, musical theater, newspaper, professional, radio and TV, and religious. Popular campus events include Black History Month, International Fair, and Health Fair.

Sports: There are 8 intramural sports for men and 8 for women. Athletic and recreation facilities include a softball field, basketball courts, table tennis, and video game room.

Disabled Students: All of the campus is accessible to disabled students. The following facilities are available: wheelchair ramps, elevators, special parking, specially equipped rest rooms, special class scheduling, lowered drinking fountains, and lowered telephones.

Services: In addition to many counseling and information services, tutoring is available in every subject.

Campus Safety and Security: Campus safety and security measures include informal discussions, pamphlets, posters, and films, emergency telephones, and lighted pathways and sidewalks. Security

guards are on duty Monday through Friday, 8 A.M. to midnight. There is 24-hour security on weekends and holidays.

Programs of Study: DeVry awards the B.S. degree. Associate degrees also are awarded. Bachelor's degrees are awarded in BUSINESS (accounting and business administration and management), COMPUTER AND PHYSICAL SCIENCE (information sciences and systems), ENGINEERING AND ENVIRONMENTAL DESIGN (electrical/electronics engineering technology). Electronics has the largest enrollment.

Required: In order to graduate, students must complete between 143 and 158 credit hours with a 2.0 minimum GPA. Course requirements vary according to program. All first-semester students take courses in business organization, computer applications, algebra, psychology, and student success strategies.

Special: Evening classes and nondegree study are possible. There are 3 national honor societies on campus. Three departments have honors programs.

Faculty/Classroom: Seventy-six percent of faculty are male; 24%, female. All teach undergraduates. The average class size in an introductory lecture is 30; in a laboratory, 30; and in a regular course offering, 30.

Admissions: About 88% of the 1993–94 applicants were accepted.

Requirements: Admissions requirements include graduation from a secondary school; the GED is also accepted. Applicants must pass the DeVry entrance exam or present satisfactory ACT, SAT I, or WPCT scores. CLEP credit is accepted.

Procedure: Freshmen are admitted to all sessions. Application deadlines are open. The application fee is $25. Notification is sent on a rolling basis. There are early decision, early admissions, and deferred admissions plans.

Transfer: Transfer students must have a minimum GPA of 2.0. Additional requirements are the same as those for freshman applicants. At least 35% of 143 to 158 credits must be completed at DeVry.

Visiting: There are regularly scheduled orientations for prospective students. There are guides for informal visits and visitors may sit in on classes. To arrange for a visit, contact Marcia Curtis, Enrollment Services Coordinator, at (312) 929–6550.

Financial Aid: In 1993–94, 75% of all students received some form of financial aid, including need-based aid. The FAFSA financial statement is required.

International Students: International students must take the TOEFL and achieve a minimum score of 550. The student must also take the college's own entrance exam; the ACT, SAT I, or WPCT may be accepted in its place.

Computers: DeVry provides computer facilities for student use. The mainframe is an IBM 3081. Laboratory facilities include IBM and IBM-compatible PCs in stand-alone and network configuration, with access to the mainframe. LANs provide access to a wide range of applications software. Hard copy from mainframe is provided through a local minicomputer and medium- and high-speed printers. Computer information systems students may access the system. It may be used during laboratory hours. There are no fees.

Graduates: In 1992–93, 333 bachelor's degrees were awarded. The most popular majors among graduates were electronics technology (70%), computer information systems and science (18%), and business administration and management (12%). Within an average freshman class, 38% graduate in 5 years. Some 80 companies recruited on campus in 1992–93. In the 1992 graduating class, 77% of all students had found employment within 6 months of graduation.

Admissions Contact: Richard Yaconis, Director of Admissions.

DEVRY INSTITUTE OF TECHNOLOGY LOMBARD
(See DeVry Institute of Technology/Addison (DuPage County))

EAST-WEST UNIVERSITY

	E-2
Chicago, IL 60605	(312) 939-0111
Full-time: 127 men, 145 women	Faculty: 8
Part-time: 4 men, 5 women	Ph.D.s: 40%
Graduate: none	Student/Faculty: 34 to 1
Year: quarters, summer session	Tuition: $5910
Application Deadline: open	Room & Board: n/app
Freshman Class: 134 applied, 121 accepted, 92 enrolled	
ACT: recommended	NONCOMPETITIVE

East-West University, founded in 1978, is a private, coeducational institution serving an entirely commuter student body. The university offers undergraduate programs in the arts and sciences, business, computer science, and engineering. The library contains 21,500 volumes and 8500 microform items, and subscribes to 95 periodicals. The campus is in an urban area. There is one building on campus.

Student Life: About 85% of undergraduates are from Illinois. Students come from 1 state and 9 foreign countries. Ninety-seven percent are from public schools; 3% from private. Seventy-five percent are African American; 13% Hispanic. The average age of freshmen is 19; all undergraduates, 20.

Housing: There are no residence halls. Alcohol is not permitted.

Activities: There are no fraternities or sororities on campus. There are 3 groups on campus, including drama, international, and student government. Popular campus events include International Day, Mother's Day Banquet, and Black History Celebration.

Sports: There is no sports program at East-West.

Disabled Students: Fifty percent of the campus is accessible to disabled students. The following facilities are available: elevators and specially equipped rest rooms.

Services: In addition to many counseling and information services, tutoring is available in most subjects. There is remedial math, reading, and writing.

Programs of Study: East-West awards the B.A. and B.S. degrees. Associate degrees also are awarded. Bachelor's degrees are awarded in BUSINESS (business administration and management), COMMUNICATIONS AND THE ARTS (communications and English), COMPUTER AND PHYSICAL SCIENCE (computer science), ENGINEERING AND ENVIRONMENTAL DESIGN (electrical/electronics engineering technology), SOCIAL SCIENCE (behavioral science). Business administration has the largest enrollment.

Required: General education requirements vary according to the degree program. To graduate, students must complete at least 180 quarter hours, including 60 in a major field, with a minimum GPA of 2.0.

Special: East-West offers co-op programs in business administration, computer and information science, electronics engineering technology, liberal arts and sciences, behavioral and social sciences, English and communications, and mathematics.

Faculty/Classroom: Seventy percent of faculty are male; 30%, female. All teach undergraduates. The average class size is 15.

Admissions: About 90% of the 1993–94 applicants were accepted.

Requirements: The ACT is recommended. Applicants must be graduates of accredited secondary schools or have earned a GED. Placement examinations are required in mathematics and English. AP and CLEP credits are accepted. Important factors used in the admissions decision are recommendations by school officials, recommendations by alumni, parents or siblings attending the school, ability to finance college education, and personality, intangible qualities.

Procedure: Freshmen are admitted to all sessions. Application deadlines are open. Application fee is $25. The college accepts all applicants. Notification is sent on a rolling basis.

Transfer: About 40 transfer students enrolled in 1993–94. East-West accepts only courses with grades of C or better. A total of 48 quarter credits out of 180 must be completed at East-West.

Visiting: There are regularly scheduled orientations for prospective students. There are guides for informal visits and visitors may sit in on classes.

Financial Aid: In 1993–94, 90% of all current freshmen and 90% of continuing students received some form of financial aid. The FAF is required.

International Students: There are currently 20 international students enrolled. The school actively recruits these students. They must take the college's own test.

Computers: The college provides computer facilities for student use. The mainframe is a Texas Instruments 930. There are 21 IBM PCs available for student use. There are no time limits on using the system. The fees are $30 per course.

Graduates: The most popular majors among graduates were business administration (65%), computer science (1%), and liberal arts and sciences (1%). Some 4 companies recruited on campus in a recent year.

Admissions Contact: Mettha M. Green, Director of Admissions.

EASTERN ILLINOIS UNIVERSITY

	E-4
Charleston, IL 61920-3099	(217) 581-2223
	(800) 252-5711 (in-state)
Full-time: 4187 men, 4974 women	Faculty: 628; IIA, --$
Part-time: 305 men, 540 women	Ph.D.s: 73%
Graduate: 509 men, 880 women	Student/Faculty: 15 to 1
Year: semesters, summer session	Tuition: $2600 ($6296)
Application Deadline: see profile	Room & Board: $2948
Freshman Class: 5597 applied, 4253 accepted, 1575 enrolled	
SAT I: required	ACT: 21	COMPETITIVE

Eastern Illinois University, founded in 1895, is a state-supported coeducational school under the jurisdiction of the Illinois Board of Governors, offering undergraduate and graduate degrees in arts and sciences and professional studies. There are 4 undergraduate schools and one graduate school. In addition to regional accreditation, EIU has baccalaureate program accreditation with AACSB, ACEJMC, AHEA,

ASLA, NASAD, NASM, NCATE, and NRPA. The library contains 905,650 volumes and more than 1.3 million microform items, and subscribes to 3200 periodicals. Computerized library sources and services include the card catalog, interlibrary loans, and database searching. Special learning facilities include a learning resource center, art gallery, radio station, and TV station. The 320-acre campus is in a small town 50 miles south of Champaign. Including residence halls, there are 70 buildings on campus.

Student Life: About 97% of undergraduates are from Illinois. Students come from 38 states, 25 foreign countries, and Canada. Ninety-two percent are white. The average age of freshmen is 19; all undergraduates, 21. Seventeen percent drop out by the end of their first year; 60% remain to graduate.

Housing: A total of 5600 students can be accommodated in college housing. College-sponsored living facilities include single-sex and coed dormitories, on-campus apartments, married-student housing, fraternity houses, and sorority houses. In addition there are honors houses. On-campus housing is guaranteed for all 4 years. Fifty-two percent of students live on campus; of those, 75% remain on campus on weekends. Upperclassmen may keep cars on campus.

Activities: About 18% of men belong to 16 national fraternities; about 16% of women belong to 12 national sororities. There are 135 groups on campus, including art, band, cheerleading, choir, computers, dance, drama, drill team, ethnic, gay, honors, international, jazz band, literary magazine, marching band, musical theater, newspaper, orchestra, pep band, political, professional, radio and TV, religious, social, social service, student government, and yearbook. Popular campus events include Parents Weekend, Greek Week, Homecoming, and an arts festival.

Sports: There are 10 intercollegiate sports for men and 8 for women, and 21 intramural sports for men and 21 for women. Athletic and recreation facilities include a swimming pool, gymnasium, and student recreation center.

Disabled Students: Seventy percent of the campus is accessible to disabled students. The following facilities are available: wheelchair ramps, elevators, special parking, specially equipped rest rooms, special class scheduling, lowered drinking fountains, and lowered telephones.

Services: In addition to many counseling and information services, tutoring is available in most subjects. In addition, there is a reader service for the blind, and remedial math, reading, and writing. An academic assistance center advises freshmen and students with undeclared majors. Term paper clinics, study skills seminars, and stress management workshops are also available.

Campus Safety and Security: Campus safety and security measures include 24-hour foot and vehicle patrol, self defense education, escort service, and informal discussions. In addition, there are pamphlets, posters, and films, emergency telephones, and lighted pathways and sidewalks.

Programs of Study: EIU awards the B.A.,B.S.,B.S.Bus.,B.S.Ed., and B.M. degrees. Master's degrees are also awarded. Bachelor's degrees are awarded in BIOLOGICAL SCIENCE (botany, environmental biology, and zoology), BUSINESS (accounting, banking and finance, hotel/motel and restaurant management, and marketing/retailing/merchandising), COMMUNICATIONS AND THE ARTS (communications, dramatic arts, English, French, German, journalism, music, and Spanish), COMPUTER AND PHYSICAL SCIENCE (chemistry, mathematics, and physics), EDUCATION (art, business, early childhood, elementary, health, home economics, middle school, music, secondary, and special), HEALTH PROFESSIONS (medical laboratory technology and speech pathology/audiology), SOCIAL SCIENCE (dietetics, economics, history, philosophy, political science/government, psychology, social science, and sociology). Business, mathematics, history, and chemistry are the strongest academically. Elementary education, psychology, and zoology have the largest enrollments.

Required: A total of 120 credit hours, with a minimum of 40 hours in upper-division courses, must be completed for graduation. The minimum GPA required for graduation is 2.0 (2.25 in education). A core curriculum of 40 to 46 hours includes courses in language, quantitative reasoning and problem solving, scientific awareness, foreign languages, cultural experience, foundations of civilizations, human behavior, social interaction, well-being, U.S. Constitution, and a senior seminar.

Special: EIU offers co-op programs in medical technology and engineering with the University of Illinois at Urbana-Champaign. Internships, study abroad, dual majors, nondegree study, B.A.-B.S. degrees in athletic training and industrial technology, and pass/fail options are available. Credit for life experience may be granted through the Board of Governors program and the Career Occupations program. There is a freshman honors program on campus, as well as 20 national honor societies. Twelve departments have honors programs.

Faculty/Classroom: Sixty-seven percent of faculty are male; 33%, female. All teach undergraduates. Graduate students teach 1% of introductory courses. The average class size in an introductory lecture is 100; in a laboratory, 20; and in a regular course offering, 40.

Admissions: About 76% of the 1993–94 applicants were accepted. The ACT scores for the 1993–94 freshman class were as follows: 39% below 21, 36% between 21 and 23, 18% between 24 and 26, 5% between 27 and 28, and 2% above 28. About 25% of the current freshmen were in the top fifth of their class; 64% were in the top two fifths.

Requirements: The SAT I or ACT is required; the ACT is preferred. Applicants must be graduates of an accredited secondary school. The GED is accepted. Thirteen academic credits are required and should include 4 years of English, 3 years each of mathematics, science, and social studies, including 1 year of U.S. history. The required minimum composite scores are 18 for the ACT and 700 for the SAT I for those students who rank in the upper 50% of their class, or 22 on the ACT and 890 for SAT I in the upper 75%. The school also recommends SAT II: Subject tests. AP and CLEP credits are accepted.

Procedure: Freshmen are admitted to all sessions. Entrance exams should be taken by the spring of the junior year. Applications should be filed no later than 10 days prior to registration for the term of enrollment. Notification is sent on a rolling basis. The application fee is $25. There is an early admissions plan.

Transfer: In 1993–94, 1155 transfer students enrolled. Transfer students must have earned 30 credit hours with a minimum GPA of 2.0. An associate degree is recommended. A total of 42 credits out of 120 must be completed at EIU.

Visiting: There are regularly scheduled orientations for prospective students, including tours with student guides and open houses. There are guides for informal visits, and visitors may sit in on classes. To arrange for a visit, contact the Admissions Office at (217) 581–2223.

Financial Aid: In a recent year, 60% of all current freshmen and 77% of continuing students received some form of financial aid. The average freshman award was $2600. Of that total, scholarships or need-based grants averaged $1000; and loans averaged $1600 ($3150 maximum). Thirty percent of undergraduate students work part-time. Average earnings from campus work for the school year are $760. The average financial indebtedness of the 1992–93 graduate was $5000. EIU is a member of CSS. The FAF, FFS or SFS, the college's own financial statement, and the FAFSA are required. The deadline for financial aid applications is April 15.

International Students: There are currently 108 international students enrolled. The school actively recruits these students. They must take the TOEFL and achieve a minimum score of 500, or achieve a proficiency level of 8 from a U.S. ESL center.

Computers: The college provides computer facilities for student use. The mainframe is an IBM 9121 model 260. There are also 700 IBM and Apple microcomputers available, and 230 of these are networked. There are also 76 LAN dumb terminals available. All students may access the system. There are no time limits on using the system and no fees.

Graduates: In 1992–93, 2169 bachelor's degrees were awarded. The most popular majors among graduates were home economics (9%), elementary education (8%), and speech communication (8%). Within an average freshman class, 46% graduate in 4 years, 55% in 5 years, and 60% in 6 years. Some 255 companies recruited on campus in 1992–93.

Admissions Contact: Dale Wolf, Director of Admissions.

ELMHURST COLLEGE
Elmhurst, IL 60126–3296

E-2
(708) 617–3226
(800) 617–1871 (out-of-state)

Full-time: 575 men, 1030 women	Faculty: 98; IIB, av$
Part-time: 427 men, 655 women	Ph.D.s: 80%
Graduate: none	Student/Faculty: 16 to 1
Year: 4–1–4, summer session	Tuition: $8612
Application Deadline: August 15	Room & Board: $3924
Freshman Class: 950 applied, 663 accepted, 267 enrolled	
SAT I or ACT: required	COMPETITIVE

Elmhurst College, founded in 1871, is a private, coeducational, liberal arts college affiliated with the United Church of Christ. In addition to regional accreditation, Elmhurst has baccalaureate program accreditation with NCATE and NLN. The library contains 212,000 volumes, 42,000 microform items, and 3350 audiovisual forms, and subscribes to 1300 periodicals. Computerized library sources and services include the card catalog, interlibrary loans, and database searching. Special learning facilities include a learning resource center, art gallery, radio station, and a 16-track, 34-channel board recording studio, an electron microscopy laboratory, and an accelerator laboratory. The 38-acre campus is in a suburban area 15 miles west of Chicago. Including residence halls, there are 17 buildings on campus.

Student Life: About 95% of undergraduates are from Illinois. Students come from 24 states, 10 foreign countries, and Canada. Eighty percent are from public schools; 20% from private. Seventy-eight percent are white. Thirty-eight percent are Catholic; 35% claim no religious affiliation; 20% are Protestant. The average age of freshmen is 18; all undergraduates, 24. Twenty-five percent drop out by the end of their first year; 64% remain to graduate.

Housing: A total of 580 students can be accommodated in college housing. College-sponsored living facilities include single-sex and coed dormitories. On-campus housing is guaranteed for all 4 years. Sixty-eight percent of students commute. All students may keep cars on campus.

Activities: About 9% of men belong to 4 national fraternities; about 12% of women belong to 1 local and 2 national sororities. There are 55 groups on campus, including art, band, cheerleading, choir, chorale, computers, dance, drama, ethnic, film, honors, jazz band, literary magazine, musical theater, newspaper, pep band, political, professional, radio and TV, religious, social, social service, student government, and yearbook. Popular campus events include Founders Day, Nightclub at Noon, Greek Games, Sunday Night at the Movies, Festival of Lessons and Carols, Conference on Student Leadership, and Midwest Jazz Festival.

Sports: There are 8 intercollegiate sports for men and 6 for women, and 4 intramural sports for men and 3 for women. Athletic and recreation facilities include a physical eductation center, weight rooms, swimming pool, and courts for tennis, racquetball, and handball.

Disabled Students: Sixty-six percent of the campus is accessible to disabled students. The following facilities are available: wheelchair ramps, elevators, special parking, specially equipped rest rooms, special class scheduling, lowered drinking fountains, and lowered telephones.

Services: In addition to many counseling and information services, tutoring is available in most subjects.

Campus Safety and Security: Campus safety and security measures include 24-hour foot and vehicle patrol, escort service, informal discussions, and pamphlets, posters, and films. In addition, there are emergency telephones and lighted pathways and sidewalks.

Programs of Study: Elmhurst awards the B.A., B.S., and B.Mus. degrees. Bachelor's degrees are awarded in BIOLOGICAL SCIENCE (biochemistry and biology/biological science), BUSINESS (accounting, banking and finance, business administration and management, business economics, international business management, management information systems, marketing/retailing/merchandising, personnel management, recreational facilities management, and transportation management), COMMUNICATIONS AND THE ARTS (arts administration/management, dramatic arts, English, fine arts, French, German, music, music business management, Spanish, and speech/debate/rhetoric), COMPUTER AND PHYSICAL SCIENCE (chemistry, computer science, mathematics, and physics), EDUCATION (art, early childhood, elementary, mathematics, music, physical, science, secondary, and special), HEALTH PROFESSIONS (nursing and speech pathology/audiology), SOCIAL SCIENCE (American studies, economics, geography, history, philosophy, political science/government, psychology, religion, religious music, sociology, and urban studies). Chemistry, physics, speech pathology, and accounting are the strongest academically. Business administration, nursing, and education-related programs have the largest enrollments.

Required: All students are required to take 4 hours each in fine arts, philosophy, theology, and literature; 12 hours in language and thought; 8 hours each in social and natural sciences; and 3 hours in physical education, including swimming. Students must maintain a 2.0 GPA and complete 132 semester hours. The total number of hours required for the major varies from 28 to 36.

Special: Internships varying from 1 month to 1 term are available in approximately 20 major fields. Students may study abroad in Spain, Germany, Italy, Austria, and Costa Rica. Elmhurst also offers a Washington semester, and a 3–2 engineering degree with the University of Illinois Institute of Technology and Northwestern University is available. Credit for life, military, and work experience, nondegree study, and pass/fail options are possible. There is a freshman honors program on campus, as well as 10 national honor societies. Twelve departments have honors programs.

Faculty/Classroom: Fifty-eight percent of faculty are male; 42%, female. All teach undergraduates and 45% both teach and do research. The average class size in an introductory lecture is 19; in a laboratory, 15; and in a regular course offering, 16.

Admissions: About 70% of the 1993–94 applicants were accepted. About 35% of the current freshmen were in the top fifth of their class; 68% were in the top two fifths. One freshman graduated first in her class.

Requirements: Elmhurst requires applicants to be in the upper 50% of their class. A minimum GPA of 2.0 is required. The SAT I or ACT is required. Candidates for admission must have completed 4 years of English, 2 years of social studies, 2 to 3 years of science, and 1 year of history. Two years of a foreign language are recommended,

as are 2 to 3 years of mathematics. AP and CLEP credits are accepted. Important factors used in the admissions decision are advanced placement or honor courses, leadership record, personality, intangible qualities, parents or siblings attending the school, and recommendations by school officials.

Procedure: Freshmen are admitted in the fall, spring, and summer. Entrance exams should be taken by the spring of the senior year. Applications should be filed by August 15 for fall entry and January 15 for spring entry, along with an application fee of $15. Notification is sent on a rolling basis. There are early admissions and deferred admissions plans.

Transfer: In 1993–4, 369 transfer students enrolled. Applicants must have a C average and be in good standing at the most recent college attended. A higher GPA is required for nursing, education, and speech pathology. A total of 36 credits out of 132 must be completed at Elmhurst.

Visiting: There are regularly scheduled orientations for prospective students, including an admissions interview, a campus tour, and faculty meetings if desired. There are guides for informal visits, and visitors may sit in on classes and stay overnight at the school. To arrange for a visit, contact Antonia Hudson, Director of Freshman Admission, at (708) 617-3226.

Financial Aid: In 1993–94, 58% of all current freshmen and 55% of continuing students received some form of financial aid. About 56% of freshmen and 52% of continuing students received need-based aid. The average freshman award was $8500. Of that total, scholarships or need-based grants averaged $2400 ($8000 maximum); loans averaged $1600 ($2625 maximum); and work contracts averaged $1000 ($1700 maximum). Sixty-one percent of undergraduate students work part-time. Average earnings from campus work for the school year are $860. The average financial indebtedness of a recent graduate was $5000. Elmhurst is a member of CSS. The FAFSA financial statement is required. The deadline for financial aid applications is April 15.

International Students: There are currently 15 international students enrolled. The school actively recruits these students. They must take the TOEFL and achieve a minimum score of 550.

Computers: The college provides computer facilities for student use. The mainframes are a Harris HCX-9, an IBM 9370, and a Harris Nighthawk. There are 32 terminals, and 100 PCs are available for student use in multiple student laboratories on campus, along with phone-in capabilities. All students may access the system. It may be used 7 days a week, 24 hours a day. There are no time limits on using the system and no fees.

Graduates: In a recent year, 745 bachelor's degrees were awarded. The most popular majors among graduates were business administration (25%), nursing (9%), and accounting (8%). Within an average freshman class, 1% graduate in 3 years, 48% in 4 years, 53% in 5 years, and 58% in 6 years. Some 30 companies recruited on campus in a recent year.

Admissions Contact: Antonia Hudson, Director of Freshman Admission.

EUREKA COLLEGE
D-3

Eureka, IL 61530   (309) 467-6350; (800) 322-3756

Full-time: 221 men, 295 women	**Faculty:** 41; IIB, --$
Part-time: 3 men, 5 women	**Ph.D.s:** 85%
Graduate: 252 men, 248 women	**Student/Faculty:** 12 to 1
Year: intensive study plan: four 8-week terms	**Tuition:** $10,955
	Room & Board: $3450

Application Deadline: open

Freshman Class: 560 applied, 454 accepted, 113 enrolled

SAT I or ACT: required   **COMPETITIVE**

Eureka College, founded in 1855, is a small, private, liberal arts college affiliated with the Christian Church (Disciples of Christ). Under the college's intensive study plan, students only take 2 or 3 courses during each 8-week term. The library contains 85,000 volumes, 3300 microform items, and 3600 audiovisual forms, and subscribes to 315 periodicals. Computerized library sources and services include interlibrary loans and database searching. Special learning facilities include a learning resource center and an art gallery. The 112-acre campus is in a small town 18 miles east of Peoria. Including residence halls, there are 23 buildings on campus.

Student Life: About 90% of undergraduates are from Illinois. Students come from 15 states and 1 foreign country. Ninety-five percent are from public schools; 5% from private. Eighty-eight percent are white. Twenty percent are Catholic. The average age of freshmen is 18; all undergraduates, 20.

Housing: A total of 451 students can be accommodated in college housing. College-sponsored living facilities include single-sex and coed dormitories, fraternity houses, and sorority houses. In addition, there are honors houses. On-campus housing is guaranteed for all 4 years. Ninety percent of students live on campus; of those, 90% re-

main on campus on weekends. Alcohol is not permitted. All students may keep cars on campus.

Activities: About 45% of men belong to 2 national fraternities; about 45% of women belong to 1 local and 2 national sororities. There are 41 groups on campus, including art, cheerleading, choir, chorale, chorus, computers, drama, ethnic, honors, international, literary magazine, newspaper, photography, political, professional, religious, social, social service, student government, and yearbook. Popular campus events include Homecoming and Founders Day.

Sports: There are 7 intercollegiate sports for men and 7 for women, and 6 intramural sports for men and 6 for women. Athletic and recreation facilities include a gymnasium, pool, weight room, tennis courts, and football, softball, and baseball fields.

Disabled Students: Twenty-five percent of the campus is accessible to disabled students. Wheelchair ramps are available for these students.

Services: In addition to many counseling and information services, tutoring is available in most subjects. There is remedial reading and writing.

Campus Safety and Security: Campus safety and security measures include informal discussions, pamphlets, posters, and films, and lighted pathways and sidewalks.

Programs of Study: Eureka awards the B.A. and B.S. degrees. Bachelor's degrees are awarded in BIOLOGICAL SCIENCE (biology/biological science), BUSINESS (accounting and business administration and management), COMMUNICATIONS AND THE ARTS (communications, dramatic arts, English, fine arts, music, and speech/debate/rhetoric), COMPUTER AND PHYSICAL SCIENCE (chemistry, computer science, mathematics, and physical sciences), EDUCATION (education, elementary, physical, science, and secondary), HEALTH PROFESSIONS (medical laboratory technology), SOCIAL SCIENCE (economics, history, philosophy, physical fitness/movement, psychology, religion, social science, and sociology). Chemistry, biology, business administration, and education are the strongest academically. Business administration and education have the largest enrollments.

Required: All students must take English composition, biological and physical sciences, general studies, mathematics, physical education, western civilization, 3 humanities courses, and 3 social science courses. A total of at least 124 hours is required for graduation, including 32 hours in the major. A minimum GPA of 2.0 is required.

Special: Cooperative programs include a 3-2 engineering degree with Illinois Institute of Technology, a B.S.N. with Mennonite College of Nursing, and medical technology with 2 area hospitals. Students may study abroad in 5 countries. Professional programs in arts management, art therapy, communications, prelaw, premedicine, preministry, and teacher education are offered. There is a freshman honors program on campus

Faculty/Classroom: All faculty teach undergraduates and do research. No introductory courses are taught by graduate students. The average class size in an introductory lecture is 25; in a laboratory, 10; and in a regular course offering, 15.

Admissions: About 81% of the 1993-94 applicants were accepted. The ACT scores for the 1993-94 freshman class were as follows: 26% below 21, 40% between 21 and 23, 15% between 24 and 26, 15% between 27 and 28, and 4% above 28. About 42% of the current freshmen were in the top fifth of their class; 73% were in the top two fifths. There were 2 National Merit semifinalists. Three freshmen graduated first in their class.

Requirements: Eureka requires applicants to be in the upper 50% of their class. A minimum GPA of 2.0 is required. The ACT and SAT I is required. Applicants should be graduates of accredited secondary schools or have the GED. AP and CLEP credits are accepted. Important factors used in the admissions decision are leadership record, extracurricular activities record, recommendations by school officials, personality, intangible qualities, and evidence of special talent.

Procedure: Freshmen are admitted to all sessions. Entrance exams should be taken by December of the senior year. Application deadlines are open. Notification is sent on a rolling basis. The application fee is $10. There is a deferred admissions plan.

Transfer: About 35 transfer students enrolled in 1993-94. Transfer applicants must have at least a 2.0 GPA in previous college work. Those with fewer than 30 hours of transferable credit must submit high school transcripts and SAT I or ACT scores. Courses with grades below C are not accepted. A total of 30 credits out of 124 must be completed at Eureka.

Visiting: There are regularly scheduled orientations for prospective students. There are guides for informal visits, and visitors may sit in on classes and stay overnight at the school. To arrange for a visit, contact The Office of Admissions at (800) 322-3756.

Financial Aid: In 1993-94, 96% of all current freshmen and 93% of continuing students received some form of financial aid. The average freshman award was $7606. Of that total, scholarships or need-based grants averaged $2412; loans averaged $2400; and work contracts averaged $780. Forty-five percent of undergraduate students work part-time. Average earnings from campus work for the school year are $1300. The average financial indebtedness of the 1992-93 graduate was $11,000. Eureka is a member of CSS. The FAFSA financial statement is required. The deadline for financial aid applications is March 1.

International Students: There are currently 21 international students enrolled. The school actively recruits these students. They must take the TOEFL and achieve a minimum score of 550.

Computers: The college provides computer facilities for student use. The mainframe is a DEC PDP 11/24. There are 22 IBM and Apple microcomputers available in the computer center and library. All students may access the system. There are no time limits on using the system and no fees.

Graduates: In an earlier year, 76 bachelor's degrees were awarded. The most popular majors among graduates were business administration (23%), elementary education (13%), and physical education (8%). Within an average freshman class, 50% graduate in 4 years. Fifteen percent of 1992 graduates were enrolled in graduate school within 6 months of graduation; 83% had found employment.

Admissions Contact: Susan R. Jordan, Dean of Admissions and Financial Aid.

GREENVILLE COLLEGE D-4

Greenville, IL 62246 (618) 664-1840; (800) 345-4440 (out-of-state)

Full-time: 374 men, 397 women	Faculty: 56; IIB, --$
Part-time: 28 men, 31 women	Ph.D.s: 53%
Graduate: none	Student/Faculty: 14 to 1
Year: 4-1-4, summer session	Tuition: $10,030
Application Deadline: open	Room & Board: $4160

Freshman Class: 479 applied, 341 accepted, 195 enrolled

SAT I Verbal/Math: 500/530 ACT: 22 COMPETITIVE

Greenville College, founded in 1892, is a coeducational, liberal arts college affiliated with the Free Methodist Church. It offers undergraduate programs in the humanities, social sciences, education, mathematics, and natural sciences. In addition to regional accreditation, Greenville has baccalaureate program accreditation with NCATE. The library contains 119,621 volumes, 10,287 microform items, and 3824 audiovisual forms, and subscribes to 578 periodicals. Computerized library sources and services include interlibrary loans and database searching. Special learning facilities include a learning resource center, art gallery, and radio station. The 12-acre campus is in a small town 50 miles east of St. Louis. Including residence halls, there are 23 buildings on campus.

Student Life: About 60% of undergraduates are from Illinois. Students come from 42 states, 11 foreign countries, and Canada. About 95% are from public schools; 5% from private. Some 84% are white. Most are Protestant. The average age of freshmen is 18; all undergraduates, 20. Approximately 31% drop out by the end of their first year; 50% remain to graduate.

Housing: A total of 624 students can be accommodated in college housing. College-sponsored living facilities include single-sex dormitories and on-campus apartments. In addition, there are language houses. On-campus housing is guaranteed for all 4 years. Some 69% of students live on campus; of those, 45% remain on campus on weekends. Alcohol is not permitted. All students may keep cars on campus.

Activities: There are no fraternities or sororities on campus. There are 20 groups on campus, including art, band, cheerleading, choir, chorale, chorus, computers, drama, ethnic, honors, musical theater, newspaper, orchestra, pep band, radio and TV, religious, social, social service, student government, and yearbook. Popular campus events include Agape Music Festival, All College Hike, and Class Retreats.

Sports: Athletic and recreation facilities include a gymnasium and the Greenville College Sports Training Annex.

Disabled Students: About 25% of the campus is accessible to disabled students. The following facilities are available: wheelchair ramps, elevators, specially equipped rest rooms, special class scheduling, and lowered drinking fountains.

Services: In addition to many counseling and information services, tutoring is available in most subjects, including general education courses, but not upper-division courses. In addition, there is remedial reading and writing. There are also supplemental instruction programs and a program for at-risk freshmen.

Campus Safety and Security: Campus safety and security measures include 24-hour foot and vehicle patrol, emergency telephones, lighted pathways and sidewalks, and alarm systems in some buildings.

Programs of Study: Greenville awards the B.A., B.S., B.Mus.Ed., and B.S.Ed. degrees. Bachelor's degrees are awarded in BIOLOGICAL SCIENCE (biology/biological science), BUSINESS (accounting, management information systems, marketing/retailing/merchandising, and recreation and leisure services), COMMUNICATIONS AND THE ARTS (art, communications, English, French, music,

and Spanish), COMPUTER AND PHYSICAL SCIENCE (chemistry, computer science, mathematics, and physics), EDUCATION (art, business, early childhood, elementary, music, physical, secondary, and special), SOCIAL SCIENCE (gerontology, history, ministries, philosophy, psychology, religion, religious music, social work, and sociology). Education, business, contemporary Christian music, biology, and psychology are the strongest programs academically and have the largest enrollments.

Required: All students must successfully complete courses in English composition, a foreign language (for the B.A.), religion, physical education, humanities, mathematics, natural sciences, social science, and philosophy. A minimum of 132 credit hours and a GPA of 2.0 are required for graduation.

Special: The college provides opportunities for dual majors, B.A.-B.S. degrees, a student-designed major in education, work-study programs, study abroad, credit by examination, internships, a general studies degree, pass/fail options, a 3-2 engineering degree with the University of Illinois, and nondegree studies. An American Studies program in Washington, D.C. is also available, and an accelerated degree program in education is offered. There is a freshman honors program on campus

Faculty/Classroom: Some 73% of faculty are male; 27%, female. All teach undergraduates. The average class size in a regular course offering is 20.

Admissions: About 71% of the 1993-94 applicants were accepted. The SAT scores for the 1993-94 freshman class were as follows: Verbal—46% below 500, 29% between 500 and 599, 22% between 600 and 700, and 2% above 700; Math—32% below 500, 37% between 500 and 599, 27% between 600 and 700, and 2% above 700. The ACT scores were 40% below 21, 25% between 21 and 23, 22% between 24 and 26, 8% between 27 and 28, and 5% above 28. About 35% of the current freshmen were in the top fifth of their class; 66% were in the top two fifths.

Requirements: Greenville requires applicants to be in the upper 50% of their class. A minimum GPA of 2.0 is required. The SAT I or ACT is required, with minimum composite scores of 750 on SAT I or 15 on the ACT. Applicants must have completed a minimum of 16 units of high school courses including 4 each in English and social studies, 3 in a foreign language, 2 in mathematics, and 1 or 2 in science. A GPA of 2.0 is required. A GED certificate will be accepted. An essay is also required. AP and CLEP credits are accepted. Important factors used in the admissions decision are advanced placement or honor courses, evidence of special talent, extracurricular activities record, personality, intangible qualities, and leadership record.

Procedure: Freshmen are admitted to all sessions. Entrance exams should be taken in the spring of the junior year. Application deadlines are open. Notification is sent on a rolling basis.

Transfer: About 67 transfer students enrolled in 1993-94. A minimum average grade of C or better is required for transfer. An associate degree will be accepted for transfer. A total of 40 credits out of 132 must be completed at Greenville.

Visiting: There are regularly scheduled orientations for prospective students. There are guides for informal visits and visitors may sit in on classes and stay overnight at the school. To arrange for a visit, contact the Admissions Office at (618) 664-1840 or (800) 345-4440 (out-of-state).

Financial Aid: In 1993-94, 87% of all current freshmen and 78% of continuing students received some form of financial aid. About 83% of freshmen and 73% of continuing students received need-based aid. The average freshman award was $7225. Of that total, scholarships or need-based grants averaged $3300 ($9910 maximum); loans averaged $3500 ($5500 maximum); and work contracts averaged $1300 ($1400 maximum). Some 47% of undergraduate students work part-time. Average earnings from campus work for the school year are $825. The average financial indebtedness of the 1992-93 graduate was $10,800. The FAFSA financial statement is required. The deadline for financial aid applications is July 1.

International Students: There are currently 18 international students enrolled.

Computers: The college provides computer facilities for student use. The mainframe is a Data General. There are also 55 to 60 microcomputers available in the library and throughout the campus. Database, spreadsheets, and word processing programs are available. All students may access the system. It may be used 8 A.M. to 10 P.M., except Sunday. There are no time limits on using the system and no fees.

Graduates: In 1992-93, 171 bachelor's degrees were awarded. The most popular majors among graduates were business/accounting (22%), education (21%), and biological sciences (11%). Within an average freshman class, 44% graduate in 4 years, 47% in 5 years, and 50% in 6 years. About 3 companies recruited on campus in 1992-93. In the 1992 graduating class, 8% of the men and 12% of the women were enrolled in graduate school within 6 months of graduation; 92% of the men and 91% of the women had found employment.

Admissions Contact: H. Kent Krober, Director of Admissions.

ILLINOIS BENEDICTINE COLLEGE
E-2
Lisle, IL 60532
(708) 960-1500

Full-time: 614 men, 614 women	Faculty: 75; IIA, --$
Part-time: 170 men, 272 women	Ph.D.s: 78%
Graduate: 410 men, 530 women	Student/Faculty: 16 to 1
Year: semesters, summer session	Tuition: $10,080
Application Deadline: open	Room & Board: $4090
Freshman Class: 603 applied, 558 accepted, 269 enrolled	
SAT I: required	ACT: 23	COMPETITIVE

Illinois Benedictine College, founded in 1887, is a private, Catholic, coeducational, liberal arts and sciences college. There is one graduate school. In addition to regional accreditation, Illinois Benedictine College has baccalaureate program accreditation with ADA and NLN. The library contains 162,874 volumes, 109,591 microform items, and 10,984 audiovisual forms, and subscribes to 700 periodicals. Computerized library sources and services include the card catalog, interlibrary loans, and database searching. Special learning facilities include a learning resource center, art gallery, and natural history museum. The 108-acre campus is in a suburban area 25 miles west of Chicago. Including residence halls, there are 9 buildings on campus.

Student Life: About 91% of undergraduates are from Illinois. Students come from 12 states, 8 foreign countries, and Canada. Fifty-three percent are from public schools; 47%, from private. Seventy-nine percent are white. Sixty-eight percent are Catholic; 12%, Protestant. The average age of freshmen is 18; all undergraduates, 24. Eight percent drop out by the end of their first year; 65% remain to graduate.

Housing: A total of 600 students can be accommodated in college housing. College-sponsored living facilities include single-sex and coed residence halls. On-campus housing is guaranteed for all 4 years. Sixty-four percent of students commute. All students may keep cars on campus.

Activities: There are no fraternities or sororities on campus. There are 30 groups on campus, including art, cheerleading, choir, chorale, chorus, computers, dance, drama, ethnic, honors, international, jazz band, literary magazine, newspaper, photography, political, professional, radio and TV, religious, social, social service, and student government. Popular campus events include Family Day, Homecoming, Spring Fest, Gospel Fest, Black History month, and multicultural awareness workshops.

Sports: There are 9 intercollegiate sports for men and 7 for women, and 16 intramural sports for men and 16 for women. Athletic and recreation facilities include a recreation center housing a main arena, pool, weight room, and dance room.

Disabled Students: Seventy-five percent of the campus is accessible to disabled students. The following facilities are available: wheelchair ramps, elevators, special parking, specially equipped rest rooms, and lowered drinking fountains.

Services: In addition to many counseling and information services, tutoring is available in every subject. In addition, there is a reader service for the blind, and remedial math, reading, and writing.

Campus Safety and Security: Campus safety and security measures include 24-hour foot and vehicle patrol, self-defense education, escort service, and informal discussions. In addition, there are pamphlets, posters, and films, emergency telephones, and lighted pathways and sidewalks.

Programs of Study: Illinois Benedictine College awards the B.A. and B.S. degrees. Master's degrees are also awarded. Bachelor's degrees are awarded in BIOLOGICAL SCIENCE (biochemistry, biology/biological science, and nutrition), BUSINESS (accounting, banking and finance, business economics, international business management, management science, and marketing/retailing/merchandising), COMMUNICATIONS AND THE ARTS (communications and Spanish), COMPUTER AND PHYSICAL SCIENCE (chemistry, computer science, mathematics, and physics), EDUCATION (elementary, physical, and special), ENGINEERING AND ENVIRONMENTAL DESIGN (engineering, engineering and applied science, and preengineering), HEALTH PROFESSIONS (health care administration, health science, medical laboratory technology, nuclear medical technology, nursing, predentistry, premedicine, prepharmacy, and preveterinary science), SOCIAL SCIENCE (economics, history, philosophy, political science/government, prelaw, psychology, religious studies, social science, and sociology). Chemistry, biochemistry, business and economics, and physics are the strongest academically. Business economics, biology, accounting, and psychology have the largest enrollments.

Required: To graduate, students must demonstrate mathematical, logical, oral, and written skills. They must complete 120 semester hours, including 36 credit hours in their major and maintain a minimum GPA of 2.0. In addition, they must take 18 hours in arts and humanities, including 2 courses in religious studies and 1 in philosophy, 12 hours in social sciences, and 9 hours in natural science.

Special: There is cross-registration with North Central College and Aurora University. Internships are available in most majors, and study abroad in many countries can be arranged. There are 3–2 preengineering degrees with the universities of Illinois, Detroit, Marquette, and Notre Dame, and an engineering degree with Illinois Institute of Technology. Preprofessional programs including prepodiatry, prephysical therapy, and prenursing are offered. Work-study programs with a number of surrounding firms and credit for work and life experience also are available. There is a freshman honors program on campus, as well as 11 national honor societies.

Faculty/Classroom: Sixty percent of faculty are male; 40%, female. All teach undergraduates. No introductory courses are taught by graduate students. The average class size in an introductory lecture is 25; in a laboratory, 15; and in a regular course offering, 20.

Admissions: About 93% of the 1993–94 applicants were accepted. The ACT scores for the 1993–94 freshman class were as follows: 34% below 21, 23% between 21 and 23, 25% between 24 and 26, 9% between 27 and 28, and 9% above 28. About 41% of the current freshmen were in the top fifth of their class; 70% were in the top two fifths. Five freshmen graduated first in their class.

Requirements: Illinois Benedictine College requires applicants to be in the upper 50% of their class. A minimum GPA of 2.0 is required. The SAT I or ACT is required. To be admitted, students must complete 4 years of English, 2 years of a foreign language, and 1 year each of history, algebra, geometry, and laboratory science. AP and CLEP credits are accepted.

Procedure: Freshmen are admitted in the fall and spring. Application deadlines are open. Application fee is $15. Notification is sent on a rolling basis. There is an early decision plan. The application fee is $15. Thirty-one early decision candidates were accepted for the 1993–94 class.

Transfer: About 260 transfer students enrolled in 1993–94. Transfer students must have a C average. A minimum GPA of 2.0 is necessary and an interview is required in some cases. Students who have completed fewer than 20 semester hours must submit SAT I or ACT scores.

Visiting: There are regularly scheduled orientations for prospective students, including a 'Visit Day' each semester. There are guides for informal visits, and visitors may sit in on classes and stay overnight at the school. To arrange for a visit, contact the Admissions Office at (708) 960–1500, ext. 4000.

Financial Aid: In 1993–94, 94% of all current freshmen and 98% of continuing students received some form of financial aid. About 52% of freshmen and 55% of continuing students received need-based aid. The average freshman award was $7761. Of that total, scholarships or need-based grants averaged $5092 ($11,200 maximum); loans averaged $2885 ($6000 maximum); and work contracts averaged $1095 ($3000 maximum). Forty percent of undergraduate students work part-time. Average earnings from campus work for the school year are $1095. The average financial indebtedness of the 1992–93 graduate was $6000. Illinois Benedictine College is a member of CSS. The FAF, FFS, or SFS is required.

International Students: There are currently 40 international students enrolled. The school actively recruits these students. They must take the TOEFL and achieve a minimum score of 550. The student must also take the SAT I or the ACT.

Computers: The college provides computer facilities for student use. The mainframe is a Sequent Symmetry 516. There are also 60 microcomputers available in 2 laboratories that may be accessed via modem. All students may access the system all day through the microcomputer laboratories from 8 A.M. Monday through Friday and from 10 A.M. on weekends, or 24 hours a day through personal modems at home or in residence halls. There are no time limits on using the system and no fees.

Graduates: In 1992–93, 340 bachelor's degrees were awarded. The most popular majors among graduates were biology (11%), business/economics (11%), and accounting (9%). Within an average freshman class, 54% graduate in 4 years and 55% in 5 years. Some 40 companies recruited on campus in 1992–93. In the 1992 graduating class, 13% of both the men and the women were enrolled in graduate school within 6 months of graduation; 82% of both the men and the women had found employment.

Admissions Contact: Jane L. Smith, Director of Admissions.

ILLINOIS BOARD OF REGENTS

The Illinois Board of Regents, established in 1967, is the governing board for the public system consisting of the Illinois State University in Normal, Northern Illinois University in DeKalb, and Sangamon State University in Springfield. It is one of 4 governing boards in Illinois, and its chief administrator is the Chair of the board. Its standing committees address issues and policy concerning academic and student affairs, finance and facilities, personnel and operations, and audit of the regency universities at an initial stage. The total enrollment in a recent year of all 3 campuses was 51,522; there were 2500 facul-

ty members. Altogether there are 143 baccalaureate, 122 master's, and 28 doctoral programs offered in Illinois Board of Regents. Profiles of the 4-year campuses are included in this chapter in alphabetical order with other Illinois schools.

ILLINOIS COLLEGE   C-3
Jacksonville, IL 62650   (217) 245-3030

Full-time: 432 men, 477 women	Faculty: 60; IIB, +$
Part-time: 16 men, 12 women	Ph.D.s: 70%
Graduate: none	Student/Faculty: 15 to 1
Year: semesters	Tuition: $7550
Application Deadline: August 15	Room & Board: $3650
Freshman Class: 894 applied, 787 accepted, 262 enrolled	
SAT I Verbal/Math: 470/545	ACT: 23 COMPETITIVE

Illinois College, founded in 1829, is a liberal arts institution related to the Presbyterian Church (USA) and the United Church of Christ. The library contains 130,000 volumes and subscribes to 600 periodicals. Special learning facilities include an art gallery, theater, and television studio. The 62-acre campus is in a rural area 35 miles west of Springfield. Including residence halls, there are 24 buildings on campus.

Student Life: About 93% of undergraduates are from Illinois. Students come from 15 states and 4 foreign countries. Ninety-five percent are white. Forty percent are Catholic; 25% claim no religious affiliation; 20% Protestant. The average age of freshmen is 18; all undergraduates, 20. Fifteen percent drop out by the end of their first year; 55% remain to graduate.

Housing: A total of 700 students can be accommodated in college housing. College-sponsored living facilities include single-sex and coed dormitories and on-campus apartments. In addition, there are honors houses. On-campus housing is guaranteed for all 4 years. Seventy-five percent of students live on campus; of those, 75% remain on campus on weekends. All students may keep cars on campus.

Activities: About 35% of men belong to 4 local fraternities; about 35% of women belong to 3 local sororities. There are 37 groups on campus, including band, cheerleading, choir, chorale, computers, drama, ethnic, honors, international, literary magazine, newspaper, photography, political, radio and TV, religious, social, social service, student government, and yearbook. Popular campus events include Osage Orange Picnic, Homecoming Parade and Follies, Honors Convocation, Honors Retreat, McGaw Fine Arts Series, Spring Weekend, and lectures in the arts.

Sports: There are 9 intercollegiate sports for men and 7 for women, and 5 intramural sports for men and 5 for women. Athletic and recreation facilities include a game room, a gymnasium with 2 basketball and 3 squash and handball courts, volleyball and badminton courts, a swimming pool, a fitness center, playing fields, an all-weather track, and 8 tennis courts.

Disabled Students: Eighty percent of the campus is accessible to disabled students. The following facilities are available: wheelchair ramps, elevators, special parking, specially equipped rest rooms, and lowered drinking fountains.

Services: In addition to many counseling and information services, tutoring is available in some subjects, including accounting, chemistry, computer science, economics, English, French, German, Japanese, mathematics, Russian, and Spanish.

Campus Safety and Security: Campus safety and security measures include self defense education, escort service, shuttle buses, and informal discussions. In addition, there are pamphlets, posters, and films, emergency telephones, lighted pathways and sidewalks, and foot patrol from 10 P.M. to 8 A.M.

Programs of Study: IC awards the B.A. and B.S. degrees. Bachelor's degrees are awarded in BIOLOGICAL SCIENCE (biology/biological science), BUSINESS (accounting and business administration and management), COMMUNICATIONS AND THE ARTS (broadcasting, communications, dramatic arts, English, fine arts, French, German, music, Spanish, and speech/debate/rhetoric), COMPUTER AND PHYSICAL SCIENCE (chemistry, computer science, information sciences and systems, mathematics, and physics), EDUCATION (elementary, foreign languages, physical, science, and secondary), HEALTH PROFESSIONS (medical laboratory technology), SOCIAL SCIENCE (economics, history, international relations, philosophy, political science/government, prelaw, psychology, religion, social work, and sociology). Computer science, mathematics, and history/political science are the strongest academically. Business administration and education have the largest enrollments.

Required: To graduate, all students must fulfill general graduation and convocation requirements and complete at least 120 semester hours. A 2.0 GPA is required. Attendance at graduation is mandatory.

Special: The college offers internships through the departments of communications and theater, computer science and information systems, economics and business administration, and English and political science, study-abroad programs in 5 countries, on- and off-

campus work-study programs, and B.A.-B.S. degrees. Also available are student-designed and dual majors, a 3–2 engineering degree with the University of Illinois or Washington University, a 3–2 nursing program, a cooperative program with the Mennonite College of Nursing, and a 3–2 occupational therapy program with Washington University. Nondegree study, an Intercultural Exchange Program with Ritsumeikan University in Kyoto, Japan, the Model Illinois Government and Model United Nations simulations, the Urban Studies Program of Associated Colleges of the Midwest in Chicago, and Asian-oriented courses through the Illinois Inter-Institutional Council for Asian and Middle Eastern Studies are offered. There are 9 national honor societies on campus, including Phi Beta Kappa. Eight departments have honors programs.

Faculty/Classroom: Sixty-six percent of faculty are male; 34%, female. All teach undergraduates. The average class size in an introductory lecture is 70; in a laboratory, 25; and in a regular course offering, 25.

Admissions: About 88% of the 1993–94 applicants were accepted. The SAT scores for the 1993–94 freshman class were as follows: Verbal—53% below 500, 35% between 500 and 599, 8% between 600 and 700, and 4% above 700; Math—42% below 500, 15% between 500 and 599, 27% between 600 and 700, and 16% above 700. The ACT scores were 24% below 21, 35% between 21 and 23, 21% between 24 and 26, 13% between 27 and 28, and 7% above 28. About 49% of the current freshmen were in the top fifth of their class; 72% were in the top two fifths. There were 2 National Merit finalists and 5 semifinalists. About 10 freshmen graduated first in their class.

Requirements: IC requires applicants to be in the upper 50% of their class. The SAT I or ACT is required. Applicants must be graduates of an accredited secondary school or have a GED certificate. Students should have completed at least 15 academic credits, including 3 in English and 7 from the following: English, foreign language, history, laboratory science, mathematics, and social studies. Recommendations from high school officials and 2 personal references are required. AP and CLEP credits are accepted.

Procedure: Freshmen are admitted to all sessions. Entrance exams should be taken in the spring of the junior year. Applications should be filed by August 15 for fall entry and December 15 for spring entry, along with an application fee of $10. Notification is sent on a rolling basis.

Transfer: About 57 transfer students enrolled in 1993–94. Transfer students must have a minimum 2.0 GPA and submit SAT I or ACT scores and transcripts of completed college work. A total of 60 credits out of 120 must be completed at IC.

Visiting: There are regularly scheduled orientations for prospective students. There are guides for informal visits, and visitors may sit in on classes and stay overnight at the school. To arrange for a visit, contact the Admissions Office at (217) 245-3030.

Financial Aid: In 1993–94 93% of all current freshmen and 94% of continuing students received some form of financial aid. About 75% of freshmen and 74% of continuing students received need-based aid. The average freshman award was $6876. Of that total, scholarships or need-based grants averaged $4165 ($12,410 maximum); loans averaged $2520 ($4125 maximum); and work contracts averaged $765 ($1000 maximum). Thirty-two percent of undergraduate students work part-time. Average earnings from campus work for the school year are $730. The average financial indebtedness of the 1992–93 graduate was $7800. The FAF and FAFSA are required. The deadline for financial aid applications is May 1.

International Students: There are currently 9 international students enrolled. They must take the TOEFL and achieve a minimum score of 500.

Computers: The college provides computer facilities for student use. The mainframe is a Prime 2755. There are 30 workstations for the Prime computer. A computer laboratory includes 16 386 PCs that are utilized by business administration, English, mathematics, and computer science departments. The learning center houses 2 computer laboratories with 31 386 PCs that are linked together with the Novell local area network. All students may access the system. It may be used from 7 A.M. to 1 A.M. There are no time limits on using the system and no fees.

Graduates: In 1992–93 163 bachelor's degrees were awarded. The most popular majors among graduates were business administration (29%), education (15%), and computer science (10%). Within an average freshman class, 1% graduate in 3 years, 50% in 4 years, 54% in 5 years, and 55% in 6 years. Some 45 companies recruited on campus in 1992–93. In the 1992 graduating class, 19% of all students were enrolled in graduate school within 6 months of graduation; 75% of all graduates had found employment.

Admissions Contact: Gale Vaughn, Director of Enrollment.

ILLINOIS INSTITUTE OF TECHNOLOGY   E-2

Chicago, IL 60616   (312) 567-3025; (800) 448-2329 (out-of-state)

Full-time: 1451 men, 460 women	Faculty: 284; I, -$
Part-time: 538 men, 88 women	Ph.D.s: 90%
Graduate: 3415 men, 1075 women	Student/Faculty: 7 to 1
Year: semesters, summer session	Tuition: $13,750
Application Deadline: March 15	Room & Board: $4540
Freshman Class: 1647 applied, 1363 accepted, 480 enrolled	
SAT I Verbal/Math: 510/610	ACT: 25 **VERY COMPETITIVE**

Illinois Institute of Technology, founded in 1890, is a private institution offering undergraduate programs in architecture and planning, sciences and letters, engineering, business administration, and design. There are 5 undergraduate and 2 graduate schools. In addition to regional accreditation, IIT has baccalaureate program accreditation with ABET. The library contains 800,000 volumes and subscribes to 3550 periodicals. Computerized library sources and services include the card catalog, interlibrary loans, and database searching. Special learning facilities include a learning resource center and radio station. The 120-acre campus is in an urban area. Including residence halls, there are 31 buildings on campus.

Student Life: About 52% of undergraduates are from out-of-state, mostly the Midwest. Students come from 49 states, 72 foreign countries, and Canada. Seventy percent are from public schools; 30% from private. Sixty percent are white; 11% African American; 10% foreign nationals; 10% Hispanic. Sixty percent are Protestant; 40% Catholic. The average age of freshmen is 19; all undergraduates, 20. Fifteen percent drop out by the end of their first year; 55% remain to graduate.

Housing: A total of 840 students can be accommodated in college housing. College-sponsored living facilities include single-sex and coed dormitories, on-campus apartments, married-student housing, and fraternity houses. On-campus housing is guaranteed for the freshman year only and is available on a first-come, first-served basis. Priority is given to out-of-town students. Seventy percent of students live on campus. All students may keep cars on campus.

Activities: About 27% of men belong to 9 national fraternities; about 10% of women belong to 1 local and 1 national sorority. There are 75 groups on campus, including cheerleading, choir, computers, drama, ethnic, honors, international, jazz band, literary magazine, newspaper, professional, radio and TV, religious, social, student government, and yearbook. Popular campus events include International Fest, Winterfest, Reggae Day, Comedy Clubs, and Casino Night.

Sports: There are 5 intercollegiate sports for men and 5 for women, as well as an intramural program. Athletic and recreation facilities include tennis, basketball, racquetball, and squash courts, a swimming pool, a weight room, a bowling alley, and a game room.

Disabled Students: The entire campus is accessible to disabled students. The following facilities are available: wheelchair ramps, elevators, special parking, specially equipped rest rooms, and lowered drinking fountains.

Services: In addition to many counseling and information services, tutoring is available in some subjects, mainly freshman courses. There also is a reader service for the blind, and remedial math, reading, and writing.

Campus Safety and Security: Campus safety and security measures include 24-hour foot and vehicle patrol, escort service, shuttle buses, and informal discussions. In addition, there are pamphlets, posters, and films, emergency telephones, and lighted pathways and sidewalks.

Programs of Study: IIT awards the B.A., B.S., B.Arch., and B.B.A. degrees. Master's and doctoral degrees also are awarded. Bachelor's degrees are awarded in BIOLOGICAL SCIENCE (biology/biological science), BUSINESS (business administration and management and investments and securities), COMMUNICATIONS AND THE ARTS (design and English), COMPUTER AND PHYSICAL SCIENCE (chemistry, computer science, mathematics, and physics), ENGINEERING AND ENVIRONMENTAL DESIGN (aeronautical engineering, architecture, chemical engineering, civil engineering, computer engineering, electrical/electronics engineering, mechanical engineering, and metallurgical engineering), HEALTH PROFESSIONS (premedicine), SOCIAL SCIENCE (history, political science/government, prelaw, psychology, and sociology). Architecture and mechanical, aerospace, and electrical engineering have the largest enrollments.

Required: To graduate, students must have completed a total of 126 to 142 credit hours with a minimum GPA of 2.0. General education requirements consist of 12 hours each of social studies and humanities, including 1 course each in English composition and industrial culture, 11 hours of science, and 8 hours of mathematics.

Special: The school offers numerous internships and co-op programs, study abroad in France and Scotland, a 3–2 engineering degree with Saint Xavier College, and accelerated degree programs in

prelaw and premedicine. There is a freshman honors program on campus.

Faculty/Classroom: Eighty-six percent of faculty are male; 14%, female. No introductory courses are taught by graduate students. The average class size in a regular course offering is 25.

Admissions: About 83% of the 1993–94 applicants were accepted. The SAT scores for the 1993–94 freshman class were as follows: Verbal—41% below 500, 44% between 500 and 599, 13% between 600 and 700, and 2% above 700; Math—10% below 500, 32% between 500 and 599, 39% between 600 and 700, and 19% above 700. The ACT scores were 16% below 21, 22% between 21 and 23, 27% between 24 and 26, 23% between 27 and 28, and 12% above 28. About 85% of the current freshmen were in the top fifth of their class; 97% were in the top two fifths. There were 4 National Merit finalists.

Requirements: The SAT I or ACT is required. In addition, graduation from an accredited secondary school or satisfactory scores on the GED are required for admission. The school requires 16 academic credits or 16 Carnegie units, including 4 units each of English and mathematics, 2 of science, and 1 of history. Students in the 7-year honors program in engineering and medicine are recommended to take SAT II: Subject tests in writing, mathematics, and chemistry. An interview is recommended and an essay is required of all students. AP credits are accepted. Important factors used in the admissions decision are advanced placement or honor courses, personality, intangible qualities, leadership record, evidence of special talent, and parents or siblings attending the school.

Procedure: Freshmen are admitted fall and spring. Entrance exams should be taken by December of the senior year. Early decision applications should be filed by December 1; regular applications, by March 15 for fall entry, along with an application fee of $30. Notification is given by phone at the time of decision. There is an early decision plan.

Transfer: A total of 149 transfer students enrolled in 1993–94. A 3.0 GPA is required. A total of 45 credits out of 126 to 142 must be completed at IIT.

Visiting: There are regularly scheduled orientations for prospective students, including accompanying current students, visits to classes, and department receptions. There are guides for informal visits and visitors may sit in on classes and stay overnight at the school. To arrange for a visit, contact Al Evon at (312) 567–3025 or (800) 448–2329 (out-of-state).

Financial Aid: In 1993–94, 90% of all current freshmen and 80% of continuing students received some form of financial aid. About 85% of freshmen and 80% of continuing students received need-based aid. The average freshman award was $14,630. Of that total, scholarships or need-based grants averaged $6000 ($14,480 maximum); loans averaged $2625 ($4200 maximum); and work contracts averaged $1500 (maximum). Sixteen percent of undergraduate students work part-time. Average earnings from campus work for the school year are $1500. The average financial indebtedness of the 1992–93 graduate was $12,000. IIT is a member of CSS. The college's own financial statement and the FAFSA are required. The deadline for financial aid applications is April 1.

International Students: There are currently 447 international students enrolled. The school actively recruits these students. They must take the TOEFL and achieve a minimum score of 550.

Computers: IIT provides computer facilities for student use. The mainframes are a DEC VAX 3600 and a Prime 9755. There are also 300 Zenith, AT&T, IBM, Tandy, and Apple Macintosh microcomputers available in academic buildings. All students may access the system. There are no time limits on using the system and no fees.

Graduates: In an earlier year, 476 bachelor's degrees were awarded. Within an average freshman class, 58% graduate in 5 years. Some 125 companies recruited on campus in an earlier year. In a recent graduating class, 14% of the men and 5% of the women were enrolled in graduate school within 6 months of graduation; 90% of all students had found employment.

Admissions Contact: Carole Snow, Dean of Admissions and Financial Aid.

ILLINOIS STATE UNIVERSITY D-3

Normal, IL 61761 (309) 438–2181; (800) 366–2478 (out-of-state)

Full-time: 7040 men, 8623 women	Faculty: 809; I, --$
Part-time: 814 men, 927 women	Ph.D.s: 83%
Graduate: 1189 men, 1728 women	Student/Faculty: 19 to 1
Year: semesters, summer session	Tuition: $3253 ($8203)
Application Deadline: open	Room & Board: $3160
Freshman Class: 8685 applied, 6694 accepted, 2407 enrolled	
SAT I: required	ACT: 22 COMPETITIVE

Illinois State University, founded in 1857, is a public institution offering instruction through schools of applied science and technology, arts and sciences, business, education, and fine arts. There are 5 undergraduate schools and one graduate school. In addition to regional accreditation, ISU has baccalaureate program accreditation with AACSB, ADA, AHEA, CSWE, NASAD, NASM, NCATE, and NRPA. The library contains 1,400,000 volumes, 1,700,000 microform items, and 29,100 audiovisual forms, and subscribes to 9619 periodicals. Computerized library sources and services include the card catalog, interlibrary loans, and database searching. Special learning facilities include a learning resource center, art gallery, natural history museum, planetarium, and radio station. The 850-acre campus is in a small town 125 miles south of Chicago and 180 miles north of St. Louis, Missouri. Including residence halls, there are 100 buildings on campus.

Student Life: About 99% of undergraduates are from Illinois. Students come from 44 states, 53 foreign countries, and Canada. Eighty-seven percent are white. The average age of freshmen is 18; all undergraduates, 21. Twenty-six percent drop out by the end of their first year; 54% remain to graduate.

Housing: A total of 7848 students can be accommodated in college housing. College-sponsored living facilities include single-sex and coed dormitories and on-campus apartments. In addition there are honors houses and special-interest houses. On-campus housing is available on a first-come, first-served basis. Fifty percent of students commute. Alcohol is not permitted. All students may keep cars on campus.

Activities: About 7% of men belong to 26 national fraternities; about 5% of women belong to 17 national sororities. There are 270 groups on campus, including art, band, cheerleading, chess, choir, chorale, chorus, computers, dance, drama, drill team, ethnic, film, gay, honors, international, jazz band, literary magazine, marching band, musical theater, newspaper, opera, orchestra, pep band, photography, political, professional, radio and TV, religious, social, social service, student government, symphony, and yearbook. Popular campus events include a Shakespeare festival, Homecoming, Parents Weekend, Festival ISU, Career Day, Ewing Festival, International Fair, and Madrigal Dinners.

Sports: There are 10 intercollegiate sports for men and 10 for women, and 26 intramural sports for men and 26 for women. Athletic and recreation facilities include a student recreational building, a basketball arena, a football stadium, a field house, baseball diamonds, tennis courts, Olympic-size pools, an 18-hole golf course, a soccer and softball field, and a bowling and billiards center.

Disabled Students: Ninety-nine percent of the campus is accessible to disabled students. The following facilities are available: wheelchair ramps, elevators, special parking, specially equipped rest rooms, special class scheduling, lowered drinking fountains, lowered telephones, and telecommunication device.

Services: In addition to many counseling and information services, tutoring is available in every subject. In addition, there is a reader service for the blind, remedial math, reading, and writing, interpreters for hearing impaired, note takers, and taped lectures.

Campus Safety and Security: Campus safety and security measures include 24-hour foot and vehicle patrol, escort service, informal discussions, and pamphlets, posters, and films. In addition, there are emergency telephones and lighted pathways and sidewalks.

Programs of Study: ISU awards the B.A., B.S., B.F.A., B.S.Ed., B.Mu., and B.Mu.E. degrees. Master's and doctoral degrees also are awarded. Bachelor's degrees are awarded in AGRICULTURE (agriculture), BIOLOGICAL SCIENCE (biology/biological science), BUSINESS (accounting, business administration and management, finance, international business management, management science, and marketing/retailing/merchandising), COMMUNICATIONS AND THE ARTS (art, communications, dance, dramatic arts, English, French, German, music, music performance, public relations, Spanish, and speech/debate/rhetoric), COMPUTER AND PHYSICAL SCIENCE (chemistry, computer science, geology, mathematics, and physics), EDUCATION (business, early childhood, elementary, health, middle school, music, physical, and special), ENGINEERING AND ENVIRONMENTAL DESIGN (industrial engineering technology), HEALTH PROFESSIONS (environmental health science, health care administration, medical laboratory technology, and speech pathology/audiology), SOCIAL SCIENCE (anthropology, criminal justice, economics, fashion design and technology, geography, history, home economics, parks and recreation management, philosophy, political science/government, psychology, Russian and Slavic studies, safety management, social science, social work, and sociology). Elementary education, special education, and accounting have the largest enrollments.

Required: Students must complete 48 hours of university studies requirements, English language and composition, and a total of 120 credits hours with a minimum GPA of 2.0. In addition, they must pass a writing examination and Constitution examination.

Special: There are numerous cooperative programs and internships, dual majors, study abroad in 11 countries, a general studies degree, student-designed majors, a 3–2 engineering program with the University of Illinois, and work-study programs both on campus and with nonprofit organizations. Pass/fail options are available and credit is

given for military experience. ISU is part of the National Student Exchange, enabling qualifying juniors and seniors to study for up to one year at one of several hundred colleges around the country. There is a freshman honors program on campus, as well as 2 national honor societies, including Phi Beta Kappa. Forty-three departments have honors programs.

Faculty/Classroom: Sixty-six percent of faculty are male; 34%, female. Graduate students teach 1% of introductory courses. The average class size in an introductory lecture is 48; in a laboratory, 20; and in a regular course offering, 26.

Admissions: About 77% of the 1993–94 applicants were accepted. The ACT scores for the 1993–94 freshman class were as follows: 33% below 21, 34% between 21 and 23, 22% between 24 and 26, 7% between 27 and 28, and 4% above 28. About 26% of the current freshmen were in the top fifth of their class; 64% were in the top two fifths. There were 7 National Merit finalists.

Requirements: ISU requires applicants to be in the upper 75% of their class. The SAT I or ACT is required. Applicants must be graduates of an accredited secondary school or have a GED. Admission is based on a combination of factors, including class rank and ACT or SAT I score. AP and CLEP credits are accepted.

Procedure: Freshmen are admitted to all sessions. Entrance exams should be taken in the fall semester of the junior year of high school. Application deadlines are open. Notification is sent within 1 week of receipt of application. There is an early admissions plan.

Transfer: In 1993–94, 1992 transfer students enrolled. Graduates of Illinois community colleges holding associate degrees are admitted pending receipt of transcripts. Other students must meet the requirements for beginning freshmen with a minimum 2.0 GPA. A total of 30 credits out of 120 must be completed at ISU.

Visiting: There are regularly scheduled orientations for prospective students. There are guides for informal visits, and visitors may sit in on classes. To arrange for a visit, contact the Admissions Office at (309) 438–2181.

Financial Aid: ISU is a member of CSS. The FAF, FFS or SFS, and AFSA or AFSSA are required. The deadline for financial aid applications is March 1.

International Students: There are currently 349 international students enrolled. The school actively recruits these students. They must take the TOEFL and achieve a minimum score of 550.

Computers: The school provides computer facilities for student use. The mainframe is a Hitachi EX/80. Mainframe terminals are in various locations across campus, and 120 terminals are placed for student access. There are also 1039 microcomputers placed in laboratories and dormitories across campus. With the purchase of a Compucard for $30 per semester, they can be accessed by those students taking courses involving computer use. It may be used 24 hours a day. There are no time limits on using the system.

Graduates: In 1992–93, 4171 bachelor's degrees were awarded. The most popular majors among graduates were marketing (6%), elementary education (5%), and finance (4%). Within an average freshman class, 22% graduate in 4 years, 49% in 5 years, and 54% in 6 years. Some 400 companies recruited on campus in 1992–93.

Admissions Contact: Dave Snyder, Director of Enrollment Management.

ILLINOIS WESLEYAN UNIVERSITY

D-3

Bloomington, IL 61702–2900

(309) 556–3031
(800) 332–2498 (out-of-state)

Full-time: 847 men, 971 women	Faculty: 143; IIB, +$
Part-time: 6 men, 17 women	Ph.D.s: 86%
Graduate: none	Student/Faculty: 13 to 1
Year: 4–1–4, summer session	Tuition: $14,460
Application Deadline: March 1	Room & Board: $4130
Freshman Class: 3050 applied, 1342 accepted, 462 enrolled	
SAT I Verbal/Math: 534/617	ACT: 28 HIGHLY COMPETITIVE +

Illinois Wesleyan University, founded in 1850 and affiliated with the United Methodist Church, is a private institution offering programs in liberal arts, fine arts, and nursing. In addition to regional accreditation, Illinois Wesleyan has baccalaureate program accreditation with AACSB, NASM, and NLN. The 2 libraries contain 201,000 volumes, 108,518 microform items, and 17,260 audiovisual forms, and subscribe to 1267 periodicals. Computerized library sources and services include interlibrary loans and database searching. Special learning facilities include an art gallery, radio station, natural history preserve, observatory, multicultural center, and 20-acre tract of virgin timberland. The 60-acre campus is in a suburban area 140 miles from Chicago. Including residence halls, there are 52 buildings on campus.

Student Life: About 82% of undergraduates are from Illinois. Students come from 35 states and 33 foreign countries. Eighty-three percent are from public schools; 17% from private. Eighty-six percent are white. Sixty-five percent are Protestant; 28% Catholic. The average

age of freshmen is 18; all undergraduates, 20. Five percent drop out by the end of their first year; 80% remain to graduate.

Housing: A total of 1200 students can be accommodated in college housing. College-sponsored living facilities include single-sex and coed dormitories, fraternity houses, and sorority houses. In addition, there is an international house. On-campus housing is guaranteed for all 4 years. Eighty-six percent of students live on campus; of those, 80% remain on campus on weekends. Alcohol is not permitted. All students may keep cars on campus.

Activities: About 24% of men belong to 6 national fraternities; about 24% of women belong to 5 national sororities. There are 75 groups on campus, including band, chess, choir, chorale, chorus, dance, drama, ethnic, gay, honors, international, jazz band, literary magazine, marching band, musical theater, newspaper, opera, orchestra, pep band, political, professional, religious, social, social service, student government, symphony, and yearbook. Popular campus events include Dads Day, Mothers Day, Homecoming, the Fine Arts Festival, the Titan Games, and the Contemporary Music Symposium.

Sports: There are 10 intercollegiate sports for men and 7 for women, and 7 intramural sports for men and 7 for women. Athletic and recreation facilities include a natatorium with a swimming pool, 1- and 2-meter diving boards, weight and exercise equipment, a gymnasium, a dance studio, a field house with a basketball court and a weight room, and a student center with a lounge and a game room.

Disabled Students: Ninety percent of the campus is accessible to disabled students. The following facilities are available: wheelchair ramps, elevators, special parking, specially equipped rest rooms, special class scheduling, and lowered drinking fountains.

Services: In addition to many counseling and information services, tutoring is available in every subject. Assistance in writing and study skills is also available.

Campus Safety and Security: Campus safety and security measures include 24-hour foot and vehicle patrol, escort service, informal discussions, and pamphlets, posters, and films. In addition, there are emergency telephones and lighted pathways and sidewalks. A campus safety committee, headed by the dean of students and composed of students, faculty, and staff, meets twice a semester to review security measures and recommend changes.

Programs of Study: Illinois Wesleyan awards the B.A., B.S., B.F.A., B.Mus.Ed., B.Sacred Mus., and B.S.N. degrees. Bachelor's degrees are awarded in BIOLOGICAL SCIENCE (biology/biological science), BUSINESS (accounting, banking and finance, business administration and management, and international business management), COMMUNICATIONS AND THE ARTS (dramatic arts, English, fine arts, French, German, Japanese, music, Russian, and Spanish), COMPUTER AND PHYSICAL SCIENCE (chemistry, computer science, mathematics, natural sciences, and physics), EDUCATION (elementary), HEALTH PROFESSIONS (medical laboratory technology), SOCIAL SCIENCE (economics, history, international studies, philosophy, political science/government, psychology, religion, and sociology). Business and economics, fine arts, and physical sciences are the strongest academically. Biology/physical science, nursing, music, and business have the largest enrollments.

Required: A total of 35 to 37 course units is required for the bachelor's degree. General education requirements include 4 course units in humanities, 3 each in natural and social sciences and mathematics, 2 in physical education, and 1 each in fine arts and writing. A minimum GPA of 2.0, at least 9 courses in the major, and at least 11 in upper-division courses are required.

Special: There are several co-op programs, including a 3–2 degree in forestry and environmental studies with Duke University; a 2–2 engineering degree with the University of Illinois; and 3–2 engineering programs with a number of universities. Illinois Wesleyan also offers work-study, internships, study abroad, Washington and United Nations semesters, dual and student-designed majors, and pass/fail options. There are 15 national honor societies on campus.

Faculty/Classroom: Fifty-nine percent of faculty are male; 41%, female. All teach undergraduates and 70% also do research. The average class size in an introductory lecture is 50; in a laboratory, 15; and in a regular course offering, 16.

Admissions: About 44% of the 1993–94 applicants were accepted. The SAT scores for the 1993–94 freshman class were as follows: Verbal—34% below 500, 36% between 500 and 599, 28% between 600 and 700, and 2% above 700; Math—7% below 500, 32% between 500 and 599, 41% between 600 and 700, and 20% above 700. The ACT scores were 7% between 21 and 23, 26% between 24 and 26, 28% between 27 and 28, and 39% above 28. About 78% of the current freshmen were in the top fifth of their class; 99% were in the top two fifths. There were 23 National Merit finalists. A total of 29 freshmen graduated first in their class.

Requirements: Illinois Wesleyan requires applicants to be in the upper 25% of their class. A minimum GPA of 3.0 and the SAT I are required. In addition, applicants should graduate from an accredited secondary school, though a GED may be accepted. Fifteen academic credits are required and should include 4 units of English, 3 each of

natural science, mathematics, and foreign language, and 2 of social science. An audition is required for drama and music majors. AP and CLEP credits are accepted. Important factors used in the admissions decision are advanced placement or honor courses, leadership record, personality, intangible qualities, evidence of special talent, and extracurricular activities record.

Procedure: Freshmen are admitted to all sessions. Applications should be filed by March 1 for fall entry. Notification is sent on a rolling basis. There are early admissions and deferred admissions plans.

Transfer: Nine transfer students enrolled in 1993–94. Applicants must submit all high school and college transcripts. A GPA of at least 2.0 is required. A total of 13 course units out of 35 to 37 must be completed at Illinois Wesleyan.

Visiting: There are regularly scheduled orientations for prospective students, including a 1 1/2 day session in the summer in which students meet with advisors to plan course work and with students and staff to become better acquainted with Illinois Wesleyan. There are guides for informal visits and visitors may sit in on classes and stay overnight at the school. To arrange for a visit, contact the Admissions Office at (309) 556–3031 or (800) 332–2498.

Financial Aid: In 1993–94, 82% of all current freshmen and 84% of continuing students received some form of financial aid. About 63% of freshmen and 64% of continuing students received need-based aid. The average freshman award was $11,662. Of that total, scholarships or need-based grants averaged $7715 ($13,295 maximum); loans averaged $2839 ($3200 maximum); and work contracts averaged $1708 ($1360 maximum). Fifty-eight percent of undergraduate students work part-time. Average earnings from campus work for the school year are $1108. The average financial indebtedness of the 1992–93 graduate was $12,300. Illinois Wesleyan is a member of CSS. The FAF and FAFSA are required. The deadline for financial aid applications is March 1.

International Students: There are currently 91 international students enrolled. The school actively recruits these students. They must take the TOEFL and achieve a minimum score of 550. The student must also achieve a minimum composite score of 1000 on the SAT I or 22 on the ACT.

Computers: The university provides computer facilities for student use. The mainframe is an IBM AS400. There are more than 100 IBM, Apple Macintosh, and other microcomputers available in various computer laboratories.

Graduates: In 1992–93, 382 bachelor's degrees were awarded. The most popular majors among graduates were business administration (12%), biology (10%), and history (9%). Within an average freshman class, 2% graduate in 3 years, 80% in 4 years, and 81% in 5 years. Some 60 companies recruited on campus in 1992–93. In the 1992 graduating class, 29% of all students were enrolled in graduate school within 6 months of graduation; 70% of all students had found employment.

Admissions Contact: James R. Ruoti, Dean of Admissions.

JUDSON COLLEGE
Elgin, IL 60123–1498

E-1
(708) 695–2500
(800) TRYJDSN (out-of-state)

Full-time: 220 men, 291 women
Part-time: 39 men, 52 women
Graduate: none
Year: 4–1–4, summer session
Application Deadline: open
Freshman Class: 238 applied, 228 accepted, 115 enrolled
ACT: 21

Faculty: 40; IIB, -$
Ph.D.s: 54%
Student/Faculty: 13 to 1
Tuition: $9225
Room & Board: $4400

COMPETITIVE

Judson College, founded in 1963 and affiliated with the American Baptist Church, is a liberal arts and teachers college stressing Christian faith and Christian living. The library contains 90,000 volumes, 27,000 microform items, and 17,000 audiovisual forms, and subscribes to 500 periodicals. Computerized library sources and services include interlibrary loans and database searching. Special learning facilities include an art gallery and radio station. The 80-acre campus is in a suburban area 40 miles west of Chicago. Including residence halls, there are 14 buildings on campus.

Student Life: About 73% of undergraduates are from Illinois. Students come from 14 states and 9 foreign countries. Eighty-five percent are white. Most are Protestant. The average age of all undergraduates is 20. Thirty percent drop out by the end of their first year; 47% remain to graduate.

Housing: A total of 394 students can be accommodated in college housing. College-sponsored living facilities include single-sex dormitories and on-campus apartments. On-campus housing is guaranteed for all 4 years and is available on a first-come, first-served basis. Fifty-eight percent of students live on campus; of those, 35% remain on campus on weekends. Alcohol is not permitted. All students may keep cars on campus.

Activities: There are no fraternities or sororities. There are many groups and organizations on campus, including art, cheerleading, choir, drama, ethnic, literary magazine, newspaper, pep band, political, radio and TV, religious, social, social service, student government, and yearbook. Popular campus events include College Fair, Spiritual Environment Enrichment Week, Homecoming, Parents Weekend, Christmas by Candlelight, Youth Conference, Spring and Athletic Banquets, Day of Prayer, Day of Missions, art exhibits, plays, musicals, concerts, lectures, and films.

Sports: There are 4 intercollegiate sports for men and 5 for women, and 9 intramural sports for men, 8 for women, and 2 coed. Athletic and recreation facilities include a fitness center, a 1500-seat gymnasium, a soccer field, baseball and softball diamonds, lighted tennis courts, racquetball and handball court, indoor and outdoor running tracks, and a Nautilus and free-weight facility.

Disabled Students: Eighty percent of the campus is accessible to disabled students. The following facilities are available: wheelchair ramps, elevators, special parking, specially equipped rest rooms, special class scheduling, and lowered drinking fountains and telephones.

Services: In addition to many counseling and information services, tutoring is available in some subjects, including core courses. There is also a reader service for the blind, and remedial math, reading, and writing.

Campus Safety and Security: Campus safety and security measures include 24-hour foot and vehicle patrol and lighted pathways and sidewalks.

Programs of Study: Judson awards the B.A. degree. Bachelor's degrees are awarded in BIOLOGICAL SCIENCE (biology/biological science), BUSINESS (accounting, business administration and management, and international business management), COMMUNICATIONS AND THE ARTS (communications, dramatic arts, English, fine arts, and speech/debate/rhetoric), COMPUTER AND PHYSICAL SCIENCE (computer science), EDUCATION (elementary, English, mathematics, music, physical, science, and secondary), ENGINEERING AND ENVIRONMENTAL DESIGN (preengineering), HEALTH PROFESSIONS (medical laboratory technology, nursing, predentistry, premedicine, and sports medicine), SOCIAL SCIENCE (anthropology, history, prelaw, psychology, and sociology). Chemistry, premedicine, computer information science, art, and business are the strongest academically. Education, art, and business have the largest enrollments.

Required: Most students must have a GPA of 2.0; education majors must have a 2.5. Students must complete at least 126 credit hours, including 45 to 66 in the major, and take the college's core courses of Bible study, writing, speech, literature, mathematics, science, history, fine arts, human relations, and physical education, as well as a course in either anthropology, psychology, or sociology.

Special: The college has co-op programs with North Park College, Rush University, and the Mennonite College of Nursing, cross-registration with the Christian College Coalition, and work-study programs with many businesses. Students may serve internships in art and business, take a Washington semester, a film studies semester in Hollywood, an ecology studies semester at Sable Institute in Michigan, or study abroad in Russia, Egypt, the Dominican Republic, and Israel. The college allows dual majors, student-designed majors, and accelerated degrees in business leadership and management. There are pass/fail options for courses outside the major. There is one national honor society on campus.

Faculty/Classroom: Ninety-five percent of faculty are male; 5%, female. Eighty percent teach undergraduates and 20% both teach and do research. The average class size in an introductory lecture is 28 and in a laboratory, 9.

Admissions: About 96% of the 1993–94 applicants were accepted. The ACT scores for the 1993–94 freshman class were as follows: 47% below 21, 26% between 21 and 23, 24% between 24 and 26, 2% between 27 and 28, and 2% above 28. About 21% of the current freshmen were in the top fifth of their class; 49% were in the top two fifths. Three freshmen graduated first in their class.

Requirements: Judson requires applicants to be in the upper 50% of their class. A minimum GPA of 2.0 is required. The ACT, with a minimum score of 18, or the SAT I is required. Graduation from secondary school is required. A minimum of 15 academic units is recommended. The college requires submission of an essay and recommends an interview. The GED is accepted. AP and CLEP credits are accepted. Important factors in the admissions decision are advanced placement or honor courses, recommendations by school officials, leadership record, extracurricular activities record, and personality and intangible qualities.

Procedure: Freshmen are admitted to all sessions. Entrance exams should be taken in spring of the junior year or fall of the senior year. Application deadlines are open. Application fee is $20. Notification is sent on a rolling basis.

Transfer: About 90 transfer students enrolled in 1993–94. Students with fewer than 30 hours of college credit must submit high school transcripts showing a GPA of at least 2.0, as well as ACT results with

a composite score of at least 18. Transfer students with more than 30 hours must have a GPA of at least 2.0. A total of 30 credits out of 126 must be completed at Judson.

Visiting: There are regularly scheduled orientations for prospective students, including a tour, class visits, a chapel visit, and individual meetings with professors, coaches, and other advisors. There are guides for informal visits and visitors may sit in on classes and stay overnight at the school. To arrange for a visit, contact the Enrollment Services Office at (708) 695-2500.

Financial Aid: In 1993-94, 96% of all current freshmen and 97% of continuing students received some form of financial aid. About 80% of freshmen and 82% of continuing students received need-based aid. The average freshman award was $9800. Of that total, scholarships or need-based grants averaged $4500 ($8000 maximum); loans averaged $2100 ($3625 maximum); and work contracts averaged $1200 ($2000 maximum). Seventy-five percent of undergraduate students work part-time. Average earnings from campus work for the school year are $800. The average financial indebtedness of the 1992-93 graduate was $8200. Judson is a member of CSS. The college's own financial statement and the FAFSA are required. The deadline for financial aid applications is May 1.

International Students: There are currently 6 international students enrolled. They must take the TOEFL and achieve a minimum score of 500. The student must also take the SAT I or the ACT.

Computers: The college provides computer facilities for student use. Thirty IBM, AT&T, and Apple Macintosh microcomputers are available in the computer laboratory. There are no time limits on using the system and no fees.

Graduates: About 100 bachelor's degrees were awarded in an earlier year. Within an average freshman class, 37% graduate in 4 years.

Admissions Contact: Matthew S. Osborne, Director of Enrollment Services.

KENDALL COLLEGE
E-1
Evanston, IL 60201   (708) 866-1304

Full-time: 285 men, 218 women	Faculty: 23; IIB, --$
Part-time: 26 men, 31 women	Ph.D.s: 33%
Graduate: none	Student/Faculty: 22 to 1
Year: quarters, summer session	Tuition: $7800
Application Deadline: open	Room & Board: $4851
Freshman Class: 275 applied, 258 accepted, 231 enrolled	
SAT I or ACT: required	LESS COMPETITIVE

Kendall College, founded in 1934, is a private coeducational institution affiliated with the Methodist Church. It offers programs in liberal arts, business, and professional training, as well as culinary arts. The library contains 33,000 volumes, 500 microform items, and 50 audiovisual forms, and subscribes to 210 periodicals. Computerized library sources and services include interlibrary loans and database searching. Special learning facilities include an American Indian museum. The 1-acre campus is in an urban area 3 miles north of Chicago. Including residence halls, there are 5 buildings on campus.

Student Life: About 89% of undergraduates are from Illinois. Students come from 5 states and 5 foreign countries. Seventy percent are from public schools; 30% from private. Seventy-eight percent are white; 16% African American. Eighteen percent are Protestant; 15% Catholic; 12% Jewish. The average age of freshmen is 19; all undergraduates, 23. Five percent drop out by the end of their first year; 25% remain to graduate.

Housing: A total of 250 students can be accommodated in college housing. College-sponsored living facilities include single-sex dormitories. On-campus housing is guaranteed for all 4 years. Fifty-five percent of students commute. Alcohol is not permitted. All students may keep cars on campus.

Activities: There are no fraternities or sororities on campus. There are several groups on campus, including computers, honors, newspaper, professional, social service, student government, and yearbook. Popular campus events include Bastille Day, Spring Dance, May Day, and Halloween Dance.

Sports: There are 2 intramural sports for men and 2 for women.

Disabled Students: Seventy-five percent of the campus is accessible to disabled students. The following facilities are available: elevators, special parking, and specially equipped rest rooms.

Services: In addition to many counseling and information services, tutoring is available in most subjects, including mathematics, human services, and business. In addition, there is remedial math, reading, and writing.

Campus Safety and Security: Campus safety and security measures include 24-hour foot and vehicle patrol and lighted pathways and sidewalks.

Programs of Study: Kendall awards the B.A. degree. Associate degrees also are awarded. Bachelor's degrees are awarded in BUSINESS (business administration and management, hospitality management services, and hotel/motel and restaurant management), COMMUNICATIONS AND THE ARTS (communications), EDUCA-TION (early childhood), SOCIAL SCIENCE (American studies, social science, and social work). Business and human services are the strongest academically. Culinary arts and hospitality management have the largest enrollments.

Required: All students must complete 184 quarter hours. A 2.0 GPA is required to graduate.

Special: Cross-registration is available with National-Louis University. There are internships in culinary arts, hospitality management, human services, and early childhood education, as well as cross registration with the National College of Education. The majority of degrees stress internships. Work-study programs and student-designed majors are also available. There is a freshman honors program on campus, as well as 2 national honor societies, including Phi Beta Kappa. Two departments have honors programs.

Faculty/Classroom: Sixty-one percent of faculty are male; 39%, female. All teach undergraduates, 25% do research, and 25% do both. The average class size in an introductory lecture is 25; in a laboratory, 15; and in a regular course offering, 13.

Admissions: About 94% of the 1993-94 applicants were accepted. About 8% of the current freshmen were in the top fifth of their class; 40% were in the top two fifths.

Requirements: A minimum GPA of 2.0 is required. The SAT I or ACT is required. The minimum acceptable score on the SAT I is 400 verbal, 400 mathematics; on the ACT, the minimum score is 15. However, there is a placement test for students who do not meet the minimum requirement. Applicants should be graduates of an accredited secondary school or have a GED. They should prepare with 4 years of high school mathematics, two years each of history, science, and social studies, and 1 year of a foreign language. An interview is recommended. Important factors used in the admissions decision are advanced placement or honor courses, recommendations by school officials, recommendations by alumni, leadership record, and evidence of special talent.

Procedure: Freshmen are admitted to all sessions. Entrance exams should be taken as soon as requested. Application deadlines are open. Application fee is $30. Notification is sent on a rolling basis within 2 weeks of acceptance. There is a deferred admissions plan.

Transfer: About 50 transfer students enrolled in 1993-94. The minimum GPA for transfer applicants is 2.0. An interview is recommended. A total of 84 quarter-hour credits out of 184 must be completed at Kendall.

Visiting: There are regularly scheduled orientations for prospective students. There are guides for informal visits and visitors may sit in on classes and stay overnight at the school. To arrange for a visit, contact the Admissions Office at (708) 866-1304.

Financial Aid: In 1993-94, 73% of all current freshmen and 85% of continuing students received some form of financial aid. About 35% of freshmen and 80% of continuing students received need-based aid. The average freshman award was $5500. Of that total, scholarships or need-based grants averaged $4000 ($6700 maximum); loans averaged $1500 ($2625 maximum); and work contracts averaged $1200 ($1800 maximum). Average earnings from campus work for the school year are $1800. Kendall is a member of CSS. The FAF is required. The deadline for financial aid applications is June 1.

International Students: There are currently 16 international students enrolled. They must take the TOEFL or the college's own test and achieve a minimum score on the TOEFL of 500. The student must also take the SAT I or the ACT.

Computers: The college provides computer facilities for student and academic use. IBM PS/2 microcomputers are available in the computer laboratory. All students may access the system when there are no computer classes in the laboratory. There are no time limits on using the system and no fees.

Graduates: In an earlier year, 27 bachelor's degrees were awarded. Some 60 companies recruited on campus that year. Within an average freshman class, 55% graduate in 4 years. In the 1992 graduating class, half of the students had found employment within 6 months of graduation.

Admissions Contact: Ralph Starenko, Director of Enrollment Management.

KNOX COLLEGE
C-2
Galesburg, IL 61401   (309) 343-0112, ext. 123
       (800) 678-KNOX (out-of-state)

Full-time: 461 men, 506 women	Faculty: 79; IIB, +$
Part-time: 12 men, 12 women	Ph.D.s: 94%
Graduate: none	Student/Faculty: 12 to 1
Year: trimesters	Tuition: $15,132
Application Deadline: February 15	Room & Board: $3858
Freshman Class: 1040 applied, 845 accepted, 286 enrolled	
SAT I Verbal/Math: 570/530	ACT: 25 VERY COMPETITIVE

Knox College, founded in 1837, is an independent, coeducational liberal arts college. The 3 libraries contain 261,633 volumes, 44,282 microform items, and 3000 audiovisual forms, and subscribe to 750

periodicals. Computerized library sources and services include inter-library loans and database searching. Special learning facilities include a learning resource center, natural history museum, radio station, and a 760-acre biological field station near the campus. The 70-acre campus is in a small town 180 miles southwest of Chicago. Including residence halls, there are 27 buildings on campus.

Student Life: About 57% of undergraduates are from Illinois. Students come from 40 states and 29 foreign countries. Some 78% are white. About 51% claim no religious affiliation; 28% Protestant; 17% Catholic. The average age of freshmen is 18; all undergraduates, 20. Approximately 17% drop out by the end of their first year; 75% remain to graduate.

Housing: A total of 886 students can be accommodated in college housing. College-sponsored living facilities include single-sex and coed dormitories, on-campus apartments, and fraternity houses. In addition, there are special interest houses. On-campus housing is guaranteed for all 4 years. Some 91% of students live on campus; of those, 90% remain on campus on weekends. All students may keep cars on campus.

Activities: About 35% of men belong to 5 national fraternities; about 15% of women belong to 2 national sororities. There are more than 60 groups on campus, including art, band, chess, choir, chorus, computers, dance, drama, ethnic, gay, honors, international, jazz band, literary magazine, newspaper, opera, orchestra, pep band, photography, political, professional, radio, religious, social, social service, student government, symphony, and yearbook. Popular campus events include International Fair, Black Culture Month, Flunk Day, and Pumphandle.

Sports: There are 11 intercollegiate sports for men and 10 for women, and 13 intramural sports for men and 10 for women. Athletic and recreation facilities include 5 outdoor playing fields, 2 gymnasiums, a swimming pool, tennis courts, and an outdoor track. The campus stadium seats 5000; the gymnasium, 3000. There are sports clubs in badminton, fencing, lacrosse, and water polo. A new field house contains a 200-meter indoor track, tennis and volleyball courts, and multiuse space.

Disabled Students: About 60% of the campus is accessible to disabled students. The following facilities are available: wheelchair ramps, elevators, special parking, and specially equipped rest rooms.

Services: In addition to many counseling and information services, tutoring is available in most subjects. In addition, there is a reader service for the blind.

Campus Safety and Security: Campus safety and security measures include escort service, informal discussions, pamphlets, posters, and films, and emergency telephones. In addition, there are lighted pathways and sidewalks and paid professional security that patrols on foot and by vehicle from 4 P.M. to 8 A.M. weeknights and 24 hours daily on weekends.

Programs of Study: Knox awards the B.A. degree. Bachelor's degrees are awarded in BIOLOGICAL SCIENCE (biochemistry and biology/biological science), COMMUNICATIONS AND THE ARTS (art history and appreciation, classics, creative writing, dramatic arts, English, French, German, literature, modern language, music, Russian, Spanish, and studio art), COMPUTER AND PHYSICAL SCIENCE (chemistry, computer science, mathematics, and physics), EDUCATION (elementary and secondary), SOCIAL SCIENCE (American studies, anthropology, economics, German area studies, history, international relations, philosophy, political science/government, psychology, Russian and Slavic studies, and sociology). Sciences, biology, chemistry, mathematics, English, writing, history, and political science are the strongest programs academically. Economics, political science, biology, chemistry, English, writing, and psychology have the largest enrollments.

Required: Students must complete a 2-term interdisciplinary preceptorial emphasizing written and oral thinking; 1 unit is taken the freshman year, the other is completed the junior or senior year. Distribution requirements include 2 courses each in humanities and fine arts, social sciences, and mathematics and natural sciences. Foreign language proficiency requirements must also be met. A total of 36 courses, including 9 to 11 in the major, with a minimum GPA of 2.0, is required in order to graduate.

Special: The normal academic load is 3 courses per term, with 3 terms per year. Cooperative programs are offered with Washington University in St. Louis in architecture, business administration, and engineering; Columbia University in engineering and law; University of Illinois at Urbana-Champaign and Rensselaer Polytechnic Institute in engineering; Rush University in medicine, nursing, and medical technology; Duke University in forestry and environmental management; and University of Chicago in law and social work. Study abroad is available in 16 countries. Other programs include a Washington semester, an urban studies semester, science and library research programs, work-study programs, and numerous internships. Dual majors, student-designed majors, and pass/fail options are available. Early admission to Rush Medical College or the University of Chicago Graduate School of Business is possible. Nondegree study is possi-

ble. There are 4 national honor societies on campus, including Phi Beta Kappa. Four departments have honors programs.

Faculty/Classroom: Some 76% of faculty are male; 24%, female. All teach and do research. The average class size in an introductory lecture is 28; in a laboratory, 25; and in a regular course offering, 17.

Admissions: About 81% of the 1993–94 applicants were accepted. The SAT scores for the 1993–94 freshman class were as follows: Verbal—31% below 500, 43% between 500 and 599, 22% between 600 and 700, and 4% above 700; Math—23% below 500, 28% between 500 and 599, 37% between 600 and 700, and 12% above 700. The ACT scores were 7% below 21, 19% between 21 and 23, 26% between 24 and 26, 24% between 27 and 28, and 24% above 28. About 69% of the current freshmen were in the top fifth of their class; 92% were in the top two fifths. There were 4 National Merit finalists. About 13 freshmen graduated first in their class.

Requirements: The SAT I or ACT is required. In addition, applicants should be graduates of an accredited secondary school with 15 academic credits, including 4 in English, 3 each in mathematics, science, history, and social studies, and 2 in foreign language. An essay is part of the application process. An interview is recommended. AP and CLEP credits are accepted. Important factors used in the admissions decision are advanced placement or honor courses, recommendations by school officials, extracurricular activities record, geographic diversity, and leadership record.

Procedure: Freshmen are admitted to all sessions. Entrance exams should be taken by December 15. Early action applications should be filed by December 1; regular applications, by February 15 for fall entry, November 1 for winter entry, and February 1 for spring entry, along with an application fee of $25. Notification of early action is sent December 31; regular decision, March 31. There are early admissions and deferred admissions plans.

Transfer: About 38 transfer students enrolled in 1993–94. A 2.75 GPA is required. An interview is recommended. A total of 13 courses out of 36 must be completed at Knox.

Visiting: There are regularly scheduled orientations for prospective students, including 2 in fall, 2 in winter, and 2 in spring. There are guides for informal visits and visitors may sit in on classes and stay overnight at the school. To arrange for a visit, contact the Admissions Office at (309) 343–0112, ext. 123 or (800) 678-KNOX.

Financial Aid: In 1993–94, 92% of all current freshmen and 88% of continuing students received some form of financial aid. About 81% of freshmen and 76% of continuing students received need-based aid. The average freshman award was $14,735. Of that total, scholarships or need-based grants averaged $10,468 ($14,955 maximum); loans averaged $3100 ($3625 maximum); and work contracts averaged $1167 ($1275 maximum). Some 66% of undergraduate students work part-time. Average earnings from campus work for the school year are $825. The average financial indebtedness of the 1992–93 graduate was $10,500. Knox is a member of CSS. The FAF and FAFSA are required. The deadline for financial aid applications is March 1.

International Students: There are currently 75 international students enrolled. The school actively recruits these students. They must take the TOEFL and achieve a minimum score of 550.

Computers: The college provides computer facilities for student use. The mainframes are a DEC VAX 3600, DEC VAX 11/750, and an HP 9000/G30. In addition, there is a PC microcomputer laboratory with 23 terminals in the social sciences building, Apple Macintosh and PC laboratories in the science building with about 40 terminals, and additional PC, Macintosh, and SUN workstations scattered throughout the campus within departments. All students may access the system. There are no time limits on using the system and no fees.

Graduates: In 1992–93, 233 bachelor's degrees were awarded. The most popular majors among graduates were political science (12%) and chemistry, biology, economics, psychology, (9% each). Within an average freshman class, 69% graduate in 4 years, 75% in 5 years, and 75% in 6 years. Some 37 companies recruited on campus in 1992–93. In the 1992 graduating class, about 28% of men and women enrolled in graduate school within 6 months of graduation; 53% of them had found employment.

Admissions Contact: Paul Steenis, Director of Admissions.

LAKE FOREST COLLEGE

E-1

Lake Forest, IL 60045–2239 — (708) 234–3100; (800) 828-4751

Full-time: 458 men, 511 women	Faculty: 80; IIB, +$
Part-time: 10 men, 25 women	Ph.D.s: 95%
Graduate: 5 men, 17 women	Student/Faculty: 12 to 1
Year: semesters, summer session	Tuition: $16,175
Application Deadline: March 1	Room & Board: $3785
Freshman Class: 979 applied, 633 accepted, 271 enrolled	
SAT I or ACT: required	VERY COMPETITIVE

Lake Forest College, founded in 1857, is a liberal arts institution affiliated with the Presbyterian Church. The 2 libraries contain 374,543 volumes, 24,473 microform items, and 10,756 audiovisual forms, and

subscribe to 1300 periodicals. Computerized library sources and services include the card catalog, interlibrary loans, and database searching. Special learning facilities include an art gallery, radio station, multimedia language laboratory, and electronic music studio with practice rooms. The 107-acre campus is in a suburban area 30 miles north of Chicago. Including residence halls, there are 30 buildings on campus.

Student Life: About 69% of undergraduates are from out-of-state, mostly the Midwest. Students come from 47 states, 17 foreign countries, and Canada. Seventy-eight percent are from public schools; 22% from private. Eighty-eight percent are white. The average age of freshmen is 18; all undergraduates, 20. Eleven percent drop out by the end of their first year; 78% remain to graduate.

Housing: A total of 847 students can be accommodated in college housing. College-sponsored living facilities include single-sex and coed dormitories. In addition, there are honors houses, special interest houses, and options for 24-hour quiet hours and substance-free housing. On-campus housing is guaranteed for all 4 years. Eighty-one percent of students live on campus; of those, 98% remain on campus on weekends. Upperclassmen may keep cars on campus.

Activities: About 30% of men belong to 3 local fraternities and 1 national fraternity; about 23% of women belong to 3 local sororities. There are 46 groups on campus, including art, cheerleading, chess, choir, chorus, computers, drama, ensembles, ethnic, film, gay, honors, international, jazz band, literary magazine, newspaper, pep band, photography, political, professional, radio and TV, religious, social, social service, student government, and yearbook. Popular campus events include Festival of Ra, Big Chill Weekend, Visiting Woodrow Wilson Fellow, and Poet-in-Residence, Writer-in-Residence, Artist-in-Residence, and Fulbright Scholar-in-Residence programs.

Sports: There are 8 intercollegiate sports for men and 7 for women, and 8 intramural sports for men and 8 for women. Athletic and recreation facilities include a gymnasium, tennis courts, 2 indoor and 1 outdoor basketball court, and 5 racquetball, 3 handball, 2 squash, and 1 outdoor sand volleyball court, weight and exercise rooms, a pool, an indoor ice rink, and baseball, football, soccer, and intramural fields.

Disabled Students: Ninety-five percent of the campus is accessible to disabled students. The following facilities are available: wheelchair ramps, elevators, special parking, specially equipped rest rooms, special class scheduling, lowered drinking fountains, and lowered telephones.

Services: In addition to many counseling and information services, tutoring is available in most subjects.

Campus Safety and Security: Campus safety and security measures include 24-hour foot and vehicle patrol, self defense education, escort service, and shuttle buses. In addition, there are informal discussions, pamphlets, posters, and films, emergency telephones, and lighted pathways and sidewalks.

Programs of Study: Lake Forest awards the B.A. degree. Master's degrees also are awarded. Bachelor's degrees are awarded in BIOLOGICAL SCIENCE (biology/biological science), BUSINESS (business economics), COMMUNICATIONS AND THE ARTS (English, fine arts, French, German, music, and Spanish), COMPUTER AND PHYSICAL SCIENCE (chemistry, computer science, mathematics, and physics), EDUCATION (elementary and secondary), HEALTH PROFESSIONS (medical laboratory technology and nursing), SOCIAL SCIENCE (anthropology, economics, history, international relations, philosophy, political science/government, psychology, and sociology). Economics, psychology, English, and politics have the largest enrollments.

Required: All students are required to complete 32 courses with a minimum GPA of 2.0. General education requirements include 3 courses in natural sciences and mathematics, 2 cultural diversity courses, and 1 course each in freshman studies, freshman writing, humanities, social science, and senior studies.

Special: Lake Forest offers cross-registration with Barat College and Associated Colleges of the Midwest, an extensive internship program, and study abroad in 10 countries. Dual, student-designed, and interdisciplinary majors, including American studies, Asian studies, area studies, art (studio and art history), comparative literature, and environmental studies are available. There is a Washington semester with American University and a work-study program. A 3–2 engineering degree with Washington University at St. Louis and a 2–2 nursing or medical technology degree with Rush University are offered. A pass/fail option is available. There is a freshman honors program on campus, as well as 10 national honor societies, including Phi Beta Kappa.

Faculty/Classroom: Fifty-nine percent of faculty are male; 41%, female. All both teach and do research. No introductory courses are taught by graduate students. The average class size in an introductory lecture is 27; in a laboratory, 11; and in a regular course offering, 18.

Admissions: About 65% of the 1993–94 applicants were accepted. The SAT scores for the 1993–94 freshman class were as follows: Verbal—46% below 500, 36% between 500 and 599, 16% between 600 and 700, and 2% above 700; Math—40% below 500, 36% between 500 and 599, 19% between 600 and 700, and 5% above 700. The ACT scores were 16% below 21, 23% between 21 and 23, 30% between 24 and 26, 17% between 27 and 28, and 14% above 28. About 54% of the current freshmen were in the top fifth of their class; 81% were in the top two fifths. There were 3 National Merit finalists and 8 semifinalists. About 4 freshmen graduated first in their class.

Requirements: The SAT I or ACT is required. Applicants are advised to complete 16 academic credits, including 4 in English, 2 to 4 each in social and natural sciences, 3 in mathematics, and study in 1 or more foreign languages. A GED is accepted. An interview is encouraged. AP credits are accepted. Important factors used in the admissions decision are advanced placement or honor courses, evidence of special talent, recommendations by school officials, extracurricular activities record, and leadership record.

Procedure: Freshmen are admitted fall and winter. Entrance exams should be taken in the junior or senior year. Early decision applications should be filed by January 1; regular applications, by March 1 for fall entry and December 15 for winter entry, along with an application fee of $20. Notification is sent on a rolling basis. There are early decision, early admissions, and deferred admissions plans. About 58 early decision candidates were accepted for the 1993–94 class. A waiting list is an active part of the admissions procedure.

Transfer: About 62 transfer students enrolled in 1993–94. Transfer applicants should have a minimum C average in all college work and be in good standing with their previous institution. High school and college transcripts and a letter of recommendation from the academic dean or a teacher at the most recent college attended are required. A total of 16 courses out of 32 must be completed at Lake Forest.

Visiting: There are guides for informal visits, and visitors may sit in on classes and stay overnight at the school. To arrange for a visit, contact the Admissions Office at (708) 234–3100 or (800) 828–4751.

Financial Aid: In 1993–94 72% of all current freshmen and 67% of continuing students received some form of financial aid. About 71% of freshmen and 67% of continuing students received need-based aid. The average freshman award was $15,697. Of that total, scholarships or need-based grants averaged $12,347 ($18,550 maximum); loans averaged $2000 ($2500 maximum); and work contracts averaged $1350 ($1600 maximum). Seventy-two percent of undergraduate students work part-time. Average earnings from campus work for the school year are $1400. The average financial indebtedness of the 1992–93 graduate was $5400. Lake Forest is a member of CSS. The college's own financial statement and the FAFSA are required. The deadline for financial aid applications is March 1.

International Students: There are currently 35 international students enrolled. The school actively recruits these students. They must take the TOEFL and achieve a minimum score of 550. The student must also take the SAT I or the ACT.

Computers: The college provides computer facilities for student use. The mainframes are a DEC VAX 4300, 4100, 3180, and 4060. There are 55 terminals that access the mainframe, 30 of which are available for student use. There are also more than 100 microcomputers in 11 computer laboratories in residence halls and academic buildings available for student use. The residence hall microcomputers have word-processing, database-management, and spreadsheet software capabilities. Internet network hookups in residence hall rooms are possible at no charge. All students may access the system. It may be used 24 hours a day, 7 days a week. There are no time limits on using the system and no fees.

Graduates: In 1992–93 250 bachelor's degrees were awarded. The most popular majors among graduates were business/economics (23%), psychology (14%), and English (10%). Within an average freshman class, 5% graduate in 3 years, 76% in 4 years, 78% in 5 years, and 78% in 6 years. Some 62 companies recruited on campus in 1992–93. In the 1992 graduating class, 13% of the men and 26% of the women were enrolled in graduate school within 6 months of graduation.

Admissions Contact: William G. Motzer, Director of Admissions.

LEWIS UNIVERSITY

E-2

Romeoville, IL 60441

(815) 838-0500

Full-time: 1096 men, 1096 women	**Faculty:** 122; IIA, --$
Part-time: 711 men, 711 women	**Ph.D.s:** 58%
Graduate: 382 men, 347 women	**Student/Faculty:** 18 to 1
Year: semesters, summer session	**Tuition:** $10,297
Application Deadline: open	**Room & Board:** $4500
Freshman Class: n/av	
ACT: required	**LESS COMPETITIVE**

Lewis University, founded in 1932, is a private institution affiliated with the Roman Catholic Church and offering programs in liberal and fine arts, aviation, business, religion, and teacher preparation. There are 3 undergraduate and 6 graduate schools. In addition to regional accreditation, Lewis has baccalaureate program accreditation with NLN. The library contains 150,000 volumes. Computerized library

sources and services include the card catalog. Special learning facilities include a learning resource center, art gallery, radio station, TV station, and aviation building. The 400-acre campus is in a suburban area 35 miles southwest of Chicago. Including residence halls, there are 16 buildings on campus.

Student Life: Almost all undergraduates are from Illinois. Students come from 20 states, 9 foreign countries, and Canada. Sixty percent are from public schools; 40% from private. Seventy-five percent are white; 18% African American. Seventy-five percent are Catholic; 25% Protestant. The average age of freshmen is 18; all undergraduates, 24. Fifteen percent drop out by the end of their first year; 40% remain to graduate.

Housing: A total of 800 students can be accommodated in college housing. College-sponsored living facilities include single-sex and coed dormitories. On-campus housing is guaranteed for all 4 years. Sixty-seven percent of students commute. All students may keep cars on campus.

Activities: About 10% of men and about 5% of women belong to 5 local and 3 national fraternities; about 10% of women belong to 4 local and 4 national sororities. There are 20 groups on campus, including band, cheerleading, choir, chorale, chorus, drama, ethnic, honors, international, jazz band, newspaper, orchestra, pep band, political, professional, radio and TV, religious, social service, and student government. Popular campus events include Lewis Fall Festival and Homecoming in the Spring.

Sports: There are 8 intercollegiate sports each for men and women, and 10 intramural sports each. Athletic and recreation facilities include a sports center, 2 gymnasiums, and an athletic field.

Disabled Students: Most of the campus is accessible to disabled students. The following facilities are available: wheelchair ramps, elevators, special parking, specially equipped rest rooms, special class scheduling, lowered drinking fountains, and lowered telephones.

Services: In addition to many counseling and information services, tutoring is available in most subjects. There is also remedial math, reading, and writing. The University Success Program provides assistance to those students who do not meet the scholastic requirements.

Campus Safety and Security: Campus safety and security measures include 24-hour foot and vehicle patrol, escort service, informal discussions, and pamphlets, posters, and films. In addition, there are emergency telephones and lighted pathways and sidewalks.

Programs of Study: Lewis awards the B.A. and B.S. degrees. Associate and master's degrees also are awarded. Bachelor's degrees are awarded in BIOLOGICAL SCIENCE (biology/biological science), BUSINESS (accounting, banking and finance, business administration and management, business economics, management information systems, and marketing/retailing/merchandising), COMMUNICATIONS AND THE ARTS (art, broadcasting, communications, English, journalism, music, and speech/debate/rhetoric), COMPUTER AND PHYSICAL SCIENCE (chemistry, computer science, mathematics, and physics), EDUCATION (art, business, elementary, middle school, music, and secondary), ENGINEERING AND ENVIRONMENTAL DESIGN (aviation administration/management and preengineering), HEALTH PROFESSIONS (nursing, physical therapy, predentistry, premedicine, and prepharmacy), SOCIAL SCIENCE (criminal justice, economics, history, liberal arts/general studies, philosophy, political science/government, prelaw, psychology, religion, social work, and sociology). Aviation, communications, criminal social justice, business, and nursing are the strongest academically. Aviation, criminal social justice, nursing, and business have the largest enrollments.

Required: All students must earn 128 credit hours in courses acceptable for graduation, with one third of these courses in the core curriculum. At least 4 upper-division courses must be taken in the major. Students must maintain a minimum GPA of 2.0.

Special: Lewis offers a general education degree, co-op programs, internships, student-designed majors, a B.A.-B.S. degree, pass/fail options, dual majors, work-study programs, and nondegree study. The aviation program permits graduates to qualify for the FAA Airframe and Powerplant certificate.

Faculty/Classroom: Sixty-seven percent of faculty are male; 33%, female.

Requirements: The ACT is required, with a minimum composite score of 20. Applicants should be graduates of an accredited secondary school. The GED is accepted. Students should have achieved an academic rank in the upper half of the graduating class and a minimum average of C. Students should have 15 units, consisting of 3 in English and 12 in other college-preparatory subjects. AP and CLEP credits are accepted.

Procedure: Freshmen are admitted to all sessions. Entrance exams should be taken prior to enrollment. Application deadlines are open. The application fee is $25. Notification is sent on a rolling basis.

Transfer: About 400 transfer students enrolled in 1993–94. Applicants must have a 2.0 GPA in transferable course work of at least 12 semester hours. A total of 32 credits out of 128 must be completed at Lewis.

Visiting: There are regularly scheduled orientations for prospective students. There are guides for informal visits and visitors may sit in on classes and stay overnight at the school. To arrange for a visit, contact the Admissions Office at (815) 838–0500.

Financial Aid: In 1993–94, 80% of all current freshmen received some form of financial aid. About 75% of freshmen received need-based aid. The average freshman award was $8700. Of that total, scholarships or need-based grants averaged $5100 ($12,492 maximum); loans averaged $1600 ($2625 maximum); and work contracts averaged $1500 ($2000 maximum). Average earnings from campus work for the school year are $1400. The average financial indebtedness of the 1992–93 graduate was $9000. Lewis is a member of CSS. The FAFSA is required. The deadline for financial aid applications is April 1.

International Students: The school actively recruits these students. They must take the TOEFL and achieve a minimum score of 500.

Computers: The college provides computer facilities for student use. The mainframes are a Prime 9750 and 9655, and an IBM unit. All students may access the system. There are no time limits. The fees are $15.

Admissions Contact: Frank Palmasani, Admissions Officer.

LOYOLA UNIVERSITY OF CHICAGO E-2

Chicago, IL 60611 (312) 915–6500; (800) 262–2373 (out-of-state)

Full-time: 2079 men, 3165 women	Faculty: 606; I, av$
Part-time: 1228 men, 2189 women	Ph.D.s: 93%
Graduate: 2248 men, 3452 women	Student/Faculty: 9 to 1
Year: semesters, summer session	Tuition: $10,570
Application Deadline: July 13	Room & Board: $5310
Freshman Class: 3579 applied, 2959 accepted, 855 enrolled	
SAT I Verbal/Math: 480/520	ACT: 24 COMPETITIVE +

Loyola University of Chicago, founded in 1870, is a private Roman Catholic university offering undergraduate curricula in the arts and sciences, business, nursing, social work, and education. There are 5 undergraduate and 9 graduate schools. In addition to regional accreditation, Loyola has baccalaureate program accreditation with AACSB, CSWE, NCATE, and NLN. The 3 libraries contain 1.3 million volumes, 1 million microform items, and 9192 audiovisual forms, and subscribe to 10,229 periodicals. Computerized library sources and services include the card catalog, interlibrary loans, and database searching. Special learning facilities include a learning resource center, art gallery, radio station, nursing resource center, theater, seismograph station, and electron microscope. The 105-acre campus is in an urban area of Chicago. Including residence halls, there are 130 buildings on campus.

Student Life: About 83% of undergraduates are from Illinois. Students come from 50 states, 70 foreign countries, and Canada. Sixty-one percent are from public schools; 39% from private. Seventy-three percent are white; 10% Asian American. Sixty-two percent are Catholic; 11% Protestant. The average age of freshmen is 18; all undergraduates, 20.7. Nineteen percent drop out by the end of their first year; 65% remain to graduate.

Housing: A total of 1985 students can be accommodated in college housing. College-sponsored living facilities include single-sex and coed dormitories and on-campus apartments. In addition, there are special interest houses, a 24-hour quiet center, and a living-learning center. On-campus housing is guaranteed for all 4 years. Seventy-five percent of students commute. All students may keep cars on campus.

Activities: About 8% of men belong to 1 local and 5 national fraternities; about 7% of women belong to 8 national sororities. There are 136 groups on campus, including cheerleading, choir, chorus, drama, ethnic, gay, honors, international, jazz band, literary magazine, musical theater, newspaper, political, professional, radio and TV, religious, social, social service, and student government. Popular campus events include Hunger Week, Orientation, Harmony Colors Festival, President's Ball, Valentines Ball, and Spring Fling.

Sports: There are 6 intercollegiate and 22 intramural sports each for men and women. Athletic and recreation facilities include racquetball courts, a dance studio, swimming pools, saunas, an elevated jogging track, and weight rooms.

Disabled Students: Ninety-five percent of the campus is accessible to disabled students. The following facilities are available: wheelchair ramps, elevators, special parking, specially equipped rest rooms, special class scheduling, lowered drinking fountains, and lowered telephones.

Services: In addition to many counseling and information services, tutoring is available in some subjects, including general education courses. There is a reader service for the blind and remedial writing, with a writing center available for student use.

Campus Safety and Security: Campus safety and security measures include 24-hour foot and vehicle patrol, self defense education, escort service, and shuttle buses. In addition, there are informal discussions, pamphlets, posters, and films, emergency telephones, and lighted pathways and sidewalks.

Programs of Study: Loyola awards the B.A., B.S., B.A.Classics, B.B.A., B.S.Ed., and B.S.N. degrees. Master's and doctoral degrees also are awarded. Bachelor's degrees are awarded in BIOLOGICAL SCIENCE (biology/biological science), BUSINESS (accounting, banking and finance, business administration and management, business economics, marketing/retailing/merchandising, and personnel management), COMMUNICATIONS AND THE ARTS (communications, dramatic arts, English, fine arts, French, German, Greek, Italian, Latin, linguistics, and Spanish), COMPUTER AND PHYSICAL SCIENCE (chemistry, computer science, mathematics, and physics), EDUCATION (early childhood, elementary, and special), HEALTH PROFESSIONS (nursing, predentistry, premedicine, and preveterinary science), SOCIAL SCIENCE (anthropology, classical/ancient civilization, criminal justice, economics, history, philosophy, political science/government, psychology, religion, social work, sociology, and theological studies). Biology, psychology, communications, and business have the largest enrollments.

Required: In order to graduate, students must have a total of 128 credit hours with a minimum GPA of 2.0. The number of hours required in the major varies. For the core requirement, all students must take 6 hours each of English composition and humanities and 9 hours each of theology, philosophy, and social sciences.

Special: Sophomores and juniors may study in Italy or Mexico. Dual majors, a Washington semester, nondegree study, and pass/fail options are available. The school also offers a 2–3 engineering degree with the University of Illinois at Urbana-Champaign. For working adults, Mundelein College offers fully accredited programs leading to baccaulaureate degrees in arts and sciences, business, and education. There is a freshman honors program on campus. All disciplines in arts and sciences and nursing have honors programs.

Faculty/Classroom: Sixty-six percent of faculty are male; 34%, female. All teach undergraduates and do research. No introductory courses are taught by graduate students. The average class size in an introductory lecture is 25; in a laboratory, 18; and in a regular course offering, 15.

Admissions: About 83% of the 1993–94 applicants were accepted. The SAT scores for the 1993–94 freshman class were as follows: Verbal—55% below 500, 33% between 500 and 599, 11% between 600 and 700, and 1% above 700; Math—37% below 500, 40% between 500 and 599, 21% between 600 and 700, and 2% above 700. The ACT scores were 17% below 21, 32% between 21 and 23, 29% between 24 and 26, 13% between 27 and 28, and 9% above 28. About 43% of the current freshmen were in the top fifth of their class; 77% were in the top two fifths. Nine freshmen graduated first in their class.

Requirements: The SAT I or ACT is required. In addition, graduation from an accredited secondary school or satisfactory scores on the GED are required for admission. Thirteen academic credits are required, including 3 of English, 2 of mathematics, and 1 each of science and social studies. An interview is recommended but an essay is not required. AP and CLEP credits are accepted. Important factors used in the admissions decision are advanced placement or honor courses, evidence of special talent, leadership record, recommendations by school officials, and extracurricular activities record.

Procedure: Freshmen are admitted to all sessions. Entrance exams should be taken as early as possible, normally in the spring of the junior year. Applications should be filed by July 13 for fall entry and December 1 for spring entry, along with an application fee of $25. Notification is sent 2 to 3 weeks after receipt of the completed application.

Transfer: About 440 transfer students enrolled in 1993–94. Applicants must have 20 transferable semester hours of credit, with a minimum GPA of 2.0 for the schools of arts and sciences and education. A minimum GPA of 2.5 is required for the schools of nursing and business administration. A total of 32 credits out of 128 must be completed at Loyola.

Visiting: There are regularly scheduled orientations for prospective students, including interviews and tours; students may attend classes if previous arrangements have been made. There are guides for informal visits and visitors may sit in on classes and stay overnight at the school. To arrange for a visit, contact the Undergraduate Admissions Office at (312) 508–3075.

Financial Aid: In 1993–94, 70% of all current freshmen and 75% of continuing students received some form of financial aid. About 51% of freshmen and 55% of continuing students received need-based aid. The average freshman award was $7995. Of that total, scholarships or need-based grants averaged $3370 ($6980 maximum); loans averaged $2125 ($4625 maximum); and work contracts averaged $1358 ($2000 maximum). Ninety percent of undergraduate students work part-time. Average earnings from campus work for the school year are $2000. The average financial indebtedness of the 1992–93 graduate was $6000. Loyola is a member of CSS. The FAF is required. The deadline for financial aid applications is February 15.

International Students: There are currently 339 international students enrolled. Applicants must take the TOEFL and achieve a minimum score of 500. The student must also take the SAT I or the ACT.

Computers: Loyola provides computer facilities for student use. The mainframe is an IBM 3081K. More than 190 microcomputers, networked to commonly used microsoftware packages, are available. More than 75 dump terminals access the mainframe computer for heavy-duty analytical packages. All students may access the system whenever facilities are available. There are no time limits on using the system and no fees.

Graduates: In 1992–93, 1614 bachelor's degrees were awarded. The most popular majors among graduates were psychology (12%), communication (10%), and biology (7%). Within an average freshman class, 1% graduate in 3 years, 38% in 4 years, 59% in 5 years, and 65% in 6 years. Some 360 companies recruited on campus in 1992–93.

Admissions Contact: Edward Moore, Acting Director.

MACMURRAY COLLEGE
C-3

Jacksonville, IL 62650   (217) 479–7056; (800) 252–7485 (in-state)

Full-time: 272 men, 356 women	Faculty: 52; IIB, --$
Part-time: 27 men, 36 women	Ph.Ds: 50%
Graduate: none	Student/Faculty: 12 to 1
Year: 4–1–4, summer session	Tuition: $9160
Application Deadline: July 15	Room & Board: $3640
Freshman Class: 740 applied, 558 accepted, 157 enrolled	
ACT: 20	**COMPETITIVE**

MacMurray College, founded in 1846, is a private liberal arts institution affiliated with the United Methodist Church. In addition to regional accreditation, MacMurray has baccalaureate program accreditation with CSWE and NLN. The library contains 145,000 volumes and subscribes to 300 periodicals. Computerized library sources and services include interlibrary loans. Special learning facilities include an art gallery. The 60-acre campus is in a small town 30 miles west of Springfield. Including residence halls, there are 16 buildings on campus.

Student Life: About 84% of undergraduates are from Illinois. Students come from 18 states and 4 foreign countries. Ninety percent are from public schools; 10% from private. Ninety-one percent are white. Sixty-two percent are Protestant; 28% Catholic; 10% claim no religious affiliation. The average age of all undergraduates is 20. Twenty-two percent drop out by the end of their first year; 45% remain to graduate.

Housing: A total of 725 students can be accommodated in college housing. College-sponsored living facilities include single-sex and coed dormitories. On-campus housing is guaranteed for all 4 years. Eighty percent of students live on campus; of those, 80% remain on campus on weekends. Alcohol is not permitted. All students may keep cars on campus.

Activities: About 10% of men belong to 1 national fraternity. There are no sororities on campus. There are 40 groups on campus, including band, cheerleading, choir, chorale, chorus, dance, ethnic, honors, literary magazine, musical theater, newspaper, orchestra, pep band, photography, political, professional, religious, social, social service, student government, and yearbook. Popular campus events include Homecoming and Spring Formal.

Sports: There are 7 intercollegiate sports for men and 6 for women, and 10 intramural sports for men and 10 for women. Athletic and recreation facilities include a gymnasium, 3 basketball courts, a competition-size swimming pool, a weight room, a wrestling room, dance studios, and a game room and TV lounge.

Disabled Students: The following facilities are available: wheelchair ramps, elevators, special parking, and specially equipped rest rooms.

Services: In addition to many counseling and information services, tutoring is available in every subject. The college provides services to visually and hearing-impaired students through interpreters, readers, and notetakers.

Campus Safety and Security: Campus safety and security measures include escort service, informal discussions, pamphlets, posters, and films, and lighted pathways and sidewalks. In addition, there are evening patrols and evening sign-in at dorms.

Programs of Study: MacMurray awards the B.A., B.S., and B.S.N. degrees. Associate degrees also are awarded. Bachelor's degrees are awarded in BIOLOGICAL SCIENCE (biology/biological science), BUSINESS (accounting, business administration and management, management information systems, and marketing/retailing/merchandising), COMMUNICATIONS AND THE ARTS (art, English, fine arts, French, journalism, music, and Spanish), COMPUTER AND PHYSICAL SCIENCE (chemistry, computer science, mathematics, and physics), EDUCATION (education of the deaf and hearing impaired, elementary, music, science, secondary, and special), ENGINEERING AND ENVIRONMENTAL DESIGN (preengineering), HEALTH PROFESSIONS (nursing, predentistry, premedicine, and preveterinary science), SOCIAL SCIENCE (criminal justice, history, philosophy, political science/government, prelaw, psychology, and social work). Education of the hearing impaired, English, nursing, and

premedicine are the strongest academically. Business, education, nursing, and criminal justice have the largest enrollments.

Required: In order to graduate, a student must complete 128 semester hours and 2 January term courses, with a minimum GPA of 2.0. All students must take 9 semester hours in rhetorical skills, and a 5-course sequence on Western civilization and world culture. In addition, students must satisfy the requirements of the Breadth Component, a 16-hour distribution of non-major courses. Proficiency examinations in mathematics and composition must be taken by all students before the end of the junior year.

Special: The school has co-op programs in all majors and cross-registration with 5 colleges through the West Central Illinois Foreign Language Consortium. A 3–2 engineering degree with Washington and Columbia universities, a Washington semester, internships in all majors, work-study programs, dual majors, and pass/fail options are available. Students may study abroad in England, Germany, Japan, or Russia. A 3–2 preoccupational therapy program is also available with Washington University. There are 2 national honor societies on campus.

Faculty/Classroom: Sixty-five percent of faculty are male; 35%, female. All teach undergraduates. The average class size in an introductory lecture is 40; in a laboratory, 25; and in a regular course offering, 20.

Admissions: About 75% of the 1993–94 applicants were accepted. The ACT scores for the 1993–94 freshman class were as follows: 61% below 21, 18% between 21 and 23, 12% between 24 and 26, 5% between 27 and 28, and 4% above 28. About 24% of the current freshmen were in the top fifth of their class; 46% were in the top two fifths. Two freshmen graduated first in their class.

Requirements: MacMurray requires applicants to be in the upper 70% of their class. A minimum GPA of 2.1 and either the SAT I or the ACT are required. Applicants must be graduates of an accredited secondary school. The GED is accepted. Secondary school courses should include 4 years of English, 3 of mathematics, and 2 each of science, foreign language, and social studies. AP and CLEP credits are accepted. Important factors used in the admissions decision are recommendations by school officials, advanced placement or honor courses, personality, intangible qualities, extracurricular activities record, and leadership record.

Procedure: Freshmen are admitted fall, winter, and spring. Entrance exams should be taken in the spring of the junior year. Applications should be filed by July 15 for fall entry, December 1 for winter entry, and January 15 for spring entry, along with an application fee of $10. Notification is sent on a rolling basis. There are early admissions and deferred admissions plans.

Transfer: A total of 49 transfer students enrolled in 1993–94. Transfer students must have a minimum GPA of 2.0. Nursing applicants must have a GPA of 2.75 and a minimum score of 20 on the ACT. Completion of the school's transfer evaluation form is also required. A total of 30 credits out of 128 must be completed at MacMurray.

Visiting: There are regularly scheduled orientations for prospective students, including a financial aid conference, a tour, and faculty appointments. There are guides for informal visits and visitors may sit in on classes and stay overnight at the school. To arrange for a visit, contact the Office of Admissions at (217) 479–7056 or (800) 252–7485 (in-state).

Financial Aid: In 1993–94, 85% of all current freshmen and 91% of continuing students received some form of financial aid. About 83% of all students received need-based aid. The average freshman award was $8447. Of that total, scholarships or need-based grants averaged $4925 ($12,800 maximum); loans averaged $3042 ($6700 maximum); and work contracts averaged $480 ($1000 maximum). Forty-six percent of undergraduate students work part-time. Average earnings from campus work for the school year are $628. The average financial indebtedness of the 1992–93 graduate was $7840. MacMurray is a member of CSS. The FAFSA is required. Financial aid applications are accepted on a rolling basis.

International Students: There are currently 5 international students enrolled. International students must take the TOEFL and achieve a minimum score of 500.

Computers: The college provides computer facilities for student use. The mainframes are a DEC VAX 11/750 and an IBM RS/6000. There are also 18 IBM and 8 Apple IIe microcomputers and 15 mainframe terminals available in computer laboratories and the library. Word processing and spreadsheets are available. All students may access the system. It may be used from 8 A.M. to 10 P.M. Monday through Friday and on Saturday and Sunday afternoons. There are no time limits on using the system and no fees.

Graduates: In 1992–93, 101 bachelor's degrees were awarded. The most popular majors among graduates were nursing (11%), social work (9%), and special education of the hearing impaired (9%). Within an average freshman class, 28% graduate in 4 years, 40% in 5 years, and 44% in 6 years. Some 7 companies recruited on campus in 1992–93. In the 1992 graduating class, 4% of the men and 8% of

the women were enrolled in graduate school within 6 months of graduation; 38% of the men and 47% of the women had found employment.

Admissions Contact: Dr. Ed Hockett, Dean of Admissions.

MCKENDREE COLLEGE
C-5
Lebanon, IL 62254
(618) 537–4481
(800) BEARCAT (in-state and Missouri)

Full-time: 360 men, 466 women	**Faculty:** 47; IIB, -$
Part-time: 234 men, 390 women	**Ph.D.s:** 72%
Graduate: none	**Student/Faculty:** 18 to 1
Year: semesters, summer session	**Tuition:** $7460
Application Deadline: open	**Room & Board:** $3440
Freshman Class: 1285 applied, 706 accepted, 124 enrolled	
SAT I: recommended	**ACT:** 21 COMPETITIVE

McKendree College, founded in 1828, is the oldest college in Illinois. It is a private liberal arts, professional, business, and teachers college affiliated with the United Methodist Church. In addition to regional accreditation, McKendree has baccalaureate program accreditation with NLN. The library contains 65,310 volumes, 16,932 microform items, and 2374 audiovisual forms, and subscribes to 460 periodicals. Computerized library sources and services include the card catalog, interlibrary loans, and database searching. Special learning facilities include a learning resource center, a greenhouse, and archives. The 30-acre campus is in a small town 25 miles east of St. Louis. Including residence halls, there are 21 buildings on campus.

Student Life: About 96% of undergraduates are from Illinois. Students come from 4 states, 2 foreign countries, and Canada. Eighty-six percent are white; 10%, African American. Thirty-nine percent are Protestant; 31%, Catholic. The average age of freshmen is 17; all undergraduates, 24. Five percent drop out by the end of their first year; 52% remain to graduate.

Housing: A total of 350 students can be accommodated in college housing. College-sponsored living facilities include single-sex and coed dormitories and on-campus apartments. On-campus housing is guaranteed for all 4 years. Seventy-five percent of students commute. Alcohol is not permitted. All students may keep cars on campus.

Activities: About 15% of men and about 3% of women belong to 4 local fraternities; about 18% of women belong to 1 national and 3 local sororities. There are 42 groups on campus, including cheerleading, choir, chorus, computers, drama, ethnic, honors, international, literary magazine, musical theater, newspaper, photography, political, professional, religious, social, social service, student government, and yearbook. Popular campus events include Homecoming, Nightabout Town, Model United Nations, Brown Bag forum, Christmas dinner and dance, Family Festival, and All-School Picnic.

Sports: There are 4 intercollegiate sports for men and 5 for women, and 8 intramural sports for men and 8 for women. Athletic and recreation facilities include a 1600-seat gymnasium, tennis courts, outdoor fields, and a student center with table tennis and billiards.

Disabled Students: Seventy-five percent of the campus is accessible to disabled students. The following facilities are available: wheelchair ramps, elevators, special parking, specially equipped rest rooms, special class scheduling, and lowered drinking fountains.

Services: In addition to many counseling and information services, tutoring is available in every subject. In addition, there is remedial reading.

Campus Safety and Security: Campus safety and security measures include 24-hour foot and vehicle patrol, escort service, informal discussions, and pamphlets, posters, and films. In addition, there are lighted pathways and sidewalks.

Programs of Study: McKendree awards the B.A., B.S., B.B.A., B.F.A., B.S.Ed., and B.S.N. degrees. Associate degrees are also are awarded. Bachelor's degrees are awarded in BIOLOGICAL SCIENCE (biology/biological science, botany, and microbiology), BUSINESS (accounting, business administration and management, and marketing/retailing/merchandising), COMMUNICATIONS AND THE ARTS (communications, English, fine arts, organizational communication, and speech/debate/rhetoric), COMPUTER AND PHYSICAL SCIENCE (chemistry, computer science, and mathematics), EDUCATION (art, business, elementary, physical, and secondary), HEALTH PROFESSIONS (medical laboratory technology, nursing, predentistry, and premedicine), SOCIAL SCIENCE (criminal justice, international relations, political science/government, prelaw, psychology, religion, social science, and sociology). Business has the largest enrollment.

Required: To graduate, students must complete 128 semester hours, including 40 hours in the core curriculum, with a minimum GPA of 2.0. A writing proficiency examination must be taken.

Special: McKendree offers internships, work-study programs, study abroad in England, and a Washington semester. Dual and student-designed majors and nondegree study are also available. There is a freshman honors program on campus, as well as 5 national honor societies.

Faculty/Classroom: Fifty-seven percent of faculty are male; 43%, female. All teach undergraduates. The average class size in an introductory lecture is 40; in a laboratory, 15; and in a regular course offering, 20.

Admissions: About 55% of the 1993–94 applicants were accepted. The ACT scores for the 1993–94 freshman class were as follows: 51% below 21, 26% between 21 and 23, 13% between 24 and 26, 4% between 27 and 28, and 6% above 28. About 36% of the current freshmen were in the top fifth of their class; 60% were in the top two fifths. Three freshmen graduated first in their class.

Requirements: McKendree requires applicants to be in the upper 50% of their class. A minimum GPA of 2.2 is required. The SAT I or ACT is recommended. Students must be high school graduates or submit the GED certificate. CLEP credit is accepted. Important factors used in the admissions decision are leadership record, personality, intangible qualities, ability to finance college education, recommendations by school officials, and extracurricular activities record.

Procedure: Freshmen are admitted in the fall and spring. Application deadlines are open. Notification is sent on a rolling basis. There are early admissions and deferred admissions plans.

Transfer: In 1993–94, 126 transfer students enrolled. Transfer students must have a minimum 2.0 GPA from their previously attended college. A total of 32 credits out of 128 must be completed at McKendree.

Visiting: There are regularly scheduled orientations for prospective students, consisting of V.I.P. days (Visit In Person), where at least one faculty member from each division and several departments answer questions. Student-led tours of the campus and various other events are also available. There are guides for informal visits, and visitors may sit in on classes and stay overnight at the school. To arrange for a visit, contact the Admissions Office at (618) 537–4481, ext. 121, or (800) BEARCAT.

Financial Aid: In 1993–94, 90% of all current freshmen and 60% of continuing students received some form of financial aid. About 70% of freshmen and 40% of continuing students received need-based aid. The average freshman award was $6100. Of that total, scholarships or need-based grants averaged $3000; loans averaged $2000; and work contracts averaged $1100. Twenty percent of undergraduate students work part-time. Average earnings from campus work for the school year are $1050. The average financial indebtedness of the 1992–93 graduate was $4500. McKendree is a member of CSS.

International Students: There are currently 29 international students enrolled. The school actively recruits these students. They must take the TOEFL or the college's own test and achieve a minimum score on the TOEFL of 520.

Computers: The college provides computer facilities for student use. The mainframes are an AT&T 3B2 and a Prime EXL 320. The college provides computer facilities for academic use, including shared student systems from more than 210 terminals on campus, and 190 in individual dorm rooms. Students may use any of the microcomputers in 4 laboratories on campus, and another 40 microcomputers in 2 laboratories at remote centers. All students may access the system. There are no time limits on using the system. All students pay a computer resource fee.

Graduates: In 1992–93, 360 bachelor's degrees were awarded. The most popular majors among graduates were business administration (47%), nursing (12%), and computer science (9%). Within an average freshman class, 30% graduate in 4 years, 8% in 5 years, and 3% in 6 years. Ten percent of 1992 graduates were enrolled in graduate school within 6 months of graduation; 78% had found employment.

Admissions Contact: Sue Cordon, Director of Admissions.

MILLIKIN UNIVERSITY   D-3
Decatur, IL 62522   (217) 424–6210; (800) 373–7733 (out-of-state)

Full-time: 767 men, 1021 women	**Faculty:** 125; IIB, av$
Part-time: 31 men, 64 women	**Ph.D.s:** 77%
Graduate: none	**Student/Faculty:** 14 to 1
Year: semesters, summer session	**Tuition:** $11,331
Application Deadline: open	**Room & Board:** $4168
Freshman Class: 1439 applied, 1270 accepted, 456 enrolled	
SAT I Verbal/Math: 500/530	**ACT: 23** COMPETITIVE

Millikin University, founded in 1901, is a private coeducational university affiliated with the Presbyterian Church, offering undergraduate programs in arts and sciences, nursing, fine arts, and business. There are 4 undergraduate schools. In addition to regional accreditation, Millikin has baccalaureate program accreditation with NASM and NLN. The library contains 147,921 volumes, 18,679 microform items, and 6945 audiovisual forms, and subscribes to 1002 periodi-

cals. Computerized library sources and services include the card catalog, interlibrary loans, and database searching. Special learning facilities include a learning resource center, art gallery, radio station, a television laboratory, a computer imaging center, an audio/video recording studio, and a museum of decorative arts. The 40-acre campus is in a suburban area 180 miles southwest of Chicago and 120 miles northeast of St. Louis, Missouri. Including residence halls, there are 26 buildings on campus.

Student Life: About 87% of undergraduates are from Illinois. Students come from 27 states and 6 foreign countries. Eighty-five percent are from public schools; 15% from private. Ninety-three percent are white. Fifty-five percent are Protestant; 27% Catholic; 11% claim no religious affiliation. The average age of freshmen is 18; all undergraduates, 21. Fourteen percent drop out by the end of their first year; 64% remain to graduate.

Housing: A total of 900 students can be accommodated in college housing. College-sponsored living facilities include single-sex and coed dormitories and on-campus apartments. In addition there are honors houses, Greek houses provided by their own organizations, and smoke-free floors in residence halls. On-campus housing is available on a first-come, first-served basis. Sixty-seven percent of students live on campus; of those, 80% remain on campus on weekends. Upperclassmen may keep cars on campus.

Activities: About 27% of men belong to 5 national fraternities; about 25% of women belong to 4 national sororities. There are 68 groups on campus, including band, cheerleading, choir, chorale, chorus, computers, dance, drama, ethnic, gay, honors, international, jazz band, literary magazine, marching band, musical theater, newspaper, opera, orchestra, pep band, political, professional, radio and TV, religious, social, social service, student government, symphony, and yearbook. Popular campus events include Springfest, Greek Week, Homecoming, University Center Board, Fall Family Weekend, Religious Emphasis Week, Diversity Week, Lecture/Artists Series, Council on Global Issues, and Christmas Cookie Party.

Sports: There are 10 intercollegiate sports for men and 7 for women, and 10 intramural sports for men and 10 for women. Athletic and recreation facilities include a physical education center with a pool, a fitness center, tennis courts, a sand volleyball court, and a playing field for football and track.

Disabled Students: Seventy-five percent of the campus is accessible to disabled students. The following facilities are available: wheelchair ramps, elevators, special parking, specially equipped rest rooms, special class scheduling, lowered drinking fountains, and lowered telephones.

Services: In addition to many counseling and information services, tutoring is available in most subjects. A writing center and a basic review course in English fundamentals are available.

Campus Safety and Security: Campus safety and security measures include 24-hour foot and vehicle patrol, self defense education, escort service, and informal discussions. In addition, there are pamphlets, posters, films, emergency telephones, and lighted pathways and sidewalks. Security also provides escorts for students.

Programs of Study: Millikin awards the B.A., B.S., B.F.A., B.M., and B.S.N. degrees. Bachelor's degrees are awarded in BIOLOGICAL SCIENCE (biology/biological science), BUSINESS (accounting, banking and finance, business administration and management, business economics, international business management, marketing/retailing/merchandising, and personnel management), COMMUNICATIONS AND THE ARTS (communications, creative writing, dramatic arts, English, fine arts, and music), COMPUTER AND PHYSICAL SCIENCE (chemistry, computer science, information sciences and systems, mathematics, and physics), EDUCATION (art, elementary, foreign languages, middle school, music, physical, science, and secondary), ENGINEERING AND ENVIRONMENTAL DESIGN (commercial art), HEALTH PROFESSIONS (nursing, predentistry, and premedicine), SOCIAL SCIENCE (economics, history, philosophy, political science/government, prelaw, psychology, religion, social science, and sociology). Business, fine arts, nursing, biology, chemistry, education, and preprofessional are the strongest academically. Accounting, art, biology, business administration, elementary education, music, and nursing have the largest enrollments.

Required: Requirements for graduation include courses in communication, library research, humanities, cultural heritage, fine arts, natural science/mathematics, and social science. The minimum GPA is 2.0. Students must complete 124 to 136 credit hours, with 33 to 48 in the major.

Special: Millikin offers internships, a Washington semester through American University, study abroad at 20 foreign sites, student-designed majors, a 3–2 engineering degree with Washington University, B.A.-B.S. degrees, credit by examination, and pass/fail options. Students are also offered a United Nations semester at Drew University, affiliate research with the U.S. Department of Energy, and affiliate agreements in occupational therapy and medical technology. There is a freshman honors program on campus, as well as 17 national honor societies. Eleven departments have honors programs.

Faculty/Classroom: Sixty-eight percent of faculty are male; 32%, female. All teach undergraduates and do research. The average class size in an introductory lecture is 23; in a laboratory, 14; and in a regular course offering, 21.

Admissions: About 88% of the 1993–94 applicants were accepted. The SAT scores for the 1993–94 freshman class were as follows: Verbal—44% below 500, 40% between 500 and 599, and 16% between 600 and 700; Math—27% below 500, 49% between 500 and 599, 19% between 600 and 700, and 5% above 700. The ACT scores were 16% below 21, 36% between 21 and 23, 21% between 24 and 26, 16% between 27 and 28, and 11% above 28. About 55% of the current freshmen were in the top fifth of their class; 82% were in the top two fifths. There was 1 National Merit finalist and 8 semifinalists. Twenty-six freshmen graduated first in their class.

Requirements: Millikin requires applicants to be in the upper 50% of their class. A minimum GPA of 2.0 is required. The SAT I or ACT is required, with minimum acceptable scores of 450 verbal, 450 mathematics on the SAT I and 20 on the ACT. Applicants should be graduates of an accredited secondary school or have a GED. They should prepare with 4 units of high school English, 2 of foreign language, and 3 each of history, mathematics, and science. An audition is required for music-theater, music, or theater majors. A portfolio is required for art majors. AP and CLEP credits are accepted. Important factors used in the admissions decision are evidence of special talent(s), extracurricular activities record, leadership record, recommendations by school officials, and advanced placement or honor courses.

Procedure: Freshmen are admitted to all sessions. Entrance exams should be taken in April. Application deadlines are open. The application fee is $25. Notification is sent on a rolling basis.

Transfer: About 89 transfer students enrolled in 1993–94. Transfer students must provide official transcripts from previous institutions, must be in good standing at the previous institution, and must have earned at least a C average in all college study previously attempted. Submission of official high school transcripts and testing is requested. A total of 33 credits of the last 45 out of 124 to 136 credits must be completed at Millikin.

Visiting: There are regularly scheduled orientations for prospective students, consisting of an opening session, an honors presentation, an academic interest session, a parents session, a student life panel, and campus tours. There is also an opportunity for students to audition or have portfolios reviewed. There are guides for informal visits and visitors may sit in on classes and stay overnight at the school. To arrange for a visit, contact the Admissions Office at (217) 424–6210 or (800) 373–7733.

Financial Aid: In 1993–94 90% of all current freshmen and 87% of continuing students received some form of financial aid. About 85% of all students received need-based aid. The average freshman award was $12,500. Of that total, scholarships or need-based grants averaged $9200 ($11,700 maximum); loans averaged $2500 ($2900 maximum); and work contracts averaged $800 ($1000 maximum). Fifty percent of undergraduate students work part-time. Average earnings from campus work for the school year are $765. The average financial indebtedness of the 1992–93 graduate was $10,200. Millikin is a member of CSS. The FAF is required. The deadline for financial aid applications is May 1.

International Students: There are currently 18 international students enrolled. The school actively recruits these students. They must take the TOEFL and achieve a minimum score of 550.

Computers: The college provides computer facilities for student use. The mainframe is a DEC MicroVax 3800. The mainframe is accessed directly via a LAN of approximately 90 IBM-compatible 286/386 PCs, which is used to support programming, database, spreadsheet, word processing, graphics, statistical/financial analysis, and business simulation. All students may access the system. There are no time limits and no fees.

Graduates: In 1992–93, 420 bachelor's degrees were awarded. The most popular majors among graduates were nursing (8%), communication (7%), and biology (7%). Within an average freshman class, 63% graduate in 5 years. Some 66 companies recruited on campus in 1992–93. Twenty-one percent of all the 1992 graduates were enrolled in graduate school within six months of graduation; 98% had found employment.

Admissions Contact: Lin Stoner, Dean of Admission.

MONMOUTH COLLEGE
C-2
Monmouth, IL 61462

(309) 457–2131
(800) 74-SCOTS (out-of-state)

Full-time: 325 men, 343 women	Faculty: 48; IIB, -$
Part-time: 4 men, 5 women	Ph.D.s: 90%
Graduate: none	Student/Faculty: 14 to 1
Year: semesters	Tuition: $13,200
Application Deadline: open	Room & Board: $4100
Freshman Class: 635 applied, 591 accepted, 261 enrolled	
ACT: 24	COMPETITIVE +

Monmouth College, founded in 1853, is a private, coeducational, liberal arts institution affiliated with the Presbyterian Church (U.S.A.). The library contains 230,000 volumes, 68,000 microform items, and 1300 audiovisual forms, and subscribes to 635 periodicals. Computerized library sources and services include the card catalog and interlibrary loans. Special learning facilities include a learning resource center, art gallery, radio station, TV station, a biology field station on the Mississippi River, and a prairie plot of native flora. The 45-acre campus is in a small town 45 miles south of Rock Island and Moline. Including residence halls, there are 25 buildings on campus.

Student Life: About 79% of undergraduates are from Illinois. Students come from 17 states, 7 foreign countries, and Canada. Ninety percent are from public schools; 10% from private. Eighty-eight percent are white. Sixty percent are Protestant; 30% Catholic; 10% claim no religious affiliation. The average age of freshmen is 18; all undergraduates, 20. Twenty percent drop out by the end of their first year; 60% remain to graduate.

Housing: A total of 916 students can be accommodated in college housing. College-sponsored living facilities include single-sex dormitories and fraternity houses. On-campus housing is guaranteed for all 4 years. Ninety-six percent of students live on campus; of those, 75% remain on campus on weekends. All students may keep cars on campus.

Activities: About 50% of men belong to 3 national fraternities; about 50% of women belong to 3 national sororities. There are 45 groups on campus, including art, bagpipe band, band, cheerleading, choir, chorus, computers, drama, ethnic, honors, international, jazz band, literary magazine, musical theater, newspaper, orchestra, pep band, photography, political, professional, radio and TV, religious, social, social service, student government, and yearbook. Popular campus events include Homecoming, Greek Week, Women's Week, Martin Luther King Day, and Sibling Weekend.

Sports: There are 7 intercollegiate sports for men and 6 for women, and 12 intramural sports for men and 12 for women. Athletic and recreation facilities include football, baseball, soccer, and softball fields; a track, 2 gymnasiums, a pool, 2 racquetball courts, and weight rooms.

Disabled Students: Twenty percent of the campus is accessible to disabled students. The following facilities are available: special parking, specially equipped rest rooms, and special class scheduling.

Services: In addition to many counseling and information services, tutoring is available in most subjects. There is also remedial reading and writing.

Campus Safety and Security: Campus safety and security measures include informal discussions, pamphlets, posters, and films, emergency telephones, and lighted pathways and sidewalks. In addition, there are 12-hour foot and vehicle patrols.

Programs of Study: MC awards the B.A. degree. Bachelor's degrees are awarded in BIOLOGICAL SCIENCE (biology/biological science), BUSINESS (accounting, business administration and management, and business economics), COMMUNICATIONS AND THE ARTS (classics, communications, dramatic arts, English, Greek, Latin, music, and Spanish), COMPUTER AND PHYSICAL SCIENCE (chemistry, computer programming, computer science, mathematics, and physics), EDUCATION (elementary, physical, secondary, and special), ENGINEERING AND ENVIRONMENTAL DESIGN (environmental science), SOCIAL SCIENCE (history, philosophy, political science/government, psychology, religion, and sociology). Education, sciences, business, and English are the strongest academically. Business and education have the largest enrollments.

Required: To graduate, all students must complete 124 credit hours, 36 of them with a minimum GPA of 2.0. A major program, the total credit hours of which average 12, must be completed with a minimum of C in all courses. Students must also take 5 components of the general education program and pass the freshman seminar.

Special: Monmouth offers 3–2 nursing programs with Rush and Mennonite Hospitals, a co-op program in physical and occupational therapy with Washington University in St. Louis, and a 3–2 engineering degree with Washington University, Case Western Reserve, and the University of Southern California. A variety of internships and a Washington semester are offered, and students have the opportunity to study in 14 countries in Europe, Asia, and Africa. Dual and student-

designed synoptic majors are available. There is a freshman honors program on campus, as well as 12 national honor societies.

Faculty/Classroom: Seventy percent of faculty are male; 30%, female. All teach undergraduates. The average class size in an introductory lecture is 18; in a laboratory, 15; and in a regular course offering, 13.

Admissions: About 93% of the 1993–94 applicants were accepted. The ACT scores for the 1993–94 freshman class were as follows: 18% below 21, 21% between 21 and 23, 43% between 24 and 26, 8% between 27 and 28, and 10% above 28. About 45% of the current freshmen were in the top fifth of their class; 65% were in the top two fifths. There were 2 National Merit semifinalists. About 7 freshmen graduated first in their class.

Requirements: MC requires applicants to be in the upper 50% of their class. A minimum GPA of 2.0 is required. Either the SAT I, with a recommended minimum composite score of 900, or the ACT, with a recommended minimum composite score of 18, is required. Applicants must be graduates of accredited high schools and have completed 4 years of English, 3 each of mathematics and social studies, 2 each of science, including 1 of laboratory, and a foreign language, and 1 of history. A GED is also accepted. AP and CLEP credits are accepted. Important factors used in the admissions decision are advanced placement or honor courses, evidence of special talent(s), recommendations by school officials, leadership record, and extracurricular activities record.

Procedure: Freshmen are admitted to all sessions. Entrance exams should be taken by spring of the junior year. Application deadlines are open. There is an early admissions plan.

Transfer: About 57 transfer students enrolled in 1993–94. Students must have completed at least 1 year with a minimum GPA of 2.5. A minimum composite score of 900 on the SAT I or 18 on the ACT is recommended. A total of 60 credits out of 124 must be completed at MC.

Visiting: There are regularly scheduled orientations for prospective students. There are guides for informal visits and visitors may sit in on classes and stay overnight at the school. To arrange for a visit, contact the Admissions Office at (800) 747–2687.

Financial Aid: In 1993–94, all current freshmen and 98% of continuing students received some form of financial aid. About 97% of all students received need-based aid. The average freshman award was $12,050. Of that total, scholarships or need-based grants averaged $9948 ($14,400 maximum); loans averaged $2586 ($3000 maximum); and work contracts averaged $606 ($1350 maximum). Fifty percent of undergraduate students work part-time. Average earnings from campus work for the school year are $1020. The average financial indebtedness of the 1992–93 graduate was $13,000. MC is a member of CSS. The FAFSA is required. The deadline for financial aid applications is September 1.

International Students: There are currently 26 international students enrolled. The school actively recruits these students. They must take the TOEFL and achieve a minimum score of 550.

Computers: The college provides computer facilities for student use. The mainframe is a DEC VAX 11/750 and an IBM RSTS/6000 Model 520. There are also 50 IBM 80, 88, 386, and 486 microcomputers available for student use. All students may access the system. It may be used from 8 A.M. to 12 midnight. There are no time limits and no fees.

Graduates: In an earlier year, 154 bachelor's degrees were awarded. The most popular majors among graduates were business (22%), education (20%), and sciences (18%). Within an average freshman class, 60% graduate in 4 years. Some 15 companies recruited on campus in 1992–93. In the 1992 graduating class, 12% of the men and 13% of the women were enrolled in graduate school within 6 months of graduation; 38% of the men and 44% of the women had found employment.

Admissions Contact: Richard Valentine, Dean of Admissions.

NAES COLLEGE
E-2
Chicago, IL 60659   (312) 761–3808

Full-time: 75 men and women	Faculty: 3
Part-time: 13 men and women	Ph.Ds: 20%
Graduate: none	Student/Faculty: 25 to 1
Year: semesters, summer session	Tuition: $4200
Application Deadline: open	Room & Board: n/app
Freshman Class: n/av	
SAT I or ACT: not required	SPECIAL

NAES College, founded in 1974, is an independent coeducational institution offering a program in community studies for Native Americans employed in Indian programs and agencies. The multicampus college has evening classes. There are 4 undergraduate schools. The library contains 13,000 volumes, 5 microform items, and 500 audiovisual forms, and subscribes to 55 periodicals. Computerized library sources and services include the card catalog. The 1-acre campus is in an urban area in Chicago. There is one building on campus.

Student Life: All undergraduates are from Illinois. All are from public schools. Ninety-six percent are Native American/Eskimo. The average age of freshmen is 34; all undergraduates, 37. About 85% of freshmen remain to graduate.

Housing: There are no residence halls. All students commute. Alcohol is not permitted. All students may keep cars on campus.

Activities: There are no fraternities or sororities on campus.

Sports: There is no sports program at NAES.

Disabled Students: The entire campus is accessible to disabled students and special class scheduling is available.

Services: In addition to many counseling and information services, tutoring is available in most subjects.

Campus Safety and Security: Campus safety and security measures include pamphlets, posters, and films, emergency telephones, and lighted pathways and sidewalks.

Programs of Study: NAES awards the B.A. degree in SOCIAL SCIENCE (community services).

Required: In order to graduate, students must maintain a 2.0 GPA and complete 120 credit hours, including a core curriculum of 6 6-credit courses, with 54 hours in the major. Students are required to complete courses in art, mathematics, science, English literature, tribal language, composition, and speech, and to demonstrate computer competence. A field project in the American Indian community is also required.

Special: Cross-registration with Northeastern Illinois University is available and students may receive credit for prior learning.

Faculty/Classroom: Sixty-one percent of faculty are male; 39%, female. The average class size in an introductory lecture is 10 and in a regular course offering, 10.

Requirements: The SAT I or ACT is not required. Applicants must be graduates of an accredited secondary school or have a GED certificate and be employed or be a volunteer at an Indian organization or agency that serves Indian people in the community where the campus is located or in which the student lives. Applicants must be at least 24 years old or have an associate of art or science degree, or have completed at least 60 semester hours of transferable credit. CLEP credit is accepted. Important factors used in the admissions decision are leadership record, extracurricular activities record, recommendations by school officials, recommendations by alumni, and geographic diversity.

Procedure: Freshmen are admitted to all sessions. Application deadlines are open. The college accepts all applicants. Notification is sent on a rolling basis. There is an early admissions plan.

Transfer: Fourteen transfer students enrolled in 1993–94. Transfer students must satisfy the same requirements as other applicants. A total of 54 credits out of 120 must be completed at NAES.

Visiting: There are regularly scheduled orientations for prospective students. Visitors may sit in on classes. To arrange for a visit, contact the Campus Administrator at (312) 761–3808.

Financial Aid: In an earlier year, 88% of all current freshmen and 82% of continuing students received some form of financial aid. About 78% of freshmen and 81% of continuing students received need-based aid. Scholarships or need-based grants averaged $1800 ($2700 maximum); loans averaged $2100 ($2625 maximum); and work contracts averaged $2300 ($4600 maximum). All undergraduate students work part-time. The average financial indebtedness of an earlier year's graduate was $375. NAES is a member of CSS. The FAF, FFS, or SFS, and FAFSA are required. The deadline for financial aid applications is rolling.

Computers: The college provides computer facilities for student use. PCs are available in class and for individual use. All students may access the system 9 A.M. to 8 P.M. There are no time limits on using the system and no fees.

Graduates: In an earlier year, 20 bachelor's degrees were awarded. Within an average freshman class, 70% graduate in 5 years. In the 1992 graduating class, 15% of the men and 15% of the women were enrolled in graduate school within 6 months of graduation.

Admissions Contact: Campus Administrator.

NATIONAL-LOUIS UNIVERSITY
E-1
Evanston, IL 60201   (708) 475–1100; (800) 443–5522 (out-of-state)

Full-time: 818 men, 1690 women	Faculty: 253; IIA, --$
Part-time: 112 men, 393 women	Ph.Ds: 70%
Graduate: 623 men, 3472 women	Student/Faculty: 10 to 1
Year: quarters, summer session	Tuition: $9090
Application Deadline: open	Room & Board: $4128
Freshman Class: 513 applied, 347 accepted, 279 enrolled	
SAT I or ACT: required	COMPETITIVE

National-Louis University, founded in 1886, is an independent institution offering programs in education, liberal arts, health science, business, and human services for the traditional and the adult student. Two additional Chicago-area campuses, in Lombard and in the Chicago Loop, accommodate commuters, and academic centers in Virginia, Missouri, Georgia, Florida, Wisconsin, and Germany offer se-

lected programs for working adults. There are 3 undergraduate and 3 graduate schools. In addition to regional accreditation, NLU has baccalaureate program accreditation with CAHEA. The 4 libraries contain 153,000 volumes, 1,100,000 microform items, and 3527 audiovisual forms, and subscribe to 1700 periodicals. Computerized library sources and services include the card catalog, interlibrary loans, and database searching. Special learning facilities include a learning resource center and a pre-K through 8 elementary demonstration school. The 12-acre campus is in a suburban area 12 miles north of Chicago. Including residence halls, there are 3 buildings on campus.

Student Life: About 83% of undergraduates are from Illinois. Students come from 28 states. Seventy-five percent are white; 13% African American. The average age of freshmen is 24; all undergraduates, 34. Fifteen percent drop out by the end of their first year; 45% remain to graduate.

Housing: A total of 200 students can be accommodated in college housing. College-sponsored living facilities include coed dormitories. On-campus housing is available on a first-come, first-served basis. Priority is given to out-of-town students. Ninety-seven percent of students commute. Upperclassmen may keep cars on campus.

Activities: About 1% of women belong to 1 national sorority. There are no fraternities on campus. There are 30 groups on campus, including chorus, drama, ethnic, honors, musical theater, newspaper, professional, religious, student government, and yearbook. Popular campus events include a boat trip on Lake Michigan and an annual dinner dance.

Sports: There are 4 intramural sports for men and 6 for women. Athletic and recreation facilities include a 300-seat gymnasium, a 700-seat auditorium, and a swimming pool.

Disabled Students: Ninety percent of the campus is accessible to disabled students. The following facilities are available: wheelchair ramps, elevators, and special parking.

Services: In addition to many counseling and information services, tutoring is available in some subjects. In addition, there is remedial math, reading, and writing. A center for academic development provides services to academically at-risk students.

Campus Safety and Security: Campus safety and security measures include shuttle buses, informal discussions, and lighted pathways and sidewalks.

Programs of Study: NLU awards the B.A., B.S. degrees. Master's and doctoral degrees also are awarded. Bachelor's degrees are awarded in BUSINESS (accounting, business administration and management, management science, and sports management), COMMUNICATIONS AND THE ARTS (art, dramatic arts, English, and fine arts), COMPUTER AND PHYSICAL SCIENCE (information sciences and systems, mathematics, radiological technology, and science), EDUCATION (early childhood, elementary, and middle school), HEALTH PROFESSIONS (health care administration, medical laboratory technology, radiation therapy, and respiratory therapy), SOCIAL SCIENCE (anthropology, community services, counseling psychology, crosscultural studies, human development, human services, psychology, and social science). Education and business are the strongest academically. Management and education have the largest enrollments.

Required: Students must take courses in humanities, natural sciences, and behavioral sciences. Other course requirements vary by program. All students must pass an English competency writing examination. A minimum 2.0 GPA and 180 quarter hours, including 45 in the major, are required to graduate.

Special: NLU offers internships in some business-related programs, summer study abroad, credit by examination and for experiential learning, and limited nondegree and pass/fail options. There are special completion programs for adults in management, applied behavioral science, and health care leadership. There is one national honor society on campus, Phi Beta Kappa.

Faculty/Classroom: Thirty-two percent of faculty are male; 68%, female. Seventy-five percent teach undergraduates and 25% both teach and do research. No introductory courses are taught by graduate students. The average class size in an introductory lecture is 35 and in a regular course offering, 13.

Admissions: About 68% of the 1993–94 applicants were accepted. The ACT scores for the 1993–94 freshman class were as follows: 91% below 21 and 9% between 21 and 23. About 17% of the current freshmen were in the top fifth of their class; 41% were in the top two fifths.

Requirements: NLU requires applicants to be in the upper 50% of their class. The SAT I, with a minimum composite score of 750, or the ACT, with a minimum composite score of 19, is required. Applicants should graduate from an accredited secondary school with 15 academic credits including 4 in English, 3 in social studies, and 2 each in mathematics and science. The GED is accepted. Two letters of recommendation, with 1 from the high school counselor recommended, are required; an interview is strongly encouraged. AP and CLEP credits are accepted. Important factors used in the admissions deci-

sion are personality, intangible qualities, leadership record, advanced placement or honor courses, evidence of special talent, and extracurricular activities record.

Procedure: Freshmen are admitted fall, winter, and spring. Entrance exams should be taken the winter before application. Application deadlines are open. Application fee is $25. There are early decision, early admissions, and deferred admissions plans.

Transfer: About 426 transfer students enrolled in 1993–94. A minimum GPA of 2.0 is required. Transfer applicants must be in good standing at the college previously attended. Official transcripts from previously attended colleges, and letters of recommendation, are required. Personal interviews are strongly encouraged. A total of 45 credits out of 180 must be completed at NLU.

Visiting: There are regularly scheduled orientations for prospective students, including campus tours, meeting with students and key administrators, attending typical campus entertainment, and visiting classes. There are guides for informal visits and visitors may sit in on classes. To arrange for a visit, contact Joseph Baglio, Vice President for Student Affairs, at (708) 475–1100.

Financial Aid: In 1993–94 92% of all current freshmen and 85% of continuing students received some form of financial aid. About 90% of continuing students received need-based aid. Scholarships or need-based grants averaged $3000; and loans averaged $2300. One percent of undergraduate students work part-time. Average earnings from campus work for the school year are $1800. The average financial indebtedness of the 1992–93 graduate was $7000. NLU is a member of CSS. The FAFSA financial statement is required. The deadline for financial aid applications is July 15.

International Students: There are currently 4 international students enrolled. They must take the college's own test.

Computers: The college provides computer facilities for student use. There are 215 Apple Macintosh and IBM microcomputers available in 20 computer laboratories located at the 3 campuses and many academic centers. Students whose classes require computer use may access the mainframe.

Graduates: In 1992–93 890 bachelor's degrees were awarded. The most popular majors among graduates were management (64%), applied behavioral sciences (19%), and elementary education (12%). Within an average freshman class, 20% graduate in 4 years, 35% in 5 years, and 49% in 6 years. In the 1992 graduating class, 30% of the men and 30% of the women were enrolled in graduate school within 6 months of graduation; 80% of the men and 80% of the women had found employment.

Admissions Contact: Randall Berd, Director of On-Campus Student Enrollment.

NORTH CENTRAL COLLEGE E-2
Naperville, IL 60566 (708) 420–3414

Full-time: 602 men, 708 women	Faculty: 97; IIB, av$
Part-time: 331 men, 435 women	Ph.D.s: 71%
Graduate: 377 men and women	Student/Faculty: 14 to 1
Year: trimesters, summer session	Tuition: $11,286
Application Deadline: open	Room & Board: $4212
Freshman Class: 1127 applied, 884 accepted, 308 enrolled	
SAT I Verbal/Math: 483/556	ACT: 25 VERY COMPETITIVE

North Central College, founded in 1861, is a private liberal arts institution affiliated with the United Methodist Church. There are 4 graduate schools. The library contains 110,000 volumes and subscribes to 800 periodicals. Computerized library sources and services include the card catalog, interlibrary loans, and database searching. Special learning facilities include an art gallery and radio station. The 54-acre campus is in a suburban area 30 miles west of Chicago. Including residence halls, there are 24 buildings on campus.

Student Life: About 78% of undergraduates are from Illinois. Students come from 27 states and 6 foreign countries. Eighty-eight percent are white. Thirty-seven percent are Catholic; 22% Protestant; 18% claim no religious affiliation. The average age of freshmen is 18. Twelve percent drop out by the end of their first year; 77% remain to graduate.

Housing: A total of 845 students can be accommodated in college housing. College-sponsored living facilities include single-sex and coed dormitories and on-campus apartments. In addition, there are special interest houses. On-campus housing is guaranteed for all 4 years. Sixty-four percent of students live on campus; of those, 75% remain on campus on weekends. All students may keep cars on campus.

Activities: There are no fraternities or sororities on campus. There are 35 groups on campus, including art, band, cheerleading, choir, chorus, drama, ethnic, honors, international, jazz band, literary magazine, musical theater, newspaper, pep band, photography, political, professional, radio and TV, religious, social, social service, student government, and yearbook. Popular campus events include Homecoming, Moms Day, Dads Day, Winter Carnival, and Spring Fling.

Sports: There are 10 intercollegiate sports for men and 7 for women, and 9 intramural sports for men and 8 for women. Athletic and recreation facilities include an indoor track, outdoor track, weight room, football stadium, baseball field, soccer field, swimming pool, and tennis courts.

Disabled Students: Ten percent of the campus is accessible to disabled students. Special parking is available for these students.

Services: In addition to many counseling and information services, tutoring is available in most subjects. There also is remedial math, reading, and writing.

Campus Safety and Security: Campus safety and security measures include self defense education, escort service, informal discussions, and pamphlets, posters, and films. In addition, there are lighted pathways and sidewalks and a 24-hour foot patrol.

Programs of Study: North Central awards the B.A. and B.S. degrees. Master's degrees also are awarded. Bachelor's degrees are awarded in BIOLOGICAL SCIENCE (biology/biological science and zoology), BUSINESS (accounting, banking and finance, business administration and management, international business management, and marketing/retailing/merchandising), COMMUNICATIONS AND THE ARTS (broadcasting, classics, communications, English, fine arts, French, German, Japanese, music, Spanish, and speech/debate/rhetoric), COMPUTER AND PHYSICAL SCIENCE (chemistry, computer science, mathematics, and physics), EDUCATION (elementary and secondary), ENGINEERING AND ENVIRONMENTAL DESIGN (preengineering), HEALTH PROFESSIONS (nursing, predentistry, premedicine, and preveterinary science), SOCIAL SCIENCE (anthropology, economics, history, philosophy, political science/government, prelaw, psychology, religion, social science, and sociology). Physical sciences and preprofessional studies are the strongest academically. Business and computer science have the largest enrollments.

Required: All students must take foundation courses in 9 areas as well as 3 terms of physical education. A GPA of 2.0 and a total of 36 courses are required for graduation, with 11 to 13 courses taken in the major.

Special: North Central offers co-op programs in medical technology, nursing, and physical therapy, cross-registration with Illinois Benedictine and Elmhurst colleges and Aurora University, a Washington semester, and study abroad in more than 60 countries. Internships in all subject areas, work-study programs, a 3–2 engineering degree with Washington and Marquette universities and the universities of Illinois and Minnesota, credit for life experience, and nondegree study are available. Students may pursue a B.A.-B.S. degree in all business areas, and in psychology and physical science. Dual majors, a general studies degree, and student-designed majors are also offered. There is a freshman honors program on campus, as well as 2 national honor societies.

Faculty/Classroom: Fifty-nine percent of faculty are male; 41%, female. All teach undergraduates. No introductory courses are taught by graduate students. The average class size in an introductory lecture is 23; in a laboratory, 10; and in a regular course offering, 16.

Admissions: About 78% of the 1993–94 applicants were accepted. The SAT scores for the 1993–94 freshman class were as follows: Verbal—51% below 500, 37% between 500 and 599, and 12% between 600 and 700; Math—25% below 500, 34% between 500 and 599, 25% between 600 and 700, and 7% above 700. The ACT scores were 20% below 21, 22% between 21 and 23, 24% between 24 and 26, 22% between 27 and 28, and 12% above 28. About 51% of the current freshmen were in the top fifth of their class; 83% were in the top two fifths. There were 3 National Merit finalists.

Requirements: North Central requires applicants to be in the upper 50% of their class. The ACT is preferred but the SAT I will be accepted. A composite score of 18 is required on the ACT and a minimum score of 400 is required on both sections of the SAT I. Applicants must be graduates of an accredited secondary school. The GED is accepted. The required secondary school courses are 4 years of English, 3 each of mathematics and science, and 2 each of a foreign language, history, and social studies. The school recommends an interview for all applicants. An essay is not required. AP and CLEP credits are accepted. Important factors used in the admissions decision are leadership record, extracurricular activities record, advanced placement or honor courses, evidence of special talent, and geographic diversity.

Procedure: Freshmen are admitted fall, winter, and spring. Entrance exams should be taken in spring of junior year or fall of senior year. Application deadlines are open. The application fee is $20. Notification of early decision and regular decision is sent on a rolling basis. There are early decision, early admissions, and deferred admissions plans.

Transfer: A total of 240 transfer students enrolled in 1993–94. Applicants require a 2.0 GPA from the previous school and an interview. A total of 9 courses out of 36 must be completed at North Central.

Visiting: There are regularly scheduled orientations for prospective students, including freshman sessions scheduled during the summer. There are guides for informal visits and visitors may sit in on classes and stay overnight at the school. To arrange for a visit, contact the Admissions Office at (708) 420–3414.

Financial Aid: In 1993–94, 94% of all current freshmen and 61% of continuing students received some form of financial aid. About 75% of freshmen and 70% of continuing students received need-based aid. The average freshman award was $9479. Of that total, scholarships or need-based grants averaged $6741; loans averaged $1647; and work contracts averaged $1091. Fifty-five percent of undergraduate students work part-time. Average earnings from campus work for the school year are $748. The average financial indebtedness of the 1992–93 graduate was $8447. North Central is a member of CSS. The college's own financial statement and the FAFSA are required. The deadline for financial aid applications is September 1.

International Students: There are currently 17 international students enrolled. The school actively recruits these students. They must take the TOEFL and achieve a minimum score of 500.

Computers: The college provides computer facilities for student use. The mainframe is a DEC VAX 11/750. Students may use computers located in the on-campus center, computer laboratories, and the library, with a total of 110 terminals and PCs available. All students may access the system during specified hours in the computer center. There are no time limits on using the system and no fees.

Graduates: In a recent year, 453 bachelor's degrees were awarded. The most popular majors among graduates were business management (19%), computer science (18%), and psychology (7%).

Admissions Contact: Marguerite Waters, Director of Admission.

NORTH PARK COLLEGE
Chicago, IL 60625–4987

E-2

(312) 583–2700
(800) 888–6728 (out-of-state)

Full-time: 396 men, 483 women	Faculty: 61; IIB, --$
Part-time: 39 men, 116 women	Ph.Ds: 72%
Graduate: 201 men, 182 women	Student/Faculty: 14 to 1
Year: semesters, summer session	Tuition: $11,990
Application Deadline: open	Room & Board: $2320
Freshman Class: 439 applied, 344 accepted, 172 enrolled	
SAT I Verbal/Math: 465/535	ACT: 21	COMPETITIVE

North Park College, founded in 1891, is a private college affiliated with the Evangelical Covenant Church and offers undergraduate programs in the arts and sciences, business, music, and education. There is one graduate school. The 2 libraries contain 210,000 volumes, 3304 microform items, and 5000 audiovisual forms, and subscribe to 950 periodicals. Computerized library sources and services include database searching. Special learning facilities include a learning resource center, art gallery, and herbarium. The 30-acre campus is in an urban area 10 miles north of downtown Chicago. Including residence halls, there are 25 buildings on campus.

Student Life: About 55% of undergraduates are from Illinois. Students come from 36 states, 27 foreign countries, and Canada. Sixty-eight percent are white; 10% foreign nationals. The average age of freshmen is 18; all undergraduates, 21.6. Twenty percent drop out by the end of their first year; 60% remain to graduate.

Housing: A total of 631 students can be accommodated in college housing. College-sponsored living facilities include single-sex dormitories, on-campus apartments, off-campus apartments, and married-student housing. In addition, there are special interest houses and an international living center. On-campus housing is guaranteed for all 4 years. Sixty percent of students live on campus; of those, 83% remain on campus on weekends. Alcohol is not permitted. All students may keep cars on campus.

Activities: There are no fraternities or sororities on campus. There are 27 groups on campus, including art, band, cheerleading, choir, chorale, chorus, computers, drama, ethnic, honors, international, jazz band, literary magazine, musical theater, newspaper, opera, orchestra, pep band, photography, political, professional, religious, social, social service, student government, symphony, and yearbook. Popular campus events include dances, concerts, and film festivals.

Sports: There are 8 intercollegiate sports for men and 6 for women, and 3 intramural sports for men and 3 for women. Athletic and recreation facilities include football, baseball, track, and soccer fields, tennis courts, a weight room, a gymnasium, a fitness center, and a swimming pool.

Disabled Students: The following facilities are available: wheelchair ramps and elevators.

Services: In addition to many counseling and information services, tutoring is available in every subject. There also is a reader service for the blind, and remedial math, reading, and writing.

Campus Safety and Security: Campus safety and security measures include 24-hour foot and vehicle patrol, self defense education, escort service, and informal discussions. In addition, there are pamphlets, posters, and films and lighted pathways and sidewalks.

Programs of Study: North Park awards the B.A., B.S., B.Mus., and B.S.Med.Tech. degrees. Master's and doctoral degrees also are awarded. Bachelor's degrees are awarded in BIOLOGICAL SCIENCE (biology/biological science), BUSINESS (accounting, banking and finance, business administration and management, international business management, and marketing/retailing/merchandising), COMMUNICATIONS AND THE ARTS (communications, English, fine arts, German, music, and Spanish), COMPUTER AND PHYSICAL SCIENCE (chemistry, mathematics, and physics), EDUCATION (early childhood, elementary, and secondary), ENGINEERING AND ENVIRONMENTAL DESIGN (engineering), HEALTH PROFESSIONS (medical laboratory technology, nursing, occupational therapy, physical therapy, predentistry, and premedicine), SOCIAL SCIENCE (anthropology, economics, history, international relations, philosophy, political science/government, prelaw, psychology, religion, social science, and sociology). Music, sciences, premedicine, liberal arts, nursing, and education are the strongest academically. Nursing, education, psychology, and business administration have the largest enrollments.

Required: Students must successfully complete 120 semester hours with a minimum 2.0 GPA. The required number of hours in the major varies. Students must meet a general requirement of 17 core courses.

Special: Cross-registration with Christian College Coalition schools is possible. Opportunities are provided for a co-op program in occupational therapy, internships, work-study, a Washington semester, 3–2 engineering degrees, accelerated degree programs in organization management and nursing, credit by examination, dual majors, student-designed majors, B.A.-B.S. degrees, pass/fail options, and study abroad. There is a freshman honors program on campus, as well as 6 national honor societies. All departments have honors programs.

Faculty/Classroom: Fifty-five percent of faculty are male; 45%, female. All teach undergraduates. No introductory courses are taught by graduate students. The average class size in an introductory lecture is 35; in a laboratory, 20; and in a regular course offering, 25.

Admissions: About 78% of the 1993–94 applicants were accepted. The SAT scores for the 1993–94 freshman class were as follows: Verbal—66% below 500, 26% between 500 and 599, and 9% between 600 and 700; Math—43% below 500, 21% between 500 and 599, 31% between 600 and 700, and 5% above 700. The ACT scores were 47% below 21, 21% between 21 and 23, 15% between 24 and 26, 9% between 27 and 28, and 8% above 28. About 20% of the current freshmen were in the top fifth of their class; 51% were in the top two fifths. There was 1 National Merit finalist and 1 semifinalist. Three freshmen graduated first in their class.

Requirements: A minimum GPA of 2.0 and either the SAT I or the ACT are required. Graduation from an accredited secondary school is required; a GED will be accepted. Students should have completed course work in a foreign language, 4 years of English, and 3 years each of mathematics, science, and social studies. Recommendations from teachers, an essay, and an audition are required. An interview is recommended. AP and CLEP credits are accepted. Important factors used in the admissions decision are recommendations by school officials, leadership record, ability to finance college education, extracurricular activities record, and advanced placement or honor courses.

Procedure: Freshmen are admitted to all sessions. Entrance exams should be taken during senior year. Application deadlines are open. The application fee is $20. Notification is sent on a rolling basis. There is an early admissions plan.

Transfer: A total of 114 transfer students enrolled in 1993–94. To be eligible for transfer admission, students must submit a reference from a faculty member, counselor, or administrator, and official transcripts from the previous college, and must have maintained a minimum GPA of 2.0. An interview is also recommended. A total of 30 credits out of 120 must be completed at North Park.

Visiting: There are regularly scheduled orientations for prospective students. There are guides for informal visits and visitors may sit in on classes and stay overnight at the school. To arrange for a visit, contact the Campus Visitation Coordinator at (312) 583–2700, ext. 4500, or (800) 888–6728 (out-of-state).

Financial Aid: In 1993–94, 91% of all current freshmen and 85% of continuing students received some form of financial aid. About 79% of freshmen and 75% of continuing students received need-based aid. The average freshman award was $9086. Of that total, scholarships or need-based grants averaged $4795 ($8400 maximum); loans averaged $3201 ($4200 maximum); and work contracts averaged $1229 ($1500 maximum). The average financial indebtedness of the 1992–93 graduate was $7500. North Park is a member of CSS. The FAF or FFS, the college's own financial statement, and student and parent federal income tax returns are required. The deadline for financial aid applications is August 15.

International Students: There are currently 115 international students enrolled. The school actively recruits these students. They must take the TOEFL and achieve a minimum score of 550. The student must also take the SAT I or the ACT.

Computers: The college provides computer facilities for student use. The mainframes are a DEC VAX 3100 and a DEC 5500. There are also 120 terminals as well as Apple Macintosh and IBM PC/AT microcomputers in the computer laboratory. All students may access the system 24 hours per day, 7 days per week. There are no time limits on using the system and no fees.

Graduates: In 1992–93, 201 bachelor's degrees were awarded. The most popular majors among graduates were nursing (26%), psychology (18%), and English (15%). Within an average freshman class, 60% graduate in 4 years and 65% in 5 years. Some 300 companies recruited on campus in 1992–93. In a recent graduating class, 12% of all students enrolled in graduate school within 6 months of graduation; 80% of the men and 84% of the women had found employment.

Admissions Contact: John Schafer, Dean of Admissions.

NORTHEASTERN ILLINOIS UNIVERSITY   E-2
Chicago, IL 60625   (312) 794–2600

Full-time: 1604 men, 2309 women	**Faculty:** 300; IIA, --$
Part-time: 1547 men, 1994 women	**Ph.D.s:** 72%
Graduate: 915 men, 1924 women	**Student/Faculty:** 13 to 1
Year: semesters, summer session	**Tuition:** $1955 ($5651)
Application Deadline: August 1	**Room & Board:** n/app
Freshman Class: 2326 applied, 1573 accepted, 821 enrolled	
SAT I or ACT: required	**COMPETITIVE**

Northeastern Illinois University, founded in 1867, is a public liberal arts institution offering degree programs in the arts and sciences, business management, and education. There are 4 undergraduate schools and one graduate school. In addition to regional accreditation, Northeastern has baccalaureate program accreditation with NCATE. The library contains 550,000 volumes, 1 million microform items, and 1 million audiovisual forms, and subscribes to 1 million periodicals. Computerized library sources and services include interlibrary loans and database searching. Special learning facilities include a learning resource center and radio station. The 63-acre campus is in an urban area in northwest Chicago. There are 10 buildings on campus.

Student Life: About 99% of undergraduates are from Illinois. Students come from 22 states and 9 foreign countries. Fifty-five percent are from public schools; 27% from private. Sixty-eight percent are white; 12% Hispanic; 11% African American. The average age of freshmen is 20; all undergraduates, 28. Forty-five percent drop out by the end of their first year; 36% remain to graduate.

Housing: There are no residence halls. All students commute. Alcohol is not permitted. All students may keep cars on campus.

Activities: There are 1 national and 2 local fraternities and 1 local sorority. There are 70 groups on campus, including art, band, cheerleading, chess, choir, chorus, computers, dance, drama, ethnic, film, honors, international, jazz band, literary magazine, newspaper, opera, orchestra, photography, political, professional, radio and TV, religious, social, social service, student government, and yearbook. Popular campus events include International Day, fairs, the Visiting Lecture Series, and dances.

Sports: There are 5 intercollegiate sports for men and 5 for women, and 6 intramural sports for men and 5 for women. Athletic and recreation facilities include basketball, tennis, and racquetball courts; indoor and outdoor tracks; a pool; a weight room; and football, baseball, and softball fields.

Disabled Students: Ninety percent of the campus is accessible to disabled students. The following facilities are available: wheelchair ramps, elevators, special parking, specially equipped rest rooms, lowered drinking fountains, and lowered telephones.

Services: In addition to many counseling and information services, tutoring is available in most subjects. There is also a reader service for the blind, and remedial math, reading, and writing.

Campus Safety and Security: Campus safety and security measures include 24-hour foot and vehicle patrol, escort service, pamphlets, posters, and films, and emergency telephones. In addition, there are lighted pathways and sidewalks.

Programs of Study: Northeastern awards the B.A. and B.S. degrees. Master's degrees also are awarded. Bachelor's degrees are awarded in BIOLOGICAL SCIENCE (biology/biological science), BUSINESS (accounting, banking and finance, business administration and management, marketing/retailing/merchandising, and recreation and leisure services), COMMUNICATIONS AND THE ARTS (English, fine arts, French, linguistics, music, Spanish, and speech/debate/rhetoric), COMPUTER AND PHYSICAL SCIENCE (chemistry, earth science, geology, information sciences and systems, mathematics, and physics), EDUCATION (bilingual/bicultural, early childhood, elementary, physical, secondary, and special), ENGINEERING AND ENVIRONMENTAL DESIGN (environmental science), SOCIAL

SCIENCE (anthropology, criminal justice, economics, geography, history, philosophy, political science/government, psychology, social science, social work, and sociology). Education, business, and computer science are the strongest academically and have the largest enrollments.

Required: All students are required to take at least 120 semester hours, including 42 of foundational general education, 30 to 60 in the major, and 12 each in social and natural sciences, 9 in humanities, 6 in fine arts, and 3 in interdisciplinary courses. An overall GPA of 2.0 is required for graduation, with an overall GPA and college major GPA of 2.5 required within the colleges of business management and education.

Special: Alternative degree and nondegree programs are available, as is cross-registration with Governors State University. Some departments offer internships. A dual major in elementary and early childhood or special education is offered. There are pass/fail options. There is a freshman honors program on campus, as well as 1 national honor society. Eighteen departments have honors programs.

Faculty/Classroom: Sixty-three percent of faculty are male; 37%, female. Ninety percent teach undergraduates. No introductory courses are taught by graduate students. The average class size in an introductory lecture is 80; in a laboratory, 20; and in a regular course offering, 30.

Admissions: About 68% of the 1993–94 applicants were accepted. The ACT scores for the 1993–94 freshman class were as follows: 52% below 21, 42% between 21 and 23, 3% between 24 and 26, 2% between 27 and 28, and 1% above 28. About 16% of the current freshmen were in the top fifth of their class; 49% were in the top two fifths.

Requirements: Northeastern requires applicants to be in the upper 50% of their class. The SAT I or ACT is required for freshmen under 21 years of age. A minimum ACT composite score of 19 is required. Applicants must have graduated from a regionally accredited high school or passed the GED. High school preparation should total at least 12 credits, including 4 years in English, 3 each in mathematics, sciences, and social studies, and 2 of foreign language, music, art, fine arts, or vocational education (only 1 vocational course is accepted). AP and CLEP credits are accepted. Important factors used in the admissions decision are evidence of special talent, advanced placement or honor courses, recommendations by school officials, recommendations by alumni, and parents or siblings attending the school.

Procedure: Freshmen are admitted to all sessions. Applications should be filed by August 1 for fall entry, December 1 for winter entry, April 1 for spring entry, and June 1 for summer entry. Notification is sent on a rolling basis. There is a deferred admissions plan.

Transfer: A total of 1054 transfer students enrolled in an earlier year. Applicants are considered if they have completed at least 30 semester hours of study with a C average. Those with fewer than 30 hours of credit must meet freshman admissions requirements. A total of 30 credits out of 120 must be completed at Northeastern.

Visiting: There are guides for informal visits and visitors may sit in on classes. To arrange for a visit, contact the School and College Relations Office at (312) 794–2600.

Financial Aid: In an earlier year, 36% of all current freshmen and 47% of continuing students received some form of financial aid. Scholarships or need-based grants averaged $1059 ($5345 maximum); loans averaged $1551 ($3577 maximum); and work contracts averaged $1393 ($3792 maximum). Thirteen percent of undergraduate students work part-time. The average financial indebtedness of an earlier graduate was $6000. The FAF, FFS, or SFS, the college's own financial statement, and the Singlefile Form are required. The deadline for financial aid applications is April 2.

International Students: There are currently 200 international students enrolled. International students must take the TOEFL and achieve a minimum score of 500.

Computers: Northeastern provides computer facilities for student use. Eighty IBM, Apple, Digital, and Zenith microcomputers are available in classroom buildings and the library. Those students enrolled in specific courses or doing research may access the system at posted times, which vary from 12 to 15 hours daily. There are no time limits on using the system and no fees.

Graduates: In an earlier year, 949 bachelor's degrees were awarded. Some 100 companies recruited on campus.

Admissions Contact: Miriam Rivera, Director of Admissions and Records.

NORTHERN ILLINOIS UNIVERSITY   D-2

DeKalb, IL 60115   (815) 753–0446; (800) 892–3050 (in-state)
Full-time: 6910 men, 7916 women   Faculty: 1049; I, --$
Part-time: 886 men, 1093 women   Ph.D.s: 85%
Graduate: 2753 men, 3619 women   Student/Faculty: 14 to 1
Year: semesters, summer session   Tuition: $3342 ($8292)
Application Deadline: August 1   Room & Board: $3066
Freshman Class: 10,706 applied, 7219 accepted, 2397 enrolled
ACT: 22   **COMPETITIVE**

Northern Illinois University, founded in 1895, is a publicly funded coeducational institution offering undergraduate and graduate programs in a comprehensive range of disciplines. There are 6 undergraduate and 2 graduate schools. In addition to regional accreditation, NIU has baccalaureate program accreditation with AACSB, ACEJMC, APTA, ASLA, CAHEA, ASAD, NASM, NCATE, and NLN. The 2 libraries contain 1 million volumes, 1 million microform items, and 35,000 audiovisual forms, and subscribe to 9500 periodicals. Computerized library sources and services include interlibrary loans and database searching. Special learning facilities include an art gallery, radio station, TV station, and an anthropology museum. The 515-acre campus is in a small town 65 miles west of Chicago. Including residence halls, there are 55 buildings on campus.

Student Life: About 93% of undergraduates are from Illinois. Students come from 50 states, 95 foreign countries, and Canada. Eighty-four percent are from public schools; 16%, from private. Eighty-one percent are white. Forty-seven percent are Catholic; 31%, Protestant; 14% claim no religious affiliation. The average age of freshmen is 18; all undergraduates, 21.9. Twenty-two percent drop out by the end of their first year; 55% remain to graduate.

Housing: A total of 7657 students can be accommodated in college housing. College-sponsored living facilities include single-sex and coed dormitories, on-campus apartments, and married-student housing. In addition there are honors houses, language houses, and special interest houses in law, computer science, music, political science, and health professions. On-campus housing is guaranteed for the freshman year only and is available on a first-come, first-served basis. All students may keep cars on campus.

Activities: About 15% of men belong to 19 national fraternities; about 11% of women belong to 14 national sororities. There are 187 groups on campus, including art, band, cheerleading, chess, choir, chorale, chorus, computers, dance, drama, drill team, ethnic, film, gay, honors, international, jazz band, literary magazine, marching band, musical theater, newspaper, orchestra, pep band, photography, political, professional, radio and TV, religious, social service, student government, symphony, and yearbook. Popular campus events include Unity in Diversity Week, Greek Week, Springfest, Homecoming, Parents Weekend, Comedy Week, Black Heritage Month, Women's History Week, and Gay Awareness Day.

Sports: There are 8 intercollegiate sports for men and 8 for women, and 15 intramural sports for men and 15 for women. Athletic and recreation facilities include a sports stadium, a recreation center and field house with facilities for basketball, volleyball, badminton, table tennis, tennis, raquetball/handball, and weight training, 2 swimming pools, and a 3-dome jogging track.

Disabled Students: Seventy-five percent of the campus is accessible to disabled students. The following facilities are available: wheelchair ramps, elevators, special parking, specially equipped rest rooms, special class scheduling, lowered drinking fountains, lowered telephones, and special housing and transportation.

Services: In addition to counseling and information services, formal tutoring is provided for eligible students.

Campus Safety and Security: Campus safety and security measures include emergency telephones and lighted pathways and sidewalks.

Programs of Study: NIU awards the B.A., B.S., B.F.A., B.G.S., B.M., and B.S.Ed. degrees. Master's and doctoral degrees also are awarded. Bachelor's degrees are awarded in BIOLOGICAL SCIENCE (biology/biological science), BUSINESS (accounting, banking and finance, business administration and management, marketing/retailing/merchandising, and personnel management), COMMUNICATIONS AND THE ARTS (communications, dramatic arts, English, fine arts, French, German, journalism, music, Russian, and Spanish), COMPUTER AND PHYSICAL SCIENCE (atmospheric sciences and meteorology, chemistry, computer science, geology, mathematics, and physics), EDUCATION (art, business, early childhood, elementary, home economics, industrial arts, and music), ENGINEERING AND ENVIRONMENTAL DESIGN (electrical/electronics engineering, engineering technology, industrial engineering, and mechanical engineering), HEALTH PROFESSIONS (medical laboratory technology, nursing, physical therapy, and speech pathology/audiology), SOCIAL SCIENCE (anthropology, child care/child and family studies, dietetics, economics, geography, history, liberal arts/general studies,

philosophy, political science/government, psychology, and sociology). Business, engineering, and sciences are the strongest academically. Business, education, and communications have the largest enrollments.

Required: In order to graduate, students must have a minimum of 124 credit hours and a minimum GPA of 2.0. All students must take English 103 and 104 and Communication Studies 100. In addition, they must take Mathematics 101 or obtain at least a C in Mathematics 155, 201, 206, 210, 211, or 229. The school also requires that students complete 29 hours in distributive studies areas, consisting of 9 to 12 hours in the humanities and arts, 7 to 11 hours in science and mathematics, 6 to 9 hours in social science, and 3 to 6 hours in interdisciplinary studies.

Special: NIU offers internships in several areas. Students may study abroad in 10 countries. A physics/engineering degree is offered in cooperation with the University of Illinois. Either a B.A. or a B.S. may be obtained in the social science programs. Work-study programs, a general studies degree, pass/fail option, and student-designed majors are available. There is a freshman honors program on campus, as well as 5 national honor societies. Sixteen departments have honors programs.

Faculty/Classroom: Sixty-two percent of faculty are male; 38%, female. Graduate students teach 20% of introductory courses. The average class size in an introductory lecture is 37; in a laboratory, 17; and in a regular course offering, 30.

Admissions: About 67% of the 1993-94 applicants were accepted. The ACT scores for the 1993-94 freshman class were as follows: 29% below 21, 31% between 21 and 23, 26% between 24 and 26, 9% between 27 and 28, and 5% above 28. About 26% of the current freshmen were in the top fifth of their class; 65% were in the top two fifths.

Requirements: NIU requires applicants to be in the upper 66% of their class. The ACT is required. Students must have a minimum score of 19 on the ACT and be in the top half of their class, or have an ACT score of 23 and be in the upper two thirds of their class. Graduation from an accredited secondary school or satisfactory scores on the GED are required for admission. Secondary school courses must include 4 years of English and 2 to 3 years each of mathematics, science, and social studies. In addition, students must have completed 1 to 2 years of art, film, foreign language, music, or theater. AP and CLEP credits are accepted.

Procedure: Entrance exams should be taken during the junior year. Applications should be filed by August 1 for fall entry, December 15 for spring entry, and May 15 for summer entry. Notification is sent on a rolling basis. A waiting list is an active part of the admissions procedure.

Transfer: In 1993-94, 2239 transfer students enrolled. Transfer students with 13 or more credit hours must have a minimum GPA of 2.0. The core competency requirement in English, mathematics, and speech must be satisfied by all transfer students. A total of 30 credits out of 124 must be completed at NIU.

Visiting: There are regularly scheduled orientations for prospective students. There are guides for informal visits, and visitors may stay overnight at the school. To arrange for a visit, contact the Office of Orientation and Student Assistance at (815) 753-1535.

Financial Aid: In 1993-94, 61% of all current freshmen and 70% of continuing students received some form of financial aid. About 38% of freshmen and 39% of continuing students received need-based aid. The average freshman award was $4000. Of that total, scholarships or need-based grants averaged $3600 ($5000 maximum); loans averaged $1000 ($4500 maximum); and work contracts averaged $700 ($2000 maximum). Twenty-three percent of undergraduate students work part-time. The average financial indebtedness of the 1992-93 graduate was $8000. NIU is a member of CSS. The FAF is required. The deadline for financial aid applications is March 1.

International Students: There are currently 237 international students enrolled. They must take the TOEFL and achieve a minimum score of 500.

Computers: The college provides computer facilities for student use. The mainframe is an Amdahl 5870. There are also 225 CRT terminals and 300 IBM compatible, Apple, and Apple Macintosh microcomputers available throughout the campus. All students may access the system. Computer laboratories are open more than 150 hours per week. There are no time limits on using the system and no fees.

Graduates: In 1992-93, 3559 bachelor's degrees were awarded. The most popular majors among graduates were marketing (7%), accountancy (6%), and communication studies (6%). Within an average freshman class, 22% graduate in 4 years, 49% in 5 years, and 54% in 6 years. More than 600 companies recruited on campus in a recent year. In the 1992 graduating class, 4% of the men and 6% of the women were enrolled in graduate school within 6 months of graduation; 35% of the men and 45% of the women had found employment.

Admissions Contact: Daniel Oborn, Director of Admissions.

NORTHWESTERN UNIVERSITY E-1
Evanston, IL 60208 (708) 491-7271

Full-time: 3717 men, 3732 women	Faculty: 851; I, +$
Part-time: 33 men, 14 women	Ph.D.s: 100%
Graduate: 2642 men, 1916 women	Student/Faculty: 9 to 1
Year: quarters, summer session	Tuition: $15,804
Application Deadline: January 1	Room & Board: $5289

Freshman Class: 12,281 applied, 5260 accepted, 1902 enrolled
SAT I: Verbal/Math 600/670   ACT: 29   **MOST COMPETITIVE**

Northwestern University, founded in 1851, is an independent, non-profit, coeducational, liberal arts institution offering undergraduate study in the arts and sciences, education and social policy, journalism, music, speech, and engineering and applied science. There are 6 undergraduate and 7 graduate schools. In addition to regional accreditation, Northwestern has baccalaureate program accreditation with AACSB, ABET, ACEJMC, ADA, APTA, ASLA, and NASM. The 3 libraries contain 3,600,000 volumes, 2,500,000 microform items, and 526,792 audiovisual forms, and subscribe to 37,412 periodicals. Computerized library sources and services include the card catalog, interlibrary loans, and database searching. Special learning facilities include an art gallery, planetarium, radio station, and TV station. The 231-acre campus is in a suburban area 12 miles north of Chicago on the shore of Lake Michigan. Including residence halls, there are 174 buildings on campus.

Student Life: About 73% of undergraduates are from out-of-state, mostly the Midwest. Students come from 50 states, 87 foreign countries, and Canada. Seventy-five percent are from public schools; 25%, from private. Seventy-four percent are white; 15%, Asian American. Thirty-two percent are Protestant; 25%, Catholic; 18% claim no religious affiliation; 13%, Jewish; 12% Buddhist, Muslim, and others. The average age of freshmen is 18; all undergraduates, 20. Six percent drop out by the end of their first year; 89% remain to graduate.

Housing: A total of 4200 students can be accommodated in college housing. College-sponsored living facilities include single-sex and coed dormitories, fraternity houses, and sorority houses. In addition there are language houses and special interest houses. On-campus housing is guaranteed for the freshman year only and is available on a lottery system for upperclassmen. Seventy-five percent of students live on campus; of those, 95% remain on campus on weekends. Upperclassmen may keep cars on campus.

Activities: About 35% of men belong to 26 national fraternities; about 39% of women belong to 16 national sororities. There are 191 groups on campus, including band, cheerleading, chess, choir, chorale, chorus, dance, drama, ethnic, film, gay, honors, international, jazz band, literary magazine, marching band, musical theater, newspaper, opera, orchestra, pep band, photography, political, professional, radio and TV, religious, social, social service, student government, symphony, and yearbook. Popular campus events include Waa-Mu, Pumpkin Prom, Armadillo Day, and Dance Marathon.

Sports: There are 7 intercollegiate sports for men and 8 for women, and 36 intramural sports for men and 32 for women. Athletic and recreation facilities include a stadium, arena, gymnasium, boat house, and recreation and sports centers housing basketball, volleyball, tennis, racquetball, swimming, badminton, weight training, jogging, squash, and fitness activities.

Disabled Students: Eighty-five percent of the campus is accessible to disabled students. The following facilities are available: wheelchair ramps, elevators, special parking, specially equipped rest rooms, special class scheduling, lowered drinking fountains, and lowered telephones.

Services: In addition to many counseling and information services, tutoring is available in every subject. In addition, there is a reader service for the blind.

Campus Safety and Security: Campus safety and security measures include 24-hour foot and vehicle patrol, escort service, shuttle buses, and informal discussions. In addition, there are pamphlets, posters, films, emergency telephones, lighted pathways and sidewalks, and a security lock system in the dormitories.

Programs of Study: Northwestern awards the B.A., B.A.M., B.M., B.M.E., B.S.E., B.S.Ed., B.S.J., and B.S.Sp. degrees. Master's and doctoral degrees also are awarded. Bachelor's degrees are awarded in BIOLOGICAL SCIENCE (biology/biological science, ecology, molecular biology, and neurosciences), COMMUNICATIONS AND THE ARTS (applied music, art, art history and appreciation, broadcasting, classics, communications, comparative literature, dramatic arts, English, film arts, fine arts, French, German, Greek, Italian, journalism, Latin, linguistics, music, music history and appreciation, music theory and composition, percussion, performing arts, piano/organ, Portuguese, radio/television technology, Slavic languages, Spanish, speech/debate/rhetoric, strings, theater design, voice, and winds), COMPUTER AND PHYSICAL SCIENCE (applied mathematics, astronomy, chemistry, computer science, geology, information sciences and systems, mathematics, physics, and statistics), EDUCATION (art,

education, English, foreign languages, music, science, secondary, and social science), ENGINEERING AND ENVIRONMENTAL DESIGN (biomedical engineering, chemical engineering, civil engineering, computer engineering, electrical/electronics engineering, engineering, environmental engineering, environmental science, industrial engineering, manufacturing engineering, materials science, and mechanical engineering), HEALTH PROFESSIONS (predentistry, premedicine, and speech pathology/audiology), SOCIAL SCIENCE (African American studies, American studies, anthropology, cognitive science, economics, geography, Hispanic American studies, history, human development, international studies, Middle Eastern studies, philosophy, political science/government, prelaw, psychology, religion, sociology, and urban studies). Journalism, speech, physical and life sciences, and social sciences are the strongest academically. Economics, political science, and engineering have the largest enrollments.

Required: Requirements for graduation vary by school and degree program. Students must maintain a minimum 2.0 GPA and complete a total of 45 to 48 quarter courses.

Special: The university offers cooperative engineering programs throughout the country, internships in arts, journalism, and teaching, study abroad at 12 universities around the world, a Washington semester, and numerous work-study programs both on and off campus. Also available are accelerated degree programs in medical and dental education, an integrated science program, an interdisciplinary study in mathematical methods in social sciences, a variety of dual and student-designed majors, pass/fail options, and a teaching newspaper and television program. There is a freshman honors program on campus, as well as 36 national honor societies, including Phi Beta Kappa.

Faculty/Classroom: Seventy-eight percent of faculty are male; 22%, female. Eighty-eight percent teach undergraduates and 95% do research. Graduate students teach 6% of introductory courses. The average class size in an introductory lecture is 40; in a laboratory, 15; and in a regular course offering, 26.

Admissions: About 43% of the 1993–94 applicants were accepted. The SAT scores for the 1993–94 freshman class were as follows: Verbal—13% below 500, 43% between 500 and 599, 38% between 600 and 700, and 6% above 700; Math—5% below 500, 18% between 500 and 599, 44% between 600 and 700, and 33% above 700. The ACT scores were 4% between 21 and 23, 14% between 24 and 26, 21% between 27 and 28, and 61% above 28. About 95% of the current freshmen were in the top fifth of their class; 99% were in the top two fifths. There were 97 National Merit finalists. Some 173 freshmen graduated first in their class.

Requirements: The SAT I or ACT is required. Applicants must be graduates of an accredited secondary school or have a GED certificate, and have completed a total of 16 units, including 4 units of English, 2 or 3 units each of a foreign language and history, 3 units of mathematics, and 2 units of laboratory sciences. SAT II: Subject tests are required for the accelerated honors program in medical education and the integrated science program. Auditions are required for applicants to the School of Music. AP credits are accepted. Important factors used in the admissions decision are recommendations by school officials, advanced placement or honor courses, leadership record, extracurricular activities record, and evidence of special talent.

Procedure: Freshmen are admitted to all sessions. Entrance exams should be taken by December of the senior year. Early decision applications should be filed by November 1; regular applications, by January 1 for fall entry, November 1 for winter entry, February 1 for spring entry, and May 1 for summer entry, along with an application fee of $45. Notification of early decision is sent December 15; regular decision, April 15. There are early decision and deferred admissions plans. About 354 early decision candidates were accepted for the 1993–94 class. A waiting list is an active part of the admissions procedure, with about 3% of all applicants on the list.

Transfer: In 1993–94, 104 transfer students enrolled. Transfer students need a minimum 3.0 GPA, SAT I or ACT scores, high school record, 3 essays, and the dean's reference form. Applicants are required to have a minimum of one year of completed college work to apply to Northwestern. An interview is recommended. A total of 23 quarter courses out of 45 to 48 must be completed at Northwestern.

Visiting: There are regularly scheduled orientations for prospective students, including daily information sessions Monday through Friday. Visitors may sit in on classes and stay overnight at the school. To arrange for a visit, contact the Admissions Office at (708) 491-7271.

Financial Aid: In 1993–94, 55% of all current freshmen and 60% of continuing students received some form of financial aid. About 50% of freshmen and 56% of continuing students received need-based aid. The average freshman award was $13,300. Of that total, scholarships or need-based grants averaged $8800 ($14,000 maximum); loans averaged $2940 ($3625 maximum); and work contracts averaged $1550 ($2000 maximum). Forty percent of undergraduate students work part-time. Average earnings from campus work for the

school year are $1200. The average financial indebtedness of the 1992–93 graduate was $10,800. Northwestern is a member of CSS. The FAF, FAFSA, and tax returns under certain conditions are required. The deadline for financial aid applications is February 15.

International Students: There are currently 145 international students enrolled. The school actively recruits these students. They must take the TOEFL and achieve a minimum score of 600. The student must also take the SAT I or the ACT.

Computers: The college provides computer facilities for student use. The mainframe is an IBM 3090/180J. There are 250 microcomputers and workstations available at 6 locations throughout the campus. A campuswide information service, electronic mail, and Internet are also available. All students may access the system. It may be used 24 hours per day. There are no time limits on using the system and no fees. It is strongly recommended that engineering students provide personal computers.

Graduates: In 1992–93, 1965 bachelor's degrees were awarded. The most popular majors among graduates were economics (10%), history (7%), and political science (7%). Within an average freshman class, 4% graduate in 3 years, 83% in 4 years, 87% in 5 years, and 88% in 6 years. Some 475 companies recruited on campus in 1992–93. In the 1992 graduating class, 40% of both men and women were enrolled in graduate school within 6 months of graduation; 55% had found employment.

Admissions Contact: Carol Lunkenheimer, Admissions Office.

OLIVET NAZARENE UNIVERSITY E-2

Kankakee, IL 60901-0592 (815) 939-5203

Full-time: 1558 men and women	Faculty: 80; IIA, --$
Part-time: 357 men and women	Ph.D.s: 52%
Graduate: 279 men and women	Student/Faculty: 19 to 1
Year: semesters, summer session	Tuition: $7836
Application Deadline: August 1	Room & Board: $4140
Freshman Class: 840 applied, 803 accepted, 425 enrolled	
ACT: 22	COMPETITIVE

Olivet Nazarene University, established in 1907, is a nonprofit, private, comprehensive institution affiliated with the Church of the Nazarene. Its programs emphasize the liberal arts, business, communication, health science, art and fine arts, engineering, music, Bible and religious studies, and teacher preparation in an atmosphere of Christian culture. There is one graduate school. In addition to regional accreditation, Olivet has baccalaureate program accreditation with ADA, NASM, NCATE, and NLN. The library contains 150,000 volumes, 38,800 microform items, and 4800 audiovisual forms, and subscribes to 900 periodicals. Computerized library sources and services include the card catalog and database searching. Special learning facilities include a learning resource center, art gallery, natural history museum, planetarium, and radio station. The 168-acre campus is in a small town 60 miles south of Chicago. Including residence halls, there are 29 buildings on campus.

Student Life: About 76% of undergraduates are from out-of-state, mostly the Midwest. Students come from 40 states, 37 foreign countries, and Canada. Ninety-one percent are white. Most are Protestant. Fifteen percent drop out by the end of their first year.

Housing: A total of 1330 students can be accommodated in college housing. College-sponsored living facilities include single-sex dormitories. On-campus housing is guaranteed for all 4 years. Seventy percent of students live on campus; of those, 80% remain on campus on weekends. Alcohol is not permitted. All students may keep cars on campus.

Activities: There are no fraternities or sororities on campus. There are 32 groups on campus, including art, band, cheerleading, choir, chorale, chorus, computers, drama, honors, international, jazz band, literary magazine, newspaper, orchestra, pep band, political, professional, radio, religious, social, social service, student government, and yearbook. Popular campus events include Homecoming, Parents Weekend, Halloween Party, and Lipsynch Contest.

Sports: There are 8 intercollegiate sports for men and 5 for women, and 7 intramural sports for men and 7 for women. Athletic and recreation facilities include a 3000-seat gymnasium with basketball, volleyball, and racquetball courts, a pool, a weight-lifting room, and an indoor track; a 2500-seat stadium with a track; and an athletic park with softball, baseball, and soccer fields, a jogging track, track and field facilities, an ice rink, and tennis courts.

Disabled Students: The following facilities are available: wheelchair ramps, elevators, special parking, specially equipped rest rooms, lowered drinking fountains, and lowered telephones.

Services: In addition to many counseling and information services, tutoring is available in economics, psychology, sociology, chemistry, and Old and New Testament studies. There is also a tutoring referral service in all subjects, and remedial math and writing.

Campus Safety and Security: Campus safety and security measures include an on-campus security service.

Programs of Study: Olivet awards the B.A., B.S., and B.Th. degrees. Associate and master's degrees also are awarded. Bachelor's degrees are awarded in BIOLOGICAL SCIENCE (biology/biological science, botany, and zoology), BUSINESS (accounting, banking and finance, business administration and management, business economics, hotel/motel and restaurant management, and marketing/retailing/merchandising), COMMUNICATIONS AND THE ARTS (broadcasting, communications, English, fine arts, French, journalism, music, Spanish, and speech/debate/rhetoric), COMPUTER AND PHYSICAL SCIENCE (chemistry, computer science, geology, information sciences and systems, mathematics, and physics), EDUCATION (art, business, early childhood, elementary, foreign languages, health, home economics, music, science, and secondary), ENGINEERING AND ENVIRONMENTAL DESIGN (engineering), HEALTH PROFESSIONS (medical laboratory technology, nursing, predentistry, and premedicine), SOCIAL SCIENCE (dietetics, economics, history, philosophy, political science/government, prelaw, psychology, religion, social science, social work, and sociology). Business administration has the largest enrollment.

Required: To graduate, students must complete 128 semester hours of credit, with fulfillment of a major and a minimum of 40 hours of credit in upper-division courses, and maintain a minimum GPA of 2.0. The required general education studies, 53 to 64 hours, include 12 credit hours of Christianity, 9 to 10 of communication, 9 of social sciences, 7 to 14 of natural science and mathematics, 6 to 8 of international culture, 6 of literature and the arts, and 4 to 5 of personal health. Participation in the Senior Outcomes testing program in general education is required.

Special: Special academic programs include a work-study program, a 3–2 engineering degree with other institutions, a general studies degree, and a joint Army-ROTC program with Wheaton College. There are 6 national honor societies on campus. Five departments have honors programs.

Faculty/Classroom: Sixty-six percent of faculty are male; 34%, female.

Admissions: About 96% of the 1993–94 applicants were accepted.

Requirements: Olivet requires applicants to be in the upper 75% of their class. A minimum GPA of 2.0 is required. The ACT is required, with a minimum score of 16. Other admissions requirements include graduation from an accredited secondary school, with 3 units each of English, mathematics, foreign language, and natural science or social science, and an additional 2 of either mathematics, foreign language, natural science, or social science. The GED also is accepted. Two certificates of recommendation must be submitted. AP and CLEP credits are accepted.

Procedure: Freshmen are admitted fall and spring. Entrance exams should be taken during the spring of the junior year or during the senior year. Applications should be filed by August 1 for fall entry, January 1 for spring entry, and June 1 for summer entry. Notification is sent on a rolling basis.

Transfer: Transcripts of all college work must be submitted. A total of 30 credits out of 128 must be completed at Olivet.

Visiting: There are regularly scheduled orientations for prospective students. There are guides for informal visits and visitors may sit in on classes and stay overnight at the school. To arrange for a visit, contact the Campus Visit Coordinator in the Admissions Office at (815) 939–5203.

Financial Aid: In an earlier year, 80% of all students received some form of financial aid. Scholarships or need-based grants averaged $1000 ($2706 maximum); loans averaged $3000 ($4125 maximum); and work contracts averaged $850 ($1000 maximum). Fifty percent of undergraduate students work part-time. The average financial indebtedness of an earlier graduate was $7700. Olivet is a member of CSS. The FAF and the college's own financial statement are required. The deadline for financial aid applications is March 1.

International Students: There are currently 75 international students enrolled. The school actively recruits these students. They must take the TOEFL or the University of Michigan Language Test and achieve a minimum score on the TOEFL of 500. The student must also take the ACT.

Computers: The university provides computer facilities for student use. The mainframe is an AT&T 3B2/400. There are 50 terminals attached to the mainframe and 30 IBM PC and IBM PS/2 Model 30 microcomputers available in the computer laboratory. There is also an Apple Macintosh laboratory with 15 microcomputers. Some laboratories are limited to students in particular courses; some machines are open to all students for use. The system may be used during working hours and at night for backlogs. There are no time limits on using the system and no fees.

Graduates: In 1992–93, 383 bachelor's degrees were awarded.

Admissions Contact: John Mongerson, Director of Admissions.

PRINCIPIA COLLEGE
Elsah, IL 62028

C-4

(618) 374–2131, ext. 5176
(800) 851–1084 (out-of-state)

Full-time: 241 men, 305 women	**Faculty:** 49; IIB, av$
Part-time: none	**Ph.D.s:** 51%
Graduate: none	**Student/Faculty:** 11 to 1
Year: quarters	**Tuition:** $12,567
Application Deadline: August 1	**Room & Board:** $5232
Freshman Class: 207 applied, 184 accepted, 129 enrolled	
SAT I Verbal/Math: 496/548	**COMPETITIVE**

Principia College, founded in 1910, is a coeducational liberal arts and sciences college for Christian Scientists. The library contains 196,000 volumes, 183,000 microform items, and 6500 audiovisual forms, and subscribes to 900 periodicals. Computerized library sources and services include the card catalog and database searching. Special learning facilities include a learning resource center, art gallery, natural history museum, and radio station. The 2600-acre campus is in a rural area 30 miles northeast of St. Louis. Including residence halls, there are 30 buildings on campus.

Student Life: About 87% of undergraduates are from out-of-state, mostly the West. Students come from 41 states, 18 foreign countries, and Canada. Sixty-five percent are from public schools; 35% from private. Ninety-seven percent are white. All are Christian Scientists. The average age of freshmen is 18; all undergraduates, 21. Eleven percent drop out by the end of their first year; 75% remain to graduate.

Housing: A total of 611 students can be accommodated in college housing. College-sponsored living facilities include single-sex dormitories, on-campus apartments, off-campus apartments, and married-student housing. In addition, there are language houses and special interest houses. On-campus housing is guaranteed for all 4 years. Ninety-seven percent of students live on campus; of those, 98% remain on campus on weekends. Alcohol is not permitted. All students may keep cars on campus.

Activities: There are no fraternities or sororities on campus. There are 25 groups on campus, including art, cheerleading, choir, chorus, computers, dance, drama, film, international, jazz band, literary magazine, musical theater, newspaper, orchestra, photography, political, radio and TV, religious, student government, and yearbook. Popular campus events include athletic events, dances, and drama and dance performances.

Sports: There are 9 intercollegiate and 5 intramural sports each for men and women. Athletic and recreation facilities include 2 gymnasiums, a pool, indoor and outdoor tennis courts, squash and racquetball courts, a weight room, and a playing field.

Disabled Students: Sixty percent of the campus is accessible to disabled students. The following facilities are available: wheelchair ramps, elevators, specially equipped rest rooms, and lowered drinking fountains.

Services: Student writing tutors are available.

Campus Safety and Security: Campus safety and security measures include 24-hour foot and vehicle patrol, informal discussions, emergency telephones, and lighted pathways and sidewalks.

Programs of Study: Principia awards the B.A. and B.S. degrees. Bachelor's degrees are awarded in BIOLOGICAL SCIENCE (biology/biological science), BUSINESS (business administration and management, business economics, and sports management), COMMUNICATIONS AND THE ARTS (communications, dramatic arts, English, fine arts, French, German, music, and Spanish), COMPUTER AND PHYSICAL SCIENCE (chemistry, computer science, mathematics, and physics), EDUCATION (elementary and secondary), ENGINEERING AND ENVIRONMENTAL DESIGN (engineering and environmental science), SOCIAL SCIENCE (anthropology, history, international relations, philosophy, political science/government, religion, Russian and Slavic studies, and sociology). Russian, German, physics, mathematics, and art history are the strongest academically. Business administration, education, mass communication, biology, and English have the largest enrollments.

Required: All students must complete a minimum of 180 quarter hours with at least a 2.0 overall GPA, including courses in foreign language, literature, arts, religion and philosophy, history, social science, mathematics, and natural sciences. In addition, students must be certified as proficient in written English, pass a moral reasoning seminar, and earn 4 credits in aquatic, individual, and team team physical education activities, one of which may be earned by examination.

Special: Students may design their own majors, study abroad or in Washington, D.C., or pursue a B.A.-B.S. degree. Internships, work-study, and an interdisciplinary major, world perspectives, are available. A 3–2 engineering program with Washington University in St. Louis, Southern Illinois University at Carbondale, and the University of Southern California is also possible. There is a freshman honors program on campus, as well as 1 national honor society. One department has an honors program.

Faculty/Classroom: Sixty-three percent of faculty are male; 37%, female. All teach undergraduates. The average class size in an introductory lecture is 14; in a laboratory, 10; and in a regular course offering, 14.

Admissions: About 89% of the 1993-94 applicants were accepted. The SAT scores for the 1993-94 freshman class were as follows: Verbal—60% below 500, 25% between 500 and 599, 17% between 600 and 700, and 1% above 700; Math—26% below 500, 36% between 500 and 599, 27% between 600 and 700, and 8% above 700. About 23% of the current freshmen were in the top fifth of their class; 44% were in the top two fifths. Three freshmen graduated first in their class.

Requirements: A minimum GPA of 2.0 is required. SAT I or ACT scores and an essay are required; SAT II: Subject tests in foreign language and mathematics are recommended. High school preparation should include 4 years of English, 3 of mathematics (including algebra II), 2 to 3 of a foreign language, and 2 of natural sciences, history or social sciences, and electives. AP and CLEP credits are accepted. Important factors used in the admissions decision are personality, intangible qualities, extracurricular activities record, evidence of special talent, advanced placement or honor courses, and recommendations by alumni.

Procedure: Freshmen are admitted to all sessions. Entrance exams should be taken in the spring or early summer of junior year. Applications should be filed by August 1 for fall entry, December 15 for winter entry, and March 1 for spring entry, along with an application fee of $35. Notification is sent on a rolling basis. There is a deferred admissions plan.

Transfer: Thirty-six transfer students enrolled in 1993-94. A total of 45 quarter hours out of 180 must be completed at Principia.

Visiting: There are regularly scheduled orientations for prospective students, including visiting classes, living in a dormitory, and meeting professors and students. Visitors at other times may sit in on classes and stay overnight at the school. To arrange for a visit, contact the Director of Hospitality at (800) 851-1084.

Financial Aid: In 1993-94, 95% of all current freshmen and 78% of continuing students received some form of financial aid. About 81% of freshmen and 72% of continuing students received need-based aid. The average freshman award was $9694. Of that total, scholarships or need-based grants averaged $7921 ($17,799 maximum); and loans averaged $1773 ($4625 maximum). Nearly all undergraduate students work part-time. Principia is a member of CSS. The FAF and the college's own financial statement are required.

International Students: There are currently 49 international students enrolled. The school actively recruits these students. They must take the TOEFL and achieve a minimum score of 525. The student must also take the SAT I and achieve a minimum composite score of 800.

Computers: The college provides computer facilities for student use. The mainframe is an HP 3000. Five academic buildings have computer facilities for student use. Approximately 85 computer workstations are available for students as microcomputers and/or remote terminals of the college mainframe computer. All students may access the system 24 hours a day. There are no time limits on using the system and no fees.

Graduates: In 1992-93, 156 bachelor's degrees were awarded. The most popular majors among graduates were English (19%), business administration (13%), and history (9%). Within an average freshman class, 65% graduate in 4 years and 75% in 5 years. Some 49 companies recruited on campus in 1992-93.

Admissions Contact: Martha Green Quirk, Director of Admissions and Enrollment.

QUINCY COLLEGE
(See Quincy University)

QUINCY UNIVERSITY
(Formerly Quincy College)   B-3
Quincy, IL 62301

(217) 222-8020, ext. 215
(800) 688-4295 (out-of-state)

Full-time: 540 men, 530 women	Faculty: 68; IIB, -$
Part-time: 34 men, 50 women	Ph.D.s: 69%
Graduate: 26 men, 22 women	Student/Faculty: 16 to 1
Year: semesters, summer session	Tuition: $9742
Application Deadline: open	Room & Board: $3904
Freshman Class: 1025 applied, 707 accepted, 297 enrolled	
ACT: 23	**VERY COMPETITIVE**

Quincy University was established in 1860 and is a private, coeducational liberal arts university, conducted by the Franciscan Friars of the Roman Catholic Church. There is one undergraduate and 2 graduate schools. In addition to regional accreditation, Quincy has baccalaureate program accreditation with AACSB and NASM. The library contains 225,965 volumes, 130,261 microform items, and 3122 audiovi-

sual forms, and subscribes to 645 periodicals. Computerized library sources and services include the card catalog, interlibrary loans, and database searching. Special learning facilities include an art gallery, radio station, and TV station. The 75-acre campus is in a small town 120 miles north of St. Louis and 280 miles south of Chicago. Including residence halls, there are 41 buildings on campus.

Student Life: About 69% of undergraduates are from Illinois. Students come from 29 states and 8 foreign countries. Forty-eight percent are from public schools; 52%, from private. Ninety-one percent are white. Sixty-two percent are Catholic; 27%, Protestant. The average age of freshmen is 18; all undergraduates, 22. Twelve percent drop out by the end of their first year; 64% remain to graduate.

Housing: A total of 1058 students can be accommodated in college housing. College-sponsored living facilities include single-sex and coed dormitories, on-campus apartments, and married-student housing. In addition there are honors houses and special interest houses. On-campus housing is guaranteed for all 4 years. Seventy percent of students live on campus; of those, 90% remain on campus on weekends. All students may keep cars on campus.

Activities: There are no fraternities or sororities on campus. There are 41 groups on campus, including bagpipe band, band, cheerleading, chess, choir, chorale, chorus, computers, drama, ethnic, honors, jazz band, literary magazine, musical theater, newspaper, orchestra, pep band, political, professional, radio and TV, religious, social, social service, student government, and yearbook. Popular campus events include Fall Fest/Parents Weekend, cultural field trips, Hogwild Weekend, Septemberfest, Little Brother/Little Sister Weekend, dinner theater, float trip, ski trip, Founders Day, community service trips, and airband.

Sports: There are 6 intercollegiate sports for men and 5 for women, and 7 intramural sports for men and 7 for women. Athletic and recreation facilities include 2 gymnasiums, a football/baseball stadium, a soccer stadium, a weight room, the college athletic field, and outdoor basketball/volleyball courts.

Disabled Students: Ninety percent of the campus is accessible to disabled students. The following facilities are available: wheelchair ramps, elevators, special parking, specially equipped rest rooms, special class scheduling, lowered drinking fountains, and lowered telephones.

Services: In addition to many counseling and information services, tutoring is available in most subjects, including peer teachers for the most challenging lower division courses. There is a reader service for the blind and remedial writing. Skill development and motivation workshops and courses are available.

Campus Safety and Security: Campus safety and security measures include shuttle buses, informal discussions, pamphlets, posters, films, and lighted pathways and sidewalks.

Programs of Study: Quincy awards the B.A., B.S., and B.F.A. degrees. Associate and master's degrees also are awarded. Bachelor's degrees are awarded in BIOLOGICAL SCIENCE (biology/biological science), BUSINESS (accounting, banking and finance, business administration and management, human resources, marketing/retailing/merchandising, and sports management), COMMUNICATIONS AND THE ARTS (art, arts administration/management, communications, English, music, and music business management), COMPUTER AND PHYSICAL SCIENCE (chemistry, computer science, information sciences and systems, and mathematics), EDUCATION (art, elementary, music, physical, science, secondary, and special), HEALTH PROFESSIONS (medical laboratory technology and sports medicine), SOCIAL SCIENCE (history, humanities, international studies, philosophy, political science/government, psychology, religious education, social work, sociology, and theological studies). Business, accounting, science, computer science, and education are the strongest academically. Business management, elementary education, accounting, and communication have the largest enrollments.

Required: Each student is required to complete a minimum of 120 credit hours, with a minimum of 27 hours in the major. In addition, students must complete required courses in rhetoric, science, social sciences, humanities, fine arts, theology, and physical education, and maintain a GPA of 2.0. Minimum distribution requirements include 39 upper level hours, 30 hours in residence, and at least 56 hours from a four year college.

Special: Dual majors, study abroad, credit by examination, and upperclass and early exploratory internships are available. Pass/fail options, credit for life experience, student-designed majors and a 3-2 degree with Washington University in St. Louis are also offered. There is a freshman honors program on campus, as well as 5 national honor societies. One department has an honors program.

Faculty/Classroom: Seventy percent of faculty are male; 30%, female. All teach undergraduates and 12% both teach and do research. No introductory courses are taught by graduate students. The average class size in an introductory lecture is 40; in a laboratory and a regular course offering, 20.

Admissions: About 69% of the 1993–94 applicants were accepted. The SAT scores for the 1993–94 freshman class were as follows: Verbal—24% below 500, 60% between 500 and 599, 15% between 600 and 700, and 1% above 700; Math—8% below 500, 64% between 500 and 599, 24% between 600 and 700, and 4% above 700. The ACT scores were 16% below 21, 15% between 21 and 23, 37% between 24 and 26, 20% between 27 and 28, and 12% above 28. About 47% of the current freshmen were in the top fifth of their class; 81% were in the top two fifths. Nine freshmen graduated first in their class.

Requirements: Quincy requires applicants to be in the upper 50% of their class. A minimum GPA of 2.0 is required. The SAT I with a minimum score of 425 verbal and 425 mathematics, or the ACT with a minimum composite score of 20, is required. A GED will be accepted. College preparatory courses totaling 16 credits should have been completed and distributed as follows: 4 years of English, 3 years each of mathematics and science, and 2 years each of a foreign language, history, and social studies. Art students must submit a portfolio, and music students are required to audition. AP and CLEP credits are accepted. Important factors used in the admissions decision are recommendations by school officials, evidence of special talent, advanced placement or honor courses, leadership record, and extracurricular activities record.

Procedure: Freshmen are admitted to all sessions. Entrance exams should be taken in October of the senior year. Application deadlines are open. Notification is sent on a rolling basis.

Transfer: A total of 78 transfer students enrolled in 1993–94. Transfer students must have a minimum GPA of 2.0. Grades of C or better transfer for credit. A total of 30 credits out of 120 must be completed at Quincy.

Visiting: There are regularly scheduled orientations for prospective students, including several weekend advising/registration programs throughout the summer, and a freshman orientation program beginning the weekend before classes start and continuing for two weeks. There are guides for informal visits, and visitors may sit in on classes and stay overnight at the school. To arrange for a visit, contact the Admissions Office at (217) 228–5215.

Financial Aid: In 1993–94, 98% of all current freshmen and 95% of continuing students received some form of financial aid. About 73% of freshmen and 71% of continuing students received need-based aid. The average freshman award was $10,306. Of that total, scholarships or need-based grants averaged $7181 ($13,646 maximum); loans averaged $2625 ($3225 maximum); and work contracts averaged $500 ($1000 maximum). Thirty-three percent of undergraduate students work part-time. Average earnings from campus work for the school year are $675. Quincy is a member of CSS. The FAFSA financial statement is required.

International Students: There are currently 10 international students enrolled. They must take the TOEFL and achieve a minimum score of 550.

Computers: The university provides computer facilities for student use. The mainframes are an AT&T 3B2 500 and a DEC PDP 11/44. A total of 132 personal computers and 192 student workstations are available. The main academic building houses separate laboratories for each mainframe system, as well as a Starlon Network serving 34 microcomputers and a Novell Network serving 60 microcomputers. The library also houses laboratories accessing each mainframe, and a microcomputer laboratory. Additionally, residence halls and honors houses have microcomputer laboratories. All students may access the system. There are no time limits on using the system and no fees.

Graduates: In 1992–93, 233 bachelor's degrees were awarded. The most popular majors among graduates were elementary education (10%), marketing (9%), and management (8%). Within an average freshman class, 60% graduate in 4 years, 64% in 5 years, and 65% in 6 years. Some 22 companies recruited on campus in 1992–93. In the 1992 graduating class, 98% had found employment within 6 months of graduation.

Admissions Contact: Patrick Olwig, Admissions Officer.

ROCKFORD COLLEGE

D-1

Rockford, IL 61108   (815) 226–4050; (800) 892–2984 (out-of-state)

Full-time: 327 men, 571 women	Faculty: 80; IIB, --$
Part-time: 119 men, 245 women	Ph.D.s: 63%
Graduate: 173 men, 175 women	Student/Faculty: 11 to 1
Year: semesters, summer session	Tuition: $11,500
Application Deadline: open	Room & Board: $3800
Freshman Class: 591 applied, 505 accepted, 218 enrolled	
SAT I: 500/536	ACT: 21 **COMPETITIVE**

Rockford College, founded in 1847, is a private coeducational institution offering undergraduate and graduate instruction in liberal arts and professional programs. There are 2 graduate schools. In addition to regional accreditation, Rockford has baccalaureate program accreditation with NLN. The library contains 162,219 volumes, 2550 microform items, and 4700 audiovisual forms, and subscribes to 900 periodicals. Computerized library sources and services include interlibrary loans and database searching. Special learning facilities include an art gallery and radio station. The 130-acre campus is in a suburban area 90 miles west of Chicago. Including residence halls, there are 26 buildings on campus.

Student Life: About 86% of undergraduates are from Illinois. Students come from 25 states and 16 foreign countries. Seventy-five percent are from public schools; 25% from private. Eighty-five percent are white. Sixty-three percent are Protestant; 35% Catholic. The average age of freshmen is 19; all undergraduates, 22. Thirty-eight percent drop out by the end of their first year.

Housing: A total of 600 students can be accommodated in college housing. College-sponsored living facilities include single-sex and coed dormitories. In addition, there is family housing. On-campus housing is guaranteed for the freshman year only, is available on a first-come, first-served basis, and is available on a lottery system for upperclassmen. Fifty percent of students live on campus; of those, 75% remain on campus on weekends. All students may keep cars on campus.

Activities: There are no fraternities or sororities on campus. There are 26 groups on campus, including art, cheerleading, chorus, dance, drama, drill team, ethnic, honors, international, literary magazine, musical theater, newspaper, professional, radio and TV, religious, social, social service, student government, and yearbook. Popular campus events include Homecoming, Snowball Dance, Kids and Sibs Weekend, Family Weekend, Senior Day, Women's History Month, Career Fair, and Scholarship Ball.

Sports: There are 6 intercollegiate sports for men and 6 for women, and 14 intramural sports for men and 14 for women. Athletic and recreation facilities include a swimming pool, athletic fields, tennis courts, and a fitness center with free weights and Nautilus weight rooms.

Disabled Students: Eighty percent of the campus is accessible to disabled students. The following facilities are available: wheelchair ramps, elevators, special parking, specially equipped rest rooms, special class scheduling, and lowered drinking fountains.

Services: In addition to many counseling and information services, tutoring is available in most subjects. There is a reader service for the blind, and remedial math, reading, and writing. Diagnostic testing is available.

Campus Safety and Security: Campus safety and security measures include 24-hour foot and vehicle patrol, escort service, informal discussions, and pamphlets, posters, and films. In addition, there are emergency telephones and lighted pathways and sidewalks.

Programs of Study: Rockford awards the B.A., B.S., B.F.A., and B.S.N. degrees. Master's degrees also are awarded. Bachelor's degrees are awarded in BUSINESS (accounting and business administration and management), COMMUNICATIONS AND THE ARTS (art, art history and appreciation, classical languages, dramatic arts, English, fine arts, French, German, music, and Spanish), COMPUTER AND PHYSICAL SCIENCE (chemistry, computer science, mathematics, and science), EDUCATION (early childhood, elementary, and physical), ENGINEERING AND ENVIRONMENTAL DESIGN (preengineering), HEALTH PROFESSIONS (nursing, predentistry, premedicine, prepharmacy, and preveterinary science), SOCIAL SCIENCE (anthropology, criminal justice, economics, history, humanities, philosophy, political science/government, prelaw, psychology, social science, sociology, and urban studies). Business, education, psychology, nursing, and English have the largest enrollments.

Required: In order to graduate, students must have a total of 124 credit hours and a minimum GPA of 2.0. The required hours for each major varies between 30 and 40 hours. Students are required to take 12 hours each of social studies and a foreign language, 8 hours each of language, literature, science, and mathematics, 6 hours each of English and art, and 2 hours of physical education. Requirements for some degree programs may vary. All students must complete a senior seminar project and must demonstrate proficiency in writing or public speaking, either by examination or by enrollment in a course that meets the requirement.

Special: The school offers junior and senior year internships, study abroad in 6 countries, a Washington semester at American University, and work-study programs. Accelerated degree programs, dual majors, student-designed majors, nondegree study, and a 3–2 engineering degree with Washington University in St. Louis, University of Southern California, University of Illinois, and Illinois Institute of Technology also are available. There is a freshman honors program on campus, as well as 5 national honor societies, including Phi Beta Kappa.

Faculty/Classroom: Seventy percent of faculty are male; 30%, female. All teach undergraduates. No introductory courses are taught by graduate students. The average class size in an introductory lecture is 25; in a laboratory, 12; and in a regular course offering, 25.

Admissions: About 85% of the 1993–94 applicants were accepted. The SAT scores for the 1993–94 freshman class were as follows: Verbal—88% below 500, 5% between 500 and 599, and 7% between 600 and 700; Math—59% below 500, 29% between 500 and 599,

and 12% between 600 and 700. The ACT scores were 21% below 21, 55% between 21 and 23, and 24% between 24 and 26. About 38% of the current freshmen were in the top fifth of their class; 66% were in the top two fifths. There was 1 National Merit finalist.

Requirements: Rockford requires applicants to be in the upper 50% of their class. A minimum GPA of 2.5 is required. The SAT I or ACT is required. Graduation from an accredited secondary school or satisfactory scores on the GED are required for admission. Sixteen academic credits are required, including 4 years of English 2 years of mathematics, and 1 year each of a foreign language, history, and laboratory science. An essay and an interview are recommended. For music students, an audition is recommended. AP and CLEP credits are accepted. Important factors used in the admissions decision are recommendations by school officials, leadership record, extracurricular activities record, evidence of special talent, and geographic diversity.

Procedure: Freshmen are admitted to all sessions. Entrance exams should be taken by fall of senior year. Application deadlines are open. The application fee is $35. Notification is sent on a rolling basis. There are early admissions and deferred admissions plans.

Transfer: A total of 182 transfer students enrolled in 1993–94. Transfer students must have a minimum GPA of 2.0. Nursing transfer students' minimum GPA is 2.5. A total of 30 credits out of 124 must be completed at Rockford.

Visiting: There are regularly scheduled orientations for prospective students, consisting of a tour, a meeting with faculty members and other students, and social programs. A week-long orientation program is required for all freshman the week before fall classes begin. There are guides for informal visits and visitors may sit in on classes. To arrange for a visit, contact the Admissions Office at (800) 892–2984.

Financial Aid: In 1993–94, 96% of all students received some form of financial aid. Rockford is a member of CSS.

International Students: There are currently 29 international students enrolled. The school actively recruits these students. They must take the TOEFL and achieve a minimum score of 550. Students may be admitted conditionally, and then tested for English proficiency. The student must also take the SAT I or the ACT (preferred) and achieve minimum SAT I scores of 350 verbal, 350 math, or 18 on the ACT.

Computers: The college provides computer facilities for student use. The mainframe is an IBM 4341. All students may use the computer laboratory located in the science building. All students may access the system 24 hours per day. There are no time limits on using the system and no fees.

Graduates: In 1992–93, 247 bachelor's degrees were awarded. The most popular majors among graduates were business (26%), nursing (10%), and education (10%). Within an average freshman class, 52% graduate in 4 years, 28% in 5 years, and 6% in 6 years. Some 69 companies recruited on campus in 1992–93. In the 1992 graduating class, 17% of men and women were enrolled in graduate school within 6 months of graduation; 57% had found employment.

Admissions Contact: Kelly Sartorius, Director of Admission and Financial Aid Records.

ROOSEVELT UNIVERSITY
Chicago, IL 60605

E-2

(312) 341-3515

Full-time: 724 men, 976 women	Faculty: 155; IIA, --$
Part-time: 1126 men, 1770 women	Ph.D.s: 70%
Graduate: 756 men, 1229 women	Student/Faculty: 11 to 1
Year: semesters, summer session	Tuition: $7408
Application Deadline: open	Room & Board: $4960
Freshman Class: n/av	
SAT I Verbal/Math: 440/440	ACT: 20 COMPETITIVE

Roosevelt University, founded in 1945, is a private liberal arts institution. There are 5 undergraduate and 5 graduate schools. In addition to regional accreditation, Roosevelt has baccalaureate program accreditation with NASM and NCATE. The library contains 405,000 volumes, 130,000 microform items, and 10,000 audiovisual forms, and subscribes to 1600 periodicals. Computerized library sources and services include the card catalog, interlibrary loans, and database searching. Special learning facilities include a learning resource center, a planetarium, and a radio station. The campus is in an urban area in downtown Chicago. Including residence halls, there are 2 buildings on campus.

Student Life: About 90% of undergraduates are from Illinois. Students come from 13 states and 60 foreign countries. Sixty-five percent are white; 25% African American. The average age of freshmen is 21; all undergraduates, 23.

Housing: A total of 325 students can be accommodated in college housing. College-sponsored living facilities include coed dormitories. On-campus housing is available on a first-come, first-served basis. Ninety-four percent of students commute.

Activities: About 1% of men and women belong to 1 local fraternity or sorority. There are 45 groups on campus, including band, choir, chorale, chorus, computers, drama, ethnic, honors, international, jazz band, literary magazine, musical theater, newspaper, opera, orchestra, political, professional, religious, student government, and symphony.

Sports: There are 7 intramural sports for men and 3 for women. Athletic and recreation facilities include a fitness center and a recreational gymnasium.

Disabled Students: All of the campus is accessible to disabled students. The following facilities are available: wheelchair ramps, elevators, specially equipped rest rooms, and lowered telephones.

Services: In addition to many counseling and information services, tutoring is available in most subjects. There is also remedial math, reading, and writing.

Campus Safety and Security: Campus safety and security measures include shuttle buses and lighted pathways and sidewalks.

Programs of Study: Roosevelt awards the B.A., B.S., B.A. Computer Science, B.A.Ed., B.A. Hospitality Mgt., B.F.A., B.M., B.S.B.A., and B.G.S. degrees. Master's and doctoral degrees are also awarded. Bachelor's degrees are awarded in BIOLOGICAL SCIENCE (biology/biological science), BUSINESS (accounting, banking and finance, business administration and management, business economics, hotel/motel and restaurant management, management science, marketing/retailing/merchandising, and personnel management), COMMUNICATIONS AND THE ARTS (art history and appreciation, broadcasting, dramatic arts, English, French, journalism, music, music performance, musical theater, public relations, Spanish, and speech/debate/rhetoric), COMPUTER AND PHYSICAL SCIENCE (actuarial science, chemistry, computer science, information sciences and systems, and mathematics), EDUCATION (business, early childhood, elementary, science, and secondary), ENGINEERING AND ENVIRONMENTAL DESIGN (electrical/electronics engineering technology, environmental science, and interior design), HEALTH PROFESSIONS (allied health, cytotechnology, medical laboratory technology, nuclear medical technology, predentistry, premedicine, prepharmacy, and preveterinary science), SOCIAL SCIENCE (African American studies, American studies, economics, history, international studies, philosophy, political science/government, prelaw, psychology, public administration, social science, and sociology). Journalism, accounting, psychology, music, theater, hospitality, and computer science are the strongest academically.

Required: For graduation, students must complete 120 credit hours, including 54 in the major, with a minimum GPA of 2.0. The core curriculum requires classes in the social sciences, natural sciences, and humanities, including English 101 and 102.

Special: Roosevelt offers internships in approximately 20 subject areas, on-campus work-study, study abroad, dual and student-designed majors, pass/fail options, and noncredit courses. Adults over 25 years of age may earn a Bachelor of General Studies through an accelerated degree program. Credit for life, military, and work experience is available in some majors through continuing education. There is a freshman honors program on campus, as well as 4 national honor societies. Twenty departments have honors programs.

Faculty/Classroom: All faculty teach undergraduates. No introductory courses are taught by graduate students.

Admissions: About 60% of the 1992–93 applicants were accepted. The SAT scores for the 1993–94 freshman class were as follows: Verbal—71% below 500 and 29% between 500 and 599; Math—57% below 500 and 43% between 500 and 599. The ACT scores were 68% below 21, 18% between 21 and 23, 5% between 24 and 26, 7% between 27 and 28, and 1% above 28. About 30% of the current freshmen were in the top fifth of their class; 70% were in the top two fifths.

Requirements: Roosevelt requires applicants to be in the upper 50% of their class. A minimum GPA of 2.5 is required. The SAT I or ACT is required. Students must have completed 15 units, including 4 of English, 3 of mathematics, 2 each of science, social studies, and foreign language, and 1 each of history and electives. An interview is recommended for all applicants, and an audition is required for music and theater candidates. AP and CLEP credits are accepted. Important factors used in the admissions decision are advanced placement or honor courses, evidence of special talent, extracurricular activities record, recommendations by school officials, and recommendations by alumni.

Procedure: Freshmen are admitted to all sessions. Application deadlines are open. Application fee is $25. Notification is sent on a rolling basis. There are early decision, early admissions, and deferred admissions plans.

Transfer: About 960 transfer students enrolled in a recent year. Applicants must have earned a minimum GPA of 2.0 in all accredited college course work. A total of 30 credits out of 120 must be completed at Roosevelt.

Visiting: There are regularly scheduled orientations for prospective students, including open houses and Transfer Days. There are guides for informal visits and visitors may sit in on classes. To arrange for a visit, contact the Undergraduate Admissions Office at (312) 341-3515.

Financial Aid: In a recent year, 65% of all students received some form of financial aid. Scholarships or need-based grants averaged $2200 ($6800 maximum); loans averaged $2800 ($4000 maximum); and work contracts averaged $950 ($2000 maximum). Seventy percent of undergraduate students work part-time. Average earnings from campus work for the school year are $650. The average financial indebtedness of the 1992–93 graduate was $3400. Roosevelt is a member of CSS. The FFS is required. The deadline for financial aid applications is rolling.

International Students: The school actively recruits international students. They must take the college's own test.

Computers: The college provides computer facilities for student use. The mainframe is an IBM ES/9000 model 30. Apple Macintosh SE and other microcomputers are available. All students may access the system. It may be used 9:30 A.M. to 10:30 P.M. Students are limited to 1 hour of computer time when demand is great. There are no fees.

Graduates: In a recent year, 300 bachelor's degrees were awarded. Five companies recruited on campus in that year.

Admissions Contact: William Smyser, Director of Admissions.

ROSARY COLLEGE
River Forest, IL 60305

E-2

(708) 524-6800
(800) 828-8475 (out-of-state)

Full-time: 154 men, 470 women	Faculty: 60; IIB, av$
Part-time: 83 men, 184 women	Ph.D.s: 70%
Graduate: 314 men, 715 women	Student/Faculty: 10 to 1
Year: semesters, summer session	Tuition: $10,550
Application Deadline: open	Room & Board: $4490
Freshman Class: 434 applied, 321 accepted, 141 enrolled	
ACT: 22	COMPETITIVE

Rosary College, founded in 1901, is an independent liberal arts college affiliated with the Roman Catholic Church and sponsored by the Sinsinawa Dominicans. There are 3 graduate schools. In addition to regional accreditation, Rosary has baccalaureate program accreditation with ADA. The library contains 292,000 volumes, 10,589 microform items, and 6018 audiovisual forms, and subscribes to 1062 periodicals. Computerized library sources and services include the card catalog, interlibrary loans, and database searching. Special learning facilities include an art gallery, radio station, and a language laboratory. The 30-acre campus is in a suburban area 10 miles west of Chicago. Including residence halls, there are 8 buildings on campus.

Student Life: About 95% of undergraduates are from Illinois. Students come from 17 states and 15 foreign countries. Fifty percent are from public schools; 50% from private. Seventy-eight percent are white. Fifty-five percent are Catholic; 23% Protestant; 10% claim no religious affiliation. The average age of freshmen is 18; all undergraduates, 24. Nineteen percent drop out by the end of their first year; 65% remain to graduate.

Housing: A total of 311 students can be accommodated in college housing. College-sponsored living facilities include coed dormitories. In addition there is an international wing. On-campus housing is guaranteed for all 4 years. Sixty percent of students commute. All students may keep cars on campus.

Activities: There are no fraternities or sororities on campus. There are 20 groups on campus, including art, cheerleading, chess, chorus, computers, ethnic, honors, international, literary magazine, newspaper, pep band, photography, political, professional, radio and TV, religious, social, social service, and student government. Popular campus events include Founders Day, Spring Fling, and Candle and Rose Ceremony.

Sports: There are 4 intercollegiate sports for men and 3 for women, and 10 intramural sports for men and 10 for women. Athletic and recreation facilities include a gymnasium, indoor running track, indoor swimming pool, training room, fitness center, dance room, and racquetball courts.

Disabled Students: The entire campus is accessible to disabled students. The following facilities are available: wheelchair ramps, elevators, special parking, specially equipped rest rooms, special class scheduling, and lowered drinking fountains.

Services: In addition to many counseling and information services, tutoring is available in most subjects. There is remedial math and writing.

Campus Safety and Security: Campus safety and security measures include 24-hour foot and vehicle patrol, escort service, informal discussions, and pamphlets, posters, and films. In addition, there are emergency telephones, lighted pathways and sidewalks, and door alarms.

Programs of Study: Rosary awards the B.A. degree. Master's degrees also are awarded. Bachelor's degrees are awarded in BIOLOGICAL SCIENCE (biochemistry and biology/biological science), BUSINESS (accounting, business administration and management, fashion merchandising, and international business management), COMMUNICATIONS AND THE ARTS (art, communications, English, fine arts, French, German, Italian, public relations, Spanish, and technical and business writing), COMPUTER AND PHYSICAL SCIENCE (chemistry, computer science, and mathematics), EDUCATION (home economics), SOCIAL SCIENCE (American studies, dietetics, economics, European studies, fashion design and technology, food production/management/services, history, Latin American studies, philosophy, political science/government, psychology, religion, social science, and sociology). English, psychology, communication arts and sciences, and languages are the strongest academically. Business administration, psychology, communication, accounting, and English have the largest enrollments.

Required: In order to graduate, students must complete a total of 124 credits hours with a minimum GPA of 2.0. A total of 30 to 56 hours is required in the major. All students must demonstrate proficiency, through a placement examination or the completion of specified courses, in English composition, mathematics, and library skills. In addition, students must take a 3-semester, interdisciplinary freshman seminar, and 1 course each in science, history, fine arts, literature, humanities, religious studies, and philosophy and in a foreign language or multicultural course.

Special: Co-op programs in medical technology and nursing with Rush University, cross-registration with Concordia University, internships, study abroad in 5 countries, and a Washington semester are offered. Student-designed majors and interdisciplinary majors, including computer information systems, mathematics and computer science, and environmental science, credit for prior learning, and pass/fail options are possible. There is a freshman honors program on campus, as well as 11 national honor societies.

Faculty/Classroom: Forty-eight percent of faculty are male; 52%, female. All teach undergraduates. No introductory courses are taught by graduate students. The average class size in an introductory lecture is 27; in a laboratory, 12; and in a regular course offering, 18.

Admissions: About 74% of the 1993–94 applicants were accepted. The ACT scores for the 1993–94 freshman class were as follows: 47% below 21, 21% between 21 and 23, 20% between 24 and 26, 9% between 27 and 28, and 3% above 28. About 40% of the current freshmen were in the top fifth of their class; 70% were in the top two fifths. Five freshmen graduated first in their class.

Requirements: Rosary requires applicants to be in the upper 50% of their class. A minimum GPA of 2.5 is required. The SAT I or ACT is required. Graduation from an accredited secondary school or satisfactory scores on the GED are required for admission. The school requires 14 academic credits or 16 Carnegie units. High school courses should include English, mathematics, foreign language, social science, and laboratory science. An essay is required and an interview is recommended. AP and CLEP credits are accepted. Important factors used in the admissions decision are advanced placement or honor courses, leadership record, recommendations by school officials, extracurricular activities record, and evidence of special talent.

Procedure: Freshmen are admitted to all sessions. Entrance exams should be taken in the junior year. Application deadlines are open. Notification is sent two weeks after application file is completed. The application fee is $20. There is a deferred admissions plan.

Transfer: About 140 transfer students enrolled in 1993–94. Transfer students must have a minimum of 12 credit hours with a GPA of 2.3. An interview is recommended. The high school record will be evaluated if GPA is below 2.3 at the previous college. A total of 34 credits out of 124 must be completed at Rosary.

Visiting: There are regularly scheduled orientations for prospective students, consisting of visiting days and 2 Sunday open house programs per year. There are guides for informal visits and visitors may sit in on classes and stay overnight at the school. To arrange for a visit, contact the Admissions Office at (708) 524-6800.

Financial Aid: In 1993–94 80% of all current freshmen and 65% of continuing students received some form of financial aid. About 70% received need-based aid. The average freshman award was $9002. Of that total, scholarships or need-based grants averaged $5172 ($10,500 maximum); loans averaged $2430 ($3000 maximum); and work contracts averaged $1400 ($1800 maximum). Eighty percent of undergraduate students work part-time. Average earnings from campus work for the school year are $1300. The average financial indebtedness of the 1992–93 graduate was $8000. Rosary is a member of CSS. The FAF, tax returns, and the FAFSA are required. The deadline for financial aid applications is rolling.

International Students: There are currently 31 international students enrolled. The school actively recruits these students. They must take the TOEFL and achieve a minimum score of 550.

Computers: The college provides computer facilities for student use. The mainframe is a DEC VAX 8400. Nineteen PCs can access the mainframe and microcomputers are available in computer laboratories and classrooms. Students enrolled in special classes may access the system, as well as students who pay for personal accounts. There are no additional fees. It may be used 92 hours per week at the computer center, or 7 days a week, 24 hrs a day with a modem. When all terminals are occupied, there is a 1-hour limit.

Graduates: In 1992–93 182 bachelor's degrees were awarded. The most popular majors among graduates were business (20%), accounting (12%), and communication arts and sciences (8%). Within an average freshman class, 55% graduate in 4 years and 65% in 5 years. In the 1992 graduating class, 2% of the men and 7% of the women were enrolled in graduate school within 6 months of graduation; 22% of the men and 62% of the women had found employment.

Admissions Contact: Hildegarde Schmidt, Dean of Admissions and Financial Aid.

SAINT XAVIER COLLEGE
(See Saint Xavier University)

SAINT XAVIER UNIVERSITY
(Formerly Saint Xavier College)   E-2
Chicago, IL 60655   (312) 298–3050; (800) 462–9288 (out-of-state)

Full-time: 1363 men and women	Faculty: 176; IIB, av$
Part-time: 1033 men and women	Ph.D.s: 61%
Graduate: 2012 men and women	Student/Faculty: 8 to 1
Year: 4–1–4, summer session	Tuition: $10,340
Application Deadline: August 15	Room & Board: $4360
Freshman Class: 715 applied, 646 accepted, 313 enrolled	
SAT I or ACT: required	COMPETITIVE

Saint Xavier University is a private, coeducational institution founded by the Sisters of Mercy in 1846 and affiliated with the Roman Catholic Church. There are 4 undergraduate and 4 graduate schools. In addition to regional accreditation, Saint Xavier has baccalaureate program accreditation with NASM and NLN. The library contains 116,000 volumes and 57,791 microform items, and subscribes to 585 periodicals. Computerized library sources and services include the card catalog, interlibrary loans, and database searching. Special learning facilities include a learning resource center, art gallery, radio station, speech and language, learning disabilities, and reading clinics, learning assistance center, and ESL program. The 50-acre campus is in an urban area 15 miles southwest of Chicago's loop. Including residence halls, there are 5 buildings on campus.

Student Life: About 93% of undergraduates are from Illinois. Students come from 7 states, 19 foreign countries, and Canada. Fifty percent are from public schools; 50% from private. Seventy-nine percent are white; 12% African American. Eighty percent are Catholic; 16% Protestant. The average age of freshmen is 22; all undergraduates, 27.

Housing: A total of 350 students can be accommodated in college housing. College-sponsored living facilities include single-sex and coed dormitories. On-campus housing is guaranteed for all 4 years. Ninety percent of students commute. Alcohol is not permitted. All students may keep cars on campus.

Activities: There are no fraternities or sororities on campus. There are 30 groups on campus, including art, band, cheerleading, choir, chorus, drama, ethnic, film, honors, international, jazz band, literary magazine, marching band, musical theater, newspaper, opera, pep band, political, professional, radio and TV, religious, student government, and yearbook. Popular campus events include Xavierfest, an ethnic food fest, Homecoming, Boat Bash, Octoberfest, and Irishfest.

Sports: There are 4 intercollegiate sports for men and 3 for women, and 4 intramural sports for men and 4 for women. Athletic and recreation facilities include a 100-seat gymnasium, baseball and softball diamonds, and a new outdoor sports facility and football field.

Disabled Students: Ninety-eight percent of the campus is accessible to disabled students. The following facilities are available: wheelchair ramps, elevators, special parking, specially equipped rest rooms, special class scheduling, and lowered drinking fountains.

Services: In addition to many counseling and information services, tutoring is available in every subject.

Campus Safety and Security: Campus safety and security measures include 24-hour foot and vehicle patrol, escort service, and lighted pathways and sidewalks.

Programs of Study: Saint Xavier awards the B.A., B.S., B.F.A., and B.M. degrees. Master's degrees also are awarded. Bachelor's degrees are awarded in BIOLOGICAL SCIENCE (biology/biological science), BUSINESS (accounting, banking and finance, business administration and management, international business management, marketing/retailing/merchandising, and personnel management), COMMUNICATIONS AND THE ARTS (communications, English, fine arts, French, music, and Spanish), COMPUTER AND PHYSICAL

SCIENCE (chemistry, computer science, and mathematics), EDUCATION (art, early childhood, elementary, foreign languages, middle school, music, science, and secondary), ENGINEERING AND ENVIRONMENTAL DESIGN (aeronautical engineering, chemical engineering, and mechanical engineering), HEALTH PROFESSIONS (nursing, predentistry, premedicine, prepharmacy, and speech pathology/audiology), SOCIAL SCIENCE (criminal justice, history, philosophy, political science/government, prelaw, psychology, religion, social science, and sociology). Business, nursing, and education are the strongest programs academically and have the largest enrollments.

Required: To graduate, the student must complete 120 credit hours, including the school's 57-semester-hour core curriculum, and earn a GPA of 2.0. The credit hours required in the student's major vary by subject.

Special: The college offers internships, study in France, Ireland, and Italy, and 2–2 engineering degrees with the Illinois Institute of Technology.

Faculty/Classroom: Thirty-eight percent of faculty are male; 62%, female. All teach undergraduates.

Admissions: About 90% of the 1993–94 applicants were accepted.

Requirements: Saint Xavier requires applicants to be in the upper 50% of their class. A minimum GPA of 2.5 is required. The SAT I or ACT is required. In addition, students must be graduates of an accredited secondary school and have earned 16 specific academic credits, including 2 years of a foreign language, 3 each of mathematics and academic electives, and 4 each of English and the natural and social sciences. The GED is accepted. AP and CLEP credits are accepted.

Procedure: Freshmen are admitted fall and spring. Entrance exams should be taken during the spring of the junior year. Applications should be filed by August 15 for fall entry and January 15 for spring entry, along with an application fee of $20. Notification is sent on a rolling basis.

Transfer: About 343 transfer students enrolled in 1993–94. Transfer applicants must have completed 30 semester hours with a GPA of 2.5. An interview is recommended. A total of 30 credits out of 120 must be completed at Saint Xavier.

Visiting: There are regularly scheduled orientations for prospective students. There are guides for informal visits, and visitors may sit in on classes and stay overnight at the school. To arrange for a visit, contact the Director of Admissions at (312) 298–3050.

Financial Aid: In an earlier year, 76% of all freshmen and 66% of continuing students received some form of financial aid. Scholarships or need-based grants averaged $3000 ($5120 maximum); loans averaged $1900 ($5440 maximum); and work contracts averaged $1000 ($1440 maximum). Ninety percent of undergraduate students work part-time. The average financial indebtedness of the an earlier year's graduate was $3588. Saint Xavier is a member of CSS. The FAF and FAFSA are required.

International Students: There are currently 29 international students enrolled. The school actively recruits these students. They must take the TOEFL and achieve a minimum score of 550.

Computers: The college provides computer facilities for student use. The mainframe is a DEC VAX 11/750. All students may access the system. There are no time limits on using the system. The fees are $10.

Graduates: In 1992–93 352 bachelor's degrees were awarded. The most popular majors among graduates were business administration (24%), nursing (16%), and accounting (9%).

Admissions Contact: Evelyn McKenna, Director of Admissions.

SCHOOL OF THE ART INSTITUTE OF CHICAGO
                                                                      E-2
Chicago, IL 60603   (312) 899–5219; (800) 232–7242 (out-of-state)

Full-time: 565 men, 616 women	Faculty: 94; IIA, --$
Part-time: 60 men, 129 women	Ph.D.s: 83%
Graduate: 125 men, 246 women	Student/Faculty: 13 to 1
Year: 4–1–4, summer session	Tuition: $13,380
Application Deadline: August 15	Room: $4230–5130
Freshman Class: 780 applied, 547 accepted, 204 enrolled	
SAT I or ACT: required	SPECIAL

The School of the Art Institute of Chicago, founded in 1866, is a private institution affiliated with the museum of the Art Institute of Chicago. The school offers training in the fine arts and design. There is one graduate school. In addition to regional accreditation, the Art Institute has baccalaureate program accreditation with NASAD. The 2 libraries contain 400,000 volumes and 2300 audiovisual forms, and subscribe to 450 periodicals. Computerized library sources and services include the card catalog, interlibrary loans, and database searching. Special learning facilities include a learning resource center and art gallery. The campus is in an urban area in downtown Chicago. Including residence halls, there are 3 buildings on campus.

Student Life: About 58% of undergraduates are from Illinois. Students come from 37 states, 35 foreign countries, and Canada. Seventy-seven percent are white. The average age of freshmen is 20; all undergraduates, 21.

Housing: A total of 206 students can be accommodated in college housing. College-sponsored living facilities include coed dormitories and off-campus apartments. On-campus housing is available on a first-come, first-served basis. Priority is given to out-of-town students. Eighty-four percent of students commute. Alcohol is not permitted. All students may keep cars on campus.

Activities: There are no fraternities or sororities on campus. There are 12 groups on campus, including art, ethnic, film, gay, international, literary magazine, newspaper, photography, political, religious, social service, and student government. Popular campus events include film center screenings, visiting artist lectures, and exhibitions/openings at galleries.

Sports: There is no sports program at the Art Institute.

Disabled Students: All of the campus is accessible to disabled students. The following facilities are available: wheelchair ramps, elevators, special parking, specially equipped rest rooms, special class scheduling, lowered drinking fountains, and lowered telephones.

Services: In addition to many counseling and information services, tutoring is available in every subject, as well as for the learning-disabled. There also is remedial reading and writing.

Campus Safety and Security: Campus safety and security measures include 24-hour foot and vehicle patrol, informal discussions, pamphlets, posters, and films, and emergency telephones.

Programs of Study: The Art Institute awards the B.F.A. and B.Int.Arch. degrees. Master's degrees also are awarded. Bachelor's degrees are awarded in COMMUNICATIONS AND THE ARTS (ceramic art and design, design, fiber/textiles/weaving, film arts, painting, photography, printmaking, sculpture, and visual and performing arts), EDUCATION (art), ENGINEERING AND ENVIRONMENTAL DESIGN (interior design), SOCIAL SCIENCE (fashion design and technology).

Required: All students must complete 132 credit hours, including 72 of studio courses, 30 of liberal arts, 18 of art history, and 12 of electives. The minimum passing grade in all courses is C. All students are required to take art history, English literature, and English composition, as well as 2-, 3-, and 4-dimensional studio.

Special: The school offers internships, student-designed majors, non-degree study, pass/fail options, visual arts co-op programs, cross-registration with Roosevelt University, and cooperative work-study with the Art Institute of Chicago, Arthur Anderson and Co., and 'Chicago' magazine. Study abroad in 11 countries, dual and student-designed majors, and a B.A.-B.S. degree are possible.

Faculty/Classroom: Sixty-one percent of faculty are male; 38%, female. All teach undergraduates. Graduate students teach 20% of introductory courses. The average class size in an introductory lecture is 25.

Admissions: About 70% of the 1993–94 applicants were accepted.

Requirements: The SAT I or ACT is required, with a minimum score of 420 on the verbal section of the SAT I or a composite score of 18 on the ACT. Applicants must be graduates of an accredited secondary school. The GED is accepted. All students must submit a portfolio and an essay. An interview is recommended. AP and CLEP credits are accepted. Important factors used in the admissions decision are evidence of special talent, personality, intangible qualities, recommendations by school officials, leadership record, and extracurricular activities record.

Procedure: Freshmen are admitted fall and spring. Entrance exams should be taken during the senior year of high school. Applications should be filed by August 15 for fall entry and January 15 for spring entry, along with an application fee of $45. Notification is sent on a rolling basis.

Transfer: A total of 233 transfer students enrolled in 1993–94. Applicants must take the SAT I or ACT. A minimum score of 420 is required on the verbal section of the SAT I or a minimum composite score of 18 on the ACT. Students must submit a portfolio. A total of 36 credits out of 132 must be completed at the Art Institute.

Visiting: There are regularly scheduled orientations for prospective students. There are guides for informal visits. To arrange for a visit, contact the Office of Admissions at (800) 232–7242.

Financial Aid: In a recent year, 67% of all students received some form of financial aid. About 64% of all students received need-based aid. The average freshman award was $10,861. Of that total, scholarships or need-based grants averaged $5112; loans averaged $3142; and work contracts averaged $2607. Seventy-seven percent of undergraduate students work part-time. Average earnings from campus work for the school year are $1818. The Art Institute is a member of CSS. The FAF and the college's own financial statement are required. The deadline for financial aid applications is April 1.

International Students: There are currently 141 international students enrolled. The school actively recruits these students. They must take the TOEFL and achieve a minimum score of 525. The student must also take the SAT I, the ACT, or the college's own entrance exam.

Computers: The school provides computer facilities for student use. There are 22 Apple Macintosh computers and 6 printers available in a general access laboratory. All students may access the system. There are no time limits on using the system and no fees.

Graduates: In a recent year, 271 bachelor's degrees were awarded in fine arts.

Admissions Contact: Ellen Cohen, Director of Admissions.

SHIMER COLLEGE
C-1
Waukegan, IL 60079 (708) 623–8400

Full-time: 59 men, 48 women	**Faculty:** 16
Part-time: 3 men, 9 women	**Ph.D.s:** 81%
Graduate: none	**Student/Faculty:** 7 to 1
Year: semesters, summer session	**Tuition:** $11,200
Application Deadline: August 1	**Room & Board:** $1650
Freshman Class: 59 applied, 57 accepted, 42 enrolled	
SAT I or ACT: recommended	**NONCOMPETITIVE**

Shimer College, founded in 1853, is a private liberal arts college with a curriculum based on original sources and a Socratic method employing discussion classes of 12 or fewer students. The library contains 200,000 volumes. Computerized library sources and services include the card catalog, interlibrary loans, and database searching. The 3-acre campus is in a suburban area 40 miles north of Chicago and 40 miles south of Milwaukee. Including residence halls, there are 10 buildings on campus.

Student Life: About 67% of undergraduates are from Illinois. Students come from 22 states and 2 foreign countries. Seventy-five percent are from public schools; 25% from private. Seventy-nine percent are white; 11% African American. The average age of freshmen is 21.3; all undergraduates, 24.4. Six percent drop out by the end of their first year; 50% remain to graduate.

Housing: A total of 47 students can be accommodated in college housing. College-sponsored living facilities include coed dormitories. On-campus housing is guaranteed for the freshman year only and is available on a first-come, first-served basis. Priority is given to out-of-town students. Sixty percent of students commute. All students may keep cars on campus.

Activities: There are no fraternities or sororities on campus. There are some groups and organizations on campus, including art, chess, computers, drama, literary magazine, newspaper, photography, and student government. Popular campus events include community lunch and poetry reading.

Sports: There are 2 intramural sports for men and 2 for women. Athletic and recreation facilities include a gym and a pool.

Services: In addition to many counseling and information services, tutoring is available in every subject.

Campus Safety and Security: Campus safety and security measures include informal discussions.

Programs of Study: Shimer awards the B.A. and B.S. degrees. Bachelor's degrees are awarded in COMPUTER AND PHYSICAL SCIENCE (natural sciences), SOCIAL SCIENCE (history, humanities, philosophy, prelaw, and social science). Humanities and social sciences are the strongest academically. Humanities has the largest enrollment.

Required: To graduate, students must earn 125 credit hours with a GPA of 2.0, complete 2 comprehensive exams, and submit a thesis. The school requires 60 credit hours in the major for the B.S. degree, 40 for the B.A.; 65 in the core curriculum for the B.S., 85 for the B.A.

Special: Shimer offers cross-registration with Barat College, internships in all areas of study, and study abroad at Oxford. There is an accelerated degree program, a B.A.-B.S. degree, dual majors, student-designed majors, and a general studies degree available. Nondegree study and pass/fail options are possible. All instruction is done using original sources and through small class discussions among 6 to 12 students.

Faculty/Classroom: Seventy-two percent of faculty are male; 28%, female. All teach undergraduates. The average class size in a regular course offering is 7.

Admissions: About 97% of the 1993–94 applicants were accepted. About 40% of the current freshmen were in the top fifth of their class; 80% were in the top two fifths. There was 1 National Merit semifinalist.

Requirements: The SAT I or ACT is recommended. Requirements are highly individualized. Essays and an interview are required. Important factors used in the admissions decision are personality, intangible qualities, leadership record, extracurricular activities record, geographic diversity, and recommendations by school officials.

Procedure: Freshmen are admitted fall and spring. Early decision applications should be filed by December 1; regular applications, by August 1 for fall entry and January 1 for winter entry, along with an application fee of $10. Notification of early decision is sent December 15; regular decision, on a rolling basis. There are early decision, early admissions, and deferred admissions plans. A waiting list is an ac-

tive part of the admissions procedure, with about 15% of applicants on the list.

Transfer: Ten transfer students enrolled in 1993–94. Transfer students are required to have an interview. A total of 60 credits out of 125 must be completed at Shimer.

Visiting: There are regularly scheduled orientations for prospective students, consisting of class visits, lunch, and a financial aid interview. There are guides for informal visits and visitors may sit in on classes and stay overnight at the school. To arrange for a visit, contact David B. Buchanan, Director of Admissions at (708) 623–8400.

Financial Aid: In an earlier year, 95% of all students received some form of financial aid. About 88% of freshmen and 90% of continuing students received need-based aid. The average freshman award was $4200. Of that total, scholarships or need-based grants averaged $3000 ($6400 maximum); loans averaged $3000 ($6000 maximum); and work contracts averaged $1200 ($2000 maximum). Fifty-two percent of undergraduate students work part-time. Average earnings from campus work for the school year are $900. The average financial indebtedness of the 1992–93 graduate was $14,500. Shimer is a member of CSS. The FAF is required. The deadline for financial aid applications is July 30.

International Students: There are currently 2 international students enrolled. The school actively recruits these students.

Computers: The college provides computer facilities for student use. There are PCs available. All students may access the system between 9 A.M. and 10 P.M. There are no time limits on using the system and no fees.

Graduates: In 1992–93, 2 bachelor's degrees were awarded. The most popular majors among graduates were humanities (95%) and social sciences (5%). Within an average freshman class, 7% graduate in 3 years, 79% in 4 years, and 14% in 5 years.

Admissions Contact: David B. Buchanan, Director of Admissions.

SOUTHERN ILLINOIS UNIVERSITY

The Southern Illinois University, established in 1965, is a public system in Illinois. It is governed by a board of trustees, whose chief administrator is the chancellor. The primary goal of the system is to create and sustain the internal and external conditions that enable the campuses to fulfill their missions with excellence. The main priorities are to achieve and maintain excellence in teaching, research, and service; to achieve and maintain cultural diversity; and to provide educational opportunity to the disadvantaged. The total enrollment in fall 1993 of both campuses was 35,144; there were 1935 instructional faculty members. Altogether there are 114 baccalaureate, 94 master's, and 31 doctoral programs offered at Southern Illinois University. Profiles of the 4-year campuses are included in this chapter in alphabetical order with other Illinois schools.

SOUTHERN ILLINOIS UNIVERSITY AT CARBONDALE

Carbondale, IL 62901   **D-5**
                            (618) 536–4405

Full-time: 10,157 men, 6746 women	**Faculty:** 1259; I, --$
Part-time: 1484 men, 1015 women	**Ph.D.s:** 69%
Graduate: 2258 men, 2221 women	**Student/Faculty:** 13 to 1
Year: semesters, summer session	**Tuition:** $3052 ($7552)
Application Deadline: open	**Room & Board:** $3182
Freshman Class: 9907 applied, 6089 accepted, 2243 enrolled	
ACT: 22	**COMPETITIVE**

Southern Illinois University at Carbondale, founded in 1869, is a public institution that is part of the Southern Illinois University. The multi-campus university offers undergraduate programs in agriculture, business and administration, education, engineering, liberal arts, mass communication and media arts, science, social work, and technical careers. There are 9 undergraduate and 3 graduate schools. In addition to regional accreditation, SIUC has baccalaureate program accreditation with AACSB, ABET, ABFSE, ACEJMC, ADA, APTA, CAHEA, CSWE, FIDER, NASAD, NASM, NCATE, NLN, NRPA, and SAF. The 2 libraries contain 2,000,000 volumes, 2,500,000 microform items, and 30,161 audiovisual forms, and subscribe to 22,075 periodicals. Computerized library sources and services include the card catalog, interlibrary loans, and database searching. Special learning facilities include a learning resource center, art gallery, natural history museum, radio station, TV station, a student-run newspaper, farms and timberlands, greenhouses, livestock facilities, an archeological center, an aviation program, a crime study center, and a wildlife laboratory. The 1128-acre campus is in a small town 96 miles southeast of St. Louis. Including residence halls, there are 256 buildings on campus.

Student Life: About 81% of undergraduates are from Illinois. Students come from 48 states, 115 foreign countries, and Canada. Eighty-seven percent are from public schools; 13% from private. Seventy-four percent are white; 12% African American. The average

age of all undergraduates is 24. Thirty-two percent drop out by the end of their first year; 43% remain to graduate.

Housing: A total of 5400 students can be accommodated in college housing. College-sponsored living facilities include single-sex and coed dormitories, fraternity houses, and sorority houses. In addition there are honors houses and family housing, an engineering residence hall, rooms for students with disabilities, over-21 residence halls, and residence halls that stay open during breaks. On-campus housing is available on a first-come, first-served basis. Seventy percent of students commute. Upperclassmen may keep cars on campus.

Activities: About 4% of men belong to 17 national fraternities; about 2% of women belong to 7 national sororities. There are 350 groups on campus, including art, band, cheerleading, chess, choir, chorale, chorus, computers, dance, drama, drill team, drum and bugle corps, ethnic, film, gay, honors, international, jazz band, marching band, musical theater, newspaper, opera, orchestra, photography, political, professional, radio and TV, religious, social, social service, student government, symphony, and yearbook. Popular campus events include Homecoming, Parents Day, Cardboard Boat Races, Springfest, Sports Fest, New Student Orientation, International Festival, Black History Month, and Hispanic Month.

Sports: There are 9 intercollegiate sports for men and 9 for women, and 48 intramural sports for men and 48 for women. Athletic and recreation facilities include a 17,324-seat stadium, a 10,014-seat arena, a women's softball field, a 700-seat gymnasium, boat docks, tennis courts, and a cross-country course. The student recreation center houses an Olympic-size pool, indoor tracks, racquetball and handball courts, aerobics equipment, and a weight room.

Disabled Students: Ninety-nine percent of the campus is accessible to disabled students. The following facilities are available: wheelchair ramps, elevators, special parking, specially equipped rest rooms, and lowered drinking fountains and telephones. The university provides classroom and residence hall accommodations for students with physical disabilities.

Services: In addition to many counseling and information services, tutoring is available in most subjects. In addition, there is a reader service for the blind, new student orientation, a mentoring program, a writing skills laboratory, and pre-major advisement.

Campus Safety and Security: Campus safety and security measures include 24-hour foot and vehicle patrol, self-defense education, escort service, and shuttle buses. In addition, there are informal discussions, pamphlets, posters, films, emergency telephones, lighted pathways and sidewalks, a 72-person full-time security department, a residence hall security system, and 911 call-boxes.

Programs of Study: SIUC awards the B.A., B.S., B.F.A., and B.Mus. degrees. Associate, master's, and doctoral degrees also are awarded. Bachelor's degrees are awarded in AGRICULTURE (agricultural business management, agriculture, animal science, forestry and related sciences, and horticulture), BIOLOGICAL SCIENCE (biochemistry, biology/biological science, botany, microbiology, physiology, and zoology), BUSINESS (accounting, banking and finance, business administration and management, business economics, hotel/motel and restaurant management, international business management, marketing/retailing/merchandising, and personnel management), COMMUNICATIONS AND THE ARTS (advertising, broadcasting, classics, design, dramatic arts, English, film arts, fine arts, French, journalism, languages, linguistics, music, photography, Russian, Spanish, and speech/debate/rhetoric), COMPUTER AND PHYSICAL SCIENCE (chemistry, computer programming, computer science, geology, mathematics, physics, and radiological technology), EDUCATION (art, business, early childhood, elementary, foreign languages, health, home economics, music, physical, science, secondary, social studies, special, and vocational), ENGINEERING AND ENVIRONMENTAL DESIGN (architecture, civil engineering, electrical/electronics engineering, engineering, engineering technology, industrial engineering technology, mechanical engineering, and mining and mineral engineering), HEALTH PROFESSIONS (dental hygiene, dental laboratory technology, physical therapy, predentistry, premedicine, preveterinary science, respiratory therapy, and speech pathology/audiology), and SOCIAL SCIENCE (anthropology, clothing and textiles management/production/services, criminal justice, dietetics, economics, food science, geography, history, international relations, liberal arts/general studies, paralegal studies, parks and recreation management, philosophy, political science/government, prelaw, psychology, social science, social work, and sociology). Business, engineering, and education are the strongest academically. Elementary education, criminal justice, psychology, electrical engineering, accounting, radio and television, speech communication, advanced technical studies, cinema and photography, and journalism have the largest enrollments.

Required: In order to graduate, all students must meet the university and program requirements, maintain a minimum 2.0 GPA, and complete a minimum of 120 semester hours. The total number of hours in the major varies, and students must complete general education course requirements.

Special: The university offers internships through the Washington center and study abroad in 100 study sites, including Europe, Africa, Latin American, China, and the West Bank. Also available are a Washington semester, work-study programs, accelerated degree programs, dual majors, B.A.-B.S. degrees in chemistry, geography, geology, and zoology, and the University Studies degree. The College of Technical Careers offers technically oriented programs, co-op programs, and work-study for the A.A.S. and B.S. degrees. Nondegree study is available through the Community Listeners Permit and Elderhostel. There is a freshman honors program on campus, as well as 36 national honor societies. Seventeen departments have honors programs.

Faculty/Classroom: Sixty-six percent of faculty are male; 34%, female. Graduate students teach 65% of introductory courses. The average class size in an introductory lecture is 75; in a laboratory, 25; and in a regular course offering, 20.

Admissions: About 61% of the 1993–94 applicants were accepted. The ACT scores for the 1993–94 freshman class were as follows: 39% below 21, 35% between 21 and 23, 16% between 24 and 26, 9% between 27 and 28, and 1% above 28. About 21% of the current freshmen were in the top fifth of their class; 48% were in the top two fifths. There was 1 National Merit finalist and 3 semifinalists. Thirty-five freshmen graduated first in their class.

Requirements: SIUC requires applicants to be in the upper 50% of their class. The ACT is required. Applicants must be graduates of an accredited secondary high school or have a GED certificate, plus 11 academic units, 11 Carnegie units, 4 years of English, 3 years each of mathematics, laboratory science, and social science, and 2 years of electives, which may include art, music, foreign language, or vocational education. For general admission, a minimum composite score of 20 on the ACT, or 18 ACT and rank in the top half of the graduating class, is required. Some programs require additional materials and/or screening, and higher ACT scores and higher class rank. AP and CLEP credits are accepted. Important factors used in the admissions decision are advanced placement or honors courses, recommendations by school officials, recommendations by alumni, personality, intangible qualities, and parents or siblings who attended the school.

Procedure: Freshmen are admitted to all sessions. Entrance exams should be taken during spring of the junior year. Application deadlines are open. Notification is sent on a rolling basis.

Transfer: About 2400 transfer students enrolled in a recent year. All transfer students must have a minimum 2.0 GPA on a 4-point scale. Students are required to meet freshman admission requirements if they are under 21 years old and have fewer than 26 credit hours of acceptable transfer work. A total of 60 credits out of 120 must be completed at SIUC.

Visiting: There are regularly scheduled orientations for prospective students, including admissions counseling, academic program exhibits, student organization exhibits, workshops on financial aid and housing, and tours of the campus and residence halls. Visitors may sit in on classes with the instructors' permission. To arrange for a visit, contact New Student Admission Services at (618) 536–4405.

Financial Aid: In 1993–94, 85% of all students received some form of financial aid. About 70% of all students received need-based aid. The average freshman award was $6300. Of that total, scholarships or need-based grants averaged $2450 ($5952 maximum); loans averaged $2000 ($2625 maximum); and work contracts averaged $1750 ($3600 maximum). Sixty-five percent of undergraduate students work part-time. Average earnings from campus work for the school year are $1400. The average financial indebtedness of the 1992–93 graduate was $5725. The FAF, FFS or SFS and or any federally approved form is required. The deadline for financial aid applications is April 1.

International Students: There are currently 2193 international students enrolled. They must take the TOEFL and achieve a minimum score of 520. Students must also complete their own countries' standardized college entrance examination.

Computers: The college provides computer facilities for student use. The mainframe is an IBM 9021–500. Students may use more than 300 microcomputers or terminals that are networked at 3 computing learning centers. Other departments on campus also have laboratories connected to the mainframe. All students may access the system. It may be used all the time, all year. There are no time limits on using the system and no fees.

Graduates: In 1992–93, 5009 bachelor's degrees were awarded. The most popular majors among graduates were advanced technical studies (4%), marketing (3%), and psychology (3%). Within an average freshman class, 1% graduate in 3 years, 19% in 4 years, 37% in 5 years, and 42% in 6 years. Some 148 companies recruited on campus in 1992–93.

Admissions Contact: New Student Admissions Services.

SOUTHERN ILLINOIS UNIVERSITY AT EDWARDSVILLE
C-4

Edwardsville, IL 62026–1047

(618) 692-3705

(800) 447-SIUE (in-state)

Full-time: 2696 men, 3367 women
Part-time: 1129 men, 1421 women
Graduate: 1215 men, 1435 women
Year: early semesters, summer session
Application Deadline: August 1
Freshman Class: 2540 applied, 2195 accepted, 994 enrolled
ACT: 21

Faculty: 506; IIA, av$
Ph.D.s: 81%
Student/Faculty: 12 to 1
Tuition: $2670 ($6124)
Room & Board: $3427

LESS COMPETITIVE

Southern Illinois University at Edwardsville, founded in 1957, is part of the Southern Illinois University system and offers undergraduate programs in business, education, engineering, fine arts and communications, humanities, nursing, sciences, and social sciences. There are 8 undergraduate and 2 graduate schools. In addition to regional accreditation, SIUE has baccalaureate program accreditation with AACSB, ABET, ADA, CAHEA, CSWE, NASM, NCATE, and NLN. The 3 libraries contain 775,254 volumes, 1,226,907 microform items, and 36,620 audiovisual forms, and subscribe to 6029 periodicals. Computerized library sources and services include the card catalog, interlibrary loans, and database searching. Special learning facilities include a learning resource center, art gallery, and radio station. The 2664-acre campus is in a rural area 18 miles northeast of St Louis. Including residence halls, there are 135 buildings on campus.

Student Life: About 87% of undergraduates are from Illinois. Students come from 36 states, 58 foreign countries, and Canada. Eighty-one percent are white; 16% African American. The average age of freshmen is 19; all undergraduates, 25. Twenty-eight percent drop out by the end of their first year.

Housing: A total of 2000 students can be accommodated in college housing. College-sponsored living facilities include coed dormitories, on-campus apartments, and married-student housing. On-campus housing is available on a first-come, first-served basis. Priority is given to out-of-town students. All students may keep cars on campus.

Activities: About 3% of men belong to 9 national fraternities; about 4% of women belong to 6 national sororities. There are 130 groups on campus, including art, band, cheerleading, choir, chorale, chorus, dance, drama, ethnic, film, gay, honors, international, jazz band, literary magazine, musical theater, newspaper, opera, orchestra, pep band, political, professional, radio and TV, religious, social, social service, student government, and symphony. Popular campus events include Springfest, Welcome Week, Homecoming, and the Arts and Issues Series.

Sports: There are 8 intercollegiate sports for men and 6 for women, and 11 intramural sports each. Athletic and recreation facilities include the Vadalabene Center and Student Fitness Center, which offer racquetball, basketball, aquatics, volleyball, indoor track, and weight training; the University Center; an outdoor swimming pool; and a lake for canoeing and sailing. A new, world-class outdoor track and field and soccer stadium is being completed.

Disabled Students: The entire campus is accessible to disabled students. The following facilities are available: wheelchair ramps, elevators, special parking, specially equipped rest rooms, special class scheduling, lowered drinking fountains, lowered telephones, a Visualtek large-screen TV, Kurzweil Readers, and test-taking facilities.

Services: In addition to many counseling and information services, tutoring is available in most subjects. There is also remedial math, reading, and writing.

Campus Safety and Security: Campus safety and security measures include 24-hour foot and vehicle patrol, self-defense education, escort service, and shuttle buses. In addition, there are informal discussions, pamphlets, posters, films, emergency telephones, and lighted pathways and sidewalks.

Programs of Study: SIUE awards the B.A., B.S., B.F.A., B.L.S., B.M., B.S.A., and B.S.E. degrees. Master's degrees also are awarded. Bachelor's degrees are awarded in BIOLOGICAL SCIENCE (biology/biological science), BUSINESS (accounting, business administration and management, and business economics), COMMUNICATIONS AND THE ARTS (broadcasting, communications, dance, dramatic arts, English, fine arts, French, German, journalism, music, Spanish, and speech/debate/rhetoric), COMPUTER AND PHYSICAL SCIENCE (chemistry, computer science, mathematics, and physics), EDUCATION (art, early childhood, elementary, health, music, secondary, and special), ENGINEERING AND ENVIRONMENTAL DESIGN (civil engineering, construction engineering, electrical/electronics engineering, industrial engineering, and mechanical engineering), HEALTH PROFESSIONS (nursing and speech pathology/audiology), and SOCIAL SCIENCE (anthropology, economics, geography, history, philosophy, political science/government, psychology, social work, and sociology). The School of Business has the largest enrollment.

Required: To graduate, students must complete a total of 124 semester hours with a minimum GPA of 2.0. Students must fulfill general education requirements, including 9 hours of mathematics/science, and complete a rising junior paper and a senior project.

Special: SIUE offers cross-registration with the University of Missouri at St. Louis, co-op programs, internships, work-study programs, dual majors, study-abroad programs in 4 countries, and a liberal studies degree. There is a freshman honors program on campus, as well as 9 national honor societies. Fifteen departments have honors programs.

Faculty/Classroom: Seventy-two percent of faculty are male; 28%, female.

Admissions: About 86% of the 1993–94 applicants were accepted. The ACT scores for the 1993–94 freshman class were as follows: 50% below 21, 26% between 21 and 23, 15% between 24 and 26, 6% between 27 and 28, and 3% above 28. About 32% of the current freshmen were in the top fifth of their class; 65% were in the top two fifths. Eleven freshmen graduated first in their class.

Requirements: The ACT is required. Applicants must be graduates of an accredited secondary school or have a GED certificate. They must have completed 15 academic credits, based on 2 years of any combination of art, foreign language, music, and vocational education; at least 2 years of government and/or history plus 1 more year of social studies; 3 years each of mathematics and laboratory science; and 4 years of English. CLEP credit is accepted.

Procedure: Freshmen are admitted fall, spring, and summer. Entrance exams should be taken prior to high school graduation. Applications should be filed by August 1 for fall entry, December 19 for spring entry, and May 2 for summer entry. Notification is sent on a rolling basis.

Transfer: About 1150 transfer students enrolled in 1993–94. Applicants must have a minimum 2.0 GPA in at least 16 semester hours earned. A total of 30 semester hours out of 124 must be completed at SIUE.

Visiting: There are regularly scheduled orientations for prospective students. There are guides for informal visits and visitors may sit in on classes. To arrange for a visit, contact the Student Recruitment Office at (618) 692-3705, (800) 447-SIUE (in-state), or (314) 231-SIUE (within the St. Louis area).

Financial Aid: In 1993–94 53% of all current freshmen and 60% of continuing students received some form of financial aid. About 50% of all students received need-based aid. The average freshman award was $5970. Of that total, scholarships or need-based grants averaged $1370 ($2200 maximum); loans averaged $2000 ($2625 maximum); and work contracts averaged $2600 (maximum). Twenty percent of undergraduate students work part-time. Average earnings from campus work for the school year are $2700. The average financial indebtedness of the 1992–93 graduate was $10,500. The deadline for financial aid applications is open.

International Students: There are currently 135 international students enrolled. The school actively recruits these students. They must take the TOEFL and achieve a minimum score of 550.

Computers: The college provides computer facilities for student use. The mainframe is an IBM 9121/511. There are also 300 PCs and terminals located in classrooms and computer laboratories. All students may access the system. It may be used daily at designated hours. There are no time limits on using the system and no fees.

Graduates: In 1992–93, 1444 bachelor's degrees were awarded. The most popular majors among graduates were business administration (20%), nursing (10%), and elementary education (7%). Within an average freshman class, 12% graduate in 4 years, 28% in 5 years, and 34% in 6 years. Some 63 companies recruited on campus.

Admissions Contact: Student Recruitment.

TRINITY CHRISTIAN COLLEGE
Palos Heights, IL 60463

E-2

(708) 597-3000
(800) 748-0085 (out-of-state)

Full-time: 545	Faculty: 40; IIB, -$
Part-time: 63	Ph.D.s: 50%
Graduate: none	Student/Faculty: 14 to 1
Year: 4-1-4	Tuition: $9460
Application Deadline: August 15	Room & Board: $3800
Freshman Class: n/av	
ACT: 22	**COMPETITIVE**

Trinity Christian College, founded in 1959, is a private coeducational college offering programs in art, business, health science, liberal arts, music, religion, and teacher preparation. In addition to regional accreditation, Trinity has baccalaureate program accreditation with NLN. The library contains 55,000 volumes, 20,000 microform items, and 100 audiovisual forms, and subscribes to 50 periodicals. Computerized library sources and services include the card catalog and interlibrary loans. Special learning facilities include a learning resource center, art gallery, and a Dutch heritage collection. The 53-

acre campus is in a suburban area 20 miles southwest of Chicago. Including residence halls, there are 14 buildings on campus.

Student Life: About 64% of undergraduates are from Illinois. Students come from 18 states, 6 foreign countries, and Canada. Some 35% are from public schools; 65% from private. About 89% are white. Most are Protestant. The average age of freshmen is 19; all undergraduates, 22. Approximately 32% drop out by the end of their first year; 44% remain to graduate.

Housing: A total of 390 students can be accommodated in college housing. College-sponsored living facilities include single-sex dormitories and on-campus apartments. On-campus housing is guaranteed for all 4 years. 65% of students live on campus; of those, 45% remain on campus on weekends. Alcohol is not permitted. All students may keep cars on campus.

Activities: There are no fraternities or sororities. There are many groups and organizations on campus, including art, band, choir, chorale, drama, ethnic, newspaper, pep band, photography, political, radio and TV, religious, social, social service, student government, and yearbook.

Sports: Athletic and recreation facilities include a gymnasium, track, and stadium.

Disabled Students: About 95% of the campus is accessible to disabled students. The following facilities are available: wheelchair ramps, elevators, special parking, specially equipped rest rooms, and lowered drinking fountains.

Services: In addition to many counseling and information services, tutoring is available in every subject.

Campus Safety and Security: Campus safety and security measures include 24-hour foot and vehicle patrol, escort service, and lighted pathways and sidewalks.

Programs of Study: Trinity awards the B.A. and B.S. degrees. Bachelor's degrees are awarded in BIOLOGICAL SCIENCE (biology/biological science), BUSINESS (accounting, banking and finance, and marketing/retailing/merchandising), COMMUNICATIONS AND THE ARTS (communications, English, fine arts, and music), COMPUTER AND PHYSICAL SCIENCE (chemistry and computer science), EDUCATION (art, business, elementary, middle school, music, science, secondary, and special), HEALTH PROFESSIONS (nursing, predentistry, and premedicine), SOCIAL SCIENCE (history, philosophy, prelaw, psychology, religion, and sociology). Business, education, and nursing are the strongest programs academically and have the largest enrollments.

Required: All students must take 9 courses in English, 6 each in philosophy and history, and 4 in theology, as well as distribution requirements in intersocietal studies, natural sciences, social sciences, fine arts, mathematics, and physical education. Students must complete 125 credit hours and maintain a minimum 2.0 average in order to graduate.

Special: Students may have various part-time or full-time internships in their major field. There are study abroad programs in the Netherlands, Spain, and Germany. Pass/fail options exist.

Faculty/Classroom: Some 70% of faculty are male; 30%, female. All teach undergraduates and do research. The average class size in an introductory lecture and in a laboratory is 25.

Admissions: About 33% of the current freshmen were in the top fifth of their class; 78% were in the top two fifths. Three freshmen graduated first in their class.

Requirements: Trinity requires applicants to be in the upper 60% of their class. A minimum GPA of 2.1 is required. The ACT, with a recommended score of 19, or the SAT I is required. Applicants should graduate from an accredited high school or have a GED. They should prepare with 3 or 4 years of high school English, 3 years of mathematics, science, or social studies, or 2 years each of a combination of 2 subject areas chosen among foreign language, mathematics, science or social studies. An interview is required in some situations. AP and CLEP credits are accepted. Important factors used in the admissions decision are advanced placement or honor courses, recommendations, leadership record, and extracurricular activities record.

Procedure: Freshmen are admitted in the fall and spring. Entrance exams should be taken during the last semester of the junior year. Applications should be filed by August 15 for fall entry and January 15 for spring entry, along with an application fee of $15. Notification is sent on a rolling basis.

Transfer: About 66 transfer students enrolled in 1993–94. Transfer applicants must have 24 hours of acceptable credits and a minimum 2.0 GPA. Transfer associate degrees are recognized. A total of 30 credits out of 125 must be completed at Trinity.

Visiting: There are regularly scheduled orientations for prospective students, including tour, interview, seminar, and class visit. There are guides for informal visits and visitors may sit in on classes and stay overnight at the school. To arrange for a visit, contact Admissions at (708) 597-3000.

Financial Aid: In an earlier year, 90% of all students received some form of financial aid. About 50% received need-based aid. The average freshman award was $4117. Some 50% of undergraduate stu-

dents work part-time. Average earnings from campus work for the school year are $1300. Trinity is a member of CSS. The FAF, FFS, or SFS are accepted; the FAF is recommended. The deadline for financial aid applications is February 15.

International Students: There are currently 11 international students enrolled. They must take the TOEFL and achieve a minimum score of 500. The ACT is recommended, with a minimum score of 19.

Computers: The college provides computer facilities for student use. The mainframe is an IBM. There is a computer laboratory of IBM-compatible PCs. All students may access the system. There are no time limits on using the system and no fees.

Graduates: In a recent year, 92 bachelor's degrees were awarded. The most popular majors among graduates were business administration (25%), education (21%), and nursing (17%). Within an average freshman class, 42% graduate in 4 years and 3% in 5 years.

Admissions Contact: Jon F. Bontekoe, Director of Admissions.

TRINITY COLLEGE
E-1
Deerfield, IL 60015   (708) 317-7000; (800) 822-3225 (out-of-state)

Full-time: 325 men, 353 women	Faculty: 41; IIB, --$
Part-time: 21 men, 40 women	Ph.D.s: 57%
Graduate: none	Student/Faculty: 17 to 1
Year: semesters, summer session	Tuition: $9900
Application Deadline: open	Room & Board: $4110
Freshman Class: 508 applied, 485 accepted, 261 enrolled	
ACT: 22	COMPETITIVE

Trinity College, established in 1897 by the Evangelical Free Church, is a coeducational, Christian liberal arts institution. The 2 libraries contain 205,000 volumes, 63,875 microform items, and 4352 audiovisual forms, and subscribe to 1700 periodicals. The 120-acre campus is in a suburban area 20 miles north of Chicago. Including residence halls, there are 12 buildings on campus.

Student Life: About 52% of undergraduates are from out-of-state, mostly the Midwest. Students come from 28 states and 3 foreign countries. Eighty-four percent are white. The average age of freshmen is 18; all undergraduates, 21. Twenty-six percent drop out by the end of their first year; 56% remain to graduate.

Housing: A total of 750 students can be accommodated in college housing. College-sponsored living facilities include single-sex dormitories, off-campus apartments, and married-student housing. On-campus housing is guaranteed for all 4 years. Eighty percent of students live on campus; of those, 75% remain on campus on weekends. Alcohol is not permitted. All students may keep cars on campus.

Activities: There are no fraternities or sororities on campus. There are 10 groups on campus, including art, band, cheerleading, choir, computers, debate, drama, ethnic, honors, international, jazz band, literary magazine, newspaper, pep band, political, religious, social service, student government, and yearbook. Popular campus events include Homecoming, Santa Lucis Festival, Spring Banquet, Spring Pops Concert, Fine Arts Series, Christian Life Week, World Christian Week, Missions Week, and Black History Month.

Sports: There are 10 intercollegiate sports for men and 7 for women, and 6 intramural sports for men and 6 for women. Athletic and recreation facilities include a sports complex, football and soccer fields, and 6 outdoor tennis courts. Students have use of a nearby indoor tennis and racquetball club.

Disabled Students: Seventy percent of the campus is accessible to disabled students. The following facilities are available: wheelchair ramps, elevators, special parking, specially equipped rest rooms, and special class scheduling.

Services: In addition to many counseling and information services, tutoring is available in every subject. There is remedial math, reading, and writing.

Campus Safety and Security: Campus safety and security measures include 24-hour foot and vehicle patrol, informal discussions, and lighted pathways and sidewalks.

Programs of Study: Trinity awards the B.A. degree. Bachelor's degrees are awarded in BIOLOGICAL SCIENCE (biology/biological science), BUSINESS (accounting, business administration and management, business economics, marketing/retailing/merchandising, and personnel management), COMMUNICATIONS AND THE ARTS (communications, creative writing, English, and music), COMPUTER AND PHYSICAL SCIENCE (chemistry, computer science, information sciences and systems, and mathematics), EDUCATION (elementary, music, science, and secondary), HEALTH PROFESSIONS (predentistry and premedicine), SOCIAL SCIENCE (history, philosophy, prelaw, psychology, religion, sociology, and youth ministry). English, Bible, education, and youth ministry are the strongest academically. Business, Bible, psychology, and education have the largest enrollments.

Required: To graduate, all students are required to complete 126 semester hours, including 60 general education hours and a variable number in the major. A GPA of 2.0 is required. Chapel attendance, Christian service, Bible study, science, and physical education are also required. In addition, students must pass an examination in English usage.

Special: Students can cross-register with the Christian College Consortium and at Trinity Evangelical Divinity School. Trinity offers three levels of internships, an opportunity through the American Studies Program to spend a semester in Washington, and work-study programs. Dual majors, a general studies degree, and nondegree study are offered. There is a freshman honors program on campus, as well as 1 national honor society.

Faculty/Classroom: Sixty-six percent of faculty are male; 34%, female. All teach undergraduates. The average class size in an introductory lecture is 40; in a laboratory, 20; and in a regular course offering, 15.

Admissions: About 95% of the 1993-94 applicants were accepted. The ACT scores for the 1993-94 freshman class were as follows: 37% below 21, 33% between 21 and 23, 25% between 24 and 26, 5% between 27 and 28, and 3% above 28. About 36% of the current freshmen were in the top fifth of their class; 57% were in the top two fifths. About 3 freshmen graduated first in their class.

Requirements: Trinity requires applicants to be in the upper 50% of their class. A minimum GPA of 2.5 is required. The SAT I or ACT (preferred) is required, with a minimum composite score on the ACT of 19; on the SAT I, 740. Applicants should be graduates of accredited high schools and have completed 15 academic credits, including 2 each in art, a foreign language, mathematics, music, science, and social studies, and 3 in English. A GED is accepted. Recommendations from a pastor must be submitted. AP and CLEP credits are accepted. Important factors used in the admissions decision are personality, intangible qualities, leadership record, advanced placement or honor courses, evidence of special talent, and recommendations by alumni.

Procedure: Freshmen are admitted fall and spring. Application deadlines are open. The fee is $20. Notification is sent on a rolling basis.

Transfer: About 96 transfer students enrolled in 1993-94. Transfer applicants must submit college transcripts. A total of 30 credits out of 126 must be completed at Trinity.

Visiting: There are regularly scheduled orientations for prospective students. There are guides for informal visits and visitors may sit in on classes and stay overnight at the school. To arrange for a visit, contact the Admissions Office at (708) 317-7000 or (800) 822-3225 (out-of-state).

Financial Aid: In a recent year, 87% of all freshmen and continuing students received some form of financial aid. Scholarships or need-based grants averaged $3952 ($10,670 maximum); loans averaged $2179 ($5600 maximum); and work contracts averaged $1603 ($3800 maximum). Sixty-five percent of undergraduate students work part-time. The average financial indebtedness of a recent year's graduate was $7100. Trinity is a member of CSS. The FAF and FAFSA are required.

International Students: There are currently 26 international students enrolled. They must take the TOEFL and achieve a minimum score of 500. The student must also take the SAT I or the ACT.

Computers: The college provides computer facilities for student use, including 25 microcomputers for academic use. All students may access the system. There are no time limits on using the system. The fees are $25.

Graduates: In a recent year, 111 bachelor's degrees were awarded. The most popular majors among graduates were education (18%), business (12%), and youth ministry (10%). In an earlier graduating class, 2% of the men and 1% of the women were enrolled in graduate school within 6 months of graduation.

Admissions Contact: Gary Larson, Director of Admissions and Financial Aid.

UNIVERSITY OF CHICAGO
E-2
Chicago, IL 60637   (312) 702-8650

Full-time: 1924 men, 1442 women	Faculty: 1855; I, + +$
Part-time: 32 men, 19 women	Ph.D.s: 100%
Graduate: 4686 men, 2782 women	Student/Faculty: 2 to 1
Year: quarters, summer session	Tuition: $18,387
Application Deadline: January 15	Room & Board: $6130
Freshman Class: 6335 applied, 2994 accepted, 922 enrolled	
SAT I or ACT: required	MOST COMPETITIVE

The University of Chicago, founded in 1891, is a private, coeducational liberal arts institution offering undergraduate and graduate programs with emphases on the biological and physical sciences, the humanities, and the social sciences. There are 10 graduate schools. In addition to regional accreditation, Chicago has baccalaureate program accreditation with NCATE. The 8 libraries contain 5.5 million volumes, 2 million microform items, 15,000 audiovisual forms, and subscribe to 47,000 periodicals. Computerized library sources and services include the card catalog, interlibrary loans, and database searching. Special learning facilities include a learning resource cen-

ter, art gallery, radio station, film studies center, language laboratories, and museum of Near Eastern antiquities. The 175-acre campus is in an urban area in downtown Chicago. Including residence halls, there are more than 200 buildings on campus.

Student Life: About 73% of undergraduates are from out-of-state, mostly the Midwest. Students come from 50 states, 70 foreign countries, and Canada. Some 69% are from public schools; 31% from private. About 64% are white; 26% Asian American. The average age of freshmen is 18; all undergraduates, 20. About 88% of freshmen remain to graduate.

Housing: A total of 2267 students can be accommodated in college housing. College-sponsored living facilities include coed dormitories, on-campus apartments, and married-student housing. In addition, there is an international house. On-campus housing is guaranteed for all 4 years. Some 66% of students live on campus; of those, 97% remain on campus on weekends. All students may keep cars on campus.

Activities: About 10% of men belong to 9 national fraternities; about 3% of women belong to 2 national sororities. There are more than 150 groups on campus, including art, bagpipe band, band, cheerleading, chess, choir, chorus, computers, dance, drama, ethnic, film, gay, honors, international, jazz band, literary magazine, musical theater, newspaper, orchestra, pep band, photography, political, radio and TV, religious, social, social service, student government, symphony, and yearbook. Popular campus events include Summer Breeze Festival, Kuviasungnerk Winter Festival, Festival of the Arts, and Spring Scavenger Hunt.

Sports: There are 11 intercollegiate sports for men and 9 for women, and 18 intramural sports for men and 18 for women. Athletic and recreation facilities include a gymnasium, field house, 400-seat stadium, 1500-seat arena, and student activities center housing a movie theater, TV and pool rooms, and a pub.

Disabled Students: The entire campus is accessible to disabled students. The following facilities are available: wheelchair ramps, elevators, special parking, specially equipped rest rooms, special class scheduling, lowered drinking fountains, and lowered telephones.

Services: In addition to many counseling and information services, tutoring is available in some subjects, including mathematics, physics, chemistry, writing, and biology. In addition, there is a reader service for the blind and remedial math.

Campus Safety and Security: Campus safety and security measures include 24-hour foot and vehicle patrol, escort service, shuttle buses, and informal discussions. In addition, there are pamphlets, posters, films, emergency telephones, and lighted pathways and sidewalks.

Programs of Study: Chicago awards the B.A. and B.S. degrees. Master's and doctoral degrees also are awarded. Bachelor's degrees are awarded in BIOLOGICAL SCIENCE (biochemistry and biology/biological science), COMMUNICATIONS AND THE ARTS (art history and appreciation, classics, English, fine arts, German, linguistics, music, and Russian), COMPUTER AND PHYSICAL SCIENCE (chemistry, mathematics, physics, and statistics), SOCIAL SCIENCE (anthropology, Asian/Oriental studies, economics, geography, history, Latin American studies, medieval studies, Near Eastern studies, philosophy, political science/government, psychology, religion, and sociology). Biology, philosophy, chemistry, physics, mathematics, political science, and English are the strongest programs academically. Biology, economics, political science, English, history, and psychology have the largest enrollments.

Required: In order to graduate, students must complete 42 quarter courses. The core curriculum includes year-long sequences in humanities, social sciences, biological and physical sciences, civilization, and foreign languages. Also required are 2 quarters of mathematics, 1 of art or music, and 1 year of noncredit physical education. A major requires 9 to 13 courses; students must have an overall GPA of 1.75, with a 2.0 in the major.

Special: Special academic programs include international, national, and local internships in most disciplines as well as a summer internship in Washington, study abroad in Spain, England, France, Germany, Italy, Japan, Czech Republic, Mexico, Hong Kong, Costa Rica, Zimbabwe, and Russia, and work-study in most departments on campus. There are 3-2 programs available through the schools of law, business, social service administration, and public policy. B.A.-B.S. and general studies degrees are offered, as are student designed majors. Nondegree study and pass/fail options are possible. There are 2 national honor societies on campus, including Phi Beta Kappa.

Faculty/Classroom: Some 81% of faculty are male; 19%, female. All teach undergraduates and do research. Graduate students teach 10% of introductory courses. The average class size in an introductory lecture is 25; in a laboratory, 10; and in a regular course offering, 25.

Admissions: About 47% of the 1993–94 applicants were accepted. The SAT scores for the 1993–94 freshman class were as follows: Verbal—9% below 500, 23% between 500 and 599, 49% between 600 and 699, and 19% above 699; Math—2% below 500, 13% between 500 and 599, 38% between 600 and 699, and 47% above 699. The

ACT scores were 2% between 17 and 20, 9% between 21 and 24, 45% between 25 and 29, and 44% above 30. About 89% of the current freshmen were in the top fifth of their class; 99% were in the top two fifths. There were 105 National Merit finalists.

Requirements: The SAT I or ACT is required. Other admissions criteria include a recommended secondary school curriculum of 4 years of English, 3 to 4 years each of history, social studies, mathematics, and science, and 2 to 3 years of a foreign language. The GED is accepted. An essay must be submitted, and an interview is recommended. AP credits are accepted. Important factors used in the admissions decision are advanced placement or honor courses, personality, intangible qualities, evidence of special talent, leadership record, and extracurricular activities record.

Procedure: Freshmen are admitted in the fall. Entrance exams should be taken during the senior year. Early decision applications should be filed by November 15; regular applications, by January 15 for fall entry, along with an application fee of $55. Notification of early decision is sent December 15; regular decision, April 1. There are early decision, early admissions, and deferred admissions plans. About 150 early decision candidates were accepted for the 1993–94 class. A waiting list is an active part of the admissions procedure, with about 5% of applicants on the list.

Transfer: About 193 transfer students enrolled in 1993–94. A total of 18 quarter courses out of 42 must be completed at Chicago.

Visiting: There are regularly scheduled orientations for prospective students, including meeting with an admissions counselor, meeting students, sitting in on classes, visiting faculty, and staying in a residence hall. There are guides for informal visits and visitors may sit in on classes and stay overnight at the school. To arrange for a visit, contact Rebecca Snyder, Assistant Director of Admissions at (312) 702-8658.

Financial Aid: In 1993–94, 80% of all students received some form of financial aid. About 61% of freshmen and 56% of continuing students received need-based aid. The average freshman award was $16,448. Of that total, scholarships or need-based grants averaged $9632 ($21,000 maximum); loans averaged $2110 ($2450 maximum); and work contracts averaged $1737 ($2100 maximum). Some 60% of undergraduate students work part-time. Average earnings from campus work for the school year are $2100. The average financial indebtedness of the 1992–93 graduate was $10,000. Chicago is a member of CSS. The FAF and the college's own financial statement are required. The deadline for financial aid applications is February 1.

International Students: There are currently 108 international students enrolled. The school actively recruits these students. They must take the TOEFL, and also the SAT I or the ACT.

Computers: The college provides computer facilities for student use. The mainframe is an Amdahl 5880; there are 2 Sun minicomputers, and a Silicon Graphics 4D/240 minicomputer. Students are able to access the Amdahl or the Suns through personal user accounts. In addition, there are 7 public computer clusters with IBM PCs and Apple Macintoshes as well as computer clusters in many of the residence halls. All residence hall rooms are linked to the campus computer network. All students may access the system. It may be used anytime. There are no time limits on using the system and no fees.

Graduates: In 1992–93, 714 bachelor's degrees were awarded. The most popular majors among graduates were biological sciences (10%), economics (10%), and English (9%). Within an average freshman class, 4% graduate in 3 years, 75% in 4 years, and 88% in 5 years. Some 96 companies recruited on campus in 1992–93. In the 1992 graduating class, 33% of men and women enrolled in graduate school within 6 months of graduation; 61% had found employment.

Admissions Contact: Theodore O'Neill, Dean of College Admissions.

UNIVERSITY OF ILLINOIS

The University of Illinois, established in 1867, is a public system. It is governed by a board of trustees, whose chief administrator is the president. The primary goal of the system is to provide undergraduate and graduate education, conduct research, and provide public service. There is a 4-year campus located in Chicago and one in Urbana-Champaign. The total enrollment in fall 1993 of both campuses was 61,606; there were 4860 faculty members. Altogether there are 173 baccalaureate, 198 master's, and 131 doctoral programs offered at University of Illinois. Profiles of the 4-year campuses are included in this chapter in alphabetical order with other Illinois schools.

UNIVERSITY OF ILLINOIS AT CHICAGO
Chicago, IL 60680

E-2
(312) 996-0952

Full-time: 6564 men, 6954 women
Part-time: 1474 men, 1442 women
Graduate: 4065 men, 4671 women
Year: semesters, summer session
Application Deadline: February 28
Freshman Class: 8384 applied, 5727 accepted, 2710 enrolled
ACT: 21

Faculty: 1004; I, -$
Ph.D.s: 82%
Student/Faculty: 13 to 1
Tuition: $3445 ($7898)
Room & Board: $4988

COMPETITIVE

The University of Illinois at Chicago, founded in 1946, is a public, primarily commuter institution with degree programs in the liberal arts, art and fine arts, business, engineering, architecture, health sciences, music, teacher preparation, social work, and preprofessional training. There are 8 undergraduate schools and 1 graduate school. In addition to regional accreditation, UIC has baccalaureate program accreditation with AACSB, ABET, ACPE, ADA, APTA, CSWE, NAAB, NASAD, and NLN. The 5 libraries contain 1,782,637 volumes, 2,112,590 microform items, and 417,189 audiovisual forms, and subscribe to 21,119 periodicals. Computerized library sources and services include the card catalog, interlibrary loans, and database searching. Special learning facilities include a learning resource center, art gallery, the Jane Addams Hull House, which is a restored settlement house, and the James Woodworth Prairie Reserve. The 183-acre campus is in an urban area just west of downtown Chicago. Including residence halls, there are 78 buildings on campus.

Student Life: About 95% of undergraduates are from Illinois. Students come from 44 states, 49 foreign countries, and Canada. Sixty percent are from public schools; 40% from private. Fifty percent are white; 18% Asian American; 16% Hispanic; 11% African American. The average age of freshmen is 18.4; all undergraduates, 22.5. Thirty percent drop out by the end of their first year; 40% remain to graduate.

Housing: A total of 2450 students can be accommodated in college housing. College-sponsored living facilities include coed dormitories. In addition there are honors floors, special interest floors, and the President's Award House. On-campus housing is available on a first-come, first-served basis. Ninety percent of students commute. All students may keep cars on campus.

Activities: About 2% of men belong to 8 national fraternities; about 2% of women belong to 5 national sororities. There are 148 groups on campus, including art, band, cheerleading, choir, chorus, computers, dance, drama, ethnic, gay, honors, international, jazz band, literary magazine, newspaper, political, professional, religious, social, social service, and student government. Popular campus events include Friday Night Live in Inner Circle, Tuesdays-Musical Events, Monthly Fine Arts Series, Cultural Festival (Spring), UIC Jazz Festival, and UIC Blues Cabaret.

Sports: There are 8 intercollegiate sports for men and 7 for women, and 10 intramural sports for men and 10 for women. Athletic and recreation facilities include a sports pavilion, a sports and fitness center, and a recreation center; there is a 10,000-seat gymnasium, a 12,000-seat arena, 3 pools, racquetball and tennis courts, a baseball field, a bowling alley, indoor and outdoor tracks, and weight rooms.

Disabled Students: Seventy-five percent of the campus is accessible to disabled students. The following facilities are available: wheelchair ramps, elevators, special parking, specially equipped rest rooms, special class scheduling, lowered drinking fountains, and lowered telephones.

Services: In addition to many counseling and information services, tutoring is available in most subjects. There also is a reader service for the blind, and remedial math, reading, and writing.

Campus Safety and Security: Campus safety and security measures include 24-hour foot and vehicle patrol, self defense education, escort service, and shuttle buses. In addition, there are informal discussions, pamphlets, posters, and films, emergency telephones, and lighted pathways and sidewalks.

Programs of Study: UIC awards the A.B., B.S., B.Arch., B.F.A., B.S.C.E., B.S.Ch.E., B.S.C.S. and E., B.S.E.E., B.S.E.M., B.S.E.M.A.N., B.S.M.E., B.S.N., and B.S.W. degrees. Master's and doctoral degrees also are awarded. Bachelor's degrees are awarded in BIOLOGICAL SCIENCE (biochemistry, biology/biological science, and nutrition), BUSINESS (accounting, banking and finance, business administration and management, business statistics, management science, and marketing/retailing/merchandising), COMMUNICATIONS AND THE ARTS (art history and appreciation, classics, design, French, German, graphic design, industrial design, Italian, literature, music, photography, Polish, Russian, Spanish, speech/debate/rhetoric, and studio art), COMPUTER AND PHYSICAL SCIENCE (chemistry, computer management, computer science, geology, information sciences and systems, mathematics, physics, and statistics), EDUCATION (art, education, elementary, English, foreign languages, mathematics, physical, science, secondary, and social studies), ENGINEERING AND ENVIRONMENTAL DESIGN (architectural engineering, archi-

tecture, bioengineering, chemical engineering, civil engineering, computer engineering, electrical/electronics engineering, engineering, engineering management, engineering mechanics, engineering physics, industrial engineering technology, materials science, mechanical engineering, and metallurgical engineering), HEALTH PROFESSIONS (health care administration, medical laboratory science, nursing, occupational therapy, physical therapy, and predentistry), SOCIAL SCIENCE (African American studies, anthropology, classical/ancient civilization, criminal justice, criminology, economics, geography, history, Judaic studies, Latin American studies, philosophy, political science/government, psychology, social work, and sociology). Mathematics, nursing, philosophy, and sciences are the strongest academically. Accounting, engineering, and psychology have the largest enrollments.

Required: Students must demonstrate proficiency in English through either course work or testing, and complete 24 hours of general education including 6 hours each of humanities, social sciences, and natural sciences; the remaining 6 may be spread across the 3 categories. A minimum overall GPA of 3.0 on a 5.0 scale is required. Total number of hours to graduate varies by major but is always at least 120.

Special: UIC offers a wide variety of co-op and program internships, work-study with some 70 on- and off-campus employers, and study-abroad opportunities at accredited foreign universities as well as special programs in France, Italy, Canada, Austria, Spain, and Mexico. There is cross-registration with the City Colleges of Chicago. Dual majors, interdisciplinary majors, including architectural studies, communications and theater, French business studies, mathematics and computer science, and information and decision sciences, and student-designed majors are offered. Students may pursue a 3-2 engineering degree with Chicago State Eastern Illinois, Illinois State, Northeastern Illinois, and Western Illinois universities. Up to 4 semester hours of credit may be granted for military experience. Nondegree study and pass/fail options are available. There is a freshman honors program on campus, as well as 10 national honor societies, including Phi Beta Kappa. UIC has an Honors College.

Faculty/Classroom: Seventy percent of faculty are male; 30%, female. Fifty percent teach undergraduates and all do research. The average class size in an introductory lecture is 126; in a laboratory, 26; and in a regular course offering, 31.

Admissions: About 68% of the 1993–94 applicants were accepted. The ACT scores for the 1993–94 freshman class were as follows: 49% below 21, 28% between 21 and 23, 15% between 24 and 26, 5% between 27 and 28, and 3% above 28. About 40% of the current freshmen were in the top fifth of their class; 73% were in the top two fifths. Three freshmen graduated first in their class.

Requirements: UIC requires applicants to be in the upper 70% of their class. The SAT I or ACT is required. Other admission requirements include graduation from an accredited secondary school; the GED also is accepted. The recommended secondary school curriculum varies according to the college program to be followed, but 16 high school credits are required. AP and CLEP credits are accepted. Important factors used in the admissions decision are evidence of special talent, advanced placement or honor courses, geographic diversity, recommendations by school officials, and leadership record.

Procedure: Freshmen are admitted to all sessions. Entrance exams should be taken in the spring of the junior year or the fall of the senior year. Applications should be filed by February 28 for fall entry, October 29 for spring entry, and April 15 for summer entry, along with an application fee of $30. Notification is sent on a rolling basis. There are early admissions and deferred admissions plans.

Transfer: A total of 2159 transfer students enrolled in 1993–94. Transferable hours and minimum GPA vary according to program. A total of 45 credits out of 120 must be completed at UIC.

Visiting: There are regularly scheduled orientations for prospective students, consisting of a general meeting, a college meeting, campus tours, and an admissions video. There are guides for informal visits and visitors may sit in on classes. To arrange for a visit, contact the Office of Undergraduate Admissions at (312) 996-4350.

Financial Aid: In a recent year, 66% of all current freshmen and 59% of continuing students received some form of financial aid. About 62% of freshmen and 53% of continuing students received need-based aid. The average freshman award was $4900. Twenty-one percent of undergraduate students work part-time. Average earnings from campus work for the school year are $1994. The FAF, FFS, or SFS is required. The deadline for financial aid applications is November 1.

International Students: There are currently 334 international students enrolled. Applicants must take the TOEFL or the University of Michigan Language Test and achieve a minimum score on the TOEFL of 480. Those entering as freshmen must also take the SAT I or ACT, with a minimum ACT score of 12 required.

Computers: UIC provides computer facilities for student use. The mainframe is an IBM 3090–300J. Numerous terminals and microcomputers are located in laboratories, classrooms, libraries, and residence

halls throughout the campus. All students may access the system 24 hours daily. There are no time limits on using the system and no fees.

Graduates: In 1992–93, 2533 bachelor's degrees were awarded. The most popular majors among graduates were accounting (8%), psychology (7%), and biological sciences (5%). Within an average freshman class, 11% graduate in 4 years and 26% in 5 years. A total of 175 companies recruited on campus in 1992–93. In the 1992 graduating class, 14% of all students were enrolled in graduate school within 6 months of graduation; 68% of all students had found employment.

Admissions Contact: Marilyn Fiduccia, Executive Director.

UNIVERSITY OF ILLINOIS AT URBANA-CHAMPAIGN
Urbana, IL 61801
E–3
(217) 333–0302

Full-time: 14,204 men, 11,218 women	Faculty: 1549; I, av$
Part-time: 531 men, 380 women	Ph.D.s: 93%
Graduate: 5973 men, 4130 women	Student/Faculty: 16 to 1
Year: semesters, summer session	Tuition: $3406 ($7658)
Application Deadline: January 1	Room & Board: $4358
Freshman Class: 14,939 applied, 11,652 accepted, 5692 enrolled	
SAT I or ACT: required	**HIGHLY COMPETITIVE**

The University of Illinois at Urbana-Champaign, founded in 1867, is the oldest and largest campus in the University of Illinois system, offering some 150 undergraduate and more than 100 graduate degree programs. There are 10 undergraduate and 3 graduate schools. In addition to regional accreditation, Illinois has baccalaureate program accreditation with AACSB, ABET, ACEJMC, ASLA, CSWE, NAAB, NASAD, NASM, NCATE, and SAF. The 39 libraries contain 8,096,040 volumes, 3.3 million microform items, and 64,605 audiovisual forms, and subscribe to 93,851 periodicals. Computerized library sources and services include the card catalog, interlibrary loans, and database searching. Special learning facilities include an art gallery, natural history museum, radio station, TV station, language learning laboratory, performing arts center, and graphic technologies laboratory. The 705-acre campus is in a small city 130 miles south of Chicago. Including residence halls, there are 185 buildings on campus.

Student Life: About 93% of undergraduates are from Illinois. Students come from 50 states, 116 foreign countries, and Canada. Seventy-four percent are white; 12% Asian American. The average age of freshmen is 18.4; all undergraduates, 20.4. Nine percent drop out by the end of their first year; 79% remain to graduate.

Housing: A total of 9000 students can be accommodated in college housing. College-sponsored living facilities include coed dormitories, on-campus apartments, married-student housing, fraternity houses, and sorority houses. In addition, there are language houses, special interest houses, and privately owned residence halls. On-campus housing is available on a first-come, first-served basis. All students may keep cars on campus.

Activities: About 22% of men belong to 3 local and 53 national fraternities; about 26% of women belong to 3 local and 25 national sororities. There are 700 groups on campus, including art, band, cheerleading, chess, choir, chorale, chorus, computers, dance, drama, drill team, ethnic, film, gay, honors, international, jazz band, literary magazine, marching band, musical theater, newspaper, opera, orchestra, pep band, photography, political, professional, radio and TV, religious, social, social service, student government, symphony, and yearbook. Popular campus events include Homecoming, Quad Day to introduce campus organizations, Dads Weekend, Moms Weekend, and Commencement.

Sports: There are 10 intercollegiate sports for men and 8 for women, and 33 intramural sports for men and 32 for women. Athletic and recreation facilities include one of the world's largest intramural sports and recreation buildings, numerous student union facilities, and acres of outdoor playing fields. Memorial Football Stadium seats 69,000 and Assembly Hall seats 16,000 for basketball games, concerts, and special events.

Disabled Students: The entire campus is accessible to disabled students. The following facilities are available: wheelchair ramps, elevators, special parking, specially equipped rest rooms, special class scheduling, lowered drinking fountains, lowered telephones, and housing.

Services: In addition to many counseling and information services, tutoring is available in every subject. There also is a reader service for the blind. Transportation and rehabilitation services are offered.

Campus Safety and Security: Campus safety and security measures include 24-hour foot and vehicle patrol, self defense education, escort service, and shuttle buses. In addition, there are informal discussions, pamphlets, posters, and films, emergency telephones, lighted pathways and sidewalks, and safety presentations and evaluations by campus police.

Programs of Study: Illinois awards the A.B., B.S., B.Arch., B.A.U.P., B.F.A., B.Land.Arch., B.Mus., B.S.W., and B.V.M. degrees. Master's and doctoral degrees also are awarded. Bachelor's degrees are awarded in AGRICULTURE (agriculture, animal science, forestry and related sciences, horticulture, and soil science), BIOLOGICAL SCIENCE (biochemistry), BUSINESS (accounting, banking and finance, business administration and management, hotel/motel and restaurant management, and recreation and leisure services), COMMUNICATIONS AND THE ARTS (advertising, applied art, art history and appreciation, crafts, dance, dramatic arts, graphic design, industrial design, journalism, media arts, music, painting, photography, and sculpture), COMPUTER AND PHYSICAL SCIENCE (chemistry, computer science, geology, and physics), EDUCATION (agricultural, art, business, early childhood, education of the mentally handicapped, elementary, English, foreign languages, health, home economics, mathematics, music, physical, science, secondary, social studies, and speech correction), ENGINEERING AND ENVIRONMENTAL DESIGN (aeronautical engineering, agricultural engineering, architecture, ceramic engineering, chemical engineering, city/community/regional planning, civil engineering, computer engineering, electrical/electronics engineering, engineering, engineering mechanics, engineering physics, industrial engineering technology, landscape architecture/design, mechanical engineering, metallurgical engineering, and nuclear engineering), HEALTH PROFESSIONS (speech pathology/audiology), SOCIAL SCIENCE (economics, family/consumer studies, food production/management/services, food science, home economics, liberal arts/general studies, and social work). Psychology, accountancy, electrical engineering, biology, and civil engineering have the largest enrollments.

Required: All students must demonstrate proficiency in the use of the English language, complete 6 hours each in humanities, social sciences, and natural sciences, and maintain a minimum GPA of 3.0 on a 5.0 scale. Minimum hours needed to graduate range from 120 to 132, depending on the major.

Special: Illinois offers cooperative engineering programs with 30 Midwestern liberal arts colleges; 16 summer, semester, and full-year programs abroad and numerous exchange opportunities; and cross-registration with Parkland College. Unusual opportunities include a leisure studies semester in Scotland and a summer parliamentary internship in London. A dual degree in liberal arts and engineering is offered, as well as student-designed majors and a 3–2 engineering program with numerous universities. On-campus work-study and pass/fail options are possible. There is a freshman honors program on campus.

Faculty/Classroom: Eighty percent of faculty are male; 20%, female. Ninety-eight percent teach undergraduates and all do research. The average class size in an introductory lecture is 125; in a laboratory, 18; and in a regular course offering, 29.

Admissions: About 78% of the 1993–94 applicants were accepted. The ACT scores for the 1993–94 freshman class were as follows: 5% below 21, 12% between 21 and 23, 29% between 24 and 26, 32% between 27 and 29, and 22% above 29. About 82% of the current freshmen were in the top fifth of their class; 96% were in the top two fifths. There were 43 National Merit finalists. A total of 564 freshmen graduated first in their class.

Requirements: The ACT or SAT I is required. Applicants should be graduates of accredited secondary schools or have the GED. High school preparation must include 4 years of English, 3 or more of mathematics, 2 each of laboratory science and social studies, and, for most programs, 2 of foreign languages. A personal essay is optional. Visual arts applicants must submit a portfolio; performing arts applicants are required to audition. AP and CLEP credits are accepted. Important factors used in the admissions decision are evidence of special talent, advanced placement or honor courses, geographic diversity, recommendations by school officials, and leadership record.

Procedure: Freshmen are admitted fall and spring. Entrance exams should be taken by spring of the junior year, and no later than October of the senior year. Applications should be filed by January 1 for fall entry and November 1 for spring entry, along with an application fee of $30. Notification is sent February 20. There is a deferred admissions plan.

Transfer: A total of 1155 transfer students enrolled in 1993–94. Transfer application requirements differ by degree program. Generally, students transferring from the Chicago campus should have junior standing of 60 hours; students from other institutions must have at least a C average in previous college work. Admission is also subject to the number of places available. A total of 30 credits out of 120 to 132 must be completed at Illinois.

Visiting: There are regularly scheduled orientations for prospective students, consisting of presentations given by the admissions staff at 10 A.M. and 1 P.M. daily on weekdays; a videotape of the campus is shown and tours are provided. There are guides for informal visits and visitors may sit in on classes. To arrange for a visit, contact the Campus Visitors Center at (217) 333–0824.

Financial Aid: In 1993–94, 82% of all current freshmen and 80% of continuing students received some form of financial aid. About 50% of all students received need-based aid. The average freshman award was $5500. Of that total, scholarships or need-based grants averaged $2090 ($5625 maximum); loans averaged $1925 ($2600 maximum); and work contracts averaged $1485. Fifty-three percent of undergraduate students work part-time. Average earnings from campus work for the school year are $700. The average financial indebtedness of the 1992–93 graduate was $6340. Illinois is a member of CSS. The college's own financial statement and the FAFSA are required. The deadline for financial aid applications is March 15.

International Students: There are currently 350 international students enrolled. Applicants must take the TOEFL or the University of Michigan Language Test and achieve a minimum score on the TOEFL of 550.

Computers: Illinois provides computer facilities for student use. The mainframes are an IBM RS6000/540, an IBM 380, a Sequent Symmetry S81, and a Convex C240. About 8000 computer workstations are located in classrooms, laboratories, and residence halls across campus. All students may access the system 24 hours a day. There are no time limits on using the system and no fees.

Graduates: In 1992–93, 5779 bachelor's degrees were awarded. The most popular majors among graduates were psychology (6%), biology (5%), and accounting (5%). Within an average freshman class, 1% graduate in 3 years, 52% in 4 years, 76% in 5 years, and 79% in 6 years. Some 1200 companies recruited on campus in 1992–93. In the 1992 graduating class, 40% of all students enrolled in graduate school within 6 months of graduation; 69% of all students had found employment.

Admissions Contact: Tammie Bouseman, Assistant Director for Undergraduate Admissions.

VANDERCOOK COLLEGE OF MUSIC E-2
Chicago, IL 60616–3886   (312) 225–6288
                                    (800) 448–2655 (out-of-state)

Full-time: 29 men, 20 women	Faculty: 11
Part-time: 1 man, 2 women	Ph.Ds: 70%
Graduate: 59 men, 32 women	Student/Faculty: 4 to 1
Year: semesters	Tuition: $8930
Application Deadline: June 1	Room & Board: $4600
Freshman Class: 28 applied, 25 accepted, 19 enrolled	
ACT: 20	**SPECIAL**

VanderCook College of Music, founded in 1909, is the only private institution in the United States devoted solely to the preparation of music educators. In addition to regional accreditation, VCM has baccalaureate program accreditation with NASM. The library contains 20,000 volumes, 2000 microform items, and 5000 audiovisual forms, and subscribes to 80 periodicals. Special learning facilities include a learning resource center. The 1-acre campus is in an urban area 3 miles from the center of Chicago. Including residence halls, there is 1 building on campus.

Student Life: About 60% of undergraduates are from Illinois. Students come from 11 states. Eighty percent are from public schools; 20% from private. Sixty-three percent are white; 32% African American. The average age of freshmen is 19; all undergraduates, 21. Eight percent drop out by the end of their first year; 80% remain to graduate.

Housing: College-sponsored living facilities include single-sex and coed dormitories. On-campus housing is guaranteed for all 4 years. Alcohol is not permitted. All students may keep cars on campus.

Activities: About 20% of men belong to 2 local and 1 national fraternity; about 20% of women belong to 2 local and 1 national sorority. There are a number of groups on campus, including band, choir, chorale, chorus, jazz band, orchestra, pep band, religious, and student government.

Sports: There is no sports program at VCM. Athletic and recreation facilities include a swimming pool, a gymnasium, and tennis courts.

Disabled Students: The following facilities are available: special parking and special class scheduling.

Campus Safety and Security: Campus safety and security measures include 24-hour foot and vehicle patrol, self defense education, escort service, and informal discussions. In addition, there are emergency telephones and lighted pathways and sidewalks.

Programs of Study: VCM awards the B.M.Ed. degree. Master's degrees also are awarded. Bachelor's degrees are awarded in EDUCATION (music).

Required: To graduate, students must complete a total of 134 semester hours distributed in the 5 major categories of general education, professional education, applied music performance, fundamentals and theory, and music education. They must also pass performance proficiency examinations on 17 instruments and a vocal proficiency examination.

Faculty/Classroom: Forty-four percent of faculty are male; 56%, female. All teach undergraduates. No introductory courses are taught by graduate students. The average class size in an introductory lecture is 15; in a laboratory, 15; and in a regular course offering, 15.

Admissions: About 89% of the 1993–94 applicants were accepted. About 20% of the current freshmen were in the top fifth of their class; 80% were in the top two fifths. There was 1 National Merit semifinalist.

Requirements: VCM requires applicants to be in the upper 50% of their class. A minimum GPA of 2.0 is required. The SAT I or the ACT is required, with a minimum composite score of 900 on the SAT I or 18 on the ACT. Graduation from an accredited secondary school or a satisfactory score on the GED is required for admission. Secondary school courses must include 1 unit each of history and art, 3 each of English and science, 2 each of mathematics, social studies, music, and a foreign language. An audition and an interview are required. AP and CLEP credits are accepted. Important factors used in the admissions decision are evidence of special talent, recommendations by alumni, extracurricular activities record, parents or siblings attending the school, and leadership record.

Procedure: Freshmen are admitted fall and spring. Entrance exams should be taken during the junior year. Early decision applications should be filed by December 1; regular applications, by June 1 for fall entry and October 1 for winter entry, along with an application fee of $25. Notification of early decision is sent in January; regular decision, on a rolling basis. There are early decision and deferred admissions plans. Eight early decision candidates were accepted for the 1993–94 class.

Transfer: Nine transfer students enrolled in 1993–94. Transfer students must have a minimum GPA of 2.5. An audition and an interview are required. Courses taken at other institutions in performance, theory, and history must be validated.

Visiting: There are regularly scheduled orientations for prospective students. There are guides for informal visits and visitors may sit in on classes and stay overnight at the school. To arrange for a visit, contact the Admissions Counselor at (312) 225–6288.

Financial Aid: In 1993–94, 95% of all current freshmen and 90% of continuing students received some form of financial aid. About 70% of freshmen and 75% of continuing students received need-based aid. The average freshman award was $2000. Of that total, scholarships or need-based grants averaged $2100 ($5000 maximum); and loans averaged $2500 (maximum). Sixty percent of undergraduate students work part-time. Average earnings from campus work for the school year are $1000. The average financial indebtedness of the 1992–93 graduate was $6000. VCM is a member of CSS. The FAFSA financial statement is required. The deadline for financial aid applications is June 1.

International Students: They must take the TOEFL and achieve a minimum score of 500.

Computers: The college provides computer facilities for student use. Apple Macintosh microcomputers are available. All students may access the system.

Graduates: In 1992–93, 10 bachelor's degrees were awarded in music education. Within an average freshman class, 90% graduate in 4 years and 10% in 5 years. In the 1992 graduating class, 50% of the graduates had found employment within 6 months of graduation.

Admissions Contact: Ann Zajec, Admissions Counselor.

WEST SUBURBAN COLLEGE OF NURSING E-2
Oak Park, IL 60302   (708) 209–3100; (800) 285–2668

Full-time: 176 men and women	Faculty: 14
Part-time: 62 men and women	Ph.Ds: 23%
Graduate: none	Student/Faculty: 13 to 1
Year: quarters, summer session	Tuition: $9575
Application Deadline: open	Room & Board: $4035
Freshman Class: 45 applied, 31 accepted, 4 enrolled	
ACT: 23	**VERY COMPETITIVE**

West Suburban College of Nursing, founded in 1982, is a private, nonsectarian college of nursing offering a joint-degree program with Concordia University in River Forest. In addition to regional accreditation, West Sub has baccalaureate program accreditation with NLN. The library contains 3000 volumes and 1000 audiovisual forms, and subscribes to 350 periodicals. Computerized library sources and services include the card catalog, interlibrary loans, and database searching. The 20-acre campus is in a suburban area 10 miles west of downtown Chicago. There is one building on campus.

Student Life: About 80% of undergraduates are from Illinois. Students come from 10 states and 1 foreign country. Sixty percent are from public schools; 40% from private. Seventy-three percent are white; 15% African American; 10% Asian American. The average age of freshmen is 18; all undergraduates, 25. About 70% of freshmen remain to graduate.

Housing: There are no residence halls. On-campus housing is provided at Concordia University and is guaranteed for all 4 years. Fifty percent of students live on campus. Alcohol is not permitted. All students may keep cars on campus.

Activities: There are no fraternities or sororities on campus. There are many groups and organizations on campus, including band, cheerleading, choir, chorus, drama, musical theater, newspaper, orchestra, photography, professional, radio and TV, religious, social, social service, student government, and yearbook.

Sports: There is no sports program at West Sub.

Disabled Students: Lowered drinking fountains are available.

Services: Remedial math, reading, and writing is available.

Campus Safety and Security: Campus safety and security measures include escort service, shuttle buses, and lighted pathways and sidewalks.

Programs of Study: West Sub awards the B.S. degree. Bachelor's degrees are awarded in HEALTH PROFESSIONS (nursing).

Required: In order to graduate, students must have a total of 192 quarter hours with a minimum GPA of 2.0. Seventy-two quarter hours are required in major. All students must take courses in nursing, psychology, sociology, chemistry, anatomy, physiology, microbiology, statistics, physical education, humanities, communications skills, and theology.

Faculty/Classroom: All of faculty are female and all teach undergraduates. The average class size in an introductory lecture is 25; in a laboratory, 6; and in a regular course offering, 12.

Admissions: About 69% of the 1993–94 applicants were accepted.

Requirements: West Sub requires applicants to be in the upper 33% of their class. A minimum GPA of 2.3 is required. The ACT is required. Graduation from an accredited secondary school or satisfactory scores on the GED are required for admission. Sixteen academic credits are required, including 4 years of English and 1 unit each in chemistry and biology, as well as courses in mathematics, history, and social studies. The ACT is required, with a minimum composite score of 20 recommended. A personal recommendation and an essay are also required. AP and CLEP credits are accepted. Important factors used in the admissions decision are recommendations by school officials, advanced placement or honor courses, personality, intangible qualities, parents or siblings attending the school, and recommendations by alumni.

Procedure: Freshmen are admitted to all sessions. Entrance exams should be taken in the spring of the junior year. Application deadlines are open. Application fee is $25. Notification is sent on a rolling basis.

Transfer: About 50 transfer students enrolled in a recent year. Transfer students must have a minimum GPA of 2.3 on all colleges courses completed. An interview is recommended. A total of 56 quarter credits out of 192 must be completed at West Sub.

Visiting: There are regularly scheduled orientations for prospective students, including open houses. There are guides for informal visits and visitors may sit in on classes and stay overnight at the school. To arrange for a visit, contact the Admissions Office at (708) 209–3100.

Financial Aid: In a recent year, 80% of all current freshmen and 80% of continuing students received some form of financial aid. West Sub is a member of CSS. The FAF is required. The deadline for financial aid applications is May 1.

International Students: Students must take the University of Michigan Language Test or the TOEFL (minimum score of 525 required). They must also take the ACT.

Computers: The college provides computer facilities for student use. Available computers are located on the Concordia University campus.

Graduates: In 1992–93, 28 bachelor's degrees were awarded. In the 1992 graduating class, all graduates had found employment within 6 months of graduation.

Admissions Contact: Edward Pryor, Director of Admissions.

WESTERN ILLINOIS UNIVERSITY
Macomb, IL 61455

C-3

(309) 298–3157

Full-time: 4806 men, 4209 women	Faculty: 635; IIA, --$
Part-time: 705 men, 744 women	Ph.D.s: 66%
Graduate: 954 men, 1459 women	Student/Faculty: 14 to 1
Year: semesters, summer session	Tuition: $2198 ($5894)
Application Deadline: August 10	Room & Board: $3043
Freshman Class: 6491 applied, 5027 accepted, 1563 enrolled	
ACT: 22	**LESS COMPETITIVE**

Western Illinois University, founded in 1899, is a state institution with 6 colleges and a school of graduate and international studies. In addition to regional accreditation, Western has baccalaureate program accreditation with AACSB, ADA, NASM, NCATE, and NRPA. The library contains 680,000 volumes, 900,000 microform items, and 450,000 audiovisual forms, and subscribes to 3700 periodicals. Computerized library sources and services include the card catalog, interlibrary loans, and database searching. Special learning facilities include a learning resource center, art gallery, natural history museum, radio station, and TV station. The 1050-acre campus is in a rural area 80 miles west of Peoria and 150 miles north of St. Louis. Including residence halls, there are 53 buildings on campus.

Student Life: About 93% of undergraduates are from Illinois. Students come from 34 states, 52 foreign countries, and Canada. Eighty-five percent are from public schools; 15% from private. Eighty-one percent are white. Sixty-six percent are Protestant; 32% Catholic. The average age of freshmen is 18; all undergraduates, 22.8. Twenty percent drop out by the end of their first year; 48% remain to graduate.

Housing: A total of 5200 students can be accommodated in college housing. College-sponsored living facilities include single-sex and coed dormitories, on-campus apartments, and married-student housing. In addition there are honors and special interest houses, and academic majors, honors, and wellness floors in residential halls. On-campus housing is guaranteed for all 4 years. Alcohol is not permitted. All students may keep cars on campus.

Activities: About 13% of men belong to 20 national fraternities; about 10% of women belong to 22 national sororities. There are 240 groups on campus, including art, band, cheerleading, chess, choir, chorale, chorus, computers, dance, drama, drill team, drum and bugle corps, ethnic, gay, honors, international, jazz band, literary magazine, marching band, musical theater, newspaper, orchestra, pep band, photography, political, professional, radio and TV, religious, social, social service, student government, symphony, and yearbook. Popular campus events include Homecoming, Family Weekend, Summer Music Theater, International Bazaar, Art Gallery, and concerts and recitals.

Sports: There are 10 intercollegiate sports for men and 8 for women, and 22 intramural sports for men and 21 for women. Athletic and recreation facilities include a 9-hole golf course, tennis courts, a football field, a basketball court, and a swimming pool.

Disabled Students: Ninety-five percent of the campus is accessible to disabled students. The following facilities are available: wheelchair ramps, elevators, special parking, specially equipped rest rooms, special class scheduling, lowered drinking fountains, and lowered telephones.

Services: In addition to many counseling and information services, tutoring is available in most subjects, including English, mathematics, reading, business, and science. In addition, there is a reader service for the blind, and remedial math, reading, and writing.

Campus Safety and Security: Campus safety and security measures include 24-hour foot and vehicle patrol, self defense education, escort service, and informal discussions. In addition, there are pamphlets, posters, and films, emergency telephones, lighted pathways and sidewalks, and a beacon system.

Programs of Study: Western awards the B.A., B.S., B.B., B.F.A., B.S.Ed., and B.S.W. degrees. Master's degrees also are awarded. Bachelor's degrees are awarded in AGRICULTURE (agriculture and forestry and related sciences), BIOLOGICAL SCIENCE (biology/biological science), BUSINESS (accounting, banking and finance, business administration and management, management science, marketing/retailing/merchandising, personnel management, and transportation management), COMMUNICATIONS AND THE ARTS (communications, dramatic arts, English, fine arts, French, German, music, and Spanish), COMPUTER AND PHYSICAL SCIENCE (chemistry, computer science, geology, mathematics, and physics), EDUCATION (bilingual/bicultural, business, early childhood, elementary, health, home economics, industrial arts, secondary, and special), ENGINEERING AND ENVIRONMENTAL DESIGN (industrial engineering technology and preengineering), HEALTH PROFESSIONS (health science, medical laboratory technology, predentistry, premedicine, prepharmacy, preveterinary science, and speech pathology/audiology), SOCIAL SCIENCE (corrections, criminal justice, economics, geography, history, parks and recreation management, philosophy, political science/government, prelaw, psychology, and sociology). Accounting, chemistry, human resource management, music, and operations management are the strongest academically. Communication arts and sciences, law enforcement, and elementary education have the largest enrollments.

Required: In order to graduate, all students must complete at least 120 credit hours and have a minimum 2.0 GPA. Students must take 44 hours in the fields of basic skills, well being, natural science and mathematics, historical and social foundations, and humanities. A writing examination is also required.

Special: The university offers internships in business, law enforcement, and physical training, study abroad in 2 countries, dual majors, student-designed majors, and independent study through the Experimental Studies, the Board of Governors B.A., and the Kaskaskia programs. The Board of Governors degree program offers credit for work experience. Also available are a field campus and a life science station on the Mississippi river, a 3–2 engineering program with the University of Illinois, and a premedical program with Southern Illinois University at Carbondale. There is a freshman honors program on

campus, as well as 30 national honor societies. Thirty-seven departments have honors programs.

Faculty/Classroom: Sixty-six percent of faculty are male; 34%, female. Ninety-five percent teach undergraduates, 90% do research and also teach. The average class size in an introductory lecture is 40; in a laboratory, 25; and in a regular course offering, 28.

Admissions: About 77% of the 1993–94 applicants were accepted. The ACT scores for the 1993–94 freshman class were as follows: 54% below 21, 28% between 21 and 23, 12% between 24 and 26, 4% between 27 and 28, and 2% above 28. About 19% of the current freshmen were in the top fifth of their class; 48% were in the top two fifths. Ten freshmen graduated first in their class.

Requirements: Western requires applicants to be in the upper 50% of their class. The SAT I, minimum composite score of 700, or the ACT, minimum composite score of 18, is required in the admissions decision and for placement purposes. Students must have completed 3 years of English (4 are recommended), 2 years each of mathematics, science, and social studies, and 2 electives in a foreign language or fine arts. The Academic Services is a multicultural recruitment and supportive admissions program for selected students who do not meet freshman or transfer requirements. AP and CLEP credits are accepted. Important factors used in the admissions decision are advanced placement or honor courses, evidence of special talent, recommendations by school officials, geographic diversity, and leadership record.

Procedure: Freshmen are admitted fall, spring, and summer. Entrance exams should be taken no later than April of the senior year. Early decision applications should be filed by August 15; regular applications, by August 10 for fall entry, December 5 for spring entry, and June 1 for summer entry. Notification is sent on a rolling basis. There are early decision, early admissions, and deferred admissions plans.

Transfer: A total of 1358 transfer students enrolled in 1993–94. Students transferring fewer than 24 semester credits or 36 quarter credits must submit a high school transcript or GED certificate, have scored at least 22 on the ACT, and be in good standing at their last school. A minimum 2.0 GPA is required. A total of 30 credits out of 120 must be completed at Western.

Visiting: There are regularly scheduled orientations for prospective students. There are guides for informal visits and visitors may sit in on classes and stay overnight at the school. To arrange for a visit, contact the Admissions Office at (309) 298-3157.

Financial Aid: In a recent year, 62% of all current freshmen and 64% of continuing students received some form of financial aid. The average freshman award was $3200. The FFS is required. The deadline for financial aid applications is July 1.

International Students: There are currently 565 international students enrolled. The school actively recruits these students. They must take the TOEFL, the University of Michigan Language Test, or the college's own test and achieve a minimum score on the TOEFL of 550.

Computers: The university provides computer facilities for student use. The mainframes are a CDC CYBER 170, an IBM 4381, a PDP 11/44, and an IBM 3090. Computer access is available through the library, various residence halls, and the College of Business laboratory. All students may access the system 8 A.M. to 10 P.M. There are no time limits; the fees are $35 per semester.

Graduates: In 1992–93, 2233 bachelor's degrees were awarded. The most popular majors among graduates were law enforcement (12%), communication arts and sciences (8%), and recreation, park and tourism administration (5%). Within an average freshman class, 21% graduate in 4 years, 39% in 5 years, and 45% in 6 years. Some 250 companies recruited on campus in 1992–93. In the 1992 class, 15% of the students were enrolled in graduate school within 6 months of graduation.

Admissions Contact: Admissions Office.

WHEATON COLLEGE
E-2

Wheaton, IL 60187-5593

(708) 752-5005
(800) 222-2419 (out-of-state)

Full-time: 1036 men, 1164 women	Faculty: 149; IIA, av$
Part-time: 23 men, 33 women	Ph.D.s: 85%
Graduate: 164 men, 155 women	Student/Faculty: 15 to 1
Year: semesters, summer session	Tuition: $10,640
Application Deadline: February 15	Room & Board: $4070
Freshman Class: 1432 applied, 920 accepted, 548 enrolled	
SAT I or ACT: required	HIGHLY COMPETITIVE

Wheaton College, founded in 1860, is a nonprofit, private, coeducational, nondenominational institution committed to providing students with a Christian education. Basically a liberal arts school, it offers undergraduate programs in business, the arts and fine arts, music, teacher preparation, and religious and Bible studies. There is one graduate school. In addition to regional accreditation, Wheaton has baccalaureate program accreditation with NASM and NCATE. The 2 libraries contain 375,828 volumes, 310,672 microform items, and 25,917 au-

diovisual forms, and subscribe to 2209 periodicals. Computerized library sources and services include the card catalog, interlibrary loans, and database searching. Special learning facilities include a radio station and a communications resource center with TV and audio studios. The 80-acre campus is in a suburban area 25 miles west of Chicago. Including residence halls, there are 35 buildings on campus.

Student Life: About 78% of undergraduates are from out-of-state, mostly the Midwest. Students come from 50 states, 8 foreign countries, and Canada. Seventy-one percent are from public schools; 29% from private. Ninety percent are white. Most are Protestant. The average age of freshmen is 18; all undergraduates, 20. Eight percent drop out by the end of their first year; 81% remain to graduate.

Housing: A total of 1879 students can be accommodated in college housing. College-sponsored living facilities include single-sex dormitories, on-campus apartments, and married-student housing. In addition, the college owns and rents houses to groups of students. On-campus housing is guaranteed for all 4 years. Eighty-five percent of students live on campus; of those, 97% remain on campus on weekends. Alcohol is not permitted. Upperclassmen may keep cars on campus.

Activities: There are no fraternities or sororities on campus. There are 37 groups on campus, including band, cheerleading, chess, choir, chorale, chorus, computers, dance, drama, drill team, ethnic, international, jazz band, literary magazine, newspaper, orchestra, pep band, political, radio and TV, religious, social, social service, student government, symphony, and yearbook. Popular campus events include Homecoming, Octoberfest, Air Jam, Springfest, and an artist concert series.

Sports: There are 10 intercollegiate sports for men and 8 for women, and 12 intramural sports for men and 12 for women. Athletic and recreation facilities include a 7000-seat football stadium, a 3200-seat gymnasium, a soccer stadium, a track, several fields, including 1 for baseball, a weight room, and a fitness center with a pool.

Disabled Students: Fifty percent of the campus is accessible to disabled students. The following facilities are available: wheelchair ramps, elevators, special parking, specially equipped rest rooms, and special class scheduling.

Services: In addition to counseling and information services, there is a reader service for the blind and a writing center.

Campus Safety and Security: Campus safety and security measures include 24-hour foot and vehicle patrol, self defense education, escort service, and informal discussions. In addition, there are pamphlets, posters, and films, emergency telephones, and lighted pathways and sidewalks.

Programs of Study: Wheaton awards the B.A., B.S., B.M., and B.M.A. degrees. Master's and doctoral degrees also are awarded. Bachelor's degrees are awarded in BIOLOGICAL SCIENCE (biology/biological science), BUSINESS (business economics), COMMUNICATIONS AND THE ARTS (communications, English, fine arts, French, German, languages, music, and Spanish), COMPUTER AND PHYSICAL SCIENCE (chemistry, computer science, geology, mathematics, and physics), EDUCATION (elementary, foreign languages, music, physical, science, and secondary), ENGINEERING AND ENVIRONMENTAL DESIGN (environmental studies), SOCIAL SCIENCE (archeology, biblical studies, economics, history, interdisciplinary studies, philosophy, political science/government, psychology, religion, and sociology). Chemistry, mathematics, psychology, literature, archeology, and philosophy are the strongest academically. Literature, psychology, music, biology, business/economics, and biblical studies have the largest enrollments.

Required: To graduate, students must complete 124 semester hours, 36 in upper-division courses, with a varying number of hours in a major, and maintain at least a 2.0 GPA. Specific disciplines include foreign language, mathematics, speech, writing, and Bible studies; distribution requirements include fine arts, history, literature, sciences, physical sciences, philosophy, other cultures, social sciences, and physical education.

Special: Special academic programs include internships, study abroad in 6 countries, and a Washington semester. There are several accelerated degree programs, dual majors in all areas, and student-designed majors. A 3–2 engineering degree is offered with the Illinois Institute of Technology, University of Illinois, Case Western Reserve University School of Engineering, and Washington University School of Engineering and Applied Science; transfer to other engineering schools is also possible. A 3–2 nursing degree is offered with Emory University, Goshen Nursing School, University of Rochester, and Rush University. Pass/fail options are available. There are 10 national honor societies on campus. Seventeen departments have honors programs.

Faculty/Classroom: Seventy-eight percent of faculty are male; 22%, female. Ninety-six percent teach undergraduates. No introductory courses are taught by graduate students. The average class size in an introductory lecture is 31; in a laboratory, 20; and in a regular course offering, 23.

Admissions: About 64% of the 1993–94 applicants were accepted. The SAT scores for the 1993–94 freshman class were as follows: Verbal—20% below 500, 41% between 500 and 599, 32% between 600 and 700, and 5% above 700; Math—5% below 500, 36% between 500 and 599, 41% between 600 and 700, and 17% above 700. The ACT scores were 1% below 21, 11% between 21 and 23, 25% between 24 and 26, 22% between 27 and 28, and 39% above 28. About 77% of the current freshmen were in the top fifth of their class; 93% were in the top two fifths. There were 33 National Merit finalists.

Requirements: The SAT I or ACT is required. Other admissions requirements include graduation from an accredited secondary school; the GED is also accepted. Eighteen secondary school credits are needed, including 15 from English, math, science, social science, and a foreign language; applicants are expected to have 2 years of a foreign language. SAT II: Subject tests are recommended. An essay and interview are required; music conservatory applicants must audition. Recommendations must be submitted as well. AP and CLEP credits are accepted. Important factors used in the admissions decision are advanced placement or honor courses, recommendations by school officials, evidence of special talent, personality, intangible qualities, and extracurricular activities record.

Procedure: Freshmen are admitted to all sessions. Entrance exams should be taken before the application deadline. Applications should be filed by February 15 for fall entry, October 1 for spring entry, and February 15 for summer entry, along with an application fee of $30. A waiting list is an active part of the admissions procedure, with about 15% of applicants on the list.

Transfer: A total of 78 transfer students enrolled in 1993–94. Transfer students should have a recommended minimum of 15 credit hours and a GPA of at least 3.0. An interview is mandatory. A total of 32 credits out of 124 must be completed at Wheaton.

Visiting: There are regularly scheduled orientations for prospective students, consisting of presentations by faculty, administrators, students, financial aid, and admissions staff, as well as social activities.

There are guides for informal visits and visitors may sit in on classes and stay overnight at the school. To arrange for a visit, contact the Admissions Office at (708) 752-5600.

Financial Aid: In 1993–94, 77% of all current freshmen and 60% of continuing students received some form of financial aid. About 58% of freshmen and 51% of continuing students received need-based aid. The average freshman award was $9109. Of that total, scholarships or need-based grants averaged $4763 ($10,000 maximum); loans averaged $2891 ($4325 maximum); and work contracts averaged $1200 (maximum). Forty-three percent of undergraduate students work part-time. Average earnings from campus work for the school year are $1000. The average financial indebtedness of the 1992–93 graduate was $10,000. Wheaton is a member of CSS. The FAFSA financial statement is required. The deadline for financial aid applications is March 15.

International Students: There are currently 48 international students enrolled. The school actively recruits these students. They must take the TOEFL and achieve a minimum score of 550.

Computers: The college provides computer facilities for student use. The mainframes are a DEC MicroVAX and DEC ULTRIX/RISC minicomputers. Also available are 73 IBM-compatible and Apple Macintosh microcomputers in a laboratory with print services and file servers, all of which have network access. All students may access the system 2 hours at one sitting if there is a waiting list; otherwise, there is no limit. There are no fees.

Graduates: In a recent year, 554 bachelor's degrees were awarded. The most popular majors among graduates were psychology (10%), business/economics (10%), and literature (10%). Within an average freshman class, 72% graduate in 4 years, 78% in 5 years, and 83% in 6 years. Some 63 companies recruited on campus in 1992–93. In the 1992 graduating class, 28% of all students were enrolled in graduate school within 6 months of graduation; 77% had found employment.

Admissions Contact: Daniel Crabtree, Director of Admissions.

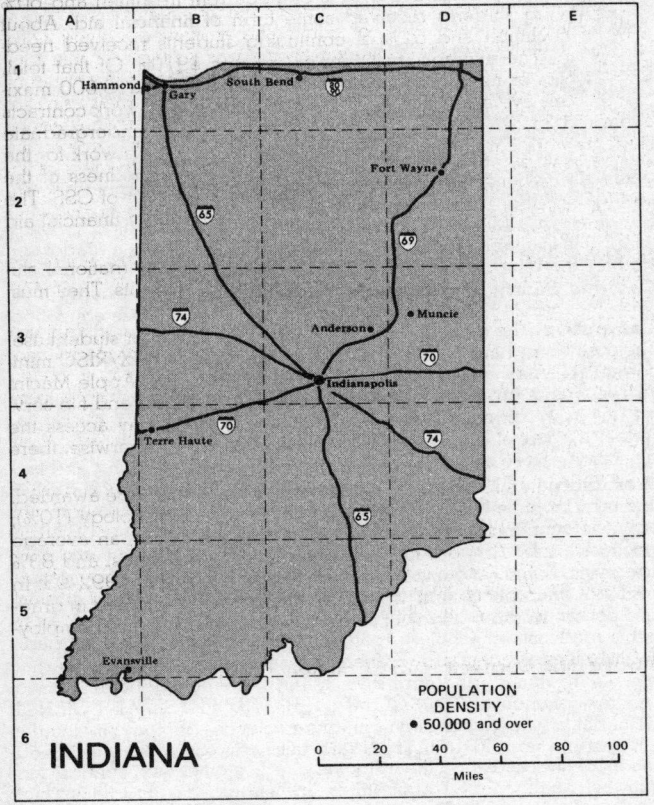

POPULATION DENSITY
● 50,000 and over

0   20   40   60   80   100
Miles

INDIANA

ANDERSON UNIVERSITY

C-3

Anderson, IN 46012   (317) 641–4080; (800) 428–6414 (out-of-state)

Full-time: 780 men, 1039 women	Faculty: 131; IIB, --$
Part-time: 98 men, 184 women	Ph.Ds: 61%
Graduate: 121 men, 34 women	Student/Faculty: 14 to 1
Year: semesters, summer session	Tuition: $9520
Application Deadline: open	Room & Board: $3400

Freshman Class: 1352 applied, 1008 accepted, 466 enrolled
SAT I Verbal/Math: 423/462   ACT: 21   **COMPETITIVE**

Anderson University, founded in 1917, is a private, liberal arts institution affiliated with the Church of God. The university offers programs in theoretical and applied science, social and professional studies, and arts, culture, and religion. There are 2 undergraduate schools and one graduate school. In addition to regional accreditation, Anderson has baccalaureate program accreditation with CSWE, NASM, NCATE, and NLN. The library contains 215,800 volumes, 184,890 microform items, and 12,000 audiovisual forms, and subscribes to 928 periodicals. Computerized library sources and services include the card catalog and interlibrary loans. Special learning facilities include a learning resource center, art gallery, radio station, and the Museum of the Bible and the Ancient Near East. The 100-acre campus is in a suburban area 40 miles northeast of Indianapolis. Including residence halls, there are 26 buildings on campus.

Student Life: About 61% of undergraduates are from Indiana. Students come from 42 states, 11 foreign countries, and Canada. Ninety-two percent are white. Seventy-four percent are Protestant; 21% claim no religious affiliation. The average age of freshmen is 20; all undergraduates, 23. Eighteen percent drop out by the end of their first year; 49% remain to graduate.

Housing: A total of 1164 students can be accommodated in college housing. College-sponsored living facilities include single-sex dormitories, on-campus apartments, off-campus apartments, and married-student housing. On-campus housing is guaranteed for all 4 years. Fifty-one percent of students live on campus; of those, 50% remain on campus on weekends. Alcohol is not permitted. All students may keep cars on campus.

Activities: There are no fraternities or sororities on campus. There are 41 groups on campus, including art, cheerleading, chorale, drama, ethnic, film, honors, international, jazz band, literary magazine, musical theater, newspaper, orchestra, photography, political, radio

and TV, religious, social, social service, student government, and yearbook. Popular campus events include Homecoming, Christmas Carols, Vision/Revision, Celebration Weekend, and Black Awareness.

Sports: There are 8 intercollegiate sports for men and 7 for women, and 7 intramural sports for men and 6 for women. Athletic and recreation facilities include 2 gymnasiums, football, baseball/softball, and soccer fields, an 8-lane all-weather track, tennis courts, a bowling alley, and a game room. The campus stadium seats 4,200 and the indoor gymnasium seats 2,400.

Disabled Students: Eighty-five percent of the campus is accessible to disabled students. The following facilities are available: wheelchair ramps, elevators, special parking, specially equipped rest rooms, special class scheduling, and lowered drinking fountains.

Services: In addition to many counseling and information services, tutoring is available in most subjects. In addition, there is a reader service for the blind, and remedial math, reading, and writing.

Campus Safety and Security: Campus safety and security measures include 24-hour foot and vehicle patrol, self defense education, escort service, and informal discussions. In addition, there are pamphlets, posters, and films, emergency telephones, lighted pathways and sidewalks. Indiana State police academy graduates are security officers.

Programs of Study: Anderson awards the B.A. and B.S.N. degrees. Associate and master's degrees also are awarded. Bachelor's degrees are awarded in BIOLOGICAL SCIENCE (biology/biological science), BUSINESS (accounting, banking and finance, business administration and management, marketing/retailing/merchandising, and sports management), COMMUNICATIONS AND THE ARTS (communications, dramatic arts, English, fine arts, French, German, graphic design, music business management, music performance, and Spanish), COMPUTER AND PHYSICAL SCIENCE (chemistry, computer science, mathematics, and physics), EDUCATION (art, elementary, foreign languages, music, physical, and science), HEALTH PROFESSIONS (medical laboratory technology, nursing, predentistry, and premedicine), SOCIAL SCIENCE (criminal justice, economics, history, philosophy, political science/government, prelaw, psychology, religion, social work, and sociology). Physical sciences are the strongest academically. Business and education have the largest enrollments.

Required: Requirements for graduation include the general education core, consisting of 55 hours, a minimum 2.0 GPA overall and in the major, 124 total credit hours, and a minimum of 36 hours in the major. All students must complete a liberal arts seminar. The last 24 credit hours must be taken in residence.

Special: Anderson offers co-op programs with Purdue University, internships through the Center for Public Service, study abroad in 25 countries through the International Studies Program, and a Washington semester. Also available are credit for military experience and pass/fail options. Courses in electronic engineering may be taken through the Purdue Anderson campus. There is a freshman honors program on campus, as well as 12 national honor societies. Ten departments have honors programs.

Faculty/Classroom: Sixty-four percent of faculty are male; 36%, female. Ninety-four percent teach undergraduates. The average class size in an introductory lecture is 34; in a laboratory, 16; and in a regular course offering, 16.

Admissions: About 75% of the 1993–94 applicants were accepted. The SAT I scores for the 1993–94 freshman class were as follows: Verbal—77% below 500, 19% between 500 and 599, and 4% between 600 and 700; Math—62% below 500, 27% between 500 and 599, 10% between 600 and 700, and 1% above 700. The ACT scores were 47% below 21, 26% between 21 and 23, 15% between 24 and 26, 7% between 27 and 28, and 5% above 28. About 42% of the current freshmen were in the top fifth of their class; 64% were in the top two fifths.

Requirements: A minimum GPA of 2.0 is required. The SAT I or ACT is required. In addition, applicants must be graduates of an accredited secondary school or have a GED certificate, and submit a photograph, references, and a health form. AP and CLEP credits are accepted. Important factors used in the admissions decision are leadership record, parents or siblings attending the school, personality, intangible qualities, advanced placement or honor courses, and evidence of special talent.

Procedure: Freshmen are admitted fall and spring. Entrance exams should be taken in the fall of the junior year. Application deadlines are open. Application fee is $20. Notification of early decision is sent in December; regular decision, on a rolling basis. There are early de-

cision and early admissions plans. About 25 early decision candidates were accepted for the 1993–94 class.

Transfer: About 137 transfer students enrolled in 1993–94. Transfer applicants must have a minimum 2.0 GPA, SAT I or ACT scores, and transcripts for all previously attended colleges. A total of 24 credits out of 124 must be completed at Anderson.

Visiting: There are regularly scheduled orientations for prospective students. There are guides for informal visits and visitors may sit in on classes and stay overnight at the school. To arrange for a visit, contact the Admissions Office at (800) 425–6414 or (317) 641–4080 (local).

Financial Aid: In 1993–94, 90% of all students received some form of financial aid. About 70% received need-based aid. The average freshman award was $6800. Of that total, scholarships or need-based grants averaged $3260 ($7500 maximum); loans averaged $2160 ($5500 maximum); and work contracts averaged $1800. Forty-one percent of undergraduate students work part-time. Average earnings from campus work for the school year are $1800. The average financial indebtedness of the 1992–93 graduate was $10,000. Anderson is a member of CSS. The FAF, FFS or SFS is required. The deadline for financial aid applications is March 1.

International Students: There are currently 27 international students enrolled. They must take the TOEFL and achieve a minimum score of 550. The student must also take the SAT I.

Computers: The college provides computer facilities for student use. The mainframes are an HP 3000/948 and an HP 9000/832. The mainframes are accessible throughout the campus, either through a local area network or by modem. All students may access the system. There are no time limits on using the system and no fees.

Graduates: In 1992–93 260 bachelor's degrees were awarded. The most popular majors among graduates were elementary education (12%), marketing (10%), and business and management (10%). Within an average freshman class, 10% graduate in 3 years, 40% in 4 years, 47% in 5 years, and 51% in 6 years. In the 1992 graduating class, 21% of the men and 21% of the women were enrolled in graduate school within 6 months of graduation.

Admissions Contact: Admissions Counselor.

BALL STATE UNIVERSITY
B-3

Muncie, IN 47306 (317) 285-8300; (800) 482-4BSU (in-state)

Full-time: 7496 men, 8652 women	Faculty: 948; I, --$
Part-time: 924 men, 1283 women	Ph.D.s: 66%
Graduate: 1025 men, 1337 women	Student/Faculty: 17 to 1
Year: semesters, summer session	Tuition: $2656 ($6584)
Application Deadline: March 1	Room & Board: $3376
Freshman Class: 9361 applied, 7601 accepted, 3849 enrolled	
SAT I Verbal/Math: 422/473	ACT: 21 **LESS COMPETITIVE**

Ball State University, founded in 1918, is a public university offering undergraduate and graduate programs through 8 colleges in applied sciences and technology, architecture and planning, business, fine arts, sciences and humanities, and teacher education. There are 8 undergraduate schools and one graduate school. In addition to regional accreditation, Ball State has baccalaureate program accreditation with AACSB, ACEJMC, ADA, AHEA, CAHEA, CSWE, NASM, and NLN. The 3 libraries contain 1,051,018 volumes, 280,947 microform items, and 502,787 audiovisual forms, and subscribe to 3847 periodicals. Computerized library sources and services include the card catalog, interlibrary loans, and database searching. Special learning facilities include a learning resource center, art gallery, natural history museum, planetarium, radio station, TV station, and research centers in solar energy, human performance, international programs, and global security. The 955-acre campus is in an urban area 56 miles northwest of Indianapolis. Including residence halls, there are 57 buildings on campus.

Student Life: About 89% of undergraduates are from Indiana. Students come from 50 states, 91 foreign countries, and Canada. About 90% are white. The average age of freshmen is 19; all undergraduates, 20. Some 23% drop out by the end of their first year; 50% remain to graduate.

Housing: A total of 6200 students can be accommodated in college housing. College-sponsored living facilities include single-sex and coed dormitories, on-campus apartments, married-student housing, and fraternity houses. In addition there are honors houses, language houses, special interest houses, and Wellness Halls. On-campus housing is guaranteed for the freshman year only. Alcohol is not permitted. All students may keep cars on campus.

Activities: About 13% of men belong to 20 national fraternities; about 13% of women belong to 1 local and 18 national sororities. There are 290 groups on campus, including art, band, cheerleading, chess, choir, chorale, chorus, computers, dance, drama, drill team, ethnic, film, gay, honors, international, jazz band, literary magazine, marching band, musical theater, newspaper, orchestra, pep band, photography, political, professional, radio and TV, religious, social, social service, student government, symphony, and yearbook. Popu-

lar campus events include Homecoming, Bike-a-thon, Watermelon Bust, Unity Week, and Family Weekend.

Sports: There are 9 intercollegiate sports for men and 9 for women, and 43 intramural sports for men and 41 for women. Athletic and recreation facilities include an 11,500-seat basketball and volleyball arena, two gymnasiums, a field sports building, tennis courts, and an aquatic center. The campus stadium seats 16,320.

Disabled Students: About 90% of the campus is accessible to disabled students. The following facilities are available: wheelchair ramps, elevators, special parking, specially equipped rest rooms, special class scheduling, lowered drinking fountains, lowered telephones, special resource guide, accessibility map (including tactile), and text telephones (TDD) in all key offices.

Services: In addition to many counseling and information services, tutoring is available in most subjects. In addition, there is a reader service for the blind, and remedial math, reading, and writing.

Campus Safety and Security: Campus safety and security measures include 24-hour foot and vehicle patrol, self defense education, escort service, and shuttle buses. In addition, there are informal discussions, pamphlets, posters, and films, emergency telephones, and lighted pathways and sidewalks.

Programs of Study: Ball State awards the B.A., B.S., B.F.A., B.G.S., B.Land.Arch., B.Mus., and B.Urban Planning and Development degrees. Associate, master's, and doctoral degrees also are awarded. Bachelor's degrees are awarded in AGRICULTURE (fishing and fisheries and natural resource management), BIOLOGICAL SCIENCE (biology/biological science, botany, cell biology, genetics, microbiology, molecular biology, wildlife biology, and zoology), BUSINESS (accounting, banking and finance, business administration and management, business economics, insurance, international business management, management science, marketing/retailing/merchandising, and personnel management), COMMUNICATIONS AND THE ARTS (art, broadcasting, Chinese, communications, dance, dramatic arts, English, film arts, fine arts, French, German, graphic design, journalism, Latin, music, photography, Spanish, speech/debate/rhetoric, and telecommunications), COMPUTER AND PHYSICAL SCIENCE (actuarial science, chemistry, computer science, geology, mathematics, and physics), EDUCATION (art, business, early childhood, education of the deaf and hearing impaired, elementary, foreign languages, health, home economics, industrial arts, middle school, music, science, secondary, and special), ENGINEERING AND ENVIRONMENTAL DESIGN (architecture, environmental design, landscape architecture/design, and urban planning technology), HEALTH PROFESSIONS (medical laboratory technology, nursing, predentistry, premedicine, prepharmacy, and speech pathology/audiology), SOCIAL SCIENCE (anthropology, criminal justice, dietetics, economics, food production/management/services, food science, geography, history, parks and recreation management, philosophy, physical fitness/movement, political science/government, prelaw, psychology, religion, social work, and sociology). Architecture, business, education, and telecommunications are the strongest programs academically. Elementary education and business have the largest enrollments.

Required: All students must take at least 126 credits and maintain a 2.0 GPA for graduation. Required courses are in English composition, mathematics, speech, history, physical sciences, social or behavioral sciences, humanities or fine arts, global studies, and 3 hours of physical education. In addition, all juniors must pass a writing competency examination.

Special: Nearly all undergraduate disciplines offer internships. Study abroad is possible at the university's London center and in 20 other programs; students may also spend a semester in Washington, D.C. Work-study programs are available. Most disciplines offer dual majors. There is a 3–2 program in engineering, an award-winning program in private enterprise, a general studies degree, nondegree study, and pass/fail options. There is a freshman honors program on campus, as well as 40 national honor societies.

Faculty/Classroom: Some 62% of faculty are male; 38%, female. Almost 98% teach undergraduates, 75% do research, and 73% do both. The average class size in an introductory lecture is 50; in a laboratory, 18; and in a regular course offering, 30.

Admissions: About 81% of the 1993–94 applicants were accepted. The SAT scores for the 1993–94 freshman class were as follows: Verbal—81% below 500, 16% between 500 and 599, 2% between 600 and 700, and 1% above 700; Math—61% below 500, 28% between 500 and 599, 10% between 600 and 700, and 1% above 700. The ACT scores were 49% below 21, 21% between 21 and 23, 16% between 24 and 26, 8% between 27 and 28, and 6% above 28. About 29% of the current freshmen were in the top fifth of their class; 59% were in the top two fifths. There were 4 National Merit finalists. About 38 freshmen graduated first in their class.

Requirements: Ball State requires applicants to be in the upper 50% of their class. The SAT I, with a minimum composite score of 800, or the ACT, with a minimum composite score of 19, is required. Applicants should be high school graduates or hold the GED. Secondary

preparation should include 4 years of English, 3 to 4 years of mathematics, 2 to 3 each of history, social science, speech, foreign language, and fine arts, and 2 years of science. A personal essay and an interview are recommended but not required. AP and CLEP credits are accepted. Important factors used in the admissions decision are advanced placement or honor courses, leadership record, evidence of special talent, recommendations by school officials, and geographic diversity.

Procedure: Freshmen are admitted in the fall, spring, and summer. Entrance exams should be taken during spring of the junior year or early in the senior year. Applications should be filed by March 1 for fall entry, December 1 for spring entry, and April 1 for summer entry, along with an application fee of $15. Notification is sent on a rolling basis. There is a deferred admissions plan.

Transfer: About 779 transfer students enrolled in 1993–94. Transfer applicants should have earned a 2.0 GPA on a 4.0 scale (as computed by Ball State) to be considered for admission. Official high school transcripts or GED score reports and official transcripts from each postsecondary institution are required. SAT I or ACT scores, if available, are required. If the student is a nontraditional student (over the age of 23), SAT I or ACT may not be required. A total of 63 credits out of 126 to 165 must be completed at Ball State.

Visiting: There are regularly scheduled orientations for prospective students, including a 2-day program (date assigned by Admissions) to familiarize the students with the campus and get them registered for classes. There are guides for informal visits and visitors may sit in on classes and stay overnight at the school. To arrange for a visit, contact the University Visit Center at (317) 285–5683 (out-of-state) or (800) 482–4BSU, ext. 5683 (in-state).

Financial Aid: In 1993–94, 40% of all current freshmen and 26% of continuing students received some form of financial aid. About 27% of freshmen and 17% of continuing students received need-based aid. Some 32% of undergraduate students work part-time. Average earnings from campus work for the school year are $1056. Ball State is a member of CSS. The FAF and the college's own financial statement are required. The deadline for financial aid applications is March 1.

International Students: There are currently 397 international students enrolled. The school actively recruits these students. They must take the TOEFL and achieve a minimum score of 550.

Computers: The college provides computer facilities for student use. The mainframes are an IBM and VAX cluster. There are more than 2,000 computer work stations on campus; 15 public-access computer laboratories are available to students in 11 academic buildings. The 2 mainframe computers have about 200 terminals that can be accessed by students. More than 300 microcomputers (IBM-PC, Apple II, Zenith, AT&T, and Macintosh) are available for student use. All students may access the system. It may be used at any time except Fridays from 5 P.M. to Saturdays at 8 A.M. There are no time limits on using the system and no fees.

Graduates: In 1992–93, 3293 bachelor's degrees were awarded. Some 256 companies recruited on campus in 1992–93.

Admissions Contact: Ruth Vedvik, Director of Admissions.

BETHEL COLLEGE
Mishawaka, IN 46545

C-1

(219) 259–8511
(800) 422–4101 (out-of-state)

Full-time: 312 men, 421 women	Faculty: 53; IIB, --$
Part-time: 133 men, 269 women	Ph.D.s: 48%
Graduate: 22 men, 1 women	Student/Faculty: 14 to 1
Year: semesters, summer session	Tuition: $8700
Application Deadline: open	Room & Board: $2950
Freshman Class: 492 applied, 415 accepted, 267 enrolled	
SAT I Verbal/Math: 453/490	ACT: 22	COMPETITIVE

Bethel College, founded in 1947, is a private, coeducational institution affiliated with the Missionary Church, offering a liberal arts education with a Christian perspective. In addition to regional accreditation, Bethel has baccalaureate program accreditation with NLN. The library contains 73,686 volumes, 3849 microform items, and 3025 audiovisual forms, and subscribes to 415 periodicals. Computerized library sources and services include the card catalog, interlibrary loans, and database searching. Special learning facilities include a learning resource center and radio station. The 62-acre campus is in a suburban area 90 miles west of Chicago, Illinois. Including residence halls, there are 23 buildings on campus.

Student Life: About 82% of undergraduates are from Indiana. Students come from 23 states, 7 foreign countries, and Canada. Eighty-seven percent are from public schools. Eighty-five percent are white; 13%, African American. Eighty-two percent are Protestant; 11%, Catholic. The average age of freshmen is 18; all undergraduates, 27.6.

Housing: A total of 368 students can be accommodated in college housing. College-sponsored living facilities include single-sex dormitories and on-campus apartments. On-campus housing is guaranteed for all 4 years. Seventy percent of students commute. Alcohol is not permitted. All students may keep cars on campus.

Activities: There are no fraternities or sororities on campus. There are many groups and organizations on campus, including art, band, cheerleading, chess, choir, chorale, computers, drama, international, newspaper, pep band, professional, radio and TV, religious, social, social service, student government, and yearbook. Popular campus events include Homecoming, Christmas Banquet, and Junior Senior Banquet.

Sports: There are 6 intercollegiate sports for men and 5 for women, and 8 intramural sports for men and 8 for women. Athletic and recreation facilities include a gymnasium, soccer and baseball fields, and tennis and basketball courts.

Disabled Students: Seventy percent of the campus is accessible to disabled students. The following facilities are available: wheelchair ramps, elevators, special parking, specially equipped rest rooms, and lowered drinking fountains.

Services: In addition to many counseling and information services, tutoring is available in every subject. There is also remedial math, reading, and writing.

Campus Safety and Security: Campus safety and security measures include self-defense education, informal discussions, pamphlets, posters, films, and lighted pathways and sidewalks.

Programs of Study: Bethel awards the B.A., B.S., and B.S.N. degrees. Associate and master's degrees also are awarded. Bachelor's degrees are awarded in BIOLOGICAL SCIENCE (biology/biological science), BUSINESS (accounting and business administration and management), COMMUNICATIONS AND THE ARTS (art, communications, English, and music), COMPUTER AND PHYSICAL SCIENCE (chemistry and mathematics), EDUCATION (business, elementary, music, science, and secondary), ENGINEERING AND ENVIRONMENTAL DESIGN (aeronautical engineering, chemical engineering, civil engineering, electrical/electronics engineering, mechanical engineering, and metallurgical engineering), HEALTH PROFESSIONS (nursing, predentistry, and premedicine), SOCIAL SCIENCE (biblical studies, ministries, parks and recreation management, psychology, religion, and social science). Education, nursing, business, and Christian ministries are the strongest academically and have the largest enrollments.

Required: To graduate, students must complete 124 credits, including 24 to 52 in the major, with a minimum 2.0 GPA. Also required are 4 semesters of physical education, 10 credits in Bible and religion, courses in communication skills, social science and history, fine arts and humanities, and natural sciences and mathematics, and a course called Lifelong Physical Awareness.

Special: A cooperative program is offered with the University of Notre Dame, and students may cross-register for courses at various local colleges. Special degree programs include a B.A.-B.S. in engineering, a 3–2 engineering degree with Notre Dame, a liberal arts degree, and an accelerated degree in organizational management (for students age 25 and over). Bethel also offers nondegree courses, a pass/fail option, business and computer internships, study in Ecuador and Jamaica, dual majors, and work-study programs.

Faculty/Classroom: Fifty-five percent of faculty are male; 45%, female. All teach undergraduates. No introductory courses are taught by graduate students. The average class size in an introductory lecture is 75; in a laboratory, 15; and in a regular course offering, 20.

Admissions: About 84% of the 1993–94 applicants were accepted. The ACT scores for the 1993–94 freshman class were as follows: 44% below 21, 20% between 21 and 23, 16% between 24 and 26, 8% between 27 and 28, and 12% above 28. About 30% of the current freshmen were in the top fifth of their class; 56% were in the top two fifths.

Requirements: Bethel suggests that applicants be in the upper 50% of their class. A minimum GPA of 2.0 is suggested. The SAT I or ACT is required, with recommended minimum scores of 360 each on the verbal and math part of SAT I, and 17 to 18 on the ACT. Applicants should be graduates of accredited secondary schools or have the GED. Required secondary school credits include 4 units in English and 2 units each in a foreign language, mathematics, laboratory science, and social science. Chemistry is required for nursing majors. An interview is recommended. An audition is required of music program applicants. AP and CLEP credits are accepted. Important factors used in the admissions decision are leadership record, advanced placement or honor courses, personality, intangible qualities, extracurricular activities record, and evidence of special talent.

Procedure: Freshmen are admitted to all sessions. Entrance exams should be taken as early as possible in the junior or senior year. Application deadlines are open. Notification is sent on a rolling basis. The application fee is $25. There are early admissions and deferred admissions plans.

Transfer: A total of 67 transfer students enrolled in 1993–94. Grades of C or better are eligible for transfer; students without a minimum GPA of 2.0 may be admitted on probation. Other admission re-

quirements are the same as for entering freshmen. At least 30 credits out of 124 must be completed at Bethel.

Visiting: There are regularly scheduled orientations for prospective students, including overnight visits. There are guides for informal visits, and visitors may sit in on classes and stay overnight at the school. To arrange for a visit, contact the Admissions Office at (219) 259–8511 or (800) 422–4101 (out-of-state).

Financial Aid: In 1993–94, 85% of all students received need-based aid. Scholarships or need-based grants averaged $1315 ($8700 maximum); loans averaged $2652 ($7000 maximum); and work contracts averaged $800 ($1400 maximum). Thirty-five percent of undergraduate students work part-time. Average earnings from campus work for the school year are $800. The average financial indebtedness of the 1992–93 graduate was $15,000. Bethel is a member of CSS. The FAF, the college's own financial statement, and the SAR are required. The deadline for financial aid applications is March 1.

International Students: There are currently 5 international students enrolled. They must take the TOEFL and achieve a minimum score of 540.

Computers: The college provides computer facilities for student use. The mainframe is an IBM AS400. There are 22 IBM or IBM-compatible and Apple Macintosh microcomputers. Stand-alone PCs can be found in some residence halls. All students may access the system 24 hours from the dormitories and from 7 A.M. to 11 P.M. in the computer laboratories. There are no time limits on using the system. The fee is $30.

Graduates: In 1992–93, 163 bachelor's degrees were awarded. The most popular majors among graduates were elementary education (14%), business administration (7%), and nursing (4%).

Admissions Contact: Steve Matteson, Director of Admissions.

BUTLER UNIVERSITY
Indianapolis, IN 46208

C-3

(317) 283–9255
(800) 368–6852 (out-of-state)

Full-time: 1071 men, 1547 women	**Faculty:** 210; IIA, -$
Part-time: 36 men, 85 women	**Ph.D.s:** 81%
Graduate: 438 men, 556 women	**Student/Faculty:** 12 to 1
Year: semesters, summer session	**Tuition:** $12,280
Application Deadline: August 1	**Room & Board:** $3930
Freshman Class: 2364 applied, 2038 accepted, 700 enrolled	
ACT: 25	**COMPETITIVE**

Butler University, founded in 1855, is an independent, coeducational institution offering undergraduate and graduate programs in liberal arts and sciences, business administration, fine arts, and pharmacy. There are 5 undergraduate schools and one graduate school. In addition to regional accreditation, Butler has baccalaureate program accreditation with ACPE, NASM, and NCATE. The 2 libraries contain 282,195 volumes, 218,207 microform items, and 12,128 audiovisual forms, and subscribe to 2835 periodicals. Computerized library sources and services include the card catalog, interlibrary loans, and database searching. Special learning facilities include a learning resource center, planetarium, TV station, an observatory, and a writer's studio. The 290-acre campus is in a suburban area 5 miles from downtown Indianapolis. Including residence halls, there are 19 buildings on campus.

Student Life: About 75% of undergraduates are from Indiana. Students come from 40 states, 37 foreign countries, and Canada. Seventy-eight percent are from public schools; 22% from private. Ninety-three percent are white. Fifty-four percent are Protestant; 28% Catholic; 10% claim no religious affiliation. The average age of freshmen is 18; all undergraduates, 20. Six percent drop out by the end of their first year; 65% remain to graduate.

Housing: A total of 2100 students can be accommodated in college housing. College-sponsored living facilities include single-sex and coed dormitories, fraternity houses, and sorority houses. On-campus housing is guaranteed for all 4 years. Seventy-six percent of students live on campus; of those, 50% remain on campus on weekends. Alcohol is not permitted. All students may keep cars on campus.

Activities: About 26% of men belong to 7 national fraternities; about 22% of women belong to 7 national sororities. There are 70 groups on campus, including band, cheerleading, choir, chorale, chorus, dance, drama, drill team, ethnic, gay, honors, international, jazz band, literary magazine, marching band, musical theater, newspaper, opera, orchestra, pep band, photography, professional, radio and TV, religious, social service, student government, symphony, and yearbook. Popular campus events include Homecoming, Geneva Stunts, Spring Sing, and Spring Weekend.

Sports: There are 9 intercollegiate sports for men and 8 for women, and 12 intramural sports for men and 12 for women. Athletic and recreation facilities include a 10,000-seat field house, a football stadium, tennis courts, indoor and outdoor tracks, a weight-training room, an indoor pool, and an aerobics/exercise room.

Disabled Students: Seventy-five percent of the campus is accessible to disabled students. The following facilities are available: wheelchair ramps, elevators, special parking, specially equipped rest rooms, and special class scheduling.

Services: In addition to many counseling and information services, tutoring is available. In addition, there is a reader service for the blind.

Campus Safety and Security: Campus safety and security measures include 24-hour foot and vehicle patrol, self defense education, escort service, and informal discussions. In addition, there are pamphlets, posters, and films, emergency telephones, and lighted pathways and sidewalks.

Programs of Study: Butler awards the B.A., B.S., B.F.A., and B.M. degrees. Master's degrees also are awarded. Bachelor's degrees are awarded in BIOLOGICAL SCIENCE (biology/biological science), BUSINESS (accounting, banking and finance, and marketing/retailing/merchandising), COMMUNICATIONS AND THE ARTS (arts administration/management, broadcasting, communications, dance, dramatic arts, English, French, German, Greek, journalism, Latin, music, music business management, music performance, music theory and composition, performing arts, Spanish, and speech/debate/rhetoric), COMPUTER AND PHYSICAL SCIENCE (actuarial science, chemistry, computer science, mathematics, and physics), EDUCATION (elementary, music, and secondary), ENGINEERING AND ENVIRONMENTAL DESIGN (environmental science), HEALTH PROFESSIONS (pharmacy and speech pathology/audiology), SOCIAL SCIENCE (economics, history, international studies, philosophy, political science/government, psychology, religion, and sociology). Pharmacy, chemistry, and English are the strongest academically. Business, education, and pharmacy have the largest enrollments.

Required: The core curriculum includes specific courses in English, speech, computer literacy, physical education, and interdisciplinary studies, as well as distribution requirements in humanities, fine arts, social science, natural science, and quantitative reasoning. In order to graduate, students must complete 126 to 166 semester hours with a minimum GPA of 2.0.

Special: Butler offers cross-registration with the 4 other members of the Consortium for Urban Education, co-op programs in business administration, and internships in pharmacy and arts administration. Study-abroad programs in 6 countries, a 3–2 degree program in engineering and forestry, work-study programs, dual majors, student-designed majors, a general studies degree, pass/fail options, and nondegree study are available. There is a freshman honors program on campus, as well as 5 national honor societies. Fourteen departments have honors programs.

Faculty/Classroom: Seventy-three percent of faculty are male; 27%, female. Ninety-six percent teach undergraduates and 75% both teach and do research. No introductory courses are taught by graduate students. The average class size in an introductory lecture is 32; in a laboratory, 20; and in a regular course offering, 18.

Admissions: About 86% of the 1993–94 applicants were accepted. The SAT scores for the 1993–94 freshman class were as follows: Verbal—54% below 500, 35% between 500 and 599, 9% between 600 and 700, and 2% above 700; Math—30% below 500, 40% between 500 and 599, 26% between 600 and 700, and 4% above 700. The ACT scores were 14% below 21, 25% between 21 and 23, 29% between 24 and 26, 16% between 27 and 28, and 16% above 28. About 61% of the current freshmen were in the top fifth of their class; 84% were in the top two fifths. There were 9 National Merit finalists and 9 semifinalists. About 31 freshmen graduated first in their class.

Requirements: Butler requires applicants to be in the upper 50% of their class. A minimum GPA of 2.0 is required. Applicants should be graduates of an accredited secondary school, but Butler will consider talented or gifted students without a diploma. Students should have earned at least 17 academic units, based on 4 years of English, 2 each of a foreign language, history, and social science, and 3 each of mathematics, laboratory science, and electives. An audition is required for dance, music, and theater majors, and an interview is required for radio/tv majors. Butler uses a comparative index of entrance exam scores and class rank to help predict academic success. AP and CLEP credits are accepted. Important factors used in the admissions decision are advanced placement or honor courses, evidence of special talent, parents or siblings attending the school, recommendations by alumni, and leadership record.

Procedure: Freshmen are admitted to all sessions. Entrance exams should be taken during the junior year. Applications should be filed by August 1 for fall entry, January 15 for spring entry, and June 1 for summer entry, along with an application fee of $25. Notification is sent on a rolling basis. There is an early admissions plan.

Transfer: A total of 124 transfer students enrolled in 1993–94. Transfer applicants who have completed more than 12 hours of college work must present transcripts from all previous colleges attended, indicating good standing and a minimum GPA of 2.0. Those students with fewer than 12 hours must also submit SAT I or ACT scores

and high school transcripts. A total of 30 credits out of 126 must be completed at Butler.

Visiting: There are regularly scheduled orientations for prospective students, including a campus tour, faculty visit, and financial aid interview. There are guides for informal visits and visitors may sit in on classes and stay overnight at the school. To arrange for a visit, contact the Admissions Office at (317) 283–9255.

Financial Aid: In 1993–94, 82% of all current freshmen and 74% of continuing students received some form of financial aid. About 63% of freshmen and 52% of continuing students received need-based aid. The average freshman award was $8075. Of that total, scholarships or need-based grants averaged $5550 ($16,430 maximum); loans averaged $3472 ($11,833 maximum); and work contracts averaged $1000 ($1800 maximum). Twenty-five percent of undergraduate students work part-time. Average earnings from campus work for the school year are $800. The average financial indebtedness of the 1992–93 graduate was $10,000. Butler is a member of CSS. The FAF and the college's own financial statement are required. The deadline for financial aid applications is March 1.

International Students: There are currently 45 international students enrolled. The school actively recruits these students. They must take the TOEFL and achieve a minimum score of 550.

Computers: The university provides computer facilities for student use. The mainframe is a DEC VAX 6610. Ethernet fiber-optic technology connects all Macintosh and MS/DOS computers (150 in laboratories for students) to the mainframe. All students may access the system 24 hours a day. There are no time limits on using the system and no fees.

Graduates: In 1992–93, 580 bachelor's degrees were awarded. The most popular majors among graduates were pharmacy (15%), marketing (10%), and elementary education (7%). Within an average freshman class, 50% graduate in 4 years, 62% in 5 years, and 65% in 6 years. Some 122 companies recruited on campus in 1992–93. In the 1992 graduating class, 5% of the men and 8% of the women were enrolled in graduate school within 6 months of graduation; 75% of the men and 65% of the women had found employment.

Admissions Contact: O'Neal Turner, Dean of Admission.

CALUMET COLLEGE OF ST. JOSEPH

B-1

Whiting, IN 46394   (219) 473–4215

Full-time: 188 men, 282 women	Faculty: 30; IIB, --$
Part-time: 213 men, 414 women	Ph.D.s: 50%
Graduate: none	Student/Faculty: 14 to 1
Year: semesters, summer session	Tuition: $3585
Application Deadline: open	Room & Board: n/app
Freshman Class: 153 applied, 106 accepted, 85 enrolled	
SAT I or ACT: required	COMPETITIVE

Calumet College of St. Joseph, founded in 1951, is a private coeducational Catholic institution offering commuting students a liberal arts education in a Christian environment. The library contains 121,143 volumes, 3761 microform items, and 1958 audiovisual forms, and subscribes to 213 periodicals. Computerized library sources and services include interlibrary loans and database searching. Special learning facilities include a learning resource center and art gallery. The 256-acre campus is in an urban area 15 miles southeast of Chicago in Northwest Indiana. There is one building on campus.

Student Life: About 70% of undergraduates are from Indiana. Students come from 2 states. Sixty-five percent are from public schools; 35% from private. Fifty-five percent are white; 22% African American; 15% Hispanic. Most are Catholic. The average age of freshmen is 21; all undergraduates, 35. Fifteen percent drop out by the end of their first year; 58% remain to graduate.

Housing: There are no residence halls. All students commute. Alcohol is not permitted. All students may keep cars on campus.

Activities: There are no fraternities or sororities on campus. There are 15 groups on campus, including drama, ethnic, musical theater, newspaper, photography, professional, social, and student government. Popular campus events include Thanksgiving Ethnic Fest.

Sports: There are 4 intramural sports for men and 4 for women. Athletic and recreation facilities include a gymnasium and the Marktown Diamond.

Disabled Students: All of the campus is accessible to disabled students. The following facilities are available: wheelchair ramps, elevators, special parking, and specially equipped rest rooms.

Services: In addition to many counseling and information services, tutoring is available in every subject. There is also remedial math, reading, and writing, and career services and placement.

Campus Safety and Security: Campus safety and security measures include emergency telephones and lighted pathways and sidewalks.

Programs of Study: Cal College awards the B.A., B.S., B.S.Ed., and B.S.M.T degrees. Associate degrees also are awarded. Bachelor's degrees are awarded in BIOLOGICAL SCIENCE (biology/biological science), BUSINESS (accounting and business administration and management), COMMUNICATIONS AND THE ARTS (communications, English, and fine arts), COMPUTER AND PHYSICAL SCIENCE (information sciences and systems and science), EDUCATION (art, business, elementary, science, secondary, and social science), ENGINEERING AND ENVIRONMENTAL DESIGN (computer engineering and industrial administration/management), HEALTH PROFESSIONS (medical laboratory technology), SOCIAL SCIENCE (addiction studies, criminal justice, economics, history, liberal arts/general studies, philosophy, political science/government, psychology, social science, social work, sociology, and theological studies). Managment, accounting, and criminal justice are the strongest academically. Management, accounting, and computer information systems have the largest enrollments.

Required: All students must complete 64 semester hours of general education courses, including English composition, economics, speech, theology, philosophy, communication and fine arts, science and mathematics, and social and behavioral science. A total of 124 semester hours with a minimum GPA of 2.0 is required in order to graduate.

Special: The college offers a cooperative 3–1 baccalaureate degree in medical technology with the schools of St. Margaret-Mercy Hospital in Indiana where students complete their study and a clinical internship. An accelerated degree completion program in organizational management is possible in 13 months for those with 60 college credits. The LEAP program offers credit for life experience. A general studies degree, pass/fail options, and nondegree study are possible.

Faculty/Classroom: Sixty-nine percent of faculty are male; 31%, female. All teach undergraduates. The average class size in an introductory lecture is 25; in a laboratory, 20; and in a regular course offering, 20.

Admissions: About 69% of the 1993–94 applicants were accepted.

Requirements: Cal College requires applicants to be in the upper 50% of their class. A minimum GPA of 2.0 is required. The SAT I or ACT is required for applicants who have graduated from High School within the prior 2 years. Applicants should have completed 15 Carnegie units or GED equivalent, including 4 years of high school English, 3 to 4 of mathematics, 2 to 3 of science, and 2 of social studies. An essay and an interview are recommended. Vocabulary and Reading Assessment Test Required. CLEP credit is accepted. Important factors used in the admissions decision are advanced placement or honor courses, leadership record, personality, intangible qualities, recommendations by school officials, and extracurricular activities record.

Procedure: Freshmen are admitted to all sessions. Entrance exams should be taken by May of the junior year. Application deadlines are open. Application fee is $25. Notification is sent on a rolling basis. There are early decision, early admissions, and deferred admissions plans. About 1 early decision candidates were accepted for the 1993–94 class.

Transfer: About 122 transfer students enrolled in 1993–94. A 2.0 GPA is required. An interview is recommended. Vocabulary and Reading Assessment Test is required. A total of 30 credits out of 126 must be completed at Cal College.

Visiting: There are regularly scheduled orientations for prospective students. There are guides for informal visits and visitors may sit in on classes. To arrange for a visit, contact Cindy Hillman at (219) 473–4216.

Financial Aid: In 1993–94, 70% of all students received some form of financial aid. Scholarships or need-based grants averaged $2100 ($2700 maximum). Seventy-one percent of undergraduate students work part-time. Average earnings from campus work for the school year are $1800. The average financial indebtedness of the 1992–93 graduate was $4000. Cal College is a member of CSS. The FAF and the college's own financial statement is required. The deadline for financial aid applications is August 1.

International Students: They must take the TOEFL and achieve a minimum score of 600. The student must also take the college's own entrance exam.

Computers: The college provides computer facilities for student use. The mainframe is a Prime 2755. All students may access the system. It may be used Monday through Friday from 8 A.M. to 10 P.M., except during class laboratory times. There are no time limits on using the system. The fees are $30.

Graduates: In 1992–93 213 bachelor's degrees were awarded. Some 50 companies recruited on campus in 1992–93. In the 1992 graduating class, 3% were enrolled in graduate school within 6 months of graduation.

Admissions Contact: Cindy Hillman, Director of Enrollment Management.

DEPAUW UNIVERSITY
B-3
Greencastle, IN 46135

(317) 658-4006

(800) 447-2495 (out-of-state)

Full-time: 888 men, 1059 women	Faculty: 156; IIB, +$
Part-time: 9 men, 27 women	Ph.D.s: 94%
Graduate: none	Student/Faculty: 12 to 1
Year: 4-1-4	Tuition: $13,700
Application Deadline: February 15	Room & Board: $4830
Freshman Class: 2073 applied, 1721 accepted, 531 enrolled	
SAT I or ACT: required	**VERY COMPETITIVE**

DePauw University, founded in 1837, is a private, coeducational institution affiliated with the United Methodist Church. It offers programs in the fields of liberal arts and music. There are 2 undergraduate schools. In addition to regional accreditation, DePauw has baccalaureate program accreditation with NASM and NCATE. The 3 libraries contain 271,129 volumes, 314,759 microform items, and 7897 audiovisual forms, and subscribe to 1249 periodicals. Computerized library sources and services include database searching. Special learning facilities include a learning resource center, art gallery, natural history museum, radio station, TV station, observatory, and nature preserve. The 175-acre campus is in a small town 45 miles west of Indianapolis. Including residence halls, there are 55 buildings on campus.

Student Life: About 60% of undergraduates are from out-of-state, mostly the Midwest. Students come from 45 states, 25 foreign countries, and Canada. Eighty-three percent are from public schools; 17% from private. Eighty-six percent are white. Sixty percent are Protestant; 21% Catholic. The average age of freshmen is 18; all undergraduates, 20. Ten percent drop out by the end of their first year; 79% remain to graduate.

Housing: A total of 2163 students can be accommodated in college housing. College-sponsored living facilities include coed dormitories, fraternity houses, and sorority houses. In addition there are special interest houses. On-campus housing is guaranteed for all 4 years. Ninety-three percent of students live on campus; of those, 95% remain on campus on weekends. Alcohol is not permitted. All students may keep cars on campus.

Activities: About 82% of men belong to 13 national fraternities; about 78% of women belong to 10 national sororities. There are 65 groups on campus, including band, cheerleading, chess, choir, chorale, chorus, computers, dance, drama, ethnic, film, honors, international, jazz band, literary magazine, musical theater, newspaper, opera, orchestra, pep band, political, professional, radio and TV, religious, social, social service, student government, symphony, and yearbook. Popular campus events include Little 500, Monon Bell, Old Gold Day, Fall Fest, Community Day, and fraternity and sorority philanthropies.

Sports: There are 10 intercollegiate sports for men and 9 for women, and 12 intramural sports for men and 11 for women. Athletic and recreation facilities include a recreation center, a 4,000-seat stadium, baseball, soccer, and field hockey fields, 3 basketball courts, indoor/outdoor tennis courts and tracks, a pool, weight training rooms, volleyball and badminton courts, and a 3,200-seat indoor gymnasium.

Disabled Students: Partial accessibility is provided to buildings, classrooms, laboratories, and residences for disabled people.

Services: In addition to many counseling and information services, tutoring is available in most subjects. There is a reader service for the blind.

Campus Safety and Security: Campus safety and security measures include 24-hour foot and vehicle patrol, escort service, informal discussions, and pamphlets, posters, and films. In addition, there are emergency telephones and lighted pathways and sidewalks.

Programs of Study: DePauw awards the B.A. and B.Mu. degrees. Bachelor's degrees are awarded in BIOLOGICAL SCIENCE (biology/biological science), COMMUNICATIONS AND THE ARTS (art history and appreciation, classical languages, communications, English, English literature, French, German, languages, Latin, music, music business management, music performance, romance languages, Spanish, and studio art), COMPUTER AND PHYSICAL SCIENCE (chemistry, computer science, earth science, geology, mathematics, and physics), EDUCATION (elementary, music, and physical), ENGINEERING AND ENVIRONMENTAL DESIGN (preengineering), HEALTH PROFESSIONS (medical technology), SOCIAL SCIENCE (anthropology, Asian studies, classical/ancient civilization, economics, geography, history, interdisciplinary women's studies, philosophy, political science/government, psychology, religion, Russian and Slavic studies, and sociology). English, political science, and communications have the largest enrollments.

Required: Students must demonstrate competence in oral communications, quantitative reasoning, and writing. Successful completion of 31 courses totaling 124 semester hours is required for graduation. In addition, students must fulfill distribution requirements in natural sciences and mathematics, social and behavioral sciences, literature

and the arts, historical and philosophical understanding, foreign language, and self-expression.

Special: The university offers dual majors in any 2 disciplines, internships for honors programs and winter term projects, unlimited study-abroad options through cooperative arrangements with other universities, pass/fail options, and credit by departmental examination and for military experience. Also available are 3-2 engineering degrees with Case Western Reserve University, Columbia University, Georgia Institute of Technology, and Washington University, and a 3-2 nursing program with Rush University. The Media Fellows, Management Fellows, and Science Research Fellows Programs offer majors in any discipline, plus a semester-long internship. There is a freshman honors program on campus, as well as 12 national honor societies, including Phi Beta Kappa.

Faculty/Classroom: Seventy-two percent of faculty are male; 28%, female. All teach undergraduates. The average class size in a regular course offering is 18.

Admissions: About 83% of the 1993-94 applicants were accepted. The SAT scores for the 1993-94 freshman class were as follows: Verbal—40% below 500, 39% between 500 and 599, 20% between 600 and 700, and 1% above 700; Math—18% below 500, 36% between 500 and 599, 36% between 600 and 700, and 10% above 700. The ACT scores were 5% below 21, 20% between 21 and 23, 31% between 24 and 26, 22% between 27 and 28, and 22% above 28. About 69% of the current freshmen were in the top fifth of their class; 92% were in the top two fifths. There were 11 National Merit finalists.

Requirements: The SAT I or ACT is required. Graduation from an accredited secondary school or a GED is required for admission. Course distribution must include 4 in English, 2 to 4 in a foreign language, 3 to 4 each in mathematics, social studies, and science, with 2 or more of these in laboratory science. An essay is required, and an interview is strongly recommended. Applicants for the School of Music must audition. AP and CLEP credits are accepted. Important factors used in the admissions decision are advanced placement or honor courses, leadership record, recommendations by school officials, evidence of special talent, and extracurricular activities record.

Procedure: Freshmen are admitted fall and spring. Entrance exams should be taken as early as possible. Applications should be filed by February 15 for fall entry, along with an application fee of $25. Notification is sent April 1. There are early notification, early admissions, and deferred admissions plans. A waiting list is an active part of the admissions procedure.

Transfer: Fifteen transfer students enrolled in 1993-94. Transfer students must submit either SAT I or ACT scores. High school and college transcripts are required, and a minimum GPA on previous college work of 3.0 is preferred. A total of 31 credits out of 124 must be completed at DePauw.

Visiting: There are regularly scheduled orientations for prospective students, consisting of day-long student/parent programs. There are guides for informal visits and visitors may sit in on classes and stay overnight at the school. To arrange for a visit, contact Sue Schoenfeld, Admissions Coordinator, at (800) 447-2495.

Financial Aid: In 1993-94, 75% of all current freshmen and 64% of continuing students received some form of financial aid. About 61% of freshmen and 44% of continuing students received need-based aid. The average freshman award was $11,762. Of that total, scholarships or need-based grants averaged $8140 ($16,530 maximum); loans averaged $2836 ($4875 maximum); and work contracts averaged $986 ($1300 maximum). Twenty-eight percent of undergraduate students work part-time. Average earnings from campus work for the school year are $580. The average financial indebtedness of the 1992-93 graduate was $9044. DePauw is a member of CSS. The FAF is required. The deadline for financial aid applications is February 15.

International Students: There are currently 60 international students enrolled. The school actively recruits these students. They must take the TOEFL and achieve a minimum score of 500 or the SAT I or ACT.

Computers: The university provides computer facilities for student use. The mainframe is a DEC VAX 11/780. More than 60 terminals are accessible to the mainframe, and 75 PCs are available for student use. Seminars are taught regularly, and any student can have a computer account. Locations include the computer center, library, residence halls, fraternities, sororities, and all academic offices. There are no time limits on using the system and no fees.

Graduates: In 1992-93, 518 bachelor's degrees were awarded. The most popular majors among graduates were communications (12%), history (11%), and economics (10%). Within an average freshman class, 73% graduate in 4 years, 78% in 5 years, and 79% in 6 years. Some 62 companies recruited on campus in 1992-93. In the 1992 graduating class, 28% of the men and 27% of the women were enrolled in graduate school within 6 months of graduation; 70% of men and women had found employment.

Admissions Contact: David C. Murray, Director of Admissions.

EARLHAM COLLEGE
D-3

Richmond, IN 47374   (317) 983-1600; (800) 327-5426 (out-of-state)

Full-time: 447 men, 581 women	Faculty: 90; IIB, +$
Part-time: 5 men, 8 women	Ph.D.s: 90%
Graduate: none	Student/Faculty: 11 to 1
Year: trimesters	Tuition: $15,327
Application Deadline: February 15	Room & Board: $4056

Freshman Class: 1358 applied, 1006 accepted, 274 enrolled
SAT I Verbal/Math: 540/560   ACT: 26   **VERY COMPETITIVE**

Earlham College, established in 1847 by the Society of Friends, is a private liberal arts college that emphasizes Quaker values. It offers undergraduate programs in humanities, fine arts, social sciences, languages, music, and natural sciences. The 2 libraries contain 338,740 volumes, 170,590 microform items, and 5600 audiovisual forms, and subscribe to 1276 periodicals. Computerized library sources and services include the card catalog, interlibrary loans, and database searching. Special learning facilities include a learning resource center, art gallery, natural history museum, planetarium, radio station, observatory, herbarium, and greenhouse. The 800-acre campus is in a suburban area 70 miles east of Indianapolis and 40 miles west of Dayton, Ohio. Including residence halls, there are 37 buildings on campus.

Student Life: About 85% of undergraduates are from out-of-state, mostly the Midwest. Students come from 46 states and 16 foreign countries. Seventy-two percent are from public schools; 18% from private. Eighty-two percent are white. The average age of freshmen is 18; all undergraduates, 20. Nine percent drop out by the end of their first year; 76% remain to graduate.

Housing: A total of 973 students can be accommodated in college housing. College-sponsored living facilities include coed dormitories, off-campus apartments, and married-student housing. In addition, there are language houses, special interest houses, the Jewish student and black student cultural centers, a peace studies house, and a small working farm. On-campus housing is guaranteed for all 4 years. Eighty-five percent of students live on campus; of those, 90% remain on campus on weekends. Alcohol is not permitted. All students may keep cars on campus.

Activities: There are no fraternities or sororities on campus. There are 60 groups on campus, including cheerleading, chess, choir, chorale, chorus, computers, dance, drama, ethnic, gay, international, jazz band, literary magazine, musical theater, newspaper, photography, political, radio, religious, social, social service, student government, and yearbook. Popular campus events include an Elizabethan celebration, Reggae Festival, African/African American celebration, lip sync contest, Japanese Spring Festival, Homecoming, and May Day.

Sports: There are 7 intercollegiate sports for men and 8 for women, and 8 intramural sports for men and 9 for women. Athletic and recreation facilities include a field house, with weight-training area, 25-meter pool, climbing wall, physical therapy room, and racquetball, handball, tennis, basketball, and volleyball courts. Outdoor facilities include a turf football field, 8 all-weather tennis courts, a trail for cross-country running and skiing, and baseball, softball, soccer, lacrosse, and field hockey fields. The campus stadium seats 2500, the indoor gymnasium 1750, and the auditorium/arena 1750.

Disabled Students: Eighty percent of the campus is accessible to disabled students. The following facilities are available: wheelchair ramps, elevators, special parking, and specially equipped rest rooms.

Services: In addition to many counseling and information services, tutoring is available in every subject. There also is a reader service for the blind.

Campus Safety and Security: Campus safety and security measures include 24-hour foot and vehicle patrol, self defense education, escort service, and shuttle buses. In addition, there are informal discussions, pamphlets, posters, and films, and lighted pathways and sidewalks.

Programs of Study: Earlham awards the B.A. degree. Bachelor's degrees are awarded in BIOLOGICAL SCIENCE (biology/biological science), BUSINESS (business administration and management), COMMUNICATIONS AND THE ARTS (dramatic arts, English, fine arts, French, German, Japanese, music, and Spanish), COMPUTER AND PHYSICAL SCIENCE (chemistry, computer science, geology, mathematics, and physics), EDUCATION (education), ENGINEERING AND ENVIRONMENTAL DESIGN (environmental science), SOCIAL SCIENCE (African American studies, anthropology, economics, history, human development, international relations, peace studies, philosophy, political science/government, psychology, religion, social science, sociology, and women's studies). Natural sciences, psychology, English, and Japanese studies are the strongest academically. Biology, English, and psychology have the largest enrollments.

Required: In order to graduate, all students must complete courses in humanities, mathematics, foreign language, fine arts, the natural sciences, religion/philosophy, and physical education. Students must also maintain a minimum GPA of 2.0 and complete a total of 36 course credits, including 8 to 12 in the major. A comprehensive examination is required.

Special: Opportunities are provided for dual majors, cross-registration with Indiana University, internships, work-study programs, nondegree study, and student-designed majors. Study abroad is available in 12 countries in Asia, Africa, and South America, and in the former Soviet Union, Mexico, and Jerusalem. Preprofessional and professional options are offered in architecture, business, forestry, law, medicine, and nursing. Special programs are also available in museum studies and wilderness studies. There is a 3–2 engineering degree with Case Western Reserve and Columbia universities, University of Rochester, Rensselaer Polytechnic Institute, and University of Michigan. There is 1 national honor society on campus, Phi Beta Kappa.

Faculty/Classroom: Fifty-eight percent of faculty are male; 42%, female. All teach undergraduates and 75% also do research. The average class size in an introductory lecture is 40; in a laboratory, 15; and in a regular course offering, 18.

Admissions: About 74% of the 1993–94 applicants were accepted. The SAT scores for the 1993–94 freshman class were as follows: Verbal—32% below 500, 40% between 500 and 599, 24% between 600 and 700, and 4% above 700; Math—25% below 500, 38% between 500 and 599, 29% between 600 and 700, and 8% above 700. The ACT scores were 13% below 21, 17% between 21 and 23, 22% between 24 and 26, 29% between 27 and 28, and 19% above 28. About 50% of the current freshmen were in the top fifth of their class; 80% were in the top two fifths. There were 5 National Merit finalists and 19 semifinalists. Sixteen freshmen graduated first in their class.

Requirements: A minimum GPA of 2.5 and either the SAT I or ACT is required. Graduation from an accredited secondary school is required; a GED will be accepted. Students must have completed at least 15 academic credits, including 4 years of English, 3 of mathematics, and 2 each of science, history, social studies, and a foreign language. Students are required to submit an essay and letters of recommendation from a teacher and guidance counselor. An interview is recommended. AP and CLEP credits are accepted. Important factors used in the admissions decision are advanced placement or honor courses, evidence of special talent, recommendations by school officials, personality, intangible qualities, and leadership record.

Procedure: Freshmen are admitted in the fall. Entrance exams should be taken during the spring of the junior year or early fall of the senior year. Early decision applications should be filed by December 1; regular applications, by February 15 for fall entry, November 15 for winter entry, and February 15 for spring entry, along with an application fee of $30. Notification of early decision is sent December 15; regular decision, April 2. There are early decision, early admissions, and deferred admissions plans. About 43 early decision candidates were accepted for the 1993–94 class. A waiting list is an active part of the admissions procedure, with about 5% of applicants on the list.

Transfer: A total of 36 transfer students enrolled in 1993–94. Applicants must take the SAT I or ACT and have a minimum GPA of 2.5. An interview is recommended. One year, or a total of 9 course credits out of 36, must be completed at Earlham.

Visiting: There are regularly scheduled orientations for prospective students, including class visitation, an admissions interview, and a tour. There are guides for informal visits and visitors may sit in on classes and stay overnight at the school. To arrange for a visit, contact the Admissions Office at (800) 327-5426.

Financial Aid: In 1993–94, 65% of all current freshmen and 70% of continuing students received some form of financial aid. About 59% of freshmen and 65% of continuing students received need-based aid. The average freshman award was $14,471. Of that total, scholarships or need-based grants averaged $9050 ($17,208 maximum); loans averaged $2785 ($4625 maximum); and work contracts averaged $1200 ($1275 maximum). Sixty percent of undergraduate students work part-time. Average earnings from campus work for the school year are $720. The average financial indebtedness of the 1992–93 graduate was $8750. Earlham is a member of CSS. The FAF and the FAFSA are required. The deadline for financial aid applications is March 1.

International Students: There are currently 47 international students enrolled. The school actively recruits these students. They must take the TOEFL and achieve a minimum score of 550.

Computers: The college provides computer facilities for student use. The mainframe is a DEC VAX 4000–200. Students may access the mainframe through modems, or they may use 35 terminal connections via dumb terminals or terminal emulators. All students may access the system 24 hours per day. There are no time limits on using the system and no fees.

Graduates: In 1992–93, 228 bachelor's degrees were awarded. The most popular majors among graduates were biology (14%), English (11%), and psychology (6%). Within an average freshman class, 66% graduate in 4 years and 72% in 5 years. Some 45 companies recruited on campus in 1992–93. In the 1992 graduating class, 28% of the

men and 23% of the women were enrolled in graduate school within 6 months of graduation; 72% of the men and 77% of the women had found employment.

Admissions Contact: Robert deVeer, Dean of Admissions.

FRANKLIN COLLEGE OF INDIANA   C-4

Franklin, IN 46131   (317) 738–8062; (800) 852–0232 (out-of-state)

Full-time: 381 men, 459 women	Faculty: 60; IIB, av$
Part-time: 26 men, 42 women	Ph.D.s: 80%
Graduate: none	Student/Faculty: 14 to 1
Year: 4–1–4, summer session	Tuition: $10,100
Application Deadline: open	Room & Board: $3870

Freshman Class: 804 applied, 632 accepted, 281 enrolled

SAT I Verbal/Math: 481/532   ACT: 22   **COMPETITIVE**

Franklin College of Indiana, founded in 1834, is a private, coeducational liberal arts college affiliated with the American Baptist Churches, USA. In addition to regional accreditation, Franklin has baccalaureate program accreditation with NCATE. The library contains 109,066 volumes, 14,285 microform items, and 3786 audiovisual forms, and subscribes to 583 periodicals. Computerized library sources and services include the card catalog and interlibrary loans. Special learning facilities include a radio station and a TV station. The 74-acre campus is in a small town 20 miles south of Indianapolis. Including residence halls, there are 20 buildings on campus.

Student Life: About 90% of undergraduates are from Indiana. Students come from 11 states and 12 foreign countries. Ninety-seven percent are white. Fifty-three percent are Protestant; 25% claim no religious affiliation; 15% are Catholic. The average age of freshmen is 18; all undergraduates, 20. Twenty-six percent drop out by the end of their first year; 70% remain to graduate.

Housing: A total of 670 students can be accommodated in college housing. College-sponsored living facilities include single-sex dormitories and fraternity houses. On-campus housing is available on a first-come, first-served basis and is available on a lottery system for upperclassmen. Eighty-one percent of students live on campus. All students may keep cars on campus.

Activities: About 50% of men belong to 5 national fraternities; about 50% of women belong to 3 national sororities. There are 60 groups on campus, including art, cheerleading, choir, chorus, dance, drama, ethnic, film, honors, international, literary magazine, musical theater, newspaper, pep band, photography, political, professional, radio and TV, religious, social, social service, student government, and yearbook. Popular campus events include Fall Fever and Spring Fever Days, Annual Kite Carnival, Greek Week, Variety Show, Monte Carlo Night, and Black History Month.

Sports: There are 8 intercollegiate sports each for men and women, and 4 intramural sports each for men and women. Athletic and recreation facilities include athletic and soccer fields, tennis courts, a physical education center, and a fitness center.

Disabled Students: All of the campus is accessible to disabled students. The following facilities are available: wheelchair ramps, elevators, special parking, specially equipped rest rooms, special class scheduling, lowered drinking fountains, and specially equipped dormitory rooms.

Services: In addition to many counseling and information services, tutoring is available in most subjects. In addition, there is a reader service for the blind, and remedial math, reading, and writing.

Campus Safety and Security: Campus safety and security measures include 24-hour foot and vehicle patrol, escort service, pamphlets, posters, and films, and emergency telephones. In addition, there are lighted pathways and sidewalks.

Programs of Study: Franklin awards the B.A. degree. Associate degrees are also awarded. Bachelor's degrees are awarded in BIOLOGICAL SCIENCE (biology/biological science), BUSINESS (accounting, banking and finance, business economics, international business management, management science, and marketing/retailing/merchandising), COMMUNICATIONS AND THE ARTS (advertising, broadcasting, communications, English, fine arts, French, journalism, and Spanish), COMPUTER AND PHYSICAL SCIENCE (chemistry, computer science, information sciences and systems, mathematics, and physics), EDUCATION (art, business, elementary, middle school, and secondary), ENGINEERING AND ENVIRONMENTAL DESIGN (engineering), HEALTH PROFESSIONS (medical laboratory technology, nursing, occupational therapy, predentistry, and premedicine), SOCIAL SCIENCE (Canadian studies, economics, history, philosophy, political science/government, prelaw, psychology, religion, and sociology). Natural sciences is the strongest academically. Journalism, business, and education have the largest enrollments.

Required: Requirements for graduation include 96 core curriculum hours, including general education, winter term and related field and activity courses; a minimum of 24 hours in the major; and 136 total credit hours. Each student must maintain a minimum GPA of 2.0, and must pass the Senior Competency Test, which is administered by the department in which the student completes a major.

Special: Cooperative programs in nursing, political science, Canadian studies, forestry and engineering are available, as are January and summer internships. Study abroad in 10 countries and cross-registration with Indiana University/Purdue University at Indianapolis, Marian College, and the University of Indianapolis are permitted. A 3–2 engineering degree with Washington University at St. Louis is possible. There is a freshman honors program on campus, as well as 6 national honor societies. Six departments have honors programs.

Faculty/Classroom: Sixty-two percent of faculty are male; 38%, female. All teach undergraduates. The average class size in an introductory lecture is 18; in a laboratory, 15; and in a regular course offering, 18.

Admissions: About 79% of the 1993–94 applicants were accepted. The SAT scores for the 1993–94 freshman class were as follows: Verbal—55% below 500, 35% between 500 and 599, 10% between 600 and 700, and 1% above 700; Math—33% below 500, 38% between 500 and 599, 27% between 600 and 700, and 3% above 700. About 53% of the current freshmen were in the top fifth of their class; 85% were in the top two fifths. There were 4 National Merit semifinalists. Seven freshmen graduated first in their class.

Requirements: Franklin requires applicants to be in the upper 50% of their class. A minimum GPA of 2.0 is required. The SAT I or ACT is required. Candidates for admission must have completed 4 years of English, 3 to 4 of mathematics, 2 to 3 of science, 2 each of art and music, social studies, and a foreign language, and completed typing and basic computing skill courses. The GED is accepted, and an essay is required. AP and CLEP credits are accepted. Important factors used in the admissions decision are recommendations by school officials, evidence of special talent, leadership record, advanced placement or honor courses, and extracurricular activities record.

Procedure: Freshmen are admitted to all sessions. Entrance exams should be taken during summer orientation. Application deadlines are open. Application fee is $15. Notification is sent on a rolling basis. A waiting list is an active part of the admissions procedure.

Transfer: About 20 transfer students enrolled in 1993–94. Transfer students must have at least a 2.0 cumulative GPA. A total of 30 credits out of 136 must be completed at Franklin.

Visiting: There are regularly scheduled orientations for prospective students, including academic presentations, admissions and financial presentations, a student life presentation, campus tours, lunch, and opportunities to talk to professors and sit in on a class. There are guides for informal visits and visitors may sit in on classes and stay overnight at the school. To arrange for a visit, contact the Admissions Office at (800) 852–0232.

Financial Aid: In 1993–94, 95% of all current freshmen and 92% of continuing students received some form of financial aid. About 71% of freshmen and 69% of continuing students received need-based aid. The average freshman award was $8500. Of that total, scholarships or need-based grants averaged $3400 ($13,970 maximum); loans averaged $2381 ($2625 maximum); and work contracts averaged $900 ($1320 maximum). Forty-two percent of undergraduate students work part-time. Average earnings from campus work for the school year are $900. The average financial indebtedness of the 1992–93 graduate was $7000. Franklin is a member of CSS. The FAF and the FAFSA are required. The deadline for financial aid applications is March 1.

International Students: There are currently 16 international students enrolled. They must take the TOEFL and achieve a minimum score of 550.

Computers: The college provides computer facilities for student use. The mainframe is a MicroVAX II. There are also 72 Z159 microcomputers in laboratories in the computer center, library, and other campus buildings. Those students involved with programming and statistics courses may access the system. It may be used 8 A.M. to midnight. There are no time limits on using the system and no fees.

Graduates: In 1992–93, 120 bachelor's degrees were awarded. Within an average freshman class, 80% graduate in 4 years and 100% in 5 years. Some 22 companies recruited on campus in 1992–93. In the 1992 graduating class, 78% of all graduates had found employment within 6 months of graduation.

Admissions Contact: B. Stephen Richards, Dean of Enrollment Management.

GOSHEN COLLEGE   C-1

Goshen, IN 46526   (219) 535–7535; (800) 348–7422

Full-time: 416 men, 540 women	Faculty: 85; IIB, --$
Part-time: 58 men, 108 women	Ph.D.s: 62%
Graduate: none	Student/Faculty: 11 to 1
Year: semesters, summer session	Tuition: $8770
Application Deadline: August 15	Room & Board: $3590

Freshman Class: 550 applied, 460 accepted, 236 enrolled

SAT I Verbal/Math: 487/519   **COMPETITIVE**

Goshen College, founded in 1894, is a private, coeducational liberal arts institution affiliated with the Mennonite Church. In addition to re-

gional accreditation, Goshen has baccalaureate program accreditation with CSWE, NCATE, and NLN. The library contains 120,000 volumes, 100 microform items, and 1500 audiovisual forms, and subscribes to 800 periodicals. Computerized library sources and services include interlibrary loans and database searching. Special learning facilities include a learning resource center, art gallery, and radio station. The 135-acre campus is in a small town 120 miles east of Chicago. Including residence halls, there are 24 buildings on campus.

Student Life: About 59% of undergraduates are from out-of-state, mostly the Midwest. Students come from 35 states, 29 foreign countries, and Canada. Seventy-seven percent are from public schools; 23% from private. Eighty-five percent are white. Most are Protestant. The average age of freshmen is 19.7; all undergraduates, 21.2. Nine percent drop out by the end of their first year; 62% remain to graduate.

Housing: A total of 696 students can be accommodated in college housing. College-sponsored living facilities include coed dormitories, off-campus apartments, and married-student housing. In addition, there are special interest houses. On-campus housing is guaranteed for all 4 years. Sixty-four percent of students live on campus; of those, 80% remain on campus on weekends. Alcohol is not permitted. All students may keep cars on campus.

Activities: There are no fraternities or sororities on campus. There are 20 groups on campus, including chess, choir, chorale, drama, ethnic, international, jazz band, newspaper, opera, orchestra, professional, radio and TV, religious, social service, student government, and yearbook. Popular campus events include Carnival, Ethnic Fair, Homecoming, and Maple Leaf Festival.

Sports: There are 7 intercollegiate sports for men and 6 for women, and 8 intramural sports for men and 7 for women. Athletic and recreation facilities include a new fitness center with an indoor track and swimming pool, 3 basketball courts, a soccer field, tennis courts, and a sand volleyball court.

Disabled Students: Seventy-five percent of the campus is accessible to disabled students. The following facilities are available: wheelchair ramps, elevators, special parking, specially equipped rest rooms, special class scheduling, lowered drinking fountains, and lowered telephones.

Services: In addition to many counseling and information services, tutoring is available in every subject. There is also a reader service for the blind, and remedial math, reading, and writing.

Campus Safety and Security: Campus safety and security measures include self defense education, escort service, informal discussions, and lighted pathways and sidewalks.

Programs of Study: Goshen awards the B.A. and B.S.N degrees. Bachelor's degrees are awarded in BIOLOGICAL SCIENCE (biology/biological science), BUSINESS (accounting and business administration and management), COMMUNICATIONS AND THE ARTS (communications, dramatic arts, English, German, music, and Spanish), COMPUTER AND PHYSICAL SCIENCE (chemistry, computer programming, mathematics, natural sciences, and physics), EDUCATION (art, business, early childhood, elementary, foreign languages, middle school, music, physical, science, secondary, and teaching English as a second language/foreign language), ENGINEERING AND ENVIRONMENTAL DESIGN (preengineering), HEALTH PROFESSIONS (nursing, predentistry, premedicine, prepharmacy, and preveterinary science), SOCIAL SCIENCE (biblical studies, economics, history, psychology, religion, social work, and sociology). Business, education, nursing, and premedicine have the largest enrollments.

Required: All students must complete the general education program, including courses in literature and communication, fine arts, Bible, religion, philosophy, natural science, social science, and history, 1 hour of fitness, and 12 hours of international education in the Study Service Term. A total of 120 (B.A.) to 124 (B.S.N.) credit hours with a minimum GPA of 2.0 is required in order to graduate.

Special: A year abroad internship in the required Study Service Term is possible in Indonesia, Germany, Ivory Coast, Costa Rica, and the Dominican Republic. Cross-registration is offered with member colleges of the Northern Indiana Consortium for Education. A Washington semester, dual majors, student-designed majors, and a 3–2 engineering degree with the University of Illinois, Washington University in St. Louis, Pennsylvania State, and Case Western Reverse University are available. Credit for life experience, pass/fail options, and nondegree study are possible.

Faculty/Classroom: Fifty-nine percent of faculty are male; 41%, female. All teach and do research. The average class size in an introductory lecture is 17; in a laboratory, 17; and in a regular course offering, 17.

Admissions: About 84% of the 1993–94 applicants were accepted. The SAT scores for the 1993–94 freshman class were as follows: Math—45% below 500, 32% between 500 and 599, 16% between 600 and 700, and 7% above 700. About 30% of the current freshmen were in the top fifth of their class; 62% were in the top two fifths.

There were 5 National Merit finalists. Sixteen freshmen graduated first in their class.

Requirements: Goshen requires applicants to be in the upper 50% of their class. A minimum GPA of 2.0 is required. The SAT I or ACT is required. Applicants should be graduates of an accredited secondary school or have the GED equivalent, with 4 years of high school English, 2 to 4 years of mathematics, and 2 years each of foreign language, science, history, and social studies. An interview is recommended. AP and CLEP credits are accepted. Important factors used in the admissions decision are advanced placement or honor courses, recommendations by school officials, recommendations by alumni, leadership record, and evidence of special talent.

Procedure: Freshmen are admitted to all sessions. Entrance exams should be taken by fall of the senior year. Applications should be filed by August 15 for fall entry, December 15 for winter entry, and April 15 for spring entry, along with an application fee of $15. Notification is sent on a rolling basis.

Transfer: A total of 53 transfer students enrolled in 1993–94. A total of 30 credits out of 120 to 124 must be completed at Goshen.

Visiting: There are regularly scheduled orientations for prospective students, consisting of a campus tour, parents session, financial aid session, and student panel. There are guides for informal visits and visitors may sit in on classes and stay overnight at the school. To arrange for a visit, contact the Admissions Office at (800) 348–7422 or (219) 535–7535.

Financial Aid: In a recent year, 87% of all current freshmen and 85% of continuing students received some form of financial aid. About 87% of freshmen and 85% of continuing students received need-based aid. The average freshman award was $5000. Of that total, scholarships or need-based grants averaged $1450 ($2000 maximum). Seventy percent of undergraduate students work part-time. Goshen is a member of CSS. The FAF and the college's own financial statement are required. The deadline for financial aid applications is March 1.

International Students: There are currently 58 international students enrolled. The school actively recruits these students. They must take the TOEFL and achieve a minimum score of 550.

Computers: The college provides computer facilities for student use. The mainframe is a DEC VAX 11/750. There are 2 computer laboratories available to all students. All students may access the system Monday through Friday 8 a.m to 11 P.M. and 12:30 to 5:30 p.m on weekends. There are no time limits on using the system and no fees.

Graduates: In 1992–93, 246 bachelor's degrees were awarded. The most popular majors among graduates were business (22%), nursing (10%), and education (9%). Some 15 companies recruited on campus in 1992–93. In the 1992 graduating class, 11% of the men and 9% of the women were enrolled in graduate school within 6 months of graduation.

Admissions Contact: Martha Lehman, Director of Admissions.

GRACE COLLEGE
Winona Lake, IN 46590

C-2

(219) 372–5128
(800) 54-GRACE (out-of-state)

Full-time: 276 men, 342 women	Faculty: 30
Part-time: 64 men, 49 women	Ph.D.s: 43%
Graduate: none	Student/Faculty: 21 to 1
Year: semesters, summer session	Tuition: $8450
Application Deadline: August 1	Room & Board: $3670
Freshman Class: 548 applied, 428 accepted, 190 enrolled	
ACT: 22	COMPETITIVE

Grace College, founded in 1948, is a Christian liberal arts institution affiliated with the Fellowship of Grace Brethren Churches. In addition to regional accreditation, Grace has baccalaureate program accreditation with NCATE. The library contains 136,700 volumes, 42,000 microform items, and 2545 audiovisual forms, and subscribes to 560 periodicals. The 150-acre campus is in a rural area 40 miles west of Fort Wayne. Including residence halls, there are 14 buildings on campus.

Student Life: About 59% of undergraduates are from out-of-state, mostly the Midwest. Students come from 31 states, 14 foreign countries, and Canada. Sixty-nine percent are from public schools; 31% from private. Ninety-five percent are white. Most are Protestant. The average age of freshmen is 18; all undergraduates, 22.6. Twenty percent drop out by the end of their first year; 70% remain to graduate.

Housing: A total of 516 students can be accommodated in college housing. College-sponsored living facilities include single-sex dormitories. On-campus housing is guaranteed for the freshman year only and is available on a first-come, first-served basis. Priority is given to out-of-town students. Seventy percent of students live on campus; of those, 80% remain on campus on weekends. Alcohol is not permitted. All students may keep cars on campus.

Activities: There are no fraternities or sororities on campus. There are 10 groups on campus, including band, cheerleading, choir, drama, newspaper, pep band, religious, social, student government, and

yearbook. Popular campus events include Fall Fest, Heart of the Holidays, Evening in December, Homecoming, and VIP Days.

Sports: There are 6 intercollegiate sports for men and 4 for women, and 4 intramural sports for men and 2 for women. Athletic and recreation facilities include a gymnasium, a playing field, and tennis courts.

Disabled Students: Eighty percent of the campus is accessible to disabled students. The following facilities are available: wheelchair ramps, elevators, special parking, and specially equipped rest rooms.

Services: In addition to many counseling and information services, tutoring is available in every subject. There is also remedial writing.

Campus Safety and Security: Campus safety and security measures include lighted pathways and sidewalks.

Programs of Study: Grace awards the B.A. and B.S. degrees. Associate degrees are also awarded. Bachelor's degrees are awarded in BIOLOGICAL SCIENCE (biology/biological science), BUSINESS (accounting, business administration and management, and management information systems), COMMUNICATIONS AND THE ARTS (art, communications, English, French, German, graphic design, music, Russian, and Spanish), COMPUTER AND PHYSICAL SCIENCE (mathematics and science), EDUCATION (art, business, elementary, English, foreign languages, mathematics, music, physical, and science), HEALTH PROFESSIONS (predentistry and premedicine), SOCIAL SCIENCE (counseling psychology, criminal justice, ministries, prelaw, psychology, religion, and sociology). Biology, psychology, business, and elementary education are the strongest academically. Business, psychology, and elementary education have the largest enrollments.

Required: To graduate, all students must complete 124 hours, including 36 to 54 in the major, and have a minimum GPA of 2.0. There is a required core curriculm of 63 to 64 hours consisting of languages/literature, religion/philosophy, education, social sciences, natural sciences, and a liberal arts seminar.

Special: Grace has a cooperative program in engineering with Tri-State University. Students may study abroad in France, Germany, the former Soviet Union, and Spain. A B.A.-B.S. degree is available in all majors except languages, English, and biblical studies. There is one national honor society on campus.

Faculty/Classroom: Sixty-eight percent of faculty are male; 32%, female. All teach undergraduates. The average class size in an introductory lecture is 36; in a laboratory, 14; and in a regular course offering, 13.

Admissions: About 78% of the 1993–94 applicants were accepted. About 35% of the current freshmen were in the top fifth of their class; 61% were in the top two fifths.

Requirements: Grace requires applicants to be in the upper 50% of their class. A minimum GPA of 2.0 is required. The ACT, with a minimum composite score of 15, or the SAT I is required. Applicants must have completed 15 Carnegie units, including 4 of English, 2 each of a foreign language and social studies, 3 each of mathematics and science, and 1 of history. A GED is accepted. AP and CLEP credits are accepted. Important factors used in the admissions decision are advanced placement or honor courses, leadership record, personality, intangible qualities, evidence of special talent, and extracurricular activities record.

Procedure: Freshmen are admitted to all sessions. Entrance exams should be taken in October, December, or February. Applications should be filed by August 1 for fall entry and December 1 for spring entry, along with an application fee of $20. Notification is sent on a rolling basis. There is a deferred admissions plan.

Transfer: A total of 43 transfer students enrolled in 1993–94. A total of 30 credits out of 124 must be completed at Grace.

Visiting: There are regularly scheduled orientations for prospective students. There are guides for informal visits and visitors may sit in on classes and stay overnight at the school. To arrange for a visit, contact Visitors Center at (219) 372-5577.

Financial Aid: In 1993–94, 70% of all current freshmen and 95% of continuing students received some form of financial aid. About 70% of freshmen and 83% of continuing students received need-based aid. The average freshman award was $7448. Of that total, scholarships or need-based grants averaged $2875 ($4800 maximum); loans averaged $3800 ($7000 maximum); and work contracts averaged $800 ($1600 maximum). Forty percent of undergraduate students work part-time. Average earnings from campus work for the school year are $1200. The average financial indebtedness of the 1992–93 graduate was $10,000. Grace is a member of CSS. The FAF and the college's own financial statement are required. The deadline for financial aid applications is April 1.

International Students: There are currently 25 international students enrolled. They must take the TOEFL and achieve a minimum score of 500. The student must also take the SAT I or the ACT.

Computers: The college provides computer facilities for student use. The mainframe is a DEC MicroVax II. There are 8 DEC terminals, 16 PCs on a Novell Network, and 5 PCs on a PEER to PEER network available in laboratories. All students may access the system when the classrooms and laboratories are open. There are no time limits on using the system and no fees.

Graduates: In 1992–93, 119 bachelor's degrees were awarded. The most popular majors among graduates were psychology (18%), elementary education (17%), and business administration (10%). Within an average freshman class, 10% graduate in 3 years, 47% in 4 years, 7% in 5 years, and 6% in 6 years. Some 22 companies recruited on campus in 1992–93. In the 1992 graduating class, 9% of the men and 6% of the women were enrolled in graduate school within 6 months of graduation; 38% of the men and 43% of the women had found employment.

Admissions Contact: Ron Henry, Dean of Enrollment.

HANOVER COLLEGE

D-5

Hanover, IN 47243 (812) 866-7026

Full-time: 500 men, 550 women	**Faculty:** 82; IIB, +$
Part-time: 5 men, 7 women	**Ph.D.s:** 80%
Graduate: none	**Student/Faculty:** 13 to 1
Year: 4-4-1	**Tuition:** $7750
Application Deadline: March 15	**Room & Board:** $3200
Freshman Class: 1006 applied, 815 accepted, 344 enrolled	
SAT I: 505/535	**ACT:** 25 **VERY COMPETITIVE**

Hanover College, founded in 1827 and the oldest private college in Indiana, is a liberal arts school affiliated with the United Presbyterian Church. The library contains 325,000 volumes, 142,000 microform items, and 10,000 audiovisual forms, and subscribes to 900 periodicals. Computerized library sources and services include the card catalog and interlibrary loans. Special learning facilities include a learning resource center, a planetarium, a radio station, a TV station, and a geology museum. The 650-acre campus is in a rural area 45 miles north of Louisville, Kentucky. Including residence halls, there are 34 buildings on campus.

Student Life: About 60% of undergraduates are from Indiana. Students come from 30 states, 15 foreign countries, and Canada. Eighty-five percent are from public schools; 15% from private. Ninety-six percent are white. Sixty-seven percent are Protestant; 30% Catholic. The average age of freshmen is 18; all undergraduates, 20.5. Eight percent drop out by the end of their first year; 60% remain to graduate.

Housing: A total of 1050 students can be accommodated in college housing. College-sponsored living facilities include single-sex dormitories, fraternity houses, and sorority houses. In addition there is a multicultural center. On-campus housing is guaranteed for all 4 years. Ninety-five percent of students live on campus; of those, 70% remain on campus on weekends. Alcohol is not permitted. Upperclassmen may keep cars on campus.

Activities: About 62% of men belong to 5 national fraternities; about 62% of women belong to 4 national sororities. There are 24 groups on campus, including band, cheerleading, choir, chorus, computers, dance, drama, film, honors, international, jazz band, literary magazine, musical theater, newspaper, orchestra, pep band, photography, political, professional, radio and TV, religious, social, social service, student government, and yearbook. Popular campus events include the community artist series and the foreign film series.

Sports: There are 8 intercollegiate sports for men and 6 for women, and 10 intramural sports for men and 8 for women. Athletic and recreation facilities include a 5000-seat stadium; a 750-seat arena; 2 gymnasiums, the larger of which seats 3000; a weight room; a handball court; a swimming pool; a bowling alley; and a billiards room.

Disabled Students: Seventy-five percent of the campus is accessible to disabled students. The following facilities are available: wheelchair ramps, elevators, special parking, lowered drinking fountains, and lowered telephones.

Services: In addition to many counseling and information services, tutoring is available in most subjects. In addition, there is remedial writing.

Campus Safety and Security: Campus safety and security measures include 24-hour foot and vehicle patrol, escort service, informal discussions, and pamphlets, posters, and films. In addition, there are emergency telephones and lighted pathways and sidewalks.

Programs of Study: Hanover awards the B.A. degree. Bachelor's degrees are awarded in BIOLOGICAL SCIENCE (biology/biological science), BUSINESS (business administration and management and business economics), COMMUNICATIONS AND THE ARTS (art, broadcasting, communications, dramatic arts, English, film arts, French, German, music, Spanish, and telecommunications), COMPUTER AND PHYSICAL SCIENCE (chemistry, computer science, geology, mathematics, and physics), EDUCATION (art, elementary, foreign languages, music, physical, science, and secondary), HEALTH PROFESSIONS (predentistry, premedicine, and speech pathology/audiology), SOCIAL SCIENCE (anthropology, economics, history, international relations, philosophy, political science/government, prelaw, psychology, religion, and sociology). Psychology, biology, and chemistry are the strongest academically. Business administration has the largest enrollment.

Required: The college requires its students to complete the core curriculum of a foreign language, philosophy, physical edcuation, fine arts, English, 2 social sciences, 2 physical sciences, speech, and history. Students must complete 36 courses, including 8 to 12 in the major, maintain a GPA of 2.0, pass a comprehensive examination, and participate in a culminations experience in the major.

Special: The college offers a 3–2 engineering degree with Washington University in St. Louis, a B.A.-B.S. degree in engineering, internships, study abroad, a Washington semester, and dual majors. In addition, there is cross-registration with the Spring Term Consortium, the University of Indianapolis, and Alma, Elmira, Northland, Transylvania, Wartburg, and William Woods colleges. There are 4 national honor societies on campus. Four departments have honors programs.

Faculty/Classroom: Seventy-five percent of faculty are male; 25%, female. All teach undergraduates. The average class size in an introductory lecture is 50; in a laboratory, 30; and in a regular course offering, 25.

Admissions: About 81% of the 1993–94 applicants were accepted. The SAT scores for the 1993–94 freshman class were as follows: Verbal—41% below 500, 50% between 500 and 599, 8% between 600 and 700, and 1% above 700; Math—36% below 500, 54% between 500 and 599, 8% between 600 and 700, and 2% above 700. The ACT scores were 5% below 21, 20% between 21 and 23, 53% between 24 and 26, 19% between 27 and 28, and 3% above 28. About 59% of the current freshmen were in the top fifth of their class; 94% were in the top two fifths. There were 2 National Merit finalists and 8 semifinalists. Six freshmen graduated first in their class.

Requirements: Hanover requires applicants to be in the upper 50% of their class. The SAT I, with a composite score of 1000, or the ACT, with a composite score of 22, is required. The college requires 16 academic credits and 12 Carnegie units from an accredited secondary school, including 4 years of English and 2 each of a foreign language, mathematics, science, and either history or social studies. The GED is accepted. The college also requires a foreign language achievement test, as well as an essay; an interview is recommended. AP credits are accepted. Important factors used in the admissions decision are advanced placement or honor courses, evidence of special talent, leadership record, recommendations by school officials, and extracurricular activities record.

Procedure: Freshmen are admitted fall and winter. Entrance exams should be taken late in the spring of the junior year. Applications should be filed by March 15 for fall entry and November 15 for winter entry, along with an application fee of $20. Notification is sent within 30 days of receipt of application. There is a deferred admissions plan. A waiting list is an active part of the admissions procedure, with about 10% of applicants on the list.

Transfer: Twenty-eight transfer students enrolled in 1993–94. Transfer students must submit transcripts from all colleges attended and must have at least a 2.5 GPA. The student must have taken either the SAT I or ACT, with a minimum composite score of 1000 on the SAT I or 24 on the ACT. A total of 17 courses must be completed at Hanover.

Visiting: There are guides for informal visits, and visitors may sit in on classes and stay overnight at the school. To arrange for a visit, contact the Office of Admissions at (812) 866–7021.

Financial Aid: In a recent year, 65% of all current freshmen and 65% of continuing students received some form of financial aid. About 65% of freshmen and 65% of continuing students received need-based aid. The average freshman award was $5000. Of that total, scholarships or need-based grants averaged $3400 ($6500 maximum); loans averaged $1590 ($2625 maximum); and work contracts averaged $400 ($1000 maximum). Twenty-three percent of undergraduate students work part-time. Average earnings from campus work for the school year are $600. The average financial indebtedness of the 1992–93 graduate was $5000. Hanover is a member of CSS. The FAF, the college's own financial statement, and the FAFSA are required. The deadline for financial aid applications is April 15.

International Students: There are currently 24 international students enrolled. They must take the TOEFL and achieve a minimum score of 500.

Computers: The college provides computer facilities for student use. The mainframe is a DEC VAX 4000. An MS-DOS-based and a Macintosh-based microcomputer network are available for student use. All students may access the system. It may be used 8 A.M. to 11 P.M. Monday through Thursday, 8 A.M. to 5 P.M. Friday, 8 A.M. to 5 P.M. Saturday, and 8 A.M. to 11 P.M. Sunday. There are no time limits on using the system and no fees.

Graduates: In 1992–93, 200 bachelor's degrees were awarded. The most popular majors among graduates were business administration (24%), communication (14%), and sociology (10%). Within an average freshman class, 60% graduate in 4 years and 65% in 5 years. Some 84 companies recruited on campus in 1992–93. In the 1992 graduating class, 45% of all graduates were enrolled in graduate school within 6 months of graduation; 50% had found employment.

Admissions Contact: C. Eugene McLemore, Director of Admissions.

HUNTINGTON COLLEGE
Huntington, IN 46750

D-2

(219) 356–6000
(800) 642–6493 (out-of-state)

Full-time: 231 men, 242 women	**Faculty:** 38; IIB, -$
Part-time: 23 men, 35 women	**Ph.D.s:** 66%
Graduate: 45 men, 2 women	**Student/Faculty:** 12 to 1
Year: 4-1-4, summer session	**Tuition:** $9490
Application Deadline: open	**Room & Board:** $3730
Freshman Class: 494 applied, 430 accepted, 150 enrolled	
SAT I Verbal/Math: 450/450	**ACT:** 21 **COMPETITIVE**

Huntington College, founded in 1897, is a private, coeducational, liberal arts college affiliated with the Church of the United Brethren in Christ. The library contains 144,006 volumes, 4177 microform items, and 3661 audiovisual forms, and subscribes to 487 periodicals. Computerized library sources and services include interlibrary loans and database searching. Special learning facilities include a learning resource center, art gallery, radio station, TV station, and a writing center. The 170-acre campus is in a small town 20 miles southwest of Fort Wayne. Including residence halls, there are 25 buildings on campus.

Student Life: About 64% of undergraduates are from Indiana. Students come from 15 states, 13 foreign countries, and Canada. Ninety-five percent are from public schools; 5% from private. Ninety-eight percent are white. Most are Protestant. The average age of freshmen is 19; all undergraduates, 21. Thirty percent drop out by the end of their first year; 44% remain to graduate.

Housing: A total of 499 students can be accommodated in college housing. College-sponsored living facilities include single-sex dormitories, on-campus apartments, and married-student housing. On-campus housing is guaranteed for all 4 years. Seventy-one percent of students live on campus; of those, 45% remain on campus on weekends. Alcohol is not permitted. All students may keep cars on campus.

Activities: About 2% of men belong to 1 local fraternity; about 2% of women belong to 1 local sorority. There are 24 groups on campus, including art, cheerleading, choir, chorale, chorus, computers, drama, honors, international, jazz band, literary magazine, musical theater, newspaper, orchestra, pep band, photography, radio and TV, religious, social service, student government, symphony, and yearbook. Popular campus events include Afro-American Week, the Artist-Lecture series, concerts, and recitals.

Sports: There are 7 intercollegiate sports for men and 6 for women, and 7 intramural sports for men and 6 for women. Athletic and recreation facilities include a field house with an indoor running track, 3 basketball courts, indoor and outdoor tennis courts, a swimming pool, softball and baseball diamonds, an outdoor track, and soccer and intramural fields.

Disabled Students: Ninety percent of the campus is accessible to disabled students. Elevators and special parking are available.

Services: In addition to many counseling and information services, tutoring is available in some subjects, including English and mathematics.

Campus Safety and Security: Campus safety and security measures include 24-hour foot and vehicle patrol and lighted pathways and sidewalks.

Programs of Study: Huntington awards the B.A., B.S., and B.Mus. degrees. Associate and master's degrees also are awarded. Bachelor's degrees are awarded in BIOLOGICAL SCIENCE (biology/biological science), BUSINESS (accounting, business administration and management, and business economics), COMMUNICATIONS AND THE ARTS (art, broadcasting, communication and theater arts, English, fine arts, music, and performance), COMPUTER AND PHYSICAL SCIENCE (chemistry, computer information science, and mathematics), EDUCATION (art, biology, business, chemistry, education, elementary, English, history/social studies, mathematics, middle school, music, physical, psychology/social studies, secondary, and sociology/social studies), HEALTH PROFESSIONS (medical laboratory technology and premedicine), SOCIAL SCIENCE (Bible and religion, economics, history, ministries, parks and recreation management, philosophy, prelaw, psychology, and sociology). Mathematics is the strongest academically. Business has the largest enrollment.

Required: Students must complete a minimum of 128 credit hours and maintain a GPA of 2.0 overall and in the major. Students must pass an English competency exam, complete a program in general education, and take 36 hours in upper-division courses numbered 300 or above, 2 hours of physical education, and 3 January term courses in at least 2 departments.

Special: Various companies in the area offer internships and ARA offers a work-study program. Students may study abroad in England, Cost Rica, Jamaica, and Israel. A Washington semester, a Hollywood semester, dual majors, correspondence courses with other schools, and pass/fail options are available. There is a freshman honors pro-

gram on campus, as well as one national honor society, Phi Beta Kappa.

Faculty/Classroom: Seventy-one percent of faculty are male; 29%, female. All teach undergraduates and 15% also do research. No introductory courses are taught by graduate students. The average class size in an introductory lecture is 35; in a laboratory, 15; and in a regular course offering, 22.

Admissions: About 87% of the 1993–94 applicants were accepted. The SAT scores for the 1993–94 freshman class were as follows: Verbal—65% below 500, 34% between 500 and 599, and 1% between 600 and 700; Math—59% below 500, 38% between 500 and 599, 2% between 600 and 700, and 1% above 700. The ACT scores were 61% below 21, 31% between 21 and 23, 5% between 24 and 26, 2% between 27 and 28, and 1% above 28. There were 3 National Merit finalists. Three freshmen graduated first in their class.

Requirements: Huntington requires applicants to be in the upper 50% of their class. A minimum GPA of 2.3 is required. The SAT I or ACT is required. Secondary school courses should include 4 years of English, 2 of college-preparatory mathematics, and 3 of social studies, including 1 each of American and world history. Two recommendations are required. AP and CLEP credits are accepted. Important factors used in the admissions decision are recommendations by school officials, personality, intangible qualities, recommendations by alumni, parents or siblings attending the school, and leadership record.

Procedure: Freshmen are admitted to all sessions. Entrance exams should be taken during the fall semester of the senior year. Application deadlines are open. The application fee is $15. Notification is sent on a rolling basis. There is an early admissions plan.

Transfer: About 25 transfer students enrolled in 1993–94. Transfer applicants should be in good standing at the college previously attended and have maintained a GPA of 2.0. Courses with a grade of C or better transfer. The last of 30 credits or a minimum of 90 out of 128 must be completed at Huntington.

Visiting: There are regularly scheduled orientations for prospective students, available on 3 days notice. There are guides for informal visits and visitors may sit in on classes and stay overnight at the school. To arrange for a visit, contact Angie Gaier at (800) 642–6493.

Financial Aid: In an earlier year, 91% of all current freshmen and 92% of continuing students received some form of financial aid. About 90% of freshmen and 88% of continuing students received need-based aid. The average freshman award was $4000. Of that total, scholarships or need-based grants averaged $4851 ($10,060 maximum); loans averaged $2000 ($4875 maximum); and work contracts averaged $800 ($1500 maximum). Twenty-six percent of undergraduate students worked part-time. Average earnings from campus work for the school year was $800. The average financial indebtedness of the graduate was $7800. Huntington is a member of CSS. The FAF or FFS is required. The deadline for financial aid applications is March 1.

International Students: There are currently 26 international students enrolled. The school actively recruits these students. They must take the TOEFL and achieve a minimum score of 525.

Computers: The college provides computer facilities for student use. The mainframes are a DEC PDP 11/44 and a DEC VAX 11/750. There are also 50 IBM and Apple microcomputers in classroom buildings. All students may access the system from 9 A.M. to 11 P.M. Monday through Thursday, 9 A.M. to 5 P.M. Friday, and 9 A.M. to 2 P.M. Saturday. There are no time limits on using the system and no fees.

Graduates: In an earlier year, 75 bachelor's degrees were awarded. The most popular majors among graduates were business (15%), theology (13%), and elementary education (12%). Within an average freshman class, 1% graduate in 3 years and 41% in 4 years. Some 26 companies recruited on campus in an earlier year. In that graduating class, 8% of the students were enrolled in graduate school and 39% of the men and 42% of the women had found employment within 6 months of graduation.

Admissions Contact: Dean of Admissions and Financial Aid.

INDIANA INSTITUTE OF TECHNOLOGY   D-2
Fort Wayne, IN 46803-1297   **(219) 422–5561, ext. 251**
            (800) 937–2448

Full-time: 367 men, 110 women	Faculty: 22
Part-time: 243 men, 359 women	Ph.D.s: 50%
Graduate: none	Student/Faculty: 22 to 1
Year: semesters, summer session	Tuition: $8120
Application Deadline: open	Room & Board: $3690
Freshman Class: 1052 applied, 978 accepted, 170 enrolled	
SAT I Verbal/Math: 446/491	**COMPETITIVE**

Indiana Institute of Technology, established in 1930, is a private institution offering undergraduate degrees in business, engineering, and science. There are 2 undergraduate schools. The library contains 46,000 volumes and 20,000 microform items, and subscribes to 200 periodicals. Computerized library sources and services include the card catalog, interlibrary loans, and database searching. Special learning facilities include a learning resource center. The 25-acre campus is in an urban area 150 miles east of Chicago. Including residence halls, there are 10 buildings on campus.

Student Life: About 65% of undergraduates are from out-of-state, mostly the Midwest. Students come from 22 states and 23 foreign countries. Ninety-five percent are from public schools; 5% from private. Fifty-five percent are white; 20% African American; 15% foreign nationals. The average age of freshmen is 18; all undergraduates, 26. Thirty percent drop out by the end of their first year; 40% remain to graduate.

Housing: A total of 400 students can be accommodated in college housing. College-sponsored living facilities include dormitories, on-campus apartments, and fraternity houses. On-campus housing is guaranteed for the freshman year only and is available on a first-come, first-served basis. Priority is given to out-of-town students. Alcohol is not permitted. All students may keep cars on campus.

Activities: About 15% of men belong to 5 national fraternities; about 2% of women belong to 1 local and 1 national sorority. There are 30 groups on campus, including cheerleading, chess, computers, ethnic, international, newspaper, professional, religious, social, social service, and student government.

Sports: There are 3 intercollegiate sports for men and 1 for women, and 6 intramural sports each for men and women. Athletic and recreation facilities include basketball, badminton, and volleyball courts and a weight room.

Disabled Students: Five percent of the campus is accessible to disabled students. The following facilities are available: wheelchair ramps, special parking, specially equipped rest rooms, lowered drinking fountains, and lowered telephones.

Services: In addition to many counseling and information services, tutoring is available in most subjects. There is remedial math, reading, and writing.

Programs of Study: Indiana Tech awards the B.S., B.S.C.S., B.S.E.E., and B.S.M.E. degrees. Associate degrees are also awarded. Bachelor's degrees are awarded in BUSINESS (accounting and business administration and management), COMMUNICATIONS AND THE ARTS (technical and business writing), COMPUTER AND PHYSICAL SCIENCE (computer programming, computer science, and information sciences and systems), ENGINEERING AND ENVIRONMENTAL DESIGN (civil engineering, computer engineering, electrical/electronics engineering, electrical/electronics engineering technology, engineering, engineering management, and mechanical engineering), HEALTH PROFESSIONS (recreation therapy), SOCIAL SCIENCE (human services and parks and recreation management). Engineering and computer science are the strongest academically. Engineering has the largest enrollment.

Required: In order to graduate, students must complete a minimum of 120 credit hours, including at least 35 in major, with a 2.0 minimum GPA. General education distribution requirements include 9 hours in English and at least 18 hours in social science/humanities. All students must complete a competency assessment in 4 areas: communication skills, humanities/social science, support knowledge, and the major.

Special: The school offers co-op programs in business administration and computer science, work-study programs, and an accelerated degree program in business administration and human services. Credit for life experience is offered through the Extended Studies Program. Dual majors, nondegree study, and pass/fail options are available. There is one national honor society on campus.

Faculty/Classroom: Eighty-five percent of faculty are male; 15%, female. The average class size in an introductory lecture is 30; in a laboratory, 22; and in a regular course offering, 21.

Admissions: About 93% of the 1993–94 applicants were accepted.

Requirements: Indiana Tech requires applicants to be in the upper 50% of their class. A minimum GPA of 2.0 is required. The SAT I or ACT is required. Applicant must be a graduate of an accredited secondary school. The GED is accepted. Twelve academic credits are required, including 4 to 6 units of social studies, 4 units of English, 3 to 6 units of mathematics, and 2 units of a laboratory science. An interview is recommended. AP and CLEP credits are accepted. Important factors used in the admissions decision are recommendations by alumni, extracurricular activities record, personality, intangible qualities, parents or siblings attending the school, and leadership record.

Procedure: Freshmen are admitted fall, winter, and summer. Application deadlines are open. Application fee is $25. Notification is sent on a rolling basis. There are early decision, early admissions, and deferred admissions plans.

Transfer: About 40 transfer students enrolled in 1993–94. Applicants must be in good standing and have a minimum GPA of 2.0. The SAT I is recommended. A total of 30 credits out of 120 must be completed at Indiana Tech.

Visiting: There are regularly scheduled orientations for prospective students. There are guides for informal visits and visitors may sit in on classes. To arrange for a visit, contact Kathleen Stahl at (800) 937–2448.

Financial Aid: In 1993–94, 80% of all current freshmen and 70% of continuing students received some form of financial aid. Thirty percent of undergraduate students work part-time. Average earnings from campus work for the school year are $650. The FAFSA financial statement is required. The deadline for financial aid applications is March 1.

International Students: The school actively recruits these students. They must take the TOEFL or the college's own test and achieve a minimum score on the TOEFL of 500. The student must also take the SAT I or the ACT.

Computers: The college provides computer facilities for student use. The mainframe is a DEC VAX 3400. Students have access to computer facilities in laboratories. The college also provides 40 PC workstations and 22 mainframe terminals, and leases over 150 PCs to students. All students may access the system. It may be used Monday through Friday, 8 A.M. to 10 P.M. There are no time limits on using the system and no fees.

Graduates: In 1992–93, 71 bachelor's degrees were awarded. The most popular majors among graduates were business (30%), engineering (28%), and computer science (20%). Within an average freshman class, 50% graduate in 4 years, 40% in 5 years, and 3% in 6 years. Some 10 companies recruited on campus in 1992–93. In the 1992 graduating class, 5% of all graduates were enrolled in graduate school within 6 months of graduation; 80% of the men and 70% of the women had found employment.

Admissions Contact: Donald St. Clair, Director of Admissions.

INDIANA STATE UNIVERSITY
B-4

Terre Haute, IN 47809   (812) 237–2121; (800) 742–0891 (in-state)

Full-time: 4339 men, 4260 women	Faculty: 646; I, --$
Part-time: 844 men, 1105 women	Ph.Ds: 61%
Graduate: 763 men, 870 women	Student/Faculty: 13 to 1
Year: semesters, summer session	Tuition: $2622 ($6410)
Application Deadline: August 15	Room & Board: $3588
Freshman Class: 5659 applied, 4761 accepted, 2377 enrolled	
SAT I or ACT: required	COMPETITIVE

Indiana State University, founded in 1865, is a publicly supported institution offering undergraduate and graduate study in liberal arts and sciences, business, health, physical education, and recreation, education, and nursing technology. There are 6 undergraduate schools and one graduate school. In addition to regional accreditation, ISU has baccalaureate program accreditation with AACSB, ADA, AHEA, CAHEA, NASAD, NASM, NCATE, NLN, and NRPA. The 3 libraries contain 1,160,450 volumes, 853,470 microform items, and 24,616 audiovisual forms, and subscribe to 5663 periodicals. Computerized library sources and services include the card catalog and database searching. Special learning facilities include a learning resource center, art gallery, planetarium, radio station, TV station, and Afro-American Cultural Center. The 92-acre campus is in an urban area 75 miles west of Indianapolis. Including residence halls, there are 55 buildings on campus.

Student Life: About 89% of undergraduates are from Indiana. Students come from 50 states, 70 foreign countries, and Canada. Ninety-five percent are from public schools; 5% from private. Eighty-six percent are white. The average age of freshmen is 19; all undergraduates, 22. Thirty-two percent drop out by the end of their first year; 40% remain to graduate.

Housing: A total of 4400 students can be accommodated in college housing. College-sponsored living facilities include single-sex and coed dormitories and married-student housing. In addition, there are honors houses, special interest houses, and a sorority residence. On-campus housing is guaranteed for all 4 years. Sixty-five percent of students commute. Alcohol is not permitted. All students may keep cars on campus.

Activities: About 18% of men belong to 21 national fraternities; about 11% of women belong to 13 national sororities. There are 200 groups on campus, including art, band, cheerleading, choir, chorale, chorus, drama, drill team, ethnic, gay, honors, international, jazz band, marching band, musical theater, newspaper, opera, orchestra, pep band, political, professional, radio and TV, religious, social, social service, student government, symphony, and yearbook. Popular campus events include a Contemporary Music Festival, the Bass Fishing Institute, Homecoming, Tandemonia, Greek Week, Theaterfest, Black History Month, and Donaghy Day.

Sports: There are 7 intercollegiate sports for men and 7 for women, and 27 intramural sports for men and 25 for women. Athletic and recreation facilities include a 20,000-seat football stadium, a 10,000-seat basketball arena, 2 softball diamonds, a baseball field, 2 indoor and outdoor tracks, 2 pools, indoor and outdoor basketball and tennis courts, racquetball, sand volleyball, and volleyball courts, a physical fitness center with weight training facilities, a 9-hole golf course, and 3 fitness and wellness facilities located in 2 residence halls and the student union.

Disabled Students: The entire campus is accessible to disabled students. The following facilities are available: wheelchair ramps, elevators, special parking, specially equipped rest rooms, special class scheduling, lowered drinking fountains, lowered telephones, and special dining hall facilities.

Services: In addition to many counseling and information services, tutoring is available in most subjects. There is a reader service for the blind, as well as a learning skills center, an academic advisement center, and student support services.

Campus Safety and Security: Campus safety and security measures include 24-hour foot and vehicle patrol, self defense education, escort service, and informal discussions. In addition, there are pamphlets, posters, and films, emergency telephones, lighted pathways and sidewalks, and bicycle and car registration.

Programs of Study: ISU awards the B.A., B.S., B.F.A., B.M., and B.S.W. degrees. Associate, master's, and doctoral degrees also are awarded. Bachelor's degrees are awarded in BIOLOGICAL SCIENCE (biology/biological science), BUSINESS (accounting, banking and finance, business administration and management, hotel/motel and restaurant management, insurance, management information systems, marketing and distribution, marketing/retailing/merchandising, office supervision and management, recreation and leisure services, and sports management), COMMUNICATIONS AND THE ARTS (art history and appreciation, broadcasting, communications, dramatic arts, English, film arts, fine arts, French, German, journalism, Latin, music, Russian, Spanish, and studio art), COMPUTER AND PHYSICAL SCIENCE (chemistry, computer science, geology, mathematics, and physics), EDUCATION (art, business, early childhood, educational media, elementary, foreign languages, health, home economics, industrial arts, middle school, music, physical, science, secondary, social studies, and special), ENGINEERING AND ENVIRONMENTAL DESIGN (aeronautical technology, airline piloting and navigation, computer technology, construction technology, electrical/electronics engineering technology, industrial engineering technology, interior design, manufacturing technology, mechanical engineering technology, and preengineering), HEALTH PROFESSIONS (environmental health science, medical laboratory technology, nursing, predentistry, premedicine, prepharmacy, preveterinary science, and speech pathology/audiology), SOCIAL SCIENCE (African American studies, anthropology, child care/child and family studies, criminology, dietetics, economics, food science, geography, history, home economics, interdisciplinary studies, liberal arts/general studies, parks and recreation management, philosophy, political science/government, prelaw, psychology, religion, safety management, social work, sociology, textiles and clothing, and urban studies). Safety management, criminology, business, education, technology, nursing, and athletic training are the strongest academically. Criminology, accounting, and elementary education have the largest enrollments.

Required: All students must complete a minimum of 48 credit hours in the general education program. The program requires 11 to 17 credit hours in basic studies, which includes English composition, communications, mathematics, and physical education, and 36 hours in liberal studies courses. A minimum GPA of 2.0 and a total of 124 credit hours are required for graduation. In addition, all students must have a distribution of hours in upper-division courses.

Special: The school has cross-registration with the Rose-Hulman Institute of Technology and Saint Mary-of-the-Woods College. Internships are available in athletic training, criminology, environmental health, political science, safety management, and sports studies. There is a co-op program, and summer and winter work-study is available. The school offers a general studies degree, credit for life experience, and nondegree study. There is a freshman honors program on campus.

Faculty/Classroom: Sixty-seven percent of faculty are male; 33%, female. Graduate students teach 5% of introductory courses. The average class size in an introductory lecture is 35; in a laboratory, 25; and in a regular course offering, 27.

Admissions: About 84% of the 1993–94 applicants were accepted. About 27% of the current freshmen were in the top fifth of their class; 58% were in the top two fifths. About 12 freshmen graduated first in their class.

Requirements: ISU requires applicants to be in the upper 50% of their class. A minimum GPA of 2.0 is required. The SAT I or ACT is required. The applicant must be a graduate of an accredited secondary school. The GED is accepted. An essay is not required. Applicants will be reviewed based on a combination of class rank, grade point average, strength of curriculum, academic progress, and standardized test scores. Those students who rank in the top 50% of their class are routinely admitted, while those in the bottom 50% of their class are reviewed on an individual basis. (Routine admission does not guarantee admission to specific majors.) AP and CLEP credits are accepted. Important factors used in the admissions decision are advanced placement or honor courses, leadership record, extracurricu-

lar activities record, evidence of special talent, and recommendations by school officials.

Procedure: Freshmen are admitted to all sessions. Entrance exams should be taken before January 1. Applications should be filed by August 15 for fall entry, December 15 for spring entry, and May 1 for summer entry, along with an application fee of $20. Notification is sent on a rolling basis. A waiting list is an active part of the admissions procedure, with about 30% of applicants on the list.

Transfer: About 670 transfer students enrolled in 1993-94. Transfer students must have a minimum GPA of 2.0. A total of 30 credits out of 124 must be completed at ISU.

Visiting: There are regularly scheduled orientations for prospective students, consisting of Sycamore Preview Days, which include campus tours, opportunities to meet with academic advisers in the majors students are considering, and formal sessions with representatives from financial aid and the career center as well as current students. There are guides for informal visits, and visitors may sit in on classes and stay overnight at the school. To arrange for a visit, contact the Office of Admissions at (800) 742-0891 (in-state).

Financial Aid: In an earlier year, 50% of all freshmen and 48% of continuing students received some form of financial aid. Seventy percent of undergraduate students work part-time. The average financial indebtedness of an earlier year's graduate was $1829. ISU is a member of CSS. The FAF, the college's own financial statement, and FAFSA are required. The deadline for financial aid applications is March 1.

International Students: There are currently 671 international students enrolled. The school actively recruits these students. They must take the TOEFL.

Computers: The college provides computer facilities for student use. The mainframes are an IBM 4381 Model 23 and 13 and a DEC VAX 8350. Students have 24-hour access to terminals located at the central computer center, most academic buildings, and residence halls. Students may use the mainframe to access university software (DOS, WordPerfect, and Lotus). All students may access the system. There are no time limits on using the system and no fees.

Graduates: In 1992-93 1447 bachelor's degrees were awarded. The most popular majors among graduates were criminology (8%), elementary education (6%), and business administration (5%). Within an average freshman class, 3% graduate in 3 years, 20% in 4 years, 33% in 5 years, and 37% in 6 years. Some 128 companies recruited on campus in 1992-93. In the 1992 graduating class, 14% of all students were enrolled in graduate school within 6 months of graduation; 74% all graduates had found employment.

Admissions Contact: Richard J. Riehl, Director of Admissions.

INDIANA UNIVERSITY

The Indiana University system, established in 1820, is a public system in Indiana. It is governed by a board of trustees, whose chief administrator is the president. The primary goals of the system are research, teaching, and service. The main priorities are undergraduate education, research, graduate education, and economical growth and access to education. The total enrollment of all 8 campuses generally exceeds 93,000, with nearly 4000 faculty members. Altogether there are 313 baccalaureate, 207 master's, and 108 doctoral programs offered within the system. Four-year campuses are located in Bloomington, Kokomo, South Bend, Gary, New Albany, and Richmond. The Indianapolis and Fort Wayne campuses are operated jointly with Purdue University. Profiles of the 6 campuses are included in this chapter in alphabetical order with other Indiana schools.

INDIANA UNIVERSITY AT KOKOMO   C-2
Kokomo, IN 46904-9003
(317) 455-9217

Full-time, part-time: 3800 men and women	Faculty: 66; IIB, av$
	Ph.D.s: n/av
Graduate: none	Student/Faculty: n/av
Year: semesters, summer session	Tuition: $2069 ($5264)
Application Deadline: see profile	Room & Board: n/app
Freshman Class: n/av	**COMPETITIVE**

Indiana University at Kokomo, founded in 1945 and part of the Indiana University System, offers a wide range of programs that emphasize liberal arts, health science, and business. In addition to regional accreditation, IUK has baccalaureate program accreditation with ABET. The library contains 140,000 volumes and 150,000 microform items, and subscribes to 900 periodicals. Special learning facilities include a learning resource center. The 57-acre campus is in a small town 45 miles north of Indianapolis. There are 4 buildings on campus.

Housing: There are no residence halls; all students commute.

Activities: There are some groups and organizations on campus, including chorale, computers, drama, newspaper, social service, and student government.

Disabled Students: The following facilities are available: wheelchair ramps, elevators, special parking, specially equipped rest rooms, special class scheduling, lowered drinking fountains, and lowered telephones.

Services: In addition to many counseling and information services, tutoring is available in most subjects. In addition, there is remedial math, reading, and writing. Students who do not meet regular admissions standards can be admitted under the Guided Study Program, which includes courses in basic skills as needed, counseling and tutoring, and a seminar on studying problems.

Programs of Study: IUK awards the B.A., B.S., B.S.Bus., B.S.Ed., B.S.Med.Tech., B.S.N. and B.G.S. degrees. Associate and master's degrees are also awarded. Bachelor's degrees are awarded in BIOLOGICAL SCIENCE (biology/biological science), BUSINESS (accounting, business administration and management, and labor studies), COMMUNICATIONS AND THE ARTS (communications, English, and speech/debate/rhetoric), COMPUTER AND PHYSICAL SCIENCE (data processing, information sciences and systems, and mathematics), EDUCATION (elementary and middle school), HEALTH PROFESSIONS (medical laboratory technology and nursing), SOCIAL SCIENCE (behavioral science, humanities, liberal arts/general studies, social science, and sociology).

Required: All students must maintain a minimum GPA of 2.0 and complete 120 credit hours; they must also demonstrate English competency.

Special: Student-designed majors, a general studies degree, study abroad, joint programs with other Indiana University campuses and with Purdue University, pass/fail options, nondegree study, and credit for military experience and by examination are available.

Requirements: IUK requires applicants to be in the upper 50% of their class. The SAT I or ACT is required, with a recommended composite score on the SAT of 780; on the ACT, 18. Admission requirements include 28 academic credits, including 4 years in English, and 20 or more in mathematics, social studies, science, and foreign languages. The GED is accepted. CLEP credit is accepted.

Procedure: Entrance exams should be taken prior to registration. Application should be submitted no later than 3 weeks prior to the start of each semester. The application fee is $30. Notification is sent on a rolling basis. There is an early admissions plan.

Transfer: Transfer applicants must have a minimum GPA of 2.0 and clear records of good conduct from previously attended colleges.

Visiting: There are regularly scheduled orientations for prospective students. To arrange for a visit, contact the Admissions Office at (317) 455-9389.

Financial Aid: The FAF and the college's own financial statement are required. The deadline for financial aid applications is March 1.

International Students: Students must take the TOEFL and the SAT I.

Computers: Computers are available at Indiana University's Bloomington and Indianapolis campuses. All students may access the system. It may be used at designated hours. There are no time limits on using the system.

Admissions Contact: Tom Kent Bumgardner, Director of Admissions.

INDIANA UNIVERSITY BLOOMINGTON   C-4
Bloomington, IN 47405
(812) 855-3512

Full-time: 11,363 men, 13,251 women	Faculty: 1405; I, -$
Part-time: 753 men, 876 women	Ph.D.s: 87%
Graduate: 3945 men, 3533 women	Student/Faculty: 18 to 1
Year: semesters, summer session	Tuition: $2762 ($8960)
Application Deadline: February 15	Room & Board: $3733
Freshman Class: 16,587 applied, 13,243 accepted, 5873 enrolled	
SAT I Verbal/Math: 466/530	ACT: 24 **VERY COMPETITIVE**

Indiana University Bloomington, founded in 1820, is a comprehensive institution that is part of the Indiana University System. The university offers undergraduate programs in arts and sciences, allied health sciences, business, dentistry, education, health, physical education, recreation, journalism, music, nursing, optometry, public and environmental affairs, and social work. There are 12 undergraduate and 9 graduate schools. In addition to regional accreditation, IU has baccalaureate program accreditation with ACEJMC, APTA, CAHEA, NASM, NCATE, and NLN. The 35 libraries contain 5,438,860 volumes, 3,260,559 microform items, and 292,422 audiovisual forms and subscribe to 39,755 periodicals. Computerized library sources and services include the card catalog, interlibrary loans, and database searching. Special learning facilities include a learning resource center; art, natural history, and geology museums; planetarium; radio and TV stations; observatories; outdoor educational facility; university archives; rare book library; and center for excellence in education. The 1860-acre campus is in a small town 50 miles south of Indianapolis. Including residence halls, there are more than 100 buildings on campus.

Student Life: About 69% of undergraduates are from Indiana. Students come from 50 states, 122 foreign countries, and Canada. Eighty-four percent are white. The average age of freshmen is 18; all undergraduates, 20. Thirteen percent drop out by the end of their first year; 66% remain to graduate.

Housing: A total of 11,729 students can be accommodated in college housing. College-sponsored living facilities include single-sex and coed dormitories and married-student housing. In addition there are honors houses, language houses, and special interest houses. On-campus housing is guaranteed for all 4 years. Alcohol is not permitted. All students may keep cars on campus.

Activities: About 12% of men belong to 34 national fraternities; about 11% of women belong to 27 national sororities. There are 252 groups on campus, including art, band, cheerleading, chess, choir, chorale, chorus, computers, dance, drama, drill team, ethnic, film, gay, honors, international, jazz band, literary magazine, marching band, musical theater, newspaper, opera, orchestra, pep band, photography, political, professional, radio and TV, religious, social, social service, student government, symphony, and yearbook. Popular campus events include Homecoming, Greekfest, Madrigals, Little 500, IU Sing, Spirit of Sport All-Nighter, Founders Day, operas, touring troupes shows, and campus theater events.

Sports: There are 11 intercollegiate sports for men and 10 for women, and 30 intramural sports for men and 30 for women. Athletic and recreation facilities include a 52,000-seat football stadium, 18,000-seat soccer/bicycle stadium, 18,000-seat indoor gymnasium, 2,300-seat auditorium, assembly hall, indoor/outdoor pools, and tennis pavilion.

Disabled Students: Ninety-five percent of the campus is accessible to disabled students. The following facilities are available: wheelchair ramps, elevators, special parking, specially equipped rest rooms, special class scheduling, lowered drinking fountains, lowered telephones, and scheduled transportation.

Services: In addition to many counseling and information services, tutoring is available in most subjects. In addition, there is a reader service for the blind, and remedial math, reading, and writing. Skills workshops are also offered.

Campus Safety and Security: Campus safety and security measures include 24-hour foot and vehicle patrol, self defense education, escort service, and shuttle buses. In addition, there are informal discussions, pamphlets, posters, and films, emergency telephones, lighted pathways and sidewalks, and safety awareness education.

Programs of Study: IU awards the B.A., B.S., B.F.A., B.M., B.M.E., and B.S.G.S. degrees. Associate, master's, and doctoral degrees also are awarded. Bachelor's degrees are awarded in AGRICULTURE (plant science), BIOLOGICAL SCIENCE (biochemistry, biology/biological science, and microbiology), BUSINESS (accounting, apparel and accessories marketing, banking and finance, business administration and management, business economics, business systems analysis, insurance, marketing/retailing/merchandising, personnel management, real estate, recreation and leisure services, and transportation management), COMMUNICATIONS AND THE ARTS (broadcasting, classics, communications, comparative literature, dance, dramatic arts, English, fine arts, folklore and mythology, French, German, Italian, journalism, linguistics, music, Spanish, speech/debate/rhetoric, and telecommunications), COMPUTER AND PHYSICAL SCIENCE (astronomy, chemistry, computer science, geology, mathematics, and physics), EDUCATION (early childhood, elementary, middle school, physical, secondary, and special), ENGINEERING AND ENVIRONMENTAL DESIGN (environmental science and interior design), HEALTH PROFESSIONS (cytotechnology, dental hygiene, medical technology, nursing, occupational therapy, optometry, physical therapy, predentistry, public health, radiological science, recreation therapy, and respiratory therapy), SOCIAL SCIENCE (African American studies, anthropology, criminal justice, dietetics, East Asian studies, economics, geography, history, human development, Jewish studies, Near Eastern studies, parks and recreation management, philosophy, political science/government, psychology, public administration, religion, Russian and Slavic studies, social science, social work, sociology, and urban studies). Sciences, music, business, and journalism are the strongest academically. Business, education, psychology, biology, and music have the largest enrollments.

Required: The general requirements for graduation include courses in English and writing, mathematics, foreign language, arts and humanities, social and behavioral sciences, natural sciences, and culture studies. Students usually must complete 122 credit hours, with approximately 36 hours in the major. Many degrees have intensive writing requirements, and the minimum GPA requirement varies by department. Liberal arts requirements are common throughout all degree programs.

Special: IU offers cooperative programs with universities in many countries, including the People's Republic of China, a variety of internships, and study abroad in more than 25 countries. A Washington semester in various majors such as political science, work-study programs, B.A.-B.S. degrees in the sciences and liberal arts, dual majors, and the general studies degree through the School of Continuing Studies are available. Student-designed majors through the Individualized Major Program, credit for military experience, nondegree study through the School of Continuing Studies, and pass/fail options also are available. There is a freshman honors program on campus, as well as 8 national honor societies, including Phi Beta Kappa. Most departments have honors programs.

Faculty/Classroom: Seventy-six percent of faculty are male; 24%, female.

Admissions: About 80% of the 1993-94 applicants were accepted. The SAT scores for the 1993-94 freshman class were as follows: Verbal—63% below 500, 29% between 500 and 599, 7% between 600 and 700, and 1% above 700; Math—35% below 500, 39% between 500 and 599, 22% between 600 and 700, and 5% above 700. The ACT scores were 17% below 21, 51% between 21 and 25, and 33% between 26 and 36. Test scores are rarely a factor in evaluating applications. About 50% of the current freshmen were in the top fifth of their class; 88% were in the top two fifths. Eighty-five freshmen graduated first in their class.

Requirements: The SAT I or ACT is required. Applicants must be graduates of an accredited secondary high school or have a GED certificate. SAT II: Subject tests and AP tests are recommended for credit and placement. Auditions for music majors are required. An interview is recommended. AP and CLEP credits are accepted. Important factors used in the admissions decision are evidence of special talent, advanced placement or honor courses, recommendations by school officials, parents or siblings attending the school, and geographic diversity.

Procedure: Freshmen are admitted to all sessions. Entrance exams should be taken during junior year. Applications should be filed by February 15 for fall entry, November 1 for winter entry, and February 15 for summer entry, along with an application fee of $30. Notification is sent on a rolling basis, 6 to 8 weeks after receipt of completed application. There is a deferred admissions plan.

Transfer: About 680 transfer students enrolled in 1993-94. Transfer students with a year or more of college work must meet transfer requirements. Applicants with less than a year must meet beginner standards based on residency. All applicants who are residents must have a minimum 2.3 GPA, or 2.7 for nonresidents. The SAT I or ACT is required except for students who graduated from high school more than 2 years before applying. Prerequisites vary per school. An interview is recommended. A total of 30 credits out of 122 must be completed at IU.

Visiting: There are regularly scheduled orientations for prospective students, including counseling regarding an admissions decision and answering students' questions. There are guides for informal visits and visitors may sit in on classes and stay overnight at the school. To arrange for a visit, contact the Scheduling Director at (812) 855-3512.

Financial Aid: In 1993-94 60% of all current freshmen and 64% of continuing students received some form of financial aid. About 50% of freshmen and 52% of continuing students received need-based aid. The average freshman award was $4704. Of that total, scholarships or need-based grants averaged $1690 ($13,520 maximum); loans averaged $2253 ($15,786 maximum); and work contracts averaged $336 ($1500 maximum). The average financial indebtedness of the 1992-93 graduate was $11,234. IU is a member of CSS. The college's own financial statement and FAFSA are required. The deadline for financial aid applications is March 1.

International Students: There are currently 2385 international students enrolled. They must take the TOEFL as well as SAT I or the ACT.

Computers: The college provides computer facilities for student use. The mainframes include an Amdahl 5995-1400A, DEC VAXs and DEC AXPs with Digital DEC Systems, and two HP Apollo 735s. More than 1,200 microcomputers are available for student use. Students have varying degrees of access to the system depending on need, 24 hours a day. There are no time limits. The fee is $100 per semester for freshmen.

Graduates: In 1992-93 5534 bachelor's degrees were awarded. The most popular majors among graduates were arts and sciences (54%), business (21%), and education (9%). Within an average freshman class, 47% graduate in 4 years, 64% in 5 years, and 66% in 6 years. Some 800 companies recruited on campus in 1992-93.

Admissions Contact: Robert S. Magee, Director of Admissions.

INDIANA UNIVERSITY EAST
D-3

Richmond, IN 47374–1289   (317) 973–8208; (800) 959-EAST

Full-time: 315 men, 675 women

Part-time: 422 men, 964 women

Graduate: 7 men, 25 women

Year: semesters, summer session

Application Deadline: August 11

Freshman Class: 835 applied, 835 accepted, 616 enrolled

SAT I: Verbal/Math 374/411   ACT: 19   **NONCOMPETITIVE**

Faculty: 72; IIB, --$

Ph.D.s: 66%

Student/Faculty: 14 to 1

Tuition: $2044 ($5053)

Room & Board: n/app

Indiana University East, established in 1971, is a public, coeducational institution serving a commuter student body. The university offers undergraduate degree programs in humanities, natural science and mathematics, behavioral and social sciences, education, business and technology, nursing, public and environmental affairs, social work, and continuing studies. There are 9 undergraduate schools. In addition to regional accreditation, Indiana University East has baccalaureate program accreditation with NLN. The library contains 55,567 volumes, 36,167 microform items, and 8818 audiovisual forms, and subscribes to 621 periodicals. Computerized library sources and services include the card catalog, interlibrary loans, and database searching. Special learning facilities include an art gallery. The 194-acre campus is in a small town 40 miles west of Dayton, Ohio. There are 2 buildings on campus.

Student Life: About 98% of undergraduates are from Indiana. Students come from 2 foreign countries. Ninety-five percent are white. The average age of all undergraduates is 29.

Housing: There are no residence halls. All students commute. Alcohol is not permitted.

Activities: There is 1 national fraternity and no sororities on campus. There are 20 groups on campus, including art, drama, ethnic, literary magazine, newspaper, photography, political, professional, social, social service, and student government. Popular campus events include fall and spring festivals and a Wednesday lunch program.

Sports: There is 1 intercollegiate sport for men, and 6 intramural sports for men and 4 for women. Athletic and recreation facilities include a softball field, tennis courts, a sand volleyball court, and a field house rented from the community.

Disabled Students: Ninety-eight percent of the campus is accessible to disabled students. The following facilities are available: wheelchair ramps, elevators, special parking, specially equipped rest rooms, lowered drinking fountains, and lowered telephones.

Services: In addition to many counseling and information services, tutoring is available in some subjects, including several freshman-level courses. In addition, there is a reader service for the blind, and remedial math, reading, and writing.

Campus Safety and Security: Campus safety and security measures include escort service, informal discussions, pamphlets, posters, films, lighted pathways and sidewalks. In addition, there is a 14-hour foot and vehicle patrol.

Programs of Study: Indiana University East awards the B.A., B.S., B.G.S., B.S.B.A., B.S.Ed., and B.S.N. degrees. Associate degrees also are awarded. Bachelor's degrees are awarded in BUSINESS (accounting and business administration and management), COMMUNICATIONS AND THE ARTS (English), EDUCATION (elementary and secondary), HEALTH PROFESSIONS (nursing), SOCIAL SCIENCE (behavioral science and liberal arts/general studies). Nursing, business, and education have the largest enrollments.

Required: In order to graduate, students must satisfactorily complete an English composition course, demonstrate computer literacy, and complete a minimum of 120 semester hours with a GPA of at least 2.0.

Special: The degree program in business supervision is implemented through the Purdue Statewide Technology System. IU East also offers a general studies degree, cross-registration with Earlham College, an internship in social work, pass/fail options, study abroad through Indiana University Bloomington, and credit for life experience. Nondegree study is possible. There is one national honor society on campus.

Faculty/Classroom: Forty-seven percent of faculty are male; 53%, female. All teach undergraduates. No introductory courses are taught by graduate students. The average class size in an introductory lecture is 19; in a laboratory, 24; and in a regular course offering, 19.

Admissions: All of the 1993–94 applicants were accepted. The SAT scores for the 1993–94 freshman class were as follows: Verbal—94% below 500, 5% between 500 and 599, and 1% between 600 and 700; Math—79% below 500, 16% between 500 and 599, and 5% between 600 and 700. The ACT scores were 66% below 21, 25% between 21 and 23, 5% between 24 and 26, and 4% between 27 and 28. About 18% of the current freshmen were in the top fifth of their class; 39% were in the top two fifths. Two freshmen graduated first in their class.

Requirements: Indiana University East requires applicants to be in the upper 50% of their class. A minimum GPA of 2.0 is required. Either the SAT I or ACT is required for applicants who have graduated from high school in the preceding 3 years. Applicants must be graduates of accredited secondary schools or have earned a GED. They must have completed 28 academic credits, including 8 in English, 6 in mathematics, 4 in social studies, and 2 in science, as well as an additional 8 semesters of academic study. Four credits in a foreign language are recommended. AP and CLEP credits are accepted.

Procedure: Freshmen are admitted to all sessions. Entrance exams should be taken during the junior or senior year. Applications should be filed by August 11 for fall entry and December 15 for spring entry, along with an application fee of $25. The college accepts all applicants.

Transfer: Some 78 transfer students enrolled in 1993–94. A total of 30 credits out of 120 must be completed at Indiana University East.

Visiting: There are regularly scheduled orientations for prospective students, including tours, counseling, registration, and financial aid sessions. There are guides for informal visits and visitors may sit in on classes. To arrange for a visit, contact the Admissions Office at (317) 973-8208.

Financial Aid: In 1993–94, 55% of all current freshmen and 65% of continuing students received some form of financial aid. About 72% of freshmen and 65% of continuing students received need-based aid. The average freshman award was $2000. Of that total, scholarships or need-based grants averaged $500 ($1000 maximum); loans averaged $1000 ($2625 maximum); and work contracts averaged $800 ($1600 maximum). Three percent of undergraduate students work part-time. Indiana University East is a member of CSS. The college's own financial statement and FAFSA are required. The deadline for financial aid applications is March 1.

International Students: There are currently 5 international students enrolled. They must take the TOEFL. The student must also take the SAT I, ACT, or the college's own entrance exam.

Computers: The university provides computer facilities for student use. There are 70 networked microcomputers in 7 public laboratories connected to Internet. All students may access the system during the operating hours of the university. There are no time limits on using the system. The fees are $30 per semester for full-time students.

Graduates: In 1992–93, 115 bachelor's degrees were awarded. The most popular majors among graduates were education (27%), nursing (27%), and general studies (16%).

Admissions Contact: Patricia E. Lemmons, Director of Admissions and Financial Aid.

INDIANA UNIVERSITY NORTHWEST
B-1

Gary, IN 46408   (219) 980–6991; (800) 437–5409 (in-state)

Full-time: 945 men, 1754 women

Part-time: 758 men, 1408 women

Graduate: 210 men, 388 women

Year: semesters, summer session

Application Deadline: July 15

Freshman Class: 2236 applied, 1784 accepted, 1246 enrolled

SAT I: required   **COMPETITIVE**

Faculty: 187; IIA, --$

Ph.D.s: 63%

Student/Faculty: 14 to 1

Tuition: $2310 ($5781)

Room & Board: n/app

Indiana University Northwest, established in 1959, is one of 8 campuses of the Indiana University system. A public, coeducational commuter school, it offers liberal arts and professional programs. There are 8 undergraduate and 3 graduate schools. In addition to regional accreditation, IUN has baccalaureate program accreditation with AACSB, NCATE, and NLN. The library contains 203,948 volumes, 161,720 microform items, and 859 audiovisual forms, and subscribes to 1100 periodicals. Computerized library sources and services include interlibrary loans. Special learning facilities include a learning resource center and an art gallery. The 33-acre campus is in an urban area 30 miles southeast of Chicago. There are 12 buildings on campus.

Student Life: Nearly all undergraduates are from Indiana. Ninety-nine percent are from public schools; 1% from private. Sixty-nine percent are white; 21% African American. The average age of freshmen is 26. About 73% of freshmen remain to graduate.

Housing: There are no residence halls. All students commute and all may keep cars on campus. Alcohol is not permitted.

Activities: There are 65 groups on campus, including chess, drama, ethnic, honors, literary magazine, musical theater, newspaper, political, professional, social, and student government. Popular campus events include Fun Days, Springfest, film festivals, Student/Faculty Dinner Dance, and Health Fair.

Sports: There are 7 intramural sports for men and 6 for women.

Disabled Students: Ninety percent of the campus is accessible to disabled students. The following facilities are available: wheelchair ramps, elevators, special parking, specially equipped rest rooms, special class scheduling, lowered drinking fountains, and lowered telephones.

Services: In addition to many counseling and information services, tutoring is available in some subjects. There are also note takers for hearing-impaired students. In addition, there is a reader service for the blind, and remedial math, reading, and writing.

Campus Safety and Security: Campus safety and security measures include 24-hour foot and vehicle patrol, escort service, emergency telephones, and lighted pathways and sidewalks.

Programs of Study: IUN awards the B.S., B.A., and B.G.S. degrees. Associate and master's degrees also are awarded. Bachelor's degrees are awarded in BIOLOGICAL SCIENCE (biology/biological science), BUSINESS (accounting, business administration and management, and labor studies), COMMUNICATIONS AND THE ARTS (communications, dramatic arts, English, fine arts, French, and Spanish), COMPUTER AND PHYSICAL SCIENCE (actuarial science, chemistry, data processing, geology, and mathematics), EDUCATION (elementary and secondary), HEALTH PROFESSIONS (medical laboratory technology and nursing), SOCIAL SCIENCE (African American studies, criminal justice, economics, history, philosophy, political science/government, psychology, public administration, and sociology). Business and nursing are the strongest academically and have the largest enrollments.

Required: Each division sets its own degree requirements. All students must maintain a minimum GPA of 2.0 and complete of least 120 credit hours to graduate.

Special: IUN offers study abroad in 25 countries, credit for life, military, and work experience, nondegree study, and pass/fail options. There is a freshman honors program on campus, as well as 7 national honor societies.

Faculty/Classroom: Sixty-three percent of faculty are male; 37%, female. The average class size in an introductory lecture is 21; in a laboratory, 14; and in a regular course offering, 18.

Admissions: About 80% of the 1993–94 applicants were accepted. Three freshmen graduated first in their class.

Requirements: IUN requires applicants to be in the upper 50% of their class. A minimum GPA of 2.0 is required. The SAT I is required, with a minimum composite score of 860. Applicants must be graduates of an accredited secondary school. The GED is accepted. The university recommends an interview. AP and CLEP credits are accepted.

Procedure: Freshmen are admitted fall and spring. Entrance exams should be taken as early as possible. Applications should be filed by July 15 for fall entry, December 15 for spring entry, and May 15 for summer entry, along with an application fee of $25. Notification is sent on a rolling basis. There is a deferred admissions plan.

Transfer: Residents of Indiana must have a 2.0 GPA. Out-of-state transfers must have a C + average or higher. Either the SAT I or ACT is recommended. Grades of C or better transfer for credit. Transfers are admitted every term. A total of 30 credits out of 120 must be completed at IUN.

Visiting: There are regularly scheduled orientations for prospective students. There are guides for informal visits and visitors may sit in on classes. To arrange for a visit, contact the Admissions Office at (219) 980–6991.

Financial Aid: In a recent year, 49% of all current freshmen and 51% of continuing students received some form of financial aid. About 38% of freshmen and 62% of continuing students received need-based aid. The average freshman award was $4575. Ten percent of undergraduate students work part-time. Average earnings from campus work for the school year are $1200. The average financial indebtedness of the 1992–93 graduate was $7000. IUN is a member of CSS. The college's own financial statement and FAFSA are required. The deadline for financial aid applications is March 1.

International Students: International students must take the TOEFL, along with SAT I or the ACT.

Computers: The university provides computer facilities for student use. The mainframe is a Prime 9955 II. There are also IBM PC, Apple Macintosh, and Apple II microcomputers available in laboratories and offices. Students enrolled in computer classes may access the system anytime. There are no time limits on using the system.

Graduates: In 1992–93, 387 bachelor's degrees were awarded. The most popular majors among graduates were business (30%), education (14%), and nursing (12%). Within an average freshman class, 16% graduate in 4 years, 28% in 5 years, and 32% in 6 years. Some 40 companies recruited on campus in 1992–93. In the 1992 graduating class, 22% of the men and 10% of the women were enrolled in graduate school within 6 months of graduation; 83% of the men and 74% of the women had found employment.

Admissions Contact: William D. Lee, Director of Admissions.

INDIANA UNIVERSITY SOUTHEAST
New Albany, IN 47150-6405

C-5
(812) 941–2212
(800) 852–8835 (in-state)

Full-time: 1091 men, 1637 women
Part-time: 1100 men, 1650 women
Graduate: 140 men, 242 women
Year: semesters, summer session
Application Deadline: open
Freshman Class: 1577 accepted, 1211 enrolled
SAT I Verbal/Math: 390/420

Faculty: 140; IIA, -$
Ph.D.s: 85%
Student/Faculty: 19 to 1
Tuition: $2260 ($5731)
Room & Board: n/app

LESS COMPETITIVE

Indiana University Southeast, established in 1941, is a state-supported institution, part of the Indiana University System, and offers undergraduate and graduate programs in humanities, social sciences, natural sciences, business and economics, education, general studies, and nursing. There are 7 undergraduate and 2 graduate schools. In addition to regional accreditation, IUS has baccalaureate program accreditation with AACSB, NCATE, and NLN. The library contains 250,000 volumes, 225,000 microform items, and 15,000 audiovisual forms, and subscribes to 1200 periodicals. Computerized library sources and services include the card catalog, interlibrary loans, and database searching. Special learning facilities include an art gallery. The 177-acre campus is in a suburban area. There are 9 buildings on campus.

Student Life: About 99% of undergraduates are from Indiana. Students come from 6 states and 16 foreign countries. Ninety-seven percent are white.

Housing: There are no residence halls; all students commute. Alcohol is not permitted.

Activities: About 2% of men belong to 2 national fraternities; about 2% of women belong to 3 national sororities. There are 50 groups on campus, including art, band, cheerleading, choir, chorus, computers, drama, ethnic, film, gay, honors, literary magazine, newspaper, orchestra, political, religious, social, and student government.

Sports: There are 2 intercollegiate sports each for men and women, and 3 intramural sports each for men and women. Athletic and recreation facilities include a 1600-seat activities building with a basketball court; facilities for jogging, badminton, volleyball, weight lifting, and gymnastics; 6 tennis courts; baseball and softball fields; paved play areas; and playing fields.

Disabled Students: All of the campus is accessible to disabled students. The following facilities are available: wheelchair ramps, elevators, special parking, specially equipped rest rooms, lowered drinking fountains, lowered telephones, and special accommodations as needed.

Services: In addition to many counseling and information services, tutoring is available in every subject. In addition, there is a reader service for the blind, and remedial math, reading, and writing.

Campus Safety and Security: Campus safety and security measures include 24-hour foot and vehicle patrol, self-defense education, pamphlets, posters, films, and emergency telephones. In addition, there are lighted pathways and sidewalks and a police department on campus.

Programs of Study: IUS awards the B.A., B.S., and B.G.S. degrees. Associate and master's degrees also are awarded. Bachelor's degrees are awarded in BIOLOGICAL SCIENCE (biology/biological science), BUSINESS (accounting, banking and finance, business administration and management, business economics, and marketing/retailing/merchandising), COMMUNICATIONS AND THE ARTS (communications, English, fine arts, and music), COMPUTER AND PHYSICAL SCIENCE (chemistry, computer science, and mathematics), EDUCATION (elementary, secondary, and special), HEALTH PROFESSIONS (nursing), SOCIAL SCIENCE (geography, history, liberal arts/general studies, philosophy, political science/government, psychology, and sociology).

Required: Students must complete 120 credit hours, with 30 of these hours in upper-level courses and at least 25 in the major and must maintain a minimum cumulative GPA of 2.0. In addition, all students must complete a core curriculum that includes courses in English composition, mathematics, computer literacy, arts and humanities, social sciences, and natural sciences and mathematics.

Special: Cross-registration with Metroversity is possible, and opportunities are provided for study abroad, internships, work-study programs, dual majors, a general studies degree, credit by examination, nondegree study, and pass/fail options. There are 8 national honor societies on campus.

Requirements: The SAT I, with minimum scores of 400 verbal and 400 mathematics or the ACT, with a minimum composite score of 19, is required. These test requirements are waived if the applicant has been out of high school for 3 or more years. Graduation from an accredited secondary school is required; a GED will be accepted. Applicants must complete 28 semesters of college-preparatory courses, distributed as follows: 8 semesters in English (1 in journalism and 1 in speech may be included), 6 in mathematics (Algebra I, Algebra II,

and geometry), 4 in social science (economics, government, history, psychology, or sociology), 2 in laboratory science (biology, chemistry, or physics), and 8 in some combination of foreign language; additional mathematics, laboratory science, or social science; computer science; and other courses of a college preparatory nature. AP and CLEP credits are accepted.

Procedure: Freshmen are admitted to all sessions. Entrance exams should be taken during high school. Application deadlines are open. Application fee is $25. Notification is sent on a rolling basis. There is an early admissions plan.

Transfer: A GPA of 2.0 is required for Indiana residents; 2.5 for out-of-state applicants. If the student has fewer than 26 transferable semester hours, the high school record should reflect compliance with freshman admission requirements. A total of 26 credits out of 120 must be completed at IUS.

Visiting: There are regularly scheduled orientations for prospective students, including an opportunity for students to apply for admission, financial aid, and scholarships, a faculty perspective, a student perspective, and a campus tour. There are guides for informal visits and visitors may sit in on classes. To arrange for a visit, contact the Office of Admissions at (812) 941–2212 or (800) 852–8835 (in-state).

Financial Aid: IUS is a member of CSS. The college's own financial statement and the FAFSA are required. The deadline for financial aid applications is March 1.

International Students: They must take the TOEFL and achieve a minimum score of 550. The student must also take special tests as directed (GRE, GMAT, SAT, etc.).

Computers: The college provides computer facilities for student use. All students have access to the Indiana University Computing Network, notably, the DEC VAX and IBM 3090 series computers. There is a local area network with several general and specialized computing applications on Apple and IBM microcomputers. All students may access the system. There are no time limits on using the system and no fees.

Admissions Contact: David B. Campbell, Director of Admissions.

INDIANA UNIVERSITY-PURDUE UNIVERSITY AT FORT WAYNE

Fort Wayne, IN 46805
D-2
(219) 481–6812

Full-time: 2261 men, 2768 women	Faculty: 330; IIA, --$
Part-time: 2722 men, 3950 women	Ph.D.s: 80%
Graduate: 750 men and women	Student/Faculty: 15 to 1
Year: semesters, summer session	Tuition: $2500 ($5800)
Application Deadline: August 1	Room & Board: n/app
Freshman Class: 2336 applied, 2192 accepted, 1942 enrolled	
SAT I Verbal/Math: 406/457	LESS COMPETITIVE

Indiana University at Fort Wayne, founded in 1917, joined Purdue University at Fort Wayne when it was founded in 1964. The combined school, a state-controlled institution, offers programs in liberal arts, science, business education, and health sciences. There are 7 undergraduate and 5 graduate schools. In addition to regional accreditation, IPFW has baccalaureate program accreditation with AACSB, ABET, ADA, NASM, NCATE, and NLN. The library contains 216,116 volumes, 217,000 microform items, and 3505 audiovisual forms, and subscribes to 49,000 periodicals. Computerized library sources and services include the card catalog and database searching. Special learning facilities include a learning resource center, art gallery, radio station, and TV station. The 410-acre campus is in a suburban area 113 miles north of Indianapolis. There are 11 buildings on campus.

Student Life: About 95% of undergraduates are from Indiana. Students come from 37 states and 45 foreign countries. Eighty percent are from public schools. Ninety-five percent are white. The average age of freshmen is 23; all undergraduates, 27.

Housing: There are no residence halls; all students commute. Alcohol is not permitted.

Activities: About 1% of men belong to 2 local fraternities; about 1% of women belong to 2 local sororities. There are 30 groups on campus, including cheerleading, choir, drama, ethnic, honors, international, musical theater, newspaper, religious, and student government.

Sports: There are 7 intercollegiate sports for men and 5 for women, and 11 intramural sports each for men and women. Athletic and recreation facilities include a par course, a physical fitness center, baseball and soccer fields, a gymnasium, 3 basketball courts, an indoor track, a weight room, 4 racquetball courts, 1 Wallyball court, and a fencing and dance room.

Disabled Students: All of the campus is accessible to disabled students. The following facilities are available: wheelchair ramps, elevators, special parking, specially equipped rest rooms, lowered drinking fountains, and lowered telephones.

Services: In addition to many counseling and information services, tutoring is available in most subjects. In addition, there is remedial math, reading, and writing.

Campus Safety and Security: Campus safety and security measures include 24-hour foot and vehicle patrol, escort service, pamphlets, posters, and films, and emergency telephones.

Programs of Study: IPFW awards the B.A., B.S., B.F.A., B.G.S., B.Mus., B.Mus.Ed., B.S.C., B.S.E., and B.S.Ed. degrees. Associate and master's degrees also are awarded. Bachelor's degrees are awarded in BIOLOGICAL SCIENCE (biology/biological science), BUSINESS (accounting, banking and finance, business economics, marketing/retailing/merchandising, and personnel management), COMMUNICATIONS AND THE ARTS (broadcasting, communications, English, fine arts, French, German, Spanish, speech/debate/rhetoric, and telecommunications), COMPUTER AND PHYSICAL SCIENCE (chemistry, computer programming, computer science, earth science, geology, information sciences and systems, mathematics, and physics), EDUCATION (elementary, foreign languages, music, science, and secondary), ENGINEERING AND ENVIRONMENTAL DESIGN (electrical/electronics engineering, engineering, engineering technology, industrial engineering, and mechanical engineering), HEALTH PROFESSIONS (nursing, predentistry, premedicine, and speech pathology/audiology), SOCIAL SCIENCE (anthropology, criminal justice, economics, history, philosophy, political science/government, prelaw, psychology, public administration, social science, and sociology). Business has the largest enrollment.

Required: All students must complete 120 credits and take English composition in order to graduate.

Special: There are continuing education, co-op, and work-study programs, as well as study abroad in France, Spain, Austria, and Germany. A general studies degree, student-designed majors, and credit for military experience are available, as is a 5-year B.A.-B.S. degree in languages, history, political science, and education. Nondegree study and pass/fail options are possible. There is a freshman honors program on campus.

Faculty/Classroom: Sixty-eight percent of faculty are male; 32%, female. The average class size in an introductory lecture is 50.

Admissions: About 94% of the 1993–94 applicants were accepted. About 18% of the current freshmen were in the top fifth of their class; 52% were in the top two fifths.

Requirements: IPFW requires applicants to be in the upper 50% of their class. The SAT I, with a minimum composite score of 800, or the ACT is required. In addition, applicants should have 26 academic credits, including 4 years of English, 3 of mathematics, 2 of science, and 1 each of history, social studies, and foreign language. The GED is accepted. An interview is recommended. AP credits are accepted. Important factors used in the admissions decision are recommendations by school officials, evidence of special talent, advanced placement or honor courses, extracurricular activities record, and recommendations by alumni.

Procedure: Freshmen are admitted fall and spring. Applications should be filed by August 1 for fall entry, December 15 for spring entry, and May 1 for summer entry, along with an application fee of $20. Notification is sent on a rolling basis.

Transfer: Transfer applicants must have a minimum GPA of 2.0. Grades of C or better transfer for credit. A total of 32 credits out of 120 must be completed at IPFW.

Visiting: There are regularly scheduled orientations for prospective students. There are guides for informal visits and visitors may sit in on classes. To arrange for a visit, contact the Admissions Office at (219) 481–6812.

Financial Aid: In an earlier year, 80% of all current freshmen received some form of financial aid. Scholarships or need-based grants averaged $500 ($2000 maximum); loans averaged $500 ($2500 maximum); and work contracts averaged $300 ($1000 maximum). IPFW is a member of CSS. The FAF is required. The deadline for financial aid applications is March 1.

International Students: There are currently 183 international students enrolled. The school actively recruits these students. They must take the University of Michigan Language Test. The student must also take the SAT I (and score a minimum of 800) or the ACT.

Computers: The college provides computer facilities for student use. The mainframe is an IBM 4381. PCs are also available. All students may access the system. There are no time limits on using the system. The fee is $19.

Graduates: In an earlier year, 637 bachelor's degrees were awarded.

Admissions Contact: Cornelius C. Fullove, Assistant Director of Admissions.

INDIANA UNIVERSITY-PURDUE UNIVERSITY AT INDIANAPOLIS

C-3

Indianapolis, IN 46202-5143

(317) 274-4591

Full-time: 3800 men, 5416 women
Part-time: 4475 men, 67 women
Graduate: 3400 men, 3760 women
Year: semesters, summer session
Application Deadline: June 1
Freshman Class: 4652 applied, 3688 accepted, 2316 enrolled
SAT I Verbal/Math: 380/420

Faculty: 561; IIA, av$
Ph.D.s: 89%
Student/Faculty: 16 to 1
Tuition: $2862 ($8137)
Room & Board: $3000

ACT: 19   **LESS COMPETITIVE**

The Indianapolis campus, founded in 1946, has offered undergraduate and graduate instruction under the auspices of both Purdue and Indiana Universities since 1969. The state-controlled, coeducational institution serves a primarily commuter student body and offers degree programs in the arts and sciences, business, education, engineering and technology, health science, religious studies, and professional training. There are 17 undergraduate and 5 graduate schools. In addition to regional accreditation, IUPUI has baccalaureate program accreditation with ABET, ACCE, ACEJMC, APTA, CAHEA, CSWE, NASAD, NASM, NCATE, and NLN. The 5 libraries contain 1,018,987 volumes and 1,597,906 microform items and subscribe to 12,387 periodicals. Special learning facilities include an art gallery, 85-acre medical center, and electronic classroom. The 370-acre campus is in an urban area. Including residence halls, there are 56 buildings on campus.

Student Life: About 99% of undergraduates are from Indiana. Students come from 40 states, 80 foreign countries, and Canada. Eighty-seven percent are white. The average age of freshmen is 21.2; all undergraduates, 26.8.

Housing: A total of 350 students can be accommodated in college housing. College-sponsored living facilities include coed dormitories, on-campus apartments, off-campus apartments, and married-student housing. In addition there are special interest houses. On-campus housing is available on a first-come, first-served basis. Ninety-eight percent of students commute. Alcohol is not permitted. All students may keep cars on campus.

Activities: About 1% of men belong to 2 national fraternities; about 1% of women belong to 2 national sororities. There are 202 groups on campus, including cheerleading, chorus, drama, ethnic, honors, international, newspaper, pep band, political, professional, religious, social, social service, student government, and yearbook. Popular campus events include Ice Cream Social and Activities, Spring Dance, and Career Day.

Sports: There are 4 intercollegiate sports for men and 4 for women, and 13 intramural sports for men and 11 for women. Athletic and recreation facilities include a 12,000-seat track and field stadium, a 3-pool natatorium, softball fields, a tennis center, and the National Institute for Fitness and Sport.

Disabled Students: The entire campus is accessible to disabled students. The following facilities are available: wheelchair ramps, elevators, special parking, specially equipped rest rooms, special class scheduling, lowered drinking fountains, lowered telephones, classroom aids, and sign language interpreters.

Services: In addition to many counseling and information services, tutoring is available in some subjects. In addition, there is a reader service for the blind, and remedial math, reading, and writing.

Campus Safety and Security: Campus safety and security measures include 24-hour foot and vehicle patrol, self defense education, escort service, and shuttle buses. In addition, there are informal discussions, pamphlets, posters, and films, emergency telephones, and lighted pathways and sidewalks.

Programs of Study: IUPUI awards the B.A., B.S., B.A.E., B.F.A., B.G.S., B.S.E., B.S.E.E., B.S.M.E., and B.S.W. degrees. Associate, master's, and doctoral degrees also are awarded. Bachelor's degrees are awarded in BIOLOGICAL SCIENCE (biology/biological science), BUSINESS (accounting, banking and finance, business administration and management, human resources management, insurance, labor studies, marketing/retailing/merchandising, real estate, and supervision), COMMUNICATIONS AND THE ARTS (art history and appreciation, ceramic art and design, communications, English, fine arts, French, German, journalism, painting, photography, printmaking, sculpture, Spanish, and visual communications), COMPUTER AND PHYSICAL SCIENCE (chemistry, computer science, geology, mathematics, and physics), EDUCATION (art, elementary, physical, secondary, and social studies), ENGINEERING AND ENVIRONMENTAL DESIGN (computer integrated manfacturing technology, computer technology, construction technology, electrical/electronics engineering, electrical/electronics engineering technology, engineering, environmental science, mechanical engineering, mechanical engineering technology, and woodworking), HEALTH PROFESSIONS (cytotechnology, dental hygiene, environmental health science, health care administration, health information administration, medical imaging technology, nuclear medicine, nursing, occupation-

al therapy, physical therapy, radiation therapy, and respiratory therapy), SOCIAL SCIENCE (anthropology, criminal justice, economics, geography, history, liberal arts/general studies, philosophy, political science/government, psychology, religion, social work, and sociology). Engineering and technology, nursing, education, and liberal arts have the largest enrollments.

Required: All students must complete a computer course toward the 122 to 126 credits required for the bachelor's degree.

Special: There is a metropolitan studies program for career work in the city. IUPUI also offers study abroad, combined B.A.-B.S. degree programs, internships, work-study programs, dual majors, student-designed majors, interdisciplinary majors such as business economics and public policy, health occupations education, and interdisciplinary engineering, nondegree study, and several nontraditional programs for adult learners. There is a freshman honors program on campus, as well as 2 national honor societies. Two departments have honors programs.

Faculty/Classroom: Seventy-three percent of faculty are male; 27%, female. The average class size in an introductory lecture is 27 and in a laboratory, 18.

Admissions: About 79% of the 1993–94 applicants were accepted. The SAT scores for the 1993–94 freshman class were as follows: Verbal—89% below 500, 9% between 500 and 599, and 2% between 600 and 700; Math—75% below 500, 19% between 500 and 599, 5% between 600 and 700, and 1% above 700. The ACT scores were 68% below 21, 20% between 21 and 23, 8% between 24 and 26, 3% between 27 and 28, and 1% above 28. About 16% of the current freshmen were in the top fifth of their class; 39% were in the top two fifths. Three freshmen graduated first in their class.

Requirements: IUPUI requires applicants to be in the upper 50% of their class. The SAT I or ACT, with average scores, is required. Applicants should be graduates of an accredited high school and should have completed 14 Carnegie units, including 4 in English, 3 in mathematics, 2 in social studies, and 1 laboratory science. AP and CLEP credits are accepted. Recommendations by school officials is an important factor used in the admission decision.

Procedure: Freshmen are admitted to all sessions. Entrance exams should be taken by the end of junior year or fall of senior year. Applications should be filed by June 1 for fall entry and October 1 for spring entry, along with an application fee of $25. Notification is sent on a rolling basis.

Transfer: Nearly 1200 transfer students enrolled in 1993–94. Transfers who are Indiana residents must present a minimum GPA of 2.0 in all previous college work; out-of-state residents need a minimum 2.5. All applicants must be in good standing at their former schools. A total of 30 credits out of 122 to 126 must be completed at IUPUI.

Visiting: There are regularly scheduled orientations for prospective students, consisting of a campus tour, video, and talks with students. There are guides for informal visits and visitors may sit in on classes. To arrange for a visit, contact Orientation Services at (317) 274-4240.

Financial Aid: In 1993–94, 49% of all current freshmen and 43% of continuing students received some form of financial aid. About 48% of freshmen and 42% of continuing students received need-based aid. The average freshman award was $2958. Of that total, scholarships or need-based grants averaged $1881; loans averaged $2845; and work contracts averaged $1319. Average earnings from campus work for the school year are $2067. IUPUI is a member of CSS. The FAFSA financial statement is required. The deadline for financial aid applications is March 1.

International Students: There are currently 263 international students enrolled. They must take the TOEFL and achieve a minimum score of 500.

Computers: The college provides computer facilities for student use. The mainframes are an IBM 4341 and 2 DEC 2060s. Microcomputers are available for all students. All students may access the system up to 24 hours a day in some clusters. There are no time limits on using the system. The fees are $75 per semester.

Graduates: In 1992–93 1956 bachelor's degrees were awarded. The most popular majors among graduates were business (16%), engineering and technology (13%), and nursing (13%).

Admissions Contact: Alan N. Crist, Director of Admissions.

INDIANA UNIVERSITY SOUTH BEND

C-1

South Bend, IN 46634

(219) 237-IUSB

Full-time: 967 men, 1720 women
Part-time: 1231 men, 2188 women
Graduate: 532 men, 944 women
Year: semesters, summer session
Application Deadline: July 1
Freshman Class: 1250 applied, 1100 accepted, 980 enrolled
SAT I Verbal/Math: 420/437

Faculty: 175; IIA, -$
Ph.D.s: 95%
Student/Faculty: 15 to 1
Tuition: $2141 ($5624)
Room & Board: n/app

LESS COMPETITIVE

Indiana University at South Bend, a coeducational commuter institution of the state-supported university system, was founded in 1940 and offers undergraduate programs in arts and sciences, business and economics, dental health, education, music, nursing, and public and environmental affairs. There are 9 undergraduate and 7 graduate schools. In addition to regional accreditation, IUSB has baccalaureate program accreditation with NLN. The library contains 250,000 volumes and 277,455 microform items, and subscribes to 1843 periodicals. Computerized library sources and services include the card catalog, interlibrary loans, and database searching. Special learning facilities include a learning resource center and art gallery. The 40-acre campus is in a suburban area 90 miles east of Chicago. There are 7 buildings on campus.

Student Life: About 95% of undergraduates are from Indiana. Students come from 44 foreign countries. Eighty-five percent are from public schools; 15% from private. Ninety percent are white. The average age of freshmen is 24; all undergraduates, 26. Forty-eight percent drop out by the end of their first year; 30% remain to graduate.

Housing: There are no residence halls. College-sponsored living facilities include off-campus apartments. All students commute. Alcohol is not permitted.

Activities: There is 1 national fraternity. There are no sororities on campus. There are 20 groups on campus, including art, cheerleading, chorus, drama, ethnic, film, gay, honors, international, jazz band, literary magazine, musical theater, newspaper, orchestra, professional, religious, social, social service, student government, and symphony. Popular campus events include Job Fair and club days.

Sports: There is 1 intercollegiate sport for men and 2 for women, and 8 intramural sports for men and 8 for women. Athletic and recreation facilities include a running club for men and women.

Disabled Students: Ninety-five percent of the campus is accessible to disabled students. The following facilities are available: wheelchair ramps, elevators, special parking, specially equipped rest rooms, special class scheduling, lowered drinking fountains, and lowered telephones.

Services: In addition to many counseling and information services, tutoring is available in every subject. There is remedial math, reading, and writing.

Campus Safety and Security: Campus safety and security measures include 24-hour foot and vehicle patrol, escort service, informal discussions, and pamphlets, posters, and films. In addition, there are emergency telephones and lighted pathways and sidewalks.

Programs of Study: IUSB awards the B.S., B.A., B.M., and B.M.E. degrees. Associate and master's degrees also are awarded. Bachelor's degrees are awarded in BIOLOGICAL SCIENCE (biology/biological science), BUSINESS (accounting, business administration and management, and marketing/retailing/merchandising), COMMUNICATIONS AND THE ARTS (communications, dramatic arts, English, fine arts, French, German, piano/organ, Spanish, and speech/debate/rhetoric), COMPUTER AND PHYSICAL SCIENCE (chemistry, computer science, mathematics, and physics), EDUCATION (early childhood, elementary, middle school, music, science, secondary, and special), ENGINEERING AND ENVIRONMENTAL DESIGN (industrial administration/management), HEALTH PROFESSIONS (dental hygiene, nursing, predentistry, and premedicine), SOCIAL SCIENCE (criminal justice, economics, history, philosophy, political science/government, prelaw, psychology, public affairs, and sociology). Accounting, management, marketing, psychology, biology, and political science are the strongest academically. Accounting, marketing, elementary education, and management have the largest enrollments.

Required: All students must complete divisional requirements and general education and concentration courses, including English composition. A total of 120 to 123 semester hours, with a minimum GPA of 2.0, is required to graduate.

Special: Cross-registration with member colleges of the Northern Indiana Consortium for Education is available. Internships are offered in social service and public affairs. Study abroad, including a student exchange program with the University of Vister in Northern Ireland, is offered. A B.G.S., student-designed majors, credit for life experience, and pass/fail options are available. Nondegree study is permitted. There is a freshman honors program on campus.

Faculty/Classroom: Sixty-five percent of faculty are male; 35% female. Ninety-five percent teach undergraduates. No introductory courses are taught by graduate students. The average class size in an introductory lecture and in a laboratory is 40; in a regular course offering, 30.

Admissions: About 88% of the 1993–94 applicants were accepted. The SAT scores for the 1993–94 freshman class were as follows: Verbal—88% below 500, 11% between 500 and 599, and 1% between 600 and 700; Math—74% below 500, 19% between 500 and 599, 6% between 600 and 700, and 1% above 700. About 10% of the current freshmen were in the top fifth of their class; 40% were in the top two fifths.

Requirements: IUSB requires applicants to be in the upper 50% of their class. A minimum GPA of 2.0 is required. The SAT I is required. Applicants should have completed 13 Carnegie units or GED equivalent. An interview is recommended. CLEP credit is accepted. Important factors used in the admissions decision are recommendations by school officials, extracurricular activities record, leadership record, evidence of special talent, and personality, intangible qualities.

Procedure: Freshmen are admitted to all sessions. Entrance exams should be taken 1 year to 6 months before entering the university. Applications should be filed by July 1 for fall entry, November 1 for spring entry, and April 1 for summer entry, along with an application fee of $25. Notification is sent on a rolling basis.

Transfer: About 1000 transfer students enrolled in 1993–94. A 2.0 GPA is required. A total of 30 credits out of 120 to 123 must be completed at IUSB.

Visiting: There are regularly scheduled orientations for prospective students, including a visit to the admissions office, a campus tour, meetings with professors, and information on financial aid. There are guides for informal visits and visitors may sit in on classes. To arrange for a visit, contact the Admissions Office at (219) 237-4496 or (219) 237-IUSB.

Financial Aid: In an earlier year 25% of all current freshmen and 30% of continuing students received some form of financial aid. Scholarships or need-based grants averaged $600 ($2400 maximum); and loans averaged $1200 ($2400 maximum). Eighty-five percent of undergraduate students work part-time. IUSB is a member of CSS. The FAF is required. The deadline for financial aid applications is March 1.

International Students: There are currently about 200 international students enrolled. The school actively recruits these students. They must take the TOEFL and achieve a minimum score of 550.

Computers: The college provides computer facilities for student use. The mainframe system is a Sun, which can be accessed through computer laboratories and networks. There are more than 200 microcomputers available for student use. All students may access the system. It may be used 7 days a week. There are no time limits on using the system but there is a $50 technology fee per semester.

Graduates: In a recent year, 817 bachelor's degrees were awarded. Within an average freshman class, 15% graduate in 4 years, 25% in 5 years, and 25% in 6 years. Some 25 companies recruited on campus in an earlier year.

Admissions Contact: Director of Admissions.

INDIANA WESLEYAN UNIVERSITY

C-2

Marion, IN 46953–9980

(317) 674-6901
(800) 332-6901 (out-of-state)

Full-time, part-time: 1888 men, 2819 women
Graduate: 670 men, 430 women
Year: 4–1–4, summer session
Application Deadline: open
Freshman Class: 1290 applied, 700 accepted, 366 enrolled
SAT I Verbal/Math: 408/455

Faculty: 90; IIB, --$
Ph.D.s: n/av
Student/Faculty: n/av
Tuition: $8660
Room & Board: $3672
ACT: 21

COMPETITIVE

Indiana Wesleyan University, founded in 1920, is a private, coeducational institution affiliated with the Wesleyan Methodist Church. The university offers undergraduate programs in the arts and sciences, business, education, fine arts, nursing, professional training, and religious studies. There are 7 undergraduate schools and one graduate school. In addition to regional accreditation, IWU has baccalaureate program accreditation with CAHEA, CSWE, and NLN. The library contains 130,000 volumes and 7382 microform items, and subscribes to 977 periodicals. Computerized library sources and services include database searching. Special learning facilities include a learning resource center. The 62-acre campus is in a suburban area 60 miles north of Indianapolis. Including residence halls, there are 20 buildings on campus.

Student Life: About 70% of undergraduates are from Indiana. Students come from 3 foreign countries. Ninety-five percent are white. Most are Protestant. About 46% of freshmen remain to graduate.

Housing: College-sponsored living facilities include single-sex and coed dormitories and on-campus apartments. On-campus housing is available on a first-come, first-served basis. Alcohol is not permitted. All students may keep cars on campus.

Activities: There are no fraternities or sororities on campus. There are 25 groups on campus, including choir, chorale, drama, honors, international, newspaper, opera, political, religious, social service, student government, and yearbook.

Sports: Athletic and recreation facilities include a gymnasium, racquetball courts, a weight room, and playing fields.

Disabled Students: Sixty percent of the campus is accessible to disabled students. The following facilities are available: wheelchair ramps, elevators, special parking, specially equipped rest rooms, and lowered drinking fountains.

Services: In addition to many counseling and information services, tutoring is available in most subjects. In addition, there is remedial reading and writing.

Programs of Study: IWU awards the B.A. and B.S. degrees. Associate and master's degrees are also awarded. Bachelor's degrees are awarded in BIOLOGICAL SCIENCE (biology/biological science), BUSINESS (accounting, banking and finance, business administration and management, marketing/retailing/merchandising, and recreational facilities management), COMMUNICATIONS AND THE ARTS (applied music, art, communications, creative writing, English, fine arts, music, Spanish, and studio art), COMPUTER AND PHYSICAL SCIENCE (chemistry, computer management, mathematics, and science), EDUCATION (art, elementary, English, music, nursing, physical, science, and social studies), HEALTH PROFESSIONS (medical laboratory technology, optometry, predentistry, premedicine, prepharmacy, and preveterinary science), SOCIAL SCIENCE (biblical studies, criminal justice, economics, history, ministries, political science/government, psychology, religion, religious education, religious music, social studies, social work, and sociology).

Required: Students must attend chapel services 3 times a week. General education requirements include humanities, biblical literature, English, history/social science, science/mathematics, intercultural experience, physical education, and either foreign language for the B.A. or computer literacy for the B.S. To graduate, students must complete at least 124 semester hours, including 40 in a major field of study, with a minimum GPA of 2.0 overall and 2.25 in the major.

Special: Students may study abroad in Europe, Mexico, Israel, and Haiti. IWU also offers internships, co-op programs with the Wesleyan Urban Coalition of Christian colleges, cross-registration with Taylor University, a Washington semester, work-study programs, pass/fail options, and nondegree study. Adult learners may earn credit for life experience toward bachelor's degrees in business through the LEAP program. There are 2 national honor societies on campus. Two departments have honors programs.

Admissions: About 54% of the 1993–94 applicants were accepted.

Requirements: A minimum GPA of 2.0 is required. Applicants should be graduates of accredited secondary schools or have earned a GED. The university requires 10 units of college preparatory study that includes courses in English, science, social science, mathematics, and foreign language. Recommendations also are required as is the SAT I or the ACT. AP and CLEP credits are accepted.

Procedure: Freshmen are admitted to all sessions. Entrance exams should be taken in the junior year or early in the senior year. Application deadlines are open. Application fee is $15. Notification is sent on a rolling basis. There are early admissions and deferred admissions plans.

Transfer: In addition to standard admission requirements, transfers must submit transcripts of all previous college work and be in good standing at their former school. A total of 60 credits out of 124 must be completed at IWU.

Visiting: There are regularly scheduled orientations for prospective students, including an appointment with an admissions counselor or a professor in the student's field of interest, if desired. There are guides for informal visits and visitors may sit in on classes and stay overnight at the school. To arrange for a visit, contact the Admissions Office at (317) 677–2138 or (800) 332–6901, ext. 138.

Financial Aid: Thirty percent of undergraduate students work part-time. IWU is a member of CSS. The college's own financial statement and FAFSA are required. The deadline for financial aid applications is April 1.

International Students: They must take the TOEFL and achieve a minimum score of 550.

Computers: The college provides computer facilities for student use. The mainframe is a DEC PDP 11/34. In addition to IBM and Apple computer laboratories, there is an academic computer center. A MicroVAX II minicomputer is available for programming for class assignments. Those students majoring in computer information systems may access the system. It may be used from 8 A.M. to 10 P.M. There are no time limits on using the system.

Admissions Contact: Charles Mealy, Director of Admissions.

MANCHESTER COLLEGE

C-2

North Manchester, IN 46962–0365 (219) 982–5055

Full-time: 464 men, 456 women	Faculty: 81; IIB, -$
Part-time: 31 men, 32 women	Ph.D.s: 66%
Graduate: 8 men, 10 women	Student/Faculty: 11 to 1
Year: 4–1-4, summer session	Tuition: $9600
Application Deadline: open	Room & Board: $3640
Freshman Class: 967 applied, 836 accepted, 241 enrolled	
SAT I Verbal/Math: 432/512	ACT: 22 LESS COMPETITIVE

Manchester College, established in 1889, is a private college affiliated with the Church of the Brethren and offering major programs in the arts and sciences, business and economics, premedicine, and education. There is one graduate school. In addition to regional accreditation, Manchester has baccalaureate program accreditation with CSWE and NCATE. The library contains 162,000 volumes and 4500 audiovisual forms, and subscribes to 800 periodicals. Computerized library sources and services include interlibrary loans. Special learning facilities include a learning resource center, planetarium, radio station, and nature preserve. The 124-acre campus is in a small town 35 miles west of Fort Wayne. Including residence halls, there are 44 buildings on campus.

Student Life: About 87% of undergraduates are from Indiana. Students come from 20 states, 9 foreign countries, and Canada. Ninety-nine percent are from public schools; 1% from private. Ninety-two percent are white. Seventy-eight percent are Protestant; 11% Catholic; 10% claim no religious affiliation. The average age of freshmen is 19; all undergraduates, 20. About 59% of freshmen remain to graduate.

Housing: A total of 1098 students can be accommodated in college housing. College-sponsored living facilities include single-sex and coed dormitories. In addition, there are special interest houses, including the AAFRO House providing social, cultural, and educational opportunities to African-American students. On-campus housing is guaranteed for all 4 years. Seventy-eight percent of students live on campus; of those, 75% remain on campus on weekends. Alcohol is not permitted. All students may keep cars on campus.

Activities: There are no fraternities or sororities on campus. There are 48 groups on campus, including band, cheerleading, choir, chorale, computers, drama, ethnic, honors, international, jazz band, literary magazine, musical theater, newspaper, orchestra, pep band, photography, political, professional, radio and TV, religious, social, social service, student government, and yearbook. Popular campus events include Parents Weekend, Sibling Weekend, Friends Weekend, Homecoming, Camp Mack Day, May Day, and an international fair.

Sports: There are 9 intercollegiate sports for men and 6 for women, and 12 intramural sports for men and 12 for women. Athletic and recreation facilities include a physical education and recreation center with an 1800-seat gymnasium; racquetball and tennis courts; facilities for track and cross country; and fields for baseball, soccer, and football.

Disabled Students: Twenty percent of the campus is accessible to disabled students. The following facilities are available: elevators, special parking, special class scheduling, lowered drinking fountains, and lowered telephones.

Services: In addition to many counseling and information services, tutoring is available in every subject. There is also a reader service for the blind; remedial math, reading, and writing; a learning center with an academic assistance program; and workshops to enhance study and learning skills, and time and project management.

Campus Safety and Security: Campus safety and security measures include 24-hour foot and vehicle patrol, escort service, informal discussions, and emergency telephones. In addition, there are lighted pathways and sidewalks.

Programs of Study: Manchester awards the B.A. and B.S. degrees. Associate and master's degrees also are awarded. Bachelor's degrees are awarded in BIOLOGICAL SCIENCE (biochemistry and biology/biological science), BUSINESS (accounting, banking and finance, business administration and management, business economics, and international business management), COMMUNICATIONS AND THE ARTS (broadcasting, communications, dramatic arts, English, French, German, music, and Spanish), COMPUTER AND PHYSICAL SCIENCE (chemistry, computer science, mathematics, and physics), EDUCATION (art, business, early childhood, elementary, foreign languages, health, middle school, music, science, and secondary), ENGINEERING AND ENVIRONMENTAL DESIGN (engineering), HEALTH PROFESSIONS (medical laboratory technology and.nursing), SOCIAL SCIENCE (anthropology, criminal justice, economics, history, philosophy, political science/government, psychology, religion, social work, and sociology). Education, accounting, biology/chemistry, and sociology/social work are the strongest academically. Education, accounting, and communication studies have the largest enrollments.

Required: Students must complete a general studies curriculum, including requirements in humanities, social sciences, and natural sciences, as well as specific courses in English composition, public communication, Western civilization, and physical fitness. In order to graduate, students must complete a minimum of 128 semester hours, including 26 to 52 in a major, with a GPA of at least 2.0 (2.5 for the education major). A comprehensive exam in the major is also required.

Special: The college offers cooperative programs in nursing and engineering science. The Brethren Colleges Abroad program allows study abroad in Ecuador, China, England, France, Germany, Japan, and Spain. Manchester also offers B.A.-B.S. degrees, internships, work-study programs, dual majors, student-designed majors, a 3-2 engineering program, pass/fail options, and nondegree study. Other special academic features include independent study, required study in non-Western culture, and interdisciplinary programs in both peace studies and environmental studies. There is a freshman honors program on campus, as well as 1 national honor society. All departments have honors programs.

Faculty/Classroom: Seventy-three percent of faculty are male; 27%, female. All teach undergraduates and 5% both teach and do research. No introductory courses are taught by graduate students. The average class size in an introductory lecture is 30; in a laboratory, 15; and in a regular course offering, 20.

Admissions: About 86% of the 1993-94 applicants were accepted. The SAT scores for the 1993-94 freshman class were as follows: Verbal—74% below 500, 20% between 500 and 599, 5% between 600 and 700, and 1% above 700; Math—45% below 500, 37% between 500 and 599, 17% between 600 and 700, and 1% above 700. The ACT scores were 45% below 21, 25% between 21 and 23, 19% between 24 and 26, 7% between 27 and 28, and 5% above 28. About 43% of the current freshmen were in the top fifth of their class; 73% were in the top two fifths. There were 2 National Merit semifinalists. Four freshmen graduated first in their class.

Requirements: Manchester requires applicants to be in the upper 50% of their class. The SAT I or ACT is recommended. Entrance examination scores should include a minimum SAT I composite of 800, with 400 on each part, or ACT composite of 18. Students are encouraged to submit SAT II: Subject test scores and arrange for an interview. Each application is reviewed on an individual basis. The GED is accepted. For high school students, the college recommends completion of 28 academic credits, based on 4 years each of English, mathematics, and science, and 2 years each of foreign language, history, and social studies. AP and CLEP credits are accepted. Important factors used in the admissions decision are recommendations by school officials, leadership record, advanced placement or honor courses, personality, intangible qualities, and extracurricular activities record.

Procedure: Freshmen are admitted fall, winter, and spring. Entrance exams should be taken by November of the senior year. Application deadlines are open. The application fee is $20. Notification is sent on a rolling basis. There is an early admissions plan.

Transfer: A total of 53 transfer students enrolled in 1993-94. Applicants must present a minimum GPA of 2.0 in all previous college work. A total of 96 credits out of 128 must be completed at Manchester.

Visiting: There are regularly scheduled orientations for prospective students, including course registration, housing preference designation, and placement testing. There are guides for informal visits and visitors may sit in on classes and stay overnight at the school. To arrange for a visit, contact Jill Biehl, Secretary, at (219) 982-5055.

Financial Aid: In a recent year, 97% of all current freshmen received some form of financial aid. About 87% of freshmen received need-based aid. The average freshman award was $9600. Of that total, scholarships or need-based grants averaged $6480 ($9330 maximum); loans averaged $2950; and work contracts averaged $850 ($1200 maximum). Fifty-three percent of undergraduate students work part-time. Average earnings from campus work for the school year are $850. The average financial indebtedness of the 1992-93 graduate was $7500. Manchester is a member of CSS. The FAFSA is required.

International Students: There are currently 32 international students enrolled. International students must take the TOEFL and achieve a minimum score of 550.

Computers: The college provides computer facilities for student use. The mainframe is an IBM AS400. Microcomputers are available in various academic buildings; in addition, various departments have computer laboratories for students. All students may access the system at any time. There are no time limits on using the system and no fees.

Graduates: In 1992-93, 217 bachelor's degrees were awarded. The most popular majors among graduates were business administration (18%), education (18%), and accounting (18%). Within an average freshman class, 50% graduate in 4 years and 60% in 5 years. Some 22 companies recruited on campus in 1992-93. In the 1992 graduating class, 14% of all students were enrolled in graduate school within 6 months of graduation; 34% of the men and 47% of the women had found employment.

Admissions Contact: David McFadden, Dean of Enrollment Management.

MARIAN COLLEGE
Indianapolis, IN 46222 (317) 929-0321; (800) 772-7264 (in-state)

C-3

Full-time: 312 men, 611 women	Faculty: 79; IIB, --$
Part-time: 67 men, 360 women	Ph.D.s: 36%
Graduate: none	Student/Faculty: 12 to 1
Year: semesters, summer session	Tuition: $9320
Application Deadline: open	Room & Board: $3616
Freshman Class: 770 applied, 542 accepted, 238 enrolled	
SAT I Verbal/Math: 420/466	**COMPETITIVE**

Marian College, an independent, coeducational institution, was founded in 1851 by the Sisters of St. Francis and is today affiliated with the Roman Catholic Church. The college offers undergraduate programs in the arts and sciences, business, education, fine arts, and the health professions. In addition to regional accreditation, Marian has baccalaureate program accreditation with ADA, AHEA, CAHEA, NCATE, and NLN. The library contains 130,000 volumes and subscribes to 588 periodicals. Computerized library sources and services include interlibrary loans and database searching. Special learning facilities include a learning resource center and the 35-acre Wetlands Ecology Laboratory. The 114-acre campus is in an urban area 6 miles from downtown Indianapolis. Including residence halls, there are 22 buildings on campus.

Student Life: About 94% of undergraduates are from Indiana. Students come from 18 states, 18 foreign countries, and Canada. Seventy percent are from public schools; 30% from private. Eighty-four percent are white; 13% African American. Forty-three percent are Catholic; 42% Protestant. The average age of freshmen is 20.1; all undergraduates, 23.3. Ten percent drop out by the end of their first year; 65% remain to graduate.

Housing: A total of 600 students can be accommodated in college housing. College-sponsored living facilities include single-sex and coed dormitories, on-campus apartments, and married-student housing. In addition there are academic houses. On-campus housing is guaranteed for all 4 years. Sixty percent of students commute. Alcohol is not permitted. All students may keep cars on campus.

Activities: There are no fraternities or sororities on campus. There are 25 groups on campus, including art, band, cheerleading, choir, chorale, chorus, computers, drama, ethnic, honors, international, jazz band, literary magazine, musical theater, newspaper, pep band, photography, political, professional, religious, social, social service, student government, and yearbook. Popular campus events include Knightly Music Awards, Mock Rock, and Homecoming.

Sports: There are 7 intercollegiate sports for men and 6 for women, and 12 intramural sports for men and 12 for women. Athletic and recreation facilities include varsity and intramural gymnasiums, racquetball courts, a weight-training room, and a physical education assessment lab.

Disabled Students: The entire campus is accessible to disabled students. The following facilities are available: wheelchair ramps, elevators, special parking, and special class scheduling.

Services: In addition to many counseling and information services, tutoring is available in most subjects. There is a reader service for the blind and remedial math and writing. Study skills training is also offered.

Campus Safety and Security: Campus safety and security measures include 24-hour foot and vehicle patrol, escort service, shuttle buses, and informal discussions. In addition, there are pamphlets, posters, and films, emergency telephones, and lighted pathways and sidewalks.

Programs of Study: Marian awards the B.A. and B.S. degrees. Associate degrees also are awarded. Bachelor's degrees are awarded in BIOLOGICAL SCIENCE (biology/biological science), BUSINESS (accounting, banking and finance, business administration and management, and fashion merchandising), COMMUNICATIONS AND THE ARTS (art history and appreciation, dramatic arts, English, French, German, music, Spanish, speech/debate/rhetoric, and studio art), COMPUTER AND PHYSICAL SCIENCE (chemistry and mathematics), EDUCATION (early childhood, elementary, physical, and special), HEALTH PROFESSIONS (allied health and nursing), SOCIAL SCIENCE (dietetics, history, philosophy, psychology, religious education, sociology, and theological studies). Nursing, business administration, and education have the largest enrollments.

Required: To graduate, students must complete 128 semester hours, including 30 to 40 in the major, with a minimum GPA of 2.0 overall and 2.5 in the major. Students must complete 12 hours of introductory courses in English composition, philosophy, speech, and theology, as well as 39 to 54 hours of distribution requirements beyond the introductory level in humanities, sciences, and languages. Attendance

at 12 out of 16 convocations over a 4-year period is required, as well as a comprehensive exam or seminar in the major field.

Special: Cross-registration with neighboring colleges is available to students in technical fields of study. Marian also offers study abroad, cooperative work-study programs for business majors, a 3–2 engineering degree with the University of Detroit, independent study, and an accelerated degree program in nursing. Dual and student-designed majors, and pass/fail options are also available. There is a freshman honors program on campus, as well as 8 national honor societies.

Faculty/Classroom: Forty-six percent of faculty are male; 54%, female. All teach undergraduates. The average class size in an introductory lecture, a laboratory, and a regular course offering is 15.

Admissions: About 70% of the 1993–94 applicants were accepted. The SAT scores for the 1993–94 freshman class were as follows: Verbal—87% below 500, 10% between 500 and 599, and 3% between 600 and 700; Math—65% below 500, 25% between 500 and 599, 9% between 600 and 700, and 1% above 700. About 38% of the current freshmen were in the top fifth of their class; 76% were in the top two fifths. There was 1 National Merit finalist and 1 semifinalist. Three freshmen graduated first in their class.

Requirements: A minimum GPA of 2.0 is required. The SAT I or ACT is required. Applicant must be a graduate of an accredited secondary school or have a GED. Marian requires 16 academic units, including 3 units in English, 2 units each in a foreign language and mathematics, of which algebra and geometry are recommended, and 1 unit each in a laboratory science and social studies. Students must also submit recommendations by school officials. AP and CLEP credits are accepted. Important factors used in the admissions decision are recommendations by school officials, recommendations by alumni, leadership record, advanced placement or honor courses, and parents or siblings attending the school.

Procedure: Freshmen are admitted to all sessions. Application deadlines are open. The application fee is $20. Notification is sent on a rolling basis.

Transfer: A total of 148 transfer students enrolled in 1993–94. In addition to meeting standard admission requirements, applicants must submit transcripts of all college work and be in good standing at their former school. Students transferring fewer than 30 credit hours must have a 1.75 GPA; those having more than 30 hours must have a 2.0 GPA. A total of 30 credits out of 128 must be completed at Marian.

Visiting: There are regularly scheduled orientations for prospective students, including a campus tour, visits with faculty, and financial aid information. There are guides for informal visits and visitors may sit in on classes and stay overnight at the school. To arrange for a visit, contact the Admissions Office at (317) 929–0321.

Financial Aid: In 1993–94, 92% of all current freshmen and 75% of continuing students received some form of financial aid. About 87% of freshmen and 90% of continuing students received need-based aid. The average freshman award was $8807. Of that total, scholarships or need-based grants averaged $5855 ($9200 maximum); loans averaged $2656 ($4125 maximum); and work contracts averaged $296 ($1000 maximum). Sixty percent of undergraduate students work part-time. Average earnings from campus work for the school year was $700. The average financial indebtedness of the 1992–93 graduate was $10,000. Marian is a member of CSS. The FAF and the college's own financial statement are required. The deadline for financial aid applications is March 1.

International Students: There are currently 26 international students enrolled. The school actively recruits these students. They must take the TOEFL and achieve a minimum score of 550. The student must also take the SAT I or the ACT.

Computers: The college provides computer facilities for student use. Microcomputers are in both stand-alone and networked configurations in several computer laboratories, the language laboratory, the library, and computerized classrooms. All students may access the system. The fees are $40 per semester.

Graduates: In 1992–93, 149 bachelor's degrees were awarded. The most popular majors among graduates were business administration (19%), nursing (16%), and education (10%).

Admissions Contact: Brent E. Smith, Dean, Enrollment Management.

MARTIN UNIVERSITY
Indianapolis, IN 46218

C-3

(317) 543–3238

Full-time: 280 men, 320 women	Faculty: 30
Part-time: 60 men, 40 women	Ph.Ds: 55%
Graduate: 7 men, 21 women	Student/Faculty: 20 to 1
Year: semesters, summer session	Tuition: $4830
Application Deadline: open	Room & Board: n/app
Freshman Class: 150 applied, 148 accepted, 135 enrolled	
SAT I or ACT: not required	**NONCOMPETITIVE**

Martin University, established in 1977, is a private liberal arts institution offering undergraduate programs primarily to low-income minority-group adults. It also offers graduate degrees in community psychology and urban ministry studies. There are 2 graduate schools. Computerized library sources and services include interlibrary loans and database searching. Special learning facilities include a learning resource center and English and mathematics laboratories. The 8-acre campus is in an urban area in the city of Indianapolis. There are 10 buildings on campus.

Student Life: Nearly all undergraduates are from Indiana. Students come from 4 foreign countries. Ninety percent are from public schools; 10% from private. Ninety percent are African American. The average age of freshmen is 43; all undergraduates, 40. Ten percent drop out by the end of their first year; 65% remain to graduate.

Housing: There are no residence halls; all students may keep cars on campus. Alcohol is not permitted.

Activities: There are no fraternities or sororities on campus. There are some groups and organizations on campus, including choir, computers, newspaper, opera, and social service. Popular campus events include internal and external conferences, Dr. Martin Luther King, Jr.'s birthday, St. Martin de Porres Feast Day, Madrigal, Fine Arts Festival, and Accountability to the Community.

Sports: There is no sports program at Martin U.

Disabled Students: Ninety percent of the campus is accessible to disabled students. The following facilities are available: wheelchair ramps, elevators, special parking, and specially equipped rest rooms.

Services: In addition to many counseling and information services, tutoring is available in most subjects. In addition, there is remedial math, reading, and writing, and addiction services.

Campus Safety and Security: Campus safety and security measures include 24-hour foot and vehicle patrol.

Programs of Study: Martin U awards the B.A. and B.S. degrees. Master's degrees also are awarded. Bachelor's degrees are awarded in BIOLOGICAL SCIENCE (biology/biological science), BUSINESS (accounting, business administration and management, insurance, and marketing/retailing/merchandising), COMMUNICATIONS AND THE ARTS (communications, English, fine arts, music, and piano/organ), COMPUTER AND PHYSICAL SCIENCE (chemistry and mathematics), EDUCATION (early childhood, education, and vocational), ENGINEERING AND ENVIRONMENTAL DESIGN (computer technology), HEALTH PROFESSIONS (nursing), SOCIAL SCIENCE (African American studies, behavioral science, community services, counseling psychology, criminal justice, history, humanities, political science/government, psychology, religion, and sociology). Humanities and psychology are the strongest academically. Business has the largest enrollment.

Required: Students must successfully complete 134 credits, including 36 in the humanities, 12 in English, 9 in social science, and 6 in mathematics, with at least 36 in the major, and must maintain a minimum GPA of 2.0. Required courses also include computer science, logic, and world consciousness. A foreign language is required for the B.A. Students must complete a final project in their major.

Special: Cross-registration is permitted with 7 schools in the Consortium of Urban Education in the area. Opportunities are provided for internships, student-designed majors, and credit based on assessment of prior learning. One department has an honors program.

Faculty/Classroom: Fifty-five percent of faculty are male; 45%, female. All teach undergraduates and 10% do research. No introductory courses are taught by graduate students. The average class size in an introductory lecture is 10 and in a laboratory, 8.

Admissions: About 99% of the 1993–94 applicants were accepted.

Requirements: The SAT I and ACT are not required. Graduation from an accredited secondary school is required; a GED will be accepted. No specific number of academic credits are required. An essay, an interview, and diagnostic testing are required. CLEP credit is accepted. Important factors used in the admissions decision are recommendations by school officials, recommendations by alumni, personality, intangible qualities, parents or siblings attending the school, and leadership record.

Procedure: Freshmen are admitted to all sessions. Entrance exams should be taken at the time of admission. Application deadlines are open. The application fee is $10. The college accepts all applicants. Notification is sent on a rolling basis.

Transfer: About 130 transfer students enrolled in a recent year. Transfers are accepted from accredited regional schools. A total of 34 credits out of 134 must be completed at Martin U.

Visiting: There are regularly scheduled orientations for prospective students, consisting of 4 three-hour sessions. There are guides for informal visits, and visitors may sit in on classes. To arrange for a visit, contact the Admissions Office at (3l7) 543–3238.

Financial Aid: In an earlier year, 80% of all current freshmen and 80% of continuing students received some form of financial aid. About 80% of freshmen received need-based aid. The average freshman award was $2700. Of that total, scholarships or need-based grants averaged $200 ($2500 maximum). Two percent of undergraduate students work part-time. Average earnings from campus work for the school year are $1500. In an earlier year, the average financial

indebtedness of graduates was $2500. The FAF is required. The deadline for financial aid applications is September 1.

International Students: There are currently 6 international students enrolled. They must take the TOEFL and achieve a minimum score of 550.

Computers: The college provides computer facilities for student use. The mainframe is an IBM/34. There are also 20 IBM microcomputers available with an assistant on duty. All students may access the system. There are no time limits on using the system and no fees.

Graduates: In a recent year, 73 bachelor's degrees were awarded. The most popular majors among graduates were business administration (20%), sociology (18%), and religious studies (11%). Within an average freshman class, 60% graduate in 3 years, 30% in 4 years, 5% in 5 years, and 5% in 6 years. Some 5 companies recruited on campus in 1992–93. In a recent graduating class, 12% of the men and 18% of the women were enrolled in graduate school within 6 months of graduation; all graduates had found employment.

Admissions Contact: Bobbye Jean Craig, Director of Enrollment Management.

OAKLAND CITY COLLEGE
A-5

Oakland City, IN 47660   (812) 749–1222; (800) 737–5125 (in-state)

Full-time: 382 men, 313 women	Faculty: 30; IIB, --$
Part-time: 64 men, 129 women	Ph.D.s: 45%
Graduate: 14 men, 2 women	Student/Faculty: 23 to 1
Year: semesters, summer session	Tuition: $7066
Application Deadline: open	Room & Board: $3150
Freshman Class: 98 enrolled	
SAT I Verbal/Math: 370/370	ACT: 20 LESS COMPETITIVE

Oakland City College, founded in 1885, is a private liberal arts college affiliated with the General Association of General Baptists. There are 2 graduate schools. In addition to regional accreditation, OCC has baccalaureate program accreditation with NCATE. The library contains 75,000 volumes and 18,000 microform items, and subscribes to 350 periodicals. Computerized library sources and services include the card catalog and interlibrary loans. Special learning facilities include a learning resource center. The 20-acre campus is in a small town 30 miles north of Evansville, Illinois. Including residence halls, there are 11 buildings on campus.

Student Life: About 88% of undergraduates are from Indiana. Students come from 17 states and 1 foreign country. Ninety percent are from public schools; 10% from private. Ninety-seven percent are white. Seventy-six percent are Protestant; 13% Catholic. The average age of freshmen is 19; all undergraduates, 24. Thirty percent drop out by the end of their first year; 70% remain to graduate.

Housing: A total of 246 students can be accommodated in college housing. College-sponsored living facilities include single-sex dormitories. On-campus housing is guaranteed for all 4 years. Sixty-three percent of students commute. Alcohol is not permitted. All students may keep cars on campus.

Activities: There are no fraternities or sororities on campus. There are 18 groups on campus, including art, cheerleading, chess, choir, chorus, computers, drama, honors, international, musical theater, newspaper, pep band, photography, professional, religious, social, social service, student government, and yearbook. Popular campus events include Homecoming, Fall Festival Week, Spring Fling, and Freedom Week.

Sports: There are 4 intercollegiate sports for men and 5 for women, and 25 intramural sports each. Athletic and recreation facilities include a gymnasium, a health and physical education center with a 1400-seat gymnasium, and a playing field.

Disabled Students: The entire campus is accessible to disabled students. The following facilities are available: wheelchair ramps, special parking, specially equipped rest rooms, and lowered drinking fountains.

Services: In addition to many counseling and information services, tutoring is available in every subject. There is also a reader service for the blind, and remedial math, reading, and writing.

Campus Safety and Security: Campus safety and security measures include self-defense education, informal discussions, pamphlets, posters, and films, and emergency telephones. In addition, there are lighted pathways and sidewalks.

Programs of Study: OCC awards the B.A. and B.S. degrees. Associate and master's degrees also are awarded. Bachelor's degrees are awarded in BIOLOGICAL SCIENCE (biology/biological science), BUSINESS (accounting and business administration and management), COMMUNICATIONS AND THE ARTS (English, fine arts, and music), COMPUTER AND PHYSICAL SCIENCE (chemistry, computer programming, computer science, and mathematics), EDUCATION (art, business, elementary, middle school, music, science, and secondary), HEALTH PROFESSIONS (premedicine), and SOCIAL SCIENCE (prelaw and religion). Education is the strongest academically and has the largest enrollment.

Required: Liberal arts students must take a general studies core, including 1 computer science course and 2 hours of physical education. A minimum GPA of 2.0 (2.5 in the major) and 120 total semester hours are needed.

Special: OCC offers campus work-study programs, an accelerated business-degree program, a B.A.-B.S. degree, dual majors, credit for significant work or service experience, nondegree study, pass/fail options, and a general studies degree. There are 3 national honor societies on campus.

Faculty/Classroom: All faculty teach undergraduates. The average class size in an introductory lecture is 20; in a laboratory, 16; and in a regular course offering, 20.

Admissions: The SAT scores for the 1993–94 freshman class were as follows: Verbal—77% below 500, 17% between 500 and 599, and 6% between 600 and 700; Math—85% below 500, 11% between 500 and 599, and 4% between 600 and 700. The ACT scores were 67% below 21, 21% between 21 and 23, 5% between 24 and 26, 3% between 27 and 28, and 4% above 28. About 19% of the current freshmen were in the top fifth of their class; 50% were in the top two fifths.

Requirements: OCC requires applicants to be in the upper 50% of their class. A minimum GPA of 2.0 is needed. The SAT I or ACT is required, with a minimum SAT I composite score of 700 or ACT composite score of 18. Preparatory programs usually include 4 units of English, 2 each of social science and science, 2 to 4 of a foreign language, and 3 to 4 of mathematics. An interview is recommended. The GED is accepted. AP and CLEP credits are accepted. Important factors used in the admissions decision are personality, intangible qualities, evidence of special talent, extracurricular activities record, leadership record, and advanced placement or honor courses.

Procedure: Freshmen are admitted to all sessions. Entrance exams should be taken in the fall of the senior year. The application deadlines are open. Application fee is $25. Notification is sent on a rolling basis. There is a deferred admissions plan.

Transfer: Transfer applicants need a minimum GPA of 2.0 and scores of 700 on the SAT I or 18 on the ACT. An interview is recommended. A total of 35 semester hours out of 120 must be completed at OCC.

Visiting: There are regularly scheduled orientations for prospective students. There are guides for informal visits and visitors may sit in on classes and stay overnight at the school. To arrange for a visit, contact the Admissions Office at (812) 749–1222 or (800) 737–5125 (in-state).

Financial Aid: In 1993–94, 93% of all current freshmen and 88% of continuing students received some form of financial aid. Scholarships or need-based grants averaged $1800 ($3450 maximum); loans averaged $2000 ($5500 maximum); and work contracts averaged $1400 ($2800 maximum). Seventy-seven percent of undergraduate students work part-time. Average earnings from campus work for the school year are $1400. OCC is a member of CSS. The college's own financial statement and the FAFSA are required. The deadline for financial aid applications is March 1.

International Students: There are currently 6 international students enrolled. The school actively recruits these students. They must take the TOEFL and achieve a minimum score of 500. The student must also take the SAT I or the ACT.

Computers: The college provides computer facilities for student use. All students may access the system. There are no time limits on using the system and no fees.

Admissions Contact: Faye Camp, Director of Admissions.

PURDUE UNIVERSITY

Purdue University, established in 1869, is a land-grant system in Indiana. It is governed by a board of trustees, whose chief administrator is the president. The primary goal of the system is to provide quality education to the citizens of Indiana. The main priorities are teaching, research, and public service. Altogether there are 212 baccalaureate, 59 master's, and 54 doctoral programs offered at Purdue Univeristy. The total enrollment in a recent year of all 5 campuses was 60,550; there were 2260 faculty members on the main campus at West Lafayette. There are 4-year campuses in Hammond and West Lafayette. The Indianapolis and Fort Wayne campuses are operated jointly with Indiana University. Profiles of the 4-year campuses are included in this chapter in alphabetical order with other Indiana schools.

PURDUE UNIVERSITY CALUMET

Hammond, IN 46323

B-1

(219) 989–2213

(800) 228–0799, ext. 2213 (Illinois)

Full-time: 1943 men, 2282 women
Part-time: 1929 men, 2416 women
Graduate: 286 men, 562 women
Year: semesters, summer session
Application Deadline: open
Freshman Class: 1790 applied, 1760 accepted, 1650 enrolled
SAT I Verbal/Math: 450/425

Faculty: 238; IIA, --$
Ph.Ds: 56%
Student/Faculty: 18 to 1
Tuition: $2374 ($5521)
Room & Board: n/app

NONCOMPETITIVE

Purdue University/Calumet, established in 1946, is a public, coeducational commuter institution offering undergraduate degrees in general studies, liberal arts, and professional studies. There are 2 undergraduate schools and one graduate school. In addition to regional accreditation, Purdue Cal has baccalaureate program accreditation with ABET, NCATE, and NLN. The library contains 200,000 volumes, 460,000 microform items, and 227 audiovisual forms, and subscribes to 1640 periodicals. Special learning facilities include an art gallery, a computer education building, and an educational media laboratory. The 130-acre campus is in an urban area 25 miles southeast of Chicago. There are 11 buildings on campus.

Student Life: About 91% of undergraduates are from Indiana. Students come from 7 states, 3 foreign countries, and Canada. Ninety percent are from public schools; 10% from private. Eighty-two percent are white. The average age of freshmen is 20; all undergraduates, 27.

Housing: There are no residence halls; all students commute. Alcohol is not permitted. All students may keep cars on campus.

Activities: There are 3 national fraternities and 3 national sororities. There are 45 groups on campus, including cheerleading, chorus, computers, drama, ethnic, honors, literary magazine, musical theater, newspaper, political, professional, religious, social service, and student government. Popular campus events include Homecoming, Orientation, Latin Culture Month, and Black History Month.

Sports: There is 1 intercollegiate sport for men and 2 for women, and 4 intramural sports for men and 4 for women. Athletic and recreation facilities include a 1500-seat gymnasium, racquetball courts, a baseball field, a running track, a weight room, and a total fitness center.

Disabled Students: Eighty percent of the campus is accessible to disabled students. The following facilities are available: wheelchair ramps, elevators, special parking, specially equipped rest rooms, special class scheduling, and lowered drinking fountains and telephones. There are electric door openers on all but one student building.

Services: In addition to many counseling and information services, tutoring is available in most subjects. In addition, there is a reader service for the blind, and remedial math, reading, and writing.

Campus Safety and Security: Campus safety and security measures include 24-hour foot and vehicle patrol, escort service, informal discussions, and pamphlets, posters, and films. In addition, there are emergency telephones and lighted pathways and sidewalks.

Programs of Study: Purdue Cal awards the B.A., B.S., B.S.Ch., and B.S.E. degrees. Associate and master's degrees also are awarded. Bachelor's degrees are awarded in BIOLOGICAL SCIENCE (biology/biological science, biotechnology, microbiology, and zoology), BUSINESS (accounting, banking and finance, business economics, hotel/motel and restaurant management, and marketing/retailing/merchandising), COMMUNICATIONS AND THE ARTS (broadcasting, communications, English, French, German, and Spanish), COMPUTER AND PHYSICAL SCIENCE (chemistry, computer programming, computer science, information sciences and systems, mathematics, and physics), EDUCATION (early childhood, elementary, foreign languages, science, and secondary), ENGINEERING AND ENVIRONMENTAL DESIGN (computer engineering, computer technology, construction technology, electrical/electronics engineering, electrical/electronics engineering technology, engineering, engineering technology, industrial engineering technology, mechanical engineering, and mechanical engineering technology), HEALTH PROFESSIONS (medical laboratory technology, nursing, optometry, physical therapy, predentistry, premedicine, prepharmacy, and preveterinary science), SOCIAL SCIENCE (criminal justice, history, international relations, philosophy, political science/government, prelaw, psychology, social work, and sociology). Engineering, nursing, behavioral sciences, education, and management are the strongest academically. Engineering, business, nursing, technologies, and behavioral sciences have the largest enrollments.

Required: Graduation requirements vary depending on the program. The total number of credit hours required for a degree varies from 126 to 136, with 24 to 73 in the major. All students must take English composition and 36 hours of general education courses and maintain a C average.

Special: Some cooperative programs, internships, and work-study programs are available to students. Purdue Cal offers cross-registration in philosophy, study in Spain, and credit for life, military, and work experience, as well as nondegree study and pass/fail options. There is a freshman honors program on campus

Faculty/Classroom: The average class size in an introductory lecture is 24; in a laboratory, 24; and in a regular course offering, 24.

Admissions: About 98% of the 1993–94 applicants were accepted. Eighteen freshmen graduated first in their class.

Requirements: Purdue Cal requires applicants to be in the upper 67% of their class. A minimum GPA of 2.0 is required. The SAT I or ACT is required. Students may request the SAT II in writing. The SAT II in mathematics is required. Applicants must be graduates of an accredited secondary school. The GED is accepted. Thirty-three Carnegie units are required for admission. Required courses vary, depending on the curriculum, and include 3 or 4 years of English, 2 or 3 years of mathematics, 2 years of foreign language, and 1 year of history or social studies. AP and CLEP credits are accepted. Important factors used in the admissions decision are recommendations by school officials, recommendations by alumni, personality, intangible qualities, parents or siblings attending the school, and advanced placement or honor courses.

Procedure: Freshmen are admitted to all sessions. Entrance exams should be taken between November and March of the senior year. Application deadlines are open. The college accepts all applicants. Notification is sent on a rolling basis.

Transfer: About 400 transfer students enrolled in a recent year. Applicants must have a minimum GPA of 2.0 for transfer credit. A total of 36 to 46 credits out of 126 to 136 must be completed at Purdue Cal.

Visiting: There are regularly scheduled orientations for prospective students. There are guides for informal visits and visitors may sit in on classes. To arrange for a visit, contact the Media Service Office, Admissions, or the academic departments at (219) 989–2289.

Financial Aid: In a recent year, 34% of all current freshmen and 32% of continuing students received some form of financial aid. Scholarships or need-based grants averaged $850 ($2380 maximum); loans averaged $1700 ($2625 maximum); and work contracts averaged $1350 ($1500 maximum). Eighty-three percent of undergraduate students work part-time. The average financial indebtedness of recent graduates was $4600. Purdue Cal is a member of CSS. The FAF is required. The deadline for financial aid applications is March 1.

International Students: There are currently 5 international students enrolled. They must take the TOEFL. The student must also take the SAT I or the ACT and achieve a minimum composite score of 500 on the SAT I.

Computers: The college provides computer facilities for student use. The mainframes are an IBM 4341/LI, 2 DEC VAX 11/780S, and a DEC VAX 8600. Numerous microcomputers are available. All students may access the system. There are no time limits on using the system and no fees.

Graduates: In a recent year, 570 bachelor's degrees were awarded. Some 64 companies recruited on campus in a recent year. In the 1992 graduating class, 8% of the men and 10% of the women were enrolled in graduate school within 6 months of graduation.

Admissions Contact: Patricia W. Grady, Acting Director.

PURDUE UNIVERSITY WEST LAFAYETTE

West Lafayette, IN 47907

B-3

(317) 494–1776

Full-time: 14,838 men, 11,112 women
Part-time: 1251 men, 1263 women
Graduate: 4170 men, 2527 women
Year: semesters, summer session
Application Deadline: see profile
Freshman Class: 21,804 applied, 18,744 accepted, 5874 enrolled
SAT I Verbal/Math: 453/545

Faculty: 2145; I, av$
Ph.Ds: 99%
Student/Faculty: 12 to 1
Tuition: $2696 ($8848)
Room & Board: $3940

ACT: 24

COMPETITIVE

Purdue University, founded in 1869, is a publicly supported institution offering undergraduate and graduate degrees in a wide range of subjects with an emphasis on engineering, business, communications, arts, and social science. There are 12 undergraduate and 11 graduate schools. In addition to regional accreditation, Purdue has baccalaureate program accreditation with AACSB, ABET, ACCE, ACPE, ADA, ASLA, FIDER, NCATE, NLN, and SAF. The 14 libraries contain 2,076,302 volumes, 2,061,467 microform items, and 13,861 audiovisual forms, and subscribe to 14,139 periodicals. Computerized library sources and services include the card catalog, interlibrary loans, and database searching. Special learning facilities include a learning resource center, an art gallery, and a radio station. The 1565-acre campus is in a suburban area 65 miles northwest of Indianapolis. Including residence halls, there are 156 buildings on campus.

Student Life: About 73% of undergraduates are from Indiana. Students come from 50 states, 109 foreign countries, and Canada. Eighty-three percent are white. Fifty-six percent claim no religious affiliation; 24% are Protestant; 17% Catholic. The average age of freshmen is 18; all undergraduates, 21. Twelve percent drop out by the end of their first year; 68% remain to graduate.

Housing: A total of 11,082 students can be accommodated in college housing. College-sponsored living facilities include single-sex and coed dormitories, on-campus apartments, married-student housing, fraternity houses, and sorority houses. On-campus housing is available on a first-come, first-served basis. Alcohol is not permitted. Upperclassmen may keep cars on campus.

Activities: About 20% of men belong to 48 national fraternities; about 18% of women belong to 1 local and 23 national sororities. There are 528 groups on campus, including band, cheerleading, chess, choir, chorale, chorus, computers, dance, drama, ethnic, gay, honors, international, jazz band, literary magazine, marching band, newspaper, orchestra, pep band, photography, political, professional, radio and TV, religious, social, social service, student government, symphony, and yearbook. Popular campus events include Grand Prix Race, Old Masters, and University Sing.

Sports: There are 8 intercollegiate sports for men and 7 for women, and 26 intramural sports for men and 24 for women. Athletic and recreation facilities include a 14,000-seat arena, a 69,000-seat stadium, an intercollegiate athletic facility, a recreational gymnasium, a fieldhouse, an athletic center, intramural playing fields, 2 golf courses, and baseball, softball, and track fields.

Disabled Students: Eighty percent of the campus is accessible to disabled students. The following facilities are available: wheelchair ramps, elevators, special parking, specially equipped rest rooms, special class scheduling, lowered drinking fountains, lowered telephones, and a lab with assistive technology and special computers.

Services: In addition to many counseling and information services, tutoring is available in every subject. There is also remedial math, reading, and writing.

Campus Safety and Security: Campus safety and security measures include 24-hour foot and vehicle patrol, escort service, informal discussions, and pamphlets, posters, and films. In addition, there are emergency telephones and lighted pathways and sidewalks.

Programs of Study: Purdue awards the B.A., B.S., B.F.A., B.P.E, B.S.A.E., B.S.C.E., B.S. Chem, B.S.Ch.E., B.S.E., B.S.E.E., B.S. Forestry, B.S.I.E., B.S.I.M., B.S.L.A., B.S.M.E., B.S. Pharm, and B.S. Surv./Topog. degrees. Associate's, master's, and doctoral degrees are also awarded. Bachelor's degrees are awarded in AGRICULTURE (agriculture, animal science, horticulture, and wildlife management), BIOLOGICAL SCIENCE (biochemistry, biology/biological science, entomology, microbiology, molecular biology, neurosciences, plant physiology, and zoology), BUSINESS (accounting, business economics, hotel/motel and restaurant management, and management science), COMMUNICATIONS AND THE ARTS (advertising, art history and appreciation, communications, comparative literature, creative writing, dramatic arts, English, film arts, fine arts, French, German, linguistics, photography, public relations, Russian, Spanish, and telecommunications), COMPUTER AND PHYSICAL SCIENCE (actuarial science, applied mathematics, atmospheric sciences and meteorology, chemistry, computer programming, computer science, earth science, geology, geophysics and seismology, mathematics, paleontology, physics, and statistics), EDUCATION (art, early childhood, elementary, health, home economics, middle school, physical, science, secondary, social studies, and special), ENGINEERING AND ENVIRONMENTAL DESIGN (aeronautical engineering, agricultural engineering, aviation computer technology, chemical engineering, civil engineering, computer engineering, construction engineering, electrical/electronics engineering, electrical/electronics engineering technology, engineering, engineering technology, environmental science, graphic arts technology, industrial engineering, industrial engineering technology, interior design, landscape architecture/design, materials engineering, mechanical engineering, mechanical engineering technology, nuclear engineering, and surveying engineering), HEALTH PROFESSIONS (community health work, medical laboratory technology, nursing, pharmacy, predentistry, premedicine, preveterinary science, and speech pathology/audiology), SOCIAL SCIENCE (African American studies, American studies, anthropology, criminal justice, dietetics, economics, food science, history, medieval studies, parks and recreation management, philosophy, political science/government, prelaw, psychology, religion, and sociology). Engineering, actuarial science, industrial management, and physical sciences are the strongest academically. Engineering, liberal arts, and technology have the largest enrollments.

Required: All students pursuing a bachelor's degree must complete approximately 128 hours and earn a minimum GPA of 2.0. In most majors, students must take courses in English, mathematics, science, computer sciences, and social science.

Special: Cooperative programs are available in engineering, technology, agriculture, management, science, and consumer and family sciences. Cross-registration with Purdue's regional campuses, numerous internships, study abroad, an accelerated-degree program in management, dual majors, student-designed majors, nondegree study, and pass/fail options are also offered. There is a freshman honors program on campus. Ten departments have honors programs.

Faculty/Classroom: Eighty-seven percent of faculty are male; 13%, female. Sixty-six percent teach undergraduates and 34% do research. Graduate students teach 58% of introductory courses. The average class size in an introductory lecture is 150; in a laboratory, 20; and in a regular course offering, 25.

Admissions: About 86% of the 1993–94 applicants were accepted. The SAT scores for the 1993–94 freshman class were as follows: Verbal—69% below 500, 25% between 500 and 599, and 6% between 600 and 700; Math—31% below 500, 36% between 500 and 599, 27% between 600 and 700, and 7% above 700. The ACT scores were 17% below 21, 25% between 21 and 23, 29% between 24 and 26, 14% between 27 and 28, and 14% above 28. About 54% of the current freshmen were in the top fifth of their class; 85% were in the top two fifths.

Requirements: The SAT I or ACT is required, and, although for most students there are no required minimum scores, students applying to the School of Engineering should have a minimum score of 400 verbal and 500 math on the SAT I or 23 math and 21 verbal on the ACT. Purdue recommends that most students have 15 semester credits including 4 years of English, 2 to 4 years of mathematics, and 1 to 3 years of science before applying. The GED is accepted. AP and CLEP credits are accepted. Important factors used in the admissions decision are advanced placement or honor courses, recommendations by school officials, parents or siblings attending the school, recommendations by alumni, and personality and other intangible qualities.

Procedure: Freshmen are admitted to all sessions. Entrance exams should be taken at the end of the junior year. Applications should be filed by November 15 for general flight technology and nursing, and December 15 for veterinary technology, along with an application fee of $30. Notification is sent on a rolling basis.

Transfer: About 1130 transfer students enrolled in 1993–94. Transfer students must file a regular application at least 30 days before start of the semester and submit SAT I/ACT results and high school and college transcripts. Students must be in good academic standing and meet the same subject-matter requirements as a beginning student. Minimum grade point varies by program but must be at least a C average; many programs require a higher average. Thirty-two credits, including one quarter of major requirements, out of a total of 128 credits must be completed at Purdue.

Visiting: There are regularly scheduled orientations for prospective students, including fall and spring preview days which consist of an admissions, financial aid, and housing information session; program sessions; a campus tour; and ROTC, band, and dormitory visits. The Summer Visitors Program consists of a counselors' orientation, campus visits, and a residence hall visit. There are guides for informal visits and visitors may sit in on classes. To arrange for a visit, contact the Office of Admissions at (317) 494–1776.

Financial Aid: In 1993–94, 60% of all current freshmen and 45% of continuing students received some form of financial aid. About 43% of freshmen and 45% of continuing students received need-based aid. The average freshman award was $7574. Of that total, scholarships or need-based grants averaged $1924 ($4300 maximum); loans averaged $5369 ($8125 maximum); and work contracts averaged $280 ($1700 maximum). Twenty-nine percent of undergraduate students work part-time. Average earnings from campus work for the school year are $980. The average financial indebtedness of the 1992–93 graduate was $9274. Purdue is a member of CSS. The FFS and the college's own financial statement are required. The deadline for financial aid applications is March 1.

International Students: There are currently 2498 international students enrolled. They must take the TOEFL and achieve a minimum score of 550.

Computers: The college provides computer facilities for student use. The mainframes are an IBM 3090/180E and Sequent Symmetry S81s. Several microcomputer laboratories are available on campus, and users can also access the systems via dial-modems from the residence halls. All students may access the system. It may be used 24 hours daily. There are no time limits on using the system and no fees.

Graduates: In 1992–93 5872 bachelor's degrees were awarded. The most popular majors among graduates were communications (7%), electrical engineering (5%), and elementary education (4%). Within an average freshman class, 1% graduate in 3 years, 30% in 4 years, 60% in 5 years, and 65% in 6 years. Some 560 companies recruited on campus in a recent year. In the 1992 graduating class, 20% of all graduates were enrolled in graduate school within 6 months of graduation; 52% found employment.

Admissions Contact: William Murray, Director of Admissions.

ROSE-HULMAN INSTITUTE OF TECHNOLOGY   B-4
Terre Haute, IN 47803   (812) 877-1511
                                        (800) 878-7448 (out-of-state)

Full-time: 1300 men	Faculty: 95; IIB, +$
Part-time: none	Ph.D.s: 93%
Graduate: 60 men, 5 women	Student/Faculty: 14 to 1
Year: quarters	Tuition: $12,500
Application Deadline: March 1	Room & Board: $3900
Freshman Class: 3320 applied, 1983 accepted, 381 enrolled	
SAT I Verbal/Math: 540/670	ACT: 30 **HIGHLY COMPETITIVE**

Rose-Hulman Institute of Technology, founded in 1874, is a private college for men emphasizing engineering and science; it plans to be coeducational beginning fall 1995. There is one graduate school. In addition to regional accreditation, Rose-Hulman has baccalaureate program accreditation with ABET. The library contains 55,000 volumes, and subscribes to 400 periodicals. Computerized library sources and services include the card catalog, interlibrary loans, and database searching. Special learning facilities include a learning resource center, art gallery, and radio station. The 130-acre campus is in a suburban area 3 miles east of Terre Haute. Including residence halls, there are 17 buildings on campus.

Student Life: About 60% of undergraduates are from Indiana. Students come from 43 states, 12 foreign countries, and Canada. Seventy-five percent are from public schools; 25% from private. Ninety-five percent are white. Fifty-five percent are Protestant; 34% Catholic; 10% claim no religious affiliation. The average age of freshmen is 18; all undergraduates, 22. Ten percent drop out by the end of their first year; 75% remain to graduate.

Housing: A total of 750 students can be accommodated in college housing. College-sponsored living facilities include fraternity houses. On-campus housing is guaranteed for the freshman year only, is available on a first-come, first-served basis, and is available on a lottery system for upperclassmen. Seventy percent of students live on campus. All students may keep cars on campus.

Activities: About 45% of men belong to 8 national fraternities. There are no sororities on campus. There are 50 groups on campus, including band, cheerleading, chess, chorus, computers, drama, drill team, honors, international, jazz band, literary magazine, newspaper, pep band, photography, political, radio and TV, religious, social, social service, student government, and yearbook. Popular campus events include art shows, concerts, and plays.

Sports: Athletic and recreation facilities include a field house and a recreational center.

Disabled Students: Ninety-five percent of the campus is accessible to disabled students. The following facilities are available: wheelchair ramps, elevators, special parking, specially equipped rest rooms, and special class scheduling.

Services: In addition to many counseling and information services, tutoring is available in most subjects.

Campus Safety and Security: Campus safety and security measures include 24-hour foot and vehicle patrol, informal discussions, pamphlets, posters, and films, and emergency telephones. In addition, there are lighted pathways and sidewalks.

Programs of Study: Rose-Hulman awards the B.S. degree. Master's degrees are also awarded. Bachelor's degrees are awarded in COMPUTER AND PHYSICAL SCIENCE (chemistry, computer science, mathematics, optics, and physics), ENGINEERING AND ENVIRONMENTAL DESIGN (chemical engineering, civil engineering, computer engineering, electrical/electronics engineering, and mechanical engineering), SOCIAL SCIENCE (economics). Engineering and science are the strongest academically. Electrical engineering has the largest enrollment.

Required: All students must complete at least 196 quarter credit hours with a minimum GPA of 2.0 and 36 hours in the humanities and social sciences. Freshmen are required to take calculus, chemistry, computer programming, and physics. In addition, 20% of all academic work must be in humanities and social sciences.

Special: The institute offers independent study, cross-registration with Indiana State University, summer industrial internships, study abroad in 8 countries, and dual majors. Pass/fail options also are available. There are 2 national honor societies on campus.

Faculty/Classroom: Ninety-five percent of faculty are male; 5%, female. All teach undergraduates. No introductory courses are taught by graduate students. The average class size in an introductory lecture is 45; in a laboratory, 25; and in a regular course offering, 24.

Admissions: About 60% of the 1993–94 applicants were accepted. The SAT I scores for the 1993–94 freshman class were as follows: Verbal—31% below 500, 47% between 500 and 599, 18% between 600 and 700, and 4% above 700; Math—19% between 500 and 599, 47% between 600 and 700, and 34% above 700. The ACT scores were 5% between 27 and 28 and 95% above 28. About 96% of the current freshmen were in the top fifth of their class; 100% were in the top two fifths. There were 25 National Merit finalists and 40 semifinalists. About 25 freshmen graduated first in their class.

Requirements: Rose-Hulman requires applicants to be in the upper 25% of their class. The SAT I or ACT is required. Candidates should have at least 16 units of credit including 4 in English, 1 each in mathematics, chemistry, physics, and electives, and 2 in social sciences. The SAT I, minimum score of 1000 composite, 400 verbal and 550 mathematics, or ACT, minimum of 22 in English and 26 in mathematics is required. An essay and interview are recommended. AP credits are accepted. Important factors used in the admissions decision are advanced placement or honor courses, personality, intangible qualities, evidence of special talent, leadership record, and extracurricular activities record.

Procedure: Freshmen are admitted in the fall. Entrance exams should be taken in the fall of the senior year or spring of the junior year. Applications should be filed by March 1 for fall entry, along with an application fee of $20. Notification is sent within 3 weeks of receipt of completed application on a rolling basis.

Transfer: About 18 transfer students enrolled in 1993–94. Applicants need 1 year each of calculus and chemistry and a minimum GPA of 3.0. An interview is recommended.

Visiting: There are regularly scheduled orientations for prospective students, including an interview, campus tour, and academic meetings. Visitors may sit in on classes and stay overnight at the school. To arrange for a visit, contact Admissions Office at (812) 877-1511.

Financial Aid: In 1993–94, 90% of all current freshmen and 90% of continuing students received some form of financial aid. About 80% of freshmen and 80% of continuing students received need-based aid. The average freshman award was $9000. Of that total, scholarships or need-based grants averaged $2000 ($5000 maximum); loans averaged $3500 ($5500 maximum); and work contracts averaged $1000 (maximum). Forty-five percent of undergraduate students work part-time. Average earnings from campus work for the school year are $1000. The average financial indebtedness of the 1992–93 graduate was $14,000. Rose-Hulman is a member of CSS. The FAF and the college's own financial statement are required. The deadline for financial aid applications is March 1.

International Students: There are currently 50 international students enrolled. They must take the TOEFL and achieve a minimum score of 550. The student must also take the SAT I or the ACT.

Computers: The college provides computer facilities for student use. The mainframe is a DEC VAX 6320. There are also some 400 microcomputers available on campus. All students may access the system. There are no time limits or fees.

Graduates: In 1992–93, 281 bachelor's degrees were awarded. The most popular majors among graduates were mechanical engineering (22%), electrical engineering (20%), and chemical engineering (15%). Within an average freshman class, 98% graduate in 4 years and 2% in 5 years. Some 325 companies recruited on campus in a recent year. In an earlier graduating class, 15% of the students were enrolled in graduate school within 6 months of graduation; 88% had found employment.

Admissions Contact: Charles G. Howard, Dean of Admissions.

SAINT FRANCIS COLLEGE   D-2
Fort Wayne, IN 46808   (219) 434-3279
                                        (800) 729-4732 (out-of-state)

Full-time: 147 men, 366 women	Faculty: 40; IIB, --$
Part-time: 61 men, 186 women	Ph.D.s: 78%
Graduate: 64 men, 137 women	Student/Faculty: 13 to 1
Year: semesters, summer session	Tuition: $8032
Application Deadline: August	Room & Board: $3630
Freshman Class: 213 applied, 166 accepted, 99 enrolled	
SAT I Verbal/Math: 400/450	ACT: 21 **COMPETITIVE**

St. Francis College is a Roman Catholic liberal arts college founded in 1890 by the sisters of St. Francis. In addition to regional accreditation, SFC has baccalaureate program accreditation with CAHEA, CSWE, NCATE, and NLN. The library contains 84,225 volumes and 510,000 microform items, and subscribes to 475 periodicals. Computerized library sources and services include the card catalog, interlibrary loans, and database searching. Special learning facilities include a learning resource center, art gallery, planetarium, and TV station. The 70-acre campus is in a suburban area west of Fort Wayne. Including residence halls, there are 13 buildings on campus.

Student Life: About 77% of undergraduates are from Indiana. Students come from 9 states and 2 foreign countries. 79% are from public schools; 21% from private. Some 84% are white. Nearly 42% are Catholic; 33%, Protestant. The average age of freshmen is 23; all undergraduates, 26. About 36% drop out by the end of their first year; 48% remain to graduate.

Housing: A total of 200 students can be accommodated in college housing. College-sponsored living facilities include single-sex dormitories. On-campus housing is guaranteed for the freshman year only and is available on a first-come, first-served basis. Some 75% of stu-

dents commute. Alcohol is not permitted. All students may keep cars on campus.

Activities: About 5% of women belong to 1 local sorority. There are no fraternities on campus. There are 19 groups on campus, including art, cheerleading, drama, radio and TV, religious, social, social service, student government, and yearbook. Popular campus events include Homecoming, Little Regatta, and Spring Fling.

Sports: Athletic and recreation facilities include a gymnasium with 2 basketball courts or 3 volleyball courts, a weight room, a baseball diamond, and a beach volleyball pit.

Disabled Students: Almost 85% of the campus is accessible to disabled students. The following facilities are available: wheelchair ramps, elevators, special parking, and specially equipped rest rooms.

Services: In addition to many counseling and information services, tutoring is available in most subjects. In addition, there is remedial math, reading, and writing, plus help for the learning disabled, individual counseling, and peer tutoring.

Campus Safety and Security: Campus safety and security measures include 24-hour foot and vehicle patrol, escort service, pamphlets, posters, and films, and lighted pathways and sidewalks.

Programs of Study: SFC awards the B.A., B.S., A.A., A.S., B.B.A., B.L.S., B.S.Ed., B.S.N., and B.S.W. degrees. Associate and master's degrees also are awarded. Bachelor's degrees are awarded in BIOLOGICAL SCIENCE (biology/biological science), BUSINESS (accounting and business administration and management), COMMUNICATIONS AND THE ARTS (communications, English, and fine arts), COMPUTER AND PHYSICAL SCIENCE (chemistry and science), EDUCATION (art, business, elementary, English, health, science, secondary, social studies, and special), ENGINEERING AND ENVIRONMENTAL DESIGN (commercial art and environmental science), HEALTH PROFESSIONS (medical laboratory technology, nursing, predentistry, and premedicine), SOCIAL SCIENCE (American studies, prelaw, psychology, religion, social science, and social work). Commercial art, nursing, and biological sciences are the strongest programs academically. Business, art, and nursing have the largest enrollments.

Required: All students must complete courses in humanities, social and behavioral science, religious studies, life and physical sciences, oral and written communication, physical education, computer science, and reading. In order to graduate, 128 semester hours with a minimum GPA of 2.0 and 30 hours in the major are required, depending on the degree and major.

Special: Internships in commercial art, business, and social work, on-campus work-study programs, and nondegree study are available. Students also can receive credit for life experience. There is a freshman honors program on campus, as well as 1 national honor society.

Faculty/Classroom: Some 55% of faculty are male; 45%, female. All teach undergraduates. No introductory courses are taught by graduate students. The average class size in an introductory lecture is 16; in a laboratory, 15; and in a regular course offering, 11.

Admissions: About 78% of the 1993–94 applicants were accepted. The SAT scores for the 1993–94 freshman class were as follows: Verbal—93% below 500 and 7% between 500 and 599; Math—64% below 500, 32% between 500 and 599, and 4% between 600 and 700. The ACT scores were 34% below 21, 44% between 21 and 23, 12% between 24 and 26, and 9% between 27 and 28. About 29% of the current freshmen were in the top fifth of their class; 45% were in the top two fifths.

Requirements: SFC requires applicants to be in the upper 50% of their class. A minimum GPA of 2.0 is required. The SAT I or ACT is required, with a minimum composite score of 800 on the SAT I or 19 on the ACT. They also must rank in the top half of their class, and carry a 2.0 cumulative GPA. While no set pattern of high school subjects is required for admission, 4 years of English, 2 each of mathematics and science, and 1 of social studies are suggested. An essay is required. AP and CLEP credits are accepted. Important factors used in the admissions decision are recommendations by school officials and ability to finance college education.

Procedure: Freshmen are admitted to all sessions. Entrance exams should be taken in the spring of the junior year or fall of the senior year. Applications should be filed by August for fall entry and May for summer entry. Notification is sent on a rolling basis. There is a deferred admissions plan.

Transfer: Transfer students need a minimum GPA of 2.0 and must submit all college transcripts. A total of 32 credits out of 128 must be completed at SFC.

Visiting: There are regularly scheduled orientations for prospective students, including meeting with faculty and staff and student tours. There are guides for informal visits and visitors may sit in on classes and stay overnight at the school. To arrange for a visit, contact the Admissions Office at (219) 434–3279 or (800) 729–4732.

Financial Aid: In 1993–94, all current freshmen and 84% of continuing students received some form of financial aid. About 75% of continuing students received need-based aid. The average freshman award was $6702. Of that total, scholarships or need-based grants

averaged $2112; loans averaged $3314; and work contracts averaged $427. About 20% of undergraduate students work part-time. The average financial indebtedness of the 1992–93 graduate was $5864. SFC is a member of CSS. The college's own financial statement and FAFSA are required. The deadline for financial aid applications is July.

International Students: There are currently 30 international students enrolled. They must take the TOEFL and achieve a minimum score of 500.

Computers: The college provides computer facilities for student use. The mainframe is an IBM. All students may access the system. It may be used 6 days a week. There are no time limits on using the system and no fees.

Graduates: In 1992–93, 95 bachelor's degrees were awarded. The most popular majors among graduates were education (24%), business (17%), and nursing (12%). In the 1992 graduating class, 5% of all students were enrolled in graduate school within 6 months of graduation; 88% of all graduates had found employment.

Admissions Contact: Scott B. Flanagan, Director of Admissions.

SAINT JOSEPH'S COLLEGE
B-2

Rensselaer, IN 47978 (219) 866–6170; (800) 447–8781 (out-of-state)

Full-time: 411 men, 404 women	**Faculty:** 53; IIB, -$
Part-time: 28 men, 199 women	**Ph.D.s:** 67%
Graduate: 4 men, 12 women	**Student/Faculty:** 15 to 1
Year: semesters, summer session	**Tuition:** $10,830
Application Deadline: open	**Room & Board:** $3900
Freshman Class: 920 applied, 777 accepted, 225 enrolled	
SAT I Verbal/Math: 432/500	**ACT:** 23 **COMPETITIVE**

St. Joseph's College, founded in 1889, is a private Catholic institution providing a 4-year core curriculum in general education with an interdisciplinary approach. There is one graduate school. In addition to regional accreditation, the college has baccalaureate program accreditation with NCATE. The library contains 165,000 volumes, 41,541 microform items, and 21,182 audiovisual forms, and subscribes to 797 periodicals. Computerized library sources and services include the card catalog, interlibrary loans, and database searching. Special learning facilities include a radio station and TV station. The 340-acre campus is in a small town 83 miles south of Chicago, Illinois, and 90 miles north of Indianapolis. Including residence halls, there are 22 buildings on campus.

Student Life: About 72% of undergraduates are from Indiana. Students come from 25 states, 5 foreign countries, and Canada. Sixty-five percent are from public schools; 35% from private. Ninety-two percent are white. Fifty-one percent are Catholic; 35% Protestant. The average age of freshmen is 19; all undergraduates, 24. Twenty percent drop out by the end of their first year; 60% remain to graduate.

Housing: A total of 950 students can be accommodated in college housing. College-sponsored living facilities include single-sex dormitories. On-campus housing is guaranteed for all 4 years. Seventy-one percent of students live on campus; of those, 65% remain on campus on weekends. Alcohol is not permitted. All students may keep cars on campus.

Activities: There are no fraternities or sororities on campus. There are 43 groups on campus, including art, band, cheerleading, choir, chorus, computers, drama, ethnic, honors, jazz band, literary magazine, marching band, musical theater, newspaper, orchestra, pep band, photography, political, professional, radio and TV, religious, social, social service, student government, and yearbook. Popular campus events include the Little 500 Go-Kart Race, Homecoming, and Parents Weekend.

Sports: There are 8 intercollegiate and 10 intramural sports each for men and women. Athletic and recreation facilities include a field house, a 2500-seat gymnasium, and a recreation center.

Disabled Students: Thirty percent of the campus is accessible to disabled students. The following facilities are available: wheelchair ramps, elevators, special parking, specially equipped rest rooms, special class scheduling, lowered drinking fountains, and lowered telephones.

Services: In addition to many counseling and information services, tutoring is available in every subject. There also is a reader service for the blind, and remedial math, reading, and writing.

Campus Safety and Security: Campus safety and security measures include 24-hour foot and vehicle patrol, escort service, informal discussions, pamphlets, posters, and films. In addition, there are lighted pathways and sidewalks.

Programs of Study: The college awards the B.A., B.S., and B.B.A. degrees. Associate and master's degrees also are awarded. Bachelor's degrees are awarded in BIOLOGICAL SCIENCE (biology/biological science), BUSINESS (accounting, banking and finance, business administration and management, business economics, and marketing/retailing/merchandising), COMMUNICATIONS AND THE ARTS (communications, English, journalism, and music), COMPUTER AND PHYSICAL SCIENCE (computer programming, comput-

er science, and mathematics), EDUCATION (business, elementary, middle school, music, science, and secondary), HEALTH PROFESSIONS (nursing, predentistry, and premedicine), SOCIAL SCIENCE (economics, history, political science/government, prelaw, psychology, and religion). Business administration, computer science, psychology, and communications are the strongest academically. Business administration has the largest enrollment.

Required: Students must complete 45 hours in the general education program and 36 hours in the major. A total of 120 credit hours with a minimum GPA of 2.0 is required to graduate.

Special: Internships in business and accounting, a Washington semester, and study abroad are available. Dual majors, a 3–2 engineering degree, credit for life, military, and work experience, nondegree study, and pass/fail options are offered. The core program consists of lectures and discussions over a 4-year period. There is a freshman honors program on campus, as well as 1 national honor society. One department has an honors program.

Faculty/Classroom: Eighty percent of faculty are male; 20%, female. All members both teach undergraduates and do research. No introductory courses are taught by graduate students. The average class size is 15.

Admissions: About 84% of the 1993–94 applicants were accepted. The SAT I scores for the 1993–94 freshman class were as follows: Verbal—83% below 500, 15% between 500 and 599, and 1% between 600 and 700; Math—59% below 500, 28% between 500 and 599, 11% between 600 and 700, and 1% above 700. The ACT scores were 9% below 18, 50% between 18 and 23, 34% between 24 and 29, and 7% above 29. About 37% of the current freshmen were in the top fifth of their class; 62% were in the top two fifths. Four freshmen graduated first in their class.

Requirements: The college requires applicants to be in the upper 50% of their class. A minimum grade average of C+ is required. The SAT I or ACT is required, with recommended minimum scores of 440 verbal and 460 math on the SAT I, or 19 on the ACT. Applicants should be graduates of an accredited secondary school or have earned the GED. They should have completed 15 academic credits, 10 of which must be from the following academic fields: English, foreign language, social studies, mathematics, and natural sciences. An interview is recommended. AP credits are accepted. Important factors used in the admissions decision are advanced placement or honor courses, leadership record, evidence of special talent, recommendations by school officials, and personality, intangible qualities.

Procedure: Freshmen are admitted fall and winter. Entrance exams should be taken by January of the senior year. Application deadlines are open. The application fee is $15. Notification is sent on a rolling basis, within 2 weeks. There is a deferred admissions plan.

Transfer: A total of 29 transfer students enrolled in 1993–94. Applicants must have a minium GPA of 2.0. A minimum composite score of 900 on the SAT I or 19 on the ACT is recommended. Grades of C or better transfer for credit. A total of 30 credits out of 120 must be completed at the college.

Visiting: There are regularly scheduled orientations for prospective students, consisting of Discover Days and VIP Days. There are guides for informal visits and visitors may sit in on classes and stay overnight at the school. To arrange for a visit, contact the Admissions Office.

Financial Aid: In 1993–94, 89% of all current freshmen and 70% of continuing students received some form of financial aid. About 81% of freshmen and 74% of continuing students received need-based aid. The average freshman award was $8435. Of that total, scholarships or need-based grants averaged $5150 ($7400 maximum); loans averaged $1200 ($2625 maximum); and work contracts averaged $1200 ($1500 maximum). Thirty-five percent of undergraduate students work part-time. Average earnings from campus work for the school year are $1200. The average financial indebtedness of the 1992–93 graduate was $9400. The college is a member of CSS. The FAF, the college's own financial statement, and the FAFSA are required. The deadline for financial aid applications is March 1.

International Students: There are currently 5 international students enrolled. Applicants must take the TOEFL and achieve a minimum score of 550. The student must also take the SAT I or the ACT.

Computers: The college provides computer facilities for student use. The mainframe is a Prime. Centrally located laboratories house Zenith and Apple Macintosh microcomputers with SUN workstations, laser printers, image scanners, and a desktop publishing center. All students may access the system. It may be used from 7:30 A.M. to midnight, or by special request. There are no time limits on using the system. The fees are $10.

Graduates: In 1992–93, 186 bachelor's degrees were awarded. The most popular majors among graduates were business administration (21%), psychology (8%), and elementary education (7%). Within an average freshman class, 60% graduate in 4 years. A total of 62 companies recruited on campus in 1992–93.

Admissions Contact: Brian Kesse, Dean of Admissions.

SAINT MARY'S COLLEGE
C-1

Notre Dame, IN 46556
(219) 284-4587

Full-time: 1538 women	Faculty: 117; IIB, av$
Part-time: 3 men, 24 women	Ph.Ds: 95%
Graduate: none	Student/Faculty: 13 to 1
Year: semesters	Tuition: $12,799
Application Deadline: March 1	Room & Board: $4244
Freshman Class: 888 applied, 734 accepted, 393 enrolled	
SAT I Verbal/Math: 489/538	ACT: 25 VERY COMPETITIVE

Saint Mary's College, established in 1844, was founded and sponsored by the Congregation of the Sisters of the Holy Cross. It is a Catholic comprehensive college for women in the liberal arts tradition. In addition to regional accreditation, Saint Mary's College has baccalaureate program accreditation with NASAD, NASM, NCATE, and NLN. The library contains 192,000 volumes, 5502 microform items, and 2361 audiovisual forms, and subscribes to 790 periodicals. Computerized library sources and services include the card catalog and database searching. Special learning facilities include an art gallery. The 275-acre campus is in a suburban area 90 miles east of Chicago. Including residence halls, there are 14 buildings on campus.

Student Life: About 80% of undergraduates are from out-of-state, mostly the Midwest. Students come from 48 states and 14 foreign countries. Forty-eight percent are from public schools; 52% from private. Ninety-five percent are white. Most are Catholic. The average age of freshmen is 18; all undergraduates, 20. Two percent drop out by the end of their first year; 78% remain to graduate.

Housing: A total of 1575 students can be accommodated in college housing. College-sponsored living facilities include dormitories. On-campus housing is guaranteed for all 4 years. Eighty-nine percent of students live on campus; of those, 85% remain on campus on weekends. All students may keep cars on campus.

Activities: There are 51 groups on campus, including band, cheerleading, choir, chorus, dance, drama, ethnic, international, literary magazine, marching band, newspaper, political, professional, religious, social, social service, student government, and yearbook. Popular campus events include Fall Fest, Winter Carnival, spring celebration, and parents weekends.

Sports: There are 7 intercollegiate and 10 intramural sports. Athletic and recreation facilities include an athletic center, outdoor tennis courts, soccer field, and swimming pool.

Disabled Students: Ninety-nine percent of the campus is accessible to disabled students. The following facilities are available: wheelchair ramps, elevators, special parking, specially equipped rest rooms, and lowered drinking fountains.

Services: In addition to many counseling and information services, tutoring is available in most subjects. There also is a writing center.

Campus Safety and Security: Campus safety and security measures include 24-hour foot and vehicle patrol, self defense education, escort service, and shuttle buses. In addition, there are informal discussions, pamphlets, posters, and films, emergency telephones, and lighted pathways and sidewalks.

Programs of Study: Saint Mary's College awards the B.A., B.S., B.B.A., B.F.A., and B.Mus. degrees. Bachelor's degrees are awarded in BIOLOGICAL SCIENCE (biology/biological science), BUSINESS (business administration and management), COMMUNICATIONS AND THE ARTS (art, communications, dramatic arts, English, fine arts, French, music, and Spanish), COMPUTER AND PHYSICAL SCIENCE (chemistry and mathematics), EDUCATION (elementary), HEALTH PROFESSIONS (nursing), SOCIAL SCIENCE (economics, history, humanities, philosophy, political science/government, psychology, religion, social work, and sociology). Art, business, English, humanistic studies, and the sciences are the strongest academically. Business has the largest enrollment.

Required: Students must successfully complete 128 credits, with at least 24 in the major, and must maintain a minimum GPA of 2.0. Students must also complete distribution requirements in fine arts, history, language, literature, mathematics, philosophy, science, religion, and other selected disciplines. Advanced proficiency in composition within the student's major must be demonstrated, and a comprehensive examination in the major area is required by the end of the senior year.

Special: Cross-registration is permitted with the University of Notre Dame and a consortium of 6 northern Indiana colleges. Opportunities are provided for internships, a Washington semester, accelerated degree programs, dual and student-designed majors, a 3–2 engineering degree with the University of Notre Dame, nondegree study, pass/fail options, and study abroad in Rome, Ireland, and India. There are 4 national honor societies on campus. Two departments have honors programs.

Faculty/Classroom: Forty-four percent of faculty are male; 56%, female. All teach undergraduates and 85% also do research. The average class size in an introductory lecture is 24; in a laboratory, 14; and in a regular course offering, 20.

Admissions: About 83% of the 1993–94 applicants were accepted. The SAT I scores for the 1993–94 freshman class were as follows: Verbal—54% below 500, 39% between 500 and 599, and 6% between 600 and 700; Math—28% below 500, 45% between 500 and 599, 26% between 600 and 700, and 1% above 700. The ACT scores were 8% below 21, 23% between 21 and 23, 38% between 24 and 26, 19% between 27 and 28, and 12% above 28. About 56% of the current freshmen were in the top fifth of their class; 89% were in the top two fifths. Ten freshmen graduated first in their class.

Requirements: The SAT I or ACT is required, as are SAT II: Subject tests in writing, mathematics, and foreign language. Graduation from an accredited secondary school is required; a GED will be accepted. Applicants must have completed 16 academic credits, including 4 in English, 2 in a foreign language, 2 in history or social studies, 3 in mathematics, 1 in science, and the remainder from college preparatory electives in the above areas. An essay is required. AP and CLEP credits are accepted. Important factors used in the admissions decision are advanced placement or honor courses, evidence of special talent, leadership record, extracurricular activities record, and recommendations by school officials.

Procedure: Freshmen are admitted fall and spring. Entrance exams should be taken between March of the junior year and December of the senior year. Early decision applications should be filed by November 15; regular applications, by March 1 for fall entry and November 15 for spring entry, along with an application fee of $30. Notification of early decision is sent December 15; regular decision, on a rolling basis. There are early decision, early admissions, and deferred admissions plans. About 160 early decision candidates were accepted for the 1993–94 class.

Transfer: About 50 transfer students enrolled in 1993–94. Students must submit a transcript from high school and each previous college attended, along with an essay, a recommendation from a college advisor, and SAT I or ACT test scores if the student has fewer than 30 semester hours of transferable credit. All transfer applicants must have maintained a minimum GPA of 3.0. An interview is recommended. A total of 60 credits out of 128 must be completed at Saint Mary's College.

Visiting: There are regularly scheduled orientations for prospective students, including campus tours and visits with admissions and financial aid counselors, faculty, and athletic staff. There are guides for informal visits and visitors may sit in on classes and stay overnight at the school. To arrange for a visit, contact the Campus Visit Coordinator at (219) 284-4587.

Financial Aid: In 1993–94, 62% of all current freshmen and 55% of continuing students received some form of financial aid. About 59% of freshmen and 52% of continuing students received need-based aid. The average freshman award was $11,012. Of that total, scholarships or need-based grants averaged $5637 ($12,000 maximum); loans averaged $2526 ($4875 maximum); and work contracts averaged $1400 ($2300 maximum). Forty percent of undergraduate students work part-time. Average earnings from campus work for the school year are $1400. The average financial indebtedness of the 1992–93 graduate was $12,454. Saint Mary's College is a member of CSS. The FAF, FAFSA, and parent's and student's federal tax returns are required. The deadline for financial aid applications is March 1.

International Students: There are currently 17 international students enrolled. The school actively recruits these students. They must take the TOEFL. The student must also take the SAT I or the ACT.

Computers: The college provides computer facilities for student use. The mainframe is an HP Model 827. There are 80 access terminals to the mainframe and 100 PC-compatible and Apple Macintosh microcomputers in the computer laboratory and various sites around campus. A variety of education-related software is available for college-related work. All students may access the system 24 hours a day, 7 days a week. There are no time limits on using the system and no fees.

Graduates: In a recent year, 459 bachelor's degrees were awarded. The most popular majors among graduates were business administration (16%), communication (12%), and political science (8%). Within an average freshman class, 1% graduate in 3 years, 72% in 4 years, 76% in 5 years, and 78% in 6 years. A total of 123 companies recruited on campus in a recent year. In a recent graduating class, 22% of the women were enrolled in graduate school within 6 months of graduation; 77% of the women had found employment.

Admissions Contact: Mary Pat Nolan, Director of Admissions.

SAINT MARY-OF-THE-WOODS COLLEGE
St. Mary-of-the-Woods, IN 47876

B-4

(812) 535-5106
(800) 926-SMWC (out-of-state)

Full-time: 300 women	**Faculty:** 51; IIB, --$
Part-time: 750 women	**Ph.D.s:** 25%
Graduate: 100 women	**Student/Faculty:** 6 to 1
Year: semesters	**Tuition:** $10,300
Application Deadline: open	**Room & Board:** $4130
Freshman Class: n/av	
SAT I or ACT: required	**NONCOMPETITIVE**

Saint Mary-of-the Woods, founded in 1840, is a private, liberal arts women's college affiliated with the Roman Catholic Church. In addition to regional accreditation, the Woods has baccalaureate program accreditation with NASM. The library contains 142,000 volumes and 1676 microform items, and subscribes to 460 periodicals. Computerized library sources and services include the card catalog. Special learning facilities include a learning resource center and an art gallery. The 67-acre campus is in a rural area 5 miles northwest of Terre Haute. Including residence halls, there are 10 buildings on campus.

Student Life: About 65% of undergraduates are from Indiana. Seventy percent are from public schools. The average age of freshmen is 18; all undergraduates, 32. Ten percent drop out by the end of their first year; 65% remain to graduate.

Housing: A total of 500 students can be accommodated in college housing. In addition, housing for student mothers with young children is available. On-campus housing is guaranteed for all 4 years. Alcohol is not permitted. All students may keep cars on campus.

Activities: There are no fraternities on campus. There are many groups and organizations on campus, including band, chorale, chorus, computers, drama, ethnic, international, literary magazine, musical theater, orchestra, religious, social service, student government, and yearbook. Popular campus events include Fugua Day, Ring Day, Christmas at The Woods, Pops Concert, Fall Play, Spring Play, Spring Concert, and Fall Classic.

Sports: Athletic and recreation facilities include stables, an athletic field, a gymnasium, tennis courts, a pool, a weight room, a fitness course, and a volleyball pit.

Disabled Students: Fifty percent of the campus is accessible to disabled students. The following facilities are available: wheelchair ramps, elevators, special parking, specially equipped rest rooms, and special class scheduling.

Services: In addition to many counseling and information services, tutoring is available in most subjects.

Campus Safety and Security: Campus safety and security measures include 24-hour foot and vehicle patrol, informal discussions, pamphlets, posters, films, and lighted pathways and sidewalks.

Programs of Study: The Woods awards the B.A. and B.S. degrees. Associate and master's degrees are also awarded. Bachelor's degrees are awarded in BIOLOGICAL SCIENCE (biology/biological science), BUSINESS (accounting, business administration and management, and marketing/retailing/merchandising), COMMUNICATIONS AND THE ARTS (English, fine arts, journalism, languages, and music), COMPUTER AND PHYSICAL SCIENCE (computer science, information sciences and systems, and mathematics), EDUCATION (art, early childhood, elementary, foreign languages, middle school, music, science, secondary, and special), HEALTH PROFESSIONS (predentistry and premedicine), SOCIAL SCIENCE (philosophy, political science/government, prelaw, psychology, social science, and social work). Paralegal, music therapy, and equine studies are the strongest academically. Education and business have the largest enrollments.

Required: All students must complete a 61-credit-hour general studies curriculum, which includes a freshman course in lifelong learning; courses in writing, speech, physical education, computer science, and mathematics; and selected courses in religion, fine arts, philosophy, science, and social sciences. A computer course is also required. Completion of 124 credit hours with a minimum GPA of 2.0 is necessary for graduation.

Special: The college offers cross-registration with Indiana State University, student-designed majors, study abroad in Spain or Taiwan, a B.A.-B.S. degree, internships, pass/fail options, on-campus work-study, and nondegree study. The Women's External Degree program, offering 19 majors, provides educational opportunities to women over 22 years of age who study mostly at home.

Admissions: Three freshmen graduated first in their class.

Requirements: The SAT I or ACT is required. Candidates should be graduates of an accredited secondary school. The GED is accepted. It is preferred that students have 4 years of English and 2 years each of a foreign language, history, science, and social science. An essay is required and a portfolio, audition, and interview are recommended for creative arts scholarships. AP and CLEP credits are accepted. Important factors used in the admissions decision are recommendations by school officials, leadership record, evidence of special

talent, advanced placement or honor courses, and recommendations by alumni.

Procedure: Freshmen are admitted fall and winter. Entrance exams should be taken in December or January of the senior year. Application deadlines are open. Application fee is $30. The college accepts all applicants. Notification is sent on a rolling basis. There are early decision, early admissions, and deferred admissions plans. About 10 early decision candidates were accepted for the 1993–94 class.

Transfer: Transfer students should be in good academic standing at their most recent institution.

Visiting: There are regularly scheduled orientations for prospective students. There are guides for informal visits and visitors may sit in on classes and stay overnight at the school. To arrange for a visit, contact the Office of Admissions at (812) 535–5106 or (800) 926-SMWC.

Financial Aid: In a recent year, 84% of continuing students received some form of financial aid. Average earnings from campus work for the school year are $500. The FAF, FFS or SFS is required.

International Students: They must take the TOEFL and achieve a minimum score of 500. The SAT I or the ACT is recommended.

Computers: The college provides computer facilities for student use. The mainframe is an IBM. The mainframe computer is accessible only to students enrolled in the computer science sequence; any student may use the microcomputers. There are no time limits on using the system and no fees.

Admissions Contact: Office of Admissions.

SAINT MEINRAD COLLEGE

C–5

St. Meinrad, IN 47577

(812) 357–6575; (800) 752–9384

Full-time: 134 men	Faculty: 28
Part-time: none	Ph.D.s: 90%
Graduate: none	Student/Faculty: 5 to 1
Year: semesters, with January interterm	Tuition: $6076
	Room & Board: $4226

Application Deadline: July 1

Freshman Class: 67 applied, 45 accepted, 37 enrolled

SAT I or ACT: required

COMPETITIVE

Saint Meinrad College, founded in 1857, is a private, liberal arts men's college affiliated with the Roman Catholic Church. The library contains 140,000 volumes, 5000 microform items, and 3400 audiovisual forms, and subscribes to 565 periodicals. Computerized library sources and services include the card catalog, interlibrary loans, and database searching. Special learning facilities include a learning resource center, radio station, and TV station. The 350-acre campus is in a rural area 50 miles east of Evansville. Including residence halls, there are 15 buildings on campus.

Student Life: About 75% of undergraduates are from out-of-state, mostly the Midwest. Students come from 24 states, 3 foreign countries, and Canada. Seventy percent are from public schools; 30% from private. Seventy-one percent are white; 20% Hispanic. Most are Catholic. The average age of freshmen is 18; all undergraduates, 21. Thirty percent drop out by the end of their first year.

Housing: A total of 167 students can be accommodated in college housing. College-sponsored living facilities include dormitories. On-campus housing is guaranteed for all 4 years. All students live on campus; of those, 70% remain on campus on weekends. All students may keep cars on campus.

Activities: There are many groups and organizations on campus, including choir, chorus, drama, ethnic, film, honors, literary magazine, newspaper, photography, radio and TV, religious, social, social service, and student government. Popular campus events include Family Weekend, Sounds of Spring, and Heritage Days.

Sports: Athletic and recreation facilities include swimming lakes, a soccer/baseball field, basketball gymnasiums, a weight and nautilus room, handball/racquetball courts, 8 tennis courts, and access to a private golf course.

Disabled Students: Fifty percent of the campus is accessible to disabled students. The following facilities are available: wheelchair ramps, elevators, and specially equipped rest rooms.

Services: In addition to many counseling and information services, tutoring is available in most subjects. There is also remedial math, reading, and writing.

Campus Safety and Security: Campus safety and security measures include lighted pathways and sidewalks and an evening security patrol.

Programs of Study: Saint Meinrad awards the B.A. and B.S. degrees. Bachelor's degrees are awarded in COMMUNICATIONS AND THE ARTS (English and Spanish), COMPUTER AND PHYSICAL SCIENCE (natural sciences), SOCIAL SCIENCE (history, liberal arts/general studies, philosophy, and psychology). Philosophy and history are the strongest academically. English has the largest enrollment.

Required: To graduate, students must complete 128 credit hours, including 28 in the major and 18 in a minor, with a minimum GPA of 2.0. A thesis and a comprehensive exam are required.

Special: A B.A.-B.S. degree in natural science is possible. All departments have honors programs.

Faculty/Classroom: Eighty-five percent of faculty are male; 15%, female. All teach undergraduates. The average class size in an introductory lecture is 25; in a laboratory, 10; and in a regular course offering, 7.

Admissions: About 67% of the 1993–94 applicants were accepted. The ACT scores for the 1993–94 freshman class were as follows: 46% below 21, 36% between 21 and 23, 4% between 24 and 26, 11% between 27 and 28, and 4% above 28. There was 1 National Merit semifinalist.

Requirements: The SAT I or ACT is required. Graduation from an accredited secondary school or the GED is required. Two recommendations, an essay, and an interview are recommended. AP and CLEP credits are accepted. Important factors used in the admissions decision are leadership record, extracurricular activities record, personality, intangible qualities, advanced placement or honor courses, and evidence of special talent.

Procedure: Freshmen are admitted in the fall and spring. Entrance exams should be taken in the fall of the senior year. Applications should be filed by July 1 for fall entry and December 1 for spring entry, along with an application fee of $10. Notification is sent on a rolling basis. There is a deferred admissions plan.

Transfer: About 15 transfer students enrolled in 1993–94. Transfer students need a minimum GPA of 2.0 and evidence of involvement in extracurricular activities. At least 30 credits out of 128 must be completed at Saint Meinrad.

Visiting: There are regularly scheduled orientations for prospective students, which include attending classes, meeting with faculty, participating in service projects and religious activities, and a financial aid presentation. There are guides for informal visits, and visitors may sit in on classes and stay overnight at the school. To arrange for a visit, contact the Enrollment Office at (800) 752–9384.

Financial Aid: In 1993–94, 97% of all students received some form of financial aid. About 85% of freshmen and 80% of continuing students received need-based aid. The average freshman award was $7500. Of that total, scholarships or need-based grants averaged $4100 ($7500 maximum); loans averaged $2500 ($2900 maximum); and work contracts averaged $900. Sixty percent of undergraduate students work part-time. Average earnings from campus work for the school year are $900. The average financial indebtedness of the 1992–93 graduate was $10,500. Saint Meinrad is a member of CSS. The FAF, FFS, or SFS is required. The deadline for financial aid applications is March 1 for Indiana residents.

International Students: International applicants must take the TOEFL and the SAT I or the ACT.

Computers: The college provides computer facilities for student use. The mainframe is an IBM. There are 12 networked IBMs and Macintoshes in the computer center and 3 networked computers in the library. All students may access the system. There are no time limits on using the system and no fees.

Graduates: In 1992–93, 21 bachelor's degrees were awarded. The most popular majors among graduates were English (30%), Spanish (25%), and natural science (15%). Within an average freshman class, 5% graduate in 3 years, 90% in 4 years, and 5% in 5 years. Some 6 companies recruited on campus in 1992–93. In the 1992 graduating class, 70% of graduates were enrolled in graduate school within 6 months of graduation; 30% had found employment.

Admissions Contact: Rev. Jonathan Fassero, Assistant Director of Enrollment.

TAYLOR UNIVERSITY

D–3

Upland, IN 46989–1001

(317) 998–5208

(800) 882–3456 (out-of-state)

Full-time: 845 men, 918 women	Faculty: 99; IIB, –$
Part-time: 34 men, 52 women	Ph.D.s: 65%
Graduate: none	Student/Faculty: 18 to 1
Year: 4–1–4, summer session	Tuition: $10,650
Application Deadline: open	Room & Board: $3800
Freshman Class: 1769 applied, 1092 accepted, 437 enrolled	
SAT I Verbal/Math: 546/556	ACT: 25 **VERY COMPETITIVE**

Taylor University, founded in 1846, is a Christian interdenominational liberal arts institution. In addition to regional accreditation, Taylor has baccalaureate program accreditation with CSWE, NASM, and NCATE. The library contains 160,000 volumes, 18,062 microform items, and 5076 audiovisual forms, and subscribes to 750 periodicals. Computerized library sources and services include the card catalog, interlibrary loans, and database searching. Special learning facilities include a learning resource center, art gallery, radio station, TV station, and a 65-acre arboretum. The 250-acre campus is in a rural area 65 miles north of Indianapolis. Including residence halls, there are 26 buildings on campus.

Student Life: About 67% of undergraduates are from out-of-state, mostly the Midwest. Students come from 49 states, 12 foreign countries, and Canada. About 79% are from public schools; 21% from private. Almost 93% are white. Most are Protestant. The average age of freshmen is 18; all undergraduates, 21. About 3% drop out by the end of their first year; 75% remain to graduate.

Housing: A total of 1509 students can be accommodated in college housing. College-sponsored living facilities include single-sex dormitories, off-campus apartments, and married-student housing. On-campus housing is guaranteed for all 4 years. Some 80% of students live on campus; of those, 90% remain on campus on weekends. Alcohol is not permitted. All students may keep cars on campus.

Activities: There are no fraternities or sororities. There are many groups and organizations on campus, including art, band, cheerleading, choir, chorale, chorus, computers, drama, ethnic, film, honors, international, jazz band, literary magazine, musical theater, newspaper, opera, orchestra, pep band, photography, political, professional, radio and TV, religious, social, social service, student government, symphony, and yearbook. Popular campus events include Taylorthon, World Opportunities Week, and Youth Conference.

Sports: There are 8 intercollegiate sports for men and 6 for women, and 14 intramural sports for men and 14 for women. Athletic and recreation facilities include a gymnasium, a field house, a wellness center, tennis courts, racquetball courts, and a track.

Disabled Students: Some 80% of the campus is accessible to disabled students. The following facilities are available: wheelchair ramps, elevators, special parking, specially equipped rest rooms, lowered drinking fountains, and lowered telephones.

Services: In addition to many counseling and information services, tutoring is available in most subjects. There are also a reader service for the blind, and remedial math, reading, and writing programs.

Campus Safety and Security: Campus safety and security measures include 24-hour foot and vehicle patrol, escort service, and lighted pathways and sidewalks.

Programs of Study: Taylor awards the B.A., B.S., and B.Mus. degrees. Associate degrees also are awarded. Bachelor's degrees are awarded in BIOLOGICAL SCIENCE (biology/biological science), BUSINESS (accounting, business administration and management, and recreation and leisure services), COMMUNICATIONS AND THE ARTS (communications, English, French, music, public relations, and Spanish), COMPUTER AND PHYSICAL SCIENCE (chemistry, computer science, mathematics, natural sciences, and physics), EDUCATION (art, elementary, music, physical, and secondary), ENGINEERING AND ENVIRONMENTAL DESIGN (computer graphics, environmental science, and preengineering), HEALTH PROFESSIONS (medical laboratory technology, predentistry, and premedicine), SOCIAL SCIENCE (biblical studies, criminal justice, economics, history, international studies, philosophy, political science/government, prelaw, psychology, religion, religious education, social work, and sociology). Computer science, premedicine, and environmental science are the strongest programs academically. Business has the largest enrollment.

Required: Students must complete 128 credits and maintain a minimum GPA of 2.0 overall and 2.3 in the major. In addition to the requirements of the student's major, each student must complete 2 classes each in computer science and fine arts, and classes in public speaking, Bible literature, fitness for life, a freshman seminar, and senior capstone.

Special: Opportunities are provided for internships, cooperative programs, a Washington semester, study abroad, work-study programs, dual majors, student-designed majors, B.A.-B.S. degrees, and a 3-2 engineering degree with Washington University, St. Louis. There is a freshman honors program on campus.

Faculty/Classroom: Some 75% of faculty are male; 25%, female. All teach undergraduates. The average class size in an introductory lecture is 25; in a laboratory, 15; and in a regular course offering, 25.

Admissions: About 62% of the 1993–94 applicants were accepted. The SAT scores for the 1993–94 freshman class were as follows: Verbal—27% below 500, 38% between 500 and 599, 31% between 600 and 700, and 5% above 700. Math—28% below 500, 37% between 500 and 599, 29% between 600 and 700, and 6% above 700. About 67% of the current freshmen were in the top fifth of their class; 88% were in the top two fifths. There were 10 National Merit finalists. About 37 freshmen graduated first in their class.

Requirements: Taylor requires applicants to be in the upper 40% of their class. A minimum GPA of 2.8 is required. The SAT I or the ACT is required, with composite scores of 1000 on the SAT I and 24 on the ACT recommended. Graduation from an accredited secondary school is required; a GED will be accepted. It is recommended that applicants complete the following college-preparatory courses: 4 years of English, 3 each of mathematics and science, and 2 each of social studies and a foreign language. An interview is recommended for all students, and an audition is required for music majors. AP and CLEP credits are accepted. Important factors used in the admissions decision are recommendations by school officials, extracurricular activities record, advanced placement or honor courses, leadership record, and evidence of special talent.

Procedure: Freshmen are admitted in the fall and spring. Entrance exams should be taken at least 15 days before the beginning of the term. Application deadlines are open. The application fee is $20. Notification is sent on a rolling basis. There are early admissions and deferred admissions plans. A waiting list is an active part of the admissions procedure, with about 25% of applicants on the list.

Transfer: About 49 transfer students enrolled in 1993–94. To be eligible for transfer, students must have maintained a minimum GPA of 2.5 and have completed at least 12 credit hours at the previous college. An interview is recommended. A total of 48 credit hours out of 128 must be completed at Taylor, including half of the major credits.

Visiting: There are regularly scheduled orientations for prospective students, including a campus tour, lunch, class meetings, faculty meetings, a financial aid session, and an admissions interview. There are guides for informal visits and visitors may sit in on classes and stay overnight at the school. To arrange for a visit, contact Stephen R. Mortland, Campus Visit Coordinator, at (317) 998–5208 or (800) 882–3456 (out-of-state).

Financial Aid: In 1993–94, 92% of all current freshmen and 78% of continuing students received some form of financial aid. About 65% of all students received need-based aid. The average freshman award was $8500. Of that total, scholarships or need-based grants averaged $4850; loans averaged $2650 ($4125 maximum); and work contracts averaged $1000 ($1500 maximum). Some 42% of undergraduate students work part-time. Average earnings from campus work for the school year are $1030. The average financial indebtedness of the 1992–93 graduate was $9326. Taylor is a member of CSS. The college's own financial statement and FAFSA are required. The deadline for financial aid applications is March 1.

International Students: There are currently 44 international students enrolled. The school actively recruits these students. They must take the TOEFL and achieve a minimum score of 550. The student must also take the SAT I or the ACT. The school will accept the TOEFL in lieu of the SAT I.

Computers: The college provides computer facilities for student use. The mainframe is a DEC PDP/11/70 and a Microvax 3600. There are also microcomputers at sites throughout the campus in a ratio of 1 computer for each 13 students. All students may access the system. There are no time limits on using the system and no fees.

Graduates: In a recent year, 309 bachelor's degrees were awarded. The most popular majors among graduates were business (20%), elementary education (18%), and psychology (10%). Some 25 companies recruited on campus in a recent year.

Admissions Contact: Stephen Mortland, Campus Visit Coordinator.

TRI-STATE UNIVERSITY   D-1

Angola, IN 46703   (219) 665–4139; (800) 347–4TSU (in-state)

Full-time: 695 men, 282 women	Faculty: 65; IIB, –$
Part-time: 55 men, 42 women	Ph.D.s: 65%
Graduate: none	Student/Faculty: 15 to 1
Year: quarters, summer session	Tuition: $9588–10,288
Application Deadline: open	Room & Board: $4200
Freshman Class: 1374 applied, 1204 accepted, 346 enrolled	
SAT I Verbal/Math: 410/510	ACT: 22 LESS COMPETITIVE

Tri-State University, founded in 1884, is a private, independent, coeducational university with schools of engineering, business, and arts and sciences. There are 3 undergraduate schools. In addition to regional accreditation, Tri-State has baccalaureate program accreditation with ABET. The library contains 149,000 volumes, 7000 microform items, and 943 audiovisual forms, and subscribes to 570 periodicals. Computerized library sources and services include interlibrary loans and database searching. Special learning facilities include a radio station. The 200-acre campus is in a rural area 30 miles north of Ft. Wayne. Including residence halls, there are 25 buildings on campus.

Student Life: About 52% of undergraduates are from Indiana. Students come from 23 states and 26 foreign countries. Sixty-seven percent are from public schools. Eighty-five percent are white; 11% foreign nationals. The average age of freshmen is 18; all undergraduates, 20. Eleven percent drop out by the end of their first year; 51% remain to graduate.

Housing: A total of 632 students can be accommodated in college housing. College-sponsored living facilities include single-sex and coed dormitories, married-student housing, fraternity houses, and sorority houses. On-campus housing is guaranteed for all 4 years. Fifty-seven percent of students commute. Alcohol is not permitted. All students may keep cars on campus.

Activities: About 22% of men belong to 9 national fraternities; about 13% of women belong to 5 local sororities and 1 national sorority. There are 20 groups on campus, including cheerleading, computers, drama, ethnic, honors, international, literary magazine, newspaper,

pep band, political, professional, radio and TV, religious, social service, student government, and yearbook.

Sports: There are 9 intercollegiate sports for men and 9 for women, and 6 intramural sports for men and 5 for women. Athletic and recreation facilities include a gymnasium with a pool, indoor and outdoor tracks, basketball and racquetball courts, and an 18-hole golf course.

Disabled Students: The following facilities are available: wheelchair ramps, elevators, special parking, specially equipped rest rooms, special class scheduling, and lowered telephones.

Services: In addition to many counseling and information services, tutoring is available in some subjects, including mathematics, business, engineering, accounting, and English. In addition, there is remedial math.

Campus Safety and Security: Campus safety and security measures include 24-hour foot and vehicle patrol and pamphlets, posters, and films.

Programs of Study: Tri-State awards the B.A. and B.S. degrees. Associate degrees also are awarded. Bachelor's degrees are awarded in BIOLOGICAL SCIENCE (biology/biological science), BUSINESS (accounting, business administration and management, management science, marketing/retailing/merchandising, and office supervision and management), COMMUNICATIONS AND THE ARTS (communications and English), COMPUTER AND PHYSICAL SCIENCE (chemistry, computer science, information sciences and systems, mathematics, and physical sciences), EDUCATION (business, elementary, mathematics, physical, science, secondary, and social science), ENGINEERING AND ENVIRONMENTAL DESIGN (aeronautical engineering, chemical engineering, civil engineering, electrical/electronics engineering, engineering management, environmental science, industrial administration/management, and mechanical engineering), HEALTH PROFESSIONS (premedicine), SOCIAL SCIENCE (criminal justice, economics, history, and social science). Engineering and elementary education have the largest enrollments.

Required: Candidates for graduation must complete 186 to 206 quarter hours with 60 in the major and a minimum overall GPA of 2.0. Required courses vary by degree sought. All students must complete 6 credits of physical education.

Special: Cooperative education programs are available in engineering, business, and computer science, and opportunities exist for internships, work-study programs with the university, and student-designed majors. Nondegree study is possible. There is a freshman honors program on campus, as well as 11 national honor societies. One department has an honors program.

Faculty/Classroom: Eighty-seven percent of faculty are male; 13%, female. All teach undergraduates and 10% do research. The average class size in an introductory lecture is 30; in a laboratory, 18; and in a regular course offering, 18.

Admissions: About 88% of the 1993–94 applicants were accepted. The SAT scores for the 1993–94 freshman class were as follows: Verbal—84% below 500, 13% between 500 and 599, and 3% between 600 and 700; Math—42% below 500, 36% between 500 and 599, 19% between 600 and 700, and 3% above 700. The ACT scores were 43% below 21, 27% between 21 and 23, 20% between 24 and 26, 8% between 27 and 28, and 2% above 28. About 29% of the current freshmen were in the top fifth of their class; 60% were in the top two fifths. Two freshmen graduated first in their class.

Requirements: A minimum GPA of 2.0 is required. The SAT I or ACT is required. Candidates for admission should be graduates of accredited secondary schools. The GED is also accepted. Most students should have 4 years of English and 2 years each of science, social studies, and mathematics. AP and CLEP credits are accepted. Important factors used in the admissions decision are evidence of special talent, personality, intangible qualities, leadership record, recommendations by school officials, and advanced placement or honor courses.

Procedure: Freshmen are admitted to all sessions. Entrance exams should be taken in the junior or senior year. Application deadlines are open; the fee is $20. Notification is sent on a rolling basis. There are early admissions and deferred admissions plans.

Transfer: In 1993–94, 56 transfer students enrolled. In addition to meeting the university's requirements for freshmen, applicants must have satisfactory records from previous institutions. A total of 45 quarter credits out of 186 to 206 must be completed at Tri-State.

Visiting: There are regularly scheduled orientations for prospective students, including breakfast, meetings with college faculty and administrators, and a campus tour. There are guides for informal visits and visitors may sit in on classes. To arrange for a visit, contact the Office of Admission at (219) 665–4139 or (800) 347–4TSU (in-state).

Financial Aid: In a recent year, 73% of all current freshmen and 62% of continuing students received some form of financial aid. About 54% of freshmen and 51% of continuing students received need-based aid. The average freshman award was $5318. Of that total, scholarships or need-based grants averaged $2258 ($8000 maximum); loans averaged $1860 ($2400 maximum); and work contracts averaged $1200 ($3000 maximum). Eighteen percent of undergraduate students work part-time. Average earnings from campus work for the school year are $750. The FAF, FFS, and FAFSA are required. The deadline for financial aid applications is March 1.

International Students: There are currently 118 international students enrolled. The school actively recruits these students. Applicants not transferring credits in mathematics or English must be tested in those subjects.

Computers: The university provides computer facilities for student use. The mainframe is a DEC VAX 6310. Some 100 terminals or microcomputers are situated in 6 laboratories across campus. All students may access the system. There are no time limits on using the system and no fees.

Graduates: In 1992–93, 222 bachelor's degrees were awarded. The most popular majors among graduates were mechanical engineering (28%), electrical engineering (11%), and civil engineering (7%). Within an average freshman class, 32% graduate in 4 years, 51% in 5 years, and 9% in 6 years. Some 38 companies recruited on campus in 1992–93. In the 1992 graduating class, 10% of the students enrolled in graduate school within 6 months of graduation; 85% had found employment.

Admissions Contact: Kim R. Bryan, Director of Admission.

UNIVERSITY OF EVANSVILLE
Evansville, IN 47702–0329

A-5
(812) 479–2468
(800) 423–8633 (out-of-state)

Full-time: 1130 men, 1515 women	**Faculty:** 172; IIA, -$
Part-time: 112 men, 141 women	**Ph.D.s:** 81%
Graduate: 21 men, 90 women	**Student/Faculty:** 15 to 1
Year: semesters, summer session	**Tuition:** $11,130
Application Deadline: February 15	**Room & Board:** $4170
Freshman Class: 2096 applied, 1626 accepted, 694 enrolled	
SAT I Verbal/Math: 498/538	**ACT:** 25 **VERY COMPETITIVE**

The University of Evansville, founded in 1854, is a private, coeducational institution affiliated with the United Methodist Church. The university offers undergraduate degree programs in arts and sciences, business administration, education, engineering and computing sciences, fine arts, and nursing and health sciences. There are 6 undergraduate schools and one graduate school. In addition to regional accreditation, UE has baccalaureate program accreditation with ABET, APTA, NASM, NCATE, and NLN. The library contains 233,412 volumes, 291,407 microform items, and 4030 audiovisual forms, and subscribes to 1162 periodicals. Computerized library sources and services include interlibrary loans and database searching. Special learning facilities include a learning resource center and radio station. The 75-acre campus is in an urban area 120 miles west of Louisville, Kentucky. Including residence halls, there are 38 buildings on campus.

Student Life: About 56% of undergraduates are from Indiana. Students come from 48 states, 40 foreign countries, and Canada. Ninety-four percent are from public schools; 6% from private. Eighty-eight percent are white. Fifty-six percent are Protestant; 21% Catholic; 22% claim no religious affiliation. The average age of freshmen is 19; all undergraduates, 20. Seventeen percent drop out by the end of their first year; 60% remain to graduate.

Housing: A total of 1600 students can be accommodated in college housing. College-sponsored living facilities include single-sex and coed dormitories, on-campus apartments, off-campus apartments, and fraternity houses. In addition there are special interest houses, including an international house. On-campus housing is guaranteed for all 4 years. Sixty percent of students live on campus; of those, 80% remain on campus on weekends. Alcohol is not permitted. All students may keep cars on campus.

Activities: About 21% of men belong to 6 national fraternities; about 20% of women belong to 4 national sororities. There are 101 groups on campus, including art, band, cheerleading, choir, chorale, chorus, computers, drama, drill team, ethnic, film, honors, international, jazz band, literary magazine, marching band, musical theater, newspaper, orchestra, pep band, photography, political, professional, radio and TV, religious, social, social service, student government, and yearbook. Popular campus events include Homecoming, Musical Madness, Greek Weekend, Bike Race, Winter Whispers Dance, International Bazaar, intramurals, and Christmas Vespers.

Sports: There are 8 intercollegiate sports for men and 7 for women, and 15 intramural sports for men and 14 for women. Athletic and recreation facilities include an athletic center, a 2000-seat stadium, a 3000-seat playing field, a baseball diamond, and practice facilities.

Disabled Students: Fifty percent of the campus is accessible to disabled students. The following facilities are available: wheelchair ramps, elevators, special parking, and specially equipped rest rooms.

Services: In addition to many counseling and information services, tutoring is available in most subjects. In addition, there is a reader service for the blind and remedial writing.

Campus Safety and Security: Campus safety and security measures include 24-hour foot and vehicle patrol, escort service, informal discussions, and pamphlets, posters, and films. In addition, there are emergency telephones and lighted pathways and sidewalks.

Programs of Study: UE awards the B.A., B.S., B.F.A., B.L.S., B.M., and B.M.E. degrees. Associate and master's degrees also are awarded. Bachelor's degrees are awarded in BIOLOGICAL SCIENCE (biology/biological science), BUSINESS (accounting, banking and finance, business administration and management, international business management, management science, and marketing/retailing/merchandising), COMMUNICATIONS AND THE ARTS (advertising, art, art history and appreciation, communications, creative writing, dramatic arts, English, fine arts, French, German, graphic design, journalism, literature, music, music business management, music performance, public relations, Spanish, studio art, telecommunications, theater, theater design, and theater management), COMPUTER AND PHYSICAL SCIENCE (chemistry, computer programming, computer science, mathematics, and physics), EDUCATION (art, business, elementary, English, mathematics, middle school, music, physical, science, secondary, social studies, and special), ENGINEERING AND ENVIRONMENTAL DESIGN (civil engineering, commercial art, computer engineering, electrical/electronics engineering, engineering management, environmental science, land use management and reclamation, and mechanical engineering), HEALTH PROFESSIONS (medical laboratory technology, music therapy, nursing, physical therapy, and premedicine), SOCIAL SCIENCE (archeology, economics, history, international studies, liberal arts/general studies, paralegal studies, philosophy, physical fitness/movement, political science/government, prelaw, psychobiology, psychology, religion, sociology, and theological studies). Business, engineering, and education have the largest enrollments.

Required: To graduate, students must complete at least 124 semester hours with a minimum 2.0 GPA, generally with 36 to 40 hours in the major. All students must take a core of 9 hours of world cultures, 7 of natural sciences, 6 each of humanities/fine arts, foreign language, and social sciences, and 3 each of mathematics and senior seminar. Two years of foreign language are required for the B.A. A demonstration of writing proficiency and completion of the fitness/wellness course are required for graduation.

Special: Students may study abroad in the United Kingdom and Germany. UE also offers cooperative programs in engineering with various industries, internships in such fields as communications and business, credit for life experience through the Center for Continuing Education, student-designed majors, and pass/fail options in elective courses. There is a freshman honors program on campus, as well as 18 national honor societies. Twenty departments have honors programs.

Faculty/Classroom: Seventy-two percent of faculty are male; 28%, female. All teach undergraduates. The average class size in an introductory lecture is 30.

Admissions: About 78% of the 1993–94 applicants were accepted. The SAT scores for the 1993–94 freshman class were as follows: Verbal—48% below 500, 37% between 500 and 599, 14% between 600 and 700, and 1% above 700; Math—29% below 500, 44% between 500 and 599, 24% between 600 and 700, and 3% above 700. The ACT scores were 13% below 21, 25% between 21 and 23, 28% between 24 and 26, 18% between 27 and 28, and 16% above 28. About 58% of the current freshmen were in the top fifth of their class; 86% were in the top two fifths. There were 6 National Merit finalists. Thirty freshmen graduated first in their class.

Requirements: UE requires applicants to be in the upper 50% of their class. A minimum GPA of 2.0 is required. Students must submit a minimum SAT I composite score of 800 (400 each on the verbal and math) or ACT composite score of 20. Applicants must be graduates of accredited secondary schools or have earned a GED. The university recommends completion of 4 credits each of English, mathematics, and science, 2 each of foreign language, history, and social studies, and 1 each of art and music. A personal essay is required and an interview is recommended for all applicants. Art majors must also present a portfolio, and music and theater majors must audition. AP and CLEP credits are accepted. Important factors used in the admissions decision are recommendations by school officials, leadership record, evidence of special talent, advanced placement or honor courses, and recommendations by alumni.

Procedure: Freshmen are admitted fall and spring. Entrance exams should be taken by December of the senior year. Early decision applications should be filed by December 1; regular applications, by February 15 for fall entry, along with an application fee of $30. Notification of early decision is sent December 15; regular decision, on a rolling basis. There is also a deferred admission plan.

Transfer: About 180 transfer students enrolled in 1993–94. Transfer applicants must have a GPA of 2.0 in all previous college work. A total of 63 credits out of 124 must be completed at UE.

Visiting: There are regularly scheduled orientations for prospective students. There are guides for informal visits and visitors may sit in on classes and stay overnight at the school. To arrange for a visit, contact the Admissions Office at (800) 992–5877 (in-state) or (800) 423–8633(out-of-state).

Financial Aid: In 1993–94, 96% of all current freshmen and 90% of continuing students received some form of financial aid. About 73% of freshmen and 72% of continuing students received need-based aid. The average freshman award was $8460. Of that total, scholarships or need-based grants averaged $6642 ($11,960 maximum); loans averaged $2916 ($8500 maximum); and work contracts averaged $1000 ($1500 maximum). Twenty-five percent of undergraduate students work part-time. Average earnings from campus work for the school year are $1140. The average financial indebtedness of the 1992–93 graduate was $10,809. UE is a member of CSS. The FAF and FAFSA are required. The deadline for financial aid applications is March 1.

International Students: There are currently 177 international students enrolled. The school actively recruits these students. They must take the TOEFL and achieve a minimum score of 500.

Computers: The college provides computer facilities for student use. There are 3 computer laboratories in a LAN with terminals connected to the mainframe. Computers are networked using Novell servers. All students may access the system. It may be used 7 days per week, usually until 11 P.M. There are no time limits on using the system and no fees. It is recommended that students in some courses have personal computers.

Graduates: In 1992–93, 469 bachelor's degrees were awarded. The most popular majors among graduates were business (19%), engineering (13%), and communications (8%). Within an average freshman class, 60% graduate in 4 years and 64% in 5 years. Some 40 companies recruited on campus in 1992–93. In the 1992 graduating class, 20% of all graduates were enrolled in graduate school within 6 months of graduation; 70% had found employment.

Admissions Contact: Director of Admissions.

UNIVERSITY OF INDIANAPOLIS
Indianapolis, IN 46227–3697

C-3

(317) 788-3216
(800) 232-8634 (in-state)

Full-time: 548 men, 870 women	Faculty: 111; IIA, --$
Part-time: 362 men, 1280 women	Ph.D.s: 53%
Graduate: 289 men, 418 women	Student/Faculty: 13 to 1
Year: 4-4-1, summer session	Tuition: $10,590
Application Deadline: open	Room & Board: $3920
Freshman Class: 1940 applied, 1644 accepted, 539 enrolled	
SAT I: Verbal/Math 432/487	ACT: 21 COMPETITIVE

The University of Indianapolis, established in 1902, is a private liberal arts school affiliated with the United Methodist Church. It provides undergraduate and graduate studies with an emphasis on education, business, nursing, and arts and sciences. There are 4 undergraduate and 3 graduate schools. In addition to regional accreditation, U of I has baccalaureate program accreditation with APTA, NASM, NCATE, and NLN. The library contains 165,000 volumes and 5500 microform items, and subscribes to 1300 periodicals. Computerized library sources and services include the card catalog, interlibrary loans, and database searching. Special learning facilities include a learning resource center, art gallery, planetarium, radio station, TV station, and an archaelogy laboratory. The 60-acre campus is in a suburban area on the south side of Indianapolis. Including residence halls, there are 11 buildings on campus.

Student Life: About 89% of undergraduates are from Indiana. Students come from 26 states, 40 foreign countries, and Canada. Eighty-seven percent are white. Sixty percent are Protestant; 20% Catholic; 10% claim no religious affiliation. The average age of freshmen is 18; all undergraduates, 25. Thirty-five percent drop out by the end of their first year; 50% remain to graduate.

Housing: A total of 800 students can be accommodated in college housing. College-sponsored living facilities include single-sex and coed dormitories, on-campus apartments, and married-student housing. On-campus housing is available on a first-come, first-served basis. Fifty-five percent of students live on campus. Alcohol is not permitted. All students may keep cars on campus.

Activities: There are no fraternities or sororities on campus. There are 25 groups on campus, including art, cheerleading, chess, choir, chorale, chorus, computers, drama, ethnic, honors, international, jazz band, literary magazine, musical theater, newspaper, orchestra, pep band, professional, radio and TV, religious, social, social service, student government, and yearbook. Popular campus events include Brown County Day, Cyclerama, and Homecoming Week.

Sports: There are 11 intercollegiate sports for men and 9 for women, and 6 intramural sports for men and 6 for women. Athletic and recreation facilities include a health and fitness center with a 3500-seat gymnasium, an Olympic-size swimming pool, racquetball courts, a weight room, and a dance studio.

Disabled Students: Seventy-five percent of the campus is accessible to disabled students. The following facilities are available: wheelchair ramps, elevators, special parking, specially equipped rest rooms, special class scheduling, lowered drinking fountains, and lowered telephones.

Services: In addition to many counseling and information services, tutoring is available in most subjects. In addition, there is also remedial math and writing.

Campus Safety and Security: Campus safety and security measures include 24-hour foot and vehicle patrol, self defense education, escort service, and emergency telephones. In addition, there are lighted pathways and sidewalks.

Programs of Study: U of I awards the B.A. and B.S. degrees. Associate and master's degrees also are awarded. Bachelor's degrees are awarded in BIOLOGICAL SCIENCE (biology/biological science), BUSINESS (accounting, banking and finance, business administration and management, business economics, international business management, management information systems, marketing/retailing/merchandising, and sports management), COMMUNICATIONS AND THE ARTS (art history and appreciation, broadcasting, communications, English, fine arts, French, German, journalism, music, Spanish, speech/debate/rhetoric, and theater design), COMPUTER AND PHYSICAL SCIENCE (chemistry, computer information sciences and systems, earth science, mathematics, and physics), EDUCATION (art, business, elementary, foreign languages, middle school, music, physical, science, and secondary), ENGINEERING AND ENVIRONMENTAL DESIGN (electrical/electronics engineering and industrial administration/management), HEALTH PROFESSIONS (art therapy, medical laboratory technology, nursing, occupational therapy, physical therapy, predentistry, and premedicine), SOCIAL SCIENCE (anthropology, criminal justice, history, philosophy, political science/government, prelaw, psychology, religion, social science, social work, and sociology). Business and nursing are the strongest academically. Business has the largest enrollment.

Required: All undergraduate students must complete at least 124 hours, including 24 hours or more in the major with a GPA of 2.0 or better. Requirements include a core curriculum in which 8 learning goals must be met. Students must also take health and physical education courses and participate in a convocation and 1 spring term.

Special: Cross-registration is offered in conjunction with 6 area colleges. Cooperative programs in medical technology and physics and electrical or mechanical engineering are available. Internships and various work-study programs, study abroad, dual majors, accelerated programs, and pass/fail options are available. Students may take nondegree study in the Center for Continuing Education and Management Development. A fleximester, which is a 3-week spring term and two 7-week summer sessions, also is offered. There is a freshman honors program on campus, as well as 9 national honor societies. Five departments have honors programs.

Faculty/Classroom: Fifty-three percent of faculty are male; 47%, female. All teach undergraduates. No introductory courses are taught by graduate students. The average class size in an introductory lecture, in a laboratory, and in a regular course offering is 20.

Admissions: About 85% of the 1993–94 applicants were accepted. About 43% of the current freshmen were in the top fifth of their class; 71% were in the top two fifths.

Requirements: U of I requires applicants to be in the upper 50% of their class. A minimum GPA of 2.0 is required. The SAT I or ACT is required, with a minimum SAT I composite of 800 (400 verbal and 400 math) or ACT composite of 20. Each applicant should have at least 24 academic credits, including at least 12 units total from English and literature (not including speech), history, foreign language, mathematics, laboratory science, and social studies. The GED is accepted. An interview is recommended. AP and CLEP credits are accepted. College preparatory course work, high school GPA and class rank, SAT I or ACT scores, and recommendations by school officials are important factors used in the admissions decision.

Procedure: Freshmen are admitted to all sessions. Application deadlines are open and there is a $20 application fee. Notification is sent on a rolling basis. There are early admissions and deferred admissions plans.

Transfer: About 125 transfer students enrolled in a recent year. No ACT or SAT I is needed if applicants have a GPA of C and 20 semester hours of credit. A total of 30 credits out of 124 must be completed at U of I.

Visiting: There are guides for informal visits and visitors may sit in on classes and stay overnight at the school. To arrange for a visit, contact the Admissions Office at (317) 788–3216.

Financial Aid: In 1993–94, 82% of all current freshmen and 82% of continuing students received some form of financial aid. About 65% of freshmen and 65% of continuing students received need-based aid. Fifty percent of undergraduate students work part-time. Average earnings from campus work for the school year are $1200. U of I is a member of CSS. The college's own financial statement, parent and student tax returns, and the FAFSA are required. The deadline for financial aid applications is March 1.

International Students: There are currently 112 international students enrolled. They must take the TOEFL and achieve a minimum score of 500. The student must also take the SAT I (minimum composite score 800) or the ACT (minimum score 20).

Computers: The university provides computer facilities for student use. The mainframe is a DEC VAX 4300. There are both Apple Macintosh and IBM laboratories available to students in 5 of 7 academic buildings. All students may access the system 7 days per week. There are no time limits on using the system and no fees.

Graduates: In 1992–93, 277 bachelor's degrees were awarded. The most popular majors among graduates were business (36%), education (15%), and nursing (8%). Within an average freshman class, 4% graduate in 3 years, 44% in 4 years, 52% in 5 years, and 52% in 6 years. Some 45 companies recruited on campus in an earlier year.

Admissions Contact: Mark T. Weigand, Director of Admissions.

UNIVERSITY OF NOTRE DAME
C-1
Notre Dame, IN 46556   (219) 631-7505

Full-time: 4500 men, 3100 women	Faculty: 610; I, +$
Part-time: none	Ph.D.s: 95%
Graduate: 1480 men, 820 women	Student/Faculty: 12 to 1
Year: semesters, summer session	Tuition: $16,000
Application Deadline: January 6	Room & Board: $4150
Freshman Class: 7700 applied, 3700 accepted, 1900 enrolled	
SAT I Verbal/Math: 580/670	MOST COMPETITIVE

The University of Notre Dame, founded in 1842, is a private, coeducational institution affiliated with the Roman Catholic Church, offering undergraduate programs in architecture, arts and letters, business administration, engineering, and science. There are 5 undergraduate and 3 graduate schools. In addition to regional accreditation, Notre Dame has baccalaureate program accreditation with AACSB, ABET, NAAB, NASAD, and NCATE. The 9 libraries contain 2 million volumes, 2.5 million microform items, and 11,200 audiovisual forms, and subscribe to 20,500 periodicals. Computerized library sources and services include the card catalog, interlibrary loans, and database searching. Special learning facilities include a learning resource center, art gallery, radio station, TV station, and the Snite Museum of Art. The 1250-acre campus is in a suburban area 90 miles east of Chicago. Including residence halls, there are 99 buildings on campus.

Student Life: About 91% of undergraduates are from out-of-state, mostly the Midwest. Students come from 50 states, 40 foreign countries, and Canada. Fifty-four percent are from public schools; 46% from private. Eighty-four percent are white. Eighty-five percent are Catholic; 10% Protestant. The average age of freshmen is 18; all undergraduates, 20. One percent drop out by the end of their first year; 93% remain to graduate.

Housing: A total of 6400 students can be accommodated in college housing. College-sponsored living facilities include single-sex dormitories and married-student housing. On-campus housing is guaranteed for the freshman year only, is available on a first-come, first-served basis, and is available on a lottery system for upperclassmen. Eighty-five percent of students live on campus; of those, 75% remain on campus on weekends. Upperclassmen may keep cars on campus.

Activities: There are no fraternities or sororities on campus. There are 200 groups on campus, including art, bagpipe band, band, cheerleading, chess, choir, chorale, chorus, dance, drama, drill team, ethnic, film, honors, international, jazz band, literary magazine, marching band, musical theater, newspaper, orchestra, pep band, photography, political, professional, radio and TV, religious, social, social service, student government, symphony, and yearbook. Popular campus events include An Tostal, a spring festival, home football weekends, the Collegiate Jazz Festival, and the Multicultural Festival.

Sports: There are 12 intercollegiate sports for men and 10 for women, and 17 intramural sports for men and 12 for women. Athletic and recreation facilities include an athletic and convocation center with an 11,500-seat basketball arena and hockey arena, a tennis pavilion, a golf course, an indoor sports center, and an aquatic center. The campus stadium seats 59,075. There are also several general purpose playing fields, stadiums for track, lacrosse, and baseball, and soccer and softball fields.

Disabled Students: Eighty percent of the campus is accessible to disabled students. The following facilities are available: wheelchair ramps, elevators, special parking, specially equipped rest rooms, special class scheduling, lowered drinking fountains, and lowered telephones.

Services: In addition to many counseling and information services, tutoring is available in most subjects.

Campus Safety and Security: Campus safety and security measures include 24-hour foot and vehicle patrol, self-defense education, escort service, and shuttle buses. In addition, there are informal discussions, pamphlets, posters, films, emergency telephones, and lighted pathways and sidewalks.

Programs of Study: Notre Dame awards the B.A., B.S., A.B., B.Arch., B.B.A., B.F.A., and B.Mus. degrees. Master's and doctoral degrees also are awarded. Bachelor's degrees are awarded in BIOLOGICAL SCIENCE (biochemistry, biology/biological science, and microbiology), BUSINESS (accounting, banking and finance, business administration and management, management science, and marketing/retailing/merchandising), COMMUNICATIONS AND THE ARTS (classics, communications, design, dramatic arts, English, film arts, fine arts, French, German, Greek, Italian, Japanese, Latin, literature, music, photography, Russian, and Spanish), COMPUTER AND PHYSICAL SCIENCE (chemistry, computer science, geoscience, information science and systems, mathematics, and physics), EDUCATION (foreign languages, science, and secondary), ENGINEERING AND ENVIRONMENTAL DESIGN (aeronautical engineering, architectural engineering, chemical engineering, civil engineering, computer engineering, electrical engineering, environmental engineering, and mechanical engineering), HEALTH PROFESSIONS (predentistry and premedicine), SOCIAL SCIENCE (African American studies, American studies, anthropology, economics, history, international relations, medieval studies, philosophy, political science/government, prelaw, psychology, sociology, theological studies, and urban studies). Engineering, architecture, philosophy, physical sciences, accountancy, English, theology, and biological sciences are the strongest academically. Accounting, government, and English have the largest enrollments.

Required: All students must complete courses in English, philosophy, science, history, theology, mathematics, social science, and physical education. A total of 120 semester hours with a minimum GPA of 2.0 is required to graduate.

Special: Cross-registration is offered with Saint Mary's College. Study abroad is possible in France, Austria, Australia, Chile, Mexico, Japan, Spain, Ireland, Rome, Cairo, Jerusalem, and London. A 5-year arts and letters/engineering B.A.-B.S. degree is offered. There is a Program of Liberal Studies centered on the discussion of great books. Internships, an accelerated degree program, dual majors, 3–2 engineering degrees, and pass/fail options are available. There is a freshman honors program on campus, as well as 15 national honor societies, including Phi Beta Kappa. Two colleges have honors programs.

Faculty/Classroom: Seventy-five percent of faculty are male; 25%, female. Ninety-five percent teach undergraduates, 95% do research, and 90% do both. Graduate students teach 10% of introductory courses. The average class size in an introductory lecture is 100; in a laboratory, 30; and in a regular course offering, 40.

Admissions: About 48% of the 1993–94 applicants were accepted. The SAT scores for the 1993–94 freshman class were as follows: Verbal—13% below 500, 48% between 500 and 599, 34% between 600 and 700, and 5% above 700; Math—3% below 500, 19% between 500 and 599, 48% between 600 and 700, and 30% above 700. About 94% of the current freshmen were in the top fifth of their class; 98% were in the top two fifths. Of the current freshmen, 225 graduated first in their class.

Requirements: The SAT I or ACT is required. Applicants should be graduates of an accredited secondary school with 16 Carnegie credits completed, including 4 years of English, 3 of mathematics, and 2 each of science, foreign language, and history. The SAT II: Subject test in a foreign language is recommended. An essay is part of the application process. An audition or a portfolio is recommended for some majors. AP credits are accepted. Important factors used in the admissions decision are personality, intangible qualities, leadership record, extracurricular activities record, evidence of special talent, and advanced placement or honor courses.

Procedure: Freshmen are admitted in the fall. Entrance exams should be taken by the fall of the senior year. Early decision applications should be filed by November 1; regular applications, by January 6 for fall entry, along with an application fee of $35. Notification of early decision is sent December 15; regular decision, April 2. There are early decision and deferred admissions plans. About 600 early decision candidates were accepted for the 1993–94 class. A waiting list is an active part of the admissions procedure, with about 7% of applicants on the list.

Transfer: About 150 transfer students enrolled in 1993–94. Applicants should have completed at least 27 semester hours of transferable credit and maintained a 3.5 GPA in all courses. Admission depends on openings in each undergraduate college. A total of 60 credits out of 120 must be completed at Notre Dame.

Visiting: There are regularly scheduled orientations for prospective students, including small group sessions for students, larger sessions for parents, and tours for all. Visitors may sit in on classes and stay overnight at the school. To arrange for a visit, contact the Admissions receptionist at (219) 631-7505.

Financial Aid: In 1993–94, 65% of all students received some form of financial aid. About 41% of freshmen and 41% of continuing students received need-based aid. The average freshman award was $9000. Of that total, scholarships or need-based grants averaged $4500 ($14,000 maximum); loans averaged $3300 ($4875 maxi-

mum); and work contracts averaged $1200 ($1800 maximum). Fifty percent of undergraduate students work part-time. Average earnings from campus work for the school year are $1200. The average financial indebtedness of the 1992–93 graduate was $15,000. Notre Dame is a member of CSS. The FAF and federal income tax return are required. The deadline for financial aid applications is February 28.

International Students: There are currently 100 international students enrolled. The school actively recruits these students. They must take the TOEFL and achieve a minimum score of 550. The student must also take the SAT I or the ACT.

Computers: The college provides computer facilities for student use. The mainframes are a Prime 9950, a DEC VAX 750, a Convex C240, and an IBM 9121/260. There are 454 workstations in 10 locations. All students may access the system. It may be used 24 hours a day. There are no time limits on using the system and no fees.

Graduates: In 1992–93, 1890 bachelor's degrees were awarded. The most popular majors among graduates were accountancy (13%), government and international studies (9%), and English (8%). Within an average freshman class, 92% graduate in 4 years, 93% in 5 years, and 94% in 6 years. Some 350 companies recruited on campus in 1992–93. In the 1992 graduating class, 32% of all graduates were enrolled in graduate school within 6 months of graduation; 63% had found employment.

Admissions Contact: Kevin M. Rooney, Director of Admissions.

UNIVERSITY OF SOUTHERN INDIANA A-5
Evansville, IN 47712 (812) 464-1765; (800) 467-1965 (in-state)

Full-time: 1689 men, 2417 women	Faculty: 112; IIA, --$
Part-time: 936 men, 1723 women	Ph.D.s: 58%
Graduate: 151 men, 105 women	Student/Faculty: 37 to 1
Year: semesters, summer session	Tuition: $2060 ($4993)
Application Deadline: August 15	Room & Board: $1660
Freshman Class: 2678 accepted, 1451 enrolled	
SAT I: Verbal/Math 392/436	ACT: 17 NONCOMPETITIVE

The University of Southern Indiana, founded in 1965, is a public, coeducational institution offering undergraduate programs in business, education and human service, liberal arts, nursing and health professions, and science and engineering technology. There are 6 undergraduate schools and one graduate school. In addition to regional accreditation, USI has baccalaureate program accreditation with ABET and NCATE. The library contains 166,000 volumes, 220,000 microform items, and 4500 audiovisual forms, and subscribes to 715 periodicals. Computerized library sources and services include the card catalog, interlibrary loans, and database searching. Special learning facilities include a learning resource center, radio station, and TV station. The 300-acre campus is in a suburban area 150 miles south of Indianapolis. Including residence halls, there are 35 buildings on campus.

Student Life: About 95% of undergraduates are from Indiana. Students come from 22 states, 36 foreign countries, and Canada. Ninety-five percent are white. The average age of freshmen is 18. Twenty percent drop out by the end of their first year.

Housing: A total of 1300 students can be accommodated in college housing. College-sponsored living facilities include single-sex and coed on-campus apartments. On-campus housing is guaranteed for all 4 years. Eighty percent of students commute. Alcohol is not permitted. All students may keep cars on campus.

Activities: About 15% of men belong to 5 national fraternities; about 5% of women belong to 3 national sororities. There are 62 groups on campus, including art, cheerleading, chorus, computers, dance, drama, ethnic, film, honors, international, literary magazine, musical theater, newspaper, pep band, photography, political, professional, radio and TV, religious, social, social service, student government, and yearbook. Popular campus events include Eagle Gran Prix Bike Race and Homecoming.

Sports: Athletic and recreation facilities include a physical activities center with a swimming pool and a 3000-seat multipurpose arena.

Disabled Students: Ninety percent of the campus is accessible to disabled students. The following facilities are available: wheelchair ramps, elevators, special parking, specially equipped rest rooms, and student assistance through the counseling center.

Services: In addition to many counseling and information services, tutoring is available in some subjects, including English and mathematics. In addition, there is remedial math, reading, and writing.

Campus Safety and Security: Campus safety and security measures include 24-hour foot and vehicle patrol, escort service, shuttle buses, and pamphlets, posters, and films. In addition, there are emergency telephones and lighted pathways and sidewalks.

Programs of Study: USI awards the B.A. and B.S. degrees. Associate and master's degrees also are awarded. Bachelor's degrees are awarded in BIOLOGICAL SCIENCE (biology/biological science and biophysics), BUSINESS (accounting, banking and finance, business administration and management, business economics, and

marketing/retailing/merchandising), COMMUNICATIONS AND THE ARTS (broadcasting, communications, dramatic arts, English, German, journalism, Spanish, and speech/debate/rhetoric), COMPUTER AND PHYSICAL SCIENCE (chemistry, mathematics, and physics), EDUCATION (art, business, early childhood, elementary, middle school, science, and secondary), ENGINEERING AND ENVIRONMENTAL DESIGN (engineering technology), HEALTH PROFESSIONS (nursing, predentistry, and premedicine), SOCIAL SCIENCE (criminal justice, economics, history, philosophy, political science/government, prelaw, psychology, social work, and sociology). Business, education, and liberal arts have the largest enrollments.

Required: For graduation, 124 credit hours must be completed with a cumulative 2.0 GPA. All students are required to take courses in humanities and the arts, science and mathematics, and social and behavioral sciences.

Special: Students may participate in cooperative programs, internships in business and communications, and work-study programs. Study abroad, dual majors, pass/fail options, and B.A.-B.S. degrees are possible.

Faculty/Classroom: The average class size in an introductory lecture is 100; in a laboratory, 35; and in a regular course offering, 20.

Admissions: The SAT scores for the 1993–94 freshman class were as follows: Verbal—89% below 500, 8% between 500 and 599, and 3% between 600 and 700; Math—75% below 500, 20% between 500 and 599, and 5% between 600 and 700. About 11% of the current freshmen were in the top fifth of their class; 64% were in the top two fifths.

Requirements: A minimum GPA of 2.0 is required. Students must take either the SAT I or ACT. Applicants must be graduates of an accredited secondary school, with a minimum GPA of 2.0. The GED is accepted. An interview is recommended if the student is below admissions standards. AP and CLEP credits are accepted. Important factors used in the admissions decision are advanced placement or honor courses, evidence of special talent, leadership record, extracurricular activities record, and personality, intangible qualities.

Procedure: Freshmen are admitted to all sessions. Applications should be filed by August 15 for fall entry, January 1 for spring entry, and June 1 for summer entry. The college accepts all applicants. Notification is sent on a rolling basis. There is a deferred admissions plan. A waiting list is an active part of the admissions procedure.

Transfer: About 610 transfer students enrolled in 1993–94. Grades of C and above will transfer for credit. D will transfer only if the cumulative GPA is above 2.0. A total of 30 credits out of 124 must be completed at USI.

Visiting: There are regularly scheduled orientations for prospective students, including meetings with counselors and faculty and campus tours. There are guides for informal visits and visitors may sit in on classes and stay overnight at the school. To arrange for a visit, contact Leanne Crane, Office of Admissions at (812) 464-1765.

Financial Aid: In an earlier year, 48% of all current freshmen and 44% of continuing students received some form of financial aid. About 47% of freshmen received need-based aid. The average freshman award was $1850. Of that total, scholarships or need-based grants averaged $1200 ($2400 maximum); loans averaged $2000 ($4000 maximum); and work contracts averaged $1500 ($2500 maximum). Forty-eight percent of undergraduate students work part-time. The average financial indebtedness of a recent graduate was $3000. USI is a member of CSS. The FAF is required. The deadline for financial aid applications is March 1.

International Students: There are currently 50 international students enrolled. They must take the TOEFL and achieve a minimum score of 500. The student must also take the SAT I or the ACT.

Computers: The university provides computer facilities for student use. The mainframes are an IBM 4381 and IBM 4361. All students may access the system. There are no time limits on using the system and no fees.

Graduates: In a recent year, 516 bachelor's degrees were awarded. The most popular majors among graduates were elementary education (24%), business administration (13%), and accounting (10%). Within an average freshman class, 25% graduate in 5 years. Some 67 companies recruited on campus in a recent year.

Admissions Contact: Timothy K. Buecher, Dean of Admissions.

VALPARAISO UNIVERSITY

B-1

Valparaiso, IN 46383 (219) 464-5011; (800) 348-2611 (out-of-state)

Full-time: 1122 men, 1418 women	Faculty: 230; IIA, -$
Part-time: 54 men, 144 women	Ph.D.s: 72%
Graduate: 349 men, 412 women	Student/Faculty: 11 to 1
Year: semesters, 2 summer sessions	Tuition: $11,720
Application Deadline: open	Room & Board: $3090
Freshman Class: 2466 applied, 2071 accepted, 723 enrolled	
SAT I or ACT: required	**VERY COMPETITIVE**

Valparaiso University, founded in 1859, is a private, coeducational institution affiliated with the Lutheran Church. The university offers degree programs in arts and sciences, business administration, engineering, and nursing. There are 5 undergraduate and 2 graduate schools. In addition to regional accreditation, Valparaiso has baccalaureate program accreditation with AACSB, ABET, CSWE, NASM, NCATE, and NLN. The 2 libraries contain 438,000 volumes, 122,000 microform items, and 5200 audiovisual forms, and subscribe to 1440 periodicals. Computerized library sources and services include the card catalog, interlibrary loans, and database searching. Special learning facilities include an art gallery, a planetarium, radio and TV stations, an observatory, a weather station, a center for visual and performing arts, and a nuclear laboratory. The 310-acre campus is in a small town 50 miles southeast of Chicago, Illinois. Including residence halls, there are 72 buildings on campus.

Student Life: About 59% of undergraduates are from out-of-state, mostly the Midwest. Students come from 47 states, 37 foreign countries, and Canada. Eighty percent are from public schools; 20% from private. Ninety-one percent are white. Fifty-nine percent are Protestant; 23% Catholic. The average age of freshmen is 18; all undergraduates, 20. Ten percent drop out by the end of their first year; 65% remain to graduate.

Housing: A total of 2058 students can be accommodated in college housing. College-sponsored living facilities include single-sex and coed dormitories, on-campus apartments, off-campus apartments, fraternity houses, and sorority houses. In addition there are language houses. On-campus housing is guaranteed for all 4 years. Eighty-four percent of students live on campus; of those, 80% remain on campus on weekends. Alcohol is not permitted. Upperclassmen may keep cars on campus.

Activities: About 48% of men belong to 12 national fraternities; about 40% of women belong to 8 local sororities. There are 150 groups on campus, including band, cheerleading, chess, choir, chorale, chorus, computers, dance, drama, ethnic, honors, international, jazz band, literary magazine, musical theater, newspaper, orchestra, pep band, photography, political, professional, radio and TV, religious, social, social service, student government, symphony, and yearbook. Popular campus events include the Christmas Concert, the Madrigal Dinner, the Jazz Festival, Martin Luther King Day, the film series, theater productions, coffee houses, Union night clubs, athletic events, Parents Weekend, Siblings Weekend, the Heritage Festival, and Spring Weekend.

Sports: There are 9 intercollegiate sports for men and 7 for women, and 20 intramural sports for men and 20 for women. Athletic and recreation facilities include an athletics-recreation center that houses a 4800-seat gymnasium, racquetball courts, weight rooms, swimming pools, basketball courts, and an indoor track. Other athletic and recreation facilities include a 5000-seat football and soccer stadium, baseball and track fields, a cross-country course, bowling alleys, game rooms, and an outdoor recreation center.

Disabled Students: Fifty-five percent of the campus is accessible to disabled students. The following facilities are available: wheelchair ramps, elevators, special parking, specially equipped rest rooms, and special class scheduling.

Services: In addition to many counseling and information services, tutoring is available in every subject. A Writing Center provides assistance.

Campus Safety and Security: Campus safety and security measures include 24-hour foot and vehicle patrol, self-defense education, escort service, and shuttle buses. In addition, there are informal discussions, pamphlets, posters, and films, emergency telephones, and lighted pathways and sidewalks.

Programs of Study: Valparaiso awards the B.A., B.S., B.Mus., B.Mus.Ed., B.S.Acc., B.S.Bus.Adm., B.S.C.E., B.S.Comp.Eng., B.S.Ed., B.S.E.E., B.S.F.A., B.S.M.E., B.S.N., B.S.P.E., and B.S.W. degrees. Associate, master's, and doctoral degrees also are awarded. Bachelor's degrees are awarded in BIOLOGICAL SCIENCE (biology/biological science), BUSINESS (accounting, banking and finance, business administration and management, international economics, marketing/retailing/merchandising, and personnel management), COMMUNICATIONS AND THE ARTS (broadcasting, classics, communications, dramatic arts, English, fine arts, French, German, Greek, journalism, Latin, music, photography, and Spanish), COMPUTER AND PHYSICAL SCIENCE (astronomy, atmospheric sciences and meteorology, chemistry, computer science, geology, mathematics, and physics), EDUCATION (elementary, foreign languages, middle school, music, science, and secondary), ENGINEERING AND ENVIRONMENTAL DESIGN (civil engineering, computer engineering, electrical/electronics engineering, engineering, and mechanical engineering), HEALTH PROFESSIONS (nursing, predentistry, premedicine, and speech pathology/audiology), SOCIAL SCIENCE (American studies, economics, geography, history, international public service, philosophy, political science/government, prelaw, psychology, religion, social work, and sociology). Premedicine, physics, mathematics, engineering, and chemistry are the strongest academically. Communication, education, business, engineering, and nursing have the largest enrollments.

Required: General education requirements include 12 credit hours of natural science, 10 of English, 9 of religion, 6 of social analysis, 3 each of history and non-Western Third World studies, and 2 of physical education. The required core curriculum includes History 100, English 100, Theology 100, and Freshman Seminar. To graduate, students must complete at least 124 credit hours, including 32 in a major field, with a GPA of at least 2.0.

Special: Valparaiso maintains cooperative programs in most majors, including one in urban studies with the Association of Midwest Colleges, as well as a United Nations semester with Drew University and a Washington semester with American University. Students may study abroad in England, Germany, Mexico, France, Greece, Namibia, Japan, and China. Internships, the B.A.-B.S. degree, work-study programs, dual majors, student-designed majors, an accelerated degree program in several majors, pass/fail options, and nondegree study are also available. Other special academic features include Christ College, which is an autonomous honors college. There is a freshman honors program on campus, as well as 5 national honor societies.

Faculty/Classroom: Seventy-two percent of faculty are male; 28%, female. All teach undergraduates. No introductory courses are taught by graduate students. The average class size in an introductory lecture is 40; in a laboratory, 20; and in a regular course offering, 20.

Admissions: About 84% of the 1993–94 applicants were accepted. The SAT scores for the 1993–94 freshman class were as follows: Verbal—43% below 500, 36% between 500 and 599, 19% between 600 and 700, and 3% above 700; Math—17% below 500, 33% between 500 and 599, 35% between 600 and 700, and 15% above 700. The ACT scores were 3% below 21, 18% between 21 and 23, 29% between 24 and 26, 20% between 27 and 28, and 30% above 28. About 72% of the current freshmen were in the top fifth of their class; 94% were in the top two fifths. There were 11 National Merit finalists. Thirty-nine freshmen graduated first in their class.

Requirements: The SAT I or ACT is required. Applicants must be graduates of accredited secondary schools or have earned a GED. The university requires completion of 4 years of English, 3 of mathematics, 1 of history, and 2 each of foreign language, laboratory science, and social science. An essay and an interview are recommended for all applicants, and an audition is required for music majors. AP and CLEP credits are accepted. Important factors used in the admissions decision are advanced placement or honor courses, leadership record, evidence of special talent, extracurricular activities record, and recommendations by school officials.

Procedure: Freshmen are admitted to all sessions. Entrance exams should be taken prior to the senior year. Application deadlines are open. The application fee is $30. Notification is sent on a rolling basis. There are early admissions and deferred admissions plans.

Transfer: About 180 transfer students enrolled in 1993–94. A minimum GPA of 2.0 is required for all college work. If the applicant has completed fewer than 24 credit hours, entrance examination scores are required. An interview is recommended. A total of 30 credits out of 124 must be completed at Valparaiso.

Visiting: There are regularly scheduled orientations for prospective students, including a campus tour conducted by a current student, an interview with a counselor, and the option to meet with professors. There are guides for informal visits, and visitors may sit in on classes and stay overnight at the school. To arrange for a visit, contact the Admissions Office at (800) 348–2611 or (219) 464–5011.

Financial Aid: In a recent year, 80% of all current freshmen and 80% of continuing students received some form of financial aid. About 70% of freshmen and 67% of continuing students received need-based aid. The average freshman award was $9286. Of that total, scholarships or need-based grants averaged $5032 ($10,305 maximum); loans averaged $3654 ($5125 maximum); and work contracts averaged $600 ($1200 maximum). Forty percent of undergraduate students work part-time. Average earnings from campus work for the school year are $900. The average financial indebtedness of the 1992–93 graduate was $9500. Valparaiso is a member of CSS. The FAF, the college's own financial statement, and the FAFSA are required. The deadline for financial aid applications is March 1.

International Students: There are currently 103 international students enrolled. The school actively recruits these students. They must take the TOEFL and achieve a minimum score of 550.

Computers: The college provides computer facilities for student use. The mainframe is a DEC VAX 4000 Model 300. More than 325 computers, including 20 Apple Macintosh II ci, 45 Apple Macintosh, 10 IBM PS/2, and 15 Zenith 286 LP microcomputers, a microlab network of Sun workstations and IBM and Zenith PCs, and 2 microcomputer laboratories are available to students at various locations throughout the campus. There are also 24-hour residential computer clusters. Word processing, databases, spreadsheets, e-mail, Galileo, and Internet are available. All students may access the system. It may be used 7 days per week. There are no time limits on using the system and no fees. It is recommended that students in electrical and computer engineering have personal computers. IBM-compatible PCs are recommended.

Graduates: In 1992–93, 705 bachelor's degrees were awarded. The most popular majors among graduates were nursing (12%), business administration (9%), and elementary education (6%). Within an average freshman class, 1% graduate in 3 years, 55% in 4 years, 70% in 5 years, and 73% in 6 years. Some 56 companies recruited on campus in 1992–93. In the 1992 graduating class, 20% of all graduates were enrolled in graduate school within 6 months of graduation; 63% had found employment.

Admissions Contact: Office of Admissions.

WABASH COLLEGE
B-3

Crawfordsville, IN 47933–0352

(317) 364–4225
(800) 345–5385 (in-state)

Full-time: 804 men	Faculty: 79; IIB, +$
Part-time: 5 men	Ph.D.s: 89%
Graduate: none	Student/Faculty: 10 to 1
Year: semesters	Tuition: $12,250
Application Deadline: March 1	Room & Board: $4000
Freshman Class: 737 applied, 623 accepted, 256 enrolled	
SAT I Verbal/Math: 510/600	**VERY COMPETITIVE**

Wabash College, founded in 1832, is a private, liberal arts men's college with a strong emphasis on preprofessional programs. The library contains 227,800 volumes, 8182 microform items, and 6441 audiovisual forms, and subscribes to 864 periodicals. Computerized library sources and services include interlibrary loans and database searching. Special learning facilities include an art gallery. The 50-acre campus is in a small town 45 miles northwest of Indianapolis. Including residence halls, there are 32 buildings on campus.

Student Life: About 75% of undergraduates are from Indiana. Students come from 32 states and 26 foreign countries. Eighty-four percent are white. The average age of freshmen is 18; all undergraduates, 20. Eleven percent drop out by the end of their first year; 75% remain to graduate.

Housing: A total of 761 students can be accommodated in college housing. College-sponsored living facilities include dormitories and fraternity houses. In addition, there is an international house. On-campus housing is guaranteed for all 4 years. Ninety-two percent of students live on campus; of those, 67% remain on campus on weekends. All students may keep cars on campus.

Activities: About 75% of men belong to 10 national fraternities. There are 40 groups on campus, including art, band, chess, choir, chorus, computers, drama, ethnic, gay, honors, international, jazz band, language, literary magazine, musical theater, newspaper, orchestra, pep band, political, professional, radio and TV, religious, social, student government, and yearbook. Popular campus events include Pan-Hel weekend, Fall Bash, and Chapel Sing.

Sports: There are 10 intercollegiate and 22 intramural sports. Athletic and recreation facilities include a 4,200-seat stadium, indoor and outdoor tennis courts, football, baseball, and soccer fields, a swimming pool, an all-weather track, a wrestling room, a weight room, and racquetball and handball courts.

Disabled Students: Thirty percent of the campus is accessible to disabled students. The following facilities are available: wheelchair ramps, elevators, special parking, specially equipped rest rooms, and lowered drinking fountains. A counseling service is provided for handicapped students.

Services: In addition to many counseling and information services, tutoring is available in most subjects, and there is a typing/reading service for blind students.

Campus Safety and Security: Campus safety and security measures include lighted pathways and sidewalks and night watchmen.

Programs of Study: Wabash awards the A.B. degree. Bachelor's degrees are awarded in BIOLOGICAL SCIENCE (biology/biological science), COMMUNICATIONS AND THE ARTS (classics, dramatic arts, English, fine arts, French, German, Greek, Latin, music, Spanish, and speech/debate/rhetoric), COMPUTER AND PHYSICAL SCIENCE (chemistry, mathematics, and physics), SOCIAL SCIENCE (economics, history, philosophy, political science/government, psychology, and religion). Premedicine and prelaw are the strongest programs academically. Psychology, history, English, and economics have the largest enrollments.

Required: All students must complete at least 4 courses in behavorial science, natural science, and mathematics; 3 courses in literature and fine arts; and 2 courses in history, philosophy, or religion. Students also must maintain a 2.0 GPA for 136 credit hours, which include a freshman tutorial and 2 cultures and traditions courses. The student must pass a written examination in his major as well as a senior oral examination and must demonstrate proficiency in English and proficiency in a foreign language at a level equivalent to 2 college courses.

Special: Internships, study abroad in 14 countries, and a Washington semester with American University are available. In addition, dual majors and a 3–2 engineering program and a 3–2 law program with Columbia University and Washington University in St. Louis are of-

fered. There are 9 national honor societies on campus, including Phi Beta Kappa.

Faculty/Classroom: Ninety percent of faculty are male; 10%, female. All teach undergraduates. The average class size in an introductory lecture is 30; in a laboratory, 20; and in a regular course offering, 11.

Admissions: About 85% of the 1993–94 applicants were accepted. The SAT scores for the 1993–94 freshman class were as follows: Verbal—40% below 500, 38% between 500 and 599, 20% between 600 and 700, and 2% above 700; Math—15% below 500, 35% between 500 and 599, 36% between 600 and 700, and 14% above 700. About 68% of the current freshmen were in the top fifth of their class; 92% were in the top two fifths. There were 11 National Merit finalists and 3 semifinalists. Ten freshmen graduated first in their class.

Requirements: The SAT I or ACT is required. Wabash recommends applicants have 4 courses in English, 3 in mathematics, and 2 each in foreign language, science, and social studies. In addition, an essay is required and an interview is recommended. AP and CLEP credits are accepted. Important factors used in the admissions decision are advanced placement or honor courses, recommendations by school officials, parents or siblings attending the school, evidence of special talent, and leadership record.

Procedure: Freshmen are admitted in the fall and spring. Entrance exams should be taken by the spring of the junior year or the fall of the senior year. Applications should be filed by March 1 for fall entry and December 1 for spring entry, along with an application fee of $15. Notification is sent on a rolling basis. There is a deferred admissions plan.

Transfer: About 16 transfer students enrolled in 1993–94. Wabash strongly considers the overall high school and college background of applicants. A minimum GPA of 2.5 is required. A total of 68 credits out of 136 must be completed at Wabash.

Visiting: There are regularly scheduled orientations for prospective students, consisting of a welcome, panel discussions on liberal arts, interest sessions, extracurricular and cocurricular activities, off-campus study, financial aid, and fraternities, a tour, lunch, and an opportunity to meet faculty, coaches, and alumni. There are guides for informal visits and visitors may sit in on classes and stay overnight at the school. To arrange for a visit, contact the Admissions Office at (800) 345–5385.

Financial Aid: In 1993–94 94% of all current freshmen and 83% of continuing students received some form of financial aid. About 74% of freshmen and 65% of continuing students received need-based aid. The average freshman award was $9755. Of that total, scholarships or need-based grants were $16,450 maximum, loans were $2,625 maximum, and work contracts were $500 maximum. Seventy percent of undergraduate students work part-time. Average earnings from campus work for the school year are $600. Wabash is a member of CSS. The FAF and federal tax form are required. The deadline for financial aid applications is March 1.

International Students: There are currently 43 international students enrolled. They must take the TOEFL and score at least 550 or the University of Michigan Language Test.

Computers: The college provides computer facilities for student use. The mainframes are a DEC MicroVax 3400 and a VAX 4000, Model 1100. More than 80 personal computers and 2 terminals are available exclusively for student use in a computer center, the library, 3 classrooms, and all departments. All are connected by a LAN and to Internet. All students may access the system 24 hours per day. There are no time limits on using the system and no fees.

Graduates: In 1992–93 178 bachelor's degrees were awarded. The most popular majors among graduates were history (15%), economics (12%), and English (11%). Within an average freshman class, 75% graduate in 4 years. Some 21 companies recruited on campus in 1992–93. In the 1992 graduating class, 43% of the men were enrolled in graduate school within 6 months of graduation; 37% of the men had found employment.

Admissions Contact: Greg Birk, Director of Admissions.

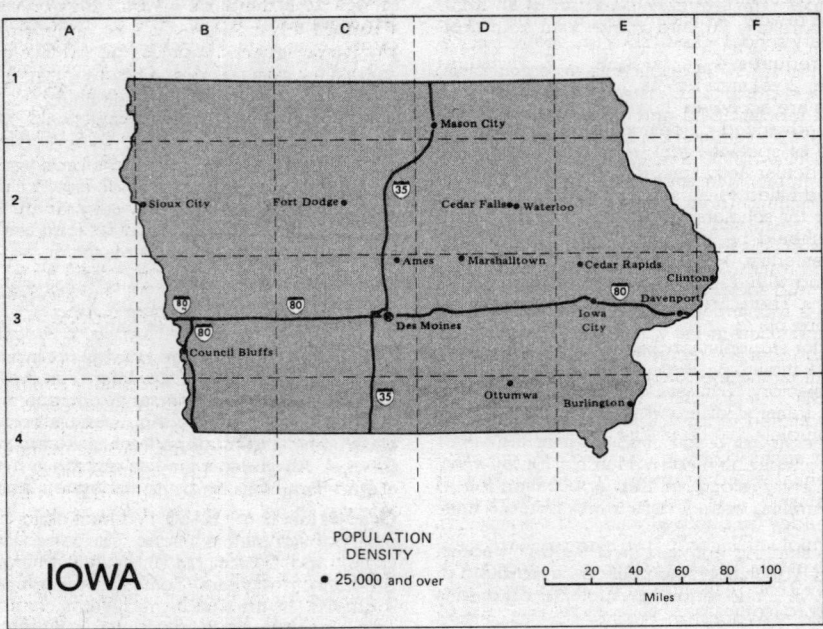

POPULATION
DENSITY

● 25,000 and over

0   20   40   60   80   100
Miles

IOWA

BRIAR CLIFF COLLEGE
B-2

Sioux City, IA 51104–2100

(712) 279–5200
(800) 662–3303 (out-of-state)

Full-time: 258 men, 480 women	**Faculty:** 64; IIB, --$
Part-time: 108 men, 322 women	**Ph.D.s:** 65%
Graduate: none	**Student/Faculty:** 12 to 1
Year: trimesters, summer sessions	**Tuition:** $9930
Application Deadline: September 1	**Room & Board:** $3445
Freshman Class: 392 applied, 351 accepted, 155 enrolled	
SAT I Verbal/Math: 385/410	**ACT:** 22 **COMPETITIVE**

Briar Cliff College, founded in 1930, is private, Catholic-Franciscan, coeducational, liberal arts institution. In addition to regional accreditation, Briar Cliff has baccalaureate program accreditation with AACSB, CSWE, and NLN. The library contains 100,773 volumes and 31,397 microform items, and subscribes to 529 periodicals. Computerized library sources and services include interlibrary loans and database searching. Special learning facilities include a learning resource center, art gallery, radio station, TV station, and a cadaver laboratory. The 70-acre campus is in a suburban area of Sioux City. Including residence halls, there are 10 buildings on campus.

Student Life: About 74% of undergraduates are from Iowa. Students come from 25 states, 10 foreign countries, and Canada. Sixtynine percent are from public schools; 31% from private. Ninety-two percent are white. Thirty-nine percent are Catholic; 36% claim no religious affiliation; 24% are Protestant. The average age of freshmen is 18; all undergraduates, 26. Twelve percent drop out by the end of their first year; 51% remain to graduate.

Housing: A total of 553 students can be accommodated in college housing. College-sponsored living facilities include single-sex and coed dormitories. On-campus housing is guaranteed for all 4 years. Sixty-two percent of students live on campus. All students may keep cars on campus.

Activities: There are no fraternities or sororities on campus. There are 27 groups on campus, including art, cheerleading, choir, chorus, computers, drama, drill team, ethnic, film, international, jazz band, literary magazine, musical theater, newspaper, photography, professional, radio and TV, religious, social, social service, and student government. Popular campus events include Golden Harvest, Homecoming, Winterfest, St. Francis Day, Founders Day, Senior Prom, Spring Fling, Welcome Week, International Dinner, and Little Brother/Little Sister Weekend.

Sports: There are 4 intercollegiate sports for men and 5 for women, and 15 intramural sports for men and 15 for women. Athletic and recreation facilities include baseball, softball, and soccer fields and a recreation center with 2 racquetball courts, a running track, tennis courts, 2 basketball/volleyball courts, and weight-lifting facilities.

Disabled Students: Ninety percent of the campus is accessible to disabled students. The following facilities are available: wheelchair ramps, elevators, special parking, specially equipped rest rooms, and lowered drinking fountains.

Services: In addition to many counseling and information services, tutoring is available in every subject. There is also remedial math, reading, and writing.

Campus Safety and Security: Campus safety and security measures include 24-hour foot and vehicle patrol, emergency telephones, and lighted pathways and sidewalks.

Programs of Study: Briar Cliff awards the B.A., B.S., and B.S.N. degrees. Associate degrees also are awarded. Bachelor's degrees are awarded in BIOLOGICAL SCIENCE (biology/biological science), BUSINESS (accounting, business administration and management, and human resources), COMMUNICATIONS AND THE ARTS (communications, dramatic arts, English, fine arts, music, and Spanish), COMPUTER AND PHYSICAL SCIENCE (chemistry, computer science, and mathematics), EDUCATION (elementary, health, and secondary), ENGINEERING AND ENVIRONMENTAL DESIGN (preengineering), HEALTH PROFESSIONS (medical laboratory technology, nursing, occupational therapy, physical therapy, predentistry, premedicine, and prepharmacy), SOCIAL SCIENCE (history, prelaw, psychology, social work, sociology, and theological studies). Accounting, nursing, psychology, and premedicine are the strongest academically. Business administration and psychology have the largest enrollments.

Required: To graduate, students must complete a minimum of 120 semester hours with at least 36 in the major. The college requires 10 general education foundation courses and six 1-hour independent research courses. A GPA of 2.0 with no more than one D in the major must be maintained, and proficiency in standard English expression and oral communication skills must be demonstrated.

Special: Internships, including those in Chicago and Washington, study abroad, dual majors, work-study programs, student-designed majors, interdisciplinary majors, and pass/fail options are available. Students may earn a 3–2 engineering degree with Iowa State University. Three departments have honors programs.

Faculty/Classroom: Fifty-six percent of full-time faculty are male; 44%, female. All full-time faculty teach undergraduates. The average class size in an introductory lecture is 30; in a laboratory, 15; and in a regular course offering, 20.

Admissions: About 90% of the 1993–94 applicants were accepted. The SAT scores for the 1993–94 freshman class were as follows: Verbal—83% below 500 and 17% between 600 and 700; Math—83% below 500 and 17% between 600 and 700. The ACT scores were 35% below 21, 29% between 21 and 23, 23% between 24 and 26, 6% between 27 and 28, and 7% above 28. About 36% of the current freshmen were in the top fifth of their class; 66% were in the top two fifths. One freshman graduated first in class.

Requirements: Briar Cliff requires applicants to be in the upper 90% of their class. A minimum GPA of 2.0 is required. The ACT or SAT I is required; the ACT is recommended, and a score of 19 qualifies for automatic acceptance review. Applicants need not be graduates of an accredited secondary school. The GED is accepted. Admission to freshman standing requires 4 years each of English and mathematics, 3 years science, 2 years of history, and 1 year of social studies. AP and CLEP credits are accepted. Important factors used in the admissions decision are advanced placement or honor courses, leadership record, evidence of special talent, recommendations by school officials, and extracurricular activities record.

Procedure: Freshmen are admitted to all sessions. Entrance exams should be taken by October for scholarship consideration, by April for admission. Applications should be filed by September 1 for fall entry, November 1 for winter entry, March 1 for spring entry, and June 1 for summer entry, along with an application fee of $20. Notification is sent on a rolling basis. There are early decision, early admissions, and deferred admissions plans.

Transfer: A total of 53 transfer students enrolled in 1993–94. Applicants for transfer must have a minimum GPA of 2.0 with at least 10 credit hours earned and satisfactory dismissal from the previous institution. Grades of D or better transfer for credit. The last 30 semester hours out of 120 must be completed at Briar Cliff.

Visiting: There are regularly scheduled orientations for prospective students, including a presidential welcome, meeting with faculty and student panels, luncheon, campus tours, a slide show, and financial aid information. There are guides for informal visits and visitors may sit in on classes and stay overnight at the school. To arrange for a visit, contact the Admissions Office at (800) 662–3303 or (712) 279–5200.

Financial Aid: In 1993–94, 97% of all current freshmen and 98% of continuing students received some form of financial aid. About 90% of freshmen and 92% of continuing students received need-based aid. The average freshman award was $8400. Of that total, scholarships or need-based grants averaged $3000 ($13,375 maximum); loans averaged $3500 ($5500 maximum); and work contracts averaged $1500 ($3000 maximum). All undergraduate students work part-time. Average earnings from campus work for the school year are $1200. The average financial indebtedness of the 1992–93 graduate was $14,000. Briar Cliff is a member of CSS. The FAF, FFS, or SFS is required. The deadline for financial aid applications is open.

International Students: There are currently 25 international students enrolled. The school actively recruits these students. They must take the TOEFL or the University of Michigan Language Test and achieve a minimum score on the TOEFL of 500.

Computers: The college provides computer facilities for student use. The mainframes are 2 DEC MicroVAX 3100 computers and an IBM system/36. In addition, there are 46 workstations located in writing laboratories in each residence hall and the computer center. A portable workstation can be attached at 70 locations around campus. All students may access the system 24 hours each day. There are no time limits on using the system. There is an information fee, but no direct user fee.

Graduates: In 1992–93, 222 bachelor's degrees were awarded. The most popular majors among graduates were business administration (33%), social sciences (10%), and health professions (10%). Within an average freshman class, 45% graduate in 4 years, 46% in 5 years, and 1% in 6 years. Some 24 companies recruited on campus in 1992–93. In the 1992 graduating class, 12% of men and women had enrolled in graduate school within 6 months of graduation; 82% had found employment.

Admissions Contact: Sharisue Wilcoxon, Executive Director of Marketing and Admissions.

BUENA VISTA COLLEGE
B-2

Storm Lake, IA 50588

(712) 749–2235; (800) 383–9600

Full-time: 475 men, 493 women	Faculty: 68; IIB, av$
Part-time: 22 men, 33 women	Ph.D.s: 65%
Graduate: none	Student/Faculty: 14 to 1
Year: 4-1-4, summer session	Tuition: $12,565
Application Deadline: May 1	Room & Board: $3585
Freshman Class: 860 applied, 688 accepted, 285 enrolled	
SAT I: 515/585	ACT: 24 **VERY COMPETITIVE**

Buena Vista College, founded in 1891, is a private, coeducational institution affiliated with the Presbyterian Church (USA). The college offers undergraduate degree programs in business, education, communication and arts, science, social science, philosophy, and religion. Programs emphasize career education with a liberal arts foundation. There are 5 undergraduate schools. In addition to regional accreditation, Buena Vista has baccalaureate program accreditation with CSWE and NCATE. The library contains 130,000 volumes, 15,000 microform items, and 5000 audiovisual forms, and subscribes to 660 periodicals. Computerized library sources and services include interlibrary loans and database searching. Special learning facilities include a learning resource center, art gallery, radio station, TV station,

and student newspaper desktop production laboratory. The 60-acre campus is in a small town 65 miles east of Sioux City. Including residence halls, there are 14 buildings on campus.

Student Life: About 78% of undergraduates are from Iowa. Students come from 19 states and 10 foreign countries. Eighty percent are from public schools; 20% from private. Ninety-three percent are white. Fifty percent are Protestant; 45% Catholic. The average age of freshmen is 18; all undergraduates, 20. Twenty-two percent drop out by the end of their first year; 60% remain to graduate.

Housing: A total of 835 students can be accommodated in college housing. College-sponsored living facilities include single-sex and coed dormitories and on-campus apartments. In addition, there are honors houses, language houses, and cottages adjacent to campus that group upperclassmen by major, sport, or other similar interest. On-campus housing is guaranteed for all 4 years. Ninety percent of students live on campus. All students may keep cars on campus.

Activities: About 5% of men belong to 1 local and 1 national fraternity; about 5% of women belong to 1 local and 1 national sorority. There are 50 groups on campus, including art, band, cheerleading, choir, chorale, chorus, computers, drama, drill team, film, honors, international, jazz band, literary magazine, marching band, newspaper, orchestra, pep band, political, professional, radio and TV, religious, social, social service, student government, and yearbook. Popular campus events include Homecoming, Winter Olympics, Academic and Cultural Events Series, and Buenafication Day.

Sports: There are 8 intercollegiate sports for men and 7 for women, and 10 intramural sports for men and 10 for women. Athletic and recreation facilities include a 380-seat natatorium, 1000-seat auditorium, 4000-seat stadium, field house with 4000-seat gymnasium, and playing fields for basketball, volleyball, football, tennis, swimming, softball, baseball, track, racquetball, weight training, and other recreational activities.

Disabled Students: Ninety percent of the campus is accessible to disabled students. The following facilities are available: wheelchair ramps, elevators, special parking, specially equipped rest rooms, special class scheduling, lowered drinking fountains, and lowered telephones.

Services: In addition to many counseling and information services, tutoring is available in most subjects. There is remedial math, reading, and writing.

Campus Safety and Security: Campus safety and security measures include self defense education, escort service, informal discussions, and pamphlets, posters, and films. In addition, there are emergency telephones, lighted pathways and sidewalks, and and an enhanced 911 system on campus.

Programs of Study: Buena Vista awards the B.A. and B.S. degrees. Bachelor's degrees are awarded in BIOLOGICAL SCIENCE (biology/biological science), BUSINESS (accounting, banking and finance, business administration and management, business economics, international business management, and marketing/retailing/merchandising), COMMUNICATIONS AND THE ARTS (arts administration/management, communications, English, music, Spanish, and speech/debate/rhetoric), COMPUTER AND PHYSICAL SCIENCE (chemistry, computer programming, computer science, mathematics, and physics), EDUCATION (art, business, elementary, foreign languages, middle school, music, science, secondary, and special), SOCIAL SCIENCE (criminal justice, economics, history, philosophy, political science/government, psychology, religion, social science, and social work). Mass communication, business, education, and science are the strongest academically. Business, science, and education have the largest enrollments.

Required: All students must complete 3 semester hours of fine arts and 6 semester hours each of natural sciences, humanities, social sciences, communication, and writing. In addition, students must successfully complete English 100 and 200, demonstrate proficiency by examination in mathematics and writing, and participate in the Academic and Cultural Events Series. The bachelor's degree requires a minimum of 128 semester hours, including 30 to 62 hours in the major, with a GPA of at least 2.0, 2.5 for education majors.

Special: Special academic offerings include a Florida internship for business students, a work-study program with the Marriott hotel chain, and a 3–2 engineering degree program with Washington University in St. Louis. Students may study abroad in Japan, Taiwan, Australia, and Europe. Buena Vista offers student-designed majors, credit for life experience, and pass/fail options in courses outside the major field. Nondegree study is possible. Internships are required in many majors and encouraged in most. The J. Leslie Rollins Fellowship allows 1 or 2 students each year to design an internship anywhere in the world. There is a freshman honors program on campus, as well as 1 national honor society.

Faculty/Classroom: Sixty-six percent of faculty are male; 34%, female. All teach undergraduates. The average class size in an introductory lecture is 35; in a laboratory, 18; and in a regular course offering, 22.

Admissions: About 80% of the 1993-94 applicants were accepted. The SAT scores for the 1993-94 freshman class were as follows: Verbal—35% below 500, 61% between 500 and 599, 3% between 600 and 700, and 1% above 700; Math—28% below 500, 64% between 500 and 599, and 8% between 600 and 700. The ACT scores were 10% below 21, 34% between 21 and 23, 26% between 24 and 26, 18% between 27 and 28, and 12% above 28. About 41% of the current freshmen were in the top fifth of their class; 77% were in the top two fifths. There were 18 National Merit semifinalists. About 19 freshmen graduated first in their class.

Requirements: Buena Vista requires applicants to be in the upper 50% of their class. A minimum GPA of 2.8 is required. The ACT is recommended, but SAT I or PSAT scores may be submitted instead. Minimum scores should be 21 on the ACT or 950 on the SAT, with 475 on each part. Applicants must be graduates of an accredited secondary school or have earned a GED. The college requires 13 academic credits, including 4 of English, and 3 each of mathematics, social studies, and science. SAT II: Subject tests and an interview are recommended. AP and CLEP credits are accepted. Important factors used in the admissions decision are advanced placement or honor courses, leadership record, evidence of special talent, parents or siblings attending the school, and recommendations by alumni.

Procedure: Freshmen are admitted to all sessions. Entrance exams should be taken during the spring of the junior year or October of the senior year. Early decision applications should be filed by December 15; regular applications, by May 1 for fall entry, December 31 for winter entry, February 1 for spring entry, and May 15 for summer entry, along with an application fee of $25. Notification of early decision is sent January 15; regular decision, on a rolling basis. There are early decision, early admissions, and deferred admissions plans. About 150 early decision candidates were accepted for the 1993-94 class.

Transfer: About 63 transfer students enrolled in 1993-94. A high school diploma and a minimum GPA of 3.0 from the applicant's college are required. A total of 30 credits out of 128 must be completed at Buena Vista.

Visiting: There are regularly scheduled orientations for prospective students. Visitors meet with a faculty representative in their area of interest and coaches or representatives of activities in which they are interested. They tour the campus and meet with an admissions counselor. There are guides for informal visits, and visitors may sit in on classes and stay overnight at the school. To arrange for a visit, contact the Director of Admissions at (800) 383-9600.

Financial Aid: In 1993-94, 97% of all current freshmen and 94% of continuing students received some form of financial aid. About 89% of freshmen and 89% of continuing students received need-based aid. The average freshman award was $10,400. Of that total, scholarships or need-based grants averaged $6900 ($8000 maximum); loans averaged $3000 ($4125 maximum); and work contracts averaged $500 ($1200 maximum). All undergraduate students work part-time. Average earnings from campus work for the school year are $500. The average financial indebtedness of the 1992-93 graduate was $11,000. Buena Vista is a member of CSS. The FAF, FFS or SFS is required. The deadline for financial aid applications is April 15.

International Students: There are currently 40 international students enrolled. The school actively recruits these students. They must take the TOEFL or the Comprehensive English Language Test and achieve a minimum score on the TOEFL of 500. The student must also take the college's own entrance exam.

Computers: The college provides computer facilities for student use. The mainframe is a DEC VAX 6320. There are IBM and Macintosh laboratories located in the main computer center in the Harold Walter Siebens Business Forum. Some 35 to 40 terminals are located in the library, the residence hall lounges, and various other locations. Access to the Internet and electronic mail is available to students. All students may access the system. There are no time limits on using the system and no fees.

Graduates: In 1992-93, 657 bachelor's degrees were awarded. The most popular majors among graduates were business (41%), education (29%), and social/sciences (21%). Within an average freshman class, 3% graduate in 3 years, 52% in 4 years, 62% in 5 years, and 63% in 6 years. Some 50 companies recruited on campus in 1992-93.

Admissions Contact: Jo Loonan, Director of Admissions.

CENTRAL COLLEGE   D-3

Pella, IA 50219   (515) 628-5285; (800) 458-5503

Full-time: 604 men, 751 women	**Faculty:** 81; IIB, av$
Part-time: 17 men, 23 women	**Ph.D.s:** 86%
Graduate: none	**Student/Faculty:** 17 to 1
Year: 3 terms, summer session	**Tuition:** $10,365
Application Deadline: July 1	**Room & Board:** $3660
Freshman Class: 1294 applied, 1124 accepted, 401 enrolled	
SAT I or ACT: required	**VERY COMPETITIVE**

Central College, founded in 1853, is a private, coeducational institution affiliated with the Reformed Church in America. The college offers undergraduate degree programs in applied arts, behavioral sciences, cross-cultural studies, fine arts, humanities, and natural sciences. In addition to regional accreditation, Central has baccalaureate program accreditation with NASM and NCATE. The 4 libraries contain 175,000 volumes, 30,359 microform items, and 3865 audiovisual forms, and subscribe to 930 periodicals. Computerized library sources and services include the card catalog, interlibrary loans, and database searching. Special learning facilities include a learning resource center, art gallery, radio station, and a fiberoptic classroom. The 133-acre campus is in a suburban area 45 miles southeast of Des Moines. Including residence halls, there are 45 buildings on campus.

Student Life: About 79% of undergraduates are from Iowa. Students come from 31 states and 18 foreign countries. Ninety-seven percent are from public schools; 3% from private. Ninety-three percent are white. Seventy-three percent are Protestant; 19% Catholic. The average age of freshmen is 18; all undergraduates, 20. Seventeen percent drop out by the end of their first year; 70% remain to graduate.

Housing: A total of 1307 students can be accommodated in college housing. College-sponsored living facilities include single-sex and coed dormitories, on-campus apartments, married-student housing, fraternity houses, and sorority houses. In addition, there are honors houses, language houses, and special interest houses. On-campus housing is guaranteed for all 4 years. Eighty-nine percent of students live on campus; of those, 70% remain on campus on weekends. Alcohol is not permitted. All students may keep cars on campus.

Activities: About 12% of men belong to 4 local fraternities; about 5% of women belong to 2 local sororities. There are 30 groups on campus, including art, band, cheerleading, choir, chorus, drama, drill team, ethnic, gay, honors, international, jazz band, literary magazine, marching band, musical theater, newspaper, opera, orchestra, pep band, photography, political, professional, radio and TV, religious, social, social service, student government, symphony, and yearbook. Popular campus events include Homecoming, Career Day, Interdisciplinary Research Symposium, Academic Seminar, Cultural Series, and Student Conference on Global Awareness.

Sports: There are 9 intercollegiate sports for men and 7 for women, and 12 intramural sports for men and 11 for women. Athletic and recreation facilities include an athletic complex, with a 7000-seat stadium and 2500-seat gymnasium, a 700-seat auditorium, a golf driving range, several practice and competition fields, tennis courts, and a field house with an indoor track.

Disabled Students: Eighty percent of the campus is accessible to disabled students. The following facilities are available: wheelchair ramps, elevators, special parking, specially equipped rest rooms, special class scheduling, lowered drinking fountains, and lowered telephones.

Services: In addition to many counseling and information services, tutoring is available in every subject. There is also a reader service for the blind.

Campus Safety and Security: Campus safety and security measures include 24-hour foot and vehicle patrol, escort service, informal discussions, and pamphlets, posters, and films. In addition, there are emergency telephones and lighted pathways and sidewalks.

Programs of Study: Central awards the B.A. degree. Bachelor's degrees are awarded in BIOLOGICAL SCIENCE (biology/biological science), BUSINESS (accounting, business administration and management, and international business management), COMMUNICATIONS AND THE ARTS (communications, dramatic arts, English, fine arts, French, German, languages, linguistics, music, and Spanish), COMPUTER AND PHYSICAL SCIENCE (chemistry, computer science, mathematics, and physics), EDUCATION (elementary, music, and secondary), ENGINEERING AND ENVIRONMENTAL DESIGN (environmental science and preengineering), HEALTH PROFESSIONS (health), SOCIAL SCIENCE (anthropology, economics, history, international studies, philosophy, political science/government, prelaw, psychology, religion, sociology, and urban studies). Political science, international studies, and religion/philosophy are the strongest academically. Economics, accounting, international business, and education have the largest enrollments.

Required: General education requirements include 10 quarter hours of humanities and 5 quarter hours each of behavioral sciences, cross-cultural studies, fine arts, and natural sciences, and 1 course in religion. Each department also establishes a communication skill requirement. To graduate, students must complete a minimum of 180 quarter hours (36 courses), including 40 to 90 in a major field, with a GPA of at least 2.0.

Special: Nearly half the students participate in study abroad programs in China, London, Paris, Vienna, Mexico, Spain, Wales, and the Netherlands. Central also offers a Washington semester, a Chicago program, numerous internship opportunities, and work-study. A B.A.-B.S. degree in engineering, a 3–4 program in architecture, and a 3–2 degree program in engineering are offered with Washington University in St. Louis. A general studies degree, student-designed majors, and pass/fail no credit options are possible. There is a freshman honors program on campus, as well as 1 national honor society.

Faculty/Classroom: Fifty-eight percent of faculty are male; 42%, female. All teach undergraduates and 40% both teach and do research. The average class size in an introductory lecture is 25; in a laboratory, 19; and in a regular course offering, 20.

Admissions: About 87% of the 1993–94 applicants were accepted. The ACT scores for the 1993–94 freshman class were as follows: 21% below 21, 24% between 21 and 23, 28% between 24 and 26, 15% between 27 and 28, and 12% above 28. About 55% of the current freshmen were in the top fifth of their class; 85% were in the top two fifths. There were 3 National Merit finalists and 7 semifinalists. About 24 freshmen graduated first in their class.

Requirements: Central requires applicants to be in the upper 50% of their class. The ACT (preferred) or SAT I is required. Applicants must be graduates of an accredited secondary school or have earned a GED. Central requires 16 academic credits and recommends that they include 4 years of English, 2 of foreign language, and 3 each of laboratory science, social studies, and mathematics, including 2 in algebra and 1 in geometry. An interview is required, and an essay is recommended. AP and CLEP credits are accepted. Important factors used in the admissions decision are evidence of special talent, advanced placement or honor courses, leadership record, extracurricular activities record, and recommendations by school officials.

Procedure: Freshmen are admitted to all sessions. Entrance exams should be taken in the spring of the junior year. Applications should be filed by July 1 for fall entry, September 1 for winter entry, February 1 for spring entry, and May 1 for summer entry, along with an application fee of $20. Notification is sent on a rolling basis. There is a deferred admissions plan.

Transfer: About 44 transfer students enrolled in 1993–94. Each transfer student is considered individually. Interviews are encouraged. A total of 90 quarter hours out of 180 must be completed at Central.

Visiting: There are regularly scheduled orientations for prospective students, including a campus tour, a registration session with an academic advisor, and presentations by the academic dean, student life dean, financial aid director, and admission staff. There are guides for informal visits, and visitors may sit in on classes and stay overnight at the school. To arrange for a visit, contact the Admission Office at (800) 458–5503.

Financial Aid: In 1993–94 96% of all current freshmen and 97% of continuing students received some form of financial aid. About 84% of freshmen and 77% of continuing students received need-based aid. The average freshman award was $8213. Of that total, scholarships or need-based grants averaged $5031 ($13,000 maximum); loans averaged $3024 ($4125 maximum); and work contracts averaged $900 ($1500 maximum). Eighty percent of undergraduate students work part-time. Average earnings from campus work for the school year were $600. The average financial indebtedness of the 1992–93 graduate was $8569. Central is a member of CSS. The FAF, FFS or SFS is required. The deadline for financial aid applications is April 1.

International Students: There are currently 62 international students enrolled. The school actively recruits these students. They must take the TOEFL and achieve a minimum score of 530.

Computers: The college provides computer facilities for student use. The mainframe is a DEC VAX 3400 and an AT&T 382/4000. There are also 5 VAX 3100 workstations, 63 terminals, and 159 microcomputers located in 7 laboratories across campus. Languages supported include Pascal, COBOL, C, PROLOG, LISP, BASIC, FORTRAN, Ada, and Modula-2. Statistical packages available are Minitab and SPSS. Also used are WordPerfect for word processing and SuperCalc 4 for spreadsheet applications. All students may access the system. There are no time limits on using the system and no fees.

Graduates: In 1992–93 389 bachelor's degrees were awarded. The most popular majors among graduates were elementary education (14%), business management (11%), and general studies (8%). Within an average freshman class, 2% graduate in 3 years, 61% in 4 years, and 67% in 5 years. Some 85 companies recruited on campus in 1992–93. In the 1992 graduating class, 15% of the men and 13% of

the women were enrolled in graduate school within 6 months of graduation; 100% of the men and 100% of the women had found employment.

Admissions Contact: Eric Sickler, Vice President for Admission and Marketing.

CLARKE COLLEGE
E-2

Dubuque, IA 52001	(319) 588-6316; (800) 383-2345
Full-time: 192 men, 412 women	Faculty: 57; IIB, --$
Part-time: 97 men, 253 women	Ph.D.s: 68%
Graduate: 1 man, 25 women	Student/Faculty: 11 to 1
Year: semesters, summer session	Tuition: $10,455
Application Deadline: open	Room & Board: $3495
Freshman Class: 460 applied, 340 accepted, 208 enrolled	
ACT: 24	COMPETITIVE +

Clarke College, established in 1843, is a nonprofit, private, Catholic institution. A strong focus on the liberal arts underlies all majors and preprofessional programs. In addition to regional accreditation, Clarke has baccalaureate program accreditation with NASM, NCATE, and NLN. The library contains 102,216 volumes, 8000 microform items, and 44,060 audiovisual forms, and subscribes to 684 periodicals. Computerized library sources and services include the card catalog, interlibrary loans, and database searching. Special learning facilities include a learning resource center, art gallery, planetarium, and an art slide library. The 60-acre campus is in an urban area 180 miles west of Chicago. Including residence halls, there are 12 buildings on campus.

Student Life: About 50% of undergraduates are from out-of-state, mostly the Midwest. Students come from 15 states and 6 foreign countries. Seventy-two percent are from public schools; 28% from private. Eighty-nine percent are white. Sixty-four percent are Catholic; 20% Protestant; 13% claim no religious affiliation. The average age of freshmen is 20.9; all undergraduates, 23.8. Fourteen percent drop out by the end of their first year; 63% remain to graduate.

Housing: A total of 399 students can be accommodated in college housing. College-sponsored living facilities include single-sex and coed dormitories. In addition, there are special interest houses and a dormitory housing only upperclassmen. On-campus housing is guaranteed for all 4 years. Fifty-nine percent of students live on campus; of those, 80% remain on campus on weekends. All students may keep cars on campus.

Activities: There are no fraternities or sororities on campus. There are 41 groups on campus, including art, band, cheerleading, choir, chorus, computers, dance, drama, drill team, ethnic, honors, international, jazz band, literary magazine, musical theater, newspaper, pep band, photography, political, professional, religious, social, social service, student government, symphony, and yearbook. Popular campus events include Homecoming, New Year's Dance, Midnight Pancake Breakfast, Valentine's Dance, Christmas Dinner, Peace and Justice Week, Brother/Sister Weekend, and Parents Weekend.

Sports: There are 8 intercollegiate sports for men and 8 for women, and 15 intramural sports for men and 15 for women. Athletic and recreation facilities include a 1000-seat gymnasium, a 700-seat arena, an indoor track, a swimming pool, a soccer field, basketball, volleyball, and tennis courts, a fitness trail, and a weight/exercise room. There are 2 ski courses nearby and a municipal golf course next to the campus.

Disabled Students: Ninety-five percent of the campus is accessible to disabled students. The following facilities are available: wheelchair ramps, elevators, special parking, specially equipped rest rooms, and lowered drinking fountains.

Services: In addition to many counseling and information services, tutoring is available in every subject. There is remedial math, reading, and writing.

Campus Safety and Security: Campus safety and security measures include 24-hour foot and vehicle patrol, informal discussions, pamphlets, posters, films, lighted pathways and sidewalks.

Programs of Study: Clarke awards the B.A., B.S., and B.F.A. degrees. Associate and master's degrees also are awarded. Bachelor's degrees are awarded in BIOLOGICAL SCIENCE (biology/biological science and molecular biology), BUSINESS (accounting, business administration and management, and marketing management), COMMUNICATIONS AND THE ARTS (advertising, art, art history and appreciation, communications, dramatic arts, English, fine arts, French, music, Spanish, and studio art), COMPUTER AND PHYSICAL SCIENCE (chemistry, computer science, information sciences and systems, and mathematics), EDUCATION (art, business, early childhood, education of the mentally handicapped, elementary, music, physical, secondary, and special), HEALTH PROFESSIONS (medical laboratory technology and nursing), SOCIAL SCIENCE (history, philosophy, political science/government, psychology, religion, social work, and sociology). Art, drama, chemistry, computer science, education, nursing, and human biology are the strongest academical-

ly. Business, computer science, education, art, nursing, and human biology have the largest enrollments.

Required: To graduate, all students must complete 124 semester hours, with 30 to 70 hours in the major, and maintain a GPA of 2.0. Students must complete courses in logic, composition, speech, research, and thinking skills, must demonstrate computer literacy, and must take Senior Performance, an integrative studies course in the major. The 54-hour core curriculum also includes 9 hours each of science, social sciences, and humanities, and 6 hours each of religious studies, multicultural studies, and philosophy.

Special: There are cooperative programs in all majors, cross-registration with Loras College and the University of Dubuque, and study abroad. Internships are available in physical therapy, chemistry, biology, and communications, and there is an accelerated degree program in business management, communications, nursing, advertising, and computer information systems, and a B.A.-B.S. degree in biology, chemistry, psychology, and computer science, as well as a B.F.A.-B.A. in art. There are also on-campus work-study programs, dual majors, student-designed majors, and a 3–2 engineering degree with Washington University of St. Louis and University of Southern California. There is a freshman honors program on campus, as well as 4 national honor societies. Three departments have honors programs.

Faculty/Classroom: Thirty-eight percent of faculty are male; 62%, female. All teach undergraduates, 3% do research, and 18% do both. No introductory courses are taught by graduate students. The average class size in an introductory lecture is 25; in a laboratory, 16; and in a regular course offering, 18.

Admissions: About 74% of the 1993–94 applicants were accepted. The ACT scores for the 1993–94 freshman class were as follows: 23% below 21, 31% between 21 and 23, 27% between 24 and 26, 11% between 27 and 28, and 8% above 28. About 37% of the current freshmen were in the top fifth of their class; 66% were in the top two fifths.

Requirements: Clarke requires applicants to be in the upper 50% of their class. A minimum GPA of 2.0 is required. The SAT I or ACT is required. In addition, students must submit an essay and a recommendation from a teacher or counselor. An interview is recommended. High school courses should include 4 years of English, 3 of mathematics, 2 each of history/social science, a foreign language, and science (3 years of science is recommended, 4 for human biology majors). AP and CLEP credits are accepted. Important factors used in the admissions decision are recommendations by school officials, advanced placement or honor courses, evidence of special talent, leadership record, and extracurricular activities record.

Procedure: Freshmen are admitted to all sessions. Entrance exams should be taken in the spring of the junior year or the fall of the senior year. Application deadlines are open. Notification is sent about 3 weeks after receipt of the application. The application fee is $20. There are early admissions and deferred admissions plans.

Transfer: A total of 77 transfer students enrolled in 1993–94. Transfer students must have a high school diploma or a GED and at least 24 college credits with a 2.0 GPA. A total of 30 credits out of 124 must be completed at Clarke.

Visiting: There are regularly scheduled orientations for prospective students, including a welcome from the president, an academic presentation, a campus tour, meetings with faculty, a student life panel, lunch, a financial aid and admissions presentation. There are guides for informal visits, and visitors may sit in on classes and stay overnight at the school. To arrange for a visit, contact the Admissions Office at (800) 383-2345.

Financial Aid: In 1993–94, 93% of all current freshmen and 71% of continuing students received some form of financial aid. About 78% of freshmen and 62% of continuing students received need-based aid. The average freshman award was $8698. Of that total, scholarships or need-based grants averaged $5938 ($11,265 maximum); loans averaged $3035 ($5300 maximum); and work contracts averaged $1467 ($2100 maximum). Twenty-four percent of undergraduate students work part-time. Average earnings from campus work for the school year are $1414. The average financial indebtedness of the 1992–93 graduate was $7417. Clarke is a member of CSS. The FAF or FFS and FAFSA are required. The deadline for financial aid applications is March 15.

International Students: There are currently 13 international students enrolled. They must take the TOEFL and achieve a minimum score of 550. The student must also take the SAT I and achieve a minimum score of 900.

Computers: The college provides computer facilities for student use. The mainframes are an IBM 9370 Model 60 and an IBM RS 6000 Model 340. In addition, there are 84 microcomputers located in laboratories for student use. All of these have mainframe access in addition to their use as microcomputers; 14 of these are networked. All students may access the system 24 hours a day, 7 days a week. There are no time limits on using the system and no fees.

Graduates: In 1992–93 130 bachelor's degrees were awarded. The most popular majors among graduates were business/accounting (20%), computer science (15%), and communications (12%). Within an average freshman class, 63% graduate in 4 years, 70% in 5 years, and 73% in 6 years. Some 64 companies recruited on campus in 1992–93. Of the 1992 graduating class, 7% were enrolled in graduate school within 6 months of graduation.

Admissions Contact: Bobbe Ames, Vice President of Institutional Marketing/Recruitment.

COE COLLEGE
E-3
Cedar Rapids, IA 52402

(319) 399-8500
(800) 332-8404 (out-of-state)

Full-time: 513 men, 614 women
Part-time: 90 men, 115 women
Graduate: 8 men, 14 women
Year: 4–1–4, summer session
Application Deadline: open
Freshman Class: 1006 applied, 742 accepted, 275 enrolled
SAT I Verbal/Math: 520/560

Faculty: 83; IIB, +$
Ph.D.s: 85%
Student/Faculty: 14 to 1
Tuition: $12,805
Room & Board: $4280

ACT: 25   **VERY COMPETITIVE**

Coe College, founded in 1851, is a private, liberal arts college affiliated with the United Presbyterian Church. In addition to regional accreditation, Coe has baccalaureate program accreditation with NASM and NCATE. The 2 libraries contain 180,448 volumes, 35,328 microform items, and 6031 audiovisual forms, and subscribe to 870 periodicals. Computerized library sources and services include the card catalog, interlibrary loans, and database searching. Special learning facilities include a learning resource center, art gallery, planetarium, and an ornithological wing. The 55-acre campus is in an urban area 225 miles west of Chicago, Illinois. Including residence halls, there are 18 buildings on campus.

Student Life: About 58% of undergraduates are from Iowa. Students come from 35 states and 20 foreign countries. Eighty-five percent are from public schools; 15% from private. Eighty-seven percent are white. The average age of freshmen is 18; all undergraduates, 20. Eighteen percent drop out by the end of their first year; 70% remain to graduate.

Housing: A total of 890 students can be accommodated in college housing. College-sponsored living facilities include single-sex and coed dormitories and on-campus apartments. In addition, there are special interest houses. On-campus housing is guaranteed for all 4 years. Eighty percent of students live on campus; of those, 75% remain on campus on weekends. All students may keep cars on campus.

Activities: About 30% of men belong to 4 national fraternities; about 30% of women belong to 3 national sororities. There are 50 groups on campus, including art, band, cheerleading, choir, chorale, chorus, computers, dance, drama, ethnic, honors, international, jazz band, literary magazine, musical theater, newspaper, orchestra, pep band, political, professional, religious, social, social service, student government, symphony, and yearbook. Popular campus events include Homecoming, Coe Olympics, International Student Banquet and Cultural Show, Flunk Day, Multicultural Awareness, Minnesota Theatrical Group performances, art shows, and convocations.

Sports: There are 11 intercollegiate sports for men and 9 for women, and 8 intramural sports for men and 8 for women. Athletic and recreation facilities include a racquet center with 4 indoor and 6 outdoor tennis, 4 racquetball, and 2 squash courts, and a 200-meter indoor track. There also are a 400-meter outdoor track, a softball diamond, and an 1100-seat football/soccer stadium.

Disabled Students: Twenty-five percent of the campus is accessible to disabled students. The following facilities are available: wheelchair ramps, elevators, special parking, and specially equipped rest rooms.

Services: In addition to many counseling and information services, tutoring is available in most subjects. There is a reader service for the blind. A writing center and an educational support program are also available.

Campus Safety and Security: Campus safety and security measures include 24-hour foot and vehicle patrols, escort service, informal discussions, and pamphlets, posters, and films. In addition, there are emergency telephones and lighted pathways and sidewalks.

Programs of Study: Coe awards the B.A., B.Mus., and B.S.N. degrees. Master's degrees also are awarded. Bachelor's degrees are awarded in BIOLOGICAL SCIENCE (biology/biological science), BUSINESS (accounting and business administration and management), COMMUNICATIONS AND THE ARTS (art, dramatic arts, English, French, German, literature, music, and Spanish), COMPUTER AND PHYSICAL SCIENCE (chemistry, computer science, mathematics, physics, and science), EDUCATION (elementary, music, physical, and secondary), ENGINEERING AND ENVIRONMENTAL DESIGN (preengineering), HEALTH PROFESSIONS (medical laboratory technology, nursing, predentistry, and premedicine), and SOCIAL SCIENCE (African American studies, American studies, Asian/Oriental studies, classical/ancient civilization, economics, history, interdisci-

plinary studies, philosophy, political science/government, prelaw, psychology, religion, and sociology). Biology, psychology, chemistry, physics, business administration, economics, and English are the strongest academically. Business administration, psychology, and English have the largest enrollments.

Required: All students must take 4 writing-emphasis courses, a first-year seminar course, a comprehensive exam in psychology, and a distribution of courses in fine arts, natural science, social science, and Western and foreign culture. A minimum of 36 course credits and a 2.0 GPA are required. Students in an honors program must submit a thesis, and psychology majors must pass a comprehensive exam.

Special: Cross-registration with nearby Mount Mercy College and the University of Iowa, cooperative 3–2 degree programs with Washington University in St. Louis in engineering, and programs in architecture, occupational therapy, and social services administration are available. Internships, study abroad in 8 countries, nondegree study, and dual and student-designed majors also are possible. There are also Washington and New York semesters. Core-course instructors provide an ongoing 6-week orientation for freshmen. There is a freshman honors program on campus, as well as 5 national honor societies, including Phi Beta Kappa. In addition, all departments have honors programs.

Faculty/Classroom: Seventy-one percent of faculty are male; 29%, female. All teach undergraduates, 90% do research, and 90% do both. No introductory courses are taught by graduate students. The average class size in an introductory lecture is 20; in a laboratory, 15; and in a regular course offering, 18.

Admissions: About 74% of the 1993–94 applicants were accepted. The SAT scores for the 1993–94 freshman class were as follows: Verbal—48% below 500, 38% between 500 and 599, and 14% between 600 and 700; Math—29% below 500, 36% between 500 and 599, 27% between 600 and 700, and 8% above 700. The ACT scores were 15% below 21, 29% between 21 and 23, 30% between 24 and 26, 13% between 27 and 28, and 13% above 28. About 50% of the current freshmen were in the top fifth of their class; 85% were in the top two fifths. Five freshmen in a recent year graduated first in their class.

Requirements: Coe requires applicants to be in the upper 50% of their class. A minimum GPA of 2.5 is required. The SAT I or ACT is required. Coe recommends that applicants have 4 years in English, 3 in mathematics, and 2 each in foreign language, history, science, and social studies. All students must also submit an essay. In addition, fine arts students need a portfolio or audition. The GED is accepted. AP and CLEP credits are accepted. Important factors used in the admissions decision are advanced placement or honors courses, recommendations by school officials, leadership record, extracurricular activities record, and personality, intangible qualities.

Procedure: Freshmen are admitted fall and spring. Entrance exams should be taken in the spring of the junior year or the fall of the senior year. Application deadlines are open. Application fee is $25. Notification of early decision is sent December 15; regular decision, on a rolling basis. There are early decision, early admissions, and deferred admissions plans. About 20 early decision candidates were accepted for the 1993–94 class.

Transfer: About 79 transfer students enrolled in 1993–94. Transfer applicants must be high school graduates, have a minimum GPA of 2.5, and submit either SAT I or ACT scores. An associate degree and an interview also are recommended. A total of 9 course credits out of 36 must be completed at Coe.

Visiting: There are regularly scheduled orientations for prospective students. There are guides for informal visits, and visitors may sit in on classes and stay overnight at the school. To arrange for a visit, contact Sharon Fair, Campus Visit Coordinator, at (800) 332–8404.

Financial Aid: In 1993–94, 90% of all current freshmen and 89% of continuing students received some form of financial aid. About 85% of freshmen and 82% of continuing students received need-based aid. The average freshman award was $11,989. Of that total, scholarships or need-based grants averaged $7714 ($12,680 maximum); loans averaged $3375 ($4625 maximum); and work contracts averaged $900 ($1350 maximum). Forty-seven percent of undergraduate students work part-time. Average earnings from campus work for the school year are $850. The average financial indebtedness of recent graduates was $9950. Coe is a member of CSS. The FAFSA financial statement is required. The deadline for financial aid applications is March 1.

International Students: There are currently 66 international students enrolled. The school actively recruits these students. They must take the TOEFL and achieve a minimum score of 500. The student must also take the SAT I or the ACT.

Computers: The college provides computer facilities for student use. The mainframe is an IBM 36. Students may access the campus network from approximately 80 PCs located in 5 laboratories on campus. All students may access the system, which is available 15 hours per day. There are no time limits on students' use of the system and no fees.

Graduates: In 1992–93, 221 bachelor's degrees were awarded. The most popular majors among graduates were economics and business administration (28%), psychology (12%), and biology (7%). Within an average freshman class, 1% graduate in 3 years, 68% in 4 years, 73% in 5 years, and 73% in 6 years. Some 70 companies recruited on campus in 1992–93. In the 1992 graduating class, 12% of the men and 14% of the women were enrolled in graduate school within 6 months of graduation; 32% of the men and 34% of the women had found employment.

Admissions Contact: Michael White, Vice President for Admissions and Financial Aid.

CORNELL COLLEGE
Mount Vernon, IA 52314

E-3

(319) 895–4215
(800) 747–1112 (out-of-state)

Full-time: 478 men, 662 women	Faculty: 75; IIB, +$
Part-time: 4 men, 6 women	Ph.D.s: 76%
Graduate: none	Student/Faculty: 15 to 1
Year: see profile	Tuition: $14,228
Application Deadline: March 1	Room & Board: $4197

Freshman Class: 1538 applied, 1329 accepted, 383 enrolled
SAT I Verbal/Math: 520/560   ACT: 25   **VERY COMPETITIVE**

Cornell College, founded in 1853, is a nonprofit, independent institution affiliated with the United Methodist Church. Its emphases are on the liberal arts, business, art and fine arts, health science, music, and teacher preparation. Cornell has a one-course-at-a-time calendar in which the year is divided into nine 3 1/2 week terms. The 2 libraries contain 185,000 volumes, 143,424 microform items, and 8554 audiovisual forms, and subscribe to 579 periodicals. Computerized library sources and services include the card catalog, interlibrary loans, and database searching. Special learning facilities include a learning resource center, art gallery, natural history museum, and radio station. The 129-acre campus is in a small town 15 miles east of Cedar Rapids and 20 miles north of Iowa City. Including residence halls, there are 41 buildings on campus.

Student Life: About 73% of undergraduates are from out-of-state, mostly the Midwest. Students come from 44 states and 17 foreign countries. Eighty-five percent are from public schools. Ninety-one percent are white. The average age of freshmen is 18; all undergraduates, 20. Twenty-four percent drop out by the end of their first year; 65% remain to graduate.

Housing: A total of 1020 students can be accommodated in college housing. College-sponsored living facilities include single-sex and coed dormitories, on-campus apartments, and off-campus apartments. In addition there are language houses, special interest houses, and accommodations for both the Women's and Men's Affinity Program members. On-campus housing is guaranteed for all 4 years. Ninety-three percent of students live on campus; of those, 85% remain on campus on weekends. All students may keep cars on campus.

Activities: About 35% of men belong to 7 local fraternities; about 35% of women belong to 6 local sororities. There are 70 groups on campus, including art, band, cheerleading, chess, choir, chorale, chorus, computers, dance, drama, ethnic, gay, honors, international, jazz band, literary magazine, musical theater, newspaper, opera, orchestra, pep band, photography, political, professional, religious, social, social service, student government, and yearbook. Popular campus events include Homecoming, Parents Weekend, Winter Weekend, the Yacht Club Variety Show, and Block Break Weekends.

Sports: There are 10 intercollegiate sports for men and 8 for women, and 15 intramural sports for men and 15 for women. Athletic and recreation facilities include an 1800-seat stadium and a 1700-seat gymnasium; football, track, and baseball facilities; a sports center with racquetball, volleyball, basketball, and tennis courts; a track; a weight room; a pool; a sauna; batting cages; and facilities for soccer.

Disabled Students: Twenty percent of the campus is accessible to disabled students. The following facilities are available: wheelchair ramps, elevators, special parking, specially equipped rest rooms, and special class scheduling.

Services: In addition to many counseling and information services, tutoring is available in every subject. There is a reader service for the blind, and remedial math, reading, and writing.

Campus Safety and Security: Campus safety and security measures include 24-hour foot and vehicle patrol, self defense education, escort service, and informal discussions. In addition, there are pamphlets, posters, and films, emergency telephones, lighted pathways and sidewalks, and and the safety-oriented campus organizations: SAFE (Students for an Assault-Free Environment) and STEPS (Students to Escort People Safely).

Programs of Study: Cornell awards the B.A., B.M., B.Ph., and B.S.S. degrees. Bachelor's degrees are awarded in BIOLOGICAL SCIENCE (biology/biological science), BUSINESS (international business management), COMMUNICATIONS AND THE ARTS (dramatic arts, English, fine arts, French, German, languages, music, Russian, Spanish, and speech/debate/rhetoric), COMPUTER AND PHYSICAL SCI-

ENCE (chemistry, computer science, geology, mathematics, and physics), EDUCATION (art, elementary, foreign languages, music, science, and secondary), ENGINEERING AND ENVIRONMENTAL DESIGN (environmental science), HEALTH PROFESSIONS (occupational therapy), SOCIAL SCIENCE (anthropology, classical/ancient civilization, economics, history, international relations, Latin American studies, medieval studies, philosophy, political science/government, psychology, religion, Russian and Slavic studies, sociology, urban studies, and women's studies). Economics and business, education, English, psychology, politics, history, and biology have the largest enrollments.

Required: To graduate, all students must complete 32 course credits (128 semester hours), with 7 to 15 in a faculty-approved major, and maintain at least a 2.0 GPA. Course requirements include 3 in humanities, 2 each in science and social science, 1 each in fine arts and mathematics, and 1 to 4 in a foreign language. Bachelor's degree candidates must take physical education.

Special: Special academic programs include 25 study-abroad opportunities and internships, including a Washington Center Internship. There is an accelerated degree program in all majors, as well as dual majors in all areas. Student-designed majors are available, and interdepartmental/interdisciplinary majors include biochemistry and molecular biology and origins of behavior. There is a 3–2 engineering program, a 3–4 architecture program, and a 3–2 occupational therapy program with Washington University in St. Louis; a 3–2 social services program with the University of Chicago; a 3–2 forestry and environmental management program with Duke University; and a 3–2 natural resource management program with the University of Michigan. Nondegree study is possible, as are pass/fail options, with restrictions. There are 8 national honor societies on campus, including Phi Beta Kappa.

Faculty/Classroom: Seventy-eight percent of faculty are male; 22%, female. All teach undergraduates and 30% also do research. The average class size in an introductory lecture is 22; in a laboratory, 18; and in a regular course offering, 16.

Admissions: About 86% of the 1993–94 applicants were accepted. The SAT scores for the 1993–94 freshman class were as follows: Verbal—40% below 500, 35% between 500 and 599, 21% between 600 and 700, and 4% above 700; Math—25% below 500, 45% between 500 and 599, 22% between 600 and 700, and 8% above 700. The ACT scores were 10% below 21, 17% between 21 and 23, 34% between 24 and 26, 18% between 27 and 28, and 21% above 28. About 57% of the current freshmen were in the top fifth of their class; 84% were in the top two fifths.

Requirements: Cornell requires applicants to be in the upper 50% of their class. A minimum GPA of 2.5 is required. The SAT I or ACT is required. Applicants must be graduates of an accredited secondary school, with a recommended 4 years each of English and history/social studies, 3 each of mathematics and science, 2 to 4 of a foreign language, and 1 each of art and music. The GED is accepted. An essay is required and an interview is advised. AP and CLEP credits are accepted. Important factors used in the admissions decision are leadership record, evidence of special talent, recommendations by school officials, advanced placement or honors courses, and extracurricular activities record.

Procedure: Freshmen are admitted fall and winter. Entrance exams should be taken in the spring of the junior year. Early decision applications should be filed by December 1; regular applications, by March 1 for fall entry, along with an application fee of $25. Notification of early decision is sent December 20; regular decision, April 1. There are early decision and deferred admissions plans. About 355 early decision candidates were accepted for the 1993–94 class. A waiting list is an active part of the admissions procedure, with about 10% of applicants on the list.

Transfer: About 21 transfer students enrolled in 1993–94. Transfer applicants must have a minimum GPA of 3.0 and a recommended 30 semester hours earned in course work parallel to that of Cornell's. An interview is advised. A total of 8 courses must be completed at Cornell.

Visiting: There are regularly scheduled orientations for prospective students, consisting of video and campus tours and meetings with an informational panel, a student panel, and financial aid staff. There are guides for informal visits and visitors may sit in on classes and stay overnight at the school. To arrange for a visit, contact Judy Penn, Visit Coordinator, at (800) 747–1112.

Financial Aid: In 1993–94, 80% of all current freshmen and 75% of continuing students received some form of financial aid. About 68% of all students received need-based aid. The average freshman award was $13,000. Of that total, scholarships or need-based grants averaged $8986 ($12,240 maximum); loans averaged $3125 ($3625 maximum); and work contracts averaged $889 ($1200 maximum). Sixty percent of undergraduate students work part-time. Average earnings from campus work for the school year are $1200. The average financial indebtedness of recent graduates was $10,000.

Cornell is a member of CSS. The FAF, FFS or SFS is required. The deadline for financial aid applications is March 1.

International Students: There are currently 27 international students enrolled. The school actively recruits these students. They must take the TOEFL and achieve a minimum score of 500.

Computers: The college provides computer facilities for student use. The mainframe is a VAXstation 3100 and a MicroVAX 3300 clustered. There is a dedicated laboratory with 12 Apollo/HP workstations running under the UNIX operating system. There are also 150 microcomputers in laboratories in academic buildings, the library, and the Commons for student use. All academic computer facilities have access to the Internet system. Students may also access the system by modem. All students may access the system. It may be used from 6 A.M. to 11 P.M. There are no time limits on each student's use of the system and no fees.

Graduates: In 1992–93 249 bachelor's degrees were awarded. The most popular majors among graduates were economics and business (11%), psychology (9%), and education (8%). Within an average freshman class, 65% graduate in 4 years. Some 60 companies recruited on campus in 1992–93.

Admissions Contact: Kevin W. Crockett, Dean of Admissions and Enrollment Management.

DORDT COLLEGE
B-1
Sioux Center, IA 51250

(712) 722–6080
(800) 34-DORDT (out-of-state)

Full-time: 525 men, 579 women	Faculty: 75; IIB, -$
Part-time: 14 men, 42 women	Ph.D.s: 60%
Graduate: none	Student/Faculty: 15 to 1
Year: semesters	Tuition: $9250
Application Deadline: August 15	Room & Board: $2440
Freshman Class: 604 applied, 562 accepted, 323 enrolled	
ACT: 23	COMPETITIVE

Dordt College, founded in 1955, is a private, coeducational institution affiliated with the Christian Reformed Church. The curriculum, which is designed to reflect the principles of the Christian faith, leads to degrees in liberal arts, agriculture, art, music, business, engineering, and teaching preparation. In addition to regional accreditation, Dordt has baccalaureate program accreditation with ABET and CSWE. The library contains 12,157 volumes, 14,819 microform items, and 3616 audiovisual forms, and subscribes to 489 periodicals. Special learning facilities include a learning resource center, planetarium, radio station, and 2 observatories, as well as a 160-acre agriculture stewardship center just north of the campus. The 45-acre campus is in a rural area 42 miles north of Sioux City. Including residence halls, there are 18 buildings on campus.

Student Life: About 62% of undergraduates are from out-of-state, mostly the Midwest. Students come from 33 states, 9 foreign countries, and Canada. Forty percent are from public schools; 60% from private. Ninety-five percent are white. Most are Protestant. The average age of freshmen is 18; all undergraduates, 20. Fifteen percent drop out by the end of their first year; 55% remain to graduate.

Housing: A total of 850 students can be accommodated in college housing. College-sponsored living facilities include single-sex and coed dormitories, on-campus apartments, off-campus apartments, and married-student housing. On-campus housing is guaranteed for all 4 years. Eighty percent of students live on campus; of those, 75% remain on campus on weekends. Alcohol is not permitted. All students may keep cars on campus.

Activities: There are no fraternities or sororities on campus. There are 15 groups on campus, including band, cheerleading, choir, chorale, computers, dance, international, jazz band, literary magazine, newspaper, opera, orchestra, radio and TV, religious, social, social service, student government, and yearbook. Popular campus events include Homecoming in February.

Sports: There are 7 intercollegiate sports for men and 6 for women, and 10 intramural sports for men and 10 for women. Athletic and recreation facilities include a 2500-seat gymnasium with 2 courts, a racquetball court, a weight room, soccer and other playing fields, and an indoor pool adjacent to the campus.

Disabled Students: Ninety percent of the campus is accessible to disabled students. The following facilities are available: elevators, specially equipped rest rooms, special class scheduling, lowered drinking fountains, and lowered telephones.

Services: In addition to many counseling and information services, tutoring is available in most subjects.

Campus Safety and Security: Campus safety and security measures include lighted pathways and sidewalks.

Programs of Study: Dordt awards the B.A., B.S., and B.S.W. degrees. Associate degrees also are awarded. Bachelor's degrees are awarded in BIOLOGICAL SCIENCE (biology/biological science), BUSINESS (accounting and business administration and management), COMMUNICATIONS AND THE ARTS (broadcasting, communications, dramatic arts, English, fine arts, journalism, languages, mu-

sic, and speech/debate/rhetoric), COMPUTER AND PHYSICAL SCIENCE (chemistry, computer programming, computer science, information sciences and systems, mathematics, and physics), EDUCATION (art, business, elementary, foreign languages, music, and secondary), ENGINEERING AND ENVIRONMENTAL DESIGN (chemical engineering, electrical/electronics engineering, engineering, and mechanical engineering), HEALTH PROFESSIONS (medical laboratory technology, predentistry, and premedicine), SOCIAL SCIENCE (history, philosophy, political science/government, prelaw, psychology, religion, social science, social work, and sociology). Engineering is the strongest academically. Education has the largest enrollment.

Required: All students must complete a college introductory course and a distribution of 14 other courses in the various academic disciplines, including General Education 300. Proficiency requirements must be met in computer science, mathematics, and physical education. To graduate, students must complete a minimum of 40 courses with a GPA of at least 2.0.

Special: Students may study abroad in 7 countries. Dordt also offers a Washington semester, a Chicago Metro semester, numerous internships in all majors, and pass/fail options.

Faculty/Classroom: Ninety percent of faculty are male; 10%, female. All teach undergraduates. The average class size in an introductory lecture is 30; in a laboratory, 20; and in a regular course offering, 15.

Admissions: About 93% of the 1993–94 applicants were accepted. The ACT scores for the 1993–94 freshman class were as follows: 20% below 21, 31% between 21 and 23, 21% between 24 and 26, 19% between 27 and 28, and 9% above 28. About 42% of the current freshmen were in the top fifth of their class; 73% were in the top two fifths. There were 7 National Merit finalists and 7 semifinalists. About 5 freshmen graduated first in their class.

Requirements: A minimum GPA of 2.0 is required. The ACT is required. Applicants must be graduates of accredited secondary schools or have earned a GED. The college requires 18 academic credits, including 4 in English and 2 each in foreign language, mathematics, science, and social studies. AP and CLEP credits are accepted. Important factors used in the admissions decision are advanced placement or honor courses, parents or siblings attending the school, leadership record, evidence of special talent, and recommendations by school officials.

Procedure: Freshmen are admitted fall and spring. Entrance exams should be taken by October of the senior year and no later than April. Applications should be filed by August 15 for fall entry, along with an application fee of $10. Notification is sent on a rolling basis.

Transfer: About 45 transfer students enrolled in 1993–94. A total of 60 credits must be completed at Dordt.

Visiting: There are regularly scheduled orientations for prospective students. There are guides for informal visits, and visitors may sit in on classes and stay overnight at the school. To arrange for a visit, contact the Admissions Office at (800) 34-DORDT.

Financial Aid: In 1993–94 98% of all current freshmen and 98% of continuing students received some form of financial aid. The average freshman award was $7600. Of that total, scholarships or need-based grants averaged $1100 ($2500 maximum); loans averaged $2000 ($4000 maximum); and work contracts averaged $1000 (maximum). Eighty percent of undergraduate students work part-time. Average earnings from campus work for the school year are $1000. The average financial indebtedness of the 1992–93 graduate was $4500. The FAF or FFS is required. The deadline for financial aid applications is April 15.

International Students: There are currently 150 international students enrolled. The school actively recruits these students. They must take the TOEFL and achieve a minimum score of 500. They must also take the ACT.

Computers: The college provides computer facilities for student use. Dordt provides 100 IBM, Apple, and Altos microcomputers for academic use. All students may access the system. There are no time limits on using the system and no fees.

Graduates: In 1992–93 224 bachelor's degrees were awarded. The most popular majors among graduates were education (38%), business (17%), and social work (9%). Within an average freshman class, 54% graduate in 4 years and 55% in 5 years. Some 25 companies recruited on campus in 1992–93. In the 1992 graduating class, 12% of the men and 4% of the women were enrolled in graduate school within 6 months of graduation; 95% of the men and 95% of the women had found employment.

Admissions Contact: Quentin Van Essen, Director of Admissions.

DRAKE UNIVERSITY
C-3

Des Moines, IA 50311 (515) 271-3181; (800) 44-DRAKE

Full-time: 1486 men, 1983 women	**Faculty:** 275; IIA, av$
Part-time: 248 men, 543 women	**Ph.D.s:** 93%
Graduate: 965 men, 1108 women	**Student/Faculty:** 13 to 1
Year: semesters, summer session	**Tuition:** $12,780
Application Deadline: March 1	**Room & Board:** $4415
Freshman Class: 2804 applied, 2574 accepted, 832 enrolled	
SAT I Verbal/Math: 490/550	**ACT:** 25 **VERY COMPETITIVE**

Drake University, founded in 1881, is a private, coeducational institution offering undergraduate and graduate programs in arts and sciences, business and public administration, pharmacy and health sciences, journalism and mass communication, education, and fine arts. There are 6 undergraduate and 2 graduate schools. In addition to regional accreditation, Drake has baccalaureate program accreditation with AACSB, ACEJMC, ACPE, NASAD, NASM, and NCATE. The 2 libraries contain 580,000 volumes, 550,000 microform items, and 6000 audiovisual forms, and subscribe to 2400 periodicals. Computerized library sources and services include the card catalog, interlibrary loans, and database searching. Special learning facilities include a learning resource center, art gallery, radio station, TV station, observatory, and Henry G. Harmon Fine Arts Center. The 120-acre campus is in a suburban area. Including residence halls, there are 48 buildings on campus.

Student Life: About 67% of undergraduates are from out-of-state, mostly the Midwest. Students come from 49 states, 50 foreign countries, and Canada. Some 85% are from public schools; 15% from private. About 85% are white. About 36% are Protestant; 25% claim no religious affiliation; 22%, Catholic. The average age of freshmen is 18; all undergraduates, 21. Some 20% drop out by the end of their first year; 67% remain to graduate.

Housing: A total of 1850 students can be accommodated in college housing. College-sponsored living facilities include coed dormitories, married-student housing, fraternity houses, and sorority houses. On-campus housing is guaranteed for all 4 years. About 53% of students live on campus; of those, 92% remain on campus on weekends. All students may keep cars on campus.

Activities: About 35% of men belong to 11 national fraternities; about 28% of women belong to 10 national sororities. There are 108 groups on campus, including art, band, cheerleading, chess, choir, chorale, chorus, computers, dance, drama, ethnic, film, gay, honors, international, jazz band, literary magazine, marching band, musical theater, newspaper, opera, orchestra, pep band, photography, political, professional, radio and TV, religious, social, social service, student government, symphony, and yearbook. Popular campus events include Drake Relays, Supreme Court Days, Homecoming, and Parents Weekend.

Sports: There are 8 intercollegiate sports for men and 6 for women, and 25 intramural sports for men and 25 for women. Athletic and recreation facilities include a field house with indoor track, handball and racquetball courts; a stadium for football, soccer, and track and field; and a recreation and convention center with a swimming pool, an aerobics room, a weight room, indoor and outdoor tracks, outdoor tennis courts, and an intramural field.

Disabled Students: About 80% of the campus is accessible to disabled students. The following facilities are available: wheelchair ramps, elevators, special parking, specially equipped rest rooms, special class scheduling, lowered drinking fountains, lowered telephones, a scanner voice printer, and a disabled student organization.

Services: In addition to many counseling and information services, tutoring is available in every subject. There is also a reader service for the blind.

Campus Safety and Security: Campus safety and security measures include 24-hour foot and vehicle patrol, self defense education, escort service, and shuttle buses. In addition, there are informal discussions, pamphlets, posters, films, emergency telephones, and lighted pathways and sidewalks.

Programs of Study: Drake awards the B.A., B.S., B.A.Journ. and Mass Comm., B.Art., B.Art Ed., B.F.A., B.Mus., B.Mus.Ed., B.S.B.A., B.S. Ed, B.S.N., B.S.Pharm., B.S. Public Admin. degrees. Master's and doctoral degrees also are awarded. Bachelor's degrees are awarded in BIOLOGICAL SCIENCE (biology/biological science and marine science), BUSINESS (accounting, banking and finance, business administration and management, insurance, and marketing/retailing/merchandising), COMMUNICATIONS AND THE ARTS (advertising, art history and appreciation, broadcasting, communications, design, dramatic arts, English, fine arts, French, German, graphic design, journalism, languages, music, music business management, music theory and composition, public relations, Spanish, and speech/debate/rhetoric), COMPUTER AND PHYSICAL SCIENCE (actuarial science, chemistry, computer science, earth science, mathematics, and physics), EDUCATION (art, business, early childhood, elementary, English, foreign languages, journalism, mathematics, middle

school, music, reading, science, secondary, social science, and social studies), ENGINEERING AND ENVIRONMENTAL DESIGN (environmental science, interior design, and military science), HEALTH PROFESSIONS (medical laboratory technology, nursing, pharmacy, predentistry, and premedicine), SOCIAL SCIENCE (economics, geography, history, international relations, Latin American studies, philosophy, political science/government, prelaw, psychology, public administration, religion, social science, and sociology). Natural sciences, social sciences, business, and journalism have the largest enrollments.

Required: Undergraduates must complete course requirements within their school, including composition, language and communication skills, humanities, natural science, and social science. For graduation, 124 credit hours are required with 27 to 36 hours in the major. In pharmacy, 158 are required. The minimum GPA is 2.0.

Special: Cooperative programs are available in marine science, physics/engineering, and medical technology. Study abroad is available in 35 countries and at sea. The university offers cross-registration, internships, a Washington semester, and work-study programs. Dual majors, B.A.-B.S. degrees, a 3–2 engineering degree, student-designed majors, accelerated degree programs, credit for life, military, and work experience, and nondegree study are possible. Students may take a maximum of 12 hours of course work on a credit/no credit basis. Drake emphasizes the use of computer technology. All schools and colleges incorporate computers into their courses of study. There is a freshman honors program on campus, as well as 26 national honor societies, including Phi Beta Kappa.

Faculty/Classroom: Some 73% of faculty are male; 28%, female. About 80% teach undergraduates, 90% do research, and 85% do both. No introductory courses are taught by graduate students. The average class size in an introductory lecture is 100; in a laboratory, 20; and in a regular course offering, 45.

Admissions: About 92% of the 1993–94 applicants were accepted. The ACT scores for the 1993–94 freshman class were as follows: 12% below 21, 22% between 21 and 23, 28% between 24 and 26, 17% between 27 and 28, and 21% above 28. About 62% of the current freshmen were in the top fifth of their class; 84% were in the top two fifths. There were 12 National Merit finalists. About 52 freshmen graduated first in their class.

Requirements: Drake requires applicants to be in the upper 50% of their class. A minimum GPA of 2.0 is required. The SAT I or ACT is required. Applicants must be graduates of an accredited secondary school. The GED is accepted. Students must have completed 4 years of English, 2 years of mathematics, and 10 other units to be selected from English, foreign languages, social studies, mathematics, laboratory sciences, and others. A portfolio is required for art majors and for those seeking scholarship consideration. An audition is necessary prior or to registration for music classes and scholarships. Tapes are accepted. AP and CLEP credits are accepted. Important factors used in the admissions decision are recommendations by school officials, leadership record, extracurricular activities record, advanced placement or honor courses, and evidence of special talent.

Procedure: Freshmen are admitted to all sessions. Entrance exams should be taken during spring of the junior year or early fall of the senior year. Applications should be filed by March 1 for fall entry and December 1 for spring entry, along with an application fee of $25. Notification is sent on a rolling basis. There are early admissions and deferred admissions plans.

Transfer: About 339 transfer students enrolled in 1993–94. Transfer students must have a minimum GPA of 2.0 and have completed 12 credit hours for evaluation. Grades of C or better transfer for credit. There is no assurance that all courses transferred will apply toward the major requirement. The final 30 hours must be completed in residence. For a degree, 124 semester hours are required, 158 in pharmacy. Transfer students are admitted in fall, spring, and summer. A total of 30 credits out of 124 must be completed at Drake.

Visiting: There are regularly scheduled orientations for prospective students, including an opportunity for students and parents to confer with professors in their area of interest, meetings with students, and attending information sessions on academic programs, financial aid, housing, and campus information. Also included are a walking tour of campus and lunch. There are guides for informal visits and visitors may sit in on classes and stay overnight at the school. To arrange for a visit, contact Visit Coordinator, Office of Admission at (515) 271-3181 or (800) 44-DRAKE.

Financial Aid: In 1993–94, 75% of all students received some form of financial aid. About 55% of all students received need-based aid. The average freshman award was $13,000. Of that total, scholarships or need-based grants averaged $8000 ($10,720 maximum); loans averaged $3400 ($4875 maximum); and work contracts averaged $1600. Some 53% of undergraduate students work part-time. Average earnings from campus work for the school year are $1000. The average financial indebtedness of the 1992–93 graduate was $13,400. Drake is a member of CSS. The FAF, FFS, FAFSA, and

Singlefile Form (preferred) are required. The deadline for financial aid applications is March 1.

International Students: There are currently 167 international students enrolled. The school actively recruits these students. They must take the TOEFL and achieve a minimum score of 530.

Computers: The college provides computer facilities for student use. The mainframe is a DEC VAX 8650. In addition, every freshman residence hall room has a Macintosh computer and a printer, and there are many microcomputer and central computing nodes located throughout the campus and in departmental computer laboratories. A data network permits students to access a variety of services from their rooms, including the campuswide information system, the on-line library catalog, and a number of statistical packages. All students may access the system. There are no time limits on using the system and no fees.

Graduates: In 1992–93, 785 bachelor's degrees were awarded. The most popular majors among graduates were pharmacy (12%), psychology (8%), and marketing/management (8%). Within an average freshman class, 67% graduate in 5 years. Some 108 companies recruited on campus in 1992–93. In the 1992 graduating class, 8% of the men and 6% of the women were enrolled in graduate school within 6 months of graduation.

Admissions Contact: Thomas F. Willoughby, Director of Admission.

GRACELAND COLLEGE
Lamoni, IA 50140

C-4
(515) 784-5196
(800) 638-0053, (800) 346-9208 (out-of-state)

Full-time: 483 men, 513 women	Faculty: 70; IIB, --$
Part-time: 23 men, 86 women	Ph.D.s: 63%
Graduate: none	Student/Faculty: 14 to 1
Year: 4–1–4, summer session	Tuition: $8680
Application Deadline: August 15	Room & Board: $2920
Freshman Class: 564 applied, 422 accepted, 248 enrolled	
SAT I Verbal/Math: 447/502	ACT: 22 **COMPETITIVE**

Graceland College, established in 1895, is a private liberal arts college affiliated with the Reorganized Church of Jesus Christ of the Latter-day Saints. In addition to regional accreditation, Graceland has baccalaureate program accreditation with NCATE and NLN. The library contains 110,559 volumes, 3774 microform items, and 834 audiovisual forms, and subscribes to 697 periodicals. Computerized library sources and services include the card catalog, interlibrary loans, and database searching. Special learning facilities include a learning resource center and art gallery. The 160-acre campus is in a small town 80 miles south of Des Moines. Including residence halls, there are 20 buildings on campus.

Student Life: About 69% of undergraduates are from out-of-state, mostly the Midwest. Students come from 39 states, 21 foreign countries, and Canada. Eighty-two percent are white; 10% foreign nationals. Most are Protestant. The average age of freshmen is 18; all undergraduates, 22. Twenty-two percent drop out by the end of their first year; 40% remain to graduate.

Housing: A total of 650 students can be accommodated in college housing. College-sponsored living facilities include single-sex dormitories and married-student housing. On-campus housing is guaranteed for all 4 years and is available on a first-come, first-served basis. Sixty-four percent of students live on campus; of those, 60% remain on campus on weekends. Alcohol is not permitted. All students may keep cars on campus.

Activities: There are no fraternities or sororities on campus. There are 35 groups on campus, including band, cheerleading, choir, chorus, computers, drama, drill team, ethnic, honors, international, jazz band, marching band, musical theater, newspaper, orchestra, pep band, political, religious, social, social service, student government, and yearbook. Popular campus events include Renaissance Week, Homecoming, Cakes and Caroling, Ice Cream Festival, Community in Revue, and Final Fling.

Sports: There are 8 intercollegiate sports for men and 7 for women, and 16 intramural sports for men and 16 for women. Athletic and recreation facilities include an outdoor track, a football field, tennis courts, a physical education center with an indoor junior Olympic-size pool, 3 basketball courts, an indoor track, and a weight room.

Disabled Students: Seventy percent of the campus is accessible to disabled students. The following facilities are available: wheelchair ramps, elevators, special parking, specially equipped rest rooms, special class scheduling, and lowered drinking fountains.

Services: In addition to many counseling and information services, tutoring is available in most subjects. There is remedial math, reading, and writing.

Campus Safety and Security: Campus safety and security measures include 24-hour foot and vehicle patrol, informal discussions, pamphlets, posters, films, and emergency telephones. In addition, there are lighted pathways and sidewalks and night security personnel.

Programs of Study: Graceland awards the B.A., B.S., and B.S.N. degrees. Bachelor's degrees are awarded in BIOLOGICAL SCIENCE (biology/biological science), BUSINESS (accounting, business administration and management, business economics, and recreation and leisure services), COMMUNICATIONS AND THE ARTS (communications, dramatic arts, English, French, German, graphic design, music, Spanish, speech/debate/rhetoric, and studio art), COMPUTER AND PHYSICAL SCIENCE (chemistry, computer science, information sciences and systems, mathematics, physics, and science), EDUCATION (elementary, music, and physical), ENGINEERING AND ENVIRONMENTAL DESIGN (commercial art and computer engineering), HEALTH PROFESSIONS (medical laboratory technology, nursing, predentistry, and premedicine), SOCIAL SCIENCE (addiction studies, economics, history, international studies, liberal arts/general studies, philosophy, prelaw, psychology, religion, social science, and sociology). English, art, philosophy and religion, and theater are the strongest academically. Business administration, education, and nursing have the largest enrollments.

Required: To graduate, students must complete courses in humanities, social sciences, history/political science, and mathematics/computer science. Among the specific courses required are freshman and junior composition, physical education, humanities, and speech communication. A total of 128 credit hours are needed, with an average of 40 hours in the major. Students must maintain a minimum 2.0 GPA in their major.

Special: Internships are required in education, recreation, communications, and publications design. The college offers study abroad, B.A.-B.S. degrees, dual majors, student-designed majors, and a general studies degree. Credit for life, military, or work experience is possible in the Liberal Studies program. A pass/fail option is available for one course each semester. The college offers nondegree study, home study in addiction studies and nursing, and a program for students with learning disabilities. There is a freshman honors program on campus, as well as 3 national honor societies.

Faculty/Classroom: Sixty-seven percent of faculty are male; 33%, female. All both teach and do research. The average class size in an introductory lecture is 26; in a laboratory, 26; and in a regular course offering, 16.

Admissions: About 75% of the 1993–94 applicants were accepted. The SAT scores for the 1993–94 freshman class were as follows: Verbal—68% below 500, 23% between 500 and 599, and 9% between 600 and 700; Math—50% below 500, 32% between 500 and 599, 16% between 600 and 700, and 2% above 700. The ACT scores were 43% below 21, 39% between 21 and 25, 14% between 26 and 29, and 4% between 30 and 36. About 41% of the current freshmen were in the top fifth of their class; 74% were in the top two fifths.

Requirements: Graceland requires applicants to be in the upper 50% of their class. A minimum GPA of 2.0 is required. The SAT or ACT is required, with a minimum composite score of 840 on the SAT I or 21 on the ACT. Applicants must be graduates of an accredited secondary school. The GED is accepted. An interview is recommended. AP and CLEP credits are accepted. Important factors used in the admissions decision are evidence of special talent, leadership record, extracurricular activities record, advanced placement or honors courses, and personality, intangible qualities.

Procedure: Freshmen are admitted to all sessions. Entrance exams should be taken in the junior or senior year. Applications should be filed by August 15 for fall entry and November 15 for spring entry, along with an application fee of $20. Notification is sent on a rolling basis.

Transfer: About 127 transfer students enrolled in 1993–94. Transfer applicants must have a minimum GPA of 2.0. Grades of D or better transfer for credit. Of the 128 credits required for graduation, 53 must be completed at the college. Transfer students are admitted every term.

Visiting: There are regularly scheduled orientations for prospective students. There are guides for informal visits, and visitors may sit in on classes and stay overnight at the school. To arrange for a visit, contact Daphne Morrison at (515) 784-5116.

Financial Aid: In 1993–94, 90% of all students received some form of financial aid. About 54% of freshmen and 62% of continuing students received need-based aid. The average freshman award was $9271. Of that total, scholarships or need-based grants averaged $6050 ($11,600 maximum); loans averaged $3453 ($10,000 maximum); and work contracts averaged $1150 ($3200 maximum). Forty-three percent of undergraduate students work part-time. Average earnings from campus work for the school year are $1152. Graceland is a member of CSS. The FAF is required. The deadline for financial aid applications is April 15.

International Students: There are currently 106 international students enrolled. The school actively recruits these students. They must take the TOEFL and achieve a minimum score of 450.

Computers: The college provides computer facilities for student use. The mainframe is an HP 5000. There are access terminals in the computer engineering laboratory and in the computer center. In addition, there are 3 microcomputer laboratories. Computer engineering majors may access the system. It may be used 24 hours a day. There are no time limits and no fees.

Graduates: In 1992–93, 253 bachelor's degrees were awarded. The most popular majors among graduates were nursing (33%), business administration (15%), and education (11%). Within an average freshman class, 27% graduate in 4 years, 39% in 5 years, and 40% in 6 years. Seven companies recruited on campus in 1992–93. In the 1992 graduating class, 6% of all students were enrolled in graduate school within 6 months of graduation; 24% of the men and 52% of the women had found employment.

Admissions Contact: Bonita A. Booth, Dean of Admissions.

GRAND VIEW COLLEGE   C-3

Des Moines, IA 50316–1599   (515) 263–2800; (800) 444–6083

Full-time: 365 men, 653 women	Faculty: 75; IIB, --$
Part-time: 142 men, 223 women	Ph.D.s: 35%
Graduate: none	Student/Faculty: 14 to 1
Year: 4–4–1, summer session	Tuition: $9870
Application Deadline: September 1	Room & Board: $3360
Freshman Class: 423 applied, 398 accepted, 183 enrolled	
SAT I or ACT: recommended	NONCOMPETITIVE

Grand View College, founded in 1896, is a private, coeducational, liberal arts college affiliated with the Evangelical Lutheran Church in America. In addition to regional accreditation, Grand View has baccalaureate program accreditation with NLN. The library contains 100,000 volumes, 35,000 microform items, and 2000 audiovisual forms, and subscribes to 715 periodicals. Computerized library sources and services include interlibrary loans. Special learning facilities include a learning resource center and radio station. The 25-acre campus is in a residential area of Des Moines. Including residence halls, there are 19 buildings on campus.

Student Life: About 97% of undergraduates are from Iowa. Students come from 12 states and 14 foreign countries. Ninety-one percent are white. Seventy percent are Protestant, 20% are Catholic. The average age of all undergraduates is 24.7. Seven percent drop out by the end of their first year; 62% remain to graduate.

Housing: A total of 258 students can be accommodated in college housing. College-sponsored living facilities include single-sex dormitories and on-campus apartments. On-campus housing is guaranteed for all 4 years. All students may keep cars on campus.

Activities: There are no fraternities or sororities on campus. There are many groups and organizations on campus, including art, choir, drama, ethnic, honors, international, literary magazine, newspaper, photography, professional, radio and TV, religious, social service, and student government. Popular campus events include Studenterfest and Tivolifest.

Sports: There are 5 intercollegiate sports for men and 4 for women, and 8 intramural sports for men and 8 for women. Athletic and recreation facilities include a 1200-seat physical education building with facilities for varsity athletics and recreation programs, tennis courts, and an athletic field.

Disabled Students: Ninety percent of the campus is accessible to disabled students. The following facilities are available: wheelchair ramps, elevators, special parking, specially equipped rest rooms, special class scheduling, and lowered drinking fountains. Support services for the disabled are available in the Academic Support office.

Services: In addition to many counseling and information services, tutoring is available in every subject. Support services for the blind also are available.

Campus Safety and Security: Campus safety and security measures include escort service and lighted pathways and sidewalks.

Programs of Study: Grand View awards the B.A. and B.S.N. degrees. Associate degrees also are awarded. Bachelor's degrees are awarded in BIOLOGICAL SCIENCE (biology/biological science), BUSINESS (accounting and business administration and management), COMMUNICATIONS AND THE ARTS (broadcasting, communications, English, journalism, and visual and performing arts), COMPUTER AND PHYSICAL SCIENCE (computer programming, computer science, and mathematics), EDUCATION (business, elementary, middle school, science, and secondary), ENGINEERING AND ENVIRONMENTAL DESIGN (commercial art), HEALTH PROFESSIONS (nursing, predentistry, and premedicine), SOCIAL SCIENCE (history, political science/government, social science, and social work).

Required: Students must complete core requirements, including courses in English, public speaking, other culture encounter, religion or philosophy, history or other humanities, laboratory science, and social science. Students must complete at least 124 hours of work, including 60 hours in courses other than the major and 24 hours in the major. Students must maintain an overall GPA of 2.0 and a 2.2 GPA in the major.

Special: Co-op programs, cross-registration with Drake University, student-designed majors, study abroad, and internships for a majority of majors are available. Dual majors, a B.A.-B.S. degree, work-study programs, and accelerated degree programs in business administration and accounting are offered. Nondegree study, a general studies degree, and pass/fail options are possible. There are 3 national honor societies on campus.

Faculty/Classroom: Fifty-one percent of faculty are male; 49%, female. All teach undergraduates. The average class size in an introductory lecture is 25; in a laboratory, 15; and in a regular course offering, 25.

Admissions: About 94% of the 1993-94 applicants were accepted. The ACT scores for a recent freshman class were as follows: 35% below 21, 40% between 21 and 23, 15% between 24 and 26, 5% between 27 and 28, and 5% above 28. About 10% of the current freshmen were in the top fifth of their class; 40% were in the top two fifths.

Requirements: The ACT, with a minimum recommended score of 16, or the SAT I is recommended. Students should be graduates of an accredited secondary school. The GED is also accepted. Students should have completed 4 courses in English, 2 courses in a foreign language, and 3 courses each in mathematics, science, and social science. AP and CLEP credits are accepted.

Procedure: Entrance exams should be taken during the second semester of the junior year. Applications should be filed by September 1 for fall entry and January 1 for winter entry, along with an application fee of $15. The college accepts all applicants. Notification is sent on a rolling basis.

Transfer: About 172 transfer students enrolled in 1993-94. Applicants must submit transcripts from each college attended. A total of 30 credits out of 124 must be completed at Grand View.

Visiting: There are regularly scheduled orientations for prospective students. There are guides for informal visits, and visitors may sit in on classes and stay overnight at the school. To arrange for a visit, contact the Admissions Office at (515) 263-2800 or (800) 444-6083.

Financial Aid: In 1993-94, 75% of all current freshmen and 75% of continuing students received some form of financial aid. About 70% of freshmen and 80% of continuing students received need-based aid. The average freshman award was $7000. Of that total, scholarships or need-based grants averaged $3000 ($8000 maximum); loans averaged $2625 ($3625 maximum); and work contracts averaged $1400 ($1500 maximum). Thirteen percent of undergraduate students work part-time. Average earnings from campus work for the school year are $1000. The college's own financial statement and FAFSA are required. The deadline for financial aid applications is April 15.

International Students: There are currently 16 international students enrolled. They must take the TOEFL or the University of Michigan Language Test and achieve a minimum score on the TOEFL of 500.

Computers: The college provides computer facilities for student use. The mainframes are 2 DEC PDP 11 minicomputers and a DEC VAX 3800. There are also more than 150 terminals and microcomputers available for student use in classrooms, faculty offices, and administrative offices. All students may access the system. There are no time limits on using the system and no fees.

Graduates: In 1992-93 258 bachelor's degrees were awarded. The most popular majors among graduates were business administration (26%), nursing (14%), and human services (9%). Some 36 companies recruited on campus in 1992-93.

Admissions Contact: Lori S. Hanson, Director of Admissions.

GRINNELL COLLEGE

D-3

Grinnell, IA 50112   (515) 269-3600; (800) 247-0113 (in-state)

Full-time: 626 men, 696 women	Faculty: 138; IIB, +$
Part-time: none	Ph.D.s: 96%
Graduate: none	Student/Faculty: 10 to 1
Year: semesters	Tuition: $15,688
Application Deadline: February 1	Room & Board: $4618
Freshman Class: 1861 applied, 1389 accepted, 432 enrolled	
SAT I Verbal/Math: 600/650	ACT: 29 HIGHLY COMPETITIVE +

Grinnell College, founded in 1846, is a private, coeducational institution that offers undergraduate degree programs in the arts and sciences. The 3 libraries contain 352,555 volumes, 6005 microform items, and 12,000 audiovisual forms, and subscribe to 2452 periodicals. Computerized library sources and services include the card catalog, interlibrary loans, and database searching. Special learning facilities include an observatory, a physics museum, a print and drawing gallery, and a student-run radio station. The 95-acre campus is in a small town 55 miles east of Des Moines. Including residence halls, there are 57 buildings on campus.

Student Life: About 85% of undergraduates are from out-of-state, mostly the Midwest. Students come from 46 states and 40 foreign countries. Seventy-five percent are from public schools; 12% from private. Seventy-eight percent are white; 10% foreign nationals. The av-

erage age of freshmen is 18; all undergraduates, 20. Two percent drop out by the end of their first year; 83% remain to graduate.

Housing: A total of 1140 students can be accommodated in college housing. College-sponsored living facilities include single-sex and coed dormitories. In addition, there are language houses and special interest houses. On-campus housing is available on a lottery system for upperclassmen. Eighty-six percent of students live on campus; of those, 96% remain on campus on weekends. All students may keep cars on campus.

Activities: There are no fraternities or sororities on campus. There are 105 groups on campus, including art, choir, chorale, chorus, computers, dance, drama, ethnic, gay, honors, international, jazz band, literary magazine, musical theater, newspaper, orchestra, political, radio and TV, religious, social service, student government, and yearbook. Popular campus events include Peace Day, Black Awareness Week, International Student Organization (ISO) Food Bazaar, James Hall Ball, Gay and Lesbian Pride Week, and Loose Hall Ball and Waltz.

Sports: There are 10 intercollegiate sports for men and 9 for women, and 5 intramural sports for men and 4 for women. Athletic and recreation facilities include a physical education complex, a gymnasium, 3 sports fields, a track, a softball field, and 3 intramural fields.

Disabled Students: Sixty-five percent of the campus is accessible to disabled students. The following facilities are available: wheelchair ramps, elevators, special parking, specially equipped rest rooms, special class scheduling, lowered drinking fountains, and lowered telephones.

Services: In addition, there is a reader service for the blind.

Campus Safety and Security: Campus safety and security measures include escort service, informal discussions, pamphlets, posters, films, and emergency telephones. In addition, there are lighted pathways and sidewalks, daytime police patrols, fire drills, and a safety committee. Security information and reports are released to the entire campus when incidents occur.

Programs of Study: Grinnell awards the B.A. degree. Bachelor's degrees are awarded in BIOLOGICAL SCIENCE (biology/biological science), COMMUNICATIONS AND THE ARTS (Chinese, classics, dramatic arts, English, fine arts, French, German, music, Russian, and Spanish), COMPUTER AND PHYSICAL SCIENCE (chemistry, computer science, mathematics, physics, and science), SOCIAL SCIENCE (American studies, anthropology, economics, history, philosophy, political science/government, psychology, religion, and sociology). Foreign languages, English, mathematics, physical and life sciences, social sciences, and humanities are the strongest academically. Biology, economics, English, and history have the largest enrollments.

Required: All students are required to take research and writing tutorials. All students must also complete a major field, which includes between 32 and 48 credits in most departments. Of the total 124 credits needed for the bachelor's degree, no more than 48 may be earned in any one department or 92 in any one division, and a minimum 2.0 GPA must be maintained.

Special: Students may participate in study-abroad programs in 29 countries or in off-campus studies throughout the United States. Grinnell offers cooperative programs in architecture with Washington University in St. Louis and in engineering with California Institute of Technology, Rensselaer Polytechnic Institute, and Washington University in St. Louis. There is also an extensive internship program, a general studies degree in science, student-designed majors, a 3-2 engineering degree program, and pass/fail options in selected courses. Grinnell's special `plus-2' option permits students to add 2 credits to a regular course through independent study. Students also may pursue one of 9 interdisciplinary concentrations in addition to their major. Accelerated degree programs of 6 to 7 semesters may be approved on an individual basis. There are 2 national honor societies on campus, including Phi Beta Kappa.

Faculty/Classroom: Sixty-three percent of faculty are male; 37%, female. All faculty both teach and do research. The average class size in an introductory lecture is 21; in a laboratory, 18; and in a regular course offering, 13.

Admissions: About 75% of the 1993-94 applicants were accepted. The SAT scores for the 1993-94 freshman class were as follows: Verbal—8% below 500, 36% between 500 and 599, 46% between 600 and 700, and 10% above 700; Math—4% below 500, 21% between 500 and 599, 52% between 600 and 700, and 23% above 700. The ACT scores were 1% below 21, 5% between 21 and 23, 14% between 24 and 26, 27% between 27 and 28, and 53% above 28. About 83% of the current freshmen were in the top fifth of their class; 90% were in the top two fifths. There were 17 National Merit finalists. About 30 freshmen graduated first in their class.

Requirements: The SAT I or the ACT is required. Applicants must be graduates of accredited secondary schools. The college requires 16 Carnegie units, including 4 in English and 3 each in mathematics, science, and social studies, with the remaining 3 units recommended to be in a foreign language. An essay is required and an interview is

recommended. AP credits are accepted. Important factors used in the admissions decision are advanced placement or honor courses, recommendations by school officials, leadership record, extracurricular activities record, and evidence of special talent.

Procedure: Freshmen are admitted in the fall. Entrance exams should be taken during the second semester of the junior year or early in the fall semester of the senior year. Early decision applications should be filed by November 20; regular applications, by February 1 for fall entry, along with an application fee of $25. Notification of early decision is sent December 15; regular decision, April 1. There are early decision, early admissions, and deferred admissions plans. About 110 early decision candidates were accepted for the 1993–94 class. A waiting list is an active part of the admissions procedure, with about 4% of applicants on the list.

Transfer: About 50 transfer students enrolled in 1993–94. A total of 62 credits out of 124 must be completed at Grinnell.

Visiting: There are regularly scheduled orientations for prospective students, consisting of a campus tour, an interview with a member of the Admissions Office, an opportunity to attend classes, overnight accommodations, and complimentary meals. There are guides for informal visits. To arrange for a visit, contact the Admissions Office at (515) 269–3600.

Financial Aid: In 1993–94, 86% of all current freshmen and 75% of continuing students received some form of financial aid. About 69% of freshmen and 57% of continuing students received need-based aid. The average freshman award was $12,258. Of that total, scholarships or need-based grants averaged $10,245 ($21,090 maximum); loans averaged $3583 ($4875 maximum); and work contracts averaged $952 ($1192 maximum). Fifty-six percent of undergraduate students work part-time. Average earnings from campus work for the school year are $1000. The average financial indebtedness of the 1992–93 graduate was $8911. Grinnell is a member of CSS. The college's own financial statement and the FAFSA are required. The deadline for financial aid applications is February 1.

International Students: There are currently 144 international students enrolled. The school actively recruits these students. They must take the TOEFL and achieve a minimum score of 550. The student must also take the SAT I or the ACT.

Computers: The college provides computer facilities for student use. The mainframes are a DEC VAX 8600 and a DEC VAX 6420. there are 365 microcomputers, workstations, and terminals located in residence halls and academic buildings. All students may access the system. It may be used 24 hours a day. There are no time limits on using the system and no fees.

Graduates: In 1992–93, 349 bachelor's degrees were awarded. The most popular majors among graduates were history (13%), political science (12%), and English (9%). Within an average freshman class, 77% graduate in 4 years, 83% in 5 years, and 83% in 6 years. Twelve companies recruited on campus in 1992–93. In the 1992 graduating class, 30% of all graduates were enrolled in graduate school within 6 months of graduation; 45% had found employment.

Admissions Contact: Vince Cuseo, Director of Admission.

IOWA STATE UNIVERSITY

C-3

Ames, IA 50011–2010   (515) 294–5836; (800) 262–3810 (in-state)

Full-time: 11,175 men, 7867 women	Faculty: 1191; I, -$
Part-time: 856 men, 731 women	Ph.D.s: 88%
Graduate: 2756 men, 1727 women	Student/Faculty: 16 to 1
Year: semesters, summer session	Tuition: $2352 ($7386)
Application Deadline: August 19	Room & Board: $3104
Freshman Class: 8427 applied, 7424 accepted, 3441 enrolled	
SAT I or ACT: required	**COMPETITIVE**

Iowa State University, established in 1858, is a public, coeducational land-grant institution offering graduate and undergraduate programs in agriculture, business, design, education, engineering, family and consumer sciences, and liberal arts and sciences. There are 8 undergraduate schools and one graduate school. In addition to regional accreditation, Iowa State has baccalaureate program accreditation with AACSB, ABET, ACEJMC, ADA, AHEA, ASLA, CSWE, FIDER, NAAB, NASM, and SAF. The library contains 1.9 million volumes, 2 million microform items, and 52,000 audiovisual forms, and subscribes to 21,000 periodicals. Computerized library sources and services include the card catalog, interlibrary loans, and database searching. Special learning facilities include an art gallery, natural history museum, planetarium, radio station, and TV station. The 1770-acre campus is in a suburban area 30 miles north of Des Moines.

Student Life: About 76% of undergraduates are from Iowa. Students come from 50 states, 118 foreign countries, and Canada. About 92% are from public schools; 8% from private. Some 83% are white; 11% foreign nationals. The average age of freshmen is 18; all undergraduates, 21.8. Approximately 18% drop out by the end of their first year; 62% remain to graduate.

Housing: A total of 9788 students can be accommodated in college housing. College-sponsored living facilities include single-sex and coed dormitories, on-campus apartments, married-student housing, fraternity houses, and sorority houses. In addition, there are honors houses, language houses, special interest houses, nonalcoholic houses, and cross-cultural houses. On-campus housing is guaranteed for all 4 years. Alcohol is not permitted. All students may keep cars on campus.

Activities: About 17% of men belong to 1 local and 36 national fraternities; about 16% of women belong to 19 national sororities. There are 500 groups on campus, including art, band, cheerleading, chess, choir, chorale, chorus, computers, dance, drama, drum and bugle corps, ethnic, film, gay, honors, international, jazz band, literary magazine, marching band, musical theater, newspaper, orchestra, pep band, photography, political, professional, radio and TV, religious, social, social service, student government, symphony, and yearbook. Popular campus events include VEISHEA (student-sponsored spring festival), Honors Week, International Week, Engineers Week, Parents Weekend, Homecoming, Greek Week, Women's Week, and Residence Hall Week.

Sports: There are 10 intercollegiate sports for men and 9 for women, and 40 intramural sports for men and 40 for women. Athletic and recreation facilities include a coliseum, stadium/field, baseball and softball complex, track complex, gymnasium, ice center, physical education building, and recreation center.

Disabled Students: Almost 99% percent of the campus is accessible to disabled students. The following facilities are available: wheelchair ramps, elevators, special parking, specially equipped rest rooms, special class scheduling, lowered drinking fountains, lowered telephones, Kiersweil Reader, enlargement services, and talking and braille text from Iowa Commission for the Blind.

Services: In addition to many counseling and information services, tutoring is available in most subjects. In addition, there is a reader service and notetakers for the blind.

Campus Safety and Security: Campus safety and security measures include 24-hour foot and vehicle patrol, self defense education, escort service, and shuttle buses. In addition, there are informal discussions, pamphlets, posters, and films, emergency telephones, and lighted pathways and sidewalks.

Programs of Study: Iowa State awards the B.A, B.S., B.Arch., B.B.A., B.F.A., B.L.A., B.L.S., and B.Mus. degrees. Master's and doctoral degrees also are awarded. Bachelor's degrees are awarded in AGRICULTURE (agricultural business management, agricultural mechanics, agriculture, agronomy, animal science, dairy science, fishing and fisheries, forestry and related sciences, horticulture, international agriculture, plant protection (pest management), and plant science), BIOLOGICAL SCIENCE (biochemistry, biology/biological science, biophysics, botany, entomology, genetics, microbiology, nutrition, plant pathology, wildlife biology, and zoology), BUSINESS (accounting, banking and finance, business administration and management, fashion merchandising, hotel/motel and restaurant management, management science, marketing/retailing/merchandising, recreation and leisure services, and transportation management), COMMUNICATIONS AND THE ARTS (advertising, communications, design, English, fine arts, French, German, graphic design, illustration, journalism, linguistics, music, Russian, Spanish, and speech/debate/rhetoric), COMPUTER AND PHYSICAL SCIENCE (atmospheric sciences and meteorology, chemistry, computer science, earth science, geology, mathematics, physics, and statistics), EDUCATION (agricultural, art, early childhood, elementary, health, home economics, industrial arts, middle school, music, physical, science, and secondary), ENGINEERING AND ENVIRONMENTAL DESIGN (aeronautical engineering, agricultural engineering, architecture, ceramic engineering, chemical engineering, city/community/regional planning, civil engineering, computer engineering, construction engineering, electrical/electronics engineering, engineering, engineering technology, environmental science, food services technology, housing and the near environment, industrial engineering technology, interior design, landscape architecture/design, mechanical engineering, metallurgical engineering, and naval science), SOCIAL SCIENCE (anthropology, child care/child and family studies, child psychology/development, dietetics, economics, family and community services, family/consumer resource management, family/consumer studies, fashion design and technology, food production/management/services, food science, history, international relations, liberal arts/general studies, philosophy, political science/government, psychology, religion, social work, sociology, and textiles and clothing). Engineering, business, agriculture, education, psychology, journalism and mass communication, and art and design have the largest enrollments.

Required: A minimum of 124 1/2 credit hours and a minimum GPA of 2.0 are required for graduation. The total number of credits required in the major varies. All students must take Freshman English and library instruction.

Special: The university offers cooperative programs in engineering, graphic design, forestry and wildlife biology, and animal ecology, internships, study abroad in 70 countries, and cross-registration with the Universities of Iowa and Northern Iowa. Dual majors, the B.A.-B.S. degree, student-designed majors, and accelerated degree programs are available. Interdisciplinary studies available include agricultural biochemistry, agricultural systems technology, animal ecology, public service and administration in agriculture, and engineering operations. There is a Washington semester, work-study programs, nondegree study, and pass/no pass options. There is a freshman honors program on campus, as well as 15 national honor societies, including Phi Beta Kappa. Up to 7 departments have honors programs.

Faculty/Classroom: Some 76% percent of faculty are male; 24%, female. Almost 75% teach undergraduates. Graduate students teach 24% of introductory courses. The average class size in a regular course offering is 30.

Admissions: About 88% of the 1993–94 applicants were accepted. The SAT scores for the 1993–94 freshman class were as follows: Verbal—64% below 500, 24% between 500 and 599, 11% between 600 and 700, and 1% above 700; Math—35% below 500, 29% between 500 and 599, 24% between 600 and 700, and 12% above 700. The ACT scores were 17% below 21, 26% between 21 and 23, 30% between 24 and 26, 13% between 27 and 28, and 14% above 28. About 49% of the current freshmen were in the top fifth of their class; 81% were in the top two fifths. There were 63 National Merit finalists. About 144 freshmen graduated first in their class.

Requirements: Iowa State requires applicants to be in the upper 50% of their class, from an accredited secondary school. Either the SAT I or ACT is required. The GED is accepted. For admission to freshman standing, students must have completed 4 years of English, 3 each of mathematics and science, 2 to 3 of social studies and, for the College of Liberal Arts and Studies, 2 years of a single foreign language. AP and CLEP credits are accepted. Leadership record is an important factor used in the admission decision.

Procedure: Freshmen are admitted in the fall, spring, and summer. Entrance exams should be taken during spring of the junior year in high school. Applications should be filed by August 19 for fall entry, January 13 for spring entry, and June 12 for summer entry, along with an application fee of $20. Notification is sent within 2 to 3 weeks after materials are received. There is a deferred admissions plan.

Transfer: About 1672 transfer students enrolled in 1993–94. Transfer applicants must have a minimum GPA of 2.0 and a minimum of 24 semester credits of acceptable transfer coursework. A total of 32 credits out of at least 124 1/2 must be completed at Iowa State.

Visiting: There are regularly scheduled orientations for prospective students, including presentations on academics, admissions, residence hall living, fraternity and sorority life, and financial aid. There is also a group session with an adviser and tours of the campus. There are guides for informal visits and visitors may sit in on classes and stay overnight at the school. To arrange for a visit, contact Linda Steensland, Admissions Office at (800) 262–3810.

Financial Aid: In 1993–94, 75% of all current freshmen and continuing students received some form of financial aid. About 70% of freshmen received need-based aid. Scholarships or need-based grants averaged $2875 ($4000 maximum); loans averaged $4410 ($4425 maximum); and work contracts averaged $1700 ($2000 maximum). Some 25% of undergraduate students work part-time. Average earnings from campus work for the school year are $1835. The average financial indebtedness of the 1992–93 graduate was $7500. Iowa State is a member of CSS. The FAFSA financial statement is required. The deadline for financial aid applications is March 1.

International Students: There are currently 2692 international students enrolled. The school actively recruits these students. They must take the TOEFL and achieve a minimum score of 500.

Computers: The college provides computer facilities for student use. The mainframe is an HDS/9180. Students may register with the Computation Center to access the VAX system, WYLBUR, and Project Vincent through the mainframe computer. Engineering students also have access to the engineering VAX cluster. Approximately 1000 terminals and microcomputers are available in various buildings across campus. Terminals are also available in the residence halls and students owning computers may access the mainframe through hook-up points in their residence hall rooms. All students may access the system. It may be used at various hours, depending on location. There are 7 24-hour locations. There are no time limits on using the system. The fees are $80 per year, except for engineering and computer science students, who pay $200 per year.

Graduates: In 1992–93, 3948 bachelor's degrees were awarded. The most popular majors among graduates were business (16%), engineering (16%), and agriculture (11%). Within an average freshman class, 55% graduate in 5 years and 63% in 6 years. In the 1992 graduating class, 17% of men and women were enrolled in graduate school within 6 months of graduation; 79% had found employment.

Admissions Contact: Phil Caffrey, Assistant Director of Admissions.

IOWA WESLEYAN COLLEGE

E-4

Mount Pleasant, IA 52641

(319) 385–6231
(800) 582–2383 (out-of-state)

Full-time: 242 men, 266 women	Faculty: 48; IIB, --$
Part-time: 151 men, 269 women	Ph.D.s: 51%
Graduate: none	Student/Faculty: 11 to 1
Year: 4–1–4, summer session	Tuition: $9850
Application Deadline: open	Room & Board: $3400
Freshman Class: 432 applied, 254 accepted, 88 enrolled	
ACT: 21	**COMPETITIVE**

Iowa Wesleyan College, founded in 1842, is a private, coeducational institution affiliated with the United Methodist Church. The college offers undergraduate degree programs in business, education, fine arts, human studies, language and literature, nursing, and science. There are 7 undergraduate schools. In addition to regional accreditation, Wesleyan has baccalaureate program accreditation with NLN. The library contains 108,000 volumes and 2900 microform items, and subscribes to 600 periodicals. Computerized library sources and services include interlibrary loans and database searching. Special learning facilities include a learning resource center, art gallery, and radio station. The 60-acre campus is in a small town 45 miles south of Iowa City. Including residence halls, there are 16 buildings on campus.

Student Life: About 78% of undergraduates are from Iowa. Students come from 13 states, 8 foreign countries, and Canada. Ninety-seven percent are from public schools; 3% from private. Eighty percent are white; 10% foreign nationals. Forty-three percent are Protestant; 11% Catholic. The average age of freshmen is 19. Twenty percent drop out by the end of their first year; 50% remain to graduate.

Housing: A total of 455 students can be accommodated in college housing. College-sponsored living facilities include single-sex dormitories. On-campus housing is guaranteed for all 4 years. Fifty-nine percent of students live on campus. All students may keep cars on campus.

Activities: About 5% of men belong to 1 national fraternities; about 10% of women belong to 2 national sororities. There are 30 groups on campus, including art, band, cheerleading, choir, chorus, ethnic, film, honors, international, jazz band, literary magazine, newspaper, orchestra, pep band, photography, professional, radio and TV, religious, social, student government, symphony, and yearbook. Popular campus events include Forum, Winterfest, and Spring Thing.

Sports: There are 7 intercollegiate sports for men and 7 for women, and 11 intramural sports for men and 11 for women. Athletic and recreation facilities include a 32-acre complex with baseball, softball, and football fields and an all-weather quarter-mile track. There is also a gymnasium, a remodeled swimming pool area, and a new basketball court area.

Disabled Students: Fifteen percent of the campus is accessible to disabled students. The following facilities are available: wheelchair ramps, elevators, special parking, and special class scheduling.

Services: In addition to many counseling and information services, tutoring is available in every subject. In addition, there is a reader service for the blind and remedial writing.

Campus Safety and Security: Campus safety and security measures include 24-hour foot and vehicle patrol, self defense education, escort service, and informal discussions. In addition, there are pamphlets, posters, and films, emergency telephones, and lighted pathways and sidewalks.

Programs of Study: Wesleyan awards the B.A., B.S., B.G.S., B.M.E., and B.S.N. degrees. Bachelor's degrees are awarded in BIOLOGICAL SCIENCE (biology/biological science and life science), BUSINESS (accounting and business administration and management), COMMUNICATIONS AND THE ARTS (communications, English, fine arts, and music), COMPUTER AND PHYSICAL SCIENCE (chemistry, computer science, and mathematics), EDUCATION (art, early childhood, elementary, music, physical, science, and secondary), ENGINEERING AND ENVIRONMENTAL DESIGN (preengineering), HEALTH PROFESSIONS (nursing and predentistry), SOCIAL SCIENCE (criminal justice, prelaw, psychology, and sociology). Education is the strongest academically. Business has the largest enrollment.

Required: General education requirements include 5 semester hours of mathematics/science and 3 each of history/political science, religion/philosophy, social science, literature, and fine arts. Students must also demonstrate proficiency in composition, satisfy a safety and survival requirement, and successfully complete English 100 and 102, a life and health course, and a responsible social involvement project. A minimum of 124 semester hours is required for the bachelor's degree.

Special: The college maintains a cooperative program with Southeastern Community College. There are also internships in every major, a study-abroad program in Mexico, a general studies degree, credit in nursing through challenge examinations, and satisfactory/unsatisfactory grade options. There are 4 national honor societies on campus.

Faculty/Classroom: Forty-nine percent of faculty are male; 51%, female. All teach undergraduates and 20% do research. The average class size in an introductory lecture is 20; in a laboratory, 12; and in a regular course offering, 16.

Admissions: About 59% of the 1993–94 applicants were accepted.

Requirements: Wesleyan requires applicants to be in the upper 60% of their class. The ACT is required. Applicants must be graduates of accredited secondary schools or have earned a GED. AP and CLEP credits are accepted.

Procedure: Freshmen are admitted fall, winter, and spring. Entrance exams should be taken in August, December, or January of the senior year. Application deadlines are open; there is a $15 application fee. Notification is sent on a rolling basis. There are early decision, early admissions, and deferred admissions plans.

Transfer: About 88 transfer students enrolled in a recent year. A minimum GPA of 2.0 is required. Applicants are also encouraged to take either the SAT I or ACT. A total of 30 credits out of 124 must be completed at Wesleyan.

Visiting: There are regularly scheduled orientations for prospective students, including meeting with admissions, financial aid, and academic staff, as well as social activities. There are guides for informal visits and visitors may sit in on classes and stay overnight at the school. To arrange for a visit, contact the Admissions Office at (800) 582-2383.

Financial Aid: In an earlier year, 92% of all current freshmen and 87% of continuing students received some form of financial aid. The average freshman award was $7500. Of that total, scholarships or need-based grants averaged $1500 ($9000 maximum); loans averaged $2200 ($2625 maximum); and work contracts averaged $600 ($1000 maximum). Eighty-three percent of undergraduate students work part-time. The average financial indebtedness of previous graduates was $8027. Wesleyan is a member of CSS. The FAF or FFS is required. The deadline for financial aid applications is April 1.

International Students: There are currently 18 international students enrolled. The school actively recruits these students. They must take the TOEFL and achieve a minimum score of 500.

Computers: The college provides computer facilities for student use. The mainframe is a DEC VAX 11/750. There are also a number of microcomputers in the library. Students in FORTRAN or COBOL courses may access the system. It may be used 6 a.m to midnight. There are no time limits on using the system and no fees.

Graduates: In an earlier year, 115 bachelor's degrees were awarded, and 5 companies recruited on campus. In a typical graduating class, 92% of the students had found employment within 6 months of graduation.

Admissions Contact: Director of Admissions.

LORAS COLLEGE
E-2

Dubuque, IA 52001   (319) 588-7235; (800) 24-LORAS (out-of-state)

Full-time: 828 men, 835 women	Faculty: 115; IIB, -$
Part-time: 104 men, 147 women	Ph.D.s: 60%
Graduate: 26 men, 55 women	Student/Faculty: 14 to 1
Year: semesters, summer session	Tuition: $10,500
Application Deadline: open	Room & Board: $3660
Freshman Class: 1495 applied, 1185 accepted, 527 enrolled	
ACT: 22	COMPETITIVE

Loras College, founded in 1839, is a Roman Catholic liberal arts institution offering degree programs in humanities, social and behavioral studies, natural sciences, philosophy and religious studies, and professional studies. The library contains 236,824 volumes, 72,140 microform items, and 1100 audiovisual forms, and subscribes to 908 periodicals. Computerized library sources and services include the card catalog, interlibrary loans, and database searching. Special learning facilities include a learning resource center, planetarium, radio station, and TV station. The 60-acre campus is in an urban area. Including residence halls, there are 14 buildings on campus.

Student Life: About 60% of undergraduates are from Iowa. Students come from 25 states, 14 foreign countries, and Canada. Some 65% are from public schools; 35% from private. Almost 90% are white. Most are Catholic. The average age of freshmen is 18; all undergraduates, 21. About 15% drop out by the end of their first year; 55% remain to graduate.

Housing: A total of 1040 students can be accommodated in college housing. College-sponsored living facilities include single-sex and coed dormitories, on-campus apartments, and off-campus apartments. On-campus housing is guaranteed for all 4 years. About 54% of students live on campus. All students may keep cars on campus.

Activities: About 15% of men belong to 1 local and 1 national fraternity; about 5% of women belong to 2 local sororities. There are 70 groups on campus, including band, cheerleading, choir, chorus, drama, honors, jazz band, literary magazine, newspaper, pep band, photography, political, professional, radio and TV, religious, social service, student government, and yearbook. Popular campus events include Homecoming, Parents Weekend, Tri-College Free Day, retreats, Awareness Week, and Career Day and Opportunity.

Sports: There are 11 intercollegiate sports for men and 9 for women, and 80 intramural sports for men and 80 for women. Athletic and recreation facilities include 3 gymnasiums, a swimming pool, and an 8-lane Olympic indoor/outdoor track. The campus stadium seats 3000.

Disabled Students: The following facilities are available: wheelchair ramps, elevators, special parking, specially equipped rest rooms, special class scheduling, lowered drinking fountains, and lowered telephones.

Services: In addition to many counseling and information services, tutoring is available in every subject. There is also remedial math and writing.

Campus Safety and Security: Campus safety and security measures include 24-hour foot and vehicle patrol, escort service, and lighted pathways and sidewalks.

Programs of Study: Loras awards the B.A. and B.S. degrees. Associate and master's degrees also are awarded. Bachelor's degrees are awarded in BIOLOGICAL SCIENCE (biology/biological science), BUSINESS (accounting, banking and finance, business administration and management, marketing/retailing/merchandising, and personnel management), COMMUNICATIONS AND THE ARTS (broadcasting, English, journalism, music, and speech/debate/rhetoric), COMPUTER AND PHYSICAL SCIENCE (chemistry, computer science, mathematics, and physics), EDUCATION (art, early childhood, elementary, foreign languages, middle school, music, science, secondary, and special), HEALTH PROFESSIONS (medical laboratory technology, predentistry, and premedicine). Biology, English (writing), finance/accounting, and radio/TV have the largest enrollments.

Required: In order to graduate, students must complete a total of 120 credit hours (36 in most majors) with a minimum GPA of 2.0. Distribution requirements include 15 credits in humanities, 12 each in social and behavioral sciences, mathematics, science, philosophy and religion, and electives. A thesis and/or comprehensive examination are required.

Special: The college offers cross-registration with Clarke College and the University of Dubuque and study abroad in England. Also available are various internships, on-campus work-study programs, the 3–2 engineering degree, pass/fail options, combined liberal arts-preprofessional programs, and adult degree programs. There is a freshman honors program on campus, as well as 4 national honor societies. There is an opportunity for an honors degree in every department.

Faculty/Classroom: Some 82% of faculty are male; 18%, female. The average class size in an introductory lecture is 25.

Admissions: Nearly 79% of the 1993–94 applicants were accepted. About 34% of the current freshmen were in the top fifth of their class; 60% were in the top two fifths. About 30 freshmen graduated first in their class.

Requirements: A minimum GPA of 2.0 is required. The ACT is recommended. Applicants must be graduates of an accredited secondary school or have a GED certificate, and have completed 4 units of English, 3 each of mathematics, science, social studies, and history, and 2 of foreign language. An essay and an interview are recommended. AP and CLEP credits are accepted. Important factors used in the admissions decision are advanced placement or honor courses, recommendations by school officials, evidence of special talent, leadership record, and recommendations by alumni.

Procedure: Freshmen are admitted in the fall and spring. Entrance exams should be taken in April or June before the senior year or October of the senior year. Application deadlines are open. The application fee is $25. Notification is sent on a rolling basis. There is an early admissions plan.

Transfer: About 89 transfer students enrolled in 1993–94. Transfer students must have a minimum 2.0 GPA and submit transcripts of previous college work. Other requirements apply. A total of 30 credits out of 120 must be completed at Loras.

Visiting: There are regularly scheduled orientations for prospective students, consisting of 4 visitation days for all students, and 7 programs for specific geographic locations. There are guides for informal visits and visitors may sit in on classes and stay overnight at the school. To arrange for a visit, contact Admissions at (800) 245-6727.

Financial Aid: In 1993–94, 89% of all current freshmen and 65% of continuing students received some form of financial aid. About 70% of freshmen and 60% of continuing students received need-based aid. The average freshman award was $10,257. Of that total, scholarships or need-based grants averaged $7690 ($10,500 maximum); loans averaged $2051 ($3500 maximum); and work contracts averaged $516 ($1200 maximum). Some 60% of undergraduate students work part-time. Average earnings from campus work for the school year are $840. The average financial indebtedness of the 1992–93 graduate was $6363. Loras is a member of CSS. The FAF, FFS or SFS is required. The deadline for financial aid applications is April 15.

International Students: There are currently 55 international students enrolled.

Computers: The college provides computer facilities for student use. The mainframe is a Prime 2250. There are microcomputers available throughout the campus. All students may access the system. All computer equipment is available for student use on most days until 11 P.M. There are no time limits on using the system and no fees.

Graduates: In 1992–93, 274 bachelor's degrees were awarded. The most popular majors among graduates were business (35%), social science (15%), and education (12%). Within an average freshman class, 55% graduate in 4 years. Some 40 companies recruited on campus in 1992–93. In the 1992 graduating class, 15% of all graduates were enrolled in graduate school within 6 months of graduation; 94% of all graduates had found employment within 1 year.

Admissions Contact: Kelly Myers, Admissions Director.

LUTHER COLLEGE

E-1

Decorah, IA 52101

(319) 387-1287; (800) 458-8437

Full-time: 921 men, 1348 women	Faculty: 150; IIB, av$
Part-time: 25 men, 60 women	Ph.D.s: 85%
Graduate: none	Student/Faculty: 15 to 1
Year: 4-1-4, summer session	Tuition: $12,375
Application Deadline: March 1	Room & Board: $3525
Freshman Class: 1549 applied, 1392 accepted, 587 enrolled	
SAT: 520/590	ACT: 25 VERY COMPETITIVE

Luther College, affiliated with the Evangelical Lutheran Church in America, is a coeducational liberal arts institution founded in 1861. In addition to regional accreditation, Luther has baccalaureate program accreditation with CSWE, NASM, NCATE, and NLN. The library contains 291,500 volumes, 17,000 microform items, and 26,800 audiovisual forms, and subscribes to 1580 periodicals. Computerized library sources and services include the card catalog, interlibrary loans, and database searching. Special learning facilities include a learning resource center, art gallery, natural history museum, planetarium, and radio station. The 800-acre campus is in a small town 70 miles south of Rochester, Minnesota. Including residence halls, there are 22 buildings on campus.

Student Life: About 61% of undergraduates are from out-of-state, mostly the Midwest. Students come from 35 states, 46 foreign countries, and Canada. Ninety percent are from public schools; 10% from private. Ninety-two percent are white. Seventy-one percent are Protestant; 13% Catholic. The average age of freshmen is 18; all undergraduates, 21. Three percent drop out by the end of their first year; 77% remain to graduate.

Housing: A total of 2023 students can be accommodated in college housing. College-sponsored living facilities include coed dormitories, on-campus apartments, off-campus apartments, and married-student housing. In addition, there are language houses. On-campus housing is guaranteed for all 4 years. Eighty-one percent of all students live on campus; of those, 85% remain on campus on weekends. All students may keep cars on campus.

Activities: About 7% of men belong to 9 local fraternities; about 9% of women belong to 6 local sororities. There are 74 groups on campus, including art, band, cheerleading, choir, chorale, chorus, computers, dance, drama, ethnic, honors, international, jazz band, literary magazine, musical theater, newspaper, opera, orchestra, pep band, photography, political, professional, radio and TV, religious, social, social service, student government, symphony, and yearbook. Popular campus events include the 2 annual performances of Handel's Messiah (with full orchestra and 1000-voice choir) and the Ethnic Arts Fair.

Sports: There are 10 intercollegiate sports for men and 9 for women, and 41 intramural sports for men and 41 for women. Athletic and recreation facilities include 4 hardwood basketball courts, an indoor swimming pool, a weight room, a dance studio, bowling lanes, 5 downhill ski runs, a 4000-seat stadium and 3500-seat gymnasium, 6 indoor tennis courts, 4 racquetball courts, an indoor 6-lane 200-meter track, an outdoor 8-lane polyurethane 400-meter track, and 13 outdoor tennis courts.

Disabled Students: Ninety-five percent of the campus is accessible to disabled students. The following facilities are available: wheelchair ramps, elevators, special parking, specially equipped rest rooms, lowered drinking fountains, and lowered telephones.

Services: In addition to many counseling and information services, tutoring is available in every subject. There is a reader service for the blind, and remedial math, reading, and writing.

Campus Safety and Security: Campus safety and security measures include 24-hour foot and vehicle patrol, self defense education, escort service, and informal discussions. In addition, there are pamphlets, posters, and films, emergency telephones, and lighted pathways and sidewalks.

Programs of Study: Luther awards the B.A. degree. Bachelor's degrees are awarded in BIOLOGICAL SCIENCE (biology/biological science), BUSINESS (accounting and management information systems), COMMUNICATIONS AND THE ARTS (communications, dance, English, fine arts, French, German, Greek, Latin, music, and speech/debate/rhetoric), COMPUTER AND PHYSICAL SCIENCE (chemistry, computer science, mathematics, and physics), EDUCATION (art, early childhood, elementary, foreign languages, health, music, science, secondary, and special), ENGINEERING AND ENVIRONMENTAL DESIGN (preengineering), HEALTH PROFESSIONS (medical laboratory technology, nursing, occupational therapy, physical therapy, predentistry, and premedicine), SOCIAL SCIENCE (African American studies, anthropology, biblical languages, economics, history, international relations, political science/government, prelaw, psychology, Russian studies, Scandinavian studies, social work, and sociology). Biology, music, management, and psychology are the strongest academically. Biology, management, and psychology have the largest enrollments.

Required: Students must complete 11 hours of interdisciplinary English and history (called 'Paideia'), 9 hours of religion/philosophy, 2 of physical education, 3 of fine arts, 6 of foreign language or culture, 8 of natural science, and 7 of social sciences. The B.A. requires 128 semester hours with at least a GPA of 2.0 in the major. A senior research paper in the major is required. Math proficiency is also required.

Special: Internships in all disciplines, work-study programs, a Washington semester, study-abroad in numerous countries, pass/fail options, student-designed and dual majors, and 3–2 engineering degrees with Washington University in St. Louis and the University of Minnesota are available. There is a freshman honors program on campus, as well as 5 national honor societies, including Phi Beta Kappa. Two departments have honors programs.

Faculty/Classroom: Sixty-three percent of faculty are male; 37%, female. All teach undergraduates. The average class size in an introductory lecture is 28; in a laboratory, 12; and in a regular course offering, 20.

Admissions: About 90% of the 1993–94 applicants were accepted. The SAT scores for the 1993–94 freshman class were as follows: Verbal—36% below 500, 43% between 500 and 599, 19% between 600 and 700, and 2% above 700; Math—14% below 500, 37% between 500 and 599, 36% between 600 and 700, and 13% above 700. The ACT scores were 8% below 21, 25% between 21 and 23, 28% between 24 and 26, 22% between 27 and 28, and 17% above 28. About 64% of the current freshmen were in the top fifth of their class; 88% were in the top two fifths. There were 4 National Merit finalists. About 42 freshmen graduated first in their class.

Requirements: Luther requires applicants to be in the upper 50% of their class. A minimum GPA of 2.5 is required. The SAT I or ACT is required. Applicants should have 4 years of English, 3 each of mathematics and social studies, and 2 of science. An essay is required, and an interview is recommended. The GED is accepted. AP and CLEP credits are accepted. Important factors used in the admissions decision are advanced placement or honor courses, evidence of special talent, extracurricular activities record, recommendations by school officials, and leadership record.

Procedure: Freshmen are admitted to all sessions. Entrance exams should be taken by fall of the senior year. Applications should be filed by March 1 for fall entry, December 1 for winter entry, and January 1 for spring entry, along with an application fee of $20. Notification is sent on a rolling basis. There are early admissions and deferred admissions plans.

Transfer: About 72 transfer students enrolled in 1993–94. Transfer students must meet the same high school standards and SAT I or ACT scores as entering freshmen plus have a minimum GPA of 2.5 in parallel college course work. A total of 32 credits out of 128 must be completed at Luther.

Visiting: There are regularly scheduled orientations for prospective students. There are guides for informal visits, and visitors may sit in on classes and stay overnight at the school. To arrange for a visit, contact the Admissions Office at (319) 387-1287 or (800) 458-8437.

Financial Aid: In 1993–94 88% of all current freshmen and 84% of continuing students received some form of financial aid. About 66% of freshmen and 63% of continuing students received need-based aid. The average freshman award was $8877. Of that total, scholarships or need-based grants averaged $4550 ($7000 maximum); loans averaged $3027 ($4680 maximum); and work contracts averaged $1300 ($1500 maximum). Sixty percent of undergraduate students work part-time. Average earnings from campus work for the school year are $1200. The average financial indebtedness of the 1992–93 graduate was $8762. Luther is a member of CSS. The FAF or FFS is required. The deadline for financial aid applications is March 1.

International Students: There are currently 141 international students enrolled. The school actively recruits these students. They must take the TOEFL and achieve a minimum score of 550. The student must also take the SAT I or the ACT.

Computers: The college provides computer facilities for student use. The mainframe is an HP 3000. Students have access to computers in several clusters around campus. About 250 computers and 45 terminals, many of which are connected to the campus network, are available for student use. A gateway to the Internet is also on the campus network. All students may access the system. It may be used 8 A.M. to midnight with provision for extending. There are no time limits on using the system and no fees. Luther supports IBM and Macintosh computers and helps with purchase arrangements.

Graduates: In 1992–93 497 bachelor's degrees were awarded. The most popular majors among graduates were management (13%), biology (12%), and psychology (7%). Within an average freshman class, 75% graduate in 4 years and 78% in 5 years. Some 114 companies recruited on campus in 1992–93. In the 1992 graduating class, 10% of the men and 11% of the women were enrolled in graduate school within 6 months of graduation; 71% of the men and 79% of the women had found employment.

Admissions Contact: David Sallee, Dean for Enrollment.

MAHARISHI INTERNATIONAL UNIVERSITY E-4
Fairfield, IA 52557–1155 | (515) 472–1166 or (515) 472–2565

Full-time: 181 men, 170 women	**Faculty:** 102
Part-time: 14 men, 13 women	**Ph.D.s:** 75%
Graduate: 130 men, 120 women	**Student/Faculty:** 4 to 1
Year: semesters	**Tuition:** $10,906
Application Deadline: open	**Room & Board:** $2760
Freshman Class: 74 applied, 51 accepted, 41 enrolled	
SAT I or ACT: recommended	**COMPETITIVE**

Maharishi International University, established in 1971, is a private institution offering undergraduate and graduate programs through the College of Arts and Sciences, coupled with the practice of transcendental meditation, in which all students and faculty are required to participate. There is one undergraduate and one graduate school. The library contains 144,000 volumes, 49,374 microform items, and 10,703 audiovisual forms, and subscribes to 1438 periodicals. Computerized library sources and services include the card catalog, interlibrary loans, and database searching. Special learning facilities include a learning resource center, an art gallery, a radio station, theaters, and studios for ceramics, drawing, and painting. The 262-acre campus is in a small town 114 miles southeast of Des Moines. Including residence halls, there are 78 buildings on campus.

Student Life: About 74% of undergraduates are from out-of-state, mostly the Middle Atlantic. Students come from 33 states, 69 foreign countries, and Canada. Fifty-two percent are foreign nationals; 42% white. The average age of freshmen is 23.1; all undergraduates, 26. Forty-four percent drop out by the end of their first year; 57% remain to graduate.

Housing: A total of 898 students can be accommodated in college housing. College-sponsored living facilities include single-sex dormitories and married-student housing. On-campus housing is guaranteed for all 4 years. Seventy-eight percent of students live on campus; of those, 96% remain on campus on weekends. Alcohol is not permitted. All students may keep cars on campus.

Activities: There are no fraternities or sororities on campus. There are 20 groups on campus, including art, chess, chorale, dance, drama, ethnic, international, musical theater, newspaper, radio, religious, social service, student government, and yearbook. Popular campus events include sports festivals, seasonal celebrations, national day celebrations for international organizations, and International Cultural Exchange Festival.

Sports: There are 2 intercollegiate sports for men and 1 for women, and 16 intramural sports for men and 13 for women. Athletic and recreation facilities include indoor tennis, basketball, and volleyball courts, a gymnasium, a weight-training room, a field house, a swimming pool, a table tennis room, an outdoor fitness trail, cross-country ski trails, camping facilities, baseball batting and golf driving cages, a golf putting range, an indoor 4-lane jogging track, and a dance studio.

Disabled Students: All of the campus is accessible to disabled students. The following facilities are available: wheelchair ramps, special parking, specially equipped rest rooms, and lowered telephones.

Services: In addition to many counseling and information services, tutoring is available in every subject. In addition, there is remedial math, reading, and writing.

Campus Safety and Security: Campus safety and security measures include 24-hour foot and vehicle patrol, escort service, informal discussions, and emergency telephones. In addition, there are lighted pathways and sidewalks.

Programs of Study: MIU awards the B.A., B.S., and B.F.A. degrees. Associate's, master's, and doctoral degrees also are awarded. Bachelor's degrees are awarded in BIOLOGICAL SCIENCE (biochemistry and biology/biological science), BUSINESS (business administration and management), COMMUNICATIONS AND THE ARTS (fine arts and literature), COMPUTER AND PHYSICAL SCIENCE (chemistry, computer science, mathematics, and physics), ENGINEERING AND ENVIRONMENTAL DESIGN (electrical/electronics engineering, electrical/electronics engineering technology, and electromechanical technology), SOCIAL SCIENCE (political science/government and psychology). Physics and engineering are the strongest academically. Science of creative intelligence, business, art, and literature have the largest enrollments.

Required: Students must complete 160 credit units, with a minimum of 60 credits in the major, and must also complete the core course program of 24 credit units. All students must maintain a minimum GPA of 2.5. Additional requirements include physical education courses and the Science of Creative Intelligence course with its applied aspect, the transcendental meditation program, as well as courses in mathematics proficiency and writing proficiency. The 44-week school year and block scheduling system allow students to take one course at a time.

Special: Opportunities are provided for internships, B.A.-B.S. degrees, study abroad, and nondegree study. Programs are offered in the science of creative intelligence and Maharishi Ayur-ved. There is a freshman honors program on campus.

Faculty/Classroom: Seventy-three percent of faculty are male; 27%, female. All teach undergraduates and 50% both teach and do research. The average class size in an introductory lecture is 50; in a laboratory, 6; and in a regular course offering, 10.

Admissions: About 69% of the 1993–94 applicants were accepted. About 10% of the current freshmen were in the top fifth of their class; 15% were in the top two fifths. There was 1 National Merit finalist.

Requirements: A minimum GPA of 2.5 is required. The SAT I or ACT is recommended. Graduation from an accredited secondary school or a GED is required. An essay and 2 personal recommendations are required. An interview is recommended. AP and CLEP credits are accepted. Important factors used in the admissions decision are recommendations by school officials, personality, intangible qualities, advanced placement or honor courses, evidence of special talent, and recommendations by alumni.

Procedure: Freshmen are admitted fall and spring. Application deadlines are open. Application fee is $25. Notification is sent on a rolling basis.

Transfer: About 40 transfer students enrolled in 1993–94. A total of 60 credits must be completed at MIU.

Visiting: There are regularly scheduled orientations for prospective students, including campus tours, visits to classes, and interviews. There are guides for informal visits and visitors may sit in on classes and stay overnight at the school. To arrange for a visit, contact the Office of Admissions at (515) 472–1166.

Financial Aid: In 1993–94, 62% of all current freshmen and 84% of continuing students received some form of financial aid. About 62% of freshmen and 84% of continuing students received need-based aid. The average freshman award was $12,578. Of that total, scholarships or need-based grants averaged $6223; loans averaged $5295 ($5625 maximum); and work contracts averaged $1060 ($1100 maximum). Seventy percent of undergraduate students work part-time. Average earnings from campus work for the school year are $1000. MIU is a member of CSS. The college's own financial statement and the FAFSA are required. The deadline for financial aid applications is August 15.

International Students: There are currently 312 international students enrolled. The school actively recruits these students. They must take the TOEFL and achieve a minimum score of 550; the University of Michigan Language Test is also accepted.

Computers: MIU provides computer facilities for student use. The mainframe is a DEC VAX 11/780. Microcomputers are available throughout the campus. Juniors and seniors may access the system. It may be used daytime and evenings. Time limits vary. There are no fees.

Graduates: In 1992–93, 64 bachelor's degrees were awarded. The most popular majors among graduates were business (25%), literature (14%), and art (11%). Within an average freshman class, 57% graduate in 5 years. Ten companies recruited on campus in 1992–93.

Admissions Contact: Harry Bright, Director of Admissions.

MORNINGSIDE COLLEGE B-2
Sioux City, IA 51106 | (712) 274–5111; (800) 831–0806

Full-time: 405 men, 547 women	**Faculty:** 66; IIB, --$
Part-time: 78 men, 150 women	**Ph.D.s:** 66%
Graduate: 25 men, 86 women	**Student/Faculty:** 14 to 1
Year: semesters, summer session	**Tuition:** $10,376
Application Deadline: open	**Room & Board:** $3520
Freshman Class: 586 applied, 533 accepted, 239 enrolled	
ACT: 22	**COMPETITIVE**

Morningside College, founded in 1894, is a private, coeducational college affiliated with the United Methodist Church, with a curriculum in the liberal arts and preprofessional and professional programs of study. In addition to regional accreditation, Morningside has bacca-

laureate program accreditation with NASM, NCATE, and NLN. The library contains 115,669 volumes, 133,552 microform items, and 4991 audiovisual forms, and subscribes to 797 periodicals. Computerized library sources and services include the card catalog, interlibrary loans, and database searching. Special learning facilities include a learning resource center, art gallery, radio station, and observatory. The 27-acre campus is in a suburban area 100 miles north of Omaha, Nebraska. Including residence halls, there are 17 buildings on campus.

Student Life: About 78% of undergraduates are from Iowa. Students come from 22 states, 10 foreign countries, and Canada. Ninety-five percent are from public schools; 5% from private. Eighty-nine percent are white. Fifty-nine percent are Protestant; 23% Catholic; 18% claim no religious affiliation. The average age of freshmen is 19; all undergraduates, 21. Twenty-six percent drop out by the end of their first year; 55% remain to graduate.

Housing: A total of 625 students can be accommodated in college housing. College-sponsored living facilities include single-sex and coed dormitories and on-campus apartments. On-campus housing is guaranteed for all 4 years. Sixty-three percent of students live on campus; of those, 64% remain on campus on weekends. All students may keep cars on campus.

Activities: About 3% of men belong to 1 national fraternity; about 5% of women belong to 2 national sororities. There are 27 groups on campus, including art, band, cheerleading, choir, chorale, computers, drama, ethnic, honors, international, jazz band, literary magazine, marching band, newspaper, orchestra, pep band, photography, political, professional, radio and TV, religious, student government, symphony, and yearbook. Popular campus events include Homecoming, Winterfest, Friday is Writing Day, and Indian Awareness Week.

Sports: There are 5 intercollegiate sports for men and 5 for women, and 24 intramural sports for men and 17 for women. Athletic and recreation facilities include an 8000-seat stadium, a football field, and a new campus recreation center with basketball, volleyball, badminton, tennis, and racquetball/handball courts, an elevated track, a weight room, and a 6-lane, 25-meter swimming pool.

Disabled Students: Eighty percent of the campus is accessible to disabled students. The following facilities are available: elevators, special parking, specially equipped rest rooms, and special class scheduling.

Services: In addition to many counseling and information services, tutoring is available in most subjects. There are support courses in reading and writing. A reader service for the blind can be arranged.

Campus Safety and Security: Campus safety and security measures include self defense education, escort service, informal discussions, pamphlets, posters, and films. In addition, there are emergency telephones and lighted pathways and sidewalks. The college is in compliance with the Crime Awareness and Campus Security Act of 1990.

Programs of Study: Morningside awards the B.A., B.S., B.Mus., B.Mus.Ed., and B.S.N. degrees. Associate and master's degrees also are awarded. Bachelor's degrees are awarded in AGRICULTURE (agricultural business management), BIOLOGICAL SCIENCE (biology/biological science), BUSINESS (accounting, business administration and management, and office supervision and management), COMMUNICATIONS AND THE ARTS (communications, dramatic arts, English, fine arts, French, music, and Spanish), COMPUTER AND PHYSICAL SCIENCE (chemistry, computer science, mathematics, and physics), EDUCATION (business, early childhood, elementary, English, music, physical, and special), ENGINEERING AND ENVIRONMENTAL DESIGN (engineering), HEALTH PROFESSIONS (nursing), SOCIAL SCIENCE (criminal justice, economics, history, Native American studies, parks and recreation management, philosophy, political science/government, psychology, religion, and sociology). Humanities and physical sciences are the strongest academically. Business administration has the largest enrollment.

Required: The total number of credit hours required for graduation is 124, with 44 hours of core curriculum in traditional liberal arts and 30 hours minimum in the major. Students must take an interdisciplinary seminar and have a minimum GPA of 2.0 to graduate.

Special: Internships, study abroad in 8 countries, a Washington semester, work-study programs, both on campus and with 5 nonprofit agencies, the B.A.-B.S. degree, dual majors, and student-designed majors are options. Also available is a professional program in engineering leading to a baccalaureate awarded by the University of Iowa, South Dakota State University, or Washington University in St. Louis. Cooperative transfer programs have been established with Iowa State University in fashion merchandising, hotel/restaurant management, and nutritional science. Pass/fail options and nondegree study are possible. Credit may be given for life, military, and work experience. There is a voluntary, interdepartmental honors program. There is a freshman honors program on campus, as well as 15 national honor societies. Ten departments have honors programs.

Faculty/Classroom: Sixty-seven percent of faculty are male; 33%, female. All teach undergraduates and 10% both teach and do research. No introductory courses are taught by graduate students. The average class size in an introductory lecture is 30; in a laboratory, 15; and in a regular course offering, 20.

Admissions: About 91% of the 1993–94 applicants were accepted. The ACT scores for the 1993–94 freshman class were as follows: 34% below 21, 32% between 21 and 23, 20% between 24 and 26, 7% between 27 and 28, and 7% above 28. About 34% of the current freshmen were in the top fifth of their class; 61% were in the top two fifths. About 8 freshmen graduated first in their class.

Requirements: Morningside requires applicants to be in the upper 50% of their class. A minimum GPA of 2.5 is required. The SAT I or ACT is required. Applicants must also be graduates of an accredited secondary school. The GED is accepted. A portfolio is required for all studio art majors and an audition for performing music majors. Applicants graduating from high school 5 years or more prior to entering college are exempted from submitting SAT I or ACT scores. AP and CLEP credits are accepted. Important factors used in the admissions decision are recommendations by school officials, evidence of special talent, advanced placement or honor courses, leadership record, and parents or siblings attending the school.

Procedure: Freshmen are admitted to all sessions. Entrance exams should be taken in the junior year. Application deadlines are open. The application fee is $15. Notification is sent on a rolling basis.

Transfer: About 109 transfer students enrolled in 1993–94. Transfer applicants must take the ACT and have an interview. A GPA of 2.0 or above transfers for credit. The college admits transfers in the fall, spring, and summer. A total of 30 credits out of 124 must be completed at Morningside.

Visiting: There are regularly scheduled orientations for prospective students, consisting of a campus tour, appointments with faculty and financial aid, and an interview with an admissions counselor. There are guides for informal visits, and visitors may sit in on classes and stay overnight at the school. To arrange for a visit, contact the Office of Admissions at (800) 831–0806.

Financial Aid: In 1993–94 79% of all current freshmen and 89% of continuing students received some form of financial aid. About 74% of freshmen and 73% of continuing students received need-based aid. The average freshman award was $11,268. Of that total, scholarships or need-based grants averaged $6744 ($13,896 maximum); loans averaged $3160 ($7625 maximum); and work contracts averaged $1364 ($1500 maximum). Ninety-three percent of undergraduate students work part-time. Average earnings from campus work for the school year are $879. The average financial indebtedness of the 1992–93 graduate was $8597. The FAFSA financial statement is required. The deadline for financial aid applications is March 1.

International Students: There are currently 36 international students enrolled. The school actively recruits these students. They must take the TOEFL. Students with TOEFL scores below 550 are reviewed on an individual basis.

Computers: The college provides computer facilities for student use. The mainframe is a Prime 5370. Students may not access the mainframe but can access an instructional network on an IBM RS6000 connected to student terminals, and some 20 PCs connected to a Novell file server. All are located in the building where computer science is taught. All students may access the system. It may be used 8 A.M. to 11 P.M. Monday through Friday and 2 P.M. to 11 P.M. Saturday and Sunday. There are no time limits on using the system and no fees. The college also provides personal computers, which are placed in each residence hall room for each residential student. These PCs are networked for communication between faculty, students, administrative offices, and the library. Campus computer laboratories are available in the library for commuter students. Rental laptop PCs are also available. Students who bring their own PCs may also access the electronic network.

Graduates: In 1992–93 213 bachelor's degrees were awarded. The most popular majors among graduates were business (35%), education (19%), and health professions (11%). Within an average freshman class, 2% graduate in 3 years and 34% in 4 years. Some 22 companies recruited on campus in a recent year. In the 1992 graduating class, 10% of the men and 8% of the women were enrolled in graduate school within 6 months of graduation; 38% of the men and 61% of the women had found employment.

Admissions Contact: Lora VanderZwaag, Director of Admissions.

freshman honors program on campus, as well as 2 national honor societies.

MOUNT MERCY COLLEGE
Cedar Rapids, IA 52402

E-3

(319) 363–8213, ext. 221
(800) 248–4504 (in-state)

Full-time: 206 men, 600 women
Part-time: 208 men, 335 women
Graduate: none
Year: 4-1-4, summer session
Application Deadline: August 15
Freshman Class: 386 applied, 331 accepted, 165 enrolled
ACT: 22

Faculty: 62; IIB, --$
Ph.D.s: 48%
Student/Faculty: 13 to 1
Tuition: $9900
Room & Board: $3330

COMPETITIVE

Mount Mercy College, founded in 1928, is a private, coeducational liberal arts institution affiliated with the Roman Catholic Church. In addition to regional accreditation, Mount Mercy has baccalaureate program accreditation with CSWE and NLN. The library contains 91,678 volumes, 1278 microform items, and 2989 audiovisual forms, and subscribes to 625 periodicals. Computerized library sources and services include interlibrary loans and database searching. Special learning facilities include a learning resource center, art gallery, and video media room. The 36-acre campus is in an urban area 230 miles west of Chicago, Illinois. Including residence halls, there are 9 buildings on campus.

Student Life: About 97% of undergraduates are from Iowa. Students come from 6 states, 10 foreign countries, and Canada. Eighty percent are from public schools; 20% from private. Ninety-seven percent are white. Fifty percent are Catholic; 40% Protestant. The average age of freshmen is 18; all undergraduates, 24. Twenty-one percent drop out by the end of their first year; 60% remain to graduate.

Housing: A total of 454 students can be accommodated in college housing. College-sponsored living facilities include coed dormitories, on-campus apartments, and off-campus apartments. In addition, there is housing for returning adult students. On-campus housing is guaranteed for all 4 years. Sixty-seven percent of students commute. All students may keep cars on campus.

Activities: There are no fraternities or sororities on campus. There are 19 groups on campus, including art, choir, chorale, chorus, computers, drama, film, honors, international, literary magazine, pep band, political, religious, social service, and student government. Popular campus events include Hillfest, Spring Fling, Family Weekend, Valentine's Day Formal, Freakers Ball, Returning Students Week, and Midnight Bowling.

Sports: There are 6 intercollegiate sports for men and 6 for women, and 10 intramural sports for men and 10 for women. Athletic and recreation facilities include a center, a 2000-seat stadium, an auditorium-gymnasium, an indoor hitting facility, a weight room, an aerobics area, and karate facilities.

Disabled Students: Ninety-five percent of the campus is accessible to disabled students. The following facilities are available: wheelchair ramps, elevators, special parking, specially equipped rest rooms, and lowered drinking fountains.

Services: In addition to many counseling and information services, tutoring is available in most subjects. There is a reader service for the blind, and remedial math, reading, and writing.

Campus Safety and Security: Campus safety and security measures include self defense education, escort service, informal discussions, and pamphlets, posters, and films. In addition, there are emergency telephones, lighted pathways and sidewalks, evening and weekend foot patrol, and cameras at residence hall entrances.

Programs of Study: Mount Mercy awards the B.A., B.S., B.A.A., B.A.S. and B.B.A. degrees. Bachelor's degrees are awarded in BIOLOGICAL SCIENCE (biology/biological science), BUSINESS (accounting, business administration and management, and marketing/retailing/merchandising), COMMUNICATIONS AND THE ARTS (English, fine arts, music, public relations, and speech/debate/rhetoric), COMPUTER AND PHYSICAL SCIENCE (computer science and mathematics), EDUCATION (art, elementary, and music), HEALTH PROFESSIONS (medical laboratory technology and nursing), SOCIAL SCIENCE (criminal justice, history, liberal arts/general studies, political science/government, psychology, religion, social work, and sociology). Nursing, social work, accounting, education, and English are the strongest academically. Administrative management, nursing, and education have the largest enrollments.

Required: To graduate, all students must complete 123 semester hours, with a varying number of hours in the major, and maintain at least a 2.0 GPA. The requirements of the concentration must be fulfilled. The 37-semester-hour general education requirement includes courses in philosophy, religious studies, humanities, arts, social and natural sciences, and mathematics.

Special: Special academic programs include internships in many majors, work-study programs on campus, and cross-registration with Coe College. A general studies degree and student-designed, interdisciplinary majors are available. Credit for prior experiential learning may be granted, and pass/fail options are possible. There is a

Faculty/Classroom: Forty-eight percent of faculty are male; 52%, female. All teach undergraduates. The average class size in an introductory lecture is 30; in a laboratory, 15; and in a regular course offering, 25.

Admissions: About 86% of the 1993–94 applicants were accepted. The ACT scores for the 1993–94 freshman class were as follows: 31% below 21, 33% between 21 and 23, 22% between 24 and 26, 8% between 27 and 28, and 6% above 28. About 41% of the current freshmen were in the top fifth of their class; 72% were in the top two fifths. About 11 freshmen graduated first in their class.

Requirements: Mount Mercy requires applicants to be in the upper 50% of their class. A minimum GPA of 2.5 is required. The SAT I, with recommended minimum scores of 400 on each section, or the ACT, with a recommended composite score of 19, is required. Other admissions requirements include graduation from an accredited secondary school, with 16 Carnegie units, including 4 of English, 2 each of mathematics and history, 1 of science, and 7 in electives. A recommendation from high school faculty or counselor and an essay or personal statement are also required. AP and CLEP credits are accepted. Important factors used in the admissions decision are recommendations by school officials, extracurricular activities record, advanced placement or honor courses, leadership record, and evidence of special talent.

Procedure: Freshmen are admitted to all sessions. Entrance exams should be taken in the junior year or the fall of the senior year. Applications should be filed by August 15 for fall entry and November 15 for winter entry, along with an application fee of $20. Notification is sent on a rolling basis. There are early admissions and deferred admissions plans.

Transfer: About 188 transfer students enrolled in 1993–94. Transfer students must have at least a 2.0 GPA. An interview is recommended. A total of 30 credits out of 123 must be completed at Mount Mercy.

Visiting: There are regularly scheduled orientations for prospective students, consisting of a presidential welcome, campus tour, student panel, faculty academic fair, tips on selecting a college, admission requirements, and student evaluation. There are guides for informal visits, and visitors may sit in on classes and stay overnight at the school. To arrange a visit, contact the Admissions Office at (319) 363–8213, ext. 221 or (800) 248–4504 (in-state).

Financial Aid: In 1993–94 85% of all current freshmen and 85% of continuing students received some form of financial aid. About 85% of freshmen and 85% of continuing students received need-based aid. The average freshman award was $9500. Of that total, scholarships or need-based grants averaged $3200 ($6400 maximum); loans averaged $3000 ($3625 maximum); and work contracts averaged $1000 (maximum). Twenty-five percent of undergraduate students work part-time. Average earnings from campus work for the school year are $1000. The average financial indebtedness of the 1992–93 graduate was $15,500. Mount Mercy is a member of CSS. The FAF, FFS or SFS, and FAFSA are required. The deadline for financial aid applications is March 1.

International Students: There are currently 12 international students enrolled. The school actively recruits these students. They must take the TOEFL and achieve a minimum score of 525.

Computers: The college provides computer facilities for student use. The mainframe is a Sun 4/280. Microcomputers and Sun workstations are networked in the new computer center with access to Internet. The computer ratio is 1 to 13 students, and there are 24-hour computer laboratories in residence halls. All students may access the system. It may be used 7 days per week, usually until 12 A.M. There are no time limits on using the system and no fees.

Graduates: In 1992–93 291 bachelor's degrees were awarded. The most popular majors among graduates were administrative management (16%), elementary education (13%), and nursing (12%). Within an average freshman class, 1% graduate in 3 years, 89% in 4 years, 98% in 5 years, and 99% in 6 years. Some 60 companies recruited on campus in 1992–93. In the 1992 graduating class, 1% of the men and 5% of the women were enrolled in graduate school within 6 months of graduation; 98% of the men and 94% of the women had found employment.

Admissions Contact: Larry D. Erenberger, Vice President for Enrollment Management.

MOUNT SAINT CLARE COLLEGE   F-3

Clinton, IA 52732   (319) 242-4153; (800) 242-4153
Full-time: 143 men, 221 women   **Faculty:** 18; IIA, --$
Part-time: 24 men, 71 women   **Ph.D.s:** 34%
Graduate: none   **Student/Faculty:** 20 to 1
Year: semesters, summer session   **Tuition:** $9270
Application Deadline: open   **Room & Board:** $3600
Freshman Class: 328 applied, 280 accepted, 95 enrolled
ACT: 20   **LESS COMPETITIVE**

Mount Saint Clare College, founded in 1918, is a private, coeducational Catholic institution offering undergraduate degree programs in liberal arts and business. The library contains 71,837 volumes, 57,418 microform items, and 2077 audiovisual forms, and subscribes to 580 periodicals. Computerized library sources and services include database searching. Special learning facilities include a learning resource center and an art gallery. The 135-acre campus is in a small town 135 miles west of Chicago. Including residence halls, there are 6 buildings on campus.

Student Life: About 53% of undergraduates are from Iowa. Students come from 9 states and 6 foreign countries. Seventy percent are from public schools; 30% from private. Eighty-eight percent are white. Forty-three percent are Catholic; 35% Protestant; 22% Buddhist, Shinto, and Orthodox. The average age of freshmen is 18. Twenty percent drop out by the end of their first year; 52% remain to graduate.

Housing: A total of 180 students can be accommodated in college housing. College-sponsored living facilities include coed dormitories. On-campus housing is guaranteed for all 4 years. Sixty-eight percent of students commute. All students may keep cars on campus.

Activities: There are no fraternities or sororities on campus. There are 14 groups on campus, including cheerleading, chorus, computers, drama, honors, international, musical theater, newspaper, religious, social, student government, and yearbook.

Sports: There are 2 intercollegiate sports for men and 4 for women, and 4 intramural sports each for men and women. Athletic and recreation facilities include soccer, football, and baseball fields, a 400-seat gymnasium, and a weight-training room.

Disabled Students: The following facilities are available: wheelchair ramps, elevators, special parking, specially equipped rest rooms, and special class scheduling.

Services: In addition to many counseling and information services, tutoring is available in most subjects.

Campus Safety and Security: There is security on campus from 9 P.M. to 1 A.M. and in the dormitory from midnight to 8 A.M.

Programs of Study: MSCC awards the B.A. degree. Associate degrees are also awarded. Bachelor's degrees are awarded in BUSINESS (accounting, business administration and management, and office supervision and management), COMPUTER AND PHYSICAL SCIENCE (computer programming), HEALTH PROFESSIONS (cytotechnology), SOCIAL SCIENCE (liberal arts/general studies). Business administration and accounting have the largest enrollments.

Required: Students must complete 122 semester hours, including 40 semester hours of general education requirements and 30 in a major, with a minimum 2.0 GPA.

Special: Special academic programs include a teacher preparatory program through cross-registration with Saint Ambrose University and Clinton Community College. MCSS also offers dual majors and limited pass/fail options. There is one national honor society on campus. One department has an honors program.

Faculty/Classroom: Forty-one percent of faculty are male; 59%, female. All teach undergraduates. The average class size in an introductory lecture is 20; in a laboratory, 15; and in a regular course offering, 20.

Admissions: About 85% of the 1993-94 applicants were accepted. The ACT scores for the 1993-94 freshman class were as follows: 60% below 21, 20% between 21 and 23, 13% between 24 and 26, 6% between 27 and 28, and 1% above 28.

Requirements: MSCC requires applicants to be in the upper 66% of their class. A minimum GPA of 1.4 is required. Applicant must be a graduate of an accredited secondary school or have earned a GED. The college requires ACT or SAT I scores as well as placement assessments in mathematics and English. AP and CLEP credits are accepted. Important factors used in the admissions decision are advanced placement or honor courses, evidence of special talent, leadership record, personality, intangible qualities, and extracurricular activities record.

Procedure: Freshmen are admitted to all sessions. Application deadlines are open. Application fee is $20. Notification is sent on a rolling basis. There are early admissions and deferred admissions plans.

Transfer: About 60 transfer students enrolled in a recent year. Applicants must have 64 semester hours of 100-level or higher courses from a 2-year school, and up to 90 semester hours maximum. A total of 30 credits out of 122 must be completed at MSCC.

Visiting: There are regularly scheduled orientations for prospective students. There are guides for informal visits and visitors may sit in on classes and stay overnight at the school. To arrange for a visit, contact the Admissions Office at (319) 242-4023.

Financial Aid: In 1993-94, 90% of all students received some form of financial aid. About 88% received need-based aid. The average freshman award was $8393. Of that total, scholarships or need-based grants averaged $5031 ($7267 maximum); loans averaged $3198 ($4625 maximum); and work contracts averaged $1065 ($1420 maximum). Thirty-five percent of undergraduate students work part-time. Average earnings from campus work for the school year are $1065. The average financial indebtedness of the 1992-93 graduate was $7400. MSCC is a member of CSS. The FAF, FFS or SFS is required. The deadline for financial aid applications is August 1.

International Students: The school actively recruits these students. They must take the TOEFL and achieve a minimum score of 450.

Computers: The college provides computer facilities for student use. MSCC provides 23 microcomputers in 4 locations for student use. All students may access the system. There are no time limits on using the system.

Graduates: In 1992-93, 30 bachelor's degrees were awarded. The most popular majors among graduates were business administration (37%), accounting (29%), and liberal arts (20%). Within an average freshman class, 47% graduate in 5 years. Some 35 companies recruited on campus in 1992-93. In the 1992 graduating class, 5% of the men and 4% of the women were enrolled in graduate school within 6 months of graduation; 40% of the men and 43% of the women had found employment.

Admissions Contact: Waunita M. Sullivan, Director of Enrollment.

NORTHWESTERN COLLEGE OF IOWA   B-2

Orange City, IA 51041   (712) 737-7130; (800) 747-4757
Full-time: 452 men, 588 women   **Faculty:** 61; IIB, --$
Part-time: 14 men, 38 women   **Ph.D.s:** 66%
Graduate: 3 men, 14 women   **Student/Faculty:** 17 to 1
Year: semesters, summer session   **Tuition:** $9250
Application Deadline: August 15   **Room & Board:** $3000
Freshman Class: 872 applied, 838 accepted, 366 enrolled
ACT: 23   **COMPETITIVE**

Northwestern College, founded in 1882, is affiliated with the Reformed Church in America and offers liberal arts and teacher education programs. In addition to regional accreditation, Northwestern has baccalaureate program accreditation with CSWE and NCATE. The library contains 130,000 volumes and 9500 microform items, and subscribes to 500 periodicals. Computerized library sources and services include the card catalog, interlibrary loans, and database searching. Special learning facilities include a learning resource center, art gallery, radio station, and TV station. The 55-acre campus is in a small town 40 miles northeast of Sioux City. Including residence halls, there are 20 buildings on campus.

Student Life: About 72% of undergraduates are from Iowa. Students come from 26 states, 16 foreign countries, and Canada. Eighty-eight percent are from public schools; 12% from private. Ninety-eight percent are white. Most are Protestant. The average age of freshmen is 18; all undergraduates, 21. Twelve percent drop out by the end of their first year; 54% remain to graduate.

Housing: A total of 900 students can be accommodated in college housing. College-sponsored living facilities include single-sex dormitories, on-campus apartments, and married-student housing. On-campus housing is guaranteed for all 4 years. Eighty-nine percent of students live on campus; of those, 60% remain on campus on weekends. Alcohol is not permitted. All students may keep cars on campus.

Activities: There are no fraternities or sororities on campus. There are 30 groups on campus, including art, band, cheerleading, choir, chorus, drama, drill team, honors, international, jazz band, literary magazine, musical theater, newspaper, orchestra, pep band, photography, political, professional, radio and TV, religious, social, social service, student government, and yearbook. Popular campus events include Winter Carnival, Spring Fest, Homecoming, and a fine arts festival.

Sports: There are 8 intercollegiate sports for men and 7 for women, and 11 intramural sports for men and 11 for women. Athletic and recreation facilities include an athletic field, a 3000-seat stadium, a 176-meter indoor track, 4 handball/racquetball courts, 4 basketball/volleyball courts, archery, and gymnastics rooms.

Disabled Students: Eighty percent of the campus is accessible to disabled students. The following facilities are available: wheelchair ramps, elevators, special parking, specially equipped rest rooms, and lowered drinking fountains.

Services: In addition to many counseling and information services, tutoring is available in most subjects. There is remedial math, reading, and writing.

Campus Safety and Security: Campus safety and security measures include informal discussions, pamphlets, posters, and films, and lighted pathways and sidewalks.

Programs of Study: Northwestern awards the B.A. and B.S.W. degrees. Associate and master's degrees also are awarded. Bachelor's degrees are awarded in BIOLOGICAL SCIENCE (biology/biological science), BUSINESS (accounting, business administration and management, and business economics), COMMUNICATIONS AND THE ARTS (communications, dramatic arts, English, fine arts, French, music, and Spanish), COMPUTER AND PHYSICAL SCIENCE (chemistry, computer science, and mathematics), EDUCATION (art, business, early childhood, elementary, foreign languages, middle school, music, physical, science, secondary, and special), HEALTH PROFESSIONS (medical laboratory technology, predentistry, and premedicine), SOCIAL SCIENCE (criminal justice, economics, history, parks and recreation management, philosophy, political science/government, prelaw, psychology, religion, social work, and sociology). Business and teacher education have the largest enrollments.

Required: All students are required to take 52 credits in the core curriculum, including courses in Bible and language, literature and writing, natural and social sciences, fine arts, and physical education. Students must maintain a 2.0 GPA for 124 total credits and pass a writing competency test.

Special: Northwestern offers numerous internships, a Washington semester, student-designed majors, and study abroad in Spain, France, and the Netherlands. There is a 3–2 engineering degree with Washington University at St. Louis, and a 2–2 nursing program with Trinity College is available. There is a freshman honors program on campus, as well as 2 national honor societies. Thirty departments have honors programs.

Faculty/Classroom: Seventy-three percent of faculty are male; 27%, female. All teach undergraduates and 69% do research. The average class size in an introductory lecture is 30 and in a laboratory, 20.

Admissions: About 96% of the 1993–94 applicants were accepted. The ACT scores for the 1993–94 freshman class were as follows: 34% below 21, 24% between 21 and 23, 24% between 24 and 26, 11% between 27 and 28, and 7% above 28. About 31% of the current freshmen were in the top fifth of their class; 74% were in the top two fifths. There were 2 National Merit finalists and 14 semifinalists. About 19 freshmen graduated first in their class.

Requirements: Northwestern requires applicants to be in the upper 67% of their class. A minimum GPA of 2.0 is required. The SAT or ACT is required. Applicants with a minimum ACT composite of 18, in the top half of their high school class, and with a 2.0 GPA are generally accepted. Applicants should be graduates of an accredited secondary school. The suggested distribution of high school courses is 4 years of English, 3 years each of mathematics and social studies, and 2 of natural science. An interview is recommended. The GED is accepted. AP and CLEP credits are accepted. Important factors used in the admissions decision are personality, intangible qualities, leadership record, evidence of special talent, advanced placement or honor courses, and recommendations by school officials.

Procedure: Freshmen are admitted fall and spring. Entrance exams should be taken in the spring of the junior year. Applications should be filed by August 15 for fall entry and January 1 for spring entry, along with an application fee of $20. Notification is sent on a rolling basis.

Transfer: About 55 transfer students enrolled in 1993–94. Transfer applicants must submit a transcript and letter of recommendation. A minimum college GPA of 2.0 is required. A total of 30 credits out of 124 must be completed at Northwestern.

Visiting: There are regularly scheduled orientations for prospective students. There are guides for informal visits, and visitors may sit in on classes and stay overnight at the school. To arrange for a visit, contact Linda Van Berkum at the Admissions Office at (712) 737-7134 or (800) 747-4757.

Financial Aid: In 1993–94 95% of all current freshmen and 95% of continuing students received some form of financial aid. About 74% of freshmen and 74% of continuing students received need-based aid. The average freshman award was $7200. Of that total, scholarships or need-based grants averaged $3100 ($9250 maximum); loans averaged $3400 ($4000 maximum); and work contracts averaged $700 ($1400 maximum). Fifty percent of undergraduate students work part-time. Average earnings from campus work for the school year are $650. The average financial indebtedness of the 1992–93 graduate was $9500. Northwestern is a member of CSS. The FAF, FFS or SFS and the college's own financial statement are required. The deadline for financial aid applications is April 1.

International Students: There are currently 58 international students enrolled. The school actively recruits these students. They must take the TOEFL and achieve a minimum score of 500.

Computers: The college provides computer facilities for student use. The mainframes are a DEC PDP 11/44 and a DEC Alpha. There are 130 terminals available in residence halls, the learning resource center, and the education and business facilities. All students may access the system. It may be used 24 hours a day in residence halls; 7 A.M. to 12 P.M. in academic buildings. There are no time limits on using the system. The fees are $30.

Graduates: In a recent year, 194 bachelor's degrees were awarded. The most popular majors among graduates were business (25%), education (23%), and biology (14%). Within an average freshman class, 2% graduate in 3 years, 34% in 4 years, 21% in 5 years, and 3% in 6 years. Some 20 companies recruited on campus in a recent year. In a recent graduating class, 12% of the men and 3% of the women were enrolled in graduate school within 6 months of graduation; 95% had found employment.

Admissions Contact: Ronald K. De Jong, Admissions Director.

SAINT AMBROSE UNIVERSITY
E-3

Davenport, IA 52803   (319) 383-8888; (800) 383-2627

Full-time: 768 men, 971 women	Faculty: 85; IIB, -$
Part-time: n/av	Ph.D.s: 95%
Graduate: 469 men, 314 women	Student/Faculty: 20 to 1
Year: semesters, summer session	Tuition: $9580
Application Deadline: open	Room & Board: $3800
Freshman Class: 979 applied, 899 accepted, 612 enrolled	
ACT: 22	COMPETITIVE

St. Ambrose University, founded in 1882, in affiliation with the Roman Catholic Church, offers degree programs through the colleges of arts and sciences, business, and human services. There also is a college-level seminary. There are 3 undergraduate and 7 graduate schools. The library contains 160,000 volumes, 105 microform items, and 3500 audiovisual forms, and subscribes to 570 periodicals. Computerized library sources and services include the card catalog, interlibrary loans, and database searching. Special learning facilities include a learning resource center, art gallery, radio station, and TV station. The 10-acre campus is in an urban area 180 miles west of Chicago. Including residence halls, there are 20 buildings on campus.

Student Life: About 60% of undergraduates are from Iowa. Sixty percent are from public schools; 40% from private. Sixty-five percent are Catholic; 35% Protestant. The average age of freshmen is 18.7; all undergraduates, 20.5. Ten percent drop out by the end of their first year; 80% remain to graduate.

Housing: A total of 800 students can be accommodated in college housing. College-sponsored living facilities include single-sex dormitories and on-campus apartments. In addition, there are townhouse residences for upper-division students. On-campus housing is guaranteed for all 4 years. Priority is given to out-of-town students. Fifty-five percent of students commute. All students may keep cars on campus.

Activities: There are no fraternities or sororities on campus. There are a number of groups on campus, including art, band, cheerleading, choir, chorale, drama, ethnic, honors, jazz band, literary magazine, newspaper, orchestra, pep band, photography, professional, radio and TV, religious, social, social service, and student government.

Sports: There are 8 intercollegiate sports for men and 7 for women, and 10 intramural sports for men and 10 for women. Athletic and recreation facilities include tennis, handball/racquetball, and volleyball courts, a swimming pool, a golf room, an archery range, a gymnasium, a weight-lifting room, and a running track.

Disabled Students: Ninety-five percent of the campus is accessible to disabled students. The following facilities are available: wheelchair ramps, elevators, and special parking.

Services: In addition to many counseling and information services, tutoring is available in most subjects. There is remedial math, reading, and writing.

Campus Safety and Security: Campus safety and security measures include 24-hour foot and vehicle patrol, escort service, pamphlets, posters, and films, and emergency telephones. In addition, there are lighted pathways and sidewalks.

Programs of Study: St. Ambrose awards the B.A., B.S., B.M., B.M.E., B.S.I.E., and B.S.O.T. degrees. Master's degrees also are awarded. Bachelor's degrees are awarded in BIOLOGICAL SCIENCE (biology/biological science), BUSINESS (accounting, business administration and management, business economics, management science, and marketing/retailing/merchandising), COMMUNICATIONS AND THE ARTS (communications, English, fine arts, French, German, music, Spanish, and speech/debate/rhetoric), COMPUTER AND PHYSICAL SCIENCE (chemistry, computer science, mathematics, and physics), EDUCATION (art, elementary, music, physical, and secondary), ENGINEERING AND ENVIRONMENTAL DESIGN (engineering physics and industrial engineering), HEALTH PROFESSIONS (health science and physical therapy), SOCIAL SCIENCE (criminal justice, economics, history, philosophy, political science/government, psychology, public administration, and sociology). Busi-

ness, accounting, computer science, and radio and television have the largest enrollments.

Required: To graduate, all students must complete at least 120 credit hours, including 45 outside the major and 30 in upper-level courses. A minimum GPA of 2.0 is required. Students must also complete developmental courses and demonstrate proficiency in English composition, mathematics, public speaking, and library skills, among other requirements.

Special: The university offers co-op and work-study programs, study abroad, internships, a 3–2 engineering degree, combined B.A.-B.S. degrees, and student-designed majors. Credit for life, military, and work experience, nondegree study, and pass/fail options also are available.

Faculty/Classroom: Fifty-five percent of faculty are male; 45%, female. No introductory courses are taught by graduate students.

Admissions: About 92% of the 1993–94 applicants were accepted. About 29 freshmen graduated first in their class.

Requirements: A minimum GPA of 2.0 is required. The ACT is required. The SAT I, with a minimum composite score of 780, may be substituted. Applicants must be graduates of an accredited secondary school and have a minimum GPA of 2.0. The GED is accepted. An interview is recommended. AP and CLEP credits are accepted. Important factors used in the admissions decision are recommendations by school officials, leadership record, parents or siblings attending the school, personality, intangible qualities, and extracurricular activities record.

Procedure: Freshmen are admitted to all sessions. Entrance exams should be taken in the spring of the junior year. Application deadlines are open. The application fee is $15. Notification is sent on a rolling basis. There are early decision and deferred admissions plans.

Transfer: About 208 transfer students enrolled in 1993–94. Applicants must have a college GPA of 2.0. A total of 30 credits out of 120 must be completed at St. Ambrose.

Visiting: There are regularly scheduled orientations for prospective students. There are guides for informal visits, and visitors may sit in on classes and stay overnight at the school. To arrange for a visit, contact the Admissions Office at (800) 383-2627.

Financial Aid: In a recent year, 90% of all current freshmen and 84% of continuing students received some form of financial aid. About 90% of freshmen and 84% of continuing students received need-based aid. The average freshman award was $6800. All undergraduate students work part-time. Average earnings from campus work for the school year are $2000. The average financial indebtedness of a recent year's graduate was $2000. St. Ambrose is a member of CSS. The college's own financial statement and FAFSA are required. The deadline for financial aid applications is March 15.

International Students: There are currently 20 international students enrolled. They must take the TOEFL and achieve a minimum score of 500.

Computers: The college provides computer facilities for student use. The mainframe is a DEC VAX. There are several microcomputer laboratories on campus. Those whose classes require the main computer may access the system. It may be used 8:30 A.M. to 9 P.M. There are no time limits on using the system and no fees.

Graduates: In 1992–93 377 bachelor's degrees were awarded. The most popular majors among graduates were business (20%), mass communications (15%), and accounting (15%). Within an average freshman class, 1% graduate in 3 years, 90% in 4 years, 7% in 5 years, and 2% in 6 years. Some 30 companies recruited on camupus. In a recent graduating class, 90% were enrolled in graduate school within 6 months of graduation; 85% had found employment.

Admissions Contact: Jeff Griebel, Associate Dean of Admissions.

SIMPSON COLLEGE

C-3

Indianola, IA 50125   (515) 961-1624; (800) 362-2454 (out-of-state)

Full-time: 538 men, 578 women	**Faculty:** 70; IIB, av$
Part-time: 206 men, 396 women	**Ph.D.s:** 73%
Graduate: none	**Student/Faculty:** 16 to 1
Year: 4-4-1, summer session	**Tuition:** $10,825
Application Deadline: see profile	**Room & Board:** $3810
Freshman Class: 1016 applied, 872 accepted, 300 enrolled	
ACT: 24	**VERY COMPETITIVE**

Simpson College, founded in 1860, is a private, coeducational, liberal arts institution affiliated with the United Methodist Church. In addition to regional accreditation, Simpson has baccalaureate program accreditation with NASM and NCATE. The 2 libraries contain 152,499 volumes, 12,675 microform items, and 3333 audiovisual forms, and subscribe to 592 periodicals. Computerized library sources and services include interlibrary loans and database searching. Special learning facilities include a learning resource center and art gallery. The 63-acre campus is in a suburban area 12 miles south of Des Moines. Including residence halls, there are 34 buildings on campus.

Student Life: About 90% of undergraduates are from Iowa. Students come from 20 states and 2 foreign countries. Nearly 96% are from public schools; 4% from private. About 97% are white. Some 64% are Protestant; 21%, Catholic; 14% claim no religious affiliation. The average age of freshmen is 18; all undergraduates, 21. About 20% drop out by the end of their first year; 61% remain to graduate.

Housing: A total of 912 students can be accommodated in college housing. College-sponsored living facilities include single-sex and coed dormitories, on-campus apartments, fraternity houses, and sorority houses. In addition there are honors houses, language houses, special interest houses, and theme houses. On-campus housing is guaranteed for all 4 years. Some 83% of students live on campus; of those, 85% remain on campus on weekends. All students may keep cars on campus.

Activities: About 36% of men belong to 1 local and 3 national fraternities; about 37% of women belong to 4 national sororities. There are 80 groups on campus, including art, band, cheerleading, choir, chorale, chorus, computers, drama, drill team, ethnic, honors, international, jazz band, literary magazine, musical theater, newspaper, opera, orchestra, pep band, political, professional, religious, social, social service, student government, and yearbook. Popular campus events include Campus Day, Homecoming Week, Greek Week, Minority Emphasis Week, All-College Sing, and Anvil Competition.

Sports: There are 8 intercollegiate sports for men and 7 for women, and 30 intramural sports for men and women. Athletic and recreation facilities include Cowles Center and Hopper Gymnasium.

Disabled Students: About 85% of the campus is accessible to disabled students. The following facilities are available: wheelchair ramps, elevators, special parking, specially equipped rest rooms, special class scheduling, and lowered drinking fountains.

Services: In addition to many counseling and information services, tutoring is available in every subject. There is also a reader service for the blind.

Campus Safety and Security: Campus safety and security measures include self defense education, escort service, informal discussions, and pamphlets, posters, and films. In addition, there are lighted pathways and sidewalks and the campus is patrolled during day and evening hours to make sure all facilities are secure.

Programs of Study: Simpson awards the B.A. and B.Mus. degrees. Bachelor's degrees are awarded in BIOLOGICAL SCIENCE (biology/biological science), BUSINESS (accounting, banking and finance, business administration and management, business economics, and international business management), COMMUNICATIONS AND THE ARTS (advertising, communications, dramatic arts, English, fine arts, French, German, music, and Spanish), COMPUTER AND PHYSICAL SCIENCE (chemistry, computer science, and mathematics), EDUCATION (art, business, early childhood, elementary, foreign languages, health, middle school, music, science, and secondary), ENGINEERING AND ENVIRONMENTAL DESIGN (preengineering), HEALTH PROFESSIONS (nursing, optometry, physical therapy, predentistry, premedicine, and preveterinary science), SOCIAL SCIENCE (criminal justice, economics, history, international relations, philosophy, political science/government, prelaw, psychology, religion, and sociology). Natural sciences, management, fine arts, education, accounting, and biology are the strongest programs academically. Management, education, and biology have the largest enrollments.

Required: Graduation requirements include at least 128 credit hours for a B.A. and 132 credit hours for a B.Mus., with a GPA of 2.0. Students must meet the requirements for Cornerstone Studies in Liberal Arts, including a senior colloquium, plus 84 hours in the major division and 30 to 42 hours in the major department. One May term course must be taken each year.

Special: Simpson offers co-op programs in engineering with Washington University and in nursing with the University of Iowa, cross-registration at American and Drew universities and at Union College, internships, a Washington semester, study abroad, and work-study programs. Also available are dual majors, student-designed majors, nondegree study, credit for life, military, and work experience, and a pass/fail option for 1 course per year. There is a freshman honors program on campus, as well as 13 national honor societies. Eight departments have honors programs.

Faculty/Classroom: Some 67% of faculty are male; 33%, female. All teach undergraduates. The average class size in an introductory lecture is 30 and in a laboratory, 12.

Admissions: About 86% of the 1993–94 applicants were accepted. The ACT scores for the 1993–94 freshman class were as follows: 13% below 21, 33% between 21 and 23, 30% between 24 and 26, 12% between 27 and 28, and 12% above 28. About 58% of the current freshmen were in the top fifth of their class; 84% were in the top two fifths. There were 2 National Merit semifinalists. About 20 freshmen graduated first in their class.

Requirements: Simpson requires applicants to be in the upper 50% of their class. The SAT I or the ACT is required. Applicants must be graduates of an accredited secondary school. The GED is accepted. Test scores, counselor recommendations, GPA, college prep course

grades, and class rank are all considered in a selective admissions process. The college requires an audition for music and theater scholarships. AP and CLEP credits are accepted. Important factors used in the admissions decision are advanced placement or honor courses, recommendations by school officials, leadership record, extracurricular activities record, and parents or siblings attending the school.

Procedure: Freshmen are admitted to all sessions. Entrance exams should be taken in the junior or senior year. The college will accept applications as long as space is available. Notification is sent on a rolling basis. There are early decision, early admissions, and deferred admissions plans.

Transfer: About 60 transfer students enrolled in 1993–94. In addition to freshmen requirements, transfer applicants are considered on the basis of college work taken and grades received. The recommended GPA is 2.5. Applicants must take either the SAT I or ACT. Grades of 2.0 and above transfer for credit. The school admits transfer students every term. A total of 32 credits out of 128 to 132 must be completed at Simpson.

Visiting: There are regularly scheduled orientations for prospective students, including a full-day orientation program scheduled 3 times during the summer, when students meet with their academic advisor, register for classes, and participate in activity information sessions. Parents are encouraged to attend. There are guides for informal visits and visitors may sit in on classes and stay overnight at the school. To arrange for a visit, contact the Office of Admissions at (800) 362–2454.

Financial Aid: In 1993–94, 97% of all current freshmen and 90% of continuing students received some form of financial aid. About 89% of freshmen and 70% of continuing students received need-based aid. The average freshman award was $11,018. Of that total, scholarships or need-based grants averaged $8297 ($11,004 maximum); loans averaged $2221 ($4625 maximum); and work contracts averaged $500 ($1000 maximum). Some 49% of undergraduate students work part-time. Average earnings from campus work for the school year are $720. The average financial indebtedness of the 1992–93 graduate was $10,710. Simpson is a member of CSS. The FAFSA financial statement is required. The deadline for financial aid applications is August 1.

International Students: There are currently 4 international students enrolled. The school actively recruits these students. They must take the TOEFL or the University of Michigan Language Test and achieve a minimum score on the TOEFL of 550.

Computers: The college provides computer facilities for student use. The mainframes are a DEC VAX 6310 and a Prime 6150. There are 200 microcomputer terminals available for student use in the library and in Carver Science Center, where computer consultants are available to assist students. All students may access the system. It may be used 24 hours a day. There are no time limits on using the system and no fees.

Graduates: In 1992–93, 285 bachelor's degrees were awarded. The most popular majors among graduates were management (22%), accounting (14%), and elementary education (11%). Within an average freshman class, 56% graduate in 4 years, 62% in 5 years, and 63% in 6 years. Some 59 companies recruited on campus in 1992–93. In the 1992 graduating class, 18% of all graduates were enrolled in graduate school within 6 months of graduation; 80% of all graduates had found employment.

Admissions Contact: John Kellogg, Vice President for Enrollment and Planning.

TEIKYO MARYCREST UNIVERSITY   E-3
Davenport, IA 52804   (319) 326–9225; (800) 728–9705

Full-time: 246 men, 442 women	Faculty: 54; IIB, --$
Part-time: 99 men, 291 women	Ph.D.s: 41%
Graduate: 30 men, 78 women	Student/Faculty: 13 to 1
Year: semesters, summer session	Tuition: $10,115
Application Deadline: open	Room & Board: $3640
Freshman Class: 499 applied, 211 accepted, 197 enrolled	
ACT: 23	**VERY COMPETITIVE**

Teikyo Marycrest University, founded in 1939, is a private liberal arts school, in the Catholic tradition, dedicated to the education of students of all faiths. In addition to regional accreditation, TMU has baccalaureate program accreditation with ADA, CSWE, and NLN. The library contains 106,000 volumes, 19,515 microform items, and 3113 audiovisual forms, and subscribes to 554 periodicals. Computerized library sources and services include the card catalog, interlibrary loans, and database searching. Special learning facilities include a learning resource center, an art gallery, a radio station, a TV station, a computer graphics laboratory, a law library, and a media center. The 20-acre campus is in an urban area 200 miles west of Chicago. Including residence halls, there are 12 buildings on campus.

Student Life: About 69% of undergraduates are from Iowa. Students come from 15 states and 19 foreign countries. Eighty-seven percent are white. Fifty-two percent are Protestant; 47% Catholic. The av-

erage age of freshmen is 18. Twenty-two percent drop out by the end of their first year; 48% remain to graduate.

Housing: A total of 350 students can be accommodated in college housing. College-sponsored living facilities include single-sex and coed dormitories and on-campus apartments. On-campus housing is guaranteed for all 4 years. Sixty-seven percent of students commute. All students may keep cars on campus.

Activities: There are no fraternities or sororities on campus. There are many groups and organizations on campus, including art, cheerleading, choir, chorale, chorus, computers, dance, drama, ethnic, honors, international, literary magazine, musical theater, newspaper, opera, photography, political, professional, radio and TV, religious, social, social service, student government, and yearbook. Popular campus events include Homecoming, Pig Roast, Winter Formal, Graduation Prom, Winter Olympics, and a performing arts series consisting of six stage performances.

Sports: There are 5 intercollegiate sports for men and 6 for women, and 5 intramural sports each for men and women. Athletic and recreation facilities include a 700-seat gymnasium and provisions for numerous sports in the athletic center.

Disabled Students: Twenty percent of the campus is accessible to disabled students. The following facilities are available: wheelchair ramps, elevators, special parking, specially equipped rest rooms, special class scheduling, and lowered drinking fountains.

Services: In addition to many counseling and information services, tutoring is available in most subjects. In addition, there is a reader service for the blind, and remedial math, reading, and writing.

Campus Safety and Security: Campus safety and security measures include self-defense education, escort service, informal discussions, and pamphlets, posters, and films. In addition, there are emergency telephones and lighted pathways and sidewalks.

Programs of Study: TMU awards the B.A., B.S., B.S.N. and B.S.W. degrees. Associate and master's degrees are also awarded. Bachelor's degrees are awarded in BIOLOGICAL SCIENCE (biology/biological science), BUSINESS (accounting, banking and finance, business administration and management, and international business management), COMMUNICATIONS AND THE ARTS (art, communications, dramatic arts, English, and visual and performing arts), COMPUTER AND PHYSICAL SCIENCE (chemistry, computer science, and mathematics), EDUCATION (early childhood, elementary, science, and secondary), ENGINEERING AND ENVIRONMENTAL DESIGN (computer graphics and environmental science), HEALTH PROFESSIONS (nursing and premedicine), SOCIAL SCIENCE (American studies, dietetics, history, international studies, prelaw, psychology, social science, and social work). Business administration, communications, computer graphics, education, nursing, social work, and computer science are the strongest academically. Business administration, education, computer graphics, and communications have the largest enrollments.

Required: All students must maintain a minimum GPA of 2.0 while taking 120 semester hours, including 45 to 65 hours in the major. Distribution requirements include a minimum of 5 semester hours each in philosophy/religious studies, natural science/mathematics, social and behavioral science, arts and literature, and foreign language. In addition, all students must take courses in oral and written communication, mathematics, and modern civilization.

Special: Cooperative programs in communications, business, history, prelaw, computer science, and nursing; and internships, cross-registration with the Teikyo University Group; work-study on campus; and study abroad in Austria, France, Japan, Germany, the Netherlands, England and other countries are possible. B.A.-B.S. degrees in numerous subjects, dual majors, student-designed majors, nondegree study, and pass/fail options are also offered. There is a freshman honors program on campus, as well as one national honor society. Three departments have honors programs.

Faculty/Classroom: Forty-five percent of faculty are male; 55%, female. No introductory courses are taught by graduate students. The average class size in an introductory lecture is 20; in a laboratory, 15; and in a regular course offering, 15.

Admissions: About 42% of the 1993–94 applicants were accepted.

Requirements: TMU requires applicants to be in the upper 50% of their class. A minimum GPA of 2.3 is required. The SAT I or ACT is required for applicants who have graduated from high school within one year of application. Applicants must be graduates of an accredited secondary school and should have earned 16 academic credits, including 4 in English, 3 in foreign language, 2 each of mathematics and social studies, and 1 in science. An interview is required; a portfolio and audition are required of art and performing arts majors. The GED is accepted. AP and CLEP credits are accepted. Important factors used in the admissions decision are recommendations by school officials, personality, intangible qualities, leadership record, evidence of special talent, and recommendations by alumni.

Procedure: Freshmen are admitted to all sessions. Application deadlines are open. Application fee is $25. Notification is sent on a rolling basis. There are early admissions and deferred admissions plans.

Transfer: About 150 transfer students enrolled in 1993–94. Transcripts from all previous institutions attended are required, as is a minimum GPA of 2.0. A total of 30 credits out of 120 must be completed at TMU.

Visiting: There are regularly scheduled orientations for prospective students, including campus tours and information presentations. There are guides for informal visits and visitors may sit in on classes and stay overnight at the school. To arrange for a visit, contact the Admissions Office at (800) 728–9705 or (319) 326–9225.

Financial Aid: In 1993–94, 87% of all current freshmen and 85% of continuing students received some form of financial aid. The average freshman award was $5400. Of that total, scholarships or need-based grants averaged $1000 ($1500 maximum); loans averaged $3625; and work contracts averaged $1300. Thirty percent of undergraduate students work part-time. Average earnings from campus work for the school year are $1300. TMU is a member of CSS. The FAF, FFS, or the college's own financial statement are required. The deadline for financial aid applications is April 1.

International Students: The school actively recruits these students. They must take the TOEFL and achieve a minimum score of 550.

Computers: The college provides computer facilities for student use. The mainframe is an IBM 9370. In addition, there are 30 microcomputers for general use and 2 computer-equipped classrooms next to the library. All students may access the system. It is available for use more than 80 hours a week. There are no time limits on using the system and no fees.

Graduates: In 1992–93, 200 bachelor's degrees were awarded. The most popular majors among graduates were business administration (22%), nursing (12%), and elementary education (11%). Within an average freshman class, 44% graduate in 4 years. Some 50 companies recruited on campus in 1992–93. In the 1992 graduating class, 2% of the men and 4% of the women were enrolled in graduate school within 6 months of graduation; 95% of the graduates had found employment.

Admissions Contact: Timothy McDonough, Assistant Vice President for Enrollment Management.

TEIKYO WESTMAR UNIVERSITY   B-2

Le Mars, IA 51031   (712) 546–2070; (800) 352–4634

Full-time: 402 men, 209 women	**Faculty:** 39; IIB, --$
Part-time: 103 men, 43 women	**Ph.D.s:** 60%
Graduate: none	**Student/Faculty:** 16 to 1
Year: see profile	**Tuition:** $12,280
Application Deadline: open	**Room & Board:** $3640
Freshman Class: 451 applied, 306 accepted, 123 enrolled	
SAT I or ACT: required	**COMPETITIVE**

Teikyo Westmar University, established in 1890, is a private, coeducational, liberal arts institution. The academic calendar consists of 2 semesters of 2 8-week terms each. The library contains 100,961 volumes, 6373 microform items, and 4957 audiovisual forms, and subscribes to 510 periodicals. Computerized library sources and services include the card catalog, interlibrary loans, and database searching. Special learning facilities include an art gallery. The 63-acre campus is in a small town 25 miles north of Sioux City. Including residence halls, there are 20 buildings on campus.

Student Life: About 61% of undergraduates are from out-of-state, mostly the Midwest. Students come from 27 states and 11 foreign countries. Fifty-two percent are white; 40% foreign nationals. Seventy-two percent claim no religious affiliation; 18% Protestant; 10% Catholic. The average age of freshmen is 18; all undergraduates, 23. Thirty-four percent drop out by the end of their first year; 45% remain to graduate.

Housing: A total of 604 students can be accommodated in college housing. College-sponsored living facilities include single-sex and coed dormitories, on-campus apartments, and married-student housing. On-campus housing is available on a first-come, first-served basis and is available on a lottery system for upperclassmen. Eighty-one percent of students live on campus; of those, 75% remain on campus on weekends. All students may keep cars on campus.

Activities: There are no fraternities or sororities on campus. There are 30 groups on campus, including band, cheerleading, chorale, computers, drama, drill team, ethnic, honors, international, jazz band, literary magazine, musical theater, newspaper, pep band, professional, radio and TV, religious, social, social service, student government, and yearbook. Popular campus events include International Cultural Festival, Black History Month, Celebrate Diversity Week, and All Campus Leadership Conference.

Sports: There are 8 intercollegiate sports for men and 6 for women, and 20 intramural sports for men and 20 for women. Athletic and recreation facilities include a physical education center for intercollegiate and intramural events, a 2200-seat basketball arena, a 1250-seat gymnasium, a weight and exercise room, an outdoor soccer complex, a football stadium, a baseball field, and a track.

Disabled Students: Fifty percent of the campus is accessible to disabled students. The following facilities are available: wheelchair ramps, elevators, special parking, specially equipped rest rooms, and special class scheduling.

Services: In addition to many counseling and information services, tutoring is available in some subjects, including mathematics, sciences, writing, German, and Japanese. There is remedial math and writing.

Campus Safety and Security: Campus safety and security measures include 24-hour foot and vehicle patrol, self defense education, escort service, and informal discussions. In addition, there are pamphlets, posters, and films, emergency telephones, and lighted pathways and sidewalks.

Programs of Study: TWU awards the B.A., B.A.S., and B.M.Ed. degrees. Bachelor's degrees are awarded in BIOLOGICAL SCIENCE (biology/biological science), BUSINESS (accounting, banking and finance, and marketing/retailing/merchandising), COMMUNICATIONS AND THE ARTS (English, fine arts, German, music, and speech/debate/rhetoric), COMPUTER AND PHYSICAL SCIENCE (computer science and mathematics), EDUCATION (music and secondary), HEALTH PROFESSIONS (physical therapy), SOCIAL SCIENCE (history, human services, psychology, religion, and sociology). Education is the strongest academically. Business and psychology have the largest enrollments.

Required: To graduate, students must complete 128 credit hours, including 30 to 48 in the major, and satisfy requirements in writing, computer science, understanding the self, understanding social institutions, mathematics, religion, science, artistic traditions, and other cultures.

Special: Internships in all fields, study abroad in 5 countries, a Washington semester, a general studies degree, B.A.-B.S. degrees, dual and student-designed majors, nondegree study, pass/fail options, and credit for life, military, and work experience are available. There are 6 national honor societies on campus. Five departments have honors programs.

Faculty/Classroom: Fifty-four percent of faculty are male; 46%, female. All teach undergraduates and 15% do research. The average class size in an introductory lecture is 40; in a laboratory, 24; and in a regular course offering, 25.

Admissions: About 68% of the 1993–94 applicants were accepted. The ACT scores for the 1993–94 freshman class were as follows: 53% below 21, 28% between 21 and 23, 14% between 24 and 26, 4% between 27 and 28, and 1% above 28. About 19% of the current freshmen were in the top fifth of their class; 48% were in the top two fifths.

Requirements: TWU requires applicants to be in the upper 50% of their class. A minimum GPA of 2.3 is required. The SAT I or ACT is required. Candidates for admission must graduate from an accredited secondary school or earn a GED. The high school program should include English, a foreign language, mathematics, science, and social studies. Requirements include 2 of the following 3: a 2.3 cumulative GPA, or the equivalent; rank in top half of graduating class; and an ACT composite score of 20 or a combined total of at least 750 on the SAT I. AP and CLEP credits are accepted. Important factors used in the admissions decision are advanced placement or honor courses, evidence of special talent, leadership record, extracurricular activities record, and recommendations by school officials.

Procedure: Freshmen are admitted fall and spring. Entrance exams should be taken by October of the senior year prior to admission. Application deadlines are open. The fee is $25. Notification is sent on a rolling basis. There is a deferred admissions plan.

Transfer: About 44 transfer students enrolled in 1993–94. Applicants must submit high school and college transcripts and relevant financial aid transcripts from all other colleges attended. A student reference form must be completed by the dean of students at the applicant's previously attended college institution. A total of 30 credits out of 128 must be completed at TWU.

Visiting: There are regularly scheduled orientations for prospective students, including meetings with appropriate faculty and an admissions counselor and a campus tour. Agendas are individualized to meet student needs. There are guides for informal visits, and visitors may sit in on classes and stay overnight at the school. To arrange for a visit, contact Pearl Molgaard at (800) 352–4634.

Financial Aid: In 1993–94 all current freshmen and 62% of continuing students received some form of financial aid. About 71% of freshmen and 62% of continuing students received need-based aid. The average freshman award was $9992. Of that total, scholarships or need-based grants averaged $6100 ($9500 maximum); loans averaged $3000 ($6625 maximum); and work contracts averaged $500 ($1200 maximum). Eighty percent of undergraduate students work part-time. Average earnings from campus work for the school year are $800. The average financial indebtedness of the 1992–93 graduate was $15,500. The FAFSA financial statement is required.

International Students: There are currently 300 international students enrolled. The school actively recruits these students. They must take the TOEFL and achieve a minimum score of 500.

Computers: The college provides computer facilities for student use. The mainframe is a VAX 4000/VAX 3100. Students at TWU have access to the LAN (local area network). Services available include word processing, databases, electronic spreadsheet, Internet, and a number of compilers. All students may access the system. It may be used 24 hours a day, 7 days a week with a modem; otherwise 8 A.M. to midnight. There are no time limits on using the system and no fees.

Graduates: In 1992-93 96 bachelor's degrees were awarded. The most popular majors among graduates were human services (36%), business (36%), and elementary education (11%). Within an average freshman class, 45% graduate in 5 years. Some 6 companies recruited on campus in 1992-93. In the 1992 graduating class, 3% of all students were enrolled in graduate school within 6 months of graduation; 54% of the men and 44% of the women had found employment.

Admissions Contact: Richard D. Phillips, Vice President for Enrollment Management.

UNIVERSITY OF DUBUQUE
E-2

Dubuque, IA 52001

(319) 589-3200; (800) 722-5583

Full-time: 333 men, 329 women	Faculty: 47; IIB, --$
Part-time: 47 men, 84 women	Ph.D.s: 70%
Graduate: 126 men, 123 women	Student/Faculty: 14 to 1
Year: semesters, summer session	Tuition: $10,530
Application Deadline: August 1	Room & Board: $3620
Freshman Class: 576 applied, 537 accepted, 137 enrolled	
SAT I Verbal/Math: 410/500	ACT: 21 LESS COMPETITIVE

The University of Dubuque, established in 1852, is a private, liberal arts institution affiliated with the Presbyterian Church (USA). Strengths in the undergraduate curriculum include environmental science, prelaw, and aviation. In addition to regional accreditation, UD has baccalaureate program accreditation with CSWE, NCATE, and NLN. The library contains 164,859 volumes, 20,739 microform items, and 2180 audiovisual forms, and subscribes to 801 periodicals. Computerized library sources and services include database searching. Special learning facilities include a learning resource center and art gallery. The 56-acre campus is in a suburban area 180 miles northwest of Chicago. Including residence halls, there are 20 buildings on campus.

Student Life: About 57% of undergraduates are from out-of-state, mostly the Midwest. Students come from 34 states and 21 foreign countries. Seventy-seven percent are white. Fifty-one percent claim no religious affiliation; 24% Catholic; 24% Protestant. The average age of freshmen is 20; all undergraduates, 24. Thirty-eight percent drop out by the end of their first year; 48% remain to graduate.

Housing: A total of 446 students can be accommodated in college housing. College-sponsored living facilities include single-sex and coed dormitories, on-campus apartments, and married-student housing. In addition, some residence halls have fraternity or sorority wings. On-campus housing is guaranteed for all 4 years. Alcohol is not permitted. All students may keep cars on campus.

Activities: About 5% of men and about 1% of women belong to 5 local and 2 national fraternities; about 3% of women belong to 3 local and 2 national sororities. There are 39 groups on campus, including cheerleading, choir, chorale, chorus, computers, dance, drama, ethnic, honors, international, musical theater, newspaper, pep band, photography, political, professional, religious, social, social service, student government, and yearbook. Popular campus events include Home Base Earth Conference, International Conference, Homecoming, SEED, Model Earth Summit, and Family Weekend.

Sports: There are 8 intercollegiate sports for men and 7 for women, and 13 intramural sports for men and 13 for women. Athletic and recreation facilities include a sports center, Chalmers field, a gymnasium, and baseball and softball fields.

Disabled Students: Fifty percent of the campus is accessible to disabled students. The following facilities are available: wheelchair ramps, elevators, special parking, specially equipped rest rooms, and lowered drinking fountains.

Services: In addition to many counseling and information services, tutoring is available in some subjects, including English, mathematics, economics, accounting, computer literacy, Spanish, and biology. There is remedial math, reading, and writing.

Campus Safety and Security: Campus safety and security measures include 24-hour foot and vehicle patrol, self defense education, escort service, and shuttle buses. In addition, there are informal discussions, pamphlets, posters, and films, emergency telephones, lighted pathways and sidewalks, and security locked residence halls.

Programs of Study: UD awards the B.A., B.S., B.B.A., and B.S.N. degrees. Associate and master's degrees also are awarded. Bachelor's degrees are awarded in BIOLOGICAL SCIENCE (biology/biological science), BUSINESS (accounting, business administration and management, and marketing/retailing/merchandising), COMMUNICATIONS AND THE ARTS (communications, English, Spanish, and speech/debate/rhetoric), COMPUTER AND PHYSICAL SCIENCE (chemistry, computer science, earth science, mathematics, physics, and science), EDUCATION (early childhood, elementary, physical, secondary, and special), ENGINEERING AND ENVIRONMENTAL DESIGN (aviation administration/management and environmental science), HEALTH PROFESSIONS (nursing and premedicine), SOCIAL SCIENCE (economics, history, international studies, philosophy, political science/government, prelaw, psychology, social work, and sociology). Business, environmental science, education, aviation management/flight operations, and prelaw are the strongest academically. Business, aviation management/flight operations, environmental science, and nursing have the largest enrollments.

Required: To graduate, students must complete 12 hours each in humanities, natural sciences, and social sciences, must fulfill specific requirements in English, literature, world history, science, mathematics, and computer science, and must complete work in a major and a minor. A total of 124 credits must be earned, with a minimum GPA of 2.0 (2.5 for education majors).

Special: The university offers cross-registration with Loras and Clarke colleges, internships, study abroad in Europe, Asia, and South America, a Washington semester, and work-study programs. B.A.-B.S. degrees, dual and student-designed majors, credit for life, military, and work experience, nondegree study, and pass/fail options are also available. B.A.-M.A. programs are offered in conjunction with the university's theological seminary. Adult degree programs and an environmental field trip to Colorado and New Mexico are available. There are 8 national honor societies on campus. Six departments have honors programs.

Faculty/Classroom: Fifty-six percent of faculty are male; 44%, female. All teach undergraduates. No introductory courses are taught by graduate students. The average class size in an introductory lecture is 22; in a laboratory, 14; and in a regular course offering, 17.

Admissions: About 93% of the 1993-94 applicants were accepted. The SAT scores for the 1993-94 freshman class were as follows: Verbal—86% below 500 and 14% between 500 and 599; Math—45% below 500, 50% between 500 and 599, and 5% between 600 and 700. The ACT scores were 34% below 21, 32% between 21 and 23, 28% between 24 and 26, 5% between 27 and 28, and 1% above 28. About 24% of the current freshmen were in the top fifth of their class; 47% were in the top two fifths. About 3 freshmen graduated first in their class.

Requirements: A minimum GPA of 2.0 is required. The SAT I or ACT is required. Applicants must graduate from an accredited secondary school with a minimum of 4 years in English, 3 in mathematics, 3 in social sciences, and 3 in natural sciences. Other academic areas, such as foreign languages, business courses, computer programming, and the fine and performing arts, are also considered. The GED is accepted. Essays and recommendations are encouraged and may be required if the ACT is less than 18 or the SAT I is less than 740. Auditions are required for music scholarship candidates. AP and CLEP credits are accepted. Important factors used in the admissions decision are leadership record, recommendations by school officials, advanced placement or honor courses, extracurricular activities record, personality, and intangible qualities.

Procedure: Freshmen are admitted to all sessions. Entrance exams should be taken before the senior year. Applications should be filed by August 1 for fall entry, January 1 for spring entry, and May 1 for summer entry, along with an application fee of $15. Notification is sent within 7 to 10 days of a completed application. There is a deferred admissions plan.

Transfer: About 115 transfer students enrolled in 1993-94. Applicants must have a minimum of 12 transferable semester hours of recognized academic work in the humanities, social sciences, or natural sciences. A minimum GPA of 2.0 is required. The applicant must have good standing at all previously attended institutions. A total of 30 credits out of 124 must be completed at UD.

Visiting: There are regularly scheduled orientations for prospective students. There are guides for informal visits, and visitors may sit in on classes and stay overnight at the school. To arrange for a visit, contact the Admissions Office at (800) 722-5583 or (319) 589-3200.

Financial Aid: In 1993-94 85% of all current freshmen and 86% of continuing students received some form of financial aid. About 74% of freshmen and 71% of continuing students received need-based aid. The average freshman award was $10,975. Of that total, scholarships or need-based grants averaged $5100 ($9300 maximum); loans averaged $3000 ($6000 maximum); and work contracts averaged $1500 ($2000 maximum). Sixty-eight percent of undergraduate students work part-time. Average earnings from campus work for the school year are $1500. The average financial indebtedness of the 1992-93 graduate was $7950. The FAFSA financial statement is required. The deadline for financial aid applications is April 19.

International Students: There are currently 137 international students enrolled. The school actively recruits these students. They must take the TOEFL and achieve a minimum score of 500.

Computers: The college provides computer facilities for student use. The mainframes are an IBM/36 Model 5360 and a DEC VAX 11/750. There are 45 microcomputers available to students in the library

and in Goldthorpe and Blades halls. IBM PS/2 Model 30 and Macintosh LC II are also available. All students may access the system. It may be used 8 A.M. to 11 P.M. There are no time limits on using the system and no fees.

Graduates: In 1992–93 121 bachelor's degrees were awarded. The most popular majors among graduates were business administration (12%), nursing (10%), and education (9%).

Admissions Contact: Christine Chapin-Tilton, Director of Undergraduate Admission.

UNIVERSITY OF IOWA
E-3

Iowa City, IA 52242–1396

Full-time: 7482 men, 7930 women
Part-time: 1315 men, 1563 women
Graduate: 4644 men, 4117 women
Year: semesters, summer session
Application Deadline: May 15
Freshman Class: 9224 applied, 8025 accepted, 3262 enrolled
SAT I or ACT: required

(319) 335-3847; (800) 553-IOWA

Faculty: 1733; I, av$
Ph.D.s: 98%
Student/Faculty: 9 to 1
Tuition: $2352 ($7740)
Room & Board: $3306

VERY COMPETITIVE

The University of Iowa, founded in 1847, is a comprehensive, public institution. Its undergraduate and graduate programs emphasize the liberal and fine arts, business, engineering, health science, and the professions. There are 6 undergraduate and 4 graduate schools. In addition to regional accreditation, Iowa has baccalaureate program accreditation with AACSB, ACEJMC, ACPE, ADA, AHEA, APTA, CAHEA, CSWE, NASM, and NLN. The 13 libraries contain 3,317,265 volumes, 5,057,309 microform items, and 20,598 audiovisual forms, and subscribe to 40,047 periodicals. Computerized library sources and services include database searching. Special learning facilities include an art gallery, natural history museum, radio station, TV station, UI hospitals and clinics, and the Iowa Center for the Arts. The 1900-acre campus is in a small town 110 miles east of Des Moines and 220 miles west of Chicago. Including residence halls, there are 101 buildings on campus.

Student Life: About 70% of undergraduates are from Iowa. Students come from 50 states, 67 foreign countries, and Canada. Ninety percent are from public schools; 10% from private. Ninety percent are white. The average age of all undergraduates is 21. Eleven percent drop out by the end of their first year; 60% remain to graduate.

Housing: A total of 6793 students can be accommodated in college housing. College-sponsored living facilities include coed dormitories and married-student housing. In addition, there are language houses, a quiet house, and upperclass floors. On-campus housing is available on a first-come, first-served basis and is available on a lottery system for upperclassmen. All students may keep cars on campus.

Activities: About 15% of men belong to 24 national fraternities; about 16% of women belong to 20 national sororities. There are 353 groups on campus, including art, bagpipe band, band, cheerleading, chess, choir, chorale, chorus, computers, dance, drama, drill team, ethnic, film, gay, honors, international, jazz band, literary magazine, marching band, musical theater, newspaper, opera, orchestra, pep band, photography, political, professional, radio and TV, religious, social, social service, student government, symphony, and yearbook. Popular campus events include Homecoming, Riverfest, and Greek Week.

Sports: There are 10 intercollegiate sports for men and 11 for women, and 29 intramural sports for men and 29 for women. Athletic and recreation facilities include a 66,000-seat stadium, a 15,500-seat arena, softball and baseball stadiums, an 18-hole golf course, a pool, basketball, racquetball, and handball courts, outdoor and indoor tennis courts, weight and fitness rooms, outdoor and indoor running tracks, a 1000-seat field hockey stadium, a field campus for hiking and cross-country skiing, and canoeing.

Disabled Students: The entire campus is accessible to disabled students. The following facilities are available: wheelchair ramps, elevators, special parking, specially equipped rest rooms, special class scheduling, lowered drinking fountains, lowered telephones, and a transportation service.

Services: In addition to many counseling and information services, tutoring is available in most subjects. There is a reader service for the blind, and remedial math, reading, and writing.

Campus Safety and Security: Campus safety and security measures include 24-hour foot and vehicle patrol, self defense education, escort service, and shuttle buses. In addition, there are informal discussions, pamphlets, posters, and films, emergency telephones, and lighted pathways and sidewalks.

Programs of Study: Iowa awards the B.A., B.S., B.B.A., B.F.A., B.L.S., B.M., B.S.E., B.S.M., B.S.N., and B.S.Ph. degrees. Master's and doctoral degrees also are awarded. Bachelor's degrees are awarded in BIOLOGICAL SCIENCE (biochemistry, biology/biological science, botany, and microbiology), BUSINESS (accounting, banking and finance, business administration and management, business economics, management science, marketing/retailing/merchandising, and recreation and leisure services), COMMUNICATIONS AND THE ARTS (art, art history and appreciation, broadcasting, classics, communications, comparative literature, dance, design, dramatic arts, English, film arts, fine arts, French, German, Greek, Italian, journalism, Latin, linguistics, music, Portuguese, Russian, Spanish, and speech/debate/rhetoric), COMPUTER AND PHYSICAL SCIENCE (actuarial science, astronomy, chemistry, computer science, geology, information sciences and systems, mathematics, physics, and statistics), EDUCATION (art, elementary, foreign languages, health, middle school, music, physical, science, and secondary), ENGINEERING AND ENVIRONMENTAL DESIGN (biomedical engineering, chemical engineering, civil engineering, computer engineering, electrical/electronics engineering, engineering, environmental engineering, industrial administration/management, industrial engineering, and mechanical engineering), HEALTH PROFESSIONS (medical laboratory technology, nuclear medical technology, nursing, pharmacy, predentistry, premedicine, and speech pathology/audiology), SOCIAL SCIENCE (African American studies, American studies, anthropology, Asian/Oriental studies, classical/ancient civilization, economics, geography, history, liberal arts/general studies, parks and recreation management, philosophy, physical fitness/movement, political science/government, prelaw, psychology, religion, Russian and Slavic studies, social science, social work, and sociology). Business administration, engineering, communication studies, psychology, and English have the largest enrollments.

Required: To graduate, students must complete at least 124 semester hours, with a GPA of 2.0. General education requirements include rhetoric, historical perspectives, foreign civilization and language, reasoning, humanities, natural and social sciences, and physical education.

Special: The University of Iowa offers cooperative education programs and internships in more than 70 academic departments, combined degree programs in liberal arts and engineering and liberal arts and medicine, and study abroad in more than 30 countries. Dual and student-designed majors, B.A.-B.S. degrees, certificate programs including Native American studies, global studies, international business, and women's studies, credit for military experience, and pass/nonpass options are also available. There is a freshman honors program on campus, as well as 20 national honor societies, including Phi Beta Kappa.

Faculty/Classroom: Seventy-nine percent of faculty are male; 21%, female.

Admissions: About 87% of the 1993–94 applicants were accepted. The ACT scores for the 1993–94 freshman class were as follows: 13% below 21, 28% between 21 and 23, 30% between 24 and 26, 14% between 27 and 28, and 15% above 28. About 43% of the current freshmen were in the top fifth of their class; 77% were in the top two fifths. There were 38 National Merit finalists. About 111 freshmen graduated first in their class.

Requirements: The SAT I or ACT is required. Iowa residents must rank in the upper 50% of their high school class (nonresidents in the upper 30%) or must meet an acceptable combination of class rank and test scores. All applicants must have completed 4 years of high school English, 3 years each of social studies and science, 3 years of mathematics (including 2 years of algebra and 1 of geometry), and 2 years of a single foreign language. Music students must audition. AP and CLEP credits are accepted.

Procedure: Freshmen are admitted to all sessions. Entrance exams should be taken in the junior year. Applications should be filed by May 15 for fall entry, November 15 for spring entry, and May 15 for summer entry, along with an application fee of $20. Notification is sent on a rolling basis. There is a deferred admissions plan.

Transfer: About 1340 transfer students enrolled in 1993–94. For the College of Liberal Arts, a GPA of at least 2.25 is required for applicants with 24 or more semester hours of credit. Those with fewer credits are considered on the same criteria as freshmen. Other colleges have different requirements. A total of 30 credits out of 124 must be completed at Iowa.

Visiting: There are regularly scheduled orientations for prospective students, including information sessions, campus tours, and visits to departments, residence halls, and classrooms. There are guides for informal visits, and visitors may sit in on classes. To arrange for a visit, contact the Admission Visitors Center at (800) 553-IOWA.

Financial Aid: In 1993–94, 65% of all students received some form of financial aid. About 26% of freshmen and 45% of continuing students received need-based aid. The average freshman award was $5100. Of that total, scholarships or need-based grants averaged $1450 ($10,886 maximum); loans averaged $1823 ($8000 maximum); and work contracts averaged $2070 ($3534 maximum). Fifty-five percent of undergraduate students work part-time. Average earnings from campus work for the school year are $2048. The average financial indebtedness of the 1992–93 graduate was $6700. Iowa is a member of CSS. The FAF, FFS, or SFS and the college's own financial statement are required.

International Students: There are currently 1874 international students enrolled. They must take the TOEFL and achieve a minimum score of 530. The student must also take the SAT I or the ACT.

Computers: The college provides computer facilities for student use. The mainframes are an IBM 3090, a DEC VAX 6410, and an Encore. There are more than 800 networked microcomputers at 26 public computer centers on campus. All students may access the system. It may be used 24 hours a day, 7 days a week. There are no time limits on using the system. The fees are included in the general student fee, but there may be additional fees set by individual departments.

Graduates: In 1992–93 3650 bachelor's degrees were awarded. The most popular majors among graduates were communication studies (8%), English (7%), and psychology (7%). Within an average freshman class, 29% graduate in 4 years, 56% in 5 years, and 60% in 6 years. Some 251 companies recruited on campus in 1992–93.

Admissions Contact: Michael Barron, Director of Admissions.

UNIVERSITY OF NORTHERN IOWA

D-2

Cedar Falls, IA 50614

(319) 273–2281
(800) 772–2037 (out-of-state)

Full-time: 4448 men, 5697 women
Part-time: 548 men, 774 women
Graduate: 479 men, 771 women
Year: semesters, summer session
Application Deadline: August 15
Freshman Class: 3808 applied, 3379 accepted, 1853 enrolled
ACT: 23

Faculty: 679; IIA, av$
Ph.D.s: 72%
Student/Faculty: 15 to 1
Tuition: $2352 ($5994)
Room & Board: $2785

COMPETITIVE

The University of Northern Iowa, established in 1876, is a public institution offering undergraduate degrees in business administration, education, humanities and fine arts, natural science, and social and behavioral sciences. There are 5 undergraduate schools and one graduate school. In addition to regional accreditation, UNI has baccalaureate program accreditation with AACSB, ACCE, ADA, AHEA, ASLA, CSWE, NASAD, NASM, and NRPA. The library contains 738,878 volumes, 618,357 microform items, and 11,394 audiovisual forms, and subscribes to 3037 periodicals. Computerized library sources and services include the card catalog, interlibrary loans, and database searching. Special learning facilities include a learning resource center, art gallery, natural history museum, planetarium, radio station, and an observatory. The university also sponsors a laboratory school, a waste reduction center, and several research institutes. The 996-acre campus is in a small town about 100 miles north of Des Moines. Including residence halls, there are 64 buildings on campus.

Student Life: About 96% of undergraduates are from Iowa. Students come from 31 states, 38 foreign countries, and Canada. Ninety-four percent are white. The average age of freshmen is 18; all undergraduates, 22. Nineteen percent drop out by the end of their first year; 56% remain to graduate.

Housing: A total of 4939 students can be accommodated in college housing. College-sponsored living facilities include single-sex and coed dormitories, on-campus apartments, and married-student housing. In addition, there are special interest houses. On-campus housing is guaranteed for all 4 years. Sixty-two percent of students commute. All students may keep cars on campus.

Activities: About 6% of men belong to 7 national fraternities; about 4% of women belong to 4 national sororities. There are 180 groups on campus, including art, band, cheerleading, choir, chorale, chorus, computers, dance, drama, ethnic, film, gay, honors, international, jazz band, marching band, musical theater, newspaper, nontraditional students, opera, orchestra, pep band, political, professional, radio and TV, religious, social, social service, student government, and yearbook. Popular campus events include Homecoming, Greek Week, Parents Weekend, Winterfest, International Food Fair, Cinco de Mayo, Diversity Week, Black History Month, Funion, and Kwanzaa.

Sports: There are 9 intercollegiate sports for men and 8 for women, and 25 intramural sports for men and 24 for women. Athletic and recreation facilities include the UNI-Dome, which houses a stadium, a field house, a basketball facility, and a physical education center.

Disabled Students: The entire campus is accessible to disabled students. The following facilities are available: wheelchair ramps, elevators, special parking, specially equipped rest rooms, special class scheduling, lowered drinking fountains, and lowered telephones.

Services: In addition to many counseling and information services, tutoring is available in some subjects, including macroeconomics, accounting, business statistics, biology, physics, physical science, chemistry, Spanish, mathematics, writing, recreation, and administration practices. In addition, there is a reader service for the blind; remedial math, reading, and writing; and a notetaking service.

Campus Safety and Security: Campus safety and security measures include 24-hour foot and vehicle patrol, escort service, informal discussions, and pamphlets, posters, and films. In addition, there are emergency telephones and lighted pathways and sidewalks.

Programs of Study: UNI awards the B.A., B.S., B.F.A., B.L.S., B.Mus., and B.T. degrees. Master's and doctoral degrees also are awarded. Bachelor's degrees are awarded in BIOLOGICAL SCIENCE (biology/biological science, biotechnology, and nutrition), BUSINESS (accounting, banking and finance, management science, marketing/retailing/merchandising, and recreation and leisure services), COMMUNICATIONS AND THE ARTS (broadcasting, communications, dramatic arts, English, fine arts, French, German, graphic design, music, music performance, music theory and composition, public relations, Spanish, speech/debate/rhetoric, and theater design), COMPUTER AND PHYSICAL SCIENCE (chemistry, computer mathematics, computer programming, computer science, earth science, geology, information sciences and systems, mathematics, physics, and science), EDUCATION (art, business, early childhood, elementary, foreign languages, health, middle school, music, physical, science, special, teaching English as a second language/foreign language, and technical), ENGINEERING AND ENVIRONMENTAL DESIGN (construction engineering, electromechanical technology, energy management technology, industrial engineering technology, and manufacturing technology), HEALTH PROFESSIONS (health care administration, medical laboratory technology, physical therapy, public health, and speech pathology/audiology), SOCIAL SCIENCE (American studies, anthropology, Asian/Oriental studies, clothing and textiles management/production/services, criminal justice, dietetics, economics, European studies, family and community services, geography, history, humanities, Latin American studies, liberal arts/general studies, philosophy, political science/government, psychology, public administration, religion, Russian and Slavic studies, social science, social work, and sociology). Accounting, elementary and special education, social work, and communicative disorders are the strongest academically. Accounting and business administration have the largest enrollments.

Required: Degree requirements include completion of 124 to 130 credits, with 47 credits in general education and 30 to 60 credits in the major. Liberal arts majors must maintain a minimum GPA of 2.0; the requirement for education majors is 2.5. Students must meet course requirements in personal wellness and foreign language, and complete a capstone course in environment, technology, and society. Education students must complete a 32-credit professional sequence.

Special: Internships and co-op programs are offered through all colleges of the university. Students may study abroad in 12 countries and may participate in a Washington semester. Interdisciplinary majors available include safety education, chemistry/marketing, design/human environment, and natural history interpretation. Cross-registration, work-study programs, a general studies degree, dual majors, student-designed majors, nondegree study, and pass/fail options are also available. There are 20 national honor societies on campus.

Faculty/Classroom: Sixty-one percent of faculty are male; 39%, female. Ninety-seven percent teach undergraduates. Graduate students teach 1% of introductory courses.

Admissions: About 89% of the 1993–94 applicants were accepted. The ACT scores for the 1993–94 freshman class were as follows: 25% below 21, 33% between 21 and 23, 25% between 24 and 26, 10% between 27 and 28, and 7% above 28. About 41% of the current freshmen were in the top fifth of their class; 81% were in the top two fifths. Sixty freshmen graduated first in their class.

Requirements: The SAT I or ACT is required. Applicants must graduate in the upper 50% of their class from an approved secondary school. The GED, with a minimum standard score of 57, is accepted. High school requirements include 4 years of English, 3 each of mathematics, social studies, and science, and 2 or more of electives, which may include foreign language and/or fine arts. AP and CLEP credits are accepted. Important factors used in the admissions decision are advanced placement or honor courses, evidence of special talent, leadership record, recommendations by school officials, and extracurricular activities record.

Procedure: Freshmen are admitted to all sessions. Entrance exams should be taken by October of the senior year. Applications should be filed by August 15 for fall entry, December 31 for spring entry, and May 15 for summer entry, along with an application fee of $20. Notification is sent on a rolling basis.

Transfer: A total of 918 transfer students enrolled in 1993–94. Applicants must have a GPA of 2.0 to 2.5, depending on the number of credits they wish to transfer. Other applicants may be admitted, on academic probation. A total of 32 credits out of 124 to 130 must be completed at UNI.

Visiting: There are guides for informal visits, and visitors may sit in on classes and stay overnight at the school. To arrange for a visit, contact the Admissions Office at (319) 273–2281 or (800) 772–2037.

Financial Aid: In 1993–94, 70% of all current freshmen and 58% of continuing students received some form of financial aid. About 65% of all students received need-based aid. The average freshman award was $3800. Of that total, scholarships or need-based grants averaged $2052 ($6886 maximum); loans averaged $2802 ($4125 maximum); and work contracts averaged $1800 ($2400 maximum).

Twenty-seven percent of undergraduate students work part-time. Average earnings from campus work for the school year are $1800. The average financial indebtedness of the 1992–93 graduate was $6500. UNI is a member of CSS. The FAF, FFS or SFS, and FAFSA are required. The deadline for financial aid applications is February 15.

International Students: There are currently 159 international students enrolled. The school actively recruits these students. They must take the TOEFL and achieve a minimum score of 550.

Computers: UNI provides computer facilities for student use. The mainframes are a DEC Alpha AXP (Cobra), an AT&T 3B2/500, and an IBM ES 9121/210. The network is available to students through 600 microcomputers, located in 7 computer centers, and through dial-in ports. All students may have accounts on the DEC system and may have Internet privileges. Around-the-clock access is available during the academic year. There are no time limits on using the system and no fees.

Graduates: In 1992–93, 2407 bachelor's degrees were awarded. The most popular majors among graduates were elementary education (14%), general studies (6%), and accounting (6%). Within an average freshman class, 32% graduate in 4 years, 27% in 5 years, and 4% in 6 years. Some 155 companies recruited on campus in 1992–93. In the 1992 graduating class, 12% of all students were enrolled in graduate school within 6 months of graduation; 67% had found employment.

Admissions Contact: Clark Elmer, Director of Admissions.

UPPER IOWA UNIVERSITY   E-2
Fayette, IA 52142

	(319) 425–5281; (800) 553–4150
Full-time: 380 men, 185 women	Faculty: 36; IIB, --$
Part-time: 5 men, 16 women	Ph.D.s: 66%
Graduate: none	Student/Faculty: 16 to 1
Year: terms	Tuition: $8840
Application Deadline: August 1	Room & Board: $3060
Freshman Class: 529 applied, 403 accepted, 152 enrolled	
SAT I Verbal/Math: 430/400	ACT: 20 **COMPETITIVE**

Upper Iowa University, founded in 1857, is a private, coeducational institution with a liberal arts focus. The library contains 75,000 volumes and 1172 microform items, and subscribes to 214 periodicals. Special learning facilities include a learning resource center. The 75-acre campus is in a rural area 65 miles north of Cedar Rapids. Including residence halls, there are 11 buildings on campus.

Student Life: About 70% of undergraduates are from Iowa. Students come from 14 states, 4 foreign countries, and Canada. Ninety percent are from public schools; 10% from private. Eighty-four percent are white. The average age of freshmen is 18; all undergraduates, 22. Thirty-five percent drop out by the end of their first year; 30% remain to graduate.

Housing: A total of 400 students can be accommodated in college housing. College-sponsored living facilities include single-sex dormitories. On-campus housing is available on a first-come, first-served basis. Seventy percent of students live on campus; of those, 65% remain on campus on weekends. All students may keep cars on campus.

Activities: About 10% of men belong to 2 local fraternities; about 5% of women belong to 2 local sororities. There are 30 groups on campus, including art, cheerleading, choir, chorus, drama, newspaper, pep band, political, social, social service, student government, and yearbook. Popular campus events include an artists series, dances, debates, and lectures.

Sports: There are 8 intercollegiate sports for men and 7 for women, and 4 intramural sports for men and 1 for women. Athletic and recreation facilities include a bowling alley and nearby cross-country skiing areas.

Campus Safety and Security: Campus safety and security measures include an escort service, informal discussions, pamphlets, posters, films, and lighted pathways and sidewalks.

Programs of Study: Upper Iowa awards the B.A. and B.S. degrees. Bachelor's degrees are awarded in AGRICULTURE (conservation management), BIOLOGICAL SCIENCE (biology/biological science), BUSINESS (accounting, business administration and management, management science, and marketing/retailing/merchandising), COMMUNICATIONS AND THE ARTS (art, communications, English, fine arts management, and music), COMPUTER AND PHYSICAL SCIENCE (computer science, mathematics, and science), EDUCATION (elementary, physical, recreation, and secondary), HEALTH PROFESSIONS (health care administration), SOCIAL SCIENCE (human services, psychology, public administration, and social science). Business, education, and preprofessional science are the strongest academically and have the largest enrollments.

Required: All students must complete at least 120 semester hours with a GPA of 2.0 overall and in the major. Distribution requirements include 9 hours each in English and speech, 6 each in arts and humanities, natural sciences, and social science, and 3 each in mathematics, computer skills, and cultures.

Special: Internships, a work-study program, a 5-year B.A.-B.S. degree, a 3-year B.A. degree in any major, and student-designed majors are available.

Faculty/Classroom: Eighty percent of faculty are male; 20%, female. All teach undergraduates and also do research. The average class size in an introductory lecture is 30; in a laboratory, 18; and in a regular course offering, 20.

Admissions: About 76% of the 1993–94 applicants were accepted. The SAT scores for the 1993–94 freshman class were as follows: Verbal—54% below 500, 44% between 500 and 599, and 2% between 600 and 700; Math—61% below 500, 37% between 500 and 599, and 2% between 600 and 700. The ACT scores were 48% below 21, 26% between 21 and 23, 14% between 24 and 26, 8% between 27 and 28, and 4% above 28. About 20% of the current freshmen were in the top fifth of their class; 45% were in the top two fifths.

Requirements: Upper Iowa requires applicants to be in the upper 50% of their class. A minimum GPA of 2.0 is required. The SAT I or ACT is required. Recommendations from counselors and extracurricular activities in school, church, and community are also considered in the admissions process. AP and CLEP credits are accepted. Important factors used in the admissions decision are leadership record, personality, intangible qualities, advanced placement or honor courses, recommendations by school officials, and recommendations by alumni.

Procedure: Freshmen are admitted to all sessions. Entrance exams should be taken in the spring of the junior year. Applications should be filed by August 1 for fall entry, along with an application fee of $15. Notification is sent on a rolling basis. There are early decision, early admissions, and deferred admissions plans.

Transfer: About 74 transfer students enrolled in 1993–94. The prime consideration for transfer students is continued good standing in an accredited institution. Credit is generally given for all lecture and laboratory courses. A total of 30 credits out of 120 must be completed at Upper Iowa.

Visiting: There are regularly scheduled orientations for prospective students, including campus tours, meals, and visits with faculty and admissions counselors. There are guides for informal visits, and visitors may sit in on classes and stay overnight at the school. To arrange for a visit, contact the Director of Admissions at (800) 553–4150.

Financial Aid: In 1993–94 93% of all current freshmen and 92% of continuing students received some form of financial aid. About 90% of freshmen and 90% of continuing students received need-based aid. The average freshman award was $9478. Of that total, scholarships or need-based grants averaged $4833; loans averaged $3625; and work contracts averaged $1020. Sixty-two percent of undergraduate students work part-time. Average earnings from campus work for the school year are $1040. The average financial indebtedness of the 1992–93 graduate was $6500. Upper Iowa is a member of CSS. The FAF, FFS or SFS and FAFSA are required. The deadline for financial aid applications is rolling.

International Students: There are currently 28 international students enrolled. They must take the TOEFL and achieve a minimum score of 550.

Computers: The college provides computer facilities for student use. The mainframe is an IBM. All students may access the system. There are no time limits on using the system.

Admissions Contact: Kent McElvania, Vice President for Enrollment Management.

WARTBURG COLLEGE   D-2
Waverly, IA 50677–0903

	(319) 352–8264
	(800) 772–2085 (out-of-state)
Full-time: 584 men, 711 women	Faculty: 88; IIB, -$
Part-time: 46 men, 59 women	Ph.D.s: 87%
Graduate: none	Student/Faculty: 15 to 1
Year: 4–4–1, summer session	Tuition: $11,080
Application Deadline: August 1	Room & Board: $3450
Freshman Class: 1145 applied, 1074 accepted, 413 enrolled	
ACT: 24	**VERY COMPETITIVE**

Wartburg College, established in 1852, is a private liberal arts institution affiliated with the Evangelical Lutheran Church in America. In addition to regional accreditation, Wartburg has baccalaureate program accreditation with CSWE, NASM, and NCATE. The library contains 140,000 volumes, 5800 microform items, and 1600 audiovisual forms, and subscribes to 725 periodicals. Computerized library sources and services include interlibrary loans and database searching. Special learning facilities include a learning resource center, art gallery, natural history museum, planetarium, radio station, and TV station. The 110-acre campus is in a small town 15 miles north of Waterloo/Cedar Falls. Including residence halls, there are 32 buildings on campus.

Student Life: About 74% of undergraduates are from Iowa. Students come from 26 states and 23 foreign countries. Eighty-nine percent are white. Seventy-eight percent are Protestant; 16% Catholic.

The average age of freshmen is 18; all undergraduates, 20. Twenty-three percent drop out by the end of their first year; 67% remain to graduate.

Housing: A total of 1055 students can be accommodated in college housing. College-sponsored living facilities include single-sex and coed dormitories. In addition, there are special interest houses. On-campus housing is guaranteed for all 4 years. Seventy-six percent of students live on campus; of those, 70% remain on campus on weekends. All students may keep cars on campus.

Activities: There are no fraternities or sororities on campus. There are 70 groups on campus, including band, cheerleading, choir, chorale, chorus, computers, drama, drill team, ethnic, honors, international, jazz band, literary magazine, newspaper, opera, orchestra, pep band, photography, political, professional, radio and TV, religious, social, student government, symphony, and yearbook. Popular campus events include Artist Series, Convocations, Outfly, Christmas with Wartburg, Homecoming, and Family Weekend.

Sports: There are 9 intercollegiate sports for men and 8 for women, and 5 intramural sports for men and 3 for women. Athletic and recreation facilities include a field house, and a physical education center with a football field, a gymnasium, handball/racquetball/squash courts, basketball or tennis/badminton/volleyball courts, an indoor track, a sauna, a weight room, and an aerobics and wrestling room.

Disabled Students: Seventy percent of the campus is accessible to disabled students. The following facilities are available: wheelchair ramps, elevators, special parking, specially equipped rest rooms, lowered drinking fountains, and lowered telephones.

Services: In addition to many counseling and information services, tutoring is available in most subjects. There also is remedial math and reading, and a writing center is available.

Campus Safety and Security: Campus safety and security measures include 24-hour foot and vehicle patrol, self defense education, escort service, and informal discussions. In addition, there are pamphlets, posters, and films, and lighted pathways and sidewalks.

Programs of Study: Wartburg awards the B.A., B.A.A., B.A.S., B.M., and B.M.E. degrees. Bachelor's degrees are awarded in BIOLOGICAL SCIENCE (biology/biological science), BUSINESS (accounting, banking and finance, business administration and management, business economics, international business management, marketing/retailing/merchandising, and recreation and leisure services), COMMUNICATIONS AND THE ARTS (broadcasting, communications, English, journalism, music, and public relations), COMPUTER AND PHYSICAL SCIENCE (chemistry, computer programming, computer science, mathematics, and physics), EDUCATION (art, elementary, foreign languages, middle school, music, science, and secondary), HEALTH PROFESSIONS (medical laboratory technology, music therapy, occupational therapy, and physical therapy), SOCIAL SCIENCE (economics, history, philosophy, political science/government, psychology, religion, social work, and sociology). Biology, business, and education have the largest enrollments.

Required: Degree requirements include a minimum cumulative and major GPA of 2.0 and completion of 36 course credits (128 semester hours), including 4 May term course credits. All students must complete the Wartburg Plan, an integrative general education program that includes courses such as Human Expression, Person and Society, Foundations of Science, Behavior, Expression, Mathematics, Natural Science, Physical Education, World View, Interdisciplinary, and Capstone.

Special: Special academic programs at Wartburg include those in leadership education and global and multicultural studies. Internships are available in all majors, with programs in Denver, Washington, D.C., and London. Study abroad in 13 countries, on-campus work-study, numerous B.A.-B.S. degrees, dual majors in any combination, and individualized majors are possible. A 3–2 engineering degree is offered with Iowa State University, the universities of Iowa and Illinois, and Washington University in St. Louis. Other 3–2 degrees are possible in medical technology, occupational therapy, and public health education. An array of experimental learning opportunities are offered. There are 8 national honor societies on campus.

Faculty/Classroom: Sixty-one percent of faculty are male; 39%, female. The average class size in an introductory lecture is 28; in a laboratory, 24; and in a regular course offering, 23.

Admissions: About 94% of the 1993–94 applicants were accepted. The SAT scores for the 1993–94 freshman class were as follows: Verbal—50% below 500, 39% between 500 and 599, and 11% between 600 and 700; Math—25% below 500, 28% between 500 and 599, 36% between 600 and 700, and 11% above 700. The ACT scores were 21% below 21, 24% between 21 and 23, 25% between 24 and 26, 15% between 27 and 28, and 14% above 28. About 58% of the current freshmen were in the top fifth of their class; 81% were in the top two fifths.

Requirements: Wartburg requires applicants to be in the upper 50% of their class. A minimum GPA of 2.2 and either the ACT or SAT I are required. Candidates for admission must be graduates of an accredited secondary school, having completed 4 years of English, 3

each of mathematics, science, and social studies, 2 of foreign language, and 1 of introduction to computers. AP and CLEP credits are accepted. Important factors used in the admissions decision are advanced placement or honor courses, recommendations by school officials, leadership record, personality, intangible qualities, and extracurricular activities record.

Procedure: Freshmen are admitted fall and winter. Entrance exams should be taken before the senior year. Applications should be filed by August 1 for fall entry and December 30 for winter entry, along with an application fee of $20. Notification is sent on a rolling basis. There is an early admissions plan.

Transfer: A total of 74 transfer students enrolled in 1993–94. Applicant must have earned an associate degree or have maintained a minimum GPA of 2.0 in previous college work for 1 year. The ACT or SAT I must be taken; the minimum acceptable ACT score is 19. A total of 7 course credits out of 36 or 25 semester hours out of 128 must be completed at Wartburg.

Visiting: There are regularly scheduled orientations for prospective students, including an introduction to academic and student life conducted by administrators, faculty, and students, and advising and registration. There are guides for informal visits and visitors may sit in on classes and stay overnight at the school. To arrange for a visit, contact the Admissions Office at (800) 772–2085.

Financial Aid: In 1993–94, 98% of all current freshmen and 95% of continuing students received some form of financial aid. About 84% of freshmen and 78% of continuing students received need-based aid. The average freshman award was $9120. Of that total, scholarships or need-based grants averaged $6170 ($8000 maximum); loans averaged $3131; and work contracts averaged $977 ($1000 maximum). Sixty-five percent of undergraduate students work part-time. Average earnings from campus work for the school year are $900. The average financial indebtedness of the 1992–93 graduate was $10,000. Wartburg is a member of CSS. The FAF, FFS, or SFS is required. The deadline for financial aid applications is May.

International Students: There are currently 65 international students enrolled. The school actively recruits these students. They must take the TOEFL or the University of Michigan Language Test and achieve a minimum score on the TOEFL of 500.

Computers: The college provides computer facilities for student use. The mainframe is a DEC VAX 11/750. All students may use the mainframe system upon approval of the computer department. Students are assigned a password and a user ID. More than 100 Apple Macintosh and PC-compatible microcomputers are also available. All students may access the system. There are no time limits on using the system and no fees.

Graduates: In 1992–93, 281 bachelor's degrees were awarded. The most popular majors among graduates were business administration (29%), biology (13%), and elementary education (12%). Within an average freshman class, 54% graduate in 4 years, 63% in 5 years, and 64% in 6 years. A total of 35 companies recruited on campus in 1992–93.

Admissions Contact: Dee Katko-Roquet, Director of Admissions.

WILLIAM PENN COLLEGE D-3

Oskaloosa, IA 52577   (515) 673–1012; (800) 779–7366 (out-of-state)

Full-time: 299 men, 301 women	Faculty: 44; IIB, --$
Part-time: 36 men, 57 women	Ph.D.s: 41%
Graduate: none	Student/Faculty: 14 to 1
Year: semesters, summer session	Tuition: $10,290
Application Deadline: August 15	Room & Board: $3110
Freshman Class: 330 applied, 290 accepted, 140 enrolled	
ACT: 19	COMPETITIVE

William Penn College, founded in 1873, is a private, coeducational, liberal arts institution affiliated with the Society of Friends (Quakers). In addition to regional accreditation, William Penn has baccalaureate program accreditation with NCATE. The library contains 90,000 volumes. Computerized library sources and services include the card catalog, interlibrary loans, and database searching. Special learning facilities include an art gallery and a radio station. The 40-acre campus is in a rural area 58 miles southeast of Des Moines. Including residence halls, there are 12 buildings on campus.

Student Life: About 85% of undergraduates are from Iowa. Students come from 26 states and 8 foreign countries. Ninety percent are from public schools. Fifty-six percent are Protestant; 31% claim no religious affiliation; 13% are Catholic. The average age of freshmen is 19; all undergraduates, 23. Thirty-five percent drop out by the end of their first year; 40% remain to graduate.

Housing: A total of 400 students can be accommodated in college housing. College-sponsored living facilities include single-sex and coed dormitories. On-campus housing is guaranteed for all 4 years. Fifty percent of students live on campus; of those, 20% remain on campus on weekends. Alcohol is not permitted. All students may keep cars on campus.

Activities: About 10% of men belong to 1 national and 3 local fraternities; about 10% of women belong to 3 local sororities. There are 20 groups on campus, including art, band, cheerleading, choir, chorale, chorus, computers, drama, ethnic, international, jazz band, literary magazine, musical theater, newspaper, orchestra, pep band, photography, religious, social service, student government, and yearbook. Popular campus events include Homecoming and Winterfest.

Sports: There are 8 intercollegiate sports for men and 7 for women, and 8 intramural sports each for men and women. Athletic and recreation facilities include a gymnasium, with 2 regulation-size basketball courts and a wrestling and weight training room.

Disabled Students: Seventy percent of the campus is accessible to disabled students. The following facilities are available: wheelchair ramps, elevators, special parking, specially equipped rest rooms, and special class scheduling.

Services: In addition to many counseling and information services, tutoring is available in some subjects, including natural sciences. In addition, there is remedial math and writing.

Campus Safety and Security: Campus safety and security measures include 24-hour foot and vehicle patrol, informal discussions, emergency telephones, and lighted pathways and sidewalks.

Programs of Study: William Penn awards the B.A. degree. Bachelor's degrees are awarded in BIOLOGICAL SCIENCE (biology/biological science), BUSINESS (accounting, business administration and management, and business economics), COMMUNICATIONS AND THE ARTS (English and music), COMPUTER AND PHYSICAL SCIENCE (computer science, earth science, and mathematics), EDUCATION (art, business, early childhood, home economics, industrial arts, middle school, music, science, and secondary), HEALTH PROFESSIONS (nursing, physical therapy, predentistry, and premedicine), SOCIAL SCIENCE (criminal justice, economics, history, peace studies, political science/government, prelaw, religion, social science, and sociology). Elementary and secondary education, industrial technology, and business are the strongest academically. Education and business have the largest enrollments.

Required: To graduate, students must complete 124 hours, with 30 to 58 hours in the major. A GPA of 2.0 overall and in major and minor courses is required. The college has general education requirements in English/communications, mathematics, natural science, social science, religion, fine arts, and philosophy. All students must take 2 physical education courses, a computer course, and a senior seminar.

Special: The college offers co-op programs in criminal justice and nursing, internships, a Washington semester, study abroad in Costa Rica and the Ukraine, work-study programs, B.A.-B.S. degrees, dual majors, student-designed majors, nondegree study, and pass/fail options. A 3–2 engineering degree with Washington University is available. There are 2 national honor societies on campus. One department has an honors program.

Faculty/Classroom: Seventy-five percent of faculty are male; 25%, female. All teach undergraduates. The average class size in an introductory lecture is 25.

Admissions: About 88% of the 1993–94 applicants were accepted. About 62% of the current freshmen were in the top fifth of their class; 80% were in the top two fifths.

Requirements: William Penn requires applicants to be in the upper 70% of their class. A minimum GPA of 2.0 is required. The SAT I or ACT is required. Applicants must be graduates of an accredited secondary school. The GED is accepted. Applicants should complete 15 high school units; the college recommends 3 to 4 units of English, and 2 units each of foreign language, history, mathematics, music, sciences, and social studies. AP and CLEP credits are accepted. Important factors used in the admissions decision are evidence of special talent, advanced placement or honor courses, leadership record, recommendations by school officials, and personality and intangible qualities.

Procedure: Freshmen are admitted to all sessions. Entrance exams should be taken late in the junior year or early in the senior year. Applications should be filed by August 15 for fall entry and January 1 for spring entry, along with an application fee of $15. Notification is sent on a rolling basis. There are early decision, early admissions, and deferred admissions plans.

Transfer: About 115 transfer students enrolled in a recent year. Transfer students must be in good standing at their previous institution. A total of 30 credits out of 124 must be completed at William Penn.

Visiting: There are regularly scheduled orientations for prospective students, including a one-day visit, meetings with faculty, student services and financial aid, plus special visits with people who share students' interests. There are guides for informal visits and visitors may sit in on classes and stay overnight at the school. To arrange for a visit, contact the Director of Admissions at (515) 673–1012.

Financial Aid: In a recent year, 98% of all students received some form of financial aid. About 95% received need-based aid. The average freshman award was $6500. Of that total, scholarships or need-based grants averaged $3000; loans averaged $2600; and work contracts averaged $900. Sixty percent of undergraduate students work part-time. Average earnings from campus work for the school year are $900. The average financial indebtedness of the 1992–93 graduate was $13,308. William Penn is a member of CSS. The FAF, FFS, or SFS is required. The deadline for financial aid applications is August 15.

International Students: There are currently 15 international students enrolled. They must take the TOEFL and achieve a minimum score of 550. The student must also take the ACT.

Computers: The college provides computer facilities for student use. The mainframe is an HP 3000. There are more than 70 terminals and PCs in the computer laboratory and library. All students may access the system. There are no time limits on using the system and no fees.

Graduates: In a recent year, 140 bachelor's degrees were awarded. The most popular majors among graduates were elementary education (19%), secondary education (19%), and business (18%). Within an average freshman class, 37% graduate in 4 years, 39% in 5 years, and 40% in 6 years. Some 35 companies recruited on campus in 1992–93. In the 1992 graduating class, 88% of the men and 79% of the women had found employment within 6 months of graduation.

Admissions Contact: Eric Otto, Director of Admissions.

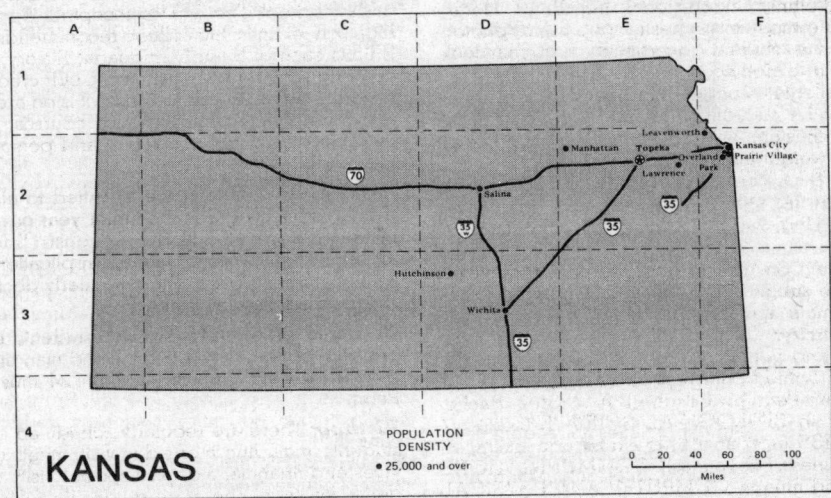

KANSAS

POPULATION DENSITY

● 25,000 and over

0 20 40 60 80 100
Miles

BAKER UNIVERSITY
Baldwin City, KS 66006

E-2

(913) 594–6451
(800) 873–4282 (out-of-state)

Full-time: 378 men, 457 women
Part-time: 12 men, 12 women
Graduate: none
Year: 4–1-4, summer session
Application Deadline: open
Freshman Class: 707 applied, 545 accepted, 256 enrolled
ACT: 22

Faculty: 63; IIB, --$
Ph.D.s: 57%
Student/Faculty: 13 to 1
Tuition: $8234
Room & Board: $4050

COMPETITIVE

Baker University, founded in 1858, is a private, liberal arts institution operated by the United Methodist Church. In addition to regional accreditation, Baker has baccalaureate program accreditation with NCATE. The library contains 65,000 volumes, 300 microform items, and 250 audiovisual forms, and subscribes to 320 periodicals. Computerized library sources and services include the card catalog, interlibrary loans, and database searching. Special learning facilities include a learning resource center, art gallery, radio station, TV station, greenhouse, and wetlands. The 26-acre campus is in a rural area 45 miles southwest of Kansas City. Including residence halls, there are 23 buildings on campus.

Student Life: About 60% of undergraduates are from Kansas. Students come from 23 states and 9 foreign countries. Ninety-five percent are from public schools; 5% from private. Eighty-nine percent are white. The average age of freshmen is 18; all undergraduates, 20. Twenty-two percent drop out by the end of their first year; 40% remain to graduate.

Housing: A total of 400 students can be accommodated in college housing. College-sponsored living facilities include single-sex and coed dormitories, on-campus apartments, fraternity houses, and sorority houses. On-campus housing is guaranteed for all 4 years. Seventy-one percent of students live on campus. Alcohol is not permitted. All students may keep cars on campus.

Activities: About 59% of men belong to 1 local and 3 national fraternities; about 61% of women belong to 4 national sororities. There are 42 groups on campus, including art, band, cheerleading, chess, choir, chorale, chorus, drama, drill team, ethnic, honors, international, jazz band, literary magazine, marching band, musical theater, newspaper, orchestra, political, professional, radio and TV, religious, and student government. Popular campus events include Maple Leaf Festival, Alumni Day, and Homecoming.

Sports: There are 7 intercollegiate sports for men and 6 for women, and 10 intramural sports for men and 10 for women. Athletic and recreation facilities include a 400-seat stadium, a 2500-seat gymnasium, practice and varsity fields for football, track, and baseball, 3 basketball courts, racquetball courts, a jogging track, and a weight room.

Disabled Students: Twenty-five percent of the campus is accessible to disabled students. The following facilities are available: wheelchair ramps, elevators, special parking, specially equipped rest rooms, special class scheduling, and lowered drinking fountains.

Services: In addition to many counseling and information services, tutoring is available in most subjects. There is also a reader service for the blind, and remedial math, reading, and writing.

Campus Safety and Security: Campus safety and security measures include lighted pathways and sidewalks.

Programs of Study: Baker awards the B.A., B.S., B.M., and B.M.E. degrees. Bachelor's degrees are awarded in BIOLOGICAL SCIENCE (biology/biological science), BUSINESS (accounting, banking and finance, business administration and management, business economics, and international business management), COMMUNICATIONS AND THE ARTS (art history and appreciation, communications, dramatic arts, English, fine arts, French, German, music, Spanish, and studio art), COMPUTER AND PHYSICAL SCIENCE (chemistry, computer science, mathematics, and physics), EDUCATION (art, business, elementary, music, and secondary), HEALTH PROFESSIONS (predentistry and premedicine), SOCIAL SCIENCE (economics, history, philosophy, political science/government, prelaw, psychology, religion, and sociology). Biology, education, business, and music are the strongest academically. Business, education, and psychology have the largest enrollments.

Required: To graduate, all students must complete 132 credit hours, including 24 to 30 hours in the major and 42 hours in 6 basic areas of study, with a minimum GPA of 2.0. Courses in physical education, computer science, and English composition are required.

Special: Internships are encouraged for students in most majors during the interim of the sophomore year. Baker also offers study abroad, B.A.-B.S. and accelerated degree programs, dual majors, pass/fail options, and credit for life, military, and work experience. A 3–2 engineering degree may be earned in conjunction with Washington University. There is a freshman honors program on campus, as well as 13 national honor societies. Nine departments have honors programs.

Faculty/Classroom: Seventy percent of faculty are male; 30%, female. All teach undergraduates, 25% also do research. The average class size in an introductory lecture is 35; in a laboratory, 20; and in a regular course offering, 24.

Admissions: About 77% of the 1993–94 applicants were accepted. The ACT scores for the 1993–94 freshman class were as follows: 29% below 21, 31% between 21 and 23, 25% between 24 and 26, 7% between 27 and 28, and 8% above 28. Thirteen freshmen graduated first in their class.

Requirements: Baker requires applicants to be in the upper 50% of their class. A minimum GPA of 2.7 is required. The SAT I or ACT is required. Candidates for admission must graduate from an accredited secondary school or earn a GED. High school course work in English, a foreign language, social studies, mathematics, and natural science is recommended. Applications of students not meeting these requirements will be reviewed, and students may be admitted on a probationary basis. AP and CLEP credits are accepted. Important factors used in the admissions decision are advanced placement or honors courses, recommendations by school officials, extracurricular activities record, leadership record, and recommendations by alumni.

Procedure: Freshmen are admitted fall and spring. Entrance exams should be taken in the fall of the senior year. Application deadlines are open. Application fee is $20. Notification is sent on a rolling basis. There are early decision, early admissions, and deferred admissions plans.

Transfer: About 50 transfer students enrolled in 1993–94. Transfer applicants must supply a high school counselor recommendation form, available from the Baker Admissions Office. An ACT or SAT I score, official high school transcript and class ranking, and official transcripts of all college courses are also required. The minimum

GPA is 2.5, and at least 15 credits must have been earned. A total of 31 credits out of 132 must be completed at Baker.

Visiting: There are regularly scheduled orientations for prospective students, consisting of a 2-day program for incoming freshmen in the fall. There are guides for informal visits, and visitors may sit in on classes and stay overnight at the school. To arrange for a visit, contact the Admissions Office at (800) 873–4282.

Financial Aid: In 1993–94, 87% of all current freshmen and 91% of continuing students received some form of financial aid. About 57% of freshmen and 55% of continuing students received need-based aid. The average freshman award was $8219. Of that total, scholarships or need-based grants averaged $4536 ($7990 maximum); loans averaged $4401 ($14,950 maximum); and work contracts averaged $1145 ($1156 maximum). Thirty-eight percent of undergraduate students work part-time. Average earnings from campus work for the school year are $1000. The average financial indebtedness of the 1992–93 graduate was $8500. Baker is a member of CSS. The FAFSA financial statement is required. The deadline for financial aid applications is March 1.

International Students: There are currently 42 international students enrolled. They must take the TOEFL and achieve a minimum score of 525.

Computers: The college provides computer facilities for student use. The mainframe is a DEC VAX. There are 24 microcomputers available for student use in the computer laboratory. In addition, there are 24 terminals in dormitories for student access to the mainframe. All students may access the system. There are no time limits on using the system and no fees.

Graduates: In 1992–93, 208 bachelor's degrees were awarded. The most popular majors among graduates were business (16%), psychology (11%), and biology (9%). Within an average freshman class, 40% graduate in 4 years and 53% in 5 years. Some 12 companies recruited on campus in 1992–93. In the 1992 graduating class, 21% of all students were enrolled in graduate school within 6 months of graduation; 70% of all students had found employment.

Admissions Contact: John D. Haynes, Director of Admissions.

BENEDICTINE COLLEGE
E-1

Atchison, KS 66002

(913) 367–5340, ext. 2474
(800) 467–5340, ext. 2474 (out-of-state)

Full-time: 420 men, 314 women	Faculty: 56; IIB, --$
Part-time: 77 men, 435 women	Ph.D.s: 54%
Graduate: 4 men, 7 women	Student/Faculty: 13 to 1
Year: semesters, summer session	Tuition: $9080
Application Deadline: August 1	Room & Board: $3750
Freshman Class: 567 applied, 556 accepted, 222 enrolled	
SAT I Verbal/Math: 435/560	ACT: 22 COMPETITIVE

Benedictine College, an independent, coeducational Roman Catholic institution, was established in 1971 by the merger of Benedict's and Mount Scholastica colleges. Benedictine offers undergraduate programs in the liberal arts and sciences, business, education, and the fine arts. In addition to regional accreditation, Benedictine has baccalaureate program accreditation with ADA, NASM, and NCATE. The library contains 310,000 volumes, 16,292 microform items, and 2000 audiovisual forms, and subscribes to 570 periodicals. Computerized library sources and services include the card catalog and interlibrary loans. Special learning facilities include a radio station. The 225-acre campus is in a small town 45 miles north of Kansas City. Including residence halls, there are 22 buildings on campus.

Student Life: About 62% of undergraduates are from Kansas. Students come from 35 states and 6 foreign countries. Sixty-five percent are from private schools. Ninety-two percent are white. Fifty-four percent are Catholic; 14% Protestant. The average age of freshmen is 18.4; all undergraduates, 20. Thirty-four percent drop out by the end of their first year; 43% remain to graduate.

Housing: A total of 1046 students can be accommodated in college housing. College-sponsored living facilities include single-sex dormitories. On-campus housing is guaranteed for all 4 years. Eighty-five percent of students live on campus. Alcohol is not permitted. All students may keep cars on campus.

Activities: There are no fraternities or sororities on campus. There are many groups and organizations on campus, including band, cheerleading, choir, chorale, computers, drama, drill team, ethnic, honors, international, jazz band, literary magazine, newspaper, orchestra, pep band, photography, political, religious, social, social service, student government, and yearbook. Popular campus events include Parents Weekend, Her Weekend, All School Mass, performing arts events, and a film series.

Sports: There are 7 intercollegiate sports for men and 7 for women, and 5 intramural sports for men and 4 for women. Athletic and recreation facilities include a gymnasium, 2 swimming pools, handball courts, a weight room, and an isometrics room.

Disabled Students: Eighty percent of the campus is accessible to disabled students. The following facilities are available: wheelchair ramps, elevators, special parking, and special class scheduling.

Services: In addition to many counseling and information services, tutoring is available in most subjects. There is remedial math, reading, and writing.

Campus Safety and Security: Campus safety and security measures include 24-hour foot and vehicle patrol, informal discussions, pamphlets, posters, films, and lighted pathways and sidewalks.

Programs of Study: Benedictine awards the B.A. and B.Mus.Ed. degrees. Associate and master's degrees also are awarded. Bachelor's degrees are awarded in BIOLOGICAL SCIENCE (biochemistry and biology/biological science), BUSINESS (accounting and business administration and management), COMMUNICATIONS AND THE ARTS (English, French, journalism, languages, Latin, music, and Spanish), COMPUTER AND PHYSICAL SCIENCE (astronomy, chemistry, computer science, information sciences and systems, mathematics, and physics), EDUCATION (elementary and special), HEALTH PROFESSIONS (health care administration), SOCIAL SCIENCE (economics, history, philosophy, political science/government, psychology, religion, social science, and sociology). Physical science, biological science, and history are the strongest academically. Business administration, education, sociology, and English have the largest enrollments.

Required: To graduate, students must complete 128 semester hours, pass a comprehensive exam in their major, and earn a minimum GPA of 2.0 overall and in the major. Core curriculum requirements include English composition and literature, foreign language, philosophy, logic, religious studies, world civilization, social science, laboratory science, mathematics, fine arts, physical education, speech, and dean's colloquium.

Special: Benedictine offers cross-registration with the 14 other members of the Kansas City Regional Council for Higher Education and study abroad in 6 countries. The school also offers a 3–2 engineering degree, a 3–2 occupational therapy program with Washington University of St. Louis, and 3–1 medical technology degree programs with area hospitals. Internships, work-study programs, dual majors, student-designed majors, pass/fail options, and nondegree study are also available. There are 4 national honor societies on campus, including Phi Beta Kappa. Four departments have honors programs.

Faculty/Classroom: Sixty percent of faculty are male; 40%, female. All teach undergraduates. No introductory courses are taught by graduate students. The average class size in an introductory lecture is 30; in a laboratory, 20; and in a regular course offering, 30.

Admissions: About 98% of the 1993–94 applicants were accepted. The SAT scores for the 1993–94 freshman class were as follows: Verbal—70% below 500, 29% between 500 and 599, and 1% between 600 and 700; Math—50% below 500, 35% between 500 and 599, 13% between 600 and 700, and 1% above 700. The ACT scores were 36% below 21, 27% between 21 and 23, 19% between 24 and 26, 9% between 27 and 28, and 9% above 28. About 34% of the current freshmen were in the top fifth of their class; 78% were in the top two fifths. About 10 freshmen graduated first in their class.

Requirements: Benedictine requires applicants to be in the upper 50% of their class. A minimum GPA of 2.0 is required. The SAT I or ACT is required. Students should have 16 academic units, including 4 in English, 3 to 4 in mathematics, 2 to 4 in foreign language and science, 2 in social science, and 1 in history. An interview is recommended. AP and CLEP credits are accepted. Important factors used in the admissions decision are advanced placement or honor courses, recommendations by school officials, recommendations by alumni, extracurricular activities record, and evidence of special talent.

Procedure: Freshmen are admitted to all sessions. Entrance exams should be taken before the July following graduation from high school. Applications should be filed by August 1 for fall entry, December 1 for spring entry, and May 1 for summer entry, along with an application fee of $25. Notification is sent on a rolling basis. There is a deferred admissions plan.

Transfer: About 43 transfer students enrolled in 1993–94. Applicants must submit transcripts from all colleges attended, a statement of courses in progress, and a reference report. A minimum GPA of 2.0 is required. A total of 30 credits out of 128 must be completed at Benedictine.

Visiting: There are regularly scheduled orientations for prospective students, consisting of an advanced placement exam, preregistration, meetings with the dean, student affairs, business office and financial aid representatives, and campus tours. The orientations are scheduled for May, June, and July. There are guides for informal visits, and visitors may sit in on classes and stay overnight at the school. To arrange for a visit, contact the Admissions Office at (913) 367–5340, ext. 2474.

Financial Aid: In an earlier year, 94% of all current freshmen received some form of financial aid. About 92% of freshmen and 96% of continuing students received need-based aid. Scholarships or need-based grants averaged $1700 ($3500 maximum); loans aver-

aged $1400 ($2265 maximum); and work contracts averaged $700 ($1000 maximum). Eighty-three percent of undergraduate students work part-time. Benedictine is a member of CSS. The FFS and the college's own financial statement are required. The deadline for financial aid applications is March 1.

International Students: There are currently 32 international students enrolled. The school actively recruits these students. They must take the TOEFL or the University of Michigan Language Test and achieve a minimum score on the TOEFL of 535.

Computers: The college provides computer facilities for student use. The mainframe is an HP 7000. There is a microcomputer laboratory comprised of 14 Apple Macintosh SEs and 4 Apple Macintosh Plus microcomputers. Smaller clusters of microcomputers are available in residence halls and the administration building. All students may access the system. It may be used 24 hours a day in residence halls, and 7:45 A.M. to 11 P.M. weekdays, with shorter hours on weekends, in microcomputer laboratories. There are no fees.

Graduates: In 1992–93 115 bachelor's degrees were awarded. The most popular majors among graduates were business administration (14%), English (9%), and education and journalism (8%). Within an average freshman class, 1% graduate in 3 years, 43% in 4 years, and 44% in 6 years. In the 1992 graduating class, 12% of the men and 5% of the women were enrolled in graduate school within 6 months of graduation; 26% of the men and 57% of the women had found employment.

Admissions Contact: James Hoffman, Dean of Enrollment Management.

BETHANY COLLEGE
D-2

Lindsborg, KS 67456   (913) 227–3311; (800) 826–2281 (out-of-state)

Full-time: 381 men, 325 women	**Faculty:** 53
Part-time: 28 men, 40 women	**Ph.D.s:** 64%
Graduate: none	**Student/Faculty:** 13 to 1
Year: 4–1–4, summer session	**Tuition:** $8105
Application Deadline: July 1	**Room & Board:** $3127
Freshman Class: 878 applied, 821 accepted, 200 enrolled	
ACT: 23	**COMPETITIVE**

Bethany College, founded in 1881, is a small, coeducational liberal arts institution affiliated with the Evangelical Lutheran Church in America. In addition to regional accreditation, Bethany has baccalaureate program accreditation with CSWE, NASM, and NCATE. The 2 libraries contain 93,789 volumes, 4288 microform items, and 1725 audiovisual forms, and subscribe to 568 periodicals. Computerized library sources and services include interlibrary loans and database searching. Special learning facilities include a learning resource center and art gallery. The 80-acre campus is in a small town 65 miles north of Wichita. Including residence halls, there are 19 buildings on campus.

Student Life: About 62% of undergraduates are from Kansas. Students come from 19 states and 10 foreign countries. Nearly 95% are from public schools. Some 87% are white. About 70% are Protestant; 15% claim no preference; 11%, Catholic. The average age of freshmen is 18; all undergraduates, 20. About 22% drop out by the end of their first year; 40% remain to graduate.

Housing: A total of 651 students can be accommodated in college housing. College-sponsored living facilities include single-sex and coed dormitories and on-campus apartments. On-campus housing is guaranteed for all 4 years. Some 88% of students live on campus; of those, 80% remain on campus on weekends. Alcohol is not permitted. All students may keep cars on campus.

Activities: About 10% of men belong to 3 local fraternities; about 10% of women belong to 3 local sororities. There are 61 groups on campus, including art, band, cheerleading, choir, chorale, computers, drama, drill team, ethnic, honors, international, jazz band, literary magazine, musical theater, newspaper, opera, orchestra, pep band, photography, political, professional, religious, social, social service, student government, symphony, and yearbook. Popular campus events include the Festival of Art and Music and Holy Week Festival.

Sports: There are 7 intercollegiate sports for men and 7 for women, and 30 intramural sports for men and 30 for women. Athletic and recreation facilities include a 1500-seat gymnasium, a 4000-seat stadium, tennis courts, a jogging track, handball/racquetball courts, and a weight training area.

Disabled Students: About 98% of the campus is accessible to disabled students. The following facilities are available: wheelchair ramps, elevators, special parking, specially equipped rest rooms, special class scheduling, and lowered drinking fountains.

Services: In addition to many counseling and information services, tutoring is available in some subjects. There is also a reader service for the blind, and remedial math, reading, and writing programs.

Campus Safety and Security: Campus safety and security measures include informal discussions, pamphlets, posters, films, and lighted pathways and sidewalks.

Programs of Study: Bethany awards the B.A. degree. Bachelor's degrees are awarded in BIOLOGICAL SCIENCE (biology/biological science), BUSINESS (accounting, business administration and management, and business economics), COMMUNICATIONS AND THE ARTS (communications, dramatic arts, English, fine arts, and music), COMPUTER AND PHYSICAL SCIENCE (chemistry and mathematics), EDUCATION (art, business, elementary, middle school, science, and secondary), HEALTH PROFESSIONS (medical laboratory technology, predentistry, and premedicine), SOCIAL SCIENCE (economics, parks and recreation management, prelaw, psychology, social science, social work, and sociology). Business and education have the largest enrollments.

Required: All students must complete 45 to 68 semester hours of general education requirements, 2 semester hours of personal wellness classes, and a junior writing proficiency exam. A total of 128 credit hours with a minimum GPA of 2.0 is required for graduation.

Special: Bethany offers co-op programs and cross-registration through the Associated Colleges of Central Kansas, and a 3–2 aerospace engineering degree with Wichita State University. Internships, a Washington semester, work-study programs, dual majors, including history-political science and religion-philosophy, student-designed majors, and limited pass/fail options are also available. There are 7 national honor societies on campus.

Faculty/Classroom: Some 74% of faculty are male; 26%, female. All teach undergraduates and 30% both teach and do research. The average class size in an introductory lecture is 50; in a laboratory, 8; and in a regular course offering, 22.

Admissions: About 94% of the 1993–94 applicants were accepted. The ACT scores for the 1993–94 freshman class were as follows: 34% below 21, 25% between 21 and 23, 22% between 24 and 26, 12% between 27 and 28, and 7% above 28. About 25% of the current freshmen were in the top fifth of their class; 66% were in the top two fifths. There were 2 National Merit semifinalists. Six freshmen graduated first in their class.

Requirements: Bethany requires applicants to be in the upper 50% of their class. A minimum GPA of 2.5 is required. Applicants should be graduates of an accredited secondary school, with 4 years of English, 3 of social studies, 2 each of mathematics and science, and 1 each of foreign language and physical education. The GED is accepted. An interview is recommended, along with a portfolio or an audition for some majors. AP and CLEP credits are accepted. Important factors used in the admissions decision are advanced placement or honor courses, leadership record, evidence of special talent, extracurricular activities record, and recommendations by school officials.

Procedure: Freshmen are admitted to all sessions. Applications should be filed by July 1 for fall entry, November 1 for winter entry, December 1 for spring entry, and April 1 for summer entry, along with an application fee of $10. Notification is sent on a rolling basis. A waiting list is an active part of the admissions procedure.

Transfer: About 71 transfer students enrolled in 1993–94. A GPA of 2.3 in 24 credit hours is required. A total of 60 credits out of 128 must be completed at Bethany.

Visiting: There are regularly scheduled orientations for prospective students. There are guides for informal visits and visitors may sit in on classes and stay overnight at the school. To arrange for a visit, contact the Office of Admissions at (913) 227–3311.

Financial Aid: In 1993–94, 97% of all current freshmen and 98% of continuing students received some form of financial aid. About 71% of freshmen and 70% of continuing students received need-based aid. The average freshman award was $6800. Of that total, scholarships or need-based grants averaged $3800 ($8000 maximum); loans averaged $2000 ($4125 maximum); and work contracts averaged $1000 ($1400 maximum). Some 50% of undergraduate students work part-time. Average earnings from campus work for the school year are $1400. The average financial indebtedness of the 1992–93 graduate was $17,250. Bethany is a member of CSS. The FAF, FFS, or SFS is required; the FFS is preferred. The deadline for financial aid applications is June 1.

International Students: There are currently 14 international students enrolled. The school actively recruits these students. They must take the TOEFL and achieve a minimum score of 525. The student must also take the SAT I or the ACT.

Computers: The college provides computer facilities for student use. The mainframe is a DEC VAX 11/750. All students may access the system. It may be used from 7 A.M. to 10 P.M. There are no time limits on using the system. The fees are $10 per semester.

Graduates: In 1992–93, 96 bachelor's degrees were awarded. The most popular majors among graduates were economics and business (24%), teaching majors (17%), and elementary education (13%). Within an average freshman class, 22% graduate in 4 years and 32% in 5 years. Some 26 companies recruited on campus in 1992–93. In the 1992 graduating class, 7% of all graduates were enrolled in graduate school within 6 months of graduation; 26% of the men and 23% of the women had found employment.

Admissions Contact: Louise Cummings-Simmons, Dean of Admissions and Financial Aid.

BETHEL COLLEGE
North Newton, KS 67117

D-3

(316) 283-2500
(800) 522-1887 (out-of-state)

Full-time: 235 men, 302 women	Faculty: 54; IIB, --$
Part-time: 41 men, 60 women	Ph.D.s: 80%
Graduate: none	Student/Faculty: 10 to 1
Year: 4-1-4, summer session	Tuition: $8180
Application Deadline: August 15	Room & Board: $3350
Freshman Class: 380 applied, 358 accepted, 197 enrolled	
ACT: 22	COMPETITIVE

Bethel College, established in 1887, is a private liberal arts institution affiliated with the Mennonite Church. In addition to regional accreditation, Bethel has baccalaureate program accreditation with CSWE and NLN. The 2 libraries contain 125,000 volumes, 2800 microform items, and 1500 audiovisual forms, and subscribe to 800 periodicals. Special learning facilities include a learning resource center, art gallery, natural history museum, radio station, and TV station. The 60-acre campus is in a suburban area 25 miles north of Wichita. Including residence halls, there are 13 buildings on campus.

Student Life: About 68% of undergraduates are from Kansas. Students come from 20 states, 16 foreign countries, and Canada. Ninety-eight percent are from public schools; 2% from private. Eighty percent are white. Most are Protestant. The average age of freshmen is 18; all undergraduates, 35. Twenty-two percent drop out by the end of their first year; 48% remain to graduate.

Housing: A total of 800 students can be accommodated in college housing. College-sponsored living facilities include single-sex and coed dormitories, off-campus apartments, and married-student housing. On-campus housing is guaranteed for all 4 years. Sixty-five percent of students live on campus; of those, 60% remain on campus on weekends. Alcohol is not permitted. All students may keep cars on campus.

Activities: There are no fraternities or sororities on campus. There are 30 groups on campus, including art, choir, chorale, chorus, computers, dance, drama, drill team, international, jazz band, literary magazine, musical theater, newspaper, orchestra, pep band, photography, radio and TV, religious, social, social service, student government, symphony, and yearbook. Popular campus events include Fall Festival, Winter Frolic, and Spring Fling.

Sports: There are 5 intercollegiate sports for men and 4 for women, and 9 intramural sports for men and 8 for women. Athletic and recreation facilities include 2 gymnasiums, a weight room, an exercise room, tennis courts, a soccer field, and an all-weather track.

Disabled Students: Seventy percent of the campus is accessible to disabled students. The following facilities are available: wheelchair ramps, elevators, special parking, specially equipped rest rooms, and lowered drinking fountains.

Services: In addition to many counseling and information services, tutoring is available in most subjects. In addition, there is a reader service for the blind, and remedial math, reading, and writing.

Campus Safety and Security: Campus safety and security measures include informal discussions and lighted pathways and sidewalks.

Programs of Study: Bethel awards the B.A. and B.S. degrees. Bachelor's degrees are awarded in BIOLOGICAL SCIENCE (biology/biological science), BUSINESS (accounting and business administration and management), COMMUNICATIONS AND THE ARTS (dramatic arts, English, German, music, and Spanish), COMPUTER AND PHYSICAL SCIENCE (chemistry, mathematics, and physics), EDUCATION (art, elementary, and secondary), HEALTH PROFESSIONS (nursing), SOCIAL SCIENCE (history, international studies, psychology, religion, social science, and social work). Nursing, history, biology, chemistry, social work, and education are the strongest academically. Nursing, education, and social work have the largest enrollments.

Required: To graduate, students must earn a total of 124 credits, including 24 to 44 in the major, 12 to 30 of those upper-level, with a GPA of 2.0. Students must also meet general education requirements in freshman seminar, English history, religion, foreign language, computer literacy, and oral communications. Distribution requirements include convocation, religious studies, natural sciences, humanities and fine arts, physical education, and recreation.

Special: Students may cross-register with Associated Colleges of Central Kansas (ACCK) institutions and Hesston College. Internships are required in many majors. Work-study programs, study abroad, dual majors, student-designed majors, and pass/fail options are also available. The college offers a 3-2 engineering degree with Washington University and a B.A.-B.S. in agriculture with Kansas State University. Two departments have honors programs.

Faculty/Classroom: Fifty-nine percent of faculty are male; 41%, female. All teach undergraduates. The average class size in an introductory lecture is 28; in a laboratory, 20; and in a regular course offering, 23.

Admissions: About 94% of the 1993-94 applicants were accepted. The ACT scores for the 1993-94 freshman class were as follows: 9% below 21, 30% between 21 and 23, 33% between 24 and 26, 18% between 27 and 28, and 10% above 28. About 30% of the current freshmen were in the top fifth of their class; 60% were in the top two fifths. Four freshmen graduated first in their class.

Requirements: Bethel requires applicants to be in the upper 33% of their class. A minimum GPA of 2.0 is required. The ACT is required. The GED is accepted. Auditions are required of candidates applying for some scholarships, and interviews are recommended for all applicants. Specific departmental requirements may vary. CLEP, AP, and International Baccalaureate credit may be awarded. Important factors used in the admissions decision are ability to finance college education, geographic diversity, parents or siblings attending the school, leadership record, and personality, intangible qualities.

Procedure: Freshmen are admitted to all sessions. Entrance exams should be taken by the fall of senior year. Applications should be filed by August 15 for fall entry, December 15 for winter entry, January 15 for spring entry, and May 15 for summer entry. Notification is sent on a rolling basis. There is an early admissions plan.

Transfer: A total of 72 transfer students enrolled in 1993-94. The entrance criteria are the same as those for freshmen. The ACT requirement may be waived for certain applicants. Thirty credits out of 124 must be completed at Bethel.

Visiting: There are regularly scheduled orientations for prospective students, including a campus tour, classroom observations, visits with faculty, an interview with an admissions counselor, lunch, and overnight residence hall lodging. There are guides for informal visits and visitors may sit in on classes and stay overnight at the school. To arrange for a visit, contact the Admissions Office at (800) 522-1887.

Financial Aid: In 1993-94, 97% of all students received some form of financial aid. About 85% of all students received need-based aid. The average freshman award was $6600. Of that total, scholarships or need-based grants averaged $3650; loans averaged $2500; and work contracts averaged $450. Thirty percent of undergraduate students work part-time. Average earnings from campus work for the school year are $1000. The average financial indebtedness of the 1992-93 graduate was $10,000. Bethel is a member of CSS. The FAF or FFS is required. The deadline for financial aid applications is February 1.

International Students: There are currently 28 international students enrolled. They must take the TOEFL and achieve a minimum score of 540.

Computers: The college provides computer facilities for student use. Thirty Apple microcomputers with printers are available in the campus computer center. All students may access the system 24 hours a day. There are no time limits on using the system and no fees.

Graduates: In 1992-93, 138 bachelor's degrees were awarded. The most popular majors among graduates were nursing (23%), education (13%), and business (10%). Some 25 companies recruited on campus in 1992-93. In the 1992 graduating class, 14% of all students were enrolled in graduate school within 6 months of graduation; 68% had found employment.

Admissions Contact: J. Michael Lamb, Director of Admissions.

EMPORIA STATE UNIVERSITY
Emporia, KS 66801

E-2

(316) 341-5465

Full-time: 1706 men, 2251 women	Faculty: 213; IIA, --$
Part-time: 246 men, 342 women	Ph.D.s: 74%
Graduate: 473 men, 1072 women	Student/Faculty: 19 to 1
Year: semesters	Tuition: $1685 ($4818)
Application Deadline: open	Room & Board: $3000
Freshman Class: 1192 applied, 1192 accepted, 853 enrolled	
ACT: 20	NONCOMPETITIVE

Emporia State University, founded in 1863, is a state-supported institution that offers undergraduate programs in liberal arts, teacher education, and vocational fields. In addition to regional accreditation, ESU has baccalaureate program accreditation with NCATE. The library contains 720,297 volumes, 754,218 microform items, and 4454 audiovisual forms, and subscribes to 1551 periodicals. Computerized library sources and services include the card catalog, interlibrary loans, and database searching. Special learning facilities include a learning resource center, art gallery, natural history museum, planetarium, TV station, theater, and geology museum. The 207-acre campus is in a small town 110 miles from Kansas City in the Bluestem Region of the Flint Hills. Including residence halls, there are 22 buildings on campus.

Student Life: About 92% of undergraduates are from Kansas. Students come from 46 states, 58 foreign countries, and Canada. Ninety-three percent are from public schools; 7% from private. Eighty-five

percent are white. The average age of freshmen is 20; all undergraduates, 23. Thirty percent drop out by the end of their first year; 50% remain to graduate.

Housing: A total of 1400 students can be accommodated in college housing. College-sponsored living facilities include single-sex and coed dormitories and on-campus apartments. In addition, there are honors houses, special interest houses, upperclass houses, and nonsmoking and alcohol-free living areas. On-campus housing is available on a first-come, first-served basis and is available on a lottery system for upperclassmen. Priority is given to out-of-town students. All students may keep cars on campus.

Activities: About 17% of men belong to 7 national fraternities; about 13% of women belong to 1 local sorority and 4 national sororities. There are 130 groups on campus, including art, band, cheerleading, choir, chorale, chorus, computers, drama, drill team, ethnic, film, gay, honors, international, jazz band, literary magazine, marching band, musical theater, newspaper, opera, orchestra, pep band, political, professional, religious, social, social service, student government, symphony, and yearbook. Popular campus events include opera productions, Homecoming, Parents Day, La Vit Sef, Scholarship Show, Flintstock, Greek Week, Campus/Community Festival, and Martin Luther King Celebration.

Sports: There are 7 intercollegiate sports for men and 7 for women, and 15 intramural sports for men and 13 for women. Athletic and recreation facilities include a 7200-seat stadium, a recreation center, an Olympic pool, 5 gymnasiums, 6 handball courts, and exercise, physical therapy, and dance rooms.

Disabled Students: The entire campus is accessible to disabled students. The following facilities are available: wheelchair ramps, elevators, special parking, specially equipped rest rooms, special class scheduling, lowered drinking fountains, and lowered telephones.

Services: In addition to many counseling and information services, there is remedial math, reading, and writing.

Campus Safety and Security: Campus safety and security measures include 24-hour foot and vehicle patrol, escort service, informal discussions, and pamphlets, posters, and films. In addition, there are emergency telephones, lighted pathways and sidewalks, motorist-assist programs, safety and self-awareness programs for students and parents, and 24-hour residence hall monitoring.

Programs of Study: ESU awards the B.A., B.S., B.F.A., B.G.S., B.Mus., B.Mus.Ed., B.S.Bus., B.S.Ed., and B.S.N. degrees. Master's and doctoral degrees also are awarded. Bachelor's degrees are awarded in BIOLOGICAL SCIENCE (biology/biological science), BUSINESS (accounting, banking and finance, business administration and management, business economics, international business management, management science, marketing/retailing/merchandising, office supervision and management, and recreation and leisure services), COMMUNICATIONS AND THE ARTS (art, communications, dramatic arts, English, linguistics, music, and speech/debate/ rhetoric), COMPUTER AND PHYSICAL SCIENCE (chemistry, computer management, computer programming, computer science, earth science, mathematics, physical sciences, and physics), EDUCATION (art, business, elementary, foreign languages, health, music, physical, recreation, and secondary), HEALTH PROFESSIONS (nursing and rehabilitation therapy), SOCIAL SCIENCE (economics, history, political science/government, psychology, social science, and sociology). Elementary education is the strongest program academically and has the largest enrollment.

Required: To graduate, students must complete at least 124 credit hours, including 40 in upper-division courses, with a minimum GPA of 2.0. Students must also pass competency exams in reading, mathematics, and writing and complete the general education program for their field of study.

Special: The university offers a co-op program in journalism with the University of Kansas, a B.S.N. program with Newman Hospital, study abroad, work-study programs, a general studies degree, and B.A.-B.S. degrees. Also available are dual and student-designed majors, 3–2 engineering degrees with Kansas State University and the University of Kansas, credit for military experience, nondegree study, independent study, evening and Saturday classes, and pass/no credit options. There is a freshman honors program on campus, as well as 1 national honor society.

Faculty/Classroom: Seventy-five percent of faculty are male; 25%, female. Ninety-eight percent teach undergraduates. Graduate students teach 35% of introductory courses. The average class size in an introductory lecture is 41; in a laboratory, 29; and in a regular course offering, 19.

Admissions: All 1993–94 applicants were accepted. The ACT scores for the 1993–94 freshman class were as follows: 57% below 21, 25% between 21 and 23, 12% between 24 and 26, 4% between 27 and 28, and 2% above 28.

Requirements: The SAT I or ACT is required. Non-Kansas residents must submit high school transcripts and may substitute SAT I scores for the ACT if the ACT isn't given in their geographic area. All applicants must be graduates of an accredited secondary school or have a GED certificate. CLEP credit is accepted.

Procedure: Freshmen are admitted to all sessions. Entrance exams should be taken prior to enrollment. Application deadlines are open. The fee is $15. The college accepts all in-state residents who apply. Notification is sent on a rolling basis. There are early decision, early admissions, and deferred admissions plans.

Transfer: Transfer students must submit official transcripts of all previous college work. The minimum GPA depends on the number of semester hours earned. Physical activity requirements must be met. A total of 30 credits out of 124 must be completed at ESU.

Visiting: There are regularly scheduled orientations for prospective students. There are guides for informal visits, and visitors may sit in on classes and stay overnight at the school. To arrange for a visit, contact the Director of Admissions at (316) 341–5465.

Financial Aid: In a recent year, 75% of all current freshmen and continuing students received some form of financial aid. About 70% of freshmen and continuing students received need-based aid. The average freshman award was $5400. Of that total, scholarships or need-based grants averaged $2610 ($2900 maximum); loans averaged $2600 ($4000 maximum); and work contracts averaged $2600 (maximum). Seventy-five percent of undergraduate students work part-time. Average earnings from campus work for the school year are $2300. The average financial indebtedness of a recent year's graduate was $5400. ESU is a member of CSS. The FFS is required. The deadline for financial aid applications is March 15.

International Students: There are currently 265 international students enrolled. The school actively recruits these students. They must take the TOEFL, the University of Michigan Language Test, or the college's own test and achieve a minimum score on the TOEFL of 525.

Computers: The college provides computer facilities for student use. The mainframe is an IBM 4381/P13. It may be used 22 hours per day. There are no time limits on using the system and no fees.

Graduates: In a recent year, 659 bachelor's degrees were awarded. The most popular majors among graduates were elementary education (19%), business administration (11%), and psychology (9%). Within an average freshman class, 20% graduate in 4 years, 31% in 5 years, and 36% in 6 years. Some 200 companies recruited on campus in 1992–93.

Admissions Contact: Dr. Barbara Tarter, Director of Admissions.

FORT HAYS STATE UNIVERSITY
C-2
Hays, KS 67601–4099   (913) 628–4187; (800) 432–0248 (in-state)

Full-time: 1722 men, 1815 women	**Faculty:** 239; IIA, --$
Part-time: 244 men, 537 women	**Ph.D.s:** 44%
Graduate: 387 men, 996 women	**Student/Faculty:** 15 to 1
Year: semesters, summer session	**Tuition:** $1734 ($4869)
Application Deadline: August 10	**Room & Board:** $2941
Freshman Class: 750 enrolled	
ACT: 21	**NONCOMPETITIVE**

Fort Hays State University, established in 1902, is a public, liberal arts institution offering programs in arts and sciences, business, education, health and life sciences, and professional study. There are 4 undergraduate and 20 graduate schools. In addition to regional accreditation, FHSU has baccalaureate program accreditation with NCATE and NLN. The library contains 314,000 volumes, 1,155,000 microform items, and 1480 audiovisual forms, and subscribes to 1600 periodicals. Computerized library sources and services include the card catalog, interlibrary loans, and database searching. Special learning facilities include a learning resource center, an art gallery, a natural history museum, a radio station, and a TV station. The 200-acre campus is in a small town 80 miles northwest of Wichita. Including residence halls, there are 40 buildings on campus.

Student Life: About 94% of undergraduates are from Kansas. Students come from 26 states, 25 foreign countries, and Canada. Ninety-five percent are from public schools; 5% from private. Ninety-four percent are white. The average age of freshmen is 18.

Housing: College-sponsored living facilities include single-sex and coed dormitories, married-student housing, fraternity houses, and sorority houses. On-campus housing is guaranteed for all 4 years. Alcohol is not permitted. All students may keep cars on campus.

Activities: About 6% of men belong to 3 national fraternities; about 3% of women belong to 3 national sororities. There are 85 groups on campus, including art, band, cheerleading, choir, chorale, chorus, computers, dance, drama, drill team, ethnic, film, gay, honors, international, jazz band, literary magazine, marching band, musical theater, newspaper, opera, orchestra, pep band, photography, political, professional, radio and TV, social, social service, student government, symphony, and yearbook. Popular campus events include Octoberfest and Parents Day.

Sports: There are 7 intercollegiate sports for men and 5 for women, and 28 intramural sports for men and 27 for women. Athletic and recreation facilities include a 7000-seat stadium, tennis courts, and a coli-

seum containing a 4600-seat basketball arena, a track, wrestling and training rooms, and gymnastics facilities.

Disabled Students: Thirty percent of the campus is accessible to disabled students. The following facilities are available: wheelchair ramps, elevators, special parking, specially equipped rest rooms, special class scheduling, lowered drinking fountains, and lowered telephones.

Services: In addition to many counseling and information services, tutoring is available in most subjects. In addition, there is remedial math and reading.

Campus Safety and Security: Campus safety and security measures include 24-hour foot and vehicle patrol, escort service, informal discussions, and emergency telephones. In addition, there are lighted pathways and sidewalks.

Programs of Study: FHSU awards the B.A., B.S., B.B.A., B.F.A., B.G.S., B.M., and B.S.A.F. degrees. Associate and master's degrees also are awarded. Bachelor's degrees are awarded in BIOLOGICAL SCIENCE (biology/biological science), BUSINESS (accounting, business administration and management, business economics, and marketing/retailing/merchandising), COMMUNICATIONS AND THE ARTS (communications, English, fine arts, and music), COMPUTER AND PHYSICAL SCIENCE (chemistry, computer science, and earth science), EDUCATION (art, elementary, foreign languages, home economics, industrial arts, and music), HEALTH PROFESSIONS (nursing), SOCIAL SCIENCE (economics, history, philosophy, political science/government, psychology, social work, and sociology). Speech pathology is the strongest academically. Communications, English, and mathematics have the largest enrollments.

Required: To graduate, students must earn an overall GPA of 2.0 for 124 credit hours, including 40 hours in upper-level study, 30 hours in the major, and 4 hours in physical education.

Special: Students may, with approval, earn their degrees through a cooperative program with FHSU and another accredited institution, or a correspondence or extension school. Cross-registration with several community colleges, internships, study-abroad, work-study programs, a 3–2 engineering degree with Kansas State University, B.A.-B.S. degrees, a general studies degree, and pass/fail options are available. There is a freshman honors program on campus, as well as 18 national honor societies.

Faculty/Classroom: Sixty-eight percent of faculty are male; 32%, female. All teach undergraduates. The average class size in an introductory lecture is 17; in a laboratory, 17; and in a regular course offering, 18.

Admissions: There were 2 National Merit semifinalists.

Requirements: The SAT I or ACT is required. Candidates for admission must graduate from an accredited secondary school or earn a GED. AP and CLEP credits are accepted.

Procedure: Freshmen are admitted to all sessions. Entrance exams should be taken in the senior year. Applications should be filed by August 10 for fall entry, December 15 for spring entry, and May 15 for summer entry, along with an application fee of $15. The college accepts all in-state residents who apply. Notification is sent on a rolling basis.

Transfer: About 400 transfer students enrolled in a recent year. Applicants must have a minimum college GPA of 2.0. A total of 30 credits out of 124 must be completed at FHSU.

Visiting: There are regularly scheduled orientations for prospective students. There are guides for informal visits and visitors may sit in on classes and stay overnight at the school. To arrange for a visit, contact Janice Chatham, Campus Tour Coordinator, at (800) 432–0248 (in-state).

Financial Aid: In an earlier year, scholarships or need-based grants averaged $375 ($5200 maximum); loans averaged $1795 ($7500 maximum); and work contracts averaged $1250 ($1500 maximum). Eighty-seven percent of undergraduate students work part-time. The average financial indebtedness of the 1992–93 graduate was $8700. The FFS and the college's own financial statement are required. The deadline for financial aid applications is March 10.

International Students: There are currently 75 international students enrolled. The school actively recruits these students. They must take the TOEFL and achieve a minimum score of 550.

Computers: The college provides computer facilities for student use. The mainframe is an IBM ES 9000 Model 9121. The system may be accessed by modem and by terminals located in dormitories and in microcomputer laboratories on campus. All students may access the system. It may be used 24 hours a day. There are no time limits on using the system and no fees.

Graduates: In a recent year, 686 bachelor's degrees were awarded.

Admissions Contact: Patricia Mahon, Director of Admissions.

FRIENDS UNIVERSITY
D-3

Wichita, KS 67213   (316) 261–5842; (800) 577–2233

Full-time: 377 men, 461 women   **Faculty:** 53; IIB, --$
Part-time: 122 men and women   **Ph.D.s:** 65%
Graduate: 203 men, 160 women   **Student/Faculty:** 16 to 1
Year: semesters, summer session   **Tuition:** $8225
Application Deadline: open   **Room & Board:** $2980
Freshman Class: 218 applied, 166 accepted, 161 enrolled
ACT: 21   **COMPETITIVE**

Friends University, established in 1898, is a coeducational institution affiliated with the Society of Friends, offering undergraduate and graduate degrees through the Colleges of Arts and Sciences, Business, and Continuing Education. There are 3 undergraduate and 5 graduate schools. In addition to regional accreditation, Friends has baccalaureate program accreditation with NASM and NCATE. The library contains 80,000 volumes, 2000 microform items, and 4033 audiovisual forms, and subscribes to 600 periodicals. Special learning facilities include an art gallery, a natural history museum, a radio station, an observatory, and an on-campus elementary school with grades K-4. The 52-acre campus is in an urban area 200 miles southwest of Kansas City. Including residence halls, there are 10 buildings on campus.

Student Life: About 90% of undergraduates are from Kansas. Students come from 16 states and 27 foreign countries. Ninety-three percent are white. Eighty-six percent are Protestant; 10% Catholic.

Housing: A total of 260 students can be accommodated in college housing. College-sponsored living facilities include single-sex dormitories, on-campus apartments, and off-campus apartments. On-campus housing is guaranteed for all 4 years. Eighty-five percent of students commute. Alcohol is not permitted. All students may keep cars on campus.

Activities: About 10% of men belong to 2 local fraternities; about 10% of women belong to 2 local sororities. There are 24 groups on campus, including art, band, cheerleading, choir, chorale, chorus, computers, dance, drama, honors, international, jazz band, marching band, opera, orchestra, pep band, photography, political, professional, religious, social, social service, student government, symphony, and yearbook. Popular campus events include Homecoming/Parents Day, Christian Emphasis Week, Cherry Carnival, Symphony of Spring, and Falcon Frenzy.

Sports: There are 6 intercollegiate sports for men and 5 for women, and 10 intramural sports for men and 9 for women. Athletic and recreation facilities include intercollegiate and intramural gymnasiums.

Disabled Students: Eighty percent of the campus is accessible to disabled students. The following facilities are available: elevators, special parking, specially equipped rest rooms, and special class scheduling.

Services: In addition to many counseling and information services, tutoring is available in most subjects.

Campus Safety and Security: Campus safety and security measures include lighted pathways and sidewalks.

Programs of Study: Friends awards the B.A., B.S., B.B.A., B.F.A., and B.Mus. degrees. Associate and master's degrees are also awarded. Bachelor's degrees are awarded in BIOLOGICAL SCIENCE (biology/biological science and zoology), BUSINESS (accounting, business administration and management, human resources, and international business management), COMMUNICATIONS AND THE ARTS (art, dance, English, fine arts, music, and Spanish), COMPUTER AND PHYSICAL SCIENCE (chemistry, computer management, computer science, mathematics, and radiological technology), EDUCATION (art, business, early childhood, elementary, foreign languages, health, music, science, secondary, and teaching English as a second language/foreign language), HEALTH PROFESSIONS (health care administration and premedicine), SOCIAL SCIENCE (history, human services, political science/government, psychology, religion, and sociology). Science is the strongest academically. Business and education have the largest enrollments.

Required: Students must complete 124 credit hours, with at least 40 hours in general education and 24 to 45 in the major. A minimum GPA of 2.0 is needed. Distribution requirements include course work in humanities, fine arts, religion and philosophy, behavioral science, and natural science. Specific requirements vary according to the major.

Special: Students may cross-register with Kansas Newman College, and they can pursue internships in their majors. A study-abroad program is available in Cancun, Mexico and several Asian countries. Friends offers an accelerated degree program in human resources management and dual majors in accounting/business administration, elementary education/early childhood education, and mathematics/computer science. A general studies degree, credit for life, military, and work experience, nondegree study, and pass/fail options are possible. There is a freshman honors program on campus, as well as one national honor society.

Faculty/Classroom: Sixty-one percent of faculty are male; 39%, female. All teach undergraduates. The average class size in an introductory lecture is 50; in a laboratory, 20; and in a regular course offering, 25.

Admissions: About 76% of the 1993–94 applicants were accepted. About 20% of the current freshmen were in the top two fifths of their class.

Requirements: The SAT I or ACT is required. Candidates for admission must graduate from an accredited secondary school or earn a GED, having completed 4 courses in English, 2 each in history and mathematics, and 1 each in science and social studies. The composite ACT score or converted SAT I score is multiplied by the high school GPA. A result of 45 is the minimum for full admission; students scoring lower may be admitted provisionally. Interviews are recommended; portfolios and auditions are advised in appropriate instances. CLEP credit is accepted.

Procedure: Freshmen are admitted to all sessions. Entrance exams should be taken in the spring of the junior year or the fall of the senior year. Application deadlines are open. Application fee is $15. Notification is sent on a rolling basis. There is an early admissions plan.

Transfer: About 100 transfer students enrolled in an earlier year. Transfer applicants with fewer than 15 semester hours must submit ACT or SAT I scores and high school and college transcripts. A total of 30 credits out of 124 must be completed at Friends.

Visiting: There are regularly scheduled orientations for prospective students. There are guides for informal visits and visitors may sit in on classes and stay overnight at the school. To arrange for a visit, contact the Admissions Office at (316) 261–5842.

Financial Aid: In an earlier year, 93% of all current freshmen and 70% of continuing students received some form of financial aid. Scholarships or need-based grants averaged $2100 ($3500 maximum); loans averaged $1700 ($4625 maximum); and work contracts averaged $700 ($2100 maximum). One-hundred percent of undergraduate students work part-time. The average financial indebtedness of the 1992–93 graduate was $6500. Friends is a member of CSS. The FFS or AFSA is required. The deadline for financial aid applications is May 1.

International Students: The school actively recruits these students. They must take the TOEFL and achieve a minimum score of 500 or the University of Michigan Language Test.

Computers: The college provides computer facilities for student use. The mainframe is an NCR Tower. There are also 35 Epson, AT&T, and IBM PCs available. All students may access the system. There are no time limits on using the system and no fees.

Graduates: In an earlier year, 301 bachelor's degrees were awarded.

Admissions Contact: Cynthia Bergman, Director of Admissions.

KANSAS NEWMAN COLLEGE

D-3

Wichita, KS 67213

(316) 942–4291, ext. 144
(800) 736–7585, ext. 144 (out-of-state)

Full-time: 260 men, 688 women
Part-time: 314 men, 551 women
Graduate: 3 men, 25 women
Year: semesters, summer session
Application Deadline: open
Freshman Class: 200 applied, 190 accepted, 98 enrolled
SAT I Verbal/Math: 442/498

Faculty: 46
Ph.D.s: 38%
Student/Faculty: 21 to 1
Tuition: $7380
Room & Board: $3260

ACT: 21   COMPETITIVE

Kansas Newman College, established in 1933, is a private, coeducational, liberal arts institution affiliated with the Roman Catholic Church. In addition to regional accreditation, KNC has baccalaureate program accreditation with NLN. The library contains 85,000 volumes, and subscribes to 550 periodicals. Computerized library sources and services include database searching. Special learning facilities include a learning resource center, an art gallery, a planetarium, and a TV station. The 53-acre campus is in an urban area. Including residence halls, there are 7 buildings on campus.

Student Life: About 90% of undergraduates are from Kansas. Students come from 17 states and 6 foreign countries. Ninety-six percent are from public schools; 4% from private. Eighty-six percent are white. Fifty-nine percent are Protestant; 41% Catholic. The average age of freshmen is 18; all undergraduates, 27.

Housing: A total of 125 students can be accommodated in college housing. College-sponsored living facilities include coed dormitories. On-campus housing is guaranteed for all 4 years. Ninety-five percent of students commute. Alcohol is not permitted. All students may keep cars on campus.

Activities: There are no fraternities or sororities on campus. There are 25 groups on campus, including cheerleading, choir, chorale, computers, drama, ethnic, honors, international, literary magazine, newspaper, pep band, political, professional, religious, social, and student government. Popular campus events include Family Weekend, Discover Newman Day, and Homecoming.

Sports: There are 3 intercollegiate sports for men and 4 for women, and 7 intramural sports for men and 6 for women. Athletic and recreation facilities include baseball, softball, and soccer fields, a weight room, and tennis courts.

Disabled Students: Ten percent of the campus is accessible to disabled students. The following facilities are available: wheelchair ramps, elevators, special parking, specially equipped rest rooms, and special class scheduling.

Services: In addition to many counseling and information services, tutoring is available in most subjects. In addition, there is remedial math and writing.

Campus Safety and Security: Campus safety and security measures include 24-hour foot and vehicle patrol, escort service, informal discussions, and pamphlets, posters, and films. In addition, there are lighted pathways and sidewalks.

Programs of Study: KNC awards the B.A., B.S., and B.S.N. degrees. Associate and master's degrees are also awarded. Bachelor's degrees are awarded in BIOLOGICAL SCIENCE (biology/biological science), BUSINESS (accounting, business administration and management, and marketing/retailing/merchandising), COMMUNICATIONS AND THE ARTS (communications, English, fine arts, and graphic design), COMPUTER AND PHYSICAL SCIENCE (chemistry, computer programming, mathematics, and statistics), EDUCATION (elementary, middle school, and secondary), ENGINEERING AND ENVIRONMENTAL DESIGN (industrial administration/management and woodworking), HEALTH PROFESSIONS (cytotechnology, health science, medical laboratory technology, nuclear medical technology, nursing, occupational therapy, predentistry, and premedicine), SOCIAL SCIENCE (addiction studies, history, pastoral studies, physical fitness/movement, prelaw, psychology, religion, and sociology). Business, nursing, health sciences and education are the strongest academically. Nursing, business and education have the largest enrollments.

Required: Degree requirements include completion of 124 credit hours, 30 of which must be upper-divisional. The number of credits required in the major varies. A minimum GPA of 2.0 is required for graduation, and students must fulfill the college's liberal arts requirement, including courses in philosophhy and theology.

Special: KNC offers cooperative programs with Washington University and Boston College and cross-registration with Friends University. Students can earn accelerated degrees in business management or education. Work-study programs are available, and credit may be conferred for life, military, and work experience. Students seeking nondegree study may enroll on a space-available basis. There are 3 national honor societies on campus.

Faculty/Classroom: Forty percent of faculty are male; 60%, female. All teach undergraduates and 1% both teach and do research. No introductory courses are taught by graduate students. The average class size in a regular course offering is 14.

Admissions: About 95% of the 1993–94 applicants were accepted. The ACT scores for the 1993–94 freshman class were as follows: 45% below 21, 29% between 21 and 23, 17% between 24 and 26, 2% between 27 and 28, and 6% above 28. About 45% of the current freshmen were in the top fifth of their class; 69% were in the top two fifths.

Requirements: A minimum GPA of 2.0 is required. The SAT I or the ACT, with a minimum composite score of 18 is required. Candidates for admission must graduate from an accredited secondary school or earn a GED, and they must have earned 23 high school academic credits. Students must complete 4 credits of English, 2 1/2 credits each of mathematics and social studies, and 2 credits each in history and science. Two credits of a foreign language are recommended. Essays and interviews are recommended for all applicants. AP and CLEP credits are accepted. Important factors used in the admissions decision are recommendations by school officials, recommendations by alumni, leadership record, advanced placement or honor courses, and parents or siblings attending the school.

Procedure: Freshmen are admitted to all sessions. Entrance exams should be taken during the spring of the junior year or fall of the senior year. Application deadlines are open. Application fee is $15. Notification is sent on a rolling basis. There are early admissions and deferred admissions plans.

Transfer: About 140 transfer students enrolled in 1993–94. A minimum GPA of 2.0 is required. A total of 30 credits out of 124 must be completed at KNC.

Visiting: There are regularly scheduled orientations for prospective students, including 8 Discover Newman Days per year. There are guides for informal visits and visitors may sit in on classes and stay overnight at the school. To arrange for a visit, contact the Admissions office at (316) 942–4291, ext. 144 or (800) 736–7585.

Financial Aid: In a recent year, 97% of all current freshmen and 70% of continuing students received some form of financial aid. About 68% of freshmen received need-based aid. The average freshman award was $6475. Ninety-seven percent of undergraduate students work part-time. Average earnings from campus work for the school year are $1300. The average financial indebtedness of the

1992–93 graduate was $5790. The X-FAFSA financial statement is required. The deadline for financial aid applications is March 15.

International Students: There are currently 15 international students enrolled. The school actively recruits these students. They must take the TOEFL and achieve a minimum score of 530.

Computers: The college provides computer facilities for student use. The mainframe is a DEC VAX II. Microcomputers are also available in the microcomputer center, library, and learning center. There are also PCs in the residence hall. All students may access the system. There are no time limits on using the system and no fees.

Graduates: In 1992–93, 250 bachelor's degrees were awarded. The most popular majors among graduates were business management (41%), business administration (17%), and elementary education (14%). Within an average freshman class, 12% graduate in 3 years, 25% in 4 years, and 27% in 5 years. In the 1992 graduating class, 98% of all graduates had found employment within 6 months of graduation.

Admissions Contact: Christine Santner, Director of Admissions.

KANSAS STATE UNIVERSITY   E-2
Manhattan, KS 66506   (913) 532–6250; (800) 432–8270 (in-state)

Full-time: 14,916 men and women	**Faculty:** 938; I, --$
Part-time: 2244 men and women	**Ph.D.s:** 77%
Graduate: 3615 men and women	**Student/Faculty:** 16 to 1
Year: semesters, summer session	**Tuition:** $1976 ($6594)
Application Deadline: open	**Room & Board:** $2840
Freshman Class: 5880 applied, 4075 accepted, 2833 enrolled	
ACT: 22	**NONCOMPETITIVE**

Kansas State University, established in 1863, is a land-grant institution offering undergraduate and graduate degrees in agriculture, arts and sciences, business, engineering, and human ecology. There are 9 undergraduate schools and one graduate school. In addition to regional accreditation, K-State has baccalaureate program accreditation with AACSB, ABET, ACCE, ADA, CSWE, FIDER, NAAB, NASM, and NCATE. The 5 libraries contain 1,277,113 volumes, 2,300,000 microform items, and 49,000 audiovisual forms, and subscribe to 8723 periodicals. Computerized library sources and services include the card catalog, interlibrary loans, and database searching. Special learning facilities include a learning resource center, art gallery, planetarium, radio station, TV station, the TRIGA MK II, nuclear reactor, a laser center, a cancer research center, and telecommunications satellite teaching. The 668-acre campus is in a suburban area 125 miles west of Kansas City. Including residence halls, there are 86 buildings on campus.

Student Life: About 87% of undergraduates are from Kansas. Students come from 50 states, 86 foreign countries, and Canada. Eighty-nine percent are from public schools; 11% from private. Eighty-seven percent are white. Fifty percent are Protestant; 25% Catholic; 22% claim no religious affiliation. The average age of freshmen is 18; all undergraduates, 21. Twenty-five percent drop out by the end of their first year; 45% remain to graduate.

Housing: A total of 4085 students can be accommodated in college housing. College-sponsored living facilities include single-sex and coed dormitories, on-campus apartments, off-campus apartments, married-student housing, fraternity houses, and sorority houses. In addition, there are honors houses and special interest houses. On-campus housing is available on a first-come, first-served basis. Alcohol is not permitted. All students may keep cars on campus.

Activities: About 21% of men belong to 30 national fraternities; about 21% of women belong to 16 national sororities. There are 340 groups on campus, including art, band, cheerleading, chess, choir, chorale, chorus, computers, dance, drama, drill team, ethnic, film, gay, honors, international, jazz band, literary magazine, marching band, musical theater, newspaper, opera, orchestra, pep band, photography, political, professional, radio and TV, religious, social, social service, student government, symphony, and yearbook. Popular campus events include Homecoming, Family Weekend, K-State Open House, Winterfest, and Racial/Ethnic Harmony Week.

Sports: There are 7 intercollegiate sports for men and 7 for women, and 45 intramural sports for men and 45 for women. Athletic and recreation facilities include indoor and outdoor tracks, baseball fields, basketball courts, a football stadium, and an indoor practice field. A multipurpose recreation facility is open 16 hours a day.

Disabled Students: Eighty percent of the campus is accessible to disabled students. The following facilities are available: wheelchair ramps, elevators, special parking, specially equipped rest rooms, special class scheduling, lowered drinking fountains, lowered telephones, and a campus shuttle service.

Services: In addition to many counseling and information services, tutoring is available in every subject. There is a reader service for the blind, and remedial math, reading, and writing.

Campus Safety and Security: Campus safety and security measures include 24-hour foot and vehicle patrol, self defense education, escort service, and informal discussions. In addition, there are pamphlets, posters, and films, emergency telephones, lighted pathways and sidewalks, televised monitors in parking lots, CPR classes, and vehicle assistance devices.

Programs of Study: K-State awards the B.A., B.S., and B.F.A. degrees. Associate, master's, and doctoral degrees also are awarded. Bachelor's degrees are awarded in AGRICULTURE (agricultural business management, agriculture, animal science, forestry and related sciences, and horticulture), BIOLOGICAL SCIENCE (biochemistry, biology/biological science, and microbiology), BUSINESS (accounting, banking and finance, business administration and management, hotel/motel and restaurant management, and marketing/retailing/merchandising), COMMUNICATIONS AND THE ARTS (advertising, communications, dramatic arts, English, French, German, journalism, music, Spanish, and speech/debate/rhetoric), COMPUTER AND PHYSICAL SCIENCE (chemistry, computer science, geology, information sciences and systems, mathematics, physics, and statistics), EDUCATION (agricultural, art, early childhood, elementary, foreign languages, music, secondary, and special), ENGINEERING AND ENVIRONMENTAL DESIGN (architectural engineering, chemical engineering, civil engineering, computer engineering, electrical/electronics engineering, engineering, engineering technology, industrial engineering technology, mechanical engineering, and nuclear engineering), HEALTH PROFESSIONS (predentistry, premedicine, and speech pathology/audiology), SOCIAL SCIENCE (anthropology, dietetics, economics, food production/management/services, food science, geography, history, parks and recreation management, philosophy, political science/government, psychology, social work, and sociology). Architecture, engineering, and accounting are the strongest academically. Journalism has the largest enrollment.

Required: To graduate, students must complete 120 to 167 credits, including 30 in the major, with a minimum GPA of 2.0. English composition, speech, and physical education are required.

Special: K-State offers a dual B.S. degree in nutrition and exercise sciences, a cooperative program with Kansas University, and a 3–2 program with Emporia State, Fort Hays State, and Pittsburg (Kansas) State universities. Cross-registration, internships, dual majors, B.A.-B.S. degrees, study abroad in more than 100 countries, nondegree study, and pass/fail options are also available. There is a freshman honors program on campus, as well as 53 national honor societies, including Phi Beta Kappa. Nine departments have honors programs.

Faculty/Classroom: Seventy-four percent of faculty are male; 26%, female.

Admissions: About 69% of the 1993–94 applicants were accepted. The ACT scores for the 1993–94 freshman class were as follows: 34% below 21, 24% between 21 and 23, 21% between 24 and 26, 10% between 27 and 28, and 11% above 28. There were 21 National Merit finalists and 5 semifinalists. About 163 freshmen graduated first in their class.

Requirements: Out-of-state applicants must rank in the upper 50% of their high school graduating class and have a minimum GPA of 2.5. KSU admits all state residents who are graduates of an accredited Kansas secondary school. No standardized tests are required. AP and CLEP credits are accepted.

Procedure: Freshmen are admitted to all sessions. Entrance exams should be taken in the junior and senior years. Application deadlines are open. The application fee is $15. The college accepts all in-state residents who apply. Notification is sent on a rolling basis.

Transfer: About 2176 transfer students enrolled in 1993–94. Transfer applicants must have a college GPA of 2.0. A total of 30 credits out of 127 must be completed at K-State.

Visiting: There are regularly scheduled orientations for prospective students, including campus tours and visits with academic advisers and admissions representatives. There are guides for informal visits, and visitors may sit in on classes and stay overnight at the school. To arrange for a visit, contact New Student Services at (800) 432–8270.

Financial Aid: In 1993–94 70% of all current freshmen and 70% of continuing students received some form of financial aid. About 56% of freshmen and 60% of continuing students received need-based aid. Twenty-one percent of undergraduate students work part-time. K-State is a member of CSS. The FFS and the college's own financial statement are required. The deadline for financial aid applications is March 15.

International Students: There are currently 1183 international students enrolled. They must take the TOEFL and achieve a minimum score of 550. Students must also take an English proficiency test at the college.

Computers: The college provides computer facilities for student use. The mainframe is an IBM 3084/Q96. There are 75 microcomputers in public laboratories and more than over 90 public terminals located at various sites across campus. The Slobourne UNIX Computer has 32 ports. All students may access the system 24 hours a day, with a limit of $200 computer dollars per week for personal accounts. All students may access the system. There are no time limits on using the system and no fees.

Graduates: In a recent year, 2583 bachelor's degrees were awarded. The most popular majors among graduates were elementary education (9%), accounting (6%), and marketing (5%). Within an average freshman class, 1% graduate in 3 years, 20% in 4 years, 42% in 5 years, and 47% in 6 years. Some 380 companies recruited on campus in a recent year.

Admissions Contact: Richard Elkins, Director of Admissions.

KANSAS WESLEYAN UNIVERSITY
Salina, KS 67401

D-2

(913) 827–5541, ext. 307
(800) 874–1154, ext. 307 (out-of-state)

Full-time: 472 men and women	Faculty: 34; IIB, --$
Part-time: 260 men and women	Ph.D.s: 65%
Graduate: none	Student/Faculty: 14 to 1
Year: 4-1-4, summer session	Tuition: $8520
Application Deadline: August 1	Room & Board: $3250
Freshman Class: 396 applied, 371 accepted, 273 enrolled	
ACT: 21	COMPETITIVE

Kansas Wesleyan, founded in 1886, is a coeducational institution affiliated with the United Methodist Church. The college offers undergraduate programs in the arts and sciences, business, and education. The library contains 72,000 volumes, and subscribes to 40 periodicals. Computerized library sources and services include the card catalog, interlibrary loans, and database searching. Special learning facilities include an art gallery, a planetarium, and a radio station. The 25-acre campus is in a small town 90 miles north of Wichita. Including residence halls, there are 10 buildings on campus.

Student Life: About 83% of undergraduates are from Kansas. Students come from 20 states, 3 foreign countries, and Canada. Ninety-two percent are from public schools; 8% from private. Eighty-two percent are white. Sixty-one percent are Protestant; 16% Catholic. The average age of freshmen is 21; all undergraduates, 24. Fifteen percent drop out by the end of their first year.

Housing: A total of 500 students can be accommodated in college housing. College-sponsored living facilities include single-sex dormitories, on-campus apartments, and married-student housing. On-campus housing is guaranteed for all 4 years. Eighty-five percent of students commute. Alcohol is not permitted. All students may keep cars on campus.

Activities: About 10% of men belong to 1 local and 1 national fraternity; about 5% of women belong to 1 local sorority. There are 38 groups on campus, including art, cheerleading, chess, choir, chorale, chorus, computers, dance, drama, ethnic, film, honors, international, literary magazine, musical theater, newspaper, photography, political, professional, radio and TV, religious, social, social service, student government, and yearbook. Popular campus events include Lilac Fete, Martin Luther King Day, Sweetheart Dance, and Rat Olympics.

Sports: There are 7 intercollegiate sports each for men and women, and 8 intramural sports for men and 6 for women. Athletic and recreation facilities include a gymnasium, a sand volleyball court, football practice and game fields, a multipurpose courtyard, a track, and a weight room.

Disabled Students: The following facilities are available: wheelchair ramps, elevators, special parking, specially equipped rest rooms, special class scheduling, and lowered drinking fountains.

Services: There is remedial math, reading, and writing available.

Campus Safety and Security: Campus safety and security measures include informal discussions, pamphlets, posters, and films, lighted pathways and sidewalks, and periodic security checks.

Programs of Study: Kansas Wesleyan awards the B.A. and B.S. degrees. Associate degrees also are awarded. Bachelor's degrees are awarded in BIOLOGICAL SCIENCE (biology/biological science), BUSINESS (accounting and business economics), COMMUNICATIONS AND THE ARTS (communications, dramatic arts, English, music, Spanish, speech/debate/rhetoric, and studio art), COMPUTER AND PHYSICAL SCIENCE (chemistry, computer science, mathematics, and physics), EDUCATION (art, music, physical, secondary, and special), HEALTH PROFESSIONS (nursing), SOCIAL SCIENCE (addiction studies, criminal justice, history, prelaw, psychology, religion, religious education, and sociology). Premedicine, nursing, preengineering, and education are the strongest academically. Education, nursing, and business have the largest enrollments.

Required: Students must demonstrate proficiency in English and mathematics and must fulfill distribution requirements in 15 liberal arts components, including environmental awareness, biblical heritage, and lifetime recreation. To graduate, students must complete at least 123 credit hours, including 30 to 40 in a major field of study, with a minimum GPA of 2.0.

Special: Cross-registration is available with other members of the Associated Colleges of Central Kansas and the Salina College Consortium. Cooperative degree programs are offered in agriculture, cytotechnology, engineering, environmental studies, and medical technology. Kansas Wesleyan also offers January interterm study trips throughout the United States and abroad, Washington D.C. and UN

semesters, internships, dual majors, student-designed majors, credit for life experience, and nondegree study. There are 5 national honor societies on campus.

Faculty/Classroom: All teach undergraduates and 15% do research. The average class size in an introductory lecture is 40; in a laboratory, 7; and in a regular course offering, 15.

Admissions: About 94% of the 1993–94 applicants were accepted. The ACT scores for the 1993–94 freshman class were as follows: 50% below 21, 31% between 21 and 23, 12% between 24 and 26, 6% between 27 and 28, and 1% above 28. About 53% of the current freshmen were in the top two fifths of their class.

Requirements: Kansas Wesleyan requires applicants to be in the upper 50% of their class. A minimum GPA of 2.5 is required. The SAT I, with a minimum composite of 700, or the ACT, with a composite of 18, is required. Applicants must be graduates of accredited secondary schools or have earned a GED. An interview is recommended. AP and CLEP credits are accepted. Important factors used in the admissions decision are evidence of special talent, advanced placement or honor courses, leadership record, personality, intangible qualities, and parents or siblings attending the school.

Procedure: Freshmen are admitted to all sessions. Entrance exams should be taken as early as possible. Applications should be filed by August 1 for fall entry, along with an application fee of $20. Notification is sent on a rolling basis. There are early decision and deferred admissions plans.

Transfer: About 120 transfer students enrolled in 1993–94. Transfers must submit transcripts from all colleges previously attended. Those students transferring fewer than 15 credit hours must submit ACT scores and a high school transcript. A minimum GPA of 2.0 is recommended. A total of 63 credits out of 123 must be completed at Kansas Wesleyan.

Visiting: There are guides for informal visits and visitors may sit in on classes and stay overnight at the school. To arrange for a visit, contact the Admissions Office at (800) 874–1154, ext. 307 or (913) 827–5541, ext. 307.

Financial Aid: In a recent year, 97% of all students received some form of financial aid. About 98% received need-based aid. The average freshman award was $7647. Kansas Wesleyan is a member of CSS. The deadline for financial aid applications is March 1.

International Students: There are currently 15 international students enrolled. The school actively recruits these students. They must take the TOEFL and achieve a minimum score of 500.

Computers: The college provides computer facilities for student use. The mainframe is a Data General MV-8000. PCs are available in the computer science laboratory. All students may access the system. It may be used at any time. There are no time limits on using the system and no fees.

Graduates: In 1992–93, 146 bachelor's degrees were awarded. Within an average freshman class, 16% graduate in 6 years. Some 7 companies recruited on campus in 1992–93. In the 1992 graduating class, 3% of all graduates were enrolled in graduate school within 6 months of graduation; 59% had found employment.

Admissions Contact: Valerie D. Robinson, Director of Admissions.

McPHERSON COLLEGE
McPherson, KS 67460

D-2

(316) 241–0731

Full-time: 182 men, 157 women	Faculty: 37; IIB, --$
Part-time: 37 men, 50 women	Ph.D.s: 54%
Graduate: none	Student/Faculty: 9 to 1
Year: 4-1-4, summer session	Tuition: $7810
	Room & Board: $3550
Freshman Class: 420 applied, 293 accepted, 95 enrolled	
ACT: required	VERY COMPETITIVE

McPherson College, founded in 1887 and affiliated with the Church of the Brethren, is a private nonprofit institution offering undergraduate programs in the arts and sciences, business, and education. The library contains 63,907 volumes, 31,223 microform items, and 3026 audiovisual forms, and subscribes to 420 periodicals. Special learning facilities include a learning resource center and and an automobile restoration center. The 23-acre campus is in a small town 60 miles north of Wichita. Including residence halls, there are 15 buildings on campus.

Student Life: About 64% of undergraduates are from Kansas. Students come from 27 states and 10 foreign countries. Ninety-nine percent are from public schools. Eighty-seven percent are white. Most are Protestant. The average age of freshmen is 18; all undergraduates, 22.

Housing: A total of 395 students can be accommodated in college housing. College-sponsored living facilities include single-sex and coed dormitories and married-student housing. On-campus housing is guaranteed for all 4 years. Fifty-eight percent of students live on campus. Alcohol is not permitted. All students may keep cars on campus.

Activities: There are no fraternities or sororities on campus. There are 44 groups on campus, including art, band, cheerleading, choir, chorus, drama, ethnic, international, musical theater, newspaper, pep band, professional, religious, social service, student government, and yearbook. Popular campus events include Mac Olympics and Homecoming.

Sports: Athletic and recreation facilities include a sport center with 2 full-size courts, 2 racquetball courts, and a fitness center.

Disabled Students: Ten percent of the campus is accessible to disabled students. The following facilities are available: wheelchair ramps, elevators, special parking, and special class scheduling.

Services: In addition to many counseling and information services, tutoring is available in most subjects.

Campus Safety and Security: Campus safety and security measures include informal discussions, pamphlets, posters, and films, emergency telephones, and lighted pathways and sidewalks.

Programs of Study: McPherson awards the B.A. and B.S. degrees. An associate's degrees also are awarded. Bachelor's degrees are awarded in AGRICULTURE (animal science), BIOLOGICAL SCIENCE (biology/biological science), BUSINESS (accounting and business administration and management), COMMUNICATIONS AND THE ARTS (communications, English, German, music, Spanish, and speech/debate/rhetoric), COMPUTER AND PHYSICAL SCIENCE (chemistry, computer programming, computer science, and mathematics), EDUCATION (art, business, early childhood, elementary, foreign languages, health, industrial arts, middle school, music, science, and secondary), HEALTH PROFESSIONS (predentistry and premedicine), SOCIAL SCIENCE (history, philosophy, prelaw, psychology, religion, social science, and sociology). Business and education have the largest enrollments.

Required: To graduate, students must complete 124 credits including 32 in the major, with 20 of the last 30 or 40 of the last 60 hours completed in residence. All students must fulfill general education requirements in speech and composition, humanities, social science, natural science, applied arts and sciences, and communications. The B.S. degree requires 8 hours of mathematics or computer science; the B.A. degree requires 8 hours of foreign language.

Special: There are cross-registration and cooperative education programs with the Associated Colleges of Central Kansas. McPherson also offers internships, study abroad in 8 countries, credit by examination, a general studies degree, and pass/fail options.

Faculty/Classroom: Sixty percent of faculty are male; 40%, female. All teach undergraduates. The average class size in an introductory lecture is 25 and in a regular course offering, 12.

Admissions: About 70% of the 1993–94 applicants were accepted. The ACT scores for the 1993–94 freshman class were as follows: 43% below 21, 23% between 21 and 23, 19% between 24 and 26, 12% between 27 and 28, and 3% above 28. About 62% of the current freshmen were in the top fifth of their class; 84% were in the top two fifths. About 4 freshmen graduated first in their class.

Requirements: McPherson requires applicants to be in the upper 33% of their class. A minimum GPA of 2.3 is required. The ACT is required. , but SAT I scores are accepted. The GED is accepted. AP and CLEP credits are accepted. Important factors used in the admissions decision are recommendations by school officials, evidence of special talent, parents or siblings attending the school, advanced placement or honor courses, and leadership record.

Procedure: Freshmen are admitted fall and spring. Entrance exams should be taken in the junior year. Application fee is $15. Notification is sent on a rolling basis.

Transfer: About 41 transfer students enrolled in 1993–94. Transfer applicants must have satisfactorily completed 12 credit hours of college course work covering 3 academic areas with a 2.25 GPA. A total of 30 credits out of 124 must be completed at McPherson.

Visiting: There are regularly scheduled orientations for prospective students, consisting of a campus tour; meetings with professors, coaches, and activity sponsors on request; attendance at a class; and meetings with admissions personnel. There are guides for informal visits and visitors may sit in on classes and stay overnight at the school. To arrange for a visit, contact the Office of Admissions at (316) 241–0731.

Financial Aid: In 1993–94 95% of all current freshmen and 95% of continuing students received some form of financial aid. About 95% of freshmen and 95% of continuing students received need-based aid. The FAFSA financial statement is required. The deadline for financial aid applications is April 1.

International Students: There are currently 21 international students enrolled. They must take the TOEFL and achieve a minimum score of 550. The student must also take the ACT.

Computers: The college provides computer facilities for student use. The mainframe is an Encore. All students may access the system. There are no time limits on using the system and no fees.

Graduates: In 1992–93 78 bachelor's degrees were awarded.

Admissions Contact: Fred Schmidt, Director of Admissions.

MIDAMERICA NAZARENE COLLEGE   F-2
Olathe, KS 66062–1899   (913) 791–3380; 800–8887, ext. 481

Full-time: 1297 men and women	Faculty: 54; IIB, --$
Part-time: 179 men and women	Ph.D.s: 39%
Graduate: none	Student/Faculty: 24 to 1
Year: semesters, summer session	Tuition: $6666
Application Deadline: open	Room & Board: $3542
Freshman Class: 286 applied, 286 accepted, 187 enrolled	
SAT I or ACT: required	NONCOMPETITIVE

MidAmerica Nazarene College, founded in 1966, is a private, coeducational, liberal arts college affiliated with the Church of the Nazarene. In addition to regional accreditation, MANC has baccalaureate program accreditation with NASM and NLN. The library contains 78,000 volumes and 130,600 microform items, and subscribes to 388 periodicals. Computerized library sources and services include the card catalog and interlibrary loans. Special learning facilities include a learning resource center. The 105-acre campus is in a suburban area 20 miles southwest of Kansas City. Including residence halls, there are 20 buildings on campus.

Student Life: About 57% of undergraduates are from Kansas. Ninety-four percent are from public schools. Most are Protestant. The average age of freshmen is 20; all undergraduates, 21. Thirty-nine percent drop out by the end of their first year; 25% graduate.

Housing: A total of 566 students can be accommodated in college housing. College-sponsored living facilities include single-sex dormitories and off-campus apartments. In addition, there are off-campus married-student apartments. On-campus housing is guaranteed for all 4 years. Fifty-two percent of students commute. Alcohol is not permitted. All students may keep cars on campus.

Activities: There are no fraternities or sororities on campus. There are numerous groups and organizations on campus, including cheerleading, choir, computers, jazz band, newspaper, pep band, professional, religious, student government, and yearbook.

Sports: Athletic and recreation facilities include a weight room, a football stadium, softball and soccer fields, tennis courts, and sand volleyball.

Disabled Students: Eighty percent of the campus is accessible to disabled students. The following facilities are available: wheelchair ramps, special parking, special class scheduling, and lowered drinking fountains.

Services: In addition to many counseling and information services, tutoring is available in most subjects. There is a reader service for the blind, and remedial math, reading, and writing.

Campus Safety and Security: Campus safety and security measures include informal discussions, lighted pathways and sidewalks, and foot and vehicle patrols.

Programs of Study: MANC awards the B.A. and B.S.N. degrees. Associate and master's degrees also are awarded. Bachelor's degrees are awarded in BIOLOGICAL SCIENCE (biology/biological science), BUSINESS (accounting and business administration and management), COMMUNICATIONS AND THE ARTS (communications, English, music, and Spanish), COMPUTER AND PHYSICAL SCIENCE (chemistry, computer science, mathematics, and physics), EDUCATION (business, early childhood, elementary, mathematics, music, physical, psychology, secondary, and social studies), SOCIAL SCIENCE (history, psychology, and religion). Nursing, management and human resources, elementary education, and business administration have the largest enrollments.

Required: All students must meet core curriculum requirements in humanities-communications, natural sciences-mathematics, social sciences, religion-philosophy, and physical education. Students must maintain a minimum GPA of 2.0 and complete 126 semester hours to graduate.

Special: The college offers nondegree study, combined B.A.-B.S. degrees in home economics and agriculture, and work-study programs.

Faculty/Classroom: Sixty-four percent of faculty are male; 36%, female.

Admissions: All 1993–94 applicants were accepted. About 38% of the current freshmen were in the top fifth of their class; 64% were in the top two fifths.

Requirements: The SAT I or ACT is required, with recommended composite scores of 18 on the ACT and 670 on the SAT I. Candidates for admission should be graduates of an accredited secondary school. The GED is also accepted. Students should have completed 15 units of study, including 4 units of English and 3 each of natural science, social studies, and mathematics. An essay is optional. AP and CLEP credits are accepted.

Procedure: Freshmen are admitted to all sessions. Entrance exams should be taken during the senior year. Application deadlines are open. The application fee is $15. The college accepts all applicants. Notification is sent on a rolling basis. There is an early admissions plan.

Transfer: Transfer applicants should have earned 10 or more hours at an accredited institution and not be on academic or disciplinary probation. A total of 30 credits out of 126 must be completed at MANC.

Visiting: There are regularly scheduled orientations for prospective students. There are guides for informal visits, and visitors may sit in on classes. To arrange for a visit, contact the Office of Admissions at (913) 791–3380 or (800) 800–8887, ext. 481.

Financial Aid: The FFS is required. The deadline for financial aid applications is June 1.

International Students: There are currently 38 international students enrolled. They must take the TOEFL and achieve a minimum score of 500.

Computers: The college provides computer facilities for student use. There are microcomputers located in the library.

Graduates: In a recent year, 257 bachelor's degrees were awarded. The most popular majors among graduates were management and human resources (34%), business administration (9%), and religion (9%). Some 15 companies recruited on campus in a recent year.

Admissions Contact: Dennis J. Troyer, Director of Admissions.

OTTAWA UNIVERSITY

Ottawa, KS 66067–3399   (913) 242–5200, ext. 5555; (800) 755–5200

Full-time: 299 men, 239 women   Faculty: IIB, --$
Part-time: 21 men, 15 women   Tuition: $7245
Graduate: none   Room & Board: $3245
Year: semesters, summer session
Application Deadline: open
Freshman Class: 881 applied, 248 accepted, 152 enrolled
ACT: 21   COMPETITIVE +

Ottawa University, founded in 1865 and affiliated with the American Baptist Churches, U.S.A., is a private, coeducational institution offering programs through the divisions of arts and humanities, natural sciences, and social and behavioral sciences. The library contains 90,000 volumes, and subscribes to 400 periodicals. Special learning facilities include a learning resource center, art gallery, and radio station. The 64-acre campus is in a small town 45 miles southwest of Kansas City. Including residence halls, there are 15 buildings on campus.

Student Life: About 55% of undergraduates are from Kansas. Students come from 21 states and 11 foreign countries. Ninety-nine percent are from public schools. Seventy-six percent are white. Sixty-one percent are Protestant; 11% Catholic. The average age of freshmen is 19; all undergraduates, 22. Fifteen percent drop out by the end of their first year; 30% remain to graduate.

Housing: A total of 428 students can be accommodated in college housing. College-sponsored living facilities include dormitories, on-campus apartments, and married-student housing. On-campus housing is guaranteed for all 4 years. Fifty-nine percent of students live on campus; of those, 65% remain on campus on weekends. Alcohol is not permitted. All students may keep cars on campus.

Activities: There are no fraternities or sororities on campus. There are many groups on campus, including cheerleading, choir, chorale, chorus, computers, drama, ethnic, honors, international, jazz band, musical theater, newspaper, orchestra, pep band, photography, professional, radio and TV, religious, social, social service, student government, and yearbook. Popular campus events include Family Day, Homecoming, Charter Day, Christmas Feast, International Dinner, Sports Banquet, Discovery Day Visitation, and Annual Alumni Auction.

Sports: There are 6 intercollegiate sports for men and 4 for women, and 12 intramural sports for men and 12 for women. Athletic and recreation facilities include a field, a sports complex, an athletic center, and a gymnasium with a wellness center.

Disabled Students: Fifty percent of the campus is accessible to disabled students. The following facilities are available: wheelchair ramps, elevators, special parking, specially equipped rest rooms, and special class scheduling.

Services: In addition to many counseling and information services, tutoring is available in most subjects. There is remedial math, reading, and writing.

Campus Safety and Security: Campus safety and security measures include pamphlets, posters, and films, lighted pathways and sidewalks, and a night security guard. In addition, students are issued individual residence hall security and room keys.

Programs of Study: Ottawa awards the B.A. degree. Bachelor's degrees are awarded in BIOLOGICAL SCIENCE (biology/biological science), BUSINESS (accounting and business administration and management), COMMUNICATIONS AND THE ARTS (communications, dramatic arts, English, fine arts, music, and speech/debate/rhetoric), COMPUTER AND PHYSICAL SCIENCE (chemistry, computer programming, information sciences and systems, and mathematics), EDUCATION (elementary), SOCIAL SCIENCE (economics, history, human services, philosophy, political science/government, psychology, religion, and sociology). English, business, and mathematics are the strongest academically. Business and teacher education have the largest enrollments.

Required: To graduate, students must complete 11 courses in 10 academic areas with a minimum GPA of 2.0. The university requires students to complete 124 semester hours, with 24 to 40 in the major. Three interdisciplinary general education seminars must be completed. In addition, students must attend 10 University Program events each semester.

Special: Internships are available, especially in business, human services, and teacher education. Student-designed majors are an option. A 3 + 1 degree in medical technology and preprofessional programs in premedicine, predentistry, prelaw, and preministry are available. There are 2 national honor societies on campus.

Faculty/Classroom: All faculty teach undergraduates. The average class size in a laboratory is 12.

Admissions: About 28% of the 1993–94 applicants were accepted. The ACT scores for the 1993–94 freshman class were as follows: 45% below 21, 32% between 21 and 23, 19% between 24 and 26, 3% between 27 and 28, and 1% above 28. About 27% of the current freshmen were in the top fifth of their class; 51% were in the top two fifths. About 4 freshmen graduated first in their class.

Requirements: Ottawa requires applicants to be in the upper 50% of their class. A minimum GPA of 2.0 is required. The SAT I or ACT is required. The GED is accepted. There are no specific high school courses required, but a sound college preparatory curriculum is highly recommended. AP and CLEP credits are accepted. Important factors used in the admissions decision are parents or siblings attending the school, recommendations by alumni, recommendations by school officials, evidence of special talent, and advanced placement or honor courses.

Procedure: Freshmen are admitted to all sessions. Entrance exams should be taken as early as possible. The application fee is $15. Application deadlines are open. Notification is sent on a rolling basis.

Transfer: About 113 transfer students enrolled in 1993–94. Transfer applicants must submit transcripts from all colleges attended and must have a 2.0 GPA and 12 hours of college credit, or else they must meet freshman requirements. A total of 30 credits out of 124 must be completed at Ottawa.

Visiting: There are regularly scheduled orientations for prospective students, including Discovery Day in the early spring, which gives prospective students a chance to meet faculty, students, and staff and to learn more about Ottawa University, the admissions process, and financial aid. There are guides for informal visits, and visitors may sit in on classes and stay overnight at the school. To arrange a visit, contact Susan Ratliff or Jean Pratt of the Admissions Office at (913) 242–5200, ext. 5555 or (800) 755–5200, ext. 1.

Financial Aid: In 1993–94 98% of all current freshmen and 95% of continuing students received some form of financial aid. About 90% of freshmen and 90% of continuing students received need-based aid. The average freshman award was $8500. Of that total, scholarships or need-based grants averaged $4300 ($6500 maximum); loans averaged $3200 ($9500 maximum); and work contracts averaged $1000 ($1400 maximum). Eighty percent of undergraduate students work part-time. Average earnings from campus work for the school year are $1000. The average financial indebtedness of the 1992–93 graduate was $10,000 to $12,000. The FFS, the college's own financial statement, and the FAFSA are required. The deadline for financial aid applications is April 1.

International Students: There are currently 66 international students enrolled. The school actively recruits these students. They must take the TOEFL or the University of Michigan Language Test and achieve a minimum score on the TOEFL of 500.

Computers: The college provides computer facilities for student use. The mainframe is an IBM A/S 400. There are 2 computer laboratories. All students may access the system.

Graduates: In a recent year, 99 bachelor's degrees were awarded. The most popular majors among graduates were business administration (19%), elementary education (18%), and communications (9%). Some 53 companies recruited on campus in 1992–93. In the 1992 graduating class, 23% of graduates were enrolled in graduate school within 6 months of graduation; 95% had found employment.

Admissions Contact: Susan Ratliff, Admissions Office Manager.

PITTSBURG STATE UNIVERSITY
Pittsburg, KS 66762

F-3

(316) 235-4251
(800) 854-PITT(7488) (out-of-state)

Full-time: 2311 men, 2180 women
Part-time: 296 men, 415 women
Graduate: 503 men, 884 women
Year: semesters, summer session
Application Deadline: open
Freshman Class: 2746 applied, 2155 accepted, 1380 enrolled
ACT: 20

Faculty: 243; IIA, --$
Ph.D.s: 54%
Student/Faculty: 18 to 1
Tuition: $1664 ($4798)
Room & Board: $2814

NONCOMPETITIVE

Pittsburg State University, founded in 1903, is a state-supported co-educational institution offering programs in arts and sciences, business, education, and technology. There are 4 undergraduate schools and one graduate school. In addition to regional accreditation, Pitt State has baccalaureate program accreditation with ABET, CSWE, NASM, NCATE, and NLN. The library contains 290,798 volumes, 516,718 microform items, and 386 audiovisual forms, and subscribes to 1368 periodicals. Computerized library sources and services include the card catalog, interlibrary loans, and database searching. Special learning facilities include a learning resource center, art gallery, planetarium, radio station, TV station, and a dedicated channel on local cable television. The 125-acre campus is in a small town 100 miles south of Kansas City. Including residence halls, there are 34 buildings on campus.

Student Life: About 84% of undergraduates are from Kansas. Students come from 45 states, 42 foreign countries, and Canada. Ninety-eight percent are from public schools; 2% from private. Seventy-seven percent are white. The average age of all undergraduates is 26.9. Twenty-two percent drop out by the end of their first year; 52% remain to graduate.

Housing: A total of 948 students can be accommodated in college housing. College-sponsored living facilities include single-sex and coed dormitories, on-campus apartments, married-student housing, fraternity houses, and sorority houses. On-campus housing is guaranteed for the freshman year only and is available on a first-come, first-served basis. Priority is given to out-of-town students. Alcohol is not permitted. All students may keep cars on campus.

Activities: About 10% of men belong to 5 national fraternities; about 6% of women belong to 3 national sororities. There are 100 groups on campus, including art, band, cheerleading, choir, chorus, computers, drama, drill team, ethnic, honors, international, jazz band, marching band, musical theater, newspaper, orchestra, pep band, photography, political, professional, radio and TV, religious, social, student government, symphony, and yearbook. Popular campus events include Homecoming, Greek Week, Multicultural Month, Welcome Week, Parents Day, and Commemoration Day.

Sports: There are 5 intercollegiate sports for men and 4 for women, and 9 intramural sports for men and 9 for women. Athletic and recreation facilities include a football stadium, a proturf track, an indoor track, a basketball arena, softball diamonds, a weight room, a dance studio, an Olympic pool, volleyball, racquetball, and badminton courts, and indoor and outdoor tennis courts.

Disabled Students: Seventy percent of the campus is accessible to disabled students. The following facilities are available: wheelchair ramps, elevators, special parking, specially equipped rest rooms, special class scheduling, lowered drinking fountains, and lowered telephones.

Services: In addition to many counseling and information services, tutoring is available in some subjects, including accounting, chemistry, foreign language, mathematics, computers, physics, psychology, reading/study, and writing. In addition, there is a reader service for the blind, and remedial math, reading, and writing. There is a student assistance center and a counseling center.

Campus Safety and Security: Campus safety and security measures include 24-hour foot and vehicle patrol, informal discussions, pamphlets, posters, and films, and lighted pathways and sidewalks.

Programs of Study: Pitt State awards the B.A., B.S., B.B.A., B.S.Ed., B.F.A., B.Gen.Studies, B.Music, B.M.Ed., B.Eng.Tech., B.Med.Tech., B.Nursing, B.Tech., and B.Voc.-Tech.Ed. degrees. Associate and master's degrees also are awarded. Bachelor's degrees are awarded in BIOLOGICAL SCIENCE (biology/biological science), BUSINESS (accounting, banking and finance, business administration and management, business economics, and marketing/retailing/merchandising), COMMUNICATIONS AND THE ARTS (broadcasting, communications, design, dramatic arts, English, fine arts, languages, music, and speech/debate/rhetoric), COMPUTER AND PHYSICAL SCIENCE (chemistry, computer programming, computer science, information sciences and systems, mathematics, and physics), EDUCATION (art, early childhood, elementary, foreign languages, home economics, industrial arts, middle school, music, science, secondary, and teaching English as a second language/foreign language), ENGINEERING AND ENVIRONMENTAL DESIGN (engineering technology, industrial engineering technology, and printing

technology), HEALTH PROFESSIONS (medical laboratory technology, nursing, predentistry, and premedicine), SOCIAL SCIENCE (geography, history, political science/government, prelaw, psychology, social science, social work, and sociology). Predentistry, premedicine, psychology, and accounting are the strongest academically. Business administration, elementary education, engineering technology, social sciences, communications, and psychology have the largest enrollments.

Required: To graduate, students must complete 124 semester hours, including 35 to 60 hours in the major, with a minimum GPA of 2.0. Courses in English, speech, mathematics, humanities, social and behavioral sciences, natural and physical sciences, producing and consuming, and lifetime fitness are required.

Special: Co-op and work-study programs, internships, a general studies degree, dual majors, a 3–2 enginering degree with Kansas and Kansas State universities, credit by examination, nondegree study, and pass/fail options are available. The university has student exchange programs with 70 countries. There is a freshman honors program on campus

Faculty/Classroom: Seventy-one percent of faculty are male; 29%, female. Ninety-six percent teach undergraduates, 83% do research, and 96% do both. Graduate students teach 5% of introductory courses. The average class size in an introductory lecture is 50; in a laboratory, 20; and in a regular course offering, 35.

Admissions: About 78% of the 1993–94 applicants were accepted. The ACT scores for the 1993–94 freshman class were as follows: 63% below 21, 15% between 21 and 23, 7% between 24 and 26, 5% between 27 and 28, and 3% above 28.

Requirements: Pitt State requires applicants to be in the upper 50% of their class. A minimum GPA of 2.0 is required. The ACT is required. The university has an open admissions policy for Kansas students who graduated from an accredited high school or have passed the GED. AP and CLEP credits are accepted.

Procedure: Freshmen are admitted fall, spring, and summer. Entrance exams should be taken before or during the first semester of the freshman year. Application deadlines are open. The application fee is $15. The college accepts all in-state residents who apply. Notification is sent on a rolling basis.

Transfer: About 739 transfer students enrolled in 1993–94. Applicants must have a college GPA of 2.0. A total of 30 credits out of 124 must be completed at Pitt State.

Visiting: There are regularly scheduled orientations for prospective students. There are guides for informal visits and visitors may sit in on classes and stay overnight at the school. To arrange for a visit, contact the Office of Admission at (316) 235-4251 or (800) 854-PITT(7488).

Financial Aid: In an earlier year, 47% of all current freshmen and 40% of continuing students received some form of financial aid. Scholarships or need-based grants averaged $785 ($6078 maximum); loans averaged $2167 ($2625 maximum); and work contracts averaged $1700 ($2278 maximum). The average financial indebtedness of an earlier year graduate was $8658. The FFS is required. The deadline for financial aid applications is March 15.

International Students: There are currently 625 international students enrolled. The school actively recruits these students. They must take the TOEFL and achieve a minimum score of 520.

Computers: The college provides computer facilities for student use. The mainframe is an IBM. Seven student laboratories can access the mainframe, E-mail, and university fiber-optic network via microcomputers. Nearly 200 workstations and more than 200 software packages are available. Bitnet and Internet are also available. All students may access the system 24 hours a day. There are no time limits and no fees.

Graduates: In 1992–93 1368 bachelor's degrees were awarded. Within an average freshman class, 23% graduate in 3 years, 40% in 4 years, and 45% in 5 years.

Admissions Contact: Office of Admission.

SAINT MARY COLLEGE
Leavenworth, KS 66048 (913) 682-5151, ext. 6118; (800) 752-7043

F-2

Full-time: 140 men, 299 women
Part-time: 188 men, 227 women
Graduate: 7 men, 14 women
Year: semesters, summer session
Application Deadline: open
Freshman Class: 351 applied, 307 accepted, 103 enrolled
ACT: 21

Faculty: 40
Ph.D.s: 50%
Student/Faculty: 11 to 1
Tuition: $7550
Room & Board: $3700

COMPETITIVE

Saint Mary College, founded in 1923, is a private, coeducational liberal arts institution affiliated with the Roman Catholic Church and sponsored by the Sisters of Charity of Leavenworth. In addition to regional accreditation, St. Mary has baccalaureate program accreditation with NCATE and NLN. The library contains 120,000 volumes and 40,000 microform items, and subscribes to 500 periodicals. Computerized library sources and services include database searching. Special learning facilities include a learning resource center. The

240-acre campus is in a small town 25 miles northwest of Kansas City, Missouri. Including residence halls, there are 10 buildings on campus.

Student Life: About 51% of undergraduates are from Kansas. Students come from 9 states and 9 foreign countries. Sixty-seven percent are from public schools; 33% from private. Sixty-three percent are white; 18% African American. Forty-six percent are Protestant; 35% Catholic; 15% claim no religious affiliation. Thirty-five percent drop out by the end of their first year; 35% remain to graduate.

Housing: A total of 400 students can be accommodated in college housing. College-sponsored living facilities include single-sex and coed dormitories. On-campus housing is guaranteed for all 4 years. Fifty-eight percent of students commute. All students may keep cars on campus.

Activities: There are no fraternities or sororities on campus. There are 14 groups on campus, including art, cheerleading, choir, chorale, chorus, computers, dance, drama, musical theater, newspaper, opera, social, social service, and student government. Popular campus events include Wyandotte Days, Fall Convocation, Founders Day, Family Weekend, Tower Power, Alternative Spring Break, Honors Convocation, and Commencement.

Sports: There are 2 intercollegiate sports for men and 4 for women, and 7 intramural sports for men and 7 for women. Athletic and recreation facilities include a 500-seat sport center, soccer and softball fields, 3 tennis courts, a sandlot volleyball court, 2 racquetball courts, a weight and exercise room, a swimming pool, dance and aerobics space, and a walking trail.

Disabled Students: Ninety percent of the campus is accessible to disabled students. The following facilities are available: wheelchair ramps, elevators, special parking, and specially equipped rest rooms.

Services: In addition to many counseling and information services, tutoring is available in most subjects.

Campus Safety and Security: Campus safety and security measures include self defense education, informal discussions, pamphlets, posters, and films, and lighted pathways and sidewalks. In addition, there are 14-hour foot and vehicle patrol and controlled access to residence halls.

Programs of Study: St. Mary awards the B.A., B.S., B.Mus., and B.S.N. degrees. Associate degree also are awarded. Bachelor's degrees are awarded in BIOLOGICAL SCIENCE (biology/biological science), BUSINESS (accounting and business administration and management), COMMUNICATIONS AND THE ARTS (art, dramatic arts, English, music, performing arts, piano, Spanish, and voice), COMPUTER AND PHYSICAL SCIENCE (chemistry, computer science, information sciences and systems, and mathematics), EDUCATION (elementary), HEALTH PROFESSIONS (medical laboratory technology and nursing), SOCIAL SCIENCE (history, human development, human services, liberal arts/general studies, political science/government, psychology, public affairs, sociology, and theological studies). Education and humanities are the strongest academically. Education and business administration have the largest enrollments.

Required: To graduate, students must complete all general education requirements and earn at least 128 credits, including 30 to 42 in the major, with a minimum GPA of 2.0. The core curriculum includes freshman humanities, colloquium in human communities, introduction to fine arts, and a senior integration project. Distribution requirements include 2 courses each in theology, philosophy, history, and social and behavioral sciences, 3 courses each in mathematics, computer science, physical science, entry-level language and literature course, plus an additional literature course, a fine arts course, an elective in arts, and 2 physical activity courses.

Special: The college offers co-op programs with the University of Kansas, cross-registration with Kansas City Regional Council for Higher Education Consortium members, a student exchange program in Tokyo at Sophia University's summer session, and study abroad in Europe. Internships, work-study programs, and pass/fail options are also available. There are 2 national honor societies on campus.

Faculty/Classroom: Thirty-five percent of faculty are male; 65%, female. All teach undergraduates. No introductory courses are taught by graduate students. The average class size in an introductory lecture is 25; in a laboratory, 15; and in a regular course offering, 12.

Admissions: About 87% of the 1993–94 applicants were accepted. About 20% of the current freshmen were in the top fifth of their class; 80% were in the top two fifths. About 2 freshmen graduated first in their class.

Requirements: A minimum GPA of 2.5 is required. The SAT I or ACT is required. Applicants should be graduates of an accredited secondary school, with a minimum GPA of 2.5. A recommendation letter is required. The GED is accepted. AP and CLEP credits are accepted. Important factors used in the admissions decision are leadership record, recommendations by school officials, recommendations by alumni, evidence of special talent, and advanced placement or honor courses.

Procedure: Freshmen are admitted fall and spring. Entrance exams should be taken in the spring of the junior year and fall of the senior year. The application fee is $20. Application deadlines are open. Notification is sent on a rolling basis.

Transfer: A college GPA of 2.0 is required. A total of 30 credits out of 128 must be completed at St. Mary.

Visiting: There are regularly scheduled orientations for prospective students, consisting of visiting classes, interviewing with faculty and financial aid representatives, and touring the campus. There are guides for informal visits, and visitors may sit in on classes and stay overnight at the school. To arrange for a visit, contact the Admissions Office at (913) 682–5151, ext. 6118 or (800) 752–7043.

Financial Aid: In 1993–94 80% of all current freshmen and 85% of continuing students received some form of financial aid. About 80% of freshmen and 80% of continuing students received need-based aid. The average freshman award was $5965. Of that total, scholarships or need-based grants averaged $3226 ($10,000 maximum); loans averaged $2604 ($5625 maximum); and work contracts averaged $797 ($1100 maximum). Thirty percent of undergraduate students work part-time. Average earnings from campus work for the school year are $838. The average financial indebtedness of the 1992–93 graduate was $3323. St. Mary is a member of CSS. The FFS or FAFSA is required.

International Students: There are currently 27 international students enrolled. The school actively recruits these students. They must take the TOEFL and achieve a minimum score of 500.

Computers: The college provides computer facilities for student use. The mainframe is an IBM AS400. Media laboratories are available for course work, and computer laboratories are available for homework. There are also some PCs in residence halls. All students may access the system. There are no time limits on using the system and no fees.

Graduates: In a recent year, 100 bachelor's degrees were awarded. The most popular majors among graduates were business administration (32%), elementary education (20%), and human services (12%). Within an average freshman class, 35% graduate in 3 years. In the 1992 graduating class, 10% of the men and 15% of the women were enrolled in graduate school within 6 months of graduation; 80% of the men and 90% of the women had found employment.

Admissions Contact: Domenic Teti, Director of Admissions.

SOUTHWESTERN COLLEGE

D-3

Winfield, KS 67156   (316) 221–8236; (800) 546–1543 (in-state)

Full-time: 233 men, 258 women	Faculty: 50; IIB, --$
Part-time: 30 men, 56 women	Ph.D.s: 90%
Graduate: 11 men, 27 women	Student/Faculty: 10 to 1
Year: 4–1–4, summer session	Tuition: $6500
Application Deadline: August 1	Room & Board: $3532
Freshman Class: 225 applied, 155 accepted, 85 enrolled	
SAT I Verbal/Math: 390/444	ACT: 21 COMPETITIVE

Southwestern College, established in 1885, is a private institution affiliated with the United Methodist Church. There is one graduate school. In addition to regional accreditation, Southwestern has baccalaureate program accreditation with CSWE, NASM, NCATE, and NLN. The library contains 125,000 volumes and 1000 microform items, and subscribes to 535 periodicals. Computerized library sources and services include the card catalog, interlibrary loans, and database searching. Special learning facilities include a learning resource center, radio station, and TV station. The 70-acre campus is in a small town 45 miles south of Wichita. Including residence halls, there are 13 buildings on campus.

Student Life: About 80% of undergraduates are from Kansas. Students come from 25 states and 4 foreign countries. Eighty-six percent are white. Twenty-six percent are members of the school's denomination. The average age of freshmen is 18; all undergraduates, 20. Thirty-nine percent drop out by the end of their first year.

Housing: A total of 386 students can be accommodated in college housing. College-sponsored living facilities include single-sex and coed dormitories, on-campus apartments, and married-student housing. In addition, there are honors houses. On-campus housing is guaranteed for all 4 years. Sixty percent of students commute. Alcohol is not permitted. All students may keep cars on campus.

Activities: There are 3 local and 2 national fraternities and 1 local and 1 national sorority. There are 32 groups on campus, including band, cheerleading, choir, chorus, drama, ethnic, honors, jazz band, newspaper, orchestra, pep band, political, radio and TV, religious, social, social service, student government, and yearbook.

Sports: There are 7 intercollegiate sports for men and 5 for women, as well as intramural sports. Athletic and recreation facilities include a 2400-seat stadium, basketball courts, playing floors, exercise rooms, a gymnasium, an indoor swimming pool, and a running track.

Disabled Students: The following facilities are available: wheelchair ramps, elevators, special parking, and specially equipped rest rooms.

Services: In addition to many counseling and information services, tutoring is available in some subjects, including English and mathematics.

Campus Safety and Security: Campus safety and security measures include lighted pathways and sidewalks.

Programs of Study: Southwestern awards the B.A., B.S., B.B.A., B.G.S., B.Mus., B.Phil., B.S.N., and B.S.W. degrees. Master's degrees also are awarded. Bachelor's degrees are awarded in BIOLOGICAL SCIENCE (biology/biological science and marine biology), BUSINESS (business administration and management), COMMUNICATIONS AND THE ARTS (English, film arts, and music), COMPUTER AND PHYSICAL SCIENCE (chemistry, computer science, and physics), EDUCATION (business, elementary, foreign languages, health, music, and secondary), HEALTH PROFESSIONS (nursing, premedicine, and respiratory therapy), SOCIAL SCIENCE (history, philosophy, prelaw, psychology, religion, social science, and social work). Natural sciences is the strongest academically. Business, natural sciences, and education have the largest enrollments.

Required: To graduate, students must earn 124 credits, fulfill all requirements of the major, and maintain a GPA of 2.0. General education requirements consist of 15 credits distributed over 6 curriculum areas. Students must also take 2 courses in a foreign language or prove proficiency, fulfill requirements in philosophy, religion, and interdisciplinary studies, and earn credit in a January term for each year of enrollment.

Special: Southwestern offers co-op programs in engineering, human resources, and manufacturing technology; internships in industry and in social and civic agencies; and study abroad in Africa, Europe, and Russia. B.A.-B.S. degrees are available in biology with Kansas State University, a 3–2 engineering degree is available with Washington University of St. Louis, and a music and theater dual major is possible. Work-study programs, credit for life, military, and work experience, nondegree study, and pass/fail options are also available. There are 7 national honor societies on campus.

Faculty/Classroom: Sixty-two percent of faculty are male; 38%, female. All teach undergraduates. No introductory courses are taught by graduate students.

Admissions: About 69% of the 1993–94 applicants were accepted. The SAT scores for the 1993–94 freshman class were as follows: Verbal—86% below 500 and 14% between 500 and 599; Math—57% below 500, 29% between 500 and 599, and 14% between 600 and 700. The ACT scores were 45% below 21, 20% between 21 and 23, 21% between 24 and 26, 10% between 27 and 28, and 3% above 28. About 32% of the current freshmen were in the top fifth of their class; 75% were in the top two fifths.

Requirements: A minimum GPA of 2.0 is required. The SAT I or ACT is required. All candidates for admission must graduate from an accredited secondary school. The GED is accepted. Interviews are recommended. AP and CLEP credits are accepted.

Procedure: Freshmen are admitted fall, spring, and summer. Applications should be filed by August 1 for fall entry, along with an application fee of $15. Notification is sent on a rolling basis. There is a deferred admissions plan.

Transfer: A total of 112 transfer students enrolled in 1993–94. Applicants must have a college GPA of 2.0. A total of 30 credits out of 124 must be completed at Southwestern.

Visiting: There are guides for informal visits and visitors may sit in on classes and stay overnight at the school. To arrange for a visit, contact the Admissions Office at (316) 221–8236 or (800) 546–1543.

Financial Aid: In a recent year, 87% of all students received some form of financial aid. Southwestern is a member of CSS. The FAF or FFS (preferred) and the college's own financial statement is required. The deadline for financial aid applications is April 1.

International Students: The school actively recruits these students. They must take the TOEFL and achieve a minimum score of 550. The student must also take the college's own entrance exam.

Computers: The college provides computer facilities for student use. The mainframe is an IBM AS/400. Those receiving permission from computer center personnel may access the system. It may be used 8 A.M. to 5 P.M. There are no time limits on using the system and no fees.

Graduates: In 1992–93, 206 bachelor's degrees were awarded. The most popular majors among graduates were business administration (22%), nursing (15%), and elementary education (9%).

Admissions Contact: Doug Mason, Director of Admissions.

STERLING COLLEGE   D-3

Sterling, KS 67579   (316) 278–2173, ext. 275; (800) 346–1017

Full-time: 227 men, 250 women	Faculty: 29
Part-time: 13 men, 27 women	Ph.D.s: n/av
Graduate: none	Student/Faculty: 16 to 1
Year: 4–1–4	Tuition: $7890
Application Deadline: February 15	Room & Board: $3100
Freshman Class: 708 applied, 419 accepted, 210 enrolled	
ACT: 22	**VERY COMPETITIVE**

Sterling College, established in 1887, is a private institution affiliated with the Presbyterian Church, U.S.A., offering undergraduate curricula in art, business, health science, liberal arts, religious studies, and teacher preparation. The library contains 84,000 volumes, 1200 microform items, and 1000 audiovisual forms, and subscribes to 450 periodicals. Special learning facilities include a museum and a theater. The 43-acre campus is in a rural area 70 miles from Wichita. Including residence halls, there are 18 buildings on campus.

Student Life: About 50% of undergraduates are from Kansas. Eighty-five percent are from public schools. Eighty-five percent are Protestant; 15% Catholic. The average age of freshmen is 18; all undergraduates, 20. Twenty percent drop out by the end of their first year; 35% graduate.

Housing: A total of 515 students can be accommodated in college housing. College-sponsored living facilities include single-sex dormitories. On-campus housing is guaranteed for all 4 years. Ninety-five percent of students live on campus; of those, 75% remain on campus on weekends. Alcohol is not permitted. All students may keep cars on campus.

Activities: There are no fraternities or sororities on campus. There are many groups and organizations on campus, including art, bagpipe band, band, choir, dance, drama, international, orchestra, pep band, political, professional, religious, social service, and student government.

Sports: There are 7 intercollegiate sports each for men and women, and 6 intramural sports each for men and women. Athletic and recreation facilities include basketball, handball, and tennis courts, a weight-training facility, an exercise deck, a swimming pool, a track and football field and stadium, a baseball diamond, a soccer field, and practice fields.

Disabled Students: Eighty-eight percent of the campus is accessible to disabled students. The following facilities are available: special parking and special class scheduling.

Services: There is remedial math, reading, and writing.

Programs of Study: Sterling awards the B.A. and B.S. degrees. Associate degrees are also awarded. Bachelor's degrees are awarded in BIOLOGICAL SCIENCE (biology/biological science), BUSINESS (accounting, business administration and management, and management information systems), COMMUNICATIONS AND THE ARTS (art, dramatic arts, English, fine arts, music, and speech/debate/rhetoric), COMPUTER AND PHYSICAL SCIENCE (chemistry, computer science, and mathematics), EDUCATION (art, business, elementary, home economics, music, physical, and secondary), HEALTH PROFESSIONS (predentistry and premedicine), SOCIAL SCIENCE (American studies, behavioral science, history, home economics, prelaw, religious education, and theological studies).

Required: To graduate, students must complete courses in college composition, writing and library research, communications, mathematics, religion and philosophy, humanities, behavioral sciences, and fine arts. They must have an overall GPA of 2.0, with 2.5 in the major. A total of 124 credit hours must be earned, with 24 to 55 hours in the major. Physical fitness and chapel/convocation requirements must also be met.

Special: Sterling offers internships, co-op programs, and work-study programs. Students may study abroad in London, Paris, Munich, Florence, and Rome and may register for junior-year programs through other colleges. A Washington semester is also available. The college offers a B.A.-B.S. degree in conjunction with Kansas State University. Dual and student-designed majors may also be pursued. Nondegree study and a pass/fail grading option are available.

Admissions: About 60% of the 1993–94 applicants were accepted. The ACT scores for the 1993–94 freshman class were as follows: 7% between 27 and 28.

Requirements: A minimum GPA of 2.2 is required. Applicants must graduate from an accredited secondary school or have a GED. An interview is recommended. The SAT I or the ACT is required. AP and CLEP credits are accepted.

Procedure: Entrance exams should be taken in the fall of senior year. Applications should be filed by February 15 for fall entry, along with an application fee of $10. Notification is sent on a rolling basis. There is an early admissions plan.

Transfer: Transfer students must maintain at least a C average. A total of 30 credits out of 124 must be completed at Sterling.

Visiting: To arrange for a visit, contact the Admissions Office at (316) 278–2173, ext. 275.
Financial Aid: Sterling is a member of CSS. The FFS is required. The deadline for financial aid applications is March 15.
International Students: Students must take the TOEFL.
Computers: The college provides computer facilities for student use. The mainframe is a Harris 800. There are also Apple microcomputers. Students with a computer ID may access the system. It may be used 16 hours per day. There are no individual time limits on using the system and no fees.
Admissions Contact: Dennis W. Dutton, Director of Admissions.

TABOR COLLEGE
D-2

Hillsboro, KS 67063   (316) 947–3121; (800) TABOR-99

Full-time: 220 men, 197 women	Faculty: 33
Part-time: 11 men, 20 women	Ph.D.s: 65%
Graduate: none	Student/Faculty: 13 to 1
Year: 4–1–4	Tuition: $8050
Application Deadline: August 15	Room & Board: $3410
Freshman Class: 323 applied, 153 accepted, 138 enrolled	
ACT: 23	**VERY COMPETITIVE**

Tabor College, established in 1908, is a private coeducational liberal arts facility affiliated with the Mennonite Brethren Church. In addition to regional accreditation, Tabor has baccalaureate program accreditation with CSWE and NASM. The library contains 70,000 volumes and 2000 audiovisual forms, and subscribes to 450 periodicals. Special learning facilities include a learning resource center and a writing center. The 26-acre campus is in a rural area 50 miles north of Wichita. Including residence halls, there are 20 buildings on campus.
Student Life: About 60% of undergraduates are from Kansas. Students come from 27 states, 4 foreign countries, and Canada. Ninety percent are from public schools; 10% from private. Ninety-two percent are white. Most are Protestant. The average age of freshmen is 18; all undergraduates, 20. Fifteen percent drop out by the end of their first year; 20% remain to graduate.
Housing: A total of 382 students can be accommodated in college housing. College-sponsored living facilities include single-sex dormitories. On-campus housing is guaranteed for all 4 years. Eighty-four percent of students live on campus; of those, 85% remain on campus on weekends. Alcohol is not permitted. All students may keep cars on campus.
Activities: There are no fraternities or sororities on campus. There are many groups and organizations on campus, including art, band, cheerleading, choir, chorale, chorus, computers, drama, ethnic, international, jazz band, musical theater, newspaper, pep band, photography, political, religious, student government, and yearbook. Popular campus events include Homecoming, Service Emphasis Week, and Mission Emphasis Week.
Sports: There are 6 intercollegiate sports for men and 5 for women, and 10 intramural sports for men and 10 for women. Athletic and recreation facilities include 4 lighted tennis courts, lighted football and baseball fields, several practice fields, a soccer field, a curbed metric all-weather track, a gymnasium with 2 playing floors, an indoor soccer court, and aerobic exercise, athletic training, and weight rooms.
Disabled Students: Forty percent of the campus is accessible to disabled students. The following facilities are available: wheelchair ramps, special parking, specially equipped rest rooms, and special class scheduling.
Services: Tutoring is available for those on academic probation.
Campus Safety and Security: Campus safety and security measures include lighted pathways and sidewalks.
Programs of Study: Tabor awards the B.A. degree. Associate degree also are awarded. Bachelor's degrees are awarded in AGRICULTURE (animal science), BIOLOGICAL SCIENCE (biology/biological science and botany), BUSINESS (accounting, business administration and management, business economics, business law, and marketing/retailing/merchandising), COMMUNICATIONS AND THE ARTS (communications, English, and music), COMPUTER AND PHYSICAL SCIENCE (chemistry, computer programming, computer science, mathematics, and physics), EDUCATION (business, elementary, health, middle school, music, physical, science, and secondary), HEALTH PROFESSIONS (medical laboratory technology), SOCIAL SCIENCE (community services, history, philosophy, psychology, religion, social work, and sociology). The sciences are the strongest academically. Business and education have the largest enrollments.
Required: All students must complete 47 to 59 hours of general education courses, including biblical and religious studies, history of diverse cultures, creative expression, natural and mathematical systems, values, social sciences, language, communication, computer literacy, physical fitness, and a college success seminar. A total of 124 credits with a minimum GPA of 2.0 is required to graduate.
Special: Co-op programs are offered with the 6-member Associated Colleges of Central Kansas. Study abroad in 4 countries is possible through the Council of Mennonite Colleges. Dual majors, student-

designed majors, and pass/fail options are available. An accelerated degree program in management organizational development also is offered. There is a freshman honors program on campus. One department has an honors program.
Faculty/Classroom: Sixty-five percent of faculty are male; 35%, female. All teach undergraduates. The average class size in an introductory lecture is 32 and in a regular course offering, 20.
Admissions: About 47% of the 1993–94 applicants were accepted. The ACT scores for the 1993–94 freshman class were as follows: 40% below 21, 20% between 21 and 23, 18% between 24 and 26, 15% between 27 and 28, and 7% above 28. There were 2 National Merit finalists and 1 semifinalist. About 7 freshmen graduated first in their class.
Requirements: A minimum GPA of 2.0 is required. The SAT I or ACT is required. An essay is required, and an interview is recommended. AP and CLEP credits are accepted. Important factors used in the admissions decision are personality, intangible qualities, and recommendations by school officials.
Procedure: Freshmen are admitted to all sessions. Entrance exams should be taken in October of the senior year. Applications should be filed by August 15 for fall entry, along with an application fee of $10. Notification is sent on a rolling basis.
Transfer: About 34 transfer students enrolled in 1993–94. A minimum 2.0 GPA is required, and an interview is recommended. A total of 30 credits out of 124 must be completed at Tabor.
Visiting: There are regularly scheduled orientations for prospective students, including a tour, admissions interview, faculty visit, class visit, and financial aid visit. If requested, an audition or tryout will be scheduled. There are guides for informal visits, and visitors may sit in on classes and stay overnight at the school. To arrange for a visit, contact Admission Counselors at (800) TABOR-99.
Financial Aid: In 1993–94 all current freshmen and all continuing students received some form of financial aid. About 74% of freshmen received need-based aid. The average freshman award was $5700. Of that total, scholarships or need-based grants averaged $3200 ($7850 maximum); loans averaged $2400; and work contracts averaged $1000 ($1500 maximum). Twenty-five percent of undergraduate students work part-time. Average earnings from campus work for the school year are $1000. The average financial indebtedness of the 1992–93 graduate was $20,000. The FAFSA and a federal income tax form are required. The deadline for financial aid applications is March 30.
International Students: There are currently 15 international students enrolled. They must take the TOEFL and achieve a minimum score of 525.
Computers: The college provides computer facilities for student use. The mainframe is a Dual 83/80. There are also 40 Zenith, Apple, and IBM-compatible microcomputers available in the administration building. All students may access the system. There are no time limits on using the system and no fees.
Graduates: In 1992–93 83 bachelor's degrees were awarded. The most popular majors among graduates were business (21%), education (18%), and sciences (12%). Within an average freshman class, 33% graduate in 4 years. Some 80 companies recruited on campus in 1992–93.
Admissions Contact: Glenn L. Lygrisse, Vice President for Enrollment Management.

UNIVERSITY OF KANSAS
E-2

Lawrence, KS 66045   (913) 864–3911

Full-time: 8970 men, 8910 women	Faculty: 1078; I, --$
Part-time: 841 men, 832 women	Ph.D.s: 96%
Graduate: 4371 men, 4938 women	Student/Faculty: 17 to 1
Year: semesters, summer session	Tuition: $1920 ($6538)
Application Deadline: February 1	Room & Board: $3280
Freshman Class: 8579 applied, 5561 accepted, 3681 enrolled	
ACT: 23	**NONCOMPETITIVE**

The University of Kansas, founded in 1866, is a public, comprehensive institution. The emphases of its programs are on the liberal arts, business, art and fine arts, music, teacher preparation, journalism, engineering, architecture, social welfare, law, and health science, including pharmacy. Its medical center campus is located in Kansas City. There are 11 undergraduate and 3 graduate schools. In addition to regional accreditation, KU has baccalaureate program accreditation with AACSB, ABET, ACEJMC, ACPE, APTA, CAHEA, CSWE, NAAB, NASAD, NASM, NCATE, and NLN. The 12 libraries contain 3,045,000 volumes, 2,510,000 microform items, and 114,000 audiovisual forms, and subscribe to 27,000 periodicals. Computerized library sources and services include the card catalog, interlibrary loans, and database searching. Special learning facilities include a learning resource center, art gallery, radio station, observatory, film studio, state-of-the-art performing arts center, and art, natural history, classics, anthropology, entomology, and invertebrate paleontology museums. The 1000-acre campus is in a small town 40 miles west of

Kansas City. Including residence halls, there are 185 buildings on campus.

Student Life: About 69% of undergraduates are from Kansas. Students come from 50 states, 112 foreign countries, and Canada. Eighty-three percent are white. The average age of freshmen is 19; all undergraduates, 22. Twenty percent drop out by the end of their first year; 55% remain to graduate.

Housing: A total of 4812 students can be accommodated in college housing. College-sponsored living facilities include single-sex and coed dormitories, on-campus apartments, off-campus apartments, and married-student housing. In addition, there are honors houses and special interest houses, including a dormitory with a fine arts emphasis. On-campus housing is available on a first-come, first-served basis. All students may keep cars on campus.

Activities: About 20% of men belong to 28 national fraternities; about 25% of women belong to 18 national sororities. There are more than 300 groups on campus, including art, band, cheerleading, choir, chorus, computers, dance, drama, drill team, ethnic, film, gay, honors, international, jazz band, literary magazine, marching band, musical theater, newspaper, opera, orchestra, pep band, photography, political, professional, radio and TV, social, social service, student government, symphony, and yearbook. Popular campus events include Parents Day, Homecoming, Graduation, Christmas Vespers, KU basketball and football events, Rock Chalk Revue, Concert Series, University Theater Series, and Hawk Week.

Sports: There are 9 intercollegiate sports for men and 9 for women, and 17 intramural sports for men and 16 for women. Athletic and recreation facilities include a field house with an indoor track and basketball and volleyball courts; a 52,000-seat football stadium with an outdoor track; a sports pavilion with an indoor football field; a health and physical education center housing 2 indoor pools, handball and racquetball courts, an indoor climbing wall, gymnasiums, and weight/exercise, gymnastics, and combative rooms; baseball, lacrosse, ultimate, cricket, football, soccer, and rugby fields; and tennis courts.

Disabled Students: Ninety percent of the campus is accessible to disabled students. The following facilities are available: wheelchair ramps, elevators, special parking, specially equipped rest rooms, special class scheduling, lowered drinking fountains, and lowered telephones.

Services: In addition to many counseling and information services, tutoring is available in most subjects. How-to sessions on study and organizational skills, workshops on note taking, and a writing center are available to students. There also is a reader service for the blind and remedial math.

Campus Safety and Security: Campus safety and security measures include 24-hour foot and vehicle patrol, shuttle buses, informal discussions, and pamphlets, posters, and films. In addition, there are emergency telephones and lighted pathways and sidewalks.

Programs of Study: KU awards the B.A., B.S., B.A.E., B.A.R.C.E., B.Arch., B.F.A., B.G.S., B.M., B.M.E., B.S.B., B.S.E., B.S.J., B.S.N., B.S.P., B.S.R., and B.S.W. degrees. Master's and doctoral degrees also are awarded. Bachelor's degrees are awarded in BIOLOGICAL SCIENCE (biochemistry, biology/biological science, cell biology, ecology, genetics, and microbiology), BUSINESS (accounting and business administration and management), COMMUNICATIONS AND THE ARTS (advertising, art, art history and appreciation, classical languages, communications, comparative literature, dance, design, dramatic arts, East Asian languages and literature, English, French, German, Italian, journalism, linguistics, media arts, music, music history and appreciation, music performance, music theory and composition, painting, printmaking, Russian, sculpture, Spanish, theater design, and voice), COMPUTER AND PHYSICAL SCIENCE (astronomy, atmospheric sciences and meteorology, chemistry, computer science, geology, geophysics and seismology, mathematics, and physics), EDUCATION (art, elementary, health, music, physical, and secondary), ENGINEERING AND ENVIRONMENTAL DESIGN (aeronautical engineering, architectural engineering, architecture, chemical engineering, civil engineering, computer engineering, electrical/electronics engineering, engineering physics, environmental science, mechanical engineering, and petroleum/natural gas engineering), HEALTH PROFESSIONS (cytotechnology, health care administration, medical laboratory technology, music therapy, nursing, occupational therapy, pharmacy, respiratory therapy, and speech pathology/audiology), SOCIAL SCIENCE (African American studies, African studies, American studies, anthropology, classical/ancient civilization, developmental psychology, Eastern European studies, economics, geography, history, humanities, Latin American studies, liberal arts/general studies, philosophy, political science/government, psychology, religion, Russian and Slavic studies, social work, sociology, and women's studies). Journalism, architecture, fine arts, pharmacy, education, and engineering are the strongest academically. Engineering, fine arts, psychology, business, journalism, and education have the largest enrollments.

Required: To graduate with a B.A. or B.G.S. degree, all students must complete at least 124 credit hours, including 20 to 40 in a major, and maintain a GPA of at least 2.0. These, as well as curricula and distribution requirements, vary according to the school and the major. English composition and literature must be taken.

Special: KU offers internships, study abroad in more than 48 countries, a Washington semester, work-study programs with the university, a cooperative program in engineering, B.A.-B.S. degrees in many combinations, interdisciplinary majors, including architectural studies and theater and film, and dual majors in any approved combination. General studies degrees are available in many areas, and student-designed majors are possible. Nondegree study and pass/fail options are offered. There is a freshman honors program on campus, as well as 12 national honor societies, including Phi Beta Kappa. There is also a university-wide honors program.

Faculty/Classroom: Seventy percent of faculty are male; 30%, female. Sixty-four percent teach undergraduates and all do research. Graduate students teach 54% of all freshman and sophomore courses. The average class size in a laboratory and in a regular course offering is 20.

Admissions: About 65% of the 1993–94 applicants were accepted. The ACT scores for the 1993–94 freshman class were as follows: 27% below 21, 26% between 21 and 23, 26% between 24 and 26, 11% between 27 and 28, and 12% above 28. About 35% of the current freshmen were in the top fifth of their class; 65% were in the top two fifths. There were 42 National Merit finalists.

Requirements: A minimum GPA of 2.0 is required. The ACT is recommended. Applicants for the College of Liberal Arts and Sciences must have at least a 3.0 GPA through the end of the junior year; have a minimum ACT composite score of 24 or SAT I composite score of 990 and at least a 2.0 GPA; or take the Kansas Regents recommended college preparatory curriculum and have at least a 2.0 GPA. Regents curriculum includes 4 years of English, 3 each of college preparatory mathematics, natural science, and social sciences, and 2 of a foreign language. The GED is accepted. Music performance students must audition. AP and CLEP credits are accepted. Important factors used in the admissions decision are recommendations by school officials, recommendations by alumni, personality, intangible qualities, parents or siblings attending the school, and leadership record.

Procedure: Freshmen are admitted to all sessions. Applications should be filed by February 1 for fall entry, December 1 for spring entry, and February 1 for summer entry, along with an application fee of $15. KU accepts all in-state residents who apply. Notification is sent on a rolling basis. There are early decision and deferred admissions plans.

Transfer: A total of 1408 transfer students enrolled in 1993–94. For entrance to the College of Liberal Arts and Sciences, transfer students must have at least 24 credit hours earned, have a minimum GPA of 2.5, and have completed English Composition I and II and college algebra. These criteria vary widely according to the schools, some of which may also consider the ACT score and course work. A total of 30 credits out of 124 must be completed at KU.

Visiting: There are regularly scheduled orientations for prospective students, consisting of a summer orientation program that includes a 1-day campus visit. There are guides for informal visits and visitors may sit in on classes and stay overnight at the school. To arrange for a visit, contact the Office of New Student Orientation or the Office of Admissions at (913) 864–3911.

Financial Aid: In 1993–94, 32% of all current freshmen and 34% of continuing students received some form of financial aid. About 25% of freshmen and 33% of continuing students received need-based aid. The average freshman award was $2753. Of that total, scholarships or need-based grants averaged $1081 ($2000 maximum); loans averaged $2594 ($4875 maximum); and work contracts averaged $1094 ($1800 maximum). Forty-two percent of undergraduate students work part-time. Average earnings from campus work for the school year are $2000. The average financial indebtedness of the 1992–93 graduate was $10,484. KU is a member of CSS. The FAFSA is required. The deadline for financial aid applications is March 1.

International Students: There are currently 1992 international students enrolled. They must take the TOEFL, the University of Michigan Language Test, the Comprehensive English Language Test, or the college's own test.

Computers: KU provides computer facilities for student use. The mainframes are an Amdahl 589/300E and a DEC VAX 9210. There are hundreds of terminals around campus in laboratories and at the computer center. Many microcomputers are also available campus-wide. All students may access the system 24 hours a day, 7 days a week. There are no time limits on using the system and no fees.

Graduates: In 1992–93, 3804 bachelor's degrees were awarded. The most popular majors among graduates were journalism (11%), general business (7%), and psychology (6%). Within an average freshman class, 25% graduate in 4 years, 49% in 5 years, and 55% in 6 years. Several hundred companies recruited on campus in

1992–93.
Admissions Contact: Deborah Castrop, Director of Admissions.

WASHBURN UNIVERSITY OF TOPEKA
E-2

Topeka, KS 66621   (913) 231–1010; (800) 332–0291 (in-state)

Full-time: 1309 men, 1848 women	Faculty: 375; IIA, av$
Part-time: 1026 men, 1679 women	Ph.Ds: 80%
Graduate: 362 men, 350 women	Student/Faculty: 12 to 1
Year: semesters, summer session	Tuition: $2642 ($4562)
Application Deadline: July 1	Room & Board: $3160
Freshman Class: n/av	
ACT: 21	NONCOMPETITIVE

Washburn University of Topeka, a public, primarily commuter institution established in 1865, offers programs in liberal arts and sciences, business, nursing, education, and technical and other career-oriented fields. There are 4 undergraduate and 3 graduate schools. In addition to regional accreditation, Washburn has baccalaureate program accreditation with CSWE, NASM, NCATE, and NLN. The 2 libraries contain 300,000 volumes and 100,000 microform items, and subscribe to 1500 periodicals. Computerized library sources and services include interlibrary loans and database searching. Special learning facilities include an art gallery, planetarium, and TV station. The 160-acre campus is in an urban area 60 miles west of Kansas City. Including residence halls, there are 18 buildings on campus.

Student Life: About 95% of undergraduates are from Kansas. Students come from 42 states and 17 foreign countries. Eighty-seven percent are from public schools; 13% from private. The average age of freshmen is 20; all undergraduates, 28. Forty percent drop out by the end of their first year; 50% remain to graduate.

Housing: A total of 170 students can be accommodated in college housing. College-sponsored living facilities include single-sex and coed dormitories, married-student housing, fraternity houses, and sorority houses. On-campus housing is available on a first-come, first-served basis. Priority is given to out-of-town students. Eighty percent of students commute. Alcohol is not permitted. All students may keep cars on campus.

Activities: About 5% of men belong to 1 local and 3 national fraternities; about 5% of women belong to 4 national sororities. There are 75 groups on campus, including art, band, cheerleading, chess, choir, chorus, computers, dance, drama, drill team, drum and bugle corps, ethnic, honors, international, jazz band, literary magazine, marching band, musical theater, newspaper, orchestra, pep band, political, professional, radio and TV, religious, social, social service, student government, and yearbook. Popular campus events include Homecoming and Greek Week.

Sports: There are 5 intercollegiate sports for men and 4 for women, as well as an intramural sports program.

Disabled Students: Ninety-five percent of the campus is accessible to disabled students. The following facilities are available: wheelchair ramps, elevators, special parking, specially equipped rest rooms, special class scheduling, lowered drinking fountains, and lowered telephones.

Services: In addition to many counseling and information services, tutoring is available in most subjects. There also is a reader service for the blind and remedial math and writing.

Campus Safety and Security: Campus safety and security measures include 24-hour foot and vehicle patrol, self defense education, and lighted pathways and sidewalks.

Programs of Study: Washburn awards the B.A., B.S., B.B.A., B.Ed., B.F.A., B.M., B.P.A., B.S.N., and B.S.W. degrees. Associate, master's, and doctoral degrees also are awarded. Bachelor's degrees are awarded in BIOLOGICAL SCIENCE (biology/biological science), BUSINESS (accounting, banking and finance, business administration and management, business economics, and marketing/retailing/merchandising), COMMUNICATIONS AND THE ARTS (communications, dance, dramatic arts, English, French, German, music, and Spanish), COMPUTER AND PHYSICAL SCIENCE (chemistry, computer programming, information sciences and systems, mathematics, and physics), EDUCATION (art, early childhood, elementary, music, and secondary), HEALTH PROFESSIONS (medical laboratory technology and nursing), SOCIAL SCIENCE (anthropology, criminal justice, economics, history, philosophy, political science/government, psychology, public administration, social work, and sociology). Business administration has the largest enrollment.

Required: To graduate, students must complete courses in the humanities, English composition, the natural sciences, and the social sciences. A minimum GPA of 2.0 is required over 124 credit hours, with 30 to 60 credit hours in the major.

Special: Washburn offers internships in numerous departments and study abroad in Holland, Denmark, Japan, and Mexico. Dual and student-designed majors, a general studies degree, credit by examination, nondegree study, and pass/fail options are also available. A 3–2 engineering degree is possible in conjunction with the University

of Kansas and Kansas State University. There is a freshman honors program on campus.

Faculty/Classroom: Sixty percent of faculty are male; 40%, female. All members both teach undergraduates and do research. No introductory courses are taught by graduate students. The average class size in an introductory lecture is 35; in a laboratory, 20; and in a regular course offering, 25.

Admissions: There was 1 National Merit finalist.

Requirements: The ACT is recommended. Applicants should be graduates of an accredited secondary school or have the GED. AP and CLEP credits are accepted.

Procedure: Freshmen are admitted to all sessions. Applications should be filed by July 1 for fall entry, December 1 for spring entry, and May 1 for summer entry. Washburn accepts all in-state residents who apply. Notification is sent on a rolling basis.

Transfer: A total of 627 transfer students enrolled in a recent year. Applicants must meet the same requirements as incoming freshmen. A total of 30 credits out of 124 must be completed at Washburn.

Visiting: There are regularly scheduled orientations for prospective students, consisting of a campus visit program Mondays through Fridays at 9:30 A.M. or 1:30 P.M. that includes a tour, visits with faculty, financial aid information, and the opportunity to have all questions answered. There are guides for informal visits and visitors may sit in on classes and stay overnight at the school. To arrange for a visit, contact Greg Moore at (913) 231–1010 or (800) 332–0291 (in-state).

Financial Aid: In 1993–94, 70% of all students received some form of financial aid. About 40% of all students received need-based aid. Scholarships or need-based grants averaged $735 ($1600 maximum); loans averaged $1800 ($5500 maximum); and work contracts averaged $1800 ($2500 maximum). Seventy percent of undergraduate students work part-time. Average earnings from campus work for the school year are $1800. The average financial indebtedness of the 1992–93 graduate was $6000. The FFS is required. The deadline for financial aid applications is March 15.

International Students: The school actively recruits these students. They must take the TOEFL and achieve a minimum score of 550.

Computers: Washburn provides computer facilities for student use. The mainframes are a Prime 9755 and an IBM AS400. Students in computer classes may access the system during a wide variety of hours. There are no time limits on using the system and no fees.

Graduates: In a recent year, 548 bachelor's degrees were awarded. The most popular majors among graduates were business (28%), education (10%), and nursing (10%). Within an average freshman class, 20% graduate in 4 years, 30% in 5 years, and 45% in 6 years.

Admissions Contact: Greg Gomez III, Director of Admissions.

WICHITA STATE UNIVERSITY
D-3

Wichita, KS 67260   (316) 689–3085; (800) 362–2594 (out-of-state)

Full-time: 3246 men, 3310 women	Faculty: 467; IIA, -$
Part-time: 2534 men, 2925 women	Ph.Ds: 87%
Graduate: 1266 men, 1609 women	Student/Faculty: 14 to 1
Year: semesters, summer session	Tuition: $1995 ($6501)
Application Deadline: open	Room & Board: $3073
Freshman Class: 2901 applied, 2236 accepted, 1200 enrolled	
ACT: 21	NONCOMPETITIVE

Wichita State University, established in 1895, is a public, coeducational institution offering programs in the liberal arts and sciences, business, engineering, education, and health professions. There are 7 undergraduate schools and one graduate school. In addition to regional accreditation, WSU has baccalaureate program accreditation with AACSB, ABET, APTA, CAHEA, CSWE, NASM, NCATE, and NLN. The library contains 952,203 volumes, 931,936 microform items, and 18,480 audiovisual forms, and subscribes to 6340 periodicals. Computerized library sources and services include the card catalog, interlibrary loans, and database searching. Special learning facilities include a learning resource center, TV station, and an electronic classroom, telecourses, the National Institute for Aviation Research, and a museum of art. The 330-acre campus is in an urban area in the metropolitan Wichita area. Including residence halls, there are 60 buildings on campus.

Student Life: About 86% of undergraduates are from Kansas. Students come from 49 states, 87 foreign countries, and Canada. Seventy-seven percent are white; 11% foreign nationals. The average age of freshmen is 19; all undergraduates, 28.7.

Housing: A total of 600 students can be accommodated in college housing. College-sponsored living facilities include dormitories, fraternity houses, and sorority houses. On-campus housing is available on a first-come, first-served basis. Ninety-six percent of students commute. Alcohol is not permitted. All students may keep cars on campus.

Activities: There are 12 national fraternities and 8 national sororities. There are 70 groups on campus, including art, band, cheerleading, chess, choir, chorus, computers, dance, drama, ethnic, film, gay, honors, international, jazz band, musical theater, newspaper, opera, or-

chestra, pep band, photography, political, professional, radio and TV, religious, social, student government, and symphony. Popular campus events include Hippodrome, International Week, Renaissance Festival, and Shocktoberest.

Sports: There are 7 intercollegiate sports for men and 8 for women, and 16 intramural sports for men and 16 for women. Athletic and recreation facilities include an arena, 2 stadiums, and a recreation and sports center.

Disabled Students: The following facilities are available: wheelchair ramps, elevators, special parking, specially equipped rest rooms, special class scheduling, lowered drinking fountains, lowered telephones, wheelchairs, and braille typewriters. Interpreters for the hearing impaired, and notetaking and typing services are also offered.

Services: In addition to many counseling and information services, tutoring is available in most subjects. There is a reader service for the blind, and remedial math, reading, and writing.

Campus Safety and Security: Campus safety and security measures include 24-hour foot and vehicle patrol, self-defense education, escort service, and shuttle buses. In addition, there are informal discussions, pamphlets, posters, films, emergency telephones, and lighted pathways and sidewalks.

Programs of Study: WSU awards the B.A., B.S., B.A.E., B.B.A., B.F.A., B.G.S., B.H.S., B.M., B.M.E., B.S.A.E., B.S.E.E., B.S.I.E., B.S.M.E., and B.S.N. degrees. Associate, master's, and doctoral degrees also are awarded. Bachelor's degrees are awarded in BIOLOGICAL SCIENCE (biology/biological science), BUSINESS (accounting, banking and finance, business administration and management, international business management, marketing/retailing/merchandising, and personnel management), COMMUNICATIONS AND THE ARTS (communications, dance, dramatic arts, English, fine arts, French, German, Latin, music, and Spanish), COMPUTER AND PHYSICAL SCIENCE (chemistry, computer programming, computer science, geology, mathematics, and physics), EDUCATION (art, early childhood, elementary, guidance, industrial arts, music, science, secondary, and special), ENGINEERING AND ENVIRONMENTAL DESIGN (aeronautical engineering, electrical/electronics engineering, engineering, industrial engineering, and mechanical engineering), HEALTH PROFESSIONS (medical laboratory technology, nursing, physical therapy, predentistry, premedicine, and speech pathology/audiology), SOCIAL SCIENCE (anthropology, criminal justice, economics, history, philosophy, political science/government, prelaw, psychology, public administration, social work, sociology, and urban studies). Aerospace engineering, engineering, business, chemistry, and applied mathematics are the strongest academically. Aerospace engineering, engineering, business, education, and health professions have the largest enrollments.

Required: To graduate, students need at least 124 credit hours, with a GPA of 2.0 to 2.5, depending on the major. Specific distribution requirements as well as department requirements must also be met.

Special: WSU offers co-op programs, internships, study abroad, work-study programs, and a Washington semester. Dual and student-designed majors, a general studies degree, credit by examination, nondegree study, and pass/fail options are also available. There is a freshman honors program on campus, as well as 38 national honor societies.

Faculty/Classroom: Seventy percent of faculty are male; 30%, female.

Admissions: About 77% of the 1993–94 applicants were accepted. There were 10 National Merit finalists.

Requirements: Applicants under 21 years of age who are Kansas residents must be graduates of an accredited secondary school or have the GED. Out-of-state applicants must have a 2.0 GPA, or at least a 21 ACT composite score, or rank in the upper half of their graduating class. AP and CLEP credits are accepted.

Procedure: Freshmen are admitted to all sessions. Application deadlines are open. The college accepts all in-state residents who apply. Notification is sent on a rolling basis. There are early admissions and deferred admissions plans.

Transfer: About 913 transfer students enrolled in 1993–94. Applicants must have a minimum GPA of 2.0 to 2.5, depending on the WSU college they wish to enter. A total of 30 credits out of 124 must be completed at WSU.

Visiting: There are regularly scheduled orientations for prospective students. There are guides for informal visits and visitors may sit in on classes and stay overnight at the school. To arrange for a visit, contact the Admissions Office at (316) 689–3085 or (800) 362–2594.

Financial Aid: In 1993–94, 24% of all current freshmen and 48% of continuing students received some form of financial aid. About 26% of freshmen and 51% of continuing students received need-based aid. The average freshman award was $842. Of that total, scholarships or need-based grants averaged $704 ($1500 maximum); loans averaged $1189 ($2625 maximum); and work contracts averaged $770 ($2200 maximum). Five percent of undergraduate students work part-time. Average earnings from campus work for the school year are $704. The average financial indebtedness of the 1992–93 graduate was $7371. The FFS is preferred. The deadline for financial aid applications is March 15.

International Students: There are currently 1373 international students enrolled. The school actively recruits these students. They must take the TOEFL and achieve a minimum score of 530.

Computers: The college provides computer facilities for student use. The mainframes are an IBM ES 9121/440 and a DEC VAX/4000. Computing laboratories are located throughout the campus. Students have access as needed and required by academic programs and courses. It may be used 24 hours a day. Students may access the system based on allocated funds. There are no fees.

Graduates: In 1992–93, 1569 bachelor's degrees were awarded. Some 174 companies recruited on campus in 1992–93.

Admissions Contact: Rita Abenh, Director of Admissions.

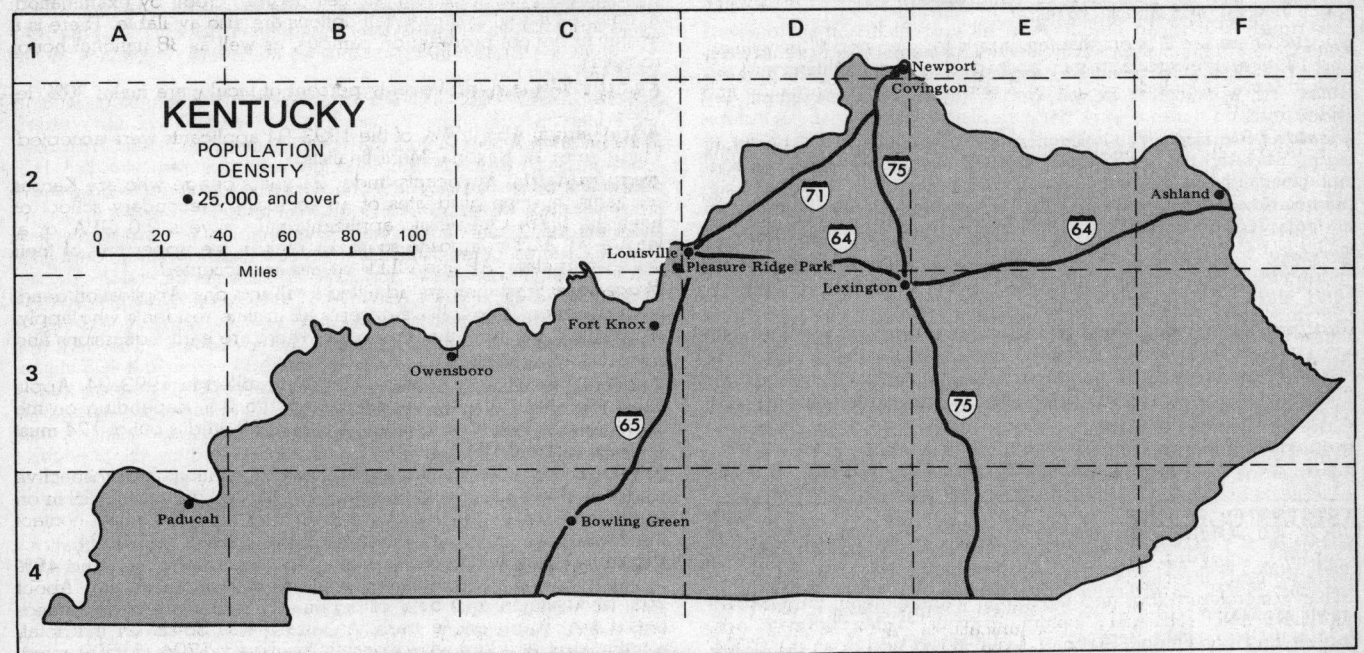

KENTUCKY
POPULATION
DENSITY
● 25,000 and over

0   20   40   60   80   100
Miles

ALICE LLOYD COLLEGE

E-4

Pippa Passes, KY 41844

(606) 368–2101, ext. 4404

Full-time: 267 men, 328 women
Part-time: 11 men, 11 women
Graduate: none
Year: semesters
Application Deadline: open
Freshman Class: 1170 applied, 611 accepted, 263 enrolled
ACT: 21

Faculty: 26; III, --$
Ph.D.s: 65%
Student/Faculty: 23 to 1
Tuition: $270
Room & Board: $2480

VERY COMPETITIVE

Alice Lloyd College, founded in 1923, is a private, liberal arts facility emphasizing Christian values and serving the Appalachian community. In addition to regional accreditation, ALC has baccalaureate program accreditation with NCATE. The library contains 62,000 volumes, 1500 microform items, and 300 audiovisual forms, and subscribes to 300 periodicals. Special learning facilities include a learning resource center, an art gallery, a radio station, and a performing arts center. The 225-acre campus is in a rural area 150 miles east of Lexington. Including residence halls, there are 35 buildings on campus.

Student Life: About 80% of undergraduates are from Kentucky. Students come from 6 states. Ninety-nine percent are from public schools; 1% from private. All are white. Most are Protestant. The average age of freshmen is 19; all undergraduates, 25. Forty percent drop out by the end of their first year; 35% remain to graduate.

Housing: A total of 426 students can be accommodated in college housing. College-sponsored living facilities include single-sex dormitories. On-campus housing is guaranteed for all 4 years. Seventy-five percent of students live on campus; of those, 10% remain on campus on weekends. Alcohol is not permitted. All students may keep cars on campus.

Activities: There are no fraternities or sororities on campus. There are several groups on campus, including cheerleading, chess, choir, drama, newspaper, pep band, photography, radio and TV, religious, social, student government, and yearbook. Popular campus events include Religious Emphasis Week, Alcohol Awareness Week, and Appalachia Day.

Sports: There are 5 intercollegiate sports each for men and women, and 11 intramural sports each for men and women. Athletic and recreation facilities include an indoor pool, weight rooms, a 1500-seat gymnasium, recreation areas, 2 tennis courts, and a baseball/athletic field.

Disabled Students: Seventy-five percent of the campus is accessible to disabled students. The following facilities are available: wheelchair ramps, elevators, special parking, and specially equipped rest rooms.

Services: In addition to many counseling and information services, tutoring is available in every subject. There is a reader service for the blind, and remedial math, reading, and writing.

Campus Safety and Security: Campus safety and security measures include security officers who are on duty 24 hours a day.

Programs of Study: ALC awards the B.A. and B.S. degrees. Associate degrees are also awarded. Bachelor's degrees are awarded in BIOLOGICAL SCIENCE (biology/biological science), BUSINESS (accounting and business administration and management), COMMUNICATIONS AND THE ARTS (English), COMPUTER AND PHYSICAL SCIENCE (mathematics), EDUCATION (elementary, middle school, physical, science, secondary, and social studies), ENGINEERING AND ENVIRONMENTAL DESIGN (preengineering), HEALTH PROFESSIONS (prepharmacy), SOCIAL SCIENCE (history). Biology, mathematics/physical science, and education are the strongest academically. Elementary education has the largest enrollment.

Required: To graduate, students must complete a work-study requirement extending through each semester and a 49-semester hour general education requirement, including physical education, composition, philosophy, and speech. A total of 128 credit hours is required.

Special: Special arrangements include a 3–2 engineering degree with the Universities of Kentucky, Louisville, and West Virginia. Credit by examination and limited work-study are possible. There is one national honor society on campus, Phi Beta Kappa.

Faculty/Classroom: Sixty percent of faculty are male; 40%, female. All teach undergraduates. The average class size in an introductory lecture is 40; in a laboratory, 10; and in a regular course offering, 17.

Admissions: About 52% of the 1993–94 applicants were accepted. The ACT scores for the 1993–94 freshman class were as follows: 29% below 21, 31% between 21 and 23, 19% between 24 and 26, 12% between 27 and 28, and 10% above 28. About 30% of the current freshmen were in the top fifth of their class; 75% were in the top two fifths.

Requirements: ALC requires applicants to be in the upper 60% of their class. A minimum GPA of 2.3 is required. Applicants must be graduates of an accredited secondary school or have a GED, having successfully completed 13 academic credits, including 4 in English and 3 each in mathematics, science, and social studies. The SAT I or the ACT is required. AP and CLEP credits are accepted. Important factors used in the admissions decision are leadership record, recommendations by school officials, evidence of special talent, and extracurricular activities record.

Procedure: Freshmen are admitted fall and spring. Entrance exams should be taken in the fall of the senior year. Application deadlines are open. Notification is sent on a rolling basis. There is a deferred admissions plan.

Transfer: About 35 transfer students enrolled in an earlier year. Transfer students must have a minimum 2.0 GPA, 2.5 for some majors, and be in good standing at their previous school. A total of 30 credits out of 128 must be completed at ALC.

Visiting: There are regularly scheduled orientations for prospective students. There are guides for informal visits and visitors may sit in on classes and stay overnight at the school. To arrange for a visit, contact Bill Melton, Director of Admissions at (606) 368–2101.

Financial Aid: In an earlier year, all current freshmen received some form of financial aid. Scholarships or need-based grants averaged $5500 ($7086 maximum); loans averaged $200 ($2000 maximum); and work contracts averaged $1072 ($1608 maximum). All undergraduate students work part-time. The average financial indebtedness of the 1992–93 graduate was $800. ALC is a member of CSS. The FAF and FAFSA are required. The deadline for financial aid applications is February 15.

International Students: The school actively recruits international students. They must take the TOEFL and achieve a minimum score of 500.

Computers: The college provides computer facilities for student use. There are 25 IBM and Apple PCs available in the computer center. Only those who are employed in offices on work-study program may access the system. There are no fees.

Graduates: In an earlier year, 87 bachelor's degrees were awarded. Some 3 companies recruited on campus that year. In the 1992 graduating class, 25% of the men and 30% of the women were enrolled in graduate school within 6 months of graduation; 75% of the men and 70% of the women had found employment.

Admissions Contact: Bill Melton, Director of Admissions.

ASBURY COLLEGE   D-3

Wilmore, KY 40390–1198   (606) 858–3511; (800) 888–1818

Full-time: 481 men, 630 women	Faculty: 69; IIB, --$
Part-time: 23 men, 23 women	Ph.D.s: 58%
Graduate: none	Student/Faculty: 16 to 1
Year: semesters, summer session	Tuition: $8445
Application Deadline: August 1	Room & Board: $2660

Freshman Class: 937 applied, 417 accepted, 321 enrolled

ACT: 24   **VERY COMPETITIVE**

Asbury College, founded in 1890, is an independent liberal arts institution emphasizing Wesleyan Christian orthodoxy. In addition to regional accreditation, Asbury has baccalaureate program accreditation with NASM. The library contains 138,228 volumes, 592 microform items, and 6901 audiovisual forms, and subscribes to 989 periodicals. Computerized library sources and services include interlibrary loans and database searching. Special learning facilities include a learning resource center, art gallery, planetarium, radio station, TV station, and media and fine arts centers. The 400-acre campus is in a rural area 20 miles south of Lexington. Including residence halls, there are 25 buildings on campus.

Student Life: About 83% of undergraduates are from out-of-state. Students come from 45 states, 14 foreign countries, and Canada. Eighty percent are from public schools; 20% from private. Most are Protestant. The average age of freshmen is 18; all undergraduates, 21. Fifteen percent drop out by the end of their first year; 65% remain to graduate.

Housing: A total of 1000 students can be accommodated in college housing. College-sponsored living facilities include single-sex dormitories, on-campus apartments, off-campus apartments, and married-student housing. On-campus housing is guaranteed for all 4 years. Seventy-eight percent of students live on campus; of those, 83% remain on campus on weekends. Alcohol is not permitted. Upperclassmen may keep cars on campus.

Activities: There are no fraternities or sororities on campus. There are a number of groups and organizations on campus, including art, band, choir, chorus, drama, jazz band, musical theater, newspaper, radio and TV, religious, student government, and yearbook.

Sports: There are 6 intercollegiate sports for men and 6 for women, and 6 intramural sports for men and 6 for women. Athletic and recreation facilities include a gymnasium, athletic fields, a track, tennis courts, an indoor swimming pool, indoor/outdoor basketball courts, a golf course, and a 1522-seat auditorium.

Disabled Students: Ten percent of the campus is accessible to disabled students. The following facilities are available: wheelchair ramps, elevators, and special class scheduling.

Programs of Study: Asbury awards the B.A. and B.S.Ed. degrees. Bachelor's degrees are awarded in BIOLOGICAL SCIENCE (biology/biological science), BUSINESS (accounting, business administration and management, and recreation and leisure services), COMMUNICATIONS AND THE ARTS (art, broadcasting, communications, English, film arts, French, journalism, music, Spanish, and speech/debate/rhetoric), COMPUTER AND PHYSICAL SCIENCE (applied mathematics, chemistry, computer science, mathematics, and physical sciences), EDUCATION (elementary, music, physical, and secondary), HEALTH PROFESSIONS (medical laboratory technology and premedicine), SOCIAL SCIENCE (biblical languages, biblical studies, history, human services, ministries, philosophy, pre-

law, psychology, social work, and sociology). Bible studies, business, and Christian ministries have the largest enrollments.

Required: To graduate, students must complete 124 to 128 semester hours, including liberal arts requirements, 8 hours of religion, and 4 hours of physical education, with a minimum GPA of 2.0 for the B.A. or 2.5 for the B.S.Ed. Students must demonstrate proficiency in English and mathematics.

Special: Asbury offers a 3–1 program in medical technology with an accredited hospital and a 3–3 program in nursing with Case Western Reserve. High school juniors may participate in a 'Credits in Escrow' program. Study abroad in England, a Washington semester, B.A.-B.S. degrees in education, dual majors, work-study, and nondegree study are available. There are credit/no credit options for seniors.

Admissions: About 45% of the 1993–94 applicants were accepted. The ACT scores for the 1993–94 freshman class were as follows: 20% below 21, 34% between 21 and 23, 31% between 24 and 26, 8% between 27 and 28, and 7% above 28. There were 4 National Merit finalists and 6 semifinalists.

Requirements: A minimum GPA of 2.3 is required. The SAT I or ACT is required, with a minimum score of 425 verbal and 405 mathematics on the SAT I or 20 on the ACT. Applicants must be graduates of an accredited secondary school. The GED is accepted. Applicants should complete 15 high school academic credits, including 4 units of English, 3 each of mathematics and social studies, and 2 each of science and a foreign language. Incoming students must take proficiency examinations in mathematics and English. AP and CLEP credits are accepted.

Procedure: Freshmen are admitted to all sessions. Applications should be filed by August 1 for fall entry, December 1 for spring entry, and April 1 for summer entry, along with an application fee of $25. Notification is sent on a rolling basis. There are early admissions and deferred admissions plans. A waiting list is an active part of the admissions procedure, with about 10% of applicants on the list.

Transfer: A total of 84 transfer students enrolled in 1993–94. Transfer applicants should have completed a minimum of 12 quarter hours or 8 semester hours, have an overall minimum GPA of 2.0, and be in good standing at the previous institution attended.

Visiting: There are guides for informal visits and visitors may sit in on classes and stay overnight at the school. To arrange for a visit, contact the Admissions Office at (606) 858–3511, ext. 2142.

Financial Aid: In an earlier year, 80% of all current freshmen received some form of financial aid. Scholarships or need-based grants averaged $600; loans averaged $1200; and work contracts averaged $600. Asbury is a member of CSS. The FAF is required. The deadline for financial aid applications is May 1.

International Students: There are currently 30 international students enrolled. They must take the TOEFL and achieve a minimum score of 550.

Computers: The college provides computer facilities for student use. The mainframes are 2 HP 3000s. There are also 150 PCs available in the Microcomputer Resource Center. The science center has an AT&T 3B2–600 computer with a local area network connecting most of the campus, a large number of PCs for use as terminals or standalones, and monitors for in-class computer display. All students may access the system. There are no time limits on using the system and no fees.

Admissions Contact: Stan F. Wiggam, Dean of Admissions.

BELLARMINE COLLEGE   D-2

Louisville, KY 40205   (502) 452–8131; (800) 274–4723 (out-of-state)

Full-time: 489 men, 709 women	Faculty: 85; IIA, --$
Part-time: 178 men, 427 women	Ph.D.s: 80%
Graduate: 201 men, 334 women	Student/Faculty: 14 to 1
Year: semesters, summer session	Tuition: $8172
Application Deadline: August 15	Room & Board: $2660

Freshman Class: 808 applied, 711 accepted, 310 enrolled

SAT I Verbal/Math: 480/530   **ACT: 23**   **COMPETITIVE**

Bellarmine College, founded in 1950, is a private liberal arts institution affiliated with the Roman Catholic Church. There are 3 undergraduate and 3 graduate schools. In addition to regional accreditation, Bellarmine has baccalaureate program accreditation with NLN. The library contains 115,730 volumes, 521,953 microform items, and 4478 audiovisual forms, and subscribes to 613 periodicals. Computerized library sources and services include the card catalog, interlibrary loans, and database searching. Special learning facilities include an art gallery. The 120-acre campus is in a suburban area in Louisville. Including residence halls, there are 15 buildings on campus.

Student Life: About 80% of undergraduates are from Kentucky. Students come from 21 states, 18 foreign countries, and Canada. Thirty-two percent are from public schools; 68% from private. Ninety-four percent are white. Sixty-five percent are Catholic; 30% Protestant. The average age of freshmen is 18.5; all undergraduates, 22. Twenty-

five percent drop out by the end of their first year; 65% remain to graduate.

Housing: A total of 450 students can be accommodated in college housing. College-sponsored living facilities include single-sex and coed dormitories. On-campus housing is guaranteed for the freshman and sophomore years only and is available on a first-come, first-served basis. Priority is given to out-of-town students. Sixty-seven percent of students commute. All students may keep cars on campus.

Activities: There are 2 national fraternities. There are no sororities on campus. There are 40 groups on campus, including art, cheerleading, choir, chorale, chorus, computers, dance, drama, ethnic, honors, international, jazz band, literary magazine, newspaper, pep band, photography, political, professional, religious, social, social service, student government, and yearbook. Popular campus events include Homecoming, Welcome Week, Kentucky Derby Week, Hillside Concerts, Midnight Breakfast, Student-Faculty Talent Show, Halloween, Ball on Bell of Louisville, and Pioneer Dance.

Sports: Athletic and recreation facilities include a basketball arena, weight rooms, indoor and outdoor tennis courts, a par-3 golf course, exercise and aerobics rooms in residence halls, a track, softball and baseball fields, and sand volleyball courts.

Disabled Students: The entire campus is accessible to disabled students. The following facilities are available: wheelchair ramps, elevators, special parking, specially equipped rest rooms, lowered drinking fountains, and lowered telephones.

Services: In addition to many counseling and information services, tutoring is available in most subjects.

Campus Safety and Security: Campus safety and security measures include 24-hour foot and vehicle patrol, self-defense education, informal discussions, and pamphlets, posters, and films. In addition, there are lighted pathways and sidewalks, foot and vehicle patrols, and security cameras in residence halls and in the parking lot.

Programs of Study: Bellarmine awards the B.A. and B.S. degrees. Master's degrees also are awarded. Bachelor's degrees are awarded in BIOLOGICAL SCIENCE (biology/biological science), BUSINESS (accounting and business administration and management), COMMUNICATIONS AND THE ARTS (communications, English, fine arts, and music), COMPUTER AND PHYSICAL SCIENCE (actuarial science, chemistry, computer science, and mathematics), EDUCATION (elementary, middle school, secondary, and special), ENGINEERING AND ENVIRONMENTAL DESIGN (computer engineering and preengineering), HEALTH PROFESSIONS (nursing, predentistry, premedicine, prepharmacy, and preveterinary science), SOCIAL SCIENCE (economics, history, philosophy, political science/government, prelaw, psychology, sociology, and theological studies). Premedicine, accounting, business, education, psychology, and philosophy are the strongest academically. Accounting, business, and nursing have the largest enrollments.

Required: In order to graduate, students must complete a total of 126 credit hours with a minimum GPA of 2.0. Between 36 and 45 hours are required in the major. All students must take the senior seminar and fulfill 60 core requirements, including English, philosophy, theology, mathematics, social sciences, and fine arts. Other required courses include art history, music appreciation, ethics, Western civilization, and world literature.

Special: Cross-registration may be arranged through Kentuckiana Metroversity, a consortium of colleges in Kentucky and southern Indiana. Bellarmine also offers study abroad in more than 40 countries, internships in all majors, a liberal studies degree, credit for life experience, pass/fail options during the junior and senior years, and a marine biology program in the Bahamas. There is a freshman honors program on campus, as well as one national honor society.

Faculty/Classroom: Fifty-nine percent of faculty are male; 41%, female. Eighty-eight percent teach undergraduates. No introductory courses are taught by graduate students. The average class size in an introductory lecture is 30; in a laboratory, 22; and in a regular course offering, 18.

Admissions: About 88% of the 1993–94 applicants were accepted. The SAT scores for the 1993–94 freshman class were as follows: Verbal—59% below 500, 29% between 500 and 599, and 12% between 600 and 700; Math—37% below 500, 42% between 500 and 599, 18% between 600 and 700, and 3% above 700. The ACT scores were 25% below 21, 28% between 21 and 23, 23% between 24 and 26, 13% between 27 and 28, and 11% above 28. About 60% of the current freshmen were in the top fifth of their class; 80% were in the top two fifths.

Requirements: Bellarmine requires applicants to be in the upper 50% of their class. A minimum GPA of 2.5 is required. The SAT I or ACT is required, with a minimum composite score of 900 on the SAT I, or a minimum composite score of 21 on the ACT. Applicants should be in the upper 50% of their high school class, with a minimum GPA of 2.5. The GED is accepted. High school courses should include 4 years of English, 3 of mathematics, and 2 each of science and social studies. An essay is required. AP and CLEP credits are accepted. Important factors used in the admissions decision are advanced place-

ment or honor courses, recommendations by school officials, personality, intangible qualities, extracurricular activities record, and leadership record.

Procedure: Freshmen are admitted to all sessions. Entrance exams should be taken by February of the senior year. Applications should be filed by August 15 for fall entry, December 15 for spring entry, and May 15 for summer entry, along with an application fee of $20. Notification is sent on a rolling basis. There are early admissions and deferred admissions plans.

Transfer: About 185 transfer students enrolled in 1993–94. Applicants must have a minimum college GPA of 2.0 and submit transcripts from all postsecondary schools attended. A total of 36 credits out of 126 must be completed at Bellarmine.

Visiting: There are regularly scheduled orientations for prospective students, including an admissions and financial aid session, class observation and attendance, a campus tour, and participation in a student panel. There are guides for informal visits and visitors may sit in on classes and stay overnight at the school. To arrange for a visit, contact the Office of Admissions at (800) 274–4723 (out-of-state) or (502) 452–8131.

Financial Aid: In 1993–94, 90% of all current freshmen and 77% of continuing students received some form of financial aid. About 65% of freshmen and 58% of continuing students received need-based aid. The average freshman award was $5194. Of that total, scholarships or need-based grants averaged $3620 ($8072 maximum); loans averaged $1650 ($4100 maximum); and work contracts averaged $2200 ($2250 maximum). Thirteen percent of undergraduate students work part-time. Average earnings from campus work for the school year are $1950. The average financial indebtedness of the 1992–93 graduate was $4000. Bellarmine is a member of CSS. The FAFSA financial statement is required. The deadline for financial aid applications is May 1.

International Students: There are currently 16 international students enrolled. They must take the TOEFL and achieve a minimum score of 500.

Computers: The college provides computer facilities for student use. All students may access the system. There are no time limits on using the system and no fees.

Graduates: In 1992–93, 265 bachelor's degrees were awarded. The most popular majors among graduates were business administration (20%), nursing (18%), and accounting (14%). Within an average freshman class, 1% graduate in 3 years, 62% in 4 years, 68% in 5 years, and 70% in 6 years. Some 55 companies recruited on campus in 1992–93. In the 1992 graduating class, 11% of the men and 9% of the women were enrolled in graduate school within 6 months of graduation; 88% of the men and 90% of the women had found employment.

Admissions Contact: R. Edwin Wilkes, Dean of Admissions.

BEREA COLLEGE
Berea, KY 40404

D-3

(606) 986–9341, ext. 5083
(800) 326–5948 (out-of-state)

Full-time: 690 men, 850 women	Faculty: 112; IIB, +$
Part-time: 16 men, 35 women	Ph.D.s: 81%
Graduate: none	Student/Faculty: 14 to 1
Year: 4-1-4, summer session	Tuition: see profile
Application Deadline: open	Room & Board: $2700
Freshman Class: 1836 applied, 599 accepted, 455 enrolled	
SAT I Verbal/Math: 465/514	ACT: 22 VERY COMPETITIVE +

Berea College, founded in 1855, is a private, coeducational liberal arts institution with a nonsectarian Christian focus. As part of the educational program, each student is expected to perform some of the labor required in maintaining the institution while carrying a normal academic load. Each student is credited with a labor grant of $2500, toward the $9600 cost of education, for participation in the student labor program. Any portion of the $9600 cost not covered by federal or state grants will be covered by a college scholarship. Fees are $183. In addition to regional accreditation, Berea has baccalaureate program accreditation with ADA, NCATE, and NLN. The 3 libraries contain 288,116 volumes, 83,450 microform items, and 3832 audiovisual forms, and subscribe to 1583 periodicals. Computerized library sources and services include the card catalog, interlibrary loans, and database searching. Special learning facilities include an art gallery, planetarium, Appalachian museum, and geology museum. The 140-acre campus is in a small town 40 miles south of Lexington. Including residence halls, there are 60 buildings on campus.

Student Life: About 52% of undergraduates are from out-of-state, mostly the South. Students come from 38 states and 52 foreign countries. Ninety-three percent are from public schools; 4% from private. Eighty-three percent are white. The average age of freshmen is 18; all undergraduates, 20. Twenty-three percent drop out by the end of their first year; 53% remain to graduate.

Housing: A total of 1327 students can be accommodated in college housing. College-sponsored living facilities include single-sex dormitories and married-student housing. On-campus housing is guaranteed for all 4 years. Eighty-three percent of students live on campus. Alcohol is not permitted. Only students with extenuating circumstances are permitted to keep cars on campus.

Activities: There are no fraternities or sororities on campus. There are 86 groups on campus, including band, cheerleading, choir, chorus, dance, drama, ethnic, honors, international, jazz band, literary magazine, newspaper, orchestra, religious, social, social service, student government, and yearbook. Popular campus events include Mountain Day and Labor Day.

Sports: There are 8 intercollegiate sports for men and 7 for women, and 6 intramural sports for men and 8 for women. Athletic and recreation facilities include 2 gymnasiums, an indoor swimming pool, 4 racquetball and 14 tennis courts, an all-weather track, and playing fields.

Disabled Students: The following facilities are available: wheelchair ramps, elevators, special parking, specially equipped rest rooms, special class scheduling, and lowered drinking fountains.

Services: In addition to many counseling and information services, there is a reader service for the blind, and remedial math, reading, and writing. The Center for Effective Communication offers individual consultation in writing, reading, listening, speaking, learning strategies and styles, and study skills.

Campus Safety and Security: Campus safety and security measures include 24-hour foot and vehicle patrol, informal discussions, pamphlets, posters, and films, and lighted pathways and sidewalks.

Programs of Study: Berea awards the B.A. and B.S. degrees. Bachelor's degrees are awarded in AGRICULTURE (agriculture), BIOLOGICAL SCIENCE (biology/biological science), BUSINESS (business administration and management and hotel/motel and restaurant management), COMMUNICATIONS AND THE ARTS (classical languages, English, French, German, music, Spanish, and theater design), COMPUTER AND PHYSICAL SCIENCE (chemistry, mathematics, and physics), EDUCATION (art, early childhood, elementary, foreign languages, home economics, industrial arts, middle school, music, physical, and secondary), HEALTH PROFESSIONS (nursing), SOCIAL SCIENCE (dietetics, economics, history, philosophy, political science/government, psychology, religion, and sociology). Business administration has the largest enrollment.

Required: To graduate, students must complete courses in physical education, health, quantitative reasoning, and natural and social sciences. One short-term (January) course for each full academic year in residence must be taken, as must a 17-course general education program. In all, students must complete 33 courses, including 8 to 12 courses in the major, with a minimum GPA of 2.0. Nursing majors must complete 35 courses.

Special: Students may study abroad in Italy, Austria, Spain, France, and Germany. Internships, work-study programs, independent majors, and dual and student-designed majors are available. A 3–2 engineering degree is offered with Washington University. All students participate in an on-campus work program 10 to 15 hours per week. There are 14 national honor societies on campus.

Faculty/Classroom: Sixty-two percent of faculty are male; 38%, female. All teach undergraduates and do research. The average class size in an introductory lecture is 25; in a laboratory, 20; and in a regular course offering, 20.

Admissions: About 33% of the 1993–94 applicants were accepted. The SAT scores for the 1993–94 freshman class were as follows: Verbal—63% below 500, 29% between 500 and 599, and 8% between 600 and 700; Math—43% below 500, 34% between 500 and 599, 21% between 600 and 700, and 2% above 700. The ACT scores were 30% below 21, 53% between 21 and 25, and 17% between 26 and 36. About 53% of the current freshmen were in the top fifth of their class; 79% were in the top two fifths.

Requirements: Berea requires applicants to be in the upper 60% of their class. The ACT or SAT I is required. Applicants should be graduates of an accredited secondary school. The GED is accepted. Financial need is a requirement for admission. Berea recommends that applicants present as part of their high school record 4 units in English, 3 in mathematics, and 2 each in science and social studies. Work in a foreign language is highly desirable. AP and CLEP credits are accepted. Important factors used in the admissions decision are ability to finance college education, leadership record, geographic diversity, personality, intangible qualities, and advanced placement or honor courses.

Procedure: Freshmen are admitted fall and spring. Entrance exams should be taken late in the junior year or early in the senior year. Application deadlines are open. The application fee is $5. Notification is sent on a rolling basis.

Transfer: A total of 53 transfer students enrolled in 1993–94. Applicants must be in good standing at the last college attended and have a minimum GPA of 2.0. A total of 8 of the last 11 courses out of 33 to 35 must be completed at Berea.

Visiting: There are regularly scheduled orientations for prospective students. Students arrive several days before classes begin and meet with advisors and administrators to become familiar with the college program. There are guides for informal visits and visitors may sit in on classes and stay overnight at the school. To arrange for a visit, contact the Admissions Office at (606) 986–9341, ext. 5083, or (800) 326–5948.

Financial Aid: In 1993–94, all students received some form of financial aid, and all students received need-based aid. The average freshman award was $14,151. Of that total, scholarships or need-based grants averaged $13,465 ($14,383 maximum); loans averaged $325 ($500 maximum); and work contracts averaged $650 (maximum). All students work part-time. Average earnings from campus work for the school year are $965. The FAFSA is required.

International Students: There are currently 104 international students enrolled. They must take the TOEFL and achieve a minimum score of 500.

Computers: The college provides computer facilities for student use. The mainframe is a Prime 6150. There are 166 microcomputers for student use located in the computer laboratory, in residence halls, and in various academic buildings. A networking system provides on-line access as well. All students may access the system 24 hours a day, 7 days a week. There are no time limits on using the system and no fees.

Graduates: In 1992–93, 307 bachelor's degrees were awarded. The most popular majors among graduates were business administration (17%), elementary education (7%), and English (7%). Within an average freshman class, 1% graduate in 3 years, 31% in 4 years, 52% in 5 years, and 53% in 6 years. Some 35 companies recruited on campus in a recent year.

Admissions Contact: John Cook, Director of Admissions.

BRESCIA COLLEGE
Owensboro, KY 42301

B-3

Full-time: 168 men, 284 women	(502) 686–4241; (800) 264–1234
Part-time: 82 men, 167 women	**Faculty:** 41; IIB, --$
Graduate: none	**Ph.D.s:** 34%
Year: semesters, summer session	**Student/Faculty:** 11 to 1
Application Deadline: open	**Tuition:** $6700
Freshman Class: 307 applied, 260 accepted, 99 enrolled	**Room & Board:** $3100
SAT I or ACT: required	**COMPETITIVE**

Brescia College, founded in 1925 as a women's junior college, became a 4-year, coeducational liberal arts institution in 1950. It is a private school affiliated with the Roman Catholic Church. The library contains 116,000 volumes and 200,000 microform items, and subscribes to 500 periodicals. Computerized library sources and services include the card catalog and interlibrary loans. Special learning facilities include an art gallery. The 6-acre campus is in an urban area 100 miles west of Louisville. Including residence halls, there are 13 buildings on campus.

Student Life: About 76% of undergraduates are from Kentucky. Students come from 4 foreign countries and Canada. Ninety-four percent are white. Sixty percent are Catholic; 40% Protestant. The average age of freshmen is 23. Thirty-three percent drop out by the end of their first year; 33% remain to graduate.

Housing: A total of 170 students can be accommodated in college housing. College-sponsored living facilities include single-sex dormitories. Seventy-nine percent of students commute. Alcohol is not permitted. All students may keep cars on campus.

Activities: There are no fraternities or sororities on campus. There are many groups and organizations on campus, including cheerleading, choir, chorus, honors, international, literary magazine, professional, religious, social service, student government, and yearbook. Popular campus events include Family Weekend.

Sports: Athletic and recreation facilities include tennis courts, a gymnasium, and a weight room.

Disabled Students: Ninety percent of the campus is accessible to disabled students. The following facilities are available: wheelchair ramps, elevators, special parking, specially equipped rest rooms, special class scheduling, lowered drinking fountains, and lowered telephones.

Services: Remedial math, reading, and writing is available.

Campus Safety and Security: Campus safety and security measures include escort service, informal discussions, emergency telephones, lighted pathways and sidewalks, and night security.

Programs of Study: Brescia awards the B.A., B.S., and B.S.W. degrees. Associate and master's degrees are also awarded. Bachelor's degrees are awarded in BIOLOGICAL SCIENCE (biology/biological science), BUSINESS (accounting, banking and finance, business administration and management, and business economics), COMMUNICATIONS AND THE ARTS (art, English, graphic design, and photography), COMPUTER AND PHYSICAL SCIENCE (chemistry, computer science, mathematics, and science), EDUCATION (art, elementary, and special), HEALTH PROFESSIONS (art therapy, med-

ical laboratory technology, and speech pathology/audiology), SOCIAL SCIENCE (history, human development, liberal arts/general studies, ministries, psychology, religion, social studies, social work, and sociology). Business courses have the largest enrollment.

Required: All students must earn 128 credit hours, 42 upper-division, while maintaining an overall GPA of 2.0 and 2.5 in the major. Distribution requirements include 18 hours in aesthetics and language and literature, 12 in social science, 9 each in fine arts and science/mathematics, 6 in religious studies, and 3 in philosophy.

Special: Brescia offers a 3–3 nursing program with Case Western University and a 2–2 engineering degree with University of Kentucky. Student-designed majors, nondegree study, dual majors, and pass/fail options are available. There is one national honor society on campus.

Faculty/Classroom: Fifty-one percent of faculty are male; 49%, female. All teach undergraduates. The average class size in a regular course offering is 12.

Admissions: About 85% of the 1993–94 applicants were accepted. The ACT scores for the 1993–94 freshman class were as follows: 36% below 21, 32% between 21 and 23, 19% between 24 and 26, 11% between 27 and 28, and 3% above 28. About 32% of the current freshmen were in the top fifth of their class; 61% were in the top two fifths.

Requirements: Brescia requires applicants to be in the upper 60% of their class. A minimum GPA of 2.0 is required. The SAT I or ACT is required. Test scores, impressions during interview, personality, and extracurricular activities also are important admissions criteria. AP and CLEP credits are accepted.

Procedure: Freshmen are admitted to all sessions. Entrance exams should be taken in March of the senior year. Application deadlines are open. Application fee is $15. Notification is sent on a rolling basis.

Transfer: About 65 transfer students enrolled in 1993–94. Transfer students must have a minimum GPA of 2.0. A total of 42 credits out of 128 must be completed at Brescia.

Visiting: Visitors may stay overnight at the school. To arrange for a visit, contact the Admissions Office at (502) 686–4241.

Financial Aid: In an earlier year, 70% of all current freshmen received some form of financial aid. Twenty percent of undergraduate students work part-time. The FAF is required. The deadline for financial aid applications is April 1.

International Students: There are currently 8 international students enrolled. They must take the TOEFL and achieve a minimum score of 500.

Computers: The college provides computer facilities for student use. There are 104 computers available with 63 networked. A computer course is required of all students. All students may access the system. There are no time limits on using the system and no fees.

Graduates: In 1992–93, 114 bachelor's degrees were awarded. The most popular majors among graduates were business (24%), accounting (11%), and elementary education (11%). Within an average freshman class, 29% graduate in 4 years, 43% in 5 years, and 50% in 6 years. In the 1992 graduating class, 3% of the men and 11% of the women were enrolled in graduate school within 6 months of graduation.

Admissions Contact: Thomas G. Green, Director of Admissions.

CAMPBELLSVILLE COLLEGE   D-3

Campbellsville, KY 42718–2799   (502) 789–5220; (800) 264–6014

Full-time: 489 men, 446 women	Faculty: 47; IIB, --$
Part-time: 66 men, 118 women	Ph.D.s: 53%
Graduate: 2 men, 36 women	Student/Faculty: 20 to 1
Year: semesters, summer session	Tuition: $5720
Application Deadline: August 1	Room & Board: $3000
Freshman Class: 848 applied, 587 accepted, 286 enrolled	
SAT I Verbal/Math: 420/450	ACT: 21 COMPETITIVE

Campbellsville College, founded in 1906, is a private, liberal arts and sciences institution affiliated with the Southern Baptist Convention. In addition to regional accreditation, Campbellsville has baccalaureate program accreditation with NASM. The library contains 108,000 volumes, 8000 microform items, and 4050 audiovisual forms, and subscribes to 500 periodicals. Computerized library sources and services include the card catalog, interlibrary loans, and database searching. Special learning facilities include a learning resource center, an art gallery, a TV station, a teacher resource center, and the Kentuckiana Collection. The 50-acre campus is in a small town 85 miles southwest of Lexington.

Student Life: About 91% of undergraduates are from Kentucky. Students come from 17 states, 8 foreign countries, and Canada. Ninety-five percent are from public schools; 1% from private. Ninety-one percent are white. Eighty-eight percent are Protestant; 12% Catholic. The average age of freshmen is 18; all undergraduates, 21. Forty percent drop out by the end of their first year.

Housing: A total of 476 students can be accommodated in college housing. College-sponsored living facilities include single-sex dormitories and married-student housing. On-campus housing is guaranteed for all 4 years. Fifty-eight percent of students commute. Alcohol is not permitted. All students may keep cars on campus.

Activities: There are no fraternities or sororities on campus. There are 28 groups on campus, including art, band, cheerleading, choir, chorale, chorus, computers, drama, ethnic, international, jazz band, literary magazine, marching band, musical theater, newspaper, pep band, photography, political, professional, radio and TV, religious, social, student government, and yearbook. Popular campus events include Homecoming, Valentine Banquet, and a Christmas celebration.

Sports: There are 8 intercollegiate sports for men and 6 for women, and 18 intramural sports for men and 10 for women. Athletic and recreation facilities include a swimming pool, a 1500-seat gymnasium, a football stadium, a baseball field, and an intramural activities center with skating facilities and large game rooms.

Disabled Students: Eighty-five percent of the campus is accessible to disabled students. The following facilities are available: wheelchair ramps, elevators, special parking, specially equipped rest rooms, and widened doorways.

Services: In addition to many counseling and information services, tutoring is available in most subjects. There is remedial math, reading, and writing.

Campus Safety and Security: Campus safety and security measures include escort service, informal discussions, pamphlets, posters, films, and lighted pathways and sidewalks. In addition, there are 12-hour foot and vehicle patrol.

Programs of Study: Campbellsville awards the B.A., B.S., B.M., and B.S.Med.Tech. degrees. Associate and master's degrees are also awarded. Bachelor's degrees are awarded in BIOLOGICAL SCIENCE (biology/biological science), BUSINESS (accounting, business administration and management, and office supervision and management), COMMUNICATIONS AND THE ARTS (art, communications, English, and music), COMPUTER AND PHYSICAL SCIENCE (chemistry, computer management, and mathematics), EDUCATION (elementary, middle school, physical, and recreation), HEALTH PROFESSIONS (medical laboratory technology), SOCIAL SCIENCE (Christian studies, history, political science/government, psychology, religious education, religious music, and sociology). Elementary education, business administration, music, and psychology have the largest enrollments.

Required: All candidates must be of good moral character. All students must complete a minimum of 128 semester hours, including 30 in the major, 21 in the minor, and 51 in general education courses. The minimum GPA is 2.5 for education majors, 2.1 for all others. All students must fulfill an English composition requirement.

Special: Legislative and public administration internships, a Washington semester, and federal work-study programs are available. The college also offers study abroad in England, France, and Israel, a 3–2 engineering degree with the University of Kentucky, dual majors, credit by exam, credit for life, military, and work experience, nondegree study, and pass/fail options. There is one national honor society on campus.

Faculty/Classroom: Fifty-six percent of faculty are male; 44%, female. All teach undergraduates. The average class size in an introductory lecture is 30; in a laboratory, 14; and in a regular course offering, 20.

Admissions: About 69% of the 1993–94 applicants were accepted. About 30% of the current freshmen were in the top fifth of their class; 68% were in the top two fifths.

Requirements: Campbellsville requires applicants to be in the upper 75% of their class. A minimum GPA of 2.0 is required. Applicants must be graduates of an accredited secondary school with a GPA of 2.0. The GED is accepted. An interview is recommended. The SAT I or ACT is required. AP and CLEP credits are accepted. Important factors used in the admissions decision are personality, intangible qualities, leadership record, extracurricular activities record, evidence of special talent, and advanced placement or honor courses.

Procedure: Freshmen are admitted to all sessions. Applications should be filed by August 1 for fall entry, along with an application fee of $10. Notification is sent on a rolling basis. There is a deferred admissions plan.

Transfer: About 80 transfer students enrolled in a recent year. Of the 128 credits needed to graduate, all students must complete one-third of the credits required for the major and the minor at the college; the last year must be completed in residence.

Visiting: There are regularly scheduled orientations for prospective students, consisting of visitation days held in October and March. There are guides for informal visits and visitors may sit in on classes and stay overnight at the school. To arrange for a visit, contact Admissions at (800) 264–6014 or (502) 789–5220.

Financial Aid: In a recent year, 89% of all students received some form of financial aid. About 62% of freshmen and 65% of continuing students received need-based aid. The average freshman award was

$5200. Of that total, scholarships or need-based grants averaged $2050 ($7680 maximum); loans averaged $1700 ($4000 maximum); and work contracts averaged $1300 ($1500 maximum). Sixty percent of undergraduate students work part-time. The average financial indebtedness of the 1992–93 graduate was $1800. Campbellsville is a member of CSS. The college's own financial statement and FAFSA are required. The deadline for financial aid applications is April 1.

International Students: The school actively recruits these students. They must take the TOEFL and achieve a minimum score of 500. The student must also take the SAT I or the ACT.

Computers: The college provides computer facilities for student use. The IBM Novell Network, with 20 workstations, is accessible to all students. The AT&T Starian Network, with 18 workstations, is available to students in computer science and science courses. More than 60 hours a week. There are no individual time limits on using the system.

Graduates: In an earlier year, 101 bachelor's degrees were awarded. The most popular majors among graduates were education (32%), business (23%), and social sciences (16%).

Admissions Contact: Trent Argo, Director of Admissions.

CENTRE COLLEGE   D-3
Danville, KY 40422   (606) 238–5350; (800) 423–6236 (out-of-state)

Full-time: 493 men, 458 women	Faculty: 84; IIB, +$
Part-time: 2 men, 3 women	Ph.D.s: 94%
Graduate: none	Student/Faculty: 11 to 1
Year: 4–2–4, summer session	Tuition: $11,600
Application Deadline: March 1	Room & Board: $4250
Freshman Class: 1006 applied, 880 accepted, 288 enrolled	
SAT I Verbal/Math: 534/575	ACT: 27 **VERY COMPETITIVE +**

Centre College, founded in 1819 by the Presbyterian Church, is an independent liberal arts and sciences institution. The library contains 200,000 volumes, 48,500 microform items, and 3000 audiovisual forms, and subscribes to 900 periodicals. Computerized library sources and services include interlibrary loans and database searching. Special learning facilities include an art gallery and a performing arts center. The 100-acre campus is in a small town 35 miles southwest of Lexington and 80 miles southeast of Louisville. Including residence halls, there are 35 buildings on campus.

Student Life: About 65% of undergraduates are from Kentucky. Students come from 40 states, 5 foreign countries, and Canada. Seventy-five percent are from public schools; 25% from private. Ninety-four percent are white. Sixty-two percent are Protestant; 20% claim no religious affiliation; 16% Catholic. The average age of freshmen is 18; all undergraduates, 20. Eleven percent drop out by the end of their first year; 73% remain to graduate.

Housing: A total of 810 students can be accommodated in college housing. College-sponsored living facilities include 14 single-sex and coed dormitories, 5 on-campus apartments, 5 fraternity houses, and 3 sorority houses. On-campus housing is guaranteed for all 4 years. Ninety-five percent of students live on campus; of those, 90% remain on campus on weekends. Alcohol is not permitted. All students may keep cars on campus.

Activities: About 65% of men belong to 6 national fraternities; about 51% of women belong to 3 national sororities. There are 75 groups on campus, including art, cheerleading, choir, chorus, dance, drama, ethnic, film, gay, honors, jazz band, literary magazine, newspaper, orchestra, pep band, photography, political, professional, radio and TV, religious, social, social service, student government, and yearbook. Popular campus events include Homecoming, Carnival, Martin Luther King Day, Family Weekend, Honors Day, and Spring Sing.

Sports: There are 17 intramural sports for men and women, and 95% of students participate. Athletic and recreation facilities include a complex with a 1,500-seat gymnasium, 3 basketball courts, 2 volleyball courts, a training room, game room, sauna, weight room, and racquetball/handball courts. There is also a 2,500 seat stadium and playing fields for football, track, and other sports, tennis courts, and fields for baseball, softball, soccer and field hockey. The natatorium has a 25-yard, 6-lane swimming pool. Golf teams compete at the local country club.

Disabled Students: Sixty-five percent of the campus is accessible to disabled students. The following facilities are available: wheelchair ramps, elevators, special parking, specially equipped rest rooms, and special class scheduling.

Services: In addition to many counseling and information services, tutoring is available in most subjects. There is a reader service for the blind.

Campus Safety and Security: Campus safety and security measures include 24-hour foot and vehicle patrol, self-defense education, escort service, and informal discussions. In addition, there are pamphlets, posters, films, emergency telephones, lighted pathways and sidewalks, a crime prevention program through notices and publications, and a working relationship with outside agencies.

Programs of Study: Centre awards the B.A., and B.S degrees. Bachelor's degrees are awarded in BIOLOGICAL SCIENCE (biochemistry, biology/biological science, and molecular biology), COMMUNICATIONS AND THE ARTS (dramatic arts, English, fine arts, French, German, music, and Spanish), COMPUTER AND PHYSICAL SCIENCE (chemistry, computer science, mathematics, and physics), EDUCATION (elementary), SOCIAL SCIENCE (anthropology, economics, history, philosophy, political science/government, psychobiology, psychology, religion, and sociology). English, economics, biology, and chemistry are the strongest academically. Economics and English have the largest enrollments.

Required: All students must earn an overall GPA of 2.0 and complete a minimum of 115 semester hours. Students also must demonstrate competency in writing, foreign lanuague, and mathematics through testing or course work. Core curriculum requirements include 3 courses in the humanities or art from the aesthetic context, 3 from the scientific/technological context, 3 from the social context, 2 from the fundamental questions context, 1 from the cross-cultural context, and 1 from the integrative context.

Special: Centre offers internships, study abroad in 9 countries, work-study, and a 3–2 engineering degree with Vanderbilt University, Washington University at St. Louis, Georgia Institute of Technology, and the University of Kentucky. Student-designed majors and interdisciplinary majors including chemical physics, secondary education certification, and prelaw and premedicine programs are available. Pass/fail options also are available. There are 8 national honor societies on campus, including Phi Beta Kappa.

Faculty/Classroom: Seventy-five percent of faculty are male; 25%, female. All teach undergraduates and also do research. The average class size in an introductory lecture is 20; in a laboratory, 25; and in a regular course offering, 17.

Admissions: About 87% of the 1993–94 applicants were accepted. The ACT scores for the 1993–94 freshman class were as follows: 4% below 21, 16% between 21 and 23, 28% between 24 and 26, 25% between 27 and 28, and 27% above 28. About 83% of the current freshmen were in the top fifth of their class; 96% were in the top two fifths. There were 11 National Merit finalists and 9 semifinalists.

Requirements: Centre requires applicants to be in the upper 50% of their class. A minimum GPA of 2.8 is required. The SAT I or ACT is required. No minimum test scores are required. Students should have completed a minimum of 15 academic credits, including 4 years each in English and mathematics, 3 years each in science and social studies, 2 years in foreign language, and 1 year in an art- or music-related course. An essay is required and an interview is strongly recommended. AP and CLEP credits are accepted. Important factors used in the admissions decision are advanced placement or honor courses, recommendations by school officials, personality, intangible qualities, evidence of special talent, and leadership record.

Procedure: Freshmen are admitted fall, winter, and spring. Entrance exams should be taken by November of the senior year. Early decision applications should be filed by November 15; regular applications, by March 1 for fall entry, December 1 for winter entry, and January 15 for spring entry, along with an application fee of $25. Notification of early decision is sent December 15; regular decision, April 1. There are early decision, early admissions, and deferred admissions plans. Fifteen early decision candidates were accepted for the 1993–94 class. A waiting list is an active part of the admissions procedure, with about 5% of applicants on the list.

Transfer: About 20 transfer students enrolled in 1993–94. Applicants for transfer must have all previous college transcripts on file and a recommendation from the dean of most recent college attended. A total of 45 credits out of 115 must be completed at Centre.

Visiting: There are regularly scheduled orientations for prospective students, including a campus tour, an interview, class visits, faculty appointments, and an overnight stay, if requested. There are guides for informal visits and visitors may sit in on classes and stay overnight at the school. To arrange for a visit, contact the Office of Admission at (800) 423–6236.

Financial Aid: In 1993–94, 84% of all current freshmen and 75% of continuing students received some form of financial aid. About 62% of freshmen and 65% of continuing students received need-based aid. The average freshman award was $10,921. Of that total, scholarships or need-based grants averaged $4464 ($7200 maximum); loans averaged $2000 ($2500 maximum); and work contracts averaged $1100 ($1500 maximum). Fifty percent of undergraduate students work part-time. Average earnings from campus work for the school year are $900. The average financial indebtedness of the 1992–93 graduate was $6326. Centre is a member of CSS. The college's own financial statement and FAFSA are required. The deadline for financial aid applications is March 1.

International Students: There are currently 5 international students enrolled. The school actively recruits these students. They must take the TOEFL and achieve a minimum score of 550.

Computers: The college provides computer facilities for student use. The mainframe is an HP 9000/8275. 80 terminals are available in the residence halls, various classroom buildings, and the library. All students may access the system. There are no time limits on using the system and no fees.

Graduates: In 1992–93, 196 bachelor's degrees were awarded. The most popular majors among graduates were economics (18%), history (15%), and English (14%). Within an average freshman class, 1% graduate in 3 years, 71% in 4 years, 73% in 5 years, and 73% in 6 years. Some 25 companies recruited on campus in 1992–93. In the 1991–92 graduating class, 34% of students were enrolled in graduate school within 6 months of graduation, and 55% of students had found employment.

Admissions Contact: John Rogers, Director of Admission.

CUMBERLAND COLLEGE E-4
Williamsburg, KY 40769

(606) 549-2200
(800) 343-1609 (out-of-state)

Full-time: 601 men, 705 women	Faculty: 104; IIB, --$
Part-time: 33 men, 89 women	Ph.D.s: 42%
Graduate: 18 men, 72 women	Student/Faculty: 13 to 1
Year: semesters, summer session	Tuition: $6230
Application Deadline: open	Room & Board: $3526
Freshman Class: 995 applied, 789 accepted, 398 enrolled	
SAT I Verbal/Math: 420/470	ACT: 21 COMPETITIVE

Cumberland College, founded in 1889, is a private, liberal arts college affiliated with the Southern Baptist Church. There is one graduate school. In addition to regional accreditation, the college has baccalaureate program accreditation with NASM. The library contains 146,000 volumes, 575,000 microform items, and 14,000 audiovisual forms, and subscribes to 1400 periodicals. Computerized library sources and services include the card catalog, interlibrary loans, and database searching. Special learning facilities include a learning resource center, art gallery, natural history museum, and TV station. The 27-acre campus is in a small town 100 miles south of Lexington and 65 miles north of Knoxville, Tennessee. Including residence halls, there are 18 buildings on campus.

Student Life: About 52% of undergraduates are from Kentucky. Students come from 27 states, 15 foreign countries, and Canada. Ninety-eight percent are from public schools; 2% from private. Ninety-one percent are white. Most are Protestant. The average age of freshmen is 18.5. Thirty-five percent drop out by the end of their first year; 65% remain to graduate.

Housing: A total of 1000 students can be accommodated in college housing. College-sponsored living facilities include single-sex dormitories. On-campus housing is guaranteed for all 4 years. Fifty-nine percent of students live on campus; of those, 60% remain on campus on weekends. Alcohol is not permitted. All students may keep cars on campus.

Activities: There are no fraternities or sororities on campus. There are 45 groups on campus, including art, band, cheerleading, choir, chorale, chorus, computers, dance, drama, drill team, ethnic, honors, international, jazz band, literary magazine, marching band, musical theater, newspaper, opera, orchestra, pep band, photography, political, professional, radio and TV, religious, social, social service, student government, and yearbook. Popular campus events include Spring Fever, Madrigal Dinner, Homecoming, Quest, fine arts concerts, Hanging of the Greens, Founders Day, lecture series, the Siler-Jones Concert, and sports competitions.

Sports: There are 9 intercollegiate sports for men and 8 for women, and 12 intramural sports for men and 12 for women. Athletic and recreation facilities include a gymnasium, an athletic/convocation complex, a game room, tennis courts, a field house, an intramural field, practice football fields, and a football, track, and soccer complex.

Disabled Students: All the campus is accessible to disabled students. The following facilities are available: wheelchair ramps, special parking, specially equipped rest rooms, special class scheduling, and lowered drinking fountains.

Services: In addition to many counseling and information services, tutoring is available in every subject. There is remedial math, reading, and writing.

Campus Safety and Security: Campus safety and security measures include 24-hour foot and vehicle patrol, escort service, informal discussions, and lighted pathways and sidewalks.

Programs of Study: The college awards the B.A., B.S., B.G.S., and B.M. degrees. Master's degrees also are awarded. Bachelor's degrees are awarded in BIOLOGICAL SCIENCE (biology/biological science), BUSINESS (accounting and business administration/ management), COMMUNICATIONS AND THE ARTS (dramatic arts, English, fine arts, music, and speech/debate/rhetoric), COMPUTER AND PHYSICAL SCIENCE (chemistry, computer programming, mathematics, and physics), EDUCATION (art, business, early childhood, elementary, health, music, physical, science, secondary, and special), ENGINEERING AND ENVIRONMENTAL DESIGN (military

science), HEALTH PROFESSIONS (health, medical laboratory technology, physical therapy, predentistry, premedicine, prepharmacy, and preveterinary science), SOCIAL SCIENCE (history, political science/government, prelaw, psychology, religion, and sociology). Biology, chemistry, history, music, mathematics, and education are the strongest academically. Business, computer information systems, and education have the largest enrollments.

Required: All students must complete 128 semester hours, including at least 30 in the major, while maintaining an overall GPA of 2.0; 2.5 for those seeking teacher certification. Distribution requirements include 2 semester hours of physical education activities, and 2 courses selected from the core groups of art, music, theater, speech, religion, English composition, literature, mathematics, and natural and social sciences.

Special: Cross-registration, summer internships, work-study programs with the college and with local businesses and educational institutions, and study abroad in 2 countries are available. B.A.-B.S. degrees and dual majors in all major fields, a general studies degree, and nondegree study are possible. There is a freshman honors program on campus, as well as 8 national honor societies. Fourteen departments have honors programs.

Faculty/Classroom: Sixty-three percent of faculty are male; 36%, female. All teach undergraduates. No introductory courses are taught by graduate students. The average class size in an introductory lecture, a laboratory, and a regular course offering is 16.

Admissions: About 79% of the 1993–94 applicants were accepted. The SAT scores for the 1993–94 freshman class were as follows: Verbal—83% below 500, 17% between 500 and 599, and 1% between 600 and 700; Math—68% below 500, 27% between 500 and 599, and 5% between 600 and 700. The ACT scores were 50% below 21, 24% between 21 and 23, 17% between 24 and 26, 6% between 27 and 28, and 3% above 28. About 33% of the current freshmen were in the top fifth of their class; 56% were in the top two fifths. Five freshmen graduated first in their class.

Requirements: A minimum GPA of 2.0 is required. The SAT I or the ACT, with composite scores of better than 16 for the ACT or 650 for the SAT I are required. Although each application is considered individually, students must have fulfilled general high school requirements of 4 years of English, 3 each of mathematics and science, and 2 each of history and social studies. Two letters of recommendation from persons other than a guidance counselor or relative, a recommendation from a guidance counselor, and a high school transcript are required. The college also recommends an interview. The GED is accepted. AP and CLEP credits are accepted. Important factors used in the admissions decision are leadership record, recommendations by school officials, advanced placement or honors courses, extracurricular activities record, and personality, intangible qualities.

Procedure: Freshmen are admitted to all sessions. Entrance exams should be taken during the summer before enrollment. Application deadlines are open. Application fee is $25. Notification is sent on a rolling basis.

Transfer: About 79 transfer students enrolled in 1993–94. In addition to fulfilling freshman requirements, transfers must have verification from their previous school that they are eligible to return. A total of 30 credits out of 128 must be completed at the college.

Visiting: There are regularly scheduled orientations for prospective students, consisting of a tour, a departmental conference, adjustment information, and general requirements. There are guides for informal visits, and visitors may sit in on classes and stay overnight at the school. To arrange for a visit, contact the Admissions Office at (800) 343-1609.

Financial Aid: In 1993–94, 90% of all current freshmen and 83% of continuing students received some form of financial aid. About 76% of all students received need-based aid. The average freshman award was $6000. Of that total, scholarships or need-based grants averaged $2144 ($5000 maximum); loans averaged $2500 ($3000 maximum); and work contracts averaged $1472 ($2000 maximum). Fifty percent of undergraduate students work part-time. Average earnings from campus work for the school year are $1640. The average financial indebtedness of the 1992–93 graduate was $8000. The college is a member of CSS. The FAFSA financial statement is required. The priority date for financial aid applications is March 1.

International Students: There are currently 37 international students enrolled. The school actively recruits these students. They must take the TOEFL or the University of Michigan Language Test and achieve a minimum score on the TOEFL of 600. The student must also take the SAT I or the ACT, and the English Placement Examination.

Computers: The college provides computer facilities for student use. The mainframe is a UNIX Sperry UNIVAC. There are also 100 IBM XT and AT, Tandy, 486 Gateway, and AT&T microcomputers available throughout the campus. All students may access the system. It may be used from 8 A.M. to 9 P.M. daily. There are no time limits on using the system and no fees.

Graduates: In 1992–93, 210 bachelor's degrees were awarded. The most popular majors among graduates were business administration (24%), elementary education (14%), and computer information systems (8%). Within an average freshman class, 1% graduate in 3 years, 14% in 4 years, 27% in 5 years, and 29% in 6 years. Some 125 companies recruited on campus in 1992–93. In the 1992 graduating class, 25% of the men and 30% of the women were enrolled in graduate school within 6 months of graduation; 80% of the men and 85% of the women had found employment.

Admissions Contact: Erica Harris, Senior Admissions Counselor.

EASTERN KENTUCKY UNIVERSITY   E-3
Richmond, KY 40475   (606) 622–2106; (800) 262–7493 (in-state)

Full-time: 5208 men, 6501 women	**Faculty:** 610; IIA, -$
Part-time: 1134 men, 1857 women	**Ph.D.s:** 65%
Graduate: 622 men, 1249 women	**Student/Faculty:** 19 to 1
Year: semesters, summer session	**Tuition:** $1700 ($4700)
Application Deadline: open	**Room & Board:** $3140
Freshman Class: 5437 applied, 5130 accepted, 2350 enrolled	
ACT: 19	**NONCOMPETITIVE**

Eastern Kentucky University, established in 1906, is a public, state-supported institution offering degree programs in the arts and sciences, business, environmental studies, health fields, and public service occupations. There are 10 undergraduate and 9 graduate schools. In addition to regional accreditation, EKU has baccalaureate program accreditation with ADA, AHEA, CSWE, FIDER, NASM, NCATE, NLN, and NRPA. The 3 libraries contain 845,977 volumes, 1.8 million microform items, and 3950 audiovisual forms, and subscribe to 4070 periodicals. Computerized library sources and services include the card catalog, interlibrary loans, and database searching. Special learning facilities include an art gallery, natural history museum, planetarium, radio station, TV station, and law enforcement complex that includes a training tank for underwater rescue and recovery. The 350-acre campus is in a small town 20 miles south of Lexington. Including residence halls, there are 75 buildings on campus.

Student Life: About 92% of undergraduates are from Kentucky. Students come from 41 states, 43 foreign countries, and Canada. Ninety percent are from public schools; 10% from private. Ninety-three percent are white. The average age of freshmen is 18; all undergraduates, 21.

Housing: A total of 6500 students can be accommodated in college housing. College-sponsored living facilities include dormitories, on-campus apartments, married-student housing, fraternity houses, and sorority houses. In addition, there are honors houses, special interest houses, and special accommodations for senior home economics students. On-campus housing is guaranteed for all 4 years. Fifty percent of students live on campus; of those, 50% remain on campus on weekends. Alcohol is not permitted. All students may keep cars on campus.

Activities: About 12% of men belong to 16 national fraternities; about 10% of women belong to 12 national sororities. There are 190 groups on campus, including art, band, cheerleading, choir, chorale, chorus, computers, dance, drama, drill team, ethnic, honors, international, jazz band, marching band, musical theater, newspaper, orchestra, pep band, photography, political, professional, radio and TV, religious, social service, student government, symphony, and yearbook. Popular campus events include Homecoming, Hanging of the Greens at Christmas, International Month, and fraternity/sorority competitions.

Sports: There are 8 intercollegiate sports for men and 7 for women, and 12 intramural sports each. Athletic and recreation facilities include 5 gymnasiums, 1 outdoor and 2 indoor swimming pools, 19 all-weather and 4 indoor tennis courts, handball courts, training rooms, a dance studio, a martial arts room, a wellness center, a 7000-seat basketball arena, a 20,000-seat stadium, an 8-lane outdoor track, a field hockey area, an 18-hole golf course, and fields for baseball, softball, and soccer.

Disabled Students: Seventy percent of the campus is accessible to disabled students. The following facilities are available: wheelchair ramps, elevators, special parking, specially equipped rest rooms, special class scheduling, and lowered drinking fountains.

Services: In addition to many counseling and information services, tutoring is available in mathematics, English, and reading. There is also a reader service for the blind, and remedial math, reading, and writing.

Campus Safety and Security: Campus safety and security measures include 24-hour foot and vehicle patrol, self defense education, escort service, and shuttle buses. In addition, there are informal discussions, pamphlets, posters, films, emergency telephones, lighted pathways and sidewalks, and 16 crime-prevention programs.

Programs of Study: EKU awards the B.A., B.S., B.B.A., B.F.A., B.I.S., B.M., B.M.Ed., B.S.N., and B.S.W. degrees. Associate and master's degrees also are awarded. Bachelor's degrees are awarded in AGRICULTURE (agriculture, fish and game management, horticul-

ture, and wildlife management), BIOLOGICAL SCIENCE (biology/biological science and microbiology), BUSINESS (accounting, banking and finance, business administration and management, business economics, fashion merchandising, insurance, marketing/retailing/merchandising, personnel management, real estate, and transportation management), COMMUNICATIONS AND THE ARTS (art, broadcasting, dramatic arts, English, fine arts, French, German, journalism, music, performing arts, public relations, Spanish, and speech/debate/rhetoric), COMPUTER AND PHYSICAL SCIENCE (chemistry, computer programming, computer science, geology, information sciences and systems, mathematics, and statistics), EDUCATION (art, business, early childhood, education of the deaf and hearing impaired, elementary, foreign languages, health, home economics, industrial arts, mathematics, middle school, music, physical, science, secondary, special, technical, and vocational), ENGINEERING AND ENVIRONMENTAL DESIGN (airline piloting and navigation, construction technology, environmental science, industrial engineering, interior design, and manufacturing technology), HEALTH PROFESSIONS (environmental health science, health care administration, medical laboratory technology, medical technology, nursing, and occupational therapy), and SOCIAL SCIENCE (anthropology, child care/child and family studies, corrections, dietetics, economics, fashion design and technology, fire protection, food production/management/services, forensic studies, geography, history, law enforcement and corrections, paralegal studies, parks and recreation management, philosophy, political science/government, psychology, religion, safety and security technology, social work, and sociology). Nursing, law enforcement, education, and business are the strongest academically. Business, education, and nursing have the largest enrollments.

Required: All students must complete between 45 and 50 hours of general education requirements, including courses in physical education, health, English, natural science, social science, and the humanities. A minimum GPA of 2.0 is required. Students must complete a total of 128 credit hours, including 45 to 60 credits in the major, with a minimum GPA of 2.0.

Special: EKU offers cooperative programs with all academic colleges, internships, and study abroad in various European countries. Students may opt for credit by examination, nondegree study, pass/fail options, student-designed and dual majors, and a general studies degree. There is a freshman honors program on campus. One department has an honors program.

Faculty/Classroom: The average class size in an introductory lecture is 30; in a laboratory, 15; and in a regular course offering, 25.

Admissions: About 94% of the 1993–94 applicants were accepted. The ACT scores for the 1993–94 freshman class were as follows: 68% below 21, 19% between 21 and 23, 7% between 24 and 26, 4% between 27 and 28, and 2% above 28. About 25% of the current freshmen were in the top fifth of their class; 59% were in the top two fifths.

Requirements: EKU requires out-of-state applicants to be in the upper 50% of their class or have an equivalent rank in ACT scores nationwide. A minimum GPA of 2.0 is needed. The ACT is required. AP and CLEP credits are accepted.

Procedure: Freshmen are admitted to all sessions. Entrance exams should be taken prior to enrollment. Application deadlines are open. The college accepts all in-state residents completing a precollege curriculum. Notification is sent within 3 weeks of receipt of the application. There is an early admissions plan.

Transfer: Transfer applicants must have a 2.0 cumulative GPA from all accredited institutions previously attended and must not have been dismissed. A total of 30 credits out of 128 must be completed at EKU.

Visiting: There are regularly scheduled orientations for prospective students, consisting of a 1-day program during the summer prior to fall enrollment. There are guides for informal visits and visitors may sit in on classes and stay overnight at the school. To arrange for a visit, contact the Admissions Office at (606) 622–2106.

Financial Aid: In an earlier year, 71% of all freshmen and 65% of continuing students received some form of financial aid. About 71% of freshmen and 65% of continuing students received need-based aid. Scholarships or need-based grants averaged $750 ($1180 maximum); loans averaged $800 ($2626 maximum); and work contracts averaged $800 ($2278 maximum). Twelve percent of undergraduate students work part-time. The average financial indebtedness of the an earlier graduate was $4500. EKU is a member of CSS. The FAF and the college's own financial statement are required. The deadline for financial aid applications is April 15.

International Students: There are currently 119 international students enrolled. The school actively recruits these students. They must take the TOEFL and achieve a minimum score of 500. The student must also take the ACT, achieving a minimum score of 21, the SAT I for those applicants from states where the SAT I is dominant.

Computers: The college provides computer facilities for student use. The mainframe is a DEC VAX. Students may access 4 different academic minicomputers over the campus network using any of the 137

terminals and 21 clusters throughout campus. In addition, there are 30 microcomputers in 1 centralized laboratory and more than 350 microcomputers in 22 college or departmental laboratories. All students may access the system. There are no time limits on using the system and no fees.

Graduates: In a recent year, 1576 bachelor's degrees were awarded.

Admissions Contact: James L. Grigsby, Director of Admissions.

GEORGETOWN COLLEGE

D-2

Georgetown, KY 40324-1696

(502) 863-8009
(800) 788-9985 (in-state)

Full-time: 499 men, 564 women	Faculty: 75; IIB, -$
Part-time: 11 men, 37 women	Ph.D.s: 72%
Graduate: 44 men, 227 women	Student/Faculty: 14 to 1
Year: semesters, summer session	Tuition: $7390
Application Deadline: open	Room & Board: $3600
Freshman Class: 727 applied, 693 accepted, 286 enrolled	
SAT I or ACT: required	COMPETITIVE

Georgetown College, founded in 1829, is a private, coeducational, liberal arts college affiliated with the Kentucky Baptist Convention. There is one graduate school. The library contains 125,707 volumes, 106,159 microform items, and 5544 audiovisual forms, and subscribes to 987 periodicals. Computerized library sources and services include the card catalog, interlibrary loans, and database searching. Special learning facilities include a learning resource center, art gallery, planetarium, and radio station. The 52-acre campus is in a small town 12 miles north of Lexington. Including residence halls, there are 25 buildings on campus.

Student Life: About 78% of undergraduates are from Kentucky. Students come from 22 states and 14 foreign countries. Ninety-two percent are from public schools; 8% from private. Ninety-five percent are white. Most are Protestant. The average age of freshmen is 18; all undergraduates, 20. Seven percent drop out by the end of their first year; 45% remain to graduate.

Housing: A total of 1050 students can be accommodated in college housing. College-sponsored living facilities include single-sex dormitories, married-student housing, fraternity houses, and sorority houses. On-campus housing is guaranteed for all 4 years. Ninety percent of students live on campus; of those, 70% remain on campus on weekends. Alcohol is not permitted. All students may keep cars on campus.

Activities: About 40% of men belong to 1 local and 4 national fraternities; about 30% of women belong to 3 national sororities. There are 60 groups on campus, including art, band, cheerleading, choir, chorale, chorus, computers, drama, honors, international, jazz band, literary magazine, musical theater, newspaper, pep band, photography, political, professional, radio and TV, religious, social, social service, student government, and yearbook. Popular campus events include Homecoming, Hanging of the Green, Festival of Song, New Student Orientation, and Parents Day.

Sports: There are 7 intercollegiate sports for men and 5 for women, and 7 intramural sports for men and 7 for women. Athletic and recreation facilities include a 3000-seat stadium, an athletic field, tennis courts, and a 1550-seat gymnasium housing a Nautilus room, a weight-lifting area, racquetball courts, and a training room.

Disabled Students: Seventy percent of the campus is accessible to disabled students. The following facilities are available: wheelchair ramps, elevators, special parking, specially equipped rest rooms, and special class scheduling.

Services: In addition to many counseling and information services, tutoring is available in every subject.

Campus Safety and Security: Campus safety and security measures include 24-hour foot and vehicle patrol, self-defense education, escort service, and informal discussions. In addition, there are pamphlets, posters, and films and lighted pathways and sidewalks.

Programs of Study: Georgetown awards the B.A., B.S., B.M., and B.M.E. degrees. Master's degrees also are awarded. Bachelor's degrees are awarded in BIOLOGICAL SCIENCE (biology/biological science), BUSINESS (accounting, banking and finance, business administration and management, business economics, international business management, management information systems, management science, marketing/retailing/merchandising, and recreation and leisure services), COMMUNICATIONS AND THE ARTS (art, communications, dramatic arts, English, French, German, music, and Spanish), COMPUTER AND PHYSICAL SCIENCE (chemistry, computer science, information sciences and systems, mathematics, and physics), EDUCATION (elementary, foreign languages, music, and physical), ENGINEERING AND ENVIRONMENTAL DESIGN (environmental science), HEALTH PROFESSIONS (medical laboratory technology and nursing), SOCIAL SCIENCE (American studies, economics, European studies, history, philosophy, political science/government, psychology, religion, religious music, and sociology). Biology, com-

puter science, and mathematics are the strongest academically. Business has the largest enrollment.

Required: All students are required to complete 56 semester hours of general education courses, including 16 in fine arts and humanities, 9 in foreign language and culture, 8 in communication, 6 each in religion, natural sciences, and social sciences, 3 in mathematics, and 2 in physical education. A total of 128 semester hours, including 33 to 60 in the major, with a minimum GPA of 2.0, is required to graduate, as is successful completion of a comprehensive exam in the major.

Special: The college offers cross-registration with the University of Kentucky and Air Force ROTC for aerospace studies. A 3-2 engineering degree is available with the Georgia Institute of Technology, University of Kentucky, and Washington University. Internships, co-op programs in mathematics and computer science, study abroad in 5 countries, work-study programs, dual and student-designed majors, and pass/fail options are available. Interdisciplinary majors include business administration/communication arts and business administration/ethics. Nondegree study is possible. There is a freshman honors program on campus, as well as 15 national honor societies. All departments have honors programs.

Faculty/Classroom: Fifty-nine percent of faculty are male; 41%, female. All teach undergraduates. No introductory courses are taught by graduate students.

Admissions: About 95% of the 1993-94 applicants were accepted. The ACT scores for the 1993-94 freshman class were as follows: 36% below 21, 31% between 21 and 23, 19% between 24 and 26, 7% between 27 and 28, and 7% above 28. About 57% of the current freshmen were in the top fifth of their class; 79% were in the top two fifths. About 19 freshmen graduated first in their class.

Requirements: Georgetown requires applicants to be in the upper 50% of their class. A minimum GPA of C in college preparatory subjects is required. The SAT I or ACT is required, as is an essay. Applicants should have completed 4 high school credits in English, 3 each in mathematics and science, 2 in a foreign language, and 1 each in social studies and history, with additional credits in electives strongly encouraged. AP and CLEP credits are accepted. Important factors used in the admissions decision are advanced placement or honor courses, evidence of special talent, leadership record, personality, intangible qualities, and extracurricular activities record.

Procedure: Freshmen are admitted fall, spring, and summer. Entrance exams should be taken from December of the junior year through October of the senior year. The application fee is $20. Application deadlines are open. Notification is sent on a rolling basis.

Transfer: About 30 transfer students enrolled in 1993-94. In addition, transfer applicants must be in good standing at the school most recently attended. A total of 30 credits out of 128 must be completed at Georgetown.

Visiting: There are regularly scheduled orientations for prospective students. There are guides for informal visits and visitors may sit in on classes and stay overnight at the school. To arrange for a visit, contact the Director of Admissions at (502) 863-8009 or (800) 788-9985 (in-state).

Financial Aid: In 1993-94, 96% of all current freshmen and 94% of continuing students received some form of financial aid. About 93% of freshmen and 92% of continuing students received need-based aid. The average freshman award was $7279. Of that total, scholarships or need-based grants averaged $2100 ($10,990 maximum); loans averaged $2600 ($8500 maximum); and work contracts averaged $1000 ($2500 maximum). Fifty percent of undergraduate students work part-time. Average earnings from campus work for the school year are $800. The average financial indebtedness of the 1992-93 graduate was $1200. Georgetown is a member of CSS. The FAF and the FAFSA are required. The deadline for financial aid applications is April 1.

International Students: There are currently 23 international students enrolled. They must take the TOEFL and achieve a minimum score of 520.

Computers: The college provides computer facilities for student use. The mainframe is an HP 9000/827. There are also 30 HP Vectra, IBM PS/2, and Apple Macintosh microcomputers, with word processing, statistical analysis, spreadsheets, programming languages, and ERIC and other databases, available in the library and department laboratories. All students may access the system. There are no time limits on using the system and no fees.

Graduates: In 1992-93, 189 bachelor's degrees were awarded. The most popular majors among graduates were marketing/finance (15%), elementary education and English (8% each), and biology, communication arts, and political science (7% each). Within an average freshman class, 32% graduate in 4 years and 45% in 6 years. Some 25 companies recruited on campus in 1992-93.

Admissions Contact: Garvel Kindrick, Director of Admissions.

KENTUCKY CHRISTIAN COLLEGE   F-2
Grayson, KY 41143   (606) 474-6613

Full-time: 235 men, 220 women	Faculty: 27
Part-time: 5 men, 16 women	Ph.D.s: 48%
Graduate: none	Student/Faculty: 17 to 1
Year: semesters, summer session	Tuition: $4288
Application Deadline: August 1	Room & Board: $3420
Freshman Class: 266 applied, 235 accepted, 169 enrolled	
SAT I Verbal/Math: 390/450	ACT: 20 LESS COMPETITIVE

Kentucky Christian College, established in 1919, is a private Bible college, affiliated with the Church of Christ, offering undergraduate programs in Christian ministry, psychology, social work, business administration, teacher education, and music. The library contains 79,634 volumes, 79 microform items, and 3547 audiovisual forms, and subscribes to 375 periodicals. Special learning facilities include a radio station. The 121-acre campus is in a rural area 20 miles from Ashland. Including residence halls, there are 10 buildings on campus.

Student Life: About 38% of undergraduates are from Kentucky. Eighty-five percent are from public schools. Ninety-eight percent are white. Most are Protestant. The average age of freshmen is 21; all undergraduates, 22. Thirty percent drop out by the end of their first year; 50% remain to graduate.

Housing: A total of 451 students can be accommodated in college housing. College-sponsored living facilities include single-sex dormitories, on-campus apartments, and married-student housing. On-campus housing is guaranteed for all 4 years. Eighty-eight percent of students live on campus. Alcohol is not permitted. All students may keep cars on campus.

Activities: There are no fraternities or sororities on campus. There are many groups and organizations on campus, including cheerleading, choir, chorus, drama, musical theater, newspaper, pep band, radio and TV, religious, social service, student government, and yearbook. Popular campus events include Madrigals, High School Days, Parents Day, Homecoming, Summer in the Son, and College Awareness Day.

Sports: Athletic and recreation facilities include a gymnasium, soccer and recreational fields, and a baseball diamond.

Disabled Students: The following facilities are available: wheelchair ramps, special parking, and specially equipped rest rooms.

Services: In addition to many counseling and information services, tutoring is available in every subject. In addition, there is remedial math, reading, and writing.

Campus Safety and Security: Campus safety and security measures include lighted pathways and sidewalks and a full-time security guard.

Programs of Study: KCC awards the B.A. and B.S. degrees. Associate degrees also are awarded. Bachelor's degrees are awarded in BUSINESS (business administration and management), COMMUNICATIONS AND THE ARTS (music), EDUCATION (elementary, middle school, and secondary), SOCIAL SCIENCE (ministries, psychology, and social work). Teacher education and ministry have the largest enrollments.

Required: To graduate, students must complete 132 semester hours with at least 30 hours in the major and a minimum GPA of 2.0. Required courses include freshman orientation, physical education, English, history, Introduction to Christian Doctrine, and Survey of Biblical Literature. Candidates for the B.A. degree must fulfill a 14-hour language requirement. All students are Bible majors; they also must complete the requirements of a second major or a minor. Students must complete a Christian service project for six semesters and also must be approved for graduation by the board of trustees.

Special: Internships, work-study programs, B.A.-B.S. degrees, and dual majors are offered. A general studies degree and nondegree study are available. One department has an honors program.

Admissions: About 88% of the 1993-94 applicants were accepted. The SAT scores for the 1993-94 freshman class were as follows: Verbal—75% below 500 and 25% between 500 and 599; Math—63% below 500, 31% between 500 and 599, and 6% between 600 and 700. The ACT scores were 56% below 21, 19% between 21 and 23, 12% between 24 and 26, 8% between 27 and 28, and 5% above 28.

Requirements: A minimum GPA of 2.0 is required. The ACT (preferred), with a minimum composite score of 13, or the SAT I with a minimum composite score of 710, is required. Applicants with lower test scores who have a high school GPA of 2.5 or higher will be considered. Applicants must graduate from an accredited secondary school or have a GED. Essays are required. AP and CLEP credits are accepted. Important factors used in the admissions decision are leadership record, advanced placement or honor courses, parents or siblings attending the school, ability to finance college education, and personality, intangible qualities.

Procedure: Freshmen are admitted to all sessions. Applications should be filed by August 1 for fall entry, along with an application fee of $25. Notification is sent on a rolling basis. There are early decision, early admissions, and deferred admissions plans.

Transfer: About 45 transfer students enrolled in 1993-94. Transfer applicants must have a cumulative GPA of 2.0. They must submit transcripts from all previous institutions, and must be in good standing at the last college attended. A total of 32 credits out of 132 must be completed at KCC.

Visiting: There are regularly scheduled orientations for prospective students, consisting of an interview, a campus tour, lunch, and attending classes. There are guides for informal visits and visitors may sit in on classes and stay overnight at the school. To arrange for a visit, contact Dee Bailey, Assistant to the Director of Admissions at (606) 474-3266.

Financial Aid: In 1993-94, 95% of all current freshmen and 80% of continuing students received some form of financial aid. About 80% of freshmen and 75% of continuing students received need-based aid. The average freshman award was $5053. Of that total, scholarships or need-based grants averaged $1403 ($4340 maximum); loans averaged $2625 ($7625 maximum); and work contracts averaged $1025 ($3700 maximum). Sixty-three percent of undergraduate students work part-time. Average earnings from campus work for the school year are $1025. The average financial indebtedness of the 1992-93 graduate was $7900. The FAFSA and the college's own financial statement are required. The deadline for financial aid applications is April 1.

Computers: The college provides computer facilities for student use. All students may access the system. There are no time limits on using the system.

Graduates: In 1992-93, 88 bachelor's degrees were awarded. The most popular majors among graduates were teacher education (33%), Christian ministry (27%), and business administration (19%). Within an average freshman class, 45% graduate in 4 years.

Admissions Contact: Sandra Deakins, Director of Admissions.

KENTUCKY STATE UNIVERSITY   D-2
Frankfort, KY 40601   (502) 227-6813; (800) 325-1716 (out-of-state)

Full-time: 713 men, 786 women	Faculty: 120; IIB, -$
Part-time: 319 men, 596 women	Ph.D.s: 52%
Graduate: 30 men, 41 women	Student/Faculty: 12 to 1
Year: semesters, summer session	Tuition: $1600 ($4600)
Application Deadline: April 15	Room & Board: $2682
Freshman Class: 1407 applied, 688 accepted, 466 enrolled	
ACT: 18 (mean)	COMPETITIVE +

Kentucky State University, founded in 1886, is a public liberal arts institution that emphasizes student involvement in seminars and course planning. In addition to regional accreditation, KSU has baccalaureate program accreditation with AACSB, ADA, AHEA, CSWE, NASM, NCATE, and NLN. The library contains 300,000 volumes, 44,260 microform items, and 12,477 audiovisual forms, and subscribes to 1209 periodicals. Computerized library sources and services include the card catalog and database searching. Special learning facilities include a learning resource center, an art gallery, and a 167-acre agricultural research farm. The 475-acre campus is in a small town 25 miles west of Lexington. Including residence halls, there are 32 buildings on campus.

Student Life: About 78% of undergraduates are from Kentucky. Ninety-nine percent are from public schools. Fifty-two percent are white; 46% African American. The average age of freshmen is 20; all undergraduates, 26. Thirty percent drop out by the end of their first year; 35% remain to graduate.

Housing: College-sponsored housing is single-sex and coed. In addition there are special interest houses. On-campus housing is guaranteed for the freshman year only and is available on a first-come, first-served basis. All students may keep cars on campus.

Activities: About 6% of men belong to 2 local and 3 national fraternities; about 4% of women belong to 3 local and 3 national sororities. There are many groups and organizations on campus, including art, band, cheerleading, chess, chorale, dance, international, literary magazine, newspaper, political, religious, social service, student government, and yearbook. Popular campus events include Homecoming, plays, lectures concerts, and talent shows.

Sports: There are 9 intercollegiate sports each for men and women, and 11 intramural sports each for men and women. Athletic and recreation facilities include a 6500-seat football stadium, an indoor swimming pool, tennis courts, a bowling alley, training and weight rooms, a field house, and baseball, track, and field complexes.

Disabled Students: The following facilities are available: wheelchair ramps, elevators, special parking, specially equipped rest rooms, lowered drinking fountains, lowered telephones, and electric doors.

Services: In addition to many counseling and information services, tutoring is available in every subject. In addition, there is a reader service for the blind, and remedial math, reading, and writing.

Programs of Study: KSU awards the B.A., B.S., B.M.Ed., and B.M.P. degrees. Associate and master's degrees are also awarded. Bachelor's degrees are awarded in BIOLOGICAL SCIENCE (biology/biological science), BUSINESS (accounting, apparel and accessories marketing, business administration and management, business economics, management science, and marketing/retailing/merchandising), COMMUNICATIONS AND THE ARTS (English, fine arts, music performance, and studio art), COMPUTER AND PHYSICAL SCIENCE (applied mathematics, chemistry, computer science, and mathematics), EDUCATION (art, early childhood, elementary, music, physical, secondary, and social studies), HEALTH PROFESSIONS (medical laboratory technology), SOCIAL SCIENCE (child psychology/development, criminal justice, history, political science/government, psychology, public administration, social work, sociology, and textiles and clothing).

Required: All students must maintain a minimum GPA of 2.0 while taking 128 semester hours, 30 to 48 in the major. Distribution requirements include 18 hours in languages and reasoning, 21 in fine arts, letter, history, and integrative studies, 12 or 13 in sciences, and 2 in health education.

Special: Co-op programs with local industry, a prelaw internship program, cross-registration with Berea College, study abroad at Oxford and Kings Colleges in England and in other countries, and work-study with the university are available. Dual-degree programs in various engineering fields with the University of Kentucky, student-designed majors, B.A.-B.S. degrees, nondegree study, and pass/fail options are offered. Credit by examination or for life or military experience is possible.

Admissions: About 49% of the 1993–94 applicants were accepted. **Requirements:** KSU requires applicants to be in the upper 50% of their class. The SAT I or ACT is required. Composite scores needed are 720 in-state and 780 out-of-state on the SAT I or 19 in-state and 20 out-of-state on the ACT. Admission is based on a combination of GPA and SAT I or ACT scores. Applicants are required to have 4 years in English, 3 in mathematics, 2 each in science and history, and 9 additional precollege curriculum classes. The GED is accepted. AP and CLEP credits are accepted.

Procedure: Freshmen are admitted to all sessions. Entrance exams should be taken from October to April. Applications should be filed by April 15 for fall entry, December 1 for spring entry, and May 1 for summer entry, along with an application fee of $15. The college accepts all in-state residents who apply. There are early admissions and deferred admissions plans.

Transfer: Transfer students must have a 2.0 minimum GPA at previous colleges. Only C grades transfer. If fewer than 30 semester credits are transferable, applicants must meet freshmen criteria. A total of 32 credits out of 128 must be completed at KSU.

Visiting: There are regularly scheduled orientations for prospective students, including tours and meetings with faculty and financial aid officers. There are guides for informal visits and visitors may sit in on classes. To arrange for a visit, contact Admissions at (502) 227–6813.

Financial Aid: In a recent year 80% of all current freshmen received some form of financial aid. Scholarships or need-based grants averaged $1500; loans averaged $2000; and work contracts averaged $1000. KSU is a member of CSS. The FAF and the college's own financial statement are required. The deadline for financial aid applications is April 15.

International Students: They must take the TOEFL and achieve a minimum score of 525. The student must also take the SAT I or the ACT.

Computers: The college provides computer facilities for student use. The mainframe is an IBM 4361 and an IBM 9375. Many IBM and Apple PCs are available in various departmental computer laboratories and in the library; some are connected to a LAN. All students may access the system. It may be used 13 hours a day. There are no individual time limits on using the system. The fees are $10 per semester.

Admissions Contact: Veronica Thomas, Associate Director of Admissions.

KENTUCKY WESLEYAN COLLEGE

Owensboro, KY 42302-1039

B-3

(502) 926–3111
(800) 999–0592 (out-of-state)

Full-time: 313 men, 349 women	Faculty: 51; IIB, --$
Part-time: 19 men, 102 women	Ph.D.s: 70%
Graduate: none	Student/Faculty: 13 to 1
Year: semesters, summer session	Tuition: $7600
Application Deadline: open	Room & Board: $3950
Freshman Class: 584 applied, 497 accepted, 175 enrolled	
SAT I Verbal/Math: 425/470	ACT: 22 COMPETITIVE

Kentucky Wesleyan College, founded in 1858, is a private, coeducational liberal arts institution affiliated with the United Methodist Church. KWC offers undergraduate programs in natural sciences, humanities and fine arts, and social sciences. Additionally, academic programs are offered in criminal justice, nursing, human resources administration, mass communication, and computer science. In addition to regional accreditation, KWC has baccalaureate program accreditation with NLN. The library contains 93,940 volumes, 49,404 microform items, and 3625 audiovisual forms, and subscribes to 453 periodicals. Computerized library sources and services include the card catalog, interlibrary loans, and database searching. Special learning facilities include a learning resource center and a radio station. The 70-acre campus is in a suburban area 95 miles southwest of Louisville. Including residence halls, there are 11 buildings on campus.

Student Life: About 77% of undergraduates are from Kentucky. Students come from 27 states, 5 foreign countries, and Canada. Ninety-three percent are from public schools; 7% from private. Ninety-six percent are white. Fifty-five percent are Protestant; 23% Catholic; 13% claim no religious affiliation. The average age of freshmen is 18; all undergraduates, 21. Thirty-four percent drop out by the end of their first year; 45% remain to graduate.

Housing: A total of 373 students can be accommodated in college housing. College-sponsored living facilities include 3 single-sex dormitories and 1 on-campus apartment. On-campus housing is guaranteed for all 4 years. Priority is given to out-of-town students. Fifty-eight percent of students commute. Alcohol is not permitted. All students may keep cars on campus.

Activities: About 23% of men belong to 3 national fraternities; about 31% of women belong to 2 national sororities. There are 31 groups on campus, including art, band, cheerleading, choir, chorale, chorus, computers, drama, ethnic, honors, literary magazine, musical theater, newspaper, pep band, professional, radio, religious, social, social service, student government, and yearbook. Popular campus events include Homecoming, Family Weekend, Little Sibling Weekend, Student Appreciation Week, Fall Greek Rush, Midnight Movie Nights, The Hanging of the Greens, All-campus Thanksgiving Dinner, Senior Banquet and Oak and Ivy Banquet, theater productions, and basketball weekends.

Sports: There are 7 intercollegiate sports for men and 7 for women, and intramural sports are offered based on student interest. Athletic and recreation facilities include a health and recreation center which houses an 800-seat gymnasium, fully equipped weight training center, racquetball courts, batting and pitching facilities for softball and baseball, and a multi-purpose auxiliary gymnasium. Outdoor facilities include a baseball park, a softball park, a soccer field, and additional practice fields for football and soccer. Varsity basketball games are played in the 5,000-seat Owensboro Sports Center.

Disabled Students: Sixty-four percent of the campus is accessible to disabled students. The following facilities are available: wheelchair ramps, elevators, special parking, specially equipped rest rooms, and special class scheduling.

Services: In addition to many counseling and information services, tutoring is available in most subjects.

Campus Safety and Security: Campus safety and security measures include 12-hour foot and vehicle patrol, escort service, informal discussions, and pamphlets, posters, and films. In addition, there are lighted pathways and sidewalks.

Programs of Study: KWC awards the B.A., B.S., B.M., B.M.E., and B.S.N. degrees. Associate degrees also are awarded. Bachelor's degrees are awarded in BIOLOGICAL SCIENCE (biology/biological science), BUSINESS (accounting, business administration and management, business economics, and human resources), COMMUNICATIONS AND THE ARTS (art, communications, dramatic arts, English, and music), COMPUTER AND PHYSICAL SCIENCE (chemistry, computer science, and physics), EDUCATION (art, elementary, middle school, music, physical, and secondary), ENGINEERING AND ENVIRONMENTAL DESIGN (preengineering), HEALTH PROFESSIONS (nursing, predentistry, and premedicine), SOCIAL SCIENCE (criminal justice, early childhood studies, history, political science/government, prelaw, psychology, and sociology). Natural sciences, education, business, and nursing are the strongest academically. Business, criminal justice, and nursing have the largest enrollments.

Required: All students are required to complete the following general education program of skills and content requirements: 9 hours each in humanities and social sciences, 8 hours in natural science, 6 hours in history, 3 hours each in religion, integrated studies and multicultural studies, and 2 hours in physical education. Students must demonstrate proficiency in math, computing, oral and written communication and foreign language. A total of 128 semester hours, including 36 in the major, with a minimum GPA of 2.0., is required in order to graduate.

Special: A cooperative program in early childhood development with Brescia College is available. Internships and student-designed majors are available in many programs and are established on an individual basis. A dual degree in engineering is offered with Auburn University and the University of Kentucky. A Washington semester and study abroad in England are also available. There are 8 national

honor societies on campus. Seven departments have honors programs.

Faculty/Classroom: Fifty-six percent of faculty are male; 44%, female. All teach undergraduates and 55% both teach and do research. The average class size in an introductory lecture is 22; in a laboratory, 10; and in a regular course offering, 15.

Admissions: About 85% of the 1993–94 applicants were accepted. The SAT scores for the 1993–94 freshman class were as follows: Verbal—77% below 500, 19% between 500 and 599, and 4% between 600 and 700; Math—59% below 500, 33% between 500 and 599, and 8% between 600 and 700. The ACT scores were 29% below 21, 30% between 21 and 23, 29% between 24 and 26, 5% between 27 and 28, and 7% above 28. About 39% of the current freshmen were in the top fifth of their class; 69% were in the top two fifths. Six freshmen graduated first in their class.

Requirements: A minimum GPA of 2.3 in core courses is required. In addition, applicants should have completed 13 high school units in college preparatory English, mathematics, science, social studies, and a foreign language, or the GED equivalent. Applicants are considered individually. Students must complete and submit ACT or SAT I scores if they have been out of high school fewer than 5 years. AP credits are accepted. Important factors used in the admissions decision are advanced placement or honor courses, leadership record, evidence of special talent, personality, intangible qualities, and extracurricular activities record.

Procedure: Freshmen are admitted fall, spring, and summer. Entrance exams should be taken during spring of the junior year and fall of the senior year. Application deadlines are open. The application fee is $15. Notification is sent on a rolling basis. There is a deferred admissions plan. A waiting list is an active part of the nursing program admissions procedure, with about 51% of applicants on the list.

Transfer: About 90 transfer students enrolled in 1993–94. Transfer applicants should have a minimum GPA of 2.0 in all course work and be in good standing at the previously attended institution. A total of 30 credits out of 128 must be completed at KWC.

Visiting: There are regularly scheduled orientations for prospective students, including a campus tour, meetings with faculty and students, and dining on campus. There are guides for informal visits and visitors may sit in on classes and stay overnight at the school. To arrange for a visit, contact the Admissions Office at (502) 926-3111, ext. 143 or (800) 999-0592.

Financial Aid: In 1993–94, 92% of all current freshmen and 90% of continuing students received some form of financial aid. About 88% of freshmen and 90% of continuing students received need-based aid. The average freshman award was $8100. Of that total, scholarships or need-based grants averaged $3000 ($7400 maximum); loans averaged $3000 ($4625 maximum); and work contracts averaged $900 ($1200 maximum). Fifty-one percent of undergraduate students work part-time. Average earnings from campus work for the school year are $900. The average financial indebtedness of the 1992–93 graduate was $11,000. KWC is a member of CSS. The FAF and the FAFSA are required. The deadline for financial aid applications is August 1.

International Students: There are currently 9 international students enrolled. They must take the TOEFL and achieve a minimum score of 500. Sat I or ACT scores are required of international students who do not have a TOEFL score or who want to play NCAA sports.

Computers: The college provides computer facilities for student use. The mainframe is an IBM AS400 Minicomputer. The campus computer network links all residential and academic buildings to a central unit. Software includes Harvard Graphics, Lotus 1-2-3, dBase IV, WordPerfect, WordStar, E-mail, Pagemaker, Corel Draw, PC Globe, PC USA, and Printshop. The system is available 24 hours a day through in-room network stations or residence hall study rooms. All students may access the system. It may be used from 8 A.M. to 11 P.M. There are no time limits on using the system. The fees are $10 per year.

Graduates: In 1992–93, 121 bachelor's degrees were awarded. The most popular majors among graduates were business (20%), criminal justice (13%), and biology (8%). Within an average freshman class, 45% graduate in 4 years and 48% in 5 years. Some 17 companies recruited on campus in 1992–93. In the 1992–93 graduating class, 58% of students were enrolled in graduate school within 6 months of graduation.

Admissions Contact: Gloria Smith Kunik, Director of Enrollment Services.

LINDSEY WILSON COLLEGE

Columbia, KY 42728   (502) 384-8100; (800) 264-0138 (in-state)   D-3

Full-time: 493 men, 513 women	Faculty: 44; IIB, --$
Part-time: 55 men, 107 women	Ph.D.s: 20%
Graduate: none	Student/Faculty: 23 to 1
Year: semesters, summer session	Tuition: $6080
Application Deadline: open	Room & Board: $3450
Freshman Class: 1089 applied, 865 accepted, 382 enrolled	
ACT: 18	**LESS COMPETITIVE**

Lindsey Wilson College, founded in 1903, is a private, coeducational liberal arts college affiliated with the United Methodist Church, offering 4 year programs in business administration, education, human services, and liberal studies. The library contains 250,828 volumes, 200,000 microform items, and 5220 audiovisual forms, and subscribes to 1260 periodicals. Computerized library sources and services include the card catalog, interlibrary loans, and database searching. Special learning facilities include a learning resource center and art gallery. The 40-acre campus is in a small town 100 miles southeast of Louisville. Including residence halls, there are 24 buildings on campus.

Student Life: About 94% of undergraduates are from Kentucky. Students come from 9 states and 12 foreign countries. Ninety percent are from public schools; 10% from private. Eighty-nine percent are white. Seventy-eight percent are Protestant; 16% claim no religious affiliation. The average age of freshmen is 19; all undergraduates, 24. Forty-five percent drop out by the end of their first year.

Housing: A total of 500 students can be accommodated in college housing. College-sponsored living facilities include single-sex dormitories, on-campus apartments, and married-student housing. In addition there are honors houses. On-campus housing is guaranteed for all 4 years. Fifty-three percent of students commute. Alcohol is not permitted. All students may keep cars on campus.

Activities: There are no fraternities or sororities on campus. There are 20 groups on campus, including art, cheerleading, choir, chorale, chorus, computers, drama, international, newspaper, pep band, political, professional, religious, social, social service, student government, and yearbook. Popular campus events include Hanging of the Greens, Homecoming, Parent Day, Tradition Day, and Founders Day.

Sports: There are 6 intercollegiate sports for men and 5 for women, and 8 intramural sports for men and 8 for women. Athletic and recreation facilities include a sports center, with a 1000-seat gymnasium, a weight training room, and the student union building.

Disabled Students: Eighty percent of the campus is accessible to disabled students. The following facilities are available: wheelchair ramps, special parking, specially equipped rest rooms, special class scheduling, and lowered drinking fountains.

Services: In addition to many counseling and information services, tutoring is available in every subject. There is remedial math, reading, and writing.

Campus Safety and Security: Campus safety and security measures include informal discussions, lighted pathways and sidewalks, and 12-hour foot and vehicle patrol.

Programs of Study: Lindsey awards the B.A. degree. Associate degrees also are awarded. Bachelor's degrees are awarded in BIOLOGICAL SCIENCE (biology/biological science), BUSINESS (accounting and business administration and management), COMMUNICATIONS AND THE ARTS (English), EDUCATION (elementary and secondary), SOCIAL SCIENCE (history, human services, liberal arts/general studies, and social work). Business, elementary education, and human services are the strongest academically. Elementary education and business have the largest enrollments.

Required: All students must complete general education core requirements, including courses in communication of ideas, mathematics, natural science, religion, humanities, fine arts, social behavioral science, and physical education, as well as a 1-hour personal development career seminar. A total of 128 semester hours, with a minimum GPA of 2.0, is required in order to graduate.

Special: Human services majors are offered a social services practicum in their field of study. Work-study programs, a general studies degree, and pass/fail options in some courses are available.

Faculty/Classroom: Forty-seven percent of faculty are male; 53%, female. The average class size in an introductory lecture is 26; in a laboratory, 20; and in a regular course offering, 26.

Admissions: About 79% of the 1993–94 applicants were accepted. The ACT scores for the 1993–94 freshman class were as follows: 40% below 21, 39% between 21 and 23, 10% between 24 and 26, 10% between 27 and 28, and 1% above 28. About 3 freshmen graduated first in their class.

Requirements: The ACT is required. Applicants should have completed 20 academic high school credits or the GED equivalent. AP and CLEP credits are accepted. Important factors used in the admissions decision are geographic diversity, recommendations by alumni,

recommendations by school officials, parents or siblings attending the school, and ability to finance college education.

Procedure: Freshmen are admitted fall and spring. Entrance exams should be taken during the junior year. Application deadlines are open. Notification is sent on a rolling basis. There is an early decision plan.

Transfer: About 89 transfer students enrolled in 1993–94. Transfer applicants are required to submit an official transcript from schools previously attended. An interview is recommended. A total of 30 credits out of 128 must be completed at Lindsey.

Visiting: There are regularly scheduled orientations for prospective students. There are guides for informal visits and visitors may sit in on classes. To arrange for a visit, contact the Admission Office at (800) 264–0138 or (502) 384–8100.

Financial Aid: In 1993–94 97% of all current freshmen and 93% of continuing students received some form of financial aid. About 95% of freshmen and 93% of continuing students received need-based aid. The average freshman award was $5000. Of that total, scholarships or need-based grants averaged $1000 ($2000 maximum); loans averaged $1500 ($2625 maximum); and work contracts averaged $800. Thirty-one percent of undergraduate students work part-time. Average earnings from campus work for the school year were $800. The average financial indebtedness of the 1992–93 graduate was $8500. Lindsey is a member of CSS. The FAF and the college's own financial statement are required. The deadline for financial aid applications is September.

International Students: There are currently 40 international students enrolled. The school actively recruits these students. They must take the TOEFL and achieve a minimum score of 490.

Computers: The college provides computer facilities for student use. The mainframe is a Data General MV/15,000. Twenty IBM PC/XT-compatibles are located in the main computing laboratory and 20 PCs are located in the English composition classroom/laboratory for word processing purposes. Mainly those enrolled in computing courses may access the system. There are no time limits on using the system and no fees.

Graduates: In a recent year, 100 bachelor's degrees were awarded. The most popular majors among graduates were elementary education (38%), business administration (35%), and human services (23%). Within an average freshman class, 15% graduate in 4 years. Some 18 companies recruited on campus in 1992–93.

Admissions Contact: Kevin A. Thompson, Director of Admissions.

MOREHEAD STATE UNIVERSITY
E-2
Morehead, KY 40351 (606) 783–2000; (800) 354–2090 (out-of-state)

Full-time: 2832 men, 3678 women	Faculty: 329; IIA, --$
Part-time: 261 men, 761 women	Ph.D.s: 54%
Graduate: 489 men, 1148 women	Student/Faculty: 20 to 1
Year: semesters, summer session	Tuition: $1800 ($4800)
Application Deadline: open	Room & Board: $2800

Freshman Class: 2961 applied, 2630 accepted, 1382 enrolled
ACT: 19   **LESS COMPETITIVE**

Morehead State University, founded in 1922, is a public, coeducational institution offering degree programs in applied science and technology, humanities, educational and behavioral sciences, and business. There are 4 undergraduate schools and one graduate school. In addition to regional accreditation, MSU has baccalaureate program accreditation with CSWE, NASM, NCATE, and NLN. The library contains 500,000 volumes, 900,000 microform items, and 102,000 audiovisual forms, and subscribes to 2000 periodicals. Computerized library sources and services include the card catalog and database searching. Special learning facilities include a learning resource center, art gallery, planetarium, radio station, TV station, a 320-acre farm complex, and a robotics laboratory. The 1044-acre campus is in a small town 60 miles east of Lexington. Including residence halls, there are 148 buildings on campus.

Student Life: About 85% of undergraduates are from Kentucky. Students come from 31 states, 33 foreign countries, and Canada. Ninety-five percent are from public schools; 5% from private. Ninety-five percent are white. The average age of freshmen is 19; all undergraduates, 21. Thirty-seven percent drop out by the end of their first year.

Housing: A total of 3801 students can be accommodated in college housing. College-sponsored living facilities include single-sex and coed dormitories, on-campus apartments, married-student housing, and fraternity houses. In addition there are honors houses and a cross-cultural house, and housing for farm students. On-campus housing is guaranteed for all 4 years. Fifty-four percent of students live on campus; of those, 30% remain on campus on weekends. Alcohol is not permitted. All students may keep cars on campus.

Activities: About 20% of men belong to 1 local and 13 national fraternities; about 20% of women belong to 7 national sororities. There are 95 groups on campus, including art, band, cheerleading, choir, chorale, chorus, computers, dance, drama, drill team, drum and bugle corps, ethnic, honors, international, jazz band, marching band,

musical theater, newspaper, orchestra, pep band, photography, political, professional, radio and TV, religious, social, social service, student government, symphony, and yearbook. Popular campus events include Homecoming, Greek Week, Parents Weekend, Black History Month, and Miss MSU Pageant.

Sports: There are 11 intercollegiate sports for men and 9 for women, and 24 intramural sports for men and 24 for women. Athletic and recreation facilities include an athletic complex, a 6500-seat gymnasium, a 10,000-seat stadium, a pool, and bowling lanes.

Disabled Students: Seventy-five percent of the campus is accessible to disabled students. The following facilities are available: wheelchair ramps, elevators, special parking, specially equipped rest rooms, special class scheduling, lowered drinking fountains, and lowered telephones.

Services: In addition to many counseling and information services, tutoring is available in most subjects. In addition, there is a reader service for the blind, and remedial math, reading, and writing.

Campus Safety and Security: Campus safety and security measures include 24-hour foot and vehicle patrol, escort service, shuttle buses, and informal discussions. In addition, there are emergency telephones and lighted pathways and sidewalks.

Programs of Study: MSU awards the A.B., B.S., B.B.A., B.M., B.M.Ed., B.S.N., B.S.W., and B.U.S. degrees. Associate and master's degrees also are awarded. Bachelor's degrees are awarded in AGRICULTURE (agriculture), BIOLOGICAL SCIENCE (biology/biological science and ecology), BUSINESS (accounting, banking and finance, business economics, management science, marketing management, and real estate), COMMUNICATIONS AND THE ARTS (advertising, communications, dramatic arts, English, journalism, music, and speech/debate/rhetoric), COMPUTER AND PHYSICAL SCIENCE (chemistry, data processing, earth science, geology, mathematics, and physics), EDUCATION (agricultural, art, business, elementary, health, home economics, industrial arts, middle school, music, physical, and special), ENGINEERING AND ENVIRONMENTAL DESIGN (industrial engineering technology and interior design), HEALTH PROFESSIONS (medical laboratory technology and nursing), SOCIAL SCIENCE (dietetics, food production/management/services, food science, geography, history, paralegal studies, philosophy, political science/government, psychology, social science, social work, sociology, and textiles and clothing). Biological sciences is the strongest academically. Elementary education has the largest enrollment.

Required: All students must complete 42 semester hours (45 for teacher certification) of general education courses, including 15 hours in communications and humanities, 12 in natural and mathematical sciences, 12 in social and behavioral sciences, and 3 in health or physical education. A total of 128 semester hours, with a minimum GPA of 2.0, is required in order to graduate.

Special: Cross-registration is offered with the University of Kentucky. Students may earn specialist certification in education. Study abroad in 3 countries, a Washington semester, a 3–2 engineering degree, dual majors, a general studies degree, credit for life experience, and pass/fail options are available. Nondegree study is possible. There is a freshman honors program on campus, as well as 9 national honor societies.

Faculty/Classroom: Sixty-five percent of faculty are male; 35%, female. No introductory courses are taught by graduate students. The average class size in an introductory lecture is 35; in a laboratory, 20; and in a regular course offering, 18.

Admissions: About 89% of the 1993–94 applicants were accepted. The ACT scores for the 1993–94 freshman class were as follows: 66% below 21, 20% between 21 and 23, 9% between 24 and 26, 3% between 27 and 28, and 2% above 28.

Requirements: A minimum GPA of 2.0 is required. The ACT (preferred) or SAT I is required. In addition, applicants should have completed the Kentucky precollege curriculum requirement. An interview is recommended. AP and CLEP credits are accepted.

Procedure: Freshmen are admitted to all sessions. Entrance exams should be taken in the spring of the junior year. Application deadlines are open. Notification is sent on a rolling basis.

Transfer: About 538 transfer students enrolled in 1993–94. Transfer applicants should have a minimum GPA of 2.0 with at least 12 credit hours earned and be in good standing at their previous institution. They must have completed a precollege curriculum or meet any deficiencies. A total of 32 credits out of 128 must be completed at MSU.

Visiting: There are regularly scheduled orientations for prospective students, consisting of registration for classes, advising, and an overview of MSU. There are guides for informal visits and visitors may sit in on classes and stay overnight at the school. To arrange for a visit, contact the Office of Admissions at (606) 783–2000.

Financial Aid: In 1993–94, 70% of all current freshmen and 68% of continuing students received some form of financial aid. About 65% of freshmen and 65% of continuing students received need-based aid. The average freshman award was $3500. Of that total, scholarships or need-based grants averaged $2000 ($4400 maximum); loans averaged $2000 ($2625 maximum); and work contracts

averaged $1302. Twenty-four percent of undergraduate students work part-time. Average earnings from campus work for the school year are $1302. The average financial indebtedness of the 1992–93 graduate was $6500. MSU is a member of CSS. The FAF and the college's own financial statement are required. The deadline for financial aid applications is April 1.

International Students: There are currently 68 international students enrolled. They must take the TOEFL or the University of Michigan Language Test and achieve a minimum score on the TOEFL of 500.

Computers: The college provides computer facilities for student use. The mainframes are 2 HP G-50s. Teaching laboratories have networked computers. All students may access the system. It may be used days and evenings. There are no time limits on using the system. The fees are $10 per semester.

Graduates: In 1992–93, 1085 bachelor's degrees were awarded. The most popular majors among graduates were elementary, reading, and special education (20%), sociology, social work, and corrections (8%), and management and marketing (8%). Within an average freshman class, 24% graduate in 4 years and 41% in 6 years. Some 500 companies recruited on campus in 1992–93.

Admissions Contact: Charles Myers, Director, Office of Admissions.

MURRAY STATE UNIVERSITY
B-4

Murray, KY 42071   (502) 762-3380

(800) 592–3977 (in-state), 272–4678 (out-of-state)

Full-time: 2811 men, 3194 women	Faculty: 300; IIA, --$
Part-time: 376 men, 591 women	Ph.Ds: 85%
Graduate: 473 men, 745 women	Student/Faculty: 20 to 1
Year: semesters, summer session	Tuition: $1780 ($4780)
Application Deadline: August 1	Room & Board: $2922
Freshman Class: 2288 applied, 1938 accepted, 1197 enrolled	
ACT: 22	COMPETITIVE

Murray State University, founded in 1922, is a publicly controlled, co-educational institution offering graduate and undergraduate degrees in business and public affairs, education, fine arts and communication, humanistic studies, industry and technology, and science. There are 6 undergraduate and 6 graduate schools. In addition to regional accreditation, MSU has baccalaureate program accreditation with AACSB, ABET, ACEJMC, ASLA, CSWE, NASAD, NASM, NCATE, and NLN. The library contains 450,000 volumes, and 2500 audiovisual forms, and subscribes to 3000 periodicals. Special learning facilities include a learning resource center, art gallery, natural history museum, radio station, TV station, and a biological station. The 232-acre campus is in a small town 130 miles northwest of Nashville.

Student Life: About 74% of undergraduates are from Kentucky. Students come from 44 states, 46 foreign countries, and Canada. Ninety percent are from public schools; 10% from private. Ninety-three percent are white. The average age of freshmen is 19; all undergraduates, 22.5. Thirty-two percent drop out by the end of their first year; 42% remain to graduate.

Housing: A total of 3200 students can be accommodated in college housing. College-sponsored living facilities include single-sex and coed dormitories and married-student housing. On-campus housing is guaranteed for all 4 years. Sixty percent of students commute. Alcohol is not permitted. All students may keep cars on campus.

Activities: About 30% of men belong to 14 national fraternities; about 30% of women belong to 1 local and 8 national sororities. There are 174 groups on campus, including art, band, cheerleading, chess, choir, chorale, chorus, computers, dance, drama, ethnic, honors, international, jazz band, literary magazine, marching band, musical theater, newspaper, orchestra, pep band, photography, political, professional, radio and TV, religious, social, student government, symphony, and yearbook.

Sports: There are 8 intercollegiate sports for men and 9 for women, and 30 intramural sports for men and 30 for women. Athletic and recreation facilities include a 16,500-seat stadium, 2 gymnasiums seating 6000, a gymnastics room, weight rooms, an indoor jogging track, racquetball courts, a swimming pool, and outdoor tennis, basketball, and volleyball courts, and _ _ course physical fitness trail.

Disabled Students: N _ ty-five percent of the campus is accessible to disabled students. The following facilities are available: wheelchair ramps, elevators, special parking, specially equipped rest rooms, special class scheduling, and lowered drinking fountains.

Services: In addition to many counseling and information services, tutoring is available in most subjects. There is also remedial math, reading, and writing available.

Campus Safety and Security: Campus safety and security measures include 24-hour foot and vehicle patrol, self defense education, escort service, and informal discussions. In addition, there are pamphlets, posters, films, emergency telephones, and lighted pathways and sidewalks.

Programs of Study: MSU awards the B.A., B.S., B.F.A., B.M., B.M.E., B.S.A., B.S.B., B.S.H.E., B.S.N., B.S.V.T.E., and B.I.S. degrees. Associate and master's degrees also are awarded. Bachelor's degrees are awarded in AGRICULTURE (agricultural mechanics, agriculture, animal science, fishing and fisheries, and horticulture), BIOLOGICAL SCIENCE (biochemistry, biology/biological science, and wildlife biology), BUSINESS (accounting, banking and finance, business administration and management, business economics, marketing/retailing/merchandising, and personnel management), COMMUNICATIONS AND THE ARTS (advertising, broadcasting, communications, dramatic arts, English, fine arts, French, German, journalism, languages, music, Spanish, and speech/debate/rhetoric), COMPUTER AND PHYSICAL SCIENCE (chemistry, computer programming, computer science, earth science, geology, mathematics, and physics), EDUCATION (agricultural, art, business, early childhood, elementary, foreign languages, health, home economics, industrial arts, middle school, music, and secondary), ENGINEERING AND ENVIRONMENTAL DESIGN (civil engineering technology, computer technology, construction technology, electrical/electronics engineering technology, and engineering technology), HEALTH PROFESSIONS (nursing, predentistry, premedicine, speech pathology/audiology, and veterinary science), SOCIAL SCIENCE (criminal justice, dietetics, economics, geography, history, parks and recreation management, philosophy, political science/government, prelaw, psychology, social work, and sociology). Premedicine, engineering, physics, and accounting are the strongest academically. Business, nursing, education, and engineering technology have the largest enrollments.

Required: All students must complete general education requirements, including 12 hours each in communications and basic skills, laboratory science, humanities, and social sciences. A total of 128 semester hours, including 30 in the major, with a minimum GPA of 2.0 are required to graduate.

Special: Cooperative programs, internships, study abroad in 14 countries through the national and international student exchange programs, dual majors, B.A.-B.S. degrees, 3–2 engineering degrees, and credit for life experience are offered. A degree in independent studies is offered. Non degree study is possible. There is a freshman honors program on campus, as well as 12 national honor societies, including Phi Beta Kappa.

Faculty/Classroom: All teach undergraduates. Graduate students teach 2% of introductory courses. The average class size in an introductory lecture is 30 and in a laboratory, 40.

Admissions: About 85% of the 1993–94 applicants were accepted. The ACT scores for the 1993–94 freshman class were as follows: 43% below 21, 28% between 21 and 23, 19% between 24 and 26, 7% between 27 and 28, and 3% above 28. About 40% of the current freshmen were in the top fifth of their class; 80% were in the top two fifths.

Requirements: MSU requires in-state applicants to be in the upper 50% of their class and out-of-state applicants to be in the upper 33% of their class. The ACT is required, with a minimum composite score of 18 in-state or 22 out-of-state. Applicants should have completed 20 high school academic credits, including 4 units in English, 3 in mathematics, 2 each in science and social studies, and 9 in electives. A portfolio or audition is required for art and music majors. An interview is recommended. AP and CLEP credits are accepted. Important factors used in the admissions decision are advanced placement or honor courses, parents or siblings attending the school, leadership record, recommendations by alumni, and recommendations by school officials.

Procedure: Freshmen are admitted to all sessions. Entrance exams should be taken before January of the enrollment year. Applications should be filed by August 1 for fall entry and December 1 for spring entry. Notification is sent on a rolling basis.

Transfer: About 643 transfer students enrolled in 1993–94. Transfer applicants must have a minimum GPA of 2.0 in at least 12 hours of degree credit. A total of 24 credits out of 128 must be completed at MSU.

Visiting: There are regularly scheduled orientations for prospective students. There are guides for informal visits and visitors may sit in on classes and stay overnight at the school. To arrange for a visit, contact the school relations office at (800) 272–4678 (out-of-state) or (800) 592–3977 (in-state).

Financial Aid: In 1993–94 60% of all current freshmen and 45% of continuing students received some form of financial aid. About 35% of freshmen received need-based aid. The average freshman award was $3322. Of that total, scholarships or need-based grants averaged $1247 ($4028 maximum); loans averaged $1710 ($2300 maximum); and work contracts averaged $1028 ($1973 maximum). Twenty percent of undergraduate students work part-time. MSU is a member of CSS. The FAF is required. The deadline for financial aid applications is February 1.

International Students: There are currently 154 international students enrolled. The school actively recruits these students. They must take the TOEFL and achieve a minimum score of 500.

Computers: The college provides computer facilities for student use. The mainframe is an IBM. Students may access the mainframe through computer laboratories in each of 6 colleges and the student center. PCs are also available at these locations. All students may access the system. There are no time limits and no fees.

Graduates: In 1992–93, 1011 bachelor's degrees were awarded. The most popular majors among graduates were early elementary education (9%), accounting (6%), and occupational safety and health (6%). Within an average freshman class, 38% graduate in 4 years, 45% in 5 years, and 50% in 6 years. Some 300 companies recruited on campus in an earlier year.

Admissions Contact: Phil Bryan, Dean of Admissions.

NORTHERN KENTUCKY UNIVERSITY D-1

Highland Heights, KY 41099   (606) 572–5220; (800) 637–9948

Full-time: 3131 men, 3899 women	Faculty: 377; IIA, --$
Part-time: 1407 men, 1848 women	Ph.D.s: 72%
Graduate: 160 men, 364 women	Student/Faculty: 19 to 1
Year: semesters, summer session	Tuition: $1720 ($4720)
Application Deadline: open	Room & Board: $2900

Freshman Class: 2582 applied, 2582 accepted, 1675 enrolled

ACT: 19   **NONCOMPETITIVE**

Northern Kentucky University, founded in 1968, is a publicly controlled institution offering programs in arts and sciences, business, and professional studies. There are 3 undergraduate and 4 graduate schools. In addition to regional accreditation, Northern has baccalaureate program accreditation with CAHEA, CSWE, NASM, and NLN. The 4 libraries contain 267,298 volumes, 31,565 microform items, and 2520 audiovisual forms, and subscribe to 1700 periodicals. Special learning facilities include a learning resource center, art gallery, radio station, TV station, and biology and geology museum. The 300-acre campus is in a suburban area 7 miles southeast of Cincinnati, Ohio. Including residence halls, there are 42 buildings on campus.

Student Life: About 76% of undergraduates are from Kentucky. Students come from 35 states, 40 foreign countries, and Canada. Ninety-seven percent are white. The average age of freshmen is 20; all undergraduates, 25.

Housing: A total of 996 students can be accommodated in college housing. College-sponsored living facilities include single-sex and coed dormitories and on-campus apartments. On-campus housing is available on a first-come, first-served basis. Priority is given to out-of-town students. Ninety-two percent of students commute. Alcohol is not permitted. All students may keep cars on campus.

Activities: About 2% of men belong to 6 national fraternities; about 2% of women belong to 4 national sororities. There are 80 groups on campus, including art, cheerleading, chorale, chorus, computers, drama, drill team, ethnic, film, gay, honors, international, jazz band, literary magazine, musical theater, newspaper, pep band, photography, political, professional, radio and TV, religious, social, social service, and student government. Popular campus events include Homecoming, Northern Noel, Music Fest, Rites of Spring, College Bowl, Greek Week, and Kentucky Awareness Week.

Sports: There are 6 intercollegiate sports for men and 5 for women, and 15 intramural sports for men and 13 for women. Athletic and recreation facilities include a 2000-seat gymnasium, baseball and soccer fields, tennis and racquetball courts, a track, a weight room, and a swimming pool.

Disabled Students: The entire campus is accessible to disabled students. The following facilities are available: elevators, special parking, specially equipped rest rooms, special class scheduling, lowered drinking fountains, and lowered telephones.

Services: In addition to many counseling and information services, tutoring is available in most subjects. There is a reader service for the blind, and remedial math, reading, and writing. There are also developmental education courses.

Campus Safety and Security: Campus safety and security measures include 24-hour foot and vehicle patrol, escort service, informal discussions, and pamphlets, posters, and films. In addition, there are emergency telephones and lighted pathways and sidewalks.

Programs of Study: Northern awards the B.A., B.S., B.Mus., B.Mus.Ed., B.S.N., and B.S.W. degrees. Associate and master's degrees also are awarded. Bachelor's degrees are awarded in BIOLOGICAL SCIENCE (biology/biological science), BUSINESS (accounting, labor studies, management science, marketing/retailing/merchandising, and organizational behavior), COMMUNICATIONS AND THE ARTS (art, dramatic arts, English, French, graphic design, journalism, music, performing arts, radio/television technology, Spanish, speech/debate/rhetoric, and studio art), COMPUTER AND PHYSICAL SCIENCE (chemistry, computer science, geology, information sciences and systems, mathematics, physics, and radiological technology), EDUCATION (art, business, elementary, industrial arts, middle school, music, physical, science, and secondary), ENGINEERING AND ENVIRONMENTAL DESIGN (construction technology, electrical/electronics engineering technology, industrial engineering

technology, manufacturing engineering, manufacturing technology, and preengineering), HEALTH PROFESSIONS (medical laboratory technology, mental health/human services, nursing, predentistry, premedicine, prepharmacy, preveterinary science, and respiratory therapy), SOCIAL SCIENCE (anthropology, economics, geography, history, international studies, philosophy, physical fitness/movement, political science/government, prelaw, psychology, public administration, social science, social work, and sociology). Education, nursing, biology, and technology fields have the largest enrollments.

Required: All students must complete 54 semester hours of general studies, including English composition, speech, and major and minor requirements. A total of 128 semester hours, with a minimum GPA of 2.0, is required to graduate.

Special: A 3–2 engineering degree is offered with the University of Kentucky. Cross-registration is possible through the Greater Cincinnati Area Consortium of colleges and universities. Study abroad in 6 countries, a Washington semester, internships for communication majors, on-campus work-study programs, an accelerated degree program, an interdisciplinary honors program, B.A.-B.S. degrees, dual majors, and pass/fail options are offered. There are co-op programs in most majors. Student-designed majors and credit for work experience are available. Nondegree study is possible. There is a freshman honors program on campus, as well as 8 national honor societies.

Faculty/Classroom: Sixty-seven percent of faculty are male; 33%, female. All teach undergraduates. No introductory courses are taught by graduate students. The average class size in a regular course offering is 26.

Admissions: All 1993–94 applicants were accepted. The ACT scores for the 1993–94 freshman class were as follows: 60% below 21, 25% between 21 and 23, 11% between 24 and 26, 3% between 27 and 28, and 1% above 28.

Requirements: The ACT is required. Students who score at least a 20 on the English and math portions of the ACT and who meet all precollege curriculum requirements, including 4 units of English, 3 units of math (algebra I, geometry, alegebra II), U.S. history, world civilization (for Kentucky residents only), and 2 units of science (biology and chemistry or physics), are granted regular admission. Others may be admitted with a stipulation or restriction on their admission. AP and CLEP credits are accepted.

Procedure: Freshmen are admitted to all sessions. Entrance exams should be taken prior to enrollment. Application deadlines are open, but the priority deadline is May 1. The fee is $25. Notification is sent on a rolling basis. There is an early admissions plan.

Transfer: About 670 transfer students enrolled in 1993–94. Students must be eligible to return to their previous institution. A total of 30 semester hours out of 128, with 9 in the major, must be completed at Northern.

Visiting: There are regularly scheduled orientations for prospective students, consisting of a 1-day program with sessions on student services and financial aid, activities, a campus tour, and academic information, advising, and registration. There are guides for informal visits, and visitors may sit in on classes and stay overnight at the school. To arrange for a visit, contact the Office of Admissions at (606) 572–5220 or (800) 637–9948.

Financial Aid: In 1993–94 33% of all current freshmen and 41% of continuing students received some form of financial aid. About 20% of freshmen and 30% of continuing students received need-based aid. The average freshman award was $2000. Of that total, scholarships or need-based grants averaged $1000 ($1720 maximum); loans averaged $2625; and work contracts averaged $1500 ($3230 maximum). Ten percent of undergraduate students work part-time. Average earnings from campus work for the school year are $2423. The average financial indebtedness of the 1992–93 graduate was $4000. The college's own financial statement and the FAFSA are required. The deadline for financial aid applications is April 1.

International Students: There are currently 152 international students enrolled. The school actively recruits these students. They must take the TOEFL and achieve a minimum score of 500.

Computers: The college provides computer facilities for student use. The mainframes are 2 DEC VAX 4000 Model 300s. Students can access the mainframes via 24 terminals in central computing laboratories and 10 in specific departments. There are 30 microcomputers in central computing laboratories and 30 dial-in modem lines available. The system may be used 24 hours a day and there are no time limits. The fees are $15 per semester.

Graduates: In 1992–93 934 bachelor's degrees were awarded. The most popular majors among graduates were elementary education (15%), psychology (8%), and accountancy (5%). Within an average freshman class, 49% graduate in 6 years. Some 98 companies recruited on campus in 1992–93.

Admissions Contact: Office of Admissions.

PIKEVILLE COLLEGE

F-3

Pikeville, KY 41501 — (606) 432-9325

Full-time: 250 men, 600 women   Faculty: 56; IIB, --$
Part-time: 20 men, 80 women   Ph.D.s: 60%
Graduate: none   Student/Faculty: 15 to 1
Year: semesters, summer session   Tuition: $5500
Application Deadline: September 1   Room & Board: $3000
Freshman Class: 378 applied, 170 enrolled
ACT: 20   **NONCOMPETITIVE**

Pikeville College, established in 1889, is a private, coeducational liberal arts institution affiliated with the Presbyterian Church. The 2 libraries contain 93,000 volumes, 14,500 microform items, and 5000 audiovisual forms, and subscribe to 355 periodicals. Computerized library sources and services include interlibrary loans and database searching. Special learning facilities include an art gallery. The 27-acre campus is in a small town 20 miles from the Virginia border in the eastern Kentucky hills. Including residence halls, there are 10 buildings on campus.

Student Life: About 90% of undergraduates are from Kentucky. Students come from 7 states and 4 foreign countries. Ninety-nine percent are from public schools. Ninety-eight percent are white. Most are Protestant. The average age of freshmen is 21; all undergraduates, 24. Thirty-five percent drop out by the end of their first year; 42% remain to graduate.

Housing: A total of 300 students can be accommodated in college housing. College-sponsored living facilities include single-sex dormitories and married-student housing. On-campus housing is guaranteed for all 4 years. Seventy-five percent of students commute. Alcohol is not permitted. All students may keep cars on campus.

Activities: There are no fraternities or sororities on campus. There are some groups and organizations on campus, including cheerleading, dance, drama, newspaper, religious, student government, and yearbook. Popular campus events include Founders Day.

Sports: There are 2 intercollegiate sports for men and 2 for women, and 4 intramural sports for men and 4 for women. Athletic and recreation facilities include a gymnasium and basketball and volleyball courts.

Disabled Students: Seventy percent of the campus is accessible to disabled students. The following facilities are available: wheelchair ramps, elevators, special parking, specially equipped rest rooms, and a new elevator from the main parking lot to the upper campus.

Services: In addition to many counseling and information services, tutoring is available in most subjects, including mathematics, English, biology, all physical sciences, and computers. There is also remedial math, reading, and writing.

Campus Safety and Security: Campus safety and security measures include 24-hour foot and vehicle patrol, shuttle buses, pamphlets, posters, and films, and lighted pathways and sidewalks.

Programs of Study: The college awards the B.A., B.S., and B.B.A. degrees. Associate degrees also are awarded. Bachelor's degrees are awarded in BIOLOGICAL SCIENCE (biology/biological science), BUSINESS (accounting and business administration and management), COMMUNICATIONS AND THE ARTS (English), COMPUTER AND PHYSICAL SCIENCE (chemistry, computer science, and mathematics), EDUCATION (business, early childhood, elementary, middle school, science, secondary, and special), HEALTH PROFESSIONS (nursing), SOCIAL SCIENCE (history, religion, and social work). Education, nursing, and biology are the strongest academically. Education has the largest enrollment.

Required: All students must complete core courses in humanities, English, social sciences, sciences, and mathematics, as well as 1 course each in religion, Appalachian studies, and computer science, and 2 in physical education. Additional requirements include 6 hours in a foreign language for the B.A. degree and a second laboratory science course for the B.S. degree. An overall GPA of 2.0, with 2.5 in the major, is required. To graduate, students must complete 120 hours, with 30 to 63 hours in the major.

Special: Students may earn up to 6 credits at other institutions while enrolled at the college. A 3-1 degree in medical technology is available in conjunction with Methodist Hospital. Business internships, B.A.-B.S. degrees, credit for life, military, and work experience, and pass/fail options are offered. Nondegree study is possible. There is a freshman honors program on campus.

Faculty/Classroom: Sixty-five percent of faculty are male; 35%, female. All teach undergraduates. The average class size in an introductory lecture is 30; in a laboratory, 10; and in a regular course offering, 20.

Admissions: The ACT scores for the 1993-94 freshman class were as follows: 31% below 21, 50% between 21 and 23, 11% between 24 and 26, 5% between 27 and 28, and 3% above 28. About 25% of the current freshmen were in the top fifth of their class; 60% were in the top two fifths. Eleven freshmen graduated first in their class.

Requirements: The ACT is required, and will be given after admission for placement purposes, as the college follows an open admissions policy. Applicants must graduate from an accredited secondary school or have a GED. An interview is recommended. AP and CLEP credits are accepted. Important factors used in the admissions decision are advanced placement or honor courses, recommendations by school officials, leadership record, parents or siblings attending the school, and personality, intangible qualities.

Procedure: Freshmen are admitted fall and spring. Applications should be filed by September 1 for fall entry and January for spring entry, along with an application fee of $10. The college accepts all applicants. Notification is sent on a rolling basis. There are early decision and early admissions plans. Sixty-seven early decision candidates were accepted for the 1993-94 class.

Transfer: Some 105 transfer students enrolled in 1993-94. Transfer applicants must be in good standing at their previously attended institution. A total of 40 credits out of 120 must be completed at the college.

Visiting: There are regularly scheduled orientations for prospective students, consisting of a campus tour and lunch. There are guides for informal visits and visitors may stay overnight at the school. To arrange for a visit, contact Dr. John Sanders at (606) 432-9325.

Financial Aid: In a recent year, 85% of all freshmen and 85% of continuing students received some form of financial aid. About 85% of freshmen and 85% of continuing students received need-based aid. The average freshman award was $2500. Of that total, scholarships or need-based grants averaged $3750 ($7000 maximum); loans averaged $2850 ($4000 maximum); and work contracts averaged $785 ($2000 maximum). Sixty percent of undergraduate students work part-time. Average earnings from campus work for the school year are $750. The FAF and the college's own financial statement are required. The deadline for financial aid applications is April.

International Students: There are currently 6 international students enrolled. They must take the TOEFL and achieve a minimum score of 500. The ACT must also be taken, for placement purposes.

Computers: The college provides computer facilities for student use. The mainframes are IBM Systems 36 and 38. There are 65 microcomputers available throughout the campus. Students taking special courses may access the system. There are no time limits on using the system and no fees.

Graduates: In 1992-93, 177 bachelor's degrees were awarded. The most popular majors among graduates were education (55%) and business (22%). Within an average freshman class, 5% graduate in 3 years, 25% in 4 years, 10% in 5 years, and 5% in 6 years. In the 1992 graduating class, 5% of the men and 5% of the women were enrolled in graduate school within 6 months of graduation; 90% of the men and 90% of the women had found employment.

Admissions Contact: Dr. John Sanders, Dean of Admissions.

SPALDING UNIVERSITY

D-2

Louisville, KY 40203 — (502) 585-7111

Full-time: 70 men, 519 women   Faculty: 61; IIB, --$
Part-time: 47 men, 216 women   Ph.D.s: 60%
Graduate: 95 men, 274 women   Student/Faculty: 10 to 1
Year: semesters, summer session   Tuition: $7896
Application Deadline: August 15   Room & Board: $2600
Freshman Class: 216 accepted, 163 enrolled
ACT: 19   **NONCOMPETITIVE**

Spalding University, established in 1814, is a private, coeducational institution affiliated with the Roman Catholic Church, offering undergraduate degrees in the arts, business, health science, preprofessional training, religious studies, and teacher preparation. There are 5 undergraduate and 4 graduate schools. In addition to regional accreditation, Spalding has baccalaureate program accreditation with CSWE, NCATE, and NLN. The library contains 154,555 volumes, 12,382 microform items, and 10,035 audiovisual forms, and subscribes to 403 periodicals. Computerized library sources and services include database searching. Special learning facilities include a learning resource center, art gallery, video production facilities, and audio recording studio. The 5-acre campus is in an urban area in downtown Louisville. Including residence halls, there are 6 buildings on campus.

Student Life: About 90% of undergraduates are from Kentucky. Students come from 19 states, 10 foreign countries, and Canada. Eighty-five percent are from public schools; 15% from private. Eighty-nine percent are white. Forty-three percent are Catholic; 40% Protestant. The average age of freshmen is 25; all undergraduates, 28. Twenty percent drop out by the end of their first year; 80% remain to graduate.

Housing: A total of 140 students can be accommodated in college housing. College-sponsored living facilities include coed dormitories. On-campus housing is guaranteed for all 4 years. Ninety percent of students commute. All students may keep cars on campus.

Activities: There are no fraternities or sororities on campus. There are 16 groups on campus, including art, cheerleading, choir, chorus, drama, ethnic, honors, international, literary magazine, newspaper, professional, religious, social, social service, and student government. Popular campus events include Halloween Dance, Holiday Reception, Founders Day, and the Rat Race.

Sports: There is 1 intercollegiate sport and 2 intramural sports each for men and women. Athletic and recreation facilities include a gymnasium and a weight and exercise room.

Disabled Students: Seventy-five percent of the campus is accessible to disabled students. The following facilities are available: wheelchair ramps, elevators, special parking, specially equipped rest rooms, and special class scheduling.

Services: In addition to many counseling and information services, tutoring is available in every subject. In addition, there is remedial math, reading, and writing.

Campus Safety and Security: Campus safety and security measures include self defense education, escort service, pamphlets, posters, and films, and lighted pathways and sidewalks.

Programs of Study: Spalding awards the B.A. and B.S. degrees. Associate, master's, and doctoral degrees also are awarded. Bachelor's degrees are awarded in BIOLOGICAL SCIENCE (biology/biological science), BUSINESS (business administration and management), COMMUNICATIONS AND THE ARTS (art, communications, and English), COMPUTER AND PHYSICAL SCIENCE (chemistry and mathematics), EDUCATION (early childhood, library science, middle school, and secondary), HEALTH PROFESSIONS (clinical science and nursing), SOCIAL SCIENCE (history, liberal arts/general studies, philosophy, psychology, religion, social work, and sociology). Nursing, education, and psychology are the strongest academically and have the largest enrollments.

Required: To graduate, students must earn 128 credits, with a maximum of 40 credits in the major for the B.A. degree and 50 credits for the B.S. degree, and a minimum overall GPA of 2.0. All students must complete 6 credits each in mathematics and computer applications, religious studies, literature, the arts, university studies, and sociology, and 3 credits each in English, communications, physics, biology, psychology, history, philosophy, and economics.

Special: Cross-registration is offered with the Kentuckiana Metroversity consortium. Internships, primarily in communications and education, and work-study programs are available. Study abroad, B.A.-B.S. degrees, dual and student-designed majors, and a liberal studies degree are offered. Credit is given for life, military, or work experience, and pass/fail options are available. Weekend College enables students to earn a bachelor's degree by attending classes only on weekends. There are 6 national honor societies on campus.

Faculty/Classroom: Thirty-five percent of faculty are male; 65%, female. Ninety-five percent teach undergraduates. No introductory courses are taught by graduate students. The average class size in an introductory lecture is 30; in a laboratory, 10; and in a regular course offering, 20.

Admissions: The ACT scores for the 1993–94 freshman class were as follows: 67% below 21, 19% between 21 and 23, 5% between 24 and 26, 5% between 27 and 28, and 2% above 28. About 25% of the current freshmen were in the top fifth of their class; 49% were in the top two fifths. Three freshmen graduated first in their class.

Requirements: A minimum GPA of 2.0 and the ACT are required. Applicants must be graduates of an accredited secondary school and should have completed 4 years of English and 2 each of a foreign language, mathematics, science, and social studies. An interview is recommended. AP and CLEP credits are accepted. Important factors used in the admissions decision are advanced placement or honor courses, recommendations by school officials, evidence of special talent, leadership record, and personality, intangible qualities.

Procedure: Freshmen are admitted to all sessions. Entrance exams should be taken by August 1. Applications should be filed by August 15 for fall entry and December 31 for spring entry, along with an application fee of $20. Notification is sent on a rolling basis. There is an early admissions plan.

Transfer: A total of 93 transfer students enrolled in 1993–94. It is preferred that applicants have a 2.5 G.P.A., but special circumstances will be considered. A total of 32 credits out of 128 must be completed at Spalding.

Visiting: There are regularly scheduled orientations for prospective students. There are guides for informal visits and visitors may sit in on classes and stay overnight at the school. To arrange for a visit, contact Dorothy Allen at (502) 585-7111.

Financial Aid: In 1993–94, 84% of all current freshmen and 92% of continuing students received some form of financial aid. About 74% of freshmen and 82% of continuing students received need-based aid. The average freshman award was $12,529. Of that total, scholarships or need-based grants averaged $2578 ($7800 maximum); loans averaged $3701 ($6625 maximum); and work contracts averaged $1584 ($2040 maximum). Seventy-seven percent of undergraduate students work part-time. Average earnings from campus work for the school year are $1271. The average financial indebtedness of the 1992–93 graduate was $13,144. Spalding is a member of CSS. The college's own financial statement and the FAFSA are required. The deadline for financial aid applications is March 15.

International Students: There are currently 13 international students enrolled. The school actively recruits these students. They must take the TOEFL and achieve a minimum score of 500. The student must also take the SAT I or the ACT.

Computers: Spalding provides computer facilities for student use. The mainframe is an HP unit. Fourteen microcomputers are available for academic use in 2 computer laboratories. There are no time limits on using the system and no fees. It is recommended that all students have personal computers.

Graduates: In 1992–93, 126 bachelor's degrees were awarded. The most popular majors among graduates were nursing (38%), business (16%), and education (16%). Within an average freshman class, 50% graduate in 4 years, 70% in 5 years, and 80% in 6 years. Some 35 companies recruited on campus in 1992–93. In the 1992 graduating class, 80% of all students had found employment within 6 months of graduation.

Admissions Contact: Dorothy Allen, Director of Admissions.

THOMAS MORE COLLEGE
D-1
Crestview Hills, KY 41017-3248

(606) 344-3332
(800) 548-7044 (in-state)

Full-time: 399 men, 412 women	**Faculty:** 67; IIB, --$
Part-time: 148 men, 340 women	**Ph.D.s:** 55%
Graduate: none	**Student/Faculty:** 12 to 1
Year: semesters, summer session	**Tuition:** $9182
Application Deadline: August 15	**Room & Board:** $3780
Freshman Class: 835 applied, 605 accepted, 286 enrolled	
SAT I or ACT: required	**COMPETITIVE**

Thomas More College, founded in 1921 as Villa Madonna College, is a private Catholic institution offering undergraduate programs in liberal arts and sciences. In addition to regional accreditation, Thomas More has baccalaureate program accreditation with CSWE and NLN. The library contains 118,000 volumes, 8300 microform items, and 1599 audiovisual forms, and subscribes to 504 periodicals. Computerized library sources and services include the card catalog, interlibrary loans, and database searching. Special learning facilities include a learning resource center. The 320-acre campus is in a suburban area 8 miles south of Cincinnati, Ohio. Including residence halls, there are 7 buildings on campus.

Student Life: About 80% of undergraduates are from Kentucky. Students come from 20 states and 6 foreign countries. Fifty-five percent are from public schools; 45% from private. Eighty-eight percent are white. Fifty percent are Catholic. The average age of freshmen is 18; all undergraduates, 20. Thirty-six percent drop out by the end of their first year; 55% remain to graduate.

Housing: A total of 250 students can be accommodated in college housing. College-sponsored living facilities include single-sex and coed dormitories. On-campus housing is guaranteed for the freshman year only. Priority is given to out-of-town students. Sixty-five percent of students commute. All students may keep cars on campus.

Activities: About 2% of men belong to 1 national fraternity. There are no sororities on campus. There are 30 groups on campus, including art, cheerleading, choir, computers, drama, ethnic, honors, literary magazine, newspaper, political, professional, religious, social, student government, and yearbook. Popular campus events include fall and spring formals, Homecoming Weekend, Spring Pig Roast, Boat Cruise, Spring Formal, Night of the Races, International Awareness Week, movies, and comedian and entertainer performances.

Sports: There are 5 intercollegiate and 3 intramural sports each for men and women. Athletic and recreation facilities include an athletic/convocation center with a 1500-seat indoor gymnasium and 2100-seat arena, plus baseball, soccer, and football fields, 16 tennis courts (8 indoor), 4 racquetball courts, a pool, a track, and weight and exercise rooms.

Disabled Students: Ninety-eight percent of the campus is accessible to disabled students. The following facilities are available: wheelchair ramps, elevators, special parking, and specially equipped rest rooms.

Services: In addition to many counseling and information services, tutoring is available in every subject. There also is remedial reading and writing.

Campus Safety and Security: Campus safety and security measures include 24-hour foot and vehicle patrol, informal discussions, pamphlets, posters, and films, and lighted pathways and sidewalks.

Programs of Study: Thomas More awards the B.A., B.S., and B.S.N. degrees. Associate degrees also are awarded. Bachelor's degrees are awarded in BIOLOGICAL SCIENCE (biology/biological science), BUSINESS (accounting, banking and finance, business administration and management, and business economics), COMMUNICATIONS AND THE ARTS (communications, dramatic arts, English, and fine arts), COMPUTER AND PHYSICAL SCIENCE (chemistry, com-

puter programming, computer science, mathematics, and physics), EDUCATION (art, business, elementary, middle school, music, science, and secondary), ENGINEERING AND ENVIRONMENTAL DESIGN (preengineering), HEALTH PROFESSIONS (medical laboratory technology, nursing, pharmacy, predentistry, premedicine, and preveterinary science), SOCIAL SCIENCE (economics, history, international studies, philosophy, political science/government, prelaw, psychology, religion, and theological studies). Sciences are the strongest academically. Business, mathematics, and sciences have the largest enrollments.

Required: All students must complete 56 to 61 hours of core requirements, including 6 credits each in English, theology, social sciences, global history, fine arts, philosophy, and natural sciences, and 3 each in foreign language, speech, and mathematics. A total of 128 credit hours, including 67 to 72 in the major, with a minimum GPA of 2.0 is required in order to graduate.

Special: There are co-op programs with the universities of Cincinnati, Dayton, Detroit, Kentucky, and Notre Dame leading to dual engineering degrees. Cross-registration is possible through the Greater Cincinnati Consortium. The college encourages dual majors. There are internships, B.A.-B.S. degrees, student-designed majors, work-study programs, credit for life experience, and pass/fail options. The Bachelor of Elected Studies degree provides adult learners with an individualized program. Nondegree study is possible.

Faculty/Classroom: All faculty members teach undergraduates. The average class size in an introductory lecture is 15; in a laboratory, 10; and in a regular course offering, 15.

Admissions: About 72% of the 1993–94 applicants were accepted. There was 1 National Merit semifinalist. Six freshmen graduated first in their class.

Requirements: The SAT I or the ACT is required, and the minimum composite score needed is 900 (450 verbal) on the SAT I or 20 on the ACT. Applicants should have completed 16 high school academic credits, including 4 years of English and 2 each of mathematics, science, social studies, and foreign language. AP and CLEP credits are accepted. Important factors used in the admissions decision are advanced placement or honor courses, leadership record, personality, intangible qualities, recommendations by school officials, and extracurricular activities record.

Procedure: Freshmen are admitted to all sessions. Entrance exams should be taken in the spring of the junior year or the fall of the senior year. Applications should be filed by August 15 for fall entry, along with an application fee of $15. Notification is sent on a rolling basis. There are early admissions and deferred admissions plans.

Transfer: A total of 36 transfer students enrolled in 1993–94. Applicants should be in good academic standing and have a minimum GPA of 2.0 in 24 semester hours earned. A total of 38 credits out of 128 must be completed at Thomas More.

Visiting: There are regularly scheduled orientations for prospective students. There are guides for informal visits and visitors may sit in on classes and stay overnight at the school. To arrange for a visit, contact the Admissions Office at (800) 548–7044 or (606) 344–3332.

Financial Aid: In an earlier year, 68% of all current freshmen received some form of financial aid. Scholarships or need-based grants averaged $1918; loans averaged $984 ($2600 maximum); and work contracts averaged $1079 ($1500 maximum). Eighteen percent of undergraduate students work part-time. Thomas More is a member of CSS. The FAF and the college's own financial statement are required. The deadline for financial aid applications is March 15.

International Students: There are currently 14 international students enrolled. Applicants must take the TOEFL or the University of Michigan Language Test and achieve a minimum score on the TOEFL of 520.

Computers: The college provides computer facilities for student use. The mainframe is a DEC MicroVAX II. There are also 30 PCs available in laboratories and classrooms. All students may access the system. There are no time limits on using the system.

Graduates: In 1992–93, 139 bachelor's degrees were awarded. Some 40 companies recruited on campus in 1992–93.

Admissions Contact: Victoria Thompson-Campbell, Director of Admissions.

TRANSYLVANIA UNIVERSITY
Lexington, KY 40508–1797

D-3

(606) 233–8242
(800) TRANSY U (out-of-state)

Full-time: 372 men, 495 women	Faculty: 65; IIB, av$
Part-time: 25 men, 26 women	Ph.D.s: 80%
Graduate: none	Student/Faculty: 13 to 1
Year: 4-4-1, summer session	Tuition: $10,670
Application Deadline: March 15	Room & Board: $4300
Freshman Class: 759 applied, 729 accepted, 243 enrolled	
SAT I Verbal/Math: 530/560	ACT: 26 VERY COMPETITIVE +

Transylvania University, founded in 1780, is an independent, coeducational liberal arts institution affiliated with the Christian Church (Dis-

ciples of Christ). The library contains 127,000 volumes, 64 microform items, and 841 audiovisual forms, and subscribes to 580 periodicals. Computerized library sources and services include the card catalog, interlibrary loans, and database searching. Special learning facilities include a learning resource center, art gallery, natural history museum, and radio station. The 30-acre campus is in an urban area 80 miles east of Louisville. Including residence halls, there are 21 buildings on campus.

Student Life: About 78% of undergraduates are from Kentucky. Students come from 28 states, 11 foreign countries, and Canada. Eighty-six percent are from public schools; 14% from private. Ninety-four percent are white. Sixty-four percent are Protestant; 19% claim no religious affiliation; 14% Catholic. The average age of freshmen is 18; all undergraduates, 19.5. Eighteen percent drop out by the end of their first year; 68% remain to graduate.

Housing: A total of 850 students can be accommodated in college housing. College-sponsored living facilities include single-sex and coed dormitories and on-campus apartments. On-campus housing is guaranteed for all 4 years. Eighty percent of students live on campus; of those, 85% remain on campus on weekends. All students may keep cars on campus.

Activities: About 58% of men belong to 4 national fraternities; about 65% of women belong to 4 national sororities. There are 51 groups on campus, including art, band, cheerleading, choir, chorus, computers, drama, ethnic, film, honors, international, jazz band, literary magazine, newspaper, pep band, political, professional, radio and TV, religious, social, social service, student government, and yearbook. Popular campus events include the Presentation Ball, Madrigal Dinner, T-Day Ball, Family Weekend, Campus Sing, and Kenan Lecture Series.

Sports: There are 5 intercollegiate and 10 intramural sports each for men and women. Athletic and recreation facilities include an 1800-seat gymnasium; a swimming pool; basketball, racquetball/handball, and tennis courts; an athletic field; and a weight room.

Disabled Students: Seventy percent of the campus is accessible to disabled students. The following facilities are available: wheelchair ramps, elevators, special parking, specially equipped rest rooms, and special class scheduling. Arrangements are made according to individual needs.

Services: In addition to many counseling and information services, tutoring is available in some subjects. There also is remedial writing.

Campus Safety and Security: Campus safety and security measures include 24-hour foot and vehicle patrol, self defense education, escort service, and shuttle buses. In addition, there are informal discussions, emergency telephones, lighted pathways and sidewalks, and a security presentation during freshman orientation.

Programs of Study: Transylvania awards the B.A. degree. Bachelor's degrees are awarded in BIOLOGICAL SCIENCE (biology/biological science), BUSINESS (business administration and management), COMMUNICATIONS AND THE ARTS (dramatic arts, English, French, music, Spanish, and studio art), COMPUTER AND PHYSICAL SCIENCE (chemistry, computer science, mathematics, and physics), EDUCATION (elementary, middle school, and secondary), SOCIAL SCIENCE (economics, history, philosophy, political science/government, psychology, religion, and sociology). Business, biology, and psychology have the largest enrollments.

Required: All students must complete general education distribution requirements in freshman studies, academic career skills, humanities, fine arts, natural sciences, mathematics/computer science, logic/linguistics, Western civilization, social sciences, modern foreign languages, non-Western civilization, and physical education. A total of 36 course units, including 10 to 15 in the major, with a minimum GPA of 2.0 is required in order to graduate.

Special: A 3–2 engineering degree with the University of Kentucky and Washington University in St. Louis is offered. Cross-registration with Spring Term Consortium schools, internships, study abroad in many countries, work-study programs, a Washington semester, dual majors, interdisciplinary majors such as sociology/anthropology, student-designed majors, and pass/fail options are available. Nondegree study is possible. There are 4 national honor societies on campus. All departments have honors programs.

Faculty/Classroom: Seventy-three percent of faculty are male; 27%, female. All teach undergraduates. The average class size in an introductory lecture is 20; in a laboratory, 15; and in a regular course offering, 16.

Admissions: About 96% of the 1993–94 applicants were accepted. The SAT scores for the 1993–94 freshman class were as follows: Verbal—41% below 500, 31% between 500 and 599, 22% between 600 and 700, and 6% above 700; Math—28% below 500, 32% between 500 and 599, 29% between 600 and 700, and 11% above 700. The ACT scores were 9% below 21, 18% between 21 and 23, 25% between 24 and 26, 16% between 27 and 28, and 32% above 28. About 75% of the current freshmen were in the top fifth of their class; 91% were in the top two fifths. There were 13 National Merit fi-

nalists and 6 semifinalists. A total of 38 freshmen graduated first in their class.

Requirements: A minimum GPA of 2.3, the SAT I or ACT, and 1 essay and 2 recommendations are required. An interview is strongly recommended. AP and CLEP credits are accepted. Important factors used in the admissions decision are recommendations by school officials, advanced placement or honor courses, leadership record, extracurricular activities record, and geographic diversity.

Procedure: Freshmen are admitted fall and winter. Entrance exams should be taken during the junior year or no later than December of the senior year. Early decision applications should be filed by November 1; regular applications, by March 15 for fall entry and November 1 for winter entry, along with an application fee of $20. Notification of early decision is sent December 1; regular decision, on a rolling basis beginning in December. There are early decision, early admissions, and deferred admissions plans. A total of 23 early decision candidates were accepted for the 1993–94 class.

Transfer: A total of 26 transfer students enrolled in 1993–94. Applicants must have a minimum GPA of 2.3 and should submit official copies of all college transcripts, 2 recommendations, and 1 essay. A high school transcript is required for those who completed high school within the previous 2 years. A total of 18 course units out of 36 must be completed at Transylvania.

Visiting: There are regularly scheduled orientations for prospective students, consisting of campus open houses in October and January for high school juniors and seniors, including a welcome program, an academic information fair, campus tours, a luncheon, a financial aid session, and prearranged admissions interviews. There are guides for informal visits and visitors may sit in on classes and stay overnight at the school. To arrange for a visit, contact the Admissions Office at (800) TRANSY U or (606) 233–8242.

Financial Aid: In 1993–94, 85% of all current freshmen and 86% of continuing students received some form of financial aid. About 53% of freshmen and 51% of continuing students received need-based aid. The average freshman award was $8713. Of that total, scholarships or need-based grants averaged $6332 ($14,970 maximum); loans averaged $1658 ($4125 maximum); and work contracts averaged $723 ($2500 maximum). Thirty-eight percent of undergraduate students work part-time. Average earnings from campus work for the school year are $1500. The average financial indebtedness of the 1992–93 graduate was $1642. Transylvania is a member of CSS. The FAF or FFS is required. The deadline for financial aid applications is April 1.

International Students: There are currently 8 international students enrolled. They must take the TOEFL and achieve a minimum score of 550.

Computers: Transylvania provides computer facilities for student use. The mainframe is an IBM 4381. There are about 110 terminals accessing the mainframe, and 210 personal computers are available. Word processing, learning programming languages, statistical software packages, and electronic mail are available. Computing facilities are available in all academic buildings and residence halls. All students may access the system 24 hours a day. There are no time limits on using the system and no fees.

Graduates: In a recent year, 210 bachelor's degrees were awarded. The most popular majors among graduates were business administration (35%), biology (13%), and psychology (11%). Within an average freshman class, 1% graduate in 3 years, 60% in 4 years, and 65% in 5 years. Twelve companies recruited on campus in a recent year. In a recent graduating class, 20% of all students were enrolled in graduate school within 6 months of graduation; 20% of all students had found employment.

Admissions Contact: Michael Suzo, Director of Admissions.

UNION COLLEGE
E-4
Barbourville, KY 40906-9989

Full-time: 346 men, 294 women	(606) 546–4223; (800) 489-8646
Part-time: 30 men, 53 women	Faculty: 49; IIB, --$
Graduate: 86 men, 217 women	Ph.D.s: 63%
Year: semesters, summer session	Student/Faculty: 13 to 1
Application Deadline: July 15	Tuition: $7000
Freshman Class: 484 applied, 384 accepted, 170 enrolled	Room & Board: $2790
SAT I Verbal/Math: 420/460	ACT: 20 COMPETITIVE

Union College, founded in 1879, is a private, coeducational liberal arts institution affiliated with the United Methodist Church. The library contains 88,000 volumes, 420 microform items, and 510 audiovisual forms, and subscribes to 434 periodicals. Computerized library sources and services include the card catalog and database searching. Special learning facilities include a learning resource center and a 1000-volume Abraham Lincoln collection. The 100-acre campus is in a small town 95 miles south of Lexington and 85 miles north of Knoxville, Tennessee. Including residence halls, there are 20 buildings on campus.

Student Life: About 69% of undergraduates are from Kentucky. Students come from 21 states, 7 foreign countries, and Canada. Ninety-three percent are from public schools; 7% from private. Eighty-nine percent are white. Twenty-nine percent are Protestant. The average age of freshmen is 19; all undergraduates, 24. Twenty-eight percent drop out by the end of their first year; 47% remain to graduate.

Housing: A total of 490 students can be accommodated in college housing. College-sponsored living facilities include single-sex dormitories, on-campus apartments, and married-student housing. On-campus housing is guaranteed for all 4 years and is available on a first-come, first-served basis. Priority is given to out-of-town students. Fifty-one percent of students live on campus; of those, 53% remain on campus on weekends. Alcohol is not permitted. All students may keep cars on campus.

Activities: There are no fraternities or sororities on campus. There are 22 groups on campus, including cheerleading, chess, choir, chorale, computers, drama, ethnic, honors, international, jazz band, literary magazine, newspaper, orchestra, pep band, professional, religious, social, social service, student government, and yearbook. Popular campus events include Parents Day, Homecoming, Daniel Boone Festival, Halloween and Valentine dances, Christmas concert, fall and spring theater productions, spring choir concert, and Wilson-Gross lecture series.

Sports: There are 8 intercollegiate sports for men and 7 for women, and 5 intramural sports for men and 3 for women. Athletic and recreation facilities include a 2800-seat campus stadium, a physical education building with a 3000-seat gymnasium, a pool, tennis courts, a weight training center, an athletic training center, a baseball stadium, and fields for football, soccer, and softball.

Disabled Students: Fifty-eight percent of the campus is accessible to disabled students. The following facilities are available: wheelchair ramps, elevators, special parking, specially equipped rest rooms, special class scheduling, lowered drinking fountains, and lowered telephones.

Services: In addition to many counseling and information services, tutoring is available in most subjects. There is a tutoring laboratory with computer support. In addition, there is remedial math, reading, and writing.

Campus Safety and Security: Campus safety and security measures include 24-hour foot and vehicle patrol and lighted pathways and sidewalks.

Programs of Study: Union awards the B.A., B.S., and B.Mus. degrees. Associate and master's degrees also are awarded. Bachelor's degrees are awarded in BIOLOGICAL SCIENCE (biology/biological science), BUSINESS (accounting, business administration and management, business law, office supervision and management, and sports management), COMMUNICATIONS AND THE ARTS (dramatic arts, English, fine arts, journalism, music, and speech/debate/rhetoric), COMPUTER AND PHYSICAL SCIENCE (chemistry, computer programming, information sciences and systems, and physics), EDUCATION (business, early childhood, elementary, middle school, music, physical science, secondary, and special), ENGINEERING AND ENVIRONMENTAL DESIGN (preengineering), SOCIAL SCIENCE (criminal justice, history, prelaw, psychology, social science, and sociology). Education, sciences, social sciences, and humanities are the strongest academically. Education, business, and social sciences have the largest enrollments.

Required: All students are required to complete a 46-credit liberal education core, including 12 to 13 hours each in basic competencies and humanities, 9 in history/behavioral sciences, and 7 to 8 in natural sciences. English composition and 3 hours of physical education also are required. A total of 128 semester hours, including 30 in the major, with a minimum GPA of 2.0 is required in order to graduate.

Special: A 3–2 engineering degree is offered with the University of Kentucky. Work-study programs, study abroad in 6 countries, and internships with area business and in sociology and psychology are available. A 16-credit-hour Appalachian studies semester, dual majors, a general studies degree, and credit for life and work experience are offered. There is a freshman honors program on campus and two departments have honors programs.

Faculty/Classroom: Fifty-two percent of faculty are male; 48%, female. All teach undergraduates. No introductory courses are taught by graduate students. The average class size in an introductory lecture is 25; in a laboratory, 16; and in a regular course offering, 15.

Admissions: About 79% of the 1993–94 applicants were accepted. The SAT scores for the 1993–94 freshman class were as follows: Verbal—87% below 500, 9% between 500 and 599, and 4% between 600 and 700; Math—75% below 500, 17% between 500 and 599, and 8% between 600 and 700. The ACT scores were 47% below 21, 29% between 21 and 23, 17% between 24 and 26, 6% between 27 and 28, and 1% above 28. About 26% of the current freshmen were in the top fifth of their class; 77% were in the top two fifths. About 9 freshmen graduated first in their class.

Requirements: Union requires applicants to be in the upper 60% of their class. A minimum GPA of 2.0 is required. The SAT I or ACT is required, as is a minimum GPA of 2.0. In addition, applicants should have completed 20 high school academic credits, including 4 years in English, 3 in mathematics, and 2 each in science, social studies, and history, as well as electives. An interview or audition is recommended. AP and CLEP credits are accepted. Important factors used in the admissions decision are evidence of special talent, geographic diversity, advanced placement or honor courses, parents or siblings attending the school, and extracurricular activities record.

Procedure: Freshmen are admitted fall, spring, and summer. Entrance exams should be taken by January of the senior year. Applications should be filed by July 15 for fall entry, December 15 for spring entry, and May 15 for summer entry, along with an application fee of $20. Notification is sent on a rolling basis. There are early admissions and deferred admissions plans.

Transfer: About 110 transfer students enrolled in 1993–94. Transfer applicants should have a minimum GPA of 2.0. A total of 30 credits out of 128 must be completed at Union.

Visiting: There are regularly scheduled orientations for prospective students, consisting of advising and registration, parents sessions, and break-out sessions. There are guides for informal visits and visitors may sit in on classes and stay overnight at the school. To arrange for a visit, contact Admissions at (800) 489-8646.

Financial Aid: In 1993–94, 86% of all current freshmen and 89% of continuing students received some form of financial aid. The average freshman award was $5460. Of that total, scholarships or need-based grants averaged $990 ($8150 maximum); loans averaged $1802 ($3825 maximum); and work contracts averaged $1008 ($1200 maximum). Thirty-six percent of undergraduate students work part-time. Average earnings from campus work for the school year are $1000. The average financial indebtedness of the 1992–93 graduate was $2132. Union is a member of CSS. The FAF is required. The deadline for financial aid applications is March 15.

International Students: There are currently 10 international students enrolled. The school actively recruits these students. They must take the TOEFL or the University of Michigan Language Test and achieve a minimum score on the TOEFL of 550.

Computers: The college provides computer facilities for student use. The mainframes are an HP3000, an AT&T, and a UNIX-based super micro. There are 55 terminals on campus located in the science center and main classroom buildings, as well as 20 Apple Macintosh microcomputers in English writing laboratories. All students may access the system. There are no time limits on using the system and no fees.

Graduates: In 1992–93, 235 bachelor's degrees were awarded. The most popular majors among graduates were education (29%), business (22%), and social sciences-sociology (13%). Within an average freshman class, 47% graduate in 4 years, 54% in 5 years, and 56% in 6 years. In the 1992 graduating class, 13% of the men and 11% of the women were enrolled in graduate school within 6 months of graduation; 57% of the men and 39% of the women had found employment.

Admissions Contact: Donald Hapward, Director of Admissions.

UNIVERSITY OF KENTUCKY

D-3

Lexington, KY 40506–0032

(606) 257-2000
(800) 432-0967 (in-state)

Full-time: 7421 men, 7324 women	Faculty: 1200; I, -$
Part-time: 1133 men, 1612 women	Ph.D.s: 98%
Graduate: 3018 men, 3094 women	Student/Faculty: 12 to 1
Year: semesters, summer session	Tuition: $2278 ($6198)
Application Deadline: June 1	Room & Board: $2874
Freshman Class: 7769 applied, 5689 accepted, 2675 enrolled	
ACT: 25	VERY COMPETITIVE

The University of Kentucky, founded in 1865, is a public, coeducational land-grant institution offering undergraduate and graduate programs in a variety of areas. There are 13 undergraduate schools and one graduate school. In addition to regional accreditation, UK has baccalaureate program accreditation with AACSB, ABET, ACEJMC, ACPE, ADA, AHEA, APTA, ASLA, CAHEA, CSWE, FIDER, NAAB, NASAD, NASM, NCATE, NLN, NRPA, and SAF. The 13 libraries contain 2,459,497 volumes, 4,614,981 microform items, and 61,767 audiovisual forms, and subscribe to 26,889 periodicals. Computerized library sources and services include the card catalog and database searching. Special learning facilities include a learning resource center, art gallery, natural history museum, radio station, and TV station. The 764-acre campus is in a suburban area 75 miles south of Cincinnati. Including residence halls, there are 350 buildings on campus.

Student Life: About 84% of undergraduates are from Kentucky. Students come from 50 states, 111 foreign countries, and Canada. Eighty-five percent are from public schools; 15% from private. Ninety percent are white. The average age of freshmen is 18; all undergrad-

uates, 22. Twenty percent drop out by the end of their first year; 50% remain to graduate.

Housing: A total of 6166 students can be accommodated in college housing. College-sponsored living facilities include single-sex and coed dormitories, on-campus apartments, married-student housing, fraternity houses, and sorority houses. In addition there are honors houses, language houses, and special interest houses. On-campus housing is available on a first-come, first-served basis. Sixty-nine percent of students commute. Alcohol is not permitted. All students may keep cars on campus.

Activities: About 16% of men belong to 22 national fraternities; about 16% of women belong to 17 national sororities. There are 230 groups on campus, including band, cheerleading, chess, choir, chorale, chorus, computers, dance, drama, drill team, ethnic, gay, honors, international, jazz band, literary magazine, marching band, musical theater, newspaper, orchestra, pep band, photography, political, professional, radio and TV, religious, social, social service, student government, symphony, and yearbook. Popular campus events include Homecoming, Little Kentucky Derby, Cultural Diversity Week, Spotlight Jazz Series, Excelsior, and Big Blue Madness.

Sports: There are 8 intercollegiate sports for men and 8 for women, and 24 intramural sports for men and 24 for women. Athletic and recreation facilities include a 58,000-seat football stadium, a 24,500-seat arena for basketball and other activities, an aquatic center and swimming pool, baseball fields, a training center, indoor tennis courts, and a field house.

Disabled Students: Eighty percent of the campus is accessible to disabled students. The following facilities are available: wheelchair ramps, elevators, special parking, specially equipped rest rooms, special class scheduling, lowered drinking fountains, and lowered telephones.

Services: In addition to counseling and information services, there is a reader service for the blind and remedial math.

Campus Safety and Security: Campus safety and security measures include 24-hour foot and vehicle patrol, self defense education, escort service, and shuttle buses. In addition, there are informal discussions, pamphlets, posters, films, emergency telephones, lighted pathways and sidewalks.

Programs of Study: UK awards the B.A., B.S., B.Arch., B.B.A., B.F.A., B.H.S., and B.M. degrees. Master's and doctoral degrees also are awarded. Bachelor's degrees are awarded in AGRICULTURE (agricultural economics, agriculture, animal science, forestry and related sciences, and horticulture), BIOLOGICAL SCIENCE (biology/biological science, botany, entomology, microbiology, and zoology), BUSINESS (accounting, banking and finance, business economics, hotel/motel and restaurant management, and marketing/retailing/merchandising), COMMUNICATIONS AND THE ARTS (advertising, art history and appreciation, arts administration/management, broadcasting, communications, dramatic arts, English, fine arts, French, German, Italian, journalism, Latin, linguistics, music, music performance, Russian, Spanish, studio art, and telecommunications), COMPUTER AND PHYSICAL SCIENCE (chemistry, computer science, geology, mathematics, and physics), EDUCATION (agricultural, art, business, early childhood, elementary, foreign languages, health, home economics, industrial arts, mathematics, middle school, music, physical, science, secondary, social studies, and special), ENGINEERING AND ENVIRONMENTAL DESIGN (chemical engineering, civil engineering, electrical/electronics engineering, landscape architecture/design, materials engineering, mechanical engineering, and mining and mineral engineering), HEALTH PROFESSIONS (medical laboratory technology, nursing, physical therapy, physician's assistant, public health, and radiological science), SOCIAL SCIENCE (anthropology, dietetics, economics, food science, geography, history, interdisciplinary studies, Latin American studies, philosophy, political science/government, psychology, social work, sociology, and textiles and clothing). Pharmacy, architecture, allied health, political science, sociology, and agriculture programs are the strongest academically. Finance, accounting, and marketing have the largest enrollments.

Required: All students must maintain at least a 2.0 GPA and complete at least 120 credit hours. Students must demonstrate competency in mathematics, foreign language, writing, and oral communications. Required studies include courses in basic skills, inference and communicative skills, disciplinary requirements, and cross-disciplinary requirements.

Special: Co-op programs are offered in engineering, business, computer science, mathematics, and agriculture. The Academic Common Market allows students in 14 southern states to study outside the university. Internships in a variety of fields, study abroad in 36 countries, work-study programs with the university and local businesses, and credit for life experience are also available. An accelerated degree program, B.A.-B.S. degrees, dual and double majors, a general studies degree, student-designed majors, a 3–2 engineering degree with several small schools in Kentucky, nondegree study, and pass/fail op-

tions are also offered. There is a freshman honors program on campus, as well as 12 national honor societies, including Phi Beta Kappa.

Faculty/Classroom: Seventy-six percent of faculty are male; 24%, female. Graduate students teach 4% of introductory courses. The average class size in an introductory lecture is 100; in a laboratory, 15; and in a regular course offering, 30.

Admissions: About 73% of the 1993–94 applicants were accepted. There were 44 National Merit finalists. About 90 freshmen graduated first in their class.

Requirements: A minimum GPA of 2.0 is required. The SAT I or ACT is required. Minimum scores vary with the GPA. Applicants must complete 11 Carnegie units, including 4 years of English, 3 of mathematics, and 2 each of science and social studies. A 4th year of mathematics, 2 years of foreign language, and 1 year of fine arts also are recommended. A portfolio is required for art studio courses, and an audition is required for music performance. AP and CLEP credits are accepted. Important factors used in the admissions decision are extracurricular activities record, leadership record, evidence of special talent, geographic diversity, and advanced placement or honor courses.

Procedure: Freshmen are admitted to all sessions. Entrance exams should be taken before Christmas of the senior year. Applications should be filed by June 1 for fall entry, along with an application fee of $15. Notification is sent on a rolling basis. There is a deferred admissions plan. A waiting list is an active part of the admissions procedure, with about 16% of applicants on the list.

Transfer: A total of 947 transfer students enrolled in 1992–93. Transfer students need a minimum GPA of 2.0. If they have fewer than 24 credit hours, they must meet freshmen admission standards. With 24 credits or more, the SAT I or ACT is not needed. A total of 30 credits out of 120 must be completed at UK.

Visiting: There are regularly scheduled orientations for prospective students, including a campus tour, an explanation of admission, housing and financial aid information, and information regarding campus activities. There are guides for informal visits and visitors may sit in on classes. To arrange for a visit, contact the UK Visitor Center at (606) 257-3595.

Financial Aid: In a recent year, 53% of all current freshmen and 52% of continuing students received some form of financial aid. Scholarships or need-based grants averaged $1920; loans averaged $1500 ($3500 maximum); and work contracts averaged $1200 ($2500 maximum). Thirty-five percent of undergraduate students work part-time. The average financial indebtedness of the 1992–93 graduate was $2500. UK is a member of CSS. The FAF and the FAFSA are required. The deadline for financial aid applications is April 1.

International Students: There are currently 1157 international students enrolled. The school actively recruits these students. They must take the TOEFL and achieve a minimum score of 525.

Computers: The university provides computer facilities for student use. The mainframes are an IBM 3090/6055, a Prime 6050, and a Convex/HP Meta Series System. There are 50 terminals to access the Prime and IBM mainframes in the UK Computing Center. There are 574 microcomputers in 13 public computer laboratories, and students may access the university system via phone modem. Several colleges also operate computer laboratories and classrooms for their students. All students may access the system 24 hours daily in the computing center and various hours in laboratories. There are no time limits on using the system and no fees.

Graduates: In 1992–93, 2780 bachelor's degrees were awarded. The most popular majors among graduates were business (21%), health professions (13%), and social science (8%). Within an average freshman class, 20% graduate in 4 years, 45% in 5 years, and 50% in 6 years. Some 550 companies recruited on campus in 1992–93.

Admissions Contact: Randy Mills, Associate Director for Recruitment.

UNIVERSITY OF LOUISVILLE
D-2

Louisville, KY 40292 (502) 588-6531; (800) 334-8635 (out-of-state)

Full-time: 21,864 men and women	Faculty: 1111; I, --$
Part-time: none	Ph.D.s: 61%
Graduate: 5819 men and women	Student/Faculty: 15 to 1
Year: semesters, summer session	Tuition: $2480 ($4980)
Application Deadline: open	Room & Board: $3468
Freshman Class: 4778 applied, 3074 accepted, 1841 enrolled	
SAT I or ACT: required	**VERY COMPETITIVE**

The University of Louisville, founded in 1798, is a public, coeducational institution offering a wide range of undergraduate and academic graduate programs. There are 8 undergraduate schools. In addition to regional accreditation, U of L has baccalaureate program accreditation with AACSB, ABET, ACEJMC, ASLA, CAHEA, NAAB, NASM, and NLN. The 5 libraries contain 1,100,000 volumes, and subscribe to 11,797 periodicals. Computerized library sources and services include the card catalog, interlibrary loans, and database searching. Special learning facilities include a learning resource center, art gallery, planetarium, and radio station. The 140-acre campus is in an urban area.

Student Life: About 91% of undergraduates are from Kentucky. Students come from 2 foreign countries. Ninety percent are from public schools. Eighty-six percent are white. The average age of freshmen is 19; all undergraduates, 27.

Housing: A total of 1100 students can be accommodated in college housing. College-sponsored living facilities include coed dormitories, on-campus apartments, off-campus apartments, married-student housing, fraternity houses, and sorority houses. On-campus housing is available on a first-come, first-served basis. Alcohol is not permitted. All students may keep cars on campus.

Activities: There are 14 local fraternities and 10 local sororities on campus. There are 50 groups on campus, including art, band, cheerleading, chess, choir, chorale, chorus, computers, dance, drama, ethnic, film, gay, honors, international, jazz band, literary magazine, marching band, musical theater, newspaper, opera, orchestra, pep band, photography, political, professional, radio and TV, religious, social, social service, student government, and symphony.

Sports: There are 8 intercollegiate sports for men and 7 for women, and 42 intramural sports for men and 37 for women. Athletic and recreation facilities include a 19,400-seat gymnasium and a football stadium.

Disabled Students: The following facilities are available: wheelchair ramps, elevators, special parking, specially equipped rest rooms, special class scheduling, lowered drinking fountains, and lowered telephones.

Services: In addition to many counseling and information services, tutoring is available in every subject.

Campus Safety and Security: Campus safety and security measures include 24-hour foot and vehicle patrol, escort service, informal discussions, and pamphlets, posters, and films. In addition, there are lighted pathways and sidewalks.

Programs of Study: U of L awards the B.A., B.S., and B.F.A. degrees. Associate, master's, and doctoral degrees also are awarded. Bachelor's degrees are awarded in BIOLOGICAL SCIENCE (biology/biological science, botany, and zoology), BUSINESS (marketing/retailing/merchandising), COMMUNICATIONS AND THE ARTS (art history and appreciation, communications, dramatic arts, English, fine arts, French, German, linguistics, music, music history and appreciation, Russian, and Spanish), COMPUTER AND PHYSICAL SCIENCE (chemistry, computer programming, computer science, geology, information sciences and systems, mathematics, and physics), EDUCATION (art, business, early childhood, elementary, foreign languages, health, middle school, music, physical, science, secondary, and teaching English as a second language/foreign language), ENGINEERING AND ENVIRONMENTAL DESIGN (chemical engineering, civil engineering, computer engineering, electrical/electronics engineering, engineering, engineering technology, industrial engineering technology, and mechanical engineering), HEALTH PROFESSIONS (dental hygiene, medical laboratory technology, medical science, nursing, and physical therapy), SOCIAL SCIENCE (American studies, anthropology, economics, geography, history, humanities, philosophy, political science/government, psychology, public administration, Russian and Slavic studies, sociology, and urban studies). Engineering is the strongest academically. The arts and sciences have the largest enrollments.

Required: Distribution requirements include at least 6 hours each in social sciences, natural sciences, the history of world civilizations, and humanities. Freshmen are required to take college writing or advanced composition, and 2 physical education courses. A total of 122 semester hours, including 46 to 60 hours in the major, with a minimum GPA of 2.5, is required in order to graduate.

Special: Cross-registration with other schools, study abroad, work-study programs, and B.A.-B.S. degrees are offered. A general studies degree, nondegree study, and pass/fail options are available. There is a freshman honors program on campus. One department has an honors program.

Faculty/Classroom: The average class size in an introductory lecture is 200 and in a laboratory, 30.

Admissions: About 64% of the 1993–94 applicants were accepted. The ACT scores for the 1993–94 freshman class were as follows: 10% below 21, 51% between 1 and 15, 20% between 16 and 21, 18% between 22 and 24, and 2% above 24. There were 18 National Merit finalists and 48 semifinalists.

Requirements: A minimum GPA of 2.0 is required. The ACT, with a minimum composite score of 20, or the SAT I, with a minimum score of 450 on each section, is required. Applicants must have 20 academic credits, including 4 units of English, 3 in mathematics, and 2 each in history, science, and social studies. AP and CLEP credits are accepted.

Procedure: Freshmen are admitted fall, spring, and summer. Entrance exams should be taken in October of the senior year. Application deadlines are open. Notification is sent on a rolling basis. The ap-

plication fee is $25. There are early decision and early admissions plans.

Transfer: Transfer students must have a minimum GPA of 2.0. A total of 30 credits out of 122 must be completed at U of L.

Visiting: There are regularly scheduled orientations for prospective students. There are guides for informal visits and visitors may sit in on classes. To arrange for a visit, contact Admissions at (800) 334–8635, ext. 6531.

Financial Aid: In a recent year, 65% of all current freshmen received some form of financial aid. About 50% of students received need-based aid. The average freshman award was $1200. Forty percent of undergraduate students work part-time. Average earnings from campus work for the school year are $750. U of L is a member of CSS. The FAF and the college's own financial statement are required. The deadline for financial aid applications is April 15.

International Students: There are currently 424 international students enrolled. They must take the TOEFL and achieve a minimum score of 550.

Computers: The college provides computer facilities for student use. All students may access the system.

Graduates: In a recent year, 3064 bachelor's degrees were awarded.

Admissions Contact: Dr. Robert Parrent, Director of Admissions for School Relations.

WESTERN KENTUCKY UNIVERSITY   C-4
Bowling Green, KY 42101

(502) 745–5422
(800) 452–3095 (in-state)

Full-time: 4746 men, 5939 women	**Faculty:** 557; IIA, --$
Part-time: 955 men, 2071 women	**Ph.Ds:** 70%
Graduate: 559 men, 1480 women	**Student/Faculty:** 19 to 1
Year: semesters, summer session	**Tuition:** $1708 ($4704)
Application Deadline: August 1	**Room & Board:** $3100
Freshman Class: 4345 applied, 3832 accepted, 2274 enrolled	
ACT: 21	**COMPETITIVE**

Western Kentucky University, founded in 1906, is a public, coeducational institution, with undergraduate and graduate programs in liberal arts, health science, business, agricultural and technical studies, art and fine arts, professional training, music, and teacher preparation. There are 5 undergraduate schools and one graduate school. In addition to regional accreditation, WKU has baccalaureate program accreditation with AACSB, ABET, ACEJMC, ADA, NASM, NCATE, NLN, and NRPA. The 4 libraries contain 833,941 volumes, 1,584,174 microform items, and 14,232 audiovisual forms, and subscribe to 5203 periodicals. Computerized library sources and services include the card catalog, interlibrary loans, and database searching. Special learning facilities include a learning resource center, planetarium, radio station, TV station, and the Kentucky Museum. The 200-acre campus is in a suburban area 65 miles north of Nashville. Including residence halls, there are 54 buildings on campus.

Student Life: About 82% of undergraduates are from Kentucky. Students come from 46 states, 36 foreign countries, and Canada. Ninety-two percent are white. The average age of freshmen is 19; all undergraduates, 23.8. Thirty-five percent drop out by the end of their first year; 44% remain to graduate.

Housing: A total of 5300 students can be accommodated in college housing. College-sponsored living facilities include single-sex and coed dormitories. On-campus housing is available on a first-come, first-served basis. Seventy-three percent of students commute. Alcohol is not permitted. All students may keep cars on campus.

Activities: About 12% of men belong to 15 national fraternities; about 13% of women belong to 10 national sororities. There are 168 groups on campus, including band, cheerleading, choir, chorale, chorus, computers, dance, drama, drill team, ethnic, gay, honors, international, jazz band, literary magazine, marching band, musical theater, newspaper, opera, orchestra, pep band, political, professional, radio and TV, religious, social, social service, student government, symphony, and yearbook. Popular campus events include Homecoming, Halloween, Hanging of the Green, Evening of Dance, and International Day.

Sports: There are 9 intercollegiate sports for men and 6 for women, and 24 intramural sports for men and 24 for women. Athletic and recreation facilities include a 19,900-seat stadium, gymnasiums, a pool, a track, a 13,500-seat arena, basketball and tennis courts, baseball and softball fields, facilities for bowling, billiards, and table tennis, a movie theater, and a night spot. There is also a student health and activities center with indoor track, weight room, aerobics studio, racquetball courts, Olympic size pool, and 4 more gymnasiums.

Disabled Students: The following facilities are available: wheelchair ramps, elevators, special parking, specially equipped rest rooms, and special services are available for students with special needs through the Student Life Office.

Services: In addition to many counseling and information services, tutoring is available in some subjects, with both departmental and freelance tutoring available. In addition, there is remedial math and writing.

Campus Safety and Security: Campus safety and security measures include 24-hour foot and vehicle patrol, self defense education, escort service, and shuttle buses. In addition, there are informal discussions, pamphlets, posters, and films, and lighted pathways and sidewalks.

Programs of Study: The University awards the B.A., B.S., B.F.A., B.M., B.S.N., and B.G.S. degrees. Associate and master's degrees also are awarded. Bachelor's degrees are awarded in AGRICULTURE (agriculture), BIOLOGICAL SCIENCE (biochemistry, biology/biological science, and genetics), BUSINESS (accounting, banking and finance, business administration and management, business economics, hotel/motel and restaurant management, and marketing/retailing/merchandising), COMMUNICATIONS AND THE ARTS (advertising, broadcasting, communications, design, dramatic arts, English, fine arts, French, German, journalism, music, photography, public relations, Spanish, and speech/debate/rhetoric), COMPUTER AND PHYSICAL SCIENCE (chemistry, computer science, earth science, geology, information sciences and systems, mathematics, and physics), EDUCATION (art, business, elementary, health, home economics, industrial arts, middle school, music, physical, science, and special), ENGINEERING AND ENVIRONMENTAL DESIGN (civil engineering technology, electrical/electronics engineering technology, engineering technology, environmental science, interior design, and mechanical engineering technology), HEALTH PROFESSIONS (health care administration, medical laboratory technology, nursing, predentistry, premedicine, public health, and speech pathology/audiology), SOCIAL SCIENCE (anthropology, dietetics, economics, geography, history, parks and recreation management, philosophy, political science/government, prelaw, psychology, religion, social science, social work, sociology, and textiles and clothing). Teacher education, journalism, and biology are the strongest academically. Accounting, elementary education, and psychology have the largest enrollments.

Required: To graduate, all students must complete at least 128 semester hours, with a varying number of hours in the major, and maintain a minimum GPA of 2.0. Curricula must include 53 to 54 semester hours of general education requirements, and 42 semester hours in upper-division courses. One Western civilization course must be taken.

Special: Internships in many areas, study abroad in 3 countries, work-study programs, and co-op programs with the universities of Louisville and Kentucky, and Eastern Kentucky University are offered. Accelerated degree programs are available in some majors. Dual majors include history and government, mathematics and physical science, and physics and engineering. A general studies degree, student-designed majors, and a 3–2 engineering degree are offered. Credit for life, military, or work experience may be granted, and non-degree study is possible. There is a freshman honors program on campus, as well as 32 national honor societies.

Faculty/Classroom: Sixty-eight percent of faculty are male; 32%, female. Graduate students teach 3% of introductory courses. The average class size in an introductory lecture is 34; in a laboratory, 20; and in a regular course offering, 26.

Admissions: About 88% of the 1993–94 applicants were accepted. The ACT scores for the 1993–94 freshman class were as follows: 51% below 21, 26% between 21 and 23, 13% between 24 and 26, 6% between 27 and 28, and 4% above 28. There were 5 National Merit semifinalists.

Requirements: A minimum GPA of 2.2 is required. The ACT, with a minimum composite score of 14 for in-state students, and 19 for out-of-state students, is required. Out-of-state students may be permitted to substitute the SAT I. Other admissions requirements include graduation from an accredited secondary school with 20 academic credits, including 4 years of English, 3 of mathematics, and 2 each of science and social studies. The GED also is accepted. AP and CLEP credits are accepted. Important factors used in the admissions decision are advanced placement or honor courses, recommendations by school officials, parents or siblings attending the school, recommendations by alumni, and evidence of special talent.

Procedure: Freshmen are admitted to all sessions. Entrance exams should be taken by fall of the senior year. Applications should be filed by August 1 for fall entry and January 1 for spring entry, along with an application fee of $15. Notification is sent on a rolling basis. There are early admissions and deferred admissions plans.

Transfer: About 910 transfer students enrolled in 1993–94. Transfer students must have a minimum GPA of 2.0 and a minimum number of credit hours earned. Two official transcripts must be presented; an interview is advised. A total of one third of the 128 credits required for the bachelor's degree must be completed at WKU.

Visiting: There are regularly scheduled orientations for prospective students. There are guides for informal visits and visitors may sit in on classes and stay overnight at the school. To arrange for a visit, contact the Office of Admissions at (502) 745-2551.

Financial Aid: In 1993–94, 61% of all current freshmen and 56% of continuing students received some form of financial aid. About 43% of freshmen and 38% of continuing students received need-based aid. The average freshman award was $3781. Of that total, scholarships or need-based grants averaged $500 ($7548 maximum); loans averaged $2934 ($5500 maximum); and work contracts averaged $1700 ($2110 maximum). Ten percent of undergraduate students work part-time. Average earnings from campus work for the school year are $1628. The average financial indebtedness of the 1992–93 graduate was $7115. The college's own financial statement and CPS Calculation are required. The deadline for financial aid applications is April 1.

International Students: There are currently 137 international students enrolled. They must take the TOEFL and achieve a minimum score of 500. The student must also take the ACT.

Computers: The college provides computer facilities for student use. The mainframes are a DEC VAX 6320 and an IBM 9121–260. More than 500 microcomputers are located in the library, student center, and most major classroom buildings. Some departments maintain their own computer laboratories. All students may access the system. It may be used during laboratory hours; anytime with individual modems. There are no time limits on using the system and no fees.

Graduates: In 1992–93, 1818 bachelor's degrees were awarded. The most popular majors among graduates were elementary education (16%), general studies (6%), and psychology (5%). Within an average freshman class, 2% graduate in 3 years, 13% in 4 years, 16% in 5 years, and 1% in 6 years. Some 171 companies recruited on campus in 1992–93.

Admissions Contact: Cheryl Chambless, Director of Admissions.

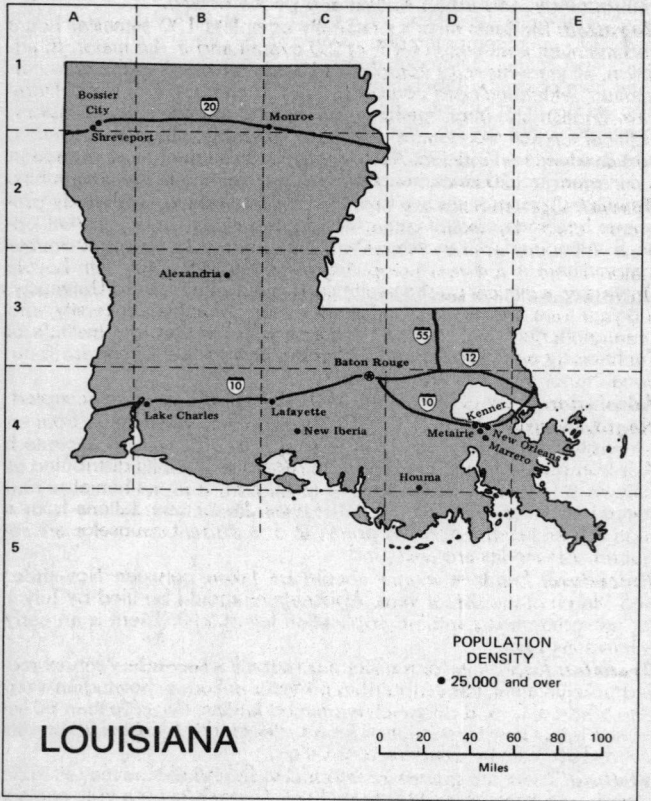

LOUISIANA

POPULATION
DENSITY

● 25,000 and over

0   20   40   60   80   100
Miles

CENTENARY COLLEGE OF LOUISIANA

Shreveport, LA 71104

A-1

(318) 869-5131
(800) 234-4448 (out-of-state)

Full-time: 345 men, 430 women	Faculty: 64; IIB, av$
Part-time: 13 men, 31 women	Ph.D.s: 92%
Graduate: 88 men, 158 women	Student/Faculty: 12 to 1
Year: 4-4-1, summer session	Tuition: $8406
Application Deadline: February 15	Room & Board: $3420
Freshman Class: 495 applied, 434 accepted, 210 enrolled	
SAT I Verbal/Math: 500/550	ACT: 25 COMPETITIVE +

Centenary College of Louisiana, founded in 1825, is a private, coeducational institution, affiliated with the United Methodist Church, offering graduate and undergraduate degrees in the liberal arts, music, business, geology, and education. There are 3 graduate schools. In addition to regional accreditation, Centenary has baccalaureate program accreditation with NASM and ACS. The 2 libraries contain 175,000 volumes, 269,000 microform items, and 888 audiovisual forms, and subscribe to 901 periodicals. Computerized library sources and services include the card catalog, interlibrary loans, and database searching. Special learning facilities include an art gallery, a radio station, and a theater. The 65-acre campus is in a suburban area 180 miles south of Dallas. Including residence halls, there are 18 buildings on campus.

Student Life: About 60% of undergraduates are from Louisiana. Students come from 23 states and 6 foreign countries. Seventy percent are from public schools; 30% from private. Eighty-six percent are white. Sixty-six percent are Protestant; 17% Catholic; 14% claim no religious affiliation. The average age of freshmen is 18; all undergraduates, 20.8. Twenty-eight percent drop out by the end of their first year; 55% remain to graduate.

Housing: A total of 676 students can be accommodated in college housing. College-sponsored living facilities include single-sex dormitories. In addition there is a women's honors house. On-campus housing is guaranteed for all 4 years. Sixty-five percent of students live on campus; of those, 70% remain on campus on weekends. Alcohol is not permitted. All students may keep cars on campus.

Activities: About 24% of men belong to 4 national fraternities; about 24% of women belong to 2 national sororities. There are 40 groups on campus, including band, cheerleading, choir, chorale, chorus, dance, drama, film, honors, jazz band, literary magazine, musical theater, newspaper, opera, orchestra, pep band, photography, political,

professional, radio and TV, religious, social, social service, student government, symphony, and yearbook. Popular campus events include the Fall Ball, April Fest, Homecoming, Dooda Parade, President's Convocation, and Founders Day.

Sports: There are 7 intercollegiate sports for men and 7 for women, and 5 intramural sports for men and 5 for women. Athletic and recreation facilities include a stadium, a 3000-seat gymnasium, and a weight room, basketball, racquetball, and tennis courts; and soccer/softball fields.

Disabled Students: Ninety percent of the campus is accessible to disabled students. The following facilities are available: wheelchair ramps, elevators, special parking, specially equipped rest rooms, special class scheduling, and lowered drinking fountains.

Services: In addition to many counseling and information services, tutoring is available in most subjects. There is a writing laboratory as well.

Campus Safety and Security: Campus safety and security measures include 24-hour foot and vehicle patrol, informal discussions, pamphlets, posters, and films, and emergency telephones. In addition, there are lighted pathways and sidewalks.

Programs of Study: Centenary awards the B.A., B.S., and B.M. degrees. Master's degrees also are awarded. Bachelor's degrees are awarded in BIOLOGICAL SCIENCE (biochemistry, biology/biological science, and biophysics), BUSINESS (accounting, business administration and management, and business economics), COMMUNICATIONS AND THE ARTS (dance, English, fine arts, music, and speech/debate/rhetoric), COMPUTER AND PHYSICAL SCIENCE (chemistry, mathematics, and physics), EDUCATION (art, elementary, foreign languages, middle school, music, science, and secondary), ENGINEERING AND ENVIRONMENTAL DESIGN (preengineering), HEALTH PROFESSIONS (occupational therapy, physical therapy, predentistry, and premedicine), SOCIAL SCIENCE (economics, history, philosophy, political science/government, prelaw, psychology, and sociology). Physical sciences, chemistry, biology, English, music, and theater/speech are the strongest academically. Business has the largest enrollment.

Required: To graduate, all students must complete 124 semester hours, with 45 in the major and 30 at the upper-division level, including a writing and speaking class in the major at the junior level, and must maintain a minimum GPA of 2.0. Core curriculum requirements include courses in the humanities and social sciences, with 2 semesters each of English, mathematics, laboratory sciences, and a foreign language. In addition, students must take courses in religion, cultural perspectives, and physical education, complete a community service project, study or live in a different culture, and fulfill career explorations.

Special: Centenary offers study abroad in 5 countries, cross-registration with Associated Colleges of the South, internships in all majors, a Washington semester, and a work-study program with the college itself. A 3-1 communication disorders degree with Louisiana State University Medical Center is possible, as is a 3-2 engineering degree with Washington University in St. Louis and Southern Methodist, Louisiana Tech, and Case Western Reserve universities. Preveterinary studies, general studies and interdisciplinary degrees, and student-designed majors are possible. There is a freshman honors program on campus, as well as 2 national honor societies. Ten departments have honors programs.

Faculty/Classroom: Seventy-five percent of faculty are male; 25% female. All teach undergraduates and 75% also do research. No introductory courses are taught by graduate students. The average class size in an introductory lecture and in a laboratory is 20 and in a regular course offering, 11.

Admissions: About 88% of the 1993-94 applicants were accepted. The SAT scores for the 1993-94 freshman class were as follows: Verbal—47% below 500, 37% between 500 and 599, 14% between 600 and 700, and 2% above 700; Math—32% below 500, 34% between 500 and 599, 33% between 600 and 700, and 1% above 700. The ACT scores were 15% below 21, 31% between 21 and 23, 20% between 24 and 26, 18% between 27 and 28, and 16% above 28. About 50% of the current freshmen were in the top fifth of their class; 72% were in the top two fifths. There were 2 National Merit finalists, and 5 freshmen who graduated first in their class.

Requirements: Centenary requires applicants to be in the upper 50% of their class. A minimum GPA of 2.5 is required. The SAT I or ACT is required. Applicants should be high school graduates with a minimum composite score of 950 on the SAT I or 20 on the ACT, although accepted students average 1050 and 24, respectively. Secondary school preparation should include 15 academic credits, including 4 of English, 3 each of mathematics and science, 2 each of a foreign language and history, 1 of social studies, and electives. An essay and an interview are required. Music students must audition; art

students are advised to present a portfolio. AP and CLEP credits are accepted. Important factors used in the admissions decision are extracurricular activities record, leadership record, advanced placement or honors courses, and evidence of special talent.

Procedure: Freshmen are admitted to all sessions. Entrance exams should be taken by the fall of the senior year. Applications should be filed by February 15 for fall entry, along with an application fee of $30. Notification is sent on a rolling basis. There are early admissions and deferred admissions plans.

Transfer: About 49 transfer students enrolled in 1993–94. Transfer applicants must have a minimum GPA of 2.0 and demonstrate good performance in a liberal arts curriculum. A total of 30 credits out of 124 must be completed at Centenary.

Visiting: There are regularly scheduled orientations for prospective students. There are guides for informal visits, and visitors may sit in on classes and stay overnight at the school. To arrange for a visit, contact Dorothy Bird Gwin at (318) 869–5131 or (800) 234–4448.

Financial Aid: In 1993–94, 84% of all current freshmen and 82% of continuing students received some form of financial aid. About 52% of freshmen and 40% of continuing students received need-based aid. The average freshman award was $7300. Of that total, scholarships or need-based grants averaged $5450 ($11,820 maximum); loans averaged $2470 ($2625 maximum); and work contracts averaged $1230 ($1300 maximum). Twenty-four percent of undergraduate students work part-time. Average earnings from campus work for the school year are $950. The average financial indebtedness of the 1992–93 graduate was $8583. Centenary is a member of CSS. The FAFSA must be submitted; the FAF is accepted. A financial statement is required. The deadline for financial aid applications is December 15.

International Students: There are currently 11 international students enrolled. The school actively recruits these students. They must take the TOEFL and achieve a minimum score of 550.

Computers: The college provides computer facilities for student use. The mainframe is an IBM System 36. There are 12 mainframe terminals in a terminal room, 50 IBMs available in the chemistry, biology, and computer laboratories, and 20 PCs in the library. Students enrolled in computer classes may access the system. It may be accessed according to availability.

Graduates: In 1992–93, 162 bachelor's degrees were awarded. The most popular majors among graduates were business (25%), life sciences (12%), and education (10%). Within an average freshman class, 40% graduate in 4 years, 51% in 5 years, and 55% in 6 years. Twelve companies recruited on campus in 1992–93.

Admissions Contact: Dorothy Bird Gwin, Dean of Enrollment Management.

DILLARD UNIVERSITY
D-4
New Orleans, LA 70122-3097 (504) 286–4670

Full-time: 1573 men and women	Faculty: 100; IIB, --$
Part-time: 2 men, 9 women	Ph.Ds: 46%
Graduate: none	Student/Faculty: 16 to 1
Year: trimesters, summer session	Tuition: $6400
Application Deadline: July 1	Room & Board: $3550
Freshman Class: 1999 applied, 1376 accepted, 651 enrolled	
ACT: 20	COMPETITIVE

Dillard University, established in 1930, is an independent, coeducational, nonsectarian liberal arts institution, affiliated with the United Church of Christ and the United Methodist Church, offering undergraduate programs in business, education, humanities, natural sciences, nursing, and social sciences. There are 6 undergraduate schools. In addition to regional accreditation, Dillard has baccalaureate program accreditation with NLN. The library contains 135,000 volumes, and subscribes to 687 periodicals. Special learning facilities include a radio station. The 35-acre campus is in an urban area in New Orleans. Including residence halls, there are 19 buildings on campus.

Housing: College-sponsored living facilities include dormitories. On-campus housing is available on a first-come, first-served basis.

Activities: There are 5 national fraternities and 5 national sororities. There are a number of groups on campus, including choir, drama, ethnic, honors, newspaper, professional, and social service.

Disabled Students: Special parking is available.

Services: In addition to many counseling and information services, tutoring is available in some subjects. There is remedial math, reading, and writing.

Programs of Study: Dillard awards the B.A., B.S., and B.S.N. degrees. Bachelor's degrees are awarded in BIOLOGICAL SCIENCE (biology/biological science), BUSINESS (accounting and business administration and management), COMMUNICATIONS AND THE ARTS (art, communications, dramatic arts, English, French, German, languages, music, Spanish, and speech/debate/rhetoric), COMPUTER AND PHYSICAL SCIENCE (chemistry, computer science, mathematics, and physics), EDUCATION (elementary, health, physical, secondary, and special), ENGINEERING AND ENVIRONMENTAL

DESIGN (cooperative engineering and preengineering), HEALTH PROFESSIONS (music therapy, nursing, and premedicine), SOCIAL SCIENCE (criminal justice, economics, history, philosophy, political science/government, psychology, religion, social welfare, sociology/anthropology, and urban studies and public policy).

Required: Students must successfully complete 130 semester hours and maintain a minimum GPA of 2.0 overall and in the major. In addition, all students must complete 44 semester hours in the core curriculum, which includes courses in English composition, world literature, English literature, mathematics, natural sciences, world history, political science, economics, university assembly, physical education, and academic orientation. Additionally, each student must engage in a minimum of 120 clock hours of volunteer service in the community.

Special: Opportunities are provided for internships, work-study programs, credit by examination, nondegree study, and pass/fail options. All social science majors are encouraged to pursue a double major. There is a 4-year co-op degree in music therapy with Loyola University, a clinical public health curriculum with Howard University, a 5-year joint degree in urban studies with Columbia University, and preengineering dual degree programs with the Georgia Institute of Technology and Auburn and Columbia universities. There are 6 national honor societies on campus.

Admissions: About 69% of the 1993–94 applicants were accepted.

Requirements: The SAT I or ACT is required. Graduation from an accredited secondary school is required; a GED will be accepted. Applicants must submit an academic record of 20 units distributed as follows: 8 in academic electives, 4 in English, 3 in mathematics and natural sciences, and 2 in social studies. Recommendations from a high school teacher and the principal or a student counselor are required. AP credits are accepted.

Procedure: Entrance exams should be taken between November and March of the senior year. Applications should be filed by July 1 for fall entry, along with an application fee of $10. There is an early admissions plan.

Transfer: Applicants for transfer must submit a secondary school record or equivalent, transcripts from previous colleges showing an average grade of C, and personal recommendations. No more than 60 semester hours may be submitted for transfer credit. A total of 70 credits out of 130 must be completed at Dillard.

Visiting: There are guides for informal visits and visitors may sit in on classes and stay overnight at the school. To arrange for a visit, contact the Director of Admissions at (504) 286–4670.

Financial Aid: In 1993–94, 90% of continuing students received some form of financial aid. The FAFSA financial statement is required. The deadline for financial aid applications is March 31.

International Students: They must take the TOEFL.

Computers: The college provides computer facilities for student use.

Admissions Contact: Mrs. Vernese B. O'Neal, Director of Admissions.

GRAMBLING STATE UNIVERSITY
B-1
Grambling, LA 71245 (318) 274–2435

Full-time: 3268 men, 4565 women	Faculty: 253; IIA, --$
Part-time: 144 men, 185 women	Ph.Ds: n/av
Graduate: 228 men, 499 women	Student/Faculty: 31 to 1
Year: semesters, summer session	Tuition: $2100 ($2975)
Application Deadline: July 15	Room & Board: $2612
Freshman Class: 5926 applied, 3126 accepted, 2162 enrolled	
ACT: 16	NONCOMPETITIVE

Grambling State University, founded in 1901, is a public, coeducational liberal arts institution. There are 6 undergraduate schools. In addition to regional accreditation, Grambling has baccalaureate program accreditation with NASM and NCATE. The library contains 249,538 volumes, 20,573 microform items, and 3908 audiovisual forms, and subscribes to 1360 periodicals. Computerized library sources and services include interlibrary loans. Special learning facilities include a radio station. The 340-acre campus is in a small town 60 miles from Shreveport. Including residence halls, there are 67 buildings on campus.

Student Life: About 58% of undergraduates are from Louisiana. Students come from 42 states and 10 foreign countries. Ninety-five percent are African American. Eighty percent are Protestant; 15% Catholic. The average age of freshmen is 18; all undergraduates, 20. About 46% of freshmen remain to graduate.

Housing: A total of 3028 students can be accommodated in college housing. College-sponsored living facilities include single-sex dormitories. In addition there are honors houses. On-campus housing is guaranteed for all 4 years. Sixty-one percent of students live on campus. Alcohol is not permitted. All students may keep cars on campus.

Activities: About 4% of men belong to fraternities; about 4% of women belong to sororities. There are some groups and organizations on campus, including band, choir, drama, marching band, newspaper, radio and TV, religious, student government, and yearbook. Pop-

ular campus events include Founders Day, Black History Month, and Springfest.

Sports: There are 9 intercollegiate sports for men and 6 for women, and 8 intramural sports for men and 6 for women. Athletic and recreation facilities include a gymnasium, tennis courts, a 25,000-seat football stadium, and an intramural center.

Disabled Students: Fifty percent of the campus is accessible to disabled students. The following facilities are available: wheelchair ramps, elevators, special parking, specially equipped rest rooms, lowered drinking fountains, and lowered telephones.

Services: In addition to counseling and information services, there is remedial math, reading, and writing.

Campus Safety and Security: Campus safety and security measures include shuttle buses, pamphlets, posters, and films, emergency telephones, 24-hour vehicle patrol, and VIP escort service.

Programs of Study: Grambling awards the B.A., B.S., B.P.A., and B.S.W. degrees. Associate, master's, and doctoral degrees also are awarded. Bachelor's degrees are awarded in BIOLOGICAL SCIENCE (biology/biological science), BUSINESS (accounting, banking and finance, business administration and management, business economics, hotel/motel and restaurant management, and marketing/retailing/merchandising), COMMUNICATIONS AND THE ARTS (broadcasting, English, fine arts, French, journalism, music, Spanish, and speech/debate/rhetoric), COMPUTER AND PHYSICAL SCIENCE (chemistry, computer science, information sciences and systems, mathematics, physics, and statistics), EDUCATION (business, early childhood, elementary, foreign languages, industrial arts, music, science, and special), ENGINEERING AND ENVIRONMENTAL DESIGN (engineering technology), HEALTH PROFESSIONS (nursing, physical therapy, predentistry, premedicine, and speech pathology/audiology), SOCIAL SCIENCE (criminal justice, geography, history, parks and recreation management, philosophy, political science/government, prelaw, psychology, public administration, social science, social work, and sociology). Business Management has the largest enrollment.

Required: To graduate, students must complete a minimum of 128 semester hours with a minimum GPA of 2.0. Students also must earn a passing grade in each part of general education integration seminars and pass the senior comprehensive competency examination.

Special: B.A.-B.S. degrees in some subjects, work-study programs, nondegree study, and a co-op program with Louisiana Tech University are offered. The university sponsors Project Rescue for disadvantaged students. There is a freshman honors program on campus, as well as 15 national honor societies.

Faculty/Classroom: Fifty-nine percent of faculty are male; 41%, female. Graduate students teach 2% of introductory courses. The average class size in an introductory lecture is 40.

Admissions: About 53% of the 1993–94 applicants were accepted. The ACT scores for the 1993–94 freshman class were as follows: 95% below 21, 3% between 21 and 23, 1% between 24 and 26, and 1% between 27 and 28. About 20% of the current freshmen were in the top fifth of their class. Two freshmen graduated first in their class.

Requirements: A minimum GPA of 2.0 is required. The SAT I or ACT is required. Applicants must be graduates of an accredited high school. The GED is accepted.

Procedure: Freshmen are admitted to all sessions. Applications should be filed by July 15 for fall entry, December 15 for spring entry, and May 15 for summer entry, along with an application fee of $5. The university accepts all in-state residents who apply. Notification is sent on a rolling basis.

Transfer: A total of 30 credits out of 128 must be completed at Grambling.

Visiting: There are regularly scheduled orientations for prospective students. There are guides for informal visits and visitors may sit in on classes. To arrange for a visit, contact Martin Lemelle at (318) 274-3138.

Financial Aid: In a recent year, 95% of all current freshmen received some form of financial aid. About 80% of freshmen received need-based aid. The Singlefile Form financial statement is required. The deadline for financial aid applications is July 1.

International Students: There are currently 103 international students enrolled. They must take the TOEFL and achieve a minimum score of 450. The student must also take the SAT I or the ACT.

Computers: The university provides computer facilities for student use. Those students enrolled in computer courses may access the system. There are no time limits on using the system and no fees.

Admissions Contact: Director of Admissions.

LOUISIANA COLLEGE
B-3

Pineville, LA 71359–0560
(318) 487-7259

Full-time: 331 men, 581 women	Faculty: 61; IIB, --$
Part-time: 41 men, 117 women	Ph.D.s: 70%
Graduate: none	Student/Faculty: 15 to 1
Year: semesters, summer session	Tuition: $4770
Application Deadline: September 6	Room & Board: $2748
Freshman Class: 1746 applied, 849 accepted, 205 enrolled	
ACT: 22	**VERY COMPETITIVE**

Lousiana College, founded in 1906, is a private, coeducational liberal arts college affiliated with the Southern Baptist Churches of Louisiana. In addition to regional accreditation, LC has baccalaureate program accreditation with NASM and NLN. The library contains 125,000 volumes, 130,000 microform items, and 900 audiovisual forms, and subscribes to 500 periodicals. Computerized library sources and services include interlibrary loans and database searching. Special learning facilities include a learning resource center and art gallery. The 81-acre campus is in a small town 1 mile northeast of Alexandria. Including residence halls, there are 16 buildings on campus.

Student Life: About 95% of undergraduates are from Louisiana. Students come from 26 states and 5 foreign countries. Some 90% are white. About 80% are Protestant; 12%, Catholic. The average age of freshmen is 20; all undergraduates, 23.3. About 12% drop out by the end of their first year; 38% remain to graduate.

Housing: A total of 542 students can be accommodated in college housing. College-sponsored living facilities include single-sex dormitories, on-campus apartments, and married-student housing. On-campus housing is guaranteed for all 4 years. Some 55% of students commute. Alcohol is not permitted. All students may keep cars on campus.

Activities: About 3% of men belong to 2 local fraternities; about 6% of women belong to 2 local sororities. There are 35 groups on campus, including art, cheerleading, choir, chorale, chorus, drama, honors, international, jazz band, literary magazine, musical theater, newspaper, opera, pep band, political, religious, student government, symphony, and yearbook. Popular campus events include Gala Christmas Eve, Cuchon de lait, Sanders Lecture Series, and Miss LC Pageant.

Sports: There are 3 intercollegiate sports for men and 3 for women, and 10 intramural sports for men and 10 for women. Athletic and recreation facilities include a field house for basketball, a baseball field, a fitness/wellness center, a jogging trail, tennis courts, an intramural soccer/football field, and an outdoor beach volleyball court.

Disabled Students: About 95% of the campus is accessible to disabled students. The following facilities are available: wheelchair ramps, elevators, special parking, and specially equipped rest rooms.

Services: In addition to many counseling and information services, tutoring is available in most subjects. There are also a reader service for the blind, and remedial math, reading, and writing programs.

Campus Safety and Security: Campus safety and security measures include 24-hour foot and vehicle patrol, self defense education, escort service, and informal discussions. In addition, there are pamphlets, posters, films, and lighted pathways and sidewalks.

Programs of Study: LC awards the B.A., B.S., B.G.S., B.M., and B.S.N. degrees. Associate degrees also are awarded. Bachelor's degrees are awarded in BIOLOGICAL SCIENCE (biology/biological science), BUSINESS (business administration and management), COMMUNICATIONS AND THE ARTS (communications, dramatic arts, music, and speech/debate/rhetoric), COMPUTER AND PHYSICAL SCIENCE (chemistry and mathematics), EDUCATION (art, business, elementary, health, science, secondary, and special), ENGINEERING AND ENVIRONMENTAL DESIGN (preengineering), HEALTH PROFESSIONS (medical laboratory technology, nursing, predentistry, premedicine, and preveterinary science), SOCIAL SCIENCE (criminal justice, economics, history, philosophy, prelaw, psychology, public administration, religion, social work, and sociology). Business, education, nursing, prelaw, premedicine, and religion are the strongest programs academically. Business, education, nursing, and biology have the largest enrollments.

Required: To graduate, students must complete 127 total credit hours, including a central core of 54 hours in all degree programs, and maintain a minimum GPA of 2.0.

Special: Dual majors, study abroad in London, interdisciplinary studies, work-study programs, nondegree study, and pass/fail options are offered. There are 11 national honor societies on campus.

Faculty/Classroom: Some 62% of faculty are male; 38%, female. All teach undergraduates.

Admissions: About 49% of the 1993–94 applicants were accepted. The ACT scores for the 1993–94 freshman class were as follows: 35% below 21, 27% between 21 and 23, 22% between 24 and 26, 10% between 27 and 28, and 6% above 28. About 51% of the current

freshmen were in the top fifth of their class; 71% were in the top two fifths. Six freshmen graduated first in their class.

Requirements: LC requires applicants to be in the upper 50% of their class. A minimum GPA of 2.0 is required. The ACT is recommended. Candidates for admission must have completed 17 units, including 4 in high school English, 3 in mathematics, 3 in science, and 3 in social studies. AP and CLEP credits are accepted. Important factors used in the admissions decision are ability to finance college education, parents or siblings attending the school, recommendations by alumni, recommendations by school officials, and geographic diversity.

Procedure: Freshmen are admitted in the fall and spring. Applications should be filed by September 6 for fall entry, January 24 for spring entry, and June 2 for summer entry. Notification is sent on a rolling basis. There is an early admissions plan.

Transfer: About 27 transfer students enrolled in a recent year. Transfer applicants must have an overall minimum GPA of 2.0. A total of 30 credits out of 127 must be completed at LC.

Visiting: There are regularly scheduled orientations for prospective students, consisting of spring and fall campus preview days, and a 2-day orientation and pre-registration in June. There are guides for informal visits and visitors may sit in on classes and stay overnight at the school. To arrange for a visit, contact the Office of Admissions at (318) 487–7259.

Financial Aid: In a recent year, 60% of all current freshmen and 78% of continuing students received some form of financial aid. About 64% of freshmen and 81% of continuing students received need-based aid. The average freshman award was $1800. Of that total, scholarships or need-based grants averaged $600 ($1000 maximum); loans averaged $2200 ($2625 maximum); and work contracts averaged $800 ($1000 maximum). Some 18% of undergraduate students work part-time. Average earnings from campus work for the school year are $800. The average financial indebtedness of a recent graduate was $8000. LC is a member of CSS. The FFS is required. The deadline for financial aid applications is May 1.

International Students: There are currently 3 international students enrolled. They must take the TOEFL and achieve a minimum score of 540. The student must also take the SAT I or the ACT and achieve a minimum combined score of 610 on the SAT I and 14 on the ACT.

Computers: The college provides computer facilities for student use. The mainframe is a DEC VAX. There are PC laboratories for Macintosh and IBM-compatible microcomputers. All students may access the system. There are no time limits on using the system and no fees.

Graduates: In a recent year, 201 bachelor's degrees were awarded. Some 35 companies recruited on campus in a recent year.

Admissions Contact: George Justice, Director of Admissions.

LOUISIANA STATE UNIVERSITY SYSTEM

The Louisiana State University System, established in 1860, is a public system in Louisiana. It is governed by a board of supervisors, whose chief administrator is the president. The primary goal of the system is to foster excellence in teaching, research, and public service. The main priorities are undergraduate education, graduate education, and economic development. The total enrollment in a recent year of all 8 campuses was 55,154; there were 3493 faculty members. Altogether there are more than 225 baccalaureate, 220 master's, and 80 doctoral programs offered in the Louisiana State University System. Four-year campuses are located in Baton Rouge, Shreveport, and New Orleans. Profiles of the 4-year campuses are included in this chapter in alphabetical order with other Louisiana schools.

LOUISIANA STATE UNIVERSITY AND AGRICULTURAL AND MECHANICAL COLLEGE

C-4

Baton Rouge, LA 70803	(504) 388–1175
Full-time: 8337 men, 7932 women	Faculty: 1218; I, --$
Part-time: 1538 men, 2233 women	Ph.D.s: 84%
Graduate: 2836 men, 2493 women	Student/Faculty: 13 to 1
Year: semesters, summer session	Tuition: $2625 ($5925)
Application Deadline: June 1	Room & Board: $2980
Freshman Class: 6000 applied, 4994 accepted, 3079 enrolled	
ACT: 23	COMPETITIVE

Louisiana State University and Agricultural and Mechanical College, a public institution founded in 1860, is part of the Louisiana State University System, offering programs in agriculture, arts and sciences, basic sciences, business administration, design, education, engineering, and music. There are 11 undergraduate and 4 graduate schools. In addition to regional accreditation, LSU A&M has baccalaureate program accreditation with AACSB, ABET, ACCE, ACEJMC, ASLA, CSWE, FIDER, NAAB, NASAD, NASM, NCATE, and SAF. The 2 libraries contain 2,709,757 volumes, 4,029,760 microform items, and 25,996 audiovisual forms, and subscribe to 16,169 periodicals. Com-

puterized library sources and services include the card catalog. Special learning facilities include a learning resource center, art gallery, natural history museum, radio station, TV station, 2 herbariums, and museums of natural science, geoscience, and rural life. The 2000-acre campus is in an urban area in Baton Rouge. Including residence halls, there are 250 buildings on campus.

Student Life: About 88% of undergraduates are from Louisiana. Students come from 51 states, 121 foreign countries, and Canada. Sixty percent are from public schools; 40% from private. Eighty-two percent are white. Forty-seven percent claim no religious affiliation; 29% Catholic; 22% Protestant. The average age of freshmen is 20.9; all undergraduates, 22.8. Twenty-five percent drop out by the end of their first year; 41% remain to graduate.

Housing: A total of 6145 students can be accommodated in college housing. College-sponsored living facilities include single-sex dormitories, on-campus apartments, married-student housing, fraternity houses, and sorority houses. In addition there are honors houses and special interest houses. On-campus housing is guaranteed for all 4 years. Seventy-five percent of students commute. All students may keep cars on campus.

Activities: About 14% of men belong to 24 national fraternities; about 14% of women belong to 14 national sororities. There are 259 groups on campus, including art, band, cheerleading, choir, chorus, computers, dance, drama, ethnic, gay, honors, international, jazz band, literary magazine, marching band, musical theater, newspaper, opera, orchestra, pep band, political, professional, radio and TV, religious, social, social service, student government, and symphony. Popular campus events include Homecoming, Rush Week, South Seas, Martin Luther King Day Celebration, and LSU Union Ice Cream/Watermelon Giveaways.

Sports: There are 8 intercollegiate sports for men and 8 for women, and 41 intramural sports for men, 40 for women, and 26 for both. Athletic and recreation facilities include an 80,140-seat football stadium; a 14,237-seat domed sports center; lighted football and baseball fields; a Chevron 400-meter track with seating for 5000; a natatorium with an 8-lane, Olympic pool and diving well; an indoor track; courts for handball, badminton, volleyball, and tennis; and a recreational sports facility that provides a multifaceted recreation sports program including aquatics, sports clubs, informal recreation, instructional sports, intramural sports, outdoor recreation, special event activities, and sports medicine.

Disabled Students: The following facilities are available: wheelchair ramps, elevators, special parking, specially equipped rest rooms, special class scheduling, lowered drinking fountains, lowered telephones, telecommunication devices for the deaf, and power doors.

Services: In addition to many counseling and information services, tutoring is available in most subjects. In addition, there is remedial math, reading, and writing.

Campus Safety and Security: Campus safety and security measures include 24-hour foot and vehicle patrol, self defense education, escort service, and shuttle buses. In addition, there are informal discussions, pamphlets, posters, and films, emergency telephones, lighted pathways and sidewalks, and specialized crime prevention programs.

Programs of Study: LSU A&M awards the B.A., B.S., B.A. in M.C., B.Arch., B.F.A., B.G.S., B.Int.Design, B.Land.Arch., B.M., B.M.E., B.S.B.A.E., B.S.C., B.S.C.E., B.S.Ch.E., B.S.E.E., B.S.F., B.S.G., B.S.I.E., B.S.M.E., and B.S.P.E. degrees. Master's and doctoral degrees also are awarded. Bachelor's degrees are awarded in AGRICULTURE (agricultural business management, agricultural economics, animal science, fishing and fisheries, and horticulture), BIOLOGICAL SCIENCE (biochemistry, botany, microbiology, nutrition, and zoology), BUSINESS (accounting, banking and finance, business administration and management, business economics, international business management, and marketing/retailing/merchandising), COMMUNICATIONS AND THE ARTS (advertising, broadcasting, design, dramatic arts, drawing, English, fine arts, French, German, graphic design, journalism, Latin, music, painting, printmaking, sculpture, Spanish, and speech/debate/rhetoric), COMPUTER AND PHYSICAL SCIENCE (chemistry, computer science, geology, mathematics, physics, and quantitative methods), EDUCATION (agricultural, business, elementary, home economics, industrial arts, and music), ENGINEERING AND ENVIRONMENTAL DESIGN (agricultural engineering, agricultural engineering technology, architecture, chemical engineering, civil engineering, computer engineering, electrical/electronics engineering, industrial engineering, industrial engineering technology, interior design, landscape architecture/design, mechanical engineering, and petroleum/natural gas engineering), HEALTH PROFESSIONS (predentistry, premedicine, and speech pathology/audiology), SOCIAL SCIENCE (anthropology, dietetics, economics, food science, geography, history, liberal arts/general studies, philosophy, political science/government, psychology, religion, Russian and Slavic studies, sociology, and textiles and clothing). Engineering and basic science are the strongest

academically. General studies, mechanical engineering, psychology, accounting, and political science have the largest enrollments.

Required: To graduate, all students must have a minimum overall 2.0 GPA in at least 128 credit hours, with 50 to 69 in the major. They must complete a general education component of 39 semester hours in approved courses in 6 major areas, including 9 hours each in humanities and natural sciences, 6 each in English composition, analytical reasoning, and social sciences, and 3 hours in the arts.

Special: Co-op programs in numerous majors, cross-registration with Southern University, study abroad, and work-study programs are offered. B.A.-B.S. degrees, dual majors, a general studies degree, nondegree study, evening school, a program of study for adult learners, and pass/fail options are available. There is a freshman honors program on campus, as well as 31 national honor societies, including Phi Beta Kappa. Seventeen departments have honors programs.

Faculty/Classroom: Seventy-five percent of faculty are male; 25%, female. Graduate students teach 21% of introductory courses. The average class size in an introductory lecture is 45; in a laboratory, 20; and in a regular course offering, 32.

Admissions: About 83% of the 1993–94 applicants were accepted. The ACT scores for the 1993–94 freshman class were as follows: 27% below 21, 26% between 21 and 23, 23% between 24 and 26, 12% between 27 and 28, and 11% above 28. About 48% of the current freshmen were in the top fifth of their class; 73% were in the top two fifths. There were 27 National Merit finalists and 27 semifinalists.

Requirements: A minimum GPA of 2.0 is required. The SAT I or ACT (preferred) is required. Applicants must be graduates of an accredited secondary school. GED certificates may be accepted in unusual circumstances. Students must have completed 4 credits in English, 3 each in mathematics, science, and social studies, 2 credits in foreign language, and 1/2 credit in computer skills. AP and CLEP credits are accepted. Important factors used in the admissions decision are advanced placement or honor courses, evidence of special talent, parents or siblings attending the school, recommendations by school officials, and recommendations by alumni.

Procedure: Freshmen are admitted to all sessions. Entering freshmen take the ACT during the first week of registration. Applications should be filed by June 1 for fall entry, December 1 for spring entry, and May 1 for summer entry, along with an application fee of $25. Notification is sent on a rolling basis. There is an early admissions plan.

Transfer: About 1100 transfer students enrolled in 1993–94. Transfer students must submit an official transcript from each previously attended school. Residents with 55 or more semester hours and all nonresidents must have a minimum 2.0 GPA. A total of 30 credits out of a minimum of 128 must be completed at LSU A&M.

Visiting: There are regularly scheduled orientations for prospective students, including an information session and a tour of campus. Department appointments can be arranged. There are guides for informal visits and visitors may sit in on classes and stay overnight at the school. To arrange for a visit, contact the Office of Recruitment and Tours at (504) 388-6652.

Financial Aid: In 1993–94, 63% of all current freshmen and 55% of continuing students received some form of financial aid. About 31% of freshmen and 28% of continuing students received need-based aid. The average freshman award was $3753. Of that total, scholarships or need-based grants averaged $1500 ($5700 maximum); loans averaged $2586 ($4000 maximum); and work contracts averaged $970 ($5000 maximum). Twenty percent of undergraduate students work part-time. Average earnings from campus work for the school year are $970. The ACT financial statement and FAFSA are required. The deadline for financial aid applications is March 1.

International Students: There are currently 1521 international students enrolled. They must take the TOEFL and achieve a minimum score of 500.

Computers: The university provides computer facilities for student use. The mainframes are an IBM 3090J, an IBM 3084, and a DEC VAX 8800. There are computer laboratories throughout the campus in department buildings and the library, with 60 IBM, and Apple microcomputers available. Students may access the system for classwork only 7 days per week, 24 hours per day. There are no time limits on using the system and no fees.

Graduates: In 1992–93, 3204 bachelor's degrees were awarded. The most popular majors among graduates were general studies (10%), psychology (7%), and accounting (6%). Within an average freshman class, 15% graduate in 4 years, 37% in 5 years, and 39% in 6 years. More than 100 companies recruited on campus in 1992–93. In the 1992 graduating class, 22% of the men and women were enrolled in graduate school within 6 months of graduation; 30% had found employment.

Admissions Contact: Lisa Harris, Director of Admissions.

LOUISIANA STATE UNIVERSITY IN SHREVEPORT

A-1

Shreveport, LA 71115   (318) 797-5061

Full-time: 1066 men, 1347 women	Faculty: 163; IIA, --$
Part-time: 561 men, 916 women	Ph.D.s: 75%
Graduate: 211 men, 364 women	Student/Faculty: 15 to 1
Year: semesters, summer session	Tuition: $1910 ($4610)
Application Deadline: July 15	Room & Board: n/app
Freshman Class: 666 applied, 666 accepted, 489 enrolled	
ACT: 20	**NONCOMPETITIVE**

Louisiana State University in Shreveport, established in 1965, is a state-supported, primarily commuter institution offering undergraduate and graduate programs through the colleges of liberal arts, business, education, and sciences. There are 4 undergraduate and 4 graduate schools. In addition to regional accreditation, LSUS has baccalaureate program accreditation with AACSB and NCATE. The library contains 206,385 volumes, 173,721 microform items, and 980 audiovisual forms, and subscribes to 2152 periodicals. Special learning facilities include a heritage center, and a museum of life sciences. The 200-acre campus is in an urban area 7 miles south of downtown Shreveport. Including residence halls, there are 7 buildings on campus.

Student Life: About 83% of undergraduates are from Louisiana. Students come from 23 states and 4 foreign countries. Ninety-five percent are from public schools. Eighty-nine percent are white; 12% African American. The average age of all undergraduates is 27. Twenty-one percent drop out by the end of their first year; 30% remain to graduate.

Housing: A total of 480 students can be accommodated in college housing. College-sponsored living facilities include on-campus apartments. On-campus housing is available on a first-come, first-served basis. Ninety-six percent of students commute. Alcohol is not permitted. All students may keep cars on campus.

Activities: About 4% of men belong to 4 national fraternities; about 3% of women belong to 3 national sororities. There are 40 groups on campus, including art, band, cheerleading, chorale, computers, drama, ethnic, honors, literary magazine, newspaper, photography, political, professional, religious, social, social service, and student government. Popular campus events include fall and spring festivals and Renaissance Festival.

Sports: There are 3 intercollegiate sports for men and 1 for women, and 16 intramural sports for men and 16 for women. Athletic and recreation facilities include tennis courts, a swimming pool, gymnasium, weight room, dance studio, football fields, softball diamonds, and a soccer field.

Disabled Students: All of the campus is accessible to disabled students. The following facilities are available: wheelchair ramps, elevators, special parking, specially equipped rest rooms, and lowered drinking fountains.

Services: There is a reader service for the blind, and remedial math, reading, and writing.

Programs of Study: LSUS awards the B.A. and B.S. degrees. Master's degrees also are awarded. Bachelor's degrees are awarded in BIOLOGICAL SCIENCE (biology/biological science), BUSINESS (accounting, banking and finance, business administration and management, business economics, and marketing/retailing/merchandising), COMMUNICATIONS AND THE ARTS (communications, English, fine arts, and speech/debate/rhetoric), COMPUTER AND PHYSICAL SCIENCE (chemistry, computer science, mathematics, and physics), EDUCATION (art, business, elementary, and secondary), HEALTH PROFESSIONS (medical laboratory technology, occupational therapy, physical therapy, predentistry, premedicine, and prepharmacy).

Required: All students must take a computer course. A minimum of 128 semester hours, with a minimum GPA of 2.0, is required for the bachelor's degree.

Special: Opportunities are provided for cross-registration with Southern University/Shreveport, internships, a Washington semester, an accelerated medical degree program for Louisiana residents, a general studies degree, credit for military service schools, nondegree study, and pass/fail options. There are 5 national honor societies on campus.

Faculty/Classroom: Thirty-eight percent of faculty are male; 62%, female. All teach undergraduates. The average class size in an introductory lecture is 30 and in a laboratory, 25.

Admissions: All of the 1993–94 applicants were accepted.

Requirements: A minimum GPA of 2.3 is required. The ACT, with a minimum composite score of 18, is required. Graduation from an accredited secondary school is required. The GED will be accepted. AP and CLEP credits are accepted.

Procedure: Freshmen are admitted to all sessions. Entrance exams should be taken by the ACT national date. Applications should be filed by July 15 for fall entry, August 5 for winter entry, December 5

for spring entry, and May 1 for summer entry, along with an application fee of $10. Notification is sent on a rolling basis.

Transfer: About 420 transfer students enrolled in 1993–94. Transfers must be in good academic standing, with a GPA of 2.0, or they may enter on probation. They must be eligible to continue at the last institution attended. A total of 30 credits out of 128 must be completed at LSUS.

Visiting: There are guides for informal visits. To arrange for a visit, contact Steve Ellis at (318) 797–5061.

Financial Aid: The FSAR financial statement is required. The deadline for financial aid applications is April 1.

International Students: There are currently 5 international students enrolled. They must take the TOEFL and achieve a minimum score of 500.

Computers: The college provides computer facilities for student use. The mainframe is an IBM 4361. Microcomputers are available for academic use in student laboratories and faculty offices. Those students who need computer access for authorized classes may access the system. There are no time limits on using the system and no fees.

Graduates: In an earlier year, 370 bachelor's degrees were awarded. Some 73 companies recruited on campus in an earlier year.

Admissions Contact: Steve Ellis, Assistant Director of Admissions/Recruitment.

LOUISIANA TECH UNIVERSITY
B-3
Ruston, LA 71272
(318) 257–3036

Full-time: 3737 men, 2983 women	Faculty: 389; IIA, --$
Part-time: 846 men, 1019 women	Ph.D.s: 66%
Graduate: 662 men, 852 women	Student/Faculty: 17 to 1
Year: quarters	Tuition: $2169 ($3624)
Application Deadline: August 15	Room & Board: $2115
Freshman Class: 2397 applied, 2144 accepted, 1525 enrolled	
SAT I or ACT: required	COMPETITIVE

Louisiana Tech University, founded in 1894, is a public, coeducational institution offering programs in arts and sciences, business, agriculture, engineering, health science, education, fine and liberal arts, and human ecology. There are 6 undergraduate and 6 graduate schools. In addition to regional accreditation, Tech has baccalaureate program accreditation with AACSB, ABET, ADA, AHEA, ASLA, CAHEA, FIDER, NAAB, NASAD, NASM, NCATE, NLN, and SAF. The library contains 349,780 volumes, 481,555 microform items, and 14,171 audiovisual forms, and subscribes to 2627 periodicals. Computerized library sources and services include interlibrary loans and database searching. Special learning facilities include a learning resource center, art gallery, natural history museum, planetarium, and radio station. The 235-acre campus is in a small town 30 miles west of Monroe and 70 miles east of Shreveport. Including residence halls, there are 58 buildings on campus.

Student Life: About 85% of undergraduates are from Louisiana. Students come from 43 states, 42 foreign countries, and Canada. Some 80% are from public schools; 20% from private. About 79% are white; 13%, African American. Some 52% are Protestant; 13%, Catholic. The average age of freshmen is 19; all undergraduates, 20. About 30% drop out by the end of their first year; 38% remain to graduate.

Housing: A total of 3989 students can be accommodated in college housing. College-sponsored living facilities include single-sex dormitories and married-student housing. On-campus housing is guaranteed for all 4 years. Some 65% of students commute. Alcohol is not permitted. All students may keep cars on campus.

Activities: About 9% of men belong to 11 national fraternities; about 12% of women belong to 5 national sororities. There are 124 groups on campus, including art, band, cheerleading, choir, chorale, chorus, computers, dance, drama, drill team, drum and bugle corps, ethnic, film, honors, international, jazz band, marching band, musical theater, newspaper, opera, orchestra, pep band, photography, political, professional, radio and TV, religious, social, social service, student government, symphony, and yearbook. Popular campus events include the International Student Festival, Spring Fling, Homecoming, and Little Theater concerts.

Sports: There are 5 intercollegiate sports for men and 5 for women, and 10 intramural sports for men and 10 for women. Athletic and recreation facilities include a football stadium, a coliseum, an intramural complex, and a natatorium.

Disabled Students: About 95% of the campus is accessible to disabled students. The following facilities are available: wheelchair ramps, elevators, special parking, specially equipped rest rooms, lowered drinking fountains, and lowered telephones.

Services: In addition to many counseling and information services, tutoring is available in some subjects. In addition, there are remedial math, reading, and writing programs.

Campus Safety and Security: Campus safety and security measures include 24-hour foot and vehicle patrol, self defense education, escort service, and informal discussions. In addition, there are lighted pathways and sidewalks.

Programs of Study: Tech awards the B.A., B.S., B. Arch., B.F.A., and B.G.S. degrees. Associate, master's, and doctoral degrees also are awarded. Bachelor's degrees are awarded in AGRICULTURE (agricultural business management, agriculture, animal science, forestry and related sciences, horticulture, and wildlife management), BIOLOGICAL SCIENCE (botany, microbiology, and zoology), BUSINESS (accounting, banking and finance, business administration and management, business economics, business systems analysis, fashion merchandising, management science, marketing/retailing/merchandising, and personnel management), COMMUNICATIONS AND THE ARTS (English, fine arts, French, journalism, music, photography, Spanish, speech/debate/rhetoric, and technical and business writing), COMPUTER AND PHYSICAL SCIENCE (chemistry, computer management, computer science, geology, mathematics, and physics), EDUCATION (art, business, early childhood, elementary, foreign languages, health, home economics, middle school, music, physical, science, secondary, and special), ENGINEERING AND ENVIRONMENTAL DESIGN (architectural engineering, biomedical engineering, chemical engineering, civil engineering, computer engineering, construction engineering, electrical/electronics engineering technology, industrial engineering, mechanical engineering, and petroleum/natural gas engineering), HEALTH PROFESSIONS (medical laboratory technology, medical records administration/services, predentistry, premedicine, and speech pathology/audiology), SOCIAL SCIENCE (dietetics, geography, history, political science/government, prelaw, psychology, social work, and sociology). Business and engineering are the strongest programs academically and have the largest enrollments.

Required: All students must complete 45 semester hours of general education courses, including 12 hours in humanities, 9 each in natural and social sciences, 6 each in English and mathematics, and 3 in arts or computer literacy. A total of 126 to 142 semester hours, with a minimum GPA of 2.0, is required to graduate.

Special: Co-op programs are available in engineering and life sciences and cross-registration with Grambling State University is offered. Internships in agriculture, engineering, dietetics, and fashion merchandising are offered. Study abroad in 2 countries, work-study programs, dual majors, a general studies degree, nondegree study, and pass/fail options are available. There is a freshman honors program on campus. Some 20 departments have honors programs.

Faculty/Classroom: About 70% of faculty are male; 30%, female. Some 95% teach undergraduates and 75% both teach and do research. Graduate students teach 2% of introductory courses. The average class size in an introductory lecture is 40; in a laboratory, 20; and in a regular course offering, 26.

Admissions: About 89% of the 1993–94 applicants were accepted. The ACT scores for the 1993–94 freshman class were as follows: 39% below 21, 26% between 21 and 23, 18% between 24 and 26, 9% between 27 and 28, and 8% above 28. About 36% of the current freshmen were in the top fifth of their class; 64% were in the top two fifths. There were 13 National Merit finalists.

Requirements: Tech requires applicants to be in the upper 50% of their class. A minimum GPA of 2.0 is required. The SAT I or the ACT is required. Applicants must be graduates of an accredited secondary school or have a GED. Students must have graduated in the upper half of their class. AP credits are accepted.

Procedure: Freshmen are admitted to all sessions. Applications should be filed by August 15 for fall entry, November 21 for winter entry, February 27 for spring entry, and May 15 for summer entry, along with an application fee of $20. Notification is sent on a rolling basis. There is an early decision plan.

Transfer: About 561 transfer students enrolled in 1993–94. Transfer applicants should have a 2.0 GPA and be eligible to enroll in the school from which they are transferring. A total of 30 credits out of 126 to 142 must be completed at Tech.

Visiting: There are regularly scheduled orientations for prospective students. There are guides for informal visits and visitors may stay overnight at the school. To arrange for a visit, contact Admissions at (318) 257–3036.

Financial Aid: In 1993–94, 77% of all students received some form of financial aid. About 46% of all students received need-based aid. Scholarships or need-based grants averaged $1500 ($7000 maximum); loans averaged $1300 ($5000 maximum); and work contracts averaged $1800. Some 22% of undergraduate students work part-time. Average earnings from campus work for the school year are $1800. The average financial indebtedness of the 1992–93 graduate was $10,000. The FAF, FFS or SFS and the college's own financial statement are required. The deadline for financial aid applications is June 1.

International Students: There are currently 151 international students enrolled. The school actively recruits these students. They must take the TOEFL and achieve a minimum score of 550.

Computers: The college provides computer facilities for student use. The mainframe is an IBM 9121–210. Computer laboratories are located within each college, with microcomputers and terminals networked to the mainframe, as well as specialized local network workstations. There are also computer laboratories located in dormitories and the central computing center. All students may access the system. It may be used 24 hours a day, 7 days a week. There are no time limits on using the system.

Graduates: In 1992–93, 1210 bachelor's degrees were awarded. The most popular majors among graduates were business management (25%), engineering (15%), and education (15%). Within an average freshman class, 17% graduate in 4 years, 35% in 5 years, and 42% in 6 years. Some 735 companies recruited on campus in 1992–93. In a recent graduating class, 25% of the men and 30% of the women were enrolled in graduate school within 6 months of graduation; 70% of the men and 65% of the women had found employment.

Admissions Contact: Karen Akin, Admissions Office.

LOYOLA UNIVERSITY
NEW ORLEANS
New Orleans, LA 70118

D-4

(504) 865–3240
(800) 4-LOYOLA (out-of-state)

Full-time: 1141 men, 1599 women	**Faculty:** 240; IIA, av$
Part-time: 217 men, 544 women	**Ph.D.s:** 87%
Graduate: 704 men, 683 women	**Student/Faculty:** 11 to 1
Year: semesters, summer session	**Tuition:** $10,560
Application Deadline: August 1	**Room & Board:** $5100
Freshman Class: 1891 applied, 1698 accepted, 719 enrolled	
SAT I Verbal/Math: 510/540	**ACT:** 25 **COMPETITIVE +**

Loyola University/New Orleans, founded in 1912, is a private, coeducational university operated by the Society of Jesus, and affiliated with the Roman Catholic Church. There are 4 undergraduate and 9 graduate schools. In addition to regional accreditation, Loyola has baccalaureate program accreditation with AACSB and NASM. The library contains 245,000 volumes, 241,000 microform items, and 2250 audiovisual forms, and subscribes to 1800 periodicals. Special learning facilities include an art gallery, radio station, and TV station. The 23-acre campus is in an urban area in New Orleans. Including residence halls, there are 26 buildings on campus.

Student Life: About 50% of undergraduates are from out-of-state, mostly the South. Students come from 50 states and 50 foreign countries. Seventy percent are white; 12% African American. Most are Catholic. The average age of freshmen is 19; all undergraduates, 23. About 41% of freshmen remain to graduate.

Housing: A total of 1053 students can be accommodated in college housing. College-sponsored living facilities include single-sex dormitories. In addition there are honors houses and special interest houses. On-campus housing is available on a first-come, first-served basis. Priority is given to out-of-town students. Seventy-five percent of students commute. All students may keep cars on campus.

Activities: About 15% of men belong to 1 local and 4 national fraternities; about 31% of women belong to 5 national sororities. There are 65 groups on campus, including art, band, choir, chorale, chorus, computers, dance, drama, ethnic, film, honors, international, jazz band, literary magazine, musical theater, newspaper, opera, orchestra, photography, political, professional, radio and TV, religious, social, social service, student government, symphony, and yearbook. Popular campus events include Mardi Gras and Oktoberfest.

Sports: There are 10 intramural sports for men and 10 for women. Athletic and recreation facilities include a recreational sports center.

Disabled Students: Sixty percent of the campus is accessible to disabled students. The following facilities are available: wheelchair ramps, elevators, special parking, specially equipped rest rooms, and lowered drinking fountains.

Services: In addition to many counseling and information services, tutoring is available in every subject.

Campus Safety and Security: Campus safety and security measures include 24-hour foot and vehicle patrol and shuttle buses.

Programs of Study: Loyola awards the B.A., B.S., B.A.S., B.B.A., B.C.J., B.L.S., B.Mus., B.Mus.Ed., and B.Mus. Therapy degrees. Master's degrees also are awarded. Bachelor's degrees are awarded in BIOLOGICAL SCIENCE (biology/biological science), BUSINESS (accounting, banking and finance, business administration and management, business economics, and marketing/retailing/merchandising), COMMUNICATIONS AND THE ARTS (broadcasting, communications, design, dramatic arts, English, fine arts, French, German, journalism, music, Russian, and telecommunications), COMPUTER AND PHYSICAL SCIENCE (chemistry, computer programming, computer science, mathematics, and physics), EDUCATION (early childhood, elementary, health, middle school, music, and secondary), HEALTH PROFESSIONS (premedicine), SOCIAL SCIENCE (criminal justice, economics, history, philosophy, political science/government, prelaw, psychology, religion, social science, and sociology). English and mathematics are the strongest academically. Communications and business administration have the largest enrollments.

Required: All students must complete a 48-credit hour core curriculum that includes courses in English composition and literature, mathematics, philosophy, science, world history, and religious studies. At total of at least 128 credit hours, with 30 in the major and a minimum GPA of 2.0, is required to graduate.

Special: Cross-registration is available with Xavier University, Notre Dame Seminary, the University of New Orleans, Tulane University, and Southern University of New Orleans. Exchange programs with Tulane University and internships with the New Orleans business community are available. Study abroad in the junior year in Italy and in the summer in Mexico are possible. Work-study programs, dual majors, student-designed majors, nondegree studies, a general studies degree, and pass/fail options are offered. There is a freshman honors program on campus, as well as 12 national honor societies. Seven departments have honors programs.

Faculty/Classroom: Seventy-four percent of faculty are male; 26%, female. All teach undergraduates. No introductory courses are taught by graduate students. The average class size in an introductory lecture is 30 and in a regular course offering, 20.

Admissions: About 90% of the 1993–94 applicants were accepted. The SAT scores for the 1993–94 freshman class were as follows: Verbal—47% below 500, 36% between 500 and 599, 16% between 600 and 700, and 1% above 700; Math—32% below 500, 43% between 500 and 599, 21% between 600 and 700, and 4% above 700. The ACT scores were 37% between 21 and 23, 32% between 24 and 26, 16% between 27 and 28, and 15% above 28. About 42% of the current freshmen were in the top fifth of their class; 72% were in the top two fifths. About 10 freshmen graduated first in their class.

Requirements: The SAT I or ACT is required. Candidates for admission must be graduates of an accredited secondary school or have a GED. They should have completed 4 units in high school English, 3 each in mathematics, science, and social sciences, and 4 academic electives. Two units in a foreign language are recommended. A portfolio is required for fine arts students, an audition for music majors, and an interview for scholarship consideration. AP and CLEP credits are accepted. Important factors used in the admissions decision are advanced placement or honor courses, recommendations by school officials, leadership record, evidence of special talent, and personality, intangible qualities.

Procedure: Freshmen are admitted to all sessions. Entrance exams should be taken during the junior and senior years. Applications should be filed by August 1 for fall entry, along with an application fee of $20. Notification is sent on a rolling basis. There are early admissions and deferred admissions plans.

Transfer: About 327 transfer students enrolled in 1993–94. Transfer applicants must have a minimum 2.25 GPA on all attempted college level work; 12 hours are needed for consideration. A total of 30 credits out of 128 must be completed at Loyola.

Visiting: There are regularly scheduled orientations for prospective students, including a class visit, department visit, student panel, tour, overnight residence, financial aid session, campus support panel, and meetings with faculty members. There are guides for informal visits and visitors may sit in on classes and stay overnight at the school. To arrange for a visit, contact the Office of Admissions at (504) 865–3240 or (800) 4-LOYOLA.

Financial Aid: In 1993–94, 63% of all current freshmen and 57% of continuing students received some form of financial aid. About 54% of freshmen and 45% of continuing students received need-based aid. The average freshman award was $9484. Of that total, scholarships or need-based grants averaged $4278 ($13,290 maximum); loans averaged $2582 ($2625 maximum); and work contracts averaged $1390 ($1800 maximum). The average financial indebtedness of the 1992–93 graduate was $13,387. Loyola is a member of CSS. The FAF is required. The deadline for financial aid applications is July 15.

International Students: There are currently 200 international students enrolled. The school actively recruits these students. They must take the college's own test and achieve a minimum score on the TOEFL of 500.

Computers: The college provides computer facilities for student use. The mainframe is an IBM 4361. There are also 100 IBM and Apple microcomputers. There are no time limits on using the system and no fees.

Graduates: In a recent year, 670 bachelor's degrees were awarded. Within an average freshman class, 56% graduate in 5 years.

Admissions Contact: Nan Massingill, Director of Admissions.

MCNEESE STATE UNIVERSITY

B-4

Lake Charles, LA 70609-2495

(318) 475-5146
(800) 622-3352 (in-state)

Full-time: 2654 men, 3367 women
Part-time: 546 men, 780 women
Graduate: 367 men, 689 women
Year: semesters, summer session
Application Deadline: July 1
Freshman Class: 1998 applied, 1978 accepted, 1518 enrolled
ACT: 19

Faculty: 297; IIA, --$
Ph.D.s: 56%
Student/Faculty: 20 to 1
Tuition: $1953 ($4163)
Room & Board: $2590

NONCOMPETITIVE

McNeese State University, founded in 1939, is a public coeducational institution offering programs in business, agriculture, engineering, education, fine arts, science, military studies, liberal arts, and nursing. There are 6 undergraduate schools and one graduate school. In addition to regional accreditation, MSU has baccalaureate program accreditation with AACSB, ABET, AHEA, NASM, NCATE, and NLN. The library contains 429,093 volumes, 543,962 microform items, and 600 audiovisual forms, and subscribes to 1557 periodicals. Computerized library sources and services include the card catalog, interlibrary loans, and database searching. Special learning facilities include an art gallery, planetarium, and a farm. The 580-acre campus is in a suburban area 120 miles west of Baton Rouge and 60 miles east of Beaumont, Texas. Including residence halls, there are 95 buildings on campus.

Student Life: About 94% of undergraduates are from Louisiana. Students come from 39 states, 32 foreign countries, and Canada. About 83% are white; 14%, African American. The average age of all undergraduates is 25. About 40% of freshmen remain to graduate.

Housing: A total of 1322 students can be accommodated in college housing. College-sponsored living facilities include single-sex and coed dormitories, on-campus apartments, and married-student housing. In addition, there are honors houses and a 12-month hall for those out-of-state and international students who cannot go home. On-campus housing is guaranteed for all 4 years. Some 90% of students commute. Alcohol is not permitted. All students may keep cars on campus.

Activities: About 5% of men belong to 8 national fraternities; about 5% of women belong to 6 national sororities. There are 74 groups on campus, including art, band, cheerleading, chorus, computers, drama, drill team, ethnic, honors, international, jazz band, marching band, musical theater, newspaper, orchestra, political, professional, radio and TV, social, social service, student government, symphony, and yearbook. Popular campus events include Spring Fling, Fall Ball, and Homecoming activities.

Sports: There are 7 intercollegiate sports for men and 7 for women, and 15 intramural sports for men and 13 for women. Athletic and recreation facilities include a football stadium, softball and intramural fields, an indoor/outdoor track, a pool, a coliseum, and a baseball complex.

Disabled Students: About 80% of the campus is accessible to disabled students. The following facilities are available: wheelchair ramps, elevators, special parking, specially equipped rest rooms, and lowered drinking fountains.

Services: There is remedial math, reading, and writing programs and a study skills course.

Campus Safety and Security: Campus safety and security measures include 24-hour foot and vehicle patrol, escort service, informal discussions, pamphlets, posters, and films. In addition, there are lighted pathways and sidewalks, security guards posted at the women's residence halls from 11 P.M. until 7 A.M., and a crime stoppers program.

Programs of Study: MSU awards the B.A., B.S., B.Mus., B.Mus.Ed., and B.S.N. degrees. Associate, specialist, and master's degrees also are awarded. Bachelor's degrees are awarded in AGRICULTURE (agricultural business management, agriculture, animal science, and wildlife management), BIOLOGICAL SCIENCE (biology/biological science, botany, ecology, microbiology, and zoology), BUSINESS (accounting, business administration and management, and marketing/retailing/merchandising), COMMUNICATIONS AND THE ARTS (broadcasting, communications, dramatic arts, English, fine arts, languages, music, and speech/debate/rhetoric), COMPUTER AND PHYSICAL SCIENCE (chemistry, computer science, geology, information sciences and systems, mathematics, physics, radiological technology, and statistics), EDUCATION (art, business, early childhood, elementary, foreign languages, guidance, health, home economics, and science), ENGINEERING AND ENVIRONMENTAL DESIGN (chemical engineering, civil engineering, electrical/electronics engineering, and mechanical engineering), HEALTH PROFESSIONS (medical laboratory technology, nursing, predentistry, and premedicine), SOCIAL SCIENCE (criminal justice, economics, history, prelaw, psychology, and sociology). Education, sciences, and liberal arts have the largest enrollments.

Required: The general requirements for graduation include 9 hours each in the humanities and natural sciences, 6 each in English, mathematics, and social sciences, 3 in arts and computer literacy, and 1 in orientation, for a total of 43 core hours. A total of 130 credit hours with a minimum GPA equivalent of C is needed.

Special: MSU offers co-op programs in engineering, internships in medical technology, radiologic technology, and education, dual majors, a general studies degree, nondegree study, and credit for military experience. There is a freshman honors program on campus, as well as 20 national honor societies.

Faculty/Classroom: Some 63% of faculty are male; 37%, female. All teach undergraduates and 30% do research.

Admissions: Nearly all of the 1993–94 applicants were accepted.
Requirements: The ACT is required. MSU accepts any Louisiana applicant with a diploma from an accredited secondary school or the GED. AP and CLEP credits are accepted.
Procedure: Freshmen are admitted to all sessions. Entrance exams should be taken prior to enrolling. Applications should be filed by July 1 for fall entry, December 1 for spring entry, and May 1 for summer entry, along with an application fee of $10. The college accepts all in-state residents who apply. Notification is sent within 14 days. There is an early admissions plan.
Transfer: About 424 transfer students enrolled in 1993–94. Transferee must be eligible for readmission to the last collegiate institution attended. A total of 30 credits out of 130 must be completed at MSU.
Visiting: There are regularly scheduled orientations for prospective students. There are guides for informal visits and visitors may sit in on classes and stay overnight at the school. To arrange for a visit, contact Penny Taylor, Enrollment Information Center at (318) 475-5504.
Financial Aid: In 1993–94, 45% of all students received some form of financial aid. About 41% of freshmen and 59% of continuing students received need-based aid. The average freshman award was $2273. Of that total, scholarships or need-based grants averaged $1557; loans averaged $1030; and work contracts averaged $549. Some 85% of undergraduate students work part-time. Average earnings from campus work for the school year are $1360. The FFS is required. The deadline for financial aid applications is May 1.
International Students: There are currently 86 international students enrolled. The school actively recruits these students. They must take the TOEFL. The student must also take the SAT I or the ACT.
Computers: The college provides computer facilities for student use. The mainframe is an IBM 9121-190. There are numerous 386, 286, XT, ATPCs, and Apple Macintosh microcomputers available in laboratories. The library houses terminals linked to MSU's computing services. The College of Science's academic computer center, the primary computing facility for computer science students, houses an IBM System/34, a PC laboratory, and terminals to access the mainframe as well as a VAX 3800-Utrix operating system. All students may access the system. It may be used during laboratory operating hours. There are no time limits on using the system and no fees.
Graduates: In 1992–93, 801 bachelor's degrees were awarded. The most popular majors among graduates were education (36%), liberal arts (14%), and science (11%). Within an average freshman class, 10% graduate in 4 years. Some 117 companies recruited on campus in 1992–93.
Admissions Contact: Kathy Bond, Admissions Counselor.

NICHOLLS STATE UNIVERSITY

D-4

Thibodaux, LA 70301

(504) 448-4507

Full-time: 2060 men, 2861 women
Part-time: 458 men, 880 women
Graduate: 240 men, 577 women
Year: semesters, summer session
Application Deadline: August 27
Freshman Class: 3679 applied, 3589 accepted, 2454 enrolled
ACT: 18

Faculty: 256; IIB, -$
Ph.D.s: 54%
Student/Faculty: 19 to 1
Tuition: $1981 ($4573)
Room & Board: $2550

NONCOMPETITIVE

Nicholls State University, established in 1948, is a public, coeducational liberal arts institution offering instruction in health sciences, fine arts, business, teacher preparation, and agricultural and technical disciplines. There are 4 undergraduate and 4 graduate schools. In addition to regional accreditation, Nicholls has baccalaureate program accreditation with AACSB, ADA, AHEA, NASM, NCATE, and NLN. The library contains 282,955 volumes, 735,607 microform items, and 2120 audiovisual forms, and subscribes to 1767 periodicals. Computerized library sources and services include interlibrary loans and database searching. Special learning facilities include a learning resource center, radio station, TV station, and centers for the study of dyslexia, women and government, and economic education. The 210-acre campus is in a small town 60 miles southwest of New Orleans. Including residence halls, there are 46 buildings on campus.
Student Life: About 98% of undergraduates are from Louisiana. Students come from 32 states, 32 foreign countries, and Canada. About 84% are from public schools. Eighty-four percent are white; 12% African American. Sixty-nine percent are Catholic; 23% Protestant. The

average age of freshmen is 19.9; all undergraduates, 24.3. Forty percent drop out by the end of their first year; 42% remain to graduate.

Housing: College-sponsored living facilities include single-sex and coed dormitories and married-student housing. In addition there are honors dormitories. On-campus housing is guaranteed for the freshman year only and is available on a first-come, first-served basis. Eighty-nine percent of students commute. All students may keep cars on campus.

Activities: About 5% of men belong to 10 national fraternities; about 4% of women belong to 6 national sororities. There are 80 groups on campus, including art, band, cheerleading, chess, choir, chorus, computers, dance, drama, drill team, ethnic, film, honors, international, literary magazine, marching band, musical theater, newspaper, pep band, photography, political, professional, radio and TV, religious, social, social service, student government, and yearbook. Popular campus events include Exam Week Breakfast, Family Day, Greek Week, Crawfish Boil, Pirogue Races, and Watermelon Party.

Sports: There are 7 intercollegiate sports for men and 7 for women, and 15 intramural sports for men and 15 for women. Athletic and recreation facilities include a stadium, 2 gymnasiums, tennis and raquetball courts, a soccer field, and a swimming pool.

Disabled Students: All of the campus is accessible to disabled students. The following facilities are available: wheelchair ramps, elevators, special parking, specially equipped rest rooms, special class scheduling, lowered drinking fountains, and lowered telephones.

Services: In addition to many counseling and information services, tutoring is available in most subjects. There is a reader service for the blind, and remedial math, reading, and writing.

Campus Safety and Security: Campus safety and security measures include 24-hour foot and vehicle patrols, self-defense education, informal discussions, and pamphlets, posters, and films. In addition, there are emergency telephones and lighted pathways and sidewalks.

Programs of Study: Nicholls awards the B.A., B.S., B.G.S., B.M., B.M.E., and B.S.N. degrees. Associate and master's degrees also are awarded. Bachelor's degrees are awarded in AGRICULTURE (agricultural business management), BIOLOGICAL SCIENCE (biology/biological science and marine biology), BUSINESS (accounting, banking and finance, business administration and management, business economics, marketing/retailing/merchandising, and personnel management), COMMUNICATIONS AND THE ARTS (communications, English, fine arts, French, music, piano/organ, and speech/debate/rhetoric), COMPUTER AND PHYSICAL SCIENCE (chemistry, computer science, geology, information sciences and systems, and mathematics), EDUCATION (art, business, early childhood, elementary, foreign languages, health, home economics, music, physical, science, and social studies), ENGINEERING AND ENVIRONMENTAL DESIGN (civil engineering technology and electrical/electronics engineering technology), HEALTH PROFESSIONS (nursing, predentistry, premedicine, and speech pathology/audiology), SOCIAL SCIENCE (dietetics, economics, history, home economics, political science/government, prelaw, psychology, and sociology). Curriculum and instruction, nursing and allied health, and general studies are the strongest academically. Nursing and allied health have the largest enrollments.

Required: All students must complete general education requirements, including 12 hours in English, a computer literacy course, 10 hours in natural sciences, 6 hours each in social sciences and mathematics, 3 hours in the arts, and 9 hours in humanities, including 2 semesters of health and physical education and 3 hours in student development. At least 130 total credit hours plus a minimum of 24 hours in the major, with a minimum GPA of 2.0, are required to graduate.

Special: Internships are offered in business areas, government, home economics, and psychology. A Washington semester including a congressional internship is available, as well as a B.A.-B.S. degree in economics, dual majors in education, and student-designed majors in general studies. Nondegree study and credit for military experience are possible. There is a seven-on/seven-off degree program for offshore-oil field workers. There is one national honor society on campus, Phi Beta Kappa. One department has an honors program.

Faculty/Classroom: Sixty-two percent of faculty are male; 38%, female. Ninety-eight percent teach undergraduates, 10% also do research. Graduate students teach 3% of introductory courses. The average class size in an introductory lecture is 31; in a laboratory, 15; and in a regular course offering, 28.

Admissions: About 98% of the 1993–94 applicants were accepted. The ACT scores for the 1993–94 freshman class were as follows: 69% below 21, 18% between 21 and 23, 10% between 24 and 26, 3% between 27 and 28, and 1% above 28. In the current freshman class there are 12 National Merit finalists. About 50 freshmen graduated first in their class.

Requirements: The ACT is required. Applicants must be graduates of an accredited secondary school or have the GED. Institutional placement tests are given for English, mathematics, and reading. AP and CLEP credits are accepted. Important factors used in the admis-

sions decision are advanced placement or honors courses, evidence of special talent, leadership record, personality, intangible qualities, and extracurricular activities record.

Procedure: Freshmen are admitted to all sessions. Entrance exams should be taken as early as possible. Early decision applications should be filed by July 13; regular applications, by August 27 for fall entry, January 22 for spring entry, and June 11 for summer entry. There is an application fee of $10. The college accepts most applicants. Notification is sent on a rolling basis. There is an early decision plan. Twenty-five early decision candidates were accepted for the 1993–94 class.

Transfer: About 340 transfer students enrolled in 1993–94. Transfer applicants must be eligible to return to the institution from which they are transferring. A total of 60 credits out of 130 must be completed at Nicholls.

Visiting: There are regularly scheduled orientations for prospective students. There are guides for informal visits, and visitors may sit in on classes and stay overnight at the school. To arrange for a visit, contact Admissions Information at (504) 448-4507.

Financial Aid: In 1993–94, 18% of all current freshmen and 39% of continuing students received some form of financial aid. About 14% of freshmen and 34% of continuing students received need-based aid. Scholarships or need-based grants averaged $500 ($3000 maximum); and loans averaged $800 ($2625 maximum). Nine percent of undergraduate students work part-time. Average earnings from campus work for the school year are $1377. The FFS is required. The deadline for financial aid applications is March 25.

International Students: There are currently 91 international students enrolled. The school actively recruits these students. They must take the TOEFL and achieve a minimum score of 500.

Computers: The college provides computer facilities for student use. The mainframe is a Unisys A6-F. There are also 200 Zenith 148, 159, and 248 microcomputers available in 7 buildings. Computer science and mathematics majors may access the system. It may be used 24 hours a day. There are no time limits and no fees.

Graduates: In 1992–93, 650 bachelor's degrees were awarded. The most popular majors among graduates were business (24%), education (23%), and general studies (19%). Within an average freshman class, 4% graduate in 4 years, 14% in 5 years, and 30% in 6 years. Some 420 companies recruited on campus in 1992–93.

Admissions Contact: Bernadette F. Dugas-Chauvin, Director of Admissions Information.

NORTHEAST LOUISIANA UNIVERSITY   C-1
Monroe, LA 71209   (318) 342-5252; (800) 372-5127 (in-state)

Full-time: 3733 men, 4985 women	Faculty: 481; IIA, --$
Part-time: 644 men, 1063 women	Ph.D.s: 56%
Graduate: 382 men, 764 women	Student/Faculty: 18 to 1
Year: semesters, summer session	Tuition: $1926 ($3774)
Application Deadline: open	Room & Board: $1980
Freshman Class: 3092 applied, 3092 accepted, 1959 enrolled	
ACT: 19	**NONCOMPETITIVE**

Northeast Louisiana University, founded in 1931, is a public, coeducational institution offering programs in liberal arts, professional studies, and business. There are 5 undergraduate schools and one graduate school. In addition to regional accreditation, NLU has baccalaureate program accreditation with AACSB, ACCE, ACPE, ADA, AHEA, ASLA, CAHEA, CSWE, NASM, NCATE, and NLN. The library contains 532,940 volumes, 435,346 microform items, and 49 audiovisual forms, and subscribes to 2935 periodicals. Computerized library sources and services include the card catalog, interlibrary loans, and database searching. Special learning facilities include a learning resource center, art gallery, planetarium, radio station, herbarium, state poison control center, and state tumor registry. The 227-acre campus is in an urban area 100 miles east of Shreveport. Including residence halls, there are 75 buildings on campus.

Student Life: About 92% of undergraduates are from Louisiana. Students come from 41 states, 42 foreign countries, and Canada. Seventy-seven percent are white; 18% African American. Fifty-six percent are Protestant; 14% Catholic. The average age of freshmen is 20.7; all undergraduates, 23.1. Thirty-eight percent drop out by the end of their first year; 34% remain to graduate.

Housing: A total of 3681 students can be accommodated in college housing. College-sponsored living facilities include single-sex and coed dormitories. In addition, there is an honors dormitory. On-campus housing is available on a first-come, first-served basis. Seventy-two percent of students commute. Alcohol is not permitted. All students may keep cars on campus.

Activities: About 3% of men belong to 7 national fraternities; about 2% of women belong to 8 national sororities. There are 172 groups on campus, including art, band, cheerleading, choir, chorale, chorus, computers, dance, drama, drill team, ethnic, film, honors, international, jazz band, literary magazine, marching band, musical theater, newspaper, opera, orchestra, pep band, photography, political, pro-

fessional, radio and TV, religious, social, social service, student government, symphony, and yearbook. Popular campus events include Homecoming, Honors Day Assembly, 'Miss Northeast' Pageant, play productions, university elections, debate and forensics, radio, Spring Fever, big-name concerts, University Arts Festival, First Amendment Open Golf Tournament, spirit groups, and the Military Ball.

Sports: There are 9 intercollegiate sports for men and 8 for women, and 100 intramural sports for men and 100 for women. Athletic and recreation facilities include a stadium, a natatorium, a coliseum, tennis courts, a softball complex, an activity center, a baseball complex, a rifle range, bowling lanes, and a bayou.

Disabled Students: All of the campus is accessible to disabled students. The following facilities are available: wheelchair ramps, elevators, special parking, specially equipped rest rooms, special class scheduling, lowered drinking fountains, and specially equipped dormitory rooms.

Services: In addition to many counseling and information services, tutoring is available in most subjects. In addition, there is remedial math, reading, and writing.

Campus Safety and Security: Campus safety and security measures include 24-hour foot and vehicle patrol, escort service, shuttle buses, and lighted pathways and sidewalks.

Programs of Study: NLU awards the B.A., B.S., B.B.A., B.F.A., B.G.S., B.M., and B.M.E. degrees. Associate, master's, and doctoral degrees also are awarded. Bachelor's degrees are awarded in AGRICULTURE (agricultural business management), BIOLOGICAL SCIENCE (biology/biological science and toxicology), BUSINESS (accounting, banking and finance, business administration and management, business economics, fashion merchandising, insurance, marketing/retailing/merchandising, and real estate), COMMUNICATIONS AND THE ARTS (broadcasting, communications, English, film arts, French, journalism, music, Spanish, and speech/debate/rhetoric), COMPUTER AND PHYSICAL SCIENCE (atmospheric sciences and meteorology, chemistry, computer programming, computer science, geology, information sciences and systems, mathematics, physics, and radiological technology), EDUCATION (art, business, early childhood, elementary, English, foreign languages, home economics, library science, mathematics, music, science, social studies, and special), ENGINEERING AND ENVIRONMENTAL DESIGN (aviation administration/management, construction, industrial administration/management, and interior design), HEALTH PROFESSIONS (dental hygiene, medical laboratory technology, nursing, occupational therapy, pharmacy, predentistry, premedicine, and speech pathology/audiology), SOCIAL SCIENCE (child care/child and family studies, criminal justice, geography, history, political science/government, prelaw, psychology, social work, and sociology). Computer science, pharmacy, and nursing are the strongest programs academically. Pharmacy, nursing, and elementary education have the largest enrollments.

Required: Students are required to take 6 hours each of English, social sciences, and mathematics, 9 each of natural sciences and humanities, and 3 of the arts. An overall minimum GPA of 2.0 is required for graduation in a total number of credits varying by degree.

Special: A co-op program in business, an internship in pharmacy, a general studies degree, nondegree study, and credit for life, military, and work experience are offered. There is a freshman honors program on campus, as well as 2 national honor societies. Five departments have honors programs.

Faculty/Classroom: Sixty percent of faculty are male; 40%, female.

Admissions: All of the 1993–94 applicants were accepted. The ACT scores for the 1993–94 freshman class were as follows: 70% below 21, 17% between 21 and 23, 9% between 24 and 26, 3% between 27 and 28, and 1% above 28.

Requirements: The ACT is required. Applicants must be graduates of an accredited high school or have a GED. CLEP credit is accepted.

Procedure: Freshmen are admitted to all sessions. Entrance exams should be taken by December 1. Application deadlines are open. Application fee is $5. The college accepts all applicants. Notification is sent on a rolling basis.

Transfer: About 810 transfer students enrolled in 1993–94. Transfer applicants must submit transcripts from previously attended institutions and should be eligible to return to the school from which they are transferring. A total of 30 credits must be completed at NLU.

Visiting: There are regularly scheduled orientations for prospective students, consisting of the mandatory PREP program, which includes campus tours, meetings with deans/advisors, class registration, and placement examinations. There are guides for informal visits and visitors may sit in on classes. To arrange for a visit, contact Patsy Rials at (318) 342–5430 or (800) 372–5127 (in-state).

Financial Aid: In 1993–94 50% of all current freshmen and 50% of continuing students received some form of financial aid. About 40% of freshmen received need-based aid. The average freshman award was $3500. Of that total, scholarships or need-based grants averaged $1500 ($2300 maximum); loans averaged $1000 ($8500 maximum); and work contracts averaged $1000 ($2200 maximum). Eleven per-

cent of undergraduate students work part-time. Average earnings from campus work for the school year are $1000. The average financial indebtedness of the 1992–93 graduate was $10,000. The Student Aid Report is required. The deadline for financial aid applications is August 1.

International Students: The school actively recruits these students. They must take the TOEFL and achieve a minimum score of 600. The student must also take the ACT.

Computers: The college provides computer facilities for student use. The mainframes are an IBM ES/900 Model 170 and a DEC VAX 6410. Some 320 Unix, VAX, IBM PC, Macintosh, and Apple microcomputers are available in student laboratories around campus. Any student whose sponsor has a rank at or above department head may access the system. There are no time limits on using the system and no fees.

Graduates: In 1992–93, 1295 bachelor's degrees were awarded. The most popular majors among graduates were pharmacy (16%), elementary education (8%), and nursing (6%). Within an average freshman class, 1% graduate in 3 years, 8% in 4 years, 20% in 5 years, and 27% in 6 years. Some 378 companies recruited on campus in 1992–93.

Admissions Contact: Dr. James Robertson, Director of Admissions.

NORTHWESTERN STATE UNIVERSITY OF LOUISIANA
Natchitoches, LA 71497

B-2

(318) 357–4503
(800) 327–1903 (out-of-state)

Full-time: 2294 men, 3450 women	Faculty: 221; IIA, --$
Part-time: 681 men, 1286 women	Ph.D.s: 63%
Graduate: 178 men, 663 women	Student/Faculty: 26 to 1
Year: semesters, summer session	Tuition: $2071 ($4081)
Application Deadline: August 12	Room & Board: $2216
Freshman Class: 2618 applied, 2612 accepted	
ACT: 19	NONCOMPETITIVE

Northwestern State University of Louisiana, founded in 1884, offers undergraduate programs in business, education, liberal arts, nursing, and science and technology. There are 13 undergraduate schools and one graduate school. In addition to regional accreditation, NSU has baccalaureate program accreditation with CAHEA, CSWE, NASM, NCATE, and NLN. The library contains 301,614 volumes, 577,021 microform items, and 1917 audiovisual forms, and subscribes to 2083 periodicals. Computerized library sources and services include the card catalog, interlibrary loans, and database searching. Special learning facilities include an art gallery, natural history museum, planetarium, radio station, and TV station. The 1000-acre campus is in a small town 50 miles northwest of Alexandria. Including residence halls, there are 36 buildings on campus.

Student Life: About 94% of undergraduates are from Louisiana. Students come from 34 states and 13 foreign countries. Seventy-three percent are white; 20% African American. The average age of freshmen is 20.8; all undergraduates, 24.8. Thirty-nine percent drop out by the end of their first year; 32% remain to graduate.

Housing: A total of 2000 students can be accommodated in college housing. College-sponsored living facilities include single-sex dormitories, on-campus apartments, married-student housing, fraternity houses, and sorority houses. In addition there are honors houses. On-campus housing is available on a first-come, first-served basis. Sixty-one percent of students commute. Alcohol is not permitted. All students may keep cars on campus.

Activities: About 16% of men belong to 8 national fraternities; about 21% of women belong to 6 national sororities. There are numerous groups on campus, including art, band, cheerleading, choir, chorale, chorus, dance, drama, drill team, ethnic, honors, jazz band, literary magazine, marching band, musical theater, newspaper, orchestra, pep band, photography, professional, radio and TV, social, student government, symphony, and yearbook. Popular campus events include Mardi Gras and Homecoming.

Sports: There are 6 intercollegiate sports for men and 4 for women, and 25 intramural sports for men and 25 for women. Athletic and recreation facilities include a 16,000-seat football stadium, a 5000-seat indoor gymnasium, sports training and basketball centers, a track, and a coliseum. The largest auditorium/arena seats 1500.

Disabled Students: The entire campus is accessible to disabled students. The following facilities are available: wheelchair ramps, elevators, special parking, specially equipped rest rooms, and lowered drinking fountains.

Services: In addition to many counseling and information services, tutoring is available in some subjects. There is also remedial math, reading, and writing.

Campus Safety and Security: Campus safety and security measures include 24-hour foot and vehicle patrol, escort service, pamphlets, posters, films, and emergency telephones. In addition, there are lighted pathways and sidewalks.

Programs of Study: NSU awards the B.A., B.S., and B.M. degrees. Associate and master's degrees also are awarded. Bachelor's degrees are awarded in BIOLOGICAL SCIENCE (biology/biological science), BUSINESS (accounting, business administration and management, marketing/retailing/merchandising, and personnel management), COMMUNICATIONS AND THE ARTS (advertising, broadcasting, English, fine arts, journalism, and music), COMPUTER AND PHYSICAL SCIENCE (information sciences and systems, mathematics, and physics), EDUCATION (art, business, early childhood, elementary, guidance, home economics, industrial arts, music, science, and secondary), ENGINEERING AND ENVIRONMENTAL DESIGN (engineering technology), HEALTH PROFESSIONS (medical laboratory technology, nursing, and speech pathology/audiology), SOCIAL SCIENCE (anthropology, history, political science/government, psychology, social science, social work, and sociology). Nursing, business, and education are the strongest academically. Business administration, nursing, and elementary teaching have the largest enrollments.

Required: In order to graduate, all students must complete an approved curriculum, the university education requirement, and a minimum 120 semester hours, with at least 30 semester hours in the major field. Distribution requirements include 12 credits each of communications and social sciences, 9 of natural sciences, 6 each of fine arts and mathematics, and 4 in personal fitness. A minimum 2.0 GPA is needed for all hours taken at NSU.

Special: NSU offers cooperative programs with local businesses, internships, study abroad on 5 continents, and work-study programs. A general studies degree, credit for experience, nondegree study, and pass/fail options are available. There is a freshman honors program on campus, as well as one national honor society, Phi Beta Kappa. One department has an honors program.

Faculty/Classroom: Fifty-three percent of faculty are male; 47%, female. Eighty-seven percent teach undergraduates, 12% do research, and 76% do both. Graduate students teach 3% of introductory courses. The average class size in an introductory lecture is 48; in a laboratory, 26; and in a regular course offering, 34.

Admissions: Nearly 100% of the 1993–94 applicants were accepted.

Requirements: The ACT is required. Applicants must be graduates of an accredited secondary school or have a GED certificate. Students must have completed 4 units of English, 3 units each of history and mathematics, and 2 units each of science and social studies. AP and CLEP credits are accepted.

Procedure: Freshmen are admitted to all sessions. Entrance exams should be taken before the semester begins. Applications should be filed by August 12 for fall entry, January 10 for spring entry, and May 10 for summer entry, along with an application fee of $5. The college accepts all applicants. Notification is sent on a rolling basis. There is an early admissions plan.

Transfer: About 410 transfer students enrolled in 1993–94. Transfer students must be eligible for readmission to their former university or college in order to enter NSU. The last 30 credits out of 120 must be completed at NSU.

Visiting: There are regularly scheduled orientations for prospective students, consisting of a campus tour, with special focus on financial aid, housing and board, academic requirements and selecting a major, registration and early registration, campus organizations and student groups, and adapting to the college. There are guides for informal visits and visitors may sit in on classes and stay overnight at the school. To arrange for a visit, contact Marsha Zulick, Director of Admissions, at (318) 357-4503.

Financial Aid: In 1993–94, 78% of all current freshmen and 61% of continuing students received some form of financial aid. Work contracts averaged $400 ($1600 maximum). Forty-five percent of undergraduate students work part-time. Average earnings from campus work for the school year are $1020. NSU is a member of CSS. The FAF or FFS is required. The deadline for financial aid applications is April 1.

International Students: There are currently 34 international students enrolled. They must take the TOEFL and achieve a minimum score of 550. The student must also take the ACT.

Computers: The university provides computer facilities for student use. The mainframes are a DEC VAX 11/785 and 11/750. PCs are available for academic use in the department of business administration, in the computer center, and in the department of mathematics and physical sciences. All students may access the system at all times. There are no time limits on using the system and no fees.

Graduates: Some 131 companies recruited on campus in 1992–93.

Admissions Contact: Marsha Zulick, Director of Admissions.

OUR LADY OF HOLY CROSS COLLEGE   D-4
New Orleans, LA 70131–7399   (504) 394-7744, ext. 126
                                    (800) 486-5422 (in-state)

Full-time: 155 men, 519 women	**Faculty:** 32; IIB, --$
Part-time: 118 men, 354 women	**Ph.D.s:** 60%
Graduate: none	**Student/Faculty:** 21 to 1
Year: semesters, summer session	**Tuition:** $4630
Application Deadline: August 16	**Room & Board:** n/app
Freshman Class: 577 applied, 297 accepted, 297 enrolled	
SAT I or ACT: required	**LESS COMPETITIVE**

Our Lady of Holy Cross College, founded in 1916, is a private, coeducational commuter college affiliated with the Roman Catholic Church. There are 6 undergraduate schools and 1 graduate school. In addition to regional accreditation, OLHCC has baccalaureate program accreditation with NLN. The library contains 56,700 volumes, 136,015 microform items, and 13,598 audiovisual forms, and subscribes to 805 periodicals. Computerized library sources and services include the card catalog, interlibrary loans, and database searching. The 40-acre campus is in an urban area in New Orleans. There is 1 building on campus.

Student Life: About 99% of undergraduates are from Louisiana. Students come from 2 states. Seventy-seven percent are white; 14% African American. Seventy percent are Catholic; 16% Protestant. The average age of freshmen is 24; all undergraduates, 28.1. Ten percent drop out by the end of their first year; 70% remain to graduate.

Housing: There are no residence halls. College-sponsored living facilities include off-campus apartments. All students commute. Alcohol is not permitted. All students may keep cars on campus.

Activities: There are no fraternities or sororities on campus. There are 11 groups on campus, including choir, chorus, computers, drama, ethnic, honors, newspaper, professional, social, social service, and student government. Popular campus events include Fall Fest, Crawfish Boil, Halloween and Christmas dances, and Homecoming.

Sports: There are 5 intramural sports for men and 4 for women.

Disabled Students: The entire campus is accessible to disabled students. The following facilities are available: wheelchair ramps, elevators, special parking, specially equipped rest rooms, lowered drinking fountains, and lowered telephones.

Services: Remedial math, reading, and writing are offered.

Campus Safety and Security: Campus safety and security measures include escort service, pamphlets, posters, and films, emergency telephones, and lighted pathways and sidewalks. In addition, there is foot patrol inside and outside of the building from 7:30 A.M. to 10 P.M.

Programs of Study: OLHCC awards the B.A. and B.S. degrees. Associate and master's degrees also are awarded. Bachelor's degrees are awarded in BIOLOGICAL SCIENCE (biology/biological science), BUSINESS (accounting and business administration and management), COMMUNICATIONS AND THE ARTS (English), EDUCATION (business, elementary, and secondary), HEALTH PROFESSIONS (health science and nursing), SOCIAL SCIENCE (behavioral science, history, and social science). Nursing is the strongest academically and has the largest enrollment.

Required: A total of 128 credit hours with 33 to 36 hours in the major, and a minimum GPA of 2.0 are required to graduate. All students must take courses in theology, philosophy, literature, English composition, mathematics, natural sciences, library orientation, social sciences, speech, fine arts, and computer science.

Special: Co-op programs in business, internships with the Navy Civilian Personnel Office, study abroad in France, and credit for life, military, and work experience are offered.

Faculty/Classroom: Ninety-eight percent of faculty teach undergraduates and 2% do research. The average class size in an introductory lecture is 25; in a laboratory, 24; and in a regular course offering, 20.

Admissions: About 51% of the 1993–94 applicants were accepted.

Requirements: A minimum GPA of 2.0 is required. The SAT I or ACT is required. AP and CLEP credits are accepted.

Procedure: Freshmen are admitted to all sessions. Entrance exams should be taken a week before registration. Applications should be filed by August 16 for winter entry, December 20 for spring entry, and May 21 for summer entry, along with an application fee of $15.

Transfer: Some 804 transfer students enrolled in 1993–94. Transfer applicants must have an overall 2.0 GPA for unconditional admission. A total of 30 credits out of 128 must be completed at OLHCC.

Visiting: There are regularly scheduled orientations for prospective students. There are guides for informal visits and visitors may sit in on classes. To arrange for a visit, contact Alan T. Flair at (504) 394-7744, ext. 126, or (800) 486-5422 (in-state).

Financial Aid: In 1993–94, 67% of all current freshmen received some form of financial aid. The average freshman award was $2625. Of that total, the maximum awards were $2300 for scholarship or need-based grants, $2500 for loans, and $1700 for work contracts.

Three percent of undergraduate students work part-time. Average earnings from campus work for the school year are $1000. The FAF and the Student Aid Report are required. The deadline for financial aid applications is June 1.

International Students: There is currently 1 international student enrolled. Such students must take the TOEFL and achieve a minimum score of 500. The student must also take the SAT I or the ACT.

Computers: The college provides computer facilities for student use. There are PCs available in a computer laboratory with 20 terminals. All students may access the system. There are no time limits and no fees.

Graduates: Within an average freshman class, 10% graduate in 4 years, 60% in 5 years, and 20% in 6 years. Some 12 companies recruited on campus in 1992–93.

Admissions Contact: Alan T. Flair, Coordinator of Admissions and Recruiting.

SOUTHEASTERN LOUISIANA UNIVERSITY D-3

Hammond, LA 70402   (504) 549–2123; (800) 222–7358 (in-state)

Full-time: 3900 men, 5883 women	Faculty: 319; IIA, --$
Part-time: 873 men, 1317 women	Ph.D.s: 65%
Graduate: 503 men, 759 women	Student/Faculty: 31 to 1
Year: semesters, summer session	Tuition: $1910 ($3854)
Application Deadline: July 15	Room & Board: $2320
Freshman Class: 3247 applied, 3149 accepted, 2306 enrolled	
ACT: 19	**NONCOMPETITIVE**

Southeastern Louisiana University, founded in 1925, is a public, coeducational university offering courses in liberal arts, fine arts, and professional studies. There are 5 undergraduate schools. In addition to regional accreditation, SLU has baccalaureate program accreditation with AACSB, CSWE, NASM, NCATE, and NLN. The library contains 290,000 volumes, 492,000 microform items, and 39,000 audiovisual forms, and subscribes to 2200 periodicals. Computerized library sources and services include the card catalog, interlibrary loans, and database searching. Special learning facilities include a learning resource center and radio station. The 365-acre campus is in a small town 46 miles northwest of New Orleans. Including residence halls, there are 50 buildings on campus.

Student Life: About 98% of undergraduates are from Louisiana. Students also come from Canada. Ninety-one percent are white. The average age of all undergraduates is 23. Fifty-three percent drop out by the end of their first year; 47% remain to graduate.

Housing: A total of 1800 students can be accommodated in college housing. College-sponsored living facilities include single-sex and coed dormitories, on-campus apartments, married-student housing, and fraternity houses. In addition, there are honors houses. On-campus housing is available on a first-come, first-served basis. Eighty percent of students commute. Alcohol is not permitted. All students may keep cars on campus.

Activities: About 5% of men belong to 1 local fraternity and 11 national fraternities; about 5% of women belong to 1 local sorority and 7 national sororities. There are 125 groups on campus, including band, choir, chorale, chorus, dance, drama, honors, jazz band, literary magazine, marching band, newspaper, orchestra, pep band, radio and TV, social, social service, student government, symphony, and yearbook.

Sports: SLU has an intercollegiate and intramural sports program.

Disabled Students: Ninety percent of the campus is accessible to disabled students. The following facilities are available: wheelchair ramps, elevators, special parking, and special class scheduling.

Services: In addition to many counseling and information services, tutoring is available in some subjects. There is also remedial math, reading, and writing.

Campus Safety and Security: Campus safety and security measures include 24-hour foot and vehicle patrol.

Programs of Study: SLU awards the B.A., B.S., B.G.S., B.M., and B.M.E. degrees. Associate and master's degrees also are awarded. Bachelor's degrees are awarded in AGRICULTURE (horticulture), BIOLOGICAL SCIENCE (biology/biological science, botany, microbiology, and zoology), BUSINESS (accounting, business administration and management, business economics, marketing/retailing/merchandising, and office supervision and management), COMMUNICATIONS AND THE ARTS (arts administration/management, communications, dance, dramatic arts, English, fine arts, French, music, Spanish, and speech/debate/rhetoric), COMPUTER AND PHYSICAL SCIENCE (chemistry, computer science, earth science, mathematics, and physics), EDUCATION (art, business, early childhood, elementary, English, foreign languages, home economics, industrial arts, mathematics, music, physical, science, social studies, and special), HEALTH PROFESSIONS (nursing, optometry, physical therapy, predentistry, premedicine, and prepharmacy), SOCIAL SCIENCE (criminal justice, family/consumer studies, history, political science/government, prelaw, psychology, social work, and sociology). Nursing has the largest enrollment.

Required: The requirements for graduation vary by academic college, but a minimum GPA of 2.0 is necessary.

Special: SLU offers a general studies degree, nondegree study, and pass/fail options. There is a freshman honors program on campus.

Admissions: About 97% of the 1993–94 applicants were accepted.

Requirements: The ACT is required. Candidates for admission should be high school graduates with a college preparatory program that includes 4 units in English, 3 each in mathematics, science, social studies, and a foreign language, 1 in fine arts, and 2 in physical education. AP and CLEP credits are accepted.

Procedure: Freshmen are admitted to all sessions. Entrance exams should be taken prior to registering for classes. Applications should be filed by July 15 for fall entry, December 1 for spring entry, and May 1 for summer entry, along with an application fee of $10. The college accepts all applicants. Notification is sent on a rolling basis.

Transfer: A total of 731 transfer students enrolled in 1993–94. Applicants must meet freshman entrance requirements.

Visiting: There are regularly scheduled orientations for prospective students. There are guides for informal visits and visitors may stay overnight at the school. To arrange for a visit, contact the High School Relations Office at (504) 549–3737.

Financial Aid: In 1993–94, 55% of all current freshmen and 55% of continuing students received some form of financial aid. The average freshman award was $6265. Of that total, scholarships or need-based grants averaged $640; loans averaged $2625; and work contracts averaged $3000. Eight percent of undergraduate students work part-time. SLU is a member of CSS. The FAF is required. The deadline for financial aid applications is April 15.

International Students: There are currently 75 international students enrolled. They must take the TOEFL and achieve a minimum score of 500. The student must also take the ACT.

Computers: The university provides computer facilities for student use. The mainframe is a DEC VAX 6000. There are also microcomputers and 600 word processors available along with terminals in the computer center. All students may access the system. There are no time limits on using the system and no fees.

Graduates: In 1992–93, 967 bachelor's degrees were awarded. Some 100 companies recruited on campus in 1992–93.

Admissions Contact: Director of Admissions.

SOUTHERN UNIVERSITY

The Southern University system, established in 1975, is a public system in Louisiana. It is governed by the Southern University Board of Supervisors and the Louisiana Board of Regents, whose chief administrator is the president. The primary goal of the system is teaching. The main priorities are teaching, public service, and research. The total enrollment of all campuses is approximately 13,000, with about 600 faculty members. Altogether, there are 144 baccalaureate, 42 master's, and 1 doctoral programs offered within the system. There are four-year campuses located in Baton Rouge and New Orleans. Profiles of those campuses are included in this chapter.

SOUTHERN UNIVERSITY AND A&M COLLEGE C-4

Baton Rouge, LA 70813   (504) 771–2430

Full-time: 2650 men, 3430 women	Faculty: 475; IIA, --$
Part-time: 970 men, 1500 women	Ph.D.s: n/av
Graduate: 746 men, 927 women	Student/Faculty: 13 to 1
Year: semesters, summer session	Tuition: $2028 ($3950)
Application Deadline: July 1	Room & Board: $2892
Freshman Class: n/av	
SAT I or ACT: required	**NONCOMPETITIVE**

Southern University and A&M College, founded in 1880, is a publicly supported, nonsectarian, land-grant institution offering degree programs in agriculture, arts and humanities, business, education, engineering, home economics, nursing, and science. There are 9 undergraduate schools and one graduate school. In addition to regional accreditation, Southern has baccalaureate program accreditation with ABET, ADA, AHEA, CSWE, NAAB, NASM, and NCATE. The library contains 700,000 volumes, 68,000 microform items, and 7000 audiovisual forms, and subscribes to 2771 periodicals. Special learning facilities include a learning resource center and the Black Heritage Collection. The 884-acre campus is in a suburban area in Baton Rouge.

Student Life: About 81% of undergraduates are from Louisiana. Students come from 48 states. Seventy-five percent are from public schools; 25% from private. Seventy-eight percent are African American; 20% white. The average age of freshmen is 18; all undergraduates, 23. Seventeen percent drop out by the end of their first year; 60% remain to graduate.

Housing: A total of 3412 students can be accommodated in college housing. College-sponsored living facilities include single-sex and coed dormitories, on-campus apartments, and married-student housing. Alcohol is not permitted.

Activities: About 8% of men belong to 4 national fraternities; about 3% of women belong to 4 national sororities. There are many groups and organizations on campus, including art, band, cheerleading, chess, choir, chorale, computers, drama, ethnic, honors, international, jazz band, marching band, newspaper, political, professional, religious, social, student government, and yearbook.

Sports: There are 19 intramural sports for men and 19 for women. Athletic and recreation facilities include a center around the main activity complex, which accommodates theater, convocations, and athletic contests.

Disabled Students: The following facilities are available: special class scheduling and special housing.

Services: In addition to many counseling and information services, tutoring is available in every subject. There is also a reader service for the blind, and remedial math, reading, and writing.

Campus Safety and Security: Campus safety and security measures include 24-hour foot and vehicle patrol, escort service, informal discussions, and pamphlets, posters, and films. In addition, there are emergency telephones.

Programs of Study: Southern awards the B.A., B.S., B.Arch., B.Mus., B.Mus.Ed., and B.S.N. degrees. Associate, master's, and doctoral degrees also are awarded. Bachelor's degrees are awarded in AGRICULTURE (agricultural business management, agricultural economics, agriculture, animal science, plant science, and soil science), BIOLOGICAL SCIENCE (biochemistry, biology/biological science, botany, microbiology, nutrition, and zoology), BUSINESS (accounting, business administration and management, and marketing/retailing/merchandising), COMMUNICATIONS AND THE ARTS (art history and appreciation, broadcasting, communications, dance, dramatic arts, English, fine arts, French, journalism, music, Spanish, speech/debate/rhetoric, and studio art), COMPUTER AND PHYSICAL SCIENCE (chemistry, computer science, mathematics, natural sciences, physics, and science), EDUCATION (agricultural, art, business, early childhood, elementary, English, foreign languages, health, home economics, industrial arts, mathematics, middle school, music, physical, recreation, science, secondary, social studies, special, and vocational), ENGINEERING AND ENVIRONMENTAL DESIGN (architecture, civil engineering, electrical/electronics engineering, engineering technology, environmental science, interior design, mechanical engineering, mechanical engineering technology, and preengineering), HEALTH PROFESSIONS (cytotechnology, health science, medical laboratory technology, nursing, occupational therapy, physical therapy, premedicine, preveterinary science, rehabilitation therapy, speech pathology/audiology, and speech therapy), and SOCIAL SCIENCE (child psychology/development, clothing and textiles management/production/services, dietetics, economics, history, political science/government, prelaw, psychology, social science, social work, and sociology). Biology, engineering, nursing, and business have the largest enrollments.

Required: All students must pass a general competency examination measuring proficiency in communication, computation, logical thinking, and general knowledge. All students also must take the GRE at the end of the junior year. To graduate, they must complete 124 semester hours with a minimum GPA of 2.0 overall and in the major.

Special: Student-designed majors, nondegree study, credit for military experience, accelerated degrees, co-op education, study abroad, internships, work-study, and an exchange program and dual majors in chemistry/chemical engineering with Louisiana State University are available. There is a freshman honors program on campus, as well as 9 national honor societies.

Requirements: A minimum GPA of 1.4 is required. To be admitted unconditionally as a freshman, SAT I or ACT scores are necessary. The school recommends that applicants have 15 Carnegie units, including 4 of English, 3 each of mathematics, social studies, science, and foreign language, and 1 of fine arts. The GED is accepted. AP and CLEP credits are accepted.

Procedure: Freshmen are admitted to all sessions. Applications should be filed by July 1 for fall entry, December 1 for spring entry, and April 1 for summer entry, along with an application fee of $5. The college accepts all applicants. There is an early admissions plan.

Transfer: Transfer students must complete at least 1 year at Southern. A total of 31 semester hours out of 124 must be completed at Southern.

Financial Aid: In an earlier year, 80% of all freshmen received some form of financial aid. The FAF or FFS is required.

International Students: International students must take the TOEFL and achieve a minimum score of 400.

Computers: The college provides computer facilities for student use. There are no time limits on using the system and no fees.

Admissions Contact: Henry Bellaire, Jr., Director of Admissions.

SOUTHERN UNIVERSITY AT NEW ORLEANS   D-4
New Orleans, LA 70126 (504) 286-5314

Full-time, part time: 4200 men and women	Faculty: 200; IIB, --$
	Ph.D.s: n/av
Graduate: 35 men, 100 women	Student/Faculty: n/av
Year: semesters, summer session	Tuition: $1452 ($3010)
Application Deadline: July 1	Room & Board: n/app
Freshman Class: n/av	
ACT: required	**NONCOMPETITIVE**

Southern University at New Orleans, established in 1956, is a public commuter institution offering programs in liberal arts and sciences, business, education, and the technologies. In addition to regional accreditation, SUNO has baccalaureate program accreditation with CSWE. The library contains 300,000 volumes. The 22-acre campus is in a suburban area. There are 10 buildings on campus. There are no residence halls.

Student Life: Ninety percent are from public schools. Fifty-eight percent drop out by the end of their first year; 20% remain to graduate.

Housing: There are no residence halls. All students commute.

Activities: There are fraternities and sororities on campus. There are 30 groups on campus, including drama, honors, international, musical theater, newspaper, political, professional, religious, student government, and yearbook.

Sports: There are 4 intercollegiate sports for men and 2 for women, as well as intramural sports. Athletic and recreation facilities include a university center housing an Olympic-size pool, a 6-lane bowling alley, and various game rooms.

Services: Personal counseling is available.

Programs of Study: SUNO awards the B.A., B.S., and B.S.W. degrees. Associate and master's degrees also are awarded. Bachelor's degrees are awarded in BIOLOGICAL SCIENCE (biology/biological science), BUSINESS (accounting, business administration and management, secretarial studies/office management, and transportation management), COMMUNICATIONS AND THE ARTS (English, fine arts, journalism, Spanish, and speech/debate/rhetoric), COMPUTER AND PHYSICAL SCIENCE (chemistry, mathematics, and physics), EDUCATION (art, business, education of the deaf and hearing impaired, elementary, English, foreign languages, mathematics, music, physical, recreation, science, secondary, and social studies), HEALTH PROFESSIONS (health care administration), and SOCIAL SCIENCE (criminal justice, economics, history, political science/government, psychology, social work, sociology, and urban studies).

Required: All students must maintain a minimum 2.0 GPA while taking at least 124 semester hours. Requirements may vary with the program. All candidates for bachelor's degrees must take the GRE (GMAT for business majors, NTE for education majors). Specific courses and a writing proficiency examination must be taken.

Special: Work-study programs with SUNO, double majors, co-op education, internships, cross-registration with the University of New Orleans and Delgado Junior College, and study abroad are available. Credit for military experience, nondegree study, and study via telecourses are possible.

Requirements: The ACT is required. The score is used for placement purposes. Candidates must be graduates of an accredited secondary school or have the GED, having earned 15 Carnegie units. AP and CLEP credits are accepted.

Procedure: Applications should be filed by July 1 for fall entry, December 15 for spring entry, and April 15 for summer entry. The college accepts all applicants. Notification is sent on a rolling basis. There are early admissions and deferred admissions plans.

Transfer: A minimum 2.0 GPA is recommended. Those with a lower GPA may be accepted on a probationary basis. Students must spend at least 1 year on campus and earn at least 31 semester hours out of at least 124 to receive a bachelor's degree.

Financial Aid: In an earlier year, 75% of all freshmen received some form of financial aid. The FAF or FFS is required.

International Students: International students must take the TOEFL and achieve a minimum score of 500. In many cases, the ACT may also be required.

Computers: The college provides computer facilities for student use. All students may access the system.

Admissions Contact: Dr. Melvin Hodges, Director of Admissions and Registrar.

TULANE UNIVERSITY

D-4

New Orleans, LA 70118

(504) 865-5731

Full-time: 2540 men, 2406 women
Part-time: 668 men, 861 women
Graduate: 2662 men, 2066 women
Year: semesters, summer session
Application Deadline: January 15
Freshman Class: 7033 applied, 5125 accepted, 1223 enrolled
SAT I Verbal/Math: 556/612

Faculty: 934; I, av$
Ph.D.s: 98%
Student/Faculty: 5 to 1
Tuition: $18,760
Room & Board: $5780

HIGHLY COMPETITIVE

Tulane University, founded in 1834, is a private, coeducational institution offering degree programs in liberal arts and sciences, business, architecture, and engineering. There are 6 undergraduate and 8 graduate schools. In addition to regional accreditation, Tulane has baccalaureate program accreditation with AACSB, ABET, ACS, CSAC, CSWE, and NAAB. The 10 libraries contain 1,946,312 volumes, 2,114,185 microform items, and 52,370 audiovisual forms, and subscribe to 17,236 periodicals. Computerized library sources and services include the card catalog, interlibrary loans, and database searching. Special learning facilities include a learning resource center, art gallery, radio station, and TV station. The 110-acre campus is in downtown New Orleans. Including residence halls, there are 75 buildings on campus.

Student Life: About 80% of undergraduates are from out-of-state, mostly the Northeast. Students come from 50 states, 64 foreign countries, and Canada. Fifty-five percent are from public schools. Eighty percent are white; 10% African American. Forty-nine percent are Catholic; 27% Protestant; 17% Jewish. The average age of freshmen is 18; all undergraduates, 20. Ten percent drop out by the end of their first year; 72% remain to graduate.

Housing: A total of 3386 students can be accommodated in college housing. College-sponsored living facilities include dormitories, on-campus apartments, and married-student housing. In addition, there are language, special interest, and international living houses. On-campus housing is guaranteed for all 4 years. Fifty-two percent of students commute. Alcohol is not permitted. All students except freshmen may keep cars on campus.

Activities: About 32% of men belong to 17 national fraternities; about 35% of women belong to 8 national sororities. There are more than 200 groups on campus, including art, band, cheerleading, chess, choir, chorale, chorus, computers, dance, drama, ethnic, gay, honors, international, jazz band, literary magazine, marching band, musical theater, newspaper, pep band, political, professional, radio and TV, religious, social, social service, student government, and yearbook. Popular campus events include the Direction Program, Homecoming, Newcomb College Spring Arts Festival, TUCP All-Niter, Mellon Program, and the Beaux Arts Ball.

Sports: There are 8 intercollegiate sports for men and 7 for women, and 30 intramural sports for men and 30 for women. Athletic and recreation facilities include a baseball diamond, a track complex, a tennis facility, and a recreation center with indoor and outdoor pools, an indoor track, squash and racquetball courts, a gymnastics area, and a weight room.

Disabled Students: Sixty percent of the campus is accessible to disabled students. The following facilities are available: wheelchair ramps, elevators, special parking, specially equipped rest rooms, lowered drinking fountains, special class scheduling when possible, and lowered telephones.

Services: In addition to many counseling and information services, tutoring is available in most subjects. There is also a reader service for the blind.

Campus Safety and Security: Campus safety and security measures include 24-hour foot and vehicle patrol, self-defense education, escort service, and shuttle buses. In addition, there are informal discussions, pamphlets, posters, and films, emergency telephones, lighted pathways and sidewalks, trained student patrols, and programs about living safely off campus. Victim resources include academic assistance, legal counseling, emergency housing, and security review of home and personal security habits.

Programs of Study: Tulane awards the B.A., B.S., B.Arch., B.F.A., B.G.S., B.S.E., and B.S.M. degrees. Associate, master's, and doctoral degrees also are awarded. Bachelor's degrees are awarded in BIOLOGICAL SCIENCE (biochemistry, cell biology, and ecology), BUSINESS (management science and sports management), COMMUNICATIONS AND THE ARTS (art history, art studio, classics, communications, dramatic arts, English, fine arts, French, German, Greek, Italian, Latin, linguistics, media arts, music, Portuguese, Russian, and Spanish), COMPUTER AND PHYSICAL SCIENCE (chemistry, computer science, earth science, geology, information sciences and systems, mathematics, and physics), EDUCATION (early childhood), ENGINEERING AND ENVIRONMENTAL DESIGN (architecture, biomedical engineering, chemical engineering, civil engineering, computer engineering, electrical/electronics engineering, engineering, environmental engineering, environmental science, and

mechanical engineering), HEALTH PROFESSIONS (exercise science, premedicine, and sports management), SOCIAL SCIENCE (American studies, anthropology, Asian/Oriental studies, economics, history, international relations, Judaic studies, Latin American studies, medieval studies, philosophy, political science/government, prelaw, psychology, Russian and Slavic studies, sociology, and women's studies). Environmental sciences, political economy, preprofessional programs, engineering, and Latin American studies are the strongest academically. English, history, psychology, biology, political science, and communications have the largest enrollments.

Required: All students in the College of Arts and Sciences must meet proficiency requirements in English, foreign language, and mathematics. They must take a distribution component, including courses in humanities and fine arts, social sciences, and sciences and mathematics. A total of 130 credits, including 32 to 40 in the major, with a minimum cumulative GPA of 2.0 is required to graduate.

Special: Cross-registration with Loyola and Xavier Universities, numerous internships, study abroad in 7 countries, work-study programs, a Washington semester, and B.A.-B.S. degrees in liberal arts, engineering, and architecture are offered. Accelerated joint degrees with Tulane's schools of medicine, law, business, and public health; student-designed, dual, and interdisciplinary majors, including art and biology, Greek and Latin, mathematical economics, political economy, and cognitive studies; and a 3-2 engineering degree with Loyola University in New Orleans are available. There is a freshman honors program on campus, as well as 32 national honor societies, including Phi Beta Kappa.

Faculty/Classroom: Seventy-seven percent of faculty are male; 23%, female. All both teach and do research. Graduate students teach 10% of introductory courses. The average class size in an introductory lecture is 30; in a laboratory, 20; and in a regular course offering, 25.

Admissions: About 73% of the 1993–94 applicants were accepted. The SAT scores for the 1993–94 freshman class were as follows: Verbal—28% below 500, 40% between 500 and 599, 26% between 600 and 700, and 6% above 700; Math—8% below 500, 35% between 500 and 599, 40% between 600 and 700, and 17% above 700. About 66% of the current freshmen were in the top fifth of their class; 92% were in the top two fifths. There were 18 National Merit finalists.

Requirements: The SAT I or ACT is required. Applicants must be graduates of an accredited secondary school or have a GED certificate. It is recommended that students have completed 4 years each of high school English and mathematics, 3 each of foreign language and social studies, and 2 of science. SAT II: Subject tests in writing, mathematics, and foreign language are recommended. An essay is required. A portfolio is recommended for architecture applicants only. AP credits are accepted. Important factors used in the admissions decision are advanced placement or honor courses, recommendations by school officials, extracurricular activities record, evidence of special talent, and parents or siblings attending the school.

Procedure: Freshmen are admitted fall and spring. Entrance exams should be taken during the spring of the junior year or the fall of the senior year. Early decision applications should be filed by November 1; regular applications, by January 15 for fall entry and November 15 for spring entry, along with an application fee of $35. Notification of early decision is sent December 15; regular decision, by April 15. There are early decision, early admissions, and deferred admissions plans. Some 741 early decision candidates were accepted for the 1993–94 class. A waiting list is an active part of the admissions procedure.

Transfer: Some 118 transfer students enrolled in 1993–94. Transfer students must submit SAT I or ACT scores, high school transcripts, proof of good standing at previously attended institutions, and transcripts of all colleges or universities attended. A minimum 3.0 GPA is mandatory. A total of 64 credits out of 130 must be completed at Tulane.

Visiting: There are regularly scheduled orientations for prospective students, including 3 on-campus Saturday programs in the fall and daily information sessions and tours Monday through Friday and Saturday mornings during the academic year. Also, selected classes are open to visitors. In the spring semester, daily, more structured programs are available. There are guides for informal visits and visitors may sit in on classes and stay overnight at the school. To arrange for a visit, contact the Office of Undergraduate Admission at (504) 865-5731.

Financial Aid: In 1993–94, 70% of all current freshmen and 56% of continuing students received some form of financial aid. About 51% of freshmen and 44% of continuing students received need-based aid. The average freshman award was $18,000. Of that total, scholarships or need-based grants averaged $13,050 ($17,250 maximum); loans averaged $3500 ($4125 maximum); and work contracts averaged $1450 ($2000 maximum). Forty-five percent of undergraduate students work part-time. Average earnings from campus work for the school year are $900. The average financial indebtedness of the

1992–93 graduate was $10,000. Tulane is a member of CSS. The FAF is required. The deadline for financial aid applications is February 1.

International Students: There are currently 928 international students enrolled. The school actively recruits these students. They must take the TOEFL or the University of Michigan Language Test. The student must also take the SAT I or the ACT.

Computers: The college provides computer facilities for student use. The mainframe is a cluster of 8 IBM RS/6000s and a Convex C210. There are 22 computer laboratories on campus, consisting of more than 250 workstations, with 150 of them connected to the university network. Access to mainframes is possible from 2 campus locations, and from residence halls rooms if the student has their own personal computer. The university network extends to all campus buildings. Each residence hall room has a data and cable TV connection. All students may access the system. It may be used 24 hours a day. There are no time limits on using the system and no fees.

Graduates: In 1992–93, 1397 bachelor's degrees were awarded. The most popular majors among graduates were English (9%), biology (9%), and psychology (8%). Within an average freshman class, 65% graduate in 4 years and 72% in 5 years. Some 305 companies recruited on campus in 1992–93.

Admissions Contact: Richard Whiteside, Dean of Admission and Enrollment Management.

UNIVERSITY OF NEW ORLEANS D-4
New Orleans, LA 70148   (504) 286-6595; (800) 833-6662 (in-state)

Full-time: 3761 men, 4397 women	Faculty: 516; IIA, -$
Part-time: 1535 men, 2108 women	Ph.D.s: 78%
Graduate: 1652 men, 2117 women	Student/Faculty: 16 to 1
Year: semesters, summer session	Tuition: $2362 ($5154)
Application Deadline: July 1	Room & Board: $3106
Freshman Class: 2406 applied, 2139 accepted, 1501 enrolled	
ACT: 21	COMPETITIVE

The University of New Orleans, founded in 1958, is a public, coeducational liberal arts institution. There are 6 undergraduate schools and one graduate school. In addition to regional accreditation, UNO has baccalaureate program accreditation with AACSB, ABET, ABFSE, NASM, and NCATE. The library contains 1,856,240 volumes, 591,545 microform items, and 19,289 audiovisual forms, and subscribes to 5909 periodicals. Computerized library sources and services include interlibrary loans and database searching. Special learning facilities include a learning resource center, art gallery, and radio station. The 345-acre campus is in an urban area in the city of New Orleans. Including residence halls, there are 26 buildings on campus.

Student Life: About 93% of undergraduates are from Louisiana. Students come from 44 states, 80 foreign countries, and Canada. Seventy-four percent are white; 13% African American. Fifty-five percent are Protestant; 42% Catholic. The average age of freshmen is 20; all undergraduates, 25. Thirty-eight percent drop out by the end of their first year; 21% remain to graduate.

Housing: A total of 732 students can be accommodated in college housing. College-sponsored living facilities include coed dormitories and married-student housing. On-campus housing is available on a first-come, first-served basis. Ninety-five percent of students commute. All students may keep cars on campus.

Activities: About 2% of men belong to 1 local and 9 national fraternities; about 2% of women belong to 7 national sororities. There are 125 groups on campus, including art, band, cheerleading, chess, choir, chorale, chorus, computers, dance, drama, ethnic, film, gay, honors, international, jazz band, literary magazine, newspaper, opera, orchestra, pep band, photography, political, professional, radio and TV, religious, social, social service, student government, and yearbook. Popular campus events include Fall Fest, and April Fest; Silver, Blue, and Something New; World's Largest Free Crawfish Boil; Alcohol and Drug Awareness Week; and Black History Month.

Sports: There are 7 intercollegiate sports for men and 7 for women, and 27 intramural sports for men and 27 for women. Athletic and recreation facilities include the UNO Lakefront Arena, Privateer Park, 12 tennis courts, a swimming pool, and a health and physical education center.

Disabled Students: Ninety-six percent of the campus is accessible to disabled students. The following facilities are available: wheelchair ramps, elevators, special parking, specially equipped rest rooms, special class scheduling, lowered drinking fountains, and lowered telephones.

Services: In addition to many counseling and information services, tutoring is available in most subjects. There is a reader service for the blind, and remedial math, reading, and writing.

Campus Safety and Security: Campus safety and security measures include 24-hour foot and vehicle patrol, escort service, informal discussions, and emergency telephones. In addition, there are lighted pathways and sidewalks.

Programs of Study: UNO awards the B.A., B.S., and B.G.S. degrees. Associate, master's, and doctoral degrees also are awarded. Bachelor's degrees are awarded in BIOLOGICAL SCIENCE (biology/biological science), BUSINESS (accounting, banking and finance, business administration and management, business economics, hotel/motel/restaurant management, marketing/retailing/merchandising, and tourism), COMMUNICATIONS AND THE ARTS (communications, dramatic arts, English, fine arts, French, languages, music, and Spanish), COMPUTER AND PHYSICAL SCIENCE (chemistry, computer science, geology, geophysics and seismology, mathematics, and physics), EDUCATION (business, elementary, English, foreign languages, mathematics, music, physical, science, and secondary), ENGINEERING AND ENVIRONMENTAL DESIGN (civil engineering, electrical/electronics engineering, marine engineering, mechanical engineering, and naval architecture and marine engineering), HEALTH PROFESSIONS (dental hygiene, medical laboratory technology, nursing, physical therapy, predentistry, premedicine, and preveterinary science), and SOCIAL SCIENCE (anthropology, economics, geography, history, philosophy, political science/government, psychology, and sociology). Business administration, accounting, and general studies have the largest enrollments.

Required: Requirements for graduation include 6 hours in English composition and literature, 6 hours in mathematics, 8 hours in science, and 12 hours in social science and the humanities. Students must complete 128 hours with a minimum GPA of 2.0 to graduate.

Special: Students may participate in co-op programs with LSU Medical Center and may cross-register with Southern University of New Orleans and Delgado Community College. Internships are required in most professional programs, and work-study programs are available with various federal agencies and private companies. Students may study abroad in Austria or France, or participate in a Washington semester. UNO also offers nondegree study, pass/fail options, and limited credit for life, military, and work experience. There is a freshman honors program on campus, as well as 12 national honor societies. Twenty-three departments have honors programs.

Faculty/Classroom: Sixty-seven percent of faculty are male; 33%, female. All teach undergraduates and 90% do research. Graduate students teach 3% of introductory courses. The average class size in an introductory lecture is 36 and in a regular course offering, 24.

Admissions: About 89% of the 1993–94 applicants were accepted. The ACT scores for the 1993–94 freshman class were as follows: 51% below 21, 28% between 21 and 23, 13% between 24 and 26, 5% between 27 and 28, and 3% above 28. About 30% of the current freshmen were in the top fifth of their class; 65% were in the top two fifths. There were 3 National Merit finalists.

Requirements: A minimum GPA of 2.0 is required. The SAT I or ACT is required. Applicants must be high school graduates with a college preparatory program of 4 units in English, 3 each in mathematics and science, 2 each in foreign language, history, and academic social studies, and half a unit in computer science. A GPA of 2.0 is required. AP and CLEP credits are accepted.

Procedure: Freshmen are admitted to all sessions. Entrance exams should be taken at least 6 months prior to enrollment. Applications should be filed by July 1 for fall entry, November 15 for spring entry, and May 1 for summer entry, along with an application fee of $20. Notification is sent on a rolling basis. There is an early admissions plan.

Transfer: Some 1051 transfer students enrolled in 1993–94. A minimum college GPA of 2.0 is required. Applicants with fewer than 24 semester hours of credit must take the SAT I or the ACT. A total of 30 credits out of 128 must be completed at UNO.

Visiting: There are regularly scheduled orientations for prospective students, including an overnight stay in the dormitories, placement testing, social activities, tours, academic advising, and registration for classes. There are guides for informal visits, and visitors may sit in on classes and stay overnight at the school. To arrange for a visit, contact the Office of Admissions at (504) 286-6595.

Financial Aid: In 1993–94, 51% of all current freshmen and 38% of continuing students received some form of financial aid. About 43% of freshmen and 33% of continuing students received need-based aid. The average freshman award was $3754. Of that total, scholarships or need-based grants averaged $3500 ($5000 maximum); loans averaged $2900 ($4000 maximum); and work contracts averaged $1600 ($2800 maximum). Eighty percent of undergraduate students work part-time. Average earnings from campus work for the school year are $2600. The average financial indebtedness of the 1992–93 graduate was $18,500. UNO is a member of CSS. The FFS and or FAFSA is required. The deadline for financial aid applications is May 1.

International Students: There are currently 318 international students enrolled. They must take the TOEFL and either the Comprehensive English Language Test or the college's own test, and must achieve a minimum score on the TOEFL of 500. The student must also take the SAT I or the ACT.

Computers: The college provides computer facilities for student use. The mainframes are 4 DEC VAX 8600s. There are 4 of these, and 680 microcomputer terminals are connected to the mainframe via the Ethernet network, which provides access to word processing languages, spreadsheets, and database systems. All students may access the system. It may be used for class assignments. There are no time limits on using the system and no fees.

Graduates: In a recent year 1238 bachelor's degrees were awarded. The most popular majors among graduates were elementary education (9%), general studies (9%), and business administration (7%). Some 200 companies have recently recruited on campus.

Admissions Contact: Office of Admissions.

UNIVERSITY OF SOUTHWESTERN LOUISIANA

C-4

Lafayette, LA 70504   (318) 231-6473

Full-time: 5476 men, 6305 women	**Faculty:** 577; I, --$
Part-time: 1264 men, 2112 women	**Ph.D.s:** 65%
Graduate: 3882 men, 747 women	**Student/Faculty:** 20 to 1
Year: semesters, summer session	**Tuition:** $1886 ($4286)
Application Deadline: open	**Room & Board:** $2082
Freshman Class: 4258 applied, 4208 accepted, 2770 enrolled	
SAT I or ACT: not required	**NONCOMPETITIVE**

The University of Southwestern Louisiana, founded in 1898, is a public coeducational institution offering undergraduate programs in liberal arts, fine arts, business, agriculture, technical disciplines, health science, engineering, and teacher preparation. There are 9 undergraduate schools and one graduate school. In addition to regional accreditation, USL has baccalaureate program accreditation with ABET, AHEA, APTA, CAHEA, CSWE, NASAD, NCATE, NLN, and NRPA. The library contains 687,142 volumes, 1,600,798 microform items, and 5396 audiovisual forms, and subscribes to 6188 periodicals. Computerized library sources and services include the card catalog, interlibrary loans, and database searching. Special learning facilities include a learning resource center, art gallery, radio station, TV station, and computer-assisted design/manufacturing center. The 1375-acre campus is in an urban area 129 miles west of New Orleans. Including residence halls, there are 195 buildings on campus.

Student Life: About 94% of undergraduates are from Louisiana. Students come from 43 states, 70 foreign countries, and Canada. Seventy-five percent are white; 17% African American. Sixty-one percent are Catholic; 22% Protestant; 15% claim no religious affiliation. Fifty percent drop out by the end of their first year; 35% remain to graduate.

Housing: A total of 3230 students can be accommodated in college housing. College-sponsored living facilities include single-sex dormitories, married-student housing, and fraternity houses. In addition, there are honors houses, special interest houses, and residence halls for athletes and for panhellenic groups. On-campus housing is guaranteed for all 4 years. Eighty-six percent of students commute. All students may keep cars on campus.

Activities: About 6% of men belong to 11 national fraternities; about 5% of women belong to 8 national sororities. There are 200 groups on campus, including band, cheerleading, choir, chorus, computers, dance, drama, drum and bugle corps, ethnic, gay, honors, international, jazz band, marching band, newspaper, opera, orchestra, photography, political, professional, radio and TV, religious, social, social service, student government, and yearbook. Popular campus events include Rajun Roar, Lagniappe Day, Homecoming, Black Expo Week, Entertainment Week, Krew of Roux Mardi Gras Parade, and Get On Board Day.

Sports: There are 8 intercollegiate sports for men and 7 for women, and 16 intramural sports for men and 16 for women. Athletic and recreation facilities include a 31,000-seat stadium, a 12,000-seat basketball arena, a gymnasium, a track, a softball park, tennis courts, various playing fields, and a health and physical education complex.

Disabled Students: Ninety percent of the campus is accessible to disabled students. The following facilities are available: wheelchair ramps, elevators, special parking, specially equipped rest rooms, special class scheduling, TDDs, and an adaptive computer laboratory with voice synthesizer, visual-tech, and brailler.

Services: In addition to many counseling and information services, tutoring is available in most subjects. In addition, there is remedial math, reading, and writing.

Campus Safety and Security: Campus safety and security measures include 24-hour foot and vehicle patrol, escort service, shuttle buses, and informal discussions. In addition, there are pamphlets, posters, and films, emergency telephones, and lighted pathways and sidewalks.

Programs of Study: USL awards the B.A., B.S., B.A.M., B.F.A., B.G.S., B.M.E., B.M.P., B.M.P.P., B.S.A., B.S.A.E., B.S.B.A., B.S.C.E., B.S.C.I.E., B.S.E.E., B.S.I.T., B.S.M.E., B.S.N., and B.S.P.E. degrees. Associate, master's, and doctoral degrees also are awarded. Bache-

lor's degrees are awarded in AGRICULTURE (animal science, horticulture, and wildlife management), BUSINESS (accounting, banking and finance, business administration and management, fashion merchandising, hotel/motel and restaurant management, management science, marketing/retailing/merchandising, personnel management, and secretarial studies/office management), COMMUNICATIONS AND THE ARTS (advertising, broadcasting, communications, dance, dramatic arts, English, fine arts, French, journalism, music, public relations, Spanish, speech/debate/rhetoric, and telecommunications), COMPUTER AND PHYSICAL SCIENCE (chemistry, computer science, geology, mathematics, physics, and statistics), EDUCATION (agricultural, art, elementary, English, foreign languages, guidance, health, home economics, industrial arts, mathematics, music, science, secondary, social studies, and special), ENGINEERING AND ENVIRONMENTAL DESIGN (agricultural engineering, chemical engineering, civil engineering, computer engineering, electrical/electronics engineering, industrial engineering, interior design, land use management and reclamation, mechanical engineering, and petroleum/natural gas engineering), HEALTH PROFESSIONS (nursing, predentistry, premedicine, and speech pathology/audiology), SOCIAL SCIENCE (anthropology, community services, criminal justice, dietetics, economics, geography, history, philosophy, political science/government, prelaw, psychology, sociology, and urban studies). Computer science, engineering, and mathematics/statistics/physical sciences are the strongest academically. Computer science, business, engineering, nursing, and general studies have the largest enrollments.

Required: Students are required to complete 47 semester hours of general education courses in the arts, literature, history, mathematics, sciences, behavioral sciences, and composition. Physical education is required in all but engineering and nursing programs. A minimum of 132 semester hours, at least 33 in the major, is required. A minimum GPA of 2.0 is needed; some majors require higher GPAs.

Special: Various internships are available, including a Washington program. Students may study in France, Canada, Belgium, Japan, and Mexico. USL also offers an accelerated degree program in nursing, B.A.-B.S. degrees, and dual majors. There is a freshman honors program on campus, as well as 6 national honor societies.

Faculty/Classroom: Sixty-six percent of faculty are male; 34%, female.

Admissions: About 99% of the 1993-94 applicants were accepted.

Requirements: Students should be graduates of accredited secondary schools or have the GED. USL recommends that students have at least 4 units in English, 3 each in mathematics, science, and social studies, 2 each in a foreign language and physical education, and 6 in electives. AP and CLEP credits are accepted.

Procedure: Freshmen are admitted to all sessions. Application deadlines are open. The application fee is $5. USL accepts all applicants. Notification is sent on a rolling basis. There are early admissions and deferred admissions plans.

Transfer: A total of 938 transfer students enrolled in 1993-94. a cumulative GPA of 2.0 is required. A total of 30 credits out of 132 must be completed at USL.

Visiting: There are regularly scheduled orientations for prospective students, including tours. There are guides for informal visits. To arrange for a visit, contact the Secretary of High School Relations at (318) 231-6553.

Financial Aid: In 1993-94, 46% of all current freshmen and 54% of continuing students received some form of financial aid. About 58% of freshmen and 51% of continuing students received need-based aid. The average freshman award was $3450. Of that total, scholarships or need-based grants averaged $400 ($6000 maximum); loans averaged $1900 ($2625 maximum); and work contracts averaged $1147 ($1912 maximum). Thirty percent of undergraduate students work part-time. Average earnings from campus work for the school year are $1147. The average financial indebtedness of an earlier graduate was $5000. USL is a member of CSS. The FFS is required. The deadline for financial aid applications is March 1.

International Students: There are currently 628 international students enrolled. The school actively recruits these students. They must take the TOEFL and achieve a minimum score of 450. Students must take SAT II: Subject tests in mathematics and writing.

Computers: USL provides computer facilities for student use. The mainframes are an IBM 3090VF and 3 Sun 4/490 Servers. About 200 terminals and Sun workstations are located in public terminal rooms and dormitories. The Sun facility provides E-mail and various network services. All students may access the system at any time. There are no time limits on using the system and no fees.

Graduates: In 1992-93, 1582 bachelor's degrees were awarded. The most popular majors among graduates were general studies (18%), business (18%), and education (17%). Within an average freshman class, 19% graduate in 4 years, 31% in 5 years, and 35% in 6 years. A total of 114 companies recruited on campus in 1992-93.

Admissions Contact: Leroy Broussard, Director of Admissions.

XAVIER UNIVERSITY OF LOUISIANA D-4

New Orleans, LA 70125 (504) 483-7388

Full-time: 912 men, 1974 women	Faculty: 188; IIA, --$
Part-time: 38 men, 54 women	Ph.D.s: 72%
Graduate: 89 men, 251 women	Student/Faculty: 15 to 1
Year: semesters, summer session	Tuition: $6600
Application Deadline: March 1	Room & Board: $3800

Freshman Class: 2097 applied, 1915 accepted, 695 enrolled

SAT I: 445/480   ACT: 20   **COMPETITIVE**

Xavier University of Louisiana, founded in 1925, is a private, coeducational, liberal arts university affiliated with the Roman Catholic Church. There are 2 undergraduate and 2 graduate schools. In addition to regional accreditation, Xavier has baccalaureate program accreditation with ACPE and NASM. The 2 libraries contain 113,000 volumes, 70,000 microform items, and 45,200 audiovisual forms, and subscribe to 1200 periodicals. Computerized library sources and services include the card catalog, interlibrary loans, and database searching. Special learning facilities include a learning resource center and TV station. The 29-acre campus is in an urban area in New Orleans. Including residence halls, there are 33 buildings on campus.

Student Life: About 66% of undergraduates are from Louisiana. Students come from 39 states, 27 foreign countries, and Canada. Sixty-eight percent are from public schools; 32% from private. Ninety percent are African American. Fifty-six percent are Protestant; 38% Catholic. The average age of freshmen is 18; all undergraduates, 22. Twenty-one percent drop out by the end of their first year; 45% remain to graduate.

Housing: A total of 799 students can be accommodated in college housing. College-sponsored living facilities include single-sex dormitories. On-campus housing is available on a first-come, first-served basis. Priority is given to out-of-town students. Seventy-three percent of students commute. Alcohol is not permitted. All students may keep cars on campus.

Activities: About 5% of men belong to 2 national fraternities; about 20% of women belong to 4 national sororities. There are 60 groups on campus, including art, band, cheerleading, chess, choir, chorus, computers, dance, drama, ethnic, honors, international, jazz band, newspaper, political, professional, radio and TV, religious, social, social service, student government, and yearbook. Popular campus events include Homecoming and Health Fair.

Sports: There is 1 intercollegiate sport for men and 1 for women, and 9 intramural sports for men and 9 for women. Athletic and recreation facilities include a gymnasium and a swimming pool.

Disabled Students: Ninety percent of the campus is accessible to disabled students. The following facilities are available: wheelchair ramps, elevators, special parking, specially equipped rest rooms, lowered drinking fountains, and lowered telephones.

Services: In addition to many counseling and information services, tutoring is available in every subject. In addition, there is remedial math, reading, and writing.

Campus Safety and Security: Campus safety and security measures include 24-hour foot and vehicle patrol, informal discussions, pamphlets, posters, and films, and emergency telephones. In addition, there are lighted pathways and sidewalks.

Programs of Study: Xavier awards the B.A., B.S., and B.M. degrees. Master's and doctoral degrees also are awarded. Bachelor's degrees are awarded in BIOLOGICAL SCIENCE (biochemistry, biology/biological science, and microbiology), BUSINESS (accounting, banking and finance, business administration and management, business economics, marketing/retailing/merchandising, and personnel management), COMMUNICATIONS AND THE ARTS (communications, English, fine arts, French, music, and Spanish), COMPUTER AND PHYSICAL SCIENCE (chemistry, computer science, mathematics, physics, and statistics), EDUCATION (art, early childhood, elementary, English, mathematics, music, physical, science, secondary, social studies, and speech correction), HEALTH PROFESSIONS (pharmacy, predentistry, premedicine, and speech pathology/audiology), SOCIAL SCIENCE (history, philosophy, political science/government, prelaw, psychology, sociology, and theological studies). Pharmacy, science, education, and English are the strongest programs academically. Pharmacy, biology, and business have the largest enrollments.

Required: Requirements for graduation include 9 units in English, 3 each in speech, mathematics, and the arts, 6 each in history, social science, language, theology, philosophy, and natural sciences, and 1 in health and physical education. Students must complete 128 to 132 total credit hours, including 24 to 54 total hours in the major. Students must maintain a minimum GPA of 2.0, take Introduction to African-American History/Culture, and pass a comprehensive examination.

Special: The university offers cooperative programs with Tulane University, Louisiana State University, University of New Orleans, University of Detroit, and Georgia Institute of Technology, as well as cross-registration with colleges of the New Orleans Consortium. Internships are available in legal, political, and pharmaceutical areas. Students may earn an accelerated degree in biology or chemistry, pursue dual majors in engineering and biostatistics, opt for nondegree study, earn a B.A.-B.S. degree in almost any combination, or earn a 3-2 engineering degree. There is a freshman honors program on campus, as well as 1 national honor society. Four departments have honors programs.

Faculty/Classroom: Sixty-two percent of faculty are male; 38%, female. Eighty-two percent teach undergraduates, 7% do research, and 40% do both. No introductory courses are taught by graduate students. The average class size in an introductory lecture is 25; in a laboratory, 21; and in a regular course offering, 21.

Admissions: About 91% of the 1993-94 applicants were accepted. The SAT scores for the 1993-94 freshman class were as follows: Verbal—74% below 500, 22% between 500 and 599, and 4% between 600 and 700; Math—59% below 500, 31% between 500 and 599, and 10% between 600 and 700. The ACT scores were 50% below 21, 19% between 21 and 23, 19% between 24 and 26, and 12% between 27 and 28. About 54% of the current freshmen were in the top fifth of their class; 77% were in the top two fifths.

Requirements: The SAT I or ACT is required. In addition, candidates for admission must have completed 4 units of English, 2 of mathematics, 1 each of science and social studies, and 8 of academic electives. AP and CLEP credits are accepted. Important factors used in the admissions decision are advanced placement or honor courses, recommendations by school officials, evidence of special talent, extracurricular activities record, and leadership record.

Procedure: Freshmen are admitted to all sessions. Entrance exams should be taken in the spring of the junior year or the fall of the senior year. Early decision applications should be filed by February 1; regular applications, by March 1 for fall entry, December 1 for spring entry, and March 1 for summer entry, along with an application fee of $25. Notification is sent on a rolling basis, beginning March 1. There is an early decision plan. About 991 early decision candidates were accepted for the 1993-94 class. A waiting list is an active part of the admissions procedure, with about 16% of applicants on the list.

Transfer: About 175 transfer students enrolled in 1993-94. Transfer applicants must submit college transcripts; high school transcripts are required of applicants with fewer than 30 transferable credits. A total of 30 credits out of 128 to 132 must be completed at Xavier.

Visiting: There are guides for informal visits and visitors may sit in on classes and stay overnight at the school. To arrange for a visit, contact Sondra Reine at (504) 483-7578.

Financial Aid: In 1993-94 84% of all current freshmen and 88% of continuing students received some form of financial aid. About 65% of freshmen and 67% of continuing students received need-based aid. The average freshman award was $6632. Of that total, scholarships or need-based grants averaged $2276 ($4300 maximum); loans averaged $3020 ($5750 maximum); and work contracts averaged $997 ($2000 maximum). Twenty-four percent of undergraduate students work part-time. Average earnings from campus work for the school year are $1000. The average financial indebtedness of the 1992-93 graduate was $25,000. Xavier is a member of CSS. The FAF or FFS, the college's own financial statement, and FAFSA are required. The deadline for financial aid applications is May 1.

International Students: There are currently 94 international students enrolled. They must take the TOEFL and achieve a minimum score of 550. The student must also take the SAT I or the ACT.

Computers: The college provides computer facilities for student use. The mainframes are an HP 3000 and an AT&T 3B15. An open laboratory in the science building has 25 terminals from which students can log on to the mainframe. In addition, computer laboratories in other buildings contain microcomputers for student use. All students may access the system. There are no time limits on using the system and no fees.

Graduates: In 1992-93, 494 bachelor's degrees were awarded. The most popular majors among graduates were natural science (30%), pharmacy (26%), and business (14%). Within an average freshman class, 20% graduate in 4 years, 35% in 5 years, and 40% in 6 years. Some 120 companies recruited on campus in 1992-93. In the 1992 graduating class, 20% of the men and 29% of the women were enrolled in graduate school within 6 months of graduation.

Admissions Contact: Winston D. Brown, Admissions Office.

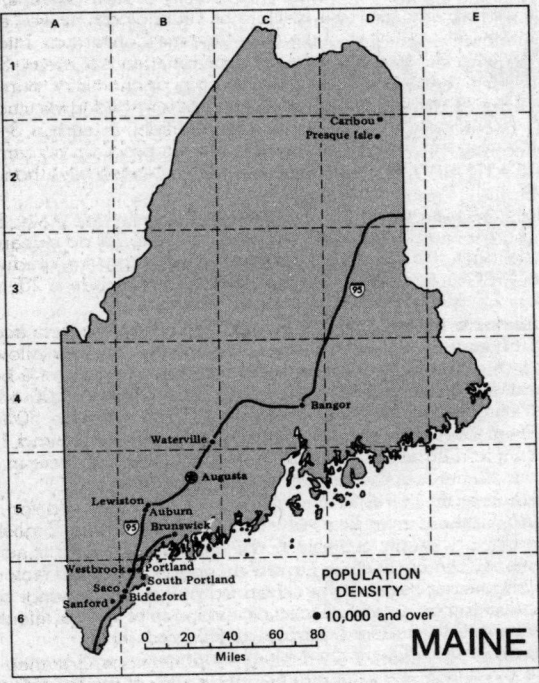

POPULATION DENSITY

● 10,000 and over

0   20   40   60   80
Miles

MAINE

BATES COLLEGE
B-5

Lewiston, ME 04240   (207) 786-6000

Full-time: 760 men, 790 women   Faculty: 151; IIB, +$
Part-time: none   Ph.D.s: 96%
Graduate: none   Student/Faculty: 10 to 1
Year: 4-4-1
Application Deadline: February 1
Freshman Class: 3600 applied, 1592 accepted, 609 enrolled
SAT I Verbal/Math: 590/640   **MOST COMPETITIVE**

Bates College, founded in 1855, is a private, coeducational liberal arts institution. The library contains 563,123 volumes, 264,781 microform items, and 19,631 audiovisual forms, and subscribes to 1841 periodicals. Computerized library sources and services include the card catalog. Special learning facilities include an art gallery, planetarium, radio station, TV station, a 574-acre mountain conservation area, the Muskie Archives, and an observatory. The 109-acre campus is in a suburban area 140 miles north of Boston. Including residence halls, there are 70 buildings on campus.

Student Life: About 88% of undergraduates are from out-of-state, mostly the Northeast. Students come from 46 states, 30 foreign countries, and Canada. Sixty-five percent are from public schools; 35% from private. Eighty-seven percent are white. The average age of freshmen is 18; all undergraduates, 20. Two percent drop out by the end of their first year; 90% remain to graduate.

Housing: A total of 1500 students can be accommodated in college housing. College-sponsored living facilities include single-sex and coed dormitories. In addition, there is an alcohol-free house. On-campus housing is guaranteed for all 4 years. Ninety-four percent of students live on campus; of those, 75% remain on campus on weekends. All students may keep cars on campus.

Activities: There are no fraternities or sororities on campus. There are 72 groups on campus, including art, chess, choir, chorale, chorus, computers, dance, drama, ethnic, film, gay, honors, international, jazz band, literary magazine, musical theater, newspaper, orchestra, photography, political, professional, radio and TV, religious, social, social service, student government, and yearbook. Popular campus events include Winter Carnival, international dinners, periodic semiformal dances, and ocean clambakes.

Sports: There are 13 intercollegiate sports for men and 14 for women, and 4 intramural sports for men and 4 for women. Athletic and recreation facilities include a pool, a field house, indoor and outdoor tracks, indoor and outdoor tennis courts, 3 basketball courts, 3 volleyball courts, football, soccer, baseball, softball, and lacrosse fields, weight rooms, dance and fencing space, squash and racquetball courts, training rooms, a rock climbing wall, and a boat house.

Disabled Students: Sixty percent of the campus is accessible to disabled students. The following facilities are available: wheelchair ramps, elevators, special parking, specially equipped rest rooms, special class scheduling, and lowered telephones.

Services: In addition to many counseling and information services, tutoring is available in every subject. There is also a reader service for the blind and remedial math and writing.

Campus Safety and Security: Campus safety and security measures include 24-hour foot and vehicle patrol, self-defense education, escort service, and informal discussions. In addition, there are pamphlets, posters, and films, emergency telephones, and lighted pathways and sidewalks.

Programs of Study: Bates awards the B.A. and B.S. degrees. Bachelor's degrees are awarded in BIOLOGICAL SCIENCE (biological chemistry and biology/biological science), COMMUNICATIONS AND THE ARTS (art, dramatic arts, East Asian languages and literature, English, French, German, music, Russian, Spanish, and speech/debate/rhetoric), COMPUTER AND PHYSICAL SCIENCE (chemistry, geology, mathematics, and physics), SOCIAL SCIENCE (African American studies, American studies, anthropology, economics, history, philosophy, political science/government, psychology, religion, sociology, and women's studies). Political science, psychology, English, biology, economics, and mathematics have the largest enrollments.

Required: Requirements for graduation include 5 courses in humanities, 3 each in natural science and social science, and 1 in physical education. The total number of hours in the major varies by department, but students should take at least 32 courses, plus 2 short terms, and maintain a minimum GPA of 2.0. A senior thesis is required.

Special: Internships, research apprenticeships, study abroad, and a Washington semester are possible. Dual, student-designed, and interdisciplinary majors, including classical and medieval studies, and a 3-2 engineering degree with Columbia University, Dartmouth College, Case Western Reserve University, Rensselaer Polytechnic Institute, and Washington University in St. Louis are available. Students in any major may graduate in 3 years and a B.A.-B.S. is possible in all majors. Students may also participate in the Williams-Mystic Seaport program in marine biology and maritime history. The 4-4-1 academic calendar includes a 5-week spring term. There is a chapter of Phi Beta Kappa on campus. Twenty-eight departments have honors programs.

Faculty/Classroom: Sixty-three percent of faculty are male; 37%, female. All both teach and do research. The average class size in a regular course offering is 16.

Admissions: About 44% of the 1993–94 applicants were accepted. The SAT scores for the 1993–94 freshman class were as follows: Verbal—4% below 500, 52% between 500 and 599, 40% between 600 and 700, and 4% above 700; Math—1% below 500, 24% between 500 and 599, 56% between 600 and 700, and 19% above 700. About 81% of the current freshmen were in the top fifth of their class; 99% were in the top two fifths.

Requirements: The SAT I or ACT is not required; submission of test scores is optional. Candidates for admission should have completed 4 years of English, 3 each of mathematics and history or social studies, and 2 each of science and foreign language. Essays are required and an interview on or off campus is strongly recommended. AP credits are accepted. Important factors used in the admissions decision are advanced placement or honor courses, evidence of special talent, leadership record, extracurricular activities record, and geographic diversity.

Procedure: Freshmen are admitted fall and winter. Early decision applications should be filed by December 1 for round 1 and January 1 for round 2; regular applications, by February 1 for fall entry and November 15 for winter entry, along with an application fee of $40. Notification of early decision is sent December 24 for round 1 and January 24 for round 2; regular decision, by April 3. There are early decision, early admissions, and deferred admissions plans. Some 219 early decision candidates were accepted for the 1993–94 class. A waiting list is an active part of the admissions procedure, with about 17% of applicants on the list.

Transfer: Some 32 transfer students enrolled in 1993–94. More weight is given to the student's college record than to high school credentials. A total of 16 courses out of at least 32 must be completed at Bates.

Visiting: There are guides for informal visits and visitors may sit in on classes and stay overnight at the school. To arrange for a visit, contact the Admissions Office at (207) 786-6000.

Financial Aid: In 1993–94, 52% of all current freshmen and 50% of continuing students received some form of financial aid. About 46% of freshmen and 45% of continuing students received need-based aid. The average freshman award was $17,300. Of that total,

scholarships or need-based grants averaged $12,525 ($22,900 maximum); loans averaged $3475 ($3750 maximum); and work contracts averaged $1300. Fifty percent of undergraduate students work part-time. Average earnings from campus work for the school year are $1300. Bates is a member of CSS. The FAF and FAFSA, and the college's own financial statement, along with parent and student tax returns and W-2 forms, are required. The deadline for financial aid applications is February 15.

International Students: There are currently 52 international students enrolled. The school actively recruits these students. They must take the TOEFL.

Computers: The college provides computer facilities for student use. The mainframe is a DEC 5000/240 and a Prime 7330 (RISC). There are 130 public microcomputers with access to the mainframe and Internet. An additional 150 microcomputers are in departmental laboratories and 75% can access the mainframe and Internet. All students may access the system. There are no time limits on using the system and no fees.

Graduates: In 1992–93, 404 bachelor's degrees were awarded. The most popular majors among graduates were political science (15%), psychology (11%), and English (10%). Within an average freshman class, 1% graduate in 3 years, 83% in 4 years, and 6% in 5 years. Some 70 companies recruited on campus in 1992–93. In the 1992 graduating class, 17% of both men and women were enrolled in graduate school within 6 months of graduation; 65% had found employment.

Admissions Contact: William C. Hiss, Vice President for Administrative Services and Dean of Admissions.

BOWDOIN COLLEGE

B-5

Brunswick, ME 04011   (207) 725-3100

Full-time: 749 men, 741 women	Faculty: 119; IIB, + +$
Part-time: 2 men, 6 women	Ph.D.s: 95%
Graduate: none	Student/Faculty: 13 to 1
Year: semesters	Tuition: $18,300
Application Deadline: January 15	Room & Board: $5855
Freshman Class: 3356 applied, 1019 accepted, 418 enrolled	
SAT I Verbal/Math: 570/640	**MOST COMPETITIVE**

Bowdoin College, established in 1794, is a private, coeducational, liberal arts institution. The 2 libraries contain 802,000 volumes, 249,200 microform items, and 5700 audiovisual forms, and subscribe to 2100 periodicals. Computerized library sources and services include the card catalog, interlibrary loans, and database searching. Special learning facilities include an art gallery, radio station, museum of art, arctic museum, language media center, and women's resource center. The 110-acre campus is in a small town 25 miles northeast of Portland. Including residence halls, there are 50 buildings on campus.

Student Life: About 85% of undergraduates are from out-of-state, mostly the Northeast. Students come from 50 states, 24 foreign countries, and Canada. Fifty-six percent are from public schools; 44% from private. Eighty-four percent are white. The average age of freshmen is 18; all undergraduates, 20. Four percent drop out by the end of their first year; 90% remain to graduate.

Housing: A total of 1101 students can be accommodated in college housing. College-sponsored living facilities include single-sex and coed dormitories, on-campus apartments, and off-campus apartments. In addition, there are special interest houses, the Wellness House, with a focus on healthful living, and an Afro-American house. On-campus housing is available on a lottery system for upperclassmen. Seventy-three percent of students live on campus; of those, 99% remain on campus on weekends. All students may keep cars on campus.

Activities: About 40% of men and about 32% of women belong to 6 local and 2 national fraternities. There are no sororities on campus. There are 60 groups on campus, including art, capella singing, choir, chorale, chorus, dance, drama, ethnic, film, gay, international, jazz band, literary magazine, marching band, musical theater, newspaper, orchestra, outing, pep band, photography, political, radio and TV, religious, social, social service, student government, and yearbook. Popular campus events include James Bowdoin Day, Parents Weekend, Ivies Weekend, Winter Weekend, Homecoming, and a pop concert series.

Sports: There are 13 intercollegiate sports for men and 14 for women, and 11 intramural sports for men and 10 for women. Athletic and recreation facilities include an arena, a field house, a swimming pool, 2 gymnasiums, indoor and outdoor track facilities, tennis and squash courts, and cross-country ski trails. There are also Nautilus, weight, and aerobics rooms, and 35 acres of playing fields for baseball, softball, lacrosse, field hockey, and soccer.

Disabled Students: Thirty-two percent of the campus is accessible to disabled students. The following facilities are available: wheelchair ramps, elevators, special parking, specially equipped rest rooms, and lowered telephones.

Services: In addition to many counseling and information services, tutoring is available in most subjects.

Campus Safety and Security: Campus safety and security measures include 24-hour foot and vehicle patrol, escort service, shuttle buses, and pamphlets, posters, and films. In addition, there are emergency telephones, lighted pathways and sidewalks, and emergency warning whistles. Residences are locked at night, and a staffed communications center is available around the clock.

Programs of Study: Bowdoin awards the A.B. and B.A. in Latin degrees. Bachelor's degrees are awarded in BIOLOGICAL SCIENCE (biochemistry, biology/biological science, and neurosciences), COMMUNICATIONS AND THE ARTS (art history and appreciation, classics, English, French, German, music, romance languages, Russian, Spanish, and studio art), COMPUTER AND PHYSICAL SCIENCE (chemistry, computer science, geology, mathematics, and physics), ENGINEERING AND ENVIRONMENTAL DESIGN (environmental science), SOCIAL SCIENCE (African American studies, anthropology, Asian/Oriental studies, classical/ancient civilization, economics, government and legal studies, history, philosophy, psychology, religion, and sociology). Natural, social, and behavioral sciences, Asian studies, and computer science are the strongest academically. Government and legal studies, history, economics, and biology have the largest enrollments.

Required: Degree requirements include 32 courses, with at least 2 semesters in natural science and mathematics, social and behavioral sciences, humanities and fine arts, and non-Eurocentric studies, and completion of major requirements.

Special: Students may take advantage of approved programs with Boston University (city semester), Williams College (Mystic Seaport), the National Theater Institute, and American University (Washington semester), among several other schools. Dual majors in any combination, study abroad in virtually any country, interdisciplinary majors, nondegree study, student-designed majors, pass/fail options, and limited credit for life, military, or work experience are also available. The college offers a 3–2 engineering degree with the California Institute of Technology and a 3–2 engineering or legal studies degree with Columbia University. There is a chapter of Phi Beta Kappa on campus.

Faculty/Classroom: Sixty-four percent of faculty are male; 36%, female. All teach undergraduates and 90% do research as well. The average class size in an introductory lecture is 50; in a laboratory, 22; and in a regular course offering, 17.

Admissions: About 30% of the 1993–94 applicants were accepted. The SAT scores for the 1993–94 freshman class were as follows: Verbal—14% below 500, 47% between 500 and 599, 36% between 600 and 700, and 3% above 700; Math—5% below 500, 27% between 500 and 599, 44% between 600 and 700, and 24% above 700. All the current freshmen were in the top fifth of their class; all were in the top two fifths. There were 4 National Merit finalists.

Requirements: The SAT I or ACT is not required. There are no specific academic requirements, but typical applicants for admission will have 4 years each of English, social studies, foreign language, and mathematics, 3 1/2 years of science, and 1 course each in art, music, and history. A high school record, 2 teacher recommendations, and an essay are required. AP credits are accepted. Important factors used in the admissions decision are recommendations by school officials, advanced placement or honor courses, evidence of special talent, leadership record, and geographic diversity.

Procedure: Freshmen are admitted in the fall. Entrance exams are utilized for counseling and placement only and may be submitted by the late summer before the freshman year. Early decision applications should be filed by November 15; regular applications, by January 15 for fall entry, along with an application fee of $40. Notification of early decision is sent December 15; regular decision, April 15. There are early decision and deferred admissions plans. Some 188 early decision candidates were accepted for the 1993–94 class. A waiting list is an active part of the admissions procedure, with about 10% of applicants on the list.

Transfer: Six transfer students enrolled in 1993–94. College grades of B or better are required to transfer. Applicants should submit high school and college transcripts, a dean's or adviser's statement from the most recent college attended, and 2 recommendations from recent professors. A total of 2 years in residence and at least 16 courses out of 32 must be completed at Bowdoin.

Visiting: There are regularly scheduled orientations for prospective students, in which they should be prepared to talk informally about their academic record, interests, talents, and goals. There are guides for informal visits and visitors may sit in on classes and stay overnight at the school. To arrange for a visit, contact the Admissions Office at (207) 725-3100.

Financial Aid: In 1993–94 43% of all current freshmen and 44% of continuing students received some form of financial aid. About 43% of freshmen and 44% of continuing students received need-based aid. The average freshman award was $14,857. Of that total, scholarships or need-based grants averaged $11,934 ($23,500 maximum);

and loans averaged $2675 ($2750 maximum). Fifty-nine percent of undergraduate students work part-time. Average earnings from campus work for the school year are $937. The average financial indebtedness of the 1992–93 graduate was $10,975. Bowdoin is a member of CSS. The FAF and the college's own financial statement are required. The deadline for financial aid applications is March 1.

International Students: There are currently 43 international students enrolled. The school actively recruits these students. They must take the TOEFL and achieve a minimum score of 600. SAT I scores must be submitted at matriculation for counseling and placement.

Computers: The college provides computer facilities for student use. The mainframes are a DEC VAX 5400 and a 8350. Approximately 90 terminals with Apple Macintosh, IBM, and Zenith microcomputers are available in 6 laboratories across the campus. All students may access the system. It may be used 24 hours a day by modem, and from 8 a.m to midnight via public terminals. There are no time limits on using the system and no fees.

Graduates: In 1992–93, 375 bachelor's degrees were awarded. The most popular majors among graduates were government and legal studies (16%), economics (12%), and English (9%). Within an average freshman class, 90% graduate in 5 years. Some 45 companies recruited on campus in 1992–93. In the 1992 graduating class, 19% of both men and women were enrolled in graduate school within 6 months of graduation; 70% had found employment.

Admissions Contact: Richard E. Steele, Dean of Admissions.

COLBY COLLEGE
B-4

Waterville, ME 04901   (207) 872-3168; (800) 723-3032 (in-state)

Full-time: 810 men, 910 women	Faculty: 141; IIB, + +$
Part-time: 17 men, 18 women	Ph.D.s: 98%
Graduate: none	Student/Faculty: 12 to 1
Year: 4–1–4	Tuition: $18,690
Application Deadline: January 15	Room & Board: $5540

Freshman Class: 2848 applied, 1319 accepted, 452 enrolled
SAT I Verbal/Math: 580/620   ACT: 27   **HIGHLY COMPETITIVE**

Colby College, founded in 1813, is a private, coeducational liberal arts college. The 3 libraries contain 467,195 volumes, 255,700 microform items, and 13,291 audiovisual forms, and subscribe to 2135 periodicals. Computerized library sources and services include the card catalog, interlibrary loans, and database searching. Special learning facilities include a learning resource center, art gallery, radio station, observatory, satellite dish, arboretum, and state wildlife management area. The 714-acre campus is in a small town 75 miles north of Portland. Including residence halls, there are 44 buildings on campus.

Student Life: About 88% of undergraduates are from out-of-state, mostly the Northeast. Students come from 48 states, 20 foreign countries, and Canada. Fifty-seven percent are from public schools; 43% from private. Ninety-one percent are white. The average age of freshmen is 18; all undergraduates, 20. Five percent drop out by the end of their first year; 87% remain to graduate.

Housing: A total of 1586 students can be accommodated in college housing. College-sponsored living facilities include coed dormitories. In addition, there are 2 substance-free and 2 quiet residence halls. On-campus housing is guaranteed for all 4 years. Ninety-two percent of students live on campus. All students may keep cars on campus.

Activities: There are no fraternities or sororities on campus. There are 95 groups on campus, including art, band, choir, chorale, chorus, computers, dance, debate, drama, emergency response, ethnic, film, gay, honors, international, jazz band, literary magazine, musical theater, newspaper, orchestra, outing, photography, political, radio, religious, social, social service, student government, symphony, women's, and yearbook. Popular campus events include Homecoming, Parents Weekend, Family Winter Weekend, Bunche Symposium, Lovejoy Convocation, Colby Outdoor Orientation Trips (COOT), Martin Luther King Day Celebration, Hispanic Awareness Month, Feminist Fortnight, and Bisexual, Gay, and Lesbian Days.

Sports: There are 15 intercollegiate sports for men and 16 for women, and 12 intramural sports for men and 12 for women. Athletic and recreation facilities include a gymnasium, field house, tennis and squash courts, track, pool, cross-country course, weight training room, sports medicine center, jogging trails, and 50 acres of playing fields.

Disabled Students: Ninety percent of the campus is accessible to disabled students. The following facilities are available: wheelchair ramps, elevators, special parking, specially equipped rest rooms, special class scheduling, and lowered telephones.

Services: In addition to many counseling and information services, tutoring is available in every subject. There is also a reader service for the blind, a writing center, and a support program for learning-disabled students.

Campus Safety and Security: Campus safety and security measures include 24-hour foot and vehicle patrol, escort service, shuttle buses, and informal discussions. In addition, there are pamphlets, posters, and films, lighted pathways and sidewalks, a women's safety

program, a property identification program, and party monitors (security officers).

Programs of Study: Colby awards the A.B. degree. Bachelor's degrees are awarded in BIOLOGICAL SCIENCE (biochemistry, biology/biological science, and cell and molecular biology/biochemistry), BUSINESS (administrative science), COMMUNICATIONS AND THE ARTS (art, art history, classics, English, fine arts, French, German, music, performing arts, Russian language and culture, Spanish, and studio art), COMPUTER AND PHYSICAL SCIENCE (chemistry, computer science, earth science, geology, mathematics, and physics), ENGINEERING AND ENVIRONMENTAL DESIGN (environmental science), SOCIAL SCIENCE (American studies, anthropology, classical civilization, East Asian cultures and languages, economics, government, history, international studies, philosophy, psychology, religious studies, and sociology). English, government, economics, biology, history, American studies, and psychology have the largest enrollments.

Required: To graduate, all students must take English composition, a foreign language, 1 year of physical education, 2 courses in natural science, and 1 course each in historical studies, arts, literature, social science, quantitative reasoning, and human diversity. The number of hours required in the major varies by department. Students must complete a total of 120 credit hours, including 2 January term courses, and maintain a GPA of 2.0.

Special: Domestic exchange programs are available with Claremont College, Howard University, American University, and Williams College under the Williams-Mystic Seaport Program. Foreign exchange programs are available through Colby or in conjunction with other colleges. Army ROTC is offered through the University of Maine/Orono. Internships, work-study programs, dual and student-designed majors, nondegree study, and limited pass/fail options are also available. A 3–2 engineering degree is offered with Case Western Reserve University, the University of Rochester, and Dartmouth College. There are 8 national honor societies on campus, including Phi Beta Kappa. Thirteen departments have honors programs.

Faculty/Classroom: Sixty percent of faculty are male; 40%, female. All both teach and do research. The average class size in a regular course offering is 17.

Admissions: About 46% of the 1993–94 applicants were accepted. The SAT scores for the 1993–94 freshman class were as follows: Verbal—10% below 500, 50% between 500 and 599, 37% between 600 and 700, and 3% above 700. The ACT scores were 3% below 21, 8% between 21 and 23, 29% between 24 and 26, 29% between 27 and 28, and 31% above 28. About 76% of the current freshmen were in the top fifth of their class; 95% were in the top two fifths. Ten freshmen graduated first in their class.

Requirements: The SAT I or ACT is required. Candidates should be high school graduates with a recommended academic program of 4 years of English, 3 each of foreign language and mathematics, and 2 each of science (including laboratory work), social studies/history, and other college-preparatory courses. AP credits are accepted. Important factors used in the admissions decision are advanced placement or honor courses, evidence of special talent, recommendations by school officials, leadership record, and parents or siblings attending the school.

Procedure: Freshmen are admitted in the fall. Entrance exams should be taken by January of the senior year. Early decision applications should be filed by November 15 for fall entry and January 1 for winter entry; regular applications, by January 15 for fall entry, along with an application fee of $45. Notification of early decision is sent December 15 for fall entry and February 15 for winter entry; regular decision, April 1. There are early decision, early admissions, and deferred admissions plans. Some 125 early decision candidates were accepted for the 1993–94 class. A waiting list is an active part of the admissions procedure, with about 5% of applicants on the list.

Transfer: Eighteen transfer students enrolled in a recent year. Transfer candidates must have a minimum GPA of 3.0 and, as a rule, have earned enough credit hours to qualify for at least sophomore standing. They must be in good academic and social standing and should submit references from a faculty member and a dean of their current school. If the SAT I or ACT has been taken, the results must be submitted as well. A total of 60 credits out of 120 must be completed at Colby.

Visiting: There are guides for informal visits and visitors may sit in on classes and stay overnight at the school. To arrange for a visit, contact the Admissions Office at (207) 872-3168.

Financial Aid: In 1993–94, 43% of all current freshmen and 38% of continuing students received some form of financial aid. About 40% of freshmen and 36% of continuing students received need-based aid. The average freshman award was $14,400. Of that total, scholarships or need-based grants averaged $11,740 ($24,000 maximum); loans averaged $1690 ($2750 maximum); and work contracts averaged $975 ($1400 maximum). Sixty-six percent of undergraduate students work part-time. Average earnings from campus work for the school year are $700. The average financial indebtedness of the

1992–93 graduate was $10,000. Colby is a member of CSS. The FAF and FAFSA, the college's own financial statement, and business and personal tax returns and balance sheets are required. The deadline for financial aid applications is January 15.

International Students: There are currently 92 international students enrolled. The school actively recruits these students. They must take the TOEFL and achieve a minimum score of 550. The student must also take the SAT I or the ACT.

Computers: The college provides computer facilities for student use. The mainframes are DEC VAX 6410, 8300, 8350, and MicroVAX 3600 models. There are 113 Apple Macintosh microcomputers available with more than 400 software titles. An academic account is automatically established for each student, with the use of E-mail strongly encouraged. Colby is a member of NEARnet, which provides access to Internet as well as commercial E-mail systems. Residence halls are linked via phone to the network. All students may access the system 24 hours a day. There are no time limits on using the system and no fees. It is advised that students have personal computers; an Apple Macintosh is recommended.

Graduates: In 1992–93, 492 bachelor's degrees were awarded. The most popular majors among graduates were government (16%), economics (12%), and English (12%). Within an average freshman class, 80% graduate in 4 years and 87% in 5 years. Some 51 companies recruited on campus in 1992–93.

Admissions Contact: Parker J. Beverage, Dean of Admissions and Financial Aid.

COLLEGE OF THE ATLANTIC
Bar Harbor, ME 04609

Full-time: 85 men, 125 women	Faculty: 18
Part-time: 6 men, 8 women	Ph.D.s: 82%
Graduate: 3 men, 3 women	Student/Faculty: 12 to 1
Year: trimesters	Tuition: $13,287
Application Deadline: March 1	Room & Board: $3860

D-5
(207) 288-5015; (800) 528-0025

Freshman Class: 256 applied, 167 accepted, 70 enrolled
SAT I Verbal/Math: 563/560
VERY COMPETITIVE

College of the Atlantic, founded in 1969, is a private, coeducational institution concerned with the study of human ecology. There is one graduate school. The library contains 28,500 volumes, 30 microform items, and 300 audiovisual forms, and subscribes to 347 periodicals. Computerized library sources and services include the card catalog, interlibrary loans, and database searching. Special learning facilities include an art gallery, natural history museum, writing center, taxidermy laboratory, and photography laboratory. The 25-acre campus is in a small town 45 miles southeast of Bangor. Including residence halls, there are 10 buildings on campus.

Student Life: About 81% of undergraduates are from out-of-state, mostly the Northeast. Students come from 29 states, 9 foreign countries, and Canada. Sixty-five percent are from public schools; 35% from private. Ninety-six percent are white. The average age of freshmen is 19; all undergraduates, 22. Ten percent drop out by the end of their first year; 65% remain to graduate.

Housing: A total of 63 students can be accommodated in college housing. College-sponsored living facilities include coed dormitories and off-campus apartments. In addition, there is a substance-free house. On-campus housing is guaranteed for the freshman year only and is available on a first-come, first-served basis. Priority is given to out-of-town students. Seventy-one percent of students commute. Alcohol is not permitted. All students may keep cars on campus.

Activities: There are no fraternities or sororities on campus. There are 25 groups on campus, including art, chess, choir, chorus, computers, drama, environmental, international, jazz band, literary magazine, musical theater, newspaper, photography, political, social, and student government. Popular campus events include the annual horseshoe tournaments, annual Bar Island Swim, Contra Dances, Halloween Party, and weekly film series.

Sports: There are 4 intramural sports for men and 3 for women. All students are members of the local YMCA and may use its pool, Nautilus equipment, and volleyball and basketball facilities, as well as nearby tennis courts. Acadia National Park offers seasonal outdoor activities.

Disabled Students: Eighty percent of the campus is accessible to disabled students. The following facilities are available: wheelchair ramps, elevators, special parking, specially equipped rest rooms, lowered drinking fountains, and lowered telephones.

Services: There is remedial math and writing.

Campus Safety and Security: Campus safety and security measures include 24-hour foot and vehicle patrol, escort service, shuttle buses, and informal discussions. In addition, there are pamphlets, posters, and films, emergency telephones, and lighted pathways and sidewalks.

Programs of Study: Bachelor's and master's degrees are awarded. Bachelor's degrees are conferred in SOCIAL SCIENCE (human ecology).

Required: Students design their own program. They must complete a total of 36 COA credits, including 3 human ecology core courses and 2 courses each in environmental science, human studies, and art and design. Also required are group study, a 3-credit internship, a human ecology essay, and participation in a 3-credit senior project.

Special: Teacher certification is offered in elementary, secondary, and science education. Students may cross-register with the University of Maine. Study abroad is available in Uruguay, Belgium, and the Czech Republic. Students may arrange a work-study program with Acadia National Park or Kids Corner day care. Pass/fail grading options are available.

Faculty/Classroom: Sixty-six percent of faculty are male; 33%, female. All teach undergraduates, 60% do research, and 60% do both. No introductory courses are taught by graduate students. The average class size in an introductory lecture is 20; in a laboratory and in a regular course offering, 14.

Admissions: About 65% of the 1993–94 applicants were accepted. The SAT scores for the 1993–94 freshman class were as follows: Verbal—11% below 500, 60% between 500 and 599, and 29% between 600 and 700; Math—22% below 500, 47% between 500 and 599, 22% between 600 and 700, and 9% above 700. About 60% of the current freshmen were in the top fifth of their class; 92% were in the top two fifths. Four freshmen graduated first in their class.

Requirements: The SAT I is recommended. Candidates for admission must be high school graduates who have completed 4 years of English, 3 to 4 of mathematics, 2 to 3 of science, 2 of a foreign language, and 1 of history. AP and CLEP credits are accepted. Important factors used in the admissions decision are personality, intangible qualities, leadership record, evidence of special talent, advanced placement or honor courses, and recommendations by school officials.

Procedure: Freshmen are admitted to all sessions. Entrance exams should be taken in the junior or senior year. Early decision applications should be filed by December 1; regular applications, by March 1 for fall entry, November 15 for winter entry, and February 15 for spring entry, along with an application fee of $35. Notification of early decision is sent December 15; regular decision, on a rolling basis. There are early decision, early admissions, and deferred admissions plans. A waiting list is an active part of the admissions procedure.

Transfer: Some 20 transfer students enrolled in a recent year. A total of 18 course credits out of 36 must be completed at COA.

Visiting: There are regularly scheduled orientations for prospective students. There are guides for informal visits and visitors may sit in on classes and stay overnight at the school. To arrange for a visit, contact Donna McFarland at (800) 528-0025 or (207) 288-5015.

Financial Aid: In 1993–94, 66% of all current freshmen and 60% of continuing students received need-based aid. The average freshman award was $10,242. Of that total, scholarships or need-based grants averaged $5611 ($12,435 maximum); loans averaged $3180 ($4000 maximum); work contracts averaged $1451 ($1800 maximum), and private scholarships averaged $1971 ($5620 maximum). Eighty-six percent of undergraduate students work part-time. Average earnings from campus work for the school year are $1600. The average financial indebtedness of the 1992–93 graduate was $8833. COA is a member of CSS. The FAF is required. The deadline for financial aid applications is May 1.

International Students: There are currently 13 international students enrolled. They must take the TOEFL and achieve a minimum score of 550.

Computers: The college provides computer facilities for student use. More than 25 microcomputers, including Dell System 220/325 and IBM XT and AT compatibles, are available in 2 computer centers and a science laboratory. The graphics laboratory contains 7 workstations and peripherals. All students may access the system. It may be used 24 hours a day. There are no time limits on using the system and no fees.

Graduates: In 1992–93, 61 bachelor's degrees were awarded. Within an average freshman class, 55% graduate in 4 years, 10% in 5 years, and 5% in 6 years. In the 1992 graduating class, 15% of the men and 20% of the women were enrolled in graduate school within 6 months of graduation; 75% had found employment.

Admissions Contact: Steve Thomas, Director of Admission and Student Services.

HUSSON COLLEGE

C-4

Bangor, ME 04401 (207) 941-7100; (800) 4-HUSSON (out-of-state)

Full-time: 348 men, 587 women	**Faculty:** 50; IIB, -$
Part-time: 195 men, 491 women	**Ph.Ds:** 30%
Graduate: 124 men, 126 women	**Student/Faculty:** 19 to 1
Year: semesters, summer session	**Tuition:** $7630
Application Deadline: open	**Room & Board:** $3880
Freshman Class: 730 applied, 633 accepted, 361 enrolled	
SAT I Verbal/Math: 383/435	**NONCOMPETITIVE**

Husson College, founded in 1898, is a private, coeducational college offering business, nursing, teaching, and other preprofessional training. There is one graduate school. In addition to regional accreditation, Husson has baccalaureate program accreditation with NLN. The library contains 34,500 volumes, 5168 microform items, and 358 audiovisual forms, and subscribes to 387 periodicals. Computerized library sources and services include interlibrary loans and database searching. Special learning facilities include a learning resource center and radio station. The 170-acre campus is in an urban area of Bangor. Including residence halls, there are 6 buildings on campus.

Student Life: About 80% of undergraduates are from Maine. Students come from 24 states, 12 foreign countries, and Canada. Ninety percent are from public schools; 10% from private. Ninety-three percent are white. The average age of freshmen is 20.4; all undergraduates, 24.1. Twenty-two percent drop out by the end of their first year.

Housing: A total of 800 students can be accommodated in college housing. College-sponsored living facilities include coed dormitories. On-campus housing is guaranteed for all 4 years. Fifty percent of students live on campus; of those, 40% remain on campus on weekends. All students may keep cars on campus.

Activities: About 7% of men belong to 2 local and 2 national fraternities; about 6% of women belong to 3 local sororities. There are 25 groups on campus, including cheerleading, computers, drama, ethnic, international, newspaper, pep band, professional, radio and TV, social, social service, student government, and yearbook. Popular campus events include Spring Fling, Winter Carnival, Greek Alumni Weekend, Chief Week, and theater productions.

Sports: There are 4 intercollegiate sports for men and 5 for women, and 8 intramural sports for men and 8 for women. Athletic and recreation facilities include a gymnasium and an athletic facility.

Disabled Students: Ninety percent of the campus is accessible to disabled students. The following facilities are available: wheelchair ramps, elevators, special parking, specially equipped rest rooms, lowered drinking fountains, and lowered telephones.

Services: In addition to many counseling and information services, tutoring is available in most subjects. There is also remedial math and writing.

Campus Safety and Security: Campus safety and security measures include informal discussions, pamphlets, posters, films, and lighted pathways and sidewalks.

Programs of Study: Husson awards the B.S. degree. Associate and master's degrees also are awarded. Bachelor's degrees are awarded in BUSINESS (accounting, banking and finance, business administration and management, court reporting, marketing/retailing/merchandising, personnel management, secretarial studies/office management, and sports management), COMPUTER AND PHYSICAL SCIENCE (computer programming), EDUCATION (business), HEALTH PROFESSIONS (nursing). Accounting and nursing are the strongest academically. Business administration has the largest enrollment.

Required: Requirements for graduation vary by program, but a total of 120 credit hours is necessary. A course in computer information systems is required in the first year for most programs. Students must maintain a minimum GPA of 2.0.

Special: Husson offers sports management and accounting internships as well as co-op programs in most majors. Study abroad, credit for life, military, and work experience, and nondegree study are also available.

Faculty/Classroom: Forty-four percent of faculty are male; 56%, female. All teach undergraduates. No introductory courses are taught by graduate students. The average class size in an introductory lecture is 30; in a laboratory, 22; and in a regular course offering, 30.

Admissions: About 87% of the 1993-94 applicants were accepted. The SAT scores for the 1993-94 freshman class were as follows: Verbal—94% below 500 and 6% between 500 and 599; Math—73% below 500, 22% between 500 and 599, and 5% between 600 and 700. About 6% of the current freshmen were in the top fifth of their class; 39% were in the top two fifths. One freshman graduated first in class.

Requirements: Husson requires applicants to be in the upper 60% of their class. A minimum GPA of 2.0 is required. The SAT I is required, as is recommendation from a high school counselor. AP and CLEP credits are accepted. Important factors used in the admissions decision are recommendations by school officials, extracurricular activities record, leadership record, advanced placement or honor courses, personality, and intangible qualities.

Procedure: Freshmen are admitted to all sessions. Entrance exams should be taken prior to enrollment. Application deadlines are open for regular admission, December 15 for early admission. The application fee is $25. The college accepts all applicants Notification is sent on a rolling basis. There are early decision, early admissions, and deferred admissions plans. About 10 early decision candidates were accepted for the 1993-94 class.

Transfer: A total of 86 transfer students enrolled in 1993-94. Transfer applicants must have a 2.0 GPA. Courses with a C grade or better transfer to Husson. A total of 30 credits out of 120 must be completed at Husson.

Visiting: There are regularly scheduled orientations for prospective students, including an interview and campus tour. There are guides for informal visits and visitors may sit in on classes and stay overnight at the school. To arrange for a visit, contact the Admissions Office at (207) 941-7100.

Financial Aid: In 1993-94, 94% of all current freshmen and 85% of continuing students received some form of financial aid. About 90% of freshmen and 68% of continuing students received need-based aid. The average freshman award was $6776. Of that total, scholarships or need-based grants averaged $3276 ($11,410 maximum); loans averaged $2892 ($12,625 maximum); and work contracts averaged $555 ($1550 maximum). All undergraduate students work part-time. Average earnings from campus work for the school year are $1302. The average financial indebtedness of the 1992-93 graduate was $12,285. Husson is a member of CSS. The FAFSA is required. The deadline for financial aid applications is open.

International Students: There are currently 10 international students enrolled. The school actively recruits these students. They must take the TOEFL and achieve a minimum score of 500; students who score less than 500 may be accepted conditionally and must enroll in a full-time intensive English program at Husson.

Computers: The college provides computer facilities for student use. The mainframe is an IBM System/36. Computer laboratories with a total of 76 microcomputer workstations are available exclusively for student use. Those enrolled in computer courses may access the system 24 hours a day, 7 days a week. There are no time limits on using the system. The fees are $40.

Graduates: In 1992-93, 384 bachelor's degrees were awarded. The most popular majors among graduates were business administration (38%), accounting (19%), and nursing (9%). Some 43 companies recruited on campus in 1992-93. In the 1992 graduating class, 1% of the students were enrolled in graduate school within 6 months of graduation.

Admissions Contact: Jane Goodwin, Director of Admissions.

MAINE COLLEGE OF ART

B-6

(Formerly Portland School of Art)

Portland, ME 04101 (207) 775-3052; (800) 639-4808 (in-state)

Full-time: 100 men, 200 women	**Faculty:** 18
Part-time: 10 men, 20 women	**Ph.Ds:** 2%
Graduate: none	**Student/Faculty:** 15 to 1
Year: semesters	**Tuition:** $10,653
Application Deadline: open	**Room & Board:** $5020
Freshman Class: n/av	
SAT I Verbal/Math: 460/450	**SPECIAL**

Maine College of Art, established in 1882, is an independent fine arts college. In addition to regional accreditation, MeCA has baccalaureate program accreditation with NASAD. The library contains 16,361 volumes and 40 audiovisual forms, and subscribes to 114 periodicals. Special learning facilities include an art gallery. The campus is in an urban area 100 miles north of Boston in downtown Portland. Including residence halls, there are 8 buildings on campus.

Student Life: About 69% of undergraduates are from Maine. Students come from 7 foreign countries and Canada. Ninety-nine percent are white. The average age of freshmen is 22; all undergraduates, 23. Thirty-three percent drop out by the end of their first year; 42% remain to graduate.

Housing: An unlimited number of students can be accommodated in college housing. College-sponsored living facilities include coed dormitories and on-campus apartments. On-campus housing is available on a first-come, first-served basis. Eighty percent of students commute. Alcohol is not permitted. All students may keep cars on campus.

Activities: There are no fraternities or sororities on campus. There are 5 groups on campus, including art, film, newspaper, and student government. Popular campus events include Halloween dance, Christmas art sale, student show, and senior show.

Sports: There is no sports program at MeCA.

Disabled Students: The available facilities include specially equipped rest rooms.

Campus Safety and Security: Campus safety and security measures include self defense education, informal discussions, and pamphlets, posters, and films.

Programs of Study: MeCA awards the B.F.A. degree. Bachelor's degrees are awarded in COMMUNICATIONS AND THE ARTS (graphic design, metal/jewelry, painting, photography, printmaking, and sculpture), ENGINEERING AND ENVIRONMENTAL DESIGN (ceramic science).

Required: All students must take 2 years in studio foundation courses (drawing and design), 1 year of English composition, 1 semester of introduction to art history, and 2 semesters of an art history survey. Total credit hours necessary are 134 with 36 class credits in the major. Students must maintain a minimum GPA of 2.0.

Special: Cross-registration with Bowdoin College and the University of New England is available, and internships utilizing professional artists and design and photography studios can be developed. The continuing studies program provides for nondegree study. The school also offers a 2-year foundation program. A minor in art history is now available.

Faculty/Classroom: Sixty-seven percent of faculty are male; 33%, female. All teach undergraduates. The average class size in an introductory lecture is 18 and in a regular course offering, 17.

Admissions: The SAT scores for the 1993–94 freshman class were as follows: Verbal—66% below 500, 28% between 500 and 599, 3% between 600 and 700, and 3% above 700; Math—72% below 500, 16% between 500 and 599, 7% between 600 and 700, and 4% above 700.

Requirements: The SAT I or ACT is required. It is recommended that candidates for admission complete 3 years of art, 4 years of English, 3 years of mathematics, and 2 years each of foreign language, science, and social studies. AP credits are accepted.

Procedure: Freshmen are admitted in the fall. Entrance exams should be taken in the fall of the senior year. Application deadlines are open. The fee is $30. Notification is sent on a rolling basis. There are early admissions and deferred admissions plans.

Transfer: About 38 transfer students enrolled in 1993–94. A total of 64 credits out of 134 must be completed at MeCA.

Visiting: There are regularly scheduled orientations for prospective students. There are guides for informal visits, and visitors may sit in on classes and stay overnight at the school. To arrange for a visit, contact Admissions at (207) 775–3052 or (800) 639–4808.

Financial Aid: In a recent year, 73% of all freshmen and 69% of continuing students received some form of financial aid. About 73% of freshmen and 67% of continuing students received need-based aid. The average freshman award was $7200. Of that total, scholarships or need-based grants averaged $3794 ($8300 maximum); loans averaged $2625 ($7125 maximum); and work contracts averaged $1000 ($1200 maximum). Thirty-one percent of undergraduate students work part-time. MeCA is a member of CSS. The FAF, the college's own financial statement, and the FAFSA are required. The deadline for financial aid applications is March 1.

International Students: There are currently 5 international students enrolled. The school actively recruits these students. They must take the TOEFL and achieve a minimum score of 500.

Computers: The college provides computer facilities for student use. Graphic design majors have full access. There are no time limits on using the system and no fees.

Graduates: In a recent year, 55 bachelor's degrees were awarded. The most popular majors among graduates were graphic design (29%), photography (20%), and jewelry and painting (15%).

Admissions Contact: Director of Admissions.

MAINE MARITIME ACADEMY

C-5

Castine, ME 04420   (207) 326–4311

(800) 443–5244 (in-state), (800) 227–8465 (out-of-state)

Full-time: 645 men, 45 women	Faculty: 45; IIB, --$
Part-time: none	Ph.D.s: 16%
Graduate: 60 men	Student/Faculty: 15 to 1
Year: see profile	Tuition: $3940 ($6885)
Application Deadline: July 1	Room & Board: $4396
Freshman Class: 675 applied, 425 accepted, 207 enrolled	
SAT I Verbal/Math: 440/510	COMPETITIVE

Maine Maritime Academy, founded in 1941, is a public, coeducational institution that qualifies students for a license in the United States Merchant Marine and confers a B.S. degree. There is one graduate school. In addition to regional accreditation, MMA has baccalaureate program accreditation with ABET. The library contains 75,381 volumes, and subscribes to 950 periodicals. Computerized library sources and services include the card catalog, interlibrary loans, and database searching. Special learning facilities include a planetarium. The 35-acre campus is in a rural area 35 miles south of Bangor on the east coast of the Penobscot Bay. Including residence halls, there are 8 buildings on campus.

Student Life: About 60% of undergraduates are from Maine. Students come from 33 states, 7 foreign countries, and Canada. Ninety-seven percent are white. The average age of freshmen is 18; all undergraduates, 22. Twenty percent drop out by the end of their first year; 70% remain to graduate.

Housing: A total of 600 students can be accommodated in college housing. College-sponsored living facilities include coed dormitories. On-campus housing is guaranteed for all 4 years. Eighty percent of students live on campus; of those, 25% remain on campus on weekends. Alcohol is not permitted. Upperclassmen may keep cars on campus.

Activities: About 6% of men and about 25% of women belong to 1 national fraternity. There are no sororities on campus. There are 26 groups on campus, including band, cheerleading, drama, drill team, ethnic, international, marching band, newspaper, pep band, photography, professional, social, social service, student government, and yearbook. Popular campus events include Daisy Day and Klondike Derby.

Sports: There are 6 intercollegiate sports for men and 2 for women, and 5 intramural sports for men and 5 for women. Athletic and recreation facilities include a weight room, an olympic pool, a field house, a bowling alley, a gymnasium, racquetball and squash courts, an aerobics room, and a multisports athletic field.

Disabled Students: The entire campus is accessible to disabled students. The following facilities are available: wheelchair ramps, elevators, special parking, and specially equipped rest rooms.

Services: In addition to many counseling and information services, tutoring is available in most subjects. There is also remedial math, reading, and writing.

Campus Safety and Security: Campus safety and security measures include 24-hour foot and vehicle patrol and medical and counseling services.

Programs of Study: MMA awards the B.S. degree. Associate and master's degrees also are awarded. Bachelor's degrees are awarded in COMPUTER AND PHYSICAL SCIENCE (oceanography), ENGINEERING AND ENVIRONMENTAL DESIGN (engineering, engineering technology, marine engineering, maritime science, and transportation technology). Marine systems engineering is the strongest academically. Marine engineering technology has the largest enrollment.

Required: A minimum GPA of 2.0 in an average of 140 total credit hours is required for graduation.

Special: The academic calendar consists of 2 semesters plus a 2 to 3 month annual training cruise. Co-op programs are possible in every major.

Faculty/Classroom: Eighty-five percent of faculty are male; 15%, female. All teach undergraduates. No introductory courses are taught by graduate students. The average class size in an introductory lecture is 30; in a laboratory, 15; and in a regular course offering, 25.

Admissions: About 63% of the 1993–94 applicants were accepted.

Requirements: MMA requires applicants to be in the upper 50% of their class. A minimum GPA of 2.0 is required. The SAT I or ACT is required. Candidates for admission must have completed 4 years of English, 3 years of mathematics, and 2 years of science. In addition, the academy recommends 1 year of a foreign language. AP and CLEP credits are accepted.

Procedure: Freshmen are admitted in the fall. Entrance exams should be taken as early as possible in the senior year. Applications should be filed by July 1 for fall entry and November 1 for spring entry, along with an application fee of $15. Notification is sent on a rolling basis. There is a deferred admissions plan.

Transfer: Some 25 transfer students enrolled in 1993–94. Transfer students must have a minimum 2.0 GPA in previous college work and meet the same prerequisites as entering freshmen.

Visiting: There are regularly scheduled orientations for prospective students. There are guides for informal visits and visitors may sit in on classes and stay overnight at the school. To arrange for a visit, contact the Admissions Office at (207) 326–4311.

Financial Aid: MMA is a member of CSS. The FAF is required. The deadline for financial aid applications is April 15.

International Students: There are currently 14 international students enrolled. They must take the TOEFL and achieve a minimum score of 550.

Computers: The college provides computer facilities for student use. PCs are available. All students may access the system. There are no time limits on using the system and no fees.

Graduates: The most popular majors among 1993 graduates were marine engineering (70%), nautical science (20%), and power engineering (10%). Within an average freshman class, 70% graduate in 4 years and 5% in 5 years. Some 60 companies recruited on campus in 1992–93. In the 1992 graduating class, 1% of the men were enrolled in graduate school within 6 months of graduation; 98% of the men and all of the women had found employment.

Admissions Contact: Director of Admissions.

PORTLAND SCHOOL OF ART
(See Maine College of Art)

SAINT JOSEPH'S COLLEGE

A-6

Windham, ME 04062-1198   (207) 892-6766; (800) 338-7057
Full-time: 265 men, 451 women   Faculty: 42; IIB, --$
Part-time: 64 men, 109 women   Ph.D.s: 86%
Graduate: none   Student/Faculty: 17 to 1
Year: semesters, summer session   Tuition: $9685
Application Deadline: June 1   Room & Board: $4850
Freshman Class: 833 applied, 582 accepted, 217 enrolled
SAT I Verbal/Math: 425/475   **COMPETITIVE**

Saint Joseph's College, founded in 1912, is a private, Roman Catholic institution offering liberal arts and preprofessional programs. In addition to regional accreditation, Saint Joe's has baccalaureate program accreditation with NLN. The library contains 74,000 volumes, 3187 microform items, and 3250 audiovisual forms, and subscribes to 497 periodicals. Computerized library sources and services include interlibrary loans and database searching. Special learning facilities include a learning resource center, radio station, and TV station. The 315-acre campus is in a rural area 16 miles west of Portland. Including residence halls, there are 18 buildings on campus.

Student Life: About 51% of undergraduates are from Maine. Students come from 14 states, 7 foreign countries, and Canada. Eighty-four percent are from public schools; 16% from private. Ninety-five percent are white. Most are Catholic. The average age of freshmen is 18; all undergraduates, 20. Nine percent drop out by the end of their first year; 76% remain to graduate.

Housing: A total of 525 students can be accommodated in college housing. College-sponsored living facilities include single-sex dormitories. On-campus housing is guaranteed for all 4 years. Seventy-three percent of students live on campus; of those, 75% remain on campus on weekends. All students may keep cars on campus.

Activities: There are no fraternities or sororities on campus. There are 25 groups on campus, including cheerleading, chess, chorale, drama, film, literary magazine, musical theater, newspaper, photography, political, professional, radio and TV, religious, social, social service, student government, and yearbook. Popular campus events include Wellness Week, Siblings Weekend, Christmas Benefit Concert, Parent's Weekend, Pentathlon, Campus Life Awards Banquet, Casino Night, Suitcase Dance, Roommate Game, Earth Day, and lip syncs.

Sports: There are 5 intercollegiate sports for men and 5 for women, and 12 intramural sports for men and 12 for women. Athletic and recreation facilities include a multipurpose gymnasium with weight and dance aerobics rooms, a private beach on Sebago Lake, a lighted athletic field for baseball, softball, and intramurals, and wooded cross-country running and ski trails.

Disabled Students: Twenty-five percent of the campus is accessible to disabled students. The following facilities are available: wheelchair ramps, elevators, special parking, specially equipped rest rooms, and lowered drinking fountains.

Services: In addition to many counseling and information services, tutoring is available in some subjects, including English, mathematics, and chemistry. There is also remedial math, reading, and writing.

Campus Safety and Security: Campus safety and security measures include 24-hour foot and vehicle patrol, informal discussions, pamphlets, posters, and films, and lighted pathways and sidewalks. In addition, there are round-the-clock security guards.

Programs of Study: Saint Joe's awards the B.A., B.S., B.S.B.A., and B.S.N. degrees. Associate and master's degrees also are awarded. Bachelor's degrees are awarded in BIOLOGICAL SCIENCE (biology), BUSINESS (accounting, business administration and management, management science, and marketing/retailing/merchandising), COMMUNICATIONS AND THE ARTS (communications and English), COMPUTER AND PHYSICAL SCIENCE (mathematics, natural sciences, and radiological technology), EDUCATION (elementary, physical, and secondary), ENGINEERING AND ENVIRONMENTAL DESIGN (environmental science), HEALTH PROFESSIONS (nursing, predentistry, premedicine, and prepharmacy), SOCIAL SCIENCE (history, philosophy, prelaw, psychology, religious studies, and sociology). Business, nursing, communications, elementary education, and biology are the strongest academically and have the largest enrollments.

Required: To graduate, all students must complete 12 hours of English, 9 of philosophy, 6 each of religious studies and history, 6 to 8 of science, and 3 each of mathematics, fine arts, and seminar studies. B.A. candidates must also have 6 hours of intermediate-level language. A total of 128 credit hours, including at least 33 in the major, must be completed with a minimum GPA of 2.0.

Special: Army ROTC is offered with the University of Southern Maine. The college also offers internships, cross-registration with Maine College of Art, study in Nova Scotia, dual majors in most pro-

grams, and limited nondegree study. Students may participate in work-study programs either on or off campus. The college has an external degree program providing directed home study in several fields. There is a 2-3 pharmacy program with the Massachusetts College of Pharmacy in Boston. There is a freshman honors program on campus, as well as 2 national honor societies. One department has an honors program.

Faculty/Classroom: Forty-six percent of faculty are male; 54%, female. All teach undergraduates. The average class size in an introductory lecture is 25; in a laboratory, 16; and in a regular course offering, 18.

Admissions: About 70% of the 1993-94 applicants were accepted. The SAT scores for the 1993-94 freshman class were as follows: Verbal—83% below 500, 16% between 500 and 599, and 1% between 600 and 700; Math—66% below 500, 28% between 500 and 599, and 6% between 600 and 700. About 27% of the current freshmen were in the top fifth of their class; 58% were in the top two fifths. Two freshmen graduated first in their class.

Requirements: A minimum C average is required, as is the SAT I. Candidates for admission must be high school graduates who have completed 4 units in English, 3 to 4 in mathematics, 2 in foreign language, and 1 to 3 each in history, science, and social studies. AP and CLEP credits are accepted. Important factors used in the admissions decision are recommendations by school officials, leadership record, advanced placement or honor courses, evidence of special talent, and extracurricular activities record.

Procedure: Freshmen are admitted fall and spring. Entrance exams should be taken by January of the senior year. Early acceptance applications should be filed by December 1; regular applications, by June 1 for fall entry and December 1 for spring entry, along with an application fee of $25. Notification of early acceptance is sent beginning in mid-December; regular decision, on a rolling basis. There are early acceptance, early admissions, and deferred admissions plans.

Transfer: Some 58 transfer students enrolled in 1993-94. Transfer students should have a minimum GPA of 2.0. A total of 32 credits out of 128 must be completed at Saint Joe's.

Visiting: There are regularly scheduled orientations for prospective students, including an open house in October and 5 group Saturday programs in the fall. There are guides for informal visits and visitors may sit in on classes; they may also stay overnight at the school on a limited basis. To arrange for a visit, contact the Admissions Office at (800) 338-7057.

Financial Aid: In 1993-94, 80% of all current freshmen and 81% of continuing students received some form of financial aid, including need-based aid. The average freshman award was $7800. Of that total, scholarships or need-based grants averaged $4000 ($9856 maximum); loans averaged $3000 ($4700 maximum); and work contracts averaged $800 ($1500 maximum). Forty-four percent of undergraduate students work part-time. Average earnings from campus work for the school year are $950. The average financial indebtedness of the 1992-93 graduate was $8300. Saint Joe's is a member of CSS. The FAF and FAFSA and income documentation are required. The deadline for financial aid applications is March 15.

International Students: There are currently 10 international students enrolled. The school actively recruits these students. They must take the TOEFL or SAT I and achieve a minimum score of 500 on the TOEFL.

Computers: The college provides computer facilities for student use. The mainframe is an AT&T 3B2/400. There are 35 microcomputer terminals available to students in the computer room, the library, and the resource center. All students may access the system. It may be used from 8 A.M. to midnight. There are no time limits on using the system and no fees.

Graduates: In 1992-93, 136 bachelor's degrees were awarded. The most popular majors among graduates were nursing (18%), education (14%), and business (13%). Within an average freshman class, 90% graduate in 4 years and 10% in 5 years. Some 18 companies recruited on campus in 1992-93. In the 1992 graduating class, 10% of the men and 14% of the women were enrolled in graduate school within 6 months of graduation; 90% of the men and 86% of the women had found employment.

Admissions Contact: Fredric V. Stone, Director of Admissions.

THOMAS COLLEGE

B-4

Waterville, ME 04901   (207) 877-0101; (800) 339-7001 (in-state)
Full-time: 50 men, 89 women   Faculty: 17; IIB, --$
Part-time: none   Ph.D.s: 25%
Graduate: none   Student/Faculty: 8 to 1
Year: semesters   Tuition: $9050
Application Deadline: open   Room & Board: $4400
Freshman Class: 346 applied, 312 accepted, 139 enrolled
SAT I Verbal/Math: 370/460   **LESS COMPETITIVE**

Thomas College, founded in 1894, is a private, coeducational college offering a business and professional education with a foundation

in liberal arts. There is one graduate school. The library contains 21,489 volumes, 1202 microform items, and 78 audiovisual forms, and subscribes to 243 periodicals. Computerized library sources and services include the card catalog, interlibrary loans, and database searching. Special learning facilities include an art gallery. The 70-acre campus is in a rural area 75 miles north of Portland. Including residence halls, there are 5 buildings on campus.

Student Life: About 87% of undergraduates are from Maine. Students come from 10 states and 4 foreign countries. Eighty-five percent are from public schools; 15% from private. Ninety-six percent are white. The average age of freshmen is 19; all undergraduates, 21. Twenty percent drop out by the end of their first year; 60% remain to graduate.

Housing: A total of 275 students can be accommodated in college housing. College-sponsored living facilities include coed dormitories and off-campus apartments. On-campus housing is guaranteed for all 4 years. Sixty percent of students live on campus; of those, 80% remain on campus on weekends. All students may keep cars on campus.

Activities: About 20% of men belong to 1 national and 2 local fraternities; about 25% of women belong to 1 national and 2 local sororities. There are 11 groups on campus, including cheerleading, chorus, computers, drama, honors, newspaper, photography, professional, religious, social, social service, student government, and yearbook. Popular campus events include Winter Carnival, Spring Fling, Olympic Day, and Captives Day.

Sports: There are 4 intercollegiate sports for men and 4 for women, and 10 intramural sports for men and 8 for women. Athletic and recreation facilities include a gymnasium, a basketball court, a weight and fitness room, soccer and softball fields, a training area, an intramural field, a skating facility, and cross-country skiing and snowshoe trails. Facilities for swimming, indoor tennis, racquetball, and hockey are available locally.

Disabled Students: Eighty percent of the campus is accessible to disabled students. The following facilities are available: special parking and specially equipped rest rooms.

Services: In addition to many counseling and information services, tutoring is available in some subjects, including accounting and mathematics.

Campus Safety and Security: Campus safety and security measures include 24-hour foot and vehicle patrol, informal discussions, pamphlets, posters, and films, and lighted pathways and sidewalks.

Programs of Study: Thomas awards the B.S. degree. Associate and master's degrees also are awarded. Bachelor's degrees are awarded in BUSINESS (accounting, business administration and management, business economics, management information systems, management science, marketing management, marketing/retailing/merchandising, and retailing), COMPUTER AND PHYSICAL SCIENCE (information sciences and systems), EDUCATION (business), SOCIAL SCIENCE (international studies). Accounting and management information systems are the strongest academically. Accounting, management, and marketing have the largest enrollments.

Required: To graduate, students must maintain a minimum GPA of 2.0, fulfill the liberal arts core requirements, and complete 120 total credit hours of study.

Special: Students may cross-register with Colby College and Kennebec Valley Technical College. There are co-op programs and internships available in most majors. The college also offers study in Canada through the New England-Quebec Exchange. A 5-year degree in business is offered. There are 2 national honor societies on campus.

Faculty/Classroom: Seventy percent of faculty are male; 30%, female. All teach undergraduates. The average class size in an introductory lecture is 25 and in a regular course offering, 15.

Admissions: About 90% of the 1993–94 applicants were accepted. About 43% of the current freshmen were in the top fifth of their class; 35% were in the top two fifths. About 2 freshmen graduated first in their class.

Requirements: Thomas requires applicants to be in the upper 50% of their class. A minimum GPA of 2.3 is required. The SAT I or ACT is required. In addition, candidates for admission be high school graduates with an academic program that includes 4 years of English and 3 years of mathematics. A letter of recommendation from a secondary school counselor is required. An interview is highly recommended. AP and CLEP credits are accepted. Important factors used in the admissions decision are advanced placement or honor courses, personality, intangible qualities, leadership record, recommendations by school officials, and extracurricular activities record.

Procedure: Freshmen are admitted fall and spring. Entrance exams should be taken by the fall of the senior year. Application deadlines are open. Application fee is $15. Notification is sent on a rolling basis. There are early admissions and deferred admissions plans.

Transfer: About 33 transfer students enrolled in 1993–94. Transfer applicants should have a minimum college GPA of 2.0. The school recommends the SAT I (with a minimum score of 400 on each section) as well as an interview. Official transcripts from all previously at-

tended post-secondary institutions are required. A total of 30 credits out of 120 must be completed at Thomas.

Visiting: There are guides for informal visits and visitors may sit in on classes. To arrange for a visit, contact the Admissions Office at (207) 873–0771 or (800) 339-7001 (in-state).

Financial Aid: In 1993–94 90% of all current freshmen and 90% of continuing students received some form of financial aid. Scholarships or need-based grants averaged $1459 ($2500 maximum); and loans averaged $3000 ($3700 maximum). Ninety-five percent of undergraduate students work part-time. The average financial indebtedness of the 1992–93 graduate was $12,000. Thomas is a member of CSS. The FAFSA financial statement is required. The deadline for financial aid applications is May 1.

International Students: There are currently 6 international students enrolled. The school actively recruits these students. They must take the TOEFL and achieve a minimum score of 500. The student must also take the SAT I.

Computers: The college provides computer facilities for student use. The mainframe is a DEC MicroVAX 3400 and MicroVAX II. Microcomputer facilities are available to students at various locations. All terminals are networked to the mainframes, one running VMS, the other, UNIX. Six PCs are also networked (virtual disk, printers); the remaining PCs are stand-alone. Desktop publishing, spreadsheet, database, word processing, graphics, presentation, and expert systems software is available. All students may access the system. It may be used 8 A.M. to 11 P.M. There are no time limits on using the system.

Graduates: In 1992–93 79 bachelor's degrees were awarded. Some 58 companies recruited on campus in 1992–93. In the 1992 graduating class, all students had found employment within 6 months of graduation.

Admissions Contact: Susan Potter, Director of Admission.

UNITY COLLEGE
C-4

Unity, ME 04988
(207) 948–3131

Full-time: 348 men, 122 women	**Faculty:** 31; IIB, --$
Part-time: none	**Ph.D.s:** 56%
Graduate: none	**Student/Faculty:** 15 to 1
Year: 4–1–4, summer session	**Tuition:** $8225 ($9325)
Application Deadline: open	**Room & Board:** $4660
Freshman Class: 425 applied, 409 accepted, 173 enrolled	
SAT I or ACT: recommended	**LESS COMPETITIVE**

Unity College, founded in 1965, is a private, independent, coeducational institution offering undergraduate programs in environmental science, natural resource management, outdoor recreation, and pre-law studies. In addition to regional accreditation, Unity has baccalaureate program accreditation with SAF. The library contains 40,000 volumes and subscribes to 651 periodicals. Computerized library sources and services include the card catalog, interlibrary loans, and database searching. Special learning facilities include a learning resource center and an art gallery. The 185-acre campus is in a rural area 18 miles east of Waterville. Including residence halls, there are 17 buildings on campus.

Student Life: About 72% of undergraduates are from out-of-state, mostly the Northeast. Students come from 28 states, 4 foreign countries, and Canada. Ninety-seven percent are from public schools; 3% from private. Ninety-nine percent are white. Fifty-seven percent are Catholic; 30% Protestant. The average age of freshmen is 18; all undergraduates, 20. Eighteen percent drop out by the end of their first year; 82% remain to graduate.

Housing: A total of 291 students can be accommodated in college housing. College-sponsored living facilities include single-sex and coed dormitories and off-campus apartments. In addition there are honors houses. On-campus housing is guaranteed for all 4 years. Eighty percent of students live on campus; of those, 80% remain on campus on weekends. All students may keep cars on campus.

Activities: There are no fraternities or sororities on campus. There are 22 groups on campus, including art, drama, literary magazine, newspaper, photography, student government, and yearbook. Popular campus events include Regional Woodsman's Meet in October.

Sports: There are 3 intercollegiate sports for men and 2 for women, and 10 intramural sports for men and 8 for women. Athletic and recreation facilities include a gymnasium, a weight training room, playing fields, a nature trail, and game rooms.

Disabled Students: Eighty percent of the campus is accessible to disabled students. The following facilities are available: wheelchair ramps, special parking, and special class scheduling.

Services: In addition to many counseling and information services, tutoring is available in every subject. In addition, there is remedial math, reading, and writing, and a full-time learning disability specialist is on staff.

Programs of Study: Unity awards the B.A. and B.S. degrees. Associate degrees also are awarded. Bachelor's degrees are awarded in AGRICULTURE (conservation and regulation and fishing and fisheries), BIOLOGICAL SCIENCE (ecology and wildlife biology), EDU-

CATION (environmental), ENGINEERING AND ENVIRONMENTAL DESIGN (environmental science and land use management and reclamation), SOCIAL SCIENCE (interdisciplinary studies, parks and recreation management, and prelaw). Aquaculture, fisheries, ecology, and wildlife biology are the strongest academically. Conservation law enforcement, wilderness-based recreation, and wildlife have the largest enrollments.

Required: General education requirements include 38 credits in English composition, oral communication, mathematics, computer science, life science, physical science, and electives, as well as 9 credits in a specialization outside the major field. Students must complete at least 120 credit hours with a minimum GPA of 2.0. An internship, thesis, or seminar is required in all bachelor's degree programs.

Special: The college offers co-op programs, credit-bearing internships, study abroad, a Washington semester, work-study programs, accelerated degree programs, dual and student-designed majors, and credit for life experience. A mentor program, in which a faculty member assists a student with research, is available to those students who earn a minimum GPA of 3.33 in their first 30 credit hours. There is a freshman honors program on campus.

Faculty/Classroom: All teach undergraduates.

Admissions: About 96% of the 1993–94 applicants were accepted.

Requirements: A minimum GPA of 2.0 is required. Applicants must be graduates of an accredited secondary school with a minimum GPA of 2.0. The GED is accepted. SAT I or ACT scores, though not required, should be submitted, if available, for placement purposes. An essay is required and an interview is recommended. AP and CLEP credits are accepted. Important factors used in the admissions decision are advanced placement or honor courses, leadership record, evidence of special talent, recommendations by school officials, and parents or siblings attending the school.

Procedure: Freshmen are admitted fall and spring. Entrance exams should be taken in the junior or senior year. Application deadlines are open. The application fee is $25. Notification is sent on a rolling basis. There are early admissions and deferred admissions plans. A waiting list is an active part of the admissions procedure.

Transfer: Sixty-one transfer students enrolled in a recent year. Applicants must present a minimum college GPA of 2.0 and are encouraged to submit SAT I scores. A total of 60 credits out of 120 must be completed at Unity.

Visiting: There are regularly scheduled orientations for prospective students. There are guides for informal visits, and visitors may sit in on classes and stay overnight at the school. To arrange for a visit, contact the Admissions Office at (207) 948-3131.

Financial Aid: In an earlier year, 90% of all current freshmen and 86% of continuing students received some form of financial aid. Unity is a member of CSS. The FAF and the college's own financial statement are required. The deadline for financial aid applications is April 15.

International Students: There are currently 8 international students enrolled. The school actively recruits these students. They must take the TOEFL and achieve a minimum score of 500.

Computers: The college provides computer facilities for student use. A network of IBM-compatible personal computers is available in the environmental science building. Apple microcomputers are available in a number of locations on campus. Apple Macintosh computers are also available. All students may access the system. There are no time limits on using the system and no fees.

Graduates: In 1992–93, 88 bachelor's degrees were awarded. Some 81 companies recruited on campus in 1992–93.

Admissions Contact: Dr. John M. B. Craig, Vice President and Dean for Admissions.

UNIVERSITY OF MAINE SYSTEM

The University of Maine system, established in 1968, is a public system. It is governed by a board of trustees, whose chief administrator is the chancellor. The primary goals of the system are teaching, research, and public service. The main priorities are to strengthen human services through programs in education, health, and social services; to provide international exchange and foreign language programs; and to conduct science and technology education and basic and applied research. The total enrollment of all 7 campuses is about 30,000, with nearly 1500 faculty members. Altogether, there are 208 baccalaureate, 75 master's, and 23 doctoral programs offered within the system. Profiles of the 4-year campuses, located at Augusta, Farmington, Fort Kent, Machias, and Presque Isle are included in this chapter.

UNIVERSITY OF MAINE

Orono, ME 04469

C-4

(207) 581-1561

Full-time: 3938 men, 3428 women	Faculty: 630; I, --$
Part-time: 736 men, 1059 women	Ph.D.s: 64%
Graduate: 927 men, 1255 women	Student/Faculty: 12 to 1
Year: semesters, summer session	Tuition: $3405 ($8805)
Application Deadline: February 1	Room & Board: $4585
Freshman Class: 5036 applied, 4589 accepted, 1741 enrolled	
SAT I Verbal/Math: 464/525	COMPETITIVE

The University of Maine, established in 1865, is a publicly funded, land-grant institution in the University of Maine System. The school has 8 undergraduate colleges: College of Arts and Humanities, College of Business Administration, College of Engineering, College of Education, College of Sciences, College of Social and Behavioral Sciences, University College, and College of Natural Resources, Forestry, and Agriculture. There is one graduate school. In addition to regional accreditation, U Maine has baccalaureate program accreditation with AACSB, ABET, AHEA, CAHEA, CSWE, NASAD, NASM, NCATE, and SAF. The library contains 730,000 volumes and 11 million microform items, and subscribes to 6900 periodicals. Computerized library sources and services include database searching. The Maine Center for the Arts houses a concert hall, an art gallery, and a natural history museum. Other learning facilities include a planetarium, a radio station, a TV station, music facilities, and 2 theaters. The 3300-acre campus is in a small town 250 miles north of Boston. Including residence halls, there are 200 buildings on campus.

Student Life: About 83% of undergraduates are from Maine. Students come from 45 states, 74 foreign countries, and Canada. Eighty percent are from public schools; 20% from private. Ninety-six percent are white. The average age of freshmen is 18; all undergraduates, 21. Twenty-five percent drop out by the end of their first year; 75% remain to graduate.

Housing: A total of 4400 students can be accommodated in college housing. College-sponsored living facilities include single-sex and coed dormitories, on-campus apartments, off-campus apartments, and married-student housing. In addition, there are honors houses, language houses, and special interest houses. On-campus housing is guaranteed for the freshman year only and is available on a first-come, first-served basis. Sixty percent of students commute. Alcohol is not permitted. All students may keep cars on campus.

Activities: About 6% of men belong to 14 national fraternities; about 4% of women belong to 7 national sororities. There are 130 groups on campus, including band, cheerleading, chess, choir, chorale, chorus, computers, dance, drama, drill team, ethnic, film, gay, honors, international, jazz band, literary magazine, marching band, musical theater, newspaper, opera, orchestra, pep band, political, professional, radio and TV, religious, social, social service, student government, symphony, and yearbook. Popular campus events include Bumstock, Maine Day, Homecoming, and Family and Friends Weekend.

Sports: There are 10 intercollegiate sports for men and 7 for women, and 22 intramural sports for men and 21 for women. Athletic and recreation facilities include a sports arena (hockey and basketball), a fitness center, baseball, soccer, field hockey, and football fields, basketball and tennis courts, a swimming pool, a weight room, an indoor track, a dance studio, an archery range, and volleyball, badminton, squash, and racquetball courts.

Disabled Students: Seventy-five percent of the campus is accessible to disabled students. The following facilities are available: wheelchair ramps, elevators, special parking, specially equipped rest rooms, special class scheduling, and lowered drinking fountains.

Services: In addition to many counseling and information services, tutoring is available in some subjects, including 100 and 200 level courses. There is a reader service for the blind and developmental courses are offered in remedial mathematics, reading, and writing.

Campus Safety and Security: Campus safety and security measures include 24-hour foot and vehicle patrol, self-defense education, escort service, and informal discussions. In addition, there are pamphlets, posters, films, emergency telephones, and lighted pathways and sidewalks.

Programs of Study: U Maine awards the B.A. and B.S. degrees. Associate, master's, and doctoral degrees are also awarded. Bachelor's degrees are awarded in AGRICULTURE (agricultural business management, agriculture, animal science, fishing and fisheries, forest engineering, forestry and related sciences, horticulture, natural resource management, wildlife management, and wood science), BIOLOGICAL SCIENCE (biochemistry, biology/biological science, botany, microbiology, molecular biology, nutrition, and zoology), BUSINESS (business administration and management), COMMUNICATIONS AND THE ARTS (communications, English, French, German, journalism, Latin, modern language, music, romance languages, Spanish, and speech/debate/rhetoric), COMPUTER AND PHYSICAL SCIENCE (chemistry, computer science, geology, mathematics, and physics), EDUCATION (art, early childhood, elementary, health, mu-

sic, physical, and secondary), ENGINEERING AND ENVIRONMEN-
TAL DESIGN (bioengineering, chemical engineering, civil engineering, computer engineering, construction technology, electrical/
electronics engineering, engineering, engineering physics, engineering technology, mechanical engineering, paper and pulp science,
and surveying engineering), HEALTH PROFESSIONS (medical laboratory technology and nursing), SOCIAL SCIENCE (anthropology,
child psychology/development, economics, food science, history,
parks and recreation management, philosophy, political science/
government, psychology, public administration, social work, and sociology). Engineering and technology, business administration, and forest resources are the strongest academically. Business administration,
education, mechanical engineering, and forestry have the largest enrollments.

Required: A minimum of 120 credit hours with a minimum GPA of
2.0 is required for graduation. Seventy-two hours must be completed
in the student's major. The distribution and curricula requirements
vary with each undergraduate college. All students are required to
take English 101.

Special: A Professional Preparation Team program is offered by the
College of Education. Cross-registration through the National Student
Exchange, internships at the upper level, a Washington semester,
work-study programs both on and off campus, a B.A.-B.S. degree,
dual majors, a general studies degree, and pass/fail options are available. Students may study abroad in more than 40 countries. Cooperative programs are available in most majors, and accelerated degree
programs may be arranged. There is a freshman honors program on
campus, as well as 9 national honor societies, including Phi Beta Kappa. Seven departments have honors programs.

Faculty/Classroom: Sixty-nine percent of faculty are male; 31%, female. The average class size in an introductory lecture is 36; in a laboratory, 15; and in a regular course offering, 22.

Admissions: About 91% of the 1993–94 applicants were accepted.
The SAT scores for the 1993–94 freshman class were as follows: Verbal—69% below 500, 25% between 500 and 599, 5% between 600
and 700, and 1% above 700; Math—38% below 500, 40% between
500 and 599, 18% between 600 and 700, and 4% above 700. About
44% of the current freshmen were in the top fifth of their class; 73%
were in the top two fifths. There were 3 National Merit finalists. Seventeen freshmen graduated first in their class.

Requirements: U Maine requires applicants to be in the upper 50%
of their class. A minimum GPA of 2.5 is required. The SAT I or the
ACT is required. In addition, applicants must be graduates of an accredited secondary school or a school approved by the state of
Maine. The GED is accepted. The number of academic or Carnegie
credits required varies according to the program. The required secondary school courses also vary with each program but should include 4 credits of English, 3 credits of mathematics, and 2 credits
each of science, social studies, a foreign language, and 3 electives.
The school recommends that students submit an essay. An audition is
required for music majors. AP and CLEP credits are accepted. Important factors used in the admissions decision are advanced placement
or honor courses, recommendations by school officials, evidence of
special talent, parents or siblings attending the school, and extracurricular activities record.

Procedure: Freshmen are admitted fall and spring. Entrance exams
should be taken by January of the senior year. Early decision applications should be filed by November 30; regular applications, by February 1 for fall entry and November 1 for spring entry, along with an
application fee of $25. Notification is sent on a rolling basis. There are
early admissions and deferred admissions plans.

Transfer: About 600 transfer students enrolled in a recent year.
Transfer students must submit transcripts of all college and high
school records. A minimum GPA of 2.0 is required. A total of 30
credits out of 120 must be completed at U Maine.

Visiting: There are regularly scheduled orientations for prospective
students, including an opening welcome, classroom visits, campus
tours, advisor sessions, and registration. There are guides for informal
visits and visitors may stay overnight at the school. To arrange for a
visit, contact the Admissions Office at (207) 581-1572.

Financial Aid: In 1993–94, 50% of all current freshmen and 57%
of continuing students received need-based aid. The average freshman award was $2418. Of that total, scholarships or need-based
grants averaged $2418 ($4900 maximum); loans averaged $1240
($5125 maximum); and work contracts averaged $1000 ($1300 max-
imum). Thirty-six percent of undergraduate students work part-time.
Average earnings from campus work for the school year are $1127.
The average financial indebtedness of a recent graduate was $6735.
U Maine is a member of CSS. The FAF is required. The deadline for
financial aid applications is March 1.

International Students: There are currently 419 international students enrolled. The school actively recruits these students. They must
take the TOEFL and achieve a minimum score of 500. The student
must also take the SAT I or the ACT.

Computers: The college provides computer facilities for student use.
The mainframe is an IBM 3090 UM/CMS. There are 3 computer clusters on campus, and microcomputers are available in the residence
halls. All students may access the system. It may be used 24 hours per
day. There are no time limits on using the system and no fees.

Graduates: In a recent year, 1381 bachelor's degrees were awarded. Within an average freshman class, 29% graduate in 5 years and
21% in 6 years. Some 124 companies recruited on campus in a recent year. In the 1992 graduating class, 30% of all graduates were
enrolled in graduate school within 6 months of graduation.

Admissions Contact: William J. Munsey, Associate Director of Admissions.

UNIVERSITY OF MAINE AT AUGUSTA
B-5

Augusta, ME 04430   (207) 621-3185; (800) 696-6000 (in-state)

Full-time: 369 men, 473 women	Faculty: 66; III, av$
Part-time: 1489 men, 2749 women	Ph.D.s: 15%
Graduate: none	Student/Faculty: 13 to 1
Year: semesters, summer session	Tuition: $2595 ($6255)
Application Deadline: open	Room & Board: n/app
Freshman Class: 1935 applied, 1590 accepted, 1060 enrolled	
SAT I or ACT: not required	**NONCOMPETITIVE**

The University of Maine at Augusta, founded in 1965, is primarily a
commuter community college in the University of Maine system.
There are 6 undergraduate schools. In addition to regional accreditation, UMA has baccalaureate program accreditation with NLN. The library contains 42,000 volumes, 42,000 microform items, and 5000
audiovisual forms, and subscribes to 400 periodicals. Computerized
library sources and services include the card catalog, interlibrary
loans, and database searching. Special learning facilities include a
learning resource center, an art gallery, and an interactive television
system. The 165-acre campus is in a small town 50 miles north of Portland. There are 12 buildings on campus.

Student Life: About 99% of undergraduates are from Maine. Students come from 15 states and 5 foreign countries. Ninety-nine percent are from public schools; 1% from private. Nearly all are white.
The average age of freshmen is 27; all undergraduates, 32.5. Forty
percent drop out by the end of their first year; 30% remain to graduate.

Housing: There are no residence halls. All students commute. Alcohol is not permitted. All students may keep cars on campus.

Activities: About 1% of men and about 1% of women belong to 1
national fraternity. There are no sororities on campus. There are 25
groups on campus, including art, band, gay, honors, international,
jazz band, literary magazine, newspaper, and student government.
Popular campus events include UMA Day, a yearly breakfast, and
community lunches.

Sports: There is 1 intercollegiate sport for men, and 5 intramural
sports each for men and women. Athletic and recreation facilities include the UMA Community Outdoor Leisure Center, which is also
open to the public. Facilities provide for seasonal activities, and feature a running and cross-country skiing trail, tennis courts, a soccer
field, and a mini-gymnasium.

Disabled Students: Ninety-five percent of the campus is accessible
to disabled students. The following facilities are available: wheelchair
ramps, elevators, special parking, specially equipped rest rooms, special class scheduling, and lowered drinking fountains and telephones.

Services: In addition to many counseling and information services,
tutoring is available in some subjects. There is a reader service for the
blind, and remedial math, reading, and writing.

Campus Safety and Security: Campus safety and security measures include pamphlets, posters, films, and lighted pathways and
sidewalks.

Programs of Study: UMA awards the B.A., B.M., and B.S.B.A. degrees. Associate degrees also are awarded. Bachelor's degrees are
awarded in BUSINESS (accounting, business administration and management, and small business management), COMMUNICATIONS
AND THE ARTS (English and music), COMPUTER AND PHYSICAL
SCIENCE (mathematics), SOCIAL SCIENCE (social science). Business administration has the largest enrollment.

Required: All students must complete at least 120 hours, 131 for
B.M. students, with a minimum GPA of 2.0. All degree programs require courses in English and communications, humanities, mathematics and computer sciences, and social sciences. Specific course requirements differ by degree program.

Special: Work-study and internship programs with local employers,
a general studies degree, nondegree study, and pass/fail options are
available. UMA administers a displaced homemakers project, offering personal and professional development training and counseling.
There is one national honor society on campus, Phi Beta Kappa. One
department has an honors program.

Faculty/Classroom: Sixty percent of faculty are male; 40%, female.
All teach undergraduates. The average class size in an introductory
lecture and regular course offering is 30; in a laboratory, 15.

Admissions: About 82% of the 1993–94 applicants were accepted.
Requirements: Applicants should have a high school diploma or the GED. Recommended secondary preparation varies according to the degree program. Students are encouraged to submit SAT I scores for placement only. Applicants for the B.M. program must audition. AP and CLEP credits are accepted.
Procedure: Freshmen are admitted to all sessions. Entrance exams should be taken in November or January of the senior year. Early decision applications should be filed by November 1; regular applications are open for fall entry, along with an application fee of $25. The college accepts all applicants. Notification of early decision is sent December 1; regular decision, on a rolling basis. There are early decision, early admissions, and deferred admissions plans. A waiting list is an active part of the admissions procedure for nursing.
Transfer: About 240 transfer students enrolled in a recent year. A total of 30 credits out of 120 to 131 must be completed at UMA.
Visiting: There are regularly scheduled orientations for prospective students during the month before the beginning of a semester. There are guides for informal visits and visitors may sit in on classes. To arrange for a visit, contact the Admissions and Records Office at (207) 621–3465.
Financial Aid: In a recent year, 55% of all current freshmen and 20% of continuing students received some form of financial aid. About 55% of freshmen and 20% of continuing students received need-based aid. The average freshman award was $2300. Of that total, scholarships or need-based grants averaged $1500 ($4000 maximum); and loans averaged $1850 ($4000 maximum). Five percent of undergraduate students work part-time. Average earnings from campus work for the school year are $2500. The average financial indebtedness of a recent graduate was $2000. UMA is a member of CSS. The FAF is required. The deadline for financial aid applications is April 1.
Computers: The university provides computer facilities for student use. The mainframes are an IBM 3033 and 4381. Terminals are available at the Student Computer Center on the main campus and at off-campus locations. All students may access the system 8 A.M. to 9:45 P.M. There are no time limits on using the system. The fees are $2 per credit hour.
Graduates: In 1992–93, 211 bachelor's degrees were awarded. The most popular major among graduates was business administration (24%).
Admissions Contact: Clark Ketcham, Director of Enrollment Services.

UNIVERSITY OF MAINE AT FARMINGTON   B-4
Farmington, ME 04938–1990   (207) 778–7050

Full-time: 606 men, 1300 women	Faculty: 10; IIB, av$
Part-time: 87 men, 257 women	Ph.D.s: 82%
Graduate: none	Student/Faculty: 17 to 1
Year: semesters, summer session	Tuition: $2910 ($6750)
Application Deadline: April 15	Room & Board: $3790
Freshman Class: 1208 applied, 803 accepted, 438 enrolled	
SAT I Verbal/Math: 437/475	COMPETITIVE

The University of Maine at Farmington is a public institution offering programs in arts and sciences, teacher education and human services. There are 2 undergraduate schools. In addition to regional accreditation, UMF has baccalaureate program accreditation with NCATE. The library contains 114,059 volumes, 49,512 microform items, and 2985 audiovisual forms, and subscribes to 713 periodicals. Computerized library sources and services include the card catalog, interlibrary loans, and database searching. Special learning facilities include a learning resource center, art gallery, radio station, an instructional media center, and an archaeology research center. The 50-acre campus is in a small town 38 miles northwest of Augusta. Including residence halls, there are 35 buildings on campus.
Student Life: About 89% of undergraduates are from Maine. Students come from 18 states and 16 foreign countries. Eighty-eight percent are from public schools; 12% from private. Ninety-seven percent are white. The average age of freshmen is 18; all undergraduates, 23.9. Twenty-nine percent drop out by the end of their first year; 68% remain to graduate.
Housing: A total of 834 students can be accommodated in college housing. College-sponsored living facilities include single-sex and coed dormitories and on-campus apartments. In addition, there is an international guest house, a language floor, and a hall for the French immersion program. On-campus housing is guaranteed for all 4 years. Sixty-three percent of students commute. All students may keep cars on campus.
Activities: There are no fraternities or sororities on campus. There are 45 groups on campus, including band, cheerleading, choir, chorus, dance, drama, film, gay, honors, international, literary magazine, musical theater, newspaper, orchestra, pep band, photography, political, professional, radio and TV, religious, social, social service, student government, and yearbook. Popular campus events include Par-

ents and Alumni weekends, Winter Carnival Weekend, Women in History Month, and Visiting Author Series.
Sports: There are 4 intercollegiate sports for men and 5 for women, and 11 intramural sports for men and 11 for women. Athletic and recreation facilities include a 500-seat gymnasium, baseball, softball, and soccer fields, a field house with an indoor jogging track, 4 multipurpose courts, a swimming pool, a weight-training center, a ski area, and mountain climbing, canoeing, and white water rafting opportunities nearby.
Disabled Students: Fifty percent of the campus is accessible to disabled students. The following facilities are available: wheelchair ramps, elevators, special parking, specially equipped rest rooms, special class scheduling, lowered drinking fountains, lowered telephones, an accessible van, an accessible swimming pool, and TDD.
Services: In addition to many counseling and information services, tutoring is available in every subject. In addition, there is a reader service for the blind, and remedial math, reading, and writing.
Campus Safety and Security: Campus safety and security measures include 24-hour foot and vehicle patrol, self defense education, escort service, and informal discussions. In addition, there are pamphlets, posters, and films, emergency telephones, and lighted pathways and sidewalks.
Programs of Study: UMF awards the B.A. B.S., B.F.A., and B.G.S. degrees. Bachelor's degrees are awarded in BIOLOGICAL SCIENCE (biology), BUSINESS (business/economics), COMMUNICATIONS AND THE ARTS (creative writing, English, music/arts, theater/arts, and visual/performing arts), COMPUTER AND PHYSICAL SCIENCE (computer mathematics, geochemistry, geology/chemistry, and mathematics), EDUCATION (early childhood, elementary, English, health, mathematics, science, secondary, social science, special: emotional disturbances, special: learning disabilities, and speical: mental retardation), ENGINEERING AND ENVIRONMENTAL DESIGN (environmental science), HEALTH PROFESSIONS (rehabilitation services and speech pathology), SOCIAL SCIENCE (geography, history, international studies, liberal arts/general studies, political science/social science, psychology, and sociology/anthropology). Elementary education, secondary education, and interdisciplinary have the largest enrollments.
Required: All students must maintain a minimum GPA of 2.0 while earning 120 semester hours, including 30 in their major. Core requirements include a foreign language, 8 hours in science, 9 each in social and behavioral sciences and the humanities, 3 each in mathematics and health and physical education, 4 in English composition, and 1 in computer science.
Special: Study abroad in 4 countries, as well as numerous opportunities through the National Student Exchange program, work-study with UMF, and student-designed majors are permitted. Internships are required in rehabilitation and health and are available in many disciplines. Also possible are a 3–2 engineering program, a program of interdisciplinary field study in physical sciences, a ski industry certificate, a French immersion program, nondegree study, and pass/fail options. There is a freshman honors program on campus, as well as 6 national honor societies. All departments have honors programs.
Faculty/Classroom: Sixty-nine percent of faculty are male; 31%, female. All teach undergraduates. The average class size in an introductory lecture is 50; in a laboratory, 18; and in a regular course offering, 25.
Admissions: About 66% of the 1993–94 applicants were accepted.
Requirements: UMF requires applicants to be in the upper 50% of their class. Applicants are required to have 16 to 19 college preparatory courses, including 4 in English, 2 each in social science and foreign language, 3 to 4 in mathematics, 2 to 3 in laboratory science, and 3 electives. An essay is required and an interview recommended. A counselor recommendation is required. The GED is accepted for older, highly motivated students. AP and CLEP credits are accepted. Important factors used in the admissions decision are advanced placement or honor courses, college preparatory courses, rank in senior class, recommendations by school officials, and leadership record.
Procedure: Freshmen are admitted fall and spring. Early action applications should be filed by December 15; regular applications, by April 15 for fall entry, along with an application fee of $25. Notification of early action is sent January 7; regular decision, on a rolling basis. There are early action and deferred admissions plans.
Transfer: About 120 transfer students enrolled in 1993–94. Transfer applicants must have a minimum GPA of 2.0 (2.5 for some majors). At least 30 credits out of 120 must be completed at UMF.
Visiting: There are regularly scheduled orientations for prospective students, including sessions on financial aid, majors, and the admissions process. There are guides for informal visits and visitors may sit in on classes. To arrange for a visit, contact the Admissions Office at (207) 778–7050.
Financial Aid: In 1993–94, 65% of all current freshmen and 57% of continuing students received some form of financial aid. About 70% of freshmen received need-based aid. The average freshman

award was $4600. Twenty-seven percent of undergraduate students work part-time. Average earnings from campus work for the school year are $1100. The average financial indebtedness of the 1992–93 graduate was $9012. UMF is a member of CSS. The FAFSA financial statement is required. The deadline for financial aid applications is March 1.

International Students: There are currently 34 international students enrolled. The school actively recruits these students. They must take the TOEFL and achieve a minimum score of 520.

Computers: The university provides computer facilities for student use. The mainframes are an IBM 3090, an IBM PC-RT, and a SUN SPARC station 1+. There are 110 microcomputers, 76 of which are networked. Workstations are DOS-based. There are 4 dumb terminals. Nearly all are located in the Academic Computing Center. The rest are located in departmental student laboratories. Students may access Internet and Bitnet. All students may access the system 24 hours, 7 days, for most stations. There are no time limits on using the system. There is a $90 per year instruction-related technology fee.

Graduates: In 1992–93, 360 bachelor's degrees were awarded. The most popular majors among graduates were elementary education (27%), interdisciplinary (13%), and rehabilitation services (9%). Within an average freshman class, 40% graduate in 4 years and 68% in 5 years. Some 52 companies recruited on campus in 1992–93. In the 1992 graduating class, 4% of the men and 9% of the women were enrolled in graduate school within 6 months of graduation; 25% of the men and 60% of the women had found employment.

Admissions Contact: James Collins, Admissions Office.

UNIVERSITY OF MAINE AT FORT KENT D-1

Fort Kent, ME 04743   (207) 834–3162

Full-time: 207 men, 248 women	Faculty: 32; IIB, -$
Part-time: 58 men, 116 women	Ph.D.s: 53%
Graduate: none	Student/Faculty: 14 to 1
Year: semesters, summer session	Tuition: $2685 ($6435)
Application Deadline: August 15	Room & Board: $3600
Freshman Class: 202 applied, 146 accepted, 93 enrolled	
SAT I Verbal/Math: 430/390	LESS COMPETITIVE

The University of Maine at Fort Kent, founded in 1878, is a publicly funded liberal arts institution within the University of Maine system. In addition to regional accreditation, UMFK has baccalaureate program accreditation with NLN. The library contains 50,000 volumes and subscribes to 250 periodicals. Computerized library sources and services include the card catalog, interlibrary loans, and database searching. Special learning facilities include a learning resource center, radio station, greenhouse, and biological park. The 52-acre campus is in a small town 200 miles north of Bangor. Including residence halls, there are 14 buildings on campus.

Student Life: About 76% of undergraduates are from Maine. Students come from 9 states, 4 foreign countries, and Canada. Ninety-seven percent are white. The average age of all undergraduates is 27. Forty percent drop out by the end of their first year; 35% remain to graduate.

Housing: A total of 175 students can be accommodated in college housing. College-sponsored living facilities include coed dormitories. On-campus housing is available on a first-come, first-served basis. Eighty-two percent of students commute. Alcohol is not permitted. All students may keep cars on campus.

Activities: About 10% of men belong to 2 national fraternities; about 10% of women belong to 2 national sororities. There are 25 groups on campus, including cheerleading, chorale, chorus, computers, dance, drama, environmental, international, literary magazine, literature, musical theater, newspaper, outing, professional, radio and TV, religious, and student government. Popular campus events include French Heritage Festival, Spring Meltdown, and Winter Carnival.

Sports: There are 2 intercollegiate sports for men and 2 for women, and 9 intramural sports for men and 8 for women. Athletic and recreation facilities include a gymnasium, a multipurpose room, a soccer field, and game rooms in the residence halls.

Disabled Students: Seventy-five percent of the campus is accessible to disabled students. The following facilities are available: wheelchair ramps, elevators, special parking, specially equipped rest rooms, and special class scheduling.

Services: In addition to many counseling and information services, tutoring is available in every subject. There is also a reader service for the blind, and remedial math, reading, and writing.

Campus Safety and Security: Campus safety and security measures include informal discussions, pamphlets, posters, and films, and lighted pathways and sidewalks.

Programs of Study: UMFK awards the B.A., B.S., B.S.E.S., B.S.N., and B.U.S. degrees. Associate degrees also are awarded. Bachelor's degrees are awarded in BIOLOGICAL SCIENCE (biology/biological science), BUSINESS (business administration and management), COMMUNICATIONS AND THE ARTS (English and French), COMPUTER AND PHYSICAL SCIENCE (computer science and

mathematics), EDUCATION (elementary and middle school), ENGINEERING AND ENVIRONMENTAL DESIGN (environmental science), HEALTH PROFESSIONS (nursing), SOCIAL SCIENCE (behavioral science, crosscultural studies, history, liberal arts/general studies, and social science). Environmental studies, nursing, and biology are the strongest academically. Education, nursing, and behavioral science have the largest enrollments.

Required: A minimum GPA of 2.0 and a total of 120 to 128 credit hours are required for graduation. Curricula and distribution requirements vary according to the major.

Special: Internships required for business majors, a general studies degree, a B.A.-B.S. degree in bilingual-bicultural studies, credit for life experience, and nondegree study are available. Students may cross-register with the College Universitaire St. Louis Maillet in New Brunswick. Study abroad may be arranged in Canada, France, and Mexico through the University of Maine at Farmington. Interactive television courses broadcasted from other universities are available on campus. There is 1 national honor society on campus.

Faculty/Classroom: Fifty-six percent of faculty are male; 44%, female. All teach undergraduates.

Admissions: About 72% of the 1993–94 applicants were accepted. The SAT scores for the 1993–94 freshman class were as follows: Verbal—68% below 500, 27% between 500 and 599, and 5% between 600 and 700; Math—90% below 500 and 10% between 500 and 599. About 11% of the current freshmen were in the top fifth of their class; 39% were in the top two fifths.

Requirements: The SAT I is required. Applicants should be graduates of an accredited secondary school. The GED is accepted. Required secondary school courses include 4 years of English and 2 years each of social studies and science. A foreign language is suggested. An essay and an interview are recommended. AP and CLEP credits are accepted. Important factors used in the admissions decision are recommendations by school officials, advanced placement or honor courses, evidence of special talent, extracurricular activities record, and geographic diversity.

Procedure: Freshmen are admitted fall and spring. Entrance exams should be taken before March of the senior year. Early decision applications should be filed by December 15; regular applications, by August 15 for fall entry and January 10 for spring entry, along with an application fee of $25. Notification is sent on a rolling basis. There are early decision, early admissions, and deferred admissions plans.

Transfer: Transfer students must submit transcripts from each college and secondary school attended. The SAT I and an interview are recommended. A total of 30 credits out of 120 to 128 must be completed at UMFK.

Visiting: There are regularly scheduled orientations for prospective students, including placement testing, meetings with advisers, campus tours, and get-acquainted activities. There are guides for informal visits and visitors may sit in on classes and stay overnight at the school. To arrange for a visit, contact the Admissions Office at (207) 834–3162, ext. 135.

Financial Aid: In 1993–94, 90% of all students received some form of financial aid, including need-based aid. The average freshman award was $2570. Of that total, scholarships or need-based grants averaged $1473 ($5000 maximum); and work contracts averaged $1000 ($1500 maximum). Twenty-five percent of undergraduate students work part-time. Average earnings from campus work for the school year are $1000. The average financial indebtedness of the 1992–93 graduate was $5133. UMFK is a member of CSS. The FAF and income tax forms are required. The deadline for financial aid applications to ensure priority consideration is April 1.

International Students: There are currently 116 international students enrolled. They must take the TOEFL, SAT I, or the college's own test and achieve a minimum score on the TOEFL of 500.

Computers: The college provides computer facilities for student use. The mainframe is an AT&T 3B2/400. Microcomputers are available for student use in the dormitories, the library, and 2 computer centers. All students may access the system. It may be used from 8 A.M. to 11 P.M. in the library and computer centers, and 24 hours a day in the dormitories. There are no time limits on using the system. The fees are $5.

Graduates: In 1992–93, 112 bachelor's degrees were awarded. The most popular majors among graduates were education (34%), English (12%), and nursing (8%). Within an average freshman class, 35% graduate in 4 years, 37% in 5 years, and 38% in 6 years.

Admissions Contact: Jerald R. Nadeau, Director of Admissions.

UNIVERSITY OF MAINE AT MACHIAS
E-4

Machias, ME 04654   (207) 255-3313, ext. 318

Full-time: 225 men, 408 women	Faculty: 43; IIB, -$
Part-time: 89 men, 228 women	Ph.D.s: 44%
Graduate: none	Student/Faculty: 15 to 1
Year: semesters, summer session	Tuition: $2785 ($6535)
Application Deadline: open	Room & Board: $3530
Freshman Class: 441 applied, 367 accepted, 172 enrolled	
SAT I Verbal/Math: 440/470	**COMPETITIVE**

The University of Maine at Machias, founded in 1909, is a publicly funded liberal arts institution in the University of Maine System. In addition to regional accreditation, UMM has baccalaureate program accreditation with NRPA. The library contains 82,089 volumes, 3501 microform items, and 1562 audiovisual forms, and subscribes to 524 periodicals. Computerized library sources and services include the card catalog and database searching. Special learning facilities include a learning resource center, art gallery, and aquariums for marine and aquaculture studies. The 47-acre campus is in a rural area 85 miles east of Bangor. Including residence halls, there are 8 buildings on campus.

Student Life: About 74% of undergraduates are from Maine. Students come from 21 states, 16 foreign countries, and Canada. Ninety-eight percent are from public schools; 2% from private. Ninety-six percent are white. The average age of freshmen is 20; all undergraduates, 26.5.

Housing: A total of 310 students can be accommodated in college housing. College-sponsored living facilities include single-sex and coed dormitories. On-campus housing is guaranteed for all 4 years. Sixty-seven percent of students commute. All students may keep cars on campus.

Activities: About 3% of men belong to 1 local and 1 national fraternity; about 2% of women belong to 2 local sororities and 1 national sorority. There are 25 groups on campus, including art, cheerleading, chorus, computers, dance, drama, honors, international, literary magazine, newspaper, photography, professional, religious, social service, student government, and yearbook. Popular campus events include Homecoming, Winter Carnival, Family Christmas Party, Spring Family Event, Spring Weekend, and Coffee House Events.

Sports: There are 3 intercollegiate sports for men and 2 for women, and 15 intramural sports for men and 12 for women. Athletic and recreation facilities include a gymnasium, a weight room, and a 64-acre recreational center.

Disabled Students: Sixty-five percent of the campus is accessible to disabled students. The following facilities are available: wheelchair ramps, elevators, special parking, and specially equipped rest rooms.

Services: In addition to many counseling and information services, tutoring is available in every subject. In addition, there is remedial math, reading, and writing.

Campus Safety and Security: Campus safety and security measures include informal discussions, lighted pathways and sidewalks, a keyless entry system for residence halls, and security patrol from 5 P.M. to 1 P.M. Sunday to Wednesday and from 5 p.m to 5 A.M. Thursday to Saturday.

Programs of Study: UMM awards the B.A. and B.S. degrees. Associate degrees also are awarded. Bachelor's degrees are awarded in BIOLOGICAL SCIENCE (biology/biological science and marine biology), BUSINESS (accounting, business administration and management, marketing/retailing/merchandising, and recreation management), COMMUNICATIONS AND THE ARTS (English), EDUCATION (business, early childhood, elementary, health, middle school, and secondary), ENGINEERING AND ENVIRONMENTAL DESIGN (environmental studies), SOCIAL SCIENCE (behavioral science, history, human services, psychology, social science, and social work). Elementary education, marine biology, and environmental studies are the strongest programs academically. Elementary education, marine biology, environmental studies, and business administration have the largest enrollments.

Required: A minimum of 120 credit hours and a GPA of 2.0 are required for graduation. All students must complete the core requirements of 9 credits in English, 6 in history, 4 each in arts and laboratory science, 3 each in interdisciplinary studies, computer science, and mathematics beyond algebra II, and 2 in physical education.

Special: Co-op programs, cross-registration, internships, work-study programs, an accelerated degree program, a B.A.-B.S. degree, and a general studies degree are available. The school also offers student-designed majors, credit for life experience, nondegree study, and a pass/fail option in certain courses. There is a transfer program in community health education with the University of Maine at Farmington. There is a freshman honors program on campus.

Faculty/Classroom: Sixty-two percent of faculty are male; 38%, female. All teach undergraduates. The average class size in an introductory lecture is 25; in a laboratory, 18; and in a regular course offering, 14.

Admissions: About 83% of the 1993-94 applicants were accepted. Two freshmen graduated first in their class.

Requirements: UMM requires applicants to be in the upper 50% of their class. A minimum GPA of 2.6 is required. The SAT I is required, with a minimum composite score of 900, and the ACT, with a minimum composite score of 22, is recommended. All candidates must be graduates of an accredited secondary school. The GED is accepted. Required secondary school courses include 4 years of English, 3 each of social science and mathematics, and 2 of laboratory science. Two years of foreign language, an essay, and an interview are strongly recommended. AP and CLEP credits are accepted. Important factors used in the admissions decision are advanced placement or honor courses, evidence of special talent, leadership record, recommendations by school officials, and personality, intangible qualities.

Procedure: Freshmen are admitted in the fall and spring. Application deadlines are open. Application fee is $25. Notification is sent on a rolling basis. There are early admissions and deferred admissions plans.

Transfer: About 88 transfer students enrolled in 1993-94. A minimum college GPA of 2.0 and evidence of good standing are required of transfer students. A total of 30 credits out of 120 must be completed at UMM.

Visiting: There are regularly scheduled orientations for prospective students, consisting of programs just prior to fall and spring semesters. There are guides for informal visits and visitors may sit in on classes and stay overnight at the school. To arrange for a visit, contact the Admissions Intern at (207) 255-3313, ext. 318.

Financial Aid: In a recent year, 65% of all students received some form of financial aid, including need-based aid. The average freshman award was $2500. Of that total, scholarships or need-based grants averaged $1500 ($4000 maximum); loans averaged $300 ($4000 maximum); and work contracts averaged $700 ($1000 maximum). Eighty-five percent of undergraduate students work part-time. Average earnings from campus work for the school year are $800. The average financial indebtedness of a recent year's graduate was $2500. UMM is a member of CSS. The FAF and FAFSA are required. The deadline for financial aid applications is March 1.

International Students: There are currently 81 international students enrolled. The school actively recruits these students. They must take the TOEFL or the college's own test and achieve a minimum score on the TOEFL of 500.

Computers: The college provides computer facilities for student use. The mainframes are an IBM 3090-180E/VF and an IBM 4341, linked to an AT&T 3132/400 and 500 microcomputer network. Students have access to 2 major laboratories and 2 clusters of MS-DOS microcomputers as well as 1 laboratory of Macintosh microcomputers. Machines are all on interconnected lines for fileservers and mailservers. All students have access to the mainframe as well as to Internet resources. All students may access the system. It may be used from 8 A.M. to 10 P.M. and by request. There are no time limits on using the system and no fees.

Graduates: In a recent year, 66 bachelor's degrees were awarded. The most popular majors among graduates were education (30%), business (30%), and English (10%). Within an average freshman class, 1% graduate in 3 years, 30% in 4 years, 15% in 5 years, and 5% in 6 years. Ten companies recruited on campus in a recent year. In an earlier year's graduating class, 90% of the men and 75% of the women had found employment within 6 months of graduation.

Admissions Contact: David P. Baldwin, Director of Admissions.

UNIVERSITY OF MAINE AT PRESQUE ISLE
D-2

Presque Isle, ME 04769   (207) 764-0311

Full-time: 1004 men and women	Faculty: 66
Part-time: 450 men and women	Ph.D.s: 64%
Graduate: none	Student/Faculty: 15 to 1
Year: semesters, summer session	Tuition: $3010 ($6760)
Application Deadline: August 15	Room & Board: $3364
Freshman Class: 523 applied, 378 accepted, 222 enrolled	
SAT I: required	**COMPETITIVE**

The University of Maine at Presque Isle, founded in 1903, is a public, coeducational, 3-campus institution within the University of Maine system. Interactive television connects the 3 campuses. There is one graduate school. In addition to regional accreditation, UM-Presque Isle has baccalaureate program accreditation with NRPA. The library contains 116,700 volumes and subscribes to 930 periodicals. Computerized library sources and services include the card catalog, interlibrary loans, and database searching. Special learning facilities include a learning resource center, art gallery, radio station, TV station, and theater. The 150-acre campus is in a rural area 150 miles north of Bangor. Including residence halls, there are 10 buildings on campus.

Student Life: About 92% of undergraduates are from Maine. Students come from 10 states and 8 foreign countries. Ninety percent are from public schools; 10% from private. Eighty-nine percent are white. Fifty-five percent are Catholic; 27% Protestant; 10% claim no religious affiliation. Forty-five percent drop out by the end of their first year; 28% remain to graduate.

Housing: A total of 350 students can be accommodated in college housing. College-sponsored living facilities include dormitories and on-campus apartments. On-campus housing is guaranteed for all 4 years. Seventy-nine percent of students commute. Alcohol is not permitted. All students may keep cars on campus.

Activities: There are 5 national fraternities and 5 national sororities. There are 17 groups on campus, including art, cheerleading, chess, choir, drama, honors, international, literary magazine, musical theater, newspaper, pep band, political, professional, radio, religious, social service, student government, and yearbook.

Sports: There are 4 intercollegiate sports for men and 4 for women, and 10 intramural sports for men and 10 for women. Athletic and recreation facilities include a multifunctional structure that houses a gymnasium, a weight room, physical education laboratories, a sports medicine facility, a student lounge, and an auditorium. A large playing field contains baseball, soccer, and field hockey areas and tennis courts. There are also hiking trails and a bike path.

Disabled Students: Ten percent of the campus is accessible to disabled students. The following facilities are available: wheelchair ramps, elevators, special parking, specially equipped rest rooms, and special class scheduling.

Services: In addition to many counseling and information services, tutoring is available in most subjects. There is a reader service for the blind, and remedial math, reading, and writing.

Campus Safety and Security: Campus safety and security measures include escort service, pamphlets, posters, and films, and lighted pathways and sidewalks.

Programs of Study: UM-Presque Isle awards the B.A., B.S., B.F.A., B.L.S., and B.S.W. degrees. Associate and master's degrees also are awarded. Bachelor's degrees are awarded in BIOLOGICAL SCIENCE (biology/biological science), BUSINESS (accounting, business administration and management, and recreation and leisure services), COMMUNICATIONS AND THE ARTS (dramatic arts, English, French, and speech/debate/rhetoric), COMPUTER AND PHYSICAL SCIENCE (mathematics), EDUCATION (art, elementary, English, foreign languages, health, mathematics, physical, science, secondary, and social science), ENGINEERING AND ENVIRONMENTAL DESIGN (environmental science), SOCIAL SCIENCE (behavioral science, history, humanities, political science/government, social science, and sociology). Education has the largest enrollment.

Required: Core requirements for the B.A. degree include 18 credits in humanities, 12 in social science, 10 in mathematics/science, and 3 in physical education/health. The student must complete a minimum of 60 credits in the major, with a cumulative GPA of 2.0 in 120 credit hours. Requirements for the B.S. and other degrees vary considerably with each major.

Special: The university participates in transfer programs in agriculture, physical science, and engineering with the University of Maine at Orono. There is also cross-registration with Northern Maine Technical College, study abroad in France, Ireland, and Canada, and internships in many majors. UM-Presque Isle offers work-study programs, dual and student-designed majors, and nondegree study. Students can apply for credit by examination and credit for life, military, and work experience. A credit/no credit option is available. There is a freshman honors program on campus.

Faculty/Classroom: Sixty-four percent of faculty are male; 36%, female. All teach undergraduates. The average class size in an introductory lecture is 22.

Admissions: About 72% of the 1993-94 applicants were accepted. There were 2 National Merit semifinalists.

Requirements: The SAT I is required. Applicants should have completed 16 academic credits at an accredited secondary school, including 4 in English, 2 each in mathematics, science, and social studies, and the rest in electives. A GED certificate may be substituted. The university recommends an essay and an interview for all candidates. Art majors must submit a portfolio. AP and CLEP credits are accepted. Important factors used in the admissions decision are advanced placement or honor courses, evidence of special talent, recommendations by school officials, leadership record, and extracurricular activities record.

Procedure: Freshmen are admitted to all sessions. Entrance exams should be taken by January 1. Applications should be filed by August 15 for fall entry and January 1 for spring entry, along with an application fee of $25. Notification is sent on a rolling basis. There are early decision, early admissions, and deferred admissions plans.

Transfer: About 214 transfer students enrolled in 1993-94. A GPA of 2.0 from an accredited college or university is required. It is recommended that applicants submit SAT I scores and arrange an interview. A total of 30 credits out of 120 must be completed at UM-Presque Isle.

Visiting: There are regularly scheduled orientations for prospective students. There are guides for informal visits, and visitors may sit in on classes. To arrange for a visit, contact Bev McAvaddy at (207) 764-0311, ext. 385.

Financial Aid: In 1993-94, 85% of all current freshmen and 75% of continuing students received some form of financial aid, including need-based aid. The average freshman award was $4064. UM-Presque Isle is a member of CSS. The FAF is required. The deadline for financial aid applications is June 1.

International Students: There are currently 70 international students enrolled. The school actively recruits these students. They must take the TOEFL and achieve a minimum score of 500.

Computers: The college provides computer facilities for student use. Apple and IBM microcomputers are available in the computer laboratory. Those students taking computer courses may access the system. There are no time limits on using the system and no fees.

Graduates: In 1992-93 170 bachelor's degrees were awarded. Some 10 companies recruited on campus in an earlier year.

Admissions Contact: Dr. Gerald Wuori, Director of Admission.

UNIVERSITY OF NEW ENGLAND
A-6

Biddeford, ME 04005   (207) 283-0171; (800) 477-4UNE (in-state)

Full-time: 229 men, 569 women	**Faculty:** 69; IIA, --$
Part-time: 15 men, 32 women	**Ph.D.s:** 56%
Graduate: 266 men, 322 women	**Student/Faculty:** 12 to 1
Year: 4-1-4, summer session	**Tuition:** $11,200
Application Deadline: see profile	**Room & Board:** $4875
Freshman Class: 978 applied, 833 accepted, 314 enrolled	
SAT I Verbal/Math: 430/470	**LESS COMPETITIVE**

The University of New England, founded in 1953, is a small, private coeducational institution offering undergraduate and graduate programs in liberal arts and sciences, education, and health professions. In addition to regional accreditation, UNE has baccalaureate program accreditation with APTA, CSWE, and NLN. The library contains 90,000 volumes, 5150 microform items, and 930 audiovisual forms, and subscribes to 800 periodicals. Computerized library sources and services include interlibrary loans and database searching. Special learning facilities include a learning resource center and video studio. The 125-acre campus is in a rural area 16 miles south of Portland. Including residence halls, there are 27 buildings on campus.

Student Life: About 57% of undergraduates are from Maine. Students come from 28 states, 4 foreign countries, and Canada. Ninety-eight percent are white. The average age of freshmen is 19; all undergraduates, 22. Fifteen percent drop out by the end of their first year.

Housing: A total of 380 students can be accommodated in college housing. College-sponsored living facilities include single-sex and coed dormitories, on-campus apartments, off-campus apartments, and married-student housing. In addition, there are special interest houses and a wellness house. On-campus housing is guaranteed for the freshman and sophomore years. Sixty percent of students commute. Upperclassmen and second-semester freshmen may keep cars on campus.

Activities: There are no fraternities or sororities on campus. There are 14 groups on campus, including cheerleading, chorale, drama, gay, honors, international, musical theater, newspaper, professional, religious, social, social service, student government, and yearbook. Popular campus events include Spring Fling, fall and spring semiformal dances, and a student-faculty variety show.

Sports: There are 4 intercollegiate sports for men and 5 for women, and 4 intramural sports for men and 4 for women. Athletic and recreation facilities include a 1500-seat gymnasium, a fitness center, a pool, racquetball courts, soccer and softball fields, and outdoor volleyball facilities.

Disabled Students: Eighty-five percent of the campus is accessible to disabled students. The following facilities are available: wheelchair ramps, elevators, special parking, specially equipped rest rooms, special class scheduling, lowered drinking fountains, lowered telephones, and stair climbers.

Services: In addition to many counseling and information services, tutoring is available in every subject. There is a reader service for the blind, and remedial math, reading, and writing, as well as a complete learning assistance center and a special program for the learning disabled.

Campus Safety and Security: Campus safety and security measures include 24-hour foot and vehicle patrol, escort service, shuttle buses, and informal discussions. In addition, there are pamphlets, posters, films, and lighted pathways and sidewalks. A safe-ride program provides drivers for students.

Programs of Study: UNE awards the B.A. and B.S. degrees. Associate, master's, and doctoral degrees also are awarded. Bachelor's degrees are awarded in BIOLOGICAL SCIENCE (biology/biological science and marine biology), BUSINESS (business adminis-

tration and management and sports management), EDUCATION (elementary, science, and secondary), ENGINEERING AND ENVIRONMENTAL DESIGN (environmental science), HEALTH PROFESSIONS (biomedical science, health care administration, medical laboratory technology, nursing, occupational therapy, physical therapy, predentistry, premedicine, and prepharmacy), SOCIAL SCIENCE (prelaw and psychology). Health professions and life sciences are the strongest programs academically and have the largest enrollments.

Required: A total of 129 credits with a minimum GPA of 2.0 is required for graduation. Students must take 41 credits in a liberal arts core curriculum of humanities, sciences, and social sciences, as well as 3 short winter-term courses of 3 credits each that allow for off-campus and nontraditional study. Most majors require 1-semester internships. Courses in English composition, computer science, and Western traditions are required.

Special: UNE offers cross-registration with the Greater Portland Alliance of Colleges and Universities, internships in all majors, work-study programs, study abroad, student-designed and dual majors in all departments, and a 3-4 medical program. The Freshmen Biology Learning Community provides combined studies in English and life sciences. There is one national honor society on campus.

Faculty/Classroom: Forty-nine percent of faculty are male; 51%, female. All teach undergraduates. No introductory courses are taught by graduate students. The average class size in an introductory lecture is 35; in a laboratory, 20; and in a regular course offering, 20.

Admissions: About 85% of the 1993-94 applicants were accepted. The SAT scores for the 1993-94 freshman class were as follows: Verbal—80% below 500, 17% between 500 and 599, and 3% between 600 and 700; Math—62% below 500, 29% between 500 and 599, and 9% between 600 and 700.

Requirements: The SAT I or ACT is required. Applicants should be high school graduates with 4 years of English, 3 years each of mathematics and science, and 2 years each of history and social studies. The GED is accepted. A personal interview is recommended. AP and CLEP credits are accepted. Important factors used in the admissions decision are advanced placement or honor courses, leadership record, personality, intangible qualities, extracurricular activities record, and recommendations by school officials.

Procedure: Freshmen are admitted in the fall and spring. Entrance exams should be taken in the spring of the junior year or the fall of the senior year. Regular application deadlines are open, except for the physical therapy applicant deadline of February 15. Early decision applications should be filed by November 15, along with an application fee of $30. Notification of early decision is sent December 15; regular decision is sent on a rolling basis. There are early decision, early admissions, and deferred admissions plans. A waiting list is an active part of the admissions procedure, with about 9% of all applicants on the list.

Transfer: Twenty-eight transfer students enrolled in a recent year. Transfer applicants should present a GPA of at least 2.5 in college work. An interview is recommended. At least 30 credits out of 129 must be completed at UNE.

Visiting: There are regularly scheduled orientations for prospective students, including a tour and information session, and an interview if the student has formally applied. There are guides for informal visits, and visitors may sit in on classes and stay overnight at the school. To arrange for a visit, contact the Admissions Office at (207) 283-0171, ext. 297.

Financial Aid: In 1993-94, about 82% of freshmen received need-based aid. The average freshman award was $7000. Of that total, scholarships or need-based grants averaged $1200 ($5500 maximum); loans averaged $3000 ($5625 maximum); and work contracts averaged $900 ($1600 maximum). Fifty percent of undergraduate students work part-time. Average earnings from campus work for the school year are $900. The average financial indebtedness of the 1992-93 graduate was $11,000. UNE is a member of CSS. The FAFSA financial statement is required.

International Students: There are currently 4 international students enrolled. They must take the TOEFL and achieve a minimum score of 500.

Computers: The college provides computer facilities for student use. The mainframe is a Data General C/7800. There are 32 microcomputers available in the main academic building and the library. There are no time limits on using the system and no fees.

Graduates: In 1992-93, 116 bachelor's degrees were awarded. The most popular majors among graduates were physical therapy (29%), occupational therapy (26%), and biology (16%). Within an average freshman class, 60% graduate in 4 years and 2% in 5 years. Some 80 companies recruited on campus in a recent year.

Admissions Contact: Patricia T. Cribby, Dean of Admissions.

UNIVERSITY OF SOUTHERN MAINE

B-6

Gorham, ME 04038   (207) 780-5670; (800) 800-4876

Full-time: 1691 men, 1965 women	Faculty: 312; IIA, av$
Part-time: 1701 men, 2456 women	Ph.D.s: 68%
Graduate: 584 men, 1125 women	Student/Faculty: 12 to 1
Year: semesters, summer session	Tuition: $3080 ($8360)
Application Deadline: July 15	Room & Board: $4219

Freshman Class: 2335 applied, 1933 accepted, 905 enrolled
SAT I Verbal/Math: 440/500   COMPETITIVE

The University of Southern Maine, founded in 1878, is a publicly funded multicampus liberal arts institution serving the University of Maine system. There are 6 undergraduate schools and 7 graduate programs with locations in Portland, Gorham, and Lewiston-Auburn. In addition to regional accreditation, USM has baccalaureate program accreditation with ABET, CSWE, NCATE, and NLN. The 2 libraries contain 342,278 volumes, 948,524 microform items, and 3116 audiovisual forms, and subscribe to 2486 periodicals. Computerized library sources and services include the card catalog, interlibrary loans, and database searching. Special learning facilities include a learning resource center, art gallery, planetarium, radio station, TV station, and cartography collections. The 126-acre campus is in a small town 110 miles north of Boston, Massachusetts, and 10 miles west of the urban Portland campus. Including residence halls, there are 59 buildings on campus.

Student Life: About 94% of undergraduates are from Maine. Students come from 16 states, 25 foreign countries, and Canada. Ninety-eight percent are white. The average age of all undergraduates is 27.

Housing: A total of 1332 students can be accommodated in college housing. College-sponsored living facilities include coed dormitories, on-campus apartments, married-student housing, and fraternity houses. In addition, there is a fine arts house and the Plus Program, in which students all live together, take 2 classes together, and have study groups and workshops. On-campus housing is guaranteed for all 4 years. Eighty-seven percent of students commute. All students may keep cars on campus.

Activities: There is 1 local fraternity and 4 national fraternities and 2 local and 2 national sororities. There are 60 groups on campus, including art, band, cheerleading, chess, choir, chorale, chorus, computers, dance, drama, ethnic, film, gay, honors, international, jazz band, literary magazine, musical theater, newspaper, opera, orchestra, photography, political, professional, radio and TV, religious, social, social service, student government, and yearbook. Popular campus events include Children's Holiday Party, Alcohol Awareness Week, Winter Carnival, and New Student Welcome.

Sports: There are 5 intercollegiate sports for men and 5 for women, and 13 intramural sports for men and 13 for women. Athletic and recreation facilities include gymnasiums, tennis courts, athletic fields, racquetball and squash courts, cross-country ski trails, and weight training and exercise facilities.

Disabled Students: Most of the campus is accessible to disabled students. The following facilities are available: wheelchair ramps, elevators, special parking, specially equipped rest rooms, special class scheduling, lowered drinking fountains, and lowered telephones.

Services: In addition to many counseling and information services, tutoring is available in some subjects, including English, mathematics, and introductory-level courses. In addition, there is a reader service for the blind, and remedial math, reading, and writing.

Campus Safety and Security: Campus safety and security measures include 24-hour foot and vehicle patrol, escort service, shuttle buses, and informal discussions. In addition, there are pamphlets, posters, and films, emergency telephones, and lighted pathways and sidewalks.

Programs of Study: USM awards the B.A., B.S., B.F.A., and B.Mus. degrees. Associate and master's degrees also are awarded. Bachelor's degrees are awarded in BIOLOGICAL SCIENCE (biology/biological science), BUSINESS (accounting, business administration and management, and business economics), COMMUNICATIONS AND THE ARTS (communications, English, fine arts, French, music, music performance, and theater), COMPUTER AND PHYSICAL SCIENCE (chemistry, computer science, geology, mathematics, and physics), EDUCATION (applied technical/leadership, music, and technology), ENGINEERING AND ENVIRONMENTAL DESIGN (electrical/electronics engineering, environmental science and policy, and industrial technology), HEALTH PROFESSIONS (nursing and therapeutic recreation), SOCIAL SCIENCE (criminal justice, economics, geography/anthropology, history, philosophy, political science/government, psychology, social work, and sociology). Electrical engineering, computer science, and nursing are the strongest academically. Business administration, nursing, psychology, English, and criminology have the largest enrollments.

Required: A total of 120 hours, with a minimum GPA of 2.0 and 36 to 94 hours in the major, is required for graduation. All students must fulfill the distribution requirements of the 3-part core curriculum: basic

competence, methods of inquiry and ways of knowing, and interdisciplinary studies.

Special: Cross-registration within the University of Maine system and 5 Greater Portland colleges, a Washington semester, and study abroad in more than 12 countries are offered. Internships, co-op and work-study programs, a B.A.-B.S. degree, dual and student-designed majors, credit for life experience, nondegree study, and pass/fail options are also available. There is a January intersession. There is a freshman honors program on campus, as well as 11 national honor societies, including Phi Beta Kappa. Nine departments have honors programs.

Faculty/Classroom: Sixty-eight percent of faculty are male; 32%, female. Eighty percent teach undergraduates and all do research. Graduate students teach 1% of introductory courses. The average class size in an introductory lecture is 50; in a laboratory, 20; and in a regular course offering, 25.

Admissions: About 83% of the 1993–94 applicants were accepted. The SAT scores for the 1993–94 freshman class were as follows: Verbal—76% below 500, 19% between 500 and 599, 4% between 600 and 700, and 1% above 700; Math—47% below 500, 41% between 500 and 599, 11% between 600 and 700, and 1% above 700. About 28% of the current freshmen were in the top fifth of their class; 65% were in the top two fifths.

Requirements: USM requires applicants to be in the upper 50% of their class. The SAT I or ACT is required. In addition, applicants must be graduates of an accredited secondary school. The GED is accepted. Either 41 academic credits or 20 1/2 Carnegie units are required. Secondary school courses should include 4 years of English, 3 of mathematics, 2 each of a foreign language and laboratory science, and 1 each of history and social studies. An essay is required, as are auditions for music applicants and interviews for applicants to the School of Applied Science. AP and CLEP credits are accepted. Important factors used in the admissions decision are advanced placement or honor courses, leadership record, recommendations by school officials, evidence of special talent, and personality, intangible qualities.

Procedure: Freshmen are admitted fall and spring. Entrance exams should be taken between May of the junior year and January of the senior year. Applications should be filed by July 15 for fall entry (February 1 for nursing students) and December 1 for spring entry, along with an application fee of $25. Notification is sent on a rolling basis. There is an early admissions plan.

Transfer: A total of 728 transfer students enrolled in 1993–94. Transfer applicants must have a minimum GPA of 2.0; 2.75 from non-regionally accredited institutions. Students who have fewer than 30 college credits or who have been out of high school for less than 3 years must submit SAT I scores. A total of 30 credits out of 120 must be completed at USM.

Visiting: There are regularly scheduled orientations for prospective students, including group information sessions and tours by appointment. There are guides for informal visits and visitors may sit in on classes and stay overnight at the school. To arrange for a visit, contact the Admissions Office at (207) 780–5670.

Financial Aid: In 1993–94, 60% of all students received some form of financial aid. About 58% of students received need-based aid. The average freshman award was $4200. Of that total, scholarships or need-based grants averaged $1500 ($4000 maximum); loans averaged $750 ($2250 maximum); and work contracts averaged $750 ($1800 maximum). Eighty percent of undergraduate students work part-time. Average earnings from campus work for the school year are $1200. The average financial indebtedness of the 1992–93 graduate was $7000. USM is a member of CSS. The college's own financial statement and FAFSA are required. The FAT is required for students transferring from another college or vocational school. The deadline for financial aid applications is March 1.

International Students: There are currently 70 international students enrolled. They must take the TOEFL and achieve a minimum score of 500. The student must also take the SAT I or the ACT.

Computers: The university provides computer facilities for student use. The mainframe is an IBM 4341. The mainframe is linked to the Bitnet and the Internet networks. There are about 1000 terminals and microcomputers, 250 available for student use. All students may access the system 24 hours per day. There are no time limits on using the system and no fees.

Graduates: Some 45 companies recruited on campus in 1992–93.

Admissions Contact: Susan Roberts, Director of Admissions.

WESTBROOK COLLEGE
B-6

Portland, ME 04103

(207) 797–7261

Full-time: 48 men, 216 women	Faculty: 47; III, --$
Part-time: 22 men, 68 women	Ph.D.s: n/av
Graduate: none	Student/Faculty: 6 to 1
Year: semesters	Tuition: $11,000
Application Deadline: open	Room & Board: $4900

Freshman Class: 249 applied, 181 accepted, 72 enrolled

SAT I Verbal/Math: 406/438

COMPETITIVE

Westbrook College, founded in 1831, is a private, coeducational undergraduate institution offering degree programs in health sciences, business, education, and the arts and sciences. In addition to regional accreditation, Westbrook has baccalaureate program accreditation with ADA and NLN. The library contains 50,000 volumes, 1600 microform items, and 1650 audiovisual forms, and subscribes to 500 periodicals. Computerized library sources and services include interlibrary loans and database searching. Special learning facilities include a learning resource center, an art gallery, a laboratory school, a dental hygiene clinic, and the Maine Women Writers Collection. The 50-acre campus is in a suburban area 100 miles north of Boston. Including residence halls, there are 20 buildings on campus.

Student Life: About 68% of undergraduates are from Maine. Students come from 15 states, 6 foreign countries, and Canada. Ninety percent are from public schools; 10% from private. Almost all are white. Fifty-seven percent are Catholic; 42% Protestant. The average age of freshmen is 18; all undergraduates, 21.

Housing: A total of 450 students can be accommodated in college housing. College-sponsored living facilities include dormitories. On-campus housing is guaranteed for all 4 years. Sixty percent of students live on campus. All students may keep cars on campus.

Activities: There are no fraternities or sororities on campus. There are 15 groups on campus, including art, cheerleading, computers, drama, international, musical theater, newspaper, professional, social, social service, student government, and yearbook.

Sports: Athletic and recreation facilities include an athletic center and outdoor soccer and softball fields.

Disabled Students: The following facilities are available: wheelchair ramps, special parking, specially equipped rest rooms, special class scheduling, lowered drinking fountains, and lowered telephones.

Services: In addition to many counseling and information services, tutoring is available in most subjects. There is also remedial math, reading, and writing.

Campus Safety and Security: Campus safety and security measures include 24-hour foot and vehicle patrol, escort service, informal discussions, and lighted pathways and sidewalks.

Programs of Study: Westbrook awards the B.A. and B.S. degrees. Associate degrees also are awarded. Bachelor's degrees are awarded in BUSINESS (accounting, business administration and management, and marketing/retailing/merchandising), COMMUNICATIONS AND THE ARTS (English), EDUCATION (early childhood and elementary), HEALTH PROFESSIONS (dental hygiene, medical laboratory technology, and nursing). Dental hygiene, business, and nursing are the strongest academically and have the largest enrollments.

Required: To graduate, students must complete 120 to 123 credit hours with a GPA of 2.0. A total of 60 to 62 credit hours must be taken in the common core arts and sciences distribution, along with a course in computer science.

Special: A co-op program is offered in nursing, and internships are available in every major. There is one national honor society on campus.

Faculty/Classroom: Seventy percent of faculty are male; 30%, female. All teach undergraduates. The average class size in an introductory lecture is 25; in a laboratory, 20; and in a regular course offering, 18.

Admissions: About 73% of the 1993–94 applicants were accepted. About 27% of the current freshmen were in the top fifth of their class; 62% were in the top two fifths. Two freshmen graduated first in their class.

Requirements: Westbrook requires applicants to be in the upper 45% of their class. A minimum GPA of 2.5 is required. The SAT I or ACT is required. In addition, applicants should be graduates of an accredited secondary school. The GED is accepted. Sixteen academic credits are required, including 4 years of English, 3 of mathematics, 2 each of science, social studies, foreign language, and academic electives and 1 of history. All candidates must submit an essay and recommendations. An interview is encouraged. AP and CLEP credits are accepted. Important factors used in the admissions decision are advanced placement or honor courses, recommendations by school officials, evidence of special talent, personality, intangible qualities, and leadership record.

Procedure: Freshmen are admitted fall and spring. Entrance exams should be taken by December of the senior year. The application deadlines are open. Application fee is $25. Notification is sent on a rolling basis. There is a deferred admissions plan.

Transfer: About 30 transfer students enrolled in a recent year. Transfer students should have a minimum college GPA of 2.5. The SAT I, with a minimum composite score of 800, is recommended. A total of 60 credits out of 120 to 123 must be completed at Westbrook.

Visiting: There are regularly scheduled orientations for prospective students. There are guides for informal visits and visitors may sit in on classes and stay overnight at the school. To arrange for a visit, contact the Admissions Office at (207) 797-7261.

Financial Aid: In a recent year, 82% of all current freshmen and 18% of continuing students received some form of financial aid. About 82% of students received need-based aid. The average freshman award was $7500. Of that total, scholarships or need-based grants averaged $4485; loans averaged $3607; and work contracts averaged $1154. Most undergraduate students work part-time. The average financial indebtedness of one graduate was $10,000. Westbrook is a member of CSS. The FAF, the college's own financial statement and the FAFSA are required. The deadline for financial aid applications is May 1.

International Students: There are currently 15 international students enrolled. The school actively recruits these students. They must take the TOEFL and achieve a minimum score of 450. The student must also take the SAT I or the ACT.

Computers: The college provides computer facilities for student use. The mainframe is a Data MV 600. Students have access to 3 computer laboratories, each equipped with IBM-compatible microcomputers, printers, and other peripherals. Westbrook also has an extensive library of business and scientific software applications. All students may access the system 24 hours a day in the library study room; from 9 A.M. to 10 P.M. daily in other facilities. There are no time limits on using the system. The fees are $25 per semester.

Graduates: In a recent year, 41 bachelor's degrees were awarded. The most popular majors among graduates were business (48%), dental hygiene (26%), and nursing (4%).

Admissions Contact: David Anthony, Director of Admissions.

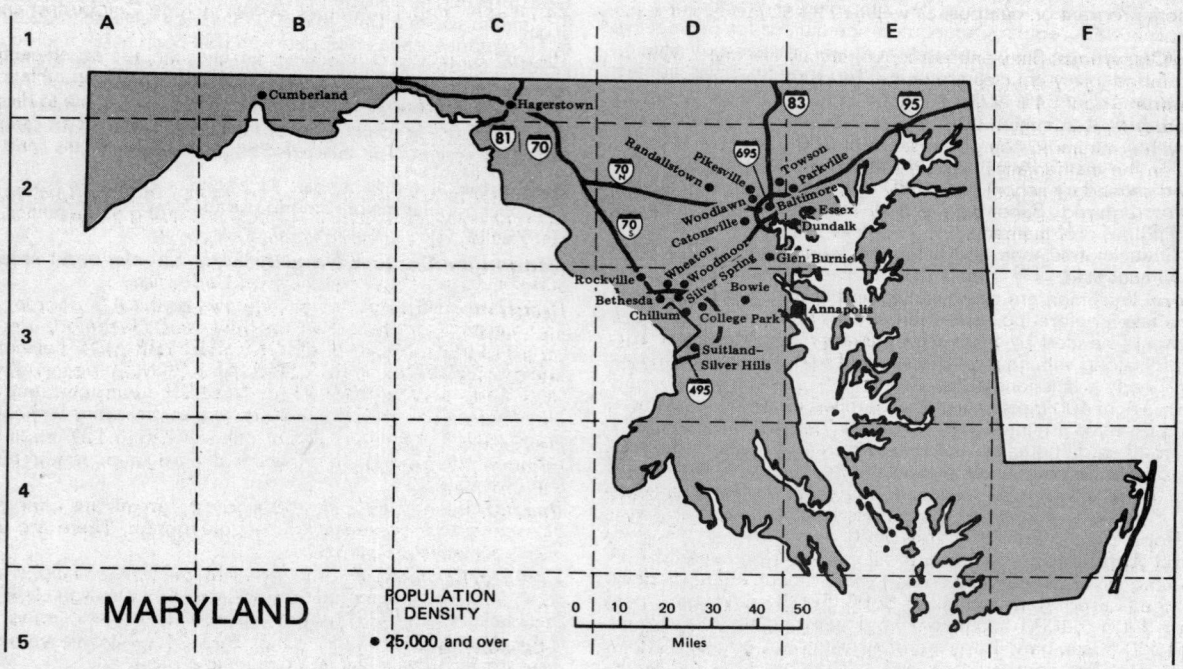

MARYLAND

POPULATION DENSITY
● 25,000 and over

0 10 20 30 40 50
Miles

BOWIE STATE UNIVERSITY

D-3

Bowie, MD 20715

(301) 464-6563

Full-time: 890 men, 1289 women
Part-time: 374 men, 715 women
Graduate: 625 men, 1053 women
Year: semesters, summer session
Application Deadline: April 1
Freshman Class: 1643 applied, 882 accepted, 407 enrolled
SAT I Verbal/Math: 357/384

Faculty: 127; IIA, --$
Ph.D.s: 50%
Student/Faculty: 17 to 1
Tuition: $3475 ($5867)
Room & Board: $3819

LESS COMPETITIVE

Bowie State University, founded in 1865, is a publicly funded institution offering undergraduate and graduate degrees in the liberal arts. The school is a part of the University of Maryland System of Higher Education. In addition to regional accreditation, Bowie State has baccalaureate program accreditation with CSWE, NCATE, and NLN. The library contains 255,282 volumes, 598,007 microform items, and 1055 audiovisual forms, and subscribes to 1287 periodicals. Computerized library sources and services include interlibrary loans. Special learning facilities include an art gallery, radio station, TV station, and the Adler-Dreikurs Institute of Human Relations. The 312-acre campus is in a suburban area 18 miles north of Washington, D.C. Including residence halls, there are 20 buildings on campus.

Student Life: About 84% of undergraduates are from Maryland. Students come from 25 states. Sixty-nine percent are African American; 22% white. The average age of freshmen is 20; all undergraduates, 22. Thirty-three percent drop out by the end of their first year; 20% remain to graduate.

Housing: A total of 965 students can be accommodated in college housing. College-sponsored living facilities include single-sex and coed dormitories. In addition there are honors houses. On-campus housing is available on a first-come, first-served basis. Priority is given to out-of-town students. Seventy-seven percent of students commute. Alcohol is not permitted. All students may keep cars on campus.

Activities: About 25% of men belong to 15 local and 11 national fraternities; about 18% of women belong to 4 national sororities. There are 40 groups on campus, including art, band, cheerleading, choir, chorale, dance, drama, honors, international, jazz band, literary magazine, marching band, newspaper, pep band, political, professional, radio and TV, religious, social, social service, student government,

and yearbook. Popular campus events include Black History Month Convocation, Parents/Founders Day, Fine Arts Festival, Honors Convocation, Commencement, and Fall Convocation.

Sports: There are 5 intercollegiate sports for men and 4 for women, and 2 intramural sports for men and 2 for women. Athletic and recreation facilities include a gymnasium, a stadium, an indoor pool, 6 tennis courts, an exercise room, a baseball field, a track, and 4 outdoor basketball courts.

Disabled Students: The following facilities are available: wheelchair ramps, elevators, special parking, specially equipped rest rooms, lowered telephones, and wide doors.

Services: In addition to counseling and information services, there is a reader service for the blind, and remedial math, reading, and writing.

Campus Safety and Security: Campus safety and security measures include 24-hour foot and vehicle patrol, self defense education, escort service, and shuttle buses. In addition, there are informal discussions, pamphlets, posters, and films, emergency telephones, and lighted pathways and sidewalks.

Programs of Study: Bowie State awards the B.A., B.S., B.S. in E., and B.S.N. degrees. Master's degrees also are awarded. Bachelor's degrees are awarded in BIOLOGICAL SCIENCE (biology/biological science), BUSINESS (business administration and management), COMMUNICATIONS AND THE ARTS (broadcasting, dramatic arts, fine arts, journalism, music, and public relations), COMPUTER AND PHYSICAL SCIENCE (computer science), EDUCATION (art, early childhood, and elementary), ENGINEERING AND ENVIRONMENTAL DESIGN (computer technology), HEALTH PROFESSIONS (nursing), SOCIAL SCIENCE (criminal justice, history, international studies, political science/government, psychology, social work, and sociology). Business administration, computer science, and elementary education have the largest enrollments.

Required: A total of 120 credit hours is required for graduation. The minimum GPA required is 1.7 to 1.9 for the freshman year and 2.0 from the sophomore year on. The number of hours that must be taken in a student's major varies. All students must complete 48 credits in general studies, including 18 credits in social science, 9 each in communication skills, humanities, and science and mathematics, 2 in education, and 1 in freshman orientation.

Special: The school offers cooperative programs, an internship in practice teaching, work-study programs, B.A.-B.S. degrees, dual majors, credit for life experience, and a 3–2 engineering degree. Dual-degree programs in engineering and dentistry are available at the University of Maryland. Cross-registration is offered with Coppin State, Morgan State, and Townson State Colleges, and the Universities of Baltimore and Maryland/Baltimore County. There is a freshman honors program on campus, as well as 12 national honor societies.

Faculty/Classroom: Sixty-one percent of faculty are male; 39%, female. No introductory courses are taught by graduate students.

Admissions: About 54% of the 1993–94 applicants were accepted.

Requirements: A minimum GPA of 2.0 is required. The SAT I is required, with a minimum composite score of 700 (350 on the verbal and 350 on the mathematics). Applicants should be graduates of an accredited secondary school. The GED is accepted. Nine Academic credits are required. Secondary school courses should include 4 years of English, 3 of mathematics, 2 each of history and social studies, and 1 each of science and a foreign language. AP and CLEP credits are accepted.

Procedure: Freshmen are admitted fall and spring. Entrance exams should be taken before the end of January for fall application. Applications should be filed by April 1 for fall entry and November 1 for spring entry, along with an application fee of $10. There are early decision and early admissions plans.

Transfer: About 400 transfer students enrolled in 1993–94. Transfer students must have a minimum GPA of 2.0. The SAT I is required if fewer than 25 credit hours are being transferred. A total of 30 credits out of 120 must be completed at Bowie State.

Visiting: There are regularly scheduled orientations for prospective students. There are guides for informal visits. To arrange for a visit, contact Hope Y. Savoy at (301) 464–6560.

Financial Aid: In 1993–94, 64% of all current freshmen and 68% of continuing students received some form of financial aid. Scholarships or need-based grants averaged $200 ($6000 maximum); loans averaged $200 ($4000 maximum); and work contracts averaged $200 ($1000 maximum). Thirty percent of undergraduate students work part-time. Average earnings from campus work for the school year are $1000. The average financial indebtedness of the 1992–93 graduate was $5619. Bowie State is a member of CSS. The FAF, the college's own financial statement, and FAFSA are required. The deadline for financial aid applications is June 1.

International Students: There are currently 183 international students enrolled. They must take the TOEFL and achieve a minimum score of 500. The student must also take the college's own entrance exam.

Computers: The university provides computer facilities for student use. The mainframe is a DEC VAX 6210. Microcomputers are available in the computing center for academic purposes. Students may request accounts on the mainframe in conjunction with course work. The system may be used by any students requiring access to a computer to complete an academic assignment. It may be used 24 hours a day. There are no time limits on using the system and no fees.

Graduates: In 1992–93, 378 bachelor's degrees were awarded. The most popular majors among graduates were business administration (33%), elementary education (9%), and nursing (7%). Within an average freshman class, 14% graduate in 5 years and 6% in 6 years.

Admissions Contact: Lawrence A. Waters, Director of Admissions.

CAPITOL COLLEGE
Laurel, MD 20708

Full-time: 248 men, 34 women	Faculty: 21; IIB, -$
Part-time: 290 men, 41 women	Ph.D.s: 1%
Graduate: 64 men, 30 women	Student/Faculty: 13 to 1
Year: semesters, summer session	Tuition: $7968
Application Deadline: open	Room & Board: $2730

D-3

(301) 953–3200; (800) 950–1992

Freshman Class: 90 applied, 80 accepted, 35 enrolled
SAT I: required

COMPETITIVE

Capitol College was originally founded in 1927 as the Capitol Radio Engineering Institute, a correspondence school. Today it is a private coeducational college offering undergraduate programs in engineering. There is one graduate school. In addition to regional accreditation, the college has baccalaureate program accreditation with ABET. The library contains 10,000 volumes and subscribes to 100 periodicals. Computerized library sources and services include the card catalog, interlibrary loans, and database searching. Special learning facilities include a learning resource center and state-of-the-art laboratories. The 52-acre campus is in a rural area 19 miles north of Washington, D.C. Including residence halls, there are 9 buildings on campus.

Student Life: About 77% of undergraduates are from Maryland. Students come from 12 states and 17 foreign countries. Sixty-two percent are white; 23% African American. The average age of freshmen is 24; all undergraduates, 29.

Housing: A total of 100 students can be accommodated in college housing. College-sponsored living facilities include coed on-campus apartments. On-campus housing is available on a first-come, first-served basis. Priority is given to out-of-town students. Eighty-seven percent of students commute. All students may keep cars on campus.

Activities: There are no fraternities or sororities on campus. There are 15 groups on campus, including chess, literary magazine, and newspaper. Popular campus events include Octoberfest and Spring Bash.

Sports: Athletic and recreation facilities include an off-campus gymnasium, a basketball court, a student center, and an athletic field.

Disabled Students: The entire campus is accessible to disabled students. The following facilities are available: wheelchair ramps, elevators, special parking, specially equipped rest rooms, and lowered drinking fountains.

Services: In addition to many counseling and information services, tutoring is available in most subjects, including mathematics, electronics, English, and developmental English.

Campus Safety and Security: Campus safety and security measures include lighted pathways and sidewalks.

Programs of Study: The college awards the B.S. degree. Associate and master's degrees also are awarded. Bachelor's degrees are awarded in COMMUNICATIONS AND THE ARTS (telecommunications), COMPUTER AND PHYSICAL SCIENCE (optics), ENGINEERING AND ENVIRONMENTAL DESIGN (computer engineering, electrical/electronics engineering, and engineering technology).

Required: A minimum GPA of 2.0 and 130 to 137 credit hours are required for graduation. Additional curriculum requirements vary with the major.

Special: Internships and work-study programs are offered through the school's Cooperative Education Program. There are 2 national honor societies on campus.

Faculty/Classroom: Seventy-eight percent of faculty are male; 22%, female. All teach undergraduates. The average class size in an introductory lecture is 22 and in a regular course offering, 22.

Admissions: About 89% of the 1993–94 applicants were accepted. One freshman was first in a graduating class.

Requirements: A minimum GPA of 2.5 is required. The SAT I is required, with a minimum composite score of 800. Applicants should be graduates of an accredited secondary school. The GED is accepted. Twenty academic credits or 20 Carnegie units are required. Secondary school courses must include 4 units of English, 3 of mathematics, and 2 each of science and social studies. An essay and an interview are recommended. AP and CLEP credits are accepted. Important factors used in the admissions decision are advanced placement or honor courses, recommendations by school officials, extracurricular activities record, recommendations by alumni, and personality, intangible qualities.

Procedure: Freshmen are admitted to all sessions. Entrance exams should be taken by March 1. Application deadlines are open. Notification is sent on a rolling basis.

Transfer: About 120 transfer students enrolled in 1993–94. Transfer students must have earned 15 college credits and a minimum GPA of 2.0. A total of 40 credits out of 130 to 137 must be completed at the college.

Visiting: There are regularly scheduled orientations for prospective students. There are guides for informal visits, and visitors may sit in on classes and stay overnight at the school. To arrange for a visit, contact the Admissions Office at (800) 950–1992.

Financial Aid: In 1993–94 46% of all current freshmen and 28% of continuing students received some form of financial aid. The average freshman award was $8325. Of that total, scholarships or need-based grants averaged $1900 ($2800 maximum); loans averaged $4625 ($7500 maximum); and work contracts averaged $1800 ($2500 maximum). The average financial indebtedness of the 1992–93 graduate was $10,000. The college is a member of CSS. The FAF is required. The deadline for financial aid applications is March 15.

International Students: There are currently 28 international students enrolled. The school actively recruits these students. They must take the TOEFL and achieve a minimum score of 500.

Computers: The college provides computer facilities for student use. The mainframe is a DEC VAX 11/750. There are also 25 Tandy, IBM PC, and TRS80 microcomputers available in laboratories. All students may access the system. There are no time limits on using the system and no fees. It is recommended that students in computer engineering technology have personal computers.

Graduates: In a recent year, 130 bachelor's degrees were awarded. The most popular major among graduates was engineering/engineering technology (79%). Some 30 companies recruited on campus in a recent year. In a recent graduating class, 5% of the men were enrolled in graduate school within 6 months of graduation; 94% of the men and 100% of the women had found employment.

Admissions Contact: Anthony Miller, Director of Admissions.

COLLEGE OF NOTRE DAME OF MARYLAND
Baltimore, MD 21210

D-2

(410) 532-5330

(800) 435-0300 (out-of-state)

Full-time: 2 men, 665 women	Faculty: 76; IIB, -$
Part-time: 195 men, 1788 women	Ph.D.s: 58%
Graduate: 54 men, 373 women	Student/Faculty: 9 to 1
Year: 4-1-4, summer session	Tuition: $10,650
Application Deadline: February 15	Room & Board: $5400
Freshman Class: 457 applied, 356 accepted, 177 enrolled	
SAT I: required	**COMPETITIVE**

The College of Notre Dame of Maryland, founded in 1873, is a private liberal arts institution primarily for women and affiliated with the Catholic Church. There is one graduate school. In addition to regional accreditation, Notre Dame has baccalaureate program accreditation with NLN. The library contains 277,450 volumes, 378,138 microform items, and 21,039 audiovisual forms, and subscribes to 1983 periodicals. Computerized library sources and services include database searching. Special learning facilities include a learning resource center, art gallery, planetarium, radio station, TV station, and graphic arts studio. The 58-acre campus is in a suburban area 10 miles north of Baltimore. Including residence halls, there are 11 buildings on campus.

Student Life: About 70% of undergraduates are from Maryland. Students come from 21 states. Fifty-eight percent are from public schools; 42% from private. Seventy-three percent are white; 12% African American. The average age of freshmen is 19. Fifteen percent drop out by the end of their first year; 70% remain to graduate.

Housing: A total of 450 students can be accommodated in college housing. College-sponsored living facilities include single-sex dormitories. On-campus housing is guaranteed for all 4 years. Sixty-five percent of students live on campus; of those, 60% remain on campus on weekends. Alcohol is not permitted. All students may keep cars on campus.

Activities: There are no fraternities or sororities on campus. There are 24 groups on campus, including art, choir, dance, drama, ethnic, honors, international, literary magazine, newspaper, political, professional, radio and TV, religious, social, social service, student government, and yearbook. Popular campus events include Honors Convocation, Antostal Day, 100 Nights, Multicultural Awareness Week, Notre Dame Day, Tree Trim, and Parents Weekend.

Sports: There are 7 intercollegiate sports for women, as well as intramural sports. Athletic and recreation facilities include a sports/activities complex that houses racquetball courts, a dance studio, a fitness center, an indoor walking track, a game room, an activities resource center, and a basketball court.

Disabled Students: The entire campus is accessible to disabled students. The following facilities are available: wheelchair ramps, elevators, special parking, specially equipped rest rooms, and lowered drinking fountains.

Services: In addition to many counseling and information services, tutoring is available in every subject.

Campus Safety and Security: Campus safety and security measures include 24-hour foot and vehicle patrol, self-defense education, escort service, and informal discussions. In addition, there are pamphlets, posters, and films and lighted pathways and sidewalks.

Programs of Study: Notre Dame awards the B.A. and B.S. degrees. Master's degrees also are awarded. Bachelor's degrees are awarded in BIOLOGICAL SCIENCE (biology/biological science), BUSINESS (accounting, banking and finance, international business management, and marketing/retailing/merchandising), COMMUNICATIONS AND THE ARTS (art history and appreciation, communications, English, graphic design, music, photography, and studio art), COMPUTER AND PHYSICAL SCIENCE (chemistry, computer science, information sciences and systems, mathematics, and physics), EDUCATION (art, early childhood, elementary, foreign languages, music, science, secondary, and special), ENGINEERING AND ENVIRONMENTAL DESIGN (preengineering), HEALTH PROFESSIONS (nursing, predentistry, premedicine, and prepharmacy), and SOCIAL SCIENCE (economics, history, international relations, liberal arts/general studies, political science/government, prelaw, psychology, and religion). Business, education, communication arts, biology, nursing, engineering, and chemistry are the strongest academically. Business, education, communication arts, psychology, and biology have the largest enrollments.

Required: To graduate, students must complete a total of 128 credit hours with a minimum GPA of 2.0 (2.5 in many majors). All students must fulfill the distribution requirements in the general education core, the major, and electives, and must demonstrate proficiencies in writing, public speaking, computer literacy, and library research. In most majors, a minimum of 42 hours is required. All students must take 2 courses in physical education, and some majors require senior practicums.

Special: The college offers cross-registration with Johns Hopkins, Towson State, and Morgan State universities; Coppin State, Goucher, and Loyola colleges; and the Maryland Institute College of Art. Study abroad, internships, dual bachelor's degrees in nursing and engineering, a 3-2 engineering degree with Johns Hopkins University and the University of Maryland, and pass/fail options are available. Notre Dame's Weekend College offers bachelor's degree programs for employed adults. There is a freshman honors program on campus, as well as 8 national honor societies. Four departments have honors programs.

Faculty/Classroom: Thirty percent of faculty are male; 70%, female. All teach undergraduates. No introductory courses are taught by graduate students. The average class size in an introductory lecture is 30; in a laboratory, 20; and in a regular course offering, 20.

Admissions: About 78% of the 1993-94 applicants were accepted. The SAT scores for the 1993-94 freshman class were as follows: Verbal—65% below 500, 24% between 500 and 599, 10% between 600 and 700, and 1% above 700; Math—50% below 500, 32% between 500 and 599, 17% between 600 and 700, and 1% above 700. About 43% of the current freshmen were in the top fifth of their class; 65% were in the top two fifths. There was 1 National Merit finalist.

Requirements: A minimum GPA of 3.0 is required. The SAT I is required. In addition, applicants should be graduates of an accredited secondary school. Eighteen academic credits are required, including 4 units of English, 3 each of mathematics and a foreign language, and 2 each of history and science, plus 4 electives. An essay is required and an interview is recommended. AP credits are accepted. Important factors used in the admissions decision are recommendations by school officials, advanced placement or honor courses, leadership record, extracurricular activities record, and evidence of special talent.

Procedure: Freshmen are admitted fall and spring. Entrance exams should be taken no later than January of the senior year. Early decision applications should be filed by November 15; regular applications, by February 15 for fall entry and December 15 for spring entry, along with an application fee of $25. Notification of early decision is sent December 1; regular decision, within 2 to 4 weeks of receipt of the completed application. There are early decision, early admissions, and deferred admissions plans.

Transfer: About 35 transfer students enrolled in 1993-94. Notre Dame requires a minimum GPA of 2.5 for transfer students but recommends a GPA of 3.0. Combined scores of 800 are required for the SAT I and 18 for the ACT. Students must also submit a letter of recommendation and an essay. A total of 60 credits out of 128 must be completed at Notre Dame.

Visiting: There are regularly scheduled orientations for prospective students, consisting of programs in June and January, each of which includes a stay in the dormitory, registration, and advisement. There are guides for informal visits and visitors may sit in on classes. Visitors may stay overnight at the school after acceptance. To arrange for a visit, contact the Office of Admissions at (800) 435-0300 (out-of-state) or (410) 532-5330.

Financial Aid: In 1993-94, 94% of all current freshmen and 90% of continuing students received some form of financial aid. About 65% of freshmen and 66% of continuing students received need-based aid. The average freshman award was $10,457. Of that total, scholarships or need-based grants averaged $7132 ($8100 maximum); loans averaged $2625 ($4000 maximum); and work contracts averaged $700 ($1200 maximum). Average earnings from campus work for the school year are $700. The average financial indebtedness of the 1992-93 graduate was $10,000. Notre Dame is a member of CSS. The FAF and the FAFSA are required. The deadline for financial aid applications is February 15.

International Students: There are currently 43 international students enrolled. The school actively recruits these students. They must take the TOEFL and achieve a minimum score of 500. The student must also take the college's own entrance examination or for placement purposes.

Computers: The college provides computer facilities for student use. The mainframe is a DEC MicroVAX II. There are 80 IBM, IBM-compatible, and Apple Macintosh microcomputer workstations located in academic and administrative buildings. All students may access the system. There are no time limits on using the system and no fees.

Graduates: In 1992-93, 315 bachelor's degrees were awarded. The most popular majors among graduates were business (30%), liberal arts (10%), and communication arts (10%). Within an average freshman class, 85% graduate in 4 years and 95% in 5 years.

Admissions Contact: Terry Boer, Director of Admissions and Enrollment Management.

COLUMBIA UNION COLLEGE
D-3

Takoma Park, MD 20912

(301) 891-4230

(800) 492-1715 (in-state), 835-4212 (out-of-state)

Full-time: 196 men, 318 women	Faculty: 48; IIB, --$
Part-time: 138 men, 328 women	Ph.D.s: 41%
Graduate: none	Student/Faculty: 11 to 1
Year: semesters, summer session	Tuition: $9750
Application Deadline: August 1	Room & Board: $3900
Freshman Class: 325 accepted, 101 enrolled	
SAT I Verbal/Math: 410/420	ACT: 23 **LESS COMPETITIVE**

Columbia Union College, founded in 1904, is a private liberal arts institution affiliated with the Seventh-day Adventist Church. In addition to regional accreditation, CUC has baccalaureate program accreditation with CAHEA and NLN. The library contains 123,104 volumes, 653 microform items, and 1965 audiovisual forms, and subscribes to 436 periodicals. Computerized library sources and services include the card catalog, interlibrary loans, and database searching. Special learning facilities include a radio station. The 19-acre campus is in a suburban area 7 miles north of Washington, D.C. Including residence halls, there are 10 buildings on campus.

Student Life: About 58% of undergraduates are from out-of-state, mostly the Middle Atlantic. Students come from 30 states, 48 foreign countries, and Canada. Thirty-one percent are from public schools; 69% from private. Forty-two percent are African American; 34% white. Sixty-three percent are Protestant; 12% Catholic. The average age of freshmen is 18; all undergraduates, 28.

Housing: A total of 440 students can be accommodated in college housing. College-sponsored living facilities include single-sex dormitories. On-campus housing is guaranteed for all 4 years. Seventy percent of students commute. Alcohol is not permitted. All students may keep cars on campus.

Activities: There are no fraternities or sororities on campus. There are 9 groups on campus, including band, choir, honors, newspaper, orchestra, radio and TV, religious, student government, and yearbook.

Sports: There are 5 intercollegiate sports for men and 5 for women, and 5 intramural sports for men and 4 for women. Athletic and recreation facilities include a swimming pool, a gymnasium, racquetball and tennis courts, a sports field, and a student lounge.

Disabled Students: One percent of the campus is accessible to disabled students. Elevators are available for these students.

Services: In addition to many counseling and information services, tutoring is available in some subjects, including all English, mathematics, and accounting courses. In addition, there is remedial math and writing.

Campus Safety and Security: Campus safety and security measures include 24-hour foot and vehicle patrol, escort service, informal discussions, and pamphlets, posters, and films.

Programs of Study: CUC awards the B.A. and B.S. degrees. Associate degrees also are awarded. Bachelor's degrees are awarded in BIOLOGICAL SCIENCE (biochemistry), BUSINESS (accounting, business administration and management, management science, and personnel management), COMMUNICATIONS AND THE ARTS (communications, English, journalism, and music), COMPUTER AND PHYSICAL SCIENCE (chemistry, computer science, information sciences and systems, and mathematics), EDUCATION (early childhood, elementary, English, and mathematics), HEALTH PROFESSIONS (health science, medical laboratory technology, nursing, predentistry, and premedicine), SOCIAL SCIENCE (history, prelaw, psychology, and religion). Business and nursing are the strongest academically and have the largest enrollments.

Required: To graduate, students must earn 120 to 128 credit hours, including 36 in the major, with a minimum GPA of 2.0. Students must take 12 hours of religion, 8 of physical sciences, natural sciences, and mathematics, 9 of social sciences, 7 of humanities, 4 of physical education and health, and 6 of practical and applied arts. Courses in English, communication, and computer science are also required.

Special: CUC offers co-op programs in business communication, computer science, English, mathematics, and nursing. Also available are internships in counseling psychology, work-study programs, a general studies degree, credit for life experience, nondegree study, pass/fail options, dual majors in engineering/chemistry and mathematics with the University of Maryland, and study abroad in France, Spain, and Austria. There is an adult evening program for degree completion as well as an external (correspondence) degree. There is a freshman honors program on campus, as well as 3 national honor societies. One department has an honors program.

Faculty/Classroom: Fifty-nine percent of faculty are male; 41%, female.

Admissions: The SAT scores for the 1993-94 freshman class were as follows: Verbal—81% below 500, 18% between 500 and 599, and 1% between 600 and 700; Math—78% below 500, 15% between 500 and 599, 6% between 600 and 700, and 1% above 700. The

ACT scores were 38% below 21, 17% between 21 and 23, 32% between 24 and 26, 10% between 27 and 28, and 3% above 28.

Requirements: CUC requires applicants to be in the upper 50% of their class. A minimum GPA of 2.5 is required. The SAT I or ACT is recommended, with a minimum composite score of 800, or at least 400 in each section, on the SAT I or 18 on the ACT. Applicants must be graduates of an accredited secondary school. The GED is accepted. Twenty-one Carnegie units are required, including 4 years of high school English and 2 each of history, mathematics, and science. An essay is recommended and an interview is required. AP and CLEP credits are accepted. Important factors used in the admissions decision are advanced placement or honor courses, leadership record, recommendations by school officials, evidence of special talent, and recommendations by alumni.

Procedure: Freshmen are admitted to all sessions. Entrance exams should be taken in the fall of the senior year. Applications should be filed by August 1 for fall entry, December 1 for spring entry, and May 1 for summer entry, along with an application fee of $15. Notification is sent on a rolling basis. There are early decision, early admissions, and deferred admissions plans. A total of 213 early decision candidates were accepted for the 1993-94 class.

Transfer: A total of 114 transfer students enrolled in 1993-94. Applicants must have at least 12 hours of college credit and a minimum GPA of 2.0. A total of 30 credits out of 120 to 128 must be completed at CUC.

Visiting: There are regularly scheduled orientations for prospective students. There are guides for informal visits and visitors may sit in on classes and stay overnight at the school. To arrange for a visit, contact the Office of College Advancement at (800) 492-1715 (in-state) or (800) 835-4212 (out-of-state).

Financial Aid: In an earlier year, 65% of all students received some form of financial aid. Scholarships or need-based grants averaged $1500 ($2000 maximum); loans averaged $2625; and work contracts averaged $1500 ($2500 maximum). Ninety-six percent of undergraduate students work part-time. The average financial indebtedness of an earlier graduate was $9160. The FAF or FFS and the college's own financial statement are required. The deadline for financial aid applications is March 31.

International Students: There are currently 45 international students enrolled. They must take the TOEFL, the University of Michigan Language Test, or the college's own test.

Computers: The college provides computer facilities for student use. The mainframes are an AT&T 3B2/400 and an HP 932. There are also 20 IBM and AT&T microcomputers available in the computer laboratory and in academic departments. Students in computer classes may access the system. It may be used 8 A.M. to midnight. There are no time limits on using the system and no fees.

Graduates: In 1992-93, 238 bachelor's degrees were awarded. The most popular majors among graduates were business (38%), allied health (22%), and health care administration (20%). Within an average freshman class, 50% graduate in 5 years.

Admissions Contact: Sheila Burnette, Director of Admissions.

COPPIN STATE COLLEGE
D-2

Baltimore, MD 21216-3698

(410) 383-5990; (800) 635-3674

Full-time: 600 men, 900 women	Faculty: 109; IIB, +$
Part-time: 200 men, 600 women	Ph.D.s: 61%
Graduate: 60 men, 200 women	Student/Faculty: 14 to 1
Year: semesters, summer session	Tuition: $2605 ($4677)
Application Deadline: July 15	Room & Board: $4540
Freshman Class: 1934 applied, 988 accepted, 567 enrolled	
SAT I Verbal/Math: 376/406	**LESS COMPETITIVE**

Coppin State College, founded in 1900, offers undergraduate programs in liberal arts, teacher education, and nursing. There are 3 undergraduate schools and one graduate school. In addition to regional accreditation, Coppin has baccalaureate program accreditation with NCATE and NLN. The library contains 200,000 volumes and 233,000 microform items, and subscribes to 715 periodicals. Computerized library sources and services include the card catalog and interlibrary loans. Special learning facilities include a learning resource center, TV station, and on-campus video production company. The 38-acre campus is in an urban area in Baltimore. Including residence halls, there are 9 buildings on campus.

Student Life: About 90% of undergraduates are from Maryland. Students come from 10 states and 5 foreign countries. Ninety percent are from public schools; 10% from private. Eighty percent are African American; 10% white. The average age of freshmen is 19; all undergraduates, 23.

Housing: A total of 300 students can be accommodated in college housing. College-sponsored living facilities include coed dormitories. In addition, the housing office maintains lists of community housing available. On-campus housing is guaranteed for all 4 years. Ninety-three percent of students commute. Alcohol is not permitted. All students may keep cars on campus.

Activities: About 45% of men belong to 10 national fraternities; about 27% of women belong to 10 national sororities. There are 40 groups on campus, including cheerleading, choir, chorus, computers, dance, drama, ethnic, film, honors, international, newspaper, political, professional, radio and TV, religious, social, social service, student government, and yearbook. Popular campus events include the Lyceum Series.

Sports: There are 7 intercollegiate sports for men and 7 for women, and 5 intramural sports for men and 5 for women. Athletic and recreation facilities include a 2,500-seat gymnasium, an indoor swimming pool, handball and racquetball courts, a soccer field, a dance studio, a weight room, a track, and a baseball field.

Disabled Students: Ninety percent of the campus is accessible to disabled students. The following facilities are available: wheelchair ramps, elevators, special parking, specially equipped rest rooms, lowered drinking fountains, lowered telephones, and individual attention for students requiring specialized materials, equipment, or instructional style accommodation.

Services: In addition to some counseling and information services, there is remedial math, reading, and writing.

Campus Safety and Security: Campus safety and security measures include 24-hour foot and vehicle patrol, escort service, pamphlets, posters, and films, and emergency telephones. In addition, there are lighted pathways and sidewalks.

Programs of Study: Coppin awards the B.A., B.S., and B.S.N. degrees. Master's degrees also are awarded. Bachelor's degrees are awarded in BIOLOGICAL SCIENCE (biology/biological science), BUSINESS (accounting, banking and finance, business administration and management, business economics, marketing management, and personnel management), COMMUNICATIONS AND THE ARTS (English), COMPUTER AND PHYSICAL SCIENCE (chemistry, computer science, mathematics, and quantitative methods), EDUCATION (elementary, English, physical, and special), ENGINEERING AND ENVIRONMENTAL DESIGN (preengineering), HEALTH PROFESSIONS (nursing, physical therapy, predentistry, and prepharmacy), SOCIAL SCIENCE (criminal justice, history, psychology, social science, social work, and sociology). Management science and education are the strongest programs academically and have the largest enrollments.

Required: To graduate, all students must have a minimum 2.0 GPA and a minimum of 120 credit hours, with 36 to 40 hours in the major. Students must complete about 50 hours of liberal arts courses in English, mathematics, speech, history, health, physical education, natural and social sciences, and philosophy. All seniors must take a standardized exit examination relevant to their major.

Special: The college offers co-op programs with Dundalk Community College and Morgan University, internships in criminal justice and sociology, and dual majors in engineering, pharmacy, physical therapy, and dentistry. Internships and work-study are also available. There is a freshman honors program on campus, as well as 1 national honor society.

Faculty/Classroom: The average class size in a regular course offering is 25.

Admissions: About 51% of the 1993–94 applicants were accepted.

Requirements: A minimum GPA of 2.0 is required. The SAT I is required. Applicants must be graduates of an accredited secondary school with a minimum GPA of 2.0, or have a GED certificate. Students must have completed 4 courses in English, 2 courses each in history, mathematics, science, and social studies, and 1 course in foreign language. Up to 15% of a freshman class may be admitted conditionally without these requirements, and those students who graduated high school more than 5 years ago will be reviewed individually. CLEP credit is accepted. Important factors used in the admissions decision are advanced placement or honor courses, extracurricular activities record, evidence of special talent, recommendations by school officials, and recommendations by alumni.

Procedure: Freshmen are admitted to all sessions. Applications should be filed by July 15 for fall entry and December 15 for spring entry, along with an application fee of $15. Notification is sent on a rolling basis. There are early decision and early admissions plans.

Transfer: About 276 transfer students enrolled in 1993–94. Transfer students must have a minimum 2.0 GPA and be in good academic standing at the former institution. Applicants with fewer than 25 credits must meet freshman requirements. A total of 30 credits out of 120 must be completed at Coppin.

Visiting: There are regularly scheduled orientations for prospective students. There are guides for informal visits, and visitors may sit in on classes. To arrange for a visit, contact Admissions at (410) 383-5990 or (410) 383-5991.

Financial Aid: In 1993–94 80% of all current freshmen and 85% of continuing students received some form of financial aid. About 70% of freshmen and 80% of continuing students received need-based aid. The average freshman award was $4500. Of that total, scholarships or need-based grants averaged $3300, and loans averaged $1200. The average financial indebtedness of the 1992–93 graduate was $4000. Coppin is a member of CSS. The FAF, FFS, or SFS and

the college's own financial statement are required. The deadline for financial aid applications is May 1.

International Students: International students must take the TOEFL and achieve a minimum score of 500.

Computers: The college provides computer facilities for student use. The mainframe is a DEC VAX 11/780. There are more than 200 personal computers available for students. All students may access the system. There are no time limits on using the system and no fees.

Graduates: In 1992–93 258 bachelor's degrees were awarded.

Admissions Contact: Allen Mosley, Director of Admissions and Recruitment.

FROSTBURG STATE UNIVERSITY
Frostburg, MD 21532

B-1

(301) 689-4201

Full-time: 1971 men, 2200 women	**Faculty:** 234; IIA, -$
Part-time: 449	**Ph.D.s:** 70%
Graduate: 778 men and women	**Student/Faculty:** 18 to 1
Year: semesters, summer session	**Tuition:** $2666 ($5296)
Application Deadline: open	**Room & Board:** $4274

Freshman Class: 2915 applied, 2226 accepted, 896 enrolled

SAT I: required

COMPETITIVE

Frostburg State University, founded in 1898, is a part of the University of Maryland system. The university offers programs through the schools of arts and humanities, business, natural and social science, and education. There are 4 undergraduate and 7 graduate schools. The library contains 245,000 volumes and 31,448 audiovisual forms, and subscribes to 1281 periodicals. Computerized library sources and services include the card catalog, interlibrary loans, and database searching. Special learning facilities include a learning resource center, art gallery, natural history museum, planetarium, and radio station. The 260-acre campus is in a small town about 150 miles west of Baltimore and northwest of Washington, D.C. Including residence halls, there are 41 buildings on campus.

Student Life: About 85% of undergraduates are from Maryland. Students come from more than 30 states. Ninety percent are white. The average age of freshmen is 18; all undergraduates, 20. Twenty percent drop out by the end of their first year.

Housing: A total of 1900 students can be accommodated in college housing. College-sponsored living facilities include single-sex and coed dormitories. In addition, there are honors houses, special interest houses, and international houses. On-campus housing is available on a first-come, first-served basis. All students may keep cars on campus.

Activities: About 15% of men belong to 8 national fraternities; about 15% of women belong to 6 national sororities. There are 150 groups on campus, including art, band, cheerleading, choir, chorale, chorus, computers, dance, drama, drill team, ethnic, honors, international, jazz band, literary magazine, marching band, musical theater, newspaper, orchestra, pep band, photography, political, professional, radio and TV, religious, social, social service, student government, symphony, and yearbook. Popular campus events include Homecoming, Parents Weekend, Siblings Weekend, and Festival of Africa.

Sports: Athletic and recreation facilities include a game room, a 3600-seat arena, a practice gymnasium, 5 athletic fields, 2 intramural fields, a swimming pool, a baseball, golf, and archery room, a dance studio, a wellness room, and 6 lighted tennis courts.

Disabled Students: The following facilities are available: wheelchair ramps, elevators, special parking, specially equipped rest rooms, special class scheduling, lowered drinking fountains, and lowered telephones.

Services: In addition to many counseling and information services, tutoring is available in every subject. There is also a reader service for the blind, and remedial math, reading, and writing.

Campus Safety and Security: Campus safety and security measures include 24-hour foot and vehicle patrol, escort service, informal discussions, and pamphlets, posters, and films. In addition, there are lighted pathways and sidewalks.

Programs of Study: FSU awards the B.A., B.S., and B.F.A. degrees. Master's degrees also are awarded. Bachelor's degrees are awarded in AGRICULTURE (wildlife management), BIOLOGICAL SCIENCE (biology/biological science), BUSINESS (accounting, business administration and management, and recreation and leisure services), COMMUNICATIONS AND THE ARTS (communications, dramatic arts, English, fine arts, graphic design, languages, music, and speech/debate/rhetoric), COMPUTER AND PHYSICAL SCIENCE (chemistry, computer science, mathematics, and physics), EDUCATION (art, business, early childhood, music, and physical), ENGINEERING AND ENVIRONMENTAL DESIGN (environmental science), SOCIAL SCIENCE (economics, geography, history, international studies, philosophy, political science/government, psychology, social science, social work, and sociology). Business, education, natural sciences, and creative and performing arts are the strongest academically. Business and education have the largest enrollments.

Required: A minimum GPA of 2.0 and 120 credit hours are required to graduate. All students must complete 6 to 9 credits in humanities and social sciences, 7 to 14 credits in natural science, and 3 to 6 credits in creative and performing arts. Courses in computer science, speech and composition, personalized health fitness, and mathematics are also required.

Special: FSU offers co-op programs with the University of Maryland, internships through individual departments, study abroad through the International Student Exchange Program, work-study and accelerated degree programs, B.A.-B.S. degrees in all majors, and dual majors in engineering. The 3–2 engineering degree is coordinated with the University of Maryland. Credit for experience, nondegree study, and pass/fail options are also available. There is a freshman honors program on campus, as well as 19 national honor societies. Sixteen departments have honors programs.

Faculty/Classroom: No introductory courses are taught by graduate students. The average class size in an introductory lecture is 30; in a laboratory, 15; and in a regular course offering, 25.

Admissions: About 76% of the 1993–94 applicants were accepted.

Requirements: A minimum GPA of 2.0 is required, as is the SAT I. In addition, applicants must be graduates of an accredited secondary school or have the GED. Secondary preparation should include 4 units of English, 3 each of mathematics and social studies, and 2 of science. An interview is recommended. AP and CLEP credits are accepted. Important factors used in the admissions decision are recommendations by school officials, extracurricular activities record, advanced placement or honor courses, evidence of special talent, and personality, intangible qualities.

Procedure: Freshmen are admitted to all sessions. Entrance exams should be taken in the junior year. Application deadlines are open. The application fee is $30. Notification is sent on a rolling basis. There is an early admissions plan. A waiting list is an active part of the admissions procedure.

Transfer: Some 399 transfer students enrolled in 1993–94. Transfer students with 12 to 29 credits must have a minimum GPA of 2.5 and provide an official high school transcript and SAT I scores. Students with 30 or more credits must have a minimum GPA of 2.0. A minimum of 30 credits out of 120 must be completed at FSU.

Visiting: There are regularly scheduled orientations for prospective students, including tours Monday through Friday at 11 A.M. and 1 P.M. There are guides for informal visits and visitors may sit in on classes. To arrange for a visit, contact the Office of Admissions at (301) 689–4201.

Financial Aid: In 1993–94, 60% of all current freshmen received some form of financial aid. About 55% of freshmen and 53% of continuing students received need-based aid. The average freshman award was $3000. Of that total, scholarships or need-based grants averaged $2000 ($5500 maximum); loans averaged $3000 ($4600 maximum); work contracts averaged $700 ($1000 maximum); and the maximum of other freshman awards was $6000. Forty percent of undergraduate students work part-time. Average earnings from campus work for the school year are $700. The FAF and the college's own financial statement are required. The deadline for financial aid applications is April 1.

International Students: The school actively recruits these students. They must take the TOEFL and achieve a minimum score of 560. The student must also take the SAT I.

Computers: The college provides computer facilities for student use. The mainframe is a VAX/VMS 4300. There are 6 laboratories with microcomputers and word processing equipment in the computer center. All students may access the system. It may be used by appointment. There are no time limits on using the system and no fees.

Graduates: In 1992–93, 601 bachelor's degrees were awarded. Some 61 companies recruited on campus.

Admissions Contact: David L. Sanford, Dean of Admissions.

GOUCHER COLLEGE
Baltimore, MD 21204   **D-2**

(410) 337–6100
(800) 638–4278 (out-of-state)

Full-time: 266 men, 586 women	Faculty: 84; IIB, av$
Part-time: 20 men, 61 women	Ph.D.s: 85%
Graduate: 5 men, 66 women	Student/Faculty: 10 to 1
Year: semesters	Tuition: $14,400
Application Deadline: February 1	Room & Board: $5895
Freshman Class: 1151 applied, 811 accepted, 245 enrolled	
SAT I Verbal/Math: 540/570	**VERY COMPETITIVE**

Goucher College, founded in 1885, is a private, coeducational liberal arts college. There is 1 graduate school. The library contains 269,262 volumes, 58,419 microform items, and 7439 audiovisual forms, and subscribes to 1114 periodicals. Computerized library sources and services include the card catalog, interlibrary loans, and database searching. Special learning facilities include a learning resource center, art gallery, research centers in politics, information technology, and media, and the Public Leadership Institute for Wo-

men. The 287-acre campus is in a suburban area 8 miles north of Baltimore. Including residence halls, there are 18 buildings on campus.

Student Life: About 51% of undergraduates are from out-of-state, mostly the Middle Atlantic. Students come from 41 states and 14 foreign countries. Seventy-one percent are from public schools; 29% from private. Seventy-eight percent are white. Forty-one percent are Protestant; 40% Catholic; 17% Jewish. The average age of freshmen is 19; all undergraduates, 21. Fifteen percent drop out by the end of their first year; 85% remain to graduate.

Housing: A total of 726 students can be accommodated in college housing. College-sponsored living facilities include single-sex and coed dormitories and on-campus apartments. In addition, there are language houses and special interest houses. On-campus housing is guaranteed for all 4 years. Seventy-five percent of students live on campus. Upperclassmen may keep cars on campus.

Activities: There are no fraternities or sororities on campus. There are 43 groups on campus, including art, chorale, chorus, dance, drama, ethnic, film, honors, international, literary magazine, musical theater, newspaper, orchestra, professional, religious, social, social service, student government, symphony, and yearbook. Popular campus events include Get into Goucher Day, Roctober Fest, Spring Fling, Hot Steel Night, and Black History Month.

Sports: There are 4 intercollegiate sports for men and 8 for women, and 12 intramural sports for men and 12 for women. Athletic and recreational facilities include a pool, weight-training room, tennis and squash courts, a dance studio, various playing fields, and a new sports center.

Disabled Students: Seventy-five percent of the campus is accessible to disabled students. The following facilities are available: wheelchair ramps, special parking, specially equipped rest rooms, and special class scheduling.

Services: In addition to many counseling and information services, tutoring is available in most subjects. There is also a reader service for the blind.

Campus Safety and Security: Campus safety and security measures include 24-hour foot and vehicle patrol, escort service, shuttle buses, and pamphlets, posters, and films. In addition, there are emergency telephones, lighted pathways and sidewalks, a whistle-alert program, and a student safety and security committee.

Programs of Study: Goucher awards the B.A. degree. Master's degrees also are awarded. Bachelor's degrees are awarded in BIOLOGICAL SCIENCE (biology/biological science), COMMUNICATIONS AND THE ARTS (communications, dance, English, French, historic preservation, music, Russian, and Spanish), COMPUTER AND PHYSICAL SCIENCE (chemistry and mathematics), EDUCATION (elementary, secondary, and special), SOCIAL SCIENCE (American studies, economics, European studies, history, international relations, philosophy, political science/government, prelaw, psychology, religion, sociology, and women's studies). Science, political science, English, and history are the strongest academically. English, psychology, communications, education, biological sciences, and political science have the largest enrollments.

Required: To graduate, all students must complete 120 semester hours, with a minimum GPA of 2.0. Requirements include 2 courses each in the arts and natural sciences, including at least 1 laboratory course, 1 course each in the humanities, social sciences, and mathematics, and the year-long common intellectual experience course for freshmen. Students are also required to demonstrate proficiency in computers, writing, and a foreign language. Other requirements include a 4-class distribution requirement in physical education and at least 3 semester hours of an off-campus experience.

Special: Students may cross-register at Johns Hopkins University, Towson State College, Loyola College, Morgan State University, the College of Notre Dame, and Baltimore Hebrew University. A wide variety of internships are available in such fields as environmental management, scientific research, legislative assistance, and counseling. Study abroad is available in England, Russia, Germany, France, and Spain. A number of field experiences and internships are offered in Washington, D.C., through the Hughes Politics Center, and ROTC is offered through other colleges. Dual majors are encouraged, and student-designed majors and pass/fail options are also available. There is a freshman honors program on campus, as well as 1 national honor society, Phi Beta Kappa. Eighteen departments have honors programs.

Faculty/Classroom: Forty-two percent of faculty are male; 48%, female. All teach undergraduates, 90% do research, and 90% do both. No introductory courses are taught by graduate students. The average class size in an introductory lecture is 25; in a laboratory, 15; and in a regular course offering, 12.

Admissions: About 70% of the 1993–94 applicants were accepted. About 52% of the current freshmen were in the top fifth of their class; 75% were in the top two fifths. Three freshmen graduated first in their class.

Requirements: The SAT I is required. SAT II: Subject tests in writing and 2 others are recommended. Applicants should be graduates of an accredited high school or have earned the GED. Secondary preparation should include at least 14 academic units, preferably 4 in English, 3 in mathematics (algebra I and II and geometry), 2 each in the same foreign language and in laboratory science, and 2 or 3 in social studies. A personal essay is required and an interview is recommended. Prospective arts majors are urged to seek an audition or submit a portfolio. AP credits are accepted. Important factors used in the admissions decision are advanced placement or honor courses, recommendations by school officials, extracurricular activities record, leadership record, and parents or siblings attending the school.

Procedure: Freshmen are admitted fall and spring. Entrance exams should be taken in spring of the junior year or fall of the senior year. Early decision applications should be filed by November 15; regular applications, by February 1 for fall entry and December 1 for spring entry, along with an application fee of $35. Notification of early decision is sent December 15; regular decision, April 1. There are early decision, early admissions, and deferred admissions plans. Sixteen early decision candidates were accepted for the 1993–94 class.

Transfer: Some 47 transfer students enrolled in a recent year. Applicants must present a GPA of at least 2.5 in 30 hours of college work. An interview, a personal essay, and recommendations from college teachers or counselors are also required. A total of 60 semester hours out of 120 must be completed at Goucher.

Visiting: There are regularly scheduled orientations for prospective students, including an academic presentation, student panel, discussions, a campus tour, an interview, and an opportunity to sit in on classes and to meet with faculty, coaches, and other staff. There are guides for informal visits and visitors may sit in on classes and stay overnight at the school. To arrange for a visit, contact the Office of Admissions at (410) 337–6100 or (800) 638–4278 (out-of-state).

Financial Aid: In 1993–94 70% of all current freshmen and 71% of continuing students received some form of financial aid. About 67% of freshmen and 52% of continuing students received need-based aid. The average freshman award was $13,000. Of that total, scholarships or need-based grants averaged $8300 ($13,000 maximum); loans averaged $2700 ($4000 maximum); and work contracts averaged $1010 ($1500 maximum). Forty-six percent of undergraduate students work part-time. Average earnings from campus work for the school year are $1200. The average financial indebtedness of the 1992–93 graduate was $9000. Goucher is a member of CSS. The FAF and FAFSA, and the college's own financial statement are required. The deadline for financial aid applications is February 15.

International Students: There are currently 16 international students enrolled. The school actively recruits these students. They must take the TOEFL and achieve a minimum score of 550. The student must also take the SAT I.

Computers: The college provides computer facilities for student use. The mainframe is a Prime 4050. There is an Apple Macintosh microcomputer laboratory as well as 150 PCs available in academic laboratories, dorms, and the library. Some are available around the clock. There are no time limits on using the system and no fees.

Graduates: In 1992–93 216 bachelor's degrees were awarded. The most popular majors among graduates were English (12%), education (10%), and psychology (8%). Within an average freshman class, 75% graduate in 4 years and 85% in 5 years. Some 18 companies recruited on campus in 1992–93. In the 1992 graduating class, 26% of both men and women were enrolled in graduate school within 6 months of graduation; 62% had found employment.

Admissions Contact: Elise A. Seraydarian, Director of Admissions.

HOOD COLLEGE
C-2

Frederick, MD 21701–8575   (301) 696–3400; (800) 922–1599

Full-time: 38 men, 672 women	Faculty: 76; IIA, --$
Part-time: 109 men, 290 women	Ph.D.s: 91%
Graduate: 343 men, 628 women	Student/Faculty: 9 to 1
Year: semesters, summer session	Tuition: $13,258
Application Deadline: March 31	Room & Board: $5752
Freshman Class: 669 applied, 565 accepted, 166 enrolled	
SAT I or ACT: required	VERY COMPETITIVE

Hood College, founded in 1893, is an independent, comprehensive college primarily for women. Distinctive for its combination of liberal arts education and professional preparation, Hood offers 31 undergraduate majors. Hood has an especially strong reputation in the sciences, and is noted for its application of computing technology to a new library, an expanded career center, and throughout the campus. There is one graduate school. In addition to regional accreditation, Hood has baccalaureate program accreditation with ADA, AHEA, and CAHEA. The library contains 164,597 volumes, 394,775 microform items, and 175,000 audiovisual forms, and subscribes to 932 periodicals. Computerized library sources and services include the card catalog, interlibrary loans, database searching, and access to Internet and CARL. Special learning facilities include a learning re-

source center, art gallery, aquatic center, child development laboratory, observatory, and energy management demonstration facility. The newest facilities include a library information technology center, which is the hub of a campus-wide computing network. The 50-acre campus is in an urban area 45 miles northwest of Washington, D.C. Including residence halls, there are 31 buildings on campus.

Student Life: About 58% of undergraduates are from Maryland. Students come from 25 states, 30 foreign countries, and Canada. Eighty-six percent are from public schools; 14% from private. Sixty-seven percent are white; 17% African American. Forty-one percent are Protestant, 13% Catholic, and 38% claim no religious affiliation. The average age of freshmen is 18; all undergraduates, 20. Eighteen percent drop out by the end of their first year; 65% remain to graduate.

Housing: A total of 600 students can be accommodated in college housing. College-sponsored living facilities include 9 single-sex dormitories. In addition, there are honors houses, language houses, and special-interest floors in the residence halls (which may change each year;) in 1993–94 there was a wellness floor and 2 nonsmoking floors. On-campus housing is guaranteed for all 4 years. Seventy-three percent of students live on campus; of those, 75% remain on campus on weekends. All students may keep cars on campus.

Activities: There are no fraternities or sororities on campus. There are 49 groups on campus, including art, choir, chorale, chorus, dance, drama, environment, ethnic, gay, honors, international, literary magazine, musical theater, newspaper, opera, political, professional, radio and TV, religious, social, social service, student government, and yearbook. Popular campus events include Hood Olympics weekend, Ring formal, Mother-Daughter and Dad-Daughter weekends, Messiah weekend, Soph Revue, Black History month, and Liberation of the Black Mind weekend.

Sports: There are 6 intercollegiate and 8 intramural sports for women. Athletic and recreation facilities include a weight-training room, an aerobics room, indoor and outdoor swimming pools, a dance studio, a mile-long par course, an archery range, a softball diamond, tennis and volleyball courts, and field hockey and lacrosse fields.

Disabled Students: Thirty-five percent of the campus is accessible to disabled students. The following facilities are available: wheelchair ramps, elevators, special parking, specially equipped rest rooms, and special class scheduling.

Services: In addition to many counseling and information services, tutoring is available in some subjects. There is also remedial math, reading, and writing. Such services as reader service for the blind and interpreters for the hearing impaired are arranged for individual students. There are also services for students with learning disabilities.

Campus Safety and Security: Campus safety and security measures include 24-hour foot and vehicle patrol, escort service, informal discussions, and pamphlets, posters, and films. In addition, there are emergency telephones, lighted pathways and sidewalks, and an electronic access control system with 24-hour monitoring in all residence halls.

Programs of Study: Hood awards the B.A., B.S., and B.B.A. degrees. Master's degrees are also awarded. Bachelor's degrees are awarded in BIOLOGICAL SCIENCE (biochemistry, biology/biological science, and nutrition), BUSINESS (business administration, management, and retailing), COMMUNICATIONS AND THE ARTS (art history, communications, English, French, German, Spanish, and studio arts), COMPUTER AND PHYSICAL SCIENCE (chemistry, computer science, information and computer sciences, and mathematics), EDUCATION (art, early childhood, English, foreign languages, history, home economics, mathematics, science, secondary, and special), ENGINEERING AND ENVIRONMENTAL DESIGN (environmental studies and interior design), HEALTH PROFESSIONS (medical laboratory technology), SOCIAL SCIENCE (economics, history, Latin American studies, law and society, philosophy, political science/government, psychobiology, psychology, religion, religion and philosphy, social work, and sociology). Biology, mathematics, art history, computer science, sociology and education are the strongest academically. Management, biology, education, communication arts, and psychology have the largest enrollments.

Required: To graduate, students must complete a total of 124 credit hours, with a minimum GPA of 2.0. A minimum of 24 to 48 hours is required in a student's major, depending on the degree being sought. All students must complete 38 to 40 credits in the core curriculum, which includes basic skills courses, courses in methods in inquiry, and interdisciplinary courses in Western civilization, non-Western civilization, and society, science and technology.

Special: The college offers a Washington semester, dual majors, student-designed majors, credit for life experience, nondegree study, pass/fail options, and cross-registration with area colleges and the Duke University Marine Sciences Education Consortium. Internships of up to 15 credits are available in all majors at more than 1000 sites throughout the United States and abroad. Students may study abroad in the Dominican Republic, Japan, Spain, France, and other countries. A 3–2 engineering degree is offered with George Washington Uni-

versity. There is a freshman honors program on campus, as well as 11 national honor societies. Students in any major may be selected to complete a senior-year departmental honors project.

Faculty/Classroom: Forty-two percent of faculty are male; 58%, female. All teach undergraduates; 50% also do research. The average class size in an introductory lecture is 17; in a laboratory, 12; and in a regular course offering, 18.

Admissions: About 84% of the 1993–94 applicants were accepted. The SAT scores for the 1993–94 freshman class were as follows: Verbal—53% below 500, 37% between 500 and 599, and 10% between 600 and 700; Math—41% below 500, 39% between 500 and 599, 19% between 600 and 700, and 1% above 700. The ACT scores were 19% below 21, 26% between 21 and 23, 19% between 24 and 26, 16% between 27 and 28, and 19% above 28. About 55% of the current freshmen were in the top fifth of their class; 77% were in the top two fifths. There was 1 National Merit finalist. Four freshmen graduated first in their class.

Requirements: Hood requires applicants to be in the upper 40% of their class. A minimum GPA of 2.5 is required. The SAT I or ACT is required. In addition, applicants should be graduates of an accredited secondary school. The GED is accepted. Hood recommends the completion of at least 16 academic credits in high school, including courses in English, social sciences, natural sciences, foreign languages, and mathematics. An essay is required and an interview is recommended. AP and CLEP credits are accepted. Important factors used in the admissions decision are advanced placement or honor courses, leadership record, evidence of special talent, recommendations by school officials, and personality, intangible qualities.

Procedure: Freshmen are admitted fall and spring. Entrance exams should be taken in spring of the junior year or fall of the senior year. There are early reply, early admission, and deferred admission plans. Early reply applications should be filed by November 15 for fall entry and January 31 for spring entry; regular applications, by March 31 and December 31, along with an application fee of $30. Notification of early reply is sent December 15 and February 15; regular decision, April 15. Some 145 early reply candidates were accepted for the 1993–94 class.

Transfer: Thirty-four transfer students enrolled in 1993–94. Applicants must have at least 12 college credits and a minimum GPA of 2.5. A total of 70 credits may be transferred. A total of 30 credits out of 124 must be completed at Hood.

Visiting: There are regularly scheduled orientations for prospective students, including tours and meetings with faculty, students, and administrators. One-day admission seminars offer the opportunity to participate in a faculty-taught seminar and an admissions interview, after which students receive an indication of their admission decision. There are guides for informal visits and visitors may sit in on classes and stay overnight at the school. To arrange for a visit, contact the Office of Admissions at (301) 696–3400 or (800) 922–1599.

Financial Aid: In 1993–94 70% of all current freshmen and 59% of continuing students received some form of financial aid. About 65% of freshmen and 55% of continuing students received need-based aid. The average freshman award was $11,000. Of that total, scholarships or need-based grants averaged $6500 ($10,000 maximum); loans averaged $3000 ($5500 maximum); and work contracts averaged $1500. Thirty-three percent of undergraduate students work part-time. Average earnings from campus work for the school year are $1400. The average financial indebtedness of the 1992–93 graduate was $11,000. Hood is a member of CSS. The FAF and FAFSA is required. The deadline for financial aid applications is March 31.

International Students: There are currently 51 international students enrolled. The school actively recruits these students. They must take the TOEFL (and achieve a minimum score of 530) or SAT I.

Computers: The college provides computer facilities for student use. The mainframe is a DEC VAX 6210. Students may use the 12 PCs in a 24-hour computing laboratory or the 16 terminals in the VAX laboratory to access the mainframe or dial in from off campus. There are 67 IBM-compatible microcomputers available in 6 student laboratories and 28 Apple and Macintosh microcomputers available in other laboratories. All students may access the system. It may be used 24 hours per day from a PC in the 24-hour computing laboratory or if student has a modem, otherwise weekdays 8:30 A.M. to 12 midnight in the terminal laboratory. There are no time limits on using the system and no fees.

Graduates: In 1992–93 261 bachelor's degrees were awarded. The most popular majors among graduates were management (17%), biology (12%), and education and psychology (11%). Within an average freshman class, 2% graduate in 3 years, 60% in 4 years, 65% in 5 years, and 68% in 6 years. Some 200 companies recruited on campus in 1992–93. In the 1992 graduating class, 30% of the women were enrolled in graduate school within 6 months of graduation; 70% of the women had found employment.

Admissions Contact: Nancy Gillece, Director of Admissions.

JOHNS HOPKINS UNIVERSITY D-2
Baltimore, MD 21218
(410) 516–8171

Full-time: 2092 men, 1244 women	Faculty: 351; I, av$
Part-time: 26 men, 9 women	Ph.D.s: 99%
Graduate: 1097 men, 735 women	Student/Faculty: 10 to 1
Year: 4–1–4, summer session	Tuition: $17,900
Application Deadline: January 1	Room & Board: $6460
Freshman Class: 8474 applied, 3436 accepted, 911 enrolled	
SAT I Verbal/Math: 610/700	ACT: 30 MOST COMPETITIVE

The Johns Hopkins University, founded in 1876, is a private, coeducational multicampus institution offering degree programs through schools of arts and sciences, engineering, international studies, nursing, medicine, hygiene and public health, and the Peabody Institute (music). There are 4 undergraduate and 8 graduate schools. In addition to regional accreditation, Johns Hopkins has baccalaureate program accreditation with ABET. The 2 libraries contain 2.3 million volumes and 28,587 audiovisual forms, and subscribe to 20,677 periodicals. Computerized library sources and services include the card catalog, interlibrary loans, and database searching. Special learning facilities include an art gallery, radio station, and TV station. The 140-acre campus is in an urban area 3 miles north of downtown Baltimore. Including residence halls, there are 33 buildings on campus.

Student Life: About 85% of undergraduates are from out-of-state, mostly the Middle Atlantic. Students come from 50 states, 24 foreign countries, and Canada. Fifty-seven percent are from public schools; 36% from private. Sixty-five percent are white; 23% Asian American. Thirty percent are Protestant; 25% claim no religious affiliation; 25% Catholic; 15% Jewish. The average age of freshmen is 18; all undergraduates, 19.5. Six percent drop out by the end of their first year; 88% remain to graduate.

Housing: A total of 2000 students can be accommodated in college housing. College-sponsored living facilities include single-sex and coed dormitories, off-campus apartments, and married-student housing. In addition, there are special interest houses. On-campus housing is available on a lottery system for upperclassmen. Eighty-one percent of students live on campus; of those, all remain on campus on weekends. Alcohol is not permitted. Upperclassmen may keep cars on campus.

Activities: About 30% of men belong to 13 national fraternities; about 25% of women belong to 3 national sororities. There are 80 groups on campus, including art, band, cheerleading, chess, choir, chorale, chorus, computers, dance, drama, ethnic, film, gay, honors, international, jazz band, literary magazine, marching band, musical theater, newspaper, opera, orchestra, pep band, photography, political, professional, radio and TV, religious, social, social service, student government, symphony, and yearbook. Popular campus events include Spring Fair, Fiji Islander, MSE Symposium, Cultural Awareness Week, and Relaxation Week.

Sports: There are 13 intercollegiate sports for men and 11 for women, and 18 intramural sports for men and 16 for women. Athletic and recreation facilities include a 4000-seat stadium, outdoor playing fields, a swimming pool and diving board, wrestling and fencing rooms, a weight room, saunas, and courts for basketball, volleyball, badminton, squash, and handball.

Disabled Students: Eighty percent of the campus is accessible to disabled students. The following facilities are available: wheelchair ramps, elevators, special parking, specially equipped rest rooms, special class scheduling, lowered drinking fountains, and lowered telephones.

Services: In addition to many counseling and information services, tutoring is available in most subjects. In addition, there is a reader service for the blind.

Campus Safety and Security: Campus safety and security measures include 24-hour foot and vehicle patrol, self defense education, escort service, and shuttle buses. In addition, there are informal discussions, pamphlets, posters, and films, emergency telephones, and lighted pathways and sidewalks.

Programs of Study: Johns Hopkins awards the B.A. and B.S. degrees. Master's and doctoral degrees also are awarded. Bachelor's degrees are awarded in BIOLOGICAL SCIENCE (biology/biological science and biophysics), COMMUNICATIONS AND THE ARTS (art history and appreciation, classics, English, French, German, and music), COMPUTER AND PHYSICAL SCIENCE (chemistry, computer science, earth science, mathematics, and physics), ENGINEERING AND ENVIRONMENTAL DESIGN (biomedical engineering, chemical engineering, civil engineering, electrical/electronics engineering, engineering, engineering mechanics, environmental engineering, materials engineering, and mechanical engineering), HEALTH PROFESSIONS (premedicine and public health), SOCIAL SCIENCE (anthropology, cognitive science, economics, history, history of science, international studies, Latin American studies, Near Eastern studies, philosophy, political science/government, prelaw, psy-

chology, sociology, and urban studies). The sciences, engineering, international studies, history, and writing seminars are the strongest academically. Biology, international studies, and biomedical engineering have the largest enrollments.

Required: Although there is no required core curriculum, all students must take 30 hours outside their major field. The B.A. requires a total of 120 hours; the B.S. in engineering programs requires 120 to 130 hours, depending on the major. A GPA of at least 2.0 is required for graduation. All students must take at least 4 courses (2 for engineers) with a writing-intensive component in order to graduate.

Special: Johns Hopkins offers an extensive array of special programs, including internships, dual majors in music and arts and sciences or engineering, cross-registration with all Baltimore-area colleges and all Johns Hopkins divisions, a cooperative 5-year civil engineering program, a student-designed Washington semester, and various multidisciplinary programs. Students may enroll at Johns Hopkins in Bologna, Italy, or Nanjing, China, or arrange programs in Europe, Africa, the Near or Far East, or Great Britain. Accelerated degrees are available in 21 fields. Students may earn combined B.A.-B.S. degrees in biomedical, computer, or mathematical engineering or a combined B.A.-B.M. through the Peabody Institute. The first freshman semester is taken on a pass/fail basis; thereafter, there are additional pass/fail options in nonmajor courses. There is a chapter of Phi Beta Kappa on campus. Most departments have honors programs.

Faculty/Classroom: Ninety-four percent of faculty are male; 6%, female. Ninety-eight percent teach undergraduates, and all do research. Graduate students teach 15% of introductory courses. The average class size in an introductory lecture is 300; in a laboratory, 50; and in a regular course offering, 30.

Admissions: About 41% of the 1993–94 applicants were accepted. The SAT scores for the 1993–94 freshman class were as follows: Verbal—8% below 500, 32% between 500 and 599, 52% between 600 and 700, and 7% above 700; Math—1% below 500, 10% between 500 and 599, 46% between 600 and 700, and 44% above 700. The ACT scores were 1% below 21, 3% between 21 and 23, 8% between 24 and 26, 29% between 27 and 28, and 59% above 28. About 92% of the current freshmen were in the top fifth of their class; 99% were in the top two fifths. There were 93 National Merit finalists and 104 semifinalists. A total of 84 freshmen graduated first in their class.

Requirements: The SAT I or ACT is required. Applicants should be graduates of an accredited secondary school or have the GED. The university recommends that secondary preparation include 4 years each of English and mathematics, 2 of a foreign language, 2 or 3 of social science or history, and at least 2, preferably 3, of laboratory science. Applicants must submit SAT II scores in writing and 2 other subjects of their choice. Two personal essays are required and an interview is recommended. AP credits are accepted. Important factors used in the admissions decision are advanced placement or honor courses, leadership record, extracurricular activities record, recommendations by school officials, and evidence of special talent.

Procedure: Freshmen are admitted in the fall. Entrance exams should be taken by January for regular decision, or November for early decision. Early decision applications should be filed by November 1; regular applications, by January 1 for fall entry, along with an application fee of $50. Notification of early decision is sent December 15; regular decision, by April. There are early decision, early admissions, and deferred admissions plans. A total of 225 early decision candidates were accepted for the 1993–94 class. A waiting list is an active part of the admissions procedure, with about 1% of applicants on the list.

Transfer: A total of 42 transfer students enrolled in 1993–94. Applicants should have sophomore or junior standing and at least a B average in previous college work. Applications must include a written essay and at least 1 letter of recommendation. High school records and standardized test scores will also be considered. Sixty credits of 120 to 130 must be completed at Johns Hopkins.

Visiting: There are regularly scheduled orientations for prospective students, including campus tours and group information sessions. There are guides for informal visits and visitors may sit in on classes and stay overnight at the school. To arrange for a visit, contact the Office of Admissions at (410) 516–8171.

Financial Aid: In 1993–94, 55% of all students received some form of financial aid; 42% received need-based aid. The average freshman award was $15,700. Of that total, scholarships or need-based grants averaged $11,000 ($19,000 maximum); loans averaged $3000 ($4500 maximum); and work contracts averaged $1700 ($1800 maximum). Fifty percent of undergraduate students work part-time. Average earnings from campus work for the school year are $1200. The average financial indebtedness of the 1992–93 graduate was $11,000. Johns Hopkins is a member of CSS. The college's own financial statement and the FAFSA are required. The deadline for financial aid applications is January 15.

International Students: There are currently 130 international students enrolled. They must take the TOEFL with a minimum score of 560 and SAT I. Applicants must also take the SAT II: writing test.

Computers: Johns Hopkins provides computer facilities for student use. The mainframes are an AT&T 3B4000, a DEC VAX 6410, and an IBM 3081. Microcomputer laboratories are available for student use in academic buildings and in some residence halls. All students may access the system 24 hours a day, 7 days a week. There are no fees.

Graduates: In 1992–93, 776 bachelor's degrees were awarded. The most popular majors among graduates were biology (14%), international studies (8%), and biomedical engineering (6%). Within an average freshman class, 4% graduate in 3 years, 80% in 4 years, 87% in 5 years, and 88% in 6 years. Some 120 companies recruited on campus in 1992–93. In the 1992 graduating class, 62% of the men and 53% of the women were enrolled in graduate school within 6 months of graduation; 37% of the men and 43% of the women had found employment.

Admissions Contact: Richard M. Fuller, Director of Admissions.

LOYOLA COLLEGE
D-2

Baltimore, MD 21210 (410) 532–5012; (800) 221–9107

Full-time: 1355 men, 1680 women	Faculty: 213; IIA, av$
Part-time: 115 men, 97 women	Ph.D.s: 88%
Graduate: 1322 men, 1652 women	Student/Faculty: 14 to 1
Year: semesters, summer session	Tuition: $11,975
Application Deadline: February 1	Room & Board: $6060
Freshman Class: 4077 applied, 3137 accepted, 751 enrolled	
SAT I Verbal/Math: 507/563	**VERY COMPETITIVE**

Loyola College, founded in 1852, is a private, coeducational liberal arts college affiliated with the Roman Catholic Church and the Jesuit tradition. It offers degree programs in arts and sciences and business and management. There are 2 undergraduate schools. In addition to regional accreditation, Loyola has baccalaureate program accreditation with AACSB and ABET. The library contains 264,145 volumes, 360,238 microform items, and 21,039 audiovisual forms, and subscribes to 2008 periodicals. Computerized library sources and services include interlibrary loans and database searching. Special learning facilities include an art gallery and radio station. The 63-acre campus is in a suburban area 3 miles from downtown Baltimore. Including residence halls, there are 22 buildings on campus.

Student Life: About 53% of undergraduates are from out-of-state, mostly the Middle Atlantic. Students come from 36 states. Fifty-four percent are from public schools; 46% from private. Ninety-one percent are white. Seventy-six percent are Catholic; 11% Protestant. The average age of freshmen is 18; all undergraduates, 20. Ten percent drop out by the end of their first year; 70% remain to graduate.

Housing: A total of 2200 students can be accommodated in college housing. College-sponsored living facilities include single-sex and coed dormitories and on-campus apartments. In addition, there are honors houses and special interest houses. On-campus housing is available on a first-come, first-served basis. Seventy-one percent of students live on campus. Alcohol is not permitted. Upperclassmen may keep cars on campus.

Activities: There are no fraternities or sororities on campus. There are 80 groups on campus, including art, band, cheerleading, chess, choir, chorale, chorus, computers, dance, drama, ethnic, film, honors, international, jazz band, literary magazine, musical theater, newspaper, orchestra, pep band, photography, political, professional, radio and TV, religious, social, social service, student government, symphony, and yearbook. Popular campus events include Parents Weekend, International Festival, Senior 100 concerts, and SYR Dance.

Sports: There are 7 intercollegiate sports for men and 7 for women, and 11 intramural sports for men and 11 for women. Athletic and recreation facilities include a pool, a sauna, a weight room, racquetball, tennis, and squash courts, a 3000-seat arena, a 2000-seat multipurpose outdoor facility, and a fitness center.

Disabled Students: Ninety-five percent of the campus is accessible to disabled students. The following facilities are available: wheelchair ramps, elevators, special parking, specially equipped rest rooms, special class scheduling, lowered drinking fountains, and lowered telephones.

Services: In addition to many counseling and information services, tutoring is available in most subjects. There is also remedial math.

Campus Safety and Security: Campus safety and security measures include 24-hour foot and vehicle patrol, escort service, shuttle buses, and informal discussions. In addition, there are pamphlets, posters, and films and lighted pathways and sidewalks.

Programs of Study: Loyola awards the B.A., B.S., B.B.A., B.S.E.E., and B.S.E.S. degrees. Master's and doctoral degrees also are awarded. Bachelor's degrees are awarded in BIOLOGICAL SCIENCE (biology/biological science), BUSINESS (accounting and business administration and management), COMMUNICATIONS AND THE ARTS (communications, creative writing, English, fine arts, French, German, Latin, and Spanish), COMPUTER AND PHYSICAL SCIENCE (chemistry, computer science, mathematics, and physics), EDUCATION (elementary and secondary), ENGINEERING AND ENVI-

RONMENTAL DESIGN (electrical/electronics engineering and engineering), HEALTH PROFESSIONS (speech pathology/audiology), SOCIAL SCIENCE (economics, history, philosophy, political science/government, psychology, sociology, and theological studies). General business, communications, accounting, psychology, and political science have the largest enrollments.

Required: All students must complete 120 hours, including 36 in the major, with at least a 2.0 GPA. The required core curriculum includes 1 course each in writing and ethics, 2 courses each in history, literature, philosophy, theology, and social science, 3 courses in mathematics, computer science, or natural science, and 2 to 4 courses in a foreign language.

Special: Loyola offers cooperative programs with Johns Hopkins and Towson State Universities, Goucher College, and the College of Notre Dame of Maryland. Credit-bearing internships are available in most majors, and there are study-abroad programs in Thailand and Belgium. There is a freshman honors program on campus, as well as 18 national honor societies. One department has an honors program.

Faculty/Classroom: Seventy percent of faculty are male; 30%, female. Ninety percent teach undergraduates, 94% do research, and 94% do both. The average class size in an introductory lecture is 130; in a laboratory, 24; and in a regular course offering, 23.

Admissions: About 77% of the 1993–94 applicants were accepted. The SAT scores for the 1993–94 freshman class were as follows: Verbal—47% below 500, 39% between 500 and 599, 13% between 600 and 700, and 1% above 700; Math—20% below 500, 46% between 500 and 599, 28% between 600 and 700, and 7% above 700. About 45% of the current freshmen were in the top fifth of their class; 77% were in the top two fifths. About 13 freshmen graduated first in their class.

Requirements: Loyola requires applicants to be in the upper 20% of their class. A minimum GPA of 3.0 is required. The SAT I is required. Applicants should have graduated from an accredited secondary school or have earned the GED. Secondary preparation should include 4 years of English, 2 to 3 each of mathematics and foreign language, 1 to 2 of natural science, and 1 of history. A personal essay is required; an interview is recommended. AP and CLEP credits are accepted. Important factors used in the admissions decision are advanced placement or honor courses, recommendations by school officials, evidence of special talent, parents or siblings attending the school, and leadership record.

Procedure: Freshmen are admitted to all sessions. Entrance exams should be taken by December of the senior year. Applications should be filed by February 1 for fall entry, December 15 for spring entry, and May 1 for summer entry, along with an application fee of $25. Notification is sent April 15. There are early admissions and deferred admissions plans. A waiting list is an active part of the admissions procedure, with about 1% of applicants on the list.

Transfer: About 141 transfer students enrolled in a recent year. Transfer applicants should have at least a 2.5 GPA and should submit SAT I scores. A total of 60 credits out of 120 must be completed at Loyola.

Visiting: There are regularly scheduled orientations for prospective students. There are guides for informal visits, and visitors may sit in on classes. To arrange for a visit, contact the Admissions Office at (410) 532-5012.

Financial Aid: In a recent year, 59% of all current freshmen and 54% of continuing students received some form of financial aid. The average freshman award was $9460. Of that total, scholarships or need-based grants averaged $5120 ($10,320 maximum); loans averaged $2940 ($3625 maximum); and work contracts averaged $1400 (maximum). Eight percent of undergraduate students work part-time. Average earnings from campus work for the school year are $1075. The average financial indebtedness of a recent year's graduate was $6640. Loyola is a member of CSS. The FAF and the college's own financial statement are required. The deadline for financial aid applications is March 1.

International Students: There are currently 50 international students enrolled. The school actively recruits these students. They must take the TOEFL and achieve a minimum score of 550. The student must also take the SAT I.

Computers: The college provides computer facilities for student use. The mainframes are 2 DEC VAX 11/785s. There are also more than 100 IBM PC, Apple IIe, and Apple Macintosh personal computers available in the science center, library, and dormitories. All students may access the system. There are no time limits on using the system and no fees.

Graduates: In a recent year, 767 bachelor's degrees were awarded. Within an average freshman class, 65% graduate in 4 years, 69% in 5 years, and 70% in 6 years. Some 245 companies recruited on campus in an earlier year.

Admissions Contact: William Bossemeyer, Director of Admissions.

MARYLAND INSTITUTE, COLLEGE OF ART D-2
Baltimore, MD 21217 (410) 225-2222

Full-time: 356 men, 436 women	Faculty: 68; IIB, --$
Part-time: 11 men, 24 women	Ph.D.s: 72%
Graduate: 39 men, 36 women	Student/Faculty: 12 to 1
Year: semesters, summer session	Tuition: $13,080
Application Deadline: March 1	Room & Board: $5340
Freshman Class: 629 applied, 399 accepted, 186 enrolled	
SAT I or ACT: see profile	SPECIAL

Maryland Institute, College of Art, founded in 1826, is a private, coeducational institution offering undergraduate and graduate degrees in art, painting, sculpture, and photography. There is one undergraduate and 5 graduate schools. In addition to regional accreditation, Maryland Institute has baccalaureate program accreditation with NASAD. The library contains 50,000 volumes and 400 audiovisual forms, and subscribes to 200 periodicals. Special learning facilities include a learning resource center and 3 art galleries, open to the public year-round, and student display spaces. The 12-acre campus is located in downtown Baltimore. Including residence halls, there are 19 buildings on campus.

Student Life: About 63% of undergraduates are from out-of-state, mostly the Northeast. Students come from 37 states, 36 foreign countries, and Canada. Eighty percent are white. The average age of freshmen is 19; all undergraduates, 21. Seventeen percent drop out by the end of their first year; 60% remain to graduate.

Housing: A total of 350 students can be accommodated in college housing. College-sponsored living facilities include coed dormitories and on-campus apartments. On-campus housing is guaranteed for the freshman year only, is available on a first-come, first-served basis, and is available on a lottery system for upperclassmen. Eighty-five percent of students live on campus; of those, 90% remain on campus on weekends. Alcohol is not permitted. All students may keep cars on campus.

Activities: There are no fraternities or sororities on campus. There are many groups on campus, including art, chess, dance, drama, ethnic, film, gay, international, literary magazine, newspaper, photography, professional, religious, social, and student government. Popular campus events include regular bus trips to galleries and museums in New York and Washington, D.C., dances, art sales, exhibition openings, film festivals, lectures, visiting artist receptions, an annual Halloween costume party, and poetry readings.

Sports: There is no sports program at Maryland Institute. Athletic and recreation facilities include classes in aerobics, dance, and karate; a nearby recreation center has volleyball, basketball, and weight-training facilities.

Disabled Students: Seventy-five percent of the campus is accessible to disabled students. The following facilities are available: wheelchair ramps, elevators, special parking, and special class scheduling.

Services: In addition to many counseling and information services, tutoring is available in all liberal arts subjects. There is remedial reading and writing.

Campus Safety and Security: Campus safety and security measures include 24-hour foot and vehicle patrol, self defense education, escort service, and shuttle buses. In addition, there are informal discussions, lighted pathways and sidewalks, guards in every building, and a security lecture as part of orientation.

Programs of Study: Maryland Institute awards the B.F.A. degree. Master's degrees also are awarded. Bachelor's degrees are awarded in COMMUNICATIONS AND THE ARTS (ceramic art and design, drawing, fiber/textiles/weaving, fine arts, graphic design, painting, photography, printmaking, and sculpture), ENGINEERING AND ENVIRONMENTAL DESIGN (interior design). Fine arts and visual communications are the strongest programs academically and have the largest enrollments.

Required: All students complete a foundation program in their first year, including courses in painting, drawing, 2- and 3-dimensional design, and liberal arts. Of a total 126 to 132 credits, students must take 84 in studio, one third of courses in liberal arts and two thirds in studio arts, with 63 to 69 credits in the major, and earn at least a 2.0 GPA. Seniors must undertake independent studio and study, a requirement often met by internships.

Special: Exchange programs are offered with Goucher College, Johns Hopkins University, Peabody Conservatory, Loyola College, or the University of Baltimore. Cross-registration is possible with any member schools in the Alliance of Independent Colleges of Art and the East Coast Art Schools consortium. Study abroad in the junior year in any of 7 countries, student-designed majors, and nondegree study in liberal arts are possible. There are work-study programs, and juniors and seniors who meet prerequisites are eligible for credit-bearing internships locally and nationally.

Faculty/Classroom: Fifty-seven percent of faculty are male; 43%, female. All teach undergraduates. No introductory courses are taught by graduate students. The average class size in an introductory lecture is 20 and in a regular course offering, 20.

Admissions: About 63% of the 1993–94 applicants were accepted.

Requirements: SAT I and/or ACT scores are required for course placement purposes only; they are not considered in the admissions decision. Applicants should have graduated from accredited secondary schools or earned the GED. No particular secondary preparation is required or recommended. Emphasis is primarily on the applicant's portfolio, which is reviewed as part of the admissions process. Applicants submit 12 to 20 pieces of their best current work in and out of school, including samples of drawing from observation. AP credits are accepted. Important factors used in the admissions decision are evidence of special talent, advanced placement or honor courses, personality, intangible qualities, recommendations by school officials, and recommendations by alumni.

Procedure: Freshmen are admitted fall and spring. Early decision applications should be filed by November 15; regular applications, by March 1 for fall entry and December 15 for spring entry, along with an application fee of $35. Notification of early decision is sent January 15; regular decision, on a rolling basis. There are early decision, early admissions, and deferred admissions plans. About 12 early decision candidates were accepted for the 1993–94 class.

Transfer: About 69 transfer students enrolled in 1993–94. Transfer applicants must submit high school and college transcripts, a personal essay, and a portfolio. An interview is recommended. A total of 62 credits out of 126 to 132 must be completed at Maryland Institute.

Visiting: There are regularly scheduled orientations for prospective students. There are guides for informal visits, and visitors may sit in on classes. To arrange for a visit, contact the Admissions Office at (410) 225–2294.

Financial Aid: In 1993–94 67% of all current freshmen and 62% of continuing students received some form of financial aid. About 64% of freshmen received need-based aid. Scholarships or need-based grants averaged $3000 ($5000 maximum); loans averaged $2625; and work contracts averaged $1110. Fifteen percent of undergraduate students work part-time. The average financial indebtedness of the 1992–93 graduate was $13,250. Maryland Institute is a member of CSS. The FAF and the college's own financial statement are required. The deadline for financial aid applications is March 15.

International Students: There are currently 48 international students enrolled. The school actively recruits these students. They must take the TOEFL and achieve a minimum score of 550.

Computers: The college provides computer facilities for student use. Microcomputers are available for use by students. There are no time limits on using the system and no fees. It is recommended that students in visual communication (graphic design/interior architecture and design) have personal computers. The Macintosh is recommended.

Graduates: In 1992–93 186 bachelor's degrees were awarded. The most popular majors among graduates were general fine arts (24%), visual communication (22%), and painting (20%).

Admissions Contact: Theresa Lynch Beobya, Dean of Admissions.

MORGAN STATE UNIVERSITY

Baltimore, MD 21239   **D-2**

Full-time: 1913 men, 2604 women	**Faculty:** 243; IIA, av$
Part-time: 341 men, 404 women	**Ph.D.s:** 80%
Graduate: 228 men, 239 women	**Student/Faculty:** 19 to 1
Year: semesters, summer session	**Tuition:** $2526 ($5062)
Application Deadline: April 15	**Room & Board:** $4840

(410) 319–3000; (800) 332–6674

Freshman Class: 5800 applied, 2881 accepted, 1316 enrolled
SAT I Verbal/Math: 410/440   **COMPETITIVE +**

Morgan State University, founded in 1867, is a comprehensive public institution offering undergraduate and graduate programs leading to liberal arts, preprofessional, and professional degrees. There are 4 undergraduate schools and one graduate school. In addition to regional accreditation, Morgan State has baccalaureate program accreditation with ABET, ADA, CSWE, NAAB, NASAD, NASM, and NCATE. The library contains 333,101 volumes, 141,733 microform items, and 37,422 audiovisual forms, and subscribes to 2526 periodicals. Computerized library sources and services include the card catalog, interlibrary loans, and database searching. Special learning facilities include a learning resource center, art gallery, radio station, and TV station. The 122-acre campus is in a suburban area in the northeast corner of Baltimore. Including residence halls, there are 30 buildings on campus.

Student Life: About 58% of undergraduates are from Maryland. Students come from 37 states and Canada. Ninety-one percent are from public schools; 9% from private. Ninety-three percent are African American. The average age of freshmen is 22; all undergraduates, 25. Thirty percent drop out by the end of their first year; 35% remain to graduate.

Housing: A total of 1700 students can be accommodated in college housing. College-sponsored living facilities include single-sex and coed dormitories and off-campus apartments. In addition, there are honors houses. On-campus housing is available on a first-come, first-served basis. Seventy-four percent of students commute. Alcohol is not permitted. All students may keep cars on campus.

Activities: About 4% of men belong to 4 national fraternities; about 3% of women belong to 4 national sororities. There are 30 groups on campus, including art, band, cheerleading, chess, choir, chorale, chorus, computers, dance, drama, drill team, ethnic, honors, international, jazz band, marching band, musical theater, newspaper, pep band, photography, political, professional, radio and TV, religious, social, social service, student government, and yearbook.

Sports: There are 6 intercollegiate sports for men and 5 for women, and 17 intramural sports for men and 16 for women. Athletic and recreation facilities include a field house, a gymnasium, a weight room, a swimming pool, tennis and racquetball courts, and various playing fields.

Disabled Students: Ninety percent of the campus is accessible to disabled students. The following facilities are available: wheelchair ramps, elevators, special parking, specially equipped rest rooms, special class scheduling, and lowered drinking fountains.

Services: In addition to many counseling and information services, tutoring is available in every subject. There is also a reader service for the blind, and remedial math, reading, and writing. There are also note takers and sign language interpreters for disabled students.

Campus Safety and Security: Campus safety and security measures include 24-hour foot and vehicle patrol, self-defense education, shuttle buses, and informal discussions. In addition, there are pamphlets, posters, and films, emergency telephones, and lighted pathways and sidewalks.

Programs of Study: Morgan State awards the A.B., B.S., and B.S.Ed. degrees. Master's and doctoral degrees also are awarded. Bachelor's degrees are awarded in BIOLOGICAL SCIENCE (biology/biological science), BUSINESS (accounting, business administration and management, management science, marketing/retailing/merchandising, and recreation and leisure services), COMMUNICATIONS AND THE ARTS (dramatic arts, English, fine arts, French, music, Spanish, speech/debate/rhetoric, and telecommunications), COMPUTER AND PHYSICAL SCIENCE (chemistry, computer programming, computer science, information sciences and systems, mathematics, and physics), EDUCATION (business, elementary, health, and physical), ENGINEERING AND ENVIRONMENTAL DESIGN (civil engineering, electrical/electronics engineering, engineering physics, industrial engineering, and preengineering), HEALTH PROFESSIONS (medical laboratory technology, mental health/human services, predentistry, premedicine, and prepharmacy), SOCIAL SCIENCE (African American studies, economics, history, home economics, human ecology, philosophy, political science/government, prelaw, psychology, religion, social work, and sociology). Engineering, chemistry, and physics are the strongest academically. Business administration, accounting, electrical engineering, and telecommunications have the largest enrollments.

Required: In order to graduate, students must complete 120 credit hours, including 74 hours in the major, with a 2.0 GPA. All students must pass speech and writing proficiency examinations prior to their senior year. The 46-credit-hour general education requirement includes courses in English, humanities, logic, history, behavioral science, science, mathematics, African American history, and health and physical education. Seniors must pass a proficiency examination in their major.

Special: Co-op programs in public and private institutions may be arranged for pharmacy honors, predentistry, premedicine, and special education students. The university also offers internships for juniors and seniors, dual majors, and preprofessional physical therapy and prelaw programs. There is a freshman honors program on campus, as well as 28 national honor societies. One department has an honors program.

Faculty/Classroom: Sixty-seven percent of faculty are male; 33%, female. All teach undergraduates, 76% do research, and 76% do both. No introductory courses are taught by graduate students. The average class size in an introductory lecture is 31; in a laboratory, 26; and in a regular course offering, 21.

Admissions: About 50% of the 1993–94 applicants were accepted. The SAT scores for the 1993–94 freshman class were as follows: Verbal—93% below 500, 7% between 500 and 599, and 1% between 600 and 700; Math—83% below 500, 15% between 500 and 599, and 2% between 600 and 700.

Requirements: A minimum GPA of 2.5 is required. The SAT I or ACT is required, with a minimum composite score of 750 on SAT I. In addition, applicants should be high school graduates, or have earned the GED, and are encouraged to have 4 years of English, 3 of mathematics, 2 each of science, social studies, and history, and 1 of a foreign language. A personal essay is recommended and, when appropriate, an audition. AP and CLEP credits are accepted. Impor-

tant factors used in the admissions decision are recommendations by school officials, evidence of special talent, parents or siblings attending the school, recommendations by alumni, and personality, intangible qualities.

Procedure: Freshmen are admitted fall and spring. Entrance exams should be taken during the junior or senior year. Applications should be filed by April 15 for fall entry and December 1 for spring entry, along with an application fee of $20. Notification is sent on a rolling basis, within 4 to 6 weeks after the completed application has been submitted. There is an early admissions plan. A waiting list is an active part of the admissions procedure, with about 35% of applicants on the list.

Transfer: About 300 transfer students enrolled in 1993–94. Applicants with fewer than 12 credits must submit SAT I scores; those with fewer than 24 credits must also submit high school transcripts. Applicants are expected to have at least a 2.0 GPA in all college work attempted and be in good academic standing at the last institution attended. A total of 30 credits out of at least 120 must be completed at Morgan State.

Visiting: There are regularly scheduled orientations for prospective students, including placement testing and academic advising. There are guides for informal visits and visitors may sit in on classes and stay overnight at the school. To arrange for a visit, contact Delores Moffatt at (410) 319-3000.

Financial Aid: In a recent year, 46% of all current freshmen and 63% of continuing students received some form of financial aid. About 46% of freshmen and 45% of continuing students received need-based aid. The average freshman award was $3562. Of that total, scholarships or need-based grants averaged $2748; loans averaged $270; and work contracts averaged $543. Thirteen percent of undergraduate students work part-time. Morgan State is a member of CSS. The FAF and the college's own financial statement are required. The deadline for financial aid applications is April 1.

International Students: There are currently 158 international students enrolled. The school actively recruits these students. They must take the TOEFL or ALIGU and achieve a minimum score of 550 on the TOEFL. The SAT I or ACT is also required except if the student has not attended any school during the preceding 3 years.

Computers: The college provides computer facilities for student use. The mainframes are a DEC VAX 11/780 and an 8300. There are also IBM and Apple Macintosh microcomputers available. Those students enrolled in courses that require such use may access the system.

Graduates: In a recent year, 497 bachelor's degrees were awarded. The most popular majors among graduates were business administration (13%), telecommunications (9%), and management (8%). Within an average freshman class, 12% graduate in 4 years and 12% in 5 years. Some 60 companies recruited on campus in a recent year.

Admissions Contact: Chelseia Harold-Miller, Director of Admission and Recruitment.

MOUNT SAINT MARY'S COLLEGE   D-1
Emmitsburg, MD 21727

(301) 447-5214
(800) 448-4347 (out-of-state)

Full-time: 588 men, 655 women	Faculty: 92; IIB, -$
Part-time: 51 men, 28 women	Ph.D.s: 84%
Graduate: 302 men, 113 women	Student/Faculty: 14 to 1
Year: semesters, summer session	Tuition: $11,725
Application Deadline: March 1	Room & Board: $6100
Freshman Class: 1321 applied, 1159 accepted, 328 enrolled	
SAT I Verbal/Math: 450/500	LESS COMPETITIVE

Mount St. Mary's College, founded in 1808, is a private coeducational liberal arts institution affiliated with the Roman Catholic Church. There are 2 graduate schools. In addition to regional accreditation, the Mount has baccalaureate program accreditation with NASDTEC. The library contains 185,000 volumes, 13,000 microform items, and 4000 audiovisual forms, and subscribes to 950 periodicals. Computerized library sources and services include interlibrary loans and database searching. Special learning facilities include a radio station and TV station. The 1400-acre campus is in a small town 50 miles northwest of Washington, D.C., and 40 miles west of Baltimore. Including residence halls, there are 25 buildings on campus.

Student Life: About 54% of undergraduates are from out-of-state, mostly the Middle Atlantic. Students come from 32 states and 14 foreign countries. Forty-nine percent are from public schools; 51% from private. Ninety percent are white. Most are Catholic. The average age of freshmen is 18; all undergraduates, 20. Ten percent drop out by the end of their first year; 75% remain to graduate.

Housing: A total of 1096 students can be accommodated in college housing. College-sponsored living facilities include single-sex and coed dormitories, on-campus apartments, and married-student housing. In addition, there are honors houses and quiet and special-interest floors. On-campus housing is guaranteed for all 4 years. Eighty-six percent of students live on campus; of those, 85% remain on campus on weekends. All students may keep cars on campus.

Activities: There are no fraternities or sororities on campus. There are 70 groups on campus, including art, cheerleading, choir, chorale, chorus, computers, drama, ethnic, honors, international, literary magazine, musical theater, newspaper, pep band, photography, political, professional, radio and TV, religious, social, social service, student government, and yearbook. Popular campus events include Spring Fling, Special Olympics, Founders Day, Open Picnic, Du Bois Lecture, and Crab Fest.

Sports: There are 9 intercollegiate sports for men and 7 for women, and 28 intramural sports for men and 28 for women. Athletic and recreation facilities include multipurpose indoor courts, a track, a pool, aerobic facilities, a sauna, a weight room, a basketball arena, lighted tennis courts, and playing fields.

Disabled Students: Sixty percent of the campus is accessible to disabled students. The following facilities are available: wheelchair ramps, elevators, special parking, specially equipped rest rooms, lowered drinking fountains, and lowered telephones.

Services: In addition to many counseling and information services, tutoring is available in every subject. There is also a reader service for the blind, and remedial math, reading, and writing, study skills and language laboratories, and a writing center.

Campus Safety and Security: Campus safety and security measures include 24-hour foot and vehicle patrol, escort service, informal discussions, and pamphlets, posters, and films. In addition, there are emergency telephones, lighted pathways and sidewalks, and access control.

Programs of Study: The Mount awards the B.A. and B.S. degrees. Master's degrees also are awarded. Bachelor's degrees are awarded in BIOLOGICAL SCIENCE (biochemistry and biology/biological science), BUSINESS (accounting and banking and finance), COMMUNICATIONS AND THE ARTS (classics, communications, English, fine arts, French, German, rhetoric and writing, and Spanish), COMPUTER AND PHYSICAL SCIENCE (chemistry and mathematics), EDUCATION (elementary), SOCIAL SCIENCE (American culture, economics, history, international studies, philosophy, political science/government, psychology, sociology, and theological studies). Business and finance, accounting, political science, and sociology have the largest enrollments.

Required: Students are required to take a 4-year, 61-credit core curriculum in liberal arts, which includes a freshman seminar, a Western civilization sequence including art and literature, and courses in humanities, science, mathematics, American culture, philosophy, theology, non-Western culture, foreign language, and ethics. Requirements total 120 credits, with 30 to 36 in the major. A 2.0 GPA is necessary for graduation.

Special: Mount St. Mary's College offers co-op programs, cross-registration with Frederick Community College, study abroad, a Washington semester, and secondary teacher certificates in English, social science, and foreign languages. Dual and student-designed majors, an interdisciplinary major in biopsychology, a general studies degree, 3–2 engineering and nursing degrees, and nondegree and accelerated study are possible. A number of independently designed internships and work-study programs and pass/fail options are available. There also is an integrated freshman-year program. There is a freshman honors program on campus, as well as 15 national honor societies. Twelve departments have honors programs.

Faculty/Classroom: Seventy-one percent of faculty are male; 29%, female. All teach undergraduates, 80% do research, and 80% do both. No introductory courses are taught by graduate students. The average class size in an introductory lecture is 25; in a laboratory, 22; and in a regular course offering, 19.

Admissions: About 88% of the 1993–94 applicants were accepted. The SAT scores for the 1993–94 freshman class were as follows: Verbal—68% below 500, 23% between 500 and 599, 8% between 600 and 700, and 1% above 700; Math—44% below 500, 41% between 500 and 599, 12% between 600 and 700, and 3% above 700. About 31% of the current freshmen were in the top fifth of their class; 58% were in the top two fifths. There were 3 National Merit semifinalists. Six freshmen graduated first in their class.

Requirements: The SAT I or ACT is required. Applicants should have graduated from an accredited secondary school or earned the GED. Secondary preparation should include 4 years of English, 3 years each of mathematics, history, natural science, and social sciences, and 2 years of a foreign language. A personal essay is required. An interview is recommended. AP and CLEP credits are accepted. Important factors used in the admissions decision are advanced placement or honor courses, evidence of special talent, extracurricular activities record, leadership record, and geographic diversity.

Procedure: Freshmen are admitted fall and spring. Entrance exams should be taken by January of the senior year. Early decision applications should be filed by December 1; regular applications, by March 1 for fall entry and December 1 for spring entry, along with an application fee of $25. Notification of early decision is sent December 15; regular decision, April 1. There are early admissions and deferred admissions plans. Some 75 early decision candidates were accepted

for the 1993–94 class. A waiting list is an active part of the admissions procedure, with about 5% of applicants on the list.

Transfer: About 40 transfer students enrolled in 1993–94. Transfer applicants should have at least a 2.5 GPA in previous college work, be in good academic and disciplinary standing, and account for all time elapsed since graduation from high school. A total of at least 30 credits out of 120 must be completed at the Mount.

Visiting: There are regularly scheduled orientations for prospective students, including information sessions on academic programs, community life, admissions, and financial aid, plus campus tours. There are guides for informal visits and visitors may sit in on classes and stay overnight at the school. To arrange for a visit, contact the Admission Office at (301) 447-5214 or (800) 448-4347 (out-of-state).

Financial Aid: In 1993–94 70% of all current freshmen and 70% of continuing students received some form of financial aid. About 63% of freshmen and 60% of continuing students received need-based aid. The average freshman award was $9555. Of that total, scholarships or need-based grants averaged $6200 ($17,825 maximum); loans averaged $2400 ($4125 maximum); and work contracts averaged $1000 ($1500 maximum). Thirty-five percent of undergraduate students work part-time. Average earnings from campus work for the school year are $1200. The average financial indebtedness of the 1992–93 graduate was $7600. The Mount is a member of CSS. The FAF and the FAFSA are required. The deadline for financial aid applications is March 15.

International Students: There are currently 25 international students enrolled. They must take the TOEFL and achieve a minimum score of 550.

Computers: The college provides computer facilities for student use. The mainframe is a Prime 9755 and a Sun Sparc Server 10. There are 60 microcomputers located in 3 laboratories throughout the campus. All students may access the system. It may be used 24 hours per day. There are no time limits on using the system and no fees. It is strongly recommended that all students have personal computers; a Dell or Apple Macintosh is recommended.

Graduates: In 1992–93 299 bachelor's degrees were awarded. The most popular majors among graduates were business and finance (30%), accounting (11%), and sociology and elementary education (8%). Within an average freshman class, 1% graduate in 3 years, 71% in 4 years, and 75% in 5 years. Some 40 companies recruited on campus in 1992–93. In the 1992 graduating class, 20% of all students were enrolled in graduate school within 6 months of graduation; 90% had found employment.

Admissions Contact: Michael Kennedy, Admission Director.

SAINT JOHN'S COLLEGE
E-3
Annapolis, MD 21404

(410) 263-2371, ext. 222
(800) 727-9238 (in-state)

Full-time: 223 men, 171 women	Faculty: 60; IIB, +$
Part-time: 2 men, 1 woman	Ph.D.s: 56%
Graduate: 30 men, 30 women	Student/Faculty: 7 to 1
Year: semesters, summer session	Tuition: $16,350
Application Deadline: see profile	Room & Board: $5450
Freshman Class: 323 applied, 278 accepted, 142 enrolled	
SAT I Verbal/Math: 630/600	VERY COMPETITIVE +

St. John's College, founded as King William's School in 1696 and chartered as St. John's in 1784, is a private, coeducational institution that offers a single, all-required curriculum sometimes called the Great Books Program. Students and faculty work together in small discussion classes without lecture courses, written finals, or emphasis on grades. The program is a rigorous interdisciplinary curriculum based on the great works of literature, mathematics, philosophy, theology, sciences, political theory, music, history, and economics. There is also a campus in Santa Fe, New Mexico. There is 1 graduate school. The 2 libraries contain 94,998 volumes, 961 microform items, and 9107 audiovisual forms, and subscribe to 124 periodicals. Computerized library sources and services include interlibrary loans. Special learning facilities include an art gallery and planetarium. The 36-acre campus is in a small town 35 miles east of Washington, D.C., and 32 miles south of Baltimore. Including residence halls, there are 16 buildings on campus.

Student Life: About 85% of undergraduates are from out-of-state, mostly the Middle Atlantic. Students come from 43 states, 14 foreign countries, and Canada. Sixty-five percent are from public schools; 35% from private. Eighty-eight percent are white. The average age of freshmen is 18; all undergraduates, 21. Seventeen percent drop out by the end of their first year; 65% remain to graduate.

Housing: A total of 291 students can be accommodated in college housing. College-sponsored living facilities include 6 coed dormitories. On-campus housing is guaranteed for the freshman year only and is available on a lottery system for upperclassmen. Seventy-five percent of students live on campus; of those, 90% remain on campus on weekends. Upperclassmen may keep cars on campus.

Activities: There are no fraternities or sororities on campus. There are 30 groups on campus, including art, chorus, computers, dance, drama, film, literary magazine, newspaper, photography, political, social service, student government, and yearbook. Popular campus events include Reality Weekend, Senior Prank, College Navy Croquet Match, concerts, and Friday night lectures.

Sports: There are 2 intercollegiate sports for men and 2 for women, and 19 intramural sports for men and 19 for women. Athletic and recreation facilities include a gymnasium with a weight room, tennis courts, a boathouse, and playing fields.

Disabled Students: Seventy percent of the campus is accessible to disabled students. The following facilities are available: wheelchair ramps, elevators, special parking, specially equipped rest rooms, special class scheduling, lowered drinking fountains, lowered telephones, and ground-floor dormitory rooms.

Services: In addition to many counseling and information services, tutoring is available in every subject. There is also a reader service for the blind and remedial math and writing.

Campus Safety and Security: Campus safety and security measures include 24-hour foot and vehicle patrol, escort service, informal discussions, and pamphlets, posters, and films. In addition, there are emergency telephones and lighted pathways and sidewalks. Adult members of the community living on campus and designated students take responsibility on freshman floors in dormitories and at student parties and other activities.

Programs of Study: St. John's awards the B.A. degree. Master's degrees also are awarded. Bachelor's degrees are awarded in SOCIAL SCIENCE (liberal arts/general studies, western civilization/culture, and Western European studies).

Required: The common curriculum, equivalent to 132 credits, covers a range of classic to modern works. Students attend small seminars; 9-week preceptorials on specific works or topics; language, music, and mathematics tutorials; and a 3-year natural sciences laboratory. Active learning occurs through discussion, translations, writing, experiment, mathematical demonstration, and musical analysis. Students take oral examinations each semester and submit annual essays. Sophomores also take a mathematics examination, juniors a French examination, and seniors an oral examination that admits them to degree candidacy. Seniors also present a final essay to the faculty and take a 1-hour public oral examination.

Special: Students in good academic standing may transfer to the Santa Fe campus at the beginning of any academic year.

Faculty/Classroom: Seventy-eight percent of faculty are male; 22%, female. All teach undergraduates. No introductory courses are taught by graduate students. The average class size in a laboratory is 15 and in a regular course offering, 15.

Admissions: About 86% of the 1993–94 applicants were accepted. The SAT scores for the 1993–94 freshman class were as follows: Verbal—9% below 500, 20% between 500 and 599, 53% between 600 and 700, and 18% above 700; Math—16% below 500, 32% between 500 and 599, 38% between 600 and 700, and 14% above 700. About 44% of the current freshmen were in the top fifth of their class; 75% were in the top two fifths. There were 3 National Merit finalists and 6 semifinalists.

Requirements: Applicants need not be high school graduates; some students are admitted before they complete high school. Test scores may be submitted, but are not required. Secondary preparation should include 4 years of English, 3 years of mathematics, and 2 years each of foreign language, science, and history. Applicants must submit written essays, which are critical to the admissions decision, and are strongly urged to schedule an interview. Important factors used in the admissions decision are recommendations by school officials, leadership record, recommendations by alumni, evidence of special talent, and advanced placement or honor courses.

Procedure: Freshmen are admitted fall and spring. Applications deadlines are open, but it is suggested that applications be filed by March 1 for fall entry and December 15 for spring entry. Notification is sent on a rolling basis. There are early admissions and deferred admissions plans.

Transfer: Some 21 transfer students enrolled in 1993–94. Transfer students may enter only as freshmen and must complete the entire program at St. John's. The admissions criteria are the same as for regular students. All 132 credits must be completed at St. John's.

Visiting: There are regularly scheduled orientations for prospective students, consisting of an overnight stay on campus, class visits, and a tour. Visitors may sit in on classes and stay overnight at the school. To arrange for a visit, contact the Admissions Office at (410) 263-2371 or (800) 727-9238 (in-state).

Financial Aid: In 1993–94 70% of all current freshmen and 69% of continuing students received some form of financial aid. About 55% of freshmen and 52% of continuing students received need-based aid. The average freshman award was $15,658. Of that total, scholarships or need-based grants averaged $11,333 ($15,000 maximum); loans averaged $2625 ($5625 maximum); and work contracts averaged $1700 (maximum). Sixty-five percent of undergraduate stu-

dents work part-time. Average earnings from campus work for the school year are $1800. The average financial indebtedness of the 1992–93 graduate was $12,000. St. John's is a member of CSS. The FAF and the college's own financial statement are required. The deadline for financial aid applications is March 1.

International Students: There are currently 19 international students enrolled. The school actively recruits these students. They must take the TOEFL and a standardized entrance examination.

Computers: The college provides computer facilities for student use. The mainframe is an IBM/36. There is a network of 11 Apple Macintosh microcomputers available for student use in a computer room and in the library. They are equipped with word-processing programs and a variety of other software. There are also 2 non-networked Apples and 3 other microcomputers for student use. Students who have demonstrated that they know the rudiments may access the system. It may be used 24 hours a day. There are no fees.

Graduates: In 1992–93 103 bachelor's degrees were awarded. Within an average freshman class, 60% graduate in 4 years, 65% in 5 years, and 70% in 6 years. Some 6 companies recruited on campus in 1992–93.

Admissions Contact: John Christensen, Director of Admissions.

SAINT MARY'S COLLEGE OF MARYLAND   E-4
St. Mary's City, MD 20686   (301) 862-0292
                                                  (800) 492-7181 (out-of-state)

Full-time: 601 men, 714 women	Faculty: 103; IIB, av$
Part-time: 80 men, 129 women	Ph.D.s: 97%
Graduate: none	Student/Faculty: 13 to 1
Year: semesters, summer session	Tuition: $4400 ($6700)
Application Deadline: January 15	Room & Board: $4500
Freshman Class: 1340 applied, 695 accepted, 286 enrolled	
SAT I Verbal/Math: 590/620	**VERY COMPETITIVE +**

Saint Mary's College of Maryland, founded in 1840, is a small public liberal arts college in the Maryland State College and University System. In addition to regional accreditation, St. Mary's has baccalaureate program accreditation with NASM. The library contains 141,395 volumes, 31,965 microform items, and 5980 audiovisual forms, and subscribes to 1542 periodicals. Computerized library sources and services include the card catalog, interlibrary loans, and database searching. Special learning facilities include a learning resource center, art gallery, radio station, and TV station. The 275-acre campus is in a rural area 70 miles south of Washington, D.C. Including residence halls, there are 34 buildings on campus.

Student Life: About 85% of undergraduates are from Maryland. Students come from 33 states, 24 foreign countries, and Canada. Eighty-two percent are from public schools; 18% from private. Eighty-four percent are white. Thirty-nine percent are Protestant; 27% Catholic; 24% claim no religious affiliation. The average age of freshmen is 18.4; all undergraduates, 21.2. Twelve percent drop out by the end of their first year; 70% remain to graduate.

Housing: A total of 956 students can be accommodated in college housing. College-sponsored living facilities include single-sex and coed dormitories and on-campus apartments. In addition there are honors houses, language houses, and special interest houses. Seventy percent of students live on campus; of those, 60% remain on campus on weekends. All students may keep cars on campus.

Activities: There are no fraternities or sororities on campus. There are 60 groups on campus, including art, band, cheerleading, chess, choir, chorale, chorus, dance, drama, ethnic, film, gay, honors, international, jazz band, literary magazine, musical theater, newspaper, orchestra, photography, political, professional, radio and TV, religious, social, social service, student government, symphony, and yearbook. Popular campus events include Homecoming, Parents Weekend, Waterfront Weekend, and dances.

Sports: There are 7 intercollegiate sports for men and 7 for women, and 6 intramural sports for men and 5 for women. Athletic and recreation facilities include basketball, volleyball, and tennis courts, a pool, training, weight, and exercise rooms, a boat house, pier, and sailing fleet, and baseball, soccer, and lacrosse fields.

Disabled Students: Eighty-six percent of the campus is accessible to disabled students. The following facilities are available: wheelchair ramps, elevators, special parking, specially equipped rest rooms, lowered drinking fountains, and lowered telephones.

Services: In addition to many counseling and information services, tutoring is available in some subjects, including mathematics, writing, physics, foreign languages, biology, chemistry, and economics. There is a reader service for the blind and remedial math and writing are available.

Campus Safety and Security: Campus safety and security measures include 24-hour foot and vehicle patrol, self defense education, escort service, and informal discussions. In addition, there are pamphlets, posters, films, emergency telephones, lighted pathways and sidewalks, and student security assistant foot patrols.

Programs of Study: St. Mary's awards the B.A. degree. Bachelor's degrees are awarded in BIOLOGICAL SCIENCE (biology/biological science), COMMUNICATIONS AND THE ARTS (dramatic arts, English, fine arts, languages, and music), COMPUTER AND PHYSICAL SCIENCE (chemistry, mathematics, natural sciences, and physics), SOCIAL SCIENCE (anthropology, economics, history, human development, philosophy, political science/government, psychology, public affairs, and public policy). Economics, psychology, and biology have the largest enrollments.

Required: Students must complete general education requirements in writing, mathematics, foreign language or creative arts, history, the arts, literature, physical, biological, behavioral, and policy sciences, philosophy, and an interdisciplinary seminar. Students must meet additional requirements in their major fields, and complete 128 semester hours with at least a 2.0 GPA.

Special: Cooperative progams are available with Towson State University and Johns Hopkins Universities. Study abroad in 5 countries, dual and student-designed majors, work-study programs, and nondegree study are possible. There are pass/fail options for some courses. Unpaid internships for credit, with placement worldwide, are also permitted. There is a freshman honors program on campus, as well as 3 national honor societies.

Faculty/Classroom: Sixty-two percent of faculty are male; 38%, female. All teach undergraduates and all do research. The average class size in an introductory lecture is 22; in a laboratory, 14; and in a regular course offering, 13.

Admissions: About 52% of the 1993–94 applicants were accepted. The SAT scores for the 1993–94 freshman class were as follows: Verbal—14% below 500, 39% between 500 and 599, 43% between 600 and 700, and 4% above 700; Math—9% below 500, 28% between 500 and 599, 54% between 600 and 700, and 9% above 700. About 64% of the current freshmen were in the top fifth of their class; 86% were in the top two fifths. There were 10 National Merit finalists and 10 semifinalists. Seventeen freshmen graduated first in their class.

Requirements: A minimum GPA of 2.0 is required. The SAT I, with a composite score of at least 1000, or the ACT is required. Applicants should have graduated from an accredited secondary school or earned the GED. Minimum high school preparation should include 4 units of English, 3 each of mathematics, social studies, and science, and 7 electives. An essay and 3 letters of recommendation are required. AP and CLEP credits are accepted. Important factors used in the admissions decision are advanced placement or honor courses, evidence of special talents, leadership record, personality, intangible qualities, and geographic diversity.

Procedure: Freshmen are admitted fall and spring. Entrance exams should be taken in May of the junior year or November of the senior year. Early decision applications should be filed by December 1; regular applications, by January 15 for fall entry, October 15 for spring entry, and February 1 for summer entry, along with an application fee of $25. Notification of early decision is sent February 1; regular decision, April 1. There are early decision and early admissions plans. About 129 early decision candidates were accepted for the 1993–94 class. A waiting list is an active part of the admissions procedure, with about 5% of applicants on the list.

Transfer: About 66 transfer students enrolled in 1993–94. Transfer applicants with a minimum of 24 credits should have at least a 2.0 GPA. Those with fewer credits should have at least a 2.5 GPA. A total of 38 credits out of 128 must be completed at St. Mary's.

Visiting: There are regularly scheduled orientations for prospective students, including group presentations, interaction with faculty and students, and campus tours. There are guides for informal visits and visitors may sit in on classes and stay overnight at the school. To arrange for a visit, contact the Admissions Office at (800) 492-7181.

Financial Aid: In 1993–94 62% of all current freshmen and 51% of continuing students received some form of financial aid. About 21% of freshmen and 14% of continuing students received need-based aid. The average freshman award was $4300. Of that total, scholarships or need-based grants averaged $2900 ($4100 maximum); loans averaged $2261 ($2625 maximum); and work contracts averaged $513 ($1300 maximum). Twenty-six percent of undergraduate students work part-time. Average earnings from campus work for the school year are $513. The average financial indebtedness of the 1992–93 graduate was $5200. St. Mary's is a member of CSS. The FAF and FAFSA are required. The deadline for financial aid applications is March 1.

International Students: There are currently 45 international students enrolled. They must take the TOEFL and achieve a minimum score of 550.

Computers: The college provides computer facilities for student use. The mainframe is a DEC MicroVAX 3100. Students can access the MicroVAX from any of the 60 DOS-based systems, 11 NeXT workstations, and 15 Macintosh microcomputers in computer laboratories. Access is also available on multi-user UNIX systems. TELNET software is the primary method of access. All students may access the system.

It may be used during all laboratory hours. There are no time limits and no fees.

Graduates: In 1992–93 349 bachelor's degrees were awarded. The most popular majors among graduates were economics (15%), biology (13%), and psychology (13%). Within an average freshman class, 1% graduate in 3 years, 57% in 4 years, 69% in 5 years, and 70% in 6 years. Some 9 companies recruited on campus in a recent year. In the graduating class, 26% of the students enrolled in graduate school within 6 months and 88% of the students found employment within 6 months of graduation.

Admissions Contact: Richard Edgar, Admissions Officer.

SALISBURY STATE UNIVERSITY   F-4
Salisbury, MD 21801   (410) 543-6161

Full-time: 1965 men, 2331 women	Faculty: 240; IIA, -$
Part-time: 445 men, 582 women	Ph.D.s: 83%
Graduate: 193 men, 440 women	Student/Faculty: 18 to 1
Year: 4-1-4, summer session	Tuition: $3026 ($5694)
Application Deadline: January 15	Room & Board: $4490
Freshman Class: 4216 applied, 2290 accepted, 736 enrolled	
SAT I Verbal/Math: 490/560	ACT: 22 COMPETITIVE +

Salisbury State University, founded in 1925, is a public, coeducational institution within the University of Maryland System. SSU offers undergraduate programs in the arts and sciences, business, education, health science, nursing, technology, and professional training. There are 4 undergraduate schools and one graduate school. In addition to regional accreditation, SSU has baccalaureate program accreditation with AHEA, CSWE, NCATE, and NLN. The library contains 254,000 volumes, 600,000 microform items, and 10,569 audiovisual forms, and subscribes to 1800 periodicals. Computerized library sources and services include the card catalog, interlibrary loans, and database searching. Special learning facilities include a learning resource center, an art gallery, a radio station, the Research Center for Delmarva History and Culture, and the Small Business Development Center Network. The 140-acre campus is in a small town 110 miles southeast of Baltimore and 100 miles east of Washington, D.C. Including residence halls, there are 35 buildings on campus.

Student Life: About 75% of undergraduates are from Maryland. Students come from 39 states, 17 foreign countries, and Canada. Seventy-five percent are from public schools; 25% from private. Ninety percent are white. The average age of freshmen is 18; all undergraduates, 20.4. Twenty percent drop out by the end of their first year; 60% remain to graduate.

Housing: A total of 1900 students can be accommodated in college housing. College-sponsored living facilities include single-sex and coed dormitories and on-campus apartments. In addition there are honors houses, special interest houses, and an international house. On-campus housing is guaranteed for all 4 years. Priority is given to out-of-town students. Fifty percent of students live on campus; of those, 68% remain on campus on weekends. Upperclassmen may keep cars on campus.

Activities: About 7% of men belong to 6 national fraternities; about 8% of women belong to 4 national sororities. There are 87 groups on campus, including art, band, cheerleading, choir, chorale, chorus, computers, dance, drama, ethnic, film, honors, international, jazz band, literary magazine, musical theater, newspaper, orchestra, political, professional, radio and TV, religious, social, social service, student government, symphony, and yearbook. Popular campus events include Homecoming, Derby Days, Family Weekend, Gullapalooza, October Fest, Spring Fling, Wellness Day, Festival of Culture, and Greek Week.

Sports: There are 9 intercollegiate sports for men and 10 for women, and 40 intramural sports for men and 40 for women. Athletic and recreation facilities include a 3000-seat stadium, a 3000-seat gymnasium, a 1000-seat arena, a swimming pool, a wrestling room, a dance studio, racquetball and indoor and outdoor tennis courts, a baseball diamond, varsity and practice fields, an all-weather track, and a Nautilus center.

Disabled Students: Ninety percent of the campus is accessible to disabled students. The following facilities are available: wheelchair ramps, elevators, special parking, specially equipped rest rooms, special class scheduling, lowered drinking fountains, lowered telephones, and special equipment for vision- or hearing-impaired students.

Services: In addition to many counseling and information services, tutoring is available in most subjects. In addition, there is a reader service for the blind, and remedial math, reading, and writing.

Campus Safety and Security: Campus safety and security measures include 24-hour foot and vehicle patrol, self-defense education, escort service, and shuttle buses. In addition, there are informal discussions, pamphlets, posters, and films, emergency telephones, and lighted pathways and sidewalks.

Programs of Study: SSU awards the B.A., B.S., B.F.A., B.S.N., and B.S.W. degrees. Master's degrees also are awarded. Bachelor's degrees are awarded in BIOLOGICAL SCIENCE (biology/biological science and marine science), BUSINESS (accounting, business administration and management, marketing/retailing/merchandising, and recreation and leisure services), COMMUNICATIONS AND THE ARTS (art, broadcasting, communications, dramatic arts, English, fine arts, French, music, Spanish, and speech/debate/rhetoric), COMPUTER AND PHYSICAL SCIENCE (chemistry, earth science, information sciences and systems, mathematics, and physics), EDUCATION (elementary, foreign languages, music, physical, science, and secondary), HEALTH PROFESSIONS (environmental health science, medical laboratory technology, nursing, predentistry, premedicine, prepharmacy, preveterinary science, and respiratory therapy), SOCIAL SCIENCE (economics, geography, history, philosophy, physical fitness/movement, political science/government, psychology, social work, and sociology). The sciences and business are the strongest academically. Biology and business administration have the largest enrollments.

Required: Students must complete 47 semester hours of general education requirements, including specific courses in English composition and literature, world civilization, and physical education. The bachelor's degree requires completion of at least 120 semester hours, including 30 or more in a major field, with a minimum GPA of 2.0.

Special: Co-operative programs in business and mathematics, cross-registration with schools in the University of Maryland System, and study abroad in various countries in Western Europe are offered. SSU also offers an Annapolis semester; a Washington semester; internships; work-study programs; accelerated degree programs; a B.A.-B.S. degree; a general studies degree; dual, interdisciplinary, and student-designed majors, including physics microelectronics; a 3–2 engineering degree with the University of Maryland at College Park, Old Dominion University, and Widener University; and pass/fail options. There is a freshman honors program on campus, as well as 14 national honor societies. Nine departments have honors programs.

Faculty/Classroom: Fifty-eight percent of faculty are male; 42%, female. All teach undergraduates and 20% both teach and do research. The average class size in an introductory lecture is 35 and in a laboratory, 18.

Admissions: About 54% of the 1993–94 applicants were accepted. The SAT scores for the 1993–94 freshman class were as follows: Verbal—55% below 500, 36% between 500 and 599, 8% between 600 and 700, and 1% above 700; Math—18% below 500, 54% between 500 and 599, 27% between 600 and 700, and 1% above 700. The ACT scores were 22% below 21, 49% between 21 and 23, 20% between 24 and 26, 5% between 27 and 28, and 4% above 28. About 43% of the current freshmen were in the top fifth of their class; 74% were in the top two fifths. Eight freshmen graduated first in their class.

Requirements: A minimum GPA of 2.0 is required. The SAT I or ACT is required, with a minimum composite score of 900 on the SAT I recommended. Applicants must be graduates of accredited secondary schools or have earned a GED. The university requires 14 academic credits or 20 Carnegie units, including 4 in English, 3 each in mathematics and social studies, of which U.S. history must be a component, and 2 each in foreign language and science. A portfolio or audition is required for specific majors. An interview is recommended for all students. AP and CLEP credits are accepted. Important factors used in the admissions decision are advanced placement or honor courses, leadership record, recommendations by school officials, extracurricular activities record, and evidence of special talent.

Procedure: Freshmen are admitted fall and spring. Entrance exams should be taken by November of the senior year. Early decision applications should be filed by December 15; regular applications, by January 15 for fall entry and January 1 for spring entry, along with an application fee of $30. Notification of early decision is sent January 15; regular decision, March 15. There are early decision and early admissions plans. A waiting list is an active part of the admissions procedure, with about 5% of applicants on the list.

Transfer: About 500 transfer students enrolled in 1993–94. Applicants must present a minimum GPA of 2.0 in at least 25 transferable credit hours earned. Students with fewer than 25 credit hours must be eligible for freshmen admission in addition to maintaining at least a 2.0 GPA in college courses. A total of 30 credits out of 120 to 125 must be completed at SSU.

Visiting: There are regularly scheduled orientations for prospective students, including presentations, tours, meetings with faculty and staff, and Saturday open house programs. There are guides for informal visits, and visitors may sit in on classes and stay overnight at the school. To arrange for a visit, contact the Admissions Office at (410) 543-6161.

Financial Aid: In 1993–94, 40% of all current freshmen and 40% of continuing students received some form of financial aid. About 25% of freshmen and 60% of continuing students received need-based aid. The average freshman award was $2700. Of that total, scholarships or need-based grants averaged $2500 ($9000 maxi-

mum); loans averaged $2500 ($4625 maximum); and work contracts averaged $1200 ($2000 maximum). Twenty-five percent of undergraduate students work part-time. Average earnings from campus work for the school year are $1800. The average financial indebtedness of the 1992–93 graduate was $5100. SSU is a member of CSS. The FAF and FAFSA are required. The deadline for financial aid applications is March 1.

International Students: There are currently 23 international students enrolled. The school actively recruits these students. They must take the TOEFL and achieve a minimum score of 550.

Computers: The college provides computer facilities for student use. The mainframes are a DEC VAX 4300, a cluster DEC VAX 8350, and a DEC VAX 6310. There are 24 VAX graphics-capable terminals connected to the mainframes that are available for student use. The library has 30 IBM-compatible microcomputers networked to a server. In addition, there are 3 computer laboratories, each containing 30 microcomputers using the Pathworks network with a MicroVAX as a server, and a third computer laboratory with a 19-station, networked Apple Macintosh laboratory, and a graphics laboratory which contains 5 DEC workstations and an academic help room. All students may access the system. It may be used 24 hours daily via modems. There are no time limits on using the system and no fees.

Graduates: In 1992–93, 1186 bachelor's degrees were awarded. The most popular majors among graduates were business (19%), elementary education (14%), and biology (8%). Within an average freshman class, 39% graduate in 4 years, 51% in 5 years, and 55% in 6 years. Some 100 companies recruited on campus in 1992–93. In the 1992 graduating class, 26% of all graduates were enrolled in graduate school within 6 months of graduation; 96% had found employment.

Admissions Contact: Jane H. Dane, Dean of Admissions.

SOJOURNER-DOUGLASS COLLEGE   D-2
Baltimore, MD 21201   (410) 276-0306

Full-time: 33 men, 142 women	Faculty: 14
Part-time: 9 men, 34 women	Ph.D.s: 18%
Graduate: none	Student/Faculty: 13 to 1
Year: trimesters	Tuition: $5265
Application Deadline: open	Room & Board: n/app
Freshman Class: n/av	
SAT I or ACT: not required	**LESS COMPETITIVE**

Sojourner-Douglass College, established in 1980, is a private institution offering undergraduate programs in administration, human and social resources, and human growth and development to a predominantly black student body. The library contains 20,000 volumes. Special learning facilities include a learning resource center. The campus is in an urban area in Baltimore.

Student Life: All undergraduates are from Maryland.

Housing: There are no residence halls. All students commute.

Activities: There are no fraternities or sororities on campus. There are some groups on campus, including newspaper and student government.

Sports: There is no sports program at Sojourner-Douglass.

Disabled Students: The following facilities are available: wheelchair ramps, elevators, and special parking.

Services: In addition to many counseling and information services, tutoring is available in some subjects, including reading, writing, mathematics, and study skills.

Programs of Study: Sojourner-Douglass awards the B.A. degree. Bachelor's degrees are awarded in BUSINESS (business administration and management and tourism), COMMUNICATIONS AND THE ARTS (broadcasting), EDUCATION (early childhood), HEALTH PROFESSIONS (health care administration), SOCIAL SCIENCE (criminal justice, gerontology, psychology, public administration, and social work).

Required: In order to graduate, students must earn 63 to 66 general education credits, with 15 credits in English literature and composition, political science, history, economics, sociology, geography, psychology, and anthropology; 12 in the humanities; 9 in natural science and mathematics; and 3 each in career planning and personal development, psychology of the black family in America, and psychology of racism. Twelve credits must be earned in a project that demonstrates competence in the major. Six credits must be earned in the sociology of work. There is also a 3-credit education seminar requirement. A total of 132 credits are needed to graduate, with 54 to 69 in the major.

Special: Credit may be granted for life, military and work experience. Faculty supervised independent study is possible for adult students.

Requirements: The SAT I or ACT is not required. Applicants must be graduates of an accredited secondary school or have a GED certificate. They must have completed 4 years of English and 2 years each of mathematics, history, and social studies. Autobiographical essays, resumes, and interviews are required.

Procedure: Freshmen are admitted to all sessions. Application deadlines are open. The application fee is $10. Notification is sent on a rolling basis.

Transfer: Transfer criteria are the same as for entering freshmen; however, transfers are not accepted to all classes.

Visiting: There are regularly scheduled orientations for prospective students. To arrange for a visit, contact the Office of Admissions at (410) 276–0306.

Financial Aid: In an earlier year, 48% of all current freshmen and 90% of continuing students received some form of financial aid. The FAF, FFS, or SFS and federal income tax forms are required. The deadline for financial aid applications is July.

Computers: The college provides computer facilities for student use.

Graduates: In an earlier year, 47 bachelor's degrees were awarded. The most popular majors among graduates were buisness and management (54%) and education (18%).

Admissions Contact: LaVerne B. Cawthorne, Coordinator of Admissions.

TOWSON STATE UNIVERSITY   D-2
Towson, MD 21204–7097   (410) 830-3333
(800) 225–5878 (in-state)

Full-time: 3787 men, 5460 women	Faculty: 459; IIA, av$
Part-time: 1496 men, 2088 women	Ph.D.s: 81%
Graduate: 431 men, 1434 women	Student/Faculty: 20 to 1
Year: 4–1–4, summer session	Tuition: $3122 ($5624)
Application Deadline: March 1	Room & Board: $4330
Freshman Class: 6151 applied, 3831 accepted, 1278 enrolled	
SAT I Verbal/Math: 467/516	**COMPETITIVE**

Towson State University, founded in 1866, is part of the University of Maryland system, offering undergraduate and graduate programs in liberal arts and sciences, allied health sciences, education, fine arts, communication, and business and economics. There are 7 undergraduate schools and one graduate school. In addition to regional accreditation, Towson State has baccalaureate program accreditation with AACSB, ASLA, NASAD, NASM, NCATE, and NLN. The library contains 536,976 volumes, 697,368 microform items, and 14,927 audiovisual forms, and subscribes to 1995 periodicals. Computerized library sources and services include the card catalog, interlibrary loans, and database searching. Special learning facilities include a learning resource center, art gallery, planetarium, radio station, TV station, curriculum center, herbarium, animal museum, observatory, and greenhouse. The 306-acre campus is in a suburban area 2 miles north of Baltimore. Including residence halls, there are 39 buildings on campus.

Student Life: About 84% of undergraduates are from Maryland. Students come from 42 states, 53 foreign countries, and Canada. Sixty-five percent are from public schools; 35% from private. Eighty-five percent are white. The average age of freshmen is 19; all undergraduates, 22.9. Eighteen percent drop out by the end of their first year; 56% remain to graduate.

Housing: A total of 3689 students can be accommodated in college housing. College-sponsored living facilities include coed dormitories, on-campus apartments, and married-student housing. In addition there are alcohol-free floors and international floors. On-campus housing is available on a first-come, first-served basis and is available on a lottery system for upperclassmen. Seventy-six percent of students commute. Upperclassmen may keep cars on campus.

Activities: About 11% of men belong to 18 national fraternities; about 10% of women belong to 13 national sororities. There are 105 groups on campus, including art, band, cheerleading, chess, choir, chorale, chorus, computers, dance, drama, drill team, ethnic, film, gay, honors, international, jazz band, literary magazine, marching band, musical theater, newspaper, orchestra, pep band, photography, political, professional, radio and TV, religious, social, social service, student government, symphony, and yearbook. Popular campus events include Homecoming, fraternity and sorority dances, Ethics Forum, Tiger Fest, Expo, and Parents Weekend.

Sports: There are 11 intercollegiate sports for men and 11 for women, and 25 intramural sports for men and 25 for women. Athletic and recreation facilities include a gymnasium with basketball and racquetball courts and a dance studio, a fitness center, a pool, a recreation center with a bowling alley and other games, playing fields, and indoor and outdoor tracks.

Disabled Students: Ninety-five percent of the campus is accessible to disabled students. The following facilities are available: wheelchair ramps, elevators, special parking, specially equipped rest rooms, special class scheduling, lowered drinking fountains, and specially equipped apartments.

Services: In addition to many counseling and information services, tutoring is available in most subjects. There is a reader service for the blind, and remedial math, reading, and writing. There are also note takers, English language and tutorial services centers, and a writing laboratory.

Campus Safety and Security: Campus safety and security measures include 24-hour foot and vehicle patrol, self-defense education, escort service, and shuttle buses. In addition, there are informal discussions, pamphlets, posters, films, emergency telephones, lighted pathways and sidewalks, and a police dog on campus.

Programs of Study: Towson State awards the B.A., B.S., and B.F.A. degrees. Master's degrees also are awarded. Bachelor's degrees are awarded in BIOLOGICAL SCIENCE (biology/biological science), BUSINESS (accounting and business administration and management), COMMUNICATIONS AND THE ARTS (communications, dance, dramatic arts, English, fine arts, French, German, music, Spanish, and speech/debate/rhetoric), COMPUTER AND PHYSICAL SCIENCE (chemistry, computer science, mathematics, natural sciences, and physics), EDUCATION (art, early childhood, education, elementary, music, and physical), HEALTH PROFESSIONS (health, medical laboratory technology, nursing, occupational therapy, and speech pathology/audiology), SOCIAL SCIENCE (economics, geography, history, interdisciplinary studies, international studies, philosophy, political science/government, psychology, social science, sociology, and women's studies). Fine arts, business, education, writing, and women's studies are the strongest academically. Business disciplines, mass communications, psychology, and elementary education have the largest enrollments.

Required: A total of 120 credits is required for most majors, including 18 core courses in the disciplines of physical education and writing, fine and performing arts, humanities, natural and mathematical sciences, and social and behavioral sciences/personal development. Students must earn a C or better in basic and advanced writing courses and at least a 2.0 GPA overall.

Special: Towson State offers a cooperative program with other institutions in the University of Maryland system, and at Loyola College, the College of Notre Dame, and Johns Hopkins University; cross-registration at more than 80 colleges through the National Student Exchange; and study abroad in most countries. Students may pursue a dual major in physics and engineering, an interdisciplinary studies degree that allows them to design their own majors, a 3–2 engineering program with the University of Maryland at College Park, or nondegree study. There are pass/fail options, extensive evening offerings, and opportunities to earn credits between semesters. There is a freshman honors program on campus as well as 20 national honor societies, including Phi Beta Kappa. Twelve departments have honors programs.

Faculty/Classroom: Sixty-six percent of faculty are male; 34%, female. Nearly all of the faculty both teach and do research. No introductory courses are taught by graduate students. The average class size in an introductory lecture is 30; in a laboratory, 24; and in a regular course offering, 25.

Admissions: About 62% of the 1993–94 applicants were accepted. The SAT scores for the 1993–94 freshman class were as follows: Verbal—71% below 500, 25% between 500 and 599, and 4% between 600 and 700; Math—44% below 500, 44% between 500 and 599, 11% between 600 and 700, and 1% above 700.

Requirements: A minimum GPA of 2.0 is required. The SAT I is required, generally with a composite score of 1000 (500 verbal and 500 math). The ACT will be accepted in lieu of SAT I. Applicants should have graduated from an accredited secondary school or earned the GED. Secondary preparation should include 4 years of English, 3 each of mathematics and social studies, and 2 each of science and foreign language. Prospective music and dance majors must audition. AP and CLEP credits are accepted. Important factors used in the admissions decision are evidence of special talent, advanced placement or honor courses, recommendations by school officials, leadership record, and extracurricular activities record.

Procedure: Freshmen are admitted in the fall and spring. Entrance exams should be taken in the junior or senior year. Applications should be filed by March 1 for fall entry and December 1 for spring entry, along with an application fee of $25. Notification is sent on a rolling basis. There is an early admissions plan. A waiting list is an active part of the admissions procedure, with about 5% of applicants on the list.

Transfer: About 1975 transfer students enrolled in 1993–94. Transfer applicants should have at least 30 academic credits. For those with fewer than 30, freshmen requirements must be met. Minimum GPA requirements range from 2.0 to 2.5, depending on the number of credits completed. At least 30 credits out of 120 must be completed at Towson State.

Visiting: There are regularly scheduled orientations for prospective students, including campus tours, a session for parents, classroom visitation, a session on the admissions process for transfers and freshmen, and a roundtable discussion. There are guides for informal visits, and visitors may sit in on classes. To arrange for a visit, contact the Admissions Office at (410) 830–3333 or (800) 225–5878.

Financial Aid: In a recent year, 41% of all current freshmen received some form of financial aid. About 31% of freshmen received need-based aid. The average freshman award was $3143. Of that total, scholarships or need-based grants averaged $1732 ($7100 maximum); loans averaged $2981 ($9100 maximum); and work contracts averaged $978 ($2000 maximum). Thirteen percent of undergraduate students work part-time. Average earnings from campus work for the school year are $1167. The average financial indebtedness of a recent year graduate was $7400. Towson State is a member of CSS. The college's own financial statement and FAFSA are required. The deadline for financial aid applications is March 15.

International Students: There are currently 196 international students enrolled. They must take the TOEFL with a minimum score of 500 and also take the SAT I or ACT. The school accepts the TOEFL as a substitute for the verbal SAT I. Graduates of the campus English language center are not required to take the TOEFL.

Computers: The college provides computer facilities for student use. The mainframe is a DEC VAX cluster consisting of a DEC VAX 8700 and a 4000. Aboout 375 microcomputers are available, 60 of which are networked. Software packages and computer languages include Pagemaker, Lotus 1–2-3, Wordperfect, BASIC, Pascal, COBOL, FORTRAN, SAS, and SPSS. All students may access the system 24 hours daily except 5 P.M. to 9 P.M. Fridays. There are no time limits and no fees.

Graduates: In 1992–93, 2744 bachelor's degrees were awarded. The most popular majors among graduates were business administration (17%), mass communications (12%), and elementary education (9%). Within an average freshman class, 24% graduate in 4 years and 54% in 5 years. Some 112 companies recruited on campus in 1992–93.

Admissions Contact: Angel Jackson, Acting Director of Admissions.

UNITED STATES NAVAL ACADEMY   E-3
Annapolis, MD 21402–5018   (410) 267–4361

Full-time: 3621 men, 504 women	Faculty: 600; IIB, +$
Part-time: none	Ph.D.s: 90%
Graduate: none	Student/Faculty: 7 to 1
Year: semesters, summer session	Tuition: see profile
Application Deadline: March 1	Room & Board: see profile
Freshman Class: n/av	
SAT I or ACT: required	**MOST COMPETITIVE**

The United States Naval Academy, founded in 1845, is a national military service college offering men and women undergraduate degree programs and professional training in aviation, engineering, and various military, maritime, and technical fields. The U.S. Navy pays for the tuition, room and board, and medical and dental care of all Naval Academy students. In addition to regional accreditation, the academy has baccalaureate program accreditation with ABET. The library contains 750,000 volumes. Computerized library sources and services include the card catalog and database searching. Special learning facilities include a learning resource center, art gallery, planetarium, radio station, TV station, propulsion laboratory, nuclear reactor, oceanographic research vessel, towing tanks, flight simulator, and naval history museum. The 329-acre campus is in a small town 30 miles southeast of Baltimore. Including residence halls, there are 21 buildings on campus.

Student Life: About 3% of undergraduates are from Maryland. Students come from 50 states and 20 foreign countries. Eighty percent are white. Fifty percent are Protestant; 49% Catholic. The average age of freshmen is 18; all undergraduates, 19. Eleven percent drop out by the end of their first year; 77% remain to graduate.

Housing: A total of 4525 students can be accommodated in college housing. College-sponsored living facilities include coed dormitories. On-campus housing is guaranteed for all 4 years. All students live on campus; of those, 75% remain on campus on weekends. Alcohol is not permitted. Upperclassmen may keep cars on campus.

Activities: There are no fraternities or sororities on campus. There are 75 groups on campus, including cheerleading, choir, chorus, computers, drama, drill team, drum and bugle corps, ethnic, honors, international, jazz band, literary magazine, musical theater, pep band, photography, professional, radio and TV, religious, social, social service, student government, and yearbook. Popular campus events include Commissioning Week, which includes the Plebe Recognition Ceremony, Ring Dance, and graduation.

Sports: There are 22 intercollegiate sports for men and 9 for women, and 23 intramural sports for men and 10 for women. Athletic and recreation facilities include an Olympic pool with a diving well for 10-meter diving boards; a wrestling arena; a 400-meter outdoor track; an indoor ice rink; 6 Nautilus and weight rooms; facilities for gymnastics, boxing, fencing, and other sports; and a 30,000-seat stadium.

Disabled Students: The entire campus is accessible to disabled students. The following facilities are available: wheelchair ramps, elevators, special parking, and specially equipped rest rooms.

Services: In addition to many counseling and information services, tutoring is available in every subject. There is remedial math, reading, and writing.

Campus Safety and Security: Campus safety and security measures include 24-hour foot and vehicle patrol, self defense education, emergency telephones, and lighted pathways and sidewalks. In addition, there are gate guards.

Programs of Study: The academy awards the B.S. degree. Bachelor's degrees are awarded in COMMUNICATIONS AND THE ARTS (English), COMPUTER AND PHYSICAL SCIENCE (chemistry, computer science, mathematics, oceanography, physics, and science), ENGINEERING AND ENVIRONMENTAL DESIGN (aeronautical engineering, electrical/electronics engineering, engineering, marine engineering, mechanical engineering, naval architecture and marine engineering, ocean engineering, and systems engineering), SOCIAL SCIENCE (economics, history, and political science/government). Mechanical engineering, mathematics, oceanography, and political science have the largest enrollments.

Required: Students must complete 140 hours, including core requirements in engineering, natural sciences, humanities, and social sciences. Physical instruction is required during all 4 years, and students must pass examinations in applied strength, long-distance running, and obstacle course each semester. During required summer sessions, students take training cruises aboard U.S. ships and submarines. Graduates must serve 5 years on active duty as commissioned officers of the Navy or Marine Corps.

Special: Study in Washington, D.C., is available during 1 semester of the senior year. A voluntary graduate program is available for those who complete requirements early and wish to begin master's work at nearby institutions, such as Georgetown or Johns Hopkins universities. Trident Scholars may spend their senior year in independent research. There are 10 national honor societies on campus. Five departments have honors programs.

Faculty/Classroom: Eighty percent of faculty are male; 20%, female. The average class size in an introductory lecture is 23; in a laboratory, 10; and in a regular course offering, 15.

Admissions: About 12% of the 1993–94 applicants were accepted.

Requirements: The SAT I or ACT is required. Candidates must be unmarried, childless U.S. citizens of good moral character, and be between 17 and 21 years of age. Candidates should have a sound secondary school background, including 4 years each of English and mathematics, 2 years of a foreign language, and 1 year each of U.S. history, world or European history, chemistry, physics, and computer literacy. To be considered for admission, candidates must obtain a nomination from an official source, such as their U.S. senator, representative, or territorial commissioner. An interview is required, and medical and physical examinations must be passed to qualify for admission. AP credits are accepted. Important factors used in the admissions decision are advanced placement or honor courses, extracurricular activities record, leadership record, recommendations by school officials, and evidence of special talent.

Procedure: Freshmen are admitted in the summer. Entrance exams should be taken after December of the junior year. Applications should be filed by March 1 for fall entry. Notification is sent on a rolling basis. There is an early decision plan.

Transfer: Transfer credit is not accepted; all students enter as freshmen.

Visiting: There are regularly scheduled orientations for prospective students, including visitation weekends for candidates likely to receive appointments. Visitors may sit in on classes.

International Students: There are currently 40 international students enrolled.

Computers: The college provides computer facilities for student use. The mainframe is a Honeywell DPS8. There are also 1500 microcomputers available in the dormitory, library, computer center, and computer laboratory. All students may access the system. There are no fees. The academy issues a personal computer to each incoming freshman.

Graduates: In a recent class, 940 bachelor's degrees were awarded. Within an average freshman class, 77% graduate in 4 years.

Admissions Contact: Candidate Guidance Office.

UNIVERSITY OF MARYLAND SYSTEM

The University of Maryland System, established in 1807, is a public system in Maryland. It is governed by a board of regents, whose chief administrator is chancellor. The primary goal of the system is research, teaching, and public service. The total enrollment in a recent year of all 11 campuses was 129,784; there were 8992 faculty members. Altogether UMS institutions offer more than 600 academic programs leading to 31 undergraduate, master's, doctoral, and pre-professional degrees. Profiles of the 4-year campuses are included in this chapter in alphabetical order with other Maryland schools.

UNIVERSITY OF MARYLAND
BALTIMORE COUNTY   D-2
Baltimore, MD 21228   (410) 455–2291

Full-time: 3303 men, 3173 women	Faculty: 384; I, --$
Part-time: 1216 men, 1376 women	Ph.D.s: 86%
Graduate: 797 men, 802 women	Student/Faculty: 17 to 1
Year: 4–1–4, summer session	Tuition: $3338 ($8594)
Application Deadline: May 1	Room & Board: $4408
Freshman Class: 4269 applied, 2594 accepted, 985 enrolled	
SAT I Verbal/Math: 500/570	ACT: 22 VERY COMPETITIVE

The University of Maryland/Baltimore County, founded in 1963 as a member of the state university system, offers a wide variety of degree programs. There are 4 undergraduate schools and one graduate school. In addition to regional accreditation, UMBC has baccalaureate program accreditation with ABET, CSWE, and NLN. The library contains 567,159 volumes, 787,373 microform items, and 21,678 audiovisual forms, and subscribes to 4114 periodicals. Computerized library sources and services include the card catalog, interlibrary loans, and database searching. Special learning facilities include a learning resource center, art gallery, radio station, and TV studio. The 485-acre campus is in a suburban area 5 miles southwest of Baltimore. Including residence halls, there are 39 buildings on campus.

Student Life: About 94% of undergraduates are from Maryland. Students come from 38 states, 71 foreign countries, and Canada. Eighty-four percent are from public schools; 16% from private. Seventy-two percent are white; 14% African American; 10% Asian American. The average age of freshmen is 19; all undergraduates, 24. Nine percent drop out by the end of their first year; 50% remain to graduate.

Housing: A total of 2227 students can be accommodated in college housing. College-sponsored living facilities include single-sex and coed dormitories and on-campus apartments. In addition, there are honors houses. On-campus housing is available on a first-come, first-served basis. Priority is given to out-of-town students. Seventy-seven percent of students commute. Alcohol is not permitted. All students may keep cars on campus.

Activities: About 8% of men belong to 12 national fraternities; about 7% of women belong to 8 national sororities. There are 88 groups on campus, including band, cheerleading, chess, choir, chorus, computers, dance, drama, ethnic, film, gay, honors, international, jazz band, literary magazine, musical theater, newspaper, orchestra, pep band, political, professional, radio and TV, religious, social, social service, student government, and symphony. Popular campus events include Quadmania, Greek Week, Gospel Extravaganza, Octoberfest, Family Day, Shakespeare-on-Wheels, Homecoming, Jazz Fest, theater productions, and Fall Frenzy.

Sports: There are 10 intercollegiate sports for men and 10 for women, and 14 intramural sports for men and 13 for women. Athletic and recreation facilities include a multipurpose field house, an aquatic center, a fitness center, tennis courts, a 4500-seat stadium, playing and practice fields, an indoor track, and an outdoor cross-country course.

Disabled Students: Ninety-five percent of the campus is accessible to disabled students. The following facilities are available: wheelchair ramps, elevators, special parking, specially equipped rest rooms, special class scheduling, lowered drinking fountains, and lowered telephones.

Services: In addition to many counseling and information services, tutoring is available in most subjects. There is a reader service for the blind, and remedial math, reading, and writing.

Campus Safety and Security: Campus safety and security measures include self defense education, escort service, shuttle buses, and pamphlets, posters, and films. In addition, there are emergency telephones, lighted pathways and sidewalks, a 24-hour police department, and a campus risk management department.

Programs of Study: UMBC awards the B.A., B.S., B.S.E., and B.S.N. degrees. Master's and doctoral degrees also are awarded. Bachelor's degrees are awarded in BIOLOGICAL SCIENCE (biochemistry and biology/biological science), BUSINESS (management information systems), COMMUNICATIONS AND THE ARTS (dramatic arts, English, fine arts, French, German, languages, music, Russian, Spanish, and visual and performing arts), COMPUTER AND PHYSICAL SCIENCE (chemistry, computer science, mathematics, and physics), EDUCATION (early childhood, elementary, and secondary), ENGINEERING AND ENVIRONMENTAL DESIGN (chemical engineering, emergency/disaster science, engineering, and mechanical engineering), HEALTH PROFESSIONS (health science and nursing), SOCIAL SCIENCE (African American studies, American studies, classical/ancient civilization, economics, geography, history, interdisciplinary studies, philosophy, political science/government, psychology, social work, and sociology). Information systems management, psychology, computer science, biological sciences, visual and performing arts, and economics have the largest enrollments.

Required: To graduate, students are required to complete at least 120 credits with a minimum GPA of 2.0. The core curriculum includes courses in arts and humanities, social sciences, mathematics and natural sciences, physical education, and modern or classical language and culture. Students must pass a basic English course with a C or better.

Special: Dual majors, student-designed majors, cooperative programs in all majors, cross-registration with several state schools, internships, study abroad, work-study programs, pass/fail options, and nondegree study are available. UMBC also offers various opportunities in interdisciplinary studies and in such fields as artificial intelligence and optical communications. There is a freshman honors program on campus, as well as 12 national honor societies. Nineteen departments have honors programs.

Faculty/Classroom: Seventy-one percent of full-time faculty are male; 29%, female. All members both teach and do research.

Admissions: About 61% of the 1993–94 applicants were accepted. The SAT scores for the 1993–94 freshman class were as follows: Verbal—49% below 500, 32% between 500 and 599, 16% between 600 and 700, and 3% above 700; Math—16% below 500, 42% between 500 and 599, 32% between 600 and 700, and 10% above 700. About 50% of the current freshmen were in the top fifth of their class; 79% were in the top two fifths. There were 3 National Merit finalists and 11 semifinalists. Eleven freshmen graduated first in their class.

Requirements: The SAT I or ACT is required. Minimum high school preparation should include 4 years of English, 3 each of social science/history and mathematics, including algebra I and II and geometry, and 2 each of laboratory sciences and a foreign language. AP and CLEP credits are accepted. Important factors used in the admissions decision are advanced placement or honor courses, evidence of special talent, recommendations by school officials, leadership record, and extracurricular activities record.

Procedure: Freshmen are admitted to all sessions. Entrance exams should be taken by fall of the senior year. Applications should be filed by May 1 for fall entry, November 25 for winter entry, December 1 for spring entry, and May 15 for summer entry, along with an application fee of $25. There is an early admissions plan. A waiting list is an active part of the admissions procedure, with about 7% of applicants on the list.

Transfer: A total of 1383 transfer students enrolled in 1993–94. Applicants should have at least a 2.2 cumulative GPA for all previous college work; those with fewer than 28 semester hours should also submit SAT I scores and the high school transcript. A total of 30 credits out of 120 must be completed at UMBC.

Visiting: There are regularly scheduled orientations for prospective students, including a group information session with an admissions counselor followed by a student-guided walking tour of campus. Saturday information sessions and campus open house are also scheduled each fall. There are guides for informal visits and visitors may sit in on classes and stay overnight at the school. To arrange for a visit, contact the Admissions Office at (410) 455–2291.

Financial Aid: In 1993–94, 68% of all current freshmen and 45% of continuing students received some form of financial aid. About 42% of freshmen and 30% of continuing students received need-based aid. The average freshman award was $2785. Of that total, scholarships or need-based grants averaged $1100 ($4000 maximum); loans averaged $1100 ($3625 maximum); and work contracts averaged $585 ($1000 maximum). Nineteen percent of undergraduate students work part-time. Average earnings from campus work for the school year are $1279. UMBC is a member of CSS. The FAFSA is required. The deadline for financial aid applications is March 1.

International Students: There are currently 158 international students enrolled. The school actively recruits these students. They must take the TOEFL and achieve a minimum score of 550.

Computers: UMBC provides computer facilities for student use. The mainframes are a DEC VAX 4000 Model 500 and an SGI CRIMSON. About 250 Apple Macintosh and MS-DOS systems microcomputers and 70 SGI graphics workstations are located in student laboratories, with some computer facilities in dormitories and various academic buildings. All are networked to the mainframes, with connectivity to Internet, Bitnet, and Gopher services. All students may access the system. There are no time limits on using the system and no fees.

Graduates: In 1992–93, 1558 bachelor's degrees were awarded. The most popular majors among graduates were psychology (11%), information systems management (11%), and nursing (8%). Within an average freshman class, 50% graduate in 6 years. Some 275 companies recruited on campus in 1992–93. In a recent graduating class, 32% of all students were enrolled in graduate school within 1 year of graduation; 87% of all students had found employment.

Admissions Contact: Mindy Hand, Director of Admissions.

UNIVERSITY OF MARYLAND COLLEGE PARK
D-3

College Park, MD 20742   (301) 314–8350

Full-time: 10,070 men, 9270 women	**Faculty:** 1267; I, av$
Part-time: 2145 men, 1846 women	**Ph.D.s:** 91%
Graduate: 4742 men, 4368 women	**Student/Faculty:** 15 to 1
Year: semesters, summer session	**Tuition:** $3179 ($8783)
Application Deadline: December 1	**Room & Board:** $5003
Freshman Class: 14,292 applied, 10,315 accepted, 3409 enrolled	
SAT I Verbal/Math: 500/580	**VERY COMPETITIVE**

The University of Maryland/College Park, founded in 1856, is a co-educational, land-grant institution, the flagship campus of the state's university system, offering undergraduate and graduate degrees through 13 undergraduate and 14 graduate schools. In addition to regional accreditation, College Park has baccalaureate program accreditation with AACSB, ABET, ACEJMC, ACPE, ADA, ASLA, CSWE, NAAB, NASM, NCATE, and NLN. The 7 libraries contain 2,174,628 volumes, 4,650,166 microform items, and 121,814 audiovisual forms, and subscribe to 20,086 periodicals. Computerized library sources and services include the card catalog, interlibrary loans, and database searching. Special learning facilities include a learning resource center, art gallery, radio station, and TV station. The 1580-acre campus is in a suburban area 9 miles northeast of Washington, D.C. Including residence halls, there are 350 buildings on campus.

Student Life: About 75% of undergraduates are from Maryland. Students come from 50 states, 110 foreign countries, and Canada. Eighty percent are from public schools; 20% from private. Seventy-two percent are white; 12% Asian American; 12% African American. Thirty percent are Protestant; 30% Catholic; 20% Jewish; 17% claim no religious affiliation. The average age of freshmen is 19; all undergraduates, 22.5. Fifteen percent drop out by the end of their first year; 56% remain to graduate.

Housing: A total of 6400 students can be accommodated in college housing. College-sponsored living facilities include single-sex and coed dormitories, on-campus apartments, fraternity houses, and sorority houses. In addition, there are honors houses, language houses, special interest houses, and an international house. On-campus housing is guaranteed for the freshman year only, is available on a first-come, first-served basis, and is available on a lottery system for upperclassmen. Seventy-three percent of students commute. Alcohol is not permitted. Upperclassmen may keep cars on campus.

Activities: About 15% of men belong to 30 national fraternities; about 15% of women belong to 20 national sororities. There are 250 groups on campus, including art, band, cheerleading, chess, choir, chorale, chorus, computers, dance, drama, drill team, ethnic, film, gay, honors, international, jazz band, literary magazine, marching band, musical theater, newspaper, opera, orchestra, pep band, photography, political, professional, radio and TV, religious, social, social service, student government, symphony, and yearbook. Popular campus events include Homecoming, University Talent Show, Panhellenic Council Show, Handel Festival, Art Attack, and International Piano Competition.

Sports: There are 12 intercollegiate sports for men and 11 for women, and 19 intramural sports for men and 19 for women. Athletic and recreation facilities include swimming pools, intramural fields, tennis, squash, racquetball, and basketball courts, a weight room, a track, a bowling alley, a 50,000-seat stadium, a 14,500-seat gymnasium, and a golf course.

Disabled Students: Eighty-five percent of the campus is accessible to disabled students. The following facilities are available: wheelchair ramps, elevators, special parking, specially equipped rest rooms, special class scheduling, lowered drinking fountains, and lowered telephones.

Services: In addition to many counseling and information services, tutoring is available in most subjects, including all 100- and 200-level courses. There is also a reader service for the blind.

Campus Safety and Security: Campus safety and security measures include 24-hour foot and vehicle patrol, escort service, shuttle buses, and informal discussions. In addition, there are pamphlets, posters, films, emergency telephones, and lighted pathways and sidewalks.

Programs of Study: College Park awards the B.A., B.S., B.L.A., and B.M. degrees. Master's and doctoral degrees also are awarded. Bachelor's degrees are awarded in AGRICULTURE (agricultural economics, agriculture, animal science, and horticulture), BIOLOGICAL SCIENCE (biochemistry, biology/biological science, botany, entomology, microbiology, and zoology), BUSINESS (accounting, banking and finance, business administration and management, business economics, management science, marketing/retailing/merchandising, personnel management, recreation and leisure services, and transportation management), COMMUNICATIONS AND THE ARTS (advertising, art history and appreciation, broadcasting,

Chinese, classics, dance, design, dramatic arts, English, film arts, fine arts, French, German, Japanese, journalism, linguistics, music, romance languages, Russian, Spanish, and speech/debate/rhetoric), COMPUTER AND PHYSICAL SCIENCE (astronomy, chemistry, computer programming, computer science, geology, mathematics, physical sciences, physics, and statistics) EDUCATION (art, business, early childhood, elementary, foreign languages, health, home economics, industrial arts, music, physical, science, and secondary), ENGINEERING AND ENVIRONMENTAL DESIGN (aeronautical engineering, agricultural engineering, architecture, chemical engineering, civil engineering, electrical/electronics engineering, engineering, fire protection engineering, interior design, landscape architecture, and mechanical engineering), HEALTH PROFESSIONS (predentistry and prepharmacy), SOCIAL SCIENCE (African American studies, American studies, anthropology, criminal justice, economics, food science, geography, history, Judaic studies, philosophy, physical fitness/movement, political science/government, psychology, social science, and sociology). Engineering, computer science, physics, art history, Spanish, education, and business management are the strongest academically. Psychology, English, engineering, government and politics, computer science, and accounting have the largest enrollments.

Required: Most programs require a minimum of 120 credits for graduation; the number of hours required in the major varies. All students must take 29 credits in a multidisciplinary core curriculum, including 10 in mathematics and science, 9 each in social science and advanced studies, and 1 diversity course. Freshman and junior composition are also required, and students must maintain a 2.0 GPA.

Special: Each of the 13 undergraduate schools offers special programs, and there is a campuswide cooperative education program. In addition, the university offers cross-registration with other colleges in the Consortium of Universities of the Washington Metropolitan Area, the B.A.-B.S. degree, dual and student-designed majors, nondegree study, an accelerated veterinary medicine program, study abroad, work-study programs with nonprofit organizations, and various internship opportunities with members of Congress and the Maryland State House, with local media, and with various federal agencies. There is a freshman honors program on campus, as well as 40 national honor societies, including Phi Beta Kappa. Thirty departments have honors programs.

Faculty/Classroom: Seventy-two percent of faculty are male; 28% female. Sixty-two percent teach undergraduates. Graduate students teach 41% of introductory courses. The average class size in an introductory lecture is 42; in a laboratory, 18; and in a regular course offering, 30.

Admissions: About 72% of the 1993–94 applicants were accepted. The SAT scores for the 1993–94 freshman class were as follows: Verbal—49% below 500, 37% between 500 and 599, 12% between 600 and 700, and 2% above 700; Math—15% below 500, 41% between 500 and 599, 33% between 600 and 700, and 11% above 700. About 53% of the current freshmen were in the top fifth of their class; 86% were in the top two fifths. There were 24 National Merit finalists.

Requirements: The SAT I is required. The university evaluates SAT I scores along with other admissions criteria. Applicants should be graduates of accredited secondary schools or have the GED. Secondary preparation should include 4 years of English, 2 of algebra and 1 of plane geometry, 2 of laboratory sciences, and 3 of history or social sciences. Prospective design and architecture majors must submit a portfolio, and music majors are required to audition. AP and CLEP credits are accepted. Important factors used in the admissions decision are advanced placement or honor courses, recommendations by school officials, evidence of special talent, parents or siblings attending the school, and leadership record.

Procedure: Freshmen are admitted fall, spring, and summer. Entrance exams should be taken at the end of the junior year or beginning of the senior year. Applications should be filed by December 1 for fall entry and December 15 for spring entry, along with an application fee of $30. Notification is sent March 15. There is an early admissions plan. A waiting list is an active part of the admissions procedure.

Transfer: Some 2736 transfer students enrolled in 1993–94. Transfer applicants from regionally accredited institutions should have attempted at least 9 credits and have earned at least a 3.0 GPA, although this requirement varies depending on space available. Applicants from Maryland community colleges may be given special consideration and admitted with lower GPAs.

Visiting: There are regularly scheduled orientations for prospective students, consisting of an information session followed by a tour. There are guides for informal visits and visitors may sit in on classes and stay overnight at the school. To arrange for a visit, contact the Undergraduate Admissions Office at (301) 314-8385.

Financial Aid: In 1993–94 51% of all current freshmen and 30% of continuing students received some form of financial aid. About 44% of freshmen and 24% of continuing students received need-based aid. The average freshman award was $4907. Of that total, scholarships or need-based grants averaged $3401 ($14,631 maximum); loans averaged $2992 ($3825 maximum); and work contracts averaged $1375 ($1500 maximum). Sixty-one percent of undergraduate students work part-time. Average earnings from campus work for the school year are $1163. College Park is a member of CSS. The FAFSA is required. The deadline for financial aid applications is February 15.

International Students: There are currently 683 international students enrolled. They must take the TOEFL and achieve a minimum score of 550. The student must also take the SAT I or the ACT.

Computers: The college provides computer facilities for student use. The mainframes are an IBM VM-CMS, a Unisys 1100, and an Ultrix. There are also 1500 microcomputers available for student use in academic buildings, computer centers, libraries, and residence halls. IBM and Apple word-processing programs are available to all registered students. The Computer Science Center supports advanced workstation and microcomputer laboratories across campus for day and evening self-study and class projects. Those students with account numbers may access the system. It may be used at any time. There are no time limits on using the system and no fees.

Graduates: In 1992–93 5240 bachelor's degrees were awarded. The most popular majors among graduates were government and politics (6%), criminal justice (5%), and accounting (5%). Within an average freshman class, 29% graduate in 4 years, 52% in 5 years, and 64% in 6 years. Some 310 companies recruited on campus in 1992–93.

Admissions Contact: Dr. Linda Clement, Director of Undergraduate Admissions.

UNIVERSITY OF MARYLAND EASTERN SHORE
F-4
Princess Anne, MD 21853

(410) 651-6410
(800) 232-UMES (in-state)

Full-time: 1041 men, 1080 women	Faculty: 88; IIA, --$
Part-time: 171 men, 120 women	Ph.D.s: 80%
Graduate: 107 men, 118 women	Student/Faculty: 24 to 1
Year: semesters, summer session	Tuition: $2674 ($7401)
Application Deadline: open	Room & Board: $3580
Freshman Class: 1680 applied, 1650 accepted, 760 enrolled	
SAT I Verbal/Math: 400/368	LESS COMPETITIVE

University of Maryland/Eastern Shore, founded in 1886, is a public university, part of the University of Maryland System, offering undergraduate and graduate programs in the arts and sciences, professional studies, and agricultural sciences. There are 3 undergraduate schools and one graduate school. The library contains 150,000 volumes. Computerized library sources and services include the card catalog, interlibrary loans, and database searching. Special learning facilities include a learning resource center, art gallery, and radio station. The 600-acre campus is in a rural area 15 miles south of Salisbury. Including residence halls, there are 30 buildings on campus.

Student Life: About 75% of undergraduates are from Maryland. Students come from 30 states and 54 foreign countries. Ninety percent are from public schools; 10% from private. Sixty-nine percent are African American; 23% white. Ninety percent are Protestant; 10% claim no religious affiliation. The average age of freshmen is 18; all undergraduates, 24. Forty percent drop out by the end of their first year; 28% remain to graduate.

Housing: A total of 1200 students can be accommodated in college housing. College-sponsored living facilities include single-sex dormitories and on-campus apartments. In addition there is a residential complex. On-campus housing is available on a first-come, first-served basis and is available on a lottery system for upperclassmen. Fifty percent of students live on campus; of those, 30% remain on campus on weekends. All students may keep cars on campus.

Activities: About 20% of men belong to 4 national fraternities; about 20% of women belong to 4 national sororities. There are 25 groups on campus, including art, band, cheerleading, choir, chorale, chorus, computers, dance, drama, drill team, ethnic, honors, international, jazz band, literary magazine, newspaper, pep band, photography, political, professional, radio and TV, religious, social, social service, student government, and yearbook. Popular campus events include Parents Day, Spring Festival, Ethnic Festival, and Homecoming.

Sports: There are 6 intercollegiate sports for men and 5 for women, and 4 intramural sports for men and 4 for women. Athletic and recreation facilities include an indoor swimming pool and a 3000-seat stadium.

Disabled Students: Twenty percent of the campus is accessible to disabled students. The following facilities are available: wheelchair ramps, elevators, special parking, specially equipped rest rooms, lowered drinking fountains, and lowered telephones.

Services: In addition to many counseling and information services, tutoring is available in every subject. There is remedial math, reading, and writing.

Campus Safety and Security: Campus safety and security measures include 24-hour foot and vehicle patrol, escort service, informal discussions, pamphlets, posters, and films. In addition, there are emergency telephones and lighted pathways and sidewalks.

Programs of Study: UMES awards the B.A., B.S., B.G.S., and B.M. degrees. Master's and doctoral degrees also are awarded. Bachelor's degrees are awarded in AGRICULTURE (agriculture and poultry science), BIOLOGICAL SCIENCE (biology/biological science), BUSINESS (accounting, business administration and management, and hotel/motel and restaurant management), COMMUNICATIONS AND THE ARTS (English), COMPUTER AND PHYSICAL SCIENCE (chemistry, computer science, and mathematics), EDUCATION (agricultural, art, business, elementary, health, home economics, industrial arts, mathematics, music, physical, science, secondary, and social science), ENGINEERING AND ENVIRONMENTAL DESIGN (aeronautical science, construction technology, engineering technology, and environmental science), HEALTH PROFESSIONS (physical therapy and rehabilitation therapy), SOCIAL SCIENCE (criminal justice, history, home economics, liberal arts/general studies, and sociology). Physical therapy is the strongest academically. Business has the largest enrollment.

Required: Students must complete 122 hours, including 36 hours in the major, 15 in communicative and quantitative skills, 9 in humanities, 7 in natural sciences, 6 in social sciences, and 4 in health and physical education. A minimum 2.0 overall GPA is required.

Special: Students may cross-register at Salisbury State University. A cooperative education program, internships, work-study programs, a general studies degree, and dual and student-designed majors are offered. Also available are an accelerated degree program and a 3–2 engineering degree with the University of Maryland/College Park. There are pass/fail options. There is a freshman honors program on campus, as well as one national honor society. Ten departments have honors programs.

Faculty/Classroom: Forty-five percent of faculty are male; 55%, female. Eighty-five percent teach undergraduates and 15% do research. Graduate students teach 1% of introductory courses. The average class size in an introductory lecture is 28; in a laboratory, 18; and in a regular course offering, 25.

Admissions: About 98% of the 1993–94 applicants were accepted. About 15% of the current freshmen were in the top fifth of their class; 45% were in the top two fifths.

Requirements: A minimum GPA of 2.5 is required. The SAT I is required. Applicants should be graduates of accredited secondary schools or have the GED. High school preparation should include 4 years of English, 3 each of social science or history and mathematics, including 2 of algebra and 1 of geometry, and 2 of laboratory science. An essay and interview are recommended. UMES recommends that prospective art education majors submit a portfolio. Students may earn credit by examination. AP and CLEP credits are accepted. Important factors used in the admissions decision are recommendations by school officials, leadership record, advanced placement or honor courses, evidence of special talent, and recommendations by alumni.

Procedure: Freshmen are admitted to all sessions. Entrance exams should be taken as early as possible. Application deadlines are open. The application fee is $25. Notification is sent on a rolling basis. There are early decision, early admissions, and deferred admissions plans.

Transfer: About 160 transfer students enrolled in 1993–94. Transfer applicants must have attempted at least 9 credits at another institution and have at least a cumulative GPA of 2.0, or have earned an associate degree or completed 56 hours of community college work.

Visiting: There are regularly scheduled orientations for prospective students. There are guides for informal visits, and visitors may sit in on classes and stay overnight at the school. To arrange for a visit, contact the Office of Recruitment at (410) 651–6178.

Financial Aid: In 1993–94, 80% of all current freshmen and 85% of continuing students received some form of financial aid. The average freshman award was $3100. UMES is a member of CSS. The FAF is required. The deadline for financial aid applications is May 1.

International Students: There are currently 103 international students enrolled. The school actively recruits these students. They must take the TOEFL and achieve a minimum score of 500. The student must also take the SAT I.

Computers: The college provides computer facilities for student use. The mainframe is an IBM 4341. About 80 microcomputers, including IBM PS/2 Models 30, 50, and 502, and AT&T 6300, are available in the library and various departments. All students may access the system. There are no time limits on using the system and no fees.

Graduates: In 1992–93, 294 bachelor's degrees were awarded. The most popular majors among graduates were business administration (16%), physical therapy (10%), and hotel and restaurant management (10%). Within an average freshman class, 25% graduate in 6 years. Some 75 companies recruited on campus in a recent year.

Admissions Contact: Rochell Peoples, Director of Admissions, Registration and Recruitment.

UNIVERSITY OF MARYLAND
UNIVERSITY COLLEGE
College Park, MD 20742–1609   D-3
      (301) 985–7265
      (800) 888–8682 (out-of-state)

Full-time: 429 men, 439 women	**Faculty:** 13
Part-time: 4692 men, 5235 women	**Ph.D.s:** n/av
Graduate: 1915 men, 1604 women	**Student/Faculty:** 67 to 1
Year: semesters, summer session	**Tuition:** $4900 ($5350)
Application Deadline: open	**Room & Board:** n/app
Freshman Class: n/av	
SAT I or ACT: not required	**NONCOMPETITIVE**

University of Maryland/University College was founded in 1947 to serve the needs of the adult continuing education student. It offers evening and weekend courses in the liberal arts and sciences and in business at more than 30 locations throughout the Washington, D.C.-Baltimore area and the state of Maryland. Computerized library sources and services include the card catalog and database searching. Special learning facilities include a learning resource center and an art gallery. The campus is in an urban area.

Student Life: About 78% of undergraduates are from Maryland. Students come from 47 states and Canada. Sixty-nine percent are white; 20% African American. The average age of all undergraduates is 32.

Housing: There are no residence halls. All students commute. Alcohol is not permitted. All students may keep cars on campus.

Activities: There are no fraternities or sororities on campus.

Sports: There is no sports program at UMUC.

Services: In addition to many counseling and information services, tutoring is available in some subjects, including mathematics, writing, and accounting. There is also a reader service for the blind. Referrals are available for tutoring in other subjects. There are fees for tutoring.

Programs of Study: UMUC awards the B.A. and B.S. degrees. Associate and master's degrees also are awarded. Bachelor's degrees are awarded in BIOLOGICAL SCIENCE (microbiology), BUSINESS (accounting, banking and finance, business administration and management, business law, management science, marketing/retailing/merchandising, and personnel management), COMMUNICATIONS AND THE ARTS (art history and appreciation, broadcasting, communications, English, fine arts, journalism, languages, and speech/debate/rhetoric), COMPUTER AND PHYSICAL SCIENCE (computer science and geology), HEALTH PROFESSIONS (health care administration), SOCIAL SCIENCE (anthropology, behavioral science, criminal justice, economics, geography, history, humanities, interdisciplinary studies, paralegal studies, philosophy, political science/government, psychology, and sociology). Business has the largest enrollment.

Required: A general education requirement of 30 semester hours includes courses in communications, humanities, social sciences, and mathematics/science. The B.A. degree requires 12 semester hours of a foreign language. A minimum 2.0 GPA and 120 credit hours are required to graduate.

Special: There are a number of work-study programs with local employers. Credit by examination, credit for life/work experience, non-degree study, and pass/fail options are available. Through UMUC's open learning program, a number of independent learning courses, including telecourses, are available. There are 4 national honor societies on campus.

Faculty/Classroom: Seventy-seven percent of faculty are male; 23%, female. All teach undergraduates.

Requirements: The SAT I or ACT is not required. Students should be graduates of an accredited secondary school or have a GED equivalent. AP and CLEP credits are accepted.

Procedure: Freshmen are admitted to all sessions. Application deadlines are open. The application fee is $25. The college accepts all applicants. Notification is sent on a rolling basis.

Transfer: A total of 30 credits out of 120 must be completed at UMUC.

Financial Aid: In an earlier year, 9% of all freshmen received some form of financial aid. About 4% of freshmen received need-based aid. The average freshman award was $2912. Of that total, scholarships or need-based grants averaged $1223 ($2300 maximum); and loans averaged $2944 ($4000 maximum). Average earnings from campus work for the school year were $3034. UMUC is a member of CSS. The FAF and FAFSA, and SAR (for Pell) are required. The priority deadline for financial aid applications is March 1.

International Students: There are currently 17 international students enrolled. They must take the TOEFL or the college's own test and achieve a minimum score on the TOEFL of 550.

Computers: The college provides computer facilities for student use. The mainframes are a 4341 Model N12, a DEC VAX 11/780, a CDC CYBER 180, and an HP 8255. There are also 153 IBM PS/2, IBM-PC, Zenith, and AT&T microcomputers available at various locations.

All students may access the system. There are no time limits and no fees.

Graduates: In a recent year, 1729 bachelor's degrees were awarded.

Admissions Contact: Admissions Office.

VILLA JULIE COLLEGE
D-2
Stevenson, MD 21153
(410) 486-7001

Full-time: 186 men, 869 women	Faculty: 51; III
Part-time: 124 men, 679 women	Ph.D.s: 36%
Graduate: none	Student/Faculty: 21 to 1
Year: semesters, summer session	Tuition: $6880
Application Deadline: open	Room & Board: $3000
Freshman Class: n/av	
SAT I Verbal/Math: 436/484	**LESS COMPETITIVE**

Villa Julie College, founded in 1947, is an independent, comprehensive college offering career preparation with a liberal arts foundation. The library contains 78,534 volumes, 15,450 microform items, and 1350 audiovisual forms, and subscribes to 510 periodicals. Computerized library sources and services include the card catalog and database searching. Special learning facilities include a learning resource center, art gallery, theater, and a video studio. The 60-acre campus is in a suburban area 10 miles northwest of Baltimore. There are 6 buildings on campus.

Student Life: About 98% of undergraduates are from Maryland. Students come from 5 states and 5 foreign countries. Seventy percent are from public schools; 30% from private. Eighty percent are white; 12% African American. Thirty-nine percent are Catholic; 29% Protestant. The average age of freshmen is 18.1; all undergraduates, 26.7.

Housing: College-sponsored living facilities include coed off-campus apartments. On-campus housing is available on a lottery system for upperclassmen with a 2.5 GPA. All students commute. Alcohol is not permitted. All students may keep cars on campus.

Activities: About 5% of women belong to 1 national sorority. There are no fraternities on campus. There are 20 groups on campus, including art, cheerleading, computers, drama, ethnic, honors, jazz band, literary magazine, newspaper, political, professional, religious, social, social service, and student government. Popular campus events include Welcome Picnic, Naval Academy Mixer, Christmas Party, art receptions, Autumn Bonfire, All-College Meetings, and College Happening.

Sports: There are 6 intercollegiate sports for men and 7 for women, and 5 intramural sports for men and 5 for women. Athletic and recreation facilities include tennis courts and an athletic field.

Disabled Students: The entire campus is accessible to disabled students. The following facilities are available: wheelchair ramps, elevators, special parking, specially equipped rest rooms, special class scheduling, and lowered drinking fountains.

Services: In addition to many counseling and information services, tutoring is available in every subject. There is remedial math, reading, and writing.

Campus Safety and Security: Campus safety and security measures include self defense education, escort service, shuttle buses, pamphlets, posters, and films. In addition, there are emergency telephones, lighted pathways and sidewalks, and 15-hour foot and vehicle patrols during VJC operating hours.

Programs of Study: VJC awards the B.S. degree. Associate degrees also are awarded. Bachelor's degrees are awarded in BUSINESS (business administration and management), COMPUTER AND PHYSICAL SCIENCE (information sciences and systems), HEALTH PROFESSIONS (nursing), SOCIAL SCIENCE (paralegal studies). Liberal arts and technology, computer information systems, business information systems, business administration, paralegal studies, computer accounting, and nursing are the strongest academically. Paralegal, computer accounting, computer information systems, business administration, and nursing have the largest enrollments.

Required: General college requirements include courses in writing and literature, communication and fine arts, philosophy and religion, social sciences, mathematics, natural science, computer information systems, physical education, and patterns of thought. A capstone course and an internship are also required. Students must complete 120 hours, including 45 to 50 hours in the major, with at least a 2.0 overall GPA.

Special: A general studies program is offered. There are cooperative education programs in several majors as well as internships and independent study opportunities. Students may earn credit by examination. Study abroad in 4 countries, a work-study program, student-designed majors, interdisciplinary majors, including liberal arts and technology, computer accounting, and business information systems, and education courses for state certification are available. Pass/fail options are also possible. There is a freshman honors program on campus, as well as 3 national honor societies.

Faculty/Classroom: Forty-seven percent of faculty are male; 53%, female. All teach undergraduates. The average class size in an introductory lecture is 20; in a laboratory, 20; and in a regular course offering, 20.

Requirements: The SAT I or ACT is required. Applicants must be graduates of an accredited secondary school. Although a secondary transcript is required, particular secondary preparation is not stipulated for all programs. Some degree programs do require specific high school courses, however. An essay and an interview are required. AP and CLEP credits are accepted. Important factors used in the admissions decision are advanced placement or honor courses, recommendations by school officials, evidence of special talent, leadership record, and extracurricular activities record.

Procedure: Freshmen are admitted fall and spring. Entrance exams should be taken between September and November of the senior year. Application deadlines are open. The application fee is $25. Notification is sent on a rolling basis. There are early admissions and deferred admissions plans. A waiting list is an active part of the admissions procedure, with about 15% of applicants on the list.

Transfer: About 130 transfer students enrolled in 1993-94. Transfer applicants must follow freshman application procedures, provide both college and secondary school transcripts, and have a minimum 2.5 GPA. Grades earned at other institutions are not included in calculating the GPA required for graduation. A total of 30 credits out of 120 must be completed at VJC.

Visiting: There are regularly scheduled orientations for prospective students, including a general overview, information on how to apply and how to finance a college education, special academic presentations, tours, meetings with faculty and students, and lunch. There are guides for informal visits and visitors may sit in on classes. To arrange for a visit, contact the Admissions Office at (410) 486-7001.

Financial Aid: In 1993-94, 76% of all current freshmen and 80% of continuing students received some form of financial aid. About 61% of freshmen and 82% of continuing students received need-based aid. The average freshman award was $4388. Of that total, scholarships or need-based grants averaged $3804 ($6440 maximum); loans averaged $2147 ($2625 maximum); and work contracts averaged $1000 ($1500 maximum). Four percent of undergraduate students work part-time. Average earnings from campus work for the school year are $1400. The average financial indebtedness of the 1992-93 graduate was $8411. VJC is a member of CSS. The college's own financial statement and FAFSA are required. The deadline for financial aid applications is March 1.

International Students: There are currently 3 international students enrolled. They must take the TOEFL and achieve a minimum score of 500.

Computers: The college provides computer facilities for student use. The mainframe is an IBM. More than 150 networked microcomputers are available for student use in classrooms and laboratories. The campuswide fiber-optic backbone provides an SNA gateway to the IBM mainframe, library card catalog access via a CD-ROM server, student dial-in from home, Macintosh connectivity, electronic mail, and hundreds of software applications in all disciplines. All students may access the system at all times. There are no time limits on using the system and no fees.

Graduates: In 1992-93, 114 bachelor's degrees were awarded. The most popular majors among graduates were business/accounting (45%), computer information systems (27%), and paralegal (26%). Some 50 companies recruited on campus in 1992-93. In the 1992 graduating class, 2% of the men and 4% of the women were enrolled in graduate school within 6 months of graduation.

Admissions Contact: Orsia F. Young, Director of Admissions and Financial Aid.

WASHINGTON COLLEGE
E-2
Chestertown, MD 21620-1197
(410) 778-7700
(800) 422-1782 (out-of-state)

Full-time: 378 men, 442 women	Faculty: 63; IIB, +$
Part-time: 21 men, 32 women	Ph.D.s: 93%
Graduate: 27 men, 74 women	Student/Faculty: 13 to 1
Year: semesters	Tuition: $13,952
Application Deadline: February 15	Room & Board: $5318
Freshman Class: 1209 applied, 902 accepted, 214 enrolled	
SAT I Verbal/Math: 516/551	ACT: 25 COMPETITIVE +

Washington College, founded in 1782, is an independent college offering programs in the liberal arts and sciences, business management, and teacher preparation. The library contains 201,576 volumes, 159,270 microform items, and 4158 audiovisual forms, and subscribes to 801 periodicals. Computerized library sources and services include the card catalog, interlibrary loans, and database searching. Special learning facilities include a learning resource center. The 112-acre campus is in a small town 75 miles from Baltimore, Philadelphia, and Washington, D.C. Including residence halls, there are 37 buildings on campus.

Student Life: About 54% of undergraduates are from Maryland. Students come from 34 states and 21 foreign countries. Fifty-eight percent are from public schools; 42% from private. Eighty-eight percent are white. Forty-one percent are Protestant; 35% Catholic; 17% claim no religious affiliation. The average age of freshmen is 18; all undergraduates, 22. Eleven percent drop out by the end of their first year; 66% remain to graduate.

Housing: A total of 700 students can be accommodated in college housing. College-sponsored living facilities include single-sex and coed dormitories and on-campus apartments. In addition, there are special interest houses, an international house, and a science house. On-campus housing is guaranteed for the freshman and sophomore years only and is available on a lottery system for upperclassmen. Eighty-five percent of students live on campus; of those, 70% remain on campus on weekends. All students may keep cars on campus.

Activities: About 20% of men belong to 3 national fraternities; about 20% of women belong to 3 national sororities. There are more than 30 groups on campus, including cheerleading, chess, chorus, computers, dance, drama, ethnic, film, gay, honors, international, jazz band, literary magazine, newspaper, opera, political, professional, religious, social, social service, student government, and yearbook. Popular campus events include fall and spring convocations, George Washington Birthday Ball, and May Day.

Sports: There are 7 intercollegiate sports for men and 8 for women, and 7 intramural sports for men and 5 for women. Athletic and recreation facilities include a swim center, a gymnasium, a field house, squash and racquetball courts, a fitness center, playing and practice fields, and a boathouse. There are riding facilities nearby.

Disabled Students: Eighty percent of the campus is accessible to disabled students. The following facilities are available: wheelchair ramps, elevators, special parking, specially equipped rest rooms, lowered drinking fountains, and lowered telephones.

Services: In addition to many counseling and information services, tutoring is available in every subject. There is remedial math and writing, a writing center, a mathematics laboratory, a study skills tutor, and peer tutors.

Campus Safety and Security: Campus safety and security measures include 24-hour foot and vehicle patrol, self defense education, escort service, and informal discussions. In addition, there are pamphlets, posters, films, emergency telephones, and lighted pathways and sidewalks.

Programs of Study: WC awards the B.A. and B.S. degrees. Master's degrees also are awarded. Bachelor's degrees are awarded in BIOLOGICAL SCIENCE (biology/biological science), BUSINESS (business administration and management), COMMUNICATIONS AND THE ARTS (dramatic arts, English, fine arts, French, German, music, and Spanish), COMPUTER AND PHYSICAL SCIENCE (chemistry, mathematics, and physics), SOCIAL SCIENCE (American studies, economics, history, humanities, international studies, philosophy, political science/government, psychology, and sociology). Psychology, English, German, and chemistry are the strongest programs academically. Business management, English, psychology, and biology have the largest enrollments.

Required: All students are required to take a year-long freshman course in English and world literature and 12 courses distributed among the social sciences, natural sciences, and humanities. The senior obligation consists of a comprehensive exam, thesis, or independent project. Students must complete 128 credit hours, including at least 32 in the major, in order to graduate. A minimum GPA of 2.0 is required.

Special: Internships are available in all majors and with the Maryland General Assembly. There is study abroad in 5 countries and a Washington semester at American University. The college offers a 3–2 engineering degree with the University of Maryland at College Park, as well as a 3–2 nursing program with Johns Hopkins University, credit by exam, and pass/fail options. There are 6 national honor societies on campus.

Faculty/Classroom: Seventy percent of faculty are male; 30%, female. Ninety-three percent teach undergraduates. No introductory courses are taught by graduate students. The average class size in an introductory lecture is 26; in a laboratory, 16; and in a regular course offering, 16.

Admissions: About 75% of the 1993–94 applicants were accepted. The SAT scores for the 1993–94 freshman class were as follows: Verbal—51% below 500, 35% between 500 and 599, 11% between 600 and 700, and 3% above 700; Math—42% below 500, 36% between 500 and 599, 20% between 600 and 700, and 2% above 700. About 60% of the current freshmen were in the top fifth of their class; 78% were in the top two fifths. There were 3 National Merit semifinalists. Ten freshmen graduated first in their class.

Requirements: WC requires applicants to be in the upper 80% of their class. A minimum GPA of 2.0 is required. The SAT I or ACT is required. Applicants must be graduates of an accredited secondary school or have a GED. Sixteen Carnegie units are required. Applicants should take high school courses in English, foreign language,

history, mathematics, science, and social studies. An essay is required; an interview is recommended. AP and CLEP credits are accepted. Important factors used in the admissions decision are advanced placement or honor courses, recommendations by school officials, leadership record, evidence of special talent, and personality, intangible qualities.

Procedure: Freshmen are admitted in the fall and spring. Entrance exams should be taken in the spring of the junior year or the fall of the senior year. Early decision applications should be filed by December 1; regular applications, by February 15 for fall entry and December 1 for spring entry, along with an application fee of $30. Notification of early decision is sent December 15; regular decision, March 1. There are early decision and early admissions plans. About 50 early decision candidates were accepted for the 1993–94 class. A waiting list is an active part of the admissions procedure, with 8 to 10% of applicants on the list.

Transfer: About 30 transfer students enrolled in 1993–94. A minimum GPA of 2.5 is required; an associate degree and interview are recommended. A total of 32 credits out of 128 must be completed at WC.

Visiting: There are regularly scheduled orientations for prospective students, consisting of individual interviews and campus tours. There are guides for informal visits and visitors may sit in on classes and stay overnight at the school. To arrange for a visit, contact the Admissions Office at (410) 778–7700.

Financial Aid: In 1993–94 65% of all current freshmen and 73% of continuing students received some form of financial aid. About 44% of freshmen and 40% of continuing students received need-based aid. The average freshman award was $12,091. Of that total, scholarships or need-based grants averaged $9086 ($14,000 maximum); loans averaged $2625 ($3825 maximum); and work contracts averaged $1145 ($1200 maximum). Forty-three percent of undergraduate students work part-time. Average earnings from campus work for the school year are $900. The average financial indebtedness of the 1992–93 graduate was $9000. WC is a member of CSS. The FAF, FAFSA, and parents'/students' federal income tax return are required. The deadline for financial aid applications is February 15.

International Students: There are currently 10 international students enrolled. The school actively recruits these students. They must take the TOEFL and achieve a minimum score of 500.

Computers: The college provides computer facilities for student use. The mainframe is a Prime 2655. Students may access the mainframe and the library collection via a campus network of more than 100 Apple Macintosh microcomputers in the library, academic buildings, and dormitories. All students may access the system. There are no time limits on using the system and no fees.

Graduates: In 1992–93 201 bachelor's degrees were awarded. The most popular majors among graduates were English (19%), psychology (17%), and business management (11%). Within an average freshman class, 60% graduate in 4 years and 65% in 5 years. Some 25 companies recruited on campus in 1992–93. In the 1992 graduating class, 12% of the men and 17% of the women were enrolled in graduate school within 6 months of graduation.

Admissions Contact: Admissions Officer.

WESTERN MARYLAND COLLEGE   D-1
Westminster, MD 21157-4390   (301) 848-7000, ext. 230
(301) 857-2230
(800) 638-5005 (out-of-state)

Full-time: 495 men, 576 women	Faculty: 75; IIB, av$
Part-time: 32 men, 66 women	Ph.D.s: 92%
Graduate: 160 men, 770 women	Student/Faculty: 14 to 1
Year: 4-1-4	Tuition: $13,750
Application Deadline: March 15	Room & Board: $5240
Freshman Class: 1205 applied, 984 accepted, 261 enrolled	
SAT I Verbal/Math: 470/520	COMPETITIVE

Western Maryland College, founded in 1867, is a private college offering programs in the liberal arts. There is 1 graduate school. In addition to regional accreditation, Western Maryland has baccalaureate program accreditation with CSWE and NASM. The library contains 180,386 volumes, more than 421,000 microform items, and 1342 audiovisual forms, and subscribes to 1148 periodicals. Computerized library sources and services include the card catalog, interlibrary loans, and database searching. Special learning facilities include an art gallery, radio station, and TV station. The 160-acre campus is in a small town 30 miles northwest of Baltimore. Including residence halls, there are 35 buildings on campus.

Student Life: About 63% of undergraduates are from Maryland. Students come from 23 states and 16 foreign countries. Eighty-nine percent are white. Forty-three percent are Protestant; 29% Catholic; 26% claim no religious affiliation. The average age of freshmen is 18; all undergraduates, 20. Nineteen percent drop out by the end of their first year; 69% remain to graduate.

Housing: A total of 1120 students can be accommodated in college housing. College-sponsored living facilities include 6 single-sex and coed dormitories and 3 on-campus apartments. In addition, there are honors houses, language houses, special interest houses, and fraternity and sorority floors. On-campus housing is guaranteed for all 4 years. Eighty-two percent of students live on campus; of those, 85% remain on campus on weekends. Upperclassmen may keep cars on campus.

Activities: About 26% of men belong to 2 local and 3 national fraternities; about 30% of women belong to 2 local and 2 national sororities. There are 70 groups on campus, including art, band, cheerleading, choir, chorale, chorus, computers, drama, ethnic, film, gay, honors, international, jazz band, literary magazine, musical theater, newspaper, orchestra, pep band, photography, political, professional, radio and TV, religious, social, social service, student government, and yearbook. Popular campus events include Homecoming, May Day, and Senior Week.

Sports: There are 10 intercollegiate sports for men and 11 for women, and 9 intramural sports for men and 9 for women. Athletic and recreation facilities include a 9-hole golf course, tennis courts, swimming pool, football stadium with track, squash/racquetball court, weight-training center, basketball and volleyball courts, and soccer, softball, and lacrosse fields.

Disabled Students: Fifty percent of the campus is accessible to disabled students. The following facilities are available: wheelchair ramps, elevators, special parking, specially equipped rest rooms, special class scheduling, lowered drinking fountains, and lowered telephones.

Services: In addition to many counseling and information services, tutoring is available in every subject. There is also a reader service for the blind, and remedial math, reading, and writing.

Campus Safety and Security: Campus safety and security measures include 24-hour foot and vehicle patrol, escort service, informal discussions, and pamphlets, posters, and films. In addition, there are emergency telephones and lighted pathways and sidewalks.

Programs of Study: Western Maryland awards the B.A. degree. Master's degrees also are awarded. Bachelor's degrees are awarded in BIOLOGICAL SCIENCE (biology/biological science), BUSINESS (business administration and management), COMMUNICATIONS AND THE ARTS (communications, English, fine arts, French, German, music, Spanish, and theater arts), COMPUTER AND PHYSICAL SCIENCE (chemistry, mathematics, and physics), EDUCATION (physical), SOCIAL SCIENCE (American studies, economics, history, philosophy, political science/government, psychology, religion, social work, and sociology). Biology, chemistry, and English are the strongest academically. Biology, business, communications, English, and psychology have the largest enrollments.

Required: Distribution requirements for all students include cross-cultural studies, fine arts, humanities, natural sciences, quantitative analysis, and social sciences. All students must take English composition, foreign language, and physical education (4 courses), and pass a mathematics proficiency examination. A total of 120 credit hours is required for graduation, including 30 to 48 in the major. The minimum GPA for graduation is 2.0.

Special: Internships are available in all majors. Study abroad is available around the world. There is a Washington semester in conjunction with American University, and 3–2 engineering programs with Washington University and the University of Maryland. The college offers work-study programs, dual and student-designed majors, credit by examination (in foreign languages), and pass/fail options. Western Maryland has a 5-year deaf education program and offers certification in elementary and secondary elementary education. There is a freshman honors program on campus, as well as 12 national honor societies, including Phi Beta Kappa. Twenty-three departments have honors programs.

Faculty/Classroom: Seventy-two percent of faculty are male; 28%, female. All both teach and do research. No introductory courses are taught by graduate students. The average class size in an introductory lecture is 30; in a laboratory, 15; and in a regular course offering, 19.

Admissions: About 82% of the 1993–94 applicants were accepted. The SAT scores for the 1993–94 freshman class were as follows: Verbal—59% below 500, 29% between 500 and 599, 11% between 600 and 700, and 1% above 700; Math—35% below 500, 42% between 500 and 599, 19% between 600 and 700, and 4% above 700. About 43% of the current freshmen were in the top fifth of their class; 67% were in the top two fifths. There were 3 National Merit finalists.

Requirements: Western Maryland requires applicants to be in the upper 50% of their class. A minimum GPA of 2.5 is required. The SAT I or ACT is required and the minimum composite SAT I score is 900. Applicants must be graduates of an accredited secondary school or have a GED. Sixteen academic credits are required, including 4 years of English, 3 years each of foreign language, mathematics, and social studies, and 2 years of a laboratory science. SAT II: Subject tests and an interview are recommended. An essay is required. AP and CLEP credits are accepted. Important factors used in the admissions decision are advanced placement or honor courses, leadership record, evidence of special talent, extracurricular activities record, and recommendations by school officials.

Procedure: Freshmen are admitted fall and spring. Entrance exams should be taken at the end of the junior year. Early decision applications should be filed by December 15; regular applications, by March 15 for fall entry and January 15 for spring entry, along with an application fee of $30. Notification of early decision is sent December 20; regular decision, February 1. There are early decision and deferred admissions plans. Thirty-one early decision candidates were accepted for the 1993–94 class.

Transfer: Some 72 transfer students enrolled in 1993–94. A minimum college GPA of 2.0 is required. If fewer than 30 credits transfer, a minimum SAT I score of 900 (composite) is required to transfer. An interview is recommended. A total of 30 credits out of 120 must be completed at Western Maryland.

Visiting: There are regularly scheduled orientations for prospective students, including meeting the president, a panel of faculty, and a panel of students. Tours of the campus for parents are conducted by faculty members; prospective students tour with current students. There are guides for informal visits and visitors may sit in on classes and stay overnight at the school. To arrange for a visit, contact the Admissions Office at (410) 857–2230 or (800) 638–5005 (out of state).

Financial Aid: In 1993–94 85% of all current freshmen and 78% of continuing students received some form of financial aid. About 67% of freshmen and 56% of continuing students received need-based aid. The average freshman award was $12,207. Of that total, the maximum scholarship or need-based grant was $4125; work contracts averaged $1298 ($1500 maximum). Thirty-four percent of undergraduate students work part-time. The average financial indebtedness of the 1992–93 graduate was $8426. Western Maryland is a member of CSS. The FAF, FAFSA, FFS or SFS, and the college's own financial statement are required. The deadline for financial aid applications is March 1.

International Students: There are currently 25 international students enrolled. The school actively recruits these students. They must take the TOEFL and achieve a minimum score of 550.

Computers: The college provides computer facilities for student use. The mainframe is a Prime 6650. Four public-access microcomputer laboratories are available. All students may access the system. It may be used 8:30 A.M. to 11 P.M. daily. There are no time limits on using the system and no fees. It is advised that students have personal computers; Apple Macintoshes, IBMs, or IBM clones are recommended.

Graduates: In 1992–93 274 bachelor's degrees were awarded. The most popular majors among graduates were business administration (18%), English (17%), and psychology (10%). Within an average freshman class, 2% graduate in 3 years, 59% in 4 years, 62% in 5 years, and 69% in 6 years. Some 49 companies recruited on campus in 1992–93. In the 1992 graduating class, 23% of both men and women were enrolled in graduate school within 6 months of graduation; 76% had found employment.

Admissions Contact: Martha O'Connell, Director of Admissions.

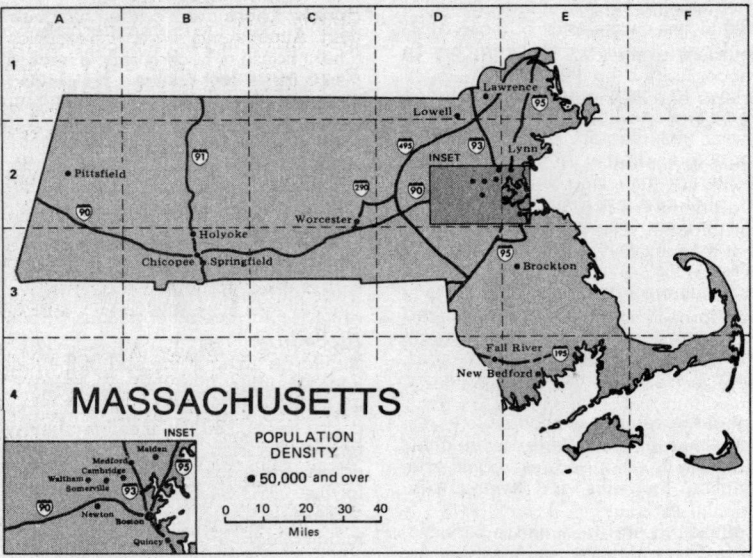

MASSACHUSETTS

INSET

POPULATION DENSITY

● 50,000 and over

0 10 20 30 40
Miles

AMERICAN INTERNATIONAL COLLEGE
B-3

Springfield, MA 01109   (413) 747–6201

Full-time: 517 men, 493 women	**Faculty:** 74
Part-time: 127 men, 199 women	**Ph.D.s:** 52%
Graduate: 193 men, 286 women	**Student/Faculty:** 14 to 1
Year: semesters, summer session	**Tuition:** $9479
Application Deadline: open	**Room & Board:** $4550

Freshman Class: 1420 applied, 1093 accepted, 290 enrolled

SAT I Verbal/Math: 426/451   **COMPETITIVE**

American International College, founded in 1885, is an independent, coeducational institution offering programs in liberal arts, business, health science, and teacher preparation. In addition to regional accreditation, AIC has baccalaureate program accreditation with NLN. The library contains 118,000 volumes, 83,700 microform items, and 1140 audiovisual forms, and subscribes to 390 periodicals. Computerized library sources and services include the card catalog and database searching. Special learning facilities include an art gallery and radio station. The 58-acre campus is in an urban area 75 miles west of Boston. Including residence halls, there are 22 buildings on campus.

Student Life: About 59% of undergraduates are from Massachusetts. Students come from 27 states, 24 foreign countries, and Canada. Sixty-four percent are from public schools; 36% from private. Seventy-five percent are white; 13% African American. Fifty-four percent are Catholic; 32% Protestant; 12% Jewish. The average age of freshmen is 18; all undergraduates, 22. Eighteen percent drop out by the end of their first year; 60% remain to graduate.

Housing: A total of 780 students can be accommodated in college housing. College-sponsored living facilities include single-sex and coed dormitories. On-campus housing is guaranteed for all 4 years. Sixty-two percent of students live on campus; of those, 55% remain on campus on weekends. Alcohol is not permitted. Upperclassmen may keep cars on campus.

Activities: About 20% of men belong to 7 local and 1 national fraternities; about 21% of women belong to 9 local and 1 national sororities. There are 40 groups on campus, including cheerleading, choir, chorale, computers, drama, ethnic, honors, international, literary magazine, musical theater, newspaper, political, professional, radio and TV, religious, social, social service, student government, and yearbook. Popular campus events include fall, winter, and spring weekends.

Sports: There are 9 intercollegiate sports for men and 5 for women, and 9 intramural sports for men and 8 for women. Athletic and recreation facilities include a gymnasium, a football stadium, tennis courts, playing fields, and a health and fitness center.

Disabled Students: Seventy percent of the campus is accessible to disabled students. The following facilities are available: wheelchair ramps, elevators, special parking, and special class scheduling.

Services: In addition to many counseling and information services, tutoring is available in every subject. There is remedial math and writing.

Campus Safety and Security: Campus safety and security measures include 24-hour foot and vehicle patrol, escort service, shuttle buses, and informal discussions. In addition, there are pamphlets, posters, films and lighted pathways and sidewalks.

Programs of Study: AIC awards the B.A., B.S., B.B.A., and B.S.N. degrees. Associate, master's, and doctoral degrees also are awarded. Bachelor's degrees are awarded in BIOLOGICAL SCIENCE (biochemistry and biology/biological science), BUSINESS (accounting, business administration and management, business economics, international business management, marketing/retailing/merchandising, and personnel management), COMMUNICATIONS AND THE ARTS (communications, English, and Spanish), COMPUTER AND PHYSICAL SCIENCE (chemistry, mathematics, and science), EDUCATION (business, early childhood, elementary, foreign languages, middle school, science, secondary, and special), HEALTH PROFESSIONS (medical laboratory technology, nursing, physical therapy, predentistry, and premedicine), SOCIAL SCIENCE (criminal justice, economics, history, international relations, liberal arts/general studies, philosophy, political science/government, prelaw, psychology, public administration, and sociology). Psychology, preprofessional, and accounting are the strongest programs academically. Accounting and criminal justice have the largest enrollments.

Required: Distribution requirements include 12 credits of social sciences, 9 of English, 8 of laboratory science, and 6 of humanities. A total of 120 credit hours is required for graduation, with 30 to 36 in the major. A minimum 2.0 GPA is required for graduation. Students must take 4 credits of physical education.

Special: Cross-registration with other colleges in the area is permitted. Internships are available in all programs, and study abroad is offered, as is a Washington semester. AIC also offers dual majors, credit by exam, credit for life/military/work experience, nondegree study, and for lower-division students, pass/fail options. There is a freshman honors program on campus, as well as 2 national honor societies.

Faculty/Classroom: Forty-one percent of faculty are male; 59%, female. All teach undergraduates, 15% do research, and 15% do both. The average class size in an introductory lecture is 26; in a laboratory, 16; and in a regular course offering, 19.

Admissions: About 77% of the 1993–94 applicants were accepted. The SAT scores for the 1993–94 freshman class were as follows: Verbal—68% below 500, 29% between 500 and 599, 2% between 600 and 700, and 1% above 700; Math—65% below 500, 33% between 500 and 599, 1% between 600 and 700, and 1% above 700. About 15% of the current freshmen were in the top fifth of their class; 64% were in the top two fifths. Four freshmen graduated first in their class.

Requirements: A minimum GPA of 2.0 is required. The SAT I is required. In addition, students must be graduates of an accredited secondary school or have a GED. They must have completed 16 academic credits of secondary school work with a minimum of 4 years of English, 2 years each of history, mathematics, and science, and 1 year of social studies. An interview is recommended. AP and CLEP credits are accepted. Important factors used in the admissions decision are recommendations by school officials, advanced placement or honor

courses, personality, intangible qualities, parents or siblings attending the school, and leadership record.

Procedure: Freshmen are admitted to all sessions. Entrance exams should be taken by March of the senior year. Application deadlines are open. Application fee is $20. Notification of early decision is sent December 15; regular decision, on a rolling basis. There are early decision, early admissions, and deferred admissions plans. About 15 early decision candidates were accepted for the 1993–94 class.

Transfer: About 87 transfer students enrolled in 1993–94. Transfer applicants must have at least a 2.0 GPA. A total of 45 credits out of 120 must be completed at AIC.

Visiting: There are regularly scheduled orientations for prospective students, including open houses with faculty, a student life panel, departmental faculty presentations, a financial aid presentation, a tour, and brunch. There are guides for informal visits and visitors may sit in on classes and stay overnight at the school. To arrange for a visit, contact the Admissions Office at (413) 747–6201.

Financial Aid: In 1993–94 69% of all current freshmen and 71% of continuing students received some form of financial aid. About 60% of freshmen and 64% of continuing students received need-based aid. The average freshman award was $6950. Of that total, scholarships or need-based grants averaged $3250 ($8500 maximum); loans averaged $2700 ($5500 maximum); and work contracts averaged $1200 ($1600 maximum). Eighty-eight percent of undergraduate students work part-time. Average earnings from campus work for the school year are $1150. The average financial indebtedness of the 1992–93 graduate was $6300. AIC is a member of CSS. The FAF, FFS or SFS, the college's own financial statement, and the FAFSA are required. The deadline for financial aid applications is April 15.

International Students: There are currently 88 international students enrolled. The school actively recruits these students. They must take the TOEFL and achieve a minimum score of 500.

Computers: The college provides computer facilities for student use. The mainframe is a DEC VAX 3100. Students may access the mainframe from the school's computer laboratories or from home via a modem. There is a cluster of DEC VAX station 3100s, DEC VT 320 terminals, and at-class microcomputers, all on an Ethernet network. All students may access the system. It may be used 7 days per week for a total of 80 hours. There are no time limits on using the system. The fees are $25 per semester.

Graduates: In 1992–93 311 bachelor's degrees were awarded. The most popular majors among graduates were accounting (11%), criminal justice (10%), and elementary education (8%). Within an average freshman class, 50% graduate in 4 years, 9% in 5 years, and 1% in 6 years. Some 36 companies recruited on campus in 1992–93. In the 1992 graduating class, 22% of the men and 20% of the women were enrolled in graduate school within 6 months of graduation; 71% of the men and 80% of the women had found employment.

Admissions Contact: Admissions Officer.

AMHERST COLLEGE
B-2

Amherst, MA 01002–5000   (413) 542–2328

Full-time: 888 men, 697 women	**Faculty:** 153; IIB, + +$
Part-time: none	**Ph.D.s:** 86%
Graduate: none	**Student/Faculty:** 10 to 1
Year: semesters	**Tuition:** $19,152
Application Deadline: December 1	**Room & Board:** $5000
Freshman Class: 4302 applied, 991 accepted, 421 enrolled	
SAT I: 639/684	**ACT:** 29 **MOST COMPETITIVE**

Amherst College, founded in 1821, is a private liberal arts college for undergraduate men and women. The 6 libraries contain 760,457 volumes, 402,352 microform items, and 25,532 audiovisual forms, and subscribe to 4357 periodicals. Computerized library sources and services include the card catalog, interlibrary loans, and database searching. Special learning facilities include an art gallery, natural history museum, planetarium, and radio station. The 1000-acre campus is in a small town 90 miles west of Boston. Including residence halls, there are 67 buildings on campus.

Student Life: About 85% of undergraduates are from out-of-state, mostly the Middle Atlantic. Students come from 50 states, 23 foreign countries, and Canada. Sixty-five percent are from public schools; 35% from private. Sixty-five percent are white; 11% Asian American. The average age of freshmen is 18; all undergraduates, 19. Two percent drop out by the end of their first year; 98% remain to graduate.

Housing: College-sponsored living facilities include single-sex and coed dormitories. In addition, there are language houses, special interest houses, and 1 cooperative house. On-campus housing is guaranteed for all 4 years. Ninety-eight percent of students live on campus; of those, 95% remain on campus on weekends. All students may keep cars on campus.

Activities: There are no fraternities or sororities on campus. There are 100 groups on campus, including choir, chorale, chorus, dance, drama, ethnic, film, gay, international, jazz band, literary magazine, musical theater, newspaper, orchestra, pep band, photography, polit-

ical, professional, radio and TV, religious, social, social service, student government, symphony, and yearbook. Popular campus events include Homecoming, Triathlon, Parents Weekend, Casino, and various cultural awareness events.

Sports: There are 12 intercollegiate sports for men and 11 for women. Athletic and recreation facilities include 2 gymnasiums, a pool, a field house, a hockey rink, a track, a Nautilus room, squash and tennis courts, a golf course, and playing fields.

Disabled Students: The following facilities are available: wheelchair ramps, elevators, special parking, specially equipped rest rooms, and special class scheduling.

Services: In addition to many counseling and information services, tutoring is available in every subject. There is also a reader service for the blind and a full-time writing counselor on staff.

Campus Safety and Security: Campus safety and security measures include 24-hour foot and vehicle patrol, escort service, shuttle buses, and informal discussions. In addition, there are pamphlets, posters, and films, emergency telephones, and lighted pathways and sidewalks.

Programs of Study: Amherst awards the B.A. degree. Bachelor's degrees are awarded in BIOLOGICAL SCIENCE (biology/biological science and neurosciences), COMMUNICATIONS AND THE ARTS (classics, dance, English, fine arts, French, German, Latin, music, Russian, and Spanish), COMPUTER AND PHYSICAL SCIENCE (astronomy, chemistry, computer science, geology, and physics), SOCIAL SCIENCE (African American studies, American studies, anthropology, Asian/Oriental studies, economics, European studies, history, philosophy, political science/government, psychology, religion, sociology, and women's studies). English, political science, economics, and psychology have the largest enrollments.

Required: To earn the B.A., all students must complete 32 courses equivalent to 128 credits, 8 of which are in the major, with at least a C average. Other than a 1-semester course in liberal studies, there are no specific course requirements.

Special: Students may cross-register at any of the rest of the members of the Five College Consortium (Smith, Mount Holyoke, and Hampshire colleges, and the University of Massachusetts, all in western Massachusetts) or members of the Twelve College Exchange Program. A number of interterm and summer internships are available. Many programs are offered abroad. Dual, student-designed, and interdisciplinary majors and work-study are possible. There are limited pass/fail options. There are 2 national honor societies on campus, including Phi Beta Kappa.

Faculty/Classroom: Seventy-one percent of faculty are male; 29%, female. All teach undergraduates and do research. The average class size in a regular course offering is 25.

Admissions: About 23% of the 1993–94 applicants were accepted. The SAT scores for the 1993–94 freshman class were as follows: Verbal—5% below 500, 20% between 500 and 599, 51% between 600 and 700, and 24% above 700; Math—1% below 500, 13% between 500 and 599, 35% between 600 and 700, and 51% above 700. About 97% of the current freshmen were in the top fifth of their class; all were in the top two fifths.

Requirements: The SAT I or the ACT, plus 3 SAT II: Subject tests, including writing, are required. Applicants should be high school graduates or have earned the GED. No specific secondary preparation is required, but Amherst strongly recommends that applicants take 4 years of English, mathematics courses including precalculus, 3 or 4 years of a foreign language, 2 years of history and social science, and at least 2 years of natural science, including a laboratory science. Two essays are required. Important factors used in the admissions decision are advanced placement or honor courses, personality, intangible qualities, extracurricular activities record, evidence of special talent, and recommendations by school officials.

Procedure: Freshmen are admitted in the fall. Entrance exams should be taken no later than December of the senior year. Early decision applications should be filed by November 15; regular applications, by December 1 for fall entry, along with an application fee of $50. Notification of early decision is sent December 15; regular decision, in early April. There are early decision and deferred admissions plans. About 136 early decision candidates were accepted for the 1993–94 class. A waiting list is an active part of the admissions procedure, with about 10% of applicants on the list.

Transfer: About 13 transfer students enrolled in 1993–94. Transfer applicants must have full sophomore standing and a minimum 3.0 GPA in previous college work. Transfers are accepted for the sophomore and junior classes only, and Amherst recommends that they submit SAT I or ACT scores, plus high school and college transcripts, and seek a personal interview. A total of 64 credits out of 128 must be completed at Amherst.

Visiting: There are guides for informal visits and visitors may sit in on classes and stay overnight at the school. Group information sessions and tours are available. To arrange for a visit, contact the Admission Office at (413) 542–2328.

Financial Aid: In 1993–94 38% of all current freshmen and 45% of continuing students received some form of financial aid. About 38% of freshmen and 45% of continuing students received need-based aid. The average freshman award was $13,450. Of that total, scholarships or need-based grants averaged $13,450; loans averaged $2623; and work contracts averaged $1220. Seventy-five percent of undergraduate students work part-time. Average earnings from campus work for the school year are $1459. The average financial indebtedness of the 1992–93 graduate was $8813. Amherst is a member of CSS. The FAF, the college's own financial statement, and the FAFSA are required. The deadline for financial aid applications is February 1.

International Students: There are currently 48 international students enrolled. They must take the TOEFL and achieve a minimum score of 600.

Computers: The college provides computer facilities for student use. The mainframe is a DEC VAX 8550. There are also 35 IBM and 5 Apple Macintosh microcomputers available in the computer center and the main library. All students may access the system 24 hours a day. There are no time limits on using the system and no fees.

Graduates: In 1992–93 427 bachelor's degrees were awarded. Within an average freshman class, 97% graduate in 5 years. Some 112 companies recruited on campus in 1992–93.

Admissions Contact: Jane Reynolds, Dean of Admission.

ANNA MARIA COLLEGE
C-2

Paxton, MA 01612

(508) 849–3300, ext. 360
(800) 344–4586 (out-of-state)

Full-time: 100 men, 300 women	**Faculty:** 33
Part-time: 60 men, 200 women	**Ph.Ds:** 37%
Graduate: 500 men, 400 women	**Student/Faculty:** 13 to 1
Year: semesters, summer session	**Tuition:** $10,775
Application Deadline: open	**Room & Board:** $5200
Freshman Class: 500 applied, 460 accepted, 139 enrolled	
SAT I Verbal/Math: 418/415	**LESS COMPETITIVE**

Anna Maria College, founded in 1946, is a private, coeducational college affiliated with the Roman Catholic Church. It offers programs in liberal and fine arts, business, and teacher preparation. There is one graduate school. In addition to regional accreditation, AMC has baccalaureate program accreditation with CSWE and NLN. The library contains 75,000 volumes and subscribes to 1000 periodicals. Special learning facilities include a learning resource center, an art gallery, and an audiovisual center. The 180-acre campus is in a suburban area 8 miles northwest of Worcester. Including residence halls, there are 11 buildings on campus.

Student Life: About 70% of undergraduates are from Massachusetts. Students come from 12 states and 6 foreign countries. Sixty-five percent are from public schools; 35% from private. Ninety-one percent are white. Fifty percent are Catholic; 43% Protestant. The average age of freshmen is 18; all undergraduates, 22. Ten percent drop out by the end of their first year; 80% remain to graduate.

Housing: A total of 290 students can be accommodated in college housing. College-sponsored living facilities include coed dormitories. On-campus housing is guaranteed for all 4 years. Sixty percent of students commute. All students may keep cars on campus.

Activities: There are no fraternities or sororities on campus. There are 22 groups on campus, including cheerleading, choir, chorus, computers, drama, ethnic, honors, international, political, professional, religious, social, social service, student government, and yearbook. Popular campus events include Harvest Weekend, Winter Semi-Formal, and Spring Variety Show.

Sports: There are 4 intercollegiate sports for men and 5 for women, and 5 intramural sports for men and 5 for women. Athletic and recreation facilities include an activities center with a basketball court, locker rooms, and weight and fitness equipment; soccer, baseball, softball, and field hockey fields; a volleyball pit; an outdoor basketball court; and a fitness trail.

Disabled Students: The entire campus is accessible to disabled students. The following facilities are available: wheelchair ramps, elevators, special parking, specially equipped rest rooms, and special class scheduling.

Services: In addition to many counseling and information services, tutoring is available in every subject through a tutoring laboratory. There is a reader service for the blind, and remedial math, reading, and writing.

Campus Safety and Security: Campus safety and security measures include 24-hour foot and vehicle patrol, informal discussions, pamphlets, posters, and films, and emergency telephones. In addition, there are lighted pathways and sidewalks.

Programs of Study: AMC awards the B.A., B.S., B.B.A., B.F.A., B.M., and B.S.N. degrees. Associate and master's degrees also are awarded. Bachelor's degrees are awarded in BIOLOGICAL SCIENCE (biology/biological science), BUSINESS (accounting, banking and finance, business administration and management, and marketing/retailing/merchandising), COMMUNICATIONS AND THE ARTS (advertising, communications, English, fine arts, illustration, music performance, and Spanish), COMPUTER AND PHYSICAL SCIENCE (computer management), EDUCATION (art, early childhood, elementary, and music), ENGINEERING AND ENVIRONMENTAL DESIGN (interior design), HEALTH PROFESSIONS (art therapy, environmental health science, medical laboratory technology, music therapy, predentistry, and premedicine), SOCIAL SCIENCE (criminal justice, liberal arts/general studies, paralegal studies, prelaw, psychology, and social work). Education, English, psychology, social work, and environmental health are the strongest academically. Education, business, and psychology/criminal justice have the largest enrollments.

Required: The 60-credit core curriculum consists of classes in English, mathematics, science, foreign language, history, philosophy, and religious studies. A total of 120 credits is required for graduation, with a minimum of 30 in the major. A 2.0 GPA is required for graduation.

Special: Cross-registration with the Worcester Consortium, internships in all majors, and a 3–2 engineering degree in conjunction with the Worcester Polytechnic Institute are available. The college offers study abroad, a Washington semester, accelerated degree programs, a general studies degree, credit by exam, some limited credit for life/military/work experience, nondegree study, and pass/fail options. There is a freshman honors program on campus.

Faculty/Classroom: Fifty percent of faculty are male; 50%, female. All teach undergraduates, and 10% also do research. No introductory courses are taught by graduate students. The average class size in an introductory lecture is 20; in a laboratory, 15; and in a regular course offering, 15.

Admissions: About 92% of the 1993–94 applicants were accepted. The SAT scores for the 1993–94 freshman class were as follows: Verbal—60% below 500 and 40% between 500 and 599; Math—60% below 500 and 40% between 500 and 599. About 20% of the current freshmen were in the top fifth of their class; 60% were in the top two fifths. Three freshmen graduated first in their class.

Requirements: The SAT I or ACT is required for traditional students. A GED is accepted. Sixteen academic units are recommended, including 4 years of English, 2 years each of foreign language, history, mathematics, and sciences, and 1 year of social studies. An interview is recommended. An essay, and, when applicable, an audition and portfolio are required. Nontraditional students who do not enroll directly from another college or high school do not need to provide SAT I or ACT test scores. AP and CLEP credits are accepted. Important factors used in the admissions decision are advanced placement or honor courses, extracurricular activities record, leadership record, evidence of special talent, and recommendations by school officials.

Procedure: Freshmen are admitted to all sessions. Entrance exams should be taken in the fall of the senior year. Application deadlines are open. The fee is $30. Notification of early decision is sent November 15; regular decision, on a rolling basis. There are early decision, early admissions, and deferred admissions plans. Two early decision candidates were accepted for the 1993–94 class.

Transfer: About 36 transfer students enrolled in 1993–94. Transfers with a minimum GPA of 2.0 are accepted for upper-division work. A total of 45 credits out of 120 must be completed at AMC.

Visiting: There are regularly scheduled orientations for prospective students. There are guides for informal visits, and visitors may sit in on classes and stay overnight at the school. To arrange for a visit, contact the Admissions Office at (508) 849–3300, ext. 360.

Financial Aid: In 1993–94 85% of all current freshmen and continuing students received some form of financial aid. About 85% of freshmen and continuing students received need-based aid. The average freshman award was $10,000. Of that total, scholarships or need-based grants averaged $5100 ($9000 maximum); loans averaged $3100 ($4000 maximum); and work contracts averaged $800 ($1200 maximum). Forty percent of undergraduate students work part-time. The average financial indebtedness of the 1992–93 graduate was $12,625. AMC is a member of CSS. The FAF, the college's own financial statement, and the income tax form 1040 and accompanying schedules are required. Deadlines for financial aid applications are open.

International Students: There are currently 27 international students enrolled. The school actively recruits these students. They must take the TOEFL and achieve a minimum score of 500.

Computers: The college provides computer facilities for student use. All students may access the system. There are no time limits on using the system and no fees.

Graduates: The most popular majors among graduates were business (20%), education (20%), and criminal justice (20%). Within an average freshman class, 75% graduate in 4 years and 85% in 5 years.

Admissions Contact: John Wilbur, Director of Admissions.

ASSUMPTION COLLEGE
Worcester, MA 01615

C-2
(508) 752-5615

Full-time: 672 men, 1023 women
Part-time: 179 men, 523 women
Graduate: 143 men, 252 women
Year: semesters, summer session
Application Deadline: March 1
Freshman Class: n/av
SAT I: required

Faculty: 108; IIB, av$
Ph.D.s: 93%
Student/Faculty: 16 to 1
Tuition: $11,595
Room & Board: $5500

LESS COMPETITIVE

Assumption College, founded in 1904, is a private, coeducational institution affiliated with the Roman Catholic Church offering programs in the liberal arts, rehabilitation, and business. There are 4 graduate schools. In addition to regional accreditation, Assumption has baccalaureate program accreditation with NLN. The library contains 197,500 volumes and 9000 microform items, and subscribes to 1150 periodicals. Special learning facilities include a learning resource center. The 150-acre campus is in a suburban area 45 miles west of Boston. Including residence halls, there are 34 buildings on campus.
Student Life: About 60% of undergraduates are from Massachusetts. Students come from 15 states, 14 foreign countries, and Canada. Forty percent are from public schools; 60% from private. Ninety-one percent are white. The average age of freshmen is 19; all undergraduates, 20. Fourteen percent drop out by the end of their first year; 80% remain to graduate.
Housing: A total of 1500 students can be accommodated in college housing. College-sponsored living facilities include single-sex dormitories and on-campus apartments. In addition, there are special interest houses and substance-free housing. On-campus housing is guaranteed for all 4 years. Ninety percent of students live on campus; of those, 85% remain on campus on weekends. All students may keep cars on campus.
Activities: There are no fraternities or sororities on campus. There are 40 groups on campus, including band, cheerleading, choir, chorale, chorus, computers, drama, ethnic, international, literary magazine, newspaper, pep band, photography, political, religious, social, social service, student government, and yearbook. Popular campus events include Spring Fest, Parents Weekend, and Alumni Weekend.
Sports: There are 10 intercollegiate sports for men and 8 for women, and 15 intramural sports for men and 15 for women. Athletic and recreation facilities include a 4400-seat gymnasium, a 3300-seat auditorium, baseball and softball diamonds, a field hockey area, a soccer field, and basketball and tennis courts. A new recreation center houses a 6-lane swimming pool, a jogging/walking track, 4 racquetball courts, an aerobics/dance studio, fully equipped bodymaster and free-weight rooms, a fitness center, and a field house with 3 multipurpose courts for basketball, volleyball, and floor hockey.
Disabled Students: Ninety percent of the campus is accessible to disabled students. The following facilities are available: wheelchair ramps, elevators, special parking, specially equipped rest rooms, special class scheduling, lowered drinking fountains, and lowered telephones.
Services: In addition to many counseling and information services, tutoring is available in every subject. In addition, there is a reader service for the blind, and remedial math, reading, and writing.
Campus Safety and Security: Campus safety and security measures include 24-hour foot and vehicle patrol, escort service, shuttle buses, and pamphlets, posters, and films. In addition, there are lighted pathways and sidewalks.
Programs of Study: Assumption awards the B.A. degree. Associate and master's degrees also are awarded. Bachelor's degrees are awarded in BIOLOGICAL SCIENCE (biology/biological science), BUSINESS (accounting, business administration and management, international business management, and marketing management), COMMUNICATIONS AND THE ARTS (classics, English, foreign languages, French, languages, and Spanish), COMPUTER AND PHYSICAL SCIENCE (chemistry, computer science, and mathematics), HEALTH PROFESSIONS (rehabilitation therapy), SOCIAL SCIENCE (economics, history, international studies, philosophy, political science/government, psychology, religion, and sociology). Business, English, political science, psychology, social and rehabilitation services, and accounting are the strongest programs academically and have the largest enrollments.
Required: Students must complete a core curriculum of 2 courses each of English composition, philosophy, and religious studies; 2 of the following 3: mathematics, a laboratory science, and a third year of a foreign language; and 1 each of literature, history, social science, and either art, music, or theater. A total of 120 semester credit hours must be completed, with 9 to 12 in the upper division of the major. A minimum 2.0 GPA is required.
Special: There are co-op programs in optometry and marine studies. Cross-registration with the Worcester Consortium and a 3–2 engineering program with Worcester Polytechnic Institute are permitted. The college offers internships, study abroad, a Washington semester,

work-study, a general studies degree, student-designed and dual majors, credit by examination, and credit for life, military, and work experience. There are 5 national honor societies on campus.
Faculty/Classroom: Sixty percent of faculty are male; 40%, female. Ninety-five percent teach undergraduates. No introductory courses are taught by graduate students. The average class size in an introductory lecture is 40; in a laboratory, 20; and in a regular course offering, 25.
Admissions: There was 1 National Merit finalist and 9 semifinalists. Eight freshmen graduated first in their class.
Requirements: The SAT I is required. In addition, all applicants must graduate from an accredited secondary school or have a GED. Fifteen academic units are required, including 4 years of English, 2 each of mathematics and foreign language, and 1 each of history and science. An essay and an interview are recommended. AP and CLEP credits are accepted. Important factors used in the admissions decision are advanced placement or honor courses, evidence of special talent, personality, intangible qualities, leadership record, and recommendations by alumni.
Procedure: Freshmen are admitted in the fall and spring. Entrance exams should be taken in May of the junior year or November of the senior year. Early decision applications should be filed by November 1; regular applications, by March 1 for fall entry and December 1 for spring entry, along with an application fee of $25. Notification of early decision is sent December 15; regular decision, on a rolling basis. There are early decision, early admissions, and deferred admissions plans. About 27 early decision candidates were accepted for the 1993–94 class. A waiting list is an active part of the admissions procedure, with about 2% of applicants on the list.
Transfer: About 65 transfer students enrolled in 1993–94. Transfer students must have maintained a minimum 2.5 GPA at their previous college. SAT I scores and high school and college transcripts are required. A total of 60 credits out of 120 must be completed at Assumption.
Visiting: There are regularly scheduled orientations for prospective students, consisting of new student orientation, a program that includes meetings with future classmates, choosing roommates, registration, testing, conferences with academic advisors, and discussions of aspects of college life. There are guides for informal visits and visitors may sit in on classes. To arrange for a visit, contact the Admissions Office at (508) 752–5615, ext. 285.
Financial Aid: In 1993–94, 69% of all current freshmen and 65% of continuing students received some form of financial aid. About 69% of freshmen and 65% of continuing students received need-based aid. The average freshman award was $8400. Of that total, scholarships or need-based grants averaged $4500; loans averaged $2625(maximum); and work contracts averaged $1000(maximum). Twenty percent of undergraduate students work part-time. Average earnings from campus work for the school year are $1000. The average financial indebtedness of the 1992–93 graduate was $10,000. Assumption is a member of CSS. The FAF is required. The deadline for financial aid applications is February 1.
International Students: There are currently 20 international students enrolled. The school actively recruits these students. They must take the TOEFL and achieve a minimum score of 550. Students may be requested to submit SAT I scores as well.
Computers: The college provides computer facilities for student use. The mainframe is a DEC VAX 3900. Students may use the Apple Macintosh and IBM microcomputers, located in microcomputer laboratory areas throughout the campus, as well as a student-dedicated mainframe. All students may access the system. There are no time limits on using the system and no fees.
Graduates: In 1992–93, 516 bachelor's degrees were awarded. The most popular majors among graduates were business management (20%), psychology (15%), and English (15%). Within an average freshman class, 72% graduate in 4 years, 76% in 5 years, and 80% in 6 years. Some 400 companies recruited on campus in 1992–93. In the 1992 graduating class, 7% of all graduates were enrolled in graduate school within 6 months of graduation; 90% of all graduates had found employment.
Admissions Contact: Dean of Admissions.

ATLANTIC UNION COLLEGE
South Lancaster, MA 01561

C-2
(508) 368-2235
(800) 282-2030 (out-of-state)

Full-time: 219 men, 315 women
Part-time: 21 men, 61 women
Graduate: none
Year: semesters, summer session
Application Deadline: August 1
Freshman Class: 340 applied, 194 accepted, 125 enrolled
SAT I Verbal/Math: 410/430

Faculty: 65
Ph.D.s: 49%
Student/Faculty: 8 to 1
Tuition: $10,600
Room & Board: $3550

ACT: 21   **LESS COMPETITIVE**

Atlantic Union College, founded in 1882, is a private, coeducational institution affiliated with the Seventh-day Adventist Church, offering

undergraduate programs in the arts and sciences, business, education, health science, nursing, and religious studies. In addition to regional accreditation, AUC has baccalaureate program accreditation with CSWE and NLN. The library contains 110,150 volumes, 8867 microform items, and 2830 audiovisual forms, and subscribes to 771 periodicals. Computerized library sources and services include database searching. Special learning facilities include a learning resource center, art gallery, and model elementary and secondary schools, and a music conservatory. The 314-acre campus is in a small town 50 miles west of Boston. Including residence halls, there are 18 buildings on campus.

Student Life: About 70% of undergraduates are from out-of-state, mostly the Northeast. Students come from 26 states, 24 foreign countries, and Canada. Thirty-seven percent are white; 28% African American; 22% Hispanic. About 39% of freshmen remain to graduate.

Housing: A total of 473 students can be accommodated in college housing. College-sponsored living facilities include single-sex dormitories, on-campus apartments, off-campus apartments, and married-student housing. On-campus housing is guaranteed for all 4 years and is available on a first-come, first-served basis. Priority is given to out-of-town students. Sixty-nine percent of students live on campus. Alcohol is not permitted. All students may keep cars on campus.

Activities: There are no fraternities or sororities on campus. There are 20 groups on campus, including art, band, cheerleading, choir, chorale, drama, ethnic, honors, musical theater, newspaper, orchestra, religious, student government, and yearbook. Popular campus events include Fall Picnic, Cultural Heritage Weeks, Fine Arts Week, Inter-school Ethics Weekend, and student forums.

Sports: There are 3 intercollegiate sports for men and 2 for women, and 5 intramural sports for men and 5 for women. Athletic and recreation facilities include a gymnasium, a field house, a swimming pool, tennis courts, and a racquetball court.

Disabled Students: The following facilities are available: elevators, special parking, and specially equipped rest rooms.

Services: In addition to many counseling and information services, tutoring is available in most subjects. There is also remedial math, reading, and writing.

Campus Safety and Security: Campus safety and security measures include self defense education, informal discussions, and lighted pathways and sidewalks.

Programs of Study: AUC awards the B.A., B.S., and B.M. degrees. Associate and master's degrees also are awarded. Bachelor's degrees are awarded in BIOLOGICAL SCIENCE (biochemistry and biology/biological science), BUSINESS (accounting, business administration and management, and office supervision and management), COMMUNICATIONS AND THE ARTS (art, English, French, music, and Spanish), COMPUTER AND PHYSICAL SCIENCE (chemistry, computer science, and mathematics), EDUCATION (art, business, early childhood, elementary, music, physical, and secondary), ENGINEERING AND ENVIRONMENTAL DESIGN (interior design), HEALTH PROFESSIONS (medical laboratory technology and nursing), SOCIAL SCIENCE (history, psychology, religion, and social work). Nursing, English, business, history, and biology are the strongest academically. Business, psychology, and education have the largest enrollments.

Required: Students must complete 12 hours each in humanities, religion/ethics, science, and social science. Foreign language proficiency, a physical education requirement, and a course in freshman rhetoric must also be fulfilled. AUC requires 128 credit hours for the bachelor's degree, with 30 to 50 in the major, and a 2.0 GPA.

Special: Students may study abroad in 4 countries. AUC also offers newspaper and biology research internships, cooperative programs in several majors, pass/fail options and nondegree study. The Summer Advantage in New England program offers precollege credit to high school honor students. There is also an adult degree program, in which most study is done at home, and in which student-designed majors are permitted. Dual majors, an accelerated degree in management and professional studies, a 1–3 engineering degree with Walla Walla College, and preprofessional curricula in dentistry, dental hygiene, medicine, respiratory therapy, radiologic technology, and veterinary medicine in conjunction with Loma Linda University are offered. There is a freshman honors program on campus. Two departments have honors programs.

Faculty/Classroom: Fifty-two percent of faculty are male; 48%, female. Ninety-nine percent teach undergraduates. The average class size in an introductory lecture is 20 and in a laboratory, 10.

Admissions: About 57% of the 1993–94 applicants were accepted. The SAT scores for the 1993–94 freshman class were as follows: Verbal—77% below 500, 13% between 500 and 599, and 10% between 600 and 700; Math—70% below 500, 23% between 500 and 599, 5% between 600 and 700, and 2% above 700. The ACT scores were 47% below 21, 9% between 21 and 23, 21% between 24 and 26, 12% between 27 and 28, and 12% above 28. There were 2 National Merit finalists.

Requirements: A minimum GPA of 2.0 is required. The SAT I or ACT is required. In addition applicants should be graduates of an accredited secondary school or hold a GED. Required academic credits include 4 years of high school English and 2 years each of a foreign language, mathematics, history, and science. AP and CLEP credits are accepted. Important factors used in the admissions decision are recommendations by school officials, recommendations by alumni, personality, intangible qualities, evidence of special talent, and extracurricular activities record.

Procedure: Freshmen are admitted fall and spring. Entrance exams should be taken during the senior year of high school. Applications should be filed by August 1 for fall entry and January 1 for spring entry, along with an application fee of $15. Notification is sent on a rolling basis.

Transfer: About 36 transfer students enrolled in 1993–94. Applicants who have completed at least 24 semester hours are not required to submit SAT I or ACT scores. Applicants from junior colleges may receive credit for up to 72 semester hours. Only a grade of C or better transfers for credit. A total of 30 credits out of 128 must be completed at AUC.

Visiting: There are regularly scheduled orientations for prospective students, portions of which include parents. There are guides for informal visits and visitors may sit in on classes and stay overnight at the school. To arrange for a visit, contact Elmer Eubanks at (508) 368–2258.

Financial Aid: In 1993–94 85% of all current freshmen and 80% of continuing students received some form of financial aid. About 70% of freshmen and 70% of continuing students received need-based aid. The average freshman award was $7000. Of that total, scholarships or need-based grants averaged $1200 ($3000 maximum); and loans averaged $2500 ($2625 maximum). One-hundred percent of undergraduate students work part-time. Average earnings from campus work for the school year are $2000. The average financial indebtedness of the 1992–93 graduate was $9000. The college's own financial statement and FAFSA are required. The deadline for financial aid applications is April 1.

International Students: The school actively recruits these students. They must take the TOEFL and achieve a minimum score of 525. The student must also take the ACT.

Computers: The college provides computer facilities for student use. The mainframe is a DEC MicroVAX II and a Novell Network. About 60 computers are available for student use in the computer laboratory and 6 terminals are available in the learning center. All students may access the system. There are no time limits or fees.

Graduates: In 1992–93 125 bachelor's degrees were awarded. The most popular majors among graduates were business administration (13%), nursing (10%), and psychology (10%).

Admissions Contact: Jim Norcliffe, Director of Admissions.

BABSON COLLEGE   D-2
Babson Park, MA 02157   (617) 239–5522; (800) 488–3696 (in-state)

Full-time: 1065 men, 615 women	**Faculty:** 114; IIB, + +$
Part-time: none	**Ph.D.s:** 93%
Graduate: 1555 men and women	**Student/Faculty:** 15 to 1
Year: semesters, summer session	**Tuition:** $16,445
Application Deadline: February 1	**Room & Board:** $6715
Freshman Class: 2007 applied, 1137 accepted, 412 enrolled	
SAT I or ACT: required	**VERY COMPETITIVE**

Babson College, founded in 1919, is a private, coeducational institution offering programs in business. There is one undergraduate and one graduate school. In addition to regional accreditation, Babson has baccalaureate program accreditation with AACSB. The library contains 118,189 volumes, 348,224 microform items, and 2176 audiovisual forms, and subscribes to 1482 periodicals. Computerized library sources and services include the card catalog and database searching. Special learning facilities include a learning resource center and art gallery. The 450-acre campus is in a suburban area 14 miles west of Boston. Including residence halls, there are 52 buildings on campus.

Student Life: About 59% of undergraduates are from out-of-state, mostly the Northeast. Students come from 41 states, 58 foreign countries, and Canada. Fifty-three percent are from public schools; 47% from private. Sixty-one percent are white; 16% foreign nationals. The average age of freshmen is 18; all undergraduates, 20. Six percent drop out by the end of their first year; 85% remain to graduate.

Housing: A total of 1300 students can be accommodated in college housing. College-sponsored living facilities include single-sex and coed dormitories, on-campus apartments, and married-student housing. In addition, there are special interest houses, substance-free living, fraternity and sorority towers, and a cultural house. On-campus housing is guaranteed for all 4 years. Eighty-two percent of students live on campus; of those, 75% remain on campus on weekends. All students may keep cars on campus.

Activities: About 10% of men and about 1% of women belong to 4 national fraternities; about 8% of women belong to 2 national sororities. There are 60 groups on campus, including art, choir, computers, dance, drama, ethnic, film, gay, honors, international, jazz band, literary magazine, musical theater, newspaper, political, professional, religious, social, social service, student government, and yearbook. Popular campus events include Homecoming, Family Weekend, Founders Day, Multicultural Week, Winter Weekend, Spring Weekend, Ocotberfest Weekend, Senior Week, and Black History Month.

Sports: There are 10 intercollegiate sports for men and 10 for women, and 12 intramural sports for men and 6 for women. Athletic and recreation facilities include a sports complex with an indoor pool, a 220-meter, 6-lane track, a 1500-seat field house, a 600-seat gymnasium with 3 basketball courts, 5 squash and 2 racquetball courts, a fitness center, a dance aerobics studio, locker rooms with saunas, and a sports medicine facility.

Disabled Students: Ninety-eight percent of the campus is accessible to disabled students. The following facilities are available: wheelchair ramps, elevators, special parking, specially equipped rest rooms, special class scheduling, lowered drinking fountains, and lowered telephones.

Services: In addition to many counseling and information services, tutoring is available in most subjects. There are writing/speech skills and mathematics/science skills centers.

Campus Safety and Security: Campus safety and security measures include 24-hour foot and vehicle patrol, escort service, shuttle buses, and informal discussions. In addition, there are pamphlets, posters, and films, emergency telephones, lighted pathways and sidewalks, and a motorist assist program.

Programs of Study: Babson awards the B.S.M. degree. Master's degrees also are awarded. Bachelor's degrees are awarded in BUSINESS (accounting, banking and finance, business administration and management, international business management, investments and securities, management information systems, management science, and marketing/retailing/merchandising), COMMUNICATIONS AND THE ARTS (communications), COMPUTER AND PHYSICAL SCIENCE (quantitative methods), SOCIAL SCIENCE (American studies and economics). Management is the strongest program academically and has the largest enrollment.

Required: Students must complete a curriculum of general management and liberal arts, with 40% in management, 40% in liberal arts, and 20% in course work in either area. A total of 128 semester hours is required for graduation. A minimum GPA of 2.0 is required. Students must take 2 semesters of physical education, a course on introduction to information processing, and a fundamental science course. Students must also fulfill a liberal arts concentration in 1 of 16 different areas.

Special: There is cross-registration with Brandeis University and Pine Manor, Wellesley, and Regis colleges. Internships in management, study abroad, dual and student-designed majors, credit by exam, and up to 8 semester hours of credit for significant work/life experience are possible. There is a freshman honors program on campus.

Faculty/Classroom: Seventy-five percent of faculty are male; 25%, female. Ninety-two percent teach undergraduates, 85% do research, and 80% do both. No introductory courses are taught by graduate students. The average class size in an introductory lecture is 37; in a laboratory, 20; and in a regular course offering, 29.

Admissions: About 57% of the 1993–94 applicants were accepted. The SAT scores for the 1993–94 freshman class were as follows: Verbal—54% below 500, 38% between 500 and 599, and 7% between 600 and 700; Math—15% below 500, 44% between 500 and 599, 34% between 600 and 700, and 7% above 700. About 58% of the current freshmen were in the top fifth of their class; 84% were in the top two fifths. Four freshmen graduated first in their class.

Requirements: The SAT I or ACT, and SAT II: Subject tests in writing and mathematics are required. In addition, applicants must be graduates of an accredited secondary school or have a GED. Sixteen academic courses are required, including 4 credits of English, 3 of mathematics, 2 of social studies, and 1 of science. A fourth year of mathematics is strongly recommended. An essay and graded paper are required. An interview is recommended. AP and CLEP credits are accepted. Important factors used in the admissions decision are advanced placement or honor courses, leadership record, evidence of special talent, extracurricular activities record, and personality, intangible qualities.

Procedure: Freshmen are admitted in the fall and spring. Entrance exams should be taken prior to application (SAT I or ACT). SAT II: Subject tests should be taken by June of the senior year. Early decision applications should be filed by December 1; regular applications, by February 1 for fall entry and November 1 for spring entry, along with an application fee of $50. Notification of early decision is sent January 1; regular decision, April 1. There are early decision and deferred admissions plans. About 69 early decision candidates were accepted for the 1993–94 class. A waiting list is an active part of the admissions procedure, with about 2% of applicants on the list.

Transfer: About 70 transfer students enrolled in 1993–94. Transfer applicants are expected to demonstrate solid academic performance at their prior institution and must submit 2 essays. A total of 64 credits out of 128 must be completed at Babson.

Visiting: There are regularly scheduled orientations for prospective students, usually consisting of personal interviews and campus tours. Group information sessions may also be available. There are guides for informal visits and visitors may sit in on classes and stay overnight at the school. To arrange for a visit, contact the Admission Office at (800) 488–3696 at least 2 weeks beforehand.

Financial Aid: In 1993–94 53% of all current freshmen and 49% of continuing students received some form of financial aid. About 50% of freshmen and 48% of continuing students received need-based aid. The average freshman award was $12,777. Of that total, scholarships or need-based grants averaged $8094 ($18,300 maximum); loans averaged $2883 ($3625 maximum); and work contracts averaged $1300 ($1800 maximum). Thirty-five percent of undergraduate students work part-time. Average earnings from campus work for the school year are $1200. The average financial indebtedness of the 1992–93 graduate was $12,050. Babson is a member of CSS. The FAF and FAFSA are required. The deadline for financial aid applications is February 1.

International Students: There are currently 344 international students enrolled. The school actively recruits these students. They must take the TOEFL and achieve a minimum score of 550. The student must also take the SAT I or the ACT. Students must take SAT II: Subject tests in mathematics and writing.

Computers: The college provides computer facilities for student use. The mainframe is a DEC VAX 6420 and a DEC VAX 8530. The VAX system is accessible through a Digital phone network on campus. Students may dial in from residence halls or use the 50 Macintosh and 250 IBM-compatible microcomputers in the computer center. All students may access the system. There are no time limits on using the system and no fees.

Graduates: In a recent year, 418 bachelor's degrees were awarded. The most popular majors among graduates were marketing (26%), accounting (16%), and finance (15%). Within an average freshman class, 1% graduate in 3 years, 84% in 4 years, 85% in 5 years, and 87% in 6 years. Some 175 companies recruited on campus in 1992–93. In the 1992 graduating class, 2% of all graduates were enrolled in graduate school within 6 months of graduation; 80% of all graduates had found employment.

Admissions Contact: Charles S. Nolan, Dean of Admissions.

BENTLEY COLLEGE
Waltham, MA 02154–4705

D-2

(617) 891–2244
(800) 523–2354 (out-of-state)

Full-time: 1789 men, 1306 women	Faculty: 191; IIA, +$
Part-time: 685 men, 848 women	Ph.D.s: 87%
Graduate: 1240 men, 947 women	Student/Faculty: 16 to 1
Year: semesters, summer session	Tuition: $12,830
Application Deadline: February 5	Room & Board: $5850
Freshman Class: 3466 applied, 2330 accepted, 640 enrolled	
SAT I Verbal/Math: 460/550	COMPETITIVE

Bentley College, founded in 1917, is a private, coeducational institution offering instruction in business and the liberal arts. There is one undergraduate and one graduate school. In addition to regional accreditation, Bentley has baccalaureate program accreditation with AACSB. The library contains 185,738 volumes, 215,100 microform items, and 3741 audiovisual forms, and subscribes to 2578 periodicals. Computerized library sources and services include interlibrary loans and database searching. Special learning facilities include a learning resource center, art gallery, planetarium, and radio station. The 110-acre campus is in a suburban area 9 miles west of Boston. Including residence halls, there are 43 buildings on campus.

Student Life: About 59% of undergraduates are from Massachusetts. Students come from 39 states, 66 foreign countries, and Canada. Seventy-four percent are from public schools. Eighty-three percent are white. The average age of freshmen is 18; all undergraduates, 20. Ten percent drop out by the end of their first year; 75% remain to graduate.

Housing: A total of 2829 students can be accommodated in college housing. College-sponsored living facilities include single-sex and coed dormitories, on-campus apartments, off-campus apartments, and married-student housing. In addition, there are special interest houses and substance-free housing. On-campus housing is guaranteed for all 4 years. Eighty percent of students live on campus; of those, 60% remain on campus on weekends. Upperclassmen may keep cars on campus.

Activities: About 15% of men belong to 3 local and 4 national fraternities; about 13% of women belong to 2 local and 4 national sororities. There are 74 groups on campus, including art, band, cheerleading, chorus, computers, dance, drama, ethnic, gay, honors, international, jazz band, literary magazine, musical theater, newspa-

per, photography, political, professional, radio and TV, religious, social, social service, student government, and yearbook. Popular campus events include Monte Carlo Night, film series, Spring Weekend, Homecoming, Spring Concert, drama production, performing art series, and distinguished lecture series.

Sports: There are 10 intercollegiate sports for men and 9 for women, and 10 intramural sports for men and 9 for women. Athletic and recreation facilities include an indoor track, tennis, racquetball, and basketball courts, a baseball batting cage, a golf cage, Nautilus machines, sauna and steam rooms, a dance studio, an indoor pool, a diving tank, a baseball diamond, softball, football, soccer, field hockey, and intramural fields, a 1500-seat stadium, and a 2800-seat indoor gymnasium, including an artificial turf practice field.

Disabled Students: Ninety-five percent of the campus is accessible to disabled students. The following facilities are available: wheelchair ramps, elevators, special parking, specially equipped rest rooms, and special class scheduling.

Services: In addition to many counseling and information services, tutoring is available in most subjects. There is remedial math, reading, and writing.

Campus Safety and Security: Campus safety and security measures include 24-hour foot and vehicle patrol, self defense education, escort service, and informal discussions. In addition, there are pamphlets, posters, and films, emergency telephones, and lighted pathways and sidewalks.

Programs of Study: Bentley awards the B.A. and B.S. degrees. Master's degrees also are awarded. Bachelor's degrees are awarded in BUSINESS (accounting, banking and finance, business economics, management science, and marketing management), COMMUNICATIONS AND THE ARTS (English), COMPUTER AND PHYSICAL SCIENCE (information sciences and systems), SOCIAL SCIENCE (economics, history, liberal arts/general studies, and philosophy). Accountancy, marketing, management, and finance have the largest enrollments.

Required: Students majoring in the B.S. degree programs take a common business core of 10 courses covering major business areas such as accounting, business law, and marketing. Students working toward the B.A. must take English composition, literature, philosophy, history, government, economics, behavioral science, mathematical science, natural science, and computer information systems. A total of 120 credit hours is required for graduation, as is a minimum GPA of 2.0. Freshmen must take physical education.

Special: There is cross-registration with Regis College, internships in all departments, and an accelerated business degree program. The college offers study abroad, student-designed majors, credit by exam, and nondegree study. There is also a minor concentration program through which business majors can broaden their exposure to the arts and sciences, and arts and science majors can minor in business or interdisciplinary topics. There is a freshman honors program on campus, as well as 2 national honor societies. Three departments have honors programs, and honors internship programs are available.

Faculty/Classroom: Seventy-two percent of faculty are male; 28%, female. The average class size in a regular course offering is 30.

Admissions: About 67% of the 1993–94 applicants were accepted. The SAT scores for the 1993–94 freshman class were as follows: Verbal—75% below 500, 22% between 500 and 599, and 3% between 600 and 700; Math—24% below 500, 46% between 500 and 599, 25% between 600 and 700, and 5% above 700. About 46% of the current freshmen were in the top fifth of their class; 85% were in the top two fifths.

Requirements: The SAT I or ACT is required. Official results of 3 SAT II: Subject tests, including writing, mathematics I or II, and any other test of the student's choice, may be substituted for the SAT I or ACT. Applicants must graduate from an accredited high school or have a GED. Sixteen academic credits are required, including 4 years each of English and mathematics, 2 years each of foreign language and social studies, and 1 year of science. In addition, 3 more years of English, mathematics, social science, laboratory science, or foreign language are required. An essay is required, and an interview is recommended. AP and CLEP credits are accepted. Important factors used in the admissions decision are recommendations by school officials, recommendations by alumni, leadership record, extracurricular activities record, and evidence of special talent.

Procedure: Freshmen are admitted fall and spring. Entrance exams should be taken no later than the January test date. Early decision applications should be filed by December 1; regular applications, by February 5 for fall entry, along with an application fee of $35. Notification of early decision is sent December 20; regular decision, April 1. There are early decision, early admissions, and deferred admissions plans. About 116 early decision candidates were accepted for the 1993–94 class. A waiting list is an active part of the admissions procedure.

Transfer: About 215 transfer students enrolled in a recent year. The SAT I, ACT, or SAT II: Subject test is required of all applicants who have completed fewer than 10 college courses. A minimum GPA of

2.5 is required to be considered. All official college transcripts must be submitted. A total of 45 credits out of 120 must be completed at Bentley.

Visiting: There are regularly scheduled orientations for prospective students, including fall, spring, and summer open house programs. Interviews are arranged by appointment; campus tours take place at regularly scheduled times each weekday. There are guides for informal visits, and visitors may sit in on classes. To arrange for a visit, contact the Office of Undergraduate Admissions at (617) 891-2244 or (800) 523-2354 (out-of-state).

Financial Aid: In a recent year, 70% of all current freshmen received some form of financial aid. About 88% of freshmen and 98% of continuing students received need-based aid. Scholarships or need-based grants averaged $4836 ($11,340 maximum); loans averaged $2722 ($17,200 maximum); and work contracts averaged $1500 ($3000 maximum). Sixty-six percent of undergraduate students work part-time. Average earnings from campus work for the school year are $1100. Bentley is a member of CSS. The FAF and both parents' and students' income tax returns are required. The deadline for financial aid applications is February 1.

International Students: There are currently 291 international students enrolled. The school actively recruits these students. They must take the TOEFL and achieve a minimum score of 550. The student must also take the SAT I or the ACT.

Computers: The college provides computer facilities for student use. The mainframes are a DEC VAX 6620 and a DEC VAX 6510. The mainframes are linked to more than 3,000 microcomputers and terminals across the campus. The network also provides worldwide access to databases and other services via Internet and dial-out modems. Five student computer laboratories contain 130 IBM-compatible and 50 Apple Macintosh microcomputers, all with network access. All students may access the system. Laboratory hours are Monday through Thursday, 8:30 A.M. to 11 P.M.; Friday, 8:30 A.M. to 9 P.M.; Saturday, 8:30 A.M. to 6 P.M.; and Sunday, noon to 11 P.M. Dial-in access is always available. There are no time limits on using the system and no fees.

Graduates: In a recent year, 965 bachelor's degrees were awarded. The most popular majors among graduates were accountancy (27%), finance (19%), and marketing (19%). Within an average freshman class, 67% graduate in 4 years and 76% in 5 years. Some 257 companies recruited on campus in a recent year. In a recent graduating class, 3% of all students were enrolled in graduate school within 6 months of graduation; 82% of the men and 87% of the women had found employment.

Admissions Contact: Joann McKenna, Director of Admissions.

BERKLEE COLLEGE OF MUSIC   E-2
Boston, MA 02215-3693

Full-time: 1872 men, 361 women	(617) 266-1400; (800) 421-0084
Part-time: 257 men, 63 women	**Faculty:** 152; IIB, av$
Graduate: none	**Ph.D.s:** 5%
Year: semesters, summer session	**Student/Faculty:** 15 to 1
Application Deadline: open	**Tuition:** $10,740
	Room & Board: $6790

Freshman Class: 1975 applied, 1516 accepted, 712 enrolled
SAT I Verbal/Math: 435/475   **SPECIAL**

Berklee College of Music, founded in 1945, is a private, coeducational institution offering programs in all areas of contemporary music, primarily American-jazz, pop, Latin, fusion, rhythm and blues, and reggae. The library contains 19,366 volumes, 3000 microform items, and 8188 audiovisual forms, and subscribes to 689 periodicals. Special learning facilities include a learning resource center, 7 recording studios, film editing, music synthesis, home recording laboratories, and 5 performance venues. The campus is in an urban area. Including residence halls, there are 9 buildings on campus.

Student Life: About 80% of undergraduates are from out-of-state, mostly the Northeast. Students come from 46 states, 75 foreign countries, and Canada. The average age of freshmen is 21; all undergraduates, 23. Forty percent drop out by the end of their first year; 60% remain to graduate.

Housing: A total of 800 students can be accommodated in college housing. College-sponsored living facilities include coed dormitories. On-campus housing is available on a first-come, first-served basis and is available on a lottery system for upperclassmen. Seventy percent of students commute. Alcohol is not permitted. All students may keep cars on campus.

Activities: There are no fraternities or sororities on campus. There are 30 groups on campus, including art, band, choir, chorale, chorus, computers, drama, ethnic, gay, international, jazz band, orchestra, professional, religious, and social. Popular campus events include International Students Fair and Concert, daily recitals and concerts, film festivals, and Singer Showcase.

Sports: There is 1 intramural sport for men and 1 for women.

Disabled Students: The following facilities are available: elevators, specially equipped rest rooms, and special class scheduling.

Services: In addition to many counseling and information services, tutoring is available in every subject.

Campus Safety and Security: Campus safety and security measures include 24-hour foot and vehicle patrol, informal discussions, pamphlets, posters, and films, and lighted pathways and sidewalks.

Programs of Study: Berklee awards the B.M. degree. Bachelor's degrees are awarded in COMMUNICATIONS AND THE ARTS (music). Performance and professional music have the largest enrollments.

Required: Students working toward a degree must take general education courses in English composition/literature, history, physical science, and social sciences. Music course programs vary by specialization. A total of 120 credits must be completed.

Special: Berklee offers cross-registration with the Pro-Arts consortium and internships in music education and music production and engineering. There are 5-year dual majors and a 4-year professional (nondegree) diploma program. Work-study programs, an accelerated-degree program, student-designed majors, and credit by exam are available.

Faculty/Classroom: Eighty-seven percent of faculty are male; 13%, female. All teach undergraduates. The average class size in an introductory lecture is 14; in a laboratory, 8; and in a regular course offering, 15.

Admissions: About 77% of the 1993–94 applicants were accepted. The SAT scores for the 1993–94 freshman class were as follows: Verbal—34% below 500, 60% between 500 and 599, 5% between 600 and 700, and 1% above 700; Math—22% below 500, 54% between 500 and 599, 20% between 600 and 700, and 4% above 700. All current freshmen were in the top two fifths of their class.

Requirements: The SAT I or ACT is required. In addition, applicants must be graduates of an accredited secondary school or have their GED. Sixteen Carnegie units are required. An audition and interview are recommended. Applicants must also submit a detailed reference letter regarding their training and experience in music, a letter from a private instructor, school music director, or professional musician. A letter of character reference is also required. AP credits are accepted. Important factors used in the admissions decision are extracurricular activities record, evidence of special talent, recommendations by alumni, recommendations by school officials, and personality, intangible qualities.

Procedure: Freshmen are admitted to all sessions. Entrance exams should be taken in the fall of the senior year. Application deadlines are open. The fee is $50. Notification is sent on a rolling basis. There are early decision and deferred admissions plans.

Transfer: About 243 transfer students enrolled in 1993–94. Applicants for transfer must go through the same application procedures as entering freshmen, as well as submit all previous college records. A total of 60 credits out of 120 must be completed at Berklee.

Visiting: There are regularly scheduled orientations for prospective students. There are guides for informal visits. To arrange for a visit, contact the Admissions Office at (617) 266–1400.

Financial Aid: The FAF or FFS and the college's own financial statement are required. The deadline for financial aid applications is March 31.

International Students: There are currently 828 international students enrolled. The school actively recruits these students.

Computers: The college provides computer facilities for student use. The mainframe is an AS400 IBM. There are more than 40 networked Apple Macintosh computers in the learning center. There are no time limits on using the system and no fees.

Graduates: In 1992–93 385 bachelor's degrees were awarded.

Admissions Contact: Director of Admissions.

BOSTON ARCHITECTURAL CENTER E-2
Boston, MA 02115 (617) 536–3170

Full-time: 425 men, 113 women	Faculty: 181
Part-time: 51 men, 31 women	Ph.D.s: 40%
Graduate: none	Student/Faculty: 3 to 1
Year: semesters, summer session	Tuition: $3372
Application Deadline: open	Room & Board: n/app
Freshman Class: 286 applied, 258 accepted, 141 enrolled	
SAT I or ACT: not required	**SPECIAL**

Boston Architectural Center, founded in 1889 as the Boston Architectural Club, is an independent, coeducational commuter institution offering 6-year programs in architecture and interior design. Students work in professional offices during the day and attend classes at night. In addition to regional accreditation, BAC has baccalaureate program accreditation with NAAB. The library contains 23,000 volumes and subscribes to 140 periodicals. The campus is in an urban area in Boston. There is 1 building on campus. There are no residence halls.

Student Life: About 60% of undergraduates are from Massachusetts. Students come from 35 states, 4 foreign countries, and Canada. Ninety-three percent are white. The average age of freshmen is 25;

all undergraduates, 27. Thirty percent drop out by the end of their first year; 25% remain to graduate.

Housing: There are no residence halls. Arrangements for housing may be made through consortium schools on a space-available basis. All students commute. Alcohol is not permitted.

Activities: There are no fraternities or sororities on campus. There are 3 groups on campus, including newspaper, professional, and student government.

Sports: There is no sports program at BAC.

Disabled Students: All of the campus is accessible to disabled students. The following facilities are available: wheelchair ramps, elevators, special parking, and specially equipped rest rooms.

Programs of Study: BAC awards the B.Arch. and B.Int.Design degrees. Bachelor's degrees are awarded in ENGINEERING AND ENVIRONMENTAL DESIGN (architecture and interior design).

Required: In order to graduate, all students must complete 177 credits. Academic credits must total 123, 93 of which must be in professional subjects and 30 in general education courses. Twenty-one credits must be earned in outside liberal arts courses, which may be taken by special arrangement at Metropolitan College of Boston University and Harvard University Extension. Students must earn 54 credits by working in architectural or interior-design offices or related fields. Academic study is divided into 3 segments, the final segment being the thesis year, which consists of 2 semesters of student-designed study under the guidance of a faculty adviser. A minimum 2.5 GPA is required.

Special: The center offers cross-registration with schools in the Professional Arts Consortium in Boston and with the Art Institute of Boston for studio and professional courses.

Faculty/Classroom: Eighty-six percent of faculty are male; 14%, female. All teach undergraduates. The average class size in an introductory lecture is 33 and in a laboratory, 8.

Admissions: About 90% of the 1993–94 applicants were accepted.

Requirements: The SAT I or ACT is not required. All applicants who have graduated from high school or have a college degree are admitted on a first-come, first-served basis. Official transcripts from previously attended secondary schools and colleges must be submitted to determine qualification for admission and advanced placement. AP and CLEP credits are accepted.

Procedure: Freshmen are admitted in the fall and spring. Application deadlines are open. The application fee is $50. The college accepts all applicants. Notification is sent on a rolling basis. A waiting list is an active part of the admissions procedure, with about 5% of applicants on the list.

Transfer: About 69 transfer students enrolled in 1993–94. Applicants for transfer must have a 2.0 GPA to receive transfer credit. A total of 47 credits out of 123 must be completed at BAC.

Visiting: There are regularly scheduled orientations for prospective students, consisting of monthly presentations. There are guides for informal visits and visitors may sit in on classes. To arrange for a visit, contact the Admissions Office at (617) 536–3170.

Financial Aid: In 1993–94 45% of all current freshmen and 40% of continuing students received some form of financial aid. About 45% of freshmen and 37% of continuing students received need-based aid. The average freshman award was $4234. Of that total, scholarships or need-based grants averaged $1265 ($2300 maximum); and loans averaged $3928 ($5500 maximum). BAC is a member of CSS. The college's own financial statement and the FAFSA are required.

International Students: There are currently 7 international students enrolled.

Computers: The college provides computer facilities for student use. There are Macintosh and IBM microcomputers available for student use. All students may access the system. There are no time limits on using the system. The fees are $44 per semester.

Graduates: In 1992–93 42 bachelor's degrees were awarded. In the 1992 graduating class, all of the men and women had found employment within 6 months of graduation.

Admissions Contact: Ellen Driscoll, Admissions Coordinator.

BOSTON COLLEGE E-2
Chestnut Hill, MA 02167 (617) 552–3100

Full-time: 4182 men, 4625 women	Faculty: 591; I, +$
Part-time: none	Ph.D.s: 95%
Graduate: 1855 men, 2442 women	Student/Faculty: 15 to 1
Year: semesters, summer session	Tuition: $16,006
Application Deadline: January 10	Room & Board: $6700
Freshman Class: 13,112 applied, 6179 accepted, 2154 enrolled	
SAT I or ACT: required	**MOST COMPETITIVE**

Boston College, founded in 1863, is an independent institution affiliated with the Roman Catholic Church and the Jesuit Order. It offers undergraduate programs in the arts and sciences, business, nursing, and education. There are 4 undergraduate and 6 graduate schools. In addition to regional accreditation, BC has baccalaureate program accreditation with AACSB, CSWE, NCATE, and NLN. The 6 libraries

contain 1,322,380 volumes and 77,390 microform items, and subscribe to 14,619 periodicals. Computerized library sources and services include the card catalog, interlibrary loans, and database searching. Special learning facilities include a learning resource center, art gallery, radio station, and TV station. The 240-acre campus is in a suburban area 6 miles west of Boston. Including residence halls, there are 88 buildings on campus.

Student Life: About 69% of undergraduates are from out-of-state, mostly the Northeast. Students come from 50 states and Canada. Fifty-eight percent are from public schools; 42% from private. Seventy-eight percent are white. Most are Catholic. The average age of freshmen is 19; all undergraduates, 20. Seven percent drop out by the end of their first year; 88% remain to graduate.

Housing: A total of 6556 students can be accommodated in college housing. College-sponsored living facilities include single-sex and coed dormitories and on-campus apartments. In addition there are honors houses, language houses, special interest houses, community and multicultural housing, quiet residences, single-sex freshmen halls, perspectives academic program housing, and a substance-free floor. On-campus housing is guaranteed for all 4 years. Seventy-four percent of students live on campus; of those, 75% remain on campus on weekends. Upperclassmen may keep cars on campus.

Activities: There are no fraternities or sororities on campus. There are 140 groups on campus, including art, band, cheerleading, chess, choir, chorale, chorus, computers, dance, drama, ethnic, film, honors, international, jazz band, literary magazine, marching band, musical theater, newspaper, orchestra, pep band, photography, political, professional, radio and TV, religious, social, social service, student government, symphony, and yearbook. Popular campus events include Harvest Night/O'Connell House, Homecoming Ball, Middlemarch Ball, Christmas Chorale, and Senior Week.

Sports: There are 17 intercollegiate sports for men and 16 for women, and 16 intramural sports for men and 14 for women. Athletic and recreation facilities include a 32,000-seat stadium, a forum that seats 8604 for basketball and 7800 for ice hockey, a field, a track, and a student recreation complex.

Disabled Students: All of the campus is accessible to disabled students. The following facilities are available: wheelchair ramps, elevators, special parking, specially equipped rest rooms, special class scheduling, lowered drinking fountains, and lowered telephones.

Services: In addition to many counseling and information services, tutoring is available in most subjects. In addition, there is a reader service for the blind and an academic development center.

Campus Safety and Security: Campus safety and security measures include 24-hour foot and vehicle patrol, self-defense education, escort service, and shuttle buses. In addition, there are informal discussions, pamphlets, posters, and films, emergency telephones, lighted pathways and sidewalks, safety seminars and safety walking tours, and whistles distributed to incoming students.

Programs of Study: BC awards the B.A. and B.S. degrees. Master's and doctoral degrees also are awarded. Bachelor's degrees are awarded in BIOLOGICAL SCIENCE (biochemistry and biology/biological science), BUSINESS (accounting, banking and finance, business administration and management, business economics, human resources, management engineering, marketing/retailing/merchandising, and operations research), COMMUNICATIONS AND THE ARTS (art history and appreciation, classics, communications, dramatic arts, English, fine arts, French, German, Greek, Italian, Latin, linguistics, music, romance languages, Spanish, and studio art), COMPUTER AND PHYSICAL SCIENCE (chemistry, computer science, geology, geophysics and seismology, information sciences and systems, mathematics, and physics), EDUCATION (early childhood, elementary, secondary, and special), ENGINEERING AND ENVIRONMENTAL DESIGN (environmental science), HEALTH PROFESSIONS (nursing), SOCIAL SCIENCE (classical/ancient civilization, economics, history, human development, philosophy, political science/government, psychology, Russian and Slavic studies, sociology, and theology). Humanities and science are the strongest academically. English, political science, and psychology have the largest enrollments.

Required: Core requirements include 2 courses each in natural science, social science, history, philosophy, and theology, and 1 course each in literature, writing, mathematics, cultural diversity, and the arts. To graduate, students must complete 114 credits (122 in nursing), including at least 30 in the major, with a minimum 1.667 GPA (1.5 in management). Computer science is required for management majors, intermediate-level foreign language proficiency for arts and sciences and management students, and a freshman writing seminar for all students.

Special: There are internship programs in communications and political science. Students may cross-register with Boston University, Brandeis University, Hebrew College, Pine Manor College, Regis College, and Tufts University. BC also offers a Washington semester with American University, work-study programs with nonprofit agencies, study abroad, dual and student-designed majors, credit by

exam, and pass/fail options. Students may pursue a 3–2 engineering program with Boston University, and accelerated programs in business, social work, and education. There are also special programs in social work and philosophy/theology, in language immersion, and in exploring fundamental questions of faith, peace, and justice. There is a freshman honors program on campus, as well as 12 national honor societies, including Phi Beta Kappa. Each of the 4 undergraduate schools has an honors program.

Faculty/Classroom: Sixty-nine percent of faculty are male; 31%, female. One-hundred percent both teach and do research. Graduate students teach 22% of introductory courses. The average class size in an introductory lecture is 100; in a laboratory, 15; and in a regular course offering, 30.

Admissions: About 47% of the 1993–94 applicants were accepted. The SAT scores for the 1993–94 freshman class were as follows: Verbal—17% below 500, 49% between 500 and 599, 32% between 600 and 700, and 2% above 700; Math—2% below 500, 23% between 500 and 599, 54% between 600 and 700, and 21% above 700.

Requirements: The SAT I or ACT is required. Students must also take SAT II: Subject tests in writing, mathematics level I or II, and any third test. Applicants must be graduates of an accredited high school, completing 4 units each of English, foreign language, and mathematics, and 2 units of science. Those students applying to the School of Nursing must complete at least 2 years of a laboratory science, including 1 year of chemistry. Applicants to the School of Management are strongly encouraged to take 4 years of mathematics. An essay is required and an interview is recommended. CLEP credit is accepted. Important factors used in the admissions decision are advanced placement or honor courses, leadership record, evidence of special talent, recommendations by school officials, and extracurricular activities record.

Procedure: Freshmen are admitted fall and spring. Entrance exams should be taken no later than January of the senior year; the December administration of the SAT II: writing is preferred. Early decision applications should be filed by November 1; regular applications, by January 10 for fall entry and November 1 for spring entry, along with an application fee of $45. Notification of early decision is sent December 15; regular decision, April 15. There are early decision, early admissions, and deferred admissions plans. About 1000 early decision candidates were accepted for the 1993–94 class. A waiting list is an active part of the admissions procedure, with about 10% to 20% of applicants on the list.

Transfer: About 270 transfer students enrolled in 1993–94. Applicants must have a current GPA of at least 2.5 and must have earned a minimum of 9 semester hours. High school transcripts, letters of recommendation, and SAT I or ACT scores are required. A total of 54 credits out of 114 must be completed at BC.

Visiting: There are regularly scheduled orientations for prospective students, consisting of group information sessions and campus tours Monday through Friday. Interviews should be scheduled 10 to 12 weeks in advance. There are guides for informal visits and visitors may sit in on classes. To arrange for a visit, contact the Office of Undergraduate Admission at (617) 552–3100.

Financial Aid: In a recent year, 61% of all current freshmen and 61% of continuing students received some form of financial aid. About 78% of freshmen and 65% of continuing students received need-based aid. The average freshman award was $15,095. Of that total, scholarships or need-based grants averaged $9818 ($14,580 maximum); loans averaged $3138 ($4625 maximum); and work contracts averaged $1471 ($1500 maximum). Twenty-four percent of undergraduate students work part-time. Average earnings from campus work for the school year are $1200. The average financial indebtedness of the 1992–93 graduate was $8719. BC is a member of CSS. The FAF, the college's own financial statement, the federal IRS income tax form, and the SAR are required. The deadline for financial aid applications is February 1.

International Students: There are currently 335 international students enrolled. They must take the TOEFL and achieve a minimum score of 550. The student must also take the SAT I or the ACT. Students must take SAT II: Subject tests in writing, mathematics level I or II, and any third test.

Computers: The college provides computer facilities for student use. The mainframes are an IBM 3090 and DEC VAX 11/785 and 8700 units. More than 200 microcomputers are available, providing database searches, optical disk references, and on-line access to catalog services. Software includes word processing, programming language, statistical analysis, graphics production, and database management packages. Printers include high-speed line printers, high-resolution dot-matrix printers, and laser printers. Professionals and students assist students with aspects of computing. All students may access the system. It may be used at all times. There are no time limits on using the system and no fees.

Graduates: In 1992–93, 2402 bachelor's degrees were awarded. The most popular majors among graduates were English (13%), finance (9%), and political science (8%). Within an average freshman class, 84% graduate in 4 years, 88% in 5 years, and 88% in 6 years. Some 311 companies recruited on campus in 1992–93. In the 1992 graduating class, 32% of the men and 24% of the women were enrolled in graduate school within 6 months of graduation; 68% of the men and 76% of the women had found employment.

Admissions Contact: John L. Mahoney, Jr., Director of Undergraduate Admission.

BOSTON CONSERVATORY

E-6

Boston, MA 02215   (617) 536–6340, ext. 16

Full-time: 262 men and women	Faculty: 17
Part-time: 29 men and women	Ph.D.s: 1%
Graduate: 125 men and women	Student/Faculty: 15 to 1
Year: semesters, summer session	Tuition: $11,975
Application Deadline: June 1	Room & Board: $5925
Freshman Class: 287 applied, 167 accepted, 67 enrolled	
SAT I Verbal/Math: 496/456	SPECIAL

The Boston Conservatory, founded in 1867, is a private college providing degree programs in music, musical theater, and dance. There are one undergraduate and 3 graduate schools. In addition to regional accreditation, the conservatory has baccalaureate program accreditation with NASM. The library contains 40,000 volumes and subscribes to 120 periodicals. Computerized library sources and services include interlibrary loans and database searching. The campus is in an urban area in the Back Bay area of Boston. Including residence halls, there are 7 buildings on campus.

Student Life: About 20% of undergraduates are from Massachusetts. Students come from 36 states, 29 foreign countries, and Canada. Ninety percent are white. The average age of freshmen is 18. Twenty-three percent drop out by the end of their first year; 44% remain to graduate.

Housing: A total of 164 students can be accommodated in college housing. College-sponsored living facilities include single-sex and coed dormitories. In addition, there are special interest and international houses. On-campus housing is guaranteed for all 4 years. Sixty-seven percent of students commute. Alcohol is not permitted. All students may keep cars on campus.

Activities: There are 1 national fraternity and 2 national sororities. There are many groups and organizations on campus, including band, choir, chorale, chorus, dance, drama, ethnic, gay, international, musical theater, newspaper, opera, orchestra, political, professional, religious, social service, student government, and yearbook. Popular campus events include Parents Weekend.

Sports: There is no sports program at the conservatory.

Disabled Students: Twenty percent of the campus is accessible to disabled students. Elevators are available for these students.

Services: In addition to many counseling and information services, tutoring is available in every subject for a fee.

Campus Safety and Security: Campus safety and security measures include 24-hour foot and vehicle patrol, self defense education, and informal discussions.

Programs of Study: The conservatory awards the B.F.A. and B.Mus. degrees. Bachelor's degrees are awarded in COMMUNICATIONS AND THE ARTS (dance, guitar, music, music performance, music theory and composition, musical theater, opera, and piano/organ), EDUCATION (music). Musical theater has the largest enrollment.

Required: All students must successfully complete the curriculum while not receiving grades of D in more than 12 credit hours. In addition, music performance majors must present recitals, music education majors must present a recital from memory, and composition majors must present a recital from memory, and composition majors must pass an exam on their primary instrument, present a portfolio of original composition, and perform a recital.

Special: There are 3 national honor societies on campus. One department has an honors program.

Faculty/Classroom: All teach undergraduates. No introductory courses are taught by graduate students. The average class size in an introductory lecture is 15; in a laboratory, 5; and in a regular course offering, 15.

Admissions: About 58% of the 1993–94 applicants were accepted. The SAT scores for the 1993–94 freshman class were as follows: Verbal—95% below 500 and 5% between 500 and 599; Math—98% below 500 and 2% between 500 and 599.

Requirements: A minimum GPA of 2.0 is required. The SAT I or ACT is recommended, and scores are reviewed. An audition is required. An academic high school diploma or GED also is required. AP and CLEP credits are accepted. Important factors used in the admissions decision are evidence of special talent, extracurricular activities record, and personality, intangible qualities.

Procedure: Freshmen are admitted in the fall and spring (music majors only). Entrance exams should be taken as early as possible. Early decision applications should be filed by December 1; regular appli-

cations, by June 1 for fall entry and December 1 for spring entry, along with an application fee of $40. Notification of early decision is sent February 1; regular decision, on a rolling basis. There are early decision, early admissions, and deferred admissions plans.

Transfer: A successful audition and a 2.0 GPA are required. Transfer credits are determined by exam or review by the division head and the dean. The high school transcript is required if fewer than 30 college credits have been earned. The number of credits that must be completed at the conservatory varies by major.

Visiting: Visitors may sit in on classes if arranged in advance. To arrange for a visit, contact the Admissions Office at (617) 536–6340, ext. 15.

Financial Aid: In an earlier year, 82% of all freshmen received some form of financial aid. The conservatory is a member of CSS. The FAF and the college's own financial statement are required. The deadline for financial aid applications is March 1.

International Students: There are currently 101 international students enrolled. The school actively recruits these students. They must take the TOEFL, with a recommended minimum score of 450, the University of Michigan Language Test, or the college's own test, upon enrollment. An audition is required.

Computers: The college provides computer facilities for student use, inlcuding Apple Macintosh microcomputers. All students may access the system when the library is open.

Admissions Contact: Allison T. Ball, Director of Enrollment and International Programs.

BOSTON UNIVERSITY

E-2

Boston, MA 02215   (617) 353–2300

Full-time: 6392 men, 7537 women	Faculty: 1018
Part-time: 291 men, 275 women	Ph.D.s: 82%
Graduate: 5203 men, 5343 women	Student/Faculty: 14 to 1
Year: semesters, summer session	Tuition: $17,650
Application Deadline: January 15	Room & Board: $6480
Freshman Class: 20,192 applied, 13,007 accepted, 3810 enrolled	
SAT I Verbal/Math: 550/600	ACT: 27 HIGHLY COMPETITIVE

Boston University, founded in 1839, is a private, coeducational institution offering undergraduate and graduate programs in basic studies, liberal arts, communications, hotel and food administration, allied health education management, and fine arts. There are 10 undergraduate and 15 graduate schools. In addition to regional accreditation, BU has baccalaureate program accreditation with AACSB, ABET, NASM, NCATE, and NLN. The 23 libraries contain 1,896,000 volumes, 3208 microform items, and 53,000 audiovisual forms, and subscribe to 28,512 periodicals. Computerized library sources and services include the card catalog, interlibrary loans, and database searching. Special learning facilities include a learning resource center, art gallery, planetarium, radio and TV stations, astronomy observatory, 20th-century archives, a theater and theater company, a scientific computing and visualization laboratory, a language laboratory, a speech, language, and hearing clinic, and a hotel food administration culinary center. The 110-acre campus is in an urban area on the Charles River in Boston's Back Bay. Including residence halls, there are 289 buildings on campus.

Student Life: About 64% of undergraduates are from out-of-state, mostly the Middle Atlantic. Students come from 50 states, 129 foreign countries, and Canada. Sixty-four percent are from public schools; 36% from private. Sixty-five percent are white; 13% Asian American; 12% foreign nationals. Thirty-nine percent are Catholic; 20% Protestant; 15% Jewish; 11% Buddhist, Hindu, Islamic, and Eastern Rite Orthodox; 15% claim no religious affiliation. The average age of freshmen is 18.8; all undergraduates, 20.9. Fifteen percent drop out by the end of their first year; 71% remain to graduate.

Housing: A total of 8530 students can be accommodated in college housing. College-sponsored living facilities include single-sex and coed dormitories, on- and off-campus apartments, and married-student housing. In addition there are honors houses, language houses, special interest houses, and international floors and houses. On-campus housing is guaranteed for the freshman year only and is available on a lottery system for upperclassmen. Fifty-five percent of students live on campus; of those, 80% remain on campus on weekends. All students may keep cars on campus.

Activities: About 5% of men belong to 7 national fraternities; about 8% of women belong to 9 national sororities. There are more than 300 groups on campus, including art, band, cheerleading, chess, choir, chorale, chorus, computers, dance, drama, ethnic, film, honors, international, jazz band, literary magazine, marching band, musical theater, newspaper, opera, orchestra, pep band, photography, political, professional, radio and TV, religious, social, social service, student government, symphony, and yearbook. Popular campus events include World Fair, Homecoming Weekend, Head of the Charles River Regatta, and the Boston Marathon.

Sports: There are 13 intercollegiate sports for men and 9 for women, and 10 intramural sports for men and 10 for women. Athletic and recreation facilities include an athletic center, 2 gymnasiums, a field, an arena, and a track and field park.

Disabled Students: Eighty-five percent of the campus is accessible to disabled students. The following facilities are available: wheelchair ramps, elevators, special parking, specially equipped rest rooms, special class scheduling, lowered drinking fountains and telephones, tactile maps, and visual fire alarms for the deaf.

Services: In addition to many counseling and information services, tutoring is available in most subjects, including liberal arts, science, engineering, and management. In addition, there is a reader service for the blind. Interpreters are available for the hearing impaired.

Campus Safety and Security: Campus safety and security measures include 24-hour foot and vehicle patrol, self-defense education, an escort service, and shuttle buses. In addition, there are informal discussions, pamphlets, posters, and films, emergency telephones, lighted pathways and sidewalks, and and a bicycle patrol system. There is a uniformed safety/security assistant on duty 24 hours a day in large residence halls and there are 48 academy-trained officers in the university police department.

Programs of Study: BU awards the B.A., B.S., B.F.A., B.L.S., B.Mus., and B.S.B.A. degrees. Master's and doctoral degrees also are awarded. Bachelor's degrees are awarded in BIOLOGICAL SCIENCE (biochemistry, biology/biological science, biophysics, marine biology, and physiology), BUSINESS (accounting, banking and finance, business administration and management, business economics, hotel/motel and restaurant management, international business management, management information systems, marketing/retailing/merchandising, operations research, and recreation and leisure services), COMMUNICATIONS AND THE ARTS (advertising, art history and appreciation, broadcasting, classics, communications, dramatic arts, English, film arts, fine arts, French, German, graphic design, Greek (classical), Greek (modern), Italian, journalism, Latin, linguistics, music history and appreciation, music performance, music theory and composition, painting, Portuguese, public relations, Russian, sculpture, Spanish, and theater design), COMPUTER AND PHYSICAL SCIENCE (astronomy, astrophysics, chemistry, computer science, geology, information sciences and systems, mathematics, physics, planetary and space science, and statistics), EDUCATION (art, bilingual/bicultural, business, drama, early childhood, education of the deaf and hearing impaired, elementary, English, foreign languages, mathematics, music, physical, school psychology, science, secondary, social foundations, social studies, special, speech correction, and teaching English as a second language/foreign language), ENGINEERING AND ENVIRONMENTAL DESIGN (aeronautical engineering, biomedical engineering, computer engineering, electrical/electronics engineering, engineering, engineering management, environmental science, industrial engineering, manufacturing engineering, mechanical engineering, and systems engineering), HEALTH PROFESSIONS (dental laboratory technology, health, health science, medical laboratory technology, occupational therapy, predentistry, premedicine, speech pathology/audiology, and sports medicine), SOCIAL SCIENCE (African studies, American studies, anthropology, archeology, East Asian studies, Eastern European studies, economics, European studies, geography, history, human services, interdisciplinary studies, international relations, Latin American studies, paralegal studies, philosophy, physical fitness/movement, political science/government, prelaw, psychology, religion, Russian and Slavic studies, social science, social work, sociology, urban studies, and Western European studies). The University Professors Program and accelerated medical program are the strongest academically. Psychology, communications, biology, management, environmental studies, and international relations have the largest enrollments.

Required: Students are required to complete 128 credit hours to qualify for graduation. Hours in the major, specific disciplines, curricula, distribution requirements, and minimum GPA vary, depending on the school or college of the university attended. All freshman students must take an English composition course unless exempted by their SAT I verbal or AP scores.

Special: Cross-registration is permitted with Brandeis University, Tufts University, Boston College, and Hebrew College in Massachusetts. Opportunities are provided for internships, co-op programs in engineering, a Washington semester, on- and off-campus work-study, accelerated degrees in medicine, physical therapy, and dentistry, B.A.-B.S. degrees, dual majors, student-designed majors, credit by exam, nondegree studies, pass/fail options, and study abroad in more than 10 countries. A 3–2 engineering degree is offered with 18 schools, and 2–2 engineering agreements with 15, plus 10 other 2–2 agreements. The University Professors Program offers a creative cross-disciplinary approach, and the College of Basic Studies offers team teaching. There is a freshman honors program on campus, as well as 10 national honor societies, including Phi Beta Kappa. All departments within the College of Liberal Arts have honors programs.

Faculty/Classroom: Seventy-three percent of faculty are male; 27%, female. Seventy-six percent teach undergraduates. Graduate students teach 21% of introductory courses. The average class size in an introductory lecture is 40; in a laboratory, 24; and in a regular course offering, 23.

Admissions: About 64% of the 1993–94 applicants were accepted. The SAT scores for the 1993–94 freshman class were as follows: Verbal—25% below 500, 47% between 500 and 599, 25% between 600 and 700, and 3% above 700; Math—9% below 500, 38% between 500 and 599, 40% between 600 and 700, and 13% above 700. The ACT scores were 3% below 21, 15% between 21 and 23, 30% between 24 and 26, 22% between 27 and 28, and 30% above 28. About 70% of the current freshmen were in the top fifth of their class; 94% were in the top two fifths. There were 47 National Merit finalists and 22 semifinalists. Eighty freshmen graduated first in their class.

Requirements: SAT I or ACT is required. SAT II: Subject tests are required for some programs and majors. Graduation from an accredited secondary school is required; a GED will be accepted. It is recommended that applicants have successfully completed 4 years each of English, mathematics, science, and social studies, and at least 3 of a foreign language. Medical, dental, management, and engineering programs require additional college-preparatory courses in high school. Applicants are evaluated on an individual basis. Emphasis is placed on their secondary school record, test scores, character, outside interests, recommendations, and other personal qualifications. An essay is required and for some programs, an interview, portfolio, or audition. AP and CLEP credits are accepted.

Procedure: Freshmen are admitted fall and spring. Entrance exams should be taken in the junior year or early in the senior year. Early decision applications should be filed by November 15; regular applications, by January 15 for fall entry and November 15 for spring entry, along with an application fee of $45. Notification of early decision is sent December 31; regular decision, March 15. There are early decision, early admissions, and deferred admissions plans. About 230 early decision candidates were accepted for the 1993–94 class. A waiting list is an active part of the admissions procedure.

Transfer: About 591 transfer students enrolled in 1993–94. SAT I or ACT scores and a high school transcript (or GED) should be submitted. A GPA of 3.0, recommendations, and an essay are also recommended. The number of credits that must be completed at the university varies by college and major.

Visiting: There are regularly scheduled orientations for prospective students, consisting of personal interviews, class visits, lunch with current students, campus tours, and information sessions. There are guides for informal visits, and visitors may sit in on classes and stay overnight at the school. To arrange for a visit, contact the Admissions Reception Center at (617) 353–2318.

Financial Aid: In 1993–94, 78% of all current freshmen received some form of financial aid. About 68% of freshmen received need-based aid. The average freshman award was $16,626. Of that total, scholarships or need-based grants averaged $12,123 ($25,000 maximum); loans averaged $3416 ($4600 maximum); and work contracts averaged $1680 ($2000 maximum). Sixty percent of undergraduate students work part-time. Average earnings from campus work for the school year are $1500. The average financial indebtedness of the 1992–93 graduate was $5230. BU is a member of CSS. The FAF and FAFSA are required. The deadline for financial aid applications is March 1.

International Students: There are currently 1752 international students enrolled. The school actively recruits these students. They must take the TOEFL and achieve a minimum score of 550. The student must also take the SAT I or the ACT. There are no minimum scores except for select programs.

Computers: The college provides computer facilities for student use. The mainframe is an IBM RS/6000 cluster. A 2800-port high-speed campus network with more than 800 public acccess terminals provides access to the mainframe and to a Connection CM 5 via terminal and workstation clusters situated throughout the campus, and via dialup facilities. A state-of-the-art computer graphics laboratory and a personal computing support center are also available to students. All students may access the system. It may be used 24 hours a day. There are no time limits on using the system and no fees.

Graduates: In 1992–93, 3430 bachelor's degrees were awarded. The most popular majors among graduates were business and management (20%), social sciences (19%), and communications (15%). Within an average freshman class, 71% graduate in 6 years.

Admissions Contact: Thomas Rajala, Director, Office of Undergraduate Admissions.

BRADFORD COLLEGE

D-1

Bradford, MA 01830   (508) 372-7161; (800) 336-6448 (out-of-state)

Full-time: 215 men, 304 women	Faculty: 35; IIB, -$
Part-time: none	Ph.D.s: 80%
Graduate: none	Student/Faculty: 15 to 1
Year: semesters, summer session	Tuition: $13,480
Application Deadline: open	Room & Board: $6120

Freshman Class: 926 applied, 715 accepted, 186 enrolled

SAT I or ACT: not required   **COMPETITIVE**

Bradford College, founded in 1803, is a private, coeducational institution offering programs in liberal arts and teacher preparation. The library contains 58,000 volumes and 86 microform items and subscribes to 236 periodicals. Computerized library sources and services include the card catalog and interlibrary loans. Special learning facilities include a learning resource center, art gallery, and radio station. The 70-acre campus is in a suburban area 35 miles north of Boston. Including residence halls, there are 14 buildings on campus.

Student Life: About 57% of undergraduates are from out-of-state, mostly the Northeast. Students come from 30 states and 28 foreign countries. Eighty percent are from public schools; 20% from private. Seventy-six percent are white. Thirty-one percent are Catholic; 21% Protestant; 11% Jewish. The average age of freshmen is 18; all undergraduates, 21. Twenty percent drop out by the end of their first year; 60% remain to graduate.

Housing: A total of 370 students can be accommodated in college housing. College-sponsored living facilities include single-sex and coed dormitories and on-campus apartments. In addition there are special interest houses. On-campus housing is guaranteed for all 4 years. Seventy-five percent of students live on campus; of those, 75% remain on campus on weekends. Alcohol is not permitted. All students may keep cars on campus.

Activities: There are no fraternities or sororities on campus. There are 23 groups on campus, including chorale, dance, drama, ethnic, film, honors, international, literary magazine, musical theater, newspaper, photography, political, radio and TV, social, social service, student government, and yearbook. Popular campus events include Spring Ball, Spring Day, Christmas Step Singing, Halloween Dracula Stories, Christmas Semiformal Dance, Earth Day, Faculty/Staff Variety Show, Student Talent Show, International Week, and Intellectual Celebration Week.

Sports: There are 3 intercollegiate sports for men and 3 for women, and 8 intramural sports for men and 8 for women. Athletic and recreation facilities include a swimming pool, weight room, gymnasium, playing fields, cross-country ski trail, and 20-station track-and-exercise facility.

Disabled Students: Wheelchair ramps and elevators are available for these students.

Services: In addition to many counseling and information services, tutoring is available in most subjects. In addition, there is remedial writing.

Campus Safety and Security: Campus safety and security measures include 24-hour foot and vehicle patrol, self defense education, escort service, and emergency telephones. In addition, there are lighted pathways and sidewalks.

Programs of Study: Bradford awards the B.A. degree. Bachelor's degrees are awarded in BUSINESS (management science), COMMUNICATIONS AND THE ARTS (fine arts), COMPUTER AND PHYSICAL SCIENCE (mathematics and natural sciences), SOCIAL SCIENCE (human development and humanities).

Required: Students must complete courses in critical inquiry, human heritage, the individual and the community, perspective on the arts, language of numbers, global perspective, nature of work, individual science and the environment, personal health and fitness, 2 additional courses in physical education or dance, and a senior seminar in ethics and values. A total of 121 credit hours and a minimum GPA of 2.0 are required for graduation.

Special: Bradford offers cross-registration with 10 area colleges, 9 internships, study abroad in 100 countries, a Washington semester, and work-study programs. Student-designed majors, credit by exam, nondegree study, and pass/fail options are also available. There is a freshman honors program on campus.

Faculty/Classroom: Sixty-five percent of faculty are male; 35%, female. All teach undergraduates. No introductory courses are taught by graduate students. The average class size in an introductory lecture is 20; in a laboratory, 10; and in a regular course offering, 15.

Admissions: About 77% of the 1993-94 applicants were accepted. About 25% of the current freshmen were in the top fifth of their class; 60% were in the top two fifths. One freshman graduated first in his/her class.

Requirements: Bradford requires applicants to be in the upper 70% of their class. A minimum GPA of 2.0 is required. The SAT I or ACT is not required. Applicants must be graduates of an accredited secondary school or have a GED. Sixteen academic credits are required, including 4 in English, 3 in mathematics, 2 in foreign language, and 1 each in science, social studies, and history. An essay is required and an interview is recommended. A portfolio is required of art and creative writing applicants. AP and CLEP credits are accepted. Important factors used in the admissions decision are advanced placement or honor courses, evidence of special talent, recommendations by school officials, leadership record, and personality, intangible qualities.

Procedure: Freshmen are admitted in the fall and spring. Entrance exams should be taken by November of the senior year. Application deadlines are open. There is no application fee. Notification is sent on a rolling basis. There are early decision and deferred admissions plans.

Transfer: About 50 transfer students enrolled in 1993-94. Official transcripts of all previous college work and a recommendation from a faculty adviser, instructor, or dean must be submitted. If fewer than 30 credits have been earned, the high school transcript must be submitted as well. Students must provide a catalog from each institution from which they wish to transfer credit. Bradford will accept a maximum of 72 credit hours from 2-year institutions for courses graded C and above. All transfer students will be expected to meet the requirements of the Bradford plan. A minimum GPA of 2.0 is required. A total of 46 credits out of 121 must be completed at Bradford.

Visiting: There are regularly scheduled orientations for prospective students, including an orientation program in June and also at the beginning of the fall term. There are guides for informal visits and visitors may sit in on classes and stay overnight at the school. To arrange for a visit, contact the Admissions Office at (800) 336-6448 or (508) 372-7161.

Financial Aid: In 1993-94 75% of all current freshmen and 70% of continuing students received some form of financial aid. About 75% of freshmen and 65% of continuing students received need-based aid. The average freshman award was $13,000. Twenty-five percent of undergraduate students work part-time. The average financial indebtedness of the 1992-93 graduate was $13,250. Bradford is a member of CSS. The FAF, the college's own financial statement, and FAFSA are required. The deadline for financial aid applications is February 15.

International Students: There are currently 75 international students enrolled. The school actively recruits these students. They must take the TOEFL and achieve a minimum score of 500.

Computers: The college provides computer facilities for student use. The mainframe is a DEC VAX. IBM and Epson microcomputers are available in the library, in 1 dormitory, and in a dedicated computer laboratory. There are no time limits on using the system and no fees.

Graduates: In 1992-93 106 bachelor's degrees were awarded. Within an average freshman class, 45% graduate in 5 years. Some 25 companies recruited on campus in a recent year.

Admissions Contact: William Dunfey, Dean of Admission.

BRANDEIS UNIVERSITY

D-2

Waltham, MA 02254-9110   (617) 736-3500

(800) 622-0622 (out-of-state)

Full-time: 1312 men, 1507 women	Faculty: 341; I, av$
Part-time: 23 men, 39 women	Ph.D.s: 93%
Graduate: 506 men, 551 women	Student/Faculty: 8 to 1
Year: semesters, summer session	Tuition: $18,955
Application Deadline: February 1	Room & Board: $6630

Freshman Class: 4186 applied, 2743 accepted, 740 enrolled

SAT I Verbal/Math: 570/610   **HIGHLY COMPETITIVE**

Brandeis University, founded in 1948, is a private, coeducational liberal arts institution. There are 4 undergraduate and 2 graduate schools. The 3 libraries contain 939,000 volumes, 826,737 microform items, and 27,397 audiovisual forms, and subscribe to 7104 periodicals. Computerized library sources and services include the card catalog, interlibrary loans, and database searching. Special learning facilities include a learning resource center, an art gallery, a radio station, a TV station, an astronomical observatory, a cultural center, a treasure hall, an art museum, and an audiovisual center. The 235-acre campus is in a suburban area 10 miles west of Boston. Including residence halls, there are 98 buildings on campus.

Student Life: About 74% of undergraduates are from out-of-state, mostly the Middle Atlantic. Students come from 50 states, 57 foreign countries, and Canada. Seventy-two percent are from public schools; 28% from private. Eighty percent are white. The average age of freshmen is 18.1; all undergraduates, 20.6. Ten percent drop out by the end of their first year; 80% remain to graduate.

Housing: A total of 2600 students can be accommodated in college housing. College-sponsored living facilities include coed dormitories, on-campus apartments, and off-campus apartments. In addition, there are special interest houses. On-campus housing is guaranteed for the freshman and sophomore years only, is available on a first-come, first-served basis, and is available on a lottery system for upperclassmen.

Ninety-one percent of students live on campus. All students may keep cars on campus.

Activities: There are no fraternities or sororities on campus. There are 130 groups on campus, including art, cheerleading, chess, choir, chorale, chorus, computers, dance, drama, ethnic, film, gay, honors, international, jazz band, literary magazine, musical theater, newspaper, orchestra, pep band, photography, political, professional, radio and TV, religious, social, social service, student government, symphony, and yearbook. Popular campus events include Bronstein Weekend, Louis Louis, Octoberfest, Homecoming, Women's Month, Black History Month, Charity Week, Tropics Night, Divali, and Chinese New Year.

Sports: There are 11 intercollegiate sports for men and 11 for women, and 10 intramural sports for men and 9 for women. Athletic and recreation facilities include a 6000-seat field house, a basketball arena, an indoor swimming pool, 3 indoor tennis courts, 10 squash and racquetball courts, an indoor track, several multipurpose rooms for fencing, aerobics, dance, and wrestling, sauna and steam rooms, Nautilus and free weight rooms, soccer and practice fields, baseball and softball diamonds, a cross-country and fitness trail, and 10 outdoor tennis courts.

Disabled Students: Sixty-five percent of the campus is accessible to disabled students. The following facilities are available: wheelchair ramps, elevators, special parking, specially equipped rest rooms, special class scheduling, lowered drinking fountains, and lowered telephones.

Services: In addition to many counseling and information services, tutoring is available in most subjects. In addition, there is a reader service for the blind, and remedial math, reading, and writing.

Campus Safety and Security: Campus safety and security measures include 24-hour foot and vehicle patrol, self defense education, escort service, and shuttle buses. In addition, there are informal discussions, pamphlets, posters, and films, emergency telephones, and lighted pathways and sidewalks.

Programs of Study: Brandeis awards the B.A. degree. Master's and doctoral degrees also are awarded. Bachelor's degrees are awarded in BIOLOGICAL SCIENCE (biochemistry, biology/biological science, and neurosciences), COMMUNICATIONS AND THE ARTS (American literature, classics, comparative literature, dramatic arts, English, English literature, fine arts, French, German, linguistics, music, Russian, and Spanish), COMPUTER AND PHYSICAL SCIENCE (chemistry, computer science, mathematics, physics, and science), SOCIAL SCIENCE (African American studies, African studies, American studies, anthropology, economics, European studies, history, history of philosophy, Judaic studies, Latin American studies, Near Eastern studies, philosophy, political science/government, psychology, and sociology). Sciences, economics, psychology, English, Near Eastern studies, and Judaic studies are the strongest programs academically. Economics, politics, English, psychology, and American studies have the largest enrollments.

Required: Students must complete 32 semester courses, including a field of concentration and the following core requirements: 1 seminar course in humanistic inquiries with a half-course writing laboratory, 1 semester course each in writing and quantitative reasoning, 3 in a foreign language, and a cluster of 3 interrelated courses. Two semesters of physical education are also required.

Special: Students may pursue interdepartmental programs in 10 different fields. Students may cross-register with Boston College, Boston University, Tufts University, and Wellesley College. Study abroad is possible in 39 countries. Internships are available in virtually every field, and a work-study program is also provided. Dual and student-designed majors can be arranged. The university also offers credit by exam, nondegree study, and pass/fail options. In the Mount Sinai Humanities and Medicine Program, students are accepted to the Mount Sinai School of Medicine for entry after freshman year and successful completion of a Brandeis degree. There is a chapter of Phi Beta Kappa on campus. All departments have honors programs.

Faculty/Classroom: Sixty-eight percent of faculty are male; 32%, female. All teach undergraduates, and do research. Graduate students teach 10% of introductory courses. The average class size in an introductory lecture is 30; in a laboratory, 20; and in a regular course offering, 15.

Admissions: About 66% of the 1993–94 applicants were accepted. The SAT scores for the 1993–94 freshman class were as follows: Verbal—18% below 500, 43% between 500 and 599, 34% between 600 and 700, and 5% above 700; Math—9% below 500, 34% between 500 and 599, 39% between 600 and 700, and 18% above 700. There were 8 National Merit finalists. Eleven freshmen graduated first in their class.

Requirements: The SAT I or ACT is required. Students submitting the SAT I score must also take 3 SAT II: Subject tests, including writing. Applicants should prepare with 4 years of high school English, 3 each of foreign language and mathematics, and 1 each of science and social studies. An essay is required, and an interview is recommended. AP credits are accepted. Important factors used in the ad-

missions decision are advanced placement or honor courses, leadership record, evidence of special talent, extracurricular activities record, and recommendations by school officials.

Procedure: Freshmen are admitted in the fall and spring. Entrance exams should be taken by the fall of the senior year. Early decision applications should be filed by January 1; regular applications, by January 1 for Part I and by February 1 for Part II for fall entry and by December 1 for spring entry, along with an application fee of $50. Notification of early decision is sent 4 weeks after application is complete; regular decision, April 15. There are early decision, early admissions, and deferred admissions plans. About 112 early decision candidates were accepted for the 1993–94 class. A waiting list is an active part of the admissions procedure, with about 3% of applicants on the list.

Transfer: About 83 transfer students enrolled in 1993–94. Major consideration is given to the quality of college-level work completed, the secondary school record, testing, professors' and deans' evaluations, and the impression made by the candidate. Because there is a 2-year residence requirement, students should apply before entering junior year. A total of 16 semester courses out of 32 must be completed at Brandeis.

Visiting: There are regularly scheduled orientations for prospective students. There are year-round student-led campus tours, and in the summer there are information sessions given by the admissions staff. There are guides for informal visits and visitors may sit in on classes and stay overnight at the school. To arrange for a visit, contact the Office of Admissions at (800) 622–0622 (out-of-state) or (617) 736–3500.

Financial Aid: In 1993–94, 60% of all current freshmen and 56% of continuing students received some form of financial aid. About 56% of freshmen and 50% of continuing students received need-based aid. The average freshman award was $18,300. Of that total, scholarships or need-based grants averaged $13,600 ($21,470 maximum); loans averaged $3500 ($4025 maximum); and work contracts averaged $1200 ($1500 maximum). Sixty-five percent of undergraduate students work part-time. Average earnings from campus work for the school year are $1100. The average financial indebtedness of the 1992–93 graduate was $14,000. Brandeis is a member of CSS. The FAF, the college's own financial statement, the FAFSA, and copies of student and parent income tax returns are required. The deadline for financial aid applications is February 15.

International Students: There are currently 133 international students enrolled. The school actively recruits these students. They must take the TOEFL and achieve a minimum score of 600. The student must also take the SAT I. SAT II: Subject tests are strongly recommended.

Computers: The college provides computer facilities for student use. The mainframe is a DEC VAXstation 3176 for undergraduate network services. There are three clusters located throughout the campus containing Macintosh and IBM-compatible computers and printers for both. All Macintoshes and some IBM-compatibles are connected to the campus network via an Ethernet Gateway, giving students access to Student Network Services accounts. The university maintains 64 Macintoshes, 13 IBM-compatibles, 2 Apple Scanners, and 21 printers. Eight modem lines are currently dedicated to the VAXstation 3176. Network access is also available in selected dormitories. All students may access the system. Students may access the system for 3 hours maximum when other students are waiting. There are no fees.

Graduates: In 1992–93, 704 bachelor's degrees were awarded. The most popular majors among graduates were politics (13%), psychology (13%), and English (11%). Within an average freshman class, 3% graduate in 3 years, 75% in 4 years, 2% in 5 years, and 2% in 6 years. Some 40 companies recruited on campus in 1992–93.

Admissions Contact: David L. Gould, Dean of Admissions.

BRIDGEWATER STATE COLLEGE
E-3
Bridgewater, MA 02325
(508) 697–1237

Full-time: 2075 men, 3050 women	Faculty: 241
Part-time: 115 men, 320 women	Ph.D.s: 76%
Graduate: 1375 men and women	Student/Faculty: 21 to 1
Year: semesters, summer session	Tuition: $3372 ($7506)
Application Deadline: March 1	Room & Board: $4146
Freshman Class: 5079 applied, 3100 accepted, 1105 enrolled	
SAT I or ACT: required	COMPETITIVE

Bridgewater State College, founded in 1840, is a state-supported college offering undergraduate and graduate programs in liberal arts, education, business, aviation science, and preprofessional studies. There are 2 undergraduate schools and one graduate school. In addition to regional accreditation, The college has baccalaureate program accreditation with CSWE and NCATE. The library contains 255,868 volumes, 77,863 microform items, and 13,942 audiovisual forms, and subscribes to 1380 periodicals. Computerized library sources and services include the card catalog, interlibrary loans, and database searching. Special learning facilities include a learning re-

source center, art gallery, radio station, TV station, an observatory, a human performance laboratory and flight simulators, and a speech/hearing/language center. The 170-acre campus is in a small town 28 miles south of Boston. Including residence halls, there are 28 buildings on campus.

Student Life: About 96% of undergraduates are from Massachusetts. Students come from 24 states, 21 foreign countries, and Canada. Eighty-six percent are from public schools; 14% from private. Ninety-four percent are white. Seventy-four percent are Catholic; 17% Protestant. The average age of freshmen is 18; all undergraduates, 26. Twenty-six percent drop out by the end of their first year; 33% remain to graduate.

Housing: A total of 1850 students can be accommodated in college housing. College-sponsored living facilities include single-sex and coed dormitories and on-campus apartments. On-campus housing is guaranteed for all 4 years. Sixty-six percent of students commute. All students may keep cars on campus.

Activities: About 9% of men and about 2% of women belong to 2 local and 5 national fraternities; about 4% of women belong to 3 national sororities. There are 90 groups on campus, including band, cheerleading, choir, chorale, computers, dance, drama, ethnic, gay, honors, international, jazz band, literary magazine, newspaper, political, professional, radio and TV, religious, social service, student government, and yearbook. Popular campus events include Convocation, Homecoming, Multiculture Day, and Christmas and spring ball.

Sports: There are 9 intercollegiate sports for men and 11 for women, and 11 intramural sports for men and 9 for women. Athletic and recreation facilities include 2 gymnasiums, a swimming pool, tennis courts, a football stadium, a 9-lane track, and soccer, lacrosse, field hockey, and baseball fields.

Disabled Students: Ninety percent of the campus is accessible to disabled students. The following facilities are available: wheelchair ramps, elevators, special parking, specially equipped rest rooms, special class scheduling, lowered drinking fountains, lowered telephones, handicapped van service, and college-operated transit system.

Services: In addition to many counseling and information services, tutoring is available in most subjects. In addition, there is a reader service for the blind, and remedial math, reading, and writing. Also available are taped texts, classroom interpreters, scribes/notetakers, testing accommodations, and a speech/hearing/language center.

Campus Safety and Security: Campus safety and security measures include 24-hour foot and vehicle patrol, self defense education, escort service, and shuttle buses. In addition, there are informal discussions, pamphlets, posters, and films, emergency telephones, lighted pathways and sidewalks, and a college-operated transit system that runs from 7 A.M. to 12 midnight, Monday through Friday.

Programs of Study: The college awards the B.A., B.S., and B.S.Ed. degrees. Master's degrees also are awarded. Bachelor's degrees are awarded in BIOLOGICAL SCIENCE (biochemistry and biology/biological science), BUSINESS (accounting, banking and finance, management science, marketing/retailing/merchandising, sports management, and transportation management), COMMUNICATIONS AND THE ARTS (communications, crafts, dramatic arts, English, fine arts, French, Spanish, and speech/debate/rhetoric), COMPUTER AND PHYSICAL SCIENCE (chemistry, computer science, earth science, geology, information sciences and systems, mathematics, and physics), EDUCATION (art, early childhood, elementary, foreign languages, health, middle school, physical, recreation, science, and secondary), ENGINEERING AND ENVIRONMENTAL DESIGN (aviation administration/management, energy management technology, and graphic arts technology), HEALTH PROFESSIONS (predentistry, premedicine, and speech pathology/audiology), SOCIAL SCIENCE (anthropology, archeology, criminology, crosscultural studies, geography, history, industrial and organizational psychology, international relations, law, paralegal studies, philosophy, physical fitness/movement, political science/government, prelaw, psychology, religion, social work, and sociology). Management science, aviation science, education, the sciences, and psychology are the strongest academically. Management science, education, communication arts, and sciences have the largest enrollments.

Required: Students are required to complete a minimum of 120 semester hours, with 30 to 36 of these hours in the major and 49 to 55 hours in liberal arts courses. Students must maintain a minimum GPA of 2.0 and must complete an introduction to information resources course.

Special: Opportunities are provided for cross-registration programs with other schools, internships in most majors, dual majors in any subject, student-designed majors, credit for military service and work experience, nondegree study, and study abroad in China, England, Canada, and West Germany. There is a freshman honors program on campus, as well as 5 national honor societies. Fourteen departments have honors programs.

Faculty/Classroom: Fifty-eight percent of faculty are male; 42%, female. All faculty teach and do research. No introductory courses are taught by graduate students. The average class size in an introductory lecture is 40; in a laboratory, 21; and in a regular course offering, 35.

Admissions: About 61% of the 1993–94 applicants were accepted. There were 18 National Merit semifinalists. One freshman graduated first in class.

Requirements: The SAT I or ACT is required. Graduation from an accredited secondary school is required; a GED will be accepted. Applicants must have successfully completed 16 Carnegie units, including 4 years of English, 3 of mathematics, 2 each of a foreign language, history, and science, and 3 in other college preparatory electives. An essay is recommended. AP and CLEP credits are accepted. Important factors used in the admissions decision are advanced placement or honor courses, recommendations by school officials, leadership record, extracurricular activities record, and evidence of special talent.

Procedure: Freshmen are admitted fall and spring. Entrance exams should be taken no later than January. Early action applications should be filed by November 15; regular applications, by March 1 for fall entry and December 1 for spring entry, along with an application fee of $10 for residents and $40 for nonresidents. Notification of early decision is sent December 15; regular decision, on a rolling basis. There are early decision and deferred admissions plans. About 70 early decision candidates were accepted for the 1993–94 class. A waiting list is an active part of the admissions procedure, with about 2% of applicants on the list.

Transfer: A total of 1044 transfer students enrolled in 1993–94. Transfer students must have maintained a minimum GPA of 2.0 at the previous college, although this alone does not guarantee admission. Priority is given to community college graduates. A total of 30 credits out of 120 must be completed at the college.

Visiting: There are regularly scheduled orientations for prospective students. Tours are available Monday through Friday at 11 A.M. and 3 P.M., and information sessions are scheduled on Fridays at 10 A.M. when college is in session. Visitations are available on a limited basis Saturdays during the fall. There are guides for informal visits and visitors may sit in on classes. To arrange for a visit, contact the Office of Admissions at (508) 697-1237.

Financial Aid: In a recent year, 48% of all current freshmen and 54% of continuing students received some form of financial aid. Scholarships or need-based grants averaged $500 ($1400 maximum); loans averaged $1000 ($2625 maximum); and work contracts averaged $1200 ($1800 maximum). The average financial indebtedness of a recent year's graduate was $4800. The college is a member of CSS. The FAF, the college's own financial statement, the parents' tax returns, and FAFSA are required. The deadline for financial aid applications is March 1.

International Students: There are currently 60 international students enrolled. They must take the TOEFL and achieve a minimum score of 550.

Computers: The college provides computer facilities for student use. The mainframes are a DEC VAX 8530 and 4000/500, a DEC MicroVAX II, a DEC Station 5000–240, a CDC Cyber 180–310, and a WANG V565. There are 300 terminals and PCs available in various laboratories and residence halls, and modem access is possible from the students' homes or offices. All students may access the system. 90 hours a week in the laboratories and 7 days a week, 24 hours a day by dial-up. There are no time limits on using the system and no fees.

Graduates: In 1992–93, 1231 bachelor's degrees were awarded. The most popular majors among graduates were management science (21%), elementary education (15%), and speech communication (9%). Within an average freshman class, 27% graduate in 4 years and 49% in 5 years.

Admissions Contact: James F. Plotner, Jr., Dean of Admissions.

CLARK UNIVERSITY
Worcester, MA 01610-1477

C-2
(508) 793-7431

Full-time: 809 men, 1090 women	Faculty: 180; IIA, +$
Part-time: 16 men, 7 women	Ph.D.s: 99%
Graduate: 359 men, 336 women	Student/Faculty: 11 to 1
Year: semesters, summer session	Tuition: $17,000
Application Deadline: February 15	Room & Board: $4400
Freshman Class: 2886 applied, 2059 accepted, 457 enrolled	
SAT I or ACT: required	VERY COMPETITIVE

Clark University, founded in 1887, is an independent liberal arts and research institution. There are 3 graduate schools. In addition to regional accreditation, Clark has baccalaureate program accreditation with AACSB. The 4 libraries contain 519,000 volumes, 60,000 microform items, and 1000 audiovisual forms, and subscribe to 1883 periodicals. Computerized library sources and services include the card catalog, interlibrary loans, and database searching. Special learning facilities include a learning resource center, art gallery, center for mu-

sic with 2 studios for electronic music, 2 theaters, magnetic resonance imaging facility, and arboretum. The 50-acre campus is in an urban area 38 miles west of Boston. Including residence halls, there are 50 buildings on campus.

Student Life: About 66% of undergraduates are from out-of-state, mostly the Northeast. Students come from 38 states, 70 foreign countries, and Canada. Sixty-six percent are from public schools; 33% from private. Sixty-three percent are white; 15% foreign nationals. Twenty-five percent claim no religious affiliation; 25% Catholic; 22% Jewish; 17% Protestant. The average age of freshmen is 18.4; all undergraduates, 20.2. Fourteen percent drop out by the end of their first year; 76% remain to graduate.

Housing: A total of 1500 students can be accommodated in college housing. College-sponsored living facilities include single-sex and coed dormitories and on-campus apartments. In addition there are language houses, special interest houses, and nonsmoking, quiet, substance awareness, global environment, and year-round houses. On-campus housing is guaranteed for all 4 years. Sixty-six percent of students live on campus. All students may keep cars on campus.

Activities: There are no fraternities or sororities on campus. There are 80 groups on campus, including chess, choir, chorale, chorus, computers, dance, drama, ethnic, film, gay, honors, international, jazz band, literary magazine, musical theater, newspaper, orchestra, photography, political, professional, radio and TV, religious, social, social service, student government, and yearbook. Popular campus events include Fall Fest, Peace Fair, Spree Day, Martin Luther King Commemoration, and Academic Spree Day.

Sports: There are 8 intercollegiate sports for men and 7 for women, and 15 intramural sports for men and 15 for women. Athletic and recreation facilities include an athletic center, with a 2000-seat gymnasium, a pool, tennis courts, outdoor fields, baseball and softball diamonds, and a boat house.

Disabled Students: The following facilities are available: wheelchair ramps, elevators, special parking, specially equipped rest rooms, special class scheduling, lowered drinking fountains, lowered telephones, and specially equipped residence rooms.

Services: In addition to many counseling and information services, tutoring is available in some subjects, including computer science, mathematics, biology, chemistry, and economics. There is also a reader service for the blind and remedial math and writing. For learning-disabled students, the university provides early orientation, alternative test-taking accommodations, note takers, individual sessions with a learning specialist, and compensatory skill training in written expression, mathematics application, and learning strategies.

Campus Safety and Security: Campus safety and security measures include 24-hour foot and vehicle patrol, self defense education, escort service, and shuttle buses. In addition, there are informal discussions, pamphlets, posters, and films, emergency telephones, and lighted pathways and sidewalks.

Programs of Study: Clark awards the B.A. degree. Master's and doctoral degrees also are awarded. Bachelor's degrees are awarded in BIOLOGICAL SCIENCE (biochemistry and biology/biological science), BUSINESS (business administration and management), COMMUNICATIONS AND THE ARTS (art history and appreciation, comparative literature, dramatic arts, English, film arts, fine arts, French, German, languages, music, romance languages, Spanish, studio art, and visual and performing arts), COMPUTER AND PHYSICAL SCIENCE (chemistry, computer science, mathematics, and physics), ENGINEERING AND ENVIRONMENTAL DESIGN (environmental science), HEALTH PROFESSIONS (predentistry and premedicine), SOCIAL SCIENCE (classical/ancient civilization, economics, geography, history, international relations, philosophy, prelaw, psychology, and sociology). Psychology, geography, environment, technology and society, physics, chemistry, and government and international relations are the strongest academically. Psychology, government and international relations, economics, and business management have the largest enrollments.

Required: Each student is required to complete 2 critical thinking courses in 2 categories of verbal expression and formal analysis, and 6 perspective-broadening courses representing the categories of aesthetics, comparative, historical, language and culture, science, and values. A student must receive passing grades in a minimum of 32 full courses, with a C- or better in at least 24 of these courses, and maintain a minimum 2.0 GPA in order to graduate.

Special: For-credit internships are available in all disciplines with private corporations and small businesses, medical centers, and government agencies. There is cross-registration with members of the Worcester Consortium, including Holy Cross and Worcester Polytechnic Institute. Clark also offers study abroad in 12 countries, a Washington semester with American University, work-study programs, dual and student-designed majors, pass/no record options, 3-2 bachelor's degree in physics and engineering with Columbia University and gerontology certificate with the Worcester Consortium for Higher Education. Integrated undergraduate/graduate programs are available in environment, technology, and society, international

development and social change, and management. High achieving, 4-year degree students at Clark are eligible for a tuition-free fifth year, to pursue an MBA, MHA, or other master's degree. There are 7 national honor societies on campus, including Phi Beta Kappa.

Faculty/Classroom: Sixty-nine percent of faculty are male; 31%, female. Ninety-five percent both teach and do research. Graduate students teach 3% of introductory courses. The average class size in an introductory lecture is 23; in a laboratory, 10; and in a regular course offering, 20.

Admissions: About 71% of the 1993-94 applicants were accepted. About 56% of the current freshmen were in the top fifth of their class; 87% were in the top two fifths. About 20 freshmen graduated first in their class.

Requirements: The SAT I or ACT is required. The SAT II in English with an essay is also required. Applicants must graduate from an accredited secondary school or have a GED. Sixteen Carnegie units are required, including 4 years of English, 3 each of mathematics and science, and 2 each of foreign language, history, and social studies. An interview is recommended. AP credits are accepted. Important factors used in the admissions decision are advanced placement or honor courses, recommendations by alumni, recommendations by school officials, personality, intangible qualities, and leadership record.

Procedure: Freshmen are admitted fall and spring. Entrance exams should be taken by November of the senior year. Early decision applications should be filed by either December 1 or January 1; regular applications, by February 15 for fall entry and November 15 for spring entry, along with an application fee of $40. Notification of early decision is sent either January 15 or February 1; regular decision, April 1. There are early decision, early admissions, and deferred admissions plans. A total of 55 early decision candidates were accepted for the 1993-94 class. A waiting list is an active part of the admissions procedure, with about 1% of applicants on the list.

Transfer: A total of 104 transfer students enrolled in 1993-94. Transfers should have a minimum GPA of about 2.8. A full semester of college course work is recommended. A total of 16 courses out of 32 must be completed at Clark.

Visiting: There are regularly scheduled orientations for prospective students. Students can make advance arrangements for visits, tours, and overnight stays; they also can talk with coaches and professors. There are guides for informal visits and visitors may sit in on classes and stay overnight at the school. To arrange for a visit, contact the Admissions Office at (508) 793-7431.

Financial Aid: In 1993-94, 65% of all current freshmen and 60% of continuing students received some form of financial aid. About 63% of freshmen and 57% of continuing students received need-based aid. The average freshman award was $15,600. Of that total, scholarships or need-based grants averaged $11,232 ($20,300 maximum); loans averaged $3120 ($4125 maximum); and work contracts averaged $1248 ($1300 maximum). Forty-seven percent of undergraduate students work part-time. Average earnings from campus work for the school year are $1100. The average financial indebtedness of the 1992-93 graduate was $16,000. Clark is a member of CSS. The FAF and FAFSA are required. The deadline for financial aid applications is February 15.

International Students: There are currently 472 international students enrolled. The school actively recruits these students. They must take the TOEFL and achieve a minimum score of 550.

Computers: Clark college provides computer facilities for student use. The mainframes are a DEC VAX 8530, a DEC VAX 6310, 2 DEC Station 5000s, and a DEC 3400 Alpha station. There are networked departmental systems in various buildings throughout campus and DOS compatible and Macintosh microcomputers in 2 public computer laboratories, with campus-wide connections to Internet and Bitnet. All students may access the system 7 days per week during scheduled hours. There are no time limits on using the system and no fees.

Graduates: In 1992-93, 551 bachelor's degrees were awarded. The most popular majors among graduates were psychology (20%), government and international relations (10%), and business management (8%). Within an average freshman class, 1% graduate in 3 years, 68% in 4 years, 75% in 5 years, and 76% in 6 years. Some 80 companies recruited on campus in 1992-93. In the 1992 graduating class, 15% of the men and 17% of the women were enrolled in graduate school within 6 months of graduation; 20% of the men and 44% of the women had found employment.

Admissions Contact: Richard Pierson, Dean of Admissions.

COLLEGE OF OUR LADY OF THE ELMS   B-3
(Formerly Elms College)
Chicopee, MA 01013   (413) 592-3189; (800) 255-ELMS (in-state)

Full-time: 12 men, 538 women	Faculty: 61; IIB, -$
Part-time: 53 men, 397 women	Ph.D.s: 70%
Graduate: 12 men, 238 women	Student/Faculty: 9 to 1
Year: semesters	Tuition: $10,974
Application Deadline: open	Room & Board: $4665

Freshman Class: 318 applied, 252 accepted, 129 enrolled
SAT I Verbal/Math: 440/420   **COMPETITIVE**

College of Our Lady of the Elms, founded in 1928, is a Catholic women's college offering undergraduate degrees in liberal arts and sciences, nursing, and social work, and graduate degrees in education. In addition to regional accreditation, Elms College has baccalaureate program accreditation with CSWE and NLN. The library contains 98,692 volumes, 65,944 microform items, and 11,911 audiovisual forms and subscribes to 730 periodicals. Computerized library sources and services include the card catalog, interlibrary loans, and database searching. Special learning facilities include a learning resource center, art gallery, and a rare book collection. The 65-acre campus is in a suburban area 2 miles north of Springfield. Including residence halls, there are 11 buildings on campus.

Student Life: About 83% of undergraduates are from Massachusetts. Students come from 11 states and 10 foreign countries. Sixty percent are from public schools; 40% from private. Eighty-eight percent are white. Seventy percent are Catholic; 15% Protestant. The average age of freshmen is 18; all undergraduates, 24. Six percent drop out by the end of their first year; 85% remain to graduate.

Housing: A total of 400 students can be accommodated in college housing. College-sponsored living facilities include single-sex dormitories. On-campus housing is guaranteed for all 4 years. Sixty percent of students live on campus; of those, 50% remain on campus on weekends. All students may keep cars on campus.

Activities: There are no fraternities or sororities on campus. There are 40 groups on campus, including art, choir, chorale, chorus, dance, drama, ethnic, honors, international, musical theater, newspaper, photography, professional, religious, social, social service, student government, and yearbook. Popular campus events include Soph Show, Cap and Gown Ring Ceremony, Spring Week, Winter Fest, Family Weekend, Christmas Vespers, and lecture series.

Sports: There are 6 intercollegiate sports for women and 6 intramural sports for women. Athletic and recreation facilities include a fitness center, a Nordic ski track, tennis courts, an indoor track, and a 1500-seat auditorium. Under construction, Maguire Center facility will include an aerobics amd weight training area, a 6-lane, 25-meter pool, a multipurpose area with a suspended indoor track, a health science laboratory, and locker rooms and showers.

Disabled Students: Forty percent of the campus is accessible to disabled students. The following facilities are available: wheelchair ramps, elevators, special parking, specially equipped rest rooms, special class scheduling, lowered drinking fountains, lowered telephones, and automated doors.

Services: In addition to many counseling and information services, tutoring is available in every subject. There is also a reader service for the blind, and remedial math, reading, and writing.

Campus Safety and Security: Campus safety and security measures include 24-hour foot and vehicle patrol, self defense education, escort service, and informal discussions. In addition, there are pamphlets, posters, and films, emergency telephones, lighted pathways and sidewalks, a safety and security manual published each year, and safety and security committee of administrators, students, faculty, and staff.

Programs of Study: Elms College awards the B.A., B.S., B.S.N., and B.S.W. degrees. Associate and master's degrees also are awarded. Bachelor's degrees are awarded in BIOLOGICAL SCIENCE (biology/biological science), BUSINESS (accounting, international business management, and marketing/retailing/merchandising), COMMUNICATIONS AND THE ARTS (arts administration/management, English, fine arts, French, and Spanish), COMPUTER AND PHYSICAL SCIENCE (chemistry, computer science, and mathematics), EDUCATION (art, bilingual/bicultural, early childhood, elementary, foreign languages, middle school, science, secondary, special, and teaching English as a second language/foreign language), HEALTH PROFESSIONS (art therapy, health science management, medical laboratory technology, nursing, predentistry, premedicine, and speech pathology/audiology), SOCIAL SCIENCE (American studies, international studies, paralegal studies, prelaw, psychology, religion, social work, and sociology). Education, business, nursing, foreign languages, social work, and speech pathology/audiology have the largest enrollments.

Required: All students must complete 120 hours with a 2.0. GPA; 30 hours are required in courses in rhetoric, computer science, history, religion, physical education, philosophy, sociology, fine arts, humanities, language, mathematics, and senior seminar.

Special: Students may cross-register at any of the Cooperating Colleges of Greater Springfield or the Consortium of Sisters of St. Joseph Schools, or study abroad in Ireland, France, and Spain. Internships are available with local hospitals, businesses, and schools. Student-designed interdepartmental majors, accelerated degree programs, work-study, dual majors, nondegree study, and pass/fail options are offered. There are 5 national honor societies on campus, including Phi Beta Kappa.

Faculty/Classroom: Thirty-five percent of faculty are male; 65%, female. All teach undergraduates and 89% both teach and do research. No introductory courses are taught by graduate students. The average class size in an introductory lecture is 30; in a laboratory, 15; and in a regular course offering, 18.

Admissions: About 79% of the 1993-94 applicants were accepted. About 50% of the current freshmen were in the top fifth of their class; 80% were in the top two fifths. There were 2 National Merit semifinalists. Two freshmen graduated first in their class.

Requirements: Elms College requires applicants to be in the upper 50% of their class. A minimum GPA of 2.0 is required. The SAT I is required. The college prefers SAT I composite scores of at least 900. Applicants should be graduates of accredited high schools or have earned the GED. Secondary preparation should include 4 units of English, 3 each of mathematics and science, and 2 each of foreign language, history, and social studies. The college recommends that potential art majors take the appropriate SAT II: Subject test and submit a portfolio, and that biology or chemistry majors take an appropriate SAT II: Subject test. A personal essay is required; an interview is recommended. AP and CLEP credits are accepted. Important factors used in the admissions decision are advanced placement or honor courses, recommendations by school officials, extracurricular activities record, parents or siblings attending the school, and recommendations by alumni.

Procedure: Freshmen are admitted in the fall and spring. Entrance exams should be taken by no later than November of the senior year. Application deadlines are open. The application fee is $25. Notification is sent on a rolling basis. There are early decision, early admissions, and deferred admissions plans. About 15 early decision candidates were accepted for the 1993-94 class.

Transfer: About 110 transfer students enrolled in a recent year. Transfer applicants must have a minimum 2.0 GPA. A total of 45 credits out of 120 must be completed at Elms College.

Visiting: There are regularly scheduled orientations for prospective students, including inteviews and tours. The college also offers an overnight program, an open house, and Applicant Day. There are guides for informal visits and visitors may sit in on classes and stay overnight at the school. To arrange for a visit, contact the Admissions Office at (800) 255-ELMS.

Financial Aid: In 1993-94 97% of all current freshmen and 97% of continuing students received some form of financial aid. About 80% of freshmen and 80% of continuing students received need-based aid. The average freshman award was $10,249. Of that total, scholarships or need-based grants averaged $4520 ($10,000 maximum); loans averaged $2625 ($3625 maximum); and work contracts averaged $1000 ($2000 maximum). Sixty percent of undergraduate students work part-time. Average earnings from campus work for the school year are $1200. The average financial indebtedness of the 1992-93 graduate was $7500. Elms College is a member of CSS. The FAF, the college's own financial statement, and FAFSA are required. The deadline for financial aid applications is February 15.

International Students: There are currently 40 international students enrolled. The school actively recruits these students. The college requires either the TOEFL, with a minimum score of 500, or the SAT I.

Computers: The college provides computer facilities for student use. The mainframe is a DEC VAX VT440. There are 50 computer terminals for student use located in the main academic building and 1 residence hall. All students may access the system Monday through Friday, 8 A.M. to 10 P.M.; Saturday and Sunday, 12 noon to 9 P.M. There are no time limits on using the system and no fees.

Graduates: In 1992-93 198 bachelor's degrees were awarded. The most popular majors among graduates were nursing (25%), education (17%), and paralegal/business (10%). Within an average freshman class, 1% graduate in 3 years, 75% in 4 years, 22% in 5 years, and 2% in 6 years. Some 20 companies recruited on campus in a recent year. In the 1992 graduating class, 28% of the women were enrolled in graduate school within 6 months of graduation; 85% of the women had found employment.

Admissions Contact: Betty Broughan, SSJ, Dean of Admissions and Financial Aid.

COLLEGE OF THE HOLY CROSS
C-2
Worcester, MA 01610
(508) 793-2443

Full-time: 1281 men, 1394 women	Faculty: 212; IIB, +$
Part-time: none	Ph.D.s: 96%
Graduate: none	Student/Faculty: 13 to 1
Year: semesters	Tuition: $17,550
Application Deadline: February 1	Room & Board: $6300
Freshman Class: 2994 applied, 1691 accepted, 659 enrolled	
SAT I Verbal/Math: 570/630	**HIGHLY COMPETITIVE**

College of the Holy Cross, founded in 1843, is a private college affiliated with the Roman Catholic Church and the Jesuit order offering programs in the liberal arts. The 3 libraries contain 485,000 volumes, 22,000 microform items, and 18,500 audiovisual forms and subscribe to 2810 periodicals. Computerized library sources and services include the card catalog, interlibrary loans, and database searching. Special learning facilities include an art gallery, radio station, greenhouses, and facilities for aquatic research. The 174-acre campus is in a suburban area 45 miles west of Boston. Including residence halls, there are 27 buildings on campus.

Student Life: About 61% of undergraduates are from out-of-state, mostly the Northeast. Students come from 43 states, 18 foreign countries, and Canada. Fifty percent are from public schools; 50% from private. Ninety-two percent are white. Most are Catholic. The average age of freshmen is 18; all undergraduates, 20. Two percent drop out by the end of their first year; 98% remain to graduate.

Housing: A total of 2092 students can be accommodated in college housing. College-sponsored living facilities include coed dormitories and off-campus apartments. In addition there are special interest houses, Fit-for-Life program housing, and First-Year program housing. On-campus housing is guaranteed for all 4 years. Eighty-five percent of students live on campus; of those, 95% remain on campus on weekends. Upperclassmen may keep cars on campus.

Activities: There are no fraternities or sororities on campus. There are 79 groups on campus, including art, band, cheerleading, chess, choir, chorale, chorus, computers, dance, drama, drill team, ethnic, film, gay, honors, international, jazz band, literary magazine, marching band, musical theater, newspaper, opera, orchestra, pep band, photography, political, professional, radio and TV, religious, social, social service, student government, and yearbook. Popular campus events include Spring Weekend, and Easy Street Night.

Sports: There are 15 intercollegiate sports for men and 15 for women, and 7 intramural sports for men and 6 for women. Athletic and recreation facilities include an omniturf playing field, baseball and football fields, indoor and outdoor running tracks, tennis, squash, and racquetball courts, a swimming pool, an ice rink, indoor crew tanks, a basketball arena, and weight and exercise rooms.

Disabled Students: Seventy-four percent of the campus is accessible to disabled students. The following facilities are available: wheelchair ramps, elevators, special parking, specially equipped rest rooms, special class scheduling, lowered drinking fountains, and lowered telephones.

Services: In addition to many counseling and information services, tutoring is available in every subject. Language laboratories and mathematics and writing workshops are available.

Campus Safety and Security: Campus safety and security measures include 24-hour foot and vehicle patrol, self defense education, escort service, and shuttle buses. In addition, there are informal discussions, pamphlets, posters, films, emergency telephones, lighted pathways and sidewalks.

Programs of Study: Holy Cross awards the A.B. degree. Bachelor's degrees are awarded in BIOLOGICAL SCIENCE (biology/biological science), COMMUNICATIONS AND THE ARTS (classics, dramatic arts, English, fine arts, French, German, Greek, Latin, music, Russian, and Spanish), COMPUTER AND PHYSICAL SCIENCE (chemistry, mathematics, and physics), SOCIAL SCIENCE (economics, European studies, history, philosophy, political science/government, psychology, religion, and sociology). English, economics, and political science have the largest enrollments.

Required: Distribution requirements include social science, natural and mathematical science, cross-cultural studies, religious and philosophical studies, historical studies and the arts, language, and literature. A total of 128 credit hours is required for graduation, with 10 to 14 in the major. The minimum GPA for graduation is 2.0.

Special: Local internships are available in health and education, law and business, journalism, social service, state and local government, scientific research, and cultural affairs. Student-designed majors, a Washington semester, and study abroad are possible. There is a 3-2 engineering program with Columbia University, Dartmouth College, and Washington University (St. Louis), and premedicine and predentistry programs are available. Students may cross-register with other universities in the Worcester Consortium for Higher Education. Non-degree study is possible. There are 11 national honor societies on campus, including Phi Beta Kappa. Three departments have honors programs.

Faculty/Classroom: Sixty-seven percent of faculty are male; 33%, female. All teach undergraduates and do research. The average class size in an introductory lecture is 27; in a laboratory, 20; and in a regular course offering, 22.

Admissions: About 56% of the 1993-94 applicants were accepted. The SAT scores for the 1993-94 freshman class were as follows: Verbal—9% below 500, 53% between 500 and 599, 35% between 600 and 700, and 3% above 700; Math—3% below 500, 30% between 500 and 599, 50% between 600 and 700, and 17% above 700. About 89% of the current freshmen were in the top fifth of their class; 100% were in the top two fifths. There were 6 National Merit finalists and 10 semifinalists. About 39 freshmen graduated first in their class.

Requirements: The SAT I is required. Applicants should be graduates of an accredited secondary school, or a GED is accepted. Applicants are recommended to prepare with courses in English, foreign language, history, mathematics, and science. An essay, 3 SAT II: Subject tests including English composition, and an interview are required. AP credits are accepted. Important factors used in the admissions decision are advanced placement or honor courses, recommendations by school officials, leadership record, evidence of special talent, and personality, intangible qualities.

Procedure: Freshmen are admitted in the fall. Entrance exams should be taken by December of the senior year. Early decision applications should be filed by November 1 and January 15; regular applications, by February 1 for fall entry, along with an application fee of $50. Notification of early decision is sent December 15 and February 15; regular decision, April 1. There are early decision, early admissions, and deferred admissions plans. About 126 early decision candidates were accepted for the 1993-94 class. A waiting list is an active part of the admissions procedure, with about 4% of applicants on the list.

Transfer: About 14 transfer students enrolled in 1993-94. Transfer students must have a minimum GPA of 3.2. The SAT I is required, as are transcripts and 2 teacher recommendations. Personal interviews are highly recommended. A total of 64 credits out of 128 must be completed at Holy Cross.

Visiting: There are regularly scheduled orientations for prospective students. There are guides for informal visits and visitors may sit in on classes and stay overnight at the school. To arrange for a visit, contact the Admissions Office at (508) 793-2443.

Financial Aid: In 1993-94 59% of all current freshmen and 56% of continuing students received some form of financial aid. About 56% of freshmen and 54% of continuing students received need-based aid. The average freshman award was $14,500. Of that total, scholarships or need-based grants averaged $9574 ($17,200 maximum); loans averaged $3517 ($3525 maximum); and work contracts averaged $1482 ($1500 maximum). Fifty-two percent of undergraduate students work part-time. Average earnings from campus work for the school year are $1190. The average financial indebtedness of a recent year's graduate was $12,600. Holy Cross is a member of CSS. The FAF and FAFSA are required. The deadline for financial aid applications is February 1.

International Students: There are currently 14 international students enrolled. The school actively recruits these students. They must take the TOEFL and achieve a minimum score of 550. The student must also take the SAT I. Students must take 3 SAT II: Subject tests, including English composition.

Computers: The college provides computer facilities for student use. The mainframes are an IBM 4381 and a DEC VAX 6320. There are 4 computer centers on campus housing 100 IBM microcomputers and 50 VAX terminals connected to the mainframe. Every dorm room has hardwire access to the mainframe system. All students may access the system 24 hours per day. There are no time limits on using the system and no fees.

Graduates: In 1992-93 670 bachelor's degrees were awarded. The most popular majors among graduates were English (13%), economics (11%), and biology (9%). Within an average freshman class, 98% graduate in 4 years and 1% in 5 years. Some 76 companies recruited on campus in a recent year. In the 1992 graduating class, 27% of the men and 24% of the women were enrolled in graduate school within 6 months of graduation; 64% of the men and 68% of the women had found employment.

Admissions Contact: Admissions Office.

CURRY COLLEGE
Milton, MA 02186-9984

E-2

(617) 333-0500, ext. 2210
(800) 669-0686 (out-of-state)

Full-time: 424 men, 456 women
Part-time: 15 men, 49 women
Graduate: 2 men, 16 women
Year: semesters, summer session
Application Deadline: April 1
Freshman Class: 1224 applied, 937 accepted, 283 enrolled
SAT I Verbal/Math: 380/420

Faculty: 68
Ph.Ds: 67%
Student/Faculty: 13 to 1
Tuition: $13,100
Room & Board: $5200

LESS COMPETITIVE

Curry College, founded in 1879, is a private liberal arts institution. There is one graduate school. In addition to regional accreditation, Curry has baccalaureate program accreditation with NLN. The library contains 110,000 volumes and 10,000 microform items and subscribes to 650 periodicals. Computerized library sources and services include InfoTrac and Internet. Special learning facilities include a learning resource center and radio station. The 120-acre campus is in a suburban area 7 miles southwest of Boston. Including residence halls, there are 40 buildings on campus.

Student Life: About 59% of undergraduates are from Massachusetts. Students come from 34 states, 19 foreign countries, and Canada. Seventy percent are from public schools; 30% from private. Seventy-five percent are white. The average age of freshmen is 18; all undergraduates, 20. Thirty-three percent drop out by the end of their first year.

Housing: A total of 600 students can be accommodated in college housing. College-sponsored living facilities include coed dormitories. On-campus housing is guaranteed for all 4 years. Priority is given to out-of-town students. Sixty-seven percent of students live on campus; of those, 60% remain on campus on weekends. All students may keep cars on campus.

Activities: There are no fraternities or sororities on campus. There are 15 groups on campus, including cheerleading, chorale, dance, drama, ethnic, film, honors, international, jazz band, literary magazine, musical theater, newspaper, photography, political, professional, radio and TV, religious, social, social service, student government, and yearbook. Popular campus events include formal dances, a concert series, guest speakers, Career Day, art exhibits, and Spring Fling.

Sports: There are 7 intercollegiate sports for men and 4 for women, and 5 intramural sports for men and 5 for women. Athletic and recreation facilities include a 500-seat gymnasium, a dance studio, 13 outdoor tennis courts, an outdoor pool, 5 athletic fields, a 1000-seat stadium, a 500-seat auditorium, and a 5000-meter cross-country trail.

Disabled Students: Elevators, special parking, and specially equipped rest rooms are available.

Services: In addition to many counseling and information services, tutoring is available in most subjects. LD tutoring and the Program for Advancement of Learning are also available. In addition, there is a reader service for the blind. General development courses in writing, reading, and mathematics are designed to develop the student's basic skills.

Campus Safety and Security: Campus safety and security measures include shuttle buses, informal discussions, pamphlets, posters, and films, and emergency telephones. In addition, there are lighted pathways and sidewalks. A campus safety office offers security services.

Programs of Study: Curry awards the B.A. and B.S.N. degrees. Master's degrees also are awarded. Bachelor's degrees are awarded in BIOLOGICAL SCIENCE (biology/biological science), BUSINESS (business administration and management), COMMUNICATIONS AND THE ARTS (communications, English, and visual and performing arts), COMPUTER AND PHYSICAL SCIENCE (chemistry and physics), EDUCATION (elementary), HEALTH PROFESSIONS (nursing), SOCIAL SCIENCE (history, justice studies, philosophy, psychology, and sociology). Nursing is the strongest academically. Business and communications have the largest enrollments.

Required: Successful completion of the required liberal arts curriculum, and a total of at least 120 semester hours (121 for nurses) with 30 in the major and a minimum 2.0 GPA are required.

Special: Curry offers internships in all majors, an accelerated degree with approval of the dean, study abroad, work-study, dual and student-designed majors, credit by exam and for life, work, and military experience, nondegree study, and pass/fail options. There are 2 national honor societies on campus. There is 1 honors program for all majors.

Faculty/Classroom: Forty-four percent of faculty are male; 56%, female. All teach undergraduates. No introductory courses are taught by graduate students. The average class size in an introductory lecture is 30; in a laboratory, 16; and in a regular course offering, 21.

Admissions: About 77% of the 1993-94 applicants were accepted. About 3% of the current freshmen were in the top fifth of their class; 12% were in the top two fifths.

Requirements: A minimum GPA of 2.0 is required. The SAT I or ACT is required, with average scores of 400 verbal, 400 mathematics on the SAT I or 18 on the ACT. Applicants must be graduates of an accredited secondary school or have a GED. Sixteen credits and Carnegie units are required, as are 4 years of English, 2 each of foreign language, history, science, and social studies, and 3 of mathematics. An essay is required, and an interview is recommended. A portfolio where appropriate is also advised. AP and CLEP credits are accepted. Important factors used in the admissions decision are recommendations by school officials, extracurricular activities record, evidence of special talent, advanced placement or honor courses, and leadership record.

Procedure: Freshmen are admitted in the fall and spring. Entrance exams should be taken in the junior year or in November of the senior year. Applications should be filed by April 1 for fall entry and December 1 for spring entry, along with an application fee of $40. Notification of early decision is sent December 15; regular decision, on a rolling basis. There are early decision, early admissions, and deferred admissions plans. About 10 early decision candidates were accepted for the 1993-94 class.

Transfer: About 102 transfer students enrolled in 1993-94. Transfer students must be in good academic standing at their previous college with a minimum GPA of 2.0. An interview is recommended. A total of 30 credits out of 120 must be completed at Curry.

Visiting: There are regularly scheduled orientations for prospective students, consisting of interviews with an admissions counselor and tours with a student. There are guides for informal visits and visitors may sit in on classes and stay overnight at the school. To arrange for a visit, contact the Admissions Office at (617) 333-0500, ext. 2210 or 2211.

Financial Aid: In 1993-94, half of all students received some form of financial aid, including need-based aid. The average freshman award was $8500. Of that total, scholarships or need-based grants averaged $4000 ($6000 maximum); loans averaged $1000 ($2000 maximum); and work contracts averaged $1200 (maximum). Ten percent of undergraduate students work part-time. Average earnings from campus work for the school year are $1500. The average financial indebtedness of the 1992-93 graduate was $8200. Curry is a member of CSS. The FAF, the college's own financial statement, and the FAFSA are required. The deadline for financial aid applications is March 15.

International Students: There are currently 36 international students enrolled. They must take the TOEFL and achieve a minimum score of 500. The student must also take the SAT I or the ACT.

Computers: The college provides computer facilities for student use. The mainframe is a DEC PDP 11/86. There are also 70 Macintosh Plus, SE, IIe, and IICX PCs in 2 library laboratories and in the learning center laboratory. Four laser printers are also available. All students may access the system. There are no time limits on using the system and no fees.

Graduates: In an earlier year, 190 bachelor's degrees were awarded. The most popular majors among graduates were business (29%), communication (22%), and nursing (13%). Within an average freshman class, 55% graduate in 5 years.

Admissions Contact: Janet Cromie Kelly, Dean of Admissions and Financial Aid.

EASTERN NAZARENE COLLEGE
Quincy, MA 02170   (617) 773-2373; (800) 88 ENC 88 (out-of-state)

E-2

Full-time: 284 men, 365 women
Part-time: 13 men, 26 women
Graduate: 87 men, 97 women
Year: 4-1-4, summer session
Application Deadline: open
Freshman Class: 409 accepted, 200 enrolled
SAT I Verbal/Math: 443/477

Faculty: 48; IIB, -$
Ph.Ds: 59%
Student/Faculty: 13 to 1
Tuition: $8765
Room & Board: $3400

LESS COMPETITIVE

Eastern Nazarene College, founded in 1918, is a private, coeducational college affiliated with the Church of the Nazarene. It offers a program in the liberal arts. There is one graduate school. In addition to regional accreditation, ENC has baccalaureate program accreditation with CSWE. The library contains 121,050 volumes and subscribes to 545 periodicals. Computerized library sources and services include interlibrary loans and database searching. Special learning facilities include a learning resource center and radio station. The 15-acre campus is in a suburban area 6 miles south of Boston. Including residence halls, there are 16 buildings on campus.

Student Life: About 55% of undergraduates are from out-of-state, mostly the Northeast. Students come from 27 states, 24 foreign countries, and Canada. Eighty-eight percent are white. Most are Protestant. The average age of freshmen is 18; all undergraduates, 20. Twenty-five percent drop out by the end of their first year; 60% remain to graduate.

Housing: A total of 638 students can be accommodated in college housing. College-sponsored living facilities include single-sex dormitories and married-student housing. On-campus housing is guaranteed for all 4 years. Seventy-five percent of students live on campus; of those, 75% remain on campus on weekends. Alcohol is not permitted. All students may keep cars on campus.

Activities: There are no fraternities or sororities on campus. There are 34 groups on campus, including band, cheerleading, choir, chorale, chorus, drama, jazz band, literary magazine, musical theater, newspaper, pep band, photography, professional, radio and TV, religious, social service, student government, and yearbook. Popular campus events include Freshmen Breakout, TWIRP Week, All School Outing, Homecoming, Kings Tournament, and Junior/Senior Banquet.

Sports: There are 5 intercollegiate sports for men and 5 for women, and 4 intramural sports for men and 5 for women. Athletic and recreation facilities include a physical education center equipped with a basketball area, batting cage, and playing courts.

Disabled Students: Sixty-five percent of the campus is accessible to disabled students. The following facilities are available: wheelchair ramps, elevators, special parking, and specially equipped rest rooms.

Services: In addition to many counseling and information services, tutoring is available in most subjects. In addition, there is remedial math, reading, and writing.

Campus Safety and Security: Campus safety and security measures include 24-hour foot and vehicle patrol, self defense education, escort service, and informal discussions. In addition, there are pamphlets, posters, and films, emergency telephones, and lighted pathways and sidewalks.

Programs of Study: ENC awards the B.A. and B.S. degrees. Associate and master's degrees also are awarded. Bachelor's degrees are awarded in BIOLOGICAL SCIENCE (biology/biological science), BUSINESS (business administration and management), COMMUNICATIONS AND THE ARTS (communications, English, French, music, music performance, and Spanish), COMPUTER AND PHYSICAL SCIENCE (chemistry, computer science, mathematics, physics, and science), EDUCATION (early childhood, education, elementary, music, science, and social science), ENGINEERING AND ENVIRONMENTAL DESIGN (computer engineering and engineering physics), HEALTH PROFESSIONS (sports therapy), SOCIAL SCIENCE (church music, general studies, history, movement arts, psychology, religion, social studies, social work, sociology, youth and Christian education, and youth ministry). Chemistry, physics, history, biology, social work, and education are the strongest academically. Education, business, and psychology have the largest enrollments.

Required: All students must complete the core curriculum of writing and rhetoric, biblical history, social science, science or mathematics, symbolic systems and intercultural awareness, philosophy and religion, and physical education. A total of 130 credits is required for the B.A. or B.S., with 32 to 40 in the major. Minimum GPA for graduation is 2.0.

Special: Internships are available in the metropolitan Boston area. Study abroad in Costa Rica, a Washington semester, a 3–2 engineering degree with Boston University, and a cooperative program with the Massachusetts College of Pharmacy are offered. Work-study programs, dual majors, credit for life/military/work experience, and pass/fail options are available. An off-campus degree-completion program for adults in business administration is offered. There is 1 national honor society on campus.

Faculty/Classroom: Seventy-two percent of faculty are male; 28%, female. Eighty-three percent teach undergraduates. No introductory courses are taught by graduate students. The average class size in an introductory lecture is 75; in a laboratory, 20; and in a regular course offering, 22.

Admissions: The SAT scores for the 1993–94 freshman class were as follows: Verbal—73% below 500, 18% between 500 and 599, and 8% between 600 and 700; Math—55% below 500, 27% between 500 and 599, 14% between 600 and 700, and 5% above 700. About 31% of the current freshmen were in the top fifth of their class; 56% were in the top two fifths. Seven freshmen graduated first in their class.

Requirements: ENC requires applicants to be in the upper 75% of their class. A minimum GPA of 2.0 is required. The SAT I is required. Applicants must be graduates of an accredited secondary school or have a GED. They must have a minimum of 16 academic credits including 4 of English, 2 to 4 of mathematics and foreign language, 1 to 4 of science, and 1 to 2 of history and social studies. Music students must audition. An essay and interview are recommended. AP and CLEP credits are accepted. Important factors used in the admissions decision are advanced placement or honor courses, recommendations by school officials, leadership record, ability to finance college education, and evidence of special talent.

Procedure: Freshmen are admitted to all sessions. Entrance exams should be taken in the spring of the junior year. Application deadlines are open. The application fee is $20. Notification is sent on a rolling basis. There is a deferred admissions plan.

Transfer: About 32 transfer students enrolled in 1993–94. A minimum 2.0 GPA is required to transfer. An interview is recommended, as is submission of a composite SAT I score of at least 800. A total of 60 credits out of 130 must be completed at ENC.

Visiting: There are regularly scheduled orientations for prospective students. There are guides for informal visits and visitors may sit in on classes and stay overnight at the school. To arrange for a visit, contact the Office of Admissions at (617) 773–2373 or (800) 88 ENC 88 (out-of-state).

Financial Aid: In a recent year, 80% of all freshmen and 78% of continuing students received some form of financial aid. The average freshman award was $6237. Of that total, scholarships or need-based grants averaged $1645 ($7270 maximum); loans averaged $2000 ($2625 maximum); and work contracts averaged $1000 ($2000 maximum). Average earnings from campus work for the school year are $2000. The average financial indebtedness of the 1992–93 graduate was $12,000. ENC is a member of CSS. The FAF and the college's own financial statement are required. The deadline for financial aid applications is March 1.

International Students: There are currently 45 international students enrolled. They must take the TOEFL and achieve a minimum score of 500.

Computers: The college provides computer facilities for student use. The mainframes are a DEC VAX 11/750 and a Plexus P/60. There are more than 30 microcomputers available for student use in the library. Access to the mainframe computers is gained by assigned password, and terminals are plentiful. All students may access the system. There are no time limits on using the system. The fees are $5.

Graduates: In 1992–93 129 bachelor's degrees were awarded. The most popular majors among graduates were education (18%), business administration (16%), and psychology (9%). Within an average freshman class, 44% graduate in 4 years and 51% in 5 years.

Admissions Contact: Bill Nichols, Director of Enrollment Management.

ELMS COLLEGE
(See College of Our Lady of the Elms)

EMERSON COLLEGE
Boston, MA 02116

E-2
(617) 578-8600

Full-time: 760 men, 1085 women	**Faculty:** 100; IIA, av$
Part-time: 140 men, 220 women	**Ph.D.s:** 80%
Graduate: 160 men, 325 women	**Student/Faculty:** 18 to 1
Year: semesters, summer session	**Tuition:** $15,112
Application Deadline: February 1	**Room & Board:** $7566
Freshman Class: n/av	
SAT I: 1000 (composite)	**LESS COMPETITIVE**

Emerson College, founded in 1880, is a private, independent, coeducational college devoted to the study of commmunications and performing arts. There are 5 graduate schools. The library contains 105,000 volumes, 17,700 microform items, and 13,000 audiovisual forms, and subscribes to 1000 periodicals. Computerized library sources and services include the card catalog, interlibrary loans, and database searching. Special learning facilities include a learning resource center, radio station, TV station, speech clinics, 5 stages, and film production facilities. The campus is in an urban area in the Beacon Hill area of Boston. Including residence halls, there are 20 buildings on campus.

Student Life: About 60% of undergraduates are from out-of-state, mostly the Northeast. Students come from 48 states, 45 foreign countries, and Canada. Ninety-one percent are white. The average age of freshmen is 18; all undergraduates, 20. Fifteen percent drop out by the end of their first year; 65% remain to graduate.

Housing: College-sponsored living facilities include coed dormitories. On-campus housing is guaranteed for all 4 years. Fifty-two percent of students live on campus; of those, all remain on campus on weekends.

Activities: About 10% of men belong to 3 local and 3 national fraternities; about 10% of women belong to 3 local and 2 national sororities. There are 48 groups on campus, including chorale, chorus, dance, drama, ethnic, film, gay, honors, international, literary magazine, musical theater, newspaper, photography, political, professional, radio and TV, religious, social, social service, student government, and yearbook. Popular campus events the include annual film showcase, Black History Month, BFA Dance Concert, the spring musical, the alumni comedy performance, the annual Emerson video award ceremony, and Hand-Me-Down-Night.

Sports: There are 7 intercollegiate sports for men and 6 for women, and 7 intramural sports each. Athletic and recreation facilities include a sailing dock, the student union, a weight room, a home basketball court, and a gymnasium.

Disabled Students: Elevators are available for disabled students.

Services: In addition to many counseling and information services, tutoring is available in most subjects. There is also remedial math, reading, and writing.

Campus Safety and Security: Campus safety and security measures include 24-hour foot and vehicle patrol, self-defense education, escort service, and shuttle buses. In addition, there are informal discussions, pamphlets, posters, and films, emergency telephones, and lighted pathways and sidewalks.

Programs of Study: Emerson awards the B.A., B.S., B.F.A., B.L.I., B.M., and B.S.Sp. degrees. Master's and doctoral degrees also are awarded. Bachelor's degrees are awarded in COMMUNICATIONS AND THE ARTS (advertising, broadcasting, communications, creative writing, dramatic arts, film arts, journalism, public relations, publishing, and speech/debate/rhetoric), HEALTH PROFESSIONS (speech pathology/audiology), and SOCIAL SCIENCE (prelaw). Mass communication, tv, radio, journalism, film, advertising, public relations, and performing arts have the largest enrollments.

Required: All students must complete 128 credit hours, with 44 to 64 in the major, and they must have a minimum GPA of 2.0 overall. The required general education curriculum consists of 12 credits in communications and 40 in liberal arts, for a total of 52 credits. A course in voice and articulation is required.

Special: Student-designed, interdisciplinary, and dual majors are available. Cross-registration is offered with the Berklee College of Music, Boston Conservatory, Massachusetts College of Art, and Museum of Fine Arts School. Many internships are possible in Boston and in Los Angeles. Emerson has nondegree study and pass/fail options, as well as study abroad in the Netherlands. There is a freshman honors program on campus, as well as 3 national honor societies.

Faculty/Classroom: Sixty-eight percent of faculty are male; 32%, female. All faculty both teach and do research. The average class size in an introductory lecture is 50; in a laboratory, 15; and in a regular course offering, 20.

Requirements: The SAT I is required, but the ACT may be substituted. In addition, candidates must be graduates of an accredited secondary school or hold a GED certificate. They must have completed 16 Carnegie units, including 4 in English and 2 each in science, social studies, and mathematics. An essay is required. Auditions and interviews are recommended. AP and CLEP credits are accepted. Important factors used in the admissions decision are advanced placement or honor courses, leadership record, evidence of special talent, recommendations by school officials, and extracurricular activities record.

Procedure: Freshmen are admitted fall and spring. Entrance exams should be taken before January of the senior year. Applications should be filed by February 1 for fall entry (March 1 for transfers) and December for spring entry, along with an application fee of $45. Applications are accepted on a rolling basis after those dates. Notification is sent on a rolling basis. There are early admissions and deferred admissions plans. A waiting list is an active part of the admissions procedure.

Transfer: About 230 transfer students enrolled in a recent year. The SAT I or ACT is required for some classes and recommended for others. Applicants must have a minimum 2.5 GPA and 2 letters of reference. A total of 32 credits out of 128 must be completed at Emerson.

Visiting: There are regularly scheduled orientations for prospective students. Visitors may sit in on classes and stay overnight at the school. To arrange for a visit, contact the Admissions Office at (617) 578-8600.

Financial Aid: In a recent year, 88% of all freshmen and 75% of continuing students received some form of financial aid. About 75% of all students received need-based aid. Scholarships or need-based grants averaged $4250 ($6500 maximum); loans averaged $3600 ($4850 maximum); and work contracts averaged $1700 ($2000 maximum). Emerson is a member of CSS. The FAF is required. The deadline for financial aid applications is March 1.

International Students: There are currently 107 international students enrolled. The school actively recruits these students. They must take the TOEFL and achieve a minimum score of 550. The student must also take the SAT I or the ACT.

Computers: The college provides computer facilities for student use. The mainframe is a DEC VAX 11/780. Many microcomputers are also available in the academic computing center. All students may access the system. It may be used weekdays 9 A.M. to 9 P.M. and weekends 12 P.M. to 8 P.M. There are no time limits on using the system and no fees.

Graduates: In an earlier year, 432 bachelor's degrees were awarded.

Admissions Contact: Jane B. Brown, Dean of Admissions.

EMMANUEL COLLEGE

E-2

Boston, MA 02115 — (617) 735-9715

Full-time: 58 men, 710 women	**Faculty:** 49; IIB, av$
Part-time: 98 men, 450 women	**Ph.D.s:** 80%
Graduate: 20 men, 135 women	**Student/Faculty:** 16 to 1
Year: semesters, summer sessions	**Tuition:** $11,973
Application Deadline: open	**Room & Board:** $5800
Freshman Class: 317 applied, 293 accepted, 145 enrolled	
SAT I or ACT: required	**LESS COMPETITIVE**

Emmanuel College, founded in 1919, is a primarily women's liberal arts college affiliated with the Roman Catholic Church. It offers programs in the fine arts, liberal arts, health sciences, engineering, business, and teacher preparation. There are 6 graduate schools. In addition to regional accreditation, The college has baccalaureate program accreditation with NLN. The library contains 98,385 volumes, 12 microform items, and 1653 audiovisual forms, and subscribes to 825 periodicals. Computerized library sources and services include interlibrary loans and database searching. Special learning facilities include a learning resource center and art gallery. The 16-acre campus is in an urban area. Including residence halls, there are 8 buildings on campus.

Student Life: About 91% of undergraduates are from Massachusetts. Students come from 18 states, 55 foreign countries, and Canada. Seventy-two percent are from public schools; 28% from private. Seventy-five percent are white. Fifty-five percent claim no religious affiliation; 34% Catholic. The average age of freshmen is 18; all undergraduates, 21. Twenty-three percent drop out by the end of their first year; 56% remain to graduate.

Housing: A total of 855 students can be accommodated in college housing. College-sponsored living facilities include single-sex dormitories. In addition there are special interest houses. On-campus housing is guaranteed for all 4 years. Seventy percent of students live on campus; of those, 40% remain on campus on weekends. Alcohol is not permitted. Upperclassmen may keep cars on campus.

Activities: There are no fraternities or sororities on campus. There are 20 groups on campus, including art, chorus, dance, drama, ethnic, honors, international, literary magazine, political, professional, religious, social, social service, student government, and yearbook. Popular campus events include Fall Carnival, semiformals, Family Weekend, Siblings Weekend, Commencement Ball, International Hospitality Night, and Spring Clambake.

Sports: There are 4 intercollegiate sports for women and 4 intramural sports for women. Athletic and recreation facilities include a 500-seat gymnasium, a training room/locker room, a fitness center, and a 500-seat auditorium. Students have access to a swimming pool and aerobic facilities.

Disabled Students: Seventy-five percent of the campus is accessible to disabled students. The following facilities are available: wheelchair ramps, elevators, special parking, specially equipped rest rooms, special class scheduling, and lowered telephones.

Services: In addition to many counseling and information services, tutoring is available in every subject. In addition, there is remedial math, reading, and writing.

Campus Safety and Security: Campus safety and security measures include 24-hour foot and vehicle patrol, self defense education, escort service, and shuttle buses. In addition, there are informal discussions, pamphlets, posters, and films, emergency telephones, and lighted pathways and sidewalks.

Programs of Study: The college awards the B.A., B.S., and B.F.A. degrees. Associate and master's degrees also are awarded. Bachelor's degrees are awarded in BIOLOGICAL SCIENCE (biochemistry and biology/biological science), BUSINESS (accounting and business administration and management), COMMUNICATIONS AND THE ARTS (art history and appreciation, communications, English, fine arts, French, languages, Spanish, and studio art), COMPUTER AND PHYSICAL SCIENCE (chemistry, mathematics, and physics), EDUCATION (art, elementary, music, and secondary), ENGINEERING AND ENVIRONMENTAL DESIGN (preengineering), HEALTH PROFESSIONS (art therapy, medical laboratory technology, nursing, predentistry, and premedicine), SOCIAL SCIENCE (economics, history, political science/government, prelaw, psychology, religion, and sociology). Education, sciences, and liberal arts are the strongest academically. Education and liberal arts have the largest enrollments.

Required: Students must complete a broad range of distribution requirements including fine arts, mathematics, writing, humanities, foreign language, philosophy, science, social science, and religious studies. A total of 128 credit hours is required, with 10 to 21 courses in the major, and a minimum GPA of 2.0 for graduation.

Special: There is cross-registration with Northeastern University, Simmons College, Wentworth Institute, and Andover-Newton Theological School. The college offers internships, study abroad, a Washington semester, work-study programs, an accelerated degree program in business administration, dual and student-designed majors, a gen-

eral studies degree, a 3–2 engineering degree, and pass/fail options. The adult learner degree program offers learning opportunities at off-campus sites for men and women age 23 and older. There are 4 national honor societies on campus. Five departments have honors programs.

Faculty/Classroom: Thirty-eight percent of faculty are male; 62%, female. All teach undergraduates and do research. The average class size in an introductory lecture is 22; in a laboratory, 15; and in a regular course offering, 18.

Admissions: About 92% of the 1993–94 applicants were accepted. About 21% of the current freshmen were in the top fifth of their class; 38% were in the top two fifths.

Requirements: The college requires applicants to be in the upper 50% of their class. A minimum GPA of 2.0 is required. The SAT I or ACT is required. Applicants must be graduates of an accredited secondary school or have a GED. Sixteen academic credits are required, including 4 years of English, 3 years each of foreign language and mathematics, and 2 years each of laboratory science and social studies. An essay and an interview are required. AP and CLEP credits are accepted. Important factors used in the admissions decision are advanced placement or honor courses, recommendations by school officials, leadership record, evidence of special talent, and extracurricular activities record.

Procedure: Freshmen are admitted fall and spring. Entrance exams should be taken by November of the senior year. Application deadlines are open. Application fee is $30. Notification of early decision is sent December 1; regular decision, on a rolling basis. There are early decision, early admissions, and deferred admissions plans. Three early decision candidates were accepted for the 1993–94 class.

Transfer: About 30 transfer students enrolled in 1993–94. Students must submit essays, college and high school transcripts, and 2 letters of recommendation. They must be financially and academically eligible to return to previously attended institution. A total of 72 credits out of 128 must be completed at the college.

Visiting: There are regularly scheduled orientations for prospective students. There are guides for informal visits and visitors may sit in on classes and stay overnight at the school. To arrange for a visit, contact the Admissions Office at (617) 735–9715.

Financial Aid: In 1993–94, 81% of all current freshmen and 73% of continuing students received some form of financial aid. About 77% of freshmen and 72% of continuing students received need-based aid. The average freshman award was $10,900. Of that total, scholarships or need-based grants averaged $6669 ($16,498 maximum); loans averaged $2900 ($4625 maximum); and work contracts averaged $1400. Thirty-two percent of undergraduate students work part-time. Average earnings from campus work for the school year are $1223. The average financial indebtedness of the 1992–93 graduate was $6700. The college is a member of CSS. The FAF and FAFSA are required. The priority deadline for financial aid applications is March.

International Students: There are currently 69 international students enrolled. The school actively recruits these students. They must take the TOEFL and achieve a minimum score of 500. The student must also take the SAT I or the ACT.

Computers: The college provides computer facilities for student use. The mainframe is a Prime 4050. IBM PS/2 and Apple microcomputers are available in the computer and academic resource centers. All students may access the system. There are no time limits on using the system and no fees.

Graduates: In 1992–93, 193 bachelor's degrees were awarded. The most popular majors among graduates were interdepartmental (14%), education (14%), and psychology (11%). Within an average freshman class, 76% graduate in 4 years, 87% in 5 years, and 92% in 6 years.

Admissions Contact: Kathleen Manning, Director of Admissions.

FITCHBURG STATE COLLEGE

C-2

Fitchburg, MA 01420

(508) 345–2151, ext. 3144

Full-time: 1223 men, 1656 women
Part-time: 713 men, 699 women
Graduate: 218 men, 699 women
Year: semesters, summer session
Application Deadline: March 1
Freshman Class: 4180 applied, 2903 accepted, 1077 enrolled
SAT I: required

Faculty: 243; IIA, --$
Ph.D.s: 61%
Student/Faculty: 12 to 1
Tuition: $3234 ($7368)
Room & Board: $3728

COMPETITIVE

Fitchburg State College, founded in 1894, is a half-residential, half-commuter college in the state system, offering programs in liberal arts, business, health sciences, and education. There is one graduate school. In addition to regional accreditation, Fitchburg has baccalaureate program accreditation with NLN. The library contains 175,798 volumes, 370,317 microform items, and 3701 audiovisual forms, and subscribes to 13,081 periodicals. Computerized library sources and services include the card catalog, interlibrary loans, and database searching. Special learning facilities include a learning resource cen-

ter, art gallery, radio station, campus school, graphics center, and TV studio. The 35-acre campus is in a small town 40 miles west of Boston. Including residence halls, there are 23 buildings on campus.

Student Life: About 96% of undergraduates are from Massachusetts. Students come from 16 states, 5 foreign countries, and Canada. Eighty percent are from public schools; 20% from private. Ninety-five percent are white. Seventy-five percent are Catholic; 20% Protestant. The average age of freshmen is 19; all undergraduates, 24. Twenty-six percent drop out by the end of their first year; 49% remain to graduate.

Housing: A total of 1467 students can be accommodated in college housing. College-sponsored living facilities include single-sex and coed dormitories and on-campus apartments. On-campus housing is guaranteed for all 4 years. Fifty percent of students live on campus; of those, 35% remain on campus on weekends. Upperclassmen may keep cars on campus.

Activities: About 10% of men belong to 5 local and 2 national fraternities; about 15% of women belong to 1 national and 4 local sororities. There are 60 groups on campus, including art, band, cheerleading, chorus, computers, drama, ethnic, film, gay, honors, international, jazz band, literary magazine, newspaper, photography, political, professional, radio and TV, religious, social, social service, student government, and yearbook. Popular campus events include the Visiting Lecture Series and Crop Day.

Sports: There are 7 intercollegiate sports for men and 6 for women, and 8 intramural sports for men and 7 for women. Athletic and recreation facilities include a 500-seat gymnasium, a track, tennis courts, intramural fields, and the Student Union.

Disabled Students: Eighty percent of the campus is accessible to disabled students. The following facilities are available: wheelchair ramps, elevators, special parking, specially equipped rest rooms, special class scheduling, lowered drinking fountains, and lowered telephones.

Services: In addition to many counseling and information services, tutoring is available in most subjects. There is also a reader service for the blind, and remedial math, reading, and writing.

Campus Safety and Security: Campus safety and security measures include 24-hour foot and vehicle patrol, self-defense education, escort service, and informal discussions. In addition, there are pamphlets, posters, and films and lighted pathways and sidewalks.

Programs of Study: Fitchburg awards the B.A., B.S., and B.S.Ed. degrees. Master's degrees also are awarded. Bachelor's degrees are awarded in BIOLOGICAL SCIENCE (biology/biological science), BUSINESS (accounting, business administration and management, management information systems, and marketing/retailing/merchandising), COMMUNICATIONS AND THE ARTS (communications, English, photography, and telecommunications), COMPUTER AND PHYSICAL SCIENCE (chemistry, computer science, earth science, and mathematics), EDUCATION (early childhood, elementary, industrial arts, middle school, secondary, and special), ENGINEERING AND ENVIRONMENTAL DESIGN (industrial engineering technology), HEALTH PROFESSIONS (medical laboratory technology, nursing, and premedicine), SOCIAL SCIENCE (community services, economics, geography, history, human services, prelaw, psychology, and sociology). Chemistry, communications, medical technology, nursing, and biology are the strongest academically. Business administration, communications, nursing, and education have the largest enrollments.

Required: All students must complete a minimum of 120 credit hours with a GPA of at least 2.0. Distribution requirements include courses from the categories of ideas and events, human behavior, literature/language arts, and the quantitative/scientific area. Two semesters of writing, 1 semester of health and fitness, and a computer literacy course are also required.

Special: Students may cross-register at any of the other state colleges. Internships in a variety of fields, study abroad, B.A.-B.S. degrees, dual majors, and a student-designed general studies major are offered. There is a freshman honors program on campus, as well as 1 national honor society. Two departments have honors programs.

Faculty/Classroom: Fifty-nine percent of faculty are male; 41%, female. Ninety-five percent teach undergraduates and 10% both teach and do research. The average class size in an introductory lecture is 30; in a laboratory, 20; and in a regular course offering, 25.

Admissions: About 69% of the 1993–94 applicants were accepted. The SAT scores for the 1993–94 freshman class were as follows: Verbal—80% below 500, 17% between 500 and 599, and 2% between 600 and 700. There was 1 National Merit finalist and 5 semifinalists. Five freshmen graduated first in their class.

Requirements: Fitchburg requires applicants to be in the upper 75% of their class. A minimum GPA of 2.0 is required. The SAT I is required. Applicants should be graduates of accredited high schools or have the GED. Secondary preparation should include 4 years of English, 3 years each of mathematics and social studies, and 2 years each of a foreign language, history, and science. A personal interview is recommended. AP and CLEP credits are accepted. Important

factors used in the admissions decision are ability to finance college education, advanced placement or honor courses, evidence of special talent, leadership record, and recommendations by school officials.

Procedure: Freshmen are admitted fall and spring. Entrance exams should be taken in the junior or senior year. Applications should be filed by March 1 for fall entry and December 1 for spring entry, along with an application fee of $10. Notification is sent on a rolling basis. There is a deferred admissions plan. A waiting list is an active part of the admissions procedure, with about 2% of applicants on the list.

Transfer: Some 361 transfer students enrolled in 1993–94. Transfer applicants should present a minimum GPA of 2.0 in at least 12 credits of transferable college work. An associate degree and personal interview are recommended. A total of 45 credits out of 120 must be completed at Fitchburg.

Visiting: There are regularly scheduled orientations for prospective students, including 5 open-house receptions. There are guides for informal visits and visitors may sit in on classes. To arrange for a visit, contact the Admissions Office at (508) 345–2151, ext. 3144, 3145, 3146, or 3147.

Financial Aid: In an earlier year, 55% of all freshmen and 50% of continuing students received some form of financial aid. About 40% of freshmen and 40% of continuing students received need-based aid. The average freshman award was $2000. Of that total, scholarships or need-based grants averaged $800 ($4100 maximum); loans averaged $1000 ($3625 maximum); and work contracts averaged $800 ($1000 maximum). Twelve percent of undergraduate students worked part-time. Average earnings from campus work for the school year were $1000. The average financial indebtedness of an earlier graduate was $1500. Fitchburg is a member of CSS. The FAF and the college's own financial statement are required. The deadline for financial aid applications is March 30.

International Students: There are currently 10 international students enrolled. They must take the TOEFL and achieve a minimum score of 500. The student must also take the SAT I.

Computers: The college provides computer facilities for student use. The mainframes are a DEC VAX 8530 and CDC CYBER 932/32. Some 200 microcomputers are also available for student use in the Computer Science building, residence halls, and elsewhere throughout the campus. All students may access the system. It may be used 24 hours daily. There are no time limits on using the system. The fees are $30.

Graduates: In 1992–93 751 bachelor's degrees were awarded. The most popular majors among graduates were education (23%), communications (12%), and nursing (10%). Within an average freshman class, 47% graduate in 4 years and 57% in 5 years. Some 21 companies recruited on campus in 1992–93. In the 1992 graduating class, 1% of all students were enrolled in graduate school within 6 months of graduation; 75% of the men and 82% of the women had found employment.

Admissions Contact: Marke Miller Vickers, Director of Admissions.

FRAMINGHAM STATE COLLEGE D-2
Framingham, MA 01701 (508) 626–4500

Full-time: 1008 men, 1768 women	Faculty: 176
Part-time: 867 men, 1207 women	Ph.D.s: 67%
Graduate: 131 men, 311 women	Student/Faculty: 16 to 1
Year: semesters, summer session	Tuition: $3154 ($7288)
Application Deadline: March 1	Room & Board: $3426

Freshman Class: 2952 applied, 1935 accepted, 535 enrolled
SAT I Verbal/Math: 428/469 **COMPETITIVE**

Framingham State College, founded in 1839, is a comprehensive public college offering 28 undergraduate majors and 14 graduate programs based on a liberal arts foundation that includes career and professional programs. There is one graduate school. In addition to regional accreditation, the college has baccalaureate program accreditation with ADA, AHEA, and NLN. The library contains 171,000 volumes, 454,000 microform items, and 5364 audiovisual forms, and subscribes to 1205 periodicals. Computerized library sources and services include the card catalog, interlibrary loans, and database searching. Special learning facilities include a learning resource center, art gallery, planetarium, radio station, greenhouse, TV studio, and an early childhood demonstration laboratory. The 73-acre campus is in a suburban area 20 miles west of Boston. Including residence halls, there are 19 buildings on campus.

Student Life: About 92% of undergraduates are from Massachusetts. Students come from 20 states, 15 foreign countries, and Canada. Eighty percent are from public schools; 20% from private. Ninety-two percent are white. The average age of freshmen is 19; all undergraduates, 21. Twenty-eight percent drop out by the end of their first year; 55% remain to graduate.

Housing: A total of 1450 students can be accommodated in college housing. College-sponsored living facilities include single-sex and coed dormitories. On-campus housing is guaranteed for all 4 years.

Sixty percent of students commute. Alcohol is not permitted. Upperclassmen may keep cars on campus.

Activities: There are no fraternities or sororities on campus. There are 40 groups on campus, including art, cheerleading, chorale, chorus, computers, drama, ethnic, gay, honors, international, literary magazine, newspaper, radio and TV, religious, social, student government, and yearbook. Popular campus events include Homecoming, Arts and Humanities Program, Lyceum Lecture Series, and New England Philharmonic Concerts (orchestra in residence).

Sports: There are 6 intercollegiate sports for men and 6 for women, and 6 intramural sports for men and 6 for women. Athletic and recreation facilities include a gymnasium; the student center provides a variety of recreational activities. Football and soccer fields and tennis and basketball courts are available on lower campus fields.

Disabled Students: Eighty percent of the campus is accessible to disabled students. The following facilities are available: wheelchair ramps, elevators, special parking, specially equipped rest rooms, and special class scheduling.

Services: There is remedial math, reading, and writing. The College Skills Center offers free tutoring in writing, mathematics, and reading. Subject tutoring may be arranged for an hourly fee.

Campus Safety and Security: Campus safety and security measures include 24-hour foot and vehicle patrol, self defense education, escort service, and shuttle buses. In addition, there are informal discussions, pamphlets, posters, and films, emergency telephones, and lighted pathways and sidewalks.

Programs of Study: The college awards the B.A. and B.S. degrees. Master's degrees also are awarded. Bachelor's degrees are awarded in BIOLOGICAL SCIENCE (biology/biological science), BUSINESS (business administration and management), COMMUNICATIONS AND THE ARTS (art history and appreciation, communications, English, fine arts, French, and Spanish), COMPUTER AND PHYSICAL SCIENCE (chemistry, computer science, earth science, and mathematics), EDUCATION (early childhood and elementary), ENGINEERING AND ENVIRONMENTAL DESIGN (preengineering), HEALTH PROFESSIONS (medical laboratory technology and nursing), SOCIAL SCIENCE (clothing and textiles management/production/services, dietetics/food and nutrition, economics, family/consumer studies/home economics, food science, geography, history, philosophy, political science/government, psychology, sociology, and textiles and clothing). Business administration, elementary/early childhood education, and psychology have the largest enrollments.

Required: All students must complete 32 courses, 20 of which must be in the major and related electives, for a total of 128 credits. General education courses include writing, mathematics, study of federal and state constitutions, 3 humanities courses, 3 social science courses, and 2 science/mathematics courses. A 2.0 GPA is required for graduation.

Special: The college offers a 2–3 preengineering program in cooperation with the University of Massachusetts at Amherst, University of Massachusetts at Lowell, and University of Massachusetts at Dartmouth. Cross-registration is possible at any of the state colleges. Study abroad in 5 countries, a Washington semester, and various internships are available. Pass/fail options are limited to 2 courses. There is a freshman honors program on campus

Faculty/Classroom: Fifty-four percent of faculty are male; 46%, female. All teach undergraduates. No introductory courses are taught by graduate students. The average class size in an introductory lecture is 25 and in a laboratory, 25.

Admissions: About 66% of the 1993–94 applicants were accepted. The SAT scores for the 1993–94 freshman class were as follows: Verbal—83% below 500, 15% between 500 and 599, and 2% between 600 and 700; Math—65% below 500, 28% between 500 and 599, and 7% between 600 and 700. About 57% of the current freshmen were in the top two fifths of their class. Two freshmen graduated first in their class.

Requirements: The SAT I is required. In addition, applicants must have a high school diploma or the GED. Secondary preparation must total 16 college preparatory credits, including 4 years of English, 3 years of mathematics, 2 years each of a foreign language and science, and 1 year each of history and social science. The recommended 3 years of electives may include additional academic subjects or art, music, or computer courses. Prospective art majors must submit a portfolio. AP and CLEP credits are accepted. Important factors used in the admissions decision are advanced placement or honor courses, leadership record, evidence of special talent, extracurricular activities record, and recommendations by school officials.

Procedure: Freshmen are admitted fall and spring. Entrance exams should be taken in spring of the junior year or fall of the senior year. Applications should be filed by March 1 for fall entry and December 1 for spring entry, along with an application fee of $10. Notification is sent on a rolling basis. There is a deferred admissions plan.

Transfer: About 482 transfer students enrolled in 1993–94. Transfer applicants with more than 30 college credits must present a GPA of at least 2.5. Those with fewer than 30 credits must meet freshman ad-

mission requirements. A total of 32 credits out of 128 must be completed at the college.

Visiting: There are regularly scheduled orientations for prospective students, including campus tours and information sessions. There are guides for informal visits and visitors may sit in on classes, if arranged in advance, and stay overnight at the school. To arrange for a visit, contact the Admissions Office at (508) 626-4500.

Financial Aid: In 1993-94 58% of all current freshmen and 30% of continuing students received some form of financial aid. About 57% of freshmen and 23% of continuing students received need-based aid. The average freshman award was $3686. Of that total, scholarships or need-based grants averaged $1175 ($2300 maximum); loans averaged $2038 ($2625 maximum); and work contracts averaged $806 ($1200 maximum). Forty percent of undergraduate students work part-time. Average earnings from campus work for the school year are $900. The average financial indebtedness of the 1992-93 graduate was $3750. The college is a member of CSS. The college's own financial statement and FAFSA are required. The deadline for financial aid applications is March 1.

International Students: There are currently 37 international students enrolled. They must take the TOEFL and achieve a minimum score of 550. The student must also take the SAT I.

Computers: The college provides computer facilities for student use. The mainframe is an ENCORE. The core of the campus network is a UNIX-based multiprocessor computer with 128 megabytes of memory and 10 gigabytes of disk storage. All computers on campus are networked and centrally maintained. Some 175 personal computers are provided by the various academic departments for specialized computing. All students may access the system. It may be used 24 hours a day, 7 days a week. There are no time limits on using the system and no fees.

Graduates: In 1992-93 669 bachelor's degrees were awarded. The most popular majors among graduates were psychology (13%), business and management (10%), and sociology (9%). Within an average freshman class, 45% graduate in 4 years, 50% in 5 years, and 55% in 6 years. Some 25 companies recruited on campus in 1992-93.

Admissions Contact: Dr. Philip M. Dooher, Dean of Admissions.

GORDON COLLEGE

Wenham, MA 01984 E-2

Full-time: 422 men, 729 women	(508) 927-2300; (800) 343-1379
Part-time: 22 men, 17 women	Faculty: 73; IIB, av$
Graduate: none	Ph.D.s: 85%
Year: semesters	Student/Faculty: 16 to 1
Application Deadline: April 15	Tuition: $12,720
Freshman Class: 674 applied, 565 accepted, 282 enrolled	Room & Board: $4070
SAT I Verbal/Math: 483/509	COMPETITIVE

Gordon College, founded in 1889, is an independent, Protestant college emphasizing a Christian approach to the liberal arts and sciences. In addition to regional accreditation, Gordon has baccalaureate program accreditation with CSWE and NASM. The library contains 232,585 volumes, 29,522 microform items, and 9234 audiovisual forms, and subscribes to 593 periodicals. Computerized library sources and services include the card catalog, interlibrary loans, and database searching. Special learning facilities include a learning resource center and art gallery. The 730-acre campus is in a small town 25 miles north of Boston. Including residence halls, there are 26 buildings on campus.

Student Life: About 68% of undergraduates are from out-of-state, mostly the Northeast. Students come from 38 states, 26 foreign countries, and Canada. Eighty-six percent are white. Most are Protestant. The average age of freshmen is 18.2; all undergraduates, 20.3. Thirteen percent drop out by the end of their first year; 66% remain to graduate.

Housing: A total of 1039 students can be accommodated in college housing. College-sponsored living facilities include single-sex dormitories and on-campus apartments. In addition there are special interest houses. On-campus housing is guaranteed for all 4 years. Eighty-seven percent of students live on campus; of those, 80% remain on campus on weekends. Alcohol is not permitted. All students may keep cars on campus.

Activities: There are no fraternities or sororities on campus. There are 35 groups on campus, including art, band, cheerleading, choir, chorus, computers, drama, ethnic, honors, international, jazz band, literary magazine, musical theater, newspaper, orchestra, photography, political, professional, religious, social, social service, student government, symphony, and yearbook. Popular campus events include Genesis Week, International Week, artists series, dances, and concerts.

Sports: There are 5 intercollegiate sports for men and 7 for women, and 19 intramural sports for men and 14 for women. Athletic and recreation facilities include a gymnasium, weight rooms, tennis courts, athletic fields, and a training room.

Disabled Students: Eighty-five percent of the campus is accessible to disabled students. The following facilities are available: wheelchair ramps, elevators, special parking, specially equipped rest rooms, special class scheduling, lowered drinking fountains, a wheelchair van, and electric doors.

Services: In addition to many counseling and information services, tutoring is available in some subjects, including mathematics, writing, and core science. Gordon also provides special advising, study skills help, support groups for some liberal arts core courses, walk-in help, and assistance finding volunteer note takers. In addition, there is remedial math, reading, and writing. There are writing and academic support centers.

Campus Safety and Security: Campus safety and security measures include 24-hour foot and vehicle patrol, escort service, informal discussions, and pamphlets, and films. In addition, there are emergency telephones and lighted pathways and sidewalks.

Programs of Study: Gordon awards the B.A., B.S., B.S.Ed., and B.Mu. degrees. Bachelor's degrees are awarded in BIOLOGICAL SCIENCE (biology), BUSINESS (accounting, business administration, and recreation and leisure services), COMMUNICATIONS AND THE ARTS (English, French, music, Spanish, and visual art), COMPUTER AND PHYSICAL SCIENCE (chemistry, computer science, mathematics, and physics), EDUCATION (early childhood, elementary, foreign languages, middle school, music, and special), SOCIAL SCIENCE (biblical studies, economics, history, international affairs, philosophy, physical fitness/movement, political studies, psychology, social work, sociology, and youth ministries). Social sciences, education, English, biblical studies, philosophy, and biology are the strongest academically. Business, English, psychology, and education have the largest enrollments.

Required: All students must complete the core curriculum, which consists of courses in the Old and New Testament, literature, philosophy, social and physical sciences, the arts, physical education, and foreign language. A total of 128 semester hours is required for graduation, 18 or more of which must be in the major. The minimum GPA for graduation is 2.0.

Special: Cooperative education and internships are promoted. There is a 3-2 engineering program with the University of Massachusetts at Lowell and a 2-2 program in allied health with the Thomas Jefferson College of Allied Health Science in Philadelphia. Cross-registration is possible with other institutions in the Northeastern Consortium of Colleges and Universities. A Washington semester, work-study, and student-designed majors are offered. Credit by examination, some limited credit for life/military/work experience, nondegree study, and pass/fail options are possible. In addition, there are off-campus study opportunities with the Christian College Consortium Visitor Program, the British Education Semester, the La Vida Wilderness Expedition, the Nova Scotia Student Exchange Program, and the Tropical Coastal Waters Program; and study abroad in England, France, Egypt, Russia, Costa Rica, Israel, and Kenya. There is a freshman honors program on campus, as well as 2 national honor societies.

Faculty/Classroom: Seventy-one percent of faculty are male; 29%, female. The average class size in an introductory lecture is 35; in a laboratory, 18; and in a regular course offering, 21.

Admissions: About 84% of the 1993-94 applicants were accepted. The SAT scores for the 1993-94 freshman class were as follows: Verbal—59% below 500, 29% between 500 and 599, 11% between 600 and 700, and 1% above 700; Math—42% below 500, 44% between 500 and 599, 12% between 600 and 700, and 2% above 700. About 44% of the current freshmen were in the top fifth of their class; 75% were in the top two fifths.

Requirements: The SAT I or ACT is required; the SAT I is preferred. In addition, applicants must graduate from an accredited secondary school or have a GED. Seventeen Carnegie units are required, including 4 English courses and 2 courses each in mathematics, science, and social studies. Foreign language is an elective that is preferred. An essay, a personal reference, and an interview are required. Music majors must audition. AP and CLEP credits are accepted. Important factors used in the admissions decision are personality, intangible qualities, advanced placement or honor courses, leadership record, evidence of special talent, and extracurricular activities record.

Procedure: Freshmen are admitted to all sessions. Entrance exams should be taken in spring of the junior year and/or fall of the senior year. Early decision applications should be filed by December 1; regular applications, by April 15 for fall entry and November 1 for spring entry, along with an application fee of $40. Notification of early decision is sent January 15; regular decision, on a rolling basis. There are early decision, early admissions, and deferred admissions plans. Fifty early decision candidates were accepted for the 1993-94 class.

Transfer: Some 77 transfer students enrolled in 1993-94. A minimum 2.5 GPA and an interview are required to transfer. College and high school transcripts (if the applicant has completed less than 1 year of full-time study), an essay, and SAT I or ACT scores are re-

quired; the SAT I is preferred. A total of 20 semster hours out of 128 must be completed at Gordon.

Visiting: There are regularly scheduled orientations for prospective students, consisting of 5 open-house programs (called Gordon Experience Days) throughout the fall, winter, and spring. There are guides for informal visits and visitors may sit in on classes and stay overnight at the school. To arrange for a visit, contact Karen Lovasco, Visitation Coordinator, at (800) 343-1379.

Financial Aid: In 1993-94 82% of all current freshmen and 83% of continuing students received some form of financial aid. About 84% of freshmen and 80% of continuing students received need-based aid. The average freshman award was $10,400. Of that total, scholarships or need-based grants averaged $4065 ($10,000 maximum); loans averaged $2500 ($4000 maximum); and work contracts averaged $1500 ($1700 maximum). Eighty-nine percent of undergraduate students work part-time. Average earnings from campus work for the school year are $1000. The average financial indebtedness of the 1992-93 graduate was $12,500. Gordon is a member of CSS. The FAF, the college's own financial statement, and the FAFSA are required. The deadline for financial aid applications is March 15.

International Students: There are currently 55 international students enrolled. They must take the TOEFL, or the SAT I or ACT.

Computers: The college provides computer facilities for student use. The mainframes are a DEC VAX 4000 and a DEC VAX 6420. There are also a number of Apple Macintosh and IBM microcomputers available in student laboratories and the computer center. Students enrolled in computer courses may access the mainframe. It may be used 24 hours a day, Monday through Saturday. There are no time limits on using the system and no fees.

Graduates: In 1992-93 266 bachelor's degrees were awarded. The most popular majors among graduates were education (19%), business administration (12%), and English (10%). Within an average freshman class, 52% graduate in 4 years and 14% in 5 years.

Admissions Contact: Pamela B. Lazarakis, Director of Admissions.

HAMPSHIRE COLLEGE
B-2

Amherst, MA 01002   (413) 582-5471

Full-time: 456 men, 623 women	Faculty: 91; IIB, +$
Part-time: none	Ph.D.s: 89%
Graduate: none	Student/Faculty: 12 to 1
Year: 4-1-4	Tuition: $20,160
Application Deadline: February 1	Room & Board: $5160
Freshman Class: 1195 applied, 1001 accepted, 309 enrolled	
SAT I or ACT: not required	**COMPETITIVE**

Hampshire College, founded in 1965, is a private college offering a liberal arts education with an emphasis on independent research, creative work, and multidisciplinary study. The library contains 111,000 volumes, 400 microform items, and 29,000 audiovisual forms and subscribes to 800 periodicals. Computerized library sources and services include the card catalog and interlibrary loans. Special learning facilities include an art gallery, TV station, multimedia center, farm center, music studio, dance studios, optics laboratory, electronics shop, integrated greenhouse and aquaculture facility, and performing arts center. The 800-acre campus is in a rural area 20 miles north of Springfield. Including residence halls, there are 28 buildings on campus.

Student Life: About 85% of undergraduates are from out-of-state, mostly the Middle Atlantic. Students come from 50 states, 21 foreign countries, and Canada. Seventy-one percent are from public schools; 29% from private. Eighty-one percent are white. The average age of freshmen is 18; all undergraduates, 20. Fourteen percent drop out by the end of their first year; 64% remain to graduate.

Housing: A total of 1100 students can be accommodated in college housing. College-sponsored living facilities include single-sex and coed dormitories and on-campus apartments. In addition there are special interest halls and special interest on-campus apartments. On-campus housing is guaranteed for all 4 years. Ninety-six percent of students live on campus. All students may keep cars on campus.

Activities: There are no fraternities or sororities on campus. There are 85 groups on campus, including art, chess, chorus, computers, dance, drama, ethnic, film, gay, international, literary magazine, marching band, musical theater, newspaper, orchestra, photography, political, radio and TV, religious, social, social service, and student government. Popular campus events include Southern Exposure, fall and spring artist series, Spring Jam, Black History Month, and Casino Night.

Sports: There are 22 intramural sports for men and 22 for women. Athletic and recreation facilities include two multipurpose sports centers housing a glass-enclosed swimming pool, a 12,000-square-foot playing floor, a 30-foot climbing wall, a weight lifting area, 4 indoor tennis courts, and a jogging track. Other facilities include soccer fields, 10 outdoor tennis courts, 2 softball diamonds, and a 2-mile nature trail.

Disabled Students: Ninety percent of the campus is accessible to disabled students. The following facilities are available: wheelchair ramps, elevators, special parking, specially equipped rest rooms, special class scheduling, and lowered drinking fountains.

Services: In addition to many counseling and information services, tutoring is available in most subjects. In addition, there is a reader service for the blind, advising center, writing and reading program, and laboratory quantitative skills program.

Campus Safety and Security: Campus safety and security measures include 24-hour foot and vehicle patrol, escort service, informal discussions, and pamphlets, posters, and films. In addition, there are lighted pathways and sidewalks, an EMT on-call program, and dormitory doors accessible by students only.

Programs of Study: Hampshire awards the B.A. degree. Bachelor's degrees are awarded in AGRICULTURE (agriculture and animal science), BIOLOGICAL SCIENCE (biology/biological science, botany, ecology, marine biology, and nutrition), COMMUNICATIONS AND THE ARTS (art history, communications, comparative literature, creative writing, dramatic arts, film arts, fine arts, journalism, linguistics, literature, music, and photography), COMPUTER AND PHYSICAL SCIENCE (chemistry, computer science, geology, mathematics, physics, and science), EDUCATION (education), ENGINEERING AND ENVIRONMENTAL DESIGN (environmental design), HEALTH PROFESSIONS (health science and premedical studies), SOCIAL SCIENCE (Black studies, American studies, anthropology, Asian studies, cognitive science, economics, family studies, history, humanities, international studies, Jewish studies, Middle Eastern studies, philosophy, political science/government, psychology, public affairs, sociology, and urban studies). Film/photography/video is the strongest academically. Social sciences has the largest enrollment.

Required: All students must complete 3 divisions of study. In Division I, Basic Studies, students work in each of Hampshire's 4 schools: Communications and Cognitive Science, Humanities and Arts, Natural Science, and Social Science. In Division II, the Concentration, they explore their field or fields of emphasis through individually designed internships or field studies. In Division III, Advanced Studies, students complete a major independent study project centered on a specific topic, question, or idea. Students must also include service to the college or the surrounding community and consider some aspect of their work from a non-Western perspective.

Special: Cross-registration is possible with colleges in the Five-College Consortium (Amherst College, the University of Massachusetts, Smith College, and Mount Holyoke). Internships, dual majors, and study abroad are offered. All majors are student-designed. Special programs and concentrations available include African studies, dance, international relations, Latin American studies, legal studies, peace studies, third world studies, and women's studies. Students may complete their programs in fewer than 4 years.

Faculty/Classroom: Fifty-seven percent of faculty are male; 43%, female. All both teach and do research. The average class size in a regular course offering is 20.

Admissions: About 84% of the 1993-94 applicants were accepted. There were 24 National Merit semifinalists. Three freshmen graduated first in their class.

Requirements: The SAT I or ACT is not required. Applicants must submit all transcripts from 9th grade on or GED/state equivalency exam results. Students are required to submit a personal statement and an analytic essay or academic paper. An interview is recommended. Important factors used in the admissions decision are personality, intangible qualities, evidence of special talent, extracurricular activities record, recommendations by school officials, and advanced placement or honor courses.

Procedure: Freshmen are admitted in the fall and spring. Early decision applications should be filed by November 15; regular applications, by February 1 for fall entry and November 15 for spring entry, along with an application fee of $40. Notification of early decision is sent December 16; regular decision, April 1. There are early decision, early admissions, and deferred admissions plans. About 43 early decision candidates were accepted for the 1993-94 class. A waiting list is an active part of the admissions procedure, with about 6% of applicants on the list.

Transfer: About 39 transfer students enrolled in 1993-94. A proposed program of study and college transcripts must be submitted.

Visiting: There are regularly scheduled orientations for prospective students, including interviews, information sessions, campus tours, open houses, and an overnight program. There are guides for informal visits and visitors may sit in on classes and stay overnight at the school. To arrange for a visit, contact the Admissions Office at (413) 582-5471.

Financial Aid: In 1993-94, 55% of all students received some form of financial aid, including need-based aid. The average freshman award was $17,905. Of that total, scholarships or need-based grants averaged $13,880 ($20,995 maximum); loans averaged $2625 (maximum); and work contracts averaged $1400 (maximum). Forty-four percent of undergraduate students work part-time. Average earn-

ings from campus work for the school year are $1500. The average financial indebtedness of the 1992–93 graduate was $12,500. Hampshire is a member of CSS. The FAF and the college's own financial statement are required. The deadline for financial aid applications is February 15.

International Students: There are currently 34 international students enrolled. The school actively recruits these students. They must take the TOEFL and achieve a minimum score of 577.

Computers: The college provides computer facilities for student use. The mainframe is a DEC VAX 11/750. Students may access the mainframe using terminals in the library or they may access it with their personal computers via modem. Microcomputers are available for use in the library, natural science, communications, and cognitive science buildings. There are 63 microcomputers available. All students may access the system. It may be used with the student's own personal computer 24 hours daily, otherwise during library hours. There are no time limits on using the system and no fees.

Graduates: In 1992–93 275 bachelor's degrees were awarded. The most popular majors among graduates were theater (7%), history (6%), and art (5%). Within an average freshman class, 11% graduate in 3 years, 86% in 4 years, 99% in 5 years, and 1% in 6 years. Some 5 companies recruited on campus in a recent year.

Admissions Contact: Audrey Y. Smith, Director of Admissions.

HARVARD UNIVERSITY
HARVARD AND RADCLIFFE COLLEGES
D-2
Cambridge, MA 02138 (617) 495–1551

Full-time: 4007 men, 2792 women	Faculty: 2167; I, + +$
Part-time: none	Ph.D.s: 100%
Graduate: 6287 men, 4624 women	Student/Faculty: 3 to 1
Year: semesters, summer session	Tuition: $18,745
Application Deadline: January 1	Room & Board: $6135
Freshman Class: 13,865 applied, 2165 accepted, 1606 enrolled	
SAT I or ACT: required	**MOST COMPETITIVE**

Harvard and Radcliffe Colleges are the undergraduate colleges of Harvard University. Founded in 1636, Harvard University also has 10 graduate schools. In addition to regional accreditation, Harvard/Radcliffe has baccalaureate program accreditation with ABET. The 97 libraries contain 13 million volumes and subscribe to 100,000 periodicals. Computerized library sources and services include the card catalog, interlibrary loans, and database searching. Special learning facilities include a learning resource center, art gallery, natural history museum, planetarium, and radio station. The 380-acre campus is in an urban area across the Charles River from Boston. Including residence halls, there are 400 buildings on campus.

Student Life: About 84% of undergraduates are from out-of-state, mostly the Middle Atlantic. Students come from 50 states, 94 foreign countries, and Canada. Sixty-five percent are from public schools; 35% from private. Fifty-four percent are white; 18% Asian American. The average age of freshman is 18. About 96% of freshmen remain to graduate.

Housing: A total of 6325 students can be accommodated in college housing. College-sponsored living facilities include coed dormitories and on-campus apartments. On-campus housing is guaranteed for all 4 years. Ninety-nine percent of students live on campus. All students may keep cars on campus.

Activities: There are no fraternities or sororities on campus. There are more than 200 groups and organizations on campus, including art, band, cheerleading, chess, choir, chorale, chorus, computers, dance, drama, ethnic, film, gay, honors, international, jazz band, literary magazine, marching band, musical theater, newspaper, opera, orchestra, pep band, photography, political, professional, radio and TV, religious, social, social service, student government, symphony, and yearbook. Popular campus events include Harvard/Yale football, Head of the Charles crew regatta, commencement, and the Cultural Rhythms Festival.

Sports: There are 21 intercollegiate sports for men and 19 for women, and 20 intramural sports for men and 14 for women. Athletic and recreation facilities include several gymnasiums and athletic centers, pools, a track, boat houses, a sailing center, a hockey rink, and various courts and playing fields.

Disabled Students: The following facilities are available: wheelchair ramps, elevators, special parking, specially equipped rest rooms, special class scheduling, lowered drinking fountains, lowered telephones, tutors, adaptive equipment in the field of information technology, TDD/TTY, shuttle van service, a student support organization called ABLE, and an adaptive technology laboratory.

Services: In addition to many counseling and information services, tutoring is available in every subject. There is also a reader service for the blind.

Campus Safety and Security: Campus safety and security measures include 24-hour foot and vehicle patrol, self-defense education, escort service, and shuttle buses. In addition, there are informal dis-

cussions, pamphlets, posters, and films, emergency telephones, and lighted pathways and sidewalks.

Programs of Study: Harvard/Radcliffe awards the A.B. and S.B. degrees. Master's degrees also are awarded. Bachelor's degrees are awarded in BIOLOGICAL SCIENCE (biochemistry, biology/biological science, and biophysics), COMMUNICATIONS AND THE ARTS (art history and appreciation, Chinese, classics, creative writing, English, fine arts, folklore and mythology, French, German, Greek, Hebrew, Italian, Japanese, Latin, linguistics, literature, music, Portuguese, Russian, and Spanish), COMPUTER AND PHYSICAL SCIENCE (applied mathematics, astronomy, chemistry, computer science, geology, geophysics and seismology, mathematics, physical sciences, physics, and statistics), ENGINEERING AND ENVIRONMENTAL DESIGN (engineering, environmental design, environmental sciences, and preengineering), SOCIAL SCIENCE (African American studies, American studies, anthropology, Asian/Oriental studies, economics, European studies, history, humanities, Middle Eastern studies, philosophy, political science/government, psychology, religion, Russian and Slavic studies, Sanskrit and Indian studies, social science, social studies, and sociology). History, English, government, mathematics, and chemistry have the largest enrollments.

Required: In 8 semesters, students must pass a minimum of 32 1-semester courses. The average course load is 4 courses per semester, but the course rate may be varied for special reasons. A typical balanced program devotes about one fourth of its courses to core curriculum requirements, one half to the concentration (or major field), and the remaining one fourth to electives.

Special: Undergraduates may cross-register at MIT and for certain courses in other schools of the university. Students may design their own concentrations or enroll for nondegree study. Study abroad may be arranged. A 3–2 engineering program and a combined A.B.-S.B. in engineering are offered. There are pass/fail options. There is a chapter of Phi Beta Kappa on campus. All departments have honors programs.

Faculty/Classroom: Eighty percent of faculty are male; 20%, female. Ninety-eight percent teach undergraduates, 97% do research, and 95% do both. No introductory courses are taught by graduate students. The average class size in a regular course offering is 25.

Admissions: About 16% of the 1993–94 applicants were accepted. About 98% of the current freshmen were in the top fifth of their class; 100% were in the top two fifths. There were 405 National Merit finalists. Some 487 freshmen graduated first in their class.

Requirements: The SAT I or ACT, and SAT II: Subject tests are required. Applicants need not be high school graduates but are expected to be well prepared academically. An essay and an interview are required, in addition to a transcript, counselor report, and 2 teacher recommendations from academic disciplines. AP credits are accepted. Important factors used in the admissions decision are recommendations by school officials, personality, intangible qualities, evidence of special talent, recommendations by alumni, and leadership record.

Procedure: Freshmen are admitted in the fall. Entrance exams should be taken by January of the senior year. Early action applications should be filed by November 1; regular applications, by January 1 for fall entry, along with an application fee of $60. Notification of early action is sent mid-December; regular action, early April. There is an early action plan. A waiting list is an active part of the admissions procedure.

Transfer: Some 120 transfer students enrolled in 1993–94. Transfer applicants must have completed at least 1 full year of daytime study in a degree-granting program at 1 institution. Students are required to submit the SAT I or ACT, 2 letters of recommendation, high school and college transcripts with a dean's report, and several essays. A total of 16 semester courses out of 32 must be completed at Harvard/Radcliffe.

Visiting: There are regularly scheduled orientations for prospective students, consisting of group information sessions and tours. There are guides for informal visits and visitors may sit in on classes and stay overnight at the school. To arrange for a visit, contact Undergraduate Admissions at (617) 495–1551.

Financial Aid: In 1993–94 79% of all current freshmen and 63% of continuing students received some form of financial aid. About 53% of freshmen and 47% of continuing students received need-based aid. The average freshman award was $18,382. Of that total, scholarships or need-based grants averaged $13,310 ($22,300 maximum); loans averaged $3363 ($3700 maximum); and work contracts averaged $1706 ($1900 maximum). Sixty-seven percent of undergraduate students work part-time. Average earnings from campus work for the school year are $1600. The average financial indebtedness of the 1992–93 graduate was $10,452. Harvard/Radcliffe is a member of CSS. The FAF, the college's own financial statement, federal tax forms, and the FAFSA are required. The deadline for financial aid applications is February 15.

International Students: There are currently 380 international students enrolled. The school actively recruits these students. They must take the TOEFL and achieve a minimum score of 600. The student

must also take the SAT I or the ACT. Students must take any 3 SAT II: Subject tests.

Computers: The college provides computer facilities for student use. All residences have Internet network access. There are also microcomputers available for use in the science center and all residence halls. All students may access the system. It may be used 24 hours per day. There are no time limits on using the system and no fees.

Graduates: In 1992–93 1675 bachelor's degrees were awarded. The most popular majors among graduates were economics (12%), government (12%), and English and American literature and languages (9%). Within an average freshman class, 96% graduate in 6 years. Some 269 companies recruited on campus in 1992–93. In the 1992 graduating class, 30% of all students were enrolled in graduate school within 6 months of graduation.

Admissions Contact: Dr. Marlyn McGrath Lewis, Director of Admissions.

HEBREW COLLEGE
D-2
Brookline, MA 02146   (617) 232–8710

Full-time: 8 men and women	Faculty: 4
Part-time: 17 men and women	Ph.D.s: 100%
Graduate: 90 men and women	Student/Faculty: 2 to 1
Year: semesters, summer session	Tuition: $4050
Application Deadline: open	Room & Board: n/app
Freshman Class: n/av	
SAT I or ACT: not required	**Less Competitive**

Hebrew College, founded in 1921, is a private, coeducational institution of Hebrew and Jewish studies providing undergraduate and graduate degrees in Judaic disciplines with an external liberal arts foundation. There are 2 graduate schools. The library contains 100,000 volumes, 2200 microform items, and 1000 audiovisual forms, and subscribes to 255 periodicals. Special learning facilities include an art gallery. The 4-acre campus is in a suburban area 2 miles west of Boston. There is one building on campus.

Student Life: About 99% of undergraduates are from Massachusetts. Students come from 3 states, 2 foreign countries, and Canada. All are white.

Housing: There are no residence halls. The college assists in finding nearby housing. All students commute. Alcohol is not permitted.

Activities: There are no fraternities or sororities on campus.

Sports: There is no sports program at the college.

Disabled Students: Seventy-five percent of the campus is accessible to disabled students.

Programs of Study: The college awards the B.H.L. and B.J.E. degrees. Master's degrees also are awarded.

Required: All students must complete a total of 120 credit hours, including 78 in Hebrew/Jewish studies, 12 electives, and 30 in liberal arts and sciences outside the colleges, and maintain a minimum 2.0 GPA.

Special: To fulfill the external liberal arts and sciences requirement, cross-registration is possible with Boston and Simmons colleges, Boston and Northeastern universities, and the University of Massachusetts. The college offers courses in Hebrew and English. There are continuing education courses, mini-courses, and 1-day institutes, and a teacher's diploma is offered.

Faculty/Classroom: No introductory courses are taught by graduate students.

Requirements: Entrance exams are not required. Admission criteria include the secondary school record and recommendations. Applicants must have a high school diploma or equivalent. A personal statement is required and an interview is encouraged.

Procedure: Freshmen are admitted to all sessions. Application deadlines are open. Notification is sent on a rolling basis.

Transfer: Courses in Hebrew and Jewish studies applicable to the college's curriculum are accepted for transfer credit. At least 54 credits out of 120 must be completed at the college.

Visiting: There are guides for informal visits and visitors may sit in on classes. To arrange for a visit, contact Norma Frankel at (617) 232–8710.

Financial Aid: The college is a member of CSS. The college's own financial statement is required.

International Students: There are currently 6 international students enrolled. They must take the TOEFL and achieve a minimum score of 550.

Computers: There are no time limits on using the system and no fees.

Admissions Contact: Norma Frankel, Registrar.

HELLENIC COLLEGE
HOLY CROSS GREEK ORTHODOX SCHOOL OF THEOLOGY
D-2
Brookline, MA 02146   (617) 731–3500, ext. 260

Full-time: 43 men, 22 women	Faculty: 14
Part-time: 2 men, 2 women	Ph.D.s: 100%
Graduate: 103 men and women	Student/Faculty: 5 to 1
Year: semesters	Tuition: $6115
Application Deadline: open	Room & Board: $4180
Freshman Class: n/av	
SAT I: required	**NONCOMPETITIVE**

Hellenic College, founded in 1937, is a private coeducational college affiliated with the Greek Orthodox Church. It offers programs in the classics, elementary education, religious studies, and human development. There is one graduate school. The library contains 102,100 volumes and 1934 microform items, and subscribes to 9756 periodicals. Computerized library sources and services include database searching. Special learning facilities include a Greek cultural center and a language laboratory. The 52-acre campus is in an urban area 4 miles southwest of Boston. Including residence halls, there are 7 buildings on campus.

Student Life: About 54% of undergraduates are from out-of-state, mostly the Midwest. Students come from 15 states, 4 foreign countries, and Canada. Ninety-seven percent are white. Most are Greek or Eastern Orthodox. The average age of freshmen is 22. Three percent drop out by the end of their first year; 93% remain to graduate.

Housing: A total of 220 students can be accommodated in college housing. College-sponsored living facilities include single-sex dormitories, on-campus apartments, and married-student housing. On-campus housing is guaranteed for all 4 years. Seventy-nine percent of students live on campus. All students may keep cars on campus.

Activities: There are no fraternities or sororities on campus. There are 9 groups on campus, including choir, ethnic, photography, religious, social, social service, student government, and yearbook. Popular campus events include Feast of the Holy Cross, Matriculation Day, Christmas Retreat, Lent, Holy Week, Annual College vs. School of Theology football game, Campus Christmas Party, and Easter dinner.

Sports: There are 4 intramural sports for men and 3 for women. Athletic and recreation facilities include a gymnasium, tennis courts, racquetball courts, and a football field.

Disabled Students: Ten percent of the campus is accessible to disabled students. The following facilities are available: wheelchair ramps and special parking.

Services: In addition to many counseling and information services, tutoring is available in some subjects, including Greek and music writing and composition. There is also remedial math, reading, and writing.

Campus Safety and Security: Campus safety and security measures include informal discussions, pamphlets, posters, and films, lighted pathways and sidewalks, and a 16-hour security patrol.

Programs of Study: The school awards the B.A. degree. Master's degrees also are awarded. Bachelor's degrees are awarded in COMMUNICATIONS AND THE ARTS (classics and Greek), EDUCATION (elementary), SOCIAL SCIENCE (religious studies). Religious studies is the strongest academically.

Required: To graduate, students must complete 128 credits, with 39 in the major, and maintain a minimum overall GPA of 2.0. General education requirements include 72 credits, with courses in English language and literature, music, history, science, philosophy, and social science.

Special: The college offers cross-registration with Boston Theological Institute and credit by examination.

Faculty/Classroom: Seventy-six percent of faculty are male; 24%, female. No introductory courses are taught by graduate students. The average class size in an introductory lecture is 75; in a laboratory, 20; and in a regular course offering, 22.

Requirements: The SAT I is required. Applicants should graduate from an accredited secondary school or have a GED. Fifteen academic credits are required, including 4 units of English, 2 each of mathematics, foreign language, and social studies, and 1 of science. An essay is required. AP and CLEP credits are accepted. Important factors used in the admissions decision are recommendations by school officials, recommendations by alumni, advanced placement or honor courses, parents or siblings attending the school, and leadership record.

Procedure: Freshmen are admitted to all sessions. Application deadlines are open. The application fee is $25. Notification is sent on a rolling basis. There is a deferred admissions plan.

Visiting: There are regularly scheduled orientations for prospective students, including observation of classroom and student life. There are guides for informal visits and visitors may sit in on classes and stay

overnight at the school. To arrange for a visit, contact Colette Chickris, Office of Admissions, at (617) 731-3500, ext. 260.

Financial Aid: In a recent year, 72% of all freshmen received some form of financial aid. About 33% of freshmen received need-based aid. The FAF and FAFSA are required. The deadline for financial aid applications is May 1.

International Students: There are currently 19 international students enrolled. They must take the TOEFL and the SAT I.

Computers: The mainframe is a 9404 AS/400 IBM Model C20.

Graduates: In a recent year, 12 bachelor's degrees were awarded.

Admissions Contact: Stephanie Skedros, Assistant Director of Admissions.

HOLY CROSS
(See College of the Holy Cross)

LESLEY COLLEGE
Cambridge, MA 02138-2790

D-2

(617) 349-8800
(800) 541-8486 (out-of-state)

Full-time: 477 women	Faculty: 39
Part-time: 19 women	Ph.D.s: 59%
Graduate: 1100 men, 4276 women	Student/Faculty: 12 to 1
Year: semesters, summer session	Tuition: $11,820
Application Deadline: April 1	Room & Board: $5300

Freshman Class: 244 applied, 198 accepted, 82 enrolled
SAT I Verbal/Math: 410/410

LESS COMPETITIVE

Lesley College, founded in 1909, is a private women's institution offering undergraduate programs in education, human services, liberal arts, and management. Nontraditional/alternative instructional delivery is offered in the graduate school and the School of Management, which are coeducational. There are 2 graduate schools. The library contains 87,600 volumes, 690,261 microform items, and 1382 audiovisual forms, and subscribes to 950 periodicals. Computerized library sources and services include the card catalog, interlibrary loans, and database searching. Special learning facilities include a learning resource center and the Kresge Center for Teaching Resources. The 5-acre campus is in an urban area 3 miles northwest of Boston. Including residence halls, there are 45 buildings on campus.

Student Life: About 60% of undergraduates are from Massachusetts. Students come from 30 states, 5 foreign countries, and Canada. Seventy are from public schools; 30% from private. Some 78% are white. The average age of freshmen is 18. Twenty-four percent drop out by the end of their first year; 60% remain to graduate.

Housing: A total of 432 students can be accommodated in college housing. College-sponsored living facilities include dormitories. In addition, there are special interest houses, an England exchange program house, and a community service house. On-campus housing is guaranteed for all 4 years. Sixty-seven percent of students live on campus.

Activities: There are no fraternities or sororities on campus. There are a number of groups on campus, including choir, chorus, drama, ethnic, gay, international, literary magazine, professional, religious, social, social service, student government, and yearbook. Popular campus events include Women's History Month, Intercultural Activity weeks, Black History Month, and Family and Friends Weekend.

Sports: There are 5 intercollegiate sports and 1 intramural sport. Athletic and recreation facilities include a gymnasium; a fitness center with Nautilus circuit, free weights, and cardiovascular equipment; and outdoor tennis courts. Students may also use an Olympic-size swimming pool at a nearby school and local playing field facilities.

Disabled Students: Eighty percent of the campus is accessible to disabled students. The following facilities are available: wheelchair ramps, elevators, special parking, specially equipped rest rooms, special class scheduling, and lowered drinking fountains.

Services: In addition to many counseling and information services, tutoring is available in most subjects. Other services include remedial math, reading, and writing and study skills.

Campus Safety and Security: Campus safety and security measures include 24-hour foot and vehicle patrol, self-defense education, escort service, and informal discussions. In addition, there are pamphlets, posters, films, emergency telephones, and lighted pathways and sidewalks.

Programs of Study: Lesley awards the B.S. and B.S.Ed. degrees. Associate, master's, and doctoral degrees also are awarded. Bachelor's degrees are awarded in BUSINESS (management science), EDUCATION (early childhood, elementary, middle school, and special), SOCIAL SCIENCE (human services and liberal arts/general studies). Education has the largest enrollment.

Required: In order to graduate, all students must complete general education requirements, including cross-cultural components in writing, critical and quantitive reasoning, multicultural and global perspectives, and leadership and ethics, plus 52 credits of distribution re-

quirements. Students need 128 total credit hours, with at least 30 hours in the major and a minimum 2.0 GPA.

Special: Cross-registration with Harvard University Extension, internships, study abroad in England, a Washington Justice semester, and on-campus work-study programs are offered. Accelerated and weekend course programs are offered for adult baccalaureate students.

Faculty/Classroom: Thirty percent of faculty are male; 70%, female. All teach undergraduates and also do research. No introductory courses are taught by graduate students.

Admissions: About 81% of the 1993-94 applicants were accepted. About 16% of the current freshmen were in the top fifth of their class; 48% were in the top two fifths.

Requirements: The SAT I or ACT is required. Applicants must be graduates of an accredited secondary school or have a GED certificate. Students must have completed 15 academic units, including 4 in English, 2 each in mathematics and foreign language, and 1 each in history and laboratory science. A writing sample is required; an interview is recommended. Three recommendations are required, including 1 personal, 1 academic, and 1 from a guidance counselor. AP and CLEP credits are accepted. Important factors used in the admissions decision are recommendations by school officials, advanced placement or honor courses, extracurricular activities record, leadership record, and personality and intangible qualities.

Procedure: Freshmen are admitted fall and spring. Entrance exams should be taken by November. There are early decision and deferred admissions plans. Early decision applications should be filed by December 1; regular applications, by April 1 for fall entry and December 15 for spring entry, along with an application fee of $35. Notification of early decision is sent December 15; regular decision, on a rolling basis. About 12 early decision candidates were accepted for the 1993-94 class.

Transfer: About 50 transfer students enrolled in a recent year. Transfer students must have at least 12 credit hours earned and a minimum 2.0 GPA. An interview is recommended. A total of 63 credits out of 128 must be completed at Lesley.

Visiting: There are regularly scheduled orientations for prospective students, including personal interviews with professional staff and student campus tours. There are guides for informal visits and visitors may sit in on classes and stay overnight at the school. To arrange for a visit, contact Valerie Brown at (617) 349-8800.

Financial Aid: In 1993-94, 87% of all current freshmen and 86% of continuing students received some form of financial aid. About 86% of freshmen and 57% of continuing students received need-based aid. The average freshman award was $10,062. Of that total, scholarships or need-based grants averaged $7382 ($13,000 maximum); loans averaged $3958 ($5500 maximum); and work contracts averaged $1194 ($1800 maximum). Forty-five percent of undergraduate students work part-time. Average earnings from campus work for the school year are $1700. The average financial indebtedness of the 1992-93 graduate was $16,000. Lesley is a member of CSS. The college's own financial statement, the FAFSA, and the state scholarship/grant form are required. The deadline for financial aid applications is March 15.

International Students: There are currently 47 international students enrolled. The school actively recruits these students. They must take the TOEFL and achieve a minimum score of 500, or 550 for the School of Management. The student must also take the SAT I or the ACT.

Computers: The college provides computer facilities for student use. The mainframe is a Prime. Over 120 microcomputers are available for use in the microcomputer center, computer laboratories, the learning center, the library, classrooms, and some dormitories. The library is part of an on-line Internet network and OCLC. There is a 24-hour work processing center. All students may access the system. It may be used during library hours primarily; the word processing center is available 24 hours a day. There are no time limits on using the system and no fees.

Graduates: The most popular majors among graduates were education (60%), human services (30%), and management (10%). Within an average freshman class, 60% graduate in 5 years. Some 63 companies recruited on campus in 1992-93. In the 1992 graduating class, 12% of graduates were enrolled in graduate school within 6 months of graduation; 90% had found employment.

Admissions Contact: Jane A. Raley, Director of Undergraduate School Admissions.

MASSACHUSETTS BOARD OF REGENTS OF HIGHER EDUCATION

The Massachusetts Board of Regents of Higher Education, established in 1980, is a public system in Massachusetts. It is governed by a 16-member board of regents appointed by the governor, whose chief administrator is the chancellor. The system is the central governing authority for the state's public higher education system. The total enrollment of all 29 campuses is approximately 170,000. Profiles of the

4-year campuses, located in Amherst, Buzzard's Bay, Bridgewater, Fitchburg, Farmingham, North Salem, North Dartmouth, Westfield, and Worcester, are included in this chapter order with other Massachusetts schools.

MASSACHUSETTS COLLEGE OF ART
E-2

Boston, MA 02115   (617) 232-1555

Full-time: 430 men, 603 women	Faculty: 66; IIB, av$
Part-time: 27 men, 68 women	Ph.Ds: 66%
Graduate: 30 men, 51 women	Student/Faculty: 16 to 1
Year: semesters, summer session	Tuition: $3940 ($8897)
Application Deadline: April 1	Room & Board: $5507
Freshman Class: 881 applied, 473 accepted, 261 enrolled	
SAT I Verbal/Math: 467/470	SPECIAL

Massachusetts College of Art, founded in 1873, is a public, coeducational institution offering undergraduate and graduate programs in art, design, and education. In addition to regional accreditation, MassArt has baccalaureate program accreditation with NASAD. The library contains 95,000 volumes, 65,000 microform items, and 1165 audiovisual forms, and subscribes to 400 periodicals. Computerized library sources and services include the card catalog and interlibrary loans. Special learning facilities include an art gallery and a computer arts learning center. The 5-acre campus is in an urban area in Boston. Including residence halls, there are 7 buildings on campus.

Student Life: About 85% of undergraduates are from Massachusetts. Students come from 24 states, 29 foreign countries, and Canada. Eighty-five percent are from public schools; 15% from private. Eighty-one percent are white. The average age of freshmen is 22; all undergraduates, 26. Fifteen percent drop out by the end of their first year.

Housing: A total of 252 students can be accommodated in college housing. College-sponsored living facilities include coed dormitories. In addition, Smith Hall was renovated specifically as a visual art college residence hall with ventilated workrooms, a visiting artist suite, and gallery space. On-campus housing is guaranteed for the freshman year only, is available on a first-come, first-served basis, and is available on a lottery system for upperclassmen. Priority is given to out-of-town students. Seventy-nine percent of students commute. All students not living in dormitories may keep cars on campus.

Activities: There are no fraternities or sororities on campus. There are more than 30 groups on campus, including art, computers, ethnic, film, gay, international, literary magazine, newspaper, photography, political, professional, radio and TV, social, social service, student government, and yearbook. Popular campus events include Eventsworks, Black History Month, First Night Ice Sculpture, fashion shows, annual art sales, gallery exhibitions and openings, visiting artist lectures, and overnight trips for special workshops and events.

Sports: There are 7 intercollegiate sports for men and 6 for women, and 8 intramural sports for men and 6 for women. Athletic and recreation facilities include a gymnasium, a wrestling room, a fitness center, and courts for squash, volleyball, and basketball.

Disabled Students: Ninety-five percent of the campus is accessible to disabled students. The following facilities are available: wheelchair ramps, elevators, special parking, specially equipped rest rooms, special class scheduling, lowered drinking fountains, and lowered telephones.

Services: There is remedial reading and writing.

Campus Safety and Security: Campus safety and security measures include 24-hour foot and vehicle patrol, self defense education, escort service, and shuttle buses. In addition, there are informal discussions, pamphlets, posters, and films, emergency telephones, and lighted pathways and sidewalks.

Programs of Study: MassArt awards the B.F.A. degree. Master's degrees also are awarded. Bachelor's degrees are awarded in COMMUNICATIONS AND THE ARTS (art history and appreciation, design, film arts, fine arts, industrial design, photography, and studio art), EDUCATION (art), ENGINEERING AND ENVIRONMENTAL DESIGN (architecture), SOCIAL SCIENCE (fashion design and technology). Painting, illustration, and graphic design have the largest enrollments.

Required: A total of 132 semester credits is required for graduation; the minimum GPA varies by major. Typically, students take 45 credits in liberal arts, 18 in studio foundation, 39 in the major, and 30 in electives. Beginning in the sophomore year, the student's work is reviewed by panels of faculty and visiting artists.

Special: MassArt offers cross-registration with several consortiums, internships for advanced students, on- and off-campus work-study programs, study-abroad and foreign-exchange programs for undergraduate and graduate students, an open major for exceptional, directed students, and dual majors in any combination of concentrations.

Faculty/Classroom: Fifty-two percent of faculty are male; 48%, female. All teach undergraduates. No introductory courses are taught by graduate students. The average class size in an introductory lecture is 23; in a laboratory, 12; and in a regular course offering, 14.

Admissions: About 54% of the 1993-94 applicants were accepted. About 31% of the current freshmen were in the top fifth of their class; 58% were in the top two fifths. There was 1 National Merit finalist and 6 semifinalists. About 2 freshmen graduated first in their class.

Requirements: The SAT I is required. In addition, applicants should be graduates of an accredited secondary school or have earned the GED. College-preparatory studies should include 4 years of English, 3 of mathematics, 2 each of social studies, science, and a foreign language, plus 3 academic electives. A personal essay and portfolio are required, and an interview and letters of reference are recommended. AP and CLEP credits are accepted. Important factors used in the admissions decision are evidence of special talent, recommendations by school officials, advanced placement or honor courses, personality, intangible qualities, and extracurricular activities record.

Procedure: Freshmen are admitted in the fall. Entrance exams should be taken in the early fall of the senior year. Early decision applications should be filed by November 1; regular applications, by April 1 for fall entry and November 1 for spring entry, along with an application fee of $10 ($40 for out-of-state students). Notification of early decision is sent December 20; regular decision, on a rolling basis from February through May. There are early decision and deferred admissions plans. A waiting list is an active part of the admissions procedure, with about 10% of applicants on the list.

Transfer: About 178 transfer students enrolled in 1993-94. Applicants must submit secondary school and postsecondary school transcripts, a statement of purpose, and a portfolio of at least 15 pieces, preferably in slides. An interview is recommended. A total of 66 semester credits out of 132 must be completed at MassArt.

Visiting: There are regularly scheduled orientations for prospective students, including an information session and a campus tour. There are guides for informal visits, and visitors may sit in on classes. To arrange for a visit, contact the Admissions Office at (617) 232-1555, ext. 235, 236, or 238.

Financial Aid: In 1993-94 38% of all current freshmen and 55% of continuing students received some form of financial aid. About 37% of freshmen and 52% of continuing students received need-based aid. Eighty-four percent of undergraduate students work part-time. Average earnings from campus work for the school year are $800. The average financial indebtedness of the 1992-93 graduate was $14,000. MassArt is a member of CSS. The FAF, FFS, or SFS and the FAFSA are required. The priority date for financial aid applications is May 1.

International Students: There are currently 74 international students enrolled. They must take the TOEFL and achieve a minimum score of 550.

Computers: The college provides computer facilities for student use. MassArt provides Amiga, Apple, Apple Macintosh, IBM, and NEC microcomputers for academic use. They are located in the computer center (CALC). The word-processing system is available to all students. The design/art systems are available to students registered for computer courses or computer access. There are no time limits on using the system. The fees are $100 per semester for students not enrolled in computer courses.

Graduates: The most popular majors among graduates were design (graphic, illustration, architectural (38%), painting (24%), and photography (15%). Some 35 companies recruited on campus in 1992-93. In the 1992 graduating class, 5% of all students were enrolled in graduate school within 6 months of graduation; 73% of all graduates had found employment.

Admissions Contact: Kay Ransdell, Associate Dean for Admissions and Retention.

MASSACHUSETTS COLLEGE OF PHARMACY AND ALLIED HEALTH SCIENCES
E-2

Boston, MA 02115   (617) 732-2850; (800) 225-5506 (out-of-state)

Full-time: 446 men, 685 women	Faculty: n/av
Part-time: 89 men, 167 women	Ph.Ds: n/av
Graduate: 23 men, 26 women	Student/Faculty: n/av
Year: quarters, summer session	Tuition: $11,632
Application Deadline: March 1	Room & Board: $6720
Freshman Class: 393 applied, 321 accepted, 116 enrolled	
SAT I or ACT: required	COMPETITIVE

The Massachusetts College of Pharmacy and Allied Health Sciences, established in 1823, is a private independent institution offering undergraduate and graduate programs in chemistry, pharmacy, nursing, and allied health sciences. In addition to regional accreditation, the college has baccalaureate program accreditation with ACPE, CAHEA, and NLN. The library contains 70,000 volumes, and subscribes to 800 periodicals. Computerized library sources and services include the card catalog, interlibrary loans, and database searching. Special learning facilities include a learning resource center and a radio station. The 2-acre campus is in an urban area 1 mile from Boston's center. There are 2 buildings on campus.

Student Life: About 60% of undergraduates are from Massachusetts. The average age of freshmen is 18; all undergraduates, 21. Twenty-one percent drop out by the end of their first year; 75% remain to graduate.

Housing: There are no residence halls.

Activities: There are 9 groups on campus, including drama, ethnic, international, newspaper, professional, student government, and yearbook.

Sports: There are 4 intercollegiate sports each for men and women, and 2 intramural sports each for men and women.

Disabled Students: Ninety percent of the campus is accessible to disabled students. The following facilities are available: wheelchair ramps, elevators, special parking, specially equipped rest rooms, and lowered drinking fountains.

Services: In addition to some personal counseling services, tutoring is provided free of charge.

Programs of Study: The college awards the B.S., B.S.Ch., B.S.H., B.S.N., B.S.Nuc.T., B.S.P., and B.S.Rad.Tech. degrees. Associate, master's, and doctoral degrees also are awarded. Bachelor's degrees are awarded in COMPUTER AND PHYSICAL SCIENCE (chemistry and radiological technology), HEALTH PROFESSIONS (allied health, nuclear medical technology, nursing, pharmacy, and premedicine), SOCIAL SCIENCE (psychology).

Required: Graduation requirements vary by program. Students must complete course work in expository writing, history and politics, psychology, sociology, interpersonal communications in the health professions, evolution of the health professions, biomedical ethics, and humanities. Quarter hours required for graduation range from 190 to 274 depending on the degree. Students must maintain a minimum quality point average of 2.0.

Special: Cross-registration for students interested in ROTC is offered at Northeastern University. Cooperative programs are available with Simmons College and Western New England College. The college offers an externship program in radiopharmacy in conjunction with Massachusetts General Hospital. Internships and work-study are possible. There are 2 national honor societies on campus.

Admissions: Eighty-two percent of the 1993–94 applicants were accepted.

Requirements: The college requires applicants to be in the upper 35% of their class. A minimum GPA of 3.0 is required. The SAT I or ACT is required. In addition, applicants must graduate from an accredited secondary school with 16 units, including 4 of English, 3 of mathematics, and 2 of laboratory science. The college additionally advises advanced chemistry or physics with laboratory and an extra unit of mathematics. Interviews are recommended. AP and CLEP credits are accepted.

Procedure: Early decision applications should be filed by November 1; regular applications, by March 1 for fall entry, along with an application fee of $25. Notification is sent on a rolling basis. There are early decision, early admissions, and deferred admissions plans.

Transfer: Transfer applicants must have a minimum GPA of 2.0. Those with 1 year or less of college must submit secondary school transcripts.

Visiting: There are regularly scheduled orientations for prospective students. To arrange for a visit, contact the Admissions Office at (617) 732–2850 or (800) 225–5506 (out-of-state).

Financial Aid: The FAF, the college's own financial statement, the CSS Needs Analysis Form, and the parents' and students' most recent federal tax form are required. The deadline for financial aid applications is April 1.

International Students: International students must take the TOEFL or the college's own test.

Computers: The college provides IBM and Leading Edge PCs for academic use by all students. They are available in the library and the laboratory and research facility.

Admissions Contact: Joan Monahan, Director of Admission and Registrar.

MASSACHUSETTS INSTITUTE OF TECHNOLOGY
D-2

Cambridge, MA 02139   (617) 253–4791

Full-time: 2962 men, 1519 women	Faculty: 953; I, + +$
Part-time: 19 men, 9 women	Ph.D.s: 99%
Graduate: 4052 men, 1229 women	Student/Faculty: 5 to 1
Year: 4–1–4	Tuition: $19,000
Application Deadline: January 1	Room & Board: $5800
Freshman Class: 6411 applied, 2140 accepted, 1081 enrolled	
SAT I or ACT: required	**MOST COMPETITIVE**

Massachusetts Institute of Technology, founded in 1861, is a private coeducational institution offering programs in architecture and planning, engineering, humanities and social science, science, health sciences, technology, and management. There are 6 undergraduate and 6 graduate schools. In addition to regional accreditation, MIT has baccalaureate program accreditation with AACSB, ABET, and NAAB. The 5 libraries contain 2,320,524 volumes, 1,969,869 microform items, and 529,231 audiovisual forms, and subscribe to 21,136 periodicals. Computerized library sources and services include the card catalog, interlibrary loans, and database searching. Special learning facilities include an art gallery, radio station, and TV station. The 146-acre campus is in an urban area 1 mile north of Boston. Including residence halls, there are 149 buildings on campus.

Student Life: About 92% of undergraduates are from out-of-state, mostly the Middle Atlantic. Students come from 50 states, 78 foreign countries, and Canada. Eighty percent are from public schools; 8% from private. Fifty percent are white; 27% Asian American. The average age of freshmen is 18; all undergraduates, 20. Two percent drop out by the end of their first year; 90% remain to graduate.

Housing: A total of 4148 students can be accommodated in college housing. College-sponsored living facilities include single-sex and coed dormitories, on-campus apartments, married-student housing, fraternity houses, and sorority houses. In addition there are language houses, special interest houses, coed fraternity houses, a cooperative house, and off-campus independent living groups, including one for women. On-campus housing is guaranteed for all 4 years. Ninety-three percent of students live on- and off-campus in institute-approved housing. Upperclassmen may keep cars on campus.

Activities: About 46% of men belong to 2 local and 28 national fraternities; about 30% of women belong to 1 local and 4 national sororities. There are 200 groups on campus, including art, band, cheerleading, chess, choir, chorale, chorus, computers, dance, drama, ethnic, film, gay, honors, international, jazz band, literary magazine, marching band, musical theater, newspaper, orchestra, photography, political, professional, radio and TV, religious, social, social service, student government, symphony, and yearbook. Popular campus events include Greek Week, Campus Preview Weekend, Spring Weekend, and 2.70 Contest.

Sports: There are 24 intercollegiate sports for men and 15 for women, and 15 intramural sports for men and 16 for women. Athletic and recreation facilities include an athletic center with indoor track, ice rink, and indoor swimming pool; a sailing pavilion and boat house; tennis courts; and softball diamonds.

Disabled Students: The following facilities are available: wheelchair ramps, elevators, special parking, specially equipped rest rooms, special class scheduling, lowered drinking fountains, lowered telephones, wheelchair lifts, and automatic doors.

Services: In addition to many counseling and information services, tutoring is available in every subject.

Campus Safety and Security: Campus safety and security measures include 24-hour foot and vehicle patrol, self-defense education, escort service, and shuttle buses. In addition, there are informal discussions, pamphlets, posters, films, emergency telephones, lighted pathways and sidewalks.

Programs of Study: MIT awards the B.S. degree. Master's and doctoral degrees also are awarded. Bachelor's degrees are awarded in BIOLOGICAL SCIENCE (biology/biological science), BUSINESS (business administration and management), COMMUNICATIONS AND THE ARTS (art and design, creative writing, French, literature, music, and Spanish), COMPUTER AND PHYSICAL SCIENCE (atmospheric sciences and meteorology, chemistry, computer science, earth science, mathematics, physics, planetary and space science, and science, technology, and society), ENGINEERING AND ENVIRONMENTAL DESIGN (aeronautical engineering, architecture, biomedical engineering, chemical engineering, civil engineering, computer engineering, electrical/electronics engineering, environmental science, materials engineering, mechanical engineering, naval architecture and marine engineering, nuclear engineering, and ocean engineering), SOCIAL SCIENCE (anthropology, cognitive science, economics, history, humanities, philosophy, political science/government, and urban studies). Architecture, management, science, engineering, and the departments of political science, economics, and linguistics are the strongest academically. Engineering has the largest enrollment.

Required: The General Institute Requirements (GIR) consist of a science requirement (1 term of chemistry, 1 term of biology, and 2 terms each of physics and calculus); a humanities, arts, and social sciences requirement consisting of 8 term subjects (of at least 9 units each) in the humanities, arts, and social sciences (3 of the 8 subjects must be chosen from a specially designated list of distribution subjects); a 2-subject Restricted Electives in Science and Technology requirement; and a laboratory requirement consisting of 1 subject of 12 units or 2 subjects of 6 units of laboratory credit. In addition, students must complete 2 phases of the writing requirement and 8 points of physical education credit (4 activities). To graduate, a student must either pass the swimming test or successfully complete a beginning swimming class. As specified for each course of study, 180 to 198 units in the student's departmental program are required beyond the GIR's for graduation, as is a minimum 3.0 GPA on a 5.0 scale.

Special: MIT offers cross-registration with Wellesley and Harvard, co-operative programs, engineering internships, junior year abroad, work-study programs, accelerated degree programs, dual majors in all fields, student-designed majors, and a 5-year joint bachelor's and master's degree in engineering through the Department of Electrical Engineering and Computer Science. A general studies degree, credit by examination, and pass/fail options are possible. Alternative programs are available to a limited number of freshmen, providing for smaller academic communities within MIT. There are 7 national honor societies on campus, including Phi Beta Kappa. Five departments have honors programs.

Faculty/Classroom: Eighty-nine percent of faculty are male; 11%, female. All both undergraduates and do research. No introductory courses are taught by graduate students.

Admissions: About 33% of the 1993–94 applicants were accepted. The SAT scores for the 1993–94 freshman class were as follows: Math—1% between 500 and 599, 14% between 600 and 700, and 83% above 700. The ACT scores were 8% between 21 and 25, 19% between 26 and 29, and 72% 30 and above. About 99% of the current freshmen were in the top fifth of their class; all were in the top two fifths. Some 241 freshmen graduated first in their class.

Requirements: The SAT I or ACT is required, as are 3 SAT II: Subject tests, including mathematics, science, and English or history. Fourteen academic units are recommended, including 4 credits of English and mathematics, 3 of laboratory science, 2 of social studies, and 1 of foreign language. The GED is accepted. An essay and interview are required. AP credits are accepted. Important factors used in the admissions decision are advanced placement or honor courses, recommendations by school officials, extracurricular activities record, evidence of special talent, and leadership record.

Procedure: Freshmen are admitted in the fall. Entrance exams should be taken by January of the senior year. Early decision applications should be filed by November 1; regular applications, by January 1 for fall entry, along with an application fee of $50. Notification of early decision is sent late December; regular decision, early April. There are early decision, early admissions, and deferred admissions plans. A waiting list is an active part of the admissions procedure, with about 6% of applicants on the list.

Transfer: Some 28 transfer students enrolled in 1993–94. Transfers must have a B average and submit transcripts and results of 3 SAT II: Subject tests, including mathematics, science, and English or history. They may apply after completing at least 1 year at another college, but not after more than 2 1/2 years.

Visiting: There are regularly scheduled orientations for prospective students, including tours, Monday to Friday, 10 A.M. or 2 P.M., followed by an information session with an admissions officer. There are guides for informal visits and visitors may sit in on classes and stay overnight at the school. To arrange for a visit, contact Robin Dey at (617) 258–5515.

Financial Aid: In 1993–94 62% of all current freshmen and 55% of continuing students received some form of financial aid. About 62% of freshmen and 55% of continuing students received need-based aid. The average freshman award was $17,770. Of that total, scholarships or need-based grants averaged $11,670 ($27,050 maximum); loans averaged $4450 ($26,350 maximum); and work contracts averaged $1650 (maximum). Fifty-five percent of undergraduate students work part-time. Average earnings from campus work for the school year are $1490. The average financial indebtedness of the 1992–93 graduate was $14,119. MIT is a member of CSS. The FAF, the college's own financial statement, FAFSA, and tax returns are required. The priority filing date for MIT's financial application is January 14; the deadline for FAF and FAFSA forms is March 1.

International Students: There are currently 373 international students enrolled. The student must take the SAT I or ACT. If the applicant's native language is not English, the TOEFL, minimum score 570, or 2 SAT II: Subject tests, 1 mathematics and 1 science, may be substituted.

Computers: The college provides computer facilities for student use. The mainframes are an IBM 3090 and a Cray X-MP, as well as UNIX and other workstations, including Digital, Sun, IBM, Silicon Graphics, and HP machines. An Athena computing environment provides approximately 600 public workstations distributed across campus. Specialized departmental computing facilities are also available. Digital-network connections are provided to dormitory rooms and living groups. All students may access the system. It may be used at all times. There are no time limits on using the system and no fees.

Graduates: In 1992–93 1100 bachelor's degrees were awarded. The most popular majors among graduates were electrical engineering (26%), mechanical engineering (14%), and chemical engineering (0%). Within an average freshman class, 80% graduate in 4 years, 89% in 5 years, and 91% in 6 years. Some 450 companies recruited on campus in 1992–93.

Admissions Contact: Admissions Officers.

MASSACHUSETTS MARITIME ACADEMY E-4
Buzzards Bay, MA 02532

(508) 830–1102
(800) 544–3411 (in-state)

Full-time: 670 men, 60 women	Faculty: 50; IIB, +$
Part-time: 17 men, 2 women	Ph.D.s: 70%
Graduate: none	Student/Faculty: 15 to 1
Year: semesters (see profile)	Tuition: $3410 ($8195)
Application Deadline: June 1	Room & Board: $4000
Freshman Class: 591 applied, 405 accepted, 260 enrolled	
SAT I: required	COMPETITIVE

The Massachusetts Maritime Academy, founded in 1891, is a public, coeducational institution that prepares graduates for qualification as officers in the U.S. Merchant Marine, U.S. Coast Guard, or U.S. Naval Reserve. A 6- to 8-week winter sea term involves the majority of students in a professional setting with travel to foreign countries included. The library contains 40,171 volumes, 11,674 microform items, and 1113 audiovisual forms and subscribes to 505 periodicals. Computerized library sources and services include interlibrary loans and database searching. Special learning facilities include a planetarium, a full bridge training simulator, an oil spill management simulator, and a liquid cargo handling simulator. The 55-acre campus is in a small town 60 miles south of Boston. Including residence halls, there are 9 buildings on campus.

Student Life: About 72% of undergraduates are from Massachusetts. Students come from 26 states and 11 foreign countries. Seventy-three percent are from public schools; 27% from private. Ninety percent are white. The average age of freshmen is 18; all undergraduates, 21. Fifteen percent drop out by the end of their first year; 70% remain to graduate.

Housing: A total of 800 students can be accommodated in college housing. College-sponsored living facilities include single-sex and coed dormitories. On-campus housing is guaranteed for all 4 years. Ninety-seven percent of students live on campus; of those, 25% remain on campus on weekends. Alcohol is not permitted. All students may keep cars on campus.

Activities: There are no fraternities or sororities on campus. There are 15 groups on campus, including band, choir, computers, drill team, jazz band, marching band, newspaper, photography, professional, religious, social service, student government, and yearbook. Popular campus events include Homecoming and Ring Dance.

Sports: There are 7 intercollegiate sports for men and 3 for women, and 13 intramural sports for men and 2 for women. Athletic and recreation facilities include a football and a baseball field, a pistol range, outdoor tennis and basketball courts, a sailing center, an Olympic-sized swimming pool, 2 weight rooms, 3 multipurpose handball courts, and wrestling courts and fitness rooms. An indoor gymnasium/auditorium seats 2500.

Disabled Students: Seventy-five percent of the campus is accessible to disabled students. The following facilities are available: wheelchair ramps, elevators, special parking, and specially equipped rest rooms.

Services: In addition to many counseling and information services, tutoring is available in most subjects.

Campus Safety and Security: Campus safety and security measures include 24-hour foot and vehicle patrol and lighted pathways and sidewalks.

Programs of Study: MMA awards the B.S. degree. Bachelor's degrees are awarded in BUSINESS (transportation management), ENGINEERING AND ENVIRONMENTAL DESIGN (marine safety and environmental protection, facilities and plant engineering, and marine engineering). Marine engineering is the strongest academically and has the largest enrollment.

Required: All students must complete 164 credit hours with a minimum of 60 hours in the major and an overall GPA of 2.0 or better. Requirements include 4 courses in physical education, 2 each in chemistry and naval science, and 1 each in algebra/trigonometry, introduction to computers, English composition, American literature, Western civilization, economics, analysis, American government, first aid, admiralty law, introduction to marine transportation, introduction to marine engineering, sea term/deck, sea term/engine, and calculus.

Special: MMA offers a junior-year internship in a commercial shipping program. Educational experience includes a minimum of 120 days aboard a training ship, with visits to foreign ports. There are cooperative programs in facilities and plant engineering and in marine safety and environmental protection. A dual major is available in marine engineering and marine transportaton.

Faculty/Classroom: Ninety-six percent of faculty are male; 4%, female. Ninety-seven percent teach undergraduates and 3% do research. The average class size in an introductory lecture is 25; in a laboratory, 12; and in a regular course offering, 22.

Admissions: About 69% of the 1993–94 applicants were accepted.

Requirements: The SAT I is required. In addition, applicants must have graduated from an accredited secondary school or hold a GED certificate. They should have completed 16 Carnegie units, including 4 in English, 3 each in mathematics and science, and 2 each in a foreign language, history, and social studies. SAT II: Subject tests are not required, but if taken, the preferred choices are mathematics, science, and English. An essay is required and an interview is strongly recommended. AP and CLEP credits are accepted. Important factors used in the admissions decision are advanced placement or honor courses, recommendations by school officials, extracurricular activities record, leadership record, and personality, intangible qualities.

Procedure: Freshmen are admitted in the fall. Early decision applications should be filed by November 1; regular applications, by June 1 for fall entry, along with an application fee of $10 (in-state) or $40 (out-of-state). Notification is sent on a rolling basis. There are early decision and deferred admissions plans.

Transfer: About 65 transfer students enrolled in a recent year. Students must have a 2.0 or better cumulative GPA. A total of 30 credits out of 164 must be completed at MMA.

Visiting: There are regularly scheduled orientations for prospective students, including a campus tour and an admissions interview. There are guides for informal visits and visitors may sit in on classes and stay overnight at the school. To arrange for a visit, contact Lieutenant Commander Fulgueras at (508) 830–1102 or (800) 544–3411 (in-state).

Financial Aid: In a recent year, 80% of all freshmen and 60% of continuing students received some form of financial aid. Loans averaged $200 ($2625 maximum); and work contracts averaged $500 ($1000 maximum). MMA is a member of CSS. The FAF and the college's own financial statement are required. The deadline for financial aid applications is May 1.

International Students: There are currently 13 international students enrolled. They must take the TOEFL and achieve a minimum score of 500. The student must also take the SAT I.

Computers: The college provides computer facilities for student use. The mainframe is a CDC Cyber 172. Microcomputers are provided for student use in the computer laboratory and dormitory. All students may access the system from 8 A.M. to 11 P.M. There are no time limits on using the system and no fees.

Graduates: In 1992–93 130 bachelor's degrees were awarded. Within an average freshman class, 75% graduate in 4 years. Some 60 companies recruited on campus in a recent year. In the 1992 graduating class, all of the men and women had found employment within 6 month of graduation.

Admissions Contact: Keith D. Rabine, Dean of Enrollment Services.

MERRIMACK COLLEGE

North Andover, MA 01845 E-2
(508) 837-5100

Full-time: 1069 men, 931 women	Faculty: 126; IIB, av$
Part-time: 448 men, 573 women	Ph.D.s: 67%
Graduate: none	Student/Faculty: 16 to 1
Year: semesters, summer session	Tuition: $11,825
Application Deadline: March 1	Room & Board: $6200
Freshman Class: n/av	
SAT I: required	**COMPETITIVE**

Merrimack College, founded in 1947 by the Augustinian clergy of the Roman Catholic Church, offers undergraduate programs in science, engineering, business administration, and liberal arts. In addition to regional accreditation, Merrimack has baccalaureate program accreditation with ABET. The library contains 150,000 volumes, 7200 microform items, and 1000 audiovisual forms, and subscribes to 900 periodicals. Computerized library sources and services include the card catalog, interlibrary loans, and database searching. Special learning facilities include a learning resource center, art gallery, planetarium, TV station, and the National Microscale Chemistry Center. The 220-acre campus is in a suburban area 25 miles north of Boston. Including residence halls, there are 30 buildings on campus.

Student Life: About 70% of undergraduates are from Massachusetts. Students come from 20 states, 20 foreign countries, and Canada. Ninety-five percent are white. Seventy-five percent are Catholic; 15% Protestant. The average age of freshmen is 18; all undergraduates, 20. Ten percent drop out by the end of their first year; 70% remain to graduate.

Housing: A total of 1171 students can be accommodated in college housing. College-sponsored living facilities include single-sex and coed dormitories and on-campus apartments. In addition, there are special interest houses. On-campus housing is guaranteed for all 4 years. Fifty-three percent of students live on campus; of those, 75% remain on campus on weekends. All students may keep cars on campus.

Activities: About 10% of men belong to 5 local fraternities; about 5% of women belong to 3 local sororities. There are 43 groups on campus, including art, ~~mputers~~, dance, drama, international, litera~~~~ ~~r~~, newspaper, photog-

raphy, political, radio and TV, religious, social, social service, student government, and yearbook. Popular campus events include Autumn Interlude, Spring Fest, Peace and Social Justice Awareness Week, Greek Week, retreat weekends, Homecoming, and Family Weekend.

Sports: There are 8 intercollegiate and 13 intramural sports each for men and women. Athletic and recreation facilities include an athletic complex with an ice rink, basketball and racquetball courts, an aerobics studio, and a new exercise room. The outdoor facilities include 2 sets of tennis courts, and baseball, softball, soccer, lacrosse, and field hockey fields.

Disabled Students: All of the campus is accessible to disabled students. The following facilities are available: wheelchair ramps, elevators, special parking, specially equipped rest rooms, special class scheduling, lowered drinking fountains, and lowered telephones.

Services: In addition to many counseling and information services, tutoring is available in every subject, and writing resource centers are available.

Campus Safety and Security: Campus safety and security measures include 24-hour foot and vehicle patrol, escort service, informal discussions, and pamphlets, posters, and films. In addition, there are emergency telephones and lighted pathways and sidewalks.

Programs of Study: Merrimack awards the B.A. and B.S. degrees. Bachelor's degrees are awarded in BIOLOGICAL SCIENCE (biology/biological science), BUSINESS (accounting, business administration and management, business economics, international business management, and marketing/retailing/merchandising), COMMUNICATIONS AND THE ARTS (English), COMPUTER AND PHYSICAL SCIENCE (chemistry, computer science, mathematics, and physics), EDUCATION (elementary, science, and secondary), ENGINEERING AND ENVIRONMENTAL DESIGN (civil engineering, computer engineering, electrical/electronics engineering, and engineering), HEALTH PROFESSIONS (allied health, medical laboratory technology, predentistry, and premedicine), SOCIAL SCIENCE (economics, history, philosophy, political science/government, prelaw, psychology, religion, and sociology). Science, engineering, business, psychology, and liberal arts are the strongest academically. Business, psychology, and liberal arts have the largest enrollments.

Required: All students are required to emphasize liberal arts with a variety of classes that must include 2 courses each in theology and philosophy, 1 each in English composition and freshman seminar, and 3 each in humanities, social science, and mathematics/science. Students must maintain a minimum GPA of 2.0 while taking a total of 120 credit hours.

Special: Merrimack offers cooperative programs in business, engineering, and computer science, cross-registration with the Northeast consortium, internships in all arts and science programs, study abroad in 7 countries, and a Washington semester at American University. Work-study programs, a 5-year combined B.A.-B.S. degree in all major fields, and dual and self-designed majors are available. General studies, nondegree study, and pass/fail options are possible.

Faculty/Classroom: Seventy-two percent of faculty are male; 28%, female. All teach undergraduates and do research. The average class size in an introductory lecture is 20.

Admissions: About 40% of the current freshmen were in the top fifth of their class; 75% were in the top two fifths. Seven freshmen graduated first in their class.

Requirements: A minimum GPA of 2.0 and the SAT I are required. For business administration, humanities, and social science majors, Merrimack recommends that applicants complete 4 units of English, 2 of social studies, 3 of mathematics, and 1 of science. For other majors, an additional mathematics course and 2 additional science courses are needed. An essay is required and an interview is recommended. Applicants should have completed 16 Carnegie units. AP and CLEP credits are accepted. Important factors used in the admissions decision are advanced placement or honor courses, recommendations by school officials, leadership record, parents or siblings attending the school, and personality, intangible qualities.

Procedure: Freshmen are admitted fall and spring. Entrance exams should be taken during spring of the junior year and fall of the senior year. Early decision applications should be filed by November 30; regular applications, by March 1 for fall entry and December 1 for spring entry, along with an application fee of $35. Notification of early decision is sent December 15; regular decision, beginning March 1. There are early decision, early admissions, and deferred admissions plans. A total of 27 early decision candidates were accepted for the 1993–94 class. A waiting list is an active part of the admissions procedure, with about 5% of applicants on the list.

Transfer: About 120 transfer students enrolled in 1993–94. Applicants must have maintained a minimum 2.0 GPA while accumulating 30 credits. The SAT I, an interview, and a letter of recommendation are recommended. A total of 60 credits out of 120 must be completed at Merrimack.

Visiting: There are regularly scheduled orientations for prospective students, including 10 information sessions on Saturdays in the fall and 4 financial aid information sessions throughout the year. There

are guides for informal visits and visitors may sit in on classes and stay overnight at the school. To arrange for a visit, contact the Office of Admissions at (508) 837-5100.

Financial Aid: In 1993-94, 82% of all current freshmen and 65% of continuing students received some form of financial aid. About 63% of freshmen and 52% of continuing students received need-based aid. The average freshman award was $10,107. Of that total, scholarships or need-based grants averaged $7300 ($17,800 maximum); loans averaged $1500 ($4125 maximum); and work contracts averaged $1000 ($2000 maximum). Sixty-eight percent of undergraduate students work part-time. Average earnings from campus work for the school year are $1300. The average financial indebtedness of the 1992-93 graduate was $15,715. Merrimack is a member of CSS. The FAF and FAFSA are required. The deadline for financial aid applications is March 1.

International Students: There are currently 35 international students enrolled. The school actively recruits these students. They must take the TOEFL and achieve a minimum score of 500.

Computers: The college provides computer facilities for student use. The mainframe is a DEC VAX 11/785. Microcomputers for academic use are available in the library, classrooms, and dormitories. All students taking computer classes may access the system. It may be used 7:30 A.M. to 11:30 P.M. There are no time limits on using the system and no fees.

Graduates: In 1992-93, 571 bachelor's degrees were awarded. The most popular majors among graduates were marketing (14%), psychology (9%), and English (7%). Within an average freshman class, 70% graduate in 4 years and 5% in 5 years. A total of 265 companies recruited on campus in 1992-93.

Admissions Contact: John W. Hamel, Acting Dean of Admissions and Financial Aid.

MONTSERRAT COLLEGE OF ART E-2

Beverly, MA 01915   (508) 922-8222; (800) 836-0487 (out-of-state)

Full-time: 141 men, 90 women	Faculty: 13
Part-time: 17 men, 24 women	Ph.D's: 38%
Graduate: none	Student/Faculty: 18 to 1
Year: terms	Tuition: $8700
Application Deadline: open	Room & Board: $3800
Freshman Class: 280 applied, 233 accepted, 105 enrolled	
SAT I or ACT: not required	SPECIAL

Montserrat College of Art, founded in 1970, is an independent, private professional college of art and design offering bachelor's degrees in painting and drawing, printmaking, graphic design, illustration, photography, and sculpture. In addition to regional accreditation, Montserrat has baccalaureate program accreditation with NASAD. The library contains 12,000 volumes and 60 audiovisual forms and subscribes to 55 periodicals. Computerized library sources and services include database searching. Special learning facilities include a learning resource center and art gallery. The 20-acre campus is in a small town 20 miles north of Boston. There are 2 buildings on campus. There are no residence halls.

Student Life: About 50% of undergraduates are from out-of-state, mostly the Northeast. Students come from 10 states and 4 foreign countries. Ninety-three percent are white. The average age of freshmen is 19; all undergraduates, 23. Ten percent drop out by the end of their first year; 46% remain to graduate.

Housing: There are no residence halls. A total of 80 students can be accommodated in college housing. College-sponsored living facilities include off-campus apartments, which are available on a first-come, first-served basis. Priority is given to out-of-town students. Alcohol is not permitted. All students may keep cars on campus.

Activities: There are no fraternities or sororities on campus. There are some groups and organizations on campus, including art, newspaper, and student government. Popular campus events include Forum Days, Halloween and Christmas parties, year-end picnic, coffee houses, open houses, and gallery openings.

Sports: There is no sports program at Montserrat.

Disabled Students: Fifty percent of the campus is accessible to disabled students. The following facilities are available: elevators, special parking, and specially equipped rest rooms. All rooms are accessible to persons in wheelchairs.

Services: In addition to many counseling and information services, tutoring is available in every subject.

Programs of Study: Montserrat awards the B.F.A. degree. Bachelor's degrees are awarded in COMMUNICATIONS AND THE ARTS (design, fine arts, illustration, painting, photography, printmaking, and sculpture).

Required: All students are required to take at least 78 credits in studio courses, and the freshman program or equivalent, which includes 42 liberal arts credits for a total of 120 credits. To enter the senior program, Montserrat students must have a portfolio. During semester-end evaluations, each student displays work from all courses and is evaluated by a faculty panel.

Special: Montserrat is a member of the Northeast Consortium of Colleges and Universities in Massachusetts, which allows students to take classes at any member college for the same cost. Noncredit study is available through the continuing education department. In addition, internships, study abroad in Italy, and dual majors are available.

Faculty/Classroom: Fifty-five percent of faculty are male; 45%, female. All teach undergraduates. The average class size in an introductory lecture is 20 and in a regular course offering, 16.

Admissions: About 83% of the 1993-94 applicants were accepted.

Requirements: The SAT I or ACT is not required. Applicants must submit a statement of purpose, a portfolio, and a high school degree, although no specific program is required. A portfolio interview is generally required. AP credits are accepted. Important factors used in the admissions decision are evidence of special talent, recommendations by school officials, recommendations by alumni, personality, intangible qualities, and leadership record.

Procedure: Freshmen are admitted in the fall and winter. Application deadlines are open. The application fee is $30. Notification of early decision is sent December 6; regular decision, on a rolling basis. There are early decision, early admissions, and deferred admissions plans. About 16 early decision candidates were accepted for an earlier class.

Transfer: About 46 transfer students enrolled in 1993-94. Transfer students are required to submit a portfolio, transcripts from a previous college, and a statement of purpose. They also must be interviewed. A total of 48 credits out of 120 must be completed at Montserrat.

Visiting: There are regularly scheduled orientations for prospective students, including tours of college studios, observation of classes, and portfolio consultations. There are guides for informal visits and visitors may sit in on classes. To arrange for a visit, contact Lena Hill, Admissions Secretary, at (508) 922-8222 or (800) 836-0487.

Financial Aid: In 1993-94 74% of all current freshmen and 57% of continuing students received some form of financial aid. About 70% of freshmen and 55% of continuing students received need-based aid. The average freshman award was $4825. Of that total, scholarships or need-based grants averaged $1400 ($3300 maximum); loans averaged $2625 (maximum); and work contracts averaged $800 (maximum). Ten percent of undergraduate students work part-time. Average earnings from campus work for the school year are $800. The average financial indebtedness of the 1992-93 graduate was $7500. Montserrat is a member of CSS. The FAF is required. The deadline for financial aid applications is April 15.

International Students: There are currently 3 international students enrolled. The school actively recruits these students. They must take the TOEFL and achieve a minimum score of 500.

Computers: The college provides computer facilities for student use. The graphic design department provides 14 Apple Macintosh computers and the illustration department has workstations for general use and for animation. Students enrolled in graphic design or illustration courses may access the system. It may be used from 8 A.M. to 11 P.M. daily. There are no time limits on using the system and no fees.

Graduates: In 1992-93 30 bachelor's degrees were awarded. The most popular majors among graduates were fine arts (54%), graphic design (33%), and illustration (13%).

Admissions Contact: James Sawyer, Director of Admissions.

MOUNT HOLYOKE COLLEGE B-3

South Hadley, MA 01075   (413) 538-2023

Full-time: 1891 women	Faculty: 198; IIB, +$
Part-time: 40 women	Ph.D's: 90%
Graduate: 17 women	Student/Faculty: 10 to 1
Year: 4-1-4	Tuition: $18,110
Application Deadline: February 1	Room & Board: $5520
Freshman Class: 1800 applied, 1314 accepted, 526 enrolled	
SAT I: 549/571	ACT: 26 VERY COMPETITIVE

Mount Holyoke, founded in 1837, is one of the oldest institutions of higher learning for women in the United States. An independent, liberal arts college, it affords students great freedom in selecting course studies. The library contains 575,000 volumes, 15,120 microform items, and 4411 audiovisual forms, and subscribes to 1800 periodicals. Special learning facilities include a learning resource center, art gallery, radio station, and an observatory, child study and language centers, and an arboretum. The 800-acre campus is in a small town 90 miles west of Boston. Including residence halls, there are 40 buildings on campus.

Student Life: About 78% of undergraduates are from out-of-state, mostly the Northeast. Students come from 48 states, 57 foreign countries, and Canada. Seventy-four percent are from public schools; 20% from private. Seventy percent are white; 14% foreign nationals. The average age of freshmen is 18; all undergraduates, 20. Five percent drop out by the end of their first year; 85% remain to graduate.

Housing: A total of 1871 students can be accommodated in college housing. College-sponsored living facilities include dormitories. In addition there are a language house. On-campus housing is guaran-

teed for all 4 years and is available on a lottery system for upperclassmen. Ninety-nine percent of students live on campus. All students may keep cars on campus.

Activities: There are no fraternities or sororities on campus. There are 70 groups on campus, including art, band, choir, chorale, chorus, computers, dance, drama, ethnic, film, gay, honors, international, literary magazine, musical theater, newspaper, orchestra, photography, political, radio and TV, religious, social, social service, student government, symphony, and yearbook. Popular campus events include Festival of Diversity, Something Every Friday entertainment series, Glascock Intercollegiate Poetry Contest, residence hall parties, and the Founders Day Ceremony.

Sports: There are 15 intercollegiate sports and 7 intramural sports. Athletic and recreation facilities include a sports complex area with indoor and outdoor tracks, playing fields, basketball, racquetball, squash, and volleyball courts, a dance studio, weight-training rooms, a 25-meter, 8-lane swimming pool, a diving pool, a hydragymnasium, an equestrian center, 18 hole golf course, field and canoe houses, and a 2500-seat amphitheater.

Disabled Students: The following facilities are available: wheelchair ramps, elevators, special parking, specially equipped rest rooms, and special class scheduling.

Services: In addition to many counseling and information services, tutoring is available in every subject. There is also a reader service for the blind available. The Writing Center helps students at all levels.

Campus Safety and Security: Campus safety and security measures include 24-hour foot and vehicle patrol, self defense education, escort service, and shuttle buses. In addition, there are pamphlets, posters, films, emergency telephones, and lighted pathways and sidewalks.

Programs of Study: Mount Holyoke awards the B.A. degree. Master's and doctoral degrees also are awarded. Bachelor's degrees are awarded in BIOLOGICAL SCIENCE (biochemistry and biology/biological science), COMMUNICATIONS AND THE ARTS (art history and appreciation, classical languages, dance, dramatic arts, English, French, German, Greek, Italian, Latin, music, romance languages, Russian, Spanish, and studio art), COMPUTER AND PHYSICAL SCIENCE (astronomy, chemistry, computer science, geology, mathematics, physics, and statistics), EDUCATION (bilingual/bicultural, early childhood, elementary, mathematics, science, and social science), SOCIAL SCIENCE (Afro-American studies, American studies, anthropology, Asian/Oriental studies, economics, European studies, geography, history, international relations, Judaic studies, Latin American studies, medieval studies, philosophy, political science/government, psychobiology, psychology, religion, sociology, and women's studies). English, politics, biology, psychology, and international relations have the largest enrollments.

Required: Students must maintain a minimum GPA of 2.0 while taking 128 total credits, with 32 to 46 in the major. Students must complete 2 courses each in the humanities, science/mathematics, and social studies, a foreign language, a course with multicultural perspective, and 6 credits in physical education. A minor field of study is necessary for those not pursuing a double major.

Special: Mount Holyoke offers students cross-registration through a 12- and 5-college exchange plan. Internships, including those in science and international studies, study-abroad in 16 countries, a Washington semester, work-study, student-designed majors, dual majors, a January program, B.A.-B.S and accelerated degrees, nondegree study, and pass/fail options also are offered. The school, in addition, emphasizes humanities and mathematics. There is a 3–2 engineering degree available with Dartmouth College. There is a freshman honors program on campus, as well as 2 national honor societies, including Phi Beta Kappa.

Faculty/Classroom: Fifty percent of faculty are male; 50%, female. All teach undergraduates. No introductory courses are taught by graduate students. The average class size in a laboratory is 12 and in a regular course offering, 15.

Admissions: About 73% of the 1993–94 applicants were accepted. About 70% of the current freshmen were in the top fifth of their class; 92% were in the top two fifths. There were 5 National Merit finalists. About 19 freshmen graduated first in their class.

Requirements: The SAT I and 3 SAT II: Subject tests with 1 in writing, or the ACT is required. The school recommends that applicants have 4 years each of English and foreign language, 3 each of mathematics and science, and 2 of social studies. An essay is required and an interview is strongly recommended. AP credits are accepted.

Procedure: Freshmen are admitted in the fall. Entrance exams should be taken before the application deadline. Applications should be filed by November 15 for early decision I, January 15 for early decision II, and February 1 for fall entry, along with an application fee of $40. Notification is sent December 15 for early decision I, February 15 for early decision II, and April 1 for regular decision. There are early decision, early admissions, and deferred admissions plans. About 110 early decision candidates were accepted in an earlier year.

Transfer: About 44 transfer students enrolled in 1993–94. A minimum GPA of 3.0, the SAT I, transcripts of secondary school or college-level work, an interview, and an essay are required of transfer applicants. A total of 64 credits out of 128 must be completed at Mount Holyoke.

Visiting: There are regularly scheduled orientations for prospective students. There are guides for informal visits and visitors may sit in on classes and stay overnight at the school. To arrange for a visit, contact the Admissions Office at (413) 538-2023.

Financial Aid: In 1993–94 69% of all current freshmen and 71% of continuing students received some form of financial aid. About 69% of freshmen and 71% of continuing students received need-based aid. The average freshman award was $18,100. Of that total, scholarships or need-based grants averaged $9000 ($14,200 maximum); loans averaged $2400 ($2500 maximum); and work contracts averaged $1300 ($1400 maximum). Sixty percent of undergraduate students work part-time. Average earnings from campus work for the school year are $925. The average financial indebtedness of the 1992–93 graduate was $9400. Mount Holyoke is a member of CSS. The FAF, the college's own financial statement and the FAFSA and parent and student tax returns are required. The deadline for financial aid applications is February 1.

International Students: There are currently 269 international students enrolled. The school actively recruits these students. They must take the TOEFL, if English is not the first language, and achieve a minimum score of 550. The student must also take SAT I or 3 SAT II: subject tests, with 1 in English composition, or ACT alone.

Computers: The college provides computer facilities for student use. The mainframe is a DEC MicroVAX and a Sun system. A computer center houses several laboratories containing various PCs and workstations. There are 4 other laboratories distributed elsewhere. Most residence halls contain word-processing facilities with 3 to 6 computers. The mainframes may be accessed via PCs connected to Ethernet or by modem. Network connections beyond the campus are through a DECnet to neighbor schools and through Bitnet and Internet to the world. All students may access the system. There are no time limits and no fees.

Graduates: In 1992–93 506 bachelor's degrees were awarded. The most popular majors among graduates were English (14%), biological sciences (9%), and politics (8%). Some 100 companies recruited on campus in an earlier year.

Admissions Contact: Anita Smith, Director of Admissions.

MOUNT IDA COLLEGE
D-2
Newton Center, MA 02159

(617) 969-7000
(800) 769-7001 (out-of-state)

Full-time: 580 men, 948 women	**Faculty:** 62
Part-time: 160 men, 213 women	**Ph.D.s:** 22%
Graduate: none	**Student/Faculty:** 25 to 1
Year: semesters, summer session	**Tuition:** $9810
Application Deadline: open	**Room & Board:** $6890
Freshman Class: 4750 applied, 4041 accepted, 795 enrolled	
SAT I or ACT: not required	**LESS COMPETITIVE**

Mount Ida College, founded in 1899, is a private, liberal arts institution offering associate degrees in more than 40 programs that transfer to the school's senior college division's 4-year program. There are 9 undergraduate schools. In addition to regional accreditation, Mount Ida has baccalaureate program accreditation with ADA. The 2 libraries contain 55,000 volumes and subscribe to 352 periodicals. Computerized library sources and services include the card catalog, interlibrary loans, and database searching. Special learning facilities include a learning resource center, radio station, TV station, communication laboratory, dark room, sewing rooms, and blueprint-making facility. The 85-acre campus is in a suburban area 8 miles west of Boston. Including residence halls, there are 15 buildings on campus.

Student Life: About 50% of undergraduates are from out-of-state, mostly the Northeast. Students come from 21 states, 44 foreign countries, and Canada. Eighty percent are from public schools. Seventy-five percent are white. The average age of freshmen is 18; all undergraduates, 19. Twenty percent drop out by the end of their first year; 60% remain to graduate.

Housing: A total of 850 students can be accommodated in college housing. College-sponsored living facilities include single-sex and coed dormitories. In addition there are honors houses. On-campus housing is guaranteed for all 4 years. Fifty percent of students live on campus; of those, 60% remain on campus on weekends. All students may keep cars on campus.

Activities: About 3% of men belong to 1 national fraternity. There are no sororities on campus. There are 20 groups on campus, including cheerleading, chess, choir, drama, ethnic, honors, international, literary magazine, newspaper, professional, radio and TV, social, student government, and yearbook. Popular campus events include a fashion show, 2 formal dances, sporting events, international dinners, senior week, and faculty lecture series.

Sports: There are 3 intercollegiate sports for men and 3 for women, and 6 intramural sports for men and 6 for women. Athletic and recreation facilities include a gymnasium and playing fields.

Disabled Students: Seventy-five percent of the campus is accessible to disabled students. The following facilities are available: wheelchair ramps, elevators, special parking, specially equipped rest rooms, and special class scheduling.

Services: In addition to many counseling and information services, tutoring is available in most subjects. There is also a program for learning disabled students, for which a fee is charged. Studies skills courses also are available.

Campus Safety and Security: Campus safety and security measures include 24-hour foot and vehicle patrol, self defense education, escort service, and shuttle buses. In addition, there are informal discussions, pamphlets, posters, and films, and lighted pathways and sidewalks.

Programs of Study: Mount Ida awards the B.A., B.S., and B.L.S. degrees. Associate degrees also are awarded. Bachelor's degrees are awarded in BUSINESS (business administration and management, fashion merchandising/marketing, funeral home management, hotel administration, and retail management), COMMUNICATIONS AND THE ARTS (graphic design, journalism and writing, and media production), EDUCATION (teacher certification öN-30), ENGINEERING AND ENVIRONMENTAL DESIGN (interior design), HEALTH PROFESSIONS (veterinary science), SOCIAL SCIENCE (bereavement counseling, criminal justice, fashion design and technology, legal studies, liberal studies, and public administration). Veterinary technology is the strongest academically. Liberal arts studies has the largest enrollment.

Required: Candidates for a bachelor's degree require 128 credits with a 2.0 GPA. All students in the junior college must complete a freshman core and physical education requirement.

Special: Internships in the form of work experience are available in each department. Work-study provided by the college, student-designed majors, study abroad in England, a general studies degree, nondegree study, and combined B.A.-B.S. degrees also are available. There is a freshman honors program on campus, as well as 2 national honor societies, including Phi Beta Kappa.

Faculty/Classroom: Thirty-nine percent of faculty are male; 61%, female. The average class size in an introductory lecture is 25; in a laboratory, 16; and in a regular course offering, 20.

Admissions: About 85% of the 1993–94 applicants were accepted.

Requirements: The SAT I or ACT is not required. Applicants are required to have 4 units of English, 3 of social studies, and 2 each of mathematics and science. A portfolio is recommended for certain programs, while an interview is recommended for all applicants. The GED is accepted. CLEP credits are accepted. Important factors used in the admissions decision are personality, intangible qualities, evidence of special talent, extracurricular activities record, recommendations by school officials, and leadership record.

Procedure: Freshmen are admitted in the fall and spring. Entrance exams should be taken as early as possible. Application deadlines are open. The application fee is $25. Notification is sent on a rolling basis. There are early admissions and deferred admissions plans.

Transfer: About 125 transfer students enrolled in a recent year. Transfer students need a minimum GPA of C and must submit college and high school transcripts. A total of 32 credits out of 128 must be completed at Mount Ida.

Visiting: There are regularly scheduled orientations for prospective students, consisting of fall and spring open houses. There are guides for informal visits and visitors may sit in on classes. To arrange for a visit, contact the Admissions Office at (617) 969–7320 or (800) 769–7001, ext. 153 (out-of-state).

Financial Aid: In 1993–94 70% of all current freshmen and 60% of continuing students received some form of financial aid. About 70% of freshmen and 60% of continuing students received need-based aid. The average freshman award was $7000. Of that total, scholarships or need-based grants averaged $3000 ($7000 maximum); loans averaged $3500 ($5500 maximum); and work contracts averaged $1500 (maximum). Sixty-five percent of undergraduate students work part-time. Average earnings from campus work for the school year are $1500. The average financial indebtedness of the 1992–93 graduate was $4000. Mount Ida is a member of CSS. The FAF, the college's own financial statement, and tax returns are required. The deadline for financial aid applications is September 1.

International Students: There are currently 60 international students enrolled. The school actively recruits these students. They must take the TOEFL.

Computers: The college provides computer facilities for student use. The mainframe is an IBM AS 400. There are 80 microcomputers for student use, including IBM, Wang, and Apple Macintosh. All students may access the system. There are no time limits on using the system and no fees.

Graduates: In 1992–93 101 bachelor's degrees were awarded. The most popular majors among graduates were liberal studies (40%), fashion merchandising (30%), and interior design (25%). Some 35 companies recruited on campus in 1992–93.

Admissions Contact: Harold Duvall or Judy Kaufmann, Co-Directors of Admissions.

NEW ENGLAND CONSERVATORY OF MUSIC

Boston, MA 02115	(617) 262–1120, ext. 430
Full-time: 153 men, 175 women	Faculty: 54
Part-time: 24 men, 45 women	Ph.D.s: 22%
Graduate: 150 men, 218 women	Student/Faculty: 6 to 1
Year: semesters	Tuition: $14,600
Application Deadline: January 15	Room & Board: $6990
Freshman Class: 425 applied, 229 accepted, 87 enrolled	
SAT I or ACT: required	SPECIAL

The New England Conservatory of Music, founded in 1867, is the oldest private school of its kind in the United States. It combines classroom study of music with an emphasis on performance for talented young musicians. There is one undergraduate and one graduate school. In addition to regional accreditation, NEC has baccalaureate program accreditation with NASM. The 3 libraries contain 70,000 volumes, 500 microform items, and 20,000 audiovisual forms, and subscribe to 250 periodicals. Computerized library sources and services include interlibrary loans. Special learning facilities include an electronic music studio. The 8-acre campus is in an urban area 2 miles south of downtown Boston. Including residence halls, there are 4 buildings on campus.

Student Life: About 71% of undergraduates are from out-of-state, mostly the Northeast. Students come from 42 states, 32 foreign countries, and Canada. Seventy-five percent are from public schools. Fifty percent are white; 10% foreign nationals. The average age of freshmen is 18; all undergraduates, 21.

Housing: A total of 168 students can be accommodated in college housing. College-sponsored living facilities include coed dormitories. On-campus housing is guaranteed for the freshman year only. Alcohol is not permitted. All students may keep cars on campus.

Activities: About 3% of men belong to fraternities; about 2% of women belong to 1 national sorority. There are 12 groups on campus, including band, choir, chorale, chorus, computers, jazz band, opera, orchestra, political, religious, student government, and symphony. Popular campus events include the annual NEC vs. Juilliard Hockey Match, visits of guest performers, 450 NEC concerts per year, the Halloween Dance, and GradFest.

Disabled Students: The following facilities are available: elevators, special parking, specially equipped rest rooms, and lowered drinking fountains.

Services: In addition to many counseling and information services, tutoring is available in most subjects.

Campus Safety and Security: Campus safety and security measures include escort service and 24-hour security at the residence hall.

Programs of Study: NEC awards the B.Mus. degree. Master's and doctoral degrees also are awarded. Bachelor's degrees are awarded in COMMUNICATIONS AND THE ARTS (applied music, jazz, music, music history and appreciation, music performance, music theory and composition, and visual and performing arts), EDUCATION (music).

Required: Requirements for graduation include a minimum 2.0 GPA and an average of 120 total credits, including at least 14 in music education.

Special: NEC offers cross-registration with Northeastern and Tufts universities and Simmons College, a 5-year, double-degree program with Tufts, a double major combining a performance major with a nonperformance area, and a diploma program in which students can focus on studio instruction in instruments or voice. Work-study also is possible, along with pass/fail options in ensemble work or recitals.

Faculty/Classroom: Seventy-two percent of faculty are male; 28%, female. The average class size in an introductory lecture is 30 and in a regular course offering, 15.

Admissions: About 54% of the 1993–94 applicants were accepted.

Requirements: The SAT I or ACT is required. In addition, applicants must be graduates of an accredited secondary school or have a GED. An essay is required, as is an audition after submitting the formal application. In some cases, taped auditions are accepted; these must be submitted with the admissions application. Applicants are expected to have reached an advanced level of performance accomplishment. AP and CLEP credits are accepted. Evidence of special talent is an important factor used in the admission decision.

Procedure: Freshmen are admitted to all sessions. Applications should be filed by January 15 for fall entry and November 15 for spring entry, along with an application fee of $60. Notification is sent by April 1. There is a deferred admissions plan. A waiting list is an active part of the admissions procedure.

Transfer: About 24 transfer students enrolled in 1993–94. Transfer students must audition and submit all college-level transcripts and a transfer statement. A total of 60 credits out of 120 must be completed at NEC.

Visiting: There are regularly scheduled orientations for prospective students, consisting of a full range of scheduled events on audition days. Visitors may sit in on classes. To arrange for a visit, contact the Admissions Office at (617) 262–1120, ext. 430.

Financial Aid: In 1993–94 56% of all current freshmen and 80% of continuing students received some form of financial aid. Scholarships or need-based grants averaged $6850; loans averaged $2500 ($4000 maximum); and work contracts averaged $1500. Eighty percent of undergraduate students work part-time. The average financial indebtedness of the 1992–93 graduate was $17,000. NEC is a member of CSS. The college's own financial statement and the FAFSA are required. The deadline for financial aid applications is January 15.

International Students: There are currently 150 international students enrolled. The school actively recruits these students. They must take the TOEFL. The student must also take the SAT I or the ACT.

Computers: The college provides computer facilities for student use. Apple Macintosh PCs, a library of music software, and synthesizers are available in the computer studio. All students may access the system. There are no time limits on using the system and no fees.

Graduates: In an earlier year, 73 bachelor's degrees were awarded.

Admissions Contact: Robert L. Annis, Dean of Enrollment Services.

NICHOLS COLLEGE

Dudley, MA 01571

C-3

(508) 943–2055

Full-time: 454 men, 243 women
Part-time: 240 men, 397 women
Graduate: 212 men, 167 women
Year: semesters, summer session
Application Deadline: open
Freshman Class: 759 applied, 701 accepted, 218 enrolled
SAT I: required

Faculty: 36
Ph.D.s: 67%
Student/Faculty: 19 to 1
Tuition: $9040
Room & Board: $5160

LESS COMPETITIVE

Nichols College, founded in 1930 as a private institution for men, became coeducational in 1971. It emphasizes business and liberal arts. There is 1 undergraduate and 1 graduate school. The library contains 60,000 volumes, 8000 microform items, and 544 audiovisual forms and subscribes to 450 periodicals. Computerized library sources and services include interlibrary loans and database searching. Special learning facilities include a learning resource center, art gallery, and radio station. The 210-acre campus is in a rural area 20 miles south of Worcester. Including residence halls, there are 44 buildings on campus.

Student Life: About 78% of undergraduates are from Massachusetts. Students come from 17 states, 7 foreign countries, and Canada. Seventy-nine percent are from public schools; 21% from private. Ninety-seven percent are white. Most are Catholic. The average age of freshmen is 18; all undergraduates, 20. Twenty percent drop out by the end of their first year; 43% remain to graduate.

Housing: A total of 602 students can be accommodated in college housing. College-sponsored living facilities include single-sex dormitories. On-campus housing is guaranteed for all 4 years. Eighty percent of students live on campus; of those, 50% remain on campus on weekends. Alcohol is not permitted. All students may keep cars on campus.

Activities: There are no fraternities or sororities on campus. There are 28 groups on campus, including cheerleading, computers, ecumenical, drama, honors, international, literary magazine, newspaper, professional, radio, student government, and yearbook. Popular campus events include Homecoming, Parents Weekend, and 100 Days Social.

Sports: There are 9 intercollegiate sports for men and 5 for women, and 7 intramural sports for men and 3 for women. Athletic and recreation facilities include a field house with basketball courts, swimming pool, sauna, and weight-training room as well as athletic training facilities. There also is a 9-hole golf course.

Disabled Students: Sixty-seven percent of the campus is accessible to disabled students. The following facilities are available: wheelchair ramps, elevators, special parking, specially equipped rest rooms, special class scheduling, and lowered drinking fountains. The college makes every effort to accommodate students with special needs.

Services: In addition to many counseling and information services, tutoring is available in most subjects.

Campus Safety and Security: Campus safety and security measures include 24-hour foot and vehicle patrol, self defense education, escort service, and informal discussions. In addition, there are pamphlets, posters, and films and lighted pathways and sidewalks.

Programs of Study: Nichols awards the B.A., B.S., and B.S. in Public Administration degrees. Associate and master's degrees also are awarded. Bachelor's degrees are awarded in BUSINESS (accounting, banking and finance, business administration and management, business economics, management information systems, and marketing/

retailing/merchandising), SOCIAL SCIENCE (history, industrial and organizational psychology, psychology, public administration, and social science). Accounting, finance, and management are the strongest academically. Accounting, finance, management, and marketing have the largest enrollments.

Required: All students must complete a program of study within 10 semesters and maintain a GPA of 2.0 overall and in their major. Students also must complete the Cultural Experience: the Arts, Sciences, and Public Policy Program, which provides cultural events each year. Business students need 33 hours of business core classes out of the total 122 hours required of all students.

Special: Internships designed with the approval of the department, study abroad at Regents College in London, a Washington semester, and a general business degree are available. Nondegree study also is offered. There are 2 national honor societies on campus. Eight departments have honors programs.

Faculty/Classroom: Seventy-seven percent of faculty are male; 23%, female. All teach undergraduates. No introductory courses are taught by graduate students. The average class size in a laboratory is 18 and in a regular course offering, 26.

Admissions: About 92% of the 1993–94 applicants were accepted.

Requirements: The SAT I is required. Four years of high school English, 3 years of mathematics, and 2 years each of science and social studies are recommended. AP and CLEP credits are accepted. Important factors used in the admissions decision are recommendations by school officials, leadership record, evidence of special talent, personality, intangible qualities, and extracurricular activities record.

Procedure: Freshmen are admitted in the fall and spring. Entrance exams should be taken by November of the senior year. Application deadlines are open. The application fee is $25. Notification is sent on a rolling basis. There are early decision, early admissions, and deferred admissions plans.

Transfer: About 33 transfer students enrolled in 1993–94. Transfer applicants need a minimum GPA of 2.0 in courses to be transferred and 30 completed college credits. A total of 30 credits out of 122 must be completed at Nichols.

Visiting: There are regularly scheduled orientations for prospective students. There are guides for informal visits and visitors may sit in on classes and stay overnight at the school. To arrange for a visit, contact the Admissions Office at (508) 943–2055.

Financial Aid: In 1993–94 80% of all current freshmen and 75% of continuing students received some form of financial aid. About 68% of freshmen and 56% of continuing students received need-based aid. The average freshman award was $9720. Of that total, scholarships or need-based grants averaged $3055 ($4500 maximum); loans averaged $4715; and work contracts averaged $1500. Twenty percent of undergraduate students work part-time. Average earnings from campus work for the school year are $750. The average financial indebtedness of the 1992–93 graduate was $13,250. Nichols is a member of CSS. The FAF is required.

International Students: There are currently 9 international students enrolled. The school actively recruits these students. They must take the TOEFL and achieve a minimum score of 500.

Computers: The college provides computer facilities for student use. The mainframe is a DEC VAX 3800. A Novelle Token Ring Network supplies programs to all students via modem. There are 246 connections in the academic center and 2 connections in every dorm room in Shamie Hall for all other students. All students may access the system 24 hours a day. There are no time limits on using the system and no fees. It is recommended that students in all programs have personal computers. The NEC 186F Ultralite Notebook, Panasonic CF-1000 Notebook, or compatible is recommended.

Graduates: In a recent year 196 bachelor's degrees were awarded. The most popular majors among graduates were management (22%), accounting (20%), and general business (15%). Within an average freshman class, 38% graduate in 4 years, 42% in 5 years, and 42% in 6 years. Some 60 companies recruited on campus in a recent year. In an earlier graduating class, 5% of the men and 5% of the women were enrolled in graduate school within 6 months of graduation; 95% of the men and 95% of the women had found employment.

Admissions Contact: Charlene L. Nemeth, Director of Admissions and Financial Aid.

NORTH ADAMS STATE COLLEGE

A-1

North Adams, MA 01247

(413) 664-4511, ext. 410
(800) 292-6632

Full-time: 683 men, 697 women	Faculty: 98; IIA, --$
Part-time: 53 men, 83 women	Ph.D.s: 60%
Graduate: none	Student/Faculty: 14 to 1
Year: semesters	Tuition: $3538 ($7672)
Application Deadline: June 1	Room & Board: $4212
Freshman Class: 1563 applied, 1001 accepted, 240 enrolled	
SAT I Verbal/Math: 427/470	**COMPETITIVE**

North Adams State College, founded in 1894, is a coeducational liberal arts college emphasizing business and education courses. In addition to regional accreditation, NASC has baccalaureate program accreditation with NCATE. The library contains 167,480 volumes, 520 microform items, and 4825 audiovisual forms, and subscribes to 510 periodicals. Computerized library sources and services include interlibrary loans. Special learning facilities include a learning resource center, radio and TV stations, and a newspaper. The 80-acre campus is in a rural area 45 miles east of Albany, New York, and 130 miles west of Boston. Including residence halls, there are 15 buildings on campus.

Student Life: About 92% of undergraduates are from Massachusetts. Students come from 16 states and Canada. Eighty percent are from public schools; 20% from private. Ninety-four percent are white. Most are Catholic. The average age of freshmen is 18; all undergraduates, 23. Eighteen percent drop out by the end of their first year; 58% remain to graduate.

Housing: A total of 1100 students can be accommodated in college housing. College-sponsored living facilities include single-sex and coed dormitories and on-campus apartments. In addition there are honors houses. On-campus housing is guaranteed for the freshman year only and is available on a lottery system for upperclassmen. Sixty percent of students live on campus; of those, 80% remain on campus on weekends. Upperclassmen may keep cars on campus.

Activities: About 5% of men belong to 4 local and 2 national fraternities; about 10% of women belong to 5 local and 2 national sororities. There are 48 groups on campus, including cheerleading, chorale, chorus, computers, dance, drama, ethnic, gay, honors, jazz band, literary magazine, musical theater, newspaper, photography, political, professional, radio and TV, religious, social, social service, student government, and yearbook. Popular campus events include Homecoming, Parents Weekend, and Winter Carnival.

Sports: There are 6 intercollegiate sports for men and 6 for women, and 7 intramural sports for men and 7 for women. Athletic and recreation facilities include the Campus Center with a swimming pool, and basketball, squash, and racquetball courts; there are also soccer, baseball, and softball fields, and weight rooms.

Disabled Students: Eighty percent of the campus is accessible to disabled students. The following facilities are available: wheelchair ramps, elevators, special parking, specially equipped rest rooms, and special class scheduling.

Services: In addition to many counseling and information services, tutoring is available in some subjects. The Tutoring Exchange Network has qualified peers tutoring small groups. There is remedial math, reading, and writing.

Campus Safety and Security: Campus safety and security measures include 24-hour foot and vehicle patrol, escort service, informal discussions, and pamphlets, posters, and films. In addition, there are lighted pathways and sidewalks.

Programs of Study: NASC awards the B.A. and B.S. degrees. Master's degrees also are awarded. Bachelor's degrees are awarded in BIOLOGICAL SCIENCE (biology/biological science), BUSINESS (business administration and management), COMMUNICATIONS AND THE ARTS (communications and English), COMPUTER AND PHYSICAL SCIENCE (chemistry, computer science, mathematics, and physics), EDUCATION (early childhood, elementary, and middle school), HEALTH PROFESSIONS (medical laboratory technology), SOCIAL SCIENCE (history, philosophy, prelaw, psychology, and sociology). Business, English, and education are the strongest academically. Business and education have the largest enrollments.

Required: All students must complete at least 120 credits including 50 in a core curriculum, and maintain a GPA of at least 2.0. Physical education and computer science courses are required.

Special: The college offers cross-registration with Williams College or Berkshire Community College, dual majors, internships, and study abroad in many countries within the International College Program. Student-designed majors, pass/fail options, nondegree study, and independent study also are available. There is one national honor society on campus. One department has an honors program.

Faculty/Classroom: Sixty-nine percent of faculty are male; 31%, female. All teach undergraduates. The average class size in an introductory lecture is 75; in a laboratory, 15; and in a regular course offering, 25.

Admissions: About 64% of the 1993-94 applicants were accepted. About 12% of the current freshmen were in the top fifth of their class; 50% were in the top two fifths.

Requirements: NASC requires applicants to be in the upper 40% of their class. A minimum GPA of 2.0 is required. The SAT I is required, with an SAT eligibility index used to determine a minimum score. Applicants should have completed 16 Carnegie units, including 4 courses in English, 3 in electives and mathematics, and 2 each in foreign language, science, and social studies. The GED is accepted. AP and CLEP credits are accepted. Important factors used in the admissions decision are advanced placement or honors courses, evidence of special talent, parents' or siblings' attendance at the school, extracurricular activities record, and leadership record.

Procedure: Freshmen are admitted fall and spring. Applications should be filed by June 1 for fall entry and January 1 for spring entry, along with an application fee of $10. Notification is sent on a rolling basis. There are early admissions and deferred admissions plans. A waiting list is an active part of the admissions procedure, with about 5% of applicants on the list.

Transfer: There were 186 transfer students enrolled in 1993-94. Transfer applicants who have a minimum of 12 semester hours from an accredited college are eligible. Students are evaluated on the basis of past college records, which must include a GPA of at least 2.0. A total of 30 credits out of 120 must be completed at NASC.

Visiting: There are regularly scheduled orientations for prospective students, including a 2-day, overnight program for students who have been accepted. There are guides for informal visits and visitors may sit in on classes. To arrange for a visit, contact the Admissions Office at (413) 664-4511, ext. 410.

Financial Aid: In 1993-94, 60% of all students received some form of financial aid. About 50% of the students received need-based aid. Average earnings from campus work for the school year are $1300. NASC is a member of CSS. The college's own financial statement and and FAFSA are required. The deadline for financial aid applications is April 1.

International Students: There are currently 2 international students enrolled. They must take the TOEFL and achieve a minimum score of 550. The applicant must also take the SAT I.

Computers: The college provides computer facilities for student use. The mainframes are a CDC Cyber 815 and a DEC VAX 1850. There are also a number of microcomputers available in the computer services facility. All students may access the system. Limitations on access to the system vary with the time of year. The fee is $25 per year.

Graduates: In 1992-93, 429 bachelor's degrees were awarded. The most popular majors among graduates were business (31%), education (21%), and English communications (14%). Within an average freshman class, 1% graduate in 3 years, 45% in 4 years, 48% in 5 years, and 50% in 6 years.

Admissions Contact: Denise C. Richardello, Director of Admissions.

NORTHEASTERN UNIVERSITY

E-2

Boston, MA 02115

(617) 373-2200

Full-time: 6686 men, 4605 women	Faculty: 810; I, -$
Part-time: 4746 men, 5344 women	Ph.D.s: 80%
Graduate: 2837 men, 2334 women	Student/Faculty: 14 to 1
Year: quarters, summer session	Tuition: $12,771
Application Deadline: open	Room & Board: $7080
Freshman Class: 11,901 applied, 8492 accepted, 2517 enrolled	
SAT I: 460/530	ACT: 22 **COMPETITIVE**

Northeastern University, founded in 1898, is a private, nonsectarian institution, offering programs that include an experiential learning component and integrate professional work experience with classroom study. The academic program requires 5 years to complete. There are 7 undergraduate and 9 graduate schools. In addition to regional accreditation, Northeastern has baccalaureate program accreditation with AACSB, ABET, ACPE, APTA, CAHEA, and NLN. The 6 libraries contain 738,193 volumes, 1,719,797 microform items, and 13,848 audiovisual forms, and subscribe to 8698 periodicals. Computerized library sources and services include the card catalog, interlibrary loans, and database searching. Special learning facilities include a learning resource center, art gallery, and radio station. The 55-acre campus is in an urban area in Boston. Including residence halls, there are 54 buildings on campus.

Student Life: About 57% of undergraduates are from Massachusetts. Students come from 47 states, 99 foreign countries, and Canada. Seventy-five percent are white. The average age of freshmen is 18; all undergraduates, 21. Twenty-nine percent drop out by the end of their first year; 43% remain to graduate.

Housing: A total of 3244 students can be accommodated in college housing. College-sponsored living facilities include single-sex and coed dormitories, on-campus apartments, and fraternity houses. In addition, there are honors houses, special interest houses, and quiet, engineering, living and learning, international, and wellness halls. On-

campus housing is guaranteed for the freshman year only and is available on a first-come, first-served basis. Sixty-five percent of students live on campus. All students may keep cars on campus.

Activities: About 9% of men belong to 5 local and 13 national fraternities; about 5% of women belong to 8 national sororities. There are 189 groups on campus, including art, band, cheerleading, chess, chorale, chorus, dance, drama, ethnic, gay, honors, international, literary magazine, marching band, newspaper, orchestra, pep band, photography, political, professional, radio and TV, religious, social, social service, student government, and yearbook. Popular campus events include Spring Fling, International Week, annual major concert, and Homecoming/Parents Weekend.

Sports: There are 12 intercollegiate sports for men and 10 for women, and 25 intramural sports for men and 25 for women. Athletic and recreation facilities include outdoor and indoor tracks, a football stadium, an indoor hockey arena, a swimming pool, indoor and outdoor tennis courts, and racquetball, volleyball, and basketball courts.

Disabled Students: Ninety-five percent of the campus is accessible to disabled students. The following facilities are available: wheelchair ramps, elevators, special parking, specially equipped rest rooms, special class scheduling, lowered drinking fountains, and lowered telephones.

Services: In addition to many counseling and information services, tutoring is available in most subjects. There is also a reader service for the blind, and remedial math, reading, and writing. A reading clinic offers a wide range of diagnostic and corrective services for a variety of reading and language problems. The Academic Assistance Center offers assistance in reading, language problems, vocabulary, note taking, test preparation, and related study skills.

Campus Safety and Security: Campus safety and security measures include 24-hour foot and vehicle patrol, escort service, emergency telephones, and lighted pathways and sidewalks. In addition, there are awareness programs on rape prevention, alcohol abuse, personal safety, and crime prevention. A state-of-the-art fire and security alarm center monitors residence halls, academic buildings, and athletic facilities.

Programs of Study: Northeastern awards the B.A., B.S., and B.Ed. degrees. Associate, master's, and doctoral degrees also are awarded. Bachelor's degrees are awarded in BIOLOGICAL SCIENCE (biology/biological science and toxicology), BUSINESS (accounting, banking and finance, business administration and management, human resources, international business management, management information systems, marketing/retailing/merchandising, personnel management, small business management, and transportation management), COMMUNICATIONS AND THE ARTS (art, broadcasting, communications, English, fine arts, French, German, Italian, journalism, linguistics, music, Russian, and Spanish), COMPUTER AND PHYSICAL SCIENCE (chemistry, computer programming, computer science, geology, information sciences and systems, mathematics, and physics), EDUCATION (early childhood, elementary, health, and physical), ENGINEERING AND ENVIRONMENTAL DESIGN (chemical engineering, civil engineering, computer engineering, electrical/electronics engineering, electrical/electronics engineering technology, engineering, engineering technology, industrial engineering, mechanical engineering, and mechanical engineering technology), HEALTH PROFESSIONS (medical laboratory technology, nursing, pharmacy, physical therapy, recreation therapy, and respiratory therapy), SOCIAL SCIENCE (African American studies, anthropology, criminal justice, economics, history, human services, parks and recreation management, philosophy, physical fitness/movement, political science/government, psychology, public administration, and sociology). Engineering, computer science, law/criminal justice, business administration, nursing, and physical science are the strongest academically. Arts and sciences, business administration, and engineering have the largest enrollments.

Required: Although each college has its own requirements, students must generally complete an upper-division writing proficiency requirement in addition to at least 176 quarter hours with a minimum GPA of 2.0.

Special: Northeastern offers many paid professional internships with area companies to integrate classroom instruction with professional experience. Cross-registration with the New England Conservatory of Music and Hebrew College, study abroad in numerous countries, a Washington semester, work-study through university, public, or private agencies, and student-designed majors in arts and sciences are offered. Nondegree adult and continuing education, and limited pass/fail options are possible. Also available are the Alternative Freshman-Year Program and Project Ujima, an academic support program designed to assist minority students. The Women in Engineering Program Office maintains a database for academic support and networking. Accelerated degrees in engineering and business are available. There is a freshman honors program on campus, as well as 25 national honor societies. All undergraduate colleges and 12 departments have honors programs.

Faculty/Classroom: Sixty-nine percent of faculty are male; 31%, female. The average class size in a regular course offering is 25.

Admissions: About 71% of the 1993–94 applicants were accepted. The SAT scores for the 1993–94 freshman class were as follows: Verbal—66% below 500, 25% between 500 and 599, 8% between 600 and 700, and 1% above 700; Math—35% below 500, 40% between 500 and 599, 20% between 600 and 700, and 5% above 700. The ACT scores were 32% below 21, 29% between 21 and 23, 18% between 24 and 26, 17% between 27 and 28, and 4% above 28. About 33% of the current freshmen were in the top fifth of their class; 64% were in the top two fifths. There were 16 National Merit finalists and 19 semifinalists. About 16 freshmen graduated first in their class.

Requirements: The SAT I or ACT is required. Northeastern recommends that applicants have 17 academic units, including 4 each in English and mathematics, and 2 each in foreign language, science, and social studies. The GED is accepted. An essay is required, and an interview is recommended. AP and CLEP credits are accepted. Important factors used in the admissions decision are recommendations by school officials, advanced placement or honor courses, leadership record, extracurricular activities record, and recommendations by alumni.

Procedure: Freshmen are admitted fall and winter. Entrance exams should be taken from October through December of the junior and senior years. Application deadlines are open; the priority date is March 1. The fee is $30. Notification is sent on a rolling basis. There are early admissions and deferred admissions plans.

Transfer: About 578 transfer students enrolled in 1993–94. Candidates applying for transfer must have a satisfactory college record. Credit is generally granted for a grade of C or better in any reasonably equivalent course. Candidates must be in good standing and must be eligible to continue in the institution they are currently attending. Emphasis is placed on the college record, but the high school record will be considered. SAT I or ACT scores are required of transfer applicants with fewer than 2 years of college. A total of 48 quarter hours out of 176 must be completed at Northeastern.

Visiting: There are regularly scheduled orientations for prospective students. There are guides for informal visits, and visitors may sit in on classes. To arrange for a visit, contact the Department of Undergraduate Admissions at (617) 373-2200.

Financial Aid: In 1993–94 71% of all current freshmen and 57% of continuing students received some form of financial aid. About 71% of freshmen and 52% of continuing students received need-based aid. The average freshman award was $9152. Of that total, scholarships or need-based grants averaged $2957 ($17,400 maximum); loans averaged $2582 ($4125 maximum); and work contracts averaged $2000 ($2150 maximum). Almost all undergraduate students work part-time. Average earnings from campus work for the school year are $1709. The average financial indebtedness of the 1992–93 graduate was $21,462. Northeastern is a member of CSS. The FAF, the FAFSA, and the state form are required; upperclassmen must submit the college's own financial statement. The deadline for financial aid applications is March 1.

International Students: There are currently 1015 international students enrolled. The school actively recruits these students. They must take the TOEFL and achieve a minimum score of 550. The student must also take the SAT I or ACT; minimum scores needed vary by and within program.

Computers: The college provides computer facilities for student use. The mainframe is a super-miniVAXcluster consisting of 2 DEC VAX 6000–440 computers. Students may gain access to the mainframe systems from on-campus computer laboratories or off-campus dial-in modems. The computers accessed are used for various computer courses, E-mail, computer conferencing, and bulletin board purposes. Students enrolled in a class that requires it may access the system. It may be used 24 hours a day. There are no time limits on using the system and no fees.

Graduates: In 1992–93 3006 bachelor's degrees were awarded. The most popular majors among graduates were criminal justice (9%), marketing (6%), and finance (6%). Within an average freshman class, 38% graduate in 5 years and 43% in 6 years. Some 216 companies recruited on campus in 1992–93. In the 1992 graduating class, 11% of all graduates were enrolled in graduate school within 6 months of graduation; 82% had found employment.

Admissions Contact: Kevin Kelly, Interim Dean and Director of Admissions.

PINE MANOR COLLEGE
E-2
Chestnut Hill, MA 02167
(617) 731-7104
(800) 762-1357 (out-of-state)

Full-time: 450 women
Part-time: none
Graduate: none
Year: semesters, summer session
Application Deadline: open
Freshman Class: 299 applied, 275 accepted, 99 enrolled
SAT I Verbal/Math: 383/396

Faculty: 33; IIB, av$
Ph.D.s: 70%
Student/Faculty: 13 to 1
Tuition: $15,700
Room & Board: $6000

LESS COMPETITIVE

Pine Manor College, established in 1911, is a private liberal arts college for women. The library contains 83,400 volumes and 8000 microform items and subscribes to 468 periodicals. Computerized library sources and services include the card catalog, interlibrary loans, and database searching. Special learning facilities include a learning resource center, radio station, TV station, and language laboratory. The 79-acre campus is in a suburban area 5 miles west of Boston. Including residence halls, there are 28 buildings on campus.

Student Life: About 79% of undergraduates are from out-of-state, mostly the Northeast. Students come from 31 states, 15 foreign countries, and Canada. Fifty-one percent are from public schools; 49% from private. Sixty-seven percent are white; 22% foreign nationals. Twenty-two percent drop out by the end of their first year.

Housing: A total of 510 students can be accommodated in college housing. College-sponsored living facilities include dormitories and on-campus apartments. In addition there are language houses, special interest houses, nonsmoking dormitories, and a quiet dormitory. On-campus housing is guaranteed for all 4 years. Eighty-five percent of students live on campus; of those, 80% remain on campus on weekends. All students may keep cars on campus.

Activities: There are no sororities on campus. There are 15 groups on campus, including chorus, dance, drama, ethnic, honors, international, literary magazine, musical theater, newspaper, political, professional, radio and TV, social service, student government, and yearbook. Popular campus events include Holiday Formal, Spring Formal, and First and Last Hurrah's.

Sports: There are 6 intercollegiate sports. Athletic and recreation facilities include a modern gym, outdoor fields, a cross-country track, tennis courts, dance studios, and a weight room.

Disabled Students: Forty percent of the campus is accessible to disabled students. The following facilities are available: wheelchair ramps, elevators, and specially equipped rest rooms.

Services: In addition to many counseling and information services, tutoring is available in every subject. In addition, there is remedial math, reading, and writing. The learning resource center has professional and peer tutoring and workshops.

Campus Safety and Security: Campus safety and security measures include escort service and shuttle buses.

Programs of Study: Pine Manor awards the B.A. degree. Associate and master's degrees also are awarded. Bachelor's degrees are awarded in BIOLOGICAL SCIENCE (biology/biological science), BUSINESS (management science), COMMUNICATIONS AND THE ARTS (art history and appreciation, communications, English, fine arts, and visual and performing arts), EDUCATION (early childhood and elementary), SOCIAL SCIENCE (American studies, psychobiology, and psychology). Management, English, and psychology are the strongest academically. Management, communications, and psychology have the largest enrollments.

Required: All students must take 2 courses each in humanities, fine and performing arts, social sciences, and natural and behavioral science, plus a mathematics competency course and 2 semesters of freshman composition. In addition, students must maintain a minimum GPA of 2.0 and take a total of 128 semester hours.

Special: Pine Manor offers cross-registration with Boston and Babson colleges, internships at more than 600 sites, and study abroad in France, England, Italy, Spain, or during a semester at sea. A Washington semester, work-study programs, dual majors, student-designed majors, nondegree study within continuing education, and pass/fail options for 2 courses each semester (except the first freshman semester) also are available. There is one national honor society on campus.

Faculty/Classroom: Forty percent of faculty are male; 60%, female. Ninety-five percent teach undergraduates. The average class size in an introductory lecture is 30; in a laboratory, 20; and in a regular course offering, 20.

Admissions: About 92% of the 1993–94 applicants were accepted. The SAT scores for the 1993–94 freshman class were as follows: Verbal—85% below 500 and 15% between 500 and 599; Math—84% below 500 and 16% between 500 and 599. The ACT scores were 50% below 21 and 50% between 21 and 23. About 10% of the current freshmen were in the top fifth of their class; 25% were in the top two fifths. One freshman graduated first in his/her class.

Requirements: A minimum GPA of 2.0 is required. Applicants are required to have taken 4 English courses and 2 in mathematics. Additional courses in foreign language, social science, natural science, and elective areas are recommended. The SAT I or ACT and an essay are also required. An interview is recommended. The GED is accepted, and the number of Carnegie units required is 16. AP and CLEP credits are accepted. Important factors used in the admissions decision are recommendations by school officials, leadership record, advanced placement or honor courses, evidence of special talent, and personality, intangible qualities.

Procedure: Freshmen are admitted in the fall and spring. Application deadlines are open. The application fee is $25. Notification is sent on a rolling basis. There are early decision and deferred admissions plans. About 11 early decision candidates were accepted for the 1993–94 class.

Transfer: About 26 transfer students enrolled in 1993–94. Pine Manor requires transfer students to submit 2 letters of recommendation (1 from a professor) and college and high school transcripts. The SAT I or ACT also is necessary. A total of 32 credits out of 128 must be completed at Pine Manor.

Visiting: There are regularly scheduled orientations for prospective students, including a campus tour. There are guides for informal visits and visitors may sit in on classes and stay overnight at the school. To arrange for a visit, contact the Admissions Office at (617) 731–7104 or (800) 762–1357 (out-of-state).

Financial Aid: In a recent year, 38% of all freshmen and 31% of continuing students received some form of financial aid. The average freshman award was $13,332. Of that total, scholarships or need-based grants averaged $6652 ($11,000 maximum); loans averaged $2625 (maximum); and work contracts averaged $1200 (maximum). Fifteen percent of undergraduate students work part-time. Average earnings from campus work for the school year are $1100. The average financial indebtedness of the 1992–93 graduate was $10,700. Pine Manor is a member of CSS. The FAF and the college's own financial statement are required. The deadline for financial aid applications is March 1.

International Students: There are currently 105 international students enrolled. The school actively recruits these students. They must take the TOEFL.

Computers: The college provides computer facilities for student use. IBM, IBM-compatible, and Apple microcomputers are available for student use in computer centers in the library and in the science, management, and art buildings. The communications center houses a computerized print media room. All students may access the system. There are no time limits on using the system. A fee of $35 is charged for computer use, but only for academic computer courses.

Graduates: In 1992–93 107 bachelor's degrees were awarded. The most popular majors among graduates were management (21%), communication (20%), and psychology (16%). Within an average freshman class, 55% graduate in 4 years and 60% in 5 years. Some 15 companies recruited on campus in an earlier year. In the 1992 graduating class, 12% of the women were enrolled in graduate school within 6 months of graduation; 60% of the women had found employment.

Admissions Contact: Mark Gonthier, Director of Admissions and Financial Aid.

REGIS COLLEGE
D-2
Weston, MA 02193
(617) 893–1820, ext. 2050; (800) 456–1820

Full-time: 581 women
Part-time: 533 women
Graduate: 46 women
Year: semesters, summer session
Application Deadline: May 1
Freshman Class: 437 applied, 381 accepted, 155 enrolled
SAT I Verbal/Math: 440/450

Faculty: 49; IIB, av$
Ph.D.s: 90%
Student/Faculty: 12 to 1
Tuition: $11,850
Room & Board: $5600

COMPETITIVE

Regis College, founded in 1927, is a private liberal arts college for women, affiliated with the Roman Catholic Church. In addition to regional accreditation, Regis has baccalaureate program accreditation with CSWE and NLN. The library contains 144,226 volumes, 30,377 microform items, and 3760 audiovisual forms, and subscribes to 825 periodicals. Computerized library sources and services include interlibrary loans. Special learning facilities include a learning resource center, art gallery, radio station, philatelic museum, and fine arts center. The 168-acre campus is in a suburban area 12 miles west of Boston. Including residence halls, there are 15 buildings on campus.

Student Life: About 86% of undergraduates are from Massachusetts. Students come from 18 states and 10 foreign countries. Sixty-nine percent are from public schools; 31% from private. Ninety percent are white. Seventy-two percent are Catholic; 11% Protestant. The average age of freshmen is 18; all undergraduates, 24. Nineteen percent drop out by the end of their first year; 69% remain to graduate.

Housing: A total of 700 students can be accommodated in college housing. College-sponsored living facilities include dormitories. On-campus housing is guaranteed for all 4 years. Seventy-three percent of students live on campus; of those, 50% remain on campus on weekends. All students may keep cars on campus.

Activities: There are 39 groups on campus, including art, choir, chorale, chorus, computers, dance, drama, ethnic, film, honors, international, literary magazine, musical theater, newspaper, photography, political, professional, radio and TV, religious, social, social service, student government, and yearbook. Popular campus events include International Month, Father/Daughter Dance, Comedy Night, Women's History Month, orientation, Spring Weekend, Oktoberfest, Christmas events, and Tower Tavern campus pub activities.

Sports: There are 9 intercollegiate sports and 10 intramural sports. Athletic and recreation facilities include a softball diamond, a soccer field, 4 tennis courts, and an athletic facility with a gymnasium, a dance studio, a Nautilus weight room, racquetball and squash courts, a pool, and a sauna and Jacuzzi.

Disabled Students: The following facilities are available: wheelchair ramps, elevators, special parking, specially equipped rest rooms, special class scheduling, lowered drinking fountains, and lowered telephones.

Services: In addition to many counseling and information services, tutoring is available in every subject. There is a reader service for the blind and remedial math and writing. There are academic support services for learning-disabled students.

Campus Safety and Security: Campus safety and security measures include 24-hour foot and vehicle patrol, self defense education, escort service, and shuttle buses. In addition, there are informal discussions, pamphlets, posters, and films, emergency telephones, and lighted pathways and sidewalks.

Programs of Study: Regis awards the B.A. and B.S.N. degrees. Bachelor's degrees are awarded in BIOLOGICAL SCIENCE (biology/biological science), BUSINESS (management science), COMMUNICATIONS AND THE ARTS (art, classics, communications, English, French, German, and Spanish), COMPUTER AND PHYSICAL SCIENCE (chemistry and mathematics), HEALTH PROFESSIONS (nursing), SOCIAL SCIENCE (economics, history, political science/government, psychology, social work, and sociology). Communication, English, political science, and psychology have the largest enrollments.

Required: All students are required to take 2 courses each in natural sciences and social sciences, 3 in humanities, and 1 each in religious studies or philosophy, physical education, and writing, a 2-semester interdisciplinary seminar as freshmen, and foreign language and mathematics skill classes. Students must maintain a minimum GPA of 2.0 and take a total of 38 credit courses, including 8 to 12 in the major.

Special: Cross-registration with Boston, Babson, and Bentley colleges and through the Sisters of St. Joseph Consortium is offered. Internships, study abroad, a Washington semester, dual and self-designed majors, work-study, nondegree study, and pass/fail options are available. There are special programs in American studies; communication; computer science; graphics; Greek, international, legal, and women's studies; and teacher-training programs. A 3–2 engineering degree is available with Worcester Polytechnic Institute. There is a freshman honors program on campus, as well as 6 national honor societies. Eighteen departments have honors programs.

Faculty/Classroom: Twenty percent of faculty are male; 80%, female. All teach undergraduates. No introductory courses are taught by graduate students. The average class size in an introductory lecture is 21; in a laboratory, 17; and in a regular course offering, 15.

Admissions: About 87% of the 1993–94 applicants were accepted. About 32% of the current freshmen were in the top fifth of their class; 55% were in the top two fifths. About 2 freshmen graduated first in their class.

Requirements: Regis requires applicants to be in the upper 50% of their class. A minimum GPA of 2.5 is required. The SAT I is required. The minimum score needed is 800, 400 each on verbal and mathematics. Applicants should have 4 years of English, 3 or 4 electives, 3 of mathematics, 2 each of foreign language and social studies, and 1 of natural science. An essay and interview are required. The GED is accepted. AP and CLEP credits are accepted. Important factors used in the admissions decision are advanced placement or honor courses, leadership record, evidence of special talent, recommendations by school officials, and extracurricular activities record.

Procedure: Freshmen are admitted fall and spring. Entrance exams should be taken during the spring or summer before enrollment. Applications should be filed by May 1 for fall entry and December 1 for spring entry, along with an application fee of $30. Notification is sent on a rolling basis. There are early admissions and deferred admissions plans. A waiting list is an active part of the admissions procedure, with about 8% of applicants on the list.

Transfer: About 37 transfer students enrolled in 1993–94. Transfer students need an admission application and fee, an official transcript of high school and college records, 2 letters of recommendation (1 from a college professor and 1 from the dean of students at the previous college), the academic catalog of the previous college attended, SAT I scores, and health records. A total of 18 courses out of 38 must be completed at Regis.

Visiting: There are regularly scheduled orientations for prospective students. There are guides for informal visits, and visitors may sit in on classes and stay overnight at the school. To arrange for a visit, contact the Admissions Office at (617) 893-1820, ext. 2050.

Financial Aid: In 1993–94 85% of all current freshmen and 46% of continuing students received some form of financial aid. About 80% of freshmen and 41% of continuing students received need-based aid. The average freshman award was $9900. Of that total, scholarships or need-based grants averaged $6000 ($14,300 maximum); loans averaged $3000 ($4625 maximum); and work contracts averaged $900 ($1200 maximum). Forty-eight percent of undergraduate students work part-time. Average earnings from campus work for the school year was $950. The average financial indebtedness of the 1992–93 graduate was $10,888. Regis is a member of CSS. The FAF, the college's own financial statement, and the FAFSA are required. The priority deadlines for financial aid applications are February 15 for fall entry and December 15 for spring entry.

International Students: There are currently 35 international students enrolled. The school actively recruits these students. They must take the TOEFL and achieve a minimum score of 500.

Computers: The college provides computer facilities for student use. The mainframe is a DEC VAX 11/780 shared with Babson College. There are also 61 IBM, Apple Macintosh, and Apple PCs available in the academic computer center, academic achievement center, science building, and education room. All students may access the system. There are no time limits on using the system and no fees.

Graduates: In 1992–93 205 bachelor's degrees were awarded. The most popular majors among graduates were communication (15%), nursing (14%), and sociology (13%). Within an average freshman class, 60% graduate in 4 years, 66% in 5 years, and 68% in 6 years. Some 33 companies recruited on campus in 1992–93. In the 1992 graduating class, 12% of students were enrolled in graduate school within 6 months of graduation; 92% of graduates had found employment.

Admissions Contact: Valerie L. Brown, Associate Director of Admissions.

SALEM STATE COLLEGE
Salem, MA 01970

E-2
(508) 741-6200

Full-time: 2395 men, 3227 women	Faculty: 292
Part-time: 3400 men, 6200 women	Ph.D.s: 65%
Graduate: 140 men, 400 women	Student/Faculty: 19 to 1
Year: semesters, summer session	Tuition: $3198 ($7332)
Application Deadline: March 1	Room & Board: $3514
Freshman Class: 4052 applied, 3140 accepted, 1283 enrolled	
SAT I Verbal/Math: 421/454	COMPETITIVE

Salem State College, founded in 1854, offers programs in liberal arts, business, education, and nursing. There are 5 undergraduate schools and one graduate school. In addition to regional accreditation, Salem State has baccalaureate program accreditation with CSWE, NASAD, NCATE, and NLN. The library contains 225,000 volumes and 300,000 microform items, and subscribes to 1340 periodicals. Special learning facilities include a learning resource center, art gallery, radio station, and TV station. The 62-acre campus is in an urban area 18 miles northeast of Boston. Including residence halls, there are 19 buildings on campus.

Student Life: About 98% of undergraduates are from Massachusetts. Students come from 20 states, 15 foreign countries, and Canada. Ninety-eight percent are from public schools; 2% from private. Ninety percent are white.

Housing: A total of 950 students can be accommodated in college housing. College-sponsored living facilities include coed dormitories and on-campus apartments. On-campus housing is guaranteed for all 4 years. Priority is given to out-of-town students. Sixty percent of students commute. All students may keep cars on campus.

Activities: There are no fraternities or sororities on campus. There are 44 groups on campus, including band, cheerleading, choir, chorale, chorus, computers, dance, drama, ethnic, gay, honors, jazz band, musical theater, newspaper, photography, political, radio and TV, religious, social, social service, student government, and yearbook. Popular campus events include Homecoming, Welcome Week, Halloween, Arts Festival, and Senior Week.

Sports: There are 8 intercollegiate sports for men and 8 for women, and 15 intramural sports for men and 15 for women. Athletic and recreation facilities include an athletic center with 27 facilities, including a 2200-seat gymnasium, a 2800-seat auditorium, an 8-lane swimming pool, 4 tennis courts, a weight room, and a dance studio.

Disabled Students: Ninety percent of the campus is accessible to disabled students. The following facilities are available: wheelchair ramps, elevators, special parking, specially equipped rest rooms, lowered drinking fountains, and lowered telephones.

Services: In addition to many counseling and information services, tutoring is available in every subject. There is also a reader service for the blind, and remedial math, reading, and writing.

Campus Safety and Security: Campus safety and security measures include shuttle buses, pamphlets, posters, and films, emergency telephones, and lighted pathways and sidewalks.

Programs of Study: Salem State awards the B.A., B.S., B.S.B.A., B.F.A., B.S.Ed., B.G.S., B.S.N., B.S.O.A., and B.S.W. degrees. Master's degrees also are awarded. Bachelor's degrees are awarded in BIOLOGICAL SCIENCE (biology/biological science), BUSINESS (accounting, banking and finance, business administration and management, and marketing/retailing/merchandising), COMMUNICATIONS AND THE ARTS (advertising, communications, design, dramatic arts, English, fine arts, and photography), COMPUTER AND PHYSICAL SCIENCE (chemistry, computer programming, earth science, geology, and mathematics), EDUCATION (art, business, education, science, and secondary), ENGINEERING AND ENVIRONMENTAL DESIGN (cartography), HEALTH PROFESSIONS (medical laboratory technology and nursing), SOCIAL SCIENCE (criminal justice, economics, geography, history, psychology, social work, and sociology). Sciences is the strongest academically. Business administration has the largest enrollment.

Required: All students are required to take a distribution of classes that includes 36 to 38 credits in humanities, sciences, and social sciences. A minimum GPA of 2.0 and a total of 127 credits, with 36 in the major, are needed. Specific courses required are English composition, speech communication, and physical education.

Special: Study abroad is available in 3 countries. Cross-registration through a consortium, internships, work-study programs, student-designed and dual majors, B.A.-B.S. degrees, and a general studies degree are offered. Life experience credit, nondegree study, and pass/fail options also are possible. There is a freshman honors program on campus, as well as 11 national honor societies. Nine departments have honors programs.

Faculty/Classroom: Sixty-four percent of faculty are male; 36%, female. The average class size in an introductory lecture is 35; in a laboratory, 20; and in a regular course offering, 30.

Admissions: About 77% of the 1993–94 applicants were accepted. About 20% of the current freshmen were in the top fifth of their class; 60% were in the top two fifths.

Requirements: Salem State requires applicants to be in the upper 50% of their class. A minimum GPA of 2.0 is required. The SAT I or ACT is required. Salem State College recommends that applicants have 16 credits earned, including 4 years of English, 3 years of mathematics, and 2 years each of foreign language, history, and laboratory science. Courses in music, art, drama, computer science, and psychology are suggested. Art majors must provide a portfolio. A GED is acceptable. Students with a GED, those out of school more than 3 years, and the learning disabled do not need the SAT I. AP and CLEP credits are accepted. Important factors used in the admissions decision are advanced placement or honor courses, evidence of special talent, leadership record, extracurricular activities record, personality, and intangible qualities.

Procedure: Freshmen are admitted in the fall. Entrance exams should be taken December of the senior year. Applications should be filed by March 1 for fall entry and December 1 for winter entry, along with an application fee of $10. Notification is sent on a rolling basis. There is a deferred admissions plan.

Transfer: About 800 transfer students enrolled in a recent year. Transfer students are required to have a minimum GPA of 2.0. A total of 30 credits out of 127 must be completed at Salem State.

Visiting: There are regularly scheduled orientations for prospective students. To arrange for a visit, contact the Admissions Office at (508) 741-6200.

Financial Aid: In a recent year, 60% of all freshmen received some form of financial aid. Scholarships or need-based grants averaged $939 ($6050 maximum); loans averaged $2012 ($7500 maximum); and work contracts averaged $1438 ($4550 maximum). The average financial indebtedness of a recent year's graduate was $2655. Salem State is a member of CSS. The FAF is required. The deadline for financial aid applications is April 15.

International Students: There are currently 65 international students enrolled. They must take the TOEFL.

Computers: The college provides computer facilities for student use. The mainframe is a CDC CYBER 170. Numerous microcomputers are available throughout the campus. Students enrolled in computer courses may access the system. There are no time limits on using the system and no fees.

Admissions Contact: Nate Bryant, Associate Director of Admissions.

SIMMONS COLLEGE
E-2
Boston, MA 02115 (617) 521-2051; (800) 345-8468

Full-time: 1144 women	Faculty: 116; IIA, av$
Part-time: 161 women	Ph.D.s: 78%
Graduate: 242 men, 1787 women	Student/Faculty: 10 to 1
Year: semesters, summer session	Tuition: $15,794
Application Deadline: February 1	Room & Board: $6740

Freshman Class: 1003 applied, 782 accepted, 295 enrolled
SAT I or ACT: required
COMPETITIVE

Simmons College, founded in 1899, supports a comprehensive education that combines the arts, sciences, and humanities with professional preparation. There are 5 graduate schools. In addition to regional accreditation, Simmons has baccalaureate program accreditation with ADA, APTA, CSWE, and NLN. The 4 libraries contain 259,645 volumes, 1384 microform items, and 1783 audiovisual forms, and subscribe to 2010 periodicals. Computerized library sources and services include the card catalog, interlibrary loans, and database searching. Special learning facilities include an art gallery, TV studio, microcomputer laboratory, foreign language laboratory, physical therapy sports laboratory, nursing laboratory, and library science technology center. ROTC (Army) is offered through Northeastern University. The 12-acre campus is in an urban area in Boston. Including residence halls, there are 26 buildings on campus.

Student Life: About 59% of undergraduates are from Massachusetts. Students come from 32 states, 33 foreign countries, and Canada. Seventy-eight percent are from public schools; 22% from private. Seventy-six percent are white. Thirty-eight percent claim no religious affiliation; 30% Catholic; 16% Protestant; 16% Jewish. The average age of freshmen is 18; all undergraduates, 20. Nineteen percent drop out by the end of their first year; 70% remain to graduate.

Housing: A total of 1016 students can be accommodated in college housing. College-sponsored living facilities include dormitories and off-campus apartments. In addition, there are special interest houses. On-campus housing is guaranteed for all 4 years. Seventy percent of students live on campus; of those, 75% remain on campus on weekends.

Activities: There are no fraternities on campus. There are 70 groups on campus, including chorale, dance, drama, ethnic, film, gay, honors, international, literary magazine, newspaper, political, professional, religious, social, student government, and yearbook. Popular campus events include Friday Teas, Father-Daughter Weekend, Mother-Daughter Weekend, Asian Awareness Week, Black-Hispanic Cultural Weekend, Parents Weekend, Fall Fest, Spring Spree, May Breakfast, Honors Convocation, Senior/Faculty Banquet, and Head of the Charles.

Sports: Athletic and recreation facilities include an 8-lane pool, a gymnasium, 2 racquetball and squash courts, rowing racks, 2 weight rooms, an aerobics room, and an indoor track.

Disabled Students: The entire campus is accessible to disabled students. The following facilities are available: wheelchair ramps, elevators, special parking, specially equipped rest rooms, special class scheduling, lowered drinking fountains, and lowered telephones.

Services: In addition to many counseling and information services, tutoring is available in some subjects, including basic freshman courses, languages, biology, chemistry, and psychology. There is remedial math and writing. The school also provides study groups, individual tutoring, help with study skills and time management, and assistance for learning-disabled and special-needs students.

Campus Safety and Security: Campus safety and security measures include 24-hour foot and vehicle patrol, self defense education, escort service, and shuttle buses. In addition, there are informal discussions, pamphlets, posters, and films, emergency telephones, lighted pathways and sidewalks, closed-circuit TV, ID card access, and security training in first response and crisis intervention.

Programs of Study: Simmons awards the B.A. and B.S. degrees. Master's and doctoral degrees also are awarded. Bachelor's degrees are awarded in BIOLOGICAL SCIENCE (biochemistry, biology/biological science, and nutrition), BUSINESS (accounting, banking and finance, international business management, management information systems, marketing management, and retailing), COMMUNICATIONS AND THE ARTS (advertising, art, arts administration/management, communications, English, French, graphic design, music, public relations, and Spanish), COMPUTER AND PHYSICAL SCIENCE (chemistry, computer science, and mathematics), EDUCATION (education, secondary, and special), ENGINEERING AND ENVIRONMENTAL DESIGN (environmental science), HEALTH PROFESSIONS (nursing, physical therapy, and premedicine), SOCIAL SCIENCE (American studies, economics, history, human services, international relations, philosophy, political science/government, pre-law, psychobiology, psychology, sociology, and women's studies). Physical therapy and international relations are the strongest academically. Nursing, biology, psychology, English, and physical therapy have the largest enrollments.

Required: To graduate, students must complete 128 semester hours, including 20 to 40 hours in the major, and maintain a minimum GPA of 1.7. They must complete 2 courses each in humanities, social sciences, and science, and 4 in liberal arts and science, as well as 1 designated writing course, 1 year of physical education, and 8 semester hours in a supervised independent learning experience or an internship. They must also show proficiency in a foreign language.

Special: Cross-registration is available with the New England Conservatory of Music, Hebrew College, Emmanual College, and Wheelock College, and study abroad in countries that include Spain, France, Italy, and England. In addition, a Washington semester at American University internship programs, a B.A.-B.S. degree, dual and student-designed majors, interdisciplinary majors, including chemistry management, work-study programs, and pass/fail options are available. A double-degree program in chemistry and pharmacy with Massachusetts College of Pharmacy and Allied Health Sciences is also possible. There is a freshman honors program on campus. All departments have honors programs.

Faculty/Classroom: Twenty-five percent of faculty are male; 75%, female. All teach undergraduates. No introductory courses are taught by graduate students. The average class size in an introductory lecture is 50; in a laboratory, 12; and in a regular course offering, 16.

Admissions: About 78% of the 1993-94 applicants were accepted. About 46% of the current freshmen were in the top fifth of their class; 80% were in the top two fifths. Two freshmen graduated first in their class.

Requirements: The SAT I or ACT is required. Simmons College recommends that applicants have 4 years of English, 3 years each of mathematics, science, and social studies, and 2 years of foreign language. An essay is required. AP and CLEP credits are accepted. Important factors used in the admissions decision are advanced placement or honor courses, recommendations by school officials, extracurricular activities record, leadership record, and evidence of special talent.

Procedure: Freshmen are admitted fall and spring. Entrance exams should be taken by February 1. Early decision applications should be filed by November 15; regular applications, by February 1 for fall entry and December 1 for spring entry, along with an application fee of $35. Notification of early decision is sent December 15; regular decision, April 15. There are early decision, early admissions, and deferred admissions plans. About 45 early decision candidates were accepted for the 1993-94 class. A waiting list is an active part of the admissions procedure.

Transfer: About 55 transfer students enrolled in 1993-94. Transfer students need a minimum GPA of 2.7, either the SAT I or ACT, at least 9 credit hours, a faculty recommendation, and the dean's report to complete their applications. A total of 48 credits out of 128 must be completed at Simmons.

Visiting: There are regularly scheduled orientations for prospective students, including a campus tour, an interview, and meetings with faculty and students. There are guides for informal visits, and visitors may sit in on classes and stay overnight at the school. To arrange for a visit, contact the Admissions Office at (617) 521-2051 or (800) 345-8468.

Financial Aid: In 1993-94 82% of all current freshmen and 64% of continuing students received some form of financial aid. About 77% of freshmen and 59% of continuing students received need-based aid. The average freshman award was $15,900. Of that total, scholarships or need-based grants averaged $12,500 ($21,846 maximum); loans averaged $2650 ($4625 maximum); and work contracts averaged $1500 (maximum). Sixty percent of undergraduate students work part-time. Average earnings from campus work for the school year are $1080. The average financial indebtedness of the 1992-93 graduate was $10,150. Simmons is a member of CSS. The FAF and the college's own financial statement are required. The deadline for financial aid applications is February 1.

International Students: There are currently 66 international students enrolled. The school actively recruits these students. They must take the TOEFL and achieve a minimum score of 550. The student must also take the SAT I.

Computers: The college provides computer facilities for student use. The mainframe is a DEC VAX network. There are 40 terminals on the academic network, including 8 in the residence halls. In addition, there are 29 microcomputers in the library. Students use the mainframe for programming, statistics, and other computations. Microcomputers are used for personal information management, including word processing and graphics. All students may access the system. There are no time limits on using the system and no fees.

Graduates: In 1992-93 338 bachelor's degrees were awarded. The most popular majors among graduates were psychology (10%), nursing (10%), and communication (9%). Within an average freshman class, 70% graduate in 4 years, 72% in 5 years, and 73% in 6 years. Some 37 companies recruited on campus in 1992-93. In the 1992 graduating class, 18% of the women were enrolled in graduate school within 6 months of graduation; 72% of the women had found

employment.

Admissions Contact: Deborah Wright, Dean of Admission.

SIMON'S ROCK COLLEGE OF BARD A-2
(Formerly Simon's Rock of Bard College)
Great Barrington, Mass 01230-9702

(413) 528-7313
(800) 235-7186 (out-of-state)

Full-time: 151 men, 150 women	Faculty: 34
Part-time: 8 men, 8 women	Ph.D.s: 94%
Graduate: none	Student/Faculty: 9 to 1
Year: 4-1-4	Tuition: $18,140
Application Deadline: June 30	Room & Board: $5620
Freshman Class: 310 applied, 180 accepted, 127 enrolled	
SAT I Verbal/Math: 570/590	**VERY COMPETITIVE +**

Simon's Rock College of Bard, founded in 1964, is a private, coeducational liberal arts school especially designed to permit students who have completed the 10th or 11th grades to enroll for collegiate studies. The library contains 55,000 volumes, 4950 microform items, and 1800 audiovisual forms, and subscribes to 350 periodicals. Special learning facilities include an art gallery, radio station, and language laboratory. The 275-acre campus is in a small town 50 miles west of Springfield. Including residence halls, there are 10 buildings on campus.

Student Life: About 93% of undergraduates are from out-of-state, mostly the Northeast. Students come from 33 states, 4 foreign countries, and Canada. Eighty-three percent are from public schools; 17% from private. Eighty-three percent are white. The average age of freshmen is 16.5; all undergraduates, 18. Fifteen percent drop out by the end of their first year; 85% remain to graduate.

Housing: A total of 288 students can be accommodated in college housing. College-sponsored living facilities include single-sex and coed dormitories and on-campus apartments. In addition, there are special interest houses. On-campus housing is guaranteed for the freshman year only and is available on a lottery system for upperclassmen. Eighty-nine percent of students live on campus; of those, 95% remain on campus on weekends. Alcohol is not permitted. Upperclassmen may keep cars on campus.

Activities: There are no fraternities or sororities on campus. There are 19 groups on campus, including art, band, chess, chorus, computers, dance, drama, ethnic, gay, international, jazz band, literary magazine, newspaper, political, religious, social, social service, student government, and yearbook. Popular campus events include Founders Day, Solstice Day, May Fest, and the Winter Dance Festival.

Sports: There are 5 intercollegiate sports for men and 3 for women, and 5 intramural sports for men and 5 for women. Athletic and recreation facilities include a gymnasium, tennis courts, athletic fields, skating ponds, and hiking trails.

Disabled Students: Eighty percent of the campus is accessible to disabled students. The following facilities are available: wheelchair ramps, specially equipped rest rooms, special class scheduling, and lowered telephones.

Services: In addition to many counseling and information services, tutoring is available in most subjects. Study skills instruction is available upon request.

Campus Safety and Security: Campus safety and security measures include 24-hour foot and vehicle patrol, informal discussions, pamphlets, posters, films, and emergency telephones. In addition, there are lighted pathways and sidewalks.

Programs of Study: Simon's Rock awards the B.A. degree. Associate degrees also are awarded. Bachelor's degrees are awarded in COMPUTER AND PHYSICAL SCIENCE (natural sciences and quantitative methods), ENGINEERING AND ENVIRONMENTAL DESIGN (environmental science), SOCIAL SCIENCE (interdisciplinary studies, social science, and women's studies).

Required: Students must complete a writing and thinking workshop, a freshman composition course and seminar, and a cultural perspectives seminar. Distribution requirements include the arts, mathematics, natural sciences, and foreign language courses. A total of 120 credits, including an 8-credit senior thesis, and a minimum 2.0 GPA are needed to graduate.

Special: All majors are interdisciplinary: arts and aesthetics, environmental studies, intercultural studies, literary studies, natural science, quantitative studies, and social science. Independent study, internships in many fields, study abroad, a cooperative program with Bard College, pass/fail options, and a 3-2 engineering degree in conjunction with Columbia University are offered.

Faculty/Classroom: Seventy-one percent of faculty are male; 28%, female. All teach undergraduates. The average class size in a regular course offering is 11.

Admissions: About 58% of the 1993-94 applicants were accepted. The SAT scores for the 1993-94 freshman class were as follows: Verbal—19% below 500, 41% between 500 and 599, 32% between 600 and 700, and 10% above 700; Math—10% below 500, 45% be-

tween 500 and 599, 26% between 600 and 700, and 21% above 700. There were 5 National Merit finalists and 9 semifinalists.

Requirements: The SAT I or ACT is required, but the admissions committee looks more toward the required interview, essay, recommendations, and special talent. The school recommends that prospective students finish 2 years each of English, foreign languages, history, mathematics, science, and social studies. Important factors used in the admissions decision are personality, intangible qualities, evidence of special talent, extracurricular activities record, advanced placement or honor courses, and leadership record.

Procedure: Freshmen are admitted fall and spring. Entrance exams should be taken prior to March 30. Applications should be filed by June 30 for fall entry and December 15 for spring entry, along with an application fee of $25. Notification is sent within 2 weeks. There are early admissions and deferred admissions plans.

Transfer: Transfer students must be evaluated by the dean and registrar. A total of 72 credits out of 120 must be completed at Simon's Rock.

Visiting: There are regularly scheduled orientations for prospective students, including class visits, a campus tour, and an interview. There are guides for informal visits, and visitors may sit in on classes. To arrange for a visit, contact Brian R. Hopewell, Director of Admissions, at (413) 528–7313 or (800) 235–7186 (out-of-state).

Financial Aid: In 1993–94 74% of all current freshmen and 73% of continuing students received some form of financial aid. About 68% of freshmen and 70% of continuing students received need-based aid. The average freshman award was $9000. Thirty-six percent of undergraduate students work part-time. Average earnings from campus work for the school year are $1200. Simon's Rock is a member of CSS. The FAF or FFS is required. The deadline for financial aid applications is June 15.

International Students: There are currently 4 international students enrolled. The school actively recruits these students. They must take the TOEFL and achieve a minimum score of 500.

Computers: The college provides computer facilities for student use. The mainframe is a UNIX. Students may access the mainframe from PCs in their dorm or from 2 computer laboratories. All students may access the system. There are no time limits on using the system and no fees.

Graduates: In 1992–93 33 bachelor's degrees were awarded.

Admissions Contact: Brian R. Hopewell, Director of Admissions.

SIMON'S ROCK OF BARD COLLEGE
(See Simon's Rock College of Bard)

SMITH COLLEGE
Northampton, MA 01063

B-2

(413) 585–2500

Full-time: 2459 women	Faculty: 250; IIA, + +$
Part-time: 95 women	Ph.D.s: 97%
Graduate: 68 men, 378 women	Student/Faculty: 10 to 1
Year: semesters	Tuition: $18,136
Application Deadline: January 15	Room & Board: $6100

Freshman Class: 2925 applied, 1598 accepted, 632 enrolled

SAT I or ACT: required
HIGHLY COMPETITIVE

Smith College, founded in 1871 and the largest independent women's college in the United States, offers a liberal arts education. The 4 libraries contain 1.1 million volumes, 68,227 microform items, and 50,454 audiovisual forms, and subscribe to 3050 periodicals. Computerized library sources and services include the card catalog, interlibrary loans, and database searching. Special learning facilities include a learning resource center, art gallery, radio station, center for performing arts, women's history archive, and botanical gardens. The 204-acre campus is in a small town 90 miles west of Boston. Including residence halls, there are 105 buildings on campus.

Student Life: About 78% of undergraduates are from out-of-state, mostly the Middle Atlantic. Students come from 50 states, 53 foreign countries, and Canada. Seventy-one percent are from public schools; 29% from private. Seventy-four percent are white; 12% Asian American. Twenty-nine percent are Protestant; 24% Catholic; 21% claim no religious affiliation; 20% claim other, including Bahai, Buddhist, Eastern Orthodox, Hindu, Mormon, Muslim, Quaker, and Unitarian. The average age of freshmen is 18; all undergraduates, 20. Twelve percent drop out by the end of their first year; 86% remain to graduate.

Housing: A total of 2348 students can be accommodated in college housing. College-sponsored living facilities include dormitories and on-campus apartments. In addition, there are language houses and a cooperative house. On-campus housing is guaranteed for all 4 years. Ninety percent of students live on campus; of those, 80% remain on campus on weekends. Upperclassmen may keep cars on campus.

Activities: There are no sororities on campus. There are 93 groups on campus, including art, choir, chorale, chorus, computers, dance, drama, ethnic, film, gay, international, literary magazine, newspaper, orchestra, photography, political, professional, religious, social, social

service, student government, symphony, and yearbook. Popular campus events include Mountain Day, International Student Day, Spring and Harvest Weekends, Rally Day, Otelia Cromwell Day, and Diversity Day.

Sports: There are 14 intercollegiate sports and 13 intramural sports. Athletic and recreation facilities include indoor and outdoor tracks, tennis courts, riding rings, 2 gymnasiums, an indoor swimming pool with 1- and 3-meter diving boards, 2 weight-training rooms, a dance studio, an athletic training room, a human performance laboratory, and squash courts.

Disabled Students: Fifty percent of the overall campus is accessible to disabled students; 80% of academic buildings are accessible. The following facilities are available: wheelchair ramps, elevators, special parking, specially equipped rest rooms, special class scheduling, and lowered telephones.

Services: In addition to many counseling and information services, tutoring is available in every subject. There is also a reader service for the blind, and services are provided for learning-disabled students, including note taking, oral tests, readers, tutors, talking books, reading machines, tape recorders, untimed tests, and writing counselors.

Campus Safety and Security: Campus safety and security measures include 24-hour foot and vehicle patrol, self defense education, escort service, and shuttle buses. In addition, there are informal discussions, pamphlets, posters, and films, emergency telephones, and lighted pathways and sidewalks. First-year students are required to attend panel discussions on campus safety.

Programs of Study: Smith awards the A.B. degree. Master's and doctoral degrees also are awarded. Bachelor's degrees are awarded in BIOLOGICAL SCIENCE (biochemistry and biology/biological science), COMMUNICATIONS AND THE ARTS (art, classical languages, comparative literature, dance, dramatic arts, English, French language and literature, French studies, Germanic languages and literature, Greek, Italian language and literature, Latin, music, Russian literature, Spanish, and theater), COMPUTER AND PHYSICAL SCIENCE (astronomy, chemistry, computer science, geology, mathematics, and physics), EDUCATION (early childhood and elementary), SOCIAL SCIENCE (African American studies, American studies, ancient studies, anthropology, economics, French studies, history, Latin American studies, Luso-Brazilian studies, medieval studies, philosophy, political science/government, psychology, religion, Russian civilization, sociology, and women's studies). Biological sciences, psychology, economics, government, art, and English are the strongest academically. Psychology, government, and art have the largest enrollments.

Required: All students planning individual programs in consultation with faculty advisers take 64 credits outside their major and 36 to 48 credits in the major. Students must maintain a minimum 2.0 GPA in all academic work and during the senior year. A total of 128 credits is needed to graduate.

Special: Smith offers a co-op program called the Twelve College Exchange, and cross-registration with 5 area schools. Internships, including one at the Smithsonian Institution, study abroad in Italy, Geneva, Hamburg, and Paris, consortial programs in Spain, England, St. Petersburg, Rome, Japan, and South India, and a Washington semester are available. An accelerated degree program, dual and student-designed majors, nondegree study, and pass/fail options are possible. There are 3 national honor societies on campus, including Phi Beta Kappa.

Faculty/Classroom: Fifty-four percent of faculty are male; 46%, female. All both teach undergraduates and do research. No introductory courses are taught by graduate students. The average class size in an introductory lecture is 25; in a laboratory, 10; and in a regular course offering, 15.

Admissions: About 55% of the 1993–94 applicants were accepted. The SAT scores for the 1993–94 freshman class were as follows: Verbal—17% below 500, 39% between 500 and 599, 36% between 600 and 700, and 8% above 700; Math—9% below 500, 39% between 500 and 599, 42% between 600 and 700, and 10% above 700. About 81% of the current freshmen were in the top fifth of their class; 97% were in the top two fifths. About 29 freshmen graduated first in their class.

Requirements: The SAT I or ACT is required. The school highly recommends that applicants have 4 years of English, 3 years each of mathematics and a foreign language, and 2 years each of science and history. SAT II: Subject tests, especially in writing, are strongly recommended. Interviews are strongly recommended. The GED is accepted. Early admission is possible. AP credits are accepted. Important factors used in the admissions decision are advanced placement or honor courses, leadership record, recommendations by school officials, extracurricular activities record, personality, and intangible qualities.

Procedure: Freshmen are admitted in the fall. Entrance exams should be taken before January of the senior year. Early decision applications should be filed by November 15 and January 1; regular applications, by January 15 for fall entry, along with an application fee of

$45. Notification of early decision is sent December 15 and February 1; regular decision, March 30. There are early decision, early admissions, and deferred admissions plans. About 121 early decision candidates were accepted for the 1993–94 class. A waiting list is an active part of the admissions procedure.

Transfer: About 93 transfer students enrolled in 1993–94. Criteria for transfer students are similar to those for entering freshmen, with more emphasis on the college record. A total of 64 credits out of 128 must be completed at Smith.

Visiting: There are regularly scheduled orientations for prospective students. Student-guided tours are available 6 times a day, Monday through Friday, when school is in full session and on Saturday mornings from September to January. Interviews may also be scheduled during these times. There are guides for informal visits, and visitors may sit in on classes and stay overnight at the school. To arrange for a visit, contact Michelle LaPlante, Receptionist, at (413) 585–2500.

Financial Aid: In 1993–94 50% of all current freshmen and 58% of continuing students received some form of financial aid. About 50% of freshmen and 58% of continuing students received need-based aid. The average freshman award was $16,560. Of that total, scholarships or need-based grants averaged $11,370 ($20,100 maximum); loans averaged $2045 ($2500 maximum); and work contracts averaged $1,150 (maximum). Sixty-three percent of undergraduate students work part-time. Average earnings from campus work for the school year are $825. The average financial indebtedness of the 1992–93 graduate was $10,000. Smith is a member of CSS. The FAF and the college's own financial statement are required. The deadline for financial aid applications is January 15.

International Students: There are currently 164 international students enrolled. The school actively recruits these students. If the language of instruction in school is English, the SAT I is required. If the language of instruction and the language spoken at home is other than English, the TOEFL is required.

Computers: The college provides computer facilities for student use. The mainframe is comprised of 4/DEC MicroVAX 3100s. Computing facilities span the campus with public computing laboratories in several buildings joined by a campuswide local area network (LAN). Resources include more than 230 IBM and Apple Macintosh personal computers. Bitnet and Internet networks are available. All students may access the system. There are no time limits on using the system and no fees.

Graduates: In 1992–93 705 bachelor's degrees were awarded. The most popular majors among graduates were government (11%), psychology (10%), and English (9%). Within an average freshman class, 1% graduate in 3 years, 83% in 4 years, 86% in 5 years, and 86% in 6 years. Some 50 companies recruited on campus in 1992–93. In the 1992 graduating class, 20% of the women were enrolled in graduate school within 6 months of graduation; 15% of the women had found employment.

Admissions Contact: Juliet Brigham, Director of Admissions.

SPRINGFIELD COLLEGE
Springfield, MA 01109

B-3

(413) 748–3136
(800) 343–1257 (out-of-state)

Full-time: 1143 men, 1310 women	Faculty: 174
Part-time: 62 men, 116 women	Ph.D.s: 43%
Graduate: 275 men, 576 women	Student/Faculty: 14 to 1
Year: semesters, summer session	Tuition: $10,368
Application Deadline: April 1	Room & Board: $4832
Freshman Class: n/av	
SAT I: required	**LESS COMPETITIVE**

Springfield College, established in 1885, is a private liberal arts institution. There is one graduate school. In addition to regional accreditation, the college has baccalaureate program accreditation with APTA, CAHEA, and NRPA. The library contains 145,000 volumes, 500,000 microform items, and 3200 audiovisual forms, and subscribes to 925 periodicals. Special learning facilities include a radio station. The 160-acre campus is in a suburban area 26 miles north of Hartford, Connecticut. Including residence halls, there are 38 buildings on campus.

Student Life: About 70% of undergraduates are from out-of-state, mostly the Northeast. Students come from 30 states and 12 foreign countries. Eighty-three percent are from public schools; 17% from private. Ninety-three percent are white. The average age of freshmen is 18; all undergraduates, 21. Twelve percent drop out by the end of their first year; 83% remain to graduate.

Housing: A total of 1967 students can be accommodated in college housing. College-sponsored living facilities include dormitories and off-campus apartments. In addition, there is a wellness dormitory. On-campus housing is guaranteed for all 4 years. Eighty-five percent of students live on campus; of those, 75% remain on campus on weekends. Alcohol is not permitted. Upperclassmen may keep cars on campus.

Activities: There are no fraternities or sororities on campus. There are 45 groups on campus, including band, cheerleading, choir, chorus, computers, dance, drama, jazz band, musical theater, newspaper, pep band, religious, social service, student government, and yearbook. Popular campus events include Parents Weekend, Homecoming, and Stepping Up Day.

Sports: There are 14 intercollegiate sports for men and 13 for women, and 10 intramural sports each. Athletic and recreation facilities include a 2000-seat stadium, a 2000-seat gymnasium, a super-turf football/soccer/lacrosse/field hockey field, 8 tennis courts, baseball and softball fields, and free weight and Nautilus rooms.

Disabled Students: Seventy-five percent of the campus is accessible to disabled students. The following facilities are available: wheelchair ramps, elevators, special parking, specially equipped rest rooms, and lowered drinking fountains.

Services: In addition to many counseling and information services, tutoring is available in most subjects. There is also remedial writing.

Campus Safety and Security: Campus safety and security measures include 24-hour foot and vehicle patrol, self-defense education, escort service, and informal discussions. In addition, there are pamphlets, posters, and films, emergency telephones, and lighted pathways and sidewalks.

Programs of Study: The college awards the B.A. and B.S. degrees. Master's and doctoral degrees also are awarded. Bachelor's degrees are awarded in BIOLOGICAL SCIENCE (biochemistry and biology/biological science), BUSINESS (business administration and management and sports management), COMMUNICATIONS AND THE ARTS (English and fine arts), COMPUTER AND PHYSICAL SCIENCE (chemistry, information sciences and systems, and mathematics), EDUCATION (early childhood, elementary, health, middle school, physical, science, and secondary), HEALTH PROFESSIONS (art therapy, emergency medical technologies, environmental health science, health care administration, medical laboratory technology, physical therapy, physician's assistant, predentistry, premedicine, recreation therapy, and rehabilitation therapy), and SOCIAL SCIENCE (gerontology, history, human services, parks and recreation management, physical fitness/movement, political science/government, prelaw, psychology, and sociology). Physical therapy and athletic training are the strongest academically. Physical education, business, health/fitness, rehabilitation therapy, and psychology have the largest enrollments.

Required: To graduate, students must complete a total of 130 credits with a 2.0 GPA. Core requirements include 30 semester hours in English, social and natural sciences, health, religion, philosophy, and art, and 4 credits in physical education.

Special: Cross-registration may be arranged with cooperating colleges in the Greater Springfield Area. There is 1 national honor society on campus.

Faculty/Classroom: Fifty-four percent of faculty are male; 46%, female. The average class size in an introductory lecture is 250; in a laboratory, 35; and in a regular course offering, 30.

Requirements: The SAT I is required. Applicants must be graduates of an accredited secondary school and have completed 4 years of English, 2 years each of history, mathematics, and science, and 6 electives. The school accepts the GED. An essay and an interview are required. AP credits are accepted. Important factors used in the admissions decision are advanced placement or honor courses, leadership record, extracurricular activities record, parents or siblings attending the school, and recommendations by school officials.

Procedure: Freshmen are admitted fall and spring. Entrance exams should be taken in November of the senior year. Applications should be filed by April 1 for fall entry and December 1 for spring entry, along with an application fee of $25. Notification is sent on a rolling basis. There are early decision, early admissions, and deferred admissions plans. A waiting list is an active part of the admissions procedure.

Transfer: About 110 transfer students enrolled in a recent year. Grades of 2.0 transfer for credit. Transfer students are admitted in the fall and spring.

Visiting: There are guides for informal visits and visitors may sit in on classes and stay overnight at the school. To arrange for a visit, contact the Admissions Office at (413) 748–3136.

Financial Aid: In a recent year, 63% of all freshmen and 55% of continuing students received some form of financial aid. About 63% of freshmen and 55% of continuing students received need-based aid. The average freshman award was $6800. Of that total, need-based grants averaged $2644 ($10,000 maximum); loans averaged $2625 ($4000 maximum); and work contracts averaged $1000 ($4000 maximum). Twenty-seven percent of undergraduate students work part-time. The average financial indebtedness of a recent graduate was $3312. The FAF, the college's own financial statement, and tax returns for parents and the student are required. The deadline for financial aid applications is April 1.

International Students: There are currently 57 international students enrolled. They must take the TOEFL and achieve a minimum score of 500. The student must also take the SAT I.

Computers: The college provides computer facilities for student use. The mainframe is an IBM AS/400. There are also 30 Apple IIe, IBM PS/2 Model 30, and IBM PS/2 Model 25 microcomputers available for academic use. All students may access the system. There are no time limits on using the system and no fees.

Graduates: In a recent year, 524 bachelor's degrees were awarded. The most popular majors among graduates were physical education (33%), rehabilitation services (18%), and health fitness (18%). Within an average freshman class, 1% graduate in 3 years, 63% in 4 years, 7% in 5 years, and 2% in 6 years. Some 34 companies recruited on campus in an earlier year.

Admissions Contact: Fred Bartlett, Director of Admissions.

STONEHILL COLLEGE
North Easton, MA 02357

E-3

(508) 230–1373

Full-time: 885 men, 1106 women	Faculty: 117; IIB, av$
Part-time: 18 men, 14 women	Ph.D.s: 79%
Graduate: none	Student/Faculty: 17 to 1
Year: semesters, summer session	Tuition: $11,485
Application Deadline: February 15	Room & Board: $5996
Freshman Class: 3646 applied, 2300 accepted, 585 enrolled	
SAT I Verbal/Math: 480/530	ACT: 24 **VERY COMPETITIVE**

Stonehill College, founded in 1948 by the Holy Cross Fathers, is a private Roman Catholic college offering undergraduate degrees in business, liberal arts, and sciences. In addition to regional accreditation, Stonehill has baccalaureate program accreditation with NCATE. The 2 libraries contain 150,285 volumes, 49,507 microform items, and 2785 audiovisual forms and subscribe to 1138 periodicals. Computerized library sources and services include interlibrary loans and database searching. Special learning facilities include a learning resource center, radio station, and observatory. The 375-acre campus is in a suburban area 20 miles south of Boston. Including residence halls, there are 26 buildings on campus.

Student Life: About 66% of undergraduates are from Massachusetts. Students come from 25 states, 13 foreign countries, and Canada. Sixty-eight percent are from public schools; 32% from private. Ninety-six percent are white. Most are Catholic. The average age of freshmen is 18; all undergraduates, 19.5. Thirteen percent drop out by the end of their first year; 80% remain to graduate.

Housing: A total of 1500 students can be accommodated in college housing. College-sponsored living facilities include single-sex and coed dormitories. In addition there are special interest houses, townhouse residences, and international experience housing and substance free/wellness housing available by application. On-campus housing is guaranteed for all 4 years. Eighty percent of students live on campus; of those, 70% remain on campus on weekends. All students may keep cars on campus.

Activities: There are no fraternities or sororities on campus. There are 54 groups on campus, including cheerleading, choir, chorus, computers, dance, drama, film, honors, international, literary magazine, newspaper, photography, political, radio and TV, religious, social, social service, student government, and yearbook. Popular campus events include Fall Concert, Spring Weekend, Octoberfest, Irish Night, Rockin' Eve (New Year's), Halloween Mixer, Spring Semiformals, Airband, and Parents Weekend.

Sports: There are 8 intercollegiate sports for men and 7 for women, and 15 intramural sports for men and 15 for women. Athletic and recreation facilities include a 55,000-square-foot complex, which houses a fitness center, jogging track, courts for basketball, volleyball, tennis, racquetball, and squash, and an instructional program area. There are outdoor practice and playing fields and a 2,000-seat stadium.

Disabled Students: Eighty-five percent of the campus is accessible to disabled students. The following facilities are available: wheelchair ramps, elevators, special parking, specially equipped rest rooms, special class scheduling, lowered drinking fountains, lowered telephones, TDD (Telecommunication Device for the Deaf), and 8 dormitory rooms designed specifically for disabled students.

Services: In addition to many counseling and information services, tutoring is available in every subject. In addition, there is a reader service for the blind and remedial writing.

Campus Safety and Security: Campus safety and security measures include 24-hour foot and vehicle patrol, self defense education, escort service, and informal discussions. In addition, there are pamphlets, posters, and films, emergency telephones, lighted pathways and sidewalks, and weekend guest sign-in policy.

Programs of Study: Stonehill awards the B.A., B.S., and B.S.B.A. degrees. Bachelor's degrees are awarded in BIOLOGICAL SCIENCE (biology/biological science), BUSINESS (accounting, finance, management science, and marketing/retailing/merchandising), COMMUNICATIONS AND THE ARTS (communications, English, and languages), COMPUTER AND PHYSICAL SCIENCE (chemistry, computer science, and mathematics), HEALTH PROFESSIONS (health care administration and medical technology), SOCIAL SCIENCE (American studies, criminal justice, economics, history, international relations, philosophy, political science/government, psychology, public administration, religious studies, and sociology). Biology, chemistry, accounting, finance, computer science, and economics are the strongest academically. Communication, psychology, accounting, biology, and criminal justice have the largest enrollments.

Required: All students must complete a general studies core, which includes 2 semesters each of religious studies, philosophy, social institutions, literature and fine arts, and scientific inquiry courses, 1 semester of writing and quantitative techniques courses, and 1 year of foreign language. Students must complete 40 3- or 4-credit courses while maintaining a minimum GPA of 2.0.

Special: Work-study programs, internships, and a Washington semester are available. Cross-registration with 7 Massachusetts schools in the SACHEM Consortium and with Wheaton College is possible. Study abroad opportunities include international internships, an exchange program with Yaroslavl State University in the Russian Federation, a Stonehill-Quebec Exchange, a semester in Irish Studies at University College Dublin, and a Foreign Studies Program offering worldwide study abroad opportunities. Nondegree, directed, and field study are available as well as a pass/fail option for upperclassmen. Minor programs in early childhood, elementary, and secondary education lead to the state's provisional teacher certification. Multidisciplinary studies including managerial economics and math-computer science are also offered. There is a freshman honors program on campus, as well as 8 national honor societies. Four departments have honors programs.

Faculty/Classroom: Seventy-one percent of faculty are male; 29%, female. All teach undergraduates. No introductory courses are taught by graduate students. The average class size in an introductory lecture is 25; in a laboratory, 20; and in a regular course offering, 22.

Admissions: About 63% of the 1993–94 applicants were accepted. The SAT scores for the 1993–94 freshman class were as follows: Verbal—62% below 500, 32% between 500 and 599, and 6% between 600 and 700; Math—28% below 500, 50% between 500 and 599, 20% between 600 and 700, and 2% above 700. About 58% of the current freshmen were in the top fifth of their class; 92% were in the top two fifths. One freshman graduated first in his/her class.

Requirements: The SAT I or ACT is required. Applicants should be graduates of an accredited high school or have earned the GED. Secondary preparation should include 4 units of English, at least 2 units of the same foreign language, 1 each in algebra, geometry, science, and history, as well as 6 electives with no more than 3 in business subjects. An essay and guidance counselor recommendation are also required. AP and CLEP credits are accepted. Important factors used in the admissions decision are advanced placement or honor courses, evidence of special talent, leadership record, extracurricular activities record, and recommendations by school officials.

Procedure: Freshmen are admitted in the fall and spring. Entrance exams should be taken in October. Applications should be filed by February 15 for fall entry and November 1 for spring entry, along with an application fee of $40. Notification is sent by April 1. There are early admissions and deferred admissions plans. A waiting list is an active part of the admissions procedure, with about 9% of applicants on the list.

Transfer: About 40 transfer students enrolled in 1993–94. Transfer applicants must have a minimum GPA of 2.0. Official high school transcripts and college transcripts, along with catalogs with course descriptions from all colleges attended, are required. SAT I or ACT scores are required and an interview is recommended. A total of 60 credits out of 120 must be completed at Stonehill.

Visiting: There are regularly scheduled orientations for prospective students, including group information sessions and guided campus tours available by appointment throughout the year. Visitors may sit in on classes. To arrange for a visit, contact the Admissions Office at (508) 230–1373.

Financial Aid: In 1993–94 83% of all current freshmen and 74% of continuing students received some form of financial aid. About 70% of freshmen and 61% of continuing students received need-based aid. The average freshman award was $7578. Of that total, scholarships or need-based grants averaged $4881 ($18,024 maximum); loans averaged $3205 ($5625 maximum); and work contracts averaged $884 ($1200 maximum). Thirty-two percent of undergraduate students work part-time. Average earnings from campus work for the school year are $800. The average financial indebtedness of the 1992–93 graduate was $7419. Stonehill is a member of CSS. The FAF and FAFSA are required. The deadline for financial aid applications is February 15.

International Students: There are currently 27 international students enrolled. The school actively recruits these students. They must take the TOEFL and achieve a minimum score of 550. The student must also take the SAT I or the ACT.

Computers: The college provides computer facilities for student use. The mainframe is a DEC VAX 4000–300. Some 36 terminals, 50 microcomputers, and 12 printers are accessible to students. A variety of software, word processors, statistics, spreadsheets, and databases are available for student use. All students may access the system from 8 A.M. to 11:30 P.M. weekdays, from 8 A.M. to 4 P.M. on Saturday, and from 1 P.M. to midnight on Sunday. There are no time limits on using the system. The fees are $100 per computer laboratory course per semester, not to exceed $200 per semester, or $50 per semester for word processing.

Graduates: In 1992–93 499 bachelor's degrees were awarded. The most popular majors among graduates were psychology (9%), communication (9%), and accounting (9%). Within an average freshman class, 77% graduate in 4 years, 80% in 5 years, and 80% in 6 years. Some 85 companies recruited on campus in 1992–93. In the 1992 graduating class, 17% of men and women were enrolled in graduate school within 6 months of graduation; 84% had found employment.

Admissions Contact: Brian P. Murphy, Dean of Admissions and Enrollment.

SUFFOLK UNIVERSITY
Boston, MA 02108   (617) 573–8460; (800) 6 SUFFOLK (out-of-state)   **E-2**

Full-time: 1027 men, 1175 women	Faculty: 152; IIA, +$
Part-time: 325 men, 494 women	Ph.D.s: 90%
Graduate: 752 men, 590 women	Student/Faculty: 14 to 1
Year: semesters, summer session	Tuition: $9860
Application Deadline: May 1	Room & Board: $5500
Freshman Class: 1133 applied, 1037 accepted, 370 enrolled	
SAT I Verbal/Math: 400/440	**LESS COMPETITIVE**

Suffolk University, founded in 1906, is a private institution offering undergraduate degrees in liberal arts and sciences and business. There are 2 undergraduate and 3 graduate schools. In addition to regional accreditation, Suffolk has baccalaureate program accreditation with AACSB. The 2 libraries contain 282,614 volumes, 757,880 microform items, and 213 audiovisual forms and subscribe to 5027 periodicals. Computerized library sources and services include the card catalog, interlibrary loans, and database searching. Special learning facilities include a learning resource center, radio station, TV station, and satellite hook-ups. The 2-acre campus is in an urban area in the Beacon Hill area of Boston. Including residence halls, there are 8 buildings on campus.

Student Life: About 89% of undergraduates are from Massachusetts. Students come from 17 states, 62 foreign countries, and Canada. Seventy percent are from public schools; 30% from private. Sixty-nine percent are white. The average age of freshmen is 19; all undergraduates, 24. Nineteen percent drop out by the end of their first year; 57% remain to graduate.

Housing: A total of 160 students can be accommodated in college housing. College-sponsored living facilities include coed dormitories. On-campus housing is available on a first-come, first-served basis. Ninety-five percent of students commute. Alcohol is not permitted.

Activities: About 2% of men and about 2% of women belong to 1 local and 2 national fraternities; about 2% of women belong to 1 national sorority. There are 40 groups on campus, including art, cheerleading, computers, drama, ethnic, film, gay, honors, international, literary magazine, musical theater, newspaper, photography, political, professional, radio and TV, religious, social, social service, student government, and yearbook. Popular campus events include Hispanic Fiesta, Black History Month, Springfest Talent Show, Holiday Party, Commencement Ball, Spirit Day, Temple Street Fair, monthly rathskellers, Recognition Day/Night, and Leadership Banquet.

Sports: There are 7 intercollegiate sports for men and 5 for women, and 3 intramural sports for men and 3 for women. Athletic and recreation facilities include a gymnasium for basketball, volleyball, aerobics, intramurals, and indoor baseball/softball practice. Also, a fully equipped fitness center is available to the university community.

Disabled Students: Ninety percent of the campus is accessible to disabled students. The following facilities are available: wheelchair ramps, elevators, specially equipped rest rooms, special class scheduling, lowered drinking fountains, and lowered telephones.

Services: In addition to many counseling and information services, tutoring is available in most subjects. In addition, there is remedial math, reading, and writing.

Campus Safety and Security: Campus safety and security measures include 24-hour foot and vehicle patrol, escort service, informal discussions, and pamphlets, posters, and films. In addition, there are emergency telephones and lighted pathways and sidewalks.

Programs of Study: Suffolk awards the B.A., B.S., B.F.A., B.S.B.A., B.S.G.S., and B.S.J. degrees. Associate and master's degrees also are awarded. Bachelor's degrees are awarded in BIOLOGICAL SCIENCE (biochemistry, biology/biological science, and marine science), BUSINESS (accounting, banking and finance, international economics, management science, and marketing/retailing/merchandising), COMMUNICATIONS AND THE ARTS (broadcast-ing, communications, dramatic arts, English, French, journalism, public relations, Spanish, and speech/debate/rhetoric), COMPUTER AND PHYSICAL SCIENCE (chemistry, computer programming, computer science, mathematics, and physics), EDUCATION (business and elementary), ENGINEERING AND ENVIRONMENTAL DESIGN (aviation computer technology, computer engineering, and electrical/electronics engineering), HEALTH PROFESSIONS (cytotechnology and medical laboratory technology), SOCIAL SCIENCE (criminal justice, economics, history, human development, humanities, industrial and organizational psychology, paralegal studies, philosophy, political science/government, public administration, social science, and sociology). Medical biophysics and radiation biology are the strongest academically. Business, sociology, communications and speech, and government have the largest enrollments.

Required: All students must complete 122 semester hours with at least a 2.0 cumulative GPA and a minimum 2.0 GPA in the major. Distribution requirements vary by degree program.

Special: Suffolk offers numerous cooperative education and work-study programs in the Boston area. Cross-registration is offered with New England School of Arts and Design (B.F.A.), Center for International Studies in Madrid, Northeast Broadcasting School, International University in Moscow, and Stilwell School for International Studies in Chongoing, China. Study abroad in 25 countries and a full-time, one-semester internship in Washington, D.C., as well as local and international internships, are possible. A combined 3–2 engineering degree with Boston University and Case Western Reserve University, an accelerated degree program in engineering, majors in medical biophysics and radiation biology taught in collaboration with Massachusetts General Hospital, dual and student-designed majors, and a lawyer's assistant certificate program are also available. There is a freshman honors program on campus, as well as 19 national honor societies. Eight departments have honors programs.

Faculty/Classroom: Sixty-five percent of faculty are male; 35%, female. Eighty-nine percent teach undergraduates, and 76% both teach and do research. No introductory courses are taught by graduate students. The average class size in an introductory lecture is 25; in a laboratory, 17; and in a regular course offering, 23.

Admissions: About 92% of the 1993–94 applicants were accepted. The SAT scores for the 1993–94 freshman class were as follows: Verbal—84% below 500, 14% between 500 and 599, and 2% between 600 and 700; Math—69% below 500, 25% between 500 and 599, and 6% between 600 and 700. About 30% of the current freshmen were in the top fifth of their class; 53% were in the top two fifths. There was 1 National Merit finalist and 8 semifinalists. About 6 freshmen graduated first in their class.

Requirements: Suffolk requires applicants to be in the upper 60% of their class. A minimum GPA of 2.0 is required. The SAT I or ACT is required. Applicants should have a high school diploma or the GED. Recommended secondary preparation includes 4 years of English, 3 years of mathematics, 2 years each of a foreign language, history, and social studies, and 1 year of science. Exact requirements differ by degree program. A personal essay is required and an interview is recommended. AP and CLEP credits are accepted. Important factors used in the admissions decision are recommendations by school officials, personality, intangible qualities, advanced placement or honor courses, leadership record, and parents or siblings attending the school.

Procedure: Freshmen are admitted to all sessions. Entrance exams should be taken by December of the senior year. Applications should be filed by May 1 for fall entry, December 15 for spring entry, and April 15 for summer entry, along with an application fee of $30. Notification is sent on a rolling basis. There are early decision, early admissions, and deferred admissions plans.

Transfer: About 383 transfer students enrolled in 1993–94. Transfer applicants should have a minimum 2.2 GPA from an accredited college. Those with fewer than 15 college credits must submit a high school transcript. A total of 30 credits out of 122 must be completed at Suffolk.

Visiting: There are regularly scheduled orientations for prospective students. There are guides for informal visits and visitors may sit in on classes. To arrange for a visit, contact the Admissions Office at (617) 573–8460 or (800) 6 SUFFOLK.

Financial Aid: In 1993–94 67% of all current freshmen and 51% of continuing students received some form of financial aid. About 61% of freshmen and 44% of continuing students received need-based aid. The average freshman award was $5988. Of that total, scholarships or need-based grants averaged $3696 ($9800 maximum); loans averaged $2943 ($3900 maximum); and work contracts averaged $1176 ($1500 maximum). All undergraduate students work part-time. Average earnings from campus work for the school year are $1200. The average financial indebtedness of the 1992–93 graduate was $10,000. Suffolk is a member of CSS. The college's own financial statement, verification of income, and the FAFSA are required. The deadline for financial aid applications is March 1.

International Students: There are currently 330 international students enrolled. The school actively recruits these students. They must take the TOEFL or the college's own test and achieve a minimum score on the TOEFL of 500.

Computers: The college provides computer facilities for student use. The mainframe is a Prime 6350 super minicomputer. Various computer laboratories located around the campus house 175 microcomputers with access to the mainframe. There are also numerous stand-alone microcomputers available for academic use. All students may access the system. There are no time limits on using the system and no fees.

Graduates: In 1992–93 592 bachelor's degrees were awarded. The most popular majors among graduates were sociology (16%), management (15%), and finance (11%). Within an average freshman class, 1% graduate in 3 years, 47% in 4 years, 56% in 5 years, and 57% in 6 years. Some 77 companies recruited on campus in 1992–93. In the 1992 graduating class, 11% of men and women were enrolled in graduate school within 6 months of graduation; 85% had found employment.

Admissions Contact: William F. Coughlin, Director of Admissions.

TUFFS UNIVERSITY
TUFTS UNIVERSITY   **D-2**
Medford, MA 02155   (617) 627-3170

Full-time: 2172 men, 2424 women	Faculty: 346; I, +$
Part-time: none	Ph.D.s: 99%
Graduate: 1582 men, 1820 women	Student/Faculty: 13 to 1
Year: semesters, summer session	Tuition: $19,269
Application Deadline: January 1	Room & Board: $5693
Freshman Class: 7615 applied, 3605 accepted, 1205 enrolled	
SAT I Verbal/Math: 580/660	**MOST COMPETITIVE**

Tufts University, founded in 1852, is a private, coeducational institution offering undergraduate programs in liberal arts and sciences, education, and engineering. There are 2 undergraduate and 9 graduate schools. In addition to regional accreditation, Tufts has baccalaureate program accreditation with ABET, ADA, and CAHEA. The 2 libraries contain 743,000 volumes, 845,000 microform items, and 19,000 audiovisual forms, and subscribe to 5600 periodicals. Computerized library sources and services include the card catalog, interlibrary loans, and database searching. Special learning facilities include a learning resource center, art gallery, radio station, and TV station. The 140-acre campus is in a suburban area 5 miles northwest of Boston. Including residence halls, there are 167 buildings on campus.

Student Life: About 74% of undergraduates are from out-of-state, mostly the Middle Atlantic. Students come from 50 states, 62 foreign countries, and Canada. Sixty-five percent are from public schools; 25% from private; 10% from parochial. Seventy-three percent are white; 11% Asian American. The average age of freshmen is 18; all undergraduates, 20. One percent drop out by the end of their first year; 89% remain to graduate.

Housing: A total of 3550 students can be accommodated in college housing. College-sponsored living facilities include single-sex and coed dormitories, on-campus apartments, fraternity houses, and sorority houses. In addition, there are language houses, special interest houses, and cooperative houses. On-campus housing is guaranteed for the freshman and sophomore years only. Freshman and sophomores are required to live on campus or commute from home. On-campus housing is available on a lottery system for upperclassmen. Eighty percent of students live on campus. Upperclassmen may keep cars on campus.

Activities: About 15% of men belong to 10 national fraternities; about 4% of women belong to 4 national sororities. There are 130 groups on campus, including art, band, cheerleading, chess, choir, chorale, chorus, computers, dance, drama, ethnic, gay, honors, international, jazz band, literary magazine, marching band, musical theater, newspaper, orchestra, pep band, photography, political, professional, radio and TV, religious, social, social service, student government, symphony, and yearbook. Popular campus events include a dramatic arts series, national and international forums, and an international affairs symposium.

Sports: There are 16 intercollegiate sports for men and 15 for women, and 11 intramural sports for men and 9 for women. Athletic and recreation facilities include a football stadium, 2 gymnasiums, an 8-lane, all-weather track, baseball, softball, and playing fields, 9 tennis courts, a field house, an indoor cage, an indoor track, 7 squash courts, a swimming pool, a dance room, a weight room, a sauna, a sailing center, and a new exercise center.

Disabled Students: Ninety percent of the campus is accessible to disabled students. The following facilities are available: wheelchair ramps, elevators, special parking, specially equipped rest rooms, special class scheduling, lowered drinking fountains, and lowered telephones. Also available are special services as needed.

Services: In addition to many counseling and information services, tutoring is available in some subjects as needed through the Academic Resources Center. There is also a reader service for the blind.

Campus Safety and Security: Campus safety and security measures include 24-hour foot and vehicle patrol, escort service, shuttle buses, and informal discussions. In addition, there are pamphlets, posters, and films, emergency telephones, and lighted pathways and sidewalks.

Programs of Study: Tufts awards the B.A., B.S., B.S.C.E., B.S.Ch.E., B.S.E., B.S.E.E., B.S.E.S., and B.S.M.E. degrees. Master's and doctoral degrees also are awarded. Bachelor's degrees are awarded in BIOLOGICAL SCIENCE (biology/biological science), COMMUNICATIONS AND THE ARTS (art history and appreciation, classics, dramatic arts, English, French, German, Greek, Latin, music, Russian, and Spanish), COMPUTER AND PHYSICAL SCIENCE (chemistry, computer science, geology, mathematics, and physics), EDUCATION (early childhood), ENGINEERING AND ENVIRONMENTAL DESIGN (chemical engineering, civil engineering, computer engineering, electrical/electronics engineering, engineering, engineering physics, engineering science, environmental science, and mechanical engineering), SOCIAL SCIENCE (American studies, anthropology, archeology, Asian/Oriental studies, clinical psychology, economics, experimental psychology, history, international relations, philosophy, political science/government, psychobiology, psychology, religion, Russian and Slavic studies, social psychology, and sociology). English, international relations, and political science have the largest enrollments.

Required: Liberal arts students must complete 34 courses, 10 of which are in the area of concentration. Requirements include foundation courses in writing and foreign language or culture and courses in humanities, arts, social sciences, mathematics, and natural sciences. Requirements for engineering students include a total of 38 courses, 12 of which are in the area of concentration, and distribution requirements in English, mathematics and science, humanities, and social sciences.

Special: The university offers cross-registration at Swarthmore College, Boston University, Boston College, and Brandeis University, a Washington semester, and study abroad in England, Spain, France, Moscow, and Germany. Many internships are available. Double majors in the liberal arts are common; student-designed majors are possible. There are 5-year programs awarding bachelor's and master's degrees in engineering and liberal arts, a B.A.-B.F.A. program with the Museum School of Fine Arts, and a B.A.-B.M. program with the New England Conservatory of Music. Pass/fail options are offered. There are 4 national honor societies on campus, including Phi Beta Kappa.

Faculty/Classroom: Sixty percent of faculty are male; 40%, female. All both teach and do research. No introductory courses are taught by graduate students. The average class size in all course offerings is 25.

Admissions: About 47% of the 1993–94 applicants were accepted. The SAT scores for the 1993–94 freshman class were as follows: Verbal—7% below 500, 50% between 500 and 599, 40% between 600 and 700, and 3% above 700; Math—1% below 500, 17% between 500 and 599, 53% between 600 and 700, and 29% above 700. About 87% of the current freshmen were in the top fifth of their class; 97% were in the top two fifths.

Requirements: The university accepts either the SAT I and the results of 3 SAT II: Subject tests, or the ACT. Liberal arts applicants should take the SAT II: Subject test in writing and 2 others; engineering applicants should take writing, mathematics level I or II, and either physics or chemistry. In addition, all applicants should be high school graduates or hold the GED. Academic preparation is expected to include 4 years of English, 3 years each of humanities and a foreign language, 2 years each of social and natural sciences, and 1 year of history. A personal essay is required. AP credits are accepted. Important factors used in the admissions decision are strength of academic record, advanced placement or honor courses, recommendations by school officials, extracurricular activities record, leadership record, and personality, intangible qualities.

Procedure: Freshmen are admitted in the fall. Entrance exams should be taken by January of the senior year. Early decision applications should be filed by November 15 and January 1; regular applications, by January 1 for fall entry, along with an application fee of $50. Notification of early decision is sent December 15 and February 1; regular decision, April 1. There are early decision, early admissions, and deferred admissions plans. About 270 early decision candidates were accepted for the 1993–94 class. A waiting list is an active part of the admissions procedure.

Transfer: About 115 transfer students enrolled in 1993–94. Admission is competitive. Primary consideration is given to college and secondary school achievement and record of personal involvement. A total of 17 courses out of 34 must be completed at Tufts.

Visiting: There are regularly scheduled orientations for prospective students, including orientation sessions twice a day, Monday through Friday, followed by campus tours. There are orientation sessions and

tours on selected Saturday mornings during the fall. There are guides for informal visits, and visitors may sit in on classes and stay overnight at the school. To arrange for a visit, contact the Admissions Office at (617) 627-3170.

Financial Aid: In 1993-94 40% of all current freshmen and 39% of continuing students received some form of financial aid. About 37% of freshmen and 35% of continuing students received need-based aid. The average freshman award was $14,398. Of that total, scholarships or need-based grants averaged $12,233 ($23,000 maximum); loans averaged $3200 ($3625 maximum); and work contracts averaged $1400 ($1800 maximum). Forty-two percent of undergraduate students work part-time. Average earnings from campus work for the school year are $1350. Tufts is a member of CSS. The FAF, the college's own financial statement, and the FAFSA are required. The deadline for financial aid applications is February 1.

International Students: There are currently 368 international students enrolled. The school actively recruits these students. They must take the TOEFL if English is not the first language. The student must also take the ACT, or the SAT I and 3 SAT II: Subject tests.

Computers: The college provides computer facilities for student use. The mainframes are a DEC VAX 4300 and a DEC MicroVAX 3600 running VMS, and a Convex 3220 minisupercomputer running UNIX. Mainframes and PC laboratories are networked on a Tufts-wide computer network called Jumbonet. There are 150 terminals and microcomputers in 5 locations across campus, supported by 45 printers in various locations. A special computer-aided design (CAD) laboratory is available to undergraduates. All students may access the system. It may be used 24 hours a day. There are no time limits on using the system and no fees.

Graduates: In 1992-93 1144 bachelor's degrees were awarded. The most popular majors among graduates were English (15%), international relations (10%), and political science (9%). Within an average freshman class, 89% graduate in 4 years. Some 150 companies recruited on campus in 1992-93. About 30% of graduates go on directly to graduate and professional schools. After 10 years, 70% of graduates have an advanced degree.

Admissions Contact: David Cuttino, Dean of Admissions.

UNIVERSITY OF LOWELL
Lowell, MA 01854   D-1
                                          (508) 934-3939

Full-time: 3573 men, 2100 women | Faculty: 519; I, -$
Part-time: 327 men, 312 women | Ph.D.s: 79%
Graduate: 1489 men, 1074 women | Student/Faculty: 11 to 1
Year: semesters, summer session | Tuition: $4530 ($9674)
Application Deadline: open | Room & Board: $4301
Freshman Class: n/av
SAT I or ACT: required | **VERY COMPETITIVE**

The University of Lowell, founded in 1895, is a public institution offering undergraduate programs through schools or arts and sciences, engineering, health professions, management science, and music, and graduate programs in education. There are 5 undergraduate schools and one graduate school. In addition to regional accreditation, the university has baccalaureate program accreditation with AACSB, ABET, APTA, CAHEA, NASAD, NASM, NCATE, and NLN. The 3 libraries contain 400,000 volumes, 625,000 microform items, and 17,100 audiovisual forms, and subscribe to 3400 periodicals. Computerized library sources and services include the card catalog, interlibrary loans, and database searching. Special learning facilities include a radio station, many experimental and investigative laboratories, and the Research Foundation, which includes a materials testing division and centers for atmospheric research and tropical disease. The 100-acre campus is in an urban area 30 miles northwest of Boston. Including residence halls, there are 37 buildings on campus.

Student Life: About 90% of undergraduates are from Massachusetts. Students come from 20 states and 48 foreign countries. Seventy-nine percent are white. The average age of freshmen is 18.

Housing: A total of 2536 students can be accommodated in college housing. College-sponsored living facilities include dormitories, off-campus apartments, married-student housing, and special interest houses. On-campus housing is available on a first-come, first-served basis. All students may keep cars on campus.

Activities: There are no fraternities or sororities on campus. There are 85 groups on campus, including art, cheerleading, computers, drama, ethnic, international, marching band, newspaper, photography, political, professional, radio and TV, religious, social, social service, student government, and yearbook.

Sports: There are 15 intercollegiate sports for men and 10 for women, and 34 intramural sports each for men and women. Athletic and recreation facilities include a gymnasium seating 2000, a pool, weight-training facilities, and areas for gymnastics, wrestling, and judo. There are also courts for handball, squash, and tennis, and various playing fields.

Disabled Students: The following facilities are available: wheelchair ramps, elevators, special parking, specially equipped rest rooms, special class scheduling, lowered drinking fountains, and lowered telephones.

Services: In addition to many counseling and information services, tutoring is available in most subjects. There is also a reader service for the blind, and remedial math, reading, and writing.

Programs of Study: The university awards the B.A., B.S., B.F.A., B.L.A., B.M., B.S.B.A., B.S.E., B.S.E.T., B.S.I.M., and B.S.I.T. degrees. Associate, master's, and doctoral degrees also are awarded. Bachelor's degrees are awarded in BIOLOGICAL SCIENCE (biology/biological science and biotechnology), BUSINESS (accounting, banking and finance, business administration and management, business economics, marketing/retailing/merchandising, and personnel management), COMMUNICATIONS AND THE ARTS (English, fine arts, French, modern language, music, and Spanish), COMPUTER AND PHYSICAL SCIENCE (atmospheric sciences and meteorology, chemistry, computer science, geology, mathematics, physics, and statistics), EDUCATION (health and music), ENGINEERING AND ENVIRONMENTAL DESIGN (chemical engineering, civil engineering, electrical/electronics engineering, engineering technology, environmental science, industrial engineering technology, mechanical engineering, nuclear engineering, and plastics engineering), HEALTH PROFESSIONS (clinical science, medical laboratory technology, nursing, radiograph medical technology, and sports medicine), SOCIAL SCIENCE (American studies, criminal justice, economics, history, philosophy, political science/government, psychology, and sociology). Engineering and management have the largest enrollments.

Required: All students must complete a minimum of 120 credits with a 2.0 GPA. Core requirements include 6 credits of English composition, 3 credits of human values, and an area distribution requirement of 27 to 29 credits outside the major in behavioral and social science, fine arts and the humanities, and mathematics and the sciences.

Special: Cross-registration, and cooperative and work-study programs are available, as are opportunities for study abroad. The university offers a combined B.A.-B.S. in Engineering, and dual majors and nondegree study, as well as pass/fail options. There is a freshman honors program on campus, as well as 2 national honor societies.

Faculty/Classroom: Seventy-eight percent of faculty are male; 22%, female.

Requirements: A minimum GPA of 2.5 is required. The SAT I or the ACT is required. In addition, applicants should have a high school diploma or the GED. The university recommends that secondary preparation include 4 English courses, 3 courses each in social science/history and mathematics, 2 courses each in science and a foreign language, and 2 elective academic courses. Prospective music majors must audition, and an interview is recommended for all students. AP and CLEP credits are accepted.

Procedure: Freshmen are admitted in the fall and spring. Entrance exams should be taken by January of the senior year. Application deadlines are open. The application fee is $20 for Massachusetts residents, $35 for nonresidents. Notification is sent on a rolling basis. There is a deferred admissions plan.

Transfer: About 850 transfer students enrolled in an earlier year. Transfer applicants must present at least a 2.0 GPA in previous college work, and must complete at least 30 credits in residence for a bachelor's degree. Those with fewer than 30 credits must meet freshman admission requirements. A total of 30 credits out of at least 120 must be completed at the university.

Financial Aid: In an earlier class, 40% of continuing students received some form of financial aid. The university is a member of CSS. The FAF is required. The deadline for financial aid applications is May 1.

International Students: There were 444 international students enrolled in an earlier year. They must take the TOEFL. The student must also take the SAT I or the ACT.

Computers: The college provides computer facilities for student use. The mainframes are clusters of DEC VAX 6420s, 8700s, and 8800s. Some 2500 terminals, microcomputers, and workstations are linked to more than 150 multiuser systems in a campus-wide communications network. All students may access the system. There are no time limits and no fees.

Graduates: In an earlier class, 1438 bachelor's degrees were awarded. Some 234 companies recruited on campus in an earlier year.

Admissions Contact: Office of Admissions.

UNIVERSITY OF MASSACHUSETTS

The University of Massachusetts, established in 1863, is the public university system in Massachusetts. It is governed by a board of trustees and its CEO is the president. The primary goal of the university system is the coordination of campus teaching, research, and service. The main priorities are fiscal management, legal counsel, and academic and student affairs coordination and collaberation. The total

enrollment for fall 1993 of all 5 campuses was 50,151; there were 3,321 faculty members. Altogether there are 187 baccalaureate, 101 master's, and 47 doctoral programs offered in the University of Massachusetts System. Profiles of the 4-year campuses are included in this chapter in alphabetical order with other Massachusetts schools.

UNIVERSITY OF MASSACHUSETTS DARTMOUTH
North Dartmouth, MA 02747

E-4

(508) 999–8606

Full-time: 2314 men, 2264 women	Faculty: 335; IIA, av$
Part-time: 139 men, 167 women	Ph.D.s: 96%
Graduate: 194 men, 164 women	Student/Faculty: 14 to 1
Year: semesters, summer session	Tuition: $3568 ($8651)
Application Deadline: open	Room & Board: $4590
Freshman Class: 3137 applied, 2349 accepted, 999 enrolled	
SAT I Verbal/Math: 423/482	COMPETITIVE

University of Massachusetts Dartmouth is a public institution that was founded in 1895 to meet the needs of the area's textile industry. Undergraduate programs now emphasize a comprehensive college curriculum. There are 5 undergraduate and 10 graduate schools. In addition to regional accreditation, UMass Dartmouth has baccalaureate program accreditation with ABET, NASAD, and NLN. The library contains 341,165 volumes, 43,505 microform items, and 107,659 audiovisual forms, and subscribes to 2083 periodicals. Computerized library sources and services include the card catalog, interlibrary loans, and database searching. Special learning facilities include a learning resource center, art gallery, radio station, observatory, marine research vessels, and a number of cultural and research centers. The 710-acre campus is in a suburban area 60 miles south of Boston. Including residence halls, there are 20 buildings on campus.

Student Life: About 94% of undergraduates are from Massachusetts. Students come from 25 states, 27 foreign countries, and Canada. Eighty-five percent are from public schools; 15% from private. Ninety-two percent are white. The average age of freshmen is 19; all undergraduates, 20. Ten percent drop out by the end of their first year; 60% remain to graduate.

Housing: A total of 2100 students can be accommodated in college housing. College-sponsored living facilities include coed dormitories and on-campus apartments. In addition, there is a quiet house, apartment-style living, and substance-free apartments. On-campus housing is guaranteed for all 4 years. Sixty-one percent of students commute. All students may keep cars on campus.

Activities: There are no fraternities or sororities on campus. There are 100 groups on campus, including art, band, cheerleading, choir, chorale, chorus, computers, drama, ethnic, gay, honors, international, jazz band, literary magazine, musical theater, newspaper, orchestra, pep band, photography, political, professional, radio and TV, religious, ROTC (Army), social, social service, student government, symphony, and yearbook. Popular campus events include Welcome Back Week, Homecoming, Winterfest, Spring Fling Week, Cultural Awareness Week, Eisteddfod Traditional Arts Festival, and Black History Month.

Sports: There are 10 intercollegiate sports for men and 10 for women, and 7 intramural sports for men and 7 for women. Athletic and recreation facilities include a 3000-seat gymnasium, a 1850-seat football stadium, an aquatic sports center, and 13 tennis courts.

Disabled Students: Ninety percent of the campus is accessible to disabled students. The following facilities are available: wheelchair ramps, elevators, special parking, specially equipped rest rooms, special class scheduling, lowered drinking fountains, lowered telephones, mobility assistance, note takers/readers, alternative testing, and office of disabled student services.

Services: In addition to many counseling and information services, tutoring is available in most subjects through the writing/reading, science/engineering, and mathematics/business centers. There is also a reader service for the blind and remedial math and writing.

Campus Safety and Security: Campus safety and security measures include 24-hour foot and vehicle patrol, self defense education, escort service, and shuttle buses. In addition, there are pamphlets, posters, and films, emergency telephones, lighted pathways and sidewalks, and bicycle patrol.

Programs of Study: UMass Dartmouth awards the B.A., B.S., B.F.A., B.Mus., and B.S.N. degrees. Master's degrees also are awarded. Bachelor's degrees are awarded in BIOLOGICAL SCIENCE (biology/biological science and marine biology), BUSINESS (accounting, banking and finance, business administration and management, and marketing/retailing/merchandising), COMMUNICATIONS AND THE ARTS (art history and appreciation, ceramic art and design, design, English, fiber/textiles/weaving, fine arts, French, graphic design, illustration, music, painting, photography, Portuguese, printmaking, sculpture, and Spanish), COMPUTER AND PHYSICAL SCIENCE (chemistry, computer science, information sciences and systems, mathematics, and physics), EDUCATION (art and foreign languages), ENGINEERING AND ENVIRONMENTAL

DESIGN (civil engineering, computer engineering, electrical/electronics engineering, electrical/electronics engineering technology, engineering, mechanical engineering, and textile technology), HEALTH PROFESSIONS (medical laboratory science, medical laboratory technology, nursing, and premedicine), SOCIAL SCIENCE (anthropology, criminal justice, economics, history, humanities, interdisciplinary studies, philosophy, political science/government, psychology, social work, and sociology). Engineering, biology, visual design, chemistry, and nursing are the strongest academically. Psychology, sociology, English, and business have the largest enrollments.

Required: Distribution requirements vary within the individual colleges, but all students must maintain a minimum 2.0 GPA and complete 120 to 127 credit hours. Freshman English and electives in the humanities, social sciences, and physical sciences are required.

Special: The school offers a fashion-merchandising option with the Fashion Institute of Technology in New York and permits cross-registration with the SACHEM Consortium of 8 schools in Massachusetts. Study abroad in 5 countries, a co-op program, a Washington semester, internships, numerous work-study programs, dual and student-designed majors, and an accelerated program in chemistry are available. Teacher certification is available in elementary and secondary education. Nondegree study and pass/fail options are possible. Students also may receive credit for life experiences. There is a freshman honors program on campus, as well as 1 national honor society. All departments have honors programs.

Faculty/Classroom: Seventy-two percent of faculty are male; 28%, female. All teach undergraduates, and 50% both teach and do research. No introductory courses are taught by graduate students. The average class size in an introductory lecture is 25; in a laboratory, 15; and in a regular course offering, 25.

Admissions: About 75% of the 1993–94 applicants were accepted. About 24% of the current freshmen were in the top fifth of their class; 62% were in the top two fifths.

Requirements: The SAT I is required. The school recommends applicants have 4 years of English, 3 years each of mathematics and electives, 2 years each of science and foreign language, and 1 year each of social studies and U.S. history. An audition also is necessary for music majors. The GED is accepted. AP and CLEP credits are accepted. Important factors used in the admissions decision are advanced placement or honor courses, recommendations by school officials, leadership record, evidence of special talent, and extracurricular activities record.

Procedure: Freshmen are admitted fall and spring. Entrance exams should be taken during the spring of the senior year. Application deadlines are open. The fee is $20 (in-state) and $40 (out-of-state). Notification of early decision is sent December 15; regular decision, on a rolling basis. There are early decision, early admissions, and deferred admissions plans. About 27 early decision candidates were accepted for a recent class.

Transfer: About 570 transfer students enrolled in 1993–94. Transfer applicants must take the SAT I unless they graduated from high school more than 3 years prior. They must also submit previous course descriptions. An associate degree is recommended if they are from a community college. A total of 60 credits out of 120 to 127 must be completed at UMass Dartmouth.

Visiting: There are regularly scheduled orientations for prospective students, including scheduled campus tours Monday through Friday and financial and informational sessions on Tuesdays and Thursdays. There are guides for informal visits, and visitors may sit in on classes. To arrange for a visit, contact the Admissions Office at (508) 999–8606.

Financial Aid: In 1993–94 52% of all current freshmen and 49% of continuing students received some form of financial aid. Thirty percent of undergraduate students work part-time. UMass Dartmouth is a member of CSS. The FAFSA financial statement is required. The preferred filing date for financial aid applications is March 1.

International Students: There are currently 114 international students enrolled. They must take the TOEFL and the SAT I.

Computers: The college provides computer facilities for student use. The mainframes are a DEC VAX 8650 and a DEC VAX 11/785. There are several computer laboratories on campus that have more than 200 microcomputers available, and computer ports are in every dormitory room for students with their own terminal to hook into the university mainframe. All students may access the system. It may be used usually during school and evening hours as well as weekends. There are no time limits on using the system and no fees.

Graduates: In a recent year 1035 bachelor's degrees were awarded. The most popular majors among graduates were accounting (8%), humanities/social studies (7%), and management (6%). Some 400 companies recruited on campus in a recent year.

Admissions Contact: Raymond M. Barrows, Admissions Director.

UNIVERSITY OF MASSACHUSETTS AMHERST

B-2

(Formerly University of Massachussetts at Amherst)

Amherst, MA 01003 (413) 545-0222

Full-time: 8307 men, 7691 women	Faculty: 1152; I, av$
Part-time: 431 men, 477 women	Ph.D.s: 92%
Graduate: 2871 men, 2988 women	Student/Faculty: 14 to 1
Year: semesters, summer session	Tuition: $5467 ($11,813)
Application Deadline: February 15	Room & Board: $3897

Freshman Class: 14,438 applied, 12,414 accepted, 3822 enrolled

SAT I or ACT: required **LESS COMPETITIVE**

The University of Massachusetts/Amherst, established in 1863, is a land-grant, coeducational institution offering undergraduate and graduate degrees in its 9 schools and colleges. In addition to regional accreditation, UMass/Amherst has baccalaureate program accreditation with AACSB, ABET, ADA, ASLA, FIDER, NASM, NCATE, NLN, NRPA, and SAF. The 4 libraries contain 2,587,957 volumes, 1,993,325 microform items, and 12,665 audiovisual forms, and subscribe to 15,546 periodicals. Computerized library sources and services include the card catalog, interlibrary loans, and database searching. Special learning facilities include a learning resource center, art gallery, radio station, and TV station. The 1405-acre campus is in a small town 90 miles west of Boston. Including residence halls, there are 353 buildings on campus.

Student Life: About 78% of undergraduates are from Massachusetts. Students come from 48 states, 74 foreign countries, and Canada. Eighty percent are from public schools; 20% from private. Eighty-two percent are white. Sixty percent did not report their religious affiliation; 25% are Catholic. The average age of freshmen is 18; all undergraduates, 21.

Housing: A total of 10,592 students can be accommodated in college housing. College-sponsored living facilities include single-sex and coed dormitories, on-campus apartments, married-student housing, fraternity houses, and sorority houses. In addition, there are honors houses, language houses, special interest houses, as well as language corridors, a social awareness corridor, and family housing. On-campus housing is available on a lottery system for upperclassmen. Fifty-eight percent of students live on campus; of those, 80% remain on campus on weekends. All students may keep cars on campus.

Activities: About 7% of men belong to 2 local and 19 national fraternities; about 5% of women belong to 1 local sorority and 12 national sororities. There are 190 groups on campus, including art, band, cheerleading, chess, choir, chorale, chorus, computers, dance, drama, ethnic, film, gay, honors, international, jazz band, literary magazine, marching band, musical theater, newspaper, opera, orchestra, pep band, photography, political, professional, radio and TV, religious, social, social service, student government, symphony, and yearbook. Popular campus events include Mid-night Madness (first basketball practice), basketball games, Spring Pond Concert, Asian Night, International Fair, Mullins Center Events, and Homecoming.

Sports: There are 14 intercollegiate sports for men and 14 for women, and 21 intramural sports for men and 20 for women. Athletic and recreation facilities include 120 acres of playing fields, a 20,000-seat outdoor stadium, and lighted tennis courts. Indoor facilities include 3 pools, handball/squash/racquetball courts, 2 gymnastics centers, a wrestling room, a physiotherapy laboratory with steam bath and whirlpool for visiting athletes, 2 dance studios, fencing facilities, an indoor track, universals, crew tanks, weight training rooms, and the Mullins indoor sports arena, a 10,500-seat multi-purpose facility that houses 2 Olympic-size ice sheets, 7 raquetball courts, and additional athletic training facilities.

Disabled Students: All programs are made accessible through accommodations. The following facilities are available: wheelchair ramps, elevators, special parking, specially equipped rest rooms, special class scheduling, lowered drinking fountains, and lowered telephones.

Services: In addition to many counseling and information services, tutoring is available in most subjects. There is a reader service for the blind and remedial math and reading.

Campus Safety and Security: Campus safety and security measures include 24-hour foot and vehicle patrol, self defense education, escort service, and shuttle buses. In addition, there are informal discussions, pamphlets, posters, and films, emergency telephones, lighted pathways and sidewalks, and tight restrictions on residence hall access.

Programs of Study: UMass/Amherst awards the B.A., B.S., B.B.A., B.F.A., B.G.S., B.Mus., B.S.C.E., B.S.Ch.E., B.S.C.S.E., B.S.E.F., B.S.I.E.O.R., and B.S.M.E. degrees. Associate, master's, and doctoral degrees also are awarded. Bachelor's degrees are awarded in AGRICULTURE (animal science, forestry and related sciences, natural resource management, plant protection (pest management), plant science, and soil science), BIOLOGICAL SCIENCE (biochemistry, biology/biological science, entomology, microbiology, nutrition, plant pathology, and wildlife biology), BUSINESS (accounting, business administration and management, hotel/motel and restaurant management, marketing/retailing/merchandising, and sports management), COMMUNICATIONS AND THE ARTS (art history and appreciation, Chinese, classics, communications, comparative literature, dance, design, dramatic arts, English, fine arts, French, German, Italian, Japanese, journalism, linguistics, music, Portuguese, Russian, and Spanish), COMPUTER AND PHYSICAL SCIENCE (astronomy, chemistry, computer science, geology, mathematics, and physics), EDUCATION (art, early childhood, elementary, home economics, middle school, and secondary), ENGINEERING AND ENVIRONMENTAL DESIGN (chemical engineering, civil engineering, computer engineering, electrical/electronics engineering, environmental design, environmental science, industrial engineering, landscape architecture/design, and mechanical engineering), HEALTH PROFESSIONS (medical laboratory technology, nursing, predentistry, premedicine, and speech pathology/audiology), SOCIAL SCIENCE (African American studies, anthropology, economics, ethics, politics, and social policy, family/consumer studies, food science, geography, history, human development, Judaic studies, liberal arts/general studies, Near Eastern studies, philosophy, physical fitness/movement, political science/government, prelaw, psychology, Russian and Slavic studies, sociology, and women's studies). Biology, communication, economics, engineering, hotel, restaurant, and travel administration, journalism, and psychology are the strongest academically. Psychology, English, communication, and hotel, restaurant and travel administration have the largest enrollments.

Required: For graduation, students must complete 120 credit hours and maintain a minimum GPA of 2.0 overall and in the major, with at least 2 courses fulfilling a diversity requirement. The general education requirements for all students include courses in writing, the social world, the biological and physical world, mathematics, and analytic reasoning.

Special: Cross-registration with the Five-College Consortium (Smith, Mt. Holyoke, Hampshire, and Amherst College) is possible. Students may participate in co-op programs, internships in every major, study abroad in 28 countries, a Washington semester, and work-study programs in various university departments. The institution offers B.A.-B.S. degees in 99 majors, dual majors in several subjects, and student-designed majors. The University Without Walls program gives credit for life, military, and work experience. Other special academic features include the National Student Exchange Program, International Exchange Agreements, University Honors Program, Minority and Women Engineering Programs, Bilingual Collegiate Program, and the Committee for the College Education of Black and Other Minority Students. There is a freshman honors program on campus, as well as 16 national honor societies, including Phi Beta Kappa. Forty-five departments have honors programs.

Faculty/Classroom: Seventy-seven percent of faculty are male; 23%, female. The average class size in an introductory lecture is 42; in a laboratory, 18; and in a regular course offering (lectures and laboratories), 35.

Admissions: About 86% of the 1993–94 applicants were accepted. The SAT scores for the 1993–94 freshman class were as follows: Verbal—66% below 500, 27% between 500 and 599, and 7% between 600 and 700; Math—36% below 500, 40% between 500 and 599, 20% between 600 and 700, and 4% above 700. About 29% of the current freshmen were in the top fifth of their class; 65% were in the top two fifths. There were 8 National Merit finalists.

Requirements: The SAT I or ACT is required. In addition, applicants must be graduates of an accredited secondary school or have the GED. The university recommends that students complete 16 Carnegie units, including 4 years of English, 3 years of mathematics, 2 years of foreign language and laboratory science, plus 3 years of electives. Students must present a portfolio for admission to the art program, and an audition is necessary for admission to music and dance. AP and CLEP credits are accepted. Important factors used in the admissions decision are advanced placement or honor courses, evidence of special talent, recommendations by school officials, leadership record, and extracurricular activities record.

Procedure: Freshmen are admitted fall and spring. Entrance exams should be taken before February 15. Applications should be filed by February 15 for fall entry and October 15 for spring entry, along with an application fee of $20 for in-state and $35 for out-of-state. Notification is sent on a rolling basis. There is a deferred admissions plan.

Transfer: About 1270 transfer students enrolled in 1993–94. Transfer applicants with fewer than 30 credits must take the SAT I and submit an essay. Priority is given to students with an associate degree. Grades of C or better transfer for credit. A total of 45 credits out of 120 must be completed at UMASS/Amherst.

Visiting: There are regularly scheduled orientations for prospective students. There are guides for informal visits, and visitors may sit in on classes and stay overnight at the school. For tours and open houses, call New Students Program at (413) 545-2621.

Financial Aid: In 1993–94 50% of all students received some form of financial aid; 45% received need-based aid. The average freshman award was $6254. Of that total, scholarships or need-based grants averaged $1300 ($6200 maximum); loans averaged $1500 ($4800 maximum); and work contracts averaged $1200 ($1500 maximum). Fifty-eight percent of undergraduate students work part-time. Average earnings from campus work for the school year are $1600. The average financial indebtedness of the 1992–93 graduate was $6500. UMass/Amherst is a member of CSS. The FAFSA financial statement is required. The deadline for financial aid applications is March 1.

International Students: There are currently 503 international students enrolled. They must take the TOEFL and achieve a minimum score of 550. The student must also take the SAT I or the ACT.

Computers: The college provides computer facilities for student use. The mainframes are a VAXcluster (2 VAX 6420s) running VMS; 2 DEC/system 5500s running ULTRIX; a CDC CYBER 840 running NOS/VE; and a CDC 830 providing access to the CYBIS computer-aided instruction system. There are 70 IBM-compatible and 65 Apple Macintosh computers available in 4 computer classrooms that are open most of the day for walk-in use. There are also 70 terminals accessing the mainframe, which students can use for $10 a semester. Computers are also available through numerous academic departments. Access to the mainframe is available in the residence halls to students who own computers. All students may access the system and there are no time limits.

Graduates: In 1992–93 4212 bachelor's degrees were awarded. The most popular majors among graduates were English (6%), psychology (6%), and communication (5%). Within an average freshman class, 45% graduate in 4 years, 63% in 5 years, and 66% in 6 years. Some 300 companies recruited on campus in 1992–93. In the 1992 graduating class, 41% of all students planned to enroll in graduate school within 6 months after graduation; 71% of all graduates had found employment within 6 months of graduation.

Admissions Contact: Arlene Cash, Director, University Admissions Center.

UNIVERSITY OF MASSACHUSETTS BOSTON

Boston, MA 02125–3393

E-2

(617) 287-6000

Full-time: 2905 men, 3090 women	Faculty: 473; IIA, +$
Part-time: 1702 men, 2111 women	Ph.D.s: 88%
Graduate: 847 men, 1481 women	Student/Faculty: 13 to 1
Year: semesters, summer session	Tuition: $4253 ($10,601)
Application Deadline: June 15	Room & Board: n/app
Freshman Class: 2237 applied, 1496 accepted, 800 enrolled	
SAT I Verbal/Math: 420/465	COMPETITIVE

The University of Massachusetts/Boston, established in 1964, is a public, coeducational institution offering undergraduate studies in arts and sciences and in the professions. There are 4 undergraduate schools. In addition to regional accreditation, UMass Boston has baccalaureate program accreditation with NLN. The library contains 535,971 volumes, 686,369 microform items, and 1939 audiovisual forms, and subscribes to 3062 periodicals. Computerized library sources and services include the card catalog, interlibrary loans, and database searching. Special learning facilities include a learning resource center, art gallery, radio station, a tropical greenhouse, an observatory, an adaptive computer laboratory, a languages laboratory, and an applied language and mathematics center. The 177-acre campus is in an urban area 5 miles south of downtown Boston. There are 10 buildings on campus.

Student Life: About 96% of undergraduates are from Massachusetts. Students come from 25 states, 44 foreign countries, and Canada. Seventy-one percent are white; 14% African American. The average age of freshmen is 23; all undergraduates, 28. Twenty-nine percent drop out by the end of their first year; 45% remain to graduate.

Housing: There are no residence halls. All students commute. Alcohol is not permitted. All students may keep cars on campus.

Activities: There are no fraternities or sororities on campus. There are 73 groups on campus, including art, band, cheerleading, chess, chorale, chorus, computers, dance, drama, ethnic, film, gay, honors, international, jazz band, literary magazine, musical theater, newspaper, photography, political, professional, radio and TV, religious, social, social service, student government, and yearbook. Popular campus events include Convocation Day, seasonal festivals, lecture series, films, and senior events.

Sports: There are 10 intercollegiate sports for men and 5 for women, and 16 intramural sports for men and 15 for women. Athletic and recreation facilities include an athletic center with a 3500-seat gymnasium with 4 basketball courts and 2 volleyball courts, an ice rink which seats 1000, an Olympic-size swimming pool with high-dive area, a multipurpose weight room, and a sports medicine area; an 8-lane 400-meter track; 8 tennis courts; a softball diamond; 3 multipurpose

fields primarily used for football, soccer, and lacrosse; racquetball and squash courts; a boat house, dock, and a fleet of sailboats and rowing dories; and several other recreational fields.

Disabled Students: The entire campus is accessible to disabled students. The following facilities are available: wheelchair ramps, elevators, special parking, specially equipped rest rooms, special class scheduling, lowered drinking fountains, lowered telephones, amplified phones, powered doors, indoor-connected building access, accessible shuttle bus, tape recorders, adaptive computer laboratory, and center for students with disabilities.

Services: In addition to many counseling and information services, tutoring is available in every subject. In addition, there is a reader service for the blind, and remedial math, reading, and writing. There are also reading study skills workshops and a mathematics resource center available.

Campus Safety and Security: Campus safety and security measures include 24-hour foot and vehicle patrol, self defense education, escort service, and shuttle buses. In addition, there are informal discussions, pamphlets, posters, and films, emergency telephones, lighted pathways and sidewalks, Operation ID, motorist assistance, and crime prevention programs.

Programs of Study: UMass Boston awards the B.A. and B.S. degrees. Master's and doctoral degrees also are awarded. Bachelor's degrees are awarded in BIOLOGICAL SCIENCE (biology/biological science), BUSINESS (labor studies and management science), COMMUNICATIONS AND THE ARTS (classics, dramatic arts, English, fine arts, French, German, Greek (classical), Italian, Latin, music, Russian, and Spanish), COMPUTER AND PHYSICAL SCIENCE (applied mathematics, chemistry, computer science, physics, and pure mathematics), EDUCATION (physical/human performance and fitness), ENGINEERING AND ENVIRONMENTAL DESIGN (engineering physics), HEALTH PROFESSIONS (medical laboratory technology and nursing), SOCIAL SCIENCE (African American studies, anthropology, community services, criminal justice, economics, geography, gerontology, history, human services, philosophy, political science/government, psychology, sociology, and women's studies). Management, English, and psychology have the largest enrollments.

Required: For graduation, students must complete 120 credit hours (123 hours in the College of Nursing) and maintain a minimum GPA of 2.0. Distribution requirements vary by college. All students must demonstrate writing proficiency. The College of Public and Community Service uses a competency-based curriculum.

Special: Students may cross-register with Massachusetts College of Art, Bunker Hill Community College, Roxbury Community College, and Hebrew College. Cooperative programs, internships, study abroad, and work-study programs are available. The college permits student-designed majors and dual and interdisciplinary majors, including public policy, anthropology/history, biology/medical technology, philosophy/public policy, and psychology/sociology. B.A.-B.S. degrees, nondegree study, and pass/fail options are available. A 2–2 engineering program is possible with various area institutions, and the College of Public and Community Service provides social-oriented education, generally to older students. There is a freshman honors program on campus, as well as 3 national honor societies.

Faculty/Classroom: Sixty-four percent of faculty are male; 36%, female. All both teach and do research. Graduate students teach 4% of introductory courses. The average class size in an introductory lecture is 32 and in a laboratory, 29.

Admissions: About 67% of the 1993–94 applicants were accepted. The SAT scores for the 1993–94 freshman class were as follows: Verbal—78% below 500, 18% between 500 and 599, and 4% between 600 and 700; Math—64% below 500, 28% between 500 and 599, 7% between 600 and 700, and 1% above 700. About 22% of the current freshmen were in the top fifth of their class; 52% were in the top two fifths.

Requirements: UMass Boston requires applicants to be in the upper 50% of their class. A minimum GPA of 2.0 is required. The SAT I is required with a minimum composite score of 800. The ACT may be substituted for the SAT I, and SAT I scores are not required of students who have been out of high school for 3 or more years. Applicants should be graduates of an accredited secondary school. The GED is accepted. The university requires the completion of 16 Carnegie units for admission to freshmen standing, including 4 years of English, 3 of mathematics, 2 each of foreign language, science, and social studies, and 3 electives in the above academic areas or in humanities, arts, or computer science. The school recommends that applicants submit an essay. AP and CLEP credits are accepted. Important factors used in the admissions decision are advanced placement or honor courses, recommendations by school officials, personality, intangible qualities, evidence of special talent, and leadership record.

Procedure: Freshmen are admitted fall and spring. Entrance exams should be taken no later than fall of the senior year in high school. Applications should be filed by June 15 for fall entry and November 1 for spring entry, along with an application fee of $20 ($35 for nonresi-

dents). Notification is sent on a rolling basis. There is a deferred admissions plan. A waiting list is an active part of the admissions procedure.

Transfer: A total of 1666 transfer students enrolled in 1993–94. Transfer students with fewer than 30 credits must meet freshman requirements. To transfer, students must have a GPA of 2.3 (2.8 for management, nursing, and engineering applicants) or better. Grades of C or better transfer for credit. A total of 30 credits out of 120 to 123 must be completed at UMass Boston.

Visiting: There are regularly scheduled orientations for prospective students, including general information about the university and the admissions process and a tour of the campus. There are guides for informal visits and visitors may sit in on classes. To arrange for a visit, contact The Admissions Information Service at (617) 287–6016.

Financial Aid: In 1993–94, 66% of all current freshmen and 50% of continuing students received some form of financial aid. About 64% of freshmen and 50% of continuing students received need-based aid. The average freshman award was $5212. Of that total, scholarships or need-based grants averaged $2746 ($4253 maximum); loans averaged $2625 ($5500 maximum); and work contracts averaged $1507 ($2500 maximum). Fourteen percent of undergraduate students work part-time. Average earnings from campus work for the school year are $1507. The average financial indebtedness of the 1992–93 graduate was $8047. The FAF and the college's own financial statement are required. The deadline for financial aid applications is March 1.

International Students: There are currently 147 international students enrolled. They must take the TOEFL and achieve a minimum score of 500.

Computers: The university provides computer facilities for student use. The mainframes are DEC VAX models 8800, 6000–410, and 6000–510. Students may access the mainframe through terminals located in the terminal room. There are also a number of microcomputer laboratories containing Macintosh, IBM, and/or IBM-compatible microcomputers. There are 390 terminals and microcomputers that may be used by students, with most in the library and the remainder in classroom buildings. All students may access the system 24 hours daily. There are no time limits on using the system and no fees.

Graduates: In 1992–93, 1579 bachelor's degrees were awarded. The most popular majors among graduates were management (16%), English (10%), psychology (10%), and nursing (10%). Within an average freshman class, 1% graduate in 3 years, 13% in 4 years, 16% in 5 years, and 8% in 6 years. Some 36 companies recruited on campus in 1992–93.

Admissions Contact: Office of Admissions Information Service.

UNIVERSITY OF MASSACHUSSETTS AT AMHERST

(See University of Massachusetts/Amherst)

WELLESLEY COLLEGE
D-2
Wellesley, MA 02181
(617) 283–2270

Full-time: 2158 women	Faculty: 241; IIB, + +$
Part-time: 191 women	Ph.Ds: 93%
Graduate: none	Student/Faculty: 9 to 1
Year: semesters	Tuition: $17,725
Application Deadline: January 15	Room & Board: $6090
Freshman Class: 2843 applied, 1267 accepted, 579 enrolled	
SAT I Verbal/Math: 610/640	**MOST COMPETITIVE**

Wellesley College, established in 1870, is an independent liberal arts college for women. The 4 libraries contain 690,000 volumes, 60,898 microform items, and 15,092 audiovisual forms, and subscribe to 4000 periodicals. Computerized library sources and services include the card catalog, interlibrary loans, and database searching. Special learning facilities include a learning resource center, art gallery, radio station, science center, botanic greenhouse, observatory, center for developmental studies and services, and centers for research on women and child study. The 500-acre campus is in a suburban area 12 miles west of Boston. Including residence halls, there are 64 buildings on campus.

Student Life: About 79% of undergraduates are from out-of-state, mostly the Middle Atlantic. Students come from 50 states, 63 foreign countries, and Canada. Sixty-seven percent are from public schools; 33% from private. Fifty-two percent are white; 22% Asian American; 10% African American. The average age of freshmen is 18; all undergraduates, 20. Three percent drop out by the end of their first year; 87% remain to graduate.

Housing: A total of 2120 students can be accommodated in college housing. College-sponsored living facilities include dormitories. In addition, there are language houses and special interest houses. On-campus housing is guaranteed for all 4 years. Ninety-eight percent of students live on campus. Upperclassmen may keep cars on campus.

Activities: There are no sororities on campus. There are 139 groups on campus, including art, choir, computers, dance, drama, ethnic, film, gay, honors, international, jazz band, literary magazine, musical theater, newspaper, orchestra, photography, political, professional, radio and TV, religious, social, social service, student government, symphony, and yearbook. Popular campus events include Parents Weekend, Step-Singing, Hoop-Rolling, Spring Weekend, Junior Show, Christmas Vespers, and Flower Sunday.

Sports: There are 11 intercollegiate and 21 intramural sports available. Athletic and recreation facilities include an indoor pool, dance studios, a weight room, an indoor track, and courts for racquetball, squash, tennis, and volleyball.

Disabled Students: The campus is accessible to disabled students. The following facilities are available: wheelchair ramps, elevators, special parking, specially equipped rest rooms, special class scheduling, lowered drinking fountains, lowered telephones, and specially equipped dormitories.

Services: In addition to many counseling and information services, tutoring is available in every subject. There is also a reader service for the blind.

Campus Safety and Security: Campus safety and security measures include 24-hour foot and vehicle patrol, self-defense education, escort service, and shuttle buses. In addition, there are informal discussions, pamphlets, posters, and films, emergency telephones, and lighted pathways and sidewalks.

Programs of Study: Wellesley awards the B.A. degree. Bachelor's degrees are awarded in BIOLOGICAL SCIENCE (biochemistry, biology/biological science, biophysics, and evolutionary biology), COMMUNICATIONS AND THE ARTS (art history and appreciation, Chinese, dramatic arts, English, fine arts, French, German, Greek, Italian, Japanese, languages, Latin, music, Russian, Spanish, and studio art), COMPUTER AND PHYSICAL SCIENCE (astronomy, chemistry, computer science, geology, mathematics, and physics), EDUCATION (secondary), ENGINEERING AND ENVIRONMENTAL DESIGN (architectural engineering), and SOCIAL SCIENCE (African American studies, American studies, anthropology, archeology, Asian/Oriental studies, classical/ancient civilization, cognitive science, economics, European studies, history, international relations, Judaic studies, Latin American studies, medieval studies, peace studies, philosophy, political science/government, psychobiology, psychology, religion, sociology, and women's studies). Psychology, English, art history, economics, political science, biological sciences, and French have the largest enrollments.

Required: All students must complete 32 units, at least 8 of which are in the major field, with a minimum 2.0 GPA. Requirements include 3 courses each in humanities, social science, and natural science and mathematics; 1 multicultural course; 1 semester of expository writing in any department; and 8 credits in physical education. Students must also possess proficiency in a modern or ancient foreign language.

Special: Students may cross-register at MIT or Brandeis University, or participate in exchange programs with Spelman College, GA, and Mills College, CA, as well as members of the Twelve-College Exchange. Study abroad is possible in Wellesley-administered programs in various countries, in exchange programs in Russia and Japan, and at Cambridge and Oxford in England. There are summer internship programs in Boston and Washington, D.C. Dual majors, student-designed majors, nondegree study, and pass/fail options are possible. A 3–2 program with MIT awards a B.A.-B.S. degree. There are 2 national honor societies on campus, including Phi Beta Kappa. All departments have honors programs.

Faculty/Classroom: Forty-two percent of faculty are male; 58%, female. All both teach and do research. The average class size in an introductory lecture is 25; in a laboratory, 15; and in a regular course offering, 21.

Admissions: About 45% of the 1993–94 applicants were accepted. The SAT scores for the 1993–94 freshman class were as follows: Verbal—9% below 500, 32% between 500 and 599, 49% between 600 and 700, and 10% above 700; Math—6% below 500, 22% between 500 and 599, 49% between 600 and 700, and 23% above 700. About 94% of the current freshmen were in the top fifth of their class; all were in the top two fifths. Thirty freshmen graduated first in their class.

Requirements: The SAT I is required, as are 3 SAT II: Subject tests, including writing and any 2 others. Most successful applicants are high school graduates or have earned the GED and taken college-preparatory courses. There are no high school course requirements, but the college expects training in writing and interpretation of literature, at least 4 years each of mathematics and a modern or ancient language, at least 2 years of natural science, and at least 1 year of social science. A personal essay is required and an interview is recommended. AP credits are accepted. Important factors used in the admissions decision are advanced placement or honor courses, leadership record, extracurricular activities record, evidence of special talent, and recommendations by school officials.

Procedure: Freshmen are admitted in the fall. Entrance exams should be taken during spring of the junior year or fall of the senior year. Early decision applications should be filed by November 1; regular applications, by January 15 for fall entry, along with an application fee of $45. Notification of early decision is sent December 15; regular decision, April 1. There are early decision, early admissions, and deferred admissions plans. About 80 early decision candidates were accepted for the 1993–94 class. A waiting list is an active part of the admissions procedure.

Transfer: Twenty-six transfer students enrolled in 1993–94. Applicants must provide high school and college transcripts and SAT I scores. An interview is required. A total of 16 units out of 32 must be completed at Wellesley.

Visiting: There are guides for informal visits and visitors may sit in on classes and stay overnight at the school. To arrange for a visit, contact the Admissions Office at (617) 283-2270.

Financial Aid: In 1993–94, 60% of all current freshmen and 72% of continuing students received some form of financial aid. About 53% of freshmen and 55% of continuing students received need-based aid. The average freshman award was $15,959. Of that total, scholarships or need-based grants averaged $12,935 ($20,825 maximum); loans averaged $2455 ($7625 maximum); and work contracts averaged $1800 ($2000 maximum). Fifty-eight percent of undergraduate students work part-time. Average earnings from campus work for the school year are $1309. The average financial indebtedness of the 1992–93 graduate was $13,248. Wellesley is a member of CSS. The FAF, the FAFSA, the college's own financial statement, and the most recent income tax returns of the parents and the student are required. The deadline for financial aid applications is February 1.

International Students: There are currently 194 international students enrolled. The school actively recruits these students. They must take the TOEFL and achieve a minimum score of 600. The student must also take the SAT I. Students must take SAT II: Subject tests in writing and 2 other subjects.

Computers: The college provides computer facilities for student use. The mainframe is a DEC VAX 8550. Students may access the mainframe through more than 150 computer terminals located in the science center, library, and dormitories. All students may access the system. There are no time limits and no fees.

Graduates: In 1992–93, 611 bachelor's degrees were awarded. The most popular majors among graduates were political science (15%), economics (14%), and English (12%). Within an average freshman class, 82% graduate in 4 years, 86% in 5 years, and 87% in 6 years. Some 136 companies recruited on campus in 1992–93. In the 1992 graduating class, 39% of the women were enrolled in graduate school within 6 months of graduation; 61% of the women had found employment.

Admissions Contact: Janet A. Lavin, Director of Admission.

WENTWORTH INSTITUTE OF TECHNOLOGY E-2
Boston, MA 02115 (617) 442-9010, ext. 219; (800) 556-0610

Full-time: 1889 men, 294 women	**Faculty:** 116
Part-time: 20 men, 184 women	**Ph.D.s:** 90%
Graduate: none	**Student/Faculty:** 19 to 1
Year: semesters, summer session	**Tuition:** $9250
Application Deadline: June 1	**Room & Board:** $6000
Freshman Class: 1925 applied, 1603 accepted, 655 enrolled	
SAT I Verbal/Math: 370/460	**LESS COMPETITIVE**

Wentworth Institute of Technology, founded in 1904, is a private, coeducational college specializing in architecture, design, engineering, technology, and management. In addition to regional accreditation, WIT has baccalaureate program accreditation with ABET, FIDER, and NAAB. The library contains 77,000 volumes, 90 microform items, and 750 audiovisual forms, and subscribes to 500 periodicals. Computerized library sources and services include the card catalog, interlibrary loans, and database searching. Special learning facilities include a learning resource center, a welding shop, a printed-circuit laboratory, CAD/CAM/CAE laboratories, design studios, and numerically controlled manufacturing systems. The 30-acre campus is in an urban area in Boston. Including residence halls, there are 21 buildings on campus.

Student Life: About 75% of undergraduates are from Massachusetts. Students come from 22 states, 65 foreign countries, and Canada. Seventy-two percent are white. The average age of freshmen is 20; all undergraduates, 22. Thirty-three percent drop out by the end of their first year; 50% remain to graduate.

Housing: A total of 613 students can be accommodated in college housing. College-sponsored living facilities include coed dormitories and on-campus apartments. On-campus housing is available on a first-come, first-served basis. Priority is given to out-of-town students. Seventy percent of students commute. Alcohol is not permitted. All students may keep cars on campus.

Activities: There are no fraternities or sororities on campus. There are 35 groups on campus, including cheerleading, computers, ethnic, honors, international, literary magazine, newspaper, professional, religious, social, student government, and yearbook. Popular campus events include Design Lecture Series, International Student Week, Black History Month, Women's History Month, Beaux Arts Ball, National Collegiate Alcohol Awareness Week, and Campus Carnival.

Sports: There are 9 intercollegiate sports for men and 5 for women, and 9 intramural sports for men and 9 for women. Athletic and recreation facilities include gymnasiums, tennis courts, a riflery range, a weight-lifting room, and an outdoor basketball court.

Disabled Students: Thirty percent of the campus is accessible to disabled students. The following facilities are available: wheelchair ramps, elevators, special parking, specially equipped rest rooms, special class scheduling, lowered drinking fountains, and lowered telephones.

Services: In addition to many counseling and information services, free tutoring is available to all students through the learning center. A 1-year preparatory curriculum is available for students who need additional preparation before starting college.

Campus Safety and Security: Campus safety and security measures include 24-hour foot and vehicle patrol, escort service, informal discussions, and pamphlets, posters, and films. In addition, there are emergency telephones and lighted pathways and sidewalks. All campus police officers have emergency medical training.

Programs of Study: WIT awards the B.S. and B.Arch. degrees. Associate degrees also are awarded. Bachelor's degrees are awarded in COMMUNICATIONS AND THE ARTS (industrial design and technical and business writing), COMPUTER AND PHYSICAL SCIENCE (computer science), ENGINEERING AND ENVIRONMENTAL DESIGN (architectural engineering, architecture, civil engineering technology, computer engineering, construction management, construction technology, electromechanical technology, electronics engineering technology, environmental engineering, interior design, manufacturing engineering, mechanical engineering technology, and technological management). Architectural engineering technology, electronics engineering technology, and building construction technology have the largest enrollments.

Required: For a bachelor's degree, students must complete a total of 148 hours in most majors, with a minimum GPA of 2.5 in the major and 2.0 overall. An introductory computer course is required of all students.

Special: Cooperative programs, study abroad, student-designed majors, interdisciplinary majors, including engineering technology and facilities planning and management, and nondegree study are possible. Most students at the bachelor's level attend school in the summer, as most cooperative work occurs during the academic year. There is 1 national honor society on campus.

Faculty/Classroom: All faculty teach undergraduates. The average class size in an introductory lecture is 28; in a laboratory, 28; and in a regular course offering, 25.

Admissions: About 83% of the 1993–94 applicants were accepted. The SAT scores for the 1993–94 freshman class were as follows: Verbal—92% below 500, 7% between 500 and 599, and 1% between 600 and 700; Math—62% below 500, 28% between 500 and 599, and 10% between 600 and 700. About 17% of the current freshmen were in the top fifth of their class; 42% were in the top two fifths. One freshman was first in a graduating class.

Requirements: SAT I or ACT scores are required of freshmen for all programs except Tech One, the 1-year preparatory curriculum. Applicants must be graduates of an accredited secondary school or have the GED. High school course requirements vary by major. AP and CLEP credits are accepted.

Procedure: Freshmen are admitted fall and winter. Entrance exams should be taken in the spring of the junior year and/or fall of the senior year. Applications should be filed by June 1 for fall entry and December 1 for winter entry, along with an application fee of $30. Notification is sent on a rolling basis. There is a deferred admissions plan.

Transfer: About 203 transfer students enrolled in 1993–94. Requirements for transfer students vary by program. Grades of C or better transfer for credit. Transfer students are admitted for fall or winter semesters. Transfer students must take 50% of the course work in their degree program at Wentworth to graduate. Portfolios and faculty reviews are required of applicants to industrial design, interior design, and architecture programs.

Visiting: There are regularly scheduled orientations for prospective students, including a 2-day orientation with optional overnight stay. There are guides for informal visits, and visitors may sit in on classes and stay overnight at the school. To arrange for a visit, contact Gaynell Cummings, the Admissions Office, at (617) 442-9010, ext. 219 or (800) 556-0610.

Financial Aid: In 1993–94 52% of all current freshmen and 26% of continuing students received some form of financial aid. About 51% of freshmen and 26% of continuing students received need-based aid. The average freshman award was $5527. Of that total, scholar-

ships or need-based grants averaged $2246 ($9250 maximum); loans averaged $2539 ($4825 maximum); and work contracts averaged $1360 ($1600 maximum). Seventeen percent of undergraduate students work part-time. Average earnings from campus work for the school year are $960. The average financial indebtedness of the 1992–93 graduate was $6206. WIT is a member of CSS. The college's own financial statement and the FAFSA are required. The deadline for financial aid applications is March 1.

International Students: There are currently 211 international students enrolled. The school actively recruits these students. They must take the TOEFL or the University of Michigan Language Test and achieve a minimum score on the TOEFL of 520.

Computers: The college provides computer facilities for student use. The mainframe is a DEC VAX 400/300. The academic VAX may be accessed via 30 terminals and several modems, as well as from 115 networked microcomputers in various student laboratories. In addition, 70 Apple Macintosh Quadra, Centris, and IIci systems are available in student laboratories throughout the institute. All students may access the system. There are no time limits on using the system and no fees.

Graduates: In 1992–93 542 bachelor's degrees were awarded. The most popular majors among graduates were electronics engineering technology (19%), architectural engineering technology (11%), and mechanical engineering technology (10%). Some 20 companies recruited on campus in 1992–93. In the 1992 graduating class, 68% of all students had found employment within 6 months of graduation.

Admissions Contact: Samuel Burgio, Assistant Director of Admissions.

WESTERN NEW ENGLAND COLLEGE   B-3

Springfield, MA 01119   (413) 782-1321; (800) 325-1122
Full-time: 1079 men, 724 women   Faculty: 105; IIA, +$
Part-time: 650 men, 466 women   Ph.D.s: 76%
Graduate: 985 men, 770 women   Student/Faculty: 17 to 1
Year: semesters, summer session   Tuition: $9274
Application Deadline: open   Room & Board: $5400
Freshman Class: 1650 applied, 1471 accepted, 409 enrolled
SAT I Verbal/Math: 400/460   **LESS COMPETITIVE**

Western New England College, founded in 1919, is a private, nonsectarian, coeducational institution offering programs in business, engineering, liberal arts, teacher preparation, and pharmacy. There are 3 undergraduate and 2 graduate schools. In addition to regional accreditation, WNEC has baccalaureate program accreditation with ABET and CSWE. The 2 libraries contain 284,619 volumes, 1720 microform items, and 2356 audiovisual forms, and subscribe to 4361 periodicals. Computerized library sources and services include the card catalog, interlibrary loans, and database searching. Special learning facilities include an art gallery and a radio station. The 131-acre campus is in a suburban area 90 miles west of Boston. Including residence halls, there are 29 buildings on campus.

Student Life: About 54% of undergraduates are from Massachusetts. Students come from 31 states, 25 foreign countries, and Canada. Eighty-three percent are from public schools; 17% from private. Ninety-two percent are white. Sixteen percent are Catholic. The average age of freshmen is 18; all undergraduates, 21.7. Twenty-eight percent drop out by the end of their first year; 54% remain to graduate.

Housing: A total of 1256 students can be accommodated in college housing. College-sponsored living facilities include single-sex and coed dormitories, on-campus apartments, and married-student housing. In addition there are special interest houses and special interest floors, including healthful living and community service floors. On-campus housing is guaranteed for all 4 years. Fifty-seven percent of students live on campus; of those, 75% remain on campus on weekends. All students may keep cars on campus.

Activities: About 1% of men and women belong to 1 local fraternity; about 1% of women belong to 1 local sorority. There are 42 groups on campus, including art, cheerleading, computers, drama, ethnic, honors, international, literary magazine, musical theater, newspaper, pep band, photography, political, professional, religious, social, social service, student government, and yearbook. Popular campus events include Parents Weekend, Homecoming Weekend, Community Festival, Sibling Weekend, and Spring Week.

Sports: There are 11 intercollegiate sports for men and 7 for women, and 10 intramural sports for men and 7 for women. Athletic and recreation facilities include a healthful living center with facilities for basketball (2000 seats), wrestling, racquetball, squash, aerobics, fitness and volleyball, as well as a weight room, an Olympic-size pool, and a track. There is also a 1200-seat football stadium.

Disabled Students: Ninety percent of the campus is accessible to disabled students. The following facilities are available: wheelchair ramps, elevators, special parking, specially equipped rest rooms, special class scheduling, lowered drinking fountains, and lowered telephones.

Services: In addition to many counseling and information services, tutoring is available for most entry-level courses and various upper-level courses. Additional assistance is provided through the mathematics and writing centers.

Campus Safety and Security: Campus safety and security measures include 24-hour foot and vehicle patrol, escort service, informal discussions, and pamphlets, posters, and films. In addition, there are emergency telephones, lighted pathways and sidewalks, security cameras, medical response, fire response, and a comprehensive public safety awareness program.

Programs of Study: WNEC awards the B.A., B.S., B.S.B.A., B.S.E., B.S.E.E., B.S.I.E., B.S.M.E., and B.S.W. degrees. Associate, master's, and doctoral degrees also are awarded. Bachelor's degrees are awarded in BIOLOGICAL SCIENCE (biology/biological science), BUSINESS (accounting, banking and finance, business administration and management, management science, marketing/retailing/merchandising, and personnel management), COMMUNICATIONS AND THE ARTS (communications, English, and journalism), COMPUTER AND PHYSICAL SCIENCE (chemistry, computer science, information sciences and systems, mathematics, and quantitative methods), ENGINEERING AND ENVIRONMENTAL DESIGN (bioengineering, computer engineering, electrical/electronics engineering, industrial administration/management, industrial engineering, and mechanical engineering), HEALTH PROFESSIONS (pharmacy), SOCIAL SCIENCE (criminal justice, economics, history, law enforcement and corrections, political science/government, psychology, social work, and sociology). Engineering, pharmacy, sciences, and mathematics are the strongest academically. Criminal justice, marketing, and accounting have the largest enrollments.

Required: For graduation, students must complete a total of 120 credit hours, at least 30 of them at the college, with a minimum GPA of 2.0. Required courses include 2 each in English, mathematics, laboratory science, and physical education, 1 each in history and culture, and computer and college success skills courses. Other requirements vary according to the major.

Special: Students may cross-register with cooperating colleges of Greater Springfield. The college offers a 5-year pharmacy program with Massachusetts College of Pharmacy, internships, study abroad, a Washington semester, work-study programs, B.A.-B.S. degrees, an accelerated degree program, dual majors, student-designed majors, credit for life, military, and work experience, and nondegree study. Engineering students must complete a senior project. There are 5 national honor societies on campus.

Faculty/Classroom: Seventy-eight percent of faculty are male; 22%, female. All teach undergraduates. No introductory courses are taught by graduate students. The average class size in an introductory lecture and in a regular course offering is 24.

Admissions: About 89% of the 1993–94 applicants were accepted. The SAT scores for the 1993–94 freshman class were as follows: Verbal—90% below 500, 9% between 500 and 599, and 1% between 600 and 700; Math—68% below 500, 26% between 500 and 599, and 6% between 600 and 700. About 17% of the current freshmen were in the top fifth of their class; 36% were in the top two fifths.

Requirements: A minimum GPA of 2.0 is required. The SAT I or ACT is required. Applicants must be graduates of an accredited secondary school and must have completed 4 years of high school English, 2 plus years of mathematics, 1 or more years of science, and 1 year of history. An interview is recommended. AP and CLEP credits are accepted. Important factors used in the admissions decision are advanced placement or honor courses, extracurricular activities record, recommendations by school officials, leadership record, personality, and intangible qualities.

Procedure: Freshmen are admitted fall and spring. Entrance exams should be taken in the senior year. Application deadlines are open. Application fee is $30. Notification is sent on a rolling basis. There is a deferred admissions plan.

Transfer: A total of 144 transfer students enrolled in 1993–94. Transfer students must have a minimum GPA of 2.0. Grades of C or better transfer for credit. The college admits transfer students in the fall and spring. A total of 30 credits out of 120 must be completed at WNEC.

Visiting: There are regularly scheduled orientations for prospective students, including 8 open houses. There are guides for informal visits and visitors may sit in on classes and stay overnight at the school. To arrange for a visit, contact the Undergraduate Admissions Office at (800) 325-1122, ext. 1321.

Financial Aid: In 1993–94, 55% of all current freshmen and 66% of continuing students received some form of financial aid. About 55% of freshmen and 66% of continuing students received need-based aid. The average freshman award was $6468. Of that total, scholarships or need-based grants averaged $1562 ($6500 maximum); loans averaged $2078 ($4000 maximum); and work contracts averaged $1036 ($2000 maximum). Twenty-seven percent of undergraduate students work part-time. Average earnings from campus work for the school year are $1221. The average financial indebted-

ness of the 1992–93 graduate was $13,161. WNEC is a member of CSS. The college's own financial statement, federal tax returns, and FAFSA are required. The deadline for financial aid applications is April 1.

International Students: There are currently 31 international students enrolled. They must take the TOEFL and achieve a minimum score of 500. Students with the TOEFL or an associate degree need not take the SAT I or ACT.

Computers: The college provides computer facilities for student use. The mainframe is a Data II General MV 10,000. There are also 35 terminals and more than 160 microcomputers in 6 laboratories in various locations on campus. All students may access the system about 80 hours per week. There are no time limits on using the system and no fees.

Graduates: In 1992–93, 603 bachelor's degrees were awarded. The most popular majors among graduates were law enforcement (13%), management (13%), and accounting (9%). Within an average freshman class, 47% graduate in 4 years, 55% in 5 years, and 57% in 6 years. In the 1992 graduating class, 10% of the men and women were enrolled in graduate school within 6 months of graduation; 82% had found employment.

Admissions Contact: Charles R. Pollack, Dean of Enrollment Management.

WESTFIELD STATE COLLEGE
B-3

Westfield, MA 01086   (413) 568–3311; (800) 322–8401 (in-state)

Full-time: 1593 men, 1699 women	Faculty: 169
Part-time: 460 men, 496 women	Ph.D.s: 75%
Graduate: 216 men, 562 women	Student/Faculty: 19 to 1
Year: semesters, summer session	Tuition: $3069 ($7203)
Application Deadline: March 1	Room & Board: $4092
Freshman Class: 3140 applied, 2100 accepted, 823 enrolled	
SAT I: required	COMPETITIVE

Westfield State College, founded in 1838, is a public coeducational college with liberal arts and teacher- preparation programs and professional training. In addition to regional accreditation, Westfield State has baccalaureate program accreditation with NCATE. The library contains 163,500 volumes and 455,000 microform items, and subscribes to 1519 periodicals. Special learning facilities include an art gallery, radio station, and TV station. The 227-acre campus is in a rural area 15 miles west of Springfield. Including residence halls, there are 13 buildings on campus.

Student Life: About 95% of undergraduates are from Massachusetts. Students come from 14 states and 2 foreign countries. Ninety-five percent are white. The average age of freshmen is 18; all undergraduates, 20. Twenty-five percent drop out by the end of their first year; 60% remain to graduate.

Housing: A total of 1900 students can be accommodated in college housing. College-sponsored living facilities include single-sex and coed dormitories and on-campus apartments. On-campus housing is guaranteed for all 4 years. Sixty-five percent of students live on campus; of those, 70% remain on campus on weekends. Upperclassmen may keep cars on campus.

Activities: There are no fraternities or sororities on campus. There are 50 groups on campus, including art, band, cheerleading, choir, chorale, chorus, drama, ethnic, honors, jazz band, literary magazine, musical theater, newspaper, orchestra, pep band, photography, political, professional, radio and TV, religious, social service, student government, and yearbook. Popular campus events include Halloween Dance, Thank God It's Friday, Spring Weekend, Comedy Night, and Student Senate Banquet.

Sports: There are 7 intercollegiate sports for men and 7 for women, and 24 intramural sports for men and 24 for women. Athletic and recreation facilities include a track, baseball and softball fields, tennis courts, a 400-seat gymnasium, and a 5000-seat stadium.

Disabled Students: The following facilities are available: wheelchair ramps, elevators, special parking, specially equipped rest rooms, special class scheduling, and lowered telephones.

Services: In addition to many counseling and information services, tutoring is available in every subject. There is also a reader service for the blind, and remedial math, reading, and writing.

Campus Safety and Security: Campus safety and security measures include 24-hour foot and vehicle patrol, escort service, shuttle buses, and emergency telephones. In addition, there are lighted pathways and sidewalks.

Programs of Study: Westfield State awards the B.A., B.S., and B.S.E degrees. Master's degrees also are awarded. Bachelor's degrees are awarded in BIOLOGICAL SCIENCE (biology/biological science), BUSINESS (business administration and management), COMMUNICATIONS AND THE ARTS (communications, English, fine arts, French, music, and Spanish), COMPUTER AND PHYSICAL SCIENCE (chemistry, computer science, information sciences and systems, and mathematics), EDUCATION (art, business, early childhood, elementary, foreign languages, middle school, music, science, sec-

ondary, and special), SOCIAL SCIENCE (criminal justice, economics, geography, history, political science/government, psychology, social science, and urban studies). Computer science, English, and psychology are the strongest academically. Criminal justice, education, and business have the largest enrollments.

Required: Students must complete a total of 120 credit hours, with 40 credits in 7 specified area and 30 to 40 hours in the major. The college requires a 2.0 GPA overall and 2.0 in major courses. U.S. history is a required course.

Special: Students may cross-register with Cooperating Colleges of Greater Springfield. Internships are for credit only in conjunction with all major programs. The college offers study abroad in 3 countries, a Washington semester for political science majors, dual majors, and some credit for military experience.

Faculty/Classroom: Seventy-three percent of faculty are male; 27%, female. Eighty-five percent teach undergraduates. No introductory courses are taught by graduate students. The average class size in an introductory lecture is 25; in a laboratory, 12; and in a regular course offering, 25.

Admissions: About 67% of the 1993–94 applicants were accepted. The SAT scores for the 1993–94 freshman class were as follows: Verbal—86% below 500, 13% between 500 and 599, and 1% between 600 and 700; Math—70% below 500, 26% between 500 and 599, 4% between 600 and 700, and 1% above 700. About 11% of the current freshmen were in the top fifth of their class; 42% were in the top two fifths.

Requirements: Westfield State requires applicants to be in the upper 60% of their class. A minimum GPA of 2.0 is required. The SAT I is required, with a minimum score of 400 verbal and 350 mathematics. Applicants must be graduates of an accredited secondary school and must have completed 4 years of English, 3 years of mathematics (algebra I and II and geometry), 2 years each of social sciences (including 1 year of U.S history), laboratory sciences, and foreign language, and 3 years of electives. The GED is accepted. A portfolio is required for admission to the art program, and an audition is necessary for admission to the music program. AP and CLEP credits are accepted. Important factors used in the admissions decision are advanced placement or honor courses, leadership record, extracurricular activities record, evidence of special talent, and recommendations by school officials.

Procedure: Freshmen are admitted fall and spring. Entrance exams should be taken in spring of the junior year and fall of the senior year. Applications should be filed by March 1 for fall entry and November 15 for spring entry, along with an application fee of $10. Notification is sent on a rolling basis. A waiting list is an active part of the admissions procedure, with about 2% of applicants on the list.

Transfer: About 450 transfer students enrolled in 1993–94. Transfer students must have more than 24 transferable credits with a minimum GPA of 2.0 (higher for some majors). A grade of D or better with a 2.0 GPA will transfer for credit. Of the 120 credits required for a bachelor's degree, a minimum of 30 credits must be completed at the college. Transfer students are admitted in the fall and spring. A total of 30 credits out of 120 must be completed at Westfield State.

Visiting: There are regularly scheduled orientations for prospective students, including a campus tour, classroom observation, academic department presentations, lunch with faculty, staff, and students, and a question-and-answer session moderated by a panel of administrators. There are guides for informal visits. To arrange for a visit, contact the Admissions Office at (413) 568–3311, ext. 218.

Financial Aid: In 1993–94, 71% of all current freshmen and 69% of continuing students received some form of financial aid. About 72% of students received need-based aid. The average freshman award was $4686. Of that total, scholarships or need-based grants averaged $1150 ($4400 maximum); loans averaged $2435 ($3625 maximum); and work contracts averaged $300 ($1000 maximum). Twenty-one percent of undergraduate students work part-time. The average financial indebtedness of the 1992–93 graduate was $3200. Westfield State is a member of CSS. The FFS and the college's own financial statement are required. The deadline for financial aid applications is April 1.

International Students: International students must take the TOEFL and achieve a minimum score of 550. The student must also take the SAT I.

Computers: The college provides computer facilities for student use. The mainframes are a CDC Cyber 172 and 2 DEC MicroVAX IIs. There are also a number of microcomputers available for student use in laboratories. All students may access the system. There are no time limits on using the system and no fees.

Graduates: In 1992–93, 881 bachelor's degrees were awarded. The most popular majors among graduates were criminal justice (23%), elementary education (16%), and business management (15%). Within an average freshman class, 51% graduate in 4 years, 58% in 5 years, and 62% in 6 years. Some 28 companies recruited on campus in 1992–93.

Admissions Contact: Director of Admission.

WHEATON COLLEGE

Norton, MA 02766

D-3

(508) 285–8251; (800) 394–6003

Full-time: 436 men, 899 women	Faculty: 91; IIB, +$
Part-time: 6 men, 24 women	Ph.D.s: 95%
Graduate: none	Student/Faculty: 15 to 1
Year: semesters	Tuition: $17,790
Application Deadline: February 1	Room & Board: $6050
Freshman Class: 1738 applied, 1373 accepted, 417 enrolled	
SAT I: 530/550	ACT: 24	COMPETITIVE +

Wheaton College, established in 1834, is an independent, coeducational, liberal arts institution. The library contains 309,000 volumes, 39,000 microform items, and 8500 audiovisual forms, and subscribes to 1300 periodicals. Computerized library sources and services include the card catalog, interlibrary loans, and database searching. Special learning facilities include an art gallery, planetarium, radio station, and TV station. The 385-acre campus is in a rural area 35 miles south of Boston. Including residence halls, there are 80 buildings on campus.

Student Life: About 59% of undergraduates are from out-of-state, mostly the Northeast and Middle Atlantic. Students come from 40 states, 28 foreign countries, and Canada. Fifty-seven percent are from public schools; 43% from private. Eighty-four percent are white. The average age of freshmen is 18; all undergraduates, 20. Thirteen percent drop out by the end of their first year; 87% remain to graduate.

Housing: A total of 1247 students can be accommodated in college housing. College-sponsored living facilities include single-sex and coed dormitories. In addition, there are special interest houses and substance-awareness, multicultural-awareness, and international-understanding houses. On-campus housing is guaranteed for all 4 years. Ninety-six percent of students live on campus; of those, 75% remain on campus on weekends. All students may keep cars on campus.

Activities: There are no fraternities or sororities on campus. There are 57 groups on campus, including art, chess, choir, chorale, chorus, dance, drama, ethnic, film, gay, honors, international, literary magazine, musical theater, newspaper, photography, political, radio and TV, religious, social, social service, student government, and yearbook. Popular campus events include Academic Festival, Otis Social Justice Symposium and Award, lectures, concerts, Kwanzaa, Black History Month, Seder, AutumnFest, Parents Weekend, and Spring Weekend.

Sports: There are 9 intercollegiate sports for men and 13 for women, and 16 intramural sports for men and 16 for women. Athletic and recreation facilities include an 8-lane stretch pool; a field house with 5 tennis courts; 3 basketball courts; a 200-meter track; a golf/archery range and batting cage; an 850-seat gymnasium; 7 outdoor tennis courts; a running course; 2 paddle tennis courts; an outdoor golf range; an aerobics/dance studio; and a fitness center.

Disabled Students: Fifty percent of the campus is accessible to disabled students. The following facilities are available: wheelchair ramps, elevators, special parking, specially equipped rest rooms, special class scheduling, and lowered telephones.

Services: In addition to many counseling and information services, tutoring is available in most subjects. Peer tutoring is available. There is also a reader service for the blind and remedial writing, as well as note takers for hearing-impaired students.

Campus Safety and Security: Campus safety and security measures include 24-hour foot and vehicle patrol, self defense education, escort service, and informal discussions. In addition, there are pamphlets, posters, films, emergency telephones, and lighted pathways and sidewalks.

Programs of Study: Wheaton awards the A.B. degree. Bachelor's degrees are awarded in BIOLOGICAL SCIENCE (biochemistry and biology/biological science), COMMUNICATIONS AND THE ARTS (art history and appreciation, classics, creative writing, English, fine arts, French, German, Italian, literature, music, Russian, and Spanish), COMPUTER AND PHYSICAL SCIENCE (chemistry, mathematics, and physics), SOCIAL SCIENCE (American studies, anthropology, Asian/Oriental studies, classical/ancient civilization, economics, history, international relations, philosophy, political science/government, psychobiology, psychology, religion, Russian and Slavic studies, social psychology, and sociology). Arts and sciences are the strongest academically. Psychology has the largest enrollment.

Required: Among the requirements for graduation are 32 credits (4 semester hours equals a credit), with a minimum of 10 credits in the major, at least 3 of which are at the 300 level or above. Students must also fulfill general education requirements and complete 2 physical education courses. The college requires a minimum GPA of 1.67 (C-) in all courses taken in the major.

Special: Students may cross-register at Brown University and several other schools. The school offers study abroad, internship programs, B.A.-B.S. degrees, nondegree study, dual and student-designed majors, interdisciplinary majors, including mathematics and economics,

mathematics and computer science, and theater and English dramatic literature, and a Washington semester at American University. A 3–2 engineering degree is possible, as are pass/fail options. There is a freshman honors program on campus, as well as 6 national honor societies, including Phi Beta Kappa. All departments have honors programs.

Faculty/Classroom: Forty-seven percent of faculty are male; 53%, female. All teach undergraduates. The average class size in an introductory lecture is 50; in a laboratory, 20; and in a regular course offering, 19.

Admissions: About 79% of the 1993–94 applicants were accepted. The SAT scores for the 1993–94 freshman class were as follows: Verbal—30% below 500, 55% between 500 and 599, 14% between 600 and 700, and 1% above 700; Math—25% below 500, 50% between 500 and 599, 23% between 600 and 700, and 2% above 700. The ACT scores were 43% between 21 and 23 and 57% between 24 and 26. About 36% of the current freshmen were in the top fifth of their class; 65% were in the top two fifths. About 3 freshmen graduated first in their class.

Requirements: Submission of SAT I or ACT scores is optional. Upon enrollment, all students are required to submit results of the SAT II: Subject test in writing or the ACT for placement purposes. Applicants must be graduates of an accredited secondary school. Recommended courses include English with emphasis on composition skills, 4 years; foreign language and mathematics, 3 to 4 years each; social studies, 3 years; and laboratory science, 2 to 3 years. The GED is accepted. The college requires an essay and recommends an interview. AP credits are accepted. Important factors used in the admissions decision are advanced placement or honor courses, extracurricular activities record, leadership record, evidence of special talent, and parents or siblings attending the school.

Procedure: Freshmen are admitted to all sessions. Entrance exams should be taken in October and/or November. Early decision applications should be filed by November 15; early action, by December 15; regular applications, by February 1 for fall entry and November 15 for spring entry, along with an application fee of $40. Notification of early decision is sent in late December; early action, February 1; regular decision, April 1. There are early decision, early admissions, and deferred admissions plans. About 40 early decision candidates were accepted for the 1993–94 class. A waiting list is an active part of the admissions procedure, with about 5% of applicants on the list.

Transfer: About 19 transfer students enrolled in 1993–94. Transfer students must have earned a minimum of 1 semester's credit hour. The college transcript is evaluated individually for transfer of credit. A total of 16 course credits out of 32 must be completed at Wheaton.

Visiting: There are regularly scheduled orientations for prospective students, including class visits; tours; panels on financial aid, student life, and athletics; lunch with faculty; and department open houses. There are guides for informal visits, and visitors may sit in on classes and stay overnight at the school. To arrange for a visit, contact the Admission Office at (508) 285–8251 or (800) 394–6003.

Financial Aid: In 1993–94 60% of all current freshmen and 55% of continuing students received some form of financial aid. About 60% of freshmen and 55% of continuing students received need-based aid. The average freshman award was $16,125. Of that total, scholarships or need-based grants averaged $11,681 ($19,175 maximum); loans averaged $3228 ($3625 maximum); and work contracts averaged $1290 ($1300 maximum). Eighty-five percent of undergraduate students work part-time. Average earnings from campus work for the school year are $850. The average financial indebtedness of the 1992–93 graduate was $13,250. Wheaton is a member of CSS. The FAF, the college's own financial statement, and the FAFSA are required. The deadline for financial aid applications is February 15.

International Students: There are currently 63 international students enrolled. The school actively recruits these students. They must take the TOEFL and achieve a minimum score of 550.

Computers: The college provides computer facilities for student use. The mainframe is a DecServer 5000, Model 240. There are 40 computers in the academic computer center available for student use. E-mail is available through 20 public access terminals. All students may access the system. It may be used Monday through Thursday, 8:30 A.M. to 2 A.M.; Friday, 8:30 A.M. to 10 P.M.; Saturday, 10 A.M. to 10 P.M.; Sunday, 10 A.M. to 2 A.M. There are no time limits on using the system and no fees.

Graduates: In 1992–93 313 bachelor's degrees were awarded. The most popular majors among graduates were psychology (12%), English literature (9%), and political science (8%). Within an average freshman class, 70% graduate in 4 years and 74% in 5 years. Some 22 companies recruited on campus in 1992–93. In the 1992 graduating class, 22% of the men and 20% of the women were enrolled in graduate school within 6 months of graduation; 8% of the men and 28% of the women had found employment.

Admissions Contact: Gail Berson, Dean of Admission and Student Aid.

WHEELOCK COLLEGE
E-2

Boston, MA 02215-4176   (617) 734-5200, ext. 206

Full-time: 23 men, 713 women	Faculty: 50; IIA, --$
Part-time: 1 man, 28 women	Ph.Ds: 78%
Graduate: 21 men, 526 women	Student/Faculty: 15 to 1
Year: semesters	Tuition: $12,640
Application Deadline: February 15	Room & Board: $5360
Freshman Class: 399 applied, 335 accepted, 161 enrolled	
SAT I Verbal/Math: 420/440	**LESS COMPETITIVE**

Wheelock College, established in 1888, is a private institution with programs in education and human services. There is one undergraduate and one graduate school. In addition to regional accreditation, Wheelock College has baccalaureate program accreditation with CSWE and NCATE. The library contains 85,000 volumes, 318,918 microform items, and 2480 audiovisual forms, and subscribes to 675 periodicals. Computerized library sources and services include the card catalog, interlibrary loans, and database searching. Special learning facilities include an art gallery and the Wheelock Family Theater. The 9-acre campus is in an urban area in Boston. Including residence halls, there are 10 buildings on campus.

Student Life: About 52% of undergraduates are from out-of-state, mostly the Northeast. Students come from 21 states and 13 foreign countries. Seventy-seven percent are from public schools; 23% from private. Eighty-seven percent are white. The average age of freshmen is 19.2; all undergraduates, 20.1. Nineteen percent drop out by the end of their first year; 70% remain to graduate.

Housing: A total of 545 students can be accommodated in college housing. College-sponsored living facilities include single-sex and coed dormitories. In addition, there is a cooperative living house. On-campus housing is guaranteed for all 4 years. Sixty-seven percent of students live on campus. Upperclassmen may keep cars on campus.

Activities: There are no fraternities or sororities on campus. There are 25 groups on campus, including choir, chorale, drama, ethnic, honors, international, literary magazine, musical theater, newspaper, professional, religious, social, social service, student government, and yearbook. Popular campus events include Senior/Sophomore Banquet, Kid's Day, Family Weekend, Holiday Dinner, Black History Month, Winter Weekend, and Freshman Dinner.

Sports: There are 4 intercollegiate sports for women, and 1 intramural sport for men and 8 for women. Athletic and recreation facilities include a sports complex with a pool, diving boards, racquetball courts, a weight room, an indoor track, a basketball court, crew tanks, and cardiovascular equipment.

Disabled Students: The following facilities are available: wheelchair ramps, elevators, special parking, specially equipped rest rooms, special class scheduling, and lowered drinking fountains.

Services: In addition to many counseling and information services, tutoring is available in every subject. There is a reader service for the blind and remedial math and writing. In addition, academic support services provide individualized programs upon request.

Campus Safety and Security: Campus safety and security measures include escort service, informal discussions, lighted pathways and sidewalks, and and 24-hour foot patrol.

Programs of Study: Wheelock College awards the B.A., B.S., and B.S.W. degrees. Master's degrees also are awarded. Bachelor's degrees are awarded in EDUCATION (early childhood, elementary, and special), SOCIAL SCIENCE (child care/child and family studies, human development, and social work). Teaching, social work, and child life are the strongest programs academically and have the largest enrollments.

Required: To graduate, students must complete between 132 and 140 credit hours, with a minimum GPA of 2.0. The school requires at least a 32-credit major combined with a 36-credit professional studies program. Students must earn 24 credits in English composition, mathematics, human growth and development, children and their environments, freshman seminar, visual and performing arts, and 1 course in first aid. Some majors require a thesis.

Special: The school offers cross-registration with Simmons College. Internships include student teaching and social work practice, and students may pursue a dual major or a B.A.-B.S. degree. Study-abroad programs and pass/fail options are available. Students may receive credit for life and work experience. Students begin practical fieldwork in their freshman year and continue for all 4 years. There is a freshman honors program on campus, as well as 1 national honor society.

Faculty/Classroom: Twenty-three percent of faculty are male; 77%, female. All teach undergraduates, and 71% both teach and do research. No introductory courses are taught by graduate students. The average class size in an introductory lecture is 22; in a laboratory, 16; and in a regular course offering, 16.

Admissions: About 84% of the 1993-94 applicants were accepted. The SAT scores for the 1993-94 freshman class were as follows: Verbal—87% below 500, 11% between 500 and 599, and 2% between 600 and 700; Math—76% below 500, 20% between 500 and 599, and 3% between 600 and 700. About 25% of the current freshmen were in the top fifth of their class; 60% were in the top two fifths.

Requirements: The SAT I or ACT is required. In addition, applicants must be graduates of an accredited secondary school and must have completed 4 years of English, 3 years of mathematics, and 2 years each of science and history. The GED is accepted. The college requires an essay and an interview. AP and CLEP credits are accepted. Important factors used in the admissions decision are advanced placement or honor courses, evidence of special talent, personality, intangible qualities, recommendations by school officials, and extracurricular activities record.

Procedure: Freshmen are admitted fall and spring. Entrance exams should be taken in the spring of the junior year and/or the fall of the senior year. Early decision applications should be filed by December 1; regular applications, by February 15 for fall entry and December 1 for spring entry, along with an application fee of $30. Notification of early decision is sent January 1; regular decision, 1 month after receipt of application. There are early decision and deferred admissions plans. About 30 early decision candidates were accepted for the 1993-94 class.

Transfer: About 111 transfer students enrolled in 1993-94. Transfer students must have a minimum GPA of 2.0 and must present 2 letters of recommendation. Grades of C- or better transfer for credit. A total of 66 credits out of 132 to 140 must be completed at Wheelock College.

Visiting: There are guides for informal visits, and visitors may sit in on classes and stay overnight at the school. To arrange for a visit, contact the Undergraduate Admissions Office at (617) 734-5200, ext. 206.

Financial Aid: In 1993-94 87% of all current freshmen and 74% of continuing students received some form of financial aid. About 87% of freshmen and 74% of continuing students received need-based aid. The average freshman award was $10,500. Of that total, scholarships or need-based grants averaged $5475 ($10,000 maximum); loans averaged $3825; and work contracts averaged $1200. Thirty-three percent of undergraduate students work part-time. Average earnings from campus work for the school year are $800. The average financial indebtedness of the 1992-93 graduate was $15,250. Wheelock College is a member of CSS. The FAF and the college's own financial statement are required. The deadline for financial aid applications is April 15.

International Students: There are currently 12 international students enrolled. They must take the TOEFL and achieve a minimum score of 500.

Computers: The college provides computer facilities for student use. The college's 56 microcomputers are located in the computer center and in the residence halls. All students may access the system. It may be used 24 hours a day any time school is in session. There are no time limits on using the system and no fees.

Graduates: In 1992-93 223 bachelor's degrees were awarded. The most popular majors among graduates were teacher education (72%), social work (18%), and child life (10%). Within an average freshman class, 60% graduate in 4 years and 70% in 5 years. Some 17 companies recruited on campus in 1992-93. In the 1992 graduating class, 7% of all students were enrolled in graduate school within 6 months of graduation; 98% of all graduates had found employment.

Admissions Contact: Lynne E. Dailey, Director of Admissions for Recruitment and Public Relations.

WILLIAMS COLLEGE
A-1

Williamstown, MA 01267   (413) 597-2211

Full-time: 1034 men, 951 women	Faculty: 233; IIB, +$
Part-time: 13 men, 15 women	Ph.Ds: 95%
Graduate: 20 men, 33 women	Student/Faculty: 12 to 1
Year: 4-1-4	Tuition: $18,795
Application Deadline: January 1	Room & Board: $5595
Freshman Class: 4186 applied, 1245 accepted, 526 enrolled	
SAT I or ACT: required	**MOST COMPETITIVE**

Williams College, founded in 1793, is a private coeducational institution offering undergraduate degrees in liberal arts, and graduate degrees in art history and development economics. There are 2 graduate schools. The 9 libraries contain 697,023 volumes, 373,656 microform items, and 22,229 audiovisual forms and subscribe to 3024 periodicals. Computerized library sources and services include the card catalog, interlibrary loans, and database searching. Special learning facilities include a learning resource center, art gallery, planetarium, radio station, 2500-acre experimental forest, environmental studies center, the Center for Foreign Languages, Literatures, and Cultures, and the Chapin Rare Book Library. The 450-acre campus is in a small town 150 miles north of New York City and west of Boston. Including residence halls, there are 97 buildings on campus.

Student Life: About 88% of undergraduates are from out-of-state, mostly the Middle Atlantic. Students come from 50 states, 40 foreign countries, and Canada. Sixty-nine percent are from public schools; 31% from private. Seventy-four percent are white; 10% Asian American. The average age of freshmen is 18; all undergraduates, 20. Two percent drop out by the end of their first year; 95% remain to graduate.

Housing: A total of 1908 students can be accommodated in college housing. College-sponsored living facilities include single-sex and coed dormitories and on-campus co-ops. In addition there is cooperative housing in which students prepare their own meals. On-campus housing is guaranteed for all 4 years. Ninety-six percent of students live on campus; of those, 90% remain on campus on weekends. Upperclassmen may keep cars on campus.

Activities: There are no fraternities or sororities on campus. There are 115 groups on campus, including a capella singing, art, band, chess, choir, chorus, comedy, computers, dance, drama, ethnic, film, gay, handbell choir, honors, international, jazz band, literary magazine, marching band, musical theater, newspaper, orchestra, pep band, photography, political, radio and TV, religious, social service, student government, symphony, and yearbook. Popular campus events include Homecoming, Winter Carnival, Mountain Day, and Multicultural Center-sponsored activities.

Sports: There are 16 intercollegiate sports for men and 15 for women, and 17 intramural sports for men and 17 for women. Athletic and recreation facilities include 2 gymnasiums, a 50-meter pool, a dance studio, a weight room, rowing tanks, a boathouse, a golf course, playing fields, and courts for tennis, squash, and paddle tennis. The campus stadium seats 6795.

Disabled Students: Forty-five percent of the campus is accessible to disabled students. The following facilities are available: wheelchair ramps, elevators, special parking, specially equipped rest rooms, special class scheduling, lowered drinking fountains, and lowered telephones.

Services: In addition to many counseling and information services, tutoring is available in every subject. In addition, there is a reader service for the blind, and remedial math, reading, and writing. Other services include a peer health program, rape and sexual assault hotline, and 10–1 counseling service.

Campus Safety and Security: Campus safety and security measures include 24-hour foot and vehicle patrol, self defense education, escort service, and informal discussions. In addition, there are pamphlets, posters, and films, emergency telephones, and lighted pathways and sidewalks.

Programs of Study: Williams awards the B.A. degree. Master's degrees also are awarded. Bachelor's degrees are awarded in BIOLOGICAL SCIENCE (biology/biological science), COMMUNICATIONS AND THE ARTS (art, art history and appreciation, classics, dramatic arts, English, fine arts, French, German, literature, music, Russian, and Spanish), COMPUTER AND PHYSICAL SCIENCE (astronomy, astrophysics, chemistry, computer science, geology, mathematics, and physics), SOCIAL SCIENCE (American studies, anthropology, Asian/Oriental studies, economics, history, philosophy, political economy, political science/government, psychology, religion, and sociology). English and history have the largest enrollments.

Required: All students must complete 4 winter studies and 32 courses, 9 of which are in the major field, with a C- or higher. Requirements include 3 semester-long courses in each of 3 academic divisions: languages and arts, social sciences, and science and mathematics. Also required are 1 course in cultural pluralism and 4 semesters of physical education.

Special: Students may cross-register at Bennington or North Adams State and study abroad in Madrid, Oxford, Cairo, Beijing, and Kyoto, or any approved program with another college or university. Teaching and medical field experiences, dual and student-designed majors, internships, and a 3–2 engineering program with Columbia University, Renssalaer Polytechnic Institute, Massachusetts Institute of Technology, and Washington University are offered. There are pass/fail options during the Winter Term. Each department offers at least 1 Oxford-model tutorial every year. There are 2 national honor societies on campus, including Phi Beta Kappa.

Faculty/Classroom: Sixty-seven percent of faculty are male; 33%, female. All teach undergraduates and do research. No introductory courses are taught by graduate students. The average class size in an introductory lecture is 20; in a laboratory, 14; and in a regular course offering, 17.

Admissions: About 30% of the 1993–94 applicants were accepted. The SAT scores for the 1993–94 freshman class were as follows: Verbal—5% below 500, 19% between 500 and 599, 45% between 600 and 700, and 31% above 700; Math—3% below 500, 10% between 500 and 599, 35% between 600 and 700, and 52% above 700. The ACT scores were 16% between 24 and 26, 9% between 27 and 28, and 75% above 28. About 95% of the current freshmen were in the

top fifth of their class; 99% were in the top two fifths. There were 59 National Merit finalists.

Requirements: The SAT I or the ACT is required. SAT II: Subject tests in English and 2 other subjects are required. Applicants should be graduates of an accredited high school or have earned the GED. Secondary preparation should include 4 years each of English and mathematics, 3 to 4 years of foreign language, and at least 2 years each of science and social studies. A personal essay must be submitted. AP credits are accepted. Important factors used in the admissions decision are advanced placement or honor courses, recommendations by school officials, evidence of special talent, extracurricular activities record, and leadership record.

Procedure: Freshmen are admitted in the fall. Early decision applications should be filed by November 15; regular applications, by January 1 for fall entry, along with an application fee of $50. Notification of early decision is sent December 15; regular decision, April 10. There are early decision and deferred admissions plans. About 171 early decision candidates were accepted for the 1993–94 class. A waiting list is an active part of the admissions procedure, with about 18% of applicants on the list.

Transfer: About 23 transfer students enrolled in 1993–94. Transfer applicants should present a 3.5 GPA in previous college work, and must submit either SAT I or ACT scores. A total of 4 semesters must be completed at Williams.

Visiting: There are regularly scheduled orientations for prospective students, consisting of panels, forums, class visits, and campus tours. There are guides for informal visits and visitors may sit in on classes and stay overnight at the school. To arrange for a visit, contact the Purple Key Society office at (413) 597-3148.

Financial Aid: In 1993–94 37% of all current freshmen and 35% of continuing students received some form of financial aid. About 37% of freshmen and 35% of continuing students received need-based aid. The average freshman award was $16,970. Of that total, scholarships or need-based grants averaged $13,900 ($20,000 maximum); loans averaged $2200 ($2625 maximum); and work contracts averaged $1400 (maximum). Forty-six percent of undergraduate students work part-time. Average earnings from campus work for the school year are $850. The average financial indebtedness of the 1992–93 graduate was $12,000. Williams is a member of CSS. The college's own financial statement and the FAFSA are required. The deadline for financial aid applications is February 1.

International Students: There are currently 56 international students enrolled. The school actively recruits these students. They must take the TOEFL and achieve a minimum score of 600. The student must also take the SAT I or the ACT. Students must take SAT II: Subject tests in English and 2 other subjects.

Computers: The college provides computer facilities for student use. The mainframe is a DEC VAX 11/785. The Computer Center houses the mainframe, which has 40 ports, as well as 7 Sun Microsystems workstations, and 100 assorted IBM PCs, Apple Macintoshes, and graphics terminals. Additional PCs are located in the library and other academic buildings. All public-access DEC terminals and PCs are networked. All students may access the system. There are no time limits on using the system and no fees.

Graduates: In 1992–93 544 bachelor's degrees were awarded. The most popular majors among graduates were history (15%), English (12%), and poitical science (8%). Within an average freshman class, 90% graduate in 4 years and 93% in 5 years. Some 90 companies recruited on campus in a recent year. In the 1992 graduating class, 20% of the men and women were enrolled in graduate school within 6 months of graduation; 60% of the men and 69% of the women had found employment.

Admissions Contact: Director of Admissions.

WORCESTER POLYTECHNIC INSTITUTE   C-2
Worcester, MA 01609   (508) 831-5286

Full-time: 2260 men, 542 women	Faculty: 226; IIA, +$
Part-time: 73 men, 13 women	Ph.D.s: 95%
Graduate: 846 men, 208 women	Student/Faculty: 12 to 1
Year: quarters, summer session	Tuition: $15,290
Application Deadline: February 15	Room & Board: $5060
Freshman Class: 2772 applied, 2315 accepted, 682 enrolled	
SAT I: required	**HIGHLY COMPETITIVE**

Worcester Polytechnic Institute, founded in 1865, is a private, nonsectarian, coeducational institution with a unique, project-oriented program of study in engineering and other technical fields. There is also a graduate school. In addition to regional accreditation, WPI has baccalaureate program accreditation with ABET. The library contains 300,000 volumes, 785,000 microform items, and 3342 audiovisual forms, and subscribes to 1400 periodicals. Computerized library sources and services include the card catalog, interlibrary loans, and database searching. Special learning facilities include a TV station. The 62-acre campus is in a suburban area in the town of Worcester. Including residence halls, there are 30 buildings on campus.

Student Life: About 53% of undergraduates are from Massachusetts. Students come from 49 states, 60 foreign countries, and Canada. Seventy-seven percent are from public schools; 23% from private. Ninety-one percent are white. The average age of freshmen is 18; all undergraduates, 20. Six percent drop out by the end of their first year; 80% remain to graduate.

Housing: A total of 1200 students can be accommodated in college housing. College-sponsored living facilities include single-sex and coed dormitories, on-campus apartments, fraternity houses, and sorority houses. In addition there are special interest houses and quiet dormitories. On-campus housing is guaranteed for the freshman year only and is available on a lottery system for upperclassmen. Fifty percent of students live on campus. Alcohol is not permitted. Upperclassmen may keep cars on campus.

Activities: About 45% of men belong to 12 national fraternities; about 40% of women belong to 3 national sororities. There are 99 groups on campus, including art, band, cheerleading, chess, choir, chorale, chorus, computers, dance, drama, ethnic, gay, international, jazz band, literary magazine, musical theater, newspaper, orchestra, pep band, photography, political, professional, television, religious, social, social service, student government, and yearbook. Popular campus events include Homecoming, Traditions Day, and New Voices Festival.

Sports: There are 11 intercollegiate sports for men and 10 for women, and 15 intramural sports for men and 9 for women. Athletic and recreation facilities include a sports field, an auditorium, and a gymnasium.

Disabled Students: Ninety percent of the campus is accessible to disabled students. The following facilities are available: wheelchair ramps, elevators, special parking, specially equipped rest rooms, special class scheduling, and lowered drinking fountains.

Services: In addition to many counseling and information services, tutoring is available in every subject.

Campus Safety and Security: Campus safety and security measures include 24-hour foot and vehicle patrol, self-defense education, escort service, and shuttle buses. In addition, there are informal discussions, and pamphlets, posters, and films; the campus has emergency telephones, and lighted pathways and sidewalks. There is a student-run emergency medical service supervised by the campus police department.

Programs of Study: WPI awards the B.S. degree. Master's and doctoral degrees also are awarded. Bachelor's degrees are awarded in BIOLOGICAL SCIENCE (biochemistry, biology/biological science, and biotechnology), BUSINESS (management information systems), COMMUNICATIONS AND THE ARTS (English), COMPUTER AND PHYSICAL SCIENCE (chemistry, computer science, information sciences and systems, mathematics, physics, and statistics), ENGINEERING AND ENVIRONMENTAL DESIGN (aeronautical engineering, chemical engineering, civil engineering, computer engineering, electrical/electronics engineering, engineering, environmental engineering, industrial engineering, and mechanical engineering), HEALTH PROFESSIONS (predentistry, premedicine, and preveterinary science), SOCIAL SCIENCE (economics, history, and philosophy). Engineering is the strongest academically and also has the largest enrollment.

Required: For a B.S. degree, the college requires that students in science and engineering complete a minor in the humanities. Students must also complete 2 major individual projects. Distribution requirements vary according to the major, but all students must take courses in social sciences and physical education.

Special: The college offers study abroad in 8 countries. Students may cross-register with 9 colleges in the Worcester Area College Consortium. Co-op programs in all majors, internships, work-study programs, dual majors in every subject, student-designed majors, 3-2 engineering degrees, nondegree study, and pass/fail options are all available, as well as a 7-year veterinary medicine program with Tufts Medical School. There are special project centers in London, Washington, Massachusetts, San Francisco, Venice, Limerick, Zurich, and Germany. There are 10 national honor societies on campus.

Faculty/Classroom: Ninety percent of faculty are male; 10%, female. All teach undergraduates and half do research. The average class size in an introductory lecture is 35; in a laboratory, 20; and in a regular course offering, 25.

Admissions: About 84% of the 1993-94 applicants were accepted. About 79% of the current freshmen were in the top fifth of their class; 98% were in the top two fifths. There were 14 National Merit finalists. Twenty-five freshmen graduated first in their class.

Requirements: The SAT I is required. SAT II: Subject tests in writing, mathematics I or II, and a science are also required. Applicants must have completed 4 years of English, precalculus, chemistry, and physics. The GED is not accepted. Students should submit an essay, and an interview is recommended. AP and CLEP credits are accepted.

Procedure: Freshmen are admitted fall and spring. Entrance exams should be taken between April and December of the senior year. Early decision applications should be filed by December 1; regular applications, by February 15 for fall entry and November 15 for spring entry. There is an application fee of $40. Notification is sent April 1. There are early decision, early admissions, and deferred admissions plans. About 145 early decision candidates were accepted for the 1993-94 class. A waiting list is an active part of the admissions procedure.

Transfer: One hundred transfer students enrolled in 1993-94. Grades of C or better transfer for credit. A total of 2 quarter credits out of 45 must be completed at WPI.

Visiting: There are regularly scheduled orientations for prospective students, consisting of meetings and presentations from various academic and extracurricular groups. There are guides for informal visits, and visitors may sit in on classes and stay overnight at the school. To arrange for a visit, contact the Admissions Office at (508) 831-5286.

Financial Aid: In 1993-94, 81% of all current freshmen received some form of financial aid. Forty-seven percent of undergraduate students work part-time. Average earnings from campus work for the school year are $1200. WPI is a member of CSS. The FAF is required. The deadline for financial aid applications is March 1.

International Students: There are currently 96 international students enrolled. The school actively recruits these students. They must take the TOEFL and achieve a minimum score of 550. The student must also take the SAT I or the ACT and SAT II: Subject tests in writing, mathematics, and science.

Computers: The institute provides computer facilities for student use. The mainframe is an Encore Multimax 520. The UNIX-based Multimax is accessible via 8 parallel processors and a campuswide data network available in a wide range of locations, including the college computer center. The center also features 35 DECstation 3100 RISC workstations and a Bauyon Vines fileserver networked to PCs throughout campus. More than 800 IBM-compatible AT&T PC-6300 computers are available throughout the campus in general-access and specialized laboratories and computer classrooms. There is also a 32-PC documentation preparation laboratory for typesetting and desktop publishing applications. All students may access the system 24 hours daily. There are no time limits and no fees.

Graduates: In 1992-93, 637 bachelor's degrees were awarded. Some 300 companies recruited on campus in 1992-93.

Admissions Contact: Director of Admissions.

WORCESTER STATE COLLEGE

C-2

Worcester, MA 01602-2597   (508) 793-8040

Full-time: 3378 men and women	**Faculty:** 174
Part-time: 297 men and women	**Student/Faculty:** 19 to 1
Graduate: 255 men and women	**Tuition:** $2604 ($6738)
Year: semesters, summer session	**Room & Board:** $3810

Application Deadline: July 15

Freshman Class: 3580 applied, 2654 accepted, 1428 enrolled

SAT I Verbal/Math: 400/436   **LESS COMPETITIVE**

Worcester State College, established in 1874, is a public, primarily commuter institution offering undergraduate degrees in education and liberal arts and sciences. In addition to regional accreditation, the college has baccalaureate program accreditation with CAHEA and NLN. The library contains 160,000 volumes, and subscribes to 1000 periodicals. Special learning facilities include a learning resource center, a radio station, a TV station, photographic laboratories, and an audiovisual center. The 58-acre campus is in a suburban area 40 miles west of Boston. Including residence halls, there are 6 buildings on campus.

Student Life: About 98% of undergraduates are from Massachusetts. Eighty-six percent are from public schools. The average age of freshmen is 19; all undergraduates, 24. Fifteen percent drop out by the end of their first year; 40% remain to graduate.

Housing: A total of 700 students can be accommodated in college housing. College-sponsored living facilities include dormitories and on-campus apartments. Eighty-five percent of students commute. All students may keep cars on campus.

Activities: There are no fraternities or sororities on campus. There are 20 groups on campus, including drama, newspaper, radio and TV, religious, social, social service, student government, and yearbook. Popular campus events include Homecoming, Winter Carnival, Senior Week, lecture series, and Academic Honors Convocation.

Sports: Athletic and recreation facilities include an auditorium, a gymnasium, a fitness center, tennis courts, a track, baseball and softball diamonds, and football, field hockey, and all-purpose fields.

Disabled Students: Seventy-five percent of the campus is accessible to disabled students. The following facilities are available: wheelchair ramps, elevators, special parking, and specially equipped rest rooms.

Services: There is remedial math, reading, and writing.

Campus Safety and Security: Campus safety and security measures include security provided 24 hours a day by full-time officers. In addition, the dormitory is protected by a security system.

Programs of Study: The college awards the B.A., B.S., and B.S.Ed. degrees. Master's degrees also are awarded. Bachelor's degrees are awarded in BIOLOGICAL SCIENCE (biology/biological science), BUSINESS (business administration and management), COMMUNICATIONS AND THE ARTS (English, French, media arts, and Spanish), COMPUTER AND PHYSICAL SCIENCE (chemistry, computer science, mathematics, natural sciences, and physics), EDUCATION (early childhood and elementary), HEALTH PROFESSIONS (nursing, occupational therapy, and speech pathology/audiology), SOCIAL SCIENCE (economics, geography, history, psychology, sociology, and urban studies).

Required: To graduate, students must complete a foundation requirement, including English composition, the study of the U.S. and Massachusetts constitutions, physical education, and, if necessary, developmental reading, English, and mathematics. Distribution requirements include 12 credits each in humanities, social sciences, and natural sciences and mathematics, and 9 in fine arts. Students must complete 128 credits, 30 to 48 in the major, with a minimum 2.0 GPA.

Special: There is cross-registration with the Worcester Consortium for Higher Education, internships, work-study, B.A.-B.S. degrees, dual majors, ROTC programs with other schools, a 3–2 engineering degree with Worcester Polytechnic Institute, nondegree study, and a pass/fail option. There is one national honor society on campus.

Admissions: About 74% of the 1993–94 applicants were accepted. About 19% of the current freshmen were in the top fifth of their class; 55% were in the top two fifths.

Requirements: The SAT I or the ACT is required. In addition, applicants must graduate from an accredited secondary school or have a GED. They should have completed 4 years of English, 3 each of mathematics and electives, and 2 each of foreign language, laboratory science, and social studies, including 1 year of U.S. history and government. The College Board Student Descriptive Questionnaire must be submitted. AP and CLEP credits are accepted.

Procedure: Entrance exams should be taken in May of the junior year or December of the senior year. Applications should be filed by July 15 for fall entry and December 15 for spring entry, along with an application fee of $10 for residents, $40 for nonresidents. Notification is sent on a rolling basis.

Transfer: Transfer applicants must have earned a minimum of 12 college credits. A total of 30 credits out of 128 must be completed at Worcester State.

Visiting: There are regularly scheduled orientations for prospective students. To arrange for a visit, contact the Director of Admissions at (508) 793-8040.

Financial Aid: Scholarships or need-based grants averaged $400; loans averaged $600; and work contracts averaged $500. The college is a member of CSS. The FAF is required. The deadline for financial aid applications is March 1.

International Students: There are currently 70 international students enrolled.

Computers: The college provides computer facilities for student use. The mainframes are a CYBER CDC, Control Data, and DEC MicroVAX 3900. There are also PC laboratories available.

Admissions Contact: E. Jay Tierney, Director of Admissions.

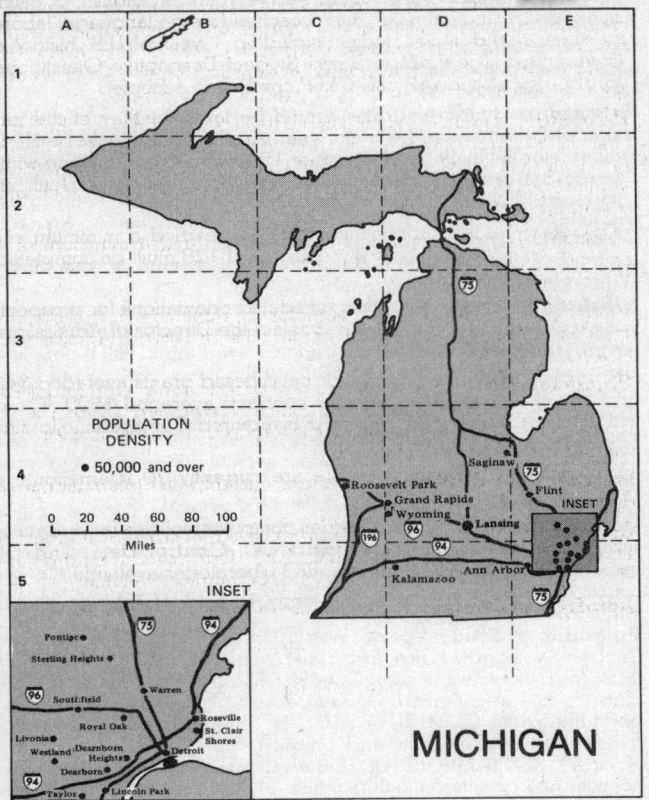

POPULATION
DENSITY

● 50,000 and over

0 20 40 60 80 100
Miles

INSET

MICHIGAN

social, social service, student government, symphony, and yearbook. Popular campus events include Welcome Week, Greek Week, major dances, BACCHUS Winter Games, Festival of Lights Week, Homecoming, Parents Weekend, Convocation, MIAA athletic events, intramurals, and the Big Friday Fall Festival.

Sports: There are 9 intercollegiate sports for men and 9 for women, and 10 intramural sports for men and 10 for women. Athletic and recreation facilities include a sport and fitness center for basketball and volleyball, a 5000-seat stadium for football, parks for baseball and softball, and tennis courts.

Disabled Students: Ninety percent of the campus is accessible to disabled students. The following facilities are available: wheelchair ramps, elevators, special parking, and specially equipped rest rooms.

Services: In addition to many counseling and information services, tutoring is available in most subjects. There is a reader service for the blind, and remedial math, reading, and writing.

Campus Safety and Security: Campus safety and security measures include 24-hour foot and vehicle patrol, self-defense education, escort service, and informal discussions. In addition, there are emergency telephones and lighted pathways and sidewalks.

Programs of Study: Adrian awards the B.A., B.S., B.B.A., B.F.A., B.M., and B.M.E. degrees. Associate degrees also are awarded. Bachelor's degrees are awarded in BIOLOGICAL SCIENCE (biology/ biological science), BUSINESS (accounting, business administration and management, international business management, management information systems, and marketing/retailing/merchandising), COMMUNICATIONS AND THE ARTS (arts administration/management, broadcasting, communications, English, fine arts, French, German, journalism, music, Spanish, and speech/debate/rhetoric), COMPUTER AND PHYSICAL SCIENCE (chemistry, computer science, earth science, mathematics, and physics), EDUCATION (art, early childhood, elementary, foreign languages, health, music, and secondary), ENGINEERING AND ENVIRONMENTAL DESIGN (environmental science), SOCIAL SCIENCE (criminal justice, economics, history, philosophy, political science/government, psychology, religion, social science, social work, and sociology). Business, teacher education, psychology, sociology, chemistry, biology, and English are the strongest academically. Business, teacher education, and biology have the largest enrollments.

Special: Co-op programs are available with the American College in London, the Fashion Institute of Technology, the Urban Life Center, the Philadelphia Urban Semester, the Washington Center, and the Appalachian Semester. The college offers cross-registration with Siena Heights College. Students may participate in internships, study abroad in 8 countries, and a Washington semester. A dual major in philosophy/religion, a 3–2 engineering degree, student-designed majors, credit for life, military, and work experience, and nondegree study are possible. Adrian offers preprofessional programs in engineering, medicine, dentistry, medical technology, law, ministry, pharmacy, physical therapy, and veterinary. There is a freshman honors program on campus as well as 17 national honor societies. Two departments have honors programs.

Faculty/Classroom: Sixty-four percent of faculty are male; 36%, female. All teach undergraduates. The average class size in an introductory lecture is 30; in a laboratory, 18; and in a regular course offering, 18.

Admissions: About 84% of the 1993–94 applicants were accepted. The ACT scores for the 1993–94 freshman class were as follows: 41% below 21, 32% between 21 and 23, 20% between 24 and 26, 3% between 27 and 28, and 4% above 28. About 45% of the current freshmen were in the top fifth of their class; 90% were in the top two fifths. Fifteen freshmen graduated first in their class.

Requirements: Adrian requires applicants to be in the upper 50% of their class. A minimum GPA of 2.5 is required. The SAT I or ACT is required. Applicants must be graduates of an accredited secondary school and have completed 15 units including 4 units of English, 2 units each of mathematics, science, and social studies, plus 5 additional units chosen from English, foreign language, history, mathematics, science and/or social studies. The GED is accepted. Each student is reviewed individually based on several criteria. An interview is recommended. AP and CLEP credits are accepted. Important factors used in the admissions decision are advanced placement or honors courses, leadership record, extracurricular activities record, personality, intangible qualities, and recommendations by school officials.

Procedure: Freshmen are admitted to all sessions. Entrance exams should be taken during the spring of junior year or fall of senior year. Applications should be filed by August 15 for fall entry, December 15 for winter entry, May 1 for spring entry, and June 15 for summer entry, along with an application fee of $15. Notification is sent on a rolling basis. There is a deferred admissions plan.

ADRIAN COLLEGE
Adrian, MI 49221

E-5

(517) 265-5161, ext. 4326
(800) 877-2246 (out-of-state)

Full-time: 509 men, 527 women
Part-time: 35 men, 64 women
Graduate: none
Year: semesters, summer session
Application Deadline: August 15
Freshman Class: 1311 applied, 1095 accepted, 339 enrolled
ACT: 23

Faculty: 70; IIB, av$
Ph.D.s: 73%
Student/Faculty: 15 to 1
Tuition: $10,800
Room & Board: $3540

COMPETITIVE

Adrian College, founded in 1845, is a private, coeducational, liberal arts and sciences institution affiliated with the United Methodist Church. The library contains 137,800 volumes, 39,580 microform items, and 2600 audiovisual forms, and subscribes to 800 periodicals. Computerized library sources and services include interlibrary loans and database searching. Special learning facilities include a learning resource center, art gallery, planetarium, radio station, and TV station. The 100-acre campus is in a small town 35 miles southwest of Ann Arbor. Including residence halls, there are 32 buildings on campus.

Student Life: About 79% of undergraduates are from Michigan. Students come from 18 states, 9 foreign countries, and Canada. Sixty-five percent are from public schools; 35% from private. Eighty-eight percent are white. Thirty-nine percent are Protestant; 30% claim no religious affiliation; 27% are Catholic. The average age of freshmen is 18; all undergraduates, 19.5. Sixteen percent drop out by the end of their first year; 58% remain to graduate.

Housing: A total of 1223 students can be accommodated in college housing. College-sponsored living facilities include single-sex and coed dormitories, and fraternity and sorority houses. In addition there are special interest houses and an alcohol-free hall, one with extended quiet hours, and one for upperclassmen only. On-campus housing is guaranteed for all 4 years. Seventy-three percent of students live on campus; of those, 50% remain on campus on weekends. All students may keep cars on campus.

Activities: About 31% of men belong to 5 national fraternities; about 25% of women belong to 3 national sororities. There are 70 groups on campus, including art, band, cheerleading, choir, chorale, chorus, computers, drama, drill team, ethnic, gay, honors, international, jazz band, literary magazine, musical theater, newspaper, orchestra, pep band, photography, political, professional, radio and TV, religious,

Transfer: There were 51 transfer students who enrolled in 1993–94. Transfer students must have an above-average GPA and provide final high school transcripts. If the student has completed less than 24 semester hours, ACT or SAT I test scores are also required. Grades of 2.0 and above transfer for credit. The college admits transfer students every semester. A total of 34 credits out of 124 must be completed at Adrian.

Visiting: There are regularly scheduled orientations for prospective students, including a visit with the admissions and financial aid representative, a meeting with professors from the applicant's area of interest, a meeting with an athletic coach if applicable, and a student-guided tour of the campus. There are guides for informal visits, and visitors may sit in on classes and stay overnight at the school. To arrange for a visit, contact the Admissions Office at (800) 877–2246 or (517) 265–5161, ext. 4326.

Financial Aid: In 1993–94, 84% of all current freshmen and 83% of continuing students received some form of financial aid. About 80% of freshmen and 81% of continuing students received need-based aid. The average freshman award was $9947. Of that total, scholarships or need-based grants averaged $7097 ($10,160 maximum); loans averaged $2958 ($5500 maximum); and work contracts averaged $1188 ($1400 maximum). Thirty-four percent of undergraduate students work part-time. The average financial indebtedness of the 1992–93 graduate was $10,400. Adrian is a member of CSS. The FAFSA financial statement is required. The deadline for financial aid applications is March 15.

International Students: There are currently 20 international students enrolled. The school actively recruits these students. They must take the TOEFL and achieve a minimum score of 500.

Computers: The college provides computer facilities for student use. The mainframe is a DEC PDP-11/44. There are computer laboratories located in various academic buildings. Students have access to 21 terminals and 40 microcomputers. All students may access the system. It may be used weekdays from 8 A.M. to 11 P.M.; weekends from 10 A.M. to 11 P.M. There are no time limits on using the system and no fees.

Graduates: In 1992–93, 241 bachelor's degrees were awarded. The most popular majors among graduates were business (20%), biology (8%), and English (7%). Within an average freshman class, 48% graduate in 4 years, 58% in 5 years, and 60% in 6 years. Thirty-six companies recruited on campus in 1992–93. In the 1992 graduating class, 24% of all students were enrolled in graduate school within 6 months of graduation; 66% had found employment.

Admissions Contact: George F. Wolf, Director of Admissions.

ALBION COLLEGE   D-5

Albion, MI 49224	**(517) 629–0321; (800) 858–6770**
Full-time: 832 men, 822 women	Faculty: 109; IIB, +$
Part-time: 13 men, 7 women	Ph.D.s: 84%
Graduate: none	Student/Faculty: 15 to 1
Year: semesters, summer session	Tuition: $13,676
Application Deadline: open	Room & Board: $4588
Freshman Class: 1899 applied, 1720 accepted, 489 enrolled	
SAT I: 530/580	ACT: 25 **VERY COMPETITIVE**

Albion College, established in 1835, is a private institution affiliated with the United Methodist Church, offering undergraduate degrees in liberal arts curricula. The library contains 472,252 volumes, 18,083 microform items, and 2701 audiovisual forms, and subscribes to 923 periodicals. Computerized library sources and services include the card catalog, interlibrary loans, and database searching. Special learning facilities include a learning resource center, art gallery, radio station, nature center, women's center, observatory, and honors program center. The 225-acre campus is in a small town 90 miles west of Detroit and 175 miles east of Chicago, Illinois. Including residence halls, there are 30 buildings on campus.

Student Life: About 85% of undergraduates are from Michigan. Students come from 30 states and 16 foreign countries. Eighty-three percent are from public schools; 17% from private. Ninety percent are white. Forty-one percent are Protestant; 27% Catholic; 19% claim no religious affiliation. The average age of freshmen is 18; all undergraduates, 20. Fourteen percent drop out by the end of their first year; 65% remain to graduate.

Housing: A total of 1600 students can be accommodated in college housing. College-sponsored living facilities include single-sex and coed dormitories, on-campus apartments, married-student housing, and fraternity houses. In addition, there are language houses, special interest houses, and special interest annexes. On-campus housing is guaranteed for all 4 years. Ninety-nine percent of students live on campus; of those, 70% remain on campus on weekends. Upperclassmen may keep cars on campus.

Activities: About 52% of men belong to 6 national fraternities; about 48% of women belong to 6 national sororities. There are 103 groups on campus, including art, band, cheerleading, choir, chorale, chorus, computers, dance, drama, ethnic, film, gay, honors, international, jazz

band, literary magazine, marching band, musical theater, newspaper, opera, orchestra, pep band, political, professional, radio and TV, religious, social, social service, student government, symphony, and yearbook. Popular campus events include Greek Week, Family Day, Homecoming, International Week, Symposium Week, Special Olympics Training Day, Briton Bash, Briton Days, Albion Performing Arts and Lecture Series, Kwanzaa, Into the Streets, and alternative fall and spring break service projects.

Sports: There are 9 intercollegiate sports for men and 9 for women, and 19 intramural sports for men and 18 for women. Athletic and recreation facilities include a stadium, an aquatic center, a gymnasium, baseball, soccer, and football fields, tennis courts, an archery range, a surfaced track, a field events area, outdoor basketball courts, practice fields, a canoeing facility, a recreation and wellness center with intramural basketball, volleyball, badminton, and tennis courts, a track, racquetball courts, a weight training room, a human performance lab, and a training/rehabilitation unit.

Disabled Students: Eighty-six percent of the campus is accessible to disabled students. The following facilities are available: wheelchair ramps, elevators, special parking, specially equipped rest rooms, special class scheduling, lowered drinking fountains, and lowered telephones.

Services: In addition to many counseling and information services, tutoring is available in most subjects. Assistance for the deaf is also available. In addition, there is a reader service for the blind and remedial math and writing. The Developing Skills Center offers individual assistance to students for study skills enhancement.

Campus Safety and Security: Campus safety and security measures include 24-hour foot and vehicle patrol, self defense education, escort service, and shuttle buses. In addition, there are informal discussions, pamphlets, posters, and films, emergency telephones, and lighted pathways and sidewalks.

Programs of Study: Albion awards the B.A. and B.F.A. degrees. Bachelor's degrees are awarded in BIOLOGICAL SCIENCE (biology/biological science), COMMUNICATIONS AND THE ARTS (English, fine arts, French, German, music, Spanish, and visual and performing arts), COMPUTER AND PHYSICAL SCIENCE (chemistry, geoscience, mathematics, and physics), EDUCATION (music and physical), SOCIAL SCIENCE (American studies, anthropology, economics, history, international studies, philosophy, political science/government, psychology, religion, and sociology). English, mathematics, computers, biology, science, and history are the strongest academically. Economics, management, English, and biology have the largest enrollments.

Required: To graduate, students must complete 12 semester hours each in social science, humanities, mathematics, and science, and 4 in fine arts, interdisciplinary studies, gender studies, and ethnic studies. Students must maintain a minimum GPA of 2.0 and complete 124 semester hours with 32 hours in the major. All students must pass a writing competence examination.

Special: Albion offers internship programs, study abroad in 17 countries, a Washington semester, and study in New York City, Philadelphia, Oak Ridge, Chicago, and the Virgin Islands. Students may earn a 3–2 engineering degree in conjunction with Columbia, Case Western Reserve, and Michigan Technological universities, and the University of Michigan. Student-designed majors, dual and interdisciplinary majors, including computational mathematics, speech communication and theater, mathematics/physics, and mathematics/economics, and pass/fail grading are possible. There is a freshman honors program on campus, as well as 4 national honor societies, including Phi Beta Kappa. Eighteen departments have honors programs.

Faculty/Classroom: Seventy-five percent of faculty are male; 25%, female. All teach undergraduates and do research. The average class size in an introductory lecture is 30; in a laboratory, 17; and in a regular course offering, 17.

Admissions: About 91% of the 1993–94 applicants were accepted. The SAT scores for the 1993–94 freshman class were as follows: Verbal—26% below 500, 43% between 500 and 599, 28% between 600 and 700, and 3% above 700; Math—16% below 500, 34% between 500 and 599, 33% between 600 and 700, and 17% above 700. The ACT scores were 16% below 21, 20% between 21 and 23, 23% between 24 and 26, 18% between 27 and 28, and 23% above 28. About 60% of the current freshmen were in the top fifth of their class; 84% were in the top two fifths. There were 18 National Merit finalists and 4 semifinalists. About 18 freshmen graduated first in their class.

Requirements: Albion requires applicants to be in the upper 66% of their class. A minimum GPA of 2.8 is required. The SAT I or the ACT is required. Applicants must graduate from an accredited secondary school or earn a GED. Completion of 15 Carnegie credits is required. A strong background in English, mathematics, and the laboratory and social sciences is recommended. AP and CLEP credits are accepted. Important factors used in the admissions decision are recommendations by school officials, advanced placement or honor

courses, evidence of special talent, personality, intangible qualities, and leadership record.

Procedure: Freshmen are admitted fall and spring. Entrance exams should be taken in April or May of the junior year. Application deadlines are open. The fee is $20. Notification is sent on a rolling basis.

Transfer: About 33 transfer students enrolled in 1993–94. Transfer applicants must submit official college transcripts. Grades of 2.0 or better will be considered for transfer credit. Albion will evaluate the applicant's course work before conferring transfer credit. A total of 48 credits out of 124 must be completed at Albion.

Visiting: There are guides for informal visits, and visitors may sit in on classes and stay overnight at the school. To arrange for a visit, contact the Admissions Office at (517) 629–0321 or (800) 858–6770.

Financial Aid: In 1993–94 87% of all current freshmen and 78% of continuing students received some form of financial aid. About 65% of freshmen and 55% of continuing students received need-based aid. The average freshman award was $9769. Of that total, scholarships or need-based grants averaged $6838 ($18,664 maximum); loans averaged $1934 ($5025 maximum); and work contracts averaged $997 ($1500 maximum). Fifty-six percent of undergraduate students work part-time. Average earnings from campus work for the school year are $818. The average financial indebtedness of the 1992–93 graduate was $10,020. Albion is a member of CSS. The FAF or FFS is required. The deadline for financial aid applications is March 1.

International Students: There are currently 25 international students enrolled. The school actively recruits these students. They must take the TOEFL and achieve a minimum score of 525.

Computers: The college provides computer facilities for student use. The mainframe is a DEC VAX 4000–200. Suites of microcomputers, including Apple Macintoshes, IBM PCs, and others are available in locations across campus. Many of these operate as stand-alones and as on-line terminals for the college's DEC VAX 4000–200 computers, but most are connected to the campus network. All students may access the system. It may be used most days and evening hours. There are no time limits on using the system and no fees.

Graduates: In 1992–93 352 bachelor's degrees were awarded. The most popular majors among graduates were economics/management (21%), history (13%), and English (13%). Within an average freshman class, 66% graduate in 4 years and 70% in 5 years. Some 27 companies recruited on campus in 1992–93. In the 1992 graduating class, 17% of the men and 43% of the women were enrolled in graduate school within 6 months of graduation.

Admissions Contact: Frank Bonta, Dean of Admissions.

ALMA COLLEGE
D-4

Alma, MI 48801 (517) 463–7139; (800) 321-ALMA (out-of-state)

Full-time: 564 men, 742 women	Faculty: 80; IIB, av$
Part-time: 11 men, 17 women	Ph.D.s: 84%
Graduate: none	Student/Faculty: 16 to 1
Year: 4-4-1, summer session	Tuition: $12,041
Application Deadline: open	Room & Board: $4334

Freshman Class: 1267 applied, 1080 accepted, 385 enrolled

ACT: 26 **VERY COMPETITIVE +**

Alma College, established in 1886, is a private, liberal arts institution affiliated with the Presbyterian Church (U.S.A.). In addition to regional accreditation, Alma has baccalaureate program accreditation with NASM. The library contains 197,700 volumes, 29,800 microform items, and 3200 audiovisual forms, and subscribes to 1100 periodicals. Computerized library sources and services include the card catalog, interlibrary loans, and database searching. Special learning facilities include a learning resource center, art gallery, planetarium, radio station, audio-visual center, and language laboratory. The 87-acre campus is in a small town 50 miles north of Lansing. Including residence halls, there are 23 buildings on campus.

Student Life: About 94% of undergraduates are from Michigan. Students come from 22 states, 11 foreign countries, and Canada. Ninety-four percent are from public schools; 6% from private. Ninety-four percent are white. Thirty-nine percent are Protestant; 31% claim no religious affiliation; 25% are Catholic. The average age of freshmen is 18; all undergraduates, 20. Twelve percent drop out by the end of their first year; 70% remain to graduate.

Housing: A total of 1173 students can be accommodated in college housing. College-sponsored living facilities include single-sex dormitories, on-campus apartments, fraternity houses, and sorority houses. In addition there are language houses and an international house for students from overseas and those who have traveled overseas. On-campus housing is guaranteed for all 4 years. Eighty-seven percent of students live on campus; of those, 60% remain on campus on weekends. All students may keep cars on campus.

Activities: About 40% of men belong to 1 local and 4 national fraternities; about 40% of women belong to 1 local and 3 national sororities. There are 89 groups on campus, including art, bagpipe band, band, cheerleading, chess, choir, computers, dance, drama, ethnic,

film, gay, honors, international, jazz band, literary magazine, marching band, musical theater, newspaper, orchestra, photography, political, professional, radio and TV, religious, social, social service, student government, symphony, and yearbook. Popular campus events include Song Fest, Homecoming, Irish Pub, Airband, Dinner Theater, and Performing Arts Series.

Sports: There are 9 intercollegiate sports for men and 9 for women, and 6 intramural sports for men and 6 for women. Athletic and recreation facilities include an indoor gymnasium and pool, an outdoor sports complex providing an artificial-turf playing field, an 8-lane track, baseball and softball fields, a weight training room, and racquetball and tennis courts.

Disabled Students: Eighty percent of the campus is accessible to disabled students. The following facilities are available: wheelchair ramps, elevators, special parking, specially equipped rest rooms, special class scheduling, lowered drinking fountains, and 2 residence halls with private baths.

Services: In addition to many counseling and information services, tutoring is available in most subjects; both individual and group tutoring are available. There is a reader service for the blind, and remedial math, reading, and writing.

Campus Safety and Security: Campus safety and security measures include informal discussions, and pamphlets, posters, and films; there are lighted pathways and sidewalks, and a 24-hour foot patrol.

Programs of Study: Alma awards the B.A., B.S., B.M., and B.F.A. degrees. Bachelor's degrees are awarded in BIOLOGICAL SCIENCE (biochemistry and biology/biological science), BUSINESS (business administration/management and international business management), COMMUNICATIONS AND THE ARTS (communications, dance, design, dramatic arts, English, fine arts, French, German, music, and Spanish), COMPUTER AND PHYSICAL SCIENCE (chemistry, computer science, information sciences and systems, mathematics, and physics), EDUCATION (elementary and secondary), SOCIAL SCIENCE (economics, history, philosophy, political science/government, psychology, religion, and sociology). Biology, history, business administration, exercise and health science, English, and psychology are the strongest academically. Business, history, biology, education, English, and psychology have the largest enrollments.

Required: Degree requirements include completion of a minimum of 136 credit hours; 148 hours are required for the B.F.A. degree, 136 to 156 for the B.M. degree. Students must attain a minimum GPA of 2.0, or 3.0 for fine arts majors. All students must demonstrate proficiency in English, communication, and computation. They must complete distribution requirements that include 4 history credits, 16 humanities credits (4 credits each in creative or performing arts, literature, philosophy, and religious studies), and 12 each in social science, and in life and physical science. The total number of credits in the major is 36 for a departmental major, 56 for an interdepartmental major, and 56 to 58 for self-designed majors.

Special: Alma offers internships in many fields, study abroad in Australia, Austria, Belgium, France, Germany, Japan, Mexico, Nigeria, Scotland, and Spain, and a Washington semester at American University. The college also offers work-study programs. Students can earn an accelerated degree in history. Dual majors, joint B.A.-B.S. degrees, and student-designed majors can be arranged in a wide variety of subjects. The college confers 3–2 engineering degrees in conjunction with the University of Michigan, Michigan Technological University, and Washington University in St. Louis. Nondegree study may be pursued, and students have a pass/fail grading option. A 4-week spring term provides intensive study in 1 course, often combined with travel. There is a freshman honors program on campus, as well as 2 national honor societies including Phi Beta Kappa. Twelve departments have honors programs.

Faculty/Classroom: Sixty-eight percent of faculty are male; 32%, female. All teach undergraduates and 13% also do research. The average class size in an introductory lecture is 25; in a laboratory, 18; and in a regular course offering, 18.

Admissions: About 85% of the 1993–94 applicants were accepted. The ACT scores for the 1993–94 freshman class were as follows: 13% below 21, 21% between 21 and 23, 27% between 24 and 26, 18% between 27 and 28, and 21% above 28. About 66% of the current freshmen were in the top fifth of their class; 91% were in the top two fifths. There were 8 National Merit finalists and 2 semifinalists. Seventeen freshmen graduated first in their class.

Requirements: A minimum GPA of 3.0 is required. The SAT I or ACT is required. Applicants must have graduated from an accredited secondary school and have earned 16 Carnegie units, including 3 years of English, and 2 each of mathematics, science, and social studies; 2 years of a foreign language are recommended. An essay is recommended, and a portfolio and audition are required for performing arts scholarships. AP and CLEP credits are accepted. Important factors used in the admissions decision are advanced placement or honors courses, recommendations by school officials, evidence of special talent, leadership record, and extracurricular activities record.

Procedure: Freshmen are admitted fall, winter, and spring. Entrance exams should be taken in the spring of junior year or the fall of senior year. Early decision applications should be filed by November 1; there is an open deadline for regular applications for fall entry. The application fee is $20. Notification of early decision is sent December 1; regular decision, on a rolling basis. There are early decision, early admissions, and deferred admissions plans. Nearly 200 early decision candidates were accepted for the 1993–94 class.

Transfer: Twenty-seven transfer students enrolled in 1993–94. Students wishing to transfer to Alma must have a minimum GPA of 3.0 from other colleges attended. A total of 34 credits out of 136 must be completed at Alma.

Visiting: There are regularly scheduled orientations for prospective students, consisting of faculty talks, tours, a meal on campus, financial aid information, and admissions sessions. There are guides for informal visits, and visitors may sit in on classes and stay overnight at the school. To arrange for a visit, contact the Admissions Office at (800) 321-ALMA.

Financial Aid: In 1993–94, 96% of all freshmen and 95% of continuing students received some form of financial aid. About 80% of freshmen and 77% of continuing students received need-based aid. The average freshman award was $8500. Of that total, scholarships or need-based grants averaged $6275 ($11,926 maximum); loans averaged $3300 ($5500 maximum); and work contracts averaged $600 ($1500 maximum). Fifty percent of undergraduate students work part-time. Average earnings from campus work for the school year are $900. The average financial indebtedness of the 1992–93 graduate was $10,000. Alma is a member of CSS. The FAFSA financial statement is required. The deadline for financial aid applications is March 1.

International Students: There are currently 16 international students enrolled. The school actively recruits these students. They must take the TOEFL and achieve a minimum score of 525.

Computers: The college provides computer facilities for student use. The mainframes are a DEC VAX 6220, a DEC VAX 8530, 2 DEC VAXstation 3100s, and a DEC VAXstation 3100 Model 76. The on-campus VAX network links 450 terminals, printers, and microcomputers across campus. Microcomputers are available in 6 residence halls, department laboratories, and the Academic Center. Macintosh, IBM PC-compatible 486DX systems, and IBM-compatible VAXmates are available. All students may access the system. It may be used at all hours. There are no time limits on using the system and no fees.

Graduates: In 1992–93, 270 bachelor's degrees were awarded. The most popular majors among graduates were business administration (23%), biology (13%), and education (9%). Within an average freshman class, 1% graduate in 3 years, 57% in 4 years, 70% in 5 years, and 70% in 6 years. Some 40 companies usually recruit on campus. In a recent graduating class, 30% of all students were enrolled in graduate school within 6 months of graduation; 65% had found employment.

Admissions Contact: John Seveland, Vice President for Enrollment and Student Affairs.

ANDREWS UNIVERSITY
Berrien Springs, MI 49104–0740   C-5

(616) 471-3303
(800) 253-2874 (out-of-state)

Full-time: 761 men, 825 women	Faculty: 255
Part-time: 124 men, 202 women	Ph.D.s: 57%
Graduate: 593 men, 363 women	Student/Faculty: 6 to 1
Year: quarters	Tuition: $10,962
Application Deadline: open	Room & Board: $3990
Freshman Class: 1130 applied, 704 accepted, 322 enrolled	
ACT: 20	NONCOMPETITIVE

Andrews University, established in 1874, is a private institution affiliated with the Seventh-Day Adventist Church offering undergraduate degrees in business, education, arts and sciences, and technology. There are 4 undergraduate and 5 graduate schools. In addition to regional accreditation, Andrews University has baccalaureate program accreditation with ADA, AHEA, APTA, CAHEA, NASM, NCATE, and NLN. The library contains 781,965 volumes, 269,385 microform items, and 44,316 audiovisual forms, and subscribes to 3004 periodicals. Special learning facilities include a natural history museum, radio station, and archeological museum. The 1600-acre campus is in a rural area 15 miles south of Benton Harbor. Including residence halls, there are 57 buildings on campus.

Student Life: About 64% of undergraduates are from out-of-state, mostly the Midwest. Students come from 48 states, 87 foreign countries, and Canada. Thirty-nine percent are from public schools; 61% from private. The average age of freshmen is 19; all undergraduates, 24. Thirty-five percent drop out by the end of their first year; 47% remain to graduate.

Housing: A total of 1705 students can be accommodated in college housing. College-sponsored living facilities include dormitories, on-campus apartments, off-campus apartments, and married-student

housing. On-campus housing is available on a first-come, first-served basis. Alcohol is not permitted. All students may keep cars on campus.

Activities: There is 1 national fraternity and 1 national sorority. There are many groups and organizations on campus, including band, choir, chorale, chorus, computers, drama, ethnic, honors, international, newspaper, professional, religious, social, social service, student government, and yearbook.

Sports: There are 6 intramural sports for men and 4 for women. Athletic and recreation facilities include a gymnasium, a pool, racquetball courts, and health clubs in 2 of the 3 dormitories.

Disabled Students: The following facilities are available: wheelchair ramps, special parking, and specially equipped rest rooms.

Services: In addition to many counseling and information services, tutoring is available in every subject. In addition, there is remedial math, reading, and writing.

Programs of Study: Andrews University awards the B.A., B.S., B.Agri., B.B.A., B.F.A., B.Mus., B.S.Art Ed., B.S.Die., B.S.El.Ed., B.S.E.T., B.S.H.S., B.S.I.T., B.S.Interiors, B.S.M.T., B.S.Rad.Tech., B.S.W., and B.T. degrees. Associate, master's, and doctoral degrees also are awarded. Bachelor's degrees are awarded in AGRICULTURE (agriculture and horticulture), BIOLOGICAL SCIENCE (biochemistry, biology/biological science, biophysics, botany, and zoology), BUSINESS (accounting, business administration and management, business economics, and marketing/retailing/merchandising), COMMUNICATIONS AND THE ARTS (communications, English, fine arts, French, German, journalism, music, and Spanish), COMPUTER AND PHYSICAL SCIENCE (chemistry, computer science, information sciences and systems, mathematics, and physics), EDUCATION (art, business, early childhood, elementary, English, foreign languages, music, science, and teaching English as a second language/foreign language), ENGINEERING AND ENVIRONMENTAL DESIGN (architecture, computer technology, construction engineering, electrical/electronics engineering, and electrical/electronics engineering technology), HEALTH PROFESSIONS (medical laboratory technology, nursing, physical therapy, predentistry, premedicine, and speech pathology/audiology), SOCIAL SCIENCE (behavioral science, economics, history, prelaw, psychology, religion, social work, and sociology). Nursing, physical therapy, education, and business have the largest enrollments.

Required: Students must complete 190 quarter credits, with a minimum of 45 quarter credits in upper-division work. Specific course requirements include religion, English, behavioral sciences, fine arts, and physical education.

Special: Students may pursue a second major in business administration. Study abroad, student-designed majors, nondegree study, and pass/fail options are available. There is a freshman honors program on campus.

Admissions: About 62% of the 1993–94 applicants were accepted. The ACT scores for the 1993–94 freshman class were as follows: 43% below 21, 20% between 21 and 23, 18% between 24 and 26, 10% between 27 and 28, and 9% above 28.

Requirements: A minimum GPA of 2.0 is required. The ACT is required. Candidates for admission must graduate from an accredited secondary school or earn a GED. Ten Carnegie units are required, and students must have completed 4 courses in English and 2 courses each in history, mathematics, and science. Interviews are recommended for all applicants. CLEP credit is accepted. Important factors used in the admissions decision are advanced placement or honor courses, leadership record, evidence of special talent, extracurricular activities record, and personality, intangible qualities.

Procedure: Entrance exams should be taken as early as possible. Application deadlines are open. Application fee is $30. The college accepts all applicants. Notification is sent on a rolling basis.

Transfer: Transfer applicants must submit a high school transcript and transcripts from all colleges attended. A maximum of 70 hours or 105 quarter credits may be transferred from a junior college toward a bachelor's degree. Credits should be relevant to the student's major at Andrews University. The minimum GPA is 2.0, and the ACT is recommended. Students must meet freshman entrance requirements if they are tranferring with less than sophomore standing from an accredited college. A total of 45 quarter credits out of 190 must be completed at Andrews University.

Visiting: There are regularly scheduled orientations for prospective students. There are guides for informal visits and visitors may sit in on classes and stay overnight at the school. To arrange for a visit, contact the Admissions Office at (616) 471-3303.

Financial Aid: Andrews University is a member of CSS. The FAF is required. The priority deadline for financial aid applications is March 1.

International Students: The school actively recruits these students. They must take the TOEFL and achieve a minimum score of 450.

Computers: The college provides computer facilities for student use. The mainframe is a Xerox Sigma 9. All students may access the system. There are no time limits on using the system and no fees.

Graduates: In a recent year, 362 bachelor's degrees were awarded.
Admissions Contact: Dr. Cyril Connelley, Director of Admissions.

AQUINAS COLLEGE
D-4
Grand Rapids, MI 49506–1799

(616) 732–4460
(800) 678–9593 (out-of-state)

Full-time: 434 men, 817 women	Faculty: 91; IIB, --$
Part-time: 234 men, 533 women	Ph.D.s: 65%
Graduate: 222 men, 236 women	Student/Faculty: 14 to 1
Year: semesters, summer session	Tuition: $10,402
Application Deadline: August 1	Room & Board: $4124
Freshman Class: 619 applied, 516 accepted, 220 enrolled	
ACT: 22	COMPETITIVE

Aquinas College, established in 1922, is a private liberal arts institution affiliated with the Roman Catholic Church and offers undergraduate and graduate degrees through day and evening programs. The library contains 105,000 volumes, 79,717 microform items, and 3800 audiovisual forms, and subscribes to 989 periodicals. Computerized library sources and services include the card catalog, interlibrary loans, and database searching. Special learning facilities include a learning resource center, art gallery, radio station, and greenhouses. The 107-acre campus is in a suburban area 6 miles east of downtown Grand Rapids. Including residence halls, there are 28 buildings on campus.

Student Life: About 97% of undergraduates are from Michigan. Students come from 11 states and 11 foreign countries. Sixty percent are from public schools; 40% from private. Eighty-eight percent are white. Fifty percent are Catholic; 16% Protestant. The average age of freshmen is 18; all undergraduates, 27. Twenty-three percent drop out by the end of their first year; 50% remain to graduate.

Housing: A total of 613 students can be accommodated in college housing. College-sponsored living facilities include single-sex and coed dormitories and on-campus apartments. In addition, there are special interest houses and service learning houses. On-campus housing is guaranteed for all 4 years. Seventy-five percent of students commute. All students may keep cars on campus.

Activities: There are no fraternities or sororities on campus. There are 138 groups on campus, including cheerleading, choir, computers, drama, ethnic, honors, international, jazz band, newspaper, photography, political, religious, social, social service, student government, and yearbook. Popular campus events include Gala Weekend, Spring Fling, Winter Fest, TGIS (Thank God It's Spring), and a jazz festival.

Sports: There are 8 intercollegiate sports for men and 9 for women, and 13 intramural sports for men and 13 for women. Athletic and recreation facilities include a gymnasium, a weight room, an indoor track, softball and soccer fields, and indoor and outdoor tennis courts.

Disabled Students: Ninety-five percent of the campus is accessible to disabled students. The following facilities are available: wheelchair ramps, elevators, special parking, specially equipped rest rooms, and special class scheduling.

Services: In addition to many counseling and information services, tutoring is available in most subjects. There is a reader service for the blind, and remedial math, reading, and writing.

Campus Safety and Security: Campus safety and security measures include 24-hour foot and vehicle patrol, escort service, informal discussions, and pamphlets, posters, and films. In addition, there are emergency telephones and lighted pathways and sidewalks.

Programs of Study: Aquinas awards the B.A., B.S., B.A.G.E., B.F.A., B.M.E., B.Mus., B.S.B.A., and B.S.I.B. degrees. Associate and master's degrees also are awarded. Bachelor's degrees are awarded in BIOLOGICAL SCIENCE (biology/biological science), BUSINESS (accounting, business administration and management, international business management, recreation and leisure services, and sports management), COMMUNICATIONS AND THE ARTS (art history and appreciation, arts administration/management, communications, drawing, English, fine arts, French, German, music, painting, photography, printmaking, sculpture, and Spanish), COMPUTER AND PHYSICAL SCIENCE (chemistry, computer programming, and mathematics), EDUCATION (elementary, physical, and secondary), ENGINEERING AND ENVIRONMENTAL DESIGN (environmental science and preengineering), HEALTH PROFESSIONS (health, medical laboratory technology, nuclear medicine technology, predentistry, and premedicine), SOCIAL SCIENCE (economics, environmental studies, geography, history, international studies, philosophy, political science/government, psychology, religion, social science, sociology, and urban studies). Business administration is the strongest program academically and has the largest enrollment.

Required: Degree requirements include completion of 124 credit hours, with 30 to 48 credits in the major, and a minimum GPA of 2.0. Distribution requirements include courses in language, communications, mathematics, aesthetics, social science, perspectives, and personal development. All freshmen are required to enroll in Freshman Experience in Humanities, and all seniors are required to enroll in a senior seminar.

Special: Students may cross-register with the Dominican Consortium. They may study abroad in Ireland, Germany, France, Spain, or Japan. Work-study programs are available. Students may pursue dual majors in business and accounting, business and sports management, or business and communication arts, and student-designed majors can be arranged. Aquinas offers a general studies degree and may confer credit for life, military, and work experience. A pass/fail grading option is available. There is a freshman honors program on campus, as well as 5 national honor societies. Five departments have honors programs.

Faculty/Classroom: Fifty-six percent of faculty are male; 44%, female. All teach undergraduates. No introductory courses are taught by graduate students. The average class size in an introductory lecture is 20; in a laboratory, 20; and in a regular course offering, 25.

Admissions: About 83% of the 1993–94 applicants were accepted. The ACT scores for the 1993–94 freshman class were as follows: 38% below 21, 25% between 21 and 23, 20% between 24 and 26, 11% between 27 and 28, and 6% above 28. About 42% of the current freshmen were in the top fifth of their class; 66% were in the top two fifths. About 5 freshmen graduated first in their class.

Requirements: A minimum GPA of 2.5 is required. The SAT I or ACT is required. The minimum composite score acceptable for the ACT is 18. In addition, candidates for admission must graduate from an accredited secondary school. Students must have completed 15 Carnegie units and 4 years of English and social studies and 3 to 4 years each of mathematics and science. Interviews are recommended for all applicants, and auditions are recommended in appropriate instances. AP and CLEP credits are accepted. Important factors used in the admissions decision are advanced placement or honor courses, leadership record, evidence of special talent, extracurricular activities record, and geographic diversity.

Procedure: Freshmen are admitted fall and winter. Entrance exams should be taken during the spring of the junior year. Applications should be filed by August 1 for fall entry and December 15 for winter entry, along with an application fee of $20. Notification is sent on a rolling basis.

Transfer: About 224 transfer students enrolled in 1993–94. Transfer applicants must have earned at least 12 credits in academic course work from an accredited junior or 4-year college with a minimum GPA of 2.0. Interviews are recommended. A total of 30 credits out of 124 must be completed at Aquinas.

Visiting: There are regularly scheduled orientations for prospective students, consisting of a tour of the campus and presentations by financial aid personnel, program directors, coaches, and faculty. There are guides for informal visits, and visitors may sit in on classes and stay overnight at the school. To arrange for a visit, contact Thomas Mikowski, Director of Admissions, at (616) 459–8281, ext. 5193.

Financial Aid: In 1993–94 98% of all current freshmen and 91% of continuing students received some form of financial aid. About 92% of freshmen and 86% of continuing students received need-based aid. The average freshman award was $10,027. Of that total, scholarships or need-based grants averaged $4898 ($11,200 maximum), and loans averaged $1975 ($2625 maximum). Forty-three percent of undergraduate students work part-time. Average earnings from campus work for the school year are $750. The average financial indebtedness of the 1992–93 graduate was $7900. Aquinas is a member of CSS. The FAF is required. The deadline for financial aid applications is June 1.

International Students: There are currently 16 international students enrolled. The school actively recruits these students. They must take the TOEFL and achieve a minimum score of 550. The student must also take the SAT I and achieve a minimum score of 1000.

Computers: The college provides computer facilities for student use. The mainframe is a DEC MicroVAX 3600. There are 17 terminals in a laboratory setting. All students may access the system. It may be used 91 hours per week during open laboratory times. There are no time limits on using the system and no fees.

Graduates: In 1992–93 330 bachelor's degrees were awarded. The most popular majors among graduates were business administration (24%), communication arts (10%), and English (8%). Within an average freshman class, 1% graduate in 3 years, 37% in 4 years, 53% in 5 years, and 55% in 6 years. Some 44 companies recruited on campus in 1992–93. In the 1992 graduating class, 18% of all students were enrolled in graduate school within 6 months of graduation; 81% of all graduates had found employment.

Admissions Contact: Thomas Mikowski, Director of Admissions.

BAKER COLLEGE
E-4

Flint, MI 48507-5508   (810) 766-4000; (800) 822-2537 (in-state)

Full-time: 700 men, 2105 women	Faculty: 36
Part-time: 376 men, 966 women	Ph.D.s: 18%
Graduate: none	Student/Faculty: 78 to 1
Year: quarters, summer session	Tuition: $5396
Application Deadline: September 19	Room & Board: $1575
Freshman Class: 1754 applied, 1754 accepted, 1432 enrolled	
ACT: recommended	NONCOMPETITIVE

Baker College, established in 1911, is an independent, coeducational institution offering undergraduate degrees in business, health science, and technical curricula. It is part of the Baker College System. In addition to regional accreditation, Baker has baccalaureate program accreditation with CAHEA. The library contains 52,000 volumes, 1057 microform items, and 186 audiovisual forms and subscribes to 165 periodicals. Computerized library sources and services include the card catalog, interlibrary loans, and database searching. Special learning facilities include a learning resource center. The 30-acre campus is in an urban area 60 miles northwest of Detroit. Including residence halls, there are 6 buildings on campus.

Student Life: About 97% of undergraduates are from Michigan. Students come from 4 foreign countries. Eighty-four percent are white; 13% African American. The average age of all undergraduates is 28.

Housing: A total of 189 students can be accommodated in college housing. College-sponsored living facilities include single-sex and coed on-campus apartments. On-campus housing is available on a first-come, first-served basis. Priority is given to out-of-town students. Ninety-eight percent of students commute. Alcohol is not permitted. All students may keep cars on campus.

Activities: There are no fraternities or sororities on campus. There are 15 groups on campus, including computers, literary magazine, professional, and social. Popular campus events include Baker College Pride Day and Martin Luther King Day.

Sports: There are 3 intramural sports for men and 3 for women. Athletic and recreation facilities include a gymnasium and a weight room.

Disabled Students: The entire campus is accessible to disabled students. The following facilities are available: wheelchair ramps, elevators, special parking, specially equipped rest rooms, lowered drinking fountains, and lowered telephones.

Services: In addition to many counseling and information services, tutoring is available in most subjects.

Campus Safety and Security: Campus safety and security measures include 24-hour foot and vehicle patrol, self defense education, escort service, and informal discussions. In addition, there are pamphlets, posters, and films and lighted pathways and sidewalks. High-traffic areas of the college are monitored by videocamera.

Programs of Study: Baker awards the B.B.A. and B.I.M. degrees. Associate degrees also are awarded. Bachelor's degrees are awarded in BUSINESS (accounting, business administration and management, marketing management, and office supervision and management), COMPUTER AND PHYSICAL SCIENCE (computer programming), ENGINEERING AND ENVIRONMENTAL DESIGN (aviation administration/management, drafting and design technology, electrical/electronics engineering technology, and interior design), HEALTH PROFESSIONS (health care administration and occupational therapy). Business administration has the largest enrollment.

Required: Degree requirements include completion of 180 to 208 quarter hours with a minimum GPA of 2.0. All students must complete mathematic and computer courses and an employment seminar.

Special: Co-op programs, internships, and dual and interdisciplinary majors, including graphic communications, are available.

Faculty/Classroom: Forty-four percent of faculty are male; 56%, female. All teach undergraduates. The average class size in a regular course offering is 24.

Admissions: All of the 1993–94 applicants were accepted.

Requirements: The ACT is recommended. There are no entrance requirements to Baker College. Students without either a high school diploma or a GED may still be admitted on the basis of Baker College test results.

Procedure: Freshmen are admitted to all sessions. Applications should be filed by September 19 for fall entry, January 3 for winter entry, March 28 for spring entry, and June 14 for summer entry, along with an application fee of $20. Notification is sent on a rolling basis.

Transfer: About 418 transfer students enrolled in 1993–94. Transcripts from all previous colleges must be submitted. Grades of C or better are eligible for transfer credit. A total of 48 quarter hours out of 180 to 208 must be completed at Baker.

Visiting: There are regularly scheduled orientations for prospective students. There are guides for informal visits, and visitors may sit in on classes. To arrange for a visit, contact the Admissions Office at (810) 766-4000 or (800) 822-2537 (in-state).

Financial Aid: In a recent year, 55% of all current freshmen and continuing students received some form of financial aid. About 55% of freshmen and continuing students received need-based aid. Five percent of undergraduate students work part-time. Baker is a member of CSS. The FAF, the FAFSA, and the college's own financial statement are required. The deadline for financial aid applications is September 1.

International Students: There are currently 5 international students enrolled. No entrance exam is required.

Computers: The college provides computer facilities for student use. The mainframe is an IBM System 36 Model B24. Some 220 networked microcomputers are available. All students may access the system. It may be used during school hours. There are no time limits on using the system and no fees.

Graduates: In 1992–93 122 bachelor's degrees were awarded. The most popular majors among graduates were management/marketing (29%), accounting (19%), and office administration (11%). Some 60 companies recruited on campus in an earlier year. In an earlier graduating class, 1% of the men were enrolled in graduate school within 6 months of graduation; 98% of all 1992 graduates found employment within 6 months of graduation.

Admissions Contact: Mark Heaton, Director of Admissions.

CALVIN COLLEGE
D-4

Grand Rapids, MI 49546   (616) 957-6106
(800) 688-0122 (out-of-state)

Full-time: 1539 men, 1862 women	Faculty: 220; IIB, +$
Part-time: 56 men, 80 women	Ph.D.s: 83%
Graduate: 93 men, 100 women	Student/Faculty: 15 to 1
Year: 4-1-4, summer session	Tuition: $9450
Application Deadline: open	Room & Board: $3570
Freshman Class: 1784 applied, 1512 accepted, 913 enrolled	
SAT I: 500/560	ACT: 24 VERY COMPETITIVE

Calvin College, established in 1876, is a private coeducational institution, affiliated with the Christian Reformed Church, offering undergraduate and graduate degrees in liberal arts. In addition to regional accreditation, Calvin has baccalaureate program accreditation with ABET, ACCE, CSWE, NASM, NCATE, and NLN. The library contains 575,000 volumes, 536,000 microform items, and 17,300 audiovisual forms and subscribes to 2700 periodicals. Computerized library sources and services include the card catalog, interlibrary loans, and database searching. Special learning facilities include a learning resource center, art gallery, radio station, TV station, ecosystem preserve, electron microscope laboratory, and observatory with a 16' telescope. The 370-acre campus is in a suburban area 7 miles southeast of downtown Grand Rapids. Including residence halls, there are 40 buildings on campus.

Student Life: About 59% of undergraduates are from Michigan. Students come from 49 states, 31 foreign countries, and Canada. Thirty-eight percent are from public schools; 62% from private. Ninety-three percent are white; 11% foreign nationals. Most are Protestant. The average age of freshmen is 18; all undergraduates, 20. Seventeen percent drop out by the end of their first year; 65% remain to graduate.

Housing: A total of 2700 students can be accommodated in college housing. College-sponsored living facilities include single-sex dormitories and on-campus apartments. In addition there are language houses and a residence hall wing designated an international house. On-campus housing is guaranteed for the freshman and sophomore years only. Fifty-seven percent of students live on campus; of those, 80% remain on campus on weekends. Alcohol is not permitted. All students may keep cars on campus.

Activities: There are no fraternities or sororities on campus. There are 36 groups on campus, including art, band, choir, chorale, chorus, computers, dance, drama, ethnic, film, international, literary magazine, musical theater, newspaper, orchestra, pep band, political, professional, radio and TV, religious, social, social service, student government, symphony, and yearbook. Popular campus events include Homecoming, Parents Weekend, the spring and fall music and art festivals, and the January lecture series.

Sports: There are 8 intercollegiate sports for men and 9 for women, and 26 intramural sports for men and 25 for women. Athletic and recreation facilities include a field house, a soccer stadium, baseball and softball diamonds, an 8-lane, 400-meter track, a Nautilus room, and the natatorium, which contains a diving pool.

Disabled Students: Eighty-five percent of the campus is accessible to disabled students. The following facilities are available: wheelchair ramps, elevators, special parking, specially equipped rest rooms, special class scheduling, lowered telephones, and dedicated accessible suites in residence halls.

Services: In addition to many counseling and information services, tutoring is available in most subjects. In addition, there is a reader service and a Braille print service for the blind, and remedial math, reading, and writing.

Campus Safety and Security: Campus safety and security measures include 24-hour foot and vehicle patrol, self defense education, escort service, and informal discussions. In addition, there are pamphlets, posters, and films, emergency telephones, lighted pathways and sidewalks, a crime alert bulletin, and reports in the school newspaper.

Programs of Study: Calvin awards the B.A., B.S., and B.F.A. degrees. Master's degrees also are awarded. Bachelor's degrees are awarded in BIOLOGICAL SCIENCE (biochemistry and biology/biological science), BUSINESS (accounting, business administration and management, business economics, and recreation), COMMUNICATIONS AND THE ARTS (art history and appreciation, communications, dramatic arts, Dutch, English, fine arts, French, German, Greek, Latin, music, and Spanish), COMPUTER AND PHYSICAL SCIENCE (chemistry, computer science, geology, mathematics, and physics), EDUCATION (art, elementary, physical, and secondary), ENGINEERING AND ENVIRONMENTAL DESIGN (civil engineering, electrical/electronics engineering, engineering, and mechanical engineering), HEALTH PROFESSIONS (medical laboratory technology, nursing, occupational therapy, predentistry, premedicine, and speech pathology/audiology), SOCIAL SCIENCE (criminal justice, economics, geography, history, philosophy, political science/government, prelaw, psychology, religion, social science, social work, and sociology). Physical sciences, English, philosophy, history, music, and engineering are the strongest academically. Education, engineering, business, and communication have the largest enrollments.

Required: Degree requirements include completion of 126 credit hours, with 28 credits in the major. All students must complete specific course work in English, religion, history, science, mathematics, communication, fine arts, psychology or sociology, economics or political science, philosophy, and physical education. A minimum GPA of 2.0 is required.

Special: A variety of dual majors and student-designed majors are available, as well as combined curriculum programs in medical laboratory technology, occupational therapy, and speech pathology. Students may study abroad in 8 countries, and they may enroll in a Washington semester and other cooperative programs in Los Angeles film studies, the Au Sable Institute, the Chicago Metropolitan program, Oregon extension, Middle East studies, and Russian studies. Internships, work-study programs, and cross-registration at Grand Valley State University, in special education, and at Reformed Bible College, in religion, are also available. A pass/fail grading option is available only during the interim semester. There is a freshman honors program on campus. Four departments have honors programs.

Faculty/Classroom: Eighty-three percent of faculty are male; 17%, female. All both teach and do research. No introductory courses are taught by graduate students. The average class size in an introductory lecture is 33; in a laboratory, 20; and in a regular course offering, 24.

Admissions: About 85% of the 1993–94 applicants were accepted. The SAT scores for the 1993–94 freshman class were as follows: Verbal—45% below 500, 35% between 500 and 599, 17% between 600 and 700, and 3% above 700; Math—26% below 500, 32% between 500 and 599, 27% between 600 and 700, and 15% above 700. The ACT scores were 16% below 21, 25% between 21 and 23, 28% between 24 and 26, 14% between 27 and 28, and 18% above 28. About 49% of the current freshmen were in the top fifth of their class; 75% were in the top two fifths. There were 20 National Merit finalists and 21 semifinalists. About 34 freshmen graduated first in their class.

Requirements: A minimum GPA of 2.5 is required. The ACT is required. Students with SAT I results will be required to take the ACT upon arrival on campus. Candidates for admission must graduate from an accredited secondary school or earn a GED and be at least 19 years of age. Completion of 12 academic credits and 20 Carnegie units is required, with a distribution of 3 to 4 units in English, 2 units each in history, mathematics, and science, and 1 or more units in social studies. Two or more units in a foreign language are also recommended. AP and CLEP credits are accepted. Important factors used in the admissions decision are recommendations by school officials, extracurricular activities record, leadership record, advanced placement or honor courses, and evidence of special talent.

Procedure: Freshmen are admitted to all sessions. Entrance exams should be taken during the spring of the junior year or the fall of the senior year. Application deadlines are open. The application fee is $25. Notification is sent on a rolling basis.

Transfer: About 132 transfer students enrolled in 1993–94. Transfer students from 4-year colleges are required to have a minimum GPA of 2.0; from 2-year colleges, 2.5. SAT I minimum requirements are 390 on the verbal section and 420 on the mathematics section. A minimum score of 20 is required on the ACT. A total of 31 credits out of 126 must be completed at Calvin.

Visiting: There are regularly scheduled orientations for prospective students, including sectionals, class visits, lunch with professors, and campus tours. There are guides for informal visits and visitors may sit in on classes and stay overnight at the school. To arrange for a visit, contact the Admissions Office at (616) 957–6106 or (800) 688–0122.

Financial Aid: In 1993–94 90% of all current freshmen and 88% of continuing students received some form of financial aid. About 70% of freshmen and 60% of continuing students received need-based aid. The average freshman award was $7500. Of that total, scholarships or need-based grants averaged $4500 ($9500 maximum); loans averaged $3400 ($4100 maximum); and work contracts averaged $1000 ($1200 maximum). Thirty percent of undergraduate students work part-time. Average earnings from campus work for the school year are $1100. The average financial indebtedness of the 1992–93 graduate was $8500. Calvin is a member of CSS. The college's own financial statement and the FAFSA are required. The deadline for financial aid applications is July 1.

International Students: There are currently 398 international students enrolled. The school actively recruits these students. They must take the TOEFL and achieve a minimum score of 550. The MTELP is required if the student scored low on the TOEFL. The student must also take the SAT I, minimum socre 390 verbal and 420 mathematics, or the ACT, minimum score 20. Exceptions are made for strong students without access to standardized exams.

Computers: The college provides computer facilities for student use. The mainframe is a Sun 670 MP. Students may access 153 IBM-compatible PCs and 112 Apple Macintoshes connected via Ethernet/Novell, as well as Suns, which are accessed via 21 Sparc workstations and 52 public terminals. All students may access the system 24 hours per day, 7 days per week. There are no time limits on using the system and no fees.

Graduates: In a recent year, 855 bachelor's degrees were awarded. The most popular majors among 1993 graduates were elementary education (10%), business (10%), and English (9%). Within an average freshman class, 45% graduate in 4 years and 65% in 5 years. Some 85 companies recruited on campus in 1992–93. In the 1992 graduating class, 32% of the men and 17% of the women were enrolled in graduate school within 6 months of graduation; 66% of the men and 80% of the women had found employment.

Admissions Contact: Thomas E. McWhertor, Director of Admissions.

CENTER FOR CREATIVE STUDIES COLLEGE OF ART AND DESIGN

E-5
Detroit, MI 48202

(313) 872-3118, ext. 204
(800) 952-ARTS (out-of-state)

Full-time, part-time: 494 men, 301 women	Faculty: 46; IIB, -$
	Ph.D.s: 15%
Graduate: none	Student/Faculty: 11 to 1
Year: semesters	Tuition: $11,230
Application Deadline: April 1	Room & Board: $4100
Freshman Class: 424 applied, 401 accepted, 203 enrolled	
SAT I Verbal/Math: 450/480	ACT: 20 SPECIAL

The Center for Creative Studies/College of Art and Design, established in 1926, is a private, independent institution offering comprehensive 4-year B.F.A. programs in crafts, fine arts, graphic communications, industrial design, and photography. In addition to regional accreditation, CCS-CAD has baccalaureate program accreditation with NASAD. The library contains 21,000 volumes and subscribes to 100 periodicals. Special learning facilities include a learning resource center and art gallery. The 11-acre campus is in an urban area 3 miles from downtown Detroit in the University Cultural Center, which includes the Detroit Institute of Arts. Including residence halls, there are 6 buildings on campus.

Student Life: About 70% of undergraduates are from Michigan. Students come from 28 states, 10 foreign countries, and Canada. Eighty-five percent are white. The average age of freshmen is 20; all undergraduates, 23. Nine percent drop out by the end of their first year; 46% remain to graduate.

Housing: A total of 175 students can be accommodated in college housing. College-sponsored living facilities include coed on-campus apartments. On-campus housing is available on a lottery system for upperclassmen. Priority is given to out-of-town students. Sixty-nine percent of students commute. Alcohol is not permitted. All students may keep cars on campus.

Activities: There are no fraternities or sororities on campus. There are 6 groups on campus, including chorus, dance, ethnic, jazz band, professional, and student government. Popular campus events include an annual student exhibition, Noel Night, Detroit Festival of the Arts, and gallery openings.

Sports: There is no sports program at CCS-CAD.

Disabled Students: Seventy-five percent of the campus is accessible to disabled students. The following facilities are available: elevators, special parking, specially equipped rest rooms, and lowered telephones.

Services: In addition to many counseling and information services, there is remedial reading and writing.

Campus Safety and Security: Campus safety and security measures include informal discussions, pamphlets, posters, and films, lighted pathways and sidewalks, and 24-hour foot patrol.

Programs of Study: CCS-CAD awards the B.F.A degree. Bachelor's degrees are awarded in COMMUNICATIONS AND THE ARTS (advertising, art direction, biomedical photography, ceramic art and design, fine arts, glass, illustration, industrial design, metal/jewelry, painting, photography, printmaking, product design, sculpture, and transportation design), ENGINEERING AND ENVIRONMENTAL DESIGN (furniture design and interior design), SOCIAL SCIENCE (textiles and clothing). Graphic communication has the largest enrollment.

Required: Degree requirements include course work in English, behavioral science, art history, history, speech, philosophy, and art and design. Students must complete 96 credits in art and design and 48 credits in liberal arts. A minimum GPA of 2.0 is required, and students must complete 144 credits to graduate, with 72 in the major.

Special: Internships are available within the student's departmental major. Credit for internships is available.

Faculty/Classroom: Sixty-seven percent of faculty are male; 33%, female. All teach undergraduates. The average class size in an introductory lecture is 20; in a laboratory, 15; and in a regular course offering, 18.

Admissions: About 95% of the 1993–94 applicants were accepted. The SAT scores for the 1993–94 freshman class were as follows: Verbal—69% below 500, 26% between 500 and 599, and 5% between 600 and 700; Math—53% below 500, 31% between 500 and 599, and 16% between 600 and 700. The ACT scores were 52% below 21, 22% between 21 and 23, 20% between 24 and 26, 2% between 27 and 28, and 4% above 28.

Requirements: A minimum GPA of 2.5 is required. The SAT I or ACT is required. Applicants must graduate from an accredited secondary school or earn a GED. An admissions interview is required for applicants living within a 250-mile radius of the school. Applicants living outside this radius will be interviewed by telephone. A portfolio of representative work is also required, and an essay is recommended. AP and CLEP credits are accepted. Important factors used in the admissions decision are evidence of special talent and advanced placement or honor courses.

Procedure: Freshmen are admitted in the fall and winter. Applications should be filed by April 1 for fall entry and December 1 for winter entry, along with an application fee of $35. Notification is sent on a rolling basis. There is a deferred admissions plan.

Transfer: About 127 transfer students enrolled in 1993–94. Transfer applicants should submit a portfolio that includes artwork done at the previous college. Transcripts and portfolio review will determine how many credits may transfer; the maximum is 72. The approval of the chairperson of the department to which the student is applying is required for transfer of studio credit. The minimum GPA is 2.0. An admissions interview for transfer students who live within a 250-mile radius of the school is required. A total of 72 credits out of 144 must be completed at CCS-CAD.

Visiting: There are regularly scheduled orientations for prospective students, including an introduction to the college by an admissions professional, a slide presentation of student work, application/financial aid information, and a campus tour. There are guides for informal visits and visitors may sit in on classes and stay overnight at the school. To arrange for a visit, contact the Admissions Office at (313) 872-3118, ext. 204, or (800) 952-ARTS.

Financial Aid: In a recent year, 62% of all freshmen and 65% of continuing students received some form of financial aid. About 59% of freshmen and 55% of continuing students received need-based aid. The average freshman award was $6225. Of that total, scholarships or need-based grants averaged $2445 ($9780 maximum); loans averaged $1500 ($2625 maximum); and work contracts averaged $1000 ($2000 maximum). Eighty percent of undergraduate students work part-time. Average earnings from campus work for the school year are $1200. The average financial indebtedness of the graduate in a recent year was $8700. CCS-CAD is a member of CSS. The FAF or FFS is required. The deadline for financial aid applications is February 15.

International Students: There are currently 22 international students enrolled. The school actively recruits these students. They must take the TOEFL and achieve a minimum score of 550.

Computers: The college provides computer facilities for student use. There are no time limits on using the system and no fees.

Graduates: In 1992–93 326 bachelor's degrees were awarded. Within an average freshman class, 46% graduate in 5 years. Some 15 companies recruited on campus in a recent year. In the 1992 graduating class, 5% of the men and 3% of the women were enrolled in graduate school within 6 months of graduation.

Admissions Contact: Eddie Kent Tallent, Assistant Dean for Enrollment Services.

CENTRAL MICHIGAN UNIVERSITY D-4

Mount Pleasant, MI 48859 (517) 774-3076

Full-time: 5866 men, 7362 women	Faculty: 667; IIA, +$
Part-time: 535 men, 752 women	Ph.D.s: 73%
Graduate: 709 men, 1155 women	Student/Faculty: 20 to 1
Year: semesters, summer session	Tuition: $2901 ($7132)
Application Deadline: March 1	Room & Board: $3836
Freshman Class: 7304 applied, 6263 accepted, 2539 enrolled	
ACT: 21	**LESS COMPETITIVE**

Central Michigan University, founded in 1892, is a public university offering programs in liberal arts, business, and health, education, and human services. There are 3 undergraduate schools and one graduate school. In addition to regional accreditation, CMU has baccalaureate program accreditation with AACSB, NASM, NCATE, and NRPA. The library contains 843,656 volumes, 1,099,215 microform items, and 267,408 audiovisual forms, and subscribes to 4940 periodicals. Computerized library sources and services include the card catalog, interlibrary loans, and database searching. Special learning facilities include a learning resource center, art gallery, natural history museum, radio station, TV station, observatory, and student newspaper. The 854-acre campus is in a small town 70 miles north of Lansing. Including residence halls, there are 54 buildings on campus.

Student Life: About 98% of undergraduates are from Michigan. Students come from 42 states and Canada. Ninety-four percent are white. The average age of freshmen is 18; all undergraduates, 20. Twenty-five percent drop out by the end of their first year; 54% remain to graduate.

Housing: A total of 6040 students can be accommodated in college housing. College-sponsored living facilities include single-sex and coed dormitories, on-campus apartments, and married-student housing. In addition, there are honors houses. On-campus housing is guaranteed for all 4 years. Alcohol is not permitted. Upperclassmen may keep cars on campus.

Activities: About 12% of men belong to 17 national fraternities; about 10% of women belong to 1 local sorority and 13 national sororities. There are 204 groups on campus, including art, cheerleading, choir, chorus, computers, dance, drama, ethnic, gay, honors, international, jazz band, literary magazine, marching band, musical theater, newspaper, orchestra, pep band, photography, political, professional, radio and TV, religious, social, social service, student government, symphony, and yearbook. Popular campus events include Student Activities Fair, CMU and You Day, Hispanic Heritage Month, Black History Month, and Big/Little Sister/Brother Weekend.

Sports: There are 8 intercollegiate sports for men and 9 for women, and 27 intramural sports for men and 26 for women. Athletic and recreation facilities include 9 flag football/soccer fields, 4 lighted softball fields, 6 outdoor tennis courts, 12 racquetball courts, 11 basketball courts, 10 volleyball courts, 16 badminton courts, 3 swimming pools, 2 saunas, an indoor track, indoor turf and tennis courts, weight rooms, and 2 auxiliary gymnasiums for floor hockey and basketball. There are additional areas for floor hockey and aerobics, a golf net, an archery range, a batting cage, and indoor soccer, together with a 12-lane bowling alley and 8 pool/billiard tables. The campus football stadium seats 20,086, the baseball stadium 4200, and the basketball gymnasium 6050.

Disabled Students: Ninety-five percent of the campus is accessible to disabled students. The following facilities are available: wheelchair ramps, elevators, special parking, specially equipped rest rooms, special class scheduling, lowered drinking fountains, and lowered telephones.

Services: In addition to many counseling and information services, tutoring is available in most subjects. There is a reader service for the blind, and remedial math, reading, and writing. Tutoring is provided free of charge to students with a GPA below 2.0.

Campus Safety and Security: Campus safety and security measures include lighted pathways and sidewalks.

Programs of Study: CMU awards the B.A., B.S., B.A.A., B.F.A., B.Indiv.S., B.Mus., B.S.B.A., and B.S.E. degrees. Master's and doctoral degrees also are awarded. Bachelor's degrees are awarded in BIOLOGICAL SCIENCE (biology/biological science), BUSINESS (accounting, banking and finance, business administration and management, court reporting, management science, marketing/retailing/merchandising, and retailing), COMMUNICATIONS AND THE ARTS (broadcasting, communications, dramatic arts, English, fine arts, French, German, journalism, languages, music, and Spanish), COMPUTER AND PHYSICAL SCIENCE (actuarial science, chemistry, computer science, earth science, geology, mathematics, physical sciences, physics, and statistics), EDUCATION (art, bilingual/bicultural, business, early childhood, education, elementary, foreign languages, guidance, health, home economics, industrial arts, middle school, music, science, secondary, and special), ENGINEERING AND ENVIRONMENTAL DESIGN (engineering technology and industrial administration/management), HEALTH PROFES-

SIONS (speech pathology/audiology and sports medicine), SOCIAL SCIENCE (anthropology, economics, geography, history, parks and recreation management, philosophy, political science/government, psychology, religion, and sociology). Elementary education, secondary education, accounting, and marketing have the largest enrollments.

Required: To graduate, students must complete 124 credit hours, including 30 in the major, with a GPA of 2.0. They must fulfill the university's distribution requirements in humanities, natural science, and social science, earn 30 hours in interpretive and area studies, and demonstrate both written and oral competency, as well as mathematics competency. A course in advanced English composition is required.

Special: CMU offers internships, study abroad in 11 countries, and dual majors in chemistry/physics and computer science/mathematics. Student-designed majors are available for a B.A. in individual studies, and there is credit for life, military, and work experience. A 3–2 engineering degree is available with Michigan Technological University. Students may take up to 25 hours for pass/fail grades. The Institute for Personal and Career Development offers external degree programs in which classes are held in the areas where students live or work, and students can get degrees without attending classes on campus. There is a freshman honors program on campus, as well as 33 national honor societies. Twenty-one departments have honors programs.

Faculty/Classroom: Sixty-five percent of faculty are male; 35%, female. Graduate students teach 1% of introductory courses. The average class size in an introductory lecture is 40; in a laboratory, 20; and in a regular course offering, 20.

Admissions: About 86% of the 1993–94 applicants were accepted. The ACT scores for the 1993–94 freshman class were as follows: 48% below 21, 30% between 21 and 23, 15% between 24 and 26, 5% between 27 and 28, and 2% above 28.

Requirements: The ACT is recommended. Applicants must be high school graduates or hold a GED. The university strongly recommends 4 years each of English and mathematics, 3 each of science and social studies, and 2 of foreign language, as well as 1 course each in computer science and fine arts. AP and CLEP credits are accepted.

Procedure: Freshmen are admitted to all sessions. Entrance exams should be taken during the junior or senior year. Applications should be filed by March 1 for fall entry, December 1 for winter entry, May 1 for spring entry, and May 1 for summer entry, along with an application fee of $25. Notification is sent on a rolling basis. There is a deferred admissions plan. A waiting list is an active part of the admissions procedure.

Transfer: About 1438 transfer students enrolled in a recent year. Transfer students must have a GPA of 2.5. A total of 30 credits out of 124 must be completed at CMU.

Visiting: There are guides for informal visits, and visitors may sit in on classes and stay overnight at the school. To arrange for a visit, contact Admissions at (517) 774–3076.

Financial Aid: In a recent year, 65% of all current freshmen and 60% of continuing students received some form of financial aid. Scholarships or need-based grants averaged $800 ($6000 maximum); loans averaged $1800 ($4000 maximum); and work contracts averaged $800 ($3000 maximum). The average financial indebtedness of a recent year's graduate was $7000. CMU is a member of CSS. The FAF is required. The deadline for financial aid applications is March 1.

International Students: There are currently 154 international students enrolled. The school actively recruits these students. They must take the TOEFL and achieve a minimum score of 520.

Computers: The college provides computer facilities for student use. The mainframe is an IBM 3090 Model 180T. There are 273 Apple Macintosh, IBM, and IBM-compatible microcomputers available for student use throughout the campus and in the dormitories; 21 different languages and softwares are applicable. All students may access the system. It may be used at any time. There are no time limits on using the system and no fees.

Graduates: In a recent year, 2936 bachelor's degrees were awarded. The most popular majors among graduates were secondary education (11%), elementary education (11%), and marketing (7%). Within an average freshman class, 1% graduate in 3 years, 18% in 4 years, 50% in 5 years, and 54% in 6 years. Some 251 companies recruited on campus in 1992–93.

Admissions Contact: Michael Owens, Director of Admissions.

CLEARY COLLEGE
Ypsilanti, MI 48197

E-5

(313) 483–4400 (Ypsilanti)
(517) 548–3670 (Howell)

Full-time: 139 men, 221 women	Faculty: 10
Part-time: 112 men, 289 women	Ph.D.s: 50%
Graduate: none	Student/Faculty: 36 to 1
Year: quarters, summer session	Tuition: $5095
Application Deadline: open	Room & Board: n/app
Freshman Class: n/av	
SAT I or ACT: not required	NONCOMPETITIVE

Cleary College, founded in 1883, is a private, coeducational institution offering undergraduate degrees in business administration. The college serves an entirely commuter student body. A second campus, similar in size and programs, is located in Howell, and there are extension sites throughout Michigan. The library contains 15,475 volumes, 1800 microform items, and 100 audiovisual forms, and subscribes to 285 periodicals. The 37-acre campus is 35 miles east of Lansing. There is one building on campus.

Student Life: All undergraduates are from Michigan. Ninety percent are from public schools; 10% from private. The average age of all undergraduates is 30.

Housing: There are no residence halls.

Activities: There are no fraternities or sororities on campus. There are some groups on campus, including newspaper, social service, and student government. Popular campus events include Spring Ball, several holiday dances, and picnics.

Sports: There is no sports program at Cleary. Athletic and recreation facilities include auditorium/gymnasium.

Disabled Students: The entire campus is accessible to disabled students. The following facilities are available: special parking, specially equipped rest rooms, lowered drinking fountains, and lowered telephones.

Services: In addition to many counseling and information services, tutoring is available in some subjects.

Programs of Study: Cleary awards the B.B.A. degree. Associate degrees are also awarded. Bachelor's degrees are awarded in BUSINESS (accounting, business administration and management, marketing/retailing/merchandising, and secretarial studies/office management).

Required: General education requirements include courses in college skills, grammar, and composition. In order to graduate, students must complete at least 180 quarter credit hours with a minimum GPA of 2.0.

Special: Cleary offers credit for life experiences and opportunities for individualized study. Nondegree study is possible.

Requirements: A minimum GPA of 2.0 is required. The SAT I or ACT is recommended. The college follows an open admissions policy. Applicants should be graduates of accredited secondary schools or have earned a GED, but those without such credentials who show potential for success may also be accepted.

Procedure: Freshmen are admitted to all sessions. Application deadlines are open. Application fee is $25. The college accepts all applicants. Notification is sent on a rolling basis.

Transfer: Applicants must submit official transcripts from all institutions previously attended. A total of 45 quarter credits out of 180 must be completed at Cleary.

Visiting: There are regularly scheduled orientations for prospective students. There are guides for informal visits and visitors may sit in on classes. To arrange for a visit, contact the Admissions Office at (313) 483–4400 (Ypsilanti), or (517) 548–3670 (Howell).

Financial Aid: Cleary is a member of CSS. The FAF is required. The deadline for financial aid applications is August 31.

International Students: Students must take the TOEFL or the University of Michigan Language Test.

Computers: The college provides computer facilities for student use. The college provides IBM PCs for academic use.

Admissions Contact: Laura LaVoie, Director of Student Recruitment.

CONCORDIA COLLEGE
Ann Arbor, MI 48105

E-5

(313) 995–7322
(800) 253–0680 (out-of-state)

Full-time: 218 men, 344 women	Faculty: 42; IIB, --$
Part-time: 5 men, 13 women	Ph.D.s: 55%
Graduate: none	Student/Faculty: 13 to 1
Year: semesters	Tuition: $9480
Application Deadline: open	Room & Board: $4180
Freshman Class: 180 applied, 171 accepted, 74 enrolled	
SAT I: 485/500	ACT: 20 COMPETITIVE

Concordia College, established in 1963, is a private institution affiliated with the Missouri Synod of the Lutheran Church, offering undergraduate degrees in the arts, business, education, and human ser-

vices. The library contains 103,138 volumes, 14,853 microform items, and 1824 audiovisual forms and subscribes to 125 periodicals. Computerized library sources and services include interlibrary loans and database searching. Special learning facilities include an art gallery. The 234-acre campus is in a suburban area 40 miles west of Detroit. Including residence halls, there are 30 buildings on campus.

Student Life: About 77% of undergraduates are from Michigan. Students come from 17 states and 2 foreign countries. Eighty-one percent are from public schools; 19% from private. Ninety percent are white. Most are Protestant. The average age of freshmen is 18. Twenty-two percent drop out by the end of their first year; 70% remain to graduate.

Housing: A total of 446 students can be accommodated in college housing. College-sponsored living facilities include single-sex dormitories and married-student housing. On-campus housing is guaranteed for all 4 years. Eighty-one percent of students live on campus; of those, 60% remain on campus on weekends. Alcohol is not permitted. All students may keep cars on campus.

Activities: There are no fraternities or sororities on campus. There are 21 groups on campus, including band, choir, chorale, chorus, computers, drama, ethnic, musical theater, newspaper, religious, social, social service, and student government. Popular campus events include Lyceum Day and Boar's Head Festival.

Sports: There are 3 intercollegiate sports for men and 3 for women, and 5 intramural sports for men and 5 for women. Athletic and recreation facilities include a soccer field, baseball and softball diamonds, tennis courts and sand volleyball courts, and a physical education building.

Disabled Students: The entire campus is accessible to disabled students. The following facilities are available: wheelchair ramps, elevators, special parking, specially equipped rest rooms, and lowered drinking fountains.

Services: In addition to many counseling and information services, tutoring is available in most subjects. There is also a reader service for the blind, and remedial math, reading, and writing.

Campus Safety and Security: Campus safety and security measures include 24-hour foot and vehicle patrol, informal discussions, and lighted pathways and sidewalks.

Programs of Study: Concordia awards the B.A. degree. Associate degrees also are awarded. Bachelor's degrees are awarded in BIOLOGICAL SCIENCE (biology/biological science), BUSINESS (business economics and human resources), COMMUNICATIONS AND THE ARTS (classical languages, communications, English, fine arts, and music), COMPUTER AND PHYSICAL SCIENCE (earth science, mathematics, and physical sciences), EDUCATION (elementary, physical, and secondary), HEALTH PROFESSIONS (health care administration), SOCIAL SCIENCE (biblical languages, history, humanities, psychology, religion, social science, and sociology). Education is the strongest academically. Teacher education, English, social science, visual arts and music, and human resources administration have the largest enrollments.

Required: Degree requirements include completion of 128 credit hours, with 30 to 36 in the major, 39 credit hours of integrated studies, and a minimum GPA of 2.0. The student must also demonstrate proficiency in foreign language, writing, speech, and mathematics.

Special: Study abroad is available in 7 countries. Accelerated degree programs are available in human resources administration and health care administration. The college confers credit for life, military, and work experience through the Division of Lifelong Learning. Nondegree study may be pursued and a pass/fail grading option is available.

Faculty/Classroom: Sixty-seven percent of faculty are male; 33%, female. All teach undergraduates. The average class size in an introductory lecture is 24; in a laboratory, 15; and in a regular course offering, 15.

Admissions: About 95% of the 1993–94 applicants were accepted. The SAT scores for the 1993–94 freshman class were as follows: Verbal—56% below 500, 41% between 500 and 599, and 3% between 600 and 700; Math—43% below 500, 25% between 500 and 599, and 32% between 600 and 700. The ACT scores were 53% below 21, 23% between 21 and 23, 17% between 24 and 26, 5% between 27 and 28, and 2% above 28. About 38% of the current freshmen were in the top fifth of their class; 58% were in the top two fifths. Two freshmen graduated first in their class.

Requirements: A minimum GPA of 2.25 is required. The SAT I or ACT is required, with the ACT preferred. Minimum ACT score must be 18. Applicants must graduate from an accredited secondary school or have a GED. Fifteen Carnegie units are required, including 3 units each in English, mathematics, and science, 2 units in social studies, and 1 unit each in art, history, and music. A portfolio is required in the Division of Lifelong Learning, and an audition is required for Kreft/Goodman Music Scholarships. AP and CLEP credits are accepted. Important factors used in the admissions decision are evidence of special talent, advanced placement or honor courses,

leadership record, recommendations by school officials, personality, and intangible qualities.

Procedure: Freshmen are admitted in the fall and winter. Application deadlines are open. The application fee is $25. Notification is sent on a rolling basis. There is a deferred admissions plan.

Transfer: About 39 transfer students enrolled in 1993–94. A GPA of 2.0 is required for transfer students; a GPA of 2.5 is required for admittance to the teacher education program. Transfer students who have earned 12 to 18 college credits are not required to take the ACT. Interviews are recommended. A total of 30 credits out of 128 must be completed at Concordia.

Visiting: There are regularly scheduled orientations for prospective students, including 3 Discover Concordia days scheduled in September, November, and April, 1 Teacher Education Info Day in February, and 1 Church Professional Weekend in March. There are guides for informal visits and visitors may sit in on classes and stay overnight at the school. To arrange for a visit, contact the Admissions Office at (313) 995–7322 or (800) 253–0680.

Financial Aid: In an earlier class, 91% of all freshmen and 89% of continuing students received some form of financial aid. In 1993–94, about 90% of all students received need-based aid. The average freshman award was $3060. Of that total, scholarships or need-based grants averaged $1300 ($8500 maximum); loans averaged $1500 ($6000 maximum); and work contracts averaged $165 ($1200 maximum). Sixty-eight percent of undergraduate students work part-time. Average earnings from campus work for the school year are $750. The average financial indebtedness of the graduate was $2978. Concordia is a member of CSS. The FAF and the college's own financial statement are required. The deadline for financial aid applications is May.

International Students: There are currently 6 international students enrolled. They must take the TOEFL or the University of Michigan Language Test and achieve a minimum score on the TOEFL of 515.

Computers: The college provides computer facilities for student use. The mainframe consists of a PC network of Apple Macintosh and IBM compatibles. More than 30 microcomputers are available for student use in the library. All students may access the system from 8 A.M. to midnight. There are no time limits on using the system and no fees.

Graduates: In 1992–93 150 bachelor's degrees were awarded. The most popular majors among graduates were human resources administration (64%), teacher education (17%), and liberal arts (10%).

Admissions Contact: Fred A. Schebor, Director of Admission.

DAVENPORT COLLEGE OF BUSINESS D-4
Grand Rapids, MI 49503 (616) 732–1200
(800) 632–9569 (out-of-state)

Full-time: 446 men, 867 women	**Faculty:** 38
Part-time: 664 men, 1478 women	**Ph.D.s:** n/av
Graduate: none	**Student/Faculty:** 35 to 1
Year: terms, summer session	**Tuition:** $6246
Application Deadline: open	**Room & Board:** $1875
Freshman Class: 1152 enrolled	
ACT: 19	**NONCOMPETITIVE**

Davenport College of Business, founded in 1866, is an independent coeducational institution specializing in business education. The library contains 35,000 volumes, 500 microform items, and 800 audiovisual forms, and subscribes to 1000 periodicals. Special learning facilities include a learning resource center. The 10-acre campus is in a suburban area 150 miles west of Detroit. Including residence halls, there are 9 buildings on campus.

Student Life: About 97% of undergraduates are from Michigan. Students come from 3 foreign countries. Ninety-seven percent are from public schools; 3% from private. Eighty-nine percent are white. The average age of all undergraduates is 25. Twenty-five percent drop out by the end of their first year.

Housing: A total of 156 students can be accommodated in college housing. College-sponsored living facilities include single-sex dormitories. On-campus housing is guaranteed for all 4 years and is available on a first-come, first-served basis. Alcohol is not permitted. All students may keep cars on campus.

Activities: There is 1 national sorority. There are no fraternities on campus. There are 12 groups on campus, including ethnic, newspaper, professional, religious, and student government. Popular campus events include Charter Day (Homecoming).

Sports: There is no sports program at Davenport.

Disabled Students: All of the campus is accessible to disabled students. The following facilities are available: wheelchair ramps, elevators, special parking, specially equipped rest rooms, special class scheduling, lowered drinking fountains, and lowered telephones.

Services: In addition to many counseling and information services, tutoring is available in most subjects, including tutoring laboratories for mathematics, English, and computers. There is also remedial math, reading, and writing, and a learning assistance center.

Campus Safety and Security: Campus safety and security measures include shuttle buses, lighted pathways and sidewalks, and and 24-hour foot patrols.

Programs of Study: Davenport awards the B.B.A. degree. Associate degrees are also awarded. Bachelor's degrees are awarded in BUSINESS (accounting, business administration and management, hotel/motel and restaurant management, and marketing/retailing/merchandising), COMPUTER AND PHYSICAL SCIENCE (computer programming). Business is the strongest academically. Accounting has the largest enrollment.

Required: Davenport requires all students to complete 184.5 credit hours, 58.5 in the major, with a minimum GPA of 2.0 overall and in career courses. The general education core consists of 72 credits, and the business core 36 credits.

Special: Davenport offers co-op programs in administrative services, sales and marketing, and paralegal studies. There are internships in most disiclines. Study abroad is available.

Faculty/Classroom: The average class size in an introductory lecture is 19; in a laboratory, 6; and in a regular course offering, 19.

Requirements: A minimum GPA of 2.0 is required. The SAT I or ACT is not required. Graduation from an accredited secondary school or a GED is accepted. An interview is recommended. CLEP credit is accepted.

Procedure: Freshmen are admitted to all sessions. Application deadlines are open. The application fee is $20. The college accepts all applicants Notification is sent on a rolling basis.

Transfer: About 2082 transfer students enrolled in 1993–94. C is the minimum grade accepted for transfer. There is a 75% maximum credit transfer for the bachelor's degree. A total of 49 credits out of 184 must be completed at Davenport.

Visiting: There are regularly scheduled orientations for prospective students. There are guides for informal visits and visitors may sit in on classes and stay overnight at the school. To arrange for a visit, contact Admissions at (616) 732-1200.

Financial Aid: In 1993–94, 83% of all students received some form of financial aid. About 76% received need-based aid. The average freshman award was $5004. Ninety-five percent of undergraduate students work part-time. Average earnings from campus work for the school year are $2200. Davenport is a member of CSS. The FAFSA financial statement is required. The deadline for financial aid applications is March 15.

International Students: There are currently 12 international students enrolled. The school actively recruits these students. They must take the TOEFL and achieve a minimum score of 500.

Computers: The college provides computer facilities for student use. The mainframe is an HP 3000/Series 58. A complete laboratory with PCs is available. All students may access the system. It may be used 8 A.M. to 12 A.M. on weekdays, and 12 P.M. to 6 P.M. on weekends. There are no time limits on using the system and no fees.

Graduates: Within an average freshman class, 40% graduate in 6 years. Some 12 companies recruited on campus in 1992–93. In the 1992 graduating class, 22% of the men were enrolled in graduate school within 6 months of graduation.

Admissions Contact: Suzanne Postema, Director of Admissions.

DETROIT COLLEGE OF BUSINESS
E-5
Dearborn, MI 48126-3799 (313) 581-4400

Full-time: 603 men, 2206 women	Faculty: 45; IIB, --$
Part-time: 578 men, 1748 women	Ph.D.s: 25%
Graduate: none	Student/Faculty: 62 to 1
Year: quarters, summer session	Tuition: $5184
Application Deadline: September 15	Room & Board: n/app
Freshman Class: 3084 applied, 3078 accepted, 1775 enrolled	
SAT I or ACT: not required	NONCOMPETITIVE

The Detroit College of Business, founded in 1962, is an independent, coeducational school offering undergraduate courses in business areas. The library contains 21,884 volumes, 2000 microform items, and 123 audiovisual forms, and subscribes to 411 periodicals. Computerized library sources and services include interlibrary loans and database searching. Special learning facilities include a learning resource center. The 17-acre campus is in a suburban area 3 miles west of Detroit. There are 3 buildings on campus.

Student Life: Nearly all of the undergraduates are from Michigan. Students come from 1 state, 5 foreign countries, and Canada. Ninety percent are from public schools; 10% from private. Forty-eight percent are African American; 42% white. The average age of freshmen is 25.5; all undergraduates, 29. Twenty-five percent drop out by the end of their first year; 40% remain to graduate.

Housing: There are no residence halls. All students commute. Alcohol is not permitted. All students may keep cars on campus.

Activities: About 1% of men and women belong to 1 national fraternity or sorority. There are many groups on campus, including accounting, Amnesty International, computers, ethnic, health occupations, newspaper, professional, student government, and yearbook.

Popular campus events include Summer Carnival and Business Olympics for high school students.

Sports: There is 1 intercollegiate sport for men, and 7 intramural sports for men and 4 for women. Athletic and recreation facilities include playing fields and nearby golf courses.

Disabled Students: Nearly all of the campus is accessible to disabled students. The following facilities are available: elevators, special parking, specially equipped rest rooms, lowered drinking fountains, and lowered telephones.

Services: In addition to many counseling and information services, tutoring is available in every subject. In addition, there is remedial math, reading, and writing.

Campus Safety and Security: Campus safety and security measures include escort service, lighted pathways and sidewalks, and and evening security service from 5 P.M. to 1 P.M. for the parking lot and buildings.

Programs of Study: DCB awards the B.B.A. degree. Associate degrees also are awarded. Bachelor's degrees are awarded in BUSINESS (accounting, applied business, banking and finance, management science, marketing/retailing/merchandising, and office supervision and management), COMPUTER AND PHYSICAL SCIENCE (computer programming and information sciences and systems), ENGINEERING AND ENVIRONMENTAL DESIGN (industrial administration/management), HEALTH PROFESSIONS (health care administration). Accounting and computer information sytems are the strongest academically. Accounting, management/marketing, and computer information systems have the largest enrollments.

Required: All students must complete 64 quarter hours of general education courses, including English or speech, mathematics, social science, and electives; 8 quarter hours of computer-related course work, including a fundamentals course; and 32 to 48 quarter hours of business core courses. A total of 196 quarter hours with at least a 2.0 GPA are needed, including a 2.0 GPA in the major.

Special: Work-study through the college, internships, dual majors, co-op programs, nondegree study, and pass-fail options are available.

Faculty/Classroom: Sixty-four percent of faculty are male; 36%, female. All teach undergraduates. The average class size in an introductory lecture is 26; in a laboratory, 20; and in a regular course offering, 26.

Admissions: All of the 1993–94 applicants were accepted.

Requirements: The GED is accepted. No entrance exams are required. AP and CLEP credits are accepted.

Procedure: Freshmen are admitted to all sessions. Applications should be filed by September 15 for fall entry, January 3 for winter entry, April 4 for spring entry, and June 27 for summer entry, along with an application fee of $20. The college accepts all applicants. Notification is sent on a rolling basis. There are early admissions and deferred admissions plans.

Transfer: About 3000 transfer students enrolled in 1993–94. A GPA of 2.0 is recommended, as is an interview. A total of 48 credits out of 196 must be completed at DCB.

Visiting: There are regularly scheduled orientations for prospective students, including organized visits by applicants or interested groups. There are guides for informal visits and visitors may sit in on classes. To arrange for a visit, contact the Director of Admissions at (313) 581-4400, ext. 210.

Financial Aid: In 1993–94, 71% of all current freshmen and 65% of continuing students received some form of financial aid. The average freshman award was $1700. Of that total, scholarships or need-based grants averaged $1700 ($4500 maximum); and loans averaged $1700 ($2600 maximum). Seventy-six percent of undergraduate students work part-time. Average earnings from campus work for the school year are $5000. The average financial indebtedness of the 1992–93 graduate was $3500. The FAF and FAFSA are required. The deadline for financial aid applications is February 1.

International Students: There are currently 6 international students enrolled. They must take the TOEFL or the University of Michigan Language Test and achieve a minimum score on the TOEFL of 550.

Computers: The college provides computer facilities for student use. The mainframe is an IBM AS/400. Twelve terminals connect to the mainframe for language programming. There are 60 microcomputers available in classroom and laboratory settings for use in program instruction and other classroom applications. Those students taking computer language classes may access the system. It may be used 8 A.M. to 10 P.M., for up to 20 hours per week. There are no fees.

Graduates: In 1992–93, 305 bachelor's degrees were awarded. The most popular majors among graduates were management (30%), accounting (20%), and computer information systems (10%). Within an average freshman class, 20% graduate in 4 years, 50% in 5 years, and 30% in 6 years. Some 29 companies recruited on campus in a recent year.

Admissions Contact: Lynda Menard, Director of Admissions.

EASTERN MICHIGAN UNIVERSITY
E-5

Ypsilanti, MI 48197   (313) 487-3060; (800) GO TO EMU

Full-time: 5524 men, 7445 women   Faculty: 687; IIA, av$
Part-time: 2509 men, 3476 women   Ph.D.s: 78%
Graduate: 1975 men, 3671 women   Student/Faculty: 19 to 1
Year: semesters, summer session   Tuition: $2718 ($6596)
Application Deadline: July 1   Room & Board: $4031
Freshman Class: 6693 applied, 5423 accepted, 2329 enrolled
ACT: 21   **COMPETITIVE**

Eastern Michigan University, founded in 1849, is a public institution offering programs in arts and sciences, business, education, health and human services, and technology. There are 5 undergraduate schools and one graduate school. In addition to regional accreditation, EMU has baccalaureate program accreditation with AACSB, ADA, AHEA, ASLA, CAHEA, CSWE, FIDER, NASM, NCATE, and NLN. The library contains 800,935 volumes, 692,593 microform items, 10,972 audiovisual forms, and subscribes to 4096 periodicals. Computerized library sources and services include the card catalog, interlibrary loans, and database searching. Special learning facilities include a learning resource center, art gallery, and radio station. The 460-acre campus is in a suburban area 8 miles east of Ann Arbor. Including residence halls, there are 112 buildings on campus.

Student Life: About 90% of undergraduates are from Michigan. Students come from 39 states, 70 foreign countries, and Canada. Eighty-four percent are white. The average age of freshmen is 19; all undergraduates, 24. Thirty percent drop out by the end of their first year; 55% remain to graduate.

Housing: A total of 4000 students can be accommodated in college housing. College-sponsored living facilities include single-sex and coed dormitories, on-campus apartments, married-student housing, fraternity houses, and sorority houses. In addition there are honors houses and special housing known as Community of Scholars, upperclass halls, and foreign student and transfer student residence areas. On-campus housing is guaranteed for the freshman year only, is available on a first-come, first-served basis, and is available on a lottery system for upperclassmen. Eighty-four percent of students commute. All students may keep cars on campus.

Activities: About 6% of men belong to 3 local and 15 national fraternities; about 4% of women belong to 2 local and 7 national sororities. There are 150 groups on campus, including art, band, cheerleading, chess, choir, chorale, chorus, computers, dance, drama, drill team, ethnic, film, gay, honors, international, jazz band, literary magazine, marching band, musical theater, newspaper, orchestra, pep band, photography, political, professional, radio and TV, religious, social, social service, student government, symphony, and yearbook. Popular campus events include Homecoming/Parents Day, Martin Luther King Birthday Celebration, Opening Night series, Family Weekend, and Little Sibs.

Sports: There are 11 intercollegiate sports for men and 9 for women, and 21 intramural sports for men and 18 for women. Athletic and recreation facilities include a stadium with a capacity of 30,000, outdoor playing fields, a field house, a student recreation and intramural center, and an outdoor facility including a lake, amphitheatre, volleyball, and lake house. The largest arena seats 6,600.

Disabled Students: Ninety-two percent of the campus is accessible to disabled students. The following facilities are available: wheelchair ramps, elevators, special parking, specially equipped rest rooms, special class scheduling, lowered drinking fountains, lowered telephones, and special housing accomodations.

Services: In addition to many counseling and information services, tutoring is available in every subject, including special seminars through the Instructional Support Center in reading, writing, study skills, and computers, and writing clinics. There is also a reader service for the blind. Notetakers and interpreters are provided for the handicapped.

Campus Safety and Security: Campus safety and security measures include 24-hour foot and vehicle patrol, self defense education, escort service, and shuttle buses. In addition, there are informal discussions, pamphlets, posters, and films, emergency telephones, and lighted pathways and sidewalks.

Programs of Study: EMU awards the B.A., B.S., B.A.E., B.A.in Language and World Business, B.B.A., B.B.E., B.F.A., B.M.E., B.M.P., B.M.T., B.S.N. degrees. Master's and doctoral degrees also are awarded. Bachelor's degrees are awarded in AGRICULTURE (forestry and related sciences), BIOLOGICAL SCIENCE (biochemistry, biology/biological science, and microbiology), BUSINESS (accounting, accounting information systems, banking and finance, business administration and management, business computer systems, business economics, business systems analysis, fashion merchandising, hospitality management services, international business management, languages and international trade, languages and world business, marketing/retailing/merchandising, personnel management, real estate, and tourism), COMMUNICATIONS AND THE ARTS (advertis-

ing, broadcasting, communications, dance, design, dramatic arts, English, film arts, fine arts, French, German, graphic design, Japanese, journalism, music, Spanish, and speech/debate/rhetoric), COMPUTER AND PHYSICAL SCIENCE (actuarial science, chemistry, computer programming, computer science, earth science, geology, information sciences and systems, mathematics, physics, and polymer science), EDUCATION (art, bilingual/bicultural, business, early childhood, elementary, foreign languages, health, home economics, industrial arts, middle school, music, physical recreation, science, secondary, special, and teaching English as a second language/foreign language), ENGINEERING AND ENVIRONMENTAL DESIGN (aviation administration/management, aviation computer technology, cartography, computer aided design, interior design, land use management and reclamation, plastics technology, and preengineering), HEALTH PROFESSIONS (medical laboratory technology, nursing, occupational therapy, predentistry, premedicine, prepharmacy, and speech pathology/audiology), SOCIAL SCIENCE (anthropology, criminal justice, dietetics, economics, food production/management/services, geography, history, international relations, parks and recreation management, philosophy, political science/government, prelaw, psychology, public administration, social science, social work, and sociology). Business, languages, sciences, communications/theater arts, and education are the strongest academically. Business, arts/sciences, teacher education, and special education have the largest enrollments.

Required: To graduate students must have a GPA of 2.0, and complete a minimum of 124 semester hours, including usually 30 in the major, and 40 or more of basic studies. Required courses include English composition, political science, computer literacy, and physical education.

Special: EMU offers internships, work-study programs, and a Washington semester, and has co-op programs and cross-registration with the University of Michigan at Ann Arbor, Concordia College, and Washtenaw Community College. Students may study abroad in more than 18 countries. EMU allows dual majors and student-designed majors, and confers a general studies degree, as well as a B.A.-B.B.A. degree in language and world business. Students may receive credit for life, military, and work experience, nondegree study is allowed, and pass/fail options are open. There is a freshman honors program on campus, as well as 11 national honor societies, including Phi Beta Kappa.

Faculty/Classroom: All teach undergraduates. Graduate students teach 2% of introductory courses. The average class size in a laboratory is 15 and in a regular course offering, 35.

Admissions: About 81% of the 1993-94 applicants were accepted. The SAT scores for the 1993-94 freshman class were as follows: Verbal—70% below 500, 25% between 500 and 599, and 5% between 600 and 700; Math—56% below 500, 38% between 500 and 599, and 6% between 600 and 700. The ACT scores were 49% below 21, 31% between 21 and 23, 11% between 24 and 26, 6% between 27 and 28, and 3% above 28.

Requirements: A minimum GPA of 2.0 is required. The ACT or the SAT I is required. A minimum composite of 17 on the ACT, and 700 on the SAT I is required. Applicants should be high school graduates, or hold a GED. The university recommends that students complete 19 academic credits in high school, consisting of 4 in English, 3 each in mathematics, science, and social studies, 2 each in foreign language and history, and 2 to 3 in other traditional college-preparatory courses. An essay is recommended. A portfolio is required for students entering an art program, and an audition is required for students entering a music program. AP and CLEP credits are accepted. Important factors used in the admissions decision are advanced placement or honor courses, evidence of special talent, recommendations by school officials, recommendations by alumni, and leadership record.

Procedure: Freshmen are admitted to all sessions. Entrance exams should be taken by November of the senior year of high school. Applications should be filed by July 1 for fall entry, November 15 for winter entry, April 11 for spring entry, and June 6 for summer entry, along with an application fee of $20. Notification is sent on a rolling basis. There is a deferred admissions plan.

Transfer: About 1957 transfer students enrolled in 1993-94. Transfer students must have at least 12 semester hours of college credit, with a GPA of 2.0. A total of 30 credits out of 124 must be completed at EMU.

Visiting: There are regularly scheduled orientations for prospective students, including information and tours. There are guides for informal visits and visitors may sit in on classes and stay overnight at the school. To arrange for a visit, contact On-Campus Programs at (800) GO TO EMU.

Financial Aid: In 1993-94 75% of all current freshmen and 60% of continuing students received some form of financial aid. About 60% of freshmen and 50% of continuing students received need-based aid. The average freshman award was $3000. Of that total, scholarships or need-based grants averaged $1650 ($8000 maximum);

loans averaged $2625 ($4425 maximum); and work contracts averaged $1800 (maximum). Forty-four percent of undergraduate students work part-time. Average earnings from campus work for the school year are $1800. The average financial indebtedness of the 1992–93 graduate was $10,000. EMU is a member of CSS. The FAF, FFS, and FAFSA financial statements are required. The deadline for financial aid applications is March 15.

International Students: There are currently 1250 international students enrolled. The school actively recruits these students. They must take the TOEFL or the University of Michigan Language Test and achieve a minimum score on the TOEFL of 500.

Computers: The college provides computer facilities for student use. There are two mainframes, a VAX 4000 and an IBM 3090. Computer laboratories and stations are available throughout the campus, in the Instructional Support Center, departmental offices, and College of Business Computer Laboratory. The system may be accessed only by students in courses which require its use. It may be used at all times. There are no time limits on using the system and no fees.

Graduates: In a recent year 2755 bachelor's degrees were awarded. The most popular majors among graduates were elementary education (7%), marketing (5%), and psychology (4%). Some 188 companies recruited on campus in 1992–93.

Admissions Contact: M. Dolan Evanovich, Director of Admissions.

FERRIS STATE UNIVERSITY

D-4

Big Rapids, MI 49307　　　　　　　　　　(616) 592–2100

Full-time: 5539 men, 3613 women	Faculty: 500; IIA, av$
Part-time: 1038 men, 998 women	Ph.D.s: 31%
Graduate: 72 men, 55 women	Student/Faculty: 18 to 1
Year: quarters, summer session	Tuition: $3237 ($6541)
Application Deadline: open	Room & Board: $3923
Freshman Class: 5381 applied, 5177 accepted, 3949 enrolled	
ACT: 18	**NONCOMPETITIVE**

Ferris State University, established in 1884, is a public institution offering day and evening courses through its School of Arts and Sciences, Education, Allied Health, Technology, Business, Pharmacy, and College of Optometry. There are 7 undergraduate and 2 graduate schools. In addition to regional accreditation, Ferris State has baccalaureate program accreditation with ABET, ACPE, ADA, AHEA, CAHEA, CSWE, and NLN. The library contains 226,282 volumes, 3,062,057 microform items, and 8560 audiovisual forms, and subscribes to 3284 periodicals. Computerized library sources and services include interlibrary loans and database searching. Special learning facilities include a learning resource center, planetarium, and tv station. The 650-acre campus is in a small town 55 miles north of Grand Rapids. Including residence halls, there are 98 buildings on campus.

Student Life: About 95% of undergraduates are from Michigan. Students come from 42 states, 37 foreign countries, and Canada. Eighty-four percent are white. The average age of freshmen is 19; all undergraduates, 22. Thirty-seven percent drop out by the end of their first year.

Housing: A total of 5250 students can be accommodated in college housing. College-sponsored living facilities include single-sex and coed dormitories, on-campus apartments, and married-student housing. On-campus housing is guaranteed for all 4 years and is available on a first-come, first-served basis. Fifty-nine percent of students commute. Upperclassmen may keep cars on campus.

Activities: About 6% of men belong to 21 national fraternities; about 4% of women belong to 10 national sororities. There are 130 groups on campus, including art, band, cheerleading, chess, choir, chorale, chorus, computers, drama, drill team, drum and bugle corps, ethnic, film, gay, honors, international, jazz band, marching band, newspaper, orchestra, pep band, photography, political, professional, radio and tv, religious, social, social service, student government, and symphony. Popular campus events include Homecoming, Little Brother/Little Sister Weekend, and Mock Rock.

Sports: There are 10 intercollegiate sports for men and 8 for women, and 21 intramural sports for men and 19 for women. Athletic and recreation facilities include a golf course, a racquetball and fitness club, an ice arena, and a 10,000-seat stadium; the largest auditorium seats 1700.

Disabled Students: The entire campus is accessible to disabled students. The following facilities are available: wheelchair ramps, elevators, special parking, specially equipped rest rooms, special class scheduling, lowered drinking fountains, and lowered telephones.

Services: In addition to many counseling and information services, tutoring is available in most subjects. There is also a reader service for the blind, and remedial math, reading, and writing.

Campus Safety and Security: Campus safety and security measures include 24-hour foot and vehicle patrol, self-defense education, escort service, and informal discussions. In addition, there are pamphlets, posters, and films, emergency telephones, and lighted pathways and sidewalks.

Programs of Study: Ferris State awards the B.S. degree. Associate, master's, and doctoral degrees are also awarded. Bachelor's degrees are awarded in BIOLOGICAL SCIENCE (biology/biological science), BUSINESS (accounting, banking and finance, business administration and management, hospitality management services, insurance, international business management, marketing/retailing/merchandising, office supervision and management, personnel management, secretarial studies/office management, and small business management), COMMUNICATIONS AND THE ARTS (advertising and public relations), COMPUTER AND PHYSICAL SCIENCE (computer programming and mathematics), EDUCATION (business, mathematics, science, and technical), ENGINEERING AND ENVIRONMENTAL DESIGN (construction management, engineering technology, plastics technology, and surveying engineering), HEALTH PROFESSIONS (health care administration, medical laboratory technology, medical records administration/services, nuclear medical technology, nursing, optometry, and pharmacy), SOCIAL SCIENCE (criminal justice and social work). Optometry and pharmacy are the strongest academically. Business administration and management have the largest enrollments.

Required: Degree requirements include a minimum 2.0 GPA, 12 quarter credit hours in English and speech communications, 9 each in the humanities and social sciences, and 7 to 8 in natural sciences. The amount of credits students must earn in the major, and the total required for graduation (180 to 200 quarter credits), varies by course of study.

Special: Ferris State offers internship, study abroad, work-study programs, accelerated degrees, dual and student-designed majors, credit for life, military, and work experience, and a pass/fail grading option. There are 6 national honor societies on campus.

Faculty/Classroom: Seventy-seven percent of faculty are male; 23%, female. The average class size in an introductory lecture is 40; in a laboratory, 18; and in a regular course offering, 30.

Admissions: About 96% of the 1993–94 applicants were accepted. The ACT scores for the 1993–94 freshman class were as follows: 76% below 21, 16% between 21 and 23, 6% between 24 and 26, and 2% between 27 and 28.

Requirements: A minimum GPA of 2.0 is required. The ACT is required. Applicants must graduate from an accredited secondary school or earn a GED. Four years each of English and mathematics, 3 years each of biophysical/physical sciences and history, 2 years each of a foreign language and fine arts, and 1 year of computer literacy are advised. Interviews are recommended. AP and CLEP credits are accepted. Recommendations by school officials is an important factor used in the admission decision.

Procedure: Freshmen are admitted to all sessions. Entrance exams should be taken prior to course registration. Application deadlines are open. Application fee is $20. The college accepts all applicants. Notification is sent on a rolling basis. A waiting list is an active part of the admissions procedure, with about 2% of applicants on the list.

Transfer: About 1300 transfer students enrolled in a recent year. A GPA of at least 2.0 is required. A total of 45 quarter credits out of 180 to 200 must be completed at Ferris State.

Visiting: There are regularly scheduled orientations for prospective students. There are guides for informal visits and visitors may sit in on classes and stay overnight at the school. To arrange for a visit, contact the Admissions Office at (616) 592–2100.

Financial Aid: In a recent year, 70% of all current freshmen and 66% of continuing students received some form of financial aid. About 58% of freshmen and 55% of continuing students received need-based aid. The average freshman award was $4700. Of that total, scholarships or need-based grants averaged $2550 ($3700 maximum); loans averaged $1100 ($4200 maximum); and work contracts averaged $1050 ($2500 maximum). Forty-three percent of undergraduate students work part-time. Average earnings from campus work for the school year are $1350. The average financial indebtedness of the 1992–93 graduate was $6400. Ferris State is a member of CSS. The FAF or FFS and FAFSA are required. The deadline for financial aid applications is April 1.

International Students: There are currently 200 international students enrolled. The school actively recruits these students. They must take the TOEFL and achieve a minimum score of 500.

Computers: The college provides computer facilities for student use. The mainframe is an IBM 3083/IX3. There are PCs available campuswide. All students may access the system. It may be used at any time; laboratories are open 16 hours daily. There are no time limits on using the system and no fees.

Graduates: In a recent year, 2042 bachelor's degrees were awarded. Some 210 companies recruited on campus.

Admissions Contact: Donald Mullens, Associate Dean.

GMI ENGINEERING & MANAGEMENT INSTITUTE

E-4

Flint, MI 48504

(313) 762–7865; (800) 955–4464

Full-time: 1874 men, 493 women	Faculty: 130; IIB, +$
Part-time: none	Ph.D.s: 65%
Graduate: 634 men, 140 women	Student/Faculty: 18 to 1
Year: alternating 12-week terms	Tuition: $11,000
Application Deadline: open	Room & Board: $3158
Freshman Class: 1538 applied, 1201 accepted, 521 enrolled	
SAT I: 510/640	ACT: 26 **HIGHLY COMPETITIVE**

GMI Engineering & Management Institute is an independent college founded in 1919 that offers a 5-year cooperative engineering program that requires students to alternate two 12-week academic terms and two 12-week work experience terms. There is one graduate school. In addition to regional accreditation, GMI has baccalaureate program accreditation with ABET. The library contains 80,000 volumes, 31,000 microform items, and 700 audiovisual forms, and subscribes to 770 periodicals. Computerized library sources and services include the card catalog, interlibrary loans, and database searching. Special learning facilities include an art gallery, radio station, TV station, and a collection of industrial history. The 45-acre campus is in a suburban area 60 miles north of Detroit. Including residence halls, there are 3 buildings on campus.

Student Life: About 51% of undergraduates are from out-of-state, mostly the Midwest. Students come from 48 states, 14 foreign countries, and Canada. Eighty-five percent are from public schools; 15% from private. Eighty percent are white. The average age of freshmen is 18; all undergraduates, 20. Ten percent drop out by the end of their first year; 75% remain to graduate.

Housing: A total of 530 students can be accommodated in college housing. College-sponsored living facilities include coed dormitories. On-campus housing is guaranteed for the freshman year only and is available on a lottery system for upperclassmen. Priority is given to out-of-town students. Alcohol is not permitted. All students may keep cars on campus.

Activities: About 60% of men belong to 14 national fraternities; about 60% of women belong to 6 national sororities. There are 60 groups on campus, including art, chorus, drama, ethnic, honors, international, jazz band, newspaper, pep band, photography, political, professional, radio and TV, religious, social, social service, student government, and yearbook. Popular campus events include Harambee, Talent Show, Greek Week, Pace cultural/entertainment series, Noon entertainment-music and comedians, 'Big Event,' SOC Weekend, Holiday Ball, Parents Weekend, and Alumni Weekend.

Sports: There are 3 intercollegiate sports for men, and 13 intramural sports for men and 10 for women. Athletic and recreation facilities include a fitness center, a gymnasium, 4 softball and 4 soccer fields, tennis courts, a sand volleyball court, and an athletic crib that has loaner equipment for most sports at no cost.

Disabled Students: All of the campus is accessible to disabled students. The following facilities are available: wheelchair ramps, elevators, special parking, specially equipped rest rooms, special class scheduling, lowered drinking fountains, and lowered telephones.

Services: In addition to many counseling and information services, tutoring is available in most subjects. Tutoring is routinely available in the residence hall and with faculty. Supplemental tutoring is coordinated through the Office of Student Retention.

Campus Safety and Security: Campus safety and security measures include 24-hour foot and vehicle patrol, self-defense education, escort service, and informal discussions. In addition, there are pamphlets, posters, films, emergency telephones, lighted pathways and sidewalks, and after-hours access (e.g., to the academic building) is easy yet secure via the tunnel from the residence hall and campus center.

Programs of Study: GMI awards the B.S.A.M., B.S.C.E., B.S.E.E., B.S.I.E., B.S.M.E., B.S.M., and B.S.M.S.E. degrees. Master's degrees also are awarded. Bachelor's degrees are awarded in BUSINESS (accounting, management information systems, and marketing/retailing/merchandising), COMPUTER AND PHYSICAL SCIENCE (applied mathematics), ENGINEERING AND ENVIRONMENTAL DESIGN (computer engineering, electrical/electronics engineering, industrial engineering, industrial engineering technology, manufacturing engineering, and mechanical engineering). Electrical engineering and mechanical engineering have the largest enrollments.

Required: Degree requirements include completion of 180 credit hours, with 60 in the major. All students must take specific courses in mathematics, chemistry, physics, communication, computers, history, and economics, and a minimum GPA of 77 on a scale of 100 is required for graduation. The GPA is determined by a formula combining the numerical grades achieved and the number of credits attempted. Most students complete a fifth year thesis project, though it can be replaced by another academic year with permission.

Special: All GMI undergraduate students participate in cooperative education work experience. Students may pursue a dual major in electrical and mechanical engineering, and student-designed majors can be arranged within the curriculum structure. There are 5 national honor societies on campus.

Faculty/Classroom: Ninety percent of faculty are male; 10%, female. All teach undergraduates, and 20% also do research. No introductory courses are taught by graduate students. The average class size in an introductory lecture is 45; in a laboratory, 21; and in a regular course offering, 28.

Admissions: About 78% of the 1993–94 applicants were accepted. The SAT scores for the 1993–94 freshman class were as follows: Verbal—46% below 500, 42% between 500 and 599, 11% between 600 and 700, and 1% above 700; Math—5% below 500, 25% between 500 and 599, 54% between 600 and 700, and 16% above 700. The ACT scores were 2% below 21, 12% between 21 and 23, 38% between 24 and 26, 25% between 27 and 28, and 23% above 28. About 78% of the current freshmen were in the top fifth of their class; 97% were in the top two fifths. Twenty-two freshmen graduated first in their class.

Requirements: The SAT I or ACT is required. Applicants must graduate from an accredited secondary school or earn a GED. Sixteen academic credits are required. Applicants must have completed 3 years of English, 3 1/2 years of mathematics, including trigonometry, and two years of laboratory science, of which at least one must be chemistry or physics (both are strongly recommended.) Corporate interviews are required in the co-op employment search process. AP and CLEP credits are accepted. Important factors used in the admissions decision are leadership record, advanced placement or honor courses, extracurricular activities record, evidence of special talent, and recommendations by school officials.

Procedure: Freshmen are admitted fall and summer. Entrance exams should be taken in the spring of the junior year and the fall of the senior year. Application deadlines are open. The application fee is $25. Notification is sent on a rolling basis. There is a deferred admissions plan.

Transfer: Sixty-two transfer students enrolled in 1993–94. Transfer applicants must have a minimum GPA of 3.0 in English, mathematics, and science, judged on the college record only. The SAT I or ACT is recommended, as is an interview.

Visiting: There are regularly scheduled orientations for prospective students, consisting of a campus video overview, a student guided tour, and an interview with staff or faculty. Meeting/open house programs are also scheduled three Saturdays a year. There are guides for informal visits, and visitors may sit in on classes and stay overnight at the school. To arrange for a visit, contact the Admissions Office at (800) 955–4464.

Financial Aid: In 1993–94, 65% of all current freshmen and 50% of continuing students received some form of financial aid. About 65% of freshmen and 52% of continuing students received need-based aid. The average freshman award was $6850. Of that total, scholarships or need-based grants averaged $2460 ($10,910 maximum); loans averaged $2625 ($6625 maximum); and work contracts averaged $800. One-hundred percent of undergraduate students work part-time. Average earnings from campus work for the school year are $500. The average financial indebtedness of the 1992–93 graduate was $14,500. GMI is a member of CSS. The FAF and the college's own financial statement are required. The deadline for financial aid applications is May 1.

International Students: There are currently 157 international students enrolled. The school actively recruits these students. They must take the TOEFL or the University of Michigan Language Test and achieve a minimum score on the TOEFL of 550.

Computers: The college provides computer facilities for student use. The mainframe is a Sun SparkServer. There are more than 100 terminals, networked PCs, and CAD workstations on campus, with limited phone access from off campus. Stand-alone and dedicated PCs and microprocessors are also available in most laboratories. All students may access the system. It may be used 24 hours per day, 7 days per week. There are no time limits on using the system and no fees.

Graduates: In a recent year, 529 bachelor's degrees were awarded. The most popular majors among graduates were mechanical engineering (41%), electrical engineering (31%), and manufacturing systems (10%). Within an average freshman class, 67% graduate in 5 years and 75% in 6 years. Some 10 companies recruited on campus in a recent year. In a recent graduating class, 10% of all graduates were enrolled in graduate school within 6 months of graduation; 98% had found employment.

Admissions Contact: Phillip D. Lavender, Director of Admissions.

GRAND RAPIDS BAPTIST COLLEGE AND SEMINARY

Grand Rapids, MI 49505–5897   D-4
(616) 949–5300, ext. 426
(800) 968-GRBC (in-state)

Full-time: 289 men, 335 women
Part-time: 37 men, 49 women
Graduate: 173 men, 15 women
Year: semesters, summer session
Application Deadline: open
Freshman Class: 282 applied, 276 accepted, 172 enrolled
ACT: 21

Faculty: 34; IIB, --$
Ph.D.s: 35%
Student/Faculty: 18 to 1
Tuition: $6340
Room & Board: $3888

COMPETITIVE

Grand Rapids Baptist College and Seminary, founded in 1941, is a liberal arts college and graduate seminary that serves the General Association of Regular Baptist Churches in the Midwest. Major undergraduate programs include business, teacher education, music, and ministry. There is one graduate school. The library contains 89,542 volumes, 145,683 microform items, and 4013 audiovisual forms, and subscribes to 652 periodicals. Computerized library sources and services include interlibrary loans and database searching. Special learning facilities include a learning resource center and radio station. The 132-acre campus is in a suburban area. Including residence halls, there are 22 buildings on campus.

Student Life: About 81% of undergraduates are from Michigan. Students come from 21 states, 4 foreign countries, and Canada. Sixty-two percent are from public schools; 38% from private. Ninety-eight percent are white. Most are Protestant. The average age of freshmen is 18; all undergraduates, 21.6. Thirty-four percent drop out by the end of their first year; 33% remain to graduate.

Housing: A total of 672 students can be accommodated in college housing. College-sponsored living facilities include single-sex dormitories, on-campus apartments, and married-student housing. On-campus housing is guaranteed for all 4 years. Fifty-five percent of students live on campus; of those, 50% remain on campus on weekends. Alcohol is not permitted. All students may keep cars on campus.

Activities: There are no fraternities or sororities on campus. There are 11 groups on campus, including band, cheerleading, choir, chorale, chorus, drama, jazz band, newspaper, pep band, religious, social service, student government, symphony, and yearbook. Popular campus events include Homecoming, Sibling Weekends, banquets, plays, musicals, and Friends Weekend.

Sports: There are 6 intercollegiate sports for men and 4 for women, and 4 intramural sports for men and 4 for women. Athletic and recreation facilities include a 750-seat gymnasium; an indoor swimming pool; a campus lake; and soccer, baseball, and softball fields.

Disabled Students: All of the campus is accessible to disabled students. The following facilities are available: wheelchair ramps, special parking, and specially equipped rest rooms.

Services: In addition to many counseling and information services, tutoring is available in most subjects. There is also remedial math and writing and a study skills class.

Campus Safety and Security: Campus safety and security measures include escort service, emergency telephones, lighted pathways and sidewalks, and foot and vehicle patrols 3 P.M. to 7 A.M. weekdays, 24 hours a day on weekends.

Programs of Study: GRBC awards the B.A., B.Mus., and B.R.E. degrees. Associate and master's degrees also are awarded. Bachelor's degrees are awarded in BIOLOGICAL SCIENCE (biology/biological science), BUSINESS (accounting, business administration and management, marketing/retailing/merchandising, and secretarial studies/office management), COMMUNICATIONS AND THE ARTS (communications, English, fine arts, music, music performance, music theory and composition, and speech/debate/rhetoric), COMPUTER AND PHYSICAL SCIENCE (information sciences and systems), EDUCATION (business, elementary, middle school, music, physical, science, and secondary), HEALTH PROFESSIONS (predentistry, premedicine, and preveterinary science), SOCIAL SCIENCE (biblical languages, biblical studies, history, interdisciplinary studies, prelaw, psychology, religion, religious education, social work, and sociology). English, music, and education are the strongest academically. Business and education have the largest enrollments.

Required: To graduate, the student must complete 129 credit hours, including 56 in the school's liberal arts core, consisting of the humanities, mathematics, social sciences, science, Bible/religion, and physical education. Specific courses include 3 physical education courses, freshman composition, rhetoric, biology, mathematics, psychology or sociology, world civilization, fine arts, philosophy, Old Testament, and inductive Bible study. The number of hours in the major varies. The student must have an overall GPA of 2.0, and 2.5 in the major, and pass a comprehensive exam.

Special: All students choose a student-ministries assignment each semester. Grand Rapids requires internships in all areas of study. Study abroad, a Washington semester, and an interdisciplinary major, missionary aviation, are available.

Faculty/Classroom: Seventy-six percent of faculty are male; 24%, female. All teach undergraduates. The average class size in an introductory lecture is 75; in a laboratory, 30; and in a regular course offering, 21.

Admissions: About 98% of the 1993–94 applicants were accepted. The ACT scores for the 1993–94 freshman class were as follows: 40% below 21, 26% between 21 and 23, 20% between 24 and 26, 9% between 27 and 28, and 5% above 28. There was 1 National Merit semifinalist. Eleven freshmen graduated first in their class.

Requirements: A minimum GPA of 2.3 is required. A minimum score of 18 is required on the ACT or 740 on the SAT I. The college requires a high school transcript or GED certificate, and recommends 15 Carnegie units, including 4 years of English, 3 each of mathematics and social sciences, and 2 of science, as well as 10 semesters of electives. The college recommends that the student appear for an interview, and requires auditions for music scholarships. A pastoral reference is required. AP and CLEP credits are accepted. Important factors used in the admissions decision are personality, intangible qualities, extracurricular activities record, leadership record, advanced placement or honor courses, and parents or siblings attending the school.

Procedure: Freshmen are admitted to all sessions. Entrance exams should be taken during the junior or senior year. Application deadlines are open. Application fee is $25. Notification is sent on a rolling basis. There is a deferred admissions plan.

Transfer: About 95 transfer students enrolled in 1993–94. The college requires high school and college transcripts from transfer students, as well as a pastor's reference. The applicant must have taken the ACT tests if under 25 years of age and with fewer than 30 hours of college credit. A total of 32 credits out of 129 must be completed at GRBC.

Visiting: There are regularly scheduled orientations for prospective students, including admissions and financial aid presentations and class visits. There are guides for informal visits and visitors may sit in on classes and stay overnight at the school. To arrange for a visit, contact the Admissions Office at (800) 968-GRBC.

Financial Aid: In 1993–94, 90% of all current freshmen and 87% of continuing students received some form of financial aid. The average freshman award was $5000. Of that total, scholarships or need-based grants averaged $1620 ($4500 maximum); loans averaged $2000 ($2625 maximum); and work contracts averaged $1500 ($2000 maximum). The average financial indebtedness of an earlier year's graduate was $5000. GRBC is a member of CSS. The FAF is required. The deadline for financial aid applications is March 1.

International Students: There are currently 6 international students enrolled. They must take the TOEFL and achieve a minimum score of 500. The student must also take the SAT I or the ACT and achieve a minimum composite score of 740 on the SAT I or 18 on the ACT.

Computers: The college provides computer facilities for student use. The mainframe is a DEC VAX 8300. Terminals are located in several buildings throughout campus for word processing and electronic mail. All students may access the system. It may be used Monday through Thursday from 8 A.M. to 11 P.M., Friday from 8 A.M. to 5 P.M., and Saturday from 1 P.M. to 5 P.M. There are no time limits on using the system and no fees.

Graduates: In 1992–93, 115 bachelor's degrees were awarded. The most popular majors among graduates were business (20%), education (16%), and Bible (10%). Some 35 companies recruited on campus in a recent year.

Admissions Contact: Rick Newberry, Director of Admissions.

GRAND VALLEY STATE UNIVERSITY

Allendale, MI 49401   D-4
(616) 895–2025; (800) 748-0246 (out-of-state)

Full-time: 3454 men, 4780 women
Part-time: 1075 men, 1544 women
Graduate: 863 men, 1668 women
Year: semesters, summer session
Application Deadline: July 31
Freshman Class: 5165 applied, 3887 accepted, 1561 enrolled
ACT: 23

Faculty: 306; IIA, av$
Ph.D.s: 76%
Student/Faculty: 27 to 1
Tuition: $2892 ($6378)
Room & Board: $3930

VERY COMPETITIVE

Grand Valley State University, founded in 1960, is a comprehensive public institution offering liberal arts and professional education. There are 12 undergraduate and 9 graduate schools. In addition to regional accreditation, Grand Valley has baccalaureate program accreditation with ABET, APTA, CSWE, NASAD, NASM, NCATE, and NLN. The library contains 438,658 volumes, 577,780 microform items, and 9816 audiovisual forms, and subscribes to 2477 periodicals. Computerized library sources and services include the card catalog, interlibrary loans, and database searching. Special learning facilities include a learning resource center, art gallery, radio station, TV station, cadaver laboratory, Great Lakes research vessel, and performance auditorium. The 900-acre campus is in a small town 12 miles west of Grand Rapids. Including residence halls, there are 53 buildings on campus.

Student Life: About 98% of undergraduates are from Michigan. Students come from 37 states, 25 foreign countries, and Canada. Seventy-five percent are from public schools; 25% from private. Ninety percent are white. The average age of freshmen is 18; all undergraduates, 23.3. Twenty-three percent drop out by the end of their first year; 44% remain to graduate.

Housing: A total of 1622 students can be accommodated in college housing. College-sponsored living facilities include coed dormitories and on-campus apartments. In addition, there are honors houses. On-campus housing is available on a first-come, first-served basis and is available on a lottery system for upperclassmen. Alcohol is not permitted. All students may keep cars on campus.

Activities: There are 1 local and 6 national fraternities and 1 local and 6 national sororities. There are 94 groups on campus, including art, band, cheerleading, chess, choir, chorale, chorus, computers, drama, ethnic, film, gay, honors, international, jazz band, literary magazine, marching band, newspaper, orchestra, pep band, photography, political, professional, radio and TV, religious, social, social service, student government, and symphony. Popular campus events include Family Day, Hispanic Awareness Week, and Black History Month.

Sports: There are 15 intercollegiate sports for men and 12 for women, and 21 intramural sports for men and 20 for women. Athletic and recreation facilities include a football stadium, baseball field, and basketball arena, as well as swimming and diving pools, an indoor track, and a weight room.

Disabled Students: Ninety-eight percent of the campus is accessible to disabled students. The following facilities are available: wheelchair ramps, elevators, special parking, specially equipped rest rooms, special class scheduling, lowered drinking fountains, and lowered telephones.

Services: In addition to many counseling and information services, tutoring is available in most subjects. In addition, there is a reader service for the blind, and remedial math, reading, and writing.

Campus Safety and Security: Campus safety and security measures include 24-hour foot and vehicle patrol, self defense education, escort service, and shuttle buses. In addition, there are informal discussions, pamphlets, posters, and films, emergency telephones, and lighted pathways and sidewalks.

Programs of Study: Grand Valley awards the B.A., B.S., B.B.A., B.F.A., B.M., B.M.E., B.S.E., B.S.N., and B.S.W. degrees. Master's degrees also are awarded. Bachelor's degrees are awarded in BIOLOGICAL SCIENCE (biology/biological science), BUSINESS (accounting, banking and finance, business administration and management, business economics, hotel/motel and restaurant management, international business management, management science, marketing/retailing/merchandising, and personnel management), COMMUNICATIONS AND THE ARTS (advertising, broadcasting, communications, design, dramatic arts, English, film arts, fine arts, journalism, languages, music, and photography), COMPUTER AND PHYSICAL SCIENCE (chemistry, computer science, geology, mathematics, and physics), EDUCATION (art, elementary, foreign languages, middle school, music, science, and secondary), ENGINEERING AND ENVIRONMENTAL DESIGN (engineering and industrial engineering technology), HEALTH PROFESSIONS (health science, medical laboratory technology, nursing, physical therapy, predentistry, and premedicine), SOCIAL SCIENCE (anthropology, criminal justice, economics, geography, history, international relations, philosophy, political science/government, prelaw, psychology, public administration, social science, social work, and sociology). Health sciences, business, psychology, and education have the largest enrollments.

Required: To graduate, students must have earned 30 credits in general education, comprised of 10 courses selected from specific groups, and have completed the university's required courses in English and mathematics, as well as the upper-division writing course. A total of 120 credits, with 36 to 60 in the major, is required.

Special: Many programs offer dual majors and internships, and most majors qualify for B.A.-B.S. degrees. There is an engineering cooperative program, a student-designed major in liberal studies, and many work-study programs. Outside opportunities include study abroad in 10 countries, and a Washington semester. There is a freshman honors program on campus, as well as 2 national honor societies.

Faculty/Classroom: Ninety-four percent teach undergraduates. No introductory courses are taught by graduate students. The average class size in an introductory lecture is 100; in a laboratory, 20; and in a regular course offering, 30.

Admissions: About 75% of the 1993–94 applicants were accepted. The ACT scores for the 1993–94 freshman class were as follows: 18% below 21, 38% between 21 and 23, 28% between 24 and 26, 10% between 27 and 28, and 6% above 28. About 45% of the current freshmen were in the top fifth of their class; 85% were in the top two fifths. Twenty-four freshmen graduated first in their class.

Requirements: A minimum GPA of 2.7 is required. Michigan residents must submit ACT test scores, nonresidents either ACT or SAT I scores. In addition, high school transcripts should indicate 4 years of English with 1 composition course, and 3 each of history, mathematics (including 2 years of algebra), science, and social studies. Foreign language is recommended. Applicants who graduated from high school more than 3 years ago need not show test results. The GED is accepted. AP and CLEP credits are accepted. Important factors used in the admissions decision are recommendations by school officials, evidence of special talent, leadership record, personality, intangible qualities, and extracurricular activities record.

Procedure: Freshmen are admitted to all sessions. Entrance exams should be taken during the junior year. Applications should be filed by July 31 for fall entry, December 1 for winter entry, April 10 for spring entry, and May 10 for summer entry, along with an application fee of $20. Notification is sent on a rolling basis. There is an early admissions plan.

Transfer: A total of 1454 transfer students enrolled in 1993–94. Transfer students must have a minimum of 30 college credits with a 2.0 GPA. A total of 30 credits out of 120 must be completed at Grand Valley.

Visiting: There are regularly scheduled orientations for prospective students. There are guides for informal visits and visitors may sit in on classes. To arrange for a visit, contact the Admissions Office at (616) 895–2025 or (800) 748–0246.

Financial Aid: In 1993–94, 68% of all current freshmen and 65% of continuing students received some form of financial aid. About 51% of freshmen and 49% of continuing students received need-based aid. The average freshman award was $4050. Of that total, scholarships or need-based grants averaged $1800 ($7022 maximum); loans averaged $1550 ($4125 maximum); and work contracts averaged $700 ($2000 maximum). Seventy-five percent of undergraduate students work part-time. Average earnings from campus work for the school year are $1500. The average financial indebtedness of the 1992–93 graduate was $4500. Grand Valley is a member of CSS. The FAFSA is required. The deadline for financial aid applications is February 15.

International Students: There are currently 60 international students enrolled. They must take the TOEFL, the University of Michigan Language Test, or the Comprehensive English Language Test and achieve a minimum score on the TOEFL of 550.

Computers: Grand Valley provides computer facilities for student use. The mainframe is an IBM E39000. There are 1500 PCs and terminals spread throughout the campus. LANs and computing laboratories are open 7 days a week, and terminals are connected to LAN and mainframe networks. All students may access the system. There are no time limits on using the system and no fees. It is recommended that all students have personal computers.

Graduates: In a recent year, 1208 bachelor's degrees were awarded. The most popular majors among graduates were health sciences (16%), business (15%), and psychology (10%). Within an average freshman class, 44% graduate in 6 years.

Admissions Contact: JoAnn Foerster, Director of Admissions.

HILLSDALE COLLEGE
D-5

Hillsdale, MI 49242   (517) 437–7341

Full-time: 529 men, 562 women	Faculty: 80
Part-time: 18 men, 30 women	Ph.D.s: 82%
Graduate: none	Student/Faculty: 14 to 1
Year: semesters, summer session	Tuition: $10,670
Application Deadline: July 15	Room & Board: $4440
Freshman Class: 935 applied, 738 accepted, 347 enrolled	
SAT I Verbal/Math: 520/550	ACT: 24 **VERY COMPETITIVE**

Hillsdale College, founded in 1844, is a private liberal arts, preprofessional, and business institution. The 2 libraries contain 175,000 volumes, 23,000 microform items, and 5500 audiovisual forms, and subscribe to 1500 periodicals. Computerized library sources and services include the card catalog, interlibrary loans, and database searching. Special learning facilities include a learning resource center and a media center, an early childhood education laboratory, an arboretum, and the 5000-book Ludwig von Miles Economic Library. The 250-acre campus is in a suburban area 120 miles southwest of Detroit. Including residence halls, there are 46 buildings on campus.

Student Life: About 55% of undergraduates are from Michigan. Students come from 38 states, 13 foreign countries, and Canada. Seventy percent are from public schools; 30% from private. Ninety-six percent are white. Forty percent are Protestant; 40% Catholic. The average age of freshmen is 18; all undergraduates, 20. Fifteen percent drop out by the end of their first year; 70% remain to graduate.

Housing: A total of 950 students can be accommodated in college housing. College-sponsored living facilities include single-sex dormitories, on-campus apartments, fraternity houses, and sorority houses. In addition there are honors houses. On-campus housing is guaranteed for all 4 years. Seventy-five percent of students live on campus;

of those, 85% remain on campus on weekends. Alcohol is not permitted. All students may keep cars on campus.

Activities: About 50% of men belong to 5 national fraternities; about 50% of women belong to 4 national sororities. There are 40 groups on campus, including art, cheerleading, choir, chorale, chorus, computers, dance, drama, drill team, ethnic, honors, international, jazz band, literary magazine, musical theater, newspaper, orchestra, pep band, photography, political, professional, radio and tv, religious, social, student government, and yearbook. Popular campus events include varsity sporting events, Parents Weekend, Homecoming, Greek Week, President's Ball, Greek formals, lectures at the Center for Constructive Alternatives, Convocation, and Siblings Weekend.

Sports: There are 8 intercollegiate sports for men and 8 for women, and 7 intramural sports for men and 7 for women. Athletic and recreation facilities include an athletic complex with a prescription turf football field; a pool; a 200-meter indoor track; a basketball arena; volleyball, handball, racquetball, and indoor tennis courts; a weight room; an outdoor Olympic track; and exercise/physiology room. The campus stadium seats 8,000; the gymnasium, 2,600.

Disabled Students: The following facilities are available: wheelchair ramps, elevators, special parking, specially equipped rest rooms, and lowered drinking fountains.

Services: In addition to many counseling and information services, tutoring is available in every subject.

Campus Safety and Security: Campus safety and security measures include informal discussions and lighted pathways and sidewalks.

Programs of Study: Hillsdale awards the B.A. and B.S. degrees. Bachelor's degrees are awarded in BIOLOGICAL SCIENCE (biology/biological science), BUSINESS (accounting, banking and finance, business administration and management, international business management, and marketing/retailing/merchandising), COMMUNICATIONS AND THE ARTS (classics, comparative literature, dramatic arts, English, fine arts, French, German, music, Spanish, and speech/debate/rhetoric), COMPUTER AND PHYSICAL SCIENCE (chemistry, mathematics, and physics), EDUCATION (art, early childhood, elementary, foreign languages, health, middle school, music, science, and secondary), ENGINEERING AND ENVIRONMENTAL DESIGN (environmental science), HEALTH PROFESSIONS (predentistry, premedicine, and preveterinary science), SOCIAL SCIENCE (American studies, Christian studies, economics, European studies, history, political science/government, prelaw, psychology, religion, social science, and sociology). History, economics, biology, business (accounting), English, and education are the strongest academically. Business, history, English, and education have the largest enrollments.

Required: To graduate, the student must complete 124 semester hours with a GPA of 2.0. Required courses include 1 year of English, 1 semester of American Heritage, 9 hours of the humanities, 8 of the natural sciences and mathematics, 6 of the social sciences, and 2 of physical education. Students must also enroll in 2 seminars at the school's Center for Constructive Alternatives. Twelve credit hours in a foreign language for a B.A. degree and 36 credit hours in mathematics and science for a B.S. degree are also required.

Special: Special academic programs include the Washington Journalism Internship at the National Journalism Center, and WHIP, the Washington-Hillsdale Intern Program, which places students in congressional or government offices. Students may study abroad in France, Germany, or Spain, and qualified students are chosen to attend Oxford University for a year. The college offers an accelerated degree, interdisciplinary majors, including political economy, 3–2 and 2–2 engineering degrees, and work-study programs at the city radio station, WCSR, and the city newspaper, the Hillsdale Daily News. There is a freshman honors program on campus, as well as 15 national honor societies. Three departments have honors programs.

Faculty/Classroom: Seventy-four percent of faculty are male; 26%, female. All teach undergraduates. The average class size in an introductory lecture is 27; in a laboratory, 7; and in a regular course offering, 20.

Admissions: About 79% of the 1993–94 applicants were accepted. The SAT scores for the 1993–94 freshman class were as follows: Verbal—43% below 500, 40% between 500 and 599, 15% between 600 and 700, and 3% above 700; Math—27% below 500, 49% between 500 and 599, 18% between 600 and 700, and 6% above 700. The ACT scores were 18% below 21, 27% between 21 and 23, 26% between 24 and 26, 14% between 27 and 28, and 15% above 28. About 60% of the current freshmen were in the top fifth of their class; 87% were in the top two fifths. There were 5 National Merit finalists and 22 semifinalists. Eleven freshmen graduated first in their class.

Requirements: Hillsdale requires applicants to be in the upper 50% of their class. A minimum GPA of 2.8 is required. The SAT I or ACT is required. In addition, the student must be a high school graduate or have earned a GED, and must have completed 4 years of English, 3 each of mathematics and science, and 2 each of history, social studies, and foreign language. The college requires an essay, and an interview is recommended. For music majors, an audition is required.

The school recommends taking SAT II: Subject tests. AP and CLP credits are accepted. Important factors used in the admissions decision are advanced placement or honor courses, leadership recoi, extracurricular activities record, recommendations by school officia, and recommendations by alumni.

Procedure: Freshmen are admitted to all sessions. Entrance exans should be taken in the spring of the junior year and/or the fall of ie senior year. Applications should be filed by July 15 for fall entry,)ecember 1 for spring entry, and April 15 for summer entry, along \ith an application fee of $15. Notification is sent on a rolling basis. Thre is an early admissions plan.

Transfer: About 50 transfer students enrolled in 1993–94. Tranfer students must have a GPA of 3.0, appear for an interview, and have a transfer evaluation form completed by the dean of students of heir school. Hillsdale also requires high school and college transcrips. A total of 24 credits out of 124 must be completed at Hillsdale.

Visiting: There are regularly scheduled orientations for prospetive students, including a spring orientation and a formal junior visitition program. There are guides for informal visits and visitors may sit n on classes and stay overnight at the school. To arrange for a visit, cotact the Admissions Office at (517) 437-7341, ext. 2327.

Financial Aid: In 1993–94, 75% of all current freshmen and 70% of continuing students received some form of financial aid. About 70% of freshmen and 65% of continuing students received need-based aid. The average freshman award was $6500. Of that total, scholarships or need-based grants averaged $5300 ($10,140 maximum); loans averaged $3200 ($6000 maximum); and work contracts averaged $1000. Sixty percent of undergraduate students work part-time. Average earnings from campus work for the school year are $1000. The average financial indebtedness of the 1992–93 graduate was $9500. Hillsdale is a member of CSS. The FAF or FFS and the FAFSA are required. The deadline for financial aid applications is April 15.

International Students: There are currently 20 international students enrolled. They must take the TOEFL, the University of Michigan Language Test, or the Comprehensive English Language Test and achieve a minimum score on the TOEFL of 500.

Computers: The college provides computer facilities for student use. The mainframe is a DEC VAX II. More than 100 microcomputers are available for student use. Laser printers are also available, along with word-processing and software workshops, electronic mail, and Internet. All students may access the system. It may be used at any time. There are no time limits on using the system and no fees.

Graduates: In 1992–93, 220 bachelor's degrees were awarded. The most popular majors among graduates were business (37%), English (16%), and history and education (13%). Within an average freshman class, 1% graduate in 3 years, 70% in 4 years, 6% in 5 years, and 1% in 6 years. Some 45 companies recruited on campus in 1992–93. In the 1992 graduating class, 20% of all students were enrolled in graduate school within 6 months of graduation; 93% had found employment.

Admissions Contact: Jeffrey S. Lantis, Director of Admissions.

HOPE COLLEGE
C-4

Holland, MI 49423   (616) 394–7850; (800) 968–7850

Full-time: 1082 men, 1423 women	**Faculty:** 182; IIB, +$
Part-time: 94 men, 114 women	**Ph.D.s:** 83%
Graduate: none	**Student/Faculty:** 14 to 1
Year: semesters, summer session	**Tuition:** $11,472
Application Deadline: open	**Room & Board:** $4156
Freshman Class: 1681 applied, 1483 accepted, 624 enrolled	
SAT I: 500/580	**ACT:** 25 **COMPETITIVE +**

Hope College, founded by Dutch pioneers in 1866, is a liberal arts institution affiliated with the Reformed Church in America. In addition to regional accreditation, Hope has baccalaureate program accreditation with NASAD, NASM, NCATE, and NLN. The 4 libraries contain 290,000 volumes, 153,504 microform items, and 18,572 audiovisual forms, and subscribe to 1950 periodicals. Computerized library sources and services include the card catalog, interlibrary loans, and database searching. Special learning facilities include a learning resource center, art gallery, radio station, TV station, academic support center, and a new modern and classical language laboratory. The 45-acre campus is in a suburban area 26 miles southwest of Grand Rapids and 5 miles east of Lake Michigan. Including residence halls, there are 105 buildings on campus.

Student Life: About 76% of undergraduates are from Michigan. Students come from 40 states, 35 foreign countries, and Canada. Ninety percent are from public schools; 10% from private. Ninety-two percent are white. Seventy-one percent are Protestant; 13% Catholic. The average age of freshmen is 18; all undergraduates, 21. Eleven percent drop out by the end of their first year; 72% remain to gradu-ate.

Housing: A total of 2044 students can be accommodated in college housing. College-sponsored living facilities include single-sex and coed dormitories, on-campus apartments, married-student housing, fraternity houses, and sorority houses. In addition there are language houses and student cottages. On-campus housing is guaranteed for all 4 years and is available on a lottery system for upperclassmen. Eighty-three percent of students live on campus; of those, 90% remain on campus on weekends. Alcohol is not permitted. All students may keep cars on campus.

Activities: About 9% of men belong to 6 local fraternities; about 10% of women belong to 6 local sororities. There are 67 groups on campus, including art, band, cheerleading, choir, chorale, chorus, computers, dance, drama, ethnic, film, honors, international, jazz band, literary magazine, musical theater, newspaper, orchestra, pep band, photography, political, professional, radio and TV, religious, social, student government, and yearbook. Popular campus events include The Pull, Homecoming, Winter Fantasia, Spring Festival, Critical Issue Symposium, Nykerk Cup Competition, Air Jam, Casino Night, and All-College Sing.

Sports: There are 9 intercollegiate sports for men and 9 for women, and 16 intramural sports for men and 13 for women. Athletic and recreation facilities include Buys Athletic Fields, Holland Civic Center, and the Dow Health and Physical Education Center, which contains gymnasiums, a running track, a swimming and diving pool, exercise rooms, a dance studio, racquetball courts, gymnastics rooms, and health-fitness equipment.

Disabled Students: Ninety-five percent of the campus is accessible to disabled students. The following facilities are available: wheelchair ramps, elevators, special parking, specially equipped rest rooms, special class scheduling, and lowered drinking fountains.

Services: In addition to many counseling and information services, tutoring is available in every subject. There is also a reader service for the blind.

Campus Safety and Security: Campus safety and security measures include 24-hour foot and vehicle patrol, escort service, shuttle buses, and informal discussions. In addition, there are pamphlets, posters, films, emergency telephones, lighted pathways and sidewalks, and free taxi services.

Programs of Study: Hope awards the B.A., B.S., B.Mus., and B.S.N. degrees. Bachelor's degrees are awarded in BIOLOGICAL SCIENCE (biochemistry and biology/biological science), BUSINESS (accounting and business administration and management), COMMUNICATIONS AND THE ARTS (communications, dance, English, fine arts, French, German, music, and Spanish), COMPUTER AND PHYSICAL SCIENCE (chemistry, computer science, geology, mathematics, and physics), EDUCATION (art, business, elementary, foreign languages, music, science, secondary, and special), HEALTH PROFESSIONS (nursing, predentistry, and premedicine), SOCIAL SCIENCE (economics, history, international relations, philosophy, political science/government, prelaw, psychology, religion, social work, and sociology). Preprofessional, biological sciences, psychology, chemistry, physics, and education are the strongest academically. Business, education, chemistry, biology, and psychology have the largest enrollments.

Required: In order to graduate, students must complete 126 semester hours with a 2.0 GPA. All students must take 59 hours of core curriculum courses, including 19 hours of cultural history and language; 8 hours of natural science; 7 hours of fundamental skills (4 hours of writing and 3 of mathematics); 6 hours each of social science, performing and fine arts, and religion; 4 hours of physical education; and 3 hours in a senior seminar.

Special: The college offers internships in all academic areas as well as on-campus work-study programs, a Washington semester, Chicago semester, New York semester, Philadelphia semester and study abroad. Students may take dual majors or work toward 3–2 engineering degrees with Michigan, Case Western, and Washington universities as well as others. There are 20 national honor societies on campus, including Phi Beta Kappa.

Faculty/Classroom: Sixty-seven percent of faculty are male; 33%, female. All teach undergraduates and 85% also do research. The average class size in an introductory lecture, in a laboratory, and in a regular course offering is 25.

Admissions: About 88% of the 1993–94 applicants were accepted. The SAT scores for the 1993–94 freshman class were as follows: Verbal—53% below 500, 32% between 500 and 599, 11% between 600 and 700, and 3% above 700; Math—28% below 500, 31% between 500 and 599, 32% between 600 and 700, and 8% above 700. The ACT scores were 13% below 21, 25% between 21 and 23, 24% between 24 and 26, 19% between 27 and 28, and 19% above 28. About 60% of the current freshmen were in the top fifth of their class; 87% were in the top two fifths. There were 9 National Merit finalists. Seventy-nine freshmen graduated first in their class.

Requirements: The SAT I or the ACT is required. The college requires a high-school transcript, which must include 4 years of English, 2 each of mathematics, a foreign language, and social science, and

1 year of a laboratory science, as well as five other academic courses. The college requires submission of an essay and recommends an interview. A portfolio or audition is required for certain majors. The GED is considered. AP and CLEP credits are accepted. Important factors used in the admissions decision are advanced placement or honor courses, leadership record, evidence of special talent, extracurricular activities record, personality, and intangible qualities.

Procedure: Freshmen are admitted in all sessions. Entrance exams should be taken during the spring of the junior year or the fall of the senior year. Application deadlines are open. Notification is sent on a rolling basis. There is a deferred admissions plan.

Transfer: About 105 transfer students enrolled in 1993–94. Transfer students must have a GPA of 2.0 in at least 1 year of liberal arts courses. A total of 32 credits out of 126 must be completed at Hope.

Visiting: There are regularly scheduled orientations for prospective students, including tours, classes, lunch with a current student, and appointments with professors. Overnight stays are also available. There are guides for informal visits and visitors may sit in on classes and stay overnight at the school. To arrange for a visit, contact the Admissions Office at (800) 968-7850.

Financial Aid: In 1993–94, 82% of all students received some form of financial aid. About 60% of freshmen and 56% of continuing students received need-based aid. The average freshman award was $11,374. Of that total, scholarships or need-based grants averaged $8145 ($15,610 maximum); loans averaged $2109 ($4125 maximum); and work contracts averaged $1120 ($1200 maximum). Seventy-three percent of undergraduate students work part-time. Average earnings from campus work for the school year are $1000. The average financial indebtedness of the 1992–93 graduate was $10,000. Hope is a member of CSS. The FAF and FAFSA are required. The deadline for financial aid applications is February 15.

International Students: There are currently 88 international students enrolled. The school actively recruits these students. They must take the TOEFL and achieve a minimum score of 550.

Computers: The college provides computer facilities for student use. The mainframe is a DEC VAX 4200. Terminals and microcomputers are located in most dormitories and academic buildings, and in the library and the student center. All students may access the system. It may be used 24 hours a day. There are no time limits on using the system and no fees.

Graduates: In 1992–93 542 bachelor's degrees were awarded. The most popular majors among graduates were business and accounting (20%), biology (8%), and education (7%). Within an average freshman class, 58% graduate in 4 years, 70% in 5 years, and 73% in 6 years. Some 54 companies recruited on campus in a recent year.

Admissions Contact: Gary Camp, Director of Admissions.

JORDAN COLLEGE D-4
Cedar Springs, MI 49319
Recognized candidate for accreditation

(616) 696-1180
(800) 968-0330

Full-time: 352 men, 940 women	Faculty: 39
Part-time: 187 men, 636 women	Ph.D.s: 9%
Graduate: none	Student/Faculty: 33 to 1
Year: semesters, summer session	Tuition: $5760
Application Deadline: open	Room & Board: n/app
Freshman Class: n/av	
SAT I or ACT: required	LESS COMPETITIVE

Jordan College, founded in 1967, is an independent, multicampus commuter institution offering undergraduate programs in business and technical fields. There are 7 undergraduate schools. The 7 libraries contain 61,000 volumes, 2100 microform items, and 400 audiovisual forms, and subscribe to 250 periodicals. Computerized library sources and services include the card catalog and database searching.

Student Life: About 99% of undergraduates are from Michigan. Students come from 10 states, 1 foreign country, and Canada. Fifty-nine percent are African American; 39% white. The average age of all undergraduates is 29. Sixty-two percent drop out by the end of their first year; 38% remain to graduate.

Housing: There are no residence halls. All students commute. Alcohol is not permitted. All students may keep cars on campus.

Activities: There are no fraternities or sororities on campus. There are some groups and organizations on campus, including choir, honors, newspaper, religious, and student government.

Disabled Students: Special parking is available for disabled students.

Services: In addition to many counseling and information services, tutoring is available in every subject. There is also remedial math, reading, and writing.

Campus Safety and Security: Campus safety and security measures include informal discussions, pamphlets, posters, and films.

Programs of Study: Jordan awards the B.A. and B.S. degrees. Associate degrees also are awarded. Bachelor's degrees are awarded in AGRICULTURE (natural resource management), ENGINEERING AND ENVIRONMENTAL DESIGN (energy management technology), SOCIAL SCIENCE (liberal arts/general studies). Engineering technologies is the strongest academically and has the largest enrollment.

Required: To graduate, students must complete 120 semester hours with a minimum GPA of 2.0. The required core curriculum includes courses in English, mathematics, and psychology.

Special: Students may cross-register at all Jordan campuses. Internships and work-study programs are available. B.A.-B.S. degrees in applied environmental technology and renewable energy engineering technology are offered. There is one national honor society on campus.

Faculty/Classroom: Thirty-seven percent of faculty are male; 63%, female. All teach undergraduates. The average class size in a regular course offering is 13.

Requirements: The SAT I or ACT is not required. Applicants must be graduates of an accredited high school or the equivalent. AP and CLEP credits are accepted. Important factors used in the admissions decision are evidence of special talent, advanced placement or honor courses, leadership record, geographic diversity, and extracurricular activities record.

Procedure: Freshmen are admitted to all sessions. Application deadlines are open. Notification is sent on a rolling basis. There are early admissions and deferred admissions plans.

Transfer: About 210 transfer students enrolled in 1993–94. At least 60 credits out of 120 must be completed at Jordan.

Visiting: There are regularly scheduled orientations for prospective students. There are guides for informal visits, and visitors may sit in on classes. To arrange for a visit, contact the Admissions Office at (616) 698–1180 or (800) 968–0330.

Financial Aid: In a recent year, 99% of all students received some form of financial aid. The average freshman award was $3600. Jordan is a member of CSS. The FAF, FFS, or SFS is required. The deadline for financial aid applications is September 1.

International Students: There are currently 2 international students enrolled. They must take the TOEFL and achieve a minimum score of 500.

Computers: Microcomputers are available to all students in the computer laboratory. There are no time limits on using the system and no fees.

Graduates: In 1992–93, 10 bachelor's degrees were awarded. Within an average freshman class, 11% graduate in 3 years and 14% in 4 years.

Admissions Contact: Director of Admissions.

KALAMAZOO COLLEGE

D-5

Kalamazoo, MI 49006–3295

Full-time: 543 men, 675 women
Part-time: none
Graduate: none
Year: quarters, summer session
Application Deadline: February 15
Freshman Class: 1240 applied, 1109 accepted, 338 enrolled
SAT I or ACT: required

(616) 337–7166; (800) 253–3602

Faculty: 91; IIB, +$
Ph.D.s: 86%
Student/Faculty: 13 to 1
Tuition: $15,135
Room & Board: $4839

HIGHLY COMPETITIVE

Kalamazoo College is a liberal arts and sciences institution founded in 1833. The library contains 301,751 volumes, 18,049 microform items, and 4512 audiovisual forms, and subscribes to 1350 periodicals. Computerized library sources and services include the card catalog, interlibrary loans, and database searching. Special learning facilities include a learning resource center, art gallery, and radio station. The 60-acre campus is in a suburban area 140 miles from Detroit and from Chicago. Including residence halls, there are 30 buildings on campus.

Student Life: About 70% of undergraduates are from Michigan. Students come from 38 states, 18 foreign countries, and Canada. Eighty percent are from public schools; 20% from private. Eighty-five percent are white. Thirty-five percent are Protestant; 30% Catholic. The average age of freshmen is 18; all undergraduates, 20. Twelve percent drop out by the end of their first year; 70% remain to graduate.

Housing: A total of 850 students can be accommodated in college housing. College-sponsored living facilities include coed dormitories. In addition there are German, French, Spanish, and Japanese language houses. On-campus housing is guaranteed for all 4 years, is available on a first-come, first-served basis, and is available on a lottery system for upperclassmen. Ninety-eight percent of students live on campus; of those, 85% remain on campus on weekends. Upperclassmen may keep cars on campus.

Activities: There are no fraternities or sororities on campus. There are 36 groups on campus, including art, band, cheerleading, choir, chorale, chorus, computers, dance, drama, ethnic, film, gay, international, jazz band, literary magazine, musical theater, newspaper, orchestra, photography, political, professional, radio and TV, religious,

social, social service, student government, symphony, and yearbook. Popular campus events include Monte Carlo Night, Quadstock, Day of Gracious Living, Spring Fling, Bahama Boogie, Senior Soiree, and Land/Sea Outdoor Adventure Orientation.

Sports: There are 8 intercollegiate sports for men and 8 for women, and 15 intramural sports for men and 13 for women. Athletic and recreation facilities include a field house that houses a 2000-seat gymnasium, basketball and volleyball courts, weight-training rooms, and a dance studio, a 1500-seat, 11-court tennis stadium, a racquet center with 4 tennis courts, 3 racquetball courts, and a squash court, a natatorium, a 4000-seat football stadium, and soccer and baseball fields.

Disabled Students: The following facilities are available: wheelchair ramps, elevators, special parking, specially equipped rest rooms, and special class scheduling.

Services: In addition to many counseling and information services, tutoring is available in most subjects. There is also a writing center and language laboratories.

Campus Safety and Security: Campus safety and security measures include 24-hour foot and vehicle patrol, self defense education, escort service, and informal discussions. In addition, there are pamphlets, posters, films, emergency telephones, lighted pathways and sidewalks, and secured residence halls with electronic entry system.

Programs of Study: Kalamazoo awards the B.A. degree. Bachelor's degrees are awarded in BIOLOGICAL SCIENCE (biology/biological science), BUSINESS (business administration and management), COMMUNICATIONS AND THE ARTS (dramatic arts, English, fine arts, French, German, music, and Spanish), COMPUTER AND PHYSICAL SCIENCE (chemistry, computer science, mathematics, and physics), HEALTH PROFESSIONS (health science and predentistry), SOCIAL SCIENCE (anthropology, history, philosophy, political science/government, prelaw, psychology, religion, and sociology). Foreign languages, international studies and commerce, health sciences, biology and chemistry are the strongest academically. Economics, business administration, English, political science, and health sciences have the largest enrollments.

Required: To graduate, students must complete 36 academic units, including 8 units in the major, with a minimum 2.0 GPA. Required courses include 4 units in social science, 3 units in natural science, computer science, or mathematics, 2 units each in literature and philosophy/religion, and 1 unit of fine arts. The college further requires completion of a senior individualized project, a credit from the liberal arts colloquium, and a passing grade on a comprehensive examination in the major. The student must also take six noncredit courses in physical education, and show proficiency in writing, as well as in a foreign language.

Special: Students may study abroad and choose from among 900 career internships in the United States, Europe, Asia, and Africa. The school offers a Washington semester, allows dual and interdisciplinary majors, for example, economics and business administration, and has cross-registration with Western Michigan University. A 3–2 engineering degree is offered with Washington University and the University of Michigan. There are accelerated 3-year programs in predentistry, premedicine, and preveterinary medicine. There are 3 national honor societies on campus, including Phi Beta Kappa.

Faculty/Classroom: Sixty-seven percent of faculty are male; 33%, female. All teach undergraduates. The average class size in an introductory lecture is 40; in a laboratory, 20; and in a regular course offering, 25.

Admissions: About 89% of the 1993–94 applicants were accepted. The SAT scores for the 1993–94 freshman class were as follows: Verbal—15% below 500, 41% between 500 and 599, 39% between 600 and 700, and 5% above 700; Math—7% below 500, 24% between 500 and 599, 46% between 600 and 700, and 23% above 700. The ACT scores were 1% below 21, 13% between 21 and 23, 31% between 24 and 26, 23% between 27 and 28, and 32% above 28. About 75% of the current freshmen were in the top fifth of their class; 97% were in the top two fifths. There were 17 National Merit finalists. Eighteen freshmen graduated first in their class.

Requirements: The SAT I or ACT is required. The college also requires a high school transcript, an essay, and teacher and counselor recommendations; an interview is recommended. AP credits are accepted. Important factors used in the admissions decision are evidence of special talent, advanced placement or honor courses, leadership record, extracurricular activities record, personality, and intangible qualities.

Procedure: Freshmen are admitted to all sessions. Entrance exams should be taken by December of the senior year. Applications should be filed by February 15 for fall entry, along with an application fee of $40. Notification is sent on a rolling basis. There are early admissions and deferred admissions plans.

Transfer: About 16 transfer students enrolled in 1993–94. Applicants must have a 2.8 GPA. A total of 9 units out of 36 must be completed at Kalamazoo.

Visiting: There are regularly scheduled orientations for prospective students, including interviews, tours, and class visits as requested. Special preview events include formal presentation of the unique K-Plan curriculum, foreign study, internship, and financial aid seminars. There are guides for informal visits and visitors may sit in on classes and stay overnight at the school. To arrange for a visit, contact the receptionist at (800) 253–3602 or (616) 337–7166.

Financial Aid: In 1993–94 80% of all current freshmen and 85% of continuing students received some form of financial aid. About 56% of freshmen and 51% of continuing students received need-based aid. The average freshman award was $11,200. Of that total, scholarships or need-based grants averaged $5485 ($11,200 maximum); loans averaged $3580 ($4875 maximum); and work contracts averaged $1075 ($1275 maximum). Thirty-eight percent of undergraduate students work part-time. Kalamazoo is a member of CSS. The FAF and FAFSA are required. The deadline for financial aid applications is February 15.

International Students: There are currently 49 international students enrolled. The school actively recruits these students. They must take the TOEFL or the University of Michigan Language Test and achieve a minimum score on the TOEFL of 550. The student must also take the SAT I or the ACT.

Computers: The college provides computer facilities for student use. The mainframe is a DEC DS 5000. There are 70 microcomputers available for student use, 10 of which are limited to physics stidents. All IBM Macintosh computers are networked on the Internet. All students may access the system. There are no time limits on using the system and no fees.

Graduates: In 1992–93 213 bachelor's degrees were awarded. The most popular majors among graduates were economics/business administration (21%), biology (13%), and English (13%). Within an average freshman class, 69% graduate in 4 years, 72% in 5 years, and 75% in 6 years.

Admissions Contact: Teresa M. Lahti, Dean of Admissions.

KENDALL COLLEGE OF ART AND DESIGN   D-4
Grand Rapids, MI 49503–3194

(616) 451–2787
(800) 676–2787 (out-of-state)

Full-time: 210 men, 203 women	Faculty: 38
Part-time: 71 men, 109 women	Ph.D.s: 33%
Graduate: none	Student/Faculty: 11 to 1
Year: semesters, summer session	Tuition: $9600
Application Deadline: open	Room & Board: n/app
Freshman Class: 196 applied, 140 accepted, 95 enrolled	
SAT I Verbal/Math: 390/390	ACT: 19 SPECIAL

The Kendall College of Art and Design, founded in 1928, is a school of design studies and the fine arts. In addition to regional accreditation, Kendall College has baccalaureate program accreditation with FIDER and NASAD. The library contains 23,000 volumes, 1000 microform items, and 3500 audiovisual forms, and subscribes to 150 periodicals. Computerized library sources and services include the card catalog. Special learning facilities include a learning resource center, art gallery, and a video studio. The 1-acre campus is in an urban area 150 miles west of Detroit. There is one building on campus.

Student Life: About 91% of undergraduates are from Michigan. Students come from 19 states, 9 foreign countries, and Canada. Eighty-eight percent are from public schools; 12% from private. Eighty-six percent are white. The average age of freshmen is 23; all undergraduates, 25. Thirty percent drop out by the end of their first year; 40% remain to graduate.

Housing: There are no residence halls. A total of 15 students can be accommodated in college-sponsored living facilities, which include single-sex off-campus apartments. All students commute. Alcohol is not permitted.

Activities: There are no fraternities or sororities on campus. There are 7 groups on campus, including art, film, international, literary magazine, newspaper, photography, professional, and student government. Popular campus events include Advising Day, pancake supper, all-campus picnic, dances, and a film festival.

Sports: There is no sports program at Kendall College.

Disabled Students: The entire campus is accessible to disabled students. The following facilities are available: wheelchair ramps, elevators, special parking, specially equipped rest rooms, lowered drinking fountains, and lowered telephones.

Services: In addition to many counseling and information services, tutoring is available in every subject. In addition, there is a reader service for the blind.

Campus Safety and Security: Campus safety and security measures include escort service, shuttle buses, informal discussions, and pamphlets, posters, and films. In addition, there are emergency telephones and lighted pathways and sidewalks.

Programs of Study: Kendall College awards the B.F.A degree. Bachelor's degrees are awarded in COMMUNICATIONS AND THE ARTS (advertising, design, fine arts, graphic design, illustration, and industrial design), ENGINEERING AND ENVIRONMENTAL DESIGN (furniture design and interior design).

Required: Students must complete 120 credit hours, to include 30 hours of liberal arts and sciences, 24 hours of a foundation studio core, 12 hours each of art and history, and up to 9 studio electives. All students must complete a graduation portfolio.

Special: Co-op programs with art agencies and in manufacturing industry are available in all majors. Cross-registration is offered through a consortium of schools of art and design. Internships are available in all majors. Study abroad may be arranged by the student and approved by the college.

Faculty/Classroom: Sixty-one percent of faculty are male; 39%, female. All teach undergraduates. The average class size in an introductory lecture is 45; in a laboratory, 20; and in a regular course offering, 20.

Admissions: About 71% of the 1993–94 applicants were accepted. The SAT scores for the 1993–94 freshman class were as follows: Verbal—89% below 500 and 11% between 500 and 599; Math—67% below 500 and 33% between 500 and 599. The ACT scores were 69% below 21, 20% between 21 and 23, 8% between 24 and 26, 2% between 27 and 28, and 1% above 28. About 9% of the current freshmen were in the top fifth of their class; 31% were in the top two fifths.

Requirements: Kendall College requires applicants to be in the upper 50% of their class. A minimum GPA of 2.0 is required. The ACT is recommended. A high school transcript is required. Scores from either the ACT or SAT I are not required if the applicant has been out of high school at least 3 years. The GED certificate is accepted. Students must submit an essay with their application. A portfolio and an interview are also recommended. Prospective students are encouraged to take courses in drawing, painting, and design in their high schools. AP and CLEP credits are accepted. Important factors used in the admissions decision are evidence of special talent, personality, intangible qualities, recommendations by school officials, recommendations by alumni, and leadership record.

Procedure: Freshmen are admitted to all sessions. Application deadlines are open. Notification is sent on a rolling basis. The application fee is $35. There are early decision, early admissions, and deferred admissions plans.

Transfer: About 80 transfer students enrolled in 1993–94. Transfer students must have a GPA of 2.25 and pass a portfolio review. An interview is recommended. A total of 60 credits out of 120 must be completed at Kendall College.

Visiting: There are regularly scheduled orientations for prospective students, including a building tour, faculty introductions, financial aid and housing information, and registration/advising. There are guides for informal visits and visitors may sit in on classes. To arrange for a visit, contact the Admissions Office at (800) 676–2787.

Financial Aid: In 1993–94 92% of all current freshmen and 80% of continuing students received some form of financial aid. About 83% of freshmen and 91% of continuing students received need-based aid. The average freshman award was $5805. Of that total, scholarships or need-based grants averaged $2945 ($4605 maximum); loans averaged $3090 ($7125 maximum); and work contracts averaged $1000 ($1500 maximum). Six percent of undergraduate students work part-time. Average earnings from campus work for the school year are $1200. The average financial indebtedness of the 1992–93 graduate was $8777. Kendall College is a member of CSS. The FAF or FFS is required. The deadline for financial aid applications is February 15.

International Students: There are currently 9 international students enrolled. They must take the TOEFL and achieve a minimum score of 500. The student must also take the SAT I or the ACT.

Computers: The college provides computer facilities with Macintosh computers for student use in classroom work and design. There are no time limits on using the system and no fees.

Graduates: In 1992–93 123 bachelor's degrees were awarded. The most popular majors among graduates were visual communication (36%), interior design (21%), and illustration (17%). Within an average freshman class, 65% graduate in 4 years, 30% in 5 years, and 5% in 6 years. Some 30 companies recruited on campus in 1992–93. In the 1992 graduating class, 2% of the men and 5% of the women were enrolled in graduate school within 6 months of graduation; 85% of the men and 85% of the women had found employment.

Admissions Contact: Geoff Kehoe, Director of Admissions.

LAKE SUPERIOR STATE UNIVERSITY D-2
Sault Sainte Marie, MI 49783

(906) 635–2231
(800) 682–4800, ext. 2231 (in-state)

Full-time, part-time: 1558 men, 1466 women	Faculty: 112; IIB, av$
	Ph.D.s: 51%
Graduate: 220 men and women	Student/Faculty: 27 to 1
Year: semesters, summer session	Tuition: $3284 ($6320)
Application Deadline: August 12	Room & Board: $4027
Freshman Class: 1406 applied, 1169 accepted, 522 enrolled	
ACT: 20	COMPETITIVE

Lake Superior State University, founded in 1946, is a business, technical, and liberal arts institution. There is one graduate school. In addition to regional accreditation, LSSU has baccalaureate program accreditation with ABET and NLN. The library contains 131,000 volumes, 164,000 microform items, and 695 audiovisual forms, and subscribes to 775 periodicals. Computerized library sources and services include the card catalog and interlibrary loans. Special learning facilities include a learning resource center, natural history museum, planetarium, radio station, fish hatchery, aquatics laboratory, and the Vermilion Nature Center. The 121-acre campus is in a small town 280 miles north of Grand Rapids. Including residence halls, there are 36 buildings on campus.

Student Life: About 75% of undergraduates are from Michigan. Students come from 18 states, 9 foreign countries, and Canada. Ninety-four percent are from public schools; 6% from private. Seventy percent are white; 23% foreign nationals. The average age of freshmen is 19; all undergraduates, 24. Thirty percent drop out by the end of their first year; 40% remain to graduate.

Housing: A total of 1198 students can be accommodated in college housing. College-sponsored living facilities include single-sex and coed dormitories, on-campus apartments, family housing, and fraternity houses. On-campus housing is guaranteed for the freshman year only, is available on a first-come, first-served basis, and is available on a lottery system for upperclassmen. Sixty-eight percent of students commute. All students may keep cars on campus.

Activities: About 10% of men belong to 1 local and 4 national fraternities; about 10% of women belong to 5 national sororities. There are 44 groups on campus, including art, cheerleading, chess, computers, ethnic, film, honors, jazz band, newspaper, orchestra, pep band, political, professional, radio and TV, religious, social, social service, student government, and yearbook. Popular campus events include Winter Carnival, Spring Fling, Beach Party, a concert series, varsity games, Snowman Burning, and Word Banishment List.

Sports: There are 5 intercollegiate sports for men and 5 for women, and 17 intramural sports for men and 15 for women. Athletic and recreation facilities include a 2800-seat gymnasium, a 3500-seat ice arena, basketball courts, indoor and outdoor tennis courts, racquetball courts, an indoor pool, weight rooms, a dance studio, and a quarter-mile, all-weather track.

Disabled Students: Eighty percent of the campus is accessible to disabled students. The following facilities are available: wheelchair ramps, elevators, special parking, specially equipped rest rooms, and lowered drinking fountains.

Services: In addition to many counseling and information services, tutoring is available in most subjects on request and free of charge. There is also remedial math and reading. There are also mathematics, reading, and writing laboratories.

Campus Safety and Security: Campus safety and security measures include 24-hour foot and vehicle patrol, self defense education, escort service, and informal discussions. In addition, there are pamphlets, posters, and films and lighted pathways and sidewalks.

Programs of Study: LSSU awards the B.A. and B.S degrees. Associate and master's degrees also are awarded. Bachelor's degrees are awarded in AGRICULTURE (fish and game management and wildlife management), BIOLOGICAL SCIENCE (biology/biological science), BUSINESS (accounting, business administration and management, hotel/motel and restaurant management, and marketing/retailing/merchandising), COMMUNICATIONS AND THE ARTS (English), COMPUTER AND PHYSICAL SCIENCE (computer science, geology, and mathematics), ENGINEERING AND ENVIRONMENTAL DESIGN (engineering technology and environmental science), HEALTH PROFESSIONS (medical laboratory technology, nursing, predentistry, premedicine, and recreation therapy), SOCIAL SCIENCE (criminal justice, economics, history, human services, parks and recreation management, political science/government, prelaw, psychology, social science, and sociology). Engineering technology, nursing, and biology are the strongest academically. Business and criminal justice have the largest enrollments.

Required: To graduate, students must complete 124 semester hours with a GPA of 2.0. Distribution requirements include 8 hours each of humanities, natural science, and social science, 6 of English, 3 of speech, and 2 of physical education. Mathematics and English competency must be met.

Special: LSSU offers internships in criminal justice, medical technology, human services, legal assistance studies, and natural resources technology; work-study programs; co-op programs in engineering technology; and cross-registration with the Canadian Colleges of Sault and Algoma. There is a freshman honors program on campus.

Faculty/Classroom: Seventy percent of faculty are male; 30%, female. No introductory courses are taught by graduate students.

Admissions: About 83% of the 1993–94 applicants were accepted. The ACT scores for the 1993–94 freshman class were as follows: 54% below 21, 24% between 21 and 23, 15% between 24 and 26, 5% between 27 and 28, and 2% above 28. About 23% of the current freshmen were in the top fifth of their class; 54% were in the top two fifths.

Requirements: A minimum GPA of 2.0 and the ACT are required. Applicants should be high school graduates with 3 years of English, 2 each of mathematics and social studies, and 1 of history. The GED is accepted. An interview is recommended. AP and CLEP credits are accepted. Important factors used in the admissions decision are recommendations by school officials, recommendations by alumni, and advanced placement or honor courses.

Procedure: Freshmen are admitted to all sessions. Applications should be filed by August 12 for fall entry and December 10 for spring entry, along with an application fee of $20. Notification is sent on a rolling basis. There is a deferred admissions plan.

Transfer: A total of 284 transfer students enrolled in 1993–94. Applicants must be eligible to return to the last institution attended, and must have an overall college GPA of 2.0. An interview is recommended. A total of 32 of the final 40 credits, out of 124, and 50% of all upper-level courses must be completed at LSSU.

Visiting: There are regularly scheduled orientations for prospective students. There are guides for informal visits and visitors may sit in on classes. To arrange for a visit, contact the Admissions Office at (800) 682–4800 (in-state) or (906) 635–2231.

Financial Aid: In 1993–94, 70% of all students received some form of financial aid. About 68% of all students received need-based aid. The average freshman award was $3800. Of that total, scholarships or need-based grants averaged $1480 ($3600 maximum); loans averaged $2200; and work contracts averaged $1400 ($2200 maximum). Thirty percent of undergraduate students work part-time. Average earnings from campus work for the school year are $1300. The average financial indebtedness of the 1992–93 graduate was $5200. The FAFSA is required. The deadline for financial aid applications is March 1.

International Students: There are currently 12 international students enrolled. They must take the TOEFL and achieve a minimum score of 550.

Computers: LSSU provides computer facilities for student use. The mainframe is a DEC VAX 6510. Students have access to a DEC MicroVAX 3400 through terminals located in the computer laboratory. There are over 190 microcomputers for student use in a number of locations across campus. All students may access the system. It may be used during laboratory hours. There are no time limits on using the system. The fees are $35 per semester.

Graduates: In 1992–93, 416 bachelor's degrees were awarded. The most popular majors among graduates were business administration (19%), criminal justice (15%), and human services (7%). Some 60 companies recruited on campus in 1992–93. In the 1992 graduating class, 85% of all students were enrolled in graduate school or had found employment within 6 months of graduation.

Admissions Contact: Bruce Johnson, Dean of Admissions.

LAWRENCE TECHNOLOGICAL UNIVERSITY E-5
Southfield, MI 48075

(313) 356–0200, ext. 3166

Full-time: 1670 men, 506 women	Faculty: 112
Part-time: 1612 men, 451 women	Ph.D.s: 68%
Graduate: 181 men, 83 women	Student/Faculty: 19 to 1
Year: semesters	Tuition: $5670
Application Deadline: August 1	Room & Board: $3800
Freshman Class: 867 applied, 695 accepted, 312 enrolled	
ACT: 22	COMPETITIVE

Lawrence Technological University, founded in 1932 as the Lawrence Institute of Technology, is a private coeducational institution university housing colleges of engineering, management, arts and science, and architecture and design. There are 4 undergraduate and 2 graduate schools. In addition to regional accreditation, LTU has baccalaureate program accreditation with ABET, FIDER, and NAAB. The library contains 70,000 volumes and 93,000 microform items, and subscribes to 1000 periodicals. Computerized library sources and services include interlibrary loans. Special learning facilities include a TV station. The 100-acre campus is in a suburban area 2 miles south of Detroit. Including residence halls, there are 8 buildings on campus.

Student Life: Most students come from the Midwest. In addition, students come from 35 foreign countries and Canada. Eighty-five percent are white.

Housing: A total of 500 students can be accommodated in college housing. College-sponsored living facilities include coed on-campus apartments. On-campus housing is guaranteed for all 4 years and is available on a first-come, first-served basis. Priority is given to out-of-town students. Ninety-five percent of students commute. Alcohol is not permitted. All students may keep cars on campus.

Activities: About 2% of men belong to 5 national fraternities; about 1% of women belong to 3 local sororities. There are 40 groups on campus, including computers, ethnic, honors, newspaper, professional, radio and TV, social, student government, and yearbook. Popular campus events include Open House, Reunion Weekend, and Greek Week.

Sports: There are 9 intramural sports for men and 6 for women. Athletic and recreation facilities include a field house, with 4 racquetball courts, a weight room, a track, and a gymnasium. The gymnasium seats 3000, an arena 350.

Disabled Students: Ninety percent of the campus is accessible to disabled students. The following facilities are available: wheelchair ramps, elevators, special parking, specially equipped rest rooms, special class scheduling, lowered drinking fountains, and lowered telephones.

Services: In addition to many counseling and information services, tutoring is available in some subjects, including mathematics, computers, science, engineering, and writing workshops.

Campus Safety and Security: Campus safety and security measures include 24-hour foot and vehicle patrol and escort service.

Programs of Study: LTU awards the B.S., B. Arch and B.F.A. degrees. Associate and master's degrees also are awarded. Bachelor's degrees are awarded in BUSINESS (accounting, banking and finance, business administration and management, and small business management), COMPUTER AND PHYSICAL SCIENCE (chemistry, computer science, mathematics, and physics), ENGINEERING AND ENVIRONMENTAL DESIGN (architecture, civil engineering, electrical/electronics engineering, engineering technology, industrial administration/management, and mechanical engineering), SOCIAL SCIENCE (humanities). Mathematics and computer science are the strongest academically. Engineering has the largest enrollment.

Required: To graduate, students must have completed, depending on the major, 180 to 202 quarter credit hours, with a GPA no lower than 2.0, or 3.0 for architectural degrees.

Special: The College of Engineering offers a work-study program. Co-op programs are available in engineering. A B.A. and any associate's degree program may be combined. There are 4 national honor societies on campus.

Faculty/Classroom: Ninety-three percent of faculty are male; 7%, female. No introductory courses are taught by graduate students. The average class size in an introductory lecture is 35; in a laboratory, 18; and in a regular course offering, 35.

Admissions: About 80% of the 1993–94 applicants were accepted. About 50% of the current freshmen were in the top two fifths of their class.

Requirements: Students must have a high school diploma and a GPA of no lower than 2.5, at least 2.0 in each subject area pertaining to their major. Applicants should have taken 4 years each of mathematics, science, English, and 3 years of social science. The GED is accepted. An interview is recommended. AP and CLEP credits are accepted. Important factors used in the admissions decision are advanced placement or honor courses, personality, intangible qualities, leadership record, ability to finance college education, and parents or siblings attending the school.

Procedure: Freshmen are admitted to all sessions. Entrance exams should be taken in the junior year. Applications should be filed by August 1 for fall entry, November 1 for winter entry, February 1 for spring entry, and May 1 for summer entry, along with an application fee of $30. Notification is sent on a rolling basis. There are early admissions and deferred admissions plans.

Transfer: About 758 transfer students enrolled in a recent year. Transfer students must have earned at least 30 credit hours (45 quarter hours), and a GPA for all college-level work no lower than 2.0, or meet all admission requirements for high school students. A total of 42 credits out of 202 must be completed at LTU.

Visiting: There are regularly scheduled orientations for prospective students. There are guides for informal visits. To arrange for a visit, contact the Admissions Office at (313) 356–0200, ext. 3166.

Financial Aid: In a recent year 45% of all current freshmen and 50% of continuing students received some form of financial aid. Scholarships or need-based grants averaged $3500; loans averaged $2000 ($2625 maximum); and work contracts averaged $1000 ($2500 maximum). Seventy-five percent of undergraduate students work part-time. The average financial indebtedness of the 1992–93 graduate was $5000. LTU is a member of CSS. The FFS is required. The deadline for financial aid applications is July 1.

International Students: There are currently 140 international students enrolled. They must take the TOEFL or the University of Michigan Language Test and achieve a minimum score on the TOEFL of 550.

Computers: The college provides computer facilities for student use. The mainframe is a Prime and a VAX Cluster. A computer center is available, as are 150 IBM clones throughout the campus. All students may access the system. It may be used 24 hours daily. There are no time limits on using the system and no fees.

Graduates: In 1992–93 766 bachelor's degrees were awarded. The most popular majors among graduates were business administration (28%), mechanical engineering (25%), and electrical engineering (23%). Some 88 companies recruited on campus in a recent year. In the 1992 graduating class, 90% of the men and 90% of the women had found employment within 6 months of graduation.

Admissions Contact: Kevin Pollock, Admissions Director.

MADONNA UNIVERSITY E-5
Livonia, MI 48150 (313) 591-5052

Full-time, part-time: 4000 men and women	Faculty: 93; IIB, av$
	Ph.D.s: 50%
Graduate: 400 men and women	Student/Faculty: n/av
Year: terms	Tuition: $4870
Application Deadline: open	Room & Board: $3676
Freshman Class: n/av	
ACT: 21	

COMPETITIVE

Madonna University, founded in 1947, is a coeducational liberal arts institution affiliated with the Roman Catholic Church. There is one graduate school. In addition to regional accreditation, the college has baccalaureate program accreditation with ADA, CSWE, NCATE, and NLN. The 2 libraries contain 112,000 volumes, 1244 microform items, and 6540 audiovisual forms, and subscribe to 1298 periodicals. Computerized library sources and services include the card catalog, interlibrary loans, and database searching. Special learning facilities include a learning resource center, art gallery, radio station, TV station, the Center for Personalized Instruction, and a computerized writing laboratory. The 48-acre campus is in a suburban area 20 miles west of Detroit. Including residence halls, there are 3 buildings on campus.

Student Life: Almost all undergraduates are from Michigan. Students come from 8 states, 11 foreign countries, and Canada. Eighty-five percent are from public schools; 15% from private. Eighty-five percent are white; 11% African American. Fifty-three percent are Catholic; 31% Protestant. The average age of all undergraduates is 24.5. Thirty-three percent drop out by the end of their first year; 67% remain to graduate.

Housing: A total of 200 students can be accommodated in the residence hall, which houses men and women in separate wings. Housing is available on a first-come, first-served basis. Almost all students commute. Alcohol is not permitted. All students may keep cars on campus.

Activities: There are no fraternities or sororities on campus. There are many groups and organizations on campus, including art, chorale, computers, ethnic, honors, newspaper, orchestra, pep band, photography, political, professional, radio and TV, religious, social, social service, student government, and symphony. Popular campus events include Founders Day, Halloween Haunt, Christmas for Kids, Donkey Basketball, and Ethnic Festival.

Sports: There is 1 intercollegiate sport for men and 3 for women, and 7 intramural sports each. Athletic and recreation facilities include an activities center, a training room, a 700-seat gymnasium, and a 300-seat arena.

Disabled Students: The entire campus is accessible to disabled students. The following facilities are available: wheelchair ramps, elevators, special parking, specially equipped rest rooms, special class scheduling, lowered drinking fountains, lowered telephones, and telecommunication devices for the deaf.

Services: In addition to many counseling and information services, tutoring is available in most subjects. There is also a reader service for the blind, and remedial math, reading, and writing.

Campus Safety and Security: Campus safety and security measures include 24-hour foot and vehicle patrol, escort service, informal discussions, and emergency telephones. In addition, there are lighted pathways and sidewalks and and an emergency car service.

Programs of Study: The college awards the B.A., B.S., B.A.S., B.S.M.T., B.S.N., and B.S.W. degrees. Associate and master's degrees also are awarded. Bachelor's degrees are awarded in BIOLOGICAL SCIENCE (biochemistry, biology/biological science, and nutrition), BUSINESS (accounting, banking and finance, business administration and management, fashion merchandising, hospitality management services, international business management, management science, and marketing/retailing/merchandising), COMMUNICATIONS AND THE ARTS (communications, English, fine arts, French, journalism, music, Spanish, technical and business writing,

and video), COMPUTER AND PHYSICAL SCIENCE (chemistry, computer science, information sciences and systems, mathematics, and natural sciences), EDUCATION (art, home economics, music, secondary, and special), ENGINEERING AND ENVIRONMENTAL DESIGN (commercial art and occupational safety and health), HEALTH PROFESSIONS (allied health, health care administration, hospice care, medical laboratory technology, nursing, and radiograph medical technology), and SOCIAL SCIENCE (child psychology/development, criminal justice, dietetics, family/consumer studies, fire science, food science, gerontology, history, home economics, interpreter for the deaf, paralegal studies, pastoral studies, psychology, public administration, religion, religious music, safety and security technology, safety management, social science, social work, and sociology). Nursing is the strongest academically. Nursing and business administration have the largest enrollments.

Required: To graduate, students must complete at least 120 semester hours with a 2.0 GPA, with 30 to 56 hours in the major (majors within the School of Business require 62 hours). A minimum of 52 hours of general education courses is required, including 25 hours in humanities, 15 hours in social science, and 12 hours in mathematics and science. All students are required to take a senior seminar.

Special: The school offers cross-registration with Marygrove and St. Mary of Orchard Lake colleges, Sacred Heart Seminary, and the University of Detroit Mercy. Students may receive credit for life, military, or work experience. The school also has affiliations with universities in Argentina, Belgium, Great Britain, Japan, Poland, and Taiwan. There is a freshman honors program on campus, as well as 5 national honor societies. Four departments have honors programs.

Faculty/Classroom: Thirty-eight percent of faculty are male; 62%, female. The average class size in an introductory lecture is 35; in a laboratory, 15; and in a regular course offering, 26.

Requirements: The SAT I or ACT is required; the ACT is preferred. In addition, students should have completed 4 years of English, 3 years of mathematics, 2 years of science, and 1 year of history, with a GPA of 2.5. The school accepts the GED. For some majors, students are asked to submit a portfolio or to appear for an interview or audition. AP and CLEP credits are accepted. Important factors used in the admissions decision are advanced placement or honor courses, recommendations by school officials, leadership record, evidence of special talent, and extracurricular activities record.

Procedure: Freshmen are admitted to all sessions. Entrance exams should be taken during either the junior or senior year. Application deadlines are open. The application fee is $25. Notification is sent on a rolling basis. A waiting list is an active part of the admissions procedure, with about 10% of applicants on the list.

Transfer: About 675 transfer students enrolled in a recent year. Transfer applicants must be in good academic and personal standing at their previous colleges. Courses completed at an accredited institution with a grade of C or better will be considered for transfer credit. The last 30 semester hours out of 120 must be completed at the college.

Visiting: There are regularly scheduled orientations for prospective students, including an interview and a tour of the campus. There are guides for informal visits and visitors may sit in on classes and stay overnight at the school. To arrange for a visit, contact the Admissions Office at (313) 591-5052.

Financial Aid: In a recent year, 25% of all students received some form of financial aid. About 25% of students received need-based aid. The average freshman award was $1200. Of that total, scholarships or need-based grants averaged $300 ($500 maximum); loans averaged $2600 ($4000 maximum); and work contracts averaged $640 ($1100 maximum). Seventy-two percent of undergraduate students work part-time. Average earnings from campus work for the school year are $2000. The average financial indebtedness of the 1992–93 graduate was $2000. the college is a member of CSS. The FAF and the college's own financial statement are required. The deadline for financial aid applications is February 15.

International Students: There are currently 75 international students enrolled. The school actively recruits these students. They must take the TOEFL and achieve a minimum score of 540, or an equivalent English proficiency test.

Computers: The college provides computer facilities for student use. The mainframe is an IBM 4341-M2. The mainframe, networked with 20 terminals that can be used for class assignments, uses COBOL, Rexx, FORTRAN, and Assembler. Sixty microcomputers are networked via a Novell LAN in the computer laboratory and the library. Library research is done via CD-ROM files and national databases. Smaller, decentralized laboratories are found in the Health Instruction Center, the tutoring center, the physics laboratory, and various faculty and staff offices. All students may access the system. It may be used 9 A.M. to 10 P.M. weekdays, 9 A.M. to 5 P.M. Saturday, and 1 P.M. to 5 P.M. Sunday. Students may access the system only 3 hours per day if others are waiting. The fees are included in the laboratory fees for certain courses.

Graduates: In a recent year, 562 bachelor's degrees were awarded. The most popular majors among graduates were business related (23%), nursing (16%), and criminal justice (8%). Some 31 companies recruited on campus. In a recent graduating class, 20% of all students were enrolled in graduate school within 6 months of graduation.

Admissions Contact: Louis E. Brohl III, Director of Admissions.

MARYGROVE COLLEGE E-5

Detroit, MI 48221-2599 (313) 862-8000 or (313) 862-5200

Full-time: 75 men, 425 women	Faculty: 56; IIB, --$
Part-time: 84 men, 416 women	Ph.D's: 70%
Graduate: 31 men, 113 women	Student/Faculty: 9 to 1
Year: semesters, summer session	Tuition: $3957 ($7704)
Application Deadline: August 15	Room & Board: $1920
Freshman Class: 320 applied, 196 accepted, 86 enrolled	
SAT I or ACT: required	**VERY COMPETITIVE**

Marygrove College, founded in 1910, is a private liberal arts institution affiliated with the Catholic Church. There is one undergraduate and one graduate school. In addition to regional accreditation, Marygrove has baccalaureate program accreditation with ADA, CAHEA, CSWE, and NCATE. The library contains 185,000 volumes and 16,535 microform items, and subscribes to 800 periodicals. Computerized library sources and services include database searching. Special learning facilities include a learning resource center and art gallery. The 68-acre campus is in an urban area 11 miles from downtown Detroit. Including residence halls, there are 7 buildings on campus.

Student Life: About 98% of undergraduates are from Michigan. Students come from 6 foreign countries and Canada. Seventy-seven percent are African American; 10% white. Fourteen percent are Protestant. The average age of all undergraduates is 32.

Housing: A total of 200 students can be accommodated in college housing. College-sponsored living facilities include coed dormitories. On-campus housing is available on a first-come, first-served basis. Eighty-nine percent of students commute. All students may keep cars on campus.

Activities: There are no fraternities or sororities on campus. There are 9 groups on campus, including art, chorale, drama, musical theater, religious, social service, and student government. Popular campus events include Honors Day, Martin Luther King Day, Black History Month, contemporary American authors lecture series, and welcome ceremony for new students.

Sports: There is no sports program at Marygrove.

Disabled Students: The following facilities are available: elevators, special parking, specially equipped rest rooms, and portable wheelchair ramps.

Services: In addition to many counseling and information services, tutoring is available in most subjects. In addition, there is remedial math, reading, and writing.

Campus Safety and Security: Campus safety and security measures include 24-hour foot and vehicle patrol, self defense education, informal discussions, and emergency telephones. In addition, there are lighted pathways and sidewalks.

Programs of Study: Marygrove awards the B.A., B.S., B.B.A., B.F.A., B.M., and B.S.W. degrees. Associate's and master's degrees also are awarded. Bachelor's degrees are awarded in BIOLOGICAL SCIENCE (biology/biological science), BUSINESS (accounting and business administration and management), COMMUNICATIONS AND THE ARTS (dance, English, fine arts, French, music, and Spanish), COMPUTER AND PHYSICAL SCIENCE (chemistry, computer science, and natural sciences), EDUCATION (art, business, early childhood, education of the emotionally handicapped, education of the mentally handicapped, elementary, music, secondary, and special), HEALTH PROFESSIONS (allied health, predentistry, and premedicine), SOCIAL SCIENCE (economics, history, home economics, humanities, philosophy, political science/government, psychology, religion, social science, social work, and sociology). Business, computer science, education, and social work have the largest enrollments.

Required: In order to graduate, students must complete 128 semester hours with a minimum GPA of 2.0. The required core program includes a first-year seminar; 18 hours in arts and letters; 12 in social sciences; 8 in mathematics and natural science (including 1 laboratory science); and courses in communications (composition, oral communication, and computer literacy). The required number of hours in the major varies.

Special: Foreign language majors may study in Europe in their junior year. A consortium program is offered with the University of Detroit Mercy, Saint Mary's College, Sacred Heart Seminary, and Madonna University. Students may earn B.A./B.S. or B.S./M.S. degrees in engineering, natural resources, and pharmacy through a co-op program with the University of Michigan. Also available are nondegree study, student-designed and dual majors, internships, pass/fail options, and work-study programs. Students may acquire credit for life experience

by documenting their achievements in a portfolio. There are 4 national honor societies on campus.

Faculty/Classroom: Thirty-one percent of faculty are male; 69%, female. All teach undergraduates, 100% do research, and 100% do both. No introductory courses are taught by graduate students. The average class size in an introductory lecture is 17 and in a laboratory, 10.

Admissions: About 61% of the 1993–94 applicants were accepted.

Requirements: A minimum GPA of 2.3 is required. The SAT I or ACT is required of all students under the age of 25. In addition, applicant must be a graduate of an accredited high school. An interview is recommended. The student's average, class rank, recommendations, and special talents are important factors in admission. Entering students must take the College Placement Examinations. AP and CLEP credits are accepted.

Procedure: Freshmen are admitted to all sessions. Applications should be filed by August 15 for fall entry, December 15 for winter entry, February 15 for spring entry, and May 15 for summer entry, along with an application fee of $15. Notification is sent on a rolling basis. There are early admissions and deferred admissions plans.

Transfer: About 55 transfer students enrolled in 1993–94. Transfer students must have a minimum 2.0 GPA. An associate degree or 24 completed credit hours and an interview are recommended. A total of 30 credits out of 128 must be completed at Marygrove.

Visiting: There are regularly scheduled orientations for prospective students, including a tour of the campus followed by college workshops, first-year-student panels, and a college financial planning seminar. There are guides for informal visits and visitors may sit in on classes and stay overnight at the school. To arrange for a visit, contact the Admissions Office at (313) 862–5200.

Financial Aid: In 1993–94 95% of all current freshmen and 95% of continuing students received some form of financial aid. About 95% of freshmen and 95% of continuing students received need-based aid. Scholarships or need-based grants averaged $1650 ($4000 maximum); loans averaged $1700 ($1000 maximum); and work contracts averaged $850 ($2000 maximum). One-hundred percent of undergraduate students work part-time. Average earnings from campus work for the school year are $1700. Marygrove is a member of CSS. The FAF, FFS or SFS is required. The deadline for financial aid applications is March 15.

International Students: There are currently 2 international students enrolled. They must take the TOEFL and achieve a minimum score of 550.

Computers: The college provides computer facilities for student use. The mainframe is a Burroughs B1000 and a Unisys AY. There is a computer center in the mathematics building. All students may access the system. Students may access the system 1 hour per day; longer use requires the permission of the Director of the Computer Learning Center. There are no fees.

Graduates: In 1992–93 152 bachelor's degrees were awarded. The most popular majors among graduates were education (10%), social work (10%), and business and management (8%). In the 1992 graduating class, 18% of the women were enrolled in graduate school within 6 months of graduation; 50% of the women had found employment.

Admissions Contact: Karin Jahn, Director of Admissions.

MICHIGAN CHRISTIAN COLLEGE
E-4
Rochester Hills, MI 48307 | (810) 650–6017
| (800) 521–6010 (out-of-state)

Full-time: 151 men, 160 women	Faculty: 23
Part-time: 30 men, 33 women	Ph.D.s: 21%
Graduate: none	Student/Faculty: 14 to 1
Year: semesters	Tuition: $5024
Application Deadline: open	Room & Board: $3070
Freshman Class: 264 applied, 179 accepted, 134 enrolled	
SAT I or ACT: required	**COMPETITIVE**

Michigan Christian College, founded in 1959, is a private, coeducational institution affiliated with the Churches of Christ. MCC offers undergraduate programs in business, human services, and Christian services. The library contains 36,938 volumes, 15,014 microform items, and 355 audiovisual forms, and subscribes to 210 periodicals. Computerized library sources and services include the card catalog, interlibrary loans, and database searching. The 83-acre campus is in a suburban area. Including residence halls, there are 10 buildings on campus.

Student Life: About 74% of undergraduates are from Michigan. Students come from 14 states, 6 foreign countries, and Canada. Eighty-one percent are white; 13% African American. Most are Protestant. The average age of all undergraduates is 23.

Housing: A total of 290 students can be accommodated in college housing. College-sponsored living facilities include single-sex dormitories. On-campus housing is available on a first-come, first-served ba-

sis. Seventy-three percent of students live on campus. Alcohol is not permitted. All students may keep cars on campus.

Activities: There are no fraternities or sororities on campus. There are a number of groups on campus, including chorus, drama, religious, social, social service, and student government. Popular campus events include Homecoming and Celebration in Song.

Sports: There are 5 intercollegiate sports each for men and women, and 6 intramural sports each for men and women. Athletic and recreation facilities include a gymnasium, soccer and baseball fields, and tennis courts.

Disabled Students: Most of the campus is accessible to disabled students. Wheelchair ramps, special parking, and specially equipped rest rooms are available.

Services: There is remedial math, reading, and writing.

Campus Safety and Security: Campus safety and security measures include lighted pathways and sidewalks and evening security guards.

Programs of Study: MCC awards the B.B.A. and B.R.E. degrees. Associate degrees also are awarded. Bachelor's degrees are awarded in BUSINESS (business administration and management, human resources, management science, and marketing management), SOCIAL SCIENCE (biblical studies, Christian studies, counseling psychology, ministries, missions, psychology, social work, sociology, and youth ministry).

Required: All students must follow a core curriculum that includes courses in Bible, communication, humanities, physical education, science, mathematics, and social science. To graduate, students must complete 128 credits with a minimum GPA of 2.0.

Special: Cross registration with Oakland University, internships, and work-study programs are offered. There is a freshman honors program on campus and 1 department has an honors program.

Faculty/Classroom: Seventy percent of faculty are male; 30%, female. Almost all teach undergraduates. The average class size in an introductory lecture is 40; in a laboratory, 10; and in a regular course offering, 20.

Admissions: About 68% of the 1993–94 applicants were accepted.

Requirements: A minimum GPA of 2.3 is required. The SAT I or ACT is required. AP and CLEP credits are accepted.

Procedure: Freshmen are admitted in the fall and spring. Entrance exams should be taken as early as possible. Application deadlines are open. Application fee is $25. Notification is sent on a rolling basis. There are early admissions and deferred admissions plans.

Transfer: About 24 transfer students enrolled in 1993–94. A 2.0 college GPA is required. A total of 32 credits out of 128 must be completed at MCC.

Visiting: There are regularly scheduled orientations for prospective students, including Junior/Senior Day in October and Celebration Saturday in February. There are guides for informal visits and visitors may sit in on classes and stay overnight at the school. To arrange for a visit, contact the Admissions Office at (800) 521–6010.

Financial Aid: The FAF, FFS, or SFS and the college's own financial statement are required. The deadline for financial aid applications is June 1.

International Students: There are currently 17 international students enrolled. The school actively recruits these students. They must take the TOEFL and achieve a minimum score of 500. The student must also take the SAT I or the ACT.

Computers: The college provides computer facilities for student use. There are PCs in the student computer laboratory. Those enrolled or previously enrolled in computer courses may access the system. There are no time limits on using the system and no fees.

Graduates: In 1992–93, 18 bachelor's degrees were awarded. The most popular majors among graduates were professional ministry (28%), counseling (28%), and Biblical studies (22%).

Admissions Contact: Toby Osburn, Dean of Enrollment Services.

MICHIGAN STATE UNIVERSITY
D-4
East Lansing, MI 48824–1046 | (517) 355–8332

Full-time: 26,935	Faculty: 4000; I, -$
Part-time: 3825	Ph.D.s: 95%
Graduate: 8983 men and women	Student/Faculty: 7 to 1
Year: semesters, summer session	Tuition: $4170 ($10,804)
Application Deadline: July 30	Room & Board: $3672
Freshman Class: 18,114 applied, 15,096 accepted, 6180 enrolled	
SAT I Verbal/Math: 458/524	ACT: 23 **COMPETITIVE**

Michigan State University, a pioneer land-grant institution, was founded in 1855. Its 14 colleges and more than 100 departments offer undergraduate and graduate degrees in more than 200 fields of study. The university's Honors College offers students an alternative education program. There are 11 undergraduate and 13 graduate schools. In addition to regional accreditation, MSU has baccalaureate program accreditation with AACSB, ABET, ACEJMC, ADA, ASLA, CAHEA, CSWE, FIDER, NASM, NCATE, NLN, and SAF. The 16 libraries contain 3.8 million volumes, 4.8 million microform items, and

30,600 audiovisual forms, and subscribe to 28,000 periodicals. Computerized library sources and services include the card catalog and database searching. Special learning facilities include a learning resource center, an art gallery, a natural history museum, a planetarium, a radio station, and a tv station. Other facilities include a botanical garden, a superconducting cyclotron laboratory, a center for environmental toxicology, a pesticide research center, and a center for computer-aided engineering and manufacturing. The 5239-acre campus is in a suburban area 80 miles west of Detroit. Including residence halls, there are 432 buildings on campus.

Student Life: About 90% of undergraduates are from Michigan. Students come from 50 states, 110 foreign countries, and Canada. Eighty percent are white. The average age of freshmen is 18; all undergraduates, 20.7. Fourteen percent drop out by the end of their first year; 66% remain to graduate.

Housing: A total of 19,749 students can be accommodated in college housing. College-sponsored living facilities include single-sex and coed dormitories, on-campus apartments, and married-student housing. In addition there are honors houses, special interest houses, and 2 residential colleges; and an international hall. On-campus housing is guaranteed for all 4 years and is available on a first-come, first-served basis. Fifty-four percent of students commute. Upperclassmen may keep cars on campus.

Activities: About 8% of men belong to 31 national fraternities; about 8% of women belong to 19 national sororities. There are 400 groups on campus, including art, band, cheerleading, chess, choir, chorale, chorus, computers, dance, drama, ethnic, film, gay, honors, international, jazz band, marching band, musical theater, newspaper, orchestra, pep band, photography, political, professional, radio and tv, religious, social, social service, student government, symphony, and yearbook. Popular campus events include MSU vs. University of Michigan football game, Homecoming; Greek Week; and Siblings Weekend.

Sports: There are 14 intercollegiate sports for men and 11 for women, and 25 intramural sports for men and 25 for women. Athletic and recreation facilities include a 76,000-seat stadium, a 4000-seat gymnasium and field house, an ice arena, and a multipurpose 15,500-seat student events center. The university also has an indoor football practice facility, 3 intramural facilities, indoor and outdoor tennis courts, ball fields, a running track, 2 golf courses, and 4 swimming pools, including 1 Olympic size outdoor pool.

Disabled Students: Seventy-five percent of the campus is accessible to disabled students. The following facilities are available: wheelchair ramps, elevators, special parking, specially equipped rest rooms, special class scheduling, lowered drinking fountains, lowered telephones, tape recorders, videotaped classes, and reading machines.

Services: In addition to many counseling and information services, tutoring is available in most subjects. In addition, there is a reader service for the blind and remedial math and writing. Note-takers are also available.

Campus Safety and Security: Campus safety and security measures include 24-hour foot and vehicle patrol, self-defense education, escort service, and shuttle buses. In addition, there are informal discussions, pamphlets, posters, and films, emergency telephones, lighted pathways and sidewalks, and campus buses.

Programs of Study: MSU awards the B.A., B.S., B.F.A., B.Land.Arch., B.Mus., and B.S. in Nursing degrees. Master's and doctoral degrees also are awarded. Bachelor's degrees are awarded in AGRICULTURE (agriculture, animal science, forestry and related sciences, horticulture, and soil science), BIOLOGICAL SCIENCE (biochemistry, biology/biological science, botany, entomology, microbiology, nutrition, and zoology), BUSINESS (accounting, business administration and management, marketing management, marketing/retailing/merchandising, and personnel management), COMMUNICATIONS AND THE ARTS (advertising, applied music, art history and appreciation, communications, English, French, German, journalism, Latin, linguistics, music, music theory and composition, Russian, Spanish, studio art, and telecommunications), COMPUTER AND PHYSICAL SCIENCE (astrophysics, chemistry, computer science, earth science, geology, mathematics, physical sciences, physics, science, and statistics), EDUCATION (agricultural, art, early childhood, elementary, environmental, foreign languages, home economics, music, physical, science, secondary, and special), ENGINEERING AND ENVIRONMENTAL DESIGN (agricultural engineering, chemical engineering, city/community/regional planning, civil engineering, computer engineering, construction management, electrical/electronics engineering, engineering, industrial administration/management, interior design, landscape architecture/design, materials engineering, and mechanical engineering), HEALTH PROFESSIONS (clinical science, medical laboratory technology, music therapy, nursing, predentistry, premedicine, and speech pathology/audiology), SOCIAL SCIENCE (American studies, anthropology, classical/ancient civilization, criminal justice, dietetics, economics, family/consumer resource management, food production/

management/services, food science, geography, history, humanities, international relations, philosophy, political science/government, pre-law, psychology, public administration, religion, social science, social work, and sociology). Teacher education, audiology and speech sciences, business, chemistry, and journalism are the strongest academically. Accounting, business administration, and psychology have the largest enrollments.

Required: To graduate, students must complete a freshman writing course and a writing course specified by the major and degree program. Students must complete the 26 credit University Integrative Studies requirement consisting of 8 credits each of arts and humanitites, and social, behavioral, and economic sciences, 7 of general science, and 3 of a transcollegiate course. Students must also demonstrate knowledge in mathematics equivalent to 4 years of college preparatory mathematics at the high school level, including 2 years of algebra, 1 year of geometry, and 1 year of either probability, trigonometry, or calculus.

Special: Special academic programs include an engineering co-op program with business and industry; internships in business, education, political science, agriculture, and communication arts; study abroad in more than 30 countries; on-campus work-study programs; and a sea semester. An accelerated degree program in all majors and student-designed majors are offered at the Honors College. Nondegree study, pass/fail options in some courses, and dual majors are possible. Educationally disadvantaged students may avail themselves of the College Achievement Admissions Program (CAAP). Cross-registration with the Committee on Institutional Cooperation schools is available. There is a freshman honors program on campus, as well as 20 national honor societies, including Phi Beta Kappa.

Faculty/Classroom: The average class size in an introductory lecture is 100; in a laboratory, 30; and in a regular course offering, 50.

Admissions: About 83% of the 1993–94 applicants were accepted. The SAT scores for the 1993–94 freshman class were as follows: Verbal—68% below 500, 23% between 500 and 599, 8% between 600 and 700, and 1% above 700; Math—40% below 500, 35% between 500 and 599, 20% between 600 and 700, and 5% above 700. The ACT scores were 24% below 21, 33% between 21 and 23, 27% between 24 and 26, 9% between 27 and 28, and 7% above 28. There were 48 National Merit finalists. About 75 freshmen graduated first in their class.

Requirements: The SAT I or ACT is required. Applicant must be a graduate of an accredited secondary school, and have completed 4 years of English, 3 years each of mathematics, and social studies, including history, and 2 years of science. The GED is accepted. Music majors must audition. AP and CLEP credits are accepted. Important factors used in the admissions decision are recommendations by school officials, advanced placement or honor courses, evidence of special talent, leadership record, and extracurricular activities record.

Procedure: Freshmen are admitted to all sessions. Entrance exams should be taken during the junior year of high school. Applications should be filed by July 30 for fall entry, December 1 for spring entry, and April 15 for summer entry, along with an application fee of $30. Notification is sent on a rolling basis. There is a deferred admissions plan. A waiting list is an active part of the admissions procedure, with about 1% of applicants on the list.

Transfer: About 1930 transfer students enrolled in 1993–94. Transfers are accepted for all classes. A minimum GPA of 2.0 is required. A total of 30 credits out of 120 must be completed at MSU.

Visiting: There are regularly scheduled orientations for prospective students, includes a presentation, a tour of the campus, and lunch. There are guides for informal visits and visitors may sit in on classes and stay overnight at the school. To arrange for a visit, contact the Student Admissions Committee at (517) 353-1615.

Financial Aid: In 1993–94, 50% of all current freshmen and 50% of continuing students received some form of financial aid. About 40% of freshmen and 40% of continuing students received need-based aid. The average freshman award was $6284. Of that total, scholarships or need-based grants averaged $1827 ($11,078 maximum); loans averaged $2046 ($16,100 maximum); and work contracts averaged $2150. Fifty-four percent of undergraduate students work part-time. Average earnings from campus work for the school year are $2400. The average financial indebtedness of the 1992–93 graduate was $7471. MSU is a member of CSS. The FAF or FFS (preferred), and the FAFSA are required. Applicants should file as early as possible.

International Students: There are currently 2431 international students enrolled. The school actively recruits these students. They must take the TOEFL, the University of Michigan Language Test, the Comprehensive English Language Test, or the college's own test.

Computers: The college provides computer facilities for student use. The mainframe is an IBM 3090, a CONVEX 220, and a 96 Node GP1000. There are more than 5000 networked microcomputers from various vendors located in 25 public microlaboratories and numerous restricted micro facilities. All students may access the system. It may

be used 16 hours a day; 7 days a week. There are no time limits on using the system and no fees.

Graduates: In 1992–93, 7273 bachelor's degrees were awarded. The most popular majors among graduates were elementary education (4%), accounting (4%), and advertising (3%). Within an average freshman class, 31% graduate in 4 years, 63% in 5 years, and 67% in 6 years. Some 1435 companies recruited on campus in 1992–93. In the 1992 graduating class, 21% of the men and 21% of all students were enrolled in graduate school within 6 months of graduation; 62% had found employment.

Admissions Contact: William H. Turner, Director of Admissions and Scholarships.

MICHIGAN TECHNOLOGICAL UNIVERSITY   B-1
Houghton, MI 49931-1295   (906) 487-2335

Full-time: 4157 men, 1367 women	Faculty: 358; IIA, av$
Part-time: 281 men, 133 women	Ph.Ds: 82%
Graduate: 498 men, 167 women	Student/Faculty: 15 to 1
Year: quarters, summer session	Tuition: $3441 ($7785)
Application Deadline: open	Room & Board: $3842

Freshman Class: 2622 applied, 2217 accepted, 1051 enrolled
SAT I Verbal/Math: 520/630   **ACT:** 26   **VERY COMPETITIVE +**

Michigan Technological University, founded in 1885, is a coeducational, state-supported institution offering degrees in engineering, liberal arts, sciences, forestry, business, and technology. There are 5 undergraduate schools and one graduate school. In addition to regional accreditation, Michigan Tech has baccalaureate program accreditation with ABET and SAF. The library contains 781,219 volumes, 367,237 microform items, and 3335 audiovisual forms, and subscribes to 4000 periodicals. Computerized library sources and services include the card catalog, interlibrary loans, and database searching. Special learning facilities include a learning resource center, radio station, and mineral museum. The 240-acre campus is in a small town 380 miles northwest of Milwaukee, Wisconsin. Including residence halls, there are 80 buildings on campus.

Student Life: About 78% of undergraduates are from Michigan. Students come from 44 states, 56 foreign countries, and Canada. Eighty-eight percent are white. The average age of freshmen is 19; all undergraduates, 21. Fifteen percent drop out by the end of their first year; 59% remain to graduate.

Housing: A total of 2870 students can be accommodated in college housing. College-sponsored living facilities include coed dormitories, on-campus apartments, and married-student housing. In addition, 1 floor is for seniors and graduate students. Also, each hall has chemical-free areas where tobacco is not allowed. On-campus housing is guaranteed for the freshman year only and is available on a first-come, first-served basis. Sixty-four percent of students commute. Alcohol is not permitted. All students may keep cars on campus.

Activities: About 11% of men belong to 4 local and 12 national fraternities; about 16% of women belong to 4 local and 4 national sororities. There are 150 groups on campus, including band, cheerleading, chess, choir, chorale, chorus, computers, drama, ethnic, film, gay, honors, international, jazz band, literary magazine, musical theater, newspaper, orchestra, pep band, photography, political, professional, radio and tv, religious, social, social service, student government, and symphony. Popular campus events include Homecoming, Winter Carnival, K-Day, and Spring Fling.

Sports: There are 7 intercollegiate sports for men and 6 for women, and 38 intramural sports for men and 38 for women. Athletic and recreation facilities include a complex with a 3250-seat ice arena and a 3100-seat gym; a lakeside golf course; a field; a tennis center; and Mount Ripley Ski Hill.

Disabled Students: Eighty-five percent of the campus is accessible to disabled students. The following facilities are available: wheelchair ramps, elevators, special parking, specially equipped rest rooms, special class scheduling, and lowered drinking fountains.

Services: In addition to many counseling and information services, tutoring is available in every subject. In addition, there is remedial math, reading, and writing.

Campus Safety and Security: Campus safety and security measures include 24-hour foot and vehicle patrol, self-defense education, escort service, and shuttle buses. In addition, there are informal discussions, pamphlets, posters, and films, emergency telephones, and lighted pathways and sidewalks.

Programs of Study: Michigan Tech awards the B.A. and B.S. degrees. Associate, master's, and doctoral degrees also are awarded. Bachelor's degrees are awarded in AGRICULTURE (forestry and related sciences), BIOLOGICAL SCIENCE (biology/biological science), BUSINESS (business administration and management and business economics), COMMUNICATIONS AND THE ARTS (communications), COMPUTER AND PHYSICAL SCIENCE (chemistry, computer science, geology, geophysics and seismology, mathematics, and physics), ENGINEERING AND ENVIRONMENTAL DESIGN (biomedical engineering, chemical engineering, civil engineering, electrical/electronics engineering, engineering, environmental engineering, geological engineering, mechanical engineering, metallurgical engineering, mining and mineral engineering, and surveying engineering), HEALTH PROFESSIONS (medical laboratory technology), SOCIAL SCIENCE (liberal arts/general studies and social science). Engineering, forestry, and physical science are the strongest academically. Mechanical, electrical, and civil engineering have the largest enrollments.

Required: To graduate, students must complete 186 to 208 credit hours, and maintain a minimum GPA of 2.0. Requirements include 12 credits each of mathematics/computer science and social science, 9 credits each of communication, science, humanities, and upper division thematic studies, and 4 credits of physical education.

Special: Michigan Tech offers co-op programs in almost all majors, internships in medical technology and secondary teacher education, study in Switzerland, Germany, Finland, and the former Soviet Union, and a B.A.-B.S. degree in scientific and technical communication. There are interinstitutional programs with Central Michigan University, Northwestern Michigan College, and Delta College. A 3–2 engineering degree is possible in conjunction with the University of Wisconsin-Superior, the College of St. Scholastica, and Adrian, Albion, Augsburg, Northland, and Mount Senario Colleges. There are 15 national honor societies on campus.

Faculty/Classroom: Eighty-three percent of faculty are male; 17%, female. All teach undergraduates, 35% do research, and 35% do both. The average class size in an introductory lecture is 96; in a laboratory, 20; and in a regular course offering, 32.

Admissions: About 85% of the 1993–94 applicants were accepted. The SAT scores for the 1993–94 freshman class were as follows: Verbal—41% below 500, 37% between 500 and 599, 21% between 600 and 700, and 1% above 700; Math—8% below 500, 29% between 500 and 599, 45% between 600 and 700, and 18% above 700. The ACT scores were 6% below 21, 19% between 21 and 23, 30% between 24 and 26, 21% between 27 and 28, and 24% above 28. About 72% of the current freshmen were in the top fifth of their class; 95% were in the top two fifths. There were 7 National Merit finalists and 17 semifinalists. About 70 freshmen graduated first in their class.

Requirements: Students are encouraged to take the SAT I, ACT, or both; scores are used for admission and placement. Admissions requirements include graduation from an accredited secondary school, with 15 academic credits. These must include 3 credits in English, 1 credit of chemistry or physics, and 3 credits in mathematics for engineering and science curricula; credits in social studies and foreign language are recommended. The GED is accepted. AP and CLEP credits are accepted. Important factors used in the admissions decision are recommendations by school officials, advanced placement or honor courses, evidence of special talent, leadership record, and extracurricular activities record.

Procedure: Freshmen are admitted to all sessions. Entrance exams should be taken in the junior year. Application deadlines are open. Application fee is $30. Notification is sent on a rolling basis. There is a deferred admissions plan.

Transfer: About 290 transfer students enrolled in 1993–94. Transfer students must have a minimum GPA of 2.5; some engineering curricula require a GPA of 3.0 or higher. The SAT I or ACT is recommended. A minimum of 36 quarter credits out of 186 to 208 must be completed at Michigan Tech.

Visiting: There are regularly scheduled orientations for prospective students, including campus tours at 10 A.M. and 2 P.M. Monday through Friday. Separate interviews are available with academic department personnel and admissions representatives. There are guides for informal visits and visitors may sit in on classes and stay overnight at the school. To arrange for a visit, contact the Admissions Office at (906) 487-2335.

Financial Aid: In 1993–94, 60% of all current freshmen and 72% of continuing students received some form of financial aid. About 32% of freshmen and 40% of continuing students received need-based aid. The average freshman award was $4170. Of that total, scholarships or need-based grants averaged $932 ($10,170 maximum); loans averaged $1888 ($4575 maximum); and work contracts averaged $1350 ($1620 maximum). Forty percent of undergraduate students work part-time. Average earnings from campus work for the school year are $1350. The average financial indebtedness of the 1992–93 graduate was $4671. Michigan Tech is a member of CSS. The FAFSA financial statement is required. The deadline for financial aid applications is March 1.

International Students: There are currently 494 international students enrolled. The school actively recruits these students. They must take the TOEFL and achieve a minimum score of 500.

Computers: The college provides computer facilities for student use. The mainframe is an IBM 4381-R14, a Sequent Balance 4000, and a UNISYS 1172. Almost every department has one or more student computing laboratories. Equipment varies but includes PCs, Apple Macintosh microcomputers, Sun workstations, laser printers, electro-

static plotters, and scanners. Software includes general productivity packages such as word processing and spreadsheets, and specialized applications, such as CAD/CAM, GIS, and publishing. All students may access the system. It may be used 24 hours a day. Students may access the system 200 hours a month with an extension of an additional 200 if required by classes. The fees vary by department.

Graduates: In 1992–93, 1129 bachelor's degrees were awarded. The most popular majors among graduates were mechanical engineering (25%), electrical engineering (22%), and civil engineering (9%). Within an average freshman class, 3% graduate in 3 years, 19% in 4 years, 52% in 5 years, and 59% in 6 years. Some 220 companies recruited on campus in 1992–93. In the 1992 graduating class, 15% of all students were enrolled in graduate school within 6 months of graduation; 81% of the men and 84% of the women had found employment.

Admissions Contact: Joseph A. Galetto, Director of Enrollment Management.

NORTHERN MICHIGAN UNIVERSITY
Marquette, MI 49855

C-2
(906) 227-2650
(800) 682-9797 (in-state and Midwest)

Full-time: 6161 men and women	Faculty: 330; IIA, av$
Part-time: 1728 men and women	Ph.D.s: 55%
Graduate: 310 men, 530 women	Student/Faculty: 19 to 1
Year: semesters, summer session	Tuition: $2521 ($4646)
Application Deadline: open	Room & Board: $3829
Freshman Class: n/av	
SAT I or ACT: required	**COMPETITIVE**

Northern Michigan University, founded in 1899, is a public, institution offering undergraduate programs in the arts and sciences, business, education, health science, human services, nursing, and technology. There are 5 undergraduate schools and one graduate school. In addition to regional accreditation, NMU has baccalaureate program accreditation with ADA, CSWE, NASM, NCATE, and NLN. The library contains 480,188 volumes, 706,425 microform items, and 7214 audiovisual forms, and subscribes to 2230 periodicals. Computerized library sources and services include the card catalog and interlibrary loans. Special learning facilities include a learning resource center, art gallery, radio station, TV station, and observatory. The 320-acre campus is in an urban area 300 miles north of Milwaukee, Wisconsin. Including residence halls, there are 50 buildings on campus.

Student Life: About 92% of undergraduates are from Michigan. Students come from 35 states, 21 foreign countries, and Canada. Ninety-five percent are white. The average age of freshmen is 19.1; all undergraduates, 24.3. Twenty-nine percent drop out by the end of their first year; 43% remain to graduate.

Housing: A total of 2500 students can be accommodated in college housing. College-sponsored living facilities include single-sex and coed dormitories, on-campus apartments, and married-student housing. In addition, there are honors houses. On-campus housing is guaranteed for all 4 years. Seventy-three percent of students commute. All students may keep cars on campus.

Activities: One percent of men and women belong to 9 national fraternities; about 1% of women belong to 5 national sororities. There are 160 groups on campus, including art, band, cheerleading, chess, choir, chorale, chorus, computers, drama, ethnic, film, gay, honors, jazz band, literary magazine, marching band, musical theater, newspaper, opera, orchestra, pep band, photography, political, professional, radio and TV, religious, social, social service, and student government. Popular campus events include Homecoming and Winfester.

Sports: There are 5 intercollegiate sports for men and 6 for women, and 14 intramural sports each. Athletic and recreation facilities include indoor and outdoor playing fields, an ice rink, a swimming pool, a diving tank, a field house, a 9000-seat stadium, a 5000-seat gymnasium, the neighboring forests and rivers, and Lake Superior.

Disabled Students: Eighty percent of the campus is accessible to disabled students. The following facilities are available: wheelchair ramps, elevators, special parking, and specially equipped rest rooms.

Services: In addition to many counseling and information services, tutoring is available in some subjects, including lower-level chemistry, mathematics, computing, biology, and foreign language. There is also remedial math, reading, and writing.

Campus Safety and Security: Campus safety and security measures include 24-hour foot and vehicle patrol, escort service, pamphlets, posters, and films, and emergency telephones. In addition, there are lighted pathways and sidewalks and and a crime prevention program with a full-time staff.

Programs of Study: NMU awards the B.A., B.S., B.F.A., B.M.Ed., B.S.N., and B.S.W. degrees. Associate and master's degrees also are awarded. Bachelor's degrees are awarded in BIOLOGICAL SCIENCE (biochemistry, biology/biological science, botany, ecology, microbiology, physiology, and zoology), BUSINESS (accounting, banking and finance, business administration and management, fashion merchandising, and marketing/retailing/merchandising), COMMUNICATIONS AND THE ARTS (broadcasting, ceramic art and design, communications, design, dramatic arts, drawing, English, film arts, fine arts, French, German, graphic design, illustration, metal/jewelry, music, painting, photography, printmaking, public relations, sculpture, Spanish, and speech/debate/rhetoric), COMPUTER AND PHYSICAL SCIENCE (chemistry, computer programming, computer science, earth science, information sciences and systems, mathematics, and physics), EDUCATION (art, business, computer, early childhood, education of the mentally handicapped, elementary, foreign languages, health, home economics, industrial arts, music, physical, science, and secondary), ENGINEERING AND ENVIRONMENTAL DESIGN (construction technology, electrical/electronics engineering technology, furniture design, industrial engineering technology, land use management and reclamation, and manufacturing technology), HEALTH PROFESSIONS (clinical science, cytotechnology, medical laboratory technology, nursing, predentistry, premedicine, preveterinary science, and speech pathology/audiology), and SOCIAL SCIENCE (corrections, criminal justice, dietetics, economics, geography, gerontology, history, international studies, parks and recreation management, philosophy, physical fitness/movement, political science/government, prelaw, psychology, public administration, social studies, social work, sociology, and water resources). Biology, chemistry, and education are the strongest academically. Business, biology, education, criminal justice, and nursing have the largest enrollments.

Required: Students must earn 40 semester credits in liberal studies requirements, including courses in humanities, composition, natural sciences/mathematics, social sciences, communications, and visual and performing arts. Graduation requirements vary by degree program; at the minimum, students must earn 124 semester credits, including 32 in a major field, with a GPA of 2.0. A writing proficiency examination is also required.

Special: There is a co-op program in ski area management with Gogebic Community College. Cross-registration is available with other Michigan universities and colleges. Students may study abroad in Europe, Latin America, and Japan. NMU also offers internships in public service and law, accelerated degree programs, dual and student-designed majors, limited pass/fail options, and nondegree study. There are 9 national honor societies on campus.

Faculty/Classroom: Seventy-one percent of faculty are male; 29%, female. Graduate students teach 2% of introductory courses. The average class size in an introductory lecture is 30; in a laboratory, 25; and in a regular course offering, 30.

Requirements: A minimum GPA of 2.3 is required. The SAT I or ACT is required, with a minimum composite score for the SAT I of 800; for the ACT, 19. Applicants must be graduates of accredited secondary schools or have earned a GED. The university requires 12 to 16 Carnegie units; recommended secondary school preparation includes 4 years each of English and mathematics, 3 of history, social studies, foreign language, and science, 2 of fine arts or performing arts, and 1 of computer instruction. An interview is recommended for all applicants. Students seeking art scholarships must submit a portfolio; those seeking music and theater scholarships must audition. AP and CLEP credits are accepted. Important factors used in the admissions decision are advanced placement or honor courses, evidence of special talent, recommendations by school officials, extracurricular activities record, and leadership record.

Procedure: Entrance exams should be taken during the year prior to enrollment. Application deadlines are open. The application fee is $25. Notification is sent on a rolling basis. There is a deferred admissions plan.

Transfer: About 610 transfer students enrolled in a recent year. Transfer applicants must present a minimum GPA of 2.0 in at least 12 semester credits of college-level work. A total of 32 semester credits out of at least 124 must be completed at NMU.

Visiting: There are regularly scheduled orientations for prospective students, including an admissions interview, a tour, and a faculty visit. Visitors may sit in on classes and stay overnight at the school. To arrange for a visit, contact the Campus Visit Office at (906) 227-1709 or (800) 682-9797 (in-state and the Midwest).

Financial Aid: In a recent year, 69% of all students received some form of financial aid. About 57% of all students received need-based aid. Scholarships or need-based grants averaged $860 ($4000 maximum); loans averaged $1400 ($4000 maximum); and work contracts averaged $900 ($2000 maximum). Forty-five percent of undergraduate students work part-time. Average earnings from campus work for the school year are $900. The average financial indebtedness of a recent graduate was $4300. NMU is a member of CSS. The FAFSA is required. The deadline for financial aid applications is February 1.

International Students: There are currently 31 international students enrolled. They must take the TOEFL and achieve a minimum score of 500. Canadian students must take the SAT I or ACT.

Computers: The college provides computer facilities for student use. The mainframe is an IBM 4381 Model R-12. There are more than 400 terminals and microcomputers located in 3 computer laboratories, the library, residence halls, and academic departments. Those students who use the computer for instruction or research may access the mainframe from 7 A.M. to midnight daily. There are no time limits. The fees are $1.25 per credit.

Graduates: In a recent year, 851 bachelor's degrees were awarded. The most popular majors among graduates were education (10%), management (9%), and criminal justice (7%). Within an average freshman class, 3% graduate in 3 years, 15% in 4 years, 34% in 5 years, and 42% in 6 years. In a recent graduating class, 12% of all students were enrolled in graduate school within 6 months of graduation; 78% of all graduates found employment.

Admissions Contact: Nancy Rehling, Director of Admissions.

NORTHWOOD INSTITUTE
(See Northwood University)

NORTHWOOD UNIVERSITY

(Formerly Northwood Institute)
Midland, MI 48640

D-4

(517) 631-1600, ext. 367
(800) 457-7878 (out-of-state)

Full-time: 791 men, 488 women	Faculty: 33
Part-time: 13 men, 11 women	Ph.D.s: 11%
Graduate: 55 men, 25 women	Student/Faculty: 39 to 1
Year: terms, summer session	Tuition: $9113
Application Deadline: open	Room & Board: $4272
Freshman Class: 1093 applied, 998 accepted, 285 enrolled	
ACT: 20	**LESS COMPETITIVE**

Northwood University, founded in 1959, is a private, nonprofit institution offering undergraduate and graduate programs in business. Campuses are located in Florida, Michigan, and Texas. The library contains 40,000 volumes and subscribes to 550 periodicals. Computerized library sources and services include interlibrary loans. Special learning facilities include an art gallery, radio station, creativity center, and Automotive Hall of Fame. The 268-acre campus is in a suburban area 135 miles north of Detroit. Including residence halls, there are 22 buildings on campus.

Student Life: About 74% of undergraduates are from Michigan. Students come from 31 states, 21 foreign countries, and Canada. Eighty-five percent are from public schools; 15% from private. Eighty-five percent are white; 12% African American. The average age of freshmen is 18; all undergraduates, 20. Thirteen percent drop out by the end of their first year; 80% remain to graduate.

Housing: A total of 1200 students can be accommodated in college housing. College-sponsored living facilities include single-sex dormitories and on-campus apartments. On-campus housing is available on a first-come, first-served basis. Sixty percent of students live on campus; of those, 60% remain on campus on weekends. Alcohol is not permitted. All students may keep cars on campus.

Activities: About 25% of men belong to 2 local and 7 national fraternities; about 25% of women belong to 3 national sororities. There are 18 groups on campus, including cheerleading, computers, drama, ethnic, honors, international, jazz band, newspaper, pep band, political, professional, radio and TV, religious, social, social service, student government, and yearbook. Popular campus events include Auto Show Weekend, Greek Week, Homecoming, Values Emphasis Week, Alcohol Awareness Week, and Salvation Army Christmas Party.

Sports: There are 9 intercollegiate sports for men and 6 for women, and 5 intramural sports for men and 5 for women. Athletic and recreation facilities include a sports center, with an 800-seat indoor gymnasium, and a 2500-seat stadium.

Disabled Students: Ninety-five percent of the campus is accessible to disabled students. The following facilities are available: wheelchair ramps, elevators, special parking, specially equipped rest rooms, and special class scheduling.

Services: In addition to many counseling and information services, tutoring is available in most subjects. In addition, there is remedial math, reading, and writing.

Campus Safety and Security: Campus safety and security measures include 24-hour foot and vehicle patrol, lighted pathways and sidewalks, and a professional security force.

Programs of Study: Northwood awards the B.B.A. degree. Associate and master's degrees also are awarded. Bachelor's degrees are awarded in BUSINESS (accounting, business administration and management, business economics, and marketing/retailing/merchandising), COMPUTER AND PHYSICAL SCIENCE (computer science and information sciences and systems), ENGINEERING AND ENVIRONMENTAL DESIGN (industrial administration/management). Accounting is the strongest academically. Business management has the largest enrollment.

Required: In order to graduate, all students must complete 180 credit hours, with 36 credit hours in the major. A minimum GPA of 2.0 must be maintained, and 6 credits of computer science management and 2 credits of executive fitness must be completed. Internships for 1 to 6 credits are required in some majors.

Special: Northwood offers on-and off-campus work-study and a competitive study-abroad program in Europe, which is based in Paris and includes extensive travel. Dual majors are available in management/automotive marketing, management/computer science, management/marketing, and management/economics. Credit for life and military work experience is possible through a plan of study. Nondegree study and pass/fail options are offered. There is a freshman honors program on campus.

Faculty/Classroom: All teach undergraduates. No introductory courses are taught by graduate students. The average class size in an introductory lecture is 25; in a laboratory, 20; and in a regular course offering, 25.

Admissions: About 91% of the 1993-94 applicants were accepted.

Requirements: Northwood requires applicants to be in the upper 75% of their class. A minimum GPA of 2.0 is required. The SAT I, with a minimum composite score of 900 (450 verbal and 450 math), or the ACT, with a minimum score of 17, is required. Other admissions requirements include graduation from an accredited secondary school. The GED is accepted. AP and CLEP credits are accepted. Important factors used in the admissions decision are leadership record, personality, intangible qualities, recommendations by alumni, recommendations by school officials, and ability to finance college education.

Procedure: Freshmen are admitted to all sessions. Entrance exams should be taken in December. Application deadlines are open. The application fee is $15. Notification is sent on a rolling basis. There are early admissions and deferred admissions plans.

Transfer: A total of 202 transfer students enrolled in 1993-94. Transfer students must have a minimum of 12 credit hours and a minimum GPA of 2.0. An associate degree and an interview are recommended. A total of 45 credits out of 180 must be completed at Northwood.

Visiting: There are regularly scheduled orientations for prospective students. There are guides for informal visits and visitors may sit in on classes and stay overnight at the school. To arrange for a visit, contact the Admissions Department at (800) 457-7878.

Financial Aid: In 1993-94, 82% of all current freshmen and 70% of continuing students received some form of financial aid. About 80% of freshmen and 69% of continuing students received need-based aid. The average freshman award was $4900. Of that total, scholarships or need-based grants averaged $4900; loans averaged $4100; and work contracts averaged $1000. Average earnings from campus work for the school year are $1000. Northwood is a member of CSS. The FAFSA is required. The deadline for financial aid applications is March 15.

International Students: There are currently 111 international students enrolled. The school actively recruits these students. They must take the TOEFL and achieve a minimum score of 500.

Computers: Northwood provides computer facilities for student use. The mainframe is an HP 3000. Computer science/management students may access the system anytime. There are no time limits on using the system. The fees are $35.

Graduates: In an earlier year, 350 bachelor's degrees were awarded. Some 300 companies recruited on campus in 1992-93. In the 1992 graduating class, 90% of all students had found employment within 6 months of graduation.

Admissions Contact: Dr. David Long, Dean of Admissions.

OAKLAND UNIVERSITY

Rochester, MI 48309-4401

E-4

(313) 370-3360

Full-time: 2360 men, 4081 women	Faculty: 359; IIA, +$
Part-time: 1368 men, 2614 women	Ph.D.s: 87%
Graduate: 890 men, 1582 women	Student/Faculty: 18 to 1
Year: semesters, summer session	Tuition: $2824 ($8210)
Application Deadline: July 15	Room & Board: $3890
Freshman Class: 3036 applied, 2576 accepted, 1170 enrolled	
ACT: 23	**VERY COMPETITIVE**

Oakland University, established in 1957, is a state-supported, liberal arts and professional institution, serving a primarily commuter student body. There are 6 undergraduate schools and one graduate school. In addition to regional accreditation, Oakland has baccalaureate program accreditation with AACSB, ABET, APTA, NCATE, and NLN. The 2 libraries contain 582,000 volumes, 989,000 microform items, and 29,000 audiovisual forms, and subscribe to 2065 periodicals. Computerized library sources and services include the card catalog, interlibrary loans, and database searching. Special learning facilities include a learning resource center, art gallery, and radio station. The 1500-acre campus is in a suburban area 25 miles north of Detroit. Including residence halls, there are 45 buildings on campus.

Student Life: About 99% of undergraduates are from Michigan. Students come from 23 states, 23 foreign countries, and Canada. Eighty-seven percent are from public schools; 13% from private. Eighty-four percent are white. Forty-four percent are Catholic; 28% Protestant; and 12% claim no religious affiliation. The average age of freshmen is 19; all undergraduates, 26. Twenty-one percent drop out by the end of their first year; 50% remain to graduate.

Housing: A total of 1421 students can be accommodated in college housing. College-sponsored living facilities include single-sex and coed dormitories and married-student housing. In addition there are honors houses, special interest houses, and a wellness dormitory. On-campus housing is guaranteed for all 4 years. Priority is given to out-of-town students. Eighty-nine percent of students commute. All students may keep cars on campus.

Activities: About 6% of men and about 1% of women belong to 1 local and 7 national fraternities; about 7% of women belong to 2 local and 7 national sororities. There are 101 groups on campus, including art, band, cheerleading, chess, choir, chorale, chorus, computers, dance, drama, ethnic, gay, honors, international, jazz band, musical theater, newspaper, orchestra, pep band, political, professional, radio and tv, religious, social, social service, student government, and symphony. Popular campus events include Welcome Back Week activities, Winter Carnival, Meadow Brook Ball, Apple Amble Marathon Run, Homecoming, African-American Celebration Month, Hispanic Week, Business Forum, and Handicap Awareness Week.

Sports: There are 7 intercollegiate sports for men and 4 for women, and 10 intramural sports for men and 10 for women. Athletic and recreation facilities include a health enhancement institute, a student center, and a sports center that includes softball and baseball diamonds, a track, soccer and touch football fields, and facilities for swimming, basketball, weight training, dance, fencing, handball, squash, racquetball, and golf.

Disabled Students: Ninety percent of the campus is accessible to disabled students. The following facilities are available: wheelchair ramps, elevators, special parking, specially equipped rest rooms, special class scheduling, lowered drinking fountains, lowered telephones, and automatic door openers.

Services: In addition to many counseling and information services, tutoring is available in every subject, including mentorship. In addition, there is a reader service for the blind and remedial math and writing.

Campus Safety and Security: Campus safety and security measures include 24-hour foot and vehicle patrol, escort service, informal discussions, and pamphlets, posters, and films. In addition, there are emergency telephones and lighted pathways and sidewalks.

Programs of Study: Oakland awards the B.A., B.S., B.G.S., B.Mus., B.S.E., and B.S.N. degrees. Master's and doctoral degrees also are awarded. Bachelor's degrees are awarded in BIOLOGICAL SCIENCE (biochemistry and biology/biological science), BUSINESS (accounting, banking and finance, business administration and management, business economics, human resources, marketing/retailing/merchandising, and personnel management), COMMUNICATIONS AND THE ARTS (art history and appreciation, Chinese, communications, English, fine arts, French, German, Japanese, journalism, linguistics, music, performing arts, Russian, and Spanish), COMPUTER AND PHYSICAL SCIENCE (chemistry, computer science, information sciences and systems, mathematics, physics, and statistics), EDUCATION (elementary and music), ENGINEERING AND ENVIRONMENTAL DESIGN (computer engineering, electrical/electronics engineering, engineering and applied science, engineering physics, industrial engineering, mechanical engineering, and systems engineering), HEALTH PROFESSIONS (environmental health science, health science, industrial hygiene, medical laboratory science, nursing, physical therapy, and predentistry), SOCIAL SCIENCE (African American studies, anthropology, East Asian studies, economics, history, Latin American studies, philosophy, political science/government, public administration, Russian and Slavic studies, sociology, and South Asian studies). Physical sciences and biological sciences are the strongest academically. Arts and sciences, business, and nursing have the largest enrollments.

Required: To graduate, students must complete 124 credit hours for a B.A. (128 for a B.Mus. or a B.S. in environmental health), including 32 to 36 in the major. A minimum GPA of 2.0 is required. The core curriculum must include 1 course each in humanities, social science, natural science, language, mathematics/logic, international studies, and Western civilization; writing proficiency must be demonstrated as well.

Special: Special academic programs include internships, cooperative programs for most disciplines, and many work-study opportunities. There are organized programs for study abroad in Japan, France, England, and Austria; independent programs can be arranged. Oakland also offers a B.A.-B.S. degree in biology and economics, a general studies program, dual majors, and nondegree study. There is a freshman honors program on campus, as well as 12

national honor societies. Twenty-three departments have honors programs.

Faculty/Classroom: Seventy percent of faculty are male; 30%, female. Ninety-nine percent teach undergraduates, 100% do research, and 99% do both. No introductory courses are taught by graduate students. The average class size in an introductory lecture is 46; in a laboratory, 18; and in a regular course offering, 40.

Admissions: About 85% of the 1993–94 applicants were accepted. The ACT scores for the 1993–94 freshman class were as follows: 18% below 21, 31% between 21 and 23, 38% between 24 and 26, 8% between 27 and 28, and 5% above 28. About 48% of the current freshmen were in the top fifth of their class; 98% were in the top two fifths. There were 5 National Merit finalists and 35 semifinalists. About 40 freshmen graduated first in their class.

Requirements: A minimum GPA of 2.5 is required. The ACT is required. Admissions requirements include graduation from an accredited secondary school and completion of 18 Carnegie units, including 4 years of English, 2 years of history, and 3 years each of mathematics, science, and social studies; 2 years of foreign language and 1 semester of computer science are recommended as well. Music and dance majors must audition. AP and CLEP credits are accepted. Important factors used in the admissions decision are advanced placement or honor courses, leadership record, evidence of special talent, personality, intangible qualities, and recommendations by school officials.

Procedure: Freshmen are admitted to all sessions. Entrance exams should be taken during the spring of the junior year or early fall of the senior year. Applications should be filed by July 15 for fall entry and December 1 for winter entry, along with an application fee of $25. Notification is sent on a rolling basis.

Transfer: About 1150 transfer students enrolled in 1993–94. Applicants must have at least a 2.5 GPA; a higher GPA is required in some majors. A total of 36 credits out of 124 to 128 must be completed at Oakland.

Visiting: There are regularly scheduled orientations for prospective students, including a review of services, academic advising, and course registration. There are guides for informal visits and visitors may sit in on classes and stay overnight at the school. To arrange for a visit, contact the Admissions Office at (313) 370–3360.

Financial Aid: In 1993–94, 32% of all current freshmen and 20% of continuing students received some form of financial aid. About 28% of freshmen and 28% of continuing students received need-based aid. The average freshman award was $4500. Of that total, scholarships or need-based grants averaged $2600 ($8000 maximum); loans averaged $700 ($2625 maximum); and work contracts averaged $1200 ($2700 maximum). Twenty percent of undergraduate students work part-time. Average earnings from campus work for the school year are $1210. Oakland is a member of CSS. The FAFSA financial statement is required. The deadline for financial aid applications is March 1.

International Students: There are currently 117 international students enrolled. They must take the TOEFL or the University of Michigan Language Test and achieve a minimum score on the TOEFL of 550.

Computers: The college provides computer facilities for student use. There are 41 mid-level computers, including various DEC models. There are 200 terminals available, accessed via DAC and VAC stations. Computer networks all over the world may be accessed through the Internet system. All students may access the system. There are no time limits on using the system and no fees.

Graduates: In 1992–93, 1643 bachelor's degrees were awarded. The most popular majors among graduates were nursing (11%), psychology (9%), and communication (8%). Within an average freshman class, 35% graduate in 4 years, 40% in 5 years, and 50% in 6 years. Some 113 companies recruited on campus in 1992–93. In the 1992 graduating class, 87% all graduates had found employment within 6 months of graduation.

Admissions Contact: Admissions Advisor.

OLIVET COLLEGE
D-4

Olivet, MI 49076   (616) 749–7631; (800) 456–7189 (in-state)

Full-time: 434 men, 289 women	**Faculty:** 46; IIB, --$
Part-time: 18 men, 35 women	**Ph.D.s:** 48%
Graduate: none	**Student/Faculty:** 16 to 1
Year: semesters, summer session	**Tuition:** $10,500
Application Deadline: open	**Room & Board:** $3500
Freshman Class: 646 applied, 612 accepted, 239 enrolled	
ACT: 18	**COMPETITIVE**

Olivet College, founded in 1844, is a private liberal arts institution affiliated with the United Church of Christ and the Congregational Christian Church. The library contains 84,000 volumes, 2400 microform items, and 500 audiovisual forms, and subscribes to 600 periodicals. Special learning facilities include a learning resource center, art gallery, planetarium, and radio station. The 45-acre campus is in a ru-

ral area 30 miles south of Lansing. Including residence halls, there are 12 buildings on campus.

Student Life: About 96% of undergraduates are from Michigan. Students come from 5 states and 4 foreign countries. Ninety-eight percent are from public schools; 2% from private. Ninety-one percent are white. Eighteen percent drop out by the end of their first year; 42% remain to graduate.

Housing: A total of 628 students can be accommodated in college housing. College-sponsored living facilities include single-sex and coed dormitories, on-campus apartments, fraternity houses, and sorority houses. In addition there are honors houses. On-campus housing is guaranteed for all 4 years. Sixty-four percent of students live on campus. Alcohol is not permitted. All students may keep cars on campus.

Activities: About 19% of men belong to 3 local fraternities; about 19% of women belong to 3 local sororities. There are 36 groups on campus, including art, band, cheerleading, choir, chorale, chorus, computers, dance, drama, ethnic, honors, international, jazz band, literary magazine, marching band, musical theater, newspaper, orchestra, pep band, photography, radio and tv, religious, social, student government, and yearbook. Popular campus events include Homecoming, Founders Day, and Stand-up.

Sports: There are 10 intercollegiate sports for men and 8 for women, and 8 intramural sports for men and 7 for women. Athletic and recreation facilities include an athletic center, football field, and gymnasium.

Disabled Students: Twenty-five percent of the campus is accessible to disabled students. The following facilities are available: wheelchair ramps, elevators, special parking, and specially equipped rest rooms.

Services: In addition to many counseling and information services, tutoring is available in most subjects. In addition, there is remedial math, reading, and writing.

Campus Safety and Security: Campus safety and security measures include 24-hour foot and vehicle patrol, self-defense education, escort service, and emergency telephones. In addition, there are lighted pathways and sidewalks.

Programs of Study: Olivet awards the B.A. and B.Mus.Ed. degrees. Bachelor's degrees are awarded in BIOLOGICAL SCIENCE (biochemistry and biology/biological science), BUSINESS (business administration and management), COMMUNICATIONS AND THE ARTS (communications, English, fine arts, journalism, music, and speech/debate/rhetoric), COMPUTER AND PHYSICAL SCIENCE (chemistry, computer science, and mathematics), EDUCATION (foreign languages, health, music, and physical), SOCIAL SCIENCE (American studies, history, psychology, social studies, and sociology). Business administration and teacher education are the strongest academically. Business administration has the largest enrollment.

Required: To graduate, students must complete 120 semester hours, 36 to 60 in the major. Their minimum GPA must be 2.0; those seeking certification must maintain a minimum 2.5 GPA in all education courses and in all courses in their major and minor fields. Also required are 18 semester hours of core, 2 of creative arts experience, 3 of a laboratory science, and 3 of mathematics or another science course.

Special: Olivet offers internships, study abroad, and student-designed and dual majors. Credit for life experience, nondegree study, a general studies major, and a professional semester program are possible. Cooperative programs in engineering with Michigan State and Western Michigan universities are also available. There are 2 national honor societies on campus, including Phi Beta Kappa.

Faculty/Classroom: Sixty-three percent of faculty are male; 37%, female. All teach undergraduates. The average class size in an introductory lecture is 30; in a laboratory, 14; and in a regular course offering, 15.

Admissions: About 95% of the 1993–94 applicants were accepted. The ACT scores for the 1993–94 freshman class were as follows: 68% below 21, 19% between 21 and 23, 10% between 24 and 26, 2% between 27 and 28, and 1% above 28.

Requirements: A minimum GPA of 2.6 is required. The ACT or SAT I is required; the minimum score considered on the ACT is 13. Students must be graduates of an accredited secondary school, with a scholastic GPA of at least 2.6 and completion of college-preparatory courses. The GED is accepted. Individual consideration is given to applicants not meeting these criteria but demonstrating other potential. AP and CLEP credits are accepted. Important factors used in the admissions decision are advanced placement or honor courses, leadership record, parents or siblings attending the school, evidence of special talent, and personality, intangible qualities.

Procedure: Freshmen are admitted fall and spring. Application deadlines are open. Application fee is $25. Notification is sent on a rolling basis.

Transfer: About 75 transfer students enrolled in an earlier year. A total of 30 semester hours out of 120 must be completed at Olivet.

Visiting: There are regularly scheduled orientations for prospective students. There are guides for informal visits and visitors may sit in on classes and stay overnight at the school. To arrange for a visit, contact the Admissions Office at (800) 456–7189 (in-state) or (616) 749–7631.

Financial Aid: In an earlier year, 90% of all current freshmen and 90% of continuing students received some form of financial aid. Scholarships or need-based grants averaged $265 ($1500 maximum); loans averaged $2900 ($4000 maximum); and work contracts averaged $900 ($1500 maximum). Ninety-eight percent of undergraduate students work part-time. Olivet is a member of CSS. The FAF or FFS, and FAFSA are required. The deadline for financial aid applications is March 15.

International Students: There are currently 4 international students enrolled. They must take the TOEFL and achieve a minimum score of 500.

Computers: The college provides computer facilities for student use. The mainframe is a DEC PDP 11/45. There are also 22 PCs available. There are no time limits on using the system and no fees.

Graduates: In 1992–93, 139 bachelor's degrees were awarded. In the 1992 graduating class, 8% all graduates were enrolled in graduate school within 6 months of graduation; 78% had found employment.

Admissions Contact: Durk Dunham, Director of Transfer/Admissions.

SAGINAW VALLEY STATE UNIVERSITY D-4
University Center, MI 48710–0001 (517) 790–4200

Full-time: 1594 men, 1993 women	**Faculty:** 175; IIA, av$
Part-time: 829 men, 1266 women	**Ph.D.s:** 82%
Graduate: 215 men, 534 women	**Student/Faculty:** 20 to 1
Year: semesters, summer session	**Tuition:** $2984 ($5983)
Application Deadline: open	**Room & Board:** $3650
Freshman Class: 1549 applied, 1349 accepted, 687 enrolled	
ACT: 21	**LESS COMPETITIVE**

Saginaw Valley State University, founded in 1963, is a state-supported institution, offering undergraduate and graduate degrees in arts and behavioral sciences, business and management, education, nursing and allied health sciences, and science, engineering, and technology. There are 5 undergraduate and 4 graduate schools. In addition to regional accreditation, SVSU has baccalaureate program accreditation with ABET, CSWE, NCATE, and NLN. The library contains 200,729 volumes, 254,097 microform items, and 20,000 audiovisual forms, and subscribes to 6083 periodicals. Computerized library sources and services include interlibrary loans and database searching. Special learning facilities include a learning resource center, art gallery, and an observatory. The 782-acre campus is in a suburban area 5 miles north of Saginaw.

Student Life: About 99% of undergraduates are from Michigan. Students come from 6 states, 20 foreign countries, and Canada. Ninety-seven percent are from public schools. Eighty-nine percent are white. The average age of all undergraduates is 26.

Housing: A total of 646 students can be accommodated in college housing. College-sponsored living facilities include coed dormitories and on-campus apartments. On-campus housing is available on a first-come, first-served basis. Ninety percent of students commute. Alcohol is not permitted. All students may keep cars on campus.

Activities: There are no fraternities or sororities on campus. There are 50 groups on campus, including band, cheerleading, choir, chorale, computers, drama, drill team, ethnic, gay, honors, jazz band, literary magazine, marching band, newspaper, orchestra, pep band, photography, professional, religious, and student government. Popular campus events include Hispanic Heritage Month, Black History Month, Comedy Night, Valley Festival of Fine Arts, and Family Day.

Sports: There are 7 intercollegiate sports for men and 6 for women, and 6 intramural sports for men and 6 for women. Athletic and recreation facilities include a health and physical education complex with an Olympic-size pool, indoor track, and racquetball courts; tennis courts; intramural, baseball, and softball fields; archery; a fitness trail; a football stadium; a golf and tee range; and horseshoe pits.

Disabled Students: Ninety-nine percent of the campus is accessible to disabled students. The following facilities are available: wheelchair ramps, elevators, special parking, specially equipped rest rooms, special class scheduling, lowered drinking fountains, lowered telephones, and electronically opened doors, and special access to the library. All buildings are interconnected on the second floor, and special provisions have been made in dormitories.

Services: In addition to many counseling and information services, tutoring is available in every subject, including most 100- and 200-level classes. In addition, there is a reader service for the blind, and remedial math, reading, and writing.

Campus Safety and Security: Campus safety and security measures include escort service, informal discussions, emergency telephones, and lighted pathways and sidewalks. In addition, the SVSU

public safety department has commissioned police officers providing police services.

Programs of Study: SVSU awards the B.A., B.S., B.B.A., B.S.E.E., B.S.M.E., B.S.N., and B.S.W. degrees. Master's degrees are also awarded. Bachelor's degrees are awarded in BIOLOGICAL SCIENCE (biochemistry and biology/biological science), BUSINESS (accounting, banking and finance, business administration and management, business economics, and marketing/retailing/merchandising), COMMUNICATIONS AND THE ARTS (communications, design, dramatic arts, English, fine arts, French, music, and Spanish), COMPUTER AND PHYSICAL SCIENCE (chemistry, computer mathematics, computer science, mathematics, optics, physical chemistry, and physics), EDUCATION (art, elementary, foreign languages, music, and secondary), ENGINEERING AND ENVIRONMENTAL DESIGN (electrical/electronics engineering, industrial administration/management, and mechanical engineering), HEALTH PROFESSIONS (medical laboratory technology, nursing, occupational therapy, predentistry, and premedicine), SOCIAL SCIENCE (criminal justice, economics, history, political science/government, prelaw, psychology, public administration, social work, and sociology). Accounting, criminal justice, management, and elementary education have the largest enrollments.

Required: Students must complete a minimum of 124 credits, including 39 in general education courses, and maintain a minimum GPA of 2.0.

Special: Opportunities are provided for student-designed majors, work-study, co-op education, credit by examination, nondegree study, pass/fail options, and study abroad in Japan, China, Mexico, Poland, Austria, and England. There is a freshman honors program on campus, as well as 4 national honor societies.

Faculty/Classroom: Thirty-one percent of faculty are male; 69%, female. All teach undergraduates. No introductory courses are taught by graduate students. The average class size in an introductory lecture is 28; in a laboratory, 19; and in a regular course offering, 27.

Admissions: About 87% of the 1993–94 applicants were accepted. The ACT scores for the 1993–94 freshman class were as follows: 54% below 21, 27% between 21 and 23, 13% between 24 and 26, 3% between 27 and 28, and 2% above 28.

Requirements: A minimum GPA of 2.5 is required. The SAT I or ACT is required. In addition, graduation from an accredited secondary school or a GED is required. Applicants should submit records of successful completion of 4 years each of English and mathematics, 3 each of social science and science, 2 each of a foreign language and fine arts, and 1 course in computer literacy. Students should have maintained a minimum GPA of 2.5 in college-preparatory courses. AP and CLEP credits are accepted.

Procedure: Freshmen are admitted to all sessions. Application deadlines are open. Application fee is $25. Notification is sent on a rolling basis, within two weeks of receipt of application.

Transfer: About 660 transfer students enrolled in 1993–94. Transfer students with fewer than 31 credits from a previous college must submit high school and college transcripts. A minimum GPA of 2.0 is needed. An interview may be required. A total of 31 credits out of a minimum of 124 must be completed at SVSU.

Visiting: There are guides for informal visits and visitors may sit in on classes and stay overnight at the school. To arrange for a visit, contact the Office of Admissions at (517) 790-4200.

Financial Aid: In 1993–94, 64% of all current freshmen and 64% of continuing students received some form of financial aid. About 50% of freshmen and 50% of continuing students received need-based aid. Scholarships or need-based grants averaged $700 ($5000 maximum); loans averaged $2000 ($5500 maximum); and work contracts averaged $1800 ($2000 maximum). Sixteen percent of undergraduate students work part-time. Average earnings from campus work for the school year are $1800. The average financial indebtedness of the 1992–93 graduate was $8000. The FAF or FFS, and FAFSA are required. The deadline for financial aid applications is April 1.

International Students: There are currently 52 international students enrolled. They must take the TOEFL or the University of Michigan Language Test and achieve a minimum score on the TOEFL of 525.

Computers: The college provides computer facilities for student use. The mainframe is an IBM 9370 Model 60 and a DEC MicroVAX II. There are also 120 IBM XT and PS/2, Zenith, and Apple IIe Macintosh PCs available in student laboratories. All students may access the system. There are no time limits on using the system and no fees.

Graduates: The most popular majors among graduates were criminal justice (9%), elementary education (9%), and accounting (9%). Some 79 companies recruited on campus in 1992–93.

Admissions Contact: James Dwyer, Director of Admissions.

SAINT MARY'S COLLEGE
E-4
Orchard Lake, MI 48324
(810) 683-0507

Full-time: 65 men, 84 women	Faculty: 18
Part-time: 62 men, 80 women	Ph.D.s: 85%
Graduate: none	Student/Faculty: 8 to 1
Year: semesters, summer session	Tuition: $5250
Application Deadline: September 1	Room & Board: $3100
Freshman Class: 110 applied, 76 accepted, 50 enrolled	
SAT I or ACT: required	COMPETITIVE

Saint Mary's College, founded in 1885, is an independent, coeducational institution affiliated with the Roman Catholic Church. The library contains 60,000 volumes and 6199 microform items, and subscribes to 450 periodicals. Special learning facilities include a learning resource center and art gallery. The 122-acre campus is in a suburban area 17 miles from Detroit. Including residence halls, there are 13 buildings on campus.

Student Life: About 95% of undergraduates are from Michigan. Students come from 11 states, 7 foreign countries, and Canada. Seventy percent are from public schools; 30% from private. Ninety-one percent are white. Sixty percent are Catholic; 34% Protestant. The average age of freshmen is 19; all undergraduates, 29. Thirty-one percent drop out by the end of their first year; 20% remain to graduate.

Housing: A total of 150 students can be accommodated in college housing. College-sponsored living facilities include single-sex dormitories. On-campus housing is guaranteed for all 4 years. Eighty-five percent of students commute. Alcohol is not permitted. All students may keep cars on campus.

Activities: About 15% of men belong to fraternities; about 20% of women belong to 2 national sororities. There are a number of groups on campus, including chorale, dance, drama, ethnic, honors, literary magazine, newspaper, religious, social service, student government, and yearbook.

Sports: There are 5 intramural sports for men and 5 for women. Athletic and recreation facilities include a stadium, 2 gymnasiums, a weight room, an outdoor track, and baseball, football, and soccer fields.

Disabled Students: Eighty percent of the campus is accessible to disabled students. The following facilities are available: wheelchair ramps, special parking, and specially equipped rest rooms.

Services: In addition to many counseling and information services, tutoring is available in most subjects. In addition, there is remedial math, reading, and writing.

Campus Safety and Security: Campus safety and security measures include informal discussions, pamphlets, posters, and films, emergency telephones, and lighted pathways and sidewalks.

Programs of Study: Saint Mary's awards the B.A., B.S., B.G.S., and B.H.S. degrees. Bachelor's degrees are awarded in BIOLOGICAL SCIENCE (biology/biological science), BUSINESS (business administration and management), COMMUNICATIONS AND THE ARTS (communications, English, and modern language), COMPUTER AND PHYSICAL SCIENCE (chemistry, computer science, and radiological technology), EDUCATION (education), HEALTH PROFESSIONS (health science and premedicine), SOCIAL SCIENCE (human services, philosophy, prelaw, psychology, religious education, social science, sociology, and theological studies). Premedicine, communication arts, theology, and business administration are the strongest academically. Business, communication arts, psychology, and human services have the largest enrollments.

Required: To graduate, students must complete 120 credit hours, with 30 to 36 hours in the major and a minimum GPA of 2.0. All students must take 60 hours of core curriculum courses in the following areas: communications, ultimate meaning and value, interpretation and analysis of the arts, historical consciousness, social science, natural science, and mathematics. The college requires that students demonstrate writing proficiency.

Special: The college offers co-op programs with colleges in the Detroit Area Consortium of Catholic Colleges. Internships, study abroad, dual majors, a general studies degree, directed study, and nondegree study are available. A program in Polish studies is offered at the school's Center of Polish Studies and Culture.

Faculty/Classroom: Forty percent of faculty are male; 60%, female. All teach undergraduates.

Admissions: About 69% of the 1993–94 applicants were accepted.

Requirements: A minimum GPA of 2.5 is required. The SAT I or the ACT is required. The required minimum composite scores are 900 on the SAT I and 19 on the ACT. Applicants must be graduates of an accredited secondary school. The GED is accepted. Students must complete 16 high school academic credits. CLEP credit is accepted. Important factors used in the admissions decision are leadership record, evidence of special talent, recommendations by school officials, personality, intangible qualities, and advanced placement or honor courses.

Procedure: Applications should be filed by September 1 for fall entry, December 15 for spring entry, and May 1 for summer entry, along with an application fee of $20. Notification is sent on a rolling basis. There are early decision and early admissions plans.

Transfer: Applicant must have a minimum GPA of 2.5. The ACT is required unless the student is classified as a nontraditional student or has 24 or more semester hours of college credit. A total of 30 credits out of 120 must be completed at Saint Mary's.

Visiting: There are regularly scheduled orientations for prospective students. There are guides for informal visits and visitors may sit in on classes and stay overnight at the school. To arrange for a visit, contact the Office of Enrollment Services at (810) 683-0508.

Financial Aid: In 1993–94, 55% of all current freshmen received some form of financial aid. About 55% of freshmen received need-based aid. The average freshman award was $3200. Saint Mary's is a member of CSS. The FAF and the college's own financial statement are required. The deadline for financial aid applications is January 15.

International Students: International students must take the TOEFL or the University of Michigan Language Test and achieve a minimum score on the TOEFL of 500.

Computers: The college provides computer facilities for student use. The mainframe is an IBM-36. The college makes available a substantial number of IBM PCs for students. There are no time limits on using the system and no fees.

Graduates: In 1992–93, 38 bachelor's degrees were awarded. The most popular majors among graduates were business administration (20%), psychology (15%), and communication arts (11%).

Admissions Contact: Darrell Brockway, Dean of Enrollment Services.

SIENA HEIGHTS COLLEGE
Adrian, MI 49221

E-5

(517) 263-0731, ext. 214
(800) 521-0009 (in-state)

Full-time: 284 men, 402 women	Faculty: 70; IIB, --$
Part-time: 92 men, 176 women	Ph.D.s: 60%
Graduate: 40 men, 117 women	Student/Faculty: 10 to 1
Year: semesters, summer session	Tuition: $8820
Application Deadline: August 15	Room & Board: $3700
Freshman Class: 465 applied, 420 accepted, 188 enrolled	
SAT I or ACT: required	**COMPETITIVE**

Siena Heights College, founded in 1919, is a private liberal arts institution affiliated with the Roman Catholic Church. In addition to regional accreditation, Siena Heights has baccalaureate program accreditation with NASAD. The library contains 112,049 volumes, 24,214 microform items, and 4730 audiovisual forms, and subscribes to 451 periodicals. Computerized library sources and services include the card catalog, interlibrary loans, and database searching. Special learning facilities include a learning resource center and an art gallery. The 140-acre campus is in a small town 75 miles southwest of Detroit. Including residence halls, there are 11 buildings on campus.

Student Life: About 85% of undergraduates are from Michigan. Students come from 15 states, 10 foreign countries, and Canada. Eighty percent are from public schools; 20% from private. Some 88% are white. The average age of freshmen is 18; all undergraduates, 25. Thirty-two percent drop out by the end of their first year.

Housing: A total of 450 students can be accommodated in college housing. College-sponsored living facilities include coed dormitories. On-campus housing is available on a first-come, first-served basis and is available on a lottery system for upperclassmen. About 50% of students commute. Alcohol is not permitted. All students may keep cars on campus.

Activities: About 5% of men belong to fraternities; about 5% of women belong to sororities. There are 30 groups on campus, including art, cheerleading, choir, chorale, chorus, computers, drama, ethnic, international, jazz band, literary magazine, newspaper, religious, social, and student government. Popular campus events include Parents Weekend, Alumni Weekend, International Dinner, athletic banquets, Madrigal Dinner, chorale concerts, Torch Night, and Fall Fling/Spring Fest.

Sports: There are 8 intercollegiate sports for men and 6 for women, and 6 intramural sports each for men and women. Athletic and recreation facilities include a 57,000-square-foot student activity center, which houses 1 volleyball, 2 basketball, and 5 tennis courts, a 200-meter track, a baseball batting cage, training and exercise rooms, ballrooms, and a union. The indoor gymnasium seats 4000.

Disabled Students: Twenty percent of the campus is accessible to disabled students. Elevators and special parking are available for these students.

Services: In addition to many counseling and information services, tutoring is available in most subjects.

Campus Safety and Security: Campus safety and security measures include 24-hour foot and vehicle patrol, self-defense education, informal discussions, pamphlets, posters, and films. In addition, there are emergency telephones and lighted pathways and sidewalks.

Programs of Study: Siena Heights awards the B.A., B.S., B.A.S., and B.F.A. degrees. Associate and master's degrees also are awarded. Bachelor's degrees are awarded in BIOLOGICAL SCIENCE (biology/biological science), BUSINESS (accounting, business administration and management, fashion merchandising, and hotel/motel and restaurant management), COMMUNICATIONS AND THE ARTS (communications, English, fine arts, music, and Spanish), COMPUTER AND PHYSICAL SCIENCE (chemistry, information sciences and systems, mathematics, and natural sciences), EDUCATION (art, business, elementary, and music), HEALTH PROFESSIONS (premedicine), SOCIAL SCIENCE (American studies, criminal justice, history, humanities, liberal arts/general studies, philosophy, psychology, public administration, religion, social science, and sociology). Art, business, biology, mathematics, and education are the strongest academically. Business, art, and social services have the largest enrollments.

Required: In order to graduate, students must complete 120 semester hours, including 30 hours in the major, and maintain at least a 2.0 GPA. A core curriculum of 33 to 35 semester hours is required, including 2 courses in English composition and 1 each in literature, mathematics, science, fine/performing arts, social science, history, philosophy, and religious studies. A seminar in education is also required.

Special: Special academic programs include 2–2 engineering co-op programs with the University of Detroit and the University of Michigan, a 2–2 business administration program at Lake Michigan College, internships in the major, study abroad in Siena, Italy for art students, and on- and off-campus work study. Also offered are dual, inverted, and student-designed majors, B.A.-B.S. degrees, and a general studies degree. Credit for life, military, and work experience and nondegree study are possible. Three-year bachelor's degrees may be earned, and a directed student-teaching program is available for education majors. Flexible learning formats include weekend and evening courses, two-month class cycles, and extended weekend course for out-of-town and out-of-state students. There is a freshman honors program on campus

Faculty/Classroom: Forty-three percent of faculty are male; 57%, female. No introductory courses are taught by graduate students. The average class size in a regular course offering is 15.

Admissions: About 90% of the 1993–94 applicants were accepted. The ACT scores for the 1993–94 freshman class were as follows: 53% below 21, 28% between 21 and 23, 12% between 24 and 26, 5% between 27 and 28, and 2% above 28. Two freshmen graduated first in their class.

Requirements: A minimum GPA of 2.3 is required. The SAT I or ACT is required, with a minimum score of 17 on the ACT. Admissions requirements include graduation from an accredited secondary school. The GED is accepted. An essay is required, and an interview is recommended. AP and CLEP credits are accepted. Important factors used in the admissions decision are recommendations by school officials, parents or siblings attending the school, recommendations by alumni, advanced placement or honor courses, and extracurricular activities record.

Procedure: Freshmen are admitted to all sessions. SAT I or ACT scores should be available when the application is filed. Comprehensive tests are also taken at orientation. Applications should be filed by August 15 for fall entry, December 1 for winter entry, and May 1 for summer entry, along with an application fee of $15. Notification is sent on a rolling basis. There is a deferred admissions plan.

Transfer: About 50 transfer students enrolled in a recent year. Applicants must have a minimum 2.0 GPA. High school and college transcripts must be submitted. A total of 30 credits out of 120 must be completed at Siena Heights.

Visiting: There are regularly scheduled orientations for prospective students. There are guides for informal visits and visitors may sit in on classes and stay overnight at the school. To arrange for a visit, contact the Admissions Office at (517) 263-0731, ext. 214.

Financial Aid: In a recent year, 84% of all current freshmen and 86% of continuing students received some form of financial aid. About 77% of students received need-based aid. The average freshman award that year was $3745. Of that total, scholarships or need-based grants averaged $1890 ($3100 maximum); loans averaged $1400 ($2625 maximum); and work contracts averaged $1260 ($1275 maximum). Twenty percent of undergraduate students work part-time. The average financial indebtedness of a recent graduate was $5650. Siena Heights is a member of CSS. The FAF or FFS is required. The deadline for financial aid applications is August 1.

International Students: There are currently 30 international students enrolled. They must take the TOEFL and achieve a minimum score of 500. The student must also take the SAT I or the ACT.

Computers: The college provides computer facilities for student use. The mainframe is an IBM-RS/6000 320H. The microcomputer laboratory has Apple Macintosh and IBM computers for student use. All students may access the system. There are no time limits on use. The fees are $6 per semester hour.

Graduates: In a recent year, 393 bachelor's degrees were awarded. The most popular majors among graduates were allied health electronics (38%), business administration (24%), and general studies (11%). Within an average freshman class, 10% graduate in 3 years, 30% in 4 years, and 40% in 5 years. Some 30 companies recruited on campus in a recent year.

Admissions Contact: Richard J. De Loof, Director of Admissions.

SPRING ARBOR COLLEGE
D-5

Spring Arbor, MI 49283

(517) 750–1200, ext. 1470
(800) 968–0011 (out-of-state)

Full-time: 309 men, 425 women	Faculty: 60; IIB, --$
Part-time: 49 men, 136 women	Ph.D.s: 42%
Graduate: none	Student/Faculty: 12 to 1
Year: 4-1-4, summer session	Tuition: $8706
Application Deadline: open	Room & Board: $3550
Freshman Class: 401 applied, 361 accepted, 181 enrolled	
SAT I or ACT: required	**COMPETITIVE**

Spring Arbor College, founded in 1873, is a private, coeducational institution affiliated with the Free Methodist Church. It offers undergraduate programs in fine arts, humanities, philosophy, religion, natural science, social science, and education. In addition to regional accreditation, Spring Arbor has baccalaureate program accreditation with CSWE and NCATE. The library contains 84,597 volumes, 58,303 microform items, and 3918 audiovisual forms, and subscribes to 1252 periodicals. Computerized library sources and services include the card catalog, interlibrary loans, and database searching. Special learning facilities include a learning resource center, radio station, and tv production facilities and equipment. The 70-acre campus is in a small town 8 miles west of Jackson. Including residence halls, there are 27 buildings on campus.

Student Life: About 89% of undergraduates are from Michigan. Students come from 16 states, 9 foreign countries, and Canada. Eighty-three percent are from public schools; 17% from private. Ninety-three percent are white. Sixty-two percent are Protestant; 24% claim no religious affiliation. Twenty-seven percent drop out by the end of their first year; 37% remain to graduate.

Housing: A total of 483 students can be accommodated in college housing. College-sponsored living facilities include single-sex dormitories and married-student housing. On-campus housing is guaranteed for all 4 years. Fifty-one percent of students live on campus; of those, 65% remain on campus on weekends. Alcohol is not permitted. All students may keep cars on campus.

Activities: There are no fraternities or sororities on campus. There are 21 groups on campus, including band, cheerleading, choir, chorale, drama, ethnic, honors, international, jazz band, newspaper, pep band, radio and tv, religious, social, social service, student government, and yearbook. Popular campus events include Arbor Games, Midnight Breakfast, Spring Banquet, and the Lip Sync Contest.

Sports: There are 7 intercollegiate sports for men and 7 for women, and 7 intramural sports for men and 5 for women. Athletic and recreation facilities include a 500-seat stadium, a 2600-seat gymnasium, all-weather and indoor tracks, tennis courts, a basketball court, an Olympic-size pool, a weight-training room with exercise equipment, and baseball and soccer fields.

Disabled Students: Seventy-five percent of the campus is accessible to disabled students. The following facilities are available: wheelchair ramps, elevators, special parking, specially equipped rest rooms, lowered drinking fountains, and lowered telephones.

Services: Remedial math, reading, and writing are available.

Campus Safety and Security: Campus safety and security measures include self-defense education, escort service, informal discussions, and lighted pathways and sidewalks. In addition, there is a night security guard.

Programs of Study: Spring Arbor awards the B.A. and B.S.W. degrees. Associate degrees are also awarded. Bachelor's degrees are awarded in BIOLOGICAL SCIENCE (biochemistry and biology/biological science), BUSINESS (accounting, business administration and management, and business economics), COMMUNICATIONS AND THE ARTS (art, communications, English, fine arts, French, music, Spanish, and speech/debate/rhetoric), COMPUTER AND PHYSICAL SCIENCE (chemistry, computer science, mathematics, and physics), SOCIAL SCIENCE (history, ministries, philosophy, physical fitness/movement, psychology, religion, religious music, social science, social work, and sociology). Communications, natural sciences, art, and teacher education are the strongest academically. Education, business, exercise and sport science, psychology, biology, and communications have the largest enrollments.

Required: Students must complete 4 Christian perspective courses, including cross-cultural studies, writing skills, speech, and physical fitness. Liberal arts requirements are in fine arts, humanities, natural science/mathematics, philosophy/religion, and social science. To graduate, at least 124 semester hours, 30 to 48 in the major, with a minimum GPA of 2.0 overall and 2.2 in the major are needed.

Special: Each student participates in a cross-cultural experience, which includes travel to a foreign country or to an urban center in the United States. Additional study-abroad opportunities can be arranged. A Washington semester is available through the American Studies Program. The college also offers cross-registration with the Christian College Coalition, work-study, dual and student-designed majors, pass/fail options, and nondegree study. Alternative programs for adult learners provide field-based study and assign credit for life experience; an accelerated B.A. program for such students is also offered. There is one national honor society on campus. Ten departments have honors programs.

Faculty/Classroom: Sixty-four percent of faculty are male; 36%, female. The average class size in a regular course offering is 15.

Admissions: About 90% of the 1993–94 applicants were accepted. The ACT scores for the 1993–94 freshman class were as follows: 49% below 21, 24% between 21 and 23, 16% between 24 and 26, 5% between 27 and 28, and 6% above 28. About 29% of the current freshmen were in the top fifth of their class; 56% were in the top two fifths. There were 5 National Merit finalists. Eight freshmen graduated first in their class.

Requirements: A minimum GPA of 2.6 is required. The SAT I or ACT is required. Minimum composite scores recommended are 710 on the SAT I (360 verbal and 350 mathematics) or 20 on the ACT. Applicants must be graduates of accredited secondary schools or have a GED. An interview is advised. AP and CLEP credits are accepted. Important factors used in the admissions decision are personality, intangible qualities, parents or siblings attending the school, leadership record, extracurricular activities record, and advanced placement or honor courses.

Procedure: Freshmen are admitted to all sessions. Entrance exams should be taken in spring of the junior year or fall of the senior year. Application deadlines are open. The application fee is $15. Notification is sent on a rolling basis. There are early admissions and deferred admissions plans.

Transfer: About 70 transfer students enrolled in 1993–94. Applicants should have a minimum GPA of 2.0 and are encouraged to arrange for an interview. A total of 30 credits out of 124 must be completed at Spring Arbor.

Visiting: There are regularly scheduled orientations for prospective students, including a tour, class and chapel attendance, lunch, and attending a student panel discussion. There are guides for informal visits and visitors may sit in on classes and stay overnight at the school. To arrange for a visit, contact the Admissions Office at (800) 968–0011.

Financial Aid: In 1993–94, 90% of all current freshmen and 90% of continuing students received some form of financial aid. About 90% of freshmen and 90% of continuing students received need-based aid. Scholarships or need-based grants averaged $4509 ($6200 maximum); loans averaged $6190 ($8500 maximum); and work contracts averaged $515 ($1850 maximum). Twenty-nine percent of undergraduate students work part-time. Average earnings from campus work for the school year are $810. Spring Arbor is a member of CSS. The FAFSA financial statement is required.

International Students: There are currently 34 international students enrolled. The school actively recruits these students. They must take the TOEFL or the University of Michigan Language Test and achieve a minimum score on the TOEFL of 525.

Computers: The college provides computer facilities for student use. Computers in the Learning Center may be accessed by anyone, those in the science building by students enrolled in computer or mathematics classes, and those in the student center by students registered with a particular professor to use the equipment. There are no time limits on using the system. The fees are $20.

Graduates: In a recent year, 135 bachelor's degrees were awarded. The most popular majors among graduates were business administration (16%), elementary education (14%), and psychology (10%). Within an average freshman class, 28% graduate in 4 years and 10% in 5 years. In a recent graduating class, 4% of the men and 5% of the women were enrolled in graduate school within 6 months of graduation; 34% of the men and 48% of the women had found employment.

Admissions Contact: Steve W. Schippers, Director of Admissions.

UNIVERSITY OF DETROIT MERCY

E-5

Detroit, MI 48219–0900 (313) 993–1245

Full-time: 959 men, 1190 women
Part-time: 558 men, 1659 women
Graduate: 1638 men, 1459 women
Year: semesters, summer session
Application Deadline: April 1
Freshman Class: 1230 applied, 913 accepted, 423 enrolled
SAT I Verbal/Math: 440/510

Faculty: 214
Ph.D.s: 81%
Student/Faculty: 10 to 1
Tuition: $10,600
Room & Board: $4120

ACT: 22 **COMPETITIVE**

University of Detroit Mercy, founded in 1877, is a private, independent coeducational institution affiliated with the Jesuits and Sisters of Mercy. It offers undergraduate programs in liberal arts, education and human services, business administration, engineering and science, architecture, and nursing and health sciences. There are 8 undergraduate and 5 graduate schools. In addition to regional accreditation, U of DM has baccalaureate program accreditation with AACSB, ABET, ADA, CSWE, NAAB, and NLN. The 4 libraries contain 784,696 volumes, 735,630 microform items, and 12,203 audiovisual forms, and subscribe to 5355 periodicals. Special learning facilities include a learning resource center and radio station. The 70-acre campus is in an urban area 7 miles north of downtown Detroit. Including residence halls, there are 43 buildings on campus.

Student Life: About 93% of undergraduates are from Michigan. Students come from 24 states, 27 foreign countries, and Canada. Fifty-two percent are white; 41% African American. Thirty percent are a variety of denominations and religions; 30% Catholic; 24% claim no religious affiliation; 16% Protestant. The average age of freshmen is 18; all undergraduates, 29. Nineteen percent drop out by the end of their first year; 55% remain to graduate.

Housing: A total of 1,000 students can be accommodated in college housing. College-sponsored living facilities include coed dormitories and married-student housing. In addition, there is a freshman residence program. On-campus housing is guaranteed for all 4 years and is available on a first-come, first-served basis. Eighty-six percent of students commute. All students may keep cars on campus.

Activities: About 12% of men belong to 3 national fraternities; about 12% of women belong to 3 national sororities. There are 60 groups on campus, including cheerleading, chorale, computers, drama, ethnic, honors, international, literary magazine, newspaper, pep band, political, professional, radio and tv, religious, social, social service, student government, and yearbook. Popular campus events include Titan Fest, Homecoming, Engineering Week, and Architecture Week.

Sports: There are 9 intercollegiate sports for men and 7 for women, and 11 intramural sports for men and 11 for women. Athletic and recreation facilities include soccer, softball, and baseball fields, a fitness center, Calahan Hall, and a game room in the Student Union.

Disabled Students: Fifty percent of the campus is accessible to disabled students. The following facilities are available: wheelchair ramps, elevators, special parking, and special class scheduling.

Services: In addition to many counseling and information services, tutoring is available in some subjects, including all freshman courses and many other courses. There is also remedial math, reading, and writing.

Campus Safety and Security: Campus safety and security measures include 24-hour foot and vehicle patrol, self-defense education, escort service, and informal discussions. In addition, there are pamphlets, posters, and films, emergency telephones, and lighted pathways and sidewalks.

Programs of Study: U of DM awards the B.A., B.S., B.Arch., B.B.A., B.C.E., B.Ch.E., B.E.E., B.En., B.F.A., B.M.E., B.S.Ed., B.S.N., and B.S.W. degrees. Associate, master's, and doctoral degrees also are awarded. Bachelor's degrees are awarded in BIOLOGICAL SCIENCE (biochemistry and biology/biological science), BUSINESS (accounting, banking and finance, business administration and management, and business economics), COMMUNICATIONS AND THE ARTS (communications, dramatic arts, English, journalism, and languages), COMPUTER AND PHYSICAL SCIENCE (chemistry, computer science, information sciences and systems, mathematics, and polymer science), EDUCATION (art, business, early childhood, elementary, guidance, health, middle school, music, science, secondary, and special), ENGINEERING AND ENVIRONMENTAL DESIGN (architectural engineering, chemical engineering, civil engineering, electrical/electronics engineering, engineering, mechanical engineering, and plastics technology), HEALTH PROFESSIONS (nursing, predentistry, and premedicine), SOCIAL SCIENCE (criminal justice, economics, history, international relations, philosophy, political science/government, prelaw, psychology, public administration, religion, social work, and sociology). Engineering, nursing, and business administration are the strongest academically. Business administration, nursing, mechanical engineering, and health services administration have the largest enrollments.

Required: Students must successfully complete at least 126 credit hours, including a core curriculum, and maintain a minimum GPA of 2.0. Required courses include English composition, religion, philosophy, and speech fundamentals.

Special: Cooperative education is mandatory for engineering and architecture majors and is optional for others. Cross-registration is available with a consortium of Catholic colleges in the Detroit area. There are internships, and a B.A.-B.S. degree is available for mathematics, chemistry, and biology majors. An accelerated 6-year degree program in dentistry is provided. Study abroad is available in England, Italy, Poland, Israel, and China. Academic exploration courses are provided to help students who are undecided about a future vocation. There is a freshman honors program on campus, as well as 5 national honor societies. The university's honor program is interdepartmental.

Faculty/Classroom: Sixty-six percent of faculty are male; 34%, female. Seventy-three percent both teach and do research. Graduate students teach 4% of introductory courses. The average class size in an introductory lecture is 27 and in a regular course offering, 26.

Admissions: About 74% of the 1993–94 applicants were accepted. The SAT scores for the 1993–94 freshman class were as follows: Verbal—72% below 500, 22% between 500 and 599, and 7% between 600 and 700; Math—47% below 500, 27% between 500 and 599, and 26% between 600 and 700. The ACT scores were 45% below 21, 17% between 21 and 23, 22% between 24 and 26, 10% between 27 and 28, and 7% above 28. About 43% of the current freshmen were in the top fifth of their class; 66% were in the top two fifths. Six freshmen graduated first in their class.

Requirements: A minimum GPA of 2.5 is required. The SAT I or ACT is required. Graduation from an accredited secondary school is required; a GED will be accepted. Students must submit 16 academic credits, which should include, as a minimum, 4 units of English, 2 of mathematics, 2 of history or social studies, and 1 of natural science. Remaining credits should be distributed in a foreign language, music, art, speech, and other college preparatory electives. An interview is recommended. AP and CLEP credits are accepted.

Procedure: Freshmen are admitted to all sessions. Entrance exams should be taken during the junior or senior year. Applications should be filed by April 1 for fall entry and December 1 for winter entry, along with an application fee of $25. Notification is sent on a rolling basis. There is an early admissions plan.

Transfer: About 550 transfer students enrolled in 1993–94. Transfer applicants with fewer than 24 semester hours of credit at an accredited institution must submit SAT I or ACT scores and have maintained a minimum GPA of 2.0. If the student is over 23 years of age, the SAT I/ACT scores need not be submitted. A total of 32 credits out of 126 must be completed at U of DM.

Visiting: There are regularly scheduled orientations for prospective students, including a look at student life, testing and advising, and registration. There are guides for informal visits and visitors may sit in on classes and stay overnight at the school. To arrange for a visit, contact the Admissions Office at (313) 993–1245.

Financial Aid: In 1993–94, 85% of all current freshmen and 70% of continuing students received some form of financial aid. About 77% of freshmen and 55% of continuing students received need-based aid. The average freshman award was $12,225. Of that total, scholarships or need-based grants averaged $8200 ($11,100 maximum); loans averaged $2025 ($4425 maximum); and work contracts averaged $2000. Twenty-five percent of undergraduate students work part-time. Average earnings from campus work for the school year are $2000. The average financial indebtedness of the 1992–93 graduate was $8000. U of DM is a member of CSS.

International Students: There are currently 292 international students enrolled. The school actively recruits these students. They must take the college's own test.

Computers: The college provides computer facilities for student use. The mainframe is a Unisys A3K. Microcomputers are available throughout the campus. All students may access the system. There are no time limits on using the system. The fees are $15 per credit hour to students registered in computer courses.

Graduates: In 1992–93, 769 bachelor's degrees were awarded. The most popular majors among graduates were health sciences (25%), business (20%), and engineering (9%). Within an average freshman class, 4% graduate in 3 years, 32% in 4 years, 46% in 5 years, and 51% in 6 years.

Admissions Contact: Dr. Robert Johnson, Dean, Enrollment Management.

UNIVERSITY OF MICHIGAN

The University of Michigan, established in 1817, is a private system in Michigan. It is governed by a board of regents, whose chief administrator is president. The primary goal of the system is to offer high-quality education commensurate with the diverse components of a large state supported university. Four-year campus are separate enti-

ties with a high degree of autonomy. Profiles of the 4-year campuses are included in this chapter in alphabetical order with other Michigan schools.

UNIVERSITY OF MICHIGAN
ANN ARBOR
E-5

Ann Arbor, MI 48109 (313) 764-7433

Full-time: 11,637 men, 10,408 women	Faculty: 2713; I, +$
Part-time: 682 men, 657 women	Ph.D.s: 95%
Graduate: 7887 men, 5574 women	Student/Faculty: 8 to 1
Year: trimesters, summer session	Tuition: $4879 ($15,145)
Application Deadline: February 1	Room & Board: $4549
Freshman Class: 19,152 applied, 12,940 accepted, 4893 enrolled	
SAT I or ACT: required	HIGHLY COMPETITIVE +

The University of Michigan/Ann Arbor, founded in 1817, is the main campus of the University of Michigan. The public, coeducational institution offers undergraduate programs in the arts and sciences, architecture, business administration, education, engineering, fine arts, natural resources, nursing, professional studies, and military training. There are 12 undergraduate and 18 graduate schools. In addition to regional accreditation, UM has baccalaureate program accreditation with AACSB, ABET, ACEJMC, ACPE, ADA, ASLA, CSWE, NAAB, NASM, NCATE, NLN, and SAF. The 23 libraries contain 6,527,636 volumes, 4,905,227 microform items, and 29,612 audiovisual forms, and subscribe to 70,691 periodicals. Computerized library sources and services include the card catalog, interlibrary loans, and database searching. Special learning facilities include a learning resource center, art gallery, natural history museum, planetarium, radio station, and archaeology museum, botanical gardens, and 2 historical museums. The 2665-acre campus is in a suburban area 50 miles west of Detroit. Including residence halls, there are 203 buildings on campus.

Student Life: About 69% of undergraduates are from Michigan. Students come from 50 states, 68 foreign countries, and Canada. Eighty percent are from public schools; 11% from private. Seventy-five percent are white; 10% Asian American. The average age of freshmen is 18.2; all undergraduates, 19.9. Six percent drop out by the end of their first year; 85% remain to graduate.

Housing: A total of 11,592 students can be accommodated in college housing. College-sponsored living facilities include single-sex and coed dormitories, on-campus apartments, married-student housing, fraternity houses, and sorority houses. In addition there are honors houses, language houses, and special interest houses. On-campus housing is guaranteed for the freshman year only, and is available on a lottery system for upperclassmen. Eighty percent of students live on campus; of those, 95% remain on campus on weekends. All students may keep cars on campus.

Activities: About 25% of men belong to 1 local and 42 national fraternities; about 25% of women belong to 1 local and 24 national sororities. There are more than 400 groups on campus, including art, band, cheerleading, chess, choir, chorale, chorus, computers, dance, drama, ethnic, film, gay, honors, international, jazz band, literary magazine, marching band, musical theater, newspaper, opera, orchestra, pep band, photography, political, professional, radio and tv, religious, social, social service, student government, symphony, and yearbook. Popular campus events include Martin Luther King Day, Native American Powwow, and a Holocaust conference.

Sports: There are 11 intercollegiate sports for men and 10 for women, and 34 intramural sports for men and 34 for women. Athletic and recreation facilities include a 101,107-seat stadium, a 1000-seat gymnasium, an indoor track and tennis complex, an indoor practice center, 3 recreational buildings, 2 golf courses, a natatorium and separate swimming pool, an ice arena, and several other athletic arenas, the largest of which seats 13,000.

Disabled Students: Seventy-five percent of the campus is accessible to disabled students. The following facilities are available: wheelchair ramps, elevators, special parking, specially equipped rest rooms, special class scheduling, lowered drinking fountains, lowered telephones, para-transit service, specially equipped vans, talking calculators, telecommunication devices for the deaf, and an adaptive technology computing site that includes a high-speed scanner, voice input and voice output, braille display and large-print screens, and a braille printer.

Services: In addition to many counseling and information services, tutoring is available in some subjects, including introductory English and mathematics. In addition, there is a reader service for the blind.

Campus Safety and Security: Campus safety and security measures include 24-hour foot and vehicle patrol, escort service, shuttle buses, and informal discussions. In addition, there are pamphlets, posters, and films, emergency telephones, lighted pathways and sidewalks, and a night-owl bus service, and officer bicycle patrols.

Programs of Study: UM awards the A.B., B.S., B.A.Ed., B.Bus.Admin., B.F.A., B.Gen.Studies, B.Mus., B.Mus.Arts., B.S.Chem., B.S.Dent.Hyg., B.S.Ed., B.S.Eng., B.S.Med.Chem., B.S.Nat.Resources, B.S.Nursing, and B.S.Pharm. degrees. Master's and doctoral degrees also are awarded. Bachelor's degrees are awarded in AGRICULTURE (fishing and fisheries, forestry and related sciences, and natural resource management), BIOLOGICAL SCIENCE (biology/biological science, biophysics, botany, cell biology, microbiology, nutrition, wildlife biology, and zoology), BUSINESS (business administration and management, recreation and leisure services, and sports management), COMMUNICATIONS AND THE ARTS (applied music Arabic, art history and appreciation, ceramic art and design, Chinese, communications, comparative literature, creative writing, dance, design, dramatic arts, English, film arts, French, German, graphic design, Greek, Hebrew, industrial design, Italian, Japanese, jazz, journalism, Latin, linguistics, literature, media arts, metal/jewelry, music, music history and appreciation, music theory and composition, musical theater, painting, percussion, performing arts, photography, piano/organ, printmaking, romance languages, Russian, sculpture, Spanish, speech/debate/rhetoric, strings, voice, and winds), COMPUTER AND PHYSICAL SCIENCE (applied mathematics, astronomy, atmospheric sciences and meteorology, chemistry, computer science, geology, mathematics, oceanography, physics, and statistics), EDUCATION (art, elementary, environmental, music, physical, secondary, and special), ENGINEERING AND ENVIRONMENTAL DESIGN (aeronautical engineering, architecture, chemical engineering, civil engineering, computer engineering, electrical/electronics engineering, engineering, engineering and applied science, engineering physics, environmental design, environmental engineering, environmental science, industrial engineering, interior design, landscape architecture/design, mechanical engineering, naval architecture and marine engineering, nuclear engineering, and textile technology), HEALTH PROFESSIONS (biomedical science, dental hygiene, nursing, and pharmacy), SOCIAL SCIENCE (African American studies, African studies, American studies, Asian/Oriental studies, biblical languages, biblical studies, classical/ancient civilization, economics, geography, Hispanic American studies, history, human ecology, humanities, Islamic studies, Judaic studies, Latin American studies, liberal arts/general studies, medieval studies, Near Eastern studies, philosophy, physical fitness/movement, political science/government, psychology, religion, Russian and Slavic studies, Scandinavian studies, social science, sociology, Western European studies, and women's studies). The classics, English, political science, psychology, sociology, and engineering (aerospace, industrial, nuclear), are the strongest academically. Liberal arts, psychology, English, political science, and engineering have the largest enrollments.

Required: Academic requirements vary by program. For the College of Literature, Science, and the Arts, students must fulfill requirements in both English composition and race and ethnicity (1 course) and must complete 2 years of foreign language and 9 semester hours each of humanities, social science, and natural science/mathematics. To graduate, students must complete 120 to 128 semester hours, including 24 to 30 in a major field, with a minimum GPA of 2.0.

Special: A co-op program in engineering and cross-registration with Big Ten institutions and the University of Chicago are available, as are study abroad in more than 18 countries and a Washington semester. An accelerated degree program in medicine, B.A.-B.S. degrees, and dual and student-designed majors are permitted, and a 3–2 engineering degree with several colleges and universities is possible. Interdisciplinary majors offered include anthropology-zoology, mathematics engineering, music and technology, natural resources-biophysical/sociobehavioral/biometry, materials and metallurgical engineering, materials science and engineering, and social anthropology. Interdisciplinary liberal arts programs offering small group living/learning environments are available in the Residential College and the Pilot Program. There is a freshman honors program on campus, as well as 14 national honor societies, including Phi Beta Kappa. All literature, science, and arts departments have honors programs.

Faculty/Classroom: Seventy-seven percent of faculty are male; 23%, female. One-hundred percent both teach and do research. The average class size in a regular course offering is 28.

Admissions: About 68% of the 1993–94 applicants were accepted. The SAT scores for the 1993–94 freshman class were as follows: Verbal—27% below 500, 44% between 500 and 599, 26% between 600 and 700, and 3% above 700; Math—7% below 500, 23% between 500 and 599, 43% between 600 and 700, and 27% above 700. The ACT scores were 4% below 21, 10% between 21 and 23, 24% between 24 and 26, 29% between 27 and 28, and 33% above 28. About 87% of the current freshmen were in the top fifth of their class; 98% were in the top two fifths. There were 83 National Merit finalists.

Requirements: The SAT I or ACT is required. In addition, applicants must be graduates of accredited secondary schools or have earned a GED. The university requires 15 academic credits or 20 Carnegie units, including 4 in English, 3 each in mathematics (4 for engineering majors), science, and social studies, 2 in foreign language, and 5 in electives. An essay is required for all applicants. Students applying to the School of Art must submit a portfolio; those ap-

plying to the School of Music must present an audition. AP and CLEP credits are accepted. Important factors used in the admissions decision are advanced placement or honor courses, parents or siblings attending the school, evidence of special talent, geographic diversity, and leadership record.

Procedure: Freshmen are admitted to all sessions. Entrance exams should be taken at the end of the junior year or the beginning of the senior year. Applications should be filed by February 1 for fall, spring, and summer entry, and November 1 for winter entry, along with an application fee of $40. Notification is sent on a rolling basis. There are early admissions and deferred admissions plans. A waiting list is an active part of the admissions procedure.

Transfer: About 850 transfer students enrolled in 1993–94. There are no minimum qualifications for transfer applicants; the best-qualified students are admitted until all slots are filled. A total of 60 credits out of 120 to 128 must be completed at UM.

Visiting: There are regularly scheduled orientations for prospective students, including placement testing; academic counseling; course registration; social activities; and informational programs on student life, computing resources, campus safety, and career planning. There are guides for informal visits and visitors may sit in on classes and stay overnight at the school. To arrange for a visit, contact the Undergraduate Admissions Office at (313) 764–7433.

Financial Aid: In 1993–94, 35% of all current freshmen and 35% of continuing students received some form of financial aid. About 35% of freshmen and 35% of continuing students received need-based aid. The average freshman award was $6600. Of that total, scholarships or need-based grants averaged $3300 ($13,000 maximum); loans averaged $2000 ($9525 maximum); and work contracts averaged $1300 ($1800 maximum). Forty percent of undergraduate students work part-time. Average earnings from campus work for the school year are $1200. The average financial indebtedness of the 1992–93 graduate was $7000. UM is a member of CSS. The FAFSA financial statement is required. The deadline for financial aid applications is September 30.

International Students: There are currently 622 international students enrolled. They must take the TOEFL and achieve a minimum score of 560. The student must also take the SAT I or the ACT.

Computers: The college provides computer facilities for student use. The mainframe is an IBM ES/9000 Model 720. More than 40 computing sites in classroom buildings, residence halls, the library, and the student union provide access to 1800 workstations, popular software packages, printers, plotters, and intelligent and graphics terminals. In addition, 2500 workstations are maintained by individual academic units for use by their students and faculty. All students may access the system. It may be used at any time, 24 hours per day. There are no time limits on using the system and no fees.

Graduates: In 1992–93, 5408 bachelor's degrees were awarded. The most popular majors among graduates were engineering (20%), biology (5%), and psychology (5%). Within an average freshman class, 63% graduate in 4 years, 83% in 5 years, and 85% in 6 years. Some 300 companies recruited on campus in 1992–93. In the 1992 graduating class, 35% of the men and 35% of the women were enrolled in graduate school within 6 months of graduation; 58% of the men and 58% of the women had found employment.

Admissions Contact: Theodore L. Spencer, Director.

UNIVERSITY OF MICHIGAN DEARBORN
Dearborn, MI 48128   E-5
                                                        (313) 593–5100

Full-time: 1706 men, 1805 women	Faculty: 219; IIA, av$
Part-time: 1545 men, 1856 women	Ph.D.s: 83%
Graduate: 700 men, 346 women	Student/Faculty: 16 to 1
Year: semesters, summer session	Tuition: see profile
Application Deadline: open	Room & Board: n/app
Freshman Class: 1796 applied, 1303 accepted, 708 enrolled	
SAT I or ACT: required	**HIGHLY COMPETITIVE**

The University of Michigan/Dearborn, founded in 1959, is a public, comprehensive commuter institution that is part of the University of Michigan System. The emphasis of its degree programs is on the liberal arts, management, engineering, and education. Tuition for state residents is $3399 for lower-division students and $3455 for upper-division students; for nonresidents, tuition is $10,741 for lower division students and $10,929 for upper-division students. There are 4 undergraduate and 4 graduate schools. In addition to regional accreditation, UMD has baccalaureate program accreditation with ABET and NCATE. The library contains 291,719 volumes, 383,533 microform items, and 1886 audiovisual forms, and subscribes to 1612 periodicals. Computerized library sources and services include the card catalog, interlibrary loans, and database searching. Special learning facilities include a learning resource center, art gallery, natural history museum, radio station, TV station, nature preserve, Armenian research center, child development center, engineering educa-

tion and practice center; and the Henry Ford Estate, a National Historic Landmark. The 196-acre campus is in a suburban area 10 miles from Detroit. There are 20 buildings on campus.

Student Life: About 99% of undergraduates are from Michigan. Students come from 16 states, 22 foreign countries, and Canada. Seventy-four percent are from public schools; 26% from private. Eighty-five percent are white. The average age of freshmen is 18; all undergraduates, 26. Eighteen percent drop out by the end of their first year; 53% remain to graduate.

Housing: There are no residence halls; all students commute and may keep cars on campus. Alcohol is not permitted.

Activities: About 5% of men and about 1% of women belong to 7 national fraternities; about 3% of women belong to 4 national sororities. There are 92 groups on campus, including art, cheerleading, chess, choir, computers, ethnic, film, honors, international, literary magazine, newspaper, pep band, political, professional, radio and TV, religious, social, social service, and student government. Popular campus events include Martin Luther King Diversity Celebration, Black History Celebration, Women's History Month, Native American Powwow, Fallfest, Fun Flicks Interactive Video, Asian American Awareness Week, Leadership Series, Hispanic Awareness Celebration, and Breakfast with Bach.

Sports: There is 1 intercollegiate sport for men and 2 for women, and 21 intramural sports for men and 20 for women. Athletic and recreation facilities include a 1200-seat gymnasium, an ice rink, an indoor/outdoor track, a playing field, sand volleyball courts, weight and exercise rooms, and outdoor tennis courts.

Disabled Students: The entire campus is accessible to disabled students. The following facilities are available: wheelchair ramps, elevators, special parking, specially equipped rest rooms, lowered drinking fountains, and lowered telephones.

Services: In addition to many counseling and information services, tutoring is available in most subjects, including science, computer classes, composition, and mathematics. There is also a reader service for the blind, and remedial math, reading, and writing.

Campus Safety and Security: Campus safety and security measures include 24-hour foot and vehicle patrol, self-defense education, escort service, and informal discussions. In addition, there are pamphlets, posters, and films, emergency telephones, lighted pathways and sidewalks, vehicle etching, Crime Prevention Day, CPR training, and a rape awareness seminar.

Programs of Study: UMD awards the B.A., B.S., B.B.A., B.G.S., B.S.A., and B.S.E. degrees. Master's degrees also are awarded. Bachelor's degrees are awarded in BIOLOGICAL SCIENCE (biochemistry, biology/biological science, and microbiology), BUSINESS (business administration and management), COMMUNICATIONS AND THE ARTS (art history and appreciation, arts administration/management, English, fine arts, languages, music, and music history and appreciation), COMPUTER AND PHYSICAL SCIENCE (chemistry, computer science, mathematics, physics, and science), EDUCATION (business, early childhood, elementary, science, secondary, and social studies), ENGINEERING AND ENVIRONMENTAL DESIGN (computer engineering, electrical/electronics engineering, environmental science, industrial engineering, and mechanical engineering), and SOCIAL SCIENCE (American studies, anthropology, behavioral science, economics, history, humanities, international studies, liberal arts/general studies, philosophy, political science/government, psychology, public administration, social science, and sociology). Electrical engineering and business administration are the strongest academically. Mechanical engineering, prebusiness, business administration, electrical engineering, and psychology have the largest enrollments.

Required: Each college within the university has its own unique requirements.

Special: UMD offers co-op programs in engineering, business administration, and arts and sciences; internships; study abroad; work-study and accelerated degree programs; a general studies degree; and dual and student-designed majors. Nondegree study and pass/fail options are possible. There is a freshman honors program on campus.

Faculty/Classroom: Seventy-three percent of faculty are male; 27%, female. No introductory courses are taught by graduate students. The average class size in an introductory lecture is 43 and in a regular course offering, 28.

Admissions: About 73% of the 1993–94 applicants were accepted. The ACT scores for the freshman class were as follows: 2% below 21, 48% between 21 and 23, 47% between 27 and 28, and 3% above 28. About 61% of the current freshmen were in the top fifth of their class; 88% were in the top two fifths.

Requirements: A minimum GPA of 3.0 is required. The ACT, with a minimum composite score of 22, or the SAT I is required. Other admissions requirements normally include graduation from an accredited secondary school, with 4 years each in mathematics and English, 3 in science, and 2 each in art, foreign language, and history. The GED is accepted with a minimum score of 55. An essay and interview

are recommended. AP credits are accepted. Important factors used in the admissions decision are recommendations by school officials, advanced placement or honor courses, extracurricular activities record, leadership record, and evidence of special talent.

Procedure: Freshmen are admitted to all sessions. Entrance exams should be taken the spring of the junior year or the fall of the senior year. Application deadlines are open. The application fee is $30. Notification is sent on a rolling basis. There are early decision and early admissions plans.

Transfer: Some 1200 transfer students enrolled in 1993–94. Applicants are required to have 25 to 30 transferable semester/credit hours; if they have fewer than 25, the SAT I or ACT is mandatory. The required minimum GPA ranges from 2.5 to 3.0, depending on the intended major. A total of 45 credits out of 128 must be completed at UMD.

Visiting: There are regularly scheduled orientations for prospective students. There are guides for informal visits and visitors may sit in on classes. To arrange for a visit, contact the Admissions Office at (313) 593-5100.

Financial Aid: In a recent year, 2% of undergraduate students worked part-time. Average earnings from campus work for the school year were $700. UMD is a member of CSS. The FAF or FFS is required. The deadline for financial aid applications is April 1.

International Students: There are currently 48 international students enrolled. They must take the TOEFL or the University of Michigan Language Test and achieve a minimum score on the TOEFL of 550. The student must also take the SAT I or the ACT.

Computers: The college provides computer facilities for student use. There is a minicomputer with 400 networked microcomputers for students, including IBM PC, Apple Macintosh, and Sun models. All students may access the system. There are no time limits on using the system and no fees.

Graduates: In 1992–93 987 bachelor's degrees were awarded. The most popular majors among graduates were administration (12%), psychology (11%), and business administration (9%). Some 45 companies recruited on campus in 1992–93.

Admissions Contact: Carol Mack, Director of Admissions.

UNIVERSITY OF MICHIGAN FLINT
E-4
Flint, MI 48502 (313) 762-3300

Full-time: 1216 men, 1872 women
Part-time: 1037 men, 1901 women
Graduate: 196 men, 196 women
Year: semesters, summer session
Application Deadline: August 27
Freshman Class: 970 applied, 877 accepted, 551 enrolled
SAT I or ACT: required

Faculty: 184; IIA, av$
Ph.D.s: 85%
Student/Faculty: 17 to 1
Tuition: $2916 ($9534)
Room & Board: n/app

COMPETITIVE

The University of Michigan/Flint, established in 1956, is a public commuter college offering programs in the liberal arts and sciences. There are 3 undergraduate and 5 graduate schools. In addition to regional accreditation, UM-F has baccalaureate program accreditation with AACSB, APTA, NASM, NCATE, and NLN. The library contains 150,000 volumes and 50,000 microform items, and subscribes to 1000 periodicals. Computerized library sources and services include interlibrary loans. Special learning facilities include a learning resource center, art gallery, and TV station. The 40-acre campus is in an urban area 60 miles northwest of Detroit. There are 6 buildings on campus.

Student Life: About 99% of undergraduates are from Michigan. Students come from 3 states, 4 foreign countries, and Canada. Ninety-five percent are from public schools; 5% from private. Eighty-six percent are white; 10% African American. The average age of freshmen is 18; all undergraduates, 28. Twelve percent drop out by the end of their first year; 54% remain to graduate.

Housing: There are no residence halls; all students commute and may keep cars on campus. College-sponsored living facilities include off-campus apartments, fraternity houses, and sorority houses. In addition there are special interest houses. Alcohol is not permitted.

Activities: About 2% of men belong to 5 local and 2 national fraternities; about 2% of women belong to 3 local and 2 national sororities. There are 50 groups on campus, including band, chess, choir, chorale, computers, dance, drama, ethnic, gay, honors, jazz band, literary magazine, musical theater, newspaper, orchestra, political, professional, radio and TV, religious, social, social service, student government, and symphony.

Sports: There are 15 intramural sports for men and 15 for women. Athletic and recreation facilities include a recreation building housing a multipurpose gymnasium, racquetball courts, a weight-training area, and a swimming pool.

Disabled Students: Ninety percent of the campus is accessible to disabled students. The following facilities are available: wheelchair ramps, elevators, special parking, specially equipped rest rooms, lowered drinking fountains, and a telephone is available for the hearing impaired.

Services: In addition to many counseling and information services, tutoring is available in every subject. In addition, there is a reader service for the blind, and remedial math, reading, and writing.

Campus Safety and Security: Campus safety and security measures include 24-hour foot and vehicle patrol, escort service, pamphlets, posters, films, and emergency telephones. In addition, there are lighted pathways and sidewalks.

Programs of Study: UM-F awards the B.A., B.S., B.A.S., B.B.A., B.F.A., B.G.S., B.Mus.Ed., and B.S.N. degrees. Master's degrees also are awarded. Bachelor's degrees are awarded in BIOLOGICAL SCIENCE (biology/biological science), BUSINESS (accounting, banking and finance; business administration and management, and marketing/retailing/merchandising), COMMUNICATIONS AND THE ARTS (communications, dramatic arts, English, and music), COMPUTER AND PHYSICAL SCIENCE (chemistry, computer science, earth science, mathematics, and physics), EDUCATION (early childhood, elementary, foreign languages, music, science, and secondary), ENGINEERING AND ENVIRONMENTAL DESIGN (engineering), HEALTH PROFESSIONS (medical laboratory technology, nursing, physical therapy, predentistry, and premedicine), SOCIAL SCIENCE (anthropology, criminal justice, economics, geography, history, philosophy, political science/government, prelaw, psychology, public administration, social science, social work, sociology, and urban studies). Business, humanities, science, and physical therapy are the strongest academically. Business and education have the largest enrollments.

Required: In order to graduate, all students must complete 120 or more credits, depending on the degree and major, complete 30 to 70 hours in the major and satisfy its requirements, and maintain a GPA of at least 2.0. Fifty distribution requirements are needed, including courses in English composition, humanities, fine arts, social sciences, and natural science.

Special: Special arrangements include co-op programs and dual majors in all majors, cross registration with Mott Community College, internships, study abroad, and work-study. A 3–2 engineering program and a general studies degree are available. Nondegree study and pass/fail options are possible. There is a freshman honors program on campus. Thirty departments have honors programs.

Faculty/Classroom: Sixty-seven percent of faculty are male; 33%, female. All teach undergraduates. No introductory courses are taught by graduate students. The average class size in an introductory lecture is 40; in a laboratory, 20; and in a regular course offering, 25.

Admissions: About 90% of the 1993–94 applicants were accepted. The ACT scores for the 1993–94 freshman class were as follows: 32% below 21, 37% between 21 and 23, 24% between 24 and 26, 5% between 27 and 28, and 2% above 28. About 48% of the current freshmen were in the top fifth of their class; 84% were in the top two fifths. There were 15 National Merit semifinalists.

Requirements: A minimum GPA of 2.7 is required. The SAT I or ACT is required with the ACT being preferred. Graduation from an accredited secondary school, with 3 years each in English, mathematics, and science, and 2 years of social studies is required. The GED is accepted. An essay is required. The SAT II and an interview are recommended. Applied music students must audition. AP and CLEP credits are accepted. Important factors used in the admissions decision are advanced placement or honor courses, evidence of special talent, leadership record, extracurricular activities record, and recommendations by school officials.

Procedure: Freshmen are admitted to all sessions. Entrance exams should be taken in spring of the junior year. Applications should be filed by August 27 for fall entry and December 18 for winter entry, along with an application fee of $30. Notification is sent on a rolling basis. There are early admissions and deferred admissions plans.

Transfer: About 762 transfer students enrolled in 1993–94. Transfer students must have at least 12 credits and a minimum GPA of 2.0 in transferrable courses. An associate degree and an interview are recommended. A total of 45 credits out of 120 must be completed at UM-F.

Visiting: There are regularly scheduled orientations for prospective students. There are guides for informal visits and visitors may sit in on classes. To arrange for a visit, contact the Admissions Office at (313) 762-3300.

Financial Aid: In a recent year, 30% of all current freshmen and 30% of continuing students received some form of financial aid. About 30% of freshmen and 30% of continuing students received need-based aid. UM-F is a member of CSS. The FAF or FFS is required. The deadline for financial aid applications is March 15.

International Students: There are currently 7 international students enrolled. They must take the TOEFL or the University of Michigan Language Test and achieve a minimum score on the TOEFL of 550. The student must also take the SAT I or the ACT.

Computers: The college provides computer facilities for student use. The college provides microcomputers for student use. All students may access the system. There are no fees.

Graduates: In 1992–93 1066 bachelor's degrees were awarded. The most popular majors among graduates were business (22%), education (18%), and nursing (11%). Within an average freshman class, 54% graduate in 5 years. Some 70 companies recruited on campus in 1992–93.

Admissions Contact: David James, Director of Admissions.

WAYNE STATE UNIVERSITY

E-5

Detroit, MI 48202

(313) 577-3577

Full-time: 4236 men, 5648 women	Faculty: 1403; I, -$
Part-time: 4686 men, 6295 women	Ph.D.s: 85%
Graduate: 7083 men, 6997 women	Student/Faculty: 7 to 1
Year: semesters, summer session	Tuition: $2680–3130
Application Deadline: August 1	($5882–7000)
	Room & Board: n/app

Freshman Class: 4855 applied, 3477 accepted, 1772 enrolled

ACT: 20

COMPETITIVE

Wayne State University, founded in 1868, is a state-supported, non-profit, coeducational institution. Primarily a commuter college, it offers programs in the liberal arts and sciences, business, engineering, and preprofessional areas. There are 11 undergraduate and 13 graduate schools. In addition to regional accreditation, Wayne State has baccalaureate program accreditation with AACSB, ABET, ABFSE, ACPE, ADA, APTA, CAHEA, CSWE, NASM, NCATE, and NLN. The 4 libraries contain 2.4 million volumes, 2.5 million microform items, and 100,000 audiovisual forms, and subscribe to 26,000 periodicals. Special learning facilities include an art gallery, natural history museum, and radio station. The 186-acre campus is in an urban area 2 miles north of Detroit. There are 95 buildings on campus.

Student Life: About 98% of undergraduates are from Michigan. Students come from 47 states, 57 foreign countries, and Canada. Sixty-five percent are white; 23% African American. The average age of all undergraduates is 28. About 43% of freshmen remain to graduate.

Housing: There are no residence halls. College-sponsored housing is coed. All students may keep cars on campus.

Activities: There are 2 local and 8 national fraternities and 9 national sororities. There are 170 groups on campus, including band, cheerleading, chess, choir, computers, dance, ethnic, film, gay, honors, international, marching band, newspaper, political, professional, radio and tv, religious, social, social service, student government, and yearbook. Popular campus events include Student Organization Day and the International Fair.

Sports: There are 8 intercollegiate sports for men and 5 for women, and 9 intramural sports for men and 8 for women. Athletic and recreation facilities include a physical education building, various swimming pools, courts, and soccer and softball fields.

Disabled Students: All of the campus is accessible to disabled students. The following facilities are available: wheelchair ramps, elevators, special parking, specially equipped rest rooms, lowered drinking fountains, and lowered telephones.

Services: In addition to many counseling and information services, tutoring is available in every subject. In addition, there is a reader service for the blind, and remedial math, reading, and writing. Tutorial services are available through centralized counseling or academic departments.

Campus Safety and Security: Campus safety and security measures include 24-hour foot and vehicle patrol, self-defense education, escort service, and informal discussions. In addition, there are pamphlets, posters, and films, emergency telephones, and lighted pathways and sidewalks.

Programs of Study: Wayne State awards the B.A., B.S., B.A.S., B.F.A., B.I.S., B.M., B.P.A., B.S.E.T., B.S.M.S., B.S.N., B.S.W., and B.T.I.S. degrees. Master's and doctoral degrees also are awarded. Bachelor's degrees are awarded in BIOLOGICAL SCIENCE (biology/biological science), BUSINESS (accounting, banking and finance, business economics, labor studies, management information systems, management science, and marketing/retailing/merchandising), COMMUNICATIONS AND THE ARTS (art history and appreciation, broadcasting, classics, communications, dance, design, dramatic arts, English, film arts, fine arts, French, German, Greek, Hebrew, Italian, journalism, Latin, linguistics, music, music business management, music performance, music theory and composition, Polish, public relations, Russian, Slavic languages, Spanish, and speech/debate/rhetoric), COMPUTER AND PHYSICAL SCIENCE (chemistry, computer science, data processing, geology, information sciences and systems, mathematics, physics, and radiological technology), EDUCATION (art, bilingual/bicultural, business, early childhood, elementary, foreign languages, health, industrial arts, mathematics, music, physical, science, secondary, and special), ENGINEERING AND ENVIRONMENTAL DESIGN (chemical engineering, civil engineering, electrical/electronics engineering, engineer-

ing technology, industrial engineering technology, mechanical engineering, and metallurgical engineering), HEALTH PROFESSIONS (medical laboratory technology, music therapy, nursing, occupational therapy, pharmacy, and physical therapy), SOCIAL SCIENCE (African American studies, American studies, anthropology, classical/ancient civilization, criminal justice, dietetics, economics, food science, geography, history, human development, humanities, international studies, liberal arts/general studies, Mexican-American/Chicano studies, Near Eastern studies, parks and recreation management, peace studies, philosophy, political science/government, psychology, public affairs, social work, sociology, urban studies, and women's studies). Basic sciences, nursing, and English are the strongest academically. Business, engineering, and computer science have the largest enrollments.

Required: In order to graduate, students must complete at least 120 credit hours and have a minimum GPA of 2.0. All students must satisfy the university's general education requirements, which include 6 credits each in the natural sciences, social sciences, and humanities; 3 credits each in historical sciences and foreign culture, and a course providing an introduction to the university and its libraries.

Special: Special academic programs include cross-registration with Macomb University Center, internships in business, industry, or communications, study abroad in Germany, Japan, or England, and on-campus work-study programs. A general studies degree, B.A.-B.S. degrees, dual majors, and co-op programs are also available. Nondegree study and pass/fail options are possible. The College of Lifelong Learning offers televised, weekend, and evening courses. There is a freshman honors program on campus, as well as one national honor society, Phi Beta Kappa. Forty-four departments have honors programs.

Faculty/Classroom: Fifty-one percent of faculty are male; 49%, female. Sixty-two percent teach undergraduates, 92% do research, and 54% do both. Graduate students teach 13% of introductory courses. The average class size in an introductory lecture is 100; in a laboratory, 20; and in a regular course offering, 30.

Admissions: About 72% of the 1993–94 applicants were accepted. The ACT scores for the 1993–94 freshman class were as follows: 66% below 21, 18% between 21 and 23, 10% between 24 and 26, 3% between 27 and 28, and 3% above 28. About 30% of the current freshmen were in the top fifth of their class; 61% were in the top two fifths.

Requirements: A minimum GPA of 2.0 is required. The ACT is recommended. Admissions requirements include graduation from accredited secondary school; the GED with an acceptable SAT I or ACT score is also allowable. If the GPA is below 2.8, applicant must have minimum SAT I scores of 450 (verbal) and 400 (mathematics) and/or a score of 21 on the ACT. AP and CLEP credits are accepted.

Procedure: Freshmen are admitted to all sessions. If necessary, the ACT should be taken in the junior year or the SAT I in the senior year. Applications should be filed by August 1 for fall entry, December 1 for winter entry, April 1 for spring entry, and April 1 for summer entry, along with an application fee of $20. Notification is sent on a rolling basis. There is a deferred admissions plan.

Transfer: About 3000 transfer students enrolled in an earlier year. Applicants must have 30 transferable credit hours with a 3.0 GPA, and an overall minimum GPA of 2.0. A total of 30 credits out of 120 must be completed at Wayne State.

Visiting: There are guides for informal visits and visitors may sit in on classes. To arrange for a visit, contact the Office of Admissions at (313) 577-3577.

Financial Aid: In an earlier year, 75% of all current freshmen and 60% of continuing students received some form of financial aid. Thirteen percent of undergraduate students work part-time. The average financial indebtedness of an earlier year's graduate was $2601. Wayne State is a member of CSS. The college's own financial statement and FAFSA are required. The deadline for financial aid applications is May 1.

International Students: There are currently 1195 international students enrolled. They must take the TOEFL or the University of Michigan Language Test and achieve a minimum score on the TOEFL of 550.

Computers: The college provides computer facilities for student use. The mainframe is an Amdahl 5890-180E. There are 1000 IBM, Zenith, and Apple microcomputers available in the libraries, the student union, and in academic departments. All students may access the system. It may be used anytime. There are no time limits on using the system.

Graduates: In 1992–93, 2926 bachelor's degrees were awarded. The most popular majors among graduates were business administration (16%), liberal arts (16%), and education (16%). Within an average freshman class, 12% graduate in 3 years, 27% in 4 years, 37% in 5 years, and 42% in 6 years. Some 222 companies recruited on campus in 1992–93. In the 1992 graduating class, 48% of all graduates were enrolled in graduate school within 6 months of graduation; 93% had found employment.

Admissions Contact: Ronald C. Hughes, Director of Admissions.

WESTERN MICHIGAN UNIVERSITY D-5
Kalamazoo, MI 49008
(616) 387-2000

Full-time: 7578 men, 8161 women   **Faculty:** 690; I, -$

Part-time: 2010 men, 2268 women   **Ph.D.s:** 81%

Graduate: 2725 men, 3813 women   **Student/Faculty:** 23 to 1

Year: semesters, summer session   **Tuition:** $2880 ($6710)

Application Deadline: open   **Room & Board:** $3940

Freshman Class: 8565 applied, 7191 accepted, 2797 enrolled

ACT: 23   **COMPETITIVE**

Western Michigan University, founded in 1903, is a public institution offering undergraduate and graduate programs in the liberal arts and sciences, business, education, engineering, fine arts, health and human services, and preprofessional studies. There are 6 undergraduate schools and one graduate school. In addition to regional accreditation, WMU has baccalaureate program accreditation with AACSB, ABET, AHEA, ASLA, CSWE, NASAD, NASM, and NCATE. The 5 libraries contain 1,609,629 volumes, 1,232,782 microform items, and 16,214 audiovisual forms, and subscribe to 5403 periodicals. Computerized library sources and services include interlibrary loans and database searching. Special learning facilities include an art gallery, radio station, and a nuclear accelerator. The 451-acre campus is in an urban area 140 miles west of Detroit. Including residence halls, there are 118 buildings on campus.

Student Life: About 91% of undergraduates are from Michigan. Students come from 47 states, 67 foreign countries, and Canada. Ninety percent are from public schools; 10% from private. Eighty-six percent are white. Forty-nine percent claim no religious affiliation; 26% Protestant; 25% Catholic. The average age of freshmen is 18.3; all undergraduates, 21. Twenty-one percent drop out by the end of their first year; 49% remain to graduate.

Housing: A total of 6980 students can be accommodated in college housing. College-sponsored living facilities include single-sex and coed dormitories, on-campus apartments, married-student housing, fraternity houses, and sorority houses. In addition there are honors houses, special interest houses, and a wellness house, and an international house. On-campus housing is guaranteed for the freshman year only and is available on a first-come, first-served basis. Seventy percent of students commute. Alcohol is not permitted. All students may keep cars on campus.

Activities: About 9% of men belong to 2 local and 19 national fraternities; about 7% of women belong to 14 national sororities. There are 275 groups on campus, including art, band, cheerleading, chess, choir, chorale, chorus, computers, dance, drama, ethnic, gay, honors, international, jazz band, marching band, musical theater, newspaper, opera, orchestra, pep band, political, professional, radio and tv, religious, social, social service, student government, and symphony. Popular campus events include Bronco Bash, Homecoming, Native American Powwow, Spring into Wellness Week, Soap Box Derby, College Bowl, Greek Week, Hispanic Month, Black History Month, visiting scholars program, and young concert artist series.

Sports: There are 10 intercollegiate sports for men and 8 for women, and 44 intramural sports for men and 42 for women. Athletic and recreation facilities include a cross-country course; a track; a field house; baseball, softball, touch football, and soccer fields, a football stadium; an ice arena; a swimming pool; a fitness room and weight rooms; bowling lanes; a game area; an archery range; basketball, racquetball, volleyball, and tennis courts; a 30,000-seat stadium, a 7000-seat gymnasium, and a 4000-seat arena.

Disabled Students: Eighty-five percent of the campus is accessible to disabled students. The following facilities are available: wheelchair ramps, elevators, special parking, specially equipped rest rooms, special class scheduling, lowered drinking fountains, lowered telephones, and some campus apartments have been renovated for wheelchair students. A lift-equipped van is available to take handicapped students to classes.

Services: In addition to many counseling and information services, tutoring is available in some subjects. In addition, there is a reader service for the blind and remedial writing.

Campus Safety and Security: Campus safety and security measures include 24-hour foot and vehicle patrol, self-defense education, escort service, and shuttle buses. In addition, there are informal discussions, pamphlets, posters, and films, emergency telephones, and lighted pathways and sidewalks.

Programs of Study: WMU awards the B.A., B.S., B.B.A., B.F.A., B.Mus., B.S., B.S.E., B.S.Medicine, and B.S.W. degrees. Master's and doctoral degrees also are awarded. Bachelor's degrees are awarded in BIOLOGICAL SCIENCE (biology/biological science), BUSINESS (accounting, banking and finance, business administration and management, business economics, business statistics, human resources, insurance, management science, marketing/retailing/merchandising, purchasing/inventory management, real estate, retailing, and tourism), COMMUNICATIONS AND THE ARTS (advertising, art, communications, dance, dramatic arts, English, fine arts, French, German,

jazz, languages, Latin, linguistics, music, music history and appreciation, music performance, and Spanish), COMPUTER AND PHYSICAL SCIENCE (chemistry, computer science, earth science, geology, information sciences and systems, mathematics, physics, and statistics), EDUCATION (art, business, elementary, foreign languages, health, home economics, industrial arts, middle school, music, science, secondary, special, and vocational), ENGINEERING AND ENVIRONMENTAL DESIGN (aeronautical engineering, automotive technology, computer engineering, electrical/electronics engineering, industrial engineering, materials science, mechanical engineering, paper and pulp science, paper engineering, and transportation engineering), HEALTH PROFESSIONS (occupational therapy, predentistry, premedicine, and speech pathology/audiology), SOCIAL SCIENCE (anthropology, criminal justice, dietetics, economics, family/consumer studies, geography, history, human services, philosophy, political science/government, prelaw, psychology, public administration, religion, social science, social work, sociology, and water resources). Business, education, engineering, and liberal arts have the largest enrollments.

Required: Students must complete 122 semester hours, including 35 of general education courses and a minimum of 24 in the major. A minimum GPA of 2.0 is required. In addition, all students must complete 2 physical education hours, courses in science, social science, humanities, and fine arts, and 1 course in non-Western world study. Comprehensive exams are required in some departments.

Special: Cross-registration is available through the Kalamazoo Consortium. Opportunities are provided for work-study programs, student-designed majors, pass/fail options, and credit by examination. Students may study abroad in France, Germany, Spain, China, and Japan. There is a freshman honors program on campus, as well as 15 national honor societies. Thirty departments have honors programs.

Faculty/Classroom: Sixty-two percent of faculty are male; 38%, female. Ninety percent teach undergraduates. Graduate students teach 13% of introductory courses. The average class size in an introductory lecture is 45; in a laboratory, 21; and in a regular course offering, 37.

Admissions: About 84% of the 1993–94 applicants were accepted. The ACT scores for the 1993–94 freshman class were as follows: 30% below 21, 31% between 21 and 23, 24% between 24 and 26, 8% between 27 and 28, and 7% above 28. About 39% of the current freshmen were in the top fifth of their class; 68% were in the top two fifths. About 60 freshmen graduated first in their class.

Requirements: The ACT is required. Applicants must submit an official high school transcript. An audition is required for music majors. An interview may be recommended. AP and CLEP credits are accepted. Important factors used in the admissions decision are advanced placement or honor courses, recommendations by school officials, extracurricular activities record, evidence of special talent, and leadership record.

Procedure: Freshmen are admitted to all sessions. Entrance exams should be taken late in the junior year or early in the senior year. Application deadlines are open. Application fee is $25. Notification is sent on a rolling basis.

Transfer: About 2070 transfer students enrolled in 1993–94. Applicants must have a minimum GPA of 2.0 in transferable college courses. Consideration will also be given to trend of grades and recent course work. A total of 30 credits out of 122 must be completed at WMU.

Visiting: There are regularly scheduled orientations for prospective students, including an admission presentation, departmental advising, lunch, and a campus tour. Visitors may sit in on classes and stay overnight at the school. To arrange for a visit, contact the Campus Visit Coordinator at (616) 387-2000.

Financial Aid: In 1993–94, 62% of all current freshmen and 55% of continuing students received some form of financial aid. About 58% of freshmen and 56% of continuing students received need-based aid. The average freshman award was $6380. Of that total, scholarships or need-based grants averaged $2100 ($3300 maximum); loans averaged $2230 ($2625 maximum); and work contracts averaged $2050 ($2300 maximum). Twenty-nine percent of undergraduate students work part-time. Average earnings from campus work for the school year are $1550. The average financial indebtedness of the 1992–93 graduate was $6735. WMU is a member of CSS. The FAF or FFS and FAFSA are required. The deadline for financial aid applications is March 1.

International Students: There are currently 1071 international students enrolled. The school actively recruits these students. They must take the TOEFL or the University of Michigan Language Test and achieve a minimum score on the TOEFL of 500.

Computers: The college provides computer facilities for student use. The mainframe is a DEC VAX 6520. The mainframe is used for institutional and research purposes, as well as for course work. Approximately 900 terminals and microcomputers are available in classroom buildings, dormitories, and the student center. A Sun and a NeXT-based UNIX operating system are networked in laboratories for stu-

dent use. All students may access the system. Students may access the system 24 hours a day. Limits are set individually by faculty and by class. There are no fees.

Graduates: In 1992–93, 4165 bachelor's degrees were awarded. The most popular majors among graduates were finance (7%), accounting (7%), and marketing (6%). Within an average freshman class, 19% graduate in 4 years, 44% in 5 years, and 52% in 6 years. Some 140 companies recruited on campus in 1992–93. In the 1992 graduating class, 7% of all graduates were enrolled in graduate school within 6 months of graduation; 78% had found employment.

Admissions Contact: Stanley E. Henderson, Admissions Office.

WILLIAM TYNDALE COLLEGE
Farmington Hills, MI 48331
(313) 553–7200

Full-time: 127 men, 102 women	Faculty: 10; IIB
Part-time: 177 men, 136 women	Ph.D.s: 71%
Graduate: none	Student/Faculty: 23 to 1
Year: semesters, summer session	Tuition: $5320
Application Deadline: July 30	Room: $1800
Freshman Class: 153 applied, 151 accepted, 151 enrolled	
ACT: 18	**NONCOMPETITIVE**

William Tyndale College, established in 1945, is a private, liberal arts institution affiliated with the Interdenominational/Conservative Evangelical faith. There are 3 undergraduate schools. The library contains 70,000 volumes, 1500 microform items, and 5400 audiovisual forms, and subscribes to 220 periodicals. The 28-acre campus is in a suburban area 15 miles west of Detroit. There are 2 buildings on campus.

Student Life: About 98% of undergraduates are from Michigan. Students come from several states, 4 foreign countries, and Canada. Sixty-eight percent are white; 29% African American. Most are Protestant. The average age of freshmen is 29; all undergraduates, 36.

Housing: A total of 50 students can be accommodated in college housing. College-sponsored living facilities include a single-sex and coed dormitory. On-campus housing is guaranteed for all 4 years. Ninety percent of students commute. Alcohol is not permitted. All students may keep cars on campus.

Activities: There are no fraternities or sororities on campus. There are some groups and organizations including band, cheerleading, choir, chorale, drama, religious, social, student government, and yearbook. Popular campus events include New Student Retreat, Jolly Holly Hay Ride, All School Picnic, Spring Banquet, and Winterfest.

Sports: There are 3 intercollegiate sports for men and 2 for women, and 5 intramural sports for men and 5 for women.

Disabled Students: All of the campus is accessible to disabled students. The following facilities are available: wheelchair ramps, elevators, special parking, and specially equipped rest rooms.

Services: In addition to many counseling and information services, tutoring is available in every subject.

Programs of Study: WTC awards the B.A., B.R.E., and B.Th. degrees. Associate degrees also are awarded. Bachelor's degrees are awarded in COMMUNICATIONS AND THE ARTS (communications, English, and music), EDUCATION (early childhood), SOCIAL SCIENCE (crosscultural studies, psychology, religion, religious education, social science, and urban studies). Psychology and biblical stud-

ies are the strongest academically, and also have the largest enrollments.

Required: Students must complete 125 credits, with 30 to 35 in the major, and maintain a minimum GPA of 2.0. There are special curricula requirements, including 35 hours of biblical studies.

Special: Opportunities are provided for internships, portfolio credit, and nondegree study. There is one national honor society on campus.

Admissions: About 99% of the 1993–94 applicants were accepted. The ACT scores for the 1993–94 freshman class were as follows: 30% below 21, 50% between 21 and 23, 15% between 24 and 26, 3% between 27 and 28, and 2% above 28. About 25% of the current freshmen were in the top fifth of their class; 54% were in the top two fifths.

Requirements: A minimum GPA of 2.0 is required. The ACT is required, with a minimum composite score of 15. Graduation from an accredited secondary school is required; the GED is accepted. Applicants should submit an academic record that includes courses in English, mathematics, history, art, a foreign language, science, and social studies. An interview is required, and music majors must audition. CLEP credit is accepted. Important factors used in the admissions decision are parents' or siblings' attendance at the school, leadership record, advanced placement or honors courses, extracurricular activities record, and evidence of special talent.

Procedure: Freshmen are admitted to all sessions. Entrance exams should be taken in the senior year. Applications should be filed by July 30 for fall entry and December 8 for spring entry, along with an application fee of $25. There are early decision and early admissions plans. Three early decision candidates were accepted for the 1993–94 class.

Transfer: About 116 transfer students enrolled in 1993–94. A total of 75 credits out of 125 must be completed at WTC.

Visiting: There are regularly scheduled orientations for prospective students. There are guides for informal visits, and visitors may sit in on classes and stay overnight at the school. To arrange for a visit, contact Kenneth L. Grunden, Director of Enrollment Management, at (313) 553–7200.

Financial Aid: In 1993–94, 54% of all current freshmen and 58% of continuing students received some form of financial aid. About 42% of freshmen and 51% of continuing students received need-based aid. The average freshman award was $1900. Of that total, scholarships or need-based grants averaged $200 ($2300 maximum); and loans averaged $2000 ($11,500 maximum). Two percent of undergraduate students work part-time. Average earnings from campus work for the school year are $1500. The average financial indebtedness of the 1992–93 graduate was $3013. WTC is a member of CSS. The FAFSA financial statement is required. The deadline for financial aid applications is May 1.

International Students: There are currently 12 international students enrolled. The school actively recruits these students. They must take the TOEFL and achieve a minimum score of 500. The student must also take the ACT.

Computers: The college provides computer facilities for student use. There is a computer laboratory for academic students and faculty. There are no time limits on using the system and no fees.

Admissions Contact: Kenneth L. Grunden, Director of Enrollment Management.

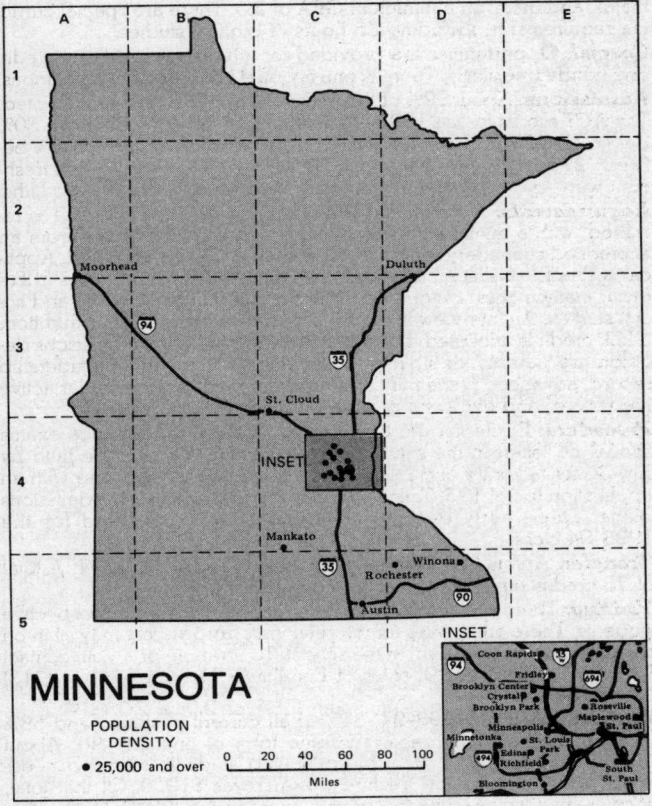

MINNESOTA

POPULATION
DENSITY

● 25,000 and over

0 20 40 60 80 100
Miles

INSET

AUGSBURG COLLEGE
Minneapolis, MN 55454

C-4

(612) 330–1001
(800) 788–5678 (out-of-state)

Full-time: 681 men, 781 women	Faculty: 128; IIB, -$
Part-time: 72 men, 114 women	Ph.D.s: 68%
Graduate: 37 men, 107 women	Student/Faculty: 11 to 1
Year: 4–1–4, summer session	Tuition: $11,404
Application Deadline: August 15	Room & Board: $4204

Freshman Class: 662 applied, 513 accepted, 257 enrolled
SAT I or ACT: required

COMPETITIVE

Augsburg College, established in 1869, is a private liberal arts institution affiliated with the Evangelical Lutheran Church in America. There is one undergraduate and 3 graduate schools. In addition to regional accreditation, Augsburg has baccalaureate program accreditation with CSWE, NASM, NCATE, and NLN. The library contains 175,000 volumes, 15,500 microform items, and 9450 audiovisual forms, and subscribes to 981 periodicals. Computerized library sources and services include the card catalog, interlibrary loans, and database searching. Special learning facilities include a learning resource center, art gallery, radio station, and TV studio. The 23-acre campus is in a residential area of downtown Minneapolis. Including residence halls, there are 39 buildings on campus.

Student Life: About 77% of undergraduates are from Minnesota. Students come from 29 states, 26 foreign countries, and Canada. Ninety percent are from public schools; 10% from private. Seventy-eight percent are white; 12% Asian American. Sixty-one percent are Protestant; 19% Catholic; 19% claim no religious affiliation. The average age of freshmen is 18; all undergraduates, 22.4.

Housing: A total of 986 students can be accommodated in college housing. College-sponsored living facilities include coed dormitories, on-campus apartments, and married-student housing. In addition, there are honors houses, special interest houses, and an international students house. On-campus housing is guaranteed for all 4 years. Seventy-nine percent of students live on campus. All students may keep cars on campus.

Activities: There are no fraternities or sororities on campus. There are 35 groups on campus, including art, band, cheerleading, choir, chorus, dance, drama, ethnic, gay, honors, international, jazz band, literary magazine, newspaper, orchestra, pep band, political, professional, radio and TV, religious, social, social service, student govern-

ment, and yearbook. Popular campus events include Days in May, Spring Affair, Mr. Urness, Advent Vespers, and the Madrigal Dinner.

Sports: There are 10 intercollegiate sports for men and 7 for women, and 7 intramural sports for men and 7 for women. Athletic and recreation facilities include a 1500-seat sports field, a 2800-seat gymnasium, tennis courts, and a double-rink ice arena.

Disabled Students: Ninety-two percent of the campus is accessible to disabled students. The following facilities are available: wheelchair ramps, elevators, special parking, specially equipped rest rooms, special class scheduling, lowered drinking fountains, and lowered telephones.

Services: In addition to many counseling and information services, tutoring is available in every subject. There are taped textbooks and adaptive computer technology, including a text scanner, speaking software, a touch tablet, and text magnification software. In addition, there is a reader service for the blind and remedial math and writing.

Campus Safety and Security: Campus safety and security measures include 24-hour foot and vehicle patrol, self defense education, escort service, and informal discussions. In addition, there are pamphlets, posters, and films and lighted pathways and sidewalks.

Programs of Study: Augsburg awards the B.A., B.S., and B.M. degrees. Master's degrees also are awarded. Bachelor's degrees are awarded in BIOLOGICAL SCIENCE (biology/biological science), BUSINESS (accounting, banking and finance, international business management, management information systems, and marketing/retailing/merchandising), COMMUNICATIONS AND THE ARTS (communications, dramatic arts, English, fine arts, French, German, music, Scandinavian languages, Spanish, and speech/debate/rhetoric), COMPUTER AND PHYSICAL SCIENCE (chemistry, computer science, mathematics, and physics), EDUCATION (art, elementary, foreign languages, health, music, science, secondary, and social studies), HEALTH PROFESSIONS (music therapy, occupational therapy, predentistry, and premedicine), SOCIAL SCIENCE (East Asian studies, economics, history, international relations, philosophy, political science/government, prelaw, psychology, religion, social work, sociology, and urban studies). Physics, chemistry, English, political science, education, social work, and music are the strongest academically. Business, communication, and education have the largest enrollments.

Required: In order to graduate, all students must have a minimum GPA of 2.0 and a total of 33 unit credits, or courses, including 11 credits in the major. A general education program of 13 to 17 courses in specific perspectives must also be followed.

Special: Special academic programs include various paid and unpaid internships in all majors; a Washington semester; study abroad in Mexico, Norway, England, and Spain; and numerous cooperative work-study programs. There are student-designed majors, cross-registration with the 5 schools in the Associated Colleges of the Twin Cities (ACTC) consortium, and dual and 3–2 engineering degrees with the universities of Northern Michigan and Minnesota. Credit for previous learning experience may be granted, and pass/fail options are possible. There is a freshman honors program on campus.

Faculty/Classroom: Fifty-three percent of faculty are male; 47%, female. All teach undergraduates. No introductory courses are taught by graduate students. The average class size in an introductory lecture is 20; in a laboratory, 9; and in a regular course offering, 20.

Admissions: About 77% of the 1993–94 applicants were accepted. The ACT scores for the 1993–94 freshman class were as follows: 53% below 21 and 21% between 21 and 23. About 32% of the current freshmen were in the top fifth of their class; 55% were in the top two fifths.

Requirements: Augsburg requires applicants to be in the upper 50% of their class. A minimum GPA of 2.5 is required. The SAT I, with minimum scores of 430 (verbal) and 430 (math), or the ACT, with a minimum composite score of 19, is required. Admissions requirements include graduation from an accredited secondary school, with 4 years of English. The GED is also accepted. An essay is required and an interview is recommended. AP and CLEP credits are accepted. Important factors used in the admissions decision are advanced placement or honor courses, leadership record, recommendations by school officials, extracurricular activities record, and evidence of special talent.

Procedure: Freshmen are admitted fall and spring. Entrance exams should be taken during the fall of the senior year. Applications should be filed by August 15 for fall entry and December 15 for spring entry, along with an application fee of $20. Notification is sent on a rolling basis. There is a deferred admissions plan.

Transfer: A total of 157 transfer students enrolled in a recent year. Applicants must have a minimum GPA of 2.0 in college course work. A total of 9 unit credits out of 33 must be completed at Augsburg.

Visiting: There are regularly scheduled orientations for prospective students, including an admissions interview, a campus tour, and academic and extracurricular activities. There are guides for informal visits and visitors may sit in on classes and stay overnight at the school. To arrange for a visit, contact the Admissions Office at (612) 330-1001 or (800) 788-5678.

Financial Aid: In 1993-94, 82% of all current freshmen and 78% of continuing students received some form of financial aid. About 79% of freshmen and 75% of continuing students received need-based aid. The average freshman award was $11,700. Of that total, scholarships or need-based grants averaged $2732 ($12,292 maximum); loans averaged $2516 ($10,000 maximum); and work contracts averaged $1760 ($2000 maximum). Eighty-five percent of undergraduate students work part-time. Average earnings from campus work for the school year are $1300. The average financial indebtedness of the 1992-93 graduate was $12,500. Augsburg is a member of CSS. The FAF or FFS, the college's own financial statement, and the FAFSA are required. The deadline for financial aid applications is August 1.

International Students: There are currently 57 international students enrolled. The school actively recruits these students. They must take the TOEFL or the University of Michigan Language Test and achieve a minimum score on the TOEFL of 520.

Computers: The college provides computer facilities for student use. The mainframes are a DEC VAX and a MicroVAX II. Approximately 40 PCs are located in the main computer center, 10 to 15 in a satellite center, and others in residence halls and in the library. All students may access the system. There are no time limits on using the system and no fees.

Graduates: In 1992-93, 320 bachelor's degrees were awarded. The most popular majors among graduates were business administration (23%), education (14%), and communications (9%). Within an average freshman class, 33% graduate in 4 years, 50% in 5 years, and 57% in 6 years. Some 60 companies recruited on campus in 1992-93. In the 1992 graduating class, 11% of all students were enrolled in graduate school within 6 months of graduation; 70% had found employment.

Admissions Contact: Director of Admissions.

BEMIDJI STATE UNIVERSITY   B-2
Bemidji, MN 56601   (218) 755-2040; (800) 652-9747 (in-state)

Full-time: 1699 men, 1767 women	Faculty: 180; IIA, -$
Part-time: 420 men, 770 women	Ph.D.s: 66%
Graduate: 113 men, 241 women	Student/Faculty: 19 to 1
Year: quarters, summer session	Tuition: $2516 ($4808)
Application Deadline: open	Room & Board: $2672
Freshman Class: 1208 applied, 877 accepted, 561 enrolled	
ACT: 21	COMPETITIVE

Bemidji State University, founded in 1919, is a public, coeducational liberal arts university. There are 3 undergraduate schools and one graduate school. In addition to regional accreditation, Bemidji State University has baccalaureate program accreditation with CSWE, NASM, and NCATE. The library contains 242,665 volumes, 28,824 microform items, and 714 audiovisual forms, and subscribes to 774 periodicals. Computerized library sources and services include the card catalog and database searching. Special learning facilities include a learning resource center, art gallery, radio station, and tv station. The 89-acre campus is in a small town 220 miles northwest of Minneapolis. Including residence halls, there are 21 buildings on campus.

Student Life: About 82% of undergraduates are from Minnesota. Students come from 46 states, 34 foreign countries, and Canada. Ninety-nine percent are from public schools. Ninety percent are white. Thirty-six percent are Catholic; 18% Protestant. The average age of freshmen is 20.1; all undergraduates, 24.6. Thirty percent drop out by the end of their first year; 40% remain to graduate.

Housing: A total of 1700 students can be accommodated in college housing. College-sponsored living facilities include single-sex and coed dormitories and on-campus apartments. In addition there are special interest houses and single-parent apartments. On-campus housing is available on a first-come, first-served basis. Alcohol is not permitted. All students may keep cars on campus.

Activities: About 2% of men belong to 2 national fraternities; about 1% of women belong to 1 national sorority. There are 80 groups on campus, including band, cheerleading, choir, chorus, computers, dance, drama, ethnic, gay, honors, international, jazz band, literary magazine, newspaper, orchestra, pep band, political, professional, radio and tv, religious, social, social service, and student government. Popular campus events include Homecoming and Funtastic Dance Follies.

Sports: There are 7 intercollegiate sports for men and 7 for women, and 7 intramural sports for men and 4 for women. Athletic and recreation facilities include a basketball gymnasium, an Olympic-size pool, a hockey arena, a football stadium, indoor and outdoor tracks, baseball and softball fields, tennis, racketball, and handball courts, weight rooms, and a dance studio.

Disabled Students: Eighty percent of the campus is accessible to disabled students. The following facilities are available: wheelchair ramps, elevators, special parking, specially equipped rest rooms, lowered drinking fountains, and lowered telephones.

Services: In addition to many counseling and information services, tutoring is available in every subject. In addition, there is a reader service for the blind, and remedial math, reading, and writing.

Campus Safety and Security: Campus safety and security measures include 24-hour foot and vehicle patrol, escort service, informal discussions, and pamphlets, posters, and films. In addition, there are emergency telephones and lighted pathways and sidewalks.

Programs of Study: Bemidji State University awards the B.A., B.S., and B.F.A. degrees. Associate and master's degrees also are awarded. Bachelor's degrees are awarded in BIOLOGICAL SCIENCE (biology/biological science), BUSINESS (accounting and business administration and management), COMMUNICATIONS AND THE ARTS (broadcasting, communications, English, fine arts, French, German, journalism, languages, music, and Spanish), COMPUTER AND PHYSICAL SCIENCE (chemistry, computer science, earth science, geology, mathematics, and physics), EDUCATION (art, early childhood, elementary, foreign languages, health, industrial arts, middle school, science, and secondary), ENGINEERING AND ENVIRONMENTAL DESIGN (industrial engineering technology), HEALTH PROFESSIONS (medical laboratory technology, nursing, predentistry, and premedicine), SOCIAL SCIENCE (community services, criminal justice, economics, geography, history, parks and recreation management, philosophy, political science/government, prelaw, psychology, social science, social work, and sociology). Business administration and elementary and secondary education have the largest enrollments.

Required: All students must complete at least 192 quarter hours, including courses in freshmen English, the humanities, social science, physical science, liberal education activities, and physical education. Students must maintain a minimum GPA of 2.0; a 2.3 GPA is required in major (2.5 for education majors).

Special: Students may participate in a common market program within the state university system. Students may study abroad in England, China, Japan, and Malaysia. Paid internships are available in many fields. Students may receive credit for life, military, and work experience. Nondegree study and pass/fail options are offered. There is a freshman honors program on campus, as well as 2 national honor societies.

Faculty/Classroom: Seventy percent of faculty are male; 30%, female. Ninety-six percent teach undergraduates. The average class size in an introductory lecture is 60; in a laboratory, 20; and in a regular course offering, 25.

Admissions: About 73% of the 1993-94 applicants were accepted. The ACT scores for the 1993-94 freshman class were as follows: 44% below 21, 34% between 21 and 23, 16% between 24 and 26, 4% between 27 and 28, and 2% above 28. About 28% of the current freshmen were in the top fifth of their class; 58% were in the top two fifths.

Requirements: Bemidji State University requires applicants to be in the upper 50% of their class. The ACT is required. AP and CLEP credits are accepted. Important factors used in the admissions decision are recommendations by school officials, advanced placement or honor courses, extracurricular activities record, leadership record, and evidence of special talent.

Procedure: Freshmen are admitted to all sessions. Entrance exams should be taken during the junior year. Application deadlines are open. Application fee is $15. Notification is sent on a rolling basis. There are early admissions and deferred admissions plans.

Transfer: About 525 transfer students enrolled in 1993-94. Applicants must have a minimum GPA of 2.0. A total of 45 quarter hours out of 192 must be completed at Bemidji State University.

Visiting: There are regularly scheduled orientations for prospective students, including an interview with an admissions counselor, a tour of the campus, and visits with faculty. There are guides for informal visits and visitors may sit in on classes and stay overnight at the school. To arrange for a visit, contact the Admissions Office at (218) 755-2040.

Financial Aid: In 1993-94, 78% of all current freshmen and 81% of continuing students received some form of financial aid. About 72% of freshmen and 72% of continuing students received need-based aid. Scholarships or need-based grants averaged $1010 ($2000 maximum); loans averaged $1759 ($4000 maximum); and work contracts averaged $1500. The college's own financial statement and Family Financial Statement are required. The deadline for financial aid applications is April 20.

International Students: There are currently 250 international students enrolled. The school actively recruits these students. They must take the TOEFL and achieve a minimum score of 550.

Computers: The college provides computer facilities for student use. The mainframe is a DEC VAX 785 and Sperry UNIVAC 1180. There are microcomputer laboratories and 135 terminals in various campus locations. Approximately 35 mainframe access terminals are located in 4 locations. All students may access the system. It may be used 18 hours a day. There are no time limits on using the system and no fees.

Graduates: In 1992–93, 774 bachelor's degrees were awarded. The most popular majors among graduates were education (30%) and business/accounting (20%). Within an average freshman class, 1% graduate in 3 years, 10% in 4 years, 29% in 5 years, and 36% in 6 years. Some 45 companies recruited on campus in 1992–93.

Admissions Contact: Paul Muller, Associate Director.

BETHEL COLLEGE
C-4
St. Paul, MN 55112   (612) 638–6242; (800) 255–8706 (out-of-state)

Full-time: 663 men, 1011 women	Faculty: 107; IIB, -$
Part-time: 34 men, 88 women	Ph.D.s: 58%
Graduate: 88 men and women	Student/Faculty: 16 to 1
Year: 4-1-4, summer session	Tuition: $11,050
Application Deadline: open	Room & Board: $4000
Freshman Class: 1361 applied, 1096 accepted, 648 enrolled	
SAT I Verbal/Math: 491/542 (mean)	ACT: 23 (mean) **COMPETITIVE**

Bethel College, established in 1871, is a private, liberal arts college affiliated with the Baptist General Conference. In addition to regional accreditation, Bethel has baccalaureate program accreditation with CSWE, NCATE, and NLN. The library contains 125,000 volumes, and subscribes to 625 periodicals. Special learning facilities include a learning resource center, an art gallery, and a radio station. The 231-acre campus is in a suburban area 10 miles north of St. Paul/Minneapolis.

Student Life: About 62% of undergraduates are from out-of-state, mostly the Midwest. Students come from 38 states. Ninety-seven percent are white.

Housing: A total of 1264 students can be accommodated in college housing. College-sponsored living facilities include single-sex dormitories. In addition, there are townhouses. On-campus housing is guaranteed for the freshman year only and is available on a lottery system for upperclassmen. Seventy percent of students live on campus; of those, 40% remain on campus on weekends. Alcohol is not permitted. All students may keep cars on campus.

Activities: There are no fraternities or sororities on campus. There are numerous groups on campus, including art, band, cheerleading, choir, chorale, chorus, drama, ethnic, literary magazine, musical theater, newspaper, orchestra, political, professional, radio and TV, religious, social, social service, student government, and yearbook.

Sports: There are 9 intercollegiate sports for men and 5 for women, and 12 intramural sports each. Athletic and recreation facilities include a gymnasium, a recreation center, a weight room, and playing fields.

Disabled Students: Eighty percent of the campus is accessible to disabled students. The following facilities are available: wheelchair ramps, elevators, special parking, specially equipped rest rooms, special class scheduling, lowered drinking fountains, and lowered telephones.

Services: In addition to many counseling and information services, tutoring is available in most subjects. There is also a reader service for the blind.

Programs of Study: Bethel awards the B.A., B.S., B.Mus., and B.Mus.Ed. degrees. Associate degrees also are awarded. Bachelor's degrees are awarded in BIOLOGICAL SCIENCE (biology/biological science), BUSINESS (accounting, banking and finance, business administration and management, and marketing/retailing/merchandising), COMMUNICATIONS AND THE ARTS (communications, dramatic arts, English, fine arts, music, Spanish, and speech/debate/rhetoric), COMPUTER AND PHYSICAL SCIENCE (chemistry, computer programming, computer science, mathematics, and physics), EDUCATION (art, business, early childhood, elementary, foreign languages, health, music, science, and secondary), ENGINEERING AND ENVIRONMENTAL DESIGN (preengineering), HEALTH PROFESSIONS (nursing, predentistry, and premedicine), and SOCIAL SCIENCE (anthropology, economics, history, international relations, philosophy, political science/government, prelaw, psychology, religion, social science, social work, and sociology). Physical sciences are the strongest academically. Business has the largest enrollment.

Required: Students must complete 122 semester credit hours, with 30 to 60 in the major and 50 in general education. Specific general education courses include Introduction to the Bible, Christianity and Western Culture, College Writing, Creativity in Fine Arts, and Physical Wellness. An overall GPA of 2.0 and a GPA of 2.25 in the major are needed.

Special: Students may arrange internships, study abroad in various countries, participate in a Washington semester with the Christian College Coalition, and select various work-study programs. Dual majors in cross-cultural studies are available. Students may design their own majors, earn a 3–2 engineering degree, and select limited pass/fail options. An adult degree completion program is offered. ROTC programs are available through other schools.

Faculty/Classroom: Seventy-three percent of faculty are male; 27%, female. The average class size in an introductory lecture is 20; in a laboratory, 20; and in a regular course offering, 20.

Admissions: About 81% of the 1993–94 applicants were accepted.

Requirements: Bethel requires applicants to be in the upper 50% of their class. The SAT I or ACT is required. The PSAT is accepted. In addition, applicants must be graduates of an accredited secondary school or have a GED. An interview is recommended. AP and CLEP credits are accepted.

Procedure: Freshmen are admitted to all sessions. Entrance exams should be taken before acceptance. Application deadlines are open. The application fee is $20. Notification is sent on a rolling basis. There is an early admissions plan.

Transfer: About 125 transfer students enrolled in a recent year. Applicants must have a minimum GPA of 2.0 and must submit all college transcripts. A total of 28 semester credit hours out of 122 must be completed at Bethel.

Visiting: There are regularly scheduled orientations for prospective students. There are guides for informal visits and visitors may sit in on classes and stay overnight at the school. To arrange for a visit, contact the Admissions Office at (612) 638–6242 or (800) 255–8706 (out-of-state).

Financial Aid: In an earlier year, 87% of all students received some form of financial aid. Scholarships or need-based grants averaged $3900 ($8500 maximum); loans averaged $2500 ($4000 maximum); and work contracts averaged $1000 ($1500 maximum). Bethel is a member of CSS. The college's own financial statement, the FAFSA, and students' and parents' most recent federal tax returns are required. The deadline for financial aid applications is April 15.

International Students: There are currently 22 international students enrolled. They must take the TOEFL and achieve a minimum score of 525.

Computers: The college provides computer facilities for student use. The mainframes are a DEC VAX 11/750 and a Pyramid 90X. The microcomputer laboratory houses 29 PCs, including Apple Macintosh, Apple II, Apple IIe, and IBM-compatible models. All students may access the system. It may be used 24 hours a day. There are no time limits on using the system and no fees.

Graduates: In an earlier year, 276 bachelor's degrees were awarded.

Admissions Contact: John C. Lassen, Director of Admissions.

CARLETON COLLEGE
C-4
Northfield, MN 55057
(507) 663–4190
(800) 995-CARL (out-of-state)

Full-time: 833 men, 845 women	Faculty: 151; IIB, +$
Part-time: none	Ph.D.s: 96%
Graduate: none	Student/Faculty: 11 to 1
Year: terms	Tuition: $18,405
Application Deadline: February 1	Room & Board: $3750
Freshman Class: 2693 applied, 1579 accepted, 489 enrolled	**HIGHLY COMPETITIVE**

Carleton College, founded in 1866, is a private, coeducational, liberal arts college. The 2 libraries contain 473,701 volumes, 130,200 microform items, and 968 audiovisual forms, and subscribe to 1431 periodicals. Computerized library sources and services include the card catalog, interlibrary loans, and database searching. Special learning facilities include a learning resource center, art gallery, radio station, and Goodsell Observatory. The 945-acre campus is in a small town 35 miles south of Minneapolis-St. Paul. Including residence halls, there are 25 buildings on campus.

Student Life: About 75% of undergraduates are from out-of-state, mostly the Midwest. Students come from 50 states, 18 foreign countries, and Canada. Seventy-six percent are from public schools; 24% from private. Eighty-three percent are white. Thirty-three percent are Protestant; 16% Catholic. The average age of freshmen is 18; all undergraduates, 20. Four percent drop out by the end of their first year.

Housing: A total of 1555 students can be accommodated in college housing. College-sponsored living facilities include single-sex and coed dormitories and off-campus apartments. In addition there are language houses and special interest houses. On-campus housing is guaranteed for all 4 years. Ninety-three percent of students live on campus; of those, 97% remain on campus on weekends.

Activities: There are no fraternities or sororities on campus. There are 100 groups on campus, including band, choir, dance, drama, ethnic, film, gay, honors, jazz band, literary magazine, musical theater, newspaper, orchestra, pep band, photography, political, professional, radio and TV, religious, social, social service, student government, and yearbook. Popular campus events include Homecoming, May Fete, and Spring Concert.

Sports: There are 12 intercollegiate sports for men and 11 for women, and 11 intramural sports for men and 9 for women. Athletic and recreation facilities include a gymnasium with an 1850-seat arena, a 6-lane swimming pool, and a wrestling room; a recreation center with a gymnasium, indoor tennis courts, a sauna, and a 5-lane swimming pool; and a 7000-seat stadium complex, with handball and racquetball courts, a baseball batting cage, and a weight room. In addition, there are baseball, softball, and soccer fields, 12 outdoor tennis courts, and 16 miles of running and ski trails in Carleton's 400-acre arboretum.

Disabled Students: Twenty-five percent of the campus is accessible to disabled students. The following facilities are available: wheelchair ramps, elevators, special parking, specially equipped rest rooms, and special class scheduling.

Services: In addition to many counseling and information services, tutoring is available in every subject. There are writing and mathematics skills assistance centers. In addition, there is a reader service for the blind.

Campus Safety and Security: Campus safety and security measures include 24-hour foot and vehicle patrol, self defense education, escort service, and informal discussions. In addition, there are pamphlets, posters, and films, emergency telephones, and lighted pathways and sidewalks.

Programs of Study: Carleton awards the B.A degree. Bachelor's degrees are awarded in BIOLOGICAL SCIENCE (biology/biological science), COMMUNICATIONS AND THE ARTS (art history and appreciation, classics, English, French, German, Greek, Latin, music, romance languages, Russian, Spanish, and studio art), COMPUTER AND PHYSICAL SCIENCE (chemistry, computer science, geology, mathematics, and physics), SOCIAL SCIENCE (African American studies, African studies, American studies, anthropology, Asian/Oriental studies, classical/ancient civilization, economics, history, international relations, Latin American studies, philosophy, political science/government, psychology, religion, and sociology). English, biology, history, economics, and political science have the largest enrollments.

Required: Students are required to demonstrate proficiency in English composition and in a foreign language, and to take 1 course centrally concerned with another culture. Four terms of physical education are required. Students must complete 210 credits or 117 semester hours, including 12 credits each from arts and literature and from history, philosophy, and religion, and 18 credits each from the social sciences and from mathematics and science. Students must maintain a minimum GPA of 2.0. The total number of hours required for the major varies by department. All seniors must complete a senior integrative exercise in their major, which may consist of a comprehensive exam, an extensive research project or paper, a public lecture, or a combination of these.

Special: Students may cross register with Saint Olaf College and pursue a variety of internships. The college offers study abroad in 25 countries and a Washington semester. Dual majors in all areas and student-designed majors are available. Students may earn a 3-2 engineering degree with Washington or Columbia universities, a 3-2 degree in nursing, and a 3-3 degree in law. Pass/fail options are offered. There is a chapter of Phi Beta Kappa on campus.

Faculty/Classroom: Sixty-eight percent of faculty are male; 32%, female. One-hundred percent both teach and do research. The average class size in an introductory lecture is 35; in a laboratory, 24; and in a regular course offering, 19.

Admissions: About 59% of the 1993–94 applicants were accepted. The SAT scores for the 1993–94 freshman class were as follows: Verbal—7% below 500, 30% between 500 and 599, 50% between 600 and 700, and 13% above 700; Math—3% below 500, 17% between 500 and 599, 46% between 600 and 700, and 34% above 700. The ACT scores were 2% below 21, 6% between 21 and 23, 16% between 24 and 26, 24% between 27 and 28, and 52% above 28. About 90% of the current freshmen were in the top fifth of their class; 98% were in the top two fifths. There were 92 National Merit finalists.

Requirements: The SAT I or ACT is required. There are no secondary school requirements, however, it is recommended that applicants have completed 4 years of English, 3 years each of mathematics and a foreign language, 2 years each of history and science, and 1 year of social studies. AP credits are accepted. Important factors used in the admissions decision are ability to finance college education, recommendations by alumni, parents or siblings attending the school, geographic diversity, and leadership record.

Procedure: Freshmen are admitted in the fall. Entrance exams should be taken before March 1. Early decision applications should be filed by November 15; regular applications, by February 1 for fall entry, along with an application fee of $30. Notification of early decision is sent December 15; regular decision, by April 15. There are early decision, early admissions, and deferred admissions plans. About 197 early decision candidates were accepted for the 1993–94 class. A waiting list is an active part of the admissions procedure.

Transfer: About 31 transfer students enrolled in 1993–94. Transfers are usually accepted for sophomore and junior classes. A 3.0 GPA is recommended. A total of 108 credits out of 210 must be completed at Carleton.

Visiting: There are guides for informal visits and visitors may sit in on classes and stay overnight at the school. To arrange for a visit, contact the Admissions Office at (507) 663–4190 or (800) 995-CARL.

Financial Aid: In 1993–94 78% of all current freshmen and 82% of continuing students received some form of financial aid. About 50% of freshmen and 49% of continuing students received need-based aid. The average freshman award was $14,590. Of that total, scholarships or need-based grants averaged $9470 ($19,620 maximum); loans averaged $2247 ($2625 maximum); and work contracts averaged $1464 ($1500 maximum). Eighty-three percent of undergraduate students work part-time. Average earnings from campus work for the school year are $1013. The average financial indebtedness of the 1992–93 graduate was $8058. Carleton is a member of CSS. The FAF and FAFSA are required. The deadline for financial aid applications is March 1.

International Students: The school actively recruits these students. They must take the TOEFL. The student must also take the SAT I, ACT, and/or TOEFL.

Computers: The college provides computer facilities for student use. The mainframes are a 2 DEC 3300s. There are 50 Macintosh Plus, H-P Vectra, and Epson Equity 1 microcomputers available in 5 public areas on campus. All students may access the system. It may be used 24 hours. There are no time limits on using the system and no fees.

Graduates: In a recent year, 456 bachelor's degrees were awarded. The most popular majors among graduates were English (13%), political science (11%), and history (11%). Within an average freshman class, 84% graduate in 4 years and 89% in 5 years. Some 55 companies recruited on campus in a recent year. In the 1992 graduating class, 24% of the men and 26% of the women were enrolled in graduate school within 6 months of graduation; 69% of the men and 68% of the women had found employment.

Admissions Contact: Paul Thiboutot, Dean of Admissions.

COLLEGE OF SAINT BENEDICT
C-3

St. Joseph, MN 56374–2099

Full-time: 1714 women	**Faculty:** 132; IIB, -$
Part-time: 53 women	**Ph.Ds:** 75%
Graduate: none	**Student/Faculty:** 13 to 1
Year: 4-1-4	**Tuition:** $11,428
Application Deadline: open	**Room & Board:** $4040

(612) 363–5308; (800) 544–1489

Freshman Class: 938 applied, 864 accepted, 511 enrolled
SAT I Verbal/Math: 490/530 **ACT:** 23 **VERY COMPETITIVE**

The College of St. Benedict, established in 1887, is a private, non-profit Roman Catholic institution offering undergraduate liberal arts study for women. It functions in conjunction with its coordinate institution, St. John's University, in Collegeville, Minnesota. In addition to regional accreditation, St. Benedict has baccalaureate program accreditation with CSWE, NCATE, and NLN. The 4 libraries contain 475,000 volumes, 77,650 microform items, and 12,000 audiovisual forms, and subscribe to 2100 periodicals. Computerized library sources and services include the card catalog, interlibrary loans, and database searching. Special learning facilities include a learning resource center, art gallery, natural history museum, planetarium, and greenhouse. The 700-acre campus is in a small town 10 miles west of St. Cloud. Including residence halls, there are 30 buildings on campus.

Student Life: About 83% of undergraduates are from Minnesota. Students come from 37 states, 11 foreign countries, and Canada. Eighty percent are from public schools; 20% from private. Ninety-four percent are white. Eighty-two percent are Catholic; 14% Protestant. The average age of freshmen is 18; all undergraduates, 20. Fifteen percent drop out by the end of their first year; 75% remain to graduate.

Housing: A total of 1450 students can be accommodated in college housing. College-sponsored living facilities include dormitories and on-campus apartments. On-campus housing is guaranteed for the freshman year only and is available on a lottery system for upperclassmen. Ninety percent of students live on campus; of those, 90% remain on campus on weekends. Alcohol is not permitted. All students may keep cars on campus.

Activities: There are no sororities on campus. There are 110 groups on campus, including art, band, choir, chorale, chorus, computers, dance, drama, ethnic, gay, honors, international, jazz band, literary magazine, musical theater, newspaper, orchestra, pep band, photography, political, professional, radio and TV, religious, social, social service, student government, symphony, and yearbook. Popular campus events include WATAB, Pinestock, and Millstream Arts Festival.

Sports: Ther are 9 intercollegiate sports and 13 intramural sports available. Athletic and recreation facilities include racquetball and tennis courts, a weight room, an indoor pool, a softball diamond, soc-

cer fields, and 30 miles of cross-country ski trails. Students have access to St. John's University facilities.

Disabled Students: Ninety percent of the campus is accessible to disabled students. The following facilities are available: wheelchair ramps, elevators, special parking, specially equipped rest rooms, special class scheduling, lowered drinking fountains, and lowered telephones.

Services: In addition to many counseling and information services, tutoring is available in every subject. There is also a writing laboratory and a mathematics skills center providing additional assistance to students.

Campus Safety and Security: Campus safety and security measures include 24-hour foot and vehicle patrol, escort service, shuttle buses, and informal discussions. In addition, there are pamphlets, posters, and films, emergency telephones, and lighted pathways and sidewalks.

Programs of Study: St. Benedict awards the B.A., B.Mus., and B.S.N. degrees. Bachelor's degrees are awarded in BIOLOGICAL SCIENCE (biology/biological science and nutrition), BUSINESS (accounting and management science), COMMUNICATIONS AND THE ARTS (art history and appreciation, classics, communications, dramatic arts, English, fine arts, French, German, Latin, music, and Spanish), COMPUTER AND PHYSICAL SCIENCE (chemistry, computer science, mathematics, natural sciences, and physics), EDUCATION (elementary), ENGINEERING AND ENVIRONMENTAL DESIGN (preengineering), HEALTH PROFESSIONS (medical laboratory technology, nursing, predentistry, premedicine, prepharmacy, and preveterinary science), and SOCIAL SCIENCE (dietetics, economics, history, humanities, liberal arts/general studies, medieval studies, peace studies, philosophy, political science/government, prelaw, psychology, social science, social work, sociology, and theological studies). Management, education, psychology, and nursing have the largest enrollments.

Required: To graduate, students must complete the core curriculum of writing, discussion, quantitative reasoning, and gender and global perspectives. Distribution requirements include 6 credits in fine arts, 5 courses in humanities, 2 courses each in natural science and social science, and 1 course in mathematics. All students must prove mathematics and foreign language proficiency. A total of 124 credits must be earned, with 40 credits in upper-division courses and an overall GPA of 2.0. Students must complete a first-year symposium and a senior seminar.

Special: Students may cross-register with St. John's and St. Cloud State universities. There are study-abroad programs in Ireland, Japan, China, South America, Scandinavia, and 6 European cities. Internships, a Washington semester, dual and student-designed majors, and liberal studies degrees may be pursued. A 3-2 engineering program is offered through several universities, and a 3-2 program in occupational therapy is available with Washington University in St. Louis, Missouri. Nondegree study and a pass/fail grading option are also available. There is a freshman honors program on campus, as well as 1 national honor society.

Faculty/Classroom: Forty percent of faculty are male; 60%, female. All both teach and do research. The average class size in an introductory lecture is 23; in a laboratory, 18; and in a regular course offering, 25.

Admissions: About 92% of the 1993-94 applicants were accepted. The SAT scores for the 1993-94 freshman class were as follows: Verbal—56% below 500, 34% between 500 and 599, 9% between 600 and 700, and 1% above 700; Math—36% below 500, 33% between 500 and 599, 29% between 600 and 700, and 1% above 700. The ACT scores were 24% below 21, 32% between 21 and 23, 24% between 24 and 26, 11% between 27 and 28, and 9% above 28. About 55% of the current freshmen were in the top fifth of their class; 82% were in the top two fifths.

Requirements: St. Benedict requires applicants to be in the upper 40% of their class. A minimum GPA of 2.8 is required. The SAT I or ACT is required. The PSAT may be substituted. Applicants must be graduates of an accredited secondary school; preparation should include 17 academic units, including 4 of English, 3 of mathematics, 2 each of a laboratory science and social studies, and 6 electives. A foreign language is recommended. Essays are required, and interviews are recommended. AP and CLEP credits are accepted. Important factors used in the admissions decision are advanced placement or honor courses, evidence of special talent, leadership record, extracurricular activities record, and recommendations by school officials.

Procedure: Freshmen are admitted to all sessions. Entrance exams should be taken during the spring of the junior year or the fall of the senior year. Application deadlines are open. The application fee is $20. Notification is sent on a rolling basis. There is a deferred admissions plan.

Transfer: About 100 transfer students enrolled in a recent year. Transfer applicants must have a minimum GPA of 2.5. The SAT I or ACT and high school transcripts are required. A total of 45 credits out of 124 must be completed at St. Benedict.

Visiting: There are regularly scheduled orientations for prospective students. There are guides for informal visits and visitors may sit in on classes and stay overnight at the school. To arrange for a visit, contact Mary Milbert, Director of Admissions, at (800) 544-1489 or (612) 363-5308.

Financial Aid: In a recent year, 80% of all students received some form of financial aid. About 72% of continuing students received need-based aid. The average freshman award was $10,460. Of that total, scholarships or need-based grants averaged $6275 ($8500 maximum); loans averaged $3035 ($4100 maximum); and work contracts averaged $1150 ($1550 maximum). Forty-seven percent of undergraduate students work part-time. Average earnings from campus work for the school year are $1300. The average financial indebtedness of a recent graduate was $9200. St. Benedict is a member of CSS. The FAF or FFS is required. The deadline for financial aid applications is July 1.

International Students: There are currently 46 international students enrolled. The school actively recruits these students. They must take the TOEFL and achieve a minimum score of 550. The student must also take the SAT I or the ACT.

Computers: The college provides computer facilities for student use. The mainframe is a DEC VAX 4000/300. There is a computer laboratory in each college residence, in numerous departments, and in 4 public access areas. All students may access the system. It may be used 24 hours per day. There are no time limits on using the system and no fees.

Graduates: In a recent year, 461 bachelor's degrees were awarded. The most popular majors among graduates were education (16%), management (12%), and psychology (9%). Within an average freshman class, 60% graduate in 4 years, 74% in 5 years, and 75% in 6 years. Some 90 companies recruited on campus. In a recent graduating class, 20% of the women were enrolled in graduate school within 6 months of graduation.

Admissions Contact: Mary Milbert, Director of Admissions.

COLLEGE OF SAINT CATHERINE   C-4

St. Paul, MN 55105	(612) 690-6505; (800) 945-4599
Full-time: 7 men, 1682 women	Faculty: 123; IIB, -$
Part-time: 17 men, 545 women	Ph.D.s: 76%
Graduate: 38 men, 296 women	Student/Faculty: 14 to 1
Year: semesters, summer session	Tuition: $11,530
Application Deadline: August 15	Room & Board: $3140
Freshman Class: 511 applied, 411 accepted, 186 enrolled	
SAT I Verbal/Math: 483/468	ACT: 22 COMPETITIVE

The College of Saint Catherine, founded in 1905, is a private, comprehensive, primarily women's college affiliated with the Roman Catholic Church. There is one graduate school. The 2 libraries contain 232,262 volumes, 35,000 microform items, and 15,000 audiovisual forms, and subscribe to 1170 periodicals. Computerized library sources and services include the card catalog, interlibrary loans, and database searching. Special learning facilities include a learning resource center and art gallery. The 110-acre campus is in an urban area. Including residence halls, there are 17 buildings on campus.

Student Life: About 87% of undergraduates are from Minnesota. Students come from 26 states and 23 foreign countries. Ninety-six percent are white. Most are Catholic. The average age of freshmen is 18; all undergraduates, 29. Twenty-seven percent drop out by the end of their first year; 41% remain to graduate.

Housing: A total of 632 students can be accommodated in college housing. College-sponsored living facilities include single-sex dormitories and on-campus apartments. On-campus housing is guaranteed for all 4 years. Sixty-five percent of students commute. All students may keep cars on campus.

Activities: There are 2 local sororities . There are no fraternities on campus. There are 40 groups on campus, including art, band, choir, chorale, chorus, drama, drill team, ethnic, honors, international, jazz band, literary magazine, musical theater, newspaper, orchestra, photography, political, professional, religious, social, social service, student government, and yearbook. Popular campus events include Fall Fest, Opening Celebration, Suitcase Dance, Student Life Week, Christmas Dance, and Dew Drop Bop.

Sports: There are 7 intercollegiate sports and 7 intramural sports for women. Athletic and recreation facilities include a new fitness facility, a gymnasium, a weight room, a swimming pool, an outdoor fitness course, tennis courts, and a softball field.

Disabled Students: Eighty-five percent of the campus is accessible to disabled students. The following facilities are available: wheelchair ramps, elevators, special parking, specially equipped rest rooms, special class scheduling, lowered drinking fountains, and lowered telephones.

Services: In addition to many counseling and information services, tutoring is available in most subjects. In addition, there is a reader service for the blind, and remedial math, reading, and writing.

Campus Safety and Security: Campus safety and security measures include 24-hour foot and vehicle patrol, self defense education, escort service, and informal discussions. In addition, there are pamphlets, posters, and films, emergency telephones, and lighted pathways and sidewalks.

Programs of Study: CSC awards the B.A. degree. Master's degrees also are awarded. Bachelor's degrees are awarded in BIOLOGICAL SCIENCE (biochemistry, biology/biological science, and nutrition), BUSINESS (accounting, business administration and management, fashion merchandising, and international economics), COMMUNICATIONS AND THE ARTS (communications, English, fine arts, French, music, Spanish, and speech/debate/rhetoric), COMPUTER AND PHYSICAL SCIENCE (chemistry, information sciences and systems, mathematics, and physics), EDUCATION (art, early childhood, elementary, home economics, and music), HEALTH PROFESSIONS (nursing and occupational therapy), SOCIAL SCIENCE (economics, family/consumer studies, history, international relations, philosophy, physical fitness/movement, political science/government, psychology, religion, social science, social studies, social work, and sociology). Business administration, nursing, education, and occupational therapy have the largest enrollments.

Required: To graduate, students must complete 128 semester credits, including a 40-credit liberal arts core and 80 credits outside the major. At least 36 hours are required in the major. Students must have a minimum 2.0 GPA and demonstrate proficiency in composition, mathematics, and computer literacy.

Special: CSC offers co-op programs with Carondelet College, the University of Minnesota, and George Washington University, and cross-registration with the Associated Colleges of the Twin Cities. Students may arrange internships, a Washington semester, and study abroad in England, France, Germany, or Japan. Dual majors are available in chemical and physics engineering. Students may receive credit for life, military, or work experience. Student-designed majors, nondegree study, and pass/fail options are available. The Weekend College offers a B.A. degree. There is a freshman honors program on campus, as well as 19 national honor societies, including Phi Beta Kappa. All departments have honors programs.

Faculty/Classroom: Twenty-six percent of faculty are male; 74%, female. All teach undergraduates. No introductory courses are taught by graduate students. The average class size in an introductory lecture is 25 and in a regular course offering, 19.

Admissions: About 80% of the 1993–94 applicants were accepted. The SAT scores for the 1993–94 freshman class were as follows: Verbal—56% below 500, 23% between 500 and 599, and 21% between 600 and 700; Math—63% below 500, 23% between 500 and 599, and 14% between 600 and 700. The ACT scores were 9% below 17, 53% between 18 and 23, 35% between 24 and 29, and 3% between 30 and 36. About 45% of the current freshmen were in the top fifth of their class; 72% were in the top two fifths. There were 3 National Merit finalists. Three freshmen graduated first in their class.

Requirements: The SAT I or ACT is required. In addition, applicants must have completed a college preparatory program, including 4 courses in English, 3 in mathematics, and 2 each in a foreign language, science, and social studies. AP and CLEP credits are accepted. Important factors used in the admissions decision are advanced placement or honor courses, recommendations by school officials, extracurricular activities record, evidence of special talent, and leadership record.

Procedure: Freshmen are admitted to all sessions. Entrance exams should be taken during the senior year. Applications should be filed by August 15 for fall entry, along with an application fee of $20. Notification is sent on a rolling basis. There are early decision, early admissions, and deferred admissions plans.

Transfer: A total of 409 transfer students enrolled in 1993–94. Transfer applicants must submit high school and college transcripts. A total of 48 credits out of 128 must be completed at CSC.

Visiting: There are regularly scheduled orientations for prospective students, including a tour, an admissions interview, and an appointment with a faculty member. There are guides for informal visits and visitors may sit in on classes and stay overnight at the school. To arrange for a visit, contact the Admissions Office at (800) 945-4599.

Financial Aid: In 1993–94, 89% of all current freshmen and 72% of continuing students received some form of financial aid. About 81% of freshmen and 68% of continuing students received need-based aid. The average freshman award was $10,221. Of that total, scholarships or need-based grants averaged $6136 ($10,221 maximum); loans averaged $2810 ($3625 maximum); and work contracts averaged $1275 ($1750 maximum). Seventy-five percent of undergraduate students work part-time. Average earnings from campus work for the school year are $1300. The average financial indebtedness of the 1992–93 graduate was $11,732. CSC is a member of CSS. The college's own financial statement and FAFSA are required. The deadline for financial aid applications is April 1.

International Students: There are currently 49 international students enrolled. The school actively recruits these students. They must take the TOEFL, the University of Michigan Language Test, or the college's own test, and achieve a minimum score on the TOEFL of 500. The SAT I is required only if the student has attended a U.S. high school either in this country or overseas.

Computers: The college provides computer facilities for student use. The mainframe is a DEC VAX 11/785. There are 165 IBM, Zenith, HP, Epson, Tandy, and Apple microcomputers available in the microcomputer center. All students may access the system 24 hours a day. There are no time limits on using the system and no fees.

Graduates: In 1992–93, 503 bachelor's degrees were awarded. The most popular majors among graduates were nursing (14%), elementary education (12%), and occupational therapy (9%). Within an average freshman class, 1% graduate in 3 years, 42% in 4 years, 15% in 5 years, and 1% in 6 years. Some 9 companies recruited on campus in 1992–93. In the 1992 graduating class, 15% of the women were enrolled in graduate school within 6 months of graduation; 82% of the women had found employment.

Admissions Contact: Mary Docken, Associate Dean of Admissions.

COLLEGE OF SAINT SCHOLASTICA   D-3
Duluth, MN 55811   (218) 723–6046; (800) 447–5444 (out-of-state)

Full-time: 380 men, 969 women	**Faculty:** 121; IIB, -$
Part-time: 74 men, 199 women	**Ph.D.s:** 76%
Graduate: 82 men, 134 women	**Student/Faculty:** 11 to 1
Year: quarters, summer session	**Tuition:** $11,280
Application Deadline: open	**Room & Board:** $3588
Freshman Class: 672 applied, 596 accepted, 278 enrolled	
SAT I Verbal/Math: 435/480	**ACT:** 23 **COMPETITIVE**

The College of St. Scholastica, founded in 1912, is a private, coeducational, liberal arts college affiliated with the Roman Catholic Church. There is one graduate school. In addition to regional accreditation, College of Saint Scholastica has baccalaureate program accreditation with APTA, CAHEA, CSWE, and NLN. The library contains 133,342 volumes and microform items, and subscribes to 779 periodicals. Computerized library sources and services include the card catalog, interlibrary loans, and database searching. Special learning facilities include a learning resource center. The 160-acre campus is in a suburban area 150 miles north of Minneapolis and St. Paul. Including residence halls, there are 12 buildings on campus.

Student Life: About 71% of undergraduates are from Minnesota. Students come from 15 states and Canada. Eighty-five percent are from public schools; 15% from private. Ninety-five percent are white. Twenty-eight percent are Catholic; 25% Protestant. The average age of freshmen is 18; all undergraduates, 21. Fifteen percent drop out by the end of their first year; 59% remain to graduate.

Housing: A total of 693 students can be accommodated in college housing. College-sponsored living facilities include coed dormitories and on-campus apartments. On-campus housing is available on a first-come, first-served basis and is available on a lottery system for upperclassmen. Sixty-seven percent of students commute. All students may keep cars on campus.

Activities: There are no fraternities or sororities on campus. There are 40 groups on campus, including cheerleading, choir, chorale, chorus, computers, dance, drama, ethnic, international, newspaper, pep band, photography, political, professional, religious, social, social service, student government, and yearbook. Popular campus events include Mayfest Week, Sports Spectacular, and Homecoming.

Sports: There are 7 intercollegiate sports for men and 7 for women, and 6 intramural sports for men and 6 for women. Athletic and recreation facilities include a recreation center.

Disabled Students: Ninety-five percent of the campus is accessible to disabled students. The following facilities are available: wheelchair ramps, elevators, special parking, specially equipped rest rooms, special class scheduling, lowered drinking fountains, and lowered telephones.

Services: In addition to many counseling and information services, tutoring is available in most subjects. In addition, there is a reader service for the blind and remedial math and writing.

Campus Safety and Security: Campus safety and security measures include 24-hour foot and vehicle patrol, self defense education, escort service, and informal discussions. In addition, there are pamphlets, posters, and films, emergency telephones, and lighted pathways and sidewalks.

Programs of Study: College of Saint Scholastica awards the B.A. degree. Master's degrees also are awarded. Bachelor's degrees are awarded in BIOLOGICAL SCIENCE (biology/biological science), BUSINESS (accounting, business administration and management, international business management, and marketing/retailing/merchandising), COMMUNICATIONS AND THE ARTS (communications, English, and music), COMPUTER AND PHYSICAL SCIENCE (chemistry, computer science, and mathematics), EDUCATION (early childhood, elementary, and secondary), HEALTH PROFESSIONS

(exercise science, health care administration, medical laboratory technology, nursing, occupational therapy, physical therapy, predentistry, premedicine, and sports medicine), SOCIAL SCIENCE (dietetics, history, home economics, ministries, pastoral studies, prelaw, psychology, religion, social work, and sociology). Health professions and management are the strongest academically. Management, nursing, physical therapy, and education have the largest enrollments.

Required: In order to graduate, students must complete 192 quarter credits with a 2.0 GPA. Seventy-two credits of general education courses are required, including 8 credits each of English composition, social science, natural science, and a foreign language; and 4 credits each of oral communication, literature, history, fine arts, philosophy, religious studies, mathematics, and cultural diversity. The hours required in the major vary. Most majors require an internship for graduation.

Special: Students may cross-register with the University of Minnesota at Duluth and the University of Wisconsin at Superior. Internships, study abroad in 3 countries, nondegree study, pass/fail options, and credit for life, military, or work experience are available.

Faculty/Classroom: Forty-three percent of faculty are male; 57%, female. All teach undergraduates. No introductory courses are taught by graduate students. The average class size in an introductory lecture is 21; in a laboratory, 15; and in a regular course offering, 13.

Admissions: About 89% of the 1993–94 applicants were accepted. The SAT scores for the 1993–94 freshman class were as follows: Verbal—77% below 500, 19% between 500 and 599, and 4% between 600 and 700; Math—61% below 500, 31% between 500 and 599, and 8% between 600 and 700. The ACT scores were 42% below 21, 22% between 21 and 23, 23% between 24 and 26, 9% between 27 and 28, and 4% above 28. About 50% of the current freshmen were in the top fifth of their class; 81% were in the top two fifths. There were 5 National Merit finalists and 10 semifinalists. Thirteen freshmen graduated first in their class.

Requirements: College of Saint Scholastica requires applicants to be in the upper 50% of their class. The SAT I or ACT is required. PSAT scores may also be submitted. AP and CLEP credits are accepted. Important factors used in the admissions decision are personality, intangible qualities, advanced placement or honor courses, recommendations by school officials, evidence of special talent, and leadership record.

Procedure: Freshmen are admitted to all sessions. Entrance exams should be taken during the junior or senior year. Application deadlines are open. The application fee is $15. Notification is sent on a rolling basis. There is an early admissions plan.

Transfer: A total of 113 transfer students enrolled in 1993–94. Applicants must have a GPA of 2.0 or a college aptitude rating score of 50 or higher. A total of 48 quarter credits out of 192 must be completed at College of Saint Scholastica.

Visiting: There are regularly scheduled orientations for prospective students, including a class placement survey, peer and academic advisement, and registration. There are guides for informal visits and visitors may sit in on classes and stay overnight at the school. To arrange for a visit, contact the Admissions Office at (218) 723–6046 or (800) 447–5444.

Financial Aid: In 1993–94, 83% of all current freshmen and 90% of continuing students received some form of financial aid. The average freshman award was $9890. Of that total, scholarships or need-based grants averaged $4945; loans averaged $3595; and work contracts averaged $1350. Sixty-five percent of undergraduate students work part-time. Average earnings from campus work for the school year are $1350. The average financial indebtedness of the 1992–93 graduate was $10,513. College of Saint Scholastica is a member of CSS. The FAFSA is required. The deadline for financial aid applications is March 15.

International Students: There are currently 20 international students enrolled. They must take the TOEFL or the University of Michigan Language Test and achieve a minimum score on the TOEFL of 550.

Computers: The college provides computer facilities for student use. The mainframes are an IBM System/36 and an AS/400. There are 80 microcomputers on network in laboratories throughout the campus. All students may access the system. It may be used 8 A.M. to midnight Monday through Thursday, 8 A.M. to 5 P.M. on Fridays, 9 A.M. to 5 P.M. on Saturdays, and 2 P.M. to 10 P.M. on Sundays. There are no time limits on using the system and no fees.

Graduates: In 1992–93, 380 bachelor's degrees were awarded. The most popular majors among graduates were management (18%), nursing (16%), and physical therapy (8%). Within an average freshman class, 1% graduate in 3 years, 38% in 4 years, 57% in 5 years, and 59% in 6 years. Five companies recruited on campus in 1992–93. In the 1992 graduating class, 20% of all students were enrolled in graduate school within 6 months of graduation; 75% of all students found employment.

Admissions Contact: Becky Urbanski-Junkert, Dean of Admissions and Student Financial Planning.

CONCORDIA COLLEGE C-4

St. Paul, MN 55104   (612) 641–8230; (800) 333–4705 (out-of-state)

Full-time: 476 men, 573 women	Faculty: 50; IIB, -$
Part-time: 65 men, 116 women	Ph.D.s: 75%
Graduate: 4 women	Student/Faculty: 21 to 1
Year: quarters, summer session	Tuition: $9720
Application Deadline: August 15	Room & Board: $3480
Freshman Class: 382 applied, 266 accepted, 139 enrolled	
ACT: recommended	COMPETITIVE

Concordia College, founded in 1893 and a unit of the Concordia University System, is a private, liberal arts institution affiliated with the Lutheran Church Missouri Synod offering programs in teacher education, business, church vocations, and the liberal arts. There is one undergraduate school. In addition to regional accreditation, Concordia/St. Paul has baccalaureate program accreditation with NCATE. The library contains 112,900 volumes, 10,800 microform items, and 5800 audiovisual forms, and subscribes to 911 periodicals. Computerized library sources and services include the card catalog and database searching. Special learning facilities include a learning resource center, art gallery, and natural history museum. The 27-acre campus is in an urban area in the Midway area of St. Paul. Including residence halls, there are 28 buildings on campus.

Student Life: About 86% of undergraduates are from Minnesota. Students come from 33 states and 4 foreign countries. Eighty-one percent are from public schools; 19% from private. Eighty-nine percent are white. Twenty-five percent are Protestant; 19% Catholic. The average age of freshmen is 18.2; all undergraduates, 23. Thirty-seven percent drop out by the end of their first year; 40% remain to graduate.

Housing: A total of 420 students can be accommodated in college housing. College-sponsored living facilities include single-sex dormitories, on-campus apartments, and married-student housing. On-campus housing is guaranteed for all 4 years. Fifty-four percent of students live on campus; of those, 40% remain on campus on weekends. Alcohol is not permitted. All students may keep cars on campus.

Activities: There are no fraternities or sororities on campus. There are 40 groups on campus, including art, band, cheerleading, choir, drama, drill team, ethnic, jazz band, musical theater, newspaper, orchestra, pep band, religious, social, student government, and yearbook. Popular campus events include Sno-Week.

Sports: There are 6 intercollegiate sports for men and 5 for women, and 8 intramural sports for men and 8 for women. Athletic and recreation facilities include a 4500-seat stadium, a 1200-seat gymnasium, and several playing fields for various sports.

Disabled Students: Ninety-five percent of the campus is accessible to disabled students. The following facilities are available: wheelchair ramps, elevators, special parking, specially equipped rest rooms, special class scheduling, lowered drinking fountains, and lowered telephones.

Services: In addition to many counseling and information services, tutoring is available in every subject. In addition, there is a reader service for the blind, and remedial math, reading, and writing.

Campus Safety and Security: Campus safety and security measures include 24-hour foot and vehicle patrol, self-defense education, escort service, and informal discussions. In addition, there are pamphlets, posters, and films, emergency telephones, and lighted pathways and sidewalks.

Programs of Study: Concordia/St. Paul awards the B.A. degree. Associate and master's degrees are also awarded. Bachelor's degrees are awarded in BIOLOGICAL SCIENCE (biology/biological science), BUSINESS (accounting, banking and finance, business administration and management, and marketing/retailing/merchandising), COMMUNICATIONS AND THE ARTS (English, fine arts, languages, literature, music, and speech/debate/rhetoric), COMPUTER AND PHYSICAL SCIENCE (mathematics, natural sciences, and physical sciences), EDUCATION (art, early childhood, elementary, English, mathematics, middle school, music, physical, science, secondary, and social studies), ENGINEERING AND ENVIRONMENTAL DESIGN (environmental science), HEALTH PROFESSIONS (premedicine), SOCIAL SCIENCE (biblical languages, economics, history, prelaw, psychology, religion, religious education, social science, and sociology). Elementary teacher education is the strongest academically. Elementary teacher education and business have the largest enrollments.

Required: In order to graduate, students must have a 2.0 GPA and complete between 192 to 212 quarter credits, including 48 to 60 in the major. A core curriculum of 71 quarter credits must include the following: 12 in religion; 10 in interdisciplinary studies; 8 in physical and biological sciences; 6 in 2 areas of art, music, or theater; and 4 each in anthropology, psychology, or sociology, in government or political science, in historical perspectives, and in literature/languages. Proficiency must be demonstrated in writing, mathematics, and physical education. A comprehensive examination must be taken during the senior year.

Special: Cross-registration with area colleges is available, as are internships in most programs. Students may study abroad in England. Work-study programs, credit for life experience, accelerated degree programs, B.A.-B.S. degrees, student-designed majors, interdisciplinary majors, including organizational management/communication, nondegree study, pass/fail options, and the substitution of 2 minors for a major are also possible.

Faculty/Classroom: Seventy-eight percent of faculty are male; 22%, female. All teach undergraduates. No introductory courses are taught by graduate students. The average class size in an introductory lecture is 25; in a laboratory, 22; and in a regular course offering, 17.

Admissions: About 70% of the 1993–94 applicants were accepted. About 24% of the current freshmen were in the top fifth of their class; 50% were in the top two fifths.

Requirements: Concordia/St. Paul requires applicants to be in the upper 50% of their class. A minimum GPA of 2.0 is required. The ACT is recommended. In addition, applicants are required to have 4 years of English, 2 each of mathematics and science, and 1 each of fine arts, history, social studies, and health or physical education. An interview and essay are recommended. Two letters of recommendation are required. The GED is accepted. AP and CLEP credits are accepted. Important factors used in the admissions decision are recommendations by school officials, advanced placement or honor courses, evidence of special talent, leadership record, and personality, intangible qualities.

Procedure: Freshmen are admitted to all sessions. Entrance exams should be taken during the senior year. Applications should be filed by August 15 for fall entry, November 15 for winter entry, February 15 for spring entry, and May 30 for summer entry, along with an application fee of $15. Notification is sent on a rolling basis. There is a deferred admissions plan.

Transfer: About 240 transfer students enrolled in 1993–94. Transfer applicants must have a 2.0 GPA. A total of 48 quarter credits out of 192 to 212 must be completed at Concordia/St. Paul.

Visiting: There are regularly scheduled orientations for prospective students, including a 3-day program before classes begin, with class visits, lunch, and meetings with professors. There are guides for informal visits and visitors may sit in on classes. To arrange for a visit, contact the Director of Admissions at (612) 641–8231.

Financial Aid: In 1993–94, 94% of all current freshmen and 72% of continuing students received some form of financial aid. About 85% of freshmen and 65% of continuing students received need-based aid. The average freshman award was $6730. Of that total, scholarships or need-based grants averaged $4038 ($14,500 maximum); loans averaged $1817 ($5625 maximum); and work contracts averaged $875 ($6600 maximum). Thirty percent of undergraduate students work part-time. Average earnings from campus work for the school year are $2000. Concordia/St. Paul is a member of CSS. The FAFSA financial statement is required. The deadline for financial aid applications is August 1.

International Students: There are currently 4 international students enrolled. They must take the TOEFL and achieve a minimum score of 500.

Computers: The college provides computer facilities for student use. The mainframe is a DEC VAX 4000/Model 200. The mathematics, science, and learning centers have a variety of Apple and IBM PCs networked to laser printers. All students may access the system. It may be used during the hours the media center and science building are open. There are no time limits on using the system and no fees.

Graduates: In 1992–93, 331 bachelor's degrees were awarded. The most popular majors among graduates were organizational management (56%), teacher education (19%), and business (6%).

Admissions Contact: Tim Utter, Director of Admissions.

CONCORDIA COLLEGE
MOORHEAD

A-2

Moorhead, MN 56562

(218) 299–3004 (collect)

Full-time: 1151 men, 1766 women	Faculty: 186; IIB, av$
Part-time: 33 men, 49 women	Ph.D.s: 63%
Graduate: none	Student/Faculty: 16 to 1
Year: semesters, summer session	Tuition: $9700
Application Deadline: open	Room & Board: $3050
Freshman Class: 2007 applied, 1808 accepted, 846 enrolled	
SAT I or ACT: required	COMPETITIVE

Concordia College, founded in 1891, is a private, liberal arts institution affiliated with the Evangelical Lutheran Church in America. In addition to regional accreditation, Concordia has baccalaureate program accreditation with ADA, CSWE, NASM, NCATE, and NLN. The library contains 273,374 volumes and 274,000 microform items, and subscribes to 1400 periodicals. Computerized library sources and services include the card catalog and interlibrary loans. Special learning facilities include a learning resource center, art gallery, radio station, and tv station. The 120-acre campus is in an urban area 240

miles northwest of Minneapolis and St. Paul. Including residence halls, there are 36 buildings on campus.

Student Life: About 64% of undergraduates are from Minnesota. Students come from 43 states, 29 foreign countries, and Canada. Ninety-four percent are from public schools; 3% from private. Ninety-seven percent are white. Seventy-nine percent are Protestant; 13% Catholic. The average age of freshmen is 18; all undergraduates, 20. Seventeen percent drop out by the end of their first year; 70% remain to graduate.

Housing: A total of 1801 students can be accommodated in college housing. College-sponsored living facilities include single-sex dormitories and on-campus apartments. In addition there are language houses. On-campus housing is available on a first-come, first-served basis and is available on a lottery system for upperclassmen. Priority is given to out-of-town students. Fifty-nine percent of students live on campus. Alcohol is not permitted. All students may keep cars on campus.

Activities: There are no fraternities or sororities on campus. There are 150 groups on campus, including art, band, cheerleading, choir, drama, drill team, ethnic, film, honors, jazz band, literary magazine, musical theater, newspaper, orchestra, pep band, political, professional, radio and tv, religious, social, social service, student government, and yearbook. Popular campus events include Homecoming, Family Weekend, Casino Night, and Winter Meltdown.

Sports: There are 10 intercollegiate sports for men and 8 for women, and 14 intramural sports for men and 14 for women. Athletic and recreation facilities include a college-owned health club, a field house with a 3500-seat gymnasium, a 6500-seat stadium, a swimming pool, 4 outdoor tennis courts, a track, a soccer field, a recreation room in the student life center, and numerous other fields and courts.

Disabled Students: The following facilities are available: wheelchair ramps, elevators, special parking, specially equipped rest rooms, special class scheduling, and lowered drinking fountains.

Services: In addition to many counseling and information services, tutoring is available in most subjects.

Campus Safety and Security: Campus safety and security measures include escort service, informal discussions, pamphlets, posters, films, and lighted pathways and sidewalks.

Programs of Study: Concordia awards the B.A. and B.M. degrees. Bachelor's degrees are awarded in BIOLOGICAL SCIENCE (biology/biological science), BUSINESS (accounting, business administration and management, and international business management), COMMUNICATIONS AND THE ARTS (advertising, classical languages, communications, dramatic arts, English, French, German, Latin, music, and Spanish), COMPUTER AND PHYSICAL SCIENCE (chemistry, computer science, mathematics, and physics), EDUCATION (art, business, elementary, foreign languages, health, home economics, middle school, music, physical, secondary, and social studies), ENGINEERING AND ENVIRONMENTAL DESIGN (preengineering), HEALTH PROFESSIONS (health, health care administration, medical laboratory technology, nursing, predentistry, premedicine, and preveterinary science), SOCIAL SCIENCE (criminal justice, dietetics, economics, history, humanities, international relations, philosophy, political science/government, prelaw, psychology, religion, social work, and sociology). Premedicine, prelaw, mathematics, and English are the strongest academically. Business administration, communications, biology, psychology, and education have the largest enrollments.

Required: All students must maintain a minimum GPA of 2.0 while taking 126 semester hours, including at least 32 in their major. Specific course needs are freshman English, introduction to liberal arts, an integration course, and 2 physical education courses. Distribution requirements include 7 courses taken from 5 areas: science and mathematics, social science, foreign language, foundation/premises of civilization, and literature/fine arts.

Special: Cross-registration with Moorhead State and North Dakota State Universities in some programs, internships, especially in Fargo, ND, Moorhead, or Minneapolis/St. Paul, study abroad in Europe, Asia, and Africa, study through an urban studies program in Chicago, and a Washington semester are available. Work-study programs with various area employers and the college, a B.A.-B.S. degree in music, dual majors in any area, and a 3–2 engineering degree at Washington University are possible. Nondegree study for special students, and pass/fail options are offered. There is a freshman honors program on campus, as well as one national honor society. Nine departments have honors programs.

Faculty/Classroom: Sixty-four percent of faculty are male; 36%, female. All teach undergraduates. The average class size in an introductory lecture is 35; in a laboratory, 18; and in a regular course offering, 25.

Admissions: About 90% of the 1993–94 applicants were accepted. The SAT scores for the 1993–94 freshman class were as follows: Verbal—54% below 500, 34% between 500 and 599, 10% between 600 and 700, and 2% above 700; Math—37% below 500, 33% between 500 and 599, 23% between 600 and 700, and 7% above 700.

The ACT scores were 23% below 21, 29% between 21 and 23, 23% between 24 and 26, 13% between 27 and 28, and 12% above 28. About 48% of the current freshmen were in the top fifth of their class; 77% were in the top two fifths. There were 12 National Merit finalists and 12 semifinalists.

Requirements: The SAT I or the ACT is required. An ACT score of 18 is recommended. Two character references also are required, and an interview is recommended. The GED is accepted. No set numbers of academic credits are needed. AP and CLEP credits are accepted. Important factors used in the admissions decision are recommendations by school officials, personality, intangible qualities, advanced placement or honor courses, leadership record, and extracurricular activities record.

Procedure: Freshmen are admitted to all sessions. Entrance exams should be taken by the first semester of the senior year. Application deadlines are open. Application fee is $20. Notification is sent on a rolling basis. There are early admissions and deferred admissions plans. A waiting list is an active part of the admissions procedure.

Transfer: About 100 transfer students enrolled in 1993–94. Transfer applicants must have a minimum 2.0 GPA. A total of 32 credits out of 126 must be completed at Concordia.

Visiting: There are regularly scheduled orientations for prospective students, including an extensive campus tour and a visit with an admissions counselor. Students may also meet with faculty members. There are guides for informal visits and visitors may sit in on classes and stay overnight at the school. To arrange for a visit, contact the Office of Admissions at (218) 299–3004.

Financial Aid: In 1993–94, 88% of all current freshmen and 83% of continuing students received some form of financial aid. About 73% of freshmen and 68% of continuing students received need-based aid. The average freshman award was $7928. Of that total, scholarships or need-based grants averaged $5010 ($12,750 maximum); loans averaged $3585 ($5625 maximum); and work contracts averaged $830 ($2500 maximum). Fifty-eight percent of undergraduate students work part-time. Average earnings from campus work for the school year are $600. The average financial indebtedness of the 1992–93 graduate was $10,225. Concordia is a member of CSS. The FAF or FFS is required.

International Students: There are currently 111 international students enrolled. The school actively recruits these students. They must take the TOEFL and achieve a minimum score of 500.

Computers: The college provides computer facilities for student use. The mainframe is a DEC VAX 11/750 and a Solborne. IBM and Apple Macintosh microcomputers are available in 3 computer laboratories on campus. Use is on a first-come, first-served basis. All students may access the system. It may be used 20 to 24 hours per day. There are no time limits on using the system and no fees.

Graduates: In 1992–93, 598 bachelor's degrees were awarded. The most popular majors among graduates were business administration (16%), communications (11%), and psychology (10%). Within an average freshman class, 59% graduate in 4 years and 66% in 5 years. Some 24 companies recruited on campus in 1992–93. In the 1992 graduating class, 91% of all graduates had found employment within 6 months of graduation.

Admissions Contact: Office of Admissions, Concordia College/Moorhead.

GUSTAVUS ADOLPHUS COLLEGE
St. Peter, MN 56082–1498

C-4
(507) 933–7676
(800) GUSTAVU(S) (out-of-state)

Full-time: 1028 men, 1253 women	Faculty: 160; IIB, av$
Part-time: 15 men, 20 women	Ph.D.s: 85%
Graduate: none	Student/Faculty: 14 to 1
Year: 4-1-4, summer session	Tuition: $12,435
Application Deadline: April 1	Room & Board: $3500
Freshman Class: 1709 applied, 1385 accepted, 634 enrolled	
SAT I Verbal/Math: 520/590	ACT: 25 **VERY COMPETITIVE**

Gustavus Adolphus College, founded in 1862, is a private, coeducational, liberal arts college affiliated with the Lutheran Church. In addition to regional accreditation, Gustavus has baccalaureate program accreditation with NASM, NCATE, and NLN. The library contains 228,554 volumes, 29,868 microform items, and 11,942 audiovisual forms, and subscribes to 1132 periodicals. Computerized library sources and services include the card catalog, interlibrary loans, and database searching. Special learning facilities include an art gallery, a radio station, and an arboretum. The 294-acre campus is in a small town 65 miles southwest of Minneapolis. Including residence halls, there are 55 buildings on campus.

Student Life: About 73% of undergraduates are from Minnesota. Students come from 39 states, 18 foreign countries, and Canada. Ninety-three percent are from public schools; 7% from private. Ninety-four percent are white. Seventy-nine percent are Protestant; 15% Catholic. The average age of freshmen is 18; all undergraduates, 20.

Nine percent drop out by the end of their first year; 76% remain to graduate.

Housing: A total of 1900 students can be accommodated in college housing. College-sponsored living facilities include coed dormitories and on-campus apartments. In addition there are language houses and special interest houses. On-campus housing is guaranteed for all 4 years. Ninety-two percent of students live on campus; of those, 85% remain on campus on weekends. Upperclassmen may keep cars on campus.

Activities: About 20% of men belong to 2 local fraternities; about 25% of women belong to 4 local sororities. There are 85 groups on campus, including band, cheerleading, choir, chorus, dance, drama, ethnic, gay, honors, international, jazz band, literary magazine, newspaper, orchestra, pep band, political, professional, radio and TV, religious, social, student government, and yearbook. Popular campus events include Christmas in Christ Chapel, Homecoming, and Frost Week.

Sports: There are 11 intercollegiate sports for men and 11 for women, and 17 intramural sports for men and 10 for women. Athletic and recreation facilities include an ice arena, an Olympic-size pool, a gymnastics area, playing fields, racquetball and tennis courts, a weight room, and an indoor running track; there are varsity and intramural fields for soccer, softball, baseball, lacrosse, rugby, and ultimate frisbee.

Disabled Students: Ninety percent of the campus is accessible to disabled students. The following facilities are available: wheelchair ramps, elevators, special parking, specially equipped rest rooms, special class scheduling, and lowered drinking fountains.

Services: In addition to many counseling and information services, tutoring is available in most subjects. There is a writing laboratory as well.

Campus Safety and Security: Campus safety and security measures include 24-hour foot and vehicle patrol, escort service, informal discussions, and emergency telephones. In addition, there are lighted pathways and sidewalks.

Programs of Study: Gustavus awards the B.A. degree. Bachelor's degrees are awarded in BIOLOGICAL SCIENCE (biochemistry and biology/biological science), BUSINESS (accounting, business administration and management, business economics, and international business management), COMMUNICATIONS AND THE ARTS (classics, communications, dance, dramatic arts, English, fine arts, French, German, music, Russian, Scandinavian languages, Spanish, and speech/debate/rhetoric), COMPUTER AND PHYSICAL SCIENCE (chemistry, computer science, geology, mathematics, and physics), EDUCATION (art, business, elementary, foreign languages, health, middle school, music, science, and secondary), HEALTH PROFESSIONS (nursing, physical therapy, predentistry, and premedicine), SOCIAL SCIENCE (anthropology, criminal justice, economics, geography, history, philosophy, political science/government, prelaw, psychology, religion, social science, and sociology). Physical science and social science are the strongest academically. Business, biology, and social science have the largest enrollments.

Required: All students are required to complete 35 courses totaling 140 semester hours, including 3 January-term courses and 1 course in physical education. Core and distribution requirements include a first-term seminar and 2 additional writing classes, 4 courses in language and humanities, 2 each in fine arts, mathematics/science, social science, and foreign culture, and 1 in religion. A minimum GPA of 2.0 is necessary for graduation. A total of 7 to 11 courses is required in the major.

Special: Co-op programs in nursing with Saint Olaf College and cross-registration with Mankato State University are available. The college offers internships, a Washington semester, study abroad, student-designed majors, nondegree study, and pass/fail options for some courses. A 3–2 engineering degree program with Washington University and the University of Minnesota is offered. The Curriculum II core offers a 12-course interdisciplinary program. There are 16 national honor societies on campus, including Phi Beta Kappa. Five departments have honors programs.

Faculty/Classroom: Seventy-three percent of faculty are male; 27%, female. All teach undergraduates. The average class size in an introductory lecture is 25; in a laboratory and in a regular course offering, 15.

Admissions: About 81% of the 1993–94 applicants were accepted. The SAT scores for the 1993–94 freshman class were as follows: Verbal—44% below 500, 29% between 500 and 599, 24% between 600 and 700, and 3% above 700; Math—21% below 500, 31% between 500 and 599, 33% between 600 and 700, and 15% above 700. The ACT scores were 10% below 21, 25% between 21 and 23, 32% between 24 and 26, 14% between 27 and 28, and 19% above 28. About 61% of the current freshmen were in the top fifth of their class; 90% were in the top two fifths. There were 22 National Merit finalists and 25 semifinalists. Thirty freshmen graduated first in their class.

Requirements: The SAT I or ACT is required. In addition, applicants must have completed 4 years of English, 3 each of mathematics and science, and 2 each of a foreign language, history, and social studies. AP credits are accepted. Important factors used in the admissions decision are advanced placement or honors courses, evidence of special talent, recommendations by school officials, personality, intangible qualities, and extracurricular activities record.

Procedure: Freshmen are admitted fall, winter, and spring. Entrance exams should be taken in the fall of the senior year. Early decision applications should be filed by November 15; regular applications, by April 1 for fall entry, December 15 for winter entry, and January 15 for spring entry, along with an application fee of $20. Notification of early decision is sent December 1; regular decision, on a rolling basis. There are early decision, early admissions, and deferred admissions plans. Some 125 early decision candidates were accepted for the 1993–94 class. A waiting list is an active part of the admissions procedure.

Transfer: About 44 transfer students enrolled in 1993–94. Transfer applicants must have earned a 2.4 GPA at their previous college. A total of 18 courses out of 35 must be completed at Gustavus.

Visiting: There are regularly scheduled orientations for prospective students, consisting of an interview, a tour, and meetings with faculty and students. There are guides for informal visits, and visitors may sit in on classes and stay overnight at the school. To arrange for a visit, contact the Admissions Office at (507) 933–7676.

Financial Aid: In 1993–94, 80% of all current freshmen and 70% of continuing students received some form of financial aid. About 78% of freshmen and 65% of continuing students received need-based aid. The average freshman award was $12,335. Of that total, scholarships or need-based grants averaged $7815; loans averaged $3120 ($4000 maximum); and work contracts averaged $1400 (maximum). Sixty-five percent of undergraduate students work part-time. Average earnings from campus work for the school year are $1100. The average financial indebtedness of the 1992–93 graduate was $10,400. Gustavus is a member of CSS. The FAFSA, FAF, or FFS is required. A financial statement is required. The deadline for financial aid applications is April 1.

International Students: There are currently 44 international students enrolled. The school actively recruits these students. They must take the TOEFL, achieving a minimum score of 550, or the University of Michigan Language Test.

Computers: The college provides computer facilities for student use. The mainframes are a DEC MicroVAX 3600 and a MicroVAX II. Students have access to 6 computer networks, some of which are connected with the Minnesota State University System. These include 55 Macintosh, 50 IBM, and 27 NeXT computers located in the library and various academic buildings. There is also an electronic music laboratory. All students may access the system. There are no time limits on using the system and no fees.

Graduates: In 1992–93, 513 bachelor's degrees were awarded. The most popular majors among graduates were biology (12%), psychology (12%), and management (11%). Within an average freshman class, 1% graduate in 3 years, 76% in 4 years, 80% in 5 years, and 80% in 6 years. About 40 companies usually recruit on campus. In an earlier graduating class, 30% of all students were enrolled in graduate school within 6 months of graduation; 60% had found employment.

Admissions Contact: Mark H. Anderson, Director of Admission.

HAMLINE UNIVERSITY
St. Paul, MN 55104–1284

C-4

(612) 641–2207
(800) 753–9753 (out-of-state)

Full-time: 642 men, 822 women	Faculty: 93; IIA, av$
Part-time: 40 men, 58 women	Ph.D.s: 93%
Graduate: 495 men, 603 women	Student/Faculty: 16 to 1
Year: 4–1–4, summer session	Tuition: $13,022
Application Deadline: April 1	Room & Board: $4100
Freshman Class: 1006 applied, 825 accepted, 328 enrolled	
SAT I Verbal/Math: 530/580	ACT: 25 **VERY COMPETITIVE**

Hamline University, founded in 1854, is a private, coeducational, liberal arts university, affiliated with the United Methodist Church. There is one undergraduate and 5 graduate schools. In addition to regional accreditation, Hamline has baccalaureate program accreditation with ACS, NASM, and NCATE. The 2 libraries contain 305,600 volumes, 157,700 microform items, and 2300 audiovisual forms, and subscribe to 3650 periodicals. Computerized library sources and services include the card catalog, interlibrary loans, and database searching. Special learning facilities include a learning resource center, art gallery, and Center for Global Environment Education, Applied Research Center, Crossroads Center, Center for Women in Government, and Jewish History Society Archives. The 44-acre campus is in an urban area between the downtowns of Minneapolis and St. Paul. Including residence halls, there are 25 buildings on campus.

Student Life: About 69% of undergraduates are from Minnesota. Students come from 40 states, 34 foreign countries, and Canada. Seventy-four percent are from public schools; 26% from private. Eighty-six percent are white. Fifty-five percent are Protestant; 24% Catholic; 12% claim no religious affiliation. The average age of freshmen is 18; all undergraduates, 21. Eighteen percent drop out by the end of their first year; 70% remain to graduate.

Housing: A total of 741 students can be accommodated in college housing. College-sponsored living facilities include coed dormitories, fraternity houses, and sorority houses. In addition there are language houses, special interest houses, and smoke-free and substance-free floors available. On-campus housing is guaranteed for all 4 years and is available on a first-come, first-served basis. Fifty-three percent of students live on campus; of those, 90% remain on campus on weekends. All students may keep cars on campus.

Activities: About 10% of men belong to 2 national fraternities; about 10% of women belong to 2 local sororities. There are 80 groups on campus, including art, band, cheerleading, chess, choir, chorale, chorus, computers, dance, drama, ethnic, gay, honors, international, jazz band, literary magazine, marching band, musical theater, newspaper, orchestra, pep band, political, professional, religious, social, social service, student government, symphony, and yearbook. Popular campus events include Homecoming, End-of-the-Year Celebration, Ethnic Fair, Snow Week, February Formal, Spring Fling, Spring Theater Festival, January Film Festival, Drew Hall Haunted House, and Halloween Dance.

Sports: There are 9 intercollegiate sports for men and 9 for women, and 8 intramural sports for men and 10 for women. Athletic and recreation facilities include the Hutton Fieldhouse.

Disabled Students: Sixty percent of the campus is accessible to disabled students. The following facilities are available: wheelchair ramps, elevators, special parking, specially equipped rest rooms, special class scheduling, lowered drinking fountains, and lowered telephones.

Services: In addition to many counseling and information services, tutoring is available in every subject. In addition, there is a reader service for the blind.

Campus Safety and Security: Campus safety and security measures include 24-hour foot and vehicle patrol, self-defense education, escort service, and informal discussions. In addition, there are pamphlets, posters, and films, emergency telephones, and lighted pathways and sidewalks.

Programs of Study: Hamline awards the B.A. degree. Master's degrees are also awarded. Bachelor's degrees are awarded in BIOLOGICAL SCIENCE (biology/biological science), BUSINESS (business administration and management and international business management), COMMUNICATIONS AND THE ARTS (communications, English, fine arts, and music), COMPUTER AND PHYSICAL SCIENCE (chemistry, mathematics, and physics), EDUCATION (art, elementary, foreign languages, music, science, and secondary), HEALTH PROFESSIONS (predentistry and premedicine), SOCIAL SCIENCE (anthropology, economics, history, international relations, philosophy, political science/government, prelaw, psychology, public administration, religion, social science, sociology, and urban studies). Prelaw, premedicine, international relations, English, psychology, and anthropology are the strongest academically. Psychology, English, and political science have the largest enrollments.

Required: To graduate, students must complete a freshman seminar; 1 course each of freshman English, computer literacy, and formal reasoning; 2 writing-intensive courses; 2 courses each in oral communication, fine arts, humanities, natural science, and social sciences; 3 courses on other cultures; 1 independent study project; and 1 course on work and liberal learning. Students must complete 32 course credits (128 semester hours) with a minimum overall GPA of 2.0.

Special: Cross-registration with Augsburg, Macalester, Saint Catherine, and Saint Thomas colleges is possible. Students may select cooperative programs, study abroad, a Washington semester with American University, student-designed majors, and pass/fail options. Students may earn a 3–2 or 4–2 engineering degree at the University of Minnesota, or pursue an accelerated 3–3 degree progam in legal studies. Work-study programs are available. There is a freshman honors program on campus, as well as 18 national honor societies, including Phi Beta Kappa. All departments have honors programs.

Faculty/Classroom: Sixty-five percent of faculty are male; 35%, female. All teach undergraduates. No introductory courses are taught by graduate students. The average class size in an introductory lecture is 27; in a laboratory, 14; and in a regular course offering, 19.

Admissions: About 82% of the 1993–94 applicants were accepted. The SAT scores for the 1993–94 freshman class were as follows: Verbal—36% below 500, 36% between 500 and 599, 20% between 600 and 700, and 8% above 700; Math—13% below 500, 47% between 500 and 599, 32% between 600 and 700, and 8% above 700. The ACT scores were 11% below 21, 26% between 21 and 23, 27% between 24 and 26, 18% between 27 and 28, and 18% above 28. About 60% of the current freshmen were in the top fifth of their class;

90% were in the top two fifths. There were 3 National Merit finalists and 22 semifinalists.

Requirements: The SAT I or ACT is required. It is recommended that candidates for admission complete 4 years of English including 1 year of college preparatory writing, 3 years each of mathematics, laboratory science, and social science, and 2 years of a foreign language. AP and CLEP credits are accepted. Important factors used in the admissions decision are advanced placement or honor courses, recommendations by school officials, leadership record, extracurricular activities record, and evidence of special talent.

Procedure: Freshmen are admitted in the fall. Entrance exams should be taken by February of the senior year. Applications should be filed by April 1 for fall entry, along with an application fee of $25. Notification of early decision is sent December 15; regular decision, on a rolling basis. There are early admissions and deferred admissions plans.

Transfer: About 140 transfer students enrolled in 1993–94. A total of 14 course credits out of 32 must be completed at Hamline.

Visiting: There are guides for informal visits and visitors may sit in on classes and stay overnight at the school. To arrange for a visit, contact the Admissions Office at (612) 641–2207 or (800) 753–9753.

Financial Aid: In 1993–94, 75% of all current freshmen and 77% of continuing students received some form of financial aid. About 73% of freshmen and 75% of continuing students received need-based aid. The average freshman award was $12,400. Of that total, scholarships or need-based grants averaged $9400 ($12,866 maximum); loans averaged $2873; and work contracts averaged $1500. Sixty-five percent of undergraduate students work part-time. Average earnings from campus work for the school year are $1500. Hamline is a member of CSS. The FAFSA financial statement is required. The deadline for financial aid applications is March 15.

International Students: There are currently 53 international students enrolled. The school actively recruits these students. They must take the TOEFL or the University of Michigan Language Test and achieve a minimum score on the TOEFL of 550.

Computers: The college provides computer facilities for student use. The mainframe is a Sequent S2000. Microcomputers are available for student use. All students may access the system. There are no time limits on using the system and no fees.

Graduates: In 1992–93, 343 bachelor's degrees were awarded. The most popular majors among graduates were psychology (14%), political science (12%), and English (10%). Within an average freshman class, 1% graduate in 3 years, 64% in 4 years, 71% in 5 years, and 71% in 6 years. In the 1992 graduating class, 25% of the men and 25% of the women were enrolled in graduate school within 6 months of graduation; 98% of the men and 98% of the women had found employment.

Admissions Contact: Dr. W. Scott Friedhoff, Dean of Admission.

MACALESTER COLLEGE

C-4

St. Paul, MN 55105   (612) 696–6357; (800) 231–7974 (out-of-state)

Full-time: 760 men, 963 women	Faculty: 125; IIB, +$
Part-time: 41 men, 72 women	Ph.D.s: 91%
Graduate: none	Student/Faculty: 14 to 1
Year: 4–1–4	Tuition: $15,208
Application Deadline: January 15	Room & Board: $4502
Freshman Class: 2939 applied, 1496 accepted, 452 enrolled	
SAT I or ACT: required	**HIGHLY COMPETITITVE**

Macalester College, founded in 1855, is a nonsectarian, liberal arts institution affiliated with the United Presbyterian Church. In addition to regional accreditation, Macalester has baccalaureate program accreditation with NASM and NCATE. The library contains 344,071 volumes, 56,377 microform items, and 8737 audiovisual forms, and subscribes to 1420 periodicals. Computerized library sources and services include the card catalog, interlibrary loans, and database searching. Special learning facilities include a learning resource center, art gallery, radio station, tv station, and a 280-acre natural history study area 25 miles from campus. The 55-acre campus is in a suburban area midway between downtown St. Paul and Minneapolis. Including residence halls, there are 35 buildings on campus.

Student Life: About 76% of undergraduates are from out-of-state, mostly the Midwest. Students come from 50 states, 83 foreign countries, and Canada. Sixty-eight percent are from public schools; 32% from private. Seventy-one percent are white; 13% foreign nationals. The average age of freshmen is 19; all undergraduates, 20. Nine percent drop out by the end of their first year; 76% remain to graduate.

Housing: A total of 1169 students can be accommodated in college housing. College-sponsored living facilities include single-sex and coed dormitories. In addition there are language houses and a vegetarian co-op, a Hebrew house, and a chemical-free floor. On-campus housing is guaranteed for the freshman year only, is available on a first-come, first-served basis, and is available on a lottery system for upperclassmen. Sixty-three percent of students live on campus; of those, 99% remain on campus on weekends. All students may keep cars on campus.

Activities: There are no fraternities or sororities on campus. There are 85 groups on campus, including art, bagpipe band, band, chess, choir, chorale, chorus, computers, dance, drama, ethnic, gay, honors, international, jazz band, literary magazine, musical theater, newspaper, opera, orchestra, pep band, political, professional, radio and tv, religious, social, social service, student government, symphony, and yearbook. Popular campus events include Scottish Country Fair, Springfest, Volunteer Service Week, Native American Week, Black History Month, International Week, and Hispanic Week.

Sports: There are 10 intercollegiate sports for men and 10 for women, and 20 intramural sports for men and 20 for women. Athletic and recreation facilities include a 2000-seat gymnasium, a 5000-seat stadium, a swimming pool, a field house, 4 racquetball courts, 6 tennis courts, a dance studio, a track, and baseball diamonds.

Disabled Students: Seventy-five percent of the campus is accessible to disabled students. The following facilities are available: wheelchair ramps, elevators, special parking, specially equipped rest rooms, special class scheduling, lowered drinking fountains, and lowered telephones.

Services: In addition to many counseling and information services, tutoring is available in every subject. In addition, there is a reader service for the blind, and remedial math, reading, and writing.

Campus Safety and Security: Campus safety and security measures include 24-hour foot and vehicle patrol, self-defense education, escort service, and informal discussions. In addition, there are pamphlets, posters, and films, emergency telephones, and lighted pathways and sidewalks.

Programs of Study: Macalester awards the B.A. degree. Bachelor's degrees are awarded in BIOLOGICAL SCIENCE (biology/biological science), COMMUNICATIONS AND THE ARTS (art, classics, communications, dramatic arts, English, French, German, linguistics, music, Russian, and Spanish), COMPUTER AND PHYSICAL SCIENCE (chemistry, computer science, geology, mathematics, and physics), ENGINEERING AND ENVIRONMENTAL DESIGN (environmental science), SOCIAL SCIENCE (anthropology, East Asian studies, economics, geography, history, international relations, Japanese studies, Latin American studies, philosophy, political science/government, psychology, religion, Russian and Slavic studies, sociology, and urban studies). Anthropology, geography, biology, history, mathematics and religious studies are the strongest academically. English, history, and psychology have the largest enrollments.

Required: All students are required to complete 136 semester hours, with 32 to 44 in the major, and an overall minimum GPA of 2.0. Required courses include 12 hours in humanities and fine arts, 8 hours each in natural science, mathematics, and social science, a first year course, a domestic course, and an international diversity course. Second language proficiency must be shown and every major requires a capstone experience.

Special: The college belongs to several consortiums, including the Associated Colleges of the Midwest and the Associated Colleges of the Twin Cities. There also are cooperative programs in liberal arts and architecture with Washington University in St. Louis, engineering with the same school and the University of Minnesota, and nursing with Rush-Presbyterian-St Luke's Medical Center in Chicago. About half of Macalester students complete internships at more than 200 sites in Minneapolis and St. Paul. Students may study abroad in China, Japan, and Europe. Credit by exam under supervision of individual instructors, nondegree study, and pass/fail options for 1 course only per semester, also are available. There are 14 national honor societies on campus, including Phi Beta Kappa.

Faculty/Classroom: Fifty-eight percent of faculty are male; 42%, female. All teach undergraduates, 90% do research, and 90% do both. The average class size in an introductory lecture is 25; in a laboratory, 15; and in a regular course offering, 19.

Admissions: About 51% of the 1993–94 applicants were accepted. The SAT scores for the 1993–94 freshman class were as follows: Verbal—8% below 500, 34% between 500 and 599, 49% between 600 and 700, and 9% above 700; Math—5% below 500, 29% between 500 and 599, 43% between 600 and 700, and 23% above 700. The ACT scores were 2% below 21, 4% between 21 and 23, 14% between 24 and 26, 27% between 27 and 28, and 54% above 28. About 79% of the current freshmen were in the top fifth of their class; 98% were in the top two fifths. There were 48 National Merit finalists.

Requirements: The SAT I or ACT is required. Applicants should have earned at least 16 academic credits, including 4 years of English and 3 each in mathematics, science, foreign language, and social studies/history. SAT II: Subject tests in mathematics, science, and languages are recommended. The college also expects applicants to have taken honors or AP courses where available. An essay is required, and an interview recommended. The GED is not accepted. AP credits are accepted. Important factors used in the admissions decision are extracurricular activities record, advanced placement or honor courses, leadership record, personality, intangible qualities, and evidence of special talent.

Procedure: Freshmen are admitted in the fall. Entrance exams should be taken the fall of the senior year. Early decision applications should be filed by November 15 and January 1; regular applications, by January 15 for fall entry, along with an application fee of $40. Notification of early decision is sent December 15 and February 7; regular decision, March 28. There are early decision, early admissions, and deferred admissions plans. About 194 early decision candidates were accepted for the 1993–94 class. A waiting list is an active part of the admissions procedure, with about 8% of applicants on the list.

Transfer: About 41 transfer students enrolled in 1993–94. Transfer students usually must present a GPA of 3.3 (B+), a secondary school transcript, and recommendations from 2 teachers and from the dean of students. In addition, the SAT I or ACT is required and an interview recommended. Transferable grades are evaluated on the basis of the nature and quality of work. Generally a grade of C or better is accepted. A total of 17 courses out of 136 semester hours must be completed at Macalester.

Visiting: There are regularly scheduled orientations for prospective students. There are guides for informal visits and visitors may sit in on classes and stay overnight at the school. To arrange for a visit, contact the Admissions Office at (612) 696–6357 or (800) 231–7974.

Financial Aid: In 1993–94, 72% of all current freshmen and 75% of continuing students received some form of financial aid. About 66% of freshmen and 70% of continuing students received need-based aid. The average freshman award was $12,200. Of that total, scholarships or need-based grants averaged $9350 ($14,300 maximum); loans averaged $1800 ($2625 maximum); and work contracts averaged $1050 ($1350 maximum). Seventy-one percent of undergraduate students work part-time. Average earnings from campus work for the school year are $1425. The average financial indebtedness of the 1992–93 graduate was $11,000. Macalester is a member of CSS. The FAF, the college's own financial statement and the FAFSA are required. The deadline for financial aid applications is February 8.

International Students: There are currently 230 international students enrolled. The school actively recruits these students. They must take the TOEFL or the University of Michigan Language Test and achieve a minimum score on the TOEFL of 550. The student must also take the SAT I or the ACT.

Computers: The college provides computer facilities for student use. The mainframe is a DEC VAX 6000–310. The central computer provides access to Internet and to Bitnet and an electronic mail capability. There are 54 microcomputers available for general student use. All students may access the system. It may be used 24 hours a day. There are no time limits on using the system and no fees.

Graduates: In 1992–93, 380 bachelor's degrees were awarded. The most popular majors among graduates were political science (13%), English (12%), and history (11%). Within an average freshman class, 65% graduate in 4 years, 75% in 5 years, and 76% in 6 years. Some 46 companies recruited on campus in 1992–93. In the 1992 graduating class, 27% of all graduates were enrolled in graduate school within 6 months of graduation; 61% had found employment.

Admissions Contact: William M. Shain, Dean of Admissions.

MANKATO STATE UNIVERSITY
C-4
Mankato, MN 56002–8400

(507) 389–1822
(800) 722–0544 (in-state)

Full-time: 5224 men, 5335 women	Faculty: 586; IIA, av$
Part-time: 787 men, 992 women	Ph.D.s: 65%
Graduate: 667 men, 920 women	Student/Faculty: 18 to 1
Year: quarters, summer session	Tuition: $2454 ($4746)
Application Deadline: open	Room & Board: $2643
Freshman Class: 3343 applied, 2727 accepted, 1589 enrolled	
ACT: required	LESS COMPETITIVE

Mankato State University, founded in 1868 and a unit of the Minnesota State University System, offers programs in the liberal arts and sciences, as well as business, education, engineering and technology, and nursing. There are 8 undergraduate schools and one graduate school. In addition to regional accreditation, Mankato State has baccalaureate program accreditation with ADA, CSWE, NASAD, NASM, NCATE, NLN, and NRPA. The library contains 1 million volumes, and subscribes to 3200 periodicals. Computerized library sources and services include the card catalog, interlibrary loans, and database searching. Special learning facilities include a learning resource center, an art gallery, and radio station. The 303-acre campus is in a rural area 85 miles southwest of Minneapolis-St. Paul. Including residence halls, there are 18 buildings on campus.

Student Life: About 88% of undergraduates are from Minnesota. Students come from 45 states, 60 foreign countries, and Canada. Ninety-five percent are white. The average age of freshmen is 18; all undergraduates, 22. Twenty-four percent drop out by the end of their first year; 50% remain to graduate.

Housing: A total of 3100 students can be accommodated in college housing. College-sponsored living facilities include coed dormitories, fraternity houses, and sorority houses. On-campus housing is guaranteed for the freshman year only, is available on a first-come, first-served basis, and is available on a lottery system for upperclassmen. Seventy-five percent of students commute. Alcohol is not permitted. All students may keep cars on campus.

Activities: About 3% of men belong to 1 local and 5 national fraternities; about 3% of women belong to 3 national sororities. There are 125 groups on campus, including art, band, cheerleading, choir, chorale, chorus, computers, dance, drama, ethnic, gay, honors, international, jazz band, literary magazine, marching band, musical theater, newspaper, opera, orchestra, pep band, photography, political, professional, radio and tv, religious, social, social service, student government, and symphony. Popular campus events include Homecoming, Spring Formal, Greek Week, and multicultural activities and celebrations.

Sports: There are 10 intercollegiate sports for men and 9 for women, and 35 intramural sports for men and 35 for women. Athletic and recreation facilities include a 7000-seat stadium, 2 gymnasiums, a field house, indoor and outdoor tracks, tennis and racquetball courts, and an indoor swimming pool.

Disabled Students: The entire campus is accessible to disabled students. The following facilities are available: wheelchair ramps, elevators, special parking, specially equipped rest rooms, and lowered drinking fountains.

Services: In addition to many counseling and information services, tutoring is available in some subjects. In addition, there is remedial math, reading, and writing. There is limited reader service for the blind.

Campus Safety and Security: Campus safety and security measures include 24-hour foot and vehicle patrol, self-defense education, escort service, and informal discussions. In addition, there are pamphlets, posters, and films, emergency telephones, lighted pathways and sidewalks, and the Night Owl Program for residence halls.

Programs of Study: Mankato State awards the B.A., B.S., B.F.A., B.Mus., B.S.E.E., and B.S.M.E. degrees. Associate and master's degrees also are awarded. Bachelor's degrees are awarded in BIOLOGICAL SCIENCE (biochemistry and biology/biological science), BUSINESS (accounting, banking and finance, business administration and management, business law, international business management, and marketing/retailing/merchandising), COMMUNICATIONS AND THE ARTS (English, journalism, and music), COMPUTER AND PHYSICAL SCIENCE (chemistry, computer science, earth science, mathematics, and physics), EDUCATION (art, business, early childhood, elementary, foreign languages, health, home economics, industrial arts, middle school, music, science, and secondary), ENGINEERING AND ENVIRONMENTAL DESIGN (electrical/electronics engineering, engineering technology, and mechanical engineering), HEALTH PROFESSIONS (medical laboratory technology, nursing, public health, and speech pathology/audiology), SOCIAL SCIENCE (anthropology, dietetics, economics, geography, history, parks and recreation management, philosophy, political science/government, psychology, social work, sociology, and urban studies). Business, sciences, accounting, computer science, psychology, and law enforcement are the strongest academically. Business and education have the largest enrollments.

Required: To graduate, students must complete 192 quarter hours of credit, with a GPA of 2.0. Most programs require 67 quarter hours of general education credits. Students must also demonstrate competency in English and mathematics.

Special: The university offers cross-registration within the Minnesota State University System. Students may serve internships, study abroad, or participate in an accelerated degree program. B.A.-B.S. and general studies degrees, dual and student-designed majors, nondegree study, and pass/fail options also are available. There is a freshman honors program on campus, as well as 7 national honor societies, including Phi Beta Kappa. One department has an honors program.

Faculty/Classroom: Sixty-eight percent of faculty are male; 32%, female. All teach undergraduates, 51% do research, and 51% do both. Graduate students teach 4% of introductory courses. The average class size in an introductory lecture is 75; in a laboratory, 25; and in a regular course offering, 28.

Admissions: About 82% of the 1993–94 applicants were accepted. About 21% of the current freshmen were in the top fifth of their class; 29% were in the top two fifths. There were 2 National Merit finalists and 1 semifinalist. About 20 freshmen graduated first in their class.

Requirements: The ACT is required. In addition, applicants must be graduates of an accredited secondary school and rank in the top 50% of their high school class or have an ACT composite score of 21 or better. AP and CLEP credits are accepted.

Procedure: Freshmen are admitted to all sessions. Entrance exams should be taken in the spring of the junior year. Application deadlines are open. Application fee is $15. Notification is sent on a rolling basis. There is a deferred admissions plan.

Transfer: About 970 transfer students enrolled in 1993–94. Transfer applicants must have a GPA of 2.0 and have completed at least 75% of all courses attempted. A total of 48 credits out of 192 must be completed at Mankato State.

Visiting: There are regularly scheduled orientations for prospective students. Visitors may sit in on classes and stay overnight at the school. To arrange for a visit, contact the Admissions Office at (507) 389–1822 or (800) 722–0544 (in-state).

Financial Aid: In 1993–94, 65% of all current freshmen and 70% of continuing students received some form of financial aid. About 70% of freshmen and 75% of continuing students received need-based aid. Thirty-five percent of undergraduate students work part-time. The FAFSA financial statement is required. The deadline for financial aid applications is July 1.

International Students: There are currently 500 international students enrolled. The school actively recruits these students. They must take the TOEFL and achieve a minimum score of 500.

Computers: The college provides computer facilities for student use. The mainframe is a Unisys 1100/92. Apple, Macintosh, and IBM microcomputers are available at several campus locations. All students may access the system. Students may access the system 2 hours per session. There are no fees.

Graduates: In an earlier year, 2002 bachelor's degrees were awarded. Within an average freshman class, 19% graduate in 4 years and 28% in 5 years. Some 375 companies recruited on campus in 1992–93.

Admissions Contact: Director of Admissions.

MINNEAPOLIS COLLEGE OF ART AND DESIGN

C-4

Minneapolis, MN 55404	(612) 874–3760; (800) 874–6223
Full-time: 252 men, 191 women	Faculty: 43; IIB, -$
Part-time: 45 men, 49 women	Ph.D.s: 65%
Graduate: 5 men, 15 women	Student/Faculty: 10 to 1
Year: semesters, summer session	Tuition: $12,012
Application Deadline: March 15	Room & Board: $3500–4000
Freshman Class: 265 applied, 202 accepted, 79 enrolled	
SAT I or ACT: required	SPECIAL

The Minneapolis College of Art and Design, founded in 1886, is a private professional college of art. In addition to regional accreditation, MCAD has baccalaureate program accreditation with NASAD. The library contains 55,000 volumes, and subscribes to 200 periodicals. Computerized library sources and services include database searching. Special learning facilities include a learning resource center and art gallery. The 7-acre campus is in an urban area 1 mile south of downtown Minneapolis. Including residence halls, there are 9 buildings on campus.

Student Life: About 70% of undergraduates are from Minnesota. Students come from 32 states, 13 foreign countries, and Canada. Eighty-eight percent are white. The average age of freshmen is 19; all undergraduates, 22. Thirty-eight percent drop out by the end of their first year.

Housing: A total of 162 students can be accommodated in college housing. College-sponsored living facilities include coed on-campus apartments. On-campus housing is available on a first-come, first-served basis. Priority is given to out-of-town students. All students may keep cars on campus.

Activities: There are no fraternities or sororities on campus. There are some groups on campus, including art, ethnic, gay, literary magazine, professional, and student government. Popular campus events include Diversity Week, Senior Show, and Halloween Party.

Sports: There is no sports program at MCAD.

Disabled Students: Ninety-five percent of the campus is accessible to disabled students. The following facilities are available: wheelchair ramps, elevators, special parking, specially equipped rest rooms, and special class scheduling.

Services: In addition to many counseling and information services, tutoring is available in most subjects.

Campus Safety and Security: Campus safety and security measures include 24-hour foot and vehicle patrol, self-defense education, escort service, and informal discussions. In addition, there are pamphlets, posters, films, emergency telephones, lighted pathways and sidewalks, and a taxi service.

Programs of Study: MCAD awards the B.F.A. degree. Master's degrees are also awarded. Bachelor's degrees are awarded in COMMUNICATIONS AND THE ARTS (design, film arts, fine arts, photography, and video), and SOCIAL SCIENCE (interdisciplinary studies). Design has the largest enrollment.

Required: All students must satisfactorily complete 120 semester credits, including 12 in foundation studies; 69 in media arts, fine arts, or design; and 39 in liberal arts. A minimum 2.0 GPA must be maintained. A senior project is required. Internships are required in media arts and recommended for other majors.

Special: MCAD offers cross-registration with Macalester College, internships, study abroad in Italy, Japan, Canada, and New Zealand, work-study programs, and student-designed interdisciplinary majors.

Faculty/Classroom: Fifty-five percent of faculty are male; 45%, female. All teach undergraduates. No introductory courses are taught by graduate students. The average class size in a regular course offering is 18.

Admissions: About 76% of the 1993–94 applicants were accepted. The SAT scores for the 1993–94 freshman class were as follows: Verbal—53% below 500, 27% between 500 and 599, 13% between 600 and 700, and 7% above 700; Math—66% below 500, 20% between 500 and 599, 7% between 600 and 700, and 7% above 700. The ACT scores were 58% below 21, 16% between 21 and 23, 12% between 24 and 26, 8% between 27 and 28, and 6% above 28.

Requirements: A minimum GPA of 2.0 is required. The SAT I or ACT is required. Applicants must have a minimum GPA of 2.0 and submit a personal statement of interest, portfolio, letter of recommendation, and transcripts. An interview is also strongly encouraged. The GED is accepted. Important factors used in the admissions decision are evidence of special talent, personality, intangible qualities, recommendations by school officials, advanced placement or honor courses, and leadership record.

Procedure: Freshmen are admitted fall and spring. Applications should be filed by March 15 for fall entry and December 1 for spring entry, along with an application fee of $35. Notification is sent on a rolling basis. There is a deferred admissions plan.

Transfer: About 70 transfer students enrolled in 1993–94. Applicants must submit a portfolio for the transfer of studio credit and an official transcript from all postsecondary schools. A minimum GPA of 2.0 is needed. A total of 45 semester credits out of 120 must be completed at MCAD.

Visiting: There are regularly scheduled orientations for prospective students, including MCAD Intro Days in February and National Portfolio Day in the fall. There are guides for informal visits and visitors may sit in on classes and, with permission, stay overnight at the school. To arrange for a visit, contact the Admissions Office at (612) 874–3760 or (800) 874–6223.

Financial Aid: In 1993–94, 72% of all current freshmen and 75% of continuing students received some form of financial aid. About 90% of freshmen and 93% of continuing students received need-based aid. Scholarships or need-based grants averaged $2500 ($4000 maximum); loans averaged $2600 ($5000 maximum); and work contracts averaged $2000. Fifteen percent of undergraduate students work part-time. Average earnings from campus work for the school year are $2000. The average financial indebtedness of the 1992–93 graduate was $12,000. MCAD is a member of CSS. The FAFSA and parent and student federal income tax forms are required. The deadline for financial aid applications is April 1.

International Students: There are currently 24 international students enrolled. They must take the TOEFL and achieve a minimum score of 500.

Computers: The college provides computer facilities for student use. The Computer Center services more than 110 workstations in 6 locations. There is software for word processing, painting, drawing, 2- and 3-dimensional design, programming, electronic imaging (digitizing), scanning, image processing, page layout prepress color separation, 2- and 3-dimensional animation, and modeling on Apple Macintosh IIcx's, a NeXT Dimension, NeXT stations, Apollo 3 AT&T Targa-based PCs, Amigas, and Silicon Graphics. All students may access the system. The fees are $60.

Graduates: In 1992–93, 123 bachelor's degrees were awarded. Within an average freshman class, 25% graduate in 4 years, 5% in 5 years, and 3% in 6 years. In the 1992 graduating class, fewer than 30% of all graduates were enrolled in graduate school within 6 months of graduation; fewer than 30% had found employment.

Admissions Contact: Rebecca Haas, Director of Admissions.

MOORHEAD STATE UNIVERSITY

A-2

Moorhead, MN 56563	(218) 236–2161
	(800) 593–7246 (out-of-state)
Full-time: 2440 men, 3812 women	Faculty: 338; IIA, -$
Part-time: 233 men, 420 women	Ph.D.s: 66%
Graduate: 116 men, 230 women	Student/Faculty: 18 to 1
Year: quarters, summer session	Tuition: $2412 ($4704)
Application Deadline: August 15	Room & Board: $2664
Freshman Class: 2164 accepted, 1242 enrolled	
ACT: 22	COMPETITIVE

Moorhead State University, founded in 1885, is a public, coeducational, liberal arts institution. There is one undergraduate and one

graduate school. In addition to regional accreditation, Moorhead State has baccalaureate program accreditation with CSWE, NASM, NCATE, and NLN. The library contains 410,162 volumes, and subscribes to 1449 periodicals. Computerized library sources and services include the card catalog, interlibrary loans, and database searching. Special learning facilities include an art gallery, planetarium, radio station, tv station, and a science center. The 104-acre campus is in a suburban area 240 miles northwest of Minneapolis-St. Paul. Including residence halls, there are 22 buildings on campus.

Student Life: About 66% of undergraduates are from Minnesota. Students come from 41 states, 30 foreign countries, and Canada. Ninety-eight percent are from public schools; 2% from private. Ninety-six percent are white. The average age of freshmen is 18; all undergraduates, 25. Thirty-one percent drop out by the end of their first year; 40% remain to graduate.

Housing: A total of 2250 students can be accommodated in college housing. College-sponsored living facilities include single-sex and coed dormitories. On-campus housing is available on a first-come, first-served basis. Sixty-seven percent of students commute. Alcohol is not permitted. All students may keep cars on campus.

Activities: About 2% of men belong to 1 local and 1 national fraternity; about 1% of women belong to 3 national sororities. There are 150 groups on campus, including art, band, cheerleading, choir, chorus, computers, dance, drama, drill team, ethnic, film, gay, honors, international, jazz band, literary magazine, musical theater, newspaper, orchestra, pep band, photography, political, professional, radio and tv, religious, social, social service, and student government. Popular campus events include Parents Day and Homecoming.

Sports: There are 7 intercollegiate sports for men and 7 for women, and 16 intramural sports for men and 14 for women. Athletic and recreation facilities include 4 gymnasiums, racquetball and volleyball courts, 2 swimming pools, indoor and outdoor tennis courts, weight and wrestling rooms, a running track, and 3 softball diamonds.

Disabled Students: The entire campus is accessible to disabled students. The following facilities are available: wheelchair ramps, elevators, special parking, specially equipped rest rooms, lowered drinking fountains, and lowered telephones.

Services: In addition to many counseling and information services, tutoring is available in every subject. In addition, there is a reader service for the blind, and remedial math, reading, and writing.

Campus Safety and Security: Campus safety and security measures include 24-hour foot and vehicle patrol, self-defense education, escort service, and informal discussions. In addition, there are pamphlets, posters, and films, emergency telephones, and lighted pathways and sidewalks.

Programs of Study: Moorhead State awards the B.A., B.S., B.F.A., B.M., B.S.N., and B.S.W. degrees. Associate and master's degrees also are awarded. Bachelor's degrees are awarded in BIOLOGICAL SCIENCE (biology/biological science), BUSINESS (accounting, banking and finance, business administration and management, hotel/motel and restaurant management, international business management, marketing/retailing/merchandising, office supervision and management, and trade and industrial supervision and management), COMMUNICATIONS AND THE ARTS (advertising, broadcasting, communications, dramatic arts, English, fine arts, French, German, journalism, music, public relations, Spanish, and speech/debate/rhetoric), COMPUTER AND PHYSICAL SCIENCE (chemistry, computer science, earth science, mathematics, and physics), EDUCATION (art, business, early childhood, elementary, foreign languages, health, industrial arts, music, science, secondary, social studies, and special), ENGINEERING AND ENVIRONMENTAL DESIGN (construction engineering and energy management technology), HEALTH PROFESSIONS (medical laboratory technology, nursing, predentistry, premedicine, prepharmacy, preveterinary science, and speech pathology/audiology), SOCIAL SCIENCE (American studies, anthropology, criminal justice, economics, geography, history, paralegal studies, philosophy, political science/government, prelaw, psychology, social science, social work, and sociology). Business, education, and mass communications have the largest enrollments.

Required: In order to graduate, students must have a 2.0 GPA and complete 192 quarter hours, including a liberal arts core of 64 credits. Required courses must include 12 hours each of natural science, social science, humanities, and communications language or symbolic systems, and 8 credits in cultural diversity. All students must take 2 courses in English composition and literature.

Special: Internships are available in most disciplines. The university offers cross-registration with North Dakota State University and Concordia College. Students may study abroad in more than 40 countries and participate in work-study programs. Student-designed and dual majors, credit for military experience, co-op programs, nondegree study, and pass/fail options are possible. There is a freshman honors program on campus. One department has an honors program.

Faculty/Classroom: Sixty-five percent of faculty are male; 35%, female. One-hundred percent both teach and do research. Graduate students teach 1% of introductory courses. The average class size in

an introductory lecture is 100; in a laboratory, 20; and in a regular course offering, 30.

Admissions: The ACT scores for the 1993–94 freshman class were as follows: 32% below 21, 37% between 21 and 23, 20% between 24 and 26, 6% between 27 and 28, and 5% above 28. About 32% of the current freshmen were in the top fifth of their class; 61% were in the top two fifths. There were 2 National Merit finalists and 12 semifinalists. Thirteen freshmen graduated first in their class.

Requirements: Moorhead State requires applicants to be in the upper 50% of their class. The SAT I or ACT is required, but the ACT is preferred. A high school diploma is required, and the GED is accepted. Applicants should rank in the upper 50% of their graduating class. AP and CLEP credits are accepted. Important factors used in the admissions decision are recommendations by school officials, leadership record, extracurricular activities record, evidence of special talent, and advanced placement or honor courses.

Procedure: Freshmen are admitted to all sessions. Entrance exams should be taken in the junior or senior year of high school. Applications should be filed by August 15 for fall entry, November 15 for winter entry, February 15 for spring entry, and May 15 for summer entry, along with an application fee of $15. Notification is sent on a rolling basis.

Transfer: About 940 transfer students enrolled in 1993–94. Applicants must submit a high school transcript or GED score and all other transcripts for post-secondary schools attended. A minimum GPA of 2.0 is necessary for transfer credit. A total of 45 quarter credits out of 192 must be completed at Moorhead State.

Visiting: There are regularly scheduled orientations for prospective students, including a campus tour, lunch, and meetings with faculty and an admissions officer. There are guides for informal visits. To arrange for a visit, contact the Admissions Office at (212) 236–2161 or (800) 593–7246.

Financial Aid: In 1993–94, 66% of all current freshmen and 70% of continuing students received some form of financial aid. About 66% of freshmen and 70% of continuing students received need-based aid. The average freshman award was $4323. Of that total, scholarships or need-based grants averaged $500 ($1000 maximum); loans averaged $2043 ($2625 maximum); and work contracts averaged $1406 ($1800 maximum). Eighty percent of undergraduate students work part-time. Average earnings from campus work for the school year are $750. The average financial indebtedness of a recent year's graduate was $6550. The FFS, the college's own financial statement, and a tax return are required. The deadline for financial aid applications is June 15.

International Students: There are currently 236 international students enrolled. They must take the TOEFL and achieve a minimum score of 500.

Computers: The college provides computer facilities for student use. The mainframe is a Data General MV20000. There are 250 Apple, Zenith, and IBM microcomputers available for student use. There are no time limits on using the system and no fees.

Graduates: In a recent year, 1200 bachelor's degrees were awarded. The most popular majors among graduates were business (24%), education (18%), and accounting (8%). Within an average freshman class, 25% graduate in 4 years and 42% in 5 years. Some 103 companies recruited on campus in a recent year. In the 1992 graduating class, 14% of the men and 11% of the women were enrolled in graduate school within 6 months of graduation; 86% of the men and 82% of the women had found employment.

Admissions Contact: Jean Lange, Director of Admissions.

NORTH CENTRAL BIBLE COLLEGE

C-4

Minneapolis, MN 55404   (612) 343–4480; (800) 289–6222

Full-time, part time: 531 men, 523 women	Faculty: 29
	Ph.D.s: 13%
Graduate: none	Student/Faculty: n/av
Year: semesters, summer session	Tuition: $5470
Application Deadline: September 1	Room & Board: $3200
Freshman Class: 701 applied, 530 accepted, 400 enrolled	
ACT: 21	**LESS COMPETITIVE**

North Central Bible College, founded in 1930 and affiliated with the Assemblies of God, is a private, coeducational college offering courses in Bible, business, music, religion, and teacher preparation. The library contains 58,120 volumes and 21 microform items, and subscribes to 392 periodicals. Special learning facilities include a radio station. The 6-acre campus is in an urban area. Including residence halls, there are 11 buildings on campus.

Student Life: About 65% of undergraduates are from out-of-state, mostly the Midwest. Ninety-four percent are white. Most are Protestant.

Housing: College-sponsored living facilities include dormitories and on-campus apartments. In addition, there are honors houses. Sixty-four percent of students commute. Alcohol is not permitted. Upperclassmen may keep cars on campus.

Activities: There are no fraternities or sororities on campus. There are 34 groups on campus, including art, band, cheerleading, choir, chorale, drama, jazz band, literary magazine, musical theater, newspaper, orchestra, political, radio and TV, student government, and yearbook. Popular campus events include All-College Picnic, Community Outreach Day, and Winter Extravaganza Days.

Sports: There are 2 intercollegiate sports each for men and women, and 3 intramural sports for men and 1 for women. Athletic and recreation facilities include Elliot Park and the Clark-Danielson College Life Center gymnasium.

Disabled Students: All of the campus is accessible to disabled students. The following facilities are available: wheelchair ramps, elevators, special parking, specially equipped rest rooms, special class scheduling, lowered drinking fountains, and lowered telephones.

Services: In addition to many counseling and information services, tutoring is available in some subjects, including English composition. There is also remedial math, reading, and writing.

Programs of Study: NCBC awards the B.A. and B.S. degrees. Associate degrees also are awarded. Bachelor's degrees are awarded in COMMUNICATIONS AND THE ARTS (communications), EDUCATION (elementary), and SOCIAL SCIENCE (behavioral science, biblical languages, ministries, pastoral studies, religion, religious education, and religious music).

Required: Students must complete at least 126 credits for the bachelor's degree. Each program has specific requirements, including general education and biblical studies core classes. Internships are required for all programs. A minimum GPA of 2.0 is required (teacher education students, 2.2). Students must take 60 or more total hours in their major.

Special: Students may study in Belgium or Kenya, earn a general studies degree, pursue nondegree study, or receive credit for life, military, or work experience.

Faculty/Classroom: Sixty-five percent of faculty are male; 35%, female.

Admissions: About 76% of the 1993–94 applicants were accepted.

Requirements: The ACT (preferred) or SAT I is required. AP and CLEP credits are accepted.

Procedure: Freshmen are admitted fall and spring. Applications should be filed by September 1 for fall entry and December 31 for spring entry. Notification is sent on a rolling basis. There is an early admissions plan.

Transfer: About 135 transfer students enrolled in a recent year. Transfer applicants must submit a completed application, a pastor's reference, a high school transcript or the GED, and college transcripts. A total of 27 credits out of 126 must be completed at NCBC.

Visiting: There are guides for informal visits and visitors may sit in on classes and stay overnight at the school. To arrange for a visit, contact Francine Argue at (612) 343–4480 or (800) 289–6222.

Financial Aid: The FFS and the college's own financial statement are required.

International Students: There are currently 30 international students enrolled. They must take the TOEFL and achieve a minimum score of 500.

Computers: The college provides computer facilities for student use. Microcomputers are available in the library.

Graduates: In an earlier year, 126 bachelor's degrees were awarded.

Admissions Contact: Dan Neary, Admissions Director.

NORTHWESTERN COLLEGE C-4
St. Paul, MN 55113 (612) 631–5111; (800) 827–6827 (out-of-state)

Full-time: 521 men, 691 women	Faculty: 61; IIB, --$
Part-time: 16 men, 14 women	Ph.D.s: 52%
Graduate: none	Student/Faculty: 20 to 1
Year: quarters, summer session	Tuition: $10,659
Application Deadline: August 15	Room & Board: $2895
Freshman Class: 620 applied, 601 accepted, 334 enrolled	
ACT: 22	COMPETITIVE

Northwestern College, founded in 1902, is a coeducational Christian college offering programs in liberal arts, business, religion, and education. In addition to regional accreditation, Northwestern has baccalaureate program accreditation with NASM. The library contains 82,000 volumes, 55,000 microform items, and 4700 audiovisual forms, and subscribes to 570 periodicals. Computerized library sources and services include the card catalog and interlibrary loans. Special learning facilities include a learning resource center, radio station, TV station, and language laboratories. The 95-acre campus is in a suburban area 5 miles north of St. Paul. Including residence halls, there are 8 buildings on campus.

Student Life: About 67% of undergraduates are from Minnesota. Students come from 35 states, 15 foreign countries, and Canada. Eighty-two percent are from public schools; 18% from private. Ninety-six percent are white. Most are Protestant. The average age of freshmen is 19; all undergraduates, 21. Eight percent drop out by the end of their first year.

Housing: A total of 850 students can be accommodated in college housing. College-sponsored living facilities include single-sex and coed dormitories and on-campus apartments. On-campus housing is available on a first-come, first-served basis. Priority is given to out-of-town students. Sixty-nine percent of students live on campus; of those, 55% remain on campus on weekends. Alcohol is not permitted. All students may keep cars on campus.

Activities: There are no fraternities or sororities on campus. There are 30 groups on campus, including art, band, cheerleading, chess, choir, chorale, chorus, drama, ethnic, international, jazz band, literary magazine, musical theater, orchestra, pep band, photography, political, professional, radio and TV, religious, social, social service, student government, and yearbook. Popular campus events include Spiritual Emphasis Week, Fine Arts Festival, Dormitory Open House, Homecoming, concerts, and drama productions.

Sports: There are 8 intercollegiate sports for men and 7 for women, and 9 intramural sports for men and 9 for women. Athletic and recreation facilities include softball, baseball, and football/soccer fields, 2 gymnasiums, a weight room, and a game room.

Disabled Students: Seventy-five percent of the campus is accessible to disabled students. The following facilities are available: wheelchair ramps, elevators, special parking, specially equipped rest rooms, special class scheduling, and lowered drinking fountains.

Services: In addition to many counseling and information services, tutoring is available in most subjects, including mathematics and English. In addition, there is remedial math, reading, and writing.

Campus Safety and Security: Campus safety and security measures include 24-hour foot and vehicle patrol, escort service, shuttle buses, and informal discussions. In addition, there are pamphlets, posters, and films, emergency telephones, and lighted pathways and sidewalks.

Programs of Study: Northwestern awards the B.A. and B.S. degrees. Associate degrees also are awarded. Bachelor's degrees are awarded in BUSINESS (accounting, banking and finance, business administration and management, human resources, international business management, marketing/retailing/merchandising, office supervision and management, and personnel management), COMMUNICATIONS AND THE ARTS (broadcasting, communications, design, English, fine arts, and music), COMPUTER AND PHYSICAL SCIENCE (computer programming and mathematics), EDUCATION (art, elementary, English, mathematics, music, physical, secondary, and social studies), HEALTH PROFESSIONS (sports medicine), SOCIAL SCIENCE (biblical studies, ministries, pastoral studies, psychology, and social science). Education, communications, business, and music are the strongest academically. Business and education have the largest enrollments.

Required: In order to graduate, students must complete 188 quarter credits with a 2.0 GPA. The number of hours required in the major varies. Core courses must include 15 to 45 credits of Bible, 16 of social science, 12 each of humanities and mathematics or natural science, 6 to 9 of English composition, 4 of speech, 3 of physical education, and 1 to 4 of computer literacy.

Special: The college offers co-op programs and 3–2 engineering degrees with the University of Minnesota and cross-registration with Bethel College. Internships in business, ministries, and broadcasting, and study abroad in 4 countries are available. Students may pursue nondegree study. One department has an honors program.

Faculty/Classroom: Fifty-five percent of faculty are male; 45%, female. All teach undergraduates. The average class size in an introductory lecture is 50; in a laboratory, 20; and in a regular course offering, 15.

Admissions: About 97% of the 1993–94 applicants were accepted. The ACT scores for the 1993–94 freshman class were as follows: 27% below 21, 26% between 21 and 23, 24% between 24 and 26, 7% between 27 and 28, and 16% above 28. About 52% of the current freshmen were in the top fifth of their class; 77% were in the top two fifths. There were 6 National Merit semifinalists. Twenty-one freshmen graduated first in their class.

Requirements: Northwestern requires applicants to be in the upper 50% of their class. A minimum GPA of 2.0 is required. The ACT is required. AP and CLEP credits are accepted. Important factors used in the admissions decision are personality, intangible qualities, recommendations by school officials, recommendations by alumni, leadership record, and extracurricular activities record.

Procedure: Freshmen are admitted to all sessions. Applications should be filed by August 15 for fall entry, along with an application fee of $15. Notification is sent on a rolling basis. There is an early admissions plan.

Transfer: A total of 97 transfer students enrolled in 1993–94. Applicants must have an average of C or better from an accredited institution. A total of 45 quarter credits out of 188 must be completed at Northwestern.

Visiting: There are regularly scheduled orientations for prospective students. There are guides for informal visits and visitors may sit in on classes and stay overnight at the school. To arrange for a visit, contact the Admissions Department at (800) 827–6827 or (612) 631–5111.

Financial Aid: In 1993–94, 95% of all students received some form of financial aid. About 85% of all students received need-based aid. The average freshman award was $9000. Of that total, scholarships or need-based grants averaged $5200 ($11,000 maximum); loans averaged $2500 ($4000 maximum); and work contracts averaged $1500 ($3000 maximum). Eighty-five percent of undergraduate students work part-time. Average earnings from campus work for the school year are $1500. The average financial indebtedness of the 1992–93 graduate was $9600. Northwestern is a member of CSS. The FAF or FFS and FAFSA are required.

International Students: There are currently 19 international students enrolled. They must take the TOEFL or the University of Michigan Language Test and achieve a minimum score on the TOEFL of 530. The student must also take the SAT I or the ACT.

Computers: The college provides computer facilities for student use. The mainframe is an IBM AS/400. There are 58 terminals available to students. All students may access the system 2 hours per session. There are no fees.

Graduates: In 1992–93, 207 bachelor's degrees were awarded. The most popular majors among graduates were elementary education (12%), marketing (10%), and psychology (8%). Within an average freshman class, 45% graduate in 4 years, 55% in 5 years, and 60% in 6 years. Some 30 companies recruited on campus in an earlier year. In the 1992 graduating class, 10% of all students were enrolled in graduate school within 6 months; 96% of all students had found employment.

Admissions Contact: Ralph D. Anderson, Dean of Admissions.

PILLSBURY BAPTIST BIBLE COLLEGE   C-5
Owatonna, MN 55060
Recognized candidate for accreditation   (507) 451–2710, ext. 274
(800) 747–4557

Full-time: 124 men, 127 women	Faculty: 27
Part-time: 14 men, 13 women	Ph.D.s: 11%
Graduate: none	Student/Faculty: 9 to 1
Year: semesters, summer session	Tuition: $4390
Application Deadline: August 25	Room & Board: $3000
Freshman Class: 158 applied, 158 accepted, 86 enrolled	
ACT: 20	NONCOMPETITIVE

Pillsbury Baptist Bible College, founded in 1957, is a private, coeducational institution affiliated with the Minnesota Baptist Association. Undergraduate programs are offered in Bible studies as well as other areas. The library contains 45,000 volumes, 1000 microform items, and 1000 audiovisual forms, and subscribes to 250 periodicals. Computerized library sources and services include database searching. Special learning facilities include a learning resource center and radio station. The 14-acre campus is in a small town 60 miles south of Minneapolis. Including residence halls, there are 10 buildings on campus.

Student Life: About 59% of undergraduates are from out-of-state, mostly the Midwest. Students come from 32 states, 4 foreign countries, and Canada. Ninety-seven percent are white. The average age of freshmen is 18; all undergraduates, 22. Seventeen percent drop out by the end of their first year; 50% remain to graduate.

Housing: A total of 500 students can be accommodated in college housing. College-sponsored living facilities include single-sex dormitories. In addition, there is a home economics house used for home economics classes. On-campus housing is guaranteed for all 4 years. Seventy-nine percent of students live on campus. Alcohol is not permitted. All students may keep cars on campus.

Activities: There are no fraternities or sororities on campus. There are 10 groups on campus, including cheerleading, choir, computers, drama, newspaper, orchestra, pep band, photography, professional, religious, social service, student government, and yearbook. Popular campus events include Harvest Home, Valentine Formal, Christmas at Pillsbury, Junior-Senior Banquet, Monroe Parker Evangelistic Services, Christian Scholar Series, Black History Month, and Nationalities in Ministry Week.

Sports: There are 5 intercollegiate sports for men and 4 for women, and 5 intramural sports for men and 5 for women.

Disabled Students: Special parking is available.

Services: In addition to many counseling and information services, tutoring is available in every subject.

Campus Safety and Security: Campus safety and security measures include pamphlets, posters, films, lighted pathways and sidewalks, and part-time security patrol.

Programs of Study: Pillsbury awards the B.A. and B.S. degrees. Associate degrees also are awarded. Bachelor's degrees are awarded in BIOLOGICAL SCIENCE (biology/biological science), BUSINESS (business administration and management and secretarial studies/

office management), COMMUNICATIONS AND THE ARTS (English, fine arts, and music), COMPUTER AND PHYSICAL SCIENCE (mathematics), EDUCATION (elementary, English, home economics, mathematics, music, physical, science, secondary, and special), SOCIAL SCIENCE (biblical studies, history, missions, religious education, and religious music). Education has the largest enrollment.

Required: All students major in Bible and must also choose a second major or 2 minors from 23 fields of study. To graduate, students must complete 128 credit hours, with a minimum of 30 hours in the major. Freshmen and sophomores must maintain a minimum GPA of 1.7; juniors and seniors, 2.0. Requirements include 60 hours in the general education core, 30 in the Bible major, 6 in Christian ministries, and Christian service in local communities.

Special: Internships in business, church ministries, and pastoral studies are available, as well as a missionary apprenticeship program in various countries.

Faculty/Classroom: Seventy-nine percent of faculty are male; 21%, female. All teach undergraduates. The average class size in an introductory lecture is 30; in a laboratory, 15; and in a regular course offering, 30.

Admissions: All of the 1993–94 applicants were accepted.

Requirements: The ACT is required. AP and CLEP credits are accepted.

Procedure: Freshmen are admitted in the fall and spring. Entrance exams should be taken in the spring before entrance. Early decision applications should be filed by October 25; regular applications, by August 25 for fall entry and January 5 for spring entry, along with an application fee of $25.

Transfer: About 15 transfer students enrolled in 1993–94. Applicants must submit transcripts from the previous institution.

Visiting: There are guides for informal visits, and visitors may sit in on classes and stay overnight at the school. To arrange for a visit, contact Larry Tindall or Shelley Lobach at (507) 451–2710, ext. 274 or 552.

Financial Aid: In 1993–94, 89% of all students received some form of financial aid. About 84% of all students received need-based aid. The average freshman award was $5245. Of that total, scholarships or need-based grants averaged $2620 ($5560 maximum); and loans averaged $2625 ($4000 maximum). Seventy-six percent of undergraduate students work part-time. The average financial indebtedness of the 1992–93 graduate was $8100. The FAFSA financial statement is required.

International Students: There are currently 4 international students enrolled. International applicants must take the ACT.

Computers: There are 25 microcomputers available for student use in a computer laboratory. Computers are also available in residence halls. The system may be used 7 A.M. to 10 P.M. weekdays, and 10 A.M. to 2 P.M. weekends. There are no time limits on using the system and no fees.

Graduates: In a recent year, 55 bachelor's degrees were awarded. The most popular majors among graduates were Bible (required major) (100%), education (40%), and general business (22%). Within an average freshman class, 50% graduate in 6 years.

Admissions Contact: Larry Tindall, Director of Admissions.

SAINT CLOUD STATE UNIVERSITY   C-3
St. Cloud, MN 56301   (612) 255–2243; (800) 369–4260 (out-of-state)

Full-time: 6019 men, 6134 women	Faculty: 635; IIA, av$
Part-time: 1019 men, 1303 women	Ph.D.s: 74%
Graduate: 471 men, 1101 women	Student/Faculty: 19 to 1
Year: quarters, summer session	Tuition: $2390 ($4682)
Application Deadline: August 10	Room & Board: $2625
Freshman Class: 3819 applied, 3164 accepted, 1841 enrolled	
ACT: 21	COMPETITIVE

Saint Cloud State University, founded in 1869, is part of the Minnesota State University system offering programs in fine and liberal arts, business, aviation, engineering, health science, and teacher preparation. There are 5 undergraduate and 5 graduate schools. In addition to regional accreditation, SCSU has baccalaureate program accreditation with AACSB, ACEJMC, CSWE, NASAD, NASM, and NCATE. The library contains 553,466 volumes, 1,532,282 microform items, and 88,469 audiovisual forms, and subscribes to 4090 periodicals. Computerized library sources and services include the card catalog, interlibrary loans, and database searching. Special learning facilities include a learning resource center, art gallery, natural history museum, planetarium, radio station, and TV station. The 158-acre campus is in a suburban area 60 miles northwest of Minneapolis. Including residence halls, there are 35 buildings on campus.

Student Life: About 92% of undergraduates are from Minnesota. Students come from 40 states, 25 foreign countries, and Canada. Ninety-five percent are from public schools; 5% from private. Ninety-four percent are white. Fifty-six percent are Protestant; 38% Catholic. The average age of freshmen is 19; all undergraduates, 22. Twenty-

five percent drop out by the end of their first year; 50% remain to graduate.

Housing: A total of 3050 students can be accommodated in college housing. College-sponsored living facilities include single-sex and coed dormitories. In addition, there are honors houses. On-campus housing is guaranteed for all 4 years. Alcohol is not permitted. All students may keep cars on campus.

Activities: About 2% of men belong to 5 national fraternities; about 2% of women belong to 5 local and 1 national sororities. There are 170 groups on campus, including art, band, cheerleading, chess, choir, chorale, chorus, computers, dance, drama, ethnic, film, gay, honors, international, jazz band, literary magazine, marching band, musical theater, newspaper, orchestra, pep band, photography, political, professional, radio and TV, religious, social, social service, student government, and symphony. Popular campus events include Homecoming, Sno Daze, and Ethnic Awareness.

Sports: There are 10 intercollegiate sports for men and 8 for women, and 37 intramural sports for men and 37 for women. Athletic and recreation facilities include an athletic hall, a national hockey center, and a playing field.

Disabled Students: Ninety-nine percent of the campus is accessible to disabled students. The following facilities are available: wheelchair ramps, elevators, special parking, specially equipped rest rooms, special class scheduling, lowered drinking fountains, and lowered telephones.

Services: In addition to many counseling and information services, tutoring is available in every subject. In addition, there is a reader service for the blind, and remedial math, reading, and writing.

Campus Safety and Security: Campus safety and security measures include 24-hour foot and vehicle patrol, self defense education, escort service, and shuttle buses. In addition, there are informal discussions, pamphlets, posters, and films, emergency telephones, and lighted pathways and sidewalks.

Programs of Study: SCSU awards the B.A., B.S., B.E.S., B.F.A., and B.Mus. degrees. Associate and master's degrees also are awarded. Bachelor's degrees are awarded in BIOLOGICAL SCIENCE (biology/biological science), BUSINESS (accounting, banking and finance, business administration and management, business economics, international business management, marketing/retailing/merchandising, and personnel management), COMMUNICATIONS AND THE ARTS (advertising, broadcasting, communications, dramatic arts, English, fine arts, journalism, languages, music, and speech/debate/rhetoric), COMPUTER AND PHYSICAL SCIENCE (atmospheric sciences and meteorology, chemistry, computer science, earth science, geology, mathematics, physics, and statistics), EDUCATION (art, early childhood, elementary, foreign languages, guidance, health, industrial arts, music, science, and secondary), ENGINEERING AND ENVIRONMENTAL DESIGN (electrical/electronics engineering), HEALTH PROFESSIONS (predentistry, premedicine, public health, and speech pathology/audiology), SOCIAL SCIENCE (anthropology, criminal justice, economics, geography, history, international relations, philosophy, political science/government, prelaw, psychology, public administration, social science, social work, sociology, and urban studies). Business, computer science, mass communications, electrical engineering, and education are the strongest programs academically. Business has the largest enrollment.

Required: Students must complete a minimum of 192 quarter hours of credit, including 70 hours of general education requirements and 48 to 101 hours in the major, and must maintain at least a 2.0 GPA. Students must complete English 162, English 163, Speech 161, 2 credits in physical education, and 16 credits each in philosophy/humanities/fine arts, natural science and mathematics, and social and behavioral science.

Special: The university offers cross-registration with Saint John's University and the College of Saint Benedict, internships in almost all majors, work-study programs, and study abroad in 7 countries. Students may take dual majors, design their own majors for a Bachelor of Elective Studies degree, and earn a general degree or a B.A.-B.S. degree in most majors, including meteorology and photographic technology. The university gives credit for military experience and allows nondegree study and pass/fail options. There is a freshman honors program on campus, as well as 4 national honor societies. One department has an honors program.

Faculty/Classroom: Seventy percent of faculty are male; 30%, female. Ninety-three percent teach undergraduates, 2% do research, and 5% do both. Graduate students teach 1% of introductory courses. The average class size in an introductory lecture is 35; in a laboratory, 20; and in a regular course offering, 30.

Admissions: About 83% of the 1993–94 applicants were accepted. The ACT scores for the 1993–94 freshman class were as follows: 45% below 21, 31% between 21 and 23, 17% between 24 and 26, 5% between 27 and 28, and 2% above 28. About 24% of the current freshmen were in the top fifth of their class; 55% were in the top two fifths. There were 12 National Merit finalists and 4 semifinalists. Five freshmen graduated first in their class.

Requirements: SCSU requires applicants to be in the upper 50% of their class. The ACT is required. AP and CLEP credits are accepted.

Procedure: Freshmen are admitted to all sessions. Entrance exams should be taken in the junior or senior year. Applications should be filed by August 10 for fall entry, November 10 for winter entry, February 1 for spring entry, and May 15 for summer entry, along with an application fee of $15. Notification is sent within 2 weeks.

Transfer: About 1300 transfer students enrolled in 1993–94. Applicants must have a minimum 2.0 GPA from their previous college. A total of 45 quarter credits out of 192 must be completed at SCSU.

Visiting: There are regularly scheduled orientations for prospective students. There are guides for informal visits and visitors may sit in on classes. To arrange for a visit, contact the Admissions Office at (612) 255–2243 or (800) 369–4260.

Financial Aid: In a recent year, 45% of all freshmen and 62% of continuing students received some form of financial aid. About 41% of freshmen and 57% of continuing students received need-based aid. The average freshman award was $2030. Of that total, scholarships or need-based grants averaged $669 ($3279 maximum); loans averaged $873 ($4000 maximum); and work contracts averaged $488 ($1800 maximum). Eighteen percent of undergraduate students work part-time. Average earnings from campus work for the school year are $827. The average financial indebtedness of a recent year's graduate was $5946. The FFS and the college's own financial statement are required.

International Students: There are currently 320 international students enrolled. The school actively recruits these students. They must take the TOEFL or the college's own test and achieve a minimum score on the TOEFL of 500.

Computers: The university provides computer facilities for student use. The mainframes include a Unisys 1100/90, an AS/400, a DEC system 5000, a DEC VAX 8550 and an 11/780, and an MVAX 3400. There are 16 computer laboratories and 650 microcomputers for student use; 175 are networked to share printers and 60 are networked to the mainframes for disk sharing and file server capabilities. All students may access the system from 8 A.M. to midnight. There are no time limits on using the system and no fees.

Graduates: In 1992–93 2596 bachelor's degrees were awarded. The most popular majors among graduates were elementary education (13%), mass communications (5%), and psychology (5%). Some 40 companies recruited on campus in 1992–93. In the 1992 graduating class, 1% of the men and 1% of the women were enrolled in graduate school within 6 months of graduation.

Admissions Contact: Sherwood Reid, Director of Admissions.

SAINT JOHN'S UNIVERSITY
Collegeville, MN 56321

B-3

(612) 363–2196
(800) 245–6467 (out-of-state)

Full-time: 1689 men, 2 women	**Faculty:** 110; IIB, av$
Part-time: 48 men, 24 women	**Ph.D.s:** 90%
Graduate: 54 men, 42 women	**Student/Faculty:** 15 to 1
Year: 4–1–4	**Tuition:** $11,428
Application Deadline: open	**Room & Board:** $3936
Freshman Class: 933 applied, 800 accepted, 444 enrolled	
SAT I Verbal/Math: 465/555	**ACT:** 23 COMPETITIVE

St. John's University, founded in 1857 by Benedictine monks, offers programs in the liberal arts. The university is a college for men but shares an academic calendar and most programs and courses with the College of St. Benedict, a college for women 4 miles away. There is one graduate school. In addition to regional accreditation, St. John's has baccalaureate program accreditation with CSWE, NCATE, and NLN. The 4 libraries contain 475,000 volumes, 77,650 microform items, and 12,000 audiovisual forms, and subscribe to 2100 periodicals. Computerized library sources and services include the card catalog, interlibrary loans, and database searching. Special learning facilities include a learning resource center, art gallery, natural history museum, radio station, observatory, and greenhouse. The 2400-acre campus is in a rural area 15 miles west of St. Cloud. Including residence halls, there are 30 buildings on campus.

Student Life: About 75% of undergraduates are from Minnesota. Students come from 42 states, 20 foreign countries, and Canada. Seventy percent are from public schools; 30% from private. Ninety-three percent are white. Seventy-eight percent are Catholic; 16% Protestant. The average age of freshmen is 18; all undergraduates, 20. Fourteen percent drop out by the end of their first year; 70% remain to graduate.

Housing: A total of 1425 students can be accommodated in college housing. College-sponsored living facilities include dormitories and on-campus apartments. On-campus housing is guaranteed for the freshman year only, is available on a first-come, first-served basis, and is available on a lottery system for upperclassmen. Eighty-five percent of students live on campus; of those, 75% remain on campus on weekends. Alcohol is not permitted. All students may keep cars on campus.

Activities: There are no fraternities on campus. There are 110 groups on campus, including art, band, chess, choir, chorale, chorus, computers, dance, drama, ethnic, honors, international, jazz band, literary magazine, musical theater, newspaper, opera, orchestra, pep band, photography, political, professional, radio and TV, religious, social, social service, student government, symphony, and yearbook. Popular campus events include Mixers, Pinestock, Swayed Pines Folk Festival, and the Lively Arts Calendar.

Sports: There are 11 intercollegiate and 15 intramural sports available. Athletic and recreation facilities include courts for basketball, racquetball, and tennis, a weight room, a swimming pool and diving platform, a hockey rink, and fields for soccer, baseball, and rugby. There is also a downhill skiing area and 5 lakes for canoeing, fishing, swimming, and rowing.

Disabled Students: Seventy-five percent of the campus is accessible to disabled students. The following facilities are available: wheelchair ramps, elevators, special parking, specially equipped rest rooms, special class scheduling, lowered drinking fountains, and lowered telephones.

Services: In addition to many counseling and information services, tutoring is available in every subject. There is also a reader service for the blind. Mathematics and writing laboratories, and study and test-taking skills instruction are available.

Campus Safety and Security: Campus safety and security measures include 24-hour foot and vehicle patrol, escort service, shuttle buses, and informal discussions. In addition, there are emergency telephones and lighted pathways and sidewalks.

Programs of Study: St. John's awards the B.A. degree. Master's degrees also are awarded. Bachelor's degrees are awarded in BIOLOGICAL SCIENCE (biology/biological science and nutrition), BUSINESS (accounting and management science), COMMUNICATIONS AND THE ARTS (art history and appreciation, classics, communications, dramatic arts, English, fine arts, French, German, Latin, music, and Spanish), COMPUTER AND PHYSICAL SCIENCE (chemistry, computer science, mathematics, natural sciences, and physics), EDUCATION (elementary), ENGINEERING AND ENVIRONMENTAL DESIGN (preengineering), HEALTH PROFESSIONS (medical laboratory technology, nursing, predentistry, premedicine, prepharmacy, and preveterinary science), and SOCIAL SCIENCE (dietetics, economics, history, humanities, liberal arts/general studies, medieval studies, peace studies, philosophy, political science/government, prelaw, psychology, social science, social work, sociology, and theological studies). Management, accounting, English, biology, and government have the largest enrollments.

Required: To graduate, students must complete 124 credit hours with a 2.0 GPA. The required core curriculum includes 6 credits in fine arts, 5 courses in humanities, 2 courses each in natural science and social science, and 1 course in mathematics. A first-year symposium and a senior seminar are also required, and students must participate in 1 approved physical activity.

Special: There is cross-registration with the College of St. Benedict and St. Cloud University. An extensive program of internships and fieldwork, including programs in Latin America, is offered. Students may design their own majors and individual learning projects and study abroad in 9 countries. A 3-2 engineering program is offered through several universities, and a 3-2 program in occupational therapy is available with Washington University in St. Louis, Missouri. Double majors, nondegree study, and pass/fail options are available. There is a freshman honors program on campus. All departments have honors programs.

Faculty/Classroom: Seventy-five percent of faculty are male; 25%, female. Ninety-eight percent teach undergraduates and 2% do research. No introductory courses are taught by graduate students. The average class size in an introductory lecture is 20; in a laboratory, 15; and in a regular course offering, 20 to 25.

Admissions: About 86% of the 1993-94 applicants were accepted. The SAT I scores for the freshman class were as follows: Verbal—59% below 500, 34% between 500 and 599, 6% between 600 and 700, and 1% above 700; Math—25% below 500, 41% between 500 and 599, 27% between 600 and 700, and 7% above 700. The ACT scores were 23% below 21, 27% between 21 and 23, 26% between 24 and 26, 14% between 27 and 28, and 10% above 28. About 37% of the current freshmen were in the top fifth of their class; 68% were in the top two fifths.

Requirements: St. John's requires applicants to be in the upper 40% of their class. A minimum GPA of 2.8 is required. The SAT I or ACT is required. The PSAT is accepted. Students should be graduates of an accredited secondary school; preparation should include 17 academic units, including 4 of English, 3 of mathematics, 2 each of science and social studies, and 6 of electives; a foreign language is recommended. A GED equivalence is accepted. AP credits are accepted. Important factors used in the admissions decision are advanced placement or honor courses, evidence of special talent, leadership record, extracurricular activities record, and recommendations by school officials.

Procedure: Freshmen are admitted to all sessions. Entrance exams should be taken by fall of the senior year. Application deadlines are open. The application fee is $20. Notification is sent on a rolling basis. There are early decision and deferred admissions plans.

Transfer: About 75 transfer students enrolled in a recent year. Transfer students are considered for admission on the combined basis of high school and college achievement. A total of 45 credits out of 124 must be completed at St. John's.

Visiting: ((NULL))There are regularly scheduled orientations for prospective students. There are guides for informal visits and visitors may sit in on classes and stay overnight at the school. To arrange for a visit, contact Mary Milbert, Director of Admissions, at (800) 245-6467 or (612) 363-2196.

Financial Aid: In a recent year, 70% of all students received some form of financial aid. About 65% of all students received need-based aid. The average freshman award was $9600. Of that total, scholarships or need-based grants averaged $4000 ($9000 maximum); loans averaged $2000 ($2625 maximum); and work contracts averaged $1500 ($1600 maximum). Forty-five percent of undergraduate students work part-time. Average earnings from campus work for the school year are $1600. The average financial indebtedness of a recent graduate was $9400. St. John's is a member of CSS. The FAF or FFS is required.

International Students: There are currently 54 international students enrolled. The school actively recruits these students. They must take the TOEFL or the University of Michigan Language Test and achieve a minimum score on the TOEFL of 500. The student must also take the SAT I or the ACT.

Computers: The college provides computer facilities for student use. The mainframe is a DEC VAX 4000/300. There are 200 terminals available in the computer center, library, and academic buildings. All students may access the system. It may be used 24 hours a day. There are no time limits on using the system and no fees.

Graduates: In a recent year, 416 bachelor's degrees were awarded. The most popular majors among graduates were business and management (27%), government (9%), and English (8%). Within an average freshman class, 60% graduate in 4 years, 67% in 5 years, and 70% in 6 years. Some 90 companies recruited on campus in a recent year. In the graduating class, 25% of the men were enrolled in graduate school within 6 months of graduation; 90% of the men had found employment.

Admissions Contact: Mary Milbert, Director of Admissions.

SAINT MARY'S COLLEGE OF MINNESOTA D-5
Winona, MN 55987-1399 (507) 457-1700
(800) 635-5987 (out-of-state)

Full-time: 660 men, 580 women	Faculty: 87; IIA, --$
Part-time: 29 men, 46 women	Ph.D.s: 61%
Graduate: 1599 men, 4167 women	Student/Faculty: 14 to 1
Year: semesters	Tuition: $10,380
Application Deadline: open	Room & Board: $3470
Freshman Class: 870 applied, 802 accepted, 367 enrolled	
SAT I or ACT: required	LESS COMPETITIVE

St. Mary's College of Minnesota, founded in 1912, is a private, coeducational, liberal arts college affiliated with the Roman Catholic Church. There is one graduate school. The library contains 148,000 volumes and 100 microform items, and subscribes to 627 periodicals. Computerized library sources and services include the card catalog and interlibrary loans. Special learning facilities include a learning resource center, art gallery, radio station, and observatory. The 400-acre campus is in a small town 110 miles southeast of Minneapolis. Including residence halls, there are 23 buildings on campus.

Student Life: About 54% of undergraduates are from out-of-state, mostly the Midwest. Students come from 45 states, 13 foreign countries, and Canada. Thirty-seven percent are from public schools; 62% from private. Eighty-nine percent are white. Seventy-eight percent are Catholic; 14% Protestant. The average age of freshmen is 18; all undergraduates, 20. Twenty-five percent drop out by the end of their first year; 62% remain to graduate.

Housing: A total of 1154 students can be accommodated in college housing. College-sponsored living facilities include single-sex and coed dormitories and on-campus apartments. In addition, there are student-directed communities, academically structured living programs for freshmen and sophomores, and a drug/alcohol/tobacco-free dorm. On-campus housing is guaranteed for all 4 years. Eighty-six percent of students live on campus; of those, 75% remain on campus on weekends. All students may keep cars on campus.

Activities: About 4% of men belong to 2 national fraternities; about 4% of women belong to 3 national sororities. There are 60 groups on campus, including art, band, cheerleading, choir, chorale, chorus, computers, dance, drama, ethnic, honors, international, jazz band, literary magazine, musical theater, newspaper, orchestra, photography, political, professional, radio and TV, religious, social, social service, and student government. Popular campus events include two annual

student talent shows, dances and formals, Casino Night, Winter Sports Weekend, and Olympic Day.

Sports: There are 8 intercollegiate sports for men and 8 for women, and 14 intramural sports for men and 13 for women. Athletic and recreation facilities include 4 basketball courts, an indoor tennis court, an indoor ice arena, 6 racquetball courts, exercise and weight rooms, and baseball, softball, and soccer fields.

Disabled Students: Forty percent of the campus is accessible to disabled students. The following facilities are available: wheelchair ramps, elevators, special parking, specially equipped rest rooms, lowered drinking fountains, and lowered telephones.

Services: In addition to many counseling and information services, tutoring is available in every subject. In addition, there is a reader service for the blind, and remedial math, reading, and writing.

Campus Safety and Security: Campus safety and security measures include 24-hour foot and vehicle patrol, escort service, shuttle buses, and informal discussions. In addition, there are pamphlets, posters, and films, emergency telephones, and lighted pathways and sidewalks.

Programs of Study: SMC awards the B.A. and B.S. degrees. Master's degrees also are awarded. Bachelor's degrees are awarded in BIOLOGICAL SCIENCE (biology/biological science and environmental biology), BUSINESS (accounting, business administration and management, and marketing/retailing/merchandising), COMMUNICATIONS AND THE ARTS (communications, communications technology, design, dramatic arts, English, fine arts, French, languages, literature, music, public relations, Spanish, speech/debate/rhetoric, and telecommunications), COMPUTER AND PHYSICAL SCIENCE (chemistry, computer science, information sciences and systems, mathematics, physics, and statistics), EDUCATION (early childhood, education, elementary, English, foreign languages, middle school, music, science, secondary, and social science), ENGINEERING AND ENVIRONMENTAL DESIGN (preengineering), HEALTH PROFESSIONS (cytotechnology, medical laboratory technology, nuclear medical technology, physical therapy, predentistry, premedicine, and preveterinary science), SOCIAL SCIENCE (criminal justice, history, human services, ministries, philosophy, political science/government, prelaw, psychology, public administration, social science, sociology, and theological studies). Business, computer science, biology, psychology, and theater are the strongest academically. Management, marketing, biology, human services, education, and psychology have the largest enrollments.

Required: Students must have a 2.0 GPA and complete a minimum of 122 semester credits, including at least 45 at the upper-division level. Students must complete 32 to 42 credits in the major and the general education program of 23 credits in core studies and 24 credits of area studies. No more than 4 hours each of music ensemble and theater activity credits may be applied toward the requirement. Students must spend their final year in academic residence, complete 2 1/2 semester-length sport activity classes (no credit), and demonstrate mathematics competency at the intermediate algebra level.

Special: Students may cross-register with Winona State University. Internships, student teaching and study abroad, work-study programs, and a Washington semester are available. The college also offers dual and student-designed majors, a 3–2 engineering degree, nondegree study, pass/fail options, and credit for life, military, and work experience. An honors program called the LaSallian Institute offers a 2-year curriculum in an area outside of the major. There is a freshman honors program on campus, as well as 10 national honor societies.

Faculty/Classroom: Seventy-nine percent of full-time faculty are male; 21%, female. Eighty-five percent teach undergraduates and 15% both teach and do research. No introductory courses are taught by graduate students. The average class size in an introductory lecture is 23; in a laboratory, 11; and in a regular course offering, 15.

Admissions: About 92% of the 1993–94 applicants were accepted. The SAT scores for the 1993–94 freshman class were as follows: Verbal—70% below 500, 23% between 500 and 599, 5% between 600 and 700, and 2% above 700; Math—55% below 500, 34% between 500 and 599, 9% between 600 and 700, and 2% above 700. The ACT scores were 48% below 20, 35% between 21 and 25, and 17% between 26 and 36. About 30% of the current freshmen were in the top fifth of their class; 47% were in the top two fifths. Eight freshmen graduated first in their class.

Requirements: SMC requires applicants to be in the upper 50% of their class. A minimum GPA of 2.0 is required. The SAT I or ACT is required. Candidates for admission should have completed 4 units of English, 3 of mathematics, 2 each of natural science and social studies, and an additional 7 of academic electives. AP and CLEP credits are accepted. Important factors used in the admissions decision are advanced placement or honor courses, leadership record, parents or siblings attending the school, personality, intangible qualities, and evidence of special talent.

Procedure: Freshmen are admitted fall and spring. Entrance exams should be taken by the fall of the senior year. Application deadlines are open. The application fee is $20. Notification is sent on a rolling basis. There is a deferred admissions plan.

Transfer: About 58 transfer students enrolled in 1993–94. Applicants must have a 2.0 GPA. A total of 60 credits out of 122 must be completed at SMC.

Visiting: There are regularly scheduled orientations for prospective students, including an interview, tour, class visit, and lunch. There are guides for informal visits and visitors may sit in on classes and stay overnight at the school. To arrange for a visit, contact the Office of Admissions at (800) 635–5987.

Financial Aid: In 1993–94, 71% of all current freshmen and 70% of continuing students received some form of financial aid. About 63% of freshmen and 60% of continuing students received need-based aid. The average freshman award was $9600. Of that total, scholarships or need-based grants averaged $4800; loans averaged $3800; and work contracts averaged $1000. Sixty-one percent of undergraduate students work part-time. Average earnings from campus work for the school year are $770. The average financial indebtedness of the 1992–93 graduate was $8800. SMC is a member of CSS. The FAFSA is required. The deadline for financial aid applications is open.

International Students: There are currently 64 international students enrolled. The school actively recruits these students. They must take the TOEFL and achieve a minimum score of 500. The student must also take the SAT I or the ACT.

Computers: The college provides computer facilities for student use. There are 125 Apple and IBM microcomputers available in computer laboratories and department areas. There are 7 NEXT workstations and 15 terminals connected to the MicroVAX system. All students may access the system. It may be used 7:30 A.M. to midnight, Monday through Thursday; 8 A.M. to 4:30 P.M., Friday; 10 A.M. to 4 P.M., Saturday; and noon to midnight, Sunday. There are no time limits on using the system and no fees.

Graduates: In 1992–93, 259 bachelor's degrees were awarded. The most popular majors among graduates were management (12%), business administration (8%), philosophy (6%), and criminal justice (6%). Within an average freshman class, 1% graduate in 3 years, 52% in 4 years, 8% in 5 years, and 1% in 6 years. Some 20 companies recruited on campus in 1992–93. In the 1992 graduating class, 18% of all students were enrolled in graduate school within 8 to 11 months of graduation; 65% of all students had found full-time employment.

Admissions Contact: Anthony M. Piscitiello, Vice President for Admissions.

SAINT OLAF COLLEGE

C-4

Northfield, MN 55057–1098 (507) 646–3025

Full-time: 1299 men, 1589 women	**Faculty:** 259; IIB, +$
Part-time: 47 men, 58 women	**Ph.D.s:** 85%
Graduate: none	**Student/Faculty:** 11 to 1
Year: 4–1–4, summer session	**Tuition:** $13,560
Application Deadline: open	**Room & Board:** $3650
Freshman Class: 2248 applied, 1673 accepted, 745 enrolled	
SAT I Verbal/Math: 530/580	**ACT:** 26 **HIGHLY COMPETITIVE**

St. Olaf College, founded in 1874, is a private, liberal arts, coeducational college affiliated with the Evangelical Lutheran Church in America. In addition to regional accreditation, St. Olaf has baccalaureate program accreditation with NASAD, NASM, NCATE, and NLN. The 4 libraries contain 428,059 volumes, 46,053 microform items, and 5533 audiovisual forms, and subscribe to 1968 periodicals. Computerized library sources and services include the card catalog, interlibrary loans, and database searching. Special learning facilities include a learning resource center, art gallery, and radio station. The 350-acre campus is in a small town 40 miles south of Minneapolis. Including residence halls, there are 29 buildings on campus.

Student Life: About 57% of undergraduates are from Minnesota. Students come from 50 states, 21 foreign countries, and Canada. Eighty percent are from public schools; 20% from private. Ninety-two percent are white. Seventy-five percent are Protestant; 14% Catholic. The average age of freshmen is 18; all undergraduates, 20. Twelve percent drop out by the end of their first year; 81% remain to graduate.

Housing: A total of 2667 students can be accommodated in college housing. College-sponsored living facilities include coed dormitories. In addition there are honors houses, language houses, and special interest houses. On-campus housing is guaranteed for all 4 years. Ninety percent of students live on campus; of those, 80% remain on campus on weekends. Alcohol is not permitted.

Activities: There are no fraternities or sororities on campus. There are 80 groups on campus, including band, cheerleading, chess, choir, dance, drama, ethnic, gay, honors, international, jazz band, literary magazine, musical theater, newspaper, opera, orchestra, pep band, photography, political, professional, radio and TV, religious,

social, social service, student government, symphony, and yearbook. Popular campus events include Christmas Festival, Black History Month, Fine Arts Week, Wellness Week, and Homecoming.

Sports: There are 13 intercollegiate sports for men and 11 for women, and 11 intramural sports for men and 11 for women. Athletic and recreation facilities include an athletic complex, a field house, and a playing field.

Disabled Students: Sixty percent of the campus is accessible to disabled students. The following facilities are available: wheelchair ramps, elevators, special parking, specially equipped rest rooms, special class scheduling, and lowered drinking fountains and telephones.

Services: In addition to many counseling and information services, tutoring is available in every subject. There is a reader service for the blind. Study sessions are available.

Campus Safety and Security: Campus safety and security measures include 24-hour foot and vehicle patrol, escort service, shuttle buses, and informal discussions. In addition, there are pamphlets, posters, and films, emergency telephones, and lighted pathways and sidewalks.

Programs of Study: St. Olaf awards the B.A. and B.Mus. degrees. Bachelor's degrees are awarded in BIOLOGICAL SCIENCE (biology/biological science), COMMUNICATIONS AND THE ARTS (art, art history and appreciation, dance, English, fine arts, French, German, Greek, Latin, music, performing arts, Russian, Scandinavian languages, Spanish, and speech/debate/rhetoric), COMPUTER AND PHYSICAL SCIENCE (chemistry, mathematics, and physics), EDUCATION (art, English, foreign languages, health, mathematics, physical, science, secondary, and social studies), ENGINEERING AND ENVIRONMENTAL DESIGN (preengineering), HEALTH PROFESSIONS (nursing, predentistry, and premedicine), SOCIAL SCIENCE (American studies, Asian/Oriental studies, classical/ancient civilization, crosscultural studies, economics, family/consumer resource management, Hispanic American studies, history, medieval studies, philosophy, political science/government, prelaw, psychology, religion, social work, sociology, urban studies, and women's studies). Mathematics, science, fine arts, and English are the strongest academically. Mathematics, economics, biology, English, and psychology have the largest enrollments.

Required: In order to graduate, students must complete 35 courses, including 6 in the major, with a 2.0 GPA. The core curriculum must include 3 courses each in religion, English composition, and a foreign language; 2 courses each in fine arts, behavioral science, natural science and mathematics, and physical education; and 1 course each in history, philosophy, literature, and crosscultural studies.

Special: Students may take co-op programs with Augsburg College and cross-register with Carleton College. The college offers study abroad in more than 27 countries, a Washington semester, and internships. An accelerated prelaw program with Columbia University is available. Students may earn a B.A.-B.S. degree in engineering with Washington University. The college offers student-designed and dual majors, a 3–2 engineering degree, nondegree study, and pass/fail options. The Paracollege allows students to design individual majors with an emphasis on tutorials and seminars. There are 13 national honor societies on campus, including Phi Beta Kappa.

Faculty/Classroom: Sixty-eight percent of faculty are male; 32%, female. All teach undergraduates, as well as do research. The average class size in a regular course offering is 21.

Admissions: About 74% of the 1993–94 applicants were accepted. The SAT scores for the 1993–94 freshman class were as follows: Verbal—38% below 500, 39% between 500 and 599, 21% between 600 and 700, and 2% above 700; Math—19% below 500, 39% between 500 and 599, 31% between 600 and 700, and 11% above 700. The ACT scores were 9% below 21, 22% between 21 and 23, 29% between 24 and 26, 20% between 27 and 28, and 20% above 28. About 62% of the current freshmen were in the top fifth of their class; 88% were in the top two fifths. There were 19 National Merit finalists. Sixty-five freshmen graduated first in their class.

Requirements: The SAT I or ACT is required. Applicants should have completed a total of 15 high school credits, including 3 credits in English and 2 credits in mathematics. Of the 15 credits, 11 must be in academic areas. AP and CLEP credits are accepted. Important factors used in the admissions decision are advanced placement or honors courses, evidence of special talent, extracurricular activities record, geographic diversity, and recommendations by alumni.

Procedure: Freshmen are admitted fall, winter, and spring. Entrance exams should be taken in the spring of the junior year or the fall of the senior year. Early decision applications should be filed by November 15. Application deadlines are open for regular decision. There is an application fee of $25. Notification of early decision is sent December 1; regular decision, on a rolling basis. There are early decision, early admissions, and deferred admissions plans. About 174 early decision candidates were accepted for the 1993–94 class.

Transfer: About 74 transfer students enrolled in 1993–94. Transfer applicants must have a 3.0 GPA at their previous institution. A total of 17 courses out of 35 must be completed at St. Olaf.

Visiting: There are regularly scheduled orientations for prospective students. Visits follow an open-house format with information sessions. There are guides for informal visits, and visitors may sit in on classes and stay overnight at the school. To arrange for a visit, contact Katie George, Visit Coordinator, at (507) 646–3025.

Financial Aid: In 1993–94, 65% of all current freshmen and 58% of continuing students received some form of financial aid. About 65% of freshmen and 62% of continuing students received need-based aid. The average freshman award was $11,924. Of that total, scholarships or need-based grants averaged $8034 ($14,110 maximum); loans averaged $2827 ($5000 maximum); and work contracts averaged $1063 ($1600 maximum). Seventy percent of undergraduate students work part-time. Average earnings from campus work for the school year are $900. The average financial indebtedness of the 1992–93 graduate was $9772. St. Olaf is a member of CSS. The college's own financial statement and FAFSA are required. The deadline for financial aid applications is March 1.

International Students: There are currently 60 international students enrolled. The school actively recruits these students. They must take the TOEFL and achieve a minimum score of 550. The student must also take the SAT I or the ACT.

Computers: The college provides computer facilities for student use. The mainframe is composed of 2 DEC VAX 11/780's. There are 54 terminals, 30 UNIX workstations, 237 microcomputers, and a variety of mini-workstations located in academic buildings and residence halls. All students may access the system. There are no time limits on using the system and no fees.

Graduates: In 1992–93, 709 bachelor's degrees were awarded. The most popular majors among graduates were economics (12%), biology (11%), and English (11%). Within an average freshman class, 73% graduate in 4 years and 81% in 5 years. Some 45 companies recruited on campus in 1992–93. In the 1992 graduating class, 22% of all students were enrolled in graduate school within 6 months of graduation; 58% had found employment.

Admissions Contact: John P. Ruohoniemi, Director of Admissions.

SOUTHWEST STATE UNIVERSITY   B-4
Marshall, MN 56258   (507) 537-6286; (800) 533-8605 (out-of-state)

Full-time: 993 men, 1098 women	Faculty: 135; IIB, +$
Part-time: 211 men, 335 women	Ph.D.s: 77%
Graduate: none	Student/Faculty: 15 to 1
Year: quarters, summer session	Tuition: $2650 ($4650)
Application Deadline: open	Room & Board: $2750
Freshman Class: 1047 applied, 938 accepted, 511 enrolled	
ACT: 20	**NONCOMPETITIVE**

Southwest State University, founded in 1963, is a public institution offering programs in liberal arts, technology, and preprofessional training. The library contains 165,000 volumes, 37,000 microform items, and 12,000 audiovisual forms, and subscribes to 800 periodicals. Computerized library sources and services include the card catalog, interlibrary loans, and database searching. Special learning facilities include an art gallery, natural history museum, planetarium, radio station, and TV station. The 216-acre campus is in a rural area 150 miles southwest of Minneapolis. Including residence halls, there are 23 buildings on campus.

Student Life: About 77% of undergraduates are from Minnesota. Students come from 27 states. Ninety-five percent are from public schools. Ninety-four percent are white. The average age of all undergraduates is 22.1. Twenty percent drop out by the end of their first year; 35% remain to graduate.

Housing: A total of 1250 students can be accommodated in college housing. College-sponsored living facilities include single-sex and coed dormitories. In addition, there are special interest houses and a quiet house. On-campus housing is guaranteed for the freshman year only. Fifty-five percent of students live on campus. Alcohol is not permitted. All students may keep cars on campus.

Activities: There are no fraternities or sororities on campus. There are 60 groups on campus, including art, band, cheerleading, chess, choir, chorus, computers, dance, drama, ethnic, honors, international, jazz band, literary magazine, marching band, newspaper, pep band, political, radio and TV, religious, student government, and symphony. Popular campus events include Prairie Festival, Rural Writer's Conference, and Homecoming.

Sports: There are 6 intercollegiate sports for men and 6 for women, as well as intramural sports. Athletic and recreation facilities include a gymnasium, baseball and softball facilities, handball and squash courts, a track, a football field, tennis courts, wrestling rooms, a weight room, an Olympic-size pool, and a 5000-seat stadium.

Disabled Students: Ninety-five percent of the campus is accessible to disabled students. The following facilities are available: wheelchair ramps, elevators, special parking, specially equipped rest rooms, special class scheduling, lowered drinking fountains, and lowered telephones.

Services: In addition to many counseling and information services, tutoring is available in most subjects. In addition, there is a reader service for the blind, and remedial math, reading, and writing.

Campus Safety and Security: Campus safety and security measures include 24-hour foot and vehicle patrol, escort service, informal discussions, pamphlets, posters, and films. In addition, there are emergency telephones in elevators and lighted pathways and sidewalks.

Programs of Study: SSU awards the B.A., B.S., and B.E.T. degrees. Associate degrees also are awarded. Bachelor's degrees are awarded in AGRICULTURE (agricultural business management), BIOLOGICAL SCIENCE (biology/biological science), BUSINESS (accounting, business administration and management, and hotel/motel and restaurant management), COMMUNICATIONS AND THE ARTS (communications, creative writing, literature, and music), COMPUTER AND PHYSICAL SCIENCE (chemistry, computer science, mathematics, and physics), EDUCATION (art, business, elementary, health, mathematics, music, and physical), ENGINEERING AND ENVIRONMENTAL DESIGN (electrical/electronics engineering technology and mechanical engineering technology), HEALTH PROFESSIONS (medical technology), SOCIAL SCIENCE (history, political science/government, psychology, social work, and sociology). Education, business administration, and accounting have the largest enrollments.

Required: To graduate, students must complete at least 192 quarter credit hours, including a common general studies curriculum, with a minimum GPA of 2.0.

Special: SSU has cooperative programs in business administration with Willmar Community College, cross-registration with 6 state universities, and an accelerated degree in business administration. SSU also offers internships in every discipline, work-study programs, study abroad in Japan, student-designed and interdisciplinary majors including speech communication and theater arts, nondegree study, pass/fail options, and credit for life, military, and work experience. There is a freshman honors program on campus, as well as 2 national honor societies.

Faculty/Classroom: Seventy-five percent of faculty are male; 25%, female. Ninety-five percent teach undergraduates.

Admissions: About 90% of the 1993–94 applicants were accepted. The ACT scores for the 1993–94 freshman class were as follows: 57% below 21, 25% between 21 and 23, 12% between 24 and 26, 3% between 27 and 28, and 3% above 28.

Requirements: SSU requires applicants to be in the upper 50% of their class. The ACT is required. Students should be graduates of an accredited secondary school or have a GED certificate. An interview is recommended. AP and CLEP credits are accepted. Important factors used in the admissions decision are recommendations by school officials, leadership record, personality, intangible qualities, advanced placement or honor courses, and evidence of special talent.

Procedure: Freshmen are admitted to all sessions. Entrance exams should be taken during the junior or senior year. Application deadlines are open. The application fee is $15. SSU accepts all applicants. Notification is sent on a rolling basis. There are early decision, early admissions, and deferred admissions plans.

Transfer: A total of 181 transfer students enrolled in 1993–94. Applicants need a minimum GPA of 2.0 in previous college-level work at an accredited institution. A total of 48 quarter credits out of 192 must be completed at SSU.

Visiting: There are regularly scheduled orientations for prospective students. There are guides for informal visits and visitors may sit in on classes and stay overnight at the school. To arrange for a visit, contact the Admissions Office at (800) 642–0684 (in-state).

Financial Aid: In 1993–94, 81% of all current freshmen and 80% of continuing students received some form of financial aid. About 82% of freshmen and 78% of continuing students received need-based aid. The average freshman award was $3043. Of that total, scholarships or need-based grants averaged $800 ($2500 maximum); loans averaged $3000 ($5500 maximum); and work contracts averaged $700 ($1200 maximum). Seventy percent of undergraduate students work part-time. Average earnings from campus work for the school year are $875. The average financial indebtedness of the 1992–93 graduate was $6100. The FFS is required. The deadline for financial aid applications is May 1.

International Students: There are currently 79 international students enrolled. The school actively recruits these students. They must take the TOEFL and achieve a minimum score of 500.

Computers: SSU provides computer facilities for student use. The mainframes are a Sperry UNIVAC 1110/91 and 1110/80, DEC VAX 11/780, Data General MV/20,000, and AT&T 3B2/500. There are also 149 Apple and IBM microcomputers available. All students may access the system 24 hours per day. There are no time limits on using the system. The fees are $1 per credit hour up to 12 credits.

Graduates: In 1992–93, 367 bachelor's degrees were awarded. The most popular majors among graduates were business administration (24%), social sciences (16%), and elementary education (10%). Within an average freshman class, 35% graduate in 6 years. Some 23

companies recruited on campus in 1992–93.

Admissions Contact: Richard Shearer, Admissions Office.

UNIVERSITY OF MINNESOTA SYSTEM

The University of Minnesota System, established in 1851, is a public system in Minnesota. It is governed by a board of regents, whose chief administrator is the president. The primary goal of the system is teaching, research, and public service. The main priorities are undergraduate education, basic and applied research, and graduate education. The total enrollment in a recent year of all 4 campuses was 67,923; there were 3357 faculty members. Altogether there are 269 baccalaureate, 235 master's, and 125 doctoral programs offered in the University of Minnesota System. Four-year campuses are located in Duluth, Morris, Crookston, and the Twin Cities. Profiles of the 4-year campuses are included in this chapter in alphabetical order with other Minnesota schools.

UNIVERSITY OF MINNESOTA CROOKSTON
Crookston, MN 56716   A-2

(218) 281–8569
(800) UMC-MINN (out-of-state)

Full-time: 473 men, 351 women	**Faculty:** 40; III, av$
Part-time: 216 men, 417 women	**Ph.D.s:** 35%
Graduate: none	**Student/Faculty:** 21 to 1
Year: trimesters	**Tuition:** $3569 ($8744)
Application Deadline: September 1	**Room & Board:** $3325
Freshman Class: 433 applied, 433 accepted, 330 enrolled	
ACT: recommended	**NONCOMPETITIVE**

University of Minnesota, Crookston, founded in 1965, is a public, coeducational institution offering undergraduate degrees in agriculture, business, and hotel, restaurant, and institutional management. In addition to regional accreditation, UMC has baccalaureate program accreditation with AACSB and ADA. The library contains 23,400 volumes. Special learning facilities include a learning resource center. The 95-acre campus is in a rural area. Including residence halls, there are 28 buildings on campus.

Student Life: About 75% of undergraduates are from Minnesota. Students come from 10 states, 8 foreign countries, and Canada. Ninety-eight percent are from public schools; 2% from private. Ninety-four percent are white. The average age of freshmen is 18; all undergraduates, 26. Forty-five percent drop out by the end of their first year.

Housing: A total of 400 students can be accommodated in college housing. College-sponsored living facilities include coed dormitories and on-campus apartments. On-campus housing is available on a first-come, first-served basis. Priority is given to out-of-town students. Fifty-five percent of students commute. Alcohol is not permitted. All students may keep cars on campus.

Activities: There are no fraternities or sororities on campus. There are some groups and organizations on campus, including choir, drama, newspaper, and yearbook. Popular campus events include Homecoming, Agriculture Activities Day, and Business Activities Day.

Sports: There are 4 intercollegiate sports for men and 3 for women, and 6 intramural sports each for men and women. Athletic and recreation facilities include a large indoor and outdoor sports complex.

Disabled Students: Ninety-five percent of the campus is accessible to disabled students. The following facilities are available: wheelchair ramps, elevators, special parking, specially equipped rest rooms, special class scheduling, lowered drinking fountains, and lowered telephones.

Services: In addition to many counseling and information services, there is a reader service for the blind, and remedial math, reading, and writing. An academic assistance center is also available.

Campus Safety and Security: Campus safety and security measures include pamphlets, posters, films, and lighted pathways and sidewalks.

Programs of Study: UMC awards the B.S. degree. Associate degrees also are awarded. Bachelor's degrees are awarded in AGRICULTURE (agricultural business management and natural resource management), BUSINESS (hotel/motel and restaurant management and management science), ENGINEERING AND ENVIRONMENTAL DESIGN (environmental engineering technology and technological management).

Required: In order to graduate, students must complete a minimum of 180 credits, with a minimum 2.0 GPA, including 72 credits in general education coursework and 108 in the major and electives. One third of credit hours (60) must be upper division coursework. An internship or field experience is also required.

Faculty/Classroom: Sixty percent of faculty are male; 40%, female. All teach undergraduates and also do research. The average class size in an introductory lecture is 40; in a laboratory, 20; and in a regular course offering, 30.

Admissions: All of the 1993–94 applicants were accepted. Six percent of the current freshmen were in the top fifth of their class; 17% were in the top two fifths.

Requirements: A minimum GPA of 1.0 is required. The ACT is recommended. Students with a high school diploma or equivalent are accepted for admission. AP and CLEP credits are accepted.

Procedure: Freshmen are admitted in the fall, winter, and spring. Recommended application deadlines are September 1 for fall entry, November 1 for winter entry, and March 1 for spring entry, along with an application fee of $25. The college accepts all applicants. Notification is sent on a rolling basis.

Transfer: About 50 transfer students enrolled in 1993–94. A total of 30 credits of the last 90 must be completed at UMC.

Visiting: There are guides for informal visits and visitors may sit in on classes and stay overnight at the school. To arrange for a visit, contact the Admissions Office at (218) 281–8569.

Financial Aid: In 1993–94, 85% of all students received some form of financial aid. About 85% of students received need-based aid. Average earnings from campus work for the school year are $900. UMC is a member of CSS. The FAFSA financial statement is required. The deadline for financial aid applications is April 15.

International Students: There are currently 40 international students enrolled. The school actively recruits these students. They must take the TOEFL and achieve a minimum score of 500.

Computers: The college provides computer facilities for student use. All full-time students pay an access fee to the local area network and are issued an IBM 486 notebook. All students may access the system. There are no time limits on using the system. The fees are $235 a quarter.

Admissions Contact: John M. Bywater, Director of Admissions.

UNIVERSITY OF MINNESOTA DULUTH

D-3

Duluth, MN 55812–2496

(218) 726–7171
(800) 232–1339 (out-of-state)

Full-time: 3120 men, 2767 women	Faculty: 325; IIA, av$
Part-time: 665 men, 589 women	Ph.Ds: 90%
Graduate: 217 men, 258 women	Student/Faculty: 18 to 1
Year: quarters, summer session	Tuition: $3137 ($8706)
Application Deadline: February 1	Room & Board: $3375
Freshman Class: 4192 applied, 3129 accepted, 1656 enrolled	
ACT: 22	COMPETITIVE

The University of Minnesota at Duluth, founded in 1947, is a liberal arts institution offering undergraduate and graduate programs as a coordinate campus of the University of Minnesota. There are 5 undergraduate and 2 graduate schools. In addition to regional accreditation, UMD has baccalaureate program accreditation with ABET, CSWE, NASM, and NCATE. The library contains 516,000 volumes, 370,900 microform items, and 10,000 audiovisual forms, and subscribes to 3500 periodicals. Computerized library sources and services include the card catalog, interlibrary loans, and database searching. Special learning facilities include a learning resource center, planetarium, radio and TV stations, an art museum, and a performing arts center. The 250-acre campus is in a suburban area 150 miles north of Minneapolis and St. Paul. Including residence halls, there are 50 buildings on campus.

Student Life: About 88% of undergraduates are from Minnesota. Students come from 33 states, 27 foreign countries, and Canada. Ninety-four percent are white. The average age of freshmen is 18; all undergraduates, 21. Twenty-three percent drop out by the end of their first year; 40% remain to graduate.

Housing: A total of 2790 students can be accommodated in college housing. College-sponsored living facilities include single-sex and coed dormitories and on-campus apartments. On-campus housing is available on a first-come, first-served basis and on a lottery system for upperclassmen. Sixty-one percent of students commute. Alcohol is not permitted. All students may keep cars on campus.

Activities: About 1% of men belong to 2 national fraternities; about 1% of women belong to 3 national sororities. There are 130 groups on campus, including band, cheerleading, choir, chorale, dance, drama, ethnic, gay, honors, international, jazz band, musical theater, newspaper, orchestra, pep band, political, professional, radio and TV, religious, social, social service, and student government. Popular campus events include Homecoming, Winter Festival, Black History Month, Hispanic Heritage Month, Latin American Awareness Week, and Women's History Month.

Sports: There are 8 intercollegiate sports for men and 6 for women, and 35 intramural sports for men and 35 for women. Athletic and recreation facilities include a multipurpose ice center, a football and track-and-field stadium, a baseball park, a softball field, a field house for track and tennis, and a gymnasium for basketball, volleyball, and wrestling. There is also a nearby country club for cross-country skiing and golf.

Disabled Students: All of the campus is accessible to disabled students. The following facilities are available: wheelchair ramps, elevators, special parking, specially equipped rest rooms, lowered drinking fountains, lowered telephones, and specially equipped residence hall rooms.

Services: In addition to many counseling and information services, tutoring is available in some subjects, including mathematics, business, economics, sciences, accounting, computer science, and writing. There is also a reader service for the blind, and remedial math, reading, and writing. Workshops and seminars are also offered in study skills, note taking, time management, test taking strategies, registration, and goal setting.

Campus Safety and Security: Campus safety and security measures include 24-hour foot and vehicle patrol, self-defense education, escort service, and pamphlets, posters, and films. In addition, there are emergency telephones, and lighted pathways and sidewalks. The campus is enclosed by tunnels.

Programs of Study: UMD awards the B.A., B.S., B.A.A., B.Ac., B.A.S., B.B.A., B.Ch.E., B.Comp.E., B.F.A., B.I.E., and B.M. degrees. Master's degrees are also awarded. Bachelor's degrees are awarded in BIOLOGICAL SCIENCE (biology/biological science), BUSINESS (business administration and management), COMMUNICATIONS AND THE ARTS (art, communications, dramatic arts, English, French, German, jazz, music, music performance, music theory and composition, and Spanish), COMPUTER AND PHYSICAL SCIENCE (chemistry, computer science, earth science, geology, mathematics, and physics), EDUCATION (art, elementary, English, foreign languages, health, home economics, mathematics, music, physical, science, and social studies), ENGINEERING AND ENVIRONMENTAL DESIGN (chemical engineering, computer engineering, and industrial engineering), HEALTH PROFESSIONS (speech pathology/audiology), SOCIAL SCIENCE (American studies, anthropology, criminology, early childhood studies, economics, geography, history, interdisciplinary studies, international studies, philosophy, political science/government, psychology, sociology, urban studies, and women's studies). Business, sciences, and engineering are the strongest academically. Business administration, communication, and psychology have the largest enrollments.

Required: To graduate, students must complete 180 to 199 quarter credits, including 2 courses in college writing and a liberal education distribution of at least 48 credits in 4 academic areas, with at least 4 credits of course work emphasizing cultural diversity and 4 emphasizing an international perspective.

Special: Students may study abroad in England, Sweden, and France. UMD also offers a 3–2 engineering degree with the University of Minnesota/Twin Cities, cross-registration with the College of St. Scholastica and the University of Wisconsin/Superior, internships, work-study programs, B.A.-B.S. degrees in several fields, dual degrees such as biochemistry and molecular biology, student-designed majors, and nondegree study. There is a freshman honors program on campus, as well as 5 national honor societies. Seven departments have honors programs.

Faculty/Classroom: Seventy-five percent of faculty are male; 25%, female. All both teach and do research.

Admissions: About 75% of the 1993–94 applicants were accepted. The ACT scores for the 1993–94 freshman class were as follows: 16% below 21, 55% between 21 and 23, 13% between 24 and 26, 12% between 27 and 28, and 3% above 28. About 35% of the current freshmen were in the top fifth of their class; 72% were in the top two fifths. Fifty freshmen graduated first in their class.

Requirements: UMD requires applicants to be in the upper 60% of their class. The ACT is required. Applicants must have completed 4 years in English, 3 each in mathematics and sciences, and 2 each in a single second language and social studies. Course work in the visual and performing arts and computer skills are recommended. Those students with a GED certificate will be admitted selectively, based on available space. AP and CLEP credits are accepted. Important factors used in the admissions decision are advanced placement or honors courses, evidence of special talent, recommendations by school officials, leadership record, and extracurricular activities record.

Procedure: Freshmen are admitted to all sessions. Entrance exams should be taken at the end of the junior year or the beginning of the senior year. Applications should be filed by February 1 for fall entry, November 1 for winter entry, and February 1 for spring entry, along with an application fee of $25. Notification is sent on a rolling basis.

Transfer: There were 448 transfer students who enrolled in 1993–94. Applicants who have attempted 40 or more quarter credits must have a 2.0 GPA and a 75% completion ratio; applicants who have attempted fewer than 40 quarter credits must have a high school rank at or above the fiftieth percentile, a 1.8 GPA in their previous college work, and a 75% completion ratio. A total of 45 quarter credits out of a total of 180–199 must be completed at UMD.

Visiting: There are regularly scheduled orientations for prospective students, including a campus tour and an appointment with school personnel, such as admissions counselors, faculty, or coaches, if re-

quested. There are guides for informal visits and visitors may sit in on classes and stay overnight at the school. To arrange for a visit, contact the Admissions Office at (800) 232–1339 (out-of-state) or (218) 726–7171.

Financial Aid: In 1993–94, 75% of all students received some form of financial aid. Twenty-five percent of undergraduate students work part-time. The FAFSA financial statement is required. The deadline for financial aid applications is March 31.

International Students: There are currently 135 international students enrolled. The school actively recruits these students. They must take the TOEFL and achieve a minimum score of 550.

Computers: The university provides computer facilities for student use. The mainframes are a DEC VAX 5900 and a Sun Sparc Center. All students may access the mainframe or equipment in the microcomputer laboratories, and they may also open an account for personal use of the Encore central system in 6 computer laboratories across the campus. The system may be used 8 A.M. to 12 P.M. weekdays; Saturday and Sunday hours are also available. There are no time limits; the fees are $60 per quarter.

Graduates: In 1992–93, 1100 bachelor's degrees were awarded. The most popular majors among graduates were business administration (17%), communications (9%), and accounting (8%). Within an average freshman class, 35% graduate in 5 years and 40% in 6 years. There were 70 companies that recruited on campus in 1992–93.

Admissions Contact: Gerald R. Allen, Registrar and Director of Student Support Services.

UNIVERSITY OF MINNESOTA
MORRIS
Morris, MN 56267–2199

B-3

(612) 589–6035
(800) 992–8863 (out-of-state)

Full-time: 857 men, 1076 women	Faculty: 118; IIB, av$
Part-time: none	Ph.D.s: 83%
Graduate: none	Student/Faculty: 16 to 1
Year: quarters, summer session	Tuition: $3645 ($10,158)
Application Deadline: March 15	Room & Board: $3180
Freshman Class: 1458 applied, 860 accepted, 588 enrolled	
SAT I Verbal/Math: 550/650	ACT: 26 **HIGHLY COMPETITIVE**

The University of Minnesota/Morris, founded in 1959, is a public, liberal arts institution within the University of Minnesota System. In addition to regional accreditation, UMM has baccalaureate program accreditation with NCATE. The library contains 155,200 volumes, 19,307 microform items, and 1600 audiovisual forms, and subscribes to 765 periodicals. Computerized library sources and services include the card catalog, interlibrary loans, and database searching. Special learning facilities include a learning resource center, an art gallery, a radio station, tv studios, and a language laboratory. The 130-acre campus is in a small town 150 miles northwest of Minneapolis. Including residence halls, there are 36 buildings on campus.

Student Life: About 80% of undergraduates are from Minnesota. Students come from 22 states and 11 foreign countries. Ninety-four percent are from public schools; 6% from private. Eighty-eight percent are white. The average age of freshmen is 18; all undergraduates, 20. Eleven percent drop out by the end of their first year; 74% remain to graduate.

Housing: A total of 1027 students can be accommodated in college housing. College-sponsored living facilities include coed dormitories and on-campus apartments. On-campus housing is guaranteed for the freshman year only and is available on a lottery system for upperclassmen. Fifty-four percent of students live on campus; of those, 60% remain on campus on weekends. All students may keep cars on campus.

Activities: About 1% of men belong to 2 national fraternities; about 1% of women belong to 1 local sorority. There are 73 groups on campus, including art, band, cheerleading, chess, choir, chorus, computers, dance, drama, ethnic, gay, honors, international, jazz band, literary magazine, musical theater, newspaper, orchestra, political, professional, radio and tv, religious, social, social service, and student government. Popular campus events include Homecoming, Cougar County Jam, Cultural Heritage Week, and Women's Week.

Sports: There are 7 intercollegiate sports for men and 6 for women, and 12 intramural sports for men and 12 for women. Athletic and recreation facilities include a 4500-seat stadium; a physical education center; 3 gymnasiums; wrestling, exercise, and weight rooms, an Olympic-size pool; handball and racquetball courts; a track; and fields for softball, baseball, soccer, and football.

Disabled Students: The following facilities are available: wheelchair ramps, elevators, special parking, specially equipped rest rooms, special class scheduling, lowered drinking fountains, and disability services coordinator.

Services: In addition to many counseling and information services, tutoring is available in every subject. In addition, there is a reader service for the blind, and remedial math, reading, and writing.

Campus Safety and Security: Campus safety and security measures include 24-hour foot and vehicle patrol, self-defense education, escort service, and pamphlets, posters, and films. In addition, there are lighted pathways and sidewalks.

Programs of Study: UMM awards the B.A. degree. Bachelor's degrees are awarded in BIOLOGICAL SCIENCE (biology/biological science), BUSINESS (business economics), COMMUNICATIONS AND THE ARTS (art history and appreciation, dramatic arts, English, French, German, music, Spanish, speech/debate/rhetoric, and studio art), COMPUTER AND PHYSICAL SCIENCE (chemistry, computer science, geology, mathematics, and physics), EDUCATION (elementary and secondary), HEALTH PROFESSIONS (premedicine), SOCIAL SCIENCE (economics, European studies, history, Latin American studies, liberal arts/general studies, philosophy, political science/government, prelaw, psychology, social science, and sociology). Studio art, psychology, and sciences are the strongest academically. Biology, education, business, and economics have the largest enrollments.

Required: In addition to 60 hours in the major, students are required to complete 90 credits of a general education curriculum, including courses in inquiry, writing, speech, computing, foreign language or equivalent, and advanced study, as well as courses focusing on the arts, the physical and abstract worlds, and the self and others. In order to graduate, students must complete at least 180 quarter credits with a minimum GPA of 2.0.

Special: UMM offers internships, study abroad, dual majors, student-designed majors, nondegree study, pass/fail options, and credit for life, military, and work experience. A program that pairs students and professors together in order to undertake creative projects is available. There is a freshman honors program on campus. All departments have honors programs.

Faculty/Classroom: Seventy-four percent of faculty are male; 26%, female. All teach undergraduates and 89% do research. The average class size in an introductory lecture is 40; in a laboratory, 20; and in a regular course offering, 22.

Admissions: About 59% of the 1993–94 applicants were accepted. The SAT scores for the 1993–94 freshman class were as follows: Verbal—29% below 500, 34% between 500 and 599, 30% between 600 and 700, and 7% above 700; Math—20% below 500, 30% between 500 and 599, 32% between 600 and 700, and 18% above 700. The ACT scores were 8% below 21, 18% between 21 and 23, 34% between 24 and 26, 23% between 27 and 28, and 17% above 28. About 83% of the current freshmen were in the top fifth of their class; 97% were in the top two fifths. There were 20 National Merit finalists and 61 semifinalists. About 91 freshmen graduated first in their class.

Requirements: UMM requires applicants to be in the upper 40% of their class. The ACT is required. Applicants should be graduates of an accredited secondary school or have a GED certificate. They must have completed 4 years of English, 3 each of mathematics and science, 2 of a single foreign language, and 1 each of social studies and American history. An interview is recommended. AP and CLEP credits are accepted. Important factors used in the admissions decision are evidence of special talent, personality, intangible qualities, advanced placement or honor courses, recommendations by school officials, and extracurricular activities record.

Procedure: Freshmen are admitted fall and winter. Entrance exams should be taken before December 1. Early decision applications should be filed by December 1; regular applications, by March 15 for fall entry and November 1 for winter entry, along with an application fee of $25. Notification of early decision is sent December 15; regular decision, April 1. There are early decision, early admissions, and deferred admissions plans. About 189 early decision candidates were accepted for the 1993–94 class.

Transfer: About 80 transfer students enrolled in 1993–94. Applicants must submit ACT scores, a high school transcript, and a college transcript reflecting a minimum GPA of 2.5. An interview is recommended. A total of 45 quarter credits out of 180 must be completed at UMM.

Visiting: There are regularly scheduled orientations for prospective students. There are guides for informal visits and visitors may sit in on classes. To arrange for a visit, contact the Admissions Office at (800) 992–8863.

Financial Aid: In a recent year, 86% of all students received some form of financial aid; 80% received need-based aid. The average freshman award was $4062. Of that total, scholarships or need-based grants averaged $1021; loans averaged $2371; and work contracts averaged $715. Seventy-eight percent of undergraduate students work part-time. Average earnings from campus work for the school year are $715. The average financial indebtedness of the 1992–93 graduate was $8000. The FAFSA financial statement is required. The deadline for financial aid applications is April 1.

International Students: International students must take the TOEFL and achieve a minimum score of 600.

Computers: The college provides computer facilities for student use. The mainframe is a DEC VAX 8350. There are also 50 IBM PC, Venus PG, and Apple Macintosh microcomputers available. All students may access the system. It may be used 24 hours per day. There are no time limits on using the system and no fees.

Graduates: In a recent year, 426 bachelor's degrees were awarded. The most popular majors among graduates were business economics (17%), psychology (12%), and education (10%). Within an average freshman class, 54% graduate in 4 years and 68% in 5 years. Some 35 companies recruited on campus in a recent year. In the 1992 graduating class, 12% of all students were enrolled in graduate school within 6 months of graduation; 42% had found employment.

Admissions Contact: Robert J. Vikander, Director of Admissions and Financial Aid.

UNIVERSITY OF MINNESOTA
TWIN CITIES
C-4

Minneapolis, MN 55455 (612) 625–2006; (800) 752–1000 (in-state)

Full-time: 8831 men, 7758 women	Faculty: 2502; I, av$
Part-time: 4421 men, 4827 women	Ph.D.s: 89%
Graduate: 7142 men, 5788 women	Student/Faculty: 7 to 1
Year: quarters	Tuition: $3282 ($8826)
Application Deadline: December 15	Room & Board: $3400
Freshman Class: 9032 applied, 5779 accepted, 3261 enrolled	
SAT I Verbal/Math: 492/570	ACT: 24 VERY COMPETITIVE

The University of Minnesota/Twin Cities, founded in 1851, is a land-grant institution offering programs in liberal and fine arts, physical and biological sciences, health sciences, education, natural resources, human ecology, business, agriculture, engineering, and preprofessional training in law, medicine, dentistry, pharmacy, and veterinary medicine. There are 18 undergraduate schools and one graduate school. In addition to regional accreditation, the university has baccalaureate program accreditation with AACSB, ABET, ABFSE, ACEJMC, ADA, APTA, ASLA, CSWE, FIDER, NAAB, NASM, NCATE, NLN, and SAF. The 5 libraries contain 4,761,630 volumes, 3,308,038 microform items, and 400,849 audiovisual forms, and subscribe to 42,304 periodicals. Computerized library sources and services include the card catalog, interlibrary loans, and database searching. Special learning facilities include a learning resource center, art gallery, natural history museum, planetarium, and radio station. The 1090-acre campus is in an urban area. Including residence halls, there are 200 buildings on campus.

Student Life: About 79% of undergraduates are from Minnesota. Students come from 50 states, 110 foreign countries, and Canada. Eighty-five percent are from public schools; 15% from private. Eighty-two percent are white. The average age of freshmen is 19.3; all undergraduates, 22.5. Eighteen percent drop out by the end of their first year; 33% remain to graduate.

Housing: A total of 4440 students can be accommodated in college housing. College-sponsored living facilities include single-sex and coed dormitories, married-student housing, fraternity houses, and sorority houses. In addition, there are special interest houses. On-campus housing is available on a first-come, first-served basis and is available on a lottery system for upperclassmen. Ninety percent of students commute. Alcohol is not permitted. All students may keep cars on campus.

Activities: There are 33 local fraternities and 18 local sororities. There are 509 groups on campus, including art, band, cheerleading, chess, choir, chorale, chorus, computers, dance, drama, ethnic, film, gay, honors, international, jazz band, literary magazine, marching band, musical theater, newspaper, orchestra, pep band, photography, political, professional, radio and TV, religious, social, social service, student government, symphony, and yearbook. Popular campus events include Homecoming.

Sports: There are 12 intercollegiate sports for men and 10 for women, and 11 intramural sports for men and 7 for women. Athletic and recreation facilities include a domed stadium, 2 gymnasiums, 2 field houses, a hockey rink, an Olympic-size aquatic center, and a new student recreation center.

Disabled Students: Seventy-five percent of the campus is accessible to disabled students. The following facilities are available: wheelchair ramps, elevators, special parking, specially equipped rest rooms, special class scheduling, lowered drinking fountains, lowered telephones, listening devices, TTY and volume-control phones, print enlargers, and adaptive computers. In addition, support groups and counselors provide assistance with all areas of university life and career planning.

Services: In addition to many counseling and information services, there is a reader service for the blind, and remedial math, reading, and writing. Test proctoring and sign language interpreters also are available.

Campus Safety and Security: Campus safety and security measures include 24-hour foot and vehicle patrol, self defense education, escort service, and shuttle buses. In addition, there are informal discussions, pamphlets, posters, and films, emergency telephones, lighted pathways and sidewalks, a 20-member university police force, and blue light phone centers.

Programs of Study: The university awards the B.A., B.S., B.Aerospace Eng., B.Agr.Eng., B.C.E., B.Ch., B.Ch.E., B.Comp.Sci., B.E.E., B.F.A., B.G.E., B.I.S., B.M., B.Materials Sci., B.Mathematics, B.M.E., B.Pcs., B.S.Bus., B.S.G., B.S. in Astrophysics, B.S. in Geophysics, B.S.N., and B.Statistics degrees. Master's and doctoral degrees also are awarded. Bachelor's degrees are awarded in AGRICULTURE (agricultural business management, agricultural economics, fishing and fisheries, forestry and related sciences, forestry production and processing, and natural resource management), BIOLOGICAL SCIENCE (biochemistry, biology/biological science, botany, cell biology, ecology, evolutionary biology, genetics, microbiology, nutrition, physiology, and wildlife biology), BUSINESS (accounting, business administration and management, management science, marketing/retailing/merchandising, recreation and leisure services, recreational facilities management, and retailing), COMMUNICATIONS AND THE ARTS (art history and appreciation, Chinese, classical languages, dance, English, film arts, French, German, Greek, Hebrew, Italian, Japanese, languages, Latin, linguistics, music, Russian, Scandinavian languages, Spanish, speech/debate/rhetoric, and studio art), COMPUTER AND PHYSICAL SCIENCE (astronomy, astrophysics, chemistry, computer science, geology, geophysics and seismology, mathematics, physics, and statistics), EDUCATION (agricultural, art, bilingual/bicultural, business, early childhood, elementary, English, home economics, industrial arts, mathematics, music, physical, science, social studies, and teaching English as a second language/foreign language), ENGINEERING AND ENVIRONMENTAL DESIGN (aeronautical engineering, agricultural engineering, architecture, chemical engineering, civil engineering, electrical/electronics engineering, environmental design, geological engineering, industrial engineering, interior design, landscape architecture/design, materials engineering, materials science, mechanical engineering, and metallurgical engineering), HEALTH PROFESSIONS (dental hygiene, medical laboratory technology, music therapy, nursing, occupational therapy, pharmacy, physical therapy, predentistry, premedicine, prepharmacy, preveterinary science, and speech pathology/audiology), SOCIAL SCIENCE (African American studies, African studies, American Indian studies, American studies, anthropology, child psychology/development, East Asian studies, economics, food science, geography, history, humanities, international relations, Mexican-American/Chicano studies, Middle Eastern studies, philosophy, political science/government, prelaw, psychology, Russian and Slavic studies, sociology, South Asian studies, textiles and clothing, urban studies, and women's studies). Chemical engineering, psychology, economics, mechanical engineering, and political science are the strongest academically. Mechanical engineering, psychology, electrical engineering, business administration, chemical engineering, history, and economics have the largest enrollments.

Required: To graduate, students must complete 180 to 190 quarter credits, including 45 in the major, with a minimum GPA of 2.0. Distribution requirements include course work in the 4 areas of physical and biological sciences; the individual and society; artistic expression; and communication, language, and symbolic systems. Other requirements vary by program.

Special: The university offers cooperative programs, cross-registration with the Minnesota Community College system, internships, study abroad in 65 countries, work-study programs both on and off campus, a B.A.-B.S. degree in all majors, a general studies degree, and dual and student-designed majors. Pass/fail options and credit for life, military, or work experience are available. There is a freshman honors program on campus, as well as 21 national honor societies, including Phi Beta Kappa. Eight departments have honors programs.

Faculty/Classroom: Seventy-nine percent of faculty are male; 21%, female. All members both teach and do research. Graduate students teach 65% of introductory courses. The average class size in an introductory lecture is 27; in a laboratory, 13; and in a regular course offering, 29.

Admissions: About 64% of the 1993–94 applicants were accepted. The SAT scores for the 1993–94 freshman class were as follows: Verbal—51% below 500, 33% between 500 and 599, 14% between 600 and 700, and 2% above 700; Math—25% below 500, 30% between 500 and 599, 32% between 600 and 700, and 14% above 700. The ACT scores were 27% below 21, 25% between 21 and 23, 25% between 24 and 26, 12% between 27 and 28, and 12% above 28. About 48% of the current freshmen were in the top fifth of their class; 76% were in the top two fifths. There were 49 National Merit finalists. A total of 137 freshmen graduated first in their class.

Requirements: The ACT or SAT I is required. The university uses a formula index in evaluating high school rank and ACT test scores. A portfolio is required for studio arts and architecture, an audition for music, and an interview for architecture and education. AP and CLEP credits are accepted. Important factors used in the admissions decision are advanced placement or honor courses, evidence of special talent, leadership record, extracurricular activities record, and recommendations by school officials.

Procedure: Freshmen are admitted to all sessions. Entrance exams should be taken by the end of the junior year or by December of the senior year. Applications should be filed by June 1st for fall entry, October 15 for winter entry, and January 15 for spring entry, along with an application fee of $25. Notification is sent on a rolling basis. There is an early admissions plan.

Transfer: A total of 4510 transfer students enrolled in 1993–94. Admission requirements vary by major/program, with a minimum 2.2 GPA needed for consideration. A total of 45 quarter credits out of 180 to 190 must be completed at the university.

Visiting: There are regularly scheduled orientations for prospective students. There are guides for informal visits and visitors may sit in on classes and stay overnight at the school. To arrange for a visit, contact Loren Anderson at (612) 625–0000.

Financial Aid: In 1993–94, 60% of all current freshmen and 65% of continuing students received some form of financial aid. About 44% of freshmen and 57% of continuing students received need-based aid. The average freshman award was $5079. Of that total, scholarships or need-based grants averaged $2710 ($8616 maximum); loans averaged $3656 ($8509 maximum); work contracts averaged $2889 ($4727 maximum); and merit awards averaged $2105 ($4000 maximum). Ninety-eight percent of undergraduate students work part-time. The average financial indebtedness of the 1992–93 graduate was $9500. The FAFSA is required. The deadline for financial aid applications is open.

International Students: There are currently 2697 international students enrolled. They must take the TOEFL, the University of Michigan Language Test, or the college's own test and achieve a minimum score on the TOEFL of 550. Residents of Minnesota or neighboring states must also take the ACT; residents of other states, the SAT I.

Computers: The university provides computer facilities for student use. The mainframes are an IBM/CMS, CDC CYBER NOSNE, NOS, EP/IX, and DEC VMS. There are about 200 terminals and 800 networked microcomputers for public use. All students may access the system. It may be used used 8 A.M. to 10 P.M. Students may access the system 2 hours per session if there are others waiting or signed on. There are no fees.

Graduates: In 1992–93, 5730 bachelor's degrees were awarded. The most popular majors among graduates were business administration (6%), psychology (6%), mechanical engineering (5%), and economics (4%). Within an average freshman class, 2% graduate in 3 years, 11% in 4 years, 38% in 5 years, and 45% in 6 years. More than 200 companies recruited on campus in 1992–93.

Admissions Contact: Admissions/Prospective Student Services.

UNIVERSITY OF SAINT THOMAS

C-4

St. Paul, MN 55105   (612) 962–6150; (800) 328–6819, ext. 2–6150

Full-time: 2031 men, 2075 women	Faculty: 191; IIA, --$
Part-time: 441 men, 541 women	Ph.D.s: 79%
Graduate: 2702 men, 2455 women	Student/Faculty: 21 to 1
Year: 4–1–4, summer session	Tuition: $11,748
Application Deadline: April 1	Room & Board: $4037
Freshman Class: 2057 applied, 1807 accepted, 831 enrolled	
SAT I Verbal/Math: 470/535	ACT: 24 COMPETITIVE +

The University of Saint Thomas, founded in 1885, is a private, liberal arts institution affiliated with the Roman Catholic Church. There are 5 graduate schools. In addition to regional accreditation, Saint Thomas has baccalaureate program accreditation with CSWE, NASM, and NCATE. The 2 libraries contain 399,529 volumes, 491,625 microform items, and 8071 audiovisual forms, and subscribe to 3328 periodicals. Computerized library sources and services include the card catalog, interlibrary loans, and database searching. Special learning facilities include a learning resource center and TV station. The 78-acre campus is in an urban area 5 miles west of St. Paul and 5 miles east of Minneapolis. Including residence halls, there are 62 buildings on campus.

Student Life: About 86% of undergraduates are from Minnesota. Students come from 32 states, 31 foreign countries, and Canada. Ninety-two percent are white. Sixty-four percent are Catholic; 21% Protestant. The average age of freshmen is 18; all undergraduates, 21. Eighteen percent drop out by the end of their first year; 66% remain to graduate.

Housing: A total of 1750 students can be accommodated in college housing. College-sponsored living facilities include single-sex dormitories and off-campus apartments. On-campus housing is available on a first-come, first-served basis and is available on a lottery system for upperclassmen. Priority is given to out-of-town students. Seventy-one percent of students commute. All students may keep cars on campus.

Activities: About 2% of men belong to 1 local fraternity and 1 national fraternity; about 2% of women belong to 2 local sororities and 1 national sorority. There are 69 groups on campus, including art, band, cheerleading, choir, computers, dance, drama, ethnic, film, gay, honors, international, jazz band, literary magazine, musical theater, newspaper, opera, orchestra, pep band, photography, political, professional, radio and TV, religious, social, social service, student government, and yearbook. Popular campus events include Homecoming and Midwinter Carnival.

Sports: There are 11 intercollegiate sports for men and 9 for women, and 13 intramural sports for men and 10 for women. Athletic and recreation facilities include a field house with a 1/10-mile track, 5 volleyball courts, a 2,000-seat gymnasium, 4 basketball courts, 4 tennis courts, 6 racquetball courts, weight training rooms, a swimming pool, squash courts, and wrestling facilities. There is a 5,000-seat football, soccer, and track stadium, a baseball diamond, and other playing fields. A second gymnasium and pool are available also.

Disabled Students: Seventy percent of the campus is accessible to disabled students. The following facilities are available: wheelchair ramps, elevators, special parking, specially equipped rest rooms, special class scheduling, lowered drinking fountains, and lowered telephones.

Services: In addition to many counseling and information services, tutoring is available in most subjects. In addition, there is a reader service for the blind, and remedial math, reading, and writing. A writing center and a reading study skills center are available.

Campus Safety and Security: Campus safety and security measures include 24-hour foot and vehicle patrol, self defense education, escort service, and shuttle buses. In addition, there are informal discussions, pamphlets, posters, and films, emergency telephones, and lighted pathways and sidewalks.

Programs of Study: Saint Thomas awards the B.A. degree. Master's and doctoral degrees also are awarded. Bachelor's degrees are awarded in BIOLOGICAL SCIENCE (biology/biological science), BUSINESS (accounting, banking and finance, business administration and management, entrepreneurial studies, international business management, marketing/retailing/merchandising, and personnel management), COMMUNICATIONS AND THE ARTS (advertising, art history and appreciation, dramatic arts, English, French, German, journalism, Latin, literature, music, public relations, Spanish, speech/debate/rhetoric, and telecommunications), COMPUTER AND PHYSICAL SCIENCE (chemistry, computer science, geology, mathematics, and physics), EDUCATION (elementary, health, and physical), SOCIAL SCIENCE (Christian studies, criminal justice, economics, geography, history, human ecology, international studies, peace studies, philosophy, physical fitness/movement, political science/government, psychology, public administration, social studies, social work, sociology, theological studies, and women's studies). Business, journalism, computer science, biology, and chemistry are the strongest academically. Business, journalism, computer science, psychology, biology, and sociology have the largest enrollments.

Required: All students must maintain a minimum GPA of 2.0 and take 33 courses, plus 1 in physical education for no credit. Distribution requirements include 1 course each in fine arts, history, and social science; 2 each in philosophy and English; and 3 each in foreign language, theology, and natural science/mathematics (1 mathematics, 1 laboratory in biology, chemistry, geology, or physics, and 1 other).

Special: Students may cross-register with Augsburg and Macalester colleges, the College of Saint Catherine, and Hamline University. Internships are offered through the higher education consortium for urban affairs in the local community. Study abroad is available in 16 countries. Work-study programs, a 3–2 engineering degree with Washington University in St. Louis, Notre Dame University, GMI Engineering and Management Institute, and the University of Minnesota, nondegree study, and pass/fail options also are available. There is a freshman honors program on campus, as well as 10 national honor societies. Two departments have honors programs.

Faculty/Classroom: Seventy-two percent of faculty are male; 28%, female. All teach undergraduates. No introductory courses are taught by graduate students. The average class size in an introductory lecture is 27; in a laboratory, 16; and in a regular course offering, 18.

Admissions: About 88% of the 1993–94 applicants were accepted. The SAT scores for the 1993–94 freshman class were as follows: Verbal—61% below 500, 29% between 500 and 599, and 10% between 600 and 700; Math—33% below 500, 42% between 500 and 599, 21% between 600 and 700, and 4% above 700. The ACT scores were 22% below 21, 31% between 21 and 23, 25% between 24 and 26, 13% between 27 and 28, and 9% above 28. About 47% of the current freshmen were in the top fifth of their class; 77% were in the top two fifths. Some 27 freshmen graduated first in their class.

Requirements: Saint Thomas requires applicants to be in the upper 40% of their class. The SAT I, with a minimum composite score of 860, the ACT, with a minimum score of 20, or the PSAT is required. In addition, Saint Thomas recommends 4 units each of English, mathematics (at least 3 are required), and foreign language, and 2 units each of science and history or social studies. An essay is required. The GED is accepted. AP and CLEP credits are accepted. Important factors used in the admissions decision are advanced placement or honor courses, evidence of special talent, leadership record, recommendations by school officials, and parents or siblings attending the school.

Procedure: Freshmen are admitted fall and spring. Entrance exams should be taken by the fall of the senior year. Applications should be filed by April 1 for fall entry and January 1 for spring entry, along with an application fee of $20. Notification is sent beginning in October. There is a deferred admissions plan.

Transfer: A total of 354 transfer students enrolled in 1993–94. Transfer applicants must have a minimum GPA of 2.3 in previous college work. A total of 32 of the last 36 credits out of a total of 132 must be completed at Saint Thomas.

Visiting: There are guides for informal visits and visitors may sit in on classes and stay overnight at the school. To arrange for a visit, contact the Admissions Office at (800) 328-6819, ext. 2-6150, or (612) 962-6150.

Financial Aid: In 1993–94, 81% of all current freshmen and 74% of continuing students received some form of financial aid. About 58% of freshmen and 53% of continuing students received need-based aid. The average freshman award was $10,634. Of that total, scholarships or need-based grants averaged $5572; loans averaged $5431; and work contracts averaged $2179. Thirty-seven percent of undergraduate students work part-time. Average earnings from campus work for the school year are $1220. The FAFSA financial statement is required. The priority deadline for financial aid applications is April 1.

International Students: There are currently 44 international students enrolled. They must take the TOEFL or the University of Michigan Language Test and achieve a minimum score on the TOEFL of 500.

Computers: The university provides computer facilities for student use. The mainframes are 2 DEC VAX 8550s, a DEC VAX 6250, and a DEC VAX 4000. There are also more than 250 IBM and Apple Macintosh microcomputers available. All students may access the system. There are no time limits on using the system and no fees.

Graduates: In 1992–93, 1141 bachelor's degrees were awarded. The most popular majors among graduates were business (43%), social sciences (19%), and communication (11%). Within an average freshman class, 46% graduate in 4 years, 66% in 5 years, and 69% in 6 years. Some 71 companies recruited on campus in 1992–93. In the 1992 graduating class, 19% of the men and women were enrolled in graduate school within 1 year of graduation; 93% had found employment.

Admissions Contact: Marla Friederichs, Director of Admissions.

WINONA STATE UNIVERSITY   D-5

Winona, MN 55987	(507) 457-5100; (800) **DIAL-WSU**
Full-time: 2400 men, 3400 women	Faculty: 300; IIB, +$
Part-time: 350 men, 550 women	Ph.D.s: 70%
Graduate: 150 men, 330 women	Student/Faculty: 19 to 1
Year: quarters, summer session	Tuition: $2500 ($4800)
Application Deadline: February 15	Room & Board: $2700
Freshman Class: 3325 applied, 2050 accepted, 1300 enrolled	
SAT I Verbal/Math: 460/490	ACT: 22 **VERY COMPETITIVE**

Winona State University, founded in 1858, is a public, liberal arts institution, and part of the Minnesota State University System. There are 5 undergraduate schools and one graduate school. In addition to regional accreditation, WSU has baccalaureate program accreditation with ABET, CSWE, NCATE, and NLN. The library contains 217,000 volumes and 703,000 microform items, and subscribes to 1400 periodicals. Computerized library sources and services include the card catalog, interlibrary loans, and database searching. Special learning facilities include a learning resource center, art gallery, radio station, and TV station. The 40-acre campus is in a small town 110 miles southeast of Minneapolis and St. Paul. Including residence halls, there are 23 buildings on campus.

Student Life: About 65% of undergraduates are from Minnesota. Students come from 40 states, 45 foreign countries, and Canada. Eighty-five percent are from public schools; 15% from private. Ninety-four percent are white. Forty percent are Protestant; 40% Catholic. The average age of freshmen is 18; all undergraduates, 23. Twenty-five percent drop out by the end of their first year; 50% remain to graduate.

Housing: A total of 2000 students can be accommodated in college housing. College-sponsored living facilities include single-sex and coed dormitories. In addition there are honors houses. On-campus housing is available on a first-come, first-served basis and is available on a lottery system for upperclassmen. Sixty-five percent of students commute. Alcohol is not permitted. All students may keep cars on campus.

Activities: About 2% of men belong to 2 national fraternities; about 2% of women belong to 1 local sorority and 1 national sorority. There are 70 groups on campus, including art, band, cheerleading, chess, choir, chorale, chorus, computers, dance, drama, ethnic, gay, honors, international, jazz band, literary magazine, musical theater, newspaper, orchestra, pep band, photography, political, professional, radio and TV, religious, social, social service, student government, and symphony.

Sports: There are 5 intercollegiate sports for men and 8 for women, and 15 intramural sports for men and 15 for women. Athletic and recreation facilities include a 4000-seat stadium, a bowling alley, 8 outdoor tennis courts, and a field house with 10 gymnasiums, 3 weight rooms, a swimming pool, indoor track and tennis facilities, and handball/racquetball courts.

Disabled Students: The entire campus is accessible to disabled students. The following facilities are available: wheelchair ramps, elevators, special parking, specially equipped rest rooms, special class scheduling, lowered drinking fountains, lowered telephones, and special apartments.

Services: In addition to many counseling and information services, tutoring is available in most subjects. There is also remedial math, reading, and writing.

Campus Safety and Security: Campus safety and security measures include 24-hour foot and vehicle patrol, self-defense education, escort service, and shuttle buses. In addition, there are informal discussions, pamphlets, posters, films, emergency telephones, and lighted pathways and sidewalks.

Programs of Study: WSU awards the B.A., B.S., B.S.E., and B.S.N. degrees. Associate and master's degrees also are awarded. Bachelor's degrees are awarded in BIOLOGICAL SCIENCE (biology/biological science), BUSINESS (accounting, banking and finance, business administration and management, business economics, marketing/retailing/merchandising, and personnel management), COMMUNICATIONS AND THE ARTS (advertising, broadcasting, communications, dramatic arts, English, fine arts, French, German, journalism, music, Spanish, and speech/debate/rhetoric), COMPUTER AND PHYSICAL SCIENCE (chemistry, computer science, earth science, geology, information sciences and systems, mathematics, physics, and statistics), EDUCATION (art, business, early childhood, elementary, foreign languages, health, music, science, secondary, and special), ENGINEERING AND ENVIRONMENTAL DESIGN (materials engineering), HEALTH PROFESSIONS (medical laboratory technology, nursing, physical therapy, predentistry, premedicine, and public health), SOCIAL SCIENCE (community services, criminal justice, economics, geography, history, international relations, paralegal studies, parks and recreation management, physical fitness/movement, political science/government, prelaw, psychology, public administration, social science, social work, and sociology).

Required: To graduate, students must complete 192 quarter hours of credit with a minimum GPA of 2.5. General education requirements include 12 credits each in humanities, science/mathematics, and social science, 8 each in English and different cultures, 4 each in speech and mathematics, and 2 in physical education.

Special: The university offers cross-registration with Saint Mary's College, study abroad in 25 countries, internship, work-study programs, student-designed majors, dual majors, pass/fail options, and credit for life, military, and work experience. Students may earn accelerated degrees in all majors and a general studies degree. There is a freshman honors program on campus, as well as 10 national honor societies. Eight departments have honors programs.

Faculty/Classroom: Sixty percent of faculty are male; 40%, female. Ninety percent teach undergraduates and 10% do research. No introductory courses are taught by graduate students. The average class size in an introductory lecture is 30 and in a regular course offering, 27.

Admissions: About 62% of the 1993–94 applicants were accepted. The ACT scores for the 1993–94 freshman class were as follows: 10% below 21, 35% between 21 and 23, 30% between 24 and 26, 15% between 27 and 28, and 10% above 28. About 25% of the current freshmen were in the top fifth of their class; 75% were in the top two fifths. There were 3 National Merit finalists and 20 semifinalists. Forty freshmen graduated first in their class.

Requirements: WSU requires applicants to be in the upper 50% of their class. The SAT I or ACT is required. Candidates should have completed 4 units of English, 1 of which may be speech; 3 each of mathematics, social studies, and science; 2 in world language; and 1 elective, preferrably in computer science. AP and CLEP credits are accepted. Important factors used in the admissions decision are advanced placement or honor courses, leadership record, evidence of special talent, extracurricular activities record, and recommendations by school officials.

Procedure: Freshmen are admitted to all sessions. Entrance exams should be taken in the junior year. Applications should be filed by February 15 for fall entry, November 9 for winter entry, February 18 for spring entry, and May 17 for summer entry, along with an application fee of $15. Notification is sent on a rolling basis. There are early admissions and deferred admissions plans.

Transfer: About 600 transfer students enrolled in 1993–94. Applicants must have completed 36 quarter hours of credit with a minimum GPA of 2.4. A total of 45 quarter credits out of 192 must be completed at WSU.

Visiting: There are regularly scheduled orientations for prospective students. There are guides for informal visits and visitors may sit in on classes and stay overnight at the school. To arrange for a visit, contact the Admissions Office at (507) 457-5100.

Financial Aid: In an earlier year, 70% of all students received some form of financial aid. The average freshman award was $3000. Of that total, scholarships or need-based grants averaged $1000 ($2500 maximum); loans averaged $1000 ($4000 maximum); and work contracts averaged $1000 ($2000 maximum). Forty percent of undergraduate students work part-time. Average earnings from campus work for the school year are $1200. The average financial indebtedness of the 1992–93 graduate was $5000. The FAFSA financial statement is required. The deadline for priority financial aid applications is April 1.

International Students: There are currently 300 international students enrolled. The school actively recruits these students. They must take the TOEFL or the University of Michigan Language Test and achieve a minimum score on the TOEFL of 550.

Computers: The university provides computer facilities for student use. The mainframes are a Unisys, DEC VAX, AS/400, and other models. There are more than 300 terminals located throughout the campus. All students may access the system 8 A.M. to 11 P.M. There are no time limits on using the system and no fees.

Graduates: In an earlier year, 900 bachelor's degrees were awarded. The most popular majors among graduates were business (25%), education (12%), and nursing (10%). Within an average freshman class, 39% graduate in 4 years, 48% in 5 years, and 52% in 6 years. Some 70 companies recruited on campus in 1992–93. In the 1992 graduating class, 5% of the men and women were enrolled in graduate school within 6 months of graduation; 80% had found employment.

Admissions Contact: J.A. Mootz, Director of Admissions.

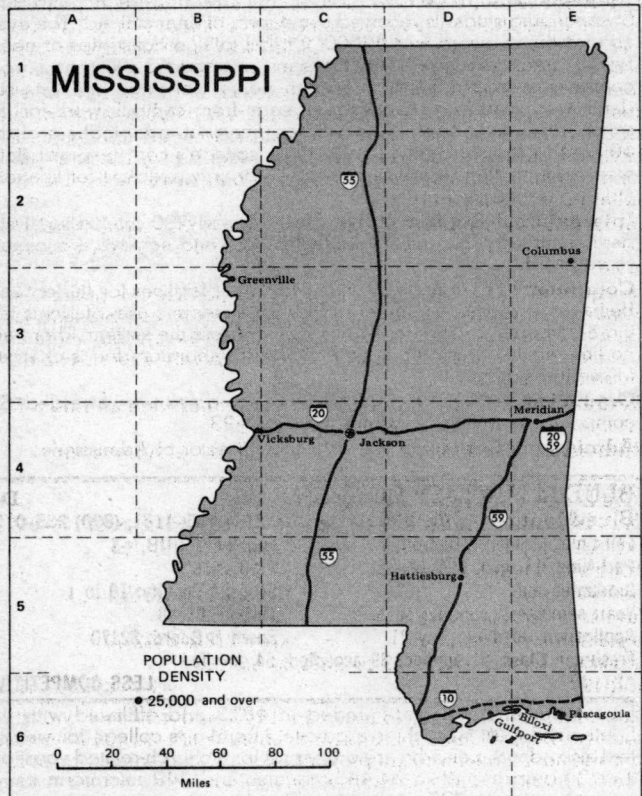

MISSISSIPPI

POPULATION
DENSITY

● 25,000 and over

0   20   40   60   80   100
Miles

ALCORN STATE UNIVERSITY
Lorman, MS 39096

B-4

(601) 877-6147, -6148
(800) 222-6790 (in-state)

Full-time: 911 men, 1415 women	**Faculty:** 176; IIB, --$
Part-time: 54 men, 181 women	**Ph.D.s:** n/av
Graduate: 50 men, 101 women	**Student/Faculty:** 13 to 1
Year: semesters, summer session	**Tuition:** $2376 ($4518)
Application Deadline: open	**Room & Board:** $2098

Freshman Class: 2883 applied, 1215 accepted, 485 enrolled
ACT: 18

COMPETITIVE +

Alcorn State University, founded in 1871, is a public institution offering programs in agriculture, the arts and sciences, business, engineering, and nursing. There is one graduate school. The 2 libraries contain 178,000 volumes, 32,399 microform items, and 4577 audiovisual forms, and subscribe to 800 periodicals. Computerized library sources and services include the card catalog and database searching. Special learning facilities include a learning resource center and radio station. The 1700-acre campus is in a rural area 44 miles south of Vicksburg. Including residence halls, there are 28 buildings on campus.

Student Life: About 80% of undergraduates are from Mississippi. Ninety-five percent are from public schools. Ninety-six percent are African American. The average age of freshmen is 18; all undergraduates, 20. Fifteen percent drop out by the end of their first year; 75% remain to graduate.

Housing: A total of 2000 students can be accommodated in college housing. College-sponsored living facilities include single-sex dormitories. On-campus housing is guaranteed for all 4 years. Almost all students live on campus; of those, 45% remain on campus on weekends. Alcohol is not permitted. All students may keep cars on campus.

Activities: About 25% of men belong to 5 local and 4 national fraternities; about 25% of women belong to 4 local and 4 national sororities. There are 40 groups on campus, including band, cheerleading, choir, chorus, drama, honors, jazz band, marching band, newspaper, photography, and yearbook. Popular campus events include Homecoming and High School Day.

Sports: There are 3 intramural sports each for men and women. Athletic and recreation facilities include a 10,000-seat stadium and a 5000-seat gymnasium.

Disabled Students: Fifteen percent of the campus is accessible to disabled students. The following facilities are available: wheelchair ramps, elevators, special parking, specially equipped rest rooms, and lowered drinking fountains.

Services: In addition to many counseling and information services, tutoring is available in most subjects. There is also remedial math, reading, and writing.

Campus Safety and Security: Campus safety and security measures include 24-hour foot and vehicle patrol, pamphlets, posters, and films, and lighted pathways and sidewalks.

Programs of Study: The university awards the B.A., B.S., B.Mus.Ed., and B.S.N. degrees. Associate and master's degrees also are awarded. Bachelor's degrees are awarded in AGRICULTURE (agricultural economics and animal science), BIOLOGICAL SCIENCE (biology/biological science), BUSINESS (accounting, business administration and management, and business economics), COMMUNICATIONS AND THE ARTS (communications and English), COMPUTER AND PHYSICAL SCIENCE (chemistry, computer science, and mathematics), EDUCATION (agricultural, business, early childhood, elementary, home economics, industrial arts, middle school, music, and secondary), ENGINEERING AND ENVIRONMENTAL DESIGN (engineering), HEALTH PROFESSIONS (nursing and premedicine), and SOCIAL SCIENCE (economics, history, political science/government, prelaw, and social science). Business has the largest enrollment.

Required: To graduate, students must complete at least 128 semester hours with a minimum GPA of 2.0. Core requirements include 12 hours of social science, 9 of natural science, 4 of physical education or military science, and 3 each of mathematics, oral communications, and creative arts, as well as 1 of student adjustment.

Special: The university offers cooperative programs, internships, and work-study programs. There is a freshman honors program on campus, as well as 1 national honor society, Phi Beta Kappa. Five departments have honors programs.

Faculty/Classroom: Ninety percent of faculty are male; 10%, female.

Admissions: About 42% of the 1993-94 applicants were accepted. The ACT scores for the 1993-94 freshman class were as follows: 45% below 21, 40% between 21 and 23, 10% between 24 and 26, 5% between 27 and 28, and 2% above 28.

Requirements: A minimum GPA of 2.0 is required. The SAT I or ACT is required. A minimum SAT I composite score of 720 or ACT score of 15 is required. In addition, applicants should be graduates of an accredited secondary school or have a GED certificate. They should have completed 4 units of English, 3 each of mathematics and science, 2 1/2 of social studies, and 1 of a required elective. Important factors used in the admissions decision are advanced placement or honor courses, leadership record, personality, intangible qualities, evidence of special talent, and parents or siblings attending the school.

Procedure: Freshmen are admitted to all sessions. Entrance exams should be taken so that scores may be submitted at the time application is made. Application deadlines are open. Notification is sent on a rolling basis. There are early decision, early admissions, and deferred admissions plans. One early decision candidate was accepted for an earlier year's class.

Transfer: About 125 transfer students enrolled in an earlier year. Applicants must have at least 6 hours of composition and 9 other transferable academic hours and have maintained an overall minimum GPA of 2.0.

Visiting: There are regularly scheduled orientations for prospective students. There are guides for informal visits and visitors may sit in on classes and stay overnight at the school. To arrange for a visit, contact Emanuel F. Barnes, Director of Admissions, at (601) 877-6147 or -6148 or (800) 222-6790 (in-state).

Financial Aid: In an earlier year, 90% of all students received some form of financial aid. Scholarships or need-based grants averaged $1700 ($3600 maximum); loans averaged $1000 ($3600 maximum). Forty-one percent of undergraduate students work part-time. The average financial indebtedness an earlier graduate was $200. the university is a member of CSS. The FAF is required. The deadline for financial aid applications is July 15.

International Students: International students must take the college's own test. The student must also take the SAT I or the ACT.

Computers: The college provides computer facilities for student use.

Admissions Contact: Emanuel F. Barnes, Director of Admissions.

BELHAVEN COLLEGE

C-4

Jackson, MS 39202

(601) 968-5940; (800) 960-5940

Full-time: 313 men, 423 women

Faculty: 34; IIB, --$

Part-time: 135 men, 212 women

Ph.D.s: 80%

Graduate: none

Student/Faculty: 22 to 1

Year: semesters, summer sessions

Tuition: $7110

Application Deadline: open

Room & Board: $2580

Freshman Class: 248 applied, 197 accepted, 121 enrolled

ACT: 24

COMPETITIVE +

Belhaven College, founded in 1883, is a private liberal arts institution affiliated with the Presbyterian Church. In addition to regional accreditation, Belhaven has baccalaureate program accreditation with NASAD and NASM. The library contains 88,127 volumes, 4898 microform items, and 2295 audiovisual forms, and subscribes to 451 periodicals. Special learning facilities include an art gallery. The 42-acre campus is in an urban area in a small city. Including residence halls, there are 12 buildings on campus.

Student Life: About 88% of undergraduates are from Mississippi. Students come from 19 states and 19 foreign countries. Eighty percent are white; 15% African American. Most are Protestant. The average age of freshmen is 18.

Housing: A total of 400 students can be accommodated in college housing. College-sponsored living facilities include single-sex dormitories. On-campus housing is guaranteed for all 4 years and is available on a first-come, first-served basis. Seventy percent of students commute. Alcohol is not permitted. All students may keep cars on campus.

Activities: There are no fraternities or sororities on campus. There are 28 groups on campus, including art, cheerleading, choir, chorus, drama, ethnic, honors, literary magazine, newspaper, political, professional, religious, social, social service, student government, and yearbook. Popular campus events include Singing Christmas Tree, concert and lecture series, Lake Day, and Homecoming.

Sports: There are 6 intercollegiate sports for men and 4 for women, and 6 intramural sports for men and 6 for women. Athletic and recreation facilities include a gymnasium, 5 tennis courts, a lake, and an intramural and soccer bowl.

Disabled Students: The following facilities are available: wheelchair ramps, special parking, and special class scheduling.

Services: There is remedial math.

Campus Safety and Security: Campus safety and security measures include 24-hour foot and vehicle patrol, escort service, informal discussions, and lighted pathways and sidewalks.

Programs of Study: Belhaven awards the B.A., B.S., and B.Mus. degrees. Bachelor's degrees are awarded in BIOLOGICAL SCIENCE (biology/biological science), BUSINESS (accounting and business administration and management), COMMUNICATIONS AND THE ARTS (art, English, music, piano/organ, and voice), COMPUTER AND PHYSICAL SCIENCE (chemistry, mathematics, and science), EDUCATION (elementary), SOCIAL SCIENCE (history, humanities, philosophy, psychology, and religion). Biology, art, and business are the strongest academically. Business has the largest enrollment.

Required: Requirements for graduation vary by degree, but students must complete at least 124 semester hours, including general education courses, with a minimum 2.0 GPA.

Special: Students may participate in various internships, including one in Washington, D.C., or in the study-travel program. Belhaven also offers B.A.-B.S. and general studies degrees, dual majors, nondegree study, pass/fail options, and work-study. Two 1-month summer sessions and two 2-week minisessions offer additional opportunities for credit. There is a freshman honors program on campus.

Faculty/Classroom: All teach undergraduates.

Admissions: About 79% of the 1993-94 applicants were accepted. About 30% of the current freshmen were in the top fifth of their class; 43% were in the top two fifths. Four freshmen graduated first in their class.

Requirements: A minimum GPA of 2.0 is required. The ACT or SAT I is required; the ACT is preferred. Applicant should be a graduate of an accredited secondary school, having completed 16 academic units, including 4 of English, 1 of history, 2 of mathematics, a recommended 2 of a foreign language, and 6 of electives. Personal recommendation is also required. AP and CLEP credits are accepted. Important factors used in the admissions decision are leadership record, advanced placement or honor courses, extracurricular activities record, evidence of special talent, personality, and intangible qualities.

Procedure: Freshmen are admitted to all sessions. Entrance exams should be taken in the junior year. Application deadlines are open. Application fee is $15. There is an early admissions plan.

Transfer: About 180 transfer students enrolled in 1993-94. Transfer applicants must have a minimum 2.0 GPA and submit all college transcripts. A total of 30 credits out of 124 must be completed at Belhaven.

Visiting: There are guides for informal visits and visitors may sit in on classes and stay overnight at the school. To arrange for a visit, contact the Admissions Office at (601) 968-5940 or (800) 960-5940.

Financial Aid: In 1993-94, 84% of all current freshmen and 92% of continuing students received some form of financial aid. The average freshman award was $3000. Of that total, scholarships or need-based grants averaged $3000; loans averaged $2000; and work contracts averaged $1360. Thirteen percent of undergraduate students work part-time. Average earnings from campus work for the school year are $1360. The average financial indebtedness of the 1992-93 graduate was $12,800. The college's own financial statement and the FAFSA are required. The priority deadline for financial aid applications is April 1.

International Students: There are currently 30 international students enrolled. They must take the TOEFL and achieve a minimum score of 500.

Computers: The college provides computer facilities for student use. Belhaven provides a number of PCs for academic use. Students taking a computer or business course may access the system. There are no time limits on using the system. A $25 laboratory fee is charged to use the system.

Graduates: In 1992-93, 201 bachelor's degrees were awarded. Six companies recruited on campus in 1992-93.

Admissions Contact: Karen Walling, Director of Admissions.

BLUE MOUNTAIN COLLEGE

D-1

Blue Mountain, MS 38610

(601) 685-4161; (800) 235-0136

Full-time: 53 men, 210 women

Faculty: 26; IIB, --$

Part-time: 18 men, 114 women

Ph.D.s: 36%

Graduate: none

Student/Faculty: 10 to 1

Year: semesters, summer session

Tuition: $3788

Application Deadline: July 31

Room & Board: $2170

Freshman Class: 91 applied, 89 accepted, 54 enrolled

ACT: 19

LESS COMPETITIVE

Blue Mountain College, founded in 1873 and affiliated with the Southern Baptist Church, is a private, liberal arts college for women that also admits men who are preparing for a church-related vocation. The 2 libraries contain 54,455 volumes and 249 microform items, and subscribe to 205 periodicals. The 44-acre campus is in a rural area 70 miles southwest of Memphis. Including residence halls, there are 14 buildings on campus.

Student Life: About 91% of undergraduates are from Mississippi. Students come from 9 states and 1 foreign country. Ninety percent are from public schools; 10% from private. Ninety-three percent are white. Most are Protestant. The average age of freshmen is 21; all undergraduates, 26. Thirty-seven percent drop out by the end of their first year; 40% remain to graduate.

Housing: A total of 250 students can be accommodated in college housing. College-sponsored living facilities include single-sex dormitories. On-campus housing is guaranteed for all 4 years and is available on a first-come, first-served basis. Seventy-seven percent of students commute. Alcohol is not permitted. All students may keep cars on campus.

Activities: There are no fraternities on campus. There are 21 groups on campus, including art, cheerleading, choir, chorale, chorus, drama, honors, musical theater, professional, religious, student government, and yearbook. Popular campus events include High School Weekend, Fall Festival, Spring Festival, Field Day, formal dinners and plays.

Sports: Athletic and recreation facilities include a gymnasium, a swimming pool, a golf course, and a softball field.

Disabled Students: Ten percent of the campus is accessible to disabled students. Wheelchair ramps are available.

Services: In addition to many counseling and information services, there is remedial writing.

Campus Safety and Security: Campus safety and security measures include lighted pathways and sidewalks.

Programs of Study: BMC awards the B.A., B.S., B.S.Ed., and B.Mus. degrees. Bachelor's degrees are awarded in BIOLOGICAL SCIENCE (biology/biological science), COMMUNICATIONS AND THE ARTS (English, fine arts, and music), COMPUTER AND PHYSICAL SCIENCE (mathematics), EDUCATION (art, business, elementary, home economics, middle school, music, science, secondary, and special), HEALTH PROFESSIONS (nursing and premedicine), SOCIAL SCIENCE (history, prelaw, psychology, and social science). Education is the strongest program academically. Elementary education has the largest enrollment.

Required: All students must take 120 semester hours, including 6 hours each of English composition, literature, history, and Bible, 3 hours of psychology, and 2 semesters of physical education. Students must maintain a minimum GPA of 2.5 for the teaching degree and 2.0 for other degrees. Majors require 30 or more hours.

Special: Students may take summer business internships. The college offers pass/fail options and dual majors. There is a freshman honors program on campus, as well as one national honor society.

Faculty/Classroom: Forty-five percent of faculty are male; 55%, female. The average class size in an introductory lecture is 20; in a laboratory, 15; and in a regular course offering, 20.

Admissions: About 98% of the 1993–94 applicants were accepted.

Requirements: A minimum GPA of 2.0 is required. The SAT I or ACT is required. In addition, BMC recommends that applicants for admission have completed 4 units of English, 2 of a foreign language, and 3 each of mathematics, science, and social studies. AP and CLEP credits are accepted. Important factors used in the admissions decision are evidence of special talent, leadership record, advanced placement or honor courses, extracurricular activities record, and recommendations by school officials.

Procedure: Entrance exams should be taken in the senior year. Applications should be filed by July 31 for fall entry, December 15 for spring entry, and May 15 for summer entry, along with an application fee of $10. Notification is sent on a rolling basis. There is an early admissions plan.

Transfer: About 70 transfer students enrolled in an earlier year. A total of 24 credits out of 120 must be completed at BMC.

Visiting: There are regularly scheduled orientations for prospective students. There are guides for informal visits and visitors may sit in on classes and stay overnight at the school. To arrange for a visit, contact the Office of Admissions at (601) 685–4161.

Financial Aid: Financial aid applications should be filed as early as possible after January 1 and before March 15. Work contracts averaged $800 (maximum). BMC is a member of CSS. The FAF is required.

International Students: There were 3 international students enrolled in a recent year. They must take the TOEFL and achieve a minimum score of 500.

Graduates: In a recent year, 77 bachelor's degrees were awarded. In an earlier graduating class, 4% of the men and 9% of the women were enrolled in graduate school within 6 months of graduation; 90% of all students had found employment.

Admissions Contact: Rhonda Cockrell, Director of Admissions.

DELTA STATE UNIVERSITY

C-2

Cleveland, MS 38733   (601) 846–4018; (800) 468–6378 (in-state)

Full-time: 1216 men, 1612 women	Faculty: 159; IIA, --$
Part-time: 169 men, 335 women	Ph.D.s: 56%
Graduate: 241 men, 268 women	Student/Faculty: 18 to 1
Year: semesters, summer session	Tuition: $2194 ($4154)
Application Deadline: open	Room & Board: $1770
Freshman Class: 967 applied, 459 enrolled	
ACT: 19	LESS COMPETITIVE

Delta State University, founded in 1924, is a public liberal arts institution offering degrees in arts and sciences, business, education, health science, and nursing. There are 4 undergraduate and 3 graduate schools. In addition to regional accreditation, DSU has baccalaureate program accreditation with AHEA, CSWE, NASAD, NASM, NCATE, and NLN. The library contains 263,891 volumes and 718,580 microform items, and subscribes to 1455 periodicals. Computerized library sources and services include the card catalog, interlibrary loans, and database searching. Special learning facilities include a learning resource center, an art gallery, a natural history museum, and a planetarium. The 274-acre campus is in a small town 110 miles south of Memphis, Tennessee, and 130 miles north of Jackson. Including residence halls, there are 42 buildings on campus.

Student Life: About 93% of undergraduates are from Mississippi. Students come from 31 states, 6 foreign countries, and Canada. Sixty-two percent of freshmen are from public schools. Seventy-six percent are white; 23% African American. The average age of freshmen is 18; all undergraduates, 25. Twenty-four percent drop out by the end of their first year; 50% remain to graduate.

Housing: A total of 1681 students can be accommodated in college housing. College-sponsored living facilities include single-sex dormitories and married-student housing. On-campus housing is guaranteed for all 4 years and is available on a first-come, first-served basis. Fifty-nine percent of students commute. Alcohol is not permitted. All students may keep cars on campus.

Activities: About 24% of men belong to 8 national fraternities; about 25% of women belong to 6 national sororities. There are 96 groups on campus, including art, band, cheerleading, choir, chorale, chorus, computers, dance, drama, drill team, ethnic, honors, jazz band, literary magazine, marching band, newspaper, opera, orchestra, pep band, political, professional, religious, social, social service, student government, and yearbook. Popular campus events include Springfest, Fallfest, Homecoming, Christmas Madrigal Feast, and Greekfest.

Sports: There are 6 intercollegiate sports for men and 5 for women, and 27 intramural sports each. Athletic and recreation facilities include a coliseum, an indoor pool, a gymnasium, a baseball field, a softball field, a football stadium, a 9-hole golf course, outdoor tennis courts, 2 intramural fields, and an outdoor walking facility.

Disabled Students: Ninety percent of the campus is accessible to disabled students. The following facilities are available: wheelchair ramps, elevators, special parking, specially equipped rest rooms, special class scheduling, lowered drinking fountains, and lowered telephones.

Services: In addition to many counseling and information services, tutoring is available in every subject. There is also remedial math, reading, and writing.

Campus Safety and Security: Campus safety and security measures include 24-hour foot and vehicle patrol, self-defense education, escort service, and informal discussions. In addition, there are pamphlets, posters, films, emergency telephones, and lighted pathways and sidewalks.

Programs of Study: DSU awards the B.A., B.S., B.B.A., B.C.A., B.F.A., B.S.C.J., B.S.E., and B.S.G.S. degrees. Master's and doctoral degrees also are awarded. Bachelor's degrees are awarded in BIOLOGICAL SCIENCE (biology/biological science), BUSINESS (accounting, banking and finance, business administration and management, fashion merchandising, insurance, marketing/retailing/merchandising, and office supervision and management), COMMUNICATIONS AND THE ARTS (art, English, music, and Spanish), COMPUTER AND PHYSICAL SCIENCE (chemistry, computer programming, and mathematics), EDUCATION (business, elementary, foreign languages, health, music, science, secondary, social studies, and special), ENGINEERING AND ENVIRONMENTAL DESIGN (aviation administration/management, aviation computer technology, and environmental science), HEALTH PROFESSIONS (medical laboratory technology, nursing, predentistry, premedicine, and speech pathology/audiology), SOCIAL SCIENCE (criminal justice, history, political science/government, psychology, social science, and social work). Biology, chemistry, mathematics, audiology and speech language pathology, and accounting are the strongest academically. Education and business have the largest enrollments.

Required: To graduate, students must complete 128 semester hours, including 33 to 40 in the major, with a minimum GPA of 2.0. General education requirements include 6 hours each of English composition, English literature, history, laboratory science, and social science; 3 hours each of fine arts, mathematics, psychology, and speech; and 2 hours of physical education.

Special: DSU offers internships in accounting, art, marketing, and management. Cross-registration is available with Westfield State College in Massachusetts. A general studies degree and nondegree study are available. There is a freshman honors program on campus, as well as 5 national honor societies.

Faculty/Classroom: Sixty-three percent of faculty are male; 37%, female. No introductory courses are taught by graduate students. The average class size in an introductory lecture is 30; in a laboratory, 24; and in a regular course offering, 30.

Admissions: The ACT scores for the 1993–94 freshman class were as follows: 63% below 21, 22% between 21 and 23, 9% between 24 and 26, 4% between 27 and 28, and 1% above 28.

Requirements: The SAT I or ACT is required. A minimum SAT I composite score of 700 or ACT score of 18 is required. The Nelson Denny Reading Test and Mathematics Placement Test must also be taken. Applicants must be graduates of an accredited secondary school or have the GED. They should have completed 4 courses in English, 3 each in mathematics and science, 2 1/2 in social studies, and 1 in a language or additional science/mathematics. AP credits are accepted.

Procedure: Freshmen are admitted to all sessions. Application deadlines are open.

Transfer: About 552 transfer students enrolled in 1993–94. A minimum GPA of 2.0 is required, and an associate degree and ACT or SAT I scores are recommended. A total of 30 credits out of 128 must be completed at DSU.

Visiting: There are regularly scheduled orientations for prospective students, including campus tours, introduction to faculty and staff, and registration for classes. There are guides for informal visits and visitors may sit in on classes and stay overnight at the school. To arrange for a visit, contact School Relations and Recruitment at (601) 846–4656.

Financial Aid: In 1993–94, 62% of all students received some form of financial aid. Scholarships or need-based grants averaged $300; loans averaged $2000 ($2625 maximum); and work contracts averaged $1500 (maximum). Ten percent of undergraduate students work part-time. The average financial indebtedness of the 1992–93 graduate was $4500. The deadline for financial aid applications is May 1.

International Students: There are currently 4 international students enrolled. They must take the TOEFL and achieve a minimum score of 525. The student must also take the SAT I or the ACT and obtain a minimum composite score of 700 on the SAT I or 15 on the ACT.

Computers: The college provides computer facilities for student use. The mainframe is an NCR Tower and an IBM RS/6000 Model 540. There are also 200 Apple and IBM-compatible microcomputers available in various locations. All students may access the system. It may be used from 8 A.M. to 11 P.M. daily. There are no time limits on using the system and no fees.

Graduates: In a recent year, 582 bachelor's degrees were awarded. The most popular majors among graduates were business (42%) and education (21%). Within an average freshman class, 45% graduate in 5 years.

Admissions Contact: Frances Short, Coordinator of Admissions.

JACKSON STATE UNIVERSITY
Jackson, MS 39217

Full-time: 2122 men, 2664 women	Faculty: 302; IIA, --$
Part-time: 229 men, 440 women	Ph.D.s: 64%
Graduate: 294 men, 597 women	Student/Faculty: 16 to 1
Year: semesters, summer session	Tuition: $2230 ($4464)
Application Deadline: August 15	Room & Board: $2766
Freshman Class: n/av	
SAT I or ACT: required	**LESS COMPETITIVE**

C-4
(601) 968–2100; (800) 848–6817

Jackson State University, founded in 1877, is a public institution with an emphasis on liberal arts, business, music, and teacher preparation. There are 4 undergraduate schools and one graduate school. In addition to regional accreditation, JSU has baccalaureate program accreditation with AACSB, CSWE, NASAD, NASM, and NCATE. The library contains 369,990 volumes and 101,192 microform items, and subscribes to 2715 periodicals. Special learning facilities include a learning resource center and a radio station. The 128-acre campus is in an urban area in Jackson. Including residence halls, there are 39 buildings on campus.

Student Life: About 72% of undergraduates are from Mississippi. Students come from 38 states and 29 foreign countries. Ninety-four percent are African American. The average age of freshmen is 18; all undergraduates, 20. Thirty-five percent drop out by the end of their first year; 37% remain to graduate.

Housing: A total of 3000 students can be accommodated in college housing. College-sponsored living facilities include single-sex dormitories, honors houses, and athletic houses. On-campus housing is available on a first-come, first-served basis. Fifty-eight percent of students commute. Alcohol is not permitted. All students may keep cars on campus.

Activities: About 5% of men belong to 4 national fraternities; about 5% of women belong to 4 national sororities. There are many groups on campus, including art, band, cheerleading, choir, dance, drama, drill team, ethnic, honors, jazz band, marching band, musical theater, newspaper, opera, orchestra, pep band, photography, political, radio and TV, religious, social service, student government, symphony, and yearbook. Popular campus events include Homecoming.

Sports: There are 7 intercollegiate sports for men and 4 for women, and 2 intramural sports each for men and women. Athletic and recreation facilities include an Olympic-size swimming pool, a gymnasium with 2 basketball courts, indoor and outdoor tennis courts, badminton and volleyball courts, a dance studio, a baseball diamond, soccer and athletic fields, an archery range, and a track.

Disabled Students: The entire campus is accessible to disabled students. The following facilities are available: wheelchair ramps, elevators, special parking, specially equipped rest rooms, lowered drinking fountains, and lowered telephones.

Services: In addition to many counseling and information services, tutoring is available in every subject. There is also remedial math, reading, and writing.

Campus Safety and Security: Campus safety and security measures include a 24-hour foot and vehicle patrol, self defense education, informal discussions, and pamphlets, posters, and films.

Programs of Study: JSU awards the B.A., B.S., B.B.A, B.M., B.M.E., B.S.Ed., and B.S.W. degrees. Master's and doctoral degrees also are awarded. Bachelor's degrees are awarded in BIOLOGICAL SCIENCE (biology/biological science), BUSINESS (accounting, banking and finance, business administration and management, marketing/retailing/merchandising, and office supervision and management), COMMUNICATIONS AND THE ARTS (art, communications, English, music, Spanish, and speech/debate/rhetoric), COMPUTER AND PHYSICAL SCIENCE (atmospheric sciences and meteorology, chemistry, computer science, mathematics, and physics), EDUCATION (business, elementary, health, industrial arts, music, and special), ENGINEERING AND ENVIRONMENTAL DESIGN (industrial engineering technology), HEALTH PROFESSIONS (predentistry and premedicine), SOCIAL SCIENCE (criminal justice, economics, history, political science/government, psychology, social science, social work, sociology, and urban studies). Computer science, biology, and accounting are the strongest programs academically. Computer science, biology, and accounting have the largest enrollments.

Required: To graduate, students must complete at least 128 semester hours with a minimum GPA of 2.0. At least 30 upper-division hours must be earned in the major. Distribution requirements include a total of 49 to 59 hours in communications, humanities and fine arts, social and behavioral sciences, natural sciences, health and physical education, and concepts for success in college.

Special: Internships with various corporations, nondegree study, work-study programs, a cooperative education program, accelerated degrees, combined B.A.-B.S. degrees, and a student-exchange program are available. JSU also offers cross-registration in military courses with Millsaps, Mississippi, Belhaven, and Hinds junior colleges. There is a freshman honors program on campus, as well as 4 national honor societies. Fourteen departments have honors programs.

Faculty/Classroom: Sixty-one percent of faculty are male; 39%, female.

Requirements: A minimum GPA of 2.0 is required. The SAT I or ACT is required. A minimum composite score of 15 on the ACT is required of in-state applicants. A minimum composite score of 16 on the ACT or 620 on the SAT I is required of out-of-state applicants. In addition, applicants must be graduates of a accredited secondary school or have a GED certificate. They must have earned 13 1/2 Carnegie units, including 4 of English, 3 each of mathematics and sciences, 2 1/2 social science, and 1 of electives. An interview is recommended. AP and CLEP credits are accepted. Important factors used in the admissions decision are recommendations by school officials, leadership record, extracurricular activities record, evidence of special talent, and advanced placement or honor courses.

Procedure: Freshmen are admitted to all sessions. Entrance exams should be taken during the first semester of the senior year. Applications should be filed by August 15 for fall entry, December 15 for spring entry, and May 15 for summer entry. Notification is sent on a rolling basis. There are early admissions and deferred admissions plans.

Transfer: About 290 transfer students enrolled in a recent year. Applicants should submit an official transcript from each institution attended, be in good standing at the last college or university attended, and have a minimum cumulative GPA of 2.0. A total of 30 semester hours out of 128 must be completed at JSU.

Visiting: There are regularly scheduled orientations for prospective students. There are guides for informal visits and visitors may sit in on classes and stay overnight at the school. To arrange for a visit, contact the Office of Admissions and Recruitment.

Financial Aid: In a recent year, 80% of all freshmen and 10% of continuing students received some form of financial aid. Scholarships or need-based grants averaged $1800. JSU is a member of CSS. The the FAFSA financial statement is required. The deadline for financial aid applications is April 15.

International Students: There were 217 international students enrolled in a recent year. The school actively recruits these students. They must take the TOEFL and achieve a minimum score of 525. The student must also take the SAT I or the ACT, with minimum composite scores of 800 and 20 respectively.

Computers: The college provides computer facilities for student use. The mainframes are 2 DEC VAX 11/780s. There are also microcomputers available throughout the campus. All students may access the system from 7 A.M. to 12 A.M., with access to microcomputers during business hours. There are no time limits and no fees.

Graduates: In a recent year, 766 bachelor's degrees were awarded. The most popular majors among graduates were business administration (11%), accounting (8%), and elementary education (7%).

Admissions Contact: Barbara Luckett, Director of Admissions.

MILLSAPS COLLEGE
Jackson, MS 39210

Full-time: 531 men, 542 women	Faculty: 90; IIB, av$
Part-time: 66 men, 113 women	Ph.D.s: 84%
Graduate: 58 men, 26 women	Student/Faculty: 12 to 1
Year: semesters, summer session	Tuition: $11,236
Application Deadline: February 1	Room & Board: $4250
Freshman Class: 905 applied, 854 accepted, 322 enrolled	
SAT I: 550/570	ACT: 26 COMPETITIVE +

C-4
(601) 974–1050; (800) 352–1050

Millsaps College, founded in 1890, is a private liberal arts institution affiliated with the United Methodist Church. There is one graduate school. In addition to regional accreditation, Millsaps has baccalaureate program accreditation with AACSB and NCATE. The library contains 249,875 volumes, 16,007 microform items, and 6617 audiovisual forms, and subscribes to 895 periodicals. Computerized library sources and services include the card catalog, interlibrary loans, and database searching. Special learning facilities include an art gallery and an observatory. The 100-acre campus is in an urban area. Including residence halls, there are 26 buildings on campus.

Student Life: About 65% of undergraduates are from Mississippi. Students come from 28 states, 3 foreign countries, and Canada. Fifty-seven percent are from public schools; 43% from private. Ninety-three percent are white. Eighty percent are Protestant; 15% Catholic. The average age of freshmen is 18; all undergraduates, 22. Fifteen percent drop out by the end of their first year; 65% remain to graduate.

Housing: A total of 865 students can be accommodated in college housing. College-sponsored living facilities include single-sex and coed dormitories and fraternity houses. On-campus housing is guaranteed for all 4 years and is available on a first-come, first-served basis. Seventy-three percent of students live on campus; of those, 75% remain on campus on weekends. All students may keep cars on campus.

Activities: About 62% of men belong to 6 national fraternities; about 61% of women belong to 5 national sororities. There are 60 groups on campus, including cheerleading, choir, chorus, drama, ethnic, honors, international, literary magazine, newspaper, religious, student government, and yearbook. Popular campus events include Major Madness, Homecoming, Student Symposium, and Tap Day.

Sports: There are 7 intercollegiate sports for men and 5 for women, and 5 intramural sports each for men and women. Athletic and recreation facilities include 6 tennis courts, a swimming pool, a jogging course, playing fields, and a physical activities center with a weight room and indoor courts for basketball, tennis, and volleyball.

Disabled Students: Eighty-six percent of the campus is accessible to disabled students. The following facilities are available: wheelchair ramps, elevators, special parking, specially equipped rest rooms, and lowered drinking fountains.

Services: In addition to many counseling and information services, tutoring is available in some subjects, including writing and mathematics.

Campus Safety and Security: Campus safety and security measures include a 24-hour foot and vehicle patrol, self defense education, an escort service, and informal discussions. In addition, there are pamphlets, posters, and films, emergency telephones, and lighted pathways and sidewalks.

Programs of Study: Millsaps awards the B.A., B.S., B.B.A., B.L.S., and B.Mus. degrees. Master's degrees also are awarded. Bachelor's degrees are awarded in BIOLOGICAL SCIENCE (biology/biological science), BUSINESS (accounting and business administration and management), COMMUNICATIONS AND THE ARTS (art, classics, dramatic arts, English, fine arts, French, music, and Spanish), COMPUTER AND PHYSICAL SCIENCE (chemistry, computer science, geology, mathematics, and physics), EDUCATION (elementary), SOCIAL SCIENCE (economics, European studies, history, philosophy, political science/government, psychology, religion, and sociology). Business administration, biology, chemistry, English, history, and psychology are the strongest programs academically. Business administration, biology, chemistry, English, and history have the largest enrollments.

Required: To graduate, students must complete 128 credit hours, with a minimum GPA of 2.0. The core curriculum includes 4 courses in humanities and 1 each in natural science, mathematics, social science, and an additional course in natural science, mathematics, or computer science. Students must successfully complete Introduction to Liberal Studies and a comprehensive exam.

Special: Multidisciplinary courses are offered to meet core requirements in the humanities and sciences. Study abroad may be arranged through several consortia. Millsaps also offers a Washington semester, internships, a B.A.-B.S. degree in most majors, and 3-2 degree programs in engineering and business administration. There are 3 national honor societies on campus, including Phi Beta Kappa. Twenty-one departments have honors programs.

Faculty/Classroom: Seventy-six percent of faculty are male; 24%, female. All teach undergraduates and 50% also do research. No introductory courses are taught by graduate students. The average class size in an introductory lecture is 30; in a laboratory, 20; and in a regular course offering, 23.

Admissions: About 94% of the 1993–94 applicants were accepted. Forty-nine percent of the current freshmen were in the top fifth of their class; 90% were in the top two fifths.

Requirements: The SAT I or ACT is required. In addition, applicants should be graduates of an accredited secondary school or have a GED certificate, and have completed at least 12 academic units, including 4 of English plus mathematics, social studies, natural sciences, or foreign languages. An essay is required. AP and CLEP credits are accepted. Important factors used in the admissions decision are advanced placement or honor courses, recommendations by school officials, leadership record, extracurricular activities record, and evidence of special talent.

Procedure: Freshmen are admitted in the fall and spring. Entrance exams should be taken in the spring of the junior year or fall of the senior year. Early decision applications should be filed by November 15; regular applications, by February 1 and March 1 for fall entry,

along with an application fee of $25. Notification for the fall semester is sent December 1, January 15, March 1, April 1, and on a weekly basis thereafter pending vacancies in the class. Applications for the spring term are considered on a weekly basis. There are early admissions and deferred admissions plans.

Transfer: About 57 transfer students enrolled in 1993–94. Applicants must have a minimum GPA of 2.0 and be in good standing at their previous school. A total of 30 credits out of 128 must be completed at Millsaps.

Visiting: There are regularly scheduled orientations for prospective students, including meetings with faculty and student services personnel. There are guides for informal visits and visitors may sit in on classes and stay overnight at the school. To arrange for a visit, contact Florence Hines at (601) 974–1050 or (800) 352–1050.

Financial Aid: In a recent year, 67% of all freshmen and 68% of continuing students received some form of financial aid. About 59% of freshmen and 52% of continuing students received need-based aid. The average freshman award was $9071. Of that total, scholarships or need-based grants averaged $5276 ($11,910 maximum); loans averaged $2500 ($6500 maximum); and work contracts averaged $700 ($1500 maximum). Ninety-two percent of undergraduate students work part-time. Average earnings from campus work for the school year were $900. The average financial indebtedness of a recent graduate was $9000. Millsaps is a member of CSS. The college's own financial statement and any federally approved financial need analysis form are required. The deadline for financial aid applications is March 1.

International Students: There were 3 international students enrolled in a recent year. They must take the TOEFL and achieve a minimum score of 550.

Computers: The college provides computer facilities for student use. The mainframes are 2 DEC VAX 4000/200s with a DEC VAX 4000/200 Server. There are also 125 terminals and networked PCs available in 8 laboratories across the campus. All students may access the system any time. Students may access the system according to the courses taken and the computer laboratory fee paid. There are no fees for basic use; for significant additional use, fees range from $25 to $70 per course.

Graduates: In a recent year, 246 bachelor's degrees were awarded. The most popular majors among graduates were English (17%), business administration (16%), and accounting (9%). Within an average freshman class, 63% graduate in 4 years, 28% in 5 years, and 3% in 6 years. Some 47 companies recruited on campus a recent year. In a recent graduating class, 19% of the men and 13% of the women were enrolled in graduate school within 6 months of graduation; 29% of the men and 34% of the women had found employment.

Admissions Contact: Florence Hines, Director of Admission.

MISSISSIPPI COLLEGE
C-4

Clinton, MS 39058   (601) 925–3240; (800) 738–1236

Full-time: 704 men, 998 women	Faculty: 134
Part-time: 234 men, 480 women	Ph.D.s: 55%
Graduate: 586 men, 739 women	Student/Faculty: 13 to 1
Year: semesters, summer session	Tuition: $5618
Application Deadline: August 15	Room & Board: $2730
Freshman Class: 594 applied, 385 accepted, 321 enrolled	
SAT I Verbal/Math: 450/450	ACT: 23 COMPETITIVE

Mississippi College, founded in 1826 and affiliated with the Southern Baptist Church, is a private institution offering degrees in liberal arts, business, education, and health sciences. There are 4 undergraduate and 2 graduate schools. In addition to regional accreditation, MC has baccalaureate program accreditation with NASM, NCATE, and NLN. The library contains 240,000 volumes, 15,704 microform items, and 9401 audiovisual forms, and subscribes to 850 periodicals. Special learning facilities include a learning resource center and radio station. The 320-acre campus is in a suburban area 5 miles west of Jackson. Including residence halls, there are 20 buildings on campus.

Student Life: About 88% of undergraduates are from Mississippi. Students come from 37 states and 11 foreign countries. Eighty-five percent are white; 13% African American. Most are Protestant. The average age of freshmen is 19; all undergraduates, 28.

Housing: A total of 1082 students can be accommodated in college housing. College-sponsored living facilities include single-sex dormitories. In addition there are married ministerial student housing. On-campus housing is guaranteed for all 4 years. Sixty-two percent of students commute. Alcohol is not permitted. All students may keep cars on campus.

Activities: There are no fraternities or sororities on campus. There are many groups and organizations on campus, including art, band, cheerleading, choir, chorale, computers, drama, honors, literary magazine, marching band, musical theater, newspaper, opera, pep band, political, professional, radio and tv, religious, social, social service, student government, and yearbook. Popular campus events include

I Love America Day, Derby Day, Spring Fever Day, and the Shakespearean Festival.

Sports: There are 6 intercollegiate sports for men and 4 for women, and 5 intramural sports for men and 5 for women. Athletic and recreation facilities include a coliseum, an 8300-seat stadium, tennis courts, soccer and softball fields, a swimming pool, and a 4000-seat gymnasium.

Disabled Students: The following facilities are available: wheelchair ramps, special parking, specially equipped rest rooms, and wide doors.

Services: In addition to many counseling and information services, tutoring is available in most subjects. There is also remedial math and writing.

Campus Safety and Security: Campus safety and security measures include 24-hour foot and vehicle patrol, escort service, and lighted pathways and sidewalks.

Programs of Study: MC awards the B.A., B.S., B.M., B.M.Ed., B.S.B.A., B.S.Ed., and B.S.N. degrees. Master's degrees are also awarded. Bachelor's degrees are awarded in BIOLOGICAL SCIENCE (biochemistry and biology/biological science), BUSINESS (accounting, banking and finance, business administration and management, business economics, business law, marketing/retailing/merchandising, and office supervision and management), COMMUNICATIONS AND THE ARTS (applied music, art, church music and organ, communications, design, English, fine arts, journalism, modern language, music, music theory and composition, and speech/debate/rhetoric), COMPUTER AND PHYSICAL SCIENCE (chemistry, computer programming, computer science, mathematics, and physics), EDUCATION (art, business, early childhood, elementary, foreign languages, home economics, music, science, and special), ENGINEERING AND ENVIRONMENTAL DESIGN (interior design), HEALTH PROFESSIONS (medical laboratory technology, nursing, pharmacy, physical therapy, predentistry, and premedicine), SOCIAL SCIENCE (criminal justice, economics, history, paralegal studies, political science/government, prelaw, psychology, religion, social science, social work, and sociology). Business and communication have the largest enrollments.

Required: To graduate, students must complete 130 credit hours, with an average of C or better in the major. The core curriculum includes English, history, religion, mathematics, fine arts, social sciences, physical education, and chapel.

Special: Cooperative programs, including a 3–2 engineering degree and a program in agriculture, are offered with the University of Mississippi, Mississippi State University, and Auburn University. MC also offers study abroad in Germany and England, work-study programs, internships, B.A.-B.S. degrees, dual majors, and credit for military experience and by examination. There is a college-wide honors program, as well as 17 national honor societies.

Faculty/Classroom: The average class size in an introductory lecture is 30; in a laboratory, 25; and in a regular course offering, 25.

Admissions: About 65% of the 1993–94 applicants were accepted. There were 13 National Merit finalists.

Requirements: The SAT I or ACT (preferred) is accepted. A minimum ACT score of 15 or SAT I composite score of 750 is required. In addition, applicants must be graduates of an accredited secondary school or have a GED certificate. A well-rounded high school program is advisable. An interview is recommended, as is a portfolio or audition for specific majors. AP and CLEP credits are accepted. Important factors used in the admissions decision are personality, intangible qualities, extracurricular activities record, leadership record, advanced placement or honor courses, and evidence of special talent.

Procedure: Freshmen are admitted to all sessions. Entrance exams should be taken by December of the senior year. Applications should be filed by August 15 for fall entry, along with an application fee of $15. Notification is sent on a rolling basis.

Transfer: Applicants must be junior college graduates or students eligible to return to the school last attended. They must have a minimum GPA of 2.0 and a score of at least 15 on the ACT or 700 on the SAT I. Transfer students will be considered as freshmen if fewer than 12 semester hours or 16 quarter hours have been completed.

Visiting: There are regularly scheduled orientations for prospective students, consisting of preview days in the fall and spring. There are guides for informal visits and visitors may sit in on classes and stay overnight at the school. To arrange for a visit, contact Jennifer Trussell, Director of Admissions, at (601) 925–3240 or (800) 738–1236.

Financial Aid: In an earlier year, 89% of all current freshmen and 75% of continuing students received some form of financial aid. Sixteen percent of undergraduate students work part-time. MC is a member of CSS. The FAF, FFS or SFS and the college's own financial statement are required. The deadline for financial aid applications is April 1.

International Students: There are currently 8 international students enrolled. The school actively recruits these students. They must take the TOEFL and achieve a minimum score of 550. The student must also take the SAT I or ACT; the ACT is preferred.

Computers: The college provides computer facilities for student use. The mainframe is an HP 3000/Series III. There are also 77 IBM, Apple, and Compaq microcomputers available in Self Hall and the Hederman Science Building. Those who have been assigned an account may access the system. It may be used from 8 A.M. to 12 A.M. Monday through Thursday, from 8 A.M. to 11 P.M. Friday, from 8 A.M. to 6 P.M. Saturday, and from 1 P.M. to 11 P.M. Sunday. There are no time limits on using the system. There is a fee only when accessing the HP 3000 via modem.

Graduates: In an earlier year, 333 bachelor's degrees were awarded. Within an average freshman class, 60% graduate in 5 years.

Admissions Contact: Director of Admissions.

MISSISSIPPI STATE UNIVERSITY E-3
Mississippi State, MS 39762   (601) 325–2224

Full-time: 5941 men, 4148 women	Faculty: 740; I, --$
Part-time: 943 men, 587 women	Ph.D.s: 77%
Graduate: 1575 men, 1163 women	Student/Faculty: 14 to 1
Year: semesters, summer session	Tuition: $2499 ($4958)
Application Deadline: August 1	Room & Board: $3130
Freshman Class: 4255 applied, 3277 accepted, 1609 enrolled	
ACT: 24	**VERY COMPETITIVE**

Mississippi State University, founded in 1878 as a land-grant institution, offers degree programs in the arts and sciences, agriculture, business and industry, education, engineering, forest resources, architecture, and preprofessional training in veterinary medicine. There are 8 undergraduate schools and one graduate school. In addition to regional accreditation, State has baccalaureate program accreditation with AACSB, ABET, AHEA, ASLA, NAAB, NASAD, NCATE, and SAF. The 3 libraries contain 865,135 volumes, 2,113,669 microform items, and 6451 audiovisual forms, and subscribe to 7189 periodicals. Computerized library sources and services include the card catalog, interlibrary loans, and database searching. Special learning facilities include an art gallery, natural history museum, planetarium, radio station, tv station, music museum, archaeology museum, and entomology museum. The 4200-acre campus is in a small town 125 miles northeast of Jackson. Including residence halls, there are 325 buildings on campus.

Student Life: About 75% of undergraduates are from Mississippi. Students come from 59 states, 79 foreign countries, and Canada. Eighty percent are white; 14% African American. The average age of freshmen is 19.2; all undergraduates, 23. Twenty-two percent drop out by the end of their first year; 42% remain to graduate.

Housing: A total of 4647 students can be accommodated in college housing. College-sponsored living facilities include single-sex and coed dormitories, on-campus apartments, married-student housing, fraternity houses, and sorority houses. In addition, there are honors houses. On-campus housing is guaranteed for all 4 years. Alcohol is not permitted. All students may keep cars on campus.

Activities: About 17% of men belong to 18 national fraternities; about 20% of women belong to 11 national sororities. There are 300 groups on campus, including band, cheerleading, chess, choir, chorale, chorus, drama, drill team, ethnic, gay, honors, international, jazz band, literary magazine, marching band, newspaper, political, professional, radio and TV, religious, social, social service, student government, symphony, and yearbook. Popular campus events include pep rallies, concerts, dance programs, MSU Discovery Days (area high school students), Christmas craft fair, Black History Week, MSU Days on the Farm (elementary school children), MSU Drama Festival, and Special Olympics.

Sports: There are 7 intercollegiate sports for men and 6 for women, and 32 intramural sports for men and 32 for women. Athletic and recreation facilities include a 41,200-seat football stadium, a 6700-seat baseball park, a 9200-seat basketball coliseum, a physical fitness complex, an all-weather track, 4 practice football fields, an 18-hole golf course, 4 basketball courts, 5 volleyball courts, 6 lighted tennis and 6 lighted racquetball courts, an outdoor swimming pool, a fitness jogging trail, and playing fields for football and softball.

Disabled Students: Ninety percent of the campus is accessible to disabled students. The following facilities are available: wheelchair ramps, elevators, special parking, specially equipped rest rooms, special class scheduling, lowered drinking fountains, and lowered telephones.

Services: In addition to many counseling and information services, tutoring is available in some subjects, including mathematics, English, and chemistry. In addition, there is a reader service for the blind; remedial math, reading, and writing; and study assistance and preparation for professional examinations.

Campus Safety and Security: Campus safety and security measures include 24-hour foot and vehicle patrol, self defense education, escort service, and informal discussions. In addition, there are pamphlets, posters, and films and lighted pathways and sidewalks.

Programs of Study: State awards the B.A., B.S., B.Arch., B.B.A., B.F.A., B.G.S., B.Land.Arch, B.Mus.Ed., B.P.A., and B.S.W. degrees. Master's and doctoral degrees also are awarded. Bachelor's degrees are awarded in AGRICULTURE (agriculture, agronomy, animal science, fishing and fisheries, forestry and related sciences, horticulture, and poultry science), BIOLOGICAL SCIENCE (biochemistry, biology/biological science, entomology, and microbiology), BUSINESS (accounting, banking and finance, business administration and management, insurance, management science, marketing management, real estate, and transportation management), COMMUNICATIONS AND THE ARTS (art, communications, English, fine arts, languages, and music), COMPUTER AND PHYSICAL SCIENCE (chemistry, computer science, geology, information sciences and systems, mathematics, and physics), EDUCATION (business, education, elementary, music, physical, secondary, and special), ENGINEERING AND ENVIRONMENTAL DESIGN (aerospace studies, architecture, bioengineering, chemical engineering, civil engineering, computer engineering, electrical/electronics engineering, industrial engineering, industrial engineering technology, landscape architecture/design, mechanical engineering, nuclear engineering, petroleum/natural gas engineering, and surveying engineering), HEALTH PROFESSIONS (medical technology and preveterinary science), SOCIAL SCIENCE (anthropology, economics, food science, history, home economics, philosophy, political science/government, psychology, social work, and sociology). Engineering, agriculture, mathematics, and preveterinary medicine are the strongest academically. General business, elementary education, and electrical engineering have the largest enrollments.

Required: The core curriculum includes 6 to 9 hours of mathematics and natural science, 6 each of humanities, English composition, fine arts, and social behavior, and 3 each of public speaking and computer literacy. The total number of hours required for graduation varies by college. A minimum GPA of 2.0 must be maintained.

Special: Cooperative programs, cross-registration with the Academic Common Market, internships, and study abroad in 7 countries are offered. Work-study programs, a Washington semester, a general studies degree, a 3–2 engineering degree, nondegree study, student-designed majors, a B.A.-B.S. degree, and pass/fail options for some courses are available. There is a freshman honors program on campus, as well as 43 national honor societies. Twenty-seven departments have honors programs.

Admissions: About 77% of the 1993–94 applicants were accepted. The ACT scores for the 1993–94 freshman class were as follows: 35% below 21, 22% between 21 and 23, 17% between 24 and 26, 10% between 27 and 28, and 16% above 28. There were 20 National Merit finalists and 23 semifinalists.

Requirements: The ACT is required. Applicants should have completed 15 academic credits, including 4 in English, 3 each in mathematics and science, 2 1/2 in social studies, 1 1/2 in a free elective, and 1 in either foreign language, higher-level mathematics, or science. Any student with an ACT score of 25 or above is exempt from high school unit requirements. Students with a GED are accepted with the required ACT. AP and CLEP credits are accepted.

Procedure: Freshmen are admitted to all sessions. Applications should be filed by August 1 for fall entry, December 15 for spring entry, and May 15 for summer entry, along with an application fee of $15. Notification is sent on a rolling basis.

Transfer: A total of 1302 transfer students enrolled in 1993–94. Applicants must submit an official transcript from each college attended, indicating a minimum GPA of 2.0, and must be in good standing at their previous school. A total of 32 credits out of 128 must be completed at State.

Visiting: There are regularly scheduled orientations for prospective students, including determining classes, meeting academic advisors, visiting faculty and administration, touring residence halls, paying tuition fees, and renting post office boxes. There are guides for informal visits and visitors may sit in on classes and stay overnight at the school. To arrange for a visit, contact Jimmy Abraham, Associate Dean of Student Services, at (601) 325-3076.

Financial Aid: State is a member of CSS. The FFS and the college's own financial statement are required. The deadline for financial aid applications is April 1.

International Students: There are currently 810 international students enrolled. They must take the TOEFL and achieve a minimum score of 525. The student must also take the SAT I and achieve a minimum composite score of 860.

Computers: State provides computer facilities for student use. The mainframes are a Unisys 2200 and 4 Sun Micro System 690s. Three of the Sun 690s are networked through 3 public laboratories and departmental facilities. All students may access the system on a timesharing basis. There are no time limits on using the system and no fees. It is recommended that students in preveterinary medicine have an Apple Macintosh personal computer and that students in architecture have a portable laptop computer.

Graduates: In 1992–93, 2231 bachelor's degrees were awarded. The most popular majors among graduates were elementary education (7%), marketing (5%), and accounting (4%). Within an average freshman class, 23% graduate in 4 years, 42% in 5 years, and 51% in 6 years. A total of 243 companies recruited on campus in 1992–93.

Admissions Contact: Jerry Inmon, Director of Admissions.

MISSISSIPPI UNIVERSITY FOR WOMEN E-2

Columbus, MS 39701 (601) 329-7106; (800) 247-0758 (in-state)

Full-time: 275 men, 1308 women	**Faculty:** 103; IIA, --$
Part-time: 290 men, 814 women	**Ph.D.s:** 53%
Graduate: 22 men, 155 women	**Student/Faculty:** 15 to 1
Year: semesters, summer session	**Tuition:** $2239 ($4381)
Application Deadline: see profile	**Room & Board:** $2217
Freshman Class: 1128 applied, 989 accepted, 501 enrolled	
ACT: recommended	**LESS COMPETITIVE**

Mississippi University for Women, founded in 1884, is a public, primarily women's institution offering degrees in liberal arts, education, business and communications, nursing, and human sciences. There are 8 undergraduate and 2 graduate schools. In addition to regional accreditation, Mississippi University for Women has baccalaureate program accreditation with AHEA, NASM, NCATE, and NLN. The library contains 938,437 volumes and 657,742 microform items, and subscribes to 1618 periodicals. Computerized library sources and services include the card catalog, interlibrary loans, and database searching. Special learning facilities include a learning resource center, art gallery, radio station, tv station, and distance learning studio. The 110-acre campus is in a small town 120 miles west of Birmingham. Including residence halls, there are 62 buildings on campus.

Student Life: About 91% of undergraduates are from Mississippi. Students come from 19 states and 1 foreign country. Seventy-nine percent are white; 20% African American. The average age of freshmen is 23; all undergraduates, 26.5.

Housing: A total of 692 students can be accommodated in college housing. College-sponsored living facilities include single-sex dormitories, on-campus apartments, and married-student housing. On-campus housing is guaranteed for all 4 years. Seventy-nine percent of students commute. Alcohol is not permitted. All students may keep cars on campus.

Activities: About 18% of men belong to 2 local and 1 national fraternities; about 22% of women belong to 12 local and 3 national sororities. There are 85 groups on campus, including art, cheerleading, choir, chorale, chorus, computers, dance, drama, ethnic, honors, jazz band, literary magazine, musical theater, newspaper, orchestra, political, radio and tv, religious, social, social service, student government, and yearbook. Popular campus events include holiday theme activities, arts and crafts shows, Mardi Gras, Oktoberfest, Nutcracker, Homecoming, and Spring Fling.

Sports: There are 4 intercollegiate sports for women, and 7 intramural sports for men and 8 for women. Athletic and recreation facilities include a gymnasium, a softball field, tennis courts, an indoor swimming pool, a gymnastics room, a weight room, a dance studio, a 3-hole pitch and putt golf course, a soccer and flag football field, and a Vita course.

Disabled Students: The following facilities are available: wheelchair ramps, elevators, special parking, and specially equipped rest rooms.

Services: Remedial math, reading, and writing are available.

Campus Safety and Security: Campus safety and security measures include 24-hour foot and vehicle patrol, escort service, informal discussions, and pamphlets, posters, and films. In addition, there are lighted pathways and sidewalks.

Programs of Study: Mississippi University for Women awards the B.A., B.S., B.F.A., B.S.N., and B.M. degrees. Associate and master's degrees also are awarded. Bachelor's degrees are awarded in BIOLOGICAL SCIENCE (biology/biological science and microbiology), BUSINESS (accounting and business administration and management), COMMUNICATIONS AND THE ARTS (broadcasting, drawing, English, fine arts, graphic design, journalism, music, and printmaking), COMPUTER AND PHYSICAL SCIENCE (chemistry, computer programming, mathematics, and physical sciences), EDUCATION (art, elementary, home economics, music, physical, secondary, and special), ENGINEERING AND ENVIRONMENTAL DESIGN (interior design), HEALTH PROFESSIONS (medical laboratory technology, nursing, and speech pathology/audiology), SOCIAL SCIENCE (child care/child and family studies, clothing and textiles management/production/services, history, paralegal studies, and social science). Biology, chemistry, English, fine arts, and teacher education are the strongest academically. Business and nursing have the largest enrollments.

Required: Students must complete 128 credit hours, 30 to 36 in a major and 2 in physical education, with a minimum GPA of 2.0.

Special: Cross-registration and a 3–2 engineering degree are with Mississippi State University. Internships in all divisions and co-op and work-study programs are available. Several combinations of dual majors, credit for experience, nondegree study, and a pass/fail option are offered. There is a freshman honors program on campus, as well as 16 national honor societies. Three departments have honors programs.

Faculty/Classroom: Thirty-eight percent of faculty are male; 62%, female. Ninety-six percent teach undergraduates. No introductory courses are taught by graduate students. The average class size in an introductory lecture is 35; in a laboratory, 23; and in a regular course offering, 25.

Admissions: About 88% of the 1993–94 applicants were accepted.

Requirements: The ACT is recommended. Prospective students should have completed 4 units of English, 3 units each of mathematics and science, 1–1/2 units in U.S. government, 1 unit in U.S. history, and 1 unit in foreign language or advanced mathematics or science. AP and CLEP credits are accepted. Important factors used in the admissions decision are recommendations by school officials, leadership record, advanced placement or honor courses, recommendations by alumni, and parents or siblings attending the school.

Procedure: Freshmen are admitted to all sessions. Entrance exams should be taken as soon as possible. Application fee is $20. The deadline for applications is 2 weeks prior to registration. Notification is sent on a rolling basis. There are early decision and early admissions plans.

Transfer: About 270 transfer students enrolled in a recent year. Applicants must have 6 semester hours of both English composition and a laboratory science, 3 of college algebra or above, and 9 of transferable electives. A total of 30 credits out of 128 must be completed at Mississippi University for Women.

Visiting: There are regularly scheduled orientations for prospective students. There are guides for informal visits and visitors may sit in on classes and stay overnight at the school. To arrange for a visit, contact the Director of Enrollment Management at (601) 329–7106.

Financial Aid: In 1993–94, 79% of all current freshmen and 81% of continuing students received some form of financial aid. About 64% of freshmen and 69% of continuing students received need-based aid. The average freshman award was $2950. Of that total, scholarships or need-based grants averaged $1250 ($6860 maximum); loans averaged $1980 ($7500 maximum); and work contracts averaged $1200 ($2750 maximum). Twenty-six percent of undergraduate students work part-time. Average earnings from campus work for the school year are $1475. The average financial indebtedness of the 1992–93 graduate was $9500. Mississippi University for Women is a member of CSS. The FAFSA financial statement is required. The deadline for financial aid applications is June 1.

International Students: There are currently 11 international students enrolled. They must take the TOEFL and achieve a minimum score of 525. The student must also take the SAT I or the ACT.

Computers: The college provides computer facilities for student use. The mainframe is an IBM 4361. The academic computing center offers access to mainframe terminals and more than 100 networked microcomputers. Computer laboratories on campus offer access to additional networked microcomputer systems. International electronic network access is available through membership in SURANET. All students may access the system. It may be used 8 A.M. to 10 P.M. There are no time limits on using the system and no fees.

Graduates: In 1992–93, 424 bachelor's degrees were awarded. The most popular majors among graduates were nursing (16%), business administration (16%), and education (10%). Some 60 companies recruited on campus in 1992–93.

Admissions Contact: Teresa Thompson, Executive Director of Enrollment Management and External Affairs.

MISSISSIPPI VALLEY STATE UNIVERSITY C-2
Itta Bena, MS 38941-1400 (601) 254-9041

Full-time: 839 men, 1478 women	Faculty: 95; IIB, --$
Part-time: 23 men, 179 women	Ph.D.s: 42%
Graduate: 3 men, 9 women	Student/Faculty: 24 to 1
Year: semesters, summer session	Tuition: $2164 ($4306)
Application Deadline: August 20	Room & Board: $1925

Freshman Class: 3537 applied, 1030 accepted, 815 enrolled
ACT: 16   **NONCOMPETITIVE**

Mississippi Valley State University, founded in 1946, offers programs in the arts and sciences, business, and education. There are 9 undergraduate departments and one graduate school. In addition to regional accreditation, MVSU has baccalaureate program accreditation with CSWE, NASAD, NASM, and NCATE. The library contains 90,000 volumes and 1000 microform items, and subscribes to 625 periodicals. Special learning facilities include a learning resource center, art gallery, radio station, and campus nursery/preschool. The 450-acre campus is in a small town 8 miles from Greenwood and 135 miles from Memphis, Tennessee. Including residence halls, there are 35 buildings on campus.

Student Life: About 90% of undergraduates are from Mississippi. Students come from 25 states and 2 foreign countries. Ninety-two percent are from public schools; 8% from private. Ninety-nine percent are African American. Most are Protestant. The average age of freshmen is 18; all undergraduates, 20. Fifteen percent drop out by the end of their first year; 40% remain to graduate.

Housing: A total of 1914 students can be accommodated in college housing. College-sponsored living facilities include single-sex dormitories. In addition, there are honors houses. On-campus housing is available on a first-come, first-served basis. Sixty-nine percent of students live on campus; of those, 55% remain on campus on weekends. Alcohol is not permitted. All students may keep cars on campus.

Activities: About 15% of men belong to 1 local and 4 national fraternities; about 20% of women belong to 1 local and 4 national sororities. There are 25 groups on campus, including art, band, cheerleading, choir, chorale, chorus, dance, drama, drill team, English, honors, jazz band, marching band, newspaper, orchestra, performing, professional, radio and TV, religious, social, student government, symphony, and yearbook. Popular campus events include Homecoming, Founders Day, Pride Day, Black History Month, and Martin Luther King Day Celebration.

Sports: There are 6 intercollegiate sports for men and 2 for women, and 10 intramural sports for men and 9 for women. Athletic and recreation facilities include a stadium for football and track, a gymnastics room, a dance studio, an indoor pool, a 2200-seat gymnasium, a basketball area, a weight-training room, and handball, squash, and paddleball courts.

Disabled Students: Ninety-nine percent of the campus is accessible to disabled students. The following facilities are available: wheelchair ramps, elevators, specially equipped rest rooms, and lowered drinking fountains.

Services: In addition to many counseling and information services, tutoring is available. In addition, there is remedial math, reading, and writing.

Campus Safety and Security: Campus safety and security measures include 24-hour foot and vehicle patrol, informal discussions, and lighted pathways and sidewalks.

Programs of Study: MVSU awards the B.A., B.S., B.M.E., and B.S.W. degrees. Master's degrees also are awarded. Bachelor's degrees are awarded in BIOLOGICAL SCIENCE (biology/biological science), BUSINESS (business administration and management), COMMUNICATIONS AND THE ARTS (English, fine arts, and speech/debate/rhetoric), COMPUTER AND PHYSICAL SCIENCE (computer science and mathematics), EDUCATION (elementary, health, industrial arts, physical, and social science), HEALTH PROFESSIONS (environmental health science), SOCIAL SCIENCE (criminal justice, political science/government, social work, and sociology). Biology, computer science, and business are the strongest academically. Criminal justice, business, and education have the largest enrollments.

Required: General education requirements include 12 semester hours in English, 6 each in social studies and laboratory science, 3 each in college algebra, speech, fine arts, psychology, and health education, and 2 in physical education or ROTC. To graduate, students must complete at least 124 credit hours with a minimum GPA of 2.0 overall and in the major.

Special: MVSU offers a special cooperative education program, internships in social work and environmental health, work-study, and nondegree study. Credit may be granted for military experience. A pass/fail option is possible. There is a freshman honors program on campus, as well as 1 national honor society.

Faculty/Classroom: Sixty-four percent of faculty are male; 36%, female. All teach undergraduates and 15% both teach and do research. No introductory courses are taught by graduate students.

Admissions: About 29% of the 1993–94 applicants were accepted. The ACT scores for the 1993–94 freshman class were as follows: 91% below 21, 6% between 21 and 23, 2% between 24 and 26, and 1% between 27 and 28. About 25% of the current freshmen were in the top fifth of their class; 50% were in the top two fifths. About 10 freshmen graduated first in their class.

Requirements: A minimum GPA of 2.0 is required. The ACT is required for Mississippi residents. Out-of-state students may submit SAT I scores. Applicants must be graduates of a secondary school and have completed 4 credits in English, 3 each in mathematics and natural sciences, 2 1/2 in social sciences, and 1 in a foreign language. The GED is accepted. AP and CLEP credits are accepted. Important factors used in the admissions decision are evidence of special talent, leadership record, advanced placement or honor courses, ability to finance college education, and recommendations by school officials.

Procedure: Freshmen are admitted to all sessions. Applications should be filed by August 20 for fall entry. The university accepts all applicants. Notification is sent on a rolling basis.

Transfer: A total of 215 transfer students enrolled in 1993–94. Transfers must have a minimum 2.0 GPA in at least 24 specified credit hours. A total of 30 credits out of 124 must be completed at MVSU.

Visiting: Campus tours with a student guide can be arranged. Visitors may sit in on classes. To arrange for a visit, contact the Dean of Students at (601) 254–9041, ext. 6515.

Financial Aid: In 1993–94, 95% of all current freshmen and 96% of continuing students received some form of financial aid. About 93% of freshmen and 92% of continuing students received need-based aid. Ninety-five percent of undergraduate students work part-time. The FAF and the college's own financial statement are required. The deadline for financial aid applications is June 1.

International Students: They must take the TOEFL and achieve a minimum score of 525.

Computers: MVSU provides computer facilities for student use. The mainframe is an IBM 4331. PCs are available in the physics laboratory. Students enrolled in computer science courses may access the system. It may be used 8 A.M. to midnight. There are no fees.

Graduates: In 1992–93, 240 bachelor's degrees were awarded. The most popular majors among graduates were criminal justice (24%), business (15%), and social work (11%). Within an average freshman class, 38% graduate in 4 years and 2% in 5 years. Some 25 companies recruited on campus in 1992–93. In the 1992 graduating class, 5% of the men and 7% of the women were enrolled in graduate school within 6 months of graduation; 60% of the men and 65% of the women had found employment.

Admissions Contact: Director of Admissions and Recruitment.

RUST COLLEGE

D-1

Holly Springs, MS 38635   (601) 252–8000, ext. 4068

Full-time, part-time: 400 men, 780 women	**Faculty:** 53; IIB, --$
	Ph.D.s: 60%
Graduate: none	**Student/Faculty:** 18 to 1
Year: see profile	**Tuition:** $4500
Application Deadline: see profile	**Room & Board:** $2100
Freshman Class: 1328 applied, 673 accepted, 282 enrolled	
ACT: 16	**LESS COMPETITIVE**

Rust College, founded in 1866, is a private, coeducational liberal arts college affiliated with the United Methodist Church. The calendar consists of four 8-week sessions and a summer session. The library contains 108,000 volumes, 5236 microform items, and 735 audiovisual forms, and subscribes to 433 periodicals. Special learning facilities include a learning resource center, radio station, and TV station. The 126-acre campus is in a small town 35 miles southeast of Memphis, Tennessee. Including residence halls, there are 23 buildings on campus.

Student Life: About 75% of undergraduates are from Mississippi. Students come from 30 states and 8 foreign countries. Ninety-five percent are African American. Most are Protestant. The average age of all undergraduates is 20.5. Thirteen percent drop out by the end of their first year; 60% remain to graduate.

Housing: A total of 808 students can be accommodated in college housing. College-sponsored living facilities include single-sex dormitories and married-student housing. On-campus housing is guaranteed for all 4 years. Seventy-five percent of students live on campus; of those, 85% remain on campus on weekends. Alcohol is not permitted. All students may keep cars on campus.

Activities: About 20% of men belong to 5 local and 5 national fraternities; about 25% of women belong to 4 local and 4 national sororities. There are 40 groups on campus, including band, cheerleading, choir, chorale, computers, drama, honors, international, marching band, newspaper, photography, political, radio and TV, religious, social service, student government, and yearbook. Popular campus events include Career Day, Founders Day, Religious Emphasis Week, and Recognition Banquet.

Sports: There are 5 intercollegiate sports for men and 3 for women, and 6 intramural sports each for men and women. Athletic and recreation facilities include a 2500-seat gymnasium, a swimming pool, tennis courts, a track, a 2000-seat stadium, a bowling alley, pool tables, and the Magic Johnson Sports Arena.

Disabled Students: The following facilities are available: wheelchair ramps, elevators, special parking, specially equipped rest rooms, and lowered drinking fountains.

Services: In addition to many counseling and information services, tutoring is available in most subjects. There is also remedial math, reading, and writing.

Campus Safety and Security: Campus safety and security measures include 24-hour foot and vehicle patrol, informal discussions, pamphlets, posters, films, and lighted pathways and sidewalks.

Programs of Study: Rust awards the B.A. and B.S. degrees. Associate degrees also are awarded. Bachelor's degrees are awarded in BIOLOGICAL SCIENCE (biology/biological science), BUSINESS (business administration and management), COMMUNICATIONS AND THE ARTS (communications, English, and music), COMPUTER

AND PHYSICAL SCIENCE (chemistry, computer science, mathematics, and physics), EDUCATION (business, elementary, and physical), SOCIAL SCIENCE (economics, history, political science/government, social work, and sociology). Business administration/management has the largest enrollment.

Required: All students must earn a minimum of 124 semester hours while maintaining a cumulative GPA of 2.0. Distribution requirements include 65 general education credits in the fields of education, humanities, science and mathematics, and a required freshman program. A minimum of 54 credits constitutes a major, and comprehensive examinations are given in all programs.

Special: Rust offers co-op programs in all areas except teacher education, internships in teaching, on-campus work-study, credit by examination, independent study, B.A.-B.S. degrees in most majors, and dual majors in a variety of science programs. There are 3–2 engineering programs available with the Georgia Institute of Technology, the Tuskegee Institute, the University of Mississippi, and Memphis State, Mississippi State, and Auburn universities. There is a freshman honors program on campus, as well as 6 national honor societies. Seven departments have honors programs.

Faculty/Classroom: Sixty-two percent of faculty are male; 38%, female. All teach undergraduates, and 19% do research as well. The average class size in a regular course offering is 30.

Admissions: About 51% of the 1993–94 applicants were accepted.

Requirements: The SAT I or ACT is required. In addition, Rust requires 16 academic credits including 4 in English, 3 each in mathematics and science, and 2 each in history, social studies, and electives. An audition, an interview, and 2 letters of recommendation are required. The GED is accepted. An essay and portfolio are recommended. AP and CLEP credits are accepted. Important factors used in the admissions decision are advanced placement or honor courses, evidence of special talent, leadership record, personality, intangible qualities, and recommendations by alumni.

Procedure: Freshmen are admitted in the fall, spring, and summer. Entrance exams should be taken prior to the second semester of the senior year. Applications should be filed for priority by July 15 for fall entry and December 15 for spring entry, along with an application fee of $10. Notification is sent on a rolling basis. There are early decision and early admissions plans.

Transfer: About 35 transfer students enrolled in a recent year. Transfer applicants with at least 15 semester hours of credit need not take the ACT or SAT I. Only C grades or better transfer. A total of 30 credits out of 124 must be completed at Rust.

Visiting: There are regularly scheduled orientations for prospective students. There are guides for informal visits and visitors may sit in on classes and stay overnight at the school. To arrange for a visit, contact Jo Ann Scott, Director of Admissions, at (601) 252–8000, ext. 4068.

Financial Aid: In a recent year, 95% of all current freshmen and 80% of continuing students received some form of financial aid. Scholarships or need-based grants averaged $720; loans averaged $719; and work contracts averaged $679. Average earnings from campus work for the school year are $1300. The average financial indebtedness of a recent graduate was $500. The FFS is required. The deadline for financial aid applications is July 15.

International Students: There were 17 international students enrolled in an earlier year. They must take the TOEFL and achieve a minimum score of 540. The student must also take the ACT.

Computers: The college provides computer facilities for student use. The mainframe is an HP 3000. Computer science majors and work-aid students may access the system at assigned times. There are no time limits on using the system and no fees.

Graduates: In a recent year, 122 bachelor's degrees were awarded. The most popular majors among graduates were business administration/management (16%), social work (11%), and early childhood education (8%). Within an average freshman class, 5% graduate in 3 years, 45% in 4 years, 30% in 5 years, and 5% in 6 years. Some 40 companies recruited on campus in a recent year.

Admissions Contact: Jo Ann Scott, Director of Admissions.

TOUGALOO COLLEGE

C-4

Tougaloo, MS 39174   (601) 977–7764

Full-time: 377 men, 743 women	**Faculty:** 66; IIB, --$
Part-time: 12 men, 21 women	**Ph.D.s:** 52%
Graduate: none	**Student/Faculty:** 17 to 1
Year: semesters	**Tuition:** $5295
Application Deadline: open	**Room & Board:** $2185
Freshman Class: 578 accepted, 311 enrolled	
ACT: 18	**LESS COMPETITIVE**

Tougaloo College, founded in 1869, is a private liberal arts institution affiliated with the United Church of Christ. The library contains 116,535 volumes, 7165 microform items, and 4251 audiovisual forms, and subscribes to 370 periodicals. Computerized library sources and services include the card catalog, interlibrary loans, and database searching. Special learning facilities include a learning resource

center and art gallery. The 500-acre campus is in a suburban area 1 mile north of Jackson. Including residence halls, there are 18 buildings on campus.

Student Life: About 87% of undergraduates are from Mississippi. Students come from 23 states and 2 foreign countries. Ninety-eight percent are from public schools; 2% from private. Nearly all are African American. Most are Baptist. The average age of freshmen is 18; all undergraduates, 20. Eighteen percent drop out by the end of their first year; 42% remain to graduate.

Housing: A total of 632 students can be accommodated in college housing. College-sponsored living facilities include single-sex dormitories. On-campus housing is available on a first-come, first-served basis. Sixty percent of students live on campus; of those, 80% remain on campus on weekends. Alcohol is not permitted. All students may keep cars on campus.

Activities: About 35% of men belong to 4 national fraternities; about 40% of women belong to 4 national sororities. There are many groups and organizations on campus, including art, cheerleading, choir, chorus, computers, honors, international, newspaper, photography, political, professional, religious, social, social service, student government, and yearbook. Popular campus events include Founders Day.

Sports: Athletic and recreation facilities include a gymnasium, a tennis court, and access to a bowling alley and a golf course.

Disabled Students: Twenty percent of the campus is accessible to disabled students. The following facilities are available: wheelchair ramps, elevators, and specially equipped rest rooms.

Services: In addition to many counseling and information services, tutoring is available in every subject. There is also remedial math, reading, and writing.

Campus Safety and Security: Campus safety and security measures include 24-hour foot and vehicle patrol, self-defense education, informal discussions, pamphlets, posters, films, emergency telephones, and lighted pathways and sidewalks.

Programs of Study: Tougaloo awards the B.A. and B.S. degrees. Associate degrees also are awarded. Bachelor's degrees are awarded in BIOLOGICAL SCIENCE (biology/biological science), COMMUNICATIONS AND THE ARTS (English and music), COMPUTER AND PHYSICAL SCIENCE (chemistry, mathematics, and physics), EDUCATION (elementary), SOCIAL SCIENCE (economics, history, political science/government, psychology, and sociology). Physical sciences is the strongest program academically. Biology and economics have the largest enrollments.

Required: To graduate, students must complete 124 credit hours, including 27 to 48 in the major, with a minimum GPA of 2.0. Students must fulfill about 56 hours of general education requirements, take computer science and physical education courses, and complete a senior paper.

Special: Tougaloo offers cooperative programs with Brown and Boston universities, study abroad in Africa, a Washington semester in conjunction with American University, internships, work-study programs, credit for military service, pass/fail options, and a 3–2 engineering degree with Georgia Tech, the universities of Mississippi and Wisconsin at Madison, and Brown, Tuskegee, and Howard universities. There is a freshman honors program on campus, as well as 3 national honor societies.

Faculty/Classroom: Fifty-five percent of faculty are male; 45%, female. All teach undergraduates.

Admissions: About 18% of the 1993–94 applicants were accepted. The ACT scores for the 1993–94 freshman class were as follows: 82% below 21, 12% between 21 and 23, 5% between 24 and 26, and 1% between 27 and 28. About 18% of the current freshmen were in the top fifth of their class; 31% were in the top two fifths.

Requirements: A minimum GPA of 2.0 is required. The SAT I or ACT is required. Candidates should be graduates of an accredited secondary school or have a GED certificate. They should have completed 3 credits of English, 2 each of mathematics and science, and 1 each of history and social studies. An interview is recommended. AP and CLEP credits are accepted. Important factors used in the admissions decision are parents or siblings attending the school, geographic diversity, extracurricular activities record, evidence of special talent, and advanced placement or honor courses.

Procedure: Freshmen are admitted in the fall. Entrance exams should be taken by March of the senior year. Application deadlines are open. Notification is sent on a rolling basis. There is an early admissions plan.

Transfer: About 50 transfer students enrolled in a recent year. Applicants must submit transcripts of all college course work and have a minimum GPA of 2.0. A total of 30 credits out of 124 must be completed at Tougaloo.

Visiting: Visitors may sit in on classes and stay overnight at the school. To arrange for a visit, contact the Office of Student Enrollment at (601) 977-7765.

Financial Aid: In a recent year, 99% of all students received some form of financial aid. All freshmen received need-based aid. The average freshman award that year was $3389. Of that total, scholarships or need-based grants averaged $3000 ($6000 maximum); loans averaged $2000 ($4000 maximum); and work contracts averaged $1115 ($2000 maximum). Ten percent of undergraduate students work part-time. Average earnings from campus work for the school year are $1045. Tougaloo is a member of CSS. The FAF, FFS or SFS is required. The deadline for financial aid applications is April 15.

International Students: There were recently 3 international students enrolled. They must take the TOEFL and achieve a minimum score of 500. The student must also take the SAT I or the ACT.

Computers: The college provides computer facilities for student use. The mainframe is a DEC. There are also Apple, IBM, and AT&T microcomputers available in the Academic Computing Center. There are no time limits on using the system and no fees.

Graduates: In a recent year, 96 bachelor's degrees were awarded. The most popular majors among graduates were biological science (29%), social sciences (15%), and psychology (12%). Within an average freshman class, 69% graduate in 5 years and 78% in 6 years. In a recent graduating class, 6% of the men and 49% of the women were enrolled in graduate school within 6 months of graduation; 7% of the men and 12% of the women had found employment.

Admissions Contact: Washington Cole, IV, Director of Admissions and Recruitment.

UNIVERSITY OF MISSISSIPPI   D-2
University, MS 38677   (601) 232-7226

Full-time: 3792 men, 3736 women	**Faculty:** 465; I, --$
Part-time: 268 men, 361 women	**Ph.D.s:** 84%
Graduate: 1243 men, 969 women	**Student/Faculty:** 16 to 1
Year: early semesters, summer session	**Tuition:** $2456 ($4916)
	Room & Board: $3300

Application Deadline: August 1
Freshman Class: 3844 applied, 3383 accepted, 1669 enrolled
SAT I or ACT: required   **COMPETITIVE**

The University of Mississippi, founded in 1844, is a public, coeducational institution offering undergraduate and graduate programs in the liberal arts, business, pharmacy, engineering, accountancy, and education. There are 6 undergraduate and 2 graduate schools. In addition to regional accreditation, the university has baccalaureate program accreditation with AACSB, ABET, ACEJMC, ACPE, ADA, AHEA, CSWE, FIDER, NASAD, NASM, and NCATE. The 5 libraries contain 1,555,359 volumes, 1,938,898 microform items, and 38,367 audiovisual forms, and subscribe to 5500 periodicals. Computerized library sources and services include the card catalog, interlibrary loans, and database searching. Special learning facilities include a learning resource center, art gallery, radio station, TV station, museum, the Center for the Study of Southern Culture, the National Center for Physical Acoustics, and Rowan Oak, the home of William Faulkner. The 2000-acre campus is in a small town 70 miles southeast of Memphis, Tennessee. Including residence halls, there are 193 buildings on campus.

Student Life: About 61% of undergraduates are from Mississippi. Students come from 44 states, 59 foreign countries, and Canada. Seventy percent are from public schools; 30% from private. Eighty-four percent are white. The average age of all undergraduates is 21.2. About 52% of freshmen remain to graduate.

Housing: A total of 4513 students can be accommodated in college housing. College-sponsored living facilities include single-sex dormitories, married-student housing, fraternity houses, and sorority houses. On-campus housing is guaranteed for all 4 years. Alcohol is not permitted. All students may keep cars on campus.

Activities: About 35% of men belong to 19 national fraternities; about 40% of women belong to 14 national sororities. There are 200 groups on campus, including art, band, cheerleading, chess, choir, chorale, chorus, computers, dance, drama, drill team, ethnic, features magazine, honors, international, jazz band, literary magazine, marching band, musical theater, newspaper, orchestra, pep band, political, professional, radio and TV, religious, social, social service, student government, symphony, and yearbook. Popular campus events include Homecoming, Festival of Southern Theater, Faulkner and Yoknapatawpha Conference, and Red and Blue Week.

Sports: There are 8 intercollegiate sports for men and 7 for women, and 35 intramural sports for men and 35 for women. Athletic and recreation facilities include a 42,000-seat football stadium, 8800-seat gymnasium, baseball diamond, indoor pool, 10 racquetball courts, 2 weight rooms, 23 tennis courts, and 3 playing fields.

Disabled Students: Twenty-five percent of the campus is accessible to disabled students. The following facilities are available: wheelchair ramps, elevators, special parking, specially equipped rest rooms, special class scheduling, lowered drinking fountains, and lowered telephones.

Services: In addition to many counseling and information services, tutoring is available in most subjects. In addition, there is a reader service for the blind, and remedial math, reading, and writing.

Campus Safety and Security: Campus safety and security measures include 24-hour foot and vehicle patrol, self defense education, escort service, and informal discussions. In addition, there are pamphlets, posters, and films, emergency telephones, lighted pathways and sidewalks, and a full-time campus safety officer.

Programs of Study: The university awards the B.A., B.S., B.Ac., B.A.E., B.A.Ed., B.A.L.M., B.B.A, B.E., B.F.A., B.Mus., B.P.A., B.S.C.E., B.S.Ch.E., B.S.C.S., B.S.E., B.S.E.E., B.S.E.S., B.S.G., B.S.G.E., B.S.H.E., B.S.J., B.S.M.E., B.S.Pharm., B.S.R., and B.S.W. degrees. Master's and doctoral degrees also are awarded. Bachelor's degrees are awarded in BIOLOGICAL SCIENCE (biology/biological science), BUSINESS (accounting, banking and finance, business administration and management, business economics, court reporting, insurance, management information systems, management science, marketing/retailing/merchandising, and real estate), COMMUNICATIONS AND THE ARTS (advertising, art, art history and appreciation, broadcasting, design, dramatic arts, English, French, German, journalism, music, Spanish, and telecommunications), COMPUTER AND PHYSICAL SCIENCE (chemistry, computer science, geology, mathematics, and physics), EDUCATION (art, early childhood, elementary, home economics, music, and special), ENGINEERING AND ENVIRONMENTAL DESIGN (chemical engineering, civil engineering, electrical/electronics engineering, engineering, geological engineering, and mechanical engineering), HEALTH PROFESSIONS (biomedical science, medical laboratory technology, pharmacy, and speech pathology/audiology), SOCIAL SCIENCE (anthropology, classical/ancient civilization, economics, history, philosophy, political science/government, psychology, public administration, social work, sociology, and Southern studies). General business, biological science, accountancy, pharmacy, and English have the largest enrollments.

Required: Students must maintain a minimum GPA of 2.0 (2.5 in teacher education) while taking 126 to 139 semester hours, including 24 to 42 in the major. Other requirements include 6 hours each of English composition and laboratory science and 3 each of college algebra and humanities and fine arts.

Special: Co-op programs with area employers, internships in journalism, study abroad in numerous countries, and work-study programs within the university are offered. Dual majors, a general studies degree, credit by examination, special testing in music and languages, credit for military experience, and limited pass/fail options also are available. There is a freshman honors program on campus, as well as 24 national honor societies.

Faculty/Classroom: Seventy percent of faculty are male; 30%, female.

Admissions: About 88% of the 1993–94 applicants were accepted. About 40% of the current freshmen were in the top fifth of their class; 70% were in the top two fifths. There were 17 National Merit finalists and 14 semifinalists.

Requirements: A minimum GPA of 2.0 is required, along with a minimum composite score of 720 on the SAT I or 18 on the ACT. Applicants need 13 1/2 academic credits, including 4 units in English, 3 in mathematics and science laboratory courses, 2 in history, a half unit in civics or government, and another unit in mathematics, science, or a foreign language. A portfolio for art majors and an audition for theater and music majors are required. The GED is not accepted. AP and CLEP credits are accepted.

Procedure: Freshmen are admitted to all sessions. Applications should be filed by August 1 for fall entry, December 1 for winter entry, and May 1 for summer entry, along with an application fee of $15. Notification is sent on a rolling basis. There are early admissions and deferred admissions plans.

Transfer: A total of 754 transfer students enrolled in 1993–94. Transfer students must have earned a minimum 2.0 GPA on previous college work. The SAT I or ACT may be required, depending on credits earned. At least 30 credits (63 to 70 from a 2-year school) out of 126 to 139 must be completed at the university.

Visiting: There are regularly scheduled orientations for prospective students, including academic information/student life discussions and tours. Class attendance and academic appointments can be arranged. There are guides for informal visits and visitors may sit in on classes; overnight stays at the school are permitted on a limited basis. To arrange for a visit, contact the Pre-Admissions Office at (601) 232-7378.

Financial Aid: In 1993–94, 66% of all current freshmen and 71% of continuing students received some form of financial aid. About 32% of freshmen received need-based aid. The average freshman award was $5767. Of that total, scholarships or need-based grants averaged $1949; loans averaged $5612; and work contracts averaged $882. Average earnings from campus work for the school year are $703. The university is a member of CSS. The FAFSA is required. The deadline for financial aid applications is March 1.

International Students: There are currently 587 international students enrolled. They must take the TOEFL and achieve a minimum score of 550. The student must also achieve a minimum composite score of 720 on the SAT I or 18 on the ACT.

Computers: The university provides computer facilities for student use. The mainframes are an SGI 40/R4400 RISC, a CDC CYBER 860, an Amdahl 5860, an IBM 3084, and Cray XMP and Cray Y-MP supercomputers. The computer center runs a 120-unit general-access laboratory housing Novell-networked PCs with mainframe connection via the campus fiber optic network. Various academic departments operate their own PC laboratories, some of which are networked and connected to the campus backbone fiber. All students may access the system 24 hours daily. There are no time limits on using the system and no fees.

Graduates: In 1992–93, 1769 bachelor's degrees were awarded. The most popular majors among graduates were business/management/accountancy (33%), education (9%), and health sciences (7%). Within an average freshman class, 1% graduate in 3 years, 33% in 4 years, 50% in 5 years, and 51% in 6 years. Some 236 companies recruited on campus in 1992–93.

Admissions Contact: Beckett Howorth, Director of Admissions.

UNIVERSITY OF SOUTHERN MISSISSIPPI D-5
Hattiesburg, MS 39406 (601) 266-5555
(800) CALL-USM (in-state)

Full-time: 3744 men, 4675 women	Faculty: 578; I, --$
Part-time: 501 men, 685 women	Ph.D.s: 77%
Graduate: 778 men, 1104 women	Student/Faculty: 15 to 1
Year: semesters, summer session	Tuition: $2392 ($4852)
Application Deadline: see profile	Room & Board: $2150
Freshman Class: 2850 applied, 2044 accepted, 1046 enrolled	
ACT: 21	COMPETITIVE

The University of Southern Mississippi, founded in 1910, is a public institution offering comprehensive degree programs. There are 6 undergraduate schools and one graduate school. In addition to regional accreditation, USM has baccalaureate program accreditation with AACSB, ABET, ACEJMC, ADA, AHEA, ASLA, CAHEA, CSWE, FIDER, NASAD, NASM, NCATE, and NLN. The 2 libraries contain 858,997 volumes, 3,066,777 microform items, and 12,414 audiovisual forms, and subscribe to 5250 periodicals. Special learning facilities include a learning resource center, art gallery, natural history museum, radio station, tv station and production studios, and music resource center. The 840-acre campus is in a suburban area 90 miles southeast of Jackson and 105 miles north of New Orleans, Louisiana. Including residence halls, there are 166 buildings on campus.

Student Life: About 83% of undergraduates are from Mississippi. Students come from 50 states, 49 foreign countries, and Canada. Eighty-five percent are from public schools. Eighty percent are white; 16% African American. The average age of freshmen is 20; all undergraduates, 25. Twenty-nine percent drop out by the end of their first year; 42% remain to graduate.

Housing: A total of 3518 students can be accommodated in college housing. College-sponsored living facilities include single-sex dormitories, married-student housing, and fraternity houses. In addition, a section in 1 dormitory is reserved for honor students. On-campus housing is guaranteed for the freshman year only and is available on a first-come, first-served basis. Sixty percent of students commute. Alcohol is not permitted. All students may keep cars on campus.

Activities: About 6% of men belong to 15 local fraternities; about 6% of women belong to 12 local sororities. There are 205 groups on campus, including art, band, cheerleading, choir, chorale, chorus, computers, dance, drama, ethnic, honors, jazz band, marching band, musical theater, opera, orchestra, pep band, photography, political, professional, radio and TV, religious, social, social service, student government, and symphony.

Sports: There are 8 intercollegiate sports for men and 7 for women, and 40 intramural sports for men and 40 for women. Athletic and recreation facilities include a football stadium, a basketball coliseum, a baseball park, tennis courts, a golf course, an equestrian center, a fitness institute, a natatorium, and playing fields for softball, flag football, and soccer.

Disabled Students: Ninety-eight percent of the campus is accessible to disabled students. The following facilities are available: wheelchair ramps, elevators, special parking, specially equipped rest rooms, special class scheduling, lowered drinking fountains, and lowered telephones.

Services: In addition to many counseling and information services, tutoring is available in most subjects. In addition, there is a reader service for the blind, and remedial math, reading, and writing.

Campus Safety and Security: Campus safety and security measures include 24-hour foot and vehicle patrol, escort service, shuttle buses, and pamphlets, posters, and films. In addition, there are emergency telephones and lighted pathways and sidewalks.

Programs of Study: USM awards the B.A., B.S., B.F.A., B.M., B.M.E., and B.S.B.A degrees. Master's and doctoral degrees also are awarded. Bachelor's degrees are awarded in BIOLOGICAL SCIENCE (biology/biological science), BUSINESS (accounting, banking and finance, business administration and management, business economics, hotel/motel and restaurant management, international business management, marketing/retailing/merchandising, and personnel management), COMMUNICATIONS AND THE ARTS (advertising, broadcasting, communications, dance, design, dramatic arts, English, fine arts, journalism, languages, music, and speech/debate/rhetoric), COMPUTER AND PHYSICAL SCIENCE (chemistry, computer science, geology, information sciences and systems, mathematics, physics, polymer science, and statistics), EDUCATION (art, business, early childhood, elementary, foreign languages, guidance, health, home economics, industrial arts, middle school, music, science, and secondary), ENGINEERING AND ENVIRONMENTAL DESIGN (architectural technology, computer technology, construction technology, electrical/electronics engineering technology, engineering technology, and mechanical engineering technology), HEALTH PROFESSIONS (medical laboratory technology, nursing, predentistry, premedicine, and speech pathology/audiology), SOCIAL SCIENCE (anthropology, criminal justice, economics, geography, history, international relations, parks and recreation management, philosophy, political science/government, prelaw, psychology, social science, social work, and sociology). Polymer science and accounting are the strongest academically. Accounting has the largest enrollment.

Required: To graduate, students must complete at least 128 semester hours, including 64 at the senior college level, with a minimum GPA of 2.0. Core requirements include courses in reasoning and communication skills, humanities and fine arts, social and behavioral sciences, and human wellness.

Special: USM offers cooperative programs with business, internships, dual majors, nondegree study, limited pass/fail options, credit for life experience, and study abroad in England, Germany, Austria, and Italy. The university also participates in the Title IV College Work-Study Program. There is a freshman honors program on campus, as well as 7 national honor societies.

Faculty/Classroom: Sixty-nine percent of faculty are male; 31%, female. All teach undergraduates and 75% do research. The average class size in an introductory lecture is 25; in a laboratory, 30; and in a regular course offering, 30.

Admissions: About 72% of the 1993–94 applicants were accepted. The ACT scores for the 1993–94 freshman class were as follows: 51% below 21, 23% between 21 and 23, 14% between 24 and 26, 7% between 27 and 28, and 5% above 28. There were 9 National Merit finalists.

Requirements: The ACT is required, with a minimum score of 15. Applicants must be graduates of an accredited secondary school or have a GED certificate. They should have completed 4 units of English, 3 each of mathematics and science, 2 1/2 of social studies, and 1 of electives. AP and CLEP credits are accepted.

Procedure: Freshmen are admitted to all sessions. Entrance exams should be taken in the fall of the senior year. Applications should be filed at least 20 days prior to registration. There are early decision and early admissions plans.

Transfer: A total of 1612 transfer students enrolled in a recent year. Applicants must be eligible to return to their previous institution. A total of 32 credits out of 128 must be completed at USM.

Visiting: There are regularly scheduled orientations for prospective students. There are guides for informal visits and visitors may sit in on classes. To arrange for a visit, contact Homer Wesley at (601) 266–5000.

Financial Aid: In an earlier year, 64% of all current freshmen and 42% of continuing students received some form of financial aid. Scholarships or need-based grants averaged $1300; loans averaged $1000; and work contracts averaged $1000. Fifteen percent of undergraduate students work part-time. The FFS is required. The deadline for financial aid applications is March 15.

International Students: There are currently 310 international students enrolled. The school actively recruits these students. They must take the TOEFL and achieve a minimum score of 525. The student must also take the ACT and achieve a minimum score of 20.

Computers: The college provides computer facilities for student use. The mainframe is a Honeywell DPS90. There are also 500 IBM, Tandy, and Zenith microcomputers available throughout the campus. All students may access the system at any time. There are no time limits on using the system and no fees.

Graduates: In a recent year, 2234 bachelor's degrees were awarded. The most popular majors among graduates were education and psychology (25%), business administration (24%), and liberal arts (20%). A total of 433 companies recruited on campus in an earlier year.

Admissions Contact: Wayne Pyle, Admissions Office.

WILLIAM CAREY COLLEGE

Hattiesburg, MS 39401-5499

D-5

(601) 582–6103
(800) 962–5991, ext. 103

Full-time: 482 men, 1056 women
Part-time: 99 men, 320 women
Graduate: 83 men, 155 women
Year: trimesters, summer session
Application Deadline: August 15
Freshman Class: 260 applied, 200 accepted, 162 enrolled
ACT: 20

Faculty: 80; IIB, --$
Ph.D.s: 57%
Student/Faculty: 19 to 1
Tuition: $4750
Room & Board: $2300

COMPETITIVE

William Carey College, founded in 1906, is a private liberal arts college affiliated with the Mississippi Baptist Convention. In addition to regional accreditation, Carey has baccalaureate program accreditation with NASM and NLN. The 2 libraries contain 110,000 volumes and 370 microform items, and subscribe to 600 periodicals. Other libraries are located at Carey's Gulf Coast and New Orleans campuses. Special learning facilities include a learning resource center. The 120-acre campus is in a small town 100 miles from New Orleans, Louisiana. Including residence halls, there are 15 buildings on campus.

Student Life: About 50% of undergraduates are from Mississippi. Ninety percent are from public schools. Most are members of the Baptist Church. The average age of freshmen is 18. Fifteen percent drop out by the end of their first year; 50% remain to graduate.

Housing: A total of 509 students can be accommodated in college housing. College-sponsored living facilities include single-sex dormitories. Fifty percent of students live on campus. All students may keep cars on campus.

Activities: There are 2 local fraternities and 2 local sororities . There are many groups and organizations on campus, including art, choir, chorale, drama, ethnic, international, literary magazine, newspaper, professional, religious, social, social service, student government, and yearbook.

Sports: Athletic and recreation facilities include a gymnasium, a baseball field, an intramural field, and tennis courts.

Disabled Students: Eighty percent of the campus is accessible to disabled students. Wheelchair ramps and special class scheduling are available.

Services: In addition to many counseling and information services, tutoring is available in every subject. There is remedial math, reading, and writing.

Campus Safety and Security: Campus safety and security measures include campus security personnel on duty 24 hours a day.

Programs of Study: Carey awards the B.A., B.S., B.F.A., B.G.S., B.L.S., B.M., B.S.B., and B.S.N. degrees. Master's degrees also are awarded. Bachelor's degrees are awarded in BIOLOGICAL SCIENCE (biology/biological science), BUSINESS (accounting, business administration and management, and business economics), COMMUNICATIONS AND THE ARTS (applied music, communications, dramatic arts, drawing, English, music, painting, public relations, Spanish, speech/debate/rhetoric, and voice), COMPUTER AND PHYSICAL SCIENCE (chemistry, information sciences and systems, mathematics, and radiological technology), EDUCATION (business, elementary, music, physical, and special), ENGINEERING AND ENVIRONMENTAL DESIGN (commercial art, interior design, and preengineering), HEALTH PROFESSIONS (medical laboratory technology, music therapy, nursing, optometry, physical therapy, predentistry, premedicine, prepharmacy, and preveterinary science), SOCIAL SCIENCE (history, liberal arts/general studies, psychology, religion, religious music, social science, and sociology).

Required: Students must complete a core group of classes, including 6 credits each in religion, English, history, social and behavioral science, and computer science, fine arts, foreign language, or natural science; 4 in laboratory science; 3 each in mathematics, fine arts, communication, and literature; and 2 in physical education. A total of 128 semester hours with a minimum 2.0 GPA overall and in the major is needed to graduate.

Special: Internships for research, study abroad by special arrangement, work-study, nondegree study, an accelerated 3-year bachelor's degree, and a cooperative 3–2 program in forestry are possible. A 6-year program in law, a 7-year cooperative program in medicine, and a 3–1 program in medical technology are available. Two-year professional programs are possible in engineering, physical therapy, medical records administration, radiological technology, optometry, and pharmacy. Upperclassmen may choose 1 pass/fail option per trisemester. There is a freshman honors program on campus

Admissions: About 77% of the 1993–94 applicants were accepted. The ACT scores for the 1993–94 freshman class were as follows: 37% below 21, 34% between 21 and 23, 16% between 24 and 26, 9% between 27 and 28, and 4% above 28. About 33% of the current freshmen were in the top fifth of their class; 60% were in the top two fifths.

Requirements: Carey requires applicants to be in the upper 60% of their class. A minimum GPA of 2.0 is required. The SAT I (recommended) or ACT is required. In addition, applicants must have

earned 16 Carnegie units, including courses in English, foreign language, social studies, science, and mathematics. The admissions committee also considers special skills or aptitudes and other evidence of academic potential. Recommendations from high school officials and college alumni, extracurricular activities, honors courses, leadership potential, and ability to pay also are considered. AP and CLEP credits are accepted.

Procedure: Freshmen are admitted to all sessions. Early decision applications should be filed by December 1; regular applications, by August 15 for fall entry, along with an application fee of $10. Notification is sent on a rolling basis. There are early decision and early admissions plans.

Transfer: Transfer students must have a minimum GPA of 1.4 for freshmen, 1.7 for sophomores, and 2.0 for juniors. A total of 30 credits out of 128 must be completed at Carey.

Visiting: Visitors may stay overnight at the school. To arrange for a visit, contact the Admissions Office at (601) 582-5051.

Financial Aid: In an earlier year, 75% of all current freshmen received some form of financial aid. Eighty percent of undergraduate students work part-time. Carey is a member of CSS. The FAF or FFS is required. The deadline for financial aid applications is February 1.

International Students: International students must take the TOEFL, and either the college's own test or the ACT and achieve a minimum score on the TOEFL of 525.

Computers: The college provides computer facilities for student use. The computer laboratory is located in the learning resource center.

Admissions Contact: Dr. Tim C. Bailey, Director of Student Marketing.

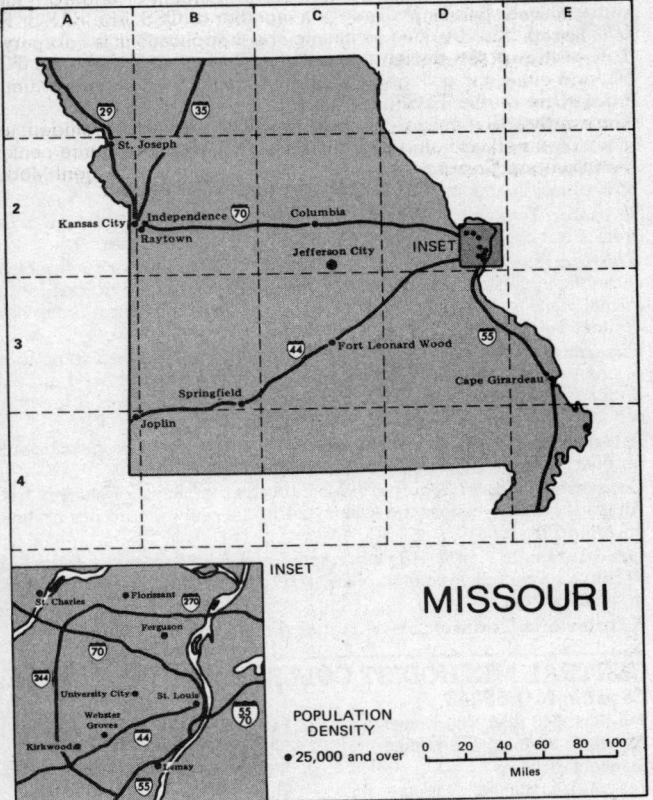

INSET

MISSOURI

POPULATION
DENSITY

● 25,000 and over

0 20 40 60 80 100
Miles

AVILA COLLEGE
Kansas City, MO 64145

A-2

(816) 942–8400, ext. 203

Full-time: 179 men, 472 women	Faculty: 54; IIB, --$
Part-time: 123 men, 367 women	Ph.D.s: 69%
Graduate: 104 men, 144 women	Student/Faculty: 12 to 1
Year: semesters, summer session	Tuition: $8530
Application Deadline: open	Room & Board: $3600
Freshman Class: 318 applied, 299 accepted, 84 enrolled	
SAT I Verbal/Math: 430/430	ACT: 21 **COMPETITIVE**

Avila College, founded in 1916, is a comprehensive liberal arts institution sponsored by the Sisters of St. Joseph of Carondelet. There are 3 graduate schools. In addition to regional accreditation, Avila has baccalaureate program accreditation with CAHEA, CSWE, and NLN. The library contains 75,000 volumes and 373,413 microform items, and subscribes to 450 periodicals. Computerized library sources and services include the card catalog, interlibrary loans, and database searching. Special learning facilities include a learning resource center, an art gallery, a 500-seat theater, a reptile collection, an interactive video library, and video production facilities. The 48-acre campus is in a suburban area in Kansas City. Including residence halls, there are 9 buildings on campus.

Student Life: About 68% of undergraduates are from Missouri. Students come from 12 states and 13 foreign countries. Ninety-one percent are from public schools; 9% from private. Eighty-three percent are white. Thirty-seven percent are Catholic. The average age of freshmen is 19; all undergraduates, 24. Eighteen percent drop out by the end of their first year; 49% remain to graduate.

Housing: A total of 230 students can be accommodated in college housing. College-sponsored living facilities include coed dormitories. On-campus housing is guaranteed for all 4 years and is available on a first-come, first-served basis. Eighty-seven percent of students commute. Alcohol is not permitted. All students may keep cars on campus.

Activities: There are no fraternities or sororities on campus. There are 21 groups on campus, including cheerleading, choir, computers, dance, drama, ethnic, honors, international, literary magazine, musical theater, newspaper, pep band, photography, political, professional, religious, social, social service, and student government. Popular campus events include Homecoming, sports and theatrical events, Family Day, and International Festival.

Sports: There are 3 intercollegiate sports for men and 4 for women, and 8 intramural sports for men and 8 for women. Athletic and recreation facilities include a field house with basketball and volleyball courts, a training room, and weight and fitness equipment. There is also an athletic complex with baseball, softball, and soccer fields, as well as tennis courts and practice fields.

Disabled Students: Eighty percent of the campus is accessible to disabled students. The following facilities are available: wheelchair ramps, elevators, special parking, specially equipped rest rooms, lowered drinking fountains, and lowered telephones.

Services: In addition to many counseling and information services, tutoring is available in some subjects, including math, sciences, English, accounting, and general/study skills. There is remedial math and writing, and a study skills center is also available.

Campus Safety and Security: Campus safety and security measures include self-defense education, and informal discussions; there are pamphlets, posters, and films, as well as lighted pathways and sidewalks. In addition, there are evening and night security patrols.

Programs of Study: Avila awards the B.A., B.S., B.F.A., B.S.B.A., B.S.M.T., B.S.N., B.S.R.T., and B.S.W. degrees. Master's degrees are also awarded. Bachelor's degrees are awarded in BIOLOGICAL SCIENCE (biology/biological science), BUSINESS (accounting, banking and finance, business administration and management, international business management, marketing/retailing/merchandising, and personnel management), COMMUNICATIONS AND THE ARTS (communications, dramatic arts, English, graphic design, music, piano/organ, and voice), COMPUTER AND PHYSICAL SCIENCE (chemistry, computer science, information sciences and systems, mathematics, natural sciences, and radiological technology), EDUCATION (art, elementary, music, and special), HEALTH PROFESSIONS (medical laboratory technology, nursing, premedicine, and respiratory therapy), SOCIAL SCIENCE (history, liberal arts/general studies, paralegal studies, political science/government, psychology, social work, sociology, and theological studies). Nursing, education, business, arts, premedicine, and science are the strongest academically. Business, education, psychology, nursing, and social work have the largest enrollments.

Required: To graduate, students must maintain a minimum GPA of 2.0 in 128 hours, with no more than 60 hours in the major. The core curriculum includes 9 hours/3 areas in economics, political science, psychology, and sociology; 9 hours/2 areas in philosophy/theology; 7 hours/2 areas in natural science, including laboratory; 6 hours in a foreign language; and 3 hours each in writing, mathematics, literature, Western civilization, and art, music, or theater. Students must also complete five communication-intensive courses; incoming freshmen must enroll in freshman seminar.

Special: Students may cross-register with the Sisters of St. Joseph College Consortium and the Kansas City Regional Council of Higher Education Consortium. Avila also offers internships, work-study, a Washington center program, and dual majors. There are 4 national honor societies on campus.

Faculty/Classroom: Thirty-seven percent of faculty are male; 63%, female. Ninety-three percent teach undergraduates and 40% both teach and do research. No introductory courses are taught by graduate students. The average class size in an introductory lecture is 18; in a laboratory, 20; and in a regular course offering, 14.

Admissions: About 94% of the 1993–94 applicants were accepted. The SAT scores for the 1993–94 freshman class were as follows: Verbal—65% below 500, 29% between 500 and 599, and 6% between 600 and 700; Math—59% below 500, 35% between 500 and 599, and 6% between 600 and 700. The ACT scores were 49% below 21, 23% between 21 and 23, 15% between 24 and 26, 7% between 27 and 28, and 9% above 28. About 30% of the current freshmen were in the top fifth of their class; 65% were in the top two fifths.

Requirements: A minimum GPA of 2.5 is required. The SAT I or ACT is required. A minimum ACT score of 20 or SAT I composite score of 850 is recommended. Applicants must be graduates of an accredited secondary school or have a GED certificate. They should have completed 16 academic units, including 4 in English, 3 in mathematics, 2 or 3 in natural and social sciences, 2 to 4 in foreign language, and 1 or 2 in fine arts. An interview is advised. AP and CLEP credits are accepted. Important factors used in the admissions decision are recommendations by school officials, extracurricular activities record, evidence of special talent, advanced placement or honors courses, and parents' or siblings' attendance at the school.

Procedure: Freshmen are admitted to all sessions. Application deadlines are open. Notification is sent on a rolling basis.

Transfer: There were 133 transfer students who enrolled in 1993–94. Applicants must have a minimum GPA of 2.0 in a recommended 24 credit hours earned. A total of 30 credits out of 128 must be completed at Avila.

Visiting: There are regularly scheduled orientations for prospective students. There are guides for informal visits, and visitors may sit in on classes and stay overnight at the school. To arrange for a visit, contact James E. Millard, Director of Admissions, at (816) 942–8400, ext. 203.

Financial Aid: In 1993–94, 96% of all current freshmen and 85% of continuing students received some form of financial aid. About 83% of freshmen and 70% of continuing students received need-based aid. The average freshman award was $8725. Of that total, scholarships or need-based grants averaged $5400 ($12,960 maximum); loans averaged $3054 ($6625 maximum); and work contracts averaged $1275. Ten percent of undergraduate students work part-time. Average earnings from campus work for the school year are $1000. The average financial indebtedness of the 1992–93 graduate was $8100. The FAF, FFS, or SFS and the FAFSA are required.

International Students: There are currently 52 international students enrolled. The school actively recruits these students. They must take the TOEFL and achieve a minimum score of 550.

Computers: The college provides computer facilities for student use. The mainframe is a Prime 2755 for administrative use. There are 34 IBM PS/2 and IBM-compatibles and 15 Apple Macintosh microcomputers located in computer laboratories, residence halls, and the library. All students may access the system. There are no time limits on using the system and no fees.

Graduates: In 1992–93, 214 bachelor's degrees were awarded. The most popular majors among graduates were information science (7%), general management (7%), and elementary education (5%). Within an average freshman class, 34% graduate in 4 years, 48% in 5 years, and 49% in 6 years. In the 1992 graduating class, 10% of all students were enrolled in graduate school within 6 months of graduation; 96% had found employment.

Admissions Contact: James E. Millard, Director of Admissions.

BARNES COLLEGE
D-2

St. Louis, MO 63110   (314) 362–4429

Full-time: 66 men, 389 women	Faculty: 37
Part-time: none	Ph.D.s: 10%
Graduate: none	Student/Faculty: 12 to 1
Year: semesters, summer session	Tuition: $6400
Application Deadline: open	Room: $600-$1500
Freshman Class: 265 applied, 161 accepted, 110 enrolled	
ACT: 21	**VERY COMPETITIVE**

Barnes College, founded in 1989, is a private, coeducational institution offering a program leading to the Bachelor of Science in Nursing degree. Computerized library sources and services include the card catalog, interlibrary loans, and database searching. Special learning facilities include a learning resource center and a nursing arts laboratory. The 2-acre campus is in an urban area. Including residence halls, there is 1 building on campus.

Student Life: About 95% of undergraduates are from Missouri. Students come from 2 foreign countries. Ninety-two percent are white. The average age of freshmen is 21; all undergraduates, 23. Eight percent drop out by the end of their first year; 80% remain to graduate.

Housing: A total of 7090 students can be accommodated in college housing. College-sponsored living facilities include coed dormitories. On-campus housing is guaranteed for all 4 years. Seventy percent of students live on campus; of those, 50% remain on campus on weekends. Alcohol is not permitted. All students may keep cars on campus.

Activities: There are no fraternities or sororities on campus. There are 2 groups on campus, including student government. Popular campus events include Student Nurse Week and Spring Dinner Dance.

Sports: There is no sports program at Barnes College.

Disabled Students: The following facilities are available: wheelchair ramps and elevators.

Services: In addition to many counseling and information services, tutoring is available in every subject. There is also remedial math and writing.

Campus Safety and Security: Campus safety and security measures include self defense education, shuttle buses, and informal discussions.

Programs of Study: Barnes College awards the B.S.N. degree. Bachelor's degrees are awarded in HEALTH PROFESSIONS (nursing).

Required: Students must earn at least 126 credit hours with a minimum GPA of 2.0. All students must complete 58 credit hours in required general education courses, and 68 in nursing.

Faculty/Classroom: Eight percent of faculty are male; 92%, female. All teach undergraduates. The average class size in an introductory lecture is 40.

Admissions: About 60% of the 1993–94 applicants were accepted. About 40% of the current freshmen were in the top fifth of their class; 70% were in the top two fifths.

Requirements: Barnes College requires applicants to be in the upper 33% of their class. A minimum GPA of 3.0 is required. The ACT is required. AP and CLEP credits are accepted. Important factors used in the admissions decision are advanced placement or honor courses, leadership record, parents or siblings attending the school, recommendations by school officials, and recommendations by alumni. A college honor society is available to students with a minimum 3.5 GPA.

Procedure: Freshmen are admitted fall and spring. Entrance exams should be taken during fall of senior year. Application deadlines are open. The application fee is $25. Notification is sent on a rolling basis. A waiting list is an active part of the admissions procedure, with about 25% of applicants on the list.

Transfer: Twelve transfer students enrolled in 1993–94. A total of 30 credits out of 126 must be completed at Barnes College.

Visiting: There are regularly scheduled orientations for prospective students, including an open house program. There are guides for informal visits and visitors may sit in on classes. To arrange for a visit, contact the Dean of Students at (314) 362–4429.

Financial Aid: In 1993–94, 70% of all students received some form of financial aid. About 65% of students received need-based aid. All undergraduate students work part-time. Barnes College is a member of CSS. The FAF, FFS or SFS is required.

International Students: There are currently 2 international students enrolled. The student must take the ACT.

Computers: The college provides computer facilities for student use. All students may access the system 24 hours daily. There are no time limits and no fees.

Graduates: In 1992–93, 26 bachelor's degrees were awarded. Within an average freshman class, 10% graduate in 3 years and 80% in 4 years.

Admissions Contact: Steve Turner, Ph.D., Dean of Students.

CENTRAL METHODIST COLLEGE
C-2

Fayette, MO 65248   (816) 248–3391

Full-time: 440 men, 480 women	Faculty: 55; IIB, --$
Part-time: 22 men, 126 women	Ph.D.s: 42%
Graduate: none	Student/Faculty: 17 to 1
Year: 4–1–4, summer session	Tuition: $8040
Application Deadline: August 24	Room & Board: $3370
Freshman Class: 677 applied, 549 accepted, 240 enrolled	
ACT: 21	**COMPETITIVE**

Central Methodist College, founded in 1855, is a private liberal arts institution affiliated with the Methodist Church. In addition to regional accreditation, CMC has baccalaureate program accreditation with NASM. The library contains 100,000 volumes and 4700 microform items, and subscribes to 200 periodicals. Computerized library sources and services include interlibrary loans and database searching. Special learning facilities include a learning resource center, natural history museum, and observatory. The 52-acre campus is in a small town 30 miles northwest of Columbia. Including residence halls, there are 22 buildings on campus.

Student Life: About 90% of undergraduates are from Missouri. Students come from 17 states and 5 foreign countries. Ninety-six percent are from public schools; 4% from private. Ninety-two percent are white. Seventy percent are Protestant; 16% claim no religious affiliation; 14% Catholic. The average age of freshmen is 18; all undergraduates, 23. Thirty-three percent drop out by the end of their first year.

Housing: A total of 850 students can be accommodated in college housing. College-sponsored living facilities include single-sex dormitories, off-campus apartments, and married-student housing. On-campus housing is guaranteed for all 4 years. Seventy-five percent of students live on campus; of those, 60% remain on campus on weekends. Alcohol is not permitted. All students may keep cars on campus.

Activities: About 40% of men belong to 6 local fraternities; about 40% of women belong to 5 local sororities. There are 30 groups on campus, including band, cheerleading, choir, chorale, chorus, computers, drama, drill team, honors, jazz band, literary magazine, marching band, newspaper, pep band, photography, political, professional, religious, social, social service, student government, and yearbook. Popular campus events include Music Festival and Homecoming.

Sports: There are 9 intercollegiate and 10 intramural sports each for men and women. Athletic and recreation facilities include a field house with a 2000-seat gymnasium, playing fields, and a recreation center.

Disabled Students: Sixty-five percent of the campus is accessible to disabled students. The following facilities are available: wheelchair ramps, elevators, special parking, specially equipped rest rooms, and lowered drinking fountains.

Services: In addition to many counseling and information services, tutoring is available in most subjects. In addition, there is remedial math, reading, and writing.

Campus Safety and Security: Campus safety and security measures include 24-hour foot and vehicle patrol, escort service, informal discussions, and pamphlets, posters, and films. In addition, there are lighted pathways and sidewalks.

Programs of Study: CMC awards the B.A., B.S., B.M., B.M.E., B.S.E., and B.S.N. degrees. Associate degrees also are awarded. Bachelor's degrees are awarded in BIOLOGICAL SCIENCE (biology/biological science), BUSINESS (accounting and business administration and management), COMMUNICATIONS AND THE ARTS (communications, dramatic arts, English, French, German, languages, music, music history and appreciation, and music theory and composition), COMPUTER AND PHYSICAL SCIENCE (chemistry, computer science, and mathematics), EDUCATION (early childhood, elementary, foreign languages, middle school, physical, science, secondary, and social science), HEALTH PROFESSIONS (nursing), SOCIAL SCIENCE (community services, economics, history, philosophy, political science/government, prelaw, psychology, religion, and social science). Sciences, music, preprofessional programs, and education are the strongest academically. Business and education have the largest enrollments.

Required: To graduate, students must complete 124 to 131 credit hours, including 15 to 40 in the major, depending on the degree sought. A minimum GPA of 2.0 is required for all but the B.S.E. and B.M.E. programs, which require a 2.5. Students must complete 48 hours of a core curriculum, demonstrate computer literacy, and take courses in physical education, religion/philosophy, and freshman orientation to college life.

Special: CMC offers cooperative programs in medical technology and physical therapy, and 3–2 engineering degrees with the University of Missouri at Rolla, the University of Evansville, Stanford University, and Washington University at St. Louis. Work-study programs, internships, study abroad in France, Germany, and Spain, dual majors, a general studies degree, and nondegree study are also available. There is a freshman honors program on campus, as well as 10 national honor societies.

Faculty/Classroom: Fifty-eight percent of faculty are male; 42%, female. All teach undergraduates. The average class size in an introductory lecture is 45; in a laboratory, 32; and in a regular course offering, 20.

Admissions: About 81% of the 1993–94 applicants were accepted. The ACT scores for the 1993–94 freshman class were as follows: 57% below 21, 20% between 21 and 23, 16% between 24 and 26, 4% between 27 and 28, and 3% above 28. About 29% of the current freshmen were in the top fifth of their class; 51% were in the top two fifths. Seven freshmen graduated first in their class.

Requirements: CMC requires applicants to be in the upper 75% of their class. A minimum GPA of 2.0 is required. The ACT is recommended, with a minimum score of 18 is advised. Those students with a GPA lower than 2.0 may write a letter of appeal and have an interview. Applicants should be graduates of an accredited secondary school or have a GED certificate. Recommended preparatory courses include 4 units of English, 3 of mathematics, and 2 each of science, social studies, and humanities. CLEP credit is accepted. Important factors used in the admissions decision are advanced placement or honor courses, evidence of special talent, parents or siblings attending the school, leadership record, and extracurricular activities record.

Procedure: Freshmen are admitted fall, winter, and summer. Early decision applications should be filed by December 31; regular applications, by August 24 for fall entry, January 18 for winter entry, and June 7 for summer entry, along with an application fee of $10. Notification is sent on a rolling basis. There are early decision, early admissions, and deferred admissions plans. Fifteen early decision candidates were accepted for the 1993–94 class.

Transfer: A total of 83 transfer students enrolled in 1993–94. Applicants must be in good academic standing at their previous college. A total of 30 credits out of 124 to 131 must be completed at CMC.

Visiting: There are regularly scheduled orientations for prospective students, including a campus tour and visits with faculty members. There are guides for informal visits and visitors may sit in on classes and stay overnight at the school. To arrange for a visit, contact Admissions/Student Affairs at (816) 248-3391.

Financial Aid: In 1993–94, 98% of all current freshmen and 90% of continuing students received some form of financial aid. About 76% of freshmen and 78% of continuing students received need-based aid. The average freshman award was $8000. Of that total, scholarships or need-based grants averaged $4875; loans averaged $2625 (maximum); and work contracts averaged $500 (maximum). Thirty-four percent of undergraduate students work part-time. Average earnings from campus work for the school year are $700. The average financial indebtedness of the 1992–93 graduate was $8000.

CMC is a member of CSS. The FFS is required. The deadline for financial aid applications is April 1.

International Students: There are currently 18 international students enrolled. The school actively recruits these students. They must take the TOEFL and achieve a minimum score of 550.

Computers: The college provides computer facilities for student use. The mainframes are a DEC VAX 3100 and an IBM 80. There are also 24 terminals and 50 microcomputers available throughout the campus. All students may access the system. It may be used during laboratory hours on an hourly basis. The fees are $100 per year.

Graduates: In a recent year, 110 bachelor's degrees were awarded. The most popular majors among graduates were elementary education (8%), business administration (7%), and nursing (6%). Some 25 companies recruited on campus. In an earlier graduating class, 21% of the men and 5% of the women were enrolled in graduate school within 6 months of graduation; 53% of the men and 74% of the women had found employment.

Admissions Contact: Office of Admissions.

CENTRAL MISSOURI STATE UNIVERSITY
B-2

Warrensburg, MO 64093
(816) 543-4290

Full-time: 3925 men, 4169 women	Faculty: 454; IIA, -$
Part-time: 758 men, 838 women	Ph.D.s: 70%
Graduate: 649 men, 943 women	Student/Faculty: 18 to 1
Year: semesters, summer session	Tuition: $2160 ($4320)
Application Deadline: open	Room & Board: $2978
Freshman Class: 4681 applied, 4101 accepted, 1613 enrolled	
ACT: 21	**LESS COMPETITIVE**

Central Missouri State University, founded in 1871, is a public liberal arts institution offering a comprehensive range of degree programs. There are 4 undergraduate schools and one graduate school. In addition to regional accreditation, Central has baccalaureate program accreditation with AHEA, CSWE, NASAD, NASM, NCATE, and NLN. The library contains 1,938,795 volumes, 1,115,161 microform items, and 13,461 audiovisual forms, and subscribes to 2870 periodicals. Computerized library sources and services include the card catalog, interlibrary loans, and database searching. Special learning facilities include a learning resource center, art gallery, radio station, TV station, and an instructional airport, a 200-acre farm, a driving/safety range, a speech and hearing clinic, and a child development laboratory. The 1052-acre campus is in a small town 50 miles southeast of Kansas City. Including residence halls, there are 50 buildings on campus.

Student Life: About 93% of undergraduates are from Missouri. Students come from 43 states, 56 foreign countries, and Canada. Ninety-four percent are from public schools; 6% from private. Eighty-seven percent are white. Fifty-eight percent are Protestant; 16% claim no religious affiliation; 15% are Catholic. The average age of all undergraduates is 22.7. Forty percent drop out by the end of their first year; 40% remain to graduate.

Housing: A total of 4482 students can be accommodated in college housing. College-sponsored living facilities include single-sex and coed dormitories, on-campus apartments, off-campus apartments, married-student housing, fraternity houses, and sorority houses. In addition there are honors houses, special interest houses, and quiet dormitories. On-campus housing is guaranteed for all 4 years. Sixty-nine percent of students commute. All students may keep cars on campus.

Activities: About 12% of men belong to 14 national fraternities; about 11% of women belong to 12 national sororities. There are 197 groups on campus, including art, band, cheerleading, chess, choir, chorale, chorus, computers, dance, drama, drill team, ethnic, gay, honors, international, jazz band, marching band, newspaper, opera, orchestra, pep band, photography, political, professional, radio and TV, religious, social, social service, student government, symphony, and yearbook. Popular campus events include Homecoming, Commencement, Parents Weekends, Greek Week, Black History Month, Madrigal Dinner, and arts events.

Sports: There are 8 intercollegiate sports for men and 6 for women, and 32 intramural sports for men and 21 for women. Athletic and recreation facilities include a 12,000-seat stadium, 3 gymnasiums, baseball and softball fields, a bowling alley, tennis courts, practice fields, and a multipurpose building that contains a swimming pool, weight rooms, and courts for basketball, racquetball, and volleyball. Pertle Springs, an outdoor recreation area, has an 18-hole golf course and facilities for swimming and other activities.

Disabled Students: Ninety-five percent of the campus is accessible to disabled students. The following facilities are available: wheelchair ramps, elevators, special parking, specially equipped rest rooms, special class scheduling, lowered drinking fountains, and lowered telephones.

Services: In addition to many counseling and information services, tutoring is available in every subject for fees. There is also a developmental reader service for the blind, and developmental remedial math, reading, and writing available.

Campus Safety and Security: Campus safety and security measures include 24-hour foot and vehicle patrol, self defense education, escort service, and informal discussions. In addition, there are pamphlets, posters, films, emergency telephones, and lighted pathways and sidewalks.

Programs of Study: Central awards the B.A., B.S., B.F.A., B.M., B.M.E., B.S.B.A., and B.S.Ed. degrees. Associate and master's degrees also are awarded. Bachelor's degrees are awarded in AGRICULTURE (agricultural business management, agricultural economics, and conservation and regulation), BIOLOGICAL SCIENCE (biology/biological science), BUSINESS (accounting, banking and finance, business administration and management, fashion merchandising, hotel/motel and restaurant management, marketing/retailing/merchandising, and personnel management), COMMUNICATIONS AND THE ARTS (broadcasting, communications, design, dramatic arts, English, film arts, fine arts, French, German, journalism, music, photography, public relations, Spanish, and speech/debate/rhetoric), COMPUTER AND PHYSICAL SCIENCE (actuarial science, chemistry, computer science, earth science, information sciences and systems, mathematics, and physics), EDUCATION (art, business, early childhood, elementary, foreign languages, home economics, industrial arts, middle school, music, science, secondary, special, and teaching English as a second language/foreign language), ENGINEERING AND ENVIRONMENTAL DESIGN (drafting and design, electrical/electronics engineering technology, engineering technology, graphic arts technology, industrial administration/management, manufacturing technology, and transportation technology), HEALTH PROFESSIONS (medical laboratory technology, nursing, predentistry, premedicine, and speech pathology/audiology), SOCIAL SCIENCE (criminal justice, dietetics, economics, geography, history, parks and recreation management, political science/government, prelaw, psychology, social science, social work, and sociology). Curriculum and instruction, criminal justice administration, management, power and transportation, mass communication, and accounting have the largest enrollments.

Required: To graduate, students must complete 124 hours, including 30 to 80 hours in the major, with a minimum GPA of 2.0. General education requirements include a total of 38 to 42 hours in humanities, social sciences, multicultural studies, technology, English and oral communications, mathematics, science, and individual development.

Special: Central offers cross-registration with the Kansas City Regional Council for Higher Education, credit and noncredit internships, study abroad in Europe, a B.A.-B.S. degree, dual and student-designed majors, credit for military service, pass/fail options, nondegree study, and a 3–2 engineering degree with the University of Missouri at Columbia and at Rolla and with the University of Kansas. There is a freshman honors program on campus, as well as 24 national honor societies.

Faculty/Classroom: Sixty-eight percent of faculty are male; 32%, female. The average class size in an introductory lecture is 35.

Admissions: About 88% of the 1993–94 applicants were accepted. The ACT scores for the 1993–94 freshman class were as follows: 55% below 21, 24% between 21 and 23, 13% between 24 and 26, 4% between 27 and 28, and 2% above 28. About 25% of the current freshmen were in the top fifth of their class; 53% were in the top two fifths. There were 2 National Merit finalists. About 5 freshmen graduated first in their class.

Requirements: Central requires applicants to be in the upper 66% of their class. The SAT I or ACT is required. Applicants must have completed 12 academic credits, including 3 in English with a writing emphasis and 2 each in mathematics, science, and social science, as well as 3 in academic electives. A foreign language and mathematics beyond algebra are recommended. AP and CLEP credits are accepted. Important factors used in the admissions decision are recommendations by alumni, advanced placement or honor courses, recommendations by school officials, extracurricular activities record, and evidence of special talents.

Procedure: Application deadlines are open. Notification is sent on a rolling basis. There are early admissions and deferred admissions plans.

Transfer: About 987 transfer students enrolled in 1993–94. Applicants must have a minimum GPA of 2.0, as indicated by an official college transcript. A total of 30 credits out of 124 must be completed at Central.

Visiting: There are regularly scheduled orientations for prospective students, including freshman orientations, which are scheduled during the summer months and are held in a two-day forum. There are guides for informal visits and visitors may sit in on classes and stay overnight at the school. To arrange for a visit, contact the Office of Admissions at (816) 543-4290.

Financial Aid: In 1993–94 71% of all current freshmen and 71% of continuing students received some form of financial aid. Nineteen percent of undergraduate students work part-time. Average earnings from campus work for the school year are $1200. The average financial indebtedness of the 1992–93 graduate was $7500. The SFS is required. The deadline for financial aid applications is March 1.

International Students: There are currently 394 international students enrolled. They must take the TOEFL and achieve a minimum score of 500.

Computers: The college provides computer facilities for student use. The mainframe is an IBM 4381 and an ES 9000 9121 Model 210. There are 150 terminals in the 2 mainframe laboratories, as well as 871 microcomputers in various buildings. All students may access the system. It may be used from 7:30 A.M. to 1 A.M. There are no time limits and no fees.

Graduates: In 1992–93 1641 bachelor's degrees were awarded. The most popular majors among graduates were curriculum and instruction (11%), management (9%), and criminal justice (7%). Within an average freshman class, 40% graduate in 4 years and 40% in 6 years. Some 111 companies recruited on campus in 1992–93. In the 1992 graduating class, 6% enrolled in graduate school within 6 months of graduation and 51% found employment within 6 months of graduation.

Admissions Contact: Delores Hudson, Director of Admissions.

COLLEGE OF THE OZARKS
B-4

Point Lookout, MO 65726

(417) 334–6411, ext. 4219
(800) 222–0525 (out-of-state)

Full-time: 590 men, 687 women	**Faculty:** 86; IIB, av$
Part-time: 83 men, 112 women	**Ph.D.s:** 53%
Graduate: none	**Student/Faculty:** 15 to 1
Year: semesters	**Tuition:** $100
Application Deadline: open	**Room & Board:** $1900
Freshman Class: 3258 applied, 430 accepted, 418 enrolled	
ACT: 21	**COMPETITIVE**

College of the Ozarks, founded in 1906, is a private, coeducational liberal arts college affiliated with the Presbyterian Church. Instead of paying tuition, students work a total of 560 hours in campus jobs and are responsible only for room and board, books, personal expenses, and an incidental fee of $100. In addition to regional accreditation, C of O has baccalaureate program accreditation with NCATE. The library contains 100,000 volumes, 15,345 microform items, and 3752 audiovisual forms, and subscribes to 797 periodicals. Computerized library sources and services include interlibrary loans and database searching. Special learning facilities include a learning resource center, art gallery, planetarium, radio station, a museum, mill, weaving studio, an airport, a firehouse, print shop, orchid greenhouses, fruitcake/jelly kitchens, and 3 farm operations. The 960-acre campus is in a small town 40 miles south of Springfield. Including residence halls, there are 82 buildings on campus.

Student Life: About 67% of undergraduates are from Missouri. Students come from 42 states and 23 foreign countries. Ninety-seven percent are from public schools. Ninety-five percent are white. Fifty-five percent are Protestant; 31% claim no religious affiliation; 10% Catholic. The average age of freshmen is 19; all undergraduates, 21. Twenty percent drop out by the end of their first year; 80% remain to graduate.

Housing: A total of 1031 students can be accommodated in college housing. College-sponsored living facilities include single-sex dormitories. In addition, student members of the volunteer fire department have living facilities in the campus fire station. On-campus housing is guaranteed for all 4 years. Seventy percent of students live on campus; of those, 80% remain on campus on weekends. Alcohol is not permitted. All students may keep cars on campus.

Activities: There are no fraternities or sororities on campus. There are 44 groups on campus, including art, band, cheerleading, chess, choir, chorale, computers, dance, department/major clubs, drama, drill team, international, jazz band, literary magazine, musical theater, newspaper, pep band, photography, political, professional, radio and tv, religious, social service, student government, and yearbook. Popular campus events include Homecoming, Fourth of July, lectures, concerts, Barnwarming, Christmas Open House, art exhibits, theater productions, and graduation.

Sports: There are 2 intercollegiate sports for men and 2 for women, and 6 intramural sports for men and 6 for women. Athletic and recreation facilities include an all-weather track, softball and baseball fields, tennis courts, volleyball, badminton and table tennis facilities, and a field house with a 4500-seat gymnasium, 3 basketball courts, an Olympic-size pool, a weight training room, racquetball courts, and a dance studio.

Disabled Students: Ninety percent of the campus is accessible to disabled students. The following facilities are available: wheelchair ramps, elevators, special parking, and specially equipped rest rooms.

Services: In addition to many counseling and information services, tutoring is available in some subjects, including mathematics and foreign language. There is also a Center for Writing and Thinking. Remedial math is also available.

Campus Safety and Security: Campus safety and security measures include 24-hour foot and vehicle patrol, informal discussions, pamphlets, posters, films, and lighted pathways and sidewalks. In addition, there is a 24-hour paramedic service on campus.

Programs of Study: C of O awards the B.A. and B.S. degrees. Bachelor's degrees are awarded in AGRICULTURE (agriculture), BIOLOGICAL SCIENCE (biology/biological science), BUSINESS (accounting, business administration and management, and hotel/motel and restaurant management), COMMUNICATIONS AND THE ARTS (communications, English, music, and theater design), COMPUTER AND PHYSICAL SCIENCE (chemistry, computer science, and mathematics), EDUCATION (art, elementary/secondary, foreign languages, home economics, industrial arts, and physical), ENGINEERING AND ENVIRONMENTAL DESIGN (aeronautical science and graphic arts technology), HEALTH PROFESSIONS (nursing), SOCIAL SCIENCE (criminal justice, dietetics, history, philosophy, political science/government, psychology, and sociology). Business administration, sciences, history, psychology, and education are the strongest academically. Business administration has the largest enrollment.

Required: General education requirements include specific courses in English, speech, religion, history and political science, mathematics, and physical education. Students must also select courses from an arts and letters, social science, and physical science distribution. B.A. candidates must complete 8 credit hours of foreign language, and B.S. candidates must complete 6 to 8 credit hours of additional physical science or mathematics. In order to graduate, all students must complete at least 124 credit hours, including 36 upper level and 30 in a major field, with a minimum GPA of 2.0.

Special: The college offers study abroad in the Netherlands, summer internships through numerous departments, work-study programs with Silver Dollar City, a 3–2 engineering degree program, student-designed interdisciplinary majors, and credit for military experience. Pass/fail grading is allowed for proficiency exams. There are 4 national honor societies on campus. Six departments have honors programs.

Faculty/Classroom: Seventy percent of faculty are male; 30%, female. All teach undergraduates. The average class size in an introductory lecture is 35; in a laboratory, 18; and in a regular course offering, 18.

Admissions: About 13% of the 1993–94 applicants were accepted. About 50% of the current freshmen were in the top fifth of their class; 80% were in the top two fifths.

Requirements: The SAT I or ACT is required. Applicants must be graduates of accredited secondary schools or have earned a GED. A physical examination and 2 recommendations (preferably from school personnel) are also required, and an interview is recommended. CLEP credit is accepted. Important factors used in the admissions decision are parents or siblings attending the school, recommendations by school officials, leadership record, recommendations by alumni, and evidence of special talent.

Procedure: Freshmen are admitted fall and spring. Entrance exams should be taken in October or December of the senior year. Application deadlines are open. Notification is sent on a rolling basis two weeks after application is reviewed. A waiting list is an active part of the admissions procedure, with about 55% of applicants on the list.

Transfer: About 92 transfer students enrolled in 1993–94. Transfer applicants must present a minimum GPA of 2.0 and may not have a previous disciplinary or loan default record. The ACT is required if the applicant has completed fewer than 31 credit hours. An interview is recommended. The dean of students at transfer college must complete a form attesting to the positive character of the applicant. All transfer students must submit a financial aid transcript. A total of 45 credits, including the final 24 credit hours, out of 124 must be completed at C of O.

Visiting: There are regularly scheduled orientations for prospective students, including College Days, an orientation provided for local area high schools. There are guides for informal visits and visitors may sit in on classes. To arrange for a visit, contact Janet Miller at (800) 222-0525.

Financial Aid: All students received need-based aid. The average freshman award was $8750. Of that total, scholarships or need-based grants averaged $6370 ($8770 maximum); and work contracts averaged $2380 (maximum). All undergraduate students work part-time. Average earnings from campus work for the school year are $2380. The average financial indebtedness of the 1992–93 graduate was $1200. The FAFSA financial statement is required. The deadline for financial aid applications is April 1.

International Students: There are currently 26 international students enrolled. They must take the TOEFL and achieve a minimum score of 550 or they may substitute ACT or SAT I scores.

Computers: The college provides computer facilities for student use. The mainframe is an IBM 4361. There are 30 Apple Macintosh and IBM XT and PS/2 microcomputers available in various laboratories and 20 word processing workstations at the Center for Writing and Thinking. Those students enrolled in computer science courses or

working in laboratories may access the system. It may be used from 8 A.M. to 10 P.M. There are no time limits and no fees.

Graduates: In 1992–93, 222 bachelor's degrees were awarded. The most popular majors among graduates were business and management (20%), elementary education (18%), and psychology (10%). Within an average freshman class, 70% graduate in 5 years. Some 400 companies recruited on campus in an earlier year. In a recent year's graduating class, 8% of the men and 6% of the women were enrolled in graduate school within 6 months of graduation; 96% of the men and 94% of the women had found employment.

Admissions Contact: Dr. Glen Cameron, Dean of Admissions.

COLUMBIA COLLEGE
C-2
Columbia, MO 65216

(314) 875-7352
(800) 231-2391 (out-of-state)

Full-time: 290 men, 400 women	**Faculty:** IIB, --$
Part-time: 85 men, 61 women	**Ph.D.s:** 65%
Graduate: none	**Student/Faculty:** 15 to 1
Year: semesters, summer session	**Tuition:** $8295
Application Deadline: open	**Room & Board:** $3700
Freshman Class: 495 applied, 273 accepted, 254 enrolled	
ACT: 21	**COMPETITIVE**

Columbia College, founded in 1851, is a private liberal arts institution affiliated with the Disciples of Christ. In addition to regional accreditation, Columbia has baccalaureate program accreditation with CSWE. The library contains 71,800 volumes, 19,336 microform items, and 2000 audiovisual forms, and subscribes to 410 periodicals. Computerized library sources and services include interlibrary loans and database searching. Special learning facilities include a learning resource center and an art gallery. The 39-acre campus is in a small town midway between St. Louis and Kansas City. Including residence halls, there are 13 buildings on campus.

Student Life: About 75% of undergraduates are from Missouri. Students come from 28 states, 18 foreign countries, and Canada. Seventy-six percent are white; 14% African American. Fifty-four percent are Protestant; 33% Catholic; 10% Jewish. The average age of freshmen is 19; all undergraduates, 22. Twelve percent drop out by the end of their first year; 46% remain to graduate.

Housing: A total of 326 students can be accommodated in college housing. College-sponsored living facilities include single-sex and coed dormitories. On-campus housing is guaranteed for all 4 years. Sixty-four percent of students commute. Alcohol is not permitted. All students may keep cars on campus.

Activities: About 3% of men belong to 1 national fraternity. There are no sororities on campus. There are 25 groups on campus, including art, cheerleading, choir, chorale, computers, drill team, honors, international, jazz band, newspaper, pep band, photography, political, professional, religious, social service, student government, and yearbook. Popular campus events include International Student Festival and holiday dances.

Sports: There are 3 intercollegiate sports for men and 2 for women, and 16 intramural sports each for men and women. Athletic and recreation facilities include a 650-seat gymnasium, softball and soccer fields, an indoor pool, a dance studio, tennis courts, and an exercise/weight room.

Disabled Students: Fifty percent of the campus is accessible to disabled students. The following facilities are available: wheelchair ramps, special parking, specially equipped rest rooms, special class scheduling, and lowered drinking fountains and telephones.

Services: In addition to many counseling and information services, tutoring is available in most subjects, including accounting, college algebra, psychology, and others as requested. There is remedial math and writing.

Campus Safety and Security: Campus safety and security measures include 24-hour foot and vehicle patrol, escort service, informal discussions, and pamphlets, posters, films. In addition, there are emergency telephones and lighted pathways and sidewalks.

Programs of Study: Columbia awards the B.A., B.S., B.A.I.S., B.F.A., and B.S.W. degrees. Associate degrees also are awarded. Bachelor's degrees are awarded in BIOLOGICAL SCIENCE (biology/biological science), BUSINESS (accounting, banking and finance, business administration and management, marketing/retailing/merchandising, real estate, and transportation and travel marketing), COMMUNICATIONS AND THE ARTS (advertising, art, English, fine arts, and illustration), COMPUTER AND PHYSICAL SCIENCE (chemistry and computer programming), EDUCATION (art, business, elementary, science, and secondary), HEALTH PROFESSIONS (predentistry and premedicine), SOCIAL SCIENCE (criminal justice, fashion design and technology, history, prelaw, psychology, and social work). Art, history/government, fashion, and education are the strongest programs academically. Business administration has the largest enrollment.

Required: To graduate, students must complete 120 semester hours, including 40 to 70 in the major, with a minimum GPA of 2.0. Distribution requirements include 18 hours in humanities, 9 in social science and basic skills such as English composition and computers, and 8 in mathematics and science.

Special: Columbia offers cross-registration through the Mid-Missouri Associated Colleges and Universities, internships, study abroad at the University of Bradford in England, a Washington semester, B.A.-B.S. degrees in business and criminal justice, an individual-studies degree, student-designed and dual majors, credit for life experience, nondegree study, and pass/fail options. There is a freshman honors program on campus, as well as 4 national honor societies. Ten departments have honors programs.

Faculty/Classroom: Fifty-two percent of faculty are male; 48%, female. All teach undergraduates. The average class size in an introductory lecture is 25; in a laboratory, 15; and in a regular course offering, 20.

Admissions: About 55% of the 1993–94 applicants were accepted. Six freshmen graduated first in their class.

Requirements: A minimum GPA of 2.0 is required. The SAT I or ACT (preferred) is required. In addition, applicants must be graduates of an accredited secondary school or have a GED certificate. AP and CLEP credits are accepted. Important factors used in the admissions decision are leadership record, advanced placement or honor courses, evidence of special talent, ability to finance college education, and extracurricular activities record.

Procedure: Freshmen are admitted to all sessions. Entrance exams should be taken in the spring of the junior year or the fall of the senior year. The application deadlines are open. Application fee is $25. Notification is sent on a rolling basis. There are early admissions and deferred admissions plans.

Transfer: About 105 transfer students enrolled in an earlier year. Transfer applicants must have a minimum GPA of 2.0 and must submit a high school transcript and ACT scores with their application. A total of 24 credits out of 120 must be completed at Columbia.

Visiting: There are regularly scheduled orientations for prospective students, including a campus tour, a workshop in financial aid, an academic/organization fair, a luncheon, and a fashion show. There are guides for informal visits and visitors may sit in on classes and stay overnight at the school. To arrange for a visit, contact the Admissions Office at (800) 231–2391, ext. 7352.

Financial Aid: In an earlier year, 30% of all current freshmen and 33% of continuing students received some form of financial aid. Loans averaged $2625 (maximum); and work contracts averaged $1000 (maximum). Seventy-five percent of undergraduate students work part-time. The average financial indebtedness of an earlier graduate was $7200. Columbia is a member of CSS. The FAF, FFS, or SFS and the college's own financial statement are required. The deadline for financial aid applications is January 31 for full tuition and room and board scholarship consideration and April 30 for all other aid.

International Students: There were 39 international students enrolled in an earlier year. The school actively recruits these students. They must take the TOEFL and achieve a minimum score of 500.

Computers: The college provides computer facilities for student use. The mainframe is a DEC VAX 3300. There are terminals located in the computer laboratory and the library. All students may access the system from 8 A.M. to 10 P.M. in the computer laboratory. There are no time limits on using the system. The fee is $35.

Graduates: In a recent year, 200 bachelor's degrees were awarded. Within an average freshman class, 35% graduate in 4 years and 45% in 5 years.

Admissions Contact: Ron Cronacher, Director of Admissions.

CULVER-STOCKTON COLLEGE

C-1

Canton, MO 63435   (314) 288–5637; (800) 537–1883 (out-of-state)

Full-time: 360 men, 632 women	Faculty: 55; IIB, --$
Part-time: 28 men, 82 women	Ph.D.s: 60%
Graduate: none	Student/Faculty: 18 to 1
Year: semesters, summer session	Tuition: $7650
Application Deadline: May 1	Room & Board: $3500
Freshman Class: 1576 applied, 1110 accepted, 275 enrolled	
ACT: 22	**COMPETITIVE**

Culver-Stockton College, established in 1853, is a private liberal arts institution affiliated with the Disciples of Christ. The library contains 132,260 volumes, 4719 microform items, and 1987 audiovisual forms, and subscribes to 867 periodicals. Special learning facilities include a learning resource center, art gallery, rare books collection, performing arts center, publications laboratory, and writing center. The 143-acre campus is in a rural area 125 miles north of St. Louis. Including residence halls, there are 19 buildings on campus.

Student Life: About 53% of undergraduates are from Missouri. Students come from 26 states and 5 foreign countries. Ninety-three percent are from public schools; 7% from private. Ninety-five percent are

white. Forty-nine percent are Protestant; 27% claim no religious affiliation; 23% Catholic. The average age of freshmen is 18; all undergraduates, 21. Twenty-nine percent drop out by the end of their first year; 47% remain to graduate.

Housing: A total of 700 students can be accommodated in college housing. College-sponsored living facilities include single-sex dormitories and sorority houses. On-campus housing is guaranteed for all 4 years. Fifty-seven percent of students live on campus; of those, 45% remain on campus on weekends. Alcohol is not permitted. All students may keep cars on campus.

Activities: About 48% of men belong to 6 national fraternities; about 27% of women belong to 3 national sororities. There are 40 groups on campus, including art, band, cheerleading, choir, chorus, drama, ethnic, honors, international, jazz band, literary magazine, musical theater, newspaper, opera, pep band, photography, professional, religious, student government, and yearbook. Popular campus events include Homecoming, Spring Formals, Spring Fling, Greek Week, Black History Month, Fall Festival, and Hoop Hysteria.

Sports: There are 6 intercollegiate sports for men and 4 for women, and 12 intramural sports for men and 12 for women. Athletic and recreation facilities include a 3500-seat football/soccer stadium, baseball field, swimming pool, jogging track, dance studio, weight room, and field house with basketball, volleyball, tennis, and racquetball courts.

Disabled Students: Thirty-five percent of the campus is accessible to disabled students. The following facilities are available: wheelchair ramps, elevators, special parking, specially equipped rest rooms, and lowered drinking fountains.

Services: In addition to many counseling and information services, tutoring is available in most subjects. In addition, there is remedial writing.

Campus Safety and Security: Campus safety and security measures include self defense education, escort service, informal discussions, and pamphlets, posters, and films. In addition, there are emergency telephones, lighted pathways and sidewalks, and nighttime security patrol.

Programs of Study: C-SC awards the B.A., B.S., B.F.A., B.M.E., and B.S.N. degrees. Bachelor's degrees are awarded in BIOLOGICAL SCIENCE (biology/biological science), BUSINESS (accounting, business administration and management, and recreational facilities management), COMMUNICATIONS AND THE ARTS (art, arts administration/management, communications, dramatic arts, English, and music), COMPUTER AND PHYSICAL SCIENCE (chemistry and mathematics), EDUCATION (art, drama, education, music, and physical), HEALTH PROFESSIONS (medical technology and nursing), SOCIAL SCIENCE (criminal justice, history, psychology, religion, and sociology). Education and nursing are the strongest academically. Nursing has the largest enrollment.

Required: To graduate, students must complete 124 credit hours, including 26 to 64 in the major, with a minimum GPA of 2.0. Distribution requirements include 3 hours in the fine arts and 6 to 9 each in humanities, natural science, social science, and mathematics and language. Specific English composition, speech, physical education, and Christian heritage courses are required.

Special: A joint-degree program in nursing is available in conjunction with Blessing-Rieman College of Nursing, a 2–2 degree in engineering with the University of Missouri/Rolla, and 3–2 degrees in engineering and in occupational therapy with Washington University at St. Louis. C-SC also offers study abroad, internships, and dual and individualized majors. A course entitled American Heritage is presented in nontraditional 5-week modules. There is a freshman honors program on campus, as well as 1 national honor society. Sixteen departments have honors programs.

Faculty/Classroom: Eighty-three percent of faculty are male; 17%, female. All teach undergraduates. The average class size in an introductory lecture is 25; in a laboratory, 18; and in a regular course offering, 19.

Admissions: About 70% of the 1993–94 applicants were accepted. The ACT scores for the 1993–94 freshman class were as follows: 31% below 21, 33% between 21 and 23, 23% between 24 and 26, 10% between 27 and 28, and 3% above 28. About 46% of the current freshmen were in the top fifth of their class; 78% were in the top two fifths. About 9 freshmen graduated first in their class.

Requirements: C-SC requires applicants to be in the upper 50% of their class. A minimum GPA of 2.0 is required. The ACT is recommended. Secondary school preparation should include 4 years of English, 2 to 4 each in mathematics and science, and 1 to 3 each in history and social studies. AP and CLEP credits are accepted. Important factors used in the admissions decision are advanced placement or honor courses, leadership record, evidence of special talent, extracurricular activities record, and parents or siblings attending the school.

Procedure: Freshmen are admitted fall and spring. Entrance exams should be taken by April of the entering school year. Applications should be filed by May 1 for fall entry and December 1 for spring entry. Notification is sent on a rolling basis.

Transfer: A total of 78 transfer students enrolled in 1993–94. Grades of C or better earned at regionally accredited institutions will be accepted if the work is relevant to the Culver curriculum. No more than 64 semester or 96 quarter hours of credit from a junior college may be transferred. A total of 30 credits out of 124 must be completed at C-SC.

Visiting: There are regularly scheduled orientations for prospective students, including campus tours and meetings with academic professors, students, coaches, extracurricular advisors, financial aid personnel, and a student life panel. There are guides for informal visits and visitors may sit in on classes and stay overnight at the school. To arrange for a visit, contact the Admissions Office at (800) 537–1883.

Financial Aid: In 1993–94, 95% of all current freshmen and 94% of continuing students received some form of financial aid. About 78% of all students received need-based aid. The average freshman award was $8500. Of that total, scholarships or need-based grants averaged $5500 ($10,150 maximum); loans averaged $2625 ($4125 maximum); and work contracts averaged $800 ($1200 maximum). Thirty-five percent of undergraduate students work part-time. Average earnings from campus work for the school year are $800. The average financial indebtedness of the 1992–93 graduate was $9500. C-SC is a member of CSS. The FFS is required. The deadline for financial aid applications is August 1.

International Students: There are currently 10 international students enrolled. The school actively recruits these students. They must take the TOEFL and achieve a minimum score of 500. The college prefers that the student also take the SAT I or ACT.

Computers: The college provides computer facilities for student use. The mainframe is an AS/400. There are 50 Apple and IBM microcomputers available in the library, computer laboratory, and various classroom buildings. All students may access the system. It may be used days, evenings, and sometimes on weekends. There are no time limits on using the system and no fees.

Graduates: In 1992–93, 209 bachelor's degrees were awarded. The most popular majors among graduates were education (23%), business administration (20%), and nursing (16%). Within an average freshman class, 30% graduate in 4 years and 6% in 5 years. Some 25 companies recruited on campus in 1992–93. In the 1992 graduating class, 6% of the men and 3% of the women were enrolled in graduate school within 6 months of graduation; 40% of the men and 53% of the women had found employment.

Admissions Contact: Betty A. Smith, Dean of Admissions.

DEACONESS COLLEGE OF NURSING
D-2

St. Louis, MO 63139   (314) 768–3044

Full-time: 24 men, 255 women
Part-time: 8 men, 104 women
Graduate: none
Year: semesters, summer session
Application Deadline: open
Freshman Class: 447 applied, 266 accepted, 134 enrolled
ACT: 22

Faculty: 19
Ph.D.s: 11%
Student/Faculty: 15 to 1
Tuition: $6160
Room & Board: $3200

VERY COMPETITIVE

Deaconess College of Nursing, established in 1889 and affiliated with the United Church of Christ, is a private college offering professional training in nursing, including an LPN to RN Bridge Program. In addition to regional accreditation, Deaconess has baccalaureate program accreditation with NLN. The library contains 8000 volumes and 130 audiovisual forms, and subscribes to 230 periodicals. Computerized library sources and services include interlibrary loans and database searching. Special learning facilities include a learning resource center, nursing archives, and nursing arts laboratory. The 15-acre campus is in an urban area 4 miles west of downtown St. Louis. Including residence halls, there are 10 buildings on campus.

Student Life: About 72% of undergraduates are from Missouri. Students come from 4 states and 2 foreign countries. Seventy-eight percent are from public schools; 22% from private. Eighty-nine percent are white. Forty-seven percent are Catholic; 38% Protestant; 15% claim no religious affiliation. The average age of freshmen is 20.6; all undergraduates, 23.2. Thirteen percent drop out by the end of their first year; 70% remain to graduate.

Housing: A total of 115 students can be accommodated in college housing. College-sponsored living facilities include single-sex dormitories and on-campus apartments. On-campus housing is guaranteed for all 4 years. Seventy-four percent of students commute. Alcohol is not permitted. All students may keep cars on campus.

Activities: There are no fraternities or sororities on campus. There are 9 groups on campus, including Ambassadors, newspaper, professional, religious, student government, student nurse, and yearbook. Popular campus events include Dedication Ceremony, Halfway Dance, Christmas Tea, Junior/Senior Dance, and Valentine Tea.

Sports: There are 2 intramural sports for men and 2 for women. Athletic and recreation facilities include a gymnasium and a weight room.

Disabled Students: Ninety percent of the campus is accessible to disabled students. The following facilities are available: wheelchair ramps, elevators, special parking, and specially equipped rest rooms.

Services: In addition to many counseling and information services, tutoring is available in some subjects, including sciences and statistics. In addition, there is remedial math, reading, and writing. Each student is assigned to a faculty academic advisor and Concern, which is professional counseling.

Campus Safety and Security: Campus safety and security measures include 24-hour foot and vehicle patrol, escort service, shuttle buses, and informal discussions. In addition, there are pamphlets, posters, and films, emergency telephones, lighted pathways and sidewalks, and a card reader security system.

Programs of Study: Deaconess awards the B.S.N. degree. Associate degrees also are awarded. Bachelor's degrees are awarded in HEALTH PROFESSIONS (nursing).

Required: To graduate with a bachelor's degree, students must complete 128 credit hours, including 59 in nursing courses. General education requirements include 30 hours of mathematics and science, 24 of liberal arts and humanities, and 12 of social science.

Special: Students may opt for credit by examination. A work-study program with Deaconess Hospital and cross registration with Fontbonne College are available.

Faculty/Classroom: Four percent of faculty are male; 96%, female. Ninety-eight percent teach undergraduates and 2% both teach and do research. The average class size in an introductory lecture is 30; in a laboratory, 20; and in a regular course offering, 25.

Admissions: About 59% of the 1993–94 applicants were accepted. The ACT scores for the 1993–94 freshman class were as follows: 33% below 21, 39% between 21 and 23, 21% between 24 and 26, 6% between 27 and 28, and 1% above 28. About 36% of the current freshmen were in the top fifth of their class; 75% were in the top two fifths.

Requirements: Deaconess prefers applicants to be in the upper 33% of their class. A minimum GPA of 2.5 is recommended. A minimum score of 21 is recommended for the ACT. Applicants must be graduates of an accredited secondary school or have a GED certificate. They should have completed 3 years each of mathematics and science and 4 years of English. An essay must be submitted. AP and CLEP credits are accepted. Important factors used in the admissions decision are advanced placement or honor courses, evidence of special talent, recommendations by school officials, recommendations by alumni, and extracurricular activities record.

Procedure: Freshmen are admitted fall and spring. Entrance exams should be taken by December of the senior year. Application deadlines are open. The application fee is $30. Notification is sent within 3 to 4 weeks after receipt of the completed application. A waiting list is an active part of the admissions procedure, with about 26% of applicants on the list.

Transfer: A total of 83 transfer students enrolled in 1993–94. Applicants must have a minimum ACT score of 20. Deaconess prefers a GPA of 2.5 or above in both college and high school course work, as well as academic ranking in the top third of the high school graduating class. A total of 30 credits out of 128 must be completed at Deaconess.

Visiting: There are regularly scheduled orientations for prospective students, consisting of an introduction to the school and program, review curriculum, admissions procedures, financial aid, and tours. There are guides for informal visits and visitors may sit in on classes and stay overnight at the school. To arrange for a visit, contact the Admissions Office at (314) 768–3044.

Financial Aid: In 1993–94, 75% of all current freshmen and 70% of continuing students received some form of financial aid. About 50% of freshmen and 50% of continuing students received need-based aid. The average freshman award was $4500. Of that total, scholarships or need-based grants averaged $1000 ($6000 maximum); loans averaged $1000 ($2000 maximum); and work contracts averaged $800 ($2000 maximum). All undergraduate students work part-time. Average earnings from campus work for the school year are $2000. The average financial indebtedness of the 1992–93 graduate was $10,000. The FAF is required. The deadline for financial aid applications is June 1.

International Students: There are currently 6 international students enrolled. They must take the TOEFL and achieve a minimum score of 500.

Computers: The college provides computer facilities for student use. There are 7 stand-alone PCs in the library and 13 networked PCs in the computer laboratory. All students may access the system. There are no time limits on using the system and no fees.

Graduates: In 1992–93, 31 bachelor's degrees were awarded. Within an average freshman class, 65% graduate in 4 years and 5% in 5 years. Four companies recruited on campus in an earlier year. In the 1992 graduating class, 5% of the women were enrolled in graduate school within 6 months of graduation; all of the students had found employment.

Admissions Contact: Barbara Bizer, Admissions Coordinator.

DEVRY INSTITUTE OF TECHNOLOGY
KANSAS CITY
Kansas City, MO 64131-3626

A-2

(816) 941-2810
(800) 821-3766 (out-of-state)

Full-time: 1206 men, 255 women	Faculty: 61
Part-time: 335 men, 111 women	Ph.D.s: n/av
Graduate: none	Student/Faculty: 24 to 1
Year: trimesters, summer session	Tuition: $5609
Application Deadline: open	Room & Board: n/app
Freshman Class: 991 applied, 912 accepted, 483 enrolled	
SAT I or ACT: see profile	**LESS COMPETITIVE**

The DeVry Institute of Technology/Kansas City, a private coeducational institution founded in 1931, joined the DeVry Institutes in 1969. One of 11 Institutes in the United States and Canada owned by Keller Graduate School of Management, the school offers undergraduate programs in business operations, electronics, engineering, telecommunications, computer information systems, and accounting. In addition to regional accreditation, DeVry has baccalaureate program accreditation with ABET. The library contains 8437 volumes, 91 microform items, and 120 audiovisual forms, and subscribes to 134 periodicals. Computerized library sources and services include the card catalog, interlibrary loans, and database searching. Special learning facilities include a learning resource center and electronics and other laboratories. The 11-acre campus is in a suburban area. There is one building on campus.

Student Life: About 52% of undergraduates are from Missouri. Students come from 8 foreign countries. Eighty-one percent are white; 14% African American. The average age of all undergraduates is 26. Fifty-three percent drop out by the end of their first year; 47% remain to graduate.

Housing: There are no residence halls. College-sponsored living facilities include off-campus apartments. All students commute. Alcohol is not permitted. All students may keep cars on campus.

Activities: There are no fraternities or sororities on campus. There are 13 groups on campus, including computers, honors, international, newspaper, photography, professional, and student government.

Sports: There are 6 intramural sports for men and 6 for women.

Disabled Students: Ninety percent of the campus is accessible to disabled students. The following facilities are available: wheelchair ramps, elevators, special parking, specially equipped rest rooms, and lowered drinking fountains.

Services: In addition to many counseling and information services, tutoring is available in every subject.

Campus Safety and Security: Campus safety and security measures include informal discussions, pamphlets, posters, and films, emergency telephones, and lighted pathways and sidewalks. In addition, security detection system is deployed when the facility is closed.

Programs of Study: DeVry awards the B.S. degree. Associate degrees also are awarded. Bachelor's degrees are awarded in BUSINESS (accounting and business administration and management), COMMUNICATIONS AND THE ARTS (telecommunications), COMPUTER AND PHYSICAL SCIENCE (information sciences and systems), ENGINEERING AND ENVIRONMENTAL DESIGN (electrical/electronics engineering technology). Electronics has the largest enrollment.

Required: In order to graduate, students must complete between 132 and 157 credit hours with a 2.0 minimum GPA. Course requirements vary according to program. All first-semester students take courses in business organization, computer applications, algebra, psychology, and student success strategies.

Special: Nondegree study and evening classes are possible. There is one national honor society on campus.

Faculty/Classroom: Seventy-eight percent of faculty are male; 22%, female. All teach undergraduates. The average class size in an introductory lecture is 30; in a laboratory, 30; and in a regular course offering, 30.

Admissions: About 92% of the 1993-94 applicants were accepted.

Requirements: Admissions requirements include graduation from a secondary school; the GED is also accepted. Applicants must pass the DeVry entrance exam or present satisfactory ACT, SAT I, or WPCT scores. CLEP credit is accepted.

Procedure: Freshmen are admitted to all sessions. Application deadlines are open. Application fee is $25. Notification is sent on a rolling basis. There are early decision and deferred admissions plans.

Transfer: Transfer students must take the DeVry entrance exam. It is recommended that applicants have math scores of at least 23 on the ACT or 480 on the SAT I. At least 35% of credits out of a total of 132 to 157 must be completed at DeVry.

Visiting: There are regularly scheduled orientations for prospective students. There are guides for informal visits. To arrange for a visit, contact Marie Gorton, New Student Coordinator at (816) 941-0430 or (800) 821-3766.

Financial Aid: In 1993-94, 80% of all current freshmen and 80% of continuing students received some form of financial aid. About 80% of freshmen and 80% of continuing students received need-based aid. DeVry is a member of CSS. The FAFSA financial statement is required.

International Students: They must take the TOEFL and achieve a minimum score of 550. The student must also take the college's own entrance exam; however the ACT, SAT I, or WPCT may be accepted in lieu of the DeVry entrance exam.

Computers: The college provides computer facilities for student use. The mainframe is an IBM 3081K. Laboratory facilities include IBM and IBM-compatible PCs in stand-alone and network configurations, with access to the mainframe. LAN provide access to a wide range of applications software. Hard copy from mainframe is provided through a local minicomputer and medium- and high-speed printers. Students in the computer information systems program may access the system. It may be used during published laboratory hours. There are no fees.

Graduates: In 1992-93, 229 bachelor's degrees were awarded. The most popular majors among graduates were electronics technology (51%), telecommunications management (25%), and computer information systems and sciences (14%). Within an average freshman class, 47% graduate in 5 years. Some 68 companies recruited on campus in 1992-93. In the 1992 graduating class, 86% of all graduates found employment within 6 months of graduation.

Admissions Contact: Gayle R. Dykes-Grimmet, Director of Admissions.

DRURY COLLEGE
Springfield, MO 65802

B-3

(417) 865-8731
(800) 922-2274 (out-of-state)

Full-time: 490 men, 575 women	Faculty: 86; IIB, av$
Part-time: 28 men, 20 women	Ph.D.s: 93%
Graduate: 98 men, 220 women	Student/Faculty: 12 to 1
Year: semesters, summer session	Tuition: $8760
Application Deadline: August 1	Room & Board: $3380
Freshman Class: 700 applied, 314 enrolled	
ACT: 25	**VERY COMPETITIVE**

Drury College, founded in 1873, is a private institution affiliated with the United Church of Christ and the Disciples of Christ. Degree programs emphasize the liberal arts, architecture, business, communications, economics, and education. There are 2 graduate schools. In addition to regional accreditation, Drury has baccalaureate program accreditation with AACSB, NAAB, and NCATE. The library contains 175,000 volumes, 58,412 microform items, and 800 audiovisual forms, and subscribes to 904 periodicals. Computerized library sources and services include the card catalog, interlibrary loans, and database searching. Special learning facilities include an art gallery, radio station, tv station, a teleconference facility, and an art and architecture slide collection. The 50-acre campus is in an urban area 200 miles southwest of St. Louis. Including residence halls, there are 19 buildings on campus.

Student Life: About 84% of undergraduates are from Missouri. Students come from 27 states, 14 foreign countries, and Canada. Eighty-eight percent are from public schools; 12% from private. Ninety-four percent are white. Sixty-two percent are Protestant; 35% claim no religious affiliation. The average age of freshmen is 18; all undergraduates, 20. Twenty-five percent drop out by the end of their first year; 52% remain to graduate.

Housing: A total of 475 students can be accommodated in college housing. College-sponsored living facilities include single-sex and coed dormitories and fraternity houses. On-campus housing is guaranteed for all 4 years. Fifty percent of students live on campus; of those, 44% remain on campus on weekends. All students may keep cars on campus.

Activities: About 39% of men belong to 4 national fraternities; about 42% of women belong to 4 national sororities. There are many groups and organizations on campus, including art, band, cheerleading, choir, chorale, chorus, computers, dance, drama, honors, jazz band, musical theater, newspaper, opera, orchestra, pep band, political, radio and tv, religious, social, social service, student government, and yearbook. Popular campus events include Homecoming, College Day, Parents Day, Fall Festival, Wellness Week, Architecture Day, Premed Day, Greek Week, Christmas Vespers, and a Freshman Convocation.

Sports: There are 5 intercollegiate sports for men and 4 for women, and 6 intramural sports for men and 6 for women. Athletic and recreation facilities include a gymnasium, tennis and racquetball courts, playing fields, an Olympic-size pool, and a health, physical education, and recreation center.

Disabled Students: Seventy-five percent of the campus is accessible to disabled students. The following facilities are available: wheelchair ramps, special parking, specially equipped rest rooms, lowered drinking fountains, and lowered telephones.

Services: In addition to many counseling and information services, tutoring is available in every subject. In addition, there is a reader service for the blind.

Campus Safety and Security: Campus safety and security measures include 24-hour foot and vehicle patrol, escort service, informal discussions, and pamphlets, posters, and films. In addition, there are emergency telephones and lighted pathways and sidewalks.

Programs of Study: Drury awards the B.A., B.S., B.Arch., B.M., B.M.Ed., and B.S.N. degrees. Associate and master's degrees also are awarded. Bachelor's degrees are awarded in BIOLOGICAL SCIENCE (biology/biological science), BUSINESS (accounting and business administration and management), COMMUNICATIONS AND THE ARTS (communications, dramatic arts, English, fine arts, French, German, music, and Spanish), COMPUTER AND PHYSICAL SCIENCE (chemistry, mathematics, and physics), EDUCATION (elementary, music, physical, secondary, and special), ENGINEERING AND ENVIRONMENTAL DESIGN (architecture), HEALTH PROFESSIONS (nursing and premedicine), SOCIAL SCIENCE (criminal justice, economics, history, philosophy, political science/government, prelaw, psychology, and sociology). Premedicine, preprofessional programs, architecture, and business are the strongest academically. Business administration, biology, communication, education, and behavior science have the largest enrollments.

Required: To graduate, students must complete 124 credit hours for all but the B.Arch. program, which requires 170. They must also maintain a minimum GPA of 2.0, complete 26 to 32 credit hours in the major (99 for architecture), and fulfill distribution requirements in science, mathematics, humanities, fine arts, foreign language, and social science, with specific classes in fitness, contemporary issues, non-Western culture, and senior seminar or research.

Special: Drury offers cross-registration with Regents College in London, a cooperative program in international business with American University, study abroad in 5 countries, internships, a Washington semester, credit by examination, nondegree study, dual majors, pass/fail options, and a 3–2 engineering degree in conjunction with the University of Missouri and Washington University in St. Louis. There is a freshman honors program on campus, as well as 3 national honor societies.

Faculty/Classroom: Seventy-six percent of faculty are male; 24%, female. All teach undergraduates. The average class size in an introductory lecture is 26; in a laboratory, 24; and in a regular course offering, 13.

Admissions: The ACT scores for the 1993–94 freshman class were as follows: 20% below 21, 28% between 21 and 23, 23% between 24 and 26, 13% between 27 and 28, and 16% above 28. About 55% of the current freshmen were in the top fifth of their class; 78% were in the top two fifths. There were 6 National Merit finalists. About 20 freshmen graduated first in their class.

Requirements: Drury requires applicants to be in the upper 50% of their class. A minimum GPA of 2.0 is required. The SAT I or ACT is required. In addition, applicants must be graduates of an accredited secondary school or have a GED certificate. Recommended high school credits include 4 units of English and at least 3 each of mathematics, natural science, and social studies. An essay and a reference from the high school counselor or principal are required. AP and CLEP credits are accepted. Important factors used in the admissions decision are recommendations by school officials, advanced placement or honor courses, parents or siblings attending the school, leadership record, and recommendations by alumni.

Procedure: Freshmen are admitted to all sessions. Entrance exams should be taken in the spring of the junior year or the fall of the senior year. Applications should be filed by August 1 for fall entry, along with an application fee of $20. Notification is sent on a rolling basis. There are early admissions and deferred admissions plans.

Transfer: About 90 transfer students enrolled in 1993–94. Applicants must have a minimum GPA of 2.0 in all college work completed. A total of 30 credits out of 124 must be completed at Drury.

Visiting: There are regularly scheduled orientations for prospective students. There are guides for informal visits and visitors may sit in on classes and stay overnight at the school. To arrange for a visit, contact Admissions at (417) 865–8731 or (800) 922–2274.

Financial Aid: In 1993–94, 85% of all current freshmen and 80% of continuing students received some form of financial aid. About 74% of freshmen and 67% of continuing students received need-based aid. The average freshman award was $4600. Of that total, scholarships or need-based grants averaged $3000 ($8500 maximum); loans averaged $600 ($4000 maximum); and work contracts averaged $1000 ($1500 maximum). Seventy-two percent of undergraduate students work part-time. Average earnings from campus work for the school year are $1200. The average financial indebtedness of the 1992–93 graduate was $5000. Drury is a member of CSS. The FAFSA financial statement is required. The deadline for financial aid applications is April 15.

International Students: There are currently 50 international students enrolled. The school actively recruits these students. They must take the TOEFL and achieve a minimum score of 500.

Computers: The college provides computer facilities for student use. The mainframe is an IBM AS400, available only to office employees. There is a computer laboratory in the library, and microcomputers are available to all students for academic use. There are no time limits on using the system and no fees.

Graduates: In 1992–93, 221 bachelor's degrees were awarded. The most popular majors among graduates were business administration (24%), communication (19%), and biology (15%). Within an average freshman class, 3% graduate in 3 years, 49% in 4 years, 52% in 5 years, and 55% in 6 years. Some 56 companies recruited on campus in a recent year. In a recent graduating class, 11% of the men and 15% of the women were enrolled in graduate school within 6 months of graduation; 26% of the men and 30% of the women had found employment.

Admissions Contact: Michael G. Thomas, Director of Admissions.

EVANGEL COLLEGE
Springfield, MO 65802

	B-3
	(417) 865–2811
Full-time: 638 men, 781 women	Faculty: 83
Part-time: 42 men, 42 women	Ph.D.s: 49%
Graduate: none	Student/Faculty: 17 to 1
Year: semesters, summer session	Tuition: $6992
Application Deadline: August 1	Room & Board: $3150
Freshman Class: 725 applied, 679 accepted, 589 enrolled	
ACT: 22	LESS COMPETITIVE

Evangel College, established in 1955, is a private coeducational instituion affiliated with the Assemblies of God. In addition to regional accreditation, Evangel has baccalaureate program accreditation with NASM and NCATE. The library contains 122,726 volumes, 25,325 microform items, and 2204 audiovisual forms, and subscribes to 655 periodicals. Special learning facilities include a learning resource center, a radio station, and a TV station. The 80-acre campus is in an urban area 225 miles west of St. Louis. Including residence halls, there are 14 buildings on campus.

Student Life: About 64% of undergraduates are from out-of-state, mostly the Midwest. Students come from 47 states, 10 foreign countries, and Canada. Ninety-four percent are from public schools; 6% from private. Ninety-five percent are white. Most are Protestant. The average age of freshmen is 18; all undergraduates, 20.1. Thirty-five percent drop out by the end of their first year; 55% remain to graduate.

Housing: A total of 1460 students can be accommodated in college housing. College-sponsored living facilities include single-sex and coed dormitories and married-student housing. In addition, there are honors floors. On-campus housing is guaranteed for all 4 years. Eighty-three percent of students live on campus; of those, all remain on campus on weekends. Alcohol is not permitted. All students may keep cars on campus.

Activities: There are no fraternities or sororities. There are many groups on campus, including band, cheerleading, choir, chorale, chorus, drama, honors, newspaper, orchestra, pep band, photography, political, professional, radio and TV, religious, student government, and yearbook. Popular campus events include College Weekend and performances of the Springfield Symphony.

Sports: There are 4 intercollegiate sports each for men and women, and 4 intramural sports each for men and women. Athletic and recreation facilities include a student activities center and a 2000-seat gymnasium.

Disabled Students: All of the campus is accessible to disabled students. Wheelchair ramps and special parking are available.

Services: In addition to many counseling and information services, tutoring is available in every subject. There is a reader service for the blind, and remedial math, reading, and writing.

Campus Safety and Security: Campus safety and security measures include 24-hour foot and vehicle patrol, escort service, and lighted pathways and sidewalks.

Programs of Study: Evangel awards the B.A., B.S., B.B.A., B.F.A., and B.M. degrees. Associate degrees also are awarded. Bachelor's degrees are awarded in BIOLOGICAL SCIENCE (biology/biological science), BUSINESS (accounting, management science, marketing/retailing/merchandising, and office supervision and management), COMMUNICATIONS AND THE ARTS (art, broadcasting, communications, design, English, journalism, music, music performance, Spanish, and speech/debate/rhetoric), COMPUTER AND PHYSICAL SCIENCE (chemistry, computer science, and mathematics), EDUCATION (business, early childhood, elementary, foreign languages, music, physical, science, secondary, and special), HEALTH PROFESSIONS (medical laboratory technology), SOCIAL SCIENCE (history, international studies, parks and recreation management, political science/government, psychology, public administration, religion, religious music, social science, social work, and soci-

ology). Business, education, music, science and technology, and communications are the strongest program academically. Business and education have the largest enrollments.

Required: All students must complete 52 general education hours including courses in physical education, computer literacy, and Bible study. A minimum GPA of 2.0 is required for graduation. Students must complete 124 credit hours with approximately 34 credit hours in the major.

Special: There is a 3–2 engineering degree available in conjunction with Washington University. Other options include work-study, credit by examination, and a Washington semester. There are 9 national honor societies on campus.

Faculty/Classroom: Sixty-two percent of faculty are male; 38%, female. All teach undergraduates. The average class size in an introductory lecture is 40 and in a regular course offering, 20.

Admissions: About 94% of the 1993–94 applicants were accepted.

Requirements: The ACT is recommended. In addition, the recommended preparatory curriculum includes 3 credits in English, 2 each in mathematics and social studies, and 1 in science. The GED is accepted. AP and CLEP credits are accepted.

Procedure: Freshmen are admitted to all sessions. Entrance exams should be taken before high school graduation. Applications should be filed by August 1 for fall entry and December 15 for spring entry, along with an application fee of $25. Notification is sent on a rolling basis.

Transfer: About 118 transfer students enrolled in a recent year. Transfer applicants must be in good standing with their previous institutions. A total of 30 credits out of 124 must be completed at Evangel.

Visiting: There are regularly scheduled orientations for prospective students. There are guides for informal visits and visitors may sit in on classes and stay overnight at the school. To arrange for a visit, contact the Office of Enrollment at (417) 865–2811.

Financial Aid: In a recent year, 86% of all current freshmen and 80% of continuing students received some form of financial aid. Work contracts averaged $1200 (maximum). Evangel is a member of CSS. The FAF is required.

International Students: There were recently 23 international students enrolled. They must take the TOEFL.

Computers: The college provides computer facilities for student use. The mainframes are a DEC VAX II/750 and DEC MicroVAX II. There are 2 computer laboratories with microcomputers available for student use. Students enrolled in computer courses may access the system. The fees are $10 per semester.

Graduates: In a recent year, 282 bachelor's degrees were awarded. Some 32 companies recruited on campus that year.

Admissions Contact: David I. Schoolfield, Executive Director of Office Enrollment.

FONTBONNE COLLEGE
St. Louis, MO 63105
D-2
(314) 889–1400

Full-time: 213 men, 542 women	**Faculty:** 55; IIB, --$
Part-time: 503 men, 272 women	**Ph.D.s:** 55%
Graduate: 221 men, 233 women	**Student/Faculty:** 14 to 1
Year: semesters, summer session	**Tuition:** $8090
Application Deadline: August 1	**Room & Board:** $4000
Freshman Class: 291 applied, 245 accepted, 126 enrolled	
ACT: 21	**COMPETITIVE**

Fontbonne College, founded in 1917, is a private institution affiliated with the Catholic Church and offering undergraduate degree programs in education, natural sciences, human environmental sciences, business, and communication and fine arts. There are 5 graduate schools. The library contains 90,000 volumes, 6000 audiovisual forms, and subscribes to 510 periodicals. Special learning facilities include a learning resource center, art gallery, and a biological field station, a broadcast center, and a communications disorder clinic. The 13-acre campus is in a suburban area 1 mile west of St. Louis. Including residence halls, there are 10 buildings on campus.

Student Life: About 90% of undergraduates are from Missouri. Students come from 14 states and 19 foreign countries. Fifty percent are from public schools; 50% from private. Seventy-four percent are white; 18% African American. Fifty-five percent are Catholic; 23% Protestant; 10% claim no religious affiliation. The average age of freshmen is 17; all undergraduates, 23. Twenty percent drop out by the end of their first year; 65% remain to graduate.

Housing: A total of 226 students can be accommodated in college housing. College-sponsored living facilities include single-sex and coed dormitories. On-campus housing is guaranteed for all 4 years. Seventy-five percent of students commute. Alcohol is not permitted. All students may keep cars on campus.

Activities: There is 1 local fraternity. There are no sororities on campus. There are 20 groups on campus, including cheerleading, choir, chorus, computers, drama, drill team, ethnic, honors, international, literary magazine, musical theater, newspaper, pep band, photography, political, professional, radio and TV, religious, social, social ser-

vice, and student government. Popular campus events include Homecoming, Spring Fest, art shows, and musical performances.

Sports: There are 4 intercollegiate sports for men and 4 for women, and 5 intramural sports for men and 5 for women. Athletic and recreation facilities include a new $3 million student activity center that houses a 2000-seat gymnasium, weight room, track, aerobics room, and cafe.

Disabled Students: The following facilities are available: wheelchair ramps, elevators, special parking, specially equipped rest rooms, and special class scheduling when possible.

Services: In addition to many counseling and information services, tutoring is available in most subjects. There is also remedial math, reading, and writing available.

Campus Safety and Security: Campus safety and security measures include self defense education, informal discussions, pamphlets, posters, films, and emergency telephones. In addition, there are lighted pathways and sidewalks and security personnel as needed.

Programs of Study: Fontbonne awards the B.A., B.S., and B.F.A. degrees. Master's degree also are awarded. Bachelor's degrees are awarded in BIOLOGICAL SCIENCE (biology/biological science), BUSINESS (accounting, banking and finance, and business administration and management), COMMUNICATIONS AND THE ARTS (art, broadcasting, communications, dramatic arts, English, fine arts, music business management, and speech/debate/rhetoric), COMPUTER AND PHYSICAL SCIENCE (computer science, information sciences and systems, and mathematics), EDUCATION (art, early childhood, education of the deaf and hearing impaired, elementary, home economics, middle school, science, secondary, and special), HEALTH PROFESSIONS (premedicine and speech pathology/audiology), SOCIAL SCIENCE (dietetics, food science, history, human services, prelaw, and social work). Education, computer science, and mathematics are the strongest academically. Business and human environmental sciences have the largest enrollments.

Required: To graduate, students must complete 128 credit hours, including 44 in general education requirements, with a minimum GPA of 2.0. The number of hours required for the major varies.

Special: Fontbonne offers cross-registration with several area colleges and a student exchange program with the Sisters of St. Joseph Consortium. There are also cooperative programs in all majors except education, internships with major companies, study abroad, work-study programs, student-designed and dual majors, credit by examination, nondegree study, pass/fail options, and B.A.-B.S. and general studies degrees. There is a freshman honors program on campus, as well as 4 national honor societies.

Faculty/Classroom: Forty-six percent of faculty are male; 54%, female. Ninety-three percent teach undergraduates and 25% also do research. The average class size in an introductory lecture is 25; in a laboratory, 12; and in a regular course offering, 12.

Admissions: About 84% of the 1993–94 applicants were accepted. The ACT scores for the 1993–94 freshman class were as follows: 31% below 21, 48% between 21 and 23, 19% between 24 and 26, 2% between 27 and 28, and 3% above 28. About 38% of the current freshmen were in the top fifth of their class; 72% were in the top two fifths. About 4 freshmen graduated first in their class.

Requirements: Fontbonne requires applicants to be in the upper 50% of their class. A minimum GPA of 2.5 is required. The SAT I or ACT is required, with a minimum SAT I composite score of 900 or ACT score of 20 recommended. Applicants must be graduates of an accredited secondary school or have a GED certificate. They must have completed 16 academic credits, including 4 in English, 3 in mathematics, 2 each in science and social studies, and 1 in history. An audition or portfolio may be required. AP and CLEP credits are accepted. Important factors used in the admissions decision are advanced placement or honor courses, extracurricular activities record, leadership record, evidence of special talents, and personality, intangible qualities.

Procedure: Freshmen are admitted to all sessions. Entrance exams should be taken prior to registration. Applications should be filed by August 1 for fall entry and January 1 for spring entry, along with an application fee of $20. Notification is sent on a rolling basis. There is an early admissions plan.

Transfer: About 132 transfer students enrolled in 1993–94. Applicants must have a minimum GPA of 2.0 and either submit ACT/SAT I scores or take a placement test. Students with fewer than 30 credits must submit a high school transcript. An interview is recommended. A total of 32 credits out of 128 must be completed at Fontbonne.

Visiting: There are regularly scheduled orientations for prospective students, including a campus tour, a financial aid presentation, and visits with faculty and current students. There are guides for informal visits and visitors may sit in on classes and stay overnight at the school. To arrange for a visit, contact the Admission Office at (314) 889–1400.

Financial Aid: In a recent year 83% of all students received some form of financial aid; and 65% students received need-based aid. The average freshman award was $7300. Of that total, scholarships or

need-based grants averaged $3100 ($7370 maximum); loans averaged $2600 ($4000 maximum); and work contracts averaged $1600 ($1780 maximum). Forty percent of undergraduate students work part-time. Average earnings from campus work for the school year are $1400. The average financial indebtedness of a recent graduate was $6000. Fontbonne is a member of CSS. The FAF or FFS, the college's own financial statement, and the FAFSA are required. The deadline for financial aid applications is April 1.

International Students: There are currently 91 international students enrolled. The school actively recruits these students. They must take the TOEFL and achieve a minimum score of 500.

Computers: The college provides computer facilities for student use. More than 22 IBM XT, IBM PS/2, and Apple microcomputers operate on a LAN network. All students may access the system. It may be used during regular hours. There are no time limits on using the system. The fee is $35.

Graduates: In 1992–93 199 bachelor's degrees were awarded. The most popular majors among graduates were business (36%), human enviromental sciences (11%), and education (10%). Some 89 companies recruited on campus in a recent year.

Admissions Contact: Peggy Musen, Director of Admission.

HANNIBAL-LAGRANGE COLLEGE

D-2

Hannibal, MO 63401 (314) 221–3113

Full-time: 189 men, 304 women	Faculty: 38; IIB, --$
Part-time: 135 men, 247 women	Ph.D.s: 37%
Graduate: none	Student/Faculty: 13 to 1
Year: semesters, summer session	Tuition: $6000
Application Deadline: open	Room & Board: $2400
Freshman Class: n/av	
ACT: 20	LESS COMPETITIVE

Hannibal-LaGrange College, founded in 1858, is a private, coeducational facility affiliated with the Southern Baptist Church. In addition to regional accreditation, H-LG has baccalaureate program accreditation with NLN. The library contains 74,835 volumes, 2742 microform items, and 5406 audiovisual forms, and subscribes to 398 periodicals. The 110-acre campus is in a small town 100 miles north of St. Louis. Including residence halls, there are 11 buildings on campus.

Student Life: About 88% of undergraduates are from Missouri. Students come from 15 states and 3 foreign countries. Almost all are white. The average age of freshmen is 22.

Housing: A total of 253 students can be accommodated in college housing. College-sponsored living facilities include dormitories and married-student housing. On-campus housing is guaranteed for all 4 years. Sixty-nine percent of students commute. Alcohol is not permitted. All students may keep cars on campus.

Activities: There are no fraternities or sororities on campus. There are 27 groups on campus, including band, cheerleading, choir, chorus, drama, honors, jazz band, newspaper, pep band, religious, social, student government, and yearbook. Popular campus events include Spring Campus Visitation Days, Homecoming, and Encounter Visitation Days.

Sports: There are 2 intercollegiate and 6 intramural sports each for men and women. Athletic and recreation facilities include a 41,000-square foot sports complex, which contains a gymnasium, weight room, aerobics room, and volleyball, tennis, and racquetball courts.

Disabled Students: Sixty-five percent of the campus is accessible to disabled students. The following facilities are available: wheelchair ramps, elevators, special parking, specially equipped rest rooms, special class scheduling, and lowered drinking fountains.

Services: In addition to many counseling and information services, tutoring is available in some subjects. There is remedial math, reading, and writing.

Campus Safety and Security: Campus safety and security measures include 24-hour foot and vehicle patrol, escort service, emergency telephones, and lighted pathways and sidewalks.

Programs of Study: H-LG awards the B.A., B.S., B.C.E., B.C.M., B.R.S., B.S.Ed., and B.S.N. degrees. Associate degrees also are awarded. Bachelor's degrees are awarded in BIOLOGICAL SCIENCE (biology/biological science), BUSINESS (accounting, banking and finance, business administration and management, marketing/retailing/merchandising, and personnel management), COMMUNICATIONS AND THE ARTS (communications, English, fine arts, and music), COMPUTER AND PHYSICAL SCIENCE (computer programming), EDUCATION (early childhood, elementary, music, and secondary), HEALTH PROFESSIONS (nursing), SOCIAL SCIENCE (criminal justice). Education, business, and nursing have the largest enrollments.

Required: All students must complete 124 credit hours with a 2.0 GPA to graduate. The major usually requires 36 or more credit hours of study. Certain general education courses are required.

Special: Internships are available for students taking courses in human services and Bible studies. Students may pursue a general studies degree, a 3–2 engineering degree, student-designed majors,

study abroad in England, credit by examination, and nondegree study. There is a freshman honors program on campus, as well as 1 national honor society.

Faculty/Classroom: The average class size in an introductory lecture is 17; in a laboratory, 18; and in a regular course offering, 16.

Admissions: Five freshmen graduated first in their class.

Requirements: The ACT is required. In addition, applicants must be graduates of an accredited secondary school or have the GED. An interview is required. AP and CLEP credits are accepted.

Procedure: Entrance exams should be taken before registration. Application deadlines are open. The application fee is $25. Notification is sent on a rolling basis. There is an early admissions plan.

Transfer: About 90 transfer students enrolled in 1993–94. Applicants must submit transcripts from all colleges attended. Students applying with fewer than 30 credit hours must also submit a high school transcript along with ACT or SAT I scores. A total of 32 credits out of 124 must be completed at H-LG.

Visiting: There are regularly scheduled orientations for prospective students, including Encounter Days which are organized tours of the campus covering financial aid, student affairs, academic areas, and lunch in the cafeteria. There are guides for informal visits and visitors may sit in on classes and stay overnight at the school. To arrange for a visit, contact the Office of Admissions at (314) 221–3113.

Financial Aid: In 1993–94, 84% of continuing students received some form of financial aid. H-LG is a member of CSS. The FFS is required. The deadline for financial aid applications is July 1.

International Students: There are currently 3 international students enrolled. They must take the TOEFL and achieve a minimum score of 520. The student must also take the ACT.

Computers: The college provides computer facilities for student use. The mainframes are an IBM AS/400, Sperry 5000/40, Data General AV620, and EXL 320, 316, and 325 units. Microcomputers are available in the technical center for all students. There are no time limits and no fees.

Graduates: In 1992–93, 94 bachelor's degrees were awarded. Some 20 companies recruited on campus in 1992–93.

Admissions Contact: Bill Creech, Dean of Admissions/Financial Aid.

HARRIS-STOWE STATE COLLEGE

D-2

St Louis, MO 63103 (314) 533–3300

Full-time: 189 men, 388 women	Faculty: 40; IIB, --$
Part-time: 277 men, 917 women	Ph.D.s: 64%
Graduate: none	Student/Faculty: 14 to 1
Year: semesters, summer session	Tuition: $1888 ($3719)
Application Deadline: open	Room & Board: n/app
Freshman Class: n/av	
SAT I or ACT: required	LESS COMPETITIVE

Harris-Stowe State College, founded in 1854, is a state-supported, commuter, coeducational institution offering undergraduate programs in teacher and urban education. In addition to regional accreditation, Harris-Stowe has baccalaureate program accreditation with NCATE. The library contains 80,000 volumes and 30,000 microform items, and subscribes to 300 periodicals. Special learning facilities include a learning resource center. The 8-acre campus is in an urban area in metropolitan St. Louis. There are 2 buildings on campus.

Student Life: Nearly all of undergraduates are from Missouri, but a few come from 2 states and 7 foreign countries. Ninety percent are from public schools; 10% from private. Seventy-three percent are African American; 36% white. The average age of all undergraduates is 28.

Housing: There are no residence halls. All students commute. Alcohol is not permitted.

Activities: There are some groups and organizations on campus, including cheerleading, chorale, dance, drama, ethnic, literary magazine, newspaper, professional, student government, and yearbook. Popular campus events include Homecoming, Mistletoe Dinner Dance, and Awards Breakfast.

Disabled Students: All of the campus is accessible to disabled students. The following facilities are available: wheelchair ramps, elevators, special parking, specially equipped rest rooms, and lowered telephones.

Services: There is remedial math, reading, and writing. tutoring.

Campus Safety and Security: Campus safety and security measures include lighted pathways and sidewalks.

Programs of Study: Harris-Stowe awards the B.S.T.E. and B.S.U.E. degrees. Bachelor's degrees are awarded in EDUCATION (early childhood, elementary, and middle school).

Required: Students are required to complete 128 to 129 semester hours, including a 40-hour core curriculum of general education courses, and must maintain a minimum GPA of 2.5.

Special: Opportunities are provided for internships as part of the degree in urban education, credit by examination, and pass/fail options in developmental courses. There are 3 national honor societies on campus.

Faculty/Classroom: All teach undergraduates.

Requirements: The SAT I or ACT is required. Applicants should have completed 14 academic units at an accredited secondary school or hold a GED.

Procedure: Entrance exams should be taken before the close of registration. Application deadlines are open. Application fee is $15. Notification is sent on a rolling basis. There is a deferred admissions plan.

Transfer: A total of 30 credits out of 129 must be completed at Harris-Stowe.

Visiting: There are guides for informal visits and visitors may sit in on classes. To arrange for a visit, contact the Director of Admissions/Academic Advisement at (314) 533-3300.

Financial Aid: In 1993–94 80% of all current freshmen and 85% of continuing students received some form of financial aid. The FAF is required.

International Students: They must take the TOEFL and achieve a minimum score of 500. The student must also take the SAT I, ACT, or or Harris-Stowe's own examination if ACT/SAT I scores are not high enough..

Computers: The college provides computer facilities for student use. Microcomputers are available for student use in the academic support center and the microcomputer laboratory. All students may access the system. There are no time limits on using the system and no fees.

Graduates: Some 30 companies recruited on campus in 1992–93.

Admissions Contact: Valerie A. Beeson, Director of Admissions/Academic Advisement.

KANSAS CITY ART INSTITUTE

Kansas City, MO 64111

A-2

(816) 931-5224
(800) 522-5224 (out-of-state)

Full-time: 527 men and women	Faculty: 48; IIB, -$
Part-time: 32 men and women	Ph.D.s: n/av
Graduate: none	Student/Faculty: 11 to 1
Year: semesters	Tuition: $12,910
Application Deadline: see profile	Room & Board: $4090–4990
Freshman Class: 675 applied, 410 accepted, 186 enrolled	
ACT: 22	SPECIAL

The Kansas City Art Institute, founded in 1885, is an independent, coeducational, professional college of art and design. In addition to regional accreditation, KCAI has baccalaureate program accreditation with NASAD. The library contains 37,000 volumes, and subscribes to 120 periodicals. Special learning facilities include a learning resource center and an art gallery. The 17-acre campus is in an urban area. Including residence halls, there are 14 buildings on campus.

Student Life: About 68% of undergraduates are from out-of-state. Students come from 40 states, 17 foreign countries, and Canada. Sixty percent are from public schools; 30% from private. The average age of freshmen is 18; all undergraduates, 21. Thirty percent drop out by the end of their first year; 42% remain to graduate.

Housing: A total of 140 students can be accommodated in college housing. College-sponsored living facilities include single-sex and coed dormitories. In addition, the Student Affairs Office offers assistance finding off-campus housing. Seventy-nine percent of students live on campus. All students may keep cars on campus.

Activities: There are no fraternities or sororities. There are some groups and organizations on campus, including literary magazine, newspaper, and yearbook. Popular campus events include dances, film series, poetry readings, exhibition openings, and visiting artist series.

Sports: There is no sports program at KCAI.

Disabled Students: Fifty percent of the campus is accessible to disabled students. Wheelchair ramps and specially equipped rest rooms are available.

Services: In addition to many counseling and information services, tutoring is available in every subject. There is remedial reading and writing.

Campus Safety and Security: Campus safety and security measures include 24-hour foot and vehicle patrol, escort service, informal discussions, pamphlets, posters, films, emergency telephones, and free taxi service.

Programs of Study: KCAI awards the B.F.A. degree. Bachelor's degrees are awarded in COMMUNICATIONS AND THE ARTS (ceramic art and design, design, fiber/textiles/weaving, fine arts, painting, photography, printmaking, sculpture, and video).

Required: Students must maintain a minimum GPA of 2.0 overall and within their studio major. A total of 129 credit hours is needed, including 81 in studio classes; 45 distributed among courses in history of Western thought, art history, literature, humanities, and other liberal arts; and 3 in electives.

Special: KCAI offers internships with major corporations such as Hallmark and Disney, independent study, work-study programs, study abroad, cross-registration, intermedia majors, an exchange program, and nondegree study.

Faculty/Classroom: All teach undergraduates.

Admissions: About 61% of the 1993–94 applicants were accepted.

Requirements: A minimum GPA of 2.0 is required. The SAT I or ACT is required. In addition, applicants must submit a portfolio consisting of 10 to 20 pieces of artwork, 2 letters of recommendation, and high school transcripts. The GED is accepted. A statement of purpose and an interview are required. AP and CLEP credits are accepted. Important factors used in the admissions decision are evidence of special talent, advanced placement or honor courses, recommendations by school officials, personality, intangible qualities, and leadership record.

Procedure: Applications should be filed for priority by February 15 for fall entry and December 1 for spring entry, along with an application fee of $25. Notification is sent on a rolling basis. There are early decision, early admissions, and deferred admissions plans. A waiting list is an active part of the admissions procedure, with about 10% of applicants on the list.

Transfer: About 40 transfer students enrolled in a recent year. Transfer applicants must submit official transcripts and a portfolio. A minimum GPA of 2.0 is required. A total of 48 credits out of 129 must be completed at KCAI.

Visiting: There are regularly scheduled orientations for prospective students, consisting of information sessions offered every other Friday. There are guides for informal visits and visitors may sit in on classes and stay overnight at the school. To arrange for a visit, contact the Admissions Office at (800) 522-5224.

Financial Aid: In a recent year, 65% of all students received some form of financial aid. Scholarships or need-based grants averaged $1500; loans averaged $1200 ($2625 maximum); and work contracts averaged $850. KCAI is a member of CSS. The FAF and student and parent IRS tax forms are required. The deadline for financial aid applications is February 15.

International Students: There were recently 21 international students enrolled. They must take the TOEFL and achieve a minimum score of 500.

Computers: The college provides computer facilities for student use. There is a computer graphics center with software for computer-generated art and design, including digital painting, image processing and composting, layout and illustration, and 3D modeling and animation. All students may access the system. There are no time limits on using the system and no fees.

Graduates: In a recent year, 78 bachelor's degrees were awarded. Some 25 companies recruited on campus. In an earlier graduating class, 37% of the men and women were enrolled in graduate school within 6 months of graduation; 80% had found employment.

Admissions Contact: Charles Van Gilder, Director of Admissions.

LINCOLN UNIVERSITY

Jefferson City, MO 65102-0029

C-2

(314) 681-5599; (800) 521-5052

Full-time: 913 men, 1106 women	Faculty: 157; IIA, --$
Part-time: 430 men, 851 women	Ph.D.s: 31%
Graduate: 100 men, 223 women	Student/Faculty: 13 to 1
Year: semesters, summer session	Tuition: $1910 ($3710)
Application Deadline: open	Room & Board: $2728
Freshman Class: 1346 applied, 1342 accepted, 659 enrolled	
ACT: 18	NONCOMPETITIVE

Lincoln University, established in 1866, is a coeducational land-grant institution offering undergraduate programs in agriculture, arts and sciences, business, applied technology, and education, and graduate programs in selected areas. There are 3 undergraduate and 3 graduate schools. In addition to regional accreditation, LU has baccalaureate program accreditation with ADA, NASM, and NCATE. The library contains 141,640 volumes, 27,109 microform items, and 1710 audiovisual forms, and subscribes to 748 periodicals. Computerized library sources and services include the card catalog, interlibrary loans, and database searching. Special learning facilities include a radio station, TV station, and and an ethnic studies center. The 152-acre campus is in a small town 125 miles east of St. Louis. Including residence halls, there are 33 buildings on campus.

Student Life: About 88% of undergraduates are from Missouri. Students come from 41 states and 21 foreign countries. Sixty-nine percent are white; 27% African American. The average age of freshmen is 20; all undergraduates, 25. Forty-four percent drop out by the end of their first year.

Housing: A total of 630 students can be accommodated in college housing. College-sponsored living facilities include single-sex dormitories. On-campus housing is guaranteed for all 4 years. Ninety percent of students commute. Alcohol is not permitted. All students may keep cars on campus.

Activities: There are 4 national fraternities and 4 national sororities. There are 28 groups on campus, including art, bagpipe band, band, cheerleading, choir, dance, drama, honors, international, jazz band, marching band, newspaper, opera, professional, radio and TV, religious, student government, and yearbook. Popular campus events include Black History Week and Unity Awards in Media.

Sports: There are 5 intercollegiate sports for men and 4 for women, and 2 intramural sports for men and 2 for women. Athletic and recreation facilities include a 5600-seat stadium and a 2500-seat gymnasium.

Disabled Students: The following facilities are available: wheelchair ramps, elevators, special parking, specially equipped rest rooms, special class scheduling, lowered drinking fountains, and lowered telephones.

Services: In addition to many counseling and information services, tutoring is available in every subject. There is also a reader service for the blind, and remedial math, reading, and writing.

Campus Safety and Security: Campus safety and security measures include 24-hour foot and vehicle patrol, self defense education, escort service, and informal discussions. In addition, there are pamphlets, posters, and films, emergency telephones, and lighted pathways and sidewalks.

Programs of Study: LU awards the B.A., B.S., B.M.Ed., and B.S.Ed. degrees. Associate and master's degrees also are awarded. Bachelor's degrees are awarded in AGRICULTURE (agriculture), BIOLOGICAL SCIENCE (biology/biological science), BUSINESS (accounting, business administration and management, marketing/retailing/merchandising, and office supervision and management), COMMUNICATIONS AND THE ARTS (art, English, French, and journalism), COMPUTER AND PHYSICAL SCIENCE (chemistry, information sciences and systems, mathematics, and physics), EDUCATION (art, business, elementary, home economics, music, physical, social science, and special), ENGINEERING AND ENVIRONMENTAL DESIGN (engineering and mechanical design technology), HEALTH PROFESSIONS (medical technology and nursing), SOCIAL SCIENCE (criminal justice, economics, history, philosophy, political science/government, psychology, public administration, and sociology). Business administration, nursing, and science have the largest enrollments.

Required: To graduate, all students must complete a total of 124 semester hours. A minimum of 30 semester hours is required for the major, with at least 18 hours in upper-division courses. Students are required to take physical education courses and must maintain a GPA of 2.0. A comprehensive exam is required in the senior year.

Special: LU offers cross-registration with the University of Missouri/Columbia and William Woods, Westminster, and Columbia colleges. Co-op programs, credit by examination, and a continuing education program are available. There is a freshman honors program on campus.

Faculty/Classroom: Sixty-one percent of faculty are male; 39%, female. Ninety-six percent teach undergraduates, 14% do research, and 4% do both. The average class size in an introductory lecture is 13.

Admissions: Almost 100% of the 1993–94 applicants were accepted. The ACT scores for the 1993–94 freshman class were as follows: 72% below 21, 16% between 21 and 23, 8% between 24 and 26, 3% between 27 and 28, and 1% above 28. About 10% of the current freshmen were in the top fifth of their class; 34% were in the top two fifths. One freshman graduated first in class.

Requirements: A minimum GPA of 2.0 is required. The ACT is recommended. Students must be graduates of an accredited secondary school or have earned the GED. CLEP credit is accepted.

Procedure: Freshmen are admitted to all sessions. Application deadlines are open. The college accepts all in-state residents who apply. Notification is sent on a rolling basis. The application fee is $17. There is an early admissions plan.

Transfer: About 236 transfer students enrolled in 1993–94. A total of 30 credits out of 124 must be completed at LU.

Visiting: There are regularly scheduled orientations for prospective students. There are guides for informal visits and visitors may sit in on classes and stay overnight at the school. To arrange for a visit, contact Enrollment Services at (314) 681–5599.

Financial Aid: Scholarships or need-based grants averaged $2070 (maximum); loans averaged $2625 (maximum); and work contracts averaged $1100 ($1400 maximum). Twelve percent of undergraduate students work part-time. Average earnings from campus work for the school year are $1000. The average financial indebtedness of the 1992–93 graduate was $1600. LU is a member of CSS. The FAF, FFS or SFS is required. The deadline for financial aid applications is March 1.

International Students: There are currently 34 international students enrolled. They must take the TOEFL or the University of Michigan Language Test and achieve a minimum score on the TOEFL of 500. The student must also take the ACT.

Computers: The university provides computer facilities for student use. The mainframes are a Unisys B5935, AL-FS, and A6-KX. The mainframes are networked and attached to the Internet. There are also 5 microcomputer laboratories with a total of 150 computers for student use. All students may access the system 8 A.M. to 10 P.M. Monday through Friday, 8 A.M. to 7 P.M. Saturday, and 9 A.M. to 2 P.M. Sunday. There are no time limits on using the system and no fees.

Graduates: In 1992–93, 283 bachelor's degrees were awarded. The most popular majors among graduates were business administration (20%), education (18%), and criminal justice (9%).

Admissions Contact: Stanford Baddley, Executive Director, Enrollment Services.

LINDENWOOD COLLEGE   D-2
St. Charles, MO 63301   (314) 949–4949

Full-time: 907 men, 1248 women	Faculty: 80; IIA, --$
Part-time: 70 men, 121 women	Ph.D.s: 68%
Graduate: 328 men, 453 women	Student/Faculty: 27 to 1
Year: semesters, summer session	Tuition: $8880
Application Deadline: open	Room & Board: $4680
Freshman Class: 1400 applied, 700 accepted, 440 enrolled	
ACT: 22	**COMPETITIVE**

Lindenwood College is a private coeducational institution that has a covenantal relationship with the Presbyterian Church. The college offers undergraduate degrees in 37 areas. There are 5 undergraduate and 9 graduate schools. In addition to regional accreditation, Lindenwood has baccalaureate program accreditation with NCATE. The library contains 132,131 volumes, 32,300 microform items, and 2500 audiovisual forms, and subscribes to 447 periodicals. Computerized library sources and services include the card catalog and interlibrary loans. Special learning facilities include a learning resource center, an art gallery, a radio station, a TV station, and a greenhouse. The 172-acre campus is in a suburban area 25 miles west of St. Louis. Including residence halls, there are 19 buildings on campus.

Student Life: About 89% of undergraduates are from Missouri. Students come from 33 states, 17 foreign countries, and Canada. Forty percent are from public schools; 60% from private. Eighty-four percent are white. Forty-nine percent are Catholic; 45% Protestant. The average age of freshmen is 18; all undergraduates, 22. Fourteen percent drop out by the end of their first year; 44% remain to graduate.

Housing: A total of 1050 students can be accommodated in college housing. College-sponsored living facilities include single-sex dormitories, on-campus apartments, married-student housing, and fraternity houses. In addition there are honors houses. On-campus housing is guaranteed for the freshman year only and is available on a first-come, first-served basis. Priority is given to out-of-town students. Seventy percent of students live on campus; of those, 60% remain on campus on weekends. Alcohol is not permitted. All students may keep cars on campus.

Activities: About 20% of men belong to 3 national fraternities; about 8% of women belong to 2 national sororities. There are 40 groups on campus, including art, band, cheerleading, chess, choir, chorale, chorus, computers, dance, drama, drill team, film, honors, international, jazz band, literary magazine, marching band, musical theater, newspaper, pep band, photography, political, radio and TV, religious, social service, student government, and yearbook. Popular campus events include Homecoming, Spring Fling, and Alumni Weekend.

Sports: There are 7 intercollegiate sports for men and 7 for women, and 6 intramural sports for men and 6 for women. Athletic and recreation facilities include outdoor and indoor pools; a gymnasium; weight rooms; a 5000-seat stadium; and softball, baseball, soccer, and track fields.

Disabled Students: Twenty percent of the campus is accessible to disabled students. The following facilities are available: wheelchair ramps, elevators, special parking, specially equipped rest rooms, special class scheduling, lowered drinking fountains, and lowered telephones.

Services: In addition to many counseling and information services, tutoring is available in every subject. There is a reader service for the blind.

Campus Safety and Security: Campus safety and security measures include 24-hour foot and vehicle patrol, escort service, informal discussions, pamphlets, posters, and films. In addition, there are emergency telephones and lighted pathways and sidewalks.

Programs of Study: Lindenwood awards the B.A., B.S., B.A.Ed., and B.F.A. degrees. Master's degrees also are awarded. Bachelor's degrees are awarded in BIOLOGICAL SCIENCE (biology/biological science), BUSINESS (business administration and management and fashion merchandising), COMMUNICATIONS AND THE ARTS (communications, dramatic arts, English, fine arts, and music), COMPUTER AND PHYSICAL SCIENCE (chemistry, computer science, and mathematics), EDUCATION (art, business, early childhood, elementary, middle school, music, science, and secondary), SOCIAL

SCIENCE (history, political science/government, prelaw, and psychology). Biology, education, mass communications, and business are the strongest academically. Business, education, mass communications, and sciences have the largest enrollments.

Required: In order to graduate, students must complete a minimum 120 credit hours, at least 42 of which must be upper-division courses, and core curriculum courses as follows: 13 hours of mathematics and science; 9 hours each of social sciences, humanities, and civilization; 6 hours of English; and 3 hours of fine arts. At least 36 hours in the major are required, as is a minimum 2.0 GPA.

Special: The college offers internships in most majors, a co-op program in computer sciences, study abroad and a Washington semester for juniors, and cross-registration with the Greater St. Louis College Consortium. The B.A.-B.S. degree, dual and student-designed majors, accelerated degree programs, 3–2 degrees in engineering and social work with Washington University in St. Louis, work-study programs, and nondegree study are also available. The college is also designed to meet the needs of working adults; there are evening and weekend classes and 5-year bachelor's programs. There are 4 national honor societies on campus.

Faculty/Classroom: All teach undergraduates. No introductory courses are taught by graduate students. The average class size in an introductory lecture is 25; in a laboratory, 20; and in a regular course offering, 20.

Admissions: About 50% of the 1993–94 applicants were accepted. The ACT scores for the 1993–94 freshman class were as follows: 39% below 21, 34% between 21 and 23, 15% between 24 and 26, 8% between 27 and 28, and 4% above 28. About 21% of the current freshmen were in the top fifth of their class; 56% were in the top two fifths. There was 1 National Merit finalist. Four freshmen graduated first in their class.

Requirements: Lindenwood requires applicants to be in the upper 50% of their class. A minimum GPA of 2.0 is required. The SAT I or ACT is required. The minimum required score on the ACT is 18. Applicants must be graduates of an accredited secondary school or have a GED. High school transcripts are required; an essay and an interview are recommended. AP and CLEP credits are accepted. Important factors used in the admissions decision are evidence of special talent, advanced placement or honor courses, leadership record, parents or siblings attending the school, and recommendations by alumni.

Procedure: Freshmen are admitted to all sessions. Application deadlines are open. Application fee is $25. Notification is sent on a rolling basis. There are early admissions and deferred admissions plans.

Transfer: About 210 transfer students enrolled in 1993–94. Transfer applicants must have a minimum GPA of 2.0. A total of 30 credits out of 120 must be completed at Lindenwood.

Visiting: There are regularly scheduled orientations for prospective students, including an admissions interview, a campus tour, and advising. There are guides for informal visits and visitors may sit in on classes and stay overnight at the school. To arrange for a visit, contact the Office of Undergraduate Admissions at (314) 949-4949.

Financial Aid: In a recent year, 90% of all students received some form of financial aid, and 50% received need-based aid. The average freshman award was $7400. Of that total, scholarships or need-based grants averaged $3500; loans averaged $2400; and work contracts averaged $1500. One-hundred-thirty-five percent of undergraduate students work part-time. Average earnings from campus work for the school year are $1500. The average financial indebtedness of the 1992–93 graduate was $9000. Lindenwood is a member of CSS. The FAFSA financial statement is required. The deadline for financial aid applications is April 30.

International Students: There are currently 40 international students enrolled. The school actively recruits these students. They must take the TOEFL or the University of Michigan Language Test and achieve a minimum score on the TOEFL of 500.

Computers: The college provides computer facilities for student use. The mainframe is a DEC VAX 11/750. There are also 65 microcomputers, 10 of which are networked, in the library and the science and business halls. All students may access the system. It may be used 8 A.M. to 11 P.M. There are no time limits on using the system and no fees.

Graduates: In 1992–93, 480 bachelor's degrees were awarded. The most popular majors among graduates were business administration (30%), communications (16%), and education (11%). Within an average freshman class, 44% graduate in 4 years and 44% in 5 years. Some 20 companies recruited on campus in 1992–93. In the 1992 graduating class, 13% of all graduates were enrolled in graduate school within 6 months of graduation; 85% had found employment.

Admissions Contact: Lise Keller, Director of Admissions.

MARYVILLE UNIVERSITY-SAINT LOUIS   D-2

St. Louis, MO 63141   (314) 576-9350; (800) MARYVLL

Full-time: 460 men, 883 women	Faculty: 82; IIA, --$
Part-time: 500 men, 1251 women	Ph.D.s: 58%
Graduate: 204 men, 466 women	Student/Faculty: 16 to 1
Year: semesters, summer session	Tuition: $8700
Application Deadline: open	Room & Board: $4200
Freshman Class: 557 applied, 375 accepted, 169 enrolled	
ACT: 24	**VERY COMPETITIVE**

Maryville University-Saint Louis, established in 1872, is a private coeducational facility offering undergraduate programs in arts and sciences, business, education, and health-related fields. There are 4 undergraduate and 2 graduate schools. In addition to regional accreditation, Maryville has baccalaureate program accreditation with APTA, FIDER, NASAD, NCATE, and NLN. The library contains 140,725 volumes, 275,025 microform items, and 5679 audiovisual forms, and subscribes to 750 periodicals. Computerized library sources and services include interlibrary loans and database searching. Special learning facilities include an art gallery and an observatory. The 130-acre campus is in a suburban area 20 miles west of downtown St. Louis. Including residence halls, there are 11 buildings on campus.

Student Life: About 95% of undergraduates are from Missouri. Students come from 16 states. Sixty-six percent are from public schools; 34% from private. Eighty-five percent are white. Thirty-two percent are Catholic; 18% Protestant. The average age of freshmen is 19; all undergraduates, 35. Twenty percent drop out by the end of their first year.

Housing: A total of 372 students can be accommodated in college housing. College-sponsored living facilities include single-sex and coed dormitories. On-campus housing is guaranteed for all 4 years. Eighty-eight percent of students commute. All students may keep cars on campus.

Activities: There are no fraternities or sororities on campus. There are 31 groups on campus, including band, cheerleading, choir, chorale, drama, ethnic, honors, international, jazz band, literary magazine, newspaper, professional, radio and TV, religious, social service, and student government. Popular campus events include Fake Greek Week, Homecoming, Love Day, Martin Luther King, Jr., Day, and Christmas Open House.

Sports: There are 7 intercollegiate sports for men and 6 for women, and 8 intramural sports for men and 8 for women. Athletic and recreation facilities include a pool, tennis courts, soccer, softball, and baseball fields, a gymnasium, and a weight table.

Disabled Students: Ninety percent of the campus is accessible to disabled students. The following facilities are available: wheelchair ramps, elevators, special parking, specially equipped rest rooms, special class scheduling, lowered drinking fountains, and lowered telephones.

Services: In addition to many counseling and information services, tutoring is available in most subjects. There is also a reader service for the blind and remedial writing.

Campus Safety and Security: Campus safety and security measures include 24-hour foot and vehicle patrol, escort service, emergency telephones, and lighted pathways and sidewalks.

Programs of Study: Maryville awards the B.A., B.S., B.F.A., and B.S.Ed. degrees. Master's degrees also are awarded. Bachelor's degrees are awarded in BIOLOGICAL SCIENCE (biology/biological science), BUSINESS (accounting, management science, and marketing/retailing/merchandising), COMMUNICATIONS AND THE ARTS (communications and studio art), COMPUTER AND PHYSICAL SCIENCE (actuarial science, chemistry, information sciences and systems, and mathematics), EDUCATION (art, early childhood, elementary, science, and secondary), ENGINEERING AND ENVIRONMENTAL DESIGN (interior design), HEALTH PROFESSIONS (health care administration, medical laboratory technology, music therapy, nursing, physical therapy, predentistry, premedicine, and preoccupational therapy), SOCIAL SCIENCE (history, political science/government, prelaw, psychology, religion, and sociology). Actuarial science and physical therapy are the strongest academically. Physical therapy, management, and nursing have the largest enrollments.

Required: All students must complete courses in the humanities, social sciences, mathematics, natural science, communications skills, and fine arts. A total of 128 credit hours is required for graduation, with 40 to 48 credit hours in the major. All students must have a minimum GPA of 2.0.

Special: Opportunities are available for co-op programs in most majors. There is cross-registration with Fontbonne, Lindenwood, and Missouri Baptist colleges, and Webster University. Students may choose internships at various St. Louis businesses. Accelerated degree programs are possible in psychology/sociology, education, and business. Other options include dual majors, study abroad in England

and Japan, a Washington semester, graduate-level courses in social work, management, and psychology, nondegree study, and pass-fail options. A 3-2 engineering degree is available in conjunction with Washington University. There is a freshman honors program on campus, as well as 6 national honor societies.

Faculty/Classroom: Forty-two percent of faculty are male; 58%, female. All teach undergraduates. No introductory courses are taught by graduate students. The average class size in a regular course offering is 30.

Admissions: About 67% of the 1993-94 applicants were accepted. The ACT scores for the 1993-94 freshman class were as follows: 25% below 21, 25% between 21 and 23, 21% between 24 and 26, 16% between 27 and 28, and 13% above 28. About 47% of the current freshmen were in the top fifth of their class; 74% were in the top two fifths. Seven freshmen graduated first in their class.

Requirements: Maryville requires applicants to be in the upper 50% of their class. A minimum GPA of 2.0 is required. The ACT, with a minimum score of 20, or the SAT I is required. Students must have graduated from an accredited secondary school with 14 academic credits or have the GED. Required preparatory courses include 4 units of English, 2 each of science and social studies, 3 each of mathematics and a foreign language, plus 8 electives. Art students must submit a portfolio. AP and CLEP credits are accepted. Important factors used in the admissions decision are advanced placement or honor courses, leadership record, recommendations by school officials, extracurricular activities record, and parents or siblings attending the school.

Procedure: Freshmen are admitted to all sessions. Application deadlines are open. The application fee is $20. Notification is sent on a rolling basis.

Transfer: About 620 transfer students enrolled in 1993-94. A minimum GPA of 2.0, higher for some majors, is required. Some majors may require ACT or SAT I scores. A total of 30 credits out of 128 must be completed at Maryville.

Visiting: There are regularly scheduled orientations for prospective students. There are guides for informal visits and visitors may sit in on classes and stay overnight at the school. To arrange for a visit, contact the Dean of Admissions and Enrollment Management at (314) 576-9350 or (800) MARYVLL.

Financial Aid: In 1993-94, 94% of all current freshmen and 45% of continuing students received some form of financial aid. About 46% of freshmen and 36% of continuing students received need-based aid. Scholarships or need-based grants averaged $2981 ($14,580 maximum); loans averaged $1562 ($14,580 maximum); and work contracts averaged $1087 ($2000 maximum). Eighteen percent of undergraduate students work part-time. Average earnings from campus work for the school year are $1224. The average financial indebtedness of the 1992-93 graduate was $7371. Maryville is a member of CSS. The FAF, FFS, or SFS, and FAFSA are required. The deadline for financial aid applications is July 31.

International Students: There are currently 215 international students enrolled. The school actively recruits these students. They must take the TOEFL and achieve a minimum score of 500.

Computers: The university provides computer facilities for student use. There are more than 150 IBM compatible, Apple II, and Macintosh microcomputers available for academic use at several computer centers and the library. All students may access the system 8 A.M. to 10 P.M. There are no time limits and no fees.

Graduates: In 1992-93, 497 bachelor's degrees were awarded. The most popular majors among graduates were management (16%), information systems (7%), and accounting (7%). Some 20 companies recruited on campus in an earlier year. In the 1992 graduating class, 96% of the men and 96% of the women had found employment within 6 months of graduation.

Admissions Contact: Martha Wade, Dean of Admissions and Enrollment Management.

MISSOURI BAPTIST COLLEGE

D-2

St. Louis, MO 63141 (314) 434-1115

Full-time: 248 men, 286 women	Faculty: 31; IIB, --$
Part-time: 413 men, 805 women	Ph.D.s: 55%
Graduate: 655 men, 1067 women	Student/Faculty: 17 to 1
Year: semesters, summer session	Tuition: $6440
Application Deadline: n/av	Room & Board: $2900
Freshman Class: 180 applied, 160 accepted, 110 enrolled	
ACT: 20	COMPETITIVE

Missouri Baptist College, established in 1964, is a private coeducational liberal arts institution affiliated with the Missouri Baptist Convention. The library contains 110,000 volumes, 5531 microform items, and 1661 audiovisual forms, and subscribes to 391 periodicals. Computerized library sources and services include database searching. Special learning facilities include an audiovisual production laboratory. The 63-acre campus is in a suburban area 15 miles west of St. Louis. Including residence halls, there are 5 buildings on campus.

Student Life: About 94% of undergraduates are from Missouri. Students come from 11 states and 17 foreign countries. Eighty percent are from public schools; 20% from private. Eighty-one percent are white; 17% African American. Sixty-five percent are Protestant; 30% Catholic. The average age of freshmen is 19; all undergraduates, 23.

Housing: A total of 114 students can be accommodated in college housing. College-sponsored living facilities include single-sex dormitories. On-campus housing is available on a first-come, first-served basis. Eighty-eight percent of students commute. Alcohol is not permitted. All students may keep cars on campus.

Activities: There are no fraternities or sororities on campus. There are 13 groups on campus, including cheerleading, choir, chorale, chorus, drama, honors, musical theater, newspaper, pep band, professional, religious, student government, and yearbook. Popular campus events include Homecoming, Spring Musical, Christmas Concert, Hanging of the Green, and Spring Banquet.

Sports: There are 7 intercollegiate sports for men and 6 for women, and 4 intramural sports for men and 4 for women. Athletic and recreation facilities include baseball, softball, and soccer fields, a gymnasium, a weight and training room, and a game room.

Disabled Students: Fifty percent of the campus is accessible to disabled students. The following facilities are available: wheelchair ramps, special parking, specially equipped rest rooms, special class scheduling, and lowered drinking fountains.

Services: There is a reader service for the blind.

Campus Safety and Security: Campus safety and security measures include lighted pathways and sidewalks and 24-hour foot patrol.

Programs of Study: Mo Bap awards the B.A., B.S., B.S.Ed., and B.S.N. degrees. Associate degrees also are awarded. Bachelor's degrees are awarded in BIOLOGICAL SCIENCE (biology/biological science), BUSINESS (accounting and business administration and management), COMMUNICATIONS AND THE ARTS (music), COMPUTER AND PHYSICAL SCIENCE (chemistry, information sciences and systems, and mathematics), EDUCATION (elementary and physical), HEALTH PROFESSIONS (nursing), SOCIAL SCIENCE (behavioral science, history, psychology, religion, religious education, social science, and sociology). Business, education, and music are the strongest academically. Business, education, and music also have the largest enrollments.

Required: All students must take courses in the humanities, social sciences, natural sciences, physical education, computer literacy, and Old and New Testament history. A minimum GPA of 2.0 is required. To graduate, students must complete a total of 128 credit hours, with a minimum of 30 hours in the major.

Special: There is cross-registration with Fontbonne, Maryville, and Lindenwood colleges and Webster University. Students may opt for credit by examination, nondegree study, student-designed majors, and a 3-2 engineering degree with the University of Missouri/Columbia or University of Missouri at Rolla. Study abroad is possible at Harlaxton College in England and internships in business and computers are available. There is one national honor society on campus. Two departments have honors programs.

Faculty/Classroom: Sixty-three percent of faculty are male; 37%, female. No introductory courses are taught by graduate students. The average class size in an introductory lecture is 28; in a laboratory, 14; and in a regular course offering, 12.

Admissions: About 89% of the 1993-94 applicants were accepted. About 14 freshmen graduated first in their class.

Requirements: Mo Bap requires applicants to be in the upper 50% of their class. A minimum GPA of 2.0 is required. The SAT I or ACT is recommended. Applicants must be graduates of an accredited secondary school. AP credits are accepted. Important factors used in the admissions decision are advanced placement or honor courses, leadership record, evidence of special talent, ability to finance college education, and personality, intangible qualities.

Procedure: Freshmen are admitted to all sessions. Early decision applications should be filed by April 1, along with an application fee of $20. For fall entry decision dates, contact the school. Notification is sent on a rolling basis. There are early decision and early admissions plans.

Transfer: About 211 transfer students enrolled in 1993-94. A total of 28 credits out of 128 must be completed at Mo Bap.

Visiting: There are guides for informal visits and visitors may sit in on classes and stay overnight at the school. To arrange for a visit, contact the Admissions Office at (314) 434-1115, ext. 232.

Financial Aid: In 1993-94, 90% of all current freshmen and 87% of continuing students received some form of financial aid. Scholarships or need-based grants averaged $2495 ($4990 maximum); loans averaged $2625 (maximum); and work contracts averaged $600 (maximum). Eighty-five percent of undergraduate students work part-time. Mo Bap is a member of CSS. The FAF or FFS, the college's own financial statement, and FAFSA are required. The deadline for financial aid applications is April 30.

International Students: There are currently 54 international students enrolled. The school actively recruits these students. They must take the TOEFL and achieve a minimum score of 500. The student must also take the ACT and achieve a minimum score of 18.
Computers: The college provides computer facilities for student use. The mainframe is a Texas Instruments 990. There are 16 IBM PCs available for academic use in the computer laboratory. All students may access the system. It may be used 9 a.m to 5 p.m by appointment. There are no time limits and no fees.
Graduates: In a recent year, 80 bachelor's degrees were awarded.
Admissions Contact: Gloria Price, Director of Admissions.

MISSOURI SOUTHERN STATE COLLEGE

A-4

Joplin, MO 64801   (417) 625-9300; (800) 492-4811 (in-state)

Full-time: 1638 men, 2012 women	Faculty: 194; IIB, av$
Part-time: 823 men, 1193 women	Ph.D.s: 47%
Graduate: none	Student/Faculty: 19 to 1
Year: semesters, summer session	Tuition: $1572 ($3074)
Application Deadline: August 23	Room & Board: $2700
Freshman Class: 1750 applied, 1725 accepted, 711 enrolled	
ACT: 20	NONCOMPETITIVE

Missouri Southern State College, founded in 1937, is a public, coeducational, primarily commuter institution offering undergraduate degree programs in the arts and sciences, business, education, psychology, and technology. There are 4 undergraduate and 4 graduate schools. In addition to regional accreditation, MSSC has baccalaureate program accreditation with NCATE and NLN. The library contains 160,384 volumes, and 387,575 audiovisual forms, and subscribes to 1215 periodicals. Computerized library sources and services include the card catalog, interlibrary loans, and database searching. Special learning facilities include a learning resource center, art gallery, radio station, tv station, a biology pond, and a nursery. The 315-acre campus is in a small town 120 miles south of Kansas City. Including residence halls, there are 39 buildings on campus.
Student Life: About 92% of undergraduates are from Missouri. Students come from 21 states, 7 foreign countries, and Canada. Ninety-eight percent are from public schools; 2% from private. Eighty-nine percent are white. Forty percent are Protestant; 40% Catholic; 15% claim no religious affiliation; 15% unknown. The average age of freshmen is 20; all undergraduates, 28. Forty percent drop out by the end of their first year; 60% remain to graduate.
Housing: A total of 560 students can be accommodated in college housing. College-sponsored living facilities include single-sex dormitories and on-campus apartments. On-campus housing is guaranteed for the freshman year only and is available on a first-come, first-served basis. Ninety-one percent of students commute. Alcohol is not permitted. All students may keep cars on campus.
Activities: About 1% of men belong to 2 local and 2 national fraternities; about 1% of women belong to 1 local and 2 national sororities. There are 59 groups on campus, including art, band, cheerleading, chess, choir, chorale, chorus, computers, drama, film, honors, international, jazz band, literary magazine, marching band, musical theater, newspaper, orchestra, pep band, photography, political, professional, radio and TV, religious, social, student government, symphony, and yearbook. Popular campus events include Spring Fling and Homecoming.
Sports: There are 5 intercollegiate sports for men and 5 for women, and 5 intramural sports for men and 4 for women. Athletic and recreation facilities include a 10,000-seat astroturf football stadium, a 4000-seat gymnasium, a 4000-seat auditorium, a swimming pool, and a weight room.
Disabled Students: Ninety-nine percent of the campus is accessible to disabled students. The following facilities are available: wheelchair ramps, elevators, special parking, specially equipped rest rooms, special class scheduling, lowered drinking fountains, and lowered telephones.
Services: In addition to many counseling and information services, tutoring is available in most subjects. There is also a reader service for the blind, and remedial math, reading, and writing available. Assistance is also provided for improving time management and test-taking skills.
Campus Safety and Security: Campus safety and security measures include 24-hour foot and vehicle patrol, self defense education, escort service, and informal discussions. In addition, there are pamphlets, posters, films, emergency telephones, and lighted pathways and sidewalks.
Programs of Study: MSSC awards the B.A., B.S., B.S.B.A, B.S.E., and B.G.S. degrees. Associate degrees also are awarded. Bachelor's degrees are awarded in BIOLOGICAL SCIENCE (biology/biological science), BUSINESS (accounting, business administration and management, business economics, and marketing/retailing/merchandising), COMMUNICATIONS AND THE ARTS (broadcasting, communications, dramatic arts, English, fine arts, music, and Spanish), COMPUTER AND PHYSICAL SCIENCE (chemistry, computer programming, information sciences and systems, mathematics, and physics), EDUCATION (art, business, early childhood, elementary, industrial arts, music, science, secondary, and special), HEALTH PROFESSIONS (medical laboratory technology, nursing, predentistry, and premedicine), SOCIAL SCIENCE (criminal justice, history, political science/government, prelaw, psychology, social science, and sociology). Business and education have the largest enrollments.
Required: General education requirements include a total of 51 credit hours, with 15 in basic studies, 12 each in science and cultural studies, 9 in humanities, and 3 in international studies. Students must also demonstrate proficiency in computer skills and writing. To graduate, students must complete at least 128 credit hours, including a minimum of 40 in the major, and present a minimum GPA of 2.0, 2.75 for the B.S.E.
Special: Students may study abroad in Oxford, England. MSSC also offers part-time accounting internships within the state, a general studies degree, and credit for life experience. Nondegree study is possible. There is a freshman honors program on campus, as well as one national honor society. Four departments have honors programs.
Faculty/Classroom: Seventy-one percent of faculty are male; 29%, female. All teach undergraduates. The average class size in an introductory lecture is 30; in a laboratory, 25; and in a regular course offering, 30.
Admissions: About 99% of the 1993-94 applicants were accepted. The ACT scores for the 1993-94 freshman class were as follows: 15% below 21, 40% between 21 and 23, 25% between 24 and 26, 15% between 27 and 28, and 5% above 28. About 20% of the current freshmen were in the top fifth of their class; 40% were in the top two fifths. There were 4 National Merit semifinalists. About 27 freshmen graduated first in their class.
Requirements: MSSC requires applicants to be in the upper 50% of their class. The ACT is required with a minimum composite score of 17. Applicants must be graduates of accredited secondary schools or have earned a GED. The college recommends completion of 16 Carnegie units in college preparatory courses. AP and CLEP credits are accepted. Important factors used in the admissions decision are advanced placement or honor courses, recommendations by school officials, ability to finance college education, parents or siblings attending the school, and recommendations by alumni.
Procedure: Freshmen are admitted to all sessions. Entrance exams should be taken during the junior year. Applications should be filed by August 23 for fall entry, January 16 for spring entry, and June 1 for summer entry, along with an application fee of $10. Notification is sent on a rolling basis. There are early decision, early admissions, and deferred admissions plans. About 20 early decision candidates were accepted for the 1993-94 class.
Transfer: About 563 transfer students enrolled in 1993-94. Applicants must present a minimum ACT composite score of 17 and a GPA of 2.0. A total of 64 credits out of 128 must be completed at MSSC.
Visiting: There are regularly scheduled orientations for prospective students, including a preenrollment tour during the summer. There are guides for informal visits and visitors may sit in on classes and stay overnight at the school. To arrange for a visit, contact Doug Carnahan at (417) 625-9300.
Financial Aid: In 1993-94 67% of all current freshmen and 7% of continuing students received some form of financial aid. About 63% of freshmen and 7% of continuing students received need-based aid. The average freshman award was $2300. Of that total, scholarships or need-based grants averaged $700 ($3000 maximum); loans averaged $1400 ($1500 maximum); and work contracts averaged $1300 ($1500 maximum). Eighty-three percent of undergraduate students work part-time. Average earnings from campus work for the school year are $2300. The average financial indebtedness of the 1992-93 graduate was $2200. MSSC is a member of CSS. The FAF or FFS, the college's own financial statement, and FAFSA are required. The deadline for financial aid applications is August 1.
International Students: There are currently 18 international students enrolled. The school actively recruits these students. They must take the TOEFL or the University of Michigan Language Test and achieve a minimum score on the TOEFL of 535. The student must also take the SAT I or the ACT and achieve a minimum score of 700 composite on the SAT I or a minimum score of 17 on the ACT.
Computers: The college provides computer facilities for student use. The mainframe is an IBM 4361. There are 350 IBM and Apple II microcomputers available for student use by appointment in the computer center and laboratory. All students may access the system. There are no time limits on using the system. The fees are $20.
Graduates: In 1992-93, 740 bachelor's degrees were awarded. The most popular majors among graduates were business (59%), education (25%), and arts and science (16%). Within an average freshman class, 54% graduate in 4 years and 73% in 5 years. Some 28 companies recruited on campus in 1992-93. In the 1992 graduating class, 16% of the men and 9% of the women were enrolled in graduate school within 6 months of graduation; 40% of the men and 42% of the

women had found employment.

Admissions Contact: Richard D. Humphrey, Director of Admissions.

MISSOURI VALLEY COLLEGE
B-2

Marshall, MO 65340   (816) 886-6924, ext. 114

Full-time: 632 men, 426 women	Faculty: 59; IIB, --$
Part-time: 45 men and women	Ph.D.s: 58%
Graduate: none	Student/Faculty: 18 to 1
Year: 4-1-4, summer session	Tuition: $9100
Application Deadline: open	Room & Board: $4950
Freshman Class: 930 applied, 783 accepted, 316 enrolled	
SAT I Verbal/Math: 380/380	ACT: 19 LESS COMPETITIVE

Missouri Valley College, founded in 1889, is a private, coeducational liberal arts college affiliated with the Presbyterian Church, U.S.A., offering programs in business, art, music, education, and religious studies. The library contains 71,000 volumes and 307 audiovisual forms, and subscribes to 400 periodicals. Special learning facilities include a learning resource center, radio station, and TV station. The 80-acre campus is in a small town 80 miles from Kansas City. Including residence halls, there are 15 buildings on campus.

Student Life: About 70% of undergraduates are from Missouri. Students come from 33 states, 10 foreign countries, and Canada. Seventy-five percent are from public schools; 25% from private. Seventy-six percent are white; 15% African American. The average age of freshmen is 19; all undergraduates, 20.

Housing: A total of 1000 students can be accommodated in college housing. College-sponsored living facilities include single-sex dormitories, on-campus apartments, married-student housing, fraternity houses, and sorority houses. In addition there are honors houses and special interest houses. On-campus housing is guaranteed for all 4 years. Eighty percent of students live on campus; of those, 70% remain on campus on weekends. Alcohol is not permitted. All students may keep cars on campus.

Activities: About 20% of men belong to 2 local and 4 national fraternities; about 15% of women belong to 1 local and 3 national sororities. There are 40 groups on campus, including art, band, cheerleading, choir, chorale, chorus, computers, dance, drama, drill team, drum and bugle corps, ethnic, film, honors, international, jazz band, literary magazine, musical theater, newspaper, orchestra, pep band, photography, radio and TV, religious, social, social service, student government, symphony, and yearbook. Popular campus events include Homecoming and Greek Week.

Sports: There are 8 intercollegiate sports for men and 7 for women, and 7 intramural sports for men and 7 for women. Athletic and recreation facilities include a 2000-seat gymnasium; tennis, basketball, and racquetball courts; a bowling alley; a football field; and a 1000-seat stadium.

Disabled Students: The following facilities are available: wheelchair ramps, elevators, special parking, and specially equipped rest rooms.

Services: In addition to counseling and information services, there is remedial math, reading, and writing.

Campus Safety and Security: Campus safety and security measures include 24-hour foot and vehicle patrol, informal discussions, pamphlets, posters, films, and emergency telephones. In addition, there are lighted pathways and sidewalks.

Programs of Study: MVC awards the B.A. and and B.S. degrees. Associate degrees also are awarded. Bachelor's degrees are awarded in AGRICULTURE (agricultural business management), BIOLOGICAL SCIENCE (biology/biological science), BUSINESS (accounting, business administration and management, and marketing/retailing/merchandising), COMMUNICATIONS AND THE ARTS (communications, dramatic arts, English, fine arts, and speech/debate/rhetoric), COMPUTER AND PHYSICAL SCIENCE (actuarial science, computer science, and mathematics), EDUCATION (elementary and physical), SOCIAL SCIENCE (economics, history, human services, philosophy, political science/government, psychology, public administration, religion, social science, and sociology). Education is the strongest academically. Business administration, physical education, and psychology have the largest enrollments.

Required: All students must complete 128 credit hours, including 35 to 40 hours in their major, with a GPA of at least 2.0. Distribution requirements include the core curriculum of English, physical education, mathematics, fine arts, and science. A computer course is strongly recommended.

Special: Student-designed majors, internships, work-study, study abroad, nondegree study, pass/fail options, a 3-2 engineering degree, dual majors, and a B.A.-B.S. degree are available. There are 3 national honor societies on campus, including Phi Beta Kappa.

Faculty/Classroom: Seventy-three percent of faculty are male; 27%, female. All teach undergraduates. The average class size in an introductory lecture is 30; in a laboratory, 25; and in a regular course offering, 28.

Admissions: About 84% of the 1993-94 applicants were accepted. The ACT scores for the 1993-94 freshman class were as follows: 50% below 21, 38% between 21 and 23, and 12% between 24 and 26. About 17% of the current freshmen were in the top fifth of their class; 50% were in the top two fifths. There were 5 National Merit semifinalists. Two freshmen graduated first in their class.

Requirements: The SAT I or ACT is recommended. Students must have graduated from an accredited secondary school or have the GED. AP and CLEP credits are accepted. Important factors used in the admissions decision are leadership record, recommendations by alumni, recommendations by school officials, parents or siblings attending the school, and advanced placement or honor courses.

Procedure: Freshmen are admitted to all sessions. Application deadlines are open, but recommended deadlines are August 15 for fall entry, December 15 for winter entry, January 15 for spring entry, and May 15 for summer entry. Application fee is $10. Notification is sent on a rolling basis.

Transfer: A minimum GPA of 2.0 is required; D grades do not transfer. A total of 64 credits out of 128 must be completed at MVC.

Visiting: There are guides for informal visits and visitors may sit in on classes and stay overnight at the school. To arrange for a visit, contact Chad Freeman, Director of Admission at (816) 886-6924.

Financial Aid: In a recent year, 98% of all students received some form of financial aid. Scholarships or need-based grants averaged $1500; loans averaged $2120; and work contracts averaged $1500. Eighty percent of undergraduate students work part-time. Average earnings from campus work for the school year are $1500. MVC is a member of CSS. The FAF, FFS, or SFS is required.

International Students: The school actively recruits international students. They must take the TOEFL and achieve a minimum score of 500. The student must also take the SAT I or the ACT, and SAT II: Subject tests.

Computers: The college provides computer facilities for student use. The mainframe is an IBM System 34. There are also 30 microcomputers available on campus. All students may access the system. There are no time limits on using the system and no fees.

Graduates: In a recent year, 128 bachelor's degrees were awarded. The most popular majors among graduates were business (42%), education (38%), and human services (12%).

Admissions Contact: Chad Freeman, Director of Admissions and Financial Aid.

MISSOURI WESTERN STATE COLLEGE
A-2

St. Joseph, MO 64507   (816) 271-4266
                              (800) 662-7041 (out-of-state)

Full-time: 1488 men, 2127 women	Faculty: 160; IIB, -$
Part-time: 540 men, 966 women	Ph.D.s: 54%
Graduate: none	Student/Faculty: 23 to 1
Year: semesters, summer session	Tuition: $1930 ($3676)
Application Deadline: August 1	Room & Board: $2454
Freshman Class: 1187 applied, 1175 accepted, 926 enrolled	
ACT: 19	NONCOMPETITIVE

Missouri Western State College, founded in 1915, is a public institution offering undergraduate degrees in the arts and sciences, business administration, education, nursing, technology, and social work. There are 2 undergraduate schools. In addition to regional accreditation, MWSC has baccalaureate program accreditation with ABET, CSWE, NASM, NCATE, and NLN. The library contains 164,883 volumes, 93,896 microform items, and 6000 audiovisual forms, and subscribes to 1374 periodicals. Computerized library sources and services include the card catalog, interlibrary loans, and database searching. Special learning facilities include a learning resource center, planetarium, and a biology nature study area. The 740-acre campus is in a suburban area 50 miles north of Kansas City. Including residence halls, there are 15 buildings on campus.

Student Life: About 91% of undergraduates are from Missouri. Students come from 28 states, 10 foreign countries, and Canada. Ninety percent are white. The average age of freshmen is 20; all undergraduates, 26. Forty-three percent drop out by the end of their first year; 39% remain to graduate.

Housing: A total of 850 students can be accommodated in college housing. College-sponsored living facilities include single-sex and coed dormitories and on-campus apartments. On-campus housing is available on a first-come, first-served basis. Eighty-three percent of students commute. Alcohol is not permitted. All students may keep cars on campus.

Activities: About 4% of men belong to 4 national fraternities; about 2% of women belong to 3 national sororities. There are 45 groups on campus, including art, band, cheerleading, choir, dance, drama, ethnic, honors, international, jazz band, marching band, musical theater, newspaper, pep band, political, professional, religious, social, social service, student government, symphony, and yearbook. Popular campus events include Spring fest, Fall Convocation, Homecoming, and Family Day.

Sports: There are 4 intercollegiate sports for men and 4 for women, and 20 intramural sports for men and 20 for women. Athletic and recreation facilities include tennis and racquetball courts, a 6000-seat football stadium, a 468-seat auditorium, a swimming pool, a jogging/walking trail, a weight-training room, a baseball field, a trapshooting range, a volleyball area, and 2 gymnasiums, the larger seating 4000.

Disabled Students: Ninety-nine percent of the campus is accessible to disabled students. The following facilities are available: wheelchair ramps, elevators, special parking, specially equipped rest rooms, lowered drinking fountains, and lowered telephones.

Services: In addition to many counseling and information services, tutoring is available in some subjects. There is also remedial math, reading, and writing available.

Campus Safety and Security: Campus safety and security measures include 24-hour foot and vehicle patrol, escort service, informal discussions, pamphlets, posters, and films. In addition, there are lighted pathways and sidewalks.

Programs of Study: MWSC awards the B.A., B.S., B.S.B.A., B.S.E., B.S.N., B.S.T., and B.S.W. degrees. Associate degrees also are awarded. Bachelor's degrees are awarded in BIOLOGICAL SCIENCE (biology/biological science), BUSINESS (accounting, business administration and management, and marketing/retailing/merchandising), COMMUNICATIONS AND THE ARTS (communications, English, fine arts, French, music, Spanish, and speech/debate/rhetoric), COMPUTER AND PHYSICAL SCIENCE (chemistry, computer programming, computer science, information sciences and systems, mathematics, and natural sciences), EDUCATION (art, early childhood, elementary, foreign languages, music, and secondary), ENGINEERING AND ENVIRONMENTAL DESIGN (commercial art and engineering technology), HEALTH PROFESSIONS (medical laboratory technology and nursing), SOCIAL SCIENCE (criminal justice, economics, history, parks and recreation management, political science/government, psychology, and social work). Physical sciences is the strongest academically. Business, education, nursing, and criminal justice have the largest enrollments.

Required: The core curriculum consists of 4 credit hours of physical health, 8 to 10 of natural sciences, 9 to 10 of humanities, 9 of social sciences, and 12 of basic skills, which include English composition, algebra, and speech. To graduate, students must complete at least 124 credit hours, 45 to 71 in the major, with a minimum GPA of 2.0.

Special: Special academic features include internships, work-study programs with local employers, dual majors, a 3–2 engineering degree program with the University of Missouri/Rolla, credit for life experience, pass/fail options, and nondegree study. There is a freshman honors program on campus, as well as 6 national honor societies. Twelve departments have honors programs.

Faculty/Classroom: Sixty-seven percent of faculty are male; 33%, female. All teach undergraduates. The average class size in an introductory lecture is 35; in a laboratory, 25; and in a regular course offering, 25.

Admissions: About 99% of the 1993–94 applicants were accepted. The ACT scores for the 1993–94 freshman class were as follows: 69% below 21, 18% between 21 and 23, 9% between 24 and 26, 2% between 27 and 28, and 1% above 28. About 20% of the current freshmen were in the top fifth of their class; 47% were in the top two fifths. About 37 freshmen graduated first in their class.

Requirements: The ACT is required. Applicants must be graduates of an accredited secondary school or have earned a GED. AP and CLEP credits are accepted.

Procedure: Freshmen are admitted to all sessions. Entrance exams should be taken at least 6 months prior to enrollment. Applications should be filed by August 1 for fall entry, December 20 for spring entry, and May 15 for summer entry, along with an application fee of $30. The college accepts all applicants.

Transfer: About 358 transfer students enrolled in 1993–94. The required GPA depends on the number of credit hours completed, but a minimum of 2.0 is standard. A total of 30 credits out of 124 must be completed at MWSC.

Visiting: There are regularly scheduled orientations for prospective students. There are guides for informal visits. To arrange for a visit, contact the Admissions office at (816) 271–4266 or (800) 662–7041.

Financial Aid: In an earlier year, 85% of continuing students received some form of financial aid. Fifty-five percent of undergraduate students work part-time. Average earnings from campus work for the school year are $1700. The FFS is required. The deadline for financial aid applications is April 1.

International Students: There are currently 8 international students enrolled. They must take the TOEFL and achieve a minimum score of 500. The student must also take the ACT.

Computers: The college provides computer facilities for student use. The mainframe is an HP 3000 Model 58 and Model 42 and an IBM RISC/6000 UNIX system. About 200 PCs are available to students. Most are located in departmental laboratories. Nearly 50 are located in other areas for general student access. About 30 terminals are also available. Students have access to E-mail and to the Internet system.

All students may access the system. There are no time limits on using the system and no fees.

Graduates: In 1992–93 553 bachelor's degrees were awarded. The most popular majors among graduates were business management (12%), nursing (11%), and elementary education (10%). Within an average freshman class, 15% graduate in 4 years, 27% in 5 years, and 34% in 6 years. In the 1992 graduating class, 15% of all students were enrolled in graduate school within 6 months of graduation; 90% of all students had found employment.

Admissions Contact: Howard McCauley, Director of Admissions.

NORTHEAST MISSOURI STATE UNIVERSITY C-1
Kirksville, MO 63501   (816) 785–4114; (800) 892–7792 (in-state)

Full-time: 2485 men, 3155 women	Faculty: 326; IIA, --$
Part-time: 111 men, 155 women	Ph.D.s: 72%
Graduate: 71 men, 176 women	Student/Faculty: 17 to 1
Year: semesters, summer session	Tuition: $2574 ($4454)
Application Deadline: November 15	Room & Board: $3080
Freshman Class: 6040 applied, 4577 accepted, 1610 enrolled	
ACT: 26	VERY COMPETITIVE +

Northeast Missouri State University, founded in 1867, is a public, liberal arts and sciences institution offering degree programs in business and accountancy, communications disorders, fine arts, health and exercise science, language and literature, mathematics and computer science, nursing, natural science, and social science. There are 7 undergraduate and 8 graduate schools. In addition to regional accreditation, NMSU has baccalaureate program accreditation with AHEA, ASLA, NASM, NCATE, and NLN. The library contains 369,848 volumes, 1,230,842 microform items, and 51,007 audiovisual forms, and subscribes to 1949 periodicals. Computerized library sources and services include the card catalog, interlibrary loans, and database searching. Special learning facilities include a learning resource center, art gallery, radio station, tv studio, biofeedback laboratory, independent learning center for nursing students, observatory, and greenhouse chamber. The 140-acre campus is in a small town 170 miles northeast of Kansas City and 200 miles north of St. Louis. Including residence halls, there are 39 buildings on campus.

Student Life: About 66% of undergraduates are from Missouri. Students come from 37 states, 50 foreign countries, and Canada. Eighty percent are from public schools; 20% from private. Ninety percent are white. Fifty percent are Protestant; 34% Catholic; 15% no affiliation, unknown affiliations or other religious affiliations. The average age of freshmen is 18.5; all undergraduates, 20. Six percent drop out by the end of their first year; 61% remain to graduate.

Housing: A total of 2927 students can be accommodated in college housing. College-sponsored living facilities include single-sex and coed dormitories, on-campus apartments, married-student housing, and sorority houses. In addition, four residential colleges are learning communities that bring students together with live-in faculty members in a residential setting. On-campus housing is guaranteed for the freshman year only and is available on a first-come, first-served basis. Fifty-two percent of students commute. Alcohol is not permitted. All students may keep cars on campus.

Activities: About 30% of men belong to 16 national fraternities; about 19% of women belong to 1 local and 6 national sororities. There are 150 groups on campus, including art, band, cheerleading, chess, choir, chorus, computers, dance, drama, drill team, ethnic, gay, honors, international, jazz band, literary magazine, marching band, musical theater, newspaper, orchestra, pep band, photography, political, professional, radio and TV, religious, social, social service, student government, and yearbook. Popular campus events include Homecoming, Dog Days (Spring Carnival), a Lyceum series, Parents Day, Greek Week, Leadership Conference, Lakeside Review (musical skit competition), NMSU Live (student talent show), Last Lecture Series, College Bowl, and Leadership Recognition Program.

Sports: There are 11 intercollegiate sports for men and 10 for women, and 26 intramural sports for men and 26 for women. Athletic and recreation facilities include a 5000-seat football stadium, a soccer field, tennis and racquetball courts, a softball diamond, a 3000-seat arena with 3 basketball courts, an Olympic-size pool, weight training rooms, and indoor and outdoor track facilities.

Disabled Students: Ninety percent of the campus is accessible to disabled students. The following facilities are available: wheelchair ramps, elevators, special parking, specially equipped rest rooms, special class scheduling, lowered drinking fountains, lowered telephones, and the swimming pool is equipped with a lift to assist physically disabled swimmers. Adaptive living arrangements are possible.

Services: In addition to many counseling and information services, tutoring is available in most subjects, including services for the hearing impaired, and a braille scanner and printer. There is also a reader service for the blind available. Services for Individuals with Disabilities provides recording, note-taking, test-taking, and advising services.

Campus Safety and Security: Campus safety and security measures include 24-hour foot and vehicle patrol, self defense education, escort service, and informal discussions. In addition, there are pamphlets, posters, films, emergency telephones, lighted pathways and sidewalks, and personal body alarms are available on a limited basis.

Programs of Study: NMSU awards the B.A., B.S., B.F.A., B.M., and B.S.N. degrees. Master's degrees also are awarded. Bachelor's degrees are awarded in AGRICULTURE (agricultural economics, agriculture, agronomy, animal science, and equestrian science), BIOLOGICAL SCIENCE (biology/biological science), BUSINESS (accounting and business administration and management), COMMUNICATIONS AND THE ARTS (art, art history and appreciation, communications, dramatic arts, English, fine arts, French, German, journalism, music, music performance, Russian, Spanish, and speech/debate/rhetoric), COMPUTER AND PHYSICAL SCIENCE (chemistry, computer science, mathematics, and physics), EDUCATION (physical and special), ENGINEERING AND ENVIRONMENTAL DESIGN (preengineering), HEALTH PROFESSIONS (health science, medical laboratory technology, medical technology, nursing, optometry, physical therapy, predentistry, premedicine, prepharmacy, preveterinary science, and speech pathology/audiology), SOCIAL SCIENCE (criminal justice, economics, history, philosophy, physical fitness/movement, political science/government, prelaw, psychology, religion, and sociology). Political science, English, biology, chemistry, mathematics, and history are the strongest academically. Business administration, biology, accounting, and psychology have the largest enrollments.

Required: Core curriculum requirements include 15 semester hours of humanities, 14 to 15 of mathematics and science, 12 of either a foreign language or additional science-based courses, 9 each of social science and communication, and 2 of either health science or military science. Students must also complete 10 to 11 semester hours of discipline-directed requirements. In order to graduate, students must complete at least 124 semester hours, including 30 in a major field, with a minimum 2.0 GPA in most divisions.

Special: Cross-registration with College Consortium for International Studies is possible and students may study abroad in 29 countries. NMSU requires internships in education and agricultural science, but also offers voluntary legislative internships at the state capitol. Work-study programs, B.A.-B.S. degrees, dual majors, student-designed majors in health and exercise science, a 3–2 engineering program with the University of Missouri's Rolla and Columbia campuses, credit for military experience, and pass/fail options for internships are available. Nondegree study is possible. There is a freshman honors program on campus, as well as 4 national honor societies. Eleven departments have honors programs.

Faculty/Classroom: Seventy percent of faculty are male; 30%, female. Ninety-seven percent teach undergraduates, 48% do research, and 48% do both. Graduate students teach 5% of introductory courses. The average class size in an introductory lecture is 47; in a laboratory, 24; and in a regular course offering, 30.

Admissions: About 76% of the 1993–94 applicants were accepted. The ACT scores for the 1993–94 freshman class were as follows: 4% below 21, 25% between 21 and 23, 34% between 24 and 26, 16% between 27 and 28, and 21% above 28. About 65% of the current freshmen were in the top fifth of their class; 92% were in the top two fifths. There were 18 National Merit finalists. About 98 freshmen graduated first in their class.

Requirements: NMSU requires applicants to be in the upper 40% of their class. A minimum GPA of 2.5 is required. The SAT I or ACT is required. NMSU prefers the ACT, with a recommended minimum score of 22. The recommended minimum composite score on the SAT I is 960 (480 on each part). Applicants must be graduates of accredited secondary schools or have earned a GED. They should have completed 4 units of English, 3 each of mathematics, science, and social studies, 2 each of foreign language, and 1 of art or music. An essay is required and an interview or visit is recommended. AP and CLEP credits are accepted. Important factors used in the admissions decision are leadership record, extracurricular activities record, evidence of special talent, advanced placement or honor courses, and parents or siblings attending the school.

Procedure: Freshmen are admitted to all sessions. Entrance exams should be taken during the spring or summer following junior year. Applications should be filed by November 15 for fall entry, November 15 for spring entry, and March 1 for summer entry. Notification of early decision is sent December 15; regular decision, on a rolling basis. There are early decision, early admissions, and deferred admissions plans. A waiting list is an active part of the admissions procedure, with about 5% of applicants on the list.

Transfer: About 199 transfer students enrolled in 1993–94. Transfer applicants must present a minimum 2.5 GPA on transferable hours and must meet minimum criteria for entering freshman. A total of 45 credits out of 124 must be completed at NMSU.

Visiting: There are regularly scheduled orientations for prospective students, including an interview with an admission counselor, a campus tour, an appointment with a faculty member in the student's major, and appointments in any areas of special interest. There are guides for informal visits and visitors may sit in on classes and stay overnight at the school. To arrange for a visit, contact the Admissions Office at (816) 785–4114 or (800) 892–7792 (in-state).

Financial Aid: In 1993–94 89% of all current freshmen and 76% of continuing students received some form of financial aid. About 32% of freshmen and 45% of continuing students received need-based aid. The average freshman award was $3283. Of that total, scholarships or need-based grants averaged $1600 ($7516 maximum); loans averaged $2800 ($4750 maximum); and work contracts averaged $833 ($2508 maximum). Sixty-seven percent of undergraduate students work part-time. Average earnings from campus work for the school year was $886. The average financial indebtedness of the 1992–93 graduate was $5796. NMSU is a member of CSS. The FAF, FFS or SFS, and FAFSA are required. The deadline for financial aid applications is April 1.

International Students: There are currently 234 international students enrolled. They must take the Comprehensive English Language Test and achieve a minimum score on the TOEFL of 500.

Computers: The college provides computer facilities for student use. The mainframe is an IBM 4361. Students have access to both mainframe and micro-based networks. All students receive free computer accounts for electronic mail and can utilize Bitnet. Computer terminals and personal computers are located in 6 academic buildings and 8 residence halls. Approximately 230 workstations are available for student use. All students may access the system. Laboratories are open until midnight in the academic buildings, residence hall laboratories have extended hours, and dial-ins with modems provide 24-hour access. There are no time limits and no fees.

Graduates: In 1992–93 1073 bachelor's degrees were awarded. The most popular majors among graduates were business administration (18%), English (10%), and psychology (9%). Within an average freshman class, 55% graduate in 4 years, 60% in 5 years, and 61% in 6 years. Some 219 companies recruited on campus in 1992–93. In the 1992 graduating class, 40% of all students were enrolled in graduate school within 6 months of graduation; 47% of all students had found employment.

Admissions Contact: Kathy Rieck, Dean of Admission and Records.

NORTHWEST MISSOURI STATE UNIVERSITY   A-1
Maryville, MO 64468   (816) 562–1162; (800) 633–1175 (out-of-state)

Full-time: 2159 men, 2582 women	Faculty: 250; IIA, --$
Part-time: 173 men, 235 women	Ph.D.s: 71%
Graduate: 199 men, 466 women	Student/Faculty: 19 to 1
Year: semesters, summer session	Tuition: $2010 ($3570)
Application Deadline: August	Room & Board: $3000
Freshman Class: 2809 applied, 2699 accepted, 1282 enrolled	
ACT: 21	**LESS COMPETITIVE**

Northwest Missouri State University, founded in 1905, is a public co-educational institution offering undergraduate courses in agriculture, science, arts and humanities, business, government, computer science, and education. There are 4 undergraduate schools and one graduate school. In addition to regional accreditation, Northwest has baccalaureate program accreditation with ADA, AHEA, NASM, and NCATE. The library contains 286,302 volumes, 15,864 microform items, and 1937 audiovisual forms, and subscribes to 3411 periodicals. Computerized library sources and services include the card catalog, interlibrary loans, and database searching. Special learning facilities include a learning resource center, art gallery, radio station, and TV station. The 175-acre campus is in a rural area 90 miles north of Kansas City. Including residence halls, there are 33 buildings on campus.

Student Life: About 58% of undergraduates are from Missouri. Students come from 39 states, 29 foreign countries, and Canada. Ninety-five percent are from public schools; 5% from private. Ninety-five percent are white. The average age of freshmen is 19; all undergraduates, 21. Fourteen percent drop out by the end of their first year; 46% remain to graduate.

Housing: A total of 2800 students can be accommodated in college housing. College-sponsored living facilities include single-sex and coed dormitories and sorority houses. On-campus housing is guaranteed for all 4 years. Fifty-three percent of students live on campus. Alcohol is not permitted. All students may keep cars on campus.

Activities: About 10% of men belong to 8 national fraternities; about 10% of women belong to 1 local and 4 national sororities. There are 200 groups on campus, including band, cheerleading, choir, chorale, computers, jazz band, literary magazine, marching band, newspaper, pep band, photography, political, radio and TV, religious, social, student government, and yearbook. Popular campus events include Homecoming, Tower Dance, Black Awareness Week, Greek Week, Intramural Finals, and Parents Weekend.

Sports: There are 6 intercollegiate sports for men and 5 for women, and 28 intramural sports for men and 28 for women. Athletic and recreation facilities include a 7000-seat stadium, 3 gymnasiums, 4 racquetball courts, a weight-lifting area, volleyball and tennis courts, dance areas, and an aquatic center with 2 pools.

Disabled Students: Ninety percent of the campus is accessible to disabled students. The following facilities are available: wheelchair ramps, elevators, special parking, specially equipped rest rooms, special class scheduling, lowered drinking fountains, and lowered telephones.

Services: In addition to many counseling and information services, tutoring is available in most subjects. There is a reader service for the blind, and remedial math, reading, and writing.

Campus Safety and Security: Campus safety and security measures include 24-hour foot and vehicle patrol, escort service, informal discussions, and pamphlets, posters, and films. In addition, there are lighted pathways and sidewalks.

Programs of Study: Northwest awards the B.A., B.S., B.F.A., B.S.Ed., B.S.El.Ed., B.S.Med.Tech., and B.Tech. degrees. Master's degrees also are awarded. Bachelor's degrees are awarded in AGRICULTURE (agricultural business management, agricultural mechanics, agriculture, animal science, conservation and regulation, forestry and related sciences, and horticulture), BIOLOGICAL SCIENCE (biology/biological science, botany, and zoology), BUSINESS (accounting, banking and finance, business economics, international business management, marketing/retailing/merchandising, and personnel management), COMMUNICATIONS AND THE ARTS (broadcasting, communications, dramatic arts, English, fine arts, French, journalism, music, public relations, Spanish, and speech/debate/rhetoric), COMPUTER AND PHYSICAL SCIENCE (chemistry, computer science, earth science, geology, information sciences and systems, mathematics, physics, and science), EDUCATION (agricultural, early childhood, education of the mentally handicapped, elementary, middle school, physical, recreation, science, secondary, special, and specific learning disabilities), ENGINEERING AND ENVIRONMENTAL DESIGN (preengineering), HEALTH PROFESSIONS (predentistry, premedicine, prepharmacy, and preveterinary science), SOCIAL SCIENCE (clothing and textiles management/production/services, economics, family/consumer resource management, food science, geography, history, home economics, humanities, philosophy, political science/government, prelaw, psychology, social science, and sociology). Education, mass communications, agriculture, and geography are the strongest academically.

Required: All students must maintain a minimum GPA of 2.0 while taking at least 124 credit hours. Distribution requirements include 6 hours in composition, 3 each in oral communications and behavioral sciences, 4 each in mathematics and physical education, 8 in natural science, 9 each in social science and humanities, and 1 in the freshman seminar.

Special: Co-op programs with the University of Missouri/Rolla, cross-registration with Missouri Western State College, campuswide internships, study abroad in England, and a Washington semester are available. Work-study programs, student-designed majors, a 3–2 engineering degree with the University of Missouri/Rolla, credit for military experience, nondegree study, and pass/fail options are possible. There are 3 national honor societies on campus.

Faculty/Classroom: Sixty-one percent of faculty are male; 39%, female. All teach undergraduates. No introductory courses are taught by graduate students. The average class size in an introductory lecture is 40; in a laboratory, 20; and in a regular course offering, 24.

Admissions: About 96% of the 1993–94 applicants were accepted. The ACT scores for the 1993–94 freshman class were as follows: 50% below 21, 22% between 21 and 23, 15% between 24 and 26, 7% between 27 and 28, and 6% above 28. About 21% of the current freshmen were in the top fifth of their class; 51% were in the top two fifths. There were 3 National Merit semifinalists.

Requirements: Northwest requires applicants to be in the upper 50% of their class. A minimum GPA of 2.0 is required. The ACT is required, with the minimum required composite score of 20 for residents, and 21 for nonresidents. Northwest recommends that applicants have 4 units each of English and mathematics, and 3 each in science and social studies. An interview is recommended. The GED is accepted. AP and CLEP credits are accepted.

Procedure: Freshmen are admitted to all sessions. Entrance exams should be taken in the fall of the senior year. Applications should be filed by August for fall entry, December for spring entry, and May for summer entry, along with an application fee of $15. Notification is sent on a rolling basis.

Transfer: About 350 transfer students enrolled in 1993–94. Transfer students must present a minimum GPA of 2.0. A total of 30 credits out of 124 must be completed at Northwest.

Visiting: There are regularly scheduled orientations for prospective students. There are guides for informal visits and visitors may sit in on classes and stay overnight at the school. To arrange for a visit, contact the Mable Cook Admissions and Visitors Center at (800) 633–1175.

Financial Aid: In a recent year, 70% of all current freshmen and 80% of continuing students received some form of financial aid. Scholarships or need-based grants averaged $500 ($2300 maximum); and loans averaged $2500 ($4000 maximum). The FFS is required. The deadline for financial aid applications is April 1.

International Students: There are currently 250 international students enrolled. They must take the TOEFL and achieve a minimum score of 500.

Computers: The college provides computer facilities for student use. The mainframes consists of 10 clustered DEC VAX computers. Students may access the mainframe from terminals located in residence halls, the library, and laboratories. Students may also use the networks available to access 6 libraries, campuses, and computers located around the country. All students may access the system. It may be used 24 hours daily. There are no time limits on using the system and no fees.

Graduates: In a recent year, 762 bachelor's degrees were awarded. Within an average freshman class, 44% graduate in 4 years, 47% in 5 years, and 50% in 6 years. Some 200 companies recruited on campus in 1992–93. In the 1992 graduating class, 52% of the men and 52% of the women were enrolled in graduate school within 6 months of graduation.

Admissions Contact: Michael D. Walsh, Executive Director of Enrollment Management.

PARK COLLEGE
A-2

Parkville, MO 64152–9974

(816) 741–2000, ext. 215
(800) 745–7275 (out-of-state)

Full-time: 350 men, 350 women	**Faculty:** 47; IIB, --$
Part-time: 70 men, 70 women	**Ph.D.s:** 65%
Graduate: 45 men, 40 women	**Student/Faculty:** 15 to 1
Year: semesters, summer session	**Tuition:** $3540
Application Deadline: open	**Room & Board:** $3780
Freshman Class: 350 applied, 295 accepted, 120 enrolled	
ACT: 20	**COMPETITIVE**

Park College, founded in 1875, is a private, coeducational institution affiliated with the Reorganized Church of Jesus Christ of Latter-day Saints. There are 2 graduate schools. The library contains 100,000 volumes and 42,000 microform items, and subscribes to 520 periodicals. Computerized library sources and services include the card catalog, interlibrary loans, and database searching. Special learning facilities include a learning resource center, art gallery, radio station, and TV station. The 800-acre campus is in a suburban area 12 miles north of Kansas City. Including residence halls, there are 17 buildings on campus.

Student Life: About 62% of undergraduates are from Missouri. Students come from 30 states, 25 foreign countries, and Canada. Eighty percent are from public schools; 20% from private. Fifty-eight percent are white; 28% African American; 15% foreign nationals; 10% Hispanic. Fifty percent are Protestant; 21% Catholic; 20% claim no religious affiliation. The average age of freshmen is 19; all undergraduates, 24. Thirty percent drop out by the end of their first year; 30% remain to graduate.

Housing: A total of 350 students can be accommodated in college housing. College-sponsored living facilities include single-sex and coed dormitories and on-campus apartments. On-campus housing is guaranteed for all 4 years. Seventy-two percent of students commute. Alcohol is not permitted. All students may keep cars on campus.

Activities: There are no fraternities or sororities on campus. There are 30 groups on campus, including art, cheerleading, choir, computers, drama, ethnic, honors, international, literary magazine, newspaper, photography, political, professional, radio and TV, religious, social, social service, student government, symphony, and yearbook. Popular campus events include Fall Harvest Festival, Spring Fling, International Week, and Christmas on the River.

Sports: There are 5 intercollegiate sports for men and 5 for women, and 3 intramural sports for men and 3 for women. Athletic and recreation facilities include a 350-seat indoor gymnasium with basketball and volleyball courts, an all-weather outdoor track, soccer and softball fields, a sports medicine room, and an outdoor sand volleyball and basketball court.

Disabled Students: Twenty percent of the campus is accessible to disabled students. The following facilities are available: wheelchair ramps, special parking, specially equipped rest rooms, special class scheduling, and lowered drinking fountains.

Services: In addition to many counseling and information services, tutoring is available in most subjects. There is also remedial math, reading, and writing available.

Campus Safety and Security: Campus safety and security measures include 24-hour foot and vehicle patrol, escort service, informal discussions, pamphlets, posters, films, and lighted pathways and sidewalks.

Programs of Study: The college awards the B.A. degree. Master's degrees also are awarded. Bachelor's degrees are awarded in BIOLOGICAL SCIENCE (biology/biological science), BUSINESS (accounting, banking and finance, business administration and management, business economics, international business management, and marketing/retailing/merchandising), COMMUNICATIONS AND THE ARTS (broadcasting, communications, design, fine arts, and journalism), COMPUTER AND PHYSICAL SCIENCE (chemistry, computer programming, computer science, and mathematics), EDUCATION (art, early childhood, elementary, middle school, science, and secondary), HEALTH PROFESSIONS (predentistry, premedicine, and sports medicine), SOCIAL SCIENCE (community services, criminal justice, economics, history, political science/government, prelaw, psychology, and sociology). Communication arts, political science/ public administration, and English are the strongest academically. Business, communication arts, education, and criminal justice have the largest enrollments.

Required: All students must complete 30 hours of general education requirements, including 2 semesters of English composition, algebra or foreign language, and a laboratory science. Students who are age 25 or under must also complete 2 credit hours of physical education. Of the 120 credit hours needed for the bachelor's degree, 45 must be completed in upper-division work and 30 to 60 in a major field, with a minimum GPA of 2.0.

Special: Cross-registration is available through a Kansas City consortium. The college also offers internships in most majors, study abroad in London, a Washington semester, a general studies degree, student-designed majors, credit for life and military experience, and pass/fail options. Nondegree study is possible. There is a freshman honors program on campus, as well as 2 national honor societies.

Faculty/Classroom: Sixty percent of faculty are male; 40%, female. All teach undergraduates, 80% do research, and 80% do both. No introductory courses are taught by graduate students. The average class size in an introductory lecture is 20; in a laboratory, 10; and in a regular course offering, 15.

Admissions: About 84% of the 1993–94 applicants were accepted. The ACT scores for the 1993–94 freshman class were as follows: 53% below 21, 29% between 21 and 23, 12% between 24 and 26, 4% between 27 and 28, and 2% above 28. About 26% of the current freshmen were in the top fifth of their class; 61% were in the top two fifths. There were 3 National Merit semifinalists. About 2 freshmen graduated first in their class.

Requirements: The college requires applicants to be in the upper 50% of their class. A minimum GPA of 2.0 is required. The ACT is required, with a minimum composite score of 20. Applicants should be graduates of accredited secondary schools or have earned a GED. An essay is recommended. AP and CLEP credits are accepted. Important factors used in the admissions decision are evidence of special talent, extracurricular activities record, parents or siblings attending the school, recommendations by school officials, and recommendations by alumni.

Procedure: Freshmen are admitted to all sessions. Entrance exams should be taken during the junior year or early in the senior year. Application deadlines are open. There is an application fee of $25. Notification is sent on a rolling basis.

Transfer: About 185 transfer students enrolled in 1993–94. The college requires a GPA of at least 2.0. A minimum ACT composite score of 20 is recommended, but is waived for students age 25 or older. A total of 24 credits out of 120 must be completed at the college.

Visiting: There are regularly scheduled orientations for prospective students, including a campus tour, lunch, an information session with a student panel, sessions on admissions, scholarships, and financial aid, and a chance to attend a class and meet with a faculty member. There are guides for informal visits and visitors may sit in on classes and stay overnight at the school. To arrange for a visit, contact Randy Condit, Director of Admissions at (800) 745-7275.

Financial Aid: In 1993–94, 90% of all current freshmen and 80% of continuing students received some form of financial aid. About 80% of freshmen and 70% of continuing students received need-based aid. The average freshman award was $6000. Of that total, scholarships or need-based grants averaged $2000 ($7320 maximum); loans averaged $2600 ($7000 maximum); and work contracts averaged $1920 ($2200 maximum). Sixty-eight percent of undergraduate students work part-time. Average earnings from campus work for the school year are $1500. The average financial indebtedness of graduates in a recent year was $10,000. The FAFSA financial statement is required. The deadline for financial aid applications is April 15.

International Students: There are currently 60 international students enrolled. The school actively recruits these students. They must take the TOEFL and achieve a minimum score of 500. The student must also take the SAT I or the ACT.

Computers: The college provides computer facilities for student use. The mainframe is an HP 9000/Series 857. There are also 20 terminals and 12 microcomputers available for student use, mostly in aca-

demic buildings and the library. Any student in a computer class may access the system. It may be used Monday through Thursday, 8 A.M. to 11 P.M.; Friday, 8 A.M. to 5 p.m; Saturday, 10 A.M. to 5 P.M.; Sunday, 12 A.M. to 5 P.M. There are no time limits on using the system. The fees are $40.

Graduates: In a recent year, 100 bachelor's degrees were awarded. The most popular majors among those graduates were business (33%), education (12%), and criminal justice (9%). Within an average freshman class, 2% graduate in 3 years, 30% in 4 years, 40% in 5 years, and 45% in 6 years. Some 15 companies usually recruited on campus. In a recent year's graduating class, 25% of all students were enrolled in graduate school within 6 months of graduation; 90% had found employment.

Admissions Contact: Randy Condit, Director of Admissions.

PARKS COLLEGE
(See Saint Louis University)

RESEARCH COLLEGE OF NURSING
A-2
Kansas City, MO 64132   (800) 842-6776

Full-time: 24 men, 252 women	**Faculty:** 30
Part-time: 32 women	**Ph.D.s:** 33%
Graduate: none	**Student/Faculty:** 9 to 1
Year: semesters	**Tuition:** $9340
Application Deadline: June 30	**Room & Board:** $4020
Freshman Class: 99 applied, 89 accepted, 39 enrolled	
ACT: 23	**COMPETITIVE**

Research College of Nursing, founded in 1980, is a private, coeducational school of nursing affiliated with Rockhurst College of Kansas City, a Jesuit-run, 25-acre liberal arts college with an enrollment of about 1500 undergraduates. Located on the campus of the Research Medical Center, the Research College of Nursing offers classes on its home campus, on the Rockhurst campus, and in a variety of health-related settings in the Kansas City area. In addition to regional accreditation, the college has baccalaureate program accreditation with NLN. The library contains 100,000 volumes and 13,194 microform items, and subscribes to 621 periodicals. Special learning facilities include a learning resource center, radio station, and the Research Psychiatric Center located on the campus of Research Medical Center. The campus is in an urban area in Kansas City.

Student Life: About 90% of undergraduates are from Missouri. Students come from 6 states and 1 foreign country. Fifty-five percent are from public schools; 45% from private. Eighty-two percent are white. Fifty percent are Protestant; 47% Catholic. The average age of freshmen is 18; all undergraduates, 22.5. Thirty percent drop out by the end of their first year.

Housing: A total of 750 students can be accommodated in the combined college housing. College-sponsored living facilities include single-sex dormitories, on-campus apartments, and fraternity houses. In addition there are special interest houses. On-campus housing is guaranteed for all 4 years. Sixty-five percent of students live on campus; of those, 60% remain on campus on weekends. All students may keep cars on campus.

Activities: There are 3 national fraternities and 2 national sororities. There are 35 groups on campus, including art, cheerleading, chess, choir, chorus, computers, drama, drill team, ethnic, honors, international, literary magazine, musical theater, newspaper, pep band, political, professional, radio and TV, religious, ROTC (Army), social, social service, student government, and yearbook.

Sports: There are 5 intercollegiate sports for men and 5 for women, and 11 intramural sports for men and 9 for women. Athletic and recreation facilities include a gymnasium, an exercise facility, a fitness center, and racquetball courts.

Disabled Students: The entire campus is accessible to disabled students. The following facilities are available: wheelchair ramps, elevators, special parking, specially equipped rest rooms, lowered drinking fountains, and lowered telephones.

Services: In addition to many counseling and information services, tutoring is available in every subject. In addition, there is a reader service for the blind and remedial writing.

Campus Safety and Security: Campus safety and security measures include 24-hour foot and vehicle patrol, informal discussions, emergency telephones, and lighted pathways and sidewalks.

Programs of Study: The college awards the B.S.N. degree. Bachelor's degrees are awarded in HEALTH PROFESSIONS (nursing).

Required: To earn a B.S.N., a student must complete a total of 128 semester hours, with 69 in liberal arts and sciences and 59 in the nursing major. A 2.25 GPA overall and in all nursing course work is required to graduate.

Special: Work-study, co-op, and accelerated degree programs are available. There is a freshman honors program on campus. One department has an honors program.

Faculty/Classroom: Two percent of faculty are male; 98%, female. All teach undergraduates. The average class size in an introductory lecture is 70; in a laboratory, 8; and in a regular course offering, 35.

Admissions: About 90% of the 1993–94 applicants were accepted. The ACT scores for the 1993–94 freshman class were as follows: 37% below 21, 28% between 21 and 23, 17% between 24 and 26, 9% between 27 and 28, and 9% above 28. About 46% of the current freshmen were in the top fifth of their class; 75% were in the top two fifths. One freshman graduated first in class.

Requirements: The college requires applicants to be in the upper 50% of their class. The SAT I or ACT is required, with a minimum composite score of 800 on the SAT I or 20 on the ACT. Applicants should graduate from an accredited secondary school or have the GED. An interview is recommended. Applicants should have completed 3 years of high school mathematics, including Algebra II, 3 years of English, and 2 years of science, including chemistry. AP and CLEP credits are accepted. Important factors used in the admissions decision are advanced placement or honor courses, recommendations by school officials, leadership record, extracurricular activities record, and evidence of special talent.

Procedure: Freshmen are admitted to all sessions. Entrance exams should be taken during the junior or senior year. Applications should be filed by June 30 for fall entry, along with an application fee of $20. Notification is sent on a rolling basis. There is a deferred admissions plan.

Transfer: About 50 transfer students enrolled in 1993–94. A minimum GPA of 2.5 is required to interview for the Research/Rockhurst Joint B.S.N. Program. Students must complete the sophomore-level nursing course before entering the junior-level clinical. Admission requires an interview along with all official transcripts. Admission for transfers is very limited. A total of 30 credits out of 128 must be completed at the college.

Visiting: There are regularly scheduled orientations for prospective students. There are 2 senior visit weekends in November, and 1 in February. There are guides for informal visits and visitors may sit in on classes and stay overnight at the school. To arrange for a visit, contact the Admission and Financial Aid Office at (816) 926–4100 or (800) 842–6776.

Financial Aid: In a recent year, 86% of all current freshmen and 70% of continuing students received some form of financial aid. Scholarships or need-based grants averaged $1684 ($8200 maximum); loans averaged $2162 ($5250 maximum); and work contracts averaged $1000 ($1500 maximum). Average earnings from campus work for the school year are $1250. The college is a member of CSS. The FAF or FFS is required. The deadline for financial aid applications is April 1.

International Students: There is currently 1 international student enrolled. They must take the TOEFL and achieve a minimum score of 550. The student must also take the SAT I (minimum score 800) or the ACT (minimum score 20).

Computers: The college provides computer facilities for student use. The mainframe is a DEC VAX 8530. Computers available for student use are in an academic building and the library. All students may access the system. There are no time limits on using the system and no fees.

Graduates: In 1992–93, 52 bachelor's degrees were awarded. In the 1992 graduating class, 7% of the men and 5% of the women were enrolled in graduate school within 6 months of graduation; all had found employment.

Admissions Contact: Leslie Mendenhall, Assistant Director of Admission.

ROCKHURST COLLEGE
Kansas City, MO 64110–2508

A-2

(816) 926–4100
(800) 842–6776 (out-of-state)

Full-time: 501 men, 626 women	Faculty: 110; IIB, -$
Part-time: 242 men, 512 women	Ph.D.s: 36%
Graduate: 386 men, 319 women	Student/Faculty: 10 to 1
Year: semesters, summer session	Tuition: $8970
Application Deadline: June 1	Room & Board: $3500

Freshman Class: 944 applied, 855 accepted, 345 enrolled
ACT: 23

COMPETITIVE

Rockhurst College, founded in 1910, is a private, Jesuit institution affiliated with the Roman Catholic Church. The college offers an undergraduate curriculum in the arts and sciences, education, health science, and business. There are 3 graduate schools. In addition to regional accreditation, Rockhurst has baccalaureate program accreditation with APTA, CAHEA, and NLN. The library contains 100,000 volumes and 13,194 microform items, and subscribes to 621 periodicals. Special learning facilities include a learning resource center, an art gallery, and a radio station. The 25-acre campus is in an urban area.

Student Life: Students come from 20 states and 10 foreign countries. Eighty-seven percent are white. Sixty-eight percent are Catholic; 21% Protestant. The average age of freshmen is 18. Nine percent drop out by the end of their first year.

Housing: A total of 639 students can be accommodated in college housing. College-sponsored living facilities include single-sex and coed dormitories fraternity houses, honors houses, and special interest houses, including those established as global studies centers. On-campus housing is guaranteed for all 4 years and is available on a first-come, first-served basis. Priority is given to out-of-town students. All students may keep cars on campus.

Activities: There are 3 national fraternities. There are no sororities on campus. There are 35 groups on campus, including art, band, cheerleading, chess, choir, chorus, computers, drama, ethnic, honors, international, literary magazine, musical theater, newspaper, political, professional, radio and TV, religious, social, social service, student government, and yearbook. Popular campus events include Fall Formal, Sadie Hawkins Day, SAE Boxer Rebellion, Christmas dances, and Plaers.

Sports: There are 2 intercollegiate sports for men and 3 for women, and 30 intramural sports each for men and women. Athletic and recreation facilities include athletic and soccer fields; tennis, handball, racquetball, badminton, basketball, and volleyball courts; a weight and exercise room; and gymnasitcs facilities.

Disabled Students: The entire campus is accessible to disabled students. The following facilities are available: wheelchair ramps, elevators, special parking, specially equipped rest rooms, lowered drinking fountains, and lowered telephones.

Services: In addition to many counseling and information services, tutoring is available in every subject. There is also a reader service for the blind and remedial writing. A writing laboratory offers assistance with any college writing task.

Programs of Study: Rockhurst awards the B.A., B.S., B.A.Elem.Ed., B.S.B.A., and B.S.N. degrees. Master's degrees also are awarded. Bachelor's degrees are awarded in BIOLOGICAL SCIENCE (biology/biological science), BUSINESS (accounting, banking and finance, business administration and management, business economics, marketing/retailing/merchandising, and personnel management), COMMUNICATIONS AND THE ARTS (communications, English, French, and Spanish), COMPUTER AND PHYSICAL SCIENCE (chemistry, computer science, information sciences and systems, mathematics, and physics), EDUCATION (elementary, foreign languages, and secondary), ENGINEERING AND ENVIRONMENTAL DESIGN (computer engineering), HEALTH PROFESSIONS (medical technology, nursing, occupational therapy, physical therapy, predentistry, and premedicine), SOCIAL SCIENCE (community services, economics, geography, history, international relations, philosophy, political science/government, prelaw, psychology, religion, sociology, and theological studies). Accounting, chemistry, biology, economics, finance, and physical therapy are the strongest programs academically. Business administration has the largest enrollment.

Required: Core requirements include 3 courses in theology or religious studies, 4 each in philosophy and humanities, and 5 each in natural sciences, social sciences, and mathematics. Students must also demonstrate proficiency in oral and written composition and expression. To graduate, students must complete at least 128 semester hours, including at least 30 in the major, with an overall GPA of 2.0.

Special: Students may participate in co-op programs, a Washington semester, and study abroad in Italy, Spain, England, Mexico, and France. Rockhurst's nursing program is conducted in cooperation with the Research College of Nursing. Cross-registration in other subjects is available through the Kansas City Regional Council for Higher Education. There are also interdisciplinary majors, and work-study programs with Hallmark Cards, Marion Labs, and AT&T. There is a freshman honors program on campus as well as a college-wide honors program.

Admissions: About 91% of the 1993–94 applicants were accepted. Seven freshmen graduated first in their class.

Requirements: A minimum GPA of 2.0 is required. The SAT I, minimum composite score of 800 (400 on each part), or the ACT, minimum standard composite score of 18 or enhanced composite score of 20, is required. In addition, applicant must be a graduate of an accredited secondary school or have earned a GED. The college requires completion of 15 academic credits, including 4 years of English, 3 to 4 of history/social science, 3 of mathematics, 2 to 4 of a foreign language, and 1 of visual or performing arts. An interview is recommended and a recommendation is required. AP and CLEP credits are accepted. Important factors used in the admissions decision are advanced placement or honor courses, recommendations by school officials, leadership record, extracurricular activities record, and evidence of special talent.

Procedure: Priority applications should be filed by June 1 for fall entry, along with an application fee of $20. Notification is sent on a rolling basis. There are early decision, early admissions, and deferred admissions plans.

Transfer: About 116 transfer students enrolled in a recent year. Transfer applicants must have a GPA of at least 2.5. An interview is recommended. All high school and college transcripts must be submitted. A total of 30 credits out of 128 must be completed at Rockhurst.

Visiting: There are regularly scheduled orientations for prospective students, including a campus tour. There are guides for informal visits and visitors may sit in on classes and stay overnight at the school. To arrange for a visit, contact the Admissions Office at (816) 926-4100.

Financial Aid: In an earlier year, 86% of all freshmen and 70% of continuing students received some form of financial aid. Scholarships or need-based grants averaged $1684 ($6850 maximum); loans averaged $2162 ($5250 maximum); and work contracts averaged $1450 ($2560 maximum). Rockhurst is a member of CSS. The FAF or FFS and FAFSA are required. The deadline for financial aid applications is March 1.

International Students: There were recently 29 international students enrolled. They must take the TOEFL and achieve a minimum score of 500. The student must also take the SAT I or the ACT.

Computers: The college provides computer facilities for student use. The mainframes are a DEC VAX 8530 and an 11/750 and a PDP 11/70. There are approximately 275 MS-DOS-based and Apple Macintosh microcomputers available in computer laboratories, classrooms, the library, and residence halls. Students who work for Computer Services may access the system. There are no time limits and no fees.

Graduates: In an earlier year, 552 bachelor's degrees were awarded. Some 85 companies recruited on campus in an earlier year. In an earlier year's graduating class, 7% of the men and 5% of the women were enrolled in graduate school within 6 months of graduation; 80% of all students had found employment.

Admissions Contact: Jack Reichmeier, Director of Admissions.

SAINT LOUIS COLLEGE OF PHARMACY

D-2

St. Louis, MO 63110   (314) 367-8700, ext. 227

Full-time: 297 men, 488 women	Faculty: 62; IIB, +$
Part-time: 14 men, 12 women	Ph.D.s: 75%
Graduate: none	Student/Faculty: 13 to 1
Year: semesters, summer session	Tuition: $7390-8890
Application Deadline: August 1	Room & Board: $4200
Freshman Class: 322 applied, 232 accepted, 148 enrolled	
SAT I or ACT: required	**VERY COMPETITIVE**

Saint Louis College of Pharmacy, founded in 1864, is a private, independent, coeducational institution providing professional pharmaceutical training through 5- and 6-year degree programs. In addition to regional accreditation, StLCOP has baccalaureate program accreditation with ACPE. The library contains 38,900 volumes, 2 microform items, and 679 audiovisual forms, and subscribes to 456 periodicals. Computerized library sources and services include interlibrary loans and database searching. Special learning facilities include a learning resource center and a modern pharmaceutics laboratory. The 5-acre campus is in an urban area 6 miles west of downtown St. Louis. Including residence halls, there are 4 buildings on campus.

Student Life: About 57% of undergraduates are from out-of-state, mostly the Midwest. Students come from 14 states, 5 foreign countries, and Canada. Eighty percent are from public schools; 20% from private. Eighty-six percent are white. The average age of freshmen is 18; all undergraduates, 22. Eighteen percent drop out by the end of their first year; 83% remain to graduate.

Housing: A total of 225 students can be accommodated in college housing. College-sponsored living facilities include coed dormitories, on-campus apartments, married-student housing, fraternity houses, and sorority houses. On-campus housing is available on a first-come, first-served basis. Priority is given to out-of-town students. Fifty percent of students commute. Alcohol is not permitted. Upperclassmen may keep cars on campus.

Activities: About 60% of men belong to 6 national fraternities; about 30% of women belong to 2 national sororities. There are 16 groups on campus, including chorale, chorus, drama, jazz band, musical theater, newspaper, orchestra, photography, professional, student government, and yearbook. Popular campus events include Street Fair on the first day of classes and 2 annual dances.

Sports: There is 1 intercollegiate sport each for men and women, and 11 intramural sports each for men and women. Athletic and recreation facilities include a student center with a gymnasium, an indoor running track, a Nautilus training facility, and aerobics facilities.

Disabled Students: The entire campus is accessible to disabled students. The following facilities are available: wheelchair ramps, elevators, special parking, specially equipped rest rooms, and lowered drinking fountains.

Services: In addition to many counseling and information services, tutoring is available in every subject.

Campus Safety and Security: Campus safety and security measures include 24-hour foot and vehicle patrol, informal discussions, emergency telephones, and lighted pathways and sidewalks.

Programs of Study: StLCOP awards the B.S.Pharm. degree. Master's and doctoral degrees also are awarded. Bachelor's degrees are awarded in HEALTH PROFESSIONS (pharmacy).

Required: The college curriculum consists of 1 year of preprofessional and 4 years of professional studies. Students must complete core curriculum requirements and demonstrate proficiency in pharmaceutical mathematics. The bachelor's degree requires completion of at least 163 credit hours, including 66 in a major field, with a minimum GPA of 2.0.

Special: Summer internships are sponsored by pharmaceutical companies throughout the country. StLCOP also offers pass/fail options and a small advisor-to-student ratio. There is a freshman honors program on campus.

Faculty/Classroom: Fifty-five percent of faculty are male; 45%, female. The average class size in an introductory lecture is 60; in a laboratory, 20; and in a regular course offering, 40.

Admissions: About 72% of the 1993-94 applicants were accepted. The ACT scores for the 1993-94 freshman class were as follows: 10% below 21, 29% between 21 and 23, 33% between 24 and 26, 16% between 27 and 28, and 12% above 28. There were 3 National Merit finalists and 15 semifinalists. Seventeen freshmen graduated first in their class.

Requirements: StLCOP requires applicants to be in the upper 50% of their class. A minimum GPA of 2.5 is required. The SAT I or ACT is required. A minimum ACT composite score of 19 is required. The SAT I is accepted in lieu of the ACT. Applicants must be graduates of accredited secondary schools where a 4-year course of study included 4 units of English and 2 to 4 units each of mathematics, science, and social studies. An interview is recommended. AP and CLEP credits are accepted. Important factors used in the admissions decision are advanced placement or honor courses, evidence of special talent, personality, intangible qualities, leadership record, and recommendations by alumni.

Procedure: Freshmen are admitted in the fall and winter. Entrance exams should be taken prior to the eighth semester of high school. Early decision applications should be filed by December 1; regular applications, by August 1 for fall entry and December 1 for winter entry, along with an application fee of $25. Notification is sent within 4 weeks of receipt of completed file. There is an early decision plan. About 94 early decision candidates were accepted for a recent class. A waiting list is an active part of the admissions procedure, with about 10% of applicants on the list.

Transfer: About 55 transfer students enrolled in a recent year. Transfer applicants must have earned at least 28 credit hours from an accredited program, including 2 semesters each of biology and chemistry past the introductory level, 2 of English composition, and 1 each of college-level calculus, philosophy, and sociology. A GPA of at least 2.5 is required. A minimum ACT composite score of 19 and an interview are recommended. A total of 97 credits out of 163 must be completed at StLCOP.

Visiting: There are regularly scheduled orientations for prospective students, including, by appointment, a tour, a financial aid session, and a personal interview. There are guides for informal visits and visitors may sit in on classes. To arrange for a visit, contact the campus admissions adviser at (314) 367-8700, ext. 264.

Financial Aid: In a recent year, 87% of all freshmen and 83% of continuing students received some form of financial aid. About 82% of freshmen and 78% of continuing students received need-based aid. The average freshman award was $5117. Of that total, scholarships or need-based grants averaged $1500 ($2400 maximum); loans averaged $2716 ($5625 maximum); and work contracts averaged $1000 ($1000 maximum). Ninety-seven percent of undergraduate students work part-time. Average earnings from campus work for the school year are $800. The average financial indebtedness of a recent graduate was $15,000. StLCOP is a member of CSS. The FAF is required. The deadline for financial aid applications is June 30.

International Students: There were recently 14 international students enrolled. They must take the TOEFL and achieve a minimum score of 550.

Computers: The college provides computer facilities for student use. All students may access the system. There are no time limits and no fees.

Graduates: In a recent year, 148 bachelor's degrees were awarded. Within an average freshman class, 85% graduate in 5 years. Some 100 companies recruited on campus in a recent year. In a recent graduating class, all students had found employment within 6 months of graduation.

Admissions Contact: Lisa Boeschen, Director of Admissions.

SAINT LOUIS UNIVERSITY

D-2

St. Louis, MO 63103

(314) 658–2500
(800) 325–6666 (out-of-state)

Full-time: 3079 men, 2926 women	Faculty: 357; I, --$
Part-time: 411 men, 614 women	Ph.D.s: 95%
Graduate: 671 men, 1196 women	Student/Faculty: 17 to 1
Year: semesters, summer session	Tuition: $10,900
Application Deadline: see profile	Room & Board: $4622
Freshman Class: 3787 applied, 3227 accepted, 1075 enrolled	
SAT I Verbal/Math: 480/550	ACT: 25 **VERY COMPETITIVE**

Saint Louis University, founded in 1818, is a private, coeducational institution affiliated with the Jesuit Order of the Roman Catholic Church. There are 8 undergraduate schools and one graduate school. In addition to regional accreditation, SLU has baccalaureate program accreditation with AACSB, ABET, ADA, AHEA, APTA, CSWE, NCATE, and NLN. The 4 libraries contain 984,557 volumes, 1,567,842 microform items, and 194,923 audiovisual forms, and subscribe to 11,654 periodicals. Computerized library sources and services include the card catalog, interlibrary loans, and database searching. Special learning facilities include a learning resource center, art gallery, and radio station. The 250-acre campus is in an urban area 3 miles west of downtown St. Louis. Including residence halls, there are 69 buildings on campus.

Student Life: About 56% of undergraduates are from Missouri. Students come from 50 states, 75 foreign countries, and Canada. Thirty-five percent are from public schools; 65% from private. Seventy percent are white. Fifty-five percent are Protestant; 44% Catholic. The average age of freshmen is 18; all undergraduates, 23. Fifteen percent drop out by the end of their first year; 65% remain to graduate.

Housing: A total of 2390 students can be accommodated in college housing. College-sponsored living facilities include single-sex and coed dormitories. In addition there are honors houses. On-campus housing is guaranteed for all 4 years. Seventy-nine percent of students commute. All students may keep cars on campus.

Activities: About 17% of men belong to 3 local and 9 national fraternities; about 9% of women belong to 5 national sororities. There are 97 groups on campus, including cheerleading, chorale, chorus, computers, drama, ethnic, gay, honors, international, musical theater, newspaper, pep band, political, professional, radio and TV, religious, social, social service, student government, and yearbook. Popular campus events include Fall Fest, Spring Fever, and Homecoming.

Sports: There are 8 intercollegiate sports for men and 7 for women, and 19 intramural sports for men and 19 for women. Athletic and recreation facilities include a 2000-seat gymnasium, a 2400-seat outdoor sports center, a 19,000-seat off-campus arena, a recreation center with multipurpose courts, a swimming pool and diving well, track facilities, and a weight-training room.

Disabled Students: Eighty-five percent of the campus is accessible to disabled students. The following facilities are available: wheelchair ramps, elevators, special parking, specially equipped rest rooms, special class scheduling, lowered drinking fountains, and lowered telephones.

Services: In addition to many counseling and information services, tutoring is available in some subjects, including mathematics, English, history, economics, and natural sciences. There is also remedial math, reading, and writing available.

Campus Safety and Security: Campus safety and security measures include 24-hour foot and vehicle patrol, self defense education, escort service, and shuttle buses. In addition, there are informal discussions, pamphlets, posters, films, emergency telephones, and lighted pathways and sidewalks.

Programs of Study: SLU awards the B.A. and B.S. degrees. Associate, master's, and doctoral degrees also are awarded. Bachelor's degrees are awarded in BIOLOGICAL SCIENCE (biology/biological science), BUSINESS (accounting, banking and finance, business administration and management, business economics, international business management, marketing/retailing/merchandising, and personnel management), COMMUNICATIONS AND THE ARTS (communications, English, fine arts, French, German, Greek, Latin, music, Russian, and Spanish), COMPUTER AND PHYSICAL SCIENCE (chemistry, computer science, earth science, geology, mathematics, and physics), EDUCATION (early childhood, elementary, secondary, and special), ENGINEERING AND ENVIRONMENTAL DESIGN (aeronautical engineering and electrical/electronics engineering), HEALTH PROFESSIONS (medical laboratory technology, nursing, physical therapy, and speech pathology/audiology), SOCIAL SCIENCE (criminal justice, economics, history, philosophy, political science/government, psychology, public administration, religion, social work, sociology, and urban studies). Physical therapy, aerospace engineering, and psychology are the strongest academically. Biology, psychology, and business have the largest enrollments.

Required: Students must complete distribution requirements in international cultures, fine arts, English, literature, science, social/behavioral science, mathematics, and history, as well as specific courses in philosophy and theology. The bachelor's degree requires completion of at least 120 credit hours, including 30 in a major field, with a minimum GPA of 2.0.

Special: Students may study abroad in Spain and France. SLU offers co-op programs through the School of Business, cross-registration with local schools, internships with local financial institutions, work-study programs on campus, an accelerated degree program in nursing, a 3–2 engineering degree program with Washington University in St. Louis, dual majors, student-designed majors, and pass/fail options. A general studies degree and credit for life experience are awarded through SLU's College of Arts and Sciences Evening Division, which also permits nondegree study. There is a freshman honors program on campus, as well as 12 national honor societies, including Phi Beta Kappa. Five colleges have honors programs.

Faculty/Classroom: Sixty-five percent of faculty are male; 35%, female. Eighty-two percent teach undergraduates and 82% both teach and do research. Graduate students teach 1% of introductory courses. The average class size in an introductory lecture is 27; in a laboratory, 20; and in a regular course offering, 23.

Admissions: About 85% of the 1993–94 applicants were accepted. The ACT scores for the 1993–94 freshman class were: 9% below 21, 21% between 21 and 23, 25% between 24 and 26, 20% between 27 and 28, and 25% above 28. About 52% of the current freshmen were in the top fifth of their class; 78% were in the top two fifths. There were 17 National Merit finalists.

Requirements: The SAT: or the ACT is required. Applicants must be graduates of accredited secondary schools or have earned a GED. The university requires a minimum of 16 academic credits, based on 4 years of English, 3 each of mathematics and electives, and 2 each of foreign language, science, and social studies. Chemistry and biology are required for nursing and allied health professions applicants. AP and CLEP credits are accepted. Important factors used in the admissions decision are advanced placement or honor courses, extracurricular activities record, leadership record, evidence of special talent, and personality, intangible qualities.

Procedure: Freshmen are admitted to all sessions. Entrance exams should be taken in the fall of the senior year. Fall application deadlines for freshmen are December 15 for physical therapy majors and August 1 for all other majors. Notification is sent on a rolling basis, 4 to 6 weeks after completed application is received. There are early admissions and deferred admissions plans.

Transfer: About 853 transfer students enrolled in 1993–94. The university recommends that transfer applicants present an associate degree or a minimum of 15 credit hours with a GPA of at least 2.0 for the colleges of Arts and Sciences, Business and Administration, and Social Service and a 2.5 GPA for the schools of Nursing and Allied Health. A total of 30 credits out of 120 must be completed at SLU.

Visiting: There are regularly scheduled orientations for prospective students, consisting of a campus tour, individual and group visits to a class or an academic department, and admissions and financial aid counseling. There are guides for informal visits and visitors may sit in on classes and stay overnight at the school. To arrange for a visit, contact Campus Visit Coordinator at (314) 658–2500 or (800) 325–6666.

Financial Aid: In 1993–94 85% of all current freshmen and 85% of continuing students received some form of financial aid. About 75% of freshmen and 75% of continuing students received need-based aid. The average freshman award was $13,738. Of that total, scholarships or need-based grants averaged $5000 ($16,000 maximum); loans averaged $3625 ($5625 maximum); and work contracts averaged $2300 (maximum). Thirty-seven percent of undergraduate students work part-time. Average earnings from campus work for the school year are $2300. The average financial indebtedness of the 1992–93 graduate was $12,430. SLU is a member of CSS. The FAFSA financial statement is required. The deadline for financial aid applications is July 1.

International Students: There are currently 1190 international students enrolled. The school actively recruits these students. They must take the TOEFL or the University of Michigan Language Test, a writing test, and achieve a minimum score on the TOEFL of 500.

Computers: The college provides computer facilities for student use. The mainframe is a DEC VAX 64100. There are about 200 microcomputers available for student use in various laboratories. All students may access the system. There are no time limits and no fees.

Graduates: In 1992–93 1436 bachelor's degrees were awarded. The most popular majors among graduates were business (30%), nursing (9%), and psychology (7%). Within an average freshman class, 1% graduate in 3 years, 50% in 4 years, 62% in 5 years, and 65% in 6 years. Some 86 companies recruited on campus in 1992–93.

Admissions Contact: Kent Hopkins, Director of Undergraduate Admissions.

SOUTHEAST MISSOURI STATE UNIVERSITY E-3
Cape Girardeau, MO 63701 (314) 651-2590
Full-time: 6151 men and women **Faculty:** 401; IIA, --$
Part-time: 1179 men and women **Ph.D.s:** 90%
Graduate: 754 men and women **Student/Faculty:** 15 to 1
Year: semesters, summer session **Tuition:** $2434 ($4366)
Application Deadline: June 1 **Room & Board:** $3420
Freshman Class: 1865 applied, 1590 accepted, 1280 enrolled
ACT: required **COMPETITIVE**

Southeast Missouri State University, founded in 1873, is a public co-educational institution offering undergraduate and graduate programs in arts and sciences, business, agriculture, education, and health. There are 5 undergraduate schools and one graduate school. In addition to regional accreditation, Southeast has baccalaureate program accreditation with NASM, NCATE, and NLN. The library contains 355,262 volumes, 71,461 microform items, and 8000 audiovisual forms, and subscribes to 2569 periodicals. Computerized library sources and services include the card catalog and interlibrary loans. Special learning facilities include a learning resource center and radio station. The 800-acre campus is in a rural area 120 miles south of St. Louis. Including residence halls, there are 51 buildings on campus.

Student Life: About 87% of undergraduates are from Missouri. Students come from 41 states, 37 foreign countries, and Canada. Eighty-seven percent are white. The average age of freshmen is 19.9; all undergraduates, 23. Thirty-four percent drop out by the end of their first year; 52% remain to graduate.

Housing: A total of 2874 students can be accommodated in college housing. College-sponsored living facilities include single-sex and coed dormitories, off-campus apartments, married-student housing, fraternity houses, and sorority houses. In addition, there are honors houses and special interest houses. On-campus housing is available on a first-come, first-served basis and is available on a lottery system for upperclassmen. Sixty-five percent of students commute. Alcohol is not permitted. All students may keep cars on campus.

Activities: About 10% of men belong to 10 national fraternities; about 12% of women belong to 9 national sororities. There are 150 groups on campus, including art, band, cheerleading, choir, drama, drill team, ethnic, gay, honors, international, jazz band, literary magazine, marching band, newspaper, orchestra, pep band, political, professional, radio and TV, religious, social, student government, and yearbook. Popular campus events include Family Weekends, Homecoming, Spring Fling, International Week, and Black History Month.

Sports: There are 6 intercollegiate sports for men and 7 for women, and 25 intramural sports each for men and women. Athletic and recreation facilities include an indoor pool and a student recreation center housing an indoor track, a climbing wall, 6 racquetball courts, 3 indoor basketball courts, a weight room, volleyball courts, and bicycle and rowing machines.

Disabled Students: Seventy percent of the campus is accessible to disabled students. The following facilities are available: wheelchair ramps, elevators, special parking, specially equipped rest rooms, special class scheduling, lowered drinking fountains, and lowered telephones.

Services: In addition to many counseling and information services, tutoring is available in most subjects. In addition, there is a reader service for the blind, and remedial math, reading, and writing.

Campus Safety and Security: Campus safety and security measures include 24-hour foot and vehicle patrol, self-defense education, escort service, and shuttle buses. In addition, there are informal discussions, pamphlets, posters, films, emergency telephones, and lighted pathways and sidewalks.

Programs of Study: Southeast awards the B.A., B.S., B.G.S., B.S.B.A., B.S.Ed., B.S.M., B.S.Mus.Ed., B.S.N., and B.S.Voc.HomeEcon.Ed. degrees. Associate and master's degrees are also awarded. Bachelor's degrees are awarded in AGRICULTURE (animal science and horticulture), BIOLOGICAL SCIENCE (biology/biological science), BUSINESS (accounting, banking and finance, business economics, and marketing/retailing/merchandising), COMMUNICATIONS AND THE ARTS (advertising, communications, English, French, music, and Spanish), COMPUTER AND PHYSICAL SCIENCE (chemistry, computer science, earth science, mathematics, and physics), EDUCATION (art, business, early childhood, elementary, industrial arts, music, secondary, and special), ENGINEERING AND ENVIRONMENTAL DESIGN (engineering technology), HEALTH PROFESSIONS (nursing, speech pathology/audiology, and sports medicine), SOCIAL SCIENCE (criminal justice, dietetics, economics, food science, geography, history, parks and recreation management, philosophy, political science/government, psychology, social work, and sociology). Teacher education is the strongest academically. Business has the largest enrollment.

Required: Students must complete 124 credit hours, with up to 64 in the major. The core curriculum includes 48 credit hours in a university studies program, as well as interdisciplinary studies, English, and mathematics. Minimum GPAs (at least 2.0) and other graduation requirements vary by program. A writing examination must also be passed.

Special: Southeast offers co-op programs in education and communication disorders, and cross-registration with Southern Illinois University. Opportunities are provided for individually arranged internships and work-study, B.A.-B.S. degree, study abroad in 48 countries, a general studies degree, dual and student-designed majors (interdisciplinary studies), credit by examination, nondegree study, and pass/fail options. A 3-2 engineering degree is possible in conjunction with the University of Missouri at Rolla or at Columbia. There is a freshman honors program on campus, as well as 4 national honor societies.

Faculty/Classroom: All faculty teach undergraduates. The average class size in an introductory lecture is 25; in a laboratory, 25; and in a regular course offering, 20.

Admissions: About 85% of the 1993-94 applicants were accepted. The ACT scores for the 1993-94 freshman class were as follows: 37% below 21, 29% between 21 and 23, 17% between 24 and 26, 7% between 27 and 28, and 10% above 28. About 37% of the current freshmen were in the top fifth of their class; 62% were in the top two fifths.

Requirements: A minimum GPA of 2.0 is required. The ACT is required. In addition, graduation from an accredited secondary school is required; the GED is accepted. Applicants should submit an academic record with 4 credits in English, 2 in algebra or higher mathematics, 2 in science, 3 in social studies, and 4 additional credits in English, mathematics, science, social studies, speech, or a foreign language. AP and CLEP credits are accepted.

Procedure: Freshmen are admitted to all sessions. Entrance exams should be taken in the spring before the fall of enrollment, but in the early fall for scholarship applicants. Early decision applications should be filed by July 1; regular applications, by June 1 for fall entry, December 15 for spring entry, and May 15 for summer entry, along with an application fee of $20. Notification is sent on a rolling basis. There are early decision and early admissions plans.

Transfer: Transcripts of the student's previous college must be submitted, listing at least 24 credits earned and a minimum GPA of 2.0. The ACT is not required. A total of 30 credits out of 124 must be completed at Southeast.

Visiting: There are regularly scheduled orientations for prospective students, including registration and icebreakers, followed by the English placement examination, academic advising, and other university information, and then the enrollment process. There are guides for informal visits and visitors may sit in on classes and stay overnight at the school. To arrange for a visit, contact the Admissions Office at (314) 651-2590.

Financial Aid: Fifteen percent of undergraduate students work part-time. Average earnings from campus work for the school year are $1500. The FFS and FAFSA are required. The deadline for financial aid applications is July 1.

International Students: There are currently 257 international students enrolled. The school actively recruits these students. They must take the TOEFL and achieve a minimum score of 550.

Computers: The college provides computer facilities for student use. The mainframe is an IBM 4381. There are also 90 terminals and microcomputers in Kent Library, Johnson Hall, Scully, and the dormitories. All students may access the system. There are no time limits on using the system and no fees.

Graduates: In a recent year, 1127 bachelor's degrees were awarded. The most popular majors among graduates were elementary education (10%), general studies (6%), and business management (1%). Within an average freshman class, 34% graduate in 4 years and 45% in 5 years. Some 48 companies recruited on campus in a recent year.
Admissions Contact: Juan Crites, Director of Admissions.

SOUTHWEST BAPTIST UNIVERSITY B-3
Bolivar, MO 65613 (417) 326-1810; (800) 526-5859
Full-time: 755 men, 1015 women **Faculty:** 92
Part-time: 215 men, 752 women **Ph.D.s:** 60%
Graduate: 63 men, 327 women **Student/Faculty:** 19 to 1
Year: 4-1-4, summer session **Tuition:** $6812
Application Deadline: open **Room & Board:** $2380
Freshman Class: 540 applied, 540 accepted, 510 enrolled
ACT: 21 **NONCOMPETITIVE**

Southwest Baptist University, founded in 1878, is a liberal arts institution affiliated with the Baptist Church. There are 5 undergraduate schools and one graduate school. In addition to regional accreditation, SBU has baccalaureate program accreditation with ADA and NASM. The library contains 99,000 volumes and 46,000 microform items, and subscribes to 1227 periodicals. Computerized library sources and services include the card catalog, interlibrary loans, and

database searching. Special learning facilities include a learning resource center and TV station. The 123-acre campus is in a rural area 28 miles north of Springfield. Including residence halls, there are 40 buildings on campus.

Student Life: About 84% of undergraduates are from Missouri. Ninety-eight percent are from public schools. Ninety-eight percent are white. Most are Protestant. The average age of freshmen is 18; all undergraduates, 22. Forty percent drop out by the end of their first year; 40% remain to graduate.

Housing: A total of 1200 students can be accommodated in college housing. College-sponsored living facilities include single-sex dormitories and on-campus apartments. On-campus housing is guaranteed for all 4 years. Alcohol is not permitted. All students may keep cars on campus.

Activities: There are no fraternities or sororities on campus. There are many groups and organizations on campus, including art, band, cheerleading, choir, chorale, chorus, drama, honors, jazz band, marching band, musical theater, newspaper, orchestra, pep band, photography, political, radio and TV, religious, social service, student government, and yearbook. Popular campus events include High School Day, Homecoming, Mozarkian, and Parents Day.

Sports: There are 12 intramural sports for men and 12 for women. Athletic and recreation facilities include a 2500-seat field house, a 1260-seat gymnasium, weight rooms, training facilities, a baseball diamond, a football stadium, an outdoor track, and 5 tennis courts. There are also fields for flag football, soccer, and softball, and a natatorium with a 25-meter swimming pool.

Disabled Students: Seventy-five percent of the campus is accessible to disabled students. The following facilities are available: wheelchair ramps, special parking, specially equipped rest rooms, special class scheduling, and lowered drinking fountains.

Services: In addition to many counseling and information services, tutoring is available in every subject.

Campus Safety and Security: Campus safety and security measures include 24-hour foot and vehicle patrol, informal discussions, emergency telephones, and lighted pathways and sidewalks.

Programs of Study: SBU awards the B.A., B.S, B.A.S., B.M., and B.S.N. degrees. Associate and master's degrees also are awarded. Bachelor's degrees are awarded in BIOLOGICAL SCIENCE (biology/biological science), BUSINESS (accounting, business administration and management, and sports management), COMMUNICATIONS AND THE ARTS (communications, dramatic arts, English, music, Spanish, and telecommunications), COMPUTER AND PHYSICAL SCIENCE (chemistry, computer science, and mathematics), EDUCATION (art, business, early childhood, elementary, music, and physical), ENGINEERING AND ENVIRONMENTAL DESIGN (commercial art), HEALTH PROFESSIONS (nursing and physical therapy), SOCIAL SCIENCE (biblical studies, economics, history, human services, ministries, political science/government, psychology, religion, religious education, religious music, social science, and sociology). Business, science, education, music, and religion are the strongest academically. Education and business have the largest enrollments.

Required: In order to graduate, students must complete 128 credit hours with a 2.0 GPA. Distribution requirements for most bachelor's degrees include 9 to 10 hours in science and mathematics, 9 in communications, 9 (12 for a B.A.) in humanities, 8 in religion, 6 in business and community leadership, 5 in personal and family development, and 3 in computer literacy. All students must take 40 hours of upper-division courses.

Special: The university offers internships, a 3–2 engineering degree with a general studies degree, a 3-year bachelor's degree, and non-degree study. Students may study abroad at Harlaxton College, Oxford University, or Regents College in England, at the National Institute for Higher Education in Ireland, and at the Korean Baptist Theological College. Work-study programs, dual majors, and a B.A.-B.S. degree are also offered. Portfolio evaluation and work experience credit are given. There is a freshman honors program on campus, as well as 2 national honor societies. Five departments have honors programs.

Faculty/Classroom: Ninety percent of faculty are male; 10%, female. All teach undergraduates. No introductory courses are taught by graduate students. The average class size in an introductory lecture is 35; in a laboratory, 60; and in a regular course offering, 20.

Admissions: All of the 1993–94 applicants were accepted. Sixteen freshmen graduated first in their class.

Requirements: The ACT is required. Applicants are required to have 13 academic credits, including a recommended 4 credits in English, 3 in mathematics, 2 each in science and social studies, and 2 selected from English, mathematics, languages, computer science, and social studies. An interview and, where applicable, an audition are recommended. The GED is accepted. AP and CLEP credits are accepted. Important factors used in the admissions decision are recommendations by school officials, advanced placement or honor courses, evidence of special talent, ability to finance college education, and leadership record.

Procedure: Freshmen are admitted to all sessions. Entrance exams may be taken at anytime. Application deadlines are open. Application fee is $25. Notification is sent on a rolling basis. There are early decision, early admissions, and deferred admissions plans.

Transfer: About 100 transfer students enrolled in a recent year. Applicants must submit official transcripts and have a minimum GPA of 2.0. Only 6 hours of D credit will be accepted. A total of 30 credits out of 128 must be completed at SBU.

Visiting: There are regularly scheduled orientations for prospective students, Prospective students are invited to visit on High School Day. There are guides for informal visits and visitors may sit in on classes and stay overnight at the school. To arrange for a visit, contact the Office of Student Services at (417) 326–1885.

Financial Aid: In a recent year, 90% of all current freshmen received some form of financial aid. Scholarships or need-based grants averaged $1500; loans averaged $2000; and work contracts averaged $800. SBU is a member of CSS. The FAF, FFS, or SFS is required. The deadline for financial aid applications is April 30.

International Students: There are currently 19 international students enrolled. They must take the TOEFL and achieve a minimum score of 550. The student must also take the SAT I or the ACT.

Computers: The university provides computer facilities for student use. The mainframe is a Prime. Microcomputers are available in academic buildings throughout campus. All students may access the system 8 A.M. to 8 P.M. daily. There are no time limits on using the system. The fee is $8.

Graduates: In a recent year, 325 bachelor's degrees were awarded. The most popular majors among graduates were education (21%), religion (13%), and social sciences (11%).

Admissions Contact: Dr. Gary Ingle, Dean of Admissions.

SOUTHWEST MISSOURI STATE UNIVERSITY   B-3
Springfield, MO 65804   (417) 836–5517
                                        (800) 492–7900 (out-of-state)

Full-time: 6192 men, 6939 women	Faculty: 672; IIA, -$
Part-time: 1534 men, 1840 women	Ph.D.s: 75%
Graduate: 540 men, 1115 women	Student/Faculty: 20 to 1
Year: semesters, summer session	Tuition: $2326 ($4516)
Application Deadline: n/av	Room & Board: $2630
Freshman Class: 6503 applied, 5254 accepted, 3204 enrolled	
ACT: 22	COMPETITIVE

Southwest Missouri State University, founded in 1905, is a public, coeducational institution offering undergraduate programs in arts and letters, business administration, humanities and social sciences, education and psychology, health and applied sciences, and science and mathematics. There are 6 undergraduate schools and one graduate school. In addition to regional accreditation, SMSU has baccalaureate program accreditation with AACSB, ADA, AHEA, ASLA, CSWE, NASM, NCATE, NLN, and NRPA. The library contains 534,000 volumes, 800,000 microform items, and 20,500 audiovisual forms, and subscribes to 4632 periodicals. Computerized library sources and services include the card catalog, interlibrary loans, and database searching. Special learning facilities include a learning resource center, art gallery, and radio station. The 225-acre campus is in a suburban area 220 miles southwest of St. Louis. Including residence halls, there are 50 buildings on campus.

Student Life: About 93% of undergraduates are from Missouri. Students come from 45 states, 49 foreign countries, and Canada. Ninety percent are from public schools; 10% from private. Ninety-four percent are white. Fifty-seven percent are Protestant; 17% Catholic. The average age of all undergraduates is 23. Twenty-nine percent drop out by the end of their first year; 45% remain to graduate.

Housing: A total of 4170 students can be accommodated in college housing. College-sponsored living facilities include single-sex and coed dormitories, on-campus apartments, fraternity houses, and sorority houses. In addition there are honors houses and wellness houses. On-campus housing is guaranteed for all 4 years. Alcohol is not permitted. All students may keep cars on campus.

Activities: About 14% of men belong to 17 national fraternities; about 10% of women belong to 10 national sororities. There are 252 groups on campus, including art, band, cheerleading, chess, choir, chorale, chorus, computers, dance, drama, drill team, ethnic, gay, honors, international, jazz band, literary magazine, marching band, musical theater, newspaper, orchestra, pep band, political, professional, radio and TV, religious, ROTC (Army), social, social service, student government, symphony, and yearbook. Popular campus events include Elizabethan Dinner, Tent Theater, African American History Month, New Student Festival, Family Weekend, Homecoming Week, Alcohol Awareness Week, Access in Motion, Spring Fling, Welcome Back Week, Leadership Conference, Greek Week, and Holly-Days.

Sports: There are 10 intercollegiate sports for men and 7 for women. Athletic and recreation facilities include a 16,600-seat stadium, a 9,000-seat arena, a 9000-seat gymnasium, a student center, an athlet-

ic center, a swimming pool, softball and practice fields, tennis courts, and bowling lanes.

Disabled Students: Ninety-five percent of the campus is accessible to disabled students. The following facilities are available: wheelchair ramps, elevators, special parking, specially equipped rest rooms, special class scheduling, lowered drinking fountains, and lowered telephones.

Services: In addition to many counseling and information services, tutoring is available in some subjects, including on demand. A reader service for the blind, and remedial math, reading, and writing are also available. There are also a mathematics center and a writing center for student use.

Campus Safety and Security: Campus safety and security measures include 24-hour foot and vehicle patrol, self defense education, escort service, and shuttle buses. In addition, there are informal discussions, pamphlets, posters, films, emergency telephones, lighted pathways and sidewalks, and a monthly newsletter.

Programs of Study: SMSU awards the B.A., B.S., B.F.A., B.M., B.S.E., B.S.N., and B.S.W. degrees. Associate and master's degrees also are awarded. Bachelor's degrees are awarded in AGRICULTURE (agriculture, agronomy, animal science, conservation and regulation, horticulture, and wildlife management), BIOLOGICAL SCIENCE (biology/biological science, cell biology, and nutrition), BUSINESS (accounting, banking and finance, business administration and management, hotel/motel and restaurant management, institutional management, insurance, marketing/retailing/merchandising, and recreation and leisure services), COMMUNICATIONS AND THE ARTS (art, broadcasting, communications, dance, design, dramatic arts, English, film arts, French, German, Latin, music, Spanish, speech/debate/rhetoric, and technical and business writing), COMPUTER AND PHYSICAL SCIENCE (chemistry, computer science, earth science, geology, information sciences and systems, mathematics, and physics), EDUCATION (agricultural, art, business, elementary, foreign languages, health, home economics, industrial arts, music, physical, science, and secondary), ENGINEERING AND ENVIRONMENTAL DESIGN (cartography, construction management, drafting and design, electrical/electronics engineering technology, engineering physics, industrial administration/management, interior design, manufacturing technology, and urban planning technology), HEALTH PROFESSIONS (medical laboratory technology, nursing, predentistry, premedicine, radiograph medical technology, respiratory therapy, and speech pathology/audiology), SOCIAL SCIENCE (child care/child and family studies, clothing and textiles management/production/services, dietetics, economics, geography, gerontology, history, parks and recreation management, philosophy, political science/government, prelaw, psychology, public administration, religion, social science, social work, and sociology). Education and business are the strongest academically and have the largest enrollments.

Required: A total of 124 to 130 semester hours, including 30 to 60 in the major, and a minimum GPA of 2.0 are required. Forty-five general education semester hours are required, to include 8 in natural sciences, 6 to 9 each in social sciences and humanties, 6 in American studies, 4 in physical education, 3 to 6 in English compostiion, and 3 each in mathematics and speech.

Special: Southwest Missouri offers co-op programs, internships, study abroad in 45 countries, and work-study programs. Also available are B.A.-B.S. degrees in 12 majors, student-designed and interdisciplinary majors, including antiquities, agriculture business and agriculture education, chemistry-biochemistry, communication management, and finance/real estate. A 3–2 engineering degree is available through the University of Missouri-Rolla. Credit for military experience, pass/not-pass options, and nondegree study are possible. There is a freshman honors program on campus, as well as 20 national honor societies.

Faculty/Classroom: Seventy percent of faculty are male; 30%, female. All teach undergraduates. Graduate students teach 4% of introductory courses.

Admissions: About 81% of the 1993–94 applicants were accepted. The ACT scores for the 1993–94 freshman class were as follows: 45% below 21, 28% between 21 and 23, 15% between 24 and 26, 5% between 27 and 28, and 7% above 28. About 30% of the current freshmen were in the top fifth of their class; 58% were in the top two fifths. There were 24 National Merit finalists. About 60 freshmen graduated first in their class.

Requirements: The ACT is required. Applicants from southwest Missouri must have an ACT composite score of 17, and other Missouri applicants must have an ACT composite score of 17 and rank in the top two thirds of their high school graduating class or have an ACT composite score of 19. Out-of-state applicants must have a 17 ACT composite score and rank in the top half of their class or have an ACT composite score of 19. AP and CLEP credits are accepted.

Procedure: Entrance exams should be taken as early as possible. Notification is sent on a rolling basis. There is a $15 application fee.

Transfer: About 953 transfer students enrolled in 1993–94. Transfer applicants must present a minimum GPA of 2.0. If they have completed less than 30 semester hours, they are also required to provide a high school transcript verifying graduation and ACT scores. A total of 30 credits out of 124 to 130 credits must be completed at SMSU.

Visiting: There are regularly scheduled orientations for prospective students, including programs preceding each semester consisting of orientation, academic advising, and enrollment for classes. There are guides for informal visits. To arrange for a visit, contact the Admissions Office at (417) 836–5517 or (800) 492–7900.

Financial Aid: In 1993–94 45% of all current freshmen and 50% of continuing students received some form of financial aid. About 35% of freshmen and 35% of continuing students received need-based aid. The average freshman award was $4259. Of that total, scholarships or need-based grants averaged $1776 ($7000 maximum); loans averaged $2433 ($5000 maximum); and work contracts averaged $50 ($1300 maximum). Fifty percent of undergraduate students work part-time. Average earnings from campus work for the school year are $1200. SMSU is a member of CSS. The FAFSA financial statement is required. The deadline for financial aid applications is March 31.

International Students: There are currently 320 international students enrolled. The school actively recruits these students. They must take the TOEFL and achieve a minimum score of 500.

Computers: The college provides computer facilities for student use. The mainframe is an IBM, a DEC, and a Prime. More than 3500 microcomputers and multiple networks with fiber optic backbone are available in computer laboratories. All students may access the system. There are no time limits and no fees.

Graduates: In 1992–93 2459 bachelor's degrees were awarded. The most popular majors among graduates were communications (8%), elementary education (8%), and marketing (7%). Within an average freshman class, 15% graduate in 4 years, 31% in 5 years, and 37% in 6 years.

Admissions Contact: Judy Geisler, Assistant Director of Admissions.

STEPHENS COLLEGE   C-2

Columbia, MO 65215   (314) 876–7207; (800) 876–7207 (in-state)

Full-time: 13 men, 580 women	Faculty: 65; IIB, --$
Part-time: 24 men, 385 women	Ph.D.s: 66%
Graduate: none	Student/Faculty: 9 to 1
Year: semesters, summer session	Tuition: $13,410
Application Deadline: August 1	Room & Board: $5050
Freshman Class: 460 applied, 420 accepted, 197 enrolled	
SAT I Verbal/Math: 460/460	ACT: 21 COMPETITIVE

Stephens College, founded in 1833, is a private college, primarily for women, offering undergraduate programs in the arts and sciences, business, education, and fine arts. The library contains 125,815 volumes, 9305 microform items, and 4811 audiovisual forms, and subscribes to 442 periodicals. Special learning facilities include a learning resource center, art gallery, radio station, and tv station. The 244-acre campus is in an urban area 126 miles west of St. Louis. Including residence halls, there are 50 buildings on campus.

Student Life: About 78% of undergraduates are from out-of-state, mostly the Southwest. Students come from 44 states and 4 foreign countries. Seventy-five percent are from public schools; 25% from private. Eighty-eight percent are white. The average age of freshmen is 19; all undergraduates, 21. Thirty percent drop out by the end of their first year; 45% remain to graduate.

Housing: College-sponsored living facilities include single-sex dormitories. In addition, there are honors houses, special interest houses for intercultural scholars and fine arts majors, and houses with designated academic floors or nonsmoking floors. On-campus housing is guaranteed for all 4 years. Ninety-five percent of students live on campus; of those, 95% remain on campus on weekends. Alcohol is not permitted. All students may keep cars on campus.

Activities: About 20% of women belong to 4 local sororities. There are no fraternities on campus. There are 25 groups on campus, including art, chorale, chorus, dance, drama, honors, international, literary magazine, musical theater, newspaper, photography, political, professional, radio and tv, religious, social, social service, student government, and yearbook. Popular campus events include the opening convocation, Honors Convocation, Haunted House, and a formal dance.

Sports: There are 4 intercollegiate sports for women and 10 intramural sports for women. Athletic and recreation facilities include a 50-seat gymnasium, a 400-seat arena, an Olympic-size pool, a 9-hole golf course, and a lake.

Disabled Students: More than 80% of the campus is accessible to disabled students. The following facilities are available: wheelchair ramps, elevators, special parking, specially equipped rest rooms, special class scheduling, lowered drinking fountains, and specially modified residence hall rooms and bathrooms.

Services: In addition to many counseling and information services, tutoring is available in most subjects, including English, mathematics, and computer science. In addition, there is remedial math.

Campus Safety and Security: Campus safety and security measures include 24-hour foot and vehicle patrol, informal discussions, emergency telephones, and lighted pathways and sidewalks.

Programs of Study: Stephens awards the B.A., B.S., and B.F.A. degrees. Associate degrees also are awarded. Bachelor's degrees are awarded in AGRICULTURE (equestrian science), BIOLOGICAL SCIENCE (biology/biological science), BUSINESS (business administration and management and fashion merchandising), COMMUNICATIONS AND THE ARTS (communications, dance, dramatic arts, English, and fine arts), COMPUTER AND PHYSICAL SCIENCE (mathematics), EDUCATION (early childhood and elementary), SOCIAL SCIENCE (fashion design and technology, philosophy, prelaw, and social science). Business, theater arts, communications, and fashion have the largest enrollments.

Required: All students must complete English 101 and 102, a mathematics course, 4 physical education activities, and a distribution of 9 courses in lower-division work, including a freshman studies course. Upper-division work includes a senior colloquium. The bachelor's degree requires completion of at least 120 semester hours, including 30 to 72 in a major field, with a minimum GPA of 2.0.

Special: Students may study abroad in England, Canada, and Spain. Stephens also offers cross-registration with the Mid-Missouri Associated Colleges and Universities, a Washington semester, dual and student-designed majors, a 3–2 occupational therapy degree program, and pass/fail options for electives. Credit for life experience is awarded to adults in the Stephens College Without Walls Program. There is a freshman honors program on campus, as well as 8 national honor societies.

Faculty/Classroom: Forty-four percent of faculty are male; 56%, female. All teach undergraduates. The average class size in an introductory lecture is 20; in a laboratory, 10; and in a regular course offering, 14.

Admissions: About 91% of the 1993–94 applicants were accepted. The SAT scores for a recent freshman class were as follows: Verbal—64% below 500, 23% between 500 and 599, 12% between 600 and 700, and 1% above 700; Math—60% below 500, 24% between 500 and 599, 15% between 600 and 700, and 1% above 700. The ACT scores were 49% below 21, 21% between 21 and 23, 14% between 24 and 26, 8% between 27 and 28, and 8% above 28. About 32% of the current freshmen were in the top fifth of their class; 54% were in the top two fifths. Five freshmen graduated first in their class.

Requirements: Stephens requires applicants to be in the upper 60% of their class. A minimum GPA of 2.0 is required. The SAT or the ACT is required. Applicants must be graduates of accredited secondary schools or have earned a GED. An essay is also required and an interview is recommended. AP and CLEP credits are accepted. Important factors used in the admissions decision are advanced placement or honor courses, leadership record, recommendations by school officials, recommendations by alumni, and geographic diversity.

Procedure: Freshmen are admitted fall and spring. Applications should be filed by August 1 for fall entry and December 31 for spring entry, along with an application fee of $25. Notification of early decision is sent December 15; regular decision, on a rolling basis. There are early decision, early admissions, and deferred admissions plans.

Transfer: About 30 transfer students enrolled in a recent year. Transfer applicants must submit official transcripts from all college work attempted or completed, as well as a recommendation from an academic college instructor. Transfers who have completed less than 1 year of college must submit an official high school transcript. A total of 36 credits out of 120 must be completed at Stephens.

Visiting: There are regularly scheduled orientations for prospective students, consisting of attendance at classes, a campus tour, an appointment with instructors, and an interview. There are guides for informal visits and visitors may sit in on classes and stay overnight at the school. To arrange for a visit, contact Darla Hickey at (800) 876-7207.

Financial Aid: In 1993–94, 70% of all students received some form of financial aid. About 60% of all students received need-based aid. The average freshman award was $14,000. Of that total, scholarships or need-based grants averaged $7500 ($15,375 maximum); loans averaged $3000 ($6250 maximum); and work contracts averaged $1800 ($2500 maximum). Forty-five percent of undergraduate students work part-time. Average earnings from campus work for the school year are $900. The average financial indebtedness of the 1992–93 graduate was $7800. Stephens is a member of CSS. The FAF, FFS, or SFS, and the FAFSA are required. The deadline for financial aid applications is March 15.

International Students: There are currently 5 international students enrolled. The school actively recruits these students. They must take the TOEFL and achieve a minimum score of 550. The student must also take the SAT I or the ACT.

Computers: The college provides computer facilities for student use. There are 24 Tandy and Apple microcomputers available in the computer laboratory. There are no time limits on using the system and no fees.

Graduates: In 1992–93, 185 bachelor's degrees were awarded. The most popular majors among graduates were fashion (20%), mass communication (20%), and theater (20%). Within an average freshman class, 15% graduate in 3 years, 40% in 4 years, and 5% in 5 years. Some 43 companies recruited on campus in 1992–93. In the 1992 graduating class, 3% of the men and 22% of the women were enrolled in graduate school within 6 months of graduation; 2% of the men and 26% of the women had found employment.

Admissions Contact: Michael Brophy, Dean of Enrollment Management.

UNIVERSITY OF MISSOURI SYSTEM

The University of Missouri system, established in 1966, is a public system in Missouri. It is governed by a board of curators, whose chief administrator is the president. The primary goals of the system are teaching, research, extension, and other public service. The main priorities are to provide the highest quality of instructional and research programs, to provide educational access to qualified students who demonstrate likelihood of academic success, and to operate in an effective and cost-efficient manner. The total enrollment of all 4 campuses usually exceeds 57,000, with more than 4800 faculty members. Altogether there are 214 baccalaureate, 228 master's, and 106 doctoral programs offered within University of Missouri system. Four-year campuses are located in Columbia, Kansas City, Rolla, and St. Louis. Profiles of those campuses are included in this chapter.

UNIVERSITY OF MISSOURI COLUMBIA

C-2

Columbia, MO 65211   (314) 882-7786; (800) 225-6075 (in-state)

Full-time: 7375 men, 7407 women	Faculty: 1552; I, --$
Part-time: 758 men, 825 women	Ph.D.s: 78%
Graduate: 2384 men, 2289 women	Student/Faculty: 10 to 1
Year: semesters, summer session	Tuition: $2934 ($8010)
Application Deadline: May 15	Room & Board: $3320
Freshman Class: 6574 applied, 4637 accepted, 2940 enrolled	
SAT I Verbal/Math: 502/564	ACT: 25 HIGHLY COMPETITIVE

The University of Missouri/Columbia, established in 1839, offers a comprehensive array of undergraduate and graduate programs as well as professional training in law, medicine, and veterinary medicine. There are 13 undergraduate and 5 graduate schools. In addition to regional accreditation, MU has baccalaureate program accreditation with AACSB, ABET, ACEJMC, ADA, AHEA, APTA, CAHEA, CSWE, FIDER, NASAD, NASM, NCATE, NLN, NRPA, and SAF. The 8 libraries contain 2.6 million volumes, 5.2 million microform items, and 11,000 audiovisual forms, and subscribe to 17,395 periodicals. Computerized library sources and services include the card catalog, interlibrary loans, and database searching. Special learning facilities include a learning resource center, art gallery, natural history museum, radio station, TV station, astronomy observatory, a natural history, geology, and entomology museum, a freedom of information center, an herbarium, and anthropology, fishery, and wildlife collections. The 1340-acre campus is in a small town 120 miles west of St. Louis and 120 miles east of Kansas City. Including residence halls, there are 300 buildings on campus.

Student Life: About 87% of undergraduates are from Missouri. Students come from 50 states, 116 foreign countries, and Canada. Ninety percent are white. Nineteen percent drop out by the end of their first year.

Housing: A total of 5367 students can be accommodated in college housing. College-sponsored living facilities include single-sex and coed dormitories, married-student housing, fraternity houses, and sorority houses. In addition there are honors/international houses, quiet houses, and graduate/professional houses. On-campus housing is guaranteed for all 4 years. Fifty-one percent of students live on campus. Alcohol is not permitted. All students may keep cars on campus.

Activities: About 25% of men belong to 35 national fraternities; about 25% of women belong to 23 national sororities. There are 374 groups on campus, including art, band, cheerleading, choir, chorale, chorus, computers, dance, drama, drill team, drum and bugle corps, ethnic, gay, honors, international, jazz band, literary magazine, marching band, musical theater, newspaper, orchestra, pep band, photography, political, professional, radio and TV, religious, ROTC (Air Force, Army), social, social service, student government, symphony, and yearbook. Popular campus events include Big Eight athletics and academic weeks.

Sports: There are 9 intercollegiate sports for men and 9 for women, and 26 intramural sports for men and 22 for women. Athletic and recreation facilities include a recreation center with more than 10 multicourts, 21 racquetball courts, a natatorium, an indoor running track, and 2 weight rooms; a 62,000-seat stadium; a 1300-seat indoor gymnasium; and an 18,000-seat auditorium.

Disabled Students: The following facilities are available: wheelchair ramps, elevators, special parking, specially equipped rest rooms, special class scheduling, lowered drinking fountains, and lowered telephones.

Services: In addition to many counseling and information services, tutoring is available in some subjects, including all sciences, mathematics, introductory economics, and introductory accounting. In addition, there is a reader service for the blind.

Campus Safety and Security: Campus safety and security measures include 24-hour foot and vehicle patrol, self defense education, escort service, and shuttle buses. In addition, there are informal discussions, pamphlets, posters, and films, emergency telephones, and lighted pathways and sidewalks.

Programs of Study: MU awards the A.B., B.S., B.E.S.,, B.F.A., B.G.S., B.H.S., B.J., B.M., B.S.Acc., B.S.Ag., B.S.AgE., B.S.B.A., B.S.ChE., B.S.CiE., B.S.E., B.S.E.E., B.S.Ed., B.S.H.E.S., B.S.I.E., B.S.M.E., B.S.CoE., B.S.F.W., B.S.F., B.S.N., and B.S.W. degrees. Master's and doctoral degrees also are awarded. Bachelor's degrees are awarded in AGRICULTURE (agricultural economics, agriculture, animal science, and horticulture), BIOLOGICAL SCIENCE (biochemistry and biology/biological science), BUSINESS (accounting, banking and finance, business administration and management, business economics, hotel/motel and restaurant management, marketing/retailing/merchandising, and real estate), COMMUNICATIONS AND THE ARTS (advertising, art history and appreciation, broadcasting, classics, communications, design, dramatic arts, English, fine arts, French, German, journalism, music, Russian, and Spanish), COMPUTER AND PHYSICAL SCIENCE (atmospheric sciences and meteorology, chemistry, computer science, geology, mathematics, physics, and statistics), EDUCATION (art, business, early childhood, education, elementary, foreign languages, guidance, home economics, industrial arts, middle school, music, secondary, and special), ENGINEERING AND ENVIRONMENTAL DESIGN (chemical engineering, civil engineering, computer engineering, electrical/electronics engineering, industrial engineering, and mechanical engineering), HEALTH PROFESSIONS (medical laboratory technology, nursing, occupational therapy, physical therapy, radiological science, respiratory therapy, and speech pathology/audiology), SOCIAL SCIENCE (anthropology, archeology, dietetics, economics, food science, geography, history, Latin American studies, parks and recreation management, philosophy, political science/government, psychology, religion, rural sociology, social science, social work, and sociology). Journalism, education, and engineering have the largest enrollments.

Required: In order to graduate, students must maintain a minimum 2.0 GPA and complete at least 120 credits, of which at least 30 must be in their major. They are required to take English 20 and Mathematics 10.

Special: Available academic programs include co-op programs and cross-registration with other schools, internships, study abroad, a Washington semester, and work-study programs. Special degrees or studies include a B.A.-B.S. degree, an accelerated degree, dual majors, a general studies degree, and student-designed majors. Nondegree study and pass/fail options are available. For highly motivated students there is an honors college and the possibility of early admission to the schools of law and medicine. The university also has an easy-access program for nondegree-seeking community residents. There is a freshman honors program on campus, as well as 25 national honor societies, including Phi Beta Kappa.

Faculty/Classroom: Seventy-six percent of faculty are male; 24%, female. The average class size in an introductory lecture is 250; in a laboratory, 23; and in a regular course offering, 22.

Admissions: About 71% of the 1993–94 applicants were accepted. The ACT scores for the 1993–94 freshman class were as follows: 13% below 21, 28% between 21 and 23, 27% between 24 and 26, 13% between 27 and 28, and 20% above 28. About 53% of the current freshmen were in the top fifth of their class; 82% were in the top two fifths. There were 21 National Merit finalists. About 160 freshmen graduated first in their class.

Requirements: The ACT is required. Students may gain probationary admission with sufficient GED scores. The usual requirements are completion of 15 Carnegie units, including 4 in English, 3 each in a foreign language (optional) and mathematics, and 2 each in history or social studies and science. Admission is determined by these 15 units and a combination of class rank and ACT score. AP and CLEP credits are accepted.

Procedure: Freshmen are admitted to all sessions. Entrance exams should be taken late in the junior year or in the senior year. Applications should be filed by May 15 for fall entry, along with an application fee of $25. Notification is sent on a rolling basis.

Transfer: A total of 1426 transfer students enrolled in a recent year. Transfer students must present 24 hours of completed college-level course work with a minimum 2.0 GPA, and show a C average in all course work attempted. An interview is recommended. A total of 45 credits out of 120 must be completed at MU.

Visiting: There are regularly scheduled orientations for prospective students, consisting of a campus tour, a visit with an admissions representative, and a visit with an academic representative on request. There are guides for informal visits and visitors may sit in on classes. To arrange for a visit, contact High School and Transfer Relations at (314) 882–2456 or (800) 225–6075 (in-state).

Financial Aid: In 1993–94, 72% of all current freshmen and 50% of continuing students received some form of financial aid. The average freshman award in a recent year was $5660. MU is a member of CSS. The FAF, FFS, or FAFSA is required. The deadline for financial aid applications is March 1.

International Students: There are currently 1111 international students enrolled. They must take the TOEFL and achieve a minimum score of 500.

Computers: The university provides computer facilities for student use. The mainframe is an IBM 3090 170 J. There are also 588 terminals for general student use, BITNET, 13 computer laboratories across campus, and residence hall computer laboratories. All students may access the system. It may be used 24 hours daily by modem; laboratory hours vary, but they are open 7 days a week. There are no time limits on using the system. A computing fee of $4.50 per credit hour is charged to fund the computer laboratories.

Graduates: In 1992–93 3803 bachelor's degrees were awarded. Within an average freshman class, 1% graduate in 3 years, 30% in 4 years, 54% in 5 years, and 56% in 6 years. Some 538 companies recruited on campus in 1992–93.

Admissions Contact: Georgeanne Porter, Director of Undergraduate Admissions.

UNIVERSITY OF MISSOURI
KANSAS CITY

A-2

Kansas City, MO 64110   (816) 235–1111

Full-time: 1614 men, 1802 women	**Faculty:** 340; I, --$
Part-time: 932 men, 1052 women	**Ph.D.s:** 94%
Graduate: 1900 men, 2558 women	**Student/Faculty:** 10 to 1
Year: semesters, summer session	**Tuition:** $2551 ($6902)
Application Deadline: July 1	**Room & Board:** $3355
Freshman Class: 1612 applied, 1051 accepted, 545 enrolled	
ACT: 25	**VERY COMPETITIVE**

The University of Missouri/Kansas City, which opened in 1933, is a public, coeducational institution offering undergraduate and graduate programs in the arts and sciences, engineering, business, education, health fields, and preprofessional studies. It offers most of the degree programs in the evening to a primarily commuter student body. There are 9 undergraduate schools and one graduate school. In addition to regional accreditation, UMKC has baccalaureate program accreditation with AACSB, ABET, ACPE, ADA, NASM, NCATE, and NLN. The 4 libraries contain 869,099 volumes, 1,657,000 microform items, and 121,884 audiovisual forms, and subscribe to 8717 periodicals. Computerized library sources and services include the card catalog, interlibrary loans, and database searching. Special learning facilities include a learning resource center, art gallery, planetarium, and radio station. The 191-acre campus is in an urban area in Kansas City. Including residence halls, there are 40 buildings on campus.

Student Life: About 77% of undergraduates are from Missouri. Students come from 48 states, 87 foreign countries, and Canada. Seventy-eight percent are white. Twenty-seven percent drop out by the end of their first year; 44% remain to graduate.

Housing: A total of 325 students can be accommodated in college housing. College-sponsored living facilities include coed dormitories. On-campus housing is available on a first-come, first-served basis. Ninety-seven percent of students commute. Alcohol is not permitted. All students may keep cars on campus.

Activities: About 2% of men belong to 4 national fraternities; about 2% of women belong to 1 local and 3 national sororities. There are 125 groups on campus, including art, band, cheerleading, chess, choir, chorale, chorus, computers, dance, drama, ethnic, gay, honors, international, jazz band, literary magazine, newspaper, opera, orchestra, photography, political, professional, radio and TV, religious, social, student government, and yearbook. Popular campus events include intramural team sports and individual tournaments, and travel programs.

Sports: There are 6 intercollegiate sports for men and 7 for women, and 19 intramural sports for men and 19 for women. Athletic and recreation facilities include a recreation center, with 5 gymnasiums; an indoor/outdoor pool, an indoor and outdoor track, a fitness center; and handball, racquetball, and squash courts. There are also recreation facilities at the University Center.

Disabled Students: Ninety-five percent of the campus is accessible to disabled students. The following facilities are available: wheelchair ramps, elevators, special parking, specially equipped rest rooms, special class scheduling, and lowered drinking fountains.

Services: There is a reader service for the blind available.

Campus Safety and Security: Campus safety and security measures include 24-hour foot and vehicle patrol, self defense education, escort service, and shuttle buses. In addition, there are informal discussions, pamphlets, posters, films, emergency telephones, and lighted pathways and sidewalks.

Programs of Study: UMKC awards the B.A., B.S., B.B.A., B.L.A., B.M., B.M.E., B.S.C.E., B.S.D.H., B.S.E.E., B.S.M.E., B.S.N., and B.S.P. degrees. Master's and doctoral degrees also are awarded. Bachelor's degrees are awarded in BIOLOGICAL SCIENCE (biology/biological science), BUSINESS (accounting and business administration and management), COMMUNICATIONS AND THE ARTS (communications, dance, dramatic arts, English, fine arts, languages, music, and speech/debate/rhetoric), COMPUTER AND PHYSICAL SCIENCE (chemistry, computer science, earth science, geology, mathematics, and physics), EDUCATION (elementary, health, music, science, and secondary), ENGINEERING AND ENVIRONMENTAL DESIGN (civil engineering, electrical/electronics engineering, and mechanical engineering), HEALTH PROFESSIONS (nursing and pharmacy), SOCIAL SCIENCE (criminal justice, economics, geography, history, philosophy, political science/government, psychology, sociology, and urban studies). Health sciences and performing arts are the strongest academically. Business has the largest enrollment.

Required: Candidates for the B.A. and B.S. degrees must complete a core curriculum that consists of courses in English, a foreign language, mathematics, philosophy, fine arts, history, literature, natural sciences, and social sciences. They must complete 120 credit hours, including 36 in their major, with a 2.0 GPA.

Special: Special academic programs include co-op programs and internships in several majors, cross-registration with the Kansas City Regional Council, study abroad in 8 countries, and numerous work-study opportunities in the Kansas City area. Special degrees include a B.A.-B.S. degree in the computer science program, a dual major in psychology and speech and hearing science, and a general studies degree offered by the adult continuing education program. The pass/fail option is available in some courses. Freshmen may enter 6-year medical and dental programs. There is a freshman honors program on campus, as well as 4 national honor societies. One department has an honors program.

Faculty/Classroom: Sixty-four percent of faculty are male; 36%, female. Seventy-five percent teach undergraduates. Graduate students teach 5% of introductory courses. The average class size in an introductory lecture is 30; in a laboratory, 16; and in a regular course offering, 24.

Admissions: About 65% of the 1993–94 applicants were accepted. The ACT scores for the 1993–94 freshman class were as follows: 22% below 21, 23% between 21 and 23, 23% between 24 and 26, 12% between 27 and 28, and 20% above 28. About 58% of the current freshmen were in the top fifth of their class; 83% were in the top two fifths. Twenty-six freshmen graduated first in their class.

Requirements: The ACT is required. A combination of the student's test score and class rank determines admissibility. Graduation from an accredited secondary school is a requirement for admission; the GED is also accepted. Required high school subjects include 4 units of English, 3 each of mathematics and social studies, 2 of science, 1 of arts, and 3 more units selected from the above subjects or from a foreign language. A portfolio is required for art majors, an audition for music majors, and an interview for only those students applying for the pharmacy degree or the 6-year medical and dental programs. AP and CLEP credits are accepted.

Procedure: Freshmen are admitted to all sessions. Entrance exams should be taken by March of the senior year. Applications should be filed by July 1 for fall entry, December 1 for spring entry, and May 1 for summer entry. Notification is sent on a rolling basis.

Transfer: About 1068 transfer students enrolled in 1993–94. A maximum of 60 semester hours from community colleges or 30 hours earned within the University of Missouri System will be accepted. Transfer students must have maintained a 2.0 GPA. The SAT I or ACT is recommended. A total of 30 credits out of 120 must be completed at UMKC.

Visiting: There are regularly scheduled orientations for prospective students, consisting of a 1-day program for new freshmen or a half-day optional program for transfer students. There are guides for informal visits. To arrange for a visit, contact the Student Life Office at (816) 235-1407.

Financial Aid: In 1993–94 59% of all current freshmen and 42% of continuing students received some form of financial aid. About 36% of freshmen and 33% of continuing students received need-based aid. The average freshman award was $5149. Of that total, scholarships or need-based grants averaged $2163 ($5149 maximum); loans averaged $2780 ($5149 maximum); and work contracts averaged $206 ($2640 maximum). Seventy-nine percent of undergraduate students work part-time. Average earnings from campus work for the school year are $2640. The FAFSA financial statement is required. The deadline for financial aid applications is March 15.

International Students: There are currently 726 international students enrolled. The school actively recruits these students. They must take the TOEFL and achieve a minimum score of 600.

Computers: The college provides computer facilities for student use. The mainframe is a DEC VAX VECTOR 6000–540. There are 176 microcomputers and 70 terminals available at various locations. All students may access the system. There are no time limits on using the system. The fees are $2.20 per credit hour.

Graduates: In 1992–93 1191 bachelor's degrees were awarded. The most popular majors among graduates were business administration (15%), elementary education (13%), and biology (13%). Within an average freshman class, 16% graduate in 4 years, 27% in 5 years, and 43% in 6 years. Some 164 companies recruited on campus in 1992–93.

Admissions Contact: Melvin Tyler, Director of Admissions.

UNIVERSITY OF MISSOURI
ROLLA
C-3

Rolla, MO 65401–0249

(314) 341-4164
(800) 522-0938 (out-of-state)

Full-time: 3036 men, 890 women	Faculty: 312; I, av$
Part-time: 373 men, 188 women	Ph.D.s: 91%
Graduate: 995 men, 201 women	Student/Faculty: 13 to 1
Year: semesters, summer session	Tuition: $3254 ($8693)
Application Deadline: July 1	Room & Board: $3475
Freshman Class: 1871 applied, 1820 accepted, 823 enrolled	
SAT I Verbal/Math: 547/655	ACT: 27　VERY COMPETITIVE +

The University of Missouri/Rolla, founded in 1870, is part of the University of Missouri System. A coeducational, public institution, it offers comprehensive undergraduate and graduate programs and confers degrees in arts and sciences, engineering, and mining and metallurgy. There are 3 undergraduate and 3 graduate schools. In addition to regional accreditation, UMR has baccalaureate program accreditation with ABET. The library contains 440,833 volumes, 365,544 microform items, and 3051 audiovisual forms, and subscribes to 1453 periodicals. Computerized library sources and services include the card catalog, interlibrary loans, and database searching. Special learning facilities include a learning resource center, radio station, a working mine, a nuclear reactor, and an observatory. The 284-acre campus is in a small town 90 miles southwest of St. Louis. Including residence halls, there are 65 buildings on campus.

Student Life: About 78% of undergraduates are from Missouri. Students come from 45 states, 37 foreign countries, and Canada. Eighty-six percent are from public schools; 14% from private. Eighty-one percent are white; 11% foreign nationals. Forty percent are Protestant; 30% claim no religious affiliation; 25% Catholic. The average age of freshmen is 18; all undergraduates, 22. Twenty-one percent drop out by the end of their first year; 50% remain to graduate.

Housing: A total of 1365 students can be accommodated in college housing. College-sponsored living facilities include single-sex and coed dormitories, on-campus apartments, and married-student housing. On-campus housing is guaranteed for the freshman and sophomore years only and is available on a first-come, first-served basis. Fifty-three percent of students live on campus. Alcohol is not permitted. All students may keep cars on campus.

Activities: About 28% of men belong to 22 national fraternities; about 20% of women belong to 5 national sororities. There are 170 groups on campus, including bagpipe band, band, cheerleading, chess, chorus, computers, drama, drill team, ethnic, honors, international, jazz band, literary magazine, marching band, musical theater, newspaper, orchestra, pep band, political, professional, radio and TV, religious, social, social service, student government, and yearbook. Popular campus events include Homecoming, St. Patrick's Day, Black Culture Month, Hispanic Culture Month, Engineering Week, Madrigal Dinners, and Greek Week.

Sports: There are 10 intercollegiate sports for men and 5 for women, and 18 intramural sports for men and 15 for women. Athletic and recreation facilities include a gymnasium, a weight room, a pool, a golf course, a track, racquetball and tennis courts, ball fields, and a 5,000-seat stadium.

Disabled Students: Ninety percent of the campus is accessible to disabled students. The following facilities are available: wheelchair ramps, elevators, special parking, specially equipped rest rooms, special class scheduling, and lowered drinking fountains.

Services: In addition to counseling and information services, there is a reader service for the blind.

Campus Safety and Security: Campus safety and security measures include 24-hour foot and vehicle patrol, escort service, informal discussions, and pamphlets, posters, and films. In addition, there are

emergency telephones, lighted pathways and sidewalks, and crime prevention and rape/sexual assault programs.

Programs of Study: UMR awards the B.A. and B.S. degrees. Master's and doctoral degrees also are awarded. Bachelor's degrees are awarded in BIOLOGICAL SCIENCE (life science), BUSINESS (management information systems), COMMUNICATIONS AND THE ARTS (English), COMPUTER AND PHYSICAL SCIENCE (applied mathematics, chemistry, computer science, geology, mathematics, and physics), ENGINEERING AND ENVIRONMENTAL DESIGN (aeronautical engineering, ceramic engineering, chemical engineering, civil engineering, electrical/electronics engineering, engineering management, geological engineering, mechanical engineering, metallurgical engineering, mining and mineral engineering, nuclear engineering, and petroleum/natural gas engineering), SOCIAL SCIENCE (economics, history, philosophy, and psychology). Engineering is the strongest academically and has the largest enrollment.

Required: Candidates for graduation must maintain at least a 2.0 GPA. A total of 120 to 132 credits, depending on the degree, is required.

Special: UMR offers co-op programs with the universities of Missouri at Columbia and St. Louis and co-op training programs in which students may work and attend school on alternating schedules. Study abroad in London, dual majors in any fields, a 3-2 engineering degree, credit for life/military/work experience, and pass/fail options in certain courses are available. There is a freshman honors program on campus, as well as 11 national honor societies. Five departments have honors programs.

Faculty/Classroom: Ninety-four percent of faculty are male; 6%, female. The average class size in an introductory lecture is 28 and in a laboratory, 17.

Admissions: About 97% of the 1993–94 applicants were accepted. The SAT scores for the 1993–94 freshman class were as follows: Verbal—35% below 500, 42% between 500 and 599, 21% between 600 and 700, and 2% above 700; Math—8% below 500, 23% between 500 and 599, 47% between 600 and 700, and 22% above 700. The ACT scores were 4% below 21, 14% between 21 and 23, 27% between 24 and 26, 17% between 27 and 28, and 38% above 28. About 67% of the current freshmen were in the top fifth of their class; 90% were in the top two fifths. There were 15 National Merit finalists. About 65 freshmen graduated first in their class.

Requirements: The SAT I or ACT is required. The sum of the high school student's class rank percentile and aptitude exam percentile must be 140 or higher. Candidates must be graduates of an accredited secondary school or have the GED. The applicant must have completed 15 academic credit units, including 4 in English, 3 in mathematics, 2 each in science and social studies, 1 in fine arts, and 3 from a foreign language, English, mathematics, science, or social studies. AP and CLEP credits are accepted. Important factors used in the admissions decision are leadership record, advanced placement or honor courses, evidence of special talent, personality, intangible qualities, and extracurricular activities record.

Procedure: Freshmen are admitted to all sessions. Applications should be filed by July 1 for fall entry, December 1 for winter entry, and May 1 for summer entry, along with an application fee of $20. Notification is sent on a rolling basis.

Transfer: A total of 328 transfer students enrolled in 1993–94. Transfer students with fewer than 24 semester hours of college-level work must apply as freshmen; those with 24 or more must have attained at least a 2.0 GPA in all college-level courses. A total of 30 credits out of 120 to 132 must be completed at UMR.

Visiting: There are regularly scheduled orientations for prospective students, including a tour with a student, admissions and financial aid counseling, and faculty and special interest contact. There are guides for informal visits and visitors may sit in on classes and stay overnight at the school. To arrange for a visit, contact Dave Allen, Director of Admissions and Financial Aid at (800) 522-0938 or (314) 341-4164.

Financial Aid: In 1993–94, 68% of all current freshmen and 51% of continuing students received some form of financial aid. About 52% of freshmen and 44% of continuing students received need-based aid. The average freshman award was $4400. Of that total, scholarships or need-based grants averaged $1600; loans averaged $1800; and work contracts averaged $1000 ($1600 maximum). Twenty-one percent of undergraduate students work part-time. Average earnings from campus work for the school year are $3856. The average financial indebtedness of the 1992–93 graduate was $8000. UMR is a member of CSS. The FAF and the college's own financial statement are required. The priority deadline for financial aid applications is March 31.

International Students: There are currently 656 international students enrolled. They must take the TOEFL and achieve a minimum score of 550. The student must also take the SAT I or the ACT.

Computers: The university provides computer facilities for student use. The mainframes are 2 IBM 4381-14 computers. All students have free access to campus mainframes and networked IBM PC and Apple Macintosh microcomputers. Also available are 160 various UNIX workstations (IBM, HP, HP/Apollo, Sun, NeXT). A complete array of software is provided on all platforms, and 24-hour service is available. About 360 Apple Macintosh and IBM-compatible computers are located at 26 locations.

Graduates: In 1992–93, 756 bachelor's degrees were awarded. The most popular majors among graduates were mechanical engineering (25%), electrical engineering (21%), and civil engineering (10%). Within an average freshman class, 10% graduate in 4 years, 26% in 5 years, and 14% in 6 years. Some 250 companies recruited on campus in 1992–93.

Admissions Contact: Dave Allen, Director of Admissions and Financial Aid.

UNIVERSITY OF MISSOURI
ST. LOUIS
St. Louis, MO 63121

D-2

(314) 553-5451

Full-time: 2238 men, 2555 women	**Faculty:** 390; I, --$
Part-time: 2005 men, 2547 women	**Ph.D.s:** 80%
Graduate: 853 men, 1513 women	**Student/Faculty:** 12 to 1
Year: semesters, summer session	**Tuition:** $2500 ($6851)
Application Deadline: July 1	**Room & Board:** $3878
Freshman Class: 1610 applied, 1051 accepted, 569 enrolled	
ACT: 22	COMPETITIVE

The University of Missouri/St. Louis, founded in 1963, is a public, coeducational institution offering undergraduate and graduate programs, and conferring degrees in arts and sciences, business, nursing, and education. There are 4 undergraduate schools and one graduate school. In addition to regional accreditation, UM-St. Louis has baccalaureate program accreditation with AACSB, CSWE, NASM, NCATE, and NLN. The 3 libraries contain 571,263 volumes and 1,497,563 microform items, and subscribe to 3000 periodicals. Special learning facilities include a learning resource center, art gallery, planetarium, and radio station. The 178-acre campus is in an urban area 10 miles north of downtown St. Louis. Including residence halls, there are 22 buildings on campus.

Student Life: About 99% of undergraduates are from Missouri. Students come from 35 foreign countries and Canada. Eighty-three percent are white; 13% African American. The average age of freshmen is 18. Thirty-eight percent drop out by the end of their first year; 60% remain to graduate.

Housing: A total of 90 students can be accommodated in college housing. College-sponsored living facilities include coed dormitories. On-campus housing is available on a first-come, first-served basis. Priority is given to out-of-town students. Ninety-nine percent of students commute. Alcohol is not permitted. All students may keep cars on campus.

Activities: There are 5 local and 5 national fraternities. There are no sororities on campus. There are 90 groups on campus, including art, band, cheerleading, chess, choir, chorale, chorus, computers, drama, ethnic, gay, honors, international, jazz band, literary magazine, newspaper, photography, political, professional, radio and TV, religious, social, social service, and student government. Popular campus events include Mirthday and Expo.

Sports: There are 6 intercollegiate sports for men and 6 for women, and 10 intramural sports for men and 10 for women. Athletic and recreation facilities include indoor handball/racquetball, basketball, volleyball, and badminton courts, wrestling, dance, and conditioning rooms, and a swimming pool; outdoors, there are intramural fields and facilities for baseball, soccer, handball, racquetball, and tennis.

Disabled Students: The following facilities are available: wheelchair ramps, elevators, special parking, specially equipped rest rooms, special class scheduling, lowered drinking fountains, and lowered telephones.

Services: In addition to many counseling and information services, tutoring is available in most subjects. In addition, there is a reader service for the blind, and remedial math, reading, and writing.

Campus Safety and Security: Campus safety and security measures include 24-hour foot and vehicle patrol, escort service, shuttle buses, and pamphlets, posters, and films. In addition, there are emergency telephones and lighted pathways and sidewalks.

Programs of Study: UM-St. Louis awards the B.A., B.S., B.G.S., B.M., B.S.A.J., B.S.B.A., B.S.Ed., B.S.N., B.S.P.A., and B.S.W. degrees. Master's and doctoral degrees also are awarded. Bachelor's degrees are awarded in BIOLOGICAL SCIENCE (biology/biological science), BUSINESS (business administration and management), COMMUNICATIONS AND THE ARTS (art history and appreciation, communications, English, French, German, music, and Spanish), COMPUTER AND PHYSICAL SCIENCE (applied mathematics, chemistry, computer science, mathematics, and physics), EDUCATION (early childhood, elementary, music, physical, secondary, and special), ENGINEERING AND ENVIRONMENTAL DESIGN (electrical/electronics engineering and mechanical engineering),

HEALTH PROFESSIONS (nursing), SOCIAL SCIENCE (anthropology, criminal justice, economics, history, philosophy, political science/government, psychology, public administration, social work, and sociology). Business, chemistry, physics, mathematics, and biology are the strongest academically. Business has the largest enrollment.

Required: To graduate, students must complete 120 credit hours, 42 of which must be in the area of general education. They must maintain a 2.0 GPA.

Special: Cross-registration with Washington University and St. Louis University, and cooperative programs in all majors are offered. Study abroad in England, France, or Germany, and a general studies degree in which credit can be earned for life, military, or work experience are available. Almost all of the degree programs are available through the Evening College. Some work-study is available. There is a freshman honors program on campus, as well as 11 national honor societies.

Admissions: About 65% of the 1993–94 applicants were accepted. The ACT scores for the 1993–94 freshman class were as follows: 35% below 21, 31% between 21 and 23, 22% between 24 and 26, 5% between 27 and 28, and 7% above 28. About 36% of the current freshmen were in the top fifth of their class; 65% were in the top two fifths.

Requirements: The SAT I or ACT is required. In addition, applicants should have a total of 15 units, including 4 in English, 3 in mathematics, 2 each in science and social studies, 1 in fine arts, and 3 in academic electives. The combined class rank and test score must be at the 75th percentile. No minimum score is used. Two units of foreign language are strongly recommended. AP and CLEP credits are accepted.

Procedure: Freshmen are admitted to all sessions. Applications should be filed by July 1 for fall entry, December 1 for winter entry, and May 1 for summer entry. Notification is sent on a rolling basis.

Transfer: A total of 1675 transfer students enrolled in 1993–94. Transfer students must have earned a minimum of 24 credit hours and maintained a minimum 2.0 GPA. A total of 30 credits out of 120 must be completed at UM-St. Louis.

Visiting: There are regularly scheduled orientations for prospective students. There are guides for informal visits and visitors may sit in on classes. To arrange for a visit, contact Rochelle DeClue at (314) 553-5450.

Financial Aid: In a recent year, 42% of all current freshmen and 35% of continuing students received some form of financial aid. Scholarships or need-based grants averaged $510 ($1700 maximum); loans averaged $1200 ($2625 maximum); and work contracts averaged $1200. UM-St. Louis is a member of CSS. The FAF or FFS is required. The FFS is preferred. The deadline for financial aid applications is March 1.

International Students: There are currently 200 international students enrolled. The school actively recruits these students. They must take the TOEFL or the college's own test and achieve a minimum score on the TOEFL of 500.

Computers: The university provides computer facilities for student use. The mainframes are an IBM 3090, 3081, and 4381P. Microcomputers are available in various computer laboratories. Students enrolled in computer courses may access the mainframe. There are no time limits on using the system and no fees.

Graduates: In a recent year, 1497 bachelor's degrees were awarded.

Admissions Contact: Director of Undergraduate Admissions.

WASHINGTON UNIVERSITY
D-2

St. Louis, MO 63130   (314) 935-6000; (800) 638-0700

Full-time: 2609 men, 2270 women	Faculty: 610; I, +$
Part-time: 594 men, 680 women	Ph.D.s: 99%
Graduate: 3042 men, 2476 women	Student/Faculty: 8 to 1
Year: semesters, summer session	Tuition: $17,776
Application Deadline: January 15	Room & Board: $5731
Freshman Class: 6894 applied, 5239 accepted, 1254 enrolled	
SAT I or ACT: required	**HIGHLY COMPETITIVE**

Washington University, founded in 1853, is a private, coeducational institution offering undergraduate and graduate programs in arts and sciences, business, architecture, engineering, and fine arts. There are 5 undergraduate and 8 graduate schools. In addition to regional accreditation, WU has baccalaureate program accreditation with AACSB, ABET, and NASAD. The 14 libraries contain 2,979,934 volumes, 2,419,941 microform items, and 34,102 audiovisual forms, and subscribe to 14,906 periodicals. Computerized library sources and services include the card catalog, interlibrary loans, and database searching. Special learning facilities include a learning resource center, art gallery, planetarium, and radio station. The 169-acre campus is in an urban area 7 miles west of downtown St. Louis. Including residence halls, there are 100 buildings on campus.

Student Life: About 88% of undergraduates are from out-of-state, mostly the Midwest. Students come from 50 states, 70 foreign countries, and Canada. Seventy percent are from public schools; 30%

from private. Seventy-three percent are white; 13% Asian American. Thirty percent are Jewish; 30% Catholic; 30% Protestant. The average age of freshmen is 18; all undergraduates, 20. Six percent drop out by the end of their first year; 85% remain to graduate.

Housing: A total of 2600 students can be accommodated in college housing. College-sponsored living facilities include single-sex and coed dormitories, on-campus apartments, off-campus apartments, and fraternity houses. In addition there are language houses, special interest suites, and language suites within residence halls. On-campus housing is guaranteed for the freshman year only, is available on a first-come, first-served basis, and is available on a lottery system for upperclassmen. Sixty percent of students live on campus; of those, 95% remain on campus on weekends. Upperclassmen may keep cars on campus.

Activities: About 30% of men belong to 12 national fraternities; about 33% of women belong to 7 national sororities. There are 170 groups on campus, including art, cheerleading, chess, choir, chorus, computers, dance, drama, ethnic, film, gay, honors, international, jazz band, literary magazine, musical theater, newspaper, opera, orchestra, pep band, photography, political, professional, radio and TV, religious, social, social service, student government, symphony, and yearbook. Popular campus events include student-run carnival, Homecoming, Air Band, cultural celebration, concerts, student-run production of African-American works, and College Bowl.

Sports: There are 9 intercollegiate sports for men and 8 for women, and 27 intramural sports for men and 26 for women. Athletic and recreation facilities include gymnasiums; a swimming pool; racquetball, tennis, handball, and squash courts; tracks; a weight room; saunas; recreational playing fields; and a football stadium.

Disabled Students: Fifty percent of the campus is accessible to disabled students. The following facilities are available: wheelchair ramps, elevators, special parking, specially equipped rest rooms, special class scheduling, lowered drinking fountains, lowered telephones, and magnification devices and hearing-assist devices.

Services: In addition to many counseling and information services, tutoring is available in every subject. In addition, there is a reader service for the blind.

Campus Safety and Security: Campus safety and security measures include 24-hour foot and vehicle patrol, self defense education, escort service, and shuttle buses. In addition, there are informal discussions, pamphlets, posters, films, emergency telephones, lighted pathways and sidewalks.

Programs of Study: WU awards the B.A., B.S., B.F.A., B.M., B.S.B.A, B.S.C.E., B.S.Ch.E., B.S.C.S., B.S.E.E., and B.S.M.E. degrees. Master's and doctoral degrees also are awarded. Bachelor's degrees are awarded in BIOLOGICAL SCIENCE (biochemistry and biology/biological science), BUSINESS (business administration and management), COMMUNICATIONS AND THE ARTS (Chinese, classics, comparative literature, dance, dramatic arts, English, fine arts, French, German, Italian, Japanese, languages, Latin, linguistics, music, photography, Russian, and Spanish), COMPUTER AND PHYSICAL SCIENCE (chemistry, computer science, earth science, mathematics, physical sciences, and physics), EDUCATION (early childhood, education of the deaf and hearing impaired, elementary, and secondary), ENGINEERING AND ENVIRONMENTAL DESIGN (architecture, chemical engineering, civil engineering, computer engineering, electrical/electronics engineering, engineering, engineering mechanics, engineering physics, geological engineering, mechanical engineering, and systems engineering), SOCIAL SCIENCE (African American studies, anthropology, archeology, Asian/Oriental studies, economics, fashion design and technology, history, humanities, international relations, Judaic studies, Latin American studies, medieval studies, philosophy, political science/government, psychology, religion, systems science, urban studies, Western European studies, and women's studies). Natural sciences, fine arts, architecture, English, business, and engineering are the strongest academically. Business and management, biology, psychology, engineering, architecture, and English have the largest enrollments.

Required: Students must complete 120 credits, and maintain a minimum GPA of 2.0. In addition, all students must complete a course in English composition and 3 courses of the major liberal arts disciplines.

Special: Opportunities are provided for cooperative programs with other schools, internships, work-study programs, study abroad, accelerated degree programs, a B.A.-B.S. engineering degree, credit by examination, nondegree study, pass/fail options, and dual and student-designed majors. There are 14 national honor societies on campus, including Phi Beta Kappa.

Faculty/Classroom: Seventy-four percent of faculty are male; 26%, female. The average class size in a regular course offering is 20.

Admissions: About 76% of the 1993–94 applicants were accepted. The SAT scores for the 1993–94 freshman class were as follows: Verbal—20% below 500, 44% between 500 and 599, 31% between 600 and 700, and 4% above 700; Math—4% below 500, 18% between 500 and 599, 50% between 600 and 700, and 26% above

700. The ACT scores were 5% between 21 and 23, 20% between 24 and 26, 21% between 27 and 28, and 53% above 28. About 84% of the current freshmen were in the top fifth of their class; 97% were in the top two fifths. There were 81 National Merit finalists and 17 semifinalists. A total of 67 freshmen graduated first in their class.

Requirements: The SAT I or ACT is required. Graduation from an accredited secondary school is required; a GED will be accepted. An essay is required from all applicants. Fine arts students may submit portfolios, but are not required to. Four years of English, 3 each of mathematics and science, 3 in social science/history, and 2 in a foreign language are recommended. Also required are recommendations from a teacher and a counselor. AP credits are accepted. Important factors used in the admissions decision are advanced placement or honor courses, evidence of special talent, leadership record, parents or siblings attending the school, and recommendations by school officials.

Procedure: Freshmen are admitted fall and spring. Entrance exams should be taken by December of the senior year. Early decision applications should be filed by January 1; regular applications, by January 15 for fall entry and November 15 for spring entry, along with an application fee of $50. Notification of early decision is sent January 15; regular decision, April 1. There are early decision and deferred admissions plans. About 117 early decision candidates were accepted for the 1993–94 class. A waiting list is an active part of the admissions procedure.

Transfer: About 180 transfer students enrolled in 1993–94. Students less than 5 years out of high school must also submit an offical transcript from secondary schools previously attended. A minimum GPA of 3.0 is required. An interview is recommended. If the students has taken the SAT I or the ACT in the last 5 years, results must be submitted. A total of 36 credits out of 120 must be completed at WU.

Visiting: There are regularly scheduled orientations for prospective students, consisting of group presentations followed by a campus tour, as well as visits to classes and clubs of interest. Visitors may sit in on classes and stay overnight at the school. To arrange for a visit, contact the Office of Undergraduate Admission at (314) 935–6000 or (800) 676–2114.

Financial Aid: In 1993–94, 52% of all current freshmen and 53% of continuing students received some form of financial aid. About 46% of freshmen and 45% of continuing students received needbased aid. The average freshman award was $16,800. Of that total, scholarships or need-based grants averaged $12,000 ($16,000 maximum); loans averaged $3300 ($4125 maximum); and work contracts averaged $1500 (maximum). Twenty-six percent of undergraduate students work part-time. Average earnings from campus work for the school year are $1500. The average financial indebtedness of the 1992–93 graduate was $13,000. WU is a member of CSS. The FAF and FAFSA are required. The deadline for financial aid applications is February 15.

International Students: There are currently 898 international students enrolled. The school actively recruits these students. They must take the TOEFL and achieve a minimum score of 550. The student must also take the SAT I or the ACT.

Computers: The university provides computer facilities for student use. The mainframe is an IBM 3081-K64. Specialized computing resources are available to students, and University Academic Computing and Networking provides numerous public terminal and personal computer facilities. The Center for Engineering Computing has 200 workstations consisting of graphics terminals, personal computers, and design workstations. The School of Business supports 2 interactive systems and provides a student laboratory with 50 personal computer workstations. In addition, University Academic Computing and Networking maintains 10 student laboratories, including 5 in the residential areas. These laboratories include personal computers and laser printers. All students may access the system 24 hours per day, 7 days per week. There are no time limits on using the system and no fees.

Graduates: In 1992–93, 1361 bachelor's degrees were awarded. The most popular majors among graduates were business (10%), psychology (9%), and English (7%). Within an average freshman class, 4% graduate in 3 years, 71% in 4 years, and 86% in 5 years. Some 287 companies recruited on campus in 1992–93.

Admissions Contact: Office of Undergraduate Admission.

WEBSTER UNIVERSITY
D-2
St. Louis, MO 63119–3194
(314) 968–7000
(800) 75-ENROL (in-state)

Full-time: 633 men, 1106 women	Faculty: 116; IIA, --$
Part-time: 424 men, 1126 women	Ph.D.s: 68%
Graduate: 3543 men, 2962 women	Student/Faculty: 15 to 1
Year: semesters, summer session	Tuition: $8560
Application Deadline: August 1	Room & Board: $4090
Freshman Class: 562 applied, 462 accepted, 226 enrolled	
SAT I Verbal/Math: 511/494	ACT: 23 COMPETITIVE

Webster University, founded in 1915, is an independent, coeducational institution with programs in fine and performing arts, liberal arts and sciences, education, nursing, and business. There is one graduate school. In addition to regional accreditation, Webster has baccalaureate program accreditation with NASM and NLN. The library contains 222,300 volumes, 78,358 microform items, and 584 audiovisual forms, and subscribes to 1232 periodicals. Computerized library sources and services include interlibrary loans. Special learning facilities include a learning resource center, art gallery, radio station, a media center, and a theater. The 47-acre campus is in a suburban area 12 miles southwest of St. Louis. Including residence halls, there are 54 buildings on campus.

Student Life: About 86% of undergraduates are from Missouri. Students come from 38 states and 18 foreign countries. Seventy-six percent are from public schools; 24% from private. Eighty-one percent are white; 13% African American. The average age of freshmen is 19.2; all undergraduates, 23.7. Twenty-four percent drop out by the end of their first year; 52% remain to graduate.

Housing: A total of 300 students can be accommodated in college housing. College-sponsored living facilities include single-sex and coed dormitories. In addition there are special interest houses and off-campus houses. On-campus housing is guaranteed for the freshman year only, is available on a first-come, first-served basis, and is available on a lottery system for upperclassmen. Priority is given to out-of-town students. Eighty percent of students commute. All students may keep cars on campus.

Activities: There are no fraternities or sororities on campus. There are 20 groups on campus, including art, band, cheerleading, choir, chorale, chorus, computers, dance, drama, ethnic, film, honors, international, jazz band, literary magazine, musical theater, newspaper, orchestra, photography, political, professional, radio, religious, social, social service, and student government. Popular campus events include Annual Ball, Spring Fest, Annual Dance Club Video Dance, Back-to-School Dance, Halloween Event, Annual Semiformal, and Wellness Fair.

Sports: There are 4 intercollegiate sports for men and 5 for women, and 5 intramural sports for men and 5 for women. Athletic and recreation facilities include tennis courts, a gymnasium, a natatorium, a fitness center, and an athletic training center.

Disabled Students: Seventy-five percent of the campus is accessible to disabled students. The following facilities are available: wheelchair ramps, elevators, special parking, specially equipped rest rooms, special class scheduling, lowered drinking fountains, telephones for the hearing impaired, and automatic door openers.

Services: In addition to many counseling and information services, tutoring is available in most subjects, including and peer tutoring. There is a reader service for the blind, and remedial math, reading, and writing.

Campus Safety and Security: Campus safety and security measures include 24-hour foot and vehicle patrol, escort service, informal discussions, pamphlets, posters, and films. In addition, there are emergency telephones and lighted pathways and sidewalks.

Programs of Study: Webster awards the B.A., B.S., B.F.A., B.S.N., B.M., and B.M.Ed. degrees. Master's and doctoral degrees also are awarded. Bachelor's degrees are awarded in BIOLOGICAL SCIENCE (biology/biological science), BUSINESS (business administration and management), COMMUNICATIONS AND THE ARTS (art, broadcasting, communications, dance, dramatic arts, jazz, languages, literature, media arts, music, music performance, music theory and composition, musical theater, performing arts, and theater design), COMPUTER AND PHYSICAL SCIENCE (computer science, information sciences and systems, mathematics, and science), EDUCATION (education and music), HEALTH PROFESSIONS (nursing), SOCIAL SCIENCE (anthropology, history and political science, international relations, philosophy, psychology, religion, social science, and sociology). Liberal arts is the strongest academically. Business has the largest enrollment.

Required: To graduate, students must complete at least 128 semester hours, with a minimum GPA of 2.0. A freshman seminar is required; otherwise, the curriculum requires specific courses within the major field of study only.

Special: Students may cross-register with Fontbonne, Maryville, Lindenwood, and Missouri Baptist Colleges, and Eden Seminary. The university offers accelerated programs, dual majors, student self-designed majors, interdisciplinary studies, a 3–2 engineering degree with the University of Missouri and Washington University, and a 3–4 architecture program with Washington University. Study abroad, nondegree study, pass/fail options, and credit for life, military, and work experience are available. There is a freshman honors program on campus

Faculty/Classroom: Fifty percent of faculty are male; 50%, female. All teach undergraduates. No introductory courses are taught by graduate students. The average class size in an introductory lecture is 25; in a laboratory, 15; and in a regular course offering, 25.

Admissions: About 82% of the 1993–94 applicants were accepted. The SAT scores for the 1993–94 freshman class were as follows: Verbal—39% below 500, 40% between 500 and 599, 20% between 600 and 700, and 1% above 700; Math—48% below 500, 43% between 500 and 599, and 9% between 600 and 700. The ACT scores were 29% below 21, 27% between 21 and 23, 29% between 24 and 26, 10% between 27 and 28, and 5% above 28. About 36% of the current freshmen were in the top fifth of their class; 66% were in the top two fifths. About 3 freshmen graduated first in their class.

Requirements: Webster requires applicants to be in the upper 50% of their class. A minimum GPA of 2.5 is required. The SAT I or ACT is required. Applicants must be graduates of an accredited secondary school. The GED is accepted. Webster recommends that students complete 16 high school academic units, including 4 units of English, 3 each of social studies/history and mathematics, and 2 each of foreign language, science, and electives. An essay is required of all students, and a portfolio or audition is required for art, dance, music, musical theater, and theater applicants. AP and CLEP credits are accepted. Important factors used in the admissions decision are recommendations by school officials, advanced placement or honor courses, leadership record, extracurricular activities record, and evidence of special talent.

Procedure: Freshmen are admitted to all sessions. Entrance exams should be taken in the spring of the junior year. Applications should be filed by August 1 for fall entry, December 15 for spring entry, and May 1 for summer entry, along with an application fee of $20. Notification is sent on a rolling basis. There are early admissions and deferred admissions plans.

Transfer: About 435 transfer students enrolled in 1993–94. Applicants for transfer must have a minimum GPA of 2.5 for college credit completed. If they have fewer than 30 transferable hours, they must submit high school transcripts. A total of 30 credits out of 128 must be completed at Webster.

Visiting: There are regularly scheduled orientations for prospective students, consisting of an open house, which includes classes, meetings with faculty, a financial aid workshop and a tour of the university. There are guides for informal visits and visitors may sit in on classes and stay overnight at the school. To arrange for a visit, contact the Admissions Office at (800) 753-6765.

Financial Aid: In 1993–94, 82% of all current freshmen and 50% of continuing students received some form of financial aid. About 82% of freshmen received need-based aid. The average freshman award was $7182. Of that total, scholarships or need-based grants averaged $4953 ($8560 maximum); loans averaged $1229 ($6625 maximum); and work contracts averaged $1000 ($2000 maximum). Average earnings from campus work for the school year were $1900. The average financial indebtedness of the 1992–93 graduate was $7000. Webster is a member of CSS. The FAF, FFS, or SFS and the college's own financial statement are required. The deadline for financial aid applications is April 1.

International Students: There are currently 106 international students enrolled. The school actively recruits these students. They must take the TOEFL and achieve a minimum score of 530. The student must also take the SAT I or the ACT.

Computers: The college provides computer facilities for student use. The mainframe is an HP 9000. There are 100 microcomputers, including IBM PC and PS/2, Apple IIe, and Macintosh, available in the main laboratory. All students may access the system. There are no time limits on using the system. Some classes charge a $5 to $10 laboratory fee.

Graduates: In 1992–93, 923 bachelor's degrees were awarded. The most popular majors among graduates were management (43%), nursing (13%), and media communications (10%). Within an average freshman class, 2% graduate in 3 years, 29% in 4 years, 41% in 5 years, and 42% in 6 years. Some 5 companies recruited on campus in 1992–93.

Admissions Contact: Charles E. Beech, Director of Admissions.

WESTMINSTER COLLEGE   C-2

Fulton, MO 65251   (314) 642–3361; (800) 475–3361 (out-of-state)

Full-time: 418 men, 284 women	Faculty: 50; IIB, -$
Part-time: 9 men, 20 women	Ph.D.s: 66%
Graduate: none	Student/Faculty: 14 to 1
Year: semesters, summer session	Tuition: $9950
Application Deadline: open	Room & Board: $3800
Freshman Class: 662 applied, 553 accepted, 184 enrolled	
SAT I Verbal/Math: 480/520	ACT: 24 COMPETITIVE +

Westminster College, founded in 1851, is a small, coeducational, liberal arts college affiliated with the Presbyterian Church. The two libraries contain 100,000 volumes, 14,000 microform items, and 2200 audiovisual forms, and subscribe to 380 periodicals. Computerized library sources and services include interlibrary loans and database searching. The 55-acre campus is in a small town 20 miles east of Columbia. Including residence halls, there are 26 buildings on campus.

Student Life: About 56% of undergraduates are from Missouri. Students come from 33 states and 7 foreign countries. Seventy percent are from public schools; 30% from private. Ninety-five percent are white. Forty-seven percent are Protestant; 20% are Catholic; 22% claim no religious affiliation. The average age of freshmen is 18; all undergraduates, 20. Twenty-three percent drop out by the end of their first year; 57% remain to graduate.

Housing: A total of 446 students can be accommodated in college housing. College-sponsored living facilities include single-sex and coed dormitories and fraternity houses. On-campus housing is guaranteed for all 4 years and is available on a first-come, first-served basis. Priority is given to out-of-town students. Ninety-six percent of students live on campus; of those, 95% remain on campus on weekends. All students may keep cars on campus.

Activities: About 74% of men belong to 6 national fraternities; about 71% of women belong to 3 national sororities. There are 56 groups on campus, including art, cheerleading, choir, chorale, chorus, drama, ethnic, honors, international, literary magazine, newspaper, photography, political, professional, religious, social, social service, student government, and yearbook. Popular campus events include Green Foundation Lecture, Alumni Weekend, Greek Games, College Bowl, Fulton Jazz Festival, Victorian Christmas at the Churchill Memorial, IBM Lecture in Business and Finance, and Woodrow Wilson Visiting National Fellow.

Sports: There are 6 intercollegiate sports for men and 7 for women, and 16 intramural sports for men and 10 for women. Athletic and recreation facilities include an 800-seat gymnasium, a weight room and a training room; baseball, softball, and soccer fields; a field sports area; a track, tennis, racquetball, and volleyball courts; a swimming pool; an indoor rifle range; and a 1500-seat auditorium/arena.

Disabled Students: Twenty-five percent of the campus is accessible to disabled students. The following facilities are available: wheelchair ramps, elevators, special parking, specially equipped rest rooms, and special class scheduling.

Services: In addition to many counseling and information services, tutoring is available in most subjects.

Campus Safety and Security: Campus safety and security measures include self defense education, escort service, informal discussions, pamphlets, posters, and films. In addition, there are lighted pathways and sidewalks.

Programs of Study: Westminster awards the B.A. and B.F.A. degrees. Bachelor's degrees are awarded in BIOLOGICAL SCIENCE (biology/biological science), BUSINESS (accounting and business administration and management), COMMUNICATIONS AND THE ARTS (dramatic arts, English, fine arts, and languages), COMPUTER AND PHYSICAL SCIENCE (chemistry, mathematics, and physics), EDUCATION (art, early childhood, elementary, foreign languages, science, and secondary), ENGINEERING AND ENVIRONMENTAL DESIGN (engineering), HEALTH PROFESSIONS (predentistry and premedicine), SOCIAL SCIENCE (anthropology, economics, history, international relations, philosophy, political science/government, psychology, religion, and sociology). English, history, political science, biology, and business administration are the strongest academically. Business, political science, and English have the largest enrollments.

Required: To graduate, students must complete 122 credit hours, including a maximum of 40 hours in their major. Core courses include 15 credits in the humanities, 12 in the social sciences, 7 in a natural science, 6 in mathematics, 4 in English, and 3 in a foreign language or culture. A 2.0 GPA in all courses is required. A student thesis or independent study is required in most majors.

Special: Westminster offers co-op programs with associated colleges of the Midwest, cross-registration with William Woods University, internships in all areas, study abroad in 15 countries, a Washington semester, a United Nations semester, and a Chicago Urban Studies Program. Student-designed majors are available as well as a 3–2 engineering degree with Washington University in St. Louis. The pass/fail option is available. There is a freshman honors program on

campus as well as 15 national honor societies. Eight departments have honors programs.

Faculty/Classroom: Seventy-four percent of faculty are male; 26%, female. All teach undergraduates. The average class size in an introductory lecture is 25; in a laboratory, 20; and in a regular course offering, 18.

Admissions: About 84% of the 1993–94 applicants were accepted. The SAT scores for the 1993–94 freshman class were as follows: Verbal—60% below 500, 27% between 500 and 599, 11% between 600 and 700, and 2% above 700; Math—38% below 500, 33% between 500 and 599, 25% between 600 and 700, and 4% above 700. The ACT scores were 23% below 21, 29% between 21 and 23, 22% between 24 and 26, 11% between 27 and 28, and 15% above 28. About 40% of the current freshmen were in the top fifth of their class; 65% were in the top two fifths. There were 2 National Merit finalists and 3 semifinalists. Nine freshmen graduated first in their class.

Requirements: The SAT I or ACT is required. Applicants must be graduates of an accredited secondary school. The GED is also accepted. Students must have completed 4 years each of social studies and English, 3 years each of mathematics and science, and 2 years each of a foreign language and history. An essay is required and an interview is recommended. AP and CLEP credits are accepted. Important factors used in the admissions decision are advanced placement or honor courses, leadership record, extracurricular activities record, recommendations by school officials, and evidence of special talent.

Procedure: Freshmen are admitted to all sessions. Application deadlines are open. Notification is sent on a rolling basis. There are early admissions and deferred admissions plans. A waiting list is an active part of the admissions procedure.

Transfer: About 51 transfer students enrolled in 1993–94. Transfer students must have taken either the ACT or SAT I and must complete at least 4 semesters at Westminster as full-time students. A total of 30 credits out of 122 must be completed at Westminster.

Visiting: There are regularly scheduled orientations for prospective students, including a 2-day/1-night stay at Westminster. There are guides for informal visits and visitors may sit in on classes and stay overnight at the school. To arrange for a visit, contact Marilyn Langley, Office of Admission, at (800) 475–3361 or (314) 642–3361.

Financial Aid: In 1993–94, 75% of all students received some form of financial aid. About 50% of freshmen and 55% of continuing students received need-based aid. The average freshman award was $10,871. Of that total, scholarships or need-based grants averaged $2285 ($9790 maximum); loans averaged $2735 ($5125 maximum); and work contracts averaged $979 ($2000 maximum). Thirty percent of undergraduate students work part-time. Average earnings from campus work for the school year are $550. Westminster is a member of CSS. The FAFSA financial statement is required. The deadline for financial aid applications is March 25.

International Students: There are currently 15 international students enrolled. The school actively recruits these students. They must take the TOEFL and achieve a minimum score of 550.

Computers: The college provides computer facilities for student use. The mainframes are a DEC VAX 4600 and a DEC VAX 3130. There are 48 Apple Macintosh, IBM PC, and Leading Edge stand-alone microcomputers available for student use. There are also 4 VT220 terminals available for student access to Internet. All students may access the system. There are no time limits on using the system and no fees.

Graduates: In 1992–93 151 bachelor's degrees were awarded. The most popular majors among graduates were business administration (25%), political science (15%), and English (12%). Within an average freshman class, 53% graduate in 4 years. Some 43 companies recruited on campus in 1992–93.

Admissions Contact: E. Norman Jones, Dean of Admissions.

WILLIAM JEWELL COLLEGE
B-2

Liberty, MO 64068

(816) 781-7700, ext. 5137
(800) 753-7009 (in-state)

Full-time: 550 men, 729 women	Faculty: 90; IIB, -$
Part-time: 30 men, 45 women	Ph.D.s: 72%
Graduate: none	Student/Faculty: 14 to 1
Year: 4-1-4	Tuition: $9720
Application Deadline: open	Room & Board: $2780
Freshman Class: 663 applied, 547 accepted, 315 enrolled	
SAT I Verbal/Math: 500/550	ACT: 24 **VERY COMPETITIVE**

William Jewell College, founded in 1849, is a small, liberal arts college affiliated with the Baptist Church, and offering undergraduate programs in the arts and sciences, business, education, and health fields. In addition to regional accreditation, the college has baccalaureate program accreditation with NASM and NLN. The library contains 198,630 volumes, 75,795 microform items, and 18,491 audiovisual forms, and subscribes to 789 periodicals. Computerized library sources and services include interlibrary loans and database search-

ing. Special learning facilities include a learning resource center, art gallery, and radio station. The 106-acre campus is in a suburban area 15 miles northeast of Kansas City. Including residence halls, there are 23 buildings on campus.

Student Life: About 75% of undergraduates are from Missouri. Students come from 34 states, 15 foreign countries, and Canada. Ninety percent are from public schools; 10% from private. Ninety-three percent are white. Seventy-four percent are Protestant; 11% Catholic; 10% claim no religious affiliation. The average age of freshmen is 18; all undergraduates, 19. Thirteen percent drop out by the end of their first year; 87% remain to graduate.

Housing: A total of 1102 students can be accommodated in college housing. College-sponsored living facilities include single-sex dormitories, on-campus apartments, married-student housing, and fraternity houses. In addition there are honors houses and and married student apartments. On-campus housing is guaranteed for all 4 years. Seventy percent of students live on campus; of those, 50% remain on campus on weekends. Alcohol is not permitted. All students may keep cars on campus.

Activities: About 35% of men belong to 4 national fraternities; about 44% of women belong to 4 national sororities. There are 74 groups on campus, including art, band, cheerleading, choir, chorale, chorus, computers, dance, drama, ethnic, honors, international, jazz band, marching band, musical theater, newspaper, opera, orchestra, pep band, photography, political, professional, radio and TV, religious, social, social service, student government, symphony, and yearbook.

Sports: There are 9 intercollegiate sports for men and 6 for women, and 14 intramural sports for men and 5 for women. Athletic and recreation facilities include a football stadium, a sports complex for baseball, soccer, and softball, and a physical education center, with facilities for basketball, racquetball, swimming, indoor track, indoor tennis, volleyball, and weight-lifting. The total seating capacity of the stadiums is 7000 and that of the indoor gymnasiums is 2000.

Disabled Students: Thirty percent of the campus is accessible to disabled students. The following facilities are available: wheelchair ramps, elevators, special parking, specially equipped rest rooms, special class scheduling, and lowered drinking fountains.

Services: In addition to many counseling and information services, tutoring is available in most subjects.

Campus Safety and Security: Campus safety and security measures include 24-hour foot and vehicle patrol, self defense education, informal discussions, pamphlets, posters, and films. In addition, there are emergency telephones and lighted pathways and sidewalks.

Programs of Study: The college awards the B.A. and B.S. degrees. Bachelor's degrees are awarded in BIOLOGICAL SCIENCE (biology/biological science), BUSINESS (accounting, business administration and management, business economics, and international business management), COMMUNICATIONS AND THE ARTS (communications, English, French, music, and Spanish), COMPUTER AND PHYSICAL SCIENCE (chemistry, computer science, and physics), EDUCATION (elementary, music, science, and secondary), HEALTH PROFESSIONS (medical laboratory technology, nursing, predentistry, and premedicine), SOCIAL SCIENCE (history, international relations, philosophy, political science/government, prelaw, psychology, religion, and sociology). Business has the largest enrollment.

Required: To graduate, students must complete a minimum of 124 credits with a minimum 2.0 GPA, fulfilling the proper core requirements for their major and degree. All students must take freshman composition, fundamentals of speech communication, orientation to physical education, a biblical studies course, a mathematics or laboratory science course, a social science course and a humanities course. Comprehensive exams in most majors are required.

Special: Internships for juniors or seniors, study abroad in Europe and Japan, and a Washington semester are offered. B.A.-B.S. degrees, dual majors of any combination, student-designed majors, or 3–2 engineering degrees with Washington University and the universities of Missouri and Kansas are available. The pass/fail option is also available. There is an interdisciplinary core curriculum, called Foundations. The Oxbridge Honors Program for major study is patterned after the teaching methods of Oxford and Cambridge. There is a freshman honors program on campus, as well as 13 national honor societies. Thirteen departments have honors programs.

Faculty/Classroom: Sixty percent of faculty are male; 40%, female. Ninety percent teach undergraduates. The average class size in an introductory lecture is 40; in a laboratory, 20; and in a regular course offering, 15.

Admissions: About 83% of the 1993–94 applicants were accepted. The SAT scores for the 1993–94 freshman class were as follows: Verbal—43% below 500, 44% between 500 and 599, 12% between 600 and 700, and 1% above 700; Math—25% below 500, 45% between 500 and 599, 23% between 600 and 700, and 7% above 700. The ACT scores were 22% below 21, 24% between 21 and 23, 24% between 24 and 26, 15% between 27 and 28, and 15% above 28. About 58% of the current freshmen were in the top fifth of their class;

86% were in the top two fifths. There were 4 National Merit finalists. Eighteen freshmen graduated first in their class.

Requirements: The SAT I or ACT is required. Students must be graduates of an accredited secondary school; the GED is also accepted. The college recommends that applicants have taken 4 English courses, 3 courses each in mathematics and science, and 2 each in foreign language and social studies. An essay is required and an interview is recommended. An audition is advised for music applicants. AP and CLEP credits are accepted. Important factors used in the admissions decision are evidence of special talent, advanced placement or honor courses, leadership record, extracurricular activities record, and personality.

Procedure: Freshmen are admitted to all sessions. Entrance exams should be taken in the junior year. Application deadlines are open. Application fee is $25. Notification is sent on a rolling basis. There are early admissions and deferred admissions plans. A waiting list is an active part of the admissions procedure, with about 1% of applicants on the list.

Transfer: About 90 transfer students enrolled in 1993–94. Transfer students must have maintained a 2.0 GPA and be in good academic standing with their former schools. Education majors must take the ACT, achieving a minimum score of 20. An interview is recommended for all students. A total of 30 credits out of 124 must be completed at the college.

Visiting: There are regularly scheduled orientations for prospective students; a personalized visit can be arranged upon request. There are guides for informal visits and visitors may sit in on classes and stay overnight at the school. To arrange for a visit, contact the Admission Office at (816) 781–7700, ext. 5137 or (800) 753–7009.

Financial Aid: In a recent year, 91% of all current freshmen and 89% of continuing students received some form of financial aid. About 62% of freshmen and 67% of continuing students received need-based aid. The average freshman award was $5850. Of that total, scholarships or need-based grants averaged $2600 ($8060 maximum); loans averaged $3000 ($4125 maximum); and work contracts averaged $1250 ($1300 maximum). Seventy percent of undergraduate students work part-time. Average earnings from campus work for the school year are $750. The average financial indebtedness of the 1992–93 graduate was $7500. The college is a member of CSS. The FAF, FFS, or SFS is required. The deadline for financial aid applications is March 15.

International Students: There are currently 5 international students enrolled. The school actively recruits these students. They must take the TOEFL or the University of Michigan Language Test and achieve a minimum score on the TOEFL of 550. The student must also take the SAT I or the ACT.

Computers: The college provides 146 IBM and Apple PCs for academic use. There are no time limits on using the system and no fees.

Graduates: The most popular majors among graduates were business (13%), psychology (11%), and education (9%). Within an average freshman class, 45% graduate in 4 years and 55% in 5 years. Some 77 companies recruited on campus in a recent year. In the 1992 graduating class, 9% of the men and 8% of the women were enrolled in graduate school within 6 months of graduation; 20% of the men and 39% of the women had found employment.

Admissions Contact: T. Edwin Norris, Director of Admission.

WILLIAM WOODS COLLEGE
(See William Woods University)

WILLIAM WOODS UNIVERSITY
(Formerly William Woods College)   C-2

Fulton, MO 65251   (314) 592-4221; (800) 995-3159 (in-state)

Full-time: 736 women	Faculty: 46; IIB, --$
Part-time: 80 women	Ph.D.s: 70%
Graduate: none	Student/Faculty: 16 to 1
Year: semesters, summer session	Tuition: $9825
Application Deadline: open	Room & Board: $4200
Freshman Class: 512 applied, 474 accepted, 234 enrolled	
SAT I Verbal/Math: 436/445	ACT: 21 LESS COMPETITIVE

William Woods University, founded in 1870, is a small liberal arts institution for women. Affiliated with the Christian Church (Disciples of Christ), it offers programs in equestrian science, international studies, education, arts and sciences, and selected preprofessional areas. There are 3 undergraduate schools. In addition to regional accreditation, William Woods has baccalaureate program accreditation with CSWE, NCATE, and NLN. The 2 libraries contain 77,853 volumes, 6760 microform items, and 1632 audiovisual forms, and subscribe to 422 periodicals. Computerized library sources and services include interlibrary loans and database searching. Special learning facilities include a learning resource center, art gallery, radio station, TV station, and laboratories for photography, sewing, foreign language,

and art. The 160-acre campus is in a small town 100 miles west of St. Louis. Including residence halls, there are 35 buildings on campus.

Student Life: About 53% of undergraduates are from Missouri. Students come from 44 states and 3 foreign countries. Eighty-six percent are from public schools; 14% from private. Ninety-seven percent are white. Fifty-nine percent are Protestant; 28% Catholic. The average age of freshmen is 18; all undergraduates, 23. Nineteen percent drop out by the end of their first year; 60% remain to graduate.

Housing: A total of 750 students can be accommodated in college housing. College-sponsored living facilities include dormitories, on-campus apartments, and sorority houses. In addition, there are special interest houses and nonsmoking, upperclassmen, and independent dormitories. On-campus housing is guaranteed for all 4 years. Eighty-eight percent of students live on campus; of those, 75% remain on campus on weekends. Alcohol is not permitted. All students may keep cars on campus.

Activities: About 53% of women belong to 4 national sororities. There are 40 groups on campus, including art, choir, chorale, chorus, computers, dance, drama, honors, international, literary magazine, musical theater, newspaper, photography, political, professional, radio and TV, religious, social, social service, and student government. Popular campus events include Oktoberfest, Greek Games, dances, Christmas dinner, horse shows, open houses, and musicals.

Sports: There are 7 intercollegiate and 8 intramural sports. Athletic and recreation facilities include a gymnasium, an indoor pool, a sand volleyball court, tennis courts, a soccer field, a weight room, a lake with a sand beach, a bowling alley, table tennis and pool tables, a boat house, and a sauna.

Disabled Students: The following facilities are available: wheelchair ramps, elevators, special parking, specially equipped rest rooms, special class scheduling, lowered drinking fountains, lowered telephones, TDD, and dormitory rooms individually equipped with special telephones and alerting devices.

Services: In addition to many counseling and information services, tutoring is available in every subject. Interpreting is provided for the deaf. Study skills improvement courses are available.

Campus Safety and Security: Campus safety and security measures include 24-hour foot and vehicle patrol, self defense education, escort service, and shuttle buses. In addition, there are informal discussions, pamphlets, posters, films, and lighted pathways and sidewalks.

Programs of Study: William Woods awards the B.A., B.F.A., and B.S.W. degrees. Associate degrees also are awarded. Bachelor's degrees are awarded in AGRICULTURE (equestrian science), BIOLOGICAL SCIENCE (biology/biological science), BUSINESS (accounting, business administration and management, business economics, fashion merchandising, and marketing/retailing/merchandising), COMMUNICATIONS AND THE ARTS (communications, design, English, fine arts, French, German, Spanish, speech/debate/rhetoric, and visual and performing arts), COMPUTER AND PHYSICAL SCIENCE (chemistry, computer science, mathematics, and physics), EDUCATION (early childhood, elementary, physical, and secondary), ENGINEERING AND ENVIRONMENTAL DESIGN (commercial art and interior design), HEALTH PROFESSIONS (premedicine), SOCIAL SCIENCE (geography, history, interpreter for the deaf, philosophy, political science/government, prelaw, psychology, social studies, social work, and sociology). Business, equestrian science, legal studies, art, and education are the strongest academically. Business, equestrian science, education, psychology, and interior design have the largest enrollments.

Required: Students must complete a minimum of 122 credits to graduate, including at least 30 in the major and the correct distribution of credits required by their degree. They must have maintained a minimum 2.0 GPA. Courses must also be taken in English, fine arts, mathematics, humanities, applied sciences, and social sciences.

Special: William Woods offers cross-registration with Westminster College, internships in various fields, study abroad, a Washington semester, and work-study. An accelerated degree program in any major, B.A.-B.S. degrees, and student-designed and dual majors are possible. Credit for life, military, and work experience and pass/fail are available. There are 8 national honor societies on campus.

Faculty/Classroom: Forty-five percent of faculty are male; 55%, female. All teach undergraduates. The average class size in an introductory lecture is 25; in a laboratory, 5; and in a regular course offering, 25.

Admissions: About 93% of the 1993–94 applicants were accepted. The SAT scores for the 1993–94 freshman class were as follows: Verbal—73% below 500, 21% between 500 and 599, 4% between 600 and 700, and 2% above 700; Math—73% below 500, 21% between 500 and 599, and 5% between 600 and 700. The ACT scores were 52% below 21, 22% between 21 and 23, 21% between 24 and 26, 4% between 27 and 28, and 1% above 28. About 28% of the current freshmen were in the top fifth of their class; 73% were in the top two fifths. There was 1 National Merit semifinalist. Four freshmen graduated first in their class.

Requirements: A minimum GPA of 2.0 is required. The SAT I or ACT is required, with a recommended composite SAT I score of 900 or ACT score of 21. Applicants must be graduates of an accredited secondary school; the GED is also accepted. They must have completed 16 course units, 11 of which must be distributed among English, a foreign language, mathematics, natural sciences, and social sciences. An essay, portfolio, and audition, where appropriate, are required, and an interview is recommended. AP and CLEP credits are accepted. Important factors used in the admissions decision are advanced placement or honor courses, leadership record, recommendations by school officials, personality, intangible qualities, and recommendations by alumni.

Procedure: Freshmen are admitted fall and winter. Entrance exams should be taken in the spring of the junior year or the fall of the senior year. The application deadlines are open. Application fee is $25. Notification is sent on a rolling basis. There is an early admissions plan.

Transfer: A total of 25 transfer students enrolled in 1993–94. The required GPA for applicants is 2.75. They must have taken the SAT I or ACT and have a minimum of 12 earned credit hours. An interview is recommended. A total of 30 credits out of 122 must be completed at William Woods.

Visiting: There are regularly scheduled orientations for prospective students, including the opportunity to talk with a member of the admissions staff, eat in the dining hall, and discuss college life with a William Woods student. There are guides for informal visits and visitors may sit in on classes and stay overnight at the school. To arrange for a visit, contact Leslie Krieger, Director of Admissions, at (314) 592–4221 or (800) 995–3159 (in-state).

Financial Aid: In 1993–94, 92% of all current freshmen and 98% of continuing students received some form of financial aid. About 75% of freshmen and 69% of continuing students received need-based aid. The average freshman award was $8989. Of that total, scholarships or need-based grants averaged $4500 ($9825 maximum); loans averaged $2625 ($4625 maximum); and work contracts averaged $1000 ($1900 maximum). Forty-five percent of undergraduate students work part-time. Average earnings from campus work for the school year are $1000. The average financial indebtedness of the 1992–93 graduate was $9200. William Woods is a member of CSS. The FAF, FFS or SFS, the college's own financial statement, and FAFSA are required. The deadline for financial aid applications is June 1.

International Students: There are currently 2 international students enrolled. The school actively recruits these students. They must take the TOEFL and achieve a minimum score of 500.

Computers: William Woods provides computer facilities for student use. Forty IBM, Apple, Macintosh, and IBM-compatibles can be found in classrooms, dormitories, and the library. E-mail and connections to Internet are also available. All students may access the system 7 days a week. There are no time limits on using the system and no fees.

Graduates: In 1992–93, 149 bachelor's degrees were awarded. The most popular majors among graduates were education (15%), equestrian science (13%), and business (13%). A total of 44 companies recruited on campus in 1992–93. In the 1992 graduating class, 10% of the women were enrolled in graduate school within 6 months of graduation; 92% of the women had found employment.

Admissions Contact: Leslie Krieger, Director of Admissions.

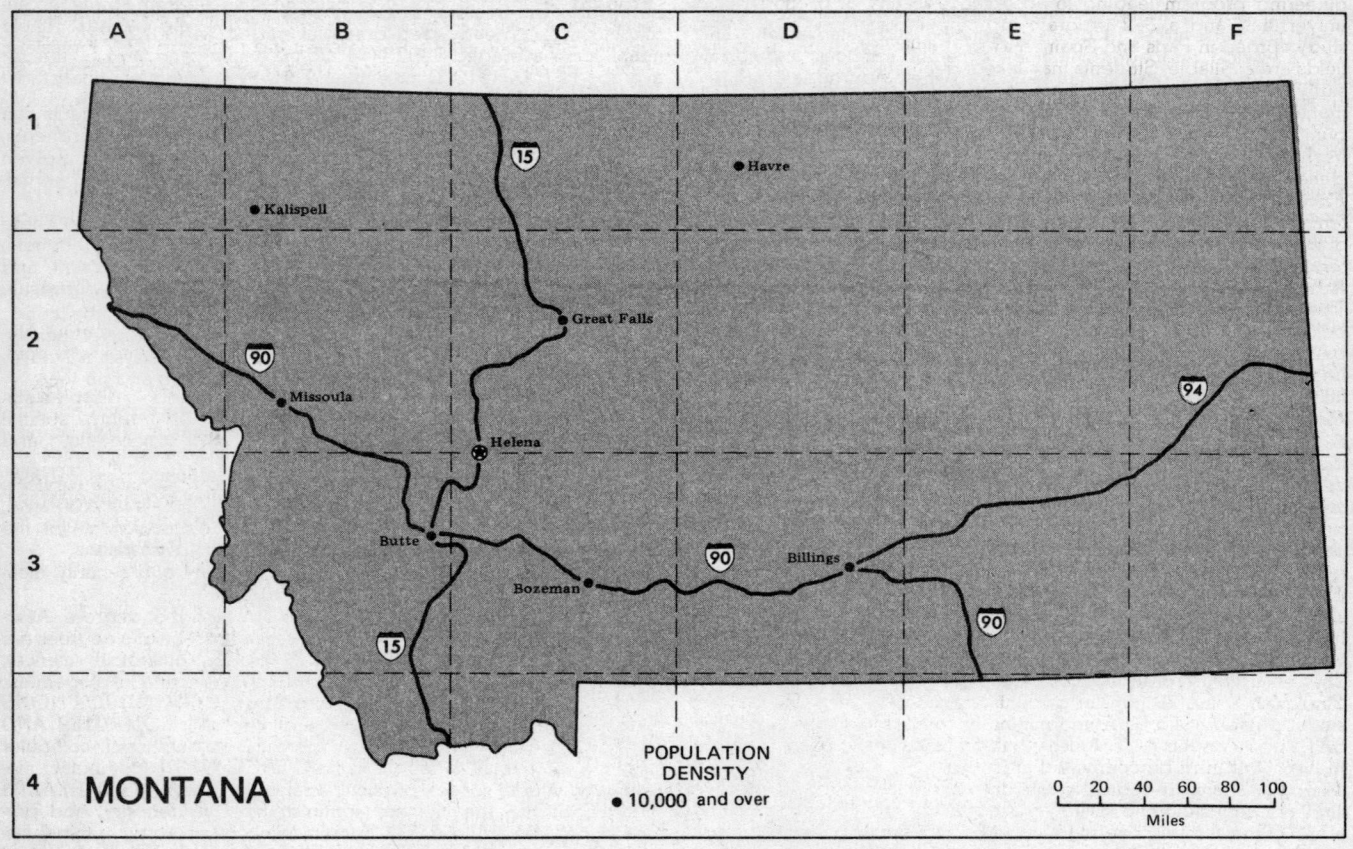

POPULATION DENSITY
● 10,000 and over

MONTANA

0 20 40 60 80 100
Miles

CARROLL COLLEGE
C-2

Helena, MT 59625   (406) 447–4384; (800) 922–3648 (in-state)
Full-time: 426 men, 667 women   **Faculty:** 74; IIB, --$
Part-time: 91 men, 231 women   **Ph.D.s:** 50%
Graduate: none   **Student/Faculty:** 15 to 1
Year: semesters   **Tuition:** $7615
Application Deadline: July 1   **Room & Board:** $3650
Freshman Class: 529 applied, 492 accepted, 261 enrolled
ACT: 23   **COMPETITIVE**

Carroll College, founded in 1909, is a small, coeducational, liberal arts college affiliated with the Roman Catholic Church. It offers undergraduate programs in arts and sciences, business, engineering, education, religion, and selected preprofessional training. In addition to regional accreditation, Carroll has baccalaureate program accreditation with CAHEA, CSWE, NLN, and NRPA. The library contains 101,000 volumes, 25,910 microform items, and 3511 audiovisual forms, and subscribes to 430 periodicals. Computerized library sources and services include interlibrary loans and database searching. Special learning facilities include a learning resource center and radio station. The 64-acre campus is in a small town 110 miles east of Missoula and 100 miles west of Bozeman. Including residence halls, there are 12 buildings on campus.

Student Life: About 70% of undergraduates are from Montana. Students come from 22 states, 20 foreign countries, and Canada. Sixty-five percent are from public schools; 35% from private. Ninety-two percent are white. Sixty percent are Catholic; 40% claim no religious affiliation. The average age of freshmen is 25; all undergraduates, 28. Twenty-six percent drop out by the end of their first year.

Housing: A total of 800 students can be accommodated in college housing. College-sponsored living facilities include single-sex and coed dormitories. On-campus housing is guaranteed for all 4 years. Fifty-eight percent of students commute. All students may keep cars on campus.

Activities: There are no fraternities or sororities on campus. There are 35 groups on campus, including cheerleading, choir, drama, ethnic, film, honors, international, jazz band, literary magazine, musical theater, newspaper, pep band, political, professional, radio, religious, social, social service, student government, and yearbook. Popular campus events include Homecoming, theme dances, Casino night, softball tournament, and concerts.

Sports: There are 2 intercollegiate sports for men and 2 for women, and 10 intramural sports for men and 10 for women. Athletic and recreation facilities include basketball, tennis, and racquetball courts, weight lifting, aerobics and dance rooms, a swimming pool, and a 4200-seat gymnasium.

Disabled Students: Seventy-five percent of the campus is accessible to disabled students. The following facilities are available: wheelchair ramps, elevators, special parking, specially equipped rest rooms, special class scheduling, and lowered drinking fountains.

Services: In addition to many counseling and information services, tutoring is available in most subjects, including writing, mathematics, statistics, economics, chemistry, accounting, anatomy, and physiology. There is also remedial math, reading, and writing.

Campus Safety and Security: Campus safety and security measures include escort service, informal discussions, and lighted pathways and sidewalks.

Programs of Study: Carroll awards the B.A. degree. Associate degrees also are awarded. Bachelor's degrees are awarded in BIOLOGICAL SCIENCE (biochemistry, biology/biological science, and combined sciences), BUSINESS (accounting and business administration and management), COMMUNICATIONS AND THE ARTS (classical languages, communications, creative writing, English, French, languages, public relations, and Spanish), COMPUTER AND PHYSICAL SCIENCE (computer science and mathematics), EDUCATION (elementary, physical, secondary, and teaching English as a second language/foreign language), ENGINEERING AND ENVIRONMENTAL DESIGN (preengineering), HEALTH PROFESSIONS (medical laboratory technology, nursing, predentistry, and premedicine), SOCIAL SCIENCE (history, international relations, philosophy, political science/government, prelaw, psychology, public administration, religion, social science, social work, and sociology). Communications, history, international relations, biology, nursing, business, education, and engineering are the strongest academically. Business has the largest enrollment.

Required: To graduate, students must complete 122 semester hours and maintain the specific GPA and credit concentration required by their major. The college's general liberal arts requirements include courses in English writing, communications, history, mathematics, and the natural and social sciences. Intermediate writing, basic communications, philosophy, theology, and the fine arts must also be taken.

Special: Carroll College offers a 3–2 program in occupational therapy in cooperation with Washington and Boston Universities, a 3–2 engineering program leading to acceptance to any of 6 cooperating universities, and a 3–2 program in computer science. Internships, study abroad in Paris and Spain, and work-study programs in certain fields are available. Students may take a dual major in any 2 fields of study, select an interdisciplinary major, such as health information management, earn credit for life, military, and work experience, or pursue nondegree study. The pass/fail option is available. There is a freshman honors program on campus, as well as 5 national honor societies, including Phi Beta Kappa.

Faculty/Classroom: Sixty-seven percent of faculty are male; 33%, female. All teach undergraduates. The average class size in an introductory lecture is 40; in a laboratory, 23; and in a regular course offering, 20.

Admissions: About 93% of the 1993–94 applicants were accepted. The ACT scores for the 1993–94 freshman class were as follows: 32% below 21, 19% between 21 and 23, 27% between 24 and 26, 12% between 27 and 28, and 10% above 28. About 50% of the current freshmen were in the top fifth of their class; 73% were in the top two fifths.

Requirements: A minimum GPA of 2.5 is required. The SAT I or ACT is required and composite scores of 800 on the SAT I or 21 on the ACT are recommended. Students must be graduates of an accredited secondary school or have a GED. An essay is required. AP and CLEP credits are accepted. Important factors used in the admissions decision are advanced placement or honor courses, recommendations by school officials, leadership record, personality, intangible qualities, and recommendations by alumni.

Procedure: Freshmen are admitted fall and spring. Entrance exams should be taken in the fall of the senior year. Applications should be filed by July 1 for fall entry and December 1 for spring entry, along with an application fee of $25. Notification is sent on a rolling basis. There is a deferred admissions plan.

Transfer: Some 29 transfer students enrolled in 1993–94. Transfer students need a 2.5 GPA and minimum composite scores of 800 on SAT I or 19 on the ACT. At least half of the semester hours required in the major must be completed at Carroll.

Visiting: There are regularly scheduled orientations for prospective students, consisting of 3 visiting sessions in the summer which include a tour of the campus, overnight housing, social activities, and preregistration for classes. Orientation takes place Thursday through Monday before the start of fall classes. There are guides for informal visits and visitors may sit in on classes and stay overnight at the school. To arrange for a visit, contact the Admissions Office at (406) 447–4384.

Financial Aid: In 1993–94 86% of all current freshmen and 63% of continuing students received some form of financial aid. About 68% of freshmen and 42% of continuing students received need-based aid. The average freshman award was $6991. Of that total, scholarships or need-based grants averaged $3812 ($11,120 maximum); loans averaged $4065 ($11,100 maximum); and work contracts averaged $1300 (maximum). Nineteen percent of undergraduate students work part-time. Average earnings from campus work for the school year are $1200. The average financial indebtedness of the 1992–93 graduate was $8420. Carroll is a member of CSS. The FAFSA is required. The deadline for financial aid applications is February 1.

International Students: There are currently 86 international students enrolled. The school actively recruits these students. They must take the TOEFL or the college's own test and achieve a minimum score on the TOEFL of 550.

Computers: The college provides computer facilities for student use. The mainframe is an IBM AS/400. There are no time limits on using the system and no fees.

Graduates: In 1992–93 151 bachelor's degrees were awarded. The most popular majors among graduates were business (13%), nursing (9%), and biology (9%).

Admissions Contact: Candace Cain, Director of Admissions.

COLLEGE OF GREAT FALLS

C-2

Great Falls, MT 59405   (406) 761–8210; (800) 848–3431 (in-state)

Full-time: 274 men, 504 women	Faculty: 44; IIB, --$
Part-time: 174 men, 352 women	Ph.D.s: 46%
Graduate: 45 men, 88 women	Student/Faculty: 18 to 1
Year: semesters, summer session	Tuition: $5240
Application Deadline: open	Room: $990
Freshman Class: 224 applied, 224 accepted, 140 enrolled	
SAT I or ACT: recommended	**NONCOMPETITIVE**

The College of Great Falls, established in 1932, is a private liberal arts institution affiliated with the Roman Catholic Church. There is one undergraduate and one graduate school. The library contains 75,000 volumes, 32,000 microform items, and 4000 audiovisual forms, and subscribes to 450 periodicals. Computerized library sources and services include the card catalog and interlibrary loans. Special learning facilities include an art gallery. The 40-acre campus is in an urban area. There are 13 buildings on campus.

Student Life: About 89% of undergraduates are from Montana. Students come from 23 states, 6 foreign countries, and Canada. Ninety percent are white. Thirty-five percent are Catholic; 27% Protestant; 12% claim no religious affiliation. The average age of freshmen is 25; all undergraduates, 29.

Housing: There are no residence halls. A total of 108 students can be accommodated in college-sponsored off-campus apartments, which are available on a first-come, first-served basis. Priority is given to out-of-town students. All students commute. Alcohol is not permitted. All students may keep cars on campus.

Activities: There are no fraternities or sororities on campus. There are 14 groups on campus, including choir, drama, ethnic, honors, newspaper, professional, religious, social, student government, and symphony. Popular campus events include Orientation Barbecue, Halloween Dance, and Intramural Festival.

Sports: There are 7 intramural sports for men and 7 for women. Athletic and recreation facilities include a gymnasium, Olympic-size pool, bowling alley, and game room.

Disabled Students: The entire campus is accessible to disabled students. The following facilities are available: wheelchair ramps, special parking, specially equipped rest rooms, special class scheduling, and lowered drinking fountains.

Services: In addition to many counseling and information services, tutoring is available in some subjects, including 100-level, 200-level, and selected 300-level courses. There is a reader service for the blind, and remedial math, reading, writing, and basic skills.

Campus Safety and Security: Campus safety and security measures include lighted pathways and sidewalks.

Programs of Study: CGF awards the B.A. and B.S. degrees. Associate and master's degrees also are awarded. Bachelor's degrees are awarded in BIOLOGICAL SCIENCE (biology/biological science), BUSINESS (accounting, business administration and management, and marketing/retailing/merchandising), COMMUNICATIONS AND THE ARTS (communications and English), COMPUTER AND PHYSICAL SCIENCE (chemistry, computer management, computer science, mathematics, and science), EDUCATION (computer, elementary, middle school, physical, science, and secondary), HEALTH PROFESSIONS (health care administration, predentistry, and premedicine), SOCIAL SCIENCE (counseling psychology, criminal justice, history, human services, liberal arts/general studies, paralegal studies, political science/government, prelaw, religion, social science, and sociology). Biology and paralegal studies are the strongest academically. Business, paralegal studies, and education have the largest enrollments.

Required: Students must complete 128 credit hours, including 30 to 42 in the major, plus 15 to 21 minor credits; maintaining a minimum GPA of 2.0. The 43-credit-hour distribution requirements include philosophy and religious studies courses.

Special: Internships are offered in sociology, criminal justice, paralegal studies, health care administration, and chemical-dependency counseling. Opportunities are provided for work-study programs, B.A.-B.S. degrees in most majors, dual majors, a general studies degree, credit by examination or for military service, and nondegree study. Specialized instruction is available through the use of videotape and telephone discussions in 14 locations throughout Montana and Canada. There is 1 national honor society on campus.

Faculty/Classroom: Fifty-nine percent of faculty are male; 41%, female. Ninety-six percent teach undergraduates. The average class size in an introductory lecture is 16; in a laboratory, 12; and in a regular course offering, 14.

Admissions: All of the 1993–94 applicants were accepted.

Requirements: The SAT I or ACT is recommended. Graduation from an accredited secondary school is required; the GED is accepted. Applicants should have 4 years of English, 3 of mathematics, and 2 each of social studies, science, and electives, including foreign language, art, music, and vocational education. An interview is recommended. AP and CLEP credits are accepted.

Procedure: Freshmen are admitted to all sessions. Entrance exams should be taken prior to registration. Application deadlines are open. The application fee is $25. The college accepts all applicants. Notification is sent on a rolling basis. There is an early admissions plan.

Transfer: Transfer applicants must be in good academic standing at another accredited college or university, and must submit official transcripts from all colleges or universities attended. Those with fewer than 30 credits must also submit an official high school transcript. A total of 30 credits out of 128 must be completed at CGF.

Visiting: There are guides for informal visits and visitors may sit in on classes. To arrange for a visit, contact the Office of Admissions and Records at (800) 848–3431 (in-state) or (406) 761–8210.

Financial Aid: In 1993–94, 70% of all students received some form of financial aid. About 65% of all students received need-based aid. The average freshman award was $4290. Of that total, scholarships or need-based grants averaged $1785 ($2300 maximum); loans av-

eraged $2505 ($2625 maximum); and work contracts averaged $2700 ($3100 maximum). Fifteen percent of undergraduate students work part-time. Average earnings from campus work for the school year are $1500. The average financial indebtedness of the 1992–93 graduate was $14,000. CGF is a member of CSS. The college's own financial statement and the FAFSA are required. The deadline for financial aid applications is August 1.

International Students: There are currently 114 international students enrolled. The school actively recruits these students. They must take the TOEFL and achieve a minimum score of 550.

Computers: The college provides computer facilities for student use. The mainframe is an AT&T 3B2/600 (minicomputer). There are also 30 AT&T, NCRs, and Apple IIe PCs available in the computer laboratory and in some faculty offices. All students may access the system 7 days a week. There are no time limits on using the system. The fees are $25.

Graduates: In 1992–93 144 bachelor's degrees were awarded. The most popular majors among graduates were criminal justice (16%), human services (13%), and elementary education (12%). Two companies recruited on campus in 1992–93. In the 1992 graduating class, 20% of the men and 11% of the women were enrolled in graduate school within 6 months of graduation; 65% of the men and 70% of the women had found employment.

Admissions Contact: Robert Hensley, Director of Admissions and Records.

EASTERN MONTANA COLLEGE   D-3
Billings, MT 59101   (406) 657-2158

Full-time: 902 men, 1578 women	**Faculty:** 150; IIA, --$
Part-time: 304 men, 563 women	**Ph.D.s:** 84%
Graduate: 108 men, 277 women	**Student/Faculty:** 17 to 1
Year: semesters, summer session	**Tuition:** $1905 ($5545)
Application Deadline: August 25	**Room & Board:** $3260
Freshman Class: 931 applied, 912 accepted, 596 enrolled	
SAT I Verbal/Math: 421/464	**ACT:** 20 **LESS COMPETITIVE**

Eastern Montana College, founded in 1927 as a teacher-training school, is a public liberal arts institution. Part of the Montana University System, it offers undergraduate programs in the arts and sciences, business and economics, education, human services, and selected preprofessional programs. There are 3 undergraduate schools and one graduate school. In addition to regional accreditation, Eastern has baccalaureate program accreditation with NASAD, NASM, and NCATE. The library contains 14,000 volumes and 650,000 microform items, and subscribes to 1000 periodicals. Computerized library sources and services include the card catalog, interlibrary loans, and database searching. Special learning facilities include a learning resource center, art gallery, and radio station. The 92-acre campus is in an urban area in Billings. Including residence halls, there are 21 buildings on campus.

Student Life: About 93% of undergraduates are from Montana. Students come from 30 states, 8 foreign countries, and Canada. Ninety-five percent are from public schools; 5% from private. Ninety-three percent are white. The average age of freshmen is 21; all undergraduates, 27.2. Thirty-five percent drop out by the end of their first year; 26% remain to graduate.

Housing: A total of 700 students can be accommodated in college housing. College-sponsored living facilities include single-sex and coed dormitories. On-campus housing is guaranteed for all 4 years. Ninety percent of students commute. Alcohol is not permitted. All students may keep cars on campus.

Activities: About 1% of men belong to 2 national fraternities; about 1% of women belong to 2 national sororities. There are 40 groups on campus, including art, band, cheerleading, choir, chorale, chorus, computers, drama, ethnic, honors, jazz band, newspaper, orchestra, pep band, political, professional, radio and TV, religious, social, social service, and student government. Popular campus events include Powwow, Homecoming, and Native American Day.

Sports: There are 4 intercollegiate sports for men and 4 for women, and 5 intramural sports for men and 5 for women. Athletic and recreation facilities include a physical education building with an Olympic-sized pool, 2 gymnasiums, a running track, weight-training equipment, and a soccer/softball field.

Disabled Students: The entire campus is accessible to disabled students. The following facilities are available: wheelchair ramps, elevators, special parking, specially equipped rest rooms, special class scheduling, lowered drinking fountains, and lowered telephones.

Services: In addition to many counseling and information services, tutoring is available in most subjects. There is also a reader service for the blind, and remedial math, reading, and writing.

Campus Safety and Security: Campus safety and security measures include 24-hour foot and vehicle patrol, escort service, informal discussions, pamphlets, posters, and films. In addition, there are emergency telephones and lighted pathways and sidewalks.

Programs of Study: Eastern awards the B.A., B.S., B.A. or B.S. in Business Administration, B.S.Ed., B.S. in Human Services, and B.S. in Rehabilitation and Related Services degrees. Associate and master's degrees also are awarded. Bachelor's degrees are awarded in BIOLOGICAL SCIENCE (biology/biological science), BUSINESS (accounting, banking and finance, business administration and management, and business economics), COMMUNICATIONS AND THE ARTS (communications, English, fine arts, German, music, and Spanish), COMPUTER AND PHYSICAL SCIENCE (chemistry, information sciences and systems, and mathematics), EDUCATION (art, business, early childhood, elementary, foreign languages, guidance, health, middle school, music, science, and secondary), SOCIAL SCIENCE (history, psychology, social science, and sociology). The sciences, business, and education are the strongest academically. Education and business have the largest enrollments.

Required: To graduate, students must have earned a minimum of 128 semester credits, including 30 in their major. They must maintain a minimum 2.0 GPA; education and human services majors must maintain a minimum 2.7 GPA. General education requirements must also be fulfilled.

Special: The college offers co-op programs, internships, work-study programs, B.A.-B.S. degrees, dual majors, nondegree study, and pass/fail options. There are 10 national honor societies on campus.

Faculty/Classroom: Sixty-seven percent of faculty are male; 33%, female. The average class size in an introductory lecture is 35 and in a laboratory, 20.

Admissions: About 98% of the 1993–94 applicants were accepted. The ACT scores for the 1993–94 freshman class were as follows: 59% below 21, 26% between 21 and 23, 12% between 24 and 26, and 3% between 27 and 28. About 26% of the current freshmen were in the top fifth of their class; 59% were in the top two fifths.

Requirements: Eastern requires applicants to be in the upper 50% of their class. A minimum GPA of 2.5 is required. The SAT I or ACT is required. Applicants must be graduates of an accredited secondary school; the GED is also accepted. The applicant must have taken 4 years of English, 3 each of social science and mathematics, and 2 each of science, foreign languages, or humanities. Students need to meet 1 of 3 criteria: be in the upper 50% of their class; have a GPA of 2.5 or better; or have minimum composite scores of 22 on the ACT or 920 on the SAT I. AP and CLEP credits are accepted. Important factors used in the admissions decision are geographic diversity, recommendations by school officials, recommendations by alumni, personality, intangible qualities, and extracurricular activities record.

Procedure: Freshmen are admitted to all sessions. Entrance exams should be taken in the senior year of high school. Applications should be filed by August 25 for fall entry, January 3 for winter entry, and May 8 for summer entry, along with an application fee of $30. Notification is sent on a rolling basis.

Transfer: About 400 transfer students enrolled in 1993–94. Out-of-state transfer students must have earned a 2.0 GPA; in-state transfer students must be in good academic standing. A total of 32 credits out of 128 must be completed at Eastern.

Visiting: There are regularly scheduled orientations for prospective students. There are guides for informal visits and visitors may sit in on classes and stay overnight at the school. To arrange for a visit, contact the Admissions and Enrollment Management Office at (406) 657-2158.

Financial Aid: In a recent year, 60% of all students received some form of financial aid. Eastern is a member of CSS. The FAF, FFS, or SFS is required. The deadline for financial aid applications is May 1.

International Students: There are currently 8 international students enrolled. They must take the TOEFL and achieve a minimum score of 525.

Computers: The college provides computer facilities for student use. The mainframe is a DEC VAX 8650. There are also 250 Apple and IBM microcomputers available on campus. All students may access the system 24 hours a day. There are no time limits on using the system. The fees are $1 per credit hour.

Graduates: In 1992–93, 611 bachelor's degrees were awarded. The most popular majors among graduates were education (51%) and business (28%). Within an average freshman class, 6% graduate in 4 years, 16% in 5 years, and 3% in 6 years.

Admissions Contact: Karen Everett, Admissions Office.

MONTANA COLLEGE OF MINERAL SCIENCE AND TECHNOLOGY

C-3

Butte, MT 59701-8997   (406) 496-4178; (800) 445-TECH (in-state)

Full-time: 953 men, 517 women	Faculty: 85; IIA, -$
Part-time: 184 men, 232 women	Ph.D.s: 69%
Graduate: 83 men, 23 women	Student/Faculty: 17 to 1
Year: semesters	Tuition: $1767 ($5743)
Application Deadline: August 1	Room & Board: $3210
Freshman Class: 572 applied, 544 accepted, 320 enrolled	
SAT I Verbal/Math: 456/554	ACT: 22 COMPETITIVE

Montana College of Mineral Science and Technology, founded in 1895, is a public coeducational institution offering programs that focus on minerals and energy engineering with related disciplines. There are 2 undergraduate schools and one graduate school. In addition to regional accreditation, Montana Tech has baccalaureate program accreditation with ABET. The library contains 49,687 volumes and 300,441 microform items, and subscribes to 450 periodicals. Special learning facilities include a learning resource center, radio station, and a mineral museum. The 56-acre campus is in a small town 260 miles east of Spokane, Washington. Including residence halls, there are 16 buildings on campus.

Student Life: About 81% of undergraduates are from Montana. Students come from 45 states, 15 foreign countries, and Canada. Ninety-eight percent are from public schools; 2% from private. Ninety-five percent are white. Most are Catholic. The average age of freshmen is 19; all undergraduates, 25. Forty percent drop out by the end of their first year; 45% remain to graduate.

Housing: A total of 340 students can be accommodated in college housing. College-sponsored living facilities include coed dormitories, off-campus apartments, and married-student housing. On-campus housing is guaranteed for the freshman year only and is available on a first-come, first-served basis. Priority is given to out-of-town students. Eighty-five percent of students commute. Alcohol is not permitted. All students may keep cars on campus.

Activities: There are no fraternities or sororities on campus. There are 35 groups on campus, including band, cheerleading, choir, computers, international, newspaper, pep band, professional, religious, student government, and yearbook. Popular campus events include M-Day, International Dinner, Homecoming, and Comedy Night.

Sports: There are 2 intercollegiate sports for men and 2 for women, and 7 intramural sports for men and 7 for women. Athletic and recreation facilities include an athletic complex housing 3 basketball courts, a 25-meter swimming pool, volleyball courts, a weight-lifting room, and 7 handball courts.

Disabled Students: Seventy-five percent of the campus is accessible to disabled students. The following facilities are available: wheelchair ramps, elevators, special parking, and specially equipped rest rooms.

Services: In addition to many counseling and information services, tutoring is available in most subjects, including mathematics, English, geology, physics, chemistry, biology, and engineering science. There is remedial math.

Campus Safety and Security: Campus safety and security measures include self defense education, informal discussions, lighted pathways and sidewalks, and a foot patrol.

Programs of Study: Montana Tech awards the B.S. degree. Associate and master's degrees also are awarded. Bachelor's degrees are awarded in COMPUTER AND PHYSICAL SCIENCE (chemistry, computer science, and mathematics), ENGINEERING AND ENVIRONMENTAL DESIGN (engineering, environmental engineering, geological engineering, geophysical engineering, metallurgical engineering, mining and mineral engineering, occupational safety and health, petroleum/natural gas engineering, technological management, and technology and public affairs). Engineering and science are the strongest programs academically and have the largest enrollments.

Required: For graduation, students must complete at least 124 semester credits (more for engineering degrees) and maintain a minimum 2.0 GPA. Requirements include 6 hours each of communications, humanities, social sciences, and physical and life sciences, and 5 hours of mathematical sciences. Engineering students must satisfy specific requirements within the individual curriculum.

Special: Montana Tech has cooperative programs with 7 other institutions. Internships are available. A student-faculty exchange program in petroleum engineering exists with the People's Republic of China. Work-study programs, 3–2 engineering degrees, credit for military experience, nondegree study, and the pass/fail option (in physical education only) are available. Two departments have honors programs.

Faculty/Classroom: The average class size in an introductory lecture is 60; in a laboratory, 30; and in a regular course offering, 30.

Admissions: About 95% of the 1993–94 applicants were accepted. The SAT scores for the 1993–94 freshman class were as follows: Verbal—65% below 500, 26% between 500 and 599, and 9% between 600 and 700; Math—32% below 500, 34% between 500 and 599, 29% between 600 and 700, and 5% above 700. The ACT scores were 28% below 21, 28% between 21 and 23, 24% between 24 and 26, 11% between 27 and 28, and 9% above 28.

Requirements: Montana Tech requires applicants to be in the upper 50% of their class. A minimum GPA of 2.5 is required. The ACT is recommended. Applicants must be graduates of an accredited secondary school. The GED is accepted. Fourteen academic credits are required, including English, 4 years; mathematics and social studies, 3 years each; science, 2 years; plus 2 years chosen from foreign language, computer science, visual and performing arts, or vocational education. Applicants must have minimum composite scores of 22 on the ACT or 920 on the SAT I or a 2.5 GPA, or be in the top half of their graduating class. Other factors regarding admissions would only be considered if the preceding standards were not met. AP and CLEP credits are accepted.

Procedure: Freshmen are admitted to all sessions. Entrance exams should be taken in the senior year. Applications should be filed by August 1 for fall entry and January 1 for spring entry, along with an application fee of $30. Notification is sent on a rolling basis. There are early admissions and deferred admissions plans.

Transfer: A total of 136 transfer students enrolled in 1993–94. Transfer applicants must have a minimum GPA of 2.0. Grades of C and above transfer for credit. A total of 30 credits out of 124 must be completed at Montana Tech.

Visiting: There are regularly scheduled orientations for prospective students, There is an official 3-day fall orientation, though visits are welcome anytime. There are guides for informal visits and visitors may sit in on classes and stay overnight at the school. To arrange for a visit, contact the Admissions Office at (406) 496-4178 or (800) 445-TECH (in-state).

Financial Aid: In 1993–94, 74% of all current freshmen and 57% of continuing students received some form of financial aid. About 62% of freshmen and 43% of continuing students received need-based aid. The average freshman award was $3380. Of that total, scholarships or need-based grants averaged $1047 ($7863 maximum); loans averaged $2539 ($11,493 maximum); and work contracts averaged $1500 (maximum). Sixty-three percent of undergraduate students work part-time. The average financial indebtedness of the 1992–93 graduate was $5737. The FAFSA financial statement is required. The deadline for financial aid applications is April 1.

International Students: There are currently 72 international students enrolled. The school actively recruits these students. They must take the TOEFL and achieve a minimum score of 525.

Computers: The college provides computer facilities for student use. Computers are integrated into every degree program. There are over 400 personal computers campuswide, most of which are connected to a DEC VAX 4000 mainframe. All students may access the system anytime. There are no time limits on using the system. All students are charged a computer-use fee at registration.

Graduates: In 1992–93, 203 bachelor's degrees were awarded. The most popular majors among graduates were computer science (32%), environmental engineering (32%), and engineering science (30%). Within an average freshman class, 1% graduate in 3 years, 40% in 4 years, 20% in 5 years, and 7% in 6 years. Some 50 companies recruited on campus in 1992–93. In the 1992 graduating class, 9% of the men and 4% of the women were enrolled in graduate school within 6 months of graduation; 85% of the men and 90% of the women had found employment.

Admissions Contact: Ed Johnson, Director of Admissions.

MONTANA STATE UNIVERSITY

C-3

Bozeman, MT 59717   (406) 994-2452

Full-time: 4896 men, 3864 women	Faculty: 524; I, --$
Part-time: 573 men, 581 women	Ph.D.s: 73%
Graduate: 536 men, 348 women	Student/Faculty: 17 to 1
Year: semesters, summer session	Tuition: $2002 ($5978)
Application Deadline: July 1	Room & Board: $3532
Freshman Class: 3500 applied, 2836 accepted, 1779 enrolled	
SAT I Verbal/Math: 440/520	ACT: 23 COMPETITIVE

Montana State University, founded in 1893, is a public, land-grant, coeducational institution offering programs in agriculture, business, arts and architecture, education, engineering, health and human development, nursing, and letters and science. There are 7 undergraduate schools and one graduate school. In addition to regional accreditation, MSU has baccalaureate program accreditation with AACSB, ABET, ADA, NAAB, NASAD, NASM, NCATE, and NLN. The 2 libraries contain 515,214 volumes, 1,308,920 microform items, and 1479 audiovisual forms, and subscribe to 5078 periodicals. Computerized library sources and services include the card catalog, interlibrary loans, and database searching. Special learning facilities in-

clude a learning resource center, art gallery, natural history museum, planetarium, radio station, and TV station. The 1170-acre campus is in a small town 140 miles west of Billings and 90 miles north of Yellowstone National Park. Including residence halls, there are 71 buildings on campus.

Student Life: About 64% of undergraduates are from Montana. Students come from 49 states, 57 foreign countries, and Canada. Ninety-two percent are white. The average age of freshmen is 19; all undergraduates, 23.1. Thirty-three percent drop out by the end of their first year; 40% remain to graduate.

Housing: A total of 3121 students can be accommodated in college housing. College-sponsored living facilities include single-sex and coed dormitories, married-student housing, fraternity houses, and sorority houses. In addition there are honors houses, international houses, and houses for older students. On-campus housing is guaranteed for the freshman year only and is available on a first-come, first-served basis. All students may keep cars on campus.

Activities: About 8% of men belong to 10 national fraternities; about 5% of women belong to 5 national sororities. There are 82 groups on campus, including art, band, cheerleading, chess, choir, chorale, chorus, computers, dance, drama, drill team, ethnic, film, gay, honors, international, jazz band, literary magazine, marching band, musical theater, newspaper, opera, orchestra, pep band, photography, political, professional, radio and TV, religious, social, social service, student government, and symphony. Popular campus events include International Food Bazaar, Jim Bridger Days, and Native-American Pow-Wow.

Sports: There are 6 intercollegiate sports for men and 8 for women, and 40 intramural sports for men, 38 for women, and 5 for both. Athletic and recreation facilities include a 14,000-seat stadium, numerous gymnasiums, handball courts, weight rooms, and 2 pools.

Disabled Students: Ninety percent of the campus is accessible to disabled students. The following facilities are available: wheelchair ramps, elevators, special parking, specially equipped rest rooms, special class scheduling, lowered drinking fountains, lowered telephones, and services through the resource center.

Services: In addition to many counseling and information services, tutoring is available in every subject. There is remedial math, reading, and writing, and a taping service for the blind and learning disabled.

Campus Safety and Security: Campus safety and security measures include 24-hour foot and vehicle patrol, self defense education, escort service, and informal discussions. In addition, there are pamphlets, posters, films and lighted pathways and sidewalks.

Programs of Study: MSU awards the B.A., B.S., B.Arch., and B.Mus.Ed. degrees. Master's and doctoral degrees also are awarded. Bachelor's degrees are awarded in AGRICULTURE (agricultural business management, agricultural economics, agronomy, animal science, horticulture, range/farm management, and soil science), BIOLOGICAL SCIENCE (biology/biological science and microbiology), BUSINESS (business administration and management), COMMUNICATIONS AND THE ARTS (art, English, media arts, modern language, and speech/debate/rhetoric), COMPUTER AND PHYSICAL SCIENCE (chemistry, computer science, earth science, mathematics, and physics), EDUCATION (agricultural, elementary, music, physical, secondary, and technical), ENGINEERING AND ENVIRONMENTAL DESIGN (agricultural engineering technology, architecture, chemical engineering, civil engineering, construction technology, electrical/electronics engineering, electrical/electronics engineering technology, industrial engineering, interior design, land use management and reclamation, mechanical engineering, and mechanical engineering technology), HEALTH PROFESSIONS (nursing), SOCIAL SCIENCE (economics, history, home economics, philosophy, political science/government, psychology, sociology, and water resources). Engineering, physical science, and architecture are the strongest academically. Business, education, and nursing have the largest enrollments.

Required: To graduate, students must complete a core curriculum of 6 credits each of multicultural studies, humanities, social science, and communications, 3 credits each of technology, fine arts, and mathematics, and 9 credits of natural sciences. The total number of credits required varies by program, with 128 being the minimum; at least one third must be in upper-division courses. A minimum 2.0 GPA is needed. Students must be officially registered in their chosen curriculum for at least 2 semesters before graduation.

Special: MSU offers internships in selected majors, study in 36 countries, B.A.-B.S. degrees, dual and interdisciplinary majors, nondegree study, and pass/fail options. There is a freshman honors program on campus. The honors program is university-wide.

Faculty/Classroom: Sixty-nine percent of faculty are male; 31%, female. Nearly all both teach and do research. Graduate students teach 1% of introductory courses. The average class size in an introductory lecture is 76; in a laboratory, 21; and in a regular course offering, 34.

Admissions: About 81% of the 1993–94 applicants were accepted. The SAT scores for the 1993–94 freshman class were as follows: Verbal—69% below 500, 26% between 500 and 599, and 5% between 600 and 700; Math—41% below 500, 34% between 500 and 599,

21% between 600 and 700, and 4% above 700. The ACT scores were 28% below 21, 30% between 21 and 23, 25% between 24 and 26, 11% between 27 and 28, and 7% above 28. About 34% of the current freshmen were in the top fifth of their class; 64% were in the top two fifths. There were 3 National Merit finalists and 5 semifinalists. A total of 64 freshmen graduated first in their class.

Requirements: MSU requires applicants to be in the upper 50% of their class. A minimum GPA of 2.5 is required. The SAT I or ACT is required. MSU requires applicants to have a minimum GPA of 2.5, rank in the upper 50% of their graduating class, or have minimum composite scores of 22 on the ACT or 920 on the SAT I. They must be graduates of an accredited secondary school. The GED is accepted. Students should have completed 4 years of English, 3 years each of social studies and mathematics, 2 years of laboratory science, and 2 years of language, computer science, visual and performing arts, or vocational education. AP and CLEP credits are accepted. Important factors used in the admissions decision are evidence of special talent, leadership record, personality, intangible qualities, extracurricular activities record, and recommendations by school officials.

Procedure: Freshmen are admitted to all sessions. Entrance exams should be taken in fall of the senior year. Applications should be filed by July 1 for fall entry, December 1 for spring entry, and May 1 for summer entry, along with an application fee of $30. Notification is sent on a rolling basis within a week of the application receipt. There is a deferred admissions plan.

Transfer: About 900 transfer students enrolled in 1993–94. Transfer students must have a minimum GPA of 2.0; grades of pass and D or better transfer for credit. A total of 30 credits out of at least 128 must be completed at MSU.

Visiting: There are regularly scheduled orientations for prospective students, including program overviews, a tour, meeting with assistant deans, course selection and class scheduling, registration, and various mini seminars. There are guides for informal visits and visitors may sit in on classes and stay overnight at the school. To arrange for a visit, contact the Office of New Student Services at (406) 994–2452.

Financial Aid: In 1993–94, 70% of students received some form of financial aid. The average freshman award was $4465. Of that total, scholarships or need-based grants averaged $1547 ($4500 maximum); loans averaged $2020 ($4875 maximum); and work contracts averaged $818 ($1800 maximum). Eighteen percent of undergraduate students work part-time. Average earnings from campus work for the school year are $1100. The average financial indebtedness of the 1992–93 graduate was $9700. MSU is a member of CSS. The FAF, FFS, or SFS, or FAFSA is required, with the FAFSA preferred. The deadline for financial aid applications is March 1.

International Students: There are currently 256 international students enrolled. They must take the TOEFL and achieve a minimum score of 525.

Computers: The university provides computer facilities for student use. The mainframes are a DEC VAX 6510 and 6520 cluster. There are 35 microcomputers in the residence hall computer rooms. Two main student computer laboratories house 46 terminals and 188 microcomputers, and departmentally controlled laboratories house 100 terminals and 400 microcomputers. All students may access the system. For instructional and personal use, each student has an account. There are no time limits on using the system. All students pay a computer fee of $1.50 per credit per semester.

Graduates: In 1992–93, 1444 bachelor's degrees were awarded. The most popular majors among graduates were engineering (21%), business (14%), and education (8%). Some 79 companies recruited on campus in 1992–93. In the 1992 graduating class, 9% of the men and women were enrolled in graduate school within 6 months of graduation; 53% had found employment.

Admissions Contact: Director, Office of New Student Services.

MONTANA UNIVERSITY SYSTEM

The Montana University system, established in 1972, is the public system in Montana. It is governed by a board of regents, whose chief administrator is the commissioner of higher education. The primary goal of the system is teaching first, then research and public service. The main priorities are funding, system structure, and transfer articulation. The total enrollment in a recent year of all 6 4-year campuses was 27,405; there were 1111 faculty members. Altogether there are 148 baccalaureate, 92 master's, and 26 doctoral programs offered in the Montana University System. Profiles of the 4-year campuses are included in this chapter in alphabetical order with other Montana schools.

NORTHERN MONTANA COLLEGE D-1

Havre, MT 59501   (406) 265–3704; (800) 662–6132

Full-time: 570 men, 599 women	Faculty: 82
Part-time: 159 men, 244 women	Ph.D.s: n/av
Graduate: 93 men, 173 women	Student/Faculty: 14 to 1
Year: semesters, summer session	Tuition: $1596 ($4716)
Application Deadline: see profile	Room & Board: $3380–3770
Freshman Class: n/av	
SAT I or ACT: required	COMPETITIVE

Northern Montana College, founded in 1929, is part of the Montana University System and offers programs in the liberal arts, teacher education, business, and technology. The library contains 100,000 volumes and 600,000 microform items, and subscribes to 650 periodicals. Special learning facilities include a radio station. The 105-acre campus is in a small town 115 miles north of Great Falls. Including residence halls, there are 21 buildings on campus.

Student Life: About 97% of undergraduates are from Montana. Ninety percent are from public schools. The average age of freshmen is 21; all undergraduates, 28.

Housing: College-sponsored living facilities include dormitories, on-campus apartments, and married-student housing. On-campus housing is guaranteed for all 4 years. Sixty percent of students live on campus. All students may keep cars on campus.

Activities: There are no fraternities or sororities on campus. There are some groups and organizations on campus, including dance, ethnic, musical theater, newspaper, pep band, religious, social service, student government, and yearbook. Popular campus events include concerts, dances, and theatrical productions.

Sports: There are 11 intramural sports for men and 9 for women. Athletic and recreation facilities include tennis courts, a swimming pool, weight and wrestling rooms, and 2 gymnasiums, the larger seating 2500. Nearby Glacier National Park offers outdoor facilities.

Disabled Students: The entire campus is accessible to disabled students. The following facilities are available: special parking and specially equipped rest rooms.

Services: In addition to many counseling and information services, tutoring is available in every subject. There is also remedial math, reading, and writing.

Programs of Study: NMC awards the B.A., B.S., B.S.Ed., and B.T. degrees. Associate and master's degrees also are awarded. Bachelor's degrees are awarded in AGRICULTURE (agricultural mechanics), BIOLOGICAL SCIENCE (biology/biological science and ecology), COMMUNICATIONS AND THE ARTS (communications, dramatic arts, English, fine arts, French, and music), COMPUTER AND PHYSICAL SCIENCE (chemistry), EDUCATION (business, elementary, industrial arts, physical, science, secondary, and social science), ENGINEERING AND ENVIRONMENTAL DESIGN (automotive technology, civil engineering technology, construction technology, drafting and design technology, electrical/electronics engineering technology, engineering technology, environmental science, and manufacturing technology), HEALTH PROFESSIONS (nursing), SOCIAL SCIENCE (history, humanities, interdisciplinary studies, Native American studies, and social science).

Required: To graduate, students must complete at least 128 credits with a minimum GPA of 2.0 overall and 2.25 in their major and minor. Distribution requirements include 12 credits each of humanities, social science, mathematics/science, and technology/applied arts. Students also must demonstrate proficiency in computing and in written and oral communication.

Special: NMC offers B.A.-B.S. and other dual-degree programs, pass/fail options, cooperative programs in most disciplines, independent study, dual majors, and work-study programs.

Requirements: NMC requires applicants to be in the upper 50% of their class. A minimum GPA of 2.5 is required. The ACT (preferred), with a minimum composite score of 20, or the SAT I, with a minimum composite score of 800, is required. Applicants must be graduates of an accredited high school, or have a GED certificate. They should have completed 4 years of English, 3 each of mathematics, including Algebra I and II and geometry, and history, including global studies and U.S. history, and 2 each of laboratory science and electives. CLEP credit is accepted.

Procedure: Freshmen are admitted to all sessions. Entrance exams should be taken prior to application. Applications should be filed at least 1 month prior to registration. The application fee is $30. There is an early admissions plan.

Transfer: Nonresidents must have a minimum GPA of 2.0. Any applicant with fewer than 12 transfer credits must submit a transcript of college work completed and meet standard freshman requirements. A total of 36 credits out of 128 must be completed at NMC.

Visiting: There are guides for informal visits and visitors may sit in on classes and stay overnight at the school. To arrange for a visit, contact the Admissions Office at (406) 265–3704 or (800) 662–6132 (in-state).

Financial Aid: In a recent year, 48% of all freshmen received some form of financial aid. Scholarships or need-based grants averaged $200; loans averaged $500; and work contracts averaged $500. Twenty percent of undergraduate students work part-time. NMC is a member of CSS. The FAF or FFS is required. The deadline for financial aid applications is March 1.

International Students: International students must take the TOEFL and achieve a minimum score of 500.

Computers: The mainframe is a DEC PDP 11/70. There are also Apple microcomputers available in various locations. All students may access the system when the buildings are open.

Admissions Contact: Kelley Palmer, Director of Admissions.

ROCKY MOUNTAIN COLLEGE D-3

Billings, MT 59102   (406) 657–1025; (800) 87-ROCKY (in-state)

Full-time: 388 men, 368 women	Faculty: 36; IIB, --$
Part-time: 36 men, 62 women	Ph.D.s: n/av
Graduate: none	Student/Faculty: 21 to 1
Year: semesters, summer session	Tuition: $8020
Application Deadline: August 15	Room & Board: $3300
Freshman Class: 480 applied, 380 accepted, 220 enrolled	
SAT I: required	COMPETITIVE

Rocky Mountain College, established in 1878, is a private, coeducational liberal arts institution affiliated with the United Church of Christ, the United Methodist Church, and the Presbyterian Church U.S.A. The library contains 70,000 volumes and 2000 audiovisual forms, and subscribes to 250 periodicals. Computerized library sources and services include interlibrary loans. Special learning facilities include a learning resource center. The 60-acre campus is in a small town 550 miles north of Denver, Colorado. Including residence halls, there are 16 buildings on campus.

Student Life: About 70% of undergraduates are from Montana. Students come from 33 states, 3 foreign countries, and Canada. Eighty-eight percent are white. The average age of freshmen is 21; all undergraduates, 24.

Housing: A total of 357 students can be accommodated in college housing. College-sponsored living facilities include coed dormitories. On-campus housing is guaranteed for all 4 years and is available on a first-come, first-served basis. Fifty-five percent of students commute. Alcohol is not permitted. All students may keep cars on campus.

Activities: There are no fraternities or sororities on campus. There are 15 groups on campus, including band, cheerleading, choir, chorale, chorus, computers, dance, drama, film, honors, jazz band, literary magazine, marching band, musical theater, newspaper, pep band, photography, professional, religious, social, social service, student government, and yearbook. Popular campus events include Convocations, Homecoming, intercollegiate athletics, Woodrow Wilson Visiting Fellow, and theater productions.

Sports: There are 3 intercollegiate and 12 intramural sports each for men and women. Athletic and recreation facilities include the Outdoor Recreation Program, which offers organized outings, a resource center, academic classes, seminars and lectures, a bicycle and ski repair shop, and an equipment rental shop. Activities include backpacking in Glacier National Park, whitewater river rafting in the Tetons, and climbing at Beartooth Mountain.

Disabled Students: Fifteen percent of the campus is accessible to disabled students. The following facilities are available: wheelchair ramps, special parking, and special class scheduling.

Services: In addition to many counseling and information services, tutoring is available in every subject. There is also a reader service for the blind, and remedial math, reading, and writing.

Campus Safety and Security: Campus safety and security measures include self defense education.

Programs of Study: The Rock awards the B.A. and B.S. degrees. Associate degrees also are awarded. Bachelor's degrees are awarded in AGRICULTURE (equestrian science), BIOLOGICAL SCIENCE (biology/biological science), BUSINESS (business administration and management and business economics), COMMUNICATIONS AND THE ARTS (dramatic arts, English, and fine arts), COMPUTER AND PHYSICAL SCIENCE (chemistry, computer mathematics, computer science, geology, and mathematics), EDUCATION (elementary, music, and physical), ENGINEERING AND ENVIRONMENTAL DESIGN (aviation administration/management), SOCIAL SCIENCE (anthropology, Christian studies, economics, history, history of philosophy, philosophy, political science/government, psychology, religion, and sociology). Business, economics, music, education, and aviation have the largest enrollments.

Required: To graduate, students must complete 124 credit hours, 24 in a major and 18 in a minor, with a minimum GPA of 2.0. There are general education requirements in humanities, the natural and social sciences, and fine arts.

Special: The college offers co-op programs, study abroad in Greece and Egypt, dual majors, individualized programs of study, a 3–2 engineering degree with Montana State University and Montana College

of Mineral Science and Technology, and credit for life, military, and work experience. Juniors and seniors may elect to take one course on a pass/fail basis each semester. There is a freshman honors program on campus.

Admissions: About 79% of the 1993–94 applicants were accepted. There were 3 National Merit finalists. Eleven freshmen graduated first in their class.

Requirements: A minimum GPA of 2.5 and the SAT I are required. Applicants must be graduates of an accredited secondary school; the GED is accepted. Students must have completed 4 units of English, 1 unit of history, and 2 units each in 3 of the following: foreign language, mathematics, natural sciences, or social sciences. The school recommends a portfolio for admission to the art program, an audition for admission to the music program, and an interview for academically weak students. AP and CLEP credits are accepted.

Procedure: Freshmen are admitted to all sessions. Applications should be filed by August 15 for fall entry and December 15 for winter entry, along with an application fee of $15. Notification is sent within 2 weeks. There are early decision, early admissions, and deferred admissions plans.

Transfer: Transfer students must have a minimum GPA of 2.0; grades of 2.0 and higher transfer for credit. Transfers are admitted every term. A total of 30 credits out of 124 must be completed at the Rock.

Visiting: There are regularly scheduled orientations for prospective students. There are guides for informal visits and visitors may sit in on classes and stay overnight at the school. To arrange for a visit, contact David Heringer, Director of Admissions, at (406) 657–1025 or (800) 87-ROCKY.

Financial Aid: In a recent year, 85% of all students received some form of financial aid. Scholarships or need-based grants averaged $1775 ($7856 maximum); loans averaged $2400 ($4125 maximum); and work contracts averaged $821 ($1000 maximum). Thirty-five percent of undergraduate students work part-time. The average financial indebtedness of a recent graduate was $8850. The Rock is a member of CSS. The FAF or FFS, the college's own financial statement, and FAFSA are required. The deadline for financial aid applications is April 1.

International Students: There are currently 44 international students enrolled. The school actively recruits these students. They must take the TOEFL or the college's own test and achieve a minimum score on the TOEFL of 500.

Computers: The college provides computer facilities for student use. The mainframe is a Prime 2755. Thirty Zenith microcomputers are available in academic buildings and the library. All students may access the system. There are no time limits on using the system and no fees.

Graduates: In a recent year, 126 bachelor's degrees were awarded.

Admissions Contact: David Heringer, Director of Admissions.

UNIVERSITY OF MONTANA
Missoula, MT 59812

B-2

(406) 243–4277

Full-time: 3697 men, 3857 women	Faculty: 436; I, --$
Part-time: 604 men, 610 women	Ph.Ds: 85%
Graduate: 2045 men and women	Student/Faculty: 17 to 1
Year: semesters, summer session	Tuition: $2033 ($6009)
Application Deadline: March 1	Room & Board: $3496
Freshman Class: 3314 applied, 2811 accepted, 2743 enrolled	
SAT I Verbal/Math: 458/489	ACT: 22 COMPETITIVE

The University of Montana, founded in 1893, is a public, coeducational institution with programs in arts and sciences, business administration, fine arts, education, forestry, journalism, and pharmacy and allied health sciences. It is part of the Montana University System. There are 6 undergraduate schools and one graduate school. In addition to regional accreditation, U of M has baccalaureate program accreditation with AACSB, ACCE, ACPE, APTA, NASAD, NASM, NCATE, and SAF. The 3 libraries contain 770,000 volumes and 280,263 microform items, and subscribe to 4958 periodicals. Computerized library sources and services include the card catalog, interlibrary loans, and database searching. Special learning facilities include an art gallery, radio station, experimental forest, biological station, and ranch. The 220-acre campus is in an urban area 200 miles east of Spokane, Washington. Including residence halls, there are 43 buildings on campus.

Student Life: About 75% of undergraduates are from Montana. Students come from 45 states, 63 foreign countries, and Canada. Eighty percent are from public schools; 20% from private. Ninety-three percent are white. The average age of freshmen is 19; all undergraduates, 25. Twenty-five percent drop out by the end of their first year; 40% remain to graduate.

Housing: A total of 2600 students can be accommodated in college housing. College-sponsored living facilities include single-sex and coed dormitories and married-student housing. In addition there are honors houses, special interest houses, an international house, and nontraditional houses. On-campus housing is guaranteed for all 4 years. Seventy-nine percent of students commute. All students may keep cars on campus.

Activities: About 10% of men belong to 7 national fraternities; about 8% of women belong to 4 national sororities. There are 111 groups on campus, including art, band, cheerleading, chess, choir, chorale, chorus, computers, dance, drill team, ethnic, gay, honors, international, jazz band, literary magazine, marching band, newspaper, opera, orchestra, pep band, political, professional, radio and TV, religious, social, social service, student government, symphony, and yearbook. Popular campus events include Forester's Day, International Wildlife Film Festival, Founders Day, International Week, Homecoming, Parents Day, Martin Luther King Day, and May Fete.

Sports: There are 6 intercollegiate sports for men and 8 for women, and 16 intramural sports for men and 12 for women. Athletic and recreation facilities include field house, a 10,000-seat gymnasium, a 12,000-seat stadium, a golf course, soccer and rugby fields, an Olympic-size pool, a game room, a climbing wall, and weight rooms.

Disabled Students: Sixty percent of the campus is accessible to disabled students. The following facilities are available: wheelchair ramps, elevators, special parking, specially equipped rest rooms, special class scheduling, lowered drinking fountains, lowered telephones, and specially equipped dormitory rooms.

Services: In addition to many counseling and information services, tutoring is available in every subject. In addition, there is a reader service for the blind, and remedial math, reading, and writing. Mentors and note takers are available.

Campus Safety and Security: Campus safety and security measures include 24-hour foot and vehicle patrol, self defense education, escort service, and informal discussions. In addition, there are pamphlets, posters, and films, emergency telephones, and lighted pathways and sidewalks.

Programs of Study: U of M awards the B.A., B.S., B.A.E., B.S.H.P.E., and B.S.M. degrees. Associate, master's, and doctoral degrees also are awarded. Bachelor's degrees are awarded in AGRICULTURE (forestry and related sciences), BIOLOGICAL SCIENCE (biology/biological science, botany, microbiology, wildlife biology, and zoology), BUSINESS (accounting, banking and finance, business administration and management, marketing/retailing/merchandising, personnel management, and small business management), COMMUNICATIONS AND THE ARTS (broadcasting, classics, communications, dance, dramatic arts, English, fine arts, French, German, Japanese, journalism, Latin, music, Russian, and Spanish), COMPUTER AND PHYSICAL SCIENCE (chemistry, computer science, geology, mathematics, and physics), EDUCATION (elementary, music, physical, science, and secondary), HEALTH PROFESSIONS (medical laboratory technology, nursing, pharmacy, physical therapy, predentistry, and premedicine), SOCIAL SCIENCE (anthropology, economics, geography, history, liberal arts/general studies, philosophy, political science/government, prelaw, psychology, social work, sociology, and women's studies). Journalism, forestry, liberal arts, and accounting are the strongest academically. Business and forestry have the largest enrollments.

Required: A total of 130 credits are required for graduation in most majors. There are competency requirements in writing, mathematics, and foreign language or symbolic systems. Distribution requirements include courses in 6 areas: expressive arts, literary and artistic studies, historical and cultural studies, social sciences, ethical and human values, and natural sciences. A minimum GPA of 2.0 must be maintained. The number of hours in the major varies; some majors require a thesis.

Special: Students may cross-register with Western Montana College. Co-op programs exist in business, communications, economics, management, and liberal studies. Internships in most majors, work-study programs with nonprofit organizations, and study abroad in 12 countries are available. The school offers a B.A.-B.S. degree in chemistry, dual majors, and pass/fail options in classes other than major requirements. A dual major in physics and computer science is possible. There is a freshman honors program on campus, as well as 3 national honor societies, including Phi Beta Kappa.

Faculty/Classroom: All faculty both teach undergraduates and do research. Graduate students teach 8% of introductory courses. The average class size in an introductory lecture is 35; in a laboratory, 25; and in a regular course offering, 35.

Admissions: About 85% of the 1993–94 applicants were accepted. The ACT scores for the 1993–94 freshman class were as follows: 5% below 21, 50% between 21 and 23, 21% between 24 and 26, 18% between 27 and 28, and 6% above 28. About 25% of the current freshmen were in the top fifth of their class; 43% were in the top two fifths.

Requirements: U of M requires applicants to be in the upper 50% of their class. A minimum GPA of 2.5 is required. A minimum composite ACT score of 22 or a minimum composite score of 920 on the SAT I is required. Applicants must be graduates of an accredited secondary school. The GED is accepted. Students should have complet-

ed 4 years of English, 3 of mathematics, 3 of social studies, 2 of laboratory science, and 2 elective credits (foreign language recommended). AP and CLEP credits are accepted. Important factors used in the admissions decision are recommendations by school officials, advanced placement or honor courses, evidence of special talent, leadership record, and geographic diversity.

Procedure: Freshmen are admitted to all sessions. Entrance exams should be taken in October, December, or February. Applications should be filed by March 1 for fall entry and November 15 for winter entry, along with an application fee of $30. Notification is sent on a rolling basis.

Transfer: About 950 transfer students enrolled in 1993–94. Applicants for transfer must have a minimum GPA of 2.0. Grades of 2.0 or better transfer for credit. A total of 30 credits out of 130 must be completed at U of M.

Visiting: There are regularly scheduled orientations for prospective students, including placement testing, advising, workshops, and social events. There are guides for informal visits and visitors may sit in on classes and stay overnight at the school. To arrange for a visit, contact New Student Services at (406) 243–6266.

Financial Aid: In 1993–94, 70% of all current freshmen and 73% of continuing students received some form of financial aid. About 75% of continuing students received need-based aid. The average freshman award was $5000. Of that total, scholarships or need-based grants averaged $1000 ($2000 maximum); loans averaged $2000 ($8500 maximum); and work contracts averaged $900 ($1500 maximum). Twenty-five percent of undergraduate students work part-time. Average earnings from campus work for the school year are $1500. The average financial indebtedness of a recent graduate was $9000. U of M is a member of CSS. The FAF or FFS is required; the FAF is preferred. The deadline for financial aid applications is March 1.

International Students: The school actively recruits international students. They must take the TOEFL and achieve a minimum score of 500.

Computers: The university provides computer facilities for student use. The mainframes are a VAX/VMS and a UNIX. Terminal rooms are located campuswide, including in dorms. Several academic departments have their own terminal rooms. There are 36 telephone lines for remote sites. Those in classes that authorize use may access the system anytime. There are no time limits on using the system and no fees.

Graduates: In 1992–93, 1706 bachelor's degrees were awarded. The most popular majors among graduates were education (8%), finance (7%), and psychology (5%). Some 38 companies recruited on campus in a recent year. In a recent graduating class, 23% of the men and women were enrolled in graduate school within 6 months of graduation; 95% had found employment.

Admissions Contact: Mike Akin, Director of Admissions.

WESTERN MONTANA COLLEGE OF THE UNIVERSITY OF MONTANA
B-3

Dillon, MT 59725   (406) 683-7331; (800) WMC-MONT (in-state)

Full-time: 479 men, 428 women	Faculty: 40; IIA, --$
Part-time: 48 men, 115 women	Ph.D.s: 42%
Graduate: none	Student/Faculty: 23 to 1
Year: semesters, summer session	Tuition: $1646 ($4950)
Application Deadline: see profile	Room & Board: n/app
Freshman Class: 332 applied, 295 accepted, 241 enrolled	
ACT: 17	COMPETITIVE

Western Montana College, established in 1898, is a land-grant, coeducational institution, part of the University of Montana system. The college emphasizes teacher education. The library contains 60,000 volumes, and subscribes to 500 periodicals. Computerized library sources and services include the card catalog, interlibrary loans, and database searching. Special learning facilities include a learning resource center, an art gallery, and a human resource center. The 20-acre campus is in a small town 60 miles south of Butte. Including residence halls, there are 20 buildings on campus.

Student Life: Most students come from Montana. Students also come from 3 foreign countries. Ninety percent are from public schools. Ninety-eight percent are white. The average age of freshmen

is 18; all undergraduates, 21. Two percent drop out by the end of their first year; 75% remain to graduate.

Housing: A total of 616 students can be accommodated in college housing. College-sponsored living facilities include dormitories and married-student housing. On-campus housing is guaranteed for all 4 years and is available on a first-come, first-served basis. All students may keep cars on campus.

Activities: There are no fraternities or sororities on campus. There are many groups on campus, including art, band, cheerleading, choir, chorale, computers, dance, drama, drill team, honors, musical theater, newspaper, pep band, political, religious, student government, and yearbook.

Sports: There are 4 intercollegiate sports for men and 3 for women, and 7 intramural sports each for men and women. Athletic and recreation facilities include a 5000-seat gymnasium, 2 basketball and 4 racquetball courts, a dance floor, tennis courts, 2 weight rooms, an aerobics room, an indoor arena, and a 3000-seat stadium.

Disabled Students: The following facilities are available: wheelchair ramps, elevators, special parking, specially equipped rest rooms, special class scheduling, and lowered drinking fountains.

Services: In addition to many counseling and information services, tutoring is available in every subject.

Programs of Study: WMC awards the B.S.Ed. degree. Associate degrees also are awarded. Bachelor's degrees are awarded in EDUCATION (art, business, early childhood, elementary, industrial arts, middle school, music, science, and secondary). Elementary education has the largest enrollment.

Required: For graduation, students must complete 128 credit hours and maintain a minimum GPA of 2.2. Other requirements vary by major.

Special: The college offers co-op programs, work-study programs, B.A.-B.S. degrees, dual majors, and pass/fail options. The Rural Education Program is designed to prepare students for teaching in 1-room schools and other rural school settings.

Faculty/Classroom: The average class size in an introductory lecture is 35.

Admissions: About 89% of the 1993–94 applicants were accepted. Eight percent of the current freshmen were in the top fifth of their class; 19% were in the top two fifths.

Requirements: A minimum GPA of 2.5 is required. The SAT I or ACT is required. New students who have not taken the ACT or SAT I must complete it during their first semester of attendance. Applicants must be graduates of an accredited secondary school. The GED is accepted. Students should have completed 4 years of English, 3 each of history and mathematics, and 1 year of science. Advanced placement or honor courses is an important factor used in the admission decision.

Procedure: Freshmen are admitted to all sessions. Applications should be filed 1 semester prior to registration. The application fee is $20. There is a deferred admissions plan.

Transfer: Transfers must have earned a minimum of 12 credit hours. Credits earned at any accredited college can be used to satisfy curriculum or degree requirements only after evaluation.

Visiting: There are guides for informal visits and visitors may sit in on classes and stay overnight at the school. To arrange for a visit, contact the Admissions Office at (406) 683-7331.

Financial Aid: In a recent year, 65% of all freshmen and 75% of continuing students received some form of financial aid. Scholarships or need-based grants averaged $350 ($1000 maximum); loans averaged $1500; and work contracts averaged $1200 ($1400 maximum). WMC is a member of CSS. The FAF is required. The deadline for financial aid applications is March 1.

International Students: There were recently 3 international students enrolled. They must take the TOEFL and achieve a minimum score of 550.

Computers: The college provides computer facilities for student use. The mainframe is a DEC PDP 11/60. Microcomputers are available in the computer learning center. All students may access the system from 8 A.M. to 10 P.M.

Admissions Contact: Michele F. O'Neill, Director of Admissions.

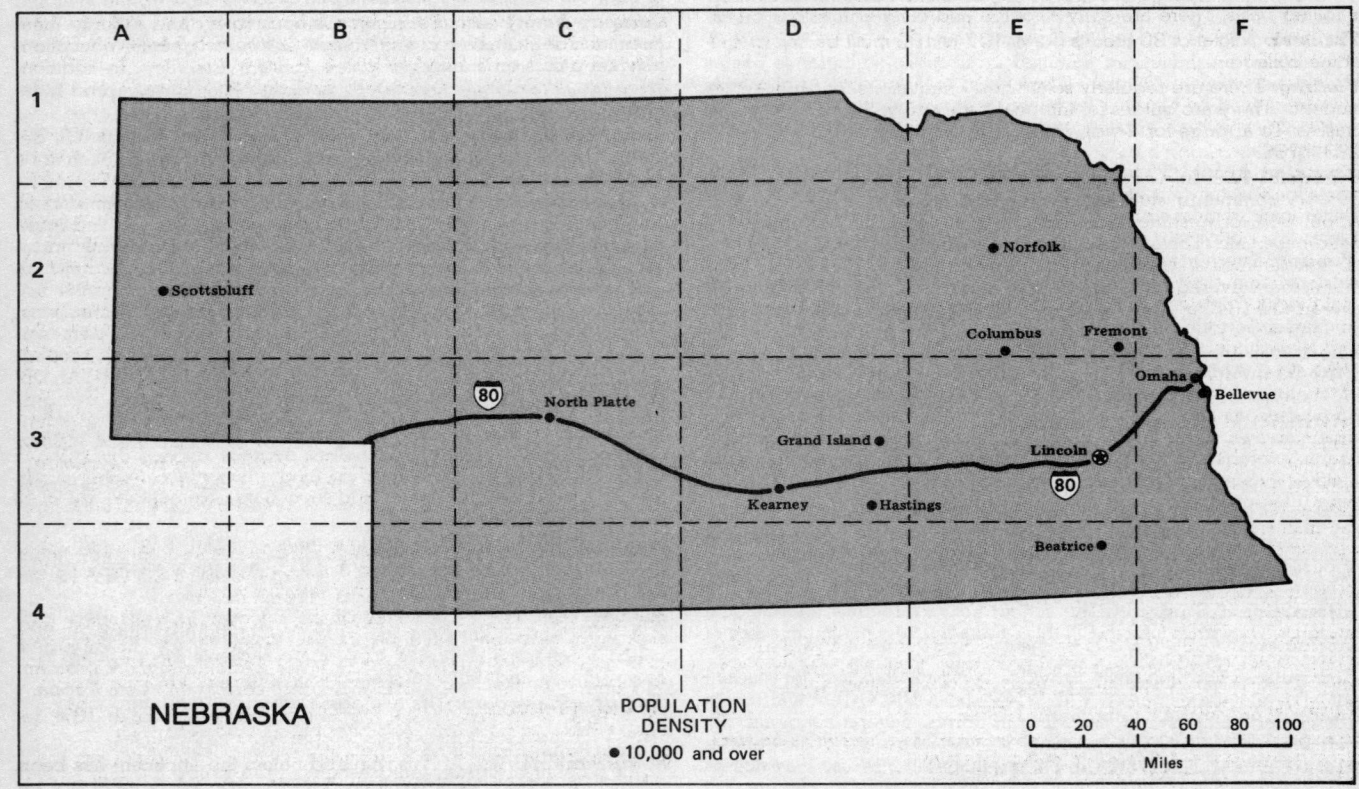

NEBRASKA

POPULATION DENSITY
● 10,000 and over

Miles
0 20 40 60 80 100

BELLEVUE COLLEGE

F-3

Bellevue, NE 68005
(402) 293-3766

Full-time: 957 men and women
Part-time: 1082 men and women
Graduate: 118 men and women
Year: trimesters, summer sessions
Application Deadline: open
Freshman Class: n/av
ACT: 21

Faculty: 40; IIB, --$
Ph.D.s: 57%
Student/Faculty: 24 to 1
Tuition: $3050
Room & Board: n/app

NONCOMPETITIVE

Bellevue College, established in 1966, is a private commuter college offering undergraduate degrees in arts and sciences, professional studies, and business. There are 3 undergraduate schools and one graduate school. The library contains 120,000 volumes and 6700 microform items, and subscribes to 507 periodicals. Computerized library sources and services include the card catalog, interlibrary loans, and database searching. Special learning facilities include a learning resource center and an art gallery. The 19-acre campus is in a suburban area 5 miles south of Omaha. There are 6 buildings on campus. There are no residence halls.

Student Life: About 95% of undergraduates are from Nebraska. Ninety percent are from public schools. Eighty-six percent are white. The average age of all undergraduates is 25. Twelve percent drop out by the end of their first year; 40% remain to graduate.

Housing: There are no residence halls. College-sponsored living facilities include on-campus apartments. Nearly all students commute. Alcohol is not permitted.

Activities: There are no fraternities or sororities on campus. There are some groups and organizations on campus, including cheerleading, newspaper, and professional. Popular campus events include Halloween and Christmas parties, Black History Month, Spring Bash, movie nights, bowling nights, and dances.

Sports: Athletic and recreation facilities include racquetball, basketball, and volleyball courts, and weight-lifting equipment.

Disabled Students: All of the campus is accessible to disabled students. The following facilities are available: wheelchair ramps, special parking, specially equipped rest rooms, and lowered drinking fountains.

Services: In addition to many counseling and information services, tutoring is available in most subjects.

Campus Safety and Security: Campus safety and security measures include self-defense education, informal discussions, pamphlets, posters, and films, and lighted pathways and sidewalks.

Programs of Study: The college awards the B.A., B.S., B.F.A., B.P.S., and B.T.S. degrees. Master's degrees are also awarded. Bachelor's degrees are awarded in BUSINESS (accounting, business administration and management, and personnel management), COMMUNICATIONS AND THE ARTS (communications, English, fine arts, and photography), COMPUTER AND PHYSICAL SCIENCE (information sciences and systems), EDUCATION (physical), SOCIAL SCIENCE (criminal justice, geography, history, philosophy, political science/government, psychology, social science, sociology, and urban studies). Business administration is the strongest academically.

Required: To graduate, students must complete the core curriculum, with coursework in communicative arts, a foreign language, art, English literature, foreign language literature, culture, civilization, music, philosophy, biology, chemistry, geology, mathematics, geography, physics, psychology, sociology, economics, history, and political science. The required distribution of core credits varies by degree program from 63 to 66, and the total number of hours in the major varies by major. Students must earn 127 to 132 credits, depending on the degree. The minimum required GPA is 2.0 overall and 2.5 in the major.

Special: Bellevue College offers cross-registration with Clarkson College, co-op programs with Clarkson and Buena Vista Colleges and Grace College of the Bible, internships, and work-study. Students may earn B.A.-B.S. degrees, and an accelerated degree program is possible in professional studies. The college permits dual majors, and composite, interdisciplinary majors are available in the social sciences and urban studies. Credit may be conferred for military experience. Nondegree study is possible. The Lockstep Degree Competition Program offers an alternative to the traditional academic structure. The School of Arts and Sciences operates on a 4-day academic week to provide flexibility. There is one national honor society on campus.

Faculty/Classroom: Ninety-one percent teach undergraduates. No introductory courses are taught by graduate students. The average class size in an introductory lecture is 35; in a laboratory, 25; and in a regular course offering, 25.

Admissions: About 20% of the current freshmen were in the top fifth of their class; 44% were in the top two fifths.

Requirements: The ACT, with a recommended minimum score of 19, or the SAT I is required for those entering college within 2 years after high school graduation; submission of ACT/SAT I scores are recommended for all others. Applicants must be graduates of an accredited secondary school or have a GED. Interviews are recommended. AP and CLEP credits are accepted.

Procedure: Freshmen are admitted to all sessions. Entrance exams should be taken in April. Application deadlines are open. Application fee is $10. The college accepts all applicants. Notification is sent on a rolling basis. There are early decision and early admissions plans.

Transfer: A total of 30 credits out of 127 to 132 must be completed at the college.

Visiting: There are regularly scheduled orientations for prospective students. There are guides for informal visits and visitors may sit in on classes. To arrange for a visit, contact the Admissions Office at (402) 293-3766.

Financial Aid: In a recent year, 88% of all current freshmen and 65% of continuing students received some form of financial aid. About 64% of freshmen and 58% of continuing students received need-based aid. The average freshman award was $4000. Of that total, scholarships or need-based grants averaged $1937 ($2400 maximum); loans averaged $1769 ($2625 maximum); and work contracts averaged $1340 ($1520 maximum). Three percent of undergraduate students work part-time. Average earnings from campus work for the school year are $1520. The average financial indebtedness of the 1992-93 graduate was $9100. the college is a member of CSS. The FAF is required. The deadline for financial aid applications is May 1.

International Students: There are currently 70 international students enrolled. The school actively recruits these students. They must take the TOEFL or the University of Michigan Language Test and achieve a minimum score on the TOEFL of 500.

Computers: The college provides computer facilities for student use. The mainframe is a Hewlett-Packard. There are 8 terminals and 25 microcomputers in the computer laboratory and computer classroom. Use is on a first-come, first-served basis. Students enrolled in classes where a computer fee is charged may use the system. There are no time limits on using the system.

Graduates: In 1992-93, 305 bachelor's degrees were awarded. The most popular majors among graduates were business and management, general (56%) and human resource management (20%).

Admissions Contact: Admissions Office.

BISHOP CLARKSON COLLEGE
(See Clarkson College)

CHADRON STATE COLLEGE
B-1
Chadron, NE 69337   (308) 432-6263; (800) 242-3766 (out-of-state)

Full-time: 763 men, 1012 women	Faculty: 92; IIB, av$
Part-time: 227 men, 369 women	Ph.D.s: 82%
Graduate: 330 men, 992 women	Student/Faculty: 19 to 1
Year: semesters, summer session	Tuition: $1575 ($2670)
Application Deadline: open	Room & Board: $2516
Freshman Class: n/av	
ACT: required	**NONCOMPETITIVE**

Chadron State College, founded in 1911, is a public, coeducational college offering programs in liberal arts and professional training. There are 4 undergraduate schools and one graduate school. In addition to regional accreditation, Chadron State has baccalaureate program accreditation with NCATE. The library contains 187,000 volumes, 220,000 microform items, and 12,000 audiovisual forms, and subscribes to 900 periodicals. Computerized library sources and services include the card catalog, interlibrary loans, and database searching. Special learning facilities include a planetarium. The 281-acre campus is in a small town 100 miles south of Rapid City, South Dakota. Including residence halls, there are 24 buildings on campus.

Student Life: About 80% of undergraduates are from Nebraska. Students come from 34 states, 8 foreign countries, and Canada. Ninety-six percent are white. The average age of freshmen is 19; all undergraduates, 30. Nineteen percent drop out by the end of their first year; 50% remain to graduate.

Housing: A total of 1200 students can be accommodated in college housing. College-sponsored living facilities include single-sex and coed dormitories and married-student housing. On-campus housing is guaranteed for all 4 years. Fifty-five percent of students commute. Alcohol is not permitted. All students may keep cars on campus.

Activities: There are no fraternities or sororities on campus. There are many groups and organizations on campus, including art, band, cheerleading, choir, ethnic, honors, international, jazz band, musical theater, newspaper, orchestra, pep band, photography, student government, symphony, and yearbook. Popular campus events include Homecoming and Spring Daze.

Sports: Athletic and recreation facilities include a 3000-seat stadium, a gymnasium, and an activity center.

Disabled Students: All of the campus is accessible to disabled students. The following facilities are available: wheelchair ramps, elevators, special parking, specially equipped rest rooms, special class scheduling, and lowered drinking fountains.

Services: In addition to many counseling and information services, tutoring is available in most subjects. In addition, there is a reader service for the blind, and remedial math, reading, and writing.

Campus Safety and Security: Campus safety and security measures include 24-hour foot and vehicle patrol, self-defense education, informal discussions, and pamphlets, posters, and films. In addition, there are emergency telephones and lighted pathways and sidewalks.

Programs of Study: Chadron State awards the B.A. and B.S. degrees. Associate and master's degrees also are awarded. Bachelor's degrees are awarded in BIOLOGICAL SCIENCE (biology/biological science), BUSINESS (accounting, business administration and management, business economics, and marketing/retailing/merchandising), COMMUNICATIONS AND THE ARTS (communications, dramatic arts, English, music, and speech/debate/rhetoric), COMPUTER AND PHYSICAL SCIENCE (chemistry, computer science, earth science, information sciences and systems, mathematics, and physics), EDUCATION (art, business, early childhood, elementary, health, home economics, middle school, music, science, secondary, and social science), ENGINEERING AND ENVIRONMENTAL DESIGN (industrial engineering technology and interior design), HEALTH PROFESSIONS (medical laboratory technology, predentistry, and premedicine), SOCIAL SCIENCE (criminal justice, history, home economics, political science/government, prelaw, psychology, social science, social work, and sociology). Education and business are the strongest academically. Education and business have the largest enrollments.

Required: For graduation, students must complete 125 credit hours and maintain a 2.0 GPA for the B.A. programs and a 2.5 GPA for the B.S. programs. Other requirements vary by major.

Special: The college offers internships, a Washington semester, and work-study programs. Dual majors and credit for life, military, and work experience are possible. There is a freshman honors program on campus, as well as one national honor society, Phi Beta Kappa.

Faculty/Classroom: Ninety percent of faculty are male; 10%, female. Graduate students teach 2% of introductory courses.

Requirements: The ACT is required unless the applicant has been out of high school for more than 5 years. Applicants need not be graduates of an accredited secondary school. The GED is accepted. High school work should include a minimum of 15 academic units, with at least 3 units in English, and others in mathematics, science, social studies, and foreign language. AP and CLEP credits are accepted. Important factors used in the admissions decision are parents or siblings attending the school, recommendations by alumni, recommendations by school officials, advanced placement or honor courses, and evidence of special talent.

Procedure: Freshmen are admitted to all sessions. Application deadlines are open. Application fee is $10. The college accepts all applicants. Notification is sent on a rolling basis. There are early decision, early admissions, and deferred admissions plans.

Transfer: About 170 transfer students enrolled in 1993-94. A maximum of 66 semester credits earned at an accredited 2-year college may be transferred. The registrar will evaluate credit earned at a 3-or 4-year college to determine the student's classification. All passing credit obtained from an institution is accepted in programs offered by the college. Transfers are admitted every term. A total of 30 credits out of 125 must be completed at Chadron State.

Visiting: There are regularly scheduled orientations for prospective students. There are guides for informal visits and visitors may sit in on classes and stay overnight at the school. To arrange for a visit, contact the Admissions Office at (308) 432-6263 or (800) 242-3766.

Financial Aid: In a recent year, 90% of all current freshmen and 80% of continuing students received some form of financial aid. About 90% of freshmen and 85% of continuing students received need-based aid. The average freshman award was $4200. Of that total, scholarships or need-based grants averaged $2100 ($2400 maximum); loans averaged $1100 ($2625 maximum); and work contracts averaged $1000 ($2200 maximum). Forty percent of undergraduate students work part-time. Average earnings from campus work for the school year are $1100. The average financial indebtedness of the 1992-93 graduate was $8350. The AFSA financial statement is required. The deadline for financial aid applications is July 1.

International Students: There are currently 17 international students enrolled. They must take the TOEFL and achieve a minimum score of 550. The student must also take the ACT.

Computers: The college provides computer facilities for student use. The mainframe is a DEC VAX 8350. Microcomputers are also available on campus. All students may access the system. It may be used 7:30 A.M. to 10:30 P.M. There are no time limits on using the system and no fees.

Graduates: In 1992-93, 286 bachelor's degrees were awarded.

Admissions Contact: Dale Williamson, Admissions Office.

CLARKSON COLLEGE

F-3

(Formerly Bishop Clarkson College)
Omaha, NE 68131   (402) 552-3041; (800) 647-5500 (in-state)

Full-time: 21 men, 146 women	Faculty: 43
Part-time: 30 men, 326 women	Ph.D.s: 36%
Graduate: 9 men, 52 women	Student/Faculty: 4 to 1
Year: semesters, summer session	Tuition: $5832
Application Deadline: May 1	Room & Board: $1750
Freshman Class: 451 applied, 288 accepted, 175 enrolled	
ACT: 19	COMPETITIVE

Clarkson College, established in 1888, is affiliated with the Episcopal Church and offers undergraduate and graduate degrees in the health care professions. There are 3 undergraduate and 2 graduate schools. In addition to regional accreditation, Clarkson has baccalaureate program accreditation with NLN. The library contains 7512 volumes, 115 microform items, and 560 audiovisual forms, and subscribes to 253 periodicals. Computerized library sources and services include the card catalog, interlibrary loans, and database searching. Special learning facilities include a learning resource center, an art gallery, and a regional medical center. The 29-acre campus is in an urban area in Omaha. Including residence halls, there are 13 buildings on campus.

Student Life: About 88% of undergraduates are from Nebraska. Students come from 10 states, 2 foreign countries, and Canada. Ninety percent are from public schools; 10% from private. Eighty-eight percent are white. Fifty percent are Catholic; 45% Protestant. The average age of freshmen is 23; all undergraduates, 29. Ten percent drop out by the end of their first year; 87% remain to graduate.

Housing: A total of 60 students can be accommodated in college housing. College-sponsored living facilities include coed on-campus apartments. On-campus housing is available on a first-come, first-served basis. Priority is given to out-of-town students. Ninety percent of students commute. Alcohol is not permitted. All students may keep cars on campus.

Activities: There is 1 national sororities. There are no fraternities on campus. There are 4 groups on campus, including chorus, professional, social, and student government. Popular campus events include dances and parties on Halloween and Christmas.

Sports: There is no sports program at Clarkson. Athletic and recreation facilities include facilities at the adjacent University of Nebraska Medical Center (basketball and volleyball courts, exercise equipment, and a weight room).

Disabled Students: Ninety-five percent of the campus is accessible to disabled students. The following facilities are available: wheelchair ramps, elevators, special parking, specially equipped rest rooms, special class scheduling, lowered drinking fountains, and lowered telephones.

Services: In addition to many counseling and information services, tutoring is available in most subjects.

Campus Safety and Security: Campus safety and security measures include 24-hour foot and vehicle patrol, self-defense education, escort service, and informal discussions. In addition, there are pamphlets, posters, and films, emergency telephones, and lighted pathways and sidewalks.

Programs of Study: Clarkson awards the B.S. and B.S.N. degrees. Associate and master's degrees also are awarded. Bachelor's degrees are awarded in COMPUTER AND PHYSICAL SCIENCE (radiological technology), HEALTH PROFESSIONS (nursing and radiograph medical technology). Radiological technology and nursing are the strongest academically. Nursing has the largest enrollment.

Required: For graduation, students must complete 128 credit hours, 68 to 74 of which are in the major, and maintain a minimum GPA of 2.0. General education requirements include courses in the humanities, English, behavioral and social sciences, science and mathematics, and physical education.

Special: A co-op program is available in nursing. Study abroad in England is possible. Credit is given for military experience, and nondegree study is possible. The distance education option allows students living a distance from the campus to complete their studies at home. Work-study programs are available. There is one national honor society on campus.

Faculty/Classroom: Twenty-one percent of faculty are male; 79%, female. All teach undergraduates. The average class size in an introductory lecture is 45; in a laboratory, 20; and in a regular course offering, 35.

Admissions: About 64% of the 1993-94 applicants were accepted. The ACT scores for the 1993-94 freshman class were as follows: 66% below 21, 22% between 21 and 23, 11% between 24 and 26, and 1% above 28. About 10% of the current freshmen were in the top fifth of their class; 23% were in the top two fifths. Three freshmen graduated first in their class.

Requirements: Clarkson requires applicants to be in the upper 50% of their class. A minimum GPA of 2.5 is required. The ACT or SAT I is required, and a minimum composite ACT score of 19 is required. The ACT is not required for applicants more than 2 years out of high school. Applicants must be graduates of an accredited secondary school. The GED is accepted. AP and CLEP credits are accepted. Important factors used in the admissions decision are advanced placement or honor courses, extracurricular activities record, evidence of special talent, leadership record, and recommendations by school officials.

Procedure: Freshmen are admitted to all sessions. Entrance exams should be taken during the junior year or first semester of the senior year. Early decision applications should be filed by March 1; regular applications, by May 1 for fall entry and November 1 for spring entry, along with an application fee of $15. Notification of early decision is sent April 1; regular decision, June 1. There is a deferred admissions plan. A waiting list is an active part of the admissions procedure, with about 5% of applicants on the list.

Transfer: About 165 transfer students enrolled in 1993-94. Transfer students must have a minimum GPA of 2.5. Grades of C or better transfer for credit. Transfers are admitted for fall and spring. An interview is sometimes required. A total of 64 credits out of 128 must be completed at Clarkson.

Visiting: There are regularly scheduled orientations for prospective students. There are guides for informal visits and visitors may sit in on classes. To arrange for a visit, contact the Admissions Office at (800) 647-5500 (in-state) or (402) 552-3041.

Financial Aid: In a recent year, 46% of all current freshmen and 52% of continuing students received some form of financial aid. About 38% of freshmen and 34% of continuing students received need-based aid. The average freshman award was $3300. Ninety-one percent of undergraduate students work part-time. Average earnings from campus work for the school year are $1200. The average financial indebtedness of the 1992-93 graduate was $8000. Clarkson is a member of CSS. The college's own financial statement and the FAFSA are required. The deadline for financial aid applications is May 30.

International Students: There are currently 4 international students enrolled. They must take the TOEFL or the University of Michigan Language Test and achieve a minimum score on the TOEFL of 600.

Computers: The college provides computer facilities for student use. The mainframe is a DEC VAX 4400. There are microcomputers, including Apple Macintosh systems, available for student use, as well as 20 IBM and MAC PCs and 10 mainframe terminals in special laboratories for their instruction and use. All students may access the system. It may be used 7 A.M. to 8:30 P.M. There are no time limits on using the system and no fees.

Graduates: In a recent year, 61 bachelor's degrees were awarded. The most popular majors among graduates were nursing (92%) and radiography (8%). Within an average freshman class, 50% graduate in 4 years, 45% in 5 years, and 5% in 6 years. In the 1992 graduating class, all of the graduates had found employment within 6 months of graduation.

Admissions Contact: Dr. D. L. Taylor, Director of Enrollment Management.

COLLEGE OF SAINT MARY

F-2

Omaha, NE 68124   (402) 399-2407; (800) 926-5534 (in-state)

Full-time: 13 men, 485 women	Faculty: 44; IIB, --$
Part-time: 61 men, 609 women	Ph.D.s: 25%
Graduate: none	Student/Faculty: 11 to 1
Year: 4-1-4, summer session	Tuition: $9000
Application Deadline: August 22	Room & Board: $3500
Freshman Class: 370 applied, 302 accepted, 121 enrolled	
ACT: 21	COMPETITIVE

College of Saint Mary, founded in 1923, is a Roman Catholic women's college, offering a program of professional training with a liberal arts component. In addition to regional accreditation, College of Saint Mary has baccalaureate program accreditation with NLN. The library contains 71,000 volumes, 250 microform items, and 5000 audiovisual forms, and subscribes to 490 periodicals. Computerized library sources and services include the card catalog, interlibrary loans, and database searching. Special learning facilities include a learning resource center and an art gallery. The 25-acre campus is in a suburban area 5 miles west of downtown Omaha. Including residence halls, there are 8 buildings on campus.

Student Life: About 88% of undergraduates are from Nebraska. Students come from 12 states. Eighty-three percent are from public schools; 17% private. Ninety-four percent are white. Most are Catholic. The average age of freshmen is 29; all undergraduates, 30. Thirty percent drop out by the end of their first year; 39% remain to graduate.

Housing: A total of 250 students can be accommodated in college housing. College-sponsored living facilities include single-sex dormitories. On-campus housing is guaranteed for all 4 years. Eighty-six percent of students commute. Alcohol is not permitted. All students may keep cars on campus.

Activities: There are no fraternities on campus. There are 12 groups on campus, including choir, computers, honors, newspaper, professional, religious, social, social service, student government, and yearbook. Popular campus events include Fine Arts Festival, Spirit Day, Founders Day, Queen of Hearts Dance, Spring Fling, and Women's History Month Celebration.

Sports: Athletic and recreation facilities include Marian Hall, a gymnasium, and an auditorium.

Disabled Students: Eighty-five percent of the campus is accessible to disabled students. The following facilities are available: wheelchair ramps, elevators, special parking, specially equipped rest rooms, special class scheduling, lowered drinking fountains, lowered telephones, and electric door openers.

Services: In addition to many counseling and information services, tutoring is available in most subjects. In addition, there is a reader service for the blind, and remedial math, reading, and writing.

Campus Safety and Security: Campus safety and security measures include 24-hour foot and vehicle patrol, self-defense education, escort service, and informal discussions. In addition, there are pamphlets, posters, and films, emergency telephones, lighted pathways and sidewalks, and camera-monitored entrances to dormitories.

Programs of Study: College of Saint Mary awards the B.A., B.S., and B.S.N. degrees. Associate degrees also are awarded. Bachelor's degrees are awarded in BIOLOGICAL SCIENCE (biology/biological science), BUSINESS (accounting, business administration and management, and human resources), COMMUNICATIONS AND THE ARTS (art, communications, English, and languages), COMPUTER AND PHYSICAL SCIENCE (chemistry, computer management, mathematics, and natural sciences), EDUCATION (early childhood, education, and special), ENGINEERING AND ENVIRONMENTAL DESIGN (computer graphics), HEALTH PROFESSIONS (medical laboratory technology, medical records administration/services, nursing, occupational therapy, physical therapy, predentistry, premedicine, and preveterinary science), SOCIAL SCIENCE (history, human services, humanities, liberal arts/general studies, paralegal studies, prelaw, and social science). Preprofessional studies is the strongest academically. Nursing has the largest enrollment.

Required: To graduate, students must complete 128 semester hours, with a minimum of 30 hours in the major and a 2.0 GPA in the major and overall. Required general education courses total 47 hours. Students must demonstrate competency in mathematics and English.

Special: The college offers some dual majors, credit for life, military, and work experience, nondegree study, and pass/fail options.

Faculty/Classroom: Twenty-one percent of faculty are male; 79%, female. All teach undergraduates. The average class size in an introductory lecture is 35 and in a regular course offering, 10.

Admissions: About 82% of the 1993–94 applicants were accepted. The ACT scores for the 1993–94 freshman class were as follows: 61% below 21, 20% between 21 and 23, 12% between 24 and 26, 6% between 27 and 28, and 1% above 28. About 33% of the current freshmen were in the top fifth of their class; 60% were in the top two fifths. Twelve freshmen graduated first in their class and 16% graduated in the top 10% of their class.

Requirements: College of Saint Mary requires applicants to be in the upper 50% of their class. A minimum GPA of 2.0 is required. The SAT I or ACT is required. Students must meet 2 out of 3 criteria: a minimum composite score of 19 on the ACT, a GPA of at least 2.0, and/or rank in the upper 50% of their class. Applicants must be graduates of an accredited secondary school. The GED is accepted. An interview is recommended. AP and CLEP credits are accepted.

Procedure: Freshmen are admitted to all sessions. Entrance exams should be taken in the junior or senior year. Applications should be filed by August 22 for fall entry and January 16 for spring entry, along with an application fee of $20. Notification is sent on a rolling basis. There is a deferred admissions plan.

Transfer: About 110 transfer students enrolled in 1993–94. Transfer applicants should have a minimum GPA of 2.0; grades of C or better transfer for credit. Students are admitted every term. A total of 30 credits out of 128 must be completed at College of Saint Mary.

Visiting: There are regularly scheduled orientations for prospective students, including touring the campus, attending financial aid and student-life presentations, and sitting in on classes of a student's choice. Visitors are College of St. Mary's guests for lunch or overnight. There are guides for informal visits and visitors may sit in on classes. To arrange for a visit, contact Sheila Haggas, Director of Enrollment Services at (402) 399-2407.

Financial Aid: In 1993–94, 95% of all current freshmen and 58% of continuing students received some form of financial aid. About 72% of freshmen and 42% of continuing students received need-based aid. The average freshman award was $8444. Of that total,

scholarships or need-based grants averaged $5432; loans averaged $3714; and work contracts averaged $1100. Twenty-six percent of undergraduate students work part-time. Average earnings from campus work for the school year are $1100. The average financial indebtedness of the 1992–93 graduate was $9608. College of Saint Mary is a member of CSS. The FAF, FFS, SFS, or the college's own financial statement and the FAFSA is required. The deadline for financial aid applications is April 1.

International Students: They must take the TOEFL and achieve a minimum score of 550.

Computers: The mainframe is an IBM AS/400. A Novell network and about 50 stand-alone microcomputers are available to students. Students in computer classes may access the system. It may be used 8 A.M. to 10 P.M., Sunday to Thursday and 8 A.M. to 5 P.M., Friday and Saturday. There are no time limits on using the system and no fees.

Graduates: In 1992–93, 250 bachelor's degrees were awarded. Some 28 companies recruited on campus in 1992–93. In the 1992 graduating class, 3% of the women were enrolled in graduate school within 6 months of graduation; 83% of the women had found employment.

Admissions Contact: Sheila Haggas, Director, Enrollment Services.

CONCORDIA COLLEGE E-3

Seward, NE 68434 (402) 643-7233; (800) 535-5494 (out-of-state)

Full-time: 358 men, 459 women	Faculty: 69; IIB, --$
Part-time: 10 men, 30 women	Ph.D.s: 60%
Graduate: 24 men, 35 women	Student/Faculty: 12 to 1
Year: 4-1-4, summer session	Tuition: $8506
Application Deadline: August 1	Room & Board: $3270

Freshman Class: 452 applied, 448 accepted, 237 enrolled
ACT: 23 **NONCOMPETITIVE**

Concordia College, founded in 1894, is a private, coeducational college owned and operated by the Lutheran Church-Missouri Synod, with degree programs in professional education and liberal arts. Among Concordia's major programs are those for professional work in the Lutheran Church: teacher education, director of Christian education, preseminary pastoral training, and church music. In addition to regional accreditation, Concordia has baccalaureate program accreditation with NCATE. The 3 libraries contain 156,135 volumes, 4000 microform items, and 12,000 audiovisual forms, and subscribe to 600 periodicals. Special learning facilities include a learning resource center, an art gallery, a natural history museum, a radio station, and an observatory. The 120-acre campus is in a small town 25 miles west of Lincoln. Including residence halls, there are 25 buildings on campus.

Student Life: About 64% of undergraduates are from out-of-state, mostly the Midwest. Students come from 37 states, 6 foreign countries, and Canada. Ninety-five percent are white. Most are Protestant. The average age of freshmen is 18; all undergraduates, 21. About 66% of freshmen remain to graduate.

Housing: A total of 748 students can be accommodated in college housing. College-sponsored living facilities include single-sex dormitories, off-campus apartments, and married-student housing. On-campus housing is guaranteed for all 4 years. Ninety-five percent of students live on campus; of those, 90% remain on campus on weekends. Alcohol is not permitted. All students may keep cars on campus.

Activities: There are no fraternities or sororities on campus. There are 35 groups on campus, including band, cheerleading, choir, chorale, chorus, computers, drama, drill team, ethnic, honors, international, jazz band, literary magazine, newspaper, orchestra, pep band, photography, professional, radio and TV, religious, social, social service, student government, and yearbook. Popular campus events include Fall Fest and Spring Weekend.

Sports: There are 8 intercollegiate sports for men and 7 for women, and 14 intramural sports for men and 14 for women. Athletic and recreation facilities include a weight-training room; an indoor pool; football, baseball, and soccer fields; and a gymnasium.

Disabled Students: Fifty percent of the campus is accessible to disabled students. The following facilities are available: wheelchair ramps, elevators, special parking, specially equipped rest rooms, lowered drinking fountains, and lowered telephones.

Services: In addition to many counseling and information services, tutoring is available in every subject. In addition, there is a reader service for the blind, and remedial math, reading, and writing.

Campus Safety and Security: Campus safety and security measures include 24-hour foot and vehicle patrol, self-defense education, escort service, and informal discussions. In addition, there are pamphlets, posters, and films and lighted pathways and sidewalks.

Programs of Study: Concordia awards the B.A., B.S., B.F.A., B.S. Med. Tech., and B.Mus. degrees. Master's degrees are also awarded. Bachelor's degrees are awarded in BIOLOGICAL SCIENCE (biology/biological science), BUSINESS (accounting, business ad-

ministration and management, and sports management), COMMUNI-
CATIONS AND THE ARTS (art, communications, dramatic arts, English, fine arts, music, and speech), COMPUTER AND PHYSICAL
SCIENCE (chemistry, computer science, mathematics, natural sciences, and physical sciences), EDUCATION (business, Christian Education, early childhood, elementary, home economics, industrial arts,
middle school, music, physical, science, secondary, and special),
HEALTH PROFESSIONS (health, medical laboratory technology, predentistry, and premedicine), SOCIAL SCIENCE (behavioral science,
geography, history, physical fitness/movement, prelaw, psychology,
and theological studies). Education, business, art, and music are the
strongest academically. Education has the largest enrollment.

Required: To graduate, students must complete a minimum of 128
credits with a GPA of at least 2.0. Required general education
courses include 11 or 12 hours of theology, 9 hours each of English/
speech, social science, and science, 6 of fine arts, 3 each of mathematics and health and physical education, and 1 hour minimum of
computer literacy.

Special: The college offers co-op programs with the University of Nebraska in Lincoln for all majors. Internships are available in education, business, and director of Christian education, B.A.-B.S. degrees,
student-designed majors, dual majors, study in England, nondegree
studies, and pass/fail options are available. There is a freshman honors program on campus. Three departments have honors programs.

Faculty/Classroom: Seventy percent of faculty are male; 30%, female. All teach undergraduates. Graduate students teach 1% of introductory courses. The average class size in an introductory lecture is
20; in a laboratory, 15; and in a regular course offering, 15.

Admissions: About 99% of the 1993-94 applicants were accepted.
There were 3 National Merit finalists. Eight freshmen graduated first
in their class.

Requirements: A minimum GPA of 2.0 is required. The SAT I or
ACT is required. A minimum composite score of 18 is recommended
for the ACT. Applicants need not be graduates of an accredited secondary school. The GED is accepted. The school strongly encourages
high school courses in art, English, foreign language, history, mathematics, music, physical education, science, and social studies. An interview is recommended. AP and CLEP credits are accepted. Important factors used in the admissions decision are recommendations by
school officials, recommendations by alumni, personality, intangible
qualities, evidence of special talent, and leadership record.

Procedure: Freshmen are admitted to all sessions. Entrance exams
should be taken in the junior or senior year. Applications should be
filed by August 1 for fall entry and January 1 for spring entry, along
with an application fee of $25. Notification is sent on a rolling basis.

Transfer: About 40 transfer students enrolled in 1993-94. Applicants for transfer should have a minimum GPA of 2.0 and a minimum
ACT score of 18. An interview is recommended. Passing grades
transfer for credit. Transfers are admitted every term. A total of 30
credits out of 128 must be completed at Concordia.

Visiting: There are regularly scheduled orientations for prospective
students, including a campus tour, sitting in on classes, visits with
professors/coaches, and an admission interview. There are guides for
informal visits and visitors may sit in on classes and stay overnight at
the school. To arrange for a visit, contact the Office of Admission at
(800) 535-5494.

Financial Aid: In 1993-94, 100% of all current freshmen and 100%
of continuing students received some form of financial aid. About
97% of freshmen and 92% of continuing students received need-
based aid. The average freshman award was $8233. Of that total,
scholarships or need-based grants averaged $4608 ($8506 maximum); loans averaged $3125 ($3625 maximum); and work contracts
averaged $500 ($1000 maximum). Eighty-five percent of undergraduate students work part-time. Average earnings from campus work for
the school year are $500. The average financial indebtedness of the
1992-93 graduate was $8000. The FAFSA financial statement is re-
quired.

International Students: There are currently 9 international students
enrolled. The school actively recruits these students. They must take
the TOEFL and achieve a minimum score of 550.

Computers: The college provides computer facilities for student use.
The mainframe is a DEC VAX 3500. More than 40 microcomputers/
terminals are available across campus. All students may access the
system. There are no time limits on using the system and no fees.

Graduates: In 1992-93, 166 bachelor's degrees were awarded. The
most popular majors among graduates were teacher education
(55%), mathematics (5%), and art (5%). Within an average freshman
class, 66% graduate in 5 years. Some 600 companies recruited on
campus in 1992-93.

Admissions Contact: Office of Admission.

CREIGHTON UNIVERSITY F-3
Omaha, NE 68178 (402) 280-2703

Full-time: 1429 men, 2021 women	**Faculty:** 225; IIA, -$
Part-time: 179 men, 465 women	**Ph.D.s:** 88%
Graduate: 1364 men, 883 women	**Student/Faculty:** 15 to 1
Year: semesters, summer session	**Tuition:** $10,252
Application Deadline: August 1	**Room & Board:** $4180
Freshman Class: 2967 applied, 2836 accepted, 876 enrolled	
ACT: 25	**VERY COMPETITIVE**

Creighton University, established in 1878, is a private Catholic coeducational institution, conducted by the Jesuits and offering undergraduate programs in arts and sciences, business, and nursing. There are
4 undergraduate and 5 graduate schools. In addition to regional accreditation, Creighton has baccalaureate program accreditation with
AACSB, ACPE, NCATE, and NLN. The 3 libraries contain 713,250
volumes, 287,561 microform items, and 17,517 audiovisual forms,
and subscribe to 9859 periodicals. Computerized library sources and
services include the card catalog, interlibrary loans, and database
searching. Special learning facilities include a learning resource center, art gallery, planetarium, radio station, and TV station. The 78-acre
campus is in an urban area northwest of downtown Omaha. Including residence halls, there are 46 buildings on campus.

Student Life: About 53% of undergraduates are from out-of-state,
mostly the Midwest. Students come from 47 states, 49 foreign countries, and Canada. Sixty percent are from public schools; 40% from
private. Eighty-five percent are white. Fifty-four percent are Catholic;
21% Protestant; 20% claim no religious affiliation. The average age of
freshmen is 18; all undergraduates, 20. Seventeen percent drop out
by the end of their first year; 67% remain to graduate.

Housing: A total of 1860 students can be accommodated in college
housing. College-sponsored living facilities include single-sex and
coed dormitories, on-campus apartments, and married-student housing. In addition there are special interest houses and Creighton
House combines independent study projects with community living
and a special interdisciplinary seminar. On-campus housing is guaranteed for all 4 years. Sixty percent of students commute. Alcohol is
not permitted. All students may keep cars on campus.

Activities: About 33% of men belong to 7 national fraternities; about
30% of women belong to 6 national sororities. There are 100 groups
on campus, including art, band, cheerleading, chess, choir, chorale,
chorus, computers, dance, drama, drill team, ethnic, film, honors, international, literary magazine, musical theater, newspaper, pep band,
photography, political, professional, radio and TV, religious, social,
social service, student government, and yearbook. Popular campus
events include Parent Weekend, Comedy Club, Homecoming, Noon
Music Series, concerts, and lectures.

Sports: There are 6 intercollegiate sports for men and 7 for women,
and 20 intramural sports for men and 20 for women. Athletic and recreation facilities include a sports complex, an outdoor artificial turf
area with baseball, softball, and soccer fields, a natural grass intercollegiate soccer facility, and a physical fitness center with courts for basketball, volleyball, badminton, or gymnastics, a pool, a weight room,
and a jogging track; another center offers practice courts and training
rooms for all intercollegiate sports.

Disabled Students: Eighty percent of the campus is accessible to
disabled students. The following facilities are available: wheelchair
ramps, elevators, special parking, specially equipped rest rooms, special class scheduling, lowered drinking fountains, and lowered telephones.

Services: In addition to many counseling and information services,
tutoring is available in most subjects. There is a reader service for the
blind, and remedial math, reading, and writing.

Campus Safety and Security: Campus safety and security measures include 24-hour foot and vehicle patrol, self defense education,
escort service, and shuttle buses. In addition, there are informal discussions, pamphlets, posters, and films, emergency telephones, and
lighted pathways and sidewalks.

Programs of Study: Creighton awards the B.A., B.S., B.F.A.,
B.S.Arts, B.S.B.A., B.S.Chem., B.S.M.T., B.S.N., B.S.O.T., B.S.Ph.,
B.S.Soc., and B.S.W. degrees. Master's and doctoral degrees also are
awarded. Bachelor's degrees are awarded in BIOLOGICAL SCI-
ENCE (biology/biological science), BUSINESS (accounting, banking
and finance, business administration and management, business economics, management information systems, marketing/retailing/
merchandising, and personnel management), COMMUNICATIONS
AND THE ARTS (communications, dramatic arts, English, fine arts,
French, German, Greek, journalism, languages, Latin, and Spanish),
COMPUTER AND PHYSICAL SCIENCE (atmospheric sciences and
meteorology, chemistry, computer science, mathematics, physics, and
statistics), EDUCATION (elementary, secondary, and special),
HEALTH PROFESSIONS (nursing, occupational therapy, pharmacy,
physical therapy, predentistry, and premedicine), SOCIAL SCIENCE
(American studies, classical/ancient civilization, economics, history,

philosophy, political science/government, prelaw, psychology, religion, social work, and sociology). Biology, psychology, nursing, and finance have the largest enrollments.

Required: For graduation, students must complete a minimum of 128 credit hours and maintain a GPA of 2.0. Each school has general education requirements.

Special: The school offers preengineering co-op programs with the University of Detroit, and Washington University in St. Louis, study abroad in London, Cork, Tokyo, and Rome, a Washington semester, internships, and work-study programs. Nursing students may take an accelerated degree program, and B.A.-B.S. degrees are possible. Dual majors, nondegree study, pass/fail options, and credit for life, military, and work experience are available. There is a freshman honors program on campus, as well as 13 national honor societies. One department has an honors program.

Faculty/Classroom: Sixty-eight percent of faculty are male; 32%, female. No introductory courses are taught by graduate students. The average class size in an introductory lecture is 29; in a laboratory, 22; and in a regular course offering, 25.

Admissions: About 96% of the 1993–94 applicants were accepted. The ACT scores for the 1993–94 freshman class were as follows: 14% below 21, 25% between 21 and 23, 30% between 24 and 26, 15% between 27 and 28, and 16% above 28. About 47% of the current freshmen were in the top fifth of their class, 68% were in the top two fifths, and 5% graduated first in their class.

Requirements: Creighton requires applicants to be in the upper 50% of their class. A minimum GPA of 2.5 is required. The SAT I or ACT is required. In addition, applicants must be graduates of an accredited secondary school. The GED is accepted. Students should have completed 16 credits, including 4 credits in English, 3 each in mathematics and electives, and 2 each in foreign language, science, and social studies. AP and CLEP credits are accepted. Important factors used in the admissions decision are recommendations by school officials, advanced placement or honor courses, leadership record, extracurricular activities record, and evidence of special talent.

Procedure: Freshmen are admitted to all sessions. Entrance exams should be taken prior to May 1 of the senior year. Applications should be filed by August 1 for fall entry and December 15 for spring entry, along with an application fee of $30. Notification is sent on a rolling basis.

Transfer: About 117 transfer students enrolled in 1993–94. Applicants for transfer must have a 2.0 GPA in a regionally accredited school. Minimum scores of 18 on the ACT or 800 on the SAT I are recommended. Grades of C or better transfer for credit. Transfers are admitted every term. A total of 48 credits out of 128 must be completed at Creighton.

Visiting: There are regularly scheduled orientations for prospective students. There are guides for informal visits and visitors may sit in on classes and stay overnight at the school. To arrange for a visit, contact the Admissions Office at (402) 280–2703.

Financial Aid: In 1993–94 86% of all current freshmen and 87% of continuing students received some form of financial aid. About 59% of freshmen and 57% of continuing students received need-based aid. The average freshman award was $8913. Of that total, scholarships or need-based grants averaged $3633 ($14,432 maximum); loans averaged $4601 ($4625 maximum); and work contracts averaged $1435 ($1500 maximum). Seventy-five percent of undergraduate students work part-time. Average earnings from campus work for the school year are $1500. The average financial indebtedness of the 1992–93 graduate was $14,617. Creighton is a member of CSS. The college's own financial statement and FAFSA are required. The deadline for financial aid applications is April 1.

International Students: There are currently 238 international students enrolled. The school actively recruits these students. They must take the TOEFL and achieve a minimum score of 500.

Computers: The college provides computer facilities for student use. The mainframe is a Unisys 220/400. There are also 250 Apple Macintosh and AT&T microcomputers available throughout the campus and in computer laboratories. All students may access the system. It may be used during computer center hours. There are no time limits on using the system and no fees.

Graduates: In 1992–93 859 bachelor's degrees were awarded. The most popular majors among graduates were psychology (9%), finance (9%), and biology (8%). Within an average freshman class, 2% graduate in 3 years, 54% in 4 years, 8% in 5 years, and 3% in 6 years. Some 102 companies recruited on campus in 1992–93. In a recent graduating class, 37% of the men and 32% of the women were enrolled in graduate school within 6 months of graduation; 62% of the men and 67% of the women had found employment.

Admissions Contact: Howard J. Bachman, Assistant Vice President.

DANA COLLEGE
Blair, NE 68008–1099

F-2
(402) 426–7222
(800) 444–3262 (out-of-state)

Full-time: 252 men, 298 women	Faculty: 37; IIB, --$
Part-time: 22 men, 44 women	Ph.D.s: 45%
Graduate: none	Student/Faculty: 15 to 1
Year: 4-1-4, summer session	Tuition: $8780
Application Deadline: open	Room & Board: $3130
Freshman Class: 504 applied, 482 accepted, 185 enrolled	
ACT: 23	COMPETITIVE

Dana College, established in 1884, is a private coeducational college affiliated with the Evangelical Lutheran Church in America. In addition to regional accreditation, the college has baccalaureate program accreditation with CSWE and NCATE. The library contains 146,000 volumes, 369 microform items, and 3050 audiovisual forms, and subscribes to 569 periodicals. Computerized library sources and services include interlibrary loans and database searching. Special learning facilities include a learning resource center, art gallery, radio station, tv station, and a theater. The 150-acre campus is in a small town 20 miles north of Omaha. Including residence halls, there are 17 buildings on campus.

Student Life: About 52% of undergraduates are from Nebraska. Students come from 26 states, 13 foreign countries, and Canada. Eighty-nine percent are white. Sixty-nine percent are Protestant; 24% Catholic. The average age of freshmen is 17.5; all undergraduates, 21. Thirty-six percent drop out by the end of their first year; 44% remain to graduate.

Housing: A total of 636 students can be accommodated in college housing. College-sponsored living facilities include single-sex and coed dormitories, on-campus apartments, and married-student housing. In addition there is a residence hall for upperclassmen. On-campus housing is guaranteed for all 4 years. Seventy percent of students live on campus; of those, 60% remain on campus on weekends. Alcohol is not permitted. All students may keep cars on campus.

Activities: There are no fraternities or sororities on campus. There are 34 groups on campus, including art, band, cheerleading, choir, chorale, chorus, dance, drama, drill team, ethnic, honors, international, jazz band, literary magazine, musical theater, newspaper, orchestra, pep band, photography, professional, radio and TV, religious, social, social service, student government, and yearbook. Popular campus events include Sights and Sounds of Christmas, Springfest, Jazzfest, and the Staley Foundation Distinguished Scholar Lecture Series.

Sports: There are 8 intercollegiate sports for men and 7 for women, and 14 intramural sports for men and 14 for women. Athletic and recreation facilities include fields for soccer, cross country, football/track, softball, and baseball, and a coliseum for basketball, swimming, tennis, racquetball, volleyball, wrestling, and weight training.

Disabled Students: Twenty-five percent of the campus is accessible to disabled students. The following facilities are available: wheelchair ramps, elevators, special parking, specially equipped rest rooms, special class scheduling, lowered drinking fountains, and lowered telephones.

Services: In addition to many counseling and information services, tutoring is available in most subjects. There is a reader service for the blind, and remedial math, reading, and writing.

Campus Safety and Security: Campus safety and security measures include escort service, informal discussions, pamphlets, posters, and films, and emergency telephones. In addition, there are lighted pathways and sidewalks a 12-hour and overnight foot patrol.

Programs of Study: The college awards the B.A. degree. Bachelor's degrees are awarded in BIOLOGICAL SCIENCE (biology/biological science), BUSINESS (accounting, banking and finance, business administration and management, and marketing/retailing/merchandising), COMMUNICATIONS AND THE ARTS (art, broadcasting, communications, dramatic arts, English, fine arts, German, graphic design, languages, music, Spanish, and speech/debate/rhetoric), COMPUTER AND PHYSICAL SCIENCE (chemistry, computer mathematics, information sciences and systems, mathematics, and science), EDUCATION (art, business, elementary, foreign languages, music, physical, science, secondary, and special), ENGINEERING AND ENVIRONMENTAL DESIGN (environmental science), HEALTH PROFESSIONS (chiropractic, health care administration, medical laboratory technology, medical science, occupational therapy, physician's assistant, predentistry, premedicine, prepharmacy, preveterinary science, and radiological science), SOCIAL SCIENCE (economics, history, humanities, liberal arts/general studies, ministries, prelaw, psychology, religion, social science, social work, and sociology). Social work, education, business, fine arts, biology, and communication are the strongest academically. Business and education have the largest enrollments.

Required: To graduate, students must complete 128 credit hours with a minimum of 30 credits in the major and a minimum GPA of 2.0. Other requirements include demonstrated competency in verbal and written communication skills, 15 core hours in liberal arts, and 18 distributive hours in 3 of 4 areas of study: human culture, human scientific inquiry, human development and organizations, and human aesthetic expression.

Special: The college offers a co-op program in ROTC with Creighton University, internships in most majors, study abroad, and work-study programs. Dual majors in mathematics/computer science, organizational communication, international communication, and speech communication and theater, a general studies degree, credit for life, military, and work experience, nondegree study, and pass/fail options are available. The Weekend College is designed primarily for working adults. There are 3 national honor societies on campus, including Phi Beta Kappa. One department has an honors program.

Faculty/Classroom: Seventy-three percent of faculty are male; 27%, female. All teach undergraduates. The average class size in an introductory lecture is 25; in a laboratory, 15; and in a regular course offering, 15.

Admissions: About 96% of the 1993–94 applicants were accepted. The ACT scores for the 1993–94 freshman class were as follows: 43% below 21, 27% between 21 and 23, 21% between 24 and 26, 6% between 27 and 28, and 3% above 28. About 25% of the current freshmen were in the top fifth of their class; 55% were in the top two fifths. There were 2 National Merit semifinalists. One freshman graduated first in her/his class.

Requirements: The college requires applicants to be in the upper 50% of their class. A minimum GPA of 2.0 is required. The ACT is preferred but the SAT I is accepted. The school recommends that students have a minimum composite score of 19 on the ACT, or 770 on the SAT I. Applicants must be graduates of an accredited secondary school. The GED is accepted. The school suggests that prospective students take college preparatory courses, including 2 years of a foreign language. An interview is recommended. AP and CLEP credits are accepted. Important factors used in the admissions decision are advanced placement or honor courses, recommendations by school officials, leadership record, personality, intangible qualities, and extracurricular activities record.

Procedure: Freshmen are admitted to all sessions. Entrance exams should be taken in the spring of the junior year or the fall of the senior year. Application deadlines are open. Notification is sent on a rolling basis. The application fee is $15. There is an early admissions plan.

Transfer: Forty-four transfer students enrolled in 1993–94. Transfer applicants must have a minimum GPA of 2.0. Grades of C or better transfer for credit. Transfer applicants with less than a 2.0 college GPA will be evaluated for acceptance based on high school performance and an interview with the admissions committee. Students are admitted every term. A total of 30 credits out of 128 must be completed at the college.

Visiting: There are regularly scheduled orientations for prospective students, including appointments with faculty, coaches, and activity directors, a campus tour, a financial aid session, an admission session, and lunch. Overnight lodging is available at no charge. There are guides for informal visits and visitors may sit in on classes. To arrange for a visit, contact the Admissions Office at (800) 444–3262 or (402) 426–7222.

Financial Aid: In 1993–94, 97% of all current freshmen and 97% of continuing students received some form of financial aid. About 78% of freshmen and 78% of continuing students received need-based aid. The average freshman award was $8500. Of that total, scholarships or need-based grants averaged $6450 ($10,600 maximum); loans averaged $3300 ($4625 maximum); and work contracts averaged $800 ($1500 maximum). Forty percent of undergraduate students work part-time. Average earnings from campus work for the school year are $750. The average financial indebtedness of the 1992–93 graduate was $11,500. The college is a member of CSS. The college's own financial statement and the FAFSA are required. The deadline for financial aid applications is April 1.

International Students: There are currently 27 international students enrolled. The school actively recruits these students.

Computers: The college provides computer facilities for student use. There are more than 40 IBM-compatible microcomputers available in the computer laboratory, business department, fine arts department, library, and residence halls. Internet is available. All students may access the system. It may be used 8 A.M. to 11 P.M., and later by appointment. There are no time limits on using the system and no fees.

Graduates: In 1992–93, 80 bachelor's degrees were awarded. The most popular majors among graduates were management (18%), marketing (11%), and communication (8%). Within an average freshman class, 32% graduate in 4 years, 43% in 5 years, and 47% in 6 years. Some 11 companies recruited on campus in 1992–93. In the 1992 graduating class, 5% of the men and 3% of the women were enrolled in graduate school within 6 months of graduation; 97% of the

men and 98% of the women had found employment.

Admissions Contact: John Schueth, Director of Admissions.

DOANE COLLEGE

E-3

Crete, NE 68333 (402) 826–8222; (800) 333–6263 (in-state)

Full-time: 388 men, 444 women	Faculty: 57; IIB, -$
Part-time: 9 men, 10 women	Ph.D.s: 70%
Graduate: 244	Student/Faculty: 15 to 1
Year: 4–1-4, summer session	Tuition: $9390
Application Deadline: June 1	Room & Board: $2830
Freshman Class: 793 applied, 709 accepted, 244 enrolled	
ACT: 23	COMPETITIVE

Doane College, founded in 1872, is a private liberal arts institution affiliated with the United Church of Christ. There is one graduate school. In addition to regional accreditation, Doane has baccalaureate program accreditation with NCATE. The library contains 197,521 volumes, 9799 microform items, and 520 audiovisual forms, and subscribes to 456 periodicals. Computerized library sources and services include interlibrary loans and database searching. Special learning facilities include a learning resource center, art gallery, radio station, and TV station. The 300-acre campus is in a small town 25 miles southwest of Lincoln. Including residence halls, there are 20 buildings on campus.

Student Life: About 80% of undergraduates are from Nebraska. Students come from 20 states and 5 foreign countries. Eighty percent are from public schools; 20% from private. Ninety-four percent are white. Sixty-three percent are Protestant; 25% Catholic; 12% claim no religious affiliation. The average age of freshmen is 18; all undergraduates, 20. Twenty percent drop out by the end of their first year; 51% remain to graduate.

Housing: A total of 690 students can be accommodated in college housing. College-sponsored living facilities include single-sex and coed dormitories, on-campus apartments, and married-student housing. In addition there are honors houses and special interest houses. On-campus housing is guaranteed for all 4 years. Eighty percent of students live on campus; of those, 60% remain on campus on weekends. All students may keep cars on campus.

Activities: About 30% of men belong to 5 local fraternities; about 36% of women belong to 4 local sororities. There are 50 groups on campus, including art, band, cheerleading, choir, chorale, chorus, computers, drama, ethnic, honors, international, jazz band, literary magazine, marching band, musical theater, newspaper, pep band, photography, political, professional, radio and tv, religious, social, social service, student government, and yearbook. Popular campus events include Parents Day, Stop Day, Homecoming, Alumni Banquet, and Commencement.

Sports: There are 8 intercollegiate sports for men and 7 for women, and 5 intramural sports for men and 4 for women. Athletic and recreation facilities include a physical education building, sports field, gymnasium, and pool.

Disabled Students: Sixty percent of the campus is accessible to disabled students. The following facilities are available: wheelchair ramps, elevators, special parking, specially equipped rest rooms, and special class scheduling.

Services: In addition to many counseling and information services, tutoring is available in every subject. There is also remedial math, reading, and writing.

Campus Safety and Security: Campus safety and security measures include escort service, informal discussions, pamphlets, posters, and films, and emergency telephones. In addition, there are lighted pathways and sidewalks.

Programs of Study: Doane awards the B.A. and B.S. degrees. Master's degrees also are awarded. Bachelor's degrees are awarded in BIOLOGICAL SCIENCE (biology/biological science), BUSINESS (accounting and business administration and management), COMMUNICATIONS AND THE ARTS (art, communications, English, English as a second/foreign language, German, music, and Spanish), COMPUTER AND PHYSICAL SCIENCE (chemistry, computer science, mathematics, and physical sciences), EDUCATION (elementary, physical, science, secondary, special, and teaching English as a second language/foreign language), ENGINEERING AND ENVIRONMENTAL DESIGN (environmental science), SOCIAL SCIENCE (economics, history, human services, international studies, political science/government, psychology, public administration, social science, and sociology). Education is the strongest academically. Business administration has the largest enrollment.

Required: The Doane Plan requires students to complete 60 to 70 credits in courses including heritage studies, contemporary issues, international/multicultural perspective, natural science, quantitative reasoning, communication, aesthetic perspective, and health and well-being. Students are also required to complete 2 hours each of physical education and computer skills in word processing, and most disciplines require a senior seminar. Students must complete 132

credit hours and have a minimum GPA of 2.0 in the major to graduate.

Special: Internships for sophomores through seniors, a Washington semester, and study abroad in numerous countries are possible. A 3–2 engineering program in conjunction with Washington at St. Louis and Columbia universities, work study, student-designed and more than 10 interdisciplinary majors, dual majors and accelerated degrees in all areas, credit by examination, nondegree study, and pass/fail options are available. Doane also offers the HELPS program, designed for Doane College graduates who wish to return as full-time students to seek further education in preparation for career advancement. There is a freshman honors program on campus, as well as 7 national honor societies. Two departments have honors programs.

Faculty/Classroom: Sixty-six percent of faculty are male; 34%, female. All teach undergraduates. No introductory courses are taught by graduate students. The average class size in an introductory lecture is 26; in a laboratory, 13; and in a regular course offering, 19.

Admissions: About 89% of the 1993–94 applicants were accepted. The ACT scores for the 1993–94 freshman class were as follows: 27% below 21, 27% between 21 and 23, 29% between 24 and 26, 10% between 27 and 28, and 7% above 28. About 39% of the current freshmen were in the top fifth of their class; 75% were in the top two fifths. About 18 freshmen graduated first in their class.

Requirements: The SAT I or ACT is required. The ACT is preferred. Applicants must be graduates of an accredited secondary school. The GED is accepted. It is recommended that 4 units of English and 3 units each of mathematics, science, and the social sciences be completed. An interview is required. Art students must submit a portfolio, and music and drama students must audition. AP and CLEP credits are accepted. Important factors used in the admissions decision are recommendations by school officials, advanced placement or honor courses, leadership record, evidence of special talent, personality, and intangible qualities.

Procedure: Freshmen are admitted fall, winter, and spring. Entrance exams should be taken by spring of the junior year. Applications should be filed by June 1 for fall entry, along with an application fee of $15. Notification is sent on a rolling basis. There are early decision, early admissions, and deferred admissions plans. Seven early decision candidates were accepted for the 1993–94 class.

Transfer: Some 24 transfer students enrolled in 1993–94. Transfer students must submit a transcript from previously attended colleges and have been in good standing. The SAT I or ACT is usually required. Grades of 2.0 or higher generally transfer for credit. A total of 30 credits out of 132 must be completed at Doane.

Visiting: There are regularly scheduled orientations for prospective students, including 4 scheduled half-day visits that incorporate a parents program. There are guides for informal visits and visitors may sit in on classes and stay overnight at the school. To arrange for a visit, contact the Admissions Office at (402) 826–8222.

Financial Aid: In 1993–94, 92% of all current freshmen and 96% of continuing students received some form of financial aid. About 82% of freshmen and 75% of continuing students received need-based aid. The average freshman award was $7550. Of that total, scholarships or need-based grants averaged $4530 ($9140 maximum); loans averaged $2640 ($3625 maximum); and work contracts averaged $380 ($1200 maximum). Fifty-one percent of undergraduate students work part-time. Average earnings from campus work for the school year are $550. The average financial indebtedness of the 1992–93 graduate was $13,561. Doane is a member of CSS. The FAF and the FAFSA are required. The deadline for financial aid applications is March 15.

International Students: There are currently 23 international students enrolled. The school actively recruits these students. They must take the TOEFL and achieve a minimum score of 550.

Computers: The college provides computer facilities for student use. The mainframes are 2 VAX 4200s and an MVAX 3100–40. Every residence hall has a microcomputer laboratory networked to the mainframe. Several large laboratories are available 70 hours a week. All students may access the system at anytime. There are no time limits on using the system and no fees.

Graduates: In 1992–93, 283 bachelor's degrees were awarded. The most popular majors among graduates were education (19%), business (14%), and accounting (8%). Within an average freshman class, 2% graduate in 3 years, 85% in 4 years, and 13% in 5 years. Some 10 companies recruited on campus in 1992–93. In the 1992 graduating class, 14% of the men and women were enrolled in graduate school within 6 months of graduation; 72% had found employment.

Admissions Contact: Dan Kunzman, Dean of Admissions.

HASTINGS COLLEGE D-3

Hastings, NE 68901   (402) 463–2402; (800) 532–7642 (out-of-state)

Full-time: 462 men, 473 women	**Faculty:** 67; IIB, --$
Part-time: 13 men, 24 women	**Ph.D.s:** 63%
Graduate: 15 men, 23 women	**Student/Faculty:** 14 to 1
Year: 4–1–4, summer session	**Tuition:** $9296
Application Deadline: July 1	**Room & Board:** $3130

Freshman Class: 814 applied, 708 accepted, 262 enrolled
ACT: 22   **COMPETITIVE**

Hastings College, founded in 1882 by the Presbyterian Church, offers programs in the liberal arts and sciences, education, business, and health professions. There is one undergraduate and one graduate school. In addition to regional accreditation, Hastings College has baccalaureate program accreditation with NASM and NCATE. The library contains 115,000 volumes, 60,000 microform items, and 1300 audiovisual forms, and subscribes to 500 periodicals. Computerized library sources and services include the card catalog, interlibrary loans, and database searching. Special learning facilities include an art gallery, a radio station, a television studio, and an observatory. The 80-acre campus is in a rural area 150 miles west of Omaha. Including residence halls, there are 25 buildings on campus.

Student Life: About 76% of undergraduates are from Nebraska. Students come from 21 states and 7 foreign countries. Ninety percent are from public schools; 10% from private. Ninety-six percent are white. Sixty percent are Protestant; 20% Catholic. The average age of freshmen is 18; all undergraduates, 22. Twenty-seven percent drop out by the end of their first year; 49% remain to graduate.

Housing: A total of 594 students can be accommodated in college housing. College-sponsored living facilities include single-sex and coed dormitories. In addition there are honors houses and off-campus houses. On-campus housing is guaranteed for all 4 years and is available on a first-come, first-served basis. Fifty-two percent of students live on campus; of those, 50% remain on campus on weekends. Alcohol is not permitted. All students may keep cars on campus.

Activities: About 20% of men belong to 4 local fraternities; about 30% of women belong to 4 local sororities. There are 60 groups on campus, including art, band, cheerleading, choir, chorus, drama, ethnic, gay, honors, jazz band, literary magazine, marching band, musical theater, newspaper, opera, orchestra, pep band, photography, political, professional, radio and tv, religious, social, social service, student government, symphony, and yearbook. Popular campus events include May Fete, Homecoming, Festival of Lessons, Carols, Artist Lecture Series, Student Symposium, and Parents Weekend.

Sports: There are 8 intercollegiate sports for men and 8 for women, and 9 intramural sports for men and 8 for women. Athletic and recreation facilities include a physical fitness center, a pool, a golf course, indoor and outdoor tennis courts, a 2200-seat stadium, a 3500-seat gymnasium, and an all-weather track.

Disabled Students: Ninety percent of the campus is accessible to disabled students. The following facilities are available: wheelchair ramps, elevators, special parking, specially equipped rest rooms, and special class scheduling.

Services: In addition to many counseling and information services, tutoring is available in most subjects, including all core subjects and most lower-division courses.

Campus Safety and Security: Campus safety and security measures include escort service, pamphlets, posters, and films, lighted pathways and sidewalks, and a night security patrol.

Programs of Study: Hastings College awards the B.A. and B.M. degrees. Master's degrees also are awarded. Bachelor's degrees are awarded in BIOLOGICAL SCIENCE (biology/biological science), BUSINESS (accounting, business administration and management, business economics, and personnel management), COMMUNICATIONS AND THE ARTS (broadcasting, communications, dramatic arts, English, fine arts, German, journalism, music, Spanish, and speech/debate/rhetoric), COMPUTER AND PHYSICAL SCIENCE (chemistry, computer science, mathematics, and physics), EDUCATION (art, business, elementary, foreign languages, music, science, secondary, and special), HEALTH PROFESSIONS (health care administration), SOCIAL SCIENCE (economics, history, human services, philosophy, political science/government, psychology, public administration, religion, social science, and sociology). Physics is the strongest academically. Business administration has the largest enrollment.

Required: Students are required to take courses in written, oral, and symbolic communication, physical and life science, foreign language, history, social and political science, literature, philosophy, religion, the fine arts, and physical education. A minimum 2.0 GPA and 127 credit hours, with 30 to 36 in the major, are required to graduate.

Special: There is a co-op program with Creighton University, a 3–2 engineering program with Columbia and Washington universities and Georgia Institute of Technology, and a 3–2 degree in occupational therapy with Boston and Washington universities. Internships, a Washington semester, work-study, dual majors in all areas, and

student-designed majors are possible. Credit by exam, credit for life/work/military experience, and pass/fail options are available. There are 9 national honor societies on campus. Six departments have honors programs.

Faculty/Classroom: Seventy-five percent of faculty are male; 25%, female. All teach undergraduates and 25% do research. No introductory courses are taught by graduate students. The average class size in an introductory lecture is 25; in a laboratory, 25; and in a regular course offering, 20.

Admissions: About 87% of the 1993–94 applicants were accepted. About 45% of the current freshmen were in the top fifth of their class; 70% were in the top two fifths. There were 3 National Merit finalists. About 20 freshmen graduated first in their class.

Requirements: Hastings College requires applicants to be in the upper 50% of their class. A minimum GPA of 2.0 is required. The SAT I or ACT is required. Applicants should graduate from an accredited secondary school with a minimum of 4 academic credits in English and 2 each in mathematics, science, social studies, and a foreign language. Generally, placement in the upper half of the graduating class, a minimum GPA of 2.0, or a composite score of 20 on the enhanced ACT is a minimal requirement for consideration for admission. AP and CLEP credits are accepted. Important factors used in the admissions decision are recommendations by school officials, personality, intangible qualities, leadership record, evidence of special talent, and advanced placement or honor courses.

Procedure: Freshmen are admitted to all sessions. Applications should be filed by July 1 for fall entry, December 1 for winter entry, January 1 for spring entry, and May 15 for summer entry, along with an application fee of $20. Notification is sent on a rolling basis. There is an early decision plan. About 100 early decision candidates were accepted for the 1993–94 class.

Transfer: About 35 transfer students enrolled in 1993–94. Transfer students must have completed course work equivalent by description to that of Hastings and have earned grades of C or better. A total of 30 credits out of 127 must be completed at Hastings College.

Visiting: There are guides for informal visits and visitors may sit in on classes and stay overnight at the school. To arrange for a visit, contact the Admissions Office at (800) 532-7642.

Financial Aid: In 1993–94, 95% of all current freshmen and 95% of continuing students received some form of financial aid. About 71% of freshmen and 77% of continuing students received need-based aid. The average freshman award was $7115. Of that total, scholarships or need-based grants averaged $4276 ($8920 maximum); loans averaged $2369 ($4625 maximum); and work contracts averaged $470 ($1200 maximum). Fifty percent of undergraduate students work part-time. Average earnings from campus work for the school year are $750. The average financial indebtedness of the 1992–93 graduate was $11,432. Hastings College is a member of CSS. The FAF, FFS or SFS, the college's own financial statement, and FAFSA are required. The deadline for financial aid applications is May 1.

International Students: There are currently 8 international students enrolled. The school actively recruits these students. They must take the TOEFL, the University of Michigan Language Test, the Comprehensive English Language Test, or the college's own test. International athletes must take a standardized test for eligibility.

Computers: The college provides computer facilities for student use. There are 38 IBM and IBM-compatible and 40 Apple microcomputers available for academic use in a computer center and throughout the college. There are no time limits on using the system and no fees.

Graduates: In 1992–93, 180 bachelor's degrees were awarded. The most popular majors among graduates were business administration (21%), education (19%), and psychology (9%). Within an average freshman class, 45% graduate in 4 years, 49% in 5 years, and 49% in 6 years. Some 27 companies recruited on campus in 1992–93. In the 1992 graduating class, 30% of the men and 20% of the women were enrolled in graduate school within 6 months of graduation; 64% of the men and 78% of the women had found employment.

Admissions Contact: Sam Rennick, Director of Admissions.

MIDLAND LUTHERAN COLLEGE   E-2
Fremont, NE 68025   (402) 721-5480; (800) 642-8382 (in-state)

Full-time: 393 men, 514 women	Faculty: 55; IIB, --$
Part-time: 43 men, 67 women	Ph.D.s: 40%
Graduate: none	Student/Faculty: 16 to 1
Year: 4-1-4, summer session	Tuition: $9550
Application Deadline: open	Room & Board: $2860
Freshman Class: 619 applied, 584 accepted, 272 enrolled	
ACT: 22	**LESS COMPETITIVE**

Midland Lutheran College, established in 1883, is a private coeducational facility affiliated with the Evangelical Lutheran Church in America. In addition to regional accreditation, Midland has baccalaureate program accreditation with NLN. The library contains 105,000 vol-

umes and 1000 audiovisual forms, and subscribes to 900 periodicals. Computerized library sources and services include interlibrary loans. Special learning facilities include a learning resource center and planetarium. The 27-acre campus is in a small town 35 miles west of Omaha. Including residence halls, there are 18 buildings on campus.

Student Life: About 75% of undergraduates are from Nebraska. Students come from 23 states and 7 foreign countries. Ninety-eight percent are from public schools; 2% from private. Ninety-two percent are white. Seventy percent are Protestant; 12% Catholic; 10% claim no religious affiliation. The average age of freshmen is 18; all undergraduates, 20. Twenty-six percent drop out by the end of their first year; 55% remain to graduate.

Housing: A total of 520 students can be accommodated in college housing. College-sponsored living facilities include single-sex and coed dormitories. On-campus housing is guaranteed for all 4 years. Fifty-eight percent of students live on campus; of those, 50% remain on campus on weekends. Alcohol is not permitted. All students may keep cars on campus.

Activities: About 40% of men belong to 4 local fraternities; about 40% of women belong to 4 local sororities. There are 36 groups on campus, including art, band, cheerleading, choir, chorus, computers, drama, drill team, ethnic, honors, jazz band, literary magazine, musical theater, newspaper, pep band, photography, professional, radio and TV, religious, social service, student government, and yearbook. Popular campus events include Journalism Day, Greek Games, Snow Week, Homecoming, and Martin Luther King Day.

Sports: There are 8 intercollegiate sports for men and 8 for women, and 4 intramural sports for men and 4 for women. Athletic and recreation facilities include a physical education center, an athletic practice field, an indoor pool, an indoor track, and a weight room.

Disabled Students: Eighty percent of the campus is accessible to disabled students. The following facilities are available: wheelchair ramps, elevators, special parking, specially equipped rest rooms, and lowered drinking fountains.

Services: In addition to many counseling and information services, tutoring is available in every subject. There is also remedial reading and writing.

Campus Safety and Security: Campus safety and security measures include escort service, informal discussions, pamphlets, posters, and films, and lighted pathways and sidewalks. In addition, security is on duty 14 hours a day and on call during night hours.

Programs of Study: Midland awards the B.A., B.S., B.B.A., and B.S.N. degrees. Associate degrees also are awarded. Bachelor's degrees are awarded in BIOLOGICAL SCIENCE (biology/biological science), BUSINESS (accounting, business administration and management, business economics, management information systems, and marketing/retailing/merchandising), COMMUNICATIONS AND THE ARTS (advertising, communications, English, fine arts, journalism, and music), COMPUTER AND PHYSICAL SCIENCE (chemistry, computer programming, computer science, and mathematics), EDUCATION (art, business, early childhood, elementary, middle school, music, science, and secondary), HEALTH PROFESSIONS (nursing, predentistry, and premedicine), SOCIAL SCIENCE (community services, economics, history, parks and recreation management, prelaw, psychology, religion, social science, and sociology). Business, journalism, education, and nursing are the strongest academically. Business, education, and nursing have the largest enrollments.

Required: To graduate, students need a total of 128 credit hours, with 36 of these in distribution requirements of the student's selection. English and speech courses are required. The total number of hours in the major varies from 34 to 48, and students must maintain a GPA of at least 2.0 overall and 2.25 in the major.

Special: Special arrangements include internships, independent study, and study abroad in France, Germany, Mexico, and several other countries in cooperation with Central College of Pella, Iowa. Other options include directed study and the pass/no credit grading system. There are 2 national honor societies on campus.

Faculty/Classroom: Sixty percent of faculty are male; 40%, female. All teach undergraduates. The average class size in a laboratory is 20 and in a regular course offering, 20.

Admissions: About 94% of the 1993–94 applicants were accepted. The ACT scores for the 1993–94 freshman class were as follows: 45% below 21, 25% between 21 and 23, 20% between 24 and 26, 6% between 27 and 28, and 4% above 28. About 38% of the current freshmen were in the top fifth of their class; 70% were in the top two fifths. Twelve freshmen graduated first in their class.

Requirements: The ACT is required. In addition, applicants should be graduates of an accredited secondary school. The GED is accepted. Recommended preparation includes 3 units of English, 2 of mathematics, and 10 of electives. An interview is recommended. AP and CLEP credits are accepted. Important factors used in the admissions decision are recommendations by school officials, personality, intangible qualities, parents or siblings attending the school, leadership record, and extracurricular activities record.

Procedure: Freshmen are admitted to all sessions. Entrance exams should be taken during fall of the senior year. Application deadlines are open. The application fee is $15. Notification is sent on a rolling basis.

Transfer: Some 108 transfer students enrolled in 1993–94. Transfer students must be in good standing at their previous college and generally have a 2.0 minimum GPA. Grades of C or higher transfer for credit. A total of 32 credits out of 128 must be completed at Midland.

Visiting: There are guides for informal visits and visitors may sit in on classes and stay overnight at the school. To arrange for a visit, contact the Admissions Office at (402) 721–5480.

Financial Aid: In 1993–94, 93% of all current freshmen received some form of financial aid. About 75% of freshmen and 80% of continuing students received need-based aid. The average freshman award was $9200. Of that total, scholarships or need-based grants averaged $3264 ($8118 maximum); loans averaged $4515 ($5625 maximum); and work contracts averaged $800 ($1200 maximum). Sixty-five percent of undergraduate students work part-time. Average earnings from campus work for the school year are $800. The average financial indebtedness of the 1992–93 graduate was $12,003. The college's own financial statement and FAFSA are required. The deadline for financial aid applications is May 1.

International Students: There are currently 19 international students enrolled. The school actively recruits these students. They must take the TOEFL and achieve a minimum score of 500.

Computers: The college provides computer facilities for student use. The mainframe is a DEC. Students have their own password for their account on the system. Terminals and printers are available in several areas of the campus for student use. All students may access the system. There are no time limits on using the system and no fees.

Graduates: In 1992–93, 177 bachelor's degrees were awarded. The most popular majors among graduates were business (30%), education (25%), and nursing (20%). Within an average freshman class, 1% graduate in 3 years, 45% in 4 years, and 6% in 5 years. Some 16 companies recruited on campus in a recent year. In an earlier graduating class, 90% of the men and women had found employment within 6 months of graduation.

Admissions Contact: Roland R. Kahnk, Vice President for Enrollment Services.

NEBRASKA METHODIST COLLEGE OF NURSING AND ALLIED HEALTH

F-3

Omaha, NE 68114   (402) 390–4879

Full-time: 278 men and women	**Faculty:** 30
Part-time: 172 men and women	**Ph.D.s:** 10%
Graduate: none	**Student/Faculty:** 9 to 1
Year: semesters, summer session	**Tuition:** $3160
Application Deadline: April 1	**Room & Board:** $1200

Freshman Class: 209 applied, 136 accepted, 130 enrolled
ACT: 21   **COMPETITIVE**

Nebraska Methodist College of Nursing and Allied Health, founded in 1891 as the Methodist School of Nursing and chartered in the state of Nebraska in 1985 with its present name, is part of the Nebraska Methodist Health Systems and is a private, coeducational, primarily commuter college offering career training in the health sciences. In addition to regional accreditation, Nebraska Methodist College has baccalaureate program accreditation with CAHEA and NLN. The library contains 8758 volumes and 655 microform items, and subscribes to 3761 periodicals. Computerized library sources and services include database searching. Special learning facilities include a learning resource center and an assessment laboratory for nursing students. The campus is in an urban area in the center of Omaha. There is 1 building on campus.

Student Life: About 95% of undergraduates are from Nebraska. Students come from 4 states. Ninety-five percent are from public schools; 5% from private. Ninety-six percent are white. The average age of freshmen is 24. Two percent drop out by the end of their first year; 85% remain to graduate.

Housing: A total of 52 students can be accommodated in college housing. College-sponsored living facilities include a coed dormitory. On-campus housing is available on a first-come, first-served basis and is available on a lottery system for upperclassmen. Priority is given to out-of-town students. Alcohol is not permitted. All students may keep cars on campus.

Activities: There are no fraternities or sororities on campus. There are 10 groups on campus, including professional, social, social service, student government, and yearbook. Popular campus events include Fall Parents Weekend, Christmas activities, Spring Dance, and Honors Convocation.

Sports: There are 3 intramural sports for men and 3 for women. Athletic and recreation facilities include an outdoor swimming pool, weight-training equipment, and a recreation area.

Disabled Students: Seventy-five percent of the campus is accessible to disabled students. Elevators are available for these students.

Services: In addition to many counseling and information services, tutoring is available in most subjects. In addition, there is remedial math, reading, and writing. Reader service for the blind is available in the metropolitan area.

Campus Safety and Security: Campus safety and security measures include self defense education and pamphlets, posters, and films.

Programs of Study: Nebraska Methodist College awards the B.S.N. degree. Associate degrees also are awarded. Bachelor's degrees are awarded in HEALTH PROFESSIONS (nursing, radiation therapy, respiratory therapy, and ultrasound technology). Nursing is the strongest program academically and has the largest enrollment.

Required: All students must complete courses in the humanities, social and behavioral sciences, and natural and applied sciences. A total of 127 credit hours is required, 55 of these in the major. Students must maintain a minimum GPA of 2.0.

Special: There is nondegree study and credit by examination. Credit by correspondence may be considered.

Faculty/Classroom: Twenty-six percent of faculty are male; 74%, female. All teach undergraduates. The average class size in an introductory lecture is 35; in a laboratory, 10; and in a regular course offering, 20.

Admissions: About 65% of the 1993–94 applicants were accepted. About 8% of the current freshmen were in the top fifth of their class; 95% were in the top two fifths. There were 2 National Merit finalists and 1 semifinalist. One freshman graduated first in the class.

Requirements: A minimum GPA of 2.0 is required. The ACT is required; the minimum acceptable score is 18. Students must be graduates of an accredited secondary school with the number of academic credits required under Nebraska state law. The GED is accepted. Students should have completed 4 years of English and 2 years each of mathematics, science, and social studies. An essay and an interview are required. AP and CLEP credits are accepted. Important factors used in the admissions decision are personality, intangible qualities, advanced placement or honor courses, leadership record, recommendations by school officials, and extracurricular activities record.

Procedure: Freshmen are admitted fall and spring. Entrance exams should be taken as early as possible. Applications should be filed by April 1 for fall entry and November 1 for spring entry, along with an application fee of $20. Notification is sent on a rolling basis.

Transfer: A total of 55 transfer students enrolled in a recent year. Applicants must have a GPA above 2.0. Grades of C and above can be transferred for credit. An interview is required, as is a minimum ACT score of 18. The senior year and a total of 36 credits out of 127 must be completed at Nebraska Methodist College.

Visiting: There are regularly scheduled orientations for prospective students. There are guides for informal visits and visitors may sit in on classes. To arrange for a visit, contact admissions representatives at (402) 390–4879.

Financial Aid: In a recent year, 82% of freshmen and 75% of continuing students received need-based aid. Scholarships or need-based grants averaged $1000 ($1000 maximum); and loans averaged $2500 ($4000 maximum). The average financial indebtedness of a recent graduate was $7000. The FAF or FFS, and the FAFSA are required. The deadline for financial aid applications is August 1.

International Students: They must take the TOEFL and achieve a minimum score of 550.

Computers: The college provides computer facilities for student use. IBM microcomputers are available in a centralized laboratory. There are no time limits on using the system and no fees.

Graduates: In a recent year, 46 bachelor's degrees were awarded. The most popular majors among graduates were nursing (65%) and respiratory care (13%). In a recent graduating class, 5% of all students were enrolled in graduate school within 6 months of graduation; all students had found employment.

Admissions Contact: Admissions Officer.

NEBRASKA WESLEYAN UNIVERSITY

E-3

Lincoln, NE 68504   (402) 465–2218; (800) 541–3818

Full-time: 653 men, 790 women	**Faculty:** 88; IIB, av$
Part-time: 55 men, 205 women	**Ph.D.s:** 83%
Graduate: none	**Student/Faculty:** 16 to 1
Year: semesters, summer session	**Tuition:** $9040
Application Deadline: March 15	**Room & Board:** $3200

Freshman Class: 969 applied, 762 accepted, 382 enrolled
ACT: 23   **COMPETITIVE**

Nebraska Wesleyan University, founded in 1887, is a private liberal arts facility affiliated with the Methodist Church. In addition to regional accreditation, NWU has baccalaureate program accreditation with CSWE, NASM, NCATE, and NLN. The library contains 171,973 volumes, 3646 microform items, and 7951 audiovisual forms, and subscribes to 751 periodicals. Computerized library sources and services

include the card catalog, interlibrary loans, and database searching. Special learning facilities include an art gallery and planetarium. The 50-acre campus is in a suburban area 50 miles west of Omaha. Including residence halls, there are 18 buildings on campus.

Student Life: About 93% of undergraduates are from Nebraska. Students come from 28 states and 10 foreign countries. Ninety-five percent are white. Sixty-six percent are Protestant; 21% Catholic. The average age of freshmen is 18; all undergraduates, 21. Fourteen percent drop out by the end of their first year; 65% remain to graduate.

Housing: A total of 549 students can be accommodated in college housing. College-sponsored living facilities include single-sex and coed dormitories. On-campus housing is guaranteed for all 4 years. Sixty percent of students commute. All students may keep cars on campus.

Activities: About 38% of men belong to 4 national fraternities; about 32% of women belong to 1 local and 2 national sororities. There are 80 groups on campus, including art, band, cheerleading, choir, chorus, drama, ethnic, gay, honors, international, jazz band, literary magazine, musical theater, newspaper, opera, orchestra, political, professional, religious, social, social service, student government, and yearbook. Popular campus events include union programs, such as dances, films, concerts, and University forum.

Sports: There are 8 intercollegiate sports for men and 8 for women, and 13 intramural sports for men and 8 for women. Athletic and recreation facilities include a physical education building and swimming pool, a stadium, a track, football and baseball fields, and tennis courts.

Disabled Students: The following facilities are available: wheelchair ramps, elevators, special parking, specially equipped rest rooms, special class scheduling, and lowered telephones.

Services: In addition to many counseling and information services, tutoring is available in some subjects, including sciences, social services, and humanities.

Campus Safety and Security: Campus safety and security measures include escort service, informal discussions, emergency telephones, and lighted pathways and sidewalks.

Programs of Study: NWU awards the B.A., B.S., B.F.A., B.M., and B.S.N. degrees. Bachelor's degrees are awarded in BIOLOGICAL SCIENCE (biology/biological science), BUSINESS (business administration), COMMUNICATIONS AND THE ARTS (applied music, art, communications, English, French, German, music, Spanish, and theater), COMPUTER AND PHYSICAL SCIENCE (chemistry, computer science, mathematics, and physics), EDUCATION (elementary, middle school, music, physical, and special), HEALTH PROFESSIONS (nursing), SOCIAL SCIENCE (economics, history, international studies, philosophy, political science/government, psychology, religion, social work, and sociology). Physical science, psychology, English, and business administration are the strongest academically. Business administration has the largest enrollment.

Required: To graduate, students must complete 56 hours of general education requirements in communication and symbolic thought, health and physical fitness, humanistic studies, fine arts, biological and physical sciences, social aspects of American culture, cultural perspectives, and attitudes and values. At least 126 credit hours, including 30 in the major, must be completed with a minimum GPA of 2.0. A senior comprehensive is also needed, consisting of a comprehensive examination in the major discipline, a thesis or independent study, or an internship or presentation of performance.

Special: NWU offers cross-registration with Union College, a Washington semester, study abroad in 35 countries, a global students major, and a department of interdisciplinary studies. Internships are available in most departments and required in many. Other options include nondegree study, pass/fail options, dual majors, credit by examination, and a 3–2 engineering degree in conjunction with Washington or Columbia Universities. There are 20 national honor societies on campus.

Faculty/Classroom: Sixty-six percent of full-time faculty are male; 35%, female. All faculty teach undergraduates. The average class size in an introductory lecture is 25; in a laboratory, 16; and in a regular course offering, 20.

Admissions: About 79% of the 1993–94 applicants were accepted. The ACT scores for the 1993–94 freshman class were as follows: 23% below 21, 31% between 21 and 23, 26% between 24 and 26, 12% between 27 and 28, and 8% above 28. About 59% of the current freshmen were in the top fifth of their class; 79% were in the top two fifths. There were 5 National Merit finalists. Some 23 freshmen graduated first in their class.

Requirements: NWU requires applicants to be in the upper 50% of their class. The ACT or SAT I is recommended, with a minimum composite score of 800 on the SAT I or 20 on the Enhanced ACT. Freshmen must be graduates of an accredited secondary school or submit the GED. An interview is recommended. AP and CLEP credits are accepted. Important factors used in the admissions decision are advanced placement or honor courses, leadership record, recommen-

dations by school officials, extracurricular activities record, and recommendations by alumni.

Procedure: Freshmen are admitted to all sessions. Entrance exams should be taken no later than December of the senior year. Early decision applications should be filed by November 15; regular applications, by March 15 for fall entry, December 15 for spring entry, and April 15 for summer entry, along with an application fee of $20. Notification of early decision is sent December 15; regular decision, April 15. There are early decision, early admissions, and deferred admissions plans. A waiting list is an active part of the admissions procedure.

Transfer: Some 63 transfer students enrolled in 1993–94. Transfer students must be in good standing at their previous school and have a minimum 2.0 GPA. A minimum of 800 on the SAT I or 20 on the ACT is recommended. Grades of C- or better transfer for credit. A total of 30 credits out of 126 must be completed at NWU.

Visiting: There are regularly scheduled orientations for prospective students, consisting of a tour, classroom visits, and meetings with faculty and financial aid and admissions personnel. There are guides for informal visits and visitors may sit in on classes and stay overnight at the school. To arrange for a visit, contact the Admissions Office at (800) 541–3818 or (402) 465–2218.

Financial Aid: In 1993–94, 95% of all current freshmen and 93% of continuing students received some form of financial aid. About 74% of freshmen and 68% of continuing students received need-based aid. The average freshman award was $6831. Of that total, scholarships or need-based grants averaged $3367 ($8894 maximum); loans averaged $3364 ($3625 maximum); and work contracts averaged $100 ($1500 maximum). Seventy percent of undergraduate students work part-time. Average earnings from campus work for the school year are $750. The average financial indebtedness of the 1992–93 graduate was $6000. The FAFSA is required.

International Students: There are currently 14 international students enrolled. The school actively recruits these students. They must take the TOEFL or the University of Michigan Language Test and achieve a minimum score on the TOEFL of 500. The SAT I or ACT is recommended, with a minimum score of 800 or 20, respectively.

Computers: The college provides computer facilities for student use. The mainframe is a Sun SPARC Server 490. The mainframe, which has 20 terminals, is available for science, mathematics, computer science, and business administration classes and research. There are also 100 microcomputers, 24 of which are networked to the mainframe, available for classes and students' personal use. All students may access the system. It may be used 80 hours per week. There are no time limits on using the system and no fees.

Graduates: In 1992–93 301 bachelor's degrees were awarded. The most popular majors among graduates were business administration (21%), biology (14%), and psychology (13%). Within an average freshman class, 1% graduate in 3 years, 50% in 4 years, 63% in 5 years, and 67% in 6 years.

Admissions Contact: Kendal E. Sieg, Director of Admissions.

PERU STATE COLLEGE　　　　　　　　　　F-3

Peru, NE 68421	(402) 872–3815; (800) 872–4412 (in-state)
Full-time and Part-time	Faculty: 48; IIB, av$
Undergraduate/Graduate	Ph.D.s: 72%
men and women: 1711	Student/Faculty: 20 to 1
Year: semesters, summer session	Tuition: $1687 ($2834)
Application Deadline: open	Room & Board: $2624
Freshman Class: 711 applied, 521 accepted, 478 enrolled	
ACT: required for out-of-state	
applicants	**NONCOMPETITIVE**

Peru State College, established in 1867 and a part of the Nebraska State College System, is a public institution offering undergraduate curricula in the arts, business, military studies, teacher preparation, and technical studies. There is one graduate school. In addition to regional accreditation, Peru State has baccalaureate program accreditation with NCATE. The library contains 102,432 volumes, 188,316 microform items, and 4352 audiovisual forms, and subscribes to 313 periodicals. Special learning facilities include an art gallery. The 103-acre campus is in a rural area 60 miles south of Omaha. Including residence halls, there are 21 buildings on campus.

Student Life: About 85% of undergraduates are from Nebraska. Students come from 12 states, 4 foreign countries, and Canada. Ninety-eight percent are from public schools. The average age of freshmen is 18; all undergraduates, 22. Twenty-eight percent drop out by the end of their first year; 50% remain to graduate.

Housing: A total of 600 students can be accommodated in college housing. College-sponsored living facilities include single-sex and coed dormitories, on-campus apartments, off-campus apartments, and married-student housing. On-campus housing is guaranteed for all 4 years. Sixty-five percent of students live on campus; of those, 27% remain on campus on weekends. Alcohol is not permitted. All students may keep cars on campus.

Activities: About 1% of men belong to 1 local and 1 national fraternities. There is 1 local sorority. There are 27 groups on campus, including art, band, cheerleading, choir, chorus, computers, drama, honors, jazz band, literary magazine, marching band, newspaper, pep band, professional, religious, social, social service, student government, and yearbook. Popular campus events include Homecoming, the Fall Formal, and the Spring Break Trip.

Sports: There are 3 intercollegiate sports for men and 3 for women, and 5 intramural sports for men and 4 for women. Athletic and recreation facilities include a health and recreation complex containing basketball and tennis courts, an indoor track, and an Olympic-sized swimming pool. Other facilities include a playing field, an activity trail, and a 2500-seat stadium.

Disabled Students: Eighty percent of the campus is accessible to disabled students. The following facilities are available: wheelchair ramps, elevators, special parking, specially equipped rest rooms, special class scheduling, lowered drinking fountains, and lowered telephones.

Services: In addition to counseling and information services, there is remedial math, reading, and writing. Tutoring is available in writing and other subjects.

Campus Safety and Security: Campus safety and security measures include 24-hour foot and vehicle patrol, informal discussions, pamphlets, posters, and films, and lighted pathways and sidewalks.

Programs of Study: Peru State awards the B.A., B.S., B.A.Ed., B.F.A.Ed., and B.T. degrees. Associate and master's degrees also are awarded. Bachelor's degrees are awarded in AGRICULTURE (natural resource management, preforestry, and wildlife ecology), BIOLOGICAL SCIENCE (biology/biological science), BUSINESS (accounting, business administration and management, management science, marketing/retailing/merchandising, and sports management), COMMUNICATIONS AND THE ARTS (dramatic arts, English, fine arts, music, music business management, and piano/organ), COMPUTER AND PHYSICAL SCIENCE (computer science, computer science business applications, computer science technical, mathematics, nuclear technology, physical sciences, and preradiological technology), EDUCATION (art, elementary, health, industrial arts, music, physical, science, secondary, and special), ENGINEERING AND ENVIRONMENTAL DESIGN (construction technology, electromechanical technology, industrial administration/management, industrial engineering technology, preengineering, and transportation technology), HEALTH PROFESSIONS (medical technology, predentistry, premedicine, prenuclear medical technology, prenursing, preoptomotry, preosteopathy, prepharmacy, prephysical therapy, prephysician's assistant, prepodiatry, preveterinary science, respiratory therapy, and speech pathology/audiology), SOCIAL SCIENCE (economics, history, human services, prelaw, psychology, social science, and sociology).

Required: In order to graduate, students must complete general education requirements in literature, communications, fine arts, social and behavioral sciences, health and hygiene, computer science, and natural sciences. Teacher education majors must have a GPA of 2.5; all others must have a GPA of 2.0. The college requires 125 credit hours for graduation. Students must also complete a physical education requirement.

Special: The college offers study-abroad opportunities, cooperative programs, and internships. Work-study programs and nondegree study are also available. Students may pursue B.A.-B.S. degrees. Dual and student-designed majors can be arranged. Credit may be granted for military experience. There are 2 national honor societies on campus.

Faculty/Classroom: No introductory courses are taught by graduate students. The average class size in an introductory lecture is 40; in a laboratory, 25; and in a regular course offering, 25.

Admissions: About 73% of the 1993–94 applicants were accepted.

Requirements: A minimum GPA of 2.0 is required. Applicants who have graduated from an accredited Nebraska secondary school will be admitted. Applicants who have earned the GED will be considered. Out-of-state applicants should have earned 16 Carnegie units and are required to take the ACT. AP and CLEP credits are accepted.

Procedure: Freshmen are admitted to all sessions. Application deadlines are open. The application fee is $10. The college accepts all in-state residents who apply. Notification is sent on a rolling basis. There are early admissions and deferred admissions plans.

Transfer: Transfer students must be in good standing with the previously attended institution. A total of 30 credits out of 125 must be completed at Peru State.

Visiting: There are regularly scheduled orientations for prospective students. There are guides for informal visits and visitors may sit in on classes and stay overnight at the school. To arrange for a visit, contact the Admissions Office at (800) 742–4412 (in-state) or (402) 872–3815.

Financial Aid: In 1993–94, 80% of all students received some form of financial aid. The average freshman award was $3800. Of that total, scholarships or need-based grants averaged $1520 ($1900 maximum); loans averaged $1520 ($1900 maximum); and work contracts averaged $570 ($760 maximum). Forty percent of undergraduate students work part-time. Average earnings from campus work for the school year are $800. The average financial indebtedness of the 1992–93 graduate was $2000. Peru State is a member of CSS. The FAF is required. The deadline for financial aid applications is April 1.

International Students: There are currently 9 international students enrolled. They must take the TOEFL and achieve a minimum score of 550.

Computers: The college provides computer facilities for student use. Peru State provides 48 Apple microcomputers in laboratories for students enrolled in computer courses. There are no time limits on using the system and no fees.

Graduates: In 1992–93 242 bachelor's degrees were awarded. Within an average freshman class, 42% graduate in 4 years and 50% in 5 years. Some 94 companies recruited on campus in 1992–93.

Admissions Contact: Curt E. Luttrell, Director of Admissions and School Relations.

UNION COLLEGE   E-3
Lincoln, NE 68506   (402) 486–2504; (800) 228–4600 (out-of-state)

Full-time: 205 men, 270 women	**Faculty:** 33; IIB, --$
Part-time: 41 men, 58 women	**Ph.D.s:** 36%
Graduate: none	**Student/Faculty:** 14 to 1
Year: semesters, summer session	**Tuition:** $8420
Application Deadline: July 30	**Room & Board:** $2640
Freshman Class: 189 applied, 188 accepted, 139 enrolled	
ACT: 21	**NONCOMPETITIVE**

Union College, established in 1891, is a nonprofit, private liberal arts institution affiliated with the Seventh-day Adventist Church. In addition to regional accreditation, Union has baccalaureate program accreditation with CSWE, NCATE, and NLN. The library contains 130,000 volumes and 1026 microform items, and subscribes to 750 periodicals. Computerized library sources and services include interlibrary loans and database searching. Special learning facilities include a learning resource center, art gallery, and state-run natural arboretum. The 26-acre campus is in a suburban area 5 miles southeast of Lincoln. Including residence halls, there are 11 buildings on campus.

Student Life: About 74% of undergraduates are from out-of-state, mostly the Midwest. Students come from 34 states and 15 foreign countries. Seventeen percent are from public schools; 83% from private. Eighty-five percent are white. The average age of freshmen is 19; all undergraduates, 21.

Housing: College-sponsored living facilities include single-sex dormitories and married-student housing. On-campus housing is guaranteed for all 4 years. Sixty-nine percent of students live on campus. Alcohol is not permitted. All students may keep cars on campus.

Activities: There are no fraternities or sororities on campus. There are 15 groups on campus, including art, band, choir, chorale, computers, honors, international, newspaper, orchestra, photography, religious, student government, and yearbook.

Sports: There is 1 intercollegiate sport for men and 1 for women, and 8 intramural sports for men and 8 for women. Athletic and recreation facilities include an Olympic-size indoor swimming pool, a weight room, tennis courts, and a sandlot volleyball court.

Disabled Students: Seventy-five percent of the campus is accessible to disabled students. The following facilities are available: wheelchair ramps, elevators, special parking, specially equipped rest rooms, and lowered telephones.

Services: There is remedial math, reading, and writing. Tutoring is available upon request.

Campus Safety and Security: Campus safety and security measures include lighted pathways and sidewalks.

Programs of Study: Union awards the B.A., B.S., B.A.T., B.Ed., B.M., and B.S.W. degrees. Associate degrees also are awarded. Bachelor's degrees are awarded in BIOLOGICAL SCIENCE (biology/biological science), BUSINESS (business administration and management), COMMUNICATIONS AND THE ARTS (communications, English, and music), COMPUTER AND PHYSICAL SCIENCE (chemistry, computer science, mathematics, and physics), EDUCATION (business, elementary, music, and secondary), HEALTH PROFESSIONS (medical laboratory technology and nursing), SOCIAL SCIENCE (history, social science, and social work). Business administration has the largest enrollment.

Required: Students must complete 124 semester hours, with fulfillment of a major, and maintain a minimum GPA of 2.0. There are 39 hours of core classes, including those in art/fine arts, computer science, English, history, mathematics, science, and philosophy/religion.

Special: Special academic programs include study abroad in Spain, France, and Austria, co-op programs with 9 Adventist institutions abroad, and cross-registration with the University of Nebraska, Nebraska Wesleyan University, and Southeast Community College.

Student-designed majors are available through the Personalized Bachelor's Degree Program. There are pass/fail options in electives for upperclassmen with a minimum cumulative GPA of 2.0. There is a freshman honors program on campus.

Faculty/Classroom: Fifty-seven percent of faculty are male; 43%, female.

Admissions: About 99% of the 1993–94 applicants were accepted. The ACT scores for the 1993–94 freshman class were as follows: 44% below 21, 22% between 21 and 23, 23% between 24 and 26, 5% between 27 and 28, and 6% above 28. There were 2 National Merit finalists.

Requirements: A minimum GPA of 2.5 and the ACT are required. Freshmen with a high school GPA below 2.5 and/or an ACT composite score below the 20th percentile will be enrolled in the freshman development program. Applicants must have graduated from an accredited secondary school with 18 academic credits, including 3 units of English and 1 unit each of mathematics, science, and history. For mathematics and science programs, 2 units of algebra and 1 unit each of geometry and trigonometry are recommended. For majors in nursing, biology, chemistry, physics, or engineering, applicants should complete physics and chemistry courses. The GED is also accepted. An essay and interview are advised, and music students should audition.

Procedure: Entrance exams should be taken by fall of the senior year. Applications should be filed by July 30 for fall entry, along with an application fee of $10. Notification is sent on a rolling basis.

Transfer: A total of 34 transfer students enrolled in 1993–94. Applicants must have a minimum GPA of 2.0. The ACT is required, and high school and college transcripts must be submitted. A total of 30 credits out of 124 must be completed at Union.

Visiting: There are guides for informal visits and visitors may sit in on classes and stay overnight at the school. To arrange for a visit, contact the Admissions Office.

Financial Aid: In a recent year, 82% of all current freshmen and 78% of continuing students received some form of financial aid. About 41% of freshmen and 49% of continuing students received need-based aid. The average freshman award was $5203. Of that total, scholarships or need-based grants averaged $3150 ($6107 maximum); loans averaged $1041 ($2625 maximum); and work contracts averaged $684 ($2800 maximum). Ninety-two percent of undergraduate students work part-time. Average earnings from campus work for the school year are $840. The average financial indebtedness of the 1992–93 graduate was $6587. Union is a member of CSS. The FAF, FFS, SFS, and FAFSA are accepted; the ASFA is preferred. The deadline for financial aid applications is June 15.

International Students: There are currently 57 international students enrolled. The school actively recruits these students. They must take the TOEFL and achieve a minimum score of 500.

Computers: The college provides computer facilities for student use. The mainframe is an HP 3000. There are also 30 microcomputers available in a computer laboratory. All students may access the system. There are no time limits on using the system and no fees.

Graduates: In an earlier year, 98 bachelor's degrees were awarded.

Admissions Contact: Timothy J. Simon, Director of Enrollment Services.

UNIVERSITY OF NEBRASKA

The University of Nebraska system, established in 1869, is a public system. It is governed by a board of regents and a central administration, whose chief administrator is the president. The primary mission and priorities of the system are teaching, research, and service. The total enrollment of all campuses exceeds 50,000, with more than 3000 faculty members. Altogether there are 263 baccalaureate, 137 master's, and 40 doctoral programs offered within the system. There are four-year campuses located in Kearney, Lincoln, and Omaha. Profiles of those campuses are included in this chapter.

UNIVERSITY OF NEBRASKA AT KEARNEY   D-3

Kearney, NE 68849	**(308) 234-8526; (800) 445-3434 (in-state)**
Full-time: 2722 men, 3042 women	Faculty: 309; IIA, -$
Part-time: 447 men, 729 women	Ph.D.s: 55%
Graduate: 360 men, 745 women	Student/Faculty: 19 to 1
Year: semesters, summer session	Tuition: $1808 ($3090)
Application Deadline: August 1	Room & Board: $2500
Freshman Class: n/av	
ACT: required	**LESS COMPETITIVE**

The University of Nebraska at Kearney, founded in 1903, is a public coeducational facility. There are 4 undergraduate schools and one graduate school. In addition to regional accreditation, UNK has baccalaureate program accreditation with ADA, CSWE, NASM, NCATE, and NLN. The library contains 249,955 volumes, 845,997 microform items, and 72,470 audiovisual forms, and subscribes to 1930 periodicals. Computerized library sources and services include the card catalog, interlibrary loans, and database searching. Special learning facilities include a learning resource center, art gallery, planetarium, radio station, and TV station. The 235-acre campus is in a small town 180 miles west of Omaha. Including residence halls, there are 32 buildings on campus.

Student Life: About 95% of undergraduates are from Nebraska. Students come from 32 states, 48 foreign countries, and Canada. Ninety-four percent are white. The average age of freshmen is 19; all undergraduates, 21. Thirty-five percent drop out by the end of their first year; 46% remain to graduate.

Housing: A total of 2200 students can be accommodated in college housing. College-sponsored living facilities include single-sex and coed dormitories, off-campus apartments, married-student housing, and sorority houses. On-campus housing is guaranteed for the freshman year only and is available on a first-come, first-served basis. Sixty percent of students commute. Alcohol is not permitted. All students may keep cars on campus.

Activities: About 4% of men belong to 7 national fraternities; about 3% of women belong to 4 national sororities. There are 140 groups on campus, including band, cheerleading, choir, chorale, chorus, computers, dance, drama, drill team, ethnic, honors, international, jazz band, marching band, musical theater, newspaper, orchestra, pep band, photography, political, radio and TV, religious, social, social service, student government, and yearbook. Popular campus events include Homecoming, Welcome Week, Bike Bowl, Senior Day, and Counseling Conference.

Sports: There are 8 intercollegiate sports for men and 7 for women, and 14 intramural sports for men and 14 for women. Athletic and recreation facilities include a field, tennis courts, and a new health and sports facility.

Disabled Students: The following facilities are available: wheelchair ramps, elevators, special parking, and specially equipped rest rooms.

Services: In addition to many counseling and information services, tutoring is available in most subjects. In addition, there is a reader service for the blind and remedial reading and writing.

Campus Safety and Security: Campus safety and security measures include 24-hour foot and vehicle patrol, pamphlets, posters, and films, emergency telephones, and lighted pathways and sidewalks.

Programs of Study: UNK awards the B.A., B.S. B.A.Ed., B.F.A., B.S.Ed., and B.G.S. degrees. Master's degrees also are awarded. Bachelor's degrees are awarded in BIOLOGICAL SCIENCE (biology/biological science), BUSINESS (accounting, banking and finance, business administration and management, business economics, management engineering, marketing/retailing/merchandising, personnel management, and tourism), COMMUNICATIONS AND THE ARTS (advertising, broadcasting, communications, dramatic arts, English, fine arts, French, German, journalism, music, Spanish, speech/debate/rhetoric, and telecommunications), COMPUTER AND PHYSICAL SCIENCE (chemistry, computer programming, computer science, earth science, information sciences and systems, mathematics, physics, and statistics), EDUCATION (art, business, early childhood, elementary, foreign languages, health, home economics, industrial arts, middle school, music, physical, science, secondary, special, and teaching English as a second language/foreign language), ENGINEERING AND ENVIRONMENTAL DESIGN (aeronautical science and industrial engineering technology), HEALTH PROFESSIONS (nursing, predentistry, and premedicine), SOCIAL SCIENCE (criminal justice, dietetics, economics, family/consumer studies, geography, history, human development, international studies, political science/government, prelaw, psychology, social science, social work, and sociology). Business administration, elementary education, and physical education have the largest enrollments.

Required: To graduate, all students must complete courses in humanities, communications, civilization, mathematics and natural sciences, and social and behavioral sciences. A minimum of 125 credit hours is required, with approximately 60 in the major. Students must maintain a GPA of 2.0 or higher.

Special: Special arrangements include internships, work-study programs, study at other U.S. colleges and universities under the auspices of the National Student Exchange Program, and study abroad through the International Student Exchange Program. Cooperative programs in some health science majors, an international studies degree, and a credit/no credit grading option are available. There is a freshman honors program on campus. One department has an honors program.

Faculty/Classroom: All faculty teach undergraduates.

Admissions: About 41% of the current freshmen were in the top quarter of their class.

Requirements: The ACT is required. Applicants must be graduates of an accredited secondary school. The GED is accepted. Applicants should have completed 4 years of high school English and 2 years each of mathematics, science, and social studies. AP and CLEP credits are accepted.

Procedure: Freshmen are admitted to all sessions. Entrance exams should be taken in the senior year. Applications should be filed by August 1 for fall entry, along with an application fee of $10. Notification is sent on a rolling basis. There is an early admissions plan.

Transfer: About 525 transfer students enrolled in a recent year. Transfer students must supply transcripts from previous institutions. If the GPA from the previous school is lower than 2.0, students will be evaluated by the Admissions Director. Transfers must show proof of honorable dismissal from the last institution attended. Grades of C and above transfer for credit. A total of 45 credits out of 125 must be completed at UNK.

Visiting: There are regularly scheduled orientations for prospective students. Visits include registration for classes and campus orientation. There are guides for informal visits and visitors may sit in on classes and stay overnight at the school. To arrange for a visit, contact the Admissions Office at (800) 445-3434 (in-state).

Financial Aid: In a recent year, 66% of all current freshmen and 53% of continuing students received some form of financial aid. About 47% of students received need-based aid. Fifty-three percent of undergraduate students work part-time. Average earnings from campus work for the school year are $1500. The average financial indebtedness of a recent graduate was $9000. The FFS is required. The deadline for financial aid applications is March 1.

International Students: There are currently 220 international students enrolled. They must take the TOEFL and achieve a minimum score of 500. The student must also take the SAT I or the ACT.

Computers: The university provides computer facilities for student use. The mainframe is a DEC VAX 8390. There are also 300 IBM and Apple microcomputers available. All students may access the system. There are no time limits on using the system and no fees.

Graduates: Within an average freshman class, 46% graduate in 6 years. Some 100 companies recruited on campus in a recent year.

Admissions Contact: Dr. Wayne Samuelson, Director of Admissions.

UNIVERSITY OF NEBRASKA AT OMAHA   F-3
Omaha, NE 68182   (402) 554-2393

Full-time: 3915 men, 4046 women	Faculty: 410; IIA, av$
Part-time: 2465 men, 2886 women	Ph.D.s: 81%
Graduate: 944 men, 1644 women	Student/Faculty: 19 to 1
Year: semesters, summer session	Tuition: $1889 ($4904)
Application Deadline: August 1	Room & Board: n/app
Freshman Class: 2825 applied, 2584 accepted, 1621 enrolled	
ACT: 20	**LESS COMPETITIVE**

The University of Nebraska at Omaha, established in 1908, is a public, commuter facility that is part of the University of Nebraska system. There are 8 undergraduate schools and one graduate school. In addition to regional accreditation, UNO has baccalaureate program accreditation with AACSB, AHEA, CSWE, and NCATE. The library contains 550,000 volumes, and subscribes to 4000 periodicals. Computerized library sources and services include interlibrary loans. Special learning facilities include a learning resource center, an art gallery, a planetarium, a radio station, and a tv station. The 90-acre campus is in a suburban area. There are 21 buildings on campus.

Student Life: About 93% of undergraduates are from Nebraska. Students come from 16 foreign countries. Eighty-four percent are from public schools; 16% from private. Ninety-three percent are white. The average age of freshmen is 18; all undergraduates, 27.

Housing: There are no residence halls. All students commute. Alcohol is not permitted.

Activities: About 1% of men belong to 9 national fraternities; about 1% of women belong to 7 national sororities. There are 100 groups on campus, including band, cheerleading, choir, chorale, chorus, dance, drama, drill team, ethnic, gay, honors, international, jazz band, marching band, newspaper, pep band, political, professional, radio and tv, religious, social, social service, and student government. Popular campus events include Celebrate UNO, Homecoming, International Week, Honors, Black History Month, and Greek Week.

Sports: There are 4 intercollegiate sports for men and 4 for women, and 16 intramural sports for men and 16 for women. Athletic and recreation facilities include a football field, a field house, and a health, physical education, and recreation building housing basketball and volleyball courts, weight rooms, and a swimming pool.

Disabled Students: The entire campus is accessible to disabled students. The following facilities are available: wheelchair ramps, elevators, special parking, specially equipped rest rooms, special class scheduling, lowered drinking fountains, and lowered telephones.

Services: In addition to many counseling and information services, tutoring is available in some subjects, including mathematics and psychology. There is also a reader service for the blind, and remedial math, reading, and writing.

Campus Safety and Security: Campus safety and security measures include 24-hour foot and vehicle patrol, self-defense education, escort service, and shuttle buses. In addition, there are emergency telephones and lighted pathways and sidewalks.

Programs of Study: UNO awards the B.A., B.S., B.B.A., B.F.A., and B.G.S. degrees. Associate, master's, and doctoral degrees also are awarded. Bachelor's degrees are awarded in BIOLOGICAL SCIENCE (biology/biological science), BUSINESS (accounting, banking and finance, business administration and management, business law, insurance, management information systems, management science, and marketing/retailing/merchandising), COMMUNICATIONS AND THE ARTS (broadcasting, communications, dramatic arts, English, fine arts, French, German, journalism, music, Spanish, and speech/debate/rhetoric), COMPUTER AND PHYSICAL SCIENCE (chemistry, computer science, geology, mathematics, physics, and statistics), EDUCATION (early childhood, elementary, health, physical, secondary, and special), ENGINEERING AND ENVIRONMENTAL DESIGN (civil engineering, engineering physics, engineering technology, industrial engineering, and mechanical engineering), HEALTH PROFESSIONS (premedicine), SOCIAL SCIENCE (African American studies, anthropology, criminal justice, economics, family/consumer studies, geography, history, home economics, interdisciplinary studies, philosophy, political science/government, prelaw, psychology, public administration, social work, sociology, textiles and clothing, and urban studies). Engineering is the strongest academically. Criminal justice has the largest enrollment.

Required: To graduate, students must complete 30 hours of distribution requirements in English and writing, mathematics, public speaking, natural and physical sciences, humanities and fine arts, social and behavioral sciences, and cultural diversity. A total of 125 credit hours is required. Students must maintain a minimum 2.0 GPA.

Special: Internships are available for business students. Cooperative programs are possible, and credit by examination is available. Students may study abroad in various European countries. There is a freshman honors program on campus. Eight departments have honors programs.

Faculty/Classroom: All teach undergraduates.

Admissions: About 91% of the 1993-94 applicants were accepted.

Requirements: The SAT I or ACT is required. In addition, students must be graduates of an accredited secondary school. The GED is accepted. Students must have completed 4 units of English and 2 units each of mathematics, social sciences, and sciences. AP and CLEP credits are accepted.

Procedure: Freshmen are admitted to all sessions. Entrance exams should be taken by the senior year. Applications should be filed by August 1 for fall entry, December 1 for spring entry, and June 1 for summer entry, along with an application fee of $10. Notification is sent on a rolling basis.

Transfer: About 2075 transfer students enrolled in 1993-94. Transfer applicants must present evidence of good standing at the last institution they attended. Grades of C or better transfer for credit. A minimum GPA of 2.0 is required. A total of 30 credits out of 125 must be completed at UNO.

Visiting: There are guides for informal visits and visitors may sit in on classes. To arrange for a visit, contact the Office of Admissions at (402) 554-2393.

Financial Aid: In 1993-94, 46% of all current freshmen and 44% of continuing students received some form of financial aid. About 37% of freshmen and 35% of continuing students received need-based aid. The average freshman award was $3290. Of that total, scholarships or need-based grants averaged $790; loans averaged $1500 ($2625 maximum); and work contracts averaged $100 ($3000 maximum). The average financial indebtedness of the 1992-93 graduate was $6000. UNO is a member of CSS. The FAF, FFS or SFS, and FAFSA are required. The deadline for financial aid applications is March 1.

International Students: There are currently 200 international students enrolled. The school actively recruits these students. They must take the TOEFL and achieve a minimum score of 500.

Computers: The college provides computer facilities for student use. The mainframe is a DEC VAX 8650. There are also microcomputers available in 16 student user rooms. All students may access the system. It may be used 24 hours per day, 7 days per week. There are no time limits on using the system and no fees.

Graduates: In 1992-93, 1519 bachelor's degrees were awarded.

Admissions Contact: John Flemming, Director of Admissions.

UNIVERSITY OF NEBRASKA-LINCOLN   E-3
Lincoln, NE 68588-0417 (402) 472-2023; (800) 742-8800 (in-state)

Full-time: 9019 men, 7611 women	Faculty: 1282; I, -$
Part-time: 1650 men, 1549 women	Ph.D.s: 80%
Graduate: 2550 men, 2316 women	Student/Faculty: 13 to 1
Year: semesters, summer session	Tuition: $2283 ($5628)
Application Deadline: August 1	Room & Board: $2995
Freshman Class: 6277 applied, 6003 accepted, 3398 enrolled	
SAT I Verbal/Math: 447/513	ACT: 22 LESS COMPETITIVE

The University of Nebraska-Lincoln, part of the University of Nebraska system, was founded in 1869 as a land-grant, four-year, coeducational facility. There are 9 undergraduate schools and one graduate school. In addition to regional accreditation, UNL has baccalaureate program accreditation with AACSB, ABET, ACCE, ACEJMC, ADA, AHEA, FIDER, NAAB, NASAD, and NCATE. The 12 libraries contain 2,164,254 volumes, 3,723,785 microform items, and 1902 audiovisual forms, and subscribe to 21,671 periodicals. Computerized library sources and services include the card catalog, interlibrary loans, and database searching. Special learning facilities include a learning resource center, an art gallery, a natural history museum, a planetarium, a radio station, a TV station, a center for mass spectrometry, an observatory, the Buros Institute of Mental Measurements, an animal sciences complex, and a center for performing arts. The 582-acre campus is in an urban area 55 miles southwest of Omaha. Including residence halls, there are 219 buildings on campus.

Student Life: About 93% of undergraduates are from Nebraska. Students come from 50 states, 109 foreign countries, and Canada. Eighty-nine percent are from public schools; 10% from private. Ninety percent are white. The average age of all undergraduates is 22.4. Twenty-eight percent drop out by the end of their first year; 51% remain to graduate.

Housing: A total of 5200 students can be accommodated in college housing. College-sponsored living facilities include single-sex and coed dormitories, on-campus apartments, married-student housing, fraternity houses, and sorority houses. In addition there are floors for modern languages, scholars, engineering, business, and journalism, and an International House. On-campus housing is guaranteed for the freshman year only and is available on a first-come, first-served basis. Fifty-seven percent of students commute. Alcohol is not permitted. All students may keep cars on campus.

Activities: About 15% of men belong to 1 local and 27 national fraternities; about 15% of women belong to 1 local and 17 national sororities. There are 289 groups on campus, including art, band, cheerleading, chess, choir, chorale, chorus, dance, drama, ethnic, film, gay, honors, international, jazz band, literary magazine, marching band, musical theater, newspaper, opera, orchestra, pep band, photography, political, professional, radio and TV, religious, social, social service, student government, symphony, and yearbook. Popular campus events include Cornstock, Walpurgisnacht, Homecoming, Parents Weekend, Freshmen Friday, and Party in the Plains.

Sports: There are 10 intercollegiate sports for men and 10 for women, and 65 intramural sports for men and 45 for women. Athletic and recreation facilities include a recreation center.

Disabled Students: Sixty-five percent of the campus is accessible to disabled students. The following facilities are available: wheelchair ramps, elevators, special parking, specially equipped rest rooms, special class scheduling, lowered drinking fountains, lowered telephones, and the Office of Handicapped Services.

Services: In addition to many counseling and information services, tutoring is available in most subjects. There is a reader service for the blind.

Campus Safety and Security: Campus safety and security measures include 24-hour foot and vehicle patrol, escort service, shuttle buses, and informal discussions. In addition, there are pamphlets, posters, films, emergency telephones, and lighted pathways and sidewalks.

Programs of Study: UNL awards the B.A., B.S., B.B.A., B.F.A., B.J., B.M., B.S.A.E., B.S.Agr., B.S.Arch., B.S.B.S.E., B.S.C.E., B.S.C.M., B.S.C.S., B.S.Ch.E., B.S.E.E., B.S.E.T., B.S.Ed., B.S.H.E., B.S.I.E., B.S.I.T., and B.S.N.R. degrees. Associate, master's, and doctoral degrees also are awarded. Bachelor's degrees are awarded in AGRICULTURE (agricultural business management, agricultural economics, agricultural mechanics, agriculture, animal science, fish and game management, horticulture, and range/farm management), BIOLOGICAL SCIENCE (biochemistry and biology/biological science), BUSINESS (accounting, banking and finance, business administration and management, business economics, hospitality management services, international business management, management science, and marketing/retailing/merchandising), COMMUNICATIONS AND THE ARTS (advertising, art, art history and appreciation, broadcasting, classics, dance, design, dramatic arts, English, fine arts, French, German, Greek, journalism, languages, Latin, music, Russian, Spanish, and speech/debate/rhetoric), COMPUTER AND PHYSICAL SCIENCE (actuarial science, atmospheric sciences and meteorology, chemistry, computer science, geology, mathematics, physics, and statistics), EDUCATION (agricultural, art, business, early childhood, education, elementary, foreign languages, guidance, health, home economics, industrial arts, middle school, music, science, secondary, and special), ENGINEERING AND ENVIRONMENTAL DESIGN (architecture, bioengineering, chemical engineering, civil engineering, computer engineering, construction management, construction technology, drafting and design technology, electrical/electronics engineering, electrical/electronics engineering technology, environmental science, industrial engineering, industrial engineering technology, manufacturing technology, and mechanical engineering), HEALTH PROFESSIONS (dental hygiene, medical laboratory technology, nursing, pharmacy, physical therapy, predentistry, prepharmacy, public health, speech pathology/audiology, and veterinary science), SOCIAL SCIENCE (anthropology, criminal justice, dietetics, economics, food science, geography, history, human development, international relations, Latin American studies, law, parks and recreation management, philosophy, political science/government, psychology, social science, social studies, social work, sociology, textiles and clothing, Western European studies, and women's studies). Biochemistry, engineering, journalism, actuarial science, and psychology are the strongest academically. Psychology, business administration, and elementary education have the largest enrollments.

Required: Each college and major has its own requirements; there are no graduation requirements that apply to all students.

Special: There is cross-registration with many schools, and co-op programs are available in the Colleges of Engineering and Technology and Argriculture. Internship opportunities abound, as do work-study programs. Accelerated degree programs, a Washington semester, B.A.-B.S. degrees, dual majors, student-designed majors, credit by examination, nondegree study, and pass/fail options are also available. There is a freshman honors program on campus, as well as 51 national honor societies, including Phi Beta Kappa. Eighteen departments have honors programs.

Faculty/Classroom: Seventy-four percent of faculty are male; 26%, female. Graduate students teach 24% of introductory courses. The average class size in an introductory lecture is 39; in a laboratory, 18; and in a regular course offering, 28.

Admissions: About 96% of the 1993-94 applicants were accepted. The SAT scores for the 1993-94 freshman class were as follows: Verbal—64% below 500, 26% between 500 and 599, 7% between 600 and 700, and 3% above 700; Math—40% below 500, 33% between 500 and 599, 19% between 600 and 700, and 8% above 700. About 33% of the current freshmen were in the top fifth of their class; 63% were in the top two fifths. There were 28 National Merit finalists.

Requirements: UNL requires applicants to be in the upper 50% of their class. The SAT I or ACT is required. Students must be graduates of an accredited secondary school. The GED is accepted. Students must have completed 3 years of English, 2 years each of mathematics, science, and social studies, and an additional year of language arts. AP and CLEP credits are accepted.

Procedure: Freshmen are admitted to all sessions. Entrance exams should be taken in April of the junior year. Applications should be filed by August 1 for fall entry and December 1 for spring entry, along with an application fee of $25. Notification is sent on a rolling basis.

Transfer: About 1100 transfer students enrolled in 1993-94. Transfer students must have a 2.0 GPA for both the cumulative average of all postsecondary facilities attended and for the most recent term of attendance. In certain majors, a higher GPA and/or extra course work may be required. A total of 30 credits must be completed at UNL.

Visiting: There are regularly scheduled orientations for prospective students, including an information session, a campus tour, a visit to areas of academic interest, and a meeting with a department representative. There are guides for informal visits and visitors may sit in on classes and stay overnight at the school. To arrange for a visit, contact High School and College Relations at (402) 472-2023 or (800) 742-8800.

Financial Aid: In 1993-94, 61% of all students received some form of financial aid. The average freshman award was $4194. Of that total, scholarships or need-based grants averaged $1450 ($6450 maximum); loans averaged $1900 ($6450 maximum); and work contracts averaged $1400. Forty-seven percent of undergraduate students work part-time. Average earnings from campus work for the school year are $1400. UNL is a member of CSS. The FFS is required. The deadline for financial aid applications is March 1.

International Students: There are currently 1521 international students enrolled. They must take the TOEFL and achieve a minimum score of 500.

Computers: The college provides computer facilities for student use. The mainframes are a DEC VAX 8800, a Cyber 930 and 6420, an IBM 4381-14, an HP 850, and an SG4D. There are also 165 microcomputers and 110 terminals in 26 public facilities. Colleges and de-

partments have additional facilities for their own students. Microcomputer facilities are in all residence halls. All facilities are part of the campus network. All students may access the system. It may be used 24 hours a day, 7 days per week. There are no time limits on using the system and no fees.

Graduates: In 1992–93, 3008 bachelor's degrees were awarded. The most popular majors among graduates were psychology (6%), elementary education (6%), and finance (5%). Within an average freshman class, 17% graduate in 4 years, 44% in 5 years, and 52% in 6 years. Some 261 companies recruited on campus in a recent year.

Admissions Contact: Lisa L. Schmidt, Director of High School and College Relations.

WAYNE STATE COLLEGE

E-2

Wayne, NE 68787   (402) 375–7000; (800) 228–9972 **(out-of-state)**

Full-time: 1232 men, 1503 women	Faculty: 130; IIA, --$
Part-time: 181 men, 264 women	Ph.D.s: 66%
Graduate: 159 men, 426 women	Student/Faculty: 21 to 1
Year: semesters, summer session	Tuition: $1690 ($2838)
Application Deadline: open	Room & Board: $2570
Freshman Class: 1375 applied, 1375 accepted, 724 enrolled	
ACT: 20	**NONCOMPETITIVE**

Wayne State College, founded in 1910, is a public, coeducational, liberal arts facility. There are 8 undergraduate schools and one graduate school. In addition to regional accreditation, the college has baccalaureate program accreditation with NCATE. The library contains 170,000 volumes, 545,000 microform items, and 6100 audiovisual forms, and subscribes to 1000 periodicals. Computerized library sources and services include the card catalog and database searching. Special learning facilities include a learning resource center, a planetarium, a radio station, a tv station, and an arboretum. The 128-acre campus is in a rural area 45 miles southwest of Sioux City, Iowa. Including residence halls, there are 25 buildings on campus.

Student Life: About 79% of undergraduates are from Nebraska. Students come from 33 states and 4 foreign countries. Ninety percent are from public schools; 10% from private. Ninety-five percent are white. Forty-nine percent are Protestant; 28% Catholic; 23% claim no religious affiliation. The average age of freshmen is 18; all undergraduates, 23. Thirty-four percent drop out by the end of their first year; 40% remain to graduate.

Housing: A total of 1600 students can be accommodated in college housing. College-sponsored living facilities include single-sex and coed dormitories. On-campus housing is guaranteed for the freshman year only; is available on a first-come, first-served basis, and is available on a lottery system for upperclassmen. Alcohol is not permitted. All students may keep cars on campus.

Activities: About 5% of men belong to 2 national fraternities; about 3% of women belong to 1 national sorority. There are 82 groups on campus, including art, band, cheerleading, chess, choir, chorus, computers, drama, drill team, ethnic, honors, international, jazz band, literary magazine, marching band, newspaper, pep band, political, professional, radio and tv, religious, social, student government, and symphony. Popular campus events include Wildcat Days (Homecoming), International Dinner, Elizabethan Dinners, and Greek Olympics.

Sports: There are 6 intercollegiate sports for men and 6 for women, and 38 intramural sports for men and 38 for women. Athletic and recreation facilities include tennis courts, softball fields, flag football fields, a gymnasium, and a 33,000-square-foot recreation center, which has an indoor track, a weight room, a pool, and handball, volleyball, basketball, and tennis courts.

Disabled Students: Ninety percent of the campus is accessible to disabled students. The following facilities are available: wheelchair ramps, elevators, special parking, specially equipped rest rooms, special class scheduling, lowered drinking fountains, lowered telephones, and a residence hall with accessibility for the disabled; in addition, the school's pool is equipped with special steps.

Services: In addition to many counseling and information services, tutoring is available in most subjects. There is a reader service for the blind.

Campus Safety and Security: Campus safety and security measures include 24-hour foot and vehicle patrol, escort service, and lighted pathways and sidewalks, and In addition, there are articles in the campus newspaper relating to safety and security.

Programs of Study: The college awards the B.A. and B.S. degrees. Master's degrees also are awarded. Bachelor's degrees are awarded in BIOLOGICAL SCIENCE (life science), BUSINESS (business administration and management and sports management), COMMUNICATIONS AND THE ARTS (communications, dramatic arts, English, fine arts, French, German, graphic design, music, Spanish, and speech/debate/rhetoric), COMPUTER AND PHYSICAL SCIENCE (chemistry, computer science, earth science, and mathematics), EDUCATION (art, business, elementary, foreign languages, health, home economics, industrial arts, music, science, and special), ENGINEERING AND ENVIRONMENTAL DESIGN (technological management),

HEALTH PROFESSIONS (health), SOCIAL SCIENCE (counseling psychology, criminal justice, early childhood studies, economics, food production/management/services, geography, history, interdisciplinary studies, international studies, parks and recreation management, political science/government, prelaw, psychology, social science, and sociology).

Required: Students must complete a specified 46-credit general education curriculum. A minimum of 125 credit hours is required for graduation, with 30 to 62 in the major and 40 in upper-division courses. Students must maintain at least a 2.0 GPA.

Special: There are co-op programs, cross-registration with Nebraska Indian Community College and Western Iowa Technical Community College, and study abroad in Denmark. Also offered are pass/fail options, credit by examination, any combination of dual majors, a B.A.-B.S. degree in certain instances, and some student-designed majors. There is a freshman honors program on campus, as well as 3 national honor societies. Seven departments have honors programs.

Faculty/Classroom: Fifty-three percent of faculty are male; 47%, female. All teach undergraduates. Graduate students teach 8% of introductory courses. The average class size in an introductory lecture is 26; in a laboratory, 19; and in a regular course offering, 26.

Admissions: All of the 1993–94 applicants were accepted. The ACT scores for the 1993–94 freshman class were as follows: 54% below 21, 24% between 21 and 23, 15% between 24 and 26, 4% between 27 and 28, and 3% above 28. About 19% of the current freshmen were in the top fifth of their class; 42% were in the top two fifths. Two freshmen graduated first in their class.

Requirements: The SAT I or ACT is required. Applicants must be graduates of an accredited secondary school. The GED is accepted. Entering freshmen must have completed 16 credits, with a recommended 4 units of English, 3 each of mathematics and social studies, and 2 each of science and foreign language. AP and CLEP credits are accepted. Important factors used in the admissions decision are advanced placement or honor courses, evidence of special talent, leadership record, extracurricular activities record, and recommendations by school officials.

Procedure: Freshmen are admitted to all sessions. Entrance exams should be taken in the spring of the junior year or fall of the senior year. The application deadlines are open. The application fee is $10. The college accepts all in-state residents who apply. Notification is sent on a rolling basis. There are early decision, early admissions, and deferred admissions plans. Six early decision candidates were accepted for the 1993–94 class.

Transfer: About 315 transfer students enrolled in 1993–94. Transfer students must have a minimum GPA of 2.0. Grades of C- and above transfer for credit. An interview is recommended. A total of 30 credits out of a minimum of 125 must be completed at the college.

Visiting: There are guides for informal visits and visitors may sit in on classes and stay overnight at the school. To arrange for a visit, contact the Admissions Office at (800) 228–9972.

Financial Aid: In 1993–94, 81% of all current freshmen and 56% of continuing students received some form of financial aid. About 62% of freshmen and 40% of continuing students received need-based aid. The average freshman award was $4320. Of that total, scholarships or need-based grants averaged $1750 ($4825 maximum); loans averaged $2450 ($4125 maximum); and work contracts averaged $1000 ($1250 maximum). The average financial indebtedness of the 1992–93 graduate was $8000. the college is a member of CSS. The FAFSA financial statement is required. The deadline for financial aid applications is May 1.

International Students: There are currently 8 international students enrolled. They must take the TOEFL and achieve a minimum score of 550.

Computers: The college provides computer facilities for student use. The mainframe is a DEC VAX 4000 Model 300. There are networked computer laboratories in the library and the education, business, applied science, and mathematics/science buildings. All students may access the system. It may be used at scheduled times and when the library is open. There are no time limits on using the system and no fees.

Graduates: In 1992–93, 433 bachelor's degrees were awarded. The most popular majors among graduates were business (30%), education (28%), and counseling (6%). Within an average freshman class, 1% graduate in 3 years, 25% in 4 years, 38% in 5 years, and 42% in 6 years. Some 35 companies recruited on campus in 1992–93.

Admissions Contact: Robert Zetocha, Director of Admissions.

YORK COLLEGE

York, NE 68467-2699	**E-3**
	(402) 362-4441; (800) 927-3435
Full-time: 206 men, 219 women	Faculty: 30; III, --$
Part-time: 23 men, 33 women	Ph.D.s: 33%
Graduate: none	Student/Faculty: 14 to 1
Year: semesters, summer session	Tuition: $4760
Application Deadline: April 15	Room & Board: $2850
Freshman Class: 240 applied, 234 accepted, 197 enrolled	
ACT: 20	**COMPETITIVE**

York College, founded in 1890, is an independent, coeducational undergraduate college administered by the Church of Christ. The library contains 50,059 volumes, and subscribes to 150 periodicals. The 40-acre campus is in a small town 45 miles west of Lincoln. Including residence halls, there are 12 buildings on campus.

Student Life: About 75% of undergraduates are from out-of-state, mostly the Midwest. Students come from 31 states, 7 foreign countries, and Canada. Ninety-six percent are from public schools; 4% from private. Ninety-three percent are white. Most are Protestant. The average age of freshmen is 18; all undergraduates, 22. Ten percent drop out by the end of their first year; 65% remain to graduate.

Housing: A total of 450 students can be accommodated in college housing. College-sponsored living facilities include single-sex dormitories. On-campus housing is guaranteed for all 4 years. Sixty-seven percent of students live on campus; of those, 85% remain on campus on weekends. Alcohol is not permitted. All students may keep cars on campus.

Activities: About 60% of men belong to 5 local fraternities; about 65% of women belong to 5 local sororities. There are 25 groups on campus, including art, chess, choir, chorus, computers, drama, honors, literary magazine, musical theater, newspaper, photography, political, professional, religious, social, social service, student government, and yearbook. Popular campus events include High School Days, Fall Musical, Lectureship, All School Banquet, SongFest, and Soul Quest.

Sports: There are 6 intercollegiate sports for men and 7 for women, and 6 intramural sports for men and 5 for women. Athletic and recreation facilities include basketball, tennis, and volleyball courts; a gymnasium; soccer, baseball, and intramural fields; and a weight room.

Services: There is remedial math and reading. Peer tutoring is available.

Campus Safety and Security: Campus safety and security measures include lighted pathways and sidewalks.

Programs of Study: York awards the B.A. and B.S.Ed. degrees. Associate degrees also are awarded. Bachelor's degrees are awarded in BUSINESS (accounting, business administration and management, and human resources), COMMUNICATIONS AND THE ARTS (English), EDUCATION (education), SOCIAL SCIENCE (biblical studies, liberal arts/general studies, and religious education). Education and business have the largest enrollments.

Required: To graduate, students must complete 128 to 130 credits with a 2.0 minimum GPA, which includes a general education requirement of 18 hours of humanities, 10 of science, 12 of social science, 10 of Bible, and 2 of physical education. The major requirements vary according to concentration.

Special: Summer internships are required in biblical studies, and work-study is available on campus. Honors and independent study are available as adjuncts to a normal course load. Study abroad in 4 countries is possible in summer session. There is a freshman honors program on campus, as well as one national honor society. Two departments have honors programs.

Faculty/Classroom: Seventy-three percent of faculty are male; 27%, female. All teach undergraduates. The average class size in an introductory lecture is 30; in a laboratory, 20; and in a regular course offering, 25.

Admissions: About 98% of the 1993-94 applicants were accepted. There was 1 National Merit semifinalist. Five freshmen graduated first in their class.

Requirements: A minimum GPA of 2.5 is required. The SAT I or ACT is required. An ACT composite score of 17 is recommended. At least 15 high school units must have been completed. AP and CLEP credits are accepted. Important factors used in the admissions decision are ability to finance college education, personality, intangible qualities, evidence of special talent, geographic diversity, and leadership record.

Procedure: Freshmen are admitted to all sessions. Entrance exams should be taken before July. Applications should be filed by April 15 for fall entry, along with an application fee of $20. Notification is sent on a rolling basis. There is an early admissions plan.

Transfer: About 30 transfer students enrolled in 1993-94. Transcripts of previous work must be submitted. An average of C or better is required.

Visiting: There are regularly scheduled orientations for prospective students, including financial aid and admissions consultations and a campus tour. There are guides for informal visits, and visitors may sit in on classes and stay overnight at the school. To arrange for a visit, contact Steddon Sikes, Director of Admissions at (402) 362-4441.

Financial Aid: In 1993-94, 93% of all current freshmen and 95% of continuing students received some form of financial aid. About 75% of freshmen and 78% of continuing students received need-based aid. The average freshman award was $5485. Ninety-two percent of undergraduate students work part-time. The FAFSA financial statement is required.

International Students: There are currently 16 international students enrolled. They must take the TOEFL and achieve a minimum score of 500. They must also take the SAT I (with a minimum composite score of 680) or the ACT.

Computers: The college provides computer facilities for student use. All students may access the system 8 A.M. to 10:30 P.M. weekdays, and various times on weekends. There are no time limits on using the system and no fees.

Graduates: In 1992-93, 9 bachelor's degrees were awarded. The most popular major among graduates was Bible (100%).

Admissions Contact: Steddon Sikes, Director of Admissions.

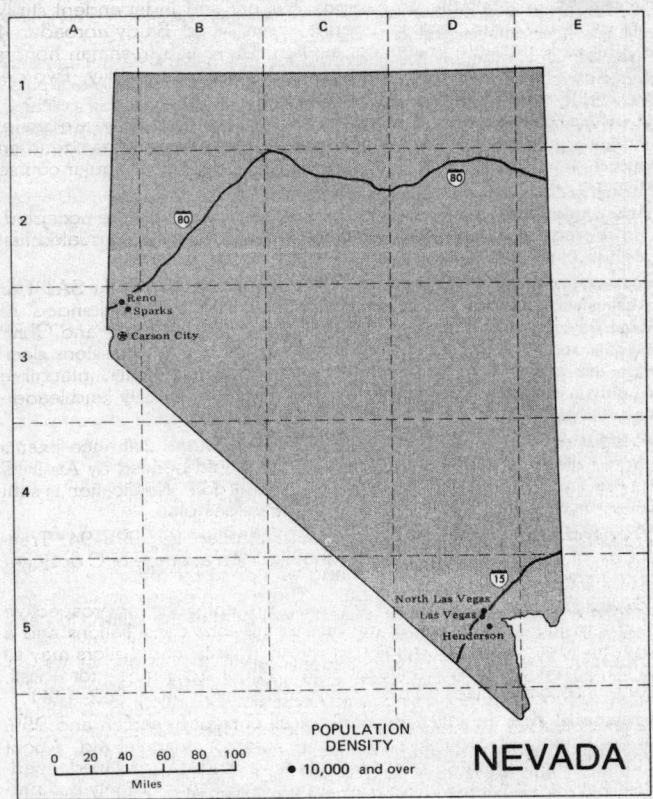

POPULATION
DENSITY

● 10,000 and over

0   20 40 60 80 100
Miles

NEVADA

SIERRA NEVADA COLLEGE

Incline Village, NV 89450

A-3

(702) 831–1314
(800) 332–8666 (out-of-state)

Full-time: 100 men, 60 women
Part-time: 170 men, 170 women
Graduate: none
Year: semesters, summer session
Application Deadline: open
Freshman Class: 150 applied, 150 accepted, 60 enrolled
ACT: 23

Faculty: 12
Ph.D.s: 60%
Student/Faculty: 13 to 1
Tuition: $9000
Room & Board: $5000

NONCOMPETITIVE

Sierra Nevada College, founded in 1969, is a private coeducational institution offering programs in liberal arts, art, business, hotel resort management, ski business management, music, and teacher preparation. The library contains 20,000 volumes and 10,000 microform items, and subscribes to 100 periodicals. Special learning facilities include an art gallery, an observatory, and a recording studio. The 17-acre campus is in a rural area 25 miles west of Reno.

Student Life: About 70% of undergraduates are from out-of-state, mostly the West. Students come from 30 states, 8 foreign countries, and Canada. Sixty percent are from public schools; 40% from private. The average age of freshmen is 19; all undergraduates, 25. Fifteen percent drop out by the end of their first year; 50% remain to graduate.

Housing: A total of 120 students can be accommodated in college housing. College-sponsored living facilities include on-campus apartments and off-campus apartments. On-campus housing is guaranteed for all 4 years and is available on a first-come, first-served basis. Priority is given to out-of-town students. Alcohol is not permitted.

Activities: There are no fraternities or sororities on campus. There are many groups and organizations on campus, including art, choir, chorale, chorus, dance, honors, international, jazz band, musical theater, newspaper, orchestra, political, student government, and symphony. Popular campus events include Bohemia Night and Nevada Day.

Sports: Athletic and recreation facilities include nearby ski areas and fields, courts for volleyball and softball, and a series of guided walks to scenic locations around the Lake Tahoe area.

Services: Remedial math, reading, and writing are available.

Programs of Study: SNC awards the B.A., B.S., and B.F.A. degrees. Bachelor's degrees are awarded in BIOLOGICAL SCIENCE (ecology), BUSINESS (business administration and management, hospitality management services, and recreational facilities management), COMMUNICATIONS AND THE ARTS (fine arts, music, and studio art), COMPUTER AND PHYSICAL SCIENCE (science), ENGINEERING AND ENVIRONMENTAL DESIGN (environmental science), SOCIAL SCIENCE (humanities).

Required: All students must complete a minimum of 120 semester hours, including 40 in the upper division, while maintaining a minimum GPA of 2.0. Students also must pass the writing proficiency examination and meet distribution requirements of the general education curriculum in 4 interdisciplinary themes: symbols, relationships with nature and humans, memberships in groups and institutions, and ethics, values, and beliefs.

Special: Student-designed majors, work-study programs, internships, credit for life experiences and volunteer community work, and nondegree study are offered.

Faculty/Classroom: Sixty percent of faculty are male; 40%, female.

Admissions: All of the 1993–94 applicants were accepted.

Requirements: SNC requires applicants to be in the upper 50% of their class. A minimum GPA of 2.0 is required. The SAT I or ACT is recommended. All applicants are reviewed individually. In addition, an essay and audition are required, and an interview is recommended. The GED is accepted. AP and CLEP credits are accepted. Important factors used in the admissions decision are ability to finance college education, advanced placement or honor courses, extracurricular activities record, personality, intangible qualities, and parents or siblings attending the school.

Procedure: Freshmen are admitted to all sessions. Entrance exams should be taken in the senior year. Application deadlines are open. Application fee is $25. Notification is sent on a rolling basis. There are early decision and deferred admissions plans.

Transfer: About 50 transfer students enrolled in a recent year. The college accepts applications from students who have completed any course at an accredited postsecondary institution. If fewer than 15 credits have been earned, the high school transcript is also needed. A total of 96 credits out of 120 must be completed at SNC.

Visiting: There are guides for informal visits and visitors may sit in on classes and stay overnight at the school. To arrange for a visit, contact Lane Murray, Director of Admissions/Retention at (800) 332–8666 or (702) 831–1314.

Financial Aid: In a recent year, 60% of all current freshmen and 60% of continuing students received some form of financial aid. About 45% of freshmen and 45% of continuing students received need-based aid. The average freshman award was $6400. Of that total, scholarships or need-based grants averaged $2900 ($10,000 maximum); loans averaged $2625 ($6625 maximum); and work contracts averaged $2000. Seventy-five percent of undergraduate students work part-time. Average earnings from campus work for the school year are $1500. The average financial indebtedness of the 1992–93 graduate was $15,000. SNC is a member of CSS. The FAF is required. The deadline for financial aid applications is July 1.

International Students: There are currently 25 international students enrolled. The school actively recruits these students. They must take the TOEFL and achieve a minimum score of 500.

Computers: The college provides computer facilities for student use. The mainframe is an IBM. All students may access the system. It may be used 8 A.M. to 9 P.M. daily. There are no time limits on using the system and no fees.

Admissions Contact: Lane Murray, Director of Admissions/Retention.

UNIVERSITY OF NEVADA SYSTEM

The University of Nevada system, established in 1865, is a public system in Nevada. It is governed by a board of regents, whose chief administrator is the chancellor. The primary goals of the system are teaching, research, and public service. The main priorities are to provide all public programs of postsecondary instruction in Nevada, to sponsor programs of basic and applied research that contribute to the cultural, economic, and social development of Nevada, and to sponsor programs of public service for citizens of the state. The total enrollment of all 7 campuses usually exceeds 63,000, with more than 1732 faculty members. Altogether, there are 135 baccalaureate, 97 master's, and 34 doctoral programs offered within University of Nevada system. There are four-year campuses in Las Vegas and Reno. Profiles of those campuses are included in this chapter.

UNIVERSITY OF NEVADA
LAS VEGAS
Las Vegas, NV 89154   **D-5**

(702) 895-3443
(800) 334-UNLV (out-of-state)

Full-time: 5110 men, 5250 women	Faculty: 617; IIA, av$
Part-time: 2870 men, 3590 women	Ph.D.s: 73%
Graduate: 1150 men, 1540 women	Student/Faculty: 17 to 1
Year: semesters, summer session	Tuition: $1705 ($6005)
Application Deadline: August 16	Room & Board: $4700

Freshman Class: 4436 applied, 3491 accepted, 2069 enrolled
SAT I Verba;/Math: 418/487   ACT: 21   **COMPETITIVE**

University of Nevada/Las Vegas, established in 1957, is a state-supported institution, offering undergraduate and graduate programs in business, education, health science, engineering, science and mathematics, hotel administration, fine and performing arts, liberal arts, and human performance and development. There are 9 undergraduate schools and one graduate school. In addition to regional accreditation, UNLV has baccalaureate program accreditation with AACSB, ABET, CSWE, NASM, NCATE, and NLN. The library contains 625,829 volumes, 1,105,960 microform items, and 78,267 audiovisual forms, and subscribes to 6000 periodicals. Computerized library sources and services include the card catalog and interlibrary loans. Special learning facilities include a learning resource center, an art gallery, a natural history museum, and a radio station. The 335-acre campus is in an urban area. Including residence halls, there are 54 buildings on campus.

Student Life: About 87% of undergraduates are from Nevada. Students come from 50 states, 51 foreign countries, and Canada. Eighty-three percent are white. The average age of all undergraduates is 24. Thirty-two percent drop out by the end of their first year.

Housing: A total of 1088 students can be accommodated in college housing. College-sponsored living facilities include single-sex and coed dormitories. In addition there are special interest houses and substance-free, study-intensive, recess housing. On-campus housing is guaranteed for the freshman year only and is available on a first-come, first-served basis. Priority is given to out-of-town students. Ninety-four percent of students commute. All students may keep cars on campus.

Activities: There are 10 national fraternities and 5 national sororities. There are 85 groups on campus, including band, cheerleading, choir, chorus, computers, dance, drama, drill team, ethnic, gay, honors, international, jazz band, marching band, musical theater, newspaper, orchestra, pep band, political, professional, radio and tv, religious, social, student government, symphony, and yearbook. Popular campus events include October Fest and Homecoming.

Sports: There are 7 intercollegiate sports for men and 7 for women, and 8 intramural sports for men and 8 for women. Athletic and recreation facilities include an arena, a football stadium, tennis courts, softball and soccer fields, raquetball courts, a weight room, and 2 gymnasiums.

Disabled Students: All of the campus is accessible to disabled students. The following facilities are available: wheelchair ramps, elevators, special parking, specially equipped rest rooms, lowered drinking fountains, and lowered telephones.

Services: In addition to many counseling and information services, tutoring is available in every subject. There is also a reader service for the blind, and remedial math, reading, and writing.

Campus Safety and Security: Campus safety and security measures include 24-hour foot and vehicle patrol, self-defense education, escort service, and shuttle buses. In addition, there are emergency telephones.

Programs of Study: UNLV awards the B.A. and B.S. degrees. Master's and doctoral degrees also are awarded. Bachelor's degrees are awarded in BIOLOGICAL SCIENCE (biology/biological science), BUSINESS (accounting, banking and finance, hotel/motel and restaurant management, management information systems, management science, and marketing/retailing/merchandising), COMMUNICATIONS AND THE ARTS (communications, dance, dramatic arts, English, fine arts, French, German, music, romance languages, and Spanish), COMPUTER AND PHYSICAL SCIENCE (chemistry, computer science, earth science, geology, mathematics, physics, and radiological technology), EDUCATION (elementary, health, physical, recreation, secondary, and special), ENGINEERING AND ENVIRONMENTAL DESIGN (architectural engineering, civil engineering, computer engineering, electrical/electronics engineering, and mechanical engineering), HEALTH PROFESSIONS (clinical science, health care administration, and nursing), SOCIAL SCIENCE (anthropology, criminal justice, economics, history, interdisciplinary studies, philosophy, political science/government, psychology, public administration, social science, social work, and sociology). Hotel administration is the strongest academically. Liberal Arts and business and economics have the largest enrollments.

Required: Students must complete 124 credits, with 45 of these credits in the student's major, and must maintain a minimum GPA of 2.0. All students must meet core requirements that include courses in English, logic and mathematics, the Constitution, social science, fine arts, science, and humanities.

Special: Opportunities are provided for internships, an accelerated degree program, B.A.-B.S. degrees, dual majors, credit by examination, credit for military service, nondegree study, pass/fail options, and study abroad in 7 countries. There is a freshman honors program on campus, as well as 16 national honor societies, including Phi Beta Kappa. Eleven departments have honors programs.

Faculty/Classroom: Seventy percent of faculty are male; 30%, female. Ninety-five percent teach undergraduates and 5% do research. The average class size in an introductory lecture is 21 and in a laboratory, 20.

Admissions: About 79% of the 1993–94 applicants were accepted. About 30 freshmen graduated first in their class.

Requirements: A minimum GPA of 2.3 is required. The SAT I or ACT is recommended. Graduation from an accredited secondary school is required. Applicants should submit an academic record distributed as follows: 4 credits in English, 3 each in history, social studies, mathematics, science, and at least one-half credit in computer studies. AP and CLEP credits are accepted. Important factors used in the admissions decision are advanced placement or honor courses, evidence of special talent, leadership record, personality, intangible qualities, and recommendations by school officials.

Procedure: Freshmen are admitted to all sessions. Applications should be filed by August 16 for fall entry, January 3 for spring entry, and June 15 for summer entry, along with an application fee of $20. Notification is sent on a rolling basis. There is an early decision plan. Notification for early decision is sent 2 weeks after the completed application is received.

Transfer: About 1720 transfer students enrolled in 1993–94. Applicants should present a minimum GPA of 2.0. and a minimum of 15 credits for transfer. The SAT I or the ACT is recommended. A total of 30 credits out of 124 must be completed at UNLV.

Visiting: There are regularly scheduled orientations for prospective students. There are guides for informal visits and visitors may sit in on classes. To arrange for a visit, contact the Admissions Office at (800) 334-UNLV.

Financial Aid: In 1993–94, 50% of all current freshmen received some form of financial aid. Seventy-five percent of undergraduate students work part-time. UNLV is a member of CSS. The FAF, FFS or SFS, U.S.A. Funds Singlefile Form, and FAFSA are required. The deadline for financial aid applications is February 15.

International Students: There are currently 377 international students enrolled. The school actively recruits these students. They must take the TOEFL or the University of Michigan Language Test and achieve a minimum score on the TOEFL of 500.

Computers: The college provides computer facilities for student use. The mainframe is a CDC CYBER 830. There are also 100 IBM, Apple, and Zenith microcomputers available in computer laboratories. All students may access the system. It may be used 24 hours a day, 7 days a week. There are no time limits on using the system. The fees are $25.

Graduates: In an earlier year, 1820 bachelor's degrees were awarded. Some 200 companies recruited on campus in 1992–93.

Admissions Contact: Larry Mason, Director of Admissions.

UNIVERSITY OF NEVADA
RENO
Reno, NV 89557   **A-3**

(702) 784-6865; (800) 622-4867 (in-state)

Full-time: 3085 men, 3040 women	Faculty: 541; I, -$
Part-time: 1148 men, 1336 women	Ph.D.s: 77%
Graduate: 1338 men, 1666 women	Student/Faculty: 11 to 1
Year: semesters, summer session	Tuition: $1665 ($5965)
Application Deadline: July 1	Room & Board: $4070

Freshman Class: 2279 applied, 1924 accepted, 1255 enrolled
SAT I Verbal/Math: 432/488   ACT: 22   **COMPETITIVE**

The University of Nevada/Reno, established in 1874, is a land-grant institution and part of the University of Nevada System. It offers programs in agriculture, arts and science, business administration, education, engineering, human and community sciences, journalism, medicine, mines, and nursing. There are 10 undergraduate schools and one graduate school. In addition to regional accreditation, UNR has baccalaureate program accreditation with AACSB, ABET, ACEJMC, AHEA, CSWE, NASM, NCATE, and NLN. The 6 libraries contain 795,000 volumes, 3.4 million microform items, and 26,000 audiovisual forms, and subscribe to 5000 periodicals. Computerized library sources and services include the card catalog, interlibrary loans, and database searching. Special learning facilities include a learning resource center, a planetarium, a radio station, and a TV station. The

200-acre campus is in an urban area north of Reno's business district. Including residence halls, there are 68 buildings on campus.

Student Life: About 82% of undergraduates are from Nevada. Students come from 46 states, 61 foreign countries, and Canada. Ninety-five percent are from public schools; 10% from private. Eighty-one percent are white. The average age of freshmen is 19; all undergraduates, 25. Thirty-three percent drop out by the end of their first year.

Housing: A total of 1149 students can be accommodated in college housing. College-sponsored living facilities include single-sex and coed dormitories, on-campus apartments, off-campus apartments, and married-student housing. In addition there are honors houses. On-campus housing is available on a first-come, first-served basis. Eighty percent of students commute. All students may keep cars on campus.

Activities: About 10% of men belong to 1 local and 10 national fraternities; about 3% of women belong to 3 national sororities. There are 100 groups on campus, including art, band, cheerleading, chess, choir, chorale, chorus, dance, drama, drill team, ethnic, film, gay, honors, international, jazz band, literary magazine, marching band, musical theater, newspaper, orchestra, pep band, photography, political, professional, radio and tv, religious, social, social service, student government, symphony, and yearbook. Popular campus events include Mackay Week, Winter Carnival, and Homecoming.

Sports: There are 8 intercollegiate sports for men and 8 for women, and 14 intramural sports for men and 11 for women. Athletic and recreation facilities include a recreation center, a stadium seating 30,000, a gymnasium seating 6,000, an auditorium seating 12,500, and an indoor events center seating 11,500.

Disabled Students: Ninety-nine percent of the campus is accessible to disabled students. The following facilities are available: wheelchair ramps, elevators, special parking, specially equipped rest rooms, special class scheduling, lowered drinking fountains, and lowered telephones.

Services: In addition to many counseling and information services, tutoring is available in most subjects. There is a reader service for the blind, and remedial math, reading, and writing. Students are mainstreamed with special services for the disabled.

Campus Safety and Security: Campus safety and security measures include 24-hour foot and vehicle patrol, escort service, shuttle buses, and lighted pathways and sidewalks.

Programs of Study: UNR awards the B.A., B.S., B.A.C.J., B.A.Ed., B.A.F.A., B.G.S., B.M., B.S.B.A., B.S.C.E., B.S.Ch., B.S.Ch.E., B.S.Comp.Sci., B.S.Ed., B.S.E.E., B.S.Eng.Phys., B.S.G., B.S.G.Eng., B.S.Geog., B.S.Geophys., B.S.H.E., B.S.M.E., B.S.Med.Sci., B.S.Met.E., B.S.Min.E., B.S.N., and B.S.Vet.Sci. degrees. Master's and doctoral degrees also are awarded. Bachelor's degrees are awarded in AGRICULTURE (agricultural economics, animal science, and natural resource management), BIOLOGICAL SCIENCE (biochemistry, biology/biological science, and nutrition), BUSINESS (accounting, banking and finance, business economics, and management science), COMMUNICATIONS AND THE ARTS (applied music, dramatic arts, English, French, German, journalism, music, Spanish, and speech/debate/rhetoric), COMPUTER AND PHYSICAL SCIENCE (chemistry, computer science, information sciences and systems, mathematics, and physics), EDUCATION (agricultural, elementary, health, music, secondary, and special), ENGINEERING AND ENVIRONMENTAL DESIGN (chemical engineering, civil engineering, electrical/electronics engineering, engineering physics, geological engineering, and mechanical engineering), HEALTH PROFESSIONS (clinical science, nursing, predentistry, premedicine, speech pathology/audiology, and veterinary science), SOCIAL SCIENCE (anthropology, child care/child and family studies, criminal justice, geography, history, international relations, philosophy, political science/government, psychology, social psychology, social work, and sociology). Chemistry and physics are the strongest academically. Business has the largest enrollment.

Required: All students must complete 124 to 134 semester credits and earn a GPA of 2.0. Core curriculum requirements include 3 to 6 credits of writing, 3 each of mathematics, social science, and fine arts, 6 each of natural science and capstone courses, and 9 of the Western tradition.

Special: Cooperative programs are available through the Cooperative Institute for Aerospace and Terrestrial Applications. The university coordinates research funded by NASA and other agencies. Internships through the engineering department and study abroad in France, Spain, and London are offered. Cross-registration through the Western Interstate Commission for Higher Education and the National Student Exchange also is possible. Work-study at the school, accelerated degree programs, numerous B.A.-B.S. degrees, dual majors, a general studies degree, student-designed majors, credit for military experience, nondegree study, and pass/fail options are available. There is a freshman honors program on campus.

Faculty/Classroom: Seventy-two percent of faculty are male; 28%, female. One-hundred percent both teach and do research.

Admissions: About 84% of the 1993–94 applicants were accepted. The SAT scores for the 1993–94 freshman class were as follows: Verbal—64% below 500, 26% between 500 and 599, 8% between 600 and 700, and 1% above 700; Math—61% below 500, 26% between 500 and 599, 8% between 600 and 700, and 5% above 700. The ACT scores were 36% below 21, 34% between 21 and 23, 17% between 24 and 26, 10% between 27 and 28, and 3% above 28. There were 2 National Merit finalists and 7 semifinalists. Three freshmen graduated first in their class.

Requirements: A minimum GPA of 2.5 is required. The SAT I or ACT is required. The ACT is preferred. In addition, applicants should have completed 13 1/2 academic credits, including 4 in English, 3 each in mathematics, science, and social studies/history, and a half credit in computer literacy. The GED is not accepted. AP and CLEP credits are accepted. Important factors used in the admissions decision are advanced placement or honor courses, recommendations by school officials, leadership record, geographic diversity, and recommendations by alumni.

Procedure: Freshmen are admitted fall and spring. Entrance exams should be taken in October for fall admission. Applications should be filed by July 1 for fall entry and November 1 for spring entry, along with an application fee of $20. Notification is sent on a rolling basis. There are early admissions and deferred admissions plans.

Transfer: About 930 transfer students enrolled in 1993–94. Transfer applicants should have a 2.0 GPA and 15 transferrable credits. A total of 32 credits out of 124 to 134 must be completed at UNR.

Visiting: There are regularly scheduled orientations for prospective students. There are guides for informal visits and visitors may sit in on classes. To arrange for a visit, contact the Office of Outreach Services/the Office for Prospective Students at (702) 784–4865.

Financial Aid: In 1993–94, 65% of all current freshmen and 30% of continuing students received some form of financial aid. Scholarships or need-based grants averaged $700 ($2500 maximum); loans averaged $1500 ($4000 maximum); and work contracts averaged $3000 ($3500 maximum). The average financial indebtedness of the 1992–93 graduate was $4000. The FFS and the college's own financial statement is required. The deadline for financial aid applications is April 15.

International Students: There are currently 209 international students enrolled. The school actively recruits these students. They must take the TOEFL and achieve a minimum score of 500.

Computers: The college provides computer facilities for student use. The mainframe is an IBM 3090. There are various computer laboratories within each college designed for local area networks as well as for networking with the mainframe. All students may access the system. There are no time limits on using the system. The fees vary per class laboratory session.

Graduates: In 1992–93, 1168 bachelor's degrees were awarded.

Admissions Contact: Dr. Melisa N. Choroszy, Director of Admissions and Registrar.

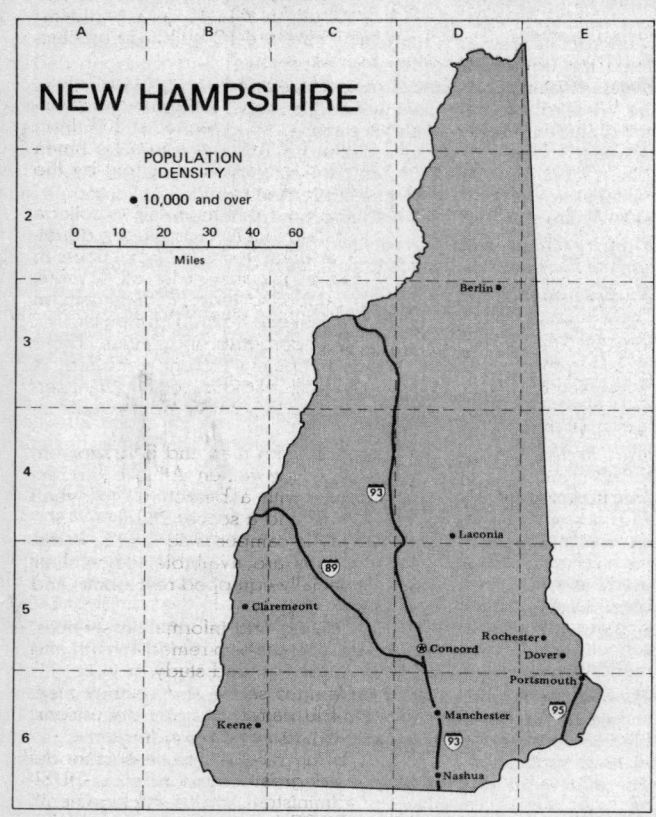

NEW HAMPSHIRE

POPULATION DENSITY

● 10,000 and over

0 10 20 30 40 60
Miles

Berlin

93

Laconia

89

Claremont

Concord Rochester
Dover
Portsmouth
93

Keene Manchester

93

Nashua

COLBY-SAWYER COLLEGE
New London, NH 03257

C-5

(603) 526-3700
(800) 272-1015 (out-of-state)

Full-time: 215 men, 435 women	Faculty: 36; IIB, --$
Part-time: 20 men and women	Ph.D.s: 70%
Graduate: none	Student/Faculty: 18 to 1
Year: semesters	Tuition: $13,375
Application Deadline: May	Room & Board: $5120
Freshman Class: 910 applied, 776 accepted, 208 enrolled	
SAT I Verbal/Math: 440/443	ACT: 20 **LESS COMPETITIVE**

Colby-Sawyer College, established in 1837, is an independent coeducational college offering a variety of undergraduate programs, including education, fine arts, nursing, business, and communications. In addition to regional accreditation, Colby-Sawyer has baccalaureate program accreditation with NLN. The library contains 70,000 volumes, 97,500 microform items, and 760 audiovisual forms, and subscribes to 580 periodicals. Special learning facilities include a learning resource center, an art gallery, a radio station, an academic development center, and a laboratory school (K-3). The 80-acre campus is in a small town 100 miles northwest of Boston. Including residence halls, there are 21 buildings on campus.

Student Life: About 70% of undergraduates are from out-of-state, mostly the Northeast. Students come from 29 states, 7 foreign countries, and Canada. Ninety-six percent are white. The average age of freshmen is 18; all undergraduates, 20. Fourteen percent drop out by the end of their first year; 65% remain to graduate.

Housing: A total of 600 students can be accommodated in college housing. College-sponsored living facilities include single-sex and coed dormitories and on-campus apartments. On-campus housing is guaranteed for all 4 years. Eighty-five percent of students live on campus; of those, 70% remain on campus on weekends. Upperclassmen may keep cars on campus.

Activities: There are no fraternities or sororities on campus. There are 22 groups on campus, including art, dance, drama, drill team, film, honors, jazz band, literary magazine, musical theater, newspaper, photography, radio and tv, social, social service, student government, and yearbook. Popular campus events include Fall and Spring Weekend and Mountain Day.

Sports: Athletic and recreation facilities include tennis courts, a fitness center, an NCAA swimming pool, an indoor track, and squash and racquetball courts.

Disabled Students: Special parking is available.

Services: In addition to many counseling and information services, tutoring is available in every subject.

Campus Safety and Security: Campus safety and security measures include 24-hour foot and vehicle patrol, escort service, shuttle buses, and informal discussions. In addition, there are pamphlets, posters, and films, emergency telephones, and lighted pathways and sidewalks.

Programs of Study: Colby-Sawyer awards the B.A., B.S., and B.F.A. degrees. Associate degrees also are awarded. Bachelor's degrees are awarded in BIOLOGICAL SCIENCE (biology/biological science), BUSINESS (business administration and management and sports management), COMMUNICATIONS AND THE ARTS (communications, design, English, and fine arts), EDUCATION (early childhood and secondary), HEALTH PROFESSIONS (nursing and sports medicine), SOCIAL SCIENCE (psychology). Education, sports science, and nursing have the largest enrollments.

Required: Required courses include writing, mathematics, and computer literacy. Four required interdisciplinary core courses are Creative Expression, Process of Discovery, Social Analysis, and Judgment and Belief. Required electives include 1 each in fine and performing arts and natural sciences and 2 each in social sciences and humanities. A total of 120 credit hours, with a minimum GPA of 2.0, is needed for graduation.

Special: There is cross-registration through the New Hampshire College and University Council. Students may choose internships (required in some majors) and study abroad in Greece, England, and various other countries. A Washington semester is available. Other options include student-designed majors, credit by examination, and a general studies degree. There is one national honor society on campus.

Faculty/Classroom: Forty-eight percent of faculty are male; 52%, female. All teach undergraduates. The average class size in a regular course offering is 17.

Admissions: About 85% of the 1993-94 applicants were accepted.

Requirements: A minimum GPA of 2.0 is required. The SAT I or ACT is required. The GED is accepted. A total of 15 college preparatory credits is recommended for admission, including 4 years of English, 2 of history, 2 of a foreign language, 2 of science, and 3 of mathematics. An essay is required, as are 2 letters of recommendation. Interviews are strongly recommended. AP and CLEP credits are accepted. Important factors used in the admissions decision are advanced placement or honor courses, leadership record, evidence of special talent, extracurricular activities record, and recommendations by school officials.

Procedure: Freshmen are admitted fall and spring. Applications should be filed by May for fall entry and November for spring entry, along with an application fee of $40. Notification is sent on a rolling basis. There is a deferred admissions plan.

Transfer: About 25 transfer students enrolled in 1993-94. College-level work will be emphasized. College transcripts, course descriptions, and a dean's form are required in addition to the standard requirements. A minimum of 30 credits out of 120 must be completed at Colby-Sawyer.

Visiting: There are regularly scheduled orientations for prospective students, including Open House in the fall and spring and a See and Ski program in the winter. There are guides for informal visits and visitors may sit in on classes. To arrange for a visit, contact the Admissions Office at (603) 526-3700.

Financial Aid: In 1993-94, 64% of all current freshmen and 68% of continuing students received some form of financial aid. About 52% of freshmen and 60% of continuing students received need-based aid. The average freshman award was $11,760. Of that total, scholarships or need-based grants averaged $9105 ($15,890 maximum); and loans averaged $2655 ($3000 maximum). Forty percent of undergraduate students work part-time. Average earnings from campus work for the school year are $840. The average financial indebtedness of the 1992-93 graduate was $8520. Colby-Sawyer is a member of CSS. The FAF, the college's own financial statement, and the FAFSA are required. The deadline for financial aid applications is February 15.

International Students: There are currently 10 international students enrolled. The school actively recruits these students. They must take the TOEFL and achieve a minimum score of 500. The student must also take the SAT I or the ACT.

Computers: The college provides computer facilities for student use. The mainframe is a DEC VAX 4300. Three student computer laboratories, comprising 45 IBM-compatible and 15 Apple Macintosh microcomputers, are available on campus.

Graduates: In 1992–93, 80 bachelor's degrees were awarded. The most popular majors among graduates were child studies (education) (23%), business (16%), and sports science (15%). Within an average freshman class, 55% graduate in 4 years and 65% in 5 years. In the 1992 graduating class, 3% of all graduates women were enrolled in graduate school within 6 months of graduation; 85% had found employment.

Admissions Contact: Office of Admissions and Financial Aid.

COLLEGE FOR LIFELONG LEARNING   E-5
(Formerly School for Lifelong Learning)
Durham, NH 03824   (603) 862–1692; (800) 582–7248 (in-state)

Full-time: 79 men, 146 women	Faculty: 300
Part-time: 341 men, 1183 women	Ph.D.s: 60%
Graduate: none	Student/Faculty: 5 to 1
Year: semesters, summer session	Tuition: $3060 ($3300)
Application Deadline: open	Room & Board: n/app
Freshman Class: n/av	
SAT I or ACT: not required	**NONCOMPETITIVE**

The College for Lifelong Learning, established as part of the University System of New Hampshire in 1972, is a state-supported, commuter institution offering undergraduate programs for adults in general and professional studies. The campus is in a small town.

Student Life: About 93% of undergraduates are from New Hampshire. Students come from 4 states and 1 foreign country.

Housing: All students commute. Alcohol is not permitted on campus.

Activities: There are no fraternities or sororities on campus.

Sports: There is no sports program at CLL.

Programs of Study: CLL awards the B.G.S. and B.P.S. degrees. Associate degrees also are awarded. Bachelor's degrees are awarded in BUSINESS (management science) and SOCIAL SCIENCE (behavioral science).

Required: Students must complete 124 credits, 30 to 36 in the major, and maintain a minimum GPA of 2.0. All students are required to complete skill courses in functional understanding, computer literacy, critical thinking, writing, mathematics, and communications.

Special: Opportunities are provided for internships through the Washington Center, cross-registration with all USNH schools, student-designed and dual majors, credit by examination, nondegree study, and pass/fail options. CLL offers programs throughout the state, in 4 regions and 12 local sites. There is one national honor society on campus.

Faculty/Classroom: Sixty percent of faculty are female. All teach undergraduates. The average class size in a regular course offering is 11.

Requirements: The SAT I or ACT is not required. A GED will be considered if submitted for admission evaluation. An interview is recommended. AP and CLEP credits are accepted.

Procedure: Application deadlines are open. Application fee is $35. The college accepts all applicants. Notification is sent on a rolling basis.

Transfer: Nearly all the students have previously attended other colleges. An interview is recommended. A total of 30 credits out of 124 must be completed at CLL.

Visiting: Visitors may sit in on classes.

Financial Aid: Financial applications are accepted on an ongoing basis. The FAF is required.

International Students: There are currently 5 international students enrolled. They must take the TOEFL and achieve a minimum score of 500.

Computers: The college provides computer facilities for student use. The mainframe is a DEC VAX. Students have no mainframe access, but may use microcomputers in 5 laboratories. There are no time limits on using the system and no fees.

Graduates: In 1992–93, 116 bachelor's degrees were awarded. The most popular majors among graduates were behavioral science (46%), management (40%), and self-designed studies (14%).

Admissions Contact: Tessa McDonnell, Admissions Office.

DANIEL WEBSTER COLLEGE   D-6
Nashua, NH 03063–1300   (603) 883–3556

Full-time: 368 men, 82 women	Faculty: 23
Part-time: 8 men, 2 women	Ph.D.s: 35%
Graduate: none	Student/Faculty: 20 to 1
Year: semesters	Tuition: $11,828
Application Deadline: open	Room & Board: $4656
Freshman Class: 585 applied, 505 accepted, 153 enrolled	
SAT I Verbal/Math: 438/490	**LESS COMPETITIVE**

Daniel Webster College, founded in 1965, is a private coeducational college offering study in the fields of aviation, business, computer sciences, and engineering. The library contains 35,000 volumes, 410 microform items, and 432 audiovisual forms, and subscribes to 250 periodicals. Computerized library sources and services include inter-library loans and database searching. Special learning facilities include a learning resource center and a flight center, a flight tower, air traffic control laboratories, flight simulators, a hangar, and 26 airplanes. The 50-acre campus is in a suburban area 45 miles northwest of Boston. Including residence halls, there are 12 buildings on campus.

Student Life: About 82% of undergraduates are from out-of-state, mostly the Northeast. Students come from 21 states, 6 foreign countries, and Canada. Eighty percent are from public schools; 20% from private. Ninety-three percent are white. The average age of freshmen is 18; all undergraduates, 20. Twenty-five percent drop out by the end of their first year; 53% remain to graduate.

Housing: A total of 380 students can be accommodated in college housing. College-sponsored living facilities include single-sex dormitories and on-campus apartments. In addition there are quiet floors in residence halls. On-campus housing is guaranteed for all 4 years. Seventy percent of students live on campus; of those, 80% remain on campus on weekends. All students may keep cars on campus.

Activities: There are no fraternities or sororities on campus. There are 16 groups on campus, including computers, honors, jazz band, literary magazine, newspaper, professional, religious, social, social service, student government, and yearbook. Popular campus events include Spring Weekend and Ski Day.

Sports: There are 4 intercollegiate sports for men and 5 for women, and 15 intramural sports for men and 10 for women. Athletic and recreation facilities include a gymnasium with a basketball/volleyball court and a weight room; tennis courts; and a soccer field.

Disabled Students: Sixty percent of the campus is accessible to disabled students. The following facilities are available: wheelchair ramps, elevators, special parking, specially equipped rest rooms, and lowered drinking fountains.

Services: In addition to many counseling and information services, tutoring is available in every subject. There is also remedial math and writing, study skills and test skills workshops, and study groups.

Campus Safety and Security: Campus safety and security measures include 24-hour foot and vehicle patrol, informal discussions, pamphlets, posters, films, and lighted pathways and sidewalks.

Programs of Study: DWC awards the B.S. degree. Associate degrees also are awarded. Bachelor's degrees are awarded in BUSINESS (accounting and business administration and management), COMPUTER AND PHYSICAL SCIENCE (computer science), ENGINEERING AND ENVIRONMENTAL DESIGN (aviation administration/management and computer technology). Aviation, computer science, and computer systems are the strongest academically. Aviation has the largest enrollment.

Required: Students must complete general education courses in communication, computer science, mathematics, and natural science, the humanities, and the social sciences. At least 120 credits, with a minimum of 30 in the major, are required for graduation. Students must maintain a minimum GPA of 2.0.

Special: There is cross-registration with the New Hampshire College and University Council. All programs offer credit by examination. Interdisciplinary majors, including aviation management/flight operations and aviation management/air traffic control are available. Study abroad, internships in aviation, business, and computer sciences, a general studies degree, and a 2–2 engineering program with the universities of New Hampshire and Massachusetts at Lowell are additional options. There is one national honor society on campus, Phi Beta Kappa.

Faculty/Classroom: Seventy-eight percent of faculty are male; 22%, female. All teach undergraduates. The average class size in an introductory lecture is 25; in a laboratory, 17; and in a regular course offering, 20.

Admissions: About 86% of the 1993–94 applicants were accepted. About 23% of the current freshmen were in the top fifth of their class; 52% were in the top two fifths. Four freshmen graduated first in their class.

Requirements: The SAT I or ACT is required of bachelor degree students and recommended to associate degree students. Applicants must be graduates of an accredited secondary school or submit the GED. Students should have taken 4 years of English, 3 years of mathematics, 2 years each of social studies and science, and 1 year of history. An essay and an interview are recommended. AP and CLEP credits are accepted. Important factors used in the admissions decision are advanced placement or honor courses, recommendations by school officials, leadership record, extracurricular activities record, and personality, intangible qualities.

Procedure: Freshmen are admitted to all sessions. Entrance exams should be taken in early fall. Application deadlines are open. Application fee is $30. Notification is sent on a rolling basis. There are early admissions and deferred admissions plans.

Transfer: About 35 transfer students enrolled in a recent year. Transfer students must have a minimum GPA of 2.0. The SAT I is required. Grades of C or better transfer for credit. A total of 30 credits out of a minimum of 120 must be completed at DWC.

Visiting: There are regularly scheduled orientations for prospective students, including a tour and an admissions interview; also available are meetings with faculty and meals. There are guides for informal visits and visitors may sit in on classes and stay overnight at the school. To arrange for a visit, contact Terry Whittum, Director of Admissions, at (603) 883–3556, ext. 224.

Financial Aid: In 1993–94, 78% of all current freshmen and 75% of continuing students received some form of financial aid. About 78% of freshmen and 73% of continuing students received need-based aid. The average freshman award was $10,060. Of that total, scholarships or need-based grants averaged $6366 ($11,800 maximum); loans averaged $2972 ($3625 maximum); and work contracts averaged $1180 ($1200 maximum). Twenty-five percent of undergraduate students work part-time. Average earnings from campus work for the school year are $1043. The average financial indebtedness of the 1992–93 graduate was $13,963. DWC is a member of CSS. The college's own financial statement and FAFSA are required. The deadline for financial aid applications is March 15.

International Students: There are currently 6 international students enrolled. They must take the TOEFL and achieve a minimum score of 500.

Computers: The college provides computer facilities for student use. The mainframes are a DEC MicroVAX 3800, DEC System 5400, and an IBM RS/6000. The 3 mainframes and more than 40 PCs, 25 of which are part of a Novell Ethernet local area network, are available to all students. All students may access the system. It may be used when the computer center is open. There are no time limits on using the system and no fees.

Graduates: In 1992–93, 161 bachelor's degrees were awarded. The most popular majors among graduates were aviation management/flight operations (28%), aviation management (19%), and business management (11%). Within an average freshman class, 3% graduate in 3 years, 27% in 4 years, 8% in 5 years, and 2% in 6 years. In the 1992 graduating class, 89% of all graduates had found employment within 6 months of graduation.

Admissions Contact: Terry Whittum, Director of Admissions.

DARTMOUTH COLLEGE
Hanover, NH 03755   **B-4**
                                               (603) 646–2875

Full-time: 2308 men, 1967 women	**Faculty:** 344; I, +$
Part-time: none	**Ph.D.s:** 92%
Graduate: 930 men and women	**Student/Faculty:** 12 to 1
Year: see profile	**Tuition:** $18,375
Application Deadline: January 1	**Room & Board:** $5979

Freshman Class: 8586 applied, 2241 accepted, 1087 enrolled
SAT I Verbal/Math: 640/710   **MOST COMPETITIVE**

Dartmouth College, chartered in 1769, is a private liberal arts institution offering a wide range of graduate and undergraduate programs. There is a year-round academic calendar of 4 10-week terms plus a summer session. There are 4 graduate schools. The 8 libraries contain 2 million volumes and 1.2 million microform items, and subscribe to 21,000 periodicals. Computerized library sources and services include the card catalog. Special learning facilities include a learning resource center, an art gallery, radio and TV stations, a center for performing arts, and an observatory. The 265-acre campus is in a small town 140 miles northwest of Boston. Including residence halls, there are 100 buildings on campus.

Student Life: About 96% of undergraduates are from out-of-state, mostly the Middle Atlantic. Students come from 50 states, 54 foreign countries, and Canada. Sixty-five percent are from public schools; 35% from private. Seventy-one percent are white. The average age of freshmen is 18; all undergraduates, 21. One percent drop out by the end of their first year; 97% remain to graduate.

Housing: A total of 3500 students can be accommodated in college housing. College-sponsored living facilities include coed dormitories, on-campus apartments, married-student housing, fraternity houses, and sorority houses. In addition there are language houses and special interest houses. On-campus housing is guaranteed for the freshman year only, is available on a first-come, first-served basis, and is available on a lottery system for upperclassmen. Ninety-five percent of students live on campus; of those, 90% remain on campus on weekends. Upperclassmen may keep cars on campus.

Activities: About 45% of men belong to 7 local and 10 national fraternities; about 40% of women belong to 3 local and 4 national sororities. There are 100 groups on campus, including art, band, cheerleading, chess, choir, chorale, chorus, computers, dance, drama, ethnic, film, gay, honors, international, jazz band, literary magazine, marching band, musical theater, newspaper, opera, orchestra, pep band, photography, political, radio and TV, religious, social, social service, student government, symphony, and yearbook. Popular campus events include Dartmouth Night/Homecoming, winter and summer carnivals, and Green Key Service Weekend.

Sports: There are 19 intercollegiate sports for men and 13 for women, and 25 intramural sports for men and 25 for women. Athletic and recreation facilities include a 2100-seat stadium, a fitness center, squash and racquetball courts, a dance studio, a 5000-seat arena, a gymnasium, a 21,000-seat football stadium, a boat house, indoor and outdoor tennis courts, a golf course, and a riding farm.

Disabled Students: The following facilities are available: wheelchair ramps, elevators, special parking, specially equipped rest rooms, special class scheduling, and lowered drinking fountains.

Services: In addition to many counseling and information services, tutoring is available in every subject. There is a reader service for the blind and an academic skills center for all students.

Campus Safety and Security: Campus safety and security measures include 24-hour foot and vehicle patrol, self-defense education, escort service, and shuttle buses. In addition, there are informal discussions, pamphlets, posters, films, emergency telephones, and lighted pathways and sidewalks.

Programs of Study: Dartmouth awards the B.A. and B.Eng. degrees. Master's and doctoral degrees also are awarded. Bachelor's degrees are awarded in BIOLOGICAL SCIENCE (biochemistry and biology/biological science), COMMUNICATIONS AND THE ARTS (art history and appreciation, Chinese, classics, comparative literature, creative writing, dramatic arts, English, film arts, fine arts, French, German, Greek, Italian, languages, Latin, literature, music, romance languages, Russian, Spanish, and visual and performing arts), COMPUTER AND PHYSICAL SCIENCE (chemistry, computer science, earth science, geology, mathematics, and physics), EDUCATION (education), ENGINEERING AND ENVIRONMENTAL DESIGN (engineering and environmental science), SOCIAL SCIENCE (African American studies, African studies, anthropology, archeology, Asian/Oriental studies, economics, geography, history, Native American studies, philosophy, political science/government, psychology, religion, Russian and Slavic studies, social science, sociology, and women's studies). History, government, engineering, and economics have the largest enrollments.

Required: All students must complete 35 courses and meet distributive requirements consisting of 12 courses outside the major, including 4 courses each from the sciences, social sciences, and humanities. Students must also elect 1 course focusing on non-Western culture, and must become proficient in at least 1 foreign language. Specific required courses include freshman English and a freshman seminar.

Special: Students may design programs using the college's unique Dartmouth Plan, which divides the academic calendar into 4 10-week terms, based on the seasons. The plan permits greater flexibility for vacations and for the 45 study abroad programs in 18 countries, including Italy, France, Scotland, the former U.S.S.R., and Brazil. Cross-registration is offered through the Twelve College Exchange Network, which includes Amherst and Mt. Holyoke. Exchange programs also exist with the University of California at San Diego, McGill University in Montreal, selected German universities, Keio University in Tokyo, and Beijing Normal University in China. There are special academic programs in Washington, D.C., and Tucson, Arizona. Students may design their own interdisciplinary majors, involving multiple departments if desired, take dual majors in all fields, or satisfy a modified major involving 2 departments, with emphasis in one. Hands-on computer science education, internships, combined B.A.-B.S. degrees, and work-study programs also are available. A 3–2 engineering degree is offered with Dartmouth's Thayer School of Engineering. There is a chapter of Phi Beta Kappa on campus.

Faculty/Classroom: Sixty-five percent of faculty are male; 35%, female. All teach undergraduates and do research. No introductory courses are taught by graduate students. The average class size in a regular course offering is 23.

Admissions: About 26% of the 1993–94 applicants were accepted. The SAT scores for the 1993–94 freshman class were as follows: Verbal—4% below 500, 24% between 500 and 599, 55% between 600 and 700, and 17% above 700; Math—1% below 500, 9% between 500 and 599, 34% between 600 and 700, and 56% above 700. About 95% of the current freshmen were in the top fifth of their class; 99% were in the top two fifths. About 175 freshmen graduated first in their class.

Requirements: The SAT I or ACT is required, as are 3 SAT II: Subject tests. Evidence of intellectual capacity, motivation, and personal integrity are prime considerations in the highly competitive admissions process, which also considers talent, accomplishment, and involvement in nonacademic areas. Course requirements are flexible, but students are urged to take English, foreign language, mathematics, laboratory science, and history. The GED is accepted. AP credits are accepted.

Procedure: Freshmen are admitted in the fall. Entrance exams should be taken no later than January of the senior year. Early decision applications should be filed by November 10; regular applications, by January 1 for fall entry, along with an application fee of $60. Notification of early decision is sent December 15; regular decision, April 2. There are early decision and deferred admissions plans. About 300

early decision candidates were accepted for the 1993–94 class. A waiting list is an active part of the admissions procedure.

Transfer: Twenty-nine transfer students enrolled in 1993–94. Transfers must demonstrate high achievement and intellectual motivation through college transcripts as well as standardized test scores and high school transcripts.

Visiting: There are regularly scheduled orientations for prospective students, including tours, group information sessions, and interviews. There are guides for informal visits and visitors may sit in on classes and stay overnight at the school. To arrange for a visit, contact the Office of Admissions at (603) 646–2875.

Financial Aid: In 1993–94, 47% of all current freshmen and 44% of continuing students received some form of financial aid including need-based aid. The average freshman award was $17,369. Of that total, scholarships or need-based grants averaged $12,614 ($24,000 maximum); loans averaged $2300; and work contracts averaged $2300. Dartmouth is a member of CSS. The FAF and the college's own financial statement are required. The application deadline is February 1.

International Students: There are currently 234 international students enrolled. The school actively recruits these students. They must take the TOEFL. The student must also take SAT I or the ACT, and any 3 SAT II: Subject tests.

Computers: The college provides computer facilities for student use. The mainframes are an IBM, a DEC, and a Honeywell. More than 7000 PCs are available for student use. Every room on campus, including dorms, is wired into the network, and all students are required to have a personal computer. The Apple Macintosh, which Dartmouth offers at a substantial discount, is recommended. All students may access the system 24 hours daily. There are no time limits and no fees.

Graduates: In 1992–93, 994 bachelor's degrees were awarded. Within an average freshman class, 97% graduate in 4 years. Some 200 companies recruited on campus in 1992–93.

Admissions Contact: Karl Furstenberg, Dean of Admissions.

FRANKLIN PIERCE COLLEGE

	C-6
Rindge, NH 03461–0060	(603) 899–4050
	(800) 437–0048 (out-of-state)

Full-time: 611 men, 570 women	Faculty: 76; IIB, av$
Part-time: 24 men, 34 women	Ph.D.s: 62%
Graduate: none	Student/Faculty: 16 to 1
Year: semesters, summer session	Tuition: $12,820
Application Deadline: open	Room & Board: $4450
Freshman Class: 5187 applied, 4471 accepted, 447 enrolled	
SAT I Verbal/Math: 403/424	**LESS COMPETITIVE**

Franklin Pierce College, founded in 1962, is a private liberal arts institution that also has an extensive continuing education program and offers bachelor's degrees from locations in Concord, Keene, Salem, Nashua, and Portsmouth in New Hampshire. The library contains 69,587 volumes, 25,600 microform items, and 1394 audiovisual forms, and subscribes to 650 periodicals. Computerized library sources and services include the card catalog, interlibrary loans, and database searching. Special learning facilities include a learning resource center, art gallery, radio station, and TV station. The 1000-acre campus is in a rural area 65 miles northwest of Boston. Including residence halls, there are 29 buildings on campus.

Student Life: About 88% of undergraduates are from out-of-state, mostly the Northeast. Students come from 28 states, 18 foreign countries, and Canada. Eighty-six percent are from public schools; 14% from private. Ninety percent are white. Thirty-seven percent are Protestant; 36% Catholic; 23% Jewish. The average age of freshmen is 19; all undergraduates, 20. Twenty-nine percent drop out by the end of their first year; 42% remain to graduate.

Housing: A total of 1075 students can be accommodated in college housing. College-sponsored living facilities include single-sex and coed dormitories, on-campus apartments, and off-campus apartments. On-campus housing is guaranteed for all 4 years. Eighty-six percent of students live on campus; of those, 70% remain on campus on weekends. All students may keep cars on campus.

Activities: There are no fraternities or sororities. There are 34 groups on campus, including art, cheerleading, chess, choir, chorale, computers, dance, drama, ethnic, gay, honors, international, jazz band, literary magazine, musical theater, newspaper, photography, political, professional, radio and TV, religious, social, social service, student government, and yearbook. Popular campus events include Winter Carnival, Spring and Fall Weekend, the performance of the Messiah, and cultural and lecture series.

Sports: There are 6 intercollegiate sports for men and 6 for women, and 10 intramural sports for men and 7 for women. Athletic and recreation facilities include a field house, a fitness center, an 800-seat gymnasium, an athletic trainer, playing fields, a lake with a beach, a fleet of sailboats, cross-country trails, and courts for tennis, basketball, and volleyball.

Disabled Students: Ninety percent of the campus is accessible to disabled students. The following facilities are available: wheelchair ramps, elevators, special parking, specially equipped rest rooms, special class scheduling, and lowered drinking fountains and telephones.

Services: In addition to many counseling and information services, tutoring is available in most subjects. There is a reader service for the blind, and remedial math, reading, and writing.

Campus Safety and Security: Campus safety and security measures include 24-hour foot and vehicle patrol, escort service, shuttle buses, and informal discussions. In addition, there are pamphlets, posters, films, emergency telephones, and lighted pathways and sidewalks.

Programs of Study: FPC awards the B.A. and B.S. degrees. Bachelor's degrees are awarded in BIOLOGICAL SCIENCE (biology/biological science), BUSINESS (accounting, banking and finance, business administration and management, international business management, management science, and marketing/retailing/merchandising), COMMUNICATIONS AND THE ARTS (advertising, broadcasting, communications, dramatic arts, English, fine arts, French, music, Spanish, and theater design), COMPUTER AND PHYSICAL SCIENCE (computer management, computer mathematics, computer science, and mathematics), EDUCATION (art, elementary, foreign languages, science, secondary, and social science), ENGINEERING AND ENVIRONMENTAL DESIGN (environmental science), HEALTH PROFESSIONS (predentistry, premedicine, and preveterinary science), SOCIAL SCIENCE (anthropology, archeology, economics, history, parks and recreation management, prelaw, psychology, social work, and sociology). Anthropology, biology, English, and psychology are the strongest academically. Communications, graphics, business, and education have the largest enrollments.

Required: Students must complete 128 semester hours with a cumulative GPA of at least 2.0 and pass examinations for writing and mathematics competency. Individual and community core requirements total 11 courses, including individual and community, college writing, integrated science, American experience, twentieth century, foundations of mathematics, experiencing the arts, ancient and medieval worlds, reason and romanticism, science of society, and a senior liberal arts seminar.

Special: Cross-registration is offered in nearly every subject through the New Hampshire College and University Council, a 13-member consortium of area institutions. Study at Richmond College in London, internships in most majors, on or off campus, and work-study through the college are possible. In addition, accelerated degree programs in all majors, dual majors in most fields, student-designed majors, credit for life experience, and nondegree study are available. There is a freshman honors program on campus, as well as 2 national honor societies.

Faculty/Classroom: Seventy-one percent of faculty are male; 29%, female. All teach undergraduates. The average class size in an introductory lecture is 25; in a laboratory, 20; and in a regular course offering, 18.

Admissions: About 86% of the 1993–94 applicants were accepted. The SAT scores for the 1993–94 freshman class were as follows: Verbal—86% below 500, 13% between 500 and 599, and 1% between 600 and 700; Math—77% below 500, 18% between 500 and 599, 4% between 600 and 700, and 1% above 700. About 11% of the current freshmen were in the top fifth of their class; 27% were in the top two fifths.

Requirements: A minimum GPA of 1.5 is required. The SAT I or ACT is required, but with no minimum score. Applicants must have earned 10 academic units or 16 Carnegie units in high school, including 4 years of English, 2 each in mathematics and science, and 1 each in history and social studies. An interview is recommended. The GED is accepted. AP and CLEP credits are accepted. Important factors in the admissions decision are recommendations by school officials, leadership record, extracurricular activities record, advanced placement or honor courses, and evidence of special talent.

Procedure: Freshmen are admitted to all sessions. Entrance exams should be taken in the fall of the senior year. Application deadlines are open. Notification is sent on a rolling basis. There are early admissions and deferred admissions plans.

Transfer: Thirty-six transfer students enrolled in 1993–94. A minimum 2.0 GPA in college work is required. Students with fewer than 30 credits must submit SAT I results (no minimum score) and official high school transcripts. A personal recommendation is necessary and an interview recommended. A total of 30 credits out of 128 must be completed at FPC.

Visiting: There are regularly scheduled orientations for prospective students, including open houses held each spring and fall; interviews and tours are available weekdays and most Saturdays. There are guides for informal visits and visitors may sit in on classes. To arrange for a visit, contact Admissions at (800) 437–0048 or (603) 899–4050.

Financial Aid: In 1993–94, 76% of all current freshmen and 73% of continuing students received some form of financial aid. About half of all students received need-based aid. The average freshman award

was $9673. Of that total, scholarships or need-based grants averaged $4811 ($5600 maximum); loans averaged $3572 ($4825 maximum); and work contracts averaged $1010 ($2100 maximum). Forty-six percent of undergraduate students work part-time. Average earnings from campus work for the school year are $760. The average financial indebtedness of the 1992–93 graduate was $12,390. FPC is a member of CSS. The FAFSA financial statement is required. The application deadline is March 15.

International Students: There are currently 43 international students enrolled. The school actively recruits these students. They must take the TOEFL and achieve a minimum score of 500.

Computers: The college provides computer facilities for student use. There are 2 DOS laboratories and 1 Apple Macintosh laboratory, both enhanced with a NOVELL network, forming a campuswide academic network. About 85 computers are available to students. Campuswide electronic mail, word processing, spreadsheets, database management, and statistics are available. All students may access the system. It may be used 16 hours daily. There are no time limits on using the system and no fees.

Graduates: In 1992–93, 217 bachelor's degrees were awarded. The most popular majors among graduates were mass communication (11%), graphic communications (11%), and education (11%). Within an average freshman class, 7% graduate in 3 years, 35% in 4 years, 48% in 5 years, and 46% in 6 years. Some 47 companies recruited on campus in 1992–93.

Admissions Contact: Thomas E. Desrosiers, Director of Admissions.

KEENE STATE COLLEGE   B-6
Keene, NH 03431   (603) 358–2276; (800) 833–4800 (tri-state area)

Full-time: 1521 men, 1959 women	Faculty: 159
Part-time: 371 men, 554 women	Ph.D.s: 75%
Graduate: 153 men, 281 women	Student/Faculty: 22 to 1
Year: semesters, summer session	Tuition: $3120 ($7960)
Application Deadline: April 1	Room & Board: $3961
Freshman Class: 3121 applied, 2446 accepted, 822 enrolled	
SAT I Verbal/Math: 424/463	**COMPETITIVE**

Keene State College, founded in 1909, is part of the public University System of New Hampshire and offers a liberal arts program that includes teacher preparation, art, and business emphases. In addition to regional accreditation, KSC has baccalaureate program accreditation with NASM and NCATE. The library contains 187,831 volumes and 567,530 microform items, and subscribes to 994 periodicals. Computerized library sources and services include the card catalog, interlibrary loans, and database searching. Special learning facilities include a learning resource center, an art gallery, a planetarium, a radio station, a TV station, and The Holocaust Resource Center. The 150-acre campus is in a suburban area 90 miles northwest of Boston. Including residence halls, there are 35 buildings on campus.

Student Life: About 62% of undergraduates are from New Hampshire. Students come from 28 states, 27 foreign countries, and Canada. Eighty percent are from public schools; 20% from private. Some 90% are white. Forty-eight percent are Catholic; 21% claim no religious affiliation; 20% are Protestant. The average age of freshmen is 19; all undergraduates, 22. Twenty-six percent drop out by the end of their first year; 54% remain to graduate.

Housing: A total of 1999 students can be accommodated in college housing. College-sponsored living facilities include single-sex and coed dormitories, on-campus apartments, married-student housing, fraternity houses, and sorority houses. In addition, there are honors, language, and special interest houses, and wellness and drug-free areas. On-campus housing is guaranteed for the freshman year only and is available on a lottery system for upperclassmen. Fifty-eight percent of students live on campus. Upperclassmen may keep cars on campus.

Activities: About 20% of men belong to 3 local and 3 national fraternities; about 20% of women belong to 2 local and 4 national sororities. There are 60 groups on campus, including art, band, cheerleading, choir, chorale, chorus, computers, dance, drama, ethnic, film, gay, honors, jazz band, musical theater, newspaper, orchestra, pep band, photography, political, professional, radio and TV, religious, social, student government, and yearbook. Popular campus events include Parent and Family Weekend, Homecoming, Winter Carnival, Spring Weekend, and Diversity Day.

Sports: There are 7 intercollegiate sports for men and 8 for women, and 10 intramural sports for men and 7 for women. Athletic and recreation facilities include a 1500-seat gymnasium, a 1000-seat stadium for soccer and field hockey, an indoor pool, a fitness center, racquetball, tennis, and squash courts, and a training room.

Disabled Students: Ninety percent of the campus is accessible to disabled students. The following facilities are available: wheelchair ramps, elevators, special parking, specially equipped rest rooms, and lowered drinking fountains and telephones.

Services: In addition to many counseling and information services, tutoring is available in most subjects. There are also writing process, reading, and math centers, and a reader service for the blind.

Campus Safety and Security: Campus safety and security measures include 24-hour foot and vehicle patrol, escort service, shuttle buses, and informal discussions. In addition, there are pamphlets, posters, films, emergency telephones, and lighted pathways and sidewalks.

Programs of Study: KSC awards the B.A., B.S., B.M. degrees. Associate and master's degrees also are awarded. Bachelor's degrees are awarded in BIOLOGICAL SCIENCE (biology/biological science), BUSINESS (sports management), COMMUNICATIONS AND THE ARTS (dramatic arts, English, fine arts, French, journalism, music, music performance, and Spanish), COMPUTER AND PHYSICAL SCIENCE (chemistry, computer mathematics, computer science, geology, and mathematics), EDUCATION (early childhood, elementary, foreign languages, home economics, industrial arts, mathematics, music, physical, science, secondary, special, and vocational), ENGINEERING AND ENVIRONMENTAL DESIGN (environmental science, industrial engineering technology, and occupational safety and health), HEALTH PROFESSIONS (sports medicine), SOCIAL SCIENCE (American studies, dietetics, geography, history, political science/government, psychology, safety management, and sociology). Education is the strongest academically. Education, management, psychology, industrial technology and safety, and fine and performing arts have the largest enrollments.

Required: All students must take 120 to 142 credits, with at least 30 hours in their major, while maintaining a minimum 2.0 GPA. Distribution requirements include 5 courses in the arts and humanities, 4 each in the social sciences, mathematics, and sciences, and 1 in English composition. Students also must demonstrate competence in mathematics.

Special: Cross-registration through New Hampshire College and the University Council, internships and co-op programs in all areas of study, study abroad in numerous countries, and work-study at the college are available. Students also may take dual and individualized majors, a general studies degree, accelerated degrees in the honors program, and a 3–2 engineering degree with Clarkson University or the University of New Hampshire. In addition, there is credit for life experience and pass/fail options. There is a freshman honors program on campus, as well as 12 national honor societies. One department has an honors program.

Faculty/Classroom: Fifty-eight percent of faculty are male; 42%, female. All teach undergraduates. No introductory courses are taught by graduate students. The average class size in an introductory lecture is 25; in a laboratory, 8; and in a regular course offering, 18.

Admissions: About 78% of the 1993–94 applicants were accepted. The SAT scores for the 1993–94 freshman class were as follows: Verbal—87% below 500, 12% between 500 and 599, and 1% between 600 and 700; Math—72% below 500, 23% between 500 and 599, and 5% between 600 and 700. About 14% of the current freshmen were in the top fifth of their class; 31% were in the top two fifths. Two freshmen graduated first in their class.

Requirements: KSC requires applicants to be in the upper 50% of their class. A minimum GPA of 2.3 is required. The SAT I (preferred) or ACT is required, with recommended scores of 450 verbal and 450 mathematics on SAT I. Applicants need at least 11 academic credits, including 4 years of English, 3 each of mathematics, science, and social studies, and 1 of history. An essay, portfolio, and audition are required for certain programs, and an interview is recommended. AP and CLEP credits are accepted. Important factors used in the admissions decision are advanced placement or honor courses, recommendations by school officials, evidence of special talent, extracurricular activities record, and leadership record.

Procedure: Freshmen are admitted in the fall and spring. Entrance exams should be taken during the spring of the junior year, or fall of the senior year. Applications should be filed by April 1 for fall entry and December 1 for spring entry. The application fee is $20 in-state and $30 for out-of-state students. Notification is sent on a rolling basis. There is a deferred admissions plan.

Transfer: A total of 314 transfer students enrolled in 1993–94. Transfer students must have a 2.0 cumulative GPA and at least 12 college credits. An interview is recommended. A total of 24 credits out of 120 to 142 must be completed at KSC.

Visiting: There are regularly scheduled orientations for prospective students, consisting of a personal interview with the professional staff and a tour. There are guides for informal visits and visitors may sit in on classes. To arrange for a visit, contact the Admissions Office at (603) 358–2276 or (800) 833–4800.

Financial Aid: In 1993–94, 65% of all current freshmen and 64% of continuing students received some form of financial aid. About 72% of freshmen and 48% of continuing students received need-based aid. The average freshman award was $6055. Of that total, scholarships or need-based grants averaged $2659 ($13,290 maximum); loans averaged $3587 ($10,600 maximum); and work con-

tracts averaged $1000 ($2500 maximum). Twenty-five percent of undergraduate students work part-time. Average earnings from campus work for the school year are $700. The average financial indebtedness of the 1992–93 graduate was $10,930. KSC is a member of CSS. The IRS tax returns and FAFSA financial statement are required. The deadline for financial aid applications is March 1.

International Students: There are currently 41 international students enrolled. They must take the TOEFL and achieve a minimum score of 500.

Computers: The college provides computer facilities for student use. The mainframe is a DEC VAX. There are 145 microcomputers available in special interest and general purpose laboratories. All students may access the system 24 hours per day. There are no time limits and no fees.

Graduates: In 1992–93, 724 bachelor's degrees were awarded. The most popular majors among graduates were business management (9%), elementary education (8%), and psychology (7%). Within an average freshman class, 38% graduate in 4 years, and 52% in 5 years. Six companies recruited on campus in 1992–93. In the 1992 graduating class, 14% of the students were enrolled in graduate school within 6 months of graduation; 46% had found employment.

Admissions Contact: Kathryn Dodge, Director of Admissions.

NEW ENGLAND COLLEGE   C-5
Henniker, NH 03242   (603) 428–2223; (800) 521–7642 (out-of-state)

Full-time: 575 men, 375 women	Faculty: 90; IIB, --$
Part-time: none	Ph.D.s: 45%
Graduate: none	Student/Faculty: 11 to 1
Year: semesters, summer session	Tuition: $12,690
Application Deadline: open	Room & Board: $5180
Freshman Class: 1103 applied, 967 accepted, 251 enrolled	
SAT I or ACT: recommended	**LESS COMPETITIVE**

New England College, founded in 1946, is an independent international institution with campuses in New Hampshire and Britain. Students may pursue numerous majors while studying at either campus. There is one graduate school. In addition to regional accreditation, N.E.C. has baccalaureate program accreditation with ABET. The library contains 100,000 volumes, 34,000 microform items, and 2000 audiovisual forms, and subscribes to 650 periodicals. Computerized library sources and services include the card catalog, interlibrary loans, and database searching. Special learning facilities include a learning resource center, art gallery, radio station, and an island off the Maine Coast for environmental research. The 212-acre campus is in a rural area 17 miles west of Concord and 80 miles north of Boston, Massachusetts. Including residence halls, there are 30 buildings on campus.

Student Life: About 85% of undergraduates are from out-of-state, mostly the Northeast. Students come from 35 states, 25 foreign countries, and Canada. Seventy percent are from public schools; 30% from private. Ninety-two percent are white. Forty percent are Protestant; 30% Jewish; 25% Catholic. The average age of freshmen is 18; all undergraduates, 20. Twenty-four percent drop out by the end of their first year; 55% remain to graduate.

Housing: A total of 500 students can be accommodated in college housing. College-sponsored living facilities include coed dormitories, on-campus apartments, fraternity houses, and sorority houses. In addition, students may choose to live in cooperative substance-free housing. On-campus housing is available on a first-come, first-served basis and is available on a lottery system for upperclassmen. Sixty percent of students live on campus; of those, 80% remain on campus on weekends. Alcohol is not permitted. All students may keep cars on campus.

Activities: About 12% of men and about 3% of women belong to 3 local fraternities; about 8% of women belong to 3 local sororities. There are 25 groups on campus, including cheerleading, drama, ethnic, film, gay, honors, international, literary magazine, musical theater, newspaper, photography, political, professional, radio, religious, social, social service, student government, and yearbook. Popular campus events include Homecoming, Winter Carnival, and Finally Fridays.

Sports: There are 6 intercollegiate sports for men and 6 for women, and 15 intramural sports for men and 15 for women. Athletic and recreation facilities include a gymnasium, field house, weight room, 26 acres of playing fields, indoor and outdoor basketball and tennis courts, cross-country ski trails, and Alpine skiing at a local ski area.

Disabled Students: Seventy percent of the campus is accessible to disabled students. The following facilities are available: wheelchair ramps, elevators, special parking, specially equipped rest rooms, and special class scheduling.

Services: In addition to many counseling and information services, tutoring is available in every subject. In addition, there is remedial math.

Campus Safety and Security: Campus safety and security measures include 24-hour foot and vehicle patrol, escort service, shuttle buses, and informal discussions. In addition, there are pamphlets, posters, and films and lighted pathways and sidewalks.

Programs of Study: N.E.C. awards the B.A., B.S., and B.S.C.E. degrees. Master's degrees also are awarded. Bachelor's degrees are awarded in BIOLOGICAL SCIENCE (biology/biological science), BUSINESS (business administration and management, international business management, and management engineering), COMMUNICATIONS AND THE ARTS (communications, dramatic arts, English, fine arts, and journalism), COMPUTER AND PHYSICAL SCIENCE (mathematics), EDUCATION (elementary, physical, and secondary), ENGINEERING AND ENVIRONMENTAL DESIGN (civil engineering and environmental science), SOCIAL SCIENCE (history, philosophy, political science/government, and psychology). Art, theater, and environmental science are the strongest academically. Business, communications, and social sciences have the largest enrollments.

Required: All students must earn a minimum GPA of 2.0 and take 120 credit hours, including an average of 30 in their major. Distribution requirements cover 9 general education areas such as those in English, humanities, mathematics, and world culture and awareness. Specific requirements include a senior project, College Writing I and II, communications skills, and a mathematics course (or passing grade on a placement test).

Special: Cross-registration is available with the New Hampshire Consortium of Universities and Colleges. Also available are internships for juniors and seniors with a GPA of 2.5, study abroad in 5 countries, work-study programs, dual majors, student-designed majors, interdisciplinary majors such as social and economic development, nondegree study, and pass/fail options. There is a freshman honors program on campus

Faculty/Classroom: Fifty-one percent of faculty are male; 49%, female. Ninety-nine percent teach undergraduates. The average class size in an introductory lecture is 22; in a laboratory, 15; and in a regular course offering, 16.

Admissions: About 88% of the 1993–94 applicants were accepted.

Requirements: N.E.C. requires applicants to be in the upper 60% of their class. A minimum GPA of 2.0 is required. The SAT I is optional. Four years of English, 3 years each of math and social studies, and 2 years each of science and electives are recommended. An essay is required and an interview is recommended. AP and CLEP credits are accepted. Important factors used in the admissions decision are personality, intangible qualities, recommendations by school officials, evidence of special talent, recommendations by alumni, and extracurricular activities record.

Procedure: Freshmen are admitted fall and spring. Application deadlines are open. Notification is sent on a rolling basis. There is an application fee of $30. There is a deferred admissions plan.

Transfer: About 41 transfer students enrolled in a recent year. Transfer students must have a minimum GPA of 2.0 from the previous college. Two academic recommendations are required, 1 from a professor, and 1 from the academic advisor. An interview is recommended. A total of 60 credits out of 120 must be completed at N.E.C.

Visiting: There are regularly scheduled orientations for prospective students, including class registration and meeting other students and faculty/staff members. There are guides for informal visits and visitors may sit in on classes and stay overnight at the school. To arrange for a visit, contact the Admissions Office, Lois Richards at (800) 521–7642.

Financial Aid: In an earlier year, 50% all students received some form of financial aid. About 44% of freshmen and 38% of continuing students received need-based aid. The average freshman award was $8500. Of that total, scholarships or need-based grants averaged $4500; loans averaged $3400; and work contracts averaged $1100. Thirty-five percent of undergraduate students work part-time. Average earnings from campus work for the school year are $600. N.E.C. is a member of CSS. The FAF and the college's own financial statement are required. The deadline for financial aid applications is March 1.

International Students: There are currently 85 international students enrolled. The school actively recruits these students. They must take the TOEFL and achieve a minimum score of 475.

Computers: The college provides computer facilities for student use. More than 30 IBM PCs are available in the computer laboratory. More than 30 Apple II microcomputers are available in the skills center and writing laboratory. All students may access the system. There are no time limits on using the system and no fees.

Graduates: In a recent year, 204 bachelor's degrees were awarded. The most popular majors among graduates were business (28%), communications (14%), and psychology (10%). Within an average freshman class, 32% graduate in 4 years and 44% in 5 years. In a recent graduating class, 10% of the men and 9% of the women were enrolled in graduate school within 6 months of graduation; 85% of all students had found employment.

Admissions Contact: Office of Admissions.

NEW HAMPSHIRE COLLEGE
D-6
Manchester, NH 03106–1045
(603) 645–9611
(800) 642–4968 (out-of-state)

Full-time: 1561 men, 1552 women	Faculty: 56; IIA, -$
Part-time: 641 men, 776 women	Ph.Ds: 50%
Graduate: 1037 men, 663 women	Student/Faculty: 56 to 1
Year: semesters, summer session	Tuition: $10,608
Application Deadline: open	Room & Board: $4634
Freshman Class: 1501 applied, 1276 accepted, 288 enrolled	
SAT I Verbal/Math: 405/455	**LESS COMPETITIVE**

New Hampshire College, founded in 1932, is a private institution offering a professional business curriculum along with liberal arts and teacher preparation courses. There is one graduate school. The library contains 78,000 volumes, 60,000 microform items, and 1917 audiovisual forms, and subscribes to 921 periodicals. Special learning facilities include a learning resource center, art gallery, tv station, and audiovisual studio. The 200-acre campus is in a suburban area 55 miles north of Boston, Massachusetts. Including residence halls, there are 22 buildings on campus.

Student Life: About 80% of undergraduates are from out-of-state, mostly the Northeast. Students come from 23 states, 67 foreign countries, and Canada. Eighty percent are from public schools; 20% from private. Ninety-six percent are white. Fifty percent are Catholic; 35% Protestant; 10% Jewish. The average age of freshmen is 19; all undergraduates, 21. Twenty-five percent drop out by the end of their first year; 55% remain to graduate.

Housing: A total of 850 students can be accommodated in college housing. College-sponsored living facilities include single-sex and coed dormitories, on-campus apartments, fraternity houses, and sorority houses. In addition, there are special interest houses, wellness housing, and a substance-free, quieter residence hall option. On-campus housing is guaranteed for all 4 years. Eighty percent of students live on campus; of those, 65% remain on campus on weekends. Alcohol is not permitted. All students may keep cars on campus.

Activities: About 10% of men belong to 2 local and 2 national fraternities; about 10% of women belong to 2 local and 2 national sororities. There are 40 groups on campus, including cheerleading, dance, drama, ethnic, honors, international, newspaper, professional, radio and tv, religious, social, student government, and yearbook. Popular campus events include Fall Weekend, Spring Weekend, Alumni Weekend, International Bazaar, and Humanities Spectrum Series.

Sports: There are 5 intercollegiate sports for men and 4 for women, and 5 intramural sports for men and 4 for women. Athletic and recreation facilities include an Olympic-size swimming pool, racquetball and tennis courts, a weight room, a hockey rink, 2 gymnasiums, several baseball fields, and soccer and softball fields.

Disabled Students: Seventy percent of the campus is accessible to disabled students. The following facilities are available: wheelchair ramps, special parking, specially equipped rest rooms, special class scheduling, lowered drinking fountains, lowered telephones, and automatic door openers.

Services: In addition to many counseling and information services, tutoring is available in every subject.

Campus Safety and Security: Campus safety and security measures include 24-hour foot and vehicle patrol, escort service, shuttle buses, and informal discussions. In addition, there are pamphlets, posters, and films, emergency telephones, lighted pathways and sidewalks, and winter driving seminars for international students.

Programs of Study: NHC awards the B.S. degree. Associate and master's degrees also are awarded. Bachelor's degrees are awarded in BUSINESS (accounting, business administration and management, hospitality management services, hotel/motel and restaurant management, international business, management science, marketing/retailing/merchandising, retailing, and sport management), COMMUNICATIONS AND THE ARTS (communications and English), COMPUTER AND PHYSICAL SCIENCE (computer programming), EDUCATION (business, English, marketing and distribution, and mathematics), ENGINEERING AND ENVIRONMENTAL DESIGN (technical management), SOCIAL SCIENCE (culinary arts, economics, humanities, and social science). Accounting, hotel management, computer information systems, marketing, and culinary arts are the strongest academically. Business administration, accounting, sport management, and international business have the largest enrollments.

Required: Students must take 120 credit hours, including a maximum of 36 in their major, while maintaining a GPA of 2.0. Distribution requirements total 69 credits from the college core, including 3 courses in writing, 2 courses each in mathematics, accounting, economics, and computer science, and other courses in communications, public speaking, statistics, and marketing.

Special: Co-op programs with the area business community are strongly promoted, as is cross-registration through the New Hampshire College and University Council. Study abroad in London, a general business studies degree with 10 different concentrations,

dual majors, accelerated degree programs in all majors, combined B.A.-B.S. degrees, credit for life experience, and nondegree study are available. There is a freshman honors program on campus, as well as 1 national honor society.

Faculty/Classroom: Seventy-five percent of faculty are male; 25%, female. All teach undergraduates. No introductory courses are taught by graduate students. The average class size in a regular course offering is 22.

Admissions: About 85% of the 1993–94 applicants were accepted. The SAT scores for the 1993–94 freshman class were as follows: Verbal—93% below 500 and 7% between 500 and 599; Math—77% below 500, 19% between 500 and 599, 3% between 600 and 700, and 1% above 700. About 6% of the current freshmen were in the top fifth of their class; 22% were in the top two fifths. Three freshmen graduated first in their class.

Requirements: The SAT I is required for all but culinary students. Students must have completed 4 years of English and 3 of mathematics. An essay is required and an interview is strongly recommended. The GED is accepted. AP and CLEP credits are accepted. Important factors used in the admissions decision are advanced placement or honor courses, personality, intangible qualities, recommendations by school officials, extracurricular activities record, and recommendations by alumni.

Procedure: Freshmen are admitted fall and spring. Application deadlines are open. Notification is sent on a rolling basis. There are early admissions and deferred admissions plans.

Transfer: Some 98 transfer students enrolled in 1993–94. Transfer applicants must have a minimum GPA of 2.0. An interview is recommended. A total of 30 credits out of 120 must be completed at NHC.

Visiting: There are regularly scheduled orientations for prospective students, including a greeting from college administrators, campus tours with students, and informal discussions with faculty. There are guides for informal visits and visitors may sit in on classes. To arrange for a visit, contact the Admission Office at (800) 642–4968 or (603) 645–9611.

Financial Aid: In 1993–94, 73% of all current freshmen and 72% of continuing students received some form of financial aid. About 70% of freshmen and 70% of continuing students received need-based aid. The average freshman award was $9000. Of that total, scholarships or need-based grants averaged $2800 ($5000 maximum); loans averaged $3200 ($4800 maximum); and work contracts averaged $1500 ($2000 maximum). Sixty-five percent of undergraduate students work part-time. Average earnings from campus work for the school year are $1780. The average financial indebtedness of the 1992–93 graduate was $13,000. NHC is a member of CSS. The FAF and the FAFSA are required. The deadline for financial aid applications is March 15.

International Students: There are currently 173 international students enrolled. The school actively recruits these students. They must take the TOEFL and achieve a minimum score of 500.

Computers: The college provides computer facilities for student use. The mainframe is an IBM 4381. There are also 178 IBM, Zenith, and HP 8088–80/286 PCs available in 3 laboratories on the main campus. All students may access the system. It may be used 15 hours daily. There are no time limits on using the system and no fees.

Graduates: In 1992–93 750 bachelor's degrees were awarded. The most popular majors among graduates were business administration (27%), accounting (12%), and marketing (11%). Within an average freshman class, 55% graduate in 4 years. Some 160 companies recruited on campus in 1992–93. In the 1992 graduating class, 3% of all students were enrolled in graduate school within 6 months of graduation; 93% had found employment.

Admissions Contact: Brad Poznanski, Director of Admission.

NOTRE DAME COLLEGE
D-6
Manchester, NH 03104
(603) 669–4298, ext. 163

Full-time: 138 men, 289 women	Faculty: 45; IIB, --$
Part-time: 116 men, 261 women	Ph.Ds: 40%
Graduate: 544 men and women	Student/Faculty: 9 to 1
Year: semesters, summer session	Tuition: $9320
Application Deadline: open	Room & Board: $4900
Freshman Class: n/av	
SAT I Verbal/Math: 440/442	**COMPETITIVE**

Notre Dame College, founded in 1950, is a private, Catholic institution providing a liberal arts education. There is one graduate school. The library contains 52,000 volumes, 3200 microform items, and 24,000 audiovisual forms, and subscribes to 270 periodicals. Computerized library sources and services include interlibrary loans. Special learning facilities include a learning resource center and radio station. The 7-acre campus is in a suburban area 2 miles north of Manchester. Including residence halls, there are 17 buildings on campus.

Student Life: About 50% of undergraduates are from out-of-state, mostly the Northeast. Students come from 12 states and 3 foreign countries. Sixty-five percent are from public schools; 35% from pri-

vate. Ninety percent are white. Eighty percent are Catholic; 16% Protestant. The average age of freshmen is 19; all undergraduates, 24. Twenty percent drop out by the end of their first year; 65% remain to graduate.

Housing: A total of 210 students can be accommodated in college housing. College-sponsored living facilities include single-sex dormitories. In addition there are substance-free facilities. On-campus housing is guaranteed for all 4 years. Sixty percent of students commute. Upperclassmen may keep cars on campus.

Activities: There are no fraternities or sororities on campus. There are 34 groups on campus, including art, choir, chorale, drama, honors, literary magazine, musical theater, newspaper, photography, political, professional, radio and TV, religious, social, social service, student government, and yearbook. Popular campus events include Family Weekend, Octoberfest, and Winter Weekend.

Sports: There are 3 intercollegiate and 3 intramural sports for men and 3 of each for women. Athletic and recreation facilities include a gymnasium, tennis courts, and a weight room.

Disabled Students: Ninety percent of the campus is accessible to disabled students. The following facilities are available: wheelchair ramps, elevators, special parking, specially equipped rest rooms, special class scheduling, and lowered telephones.

Services: In addition to many counseling and information services, tutoring is available in most subjects. There is remedial math, reading, and writing.

Campus Safety and Security: Campus safety and security measures include 24-hour foot and vehicle patrol, escort service, shuttle buses, and informal discussions. In addition, there are pamphlets, posters, films, and lighted pathways and sidewalks.

Programs of Study: NDC awards the B.A., B.S., and B.S.Ed. degrees. Associate and master's degrees also are awarded. Bachelor's degrees are awarded in BIOLOGICAL SCIENCE (biology/ biological science and microbiology), BUSINESS (business administration and management), COMMUNICATIONS AND THE ARTS (communications, English, and fine arts), COMPUTER AND PHYSICAL SCIENCE (science), EDUCATION (art, early childhood, elementary, middle school, science, secondary, special, and teaching English as a second language/foreign language), ENGINEERING AND ENVIRONMENTAL DESIGN (commercial art), HEALTH PROFESSIONS (prepharmacy), SOCIAL SCIENCE (child psychology/ development, history, paralegal studies, prelaw, psychology, and religion). Paralegal, prepharmacy, and education are the strongest academically. Education, commercial art, and communications have the largest enrollments.

Required: All students must maintain a GPA of at least 2.0 and complete 124 credit hours, with 30 in the major. Distribution requirements include 3 courses in English, 2 each in Western civilization, religious studies, natural science, foreign language, and electives, and 1 each in art, music, philosophy, mathematics, logic, or computer science, and social science.

Special: Cross-registration is available with the New Hampshire College and University Council. Internships in commercial art, communications, and management and study abroad in England and France are also available. In addition, work-study, dual majors, a general studies degree, credit for life and work experience, and nondegree study are possible. There are 2 national honor societies on campus, including Phi Beta Kappa.

Faculty/Classroom: Thirty percent of faculty are male; 70%, female. All teach undergraduates. No introductory courses are taught by graduate students. The average class size in an introductory lecture is 25; in a laboratory, 20; and in a regular course offering, 20.

Admissions: The SAT scores for the 1993–94 freshman class were as follows: Verbal—80% below 500, 16% between 500 and 599, and 4% between 600 and 700; Math—76% below 500, 17% between 500 and 599, 6% between 600 and 700, and 1% above 700. About 20% of the current freshmen were in the top fifth of their class; 55% were in the top two fifths. There were 3 National Merit semifinalists. Two freshmen graduated first in their class.

Requirements: A minimum GPA of 2.0 is required. The SAT I is required and the ACT is recommended. In addition, applicants are expected to have completed 16 academic units in high school, including 4 years of English and 2 each of foreign language, history, mathematics, science, and social studies. An essay and a portfolio are required, and an interview is recommended. The GED is accepted. AP and CLEP credits are accepted. Important factors used in the admissions decision are recommendations by school officials, advanced placement or honor courses, personality, intangible qualities, evidence of special talent, and leadership record.

Procedure: Freshmen are admitted fall and spring. Entrance exams should be taken by December of the senior year. Application deadlines are open. The application fee is $25. Notification is sent on a rolling basis. There is a deferred admissions plan.

Transfer: Fifty-three transfer students enrolled in 1993–94. Transfer applicants must have earned a cumulative GPA of 2.0 for 30 credit hours, or must take the SAT I. An interview and a recommendation

from an official from the previous school are required, and an associate degree is recommended. A total of 30 credits out of 124 must be completed at NDC.

Visiting: There are regularly scheduled orientations for prospective students. There are guides for informal visits and visitors may sit in on classes and stay overnight at the school. To arrange for a visit, contact Jane Murray at (683) 669–4288, ext. 163.

Financial Aid: In an earlier year, 90% of all current freshmen and 85% of continuing students received some form of financial aid. About 80% of all students received need-based aid. The average freshman award was $6300. Of that total, scholarships or need-based grants averaged $2000 ($6000 maximum); loans averaged $1500 ($4500 maximum); and work contracts averaged $800 ($1500 maximum). Ninety percent of undergraduate students work part-time. Average earnings from campus work for the school year are $1000. The average financial indebtedness of a recent graduate was $8000. NDC is a member of CSS. The FAF and the college's own financial statement are required. The deadline for financial aid applications is March 15.

International Students: There are currently 11 international students enrolled. They must take the TOEFL and achieve a minimum score of 500. The student must also take the SAT I or the ACT.

Computers: The college provides computer facilities for student use. Microcomputers are available for student use in the computer room. All students may access the system whenever the computer room is open, usually at least 14 hours per day. There are no time limits and no fees.

Graduates: In 1992–93, 112 bachelor's degrees were awarded. The most popular majors among graduates were education (45%), commercial art (15%), and paralegal studies (10%). Within an average freshman class, 60% graduate in 4 years and 15% in 5 years. Some 30 companies recruited on campus in an earlier year. In a recent graduating class, 3% of the men and 4% of the women were enrolled in graduate school within 6 months of graduation; 90% of the men and 92% of the women had found employment.

Admissions Contact: Joseph P. Wagner, Dean of Admissions.

PLYMOUTH STATE COLLEGE   D-4
Plymouth, NH 03264   (603) 535–2237; (800) 842–6900 (out-of-state)

Full-time: 1750 men, 1750 women	Faculty: 171; IIB, av$
Part-time: 250 men, 250 women	Ph.D.s: 88%
Graduate: 150 men, 50 women	Student/Faculty: 20 to 1
Year: semesters, summer session	Tuition: $3282 ($8122)
Application Deadline: April 1	Room & Board: $3884
Freshman Class: 4027 applied, 2902 accepted, 1135 enrolled	
SAT I Verbal/Math: 450/449	**COMPETITIVE**

Plymouth State College, founded in 1871, is a public institution and part of the University System of New Hampshire. Although historically a teacher preparation institution, it now emphasizes a liberal arts education. There are 2 graduate schools. In addition to regional accreditation, Plymouth State has baccalaureate program accreditation with NCATE and NLN. The library contains 750,000 volumes and 500,000 microform items, and subscribes to 1200 periodicals. Computerized library sources and services include the card catalog, interlibrary loans, and database searching. Special learning facilities include a learning resource center, art gallery, planetarium, and radio station. The 150-acre campus is in a small town 40 miles north of Concord. Including residence halls, there are 42 buildings on campus.

Student Life: About 60% of undergraduates are from New Hampshire. Students come from 30 states and 10 foreign countries. Ninety-five percent are from public schools. Ninety-nine percent are white. The average age of freshmen is 18; all undergraduates, 20. Fifteen percent drop out by the end of their first year; 70% remain to graduate.

Housing: A total of 2200 students can be accommodated in college housing. College-sponsored living facilities include single-sex and coed dormitories, on-campus apartments, married-student housing, fraternity houses, and sorority houses. In addition there are honors houses, language houses, and special interest houses. On-campus housing is guaranteed for all 4 years. Seventy percent of students live on campus; of those, 70% remain on campus on weekends. All students may keep cars on campus.

Activities: About 10% of men belong to 5 local and 2 national fraternities; about 10% of women belong to 7 local and 2 national sororities. There are 50 groups on campus, including art, band, cheerleading, choir, chorale, chorus, computers, dance, drama, gay, honors, international, jazz band, literary magazine, musical theater, newspaper, pep band, political, professional, radio and TV, religious, social, social service, student government, and yearbook. Popular campus events include Homecoming, Winter Carnival, and Medieval Forum.

Sports: There are 9 intercollegiate sports for men and 8 for women, and 17 intramural sports for men and 17 for women. Athletic and recreation facilities include a 5,000-seat stadium and a 2000-seat gymna

sium, playing fields, and facilities for basketball, handball, racquetball, indoor soccer, swimming, tennis, volleyball, and softball.

Disabled Students: Seventy-five percent of the campus is accessible to disabled students. The following facilities are available: wheelchair ramps, elevators, special parking, specially equipped rest rooms, and lowered drinking fountains and telephones.

Services: In addition to many counseling and information services, tutoring is available in most subjects. There is a reader service for the blind, and remedial math, reading, and writing.

Campus Safety and Security: Campus safety and security measures include 24-hour foot and vehicle patrol, self-defense education, escort service, and shuttle buses. In addition, there are informal discussions, pamphlets, posters, films, emergency telephones, and lighted pathways and sidewalks.

Programs of Study: Plymouth State awards the B.A., B.S., B.F.A., B.H.E., and B.S.Ed. degrees. Associate and master's degrees also are awarded. Bachelor's degrees are awarded in BIOLOGICAL SCIENCE (biology/biological science and environmental biology), BUSINESS (accounting, business administration and management, business economics, management science, and marketing/retailing/merchandising), COMMUNICATIONS AND THE ARTS (art history and appreciation, dramatic arts, drawing, English, fine arts, French, graphic design, literature, music, painting, printmaking, sculpture, Spanish, and studio art), COMPUTER AND PHYSICAL SCIENCE (actuarial science, atmospheric sciences and meteorology, chemistry, computer programming, computer science, and mathematics), EDUCATION (art, early childhood, elementary, English, foreign languages, guidance, health, mathematics, middle school, music, physical, recreation, science, secondary, social science, and special), ENGINEERING AND ENVIRONMENTAL DESIGN (city/community/regional planning), SOCIAL SCIENCE (anthropology, geography, history, humanities, interdisciplinary studies, medieval studies, philosophy, political science/government, psychology, public administration, social science, social work, and sociology). Business, education, health and physical education, and liberal arts have the largest enrollments.

Required: All students must maintain a minimum GPA of 2.0 while taking 122 semester hours, including 1 hour of introduction to the academic community, 2 hours of physical education, and 1 each in composition and mathematics proficiency. Distribution requirements stem from the general education program requiring 3 credits each in the perspectives of the fine and performing arts, global history, literacy, philosophy, quantitative reasoning, science, sociology, psychology, and technology.

Special: Co-op programs with the University System of New Hampshire and cross-registration with the New Hampshire College and University Council are provided. Internships both on and off campus, study abroad in 5 countries, and college work-study programs are available. Dual majors, a general studies degree, and student-designed majors are possible. There also is credit for life experience, nondegree study, and pass/fail options. There are 3 national honor societies on campus.

Faculty/Classroom: Sixty-nine percent of faculty are male; 31%, female. No introductory courses are taught by graduate students.

Admissions: About 72% of the 1993–94 applicants were accepted. The SAT scores for the 1993–94 freshman class were as follows: Verbal—80% below 500, 18% between 500 and 599, and 2% between 600 and 700; Math—66% below 500, 27% between 500 and 599, and 6% between 600 and 700. About 20% of the current freshmen were in the top fifth of their class; 50% were in the top two fifths. Five freshmen graduated first in their class.

Requirements: The SAT I is required. The college recommends that applicants have completed 4 units of English, 3 of mathematics, 2 each in foreign language, science, social studies, and history, and 1 in art. An audition for certain programs is required, and an essay is recommended. The GED is accepted. AP and CLEP credits are accepted. Important factors used in the admissions decision are advanced placement or honor courses, leadership record, recommendations by school officials, evidence of special talent, and extracurricular activities record.

Procedure: Freshmen are admitted fall and spring. Entrance exams should be taken in November. Applications should be filed by April 1 for fall entry and January 1 for spring entry, along with an application fee of $20 ($30 out-of-state). Notification is sent on a rolling basis.

Transfer: Transfer students must have a minimum GPA of 2.0 on prior work. The SAT I is required. A total of 30 credits out of 122 must be completed at Plymouth State.

Visiting: There are regularly scheduled orientations for prospective students. There are guides for informal visits and visitors may sit in on classes. To arrange for a visit, contact the Admission Office at (603) 535–2237 or (800) 842–6900.

Financial Aid: In 1993–94, 73% of all current freshmen and 49% of continuing students received some form of financial aid. About 64% of freshmen and 43% of continuing students received need-based aid. The average freshman award was $5400. Of that total,

scholarships or need-based grants averaged $2000 ($2800 maximum); loans averaged $2100 ($2750 maximum); and work contracts averaged $500 ($1300 maximum). Thirty-one percent of undergraduate students work part-time. Average earnings from campus work for the school year are $820. The average financial indebtedness of the 1992–93 graduate was $5000. Plymouth State is a member of CSS. The FAF and parent and student tax returns are required. The deadline for financial aid applications is March 1.

International Students: There are currently 75 international students enrolled. They must take the TOEFL and achieve a minimum score of 520.

Computers: The college provides computer facilities for student use. The mainframe is a DEC VAX. There are also 125 IBM, Apple IIe and Macintosh, Zenith 150, and other microcomputers available. All students may access the system. There are no time limits on using the system and no fees.

Graduates: In 1992–93, 732 bachelor's degrees were awarded. The most popular majors among graduates were management (15%), elementary education (15%), and marketing (10%). Some 54 companies recruited on campus in an earlier year. In that graduating class, 4% of all graduates were enrolled in graduate school within 6 months of graduation; 49% had found employment.

Admissions Contact: Eugene D. Fahey, Director of Admissions.

RIVIER COLLEGE
D-6

Nashua, NH 03060–5086   (603) 888–1311, exts. 506 or 507

Full-time: 82 men, 508 women	Faculty: 66; IIA, --$
Part-time: 198 men, 998 women	Ph.D.s: 60%
Graduate: 308 men, 668 women	Student/Faculty: 9 to 1
Year: semesters, summer session	Tuition: $10,070
Application Deadline: open	Room & Board: $4850
Freshman Class: 763 applied, 589 accepted, 572 enrolled	
SAT I Verbal/Math: 430/467	**LESS COMPETITIVE**

Rivier College, founded in 1933, is a Catholic, coeducational liberal arts college. There are 3 undergraduate schools and 1 graduate school. In addition to regional accreditation, Rivier has baccalaureate program accreditation with NLN. The library contains 120,440 volumes, 26,350 microform items, and 17,465 audiovisual forms, and subscribes to 600 periodicals. Computerized library sources and services include the card catalog. Special learning facilities include a learning resource center and art gallery. The 60-acre campus is in a suburban area 40 miles north of Boston. Including residence halls, there are 37 buildings on campus.

Student Life: About 78% of undergraduates are from New Hampshire. Students come from 10 states and 12 foreign countries. Eighty percent are from public schools; 20% from private. Seventy-eight percent are white. The average age of freshmen is 18; all undergraduates, 30. Nine percent drop out by the end of their first year.

Housing: A total of 250 students can be accommodated in college housing. College-sponsored living facilities include single-sex and coed dormitories. On-campus housing is guaranteed for all 4 years. Sixty percent of students commute. Alcohol is not permitted. All students may keep cars on campus.

Activities: There are no fraternities or sororities on campus. There are 23 groups on campus, including art, chorus, drama, literary magazine, newspaper, professional, religious, social, student government, and yearbook. Popular campus events include R-Aid Day, Global Awareness Week, Alcohol Awareness Week, Spirit Week, Parents and Homecoming Weekends, Black History Month, and Women's History Month.

Sports: There are 2 intercollegiate sports for men and 4 for women, and 7 intramural sports for men and 7 for women. Athletic and recreation facilities include a 300-seat gymnasium, a weight room, tennis courts, and a soccer field.

Disabled Students: Seventy-five percent of the campus is accessible to disabled students. The following facilities are available: wheelchair ramps, elevators, special parking, specially equipped rest rooms, and lowered drinking fountains.

Services: In addition to many counseling and information services, tutoring is available in some subjects, including mathematics, English, business, and languages. There is also remedial math and writing.

Campus Safety and Security: Campus safety and security measures include escort service, informal discussions, pamphlets, posters, and films, and lighted pathways and sidewalks.

Programs of Study: Rivier awards the B.A., B.S., and B.F.A. degrees. Associate and master's degrees also are awarded. Bachelor's degrees are awarded in BIOLOGICAL SCIENCE (biology/biological science), BUSINESS (accounting, business administration and management, management science, and marketing/retailing/merchandising), COMMUNICATIONS AND THE ARTS (communications, design, English, French, Spanish, and studio art), COMPUTER AND PHYSICAL SCIENCE (chemistry, computer science, and mathematics), EDUCATION (art, business, early childhood, elementary, English, foreign languages, mathematics, science, secondary, social

studies, and special), HEALTH PROFESSIONS (nursing, predentistry, premedicine, and preveterinary science), SOCIAL SCIENCE (human development, liberal arts/general studies, paralegal studies, political science/government, prelaw, psychology, social work, and sociology). Education, business, paralegal, nursing, behavioral sciences, and art have the largest enrollments.

Required: A writing sample is required at entry, and a demonstration of writing proficiency must be shown prior to graduation. Students must complete at least 120 credit hours to graduate, ordinarily consisting of 40 3-credit courses with 35 to 60 credits in the major, and must maintain a minimum GPA of 2.0. Distribution requirements include 19 core courses in basic skills of writing and reasoning, the humanities, and the sciences. These courses should include English, religion, philosophy, mathematics, history, physical and life sciences, fine arts, languages, literature, social sciences, and Western civilization.

Special: Rivier offers cross-registration through the New Hampshire College and University Council, internships in most majors, a B.A.-B.S. degree in chemistry, dual majors, a general studies degree, credit by challenge examination, nondegree study, and pass/fail options.

Faculty/Classroom: Thirty-eight percent of faculty are male; 62%, female. All teach undergraduates and 20% do research. No introductory courses are taught by graduate students. The average class size in an introductory lecture, in a laboratory, and in a regular course offering, is 15.

Admissions: About 77% of the 1993–94 applicants were accepted. The SAT scores for the 1993–94 freshman class were as follows: Verbal—80% below 500, 16% between 500 and 599, 3% between 600 and 700, and 1% above 700; Math—73% below 500, 23% between 500 and 599, and 4% between 600 and 700. About 16% of the current freshmen were in the top fifth of their class; 14% were in the top two fifths. One freshman graduated first in their class.

Requirements: The SAT I is required. In addition, it is recommended that students rank in the top third to top half of their class, depending on its size, and that they maintain a strong college preparatory curriculum. Applicants must have earned 16 academic credits, including 4 units of English, 2 each in foreign language and mathematics, 1 in science with a laboratory course, and 5 electives. An essay (and a portfolio for art majors) also is required, and an interview is recommended. Students should consult the Office of Admissions about whether the GED is accepted. AP and CLEP credits are accepted. Important factors used in the admissions decision are advanced placement or honor courses, leadership record, extracurricular activities record, recommendations by school officials, and personality, intangible qualities.

Procedure: Freshmen are admitted fall and spring. Entrance exams should be taken in the junior or senior year. Application deadlines are open, but the recommended deadlines are February 1 for fall entry and December 1 for spring entry. The application fee is $25. Notification is sent on a rolling basis, within 4 weeks of receipt of the completed application. There are early admissions and deferred admissions plans. A waiting list is an active part of the admissions procedure, with about 10% of applicants on the list.

Transfer: Some 92 transfer students enrolled in 1993–94. Transfer students must have a minimum GPA of 2.0 and submit an official high school transcript and the SAT I if they have earned fewer than 60 credits at the previous institution. A college transcript is required and an interview is recommended. A total of 30 credits out of 120 must be completed at Rivier.

Visiting: There are regularly scheduled orientations for prospective students, including a tour, class visits, and an interview with department chairs. There are guides for informal visits and visitors may sit in on classes and stay overnight at the school. To arrange for a visit, contact the Office of Admissions at (603) 888–1311, ext. 506 or 507.

Financial Aid: In a recent year, 85% of all freshmen and 80% of continuing students received some form of financial aid. About 85% of freshmen and 80% of continuing students received need-based aid. The average freshman award was $4577. Of that total, scholarships or need-based grants averaged $3715 ($7000 maximum); loans averaged $2288 ($3000 maximum); and work contracts averaged $1290 ($1600 maximum). Thirty-five percent of undergraduate students worked part-time. Average earnings from campus work for the school year were $1000. The average financial indebtedness of a recent graduate was $7000. Rivier is a member of CSS. The FAF, the college's own financial statement, and FAFSA are required. The deadline for financial aid applications is March 16.

International Students: There are currently 38 international students enrolled. The school actively recruits these students. They must take the TOEFL and achieve a minimum score of 500.

Computers: The college provides computer facilities for student use. The mainframes are a DEC VAX 8550, a DEC MicroVAX II, and a DEC VAX Server 3100. There are 30 terminals and 14 Apple Macintosh, 19 Apple IIgs, and 30 DOS-based microcomputers available for student use in programming, word processing, connection to the Ethernet/DECNET Network, and other applications. All students may access the system. It may be used Monday through Saturday and on

Sundays via modems. There are no time limits on using the system and no fees.

Graduates: In 1992–93 157 bachelor's degrees were awarded. The most popular majors among graduates were accounting (30%), education (24%), and paralegal studies (24%).

Admissions Contact: Office of Admissions.

SAINT ANSELM COLLEGE
Manchester, NH 03102

D-6
(603) 641-7500

Full-time: 823 men, 1050 women	Faculty: 116; IIB, av$
Part-time: 37 men, 57 women	Ph.D.s: 79%
Graduate: none	Student/Faculty: 16 to 1
Year: semesters, summer session	Tuition: $12,140
Application Deadline: March 15	Room & Board: $5200
Freshman Class: 2095 applied, 1553 accepted, 514 enrolled	
SAT I Verbal/Math: 481/512	COMPETITIVE

Saint Anselm College, founded in 1889, is a private Roman Catholic institution offering a liberal arts education. In addition to regional accreditation, Saint Anselm has baccalaureate program accreditation with NLN. The library contains 192,000 volumes, 16,000 microform items, and 7100 audiovisual forms, and subscribes to 1350 periodicals. Computerized library sources and services include interlibrary loans and database searching. Special learning facilities include a learning resource center, art gallery, and planetarium. The 450-acre campus is in a suburban area 50 miles north of Boston, Massachusetts. Including residence halls, there are 38 buildings on campus.

Student Life: About 80% of undergraduates are from out-of-state, mostly the Northeast. Students come from 28 states and 10 foreign countries. Sixty-five percent are from public schools; 35% from private. Ninety-eight percent are white. Eighty-seven percent are Catholic; 11% Protestant. The average age of freshmen is 18; all undergraduates, 20. Twelve percent drop out by the end of their first year; 75% remain to graduate.

Housing: A total of 1300 students can be accommodated in college housing. College-sponsored living facilities include single-sex dormitories and on-campus apartments. On-campus housing is guaranteed for all 4 years. Sixty-five percent of students live on campus; of those, 75% remain on campus on weekends. All students may keep cars on campus.

Activities: About 11% of men belong to 2 local and 1 national fraternity; about 3% of women belong to 1 local sorority. There are 51 groups on campus, including art, cheerleading, chess, choir, chorale, computers, drama, jazz band, literary magazine, newspaper, photography, political, professional, religious, social, social service, student government, and yearbook. Popular campus events include Fall Fest, Spring Olympics, New Hampshire Philharmonic Orchestra performances, Family Weekend, Jazz Festival, League of Women Voters sponsored presidential debates, and Bean Lecture Series.

Sports: There are 9 intercollegiate sports for men and 7 for women, and 14 intramural sports for men and 14 for women. Athletic and recreation facilities include a 1500-seat gymnasium; a multipurpose complex providing basketball, volleyball, tennis, and racquetball courts; a swimming pool; athletic fields; and weight and training rooms.

Disabled Students: Sixty-five percent of the campus is accessible to disabled students. The following facilities are available: wheelchair ramps, elevators, special parking, specially equipped rest rooms, special class scheduling, and lowered drinking fountains.

Services: In addition to many counseling and information services, tutoring is available in every subject. There is also a reader service for the blind.

Campus Safety and Security: Campus safety and security measures include 24-hour foot and vehicle patrol and lighted pathways and sidewalks.

Programs of Study: Saint Anselm awards the B.A. and B.S. degrees. Associate degrees also are awarded. Bachelor's degrees are awarded in BIOLOGICAL SCIENCE (biochemistry and biology/biological science), BUSINESS (accounting, business economics, and financial economics), COMMUNICATIONS AND THE ARTS (classics, English, fine arts, French, languages, and Spanish), COMPUTER AND PHYSICAL SCIENCE (chemistry, computer science, mathematics, and natural sciences), EDUCATION (secondary), HEALTH PROFESSIONS (nursing, predentistry, and premedicine), SOCIAL SCIENCE (criminal justice, economics, history, liberal studies in the Great Books, philosophy, politics, prelaw, psychology, social work, sociology, and theology). Business economics, biology, nursing, English, psychology, and history have the largest enrollments.

Required: All students must maintain a GPA of 2.0 while completing at least 40 semester courses that include 4 semesters in the humanities, 2 each in English and laboratory science, 3 each in philosophy and theology, and 2 to 4 in foreign language; 10 to 13 courses are required in the major area of study.

Special: Saint Anselm offers a 5-year liberal arts and a 3–2 engineering program in cooperation with Manhattan College, Notre Dame University, University of Massachusetts at Lowell, and Catholic Uni-

versity of America. Cross-registration is possible through the New Hampshire College and University Council. In addition, Saint Anselm offers internships in most departments, a Washington semester to qualified students, study abroad in Europe, nondegree study, and dual majors in computer science/business, computer science/mathematics, and mathematics/economics. There are 8 national honor societies on campus.

Faculty/Classroom: Sixty-four percent of faculty are male; 36%, female. All teach undergraduates. The average class size in an introductory lecture is 20; in a laboratory, 17; and in a regular course offering, 24.

Admissions: About 74% of the 1993–94 applicants were accepted. The SAT scores for the 1993–94 freshman class were as follows: Verbal—62% below 500, 34% between 500 and 599, and 4% between 600 and 700; Math—45% below 500, 43% between 500 and 599, and 12% between 600 and 700. About 32% of the current freshmen were in the top fifth of their class; 68% were in the top two fifths. There were 7 National Merit semifinalists. Four freshmen graduated first in their class.

Requirements: A minimum GPA of 2.0 is required. The SAT I or ACT is required. Applicants must have 16 academic credits and 16 Carnegie units, including 4 years of English, 3 each of mathematics and science, 2 of foreign language, and 1 each of history and social studies. An essay is required and an interview is recommended. The GED is accepted. AP and CLEP credits are accepted. Important factors used in the admissions decision are advanced placement or honor courses, leadership record, evidence of special talent, recommendations by school officials, and personality.

Procedure: Freshmen are admitted fall and spring. Entrance exams should be taken during the spring of the junior year or fall of the senior year. Early decision applications should be filed by December 1; regular applications, by March 15 for fall entry and December 1 for spring entry, along with an application fee of $25. Notification of early decision is sent December 15; regular decision, on a rolling basis beginning January 15. There are early decision and deferred admissions plans. Fifty-one early decision candidates were accepted for the 1993–94 class. A waiting list is an active part of the admissions procedure, with about 5% of applicants on the list.

Transfer: Some 41 transfer students enrolled in 1993–94. Transfer students must have a minimum GPA of 2.5 after earning at least 30 college credit hours. The SAT I is required and an interview is recommended. In addition, 2 letters of recommendation are necessary. A total of 20 courses out of at least 40 must be completed at Saint Anselm.

Visiting: There are regularly scheduled orientations for prospective students, consisting of daily individual interviews followed by a campus tour. There are guides for informal visits and visitors may sit in on classes and by apppointment, stay overnight at the school. To arrange for a visit, contact the Admissions Office at (603) 641–7500.

Financial Aid: In 1993–94 74% of all current freshmen and 77% of continuing students received some form of financial aid. About 76% of freshmen and 82% of continuing students received need-based aid. Scholarships or need-based grants averaged $5600 ($11,840 maximum); loans averaged $2366 ($2500 maximum); and work contracts averaged $800 (maximum). Fifty-two percent of undergraduate students work part-time. Average earnings from campus work for the school year are $665. The average financial indebtedness of the 1992–93 graduate was $7704. Saint Anselm is a member of CSS. The FAF and the FAFSA are required. The deadline for financial aid applications is April 15.

International Students: There are currently 11 international students enrolled. They must take the TOEFL and achieve a minimum score of 600. The student must also take the SAT I or the ACT.

Computers: The college provides computer facilities for student use. The mainframes are 2 DEC Alpha systems. Two main computer centers on campus contain 55 Apple Macintosh, 50 MS-DOS, and 11 dumb terminals. All have access to the mainframe; some are connected to the Novell Network. There are additional small centers located in the departments of psychology, biology, physics, and nursing. All students may access the system. It may be used weekdays from 8:30 A.M. and weekends from 10 A.M. Those students with dorm connections to the system have 24-hour access. There are no time limits on using the system. The fees are $25.

Graduates: In 1992–93 414 bachelor's degrees were awarded. The most popular majors among graduates were nursing (14%), history (12%), and business (11%). Within an average freshman class, 75% graduate in 4 years and 78% in 5 years. Some 83 companies recruited on campus in 1992–93. In the 1992 graduating class, 22% of all students were enrolled in graduate school within 6 months of graduation.

Admissions Contact: Donald Healy, Director of Admissions.

SCHOOL FOR LIFELONG LEARNING
(See College for Lifelong Learning)

THOMAS MOORE COLLEGE OF LIBERAL ARTS

D-6

Merrimack, NH 03054
Recognized candidate for accreditation (603) 880–8308

Full-time: 30 men, 29 women	Faculty: 5
Part-time: none	Ph.D.s: 80%
Graduate: none	Student/Faculty: 12 to 1
Year: semesters	Tuition: $6900
Application Deadline: open	Room & Board: $5000
Freshman Class: 33 applied, 33 accepted, 22 enrolled	
SAT I Verbal/Math: 526/513	**NONCOMPETITIVE**

Thomas Moore College of Liberal Arts, founded in 1978 by Roman Catholic educators, is a coeducational undergraduate institution. The 11-acre campus is in a rural area between Nashua and Manchester. Including residence halls, there are 5 buildings on campus.

Student Life: About 80% of undergraduates are from out-of-state, mostly the Northeast. Students come from 17 states, 3 foreign countries, and Canada. The average age of freshmen is 18; all undergraduates, 20.

Housing: A total of 60 students can be accommodated in college housing. College-sponsored living facilities include single-sex dormitories. On-campus housing is guaranteed for all 4 years. All students live on campus and remain on campus on weekends. Alcohol is not permitted. All students may keep cars on campus.

Activities: There are no fraternities or sororities on campus. Popular campus events include Charter Day (homecoming).

Sports: There is no sports program.

Disabled Students: Wheelchair ramps are available.

Programs of Study: Thomas Moore College of Liberal Arts awards the B.A. degree. Bachelor's degrees are awarded in COMMUNICATIONS AND THE ARTS (literature), SOCIAL SCIENCE (philosophy and political science/government).

Required: A total of 120 credit hours is required to graduate, including 48 in humanities, 12 each in writing workshop, classical languages, and mathematics and science, 6 in theology, and 3 in fine arts. At least 24 hours in the major are required. In addition, students must complete the junior and the modern language examination.

Special: A semester in Rome for sophomores is possible.

Faculty/Classroom: Eighty percent of faculty are male; 20%, female. All teach undergraduates.

Admissions: All of the 1993–94 applicants were accepted. The SAT scores for the 1993–94 freshman class were as follows: Verbal—35% below 500, 35% between 500 and 599, 24% between 600 and 700, and 6% above 700; Math—53% below 500, 18% between 500 and 599, 18% between 600 and 700, and 11% above 700.

Requirements: The SAT I or ACT is required. Graduation from high school or the GED is required. An essay and 2 letters of recommendation are required. An interview is strongly recommended. Important factors used in the admissions decision are personality, intangible qualities, evidence of special talent, leadership record, extracurricular activities record, and advanced placement or honor courses.

Procedure: Freshmen are admitted to all sessions. Application deadlines are open. The application fee is $15. Notification is sent on a rolling basis.

Transfer: Two transfer students enrolled in 1993–94. Transfer applicants must submit a transcript from all higher institutions attended.

Visiting: There are guides for informal visits and visitors may sit in on classes and stay overnight at the school. To arrange for a visit, contact Peter O'Connor, Director of Admissions at (603) 880–8308.

Financial Aid: In 1993–94, 83% of all current freshmen and 91% of continuing students received some form of financial aid. All students received need-based aid. Sixty-six percent of undergraduate students work part-time. Average earnings from campus work for the school year are $2400. Thomas Moore College of Liberal Arts is a member of CSS. The FAFSA financial statement is required.

International Students: There are currently 6 international students enrolled. The school actively recruits these students. The student must take the SAT I or the ACT.

Computers: The college provides computer facilities for student use.

Graduates: In 1992–93, 15 bachelor's degrees were awarded. The most popular majors among graduates were literature (60%), philosophy (27%), and political science (13%). Within an average freshman class, 33% graduate in 3 years and 67% in 4 years.

Admissions Contact: Peter I. O'Connor, Director of Admissions.

UNIVERSITY OF NEW HAMPSHIRE SYSTEM

The University of New Hampshire system, established in 1963, is the public university system in New Hampshire. It is governed by a board

of trustees, whose chief administrator is the chancellor. The primary goal of the system is to serve the higher educational needs of the people of New Hampshire. The main priorities are to provide a well-coordinated system of higher education, student access and diversity, and quality programs through a commitment to excellence. The total enrollment in a recent year of all 4 campuses was 29,440; there were 1008 faculty members. Altogether there are 177 baccalaureate, 67 master's, and 21 doctoral programs offered in the University of New Hampshire System. Four-year campuses are located in Durham, Keene, and Plymouth. Profiles of the 4-year campuses are included in this chapter in alphabetical order with other New Hampshire schools.

UNIVERSITY OF NEW HAMPSHIRE
Durham, NH 03824

E-5

(603) 862-1360

Full-time: 4578 men, 5644 women
Part-time: 213 men, 396 women
Graduate: 750 men, 816 women
Year: semesters, summer session
Application Deadline: February 1
Freshman Class: 9750 applied, 7640 accepted, 2529 enrolled
SAT I Verbal/Math: 476/536

Faculty: 649; I, --$
Ph.D.s: 87%
Student/Faculty: 16 to 1
Tuition: $4380 ($12,010)
Room & Board: $3862

COMPETITIVE

The University of New Hampshire, founded in 1866, is part of the public university system of New Hampshire and offers undergraduate and graduate programs in a wide range of programs, including liberal arts, engineering, physical sciences, business, economics, life sciences, agriculture, and health and human services. There are 7 undergraduate schools and one graduate school. In addition to regional accreditation, UNH has baccalaureate program accreditation with ABET, ADA, AHEA, CAHEA, NCATE, NLN, and SAF. The 5 libraries contain 1,023,000 volumes, 615,000 microform items, and 10,000 audiovisual forms, and subscribe to 6500 periodicals. Computerized library sources and services include the card catalog, interlibrary loans, and database searching. Special learning facilities include a learning resource center, art gallery, radio station, TV station, and an observatory. The 188-acre campus is in a rural area 60 miles north of Boston, Massachusetts. Including residence halls, there are 95 buildings on campus.
Student Life: About 60% of undergraduates are from New Hampshire. Students come from 49 states, 30 foreign countries, and Canada. Ninety-two percent are white. The average age of freshmen is 18.5; all undergraduates, 20.5. Seven percent drop out by the end of their first year; 87% remain to graduate.
Housing: A total of 5422 students can be accommodated in college housing. College-sponsored living facilities include single-sex and coed dormitories, on-campus apartments, and married-student housing. In addition there are honors houses, special interest houses, and an international dorm. On-campus housing is guaranteed for the freshman year only, is available on a first-come, first-served basis, and is available on a lottery system for upperclassmen. Fifty-one percent of students live on campus. Upperclassmen may keep cars on campus.
Activities: About 10% of men belong to 2 local and 7 national fraternities; about 10% of women belong to 6 national sororities. There are 100 groups on campus, including art, band, cheerleading, chess, choir, chorale, chorus, computers, dance, drama, drill team, ethnic, film, gay, honors, international, jazz band, literary magazine, marching band, musical theater, newspaper, opera, orchestra, photography, political, professional, radio and TV, religious, social, social service, student government, symphony, and yearbook. Popular campus events include International Day, concert series, Homecoming, Winter Carnival, lecture series, and athletic events.
Sports: There are 13 intercollegiate sports for men and 14 for women, and 16 intramural sports for men and 14 for women. Athletic and recreation facilities include indoor and outdoor swimming pools, tracks, tennis courts, gymnasiums, weight training, wrestling, and gymnastics rooms, a dance studio, playing fields, an indoor ice rink, and cross-country ski trails.
Disabled Students: Fifty percent of the campus is accessible to disabled students. The following facilities are available: wheelchair ramps, elevators, special parking, specially equipped rest rooms, special class scheduling, lowered drinking fountains, and lowered telephones.
Services: In addition to many counseling and information services, tutoring is available in most subjects. There is a reader service for the blind, and remedial math, reading, and writing.
Campus Safety and Security: Campus safety and security measures include 24-hour foot and vehicle patrol, self defense education, escort service, and shuttle buses. In addition, there are informal discussions, pamphlets, posters, and films, emergency telephones, and lighted pathways and sidewalks.
Programs of Study: UNH awards the B.A., B.S., B.E.T., B.F.A., B.M., and B.S.F. degrees. Associate, master's, and doctoral degrees also are awarded. Bachelor's degrees are awarded in AGRICULTURE (animal science, dairy science, equestrian science, forestry and related sciences, horticulture, plant science, soil science, and wildlife man-

agement), BIOLOGICAL SCIENCE (biochemistry, biology/biological science, entomology, microbiology, nutrition, and zoology), BUSINESS (business administration and management, hotel/motel and restaurant management, and recreation and leisure services), COMMUNICATIONS AND THE ARTS (classics, communications, dramatic arts, English, fine arts, French, German, Greek, journalism, Latin, linguistics, music, performing arts, Russian, and Spanish), COMPUTER AND PHYSICAL SCIENCE (chemistry, computer science, earth science, geology, hydrology, mathematics, and physics), EDUCATION (English, industrial arts, mathematics, physical, and vocational), ENGINEERING AND ENVIRONMENTAL DESIGN (chemical engineering, city/community/regional planning, civil engineering, computer engineering, electrical/electronics engineering, engineering technology, environmental science, and mechanical engineering), HEALTH PROFESSIONS (health care administration, medical laboratory technology, nursing, occupational therapy, and speech pathology/audiology), SOCIAL SCIENCE (anthropology, economics, family, geography, history, humanities, liberal arts/general studies, philosophy, political science/government, psychology, social work, sociology, water resources, and women's studies). English and business administration have the largest enrollments.
Required: All students must maintain a GPA of 2.0 and complete at least 128 credits, with a minimum of 36 credits and 10 classes in the major. Students must also complete general education requirements and an introductory prose writing course. Honors students and most seniors write a thesis or complete a project.
Special: Co-op programs with Cornell University in marine science are available. Extensive cross-registration is possible through the New Hampshire College and University Council, the University of New Hampshire at Manchester, and the University of California, Santa Cruz. There also is nationwide study through the National Student Exchange. Internships, study abroad throughout the world, a Washington semester, and work-study are possible. Also available are B.A.-B.S. degrees, dual majors, a general studies degree, student-designed majors, extensive 3–2 B.S./M.B.A. programs and other bachelor's/graduate degree plans, nondegree study, and pass/fail options. A 3–2 engineering degree is offered with the New Hampshire Technical Institute in Concord. There is a freshman honors program on campus. Forty-six departments have honors programs.
Faculty/Classroom: Sixty-four percent of faculty are male; 36%, female. All teach undergraduates and do research. Graduate students teach 6% of introductory courses. The average class size in an introductory lecture is 38; in a laboratory, 25; and in a regular course offering, 25.
Admissions: About 78% of the 1993–94 applicants were accepted. The SAT scores for the 1993–94 freshman class were as follows: Verbal—61% below 500, 33% between 500 and 599, and 6% between 600 and 700; Math—32% below 500, 43% between 500 and 599, 22% between 600 and 700, and 3% above 700. About 48% of the current freshmen were in the top fifth of their class; 89% were in the top two fifths.
Requirements: UNH recommends applicants to be in the upper 30% of their class. The SAT I or ACT is required, with a composite SAT I score of 1080 recommended. Applicants must have 17 academic credits, including 4 years each of English and mathematics, 3 each in science, and foreign language, and 2 in social studies. Students with a specific major in mind are encouraged to take SAT II: Subject tests relating to that major. An essay is required for all students and an informational interview recommended. For art students, a portfolio is required, as is an audition for music students. The GED is accepted. AP and CLEP credits are accepted. Important factors used in the admissions decision are advanced placement or honor courses, recommendations by school officials, extracurricular activities record, leadership record, and evidence of special talent.
Procedure: Freshmen are admitted fall and spring. Entrance exams should be taken before February 1 of the senior year. Early decision applications should be filed by December 1; regular applications, by February 1 for fall entry and November 1 for spring entry, along with an application fee of $20. Notification of early decision is sent January 15; regular decision, April 15. There are early decision and deferred admissions plans. About 923 early decision candidates were accepted for the 1993–94 class.
Transfer: About 586 transfer students enrolled in 1993–94. Transfer students must submit a GPA of 3.0 in a general education curriculum and an overall minimum GPA of 2.8. The SAT I or ACT is required, and an interview is recommended. A total of 32 credits out of 128 must be completed at UNH.
Visiting: There are regularly scheduled orientations for prospective students. There are guides for informal visits and visitors may sit in on classes. To arrange for a visit, contact the Admissions Office at (603) 862-1360.
Financial Aid: In 1993–94 63% of all current freshmen and 57% of continuing students received some form of financial aid. About 60% of freshmen and 51% of continuing students received need-based aid. The average freshman award was $6883. Of that total, scholar-

ships or need-based grants averaged $3752 ($11,790 maximum); loans averaged $3519 ($8217 maximum); and work contracts averaged $1916 ($2500 maximum). Eighty percent of undergraduate students work part-time. Average earnings from campus work for the school year are $1286. The average financial indebtedness of the 1992–93 graduate was $6100. UNH is a member of CSS. The FAFSA financial statement is required. The deadline for financial aid applications is March 1.

International Students: There are currently 250 international students enrolled. The school actively recruits these students. They must take the TOEFL and achieve a minimum score of 550. The student must also take the SAT I or the ACT.

Computers: The college provides computer facilities for student use.

The mainframes are a digital 5500 and 8820, and a DEC 4000. Each dorm is fitted with telephone lines, to enable students to access the university's mainframe. In addition, there are nearly 200 computers located in 5 clusters on the campus and open to all UNH students. All students may access the system. There are no time limits on using the system and no fees.

Graduates: In 1992–93 2322 bachelor's degrees were awarded. The most popular majors among graduates were business administration (12%), English (9%), and political science (7%). Within an average freshman class, 51% graduate in 4 years and 70% in 5 years. Some 200 companies recruited on campus in 1992–93.

Admissions Contact: Davod Kraus, Director of Admissions.

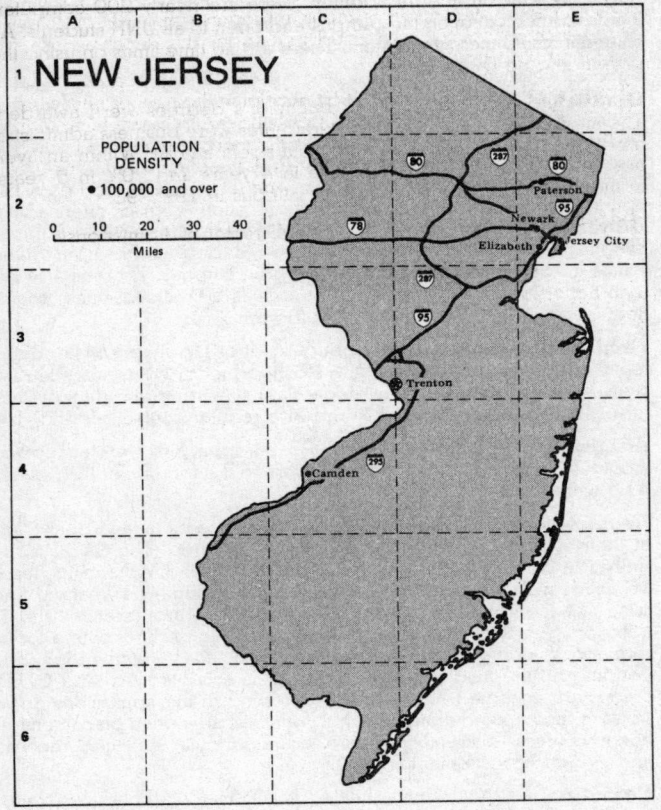

NEW JERSEY

POPULATION
DENSITY

● 100,000 and over

0 10 20 30 40
Miles

Sports: There are 6 intercollegiate sports each for men and women, and 5 intramural sports each. Athletic and recreation facilities include a 750-seat gymnasium.

Disabled Students: Two percent of the campus is accessible to disabled students. The following facilities are available: wheelchair ramps, elevators, special parking, and specially equipped rest rooms.

Services: In addition to many counseling and information services, tutoring is available in most subjects, including English, accounting, mathematics, biology, and chemistry. There is also remedial math, reading, and writing.

Campus Safety and Security: Campus safety and security measures include 24-hour foot and vehicle patrol, informal discussions, and pamphlets, posters, and films.

Programs of Study: Bloomfield awards the B.A. and B.S. degrees. Bachelor's degrees are awarded in BIOLOGICAL SCIENCE (biology/biological science), BUSINESS (accounting and business administration and management), COMMUNICATIONS AND THE ARTS (English, fine arts, French, and Spanish), COMPUTER AND PHYSICAL SCIENCE (chemistry), HEALTH PROFESSIONS (nursing), SOCIAL SCIENCE (economics, history, interdisciplinary studies, philosophy, political science/government, psychology, religion, and sociology). Nursing, prechiropractic, business, and sciences are the strongest academically. and have the largest enrollments.

Required: All students must maintain a minimum GPA of 2.0 while taking 132 credits. Distribution requirements include 4 courses from English/humanities and mathematics areas, 8 courses from culture and the arts, humanistic studies, social and behavioral science, and natural science, and 16 courses from a general education group.

Special: Student-designed majors through independent study programs and a contract program, study abroad, combined B.A.-B.S. degrees, internships, pass/fail options, dual majors, nondegree study, and work-study programs are available. Cross-registration with the University of Medicine and Dentistry of New Jersey is permitted. There are 3 national honor societies on campus. One department has an honors program.

Faculty/Classroom: Sixty percent of faculty are male; 40%, female. All teach undergraduates, and do research. The average class size in an introductory lecture is 25; in a laboratory, 18; and in a regular course offering, 25.

Admissions: About 86% of the 1993–94 applicants were accepted.

Requirements: The SAT I or ACT is required. In addition, the college requires at least 14 academic units, which should include English, mathematics, history, foreign language, and laboratory science. Candidates for the nursing major also should have a biology and a chemistry course. A personal recommendation is required. AP and CLEP credits are accepted. Important factors used in the admissions decision are leadership record, recommendations by school officials, advanced placement or honor courses, evidence of special talent, and personality, intangible qualities.

Procedure: Freshmen are admitted fall, spring, and summer. Entrance exams should be taken by December of the senior year. Application deadlines are open. Application fee is $20. Notification is sent on a rolling basis. There are early decision, early admissions, and deferred admissions plans.

Transfer: About 200 transfer students enrolled in a recent year. Transfer applicants must present a minimum GPA of 2.0 from an accredited institution and submit official transcripts from all previously attended colleges. A total of 32 credits out of 132 must be completed at Bloomfield.

Visiting: There are regularly scheduled orientations for prospective students, consisting of a campus tour, an admissions interview, and other activities by request. There are guides for informal visits and visitors may sit in on classes and stay overnight at the school. To arrange for a visit, contact the Office of Admissions at (201) 748–9000, ext. 230.

Financial Aid: In a recent year, 75% of all students received some form of financial aid. About 71% received need-based aid. The average freshman award was $5762. Of that total, scholarships or need-based grants averaged $4574 ($11,160 maximum); loans averaged $1031 ($6625 maximum); and work contracts averaged $157 ($1500 maximum). Sixty-two percent of undergraduate students work part-time. Average earnings from campus work for the school year are $1000. The average financial indebtedness of a recent graduate was $8095. Bloomfield is a member of CSS. The FAF, the college's own financial statement, and the FAFSA are required. The deadline for financial aid applications is June 1.

BLOOMFIELD COLLEGE   E-2

Bloomfield, NJ 07003   (201) 748–9000, ext. 230; (800) 216–1212

Full-time: 402 men, 910 women	**Faculty:** 42; IIB, av$
Part-time: 261 men, 421 women	**Ph.D.s:** 69%
Graduate: none	**Student/Faculty:** 31 to 1
Year: semesters, summer session	**Tuition:** $8100
Application Deadline: open	**Room & Board:** $4100

Freshman Class: 1304 applied, 1118 accepted, 279 enrolled

SAT I or ACT: required   **LESS COMPETITIVE**

Bloomfield College, founded in 1868 and affiliated with the Presbyterian Church, USA, is an independent, coeducational institution offering programs of study in fine and performing arts, professional studies, and the chemical and health sciences. In addition to regional accreditation, Bloomfield has baccalaureate program accreditation with NLN. The 3 libraries contain 60,000 volumes, 4500 microform items, and 3850 audiovisual forms, and subscribe to 352 periodicals. Computerized library sources and services include interlibrary loans and database searching. Special learning facilities include a learning resource center and art gallery. The 11-acre campus is in a suburban area 15 miles from New York City. Including residence halls, there are 28 buildings on campus.

Student Life: Most undergraduates are from New Jersey. Students come from 31 states and 15 foreign countries. Forty-four percent are African American; 40% white; 10% Hispanic. The average age of freshmen is 18; all undergraduates, 26. Twelve percent drop out by the end of their first year; 40% remain to graduate.

Housing: A total of 250 students can be accommodated in college housing. College-sponsored living facilities include single-sex and coed dormitories, fraternity houses, and sorority houses. In addition, there are honors houses and special interest houses. On-campus housing is available on a first-come, first-served basis. Priority is given to out-of-town students. Seventy-five percent of students commute. All students may keep cars on campus.

Activities: About 25% of men belong to 9 local fraternities; about 20% of women belong to 4 local sororities. There are 36 groups on campus, including cheerleading, choir, chorale, chorus, drama, ethnic, honors, international, literary magazine, newspaper, professional, religious, social service, student government, and yearbook. Popular campus events include Spring Festival.

International Students: There were recently 100 international students enrolled. They must take the TOEFL, the Comprehensive English Language Test, or the college's own test and achieve a minimum score on the TOEFL of 500.

Computers: The college provides computer facilities for student use. The mainframe is a DEC VAX 5400. Students have access to an 18-station networked laboratory. There are also 54 computers in 2 public-access facilities for student use. All students may access the system. It is available more than 70 hours a week and there are no individual time limits on using the system. The fees are $50.

Graduates: In a recent year, 157 bachelor's degrees were awarded. The most popular majors among graduates were business administration (32%), sociology (17%), and nursing (13%). Within an average freshman class, 20% graduate in 4 years and 40% in 5 years. Some 45 companies recruited on campus. In the 1992 graduating class, 80% of all graduates found employment within 6 months of graduation.

Admissions Contact: George P. Lynes, II, Dean of Admissions.

CALDWELL COLLEGE
E-2

Caldwell, NJ 07006 (201) 228-4424, ext. 220; (800) 831-9178

Full-time: 241 men, 453 women	Faculty: 57; IIB, -$
Part-time: 183 men, 685 women	Ph.D.s: 51%
Graduate: 6 men, 24 women	Student/Faculty: 12 to 1
Year: semesters, summer session	Tuition: $8460
Application Deadline: open	Room & Board: $4400
Freshman Class: 1011 applied, 604 accepted, 213 enrolled	
SAT I Verbal/Math: 450/470	**COMPETITIVE**

Caldwell College, founded in 1939, is a private coeducational school offering programs in liberal arts, science, business, fine arts, and education. It is affiliated with the Roman Catholic Church. The library contains 192,958 volumes, 2510 microform items, and 3000 audiovisual forms, and subscribes to 390 periodicals. Computerized library sources and services include the card catalog, interlibrary loans, and database searching. Special learning facilities include a learning resource center, an art gallery, a TV station, and a greenhouse. The 100-acre campus is in a suburban area 20 miles west of New York City. Including residence halls, there are 5 buildings on campus.

Student Life: About 89% of undergraduates are from New Jersey. Students come from 14 states and 20 foreign countries. Seventy percent are from public schools; 30% from private. Sixty-four percent are white; 17% foreign nationals; 10% African American. Sixty-six percent are Catholic; 20% Protestant. The average age of freshmen is 18; all undergraduates, 20. Twenty-four percent drop out by the end of their first year; 44% remain to graduate.

Housing: A total of 264 students can be accommodated in college housing. College-sponsored living facilities include coed dormitories. On-campus housing is guaranteed for all 4 years. Sixty-six percent of students commute. Alcohol is not permitted. All students may keep cars on campus.

Activities: There are no fraternities or sororities. There are 27 groups on campus, including art, cheerleading, choir, drama, ethnic, honors, international, literary magazine, newspaper, professional, radio and TV, religious, social, social service, student government, and yearbook. Popular campus events include Founders Day, Christmas Banquet, Junior Ring Ceremony, and Freshman Investiture.

Sports: There are 4 intercollegiate sports for men and 3 for women, and 6 intramural sports for men and 6 for women. Athletic and recreation facilities include a multipurpose gymnasium, a training room, tennis courts, weight rooms, playing fields, and a pool.

Disabled Students: Eighty percent of the campus is accessible to disabled students. The following facilities are available: wheelchair ramps, elevators, special parking, specially equipped rest rooms, and special class scheduling.

Services: In addition to many counseling and information services, tutoring is available in most subjects. There is a reader service for the blind, and remedial math, reading, and writing.

Campus Safety and Security: Campus safety and security measures include 24-hour foot and vehicle patrol, informal discussions, pamphlets, posters, and films, and emergency telephones. In addition, there are lighted pathways and sidewalks.

Programs of Study: Caldwell awards the B.A., B.S., and B.F.A. degrees. Master's degrees also are awarded. Bachelor's degrees are awarded in BIOLOGICAL SCIENCE (biology/biological science), BUSINESS (business administration and management), COMMUNICATIONS AND THE ARTS (art, English, fine arts, French, music, and Spanish), COMPUTER AND PHYSICAL SCIENCE (chemistry, computer information systems, computer management, computer science, and mathematics), EDUCATION (elementary), HEALTH PROFESSIONS (medical laboratory technology), SOCIAL SCIENCE (history, psychology, religion, social studies, and sociology). Business and education have the largest enrollments.

Required: Students must maintain a minimum GPA of 2.0 while taking 122 credit hours, including 30 in the major. The 55-credit core includes 15 credits in religion/philosophy, 6 each in history, English, language, social science, and mathematics, 4 in fine arts, 3 in science, 2 in communication arts, and 1 in physical education. A 3-credit course in computer science is also required.

Special: Caldwell offers co-op programs in all majors except education and medical technology; study abroad in 3 countries; a Washington semester; 1-semester internships; and work study with Mt. St. Dominic, Hill Top Day Care, and Family and Child Services of North Essex. B.A.-B.S. degrees in 19 fields, dual majors in all majors, credit for life experience in adult education, nondegree study, and pass/fail options are possible. The Continuing Education Program offers adults (23 years or older) a chance to complete degree requirements in the evening and Saturdays and the External Degree Program gives adults an opportunity to earn a degree off campus. There is a freshman honors program on campus, as well as 10 national honor societies. All departments have honors programs.

Faculty/Classroom: Thirty-eight percent of faculty are male; 62% female. All teach undergraduates. No introductory courses are taught by graduate students. The average class size in an introductory lecture is 23; in a laboratory, 13; and in a regular course offering, 16.

Admissions: About 60% of the 1993–94 applicants were accepted. About 24% of the current freshmen were in the top fifth of their class; 47% were in the top two fifths.

Requirements: Caldwell requires applicants to be in the upper 50% of their class. A minimum GPA of 2.0 is required. The SAT I is required. A composite score of 900 is recommended. Applicants need 16 academic credits or 16 Carnegie units, including 4 years in English, 2 each in foreign language, mathematics, and science, and 1 in history. A written recommendation from a high school counselor is required. A portfolio, audition, and interview are recommended, depending on the field of study. The GED is accepted. AP and CLEP credits are accepted. Important factors used in the admissions decision are recommendations by school officials, advanced placement or honor courses, leadership record, extracurricular activities record, and evidence of special talent.

Procedure: Freshmen are admitted to all sessions. Entrance exams should be taken in the fall of the senior year. Application deadlines are open. The application fee is $25. Notification is sent on a rolling basis.

Transfer: Thirty-six transfer students enrolled in 1993–94. Transfer students must have a minimum GPA of 2.0 (2.5 in teacher education). A total of 45 credits out of 122 must be completed at Caldwell.

Visiting: There are regularly scheduled orientations for prospective students, including a brief presentation by faculty and students, followed by a tour. There are guides for informal visits and visitors may sit in on classes and stay overnight at the school. To arrange for a visit, contact Admissions at (201) 228-4424.

Financial Aid: In 1993–94, 73% of all current freshmen and 61% of continuing students received some form of financial aid. About 56% of freshmen and 50% of continuing students received need-based aid. The average freshman award was $8089. Of that total, scholarships or need-based grants averaged $6331 ($8400 maximum); loans averaged $2424 ($2625 maximum); and work contracts averaged $815 ($1000 maximum). Thirty-five percent of undergraduate students work part-time. Average earnings from campus work for the school year are $607. The average financial indebtedness of the 1992–93 graduate was $7506. Caldwell is a member of CSS. The FAF is required. The deadline for financial aid applications is May 1.

International Students: There are currently 123 international students enrolled. The school actively recruits these students. They must take the TOEFL and achieve a minimum score of 500.

Computers: The college provides computer facilities for student use. The mainframe is an AS400. There are 106 IBM PC, Tandy 1000 SX, DTK, and Apple IIe and IIgs microcomputers available in the academic computing center. All students may access the system. It may be used Monday to Thursday 9 A.M. to 9:30 P.M., Friday 10:30 A.M. to 4 P.M., and weekends 1 to 5 P.M. There are no time limits and no fees.

Graduates: In 1992–93, 177 bachelor's degrees were awarded. The most popular majors among graduates were business administration (45%), psychology (12%), and education (8%). Within an average freshman class, 33% graduate in 4 years, 47% in 5 years, and 50% in 6 years. Some 14 companies recruited on campus in 1992–93. In the 1992 graduating class, 11% of all graduates were enrolled in graduate school within 6 months of graduation; 79% had found employment.

Admissions Contact: J. Raymond Sheenan, Director of Admissions.

CENTENARY COLLEGE
C-2

Hackettstown, NJ 07840   (908) 852-4696; (800) 236-8679

Full-time: 90 men, 330 women   Faculty: 36; IIB, --$

Part-time: 210 men, 290 women   Ph.Ds: 75%

Graduate: none   Student/Faculty: 12 to 1

Year: semesters, summer session   Tuition: $11,640

Application Deadline: open   Room & Board: $5400

Freshman Class: 369 applied, 312 accepted, 90 enrolled

SAT I Verbal/Math: 470/500   **LESS COMPETITIVE**

Centenary College, founded in 1867, is a private, coeducational institution affiliated with the United Methodist Church. The college offers undergraduate programs in liberal arts, business, international studies, education, equine studies, fashion, and fine arts. The library contains 65,000 volumes, 12,400 microform items, and 2600 audiovisual forms, and subscribes to 375 periodicals. Computerized library sources and services include interlibrary loans. Special learning facilities include a learning resource center, an art gallery, a radio station, a children's center, an equestrian center, and a language laboratory. The 42-acre campus is in a small town 55 miles west of New York City. Including residence halls, there are 14 buildings on campus.

Student Life: About 74% of undergraduates are from New Jersey. Students come from 15 states and 7 foreign countries. Seventy-six percent are from public schools; 24% from private. Sixty-seven percent are white; 12% African American; 11% Hispanic. Seventy-five percent claim no religious affiliation; 12% are Catholic; 10% Protestant. The average age of freshmen is 18; all undergraduates, 36. Twenty-seven percent drop out by the end of their first year; 70% remain to graduate.

Housing: A total of 460 students can be accommodated in college housing. College-sponsored living facilities include single-sex and coed dormitories. On-campus housing is guaranteed for all 4 years. Fifty-seven percent of students live on campus; of those, 50% remain on campus on weekends. All students may keep cars on campus.

Activities: About 20% of men belong to 1 local fraternity; about 60% of women belong to 3 local sororities. There are 27 groups on campus, including art, cheerleading, chorus, dance, drama, ethnic, honors, international, literary magazine, newspaper, photography, professional, radio and TV, religious, social, social service, student government, and yearbook. Popular campus events include Presidents Ball, Centenary Weekend, and Spring Fling Weekend.

Sports: There are 3 intercollegiate sports for men and 5 for women, and 3 intramural sports for men and 4 for women. Athletic and recreation facilities include a gymnasium, a fitness center and indoor pool, tennis courts, playing fields, and an equine center and stables.

Disabled Students: Twenty percent of the campus is accessible to disabled students. The following facilities are available: wheelchair ramps, special parking, specially equipped rest rooms, special class scheduling, and lowered telephones.

Services: In addition to many counseling and information services, tutoring is available in every subject. There is also remedial math, reading, and writing.

Campus Safety and Security: Campus safety and security measures include self-defense education, escort service, informal discussions, and pamphlets, posters, and films. In addition, there are lighted pathways and sidewalks.

Programs of Study: Centenary awards the B.A., B.S., and B.F.A. degrees. Associate degrees are also awarded. Bachelor's degrees are awarded in AGRICULTURE (equestrian science), BUSINESS (accounting and business administration and management), COMMUNICATIONS AND THE ARTS (communications, design, and English), COMPUTER AND PHYSICAL SCIENCE (mathematics), EDUCATION (elementary and secondary), ENGINEERING AND ENVIRONMENTAL DESIGN (interior design), SOCIAL SCIENCE (fashion design and technology, history, interdisciplinary studies, international studies, and psychology). Equine studies, business, and education are the strongest academically. Equine studies and business have the largest enrollments.

Required: Students must complete a distribution of 52 semester hours in core courses, including college seminars, as well as the required number of credits, usually about 48, for their particular major. At least 128 semester hours and a minimum GPA of 2.0 are needed to earn the bachelor's degree.

Special: Centenary requires internships in some majors. The college offers study abroad in England, student-designed majors, work-study, and a pass/fail option. Students aged 25 or older may earn life experience credits. There is a freshman honors program on campus, as well as one national honor society. All departments have honors programs.

Faculty/Classroom: Forty-eight percent of faculty are male; 52%, female. All teach undergraduates. The average class size in an introductory lecture is 25; in a laboratory, 20; and in a regular course offering, 15.

Admissions: About 85% of the 1993-94 applicants were accepted. The SAT scores for the 1993-94 freshman class were as follows: Verbal—80% below 500, 15% between 500 and 599, and 5% between 600 and 700; Math—73% below 500, 22% between 500 and 599, and 5% between 600 and 700. About 10% of the current freshmen were in the top fifth of their class; 31% were in the top two fifths.

Requirements: The SAT I or ACT is required. Minimum scores include an SAT I composite of 810, 410 verbal and 400 math, and an ACT composite of 19. Applicants must be graduates of accredited secondary schools or have earned a GED. Centenary requires 16 academic credits or Carnegie units, based on 2 years each of foreign language and history, and 4 years each of English, mathematics, and science. An essay is required, and an interview is recommended. Applicants to specific fine arts programs must also submit a portfolio. AP and CLEP credits are accepted. Important factors used in the admissions decision are extracurricular activities record, evidence of special talent, personality, intangible qualities, leadership record, and advanced placement or honor courses.

Procedure: Freshmen are admitted fall and spring. Entrance exams should be taken as early as possible in the senior year. Application deadlines are open. The application fee is $25; $50 for international students. Notification is sent on a rolling basis. There is a deferred admissions plan.

Transfer: About 80 transfer students enrolled in 1993-94. Applicants must have a minimum cumulative college GPA of 2.0 and submit proof of high school graduation or the equivalent. A total of 32 credits out of 128 must be completed at Centenary.

Visiting: There are regularly scheduled orientations for prospective students, including basic skills testing, advising, registration, and social events. There are guides for informal visits and visitors may sit in on classes and stay overnight at the school. To arrange for a visit, contact the Admissions Office at (800) 236-8679.

Financial Aid: In 1993-94, 75% of students received some form of financial aid. About 70% received need-based aid. The average freshman award was $4000. Ninety-five percent of undergraduate students work part-time. Average earnings from campus work for the school year are $800. The average financial indebtedness of the 1992-93 graduate was $7000. Centenary is a member of CSS. The college's own financial statement and the FAFSA are required. The deadline for financial aid applications is August 1.

International Students: There are currently 39 international students enrolled. The school actively recruits these students. They must take the TOEFL and achieve a minimum score of 500, or they may take the SAT I or ACT.

Computers: The college provides computer facilities for student use. The mainframe is an IBM/36. The microcomputer and CAD laboratories are available for instructional and student use. Those students enrolled in computer courses may access the mainframe during the laboratory hours specified by their course. All students have access to the microcomputer laboratory. There are no fees.

Graduates: In a recent year, 110 bachelor's degrees were awarded. Within an average freshman class, 95% graduate in 4 years and 5% in 5 years. Some 15 companies recruited on campus in a recent year.

Admissions Contact: Dennis M. Kelly, Dean of Admissions.

COLLEGE OF SAINT ELIZABETH
E-2

Morristown, NJ 07960-6989   (201) 292-6351; (800) 210-7900

Full-time: 2 men, 490 women   Faculty: 48; IIB, -$

Part-time: 150 men, 823 women   Ph.Ds: 69%

Graduate: 2 men, 21 women   Student/Faculty: 10 to 1

Year: semesters, summer session   Tuition: $10,800

Application Deadline: August 15   Room & Board: $5000

Freshman Class: 444 applied, 359 accepted, 123 enrolled

SAT I Verbal/Math: 450/470   **COMPETITIVE**

The College of St. Elizabeth, founded in 1899, is a private Roman Catholic college primarily for women. Undergraduate programs are offered in the arts and sciences, business administration, education, home economics, and upper-level nursing. In addition to regional accreditation, CSE has baccalaureate program accreditation with NLN. The library contains 187,506 volumes, 33,061 microform items, and 3402 audiovisual forms, and subscribes to 751 periodicals. Computerized library sources and services include interlibrary loans and database searching. Special learning facilities include a learning resource center and a television studio. The 188-acre campus is in a suburban area 40 miles west of New York City. Including residence halls, there are 12 buildings on campus.

Student Life: About 95% of undergraduates are from New Jersey. Students come from 5 states and 9 foreign countries. Sixty-three percent are from public schools; 37% from private. Seventy-five percent are white; 10% Hispanic. Sixty-two percent are Catholic; 10% Protestant; 21% claim no religious affiliation. The average age of freshmen is 18; all undergraduates, 25. Twenty-five percent drop out by the end of their first year; 62% remain to graduate.

Housing: A total of 352 students can be accommodated in college housing. College-sponsored living facilities include single-sex dormitories. On-campus housing is guaranteed for all 4 years. Sixty-nine percent of students live on campus; of those, 35% remain on campus on weekends. All students may keep cars on campus.

Activities: There are no fraternities or sororities. There are 24 groups on campus, including chorale, drama, ethnic, film, honors, international, literary magazine, newspaper, professional, religious, social, student government, and yearbook. Popular campus events include Oktoberfest, fall and spring picnics, International Night, Holiday Social, Sadie Hawkins Social, Junior Class Ring Ceremony, and Greek drama presentation.

Sports: There are 6 intercollegiate and 6 intramural sports for women. Athletic and recreation facilities include student center houses, a swimming pool, a sauna, a weight room, an archery range, a gymnasium, and tennis courts.

Disabled Students: Seventy-five percent of the campus is accessible to disabled students. The following facilities are available: wheelchair ramps, elevators, special parking, and specially equipped rest rooms.

Services: In addition to many counseling and information services, tutoring is available in most subjects. There is remedial math, reading, and writing.

Campus Safety and Security: Campus safety and security measures include escort service, lighted pathways and sidewalks, and patrols from dusk until dawn.

Programs of Study: CSE awards the B.A., B.S., and B.S.N. degrees. Bachelor's degrees are awarded in BIOLOGICAL SCIENCE (biology/biological science and nutrition), BUSINESS (accounting and business administration and management), COMMUNICATIONS AND THE ARTS (art, English, fine arts, French, music, and Spanish), COMPUTER AND PHYSICAL SCIENCE (chemistry, computer science, and mathematics), EDUCATION (early childhood, elementary, home economics, and special), HEALTH PROFESSIONS (nursing, predentistry, and premedicine), SOCIAL SCIENCE (economics, history, philosophy, prelaw, psychology, and sociology). Mathematics, chemistry, education, psychology, and English are the strongest academically. Business administration, education, and English have the largest enrollments.

Required: Core requirements include 2 credits in physical education, 9 in social science, 9 to 12 in mathematics and science, and 18 in specific humanities courses focusing on religion, philosophy, literature, history, and fine arts. Students must also demonstrate proficiency in writing. The bachelor's degree requires completion of at least 128 semester hours, including a minimum of 32 in a major field, with a GPA of 2.0 or better.

Special: There is cross-registration with Drew University and Fairleigh Dickinson University. CSE also offers internships, study abroad, and a Washington semester, including internships and seminars through the American University Justice Semester program. Work-study programs on campus, dual majors, credit for life experience, pass/fail options, and nondegree study are also available. Weekend College, a program geared to the working student, requires Saturday conference sessions and only 6 days of class attendance each semester. There is a freshman honors program on campus, as well as 4 national honor societies.

Faculty/Classroom: Thirty-two percent of faculty are male; 68%, female. Nearly all teach undergraduates. The average class size in a regular course offering is 15.

Admissions: About 81% of the 1993–94 applicants were accepted. The SAT scores for the 1993–94 freshman class were as follows: Verbal—66% below 500, 26% between 500 and 599, and 8% between 600 and 700; Math—57% below 500, 30% between 500 and 599, 12% between 600 and 700, and 1% above 700. About 47% of the current freshmen were in the top fifth of their class; 68% were in the top two fifths.

Requirements: CSE requires applicants to be in the upper 60% of their class. A minimum GPA of 2.0 is required. The SAT I or ACT is required. A minimum composite SAT I score of 800, 400 on each part, is recommended. Applicants must be graduates of accredited secondary schools or have earned a GED. The college requires 16 academic units, including 3 each in English, mathematics, and science, and 2 each in foreign language and history. An essay is required and an interview is recommended. AP and CLEP credits are accepted. Important factors used in the admissions decision are advanced placement or honor courses, leadership record, recommendations by school officials, personality, intangible qualities, and recommendations by alumni.

Procedure: Freshmen are admitted fall and spring. Entrance exams should be taken early in the senior year. Early decision applications should be filed by November 15; regular applications, by August 15 for fall entry and December 15 for spring entry, along with an application fee of $25. Notification of early decision is sent December 1; regular decision, on a rolling basis. There are early decision, early admissions, and deferred admissions plans. Six early decision candidates were accepted for the 1993–94 class.

Transfer: Forty-eight transfer students enrolled in 1993–94. Applicants must present a minimum GPA of 2.0 in course work from an accredited college. SAT I or ACT scores, an associate degree, and an interview are also recommended. A total of 64 credits out of 128 must be completed at CSE.

Visiting: There are regularly scheduled orientations for prospective students, including interviews, tours, and class visitation. There are guides for informal visits and visitors may sit in on classes and stay overnight at the school. To arrange for a visit, contact George P. Lynes II, Dean of Admission and Financial Aid, at (201) 292-6351.

Financial Aid: In 1993–94, 82% of all current freshmen and 79% of continuing students received some form of financial aid. About 75% of all students received need-based aid. The average freshman award was $5000. Of that total, scholarships or need-based grants averaged $5000 ($10,400 maximum); loans averaged $2625; and work contracts averaged $1100 ($1425 maximum). All undergraduate students work part-time. Average earnings from campus work for the school year are $1425. The average financial indebtedness of the 1992–93 graduate was $8000. CSE is a member of CSS. The FAF is required. The deadline for financial aid applications is April 15.

International Students: There are currently 46 international students enrolled. The school actively recruits these students. They must take the TOEFL and achieve a minimum score of 500. The student must also take the SAT I; applicants from English-speaking countries may submit scores from either the TOEFL or SAT I.

Computers: The college's computer is an AT&T 3B2 1000 Model 60 minicomputer. There are also 98 IBM, Apple IIC, and Macintosh microcomputers in various laboratories throughout the campus. Science departments have computers interfacing with equipment, and the home economics department has computer aided-design equipment for fashion and design use. Those students enrolled in computer courses may access the minicomputer 72 hours per week. It may be used when the main laboratory is open. There are no time limits and the fee is $25.

Graduates: In 1992–93, 189 bachelor's degrees were awarded. The most popular majors among graduates were business (45%), education (13%), and English (10%). Within an average freshman class, 53% graduate in 4 years, 57% in 5 years, and 62% in 6 years. Some 23 companies recruited on campus in 1992–93. In the 1992 graduating class, 14% of the women were enrolled in graduate school within 6 months of graduation; 64% had found employment.

Admissions Contact: George P. Lynes II, Dean of Admission and Financial Aid.

DREW UNIVERSITY
COLLEGE OF LIBERAL ARTS
D-2
Madison, NJ 07940   (201) 408-DREW

Full-time: 483 men, 685 women	**Faculty:** 100; IIA, +$
Part-time: 13 men, 33 women	**Ph.D.s:** 93%
Graduate: 454 men, 307 women	**Student/Faculty:** 12 to 1
Year: semesters	**Tuition:** $18,058
Application Deadline: February 15	**Room & Board:** $5348
Freshman Class: 2150 applied, 1580 accepted, 323 enrolled	
SAT I Verbal/Math: 580/630	**HIGHLY COMPETITIVE**

The College of Liberal Arts was added to Drew University in 1928 and is part of an educational complex that includes a theological school and a graduate school. Drew is a private, independent, coeducational university affiliated with the United Methodist Church. There are 2 graduate schools. The library contains 429,636 volumes, 296,414 microform items, and 3320 audiovisual forms, and subscribes to 2049 periodicals. Computerized library sources and services include the card catalog, interlibrary loans, and database searching. Special learning facilities include an art gallery, a radio station, an observatory, a photography gallery, and a TV satellite dish. The 186-acre campus is in a small town 30 miles west of New York City. Including residence halls, there are 57 buildings on campus.

Student Life: About 55% of undergraduates are from New Jersey. Students come from 40 states, 11 foreign countries, and Canada. Seventy-four percent are from public schools; 26% from private. Seventy-three percent are white. The average age of freshmen is 18; all undergraduates, 20. Ten percent drop out by the end of their first year; 72% remain to graduate.

Housing: A total of 1272 students can be accommodated in college housing. College-sponsored living facilities include single-sex and coed dormitories, on-campus apartments, and married-student housing. In addition there are language houses and special interest houses. On-campus housing is guaranteed for all 4 years. Ninety percent of students live on campus; of those, 70% remain on campus on weekends. Upperclassmen may keep cars on campus.

Activities: There are no fraternities or sororities on campus. There are 64 groups on campus, including art, cheerleading, choir, chorale, computers, dance, drama, ethnic, gay, honors, international, literary magazine, newspaper, orchestra, photography, political, professional, radio and TV, religious, social, social service, student government, and yearbook. Popular campus events include Holiday Semiformal, Annual Picnic, Multicultural Awareness Day, the New Jersey Shakespeare Festival, Women's History Month, Black History Month, Puerto Rican Heritage Month, Hispanic Heritage Month, African Emphasis Weekend, Welcome Back Bash, and Suitcases Party.

Sports: There are 7 intercollegiate sports for men and 11 for women, and 16 intramural sports for men and 16 for women. Athletic and recreation facilities include an artificial turf athletic field with a 1000-seat gymnasium, a 1000-seat auditorium, swimming pool, lighted tennis complex, weight training room, forest preserve, arboretum, and game room.

Disabled Students: The following facilities are available: wheelchair ramps, elevators, special parking, specially equipped rest rooms, special class scheduling. The main dining facility, the student center and commons, and the ground floor of every dormitory and classroom building are accessible to physically handicapped students.

Services: In addition to many counseling and information services, tutoring is available in every subject.

Campus Safety and Security: Campus safety and security measures include 24-hour foot and vehicle patrol, escort service, informal discussions, and emergency telephones. In addition, there are lighted pathways and sidewalks.

Programs of Study: Drew awards the B.A. degree. Master's and doctoral degrees also are awarded. Bachelor's degrees are awarded in BIOLOGICAL SCIENCE (biology/biological science), COMMUNICATIONS AND THE ARTS (classics, dramatic arts, English, fine arts, French, German, music, Russian, and Spanish), COMPUTER AND PHYSICAL SCIENCE (chemistry, computer science, mathematics, and physics), SOCIAL SCIENCE (American studies, anthropology, behavioral science, economics, history, philosophy, political science/government, psychobiology, psychology, religion, Russian and Slavic studies, and sociology). Biological and other physical sciences are the strongest academically. Social sciences has the largest enrollment.

Required: General education requirements include a freshman seminar, 6 credits in foreign language, 6 in natural science/mathematics distribution, 4 in performing or fine arts, and 3 each in history, religion/philosophy, economics and political systems, behavioral science, and non-Western/Third World perspectives. Students must also demonstrate computer literacy and writing proficiency. In order to graduate, students must complete at least 120 semester hours, including the required number in their particular major, with a minimum GPA of 2.0.

Special: Drew offers co-op programs with the University of Miami, the University of Hawaii, and Duke University, as well as cross-registration with the College of Saint Elizabeth and Fairleigh Dickinson University. There are also dual majors, study abroad, a Washington semester, student-designed majors, internships, field work, and 3-2 engineering programs with Washington University in St. Louis and the Stevens Institute of Technology. There are 11 national honor societies on campus, including Phi Beta Kappa.

Faculty/Classroom: Sixty percent of faculty are male; 40%, female. All teach and do research. No introductory courses are taught by graduate students. The average class size in an introductory lecture is 25; in a laboratory, 20; and in a regular course offering, 18.

Admissions: About 73% of the 1993-94 applicants were accepted. The SAT I scores for the 1993-94 freshman class were as follows: Verbal—19% below 500, 38% between 500 and 599, 35% between 600 and 700, and 8% above 700; Math—12% below 500, 29% between 500 and 599, 39% between 600 and 700, and 20% above 700. About 78% of the current freshmen were in the top fifth of their class; 92% were in the top two fifths. There were 5 National Merit finalists. About 24 freshmen graduated first in their class.

Requirements: The SAT I is required. Applicants must be graduates of accredited secondary schools or have earned a GED. The university strongly recommends 16 academic credits or Carnegie units, including 4 in English, 2 in mathematics, and 2 each in foreign language, science, and history, with the remaining 3 in additional academic courses. Three SAT II: Subject tests are recommended, including writing. An essay is also required, and an interview is recommended. AP and CLEP credits are accepted. Important factors used in the admissions decision are advanced placement or honor courses, evidence of special talent, recommendations by school officials, personality, intangible qualities, and leadership record.

Procedure: Freshmen are admitted fall and spring. Entrance exams should be taken by January of the senior year. Early decision applications should be filed by January 15; regular applications, by February 15 for fall entry and December 1 for spring entry, along with an application fee of $30. Notification is sent March 15. There are early decision, early admissions, and deferred admissions plans. About 78 ear-

ly decision candidates were accepted for the 1993-94 class. A waiting list is an active part of the admissions procedure, with about 2% of applicants on the list.

Transfer: About 33 transfer students enrolled in 1993-94. Applicants must submit satisfactory high school and college academic records and either SAT I or ACT scores. An interview is also required. A total of 60 credits out of 120 must be completed at Drew.

Visiting: There are regularly scheduled orientations for prospective students. There are guides for informal visits and visitors may sit in on classes and stay overnight at the school. To arrange for a visit, contact the Admissions Office at (201) 408-DREW.

Financial Aid: In 1993-94, 67% of continuing students received some form of financial aid. About 79% of freshmen and 56% of continuing students received need-based aid. The average freshman award was $15,142. Of that total, scholarships or need-based grants averaged $9924 ($17,568 maximum); loans averaged $3069 ($4325 maximum); and work contracts averaged $1163 ($1300 maximum). The average financial indebtedness of the 1992-93 graduate was $6783. The FAF or FFS, the college's own financial statement, and FAFSA are required. The deadline for financial aid applications is March 1.

International Students: There are currently 18 international students enrolled. They must take the TOEFL and achieve a minimum score of 550.

Computers: The college provides computer facilities for student use. The mainframes are 2 DEC VAX 11/750s and a 6330. All full-time students are provided with a laptop PC, a dot-matrix printer, and accompanying software, including DOS 6.0 and WordPerfect 5.1. An extensive software library and additional computers are located on campus. Students also have access to Internet. All students may access the system. There are no time limits on using the system and no fees.

Graduates: In 1992-93, 355 bachelor's degrees were awarded. The most popular majors among graduates were political science (22%), psychology (12%), and English (12%). Within an average freshman class, 72% graduate in 4 years and 77% in 5 years. Some 50 companies recruited on campus in 1992-93. In the 1992 graduating class, 21% of graduates were enrolled in graduate school within 6 months of graduation; 68% of graduates had found employment.

Admissions Contact: Roberto Noya, Director of Admissions.

FAIRLEIGH DICKINSON UNIVERSITY SYSTEM

The Fairleigh Dickinson University System, established in 1942, is a private system in New Jersey. It is governed by Board of Trustees, whose chief administrator is President. The primary goal of the system is Teaching/Research. The main priorities are To provide an academically challenging learning experience to prepare students for employment or enrollment in graduate and professional schools;, To promote independent thinking and collaborative learning in students as part of the educational process; and, and To cultivate a holistic, integrated living-learning experience as part of the educational process, and to foster the ideals of good citizenship and community service. The total enrollment in fall 1991 of all 2 campuses was 11,001; there were 668 faculty members. Altogether there are 38 baccalaureate, 51 master's, and 1 doctoral programs offered in Fairleigh Dickinson University System. There is a four-year campus located in Florham Park/Madison Campus.

FAIRLEIGH DICKINSON UNIVERSITY E-2

Teaneck, NJ 07666-1914 (201) 460-5267; (800) 338-8803

Full-time: 1399 men, 1376 women	Faculty: 263; IIA, av$
Part-time: 939 men, 1263 women	Ph.D.s: 81%
Graduate: 1978 men, 2114 women	Student/Faculty: 11 to 1
Year: semesters, summer session	Tuition: $11,091
Application Deadline: June 1	Room & Board: $5336
Freshman Class: 3085 applied, 1569 accepted, 462 enrolled	
SAT I Verbal/Math: 432/496	**COMPETITIVE**

Farleigh Dickinson University, founded in 1942, is an independent university consisting of 2 campuses, Teaneck/Hackensack and Florham/Madison, offering undergraduate and graduate degrees in business, arts and sciences, professional studies, public administration, and hotel, restaurant, and tourism management. There are 6 undergraduate and 6 graduate schools. In addition to regional accreditation, FDU has baccalaureate program accreditation with ABET, APTA, and NLN. The 2 libraries contain 408,415 volumes, 259,216 microform items, and 2016 audiovisual forms, and subscribe to 2277 periodicals. Special learning facilities include a learning resource center, art gallery, radio station, and TV station. The 125-acre Teaneck-Hackensack campus is in a suburban area 5 miles from New York City, and the 177-acre Florham/Madison campus is 33 miles from New York City. Including residence halls, there are 82 buildings on the combined campuses.

Student Life: About 85% of undergraduates are from New Jersey. Students come from 26 states, 43 foreign countries, and Canada. Seventy-six percent are white. The average age of freshmen is 18; all undergraduates, 27. Twenty-nine percent drop out by the end of their first year; 45% remain to graduate.

Housing: A total of 1790 students can be accommodated in college housing. College-sponsored living facilities include single-sex and coed dormitories and fraternity houses. In addition, there are special-interest houses and sports, sorority communal living, Greek life, and major houses. On-campus housing is guaranteed for all 4 years at Madison, and at Teaneck is available on a first-come, first-served basis, and is available on a lottery system for upperclassmen. Priority is given to out-of-town students. All students may keep cars on campus.

Activities: About 20% of men belong to 15 national fraternities; about 20% of women belong to 13 national sororities. There are 40 groups on campus, including art, cheerleading, choir, chorus, drama, drill team, ethnic, film, gay, honors, international, jazz band, literary magazine, newspaper, photography, political, professional, radio and TV, religious, social, social service, student government, and yearbook. Popular campus events include dances, dinner parties, concerts, Welcome Back Week, Homecoming, Greek Week, Spring Fling, Senior Week, Spring Jam, Multicultural Week, and SGA Awards Dinner.

Sports: There are 14 intercollegiate sports for men and 13 for women, and 41 intramural sports for men and 41 for women. Athletic and recreation facilities at Teaneck include include a 5,000-seat facility with a 6-lane, 200-meter track, 4 full basketball courts, and 2 volleyball courts; a soccer field; a fully equipped weight room; 6 tennis courts; a baseball field; outdoor basketball courts; and a billiard area. Madison facilities include a gymnasium seating 400; a pool, a fitness center; a training room; rehabilitation facilities; football, basketball, softball, lacrosse, and field hockey fields; 5 tennis courts; and 2 outdoor basketball courts.

Disabled Students: Forty-five percent of the campus is accessible to disabled students. The following facilities are available: wheelchair ramps, elevators, special parking, lowered telephones, and assistance for the hearing impaired.

Services: In addition to many counseling and information services, tutoring is available in every subject. There is also a reader service for the blind, and remedial math, reading, and writing. Workshops offer assistance with study skills and time management, and support services for basic-skills students and freshmen are available. There is also a regional center for learning-disabled students.

Campus Safety and Security: Campus safety and security measures include 24-hour foot and vehicle patrol, self-defense education, escort service, and informal discussions. In addition, there are pamphlets, posters, films, emergency telephones, lighted pathways and sidewalks, and a crime prevention program.

Programs of Study: FDU awards the B.A., B.S., B.S.C.L.S., B.S.Civ.E.T., B.S.Con.E.T., B.S.E.E., B.S.E.E.T., B.S.M.E.T., and B.S.N. degrees. Associate, master's, and doctoral degrees also are awarded. Bachelor's degrees are awarded in BIOLOGICAL SCIENCE (biochemistry, biology/biological science, and marine biology), BUSINESS (accounting, business administration and management, hotel/motel and restaurant management, management science, and marketing/retailing/merchandising), COMMUNICATIONS AND THE ARTS (English, fine arts, French, and Spanish), COMPUTER AND PHYSICAL SCIENCE (chemistry, computer science, mathematics, and science), ENGINEERING AND ENVIRONMENTAL DESIGN (civil engineering technology, construction technology, electrical/electronics engineering, electrical/electronics engineering technology, environmental science, and mechanical engineering technology), HEALTH PROFESSIONS (clinical science, medical laboratory technology, nursing, predentistry, premedicine, and preveterinary science), SOCIAL SCIENCE (economics, history, humanities, international studies, philosophy, political science/government, prelaw, psychology, and sociology). Business management, finance, psychology, and marketing have the largest enrollments.

Required: To graduate, students must complete a minimum of 128 credits, including 30 to 44 in the major, with a minimum 2.0 GPA. Distribution requirements include courses in English, communications, mathematics, physical education, foreign language, humanities, social and behavioral sciences, laboratory science, and an integrated, interdisciplinary university core sequence.

Special: FDU offers co-op programs in all majors, cross-registration, internships, and study abroad in more than 20 countries. A Washington semester, work-study, accelerated degrees, and student-designed majors in the humanities are possible. A 3-2 prepharmacy program with Long Island University is available. There is a freshman honors program on campus, as well as 4 national honor societies. All departments have honors programs.

Faculty/Classroom: Seventy-four percent of faculty are male; 26%, female. All teach undergraduates and 60% also do research. No introductory courses are taught by graduate students. The average class size in an introductory lecture is 24; in a laboratory, 19; and in a regular course offering, 22.

Admissions: About 51% of the 1993-94 applicants were accepted. About 27% of the current freshmen were in the top fifth of their class; 56% were in the top two fifths.

Requirements: FDU requires applicants to be in the upper 50% of their class. A minimum GPA of 2.0 is required. The SAT I or ACT is required. Applicants should be graduates of an accredited high school or have a GED certificate. They should have completed 16 academic units, including 4 in English, 3 in mathematics, 2 each in history and foreign language, 1 in a laboratory science (2 are recommended), and 4 in electives. Those students applying to science, engineering, and health sciences programs must meet additional requirements. An interview may be requested by the university. AP and CLEP credits are accepted. Important factors used in the admissions decision are advanced placement or honor courses, recommendations by school officials, leadership record, evidence of special talent, and extracurricular activities record.

Procedure: Freshmen are admitted to all sessions. Entrance exams should be taken during the spring or fall. There are early decision and early admissions plans. Early decision applications should be filed by December 1; regular applications, by June 1 for fall entry and October 15 for spring entry, along with an application fee of $35. Notification of early decision is sent January 1; regular decision, on a rolling basis. One early decision candidate was accepted for the 1993-94 class.

Transfer: About 650 transfer students enrolled in 1993-94. All transfer applicants must submit official transcripts for all college work taken. Those students with fewer than 24 credits must also submit a high school transcript or a copy of their state department of education's equivalency score. At least 32 credits out of 128 must be completed at FDU.

Visiting: There are regularly scheduled orientations for prospective students. There are guides for informal visits, and visitors may sit in on classes and stay overnight at the school. To arrange for a visit, contact the Admissions Office at (800) 338-8803.

Financial Aid: In 1993-94, 82% of all current freshmen received some form of financial aid. The average freshman award was $12,550. Of that total, scholarships or need-based grants averaged $6662 ($15,000 maximum); loans averaged $3656 ($5500 maximum); and work contracts averaged $1000 ($2000 maximum). Sixteen percent of undergraduate students work part-time. Average earnings from campus work for the school year are $1100. FDU is a member of CSS. The FAF and FAFSA are required. The deadline for financial aid applications is March 15.

International Students: There are currently 602 international students enrolled. The school actively recruits these students. They must take the TOEFL and achieve a minimum score of 500.

Computers: The college provides computer facilities for student use. The mainframes are a Prime 5370, a DEC VAX 4000/500, a Sun 4/490, and an IBM 4381. There are 6 PC laboratories at Teaneck and 6 at Madison. Each laboratory consists of 20 or more NEC 386 or 486 PCs connected to a central Novell file server and to the university-wide network, which is connected to Internet. All students may access the system. There are no time limits on using the system and no fees.

Graduates: In 1992-93, 972 bachelor's degrees were awarded. The most popular majors among graduates were business management (16%), marketing (10%), and psychology (8%). Within an average freshman class, 4% graduate in 3 years, 31% in 4 years, 45% in 5 years, and 49% in 6 years. Some 72 companies recruited on campus in 1992-93.

Admissions Contact: Dale Herold, University Director of Admissions.

FELICIAN COLLEGE

E-2

Lodi, NJ 07644

(201) 778-1029

Full-time: 70 men, 435 women	Faculty: 45; IIB, --$
Part-time: 85 men, 555 women	Ph.D.s: 75%
Graduate: none	Student/Faculty: 11 to 1
Year: semesters, summer session	Tuition: $7900
Application Deadline: open	Room & Board: n/app
Freshman Class: 779 applied, 559 accepted, 334 enrolled	
SAT I Verbal/Math: 450/450	COMPETITIVE

Felician College, founded in 1942, is a private Roman Catholic liberal arts school with concentrations in health science, teacher education, and arts and sciences. In addition to regional accreditation, Felician has baccalaureate program accreditation with CAHEA and NLN. The library contains 110,000 volumes, 10,860 microform items, and 4870 audiovisual forms, and subscribes to 553 periodicals. Computerized library sources and services include interlibrary loans. Special learning facilities include a learning resource center and a nursing clinical laboratory. The 32-acre campus is in a suburban area 10 miles east of New York City. There are 6 buildings on campus.

Student Life: About 99% of undergraduates are from New Jersey. Students come from 2 states, 6 foreign countries, and Canada. Sixty-five percent are from public schools; 35% from private. Seventy-four percent are white; 11% Hispanic. The average age of freshmen is 19; all undergraduates, 24. Nine percent drop out by the end of their first year.

Housing: There are no residence halls. All students commute and all may keep cars on campus. Alcohol is not permitted.

Activities: About 25% of men belong to 1 local fraternity; about 10% of women belong to 2 local sororities. There are 17 groups on campus, including art, choir, drama, honors, literary magazine, political, professional, religious, social, social service, and student government. Popular campus events include holiday dances, Variety Show, and commencement week activities.

Sports: There is no sports program at Felician.

Disabled Students: Ninety percent of the campus is accessible to disabled students. The following facilities are available: wheelchair ramps, elevators, special parking, specially equipped rest rooms, lowered drinking fountains, lowered telephones, and wheelchair lifts.

Services: In addition to many counseling and information services, tutoring is available in every subject. There is remedial math, reading, and writing.

Campus Safety and Security: Campus safety and security measures include 24-hour foot and vehicle patrol, lighted pathways and sidewalks, and guards on duty when school is open.

Programs of Study: Felician awards the B.A., B.S., and B.S.N. degrees. Associate degrees are also awarded. Bachelor's degrees are awarded in BIOLOGICAL SCIENCE (biology/biological science), BUSINESS (business administration and management), COMMUNICATIONS AND THE ARTS (English and fine arts), COMPUTER AND PHYSICAL SCIENCE (computer programming, mathematics, and natural sciences), EDUCATION (elementary and special), HEALTH PROFESSIONS (clinical science, medical laboratory technology, nursing, and premedicine), SOCIAL SCIENCE (history, humanities, interdisciplinary studies, prelaw, psychology, religion, and social science). Education and nursing are the strongest academically. Education and nursing have the largest enrollments.

Required: All students must earn a minimum GPA of 2.0 (2.5 in medical laboratory technology, nursing, and education), while taking 120 credit hours (128 to 130 in education), with 39 to 57 hours in their majors. Distribution requirements include 42 hours from a core curriculum, including courses in English, philosophy, religious studies, humanities, historical tradition, science, and social-cultural studies.

Special: Co-op programs are available in clinical laboratory sciences with the University of Medicine and Dentistry of New Jersey. In addition, internships for credit, work-study at the college, dual majors in education, an interdisciplinary studies degree, student-designed majors within humanities and social and behavioral sciences, weekend college, and pass/fail options are possible. There is a freshman honors program on campus

Faculty/Classroom: Thirty percent of faculty are male; 70%, female. Ninety percent teach undergraduates. The average class size in an introductory lecture is 18; in a laboratory, 20; and in a regular course offering, 11.

Admissions: About 72% of the 1993–94 applicants were accepted. About 11% of the current freshmen were in the top fifth of their class; 31% were in the top two fifths.

Requirements: A minimum GPA of 2.0 is required. The SAT I is required, with a minimum composite score of 850 recommended. The college also recommends that applicants have 16 academic credits, including 4 units in English, 3 each in mathematics and science, 2 each in foreign language and history, and 1 in social studies. An interview is required. The GED is accepted. AP and CLEP credits are accepted. Important factors used in the admissions decision are personality, intangible qualities, advanced placement or honor courses, extracurricular activities record, leadership record, and recommendations by school officials.

Procedure: Freshmen are admitted fall and spring. Application deadlines are open. The application fee is $25. Notification is sent on a rolling basis.

Transfer: About 200 transfer students enrolled in 1993–94. Transfer students must have maintained a minimum GPA of 2.0 (2.5 in medical laboratory technology, nursing, and education). An interview is recommended. Nursing majors require previous college-level laboratory science. A total of 30 credits out of 120 must be completed at Felician.

Visiting: There are guides for informal visits and visitors may sit in on classes. To arrange for a visit, contact the Admissions Office at (201) 778-1029.

Financial Aid: In 1993–94, 38% of all current freshmen and 26% of continuing students received some form of financial aid including need-based aid. Scholarships or need-based grants averaged $1000; and work contracts averaged $500. Ninety percent of undergraduate students work part-time. Felician is a member of CSS. The FAF and the college's own financial statement are required. The deadline for financial aid applications is June 1.

International Students: There are currently 23 international students enrolled. They must take the TOEFL and achieve a minimum score of 500.

Computers: The college provides computer facilities for student use. Fifty IBM and Apple microcomputers are available for academic use. All students may access the system. There are no time limits on using the system and no fees.

Graduates: In 1992–93, 106 bachelor's degrees were awarded. The most popular majors among graduates were nursing (43%), arts and sciences (30%), and education (12%).

Admissions Contact: Sr. Mary Austin Blank, Director of Admissions.

GEORGIAN COURT COLLEGE

E-4
Lakewood, NJ 08701-2697
(908) 364-2200, ext. 760
(800) 458-8422

Full-time: 62 men, 1033 women	Faculty: 81; IIB, av$
Part-time: 124 men, 661 women	Ph.D.s: 52%
Graduate: 104 men, 596 women	Student/Faculty: 14 to 1
Year: semesters, summer session	Tuition: $8700
Application Deadline: August 1	Room & Board: $3850
Freshman Class: 348 applied, 281 accepted, 124 enrolled	
SAT I Verbal/Math: 441/473	COMPETITIVE

Georgian Court College, founded in 1908, is an independent Roman Catholic college primarily for women; the evening and graduate divisions are coeducational. Undergraduate programs are offered in the arts and sciences, business administration, religion, social work, and teacher preparation. There is one graduate school. The library contains 148,190 volumes, 484,876 microform items, and 3244 audiovisual forms, and subscribes to 927 periodicals. Computerized library sources and services include the card catalog, interlibrary loans, and database searching. Special learning facilities include a learning resource center, an art gallery, and an arboretum. The 150-acre campus is in a suburban area 60 miles south of New York City. Including residence halls, there are 15 buildings on campus.

Student Life: About 99% of undergraduates are from New Jersey. Students come from 7 states and 1 foreign country. Seventy-one percent are from public schools; 29% from private. Eighty-seven percent are white. The average age of freshmen is 18.9; all undergraduates, 28.3. Fourteen percent drop out by the end of their first year; 53% remain to graduate.

Housing: A total of 308 students can be accommodated in college housing. College-sponsored living facilities include single-sex dormitories. On-campus housing is guaranteed for all 4 years. Seventy-seven percent of students commute. All students may keep cars on campus.

Activities: There are no fraternities or sororities on campus. There are 31 groups on campus, including art, band, chorale, chorus, computers, ethnic, honors, international, literary magazine, newspaper, professional, religious, social, social service, student government, and yearbook. Popular campus events include Irish Afternoon, Family Day, Court Singers, concerts, Christmas Reception, Carasaljo Ball, and SGA Bonfire.

Sports: Athletic and recreation facilities include a porcelain-faced swimming pool, a basketball court, squash and badminton courts, a volleyball court, a bowling alley, a 300-seat gymnasium, a fitness center, athletic fields, and tennis courts.

Disabled Students: Ninety percent of the campus is accessible to disabled students. The following facilities are available: wheelchair ramps, elevators, special parking, specially equipped rest rooms, special class scheduling, lowered drinking fountains, lowered telephones, and special equipment for the visually and hearing impaired.

Services: In addition to many counseling and information services, tutoring is available in most subjects. There is also remedial math, reading, and writing.

Campus Safety and Security: Campus safety and security measures include 24-hour foot and vehicle patrol, escort service, informal discussions, pamphlets, posters, and films. In addition, there are emergency telephones and lighted pathways and sidewalks.

Programs of Study: The Court awards the B.A., B.S., and B.S.W. degrees. Master's degrees also are awarded. Bachelor's degrees are awarded in BIOLOGICAL SCIENCE (biochemistry and biology/biological science), BUSINESS (accounting and business administration and management), COMMUNICATIONS AND THE ARTS (art, art history and appreciation, English, French, music, and Spanish), COMPUTER AND PHYSICAL SCIENCE (chemistry, mathematics, and physics), EDUCATION (special), SOCIAL SCIENCE (history, humanities, psychology, religion, social work, and sociology). Accounting, business administration, psychology, education, and English have the largest enrollments.

Required: General education requirements include 9 semester courses in humanities, 5 in social science, and 3 in natural science/mathematics. Students under 25 also must complete a semester

Faculty/Classroom: Thirty-one percent of faculty are male; 69%, female. Seventy-nine percent teach undergraduates and 23% both teach and do research. No introductory courses are taught by graduate students. The average class size in an introductory lecture is 16 and in a regular course offering, 16.

Admissions: About 81% of the 1993–94 applicants were accepted. The SAT scores for the 1993–94 freshman class were as follows: Verbal—86% below 500, 11% between 500 and 599, and 4% between 600 and 700; Math—66% below 500, 28% between 500 and 599, and 6% between 600 and 700. About 37% of the current freshmen were in the top fifth of their class; 73% were in the top two fifths.

Requirements: The Court requires applicants to be in the upper 50% of their class. A minimum GPA of 2.7 is required. The SAT I is required, with a minimum composite score of 750. Applicants must be graduates of accredited secondary schools or have a GED. The college requires 16 academic credits or Carnegie units, based on 4 years of English, 2 each of foreign language and mathematics, 1 each of history and a laboratory science, and 6 of academic electives. An interview is recommended for all students, and an audition is required for applied music majors. AP and CLEP credits are accepted. Important factors used in the admissions decision are advanced placement or honor courses, evidence of special talent, parents or siblings attending the school, extracurricular activities record, and recommendations by school officials.

Procedure: Freshmen are admitted in the fall and spring. Entrance exams should be taken by January of the senior year. There are early decision and early admissions plans. Early decision applications should be filed by November 15; regular applications, by August 1 for fall entry and January 1 for spring entry, along with an application fee of $30. Notification of early decision is sent December 1; regular decision, on a rolling basis. About 15 early decision candidates were accepted for the 1993–94 class.

Transfer: About 320 transfer students enrolled in a recent year. Applicants with fewer than 24 credits must fulfill all requirements for admission to the freshman class. At least 50 credits out of 132 must be completed at The Court.

Visiting: There are regularly scheduled orientations for prospective students, including visits with faculty and students, and a tour of facilities. There are guides for informal visits, and visitors may sit in on classes and stay overnight at the school. To arrange for a visit, contact Ms. Sandra Zerby, Director of Admissions at (908) 364-2200, ext. 760.

Financial Aid: In 1993–94, 93% of all current freshmen and 81% of continuing students received some form of financial aid. The average freshman award was $6050. Of that total, scholarships or need-based grants averaged $3000 ($8450 maximum); loans averaged $2300 ($6625 maximum); and work contracts averaged $750 ($1200 maximum). Eighty-five percent of undergraduate students work part-time. Average earnings from campus work for the school year are $800. The average financial indebtedness of the 1992–93 graduate was $9000. The Court is a member of CSS. The FAF, the college's own financial statement, the parent and student 1040 tax forms, and CSS Supplementary Form are required. The deadline for financial aid applications is October 1.

International Students: There is currently 1 international student enrolled. The school actively recruits these students. They must take the TOEFL and achieve a minimum score of 550.

Computers: The college provides computer facilities for student use. The Arts and Science Center has 39 networked computers in 4 laboratories, the computer center has 2 laboratories with 29 networked computers, and the library has 12 computers. The computer laboratories also include 18 nonnetworked computers. All students may access the system from 8 A.M. to 10 P.M. daily. There are no time limits on using the system and no fees.

Graduates: In 1992–93, 365 bachelor's degrees were awarded. The most popular majors among graduates were business (19%), accounting (13%), and psychology (12%). Within an average freshman class, 1% graduate in 3 years, 52% in 4 years, 60% in 5 years, and 61% in 6 years. Some 60 companies recruited on campus in a recent year. In the 1992 graduating class, 18% of all graduates were enrolled in graduate school within 6 months of graduation; 76% had found employment.

Admissions Contact: Ms. Sandra Zerby, Director of Admissions.

GLASSBORO STATE COLLEGE
(See Rowan College of New Jersey)

JERSEY CITY STATE COLLEGE
E-2

Jersey City, NJ 07305	(201) 200-3234; (800) 441-JCSC
Full-time: 1765 men, 2052 women	Faculty: 245; IIB, + +$
Part-time: 720 men, 1074 women	Ph.D.s: 64%
Graduate: 364 men, 870 women	Student/Faculty: 16 to 1
Year: semesters, summer session	Tuition: $2797 ($3945)
Application Deadline: May 1	Room & Board: $5000
Freshman Class: 2957 applied, 1423 accepted, 691 enrolled	
SAT I Verbal/Math: 430/400	LESS COMPETITIVE

Jersey City State College, founded in 1927, is a public, coeducational institution offering undergraduate programs in the arts and sciences, business administration, education, health science, upper-level nursing, and other professional fields. There are 2 undergraduate schools and one graduate school. In addition to regional accreditation, JCSC has baccalaureate program accreditation with NASAD, NASM, NCATE, and NLN. The library contains 235,773 volumes, 597,191 microform items, and 850 audiovisual forms, and subscribes to 1445 periodicals. Computerized library sources and services include the card catalog, interlibrary loans, and database searching. Special learning facilities include a learning resource center, an art gallery, radio and TV stations, a comprehensive media arts center, and a laboratory school for special-education instruction. The 17-acre campus is in an urban area 10 miles west of New York City. Including residence halls, there are 14 buildings on campus.

Student Life: About 90% of undergraduates are from New Jersey. Students come from 10 states and 40 foreign countries. Sixty percent are from public schools; 40% from private. Fifty-four percent are white; 18% African American; 14% Hispanic. The average age of freshmen is 18; all undergraduates, 24. Twenty-five percent drop out by the end of their first year; 75% remain to graduate.

Housing: A total of 267 students can be accommodated in college housing. College-sponsored living facilities include single-sex dormitories. On-campus housing is guaranteed for all 4 years. Ninety-five percent of students commute. Alcohol is not permitted. All students may keep cars on campus.

Activities: About 4% of men belong to 3 local and 4 national fraternities; about 3% of women belong to 3 local and 2 national sororities. There are 42 groups on campus, including art, band, cheerleading, choir, chorale, chorus, computers, dance, drama, ethnic, honors, international, jazz band, literary magazine, musical theater, newspaper, orchestra, photography, political, professional, radio and TV, religious, social, social service, student government, and yearbook. Popular campus events include Dean's Picnic, summer concert series, lecture series, films, coffee house entertainment, day trips to New York City for Broadway shows, winter and spring semiformals, and Club Fair.

Sports: There are 6 intercollegiate sports for men and 5 for women, and 14 intramural sports for men and 14 for women. Athletic and recreation facilities include a gymnasium, a track, a pool, a weight room, raquetball courts, and an exercise room.

Disabled Students: All of the campus is accessible to disabled students. The following facilities are available: wheelchair ramps, elevators, special parking, specially equipped rest rooms, special class scheduling, and lowered drinking fountains and telephones.

Services: In addition to many counseling and information services, tutoring is available in most subjects. There is remedial math, reading, and writing.

Campus Safety and Security: Campus safety and security measures include 24-hour foot and vehicle patrol, escort service, shuttle buses, and informal discussions. In addition, there are pamphlets, posters, and films, emergency telephones, and lighted pathways and sidewalks.

Programs of Study: JCSC awards the B.A., B.S., B.F.A., and B.S.N. degrees. Master's degrees also are awarded. Bachelor's degrees are awarded in BIOLOGICAL SCIENCE (biology/biological science), BUSINESS (accounting, banking and finance, business administration and management, marketing/retailing/merchandising, and retailing), COMMUNICATIONS AND THE ARTS (design, English, fine arts, media arts, music, photography, and Spanish), COMPUTER AND PHYSICAL SCIENCE (chemistry, computer science, earth science, geology, and mathematics), EDUCATION (art, early childhood, elementary, health, music, secondary, and special), HEALTH PROFESSIONS (medical laboratory technology, nursing, predentistry, premedicine, and public health), SOCIAL SCIENCE (criminal justice, economics, geography, history, philosophy, political science/government, prelaw, psychology, and sociology). Music, criminal justice, business, and education are the strongest academically. Art, music, and media arts have the largest enrollments.

Required: Students must complete 66 semester hours in general education courses, satisfy college requirements in English, communication, and mathematics, and complete the introductory career exploration and computer usage courses. The bachelor's degree requires completion of at least 128 semester hours, including 36 to 54 in a major field, with a minimum GPA of 2.0. Distribution requirements include 9 credits each in natural science, social science, humanities, and fine and performing arts, and 6 credits in communications and contemporary world.

Special: Co-op programs and internships in all majors are available. JCSC also offers study abroad in Europe, Africa, and South America, a Washington semester, work-study programs, a B.A.-B.S. degree program in biology, chemistry, or geoscience, and pass/fail options. Nondegree study is possible. There is a freshman honors program on campus, as well as 4 national honor societies. Four departments have honors programs.

Faculty/Classroom: Sixty-two percent of faculty are male; 38%, female. All teach undergraduates. No introductory courses are taught by graduate students. The average class size in an introductory lecture is 25; in a laboratory, 15; and in a regular course offering, 16.

Admissions: About 48% of the 1993–94 applicants were accepted. The SAT scores for the 1993–94 freshman class were as follows: Verbal—85% below 500, 13% between 500 and 599, and 2% between 600 and 700; Math—80% below 500, 15% between 500 and 599, and 5% between 600 and 700. About 20% of the current freshmen were in the top fifth of their class; 54% were in the top two fifths. Two freshmen graduated first in their class.

Requirements: JCSC requires applicants to be in the upper 50% of their class. A minimum GPA of 2.5 is required. The SAT I is required, with a recommended minimum score of 400 on each section. Applicants must be graduates of accredited secondary schools or have earned a GED. The college requires 16 Carnegie units, including 4 in English, 3 in mathematics, and 2 each in social studies and a laboratory science, with the remaining 5 units in a foreign language and additional academic courses. An essay is also required and an interview is recommended. AP and CLEP credits are accepted. Important factors used in the admissions decision are advanced placement or honor courses, leadership record, evidence of special talent, recommendations by school officials, and geographic diversity.

Procedure: Freshmen are admitted fall and spring. Entrance exams should be taken in the spring of the junior year or the fall of the senior year. Applications should be filed by May 1 for fall entry and November 1 for spring entry, along with an application fee of $20. Notification is sent on a rolling basis. There are early admissions and deferred admissions plans.

Transfer: About 860 transfer students enrolled in 1993–94. Applicants must present a minimum GPA of 2.5 in at least 12 credit hours completed at the college level. Students transferring fewer than 12 credits must also submit SAT I scores of at least 400 on each part. An interview is recommended for all transfers. A basic skills test is required for transfers with fewer than 30 credits or who have not taken English or mathematics at their previous school. A total of 36 credits out of 128 must be completed at JCSC.

Visiting: There are regularly scheduled orientations for prospective students, including a financial aid workshop and guided tour. There are guides for informal visits and visitors may sit in on classes. To arrange for a visit, contact the Admissions Office at (201) 200–3234 or (800) 441-JCSC.

Financial Aid: In 1993–94, 43% of all current freshmen and 31% of continuing students received some form of financial aid including need-based aid. The average freshman award was $5614. Of that total, scholarships or need-based grants averaged $4372 ($5140 maximum); loans averaged $2955 ($4625 maximum); and work contracts averaged $1747 ($2000 maximum). Twelve percent of undergraduate students work part-time. Average earnings from campus work for the school year are $1550. The average financial indebtedness of the 1992–93 graduate was $5048. JCSC is a member of CSS. The FAF and FAFSA are required. The deadline for financial aid applications is April 1.

International Students: Applicants must take the TOEFL and achieve a minimum score of 400, along with SAT I or the ACT.

Computers: The college provides computer facilities for student use. The mainframes are a DEC VAX 6510, a DEC VAX 8530, 3 MicroVax 3100s, and a DEC MicroVax 3800. Students are able to use the BITNET and Internet systems (as well as other network systems) and a toll-free dial-up system whereby they may use home computers and the mainframe. There are 3 computer laboratories with 75 terminals. Those students enrolled in computer science classes may access the system 24 hours a day. There are no time limits on using the system and no fees.

Graduates: In a recent year, 590 bachelor's degrees were awarded. The most popular majors among graduates were business administration (31%), criminal justice (10%), and computer science (8%). Some 350 companies recruited on campus in a recent year. In a recent graduating class, 10% of all graduates were enrolled in graduate

school within 6 months of graduation.

Admissions Contact: Samuel T. McGhee, Director of Admissions.

KEAN COLLEGE OF NEW JERSEY
E-2
Union, NJ 07083
(908) 527–2195

Full-time: 2757 men, 3902 women	Faculty: 333; IIA, +$
Part-time: 1159 men, 2415 women	Ph.D.s: 85%
Graduate: 347 men, 1291 women	Student/Faculty: 20 to 1
Year: semesters, summer session	Tuition: $2555 ($3485)
Application Deadline: June 15	Room & Board: $3840

Freshman Class: 3053 applied, 2277 accepted, 1176 enrolled
SAT I Verbal/Math: 409/470
LESS COMPETITIVE

Kean College of New Jersey, founded in 1855, is a public, coeducational, primarily commuter institution offering undergraduate programs in the arts and sciences, business, education, government, nursing, and technology. There are 4 undergraduate and 4 graduate schools. The library contains 265,000 volumes, 792,000 microform items, and 6000 audiovisual forms, and subscribes to 1200 periodicals. Special learning facilities include a learning resource center, an art gallery, a planetarium, a radio station, and a TV station. The 151-acre campus is in a suburban area 20 miles west of New York City. Including residence halls, there are 23 buildings on campus.

Student Life: About 97% of undergraduates are from New Jersey. Sixty-eight percent are white; 13% African American; 12% Hispanic. The average age of freshmen is 18; all undergraduates, 24. Twenty-three percent drop out by the end of their first year; 77% remain to graduate.

Housing: A total of 1400 students can be accommodated in college housing. College-sponsored living facilities include coed dormitories and on-campus apartments. On-campus housing is guaranteed for all 4 years. Eighty-eight percent of students commute. All students may keep cars on campus.

Activities: There are 9 local and 4 national fraternities and 13 local and 5 national sororities. There are more than 80 groups on campus, including cheerleading, chorus, computers, dance, drama, ethnic, gay, honors, international, jazz band, literary magazine, musical theater, newspaper, pep band, political, professional, radio and TV, religious, social, social service, student government, and yearbook. Popular campus events include Campus Awareness Festival and Homecoming.

Sports: There are 8 intercollegiate sports for men and 7 for women, and 8 intramural sports each for men and women. Athletic and recreation facilities include a 2000-seat stadium, 22 tennis courts, 7 playing fields, 2 gymnasiums, basketball courts, swimming pools, a track, a weight training room, pool tables, and pinball and video machines.

Disabled Students: The entire campus is accessible to disabled students. The following facilities are available: wheelchair ramps, elevators, special parking, and specially equipped rest rooms.

Services: In addition to many counseling and information services, tutoring is available in most subjects. There is remedial math, reading, and writing.

Campus Safety and Security: Campus safety and security measures include 24-hour foot and vehicle patrol, escort service, shuttle buses, and informal discussions. In addition, there are pamphlets, posters, films, emergency telephones, and lighted pathways and sidewalks.

Programs of Study: Kean awards the B.A., B.S., and B.F.A. degrees. Master's degrees also are awarded. Bachelor's degrees are awarded in BIOLOGICAL SCIENCE (biology/biological science), BUSINESS (accounting, banking and finance, business administration and management, business economics, international business management, and marketing/retailing/merchandising), COMMUNICATIONS AND THE ARTS (communications, design, dramatic arts, English, fine arts, French, music, Spanish, and studio art), COMPUTER AND PHYSICAL SCIENCE (chemistry, computer science, earth science, geology, information sciences and systems, and mathematics), EDUCATION (art, bilingual/bicultural, early childhood, elementary, foreign languages, health, industrial arts, music, science, secondary, special, and technical), ENGINEERING AND ENVIRONMENTAL DESIGN (electrical/electronics engineering and engineering management), HEALTH PROFESSIONS (medical laboratory technology, medical records administration/services, nursing, occupational therapy, and physical therapy), SOCIAL SCIENCE (criminal justice, economics, history, philosophy, political science/government, psychology, public administration, social work, and sociology). Allied health and technology are the strongest programs academically. Business has the largest enrollment.

Required: Students must complete a freshman seminar, 18 credits of core requirements, 2 upper-level writing courses, and at least 30 credits in a major field. The bachelor's degree requires completion of 124 to 129 semester hours with a minimum GPA of 2.0.

Special: Students may study abroad in 7 countries, and Kean offers cooperative programs and cross-registration with other members of the Consortium of East New Jersey. There are also dual majors in ele-

mentary education, internships in selected majors, credit for life experience, and pass/fail options. There is a freshman honors program on campus, as well as 3 national honor societies. Fifteen departments have honors programs.

Faculty/Classroom: Fifty-nine percent of faculty are male; 41%, female. The average class size in an introductory lecture is 25; in a laboratory, 15; and in a regular course offering, 17.

Admissions: About 75% of the 1993–94 applicants were accepted. The SAT scores for the 1993–94 freshman class were as follows: Verbal—91% below 500 and 9% between 500 and 599; Math—65% below 500, 30% between 500 and 599, and 5% between 600 and 700. About 24% of the current freshmen were in the top fifth of their class; 62% were in the top two fifths.

Requirements: The SAT I is required, with a minimum composite score of 900. Applicants must be graduates of accredited secondary schools or have earned a GED. College preparatory study includes 5 courses in academic electives, 4 in English, 3 in mathematics, and 2 each in science and social studies. An essay is also required and an interview is recommended. AP and CLEP credits are accepted. Important factors used in the admissions decision are leadership record, advanced placement or honor courses, recommendations by school officials, evidence of special talent, and extracurricular activities record.

Procedure: Freshmen are admitted in the fall and spring. Applications should be filed by June 15 for fall entry and November 15 for spring entry, along with an application fee of $20. Notification is sent on a rolling basis.

Transfer: About 1269 transfer students enrolled in 1993–94. Applicants must have a minimum GPA of 2.0. Those students tranferring fewer than 15 credits must also submit SAT I scores. A total of 32 credits out of 124 to 129 must be completed at Kean.

Visiting: There are regularly scheduled orientations for prospective students. To arrange for a visit, contact the Admissions Office at (908) 527–2195.

Financial Aid: In a recent year, 22% of all freshmen and 43% of continuing students received some form of financial aid. The average freshman award was $2615. Kean is a member of CSS. The FAF, the college's own financial statement, and a tax return form are required.

International Students: There are currently 224 international students enrolled. International students must take the TOEFL.

Computers: The college provides computer facilities for student use. The mainframe is a Prime 6350. The computer services department operates a Prime 6550 for academic use and a Prime 5340 for CAD/CAM use by the technology department. Major buildings are connected by a campuswide fiber-optic backbone. This network allows access to the college's Prime super minicomputers and Novell Netware file servers. More than 30 discipline-based microcomputer laboratories with software packages are located throughout the campus. All students may access the system. There are no time limits and no fees.

Graduates: In 1992–93, 1682 bachelor's degrees were awarded. The most popular majors among graduates were management science (26%), accounting (8%), and elementary education (7%). Within an average freshman class, 15% graduate in 4 years, 35% in 5 years, and 43% in 6 years.

Admissions Contact: Audley Bridges, Director of Admissions.

MONMOUTH COLLEGE
E-3
West Long Branch, NJ 07764–1898
(908) 571–3456
(800) 543–9671 (out-of-state)

Full-time: 1893 men and women
Part-time: 847 men and women
Graduate: 1228 men and women
Year: semesters, summer session
Application Deadline: March 1
Freshman Class: 2432 applied, 1881 accepted, 478 enrolled
SAT I Verbal/Math: 430/490

Faculty: 150
Ph.Ds: 70%
Student/Faculty: 13 to 1
Tuition: $11,820
Room & Board: $5000

COMPETITIVE

Monmouth College, founded in 1933, is a private, comprehensive, coeducational institution offering both undergraduate and graduate programs in the arts and sciences, business, education, upper-level nursing, technology, and professional training. There are 3 undergraduate and 7 graduate schools. In addition to regional accreditation, Monmouth has baccalaureate program accreditation with ABET, CSWE, and NLN. The library contains 237,614 volumes and 291,133 microform items, and subscribes to 1425 periodicals. Computerized library sources and services include the card catalog, interlibrary loans, and database searching. Special learning facilities include a learning resource center, an art gallery, a radio station, and a TV station. The 125-acre campus is in a suburban area 60 miles south of New York City. Including residence halls, there are 39 buildings on campus.

Student Life: About 92% of undergraduates are from New Jersey. Students come from 21 states and 52 foreign countries. Seventy-five percent are from public schools; 25% from private. Eighty-two per-

cent are white. Twenty percent drop out by the end of their first year; 50% remain to graduate.

Housing: A total of 1100 students can be accommodated in college housing. College-sponsored living facilities include single-sex and coed dormitories and on-campus apartments. On-campus housing is available on a first-come, first-served basis. Priority is given to out-of-town students. Fifty percent of students live on campus. Alcohol is not permitted. All students may keep cars on campus.

Activities: About 25% of men belong to 6 national fraternities; about 25% of women belong to 6 national sororities. There are 48 groups on campus, including art, band, cheerleading, choir, computers, dance, drama, ethnic, film, honors, international, jazz band, literary magazine, musical theater, newspaper, pep band, photography, political, professional, radio and TV, religious, social, social service, student government, symphony, and yearbook. Popular campus events include Springfest, Ebony Night, Homecoming, and Winter Ball.

Sports: There are 8 intercollegiate sports for men and 7 for women, and 11 intramural sports each for men and women. Athletic and recreation facilities include a 2800-seat gymnasium; outdoor tennis courts; baseball, softball and soccer fields; an 8-lane all-weather track; an indoor Olympic-size pool; exercise, wrestling, and weight rooms; and 3 basketball courts.

Disabled Students: Ninety percent of the campus is accessible to disabled students. The following facilities are available: wheelchair ramps, elevators, special parking, specially equipped rest rooms, special class scheduling, lowered drinking fountains, and academic assistance is provided within the classroom.

Services: In addition to many counseling and information services, tutoring is available in every subject for learning disabled and physically challenged students. There is also a reader service for the blind, and remedial math, reading, and writing. All are available upon request for others.

Campus Safety and Security: Campus safety and security measures include 24-hour foot and vehicle patrol, self-defense education, escort service, and informal discussions. In addition, there are pamphlets, posters, films, emergency telephones, lighted pathways and sidewalks, an official Monmouth College police force, and a student watch organization.

Programs of Study: Monmouth awards the B.A., B.S., B.S.N., and B.S.W. degrees. Master's degrees also are awarded. Bachelor's degrees are awarded in BIOLOGICAL SCIENCE (biology/biological science), BUSINESS (accounting, banking and finance, business administration and management, business economics, international business management, and marketing/retailing/merchandising), COMMUNICATIONS AND THE ARTS (English, fine arts, French, music, Spanish, and speech/debate/rhetoric), COMPUTER AND PHYSICAL SCIENCE (chemistry, computer science, mathematics, and physics), EDUCATION (art, early childhood, elementary, foreign languages, middle school, music, science, and secondary), HEALTH PROFESSIONS (medical laboratory technology, nursing, and premedicine), SOCIAL SCIENCE (anthropology, criminal justice, history, philosophy, political science/government, prelaw, psychology, social work, and sociology). Business, electronic engineering, and education are the strongest programs academically. Business, education, and communication have the largest enrollments.

Required: General education requirements include 6 credits each of English composition, literature, history, science/mathematics, social science, and global studies; 3 each of computer science, critical discourse, and perspectives; and 2 of physical education. Students must also pass a writing proficiency examination. In order to graduate, students must earn at least 128 credits, including 30 or more in a major, with a minimum GPA of 2.0 overall and 2.1 in the major. Education and electronic engineering majors must maintain a minimum GPA of 2.5.

Special: Students may study abroad. There are cooperative and internship programs and a Washington semester. Qualified students may pursue a 5-year B.S.-M.B.A. degree program. Monmouth also offers work-study programs, dual majors, flexible studies programs, and credit for life experience. Nondegree study is possible. There is a freshman honors program on campus, as well as 7 national honor societies.

Faculty/Classroom: Seventy-five percent of faculty are male; 25%, female. All teach undergraduates. The average class size in an introductory lecture is 25; in a laboratory, 20; and in a regular course offering, 22.

Admissions: About 77% of the 1993–94 applicants were accepted. The SAT scores for the 1993–94 freshman class were as follows: Verbal—80% below 500, 14% between 500 and 599, 5% between 600 and 700, and 1% above 700; Math—51% below 500, 35% between 500 and 599, 13% between 600 and 700, and 1% above 700. About 28% of the current freshmen were in the top fifth of their class; 59% were in the top two fifths. In a recent year, one freshman graduated first in the class.

Requirements: Monmouth requires applicants to be in the upper 50% of their class. A minimum GPA of 2.25 is required. The SAT I or ACT is required. For the SAT I, the required minimum verbal score is 450; the recommended minimum mathematics score is 450 and the composite, 900. Applicants must be graduates of accredited secondary schools or have earned a GED. The college requires 16 Carnegie units, based on 4 years of English, 2 each of mathematics and social studies, and 1 each of foreign language and science, with the remaining 6 units in any additional combination of the above. An essay and an interview are also recommended. AP credits are accepted. Important factors used in the admissions decision are advanced placement or honor courses, recommendations by school officials, personality, intangible qualities, leadership record, and extracurricular activities record.

Procedure: Freshmen are admitted in the fall, spring, and summer. Entrance exams should be taken by December of the senior year. Applications should be filed by March 1 for fall entry and January 1 for spring entry, along with an application fee of $30. Notification is sent January 19. There is a deferred admissions plan.

Transfer: About 490 transfer students enrolled in a recent year. Transfers with fewer than 30 college credits must provide a high school transcript and SAT I scores. A total of 32 credits out of at least 128 must be completed at Monmouth.

Visiting: There are regularly scheduled orientations for prospective students, including campus tours and interviews. There are guides for informal visits and visitors may sit in on classes and stay overnight at the school. To arrange for a visit, contact the Admissions Office at (908) 571-3456 or (800) 543-9671 (out-of-state).

Financial Aid: In a recent year, 64% of all current freshmen and 66% of continuing students received some form of financial aid. More than half of all students received need-based aid. The average freshman award was $10,892. Of that total, scholarships or need-based grants averaged $6500 ($10,700 maximum); loans averaged $2600 ($4300 maximum); and work contracts averaged $1800 ($2000 maximum). Eighteen percent of undergraduate students work part-time. Average earnings from campus work for the school year are $662. The average financial indebtedness of a recent graduate was $9975. Monmouth is a member of CSS. The FAF, the college's own financial statement, and parent and student 1040 federal tax forms are required. The deadline for financial aid applications is March 1.

International Students: There were recently 183 international students enrolled. The school actively recruits these students. They must take the TOEFL and achieve a minimum score of 525.

Computers: The college provides computer facilities for student use. The mainframes are a Concurrent 3250 XP, and 3260 MPS, and an AT&T 3B15, and 3B2. Microcomputers are available in the computer center and the college center. All students may access the system. There are no time limits and no fees.

Graduates: In a recent year, 518 bachelor's degrees were awarded. Some 110 companies recruited on campus that year. In a recent graduating class, 20% of all students were enrolled in graduate school within 6 months of graduation; 75% had found employment.

Admissions Contact: Christine L. Barsony, Associate Director of Admissions.

MONTCLAIR STATE COLLEGE E-2
Upper Montclair, NJ 07043-1624

(201) 655-5116
(800) 331-9205

Full-time: 2587 men, 3818 women
Part-time: 1048 men, 2135 women
Graduate: 1098 men, 2517 women
Year: semesters, summer session
Application Deadline: March 1

Faculty: 429; IIA, +$
Ph.D.s: 84%
Student/Faculty: 15 to 1
Tuition: $2845 ($4016)
Room & Board: $4694

Freshman Class: 5220 applied, 2128 accepted, 865 enrolled
SAT I Verbal/Math: 460/520

COMPETITIVE +

Montclair State College, established in 1908, is a public, coeducational institution offering programs in liberal arts and sciences, business administration, fine and performing arts, and professional studies. There are 5 undergraduate schools and one graduate school. In addition to regional accreditation, Montclair has baccalaureate program accreditation with ADA, AHEA, NASAD, NASM, NCATE, and NRPA. The library contains 434,872 volumes, 983,749 microform items, and 44,443 audiovisual forms, and subscribes to 3376 periodicals. Computerized library sources and services include interlibrary loans and database searching. Special learning facilities include a learning resource center, an art gallery, a radio station, and a psychoeducational center. The 200-acre campus is in a suburban area 15 miles west of New York City. Including residence halls, there are 35 buildings on campus.

Student Life: Most undergraduates are from New Jersey, but students also come from 15 states, 53 foreign countries, and Canada. Eighty percent are from public schools; 20% from private. Seventy-four percent are white; 12% Hispanic. Sixty percent are Catholic; 19% Protestant; 10% claim no religious affiliation. The average age of

freshmen is 18; all undergraduates, 20. Twenty percent drop out by the end of their first year; 58% remain to graduate.

Housing: A total of 2100 students can be accommodated in college housing. College-sponsored living facilities include single-sex and coed dormitories and on-campus apartments. On-campus housing is guaranteed for the freshman year only and is available on a lottery system for upperclassmen. Priority is given to out-of-town students. Eighty percent of students commute. Alcohol is not permitted. All students may keep cars on campus.

Activities: There are 100 groups on campus, including band, cheerleading, choir, chorus, drama, ethnic, honors, international, jazz band, literary magazine, marching band, newspaper, orchestra, professional, radio and TV, religious, social, social service, student government, and yearbook. Popular campus events include Carnival, Homecoming, Spring Week, and Greek Week.

Sports: There are 11 intercollegiate sports for men and 8 for women, and 10 intramural sports for men and 9 for women. Athletic and recreation facilities include a softball field, a 100-meter all-weather track, a multipurpose field, a baseball field, tennis courts, a swimming pool, a gymnasium, and a field house.

Disabled Students: Eighty-five percent of the campus is accessible to disabled students. Elevators and special parking are available.

Services: In addition to many counseling and information services, tutoring is available in most subjects. There is also remedial math, reading, and writing.

Campus Safety and Security: Campus safety and security measures include 24-hour foot and vehicle patrol, self defense education, escort service, and shuttle buses. In addition, there are informal discussions, pamphlets, posters, films, emergency telephones, lighted pathways and sidewalks, a full-time campus police force, a crime prevention officer, and crime prevention programs.

Programs of Study: Montclair awards the B.A., B.S., B.F.A., and B.Mus. degrees. Master's degrees also are awarded. Bachelor's degrees are awarded in BIOLOGICAL SCIENCE (biochemistry, biology/biological science, molecular biology, and toxicology), BUSINESS (business administration and management), COMMUNICATIONS AND THE ARTS (classics, dance, dramatic arts, English, fine arts, French, German, Italian, Latin, linguistics, music, and Spanish), COMPUTER AND PHYSICAL SCIENCE (chemistry, computer science, geoscience, mathematics, and physics), EDUCATION (business, health, home economics, physical, and technical), HEALTH PROFESSIONS (allied health, music therapy, and speech pathology/audiology), SOCIAL SCIENCE (anthropology, economics, geography, history, humanities, parks and recreation management, philosophy, political science/government, psychology, and sociology). Business administration, psychology, and English have the largest enrollments.

Required: Students must successfully complete a minimum of 128 semester hours, with 33 to 82 in the student's major, while maintaining a minimum GPA of 2.0. General education requirements include courses in communications, contemporary issues, art appreciation, a foreign language, humanities, mathematics, natural/physical science, social sciences, and multicultural awareness, as well as 1 semester hour in physical education and 2 semester hours in computer science.

Special: Cross-registration for Army ROTC credits with Seton Hall University and for Air Force ROTC with New Jersey Institute of Technology is available. Internships, co-op programs in all majors, credit by examination, pass/fail options, work-study, credit for life experience, weekend study, and study abroad in 13 countries are offered. A 5-year joint-degree program in practical anthropology is possible. There is a freshman honors program on campus. Five departments have honors programs.

Faculty/Classroom: Sixty-three percent of faculty are male; 37%, female.

Admissions: About 41% of the 1993-94 applicants were accepted. The SAT scores for the freshman class were as follows: Verbal—70% below 500, 27% between 500 and 599, and 3% between 600 and 700; Math—32% below 500, 55% between 500 and 599, 12% between 600 and 700, and 1% above 700. About 47% of the current freshmen were in the top fifth of their class; 90% were in the top two fifths. About 10 freshmen graduated first in their class.

Requirements: The SAT I is required. Applicants must submit 16 Carnegie units, including 4 in high school English, 3 to 4 in mathematics, 2 each in science, social studies, and a foreign language, and the remainder in additional courses in these fields. The GED is accepted. A portfolio, audition, and interview are required for students planning to major in fine arts, music, speech, and theater. AP and CLEP credits are accepted. Important factors used in the admissions decision are advanced placement or honor courses, leadership record, extracurricular activities record, recommendations by school officials, and evidence of special talent.

Procedure: Freshmen are admitted fall and spring. Entrance exams should be taken in November or December of the senior year. Applications should be filed by March 1 for fall entry and October 15 for spring entry, along with an application fee of $35. Notification is sent

on a rolling basis. A waiting list is an active part of the admissions procedure, with about 5% of applicants on the list.

Transfer: About 680 transfer students enrolled in a recent year. Transfer applicants must have completed a minimum of 15 credits from an accredited college, with at least a C average. A cumulative GPA of 2.5 is required; a GPA of 3.0 is required for business and computer science majors. A total of 32 semester hours out of 128 must be completed at Montclair.

Visiting: There are regularly scheduled orientations for prospective students. There are guides for informal visits. To arrange for a visit, contact the Admissions Office at (201) 655-5116.

Financial Aid: In a recent year, half of all students received some form of financial aid. About 38% received need-based aid. The average freshman award was $3500. Of that total, scholarships or need-based grants averaged $1000 ($2000 maximum); loans averaged $1250 ($2500 maximum); and work contracts averaged $500 ($1000 maximum). Ten percent of undergraduate students work part-time. Average earnings from campus work for the school year are $1000. The average financial indebtedness of a recent graduate was $5000. Montclair is a member of CSS. The FAF is required. The deadline for financial aid applications is March 1.

International Students: There are currently 279 international students enrolled. They must take the TOEFL and achieve a minimum score of 500.

Computers: The college provides computer facilities for student use. The mainframe is a DEC VAX cluster. Many IBM PC and Apple Macintosh laboratories are located throughout the campus, with about 200 terminals and PC printers. A network of Sun minicomputer systems is also available. A wide variety of general and discipline-specific software is offered. All students may access the system. There are no time limits and no fees.

Graduates: In a recent year, 1487 bachelor's degrees were awarded. The most popular majors among graduates were business administration (30%), psychology (10%), and English (9%). Within an average freshman class, 1% graduate in 3 years, 34% in 4 years, 54% in 5 years, and 57% in 6 years.

Admissions Contact: Dr. Alan L. Buechler, Director of Admissions.

NEW JERSEY INSTITUTE OF TECHNOLOGY E-2
Newark, NJ 07102-1982 (201) 596-3300; (800) 222-NJIT (in-state)

Full-time: 2784 men, 527 women	Faculty: 311; IIA, + +$
Part-time: 1368 men, 278 women	Ph.D.s: 98%
Graduate: 1900 men, 676 women	Student/Faculty: 11 to 1
Year: semesters	Tuition: $4790 ($9134)
Application Deadline: April 1	Room & Board: $5175
Freshman Class: 1879 applied, 1216 accepted, 483 enrolled	
SAT I Verbal/Math: 466/600	VERY COMPETITIVE

New Jersey Institute of Technology, founded in 1881, is a public, coeducational, technological university providing instruction, research, and public service in engineering, computer science, management, architecture, engineering technology, applied sciences, and related fields. There are 4 undergraduate schools and one graduate school. In addition to regional accreditation, NJIT has baccalaureate program accreditation with ABET, CSAB, and NAAB. The 2 libraries contain 134,500 volumes, 3723 microform items, and 200 audiovisual forms, and subscribe to 1233 periodicals. Computerized library sources and services include the card catalog, interlibrary loans, and database searching. Special learning facilities include a learning resource center and a radio station. NJIT is home to many government- and industry-sponsored laboratories and research centers, including the EPA Northeast Hazardous Substance Research Center, the Center for Transportation Studies and Research, the Center for Manufacturing Systems, the Air Emissions Research Center, the Microelectronics Research Center, and the Center for Microwave and Lightwave Engineering. The 40-acre campus is in an urban area in Newark, 10 miles west of New York City. Including residence halls, there are 24 buildings on campus.

Student Life: About 93% of undergraduates are from New Jersey. Students come from 14 states, 44 foreign countries, and Canada. Eighty percent are from public schools; 20% from private. Fifty-four percent are white; 16% Asian American; 11% foreign nationals; 10% African American. Forty-eight percent are Catholic; 19% Protestant; 18% Muslim, Buddhist, and others; 14% claim no religious affiliation. The average age of freshmen is 18; all undergraduates, 24. Twenty percent drop out by the end of their first year; 80% remain to graduate.

Housing: A total of 870 students can be accommodated in college housing. College-sponsored living facilities include coed dormitories. On-campus housing is available on a first-come, first-served basis and is available on a lottery system for upperclassmen. Priority is given to out-of-town students. Seventy-five percent of students commute. All students may keep cars on campus.

Activities: About 18% of men belong to 7 local and 11 national fraternities; about 19% of women belong to 4 local and 3 national sororities. There are 36 groups on campus, including computers, drama, ethnic, gay, honors, international, musical theater, newspaper, professional, radio and TV, religious, social, social service, student government, and yearbook. Popular campus events include Alcohol Awareness Week, Fall Holiday Celebration, Miniversity, International Students Food Festival, Black History Month, Women's History Month, Hispanic Heritage Month, Winter Holiday Celebration, Spring Week, and Greek Week.

Sports: There are 9 intercollegiate sports for men and 6 for women, and 28 intramural sports for men and 28 for women. Athletic and recreation facilities include a 1000-seat stadium, a fitness center with an indoor track, a 6-lane swimming pool, 4 tennis and 4 racquet sport courts, playing fields, bowling lanes, a table tennis and billiards area, and 3 gymnasiums, the largest of which seats 1200. NJIT also has access to the 25,000-seat Meadowlands Arena.

Disabled Students: Ninety-five percent of the campus is accessible to disabled students. The following facilities are available: wheelchair ramps, elevators, special parking, specially equipped rest rooms, special class scheduling, and lowered drinking fountains and telephones.

Services: In addition to many counseling and information services, tutoring is available in most subjects, including chemistry and physics. There is a reader service for the blind, and remedial math, reading, and writing.

Campus Safety and Security: Campus safety and security measures include 24-hour foot and vehicle patrol, self-defense education, escort service, and shuttle buses. In addition, there are informal discussions, pamphlets, posters, films, emergency telephones, and lighted pathways and sidewalks.

Programs of Study: NJIT awards the B.A., B.S., and B.Arch. degrees. Master's and doctoral degrees also are awarded. Bachelor's degrees are awarded in BUSINESS (management science), COMPUTER AND PHYSICAL SCIENCE (applied mathematics, chemistry, computer science, information science and systems, physics, and statistics and actuarial science), ENGINEERING AND ENVIRONMENTAL DESIGN (architecture, chemical engineering, civil engineering, computer engineering, electrical engineering, engineering, engineering science, engineering technology, industrial engineering, manufacturing engineering, and mechanical engineering). Architecture, engineering, computer science, management, and applied sciences are the strongest academically. Engineering has the largest enrollment.

Required: General university requirements include 9 credits of humanities and social science electives, 7 of natural sciences, 6 each of mathematics, cultural history, basic social sciences, and engineering technology, 3 each of English and management, and 2 credits of computer science. Students must also complete 2 courses in physical education. To graduate, students must earn between 124 and 164 credits, depending on the program, including 50 in the major, with a minimum GPA of 2.0 in upper-level major courses.

Special: Cross-registration is offered in conjunction with Essex County College, Rutgers University, whose Newark campus is adjacent to NJIT's, and the University of Medicine and Dentistry of New Jersey. Cooperative programs, available in all majors, include two 6-month internships. There are 3-2 engineering degree programs with Upsala College and Lincoln and Seton Hall Universities. NJIT also offers work-study programs, double, student-designed, and interdisciplinary majors, including science, technology, and society, and nondegree study. There is a freshman honors program on campus, as well as one national honor society. Eight departments have honors programs.

Faculty/Classroom: Eighty-nine percent of faculty are male; 11%, female. Ninety-five percent teach undergraduates and all do research. Graduate students teach 8% of introductory courses. The average class size in an introductory lecture is 29; in a laboratory, 27; and in a regular course offering, 28.

Admissions: About 65% of the 1993-94 applicants were accepted. The SAT scores for the 1993-94 freshman class were as follows: Verbal—64% below 500, 29% between 500 and 599, and 7% between 600 and 700; Math—4% below 500, 47% between 500 and 599, 39% between 600 and 700, and 10% above 700. About 51% of the current freshmen were in the top fifth of their class; 82% were in the top two fifths. There was 1 National Merit semifinalist. Five freshmen graduated first in their class.

Requirements: The SAT I or ACT is required; the SAT I is preferred. The SAT II: Subject test in mathematics I or II is also required. Applicants should have completed 16 secondary school units, including 4 each in English and mathematics, 2 in a laboratory science, and 6 in a distribution of social studies, foreign language, mathematics, and science courses. AP and CLEP credits are accepted. Important factors in the admissions decision are advanced placement or honor courses, recommendations by school officials, extracurricular activities record, leadership record, and personality, intangible qualities.

Procedure: Freshmen are admitted to all sessions. Entrance exams should be taken in May of the junior year or November of the senior year. Early decision applications should be filed by December 1; regular applications, by April 1 for fall entry and December 1 for spring entry, along with an application fee of $25. There is an early decision plan; notification is sent December 31. Regular decision is sent May 1. About 30 early decision candidates were accepted for the 1993–94 class. A waiting list is an active part of the admissions procedure, with about 2% of applicants on the list.

Transfer: About 440 transfer students enrolled in 1993–94. A minimum GPA of 2.0 is required, but 2.5 or higher is recommended. Engineering technology students must present an associate degree. Admission to the School of Architecture is very competitive for transfer students. Students must submit transcripts of all attempted postsecondary academic work. Applicants with fewer than 30 credits may be asked to provide SAT I and SAT II: Subject test in mathematics scores, and a high school transcript. A total of 33 credits out of 124 to 164 must be completed at NJIT.

Visiting: There are regularly scheduled orientations for prospective students, including tours and meetings with admissions personnel, students, and faculty. There are guides for informal visits and visitors may sit in on classes and stay overnight at the school. To arrange for a visit, contact Ralph Choonoo, Director of Residence Life, at (201) 596–3041.

Financial Aid: In 1993–94, 71% of all current freshmen and 58% of continuing students received some form of financial aid. About 54% of freshmen and 51% of continuing students received need-based aid. The average freshman award was $6439. Of that total, scholarships or need-based grants averaged $4345; loans averaged $1492; and work contracts averaged $602. Seventy percent of undergraduate students work part-time. Average earnings from campus work for the school year are $2333. The average financial indebtedness of the 1992–93 graduate was $3500. NJIT is a member of CSS. The FAF, the college's own financial statement, and the NJFAF are required. The deadline for financial aid applications is March 15 for fall entry and October 1 for spring entry.

International Students: There are currently 598 international students enrolled. They must take the TOEFL and achieve a minimum score of 520.

Computers: The college provides computer facilities for student use. The mainframes are an IBM, a SUN, and other models. A DEC VAX 6430 serves as the main VMS computer, and a DEC 5900 serves as the UNIX engine for academic work. All computing facilities are connected to a campuswide network, which has a fiber-optic spine between buildings; 150 computer nodes can be accessed from 2500 on-campus locations. All students may access the system. There are no time limits and no fees. All full-time freshmen are given a computer and a variety of software for their personal use, which they may purchase for a nominal fee upon graduation.

Graduates: In 1992–93 660 bachelor's degrees were awarded. The most popular majors among graduates were electrical engineering (22%), engineering technology (17%), and mechanical engineering (14%). Within an average freshman class, 40% graduate in 4 years, 55% in 5 years, and 65% in 6 years. Some 127 companies recruited on campus in 1992–93. In the 1992 graduating class, 10% of all graduates were enrolled in graduate school within 6 months of graduation; 90% had found employment.

Admissions Contact: Kathryn Kelly, Director of Admissions.

PRINCETON UNIVERSITY
D-3

Princeton, NJ 08544–0430   (609) 258–3060

Full-time: 2569 men, 1969 women	Faculty: 716; I, + +$
Part-time: none	Ph.D.s: 99%
Graduate: 1230 men, 676 women	Student/Faculty: 6 to 1
Year: semesters	Tuition: $18,940
Application Deadline: January 2	Room & Board: $5710
Freshman Class: 13,218 applied, 2042 accepted, 1151 enrolled	
SAT I: required	**MOST COMPETITIVE**

Princeton University, established in 1746, is a private institution offering degrees in the liberal arts and sciences, engineering, applied science, architecture, public and international affairs, interdisciplinary and regional studies, and the creative arts. There are 4 graduate schools. In addition to regional accreditation, Princeton has baccalaureate program accreditation with ABET and NAAB. The 20 libraries contain 5,000,000 volumes, 3,000,000 microform items, and 52,000 audiovisual forms, and subscribe to 30,000 periodicals. Computerized library sources and services include the card catalog. Special learning facilities include an art gallery, a natural history museum, a radio station, a music center, a visual and performing arts center, several theaters, an observatory, a plasma physics laboratory, and a center for environmental and energy studies. The 600-acre campus is in a small town 50 miles south of New York City. Including residence halls, there are 140 buildings on campus.

Student Life: About 86% of undergraduates are from out-of-state, mostly the Middle Atlantic. Students come from 50 states, 70 foreign countries, and Canada. Seventy-one percent are white; 10% Asian American. The average age of freshmen is 18; all undergraduates, 20. Two percent drop out by the end of their first year; 96% remain to graduate.

Housing: A total of 4400 students can be accommodated in college housing. College-sponsored living facilities include coed dormitories, on-campus apartments, and married-student housing. Freshmen and sophomores are assigned to one of 5 residential colleges; most juniors and seniors live in upperclass dormitories and select dining options such as co-ops and private clubs. On-campus housing is guaranteed for all 4 years. Ninety-eight percent of students live on campus. Alcohol is not permitted. All students may keep cars on campus.

Activities: There are no fraternities or sororities on campus. There are 200 groups on campus, including art, band, cheerleading, chess, choir, chorale, chorus, dance, drama, ethnic, film, gay, international, jazz band, literary magazine, musical theater, newspaper, opera, orchestra, pep band, photography, political, professional, radio and TV, religious, social, social service, student government, symphony, and yearbook. Popular campus events include recitals and theater productions.

Sports: There are 17 intercollegiate sports for men and 16 for women, and 53 intramural sports for men and 53 for women. Athletic and recreation facilities include a 45,000-seat football and track stadium, an 18-hole golf course, 2 gymnasiums, an Olympic swimming and diving complex, playing fields, a boat house and Olympic-level racing course for crew and sailing, a health fitness center, an ice rink, dance studios, and tennis, squash, and volleyball courts.

Disabled Students: The following facilities are available: wheelchair ramps, elevators, special parking, specially equipped rest rooms, special class scheduling, and lowered telephones.

Services: In addition to many counseling and information services, tutoring is available in every subject. There is also a reader service for the blind.

Campus Safety and Security: Campus safety and security measures include 24-hour foot and vehicle patrol, self-defense education, escort service, and shuttle buses. In addition, there are informal discussions, pamphlets, posters, films, emergency telephones, and lighted pathways and sidewalks.

Programs of Study: Princeton awards the A.B. and B.S.E. degrees. Master's and doctoral degrees also are awarded. Bachelor's degrees are awarded in BIOLOGICAL SCIENCE (biology/biological science), COMMUNICATIONS AND THE ARTS (classics, comparative literature, English, Germanic languages and literature, music, romance languages, and Slavic languages), COMPUTER AND PHYSICAL SCIENCE (astrophysics, chemistry, computer science, geology, mathematics, and physics), ENGINEERING AND ENVIRONMENTAL DESIGN (aeronautical engineering, architectural engineering, architecture, chemical engineering, civil engineering, electrical/electronics engineering, and mechanical engineering), SOCIAL SCIENCE (anthropology, archeology, East Asian studies, economics, history, international relations, Near Eastern studies, philosophy, political science/government, psychology, religion, and sociology). History, political science, and English have the largest enrollments.

Required: To graduate, students must complete 8 semesters, or academic units. Candidates for the A.B. degree must demonstrate proficiency in English composition and a foreign language and complete distribution requirements in the areas of arts and letters, natural science, social science, and history, philosophy, and religion. Candidates for the B.S.E. must satisfy the English composition requirement and, by the end of the sophomore year, complete 4 terms of mathematics, 2 of physics, and 1 each of chemistry and computer programming. A junior project and senior thesis are required of virtually all students.

Special: Princeton offers independent study, preceptorials, accelerated degree programs, a program in teacher preparation, student-proposed courses and majors, field study, study abroad, seminars, and internships in public affairs. The university operates on an honor code whereby examinations are not proctored by faculty members. There are 2 national honor societies on campus, including Phi Beta Kappa.

Faculty/Classroom: Seventy-six percent of faculty are male; 24%, female. All teach undergraduates and 90% do research. Graduate students teach 1% of introductory courses.

Admissions: About 15% of the 1993–94 applicants were accepted. The SAT scores for the 1993–94 freshman class were as follows: Verbal—2% below 500, 19% between 500 and 599, 52% between 600 and 700, and 27% above 700; Math—6% between 500 and 599, 31% between 600 and 700, and 63% above 700. About 97% of the current freshmen were in the top fifth of their class.

Requirements: The SAT I is required. The ACT is accepted. Three SAT II: Subject tests are strongly recommended. Applicants must be graduates of an accredited secondary school. Recommended college preparatory courses include 4 years each of English, mathematics,

and a foreign language; 2 years each of laboratory science and history; and some study of art, music, and, if possible, a second foreign language. An essay is required and an interview is recommended. Fine arts majors should submit an audition tape or portfolio. AP credits are accepted.

Procedure: Freshmen are admitted in the fall. Entrance exams should be taken by January of the senior year. There are early decision, early admissions, and deferred admissions plans. Early decision applications should be filed by November 1; regular applications, by January 2 for fall entry, along with an application fee of $55. Notification of early decision is sent mid-December; regular decision, early April. A waiting list is an active part of the admissions procedure, with about 3% of applicants on the list.

Transfer: Since space is limited, only those students with excellent academic records and compelling academic reasons for transferring should apply.

Visiting: There are regularly scheduled orientations for prospective students. There are guides for informal visits, and visitors may sit in on classes and stay overnight at the school. To arrange for a visit, contact Orange Key Guide Service at (609) 258-3603.

Financial Aid: In 1993–94, 43% of all current freshmen and 42% of continuing students received need-based aid. The average freshman award was $15,870. Of that total, scholarships or need-based grants averaged $11,830 ($20,000 maximum); loans averaged $2660 ($3500 maximum); and work contracts averaged $1380 ($1750 maximum). Sixty-seven percent of undergraduate students work part-time. Average earnings from campus work for the school year are $1200. The average financial indebtedness of the 1992–93 graduate was $13,000. Princeton is a member of CSS. The FAF and the college's own financial statement are required. The deadline for financial aid applications is February 1.

International Students: There are currently 273 international students enrolled. The school actively recruits these students. They must take the TOEFL and the SAT I.

Computers: The college provides computer facilities for student use. The mainframes are an IBM 3081 and a DEC VAX 8700. There are also 450 microcomputers, including Apple Macintoshes and IBM PCs, connected to a central TigerNet system. Next, Silicon Graphics, Bitnet, and Internet are available through SUN workstations. All students receive a $500 account and may access the system.

Graduates: In 1992–93, 1097 bachelor's degrees were awarded.

Admissions Contact: Fred A. Hargadon, Dean of Admissions.

RAMAPO COLLEGE OF NEW JERSEY
Mahwah, NJ 07430 D-2
(201) 529-7600

Full-time: 1413 men, 1332 women	Faculty: 131; IIB, + +$
Part-time: 866 men, 1072 women	Ph.D.s: 95%
Graduate: none	Student/Faculty: 21 to 1
Year: semesters, summer session	Tuition: $3227 ($4449)
Application Deadline: March 15	Room & Board: $4800
Freshman Class: 2131 applied, 987 accepted, 386 enrolled	
SAT I Verbal/Math: 450/510	COMPETITIVE +

Ramapo College, founded in 1971, is a public, coeducational institution offering undergraduate programs in the arts and sciences, American and international studies, business administration, and human services. Incorporated throughout the curriculum is an international, multicultural component including telecommunications and computer technology. There are 5 undergraduate schools. In addition to regional accreditation, Ramapo has baccalaureate program accreditation with CSWE. The library contains 145,614 volumes, 21,948 microform items, and 19,057 audiovisual forms, and subscribes to 1283 periodicals. Computerized library sources and services include the card catalog, interlibrary loans, and database searching. Special learning facilities include an art gallery, a radio station, and an international telecommunications satellite center. The 350-acre campus is in a suburban area 25 miles northwest of New York City. Including residence halls, there are 20 buildings on campus.

Student Life: About 81% of undergraduates are from New Jersey. Students come from 15 states and 47 foreign countries. Ninety-four percent are from public schools; 6% from private. Eighty-one percent are white. The average age of freshmen is 18; all undergraduates, 26. Twenty-five percent drop out by the end of their first year.

Housing: A total of 1100 students can be accommodated in college housing. College-sponsored living facilities include coed dormitories and on-campus apartments. In addition there are honors houses, special interest houses, and an international house. On-campus housing is guaranteed for all 4 years. Sixty percent of students commute. All students may keep cars on campus.

Activities: About 4% of men belong to 3 national fraternities; about 4% of women belong to 3 national sororities. There are 50 groups on campus, including art, cheerleading, choir, chorus, computers, drama, ethnic, gay, honors, international, jazz band, literary magazine, newspaper, political, professional, radio and TV, religious, social, social service, student government, and yearbook. Popular campus events include Welcome Week, Homecoming, African Ancestry Month, Springfest, Spring Semiformal, Earth Days, Hispanic Latino Heritage Month, International Celebration, Senior Gala, and Summer Block Party.

Sports: There are 6 intercollegiate sports for men and 5 for women, and 12 intramural sports for men and 12 for women. Athletic and recreation facilities include a 1000-seat stadium, 12 lighted tennis courts, playing fields, a 300-seat arena, a track, a 1000-seat gymnasium with a basketball court, an Olympic pool, a fitness room, and a weight training room.

Disabled Students: All of the campus is accessible to disabled students. The following facilities are available: wheelchair ramps, elevators, special parking, specially equipped rest rooms, special class scheduling, lowered drinking fountains, lowered telephones, and specially equipped residence hall units.

Services: In addition to many counseling and information services, tutoring is available in every subject. There is a reader service for the blind, and remedial math, reading, and writing.

Campus Safety and Security: Campus safety and security measures include 24-hour foot and vehicle patrol, shuttle buses, informal discussions, and pamphlets, posters, and films. In addition, there are emergency telephones and lighted pathways and sidewalks.

Programs of Study: Ramapo awards the B.A., B.S., B.S.N., and B.S.W. degrees. Bachelor's degrees are awarded in BIOLOGICAL SCIENCE (biology/biological science), BUSINESS (accounting, banking and finance, business administration and management, business economics, international business management, management information systems, management science, and marketing/retailing/merchandising), COMMUNICATIONS AND THE ARTS (communications, dramatic arts, fine arts, literature, and music), COMPUTER AND PHYSICAL SCIENCE (chemistry, computer science, mathematics, and physics), ENGINEERING AND ENVIRONMENTAL DESIGN (environmental science), HEALTH PROFESSIONS (nursing), SOCIAL SCIENCE (American studies, economics, history, international studies, law, philosophy, political science/government, psychology, social science, social work, sociology, and urban studies). Business, liberal arts, social sciences, and sciences are the strongest academically. Communications and business administration have the largest enrollments.

Required: Students must complete general education requirements of approximately 50 credits in science, social science, humanities, and English composition, as well as core requirements in their school of study and their particular major. A senior seminar is also required. In order to graduate, students must earn at least 128 credits with a minimum GPA of 2.0.

Special: Ramapo's curriculum emphasizes the interdependence of global society and includes an international dimension in all academic programs. Students may study abroad in 7 countries. Cooperative programs are available with various corporations and in 12 foreign countries. Cross-registration is possible with local state colleges. Ramapo also offers accelerated degree programs, dual majors, student-designed majors, and interdisciplinary majors, including law and society, credit for life experience, pass/fail options, and nondegree study. There is a freshman honors program on campus, as well as 5 national honor societies. All departments have honors programs.

Faculty/Classroom: Sixty-eight percent of faculty are male; 32%, female. All teach undergraduates. The average class size in an introductory lecture is 35; in a laboratory, 22; and in a regular course offering, 25.

Admissions: About 46% of the 1993–94 applicants were accepted. The SAT scores for the 1993–94 freshman class were as follows: Verbal—73% below 500, 22% between 500 and 599, and 5% between 600 and 700; Math—45% below 500, 37% between 500 and 599, 17% between 600 and 700, and 1% above 700. About 22% of the current freshmen were in the top fifth of their class; 63% were in the top two fifths. Two freshmen graduated first in their class.

Requirements: Ramapo requires applicants to be in the upper 50% of their class. A minimum GPA of 3.0 is required. The SAT I or ACT is required. Applicants must be graduates of accredited secondary schools or have earned a GED. The college requires 16 academic credits, including 4 in English, 3 in mathematics, 2 each in science and social studies, and the remaining 5 in academic electives. Students are encouraged to take 2 years of a foreign language. Students must also submit an essay. An interview is recommended. AP and CLEP credits are accepted. Important factors used in the admissions decision are advanced placement or honor courses, recommendations by school officials, extracurricular activities record, leadership record, and evidence of special talent.

Procedure: Freshmen are admitted fall and spring. Entrance exams should be taken by January of the senior year. Applications should be filed by March 15 for fall entry and December 1 for spring entry, along with an application fee of $35. Notification is sent on a rolling basis. A waiting list is an active part of the admissions procedure, with about 4% of applicants on the list.

Transfer: About 670 transfer students enrolled in 1993–94. Applicants must present a minimum GPA of 2.0; however, students applying to the School of Business with at least 45 credits must submit a GPA of 2.5. There are special requirements for social work, nursing, and communications majors. Any applicant transferring fewer than 30 credits must provide a high school transcript. SAT I scores are recommended. Associate degree recipients are encouraged to apply. A total of 45 credits out of 128 must be completed at Ramapo.

Visiting: There are regularly scheduled orientations for prospective students, including orientation, advisement, and registration. There are guides for informal visits and visitors may sit in on classes. To arrange a visit, contact the Admissions Office at (201) 529–7600.

Financial Aid: In 1993–94, 53% of all current freshmen and 39% of continuing students received some form of financial aid. About 52% of freshmen and 37% of continuing students received need-based aid. The average freshman award was $6322. Of that total, scholarships or need-based grants averaged $5387 ($8555 maximum); loans averaged $2170 ($3625 maximum); and work contracts averaged $1213 ($1500 maximum). Ninety-three percent of undergraduate students work part-time. Average earnings from campus work for the school year are $1104. The average financial indebtedness of the 1992–93 graduate was $6665. Ramapo is a member of CSS. The FAFSA financial statement is required. The deadline for financial aid applications is March 15.

International Students: There are currently 169 international students enrolled. They must take the TOEFL and achieve a minimum score of 500.

Computers: The college provides computer facilities for student use. The mainframes are a DEC VAX 8600 and a DEC MicroVAX II. In addition, 80 microcomputers are located in the residence halls and the computing laboratory. All students may access the system according to a posted schedule. There are no time limits on using the system and no fees.

Graduates: In 1992–93, 670 bachelor's degrees were awarded. The most popular majors among graduates were business administration (33%), communications (11%), and psychology (9%). Within an average freshman class, 34% graduate in 5 years and 41% in 6 years. Some 80 companies recruited on campus in 1992–93. In the 1992 graduating class, 5% of all graduates were enrolled in graduate school within 6 months of graduation.

Admissions Contact: Nancy E. Jaeger, Director of Admission.

RICHARD STOCKTON COLLEGE OF NEW JERSEY

D-5

(Formerly Stockton State College)

Pomona, NJ 08240–9988   (609) 652–4261

Full-time: 2158 men, 2277 women	Faculty: 193; IIB, +$
Part-time: 575 men, 772 women	Ph.D.s: 92%
Graduate: none	Student/Faculty: 23 to 1
Year: semesters, summer session	Tuition: $2880 ($3584)
Application Deadline: May 1	Room & Board: $4070
Freshman Class: 4019 applied, 1579 accepted, 716 enrolled	
SAT I Verbal/Math: 490/560	**VERY COMPETITIVE**

Richard Stockton College of New Jersey, founded in 1969, is a public, coeducational liberal arts, preprofessional, business, and teachers' college. In addition to regional accreditation, Stockton has baccalaureate program accreditation with APTA, CSWE, and NLN. The library contains 224,972 volumes, 298,388 microform items, and 9587 audiovisual forms, and subscribes to 1881 periodicals. Computerized library sources and services include the card catalog, interlibrary loans, and database searching. Special learning facilities include a learning resource center, an art gallery, a radio station, a TV station, an astronomical observatory, a marine science field laboratory, and a marina with a fleet of small boats. The 1600-acre campus is in a suburban area 12 miles northwest of Atlantic City. Including residence halls, there are 33 buildings on campus.

Student Life: About 97% of undergraduates are from New Jersey. Students come from 21 states, 20 foreign countries, and Canada. Sixty-five percent are from public schools; 35% from private. Eighty-five percent are white. The average age of freshmen is 18; all undergraduates, 22. Seven percent drop out by the end of their first year; 56% remain to graduate.

Housing: A total of 1862 students can be accommodated in college housing. College-sponsored living facilities include single-sex and coed dormitories and on-campus apartments. In addition, there are honors houses and special interest houses. On-campus housing is guaranteed for the freshman year only and is available on a first-come, first-served basis. Priority is given to out-of-town students. Sixty-three percent of students commute. All students may keep cars on campus.

Activities: About 19% of men belong to 1 local and 10 national fraternities; about 10% of women belong to 1 local and 6 national sororities. There are 76 groups on campus, including art, band, cheerlead-

ing, chess, choir, chorale, computers, dance, drama, ethnic, honors, international, jazz band, literary magazine, newspaper, photography, political, professional, radio and TV, religious, social, social service, and student government. Popular campus events include Comedy Club, Kwanza, Alcohol Awareness Week, Spring Challenge, Jewish Dinner, International Student Dinner, Earth Day, Spring Scholarship Benefit, Alumni Picnic, and Family Day.

Sports: There are 7 intercollegiate sports each for men and women, and 5 intramural sports each for men and women. Athletic and recreation facilities include an indoor, 6-lane swimming pool, a weight-lifting gymnasium, a multipurpose gymnasium, a sauna, steam baths, and dance studios, as well as playing fields, a 60-acre lake for fishing and canoeing, cross-country courses, bike trails, an all-weather track, and tennis, racquetball, and basketball courts.

Disabled Students: The entire campus is accessible to disabled students. The following facilities are available: wheelchair ramps, elevators, special parking, specially equipped rest rooms, special class scheduling, lowered drinking fountains, and lowered telephones.

Services: In addition to many counseling and information services, tutoring is available in most subjects. In addition, there is a reader service for the blind, and remedial math, reading, and writing. In addition, there is a skills center.

Campus Safety and Security: Campus safety and security measures include 24-hour foot and vehicle patrol, self-defense education, escort service, and shuttle buses. In addition, there are informal discussions, pamphlets, posters, films, emergency telephones, and lighted pathways and sidewalks.

Programs of Study: Stockton awards the B.A., B.S., and B.S.N. degrees. Bachelor's degrees are awarded in BIOLOGICAL SCIENCE (biology/biological science and marine science), BUSINESS (accounting, banking and finance, management science, and marketing/retailing/merchandising), COMMUNICATIONS AND THE ARTS (dance, design, dramatic arts, fine arts, and music), COMPUTER AND PHYSICAL SCIENCE (chemistry, computer programming, computer science, information sciences and systems, mathematics, and physics), ENGINEERING AND ENVIRONMENTAL DESIGN (environmental science and preengineering), HEALTH PROFESSIONS (nursing, physical therapy, public health, and speech pathology/audiology), SOCIAL SCIENCE (anthropology, criminal justice, economics, history, liberal arts/general studies, philosophy, political science/government, psychology, and social work). Sciences are the strongest academically. Business has the largest enrollment.

Required: To graduate, students must earn 128 credit hours, 32 in the general studies curriculum and at least 40 in the major, with a minumum GPA of 2.0. General studies includes 3 writing courses and freshman and senior seminars. Graduates must also satisfy writing and basic skills requirements.

Special: Stockton offers co-op programs in business, computers, and computer science, internships in all fields with a wide variety of companies, work-study with various government agencies and corporations, a Washington semester, independent study, and study abroad in 10 countries. Dual majors in all programs, student-designed majors, an accelerated degree in medicine, 3–2 engineering degrees with the New Jersey Institute of Technology and Rutgers University, and general studies degrees are offered. Nondegree study, pass/fail options, and credit for life, military, and work experience are possible. There is a freshman honors program on campus. One department has an honors program.

Faculty/Classroom: Sixty-one percent of faculty are male; 39%, female. All teach undergraduates and 70% both teach and do research. The average class size in an introductory lecture is 22; in a laboratory, 12; and in a regular course offering, 26.

Admissions: About 39% of the 1993–94 applicants were accepted. The SAT scores for the 1993–94 freshman class were as follows: Verbal—56% below 500, 37% between 500 and 599, 6% between 600 and 700, and 1% above 700; Math—21% below 500, 52% between 500 and 599, 23% between 600 and 700, and 4% above 700. About 61% of the current freshmen were in the top fifth of their class; 92% were in the top two fifths. There were 5 National Merit finalists. Five freshmen graduated first in their class.

Requirements: Stockton requires applicants to be in the upper 50% of their class. A minimum GPA of 2.5 is required. The SAT I or ACT is required. Applicants must be high school graduates; the GED is accepted. Sixteen academic credits are required, inlcuding 4 years in English, 3 each in mathematics and social studies, 2 in science, and 4 additional years of any of the above or a foreign language, or both. An essay and an interview are recommended and a portfolio or audition is necessary where appropriate. AP and CLEP credits are accepted. Important factors used in the admissions decision are advanced placement or honor courses, leadership record, evidence of special talent, recommendations by school officials, and extracurricular activities record.

Procedure: Freshmen are admitted fall and spring. Entrance exams should be taken once in the junior year, and again before January in the senior year. Early decision applications should be filed by January

15; regular applications, by May 1 for fall entry and December 1 for spring entry, along with an application fee of $25. Notification of early decision is sent January 31; regular decision, May 15. There are early decision and early admissions plans. About 82 early decision candidates were accepted for the 1993–94 class. A waiting list is an active part of the admissions procedure, with about 15% of applicants on the list.

Transfer: About 550 transfer students enrolled in a recent year. Transfer students must have earned at least 16 credits at other colleges and must submit college and high school transcripts as well as SAT I scores. A total of 32 credits out of 128 must be completed at Stockton.

Visiting: There are regularly scheduled orientations for prospective students. There are guides for informal visits and visitors may sit in on classes. To arrange for a visit, contact Enrollment Management at (609) 652–4261.

Financial Aid: In 1993–94, 64% of all current freshmen and 39% of continuing students received some form of financial aid. About 47% of freshmen and 35% of continuing students received need-based aid. The average freshman award was $4658. Of that total, scholarships or need-based grants averaged $1159 ($5700 maximum); loans averaged $2455 ($3000 maximum); and work contracts averaged $1044 ($2400 maximum). Forty-six percent of undergraduate students work part-time. Average earnings from campus work for the school year are $985. The FAFSA financial statement is required. The deadline for financial aid applications is March 1.

International Students: There are currently 123 international students enrolled. The school actively recruits these students. They must take the TOEFL and achieve a minimum score of 525.

Computers: The college provides computer facilities for student use. The mainframes are a DEC VAX 8600 and 6300, and an IBM 3090 and 4381. Students may access a network called Co Sy for conferencing and linkage to the mainframe and Internet. There are also more than 350 microcomputers in laboratories and residence halls across the campus. All students may access the system. It may be used between 8 A.M. and midnight. There are no time limits on using the system and no fees.

Graduates: In 1992–93, 1089 bachelor's degrees were awarded. The most popular majors among graduates were business and management (35%), social sciences (26%), and health professions (8%). Within an average freshman class, 49% graduate in 4 years, 52% in 5 years, and 56% in 6 years. Some 156 companies recruited on campus in 1992–93. In the 1992 graduating class, 40% of all graduates were enrolled in graduate school within 6 months of graduation; 54% had found employment.

Admissions Contact: Sal Catalfamo, Dean of Enrollment Management.

RIDER COLLEGE

D-3

Lawrenceville, NJ 08648-3099

(609) 896–5042

(800) 257–9026 (out-of-state)

Full-time: 1251 men, 1499 women

Part-time: 454 men, 856 women

Graduate: 436 men, 821 women

Year: semesters, summer session

Application Deadline: open

Freshman Class: 3586 applied, 2424 accepted, 668 enrolled

SAT I Verbal/Math: 439/501

Faculty: 226; IIA, +$

Ph.D.s: 92%

Student/Faculty: 12 to 1

Tuition: $12,950

Room & Board: $5210

COMPETITIVE

Rider College, founded in 1865, is a private coeducational institution offering undergraduate programs in business administration, education and human services, liberal arts and science, and continuing studies. There are 5 undergraduate and 2 graduate schools. In addition to regional accreditation, Rider has baccalaureate program accreditation with AACSB and NCATE. The library contains 350,000 volumes and 450,000 microform items, and subscribes to 2000 periodicals. Computerized library sources and services include the card catalog, interlibrary loans, and database searching. Special learning facilities include a learning resource center, art gallery, radio station, TV station, and journalism and sociology laboratories. The 340-acre campus is in a suburban area 3 miles north of Trenton. Including residence halls, there are 37 buildings on campus.

Student Life: About 78% of undergraduates are from New Jersey. Students come from 27 states and Canada. Seventy-nine percent are white. Forty-seven percent are Catholic; 13% Protestant. The average age of freshmen is 18; all undergraduates, 21. Nineteen percent drop out by the end of their first year; 59% remain to graduate.

Housing: A total of 2264 students can be accommodated in college housing. College-sponsored living facilities include single-sex and coed dormitories, on-campus apartments, fraternity houses, and sorority houses. In addition there are special interest houses. On-campus housing is guaranteed for all 4 years. Seventy percent of students live on campus; of those, 65% remain on campus on weekends. All students may keep cars on campus.

Activities: About 8% of men belong to 6 national fraternities; about 7% of women belong to 6 national sororities. There are 70 groups on campus, including band, cheerleading, choir, chorus, computers, drama, ethnic, film, honors, international, literary magazine, musical theater, newspaper, orchestra, pep band, photography, political, professional, radio and TV, religious, social, social service, student government, and yearbook. Popular campus events include Cranberry Day, Cranberry and White Night, and movie nights.

Sports: There are 10 intercollegiate sports for men and 9 for women, and 15 intramural sports for men and 15 for women. Athletic and recreation facilities include a gymnasium, a swimming pool, fitness center and spa, lighted outdoor multipurpose courts, and outdoor varsity and intramural fields.

Disabled Students: Thirty percent of the campus is accessible to disabled students. The following facilities are available: wheelchair ramps, elevators, special parking, specially equipped rest rooms, special class scheduling, lowered drinking fountains, and lowered telephones.

Services: In addition to many counseling and information services, tutoring is available in most subjects. There is remedial math, reading, and writing.

Campus Safety and Security: Campus safety and security measures include 24-hour foot and vehicle patrol, self defense education, escort service, and informal discussions. In addition, there are pamphlets, posters, and films, emergency telephones, and lighted pathways and sidewalks.

Programs of Study: Rider awards the B.A., B.S., and B.S.B.A. degrees. Associate and master's degrees also are awarded. Bachelor's degrees are awarded in BIOLOGICAL SCIENCE (biochemistry, biology/biological science, and marine science), BUSINESS (accounting, banking and finance, business administration and management, business economics, marketing/retailing/merchandising, organizational behavior, and personnel management), COMMUNICATIONS AND THE ARTS (advertising, communications, English, fine arts, French, German, journalism, Russian, Spanish, and speech/debate/rhetoric), COMPUTER AND PHYSICAL SCIENCE (actuarial science, chemistry, computer management, geology, mathematics, and physics), EDUCATION (business, early childhood, elementary, foreign languages, marketing and distribution, science, secondary, social studies, and teaching English as a second language/foreign language), HEALTH PROFESSIONS (predentistry and premedicine), SOCIAL SCIENCE (American studies, economics, history, philosophy, political science/government, prelaw, psychology, and sociology). Business, actuarial science, sciences, and communications are the strongest academically. Accounting, finance, communications, and psychology have the largest enrollments.

Required: All students must maintain a minimum GPA of 2.0 while taking 120 semester hours. Students also must fulfill core curriculum requirements, including 9 hours in humanities, 7 to 8 in science, 6 each of English writing and foreign language (each may be waived if proficiency is demonstrated), social sciences/communications, and history, and 3 hours in mathematics.

Special: Internships in many programs, a co-op program in marketing, work-study, study abroad in 6 countries, a B.A.-B.S. degree in all liberal arts and sciences, dual majors in education, liberal studies degree, and nondegree study are possible. There is a freshman honors program on campus, as well as 25 national honor societies. Fourteen departments have honors programs.

Faculty/Classroom: Sixty-two percent of faculty are male; 38%, female. All teach undergraduates. No introductory courses are taught by graduate students. The average class size in an introductory lecture is 50; in a laboratory, 20; and in a regular course offering, 25.

Admissions: About 68% of the 1993–94 applicants were accepted. The SAT scores for the 1993–94 freshman class were as follows: Verbal—81% below 500, 15% between 500 and 599, 3% between 600 and 700, and 1% above 700; Math—53% below 500, 32% between 500 and 599, 12% between 600 and 700, and 4% above 700. About 25% of the current freshmen were in the top fifth of their class; 50% were in the top two fifths.

Requirements: Rider requires applicants to be in the upper 50% of their class. A minimum GPA of 2.5 is required. The SAT I or ACT is required. Applicants need 16 Carnegie units, including 4 years of English. An essay and interview are recommended. An audition is required for theater scholarships. The GED is accepted. Three units of mathematics are required for prospective mathematics, science, and business majors. AP and CLEP credits are accepted. Important factors used in the admissions decision are advanced placement or honor courses, extracurricular activities record, recommendations by alumni, recommendations by school officials, and leadership record.

Procedure: Freshmen are admitted to all sessions. Entrance exams should be taken by December of the senior year. Application deadlines are open. The application fee is $35. Notification is sent on a rolling basis. There is a deferred admissions plan.

Transfer: About 210 transfer students enrolled in 1993–94. A minimum GPA of 2.0 is required for transfer applicants. If students have fewer than 30 credits, they also must submit high school transcripts and SAT I scores. An interview is recommended. A total of 30 credits out of 120 must be completed at Rider.

Visiting: There are guides for informal visits and visitors may sit in on classes. To arrange for a visit, contact the Admissions office at (800) 257-9026 or (609) 896-5042.

Financial Aid: In 1993–94, 70% of all students received some form of financial aid, including need-based aid. The average freshman award was $11,000. Of that total, scholarships or need-based grants averaged $6373 ($12,750 maximum); loans averaged $1500 ($4000 maximum); and work contracts averaged $1000 ($1500 maximum). Thirty-five percent of undergraduate students work part-time. Average earnings from campus work for the school year are $1500. Rider is a member of CSS. The FAFSA financial statement is required. The deadline for financial aid applications is March 1.

International Students: The school actively recruits these students. They must take the TOEFL and achieve a minimum score of 550. The student must also take the SAT I or the ACT.

Computers: The college provides computer facilities for student use. The mainframes are a DEC VAX 4000 and MicroVAX 3400. There are 30 networked terminals. The microcomputer laboratory facility has 24 IBM PCs available for general use and more than 200 microcomputers in departmental laboratories, many of which are networked. All students may access the system. It may be used anytime. There are no time limits on using the system and no fees.

Graduates: In a recent class 600 bachelor's degrees were awarded. Some 240 companies recruited on campus in 1992–93.

Admissions Contact: Susan C. Christian, Director of Admissions.

ROWAN COLLEGE OF NEW JERSEY C-4
(Formerly Glassboro State College)
Glassboro, NJ 08028 (609) 863-5346

Full-time: 2298 men, 3128 women	Faculty: 308; IIB, + +$
Part-time: 1319 men, 2623 women	Ph.D.s: 80%
Graduate: 391 men, 1044 women	Student/Faculty: 18 to 1
Year: semesters, summer session	Tuition: $2843 ($4743)
Application Deadline: March 15	Room & Board: $4515
Freshman Class: 3820 applied, 1430 accepted, 675 enrolled	
SAT I Verbal/Math: 486/538	**VERY COMPETITIVE**

Rowan College, founded in 1923, is a public, coeducational institution offering undergraduate programs in the arts and sciences, business administration, education, and fine and performing arts. There are 4 undergraduate schools and one graduate school. In addition to regional accreditation, Rowan College of New Jersey has baccalaureate program accreditation with NASM and NCATE. The library contains 350,800 volumes, 77,000 microform items, and 43,500 audiovisual forms, and subscribes to 1725 periodicals. Computerized library sources and services include database searching. Special learning facilities include an art gallery, a planetarium, and a radio station. The 200-acre campus is in a small town 20 miles southeast of Philadelphia. Including residence halls, there are 40 buildings on campus.

Student Life: About 98% of undergraduates are from New Jersey. Students come from 11 states and 13 foreign countries. Sixty-five percent are from public schools; 35% from private. Eighty-two percent are white; 10% African American. The average age of freshmen is 19.6; all undergraduates, 24.8. Twenty percent drop out by the end of their first year; 55% remain to graduate.

Housing: A total of 2224 students can be accommodated in college housing. College-sponsored living facilities include dormitories, on-campus apartments, off-campus apartments, and married-student housing. In addition there are honors houses. On-campus housing is available on a lottery system for upperclassmen. Priority is given to out-of-town students. Alcohol is not permitted. Upperclassmen may keep cars on campus.

Activities: About 9% of men belong to 1 local fraternity and 11 national fraternities; about 9% of women belong to 5 local and 8 national sororities. There are 150 groups on campus, including art, band, cheerleading, chess, choir, chorale, chorus, computers, dance, drama, ethnic, film, honors, international, jazz band, literary magazine, marching band, musical theater, newspaper, opera, orchestra, political, professional, radio and TV, religious, social, social service, student government, symphony, and yearbook.

Sports: There are 9 intercollegiate sports for men and 8 for women, and 7 intramural sports for men and 6 for women. Athletic and recreation facilities include a 3000-seat stadium, an 1800-seat gymnasium, a 1000-seat auditorium, a swimming pool, tennis courts, and playing fields.

Disabled Students: Ninety-five percent of the campus is accessible to disabled students. The following facilities are available: wheelchair ramps, elevators, special parking, specially equipped rest rooms, special class scheduling, lowered drinking fountains, and lowered telephones.

Services: In addition to many counseling and information services, tutoring is available in some subjects. There is also remedial math, reading, and writing.

Campus Safety and Security: Campus safety and security measures include a 24-hour foot and vehicle patrol, an escort service, informal discussions, and pamphlets, posters, and films. In addition, there are emergency telephones and lighted pathways and sidewalks.

Programs of Study: Rowan College of New Jersey awards the B.A. and B.S. degrees. Master's degrees also are awarded. Bachelor's degrees are awarded in BIOLOGICAL SCIENCE (biology/biological science), BUSINESS (accounting, business administration and management, marketing/retailing/merchandising, personnel management, and small business management), COMMUNICATIONS AND THE ARTS (broadcasting, communications, dramatic arts, English, fine arts, journalism, music, Spanish, and speech/debate/rhetoric), COMPUTER AND PHYSICAL SCIENCE (chemistry and physics), EDUCATION (early childhood, elementary, foreign languages, music, and science), SOCIAL SCIENCE (criminal justice, economics, history, political science/government, psychology, and sociology). Communications, business administration, and elementary education are the strongest programs academically. Elementary education, communications, and business administration have the largest enrollments.

Required: General education requirements include 12 to 18 semester hours of social and behavioral sciences, 12 to 16 of science and mathematics, 6 to 9 of communications, 6 of fine and performing arts, and 3 to 6 of history/humanities/language/arts. Students must also complete 6 semester hours of writing and 3 of physical education. The bachelor's degree requires completion of at least 120 semester hours, including 30 to 39 in a major field, with a minimum GPA of 2.0.

Special: Students may study abroad in 5 countries. Internships are available both with and without pay. GSC also offers accelerated degree programs and 3-2 degrees in engineering, optometry, podiatry, and pharmacy. There are also dual majors, pass/fail options and credit for military experience. There is a freshman honors program on campus.

Faculty/Classroom: Seventy-one percent of faculty are male; 29%, female. All teach undergraduates. No introductory courses are taught by graduate students. The average class size in an introductory lecture is 25; in a laboratory, 20; and in a regular course offering, 25.

Admissions: About 37% of the 1993–94 applicants were accepted. The SAT scores for the 1993–94 freshman class were as follows: Verbal—58% below 500, 34% between 500 and 599, 6% between 600 and 700, and 1% above 700; Math—28% below 500, 50% between 500 and 599, 19% between 600 and 700, and 1% above 700. About 46% of the current freshmen were in the top fifth of their class; 85% were in the top two fifths. There was 1 National Merit finalist and 27 semifinalists. Twenty-nine freshmen graduated first in their class.

Requirements: A minimum GPA of 3.0 is required. The SAT I is required with a recommended minimum composite score of 950, or no less than 450 on either part. Students submitting ACT scores should have a minimum composite score of 19. Applicants must be graduates of accredited secondary schools or have earned a GED. The college requires 16 academic credits or Carnegie units, including 4 in English, 3 each in mathematics and college preparatory electives, and 2 each in foreign language, history, and a laboratory science. An essay is required of all students, and a portfolio or audition is required for specific majors. AP and CLEP credits are accepted. Important factors used in the admissions decision are advanced placement or honor courses, evidence of special talent, leadership record, extracurricular activities record, and recommendations by school officials.

Procedure: Freshmen are admitted in the fall and spring. Entrance exams should be taken in November or December of the senior year. Applications should be filed by March 15 for fall entry and November 15 for spring entry, along with an application fee of $30. Notification is sent on a rolling basis. There is a deferred admissions plan. A waiting list is an active part of the admissions procedure, with about 5% of applicants on the list.

Transfer: About 900 transfer students enrolled in 1993–94. Applicants must present a minimum GPA of 2.0, but should present a GPA of 2.5 to be competitive. An associate degree is recommended. Students who have earned less than 30 semester hours must also submit a high school transcript and SAT I results. A total of 30 credits out of 120 must be completed at Rowan College of New Jersey.

Visiting: There are regularly scheduled orientations for prospective students, consisting of a 2-day summer program providing schedule confirmation/adjustment, student activities updates, and workshops for students and parents. There are guides for informal visits and visitors may sit in on classes. To arrange for a visit, contact Admissions at (609) 863-5346.

Financial Aid: In 1993–94, 55% of all current freshmen and 50% of continuing students received some form of financial aid. About 55% of freshmen and 50% of continuing students received need-based aid. The average freshman award was $2500. Of that total,

scholarships or need-based grants averaged $750 ($2000 maximum); loans averaged $1500 ($2500 maximum); and work contracts averaged $900 ($1500 maximum). Ten percent of undergraduate students work part-time. Average earnings from campus work for the school year are $1200. The average financial indebtedness of the 1992–93 graduate was $4000. Rowan College of New Jersey is a member of CSS. The FAF, the college's own financial statement and financial aid transcripts are required. The deadline for financial aid applications is April 1.

International Students: There are currently 69 international students enrolled. They must take the TOEFL or the University of Michigan Language Test and achieve a minimum score on the TOEFL of 500. Applicants from English-speaking countries must also submit SAT I score.

Computers: The college provides computer facilities for student use. The mainframes consist of (2) DEC VAX 8650, series 6000–410. There are also microcomputers available in academic laboratories. Students enrolled in computer science courses and seniors working on research projects may access the mainframe from 8:30 A.M. to 4:30 P.M. There are no fees.

Graduates: In 1992–93, 1452 bachelor's degrees were awarded. The most popular majors among graduates were business administration (20%), communications (17%), and elementary education (14%). Within an average freshman class, 24% graduate in 4 years, 48% in 5 years, and 55% in 6 years. Some 100 companies recruited on campus in a recent year.

Admissions Contact: Marvin G. Sills, Director of Admissions.

RUTGERS UNIVERSITY
CAMDEN COLLEGE OF ARTS AND SCIENCES   C-4
Camden, NJ 08101   (609) 225-6104

Full-time: 885 men, 1128 women	Faculty: 136; IIA, ++$
Part-time: 236 men, 318 women	Ph.D.s: 95%
Graduate: none	Student/Faculty: 15 to 1
Year: semesters, summer session	Tuition: $4198 ($7753)
Application Deadline: May 1	Room & Board: $4454
Freshman Class: 3366 applied, 1752 accepted, 232 enrolled	
SAT I Verbal/Math: 492/551	VERY COMPETITIVE

Rutgers University/Camden College of Arts and Sciences, established in 1927, is a coeducational liberal arts institution. There are 3 undergraduate and 6 graduate schools. In addition to regional accreditation, Camden College of Arts and Sciences has baccalaureate program accreditation with CAHEA, NASM, NCATE, and NLN. The 2 libraries contain 357,701 volumes, 214,499 microform items, and 207 audiovisual forms, and subscribe to 2106 periodicals. Computerized library sources and services include the card catalog, interlibrary loans, and database searching. Special learning facilities include a learning resource center, art gallery, and radio station. The 25-acre campus is in an urban area 1 mile from Philadelphia, Pennsylvania. Including residence halls, there are 20 buildings on campus.

Student Life: About 98% of undergraduates are from New Jersey. Students come from 16 states and 4 foreign countries. Seventy-nine percent are white; 13% African American. The average age of freshmen is 18.5; all undergraduates, 23.8. Twenty-one percent drop out by the end of their first year; 49% remain to graduate.

Housing: A total of 482 students can be accommodated in college housing. College-sponsored living facilities include coed dormitories and on-campus apartments. In addition there are special interest houses, and substance-free housing is available. On-campus housing is available on a first-come, first-served basis and is available on a lottery system for upperclassmen. Alcohol is not permitted. All students may keep cars on campus.

Activities: About 6% of men belong to 1 local and 2 national fraternities; about 6% of women belong to 2 local and 5 national sororities. There are 45 groups on campus, including cheerleading, computers, drama, ethnic, gay, honors, international, literary magazine, newspaper, political, professional, radio and TV, religious, social, social service, student government, and yearbook. Popular campus events include Black History Month, Women's History Month, Pioneer Week, Spring Day, and Hispanic Solidarity Week.

Sports: There are 9 intercollegiate sports for men and 5 for women, and 8 intramural sports for men and 6 for women. Athletic and recreation facilities include a 2000-seat gymnasium; a swimming pool; soccer, baseball, and softball fields; basketball, handball, racquetball, tennis, and squash courts; and a weight room.

Disabled Students: Ninety-five percent of the campus is accessible to disabled students. The following facilities are available: wheelchair ramps, elevators, special parking, specially equipped rest rooms, special class scheduling, and lowered drinking fountains and telephones. Facilities vary from building to building; however, all classes are scheduled in accessible locations for disabled students, and adaptations are made to individual needs in dormitory rooms.

Services: In addition to many counseling and information services, tutoring is available in some subjects, including introductory-level courses. There is a reader service for the blind, and remedial math, reading, and writing.

Campus Safety and Security: Campus safety and security measures include 24-hour foot and vehicle patrol, self-defense education, escort service, and shuttle buses. In addition, there are informal discussions, pamphlets, posters, films, emergency telephones, and lighted pathways and sidewalks. The police department and security guards offer additional security.

Programs of Study: Camden College of Arts and Sciences awards the B.A. and B.S. degrees. Bachelor's degrees are awarded in BIOLOGICAL SCIENCE (biochemistry and biology/biological science), BUSINESS (accounting, management science, and marketing/retailing/merchandising), COMMUNICATIONS AND THE ARTS (art, art history and appreciation, dramatic arts, English, fine arts, French, German, music, and Spanish), COMPUTER AND PHYSICAL SCIENCE (chemistry, computer science, mathematics, physics, and science), EDUCATION (elementary and secondary), ENGINEERING AND ENVIRONMENTAL DESIGN (ceramic engineering, chemical engineering, civil engineering, electrical/electronics engineering, engineering and applied science, environmental engineering, industrial engineering, and mechanical engineering), HEALTH PROFESSIONS (medical laboratory technology, nursing, predentistry, and premedicine), SOCIAL SCIENCE (African American studies, economics, history, philosophy, political science/government, prelaw, psychology, social work, sociology, and urban studies). Psychology, English, and biological sciences have the largest enrollments.

Required: For graduation, students must complete a total of 126 credits, with 30 to 48 credits in the major and a minimum GPA of 2.0. General curricular requirements include 6 credits each in English composition and history, philosophy, or religion; 9 in social science; 3 in mathematics and 3 additional in mathematics, computer science, or statistics; 6 in two interdisciplinary courses; 12 in courses offered outside the major department; 3 each in literary masterpieces and a foreign language, and an additional 3 in English or a foreign language; 6 in the natural science disciplines; and 3 in art, music, or theater arts.

Special: The college offers study abroad in 9 countries, some B.A.-B.S. degrees, and student-designed majors. Pass/fail options are available for two courses during matriculation. Students may take 2–2 and 2–3 (dual majors) programs with the College of Engineering, a 1–3 program with Cook College (agriculture), and a 2–3 program with the College of Pharmacy. There is a freshman honors program on campus, as well as 11 national honor societies. Twenty-six departments have honors programs.

Faculty/Classroom: Sixty-five percent of faculty are male; 35%, female. All teach undergraduates and 90% do research. Graduate students teach 5% of introductory courses. The average class size in a regular course offering is 32.

Admissions: About 52% of the 1993–94 applicants were accepted. The SAT scores for the 1993–94 freshman class were as follows: Verbal—55% below 500, 37% between 500 and 599, and 8% between 600 and 700; Math—19% below 500, 58% between 500 and 599, 21% between 600 and 700, and 2% above 700. About 69% of the current freshmen were in the top fifth of their class; 92% were in the top two fifths. Two freshmen graduated first in their class.

Requirements: The SAT I or ACT is required. Applicants must be graduates of an accredited secondary school. The GED is accepted. Students must have completed 16 academic credits or Carnegie units, including 4 years of English, 3 of mathematics (algebra I and II and geometry), 2 each of a foreign language and science, and 5 other approved academic subjects. AP and CLEP credits are accepted. Important factors used in the admissions decision are advanced placement or honor courses, evidence of special talent, leadership record, extracurricular activities record, and recommendations by school officials.

Procedure: Freshmen are admitted fall and spring. Entrance exams should be taken as early as possible in the junior year. Applications should be filed by May 1 for fall entry and November 30 for spring entry, along with an application fee of $40. Notification is sent on a rolling basis. There is a deferred admissions plan.

Transfer: About 460 transfer students enrolled in 1993–94. Applicants must have completed a minimum of 12 college credits with a GPA of 2.5 or better. Grades of C or better in courses that correspond in content and credit to those offered by the college transfer for credit. A total of 30 credits out of 126 must be completed at this college.

Visiting: There are regularly scheduled orientations for prospective students, including an information session with an admissions officer and a tour of the campus. Visitors may sit in on classes. To arrange for a visit, contact the Office of University Undergraduate Admissions (Camden) at (609) 225-6104.

Financial Aid: In 1993–94, 64% of all current freshmen and 47% of continuing students received some form of financial aid. About 59% of freshmen and 43% of continuing students received need-based aid. The average freshman award was $4927. Of that total, scholarships or need-based grants averaged $3750 ($10,000 maximum); loans averaged $1463 ($4000 maximum); and work contracts averaged $1167 ($1500 maximum). Eight percent of undergraduate students work part-time. Average earnings from campus work for the school year are $917. The average financial indebtedness of the 1992–93 graduate was $4655. The FAFSA financial statement is required. The deadline for financial aid applications is March 1.

International Students: There are currently 26 international students enrolled. They must take the TOEFL with a minimum score of 550 as well as SAT I or the ACT.

Computers: The college provides computer facilities for student use. The mainframes are a Sun Sparc Server 10/41 and a 10/51 MP. Terminals or networked microcomputers are located in two major academic buildings, the library, the Campus Center, and dorms; terminals provide access to the central systems as well as to the local Camden campus computers. The on-campus computer network includes on-line registration, E-mail, and access to Internet and Bitnet. All students may access the system, Monday through Thursday, 8:30 A.M. to midnight and Friday and Saturday, 9 A.M. to 5 P.M. There are no time limits on using the system. The fee is $100 per year.

Graduates: In 1992–93, 537 bachelor's degrees were awarded. The most popular majors among graduates were psychology (19%), English (12%), and nursing (8%). Within an average freshman class, 20% graduate in 4 years, 44% in 5 years, and 49% in 6 years. Some 90 companies recruited on campus in 1992–93. In the 1992 graduating class, 27% of all graduates were enrolled in graduate school within 6 months of graduation; 78% had found employment.

Admissions Contact: Dr. Deborah Bowles, Director of Admissions-Camden.

RUTGERS UNIVERSITY
COLLEGE OF ENGINEERING
New Brunswick, NJ 08903

D-3

(908) 932–3770

Full-time: 1936 men, 412 women	Faculty: 126; I, +$
Part-time: 48 men, 11 women	Ph.D.s: 95%
Graduate: none	Student/Faculty: 19 to 1
Year: semesters, summer session	Tuition: $4800 ($8742)
Application Deadline: January 15	Room & Board: $4454
Freshman Class: 3593 applied, 2499 accepted, 582 enrolled	
SAT I Verbal/Math: 514/667	HIGHLY COMPETITIVE

Rutgers University College of Engineering, founded in 1864, offers a bachelor of science program in engineering. There are 11 undergraduate and 4 graduate schools. In addition to regional accreditation, the College of Engineering has baccalaureate program accreditation with ABET. The 14 libraries contain 4,387,960 volumes, 2,630,211 microform items, and 63,879 audiovisual forms, and subscribe to 19,822 periodicals. Computerized library sources and services include the card catalog, interlibrary loans, and database searching. Special learning facilities include a learning resource center, an art gallery, radio and TV stations, a geology museum, and various research centers, laboratories, and programs. The 2686-acre campus is in a suburban area 33 miles south of New York City. Including residence halls, there are 5 buildings on campus.

Student Life: About 87% of undergraduates are from New Jersey. Students come from 22 states and 38 foreign countries. Fifty-seven percent are white; 22% Asian American. The average age of freshmen is 18.2; all undergraduates, 20.6. Eleven percent drop out by the end of their first year; 72% remain to graduate.

Housing: A total of 1582 students can be accommodated in college housing. College-sponsored living facilities include single-sex and coed dormitories and on-campus apartments. In addition, there are cultural language houses, special interest houses, a special dorm for women interested in math and sciences, and substance-free housing. On-campus housing is guaranteed for the first 2 years and is available on a lottery system for upperclassmen. Sixty-five percent of students live on campus. Alcohol is not permitted.

Activities: About 7% of men belong to 3 local and 29 national fraternities; about 3% of women belong to 4 local and 11 national sororities. There are more than 300 groups on campus, including art, band, cheerleading, chess, choir, chorale, chorus, computers, dance, drama, drill team, ethnic, film, gay, honors, international, jazz band, literary magazine, marching band, musical theater, newspaper, orchestra, pep band, political, professional, radio and TV, religious, social, social service, student government, symphony, and yearbook. Popular campus events include Engineering Open House and Science and Engineering Career Day.

Sports: There are 15 intercollegiate sports each for men and women, and 24 intramural sports each for men and women. Athletic and recreation facilities include a 23,000-seat stadium, an athletic center, a gymnasium, a swimming pool, tennis courts, beach volleyball courts, and a recreation center.

Disabled Students: Fifty-one percent of the campus is accessible to disabled students. The following facilities are available: wheelchair ramps, elevators, special parking, specially equipped rest rooms, special class scheduling, and lowered drinking fountains and telephones. Facilities available vary widely from building to building; however, all classes are scheduled in accessible locations for students with disabilities.

Services: In addition to many counseling and information services, tutoring is available in most subjects. The academic tutoring service provides specific course assistance in first- and second-level difficult courses. There is a reader service for the blind, and remedial math, reading, and writing.

Campus Safety and Security: Campus safety and security measures include 24-hour foot and vehicle patrol, self-defense education, escort service, and shuttle buses. In addition, there are informal discussions, pamphlets, posters, and films, emergency telephones, and lighted pathways and sidewalks. The police department is supplemented by security guards and student safety officers.

Programs of Study: The College of Engineering awards the B.S. degree. Master's and doctoral degrees also are awarded. Bachelor's degrees are awarded in ENGINEERING AND ENVIRONMENTAL DESIGN (bioresource engineering, ceramic engineering, chemical engineering, civil and environmental engineering, electrical/electronics engineering, engineering and applied science, industrial engineering, and mechanical engineering). Electrical engineering, mechanical engineering, and civil and environmental engineering have the largest enrollments.

Required: In order to graduate, 131 to 138 credits are required with a minimum GPA of 2.0. The core curriculum includes 16 credits of calculus for engineering; 12 credits each of analytical physics and humanities/social sciences; 6 credits of general chemistry for engineers; 3 credits each of expository writing, introduction to computers for engineers, engineering mechanics/statics, and economics; and 1 credit each of introduction to experimentation and engineering orientation lectures.

Special: The college offers study abroad in England, 2–3 dual degree programs in conjunction with other undergraduate colleges of Rutgers, and B.A.-B.S. degrees in all engineering majors and all B.A. majors offered on the New Brunswick campus. Pass/fail options are limited to 2 elective courses. Internships are offered through the engineering departments and Career Services. There is a freshman honors program on campus, as well as 7 national honor societies. Seven departments have honors programs.

Faculty/Classroom: Ninety-three percent of faculty are male; 7%, female. Graduate students teach 35% of introductory courses. The average class size in a regular course offering is 44.

Admissions: About 70% of the 1993–94 applicants were accepted. The SAT scores for the 1993–94 freshman class were as follows: Verbal—43% below 500, 39% between 500 and 599, 17% between 600 and 700, and 1% above 700; Math—1% below 500, 13% between 500 and 599, 53% between 600 and 700, and 33% above 700. About 69% of the current freshmen were in the top fifth of their class; 95% were in the top two fifths. There were 3 National Merit finalists. Five freshmen graduated first in their class.

Requirements: The SAT I or ACT is required. Applicants usually must be graduates of an accredited secondary school. The GED is accepted. Students must have completed 16 academic credits or Carnegie units, including 4 years each of English and mathematics (through precalculus), 1 year each of chemistry and physics, plus 6 other approved academic subjects. Computer programming is recommended. Students without a high school diploma, those from nonaccredited high schools, and those with academic unit entrance deficiencies must take SAT II: Subject tests in writing, mathematics, and a science. AP credits are accepted. Important factors used in the admissions decision are advanced placement or honor courses, evidence of special talent, leadership record, extracurricular activities record, and recommendations by school officials.

Procedure: Freshmen are admitted in the fall. Entrance exams should be taken no later than December of the senior year. Applications should be filed by January 15 for fall entry, along with an application fee of $40. Notification is sent April 15. There are early admissions and deferred admissions plans. A waiting list is an active part of the admissions procedure, with about 5% of applicants on the list.

Transfer: Ninety-six transfer students enrolled in 1993–94. Students with a minimum of 12 college credits are considered for transfer. Grades of C or better in courses that correspond in content and credit to ones offered at the college transfer for credit. Transfer students are admitted in both the fall and spring semesters. A total of 30 credits out of 131 to 138 must be completed at the College of Engineering.

Visiting: There are regularly scheduled orientations for prospective students, including an information session with an admissions officer followed by a bus tour with a student guide. Student-guided walking tours are also available, which include a meeting with the dean. Visi-

tors may sit in on classes. To arrange for a visit, contact the Office of University Undergraduate Admissions at (908) 932–7881.

Financial Aid: In 1993–94, 74% of all current freshmen and 61% of continuing students received some form of financial aid. About 55% of freshmen and 39% of continuing students received need-based aid. The average freshman award was $5452. Of that total, scholarships or need-based grants averaged $4174 ($10,000 maximum); loans averaged $1097 ($6000 maximum); and work contracts averaged $1203 ($1500 maximum). Ten percent of undergraduate students work part-time. Average earnings from campus work for the school year are $837. The average financial indebtedness of the 1992–93 graduate was $6181. The FAFSA financial statement is required. The deadline for financial aid applications is March 1.

International Students: There are currently 141 international students enrolled. They must take the TOEFL and achieve a minimum score of 550. The student must also take the SAT I or the ACT.

Computers: The college provides computer facilities for student use. The mainframes are a DEC VAX 8650 cluster, an IBM 3081, a Sun Sparc 670, and a SUN 4/110. Individual departments have a variety of minicomputers. Terminals on networked microcomputers are located on all campuses in the New Brunswick area. Computing services available to students include on-line class registration, E-mail, word processing, course-work assignments, and access to Internet and Bitnet. All students may access the system. It may be used 24 hours a day. Student use is limited by file space and execution length. The fee is $100 per year.

Graduates: In 1992–93, 424 bachelor's degrees were awarded. The most popular majors among graduates were electrical engineering (27%), mechanical engineering (22%), and civil and environmental engineering (18%). Within an average freshman class, 37% graduate in 4 years, 66% in 5 years, and 72% in 6 years. Some 500 companies recruited on campus in 1992–93. In the 1992 graduating class, 34% of all graduates were enrolled in graduate school within 6 months of graduation.

Admissions Contact: Dr. Elizabeth Mitchell, Assistant Vice President for University Undergraduate Admissions.

RUTGERS UNIVERSITY
COLLEGE OF NURSING

Newark, NJ 07102   E-2

(201) 648–5205

Full-time: 41 men, 347 women | Faculty: 37; IIA, + +$
Part-time: 6 men, 34 women | Ph.D.s: 95%
Graduate: none | Student/Faculty: 11 to 1
Year: semesters, summer session | Tuition: $4184 ($7739)
Application Deadline: January 15 | Room & Board: $4454
Freshman Class: 933 applied, 162 accepted, 43 enrolled
SAT I Verbal/Math: 508/575 | **VERY COMPETITIVE +**

Rutgers University/College of Nursing, founded in 1952, is a coeducational institution. There are 4 graduate schools. In addition to regional accreditation, the College of Nursing has baccalaureate program accreditation with NLN. The 4 libraries contain 591,536 volumes, 675,962 microform items, and 24,297 audiovisual forms, and subscribe to 3748 periodicals. Computerized library sources and services include the card catalog, interlibrary loans, and database searching. Special learning facilities include a learning resource center, an art gallery, a radio station, and a center for molecular and behavioral neuroscience. The 33-acre campus is in an urban area 7 miles west of New York City in downtown Newark. Including residence halls, there are 31 buildings on campus.

Student Life: About 98% of undergraduates are from New Jersey. Students come from 2 states. Forty-seven percent are white; 20% African American; 18% Asian American; 10% Hispanic. The average age of freshmen is 18.2; all undergraduates, 23.8. Fourteen percent drop out by the end of their first year; 54% remain to graduate.

Housing: A total of 141 students can be accommodated in college housing. College-sponsored living facilities include coed on-campus apartments and married-student housing. On-campus housing is available on a first-come, first-served basis. Alcohol is not permitted. All students may keep cars on campus.

Activities: There are 1 local and 4 national fraternities and 3 local and 4 national sororities. There are 85 groups on campus, including art, band, cheerleading, chess, choir, chorale, chorus, computers, drama, ethnic, gay, honors, international, jazz band, literary magazine, musical theater, newspaper, orchestra, photography, political, professional, radio and TV, religious, social, social service, student government, and yearbook. Popular campus events include monthly rap and refreshment sessions, annual holiday party, annual Research and Career Day, and an end-of-the-year picnic in May.

Sports: There is 1 intercollegiate sport for men and 4 for women, and 13 intramural sports for men and 13 for women. Athletic and recreation facilities include a 1300-seat athletic center, a tennis complex, a swimming pool, racquetball courts, a dance room, and soccer, softball, and baseball fields.

Disabled Students: Eighty percent of the campus is accessible to disabled students. The following facilities are available: wheelchair ramps, elevators, special parking, specially equipped rest rooms, special class scheduling, and lowered drinking fountains and telephones. Facilities vary widely from building to buidling; however, all classes will be scheduled in accessible locations for disabled students, and adaptations will be made to individual needs in dormitory rooms.

Services: In addition to many counseling and information services, tutoring is available in most subjects. There is a reader service for the blind, and remedial math, reading, and writing.

Campus Safety and Security: Campus safety and security measures include 24-hour foot and vehicle patrol, self-defense education, escort service, and shuttle buses. In addition, there are informal discussions, pamphlets, posters, and films, emergency telephones, and lighted pathways and sidewalks. Security guards assist Rutgers police in providing public safety services. There is also a student marshal program.

Programs of Study: The College of Nursing awards the B.S degree. Master's and doctoral degrees also are awarded. Bachelor's degrees are awarded in HEALTH PROFESSIONS (nursing).

Required: In order to graduate, students must complete 125 credits, including 70 credits in nursing, and maintain a minimum GPA of 2.0. The college also requires 27 liberal arts credits and 19 science credits.

Special: Students may cross-register with Essex County College and New Jersey Institute of Technology. The college offers a B.A.-B.S. degree. Juniors and seniors may take 1 course per term on a pass/fail basis. There is a freshman honors program on campus

Faculty/Classroom: The faculty is entirely female. The average class size in a regular course offering is 15.

Admissions: About 17% of the 1993–94 applicants were accepted. The SAT scores for the 1993–94 freshman class were as follows: Verbal—44% below 500, 52% between 500 and 599, and 4% between 600 and 700; Math—18% below 500, 52% between 500 and 599, 26% between 600 and 700, and 4% above 700. About 70% of the current freshmen were in the top fifth of their class; 100% were in the top two fifths. One freshman graduated first in his class.

Requirements: The SAT I or ACT is required. Applicants must be graduates of an accredited secondary school. The GED is accepted. Secondary school courses must include 4 years of English, 3 years of mathematics (algebra I and II and plane geometry), 1 year each of biology and chemistry, and 7 other approved academic subjects. AP and CLEP credits are accepted. Important factors used in the admissions decision are advanced placement or honor courses, evidence of special talent, leadership record, extracurricular activities record, and recommendations by school officials.

Procedure: Freshmen are admitted in the fall. Entrance exams should be taken no later than December of the senior year. Applications should be filed by January 15 for fall entry, along with an application fee of $40. Notification is sent on a rolling basis. There are early admissions and deferred admissions plans. A waiting list is an active part of the admissions procedure, with about 6% of applicants on the list.

Transfer: Eighty-seven transfer students enrolled in 1993–94. Applicants must have earned a minimum of 12 credits. Transfer students are admitted in the fall. Grades of C or better in courses that correspond in content and credit to those offered by the college transfer for credit. A total of 30 credits out of 125 must be completed at the College of Nursing.

Visiting: There are regularly scheduled orientations for prospective students, including an information session with admissions representatives and a tour of the campus. Visitors may sit in on classes. To arrange for a visit, contact the Office of University Undergraduate Admissions at (201) 648–5202.

Financial Aid: In 1993–94, 52% of all current freshmen and 50% of continuing students received some form of financial aid. About 47% of all students received need-based aid. The average freshman award was $5146. Of that total, scholarships or need-based grants averaged $3636 ($10,000 maximum); loans averaged $715 ($2625 maximum); and work contracts averaged $1230 ($1500 maximum). Nine percent of undergraduate students work part-time. Average earnings from campus work for the school year are $809. The average financial indebtedness of the 1992–93 graduate was $3140. The FAFSA financial statement is required. The deadline for financial aid applications is March 1.

International Students: There are currently 5 international students enrolled. They must score 600 on the TOEFL or take the college's own test, along with the SAT I or the ACT.

Computers: The college provides computer facilities for student use. The mainframes are a DEC VAX 8550 and a Sun Sparc 1000; individual departments also have a variety of minicomputers. All students on the Newark campus have accounts on one or the other of the local systems. Access to the local systems as well as to the New Brunswick central systems is provided to all students through networked micro/

terminal laboratories in major academic buildings on campus. There are no time limits. The fee is $100 per year.

Graduates: In 1992–93, 104 bachelor's degrees were awarded. Within an average freshman class, 42% graduate in 4 years, 52% in 5 years, and 54% in 6 years. Eighty companies recruited on campus in 1992–93. In the 1992 graduating class, 5% were enrolled in graduate school within 6 months of graduation; 98% had found employment.

Admissions Contact: John Scott, Director of Admissions—Newark.

RUTGERS UNIVERSITY
COLLEGE OF PHARMACY
New Brunswick, NJ 08903

D-3

(908) 932-3770

Full-time: 310 men, 556 women	Faculty: 52; I, +$
Part-time: 4 men, 5 women	Ph.D.s: 95%
Graduate: 9 men, 27 women	Student/Faculty: 17 to 1
Year: semesters, summer session	Tuition: $4800 ($8742)
Application Deadline: January 15	Room & Board: $4454

Freshman Class: 1591 applied, 552 accepted, 194 enrolled

SAT I Verbal/Math: 531/662 **HIGHLY COMPETITIVE**

Rutgers University/College of Pharmacy, founded in 1892, provides undergraduates with a 5-year pharmacy program. There are 11 undergraduate and 4 graduate schools. In addition to regional accreditation, the College of Pharmacy has baccalaureate program accreditation with ACPE. The 14 libraries contain 4,387,960 volumes, 2,630,211 microform items, and 63,879 audiovisual forms, and subscribe to 19,822 periodicals. Computerized library sources and services include the card catalog, interlibrary loans, and database searching. Special learning facilities include a learning resource center, an art gallery, radio and TV stations, a geology museum, a controlled drug delivery research center, and a pharmaceutical manufacturing laboratory. The 2686-acre campus is in a suburban area 33 miles south of New York City. There is 1 building on campus.

Student Life: About 87% of undergraduates are from New Jersey. Students come from 14 states, 10 foreign countries, and Canada. Forty-eight percent are white; 36% Asian American. The average age of freshmen is 18.2; all undergraduates, 20.8. Twelve percent drop out by the end of their first year; 81% remain to graduate.

Housing: A total of 536 students can be accommodated in college housing. College-sponsored living facilities include single-sex and coed dormitories and on-campus apartments. In addition, there are language and cultural houses, special interest houses, a special math/science house for women, and substance-free housing. On-campus housing is guaranteed for the first 2 years and is available on a lottery system for upperclassmen. Sixty-two percent of students live on campus. Alcohol is not permitted.

Activities: About 7% of men belong to 3 local and 29 national fraternities; about 3% of women belong to 4 local and 11 national sororities. There are 300 groups on campus, including art, band, cheerleading, chess, choir, chorale, chorus, computers, dance, drama, drill team, ethnic, film, gay, honors, international, jazz band, literary magazine, marching band, musical theater, newspaper, orchestra, pep band, political, professional, radio and TV, religious, social, social service, student government, symphony, and yearbook. Popular campus events include 2 career fairs in the fall and 1 open house in the spring, the Morton J. Rodman annual lecture is pharmacology, the David L. Cowen annual lecture—history of pharmacy, and the Roy A. Bowers annual pharmaceutical conference.

Sports: There are 15 intercollegiate sports each for men and women, and 24 intramural sports each for men and women. Athletic and recreation facilities include a 23,000-seat stadium, an athletic center, a gymnasium, a swimming pool, tennis courts, and a recreation center.

Disabled Students: Fifty-five percent of the campus is accessible to disabled students. The following facilities are available: wheelchair ramps, elevators, special parking, specially equipped rest rooms, special class scheduling, and lowered drinking fountains and telephones. Facilities vary widely from building to building; however, all classes will be scheduled in accessible locations for disabled students, and adaptations will be made to individual needs in dormitory rooms.

Services: In addition to many counseling and information services, tutoring is available in most subjects. The academic tutoring service provides specific assistance in first- and second-level difficult courses. There is remedial math, reading, and writing.

Campus Safety and Security: Campus safety and security measures include 24-hour foot and vehicle patrol, self-defense education, escort service, and shuttle buses. In addition, there are informal discussions, pamphlets, posters, and films, emergency telephones, and lighted pathways and sidewalks. The police department is supplemented by security guards and student safety officers.

Programs of Study: The College of Pharmacy awards the B.S. degree. Master's and doctoral degrees also are awarded. Bachelor's degrees are awarded in HEALTH PROFESSIONS (pharmacy).

Required: In order to graduate, students must complete 172 credit hours with a GPA of 2.0 overall and in professional courses. Students must complete 27 credits in humanities and social sciences. Required courses include microeconomics, physiology, biochemistry, general chemistry and biology, calculus, statistics, organic chemistry, physics, English composition, and professional pharmaceutical sciences. All must also complete an externship in pharmacy practice in community and hospitals.

Special: Internships include 4- or 8-week rotations in community and hospital pharmacies and in industrial research laboratories. This is the only college of pharmacy to provide industrial experience for all students. There is a freshman honors program on campus, as well as 3 national honor societies. One department has an honors program.

Faculty/Classroom: Sixty-four percent of faculty are male; 36%, female. The average class size in a regular course offering is 107.

Admissions: About 35% of the 1993–94 applicants were accepted. The SAT scores for the 1993–94 freshman class were as follows: Verbal—34% below 500, 47% between 500 and 599, and 19% between 600 and 700; Math—1% below 500, 16% between 500 and 599, 55% between 600 and 700, and 28% above 700. About 97% of the current freshmen were in the top fifth of their class; all were in the top two fifths. Four freshmen graduated first in their class. There was 1 National Achievement scholar.

Requirements: The SAT I or ACT is required. Applicants must have completed 16 high school academic credits or Carnegie units, including 4 years of English, 3 years of mathematics (algebra I and II and plane geometry), 2 years of a foreign language, 1 year each of biology and chemistry, and 5 other academic subjects. Physics is recommended. The GED is accepted. Students without a high school diploma, those from nonaccredited high schools, or those with academic unit entrance deficiencies must take SAT II: Subject tests in writing, mathematics, and a science. AP and CLEP credits are accepted. Important factors in the admissions decision are advanced placement or honor courses, evidence of special talent, leadership record, extracurricular activities record, and recommendations by school officials.

Procedure: Freshmen are admitted in the fall. Entrance exams should be taken no later than December of the senior year. Applications should be filed by January 15 for fall entry, along with an application fee of $40. Notification is sent by April 15. There are early admissions and deferred admissions plans. A waiting list is an active part of the admissions procedure, with about 11% of applicants on the list.

Transfer: Thirty-two transfer students enrolled in 1993–94. Applicants must have completed a minimum of 12 college credits. Grades of C or better in courses that correspond in content and credit to those offered by the college transfer for credit. Transfer students are admitted only in the fall. The last year of study must be completed at the College of Pharmacy.

Visiting: There are regularly scheduled orientations for prospective students, including an information session with an Admissions Officer followed by a bus tour with a student guide. Student-guided walking tours are also available. Visitors may sit in on classes. To arrange a visit, contact the Undergraduate Admissions Office at (908) 932–7881.

Financial Aid: In 1993–94, 63% of all current freshmen and 81% of continuing students received some form of financial aid. About 41% of freshmen and 51% of continuing students received need-based aid. The average freshman award was $4409. Of that total, scholarships or need-based grants averaged $3735 ($10,000 maximum); loans averaged $1377 ($7000 maximum); and work contracts averaged $1181 ($1500 maximum). Eleven percent of undergraduate students work part-time. Average earnings from campus work for the school year are $851. The average financial indebtedness of the 1992–93 graduate was $5407. The FAFSA financial statement is required. The deadline for financial aid applications is March 1.

International Students: There are currently 17 international students enrolled. They must score 550 on the TOEFL and must also take SAT I or the ACT.

Computers: The college provides computer facilities for student use. The mainframes are a DEC VAX 8650 cluster, an IBM 3081, a Sun Spare 670, and a Sun 4/110. Individual departments have a variety of minicomputers. Terminals on networked microcomputers are located on all campuses in the New Brunswick area. Computing services available to students include on-line class registration, E-mail, word processing, course-work assignments, and access to Internet and Bitnet. All students may access the system 24 hours a day. Students must observe limits on file space and execution length. The fee is $100 per year.

Graduates: In 1992–93, 130 bachelor's degrees were awarded. Within an average freshman class, 68% graduate in 5 years and 81% in 6 years. Some 500 companies recruited on campus in 1992–93. In the 1992 graduating class, 26% of all graduates were enrolled in graduate school within 6 months of graduation.

Admissions Contact: Dr. Elizabeth Mitchell, Assistant Vice President for University Undergraduate Admissions.

RUTGERS UNIVERSITY
COOK COLLEGE
New Brunswick, NJ 08903

D-3

(908) 932-3770

Full-time: 1391 men, 1183 women
Part-time: 158 men, 199 women
Graduate: none
Year: semesters, summer session
Application Deadline: January 15
Freshman Class: 7097 applied, 4006 accepted, 545 enrolled
SAT I Verbal/Math: 514/588

Faculty: 97; I, +$
Ph.D.s: 95%
Student/Faculty: 27 to 1
Tuition: $4743 ($8685)
Room & Board: $4454

HIGHLY COMPETITIVE

Rutgers University/Cook College, founded in 1864, is a coeducational residential college offering a program that emphasizes life, environmental, marine and coastal, and agricultural sciences. There are 11 undergraduate and 4 graduate schools. In addition to regional accreditation, Cook College has baccalaureate program accreditation with ADA, ASLA, and NCATE. The 14 libraries contain 4,387,960 volumes, 2,630,211 microform items, and 63,879 audiovisual forms, and subscribe to 19,822 periodicals. Computerized library sources and services include the card catalog, interlibrary loans, and database searching. Special learning facilities include a learning resource center, an art gallery, a radio station, a TV station, a geology museum, and various research centers and institutes. The 2686-acre campus is in a small town 33 miles south of New York City, New York. Including residence halls, there are 100 buildings on campus.

Student Life: About 91% of undergraduates are from New Jersey. Students come from 26 states, 15 foreign countries, and Canada. Seventy-seven percent are white; 10% Asian American. The average age of freshmen is 18.2; all undergraduates, 21.7. Seven percent drop out by the end of their first year; 75% remain to graduate.

Housing: A total of 1952 students can be accommodated in college housing. College-sponsored living facilities include single-sex and coed dormitories, on-campus apartments, special interest houses, and a substance-free house. In addition, there is a small modern residence hall where male students can reduce college expenses by helping with maintenance, ordering supplies, and preparing for meals; residents are selected on the basis of financial need. Housing is guaranteed for the first 2 years. On-campus housing is available on a lottery system for upperclassmen. Sixty-one percent of students live on campus. Upperclassmen may keep cars on campus.

Activities: About 7% of men belong to 3 local and 29 national fraternities; about 3% of women belong to 4 local and 11 national sororities. There are more than 300 groups on campus, including art, band, cheerleading, chess, choir, chorale, chorus, computers, dance, drama, drill team, ethnic, film, gay, honors, international, jazz band, literary magazine, marching band, musical theater, newspaper, orchestra, pep band, political, professional, radio and TV, religious, social, social service, student government, symphony, and yearbook. Popular campus events include Agricultural Field Day, Beach'n Boardwalk, trips to Broadway shows and cultural and sporting events, recently released films, comedy nights, cultural coffee houses, concerts, air band, Student Activities/Club Fair, and Curriculum Fest.

Sports: There are 15 intercollegiate sports each for men and women, and 24 intramural sports each for men and women. Athletic and recreation facilities include a 23,000-seat stadium, an athletic center, a gymnasium, a swimming pool, a recreation center, a weight room, and tennis and racquetball courts.

Disabled Students: Fifty-five percent of the campus is accessible to disabled students. The following facilities are available: wheelchair ramps, elevators, special parking, specially equipped rest rooms, special class scheduling, lowered drinking fountains, and lowered telephones.

Services: In addition to many counseling and information services, tutoring is available in most subjects, including first- and second-level difficult courses. In addition, there is a reader service for the blind, and remedial math, reading, and writing.

Campus Safety and Security: Campus safety and security measures include 24-hour foot and vehicle patrol, self-defense education, escort service, and shuttle buses. In addition, there are informal discussions, pamphlets, posters, and films, emergency telephones, lighted pathways and sidewalks. The police department is supplemented by security guards and student safety officers.

Programs of Study: Cook College awards the B.A. and B.S. degrees. Bachelor's degrees are awarded in AGRICULTURE (agriculture, animal science, fishing and fisheries, horticulture, natural resource management, plant science, and wildlife management), BIOLOGICAL SCIENCE (biochemistry, biology/biological science, biotechnology, botany, cell biology, ecology, entomology, evolutionary biology, genetics, microbiology, molecular biology, nutrition, and physiology), BUSINESS (business economics), COMMUNICATIONS AND THE ARTS (communications and journalism), COMPUTER AND PHYSICAL SCIENCE (atmospheric sciences and meteorology, chemistry, computer science, earth science, geology, and oceanography), EDUCATION (vocational and physical), ENGINEERING AND ENVI-

RONMENTAL DESIGN (environmental design, environmental science, and landscape architecture/design), HEALTH PROFESSIONS (biomedical science, predentistry, premedicine, preveterinary science, and public health), SOCIAL SCIENCE (food science, geography, human ecology, international studies, and physical fitness/movement). Environmental science, nutritional sciences, and environmental planning design have the largest enrollments.

Required: In order to graduate, students must complete 128 credit hours (163 credits for the 5-year bioresource engineering program), with a minimum GPA of 2.0. In addition to achieving competency in one of the programs of study offered at Cook College, all students are required to complete course work in introductory life and physical sciences, interdisciplinary/ethical analysis, the arts, human diversity, economic and political systems, oral and written communication, and experience-based education. Competence in a field includes course work in quantitative skills, computer use, and professional ethics.

Special: Cook College offers an extensive cooperative education program, independent study programs, B.A.-B.S. degrees, and a 2-3 engineering degree. Seniors may elect to take one course each semester on a pass/fail basis. Study abroad is offered in 9 countries. A wide variety of professionally oriented majors in the life, environmental, marine, coastal, and agricultural sciences is offered. There is a freshman honors program on campus, as well as 8 national honor societies.

Faculty/Classroom: Seventy-nine percent of faculty are male; 21%, female. Graduate students teach 2% of introductory courses. The average class size in a regular course offering is 38.

Admissions: About 56% of the 1993–94 applicants were accepted. The SAT scores for the 1993–94 freshman class were as follows: Verbal—42% below 500, 47% between 500 and 599, 10% between 600 and 700, and 1% above 700; Math—11% below 500, 44% between 500 and 599, 37% between 600 and 700, and 8% above 700. About 69% of the current freshmen were in the top fifth of their class; 99% were in the top two fifths. There were 4 National Merit finalists. Four freshmen graduated first in their class.

Requirements: The SAT I or ACT is required. Applicants must have completed 16 high school academic credits or Carnegie units, including 4 years of English, 3 years of mathematics (algebra I and II and geometry), and 9 other approved academic subjects. The GED is accepted. Students without a high school diploma, those from a nonaccredited high school, or those with academic unit entrance deficiencies must take SAT II: Subject tests in writing, mathematics, and one other subject. AP and CLEP credits are accepted. Important factors used in the admissions decision are advanced placement or honor courses, evidence of special talent, leadership record, extracurricular activities record, and recommendations by school officials.

Procedure: Freshmen are admitted in the fall. Entrance exams should be taken no later than December of the senior year. Applications should be filed by January 15 for fall entry, along with an application fee of $40. Notification is sent by April 15. There are early admissions and deferred admissions plans. A waiting list is an active part of the admissions procedure, with about 7% of applicants on the list.

Transfer: About 175 transfer students enrolled in 1993–94. Applicants must have completed a minimum of 12 college credits. Grades of C or better in courses that correspond in content and credit to those offered by the college transfer for credit. Transfer students are admitted in both the fall and spring semesters. A total of 40 credits out of 128 must be completed at Cook College.

Visiting: There are regularly scheduled orientations for prospective students, including an information session with an admissions officer and a bus tour with a student guide. Walking tours are also available. There are guides for informal visits and visitors may sit in on classes. To arrange for a visit, contact the Office of University Undergraduate Admissions at (908) 932-7881.

Financial Aid: In 1993–94, 67% of all current freshmen and 51% of continuing students received some form of financial aid. About 50% of freshmen and 37% of continuing students received need-based aid. The average freshman award was $5047. Of that total, scholarships or need-based grants averaged $3459 ($10,000 maximum); loans averaged $1394 ($8900 maximum); and work contracts averaged $1228 ($1500 maximum). Nine percent of undergraduate students work part-time. Average earnings from campus work for the school year are $837. The average financial indebtedness of the 1992–93 graduate was $4932. The FAFSA financial statement is required. The priority deadline for financial aid applications is March 1.

International Students: There are currently 20 international students enrolled. They must take the TOEFL and achieve a minimum score of 550. The student must also take the SAT I or the ACT.

Computers: The college provides computer facilities for student use. Central computer systems include a DEC VAX 8650 cluster, an IBM 3081, a Sun Sparc 670, and a Sun 4/110. Individual departments have a variety of minicomputers. Terminals on networked microcomputers are located on all campuses in the New Brunswick area. Computing services available to students include on-line registration, E-mail, word processing, course-work assignments, and access to Inter-

net and Bitnet. All students may access the system. It may be used 24 hours a day. Students must observe limits on file space and execution length. The fee is $100 per year.

Graduates: In 1992–93, 582 bachelor's degrees were awarded. The most popular majors among graduates were environmental science (18%), environmental and business economics (13%), and biological sciences (13%). Within an average freshman class, 42% graduate in 4 years, 69% in 5 years, and 75% in 6 years. Some 500 companies recruited on campus in 1992–93. In the 1992 graduating class, 38% of all students were enrolled in graduate school within 6 months of graduation.

Admissions Contact: Dr. Elizabeth Mitchell, Assistant Vice President for University Undergraduate Admissions.

RUTGERS UNIVERSITY
DOUGLASS COLLEGE
D-3

New Brunswick, NJ 08903   (908) 932–3770

Full-time: 2830 women	Faculty: 761; I, +$
Part-time: 160 women	Ph.D.s: 95%
Graduate: none	Student/Faculty: 4 to 1
Year: semesters, summer session	Tuition: $4341 ($7896)
Application Deadline: January 15	Room & Board: $4454

Freshman Class: 5887 applied, 3983 accepted, 659 enrolled
SAT I Verbal/Math: 497/550   **VERY COMPETITIVE**

Douglass College, founded in 1918, is a women's liberal arts institution. There are 11 undergraduate and 4 graduate schools. In addition to regional accreditation, Douglass College has baccalaureate program accreditation with AACSB, CAHEA, NASM, and NCATE. The 14 libraries contain 4,387,960 volumes, 2,630,211 microform items, and 63,879 audiovisual forms, and subscribe to 19,822 periodicals. Computerized library sources and services include the card catalog, interlibrary loans, and database searching. Special learning facilities include a learning resource center, an art gallery, a radio station, a TV station, a geology museum, and various research institutes and centers. The 2686-acre campus is in a suburban area 33 miles south of New York City, New York. Including residence halls, there are 100 buildings on campus.

Student Life: About 93% of undergraduates are from New Jersey. Students come from 23 states and 19 foreign countries. Sixty-seven percent are white; 13% Asian American; 10% African American. The average age of freshmen is 18.2; all undergraduates, 20.8. Nine percent drop out by the end of their first year; 80% remain to graduate.

Housing: A total of 2074 students can be accommodated in college housing. College-sponsored living facilities include dormitories and on-campus apartments. In addition, there are language houses, special interest houses, a substance-free house, and 7 cultural houses. On-campus housing is guaranteed for all 4 years. Sixty-four percent of students live on campus. Alcohol is not permitted. Upperclassmen may keep cars on campus.

Activities: About 3% of women belong to 4 local and 11 national sororities. There are no fraternities on campus. There are more than 300 groups on campus, including art, band, cheerleading, chess, choir, chorale, chorus, computers, dance, drama, drill team, ethnic, film, gay, honors, international, jazz band, literary magazine, marching band, musical theater, newspaper, orchestra, pep band, political, professional, radio and TV, religious, social, social service, student government, symphony, and yearbook. Popular campus events include International Weekend, Yule Log Ceremony, New Jersey Folk Festival, New Jersey Women of Achievement Awards, the annual Women's Conference, Spring Colloquium, L'Hommedien Lecture Series, and Spring Honors Assembly.

Sports: Athletic and recreation facilities include a 23,000-seat stadium, an athletic center, a gymnasium, a swimming pool, tennis courts, and a recreation center.

Disabled Students: Fifty-five percent of the campus is accessible to disabled students. The following facilities are available: wheelchair ramps, elevators, special parking, specially equipped rest rooms, special class scheduling, lowered drinking fountains, and lowered telephones.

Services: In addition to many counseling and information services, tutoring is available in most subjects, including first and second-level difficult courses. There is also remedial math, reading, and writing.

Campus Safety and Security: Campus safety and security measures include 24-hour foot and vehicle patrol, self-defense education, escort service, and shuttle buses. In addition, there are informal discussions, pamphlets, posters, films, emergency telephones, and lighted pathways and sidewalks. The police department is supplemented by security guards and student safety officers.

Programs of Study: Douglass College awards the B.A. and B.S. degrees. Bachelor's degrees are awarded in BIOLOGICAL SCIENCE (biochemistry, biology/biological science, biometrics and biostatistics, biotechnology, botany, cell biology, ecology, evolutionary biology, genetics, microbiology, neurosciences, nutrition, and physiology),

BUSINESS (accounting, banking and finance, business administration and management, labor studies, management science, and marketing/retailing/merchandising), COMMUNICATIONS AND THE ARTS (art history and appreciation, Chinese, classics, communications, comparative literature, dance, dramatic arts, English, fine arts, French, German, Greek, Italian, journalism, Latin, linguistics, music, Portuguese, Russian, Spanish, and visual and performing arts), COMPUTER AND PHYSICAL SCIENCE (atmospheric sciences and meteorology, chemistry, computer science, geology, mathematics, physics, and statistics), EDUCATION (physical), HEALTH PROFESSIONS (biomedical science, medical laboratory technology, predentistry, premedicine, and public health), SOCIAL SCIENCE (African American studies, American studies, anthropology, East Asian studies, Eastern European studies, economics, food science, geography, Hispanic American studies, history, Judaic studies, Latin American studies, Middle Eastern studies, philosophy, physical fitness/movement, political science/government, prelaw, psychology, religion, sociology, urban studies, and women's studies). Psychology, English, and communications have the largest enrollments.

Required: In order to graduate, students must complete 120 credits, with a minimum GPA of 1.95. Nine credits are required in each of 3 areas: mathematics and science, history and social science, and humanities. In addition, students must take 3 credits each in women's experience, cross-cultural perspectives, and English composition.

Special: Douglass offers an alumnae-sponsored externship program, a Washington semester, B.A.-B.S. degrees in liberal arts and engineering, dual majors, student-designed majors, 2–3 degrees with the College of Engineering, and pass/fail options. Students may study abroad in 9 countries. There is also a certificate program in international studies. There is a freshman honors program on campus, as well as one national honor society, Phi Beta Kappa. Nearly all departments have honors programs.

Faculty/Classroom: Seventy-four percent of faculty are male; 26%, female. The average class size in a regular course offering is 45.

Admissions: About 68% of the 1993–94 applicants were accepted. The SAT scores for the 1993–94 freshman class were as follows: Verbal—51% below 500, 37% between 500 and 599, 11% between 600 and 700, and 1% above 700; Math—24% below 500, 53% between 500 and 599, 21% between 600 and 700, and 2% above 700. About 53% of the current freshmen were in the top fifth of their class; 97% were in the top two fifths. Three freshmen graduated first in their class.

Requirements: The SAT I or ACT is required. Applicants must have completed 16 high school academic credits or Carnegie units, including 4 years of English, 3 years of mathematics (algebra I and II and geometry), 2 years each of science and foreign language, and 5 other academic subjects. Students without a high school diploma, those from a nonaccredited high school, or those with academic deficiencies must take SAT II: Subject tests in writing, mathematics, and one other subject. AP credits are accepted. Important factors used in the admissions decision are advanced placement or honor courses, evidence of special talent, leadership record, extracurricular activities record, and recommendations by school officials.

Procedure: Freshmen are admitted in the fall. Entrance exams should be taken no later than December of the senior year. Applications should be filed by January 15 for fall entry, along with an application fee of $40. Notification is sent on a rolling basis, with notifications completed by April 15. There are early admissions and deferred admissions plans. A waiting list is an active part of the admissions procedure, with about 5% of applicants on the list.

Transfer: About 170 transfer students enrolled in 1993–94. Applicants must have a minimum of 12 college credits. Grades of C or better in courses that correspond in content and credit to those offered at the college transfer for credit. Transfer students are admitted in both the fall and spring semesters. A total of 30 credits out of 120 must be completed at Douglass College.

Visiting: There are regularly scheduled orientations for prospective students, including an information session with an admissions officer followed by a bus tour with a student guide. Student-guided walking tours are also available and include a meeting with the dean prior to the tour. Visitors may sit in on classes. To arrange for a visit, contact the Office of University Undergraduate Admissions at (908) 932–7881.

Financial Aid: In 1993–94, 68% of all current freshmen and 56% of continuing students received some form of financial aid. About 51% of freshmen and 40% of continuing students received need-based aid. The average freshman award was $4893. Of that total, scholarships or need-based grants averaged $3513 ($10,000 maximum); loans averaged $1223 ($8833 maximum); and work contracts averaged $1195 ($1500 maximum). Seventeen percent of undergraduate students work part-time. Average earnings from campus work for the school year are $896. The average financial indebtedness of the 1992–93 graduate was $4109. Douglass College is a member of CSS. The FAFSA financial statement is required. The deadline for financial aid applications is March 1.

International Students: There are currently 39 international students enrolled. They must take the TOEFL and achieve a minimum score of 550. The student must also take the SAT I or the ACT.

Computers: The college provides computer facilities for student use. Central computer systems include a DEC VAX 8650 cluster, an IBM 3081, a Sun Sparc 670, and a Sun 4/110. Individual departments have a variety of minicomputers. Terminals on networked microcomputers are located on all campuses in the New Brunswick area. Computing services available to students include on-line class registration, E-mail, word processing, course-work assignments and access to Internet and Bitnet. All students may access the system. It may be used 24 hours a day. Students must observe limits on file space and execution length. The fee is $100 per year.

Graduates: In 1992–93, 805 bachelor's degrees were awarded. The most popular majors among graduates were psychology (18%), English (12%), and communications (9%). Within an average freshman class, 64% graduate in 4 years, 78% in 5 years, and 80% in 6 years. Some 500 companies recruited on campus in 1992–93.

Admissions Contact: Dr. Elizabeth Mitchell, Assistant Vice President for University Undergraduate Admissions.

RUTGERS UNIVERSITY
LIVINGSTON COLLEGE

New Brunswick, NJ 08903   D-3

                                           (908) 932–3770

Full-time: 2073 men, 1360 women	Faculty: 761; I, +$
Part-time: 147 men, 106 women	Ph.D.s: 90%
Graduate: none	Student/Faculty: 5 to 1
Year: semesters, summer session	Tuition: $4423 ($7978)
Application Deadline: January 15	Room & Board: $4454
Freshman Class: 11,996 applied, 7212 accepted, 661 enrolled	
SAT I Verbal/Math: 487/556	**VERY COMPETITIVE**

Livingston College, founded in 1969, is a coeducational, liberal arts, residential college. There are 11 undergraduate and 4 graduate schools. In addition to regional accreditation, Livingston College has baccalaureate program accreditation with AACSB, CAHEA, CSWE, NASM, and NCATE. The 14 libraries contain 4,387,960 volumes, 2,630,211 microform items, and 63,879 audiovisual forms, and subscribe to 19,822 periodicals. Computerized library sources and services include the card catalog, interlibrary loans, and database searching. Special learning facilities include a learning resource center, art gallery, radio station, TV station, geology museum, and various research institutes and centers. The 2686-acre campus is in a suburban area 33 miles south of New York City. Including residence halls, there are 35 buildings on campus.

Student Life: About 89% of undergraduates are from New Jersey. Students come from 26 states, 34 foreign countries, and Canada. Sixty-two percent are white; 14% African American; 12% Asian American. The average age of freshmen is 18.2; all undergraduates, 21. Thirteen percent drop out by the end of their first year; 69% remain to graduate.

Housing: A total of 1735 students can be accommodated in college housing. College-sponsored living facilities include coed dormitories and on-campus apartments. In addition there are special interest houses and substance-free housing. Housing is guaranteed for the first 2 years and is available on a lottery system thereafter. All students may keep cars on campus.

Activities: About 7% of men belong to 3 local and 29 national fraternities; about 3% of women belong to 4 local and 11 national sororities. The more than 300 groups on campus include art, band, cheerleading, chess, choir, chorale, chorus, computers, dance, drama, drill team, ethnic, film, gay, honors, international, jazz band, literary magazine, marching band, musical theater, newspaper, orchestra, pep band, political, professional, radio and TV, religious, social, social service, student government, symphony, and yearbook. Popular campus events include major concerts, comedy shows, fashion shows, poetry readings, coffee houses, global cultural programs, Halloween, Homecoming, Parents Weekend, casino nights, Springfest, MTV showcase, Comic Relief, ski trips, museum trips, and Manhattan trips.

Sports: There are 15 intercollegiate sports each for men and women, and 24 intramural sports for both. Athletic and recreation facilities include a 23,000-seat stadium, an athletic center, a gymnasium, a swimming pool, tennis courts, and a recreation center.

Disabled Students: Fifty-five percent of the campus is accessible to disabled students. The following facilities are available: wheelchair ramps, elevators, special parking, specially equipped rest rooms, special class scheduling, and lowered drinking fountains and telephone. Facilities vary widely from building to building, but all classes will be scheduled in accessible locations for disabled students, and adaptations will be made to individual needs in dormitory rooms.

Services: In addition to many counseling and information services, tutoring is available in most subjects. The academic tutoring service provides specific course assistance in first- and second-level difficult courses. There is also a reader service for the blind and remedial math, reading, and writing.

Campus Safety and Security: Campus safety and security measures include 24-hour foot and vehicle patrol, self-defense education, escort service, and shuttle buses. In addition, there are informal discussions, pamphlets, posters, films, emergency telephones, and lighted pathways and sidewalks. The police department is supplemented by security guards and student safety officers.

Programs of Study: Livingston College awards the B.A. and B.S. degrees. Bachelor's degrees are awarded in BIOLOGICAL SCIENCE (biochemistry, biology/biological science, biometrics and biostatistics, botany, cell biology, ecology, genetics, microbiology, nutrition, and physiology), BUSINESS (accounting, banking and finance, business administration and management, labor studies, management science, and marketing/retailing/merchandising), COMMUNICATIONS AND THE ARTS (art history and appreciation, Chinese, classical languages, classics, communications, comparative literature, dance, dramatic arts, English, French, German, Greek, Italian, journalism, Latin, linguistics, music, Portuguese, Russian, Spanish, and visual and performing arts), COMPUTER AND PHYSICAL SCIENCE (chemistry, computer science, geology, mathematics, physics, and statistics), HEALTH PROFESSIONS (biomedical science, medical laboratory technology, physician's assistant, predentistry, premedicine, and public health), SOCIAL SCIENCE (African American studies, American studies, anthropology, Asian/Oriental studies, criminal justice, East Asian studies, Eastern European studies, economics, geography, Hispanic American studies, history, humanities, Judaic studies, Latin American studies, Middle Eastern studies, philosophy, physical fitness/movement, political science/government, prelaw, psychology, religion, social work, sociology, urban studies, and women's studies). Psychology, economics, and political science have the largest enrollments.

Required: In order to graduate, students must complete 120 credit hours, with a minimum GPA of 1.93. Distribution requirements include 2 courses each in cultural perspectives, contemporary issues, and arts and humanities, and 1 course each in social science, natural sciences, and analytical/quantitative skills. All students must take at least 2 semesters of English composition and must show proficiency through intermediate algebra. All students must accumulate at least 30 credits at the 300/400 level.

Special: Internships, a Washington semester, accelerated degree programs, B.A.-B.S. degrees, student-designed majors, a 2–3 engineering degree, and nondegree study are available. Credit for life, military, and work experience (including summer work) is available. There are pass/fail options under certain circumstances. Students may study abroad in 9 countries. Dual degrees are offered in statistics/mathematics and math/physics/political science. There is a freshman honors program on campus and 2 national honor societies including Phi Beta Kappa. Nearly all departments have honors programs.

Faculty/Classroom: Seventy-four percent of faculty are male; 26%, female. The average class size in a regular course offering is 45.

Admissions: About 60% of the 1993–94 applicants were accepted. The SAT scores for the 1993–94 freshman class were as follows: Verbal—56% below 500, 38% between 500 and 599, 5% between 600 and 700, and 1% above 700; Math—22% below 500, 49% between 500 and 599, 26% between 600 and 700, and 3% above 700. About 42% of the current freshmen were in the top fifth of their class; 95% were in the top two fifths. Three freshmen graduated first in their class.

Requirements: The SAT I or ACT is required. Students should have completed 16 high school academic credits or Carnegie units, including 4 years of English, 3 years of mathematics (algebra I and II and geometry), 2 years each of a foreign language and a science, and 5 other approved academic subjects. The GED is accepted. Students without a high school diploma, those from a nonaccredited high school, or those with academic unit deficiencies must take SAT II: Subject tests in writing, mathematics, and one other subject. AP and CLEP credits are accepted. Important factors used in the admissions decision are advanced placement or honor courses, evidence of special talent, leadership record, extracurricular activities record, and recommendations by school officials.

Procedure: Freshmen are admitted in the fall. Entrance exams should be taken no later than December of the senior year. Applications should be filed by January 15 for fall entry, along with an application fee of $40. Notification is sent by April 15. There are early admissions and deferred admissions plans. A waiting list is an active part of the admissions procedure, with about 6% of all applicants on the list.

Transfer: About 370 transfer students enrolled in 1993–94. Students with a minimum of 12 credit hours at another institution are considered for transfer. Grades of C or better in courses that correspond in content and credit to those offered by the college transfer for credit. Transfer students are usually admitted in both the fall and spring semesters. A total of 30 credits out of 120 must be completed at Livingston College.

Visiting: There are regularly scheduled orientations for prospective students, including an information session with an admissions officer followed by a bus tour with a student guide. Student-guided walking tours are also available. Visitors may sit in on classes, with prior arrangements. To schedule a visit, contact the Office of University Undergraduate Admissions at (908) 932-7881.

Financial Aid: In 1993-94, 63% of all current freshmen and 50% of continuing students received some form of financial aid. About 55% of freshmen and 42% of continuing students received need-based aid. The average freshman award was $6225. Of that total, scholarships or need-based grants averaged $4937 ($10,000 maximum); loans averaged $975 ($8000 maximum); and work contracts averaged $1207 ($1500 maximum). Seventeen percent of undergraduate students work part-time. Average earnings from campus work for the school year are $919. The average financial indebtedness of the 1992-93 graduate was $6903. The FAFSA financial statement is required. The deadline for applications is March 1.

International Students: There are currently 81 international students enrolled. They must take the TOEFL and achieve a minimum score of 550. The student must also take the SAT I or the ACT.

Computers: The college provides computer facilities for student use. The mainframe is a central system which includes a DEC VAX 8650 cluster, an IBM 3081, a Sun Sparc 670, and a Sun 4/110. Individual departments have a variety of minicomputers. Terminals on networked microcomputers are located on all campuses in the New Brunswick area. Computing services available to students include on-line class registration, E-mail, word processing, course-work assignments, and access to Internet and Bitnet. All students may access the system 24 hours a day but must observe limits on file space and execution length. The fees are $100 per year.

Graduates: In 1992-93, 850 bachelor's degrees were awarded. The most popular majors among graduates were psychology (12%), economics (11%), and English (9%). Within an average freshman class, 40% graduate in 4 years, 64% in 5 years, and 69% in 6 years. Some 500 companies recruited on campus in 1992-93. Of the 1992 graduating class, 34% had plans for graduate school within 6 months of graduation.

Admissions Contact: Dr. Elizabeth Mitchell, Assistant Vice President for University Undergraduate Admissions.

RUTGERS UNIVERSITY
MASON GROSS SCHOOL OF THE ARTS
New Brunswick, NJ 08903

D-3

(908) 932-3770

Full-time: 184 men, 214 women	**Faculty:** 78; I, +$
Part-time: 5 men, 7 women	**Ph.D.s:** 95%
Graduate: 104 men, 120 women	**Student/Faculty:** 5 to 1
Year: semesters, summer session	**Tuition:** $4423 ($7978)
	Room & Board: $4454

Freshman Class: 1087 applied, 270 accepted, 119 enrolled
SAT I Verbal/Math: 496/530

SPECIAL

The Mason Gross School of the Arts, founded in 1976, offers programs to students of special talent and ability who wish to pursue careers in theater arts, visual arts, dance, and music. There are 11 undergraduate and 4 graduate schools. In addition to regional accreditation, Mason Gross School of the Arts has baccalaureate program accreditation with NASAD, NASM, and NCATE. The 14 libraries contain 4,387,960 volumes, 2,630,211 microform items, and 63,879 audiovisual forms, and subscribe to 19,822 periodicals. Computerized library sources and services include the card catalog, interlibrary loans, and database searching. Special learning facilities include a learning resource center, art gallery, radio station, TV station, and geology museum; dance, music, and art studios; concert and recital halls; and black-box and proscenium theaters. The 2686-acre campus is in a small town 33 miles south of New York City. Including residence halls, there are 8 buildings on campus.

Student Life: About 85% of undergraduates are from New Jersey. Students come from 17 states, 9 foreign countries, and Canada. Seventy-six percent are white. The average age of freshmen is 18.2; all undergraduates, 20.7. Twenty-four percent drop out by the end of their first year; 58% remain to graduate.

Housing: A total of 202 students can be accommodated in college housing. College-sponsored living facilities include single-sex and coed dormitories and on-campus apartments. In addition there are cultural and language houses, special interest houses, and substance-free housing. On-campus housing is available on a lottery system for upperclassmen. Fifty percent of all students live on campus.

Activities: About 7% of men belong to 3 local and 29 national fraternities; about 3% of women belong to 4 local and 11 national sororities. There are 300 groups on campus, including art, band, cheerleading, chess, choir, chorale, chorus, computers, dance, drama, drill team, ethnic, film, gay, honors, international, jazz band, literary magazine, marching band, musical theater, newspaper, orchestra, pep band, political, professional, radio and TV, religious, social, social ser-

vice, student government, symphony, and yearbook. Popular campus events include a theater subscription series, concerts, opera, dance faculty concerts, BFA and MFA visual arts thesis shows, and Summer Fest.

Sports: Two percent of all students participate in 15 intercollegiate sports for men and 15 for women. There are also 24 intramural sports for men and 24 for women. Athletic and recreation facilities include a 23,000-seat stadium, an athletic center, a gymnasium, a swimming pool, tennis courts, and a recreation center.

Disabled Students: Fifty-five percent of the campus is accessible to disabled students. The following facilities are available: wheelchair ramps, elevators, special parking, specially equipped rest rooms, special class scheduling, and lowered drinking fountains and telephones. Facilities vary widely from building to building, but all classes will be scheduled in accessible locations for students with disabilities, and adaptations will be made to individual needs in dormitory rooms.

Services: In addition to many counseling and information services, tutoring is available in most subjects. The academic tutoring service provides specific course assistance in first- and second-level difficult courses. There is also a reader service for the blind and remedial math, reading, and writing.

Campus Safety and Security: Campus safety and security measures include 24-hour foot and vehicle patrol, self defense education, escort service, and shuttle buses. In addition, there are informal discussions, pamphlets, posters, and films, emergency telephones, and lighted pathways and sidewalks. The police department is supplemented by security guards and student safety officers.

Programs of Study: Mason Gross School of the Arts awards the B.F.A and B.Mus. degrees. Master's and doctoral degrees also are awarded. Bachelor's degrees are awarded in COMMUNICATIONS AND THE ARTS (dance, dramatic arts, music, and visual and performing arts), EDUCATION (music). Music, theater arts, and visual arts have the largest enrollments.

Required: In order to graduate, students must complete 120 to 129 credits with a cumulative GPA of 2.0. The college requires 36 credits of liberal arts courses, in addition to the requirements of the major. All students must take expository writing.

Special: Mason Gross is a creative and performing arts school; three fourths of the courses are performance, studio, or critical studies classes within the chosen discipline. The college offers study abroad in 9 countries.

Faculty/Classroom: Sixty-nine percent of faculty are male; 31%, female. Graduate students teach 16% of introductory courses. The average class size in a regular course offering is 26.

Admissions: About 25% of the 1993-94 applicants were accepted. The SAT scores for the 1993-94 freshman class were as follows: Verbal—52% below 500, 39% between 500 and 599, and 9% between 600 and 700; Math—35% below 500, 44% between 500 and 599, 18% between 600 and 700, and 3% above 700. About 33% of the current freshmen were in the top fifth of their class; 61% were in the top two fifths.

Requirements: The SAT or ACT is required. Applicants should have completed 16 high school academic credits or Carnegie units, including 4 years of English, 3 years of mathematics (algebra I and II, and geometry), and 9 other approved academic subjects. The GED is accepted. Students without a high school diploma, those from nonaccredited high schools, or those with academic unit entrance deficiencies must take SAT II: subject tests in writing, mathematics, and one other subject. Two years of a foreign language are recommended. All students must audition or present a portfolio for admission. AP credits are accepted. Important factors used in the admissions decision are evidence of special talent, advanced placement or honor courses, leadership record, extracurricular activities record, and recommendations by school officials.

Procedure: Freshmen are admitted in the fall. Entrance exams should be taken no later than December of the senior year. Application deadlines are January 15 for visual arts and March 15 for theater, dance, and music. The fee is $40. Notification is sent by April 15. There are early admissions and deferred admissions plans. A waiting list is an active part of the admissions procedure, with about 9% of applicants on the list.

Transfer: About 27 transfer students enrolled in 1993-94. Applicants should have earned a minimum of 12 credit hours at another college. A portfolio and/or audition is required for admission. Grades of C or better in courses that correspond in content and credit to those offered by the college transfer for credit. Transfer students are usually admitted in the fall, but applicants may contact the Admissions Office in early October to see if spring admission is available. A total of 30 credits out of 120 must be completed at Mason Gross School of the Arts.

Visiting: There are regularly scheduled orientations for prospective students, including an information session with an admissions officer followed by a bus tour with a student guide. Walking tours are also available. Visitors may sit in on classes. To arrange for a visit, contact

the Office of University Undergraduate Admissions at (908) 932-7881.

Financial Aid: In 1993–94, 61% of all current freshmen and 58% of continuing students received some form of financial aid. About 48% of freshmen and 46% of continuing students received need-based aid. The average freshman award was $3631. Of that total, scholarships or need-based grants averaged $2812 ($10,000 maximum); loans averaged $1529 ($5000 maximum); and work contracts averaged $1227 ($1500 maximum). Thirteen percent of undergraduate students work part-time. Average earnings from campus work for the school year are $968. The average financial indebtedness of the 1992–93 graduate was $6747. The FAFSA financial statement is required. The deadline for financial aid applications is March 1.

International Students: There are currently 10 international students enrolled. They must take the TOEFL with a minimum score of 550.

Computers: The college provides computer facilities for student use. The mainframe is a central system which includes a DEC VAX 8650 cluster, an IBM 3081, a Sun Sparc 670, and a Sun 4/110. Individual departments have a variety of minicompuers. Terminals on networked microcomputers are located on all campuses in the New Brunswick area. Computing services available to students incuding on-line class registration, E-mail, word processing, course-work assignments, and access to Internet and Bitnet. All students may access the system 24 hours a day, but must observe limits on file space and execution length. The fees are $100 per year.

Graduates: In 1992–93, 85 bachelor's degrees were awarded. The most popular majors among graduates were visual arts (49%), music (22%), and dance (15%). Within an average freshman class, 41% graduate in 4 years, 55% in 5 years, and 58% in 6 years. Of all graduating seniors, 22% has plans for graduate school. Some 500 companies recruited on campus in 1992–93.

Admissions Contact: Dr. Elizabeth Mitchell, Assistant Vice President for University Undergraduate Admissions.

RUTGERS UNIVERSITY
NEWARK COLLEGE OF ARTS AND SCIENCES E-2
Newark, NJ 07102   (201) 648-5205

Full-time: 1484 men, 1638 women	**Faculty:** 184; IIA, + +$
Part-time: 276 men, 245 women	**Ph.D.s:** 95%
Graduate: none	**Student/Faculty:** 17 to 1
Year: semesters, summer session	**Tuition:** $4191 ($7746)
Application Deadline: May 1	**Room & Board:** $4454
Freshman Class: 4852 applied, 2528 accepted, 456 enrolled	
SAT I Verbal/Math: 455/529	**COMPETITIVE**

Newark College of Arts and Science, a coeducational liberal arts institution, became part of Rutgers in 1946. There are 3 undergraduate and 4 graduate schools. In addition to regional accreditation, Newark College of Arts and Sciences has baccalaureate program accreditation with AACSB, CAHEA, CSWE, and NASM. The 4 libraries contain 591,536 volumes, 675,962 microform items, and 24,497 audiovisual forms, and subscribe to 3748 periodicals. Computerized library sources and services include the card catalog, interlibrary loans, and database searching. Special learning facilities include a learning resource center, an art gallery, a TV and radio media center, a molecular and behavioral neuroscience center, and institutes of jazz studies and animal behavior. The 33-acre campus is in an urban area 7 miles west of New York City, New York, in downtown Newark. Including residence halls, there are 31 buildings on campus.

Student Life: About 95% of undergraduates are from New Jersey. Students come from 10 states. Thirty-nine percent are white; 18% African American; 16% Hispanic; 14% Asian American. The average age of freshmen is 18.5; all undergraduates, 22.3. Seventeen percent drop out by the end of their first year; 56% remain to graduate.

Housing: A total of 692 students can be accommodated in college housing. College-sponsored living facilities include coed dormitories, on-campus apartments, and married-student housing. On-campus housing is available on a first-come, first-served basis. All students may keep cars on campus.

Activities: There are 1 local and 4 national fraternities and 3 local and 4 national sororities. There are 85 groups on campus, including art, band, cheerleading, chess, choir, chorale, chorus, computers, drama, ethnic, gay, honors, international, jazz band, literary magazine, musical theater, newspaper, orchestra, photography, political, professional, radio and TV, religious, social, social service, student government, and yearbook. Popular campus events include Campus Fair, Thanksgiving for International Students, Student Talent Show, World Week, Multicultural Olympics, Black History Month, Puerto Rican Heritage Month, Pub Night, and Greek Week.

Sports: There are 5 intercollegiate sports for men and 4 for women, and 13 intramural sports each for men and women. Athletic and recreation facilities include an athletic center, a tennis complex, a swim-

ming pool, soccer, softball, and baseball fields, racquetball courts, and a dance room.

Disabled Students: Eighty percent of the campus is accessible to disabled students. The following facilities are available: wheelchair ramps, elevators, special parking, specially equipped rest rooms, special class scheduling, lowered drinking fountains, and lowered telephones.

Services: In addition to many counseling and information services, tutoring is available in most subjects. In addition, there is a reader service for the blind, and remedial math, reading, and writing.

Campus Safety and Security: Campus safety and security measures include 24-hour foot and vehicle patrol, self-defense education, escort service, and shuttle buses. In addition, there are informal discussions, pamphlets, posters, films, emergency telephones, and lighted pathways and sidewalks. Security guards assist Rutgers police in providing public safety services. There is also a student marshal program.

Programs of Study: Newark College of Arts and Sciences awards the B.A. and B.S. degrees. Bachelor's degrees are awarded in BIOLOGICAL SCIENCE (biology/biological science, botany, microbiology, and zoology), BUSINESS (accounting, banking and finance, business administration and management, management science, and marketing/retailing/merchandising), COMMUNICATIONS AND THE ARTS (art, art history and appreciation, classics, dramatic arts, English, fine arts, French, German, Italian, journalism, music, Russian, and Spanish), COMPUTER AND PHYSICAL SCIENCE (applied mathematics, applied physics, chemistry, computer science, geology, information sciences and systems, mathematics, physics, and science), ENGINEERING AND ENVIRONMENTAL DESIGN (ceramic engineering, chemical engineering, civil engineering, electrical/electronics engineering, industrial engineering, and mechanical engineering), HEALTH PROFESSIONS (clinical science, medical laboratory technology, predentistry, and premedicine), SOCIAL SCIENCE (African American studies, American studies, anthropology, criminal justice, Eastern European studies, economics, Hispanic American studies, history, humanities, Judaic studies, philosophy, political science/government, prelaw, psychology, Russian and Slavic studies, social work, sociology, and women's studies). Biology, English and mathematics have the largest enrollments.

Required: In order to graduate, students must complete 124 credit hours, including 30 or more in the major, and have a minimum GPA of 2.0. Distribution requirements include 8 credits of natural sciences, 6 each of history, literature, and social science, and 3 credits each in mathematics or natural science, fine arts, and interdisciplinary study. English composition is also required.

Special: Students may cross-register at the New Jersey Institute of Technology and the University of Medicine and Dentistry of New Jersey. Study abroad is offered in 9 countries. Internships in accounting and journalism, dual majors, student-designed majors, pass-fail options, and nondegree study are available. The college offers accelerated degree programs in business administration and criminal justice and 2–2 and 2–3 engineering degrees with the College of Engineering in New Brunswick. There is a freshman honors program on campus, as well as 12 national honor societies, including Phi Beta Kappa.

Faculty/Classroom: Seventy-one percent of faculty are male; 29%, female. Graduate students teach 28% of introductory courses. The average class size in a regular course offering is 30.

Admissions: About 52% of the 1993–94 applicants were accepted. The SAT scores for the 1993–94 freshman class were as follows: Verbal—74% below 500, 21% between 500 and 599, and 5% between 600 and 700; Math—33% below 500, 48% between 500 and 599, 17% between 600 and 700, and 2% above 700. About 49% of the current freshmen were in the top fifth of their class; 89% were in the top two fifths. Five freshmen graduated first in their class.

Requirements: The SAT I or ACT is required. Applicants must be graduates of an accredited secondary school. The GED is accepted. Sixteen academic credits or Carnegie units are required, including 4 years of English, 3 years of mathematics (alegbra I and II), 2 years each of a foreign language and science, plus 5 other approved academic subjects. AP and CLEP credits are accepted. Important factors used in the admissions decision are advanced placement or honor courses, evidence of special talent, leadership record, extracurricular activities record, and recommendations by school officials.

Procedure: Freshmen are admitted fall and spring. Entrance exams should be taken no later than February of the senior year. Applications should be filed by May 1 for fall entry and November 30 for spring entry, along with an application fee of $40. Notification is sent on a rolling basis. There are early admissions and deferred admissions plans. A waiting list is an active part of the admissions procedure, with about 7% of applicants on the list.

Transfer: About 420 transfer students enrolled in 1993–94. Applicants must have a minimum GPA of 2.5 with a minimum of 12 credit hours earned. Grades of C or better in courses that correspond in content and credit to those offered by the college transfer for credit. Transfer students are admitted in the fall and spring semesters. A total

of 30 credits out of 124 must be completed at Newark College of Arts and Sciences.

Visiting: There are regularly scheduled orientations for prospective students, including an information session with an admissions officer and a tour of the campus. Visitors may sit in on classes. To arrange for a visit, contact the Office of University Undergraduate Admissions at (201) 648-5205.

Financial Aid: In 1993–94, 56% of all current freshmen and 45% of continuing students received some form of financial aid. About 51% of freshmen and 42% of continuing students received need-based aid. The average freshman award was $4876. Of that total, scholarships or need-based grants averaged $4265 ($10,000 maximum); loans averaged $846 ($2625 maximum); and work contracts averaged $1178 ($1500 maximum). Ten percent of undergraduate students work part-time. Average earnings from campus work for the school year are $931. The average financial indebtedness of the 1992–93 graduate was $2541. The FAFSA financial statement is required. The deadline for financial aid applications is March 1.

International Students: There are currently 144 international students enrolled. They must take the TOEFL or the college's own test and achieve a minimum score on the TOEFL of 550. The student must also take the SAT I or the ACT.

Computers: The college provides computer facilities for student use. The mainframes are a Sun Sparc 1000 and a DEC VAX 8550. Individual departments also have a variety of minicomputers. All students on the Newark campus have accounts on one or the other of the local systems. Access to the local systems as well as to the New Brunswick central system is provided through networked micro/terminal laboratories in major academic buildings on the campus. Stand-alone microcomputers are also available in one of the dorms. All students may access the system. There are no time limits on using the system. The fee is $100 per year.

Graduates: In 1992–93, 754 bachelor's degrees were awarded. The most popular majors among graduates were accounting (24%), biology (10%), and management (10%). Within an average freshman class, 27% graduate in 4 years, 45% in 5 years, and 56% in 6 years. Some 194 companies recruited on campus in 1992–93.

Admissions Contact: John Scott, Director of Admissions.

RUTGERS UNIVERSITY
RUTGERS COLLEGE

D-3

New Brunswick, NJ 08903 (908) 932-3770

Full-time: 4068 men, 4162 women	Faculty: 761; I, +$
Part-time: 213 men, 139 women	Ph.D.s: 95%
Graduate: none	Student/Faculty: 11 to 1
Year: semesters, summer session	Tuition: $4387 ($7942)
Application Deadline: January 15	Room & Board: $4454
Freshman Class: 16,843 applied, 7808 accepted, 1760 enrolled	
SAT I Verbal/Math: 539/617	**HIGHLY COMPETITIVE +**

Rutgers College, founded in 1766, is a coeducational liberal arts institution and the largest residential college in the Rutgers system. There are 11 undergraduate and 4 graduate schools. In addition to regional accreditation, Rutgers College has baccalaureate program accreditation with AACSB, NASM, and NCATE. The 14 libraries contain 4,387,960 volumes, 2,630,211 microform items, and 63,879 audiovisual forms, and subscribe to 19,822 periodicals. Computerized library sources and services include the card catalog, interlibrary loans, and database searching. Special learning facilities include a learning resource center, an art gallery, a radio station, a TV station, a geology museum, and various research institutes and centers. The 2686-acre campus is in a suburban area 33 miles south of New York City, New York. Including residence halls, there are 100 buildings on campus.

Student Life: About 89% of undergraduates are from New Jersey. Students come from 40 states, 44 foreign countries, and Canada. Sixty-two percent are white; 15% Asian American; 12% Hispanic. The average age of freshmen is 18.2; all undergraduates, 20.3. Nine percent drop out by the end of their first year; 77% remain to graduate.

Housing: A total of 6838 students can be accommodated in college housing. College-sponsored living facilities include coed dormitories and on-campus apartments. In addition, there are include honors houses and special interest facilities, including Latin image (Hispanic), black experience, and language. Substance-free housing is also available. On-campus housing is available on a lottery system for upperclassmen. Fifty-seven percent of students live on campus. Alcohol is not permitted. Upperclassmen may keep cars on campus.

Activities: About 7% of men belong to 3 local and 29 national fraternities; about 3% of women belong to 4 local and 11 national sororities. There are more than 300 groups on campus, including art, band, cheerleading, chess, choir, chorale, chorus, computers, dance, drama, drill team, ethnic, film, gay, honors, international, jazz band, literary magazine, marching band, musical theater, newspaper, orchestra, pep band, political, professional, radio and TV, religious, social, so-

cial service, student government, symphony, and yearbook. Popular campus events include New Student Orientation, Spring Fest, International Festival, Latin Heritage Week, Paul Robeson Week, and Student Activities Fair.

Sports: There are 15 intercollegiate sports each for men and women, and 24 intramural sports each for men and women. Athletic and recreation facilities include a 23,000-seat stadium, an athletic center, a gymnasium, a swimming pool, tennis courts, and a recreation center.

Disabled Students: Fifty-five percent of the campus is accessible to disabled students. The following facilities are available: wheelchair ramps, elevators, special parking, specially equipped rest rooms, special class scheduling, lowered drinking fountains, and lowered telephones.

Services: In addition to many counseling and information services, tutoring is available in most subjects, including in first- and second-level difficult courses. In addition, there is a reader service for the blind, and remedial math, reading, and writing.

Campus Safety and Security: Campus safety and security measures include 24-hour foot and vehicle patrol, self-defense education, escort service, and shuttle buses. In addition, there are informal discussions, pamphlets, posters, films, emergency telephones, and lighted pathways and sidewalks. The police department is supplemented by security guards and student safety officers.

Programs of Study: Rutgers College awards the B.A. and B.S. degrees. Bachelor's degrees are awarded in BIOLOGICAL SCIENCE (biochemistry, biology/biological science, botany, cell biology, ecology, evolutionary biology, genetics, microbiology, molecular biology, nutrition, and physiology), BUSINESS (accounting, banking and finance, labor studies, management science, and marketing/retailing/merchandising), COMMUNICATIONS AND THE ARTS (art history and appreciation, Chinese, classical languages, classics, communications, comparative literature, dance, dramatic arts, English, fine arts, French, German, Greek (classical), Italian, journalism, Latin, linguistics, music, Portuguese, Russian, Spanish, and visual and performing arts), COMPUTER AND PHYSICAL SCIENCE (chemistry, computer science, geology, mathematics, physics, and statistics), HEALTH PROFESSIONS (biomedical science, predentistry, premedicine, and public health), SOCIAL SCIENCE (African studies, American studies, anthropology, criminal justice, East Asian studies, economics, geography, Hispanic American studies, history, humanities, Judaic studies, Latin American studies, Middle Eastern studies, philosophy, physical fitness/movement, political science/government, prelaw, psychology, religion, Russian and Slavic studies, sociology, urban studies, and women's studies). Psychology, English, and political science have the largest enrollments.

Required: In order to graduate, students must complete a total of 120 credit hours, including 30 hours in major, with a minimum GPA of 2.0. The general education requirements include 2 courses each in writing skills, quantitative skills, natural science, social science, and humanities, and 1 each in non-Western world and either mathematics, computer science, or statistics.

Special: Rutgers College offers internships, a Washington semester, study abroad in 9 countries, accelerated degree programs in business and engineering, and dual majors in statistics and mathematics, and history and political science. A 2–3 degree with the College of Engineering is available. There is a freshman honors program on campus, as well as 8 national honor societies, including Phi Beta Kappa.

Faculty/Classroom: Seventy-four percent of faculty are male; 26%, female. Graduate students teach 30% of introductory courses. The average class size in a regular course offering is 45.

Admissions: About 46% of the 1993–94 applicants were accepted. The SAT scores for the 1993–94 freshman class were as follows: Verbal—32% below 500, 43% between 500 and 599, 23% between 600 and 700, and 2% above 700; Math—9% below 500, 33% between 500 and 599, 42% between 600 and 700, and 16% above 700. About 82% of the current freshmen were in the top fifth of their class; 98% were in the top two fifths. There were 15 National Merit finalists. About 30 freshmen graduated first in their class.

Requirements: The SAT I or ACT is required. Applicants must have completed 16 high school credits or Carnegie units, including 4 years of English, 3 years of mathematics (algebra I and II, and plane geometry), 2 years each of a foreign language and science, and 5 other academic subjects. Students without a high school diploma, those from a nonaccredited high school, or those with academic unit deficiencies must take SAT II: Subject tests in English, mathematics, and one other subject. AP credits are accepted. Important factors used in the admissions decision are advanced placement or honor courses, evidence of special talent, leadership record, extracurricular activities record, and recommendations by school officials.

Procedure: Freshmen are admitted in the fall. Entrance exams should be taken no later than December of the senior year. Applications should be filed by January 15 for fall entry, along with an application fee of $40. Notification is sent by April 15. There are early admissions

and deferred admissions plans. A waiting list is an active part of the admissions procedure, with about 6% of applicants on the list.

Transfer: About 450 transfer students enrolled in 1993–94. Students who have completed a minimum of 12 college credits are considered for transfer. Grades of C or better in courses that correspond in content and credit to those offered by the college transfer for credit. Transfer students are admitted in both the fall and spring semesters. A total of 30 credits out of 120 must be completed at Rutgers College.

Visiting: There are regularly scheduled orientations for prospective students, including an information session with an admissions officer followed by a bus tour with a student guide. Student-guided walking tours are also available, and include a meeting with a dean prior to the tour. With prior arrangement, visitors may sit in on classes. To arrange for a visit, contact the Office of University Undergraduate Admissions at (908) 932-7881.

Financial Aid: In 1993–94, 78% of all current freshmen and 63% of continuing students received some form of financial aid. About 50% of freshmen and 39% of continuing students received need-based aid. The average freshman award was $4440. Of that total, scholarships or need-based grants averaged $3215 ($10,000 maximum); loans averaged $1184 ($9790 maximum); and work contracts averaged $1198 ($1500 maximum). Eleven percent of undergraduate students work part-time. Average earnings from campus work for the school year are $921. The average financial indebtedness of the 1992–93 graduate was $3490. The FAFSA financial statement is required. The priority deadline for financial aid applications is March 1.

International Students: There are currently 180 international students enrolled. They must take the TOEFL and achieve a minimum score of 550. The student must also take the SAT I or the ACT.

Computers: The college provides computer facilities for student use. Central computer systems include a DEC VAX 8650 cluster, an IBM 3081, a Sun Sparc 670, and a Sun 4/110. Individual departments have a variety of minicomputers. Terminals on networked microcomputers are located on all campuses in the New Brunswick area. Computing services available to students include on-line class registration, E-mail, word processing, course-work assignments, and access to Internet and Bitnet. All students may access the system. It may be used 24 hours a day. Students must observe limits on file space and execution length. The fee is $100 per year.

Graduates: In 1992–93, 2512 bachelor's degrees were awarded. The most popular majors among graduates were psychology (14%), English (14%), and political science (11%). Within an average freshman class, 58% graduate in 4 years, 74% in 5 years, and 77% in 6 years. Some 500 companies recruited on campus in 1992–93.

Admissions Contact: Dr. Elizabeth Mitchell, Assistant Vice President for University Undergraduate Admissions.

RUTGERS UNIVERSITY
UNIVERSITY COLLEGE-CAMDEN
C-4

Camden, NJ 08101   (609) 225-6104

Full-time: 136 men, 132 women	Faculty: 136; IIA, + +$
Part-time: 258 men, 304 women	Ph.D.s: 95%
Graduate: none	Student/Faculty: 6 to 1
Year: semesters	Tuition: see profile
Application Deadline: May 1	Room & Board: n/app
Freshman Class: 503 applied, 338 accepted, 69 enrolled	
SAT I or ACT: required	COMPETITIVE

Rutgers University College-Camden, established in 1934, is a coeducational, liberal arts college serving part-time and evening adult students. Tuition is $111 per credit plus an $88 per semester fee for New Jersey residents; $227 per credit plus an $88 per semester fee for out-of-state residents. There are 3 undergraduate and 6 graduate schools. In addition to regional accreditation, University College-Camden has baccalaureate program accreditation with CAHEA and NCATE. The 2 libraries contain 357,701 volumes, 214,499 microform items, and 207 audiovisual forms, and subscribe to 2106 periodicals. Computerized library sources and services include the card catalog, interlibrary loans, and database searching. Special learning facilities include an art gallery. The 25-acre campus is in an urban area 1 mile east of Philadelphia, Pennsylvania. There are 20 buildings on campus.

Student Life: About 98% of undergraduates are from New Jersey. Students come from 3 states. Seventy-three percent are white; 12% African American. The average age of freshmen is 20.4; all undergraduates, 29.7.

Housing: There are no residence halls. Alcohol is not permitted.

Activities: There are no fraternities or sororities on campus. There are 45 groups on campus, including computers, drama, ethnic, gay, honors, international, literary magazine, newspaper, political, professional, radio and TV, religious, social, social service, student government, and yearbook. Popular campus events include Black History Month, Hispanic Solidarity Week, Women's History Month, Pioneer Week, and Spring Day.

Sports: There is no sports program at University College-Camden.

Disabled Students: Ninety-five percent of the campus is accessible to disabled students. The following facilities are available: wheelchair ramps, elevators, special parking, specially equipped rest rooms, special class scheduling, lowered drinking fountains, and lowered telephones.

Services: In addition to many counseling and information services, tutoring is available in some subjects, including introductory classes. In addition, there is a reader service for the blind, and remedial math, reading, and writing.

Campus Safety and Security: Campus safety and security measures include 24-hour foot and vehicle patrol, self-defense education, escort service, and shuttle buses. In addition, there are informal discussions, pamphlets, posters, films, emergency telephones, lighted pathways and sidewalks. The police department is supplemented by security guards.

Programs of Study: University College-Camden awards the B.A. and B.S. degrees. Bachelor's degrees are awarded in BIOLOGICAL SCIENCE (biochemistry and biology/biological science), BUSINESS (accounting, management science, and marketing/retailing/merchandising), COMMUNICATIONS AND THE ARTS (art history and appreciation, dramatic arts, English, French, German, music, Spanish, and visual and performing arts), COMPUTER AND PHYSICAL SCIENCE (chemistry, computer science, mathematics, physics, and science), HEALTH PROFESSIONS (medical laboratory technology, predentistry, and premedicine), SOCIAL SCIENCE (African American studies, American studies, economics, history, philosophy, political science/government, prelaw, psychology, social work, and sociology). Computer science has the largest enrollment.

Required: To graduate, students must complete 126 credits, with 30 to 48 in the major, and maintain a minimum GPA of 2.0. A core curriculum of 60 credits is required, including 3 credits each in literary masterpieces; art, music or theater arts; foreign language, with an additional 3 credits in English or a foreign language; and mathematics, with an additional 3 credits in mathematics, computer science or statistics. Two interdisciplinary courses are required.

Special: The college offers student-designed majors, dual majors, nondegree study, and pass/fail options. Students may study abroad in 9 countries. There is a freshman honors program on campus, as well as one national honor society. Three departments have honors programs.

Faculty/Classroom: Sixty-five percent of faculty are male; 35%, female. All teach undergraduates and 90% do research. Graduate students teach 5% of introductory courses. The average class size in a regular course offering is 32.

Admissions: About 67% of the 1993–94 applicants were accepted.

Requirements: The SAT I or ACT is required, but not for students who have been out of high school for two years or more. Applicants for admission must be graduates of an accredited secondary school. The GED is accepted. Students must have completed 16 academic credits or Carnegie units, including 4 years of English, 3 years of mathematics (algebra I and II, and geometry), and 2 years of a foreign language, plus 7 additional academic units. AP and CLEP credits are accepted. Important factors used in the admissions decision are evidence of special talent, leadership record, advanced placement or honor courses, extracurricular activities record, and recommendations by school officials.

Procedure: Freshmen are admitted fall and spring. Applications should be filed by May 1 for fall entry and November 30 for spring entry, along with an application fee of $40. Notification is sent on a rolling basis. There is a deferred admissions plan.

Transfer: About 200 transfer students enrolled in 1993–94. Applicants must have a minimum GPA of 2.5 and a minimum of 12 credit hours. Grades of C or better in courses that correspond in content and credit to those offered by the college transfer for credit. Transfer students are admitted in the fall and spring semesters. Thirty of the final 40 credits out of 126 must be completed at University College-Camden.

Visiting: There are regularly scheduled orientations for prospective students, including an information session with an admissions officer and a campus tour. With prior arrangement, visitors may sit in on classes. To arrange for a visit, contact the Office of University Undergraduate Admission-Camden at (609) 225-6104.

Financial Aid: In 1993–94, 37% of all current freshmen and 17% of continuing students received some form of financial aid. About 35% of freshmen and 15% of continuing students received need-based aid. The average freshman award was $4646. Of that total, scholarships or need-based grants averaged $3823 ($10,000 maximum); loans averaged $896 ($2625 maximum); and work contracts averaged $1100 ($1200 maximum). Three percent of undergraduate students work part-time. Average earnings from campus work for the school year are $853. The average financial indebtedness of the 1992–93 graduate was $7798. The FAFSA financial statement is required. The deadline for financial aid applications is March 1.

International Students: International applicants must take the TOEFL and achieve a minimum score of 550. The student must also take the SAT I or the ACT.

Computers: The college provides computer facilities for student use. The mainframes are a Sun Sparc Server 10/41 and a 10/51 MP. Terminals or networked microcomputers are located in 2 major academic buildings, the library, the Campus Center, and dormitories, and provide access to the central systems as well as to the Camden campus computers. The on-campus computer network includes on-line registration, E-mail, and access to Internet and Bitnet. All students may access the system. There are no time limits on using the system. Part-time students are assessed a fee of $10 per semester.

Graduates: In 1992–93, 31 bachelor's degrees were awarded. The most popular majors among graduates were computer science (37%), English (30%), and psychology (17%). Some 90 companies recruited on campus in 1992–93.

Admissions Contact: Dr. Deborah Bowles, Director of Admissions-Camden.

RUTGERS UNIVERSITY
UNIVERSITY COLLEGE-NEW BRUNSWICK   D-3

New Brunswick, NJ 08903   **(908) 932-7276**

Full-time: 335 men, 345 women	Faculty: 761; I, +$
Part-time: 1148 men, 1421 women	Ph.D.s: 95%
Graduate: none	Student/Faculty: 4 to 1
Year: semesters, summer session	Tuition: see profile
Application Deadline: July 21	Room & Board: n/app
Freshman Class: n/av	
SAT I or ACT: not required	**LESS COMPETITIVE**

University College-New Brunswick, founded in 1934, is a coeducational, liberal arts school for adult part-time students. Tuition is $111 per credit plus a $79 semester fee for New Jersey residents; $227 per credit plus a $79 semester fee for out-of-state residents. There are 11 undergraduate and 4 graduate schools. In addition to regional accreditation, University College-New Brunswick has baccalaureate program accreditation with AACSB, NASM, and NCATE. The 14 libraries contain 4,387,960 volumes, 2,630,211 microform items, and 63,879 audiovisual forms, and subscribe to 19,822 periodicals. Computerized library sources and services include the card catalog, interlibrary loans, and database searching. Special learning facilities include a learning resource center, art gallery, radio station, TV station, geology museum, and various research centers. The 2686-acre campus is in a small town 33 miles south of New York City. There are 100 buildings on campus. There are no residence halls.

Student Life: About 98% of undergraduates are from New Jersey. Students come from 14 states, 15 foreign countries, and Canada. Seventy-six percent are white. The average age of all undergraduates is 30.

Housing: There are no residence halls. Alcohol is not permitted.

Activities: There are no fraternities or sororities on campus. There are 300 groups on campus, including art, band, cheerleading, chess, choir, chorale, chorus, computers, dance, drama, drill team, ethnic, film, gay, honors, international, jazz band, literary magazine, marching band, musical theater, newspaper, orchestra, pep band, political, professional, radio and TV, religious, social, social service, student government, symphony, and yearbook. Popular campus events include Homecoming, theater trips, and a picnic.

Sports: There is no sports program at University College-New Brunswick.

Disabled Students: Fifty-five percent of the campus is accessible to disabled students. The following facilities are available: wheelchair ramps, elevators, special parking, specially equipped rest rooms, special class scheduling, lowered drinking fountains, and lowered telephones. Facilities vary from building to building. All classes will be scheduled in accessible locations for disabled students, and adaptations will be made to individual needs in dormitory rooms.

Services: In addition to many counseling and information services, tutoring is available in most subjects. There is also remedial math, reading, and writing.

Campus Safety and Security: Campus safety and security measures include 24-hour foot and vehicle patrol, self-defense education, escort service, and shuttle buses. In addition, there are informal discussions, pamphlets, posters, films, emergency telephones, and lighted pathways and sidewalks. The police department is supplemented by security guards and student safety officers.

Programs of Study: University College-New Brunswick awards the B.A. and B.S. degrees. Bachelor's degrees are awarded in BIOLOGICAL SCIENCE (biochemistry, biology/biological science, botany, cell biology, ecology, evolutionary biology, genetics, microbiology, molecular biology, nutrition, and physiology), BUSINESS (accounting, banking and finance, business administration and management, labor studies, management science, and marketing/retailing/merchandising), COMMUNICATIONS AND THE ARTS (art, art history and appreciation, Chinese, classics, communications, comparative literature, dance, dramatic arts, English, fine arts, French, German, Greek, Italian, journalism, Latin, linguistics, music, Portuguese, Russian, Spanish, and visual and performing arts), COMPUTER AND PHYSICAL SCIENCE (chemistry, computer science, geology, mathematics, physics, and statistics), EDUCATION (vocational), HEALTH PROFESSIONS (biomedical science, predentistry, premedicine, and public health), SOCIAL SCIENCE (African American studies, American studies, anthropology, Asian/Oriental studies, criminal justice, economics, food science, geography, Hispanic American studies, history, humanities, Judaic studies, Latin American studies, Middle Eastern studies, philosophy, physical fitness/movement, political science/government, prelaw, psychology, religion, Russian and Slavic studies, sociology, urban studies, and women's studies). Economics, computer science, psychology, and English have the largest enrollments.

Required: In order to graduate, students must complete 120 credits, with a minimum GPA of 2.0. A liberal arts core requirement includes 6 credits of English composition and 12 credits each of humanities and social sciences and of mathematics and science.

Special: Internships are available for students majoring in administration of justice, psychology, political science, and journalism. The college offers study abroad in 10 countries. A Washington semester, B.A.-B.S. degrees, student-designed majors, nondegree study, and pass/fail options are available. There is a freshman honors program on campus, as well as 2 national honor societies, including Phi Beta Kappa. Nearly all departments have honors programs.

Faculty/Classroom: Seventy-four percent of faculty are male; 26%, female.

Requirements: Applicants must be graduates of an accredited secondary school. The GED is accepted. Students must have completed 16 academic credits or Carnegie units, including 4 years of English, 3 years of mathematics (algebra I and II and geometry), 2 years of a foreign language, and 7 additional academic units. Ordinarily, University College-New Brunswick does not admit applicants who apply within two years of high school graduation unless they have completed 24 transferable credits with a 2.5 GPA at another college. AP and CLEP credits are accepted. Important factors used in the admissions decision are leadership record, evidence of special talent, personality, intangible qualities, advanced placement or honor courses, and recommendations by school officials.

Procedure: Applications should be filed by July 21 for fall entry and December 1 for spring entry, along with an application fee of $40. Notification is sent on a rolling basis.

Transfer: About 890 transfer students enrolled in a recent year. Applicant must have a 2.5 GPA with a minimum of 24 credit hours. Grades of C or better transfer for credit. Transfers are admitted in the fall or spring. At least 30 credits out of 120 must be completed at University College-New Brunswick.

Visiting: There are regularly scheduled orientations for prospective students, including a preadmission orientation for prospective students. To arrange for a visit, contact University College Admissions at (908) 932-7276.

Financial Aid: In 1993–94, 11% of all current freshmen and 12% of continuing students received some form of financial aid. About 10% of freshmen and 11% of continuing students received need-based aid. The average freshman award was $3607. Of that total, scholarships or need-based grants averaged $2470 ($10,000 maximum); and loans averaged $2625 (maximum). Ten percent of undergraduate students work part-time. Average earnings from campus work for the school year are $1109. The average financial indebtedness of the 1992–93 graduate was $4589. The FAFSA financial statement is required. The deadline for financial aid applications is March 1.

International Students: There are currently 24 international students enrolled. They must take the TOEFL or the college's own test and achieve a minimum score on the TOEFL of 550.

Computers: The college provides computer facilities for student use. The mainframes are a DEC VAX 8650 cluster, an IBM 3081, a Sun Sparc 670, and a Sun 4/110. Individual departments have a variety of minicomputers. Terminals or networked microcomputers are campuswide. Computing services available to students include on-line registration, E-mail, and access to Internet and Bitnet. All students may access the system 24 hours per day. Students must observe limits on file space and execution length. The fees are $Part-time students are assessed a $10 fee per semester.

Graduates: In 1992–93, 358 bachelor's degrees were awarded. The most popular majors among graduates were psychology (12%), economics (10%), and English (10%). Some 500 companies recruited on campus in a recent year. In the 1992 graduating class, 32% of all graduates were enrolled in graduate school within 6 months of graduation.

Admissions Contact: Loretta Daniel, Director of Admissions.

RUTGERS UNIVERSITY
UNIVERSITY COLLEGE-NEWARK
E-2

Newark, NJ 07102　　　　　　　　　　(201) 648-5205

Full-time: 223 men, 272 women	Faculty: 184; IIA, + +$
Part-time: 686 men, 639 women	Ph.D.s: 95%
Graduate: none	Student/Faculty: 10 to 1
Year: semesters, summer session	Tuition: see profile
Application Deadline: August 1	Room & Board: n/app
Freshman Class: 296 applied, 176 accepted, 78 enrolled	
SAT I or ACT: required	COMPETITIVE

Rutgers University College-Newark, founded in 1934, is a liberal arts evening school designed for part-time adult students. Tuition is $111 per credit hour plus an $84 semester fee for New Jersey residents; $227 per credit hour plus an $84 semester fee for out-of-state residents. There are 3 undergraduate and 4 graduate schools. In addition to regional accreditation, University College-Newark has baccalaureate program accreditation with AACSB and CSWE. The 4 libraries contain 591,536 volumes, 675,962 microform items, and 24,297 audiovisual forms, and subscribe to 3748 periodicals. Computerized library sources and services include the card catalog, interlibrary loans, and database searching. Special learning facilities include a learning resource center, an art gallery, a molecular and behavioral neuroscience center, and institutes of jazz and animal behavior. The 33-acre campus is in an urban area 7 miles west of New York City, New York, in downtown Newark. There are 31 buildings on campus.

Student Life: About 97% of undergraduates are from New Jersey. Students come from 4 states. Thirty-seven percent are white; 30% African American; 14% Hispanic. The average age of freshmen is 23.2; all undergraduates, 28.6.

Housing: There are no residence halls. Alcohol is not permitted.

Activities: There are no fraternities or sororities on campus. There are 97 groups on campus, including chess, computers, ethnic, gay, honors, international, literary magazine, newspaper, political, professional, radio and TV, religious, social, social service, student government, and yearbook. Popular campus events include Campus Fair, Thanksgiving for International Students, Student Talent Show, World Week, Multicultural Olympics, Black History Month, and Puerto Rican Heritage Month.

Sports: There is no sports program at University College-Newark.

Disabled Students: Eighty percent of the campus is accessible to disabled students. The following facilities are available: wheelchair ramps, elevators, special parking, specially equipped rest rooms, special class scheduling, lowered drinking fountains, and lowered telephones.

Services: In addition to many counseling and information services, tutoring is available in most subjects. In addition, there is a reader service for the blind, and remedial math, reading, and writing.

Campus Safety and Security: Campus safety and security measures include 24-hour foot and vehicle patrol, self-defense education, escort service, and shuttle buses. In addition, there are informal discussions, pamphlets, posters, films, emergency telephones, and lighted pathways and sidewalks. Security guards assist Rutgers police in providing public safety services. There is also a student marshal program.

Programs of Study: University College-Newark awards the B.A. and B.S. degrees. Bachelor's degrees are awarded in BUSINESS (accounting, banking and finance, business administration and management, management science, and marketing/retailing/merchandising), COMMUNICATIONS AND THE ARTS (English and Spanish), COMPUTER AND PHYSICAL SCIENCE (computer science, information sciences and systems, and mathematics), EDUCATION (vocational), HEALTH PROFESSIONS (predentistry and premedicine), SOCIAL SCIENCE (criminal justice, economics, history, philosophy, political science/government, prelaw, psychology, social work, and sociology). Accounting, English, and psychology have the largest enrollments.

Required: In order to graduate, students must complete 124 credits with a minimum GPA of 2.0. Distribution requirements include 8 credits in natural science/mathematics plus 3 courses in nonlaboratory science, mathematics, or computer science; 6 credits each in history, literature, social sciences, humanities, and fine arts; 1 course in critical thinking; and 15 credits of electives. All students must take English composition.

Special: Students may cross-register with the New Jersey Institute of Technology and the University of Medicine and Dentistry of New Jersey. Internships are available in accounting and journalism. The school offers study abroad, accelerated degree programs in business administration and criminal justice, dual majors, student-designed majors, nondegree study, and pass/fail options. There is a freshman honors program on campus, as well as 12 national honor societies, including Phi Beta Kappa.

Faculty/Classroom: Seventy-one percent of faculty are male; 29%, female. The average class size in a regular course offering is 30.

Admissions: About 59% of the 1993-94 applicants were accepted.

Requirements: The SAT I or ACT is required. Students must be graduates of an accredited high school. The GED is accepted. Students should have completed 16 high school academic credits or Carnegie units, including 4 years of English, 3 of mathematics, 2 of foreign languages, and 7 other academic units. AP and CLEP credits are accepted. Important factors used in the admissions decision are advanced placement or honor courses, evidence of special talent, leadership record, extracurricular activities record, and recommendations by school officials.

Procedure: Freshmen are admitted fall and spring. Applications should be filed by August 1 for fall entry and December 1 for spring entry, along with an application fee of $40. Notification is sent on a rolling basis. There is a deferred admissions plan.

Transfer: About 240 transfer students enrolled in 1993-94. Students who have completed at least 12 credit hours at another college with a cumulative GPA of 2.0 are considered for admission as transfer students. Transfers are admitted in the fall and spring. A total of 30 credits out of 124 must be completed at University College—Newark.

Visiting: There are regularly scheduled orientations for prospective students, including an information session with an admissions counselor and a tour of the campus. With prior arrangement, visitors may sit in on classes. To arrange for a visit, contact the Office of University Undergraduate Admissions-Newark at (201) 648-5205.

Financial Aid: In 1993-94, 33% of all current freshmen and 17% of continuing students received some form of financial aid. About 30% of freshmen and 10% of continuing students received need-based aid. The average freshman award was $4603. Of that total, scholarships or need-based grants averaged $4103 ($10,000 maximum); loans averaged $899 ($2499 maximum); and work contracts averaged $1066 ($1200 maximum). Four percent of undergraduate students work part-time. Average earnings from campus work for the school year are $837. The average financial indebtedness of the 1992-93 graduate was $3369. The FAFSA financial statement is required. The deadline for financial aid applications is March 1.

International Students: There are currently 24 international students enrolled. They must take the TOEFL or the college's own test and achieve a minimum score on the TOEFL of 550.

Computers: The college provides computer facilities for student use. The mainframes are a Sun Sparc 1000 and a DEC VAX 8550. Individual departments also have a variety of minicomputers. All students on the Newark campus have accounts on one or the other of the local systems. Access to the local systems as well as to the New Brunswick central systems is provided through networked micro/terminal laboratories in major academic buildings on the campus. All students may access the system. There are no time limits on using the system. Part-time students are assessed a fee of $10 per semester.

Graduates: In 1992-93, 194 bachelor's degrees were awarded. The most popular majors among graduates were accounting (27%), management (18%), and criminal justice (8%). Some 194 companies recruited on campus in 1992-93.

Admissions Contact: John Scott, Director of Admissions-Newark.

RUTGERS, THE STATE UNIVERSITY OF NEW JERSEY

Rutgers, the State University of New Jersey, established in 1766, is a public system. It is governed by a board of governors, whose chief administrator is the president. The primary goal of the system is instruction, research, and service. The main priorities are to continue development as a distinguished comprehensive public university, to enhance undergraduate education, to strengthen graduate education and research, and to develop and improve programs to better serve New Jersey's and society's needs. Four-year campuses are located in New Brunswick, Newark, and Camden. The total enrollment in fall 1993 of all 3 campuses was 48,063; there were 1954 instructional faculty members. Altogether there are more than 100 baccalaureate, 100 master's, and 80 doctoral programs offered in Rutgers, the State University of New Jersey.

SAINT PETER'S COLLEGE
E-2

Jersey City, NJ 07306　　　　　　　　　　(201) 915-9213

Full-time: 925 men, 1056 women	Faculty: 123; IIB, av$
Part-time: 354 men, 854 women	Ph.D.s: 72%
Graduate: 205 men, 173 women	Student/Faculty: 16 to 1
Year: semesters, summer session	Tuition: $9445
Application Deadline: March 1	Room & Board: $5330
Freshman Class: 1607 applied, 1413 accepted, 616 enrolled	
SAT I Verbal/Math: 450/490	LESS COMPETITIVE

Saint Peter's College, founded in 1872, is a coeducational liberal arts and business college affiliated with the Roman Catholic Church and known as New Jersey's Jesuit College. There are 2 undergraduate

and 2 graduate schools. In addition to regional accreditation, Saint Peter's College has baccalaureate program accreditation with NLN. The library contains 272,074 volumes, 581 microform items, and 1766 audiovisual forms, and subscribes to 1347 periodicals. Special learning facilities include an art gallery and radio station. The 10-acre campus is in an urban area 2 miles west of New York City. Including residence halls, there are 20 buildings on campus.

Student Life: About 84% of undergraduates are from New Jersey. Students come from 10 states, 15 foreign countries, and Canada. Fifty percent are from public schools; 50% from private. Fifty-six percent are white; 23% Hispanic; 12% African American. Most are Catholic. Twenty-five percent drop out by the end of their first year; 55% remain to graduate.

Housing: A total of 485 students can be accommodated in college housing. College-sponsored living facilities include single-sex and coed dormitories and on-campus apartments. On-campus housing is guaranteed for all 4 years. Eighty percent of students commute. Alcohol is not permitted. Upperclassmen may keep cars on campus.

Activities: About 5% of men belong to 3 national fraternities; about 5% of women belong to 1 local sorority. There are 35 groups on campus, including cheerleading, chorus, computers, drama, ethnic, honors, international, literary magazine, newspaper, pep band, political, professional, radio and TV, religious, ROTC (Air Force, Army), social, social service, student government, and yearbook. Popular campus events include International Day, career fairs, and Homecoming.

Sports: There are 11 intercollegiate sports for men and 9 for women, and 19 intramural sports for men and 19 for women. Athletic and recreation facilities include a recreational center, a 2000-seat gymnasium, and an athletic field.

Disabled Students: Eighty percent of the campus is accessible to disabled students. The following facilities are available: wheelchair ramps, elevators, special parking, specially equipped rest rooms, lowered drinking fountains, and lowered telephones.

Services: In addition to many counseling and information services, tutoring is available in every subject. There is also a reader service for the blind, and remedial math, reading, and writing.

Campus Safety and Security: Campus safety and security measures include an escort service.

Programs of Study: Saint Peter's College awards the B.A., B.S., and B.S.N. degrees. Associate and master's degrees also are awarded. Bachelor's degrees are awarded in BIOLOGICAL SCIENCE (biochemistry and biology/biological science), BUSINESS (accounting, business administration and management, and marketing/retailing/merchandising), COMMUNICATIONS AND THE ARTS (classical languages, classics, English, fine arts, French, and Spanish), COMPUTER AND PHYSICAL SCIENCE (chemistry, computer science, mathematics, natural sciences, and physics), EDUCATION (elementary and secondary), HEALTH PROFESSIONS (health care administration, medical laboratory technology, nursing, predentistry, and premedicine), SOCIAL SCIENCE (American studies, economics, history, humanities, philosophy, political science/government, prelaw, psychology, religion, social science, sociology, and urban studies). Natural sciences and accounting are the strongest academically. Business administration, accounting, and computer sciences have the largest enrollments.

Required: To graduate, students must complete 129 credit hours, including 57 in the core curriculum, 12 in core electives, between 30 and 45 in the major, and the rest in subjects related to the major. The core curriculum consists of courses in communications, literature, mathematics, natural sciences, social science, philosophy, history, theology, fine arts, and a modern language. Students must earn a GPA of 2.0.

Special: There are co-op programs with local companies, as well as departmental programs. A Washington semester and study abroad in any of 60 countries are offered. The college also offers dual and student-designed majors, credit for life, military, and work experience, nondegree study, and pass/fail options. There is a freshman honors program on campus, as well as 9 national honor societies. One department has an honors program.

Faculty/Classroom: Seventy-eight percent of faculty are male; 22%, female. The average class size in an introductory lecture is 35; in a laboratory, 24; and in a regular course offering, 22.

Admissions: About 88% of the 1993–94 applicants were accepted. The SAT I scores for the 1993–94 freshman class were as follows: Verbal—73% below 500, 21% between 500 and 599, 5% between 600 and 700, and 1% above 700; Math—53% below 500, 35% between 500 and 599, 11% between 600 and 700, and 1% above 700. About 35% of the current freshmen were in the top fifth of their class; 53% were in the top two fifths. About 6 freshmen graduated first in their class.

Requirements: The SAT I is required. Applicants must be high school graduates or submit the GED certificate. Students should have completed 16 Carnegie units of high school study, including 4 years of English, 3 of mathematics, 2 each of science, history, and a foreign language, and another 3 of additional work in any of these subjects.

They must be in the top 50% of their high school class and present an essay and letters of recommendation. The school recommends an interview. AP and CLEP credits are accepted. Important factors used in the admissions decision are advanced placement or honor courses, leadership record, evidence of special talent, extracurricular activities record, and recommendations by school officials.

Procedure: Freshmen are admitted fall and spring. Entrance exams should be taken by the fall of the senior year. Early decision applications should be filed by February 1; regular applications, by March 1 for fall entry and December 1 for spring entry, along with an application fee of $30. Notification of early decision is sent November 15; regular decision, on a rolling basis. There are early decision, early admissions, and deferred admissions plans. About 3 early decision candidates were accepted for the 1993–94 class.

Transfer: About 26 transfer students enrolled in a recent year. The school requires a 2.0 college GPA of transfer students, as well as a high school transcript and an 800 composite SAT I score for students less than 2 years out of high school. An interview is recommended. A total of 30 credits out of 129 must be completed at Saint Peter's College.

Visiting: There are guides for informal visits and visitors may sit in on classes. To arrange for a visit, contact the Admissions Office at (201) 915–9213.

Financial Aid: In 1993–94, 80% of all current freshmen and continuing students received some form of financial aid. The average freshman award was $7000. Of that total, scholarships or need-based grants averaged $2700 ($9445 maximum); loans averaged $2000 ($3625 maximum); and work contracts averaged $1000 ($2000 maximum). Eighteen percent of undergraduate students work part-time. The average financial indebtedness of the 1992–93 graduate was $4812. Saint Peter's College is a member of CSS. The FAF is required.

International Students: There are currently 46 international students enrolled. The school actively recruits these students. They must take the TOEFL and achieve a minimum score of 500.

Computers: The college provides computer facilities for student use. The mainframes are an IBM 9370, a DEC VAX 780, 2 DEC PDP-11/44s, and a DEC PDP-11/24. There are also a number of microcomputers available in computer laboratories. All students may access the system. It may be used for remote access 24 hours a day; for local access, 8 A.M. to 10 P.M. Monday through Thursday, 8 A.M. to 5 P.M. Friday, and 9 A.M. to 2 P.M. Saturday. There are no time limits on using the system and no fees.

Graduates: In a recent year, 500 bachelor's degrees were awarded. Some 75 companies recruited on campus in a recent year.

Admissions Contact: Mary Beth Carey, Director of Admissions.

SETON HALL UNIVERSITY
South Orange, NJ 07079-2691

E-2

(201) 761-9332
(800) THE-HALL (out-of-state)

Full-time: 2174 men, 2224 women	Faculty: 299; IIA, +$
Part-time: 365 men, 555 women	Ph.D.s: 66%
Graduate: 2062 men, 2558 women	Student/Faculty: 15 to 1
Year: semesters, summer session	Tuition: $12,052
Application Deadline: March 1	Room & Board: $6254
Freshman Class: 4697 applied, 3566 accepted, 1003 enrolled	
SAT I Verbal/Math: 442/496	**LESS COMPETITIVE**

Seton Hall University, founded in 1856 by the first bishop of Newark, and affiliated with the Roman Catholic Church, has undergraduate colleges of arts and sciences, business, education and human services, and nursing. There are 4 undergraduate and 7 graduate schools. In addition to regional accreditation, Seton Hall has baccalaureate program accreditation with AACSB, CSWE, NCATE, and NLN. The 2 libraries contain 403,350 volumes, 24,250 microform items, and 14,352 audiovisual forms, and subscribe to 2163 periodicals. Computerized library sources and services include the card catalog, interlibrary loans, and database searching. Special learning facilities include a learning resource center, an art gallery, a natural history museum, and a radio station. The 58-acre campus is in a suburban area 14 miles west of New York City. Including residence halls, there are 30 buildings on campus.

Student Life: About 84% of undergraduates are from New Jersey. Students come from 36 states, 31 foreign countries, and Canada. Sixty percent are from public schools; 40% from private. Seventy-eight percent are white; 10% African American. The average age of freshmen is 18; all undergraduates, 20. Fourteen percent drop out by the end of their first year; 63% remain to graduate.

Housing: A total of 2000 students can be accommodated in college housing. College-sponsored living facilities include single-sex and coed dormitories and off-campus apartments. In addition, there are special interest houses and an all-quiet residence hall, an all-female residence hall, and modern language and transfers floors. On-campus housing is guaranteed for the freshman year only, is available on a first-come, first-served basis, and is available on a lottery system

for upperclassmen. Priority is given to out-of-town students. Fifty percent of students live on campus; of those, 70% remain on campus on weekends. Upperclassmen may keep cars on campus.

Activities: About 25% of men belong to 12 national fraternities; about 25% of women belong to 10 national sororities. There are 100 groups on campus, including art, cheerleading, choir, chorus, computers, drama, drill team, ethnic, honors, international, literary magazine, musical theater, newspaper, pep band, photography, political, professional, radio and TV, religious, social, social service, student government, and yearbook. Popular campus events include University Day, Theater-in-the-Round, lawn parties, Greek Week, International Students Day, special masses, and Welcome Weekend.

Sports: There are 10 intercollegiate sports for men and 9 for women, and 20 intramural sports each for men and women. Athletic and recreation facilities include a 3400-seat gymnasium, an indoor track, an indoor pool, a dance studio, a weight room, a soccer and baseball field, a softball field, and tennis and racquetball courts. School teams also use the Meadowlands Arena, which seats 19,759.

Disabled Students: The entire campus is accessible to disabled students. The following facilities are available: wheelchair ramps, elevators, special parking, specially equipped rest rooms, special class scheduling, lowered drinking fountains, and lowered telephones.

Services: In addition to many counseling and information services, tutoring is available in most subjects. In addition, there is a reader service for the blind, remedial math, reading, and writing, and tutorial assistance for disabled students.

Campus Safety and Security: Campus safety and security measures include 24-hour foot and vehicle patrol, informal discussions, pamphlets, posters, films, and emergency telephones. In addition, there are lighted pathways and sidewalks and paid student security attendants are posted at residence hall entrances.

Programs of Study: Seton Hall awards the B.A., B.S., B.S.Ed., and B.S.N. degrees. Master's and doctoral degrees also are awarded. Bachelor's degrees are awarded in BIOLOGICAL SCIENCE (biology/biological science), BUSINESS (accounting, banking and finance, business administration and management, business economics, and marketing/retailing/merchandising), COMMUNICATIONS AND THE ARTS (art, communications, English, French, Italian, modern language, music, and Spanish), COMPUTER AND PHYSICAL SCIENCE (chemistry, computer science, information sciences and systems, mathematics, and physics), EDUCATION (elementary, physical, and secondary), HEALTH PROFESSIONS (nursing, predentistry, and premedicine), SOCIAL SCIENCE (African American studies, anthropology, Asian/Oriental studies, classical/ancient civilization, criminal justice, economics, history, liberal arts/general studies, philosophy, political science/government, prelaw, psychology, religion, social science, social work, and sociology). Business (accounting, finance), premedical, predental, communications, and education are the strongest academically. Communications, accounting, political science, psychology, finance, biology, chemistry, and criminal justice have the largest enrollments.

Required: To graduate, students must complete at least 128 hours, including a minimum of 36 hours in the major. Students must take freshman composition, as well as courses in English, mathematics, social science, natural sciences, religious studies, and philosophy, earning a minimum GPA of 2.0 (2.5 education and human services).

Special: Co-op and work-study are possible through the College of Arts and Sciences and the School of Business, and internships are available in many arts and sciences majors. Education majors go into the field during their sophomore year. Cross-registration in engineering and 3–2 engineering degrees are offered with the New Jersey Institute of Technology and Stevens Institute of Technology. Students may take a Washington semester or study abroad in more than 100 countries. An accelerated B.S.N. degree, a 5-year B.A.-M.B.A., and a 5-year B.A.-B.S. degree in engineering are offered. Nondegree study is permitted, as are pass/fail options in electives. There is a freshman honors program on campus, as well as 20 national honor societies. All departments have honors programs.

Faculty/Classroom: Sixty-eight percent of faculty are male; 32%, female. No introductory courses are taught by graduate students. The average class size in an introductory lecture is 50; in a laboratory, 20; and in a regular course offering, 25.

Admissions: About 76% of the 1993–94 applicants were accepted. The SAT scores for the 1993–94 freshman class were as follows: Verbal—76% below 500, 19% between 500 and 599, 4% between 600 and 700, and 1% above 700; Math—52% below 500, 34% between 500 and 599, 13% between 600 and 700, and 1% above 700. About 35% of the current freshmen were in the top fifth of their class; 60% were in the top two fifths.

Requirements: The SAT I or ACT is required. A composite score of over 900 is recommended on the SAT I, with at least 450 on each part, or a minimum composite score of 24 on the ACT. Applicants must supply high school transcripts or a GED certificate. Students should have completed 16 Carnegie units of high school study, including 4 years of English, 3 of mathematics, 2 each of a foreign language and either history or social studies, and 1 of science. An essay is optional, and an interview is recommended. AP and CLEP credits are accepted. Important factors used in the admissions decision are advanced placement or honor courses, leadership record, parents or siblings attending the school, geographic diversity, and extracurricular activities record.

Procedure: Freshmen are admitted fall and spring. Entrance exams should be taken by January of the senior year. Applications should be filed by March 1 for fall entry and December 1 for spring entry, along with an application fee of $25. Notification is sent on a rolling basis, beginning after January 1. There is a deferred admissions plan. A waiting list is an active part of the admissions procedure, with about 6% of applicants on the list.

Transfer: About 260 transfer students enrolled in 1993–94. Transfer students should have earned 30 hours of college credit, with a minimum GPA of 2.5, or 2.8 for the business and science schools. The SAT I is required for students with fewer than 30 credits of college-level work at the time of application, and an interview is recommended. A total of 30 credits out of a minimum of 128 must be completed at Seton Hall.

Visiting: There are regularly scheduled orientations for prospective students, including Freshmen Preview (accepted students only), tours, meetings with department personnel, student talk, Freshman Studies talk, and financial aid and housing information. Visitors may sit in on classes. To arrange for a visit, contact the Office of Admissions at (201) 761–9332 or (800) THE-HALL (out-of-state).

Financial Aid: In 1993–94, 74% of all current freshmen and 74% of continuing students received some form of financial aid. About 70% of students received need-based aid. The average freshman award was $8700. Of that total, scholarships or need-based grants averaged $4600 ($18,000 maximum); loans averaged $3200 ($4200 maximum); and work contracts averaged $1000 ($2000 maximum). Sixteen percent of undergraduate students work part-time. Average earnings from campus work for the school year are $1000. The average financial indebtedness of the 1992–93 graduate was $10,000. Seton Hall is a member of CSS. The FAFSA financial statement is required. The deadline for financial aid applications is April 15.

International Students: There are currently 56 international students enrolled. The school actively recruits these students. They must take the TOEFL and achieve a minimum score of 550. The student must also take the college's placement tests.

Computers: The college provides computer facilities for student use. The mainframe is an IBM 4381. There are 14 computer facilities, with more than 250 networked systems and stand-alone computers. All students may access the system. Mainframe terminals are available until 11 P.M. and there are no time limits on using the system and no fees.

Graduates: In 1992–93, 1069 bachelor's degrees were awarded. The most popular majors among graduates were communications (14%), accounting (12%), and finance (8%). Within an average freshman class, 63% graduate in 6 years. In the 1992 graduating class, 30% of all graduates were enrolled in graduate school within 6 months of graduation; 56% had found employment.

Admissions Contact: Patricia L. Burgh, Dean for Enrollment Services.

STEVENS INSTITUTE OF TECHNOLOGY   E-2

Hoboken, NJ 07030   (201) 216-5194; (800) 247-7722 (out-of-state)

Full-time: 1025 men, 238 women	Faculty: 135
Part-time: 9 men, 2 women	Ph.D.s: 90%
Graduate: 1254 men, 348 women	Student/Faculty: 9 to 1
Year: semesters, summer session	Tuition: $16,690
Application Deadline: March 1	Room & Board: $5290
Freshman Class: 1768 applied, 1249 accepted, 380 enrolled	
SAT I Verbal/Math: 521/652	**VERY COMPETITIVE +**

Stevens Institute of Technology, founded in 1870, is a private, coeducational institution offering programs of study in science, computer science, engineering, and humanities. There is one graduate school. In addition to regional accreditation, Stevens has baccalaureate program accreditation with ABET. The library contains 150,000 volumes, 20 microform items, and 15,000 audiovisual forms, and subscribes to 1000 periodicals. Computerized library sources and services include the card catalog, interlibrary loans, and database searching. Special learning facilities include an art gallery, radio station, TV station, laboratory for ocean and coastal engineering, environmental laboratory, design and manufacturing institute, and telecommunications institute. The 55-acre campus is in an urban area 1 mile west of New York City. Including residence halls, there are 30 buildings on campus.

Student Life: About 67% of undergraduates are from New Jersey. Students come from 33 states and 40 foreign countries. Seventy-three percent are from public schools; 26% from private. Fifty-seven percent are white; 26% Asian American. The average age of freshmen is 18; all undergraduates, 20. Seventeen percent drop out by the end of their first year; 70% remain to graduate.

Housing: A total of 1015 students can be accommodated in college housing. College-sponsored living facilities include single-sex and coed dormitories, off-campus apartments, married-student housing, fraternity houses, and sorority houses. On-campus housing is guaranteed for all 4 years. Eighty percent of students live on campus; of those, 80% remain on campus on weekends. Upperclassmen may keep cars on campus.

Activities: About 40% of men and about 30% of women belong to 10 national fraternities; about 40% of women belong to 3 national sororities. There are 50 groups on campus, including art, band, chess, chorus, computers, drama, ethnic, international, jazz band, literary magazine, musical theater, newspaper, pep band, photography, political, professional, radio and TV, religious, social, student government, and yearbook. Popular campus events include the Fall Tech Fest and Spring Boken Festival.

Sports: There are 10 intercollegiate sports for men and 4 for women, and 18 intramural sports for men and 18 for women. Athletic and recreation facilities include a 60,000-square-foot complex with an NCAA regulation swimming pool convertible to international size, squash courts, a 1000-seat basketball arena, fitness rooms, and racquetball courts; a playing field; a student union; and several outdoor courts.

Disabled Students: Twenty-five percent of the campus is accessible to disabled students. The following facilities are available: wheelchair ramps, elevators, special parking, specially equipped rest rooms, and lowered drinking fountains.

Services: In addition to many counseling and information services, tutoring is available in every subject. There are special support programs for women.

Campus Safety and Security: Campus safety and security measures include 24-hour foot and vehicle patrol, self-defense education, escort service, and informal discussions. In addition, there are pamphlets, posters, and films, emergency telephones, and lighted pathways and sidewalks.

Programs of Study: Stevens awards the B.A., B.S., and B.E. degrees. Master's and doctoral degrees also are awarded. Bachelor's degrees are awarded in BIOLOGICAL SCIENCE (biochemistry), BUSINESS (management), COMMUNICATIONS AND THE ARTS (literature), COMPUTER AND PHYSICAL SCIENCE (chemistry, computer science, mathematics, physics, polymer engineering, science, and statistics), ENGINEERING AND ENVIRONMENTAL DESIGN (chemical engineering, civil engineering, computer engineering, electrical/electronics engineering, engineering management, engineering physics, environmental engineering, materials engineering, materials science, and mechanical engineering), SOCIAL SCIENCE (history and philosophy). Engineering is the strongest academically and has the largest enrollment.

Required: To graduate, the student must have earned at least 145 credit hours with a 2.0 GPA; the total hours in the major varies by program. The core curriculum includes courses in engineering, science, computer science, mathematics, liberal arts, and physical education.

Special: Stevens offers a 3–2 engineering degree with New York University, a work-study program within the school, co-op programs, corporate and research internships through the Undergraduate Projects in Technology and Medicine, and study abroad in Scotland or Germany. Students may undertake dual majors as well as accelerated degree programs in medicine, dentistry, and law, and can receive a B.A.-B.E. degree or a B.A.-B.S. degree in all majors. Pass/fail options are available for extra courses. Undergraduates may take graduate courses. There is a freshman honors program on campus, as well as 3 national honor societies.

Faculty/Classroom: Ninety-five percent of faculty are male; 5%, female. No introductory courses are taught by graduate students. The average class size in an introductory lecture is 100; in a laboratory, 50; and in a regular course offering, 20.

Admissions: About 71% of the 1993–94 applicants were accepted. About 66% of the current freshmen were in the top fifth of their class; 88% were in the top two fifths. There were 3 National Merit finalists and 15 semifinalists. Thirty freshmen graduated first in their class.

Requirements: Stevens requires applicants to be in the upper 20% of their class. A minimum GPA of 3.0 is required. The SAT I is required. In addition, applicants must provide high school transcripts or a GED certificate. Students should have taken 4 years of both English and mathematics, or 3 of mathematics for the management or liberal arts major. Stevens recommends either 2 or 3 SAT II: Subject tests, depending on the intended major. An interview is required. Stevens's application and catalog are on diskette, and students may apply online by computer. AP credits are accepted. Important factors used in the admissions decision are recommendations by school officials, advanced placement or honor courses, leadership record, extracurricular activities record, and personality, intangible qualities.

Procedure: Freshmen are admitted to all sessions. Entrance exams should be taken by March of the senior year. Early decision applications should be filed by November 1; regular applications, by March 1 for fall entry, November 1 for spring entry, and March 1 for summer entry, along with an application fee of $35. Notification of early decision is sent December 1; regular decision, on a rolling basis. There are early decision, early admissions, and deferred admissions plans. Twenty-three early decision candidates were accepted for the 1993–94 class.

Transfer: Some 60 transfer students enrolled in 1993–94. Transfer students must submit all college transcripts, including course descriptions. Applicants must have a GPA of 3.0, and SAT I or ACT scores are required of those with fewer than 30 hours of college credit. At least half of the required credits must be taken at Stevens.

Visiting: There are regularly scheduled orientations for prospective students. There are guides for informal visits and visitors may sit in on classes and stay overnight at the school. To arrange for a visit, contact the Admissions Office at (201) 216–5194.

Financial Aid: In 1993–94 75% of all current freshmen and 75% of continuing students received some form of financial aid. About 70% of freshmen and 70% of continuing students received need-based aid. The average freshman award was $17,850. Of that total, scholarships or need-based grants averaged $8000 ($12,500 maximum); loans averaged $7000 ($23,000 maximum); and work contracts averaged $1500 (maximum). Thirty-five percent of undergraduate students work part-time. Average earnings from campus work for the school year are $1500. The average financial indebtedness of the 1992–93 graduate was $16,000. Stevens is a member of CSS. The FAF and FAFSA are required. The deadline for financial aid applications is May 1.

International Students: There are currently 142 international students enrolled. The school actively recruits these students. They must take the TOEFL and achieve a minimum score of 550. The student must also take the SAT I.

Computers: The college provides computer facilities for student use. The mainframes are a DEC VAX 6320, an 11/785, an 8700, and an 11/780, a MicroVAX II, and several VAX 3600s. All students may access the mainframe anytime using their own computers connected to the campuswide network. There are no time limits on using the system and no fees. Stevens requires students to have a personal computer, and specifies an IBM-compatible 80486, 33 MHz or 66 MHz. The institute has a personal computer plan for $425 per year.

Graduates: In 1992–93 251 bachelor's degrees were awarded. The most popular majors among graduates were electrical engineering (23%), mechanical engineering (21%), and computer engineering (9%). Within an average freshman class, 73% graduate in 4 years and 78% in 5 years. Some 300 companies recruited on campus in 1992–93. In the 1992 graduating class, 15% of all students were enrolled in graduate school within 6 months of graduation; 91% had found employment.

Admissions Contact: Maureen Weatherall, Dean of Admissions and Financial Aid.

STOCKTON STATE COLLEGE
(See Richard Stockton College of New Jersey)

THOMAS A. EDISON STATE COLLEGE   D-3
Trenton, NJ 08608–1176   (609) 984–1150

Full-time: none	Faculty: n/app
Part-time: 5348 men, 3420 women	Ph.D.s: n/app
Graduate: none	Student/Faculty: n/app
Year: n/app	Tuition: $400 ($710)
Application Deadline: open	Room & Board: n/app
Freshman Class: 4720 applied, 4720 accepted, 2840 enrolled	
SAT I or ACT: not required	NONCOMPETITIVE

Thomas A. Edison State College, founded in 1972, is a public learner-centered institution serving the educational needs of adults in a rigorous academic program without interrupting their professional or personal lives. Students have numerous degree-completion options, including transfer of credit from other colleges, credit by examination, assessment of experiential learning, guided independent study, and credit from approved licenses, certificates, and training programs. The college has no classrooms or regular semesters; attendance is not required in the traditional college way. In addition to regional accreditation, Thomas Edison has baccalaureate program accreditation with NLN. The 2-acre campus is in an urban area 40 miles north of Philadelphia. There are 3 buildings on campus. There are no residence halls.

Student Life: About 67% of undergraduates are from New Jersey. Students come from 50 states, 66 foreign countries, and Canada. Eighty-five percent are white. The average age of all undergraduates is 38.7.

Housing: There are no residence halls.

Sports: There is no sports program at Thomas Edison.

Disabled Students: All of the campus is accessible to disabled students. The following facilities are available: wheelchair ramps, elevators, special parking, specially equipped rest rooms, and lowered drinking fountains.

Services: Alumni peer counseling and study groups for the nursing degree are among the counseling and tutorial services available.

Campus Safety and Security: Campus safety and security measures include lighted pathways and sidewalks. There is a guard on the premises 7 A.M. to 11 P.M.

Programs of Study: Thomas Edison awards the B.A., B.S., B.S.B.A., and B.S.N. degrees. Associate degrees also are awarded. Bachelor's degrees are awarded in BIOLOGICAL SCIENCE (biology/biological science), BUSINESS (business administration and management and labor studies), COMMUNICATIONS AND THE ARTS (communications, dance, dramatic arts, fine arts, journalism, languages, literature, music, and photography), COMPUTER AND PHYSICAL SCIENCE (chemistry, computer science, geology, mathematics, natural sciences, physics, and science technology), ENGINEERING AND ENVIRONMENTAL DESIGN (environmental science), HEALTH PROFESSIONS (nursing), SOCIAL SCIENCE (anthropology, archeology, economics, geography, history, human services, humanities, philosophy, political science/government, psychology, religion, social science, and sociology). The B.S. in applied science and technology, the B.S.B.A., and the B.A. have the largest enrollments.

Required: The baccalaureate student must complete at least 9 semester hours in each of 3 liberal arts areas (humanities, social sciences, and natural science/mathematics), including 1 year of English composition, and a mathematics or computer science course; 120 semester hours, 33 in the major, are required, with a minimum GPA of 2.0.

Special: Students may design their own majors and take dual majors in all degree programs except nursing. Credit for college-level knowledge gained through life, military, and work experience is readily granted. Students may receive pass/fail grades. The college will develop new programs of study when requested by students, if they fit into the school's aims/requirements. Students work on their own, proceeding at their own pace/schedule, depending on the option selected for earning credit. Thomas Edison has no semesters, though the Guided Study program is on a traditional semester calendar; the school holds 6 graduations a year.

Admissions: All of the 1993–94 applicants were accepted.

Requirements: Applicants must have a high school diploma or the equivalent and be at least 21 years old. AP and CLEP credits are accepted.

Procedure: Application deadlines are open. Application fee is $75. The college accepts all applicants. Notification is sent on a rolling basis.

Transfer: About 2840 transfer students enrolled in 1993–94. Transfers, like other students, must be at least 21 and be high school graduates or the equivalent. The granting of credit for coursework successfully completed elsewhere is an intrinsic part of the school's system. Transfer credits are awarded with the grades earned. All 120 credits may be acquired outside the college.

Visiting: There are regularly scheduled orientations for prospective students, including group information sessions/seminars. To arrange for a visit, contact Janice Toliver, Director of Admissions, at (609) 984-1150.

Financial Aid: In 1993–94, 1% of continuing students received need-based aid. The average award was $1000. Of that total, scholarships or need-based grants averaged $550; and loans averaged $450. Ninety-nine percent of undergraduate students work part-time. Thomas Edison is a member of CSS. The FAF is required. The deadline for financial aid applications is September 1.

International Students: There are currently 140 international students enrolled. They must take the TOEFL and achieve a minimum score of 500.

Computers: The college provides computer facilities for student use. The mainframes are a Wang VS 300 and a DEC VAX 4000. The Computer Assisted Lifelong Learning (CALL) Network allows students to dial in and log on to the college's computer system from home or work. Students may use electronic mail to communicate with the college, interactively register and pay fees, view copies of their records, and access informational software. Nonstudents may access information via the public bulletin board of the CALL Network. All students may access the system. It may be used at the student's convenience. There are no time limits on using the system and no fees.

Graduates: In a recent year, 495 bachelor's degrees were awarded. The most popular majors among graduates were general management (7%), social sciences (7%), and aviation (6%).

Admissions Contact: Janice Toliver, Director of Admissions.

TRENTON STATE COLLEGE D-3
Trenton, NJ 08650–4700

(609) 771-2131
(800) 345-7354 (out-of-state)

Full-time: 2010 men, 3155 women	Faculty: 311; IIA, + +$
Part-time: 316 men, 586 women	Ph.D.s: 81%
Graduate: 182 men, 761 women	Student/Faculty: 17 to 1
Year: semesters, summer session	Tuition: $3857 ($5934)
Application Deadline: March 1	Room & Board: $5228
Freshman Class: 5044 applied, 2312 accepted, 943 enrolled	
SAT I Verbal/Math: 520/590	HIGHLY COMPETITIVE

Trenton State College, founded in 1855, is a public, coeducational institution offering programs in the liberal arts, sciences, business, nursing, and education. In addition to regional accreditation, TSC has baccalaureate program accreditation with FIDER, NASM, NCATE, and NLN. The library contains 505,000 volumes, 558,000 microform items, and 10,050 audiovisual forms, and subscribes to 1566 periodicals. Computerized library sources and services include the card catalog, interlibrary loans, and database searching. Special learning facilities include a learning resource center, art gallery, planetarium, radio station, TV station, and a microscopy lab. The 250-acre campus is in a suburban area 6 miles northwest of Trenton in central New Jersey. Including residence halls, there are 36 buildings on campus.

Student Life: About 91% of undergraduates are from New Jersey. Students come from 20 states, 21 foreign countries, and Canada. Sixty-eight percent are from public schools; 32% from private. Eighty-five percent are white. Fifty-five percent are Catholic; 23% Protestant; 11% claim no religious affiliation. The average age of freshmen is 18; all undergraduates, 21.5. Four percent drop out by the end of their first year; 67% remain to graduate.

Housing: A total of 2743 students can be accommodated in college housing. College-sponsored living facilities include single-sex and coed dormitories. In addition there are study floors with extended quiet hours and an honors house. On-campus housing is available on a lottery system for upperclassmen. Fifty-three percent of students live on campus; of those, 40% remain on campus on weekends. Upperclassmen may keep cars on campus.

Activities: About 9% of men belong to 4 local and 10 national fraternities; about 9% of women belong to 3 local and 13 national sororities. There are 140 groups on campus, including art, band, cheerleading, choir, chorale, chorus, computers, dance, drama, ethnic, film, gay, honors, international, jazz band, literary magazine, musical theater, newspaper, opera, orchestra, pep band, photography, political, professional, radio and TV, religious, social, social service, student government, symphony, and yearbook. Popular campus events include Family Fest (Parents Day), Convocation, Homecoming, Black History Month, Hispanic Awareness Week, Welcome Week, Handicapable Awareness Week, International Week, Holiday Marketplace, Government Jam, Puerto Rican Heritage Month, Multicultural Lecture Series, and Feast of the Golden Lion (honoring student leaders).

Sports: There are 11 intercollegiate sports for men and 10 for women, and 11 intramural sports for men and 11 for women. Athletic and recreation facilities include a 5000-seat stadium with an astroturf field, an aquatic center, baseball and softball diamonds, an NCAA-approved all-weather track, lighted tennis courts, a 1200-seat gymnasium, and a student recreation center with tennis and racquetball courts and a weight room.

Disabled Students: Eighty-five percent of the campus is accessible to disabled students. The following facilities are available: wheelchair ramps, elevators, special parking, specially equipped rest rooms, special class scheduling, lowered drinking fountains, lowered telephones, TDD machines for the deaf, and a library room equipped for the hearing-impaired, visually impaired, and motor-impaired.

Services: In addition to many counseling and information services, tutoring is available in most subjects. There is a reader service for the blind, and remedial math, reading, and writing. The school also offers science laboratory tutoring and evaluative testing services.

Campus Safety and Security: Campus safety and security measures include 24-hour foot and vehicle patrol, escort service, informal discussions, and pamphlets, posters, and films. In addition, there are emergency telephones and lighted pathways and sidewalks.

Programs of Study: TSC awards the B.A., B.S., B.F.A., B.M., and B.S.N. degrees. Master's degrees also are awarded. Bachelor's degrees are awarded in BIOLOGICAL SCIENCE (biology/biological science), BUSINESS (accounting, banking and finance, business administration and management, business economics, management science, and marketing/retailing/merchandising), COMMUNICATIONS AND THE ARTS (communications, dramatic arts, English, fine arts, and music), COMPUTER AND PHYSICAL SCIENCE (chemistry, computer science, mathematics, physics, and statistics), EDUCATION (art, early childhood, elementary, health, music, physical, and special), ENGINEERING AND ENVIRONMENTAL DESIGN (engineering and applied science), HEALTH PROFESSIONS (nursing and speech pathology/audiology), SOCIAL SCIENCE (criminal justice, econom-

ics, history, philosophy, political science/government, psychology, and sociology). History, biology, accounting, psychology, and elementary education are the strongest academically. Art, English, elementary/early childhood education, engineering science, business administration, and nursing have the largest enrollments.

Required: To graduate, the student must earn 128 semester hours, with a minimum GPA of 2.0. The student must complete a general education curriculum that includes 26 hours in Perspectives on the World, 3 to 21 hours in Intellectual Skills, and 9 hours in Interdisciplinary Core: Understanding Humanity. A college seminar is required of first-time freshmen. The credits required in the major vary by program.

Special: TSC offers cross-registration with the New Jersey Marine Science Consortium, internships with the Big 6 accounting firms, radio and television stations, and local governments, and study abroad through the International Student Exchange program (ISEP). Nondegree study and pass/fail options are possible. The Oxford tutorial is offered in a small class setting. There is a freshman honors program on campus, as well as 9 national honor societies. Seventeen departments have honors programs.

Faculty/Classroom: Sixty-six percent of faculty are male; 34%, female. Ninety-eight percent teach undergraduates and 22% both teach and do research. No introductory courses are taught by graduate students. The average class size in a laboratory is 24 and in a regular course offering, 19.

Admissions: About 46% of the 1993–94 applicants were accepted. The SAT scores for the 1993–94 freshman class were as follows: Verbal—38% below 500, 48% between 500 and 599, 13% between 600 and 700, and 1% above 700; Math—10% below 500, 42% between 500 and 599, 38% between 600 and 700, and 11% above 700. About 90% of the current freshmen were in the top fifth of their class; 98% were in the top two fifths. There was 1 National Merit finalist and 2 semifinalists. About 50 freshmen graduated first in their class.

Requirements: The SAT I is required. Applicants must have earned 16 academic credits in high school, consisting of 4 in English, 2 each in mathematics, science, and social studies, and 6 others distributed among mathematics, science, social studies, and a foreign language. An essay is required. Art majors must submit a portfolio, and music majors must audition. The GED is accepted. AP and CLEP credits are accepted. Important factors used in the admissions decision are advanced placement or honor courses, leadership record, evidence of special talent, personality, intangible qualities, and recommendations by school officials.

Procedure: Freshmen are admitted fall and spring. Entrance exams should be taken by the end of the junior year or early in the senior year. Early decision applications should be filed by November 15; regular applications, by March 1 for fall entry, November 1 for spring entry, and May 1 for summer entry, along with an application fee of $50. Notification of early decision is sent December 15; regular decision, April 1. There are early decision and early admissions plans. About 100 early decision candidates were accepted for the 1993–94 class. A waiting list is an active part of the admissions procedure, with about 5% of applicants on the list.

Transfer: About 550 transfer students enrolled in 1993–94. Transfer students must have a minimum GPA of 3.0, and those with fewer than 33 credits must submit SAT I scores. An associate degree is recommended. A total of 45 credits out of 128 must be completed at TSC.

Visiting: There are regularly scheduled orientations for prospective students. There are guides for informal visits and visitors may sit in on classes and stay overnight at the school. To arrange for a visit, contact the Admissions Office at (609) 771–2131 or (800) 345–7354 (out-of-state).

Financial Aid: In 1993–94 55% of all current freshmen and 48% of continuing students received some form of financial aid. About 40% of all students received need-based aid. The average freshman award was $4600. Of that total, scholarships or need-based grants averaged $2600 ($9500 maximum); loans averaged $3200 ($9500 maximum); and work contracts averaged $1000 ($2000 maximum). Twenty-five percent of undergraduate students work part-time. Average earnings from campus work for the school year are $850. The average financial indebtedness of the 1992–93 graduate was $4200. TSC is a member of CSS. The FAF, the college's own financial statement, and copies of the student's and the parents' tax returns are required. The deadline for financial aid applications is May 1.

International Students: There are currently 70 international students enrolled. They must take the TOEFL and achieve a minimum score of 550. Students must also take SAT I and SAT II: engineering technology test, and pass a mathematics aptitude test.

Computers: The college provides computer facilities for student use. The mainframe is an IBM 4381-P13. There are 420 microcomputers/terminals available in 16 academic computing laboratories throughout the campus. All students may access the system. There are no time limits on using the system and no fees.

Graduates: In 1992–93 1101 bachelor's degrees were awarded. The most popular majors among graduates were elementary/early childhood education (11%), business administraton (7%), and English (7%). Within an average freshman class, 67% graduate in 5 years. Some 200 companies recruited on campus in 1992–93.

Admissions Contact: John Iacovelli, Director of Admissions and Financial Aid.

UPSALA COLLEGE
E-2

East Orange, NJ 07019   (201) 266–7191

Full-time: 1076 men and women	Faculty: 58; IIB, -$
Part-time: 412 men and women	Ph.D.s: 63%
Graduate: none	Student/Faculty: 19 to 1
Year: semesters, summer session	Tuition: $12,500
Application Deadline: June 1	Room & Board: $4700
Freshman Class: 1738 applied, 1464 accepted, 555 enrolled	
SAT I Verbal/Math: 420/440	**COMPETITIVE**

Upsala College, founded in 1893, is a private, coeducational liberal arts institution affiliated with the Evangelical Lutheran Church in America. Wirths College, a branch campus in Sussex County, offers selected bachelor-level programs. In addition to regional accreditation, Upsala has baccalaureate program accreditation with CSWE. The library contains 162,000 volumes, 1000 microform items, and 300 audiovisual forms, and subscribes to 631 periodicals. Computerized library sources and services include interlibrary loans and database searching. Special learning facilities include a learning resource center, a radio station, and a theater. The 45-acre campus is in an urban area 15 miles east of New York City. Including residence halls, there are 31 buildings on campus.

Student Life: About 80% of undergraduates are from New Jersey. Students come from 7 states, 16 foreign countries, and Canada. Seventy-eight percent are from public schools. Forty percent are white; 34% African American; 15% Asian American; 11% foreign nationals; 11% Hispanic. Fifty percent are Catholic; 23% Protestant; 26% claim no religious affiliation. The average age of freshmen is 19; all undergraduates, 24. Twenty-four percent drop out by the end of their first year; 46% remain to graduate.

Housing: A total of 500 students can be accommodated in college housing. College-sponsored living facilities include single-sex and coed dormitories. On-campus housing is guaranteed for all 4 years. Fifty percent of students live on campus; of those, 30% remain on campus on weekends. Alcohol is not permitted. All students may keep cars on campus.

Activities: About 20% of men and about 7% of women belong to 2 local and 4 national fraternities; about 50% of women belong to 4 national sororities. There are 26 groups on campus, including art, cheerleading, choir, chorus, computers, ethnic, honors, international, literary magazine, musical theater, newspaper, photography, political, professional, radio and TV, religious, social, student government, and yearbook. Popular campus events include Homecoming, theater performances, and jazz nights.

Sports: There are 8 intercollegiate sports for men and 35 for women, and 10 intramural sports each for men and women. Athletic and recreation facilities include a field, tennis courts, a 2200-seat gymnasium, a 1200-seat stadium, and a 2200-seat auditorium/arena.

Disabled Students: Half of the campus is accessible to disabled students. The following facilities are available: wheelchair ramps, elevators, special parking, specially equipped rest rooms, and special class scheduling.

Services: In addition to many counseling and information services, tutoring is available in every subject. There is also remedial math, reading, and writing.

Campus Safety and Security: Campus safety and security measures include 24-hour foot and vehicle patrol, informal discussions, pamphlets, posters, films, and emergency telephones. In addition, there are lighted pathways and sidewalks.

Programs of Study: Upsala awards the B.A., B.S., and B.S.W. degrees. Associate degrees also are awarded. Bachelor's degrees are awarded in BIOLOGICAL SCIENCE (biochemistry and biology/biological science), BUSINESS (accounting, business administration and management, international business management, and personnel management), COMMUNICATIONS AND THE ARTS (communications, English, fine arts, and Spanish), COMPUTER AND PHYSICAL SCIENCE (chemistry, computer science, information sciences and systems, and mathematics), SOCIAL SCIENCE (anthropology, economics, history, political science/government, psychology, religion, social work, and sociology). Multinational corporate studies is the strongest academically. Business administration has the largest enrollment.

Required: In order to graduate, all students must complete at least 128 credit hours (32 4-credit courses), with 32 to 56 in the major (8 4-credit courses) and a minimum 2.0 GPA. Distribution requirements include 2 courses each in foreign language, laboratory science, and area studies (non-Western), and 1 course each in art, social science, and humanities. Students also take courses in Western culture, com-

puter science, and writing-intensive courses. The New Jersey College Basic Skills Test is required.

Special: Upsala offers cooperative programs with New Jersey Institute of Technology (NJIT), Pennsylvania College of Optometry, and the University of Medicine and Dentistry of New Jersey. Internships, study abroad in 3 countries, and a Washington semester, student-designed majors, a 3–2 engineering degree with NJIT, credit for experience, pass/fail options, independent study, and an Air Force ROTC cross-registration program with NJIT are also available. There is a freshman honors program on campus.

Faculty/Classroom: Fifty-seven percent of faculty are male; 43%, female. All teach undergraduates. The average class size in an introductory lecture is 40; in a laboratory, 25; and in a regular course offering, 20.

Admissions: About 84% of the 1993–94 applicants were accepted. There was 1 National Merit finalist.

Requirements: Upsala requires applicants to be in the upper 60% of their class. A minimum GPA of 2.0 is required. The SAT I is required. Applicants should be graduates of an accredited secondary school with 16 academic credits. These include 4 years of English, 3 each of mathematics and electives, and 2 each of foreign language, history/social studies, and laboratory science. All secondary school records are required. An interview is advised and recommendations are considered. AP and CLEP credits are accepted. Important factors used in the admissions decision are advanced placement or honor courses, evidence of special talent, recommendations by school officials, geographic diversity, personality, and intangible qualities.

Procedure: Freshmen are admitted to all sessions. Entrance exams should be taken by December of the senior year. Early decision applications should be filed by May 1; regular applications, by June 1 for fall entry, along with an application fee of $30. Notification of early decision is sent December 1; regular decision, on a rolling basis. There are early decision, early admissions, and deferred admissions plans. About 10 early decision candidates were accepted for the 1993–94 class. A waiting list is an active part of the admissions procedure, with about 33% of applicants on the list.

Transfer: Applicants must have a GPA of 2.0. The SAT I and a high school transcript are required of transfers with fewer than 30 credits. A total of 32 credits out of 128 must be completed at Upsala.

Visiting: There are regularly scheduled orientations for prospective students, including an interview and campus tour. There are guides for informal visits and visitors may sit in on classes and stay overnight at the school. To arrange for a visit, contact the Admissions Department at (201) 266–7191.

Financial Aid: In a recent year, 88% of all students received some form of financial aid. About 75% received need-based aid. The average freshman award was $10,000. Of that total, scholarships or need-based grants averaged $50 ($6000 maximum); loans averaged $2625 (maximum); and work contracts averaged $1300 ($2500 maximum). All undergraduate students work part-time. Average earnings from campus work for the school year are $2000. The average financial indebtedness of a recent graduate was $2000. Upsala is a member of CSS. The FAF is required. The deadline for financial aid applications is May 15.

International Students: There are currently 80 international students enrolled. The school actively recruits these students. They must take the TOEFL and achieve a minimum score of 400. The student must also take the SAT I and the New Jersey College Basic Skills Test.

Computers: The college provides computer facilities for student use. The mainframe is a Prime. There are 2 computer rooms linked to the mainframe, and an open computer laboratory with IBM PCs and Apple Macintoshes which operates 60 hours a week. All students may access the system. There are no time limits and no fees.

Graduates: In a recent year, 200 bachelor's degrees were awarded. Within an average freshman class, 40% graduate in 4 years, 45% in 5 years, and 46% in 6 years. Some 53 companies recruited on campus. In a recent graduating class, 10% of the men and 15% of the women were enrolled in graduate school within 6 months of graduation; 75% of the men and 70% of the women had found employment.

Admissions Contact: Susan Chaplin, Director of Admissions.

WESTMINSTER CHOIR COLLEGE D-3
Princeton, NJ 08540 (609) 921-7144; (800) 96-CHOIR (out-of-state)

Full-time: 79 men, 142 women	Faculty: 40; IIA, ++$
Part-time: 15 men, 23 women	Ph.D.s: 60%
Graduate: 43 men, 61 women	Student/Faculty: 6 to 1
Year: semesters, summer session	Tuition: $13,070
Application Deadline: open	Room & Board: $5515
Freshman Class: 146 applied, 135 accepted, 73 enrolled	
SAT I Verbal/Math: 490/510	ACT: 22 SPECIAL

Westminster Choir College, founded in 1926, is a private coeducational school of music within Rider College, that focuses on undergraduate and graduate students seeking positions of music leadership in churches, schools, and communities. There is one graduate

school. In addition to regional accreditation, Westminster has baccalaureate program accreditation with NASM. The library contains 56,260 volumes, 414 microform items, and 8000 audiovisual forms, and subscribes to 175 periodicals. Computerized library sources and services include the card catalog, interlibrary loans, and database searching. Special learning facilities include a learning resource center, a music computer laboratory, and a vocal laboratory. The 23-acre campus is in a suburban area 50 miles south of New York City. Including residence halls, there are 12 buildings on campus.

Student Life: About 63% of undergraduates are from out-of-state, mostly the Middle Atlantic. Students come from 36 states, 17 foreign countries, and Canada. Seventy-five percent are white; 13% foreign nationals. The average age of freshmen is 18; all undergraduates, 20.6. Eighteen percent drop out by the end of their first year; 50% remain to graduate.

Housing: A total of 206 students can be accommodated in college housing. College-sponsored living facilities include single-sex and coed dormitories. On-campus housing is guaranteed for all 4 years. Fifty-eight percent of students live on campus; of those, 85% remain on campus on weekends. All students may keep cars on campus.

Activities: There are no fraternities or sororities on campus. There are 12 groups on campus, including choir, chorus, drama, honors, musical theater, newspaper, opera, orchestra (community), professional, radio and TV (Rider campus), religious, social, student government, and yearbook. Popular campus events include Spring Fling, Christmas at Westminster, Homecoming Dance, and concerts.

Sports: There are 2 intramural sports for men and 2 for women.

Disabled Students: Forty-two percent of the campus is accessible to disabled students. The following facilities are available: wheelchair ramps, elevators, special parking, and specially equipped rest rooms.

Services: In addition to many counseling and information services, tutoring is available in every subject. There is remedial math, reading, and writing.

Campus Safety and Security: Campus safety and security measures include escort service, emergency telephones, lighted pathways and sidewalks, and increased campus security from 6 P.M. to 6 A.M.

Programs of Study: Westminster awards the B.A. and B.M. degrees. Master's degrees also are awarded. Bachelor's degrees are awarded in COMMUNICATIONS AND THE ARTS (music, music performance, music theory and composition, piano/organ, and voice), EDUCATION (music), SOCIAL SCIENCE (religious music). Music education has the largest enrollment.

Required: All students must maintain a minimum GPA of 2.0 (2.5 for music education majors) while completing 124 semester hours, including 92 to 100 in their majors. All students also must meet English reading and writing proficiency requirements. Distribution requirements include 33 semester hours in arts and sciences with at least 1 course from each of the divisions of the department. Satisfactory performance in recital also is needed.

Special: Cross-registration with Princeton University, Rider College, and Princeton Theological Seminary, internships in church, work-study programs, dual majors in any combination of 7 majors in music, and pass/fail options are available. There is one national honor society on campus.

Faculty/Classroom: All teach undergraduates. The average class size in an introductory lecture is 18; in a laboratory, 8; and in a regular course offering, 12.

Admissions: About 92% of the 1993–94 applicants were accepted. The SAT scores for the 1993–94 freshman class were as follows: Verbal—55% below 500, 35% between 500 and 599, and 10% between 600 and 700; Math—47% below 500, 31% between 500 and 599, 18% between 600 and 700, and 4% above 700. The ACT scores were 57% below 21, 14% between 24 and 26, 14% between 27 and 28, and 15% above 28. About 34% of the current freshmen were in the top fifth of their class; 64% were in the top two fifths.

Requirements: Westminster requires applicants to be in the upper 50% of their class. A minimum GPA of 2.0 is required. The SAT I, with minimum scores of 700 composite, 300 verbal and 350 mathematics, or the ACT is required. Applicants must present 4 years each of credits in English and history, 2 in mathematics, and 1 in science. An essay and music audition are required, while an interview is recommended. The GED is accepted. AP credits are accepted. Important factors used in the admissions decision are evidence of special talent, recommendations by alumni, recommendations by school officials, advanced placement or honor courses, and personality, intangible qualities.

Procedure: Freshmen are admitted fall and spring. Entrance exams should be taken at the time of the audition. Application deadlines are open. The application fee is $35. Notification is sent on a rolling basis. There are early decision, early admissions, and deferred admissions plans.

Transfer: About 16 transfer students enrolled in a recent year. Transfer applicants must submit high school and college transcripts and 3 letters of recommendation. An audition is required. A total of 65 credits out of 124 must be completed at Westminster.

Visiting: There are regularly scheduled orientations for prospective students. There are guides for informal visits and visitors may sit in on classes. To arrange for a visit, contact the Admissions Office at (609) 921-7144 or (800) 962-4647.

Financial Aid: In 1993-94 more than 80% of all students received some form of financial aid. About 74% of freshmen and 81% of continuing students received need-based aid. Scholarships or need-based grants averaged $3000 ($12,750 maximum); loans averaged $2600 ($5000 maximum); and work contracts averaged $1000 ($1500 maximum). About 85% of undergraduate students work part-time. Average earnings from campus work for the school year are $900. The average financial indebtedness of the 1992-93 graduate was $10,240. Westminster is a member of CSS. The FAFSA financial statement is required. The deadline for financial aid applications is March 15.

International Students: There are currently 46 international students enrolled. They must take the TOEFL and achieve a minimum score of 580.

Computers: The college provides computer facilities for student use. Microcomputers are available for academic use in the music, art and sciences, and learning center computer laboratories. All students may access the system. There are no time limits on using the system and no fees.

Graduates: In 1992-93, 38 bachelor's degrees were awarded. The most popular majors among graduates were music education (47%), voice performance (18%), and church music (18%). Within an average freshman class, 36% graduate in 4 years, 47% in 5 years, and 50% in 6 years. In the 1992 graduating class, 7% of the men and 8% of the women were enrolled in graduate school within 6 months of graduation; 62% of the men and 73% of the women had found employment.

Admissions Contact: Deborah Erie, Director of Admissions.

WILLIAM PATERSON COLLEGE
Wayne, NJ 07470

E-2
(201) 595-2126

Full-time: 2609 men, 3307 women	Faculty: 311; IIB, + +$
Part-time: 766 men, 1362 women	Ph.D.s: 79%
Graduate: 222 men, 695 women	Student/Faculty: 19 to 1
Year: semesters, summer session	Tuition: $2928 ($3856)
Application Deadline: June 30	Room & Board: $4510
Freshman Class: 5485 applied, 2662 accepted, 1108 enrolled	
SAT I Verbal/Math: 428/485	ACT: 21 COMPETITIVE +

William Paterson College, founded in 1855, is a public coeducational institution comprised of schools of Arts and Communication; Education; Humanities, Management, and Social Sciences; and Science and Health. There are 4 undergraduate and 4 graduate schools. In addition to regional accreditation, WPC has baccalaureate program accreditation with ASHA, NASM, NCATE, and NLN. The library contains 307,000 volumes, 102,000 microform items, and 5300 audiovisual forms, and subscribes to 1400 periodicals. Computerized library sources and services include the card catalog, interlibrary loans, and database searching. Special learning facilities include a learning resource center, an art gallery, a radio station, a TV station, a speech and hearing clinic, computer laboratories, an academic support center, a computerized writing center, and a teleconference center. The 250-acre campus is in a suburban area 25 miles west of New York City. Including residence halls, there are 35 buildings on campus.

Student Life: About 98% of undergraduates are from New Jersey. Students come from 4 states, 15 foreign countries, and Canada. Seventy-five percent are from public schools; 25% from private. Eighty percent are white. The average age of freshmen is 18; all undergraduates, 26.

Housing: A total of 1800 students can be accommodated in college housing. College-sponsored living facilities include coed dormitories and on-campus apartments. On-campus housing is guaranteed for all 4 years. Eighty-one percent of students commute. All students may keep cars on campus.

Activities: About 10% of men belong to 3 local and 8 national fraternities; about 12% of women belong to 3 local and 11 national sororities. There are 50 groups on campus, including art, cheerleading, chorus, computers, dance, drama, ethnic, film, gay, honors, international, jazz band, literary magazine, musical theater, newspaper, opera, orchestra, photography, political, professional, radio and TV, religious, student government, and yearbook. Popular campus events include athletics, distinguished lecturer series, theater, jazz concerts, Wayne Chamber Orchestra, Midday Artist Series, Kwanza, Freshman Convocation, Homecoming, African Heritage Month, Puerto Rican Heritage Month, Latin American Week, and Springfest.

Sports: There are 7 intercollegiate sports each for men and women, and 24 intramural sports each for men and women. Athletic and recreation facilities include a recreation center with courts for basketball, tennis, racquetball, volleyball, and badminton, weight and exercise rooms, saunas and whirlpools, and a 4000-seat auditorium. The college also offers an Olympic-size pool, 8 additional tennis courts, and an athletic complex with fields for baseball, field hockey, football, soccer, softball, and track.

Disabled Students: The following facilities are available: wheelchair ramps, elevators, special parking, specially equipped rest rooms, special class scheduling, and lowered drinking fountains.

Services: In addition to many counseling and information services, tutoring is available in most subjects. There is a science enrichment center and a writing center. In addition, there is a reader service for the blind, and remedial math, reading, and writing.

Campus Safety and Security: Campus safety and security measures include 24-hour foot and vehicle patrol, shuttle buses, informal discussions, and pamphlets, posters, and films. In addition, there are emergency telephones and lighted pathways and sidewalks.

Programs of Study: WPC awards the B.A., B.S., B.F.A., and B.M. degrees. Master's degrees also are awarded. Bachelor's degrees are awarded in BIOLOGICAL SCIENCE (biology/biological science and biotechnology), BUSINESS (accounting, banking and finance, and business administration and management), COMMUNICATIONS AND THE ARTS (art history, communications, dramatic arts, English, fine arts, music, Spanish, and studio art), COMPUTER AND PHYSICAL SCIENCE (chemistry, computer science, and mathematics), EDUCATION (health, music, physical, and special), ENGINEERING AND ENVIRONMENTAL DESIGN (environmental science), HEALTH PROFESSIONS (community health work, health science, nursing, and speech pathology/audiology), SOCIAL SCIENCE (African, African American and Caribbean studies, anthropology, economics, geography, history, liberal arts/general studies, philosophy, political science/government, psychology, and sociology). Biology/biotechnology, management, English, political science, and nursing are the strongest academically. Management, communications, education, and sociology have the largest enrollments.

Required: All students must maintain a cumulative GPA of at least 2.0 and take 128 credit hours, typically including 30 to 40 in their major. General education requirements include 6 credits in art and communication, 21 in the humanities, 11 or 12 in science, and 9 in the social sciences. Also required are 1 course in health or movement science and 1 course in non-Western culture. Students also complete 6 credits of general education electives and a minimum of 9 credits of upper-level elective courses.

Special: Study abroad in 33 countries, cross-registration, internships, work-study programs on campus, accelerated degree programs, dual majors, individual curriculum design, and credit for military experience are available. Nondegree study and some pass/fail options are also possible. In the Learning Clusters Project, students experience how 3 general education courses, taken together, reinforce and better integrate each other. There is a professional program in teacher education leading to certification in early childhood, elementary, middle, and secondary education. There are 6 national honor societies on campus. Four departments have honors programs.

Faculty/Classroom: Sixty-two percent of faculty are male; 38%, female. All teach undergraduates, 40% also do research. No introductory courses are taught by graduate students. The average class size in an introductory lecture is 32; in a laboratory, 24; and in a regular course offering, 19.

Admissions: About 49% of the 1993-94 applicants were accepted. The SAT scores for the 1993-94 freshman class were as follows: Verbal—80% below 500, 15% between 500 and 599, and 2% between 600 and 700; Math—59% below 500, 37% between 500 and 599, and 7% between 600 and 700. About 24% of the current freshmen were in the top fifth of their class; 69% were in the top two fifths.

Requirements: The SAT I is required. Applicants must have 16 academic credits or Carnegie units, including 4 in English, 3 in mathematics, 2 each in science laboratory and social studies, and 5 electives such as foreign language and history. An essay and interview are recommended for some applicants, as are a portfolio and audition. The GED is accepted. AP and CLEP credits are accepted. Important factors used in the admissions decision are advanced placement or honor courses, recommendations by school officials, evidence of special talent, extracurricular activities record, personality, and intangible qualities.

Procedure: Freshmen are admitted fall and spring. Entrance exams should be taken by January 31. Early decision applications should be filed by April 1; regular applications, by June 30 for fall entry and November 1 for spring entry, along with an application fee of $20. Notification of early decision is sent January 15; regular decision, on a rolling basis. There are early decision, early admissions, and deferred admissions plans. About 84 early decision candidates were accepted for the 1993-94 class. A waiting list is an active part of the admissions procedure, with about 5% of applicants on the list.

Transfer: About 960 transfer students enrolled in 1993–94. Transfer students need a minimum GPA of 2.0 (business, nursing, and education students need a 2.5 GPA) and at least 12 credit hours earned. A total of 30 credits out of 128 must be completed at WPC.

Visiting: There are regularly scheduled orientations for prospective students, including a campus tour, guest speakers, and dissemination of printed information. There are guides for informal visits and visitors may sit in on classes. To arrange for a visit, contact the Admissions Office at (201) 595–2125.

Financial Aid: In a recent year, 44% of all freshmen and 33% of continuing students received some form of financial aid. About 36% of freshmen and 26% of continuing students received need-based aid. The average freshman award was $3591. Of that total, scholarships or need-based grants averaged $2946 ($5480 maximum); loans averaged $2272 ($5000 maximum); and work contracts averaged $792 ($3000 maximum). Forty-seven percent of undergraduate students work part-time. Average earnings from campus work for the school year are $1070. The average financial indebtedness of a re-

cent graduate was $4450. WPC is a member of CSS. The FAF and parent and student federal income tax forms are required. The deadline for financial aid applications is open.

International Students: There are currently 50 international students enrolled. They must take the TOEFL and achieve a minimum score of 550, or they may take the SAT I.

Computers: The college provides computer facilities for student use. The mainframe is an IBM 3099. There are also Zenith, Apple II, and AST Bravo/286 microcomputers available for student use. All students may access the system at all times. There are no time limits on using the system. The fee is $30.

Graduates: In 1992–93, 1560 bachelor's degrees were awarded. Within an average freshman class, 14% graduate in 4 years, 37% in 5 years, and 46% in 6 years. Some 46 companies recruited on campus in 1992–93.

Admissions Contact: Director of Admissions.

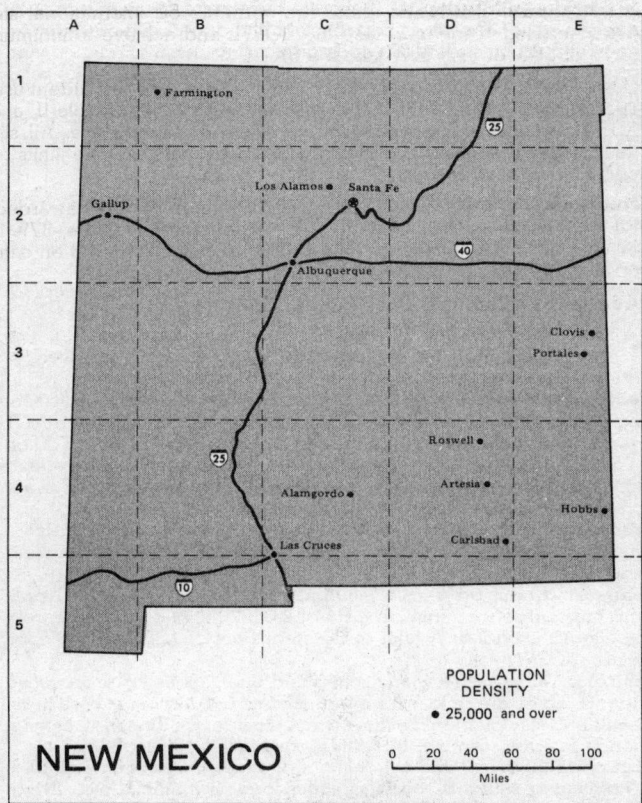

NEW MEXICO

POPULATION
DENSITY
● 25,000 and over

0 20 40 60 80 100
Miles

COLLEGE OF SANTA FE
Santa Fe, NM 87501–5634

C-2

(505) 473–6133
(800) 456–2673 (out-of-state)

Full-time: 784 men and women
Part-time: n/av
Graduate: none
Year: semesters, summer session
Application Deadline: open
Freshman Class: 535 applied, 442 accepted, 177 enrolled
SAT I Verbal/Math: 480/490

Faculty: 54; IIB, --$
Ph.D.s: 75%
Student/Faculty: 15 to 1
Tuition: $9900
Room & Board: $4108

ACT: 21 **COMPETITIVE**

The College of Santa Fe, founded in 1947 by the Christian Brothers, is a private liberal arts institution, offering undergraduate programs in social sciences, humanities, education, science and mathematics, business, visual arts, moving image arts, and performing arts. There are 8 undergraduate and 2 graduate schools. The library contains 165,000 volumes and 7268 audiovisual forms, and subscribes to 321 periodicals. Computerized library sources and services include database searching. Special learning facilities include a learning resource center, an art gallery, a professional sound stage for film and video, and a professional graphics workshop. The 118-acre campus is in a suburban area. Including residence halls, there are 40 buildings on campus.

Student Life: Students come from Canada. Sixty-three percent are white; 28% Hispanic. The average age of freshmen is 19; all undergraduates, 27. Thirty-eight percent drop out by the end of their first year; 53% remain to graduate.

Housing: A total of 404 students can be accommodated in college housing. College-sponsored living facilities include single-sex and coed dormitories. In addition, there are honors houses, an alcohol-free dormitory, and nontraditional-aged student housing. On-campus housing is guaranteed for the freshman year only. Fifty-one percent of students commute. All students may keep cars on campus.

Activities: There are no fraternities or sororities on campus. There are 22 groups on campus, including art, computers, dance, drama, ethnic, film, gay, honors, international, literary magazine, musical theater, newspaper, photography, political, radio and TV, religious, social, social service, student government, and yearbook. Popular campus events include Spring Fest, Christmas Ball, Halloween Dance, Halloween Haunted House, Timex Fitness Week, Music Fest, President's Pancake Flip, and AIDS Awareness Week.

Sports: There are 5 intramural sports for men and 5 for women. Athletic and recreation facilities include a fitness center housing a gymnasium, racquetball/squash courts, a weight room, multipurpose exercise room, and an athletic field.

Disabled Students: The entire campus is accessible to disabled students. The following facilities are available: wheelchair ramps, elevators, special parking, specially equipped rest rooms, lowered drinking fountains, lowered telephones, and lowered light switches and controls in dormitories.

Services: In addition to many counseling and information services, tutoring is available in most subjects. There is remedial math, reading, and writing.

Campus Safety and Security: Campus safety and security measures include 24-hour foot and vehicle patrol, self defense education, informal discussions, and pamphlets, posters, and films. In addition, there are emergency telephones and lighted pathways and sidewalks.

Programs of Study: CSF awards the B.A., B.S., and B.F.A. degrees. Master's degrees also are awarded. Bachelor's degrees are awarded in BIOLOGICAL SCIENCE (biology/biological science), BUSINESS (accounting and business administration and management), COMMUNICATIONS AND THE ARTS (art history and appreciation, creative writing, design, dramatic arts, English, film arts, music, and visual and performing arts), COMPUTER AND PHYSICAL SCIENCE (chemistry, computer science, information sciences and systems, and mathematics), EDUCATION (education, English, and mathematics), ENGINEERING AND ENVIRONMENTAL DESIGN (environmental science), SOCIAL SCIENCE (human services, humanities, psychology, public administration, religion, and Southwest American Studies). The arts, business, and education are the strongest academically. Performing arts, moving image arts, and visual arts have the largest enrollments.

Required: Students must successfully complete 128 credit hours, with 64 to 69 hours in the major and a minimum GPA of 2.0. The liberal arts core curriculum requires courses in science, humanities, philosophy, religious studies, English, speech, social science, physical education, and health awareness.

Special: CSF offers co-op programs in art therapy and arts and entertainment management, internships in moving image arts, performing arts, business, psychology, science, and education, and cross-registration with the Institute of American Indian Arts. Work study, study abroad in London, student-designed majors, pass/fail options, credit by examination, art studies in New York City, and credit for work experience are possible.

Faculty/Classroom: Eighty-two percent of faculty are male; 18%, female. All teach undergraduates and 10% also do research. The average class size in an introductory lecture is 25; in a laboratory, 25; and in a regular course offering, 20.

Admissions: About 83% of the 1993–94 applicants were accepted. The SAT scores for the 1993–94 freshman class were as follows: Verbal—28% below 500, 57% between 500 and 599, 13% between 600 and 700, and 2% above 700; Math—35% below 500, 52% between 500 and 599, 12% between 600 and 700, and 1% above 700. The ACT scores were 26% below 21, 47% between 21 and 23, 17% between 24 and 26, 5% between 27 and 28, and 4% above 28. About 23% of the current freshmen were in the top fifth of their class; 51% were in the top two fifths.

Requirements: A minimum GPA of 2.3 is required. The SAT I or ACT is required of students who graduated from high school within 2 years of applying to CSF. Graduation from an accredited secondary school is required. The GED is accepted. Applicants must have 16 academic credits, including 3 years of English, 2 each of mathematics, science, and social studies, 1 of foreign language, and the remainder in college-preparatory courses. Letters of recommendation are suggested. A portfolio or an audition is required for specific majors. An essay and an interview are recommended. AP and CLEP credits are accepted. Important factors used in the admissions decision are evidence of special talent, leadership record, advanced placement or honor courses, extracurricular activities record, and recommendations by school officials.

Procedure: Freshmen are admitted to all sessions. Entrance exams should be taken in the freshman year. Application deadlines are open. Notification is sent on a rolling basis. The application fee is $25. There are early admissions and deferred admissions plans.

Transfer: Applicants must submit an official high school transcript and official transcripts from all previous colleges. SAT I or ACT scores and an interview are recommended. A total of 30 credits out of 128 must be completed at CSF.

Visiting: There are regularly scheduled orientations for prospective students, including 3 Weekend Fiestas each year during which students attend campus tours, classes, departmental receptions, a meet-

ing with an admissions counselor, a campus event, and an outdoor activity. Students are housed with current students and eat in the campus dining hall. There are guides for informal visits and visitors may stay overnight at the school. To arrange for a visit, contact the Office of Admissions at (505) 473-6133 or (800) 456-2673 (out-of-state).

Financial Aid: In 1993-94 85% of all current freshmen and 72% of continuing students received some form of financial aid. About 48% of freshmen and 60% of continuing students received need-based aid. The average freshman award was $7650. Of that total, scholarships or need-based grants averaged $1500; loans averaged $1750; and work contracts averaged $2000. Twenty-five percent of undergraduate students work part-time. Average earnings from campus work for the school year are $925. The average financial indebtedness of the 1992-93 graduate was $2625. CSF is a member of CSS. The FAF, the college's own financial statement, and the FAFSA are required. The deadline for financial aid applications is March 1.

International Students: There are currently 8 international students enrolled. They must take the TOEFL and achieve a minimum score of 500.

Computers: The college provides computer facilities for student use. The mainframe is a Data General MV4000. The computer laboratory has 14 Data General terminals for programming languages and 12 microcomputers. All students may access the system. There are no time limits on using the system and no fees.

Graduates: In 1992-93 250 bachelor's degrees were awarded. The most popular majors among graduates were moving image arts (20%), art (20%), and performing arts (20%). Within an average freshman class, 2% graduate in 3 years, 53% in 4 years, 5% in 5 years, and 1% in 6 years. Some 50 companies recruited on campus in 1992-93.

Admissions Contact: Monica Martinez, Director of Admissions.

COLLEGE OF THE SOUTHWEST

E-4

Hobbs, NM 88240-9987   (505) 392-6561

Full-time: 82 men, 140 women	Faculty: 19; IIB, --$
Part-time: 39 men, 106 women	Ph.D.s: 33%
Graduate: none	Student/Faculty: 12 to 1
Year: semesters, summer session	Tuition: $3220
Application Deadline: open	Room & Board: $2500
Freshman Class: 35 applied, 31 accepted, 27 enrolled	
SAT I Verbal/Math: 390/460	ACT: 19 LESS COMPETITIVE

College of the Southwest, founded in 1962, is a private institution offering undergraduate programs in arts and sciences, business, education, and psychology. The library contains 80,000 volumes and subscribes to 131 periodicals. Special learning facilities include a learning resource center. The 162-acre campus is in a small town 110 miles southwest of Lubbock, Texas. Including residence halls, there are 9 buildings on campus.

Student Life: About 83% of undergraduates are from New Mexico. Students come from 9 states, 2 foreign countries, and Canada. Eighty-one percent are white; 16% Hispanic. The average age of freshmen is 18; all undergraduates, 27.7. Sixty-five percent drop out by the end of their first year; 34% remain to graduate.

Housing: A total of 61 students can be accommodated in college housing. College-sponsored living facilities include single-sex dormitories and on-campus apartments. On-campus housing is available on a first-come, first-served basis. Priority is given to out-of-town students. Eighty-eight percent of students commute. Alcohol is not permitted. All students may keep cars on campus.

Activities: There are no fraternities or sororities on campus. There are 7 groups on campus, including drama, honors, newspaper, professional, student government, and yearbook. Popular campus events include Homecoming and the Annual Students-in-Free-Enterprise Dinner and Award Presentation.

Sports: There are intercollegiate and intramural sports for men and women. Athletic and recreation facilities include soccer and baseball fields, a game room, and a physical fitness center with a multipurpose gymnasium, racquetball courts, and physiology laboratory.

Disabled Students: All of the campus is accessible to disabled students. The following facilities are available: wheelchair ramps, special parking, and specially equipped rest rooms.

Services: In addition to many counseling and information services, tutoring is available in most subjects. There is also remedial math and writing.

Programs of Study: CSW awards the B.A., B.S., B.A.S., B.B.A., and B.M. degrees. Bachelor's degrees are awarded in BIOLOGICAL SCIENCE (biology/biological science), BUSINESS (accounting, business administration and management, and marketing/retailing/merchandising), COMMUNICATIONS AND THE ARTS (English), COMPUTER AND PHYSICAL SCIENCE (geology, mathematics, and natural sciences), EDUCATION (elementary, physical, secondary, and special), ENGINEERING AND ENVIRONMENTAL DESIGN (land use management and reclamation), SOCIAL SCIENCE (history, politi-

cal science/government, prelaw, psychology, and sociology). Education and business are the strongest academically.

Required: To graduate, students must complete 128 semester hours with a minimum GPA of 2.0. General educaton requirements include 12 semester hours each of social science and mathematics/science, 9 each of humanities/fine arts and communications, 6 of religion, and 3 of economics, as well as a course in free enterprise and senior seminar in leadership and ethics.

Special: Internships are available for students majoring in business, psychology, and education. CSW also offers nondegree study and credit for military experience. There are 2 national honor societies on campus.

Faculty/Classroom: Sixty-three percent of faculty are male; 37%, female. All teach undergraduates. The average class size in an introductory lecture is 25; in a laboratory, 15; and in a regular course offering, 18.

Admissions: About 89% of the 1993-94 applicants were accepted. The ACT scores for the 1993-94 freshman class were as follows: 74% below 21, 10% between 21 and 23, 10% between 24 and 26, and 6% between 27 and 28. About 22% of the current freshmen were in the top fifth of their class; 65% were in the top two fifths.

Requirements: CSW requires applicants to be in the upper 50% of their class. A minimum GPA of 2.0 is required. The SAT I or the ACT is required. A minimum composite score of 18 on the ACT or 700 on the SAT I is required. Applicants must be graduates of an accredited secondary school or have a GED certificate. AP and CLEP credits are accepted.

Procedure: Freshmen are admitted to all sessions. Application deadlines are open. Application fee is $20. Notification is sent on a rolling basis.

Transfer: About 65 transfer students enrolled in 1993-94. Applicants must present a minimum GPA of 2.0 and official transcripts from all colleges attended. A total of 30 credits out of 128 must be completed at CSW.

Visiting: There are regularly scheduled orientations for prospective students. There are guides for informal visits and visitors may sit in on classes and stay overnight at the school. To arrange for a visit, contact Rhonda S. Tyler, Director of Admissions at (505) 392-6261.

Financial Aid: In 1993-94, 91% of all current freshmen and 84% of continuing students received some form of financial aid. About 63% of freshmen and 83% of continuing students received need-based aid. The average freshman award was $3633. Of that total, scholarships or need-based grants averaged $2347 ($4500 maximum); loans averaged $2991 ($3300 maximum); and work contracts averaged $1359 ($1574 maximum). Average earnings from campus work for the school year are $1318. The FAF, FFS, or SFS is required. The deadline for financial aid applications is June 15.

International Students: There are currently 5 international students enrolled. They must take the TOEFL and achieve a minimum score of 550. The student must also take the SAT I or the ACT.

Computers: The college provides computer facilities for student use. Apple and IBM-compatible microcomputers are located in the computer laboratory and science building. There are no fees.

Graduates: In 1992-93, 71 bachelor's degrees were awarded. The most popular majors among graduates were education (45%), management (14%), and psychology (12%). Within an average freshman class, 19% graduate in 5 years.

Admissions Contact: Rhonda S. Tyler, Director of Admissions.

EASTERN NEW MEXICO UNIVERSITY

E-3

Portales, NM 88130   (505) 562-2178; (800) 367-3668 (out-of-state)

Full-time: 1250 men, 1543 women	Faculty: 193; IIA, --$
Part-time: 206 men, 353 women	Ph.D.s: 84%
Graduate: 229 men, 393 women	Student/Faculty: 14 to 1
Year: semesters, summer session	Tuition: $1440 ($5280)
Application Deadline: open	Room & Board: $2510
Freshman Class: 1297 applied, 1156 accepted, 512 enrolled	
ACT: 20	COMPETITIVE

Eastern New Mexico University, founded in 1934, is a public institution offering programs in the liberal arts and sciences, as well as education, business, fine arts, and vocational and technical fields. There are 4 undergraduate schools and one graduate school. In addition to regional accreditation, the university has baccalaureate program accreditation with NASM and NCATE. The library contains 280,000 volumes and 1944 microform items, and subscribes to 1785 periodicals. Computerized library sources and services include the card catalog, interlibrary loans, and database searching. Special learning facilities include a learning resource center, a natural history museum, a radio station, a TV station, and nearby archaeological sites. The 400-acre campus is in a small town 120 miles northeast of Lubbock, Texas. Including residence halls, there are 50 buildings on campus.

Student Life: About 74% of undergraduates are from New Mexico. Students come from 50 states, 22 foreign countries, and Canada. Ninety-two percent are from public schools; 8% from private. Seventy-

six percent are white; 15% Hispanic. Forty-five percent are Protestant; 25% Catholic; 10% claim no religious affiliation. The average age of freshmen is 20. Forty-seven percent drop out by the end of their first year; 30% remain to graduate.

Housing: A total of 1600 students can be accommodated in college housing. College-sponsored living facilities include single-sex and coed dormitories, on-campus apartments, married-student housing, and honors housing. On-campus housing is guaranteed for all 4 years. Sixty-four percent of students commute. Alcohol is not permitted. All students may keep cars on campus.

Activities: About 11% of men belong to 6 national fraternities; about 5% of women belong to 2 national sororities. There are 105 groups on campus, including band, cheerleading, choir, drama, drill team, ethnic, honors, international, jazz band, literary magazine, marching band, musical theater, newspaper, orchestra, photography, political, professional, radio and TV, religious, social, social service, student government, and yearbook. Popular campus events include Homecoming, Top Dog Academy, Peanut Valley Festival, Fiesta, International, Black History, and Native American Weeks.

Sports: There are 6 intercollegiate sports each for men and women, and 18 intramural sports each. Athletic and recreation facilities include a 5200-seat arena, tennis courts, an indoor pool, and a 5300-seat stadium.

Disabled Students: Almost all of the campus is accessible to disabled students. The following facilities are available: wheelchair ramps, elevators, special parking, specially equipped rest rooms, special class scheduling, and lowered drinking fountains.

Services: In addition to many counseling and information services, tutoring is available in every subject. There is also remedial math, reading, and writing.

Campus Safety and Security: Campus safety and security measures include escort service and lighted pathways and sidewalks.

Programs of Study: The university awards the B.A., B.S., B.A.E., B.B.A., B.F.A., B.M., B.M.E., B.S.E., and B.U.S. degrees. Associate and master's degrees also are awarded. Bachelor's degrees are awarded in AGRICULTURE (agricultural business management and wildlife management), BIOLOGICAL SCIENCE (biology/biological science), BUSINESS (accounting, banking and finance, business administration and management, business economics, marketing/retailing/merchandising, and personnel management), COMMUNICATIONS AND THE ARTS (communications, dramatic arts, English, fine arts, French, journalism, music, music performance, Spanish, and speech/debate/rhetoric), COMPUTER AND PHYSICAL SCIENCE (chemistry, computer science, geology, information sciences and systems, mathematics, physics, and statistics), EDUCATION (art, business, elementary, home economics, music, physical, and special), HEALTH PROFESSIONS (medical laboratory technology), SOCIAL SCIENCE (anthropology, economics, history, political science/government, psychology, religion, and social studies). Science is the strongest program academically. Business has the largest enrollment.

Required: To graduate, students must earn 128 credit hours, 36 in the major, with a minimum GPA of 2.0. Required courses include those in English, science, mathematics, social studies, humanities, fine arts, and physical education.

Special: The school offers study abroad through the International Students Exchange Program, a general studies degree, credit for life, military, and work experience, nondegree study, and pass/fail options. There is a freshman honors program on campus, as well as 10 national honor societies.

Faculty/Classroom: Seventy-one percent of faculty are male; 29%, female. The average class size in an introductory lecture is 35; in a laboratory, 15; and in a regular course offering, 22.

Admissions: About 89% of the 1993–94 applicants were accepted.

Requirements: A minimum GPA of 2.5 is required. The SAT I or ACT is required. For regular admissions, the minimum required composite score is 20 on the ACT or 800 on the SAT I. Applicants must be high school graduates or have the GED, having earned 20 units, including 4 in English, 3 in mathematics, 2 in science, and 1 each in history, music, and social studies. Provisional and special admissions are available. AP and CLEP credits are accepted.

Procedure: Freshmen are admitted to all sessions. Entrance exams should be taken in the senior year. Application deadlines are open. The application fee is $15. Notification is sent on a rolling basis. There is an early admissions plan.

Transfer: About 130 transfer students enrolled in a recent year. Transfer students must have a minimum GPA of 2.0. A total of 30 credits out of 128 must be completed at the university.

Visiting: There are regularly scheduled orientations for prospective students. There are guides for informal visits and visitors may sit in on classes and stay overnight at the school. To arrange for a visit, contact the Admissions Office at (800) 367-3668 or (505) 562-2178.

Financial Aid: In a recent year, 60% of all freshmen and 57% of continuing students received some form of financial aid. Scholarships or need-based grants averaged $300 ($1140 maximum); loans averaged $400 ($2625 maximum); and work contracts averaged $645

($1075 maximum). Sixty-five percent of undergraduate students work part-time. The average financial indebtedness of a recent graduate was $2250. The university is a member of CSS. The FAF is required.

International Students: There are currently 82 international students enrolled. The school actively recruits these students. They must take the TOEFL and achieve a minimum score of 500.

Computers: The college provides computer facilities for student use. There are 28 Apple PCs available. There are no time limits on using the system and no fees.

Graduates: In a recent year, 828 bachelor's degrees were awarded.

Admissions Contact: Larry Brock, Associate Director of Admissions.

NEW MEXICO HIGHLANDS UNIVERSITY   D-2
Las Vegas, NM 87701   (505) 425-3593
                                       (800) 338-6648 (out-of-state)

Full-time: 742 men, 850 women	Faculty: 109; IIA, --$
Part-time: 146 men, 276 women	Ph.Ds: 75%
Graduate: 300 men, 454 women	Student/Faculty: 15 to 1
Year: semesters, summer session	Tuition: $1412 ($5168)
Application Deadline: open	Room & Board: $2360
Freshman Class: 721 applied, 499 accepted, 439 enrolled	
ACT: 18	**COMPETITIVE**

New Mexico Highlands University, founded in 1893, is a state-supported institution offering undergraduate programs in liberal and fine arts, science and technology, and professional studies. There are 3 undergraduate schools. In addition to regional accreditation, Highlands has baccalaureate program accreditation with ABET and CSWE. The library contains 498,500 volumes, and subscribes to 1200 periodicals. Computerized library sources and services include the card catalog and interlibrary loans. Special learning facilities include a learning resource center, an art gallery, a radio station, a TV station, and a video production studio. The 175-acre campus is in a small town 65 miles northeast of Santa Fe. Including residence halls, there are 38 buildings on campus.

Student Life: About 94% of undergraduates are from New Mexico. Students come from 35 states and Canada. Ninety-five percent are from public schools; 5% from private. Sixty-six percent are Hispanic; 26% white. The average age of freshmen is 18; all undergraduates, 25. Thirty-two percent drop out by the end of their first year; 25% remain to graduate.

Housing: A total of 580 students can be accommodated in college housing. College-sponsored living facilities include single-sex and coed dormitories, on-campus apartments, and married-student housing. On-campus housing is guaranteed for all 4 years. Alcohol is not permitted. All students may keep cars on campus.

Activities: There are many groups and organizations on campus, including art, band, cheerleading, choir, chorale, chorus, drama, ethnic, film, honors, international, marching band, newspaper, photography, political, radio and TV, religious, social service, student government, and yearbook. Popular campus events include Homecoming, Multicultural Week, and Career Day.

Sports: There are 4 intercollegiate sports for men and 3 for women, and 8 intramural sports each for men and women. Athletic and recreation facilities include a 5000-seat football stadium, a 3600-seat arena, an indoor swimming pool, a weight room, tennis, racquetball, and basketball courts, athletic fields, and a 9-hole golf course. Hiking and skiing are nearby.

Disabled Students: The following facilities are available: wheelchair ramps, elevators, special parking, specially equipped rest rooms, lowered drinking fountains, and lowered telephones.

Services: In addition to many counseling and information services, tutoring is available in some subjects. In addition, there is remedial math, reading, and writing.

Campus Safety and Security: Campus safety and security measures include 24-hour foot and vehicle patrol, self-defense education, escort service, and informal discussions. In addition, there are pamphlets, posters, films, emergency telephones, and lighted pathways and sidewalks.

Programs of Study: Highlands awards the B.A., B.S., B.B.A., B.F.A., B.S.E., B.S.E.T., and B.S.W. degrees. Associate and master's degrees are also awarded. Bachelor's degrees are awarded in BIOLOGICAL SCIENCE (biology/biological science), BUSINESS (accounting, business administration and management, management information systems, marketing/retailing/merchandising, recreation and leisure services, and tourism), COMMUNICATIONS AND THE ARTS (communications, English, fine arts, graphic design, journalism, music, radio/television technology, and Spanish), COMPUTER AND PHYSICAL SCIENCE (chemistry, computer programming, computer science, and mathematics), EDUCATION (elementary, music, and technical), ENGINEERING AND ENVIRONMENTAL DESIGN (computer technology, electrical/electronics engineering technology, engineering, environmental science, and preengineering), HEALTH PROFESSIONS (health, medical laboratory technology, predentistry,

premedicine, and preveterinary science), SOCIAL SCIENCE (history, physical fitness/movement, political science/government, prelaw, psychology, social work, and sociology). Engineering and physical sciences are the strongest academically. Education, business administration, and social work have the largest enrollments.

Required: Students must complete 42 to 45 credits of core curriculum requirements, including courses in English, history, science, social environment, thought and critical analysis, fine arts, literature, communicating skills, and physical education. Proficiency in language and mathematics must be demonstrated. A minimum of 128 credits, at least 30 in the major, with a GPA of at least 2.0 is required in order to graduate.

Special: Highlands offers practicum, internship, and field-study courses; cooperative programs in most majors; internships in education; minors in geology, physics, secondary education, military science, philosophy, and theater; and credit for military training. There is a freshman honors program on campus, as well as 2 national honor societies, including Phi Beta Kappa.

Faculty/Classroom: Sixty-nine percent of faculty are male; 31%, female.

Admissions: About 69% of the 1993–94 applicants were accepted. Two freshmen graduated first in their class.

Requirements: A minimum GPA of 2.0 is required. The SAT I or ACT is recommended; scores are used for placement purposes. Applicants should be graduates of an accredited secondary school; the GED is accepted. AP and CLEP credits are accepted. Important factors used in the admissions decision are advanced placement or honor courses, evidence of special talent, recommendations by school officials, extracurricular activities record, and leadership record.

Procedure: Freshmen are admitted to all sessions. Application deadlines are open. Application fee is $15. Notification is sent on a rolling basis. There are early decision, early admissions, and deferred admissions plans. About 5 early decision candidates were accepted for the 1993–94 class.

Transfer: About 140 transfer students enrolled in 1993–94. Transfer applicants with 16 or more semester credit hours must have at least a 2.0 GPA. A total of 32 credits out of at least 128 must be completed at Highlands.

Visiting: There are regularly scheduled orientations for prospective students. There are guides for informal visits and visitors may sit in on classes and stay overnight at the school. To arrange for a visit, contact the Admissions Office at (505) 454–3256 or (800) 338–6648 (out-of-state).

Financial Aid: In 1993–94, 80% of all current freshmen and 85% of continuing students received some form of financial aid. About 75% of students received need-based aid. The average freshman award was $4490. Of that total, scholarships or need-based grants averaged $2190 ($3190 maximum); and loans averaged $500 ($3625 maximum). Twenty percent of undergraduate students work part-time. Average earnings from campus work for the school year are $2000. The average financial indebtedness of the 1992–93 graduate was $4200. Highlands is a member of CSS. The FAF or FFS is required. The deadline for financial aid applications is March 1.

International Students: There are currently 22 international students enrolled. They must take the TOEFL and achieve a minimum score of 500.

Computers: The college provides computer facilities for student use. The mainframes are a DEC VAX 8350 and 6210, and a DEC MicroVAX II. The VAX cluster may be accessed through various computer laboratories located throughout the campus. All students may access the system. It may be used 24 hours daily and there are no fees.

Graduates: In 1992–93, 225 bachelor's degrees were awarded. The most popular majors among graduates were business administration (21%), elementary education (15%), and social work (7%). Within an average freshman class, 18% graduate in 4 years, 22% in 5 years, and 23% in 6 years. Some 100 companies recruited on campus in 1992–93.

Admissions Contact: John Coca, Director of Admissions.

NEW MEXICO INSTITUTE OF MINING AND TECHNOLOGY
C-3
Socorro, NM 87801   (505) 835–5424; (800) 428–8324 (out-of-state)

Full-time: 686 men, 326 women	Faculty: 95; I, --$
Part-time: 166 men, 245 women	Ph.D.s: 97%
Graduate: 222 men, 69 women	Student/Faculty: 11 to 1
Year: semesters, summer session	Tuition: $1786 ($5648)
Application Deadline: August 1	Room & Board: $3426
Freshman Class: 787 applied, 601 accepted, 233 enrolled	
SAT I Verbal/Math: 506/594	ACT: 26 COMPETITIVE +

New Mexico Institute of Mining and Technology, founded in 1889 as the New Mexico School of Mines, consists of a technical and engineering college, as well as 3 research divisions: the New Mexico Bureau of Mines and Mineral Resources, the Research and Development Division, and the Petroleum Recovery Research Center. There is one graduate school. In addition to regional accreditation, New Mexico Tech has baccalaureate program accreditation with ABET. The library contains 155,000 volumes, 71,000 microform items, and 800 audiovisual forms, and subscribes to 1025 periodicals. Computerized library sources and services include interlibrary loans and database searching. Special learning facilities include a radio station, a TV station, a mineral museum, a seismic research mine, and an atmospheric research laboratory. The 320-acre campus is in a small town 75 miles south of Albuquerque. Including residence halls, there are 27 buildings on campus.

Student Life: About 60% of undergraduates are from New Mexico. Students come from 47 states, 42 foreign countries, and Canada. Eighty-six percent are from public schools; 10% from private. Sixty-nine percent are white; 16% Hispanic; 10% foreign nationals. The average age of freshmen is 20; all undergraduates, 24. Thirty percent drop out by the end of their first year; 55% remain to graduate.

Housing: A total of 490 students can be accommodated in college housing. College-sponsored living facilities include single-sex and coed dormitories and married-student housing. In addition, there are graduate student houses. On-campus housing is guaranteed for all 4 years. Fifty-three percent of students commute. Alcohol is not permitted. All students may keep cars on campus.

Activities: There are no fraternities or sororities on campus. There are 60 groups on campus, including art, band, chess, choir, chorus, computers, ethnic, gay, honors, international, jazz band, newspaper, orchestra, political, professional, radio and TV, religious, social, student government, and symphony. Popular campus events include 49ers (a homecoming celebration), Spring Fling, and International Student Exhibit.

Sports: There are 20 intramural sports each for men and women. Athletic and recreation facilities include 2 gymnasiums, tennis courts, a swimming pool, an 18-hole golf course, and an athletic field.

Disabled Students: All of the campus is accessible to disabled students. The following facilities are available: wheelchair ramps, elevators, special parking, specially equipped rest rooms, lowered drinking fountains, and lowered telephones.

Services: In addition to many counseling and information services, tutoring is available in most subjects. In addition, there is a reader service for the blind.

Campus Safety and Security: Campus safety and security measures include 24-hour foot and vehicle patrol, escort service, informal discussions, and pamphlets, posters, and films. In addition, there are emergency telephones and lighted pathways and sidewalks.

Programs of Study: New Mexico Tech awards the B.S., and B.G.S. degrees. Associate, master's, and doctoral degrees are also awarded. Bachelor's degrees are awarded in BIOLOGICAL SCIENCE (biology/biological science), BUSINESS (business administration and management), COMMUNICATIONS AND THE ARTS (technical and business writing), COMPUTER AND PHYSICAL SCIENCE (chemistry, computer science, geology, geophysics and seismology, mathematics, and physics), ENGINEERING AND ENVIRONMENTAL DESIGN (electrical/electronics engineering, engineering, engineering mechanics, environmental engineering, environmental science, geological engineering, materials engineering, metallurgical engineering, mining and mineral engineering, and petroleum/natural gas engineering), SOCIAL SCIENCE (liberal arts/general studies and psychology). Computer science and physics are the strongest academically. Engineering, computer science, physics, environmental engineering, and electrical engineering have the largest enrollments.

Required: The student must earn at least 130 credit hours to graduate, including 42 hours of basic science, consisting in part of 10 hours of physics, and 8 each of chemistry, calculus, and biology/geology. Further distribution requirements include 9 hours each of written and spoken English, and social science, 6 hours of literature, philosophy, and the arts, a computer science course, and a senior seminar or senior design project. The hours required in the major vary by program. The student must have a GPA of 2.0.

Special: New Mexico Tech offers co-op programs in computer science and all engineering majors, cross-registration with New Mexico State, University of New Mexico, and Los Alamos National Laboratories in WERC consortium, and internships in technical communications. Dual majors in engineering, computer science, physics, and mathematics, student-designed majors in environmental science, general studies, and basic science, non-degree study, and pass/fail options are available. There is a 3–2 accelerated degree program in science or engineering and hydrology. There are 6 national honor societies on campus.

Faculty/Classroom: Eighty-eight percent of faculty are male; 12%, female. Ninety percent both teach and do research. Graduate students teach 10% of introductory courses. The average class size in an introductory lecture is 60; in a laboratory, 20; and in a regular course offering, 25.

Admissions: About 76% of the 1993–94 applicants were accepted. The SAT scores for the 1993–94 freshman class were as follows: Verbal—45% below 500, 34% between 500 and 599, 19% between 600 and 700, and 3% above 700; Math—19% below 500, 28% between 500 and 599, 35% between 600 and 700, and 18% above 700. The ACT scores were 9% below 21, 19% between 21 and 23, 24% between 24 and 26, 23% between 27 and 28, and 25% above 28. About 39% of the current freshmen were in the top fifth of their class; 73% were in the top two fifths. There were 5 National Merit finalists. Three freshmen graduated first in their class.

Requirements: A minimum GPA of 2.0 is required. The SAT I or the ACT, with a minimum score of 21, is required. Applicants must be high school graduates or present a GED certificate. Students should have earned 15 academic credits, consisting of 4 units of English, 3 each of social science and mathematics (2 beyond general mathematics), and 2 of science, including 1 of laboratory science, and electives. AP credits are accepted. Important factors used in the admissions decision are advanced placement or honor courses, recommendations by school officials, recommendations by alumni, personality, intangible qualities, and parents or siblings attending the school.

Procedure: Freshmen are admitted to all sessions. Entrance exams should be taken by December of the senior year. Applications should be filed by August 1 for fall entry and December 1 for spring entry, along with an application fee of $15. Notification is sent on a rolling basis. There are early admissions and deferred admissions plans.

Transfer: About 80 transfer students enrolled in 1993–94. Transfer students must have a GPA of 2.0 and have completed 30 semester hours of transferable credit. Those with fewer than 30 credit hours, or who have not completed freshman English, must supply ACT scores, with a minimum of 21. A total of 30 credits out of 130 must be completed at New Mexico Tech.

Visiting: There are regularly scheduled orientations for prospective students, including 2 days of get-acquainted social activities, information sessions for parents and students, and transition sessions for parents. There are guides for informal visits and visitors may sit in on classes and stay overnight at the school. To arrange for a visit, contact the Admissions Office at (505) 835–5424 or (800) 428-TECH.

Financial Aid: In 1993–94, 93% of all current freshmen and 96% of continuing students received some form of financial aid. Scholarships or need-based grants averaged $700; loans averaged $1100 ($4000 maximum); and work contracts averaged $600 ($2700 maximum). The average financial indebtedness of the 1992–93 graduate was $14,000. New Mexico Tech is a member of CSS. The FAFSA financial statement is required. The deadline for financial aid applications is March 1.

International Students: There are currently 174 international students enrolled. They must take the TOEFL and achieve a minimum score of 540.

Computers: The college provides computer facilities for student use. The mainframes are 2 SUN-3/280s. Students may access the mainframe through SUN workstations located in the computer center and in various departments across campus. Students may also access the mainframe from their rooms via modem. All students may access the system. It may be used 18 hours a day. There are no time limits on using the system. The fees are $25.

Graduates: In 1992–93, 117 bachelor's degrees were awarded. The most popular majors among graduates were environmental engineering (12%), biology (9%), and electrical, and material engineering (7%). Within an average freshman class, 38% graduate in 4 years, 55% in 5 years, and 65% in 6 years. Some 28 companies recruited on campus in 1992–93.

Admissions Contact: Admissions Office, Director of Admissions.

NEW MEXICO STATE UNIVERSITY
C-4

Las Cruces, NM 88003   (505) 646–3121; (800) 662–6678 (in-state)

Full-time: 5003 men, 4670 women	Faculty: 651; I, --$
Part-time: 1550 men, 1931 women	Ph.D.s: 80%
Graduate: 1419 men, 1215 women	Student/Faculty: 15 to 1
Year: semesters, summer session	Tuition: $1872 ($6072)
Application Deadline: 2 weeks prior to first day of classes	Room & Board: $2972

Freshman Class: 3786 applied, 2978 accepted, 1527 enrolled
ACT: required   **LESS COMPETITIVE**

New Mexico State University, founded in 1888, is a public institution offering undergraduate and graduate programs that include study in liberal arts, agriculture, art, business, engineering, health science, teacher preparation, and music. There are 6 undergraduate schools and one graduate school. In addition to regional accreditation, NMSU has baccalaureate program accreditation with AACSB, ABET, AHEA, CSWE, NASM, NCATE, and NLN. The 2 libraries contain 850,000 volumes and 400,000 microform items, and subscribe to 6700 periodicals. Computerized library sources and services include the card catalog, interlibrary loans, and database searching. Special

learning facilities include a learning resource center, art gallery, natural history museum, radio station, TV station, 289-acre experimental farm and orchard, 61,760-acre cattle and experimental ranch, and 2,160-acre recreational area in the Organ Mountains. The 5800-acre campus is in a suburban area 40 miles north of El Paso, Texas. Including residence halls, there are 124 buildings on campus.

Student Life: About 88% of undergraduates are from New Mexico. Students come from 51 states, 80 foreign countries, and Canada. Ninety percent are from public schools; 10% from private. Sixty-three percent are white; 31% Hispanic. The average age of freshmen is 18.6; all undergraduates, 24.3. Nine percent drop out by the end of their first year; 38% remain to graduate.

Housing: A total of 4000 students can be accommodated in college housing. College-sponsored living facilities include single-sex and coed dormitories, on-campus apartments, married-student housing, fraternity houses, and sorority houses. In addition there are honors houses. On-campus housing is guaranteed for all 4 years. All students may keep cars on campus.

Activities: About 6% of men and women belong to fraternities and sororities. There are 220 groups on campus, including band, cheerleading, choir, chorale, chorus, dance, drama, drill team, drum and bugle corps, ethnic, gay, honors, international, jazz band, literary magazine, marching band, musical theater, newspaper, orchestra, political, radio and TV, religious, social, social service, student government, and yearbook. Popular campus events include Chicano Week, Native American Week, Black Week, and Homecoming.

Sports: There are 8 intercollegiate sports for men and 8 for women, and 24 intramural sports for men and 24 for women. Athletic and recreation facilities include a game room, natatorium, tennis courts, playing fields, and a gymnasium. One campus stadium seats 30,342 while the other seats more than 13,000.

Disabled Students: The following facilities are available: wheelchair ramps, elevators, special parking, specially equipped rest rooms, lowered drinking fountains, and lowered telephones.

Services: In addition to many counseling and information services, tutoring is available in most subjects. There is a reader service for the blind. Remedial classes are offered at the Dona Ana Branch Community College. There is also an interpreter for the hearing impaired.

Campus Safety and Security: Campus safety and security measures include 24-hour foot and vehicle patrol, self defense education, escort service, and shuttle buses. In addition, there are informal discussions, pamphlets, posters, and films, emergency telephones, and lighted pathways and sidewalks.

Programs of Study: NMSU awards the B.A., B.S., B.Ac., B.B.A., B.C.J., B.F.A., B.G.S., B.M., B.M.Ed., B.S.A., B.S.A.E., B.S.A.T.Ed., B.S.C.H., B.S.ChE., B.S.C.I.E., B.S.Ed., B.S.E.E., B.S.E.T., B.S.G.E., B.S.H.E., B.S.H.T.S., B.S.M.E., B.S.Med.Tech., B.S.N., B.S.P.E., B.S.S., and B.S.W. degrees. Associate, master's, and doctoral degrees also are awarded. Bachelor's degrees are awarded in AGRICULTURE (agricultural business management, agriculture, animal science, fishing and fisheries, horticulture, range/farm management, and soil science), BIOLOGICAL SCIENCE (biochemistry, biology/biological science, microbiology, nutrition, and wildlife biology), BUSINESS (banking and finance, business administration and management, business economics, fashion merchandising, international business management, management information systems, marketing/retailing/merchandising, and recreational facilities management), COMMUNICATIONS AND THE ARTS (communications, dramatic arts, English, fine arts, French, German, journalism, music, Russian, and Spanish), COMPUTER AND PHYSICAL SCIENCE (chemistry, computer science, geology, mathematics, and physics), EDUCATION (elementary, home economics, music, physical, secondary, and special), ENGINEERING AND ENVIRONMENTAL DESIGN (agricultural engineering, chemical engineering, city/community/regional planning, civil engineering, electrical/electronics engineering, engineering technology, geological engineering, industrial engineering, and mechanical engineering), HEALTH PROFESSIONS (community health work, medical laboratory technology, and nursing), SOCIAL SCIENCE (anthropology, criminal justice, economics, family/consumer studies, geography, history, Latin American studies, Mexican-American/Chicano studies, philosophy, political science/government, psychology, social work, and sociology). Engineering is the strongest academically. Prebusiness has the largest enrollment.

Required: All students must complete a minimum of 128 credits including at least 50 upper-division credits. A minimum GPA of 2.0 is needed. Distribution requirements include communications, humanities, mathematics, natural sciences, and social sciences.

Special: Internships, cooperative programs in engineering, mathematics, science, teacher education, business and other majors, dual majors, work-study, nondegree study, and B.A.-B.S. degrees are available. There is cross-registration with the Dona Ana Branch Community College. There is a freshman honors program on campus

Admissions: About 79% of the 1993–94 applicants were accepted.

Requirements: A minimum GPA of 2.0 is required. The ACT is required. Applicants must score 20 on the ACT or may take the SAT I (accepted but not recommended), and submit a composite score of 780. The GED is accepted. AP and CLEP credits are accepted.

Procedure: Freshmen are admitted to all sessions. Entrance exams should be taken during the high school junior or senior year. The application fee is $10. Application deadlines are two weeks prior to the first day of classes. Notification is sent on a rolling basis. There is an early admissions plan.

Transfer: About 650 transfer students enrolled in 1993–94. Transfer applicants must have a minimum GPA of 2.0. They need 30 credits to avoid freshman admission requirements. If applicant earned 30 academic credit hours or more, ACT score will be waived. If applicant earned 48 academic credit hours or more, high school transcript will be waived. A total of 30 credits out of 128 must be completed at NMSU.

Visiting: There are regularly scheduled orientations for prospective students. There are guides for informal visits and visitors may sit in on classes. To arrange for a visit, contact the Office of Admissions at (505) 646–3121.

Financial Aid: In 1993–94, 65% of all students received some form of financial aid and need-based aid. The average freshman award was $2370. Of that total, scholarships or need-based grants averaged $1900 ($3500 maximum); loans averaged $1500 ($2625 maximum); and work contracts averaged $2000 ($2400 maximum). Forty percent of undergraduate students work part-time. The FAFSA financial statement is required. The deadline for financial aid applications is March 1.

International Students: There are currently 462 international students enrolled. They must take the TOEFL or the University of Michigan Language Test and achieve a minimum score on the TOEFL of 500.

Computers: The college provides computer facilities for student use. The mainframe is an IBM ES9000. A number of microcomputers are available in academic areas and dormitories. All students may access the system. It may be used 24 hours daily. There are no time limits on using the system and no fees.

Admissions Contact: Bill Bruner, Director of Admissions.

SAINT JOHN'S COLLEGE   C-2

Santa Fe, NM 87501   (505) 982–3691; (800) 331–5232

Full-time: 231 men, 180 women	Faculty: 45; IIB, +$
Part-time: 1 man, 1 woman	Ph.D.s: 60%
Graduate: 40 men, 44 women	Student/Faculty: 9 to 1
Year: semesters, summer session	Tuition: $16,300
Application Deadline: see profile	Room & Board: $5450
Freshman Class: 285 applied, 243 accepted, 126 enrolled	
SAT I or ACT: not required	**VERY COMPETITIVE +**

St. John's College of New Mexico, a nonsectarian, coeducational liberal arts college opened in 1964, is the sister campus of St. John's College in Annapolis, Maryland, which was founded in 1696. Students undertake a common curriculum based on a list of seminal works of Western civilization, the Great Books program. There is one graduate school. The library contains 50,000 volumes and 8620 audiovisual forms, and subscribes to 178 periodicals. Computerized library sources and services include the card catalog and interlibrary loans. Special learning facilities include an art gallery and music library. The 250-acre campus is located at an altitude of 7300 feet overlooking the city of Santa Fe and is 60 miles north of Albuquerque. Including residence halls, there are 31 buildings on campus.

Student Life: About 91% of undergraduates are from out-of-state, mostly the Southwest. Students come from 37 states, 3 foreign countries, and Canada. Sixty-eight percent are from public schools; 26% from private. Ninety percent are white. The average age of freshmen is 18; all undergraduates, 21. Seven percent drop out by the end of their first year; 66% remain to graduate.

Housing: A total of 329 students can be accommodated in college housing. College-sponsored living facilities include single-sex and coed dormitories and on-campus apartments. On-campus housing is guaranteed for the freshman year only and is available on a lottery system for upperclassmen. Seventy-five percent of students live on campus; of those, all remain on campus on weekends. All students may keep cars on campus.

Activities: There are no fraternities or sororities on campus. There are 32 groups on campus, including art, chess, choir, chorale, chorus, computers, dance, drama, film, jazz band, literary magazine, newspaper, orchestra, photography, pottery, search and rescue, social service, student government, women's literature, and yoga. Popular campus events include Reality Weekend, Senior Prank, Oktoberfest, Halloween and Christmas parties, weekend parties, and weekend films.

Sports: There are 9 intramural sports for men and 9 for women. Athletic and recreation facilities include a soccer field, a track, tennis courts, a weight room, and an outdoor basketball court.

Disabled Students: Sixty percent of the campus is accessible to disabled students. The following facilities are available: wheelchair ramps, elevators, special parking, specially equipped rest rooms, and special class scheduling.

Services: In addition to many counseling and information services, tutoring is available in every subject.

Campus Safety and Security: Campus safety and security measures include 24-hour foot and vehicle patrol, self-defense education, escort service, and shuttle buses. In addition, there are informal discussions, pamphlets, posters, and films, emergency telephones, and lighted pathways and sidewalks.

Programs of Study: St. John's awards the B.A. degree. Master's degrees also are awarded. Bachelor's degrees are awarded in SOCIAL SCIENCE (liberal arts/general studies).

Required: The college has one curriculum, based on the Great Books of the Western World, which the student must complete to graduate. It includes 4 years each of mathematics, seminar, and a language, 3 years of science, and 1 year of music. There are 2 electives in the 4 years. A total of 132 semester hours is required, and the student must have no grade below C in the senior year. An oral examination on the senior thesis is required.

Special: Internships with alumni in a wide range of fields are available and students may transfer between the Santa Fe and Annapolis campuses. Premedical studies at universities around the country and 4–1 teaching certification through the University of New Mexico are possible. Work-study programs and summer work between junior and senior years in the University of Chicago Business Fellows Program are possible.

Faculty/Classroom: Seventy-one percent of faculty are male; 29%, female. All teach undergraduates. No introductory courses are taught by graduate students. The average class size in an introductory lecture, in a laboratory, and in a regular course offering is 15.

Admissions: About 85% of the 1993–94 applicants are accepted. The SAT scores for the 1993–94 freshman class were as follows: Verbal—6% below 500, 42% between 500 and 599, 46% between 600 and 700, and 6% above 700; Math—11% below 500, 43% between 500 and 599, 38% between 600 and 700, and 8% above 700. The ACT scores were 9% between 21 and 23, 40% between 24 and 26, 39% between 27 and 28, and 12% above 28. About 28% of the current freshmen were in the top fifth of their class; 48% were in the top two fifths. Seven freshmen graduated first in their class.

Requirements: No entrance examinations are required, but may be submitted. Applicants need not be high school graduates; some students are admitted prior to completing high school. Secondary preparation should include 4 years of English, 3 years of mathematics, and 2 years each of foreign language, science, and history. Applicants must submit written essays, and are strongly urged to schedule an interview. Important factors used in the admissions decision are recommendations by school officials, leadership record, recommendations by alumni, evidence of special talent, and advanced placement or honor courses.

Procedure: Freshmen are admitted fall and spring. It is suggested that applications be filed by March 1 for fall entry and December 15 for spring entry. Notification is sent on a rolling basis. There are early admissions and deferred admissions plans.

Transfer: Some 25 transfer students enrolled in 1993–94. St. John's accepts transfers only for its freshman class, and no previous college credit is recognized. All 132 semester must be completed at St. John's.

Visiting: There are regularly scheduled orientations for prospective students, including a tour of the campus and housing, class visits, and an interview. There are guides for informal visits and visitors may stay overnight at the school. To arrange for a visit, contact the Admissions Office at (800) 331–5232.

Financial Aid: In 1993–94 65% of all current freshmen and 61% of continuing students received some form of financial aid. All freshmen received need-based aid. The average freshman award was $13,101. Of that total, scholarships or need-based grants averaged $8751 ($13,101 maximum); loans averaged $2650; and work contracts averaged $1700. Fifty-five percent of undergraduate students work part-time. Average earnings from campus work for the school year are $1900. The average financial indebtedness of the 1992–93 graduate was $12,000. St. John's is a member of CSS. The FAF, FFS or SFS and the college's own financial statement are required. The deadline for financial aid applications is March 1.

International Students: There are currently 8 international students enrolled. The school actively recruits these students. They must take the TOEFL. The student must also take the SAT I.

Computers: The college provides computer facilities for student use. There are no time limits on using the system and no fees.

Graduates: In 1992–93 74 bachelor's degrees were awarded. Within an average freshman class, 60% graduate in 4 years, 65% in 5 years, and 70% in 6 years. Some 15 companies recruited on campus in 1992–93.

Admissions Contact: Larry Clendenin, Director of Admissions.

UNIVERSITY OF NEW MEXICO
C-2

Albuquerque, NM 87131   (505) 277-2446

Full-time: 5766 men, 6691 women	Faculty: 933; I, --$
Part-time: 3220 men, 4327 women	Student/Faculty: 13 to 1
Graduate: 2530 men, 2800 women	Tuition: $1788 ($6468)
Year: semesters, summer session	Room & Board: $3516
Application Deadline: see profile	
Freshman Class: 3871 applied, 3349 accepted, 1891 enrolled	
SAT I Verbal/Math: 462/506 ACT: 22	**COMPETITIVE**

The University of New Mexico, founded in 1889, is a public university offering instruction in liberal and fine arts, business, engineering, health science, teacher preparation, and technology. In addition to the main campuses, it has 4 campuses for 2-year study and 2 for graduate study. There are 12 undergraduate and 4 graduate schools. In addition to regional accreditation, UNM has baccalaureate program accreditation with AACSB, ABET, ACPE, CAHEA, NAAB, NASM, NCATE, NLN, and NRPA. The 9 libraries contain 1,815,957 volumes, 5 million microform items, and 320,034 audiovisual forms, and subscribe to 18,230 periodicals. Computerized library sources and services include the card catalog, interlibrary loans, and database searching. Special learning facilities include a learning resource center, an art gallery, a natural history museum, a planetarium, a radio station, a TV station, a robotics laboratory, microcomputer laboratories, a photo-history collection, and a lithography institute. The 625-acre campus is in an urban area within the city of Albuquerque. Including residence halls, there are 269 buildings on campus.

Student Life: About 79% of undergraduates are from New Mexico. Students come from 50 states, 56 foreign countries, and Canada. Sixty-five percent are white; 23% Hispanic. The average age of freshmen is 18; all undergraduates, 25. About 33% of freshmen remain to graduate.

Housing: A total of 2100 students can be accommodated in college housing. College-sponsored living facilities include single-sex and coed dormitories, on-campus apartments, married-student housing, fraternity houses, and sorority houses. On-campus housing is guaranteed for all 4 years. Ninety-two percent of students commute. Alcohol is not permitted. All students may keep cars on campus.

Activities: About 2% of men belong to 10 national fraternities; about 1% of women belong to 4 national sororities. There are 245 groups on campus, including art, band, cheerleading, chess, choir, chorale, chorus, dance, drama, drill team, ethnic, film, gay, honors, international, jazz band, literary magazine, marching band, newspaper, orchestra, pep band, photography, political, professional, radio and TV, religious, social, social service, student government, symphony, and yearbook. Popular campus events include Homecoming, Spring Fiesta, Welcome Back Days, Nizhoni, and Hanging of the Greens.

Sports: There are 13 intercollegiate sports for men and 11 for women, and 32 intramural sports for men and 26 for women. Athletic and recreation facilities include 2 gymnasiums, a football field, basketball courts, 2 pools, weights, and racquetball and tennis courts. The stadium seats 30,000, the gymnasium 7000, and the largest arena 20,000.

Disabled Students: Ninety-five percent of the campus is accessible to disabled students. The following facilities are available: wheelchair ramps, elevators, special parking, specially equipped rest rooms, special class scheduling, lowered drinking fountains, and lowered telephones.

Services: In addition to many counseling and information services, tutoring is available in most subjects. In addition, there is a reader service for the blind, and remedial math, reading, and writing.

Campus Safety and Security: Campus safety and security measures include 24-hour foot and vehicle patrol, escort service, shuttle buses, and informal discussions. In addition, there are pamphlets, posters, and films, emergency telephones, and lighted pathways and sidewalks.

Programs of Study: UNM awards the B.A., B.S., B.B.A., B.F.A., and B.S.Ed. degrees. Associate, master's, and doctoral degrees also are awarded. Bachelor's degrees are awarded in BIOLOGICAL SCIENCE (biochemistry and biology/biological science), BUSINESS (accounting, banking and finance, business administration and management, international business management, marketing/retailing/merchandising, and personnel management), COMMUNICATIONS AND THE ARTS (classics, communications, dance, dramatic arts, English, fine arts, French, German, journalism, music, Portuguese, and Spanish), COMPUTER AND PHYSICAL SCIENCE (chemistry, computer science, geology, mathematics, and physics), EDUCATION (art, bilingual/bicultural, business, elementary, health, home economics, industrial arts, music, science, special, and teaching English as a second language/foreign language), ENGINEERING AND ENVIRONMENTAL DESIGN (architecture, chemical engineering, civil engineering, electrical/electronics engineering, industrial engineering, and mechanical engineering), HEALTH PROFESSIONS (medical laboratory technology, nursing, pharmacy, physical therapy, and pre-

medicine), SOCIAL SCIENCE (anthropology, criminal justice, dietetics, economics, geography, history, philosophy, political science/government, psychology, and sociology). Psychology, nursing, and elementary education have the largest enrollments.

Required: All students must take 2 English courses. A minimum of 128 credit hours is required, along with a GPA of 2.0.

Special: There is a 3-2 engineering program with the Anderson School of Management. Study abroad is available in 7 countries. The university offers cooperative programs, a Washington semester, work-study, dual and student-designed majors, a general studies degree, credit by examination, credit for military experience, nondegree study, and pass/fail options. There is a freshman honors program on campus, as well as 2 national honor societies, including Phi Beta Kappa.

Admissions: About 87% of the 1993-94 applicants were accepted. The ACT scores for the 1993-94 freshman class were as follows: 38% below 21, 30% between 21 and 23, 18% between 24 and 26, 8% between 27 and 28, and 6% above 28. About 43% of the current freshmen were in the top fifth of their class; 72% were in the top two fifths. There were 12 National Merit finalists.

Requirements: A minimum GPA of 2.0 is required. The SAT I or ACT is required. A total of 13 academic credits is required, including 4 years of English, 3 years of mathematics, and 2 years each of foreign language, natural science, and social science. A GED is accepted. AP and CLEP credits are accepted. Important factors used in the admissions decision are leadership record, evidence of special talent, advanced placement or honor courses, recommendations by school officials, and extracurricular activities record.

Procedure: Freshmen are admitted to all sessions. Entrance exams should be taken late in the junior or early in the senior year. Applications should be filed 1 month prior to start of classes, along with an application fee of $15. Notification is sent on a rolling basis. There is an early admissions plan.

Transfer: About 2630 transfer students enrolled in 1993-94. Transfer applicants must have at least a 2.0 GPA in all transferable courses. The SAT I or ACT is required. A total of 30 credits out of 128 must be completed at UNM.

Visiting: There are regularly scheduled orientations for prospective students, including academic advisement, admissions and financial aid counseling, and a tour of the campus and housing. There are guides for informal visits and visitors may sit in on classes and stay overnight at the school. To arrange for a visit, contact Student Outreach Services at (505) 277-5161.

Financial Aid: In 1993-94, 65% of all current freshmen and 50% of continuing students received some form of financial aid. About 31% of freshmen and 37% of continuing students received need-based aid. The average freshman award was $4988. Of that total, scholarships or need-based grants averaged $1564 ($5000 maximum); loans averaged $1747 ($4000 maximum); and work contracts averaged $2409 ($4000 maximum). Sixty-two percent of undergraduate students work part-time. Average earnings from campus work for the school year are $1684. The average financial indebtedness of the 1992-93 graduate was $8164. UNM is a member of CSS. The FAFSA financial statement is required. The deadline for financial aid applications is March 1.

International Students: There are currently 505 international students enrolled. They must take the TOEFL and achieve a minimum score of 550.

Computers: The college provides computer facilities for student use. The mainframes are an IBM ES9121 Model 320, an IBM 9375 Model 60, a DEC VAX 6320, a 7 DEC Station 5000/120, a 3 DEC Station 3200, and a DEC Station 5000/133. There are 345 terminals and microcomputers available in 7 computing pods and 4 classrooms in various locations. All students may access the system. There are no time limits on using the system and no fees.

Graduates: In 1992-93, 2484 bachelor's degrees were awarded. The most popular majors among graduates were university studies (10%), elementary education (6%), and psychology (5%). Within an average freshman class, 33% graduate in 6 years. Some 141 companies recruited on campus in 1992-93.

Admissions Contact: Cynthia Stuart, Director of Admissions.

WESTERN NEW MEXICO UNIVERSITY
B-4

Silver City, NM, 88062   (505) 538-6105; (800) 872-9668 (in-state)

Full-time: 240 men, 300 women	Faculty: IIB, -$
Part-time: 42 men, 80 women	Ph.D.s: 39%
Graduate: 70 men, 120 women	Student/Faculty: 7 to 1
Year: semesters, summer sessions	Tuition: $1204 ($4384)
Application Deadline: September 1	Room & Board: $2054
Freshman Class: n/av	
SAT or ACT: required	**LESS COMPETITIVE**

Western New Mexico University, founded in 1893, is a coeducational public institution offering vocational, liberal arts, science, and professional programs. There are 2 undergraduate and 3 graduate schools.

The library contains 140,000 volumes, 370,000 microform items, and 500 audiovisual forms, and subscribes to 1000 periodicals. Computerized library sources and services include database searching. Special learning facilities include a learning resource center, an art gallery, a natural history museum, and an instrumental-vocal music center with individual practice rooms. The 80-acre campus is in a small town 113 miles northwest of Las Cruces and a few minutes from Gila National Forest. Including residence halls, there are 40 buildings on campus.

Student Life: About 85% of undergraduates are from New Mexico. Students come from 7 states and 4 foreign countries. Ninety-five percent are from public schools; 5% from private. The average age of freshmen is 18; all undergraduates, 21.

Housing: A total of 285 students can be accommodated in college housing. College-sponsored living facilities include single-sex dormitories and married-student housing. On-campus housing is guaranteed for the freshman year only and is available on a first-come, first-served basis. Priority is given to out-of-town students. Fifty-six percent of students live on campus. Alcohol is not permitted. All students may keep cars on campus.

Activities: There are no fraternities or sororities on campus. There are 25 groups on campus, including band, cheerleading, choir, drama, drill team, ethnic, film, honors, jazz band, literary magazine, marching band, newspaper, photography, religious, student government, and yearbook. Popular campus events include the Great Race and Homecoming.

Sports: There are 4 intercollegiate sports each for men and women, and 23 intramural sports each for men and women. Athletic and recreation facilities include a football field and track, a 2000-seat stadium, and a physical education complex housing a 1500-seat gymnasium, basketball and handball courts, a 25-meter indoor pool, a training room, and a dance studio.

Disabled Students: The entire campus is accessible to disabled students. The following facilities are available: wheelchair ramps, elevators, special parking, and specially equipped rest rooms.

Services: In addition to many counseling and information services, tutoring is available in every subject. There is also remedial math, reading, and writing.

Programs of Study: WNMU awards the B.A., B.S., and B.A.S. degrees. Associate and master's degrees also are awarded. Bachelor's degrees are awarded in AGRICULTURE (forestry and related sciences), BIOLOGICAL SCIENCE (biology/biological science, botany, and zoology), BUSINESS (accounting, business administration and management, business law, international business management, management information systems, and marketing/retailing/merchandising), COMMUNICATIONS AND THE ARTS (English, fine arts, music, and Spanish), COMPUTER AND PHYSICAL SCIENCE (chemistry, computer science, mathematics, and science), EDUCATION (art, business, elementary, physical, science, secondary, and special), HEALTH PROFESSIONS (medical laboratory technology, predentistry, premedicine, prepharmacy, and public health), SOCIAL SCIENCE (Hispanic American studies, history, human services, humanities, physical fitnesss/movement, psychology, public adminis-

tration, social science, social work, and sociology). Social science has the largest enrollment.

Required: To graduate, students must earn at least 128 credit hours, 30 to 54 in the major, with a minimum GPA of 2.0 and complete the general education curriculum. An English course is required.

Special: WNMU offers internships, dual and student-designed majors, and on-campus work-study programs. Nondegree study, credit by examination, and a pass/fail option are possible.

Faculty/Classroom: Sixty-three percent of faculty are male; 37%, female.

Admissions: About 87% of a recent year's applicants were accepted.

Requirements: The SAT I or ACT is required. Applicants should be graduates of an accredited secondary school or present a GED. Students should have completed at least 3 units of English, 2 of social studies, including U.S. history, as well as 2 each of science and mathematics. Intermediate algebra and plane geometry are advised for students planning to enter certain fields. WNMU recommends a 2.0 GPA, but lower averages will be considered if applicants' test scores and personal recommendations are strong. CLEP credit is accepted. Important factors used in the admissions decision are leadership record, geographic diversity, extracurricular activities record, evidence of special talent, and advanced placement or honor courses.

Procedure: Freshmen are admitted to all sessions. Entrance exams should be taken before registration, preferably in the senior year. Applications should be filed by September 1 for fall entry, along with an application fee of $10. Notification is sent on a rolling basis. There is an early admissions plan.

Transfer: Transfer students must have a GPA of 2.0. Those with fewer than 32 hours of college credit must supply SAT I or ACT scores and a high school transcript. A total of 30 credits out of 128 must be completed at WNMU.

Visiting: There are regularly scheduled orientations for prospective students. There are guides for informal visits and visitors may sit in on classes and stay overnight at the school. To arrange for a visit, contact Mike Alecksen at (505) 538-6105.

Financial Aid: The FAFSA is required. The deadline for financial aid applications is April 1.

International Students: The school actively recruits these students. They must take the Comprehensive English Language Test and achieve a minimum score on the TOEFL of 550. The student must also take the SAT I or the ACT.

Computers: The college provides computer facilities for student use. The mainframes are 2 DEC VAX computers and support 100 terminals, half of which may be used by students. The computer laboratory contains 60 PCs and 15 VAX terminals. The Learning Resource Center houses 20 PCs and a DEC PDP11 with 32 terminals; word-processing software is available. Miller Library has a MICRO PDP11 with 10 terminals. Other campus locations house special-purpose computers.

Graduates: Some 50 companies recruited on campus in 1992–93.

Admissions Contact: Eric W. Gunnick, Registrar/Director of Admissions.

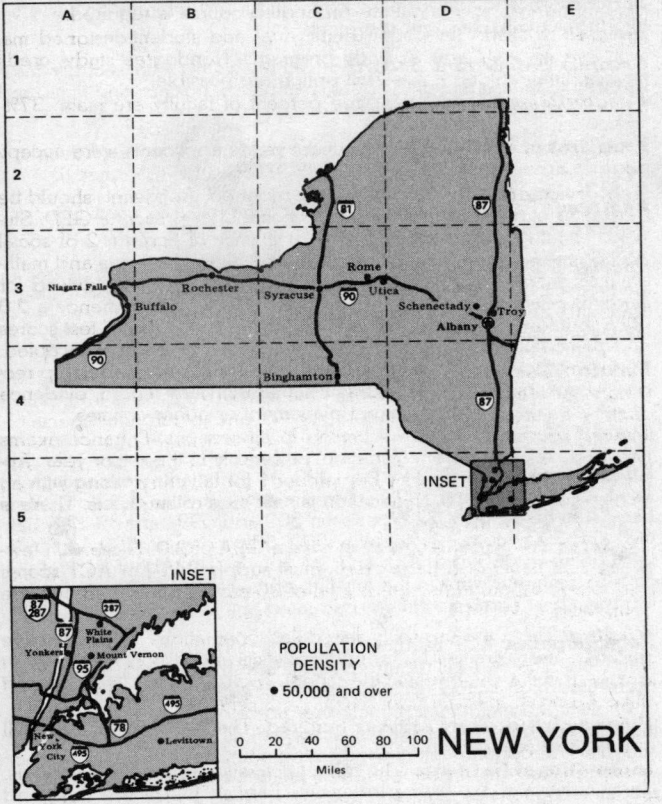

POPULATION
DENSITY
● 50,000 and over

0 20 40 60 80 100
Miles

NEW YORK

ADELPHI UNIVERSITY   D-5
Garden City, NY 11530   (516) 663–1100; (800) ADELPHI (in-state)

Full-time: 947 men, 1736 women	Faculty: 264; I, -$
Part-time: 338 men, 889 women	Ph.D.s: 75%
Graduate: 1063 men, 3221 women	Student/Faculty: 10 to 1
Year: semesters, summer session	Tuition: $12,250
Application Deadline: March 1	Room & Board: $6000
Freshman Class: 2190 applied, 1927 accepted, 512 enrolled	
SAT I Verbal/Math: 449/488	**LESS COMPETITIVE**

Adelphi University, a private, liberal arts school, was founded in 1896. There are 6 undergraduate and 6 graduate schools. In addition to regional accreditation, Adelphi has baccalaureate program accreditation with CSWE and NLN. The 2 libraries contain 473,098 volumes, 669,137 microform items, and 39,182 audiovisual forms, and subscribe to 1600 periodicals. Computerized library sources and services include the card catalog, interlibrary loans, and database searching. Special learning facilities include a learning resource center, an art gallery, a radio station, and an observatory. The 75-acre campus is in a suburban area 20 miles east of New York City. Including residence halls, there are 22 buildings on campus.

Student Life: About 87% of undergraduates are from New York. Students come from 34 states, 40 foreign countries, and Canada. Seventy-five percent are from public schools; 9% from private. Eighty percent are white; 11% African American. The average age of freshmen is 21; all undergraduates, 27. Twelve percent drop out by the end of their first year; 56% remain to graduate.

Housing: A total of 1112 students can be accommodated in college housing. College-sponsored living facilities include single-sex and coed dormitories and off-campus apartments. On-campus housing is guaranteed for all 4 years. Priority is given to out-of-town students. Seventy-eight percent of students commute. Alcohol is not permitted. All students may keep cars on campus.

Activities: About 10% of men belong to 8 national fraternities; about 8% of women belong to 1 local and 6 national sororities. There are no sororities on campus. There are 77 groups on campus, including cheerleading, chorale, computers, dance, drama, ethnic, film, honors, international, literary magazine, musical theater, newspaper, opera, orchestra, pep band, political, professional, radio and TV, religious, social, social service, student government, symphony, and yearbook. Popular campus events include Senior Week, Halloween Party, Homecoming, Fall Fest, Spring Fest, and Kwanza.

Sports: There are 7 intercollegiate sports each for men and women, and 25 intramural sports each for men and women. Athletic and recreation facilities include a 3000-seat stadium, a 600-seat gymnasium, a swimming pool, racquetball, squash, tennis, and handball courts, exercise rooms, a dance studio, a track, and playing fields for baseball, softball, and soccer.

Disabled Students: Eighty percent of the campus is accessible to disabled students. The following facilities are available: wheelchair ramps, elevators, special parking, specially equipped rest rooms, special class scheduling, lowered drinking fountains, and lowered telephones.

Services: In addition to many counseling and information services, tutoring is available in most subjects. In addition, there is a reader service for the blind, and remedial math, reading, and writing.

Campus Safety and Security: Campus safety and security measures include 24-hour foot and vehicle patrol, self-defense education, escort service, and shuttle buses. In addition, there are informal discussions, pamphlets, posters, films, emergency telephones, and lighted pathways and sidewalks. All dormitory main entrances are videotaped 24 hours a day; all dormitory doors are locked 24 hours.

Programs of Study: Adelphi awards the B.A., B.S., B.B.A., B.F.A., B.S.Ed., and B.S.S.W. degrees. Associate, master's, and doctoral degrees are also awarded. Bachelor's degrees are awarded in BIOLOGICAL SCIENCE (biochemistry and biology/biological science), BUSINESS (accounting, banking and finance, business administration and management, and management information systems), COMMUNICATIONS AND THE ARTS (art history and appreciation, communications, dance, design, dramatic arts, English, fine arts, French, languages, music, performing arts, and Spanish), COMPUTER AND PHYSICAL SCIENCE (chemistry, computer science, earth science, mathematics, natural sciences, and physics), EDUCATION (art, education of the deaf and hearing impaired, elementary, English, foreign languages, mathematics, music, physical, science, secondary, and social studies), HEALTH PROFESSIONS (nursing and speech pathology/audiology), SOCIAL SCIENCE (anthropology, economics, history, Latin American studies, liberal arts/general studies, philosophy, physical fitness/movement, political science/government, psychology, social science, social work, and sociology). Business management, nursing, psychology, and biology have the largest enrollments.

Required: All students need at least a 2.0 cumulative GPA (higher in some programs), and 120 credit hours. Distribution requirements revolve around Adelphi's core curriculum, which requires 8 credits in Modern Condition, 2 in Origin of the Modern Condition, 7 courses pertaining to nature, society and culture, and art and expression, and 3 in a senior seminar. In addition, a core composition course of 3 credits is required.

Special: Internships are available in accounting, banking and money management, and communications, among others. Study abroad is available in more than 30 countries, including Spain, France, Denmark, and England. Work-study programs, double majors, the B.A.-B.S. degree, a general studies degree, a 3–2 engineering degree, credit for life experience for adult students, nondegree study in special cases, and pass/fail options are possible. There is a freshman honors program on campus, as well as 15 national honor societies. Three departments have honors programs.

Faculty/Classroom: Sixty-three percent of faculty are male; 37%, female. The average class size in a regular course offering is 22.

Admissions: About 88% of the 1993–94 applicants were accepted. The SAT scores for the 1993–94 freshman class were as follows: Verbal—74% below 500, 25% between 500 and 599, and 1% between 600 and 700; Math—75% below 500, 23% between 500 and 599, and 2% between 600 and 700. About 27% of the current freshmen were in the top fifth of their class; 54% were in the top two fifths. One freshman graduated first in his class.

Requirements: The SAT I is required, but the ACT will be accepted. Composite scores should be 950 on the SAT I and 24 on the ACT. Applicants should have 16 academic credits, including a recommended 4 units of English, 3 each of mathematics and science, 2 or 3 in foreign language, and 4 each from history, social studies, and the fields named above. An essay is required, and an interview recommended for all applicants. A portfolio for art and technical theater candidates, an audition for music, dance, and theater candidates, or an interview for nursing candidates, is required. AP and CLEP credits are accepted. Important factors used in the admissions decision are advanced placement or honor courses, leadership record, personality, intangible qualities, recommendations by school officials, and extracurricular activities record.

Procedure: Freshmen are admitted fall and spring. Entrance exams should be taken in December of the senior year. Applications should be filed by March 1 for fall entry and November 30 for spring entry,

along with an application fee of $35. Notification is sent on a rolling basis. There are early admissions and deferred admissions plans.

Transfer: About 600 transfer students enrolled in 1993–94. A GPA of 2.5 is preferred in addition to an essay, an official high school transcript, and official records of all work completed or in progress from all previous colleges and universities. An interview is recommended for students in social work and nursing, while an audition is needed for music, dance, and theater students, and a portfolio for art and technical theater students. A total of 30 credits out of 120 must be completed at Adelphi.

Visiting: There are guides for informal visits and visitors may sit in on classes and stay overnight at the school. To arrange for a visit, contact Undergraduate Admissions at (516) 877–3050.

Financial Aid: In 1993–94, 75% of all current freshmen and 60% of continuing students received some form of financial aid. About 86% of freshmen and 50% of continuing students received need-based aid. The average freshman award was $10,110. Of that total, scholarships or need-based grants averaged $4991 ($17,000 maximum); loans averaged $2525 ($2625 maximum); and work contracts averaged $1662 ($2500 maximum). Twenty-six percent of undergraduate students work part-time. Average earnings from campus work for the school year are $1000. The college's own financial statement and FAFSA are required. The deadline for financial aid applications is March 1.

International Students: There are currently 181 international students enrolled. The school actively recruits these students. They must take the TOEFL and achieve a minimum score of 500.

Computers: The college provides computer facilities for student use. The mainframes are a DEC VAX 6420 and DEC System 5500. Students use the mainframe for course work and research. Approximately 125 terminals and microcomputers are available in various public, private, and departmental laboratories, all with access to the mainframes and PC service networks. Software support includes a variety of programming languages, color graphics, database management systems, word processing, simulations, models, and games. All students may access the system. There are no time limits on using the system and no fees.

Graduates: In 1992–93, 1026 bachelor's degrees were awarded. The most popular majors among graduates were management (15%), management/communications (12%), and elementary education (8%). Within an average freshman class, 1% graduate in 3 years, 44% in 4 years, 9% in 5 years, and 2% in 6 years. Some 74 companies recruited on campus in 1992–93.

Admissions Contact: Office of University Admissions.

ALBANY COLLEGE OF PHARMACY
D-3

Albany, NY 12208   (518) 445-7221

Full-time: 244 men, 396 women	Faculty: 40; IIB, +$
Part-time: 11 men, 21 women	Ph.D.s: 75%
Graduate: none	Student/Faculty: 16 to 1
Year: semesters	Tuition: $8700
Application Deadline: open	Room & Board: $4300
Freshman Class: 363 applied, 265 accepted, 140 enrolled	
SAT I Verbal/Math: 460/550	**VERY COMPETITIVE**

Albany College of Pharmacy, founded in 1881, is a private, coeducational, 5-year institution, a division of Union University. In addition to regional accreditation, ACP has baccalaureate program accreditation with ACPE. The library contains 8000 volumes and subscribes to 155 periodicals. Computerized library sources and services include interlibrary loans and database searching. Special learning facilities include a learning resource center. The 1-acre campus is in an urban area in downtown Albany. Including residence halls, there are 3 buildings on campus.

Student Life: About 90% of undergraduates are from New York. Students come from 10 states, 7 foreign countries, and Canada. Eighty-eight percent are white. The average age of freshmen is 18; all undergraduates, 21. Fifteen percent drop out by the end of their first year; 81% remain to graduate.

Housing: A total of 110 students can be accommodated in college housing. College-sponsored living facilities include coed off-campus apartments, which are guaranteed for the freshman year only. Priority is given to out-of-town students. Sixty-five percent of students commute. Alcohol is not permitted. Upperclassmen may keep cars on campus.

Activities: About 45% of men and about 43% of women belong to 3 national fraternities; about 30% of women belong to 1 national sorority. There are 10 groups on campus, including cheerleading, ethnic, honors, international, newspaper, photography, professional, social service, student government, and yearbook. Popular campus events include Parents Weekend, Open House, and Interview Day.

Sports: There are 5 intercollegiate sports for men and 5 for women, and 3 intramural sports for men and 3 for women. Athletic and recreation facilities include a small gymnasium on campus.

Disabled Students: All of the campus is accessible to disabled students. The following facilities are available: wheelchair ramps, elevators, special parking, and specially equipped rest rooms.

Services: In addition to many counseling and information services, tutoring is available in most subjects.

Campus Safety and Security: Campus safety and security measures include informal discussions, pamphlets, posters, and films, and lighted pathways and sidewalks.

Programs of Study: ACP awards the B.S.Pharm. degree. Bachelor's degrees are awarded in HEALTH PROFESSIONS (pharmacy).

Required: To graduate, students must complete 162 credits, including core curriculum courses, with a minimum GPA of 2.0.

Special: The college offers cross-registration with other colleges in the area, a dual major (B.S. in Pharmacy/M.S. in Health Systems Management), and work-study programs. There is 1 national honor society on campus.

Faculty/Classroom: Seventy-five percent of faculty are male; 25%, female. All teach undergraduates. The average class size in an introductory lecture is 120; in a laboratory, 30; and in a regular course offering, 125.

Admissions: About 73% of the 1993–94 applicants were accepted. The SAT scores for the 1993–94 freshman class were as follows: Verbal—72% below 500, 22% between 500 and 599, and 6% between 600 and 700; Math—21% below 500, 53% between 500 and 599, 24% between 600 and 700, and 2% above 700. About 61% of the current freshmen were in the top fifth of their class; 91% were in the top two fifths. Three freshmen graduated first in their class.

Requirements: ACP requires applicants to be in the upper 50% of their class. The SAT I is required. Applicants must be graduates of an accredited high school, with at least 17 credits consisting of 4 each of English and mathematics, including precalculus, and 3 of science, including chemistry. The GED is accepted. AP and CLEP credits are accepted. Important factors used in the admissions decision are advanced placement or honor courses, extracurricular activities record, recommendations by alumni, parents or siblings attending the school, and recommendations by school officials.

Procedure: Freshmen are admitted in the fall. Entrance exams should be taken in the junior year. Application deadlines are open. The application fee is $25. Notification is sent on a rolling basis. There are early decision and early admissions plans. About 52 early decision candidates were accepted for the 1993–94 class.

Transfer: About 43 transfer students enrolled in 1993–94. Applicants for transfer must have a GPA of 3.0. A total of 83 credits out of 162 must be completed at ACP.

Visiting: There are regularly scheduled orientations for prospective students, including a tour of the school and residence halls and a discussion of admissions requirements, financial aid, and student activities. There are guides for informal visits and visitors may sit in on classes and stay overnight at the school. To arrange for a visit, contact the Admissions Office at (518) 445–7221.

Financial Aid: In a recent year, 81% of all freshmen and 79% of continuing students received some form of financial aid. About 78% of freshmen and 74% of continuing students received need-based aid. The average freshman award was $5697. Of that total, scholarships or need-based grants averaged $1000 ($2500 maximum); loans averaged $2350 ($2625 maximum); and work contracts averaged $565 ($1500 maximum). Ninety-five percent of undergraduate students work part-time. Average earnings from campus work for the school year are $800. The average financial indebtedness of a recent year's graduate was $12,000. ACP is a member of CSS. The FFS and FAFSA are required. The deadline for financial aid applications is March 1.

International Students: There are currently 10 international students enrolled. They must take the TOEFL. The student must also take the SAT I or the ACT.

Computers: The college provides computer facilities for student use. The mainframe is a DEC VAX 11/750. A number of microcomputers are available for student use. All students may access the system 24 hours a day. There are no time limits on using the system and no fees.

Graduates: In 1992–93 119 bachelor's degrees were awarded. Within an average freshman class, 86% graduate in 5 years and 1% in 6 years. Some 50 companies recruited on campus in 1992–93.

Admissions Contact: Janis L. Fisher, Director of Admissions.

ALFRED UNIVERSITY
B-4

Alfred, NY 14802   (607) 871-2115; (800) 541-9229 (out-of-state)

Full-time: 1029 men, 801 women	Faculty: 169; IIA, -$
Part-time: 55 men, 55 women	Ph.Ds: 87%
Graduate: 187 men, 199 women	Student/Faculty: 11 to 1
Year: semesters, summer session	Tuition: $16,048; see profile
Application Deadline: February 15	Room & Board: $5006
Freshman Class: 1732 applied, 1425 accepted, 479 enrolled	
SAT I: 580/660	ACT: 27 VERY COMPETITIVE +

Alfred University, founded in 1836, is a private institution offering programs in business administration, liberal arts and sciences, engineering, and professional studies, and in art and design and ceramic engineering through the New York State College of Ceramics. Tuition for the College of Cermaics maybe as low as $6320. There are 4 undergraduate and 4 graduate schools. In addition to regional accreditation, Alfred has baccalaureate program accreditation with AACSB, ABET, and NASAD. The 2 libraries contain 323,234 volumes, 92,693 microform items, and 5149 audiovisual forms, and subscribe to 2527 periodicals. Computerized library sources and services include interlibrary loans and database searching. Special learning facilities include a learning resource center, art gallery, radio station, TV station, and observatory. The 232-acre campus is in a rural area 70 miles south of Rochester. Including residence halls, there are 53 buildings on campus.

Student Life: About 69% of undergraduates are from New York. Students come from 43 states, 31 foreign countries, and Canada. Eighty-four percent are from public schools; 16% from private. Eighty-six percent are white. The average age of freshmen is 18; all undergraduates, 20.5. Nine percent drop out by the end of their first year; 71% remain to graduate.

Housing: A total of 1350 students can be accommodated in college housing. College-sponsored living facilities include coed dormitories, on-campus apartments, fraternity houses, and sorority houses. In addition, there are honors houses and language houses. On-campus housing is guaranteed for all 4 years. Eighty-three percent of students live on campus; of those, 90% remain on campus on weekends. Alcohol is not permitted. All students may keep cars on campus.

Activities: About 30% of men belong to 2 local and 5 national fraternities; about 17% of women belong to 4 local sororities. There are 72 groups on campus, including art, band, cheerleading, chess, chorale, chorus, dance, drama, ethnic, film, gay, honors, international, jazz band, literary magazine, newspaper, orchestra, pep band, photography, political, professional, radio and tv, religious, social, social service, student government, and yearbook. Popular campus events include Alumni Weekend, Hot Dog Day, Performing Artists and Speakers Series, Family Weekend, and Homecoming.

Sports: There are 10 intercollegiate sports for men and 8 for women, and 17 intramural sports for men and 17 for women. Athletic and recreation facilities include an omniturf football surface, a soccer and lacrosse field, an Olympic-size pool, tennis courts, racquetball and squash courts, a weight room, and a dance and exercise studio. The campus stadium seats 4200, the indoor gymnasium, 3000. There is also a fitness center and facilities for horseback riding nearby.

Disabled Students: Fifty percent of the campus is accessible to disabled students. The following facilities are available: wheelchair ramps, elevators, special parking, specially equipped rest rooms, and special class scheduling.

Services: In addition to many counseling and information services, tutoring is available in most subjects. There is also a reader service for the blind, and remedial math, reading, and writing. Time management and study skills workshops and advocacy and support for students with learning and physical disabilities are available.

Campus Safety and Security: Campus safety and security measures include escort service, informal discussions, pamphlets, posters, films, and emergency telephones. In addition, there are lighted pathways and sidewalks.

Programs of Study: Alfred awards the B.A., B.S., and B.F.A. degrees. Master's and doctoral degrees also are awarded. Bachelor's degrees are awarded in BIOLOGICAL SCIENCE (biology/biological science), BUSINESS (accounting, banking and finance, business administration and management, business economics, international business management, and marketing/retailing/merchandising), COMMUNICATIONS AND THE ARTS (broadcasting, communications, design, dramatic arts, English, fine arts, French, photography, and Spanish), COMPUTER AND PHYSICAL SCIENCE (chemistry, computer science, geology, mathematics, physics, and science), EDUCATION (art, elementary, secondary, and special), ENGINEERING AND ENVIRONMENTAL DESIGN (ceramic engineering, electrical/electronics engineering, engineering, environmental science, industrial engineering, and mechanical engineering), HEALTH PROFESSIONS (health care administration, medical laboratory technology, predentistry, premedicine, and preveterinary science), SOCIAL SCIENCE (criminal justice, economics, gerontology, history, international studies, philosophy, political science/government, prelaw, psychology, public administration, and sociology). Ceramic engineering, electrical engineering, business, psychology, and education are the strongest programs academically. Ceramic engineering, accounting, psychology, art and design, and education have the largest enrollments.

Required: To graduate, students must complete 120 to 137 credits, depending on the major, with 36 to 48 credits in the major. Students must demonstrate basic competencies in writing, oral communication, mathematics, and computers. Freshmen must attend 10 freshman forums. Distribution requirements include 4 credits each of philosophy or religion, literature, art, and history, and 8 credits each of social studies and natural science. A minimum GPA of 2.0 is required.

Special: There are cooperative programs in engineering and business with Duke, Clarkson, and Columbia universities and SUNY/Brockport. There is cross-registration with the SUNY College of Technology and a 5-year program in environmental management/forestry with Duke. Alfred offers internships in all programs, extensive study abroad, Washington and Albany semesters, work-study, accelerated-degree programs, a general studies degree, student-designed majors, dual majors, credit by examination, and pass/fail options. A special feature is the New York State College of Ceramics, which offers programs and facilities in ceramic engineering and science as well as art and design. There is a freshman honors program on campus, as well as 14 national honor societies.

Faculty/Classroom: Seventy-six percent of faculty are male; 24%, female. Ninety-five percent teach undergraduates, 85% do research, and 80% do both. The average class size in an introductory lecture, a laboratory, and a regular course offering is 18.

Admissions: About 82% of the 1993–94 applicants were accepted. The SAT scores for the 1993–94 freshman class were as follows: Verbal—43% below 500, 37% between 500 and 599, 15% between 600 and 700, and 5% above 700; Math—11% below 500, 40% between 500 and 599, 35% between 600 and 700, and 14% above 700. The ACT scores were 11% below 21, 29% between 21 and 23, 26% between 24 and 26, 23% between 27 and 28, and 12% above 28. About 61% of the current freshmen were in the top fifth of their class; 89% were in the top two fifths. There were 39 National Merit finalists. Forty-nine freshmen graduated first in their class.

Requirements: The SAT I or ACT is required. A GED is accepted. A minimum of 16 Carnegie units is required, including 4 years of English and 2 to 3 years each of mathematics, history/social studies, and science. The remaining units may be in either a foreign language or any of the previously mentioned fields. An essay is required, and applicants to B.F.A. programs must submit a portfolio. Interviews are encouraged. AP and CLEP credits are accepted. Important factors used in the admissions decision are advanced placement or honor courses, personality, intangible qualities, extracurricular activities record, recommendations by school officials, and leadership record.

Procedure: Freshmen are admitted in the fall and spring. Entrance exams should be taken in the junior year. Early decision applications should be filed by December 1; regular applications, by February 15 for fall entry and December 1 for spring entry, along with an application fee of $25. Notification of early decision is sent December 15; regular decision, March 15. There are early decision, early admissions, and deferred admissions plans. About 48 early decision candidates were accepted for the 1993–94 class. A waiting list is an active part of the admissions procedure, with about 5% of applicants on the list.

Transfer: About 150 transfer students enrolled in 1993–94. Transfer applicants must have a GPA of at least 2.5. They must submit at least 1 letter of recommendation and official high school and college transcripts. Art students must submit a portfolio. A total of 30 credits out of 120 to 137 must be completed at Alfred.

Visiting: There are regularly scheduled orientations for prospective students, including a campus tour, social activities panel, financial aid presentation, faculty discussions, and on-campus interviews. There are guides for informal visits and visitors may sit in on classes and stay overnight at the school. To arrange for a visit, contact Laurie A. Richer, Acting Director of Admissions, at (800) 541-9229.

Financial Aid: In a recent year, 65% of all freshmen and 70% of continuing students received some form of financial aid. About 63% of freshmen and 60% of continuing students received need-based aid. The average freshman award in a recent year was $13,700. Of that total, scholarships or need-based grants averaged $11,100 ($18,580 maximum); loans averaged $2600 ($3500 maximum); and work contracts averaged $800 ($1200 maximum). Fifty percent of undergraduate students work part-time. Average earnings from campus work for the school year are $500. Alfred is a member of CSS. The FAF and the college's own financial statement are required. The deadline for financial aid applications is May 1.

International Students: There are currently 90 international students enrolled. The school actively recruits these students. They must take the TOEFL and achieve a minimum score of 550.

Computers: The college provides computer facilities for student use. The mainframes include 2 DEC VAX 11/785s, a VAX 8530, and 2 VAX 3100 systems. All academic and administration buildings are connected to the VAX network. There are numerous high-speed and laser printers, 4 tape drives, and multicolor pen plotters. More than 300 terminals are located across campus for student use. All students may access the system 24 hours a day, 7 days a week. There are no time limits on using the system and no fees.

Graduates: In a recent year, 474 bachelor's degrees were awarded. The most popular majors among graduates were ceramic engineering (8%), business administration (7%), and biology (5%). Within an average freshman class, 1% graduate in 3 years, 67% in 4 years, and 8% in 5 years. Some 56 companies recruited on campus in a recent year. In a recent graduating class, 10% of the men and 12% of the women were enrolled in graduate school within 6 months of graduation; 27% of the men and 39% of the women had found employment.

Admissions Contact: Laurie A. Richer, Acting Director of Admissions.

AUDREY COHEN COLLEGE D-5
(Formerly College for Human Services)
New York, NY 10014   (212) 989-2002, ext. 225
      (800) 33-THINK (in-state)

Full-time: 266 men, 677 women	Faculty: 15
Part-time: 9 men, 36 women	Ph.D.s: 90%
Graduate: 20 men, 37 women	Student/Faculty: 63 to 1
Year: 3 semesters, summer session	Tuition: $11,184
Application Deadline: August 1	Room & Board: n/app
Freshman Class: 631 applied, 531 accepted, 265 enrolled	
SAT I or ACT: not required	**LESS COMPETITIVE**

Audrey Cohen College, founded in 1964, is a private, coeducational institution offering programs in human services and business management. All bachelor's degree programs involve a combination of classwork and field work and may be completed in two years and eight months. There are 2 undergraduate schools and one graduate school. The library contains 20,170 volumes and 310 microform items, and subscribes to 201 periodicals. Computerized library sources and services include the card catalog and database searching. Special learning facilities include a learning resource center. The campus is in an urban area in New York City. There is one building on campus.

Student Life: About 95% of undergraduates are from New York. Students come from 4 states and 3 foreign countries. Sixty-eight percent are from public schools; 32% from private. Sixty percent are African American; 21% Hispanic; 12% white. The average age of freshmen is 29; all undergraduates, 32. Twenty-eight percent drop out by the end of their first year; 59% remain to graduate.

Housing: There are no residence halls; all students commute. Alcohol is not permitted.

Activities: There are no fraternities or sororities on campus. There are 5 groups on campus, including computers, gay, professional, social, social service, student government, and yearbook. Popular campus events include career fairs, admissions open house, and dean's ceremonies.

Sports: There is no sports program at the college.

Disabled Students: All of the campus is accessible to disabled students. The following facilities are available: wheelchair ramps, elevators, specially equipped rest rooms, special class scheduling, lowered drinking fountains, and lowered telephones.

Services: In addition to many counseling and information services, tutoring is available in every subject. In addition, there is remedial math, reading, and writing.

Campus Safety and Security: Campus safety and security measures include 24-hour foot and vehicle patrol and lighted pathways and sidewalks.

Programs of Study: The college awards the B.P.S. degree. Master's degrees also are awarded. Bachelor's degrees are awarded in BUSINESS (business administration and management), EDUCATION (early childhood), HEALTH PROFESSIONS (mental health/human services), SOCIAL SCIENCE (child care/child and family studies, community services, gerontology, human services, prelaw, psychology, and social work). Human services has the largest enrollment.

Required: To graduate, students must complete 128 credit hours with a minimum GPA of 2.0. The curriculum is prescribed and no electives are featured. A constructive action document based on performance in the field and mastery of course work is required each semester.

Special: Internships, work-study programs, an accelerated degree program, credit by examination, and credit for life experience are offered.

Faculty/Classroom: Forty percent of faculty are male; 60%, female. All teach undergraduates. The average class size in an introductory lecture is 25; in a laboratory, 18; and in a regular course offering, 20.

Admissions: About 84% of the 1993–94 applicants were accepted. About 15% of the current freshmen were in the top fifth of their class; 50% were in the top two fifths.

Requirements: Students must take the Test of Adult Basic Education (TABE) in English, reading, and mathematics; recent high school graduates who have a minimum composite SAT I score of 900 may present the SAT I instead. Applicants must have graduated from an accredited secondary school. The GED is accepted. An essay and an interview are required. Important factors used in the admissions decision are evidence of special talent, leadership record, personality, intangible qualities, extracurricular activities record, and recommendations by school officials.

Procedure: Freshmen are admitted to all sessions. Entrance exams should be taken in the senior year. Applications should be filed by August 1 for fall entry, December 1 for spring entry, and April 1 for summer entry, along with an application fee of $20. Notification is sent on a rolling basis.

Transfer: About 120 transfer students enrolled in 1993–94. Admission is based on current skills and abilities as measured on the entrance examination and essay. A total of 64 credits out of 128 must be completed at the college.

Visiting: There are regularly scheduled orientations for prospective students. There are guides for informal visits and visitors may sit in on classes. To arrange for a visit, contact the Admissions Office at (212) 989-2002, ext. 501, or (800) 33-THINK (in-state).

Financial Aid: In 1993–94, 80% of all current freshmen and 80% of continuing students received some form of financial aid. Scholarships or need-based grants averaged $900 ($1000 maximum); loans averaged $1500 ($6625 maximum); and work contracts averaged $1500 ($3000 maximum). Eight percent of undergraduate students work part-time. The FAF and the New York State Higher Education Financial statement are required. The deadline for financial aid applications is August 15.

International Students: They must take the TOEFL and achieve a minimum score of 550. The student must also take the TABE.

Computers: The college provides computer facilities for student use. The mainframe is a Sun 3/260. There are also 32 Unisys PW300 microcomputers available in the computer laboratory. All students may access the system. It may be used any hours the college is open. There are no time limits on using the system and no fees.

Graduates: In 1992–93, 159 bachelor's degrees were awarded. Within an average freshman class, 40% graduate in 4 years. Some 35 companies recruited on campus in an earlier year. In an earlier graduating class, 60% of all graduates were enrolled in graduate school within 6 months of graduation; 90% had found employment.

Admissions Contact: Steven Lenhart, Admissions Office.

BARD COLLEGE D-4
Annandale-on-Hudson, NY 12504   (914) 758-7472

Full-time: 501 men, 522 women	Faculty: 92; IIB, ++$
Part-time: 22 men, 23 women	Ph.D.s: 95%
Graduate: 70 men, 62 women	Student/Faculty: 11 to 1
Year: 4-1-4	Tuition: $19,239
Application Deadline: February 15	Room & Board: $6030
Freshman Class: 1857 applied, 910 accepted, 313 enrolled	
SAT I or ACT: not required	**HIGHLY COMPETITIVE**

Bard College, founded in 1860, is a private, coeducational liberal arts and sciences institution, affiliated historically with the Association of Episcopal Colleges. Discussion-oriented seminars and independent study are encouraged, tutorials are on a one-to-one basis, and most classes are kept small, with fewer than 20 students. There are 3 graduate schools. The library contains 260,000 volumes, 5670 microform items, and 4000 audiovisual forms, and subscribes to 730 periodicals. Computerized library sources and services include the card catalog, interlibrary loans, and database searching. Special learning facilities include an art gallery, a radio station, an ecology field station, the Jerome Levy International Economics Institute, the Institute for Writing and Thinking, the International Academy for Scholarship and the Arts, the Center for Curatorial Studies and Art in Contemporary Culture, and an archaeological field school. The 600-acre campus is in a rural area 100 miles north of New York City. Including residence halls, there are 70 buildings on campus.

Student Life: About 75% of undergraduates are from out-of-state. Students come from 50 states, 48 foreign countries, and Canada. Seventy percent are from public schools; 30% from private. Seventy-five percent are white; 12% foreign nationals. The average age of freshmen is 18; all undergraduates, 20. Ten percent drop out by the end of their first year; 77% remain to graduate.

Housing: A total of 809 students can be accommodated in college housing. College-sponsored living facilities include single-sex and coed dormitories. In addition, there are special interest houses. On-campus housing is guaranteed for all 4 years. Eighty-five percent of students live on campus; of those, 75% remain on campus on weekends. All students may keep cars on campus.

Activities: There are no fraternities or sororities on campus. There are 60 groups on campus, including art, band, chess, choir, chorus, computers, dance, drama, ethnic, film, gay, international, jazz band, literary magazine, newspaper, opera, orchestra, photography, political, radio and TV, religious, social, social service, student government, and yearbook. Popular campus events include Winter Carnival, Spring Festival, Comedy Night, campus outreach activities, political action activities, musical events, and senior project shows.

Sports: There are 7 intercollegiate sports for men and 6 for women, and 13 intramural sports each for men and women. Athletic and recreation facilities include a gymnasium, a pool, a student center, soccer and softball fields, squash and tennis courts, cross-country trails, bike paths, a 3000-seat auditorium, and a film center.

Disabled Students: Seventy percent of the campus is accessible to disabled students. The following facilities are available: wheelchair ramps, elevators, special parking, specially equipped rest rooms, and lowered drinking fountains and telephones.

Services: In addition to many counseling and information services, tutoring is available in most subjects. There is also a reader service for the blind.

Campus Safety and Security: Campus safety and security measures include 24-hour foot and vehicle patrol, self-defense education, escort service, and shuttle buses. In addition, there are informal discussions, pamphlets, posters, films, emergency telephones, lighted pathways and sidewalks, 24-hour volunteer emergency medical technicians, and Bard Response to Rape and Associated Violence Education (BRAVE) volunteers.

Programs of Study: Bard awards the B.A. degree. Master's degrees also are awarded. Bachelor's degrees are awarded in BIOLOGICAL SCIENCE (biology/biological science), COMMUNICATIONS AND THE ARTS (art history and appreciation, dance, dramatic arts, English, film arts, fine arts, languages, music, and photography), COMPUTER AND PHYSICAL SCIENCE (chemistry, mathematics, and physics), ENGINEERING AND ENVIRONMENTAL DESIGN (environmental science), HEALTH PROFESSIONS (predentistry and premedicine), SOCIAL SCIENCE (American studies, anthropology, Asian/Oriental studies, economics, history, history of science, philosophy, political science/government, prelaw, psychology, religion, social science, and sociology). Language and literature, the arts, and social studies have the largest enrollments.

Required: All students must complete a year-long freshman seminar, a 3-week workshop in language and thinking, a moderation process in the sophomore year where the student chooses a concentration in an academic department, a conference in the junior year, and a senior project. A distribution of at least 2 courses in each of the 4 academic divisions, including a quantitative analysis course, is required with a maximum of 84 hours in the major and a total of 124 credit hours needed.

Special: Bard offers opportunities for study abroad, internships (no academic credit), a Washington, D.C. semester, dual majors, student-designed majors, and pass/fail options. Cross-registration is available with Vassar College and SUNY/New Paltz. A 3–2 engineering degree is available with the Columbia University School of Engineering. Other 3–2 degrees are available in forestry and environmental studies, social work, architecture, city and regional planning, public health, and business administration. There are also opportunities for independent study; multicultural and ethnic studies; community, regional, and environmental studies; area studies; and the International Honors Program.

Faculty/Classroom: Sixty percent of faculty are male; 40%, female. All teach and also do research. No introductory courses are taught by graduate students. The average class size in an introductory lecture is 20; in a laboratory, 15; and in a regular course offering, 15.

Admissions: About 49% of the 1993–94 applicants were accepted. The SAT scores for the 1993–94 freshman class were as follows: Verbal—1% below 500, 43% between 500 and 599, 46% between 600 and 700, and 10% above 700; Math—1% below 500, 40% between 500 and 599, 51% between 600 and 700, and 8% above 700. About 70% of the current freshmen were in the top fifth of their class; 90% were in the top two fifths.

Requirements: Bard requires applicants to be in the upper 50% of their class. A minimum GPA of 2.5 is required. Standardized testing (SAT I and ACT) is not required. Bard places strong emphasis on the academic background and intellectual curiosity of applicants, as well as indications of the student's commitment to social and environmental concerns, independent research, volunteer work, and other important extracurricular activities. Students applying for admission are expected to have graduated from an accredited secondary school (the GED is accepted) and must submit written essays with the application. The high school record should include a full complement of college-preparatory courses. An interview is recommended. AP credits are accepted. Important factors used in the admissions decision are advanced placement or honor courses, evidence of special talent, leadership record, and recommendations by school officials.

Procedure: Freshmen are admitted in the fall and spring. There are early decision, early admissions, and deferred admissions plans. Early decision applications should be filed by December 1; regular applications, by February 15 for fall entry and December 1 for spring entry, along with an application fee of $40. Notification of early decision is sent January 1; regular decision, April 1. About 16 early decision candidates were accepted for the 1993–94 class. A waiting list is an active part of the admissions procedure, with about 10% of applicants on the list.

Transfer: About 50 transfer students enrolled in a recent year. Admission requirements are the same as for regular applicants. A minimum GPA of 3.0 and an interview are recommended. A total of 60 credits out of 124 must be completed at Bard.

Visiting: There are regularly scheduled orientations for prospective students, consisting of regularly scheduled, daily tours and interviews (each 1 hour), which are strongly recommended. There are guides for informal visits and visitors may sit in on classes with advanced notice only. Accepted candidates may stay overnight at the school after April. To arrange for a visit, contact the Admissions Office at (914) 758–7472.

Financial Aid: In 1993–94, 70% of all students received some form of financial aid. About 68% of all students received need-based aid. The average freshman award was $18,000. Of that total, scholarships or need-based grants averaged $12,820 ($25,184 maximum); loans averaged $2800 ($4125 maximum); and work contracts averaged $1500 ($2000 maximum). Fifty percent of undergraduate students work part-time. Average earnings from campus work for the school year are $1000. The average financial indebtedness of the 1992–93 graduate was $13,000. Bard is a member of CSS. The FAF and the college's own financial statement are required. The deadline for financial aid applications is February 15.

International Students: There are currently 127 international students enrolled. The school actively recruits these students. They must take the TOEFL and achieve a minimum score of 550.

Computers: The college provides computer facilities for student use. The computer center houses more than 65 networked IBM and Apple microcomputers as well as some 50 additional terminals and PCs. Others are located in the library and academic departments. All students may access the system. There are no time limits and no fees.

Graduates: In 1992–93, 218 bachelor's degrees were awarded. The most popular majors among graduates were social studies (36%), arts (29%), and languages and literature (19%). Within an average freshman class, 77% graduate in 5 years. Some 80 companies recruited on campus in 1992–93.

Admissions Contact: Mary Backlund, Director, Admissions Office.

BORICUA COLLEGE
D-5
New York, NY 10032   (212) 694–1000

Full-time: 352 men, 859 women	**Faculty:** 48
Part-time: none	**Ph.D.s:** 18%
Graduate: none	**Student/Faculty:** 25 to 1
Year: trimesters, summer session	**Tuition:** $5920
Application Deadline: August 15	**Room & Board:** n/app
Freshman Class: 1600 applied, 545 accepted, 490 enrolled	
SAT I or ACT: accepted	**VERY COMPETITIVE**

Boricua College, founded in 1974, is a private college for bilingual students, designed to meet the needs of a Spanish-speaking population. Special learning facilities include a learning resource center and an art gallery. The campus is in an urban area in Manhattan. There are 4 buildings on campus.

Student Life: All undergraduates are from New York.

Housing: There are no residence halls.

Activities: There are some groups on campus, including chorus, drama, newspaper, and student government. Popular campus events include cultural programs.

Sports: There is no sports program at Boricua.

Services: In addition to many counseling and information services, tutoring is available in most subjects.

Campus Safety and Security: Campus safety and security measures include informal discussions, pamphlets, posters, films, emergency telephones, and lighted pathways and sidewalks.

Programs of Study: Boricua awards the B.A. and B.S. degrees. Associate degrees also are awarded. Bachelor's degrees are awarded in BUSINESS (business administration and management), EDUCATION (elementary), SOCIAL SCIENCE (human services and liberal arts/general studies).

Required: To graduate, students must complete 124 credits, including a computer course.

Special: Nontraditional methods of teaching include individualized instruction, small learning groups, and independent study. Students take part in directed internships throughout their 4 years, which are related to human services, business administration, and elementary education. Study abroad in Mexico is permitted.

Faculty/Classroom: Fifty-one percent of faculty are male; 49%, female.

Admissions: About 34% of the 1993–94 applicants were accepted.

Requirements: Boricua administers its own tests to prospective students, although either the SAT I or ACT is accepted. Applicants must be graduates of an accredited secondary school. Two letters of recommendation are required. Applicants must demonstrate a working knowledge of English and Spanish to a faculty panel. Important factors used in the admissions decision are recommendations by school officials and alumni, personality, intangible qualities, parents or siblings attending the school, and leadership record.

Procedure: Freshmen are admitted fall, spring, and summer. Applications should be filed by August 15 for fall entry, January 15 for spring entry, and May 20 for summer entry, along with an application fee of $20. Notification is sent on a rolling basis. There is an early decision plan.

Transfer: Applicants with associate degrees may transfer up to 60 credits, others up to 30 credits. A total of 64 credits out of 124 must be completed at Boricua.

Visiting: There are regularly scheduled orientations for prospective students. Letters are sent to prospective students advising them of scheduled orientations. To arrange for a visit, contact the Admissions Department at (212) 694–1000.

Financial Aid: In a recent year, 99% of all students received some form of financial aid. Most awards are need-based. Boricua is a member of CSS. The FAF is required. The deadline for financial aid applications is March 31.

International Students: The student must take the college's own entrance exam.

Computers: The college provides computer facilities for student use. The mainframe is an IBM. There are computers available for student use in the computer laboratory. Those students registered in computer courses may access the system. There are no fees.

Admissions Contact: Abraham Cruz, Director of Student Services.

BROOKLYN CAMPUS OF LONG ISLAND UNIVERSITY

D-

Brooklyn, NY 11201   (718) 488–1011

Full-time: 1752 men, 3402 women	Faculty: 203; IIA, +$
Part-time: 282 men, 540 women	Ph.D.s: 75%
Graduate: 629 men, 985 women	Student/Faculty: 25 to 1
Year: semesters, summer session	Tuition: $11,000
Application Deadline: open	Room & Board: $4000
Freshman Class: 1952 applied, 1922 accepted, 987 enrolled	
SAT I Verbal/Math: 410/420	LESS COMPETITIVE

Long Island University/Brooklyn Campus, founded in 1926, is part of the Long Island University system. It is a private, coeducational institution offering programs in liberal arts and sciences, pharmacy, health professions, education, business, nursing, and special programs. It is largely a commuter school. There are 6 undergraduate and 5 graduate schools. In addition to regional accreditation, LIU has baccalaureate program accreditation with ACPE and NLN. The library contains 2,100,000 volumes, 813,544 microform items, and 7902 audiovisual forms, and subscribes to 8042 periodicals. Computerized library sources and services include the card catalog and interlibrary loans. Special learning facilities include a learning resource center, art gallery, radio station, and TV station. The 10-acre campus is in an urban area. Including residence halls, there are 8 buildings on campus.

Student Life: About 91% of undergraduates are from New York. Students come from 35 states, 21 foreign countries, and Canada. Seventy-five percent are from public schools; 25% from private. Forty-three percent are African American; 29% white; 17% Hispanic; 11% Asian American. The average age of freshmen is 21; all undergraduates, 25. Thirty-six percent drop out by the end of their first year; 61% remain to graduate.

Housing: A total of 525 students can be accommodated in college housing. College-sponsored living facilities include single-sex and coed dormitories and married-student housing. On-campus housing is available on a first-come, first-served basis. Eighty-nine percent of students commute. Alcohol is not permitted.

Activities: There are 75 groups on campus, including band, cheerleading, chess, chorale, computers, dance, ethnic, honors, international, literary magazine, newspaper, photography, political, radio and TV, religious, student government, and yearbook.

Sports: Athletic and recreation facilities include a baseball/soccer field and a basketball gymnasium.

Disabled Students: The entire campus is accessible to disabled students. The following facilities are available: wheelchair ramps, elevators, specially equipped rest rooms, special class scheduling, lowered drinking fountains, and lowered telephones.

Services: In addition to many counseling and information services, tutoring is available in most subjects. There is also remedial math, reading, and writing.

Programs of Study: LIU awards the B.A., B.S., and B.F.A. degrees. Associate, master's, and doctoral degrees also are awarded. Bachelor's degrees are awarded in BIOLOGICAL SCIENCE (biology/biological science), BUSINESS (accounting, banking and finance, business administration and management, and marketing/retailing/merchandising), COMMUNICATIONS AND THE ARTS (broadcasting, communications, English, fine arts, journalism, languages, music, and speech/debate/rhetoric), COMPUTER AND PHYSICAL SCIENCE (chemistry, computer science, information sciences and systems, and mathematics), EDUCATION (art, business, early childhood, elementary, music, science, secondary, special, and teaching English as a second language/foreign language), HEALTH PROFESSIONS (nursing, pharmacy, physical therapy, predentistry, and premedicine), SOCIAL SCIENCE (anthropology, economics, history, philosophy, political science/government, prelaw, psychology, social science, and sociology). Health professions, pharmacy, and liberal arts are the strongest academically. Health professions, liberal arts, business, and education have the largest enrollments.

Required: Proficiency courses include basic English and mathematics, English composition, and speech. Distribution requirements are 6 credits each in foreign language, mathematics, and science. Students must complete a core curriculum of 18 credits in the humanities, 12 in social sciences, 8 in natural sciences, and 6 in mathematics. A total of 128 credits is required for graduation, with 40 to 50 credits in the major, and a minimum GPA of 2.0.

Special: Accelerated degree programs are available in all majors. Students may cross-register with other LIU campuses. Internships in career-related jobs provide cooperative education credits. Study abroad, dual majors, credit for life, military, and work experience, and pass/fail options are also offered. There is a freshman honors program on campus.

Faculty/Classroom: The average class size in a regular course offering is 22.

Admissions: About 98% of the 1993–94 applicants were accepted.

Requirements: A minimum GPA of 2.0 is required. The SAT I or ACT is recommended. AP and CLEP credits are accepted. Important factors used in the admissions decision are recommendations by school officials, advanced placement or honor courses, evidence of special talent, personality, intangible qualities, and leadership record.

Procedure: Freshmen are admitted to all sessions. Entrance exams should be taken by January of the senior year. Application deadlines are open. Application fee is $30. Notification is sent on a rolling basis. There is a deferred admissions plan.

Transfer: About 880 transfer students enrolled in a recent year. A minimum GPA of 2.5 and 64 earned credit hours are required to transfer. The SAT I, an associate degree, and an interview are recommended. At least 32 credits out of 128 must be completed at LIU.

Visiting: There are regularly scheduled orientations for prospective students. Visitors may sit in on classes. To arrange for a visit, contact the Admissions Office at (718) 488–1011.

Financial Aid: In a recent year, 90% of all students received some form of financial aid. Average earnings from campus work for the school year are $750. LIU is a member of CSS. The FAF and the college's own financial statement are required. The deadline for financial aid applications is November 15.

International Students: There are currently 175 international students enrolled. The school actively recruits these students. They must take the TOEFL and achieve a minimum score of 500 and must also take the SAT I or the ACT.

Computers: The college provides computer facilities for student use. The mainframe is a DEC VAX 8600. Microcomputers are available in the library. All students may access the system during library hours. There are no time limits on using the system and no fees.

Graduates: In a recent year, 592 bachelor's degrees were awarded.

Admissions Contact: Alan B. Chaves, Admissions Office.

CANISIUS COLLEGE

A-3

Buffalo, NY 14208   (716) 888–2200; (800) 843–1517 (out-of-state)

Full-time: 1636 men, 1339 women	Faculty: 190; IIB, +$
Part-time: 287 men, 263 women	Ph.D.s: 93%
Graduate: 590 men, 805 women	Student/Faculty: 16 to 1
Year: semesters, summer session	Tuition: $10,270
Application Deadline: open	Room & Board: $5240
Freshman Class: 3182 applied, 2541 accepted, 738 enrolled	
SAT I Verbal/Math: 448/510	ACT: 23 COMPETITIVE

Canisius College, founded in 1870, is a private, coeducational Roman Catholic college in the Jesuit tradition. It offers undergraduate programs in the liberal arts and sciences and business. There are 2 undergraduate and 2 graduate schools. In addition to regional accreditation, Canisius has baccalaureate program accreditation with AACSB and NCATE. The library contains 280,507 volumes, 502,789 microform items, and 3861 audiovisual forms, and subscribes to 1845 periodicals. Computerized library sources and services include the card catalog, interlibrary loans, and database searching. Special

learning facilities include a learning resource center, planetarium, radio station, and a TV studio. The 25-acre campus is in an urban area. Including residence halls, there are 22 buildings on campus.

Student Life: About 93% of undergraduates are from New York. Students come from 22 states, 23 foreign countries, and Canada. Sixty-five percent are from public schools; 35% from private. Ninety percent are white. Fifty-nine percent are Catholic; 22% claim no religious affiliation. The average age of freshmen is 19; all undergraduates, 22. Seven percent drop out by the end of their first year; 53% remain to graduate.

Housing: A total of 928 students can be accommodated in college housing. College-sponsored living facilities include single-sex and coed dormitories and off-campus apartments. In addition there are special interest houses and and an international students house. On-campus housing is guaranteed for all 4 years. Sixty-eight percent of students commute. All students may keep cars on campus.

Activities: About 4% of men and women belong to 2 national fraternities and sororities. There are 90 groups on campus, including cheerleading, chess, chorale, computers, drama, drill team, ethnic, honors, international, jazz band, literary magazine, newspaper, pep band, political, professional, radio and TV, religious, social, social service, student government, and yearbook. Popular campus events include Fall and Spring Quad Parties, Fall and Spring Semiformals, Senior Week, Parents Weekend, Buffalo Philharmonic on Campus, Oktoberfest, Carnivale, Little Theater, International Fest, Multicultural Week, MLK celebration, and commuter awareness weeks.

Sports: There are 13 intercollegiate sports for men and 10 for women, and 13 intramural sports for men and 12 for women. Athletic and recreation facilities include an 1800-seat athletic center, with a 24-yard pool, racquetball courts, and training rooms; a 1000-seat sports complex; and a rifle range.

Disabled Students: Ninety-five percent of the campus is accessible to disabled students. The following facilities are available: wheelchair ramps, elevators, special parking, specially equipped rest rooms, automatic doors, and TDD.

Services: In addition to many counseling and information services, tutoring is available in some subjects, including in most introductory courses. There is a reader service for the blind and remedial math and writing.

Campus Safety and Security: Campus safety and security measures include 24-hour foot and vehicle patrol, escort service, shuttle buses, and informal discussions. In addition, there are pamphlets, posters, and films, emergency telephones, lighted pathways and sidewalks, and a crime prevention officer and crime-prevention programs.

Programs of Study: Canisius awards the B.A. and B.S. degrees. Associate and master's degrees also are awarded. Bachelor's degrees are awarded in BIOLOGICAL SCIENCE (biochemistry and biology), BUSINESS (accounting, banking, management, management information systems, marketing, and sports management), COMMUNICATIONS AND THE ARTS (art history, communication studies, English, French, German, languages, and Spanish), COMPUTER AND PHYSICAL SCIENCE (chemistry, computer science, mathematics, and physics), EDUCATION (business, elementary/early, English, foreign languages, mathematics, physical, science, secondary, and social studies), ENGINEERING AND ENVIRONMENTAL DESIGN (preengineering), HEALTH PROFESSIONS (medical laboratory technology, predentistry, and premedicine), SOCIAL SCIENCE (anthropology, economics, history, international relations, philosophy, political science/government, prelaw, psychology, religious studies, sociology, and urban studies). Accounting, chemistry, computer science, and biology are the strongest academically. Management, communication studies, and psychology have the largest enrollments.

Required: All students must complete a core curriculum consisting of physical education, 4 courses in general studies (literature, philosophy, and religion), and 12 courses in area studies (natural sciences, social studies, art and literature, history, philosophy, religious studies, mathematics, and languages). A minimum of 120 credit hours and a minimum GPA of 2.0 are required for graduation.

Special: Canisius offers internships, credit by examination, pass/fail options, nondegree studies, dual majors, a Washington semester, work-study programs, and study abroad in Italy, Spain, and other countries. Cooperative programs are available with the Fashion Institute of Technology in New York City and the SUNY College of Environmental Science and Forestry in Syracuse. Cross-registration is permitted with 14 schools in the Western New York Consortium of Higher Education. Canisius also offers several joint degree programs with SUNY at Buffalo Dental School and School of Pharmacy, the Ohio College of Podiatric Medicine, and the SUNY College of Optometry. There is a freshman honors program on campus, as well as 6 national honor societies. Three departments have honors programs.

Faculty/Classroom: Seventy percent of faculty are male; 30%, female. Ninety-eight percent teach undergraduates, 75% do research, and 80% do both. The average class size in an introductory lecture is 25; in a laboratory, 20; and in a regular course offering, 27.

Admissions: About 80% of the 1993–94 applicants were accepted. The SAT scores for the 1993–94 freshman class were as follows: Verbal—73% below 500, 21% between 500 and 599, and 5% between 600 and 700; Math—46% below 500, 34% between 500 and 599, 16% between 600 and 700, and 3% above 700. The ACT scores were 5% below 21, 64% between 21 and 23, 29% between 24 and 26, and 3% between 27 and 28. About 34% of the current freshmen were in the top fifth of their class; 59% were in the top two fifths. About 10 freshmen graduated first in their class.

Requirements: A minimum GPA of 3.0 is required. The SAT I or ACT is required. Minimum scores recommended are SAT I composite 800 and 21 ACT. Applicants must have graduated from an accredited secondary school (a GED will be accepted) and have acquired 4 credits in English, 2 in a foreign language, 3 to 3 1/2 in mathematics, 1 to 2 in science, 2 in social studies, and 2 1/2 to 4 in other electives. An essay and an interview are recommended. AP and CLEP credits are accepted. Important factors used in the admissions decision are advanced placement or honor courses, recommendations by school officials, evidence of special talent, leadership record, and personality, intangible qualities.

Procedure: Freshmen are admitted fall and spring. Entrance exams should be taken during the student's junior or senior year. Application deadlines are open. The application fee is $30. Notification is sent on a rolling basis. There are early admissions and deferred admissions plans.

Transfer: About 222 transfer students enrolled in 1993–94. Transfer students must present a minimum GPA of 2.0. A total of 30 credits out of 120 must be completed at Canisius.

Visiting: There are regularly scheduled orientations for prospective students, which include campus weekends, single-day visits, and overnights. There are guides for informal visits and visitors may sit in on classes and stay overnight at the school. To arrange for a visit, contact the Admissions Office at (716) 888–2200 or (800) 843–1517.

Financial Aid: In 1993–94, 91% of all current freshmen and 80% of continuing students received some form of financial aid. About 85% of freshmen and 74% of continuing students received need-based aid. The average freshman award was $10,244. Of that total, scholarships or need-based grants averaged $6337 ($9950 maximum); loans averaged $3157; and work contracts averaged $750 ($1600 maximum). Twenty percent of undergraduate students work part-time. Average earnings from campus work for the school year are $1374. The average financial indebtedness of the 1992–93 graduate was $11,790. Canisius is a member of CSS. The FAF and the FAFSA are required. The deadline for financial aid applications is March 1.

International Students: There are currently 80 international students enrolled. The school actively recruits these students. They must take the TOEFL and achieve a minimum score of 500.

Computers: The college provides computer facilities for student use. The mainframe is a DEC VAX 4000. Five computer laboratories contain 82 networked Macintoshes, 53 networked IBM-compatible and 15 VAX terminals. The laboratories are open to all currently registered students. Personal network accounts with electronic mail are available to all current students. All registered students may use PC laboratories. It may be used 24 hours a day, 7 days a week. Students may access the system for 1 hour if others are waiting. The fees are $40 for computer laboratory courses.

Graduates: In 1992–93 616 bachelor's degrees were awarded. The most popular majors among graduates were finance (9%), accounting (9%), and psychology (9%). Within an average freshman class, 41% graduate in 4 years, 53% in 5 years, and 55% in 6 years. Some 48 companies recruited on campus in 1992–93. In the 1992 graduating class, 29% of graduates were enrolled in graduate school within 6 months of graduation; 67% of graduates had found employment.

Admissions Contact: Penelope H. Lips, Director of Admissions.

CAZENOVIA COLLEGE

C-3

Cazenovia, NY 13035

(315) 655–8005

(800) 654–3210 (out-of-state)

Full-time: 342 men, 694 women	Faculty: 45; IIB, --$
Part-time: none	Ph.D.s: 100%
Graduate: none	Student/Faculty: 23 to 1
Year: 12–12–6	Tuition: $10,047
Application Deadline: open	Room & Board: $4608
Freshman Class: 4032 applied, 3463 accepted, 505 enrolled	
SAT I or ACT: required	**LESS COMPETITIVE**

Cazenovia College, founded in 1824, is a private coeducational institution offering undergraduate programs in applied arts and sciences and professional studies. The library contains 52,095 volumes, 210 microform items, and 2704 audiovisual forms, and subscribes to 456 periodicals. Computerized library sources and services include interlibrary loans and database searching. Special learning facilities include a learning resource center, an art gallery, and a radio station.

The 40-acre campus is in a rural area 18 miles southeast of Syracuse. Including residence halls, there are 19 buildings on campus.

Student Life: About 81% of undergraduates are from New York. Students come from 11 states, 5 foreign countries, and Canada. Ninety-one percent are from public schools; 9% from private. Eighty-six percent are white. The average age of freshmen is 18. Thirty-four percent drop out by the end of their first year; 81% remain to graduate.

Housing: A total of 970 students can be accommodated in college housing. College-sponsored living facilities include single-sex and coed dormitories and on-campus apartments. On-campus housing is guaranteed for all 4 years. Eighty-six percent of students live on campus; of those, 60% remain on campus on weekends. All students may keep cars on campus. Alcohol is not permitted.

Activities: There are no fraternities or sororities on campus. There are many groups and organizations on campus, including cheerleading, chorus, computers, drama, ethnic, honors, musical theater, newspaper, political, social service, student government, and yearbook. Popular campus events include Spring Day, Parents Weekend, and Athletic Events.

Sports: There are 6 intercollegiate sports for men and women, and 8 intramural sports for men and 9 for women. Athletic and recreation facilities include an athletic center which houses an Olympic-size pool, a weight room, racquetball courts, tennis courts, and a main gymnasium.

Disabled Students: Eighty-six percent of the campus is accessible to disabled students. The following facilities are available: wheelchair ramps, elevators, special parking, specially equipped rest rooms, special class scheduling, and special dormitory facilities.

Services: In addition to many counseling and information services, tutoring is available in every subject. There is a reader service for the blind, and remedial math, reading, and writing.

Campus Safety and Security: Campus safety and security measures include informal discussions, pamphlets, posters, films, emergency telephones, and lighted pathways and sidewalks. In addition, there are night foot patrol.

Programs of Study: Cazenovia awards the B.A., B.S., B.F.A., and B.P.S. degrees. Associate degrees are also awarded. Bachelor's degrees are awarded in BUSINESS (management science and retailing), COMMUNICATIONS AND THE ARTS (fine arts and graphic design), COMPUTER AND PHYSICAL SCIENCE (science technology), ENGINEERING AND ENVIRONMENTAL DESIGN (interior design), SOCIAL SCIENCE (humanities and social science). Interior design, liberal arts, and human services are the strongest programs academically. Art has the largest enrollment.

Required: A total of 127 semester credits and a GPA of 2.0 are required for the bachelor's degree. All students must take courses in speech, English composition, and physical education.

Special: Canzenovia offers internships in human services and child studies, student-designed majors, work study, B.A.-B.S. degrees in fine arts, functioning in social institutions, and science and technology, and study abroad in 2 countries. There is a freshman honors program on campus, as well as one national honor society, Phi Beta Kappa. Two departments have honors programs.

Faculty/Classroom: Thirty-eight percent of faculty are male; 62%, female. All teach undergraduates, and 1% also do research. The average class size in an introductory lecture is 45; in a laboratory, 20; and in a regular course offering, 35.

Admissions: About 86% of the 1993–94 applicants were accepted. The SAT scores for the 1993–94 freshman class were as follows: Verbal—71% below 500, 23% between 500 and 599, 5% between 600 and 700, and 1% above 700; Math—74% below 500, 21% between 500 and 599, 4% between 600 and 700, and 1% above 700. One freshman graduated first in their class.

Requirements: A minimum GPA of 2.0 is required, as is the SAT I or ACT. Applicants should be graduates of an accredited secondary school or the equivalent. AP and CLEP credits are accepted. Important factors used in the admissions decision are recommendations by school officials, personality, intangible qualities, evidence of special talent, leadership record, and advanced placement or honor courses.

Procedure: Freshmen are admitted in the fall and winter. Entrance exams should be taken by the fall of the senior year. Application deadlines are open, the application fee is $25. Notification is sent on a rolling basis. There is a deferred admissions plan. A waiting list is an active part of the admissions procedure, with about 5% of applicants on the list.

Transfer: About 90 transfer students enrolled in a recent year. Applicants must present at least 12 college credits and a GPA of 2.0.

Visiting: There are regularly scheduled orientations for prospective students, through an information mall on campus. There are guides for informal visits and visitors may sit in on classes and stay overnight at the school. To arrange for a visit, contact the Director of Admissions at (800) 654–3210.

Financial Aid: In a recent year, 87% of all students received some form of financial aid. About 87% of all students received need-based aid. The average freshman award was $8341. Of that total, scholarships or need-based grants averaged $1832 ($4000 maximum); loans averaged $3461 ($4000 maximum); and work contracts averaged $800 ($1000 maximum). Twenty-eight percent of undergraduate students work part-time. Average earnings from campus work for a recent school year were $800. The average financial indebtedness of a recent graduate was $5000. Cazenovia is a member of CSS. The FAF is required. The deadline for financial aid applications is September 15.

International Students: There are currently 5 international students enrolled. They must take the TOEFL and achieve a minimum score of 500. The SAT I or the ACT is also required.

Computers: The college provides computer facilities for student use. Students access a network designed for the computer laboratory, which houses approximately 70 microcomputers. All students may access the system daily from 8 A.M. to midnight. There are no time limits on using the system and no fees.

Graduates: In 1992–93, 28 bachelor's degrees were awarded. The most popular majors among graduates were professional studies in management (82%) and applied arts and sciences (18%). Within an average freshman class, 100% graduate in 4 years. Some 23 companies recruited on campus in 1992–93.

Admissions Contact: Director of Admissions.

CITY UNIVERSITY OF NEW YORK

The City University of New York (CUNY), established in 1847, is a public system in New York City. It is governed by a Board of Trustees, whose chief administrator is the chancellor. The primary goal of the system is to maintain and expand its commitment to academic excellence and to the provision of equal access and opportunity. The main priorities are providing access for all students who seek to enroll, ensuring student success, and enhancing instructional and research excellence. The total enrollment of all 20 campuses is about 200,000, with some 7000 faculty members. Altogether, there are 617 baccalaureate, 323 master's, and 43 doctoral programs offered within the City University of New York. Profiles of the 4-year campuses, located in New York's 5 boroughs of Manhattan, Brooklyn, Queens, Staten Island, and the Bronx, are included in this chapter.

CITY UNIVERSITY OF NEW YORK
BARUCH COLLEGE
New York, NY 10010

D-5
(212) 447–3750

Full-time: 3520 men, 4727 women	Faculty: 440
Part-time: 1698 men, 2630 women	Ph.D.s: 87%
Graduate: 1383 men, 1106 women	Student/Faculty: 19 to 1
Year: semesters, summer session	Tuition: $2562 ($5162)
Application Deadline: January 16	Room & Board: n/app
Freshman Class: 5347 applied, 2921 accepted, 1356 enrolled	
SAT I: recommended	**VERY COMPETITIVE**

Baruch College was founded in 1919 and became a separate unit of the City University of New York in 1968. It offers undergraduate programs in business and public administration, liberal arts and sciences, and education and educational services. There are 3 undergraduate and 2 graduate schools. In addition to regional accreditation, Baruch has baccalaureate program accreditation with AACSB. The library contains 412,000 volumes, 250,000 microform items, and 1000 audiovisual forms, and subscribes to 3500 periodicals. Special learning facilities include an art gallery and radio station. The campus is in New York City. There are 6 buildings on campus. There are no residence halls.

Student Life: About 90% of undergraduates are from New York. Students come from 90 foreign countries. Twenty-five percent are Asian American; 24% African American; 23% white; 20% Hispanic.

Housing: There are no residence halls. All students commute. Alcohol is not permitted.

Activities: There are no fraternities or sororities on campus. There are 97 groups on campus, including cheerleading, chess, chorus, computers, drama, ethnic, film, gay, honors, international, jazz band, literary magazine, musical theater, newspaper, photography, political, professional, radio and TV, religious, social, social service, student government, and yearbook. Popular campus events include club fairs and street fairs.

Sports: There are 7 intercollegiate sports for men and 5 for women, and 6 intramural sports for men and 5 for women. Athletic and recreation facilities include a gymnasium, a swimming pool, a weight room, and an exercise room.

Disabled Students: The entire campus is accessible to disabled students. The following facilities are available: wheelchair ramps, elevators, specially equipped rest rooms, and special class scheduling.

Services: In addition to many counseling and information services, tutoring is available in most subjects. There is also a reader service for the blind, as well as remedial math, reading, and writing. Note takers, and large-print computer screens are available.

Campus Safety and Security: Campus safety and security measures include pamphlets, posters, films, emergency telephones, and lighted pathways and sidewalks.

Programs of Study: Baruch awards the B.B.A., B.A., and B.S.Ed. degrees. Master's and doctoral degrees also are awarded. Bachelor's degrees are awarded in BUSINESS (accounting, investments and securities, management science, marketing management, marketing/retailing/merchandising, operations research, and personnel management), COMMUNICATIONS AND THE ARTS (advertising, communications, English, Hebrew, journalism, music, and Spanish), COMPUTER AND PHYSICAL SCIENCE (actuarial science, computer management, mathematics, and statistics), EDUCATION (business, early childhood, elementary, and special), SOCIAL SCIENCE (economics, history, industrial and organizational psychology, philosophy, political science/government, psychology, public administration, and sociology). Economics, English, mathematics, philosophy, psychology, management, accounting, finance, computers, and marketing are the strongest academically. Accounting has the largest enrollment.

Required: Students must complete a minimum of 128 credit hours, with at least 24 hours in the major and a minimum GPA of 2.0.

Special: The college offers internships and study abroad in Great Britain, France, Germany, Mexico, and Israel. Students may design their own liberal arts major. A federal work-study program is available, and pass/fail options are permitted for liberal arts majors. There is one national honor society on campus.

Faculty/Classroom: Fifty-nine percent of faculty are male; 41%, female.

Admissions: About 55% of the 1993–94 applicants were accepted.

Requirements: Baruch requires applicants to be in the upper 33% of their class. The SAT I is recommended, with a minimum composite score of 990. Applicants must present an official high school transcript (a GED will be accepted) indicating a minimum average grade of 80% in academic subjects. AP and CLEP credits are accepted.

Procedure: Freshmen are admitted in the fall and spring. Applications should be filed by January 16 for fall entry and October 15 for spring entry, along with an application fee of $35. Notification is sent in March and in November. There is an early admissions plan.

Transfer: About 1140 transfer students enrolled in 1993–94. Transfer students must have a minimum GPA of 2.5 for 12 to 34.9 credits submitted; a minimum GPA of 2.25 for 35 to 59.9 credits; and a minimum GPA of 2.0 for 60 or more credits. Students applying for transfer with fewer than 12 credits earned must have a minimum GPA of 2.5 and a minimum high school average of 80%. At least 32 credits out of 128 must be completed at Baruch.

Visiting: There are regularly scheduled orientations for prospective students, include meeting with an admissions counselor. There are guides for informal visits. To arrange for a visit, contact the Admissions Office at (212) 447-3750.

Financial Aid: In 1993–94, 71% of all current freshmen and 63% of continuing students received some form of financial aid. The average freshman award was $2600. Of that total, scholarships or need-based grants averaged $600 ($800 maximum); loans averaged $2000 ($2625 maximum); and work contracts averaged $900 ($1500 maximum). Six percent of undergraduate students work part-time. Average earnings from campus work for the school year are $1600. The average financial indebtedness of the 1992–93 graduate was $8400. The FAF is required. The deadline for financial aid applications is May 1.

International Students: There are currently 878 international students enrolled. They must take the TOEFL and achieve a minimum score of 500.

Computers: The college provides computer facilities for student use. The mainframe is an IBM 4381. All students may access the system. There are no fees.

Graduates: Some 350 companies recruited on campus in 1992–93.

Admissions Contact: Undergraduate Admissions Office.

CITY UNIVERSITY OF NEW YORK
BROOKLYN COLLEGE

D-5

Brooklyn, NY 11210   (718) 951-5921

Full-time: 7454 men and women	Faculty: 716
Part-time: 3382 men and women	Ph.D.s: 79%
Graduate: 2996 men and women	Student/Faculty: 10 to 1
Year: semesters, summer session	Tuition: $2450 ($5050)
Application Deadline: June 1	Room & Board: n/app
Freshman Class: 4771 applied, 3054 accepted, 1740 enrolled	
SAT I: recommended	**VERY COMPETITIVE**

Brooklyn College, established in 1930, is a publicly supported college of liberal arts, sciences, preprofessional, and professional studies. It is part of the City University of New York and serves the commuter student. There are 2 undergraduate schools and one graduate school. The library contains 912,612 volumes and 439 microform items, and subscribes to 3833 periodicals. Computerized library sources and services include the card catalog, interlibrary loans, and database searching. Special learning facilities include a learning resource center, an art gallery, a radio station, a TV station, 3 color studios, and a speech and hearing clinic. The 26-acre campus is in an urban area. There are 8 buildings on campus.

Student Life: About 92% of undergraduates are from New York. Students come from 15 states, 22 foreign countries, and Canada. Sixty percent are from public schools; 40% from private. Fifty-four percent are white; 23% African American; 10% Hispanic. The average age of freshmen is 19; all undergraduates, 21.

Housing: There are no residence halls. All students commute. Alcohol is not permitted.

Activities: About 2% of men belong to 7 national fraternities; about 2% of women belong to 2 national sororities. There are 150 groups on campus, including art, choir, chorus, computers, dance, drama, ethnic, film, gay, honors, literary magazine, musical theater, newspaper, orchestra, photography, political, professional, radio and TV, religious, social, social service, student government, symphony, and yearbook. Popular campus events include Country Fair, Fall Festival, and Black Solidarity Day.

Sports: Athletic and recreation facilities include swimming pools; a soccer field; volleyball, racquetball, squash, tennis, and basketball courts; a weight-training room; and a jogging track.

Disabled Students: All of the campus is accessible to disabled students. The following facilities are available: wheelchair ramps, elevators, special parking, specially equipped rest rooms, special class scheduling, and lowered drinking fountains.

Services: In addition to many counseling and information services, tutoring is available in every subject. There is also a reader service for the blind, and remedial math, reading, and writing.

Campus Safety and Security: Campus safety and security measures include 24-hour foot and vehicle patrol, informal discussions, pamphlets, posters, films, and emergency telephones. In addition, there are lighted pathways and sidewalks.

Programs of Study: Brooklyn College awards the B.A., B.S., B.F.A., and B.M. degrees. Master's degrees also are awarded. Bachelor's degrees are awarded in BIOLOGICAL SCIENCE (biology/biological science), BUSINESS (accounting and banking and finance), COMMUNICATIONS AND THE ARTS (art history and appreciation, broadcasting, classics, comparative literature, creative writing, dance, dramatic arts, English, film arts, French, German, Greek, Hebrew, Italian, journalism, languages, Latin, linguistics, music, Russian, Spanish, and speech/debate/rhetoric), COMPUTER AND PHYSICAL SCIENCE (chemistry, computer science, earth science, geology, information sciences and systems, mathematics, and physics), EDUCATION (art, bilingual/bicultural, early childhood, education of the deaf and hearing impaired, elementary, home economics, mathematics, music, physical, secondary, and special), HEALTH PROFESSIONS (health science, predentistry, premedicine, and speech pathology/audiology), SOCIAL SCIENCE (African studies, anthropology, archeology, economics, Hispanic American studies, history, Judaic studies, philosophy, political science/government, prelaw, psychology, religion, sociology, and urban studies). Education, TV/radio, premedicine, music, and psychology are the strongest academically. Education, business, and computer science have the largest enrollments.

Required: Ten required, interrelated courses cover the following core curriculum areas: classics, art, music, political science, sociology, history, literature, mathematics, computer science, chemistry, physics, biology, geology, philosophy, and comparative cultures. There are basic skills requirements in reading, composition, speech, and mathematics, as well as a foreign language requirement. A 2.0 GPA and a minimum of 128 credit hours, with 31 to 36 in the major, are required in order to graduate.

Special: There are numerous cooperative and cross-registration programs with colleges and universities in the area. A large variety of internships and work-study programs are available. Study abroad is possible in Israel, Paris, Puerto Rico, and Africa. Summer programs are available in London, Florence, Madrid, Tokyo, and Ireland. A B.A.-M.D. and accelerated B.A.-M.A. programs are available. A number of B.A.-B.S. degrees, dual majors, and student-designed majors are possible. Credit by examination, credit for life experience, nondegree study, and pass/fail options are offered. There is a freshman honors program on campus, as well as 11 national honor societies, including Phi Beta Kappa.

Faculty/Classroom: Seventy percent of faculty are male; 30%, female. All teach undergraduates and 80% do research. The average class size in a laboratory is 15 and in a regular course offering, 35.

Admissions: About 64% of the 1993–94 applicants were accepted.

Requirements: A minimum grade average of 80 is required. The SAT I is recommended, with a composite score of 900. The GED, with a score of 300 or higher, is accepted. Requirements are higher

for B.A.-M.D. entrants and for the scholars program. Applicants not meeting the standard requirements are eligible for admission to the City University's community colleges. AP and CLEP credits are accepted.

Procedure: Freshmen are admitted fall and spring. Entrance exams should be taken before registration. Applications should be filed by June 1 for fall entry and November 15 for spring entry, along with an application fee of $35. Notification is sent on a rolling basis. There are early admissions and deferred admissions plans.

Transfer: About 660 transfer students enrolled in a recent year. Transfer students must have a 2.0 GPA with 24 or more credits; 2.25 with 15 to 23 credits; and 2.5 with 7 to 14 credits. A total of 48 credits out of 128 must be completed at Brooklyn College.

Visiting: There are regularly scheduled orientations for prospective students. There are guides for informal visits and visitors may sit in on classes. To arrange for a visit, contact the Office of Admissions at (718) 951-5921.

Financial Aid: In 1993–94, 35% of all students received some form of financial aid. About 33% of freshmen and 37% of continuing students received need-based aid. The average freshman award was $4674. The average financial indebtedness of the 1992–93 graduate was $7000. Brooklyn College is a member of CSS. The college's own financial statement is required. The deadline for financial aid applications is March 31.

International Students: There are currently 572 international students enrolled. They must take the TOEFL and achieve a minimum score of 500.

Computers: The college provides computer facilities for student use. The mainframe is an IBM 4381. A new 150-workstation microcomputer facility includes 36 Apple Macintosh IICi computers, 82 IBM PS2/55sx computers, and 36 Sun workstations networked across 5 file servers and 3 mainframe gateways. Computer science students may access the mainframe at anytime. Students may access the system with a 1 hour limit. There are no fees.

Graduates: In an earlier year, 1471 bachelor's degrees were awarded. Some 157 companies recruited on campus.

Admissions Contact: John Fraire, Director of Admissions.

CITY UNIVERSITY OF NEW YORK
CITY COLLEGE

D-5

New York, NY 10031 (212) 650-6977

Full-time: 4457 men, 3614 women	Faculty: 592
Part-time: 1864 men, 1765 women	Ph.D.s: 85%
Graduate: 1570 men, 1562 women	Student/Faculty: 14 to 1
Year: semesters, summer session	Tuition: $2543 ($5143)
Application Deadline: January 15	Room & Board: n/app

Freshman Class: 3728 applied, 2747 accepted, 1269 enrolled

SAT I or ACT: accepted **VERY COMPETITIVE**

City College, founded in 1847, is a public liberal arts college that is part of the City University of New York. The college offers programs through 6 undergraduate and 4 graduate schools and 2 professional centers. In addition to regional accreditation, CCNY has baccalaureate program accreditation with ABFSE, NAAB, NCATE, and NLN. The 4 libraries contain 1,420,550 volumes and 15,034 audiovisual forms, and subscribe to 3000 periodicals. Computerized library sources and services include the card catalog, interlibrary loans, and database searching. Special learning facilities include an art gallery, planetarium, radio station, TV station, weather station, laser laboratories, and microwave laboratories. The 34-acre campus is in an urban area in New York City. There are 14 buildings on campus. There are no residence halls.

Student Life: About 85% of undergraduates are from New York. Students come from 52 states, 60 foreign countries, and Canada. Ninety percent are from public schools; 10% from private. Thirty-nine percent are African American; 23% Hispanic; 16% Asian American; 12% white; 10% foreign nationals. The average age of freshmen is 18; all undergraduates, 28. Twenty percent drop out by the end of their first year.

Housing: There are no residence halls. All students commute. Alcohol is not permitted.

Activities: There are 4 local fraternities and no sororities on campus. There are 100 groups on campus, including art, band, cheerleading, chess, chorus, computers, drama, ethnic, gay, honors, international, jazz band, literary magazine, newspaper, orchestra, political, professional, radio and TV, religious, social, social service, student government, and yearbook. Popular campus events include Langston Hughes Poetry Contest and Dance Theater of Harlem performances at Davis Center.

Sports: There are 11 intercollegiate sports for men and 8 for women. Athletic and recreation facilities include swimming pools, 3 gymnasiums, and a weight room.

Disabled Students: Ninety percent of the campus is accessible to disabled students. The following facilities are available: wheelchair ramps, elevators, special parking, specially equipped rest rooms, special class scheduling, lowered drinking fountains, and lowered telephones.

Services: In addition to many counseling and information services, tutoring is available in most subjects, including science, economics, and engineering. There is also a reader service for the blind, and remedial math, reading, and writing.

Campus Safety and Security: Campus safety and security measures include shuttle buses, informal discussions, pamphlets, posters, and films, and emergency telephones.

Programs of Study: CCNY awards the B.A., B.S., B.Arch., B.E., B.F.A., B.S.Ed., and B.S.N. degrees. Master's degrees also are awarded. Bachelor's degrees are awarded in BIOLOGICAL SCIENCE (biochemistry, biology/biological science, and marine science), BUSINESS (business administration and management), COMMUNICATIONS AND THE ARTS (classics, communications, comparative literature, creative writing, dance, dramatic arts, English, film arts, fine arts, French, Greek, Hebrew, languages, music, photography, and Spanish), COMPUTER AND PHYSICAL SCIENCE (chemistry, computer science, earth science, geology, mathematics, and physics), EDUCATION (art, early childhood, elementary, foreign languages, health, industrial arts, music, physical, science, secondary, special, and vocational), ENGINEERING AND ENVIRONMENTAL DESIGN (chemical engineering, civil engineering, electrical/electronics engineering, and mechanical engineering), HEALTH PROFESSIONS (nursing, predentistry, and premedicine), SOCIAL SCIENCE (African American studies, anthropology, Asian/Oriental studies, economics, geography, Hispanic American studies, history, international studies, Judaic studies, Latin American studies, philosophy, political science/government, prelaw, psychology, and sociology). Engineering, architecture, sciences, liberal arts, and nursing are the strongest programs academically. Engineering, architecture, nursing, psychology, and computer science have the largest enrollments.

Required: Students must successfully complete 128 credits, with 32 to 48 of these credits in the major, and must maintain a minimum GPA of 2.0. A core curriculum must be met, and students must complete courses in basic writing, world humanities, world civilizations, computer literacy, world arts, and United States society.

Special: Cross-registration is permitted with other City University colleges. Dual majors in law and medicine are available. Opportunities are provided for internships, a Washington semester, work-study programs, a wide variety of accelerated degree programs, credit by examination, credit for life experience, and study abroad in England, China, Germany, the Dominican Republic, Japan, France, and Nigeria. There is a freshman honors program on campus. There is a chapter of Phi Beta Kappa on campus.

Faculty/Classroom: The average class size in an introductory lecture is 175 and in a regular course offering, 25.

Admissions: About 74% of the 1993–94 applicants were accepted.

Requirements: Applicants may submit SAT I or ACT scores. A minimum composite SAT I score of 900 or an ACT score of 20 is recommended. Graduation from an accredited secondary school is generally required, but a GED will be accepted. Twelve academic credits should be presented, with a minimum grade average of 80% or graduation in the top third of the current senior class. AP credit is accepted.

Procedure: Freshmen are admitted in the fall and spring. Entrance exams should be taken prior to registration. Applications should be filed by January 15 for fall entry and October 15 for spring entry, along with an application fee of $35. Notification is sent on a rolling basis. There is an early admissions plan.

Transfer: About 990 transfer students enrolled in 1993–94. Transfer applicants must have earned a minimum of 24 credit hours and maintained a minimum GPA of 2.0. Selected programs have more competitive requirements. A total of 32 credits out of 128 and 60% of the major must be completed at CCNY.

Visiting: There are regularly scheduled orientations for prospective students. There are guides for informal visits and visitors may sit in on classes. To arrange for a visit, contact the Admissions Office.

Financial Aid: In a recent year, 70% of all current freshmen and 71% of continuing students received some form of financial aid. The average financial indebtedness of a recent year's graduate was $6500. The college's own financial statement is required.

International Students: There are currently 1786 international students enrolled. They must take the TOEFL and achieve a minimum score of 500.

Computers: The college provides computer facilities for student use. The mainframes include an IBM 4381, a DEC VAX, and a SUN. A campuswide fiber-optics network is the backbone of the network; 600 microcomputers with 450 networked are available, along with 500 dumb workstations; 50 computer languages are available. All students may access the system. There are no time limits on using the system.

Graduates: In an earlier year, 1204 bachelor's degrees were awarded. The most popular majors among graduates were electric engineering (11%), architecture (7%) and psychology (6%). Some 135 companies recruited on campus in an earlier year.

Admissions Contact: Nancy P. Campbell, Director of Enrollment Management.

CITY UNIVERSITY OF NEW YORK
COLLEGE OF STATEN ISLAND
Staten Island, NY 10314   D-5
(718) 982-2010

Full-time: 3683 men, 3266 women	Faculty: 302
Part-time: 1816 men, 3071 women	Ph.D.s: 78%
Graduate: 308 men, 906 women	Student/Faculty: 23 to 1
Year: semesters, summer session	Tuition: $2558 ($5158)
Application Deadline: September 1	Room & Board: n/app

Freshman Class: 2863 applied, 2863 accepted, 1595 enrolled
SAT I or ACT: not required   **NONCOMPETITIVE**

The College of Staten Island, founded in 1955, offers programs in liberal arts and sciences, professional studies, health sciences, and the technologies. There is one graduate school. In addition to regional accreditation, CSI has baccalaureate program accreditation with ABET, CAHEA, and NLN. The library contains 190,764 volumes, 469,597 microform items, and 7942 audiovisual forms, and subscribes to 1374 periodicals. Computerized library sources and services include the card catalog, interlibrary loans, and database searching. Special learning facilities include an art gallery and radio station. The 204-acre campus is in an urban area 5 miles south of Manhattan. There are 19 buildings on campus. There are no residence halls.

Student Life: About 95% of undergraduates are from New York. Students come from 4 states, 75 foreign countries, and Canada. Seventy-three percent are white; 10% African American. The average age of freshmen is 21.1; all undergraduates, 27.1. Thirty percent drop out by the end of their first year; 25% remain to graduate.

Housing: There are no residence halls. All students commute. Alcohol is not permitted. All students may keep cars on campus.

Activities: There are no fraternities or sororities on campus. There are 56 groups on campus, including art, cheerleading, chorus, drama, ethnic, film, gay, honors, international, jazz band, literary magazine, newspaper, photography, professional, radio and TV, religious, social, student government, and yearbook. Popular campus events include International Festival, Holiday Hip-Hop Party, Kwanzaa, and World Beat Festival.

Sports: There are 4 intercollegiate sports for men and 4 for women, and 22 intramural sports for men and 22 for women. Athletic and recreation facilities include a 1200-seat gymnasium, an outdoor baseball field, a soccer field, tennis courts, outdoor recreational basketball courts, and shuffleboard and bocce courts.

Disabled Students: Ninety percent of the campus is accessible to disabled students. The following facilities are available: wheelchair ramps, elevators, special parking, specially equipped rest rooms, special class scheduling, lowered drinking fountains, and lowered telephones.

Services: In addition to many counseling and information services, tutoring is available in most subjects. There is also a reader service for the blind, as well as remedial math, reading, and writing.

Campus Safety and Security: Campus safety and security measures include 24-hour foot and vehicle patrol, escort service, shuttle buses, and informal discussions. In addition, there are pamphlets, posters, films, emergency telephones, lighted pathways and sidewalks, and formal talks by the security director.

Programs of Study: CSI awards the B.A. and B.S. degrees. Associate, master's, and doctoral degrees also are awarded. Bachelor's degrees are awarded in BIOLOGICAL SCIENCE (biochemistry and biology/biological science), BUSINESS (accounting and business administration and management), COMMUNICATIONS AND THE ARTS (communications, dramatic arts, English, film arts, fine arts, languages, music, and Spanish), COMPUTER AND PHYSICAL SCIENCE (chemistry, computer science, mathematics, and physics), EDUCATION (education), ENGINEERING AND ENVIRONMENTAL DESIGN (engineering), HEALTH PROFESSIONS (medical laboratory technology, medical technology, nursing, and physician's assistant), SOCIAL SCIENCE (African American studies, American studies, economics, history, international studies, liberal arts/general studies, philosophy, political science/government, psychology, sociology, and women's studies). Engineering science, computer science, chemistry, nursing, and environmental science are the strongest academically. Business, nursing, and computer science have the largest enrollments.

Required: The core curriculum varies for each degree, but physical education and English are required for all. All degrees require courses from each of three areas: science/technology/mathematics; social sciences/history/philosophy; and humanities. A minimum 2.0 GPA and 128 to 136 credit hours are required to graduate.

Special: Internships are available in most fields. Study abroad is possible in Italy, Israel, France, Spain, Ecuador, Denmark, England, and Greece. There are student-designed majors and interdisciplinary majors, including computer science-mathematics, sociology-anthropology, and science, letters, and society. Credit by exam, credit for life experience, and nondegree study are available. There are 4 national honor societies on campus. Eighteen departments have honors programs.

Faculty/Classroom: Sixty-seven percent of faculty are male; 33%, female. All teach undergraduates and 80% both teach and do research. No introductory courses are taught by graduate students. The average class size in an introductory lecture is 40; in a laboratory, 24; and in a regular course offering, 25.

Admissions: All of the 1993–94 applicants were accepted.

Requirements: The SAT I and ACT are not required. All graduates of an accredited secondary school or GED equivalent are accepted for admission. Applicants must have an 80% minimum average or graduate in the upper two thirds of their class to be eligible for admission to the 4-year programs. AP and CLEP credits are accepted.

Procedure: Freshmen are admitted to all sessions. Applications should be filed by September 1 for fall entry and February 1 for spring entry, along with an application fee of $35 ($40 for transfers). The college accepts all applicants. Notification is sent on a rolling basis.

Transfer: About 640 transfer students enrolled in 1993–94. Applicants must have a 2.0 minimum GPA. At least 30 credits out of 128 must be completed at CSI.

Visiting: There are regularly scheduled orientations for prospective students, which include campus tours, presentations, and lunch. There are guides for informal visits, and visitors may sit in on classes. To arrange for a visit, contact the Office of Student Recruitment at (718) 982-2259.

Financial Aid: In an earlier year, 35% of all students need-based aid. Scholarships or need-based grants averaged $1000 ($1250 maximum); loans averaged $1800 ($5500 maximum); and work contracts averaged $1500 ($2500 maximum). Average earnings from campus work for the school year are $1300. CSI is a member of CSS. The college's own financial statement and CUNY version of the FAF are required. The deadline for financial aid applications is May 31.

International Students: There are currently 510 international students enrolled. They must take the TOEFL and achieve a minimum score of 450.

Computers: The college provides computer facilities for student use. The mainframes are an IBM 3090/200, an IBM 3081KX, and an IBM 4341. Approximately 300 microcomputers and 25 terminals are located in 14 laboratories, which vary in size from 7 workstations to 36 units. Students receive computer accounts to use the mainframe computers. All students may access the system 24 hours a day. The fee is $25.

Graduates: In 1992–93, 863 bachelor's degrees were awarded. The most popular majors among graduates were business (30%), psychology (17%), and science, letters and society (9%). Within an average freshman class, 7% graduate in 3 years, 13% in 4 years, 22% in 5 years, and 25% in 6 years. Some 70 companies recruited on campus in 1992–93.

Admissions Contact: Raymon Hulsey, Director of Admissions.

CITY UNIVERSITY OF NEW YORK
HERBERT H. LEHMAN COLLEGE
Bronx, NY 10468   D-5
(718) 960-8131

Full-time: 1536 men, 3354 women	Ph.D.s: 83%
Part-time: 1138 men, 2639 women	Student/Faculty: 13 to 1
Graduate: 469 men, 1216 women	Tuition: $2542 ($5142)
Year: semesters, summer session	Room & Board: n/app

Application Deadline: August
Freshman Class: 1877 applied, 1017 accepted, 768 enrolled
SAT I or ACT: recommended   **COMPETITIVE**

Lehman College, established in 1968 as an independent unit of the City University of New York, is a commuter institution offering programs in the arts and humanities, natural and social sciences, nursing, and professional studies. There are 5 undergraduate and 4 graduate schools. In addition to regional accreditation, Lehman has baccalaureate program accreditation with ADA, CSWE, NCATE, and NLN. The library contains 500,000 volumes and 450,000 microform items, and subscribes to 2000 periodicals. Computerized library sources and services include the card catalog. Special learning facilities include a learning resource center, an art gallery, a radio station, and a center for performing arts. The 37-acre campus is in an urban area 8 miles north of midtown Manhattan. There are 15 buildings on campus.

Student Life: Almost all undergraduates are from New York. Students come from 4 states and 70 foreign countries. Seventy-four percent are from public schools; 26% from private. Thirty-eight percent

are Hispanic; 30% white; 30% African American. Fifty-four percent are Catholic; 14% claim no religious affiliation. The average age of freshmen is 18; all undergraduates, 25.

Housing: There are no residence halls; all students commute.

Activities: There is 1 national sorority. There are no fraternities on campus. There are 54 groups on campus, including art, band, chess, choir, chorus, computers, dance, drama, ethnic, film, honors, international, literary magazine, musical theater, newspaper, professional, radio and TV, religious, social, social service, student government, and yearbook.

Sports: There are 7 intercollegiate sports for men and 6 for women, and 4 intramural sports each. Athletic and recreation facilities include 3 gymnasiums, an exercise room, a swimming pool, outdoor tennis courts, soccer and baseball fields, and a dance studio.

Disabled Students: All of the campus is accessible to disabled students. The following facilities are available: wheelchair ramps, elevators, special parking, specially equipped rest rooms, and special class scheduling.

Services: In addition to many counseling and information services, tutoring is available in every subject. There is also a reader service for the blind, and remedial math, reading, and writing. A writing center offers individual and small group tutorials and workshops.

Programs of Study: Lehman awards the B.A., B.S., and B.F.A. degrees. Master's degrees also are awarded. Bachelor's degrees are awarded in BIOLOGICAL SCIENCE (biology/biological science), BUSINESS (accounting, business administration and management, and management science), COMMUNICATIONS AND THE ARTS (communications, comparative literature, dance, English, fine arts, French, German, Greek, Hebrew, Italian, languages, Latin, linguistics, music, Russian, Spanish, and speech/debate/rhetoric), COMPUTER AND PHYSICAL SCIENCE (chemistry, computer science, geology, mathematics, and physics), EDUCATION (art, business, early childhood, elementary, foreign languages, health, home economics, music, science, and secondary), HEALTH PROFESSIONS (health care administration, nursing, predentistry, premedicine, public health, and speech pathology/audiology), SOCIAL SCIENCE (African American studies, American studies, anthropology, classical/ancient civilization, criminal justice, crosscultural studies, dietetics, economics, family/consumer studies, geography, Hispanic American studies, history, international relations, Latin American studies, philosophy, political science/government, prelaw, psychology, social work, and sociology). Economics and accounting have the largest enrollments.

Required: To graduate, students must successfully complete 128 credits, including 64 in the major, with a minimum GPA of 2.0. Requirements include 17 credits of core courses, 8 of English composition, 3 to 10 of a foreign language, 3 of oral communication, and 2 of physical fitness, as well as 22 credits distributed among courses in comparative culture, historical studies, social science, natural science, literature, art, and knowledge, self, and values. Students must demonstrate proficiency in basic reading, writing, and mathematics skills before entering the upper division.

Special: Lehman offers internships, study abroad, work-study programs, dual and student-designed majors, nondegree study, pass/fail options, and credit for life experience. A 3–2 social work degree is offered in conjunction with the senior college of CUNY, Bard, and Sarah Lawrence. Transfer programs in preengineering, prepharmacy, and preenvironmental science and forestry allow students to complete their degrees at specialized colleges or other New York universities. There is a freshman honors program on campus, as well as 21 national honor societies, including Phi Beta Kappa.

Faculty/Classroom: Fifty-eight percent of faculty are male; 42%, female. No introductory courses are taught by graduate students. The average class size in an introductory lecture is 25; in a laboratory, 12; and in a regular course offering, 18.

Admissions: About 54% of the 1993–94 applicants were accepted.

Requirements: A minimum grade average of 80 is required. This requirement may also be satisfied by an SAT I composite score of 900. The SAT I or ACT is recommended; the SAT I is preferred. Graduation from an accredited secondary school is required; a GED will be accepted. AP and CLEP credits are accepted.

Procedure: Freshmen are admitted to all sessions. Applications should be filed by August for fall entry and January for spring entry, along with an application fee of $35 for freshmen and $40 for transfer students. Notification is sent on a rolling basis. There are early admissions and deferred admissions plans.

Transfer: About 860 transfer students enrolled in an earlier year. Transfer students must submit all educational records and show a minimum GPA of 2.0 in previous college work. Applicants with fewer than 12 college credits must also have a high school average of 80 in academic subjects. A total of 38 credits out of 128 must be completed at Lehman.

Visiting: There are regularly scheduled orientations for prospective students. There are guides for informal visits and visitors may sit in on classes. To arrange for a visit, contact the Office of Enrollment Management at (718) 960–8713.

Financial Aid: In an earlier year, 75% of all freshmen and 66% of continuing students received some form of financial aid. Scholarships or need-based grants averaged $2000 ($3440 maximum); loans averaged $1000 ($2625 maximum); and work contracts averaged $800 ($2000 maximum). The average financial indebtedness of an earlier graduate was $8800. The college's own financial statement is required. The deadline for financial aid applications is May 31.

International Students: There are currently 72 international students enrolled. They must take the TOEFL with a minimum score of 500 or the college's own test.

Computers: The college provides computer facilities for student use. The mainframe is a DEC VAX 11/750. There are also Apple Macintosh and IBM microcomputers located in the Academic Computer Center and specific classrooms. A UNIX-based network includes an IBM PC/RT file server and 8 IBM 6152 RISC workstations. All students may access the system. There are no time limits and no fees.

Admissions Contact: Alberto G. Forbes, Director of Admission.

CITY UNIVERSITY OF NEW YORK HUNTER COLLEGE
New York, NY 10021   **D-5**

(212) 772–4490
(800) (212) 772–4000 (out-of-state)

Full-time: 2112 men, 5584 women	**Faculty:** n/av
Part-time: 1823 men, 4447 women	**Ph.D.s:** 83%
Graduate: 1054 men, 3370 women	**Student/Faculty:** n/av
Year: semesters, summer session	**Tuition:** $2501 ($5101)
Application Deadline: January 15	**Room:** $1600
Freshman Class: 2380 accepted, 1021 enrolled	
SAT I: recommended	**VERY COMPETITIVE**

Hunter College, a comprehensive, nonprofit, coeducational institution established in 1870, is part of the City University of New York, and is both city- and state-supported. Primarily a commuter college, the emphasis of its more than 90 undergraduate and graduate programs is on liberal arts. There are 2 undergraduate and 3 graduate schools. In addition to regional accreditation, Hunter has baccalaureate program accreditation with ADA, CSWE, NCATE, and NLN. The library contains 658,000 volumes and 12,897 microform items, and subscribes to 4100 periodicals. Special learning facilities include a learning resource center, art gallery, radio station, geography/geology laboratory, and the Academic Computing Services Laboratory. The 3-acre campus is in an urban area in New York City. Including residence halls, there are 6 buildings on campus.

Student Life: About 48% of undergraduates are from New York. Students come from 9 foreign countries and Canada. Thirty-nine percent are white; 24% African American; 23% Hispanic; 13% Asian American. The average age of freshmen is 19; all undergraduates, 28. Twenty-three percent drop out by the end of their first year; 15% remain to graduate.

Housing: A total of 500 students can be accommodated in college housing. College-sponsored living facilities include coed dormitories. On-campus housing is available on a first-come, first-served basis. Ninety-nine percent of students commute.

Activities: There are fraternities and sororities on campus. There are more than 130 groups on campus, including art, band, cheerleading, choir, chorale, chorus, drama, ethnic, film, gay, honors, international, jazz band, literary magazine, musical theater, newspaper, orchestra, political, professional, radio and TV, religious, social, social service, student government, symphony, and yearbook. Popular campus events include Major Day Fair.

Sports: There are 9 intercollegiate sports for men and 9 for women. Athletic and recreation facilities include a state-of-the art competition gymnasium, fencing, dance, and weight rooms, racquetball courts, a pool, and outdoor tennis courts.

Disabled Students: All of the campus is accessible to disabled students. The following facilities are available: wheelchair ramps, elevators, special parking, specially equipped rest rooms, special class scheduling, lowered drinking fountains, and lowered telephones. A special advisement office and a student organization are also available.

Services: In addition to many counseling and information services, tutoring is available in every subject. In addition, there is a reader service for the blind, and remedial math, reading, and writing. Tutoring above the remedial level is available. Review of graduate-level papers through the Writing Center, a Mathematics Tutoring Center above the remedial level, a computer center, and advanced tutoring for other subjects through departments is available.

Campus Safety and Security: Campus safety and security measures include self defense education, shuttle buses, pamphlets, posters, and films, and emergency telephones. In addition, there is 24-hour foot patrol.

Programs of Study: Hunter awards the B.A., B.S., B.F.A., B.Mus., and B.S.Ed degrees. Master's degrees also are awarded. Bachelor's degrees are awarded in BIOLOGICAL SCIENCE (biology/biological science and nutrition), BUSINESS (accounting), COMMUNICATIONS AND THE ARTS (Chinese, classics, communications, comparative literature, creative writing, dance, dramatic arts, English, film arts, French, German, Greek, Hebrew, Italian, languages, Latin, music, Russian, and Spanish), COMPUTER AND PHYSICAL SCIENCE (chemistry, computer science, geology, mathematics, and physics), EDUCATION (art, early childhood, elementary, foreign languages, health, middle school, music, science, and secondary), ENGINEERING AND ENVIRONMENTAL DESIGN (environmental science and preengineering), HEALTH PROFESSIONS (medical laboratory technology, nursing, physical therapy, predentistry, premedicine, and public health), SOCIAL SCIENCE (anthropology, archeology, economics, geography, Hispanic American studies, history, international relations, Judaic studies, Latin American studies, philosophy, political science/government, prelaw, psychology, religion, social science, sociology, urban studies, and women's studies). Physical therapy is the strongest program academically. Psychology has the largest enrollment.

Required: To graduate, students must complete 125 to 131 credits: the B.A., B.F.A., and B.Mus. degrees require 125; the B.S. degree requires between 125 and 131. The total number of hours in a major varies from 24 credits for a liberal arts major to 63 credits for a professional concentration; a minimum GPA of 2.0 in the major and all courses is needed. Distribution requirements include 10 to 12 credits or more of mathematics and science, depending on the major; 12 credits of social sciences; 9 credits of humanities and the arts; 6 credits of literature; 3 credits of English composition; 1 credit of physical education; and up to 12 credits of a foreign language, depending on the major.

Special: Special academic programs include internships, student-designed majors, work-study, study abroad, dual majors, and an honors program. There is cross-registration with the Mannes College of Music, Marymount Manhattan College, and the YIVO Institute. Accelerated degree programs are offered in anthropology, biopharmacology, economics, English, history, mathematics, physics, sociology, and social research. A 2–3 engineering degree with City College is also offered. There is a freshman honors program on campus, as well as a chapter of Phi Beta Kappa.

Requirements: The SAT I is recommended. Although the City University of New York accepts all New York State residents having a high school diploma from an accredited secondary school and meeting the university's health standards, applicants must have completed 15 academic credits in that secondary school, as well as have an average of 80%, be in the top third of their class, or score a minimum composite of 900 on the SAT I to be eligible for admission to the senior colleges. Those with lower averages or class ranks are eligible for admission to the university's community colleges and technical college. The GED is also accepted. AP and CLEP credits are accepted.

Procedure: Freshmen are admitted in the fall and spring. Entrance exams should be taken sometime between admissions and registration for the first semester. Applications should be filed by January 15 for fall entry and October 15 for spring entry, along with an application fee of $35. There is a deferred admissions plan.

Transfer: Students transferring with fewer than 30 credits must have at least a 2.5 GPA; those with 30 or more, at least a 2.0. All students must complete 30 of the 125 to 131 credits required for a bachelor's degree at Hunter, including half of those needed for both the major and the minor.

Visiting: There are regularly scheduled orientations for prospective students, including group preadmissions counseling, workshops, and tours. Visitors must call ahead to attend a workshop or tour. Visitors may sit in on classes. To arrange for a visit, contact the Office of Admissions at (212) 772–4490.

Financial Aid: In an earlier year, 73% of all freshmen and 70% of continuing students received some form of financial aid. Scholarships or need-based grants averaged $1500 ($2960 maximum); loans averaged $750 ($2000 maximum); and work contracts averaged $750 ($1500 maximum). Twenty-five percent of undergraduate students work part-time. The City University financial aid application form is required and the deadline is May 1.

International Students: There are currently 520 international students enrolled. They must take the TOEFL or the college's own test and achieve a minimum score on the TOEFL of 500.

Computers: The college provides computer facilities for student use. The mainframe is an IBM 3090. Students requiring the mainframe to complete course work may access the system. It may be used 24 hours a day. A 1-hour time limit is employed when students are waiting. The fees are $25.

Graduates: In a recent year, 1444 bachelor's degrees were awarded. The most popular majors among graduates were psychology (14%), English (9%), and communications (9%).

Admissions Contact: Office of Admissions.

CITY UNIVERSITY OF NEW YORK
JOHN JAY COLLEGE OF CRIMINAL JUSTICE   D-5
New York, NY 10019   (212) 237–8873

Full-time: 2632 men, 3215 women	**Faculty:** 283
Part-time: 1295 men, 1175 women	**Ph.D.s:** 85%
Graduate: 363 men, 337 women	**Student/Faculty:** 21 to 1
Year: semesters, summer session	**Tuition:** $2501 ($5101)
Application Deadline: n/av	**Room & Board:** n/app
Freshman Class: 2577 accepted, 1421 enrolled	
SAT I: recommended	**LESS COMPETITIVE**

John Jay College of Criminal Justice, established in 1964, is a liberal arts college and part of the City University of New York, with special emphasis in the fields of criminology, forensic science, correction administration, and other areas of the criminal justice system. There are 5 graduate schools. The library contains 200,000 volumes, 30,000 microform items, and 3000 audiovisual forms, and subscribes to 1300 periodicals. Computerized library sources and services include the card catalog, interlibrary loans, and database searching. Special learning facilities include an art gallery, radio station, TV station, fire science laboratory, security technology laboratory, and explosion-proof forensic science/toxicology laboratory. The 1-acre campus is in an urban area. There are 2 buildings on campus. There are no residence halls.

Student Life: About 95% of undergraduates are from New York. Eighty percent are from public schools; 20% from private. Thirty-seven percent are African American; 35% white; 22% Hispanic. The average age of freshmen is 17; all undergraduates, 27. Twenty percent drop out by the end of their first year; 40% remain to graduate.

Housing: There are no residence halls. There are off-campus dormitories. All students commute. All students may keep cars on campus.

Activities: There are no fraternities or sororities on campus. There are many groups and organizations on campus, including art, cheerleading, chess, choir, chorale, chorus, computers, dance, drama, ethnic, film, gay, honors, international, literary magazine, musical theater, newspaper, photography, political, professional, radio and TV, religious, social, social service, student government, and yearbook.

Sports: There are 5 intercollegiate sports for men and 5 for women, and 15 intramural sports for men and 15 for women. Athletic and recreation facilities include 2 gymnasiums, 2 racquetball courts, a fitness center, a swimming pool, a strength training center, and a rooftop outdoor tennis court and jogging track.

Disabled Students: Ninety-nine percent of the campus is accessible to disabled students. The following facilities are available: wheelchair ramps, elevators, special parking, specially equipped rest rooms, special class scheduling, lowered drinking fountains, and lowered telephones.

Services: In addition to many counseling and information services, tutoring is available in most subjects, including English, mathematics, and reading. In addition, there is a reader service for the blind, and remedial math, reading, and writing.

Campus Safety and Security: Campus safety and security measures include 24-hour foot and vehicle patrol, self defense education, informal discussions, and pamphlets, posters, and films. In addition, there are lighted pathways and sidewalks.

Programs of Study: John Jay awards the B.A. and B.S. degrees. Associate, master's, and doctoral degrees also are awarded. Bachelor's degrees are awarded in BIOLOGICAL SCIENCE (toxicology), COMPUTER AND PHYSICAL SCIENCE (information sciences and systems), SOCIAL SCIENCE (corrections, criminal justice, criminology, fire science, forensic studies, law enforcement and corrections, legal studies, and public administration). Forensic science is the strongest program academically. Criminal justice, police science, and legal studies have the largest enrollments.

Required: Students are required to complete 128 credit hours, with 36 to 42 of these hours in the student's major, and must maintain a minimum GPA of 2.0. One credit in physical education is required of all students.

Special: The school offers cross-registration with other schools in the City University of New York. Internships are available with the Manhattan District Attorney, the Queens Supreme Court, the New York City Police Department, the United States Marshal's Service, and the New York City Corrections Department. Opportunities are provided for work-study programs, interdisciplinary majors, including forensic psychology, pass/fail options, nondegree study, credit for life experience, and study abroad in England, Barbados, and Israel. There is a

freshman honors program on campus, as well as 1 national honor society.

Faculty/Classroom: Sixty-five percent of faculty are male; 35%, female. All teach undergraduates and 80% do research. Graduate students teach 5% of introductory courses. The average class size in an introductory lecture is 25; in a laboratory, 15; and in a regular course offering, 20.

Requirements: John Jay requires applicants to be in the upper 50% of their class. A minimum average of 75% is required. The ACT is recommended. Applicants must have graduated from an accredited secondary school or a GED certificate will be accepted. AP and CLEP credits are accepted.

Procedure: Freshmen are admitted in the fall and spring. Application fee is $30. Notification is sent on a rolling basis. There is an early admissions plan.

Transfer: About 643 transfer students enrolled in a recent year. Transfer applicants must have completed 24 credits with a cumulative GPA of 2.0. If fewer than 24 credits are presented, a high school transcript should be presented. Half of the credits required for the major must be completed at John Jay. A total of 32 credits out of 128 must be completed at John Jay.

Visiting: There are regularly scheduled orientations for prospective students, consisting of a freshman/transfer workshop. There are guides for informal visits and visitors may sit in on classes. To arrange for a visit, contact Christopher Williams at (212) 237-8868.

Financial Aid: In a recent year, 70% of all freshmen and 70% of continuing students received some form of financial aid. About 80% of freshmen and 80% of continuing students received need-based aid. The average freshman award was $1000. Five percent of undergraduate students work part-time. Average earnings from campus work for the school year are $1000. The college's own financial statement is required.

International Students: There are currently 60 international students enrolled. They must take the TOEFL and achieve a minimum score of 500.

Computers: The college provides computer facilities for student use. The mainframe is an IBM 3090/400. All students may access the system. There are no time limits on using the system. The fees are $25 per year.

Graduates: In 1992-93 683 bachelor's degrees were awarded. The most popular majors among graduates were police science (68%) and criminal justice (37%). Some 75 companies recruited on campus in 1992-93.

Admissions Contact: Dean Frank W. Maroujek.

CITY UNIVERSITY OF NEW YORK
MEDGAR EVERS COLLEGE
D-5

Brooklyn, NY 11225-2201   (718) 270-6076, ext. 3022

Full-time: 782 men, 1589 women	Faculty: 110
Part-time: 871 men, 1769 women	Ph.D.s: 70%
Graduate: none	Student/Faculty: 22 to 1
Year: semesters, summer session	Tuition: $2577
Application Deadline: open	Room & Board: n/app
Freshman Class: n/av	
SAT I or ACT: not required	**NONCOMPETITIVE**

Medgar Evers College, established in 1969 as part of the City University of New York, is an undergraduate commuter institution offering programs in business, education, natural sciences and mathematics, nursing, and social sciences. There are 6 undergraduate schools. The library contains 74,000 volumes, 40,000 microform items, and 13,000 audiovisual forms, and subscribes to 700 periodicals. Computerized library sources and services include the card catalog and interlibrary loans. Special learning facilities include a learning resource center and a radio station. The campus is in an urban area located in the Crown Heights section of Brooklyn.

Student Life: Most undergraduates are from New York. The average age of freshmen is 22; all undergraduates, 27. Twenty-five percent drop out by the end of their first year.

Housing: There are no residence halls.

Activities: There are no fraternities or sororities on campus. There are some groups on campus, including dance, ethnic, political, religious, and student government. Popular campus events include Kwaanza and Black Solidarity Day.

Sports: There are 4 intercollegiate sports for men and 3 for women, and 5 intramural sports for men and 3 for women. Athletic and recreation facilities include a swimming pool, a gymnasium, and an exercise room.

Disabled Students: Wheelchair ramps and elevators are available.

Services: There is remedial math, reading, and writing.

Programs of Study: MEC awards the B.S. degree. Associate degrees are also awarded. Bachelor's degrees are awarded in BIOLOGICAL SCIENCE (biology/biological science), BUSINESS (accounting and business administration and management),

EDUCATION (elementary and special), SOCIAL SCIENCE (psychology and public administration).

Required: To graduate, students must complete 128 credits with a minimum GPA of 2.0. The core curriculum requires a total of 42 credits in English, philosophy, speech, mathematics, liberal arts, career planning, and physical education. Students must demonstrate proficiency in basic reading, writing, and mathematics skills prior to entering their junior year.

Special: MEC offers exchange programs with other CUNY institutions, evening and weekend classes, credit for military and prior learning experience, pass/fail options, and nondegree study.

Requirements: MEC accepts all applicants who either are graduates of an accredited secondary school or have earned a GED with a score of 225 or higher. Students must meet the university's health standards. CLEP credit is accepted.

Procedure: Application deadlines are open. The application fee is $35 for freshmen and $40 for transfer students.

Transfer: Applicants must have a minimum GPA of 2.0. Those students with fewer than 24 college credits must also submit a high school transcript. A total of 32 credits out of 128 must be completed at MEC.

Financial Aid: The CUNY Student Aid Form (CSAF) financial statement is required. The deadline for financial aid applications is August 15, but students should apply as early as possible.

International Students: Students must take the TOEFL and achieve a minimum score of 475.

Computers: The college provides computer facilities for student use. The mainframe is an IBM 3033. There are also IBM PCs and Apple microcomputers available in the data processing center. All students may access the system.

Admissions Contact: An Admissions Counselor.

CITY UNIVERSITY OF NEW YORK
NEW YORK CITY TECHNICAL COLLEGE
D-5

Brooklyn, NY 11201-2983   (718) 260-5500

Full-time: 6991 men and women	Faculty: 400
Part-time: 3795 men and women	Ph.D.s: n/av
Graduate: none	Student/Faculty: 17 to 1
Year: semesters, summer session	Tuition: $2405 ($5005)
Application Deadline: January 15	Room & Board: n/app
Freshman Class: 4600 applied, 4365 accepted, 2676 enrolled	
SAT I or ACT: not required	**NONCOMPETITIVE**

New York City Technical College, founded in 1946 and made part of the City University of New York system in 1964, is an undergraduate commuter college offering day and evening programs in technology. The library contains 150,000 volumes and subscribes to 700 periodicals. Special learning facilities include a learning resource center and an art gallery. The campus is in an urban area. There are 9 buildings on campus.

Housing: There are no residence halls. Alcohol is not permitted on campus.

Activities: There are no fraternities or sororities on campus. There are 70 groups on campus, including drama, ethnic, newspaper, and professional. Popular campus events include concerts, film series, and the Presidential Lecture series.

Sports: There is no sports program at City Tech.

Services: In addition to career and personal counseling, tutoring is available in basic skills and study skills.

Programs of Study: City Tech awards the B.T. degree. Associate degrees also are awarded. Bachelor's degrees are awarded in BUSINESS (hotel/motel and restaurant management), ENGINEERING AND ENVIRONMENTAL DESIGN (graphic and printing production).

Required: Students must receive CUNY certification in reading, writing, and mathematics and complete associate degree requirements. General education requirements include selections from African-American, Puerto Rican, and Latin American studies, sciences, humanities, social sciences, and education. A total of 128 credits is required for the B.T. degree.

Special: B.A. and B.S. degrees are offered through CUNY's universitywide bachelor's exchange credits program. An alternative format program for adults offers credit for life/work experience. Nondegree study and work-study are possible.

Admissions: About 95% of the 1993-94 applicants were accepted.

Requirements: The SAT I or ACT is not required. Applicants should be graduates of an accredited secondary school or GED equivalent and meet the university's health standards. Students must first apply to the associate degree program and later to the specific bachelor degree program. AP and CLEP credits are accepted.

Procedure: Applications should be filed by January 15 for fall entry and October 15 for spring entry, along with an application fee of $30. The college accepts all applicants.

Transfer: Candidates must have an associate degree in hotel and restaurant management or graphic arts, lithographic offset technology, or the equivalent. They must meet CUNY requirements in reading, writing, and mathematics. A total of 34 credits out of 128 must be completed at City Tech.

Financial Aid: The CUNY Students Aid Form (CSAF) financial statement is required.

International Students: Applications are accepted from international students.

Admissions Contact: Arlene Floyd, Director of Admissions.

CITY UNIVERSITY OF NEW YORK
QUEENS COLLEGE
D-5

Flushing, NY 11367-1597   (718) 997-5600

Full-time, part-time: 14,100 men and women	Faculty: 665
	Ph.D.s: 87%
Graduate: 3300 men and women	Student/Faculty: n/av
Year: semesters, summer session	Tuition: $2631 ($5231)
Application Deadline: March 15	Room & Board: n/app
Freshman Class: n/av	
SAT I or ACT: see profile	**COMPETITIVE**

Queens College, founded in 1937, is a public, coeducational, commuter institution within the City University of New York system. The 2 libraries contain 630,000 volumes, 631,000 microform items, and 25,000 audiovisual forms, and subscribe to 4100 periodicals. Computerized library sources and services include the card catalog, interlibrary loans, and database searching. Special learning facilities include a learning resource center, an art gallery, a center for the performing arts, and a center for environmental teaching and research located on Long Island. The 76-acre campus is in an urban area 10 miles from Manhattan. There are more than 20 buildings on campus.

Student Life: About 90% of undergraduates are from New York. Sixty-five percent are from public schools; 35% from private. Sixty percent are white; 14% Asian American; 10% Hispanic. Forty-four percent are Catholic; 23% Jewish; 11% claim no religious affiliation; 11% are Protestant. The average age of freshmen is 18; all undergraduates, 22. Thirty percent drop out by the end of their first year; 40% remain to graduate.

Housing: There are no residence halls; all students commute and may keep cars on campus.

Activities: About 1% of men belong to 1 national fraternity. There are many groups on campus, including band, choir, chorus, ethnic, honors, jazz band, literary magazine, musical theater, newspaper, orchestra, radio and TV, religious, social service, student government, and yearbook.

Sports: There are 10 intercollegiate sports for men and 7 for women, and 7 intramural sports for men and 4 for women. Athletic and recreation facilities include a gymnasium complex, a swimming pool, dance studios, weight rooms, outdoor quarter-mile track, soccer, lacrosse and baseball fields, and 18 tennis courts.

Disabled Students: Most of the campus is accessible to disabled students. The following facilities are available: wheelchair ramps, elevators, special parking, specially equipped rest rooms, and special class scheduling.

Services: In addition to many counseling and information services, tutoring is available in most subjects. In addition, there is a reader service for the blind, and remedial math, reading, and writing.

Campus Safety and Security: Campus safety and security measures include pamphlets, posters, and films, emergency telephones, and lighted pathways and sidewalks.

Programs of Study: Queens awards the B.A., B.S., B.F.A., and B.Mus. degrees. Master's degrees are also awarded. Bachelor's degrees are awarded in BIOLOGICAL SCIENCE (biochemistry and biology/biological science), BUSINESS (accounting and labor studies), COMMUNICATIONS AND THE ARTS (communications, dance, dramatic arts, English, English as a second/foreign language, film arts, fine arts, French, German, Greek, Hebrew, Italian, Latin, music, Portuguese, Russian, Spanish, and Yiddish), COMPUTER AND PHYSICAL SCIENCE (chemistry, computer science, geology, mathematics, and physics), EDUCATION (art, early childhood, elementary, foreign languages, health, home economics, mathematics, music, physical, science, secondary, and social studies), HEALTH PROFESSIONS (predentistry, premedicine, and speech pathology/audiology), SOCIAL SCIENCE (anthropology, dietetics, economics, history, philosophy, political science/government, prelaw, psychology, sociology, and urban studies). Anthropology, biology, chemistry, and economics are the strongest academically. Accounting, elementary education, computer science, and psychology have the largest enrollments.

Required: To graduate, students must complete 128 credits with a minimum GPA of 2.0. They must fulfill requirements in the major and 35 to 40 credits of a liberal arts core curriculum.

Special: Queens offers cooperative programs in all majors, study abroad, independent study, interdisciplinary and dual majors, internships in business and liberal arts fields, a 3-2 engineering degree with Columbia University or CCNY/CUNY, pass/fail options, workstudy, and nondegree study. The SEEK program provides financial and educational resources for underprepared freshmen. There is a freshman honors program on campus.

Faculty/Classroom: Sixty-one percent of faculty are male; 39%, female. The average class size in an introductory lecture is 100 and in a regular course offering, 27.

Requirements: If the high school average is less than 80, the SAT I or ACT is required, with a composite score of 900 or 20 respectively. Either of the tests and an interview are required for scholarship and honors program candidates. Music students must audition. AP and CLEP credits are accepted.

Procedure: Freshmen are admitted fall and spring. Entrance exams should be taken in the spring of the junior year or the fall of the senior year. Applications should be filed by March 15 for fall entry and November 15 for spring entry, along with an application fee of $35. Notification is sent March 1. There is an early admissions plan.

Transfer: Applicants should have a minimum GPA of 2.5. A total of 45 credits out of 128 must be completed at Queens.

Visiting: There are regularly scheduled orientations for prospective students, including information sessions and a campus tour. To arrange for a visit, contact Diane Warmsley, Admissions Office, at (718) 997-5600.

Financial Aid: In a recent year, 50% of all students received need-based aid. Thirty-five percent of undergraduate students work part-time. The CUNY Student Aid Form (CSAF) financial statement is required. The deadline for financial aid applications is May 1.

International Students: Students must take the TOEFL or the college's own test and achieve a minimum score on the TOEFL of 500.

Computers: The college provides computer facilities for student use. The mainframe is a Hitachi Data Systems Model 8023. A computer center is available, with DEC VAX and IBM systems. Extensive microcomputer facilities are also provided throughout the campus and there are a variety of support services for PC users. Those students enrolled in computer science courses may access the system. It may be used during day and evening hours. There are no fees.

Graduates: In a recent year, 1899 bachelor's degrees were awarded. The most popular majors among graduates were accounting (16%), communication arts and sciences (11%), and elementary education (9%). Within an average freshman class, 1% graduate in 3 years, 15% in 4 years, 32% in 5 years, and 36% in 6 years. Some 100 companies recruited on campus in 1992-93.

Admissions Contact: Diane Warmsley, Admissions Office.

CITY UNIVERSITY OF NEW YORK
YORK COLLEGE
D-5

Jamaica, NY 11451   (718) 262-2165

Full-time: 1556 men, 2376 women	Faculty: 138
Part-time: 851 men, 2086 women	Ph.D.s: 67%
Graduate: none	Student/Faculty: 28 to 1
Year: 4-1-4, summer session	Tuition: $2534 ($5134)
Application Deadline: March 1	Room & Board: n/app
Freshman Class: 1200 accepted, 706 enrolled	
SAT I: recommended	**NONCOMPETITIVE**

York College, established in 1966, is a public liberal arts commuter college and part of the City University of New York. In addition to regional accreditation, York has baccalaureate program accreditation with CAHEA and CSWE. The library contains 180,000 volumes, 135,600 microform items, and 4613 audiovisual forms, and subscribes to 1425 periodicals. Computerized library sources and services include the card catalog, interlibrary loans, and database searching. Special learning facilities include a learning resource center. The 50-acre campus is in an urban area in New York City. There are 5 buildings on campus.

Student Life: About 88% of undergraduates are from New York. Students come from 20 foreign countries and Canada. Seventy-five percent are from public schools; 25% from private. Sixty-one percent are African American; 16% Hispanic; 14% white; 10% Asian American. The average age of freshmen is 19; all undergraduates, 32.

Housing: There are no residence halls. All students commute. Alcohol is not permitted. All students may keep cars on campus.

Activities: There are 64 groups on campus, including art, band, cheerleading, choir, chorus, computers, dance, drama, ethnic, international, jazz band, literary magazine, musical theater, newspaper, political, professional, radio and TV, religious, social, social service, student government, and yearbook.

Sports: There are 6 intercollegiate sports for men and 5 for women, and 5 intramural sports for men and 5 for women. Athletic and recreation facilities include a 1200-seat gymnasium, a 25-meter 6-lane

swimming pool with diving boards, a fitness center, a health risk appraisal center, and an exercise therapy room.

Disabled Students: All of the campus is accessible to disabled students. The following facilities are available: wheelchair ramps, elevators, special parking, specially equipped rest rooms, special class scheduling, lowered drinking fountains, and lowered telephones.

Services: In addition to many counseling and information services, tutoring is available in every subject. There is also a reader service for the blind, and remedial math, reading, and writing.

Campus Safety and Security: Campus safety and security measures include escort service, informal discussions, pamphlets, posters, films, and lighted pathways and sidewalks.

Programs of Study: York awards the B.A. and B.S. degrees. Bachelor's degrees are awarded in BIOLOGICAL SCIENCE (biology/biological science), BUSINESS (accounting, business administration and management, and marketing/retailing/merchandising), COMMUNICATIONS AND THE ARTS (English, French, Italian, music, Spanish, and speech/debate/rhetoric), COMPUTER AND PHYSICAL SCIENCE (chemistry, computer science, earth science, geology, information sciences and systems, mathematics, and physics), EDUCATION (art, business, early childhood, elementary, foreign languages, middle school, and secondary), HEALTH PROFESSIONS (medical laboratory technology, nursing, occupational therapy, predentistry, and premedicine), SOCIAL SCIENCE (anthropology, economics, geography, history, philosophy, political science/government, prelaw, psychology, social work, and sociology). Business, accounting, information systems management, and marketing have the largest enrollments.

Required: All students are required to complete 128 credits, including a core curriculum of 61 credits, and must maintain a minimum GPA of 2.0. Students must take a 1-credit physical education course and complete 2 semesters of English.

Special: Cross-registration with all schools in the City University of New York is permitted. Also provided are work-study programs, credit by examination, nondegree study, pass/fail options, credit for life experience, internships, cooperative programs with other schools, and study abroad in Paris.

Faculty/Classroom: Sixty percent of faculty are male; 40%, female. The average class size in an introductory lecture is 35; in a laboratory, 20; and in a regular course offering, 35.

Requirements: York requires applicants to be in the upper 66% of their class. The SAT I is recommended. Applicants must have graduated from an accredited secondary school or present a GED certificate. Students should achieve a minimum composite score of 900 on the SAT I. An audition is recommended for music majors. AP and CLEP credits are accepted.

Procedure: Freshmen are admitted fall and spring. Applications should be filed by March 1 for fall entry and November 1 for spring entry, along with an application fee of $35. The college accepts all applicants. Notification is sent on a rolling basis. There are early decision, early admissions, and deferred admissions plans.

Transfer: About 700 transfer students enrolled in 1993–94. Transfer students must present a minimum GPA of 2.0. A total of 30 credits out of 128 must be completed at York.

Visiting: There are regularly scheduled orientations for prospective students. To arrange for a visit, contact Sally Nelson, Director of Admissions, at (718) 262–2165.

International Students: There are currently 398 international students enrolled. They must take the TOEFL and achieve a minimum score of 400.

Computers: The college provides computer facilities for student use. The mainframe is an IBM 3090, 3081KX, and 4361–5. There are also 353 IBM, Apple, and Apple Macintosh microcomputers available throughout the school. Information systems management majors only may access the system. There are no time limits on using the system and no fees.

Graduates: In 1992–93, 564 bachelor's degrees were awarded.

Admissions Contact: Sally Nelson, Director of Admissions.

CLARKSON UNIVERSITY
D-2

Potsdam, NY 13699   (315) 268–6479; (800) 527–6577 (in-state)

Full-time: 1812 men, 520 women	Faculty: 151; I, av$
Part-time: 34 men, 19 women	Ph.D.s: 98%
Graduate: 294 men, 93 women	Student/Faculty: 15 to 1
Year: semesters, summer session	Tuition: $15,383
Application Deadline: February 1	Room & Board: $5322
Freshman Class: 2031 applied, 1856 accepted, 498 enrolled	
SAT I Verbal/Math: 518/612	ACT: 28 VERY COMPETITIVE +

Clarkson University, founded in 1896, is a private, coeducational institution offering undergraduate programs in engineering, management, science, and the liberal arts. There are 4 undergraduate and 4 graduate schools. In addition to regional accreditation, Clarkson has baccalaureate program accreditation with AACSB and ABET. The library contains 207,453 volumes and 253,834 microform items, and

subscribes to 2886 periodicals. Computerized library sources and services include the card catalog, interlibrary loans, and database searching. Special learning facilities include a learning resource center, natural history museum, radio station, and TV station. The 640-acre campus is in a rural area 70 miles north of Watertown, and 75 miles south of Ottawa, Canada. Including residence halls, there are 39 buildings on campus.

Student Life: About 74% of undergraduates are from New York. Students come from 33 states, 42 foreign countries, and Canada. Ninety percent are from public schools; 10% from private. Ninety percent are white. Forty percent are Catholic; 20% Protestant; 32% claim no religious affiliation. The average age of freshmen is 18; all undergraduates, 20. Fourteen percent drop out by the end of their first year; 74% remain to graduate.

Housing: A total of 1993 students can be accommodated in college housing. College-sponsored living facilities include single-sex and coed dormitories, on-campus apartments, married-student housing, fraternity houses, and sorority houses. In addition there are special interest houses. On-campus housing is guaranteed for all 4 years. Seventy-six percent of students live on campus; of those, 90% remain on campus on weekends. Alcohol is not permitted. All students may keep cars on campus.

Activities: About 23% of men belong to 5 local and 9 national fraternities; about 28% of women belong to 3 national sororities. There are 23 groups on campus, including cheerleading, chess, chorus, computers, drama, ethnic, honors, international, jazz band, literary magazine, musical theater, newspaper, orchestra, pep band, photography, professional, radio and TV, religious, social, social service, student government, and yearbook. Popular campus events include Ice Carnival.

Sports: There are 8 intercollegiate sports for men and 6 for women, and 11 intramural sports for men and 11 for women. Athletic and recreation facilities include a 3000-seat multipurpose ice arena, a gymnasium, a swimming pool, a weight room, a field house, and racquetball, paddleball, and tennis courts.

Disabled Students: Eighty-five percent of the campus is accessible to disabled students. The following facilities are available: wheelchair ramps, elevators, special parking, specially equipped rest rooms, special class scheduling, lowered drinking fountains, lowered telephones, and residence hall rooms.

Services: In addition to many counseling and information services, tutoring is available in some subjects, including accounting, biology, chemical engineering, chemistry, mathematics, mechanical engineering, physics, and psychology.

Campus Safety and Security: Campus safety and security measures include 24-hour foot and vehicle patrol, escort service, shuttle buses, and informal discussions. In addition, there are pamphlets, posters, and films, emergency telephones, and lighted pathways and sidewalks.

Programs of Study: Clarkson awards the B.S. and B.P.S. degrees. Master's and doctoral degrees also are awarded. Bachelor's degrees are awarded in BIOLOGICAL SCIENCE (biology/biological science), BUSINESS (accounting, banking and finance, business administration and management, business economics, management information systems, and marketing/retailing/merchandising), COMMUNICATIONS AND THE ARTS (technical and business writing), COMPUTER AND PHYSICAL SCIENCE (chemistry, computer science, mathematics, and physics), ENGINEERING AND ENVIRONMENTAL DESIGN (aeronautical engineering, chemical engineering, civil engineering, computer engineering, electrical/electronics engineering, environmental science, industrial administration/management, and mechanical engineering), HEALTH PROFESSIONS (premedicine), SOCIAL SCIENCE (economics, history, humanities, political science/government, psychology, social science, and sociology). Engineering, business, and sciences are the strongest academically. Engineering has the largest enrollment.

Required: Students must complete at least 120 credit hours, with a minimum GPA of 2.0, to graduate. Students must meet a foundation curriculum requirement, take the Personal Wellness unit, and meet the requirement for courses in physical education, military science, or aerospace studies.

Special: Clarkson offers cross-registration with the Associate Colleges of the St. Lawrence Valley: St. Lawrence University and Potsdam and Canton colleges. Co-op programs with industry, work-study programs, dual majors in business and liberal arts, interdisciplinary majors in engineering and management and professional studies, internships for premedical students at local hospitals, and study abroad in England, Sweden, and Canada are possible. There are 3–2 engineering programs with many institutions in the Northeast; students who participate take the first 3 years of the prescribed program at a 4-year liberal arts institution and then transfer with junior standing into one of Clarkson's 4-year engineering curricula. There are 15 national honor societies on campus, including Phi Beta Kappa.

Faculty/Classroom: Eighty-six percent of faculty are male; 14%, female. Ninety-two percent teach undergraduates and 55% do research. The average class size in an introductory lecture is 165; in a laboratory, 21; and in a regular course offering, 35.

Admissions: About 91% of the 1993–94 applicants were accepted. The SAT scores for the 1993–94 freshman class were as follows: Verbal—43% below 500, 35% between 500 and 599, 18% between 600 and 700, and 4% above 700; Math—6% below 500, 34% between 500 and 599, 49% between 600 and 700, and 12% above 700. About 61% of the current freshmen were in the top fifth of their class; 87% were in the top two fifths. There were 8 National Merit finalists. Eleven freshmen graduated first in their class.

Requirements: A minimum GPA of 3.0 is required. The SAT I is required and the ACT is recommended. The SAT II: Subject test is also recommended. Applicants must have graduated from an accredited secondary school or have the GED. An essay and interview are also recommended. AP and CLEP credits are accepted. Important factors used in the admissions decision are advanced placement or honor courses, recommendations by school officials, extracurricular activities record, leadership record, and geographic diversity.

Procedure: Freshmen are admitted fall and spring. Early decision applications should be filed by December 1; regular applications, by February 1 for fall entry and December 1 for spring entry, along with an application fee of $25. Notification is sent in February. There are early decision, early admissions, and deferred admissions plans. About 160 early decision candidates were accepted for the 1993–94 class.

Transfer: About 150 transfer students enrolled in 1993–94. Transfer students should submit transcripts from all colleges attended and must present a minimum GPA of 2.8. An associate degree will be considered, and an interview is recommended. A total of 30 credits out of 120 must be completed at Clarkson.

Visiting: There are regularly scheduled orientations for prospective students, including meetings with administration and faculty. There are guides for informal visits, and visitors may sit in on classes and stay overnight at the school. To arrange for a visit, contact the Admissions Office at (800) 527–6577 (in state) or (315) 268–6479.

Financial Aid: In 1993–94, 85% of all current freshmen and 90% of continuing students received some form of financial aid. About 65% of freshmen and 75% of continuing students received need-based aid. The average freshman award was $10,000. Of that total, scholarships or need-based grants averaged $4000; loans averaged $2000 ($4000 maximum); and work contracts averaged $1000 ($1500 maximum). Forty percent of undergraduate students work part-time. Average earnings from campus work for the school year are $1100. The average financial indebtedness of the 1992–93 graduate was $20,000. Clarkson is a member of CSS. The FAF is required. The deadline for financial aid applications is February 15.

International Students: There are currently 92 international students enrolled. The school actively recruits these students. They must take the TOEFL and achieve a minimum score of 500. Students for whom English is a second language must take a placement exam.

Computers: The college provides computer facilities for student use. The mainframes are an IBM 4381 and an RS 6000. All undergraduates are provided with an IBM PS/2 Model 25 SX. About 100 other terminals are available in clusters throughout the campus. All students may access the system. There are no time limits on using the system and no fees.

Graduates: In 1992–93, 760 bachelor's degrees were awarded. The most popular majors among graduates were mechanical engineering (19%), civil engineering (17%), and electrical engineering (17%). Within an average freshman class, 64% graduate in 4 years and 74% in 5 years. Some 150 companies recruited on campus in 1992–93. In the 1992 graduating class, 18% of all graduates were enrolled in graduate school within 6 months of graduation; 70% had found employment.

Admissions Contact: Robert A. Croot, Executive Director of Freshman Admissions.

COLGATE UNIVERSITY　　　　　　　　　　　　**C-3**
Hamilton, NY 13346　　　　　　　　　　　**(315) 824–7401**

Full-time: 1299 men, 1353 women	Faculty: 198; IIB, + +$
Part-time: 12 men, 11 women	Ph.D.s: 99%
Graduate: 8 men, 5 women	Student/Faculty: 13 to 1
Year: semesters	Tuition: $18,620
Application Deadline: January 15	Room & Board: $5400
Freshman Class: 4856 applied, 2492 accepted, 730 enrolled	
SAT I or ACT: required	**HIGHLY COMPETITIVE**

Colgate University, founded in 1819, is a private, coeducational, liberal arts institution. There is one graduate school. The 2 libraries contain 530,460 volumes, 396,396 microform items, and 6500 audiovisual forms, and subscribe to 2500 periodicals. Computerized library sources and services include interlibrary loans and database searching. Special learning facilities include an art gallery, radio station, TV station, anthropology museum, and observatory. The 1100-acre campus is in a rural area 45 miles southeast of Syracuse and 35 miles southwest of Utica. Including residence halls, there are 60 buildings on campus.

Student Life: About 67% of undergraduates are from out-of-state, mostly the Northeast. Students come from 47 states, 41 foreign countries, and Canada. Sixty-two percent are from public schools; 25% from private. Eighty-five percent are white. Most claim no religious affiliation. The average age of freshmen is 18; all undergraduates, 20. Four percent drop out by the end of their first year; 89% remain to graduate.

Housing: A total of 1675 students can be accommodated in college housing. College-sponsored living facilities include 7 coed dormitories, on-campus apartments, fraternity houses, and sorority houses. In addition there are language houses and special interest houses. On-campus housing is guaranteed for the freshman year only and is available on a lottery system for upperclassmen. Seventy-four percent of students live on campus; of those, 90% remain on campus on weekends. All students may keep cars on campus.

Activities: About 51% of men belong to 1 local and 8 national fraternities; about 41% of women belong to 5 national sororities. There are 90 groups on campus, including art, band, cheerleading, chess, choir, chorale, chorus, computers, dance, drama, ethnic, film, gay, honors, international, jazz band, literary magazine, marching band, musical theater, newspaper, orchestra, pep band, photography, political, professional, radio and TV, religious, social, social service, student government, symphony, and yearbook. Popular campus events include Homecoming, Parents Weekend, Black History Week, Peace Jam, Winter Carnival, Charity Fund Drive, Spring Party Weekend, and Global Awareness Day.

Sports: There are 12 intercollegiate sports for men and 11 for women, and 27 intramural sports for men and 27 for women. Athletic and recreation facilities include numerous athletic fields, an athletic center, a 3000-seat gymnasium, tennis and golf courses, a field house, a ski center, and a 50-meter pool. Recreational facilities include a woodworking shop.

Disabled Students: Fifteen percent of the campus is accessible to disabled students; improvements are underway. The following facilities are available: wheelchair ramps, elevators, special parking, specially equipped rest rooms, special class scheduling, and lowered drinking fountains.

Services: In addition to many counseling and information services, tutoring is available in most subjects. There is also a reader service for the blind, remedial writing, and a writing workshop.

Campus Safety and Security: Campus safety and security measures include 24-hour foot and vehicle patrol, self-defense education, escort service, and shuttle buses. In addition, there are informal discussions, pamphlets, posters, and films, emergency telephones, and lighted pathways and sidewalks.

Programs of Study: Colgate awards the B.A. degree. Master's degrees are also awarded. Bachelor's degrees are awarded in BIOLOGICAL SCIENCE (biochemistry, biology/biological science, molecular biology, and neurosciences), COMMUNICATIONS AND THE ARTS (English, fine arts, French, German, Greek, Latin, music, Russian, and Spanish), COMPUTER AND PHYSICAL SCIENCE (astronomy, chemistry, computer science, geology, geophysics and seismology, mathematics, and physics), EDUCATION (education), ENGINEERING AND ENVIRONMENTAL DESIGN (engineering), SOCIAL SCIENCE (anthropology, Asian/Oriental studies, economics, geography, history, international relations, Native American studies, peace studies, philosophy, political science/government, psychology, religion, Russian and Slavic studies, social science, sociology, and women's studies). Geology, psychology, chemistry, and English are the strongest academically. English, economics, political science, history, and psychology have the largest enrollments.

Required: To graduate, students must complete courses in a core curriculum, including 4 general education courses and 2 courses each in the natural sciences, social sciences, and humanities. A total of 32 courses is required, with 6 to 8 courses in the major. Study in a foreign language, physical education, and a swimming test are also required. Students need 1.8 GPA overall for graduation, with a 2.0 GPA in the major.

Special: Various internships, work-study, and study abroad in 15 countries are available. Students may choose accelerated degree programs, dual majors, and student-designed majors. Cross-registration is possible with Hamilton College. A 3–2 engineering degree with Columbia and Washington universities and Rensselaer Polytechnic Institute, a 3–4 architecture degree with Washington University, credit by exam, pass/fail options, co-op programs in preengineering and prearchitecture, and a Washington semester are offered. There is a freshman honors program on campus, as well as 8 national honor societies, including Phi Beta Kappa. All departments have honors programs.

Faculty/Classroom: Sixty-three percent of faculty are male; 37%, female. All teach and do research. No introductory courses are taught by graduate students. The average class size in an introductory lecture is 30; in a laboratory, 15; and in a regular course offering, 21.

Admissions: About 51% of the 1993–94 applicants were accepted. The SAT scores for the 1993–94 freshman class were as follows: Verbal—17% below 500, 46% between 500 and 599, 35% between 600 and 700, and 2% above 700; Math—6% below 500, 27% between 500 and 599, 54% between 600 and 700, and 14% above 700. The ACT scores were 1% below 21, 6% between 21 and 23, 28% between 24 and 26, 25% between 27 and 28, and 40% above 28. More than 50 freshmen graduated first in their class.

Requirements: The SAT I and SAT II: Subject tests or ACT is required. Students may submit the SAT I and SAT II: Subject tests in writing and 2 subject tests; the SAT II: Subject tests in writing and four subject tests (one of which must be mathematics); or the ACT. Two teacher recommendations, and a counselor's report are also required. An interview, though not evaluated, is recommended, and 16 or more Carnegie credits including humanities, social science, mathematics, physical science and biology, are also recommended. AP and CLEP credits are accepted. Important factors used in the admissions decision are advanced placement or honor courses, recommendations by school officials, evidence of special talent, leadership record, and extracurricular activities record.

Procedure: Freshmen are admitted fall and spring. Entrance exams should be taken in time for score reports to reach the university by January 15. Early decision applications should be filed by February 28; regular applications, by January 15 for fall entry, along with an application fee of $50. There are early decision, early admissions, and deferred admissions plans. Some 168 early decision candidates were accepted for the 1993–94 class. A waiting list is an active part of the admissions procedure.

Transfer: Twenty-six transfer students enrolled in 1993–94. The SAT I or the ACT is required, as well as high school transcripts, a dean's report, faculty recommendations and college transcripts. A total of 16 courses (of 32) must be completed at Colgate.

Visiting: There are regularly scheduled orientations for prospective students, including interviews, group sessions, and tours available throughout the year, except during final examinations and holiday recesses. There are guides for informal visits and visitors may sit in on classes and stay overnight at the school. To arrange for a visit, contact the Office of Admissions at (315) 824-7401.

Financial Aid: In 1993–94 62% of all current freshmen and 63% of continuing students received some form of financial aid. About 44% of freshmen and 43% of continuing students received need-based aid. The average freshman award was $15,600. Of that total, scholarships or need-based grants averaged $12,907 ($24,250 maximum); loans averaged $1747 ($2500 maximum); and work contracts averaged $915 ($1300 maximum). Fifty-five percent of undergraduate students work part-time. Average earnings from campus work for the school year are $1100. The average financial indebtedness of the 1992–93 graduate was $7292. Colgate is a member of CSS. The FAF and the FAFSA and the college's own financial statement are required. The deadline for financial aid applications is February 1.

International Students: There are currently 67 international students enrolled. They must take the TOEFL and achieve a minimum score of 550. The student must also take the SAT I or the ACT.

Computers: The college provides computer facilities for student use. The mainframe is a DEC VAX 11/780. There are 250 terminals on campus offering a wide variety of applications software. All students may access the system. There are no time limits on using the system and no fees.

Graduates: In 1992–93 685 bachelor's degrees were awarded. The most popular majors among graduates were English (14%), economics (12%), and history (10%). Within an average freshman class, 83% graduate in 4 years, 6% in 5 years, and 1% in 6 years. Some 82 companies recruited on campus in 1992–93. In the 1992 graduating class, 25% had enrolled in graduate school and 53% had found employment within a year of graduation.

Admissions Contact: Gary Ross, Director of Admission.

COLLEGE FOR HUMAN SERVICES
(See Audrey Cohen College)

COLLEGE OF AERONAUTICS   D-5
Flushing, NY 11371   (718) 429-6600; (800) 776-2376 (in-state)

Full-time: 1000 men, 75 women	Faculty: 57
Part-time: 80 men, 15 women	Ph.D.s: 15%
Graduate: none	Student/Faculty: 19 to 1
Year: semesters, summer session	Tuition: $5870
Application Deadline: open	Room & Board: n/app
Freshman Class: 500 applied, 475 accepted, 300 enrolled	
SAT I Verbal/Math: 400/420	NONCOMPETITIVE

The College of Aeronautics, founded in 1932, is a private, coeducational aviation school offering undergraduate degrees in aeronautical engineering technology. In addition to regional accreditation, COA has baccalaureate program accreditation with ABET. The library contains 60,000 volumes and 10,000 microform items. Computerized library sources and services include the card catalog and database searching. Special learning facilities include a learning resource center. The 6-acre campus is in an urban area at LaGuardia Airport, 4 miles east of Manhattan. There are 2 buildings on campus.

Student Life: About 95% of undergraduates are from New York. Students come from 9 states, 19 foreign countries, and Canada. Ninety-six percent are from public schools; 4% from private. Forty percent are white; 25% Hispanic; 25% African American. The average age of freshmen is 21.5; all undergraduates, 23. Twenty-seven percent drop out by the end of their first year; 59% remain to graduate.

Housing: There are no residence halls. College-sponsored living facilities include off-campus apartments, which are available on a first-come, first-served basis. Priority is given to out-of-town students. Ninety-eight percent of students commute. Alcohol is not permitted. All students may keep cars on campus.

Activities: There are no fraternities or sororities on campus. There are some groups and organizations on campus, including flying, helicopter, Hellenic, newspaper, student government, and yearbook. Popular campus events include Open House and Dance Party.

Sports: There are 3 intramural sports for men and 3 for women. Athletic and recreation facilities include nearby areas for softball, flag football, and bowling.

Disabled Students: Ninety-five percent of the campus is accessible to disabled students. The following facilities are available: wheelchair ramps, elevators, special parking, specially equipped rest rooms, special class scheduling, lowered drinking fountains, and lowered telephones.

Services: In addition to many counseling and information services, tutoring is available in most subjects. There is remedial math, reading, and writing.

Campus Safety and Security: Campus safety and security measures include 24-hour foot and vehicle patrol, informal discussions, and pamphlets, posters, and films.

Programs of Study: COA awards the B.Tech. degree. Associate degrees also are awarded. Bachelor's degrees are awarded in ENGINEERING AND ENVIRONMENTAL DESIGN (aeronautical engineering technology). Manufacturing technology is the strongest academically. Maintenance technology has the largest enrollment.

Required: All students must satisfy English, mathematics, and science requirements and fulfill appropriate licensing requirements while maintaining a GPA of at least 2.0. Students with advanced credit must complete 30 credits in residency. A total of 135 credits is required to graduate.

Faculty/Classroom: Ninety percent of faculty are male; 10%, female. All teach undergraduates. The average class size in an introductory lecture is 25; in a laboratory, 20; and in a regular course offering, 20.

Admissions: About 95% of the 1993–94 applicants were accepted. The SAT scores for the 1993–94 freshman class were as follows: Verbal—60% below 500, 30% between 500 and 599, and 8% between 600 and 700; Math—70% below 500, 23% between 500 and 599, and 5% between 600 and 700. About 18% of the current freshmen were in the top fifth of their class; 45% were in the top two fifths. Two freshmen graduated first in their class.

Requirements: The SAT I is recommended, with scores of 400 verbal and 400 mathematics. Applicants are required to have 2 years each of English and science and 3 of mathematics. An interview is also recommended. AP credits are accepted. Important factors used in the admissions decision are advanced placement or honor courses, recommendations by school officials, parents or siblings attending the school, personality, intangible qualities, and recommendations by alumni.

Procedure: Freshmen are admitted in the fall and spring. Application deadlines are open. The application fee is $25. The college accepts all applicants. Notification is sent on a rolling basis. There is an early admissions plan.

Transfer: About 45 transfer students enrolled in 1993–94. A minimum 2.0 GPA is required. A total of 30 credits out of 135 must be completed at COA.

Visiting: There are regularly scheduled orientations for prospective students prior to registration, which include a tour and academic advisement. There are guides for informal visits and visitors may sit in on classes. To arrange for a visit, contact the Admissions Office at (800) 776–2376.

Financial Aid: In a recent year, 85% of all freshmen and 82% of continuing students received some form of financial aid. About 80% of freshmen and 78% of continuing students received need-based aid. The average freshman award was $5700. Of that total, scholarships or need-based grants averaged $702 ($878 maximum); loans averaged $2633 ($2808 maximum); and work contracts averaged $2340. Eighty-five percent of undergraduate students work part-time. Average earnings from campus work for the school year are $1500. The average financial indebtedness of the 1992–93 graduate was $5040. The FAF and the college's own financial statement are required. The deadline for financial aid applications is April 15.

International Students: There are currently 50 international students enrolled. The school actively recruits these students. They must take the TOEFL and achieve a minimum score of 500.

Computers: The college provides computer facilities for student use. The mainframe is an IBM. All students may access the system. There are no time limits on using the system and no fees.

Graduates: The most popular majors among graduates were aeronautical technology-maintenance (90%) and aeronautical technology-manufacturing (10%). Within an average freshman class, 30% graduate in 3 years, 30% in 4 years, 20% in 5 years, and 20% in 6 years. Some 25 companies recruited on campus in 1992–93. In the 1992 graduating class, 80% of the men and 90% of the women had found employment within 6 months of graduation.

Admissions Contact: Donald J. Whitman, Director of Admissions.

COLLEGE OF INSURANCE   D-5
New York, NY 10007   (212) 815–9232; (800) 356–5146 (out-of-state)

Full-time: 80 men, 54 women	Faculty: 22
Part-time: 228 men, 371 women	Ph.D.s: 25%
Graduate: 124 men, 67 women	Student/Faculty: 6 to 1
Year: semesters, summer session	Tuition: $10,500
Application Deadline: May 1	Room & Board: $7100
Freshman Class: 180 applied, 108 accepted, 74 enrolled	
SAT I or ACT: required	**VERY COMPETITIVE**

The College of Insurance, founded in 1962, is a private professional school established and supported by insurance and financial service organizations. There is one undergraduate and one graduate school. The library contains 103,517 volumes and 11,068 microform items, and subscribes to 481 periodicals. The campus is in an urban area in Manhattan. Including residence halls, there is 1 building on campus.

Student Life: Students come from 18 foreign countries. Sixty-two percent are white; 17% African American; 10% Hispanic. The average age of freshmen is 18; all undergraduates, 21.

Housing: A total of 120 students can be accommodated in college housing. College-sponsored living facilities include coed dormitories. On-campus housing is available on a first-come, first-served basis. Sixty percent of students live on campus; of those, 50% remain on campus on weekends. Alcohol is not permitted.

Activities: There are no sororities on campus. There are 15 groups on campus, including band, chess, drama, international, newspaper, photography, professional, student government, and yearbook. Popular campus events include the Kick-Off Dance, Halloween Celebration, Senior Week, and a ski trip.

Sports: There is 1 intercollegiate sport for men and 1 for women, and 2 intramural sports for men and 2 for women. Athletic and recreation facilities include a weight and exercise room, and a game room.

Disabled Students: All of the campus is accessible to disabled students. The following facilities are available: elevators and specially equipped rest rooms.

Services: In addition to many counseling and information services, tutoring is available in most subjects. All tutoring is provided by professors or fellow students via a Tutorial Network Program.

Campus Safety and Security: Campus safety and security measures include 24-hour foot and vehicle patrol, emergency telephones, and lighted pathways and sidewalks.

Programs of Study: The College awards the B.S. and B.B.A. degrees. Associate and master's degrees also are awarded. Bachelor's degrees are awarded in BUSINESS (banking and finance, business administration and management, and insurance), COMPUTER AND PHYSICAL SCIENCE (actuarial science).

Required: Students must successfully complete a total of 126 credits and maintain a minimum GPA of 2.3. A liberal arts requirement must be met, as well as a business core, which includes accounting, finance, information systems, insurance, law, management, and marketing.

Special: Many students take part in a cooperative education program that allows them to work alternate semesters of full-time study and full-time work in various business companies. B.A.-B.S. degrees in insurance, finance, business, and actuarial science are available.

Admissions: About 60% of the 1993–94 applicants were accepted. The SAT scores for the 1993–94 freshman class were as follows: Verbal—43% below 500 and 47% between 500 and 599; Math—7% below 500, 40% between 500 and 599, 47% between 600 and 700, and 9% above 700. About 60% of the current freshmen were in the top fifth of their class; 40% were in the top two fifths.

Requirements: The College requires applicants to be in the upper 50% of their class. The SAT I or ACT is required, with minimum composite SAT I scores of 900 to 1200 (450 to 600 in each section), or an ACT of 25 is recommended. In addition, applicants must be graduates of an accredited secondary school or have the GED. Applicants must have completed 19 academic units, including 4 years of English and at least 3 years of college-preparatory mathematics. An essay and interview are also recommended. AP and CLEP credits are accepted. Important factors used in the admissions decision are advanced placement or honor courses, leadership record, extracurricular activities record, personality, intangible qualities, and recommendations by alumni.

Procedure: Freshmen are admitted to all sessions. Early decision applications should be filed by December 1; regular applications, by May 1 for fall entry, October 15 for spring entry, and February 15 for summer entry, along with an application fee of $30. Notification of early decision is sent December 15; regular decision, on a rolling basis. There are early decision and deferred admissions plans.

Transfer: About 21 transfer students enrolled in 1993–94. Transfer applicants must submit a high school transcript with a GPA of 3.0, combined SAT I scores of 900 to 1200, and a college transcript with a GPA of 2.5. A total of 45 credits out of 126 must be completed at The College.

Visiting: There are regularly scheduled orientations for prospective students, consisting of an interview, a tour of the school, and a chance to sit in on a class. There are guides for informal visits, and visitors may sit in on classes and stay overnight at the school. To arrange for a visit, contact Theresa Marro, Director of Admissions, at (800) 356–5146 or (212) 815–9232.

Financial Aid: In a recent year, 90% of all current freshmen and 95% of continuing students received some form of financial aid. Ninety percent of undergraduate students work part-time. The College is a member of CSS. The FAF, the college's own financial statement, and FAFSA are required.

International Students: There are currently 56 international students enrolled. They must take the TOEFL and achieve a minimum score of 550. The student must also take the SAT I or the ACT.

Computers: The college provides computer facilities for student use. The mainframe is an AS400. There is a microcomputer laboratory available 24 hours a day. There are no time limits on using the system and no fees.

Graduates: In 1992–93, 40 bachelor's degrees were awarded.

Admissions Contact: Theresa Marro, Director of Admissions.

COLLEGE OF MOUNT SAINT VINCENT   D-5
Riverdale, NY 10471   (718) 405-3400

Full-time: 147 men, 564 women	Faculty: 56; IIB, -$
Part-time: 49 men, 392 women	Ph.D.s: 77%
Graduate: 59 women	Student/Faculty: 13 to 1
Year: semesters, summer session	Tuition: $11,130
Application Deadline: February 1	Room & Board: $5600
Freshman Class: 945 applied, 648 accepted, 171 enrolled	
SAT I Verbal/Math: 454/474	ACT: 22 **COMPETITIVE**

The College of Mount Saint Vincent, founded in 1911, is a private, coeducational liberal arts institution in the Catholic tradition. There is graduate school. In addition to regional accreditation, St. Vincent has baccalaureate program accreditation with NLN. The library contains 149,000 volumes, 6028 microform items, and 5140 audiovisual forms, and subscribes to 618 periodicals. Computerized library sources and services include the card catalog, interlibrary loans, and database searching. Special learning facilities include a learning resource center, radio station, and TV station. The 70-acre campus is in a suburban area 11 miles north of midtown Manhattan. Including residence halls, there are 11 buildings on campus.

Student Life: About 84% of undergraduates are from New York. Students come from 12 states and 8 foreign countries. Thirty-nine percent are from public schools; 61% from private. Fifty-nine percent are white; 14% Hispanic; 12% African American. Most are Catholic. The

average age of freshmen is 18; all undergraduates, 20. Nine percent drop out by the end of their first year; 59% remain to graduate.

Housing: A total of 556 students can be accommodated in college housing. College-sponsored living facilities include single-sex and coed dormitories. On-campus housing is guaranteed for all 4 years. Fifty-nine percent of students live on campus; of those, 75% remain on campus on weekends. Upperclassmen may keep cars on campus.

Activities: There are no fraternities or sororities on campus. There are 30 groups on campus, including art, campus ministry, cheerleading, choir, chorus, computers, dance, drama, environmental, ethnic, film, honors, international, jazz band, literary magazine, newspaper, photography, professional, radio and TV, religious, social, social service, student government, and yearbook. Popular campus events include Annual Block Party, Battle of the Dorms, International Festival, Bachelor Auction, Spring Week, Senior Week, Talent Night, Ring Night, Family Day, and Siblings Weekend.

Sports: There are 5 intercollegiate sports for men and 7 for women, and 6 intramural sports for men and 6 for women. Athletic and recreation facilities include a gymnasium; basketball, squash, and tennis courts; a swimming pool; a weight room; a dance studio; and a recreation room.

Disabled Students: Five percent of the campus is accessible to disabled students. The following facilities are available: wheelchair ramps, elevators, special parking, specially equipped rest rooms, lowered drinking fountains, and lowered telephones.

Services: In addition to many counseling and information services, tutoring is available in most subjects, including computer science, mathematics, chemistry, biology, languages, psychology, sociology, writing, and economics. There is also a reader service for the blind, and remedial math, reading, and writing.

Campus Safety and Security: Campus safety and security measures include 24-hour foot and vehicle patrol, escort service, shuttle buses, and informal discussions. In addition, there are pamphlets, posters, and films, lighted pathways and sidewalks, and a college committee on safety and security on campus.

Programs of Study: St. Vincent awards the B.A. and B.S. degrees. Associate and master's degrees also are awarded. Bachelor's degrees are awarded in BIOLOGICAL SCIENCE (biochemistry and biology/biological science), BUSINESS (business and business administration), COMMUNICATIONS AND THE ARTS (communications, English, French, modern foreign languages, and Spanish), COMPUTER AND PHYSICAL SCIENCE (chemistry, computer science, and mathematics), EDUCATION (health and special), HEALTH PROFESSIONS (nursing), SOCIAL SCIENCE (economics, history, liberal arts/general studies, psychology, and sociology). Nursing, biology, and communications are the strongest academically. Nursing, communications, and business have the largest enrollments.

Required: All students must complete a 56-credit core curriculum with courses in humanities, social sciences, mathematics, computers, and natural sciences. A total of 120 credits for a B.A. or 126 credits for a B.S., with a minimum of 30 credits in the major, and a minimum GPA of 2.0 are required.

Special: Cross-registration with Manhattan College offers cooperative B.A. programs in international studies, philosophy, physical education, physics, religious studies, and urban affairs. Internships, work-study, study abroad in 6 countries, a 3–2 engineering degree with Manhattan College, dual majors, and student-designed majors in liberal arts are available. B.A.-B.S. degrees in computer science, health education, mathematics, and psychology, and teacher certification programs in elementary, middle school, and secondary education are possible. There is a freshman honors program on campus, as well as 15 national honor societies. Five departments have honors programs and there is a collegewide core curriculum honors track.

Faculty/Classroom: Thirty-two percent of faculty are male; 68%, female. Ninety-eight percent teach undergraduates. No introductory courses are taught by graduate students. The average class size in an introductory lecture is 25; in a laboratory, 15; and in a regular course offering, 18.

Admissions: About 69% of the 1993–94 applicants were accepted. The SAT scores for the 1993–94 freshman class were as follows: Verbal—79% below 500, 17% between 500 and 599, and 4% between 600 and 700; Math—65% below 500, 28% between 500 and 599, 6% between 600 and 700, and 1% above 700. The ACT scores were 38% below 21, 38% between 21 and 23, 13% between 27 and 28, and 13% above 28. About 36% of the current freshmen were in the top fifth of their class; 62% were in the top two fifths. Four freshmen graduated first in their class.

Requirements: St. Vincent requires applicants to be in the upper 50% of their class and to have a minimum C+ grade average. The SAT I or ACT is recommended. Applicants should have completed 4 high school academic units of English, 3 of science, 2 of mathematics and foreign language, and 1 of U.S. history, as well as electives. An essay is required, and an interview is recommended. AP and CLEP credits are accepted. Important factors used in the admissions decision are advanced placement or honor courses, recommenda-

tions by school officials, evidence of special talent, leadership record, and parents or siblings attending the school.

Procedure: Freshmen are admitted fall and spring. Entrance exams should be taken during the junior year and/or fall of the senior year. Early decision applications should be filed by November 15; regular applications, by February 1 for fall entry, along with an application fee of $25. Notification of early decision is sent December 15; regular decision, on a rolling basis. There are early decision, early admissions, and deferred admissions plans. Four early decision candidates were accepted for the 1993–94 class.

Transfer: Some 158 transfer students enrolled in 1993–94. Transfer applicants should have a minimum GPA of 2.0. Those majoring in nursing, the sciences, mathematics, or computer science need at least a 2.7 GPA. An interview is recommended. A total of 45 credits out of 120 or 126, depending on the degree, must be completed at St. Vincent.

Visiting: There are regularly scheduled orientations for prospective students, consisting of an interview with an admissions counselor, sitting in on classes, a tour of the campus, an open house, and a one-on-one with a student on campus. There are guides for informal visits and visitors may sit in on classes and stay overnight at the school. To arrange for a visit, contact the Admissions Office at (718) 405-3267.

Financial Aid: In 1993–94 88% of all current freshmen and 75% of continuing students received some form of financial aid. About 75% of freshmen and 75% of continuing students received need-based aid. The average freshman award was $9433. Of that total, scholarships or need-based grants averaged $6000 ($16,730 maximum); loans averaged $2625 ($4625 maximum); and work contracts averaged $700 ($1000 maximum). Ninety percent of undergraduate students work part-time. Average earnings from campus work for the school year are $800. The average financial indebtedness of the 1992–93 graduate was $9000. St. Vincent is a member of CSS. The FAF and the FAFSA, and the college's own financial statement are required. The deadline for financial aid applications is March 15.

International Students: There are currently 89 international students enrolled. The school actively recruits these students. They must take the TOEFL and achieve a minimum score of 550. The student must also take the SAT I or the ACT.

Computers: The college provides computer facilities for student use. Two terminals are connected to Manhattan College's DEC VAX 11/780 system via modem. Students whose course work requires mainframe use may access the system. It may be used 9:30 A.M. to 10 P.M. Monday through Thursday and 9:30 A.M. to 4 P.M. Friday and Saturday. There are no time limits on using the system and no fees. Should students be interested in buying a personal computer, an IBM or compatible is recommended.

Graduates: In 1992–93 181 bachelor's degrees were awarded. The most popular majors among graduates were nursing (28%), communications (12%), and business (11%). Within an average freshman class, 64% graduate in 4 years and 5% in 5 years. Some 5 companies recruited on campus in 1992–93. In the 1992 graduating class, 5% of the men and 13% of the women were enrolled in graduate school within 6 months of graduation; 24% of the men and 63% of the women had found employment.

Admissions Contact: Lenore Mott, Dean of Admissions and Financial Aid.

COLLEGE OF NEW ROCHELLE
New Rochelle, NY 10805

D-5

(914) 654-5452

Full-time: 10 men, 671 women	Faculty: 53; IIA, -$
Part-time: 7 men, 287 women	Ph.D.s: 66%
Graduate: 171 men, 1212 women	Student/Faculty: 13 to 1
Year: semesters, summer session	Tuition: $10,680
Application Deadline: August 15	Room & Board: $4760
Freshman Class: 600 applied, 376 accepted, 136 enrolled	
SAT I Verbal/Math: 410/420	**LESS COMPETITIVE**

The College of New Rochelle was founded in 1904 by the Ursuline order as the first Catholic college for women in New York State and is now independent. The School of Arts and Sciences offers liberal arts baccalaureate education for women only, the School of Nursing is coeducational, and the School of New Resources, an adult liberal arts baccalaureate program, is also coeducational. There are 3 undergraduate schools and one graduate school. In addition to regional accreditation, CNR has baccalaureate program accreditation with CSWE and NLN. The library contains 200,000 volumes, 274 microform items, and 5012 audiovisual forms, and subscribes to 1509 periodicals. Computerized library sources and services include the card catalog, interlibrary loans, and database searching. Special learning facilities include a learning resource center, art gallery, TV station, and the Learning Center for Nursing. The 20-acre campus is in a suburban area 12 miles north of New York City. Including residence halls, there are 20 buildings on campus.

Student Life: About 90% of undergraduates are from New York. Students come from 10 states, 12 foreign countries, and Canada. Seventy-three percent are from public schools; 27% from private. Sixty-four percent are white; 15% African American; 13% Hispanic. Seventy-nine percent are Catholic; 18% Protestant. The average age of freshmen is 18; all undergraduates, 21. Twenty percent drop out by the end of their first year; 55% remain to graduate.

Housing: A total of 550 students can be accommodated in college housing. College-sponsored living facilities include single-sex dormitories. On-campus housing is guaranteed for all 4 years. Sixty-six percent of students live on campus; of those, 50% remain on campus on weekends. Commuting students may keep cars on campus.

Activities: There are no fraternities or sororities on campus. There are 18 groups on campus, including choir, chorus, drama, ethnic, film, honors, international, literary magazine, musical theater, newspaper, photography, political, professional, radio and TV, religious, social, student government, and yearbook. Popular campus events include Junior Ring Dance, 100 and 200 days dances, Parents Weekend, Strawfest, Founders Day, Career Fair, Health Fair, World Food Day, Swimphony, and honors convocation.

Sports: Athletic and recreation facilities include a gymnasium, a dance studio, a swimming pool, a tennis court, and a Nautilus room.

Disabled Students: Twenty-five percent of the campus is accessible to disabled students. The following facilities are available: wheelchair ramps, elevators, special parking, specially equipped rest rooms, and special class scheduling.

Services: In addition to many counseling and information services, tutoring is available in every subject. In addition, there is remedial math, reading, and writing. Individual counseling and educational workshops about self-development and personal concerns are available, as are self-help materials.

Campus Safety and Security: Campus safety and security measures include 24-hour foot and vehicle patrol, self-defense education, escort service, and shuttle buses. In addition, there are informal discussions, pamphlets, posters, and films, emergency telephones, lighted pathways and sidewalks, card access into dormitories, and surveillance cameras.

Programs of Study: CNR awards the B.A., B.S., B.F.A., and B.S.N. degrees. Master's degrees also are awarded. Bachelor's degrees are awarded in BIOLOGICAL SCIENCE (biology), BUSINESS (business), COMMUNICATIONS AND THE ARTS (art history and appreciation, classics, communications, English, fine arts, French, Italian, and Spanish), COMPUTER AND PHYSICAL SCIENCE (chemistry, mathematics, and physics), EDUCATION (art, early childhood, elementary, foreign languages, middle school, and secondary), HEALTH PROFESSIONS (art therapy, nursing, predentistry, and premedicine), SOCIAL SCIENCE (economics, history, international relations, philosophy, political science, prelaw, psychology, religious studies, social work, and sociology). Nursing, business, communication, art, and psychology are the strongest academically. Nursing has the largest enrollment.

Required: Students must complete 120 credit hours, 60 to 90 in liberal arts courses, depending on the major, meet specific course distribution requirements, and maintain a minimum GPA of 2.0 to graduate. Four physical education courses are also required.

Special: CNR provides cooperative programs in all disciplines, cross-registration with Iona College, work-study programs, dual majors in all majors, interdisciplinary studies, an accelerated degree program in nursing, a Washington semester, internships, study abroad in 9 countries, nondegree study, pass/fail options, student-designed majors, and a general studies degree. There is a freshman honors program on campus.

Faculty/Classroom: Thirty-four percent of faculty are male; 68%, female. Ninety-two percent both teach and do research. The average class size in an introductory lecture is 15; in a laboratory, 10; and in a regular course offering, 15.

Admissions: About 63% of the 1993-94 applicants were accepted. The SAT scores for the 1993-94 freshman class were as follows: Verbal—88% below 500, 10% between 500 and 599, 1% between 600 and 700, and 1% above 700; Math—78% below 500, 19% between 500 and 599, and 3% between 600 and 700. About 30% of the current freshmen were in the top fifth of their class; 60% were in the top two fifths.

Requirements: The SAT I is required. Graduation from an accredited secondary school is required; the GED is accepted. Applicants must have completed 15 academic credits, with 4 in English, 3 each in mathematics, science, and social studies, and 2 in a foreign language. A portfolio is required for art majors. An essay and interview are recommended. AP credits are accepted. Important factors used in the admissions decision are advanced placement or honor courses, recommendations by school officials, recommendations by alumni, parents or siblings attending the school, and leadership record.

Procedure: Freshmen are admitted to all sessions. Entrance exams should be taken in the junior year or fall of the senior year. Early decision applications should be filed by November 1; regular applica-

tions, by August 15 for fall entry and January 10 for spring entry, along with an application fee of $20. Notification of early decision is sent December 15; regular decision, on a rolling basis. There are early decision, early admissions, and deferred admissions plans.

Transfer: About 61 transfer students enrolled in 1993-94. Transfer students must submit a transcript from their previous college, showing courses completed and a minimum GPA of 2.0. High school records and SAT I scores are required. An interview is recommended. A total of 30 credits out of 120 must be completed at CNR.

Visiting: There are guides for informal visits, and visitors may sit in on classes and stay overnight at the school. To arrange for a visit, contact the Office of Admission at (914) 654-5452.

Financial Aid: In 1993-94, 90% of all current freshmen and 90% of continuing students received some form of financial aid. About 80% of freshmen and 80% of continuing students received need-based aid. The average freshman award was $11,996. Of that total, scholarships or need-based grants averaged $7082; loans averaged $3758; and work contracts averaged $950. Sixty percent of undergraduate students work part-time. Average earnings from campus work for the school year are $950. The average financial indebtedness of the 1992-93 graduate was $5330. CNR is a member of CSS. The FAF, FFS, or SFS, the college's own financial statement, the FAFSA, and income documentation are required. The deadline for financial aid applications is open.

International Students: There are currently 16 international students enrolled. The school actively recruits these students. They must take the TOEFL and achieve a minimum score of 550. The student must also take the SAT I or ACT; the SAT I is preferred.

Computers: The college provides computer facilities for student use. The mainframe is an IBM PS 80. The computer center contains 69 PCs for student use. All students may access the system. It may be used from 8:30 A.M. to 11 P.M. daily. Students may access the system 2 hours during peak usage. There are no fees.

Graduates: In 1992-93, 166 bachelor's degrees were awarded. The most popular majors among graduates were nursing (44%), communication arts (21%), and psychology (21%). Within an average freshman class, 78% graduate in 4 years, 20% in 5 years, and 2% in 6 years. Some 32 companies recruited on campus in 1992-93. In the 1992 graduating class, 22% of all graduates were enrolled in graduate school within 6 months of graduation.

Admissions Contact: John Hine, Director of Admission.

COLLEGE OF SAINT ROSE
D-3

Albany, NY 12203   (518) 454-5150

Full-time: 472 men, 1226 women	**Faculty:** 129; IIA, --$
Part-time: 243 men, 651 women	**Ph.D.s:** 73%
Graduate: 328 men, 985 women	**Student/Faculty:** 13 to 1
Year: semesters, summer session	**Tuition:** $9442
Application Deadline: August 1	**Room & Board:** $5010
Freshman Class: 818 applied, 664 accepted, 249 enrolled	
SAT I Verbal/Math: 480/500	**COMPETITIVE**

The College of Saint Rose, established in 1920, is an independent liberal arts institution sponsored by the Sisters of St. Joseph of Carondelet. There are 4 undergraduate schools and one graduate school. The library contains 170,000 volumes and 100,000 microform items, and subscribes to 1025 periodicals. Computerized library sources and services include interlibrary loans. Special learning facilities include a learning resource center, art gallery, and TV station. The 22-acre campus is in a residential suburban area, 1 1/2 miles from downtown Albany.

Student Life: Students come from 16 states, 30 foreign countries, and Canada. Sixty percent are from public schools. Sixty-one percent are Catholic; 38% Protestant. The average age of freshmen is 18; all undergraduates, 22. About 65% of freshmen remain to graduate.

Housing: A total of 725 students can be accommodated in college housing. College-sponsored living facilities include single-sex and coed dormitories, on-campus apartments, and married-student housing. In addition, there are language houses. On-campus housing is available on a first-come, first-served basis and is available on a lottery system for upperclassmen. All students may keep cars on campus.

Activities: There are no fraternities or sororities on campus. There are 34 groups on campus, including art, cheerleading, chorale, computers, drama, ethnic, gay, international, jazz band, literary magazine, newspaper, orchestra, political, professional, religious, social, social service, student government, and yearbook.

Sports: There are 7 intercollegiate sports for men and 8 for women, and 3 intramural sports for men and 3 for women. Athletic and recreation facilities include an activities center, basketball court, weight room, and Olympic-size swimming pool.

Disabled Students: Virtually all of the campus is accessible to disabled students. The following facilities are available: wheelchair ramps, elevators, special parking, specially equipped rest rooms, low-

ered drinking fountains, lowered telephones, automatic-open doors, and braille-numbered doors and elevators.

Services: In addition to many counseling and information services, tutoring is available in most subjects, including writing, mathematics, accounting, computer, and others as needed. There is also remedial math, reading, and writing. There is also a full-time coordinator of disabled student services.

Campus Safety and Security: Campus safety and security measures include 24-hour foot and vehicle patrol, self-defense education, shuttle buses, and informal discussions. In addition, there are pamphlets, posters, and films, emergency telephones, lighted pathways and sidewalks, and a student volunteer escort service.

Programs of Study: CSR awards the B.A. and B.S. degrees. Master's degrees also are awarded. Bachelor's degrees are awarded in BIOLOGICAL SCIENCE (biology/biological science), BUSINESS (accounting and business administration and management), COMMUNICATIONS AND THE ARTS (English, graphic design, music, public relations, Spanish, and studio art), COMPUTER AND PHYSICAL SCIENCE (chemistry, computer programming, and mathematics), EDUCATION (art, elementary, English, foreign languages, mathematics, music, science, social studies, and special), HEALTH PROFESSIONS (medical laboratory technology and speech pathology/audiology), SOCIAL SCIENCE (American studies, history, interdisciplinary studies, religion, and sociology).

Required: To graduate, students must complete 122 credits with a minimum GPA of 2.0 overall and in the major; these requirements are higher for education majors. Liberal education requirements consist of 6 credits in college writing and speech and 30 credits in the humanities, science and mathematics, social science and business, and the arts. Students must also complete 2 credits in physical education.

Special: CSR offers cross-registration with the Hudson-Mohawk Consortium and the Sisters of Saint Joseph College Consortium, internships, work-study programs, study abroad in China and Italy, dual and student-designed majors, nondegree study, and pass/fail options. There are 3-2 engineering degree programs with Alfred and Clarkson Universities and Union College, as well as a 6-year law program with Albany Law School. There are 3 national honor societies on campus.

Admissions: About 81% of the 1993-94 applicants were accepted. The SAT scores for the 1993-94 freshman class were as follows: Verbal—71% below 500, 24% between 500 and 599, and 4% between 600 and 700.

Requirements: CSR requires applicants to be in the upper 50% of their class. The minimum average required is B. The SAT I or ACT is required. Applicants must be graduates of an accredited secondary school or have a GED certificate. They should have completed 16 college preparatory units. All students must submit a letter of recommendation. Art students must submit portfolios, and music students must audition. CLEP credit is accepted.

Procedure: Freshmen are admitted fall and spring. Applications should be filed by August 1 for fall entry and December 15 for spring entry, along with an application fee of $25. Notification is sent on a rolling basis. There are early admissions and deferred admissions plans.

Transfer: Some 454 transfer students enrolled in 1993-94. Applicants must submit official transcripts and catalogs from each college attended, along with a statement of honorable dismissal, a letter of recommendation, and a personal statement of the reasons for seeking transfer. Art majors must submit a portfolio and music majors must audition. A total of 60 credits out of 122 must be completed at CSR.

Visiting: There are guides for informal visits and visitors may sit in on classes and stay overnight at the school. To arrange for a visit, contact the Admissions Office at (518) 454-5150.

Financial Aid: In 1993-94 90% of all current freshmen and 85% of continuing students received some form of financial aid. About 85% of all students received need-based aid. The average freshman award was $13,575. Of that total, scholarships or need-based grants averaged $9575 ($12,000 maximum); loans averaged $3250 ($3700 maximum); and work contracts averaged $750 ($1000 maximum). Twenty percent of undergraduate students work part-time. The average financial indebtedness of the 1992-93 graduate was $12,000. CSR is a member of CSS. The college's own financial statement and the FAFSA are required. The deadline for financial aid applications is February 1.

International Students: There are currently 69 international students enrolled. They must take the TOEFL and achieve a minimum score of 500.

Computers: The college provides computer facilities for student use. The mainframe is a Sperry 2200/100. There is 24-hour access via modem from home or through 34 PCs located on campus. All students may access the system. It may be used 24 hours a day Monday through Saturday, and additional hours on Sunday. There are no time limits on using the system and no fees.

Admissions Contact: Mary O'Donnell, Dean of Admissions and Enrollment Services.

COLUMBIA UNIVERSITY

Columbia University, established in 1754, is a private system in New York. It is governed by a board of trustees, whose chief administrator is president. The primary goals of the system are teaching and research. The main priorities are providing outstanding undergraduate instruction; conducting research to develop new knowledge and methods; and training of professionals in law, business, social work, and medicine. The total enrollment in a recent year of both campuses was 19,000; there were 2100 faculty members. Altogether there are approximately 110 baccalaureate, 160 master's, and 80 doctoral programs offered at Columbia University. Profiles of the 4-year campuses are included in this chapter in alphabetical order with other New York schools.

COLUMBIA UNIVERSITY
BARNARD COLLEGE

New York, NY 10027-6598   **D-5**
                                   (212) 854-2014

Full-time: 2121 women	Faculty: 160; IIB, +$
Part-time: 69 women	Ph.D.s: 98%
Graduate: none	Student/Faculty: 13 to 1
Year: semesters	Tuition: $17,756
Application Deadline: January 15	Room & Board: $7736
Freshman Class: 2496 applied, 1402 accepted, 531 enrolled	
SAT I Verbal/Math: 600/620	ACT: 27 **HIGHLY COMPETITIVE**

Barnard College, founded in 1889, is an independent affiliate of Columbia University. It is an undergraduate women's liberal arts college. The library contains 169,500 volumes and 8000 audiovisual forms, and subscribes to 710 periodicals. Computerized library sources and services include the card catalog, interlibrary loans, and database searching. Special learning facilities include a learning resource center, art gallery, radio station, greenhouse, history of physics laboratory, child development research and study center, dance studio, modern theater, and women's research archives within a women's center. The 4-acre campus occupies 4 city blocks on Manhattan's upper west side. Including residence halls, there are 15 buildings on campus.

Student Life: About 58% of undergraduates are from out-of-state, mostly the Middle Atlantic. Students come from 47 states, 36 foreign countries, and Canada. Fifty-six percent are from public schools; 44% from private. Sixty percent are white; 25% Asian American. The average age of freshmen is 18; all undergraduates, 20. Five percent drop out by the end of their first year; 87% remain to graduate.

Housing: A total of 1900 students can be accommodated in college housing. College-sponsored living facilities include dormitories, on-campus apartments, and off-campus apartments. In addition, there are special interest houses. On-campus housing is guaranteed for all 4 years. Eighty-seven percent of students live on campus. Alcohol is not permitted. All students may keep cars on campus.

Activities: About 1% of women belong to 1 local sorority. There are 56 groups on campus, including art, band, choir, chorale, chorus, dance, drama, ethnic, film, gay, international, jazz band, literary magazine, marching band, musical theater, newspaper, opera, orchestra, photography, political, professional, radio and TV, religious, social, social service, student government, symphony, and yearbook. Popular campus events include Spring Festival, Winter Festival, Women Poets Series, The Scholar and the Feminist Conference, Celebration of Black Women, Women's History Month, Latina Month, and Founders Day.

Sports: There are 11 intercollegiate and 13 intramural sports. Athletic and recreation facilities include pools, weight rooms, gymnasiums, tennis courts, an indoor track, a boat slip, and a bowling alley.

Disabled Students: The entire campus is accessible to disabled students. The following facilities are available: wheelchair ramps, elevators, specially equipped rest rooms, lowered drinking fountains, and lowered telephones.

Services: In addition to many counseling and information services, tutoring is available in every subject. A writing room is available for students of all levels of writing ability.

Campus Safety and Security: Campus safety and security measures include 24-hour foot and vehicle patrol, escort service, shuttle buses, and informal discussions. In addition, there are pamphlets, posters, and films, emergency telephones, and lighted pathways and sidewalks.

Programs of Study: Barnard awards the B.A. degree. Bachelor's degrees are awarded in BIOLOGICAL SCIENCE (biochemistry and biology/biological science), COMMUNICATIONS AND THE ARTS (art history and appreciation, classics, dance, dramatic arts, English, French, German, Greek, Italian, languages, Latin, linguistics, music, Russian, and Spanish), COMPUTER AND PHYSICAL SCIENCE (astronomy, chemistry, computer science, mathematics, physics, and statistics), EDUCATION (elementary and secondary), ENGINEERING AND ENVIRONMENTAL DESIGN (architecture and environmental science), SOCIAL SCIENCE (American studies, anthropology, Asian

and Middle Eastern cultures, classical/ancient civilization, East Asian studies, economics, European studies, history, international studies, medieval studies, Middle Eastern studies, philosophy, political science/government, psychology, religion, sociology, urban studies, and women's studies). English, biology, foreign languages, and political science are the strongest academically. English, political science, psychology, history, and economics have the largest enrollments.

Required: A total of 120 credits is required, with a minimum GPA of 2.0. All students must take 4 semesters each of a foreign language, humanities, or social sciences outside the major, and geographic and cultural diversity courses that may satisfy the major or other requirements, 2 semesters each of laboratory science and physical education, and 1 semester each in first-year seminar, first-year English, and quantitative reasoning.

Special: Barnard offers cross-registration with Columbia College, more than 1000 internships, and study abroad worldwide. A 3–2 engineering program with the Columbia School of Engineering and double degree programs with the Juilliard School and the Jewish Theological Seminary are possible. The college offers work-study, dual and student-designed majors, and multidisciplinary majors, including Pan-African Studies and biopsychology. There is 1 national honor society on campus, Phi Beta Kappa.

Faculty/Classroom: Forty-two percent of faculty are male; 58%, female. All teach and do research. Graduate students teach 5% of the introductory courses. The average class size in an introductory lecture is 30; in a laboratory, 14; and in a regular course offering, 22.

Admissions: About 56% of the 1993–94 applicants were accepted. The SAT scores for the 1993–94 freshman class were as follows: Verbal—6% below 500, 44% between 500 and 599, 46% between 600 and 700, and 4% above 700; Math—2% below 500, 32% between 500 and 599, 55% between 600 and 700, and 11% above 700. The ACT scores were 5% between 21 and 23, 28% between 24 and 26, 37% between 27 and 28, and 30% above 28. About 82% of the current freshmen were in the top fifth of their class; 99% were in the top two fifths. There were 2 National Merit finalists and 10 semifinalists.

Requirements: The SAT I or the ACT is required. If taking the SAT I, an applicant must also take 3 SAT II: Subject tests, one of which must be in writing. A GED is accepted. Applicants should prepare with 4 years of English, 3 of mathematics, 3 or 4 of a foreign language, 2 of a laboratory science, and 1 of history. An interview is recommended. AP credits are accepted. Important factors used in the admissions decision are advanced placement or honor courses, recommendations by school officials, extracurricular activities record, and leadership record.

Procedure: Freshmen are admitted fall and spring. Entrance exams should be taken by January of the senior year. Early decision applications should be filed by November 15 for fall entry and January 2 for spring entry; regular applications, by January 15 for fall entry and November 1 for spring entry, along with an application fee of $40. Notification of early decision is sent December 15 for fall entry and February 2 for spring entry; regular decision, April 1. There are early decision and deferred admissions plans. Some 85 early decision candidates were accepted for the 1993–94 class. A waiting list is an active part of the admissions procedure, with about 15% of applicants on the list.

Transfer: Ninety-one transfer students enrolled in 1993–94. Transfer applicants must complete at least 1 college course and have a minimum GPA of 3.0. The SAT I or ACT is required. An interview is recommended. A total of 60 credits out of 120 must be completed at Barnard.

Visiting: There are regularly scheduled orientations for prospective students, consisting of open-house programs for prospective students regularly scheduled throughout the fall. There are guides for informal visits and visitors may sit in on classes and stay overnight at the school. To arrange for a visit, contact the Office of Admissions at (212) 854–2014.

Financial Aid: In 1993–94 60% of all current freshmen and 60% of continuing students received some form of financial aid. About 53% of freshmen and 50% of continuing students received need-based aid. The average freshman award was $18,840. Of that total, scholarships or need-based grants averaged $14,870 ($25,426 maximum); loans averaged $2400 ($2625 maximum); and work contracts averaged $900 ($1600 maximum). The average financial indebtedness of the 1992–93 graduate was $10,000. Barnard is a member of CSS. The FAF, the college's own financial statement, and the parents' and student's federal tax returns are required. The deadline for financial aid applications is February 1.

International Students: There are currently 86 international students enrolled. The school actively recruits these students. They must take the TOEFL and achieve a minimum score of 600. The student must also take the SAT I or ACT; applicants who take the SAT I must also take the writing or 2 other SAT II: Subject tests.

Computers: The college provides computer facilities for student use. The mainframe is a Prime 6450. All students have access to 3 academic computer laboratories that provide networked access to software, bibliographic searching, and Columbia University mainframe links. Several academic departments maintain computer laboratories for student use. All students may access the system. There are no time limits on using the system and no fees.

Graduates: In 1992–93 521 bachelor's degrees were awarded. The most popular majors among graduates were English (15%), political science (13%), and psychology (10%). Within an average freshman class, 3% graduate in 3 years, 82% in 4 years, 84% in 5 years, and 88% in 6 years. Some 55 companies recruited on campus in 1992–93. In the 1992 graduating class, 36% of the women were enrolled in graduate school within 6 months of graduation; 55% of the women had found employment.

Admissions Contact: Doris Davis, Director of Admissions.

COLUMBIA UNIVERSITY
COLUMBIA COLLEGE
D-5

New York, NY 10027   (212) 854–2521

Full-time: 1783 men, 1664 women	Faculty: 475; I, +$
Part-time: none	Ph.D.s: 100%
Graduate: none	Student/Faculty: 7 to 1
Year: semesters, summer session	Tuition: $20,147
Application Deadline: January 1	Room & Board: $6610
Freshman Class: 6756 applied, 2053 accepted, 871 enrolled	
SAT I or ACT: required	MOST COMPETITIVE

Columbia College of Columbia University, founded in 1754, is a private college offering programs in the liberal arts. There are 2 undergraduate schools. The 26 libraries contain 6 million volumes and 4 million microform items, and subscribe to 59,000 periodicals. Computerized library sources and services include the card catalog and interlibrary loans. Special learning facilities include an art gallery, planetarium, radio station, TV station, satellite linkup with the Soviet Union, geological research center, and the Nevis Laboratory Center for study of high energy particle physics. The 36-acre campus is in an urban area of New York City. Including residence halls, there are 37 buildings on campus.

Student Life: About 81% of undergraduates are from out-of-state. Students come from 50 states, 77 foreign countries, and Canada. Fifty-nine percent are from public schools; 41% from private. Sixty-six percent are white; 20% Asian American. The average age of freshmen is 17; all undergraduates, 19. Four percent drop out by the end of their first year; 90% remain to graduate.

Housing: College-sponsored living facilities include coed dormitories, on-campus apartments, fraternity houses, and sorority houses. In addition, there are language houses and special interest houses. On-campus housing is guaranteed for all 4 years. Ninety-five percent of students live on campus; of those, 85% remain on campus on weekends.

Activities: About 13% of men belong to 19 national fraternities; about 6% of women belong to 5 national sororities. There are 120 groups on campus, including art, band, cheerleading, chess, choir, chorale, chorus, computers, dance, drama, ethnic, film, gay, honors, international, jazz band, literary magazine, marching band, musical theater, newspaper, opera, orchestra, pep band, photography, political, professional, radio and TV, religious, social, social service, student government, symphony, and yearbook. Popular campus events include Columbia Fest, the Scholastic Press Conference for high school journalists, and the United Minorities Board Ethnic Festival.

Sports: There are 12 intercollegiate sports for men and 10 for women, and 43 intramural sports for men and 43 for women. Athletic and recreation facilities include a football stadium; indoor and outdoor track and field facilities; a baseball field; a soccer stadium; a recreational gymnasium with a swimming pool; tennis, squash, handball, and racquetball courts; and a boat house.

Disabled Students: The entire campus is accessible to disabled students. The following facilities are available: wheelchair ramps, elevators, special parking, specially equipped rest rooms, special class scheduling, lowered drinking fountains, lowered telephones, and chair lifts.

Services: In addition to many counseling and information services, tutoring is available in every subject. There is also a reader service for the blind.

Campus Safety and Security: Campus safety and security measures include 24-hour foot and vehicle patrol, self-defense education, escort service, and shuttle buses. In addition, there are informal discussions, pamphlets, posters, and films, emergency telephones, and lighted pathways and sidewalks.

Programs of Study: Columbia awards the A.B. degree. Bachelor's degrees are awarded in BIOLOGICAL SCIENCE (biochemistry, biology/biological science, biophysics, and microbiology), COMMUNICATIONS AND THE ARTS (art history and appreciation, classics, comparative literature, dance, dramatic arts, English, film studies, French, German, German language and literature, Greek, Italian, languages, Latin, music, Russian language and literature, Spanish lan-

guage and literature, and visual and performing arts), COMPUTER AND PHYSICAL SCIENCE (astronomy, astrophysics, chemistry, computer science, earth science, geochemistry, geology, geophysics and seismology, mathematics, physics, and statistics), ENGINEERING AND ENVIRONMENTAL DESIGN (architecture and environmental science), SOCIAL SCIENCE (African American studies, anthropology, archeology, Asian/Oriental studies, East Asian studies, economics, history, Middle East studies, philosophy, political science/government, prelaw, psychology, religion, Russian regional studies, social science, sociology, urban studies, and women's studies). English, political science, and history have the largest enrollments.

Required: All students complete a core curriculum consisting of classes in moral and religious philosophy, history, social science, art, sculpture and architecture, literature, and music of the Western tradition; additionally, 2 courses in non-Western areas are required. Distribution requirements include half a year of writing, 2 years of foreign language (unless competency can be demonstrated), 1 year of science and 1 of physical education. A total of 124 credit hours is required; usually 42 of these are in the major. The minimum required GPA is 2.0.

Special: There is a co-op program with Oxford and Cambridge Universities in England and the Kyoto Center for Japanese Studies in Japan, and cross-registration with the Juilliard School and Barnard College. Combined B.A.-B.S. degrees are offered via 3–2 or 4–1 engineering programs. The college also offers study abroad in France; work-study; dual, student-designed, and interdisciplinary majors, including regional studies and ancient studies; internships; credit by examination, and pass/fail options. There is also a 3–2 program in international affairs with the School of International and Public Affairs, and a joint 5-year program with the School of Arts, both other units of the university. There is a chapter of Phi Beta Kappa on campus.

Faculty/Classroom: Eighty percent of faculty are male; 20%, female. All both teach and do research. The average class size in an introductory lecture is 70; in a laboratory, 15; and in a regular course offering, 20.

Admissions: About 30% of the 1993–94 applicants were accepted. About 94% of the current freshmen were in the top fifth of their class.

Requirements: The SAT I or the ACT is required, and 3 SAT II: Subject tests, 1 of which must be writing, are also required. A GED is accepted. Students should prepare with 4 years of English and 3 years each of foreign language, history, mathematics, and science. An essay is required, and an interview recommended. Two academic faculty recommendations and a written evaluation or recommendation from a school official are also required. AP credits are accepted. Important factors used in the admissions decision are advanced placement or honor courses, evidence of special talent, leadership record, extracurricular activities record, and recommendations by school officials.

Procedure: Freshmen are admitted in the fall. Entrance exams should be taken in the summer of the junior year or fall of the senior year. Early decision applications should be filed by November 1; regular applications, by January 1 for fall entry, along with an application fee of $55. Notification of early decision is sent mid-December; regular decision, April 2. There are early decision, early admissions, and deferred admissions plans. Some 153 early decision candidates were accepted for the 1993–94 class. A waiting list is an active part of the admissions procedure, with about 4% of applicants on the list.

Transfer: Eighty-five transfer students enrolled in 1993–94. Transfer applicants must have completed 1 full year of college (24 credits) with a GPA of at least 3.0. They must submit high school and college transcripts. A total of 60 credits out of 124 must be completed at Columbia.

Visiting: There are regularly scheduled orientations for prospective students, consisting of group information sessions at 11 A.M. and 2 P.M., and student-led tours. There are guides for informal visits and visitors may sit in on classes and stay overnight at the school. To arrange for a visit, contact the Admissions Office at (212) 854–2521.

Financial Aid: In 1993–94 58% of all current freshmen and 60% of continuing students received some form of financial aid. About 50% of freshmen and 60% of continuing students received need-based aid. The average freshman award was $16,000. Of that total, scholarships or need-based grants averaged $10,000 ($18,000 maximum); loans averaged $2396 ($2625 maximum); and work contracts averaged $1458 ($1775 maximum). Eighty percent of undergraduate students work part-time. The average financial indebtedness of the 1992–93 graduate was $2670. Columbia is a member of CSS. The FFS, the college's own financial statement, and a business and/or divorced parents' statement are required. The deadline for financial aid applications is January 30.

International Students: There are currently 72 international students enrolled. The school actively recruits these students. They must take the TOEFL and achieve a minimum score of 600. The student must also take the SAT I or ACT, and 3 SAT II: Subject tests, 1 of them in writing.

Computers: The college provides computer facilities for student use. The mainframes are 3 Sun 4/280's, a DEC VAX 8700, and an IBM 4341. All students may access the system, and extra time can be bought.

Graduates: In 1992–93 821 bachelor's degrees were awarded. Within an average freshman class, 80% graduate in 4 years and 90% in 5 years. Some 375 companies recruited on campus in 1992–93.

COLUMBIA UNIVERSITY
SCHOOL OF ENGINEERING AND APPLIED
SCIENCE
New York, NY 10027   D-5
                                                (212) 854–2521

Full-time and part-time: 806 men, 202 women	Faculty: 100
	Ph.D.s: 100%
Graduate: 734 men, 105 women	Student/Faculty: 10 to 1
Year: semesters	Tuition: $17,944
Application Deadline: January 1	Room & Board: $6610
Freshman Class: 618 accepted, 242 enrolled	
SAT I or ACT: required	**MOST COMPETITIVE**

The School of Engineering and Applied Science of Columbia University offers undergraduate and graduate degree programs in engineering. There are 2 undergraduate and 15 graduate schools. In addition to regional accreditation, Columbia Engineering has baccalaureate program accreditation with ABET. The 27 libraries contain 170,000 volumes and subscribe to 1300 periodicals. Computerized library sources and services include the card catalog, interlibrary loans, and database searching. Special learning facilities include a radio station and TV station. The campus is in New York City.

Student Life: About 47% of undergraduates are from out-of-state, mostly the Northeast. Students come from 40 states, 48 foreign countries, and Canada. Seventy percent are from public schools. Forty-eight percent are Asian American; 38% white. The average age of freshmen is 17.7; all undergraduates, 20.5. Eleven percent drop out by the end of their first year; 84% remain to graduate.

Housing: College-sponsored living facilities include coed dormitories, off-campus apartments, married-student housing, fraternity houses, and sorority houses. In addition, there are special interest houses. On-campus housing is guaranteed for all 4 years. Ninety-two percent of students live on campus. All students may keep cars on campus.

Activities: About 7% of men belong to 14 national fraternities; about 2% of women belong to 2 local and 3 national sororities. There are many groups and organizations on campus, including band, cheerleading, chess, chorus, computers, dance, drama, ethnic, film, gay, honors, jazz band, literary magazine, marching band, musical theater, newspaper, orchestra, political, professional, radio and TV, religious, social service, student government, and yearbook. Popular campus events include Columbiafest-Spring.

Sports: There are 12 intercollegiate sports for men and 9 for women, and 20 intramural sports for men and 21 for women. Athletic and recreation facilities of Columbia University are available to students.

Disabled Students: Seventy percent of the campus is accessible to disabled students. The following facilities are available: wheelchair ramps, elevators, special parking, and specially equipped rest rooms.

Services: In addition to many counseling and information services, tutoring is available in every subject. In addition, there is a reader service for the blind, and remedial math, reading, and writing.

Campus Safety & Security: Campus safety and security measures include 24-hour foot and vehicle patrol, escort service, emergency telephones, and lighted pathways and sidewalks.

Programs of Study: Columbia Engineering awards the B.S. degree. Master's and doctoral degrees also are awarded. Bachelor's degrees are awarded in BUSINESS (operations research), COMPUTER AND PHYSICAL SCIENCE (computer science), ENGINEERING AND ENVIRONMENTAL DESIGN (chemical engineering, civil engineering, electrical/electronics engineering, engineering mechanics, industrial engineering technology, materials science, mechanical engineering, metallurgical engineering, and mining and mineral engineering). Computer science, electrial engineering, and mechanical engineering have the largest enrollments.

Required: All students must complete 128 semester hours, including calculus I to III, ordinary differential equations, 3 credits in computer science, 9 in chemistry, 15 in physics, 18 in humanities, and 2 in physical education. They must take 66 hours in the major and maintain a GPA of 2.5.

Special: Students may study at Columbia College or any of more than 80 other liberal arts colleges throughout the country in a 5-year program leading to the combined B.A.-B.S. degree. There is cross-registration with Barnard College, Teacher's College, and the Juilliard School. The school offers study abroad, internships, work-study, and pass/fail options.

Faculty/Classroom: All faculty members both teach and do research. No introductory courses are taught by graduate students.

Admissions: Three-quarters of the class had mathematics scores of 700 or higher. About half of the 1993–94 applicants were accepted. Nearly 80% of the current freshmen were in the top tenth of their graduating class; 94% were in the top fifth.

Requirements: The SAT I or ACT is required, as are SAT II: Subject tests in mathematics I or II, chemistry or physics, and writing. Applicants must be graduates of an accredited secondary school with preparation including 4 years of English, 3 or 4 of history or social science, 2 or 3 of a foreign language, 1 each of physics and chemistry, and mathematics courses through calculus. Also required are a written evaluation or recommendation from a school official (college advisor, guidance counselor) and 2 recommendations from teachers of academic classroom subjects (1 of these must be from a teacher of mathematics). An essay is required, and an interview is recommended. AP credit is accepted. Important factors used in the admissions decision are advanced placement or honor courses, evidence of special talent, extracurricular activities record, and leadership record.

Procedure: Freshmen are admitted in the fall. Entrance exams should be taken in spring of the junior year and/or fall of the senior year. Early decision applications should be filed by November 1; regular applications, by January 1 for fall entry, along with an application fee of $55. Notification of early decision is sent December 15; regular decision, April 2. There are early decision and deferred admissions plans. About 17 early decision candidates were accepted for the 1993–94 class. A waiting list is an active part of the admissions procedure.

Transfer: Transfer students numbered 14 in 1993–94. Transfer applicants should have completed 1 year each of calculus, physics, and chemistry with laboratory, in addition to appropriate liberal arts courses. A total of 60 credits out of 128 must be completed at Columbia Engineering.

Visiting: There are regularly scheduled orientations for prospective students. There are guides for informal visits and visitors may sit in on classes and stay overnight at the school. To arrange for a visit, contact the Admissions Office at (212) 854–2521.

Financial Aid: In 1993–94 93% of all current freshmen received some form of financial aid. The average freshman award was $18,000. Of that total, scholarships or need-based grants averaged $12,000. Forty-nine percent of undergraduate students work part-time. Average earnings from campus work for the school year are $1600. The average financial indebtedness of a recent year's graduate was $11,000. Columbia Engineering is a member of CSS. The FAF and the college's own financial statement are required. The deadline for financial aid applications is February 1.

International Students: There are currently 489 international students enrolled. They must take the TOEFL or the college's own test and achieve a minimum score on the TOEFL of 600. The student must also take the SAT I or the ACT. Students must take SAT II: Subject tests in writing, mathematics I or II, and physics or chemistry.

Computers: The college provides computer facilities for student use. The mainframes include a Prime, 13 DEC VAX 11/750s, 3 AT&T 3B20s, 75 AT&T 3B2 supermicros, an HP 9050, a system of HP 9900s, 2 IRIS computers, and an IBM Interactive Graphics Lab. There are also microcomputers available in laboratories and classrooms. All students may access the system 24 hours a day. There are no time limits on using the system and no fees.

Graduates: In 1992–93 214 bachelor's degrees were awarded. The most popular majors among a recent year's graduates were electrical engineering (21%), industrial engineering (18%), and mechanical engineering (18%). Some 290 companies recruited on campus in a recent year.

Admissions Contact: Admissions Officer, Office of Undergraduate Admissions.

CONCORDIA COLLEGE D-5
Bronxville, NY 10708 (914) 337–9300

Full-time: 440 men and women	Faculty: IIB, --$
Part-time: 150 men and women	Ph.D.s: n/av
Graduate: none	Student/Faculty: n/av
Year: semesters, summer session	Tuition: n/av
Application Deadline: open	Room & Board: n/av
Freshman Class: n/av	
SAT I or ACT: required	**LESS COMPETITIVE**

Concordia College, founded in 1881, is a private institution affiliated with the Lutheran Church-Missouri Synod and offering undergraduate programs in business, education, music, social work, and professional training in ministry. There are 5 undergraduate schools. In addition to regional accreditation, Concordia has baccalaureate program accreditation with CSWE. The library contains 45,000 volumes and 20,000 microform items, and subscribes to 450 periodicals. Computerized library sources and services include interlibrary loans and database searching. The 30-acre campus is in a suburban area 17 miles north of New York City. Including residence halls, there are 21 buildings on campus.

Student Life: About 67% of undergraduates are from New York. Eighteen percent drop out by the end of their first year; 20% remain to graduate.

Housing: A total of 350 students can be accommodated in college housing. College-sponsored living facilities include single-sex dormitories. Seventy percent of students live on campus. Upperclassmen may keep cars on campus.

Activities: There are no fraternities or sororities on campus. There are many groups and organizations on campus, including cheerleading, choir, chorus, drama, ethnic, literary magazine, photography, professional, religious, social service, student government, and yearbook. Popular campus events include guest lectures, dances, and dramatic presentations.

Sports: There are 5 intercollegiate sports for men and 4 for women, and 10 intramural sports each. Athletic and recreation facilities include an athletic center, a field house, indoor and outdoor tennis courts, squash/racquetball courts, a weight room, and 3 athletic fields.

Disabled Students: The following facilities are available: wheelchair ramps, special parking, specially equipped rest rooms, lowered telephones, and an elevator in the library.

Services: In addition to many counseling and information services, tutoring is available in some subjects, including reading, writing, and mathematics.

Programs of Study: Concordia awards the B.A., B.S., and B.M. degrees. Associate degrees are also awarded. Bachelor's degrees are awarded in BIOLOGICAL SCIENCE (biology/biological science), BUSINESS (business administration and management), COMMUNICATIONS AND THE ARTS (English and music), COMPUTER AND PHYSICAL SCIENCE (mathematics), EDUCATION (business, early childhood, education, elementary, music, and secondary), ENGINEERING AND ENVIRONMENTAL DESIGN (environmental science), SOCIAL SCIENCE (behavioral science, history, Judaic studies, ministries, and social work).

Required: To graduate, students must complete 122 semester hours with a minimum GPA of 2.0. General education requirements include 39 semester hours of liberal arts, 12 of integrated studies, and 18 of foundation courses in basic skills and values.

Special: A registered professional nurse program is offered in cooperation with Mount Vernon Hospital School of Nursing. Concordia also offers cross-registration with a consortium of nearby colleges, internships, an interdisciplinary studies degree, and credit for life experience. There is a freshman honors program on campus.

Requirements: The SAT I or ACT is required. Applicants should be graduates of an accredited secondary school or have a GED certificate. Concordia prefers completion of 16 academic units, including 4 of English, 2 of mathematics, 2 of history or social studies, 2 of science (at least 1 with laboratory), and 2 years of a foreign language. An interview is required, and those students applying to the music program must audition. AP and CLEP credits are accepted.

Procedure: Application deadlines are open. Application fee is $15. Notification is sent on a rolling basis. There is an early decision plan.

Transfer: A 2.5 GPA is recommended. Applicants must submit official transcripts from previous colleges attended. A total of 30 credits out of 122 must be completed at Concordia.

Visiting: There are regularly scheduled orientations for prospective students. There are guides for informal visits and visitors may sit in on classes and stay overnight at the school. To arrange for a visit, contact the Office of Admissions at (914) 337–9300, ext. 2152.

Financial Aid: Concordia is a member of CSS. The FAF is required.

International Students: The school actively recruits these students. They must take the TOEFL or the SAT I.

Computers: The college provides computer facilities for student use. There are 2 computer laboratories available.

Admissions Contact: John M. Bahr, Director of Admissions.

COOPER UNION FOR THE ADVANCEMENT OF SCIENCE AND ART D-5
New York, NY 10003–7183 (212) 353–4120

Full-time: 627 men, 309 women	Faculty: 59; IIB, + +$
Part-time: 14 men, 14 women	Ph.D.s: 60%
Graduate: 60 men, 7 women	Student/Faculty: 16 to 1
Year: semesters	Tuition: $300
Application Deadline: January 1	Room & Board: $8130
Freshman Class: 2341 applied, 294 accepted, 197 enrolled	
SAT I Verbal/Math: 600/740	**MOST COMPETITIVE**

The Cooper Union for the Advancement of Science and Art, founded in 1859, is a privately endowed coeducational institution providing tuition-free, high-quality education. It offers undergraduate and graduate degrees in architecture, art, and engineering. There are 3 undergraduate schools and one graduate school. In addition to regional accreditation, Cooper Union has baccalaureate program accreditation with ABET, NAAB, and NASAD. The library contains 97,000 vol-

umes, and subscribes to 370 periodicals. Computerized library sources and services include the card catalog, interlibrary loans, and database searching. Special learning facilities include a learning resource center and art gallery. The campus is in an urban area. Including residence halls, there are 5 buildings on campus.

Student Life: About 70% of undergraduates are from New York. Students come from 39 states, 12 foreign countries, and Canada. Eighty percent are from public schools; 20% from private. Fifty-three percent are white; 27% Asian American. The average age of freshmen is 17; all undergraduates, 20. Eight percent drop out by the end of their first year; 78% remain to graduate.

Housing: A total of 183 students can be accommodated in college housing. College-sponsored living facilities include coed off-campus apartments. On-campus housing is available on a lottery system for upperclassmen. All students may keep cars on campus.

Activities: About 20% of men belong to 2 national fraternities; about 10% of women belong to 1 local sorority. There are 45 groups on campus, including chorale, computers, ethnic, honors, literary magazine, newspaper, political, professional, religious, social, social service, student government, and yearbook. Popular campus events include Fall Festival and the end-of-the-year student art and architecture exhibit.

Sports: There are 3 intercollegiate sports for men and 3 for women, and 12 intramural sports for men and 12 for women. Athletic and recreation facilities include weight, martial arts, and fencing rooms; a swimming pool; and basketball courts.

Disabled Students: Sixty percent of the campus is accessible to disabled students. The following facilities are available: wheelchair ramps, elevators, and specially equipped rest rooms.

Services: In addition to many counseling and information services, tutoring is available in some subjects, including mathematics, physics, speech, and writing.

Campus Safety and Security: Campus safety and security measures include pamphlets, posters, and films, emergency telephones, lighted pathways and sidewalks, and community security and police.

Programs of Study: Cooper Union awards the B.S., B.Arch., B.E., and B.F.A. degrees. Master's degrees also are awarded. Bachelor's degrees are awarded in COMMUNICATIONS AND THE ARTS (drawing, fine arts, graphic design, painting, photography, printmaking, and sculpture), ENGINEERING AND ENVIRONMENTAL DESIGN (architecture, chemical engineering, civil engineering, electrical/electronics engineering, engineering, and mechanical engineering). Engineering has the largest enrollment.

Required: The 5-year architecture program requires 169 credits, including 30 in liberal arts and electives, for graduation. Art students must complete 128 credits, including 38 in liberal arts and electives, with a minimum overall GPA of 2.0 in order to graduate. A higher GPA is expected in studio work. Engineering students are required to complete a minimum of 135 credits, including a computer literacy course and 24 credits in humanities and social sciences, with a minimum GPA of 2.0.

Special: Cross-registration with the New School for Social Research, internships, study abroad in 8 countries for art students, and some pass/fail options are available. Nondegree study is possible. An accelerated degree in engineering is also available. There are 4 national honor societies on campus. One department has an honors program.

Faculty/Classroom: Seventy percent of faculty are male; 30%, female. All both teach undergraduates and do research. No introductory courses are taught by graduate students. The average class size in an introductory lecture is 30; in a laboratory, 20; and in a regular course offering, 30.

Admissions: About 13% of the 1993–94 applicants were accepted. The SAT scores for the 1993–94 freshman class were as follows: Verbal—16% below 500, 38% between 500 and 599, 39% between 600 and 700, and 7% above 700; Math—25% between 600 and 700 and 75% above 700.

Requirements: The SAT I is required. Engineering applicants must take SAT II: Subject tests in mathematics level I or level II and physics or chemistry. Graduation from an approved secondary school is required. Applicants should have completed 16 to 18 high school academic credits, depending on their major. An essay is part of the application process, and art students must submit a portfolio. Art and architecture applicants must complete a project called the homotest. AP credits are accepted. Important factors used in the admissions decision are evidence of special talent, advanced placement or honor courses, recommendations by school officials, leadership record, and recommendations by alumni.

Procedure: Freshmen are admitted in the fall. Entrance exams should be taken before February 1. Early decision applications should be filed by December 1; regular applications, by January 1 for fall entry, along with an application fee of $25. Notification of early decision is sent December 20; regular decision, on a rolling basis. There are early decision, early admissions, and deferred admissions plans. Some 33 early decision candidates were accepted for the 1993–94 class.

Transfer: Twenty-nine transfer students enrolled in a recent year. Art and architecture transfer applicants must present a portfolio and a minimum of 24 credits in studio classes. Engineering transfer applicants must submit a transcript with grades of B or better in at least 24 credits of appropriate courses.

Visiting: There are regularly scheduled orientations for prospective students, consisting of open houses and portfolio review days. To arrange for a visit, contact the Office of Admissions and Records at (212) 353–4120.

Financial Aid: In 1993–94 40% of all students received some form of financial aid. About 40% of all students received need-based aid. All students receive a full-tuition scholarship. Loans averaged $2100; work contracts averaged $3000. Cooper Union is a member of CSS. The FAF is required. The deadline for financial aid applications is May 1.

International Students: They must take the TOEFL and achieve a minimum score of 550. Freshmen must also take the SAT I; the hometest project is required for art or architecture students. Students must take SAT II: Subject tests in mathematics level I or mathematics level II, and physics or chemistry (engineering only).

Computers: The college provides computer facilities for student use. The mainframe is a DEC VAX 11/780. Five AT&T 3B minicomputers are networked to the UNIX V operating system. A DEC VAX 4200 minicomputer is available, as are more than 100 microcomputers in classrooms, laboratories, and the computer center. A computer laboratory is also affiliated with the film and video departments. All students may access the system. There are no time limits on using the system and no fees.

Graduates: In a recent year, 176 bachelor's degrees were awarded. The most popular majors among graduates were fine arts (36%), electrical engineering (19%), and architecture (13%). Within an average freshman class, 60% graduate in 4 years and 78% in 5 years. Some 40 companies recruited on campus in an earlier year. In an earlier graduating class, 40% of the men and 15% of the women were enrolled in graduate school within 6 months of graduation; all students had found employment.

Admissions Contact: Admissions Representative.

CORNELL UNIVERSITY
C-3

Ithaca, NY 14850 (607) 255-5241

Full-time: 6878 men, 5935 women	**Faculty:** 1542; I, +$
Part-time: none	**Ph.D.s:** 96%
Graduate: 3485 men, 2151 women	**Student/Faculty:** 8 to 1
Year: semesters, summer session	**Tuition:** $7482–18,226
Application Deadline: January 1	($14,162–18,226)
	Room & Board: $5963

Freshman Class: 19,227 applied, 7171 accepted, 3286 enrolled
SAT I: required **MOST COMPETITIVE**

Cornell University, founded in 1865 as a land-grant institution, consists of 7 undergraduate divisions and several professional and graduate schools. Privately supported divisions offering undergraduate programs include the College of Architecture, Art, and Planning; the College of Arts and Sciences; the College of Engineering; and the School of Hotel Administration. State-supported undergraduate divisions include the College of Agriculture and Life Sciences, the College of Human Ecology, and the School of Industrial and Labor Relations. There are 7 undergraduate and 4 graduate schools. The 15 libraries contain 5,579,629 volumes, 6,129,806 microform items, and 109,383 audiovisual items, and subscribe to 61,068 periodicals. Computerized library sources and services include the card catalog, interlibrary loans, and database searching. Special learning facilities include a learning resource center, art gallery, planetarium, bird sanctuary, 5 designated national resource centers, and 2 local optical observatories. The 745-acre campus is in a rural area 60 miles southeast of Syracuse. Including residence halls, there are 468 buildings on campus.

Student Life: About 57% of undergraduates are from out-of-state, mostly the Middle Atlantic. Students come from 50 states, 100 foreign countries, and Canada. Sixty-nine percent are white; 15% Asian American. The average age of freshmen is 18; all undergraduates, 20. Four percent drop out by the end of their first year; 85% remain to graduate.

Housing: A total of 6243 students can be accommodated in college housing. College-sponsored living facilities include single-sex and coed dormitories, on-campus apartments, married-student housing, fraternity houses, and sorority houses. In addition, there are language houses and special interest houses. On-campus housing is guaranteed for the freshman year only and is available on a lottery system for upperclassmen. Seventy-six percent of students live on campus; of those, 90% remain on campus on weekends. All students may keep cars on campus.

Activities: About 32% of men belong to 2 local and 46 national fraternities; about 28% of women belong to 1 local and 17 national sororities. There are 500 groups on campus, including art, band, cheer-

leading, choir, chorale, chorus, computers, dance, drama, drill team, drum and bugle corps, ethnic, film, gay, honors, international, literary magazine, marching band, musical theater, newspaper, orchestra, pep band, photography, political, professional, radio and TV, religious, social, social service, student government, symphony, and yearbook. Popular campus events include Green Dragon Day, Festival of Black Gospel, Greek Week, Springfest, International Student Week, Third World Festival of the Arts, Student Leadership Conference, and College Bowl.

Sports: There are 20 intercollegiate sports for men and 15 for women, and 26 intramural sports for men and 23 for women. Athletic and recreation facilities include indoor and outdoor tracks, a 5000-seat indoor gymnasium, 3 swimming pools, a 25,000-seat stadium, 16 intercollegiate fields, a bowling alley, intramural fields, a boat house, and indoor and outdoor tennis courts.

Disabled Students: Eighty-five percent of the campus is accessible to disabled students. The following facilities are available: wheelchair ramps, elevators, special parking, specially equipped rest rooms, special class scheduling, lowered drinking fountains, and lowered telephones.

Services: In addition to many counseling and information services, tutoring is available in most subjects. There is also a reader service for the blind, remedial reading, biology, and mathematics student support centers, and writing workshops.

Campus Safety and Security: Campus safety and security measures include 24-hour foot and vehicle patrol, self defense education, escort service, and shuttle buses. In addition, there are informal discussions, pamphlets, posters, films, emergency telephones, and lighted pathways and sidewalks.

Programs of Study: Cornell awards the B.A., B.S., B.Arch., and B.F.A. degrees. Master's and doctoral degrees also are awarded. Bachelor's degrees are awarded in AGRICULTURE (agricultural economics, agriculture, animal science, international agriculture, natural resource management, plant science, and soil science), BIOLOGICAL SCIENCE (biology/biological science, botany, entomology, evolutionary biology, genetics, microbiology, neurosciences, and nutrition), BUSINESS (business administration and management, hotel/motel and restaurant management, labor studies, and operations research), COMMUNICATIONS AND THE ARTS (art history and appreciation, classics, communications, comparative literature, dance, design, dramatic arts, English, fine arts, French, German, Greek, Italian, languages, Latin, linguistics, music, photography, Russian, and Spanish), COMPUTER AND PHYSICAL SCIENCE (astronomy, atmospheric sciences and meteorology, chemistry, computer science, geology, mathematics, physics, and statistics), EDUCATION (agricultural), ENGINEERING AND ENVIRONMENTAL DESIGN (architectural engineering, architecture, chemical engineering, city/community/regional planning, civil engineering, electrical/electronics engineering, engineering, engineering physics, environmental engineering technology, landscape architecture/design, materials science, and mechanical engineering), SOCIAL SCIENCE (African studies, American studies, anthropology, archeology, Asian/Oriental studies, economics, food production/management/services, food science, history, human development, human services, international studies, Near Eastern studies, philosophy, political science/government, psychology, public affairs, religion, rural sociology, Russian and Slavic studies, social science, sociology, and textiles and clothing). Engineering has the largest enrollment.

Required: All undergraduates must take 2 semesters of freshman writing seminar and 2 semesters of physical education. Graduation requirements vary by program, including a minimum of 120 credits.

Special: Co-op programs are offered in the College of Engineering and the School of Industrial and Labor Relations. Cross-registration is available with Ithaca College. Public-policy internships are available in Washington, D.C., Albany, and New York City. Study abroad is offered in more than 50 countries. B.A.-B.S. degrees, interdisciplinary/intercollegiate options, student-designed and dual majors, work-study programs, accelerated degree programs, and pass/fail options are available. Nondegree study is possible on a limited basis. There are 3 national honor societies on campus, including Phi Beta Kappa.

Faculty/Classroom: Eighty-two percent of faculty are male; 18%, female. All teach undergraduates and also do research. Graduate students teach 1% of introductory courses.

Admissions: About 37% of the 1993–94 applicants were accepted. The SAT scores for the 1993–94 freshman class were as follows: Verbal—13% below 500, 38% between 500 and 599, 42% between 600 and 700, and 7% above 700; Math—1% below 500, 12% between 500 and 599, 40% between 600 and 700, and 47% above 700. About 95% of the current freshmen were in the top fifth of their class; 99% were in the top two fifths. There were 60 National Merit finalists.

Requirements: The SAT I is required. An essay is required as part of the application process. Other requirements vary by division or program. AP credit is accepted. Important factors used in the admissions decision are recommendations by school officials, evidence of

special talent, advanced placement or honor courses, recommendations by alumni, personality, and intangible qualities.

Procedure: Freshmen are admitted fall and spring. Entrance exams should be taken by December of the senior year. Applications should be filed by January 1 for fall entry and October 15 for spring entry, along with an application fee of $60. Notification is sent mid-April. There are early decision, early admissions, and deferred admissions plans. About 691 early decision candidates were accepted for the 1993–94 class. A waiting list is an active part of the admissions procedure.

Transfer: About 462 transfer students enrolled in 1993–94. Admission requirements for transfers vary by program.

Visiting: There are regularly scheduled orientations for prospective students, including regularly scheduled tours and information sessions. There are guides for informal visits and visitors may sit in on classes and stay overnight at the school. To arrange for a visit, contact the Red Carpet Society at (607) 255-3447.

Financial Aid: In 1993–94, 60% of all current freshmen and 70% of continuing students received some form of financial aid. About 47% of freshmen and 45% of continuing students received need-based aid. The average freshman award was $11,750. Of that total, scholarships or need-based grants averaged $11,750 ($26,200 maximum); loans averaged $3850 ($5500 maximum); and work contracts averaged $1440 ($2100 maximum). Seventy-one percent of undergraduate students work part-time. Average earnings from campus work for the school year are $1499. The average financial indebtedness of the 1992–93 graduate was $10,200. Cornell is a member of CSS. The FAF and the college's own financial statement are required. The IRS form is required after enrollment. The deadline for financial aid applications is February 15.

International Students: There are currently 2458 international students enrolled. The school actively recruits these students. They must take the TOEFL and achieve a minimum score of 550. The student must also take the SAT I or ACT. Some colleges require SAT II: Subject tests.

Computers: The college provides computer facilities for student use. The mainframes are 2 IBM 3090/600s. Students have access to 7 campuswide computer centers and more than 20 departmental facilities with more than 700 microcomputers/terminals. All students may access the system. There are no time limits on using the system and no fees.

Graduates: In 1992–93, 3307 bachelor's degrees were awarded. The most popular majors among graduates were biological sciences (8%), government (5%), and agricultural business (4%). Within an average freshman class, 1% graduate in 3 years, 78% in 4 years, 87% in 5 years, and 89% in 6 years. Some 500 companies recruited on campus. In a recent year's graduating class, 32% of all graduates were enrolled in graduate school within 6 months of graduation; 54% had found employment.

Admissions Contact: Nancy Hargrave Meislahn, Director of Admissions.

D'YOUVILLE COLLEGE
Buffalo, NY 14201

Full-time: 290 men, 784 women	**Faculty:** 83; IIB, -$
Part-time: 66 men, 270 women	**Ph.Ds:** 59%
Graduate: 44 men, 342 women	**Student/Faculty:** 13 to 1
Year: semesters, summer session	**Tuition:** $8720
Application Deadline: August	**Room & Board:** $4130

A-3
(716) 881-7600; (800) 777-3921

Freshman Class: 1723 applied, 1035 accepted, 406 enrolled
SAT I Verbal/Math: 435/497   **ACT:** 22   **COMPETITIVE**

D'Youville College, founded in 1908, is a private, nonsectarian, coeducational liberal arts institution. There are 5 graduate schools. In addition to regional accreditation, D'Youville has baccalaureate program accreditation with ADA, APTA, CSWE, and NLN. The library contains 154,000 volumes, 7339 microform items, and 3490 audiovisual forms, and subscribes to 1042 periodicals. Computerized library sources and services include database searching. Special learning facilities include a learning resource center. The 7-acre campus is in an urban area 1 mile north of Buffalo. Including residence halls, there are 7 buildings on campus.

Student Life: About 76% of undergraduates are from New York. Students come from 15 states, 3 foreign countries, and Canada. Eighty percent are from public schools; 20% from private. Seventy-one percent are white; 16% foreign nationals. The average age of freshmen is 18. Twenty-three percent drop out by the end of their first year; 43% remain to graduate.

Housing: A total of 390 students can be accommodated in college housing. College-sponsored living facilities include coed dormitories. In addition there are honors floors. On-campus housing is guaranteed for all 4 years. Eighty-five percent of students commute. All students may keep cars on campus.

Activities: There are no fraternities or sororities on campus. There are 16 groups on campus, including computers, ethnic, honors, international, literary magazine, newspaper, professional, religious, social, social service, student government, and yearbook. Popular campus events include Moving Up Days, Sibling Weekend, Senior Week, Compete-A-Thon, and Family Weekend.

Sports: There is 1 intercollegiate sport for men and 2 for women, 11 intramural sports for men and 9 for women. Athletic and recreation facilities include a 125-seat indoor gymnasium, a basketball court, a swimming pool, and a weight-training room.

Disabled Students: Seventy-five percent of the campus is accessible to disabled students. The following facilities are available: wheelchair ramps, elevators, special parking, specially equipped rest rooms, and lowered telephones.

Services: In addition to many counseling and information services, tutoring is available in some subjects and is based on tutor accessibility. There is also a reader service for the blind, and remedial math, reading, and writing.

Campus Safety and Security: Campus safety and security measures include 24-hour foot and vehicle patrol, self-defense education, escort service, and informal discussions. In addition, there are pamphlets, posters, and films, emergency telephones, lighted pathways and sidewalks, a special focus program, and a security committee.

Programs of Study: D'Youville awards the B.A., B.S., B.S.N., and B.S.W. degrees. Master's degrees also are awarded. Bachelor's degrees are awarded in BIOLOGICAL SCIENCE (biology/biological science), BUSINESS (accounting, business administration and management, general business, and marketing/retailing/merchandising), COMMUNICATIONS AND THE ARTS (English and literature), EDUCATION (bilingual/bicultural, business, education of the visually handicapped, elementary, secondary, and special), HEALTH PROFESSIONS (nursing, occupational therapy, physical therapy, physician assistant, predentistry, premedicine, and preveterinary science), SOCIAL SCIENCE (dietetics, history, liberal arts/general studies, philosophy, prelaw, social work, and sociology). Education and health professions are the strongest academically. Health professions, business, and nursing have the largest enrollments.

Required: All students must complete general program and core curriculum requirements, including 5 courses in humanities, 2 each in English and natural sciences, and 1 each in philosophy or religion, history, sociology, psychology, economics or political science, mathematics and computer science. A minimum of 120 to 129 credit hours, varying by major, with a minimum GPA of 2.0 is required in order to graduate.

Special: D'Youville has cross-registration with member colleges of the Western New York Consortium. Internships, work-study programs, dual majors, and pass/fail options are available. Accelerated 5-year B.S.-M.S. programs in physical therapy, occupational therapy, and dietetics are offered. For freshmen undecided about their majors, the Career Discovery Program offers special courses, internships, and faculty advisers. There is a freshman honors program on campus, as well as 1 national honor society. Six departments have honors programs.

Faculty/Classroom: Forty-one percent of faculty are male; 59%, female. All teach undergraduates. No introductory courses are taught by graduate students. The average class size in an introductory lecture is 30; in a laboratory, 12; and in a regular course offering, 23.

Admissions: About 60% of the 1993–94 applicants were accepted. The SAT scores for the 1993–94 freshman class were as follows: Verbal—80% below 500, 19% between 500 and 599, and 1% between 600 and 700; Math—45% below 500, 45% between 500 and 599, and 10% between 600 and 700. The ACT scores were 31% below 21, 28% between 21 and 23, 25% between 24 and 26, and 16% between 27 and 28. About 29% of the current freshmen were in the top fifth of their class; 62% were in the top two fifths. There were 3 National Merit semifinalists. Five freshmen graduated first in their class.

Requirements: D'Youville requires applicants to be in the upper 50% of their class. A minimum grade average of 80 is required for most programs. The SAT I or ACT is required. Applicants should have completed 16 Carnegie units, including 4 years of high school English, 3 of social studies, and 1 each of mathematics and science; some majors require additional years of mathematics and science. The GED is accepted. An interview is recommended. AP and CLEP credits are accepted. Important factors used in the admissions decision are advanced placement or honor courses, evidence of special talent, leadership record, recommendations by school officials, and extracurricular activities record.

Procedure: Freshmen are admitted fall and spring. Applications should be filed by August for fall entry and January for spring entry, along with an application fee of $20. Notification is sent on a rolling basis. There is a deferred admissions plan.

Transfer: Some 243 transfer students enrolled in 1993–94. Transfer applicants need a minimum GPA of 2.0, or 2.5 for some programs. An interview is recommended. There are very limited openings for transfers seeking part-time studies. A total of 30 credits out of 120 to 129 must be completed at D'Youville.

Visiting: There are regularly scheduled orientations for prospective students. There are guides for informal visits and visitors may sit in on classes. To arrange for a visit, contact the Admissions Office at (716) 881-7600.

Financial Aid: In 1993–94 93% of all current freshmen and 95% of continuing students received some form of financial aid. The average freshman award was $5500. Of that total, scholarships or need-based grants averaged $5509 ($7300 maximum); loans averaged $3145 ($3500 maximum); work contracts averaged $686 ($1000 maximum); and D'Youville grants averaged $1500 (maximum). Twenty percent of undergraduate students work part-time. Average earnings from campus work for the school year are $1000. The average financial indebtedness of the 1992–93 graduate was $12,000. D'Youville is a member of CSS. The FAF is required. The deadline for financial aid applications is April 15.

International Students: There are currently 323 international students enrolled. The school actively recruits these students. They must take the TOEFL and achieve a minimum score of 500.

Computers: The college provides computer facilities for student use. There are 3 computer laboratories as well as computers located in the residence hall. Apple Macintosh and DOS computers are nonnetworked. All students may access the system. There are no time limits on using the system. There are fees for students in computer science classes.

Graduates: In 1992–93 217 bachelor's degrees were awarded. The most popular majors among graduates were nursing (25%), education (16%), and physical therapy (15%). Within an average freshman class, 1% graduate in 3 years, 24% in 4 years, 16% in 5 years, and 2% in 6 years. Some 92 companies recruited on campus in 1992–93. In the 1992 graduating class, 82% of all students were enrolled in graduate school within 6 months of graduation; 59% had found employment.

Admissions Contact: Ronald H. Dannecker, Director of Admissions and Financial Aid.

DAEMEN COLLEGE   A-3

Amherst, NY 14226   (716) 839-8225; (800) 462-7652 (in-state)

Full-time: 433 men, 824 women	**Faculty:** 68
Part-time: 116 men, 417 women	**Ph.Ds:** 78%
Graduate: 4 men, 8 women	**Student/Faculty:** 18 to 1
Year: semesters, summer session	**Tuition:** $8670
Application Deadline: open	**Room & Board:** $4350
Freshman Class: n/av	
SAT I or ACT: required	**LESS COMPETITIVE**

Daemen College, founded in 1947, is a private, coeducational institution offering programs in the liberal and fine arts, business, education, health sciences, and professional training. In addition to regional accreditation, Daemen has baccalaureate program accreditation with APTA, CAHEA, CSWE, and NLN. The library contains 135,000 volumes, 2000 microform items, and 4500 audiovisual forms, and subscribes to 850 periodicals. Computerized library sources and services include interlibrary loans and database searching. Special learning facilities include a learning resource center and art gallery. The 37-acre campus is in a suburban area 15 miles north of Buffalo. Including residence halls, there are 35 buildings on campus.

Student Life: About 88% of undergraduates are from New York. Students come from 21 states, 17 foreign countries, and Canada. Eighty-eight percent are white. The average age of freshmen is 18; all undergraduates, 20.

Housing: A total of 565 students can be accommodated in college housing. College-sponsored living facilities include single-sex dormitories and on-campus apartments. In addition there is a quiet dormitory. On-campus housing is guaranteed for all 4 years. Seventy-two percent of students commute. Alcohol is not permitted. All students may keep cars on campus.

Activities: About 14% of men belong to 1 local and 1 national fraternity; about 15% of women belong to 4 local sororities. There are 22 groups on campus, including art, cheerleading, computers, drama, ethnic, honors, international, literary magazine, newspaper, political, professional, religious, social, social service, student government, and yearbook.

Sports: There is 1 intercollegiate sport for men and 1 for women, and 4 intramural sports for men and 4 for women. Athletic and recreation facilities include a gymnasium, weight and exercise rooms, and saunas.

Disabled Students: The entire campus is accessible to disabled students. The following facilities are available: wheelchair ramps, elevators, special parking, specially equipped rest rooms, lowered drinking fountains, and lowered telephones.

Services: In addition to many counseling and information services, tutoring is available in every subject. There is remedial math, reading, and writing.

Campus Safety and Security: Campus safety and security measures include 24-hour foot and vehicle patrol, informal discussions, pamphlets, posters, and films, and lighted pathways and sidewalks. In addition, there are video monitors.

Programs of Study: Daemen awards the B.A., B.S., and B.F.A. degrees. Master's degrees also are awarded. Bachelor's degrees are awarded in BIOLOGICAL SCIENCE (biology/biological science), BUSINESS (accounting, business administration and management, and transportation management), COMMUNICATIONS AND THE ARTS (design, English, fine arts, French, graphic design, languages, and Spanish), COMPUTER AND PHYSICAL SCIENCE (chemistry, mathematics, and natural sciences), EDUCATION (art, business, elementary, English, mathematics, science, secondary, social studies, and special), HEALTH PROFESSIONS (medical laboratory technology, nursing, and physical therapy), SOCIAL SCIENCE (history, humanities, psychology, religion, and social work). Physical therapy, medical technology, and natural science are the strongest academically. Business, physical therapy, art, and education have the largest enrollments.

Required: To graduate, students must complete 122 to 144 hours with a minimum GPA of 2.0. The core curriculum includes 6 credit hours each in literature, philosophy/religion, and history/government; 3 each in composition, fine or performing arts, mathematics, science, economics/sociology, psychology, and Liberal Arts Colloquium; and 6 additional hours outside the major for most programs.

Special: Daemen offers cooperative programs in all majors, internships, cross-registration within the Western New York Consortium of Colleges and Universities, work-study programs, and study abroad in Spain, France, Canada, England, Mexico, and Poland. There are 2 national honor societies on campus, including Phi Beta Kappa.

Faculty/Classroom: Fifty-four percent of faculty are male; 46%, female. No introductory courses are taught by graduate students. The average class size in an introductory lecture is 50; in a laboratory, 16; and in a regular course offering, 20.

Requirements: The SAT I or ACT is required. Applicants must be graduates of an accredited secondary school or have the GED equivalent. Some departments have further admissions requirements, including a portfolio review for art majors and 3-year sequences of mathematics and science for all natural science programs. AP and CLEP credits are accepted. Important factors used in the admissions decision are advanced placement or honor courses, leadership record, evidence of special talent, personality, intangible qualities, and parents or siblings attending the school.

Procedure: Freshmen are admitted to all sessions. Entrance exams should be taken by the summer following the senior year. Application deadlines are open. The application fee is $15. Notification is sent on a rolling basis. There are early decision, early admissions, and deferred admissions plans. A waiting list is an active part of the admissions procedure.

Transfer: About 258 transfer students enrolled in 1993–94. Applicants must have a minimum GPA of 2.0 for most programs. A total of 30 credits out of 122 must be completed at Daemen.

Visiting: There are regularly scheduled orientations for prospective students, including a campus tour and interviews. There are guides for informal visits and visitors may sit in on classes and stay overnight at the school. To arrange for a visit, contact the Admissions Office at (716) 839–8225.

Financial Aid: In 1993–94, 97% of all current freshmen and 98% of continuing students received some form of financial aid. About 81% of freshmen and 89% of continuing students received need-based aid. The average freshman award was $4700. Of that total, scholarships or need-based grants averaged $3500 ($8800 maximum); loans averaged $2300 ($2625 maximum); and work contracts averaged $1200. Twenty-five percent of undergraduate students work part-time. Average earnings from campus work for the school year are $1200. Daemen is a member of CSS. The FAF and the college's own financial statement are required. The deadline for financial aid applications is February 15.

International Students: The school actively recruits these students. They must take the TOEFL and achieve a minimum score of 550.

Computers: The college provides computer facilities for student use. About 80 microcomputers are available in the Academic Resources Center and departmental computer laboratories. All students may access the system. There are no time limits on using the system and no fees.

Graduates: In 1992–93 245 bachelor's degrees were awarded. Some 22 companies recruited on campus in 1992–93. In the 1992 graduating class, 10% of all graduates were enrolled in graduate school within 6 months of graduation; 80% of all graduates had found employment.

Admissions Contact: Maria P. Dillard, Director of Admissions.

DOMINICAN COLLEGE D-5
Orangeburg, NY 10962 (914) 359-7800, ext. 271

Full-time: 230 men, 445 women	Faculty: 40; IIB, -$
Part-time: 224 men, 702 women	Ph.D.s: 55%
Graduate: none	Student/Faculty: 17 to 1
Year: semesters, summer session	Tuition: $8060
Application Deadline: open	Room & Board: $5540
Freshman Class: 320 applied, 310 accepted, 108 enrolled	
SAT I Verbal/Math: 370/385	**LESS COMPETITIVE**

Dominican College, founded in 1952, is an independent, coeducational Catholic institution offering undergraduate programs in business, education, liberal arts, health professions, and social sciences. In addition to regional accreditation, Dominican has baccalaureate program accreditation with CSWE and NLN. The library contains 99,735 volumes, 12,750 microform items, and 1032 audiovisual forms, and subscribes to 637 periodicals. Computerized library sources and services include interlibrary loans. Special learning facilities include a learning resource center. The 14-acre campus is in a small town 17 miles north of New York City. Including residence halls, there are 7 buildings on campus.

Student Life: About 70% of undergraduates are from New York. Students come from 10 states and 5 foreign countries. Seventy percent are from public schools; 30% from private. Eighty-six percent are white. Eighty percent are Catholic; 10% Jewish; 10% Protestant. The average age of freshmen is 19; all undergraduates, 23. Thirty percent drop out by the end of their first year; 45% remain to graduate.

Housing: A total of 120 students can be accommodated in college housing. College-sponsored living facilities include coed dormitories. On-campus housing is guaranteed for the freshman year only and is available on a first-come, first-served basis. Priority is given to out-of-town students. Ninety-two percent of students commute. Alcohol is not permitted. All students may keep cars on campus.

Activities: There are no fraternities or sororities on campus. There are 17 groups on campus, including cheerleading, chorus, computers, drama, honors, international, literary magazine, musical theater, newspaper, professional, religious, social service, student government, and yearbook. Popular campus events include Family Day, craft fairs, and the Dominican Cup Tournament (soccer).

Sports: Athletic and recreation facilities include a baseball field and a basketball court.

Disabled Students: The entire campus is accessible to disabled students. The following facilities are available: wheelchair ramps, special parking, specially equipped rest rooms, lowered drinking fountains, and lowered telephones.

Services: In addition to many counseling and information services, tutoring is available in some subjects, including English and mathematics. There is remedial math, reading, and writing.

Campus Safety and Security: Campus safety and security measures include shuttle buses, informal discussions, emergency telephones, and lighted pathways and sidewalks.

Programs of Study: Dominican awards the B.A., B.S., B.S.Ed., and B.S.N. degrees. Associate degrees also are awarded. Bachelor's degrees are awarded in BUSINESS (accounting, business administration and management, business economics, international business management, and marketing/retailing/merchandising), COMMUNICATIONS AND THE ARTS (English, languages, and Spanish), COMPUTER AND PHYSICAL SCIENCE (actuarial science and mathematics), EDUCATION (elementary, science, secondary, and special), ENGINEERING AND ENVIRONMENTAL DESIGN (preengineering), HEALTH PROFESSIONS (nursing and occupational therapy), SOCIAL SCIENCE (American studies, history, humanities, prelaw, psychology, public administration, social science, and social work). Business and nursing are the strongest academically. Business, nursing, and occupational therapy have the largest enrollments.

Required: Computer courses are required for business majors. In order to graduate, all students must complete 120 semester hours, including a general education curriculum of 36 to 39 credits. Nursing majors must maintain a minimum GPA of 2.3, while all other majors require at least a 2.0.

Special: Individualized internships in all fields, work-study programs, B.A.-B.S. degrees, dual majors, and a 3–2 engineering degree with Manhattan College are also offered. Credit for life experience is granted through submission of a portfolio. Weekend College, offered on a trimester basis, is designed to meet the needs of working adults. There is a freshman honors program on campus, as well as 3 national honor societies. Three departments have honors programs.

Faculty/Classroom: Forty-nine percent of faculty are male; 51%, female. All teach undergraduates. The average class size in a regular course offering is 16.

Admissions: About 97% of the 1993–94 applicants were accepted. The SAT scores for the 1993–94 freshman class were as follows: Verbal—65% below 500, 30% between 500 and 599, and 5% between 600 and 700; Math—55% below 500, 38% between 500 and 599,

and 7% between 600 and 700. About 15% of the current freshmen were in the top fifth of their class; 30% were in the top two fifths.

Requirements: Dominican requires applicants to be in the upper 80% of their class. A minimum grade average of 70 is required. The SAT I or ACT is required. Applicants should be graduates of an accredited secondary school or possess a GED equivalent. An interview is required, and an essay is recommended. AP and CLEP credits are accepted. Important factors used in the admissions decision are recommendations by school officials, recommendations by alumni, parents or siblings attending the school, advanced placement or honor courses, and ability to finance college education.

Procedure: Freshmen are admitted to all sessions. Entrance exams should be taken by November of the senior year. Application deadlines are open. The application fee is $25. Notification is sent on a rolling basis. There are early decision and deferred admissions plans.

Transfer: About 80 transfer students enrolled in a recent year. Transfer applicants must submit a transcript from their previous school. A minimum GPA of 2.0 is required. An interview should be scheduled. Those applying to the occupational therapy program should have completed an associate degree. A total of 30 semester hours out of 120 must be completed at Dominican.

Visiting: There are guides for informal visits and visitors may sit in on classes. To arrange for a visit, contact Louis Kern, Director of Admissions, at (914) 359-7800, ext. 271.

Financial Aid: In a recent year, 59% of all current freshmen and 63% of continuing students received some form of financial aid. About 55% of freshmen and 60% of continuing students received need-based aid. The average freshman award was $5300. Of that total, scholarships or need-based grants averaged $2000 ($6600 maximum); loans averaged $1800 ($2700 maximum); and work contracts averaged $1000 ($1200 maximum). Two percent of undergraduate students work part-time. Average earnings from campus work for the school year are $1000. Dominican is a member of CSS. The FAF and the college's own financial statement are required.

International Students: There are currently 20 international students enrolled. They must take the TOEFL and achieve a minimum score of 500. The student must also take the SAT I.

Computers: The college provides computer facilities for student use. The mainframe is a DEC MicroVAX II. There is a PC computer laboratory with access to the mainframe. All students may access the system. There are no time limits on using the system. There is a $50 laboratory fee.

Graduates: In a recent year, 262 bachelor's degrees were awarded. The most popular majors among graduates were business administration (44%), nursing (13%), and occupational therapy (12%). Within an average freshman class, 5% graduate in 3 years, 28% in 4 years, 14% in 5 years, and 1% in 6 years.

Admissions Contact: Louis Kern, Director of Admissions.

DOWLING COLLEGE

Oakdale, NY 11769-1999   **E-5**

Full-time: 472 men, 587 women	Faculty: 93
Part-time: 1126 men, 1332 women	Ph.D.s: 81%
Graduate: 694 men, 1154 women	Student/Faculty: 11 to 1
Year: 4-1-4, summer session	Tuition: $9630
Application Deadline: open	Room: $3100

(516) 244-3030; (800) DOWLING

Freshman Class: 1011 applied, 829 accepted, 410 enrolled
SAT I Verbal/Math: 420/450   **ACT: 18**   **LESS COMPETITIVE**

Dowling College, founded in 1955, is a small, independent, coeducational institution offering programs in the arts and sciences, aviation and transportation, business, and education. There are 4 undergraduate and 2 graduate schools. The library contains 161,416 volumes and 366,562 microform items, and subscribes to 1177 periodicals. Computerized library sources and services include the card catalog, interlibrary loans, and database searching. Special learning facilities include a learning resource center, an art gallery, and a radio station. The 47-acre campus is in a suburban area 50 miles east of New York City. Including residence halls, there are 10 buildings on campus.

Student Life: About 95% of undergraduates are from New York. Students come from 12 states, 4 foreign countries, and Canada. Eighty-nine percent are from public schools; 11% from private. Ninety-one percent are white. The average age of freshmen is 19; all undergraduates, 25. Thirty percent drop out by the end of their first year; 38% remain to graduate.

Housing: A total of 260 students can be accommodated in college housing. College-sponsored living facilities include coed on-campus apartments. Priority for on-campus housing is given to out-of-town students. Ninety-four percent of students commute. All students may keep cars on campus.

Activities: There are no fraternities or sororities on campus. There are 25 groups on campus, including chorus, drama, ethnic, honors, literary magazine, newspaper, orchestra, professional, radio and TV, religious, student government, and yearbook. Popular campus events

include Freshman Mixer, Holiday Party, Senior Picnic, and Spring Cotillion.

Sports: Athletic and recreation facilities include a basketball court, a weight room, tennis courts, and a fitness center.

Disabled Students: Ninety percent of the campus is accessible to disabled students. The following facilities are available: wheelchair ramps, elevators, special parking, specially equipped rest rooms, special class scheduling, lowered drinking fountains, and lowered telephones.

Services: In addition to many counseling and information services, tutoring is available in most subjects. There is also remedial math, reading, and writing.

Campus Safety and Security: Campus safety and security measures include 24-hour foot and vehicle patrol, informal discussions, pamphlets, posters, films, and emergency telephones. In addition, there are lighted pathways and sidewalks.

Programs of Study: Dowling awards the B.A., B.S., and B.B.A. degrees. Master's degrees are also awarded. Bachelor's degrees are awarded in BIOLOGICAL SCIENCE (biology/biological science and marine biology), BUSINESS (accounting, banking and finance, business administration and management, and marketing/retailing/merchandising), COMMUNICATIONS AND THE ARTS (English, fine arts, languages, music, romance languages, and speech/debate/rhetoric), COMPUTER AND PHYSICAL SCIENCE (applied mathematics, computer programming, computer science, mathematics, and natural sciences), EDUCATION (elementary, secondary, and special), ENGINEERING AND ENVIRONMENTAL DESIGN (aeronautical science and aeronautical technology), SOCIAL SCIENCE (anthropology, economics, history, humanities, psychology, and social science). Business, education, and aviation and transportation have the largest enrollments.

Required: To graduate, students must complete 120 credits with a minimum GPA of 2.0. The required 36-credit general education core includes a senior seminar.

Special: Dowling offers a B.S. in professional and liberal studies, internships, independent study, and nondegree study. There are cooperative programs with the FAA in several majors, including aeronautics and airway science. There are 6 national honor societies on campus. One department has an honors program.

Faculty/Classroom: Fifty-six percent of faculty are male; 44%, female. All teach undergraduates. No introductory courses are taught by graduate students. The average class size in an introductory lecture is 20; in a laboratory, 15; and in a regular course offering, 19.

Admissions: About 82% of the 1993-94 applicants were accepted. The SAT scores for the 1993-94 freshman class were as follows: Verbal—90% below 500, 7% between 500 and 599, 1% between 600 and 700, and 1% above 700; Math—70% below 500, 25% between 500 and 599, 3% between 600 and 700, and 1% above 700. The ACT scores were 74% below 21, 19% between 21 and 23, 4% between 24 and 26, 2% between 27 and 28, and 1% above 28. About 20% of the current freshmen were in the top fifth of their class; 68% were in the top two fifths.

Requirements: The SAT I or ACT is required; the SAT I is recommended. Applicants should be graduates of an accredited secondary school and have completed at least 16 Carnegie units, including 4 in English. An interview is required. AP and CLEP credits are accepted. Important factors used in the admissions decision are advanced placement or honor courses, evidence of special talent, recommendations by school officials, personality, intangible qualities, and extracurricular activities record.

Procedure: Freshmen are admitted fall and spring. Entrance exams should be taken by December or January of the senior year. Application deadlines are open. Application fee is $25. Notification is sent on a rolling basis. There are early admissions and deferred admissions plans.

Transfer: About 640 transfer students enrolled in 1993-94. Applicants must submit official transcripts from all colleges attended. A total of 30 credits out of 120 must be completed at Dowling.

Visiting: There are regularly scheduled orientations for prospective students, including a campus tour and meetings with enrollment services staff members. There are guides for informal visits and visitors may sit in on classes. To arrange for a visit, contact the Admissions Office at (516) 244-3030, (516) 369-5464, or (800) DOWLING.

Financial Aid: In 1993-94, 60% of all current freshmen and 75% of continuing students received some form of financial aid. About 60% of freshmen and 75% of continuing students received need-based aid. The average freshman award was $5125. Of that total, scholarships or need-based grants averaged $1025 ($9000 maximum); loans averaged $2000 ($4125 maximum); and work contracts averaged $2100 ($3000 maximum). All undergraduate students work part-time. Average earnings from campus work for the school year are $3000. The average financial indebtedness of the 1992-93 graduate was $5875. Dowling is a member of CSS. The FAF, the college's own financial statement, and the FAFSA are required. The deadline for financial aid applications is May 1.

International Students: There are currently 4 international students enrolled. They must take the TOEFL and the SAT I or the ACT.

Computers: The college provides computer facilities for student use. The mainframe is an IBM AIX. There are also Apple II and Macintosh, Dell, and IBM microcomputers located in the Academic Computing Center and Gateway. All students may access the system. It may be used 7 A.M. to 10:45 P.M. Monday through Thursday and 7 A.M. to 5 P.M. Friday through Sunday. There are no time limits on using the system and no fees.

Graduates: In 1992–93, 931 bachelor's degrees were awarded. The most popular majors among graduates were business (27%), education (18%), and liberal arts (16%). Within an average freshman class, 30% graduate in 4 years and 44% in 6 years. Some 200 companies recruited on campus in 1992–93.

Admissions Contact: Kate Rowe, Director of Admissions.

EASTMAN SCHOOL OF MUSIC

B-3

Rochester, NY 14604   (716) 274–1060

Full-time: 221 men, 257 women	Faculty: 89
Part-time: none	Ph.D.s: 80%
Graduate: 164 men, 155 women	Student/Faculty: 5 to 1
Year: semesters	Tuition: $15,435
Application Deadline: February 1	Room & Board: $6015

Freshman Class: 644 applied, 255 accepted, 130 enrolled

ACT: not required   **SPECIAL**

Eastman School of Music, founded in 1921, is a private, professional, coeducational school of music within the University of Rochester. There is one undergraduate and one graduate school. In addition to regional accreditation, Eastman has baccalaureate program accreditation with NASM. The library contains 500,000 volumes, 3800 microform items, and 60,000 audiovisual forms, and subscribes to 500 periodicals. Computerized library sources and services include the card catalog, interlibrary loans, and database searching. Special learning facilities include a learning resource center, art gallery, recording studios, and the Sibley Music Library. The 3-block campus is in an urban area in downtown Rochester. Including residence halls, there are 5 buildings on campus.

Student Life: About 73% of undergraduates are from out-of-state, mostly the Midwest. Students come from 47 states, 21 foreign countries, and Canada. Ninety percent are from public schools; 10% from private. Seventy-two percent are white; 15% foreign nationals. The average age of freshmen is 18; all undergraduates, 20. Twelve percent drop out by the end of their first year; 80% remain to graduate.

Housing: A total of 360 students can be accommodated in college housing. College-sponsored living facilities include single-sex and coed dormitories. On-campus housing is guaranteed for all 4 years. Seventy-seven percent of students live on campus; of those, 100% remain on campus on weekends. Alcohol is not permitted. All students may keep cars on campus.

Activities: About 10% of men and about 6% of women belong to 2 national fraternities; about 5% of women belong to 1 national sorority. Groups on campus include band, chorale, chorus, computers, gay, international, jazz band, literary magazine, musical theater, newspaper, opera, orchestra, religious, student government, symphony, and yearbook. Popular campus events include Christmas Sing, Spring Formal, and Halloween party.

Sports: There is no sports program at Eastman. Athletic and recreation facilities include the Zornow Sports Center and all other athletic facilities of the University of Rochester, as well as a nearby YMCA, which are available to students.

Disabled Students: The entire campus is accessible to disabled students. The following facilities are available: wheelchair ramps, elevators, special parking, specially equipped rest rooms, lowered drinking fountains, and lowered telephones.

Services: In addition to many counseling and information services, tutoring is available in every subject. In addition, there is a reader service for the blind and remedial writing.

Campus Safety and Security: Campus safety and security measures include 24-hour foot and vehicle patrol, self defense education, escort service, and shuttle buses. In addition, there are informal discussions, pamphlets, posters, and films, emergency telephones, and lighted pathways and sidewalks.

Programs of Study: Eastman awards the B.M. and B.A. degrees. Master's and doctoral degrees also are awarded. Bachelor's degrees are awarded in COMMUNICATIONS AND THE ARTS (music, music performance, and music theory and composition), EDUCATION (music). Performance has the largest enrollment.

Required: All students must complete core requirements in a major instrument or voice, music theory, music history, and Western cultural tradition, as well as English and humanities electives. A total of 122 to 136 credit hours, varying by program, with a minimum GPA of 2.0, is required in order to graduate.

Special: Eastman and the University of Rochester cooperatively offer the B.A. degree with a music concentration. All the facilities of the university are open to Eastman students. Cross-registration is also available with colleges in the Rochester Consortium. Dual majors are available in composition, music education, theory, and performance.

Faculty/Classroom: Sixty percent of faculty are male; 40%, female. One-hundred percent both teach and do research. Graduate students teach 10% of introductory courses. The average class size in an introductory lecture is 30, and in a regular course offering, 15.

Admissions: About 40% of the 1993–94 applicants were accepted.

Requirements: Applicants should be graduates of an accredited secondary school with 16 academic credits, including 4 years of English. The GED is accepted. An audition and an interview are required. Important factors used in the admissions decision are evidence of special talent, personality, intangible qualities, recommendations by alumni, leadership record, and parents or siblings attending the school.

Procedure: Freshmen are admitted fall and spring. Applications should be filed by February 1 for fall entry and December 1 for spring entry, along with an application fee of $50. Notification is sent on a rolling basis. A waiting list is an active part of the admissions procedure, with about 4% of applicants on the list.

Transfer: About 17 transfer students enrolled in 1993–94. Transfer requirements include satisfactory academic standing at the previous institution, a GPA of at least 2.0, a successful audition, and an interview.

Visiting: To arrange for a visit, contact Admissions Office at (716) 274–1060.

Financial Aid: In 1993–94 87% of all current freshmen and 85% of continuing students received some form of financial aid. About 66% of freshmen and 64% of continuing students received need-based aid. The average freshman award was $9125. Of that total, scholarships or need-based grants averaged $5200 ($15,000 maximum); loans averaged $2625 ($4000 maximum); and work contracts averaged $300 ($1200 maximum). Sixty percent of undergraduate students work part-time. Average earnings from campus work for the school year are $700. The average financial indebtedness of the 1992–93 graduate was $10,000. Eastman is a member of CSS. The college's own financial statement and FAFSA are required. The deadline for financial aid applications is February 1.

International Students: There are currently 97 international students enrolled. The school actively recruits these students. They must take the TOEFL or the college's own test and achieve a minimum score on the TOEFL of 500.

Computers: The college provides computer facilities for student use. The mainframe is a DEC VAX 8650, a DEC VAX 750, and an IBM 4381/P2. IBM and Macintosh microcomputer systems are located in residence halls, the library, and the main building. All students may access the system. Students may access the system 2 hours during peak periods. There are no fees.

Graduates: In 1992–93 98 bachelor's degrees were awarded. The most popular majors among graduates were performance (84%), music education (11%), and composition (5%). Within an average freshman class, 71% graduate in 4 years and 9% in 5 years. Some 15 companies recruited on campus in 1992–93. In the 1992 graduating class, 65% of the men and 65% of the women were enrolled in graduate school within 6 months of graduation; 59% of the men and 59% of the women had found employment.

Admissions Contact: Charles Krusenstjerna, Director of Admissions..

ELMIRA COLLEGE

C-4

Elmira, NY 14901   (607) 735–1724

Full-time: 440 men, 659 women	Faculty: 66; IIB, --$
Part-time: none	Ph.D.s: 98%
Graduate: none	Student/Faculty: 17 to 1
Year: modified (4–4–1), summer session	Tuition: $13,900
	Room & Board: $4550

Application Deadline: December 15

Freshman Class: 1457 applied, 1045 accepted, 345 enrolled

SAT I or ACT: required   **COMPETITIVE**

Elmira College, founded in 1855, is a private, coeducational liberal arts institution offering general and preprofessional programs. In addition to regional accreditation, Elmira has baccalaureate program accreditation with NLN. The library contains 349,300 volumes, 710,000 microform items, and 3900 audiovisual forms, and subscribes to 844 periodicals. Computerized library sources and services include interlibrary loans and database searching. Special learning facilities include a learning resource center, art gallery, radio station, speech and hearing clinic, and Mark Twain's study. The 40-acre campus is in a suburban area 90 miles southwest of Syracuse. Including residence halls, there are 25 buildings on campus.

Student Life: About 60% of undergraduates are from New York. Students come from 24 states, 23 foreign countries, and Canada. Sixty-five percent are from public schools; 35% from private. Eighty-four percent are white. The average age of freshmen is 18; all undergraduates, 21. Twelve percent drop out by the end of their first year; 65% remain to graduate.

Housing: A total of 1000 students can be accommodated in college housing. College-sponsored living facilities include single-sex and coed dormitories, on-campus apartments, and married-student housing. In addition, there are honors houses and quiet floors. On-campus housing is guaranteed for all 4 years. Eighty-six percent of students live on campus; of those, 75% remain on campus on weekends. All students may keep cars on campus.

Activities: There are no fraternities or sororities on campus. There are 44 groups on campus, including band, cheerleading, chorus, dance, drama, film, honors, international, literary magazine, musical theater, newspaper, pep band, political, professional, religious, social, social service, student government, and yearbook. Popular campus events include Mountain Day, Holiday Banquet, Holiday Ball, Midnight Breakfast, and Spring Weekend.

Sports: There are 6 intercollegiate and 21 intramural sports each for men and women. Athletic and recreation facilities include 2500-seat and 500-seat gymnasiums, indoor tennis facilities, a 3500-seat hockey arena, racquetball courts, a weight room, a dance studio, and a swimming pool.

Disabled Students: Twenty-five percent of the campus is accessible to disabled students. The following facilities are available: wheelchair ramps, elevators, special parking, specially equipped rest rooms, and special class scheduling.

Services: In addition to many counseling and information services, tutoring is available in most subjects.

Campus Safety and Security: Campus safety and security measures include 24-hour foot and vehicle patrol, escort service, informal discussions, and pamphlets, posters, and films. In addition, there are emergency telephones and lighted pathways and sidewalks.

Programs of Study: Elmira awards the B.A. and B.S. degrees. Bachelor's degrees are awarded in BIOLOGICAL SCIENCE (biochemistry and biology/biological science), BUSINESS (accounting, business administration and management, business economics, international business management, and marketing/retailing/merchandising), COMMUNICATIONS AND THE ARTS (classics, dramatic arts, English literature, fine arts, French, German, music, and Spanish), COMPUTER AND PHYSICAL SCIENCE (chemistry and mathematics), EDUCATION (art, elementary, foreign languages, science, and secondary), ENGINEERING AND ENVIRONMENTAL DESIGN (environmental science), HEALTH PROFESSIONS (medical laboratory technology, nursing, predentistry, and premedicine), SOCIAL SCIENCE (American studies, anthropology, criminal justice, history, human services, international studies, philosophy, political science/government, prelaw, psychology, and sociology). History, theater, and premedicine are the strongest academically. Psychology, management, and education have the largest enrollments.

Required: All students must complete general degree requirements, including communication skills, writing courses, mathematical competency, and computer literacy; a core curriculum; distribution requirements in culture and civilization, contemporary social institutions, the scientific method, the creative process, and physical education; and a field experience program. A total of 120 credit hours with a minimum GPA of 2.0 overall and in the major is required in order to graduate.

Special: The required field experience program provides a career-related internship as well as community service. A junior year abroad program, a Washington semester, an accelerated degree program, a general studies degree, student-designed majors, and pass/fail options are available. B.A.-B.S. degrees are offered in biochemistry, biology, chemistry, economics, education, environmental studies, history, mathematics, political science, and psychology. Elmira is a member of the Spring Term Consortium enabling students to take 6-week courses at participating institutions. There are 6 national honor societies on campus, including Phi Beta Kappa.

Faculty/Classroom: Sixty-four percent of faculty are male; 36%, female. All both teach and do research. The average class size in an introductory lecture is 35; in a laboratory, 10; and in a regular course offering, 20.

Admissions: About 72% of the 1993–94 applicants were accepted. The SAT scores for the 1993–94 freshman class were as follows: Verbal—63% below 500, 30% between 500 and 599, 6% between 600 and 700, and 1% above 700; Math—52% below 500, 30% between 500 and 599, 16% between 600 and 700, and 2% above 700. The ACT scores were 28% below 21, 35% between 21 and 23, 15% between 24 and 26, 9% between 27 and 28, and 13% above 28. About 42% of the current freshmen were in the top fifth of their class; 74% were in the top two fifths. About 35 freshmen graduated first in their class.

Requirements: The SAT I or ACT is required. In addition, applicants should have completed 4 years of high school English, 3 of mathematics, and 2 of science, or GED equivalent. An essay is part of the application process. An interview is strongly recommended. AP and CLEP credits are accepted. Important factors used in the admissions decision are advanced placement or honor courses, recommendations by school officials, leadership record, extracurricular activities record, and parents or siblings attending the school.

Procedure: Freshmen are admitted fall and winter. Entrance exams should be taken by January of the entry year. Early decision applications should be filed by January 15; regular applications, by December 15 for fall entry, along with an application fee of $40. Notification of early decision is sent January 31; regular decision, on a rolling basis. There are early decision, early admissions, and deferred admissions plans. A waiting list is an active part of the admissions procedure, with about 6% of applicants on the list.

Transfer: A total of 115 transfer students enrolled in 1993–94. Applicants should have a minimum GPA of 2.0. An interview is strongly recommended. A total of 30 credits out of 120 must be completed at Elmira.

Visiting: There are regularly scheduled orientations for prospective students, consisting of an open house format and overview, tour, lunch, student panel, faculty panel, general admissions and scholarship information, and optional interview. There are guides for informal visits and visitors may sit in on classes and stay overnight at the school. To arrange for a visit, contact the Admissions Office at (607) 735-1724.

Financial Aid: In 1993–94, 80% of all students received some form of financial aid. About 70% of all students received need-based aid. The average freshman award was $12,125. Of that total, scholarships or need-based grants averaged $5600 ($13,650 maximum); loans averaged $2500 ($3625 maximum); and work contracts averaged $1300 ($1400 maximum). Forty-five percent of undergraduate students work part-time. Average earnings from campus work for the school year are $900. The average financial indebtedness of the 1992–93 graduate was $11,849. Elmira is a member of CSS. The FAF is required. The deadline for financial aid applications is March 1.

International Students: There are currently 86 international students enrolled. The school actively recruits these students. They must take the TOEFL and achieve a minimum score of 500.

Computers: The college provides computer facilities for student use. The mainframe is a DEC VAX 4000–600 minicomputer. Twenty terminals provide access to the mainframe. Approximately 50 microcomputers are also available. All students may access the system. It may be used weekdays 15 hours per day, and weekends 8 to 10 hours per day. There are no time limits on using the system and no fees.

Graduates: In 1992–93, 194 bachelor's degrees were awarded. The most popular majors among graduates were elementary education (23%), psychology (15%), and business administration/marketing (12%). Within an average freshman class, 60% graduate in 4 years and 65% in 5 years. Some 20 companies recruited on campus in 1992–93. In the 1992 graduating class, 11% of the men and 31% of the women were enrolled in graduate school within 6 months of graduation; 82% of the men and 73% of the women had found employment.

Admissions Contact: William S. Neal, Dean of Admissions.

EUGENE LANG COLLEGE OF THE NEW SCHOOL FOR SOCIAL RESEARCH

D-3

(Formerly New School for Social Research)
New York, NY 10011   (212) 229-5665

Full-time: 84 men, 162 women	Faculty: 13
Part-time: 8 men, 13 women	Ph.D.s: 77%
Graduate: none	Student/Faculty: 19 to 1
Year: semesters	Tuition: $13,835
Application Deadline: February 1	Room & Board: $7310
Freshman Class: 255 applied, 198 accepted, 77 enrolled	
SAT I or ACT: required	COMPETITIVE

Eugene Lang College, established in 1976, is the liberal arts undergraduate division of the New School for Social Research. There are 3 undergraduate and 2 graduate schools within the New School. The 4 libraries contain 142,000 volumes and 65,000 microform items, and subscribe to 750 periodicals. Computerized library sources and services include the card catalog, interlibrary loans, and database searching. Special learning facilities include a learning resource center, art gallery, and environmental simulation center for urban planning and research. The 5-acre campus is in an urban area in the heart of Greenwich Village. Including residence halls, there are 14 buildings on campus.

Student Life: About 51% of undergraduates are from out-of-state, mostly the Middle Atlantic. Students come from 26 states, 12 foreign countries, and Canada. Sixty percent are from public schools; 30% from private. Eighty-two percent are white. The average age of freshmen is 19; all undergraduates, 20. Fifteen percent drop out by the end of their first year; 85% remain to graduate.

Housing: A total of 200 students can be accommodated in college housing. College-sponsored living facilities include coed dormitories and off-campus apartments. On-campus housing is guaranteed for the freshman year only, is available on a first-come, first-served basis, and is available on a lottery system for upperclassmen. Priority is given to out-of-town students. Sixty percent of students commute. Alcohol is not permitted. All students may keep cars on campus.

Activities: There are no fraternities or sororities on campus. There are many groups and organizations on campus, including chorus, dance, drama, ethnic, gay, international, jazz band, literary magazine, newspaper, political, social, social service, student government, and yearbook. Popular campus events include Lang in the City, a cultural program that makes dance, opera, Broadway, theater, and other events available to students for $5 or less; poetry readings; theater performances; dance performances; and ethnic cultural events.

Sports: There are 9 intramural sports for men and 9 for women. The intramural program is offered in conjunction with Cooper Union. A nearby gymnasium is rented or various city parks are used.

Disabled Students: The entire campus is accessible to disabled students. The following facilities are available: elevators, specially equipped rest rooms, and lowered telephones.

Services: In addition to many counseling and information services, tutoring is available in most subjects. In addition, there is remedial writing. There is a writing center.

Campus Safety and Security: Campus safety and security measures include informal discussions, pamphlets, posters, and films, and 24-hour dormitory security.

Programs of Study: Lang College awards the B.A. degree. Master's and doctoral degrees also are awarded. Bachelor's degrees are awarded in COMMUNICATIONS AND THE ARTS (creative writing, dramatic arts, and English), SOCIAL SCIENCE (economics, history, political science/government, prelaw, psychology, social science, sociology, urban studies, and women's studies). Creative writing, history, and urban studies are the strongest programs academically. Writing and drama have the largest enrollments.

Required: To graduate, students must complete 120 credit hours, with a GPA of 2.0 and a minimum of 24 hours in 1 of 5 areas of concentration: writing, literature, and the arts; urban studies; social and historical inquiry; cultural studies; and mind, nature, and value. Also required are 88 credit hours in Lang College courses and 4 credits of senior work. Required courses include a first-year writing seminar and a freshman workshop program. A senior project must be completed.

Special: Lang College offers a concentration rather than a traditional major; there is no core curriculum and students are instructed in small seminars. Students may cross-register with other New School divisions and with Mannes School of Music, Parsons School of Design, Cooper Union, Brooklyn Polytechnic Institute, and Bank Street College. A large variety of internships for credit, study abroad, a B.A./B.F.A. degree with Parsons School of Design and the New School Jazz and Contemporary Music Program, student-designed majors, nondegree study, and pass/fail options also are available.

Faculty/Classroom: Fifty percent of faculty are male; 50%, female. All teach undergraduates. The average class size in a laboratory is 15 and in a regular course offering, 15.

Admissions: About 78% of the 1993–94 applicants were accepted. The SAT scores for the 1993–94 freshman class were as follows: Verbal—26% below 500, 44% between 500 and 599, 28% between 600 and 700, and 2% above 700; Math—31% below 500, 43% between 500 and 599, 23% between 600 and 700, and 3% above 700. About 22% of the current freshmen were in the top fifth of their class; 70% were in the top two fifths.

Requirements: Lang College requires applicants to be in the upper 50% of their class. The SAT I or ACT, is required or 4 SAT II: Subject tests may be substituted for either test. Applicants must be enrolled in a strong college preparatory program. The GED is accepted. An essay and an interview are required. Art students must present a portfolio and complete a home examination, and jazz students are required to audition. AP credit is accepted. Important factors used in the admissions decision are advanced placement or honor courses, personality, intangible qualities, recommendations by school officials, evidence of special talent, and extracurricular activities record.

Procedure: Freshmen are admitted in the fall and spring. Entrance exams should be taken in May of the junior year or October of the senior year. Early decision applications should be filed by November 15; regular applications, by February 1 for fall entry and November 15 for spring entry, along with an application fee of $30. Notification of early decision is sent December 15; regular decision, April 1.

There are early decision, early admissions, and deferred admissions plans. About 15 early decision candidates were accepted for the 1993–94 class.

Transfer: About 60 transfer students enrolled in 1993–94. Applicants must have a minimum college GPA of 2.5 and must submit their high school transcript, ACT or SAT I scores (if taken in the last 5 years), and 2 recommendations. An interview is required. Grades of C or better transfer for credit. A total of 60 credits out of 120 must be completed at Lang College.

Visiting: There are regularly scheduled orientations for prospective students, including a campus tour, visits to classes, and panel discussions. There are guides for informal visits and visitors may sit in on classes. To arrange for a visit, contact the Admissions Office at (212) 229–5665.

Financial Aid: In 1993–94 77% of all current freshmen and 40% of continuing students received some form of financial aid. About 77% of freshmen and 40% of continuing students received need-based aid. The average freshman award was $12,226. Of that total, scholarships or need-based grants averaged $6974; and loans averaged $4000. Forty percent of undergraduate students work part-time. The average financial indebtedness of the 1992–93 graduate was $11,000. The FAF and FAFSA are required. The deadline for financial aid applications is March 1.

International Students: There are currently 20 international students enrolled. The school actively recruits these students. They must take the TOEFL and achieve a minimum score of 600. The student must also take the SAT I or the ACT.

Computers: The college provides computer facilities for student use. The mainframe is a Hewlett Packard. IBM and Apple microcomputers are available for student use in an academic computing center. Students can arrange for access for statistical course work and dissertation research. There are no time limits on using the system and no fees.

Graduates: In a recent year, 75 bachelor's degrees were awarded. Within an average freshman class, 85% graduate in 4 years.

Admissions Contact: Director of Admissions.

FASHION INSTITUTE OF TECHNOLOGY
STATE UNIVERSITY OF NEW YORK
New York, NY 10001–5992 D-5
(212) 760–7675

Full-time: 807 men, 3657 women	Faculty: 184; III, +$
Part-time: 1692 men, 5962 women	Student/Faculty: 24 to 1
Graduate: 10 men, 65 women	Tuition: $2310 ($5260)
Year: 4–1-4, summer session	Room & Board: $4825
Application Deadline: January 15	
Freshman Class: 4925 applied, 1949 accepted, 1657 enrolled	
SAT I: Verbal/Math 420/400	ACT: 21	SPECIAL

The Fashion Institute of Technology, founded in 1944 as part of the State University of New York, is an art and design, business, and technology college that prepares students for careers in fashion and related design professions and industries. There is one graduate school. In addition to regional accreditation, FIT has baccalaureate program accreditation with FIDER and NASAD. The library contains 105,027 volumes, 3564 microform items, 13,225 audiovisual forms, and subscribes to 588 periodicals. Special learning facilities include an art gallery, a radio station, and a design laboratory, a lighting laboratory, the Advanced Apparel Manufacturing Technology Demonstration Facility, and a computer-aided design and communications facility. The 5-acre campus is in an urban area in Manhattan. Including residence halls, there are 8 buildings on campus.

Student Life: About 84% of undergraduates are from New York. Students come from 50 states, 55 foreign countries, and Canada. Seventy-five percent are from public schools; 25% from private. Thirty-nine percent are white; 21% Asian American; 12% Hispanic; 11% foreign nationals; 10% African American. The average age of freshmen is 19; all undergraduates, 20.

Housing: A total of 1300 students can be accommodated in college housing. College-sponsored living facilities include single-sex and coed dormitories and on-campus apartments. On-campus housing is available on a lottery system for upperclassmen. Priority is given to out-of-town students. Seventy percent of students commute. Alcohol is not permitted.

Activities: There are no fraternities or sororities. There are 70 groups on campus, including art, cheerleading, chess, dance, drama, ethnic, gay, literary magazine, musical theater, newspaper, photography, political, professional, radio and TV, religious, social, social service, student government, and yearbook. Popular campus events include fashion shows, a lecture series, craft center events, and Monday night movies.

Sports: There are 4 intercollegiate sports for men and 4 for women, and 4 intramural sports for men and 4 for women. Athletic and recreation facilities include 2 gymnasiums, a dance studio, and a weight room.

Disabled Students: Nearly all of the campus is accessible to disabled students. The following facilities are available: wheelchair ramps, elevators, special parking, specially equipped rest rooms, lowered drinking fountains, lowered telephones, services/facilities for hearing impaired, and library tapes.

Services: In addition to many counseling and information services, tutoring is available in every subject. There is also remedial math, reading, and writing. The school has a special program for the learning disabled.

Campus Safety and Security: Campus safety and security measures include 24-hour foot and vehicle patrol, informal discussions, emergency telephones, and lighted pathways and sidewalks.

Programs of Study: FIT awards the B.F.A. and B.S. degrees. Associate and master's degrees also are awarded. Bachelor's degrees are awarded in BUSINESS (apparel and accessories marketing, business administration and management, and marketing/retailing/merchandising), COMMUNICATIONS AND THE ARTS (advertising, design, fiber/textiles/weaving, graphic design, historic preservation, illustration, and toy design), ENGINEERING AND ENVIRONMENTAL DESIGN (interior design), SOCIAL SCIENCE (fashion design and technology and textiles and clothing). Advertising and communications, interior design, advertising design, and marketing are the strongest academically. Fashion buying and merchandising and fashion design have the largest enrollments.

Required: To graduate, students must complete the credit and course requirements for their majors with a 2.0 GPA. Students may qualify for a degree in two ways; by earning 60 credits, with half in the major while in residence at the upper-division level; or by earning 30 credits at the upper-division level, in addition to an F.I.T. associate degree. There is a 2-credit physical education requirement.

Special: Internships are offered, and students may study abroad in England, China, France, Canada, Spain, and Italy. Nondegree study is available. One department has an honors program.

Faculty/Classroom: Forty-nine percent of faculty are male; 51%, female. The average class size in a regular course offering is 25.

Admissions: About 40% of the 1993–94 applicants were accepted. Nine percent of the current freshmen were in the top fifth of their class; 70% were in the top two fifths.

Requirements: FIT requires applicants to be in the upper 50% of their class. A minimum GPA of 2.5 is required. The SAT I or ACT is required. Applicants must be high school graduates, or have a GED certificate. An essay and, when appropriate, a portfolio are required. AP and CLEP credits are accepted. Important factors used in the admissions decision are evidence of special talent, leadership record, personality, intangible qualities, advanced placement or honor courses, and parents or siblings attending the school.

Procedure: Freshmen are admitted fall and spring. Applications should be filed by January 15 for fall entry and October 15 for spring entry, along with an application fee of $20. Notification is sent on a rolling basis beginning March 15. There is an early decision plan. A waiting list is an active part of the admissions procedure, with about 5% of applicants on the list.

Transfer: Applicant must have a GPA of 2.0 and at least 30 college credits. An interview is required for art and design applicants, as well as a portfolio when appropriate.

Visiting: There are regularly scheduled orientations for prospective students, including a presentation and group information session with a counselor. To arrange for a visit, contact the Admissions Office at (212) 760-7675.

Financial Aid: In 1993–94, 54% of all current freshmen and 52% of continuing students received some form of financial aid. About 52% of freshmen and 51% of continuing students received need-based aid. The average freshman award was $3904. Of that total, scholarships or need-based grants averaged $3181 ($6400 maximum); loans averaged $2164 ($5125 maximum); and work contracts averaged $1060 ($1400 maximum). Eighteen percent of undergraduate students work part-time. Average earnings from campus work for the school year are $1331. The average financial indebtedness of the 1992–93 graduate was $2259. FIT is a member of CSS. The FAF is required. The deadline for financial aid applications is March 15.

International Students: There are currently 252 international students enrolled. They must take the TOEFL and achieve a minimum score of 550. The student must also take the SAT I or the ACT.

Computers: The college provides computer facilities for student use. The mainframe is a DEC VAX 11/785. There are also 120 Epson, Zenith, ITT, Apple, and IBM PCs available in various academic computer laboratories. Those students enrolled in the computer course may access the system. There are no fees.

Graduates: In 1992–93 640 bachelor's degrees were awarded. Some 24 companies recruited on campus in 1992–93.

Admissions Contact: James C. Pridgeon, Director of Admissions.

FIVE TOWNS COLLEGE
Dix Hills, NY 11746   (516) 424–7000, ext. 110

Full-time: 499 men, 189 women	Faculty: 29
Part-time: 40 men, 16 women	Ph.D.s: 38%
Graduate: none	Student/Faculty: 24 to 1
Year: semesters, summer session	Tuition: $6800
Application Deadline: open	Room & Board: $4400
Freshman Class: 475 applied, 426 accepted, 322 enrolled	
SAT I Verbal/Math: 440/450	SPECIAL

Five Towns College, founded in 1972, is a private, coeducational institution offering undergraduate programs in music, business and liberal arts. The library contains 22,910 volumes, 41 microform items, and 4031 audiovisual forms, and subscribes to 360 periodicals. Computerized library sources and services include interlibrary loans and database searching. Special learning facilities include a learning resource center and 48- and 24-track recording studios, a midi studio, and a video/TV studio. The 34-acre campus is in a suburban area 18 miles east of New York City. Including residence halls, there is 1 building on campus.

Student Life: About 95% of undergraduates are from New York. Students come from 8 states and 3 foreign countries. Eighty-eight percent are from public schools; 12% from private. Seventy-two percent are white; 18% African American. The average age of freshmen is 18; all undergraduates, 20. Thirty-seven percent drop out by the end of their first year; 45% remain to graduate.

Housing: A total of 100 students can be accommodated in college housing. College-sponsored living facilities include coed dormitories. On-campus housing is guaranteed for all 4 years. Priority is given to out-of-town students. Ninety-one percent of students commute. Alcohol is not permitted. All students may keep cars on campus.

Activities: There are no fraternities or sororities on campus. There are 7 groups on campus, including band, chess, choir, chorale, chorus, honors, jazz band, musical theater, radio and TV, student government, and yearbook. Popular campus events include the Cultural Hour, the Annual Picnic, and the Annual Ski Trip.

Sports: There is no sports program at Five Towns College. Athletic and recreation facilities include a gymnasium with basketball and volleyball courts.

Disabled Students: Twenty percent of the campus is accessible to disabled students. The following facilities are available: wheelchair ramps, special parking, special class scheduling, and lowered drinking fountains and telephones.

Services: In addition to many counseling and information services, tutoring is available in most subjects. There is remedial math, reading, and writing.

Campus Safety and Security: Campus safety and security measures include 24-hour foot and vehicle patrol, shuttle buses, informal discussions, pamphlets, posters, and films. In addition, there are lighted pathways and sidewalks.

Programs of Study: Five Towns College awards the B.Mus. and B.P.S. degrees. Associate degrees also are awarded. Bachelor's degrees are awarded in COMMUNICATIONS AND THE ARTS (audio technology, jazz, music business management, music performance, music theory and composition, and video), EDUCATION (music). Music education is the strongest academically. Jazz/commercial music has the largest enrollment.

Required: To graduate, all students must complete 128 credits for a Mus.B. degree, or 120 credits for a B.P.S. degree. Students must maintain at least a C average in their major concentration and have a minimum GPA of 2.0 to graduate. Distribution requirements include 45 credits in applied music or business, 33 in liberal arts, 12 in music history, 24 in the concentration, and either 14 or 6 elective credits. The core curriculum consists of English Composition 101 and 102, Speech 101, 3 credits each of either psychology or sociology, and various upper-division liberal arts and social science courses. All music students must pass a jury examination.

Special: Cross-registration is available with schools in the Long Island Regional Advisory Council on Higher Education, and co-op programs in audio recording technology, music business, video arts, and broadcasting, and internships are possible. Work-study programs are offered on campus. Students can have dual majors in music and audio recording technology. There is one national honor society on campus.

Faculty/Classroom: Sixty-two percent of faculty are male; 38%, female. All faculty teach and do research. The average class size in an introductory lecture is 25; in a laboratory, 15; and in a regular course offering, 25.

Admissions: Most of the 1993–94 applicants were accepted. The SAT scores for the 1993–94 freshman class were as follows: Verbal—75% below 500, 20% between 500 and 599, and 5% between 600 and 700; Math—75% below 500, 19% between 500 and 599, and 5% between 600 and 700. About 10% of the current freshmen were in the top fifth of their class; 26% were in the top two fifths.

Requirements: A minimum GPA of 2.5 is required. The ACT is recommended. A minimum high school average of 75 is required. A GED with a minimum score of 250 is accepted. An interview is required for all students, and music students are required to audition. AP and CLEP credits are accepted. Important factors used in the admissions decision are advanced placement or honor courses, evidence of special talent, personality, intangible qualities, extracurricular activities record, and recommendations by school officials.

Procedure: Freshmen are admitted to all sessions. Entrance exams should be taken prior to admission. Application deadlines are open. The application fee is $25. Notification is sent on a rolling basis. There are early admissions and deferred admissions plans. A waiting list is an active part of the admissions procedure, with about 5% of applicants on the list.

Transfer: About 110 transfer students enrolled in 1993–94. Students must be in good academic standing at their former school. A total of 45 credits out of 128 must be completed at Five Towns College.

Visiting: There are regularly scheduled orientations for prospective students, including a campus tour, academic counseling, and financial aid counseling. There are guides for informal visits and visitors may sit in on classes. To arrange for a visit, contact the Admissions Office at (516) 424–7000, ext. 110.

Financial Aid: In 1993–94, 77% of all current freshmen and 80% of continuing students received some form of financial aid. About 75% of students received need-based aid. The average freshman award was $4900. Of that total, scholarships or need-based grants averaged $1820 ($6500 maximum); loans averaged $2467 ($2625 maximum); and work contracts averaged $600 ($3000 maximum). Fifty-three percent of undergraduate students work part-time. Average earnings from campus work for the school year are $1000. The average financial indebtedness of the 1992–93 graduate was $4000. The college's own financial statement and FAFSA are required.

International Students: There are currently 9 international students enrolled. The school actively recruits these students. They must take the TOEFL and achieve a minimum score of 500. The student must also take the college's own entrance exam.

Computers: The college provides computer facilities for student use. The mainframe is an IBM System 36. There are 25 terminals available in a computer laboratory. All students may access the system. It may be used during school hours. There are no time limits and no fees.

Graduates: In 1992–93, 14 bachelor's degrees were awarded. The most popular majors among graduates were music education (35%), music performance (26%), and audio recording (26%).

Admissions Contact: Jennifer Roemer, Director of Admissions.

FORDHAM UNIVERSITY

The Fordham University system, established in 1841, is a private system in New York City in the Jesuit tradition. It is governed by a board of trustees, whose chief administrator is the president. The primary goal of the system is to educate talented men and women in the liberal arts and basic sciences. The main priorities are excellence in undergraduate and selected graduate/professional programs, and commitment to teaching, research, and service. The total enrollment in fall 1993 of all 3 campuses was 14,612; there were 522 faculty members. Altogether there are 69 baccalaureate, 71 master's, and 25 doctoral programs offered at Fordham University. Profiles of the 4-year campuses are included in this chapter in alphabetical order with other New York schools.

FORDHAM UNIVERSITY
COLLEGE AT LINCOLN CENTER
New York, NY 10023

D-5
(718) 817-4000

Full-time: 925 men and women
Part-time: 1328 men and women
Graduate: none
Year: semesters
Application Deadline: February 1
Freshman Class: 825 applied, 559 accepted, 190 enrolled
SAT I Verbal/Math: 511/556

Faculty: 92; I, av$
Ph.D.s: 95%
Student/Faculty: 10 to 1
Tuition: $11,250
Room & Board: $6900

VERY COMPETITIVE

The College at Lincoln Center, established in 1968, is a private, coeducational institution within Fordham University's Jesuit tradition, offering liberal arts and preprofessional studies. There are 4 graduate schools. In addition to regional accreditation, the college has baccalaureate program accreditation with AACSB. The library contains 1,553,549 volumes and 1,850,575 microform items, and subscribes to 9958 periodicals. Computerized library sources and services include the card catalog, interlibrary loans, and database searching. Special learning facilities include a radio station. The 8-acre campus is in an urban area in New York City. Including residence halls, there are 3 buildings on campus.

Student Life: About 67% of undergraduates are from New York. Students come from 43 states, 48 foreign countries, and Canada. Thirty-six percent are from public schools; 64% from private. Seventy-

one percent are white; 15% Hispanic. Eighty-five percent are Catholic; 14% Protestant. The average age of freshmen is 18; all undergraduates, 21. Eight percent drop out by the end of their first year; 77% remain to graduate.

Housing: A total of 850 students can be accommodated in college housing. College-sponsored living facilities include coed dormitories and off-campus apartments. On-campus housing is guaranteed for all 4 years. Sixty percent of students commute.

Activities: There are no fraternities or sororities on campus. There are 130 groups on campus, including art, band, cheerleading, chorus, computers, drama, ethnic, film, honors, international, literary magazine, marching band, musical theater, newspaper, pep band, photography, political, professional, radio and TV, religious, social, social service, student government, and yearbook. Popular campus events include Homecoming and Spring Weekend.

Sports: Athletic and recreation facilities include a 6000-seat football stadium, an Olympic-size pool with a separate diving area, an indoor track, a 3200-seat gymnasium, and tennis, squash, and racquetball courts. All facilities are at the Rose Hill (Bronx) campus of the university.

Disabled Students: All of the campus is accessible to disabled students. The following facilities are available: wheelchair ramps, elevators, special parking, specially equipped rest rooms, lowered drinking fountains, and lowered telephones.

Services: In addition to many counseling and information services, tutoring is available in most subjects.

Campus Safety and Security: Campus safety and security measures include 24-hour foot and vehicle patrol, informal discussions, emergency telephones, and lighted pathways and sidewalks.

Programs of Study: The college awards the B.A. and B.S. degrees. Master's and doctoral degrees also are awarded. Bachelor's degrees are awarded in COMMUNICATIONS AND THE ARTS (art history and appreciation, comparative literature, creative writing, dramatic arts, English, film arts, French, Italian, journalism, modern language, Spanish, and studio art), COMPUTER AND PHYSICAL SCIENCE (computer science, mathematics, and natural sciences), EDUCATION (elementary and secondary), HEALTH PROFESSIONS (predentistry and premedicine), SOCIAL SCIENCE (African American studies, anthropology, economics, Hispanic American studies, history, Middle Eastern studies, philosophy, political science/government, prelaw, psychology, religion, social science, sociology, and urban studies). Philosophy, media studies, social sciences, and English are the strongest academically. Media studies, political science, and philosophy have the largest enrollments.

Required: All students must complete a core curriculum, including English literature and composition, history, philosophy, mathematics, science, theology, and foreign language. A total of 124 credit hours with a minimum GPA of 2.0 is required in order to graduate.

Special: The college offers career-oriented internships during the junior or senior year with New York City companies and institutions. Study abroad, a Washington semester, student-designed majors, and pass/fail options are available. A combined 3–2 engineering program is available with Columbia University and Case Western Reserve University. Other cooperative programs include a 3–2 in nursing with Columbia University and a 3–2 in pharmacy with Long Island University. The Life Experience program provides credit for outside learning. There is a freshman honors program on campus, as well as 2 national honor societies, including Phi Beta Kappa.

Faculty/Classroom: All teach undergraduates. The average class size in an introductory lecture is 28 and in a regular course offering, 24.

Admissions: About 68% of the 1993–94 applicants were accepted. The SAT scores for the 1993–94 freshman class were as follows: Verbal—46% below 500, 39% between 500 and 599, 14% between 600 and 700, and 1% above 700; Math—26% below 500, 49% between 500 and 599, 20% between 600 and 700, and 5% above 700. About 46% of the current freshmen were in the top fifth of their class; 78% were in the top two fifths.

Requirements: The SAT I is required. Applicants should be graduates of an accredited high school or have a GED equivalent, with 4 years of English and 3 each of mathematics, science, social studies, history, and foreign language. An essay is part of the application process, and an audition is required for theater majors. An interview is recommended. AP and CLEP credits are accepted. Important factors used in the admissions decision are advanced placement or honor courses, recommendations by school officials, extracurricular activities record, evidence of special talent, and leadership record.

Procedure: Freshmen are admitted fall and spring. Entrance exams should be taken by November of the senior year. Early decision applications should be filed by November 1; regular applications, by February 1 for fall entry and December 1 for spring entry, along with an application fee of $50. Notification of early decision is sent December 15; regular decision, March 1. There are early decision and early admissions plans. Six early decision candidates were accepted for the

1993–94 class. A waiting list is an active part of the admissions procedure.

Transfer: A total of 37 transfer students enrolled in 1993–94. A minimum 3.0 GPA is recommended. Applicants under age 21 should submit SAT I or ACT scores. An interview is recommended. A total of 64 credits out of 124 must be completed at the college.

Visiting: There are regularly scheduled orientations for prospective students. There are guides for informal visits and visitors may sit in on classes and stay overnight at the school. To arrange for a visit, contact Elizabeth Roper, Associate Director of Admissions, at (212) 636-6710.

Financial Aid: In 1993–94, 90% of all current freshmen and 88% of continuing students received some form of financial aid. About 90% of freshmen and 83% of continuing students received need-based aid. The average freshman award was $9500. Of that total, scholarships or need-based grants averaged $6600 ($11,000 maximum); loans averaged $700 ($2200 maximum); and work contracts averaged $700 ($1600 maximum). Ninety-five percent of undergraduate students work part-time. Average earnings from campus work for the school year are $1600. The average financial indebtedness of the 1992–93 graduate was $8170. The college is a member of CSS. The FAF and the college's own financial statement are required. The deadline for financial aid applications is February 1.

International Students: The school actively recruits these students. They must take the TOEFL and achieve a minimum score of 550. The student must also take the SAT I or the ACT.

Computers: The college provides computer facilities for student use. The mainframe is a DEC VAX. All students may access the system. There are no time limits on using the system and no fees.

Graduates: In 1992–93, the most popular majors among graduates were theater and drama, political science, and psychology. Within an average freshman class, 77% graduate in 4 years, 82% in 5 years, and 87% in 6 years. Some 500 companies recruited on campus in 1992–93. In the 1992 graduating class, 26% of the men and 24% of the women were enrolled in graduate school within 6 months of graduation; 92% of the men and 91% of the women had found employment.

Admissions Contact: John W. Buckley, Director of Admissions.

FORDHAM UNIVERSITY
COLLEGE OF BUSINESS ADMINISTRATION
Bronx, NY 10458

D-5

(718) 817-4000

Full-time: 1118 men and women	Faculty: 351; I, av$
Part-time: 154 men and women	Ph.D.s: 97%
Graduate: none	Student/Faculty: 3 to 1
Year: semesters, summer session	Tuition: $13,350
Application Deadline: February 1	Room & Board: $6525
Freshman Class: 826 applied, 562 accepted, 178 enrolled	
SAT I Verbal/Math: 510/552	**VERY COMPETITIVE**

The College of Business Administration, founded in 1926, is a coeducational undergraduate school of business that maintains its independent status within Fordham University, a private institution founded in 1841 in the Jesuit tradition. There are 2 graduate schools. In addition to regional accreditation, CBA has baccalaureate program accreditation with AACSB. The 2 libraries contain 1,553,549 volumes and 1,850,575 microform items, and subscribe to 9958 periodicals. Computerized library sources and services include the card catalog, interlibrary loans, and database searching. Special learning facilities include a radio station. The 85-acre campus is in an urban area in the Bronx. Including residence halls, there are 31 buildings on campus.

Student Life: About 67% of undergraduates are from New York. Students come from 43 states, 48 foreign countries, and Canada. Thirty-six percent are from public schools; 64% from private. Seventy-one percent are white; 15% Hispanic. Eighty-five percent are Catholic; 14% Protestant. The average age of all undergraduates is 19. Eight percent drop out by the end of their first year; 77% remain to graduate.

Housing: College-sponsored living facilities include coed dormitories, on-campus apartments, and off-campus apartments. In addition, there is an international house and a residential college. On-campus housing is guaranteed for all 4 years. Seventy percent of students live on campus; of those, 90% remain on campus on weekends. Upperclassmen may keep cars on campus.

Activities: There are no fraternities or sororities on campus. There are 130 groups on campus, including art, band, cheerleading, choir, chorus, computers, drama, ethnic, film, honors, international, literary magazine, marching band, musical theater, newspaper, pep band, photography, political, professional, radio and TV, religious, social, social service, student government, and yearbook. Popular campus events include Spring Weekend, Christmas Formal, and Spring Semi-formal.

Sports: There are 11 intercollegiate sports for men and 10 for women, as well as an intramural program. Athletic and recreation facilities include a 6000-seat football stadium, an Olympic-size pool with a separate diving area, an indoor track, a 3200-seat gymnasium, and tennis, squash, and racquetball courts.

Disabled Students: Eighty percent of the campus is accessible to disabled students. The following facilities are available: wheelchair ramps, elevators, and special parking.

Services: In addition to many counseling and information services, tutoring is available in most subjects.

Campus Safety and Security: Campus safety and security measures include 24-hour foot and vehicle patrol, informal discussions, emergency telephones, and lighted pathways and sidewalks.

Programs of Study: CBA awards the B.S. degree. Master's and doctoral degrees also are awarded. Bachelor's degrees are awarded in BUSINESS (accounting, banking and finance, business economics, international business management, management science, and marketing/retailing/merchandising), COMPUTER AND PHYSICAL SCIENCE (information sciences and systems). Accounting, finance, and information systems are the strongest academically. Finance, accounting, and information systems have the largest enrollments.

Required: All students must complete a core curriculum of liberal arts courses at Fordham College on the Rose Hill campus. About half the program is in liberal arts; business requirements and concentration with electives constitute the remainder of the 124 credit hours needed in order to graduate. A minimum GPA of 2.0 is required.

Special: Career-oriented internships are offered by the college during the junior or senior year with New York City companies and institutions. Study abroad, a Washington semester, student-designed majors, and pass/fail options are available. An evening program leading to the undergraduate degree is also offered. There is a freshman honors program on campus, as well as 3 national honor societies, including Phi Beta Kappa.

Faculty/Classroom: All teach undergraduates. The average class size in an introductory lecture is 28 and in a regular course offering, 24.

Admissions: About 68% of the 1993–94 applicants were accepted. The SAT scores for the 1993–94 freshman class were as follows: Verbal—44% below 500, 40% between 500 and 599, 15% between 600 and 700, and 1% above 700; Math—26% below 500, 48% between 500 and 599, 21% between 600 and 700, and 5% above 700. About 46% of the current freshmen were in the top fifth of their class; 78% were in the top two fifths.

Requirements: The SAT I is required. Applicants should be graduates of an accredited secondary school or have the GED equivalent, with 4 years of English and 3 each of mathematics, science, history, social studies, and foreign language. An essay is part of the application process. An interview is recommended. AP and CLEP credits are accepted. Important factors used in the admissions decision are advanced placement or honor courses, recommendations by school officials, extracurricular activities record, evidence of special talent, and leadership record.

Procedure: Freshmen are admitted fall and spring. Entrance exams should be taken by November of the senior year. Applications should be filed by February 1 for fall entry and December 1 for spring entry, along with an application fee of $50. Notification of early decision is sent December 15; regular decision, March 1. There are early decision, early admissions, and deferred admissions plans. Seven early decision candidates were accepted for the 1993–94 class. A waiting list is an active part of the admissions procedure.

Transfer: About 32 transfer students enrolled in 1993–94. A minimum 3.0 GPA is recommended. Applicants under age 21 should submit SAT I or ACT scores. An interview is recommended. A total of 64 credits out of 124 must be completed at CBA.

Visiting: There are regularly scheduled orientations for prospective students. There are guides for informal visits and visitors may sit in on classes and stay overnight at the school. To arrange for a visit, contact Robert Dusterberg, Assistant Director of Admissions, at (718) 817-4000.

Financial Aid: In 1993–94, 90% of all current freshmen and 88% of continuing students received some form of financial aid. About 90% of freshmen and 83% of continuing students received need-based aid. The average freshman award was $9500. Of that total, scholarships or need-based grants averaged $6600 ($11,000 maximum); loans averaged $700 ($2200 maximum); and work contracts averaged $700 ($1600 maximum). Ninety-five percent of undergraduate students work part-time. Average earnings from campus work for the school year are $1600. The average financial indebtedness of the 1992–93 graduate was $8170. CBA is a member of CSS. The FAF and the college's own financial statement are required. The deadline for financial aid applications is February 1.

International Students: The school actively recruits these students. They must take the TOEFL and achieve a minimum score of 550. The student must also take the SAT I or the ACT.

Computers: The college provides computer facilities for student use. The mainframe is a DEC VAX. All students may access the system. There are no time limits on using the system and no fees.

Graduates: Within an average freshman class, 77% graduate in 4 years, 82% in 5 years, and 87% in 6 years. Some 500 companies recruited on campus in 1992–93. In the 1992 graduating class, 26% of the men and 24% of the women were enrolled in graduate school within 6 months of graduation; 92% of the men and 91% of the women had found employment.

Admissions Contact: John W. Buckley, Director of Admissions.

FORDHAM UNIVERSITY
FORDHAM COLLEGE
D-5

Bronx, NY 10458 (718) 817–4000

Full-time: 2697 men and women	Faculty: 351; I, av$
Part-time: 164 men and women	Ph.D.s: 97%
Graduate: n/av	Student/Faculty: 8 to 1
Year: semesters, summer session	Tuition: $13,350
Application Deadline: February 1	Room & Board: $6525

Freshman Class: 2549 applied, 1753 accepted, 574 enrolled
SAT I Verbal/Math: 511/554 **VERY COMPETITIVE**

Fordham College, founded in 1841, is a private, independent coeducational liberal arts college within Fordham University's Jesuit tradition. There are 2 graduate schools. In addition to regional accreditation, Fordham College has baccalaureate program accreditation with AACSB. The 2 libraries contain 1,553,549 volumes and 1,850,575 microform items, and subscribe to 9958 periodicals. Computerized library sources and services include the card catalog, interlibrary loans, and database searching. Special learning facilities include a radio station. The 85-acre campus is in an urban area in the Bronx. Including residence halls, there are 31 buildings on campus.

Student Life: About 67% of undergraduates are from New York. Students come from 43 states and 48 foreign countries. Thirty-six percent are from public schools; 64% from private. Seventy-one percent are white; 15% Hispanic. Eighty-five percent are Catholic; 14% Protestant. The average age of freshmen is 18; all undergraduates, 19. Eight percent drop out by the end of their first year; 77% remain to graduate.

Housing: A total of 2508 students can be accommodated in college housing. College-sponsored living facilities include coed dormitories, on-campus apartments, and off-campus apartments. In addition, there is an international house and a residential college. On-campus housing is guaranteed for all 4 years. Seventy percent of students live on campus; of those, 90% remain on campus on weekends. Upperclassmen may keep cars on campus.

Activities: There are no fraternities or sororities on campus. There are 130 groups on campus, including art, band, cheerleading, choir, chorus, computers, drama, ethnic, film, honors, international, literary magazine, marching band, musical theater, newspaper, pep band, photography, political, professional, radio and TV, religious, social, social service, student government, and yearbook. Popular campus events include Spring Weekend, Christmas Formal, and Spring Semiformal.

Sports: Athletic and recreation facilities include a 6000-seat football stadium; an Olympic-size pool with a separate diving area; an indoor track; a 3200-seat gymnasium; and tennis, squash, and racquetball courts.

Disabled Students: Eighty percent of the campus is accessible to disabled students. The following facilities are available: wheelchair ramps, elevators, and special parking.

Services: In addition to many counseling and information services, tutoring is available in most subjects.

Campus Safety and Security: Campus safety and security measures include 24-hour foot and vehicle patrol, informal discussions, emergency telephones, and lighted pathways and sidewalks.

Programs of Study: Fordham College awards the B.A. and B.S. degrees. Master's and doctoral degrees also are awarded. Bachelor's degrees are awarded in BIOLOGICAL SCIENCE (biology/biological science), COMMUNICATIONS AND THE ARTS (art history and appreciation, broadcasting, classical languages, communications, English, film arts, fine arts, French, German, Greek, Italian, journalism, Latin, modern language, music, Russian, and Spanish), COMPUTER AND PHYSICAL SCIENCE (chemistry, computer science, information sciences and systems, mathematics, and physics), SOCIAL SCIENCE (African American studies, American studies, anthropology, criminal justice, economics, history, medieval studies, Middle Eastern studies, peace studies, philosophy, political science/government, psychology, Russian and Slavic studies, sociology, theological studies, urban studies, and women's studies). Communications, philosophy, history, political science, economics, and biology are the strongest academically. Communications, political science, and economics have the largest enrollments.

Required: All students must complete a core curriculum, including 2 courses each in English, history, philosophy, theology, and language, and 1 each in life science, physical science, composition, and social science. A total of 124 credits with 30 in the major and a 2.0 minimum GPA are required. A thesis is required for the honors program.

Special: Fordham College offers career-oriented internships in communications and other majors during the junior or senior year with New York City companies and institutions. A combined 3–2 engineering program is available with Columbia University and Case Western University. Study abroad, a Washington semester, dual and student-designed majors, and pass/fail options are available. There is a freshman honors program on campus, as well as 3 national honor societies, including Phi Beta Kappa.

Faculty/Classroom: All faculty teach undergraduates. The average class size in an introductory lecture is 28 and in a regular course offering, 24.

Admissions: About 69% of the 1993–94 applicants were accepted. The SAT scores for the 1993–94 freshman class were as follows: Verbal—44% below 500, 40% between 500 and 599, 15% between 600 and 700, and 1% above 700; Math—27% below 500, 48% between 500 and 599, 20% between 600 and 700, and 5% above 700. About 47% of the current freshmen were in the top fifth of their class; 78% were in the top two fifths.

Requirements: The SAT I or ACT is required, and applicants should have completed 4 years of high school English and 3 each of mathematics, science, social studies, history, and foreign language. An essay is part of the application process. An interview is recommended. AP and CLEP credits are accepted.

Procedure: Freshmen are admitted fall and spring. Entrance exams should be taken by November of the senior year. Early decision applications should be filed by November 1; regular applications, by February 1 for fall entry and December 1 for spring entry, along with an application fee of $50. Notification of early decision is sent December 15; regular decision, March 1. There are early decision, early admissions, and deferred admissions plans. Some 18 early decision candidates were accepted for the 1993–94 class. A waiting list is an active part of the admissions procedure.

Transfer: Sixty-eight transfer students enrolled in 1993–94. A 3.0 minimum GPA is recommended. Transfer applicants under age 21 should submit SAT I or ACT scores. An interview is recommended. A total of 64 credits out of 124 must be completed at Fordham College.

Visiting: There are regularly scheduled orientations for prospective students. There are guides for informal visits and visitors may sit in on classes and stay overnight at the school. To arrange for a visit, contact Robert Doslerberg, Assistant Director of Admissions, at (718) 817–4000.

Financial Aid: In 1993–94 90% of all current freshmen and 88% of continuing students received some form of financial aid. About 90% of freshmen and 83% of continuing students received need-based aid. The average freshman award was $9500. Of that total, scholarships or need-based grants averaged $6600 ($11,000 maximum); loans averaged $700 ($2200 maximum); and work contracts averaged $700 ($1600 maximum). Ninety-five percent of undergraduate students work part-time. Average earnings from campus work for the school year are $1600. The average financial indebtedness of the 1992–93 graduate was $8170. Fordham College is a member of CSS. The FAF and the college's own financial statement are required. The deadline for financial aid applications is February 1.

International Students: The school actively recruits these students. They must take the TOEFL and achieve a minimum score of 550. The student must also take the SAT I or the ACT.

Computers: The college provides computer facilities for student use. The mainframe is a DEC VAX system. All students may access it. There are no time limits on using the system and no fees.

Graduates: In 1992–93, the most popular majors among graduates were communications (8%), political science (7%), and English (6%). Within an average freshman class, 77% graduate in 4 years, 82% in 5 years, and 87% in 6 years. Some 500 companies recruited on campus in 1992–93. In the 1992 graduating class, 26% of the men and 24% of the women were enrolled in graduate school within 6 months of graduation; 92% of the men and 91% of the women had found employment.

Admissions Contact: John W. Buckley, Director of Admissions.

FRIENDS WORLD PROGRAM
E-5
Southampton, NY 11968
(516) 283–4000
(800) LIU-PLAN (out-of-state)

Full-time: 34 men, 92 women	Faculty: 14
Part-time: none	Ph.D.s: 55%
Graduate: none	Student/Faculty: 9 to 1
Year: semesters	Tuition: $11,500
Application Deadline: open	Room & Board: $5650
Freshman Class: 40 applied, 34 accepted, 14 enrolled	**LESS COMPETITIVE**

Friends World Program, founded in 1965, offers student-designed majors in the liberal arts and is located on the campus of Southampton College. It has campuses in Costa Rica, England, Israel, Kenya, India, China, and Japan, and during the 4-year program, students study at 2 or 3 of them. Much of the learning is through individually designed off-campus field experience and internships in 2 or more cultures. Students attend the Southampton campus only during their first semester. The library contains 1,000,000 volumes, 1000 microform items, and 500 audiovisual forms, and subscribes to 690 periodicals. Computerized library sources and services include the card catalog, interlibrary loans, and database searching. Special learning facilities include a learning resource center, art gallery, radio station, and a marine laboratory. The 110-acre campus is in a rural area 90 miles east of New York City. Including residence halls, there are 33 buildings on campus.

Student Life: About 75% of undergraduates are from out-of-state, mostly the Middle Atlantic. Students come from 20 states, 10 foreign countries, and Canada. Seventy-five percent are from public schools; 25% from private. Ninety percent are white. The average age of freshmen is 19; all undergraduates, 22. Twenty-five percent drop out by the end of their first year; 40% remain to graduate.

Housing: A total of 700 students can be accommodated in college housing. College-sponsored living facilities include coed dormitories. In addition there are special interest houses and All Friends World students are housed together. On-campus housing is guaranteed for all 4 years. Ninety-five percent of students live on campus; of those, 80% remain on campus on weekends. All students may keep cars on campus.

Activities: There are no fraternities or sororities on campus. There are 50 groups on campus, including art, cheerleading, drama, ethnic, honors, international, literary magazine, newspaper, political, radio and TV, religious, social service, student government, and yearbook. Popular campus events include 'Ingatherings'—weekend events where students on field internships return to campus for sharing and community meetings for college governance. There are also Multicultural Awareness activities.

Sports: There are 4 intercollegiate sports for men and 4 for women, and 4 intramural sports for men and 4 for women. Athletic and recreation facilities include a gymnasium, an outdoor swimming pool, basketball and volleyball courts, a weight room, tennis courts, and a fitness trail.

Disabled Students: Fifteen percent of the campus is accessible to disabled students. The following facilities are available: wheelchair ramps and special parking.

Services: In addition to many counseling and information services, tutoring is available in every subject, including in the study center with trained faculty. There is remedial math, reading, and writing.

Campus Safety and Security: Campus safety and security measures include 24-hour foot and vehicle patrol, self defense education, informal discussions, and pamphlets, posters, and films. In addition, there are emergency telephones and lighted pathways and sidewalks.

Programs of Study: Friends World awards the B.A. in Interdisciplinary Studies degree. Bachelor's degrees are awarded in SOCIAL SCIENCE (interdisciplinary studies).

Required: All students take courses in languages and writing and study 2 cultures other than their own. A senior thesis is required. There are no grades. A total of 120 credit hours is required, with 24 in the major subject area.

Special: There is cross-registration with Long Island University. All students carry out fieldwork and internships and live abroad. The college offers a general studies degree, and students may study a wide range of subjects that include women's studies, anthropology, politics, archaeology, comparative religions, music, rainforest ecology, alternative agriculture, and ecology. There is a freshman honors program on campus

Faculty/Classroom: Thirty-five percent of faculty are male; 35%, female. All teach undergraduates, 50% do research, and 50% do both. The average class size in an introductory lecture is 40 and in a regular course offering, 15.

Admissions: About 85% of the 1993–94 applicants were accepted.

Requirements: A minimum average of 75 is required. The SAT I or ACT is not required, but will be considered if submitted. The GED is accepted. An essay and interview are required. AP and CLEP credits are accepted. Important factors used in the admissions decision are personality, intangible qualities, extracurricular activities record, evidence of special talent, leadership record, and recommendations by school officials.

Procedure: Freshmen are admitted in the fall. Application deadlines are open. The application fee is $30. Notification is sent on a rolling basis. There are early admissions and deferred admissions plans.

Transfer: About 60 transfer students enrolled in a recent year. Transfer applicants must have earned at least 15 academic credits with a GPA of at least 2.0. An interview is required. A total of 60 credits out of 120 must be completed at Friends World.

Visiting: There are guides for informal visits and visitors may sit in on classes and stay overnight at the school. To arrange for a visit, contact the Admissions Office at (516) 283–4000, ext. 200.

Financial Aid: In 1993–94, 65% of all current freshmen and 6% of continuing students received some form of financial aid. About 45% of freshmen and 55% of continuing students received need-based aid. The average freshman award was $4000. Of that total, scholarships or need-based grants averaged $1200 ($2500 maximum); loans averaged $2600 ($4000 maximum); and work contracts averaged $400 ($600 maximum). All undergraduate students work part-time. Average earnings from campus work for the school year are $700. The average financial indebtedness of the 1992–93 graduate was $9000. Friends World is a member of CSS. The FAF and the college's own financial statement are required. The deadline for financial aid applications is July 1.

International Students: There are currently 30 international students enrolled. The school actively recruits these students. They must take the TOEFL and achieve a minimum score of 500.

Computers: The college provides computer facilities for student use. The LIU network is a node on INTERNET connecting Friends World students to computers worldwide. There are 125 PCs in 6 campus locations, a 12 to 1 student/computer ratio, and computer hook-up in all dorm rooms. All students may access the system. It may be used 24 hours/day. There are no time limits on using the system and no fees.

Graduates: In a recent year 30 bachelor's degrees were awarded. The most popular major among graduates was interdisciplinary studies (100%). Within an average freshman class, 70% graduate in 4 years, 10% in 5 years, and 20% in 6 years.

Admissions Contact: Carol Gilbert, Director of Admissions.

HAMILTON COLLEGE
C-3
Clinton, NY 13323
(315) 859–4421; (800) 843–2655

Full-time: 904 men, 742 women	Faculty: 168; IIB, +$
Part-time: 6 men, 18 women	Ph.D.s: 96%
Graduate: none	Student/Faculty: 10 to 1
Year: semesters	Tuition: $18,650
Application Deadline: January 15	Room & Board: $4850
Freshman Class: 3140 applied, 1783 accepted, 454 enrolled	
SAT I Verbal/Math: 560/610	**HIGHLY COMPETITIVE**

Hamilton College, founded in 1793, is a private, nonsectarian, liberal arts school offering undergraduate programs in the arts and sciences. The 3 libraries contain 484,634 volumes, 368,587 microform items, and 15,505 audiovisual forms, and subscribe to 1870 periodicals. Computerized library sources and services include the card catalog and database searching. Special learning facilities include an art gallery, radio station, and observatory. The 1200-acre campus is in a rural area 9 miles southwest of Utica. Including residence halls, there are 51 buildings on campus.

Student Life: About 53% of undergraduates are from out-of-state, mostly the Northeast. Students come from 43 states, 35 foreign countries, and Canada. Sixty percent are from public schools; 40% from private. Eighty-five percent are white. Thirty-three percent are Catholic; 32% Protestant; 20% claim no religious affiliation. The average age of freshmen is 18; all undergraduates, 20. Five percent drop out by the end of their first year; 90% remain to graduate.

Housing: A total of 1449 students can be accommodated in college housing. College-sponsored living facilities include coed dormitories, on-campus apartments, fraternity houses, and sorority houses. In addition, there are language houses, special interest houses, quiet floors, substance-free areas, and a cooperative. On-campus housing is guaranteed for all 4 years. Ninety-nine percent of students live on campus; of those, 95% remain on campus on weekends. Upperclassmen may keep cars on campus.

Activities: About 48% of men belong to 8 national fraternities; about 12% of women belong to 1 local and 1 national sorority. There are 60 groups on campus, including art, band, chess, choir, chorale, chorus, computers, dance, drama, ethnic, film, gay, honors, international, jazz band, literary magazine, newspaper, orchestra, photography, political, professional, radio and TV, religious, social, social service, student government, and yearbook. Popular campus events include Class and Charter Day, Winterfest, and Springfest.

Sports: There are 12 intercollegiate sports for men and 11 for women, and 26 intramural sports for men and 29 for women. Athletic and recreation facilities include a gymnasium, a field house, squash and racquetball courts, indoor and outdoor tennis courts, a football stadium, a 9-hole golf course, a swimming pool, indoor and outdoor tracks, numerous grass fields, paddle tennis courts, and an ice rink.

Disabled Students: Thirty percent of the campus is accessible to disabled students. The following facilities are available: wheelchair ramps, elevators, special parking, specially equipped rest rooms, and special class scheduling.

Services: In addition to many counseling and information services, tutoring is available in some subjects through the New York State Higher Education Opportunity Program (HEOP).

Campus Safety and Security: Campus safety and security measures include 24-hour foot and vehicle patrol, escort service, shuttle buses, and emergency telephones. In addition, there are lighted pathways and sidewalks.

Programs of Study: Hamilton awards the B.A. degree. Bachelor's degrees are awarded in BIOLOGICAL SCIENCE (biochemistry and biology/biological science), COMMUNICATIONS AND THE ARTS (classics, comparative literature, creative writing, dance, dramatic arts, English, fine arts, French, German, languages, linguistics, music, and Spanish), COMPUTER AND PHYSICAL SCIENCE (chemistry, computer science, geology, mathematics, and physics), SOCIAL SCIENCE (American studies, anthropology, Asian/Oriental studies, classical/ancient civilization, economics, history, international relations, philosophy, political science/government, psychobiology, psychology, public affairs, religion, Russian and Slavic studies, sociology, and women's studies). English, government, history, economics, and mathematics/computer science have the largest enrollments.

Required: Students must successfully complete 128 credits, with 32 to 40 of these credits in the student's major, and must maintain at least a 72 average in half the courses taken. Students are required to take 2 courses in each academic division, 3 courses designated as writing-intensive, and at least 2 courses covering human diversity and ethical issues, as well as 2 semesters of physical education. A senior project in the student's major is also required.

Special: Cross-registration is permitted with Colgate University, Syracuse University, and Utica College. Opportunities are provided for internships, a cooperative program through the Williams College-Mystic Seaport Program in Connecticut, and a Washington semester. Accelerated degree programs, dual majors, 3-2 engineering degrees, nondegree study, pass/fail options, student-designed majors, a program for early assurance of acceptance to medical school, and study abroad in many countries are offered. There are 4 national honor societies on campus, including Phi Beta Kappa.

Faculty/Classroom: Sixty-one percent of faculty are male; 39%, female. All both teach and do research.

Admissions: About 57% of the 1993-94 applicants were accepted. The SAT scores for the 1993-94 freshman class were as follows: Verbal—28% below 500, 52% between 500 and 599, 19% between 600 and 700, and 1% above 700; Math—8% below 500, 43% between 500 and 599, 39% between 600 and 700, and 10% above 700. About 73% of the current freshmen were in the top fifth of their class; 94% were in the top two fifths. Eight freshmen graduated first in their class.

Requirements: The SAT I or ACT is required. Although graduation from an accredited secondary school or a GED is desirable, and a full complement of college-preparatory courses is advised, Hamilton will consider all highly recommended candidates who demonstrate an ability and desire to perform at intellectually demanding levels. An essay is required, and an interview is recommended. AP credits are accepted. Important factors used in the admissions decision are advanced placement or honor courses, recommendations by school officials, parents or siblings attending the school, extracurricular activities record, and personality, intangible qualities.

Procedure: Freshmen are admitted in the fall. Entrance exams should be taken prior to February of the senior year. Early decision applications should be filed by November 15; regular applications, by January 15 for fall entry, along with an application fee of $40. Notification of early decision is sent December 15; regular decision, April 15. There are early decision, early admissions, and deferred admissions plans. Some 146 early decision candidates were accepted for the 1993-94 class. A waiting list is an active part of the admissions procedure, with about 7% of applicants on the list.

Transfer: Sixteen transfer students enrolled in a recent year. A total of 64 credits out of 128 must be completed at Hamilton.

Visiting: There are regularly scheduled orientations for prospective students, consisting of an interview, tour, and class visit. There are guides for informal visits and visitors may sit in on classes and stay overnight at the school. To arrange for a visit, contact the Admission Office at (315) 859-4421 or (800) 843-2655.

Financial Aid: In 1993-94 60% of all current freshmen and 65% of continuing students received some form of financial aid. About 60% of freshmen and 61% of continuing students received need-based aid. The average freshman award was $14,600. Of that total, scholarships or need-based grants averaged $11,200 ($20,800 maximum); loans averaged $2200 ($2500 maximum); and work contracts averaged $1200 ($1400 maximum). Forty-five percent of undergraduate students work part-time. Average earnings from campus work for the school year are $1400. Hamilton is a member of CSS. The FAF or FFS, FAFSA, and the college's own financial statement is required. The deadline for financial aid applications is February 1.

International Students: There are currently 88 international students enrolled. The school actively recruits these students. They must take the TOEFL and achieve a minimum score of 580. The student must also take the SAT I or the ACT.

Computers: The college provides computer facilities for student use. The mainframes are a DEC 5100, 5000/25, and 5500. Hamilton is connected to Internet and there are 100 Apple Macintosh PCs and 50 MS-DOS PCs in public computer laboratories. Students have full access to Internet. All students may access the system. It may be used more than 100 hours per week. There are no time limits on using the system and no fees.

Graduates: In 1992-93 412 bachelor's degrees were awarded. The most popular majors among graduates were history (12%), English (11%), and government (10%). Within an average freshman class, 85% graduate in 4 years and 91% in 5 years. Some 50 companies recruited on campus in 1992-93. In the 1992 graduating class, 11% of the men and 7% of the women were enrolled in graduate school within 6 months of graduation.

Admissions Contact: Douglas C. Thompson, Dean of Admissions.

HARTWICK COLLEGE
D-3

Oneonta, NY 13820-4020 (607) 431-4150; (800) 828-2200

Full-time: 673 men, 783 women	Faculty: 99; IIB, av$
Part-time: 18 men, 60 women	Ph.Ds: 87%
Graduate: none	Student/Faculty: 15 to 1
Year: 4-1-4	Tuition: $16,400
Application Deadline: February 15	Room & Board: $4550
Freshman Class: 2112 applied, 1725 accepted, 430 enrolled	
SAT I Verbal/Math: 478/524	ACT: 23 COMPETITIVE

Hartwick College, founded in 1797, is a private undergraduate liberal arts college. In addition to regional accreditation, Hartwick has baccalaureate program accreditation with NASAD, NASM, and NLN. The library contains 238,618 volumes, 47,535 microform items, and 238,618 audiovisual forms, and subscribes to 1188 periodicals. Computerized library sources and services include the card catalog, interlibrary loans, and database searching. Special learning facilities include an art gallery, radio station, 3 museums, 914-acre environmental study center, and observatory. The 375-acre campus is in a small town 75 miles southwest of Albany. Including residence halls, there are 25 buildings on campus.

Student Life: About 63% of undergraduates are from New York. Students come from 29 states, 16 foreign countries, and Canada. Seventy-five percent are from public schools; 25% from private. Ninety-three percent are white. Forty-five percent are Catholic; 27% Protestant; 14% claim no religious affiliation; and 11% are other religions. The average age of freshmen is 18; all undergraduates, 20. Eighteen percent drop out by the end of their first year; 67% remain to graduate.

Housing: A total of 1081 students can be accommodated in college housing. College-sponsored living facilities include single-sex and coed dormitories, on-campus apartments, fraternity houses, and sorority houses. In addition, there are special interest houses. On-campus housing is guaranteed for all 4 years. Seventy-one percent of students live on campus; of those, 90% remain on campus on weekends. Alcohol is not permitted. All students may keep cars on campus.

Activities: About 23% of men belong to 1 local and 3 national fraternities; about 26% of women belong to 3 local and 1 national sorority. There are 64 groups on campus, including art, band, cheerleading, choir, chorale, chorus, computers, dance, drama, ethnic, film, gay, honors, international, jazz band, literary magazine, musical theater, newspaper, orchestra, pep band, photography, political, professional, radio and TV, religious, social, social service, student government, and yearbook. Popular campus events include the Concert Series, Winter, Spring, and Fall Weekends, the Holiday Ball, Earth Day, Multicultural Month, and January thematic term.

Sports: There are 11 intercollegiate sports for men and 11 for women, and 14 intramural sports for men and 13 for women. Athletic and recreation facilities include 2 gymnasiums, an indoor pool, a dance room, athletic and training facilities, a track, courts for handball, racquetball, squash, and tennis, a Nautilus exercise gym, a fitness center, and a lighted all-weather playing field.

Disabled Students: Fifty percent of the campus is accessible to disabled students. The following facilities are available: wheelchair ramps, elevators, special parking, specially equipped rest rooms, special class scheduling, and lowered drinking fountains.

Services: In addition to many counseling and information services, tutoring is available in every subject. There is also a reader service for the blind. Writing, mathematics, and academic advising centers are available.

Campus Safety and Security: Campus safety and security measures include 24-hour foot and vehicle patrol, self-defense education, escort service, and shuttle buses. In addition, there are informal discussions, pamphlets, posters, and films, emergency telephones, and lighted pathways and sidewalks.

Programs of Study: Hartwick awards the B.A. and B.S. degrees. Bachelor's degrees are awarded in BIOLOGICAL SCIENCE (biochemistry and biology/biological science), BUSINESS (accounting and management), COMMUNICATIONS AND THE ARTS (dramatic arts, English, fine arts, languages, and music), COMPUTER AND PHYSICAL SCIENCE (chemistry, computer science, geology, information sciences and systems, mathematics, and physics), EDUCATION (music), HEALTH PROFESSIONS (medical technology and nursing), SOCIAL SCIENCE (anthropology, economics, history, philosophy, political science/government, psychology, religion, and sociology). Anthropology, art, biology, geology, history, music, and nursing are the strongest academically. Psychology has the largest enrollment.

Required: All students must complete 36 course units with at least a 2.0 GPA. Core requirements are in the study areas of continuity, interdependence, science and technology, critical thinking, effective communication, and choices. Courses are chosen from offerings in humanities, science and mathematics, social and behavioral sciences, foreign language, and physical education. A first-year seminar and a contemporary issues seminar for juniors and seniors are required. Students are strongly urged to include an off-campus learning experience.

Special: Students may design their own majors, or choose independent or directed study. Cross-registration with SUNY College at Oneonta is possible, and local internships are available. There is a January thematic term. Off-campus programs are numerous, including a Washington semester and study abroad in 30 countries. Experiential programs include Outward Bound and the National Outdoor Leadership School. All departments offer dual majors. There is a 3–2 engineering program with Clarkson or Columbia Universities, a 3–3 program with Albany Law School, and a 4–1 business program with Clarkson University. There is a freshman honors program on campus, as well as 13 national honor societies. Thirty departments have honors programs.

Faculty/Classroom: Sixty-five percent of faculty are male; 35%, female. All teach undergraduates. The average class size in an introductory lecture is 40; in a laboratory, 20; and in a regular course offering, 19.

Admissions: About 82% of the 1993–94 applicants were accepted. The SAT scores for the 1993–94 freshman class were as follows: Verbal—64% below 500, 28% between 500 and 599, 7% between 600 and 700, and 1% above 700; Math—36% below 500, 47% between 500 and 599, 15% between 600 and 700, and 2% above 700. The ACT scores were 22% below 21, 36% between 21 and 23, 24% between 24 and 26, 5% between 27 and 28, and 13% above 28. About 41% of the current freshmen were in the top fifth of their class; 69% were in the top two fifths. Twelve freshmen graduated first in their class.

Requirements: The SAT I or ACT is required. In addition, SAT II: Subject tests in writing and 1 other subject are strongly recommended. The suggested secondary school course of study includes 4 years of English and 3 years each of a foreign language, mathematics, laboratory science, and history. Hartwick also strongly recommends that applicants plan a campus visit and interview. Prospective art majors should submit a portfolio, and music majors must audition. AP and CLEP credits are accepted. Important factors used in the admissions decision are advanced placement or honor courses, evidence of special talent, extracurricular activities record, leadership record, and personality, intangible qualities.

Procedure: Freshmen are admitted to all sessions. Entrance exams should be taken in the spring of the junior year and/or the fall of the senior year. Early decision applications should be filed by January 1; regular applications, by February 15 for fall entry, December 1 for winter entry, and January 1 for spring entry, along with an application fee of $35. Notification of early decision and early notification applications is sent on a rolling basis; regular decision, on or about March 15. There are early decision, early admissions, and deferred admissions plans. Forty-one early decision candidates were accepted for the 1993–94 class.

Transfer: Some 53 transfer students enrolled in 1993–94. Transfer applicants must present a cumulative GPA of 2.5. A total of 18 course units out of 36 must be completed at Hartwick.

Visiting: There are regularly scheduled orientations for prospective students, consisting of an interview and tour, lunch, class visits, and individual meetings with financial aid representatives. There are guides for informal visits and visitors may sit in on classes and stay

overnight at the school. To arrange for a visit, contact the Admissions Office at (607) 431–4150 or (800) 828–2200.

Financial Aid: In 1993–94 85% of all current freshmen and 71% of continuing students received some form of financial aid. About 68% of freshmen and 63% of continuing students received need-based aid. The average freshman award was $12,907. Of that total, scholarships or need-based grants averaged $6915 ($16,300 maximum); loans averaged $5600 ($12,000 maximum); and work contracts averaged $1100 ($1400 maximum). Sixty-six percent of undergraduate students work part-time. Average earnings from campus work for the school year are $1400. The average financial indebtedness of the 1992–93 graduate was $13,460. Hartwick is a member of CSS. The FAF and FAFSA, and the college's own financial statement are required. The deadline for financial aid applications is February 15.

International Students: There are currently 27 international students enrolled. They must take the TOEFL and achieve a minimum score of 500.

Computers: The college provides computer facilities for student use. The mainframes are a DEC VAX 6410, 2 DEC MicroVAX 3100s, and a DEC MicroVAX II. There is a laboratory with 26 IBM-compatible 486sx computers with VGA graphics, a laboratory with 26 Apple Macintosh microcomputers, several small clusters of computers in academic buildings, and computers spread throughout the library, all connected with a campus local area network. All students may access the system. It may be used 8 A.M. to 1 A.M. weekdays, noon to 10 P.M. Saturday, noon to 1 A.M. Sunday, as well as 24 hours via dial-up. There are no time limits on using the system and no fees. Since it is required that all students have personal computers, each first-year student receives a notebook-sized computer with modem, printer, word-processing software, and access to the campus network.

Graduates: In 1992–93 309 bachelor's degrees were awarded. The most popular majors among graduates were psychology (11%), political science (11%), and management (10%). Within an average freshman class, 60% graduate in 4 years, 69% in 5 years, and 73% in 6 years. Some 30 companies recruited on campus in 1992–93. In the 1992 graduating class, 20% of all students were enrolled in graduate school within 6 months of graduation; 70% had found employment.

Admissions Contact: Karyl B. Clemens, Dean of Admissions.

HOBART AND WILLIAM SMITH COLLEGES   C-3

Geneva, NY 14456   (315) 781-3622 (Hobart) or (315) 781-3472 (William Smith)

(800) 852-2256 (Hobart) or (800) 245-0100 (William Smith)

Full-time: 953 men, 839 women	**Faculty:** 145; IIB, +$
Part-time: 1 men, 4 women	**Ph.D.s:** 98%
Graduate: none	**Student/Faculty:** 12 to 1
Year: trimesters	**Tuition:** $18,309
Application Deadline: February 15	**Room & Board:** $5616
Freshman Class: 2688 applied, 2081 accepted, 500 enrolled	
SAT I or ACT: required	**VERY COMPETITIVE**

Hobart College, a men's college founded in 1822 and affiliated with the Episcopal Church, shares campus, classes, and faculty with William Smith College, a women's nonsectarian college founded in 1908. There are 2 undergraduate schools. The library contains 306,000 volumes, 42,000 microform items, and 15,500 audiovisual forms, and subscribes to 1872 periodicals. Computerized library sources and services include the card catalog and interlibrary loans. Special learning facilities include a learning resource center, art gallery, radio station, 100-acre natural preserve, and 70-foot research vessel. The 170-acre campus is in a small town 50 miles west of Syracuse and 50 miles east of Rochester, on the north shore of Geneva Lake. Including residence halls, there are 75 buildings on campus.

Student Life: About 59% of undergraduates are from out-of-state, mostly the Northeast. Students come from 41 states, 24 foreign countries, and Canada. Fifty-eight percent are from public schools; 38% from private. Eighty-nine percent are white. Thirty percent are Protestant; 30% are Catholic; 20% claim no religious affiliation; and 15% Jewish. The average age of freshmen is 18; all undergraduates, 20. Seven percent drop out by the end of their first year; 80% remain to graduate.

Housing: A total of 1450 students can be accommodated in college housing. College-sponsored living facilities include single-sex and coed dormitories and fraternity houses. In addition, there are honors houses, language houses, special interest houses, and cooperative houses in which students plan and prepare their own meals. On-campus housing is guaranteed for all 4 years. Eighty percent of students live on campus; of those, 93% remain on campus on weekends. All students may keep cars on campus.

Activities: About 30% of men belong to 7 national fraternities. There are no sororities on campus. There are more than 70 groups on campus, including art, choir, chorale, chorus, computers, dance, drama, ethnic, film, gay, honors, international, jazz band, literary magazine, musical theater, newspaper, orchestra, photography, political, professional, radio and TV, religious, social, social service, student govern-

ment, and yearbook. Popular campus events include Folk Festival, Air Band Contest, Charter Day, Moving-up Day, Winter Carnival, and Lobster Bash.

Sports: There are 12 intercollegiate sports for men and 8 for women, and 23 intramural sports for men and 23 for women. Athletic and recreation facilities include a sport and recreation center and 2 gymnasiums.

Disabled Students: The following facilities are available: wheelchair ramps, elevators, special parking, specially equipped rest rooms, and special class scheduling.

Services: In addition to many counseling and information services, tutoring is available in every subject. There is also a reader service for the blind, and remedial math, reading, and writing. There is a counseling center staffed by 5 therapists/counselors as well as various support groups and educational workshops.

Campus Safety and Security: Campus safety and security measures include evening foot and vehicle patrol, self-defense education, evening escort service, and evening shuttle buses. In addition, there are informal discussions, pamphlets, posters, and films, emergency telephones, and lighted pathways and sidewalks.

Programs of Study: HWS awards the B.A. and B.S. degrees. Bachelor's degrees are awarded in BIOLOGICAL SCIENCE (biology/biological science), COMMUNICATIONS AND THE ARTS (Chinese, classics, dance, English, fine arts, French, German, Japanese, music, Russian, and Spanish), COMPUTER AND PHYSICAL SCIENCE (chemistry, computer science, geoscience, mathematics, and physics), ENGINEERING AND ENVIRONMENTAL DESIGN (architecture and environmental science), SOCIAL SCIENCE (American studies, anthropology, Asian/Oriental studies, economics, history, philosophy, political science/government, psychology, religion, Russian and Slavic studies, sociology, urban studies, and women's studies). Natural sciences, environmental studies, and creative writing are the strongest academically. English, economics, and political science have the largest enrollments.

Required: All first-year students take a seminar; sophomores take at least 1 bidisciplinary course. All students must fulfill distribution requirements consisting of 2 courses each in humanities, natural sciences, and social sciences by the end of the sophomore year. The Third Tier requirement may be satisfied by study abroad, upper-level bidisciplinary work, or substantial independent study of an interdisciplinary nature. A total of 36 courses is required for graduation, with 12 to 14 of these in the major, and a minimum GPA of 2.0.

Special: In their junior year, all students are encouraged to spend at least 1 term studying off campus in a study-abroad program or other form of off-campus work. Options include a United Nations term, a Washington semester, an urban semester, and prearchitecture semesters in New York, Paris, or Florence. Other study-abroad opportunities are available in more than 15 countries. There is cross-registration with the 15 members of the Rochester Area Colleges consortium. The college offers dual and student-designed majors, and 3–2 engineering degree options with Columbia University, the University of Rochester, Rensselaer Polytechnic Institute, and Dartmouth College. Credit for life/military/work experience, nondegree study, and pass/fail options may be granted. There are also M.B.A. degrees with Clarkson University and 3–4 architecture degrees with Washington University. There are 9 national honor societies on campus, including Phi Beta Kappa.

Faculty/Classroom: Sixty-six percent of faculty are male; 34%, female. All teach and do research. The average class size in an introductory lecture is 45; in a laboratory, 25; and in a regular course offering, 23.

Admissions: About 77% of the 1993–94 applicants were accepted. The SAT scores for the 1993–94 freshman class were as follows: Verbal—52% below 500, 39% between 500 and 599, and 8% between 600 and 700; Math—25% below 500, 47% between 500 and 599, 24% between 600 and 700, and 4% above 700. The ACT scores were 14% below 21, 33% between 21 and 23, 28% between 24 and 26, 13% between 27 and 28, and 12% above 28. About 54% of the current freshmen were in the top fifth of their class; 76% were in the top two fifths. Two freshmen graduated first in their class.

Requirements: The SAT I or ACT is required. SAT II: Subject tests are not required but may be considered. A GED is accepted. A total of 18 academic credits is required, including 4 years of English, 3 each of mathematics and science (including a laboratory science), and 2 each of foreign language and history. An essay is required; an interview is recommended. AP credits are accepted. Important factors used in the admissions decision are advanced placement or honor courses, recommendations by school officials, evidence of special talent, extracurricular activities record, and personality, intangible qualities.

Procedure: Freshmen are admitted in the fall. Entrance exams should be taken in the junior or senior year. Early decision applications should be filed by November 15 for Round I and January 1 for Round II; regular applications, by February 15 for fall entry, along with an application fee of $40. Notification of early decision is sent December 15 for Round I and February 1 for Round II; regular decision, April 1. There are early decision, early admissions, and deferred admissions plans. Some 91 early decision candidates were accepted for the 1993–94 class. A waiting list is an active part of the admissions procedure, with about 10% of applicants on the list.

Transfer: Fifty-nine transfer students enrolled in 1993–94. Transfer applicants must have a 3.0 GPA and have completed 1 year of college study. They are required to take the SAT I or ACT. An interview is recommended. A total of 18 courses out of 36 must be completed at HWS.

Visiting: There are regularly scheduled orientations for prospective students. There are guides for informal visits and visitors may sit in on classes and stay overnight at the school. To arrange for a visit, contact the Offices of Admissions at (800) 852–2256 (Hobart) or (800) 245–0100 (William Smith).

Financial Aid: In 1993–94 58% of all current freshmen and 57% of continuing students received some form of financial aid. About 58% of freshmen and 57% of continuing students received need-based aid. The average freshman award was $13,852. Of that total, scholarships or need-based grants averaged $11,288 ($18,000 maximum); loans averaged $2420 ($2625 maximum); and work contracts averaged $1000 ($2400 maximum). Fifty-five percent of undergraduate students work part-time. Average earnings from campus work for the school year are $972. The average financial indebtedness of the 1992–93 graduate was $10,700. HWS is a member of CSS. The FAF, the college's own financial statement, and the FAFSA are required. The deadline for financial aid applications is February 15.

International Students: There are currently 63 international students enrolled. The school actively recruits these students. They must take the TOEFL and achieve a minimum score of 500. The student must also take the SAT I or the ACT.

Computers: The college provides computer facilities for student use. The mainframe is a DEC VAX 11/785. There are 122 microcomputers, and 60 terminals directly connected to the mainframe, with 114 microcomputers networked. All students may access the system. It may be used from 9 A.M. to midnight, 7 days a week. There are no time limits on using the system and no fees.

Graduates: In 1992–93, 477 bachelor's degrees were awarded. The most popular majors among graduates were English (21%), history (12%), and individual majors (12%). Within an average freshman class, 78% graduate in 4 years and 80% in 5 years. Some 224 companies recruited on campus in 1992–93. In the 1992 graduating class, 24% of all students were enrolled in graduate school within 6 months of graduation; 76% of graduates had found employment.

Admissions Contact: Offices of Admissions.

HOFSTRA UNIVERSITY

D-5

Hempstead, NY 11550   (516) 463–6700

Full-time: 3076 men, 3458 women	**Faculty:** 402; I, av$
Part-time: 618 men, 732 women	**Ph.D.s:** 90%
Graduate: 1596 men, 2320 women	**Student/Faculty:** 16 to 1
Year: semesters, summer session	**Tuition:** $11,080
Application Deadline: February 15	**Room & Board:** $5500
Freshman Class: 7428 applied, 5860 accepted, 1498 enrolled	
SAT I Verbal/Math: 480/545	**ACT:** 25 **VERY COMPETITIVE**

Hofstra University, founded in 1935, is an independent institution offering programs in liberal arts and sciences, business, and education. There are 4 undergraduate and 7 graduate schools. In addition to regional accreditation, Hofstra has baccalaureate program accreditation with AACSB, ABET, ASLA, and NCATE. The 2 libraries contain 1.3 million volumes, 30,098 microform items, and 3986 audiovisual forms, and subscribe to 7017 periodicals. Computerized library sources and services include the card catalog and database searching. Special learning facilities include a learning resource center, art gallery, radio station, cable TV network, museum, and arboretum. The 238-acre campus is in a suburban area 25 miles east of New York City. Including residence halls, there are 104 buildings on campus.

Student Life: About 65% of undergraduates are from New York. Students come from 45 states, 64 foreign countries, and Canada. Seventy percent are from public schools; 30% from private. Eighty-one percent are white. Forty-five percent are Catholic; 30% Protestant; 18% Jewish. The average age of freshmen is 19; all undergraduates, 22. Eleven percent drop out by the end of their first year; 59% remain to graduate.

Housing: A total of 4100 students can be accommodated in college housing. College-sponsored living facilities include single-sex and coed dormitories and off-campus apartments. In addition, there are special interest houses, a living/learning center, an international house, and a freshmen center. On-campus housing is guaranteed for all 4 years. Sixty percent of students live on campus; of those, 90% remain on campus on weekends. All students may keep cars on campus.

Activities: About 14% of men belong to 6 local and 10 national fraternities; about 12% of women belong to 3 local and 7 national sororities. There are more than 100 groups on campus, including art, band, cheerleading, choir, chorale, chorus, computers, dance, drama, drill team, ethnic, film, gay, honors, international, jazz band, literary magazine, musical theater, newspaper, opera, orchestra, pep band, photography, political, professional, radio and TV, religious, social, social service, student government, symphony, and yearbook. Popular campus events include December Dutch Holiday Festival, Spring Shakespeare Festival, May Dutch Tulip Festival, Freak Formal, Mirror Stars, Italian American Festival, Homecoming, and Parents Weekend.

Sports: There are 9 intercollegiate sports for men and 8 for women, and 13 intramural sports for men and 13 for women. Athletic and recreation facilities include a physical fitness center, a recreation center, playing fields, a 7500-seat stadium, a gymnasium, and an indoor track.

Disabled Students: The entire campus is accessible to disabled students. The following facilities are available: wheelchair ramps, elevators, special parking, specially equipped rest rooms, special class scheduling, lowered drinking fountains, lowered telephones, automated door openers, and TTY visual telephones.

Services: In addition to many counseling and information services, tutoring is available in every subject. There is also a reader service for the blind, and remedial math, reading, and writing.

Campus Safety and Security: Campus safety and security measures include 24-hour foot and vehicle patrol, self-defense education, escort service, and shuttle buses. In addition, there are informal discussions, pamphlets, posters, films, emergency telephones, lighted pathways and sidewalks, and security cameras in residence halls.

Programs of Study: Hofstra awards the B.A., B.S., B.B.A., B.E., B.F.A., and B.S.Ed. degrees. Associate, master's, and doctoral degrees also are awarded. Bachelor's degrees are awarded in AGRICULTURE (natural resource management), BIOLOGICAL SCIENCE (biochemistry and biology/biological science), BUSINESS (accounting, banking and finance, business administration and management, international business management, management information systems, and marketing/retailing/merchandising), COMMUNICATIONS AND THE ARTS (art history and appreciation, broadcasting, ceramic art and design, classics, communications, dance, design, dramatic arts, English, film arts, fine arts, journalism, languages, music, painting, photography, sculpture, and speech/debate/rhetoric), COMPUTER AND PHYSICAL SCIENCE (chemistry, computer programming, computer science, geology, information sciences and systems, mathematics, natural sciences, and physics), EDUCATION (art, bilingual/bicultural, business, early childhood, elementary, foreign languages, music, physical, science, and secondary), ENGINEERING AND ENVIRONMENTAL DESIGN (computer engineering, electrical/electronics engineering, engineering, industrial engineering, and mechanical engineering), HEALTH PROFESSIONS (community health work, predentistry, premedicine, and speech pathology/audiology), SOCIAL SCIENCE (African studies, American studies, anthropology, Asian/Oriental studies, cross-cultural studies, economics, geography, history, humanities, interdisciplinary studies, Judaic studies, liberal arts/general studies, philosophy, political science/government, prelaw, psychology, social science, and sociology). Engineering, accounting, biology, and political science are the strongest academically. Accounting, communications, and psychology have the largest enrollments.

Required: Students must take 2 semesters of English and pass a writing proficiency test. A minimum of 6 credits each is required in humanities, natural sciences/mathematics, and social science. A total of 124 to 135 credit hours is required for graduation, with 30 to 84 in the major and a minimum GPA of 2.0. Foreign language study is required for the B.A., and students in New College must submit a thesis.

Special: Internships, a 3–2 engineering program with Columbia University, a Washington semester, study abroad in 7 countries, and dual and student-designed majors are offered. Credit for military and work experience and credit by examination are given. There is a January session as well as 2 summer sessions. The college offers nondegree study and pass/fail options. There is a freshman honors program on campus, as well as 17 national honor societies, including Phi Beta Kappa.

Faculty/Classroom: Sixty-one percent of faculty are male; 39%, female. Ninety-six percent teach undergraduates and 65% both teach and do research. No introductory courses are taught by graduate students. The average class size in a laboratory is 19 and in a regular course offering, 25.

Admissions: About 79% of the 1993–94 applicants were accepted. The SAT scores for the 1993–94 freshman class were as follows: Verbal—44% below 500, 45% between 500 and 599, 10% between 600 and 700, and 1% above 700; Math—25% below 500, 47% between 500 and 599, 24% between 600 and 700, and 4% above 700. The ACT scores were 11% below 21, 15% between 21 and 23, 48% between 24 and 26, 18% between 27 and 28, and 8% above 28. About 60% of the current freshmen were in the top fifth of their class;

97% were in the top two fifths. Some 48 freshmen graduated first in their class.

Requirements: The SAT I or ACT is required. Applicants should graduate from an accredited secondary school or have a GED. Preparatory work should include 4 years of English, 3 of history and social studies, 2 each of mathematics and foreign language, and 1 of science, plus 4 academic electives. An essay and interview are recommended. AP and CLEP credits are accepted. Important factors used in the admissions decision are advanced placement or honor courses, recommendations by school officials, leadership record, personality, intangible qualities, and evidence of special talent.

Procedure: Freshmen are admitted fall and spring. Entrance exams should be taken in the junior or senior year. Early decision applications should be filed by December 1; regular applications, by February 15 for fall entry and December 1 for spring entry, along with an application fee of $25. Notification of early decision is sent December 30; regular decision, on a rolling basis. There are early decision, early admissions, and deferred admissions plans. Eighty-one early decision candidates were accepted for the 1993–94 class. A waiting list is an active part of the admissions procedure, with about 5% of applicants on the list.

Transfer: Some 805 transfer students enrolled in 1993–94. Admission is based primarily on prior college work in appropriate courses within the study area. A maximum of 64 credits from a 2-year school, or 94 credits from a 4-year school is accepted. The minimum overall GPA required is 2.5. A total of 30 credits out of 124 to 135 must be completed at Hofstra.

Visiting: There are regularly scheduled orientations for prospective students, including an open house, a tour of the campus, and a program in which a prospective student spends the day with a student currently enrolled in the projected or a similar major. There are guides for informal visits and visitors may sit in on classes and stay overnight at the school. To arrange for a visit, contact the Ambassador Program at (516) 463–6796.

Financial Aid: In 1993–94 79% of all current freshmen and 75% of continuing students received some form of financial aid. About 63% of freshmen and 65% of continuing students received need-based aid. The average freshman award was $7155. Of that total, scholarships or need-based grants averaged $3330 (full tuition maximum); loans averaged $2625 ($6625 maximum); and work contracts averaged $1200 ($2500 maximum). Twelve percent of undergraduate students work part-time. Average earnings from campus work for the school year are $1250. The average financial indebtedness of the 1992–93 graduate was $12,000. Hofstra is a member of CSS. The FAF and FAFSA are required. The deadline for financial aid applications is May 1.

International Students: There are currently 319 international students enrolled. The school actively recruits these students. They must take the TOEFL; if they score lower than 550, they must take an English test upon arrival.

Computers: The college provides computer facilities for student use. The mainframes are an IBM 9121, a DEC VAX 8530, and a DEC VAX 6410. These systems provide central computing resources for teaching and research, including electronic mail, BITNET and Internet, and databases. Systems are accessible from the 300 PCs and terminals in 3 computer laboratories on campus. All students may access the system. There are no time limits on using the system and no fees.

Graduates: In 1992–93 1889 bachelor's degrees were awarded. The most popular majors among graduates were accounting (14%), marketing (11%), and psychology (11%). Within an average freshman class, 59% graduate in 5 years. Some 200 companies recruited on campus in 1992–93.

Admissions Contact: Margaret Shields, Dean of Admissions.

HOUGHTON COLLEGE
B-3
Houghton, NY 14744 (716) 567-9353; (800) 777-2556 (in-state)

Full-time: 483 men, 727 women	Faculty: 75; IIB, --$
Part-time: 5 men, 21 women	Ph.D.s: 70%
Graduate: none	Student/Faculty: 16 to 1
Year: semesters, summer session	Tuition: $9720
Application Deadline: August 1	Room & Board: $3400
Freshman Class: 949 applied, 786 accepted, 302 enrolled	
SAT I Verbal/Math: 500/535	ACT: 24 VERY COMPETITIVE

Houghton College, founded in 1883, is a private college affiliated with the Wesleyan Church. It offers programs in the liberal arts and music. In addition to regional accreditation, Houghton has baccalaureate program accreditation with NASM. The library contains 216,857 volumes and 5000 microform items, and subscribes to 822 periodicals. Computerized library sources and services include the card catalog, interlibrary loans, and database searching. Special learning facilities include an art gallery and radio station. The 1300-acre campus is in a rural area 60 miles southeast of Buffalo.

Student Life: About 61% of undergraduates are from New York. Students come from 39 states, 20 foreign countries, and Canada. Seventy-five percent are from public schools; 25% from private. Eighty-nine percent are white. Most are Protestant. The average age of freshmen is 18; all undergraduates, 20.6. Thirteen percent drop out by the end of their first year; 62% remain to graduate.

Housing: A total of 930 students can be accommodated in college housing. College-sponsored living facilities include single-sex dormitories. In addition, there are language houses and special interest houses. On-campus housing is guaranteed for the freshman year only and is available on a lottery system for upperclassmen. Priority is given to out-of-town students. Eighty-nine percent of students live on campus; of those, 80% remain on campus on weekends. Alcohol is not permitted. All students may keep cars on campus.

Activities: There are no fraternities or sororities on campus. There are 40 groups on campus, including art, band, cheerleading, choir, chorale, chorus, drama, ethnic, honors, international, jazz band, literary magazine, musical theater, newspaper, opera, orchestra, political, professional, radio and TV, religious, social service, student government, and yearbook. Popular campus events include Christian Life Emphasis Week, Homecoming, Winter Weekend, Senate Spots, and artist series.

Sports: There are 4 intercollegiate sports for men and 7 for women, and 9 intramural sports for men and 8 for women. Athletic and recreation facilities include 3 basketball and 4 racquetball courts, a swimming pool, an indoor track, a downhill ski slope, cross-country ski trails, 8 tennis courts, and an equestrian farm with an indoor riding ring. The gymnasium seats 1800, the largest auditorium/arena, 1300.

Disabled Students: Eighty percent of the campus is accessible to disabled students. The following facilities are available: wheelchair ramps, elevators, special parking, specially equipped rest rooms, special class scheduling, lowered drinking fountains, and lowered telephones.

Services: In addition to many counseling and information services, tutoring is available in some subjects, including mathematics, writing, and history. In addition, there is a reader service for the blind, remedial reading and writing, and support for learning-disabled students.

Campus Safety and Security: Campus safety and security measures include 24-hour foot and vehicle patrol, escort service, shuttle buses, and informal discussions. In addition, there are pamphlets, posters, and films, emergency telephones, and lighted pathways and sidewalks.

Programs of Study: Houghton awards the B.A., B.S., and B.M. degrees. Associate degrees also are awarded. Bachelor's degrees are awarded in BIOLOGICAL SCIENCE (biology/biological science), BUSINESS (accounting, business administration and management, and recreation and leisure services), COMMUNICATIONS AND THE ARTS (art, communications, creative writing, English, fine arts, French, music, and Spanish), COMPUTER AND PHYSICAL SCIENCE (chemistry, mathematics, physics, and science), EDUCATION (art, elementary, foreign languages, music, science, and secondary), HEALTH PROFESSIONS (medical laboratory technology, predentistry, and premedicine), SOCIAL SCIENCE (biblical studies, history, humanities, international studies, philosophy, political science/government, prelaw, psychology, religion, social science, and sociology). Biology, chemistry, religion, psychology, and art are the strongest academically. Elementary education, psychology, and business administration have the largest enrollments.

Required: Required courses include 12 hours of language, 10 each of religion, mathematics and science, English and speech, and social science, 3 of fine arts, and 2 of physical education. A total of 125 credits with at least 25 in the major and a minimum GPA of 2.0 are required to graduate.

Special: There is cross-registration with the Western New York Consortium. Internships are available in psychology, social work, business, and Christian education. Study abroad in 7 countries, a Washington semester, dual majors, and a 3–2 engineering degree with Clarkson University are offered. Credit for military experience and nondegree study are possible. There are 2 national honor societies on campus.

Faculty/Classroom: Sixty-seven percent of faculty are male; 33%, female. All teach undergraduates and 20% do research. The average class size in an introductory lecture is 45; in a laboratory, 22; and in a regular course offering, 20.

Admissions: About 83% of the 1993–94 applicants were accepted. The SAT scores for the 1993–94 freshman class were as follows: Verbal—48% below 500, 36% between 500 and 599, 14% between 600 and 700, and 2% above 700; Math—33% below 500, 39% between 500 and 599, 24% between 600 and 700, and 4% above 700. The ACT scores were 13% below 21, 35% between 21 and 23, 33% between 24 and 26, 12% between 27 and 28, and 7% above 28. About 56% of the current freshmen were in the top fifth of their class; 85% were in the top two fifths. There were 4 National Merit finalists and 1 semifinalist. A total of 25 freshmen graduated first in their class.

Requirements: Houghton requires applicants to be in the upper 50% of their class. A minimum GPA of 2.5 is required. The SAT I or ACT is required; a minimum composite score of 800 on the SAT I or 20 on the ACT is recommended. Applicants must graduate from an accredited secondary school or have a GED. A total of 16 academic credits is required, including 4 of English, 3 of social studies, and 2 each of foreign language, mathematics, and science. An essay is required. Music students must audition. An interview is recommended. AP and CLEP credits are accepted. Important factors used in the admissions decision are personality, intangible qualities, recommendations by school officials, advanced placement or honor courses, evidence of special talent, and leadership record.

Procedure: Freshmen are admitted fall and spring. Entrance exams should be taken in the spring of the junior year or fall of the senior year. Applications should be filed by August 1 for fall entry and December 1 for spring entry, along with an application fee of $25. Notification is sent on a rolling basis. There is a deferred admissions plan.

Transfer: A total of 77 transfer students enrolled in 1993–94. Applicants should have completed at least 12 credit hours of college work with a 2.5 or better GPA. A pastor's recommendation and high school transcripts must be submitted. The SAT I or ACT and an interview are recommended. A total of 30 credits out of 125 must be completed at Houghton.

Visiting: There are regularly scheduled orientations for prospective students, including a tour, admissions interview, financial aid session, class visit, and academic program sessions. There are guides for informal visits and visitors may sit in on classes and stay overnight at the school. To arrange for a visit, contact Kamala Gross, Campus Visit Coordinator, at (800) 777-2556.

Financial Aid: In 1993–94, 92% of all current freshmen and 88% of continuing students received some form of financial aid. About 85% of freshmen and 82% of continuing students received need-based aid. The average freshman award was $9017. Of that total, scholarships or need-based grants averaged $2446 ($4718 maximum); loans averaged $2421 ($4125 maximum); and work contracts averaged $900 ($1200 maximum). Fifty-five percent of undergraduate students work part-time. Average earnings from campus work for the school year are $989. The average financial indebtedness of the 1992–93 graduate was $11,250. Houghton is a member of CSS. The FAF and the college's own financial statement are required. The deadline for financial aid applications is March 15.

International Students: There are currently 55 international students enrolled. The school actively recruits these students. They must take the TOEFL and achieve a minimum score of 500.

Computers: The college provides computer facilities for student use. The mainframe is a DEC VAX 8200. There are 2 terminal laboratories, 3 microcomputer laboratories, and terminals in each residence hall. All students may access the system 24 hours a day in the residence halls, 15 hours a day in the computer laboratories. There are no time limits on using the system. The fees are $30.

Graduates: In 1992–93, 259 bachelor's degrees were awarded. The most popular majors among graduates were psychology (19%), elementary education (19%), and business administration (16%). Within an average freshman class, 2% graduate in 3 years, 56% in 4 years, 65% in 5 years, and 66% in 6 years. Some 15 companies recruited on campus in 1992–93. In the 1992 graduating class, 21% of all students were enrolled in graduate school within 6 months of graduation; 81% of the men and 84% of the women had found employment.

Admissions Contact: Timothy R. Fuller, Director of Admissions.

IONA COLLEGE
New Rochelle, NY 10801–1890

D-5
(914) 633-2503
(800) 231-IONA (in-state)

Full-time: 1863 men, 2044 women	Faculty: 218; IIA, av$
Part-time: 472 men, 1003 women	Ph.D.s: 66%
Graduate: 715 men, 929 women	Student/Faculty: 18 to 1
Year: semesters, summer session	Tuition: $10,210
Application Deadline: March 15	Room & Board: $6100
Freshman Class: 4892 applied, 3530 accepted, 913 enrolled	
SAT I Verbal/Math: 402/450	**COMPETITIVE**

Iona College, founded in 1940, is an independent, largely commuter college with a Catholic tradition, offering programs through schools of general studies, arts and science, and business. It has campuses in Rockland County and Manhattan in addition to the main campus in New Rochelle. There are 3 undergraduate and 2 graduate schools. In addition to regional accreditation, Iona has baccalaureate program accreditation with CSWE and NLN. The library contains 309,518 volumes, 90,000 microform items, and 13,399 audiovisual forms, and subscribes to 1260 periodicals. Computerized library sources and services include the card catalog, interlibrary loans, and database searching. Special learning facilities include a learning resource center, art gallery, electron microscope, speech and hearing clinic, and radio and television studios. The 35-acre campus is in a suburban

area 20 miles northeast of New York City. Including residence halls, there are 47 buildings on campus.

Student Life: About 91% of undergraduates are from New York. Students come from 22 states, 46 foreign countries, and Canada. Thirty-two percent are from public schools; 68% from private. Seventy percent are white; 16% African American; 10% Hispanic. Most are Catholic. The average age of freshmen is 18; all undergraduates, 20. Twenty-one percent drop out by the end of their first year; 63% remain to graduate.

Housing: A total of 600 students can be accommodated in college housing. College-sponsored living facilities include single-sex and coed dormitories. On-campus housing is available on a first-come, first-served basis and is available on a lottery system for upperclassmen. Priority is given to out-of-town students. Eighty-nine percent of students commute. Alcohol is not permitted. All students may keep cars on campus.

Activities: About 5% of men belong to 8 local and 2 national fraternities; about 5% of women belong to 7 local and 2 national sororities. There are 74 groups on campus, including bagpipe band, cheerleading, choir, chorale, computers, dance, drama, ethnic, honors, international, literary magazine, musical theater, newspaper, pep band, political, professional, radio and TV, religious, SADD, social, student government, various clubs for almost all majors, and yearbook. Popular campus events include Founders Day, Day of the Peacemaker, Columbus Day Carnival, and Homecoming.

Sports: There are 12 intercollegiate sports for men and 8 for women, and 5 intramural sports for men and 2 for women. Athletic and recreation facilities include an all-weather football-soccer field, a gymnasium, a Nautilus fitness center, a baseball field, saunas, a track, and a swimming pool. The campus stadium seats 1200 and the indoor gymnasium 3200.

Disabled Students: Eighty percent of the campus is accessible to disabled students. The following facilities are available: wheelchair ramps, elevators, special parking, specially equipped rest rooms, special class scheduling, lowered drinking fountains, and lowered telephones. All classes are on the first floor.

Services: In addition to many counseling and information services, tutoring is available in some subjects, including mathematics, statistics, computer science, English composition, history, Spanish, scientific and technological literacy, accounting, business, and management science. There is also a reader service for the blind and remedial math, reading, and writing as well as note-taking for challenged students.

Campus Safety and Security: Campus safety and security measures include 24-hour foot and vehicle patrol, shuttle buses, informal discussions, and pamphlets, posters, and films. In addition, there are lighted pathways and sidewalks.

Programs of Study: Iona awards the B.A., B.S., B.B.A., and B.P.S. degrees. Associate and master's degrees also are awarded. Bachelor's degrees are awarded in BIOLOGICAL SCIENCE (biology/biological science and ecology), BUSINESS (accounting, banking and finance, business administration and management, business economics, business law, management information systems, management science, and marketing/retailing/merchandising), COMMUNICATIONS AND THE ARTS (advertising, communications, dramatic arts, English, film arts, French, Italian, journalism, and Spanish), COMPUTER AND PHYSICAL SCIENCE (computer science, information sciences and systems, mathematics, and physics), EDUCATION (elementary, foreign languages, middle school, science, and secondary), HEALTH PROFESSIONS (health care administration, medical laboratory technology, predentistry, premedicine, prepharmacy, preveterinary science, and speech pathology/audiology), SOCIAL SCIENCE (criminal justice, economics, history, international relations, philosophy, political science/government, prelaw, psychology, religion, social science, social work, sociology, and urban studies). Accounting, computer science, and management information systems are the strongest academically. Communication arts, accounting, and management have the largest enrollments.

Required: The core curriculum includes 24 credits of humanities, 6 credits each of communications, social science, and science and technology, and 12 credits of natural and symbolic languages. Computer literacy is required. The total number of credits required in liberal arts is 120, with 39 to 46 in the major; the business program requires 126 credits, with 30 in the major. The minimum GPA is 2.0.

Special: There are cross-registration and co-op programs with Concordia College, Marymount College/Tarrytown, and the College of New Rochelle. There are internships for upperclassmen. Study abroad is available in Ireland, Belgium, France, Spain, Italy, and Morocco. There is work-study in Iona offices and academic departments. Students may earn a combined B.A.-B.S. degree in economics, psychology, elementary education, early secondary education, and mathematics education. The college offers dual and student-designed majors, a general studies degree, and credit by examination and for life/military/work experience. There is a freshman honors program on campus, as well as 15 national honor societies.

Faculty/Classroom: Sixty-five percent of faculty are male; 35%, female. Ninety-seven percent teach undergraduates. No introductory courses are taught by graduate students. The average class size in an introductory lecture is 28; in a laboratory and a regular course offering, 20.

Admissions: About 72% of the 1993–94 applicants were accepted. The SAT scores for the 1993–94 freshman class were as follows: Verbal—86% below 500, 11% between 500 and 599, and 3% between 600 and 700; Math—68% below 500, 25% between 500 and 599, 6% between 600 and 700, and 1% above 700. About 19% of the current freshmen were in the top fifth of their class; 41% were in the top two fifths.

Requirements: Iona requires applicants to be in the upper 60% of their class. A minimum GPA of 2.5 is required. The SAT I is required. Applicants must complete 16 academic credits, including 4 units of English, 3 of mathematics, 2 of foreign language, and 1 each of history, science, and social studies. A GED is accepted. An essay and an interview are recommended. AP and CLEP credits are accepted. Important factors used in the admissions decision are recommendations by school officials, extracurricular activities record, leadership record, personality, intangible qualities, and parents or siblings attending the school.

Procedure: Freshmen are admitted fall and spring. Entrance exams should be taken in spring of the senior year. Applications should be filed by March 15 for fall entry and January 1 for spring entry, along with an application fee of $25. Notification is sent on a rolling basis. There are early admissions and deferred admissions plans.

Transfer: Some 144 transfer students enrolled in 1993–94. Transfer applicants must have a GPA of at least 2.5, and must submit high school transcripts if they have earned less than 30 college credits. An interview is recommended. A total of 30 credits out of 120 or 126, depending on the degree, must be completed at Iona.

Visiting: There are regularly scheduled orientations for prospective students, including a meeting with an admissions counselor, a campus tour, and a variety of on-campus programs during the spring and summer. There are guides for informal visits and visitors may sit in on classes. To arrange for a visit, contact the Admissions Office at (914) 633–2502 or (800) 231-IONA (in-state).

Financial Aid: In 1993–94 87% of all current freshmen and 84% of continuing students received some form of financial aid. About 78% of freshmen and 55% of continuing students received need-based aid. The average freshman award was $8000. Of that total, scholarships or need-based grants averaged $3295 ($9990 maximum); loans averaged $2625 (maximum); work contracts averaged $1500 ($3500 maximum); and state and federal entitlements averaged $580. Nineteen percent of undergraduate students work part-time. Average earnings from campus work for the school year are $1130. The average financial indebtedness of the 1992–93 graduate was $7933. Iona is a member of CSS. The FAF or the college's own financial statement and TAP (Tuition Assistance Program) forms are required. The deadline for financial aid applications is April 15.

International Students: There are currently 92 international students enrolled. They must take the TOEFL and achieve a minimum score of 550. The student must also take SAT I or the ACT and obtain minimum scores of 700 on the SAT I and 20 on the ACT.

Computers: The college provides computer facilities for student use. The mainframe is an IBM 9121 Model 210. More than 1000 microcomputers throughout the campus provide access to local area networks and mainframe facilities. All students have unlimited access to PC software (24 hours) and mainframe facilities. There are no time limits on using the system. The fee is $20 per semester.

Graduates: In 1992–93 929 bachelor's degrees were awarded. The most popular majors among graduates were communication arts (14%), elementary education (8%), and accounting (7%). Within an average freshman class, 2% graduate in 3 years, 42% in 4 years, and 18% in 5 years. Some 62 companies recruited on campus in 1992–93. In the 1992 graduating class, 10% of the men and 14% of the women were enrolled in graduate school within 6 months of graduation; 72% of all students had found employment.

Admissions Contact: Laurie Austin, Director of Admissions.

ITHACA COLLEGE
Ithaca, NY 14850

C-3
(607) 274-3124

Full-time: 2643 men, 2969 women	Faculty: 480; IIB, +$
Part-time: 65 men, 101 women	Ph.D.s: 85%
Graduate: 57 men, 129 women	Student/Faculty: 12 to 1
Year: semesters, summer session	Tuition: $13,642
Application Deadline: March 1	Room & Board: $6037
Freshman Class: 7259 applied, 5526 accepted, 1388 enrolled	
SAT I or ACT: required	COMPETITIVE

Ithaca College, founded in 1892, is a private, coeducational college offering undergraduate and graduate programs in business, communications, health science and human performance, humanities and sciences, and music. There are 5 undergraduate schools and one

graduate school. In addition to regional accreditation, Ithaca has baccalaureate program accreditation with APTA, NASM, and NRPA. The library contains 315,051 volumes, 168,015 microform items, and 15,557 audiovisual forms, and subscribes to 2394 periodicals. Computerized library sources and services include interlibrary loans and database searching. Special learning facilities include a learning resource center, art gallery, radio station, TV station, film and photography complex, and multi-image and interactive video laboratories. The 600-acre campus is in a small town 250 miles northwest of New York City. Including residence halls, there are 60 buildings on campus.

Student Life: About 54% of undergraduates are from out-of-state, mostly the Middle Atlantic. Students come from 48 states, 53 foreign countries, and Canada. Eighty percent are from public schools; 20% from private. Ninety-three percent are white. The average age of freshmen is 18; all undergraduates, 20. Six percent drop out by the end of their first year; 69% remain to graduate.

Housing: A total of 4100 students can be accommodated in college housing. College-sponsored living facilities include single-sex and coed dormitories and on-campus apartments. In addition, there are special-interest houses. On-campus housing is guaranteed for all 4 years. Seventy-two percent of students live on campus; of those, 95% remain on campus on weekends. All students may keep cars on campus.

Activities: There are no fraternities or sororities on campus. There are 133 groups on campus, including art, chess, choir, chorale, chorus, computers, dance, drama, ethnic, film, gay, honors, international, jazz band, literary magazine, musical theater, newspaper, opera, orchestra, pep band, photography, political, professional, radio and TV, religious, social, social service, student government, and yearbook. Popular campus events include Winter Carnival, Oktoberfest, and a spring concert.

Sports: There are 12 intercollegiate sports for men and 12 for women, and 23 intramural sports for men and 23 for women. Athletic and recreation facilities include a gymnasium, a dance studio, indoor and outdoor pools, wrestling and weight rooms, baseball, football, lacrosse, field hockey, and soccer fields, a sand volleyball court, tennis courts, and a student union.

Disabled Students: The following facilities are available: wheelchair ramps, elevators, special parking, specially equipped rest rooms, special class scheduling, lowered drinking fountains, and lowered telephones.

Services: Nonremedial tutoring is available.

Campus Safety and Security: Campus safety and security measures include 24-hour foot and vehicle patrol, escort service, shuttle buses, pamphlets, posters, and films. In addition, there are emergency telephones and lighted pathways and sidewalks.

Programs of Study: Ithaca awards the B.A., B.S., B.F.A., and B.M. degrees. Master's degrees are also awarded. Bachelor's degrees are awarded in BIOLOGICAL SCIENCE (biochemistry and biology/biological science), BUSINESS (accounting, banking and finance, business administration and management, international business management, marketing/retailing/merchandising, personnel management, recreation and leisure services, and sports management), COMMUNICATIONS AND THE ARTS (art, art history and appreciation, broadcasting, communications, dramatic arts, English, film arts, fine arts, French, German, jazz, journalism, music, music performance, music theory and composition, photography, Spanish, speech/debate/rhetoric, telecommunications, and visual and performing arts), COMPUTER AND PHYSICAL SCIENCE (chemistry, computer programming, computer science, mathematics, and physics), EDUCATION (education of the deaf and hearing impaired, foreign languages, health, music, physical, science, and secondary), HEALTH PROFESSIONS (health care administration, medical records administration/services, physical therapy, predentistry, premedicine, and speech pathology/audiology), SOCIAL SCIENCE (anthropology, economics, history, parks and recreation management, philosophy, physical fitness/movement, political science/government, prelaw, psychology, religion, social studies, and sociology). Physical therapy, communications, accounting, natural sciences, and music are the strongest academically. Business, communications, psychology, English, physical therapy, and music have the largest enrollments.

Required: Students must successfully complete a minimum of 120 credit hours. In addition, each student must meet the requirements of a core curriculum, which varies with each school within the college and includes courses in the liberal arts and professional courses outside the student's major.

Special: Cross-registration is available with Cornell University. Opportunities are also provided for internships, work-study programs, dual majors, accelerated degree programs, nondegree study, pass/fail options, student-designed majors, a 3–2 engineering degree with Cornell University, a B.A.-B.S. degree, credit for life experience, and study abroad in the college's London Center and in other foreign cities. There is a freshman honors program on campus, as well as 12 national honor societies. Ten departments have honors programs.

Faculty/Classroom: Sixty-five percent of faculty are male; 35%, female. All teach undergraduates. No introductory courses are taught by graduate students. The average class size in an introductory lecture is 20; in a laboratory, 10; and in a regular course offering, 16.

Admissions: About 76% of the 1993–94 applicants were accepted. The SAT scores for the 1993–94 freshman class were as follows: Verbal—52% below 500, 38% between 500 and 599, 9% between 600 and 700, and 1% above 700; Math—24% below 500, 50% between 500 and 599, 24% between 600 and 700, and 2% above 700. About 43% of the current freshmen were in the top fifth of their class; 73% were in the top two fifths. About 15 freshmen graduated first in their class.

Requirements: The SAT I or ACT is required. In addition, applicants should be graduates of an accredited secondary school with a minimum of 16 Carnegie units, including 4 years of English, 3 each of mathematics, science, and social studies, 2 of foreign language, and other college-preparatory electives. The GED is accepted. An essay is required, as is an audition for music students. In some majors, a portfolio and an interview are recommended. AP and CLEP credits are accepted. Important factors used in the admissions decision are advanced placement or honor courses, evidence of special talent, leadership record, recommendations by school officials, and extra-curricular activities record.

Procedure: Freshmen are admitted in the fall and spring. Entrance exams should be taken in the spring of the junior year or the fall of the senior year. There are early decision, early admissions, and deferred admissions plans. Early decision applications should be filed by November 1; regular applications, by March 1 for fall entry and November 1 for spring entry, along with an application fee of $40. Notification of early decision is sent December 15; regular decision, on a rolling basis. About 215 early decision candidates were accepted for the 1993–94 class. A waiting list is an active part of the admissions procedure.

Transfer: About 150 transfer students enrolled in a recent year. Transfer applicants must submit SAT I or ACT scores, a high school transcript, and transcripts from previously attended colleges. A college minimum GPA of 2.6 is required. At least 30 credits out of 120 must be completed at Ithaca.

Visiting: There are regularly scheduled orientations for prospective students, including a campus tour and an interview with an admissions counselor. There are guides for informal visits, and visitors may sit in on classes. To arrange for a visit, contact the Director of Admissions at (607) 274–3124.

Financial Aid: In 1993–94, 55% of all students received some form of financial aid. About 65% of freshmen and 60% of continuing students received need-based aid. The average freshman award was $11,000. Of that total, scholarships or need-based grants averaged $8700 ($14,000 maximum); loans averaged $2200 ($2625 maximum); and work contracts averaged $1000 ($1500 maximum). Forty percent of undergraduate students work part-time. Average earnings from campus work for the school year are $1000. Ithaca is a member of CSS. The FAF is required. The deadline for financial aid applications is March 1.

International Students: There are currently 52 international students enrolled. They must take the TOEFL or the University of Michigan Language Test and achieve a minimum score on the TOEFL of 550. They must also take the SAT I or the ACT.

Computers: The college provides computer facilities for student use. The mainframes are a DEC VAX 11/750 and a DEC VAX 11/785. There are more than 260 microcomputers on 6 local area networks in 7 buildings across campus. All students may access the system 24 hours a day. There are no time limits on using the system and no fees.

Graduates: In a recent year, 1347 bachelor's degrees were awarded. The most popular majors among graduates were TV and radio (9%), sociology (7%), and management (7%). Within an average freshman class, 53% graduate in 4 years, 65% in 5 years, and 67% in 6 years. Some 63 companies recruited on campus in a recent year.

Admissions Contact: Dr. Peter A. Stace, Dean of Admissions and Enrollment Planning.

JEWISH THEOLOGICAL SEMINARY OF AMERICA
LIST COLLEGE OF JEWISH STUDIES
New York, NY 10027

D-5

(212) 678–8832

Full-time: 56 men, 67 women	Faculty: 60
Part-time: 1 man, 3 women	Ph.D.s: 95%
Graduate: 188 men, 184 women	Student/Faculty: 2 to 1
Year: semesters, summer session	Tuition: $6795
Application Deadline: February 15	Room & Board: $6000
Freshman Class: 80 applied, 57 accepted, 32 enrolled	
SAT I Verbal/Math: 580/600	ACT: 28 HIGHLY COMPETITIVE

The Jewish Theological Seminary/List College of Jewish Studies, founded in 1886, is a private, coeducational institution affiliated with

the Conservative branch of the Jewish faith. JTS offers undergraduate and graduate programs in all aspects of Judaica, including the Bible, rabbinics, literature, history, philosophy, education, and communal service. There is also a combined undergraduate program with Columbia University and Barnard College. There are 3 graduate schools. The 3 libraries contain 275,000 volumes and 3500 microform items, and subscribe to 750 periodicals. Computerized library sources and services include the card catalog, interlibrary loans, and database searching. Special learning facilities include a learning resource center, an art gallery, a music center, the Melton Research Center, and the Jewish Museum Archives Center. The 1-acre campus is in an urban area on the Upper West Side of Manhattan. Including residence halls, there are 6 buildings on campus.

Student Life: About 65% of undergraduates are from out-of-state, mostly the Northeast. Students come from 28 states, 5 foreign countries, and Canada. Sixty percent are from public schools; 40% from private. Ninety-seven percent are white. Most are Jewish. The average age of freshmen is 18; all undergraduates, 20. About 96% of freshmen remain to graduate.

Housing: A total of 212 students can be accommodated in college housing. College-sponsored living facilities include coed dormitories, on-campus apartments, off-campus apartments, and married-student housing. In addition, there is kosher housing. On-campus housing is guaranteed for all 4 years. Ninety-three percent of students live on campus; of those, 95% remain on campus on weekends. Alcohol is not permitted. All students may keep cars on campus.

Activities: About 12% of men belong to fraternities; about 4% of women belong to sororities. There are 24 groups on campus, including art, band, choir, chorus, computers, dance, drama, ethnic, film, gay, honors, international, literary magazine, musical theater, newspaper, photography, political, professional, radio and TV, religious, social, social service, student government, and yearbook. Popular campus events include Purim, Simchat Torah, and Orientation.

Sports: There are 3 intramural sports for men and 3 for women, and students can participate in Columbia University's intercollegiate sports program. There is a gymnasium. Students enrolled in the dual-degree program may also use the athletic/recreation facilities at Columbia University.

Disabled Students: The entire campus is accessible to disabled students. The following facilities are available: wheelchair ramps, elevators, special parking, specially equipped rest rooms, lowered drinking fountains, lowered telephones, and elevators with braille panels.

Services: In addition to many counseling and information services, tutoring is available in most subjects.

Campus Safety and Security: Campus safety and security measures include 24-hour foot and vehicle patrol, escort service, informal discussions, and pamphlets, posters, and films. In addition, there are emergency telephones and lighted pathways and sidewalks.

Programs of Study: JTS awards the B.A. degree. Master's and doctoral degrees also are awarded. Bachelor's degrees are awarded in religion.

Required: Students must take a Hebrew language requirement, 9 credits in literature, 24 in Jewish history, and 6 each in Bible, Jewish philosophy, and the Talmud. In addition, there are 60 required credits in liberal arts, including 18 credits in English, history, philosophy or social science, and mathematics or laboratory science to be completed at another college or university. A total of 156 credits (96 taken at JTS) is required for graduation, with 21 in a major field.

Special: There is a joint liberal arts program with Columbia University and a double-degree program with Barnard College, which enables students to earn 2 B.A. degrees in 4 to 4 1/2 years. Study abroad is available in Israel, England, France, and Spain. Student-designed majors, credit by exam, and nondegree study are also offered. There is a freshman honors program on campus, as well as a chapter of Phi Beta Kappa.

Faculty/Classroom: Sixty-eight percent of faculty are male; 32%, female. All teach and do research. Graduate students teach 1% of introductory courses. The average class size in an introductory lecture is 30 and in a regular course offering, 10.

Admissions: About 71% of the 1993–94 applicants were accepted. The SAT scores for the 1993–94 freshman class were as follows: Verbal—4% below 500, 54% between 500 and 599, 36% between 600 and 700, and 4% above 700; Math—4% below 500, 27% between 500 and 599, 54% between 600 and 700, and 13% above 700. There were 2 National Merit finalists and 1 semifinalist.

Requirements: A minimum GPA of 3.0 is required. The SAT I or ACT is required, as is the EN or ES SAT II: Subject tests. Applicants must be graduates of an accredited secondary school or have the GED. An essay and 2 recommendations are required. AP credits are accepted. Important factors used in the admissions decision are advanced placement or honor courses, extracurricular activities record, personality, intangible qualities, leadership record, and evidence of special talent.

Procedure: Freshmen are admitted fall and spring. Entrance exams should be taken in the spring of the junior year. Early decision applications should be filed by November 15; regular applications, by February 15 for fall entry and November 1 for spring entry, along with an application fee of $60. Notification of early decision is sent December 15; regular decision, April 1. There are early decision, early admissions, and deferred admissions plans. Ten early decision candidates were accepted for the 1993–94 class.

Transfer: Six transfer students enrolled in 1993–94. Applicants must submit SAT I or ACT scores, an essay, a high school transcript, a college transcript, and 2 academic recommendations. A minimum college GPA of 2.5 is required. An interview is recommended. A total of 48 credits out of 156 must be completed at JTS.

Visiting: There are regularly scheduled orientations for prospective students, including a tour of the campus and of Columbia University, an interview with the dean, and an overnight stay in the dormitory. There are guides for informal visits and visitors may sit in on classes and stay overnight at the school. To arrange for a visit, contact Marci Harris Blumenthal, Admissions Director, at (212) 678–8832.

Financial Aid: In 1993–94, 40% of all current freshmen and 60% of continuing students received some form of financial aid. About 40% of freshmen and 60% of continuing students received need-based aid. The average freshman award was $12,000. Of that total, scholarships or need-based grants averaged $5500 ($12,700 maximum); loans averaged $2500 ($2625 maximum). Fifteen percent of undergraduate students work part-time. JTS is a member of CSS. The FAF, the college's own financial statement, the 1040 tax forms, and the FAFSA are required. The deadline for financial aid applications is February 15.

International Students: There are currently 33 international students enrolled. They must take the TOEFL or the college's own test and achieve a minimum score on the TOEFL of 500.

Computers: Students may use Columbia University facilities. There are no time limits on using the system and no fees.

Graduates: In 1992–93 27 bachelor's degrees were awarded. Within an average freshman class, 60% graduate in 4 years and 40% in 4 1/2 to 5 years.

Admissions Contact: Marci Harris Blumenthal, Director of Admissions.

JULLIARD SCHOOL
New York, NY 10023–6590

Full-time: 200 men, 280 women	**Faculty:** 50
Part-time: none	**Ph.Ds:** n/av
Graduate: 170 men, 200 women	**Student/Faculty:** 10 to 1
Year: semesters	**Tuition:** $12,000
Application Deadline: see profile	**Room & Board:** $6900
Freshman Class: n/av	
SAT I or ACT: not required	**SPECIAL**

D-5

(212) 799–5000, ext. 223

The Juilliard School, founded in 1905, is a private professional college of dance, music, and drama. The 2 libraries contain 65,000 volumes, 1300 microform items, and 15,000 audiovisual forms, and subscribe to 175 periodicals. Computerized library sources and services include interlibrary loans. Special learning facilities include 200 practice rooms, 5 theaters, scenery and costume shops, and dance studios. All Juilliard facilities are housed in 2 buildings at Lincoln Center in Manhattan. The campus is in an urban area.

Student Life: Students come from 30 states, 30 foreign countries, and Canada. Sixty percent are white; 31% Asian American. The average age of freshmen is 18; all undergraduates, 21.

Housing: A total of 375 students can be accommodated in college housing. College-sponsored living facilities include single-sex and coed dormitories and off-campus apartments. In addition, there are single-sex, no-smoking, and no-practice (silent) floors, as well as floors for new students. On-campus housing is guaranteed (and required) for the freshman year only, is available on a first-come, first-served basis, and is available on a lottery system for upperclassmen. Fifty-two percent of students commute. All students may keep cars on campus.

Activities: There are no fraternities or sororities on campus. There are 20 groups on campus, including band, choir, chorale, chorus, dance, drama, ethnic, gay, international, jazz band, marching band, newspaper, opera, orchestra, professional, religious, social service, student government, symphony, and yearbook. Popular campus events include performances by the Juilliard Orchestra at Avery Fisher Hall, dance concerts, drama repertory, opera season, and Rite of Spring, a race around Lincoln Center by students and members of several New York cultural institutions.

Sports: There are 2 intercollegiate sports for men and 1 for women, and 2 intramural sports for men and 1 for women. Athletic and recreation facilities include a health club in the residence hall.

Disabled Students: All of the campus is accessible to disabled students. The following facilities are available: wheelchair ramps, elevators, specially equipped rest rooms, lowered drinking fountains, and lowered telephones.

Services: In addition to many counseling and information services, tutoring is available in some subjects, including ear training and literature and materials of music. There is an English laboratory for nonnative speakers.

Campus Safety and Security: Campus safety and security measures include 24-hour foot and vehicle patrol, self-defense education, informal discussions, and pamphlets, posters, and films. In addition, there are emergency telephones, lighted pathways and sidewalks, and 24-hour guards in the residence hall and the main building, videocameras, and turnstiles with ID-card access.

Programs of Study: Juilliard awards the B.Mus. and B.F.A. degrees. Master's and doctoral degrees also are awarded. Bachelor's degrees are awarded in COMMUNICATIONS AND THE ARTS (dance, dramatic arts, music and composition, piano/organ, strings, and voice). Piano, voice, and violin have the largest enrollments.

Required: Each division has its own requirements for graduation.

Special: A joint program with Columbia University and Barnard College allows students to obtain a 5-year B.A.-B.Mus. degree. Internship are available with cultural organizations in New York City. There is study abroad in music academies in England, Israel, and Russia. Work-study programs, accelerated degrees and dual majors in music, a combined B.Mus.-M.Mus. degree, nondegree study, and pass/fail options are also available.

Faculty/Classroom: Sixty-five percent of faculty are male; 35%, female. All teach undergraduates. Graduate students teach 1% of introductory courses. The average class size in a regular course offering is 12.

Admissions: About 17% of a recent year's applicants were accepted.

Requirements: A high school diploma or GED is required. Students are accepted primarily on the basis of personal auditions rather than tests. AP credits are accepted. Important factors used in the admissions decision are evidence of special talent, personality, intangible qualities, recommendations by school officials, recommendations by alumni, and parents or siblings attending the school.

Procedure: Freshmen are admitted in the fall. Application deadlines are January 7 for all drama applicants and for dance and drama applicants to meet March auditions; and March 15 for dance and music applicants to meet May auditions. Application fee is $75. Notification is sent within a month after the audition. There is an early admissions plan. A waiting list is an active part of the admissions procedure, with about 5% of applicants on the list.

Transfer: About 62 transfer students enrolled in a recent year. Transfer applicants must audition in person.

Visiting: There are regularly scheduled orientations for prospective students, including guided tours and question-and-answer sessions, Monday to Friday at 2:30 P.M. Visitors may sit in on classes and stay overnight at the school. To arrange for a visit, contact David Stull, Assistant Director of Admissions at (212) 799-5000, ext. 223.

Financial Aid: In a recent year, 87% of all current freshmen and 86% of continuing students received need-based aid. The average freshman award was $10,452. Of that total, scholarships or need-based grants averaged $4952 ($18,000 maximum); loans averaged $4000; and work contracts averaged $1500 ($5000 maximum). Eighty percent of undergraduate students work part-time. Average earnings from campus work for the school year are $1500. The average financial indebtedness of the 1992–93 graduate was $11,600. Juilliard is a member of CSS. The FAF and the college's own financial statement are required.

International Students: There were recently 300 international students enrolled. They must take the TOEFL or the college's own test. The student must also audition in person.

Graduates: In a recent year, 86 bachelor's degrees were awarded.

Admissions Contact: Office of Admissions.

KEUKA COLLEGE
Keuka Park, NY 14478

B-3

(315) 536-4411, ext. 254
(800) 54-KEUKA (out-of-state)

Full-time: 737 men and women	Faculty: 44; IIB, --$
Part-time: 14 men, 74 women	Ph.D.s: 58%
Graduate: none	Student/Faculty: 17 to 1
Year: 4-1-4, summer session	Tuition: $9310
Application Deadline: open	Room & Board: $4350
Freshman Class: 461 applied, 381 accepted, 174 enrolled	
SAT I Verbal/Math: 451/495	**COMPETITIVE**

Keuka College, founded in 1890, is an independent, coeducational college affiliated with American Baptist Churches, offering instruction in the liberal arts. In addition to regional accreditation, Keuka has baccalaureate program accreditation with AHEA, CSWE, and NLN. The library contains 150,000 volumes, 4408 microform items, and 2009 audiovisual forms, and subscribes to 388 periodicals. Computerized library sources and services include the card catalog and interlibrary loans. Special learning facilities include a learning resource center and art gallery. The 173-acre campus is in a rural area 60 miles south of Rochester. Including residence halls, there are 19 buildings on campus.

Student Life: About 94% of undergraduates are from New York. Students come from 13 states, 4 foreign countries, and Canada. Eighty percent are from public schools; 20% from private. Ninety-two percent are white. Thirty percent are Protestant. The average age of freshmen is 18; all undergraduates, 23. Twenty percent drop out by the end of their first year; 55% remain to graduate.

Housing: A total of 800 students can be accommodated in college housing. College-sponsored living facilities include single-sex and coed dormitories. On-campus housing is guaranteed for all 4 years. Sixty-nine percent of students live on campus; of those, 75% remain on campus on weekends. Alcohol is not permitted. Upperclassmen may keep cars on campus.

Activities: There are no fraternities or sororities on campus. There are 42 groups on campus, including art, cheerleading, choir, chorale, computers, dance, drama, ethnic, gay, honors, international, literary magazine, newspaper, political, professional, religious, social, social service, student government, and yearbook. Popular campus events include Spring Weekend, Freshman Theme Days, Homecoming, May Day, Fall Weekend, Parents Weekend, Moving Up, 100 Days, Freshman Stunt, and crew races.

Sports: Athletic and recreation facilities include an Olympic-sized pool, a gymnasium, and a new fitness center and weight room.

Disabled Students: The following facilities are available: wheelchair ramps, elevators, special parking, specially equipped rest rooms, and special class scheduling.

Services: In addition to many counseling and information services, tutoring is available in most subjects. There is remedial math, reading, and writing.

Campus Safety and Security: Campus safety and security measures include escort service, informal discussions, pamphlets, posters, and films, and lighted pathways and sidewalks.

Programs of Study: Keuka awards the B.A. and B.S. degrees. Bachelor's degrees are awarded in BIOLOGICAL SCIENCE (biochemistry and biology/biological science), BUSINESS (business administration and management, marketing/retailing/merchandising, and personnel management), COMMUNICATIONS AND THE ARTS (English), COMPUTER AND PHYSICAL SCIENCE (mathematics), EDUCATION (elementary, secondary, and special), HEALTH PROFESSIONS (medical laboratory technology, nursing, and occupational therapy), SOCIAL SCIENCE (history, political science/government, social work, and sociology). Occupational therapy, education, and business administration have the largest enrollments.

Required: Students must complete 1 field period combining academic study and professional experience for each year of enrollment. The core curriculum consists of 43 to 46 credits, including required courses in physical education, computer science, and integrative studies. A total of 120 credit hours is required for graduation with a minimum of 30 credits in the major and a GPA of 2.0.

Special: There are co-op programs with other members of the Rochester Area Colleges Consortium. The college offers internships, study abroad, a Washington semester, dual majors, student-designed majors, and a 3–2 engineering degree with Clarkson University. Credit is also given by exam and for work experience. There is a freshman honors program on campus, as well as 16 national honor societies, including Phi Beta Kappa.

Faculty/Classroom: Fifty percent of faculty are male; 50%, female. All teach undergraduates. The average class size in an introductory lecture is 25; in a laboratory, 12; and in a regular course offering, 25.

Admissions: About 83% of the 1993–94 applicants were accepted. The SAT scores for the 1993–94 freshman class were as follows: Verbal—77% below 500, 21% between 500 and 599, and 3% between 600 and 700; Math—50% below 500, 40% between 500 and 599, 9% between 600 and 700, and 1% above 700. About 27% of the current freshmen were in the top fifth of their class; 82% were in the top two fifths. There was 1 National Merit semifinalist. About 4 freshmen graduated first in their class.

Requirements: Keuka requires applicants to be in the upper 50% of their class. A minimum GPA of 2.8 is required. The SAT I or ACT is required. Students should graduate from an accredited secondary school with a minimum GPA of 2.8. The GED is accepted. A minimum of 15 Carnegie units is required, including 4 years of English, 3 years of history, 2 to 3 years of mathematics and science, 2 of foreign language, and 1 of social studies. An essay is required, and an interview is recommended. AP and CLEP credits are accepted. Important factors used in the admissions decision are recommendations by school officials, extracurricular activities record, leadership record, recommendations by alumni, and personality, intangible qualities.

Procedure: Freshmen are admitted fall and spring. Entrance exams should be taken in the spring of the junior year or the fall of the senior year. Application deadlines are open. The application fee is $25. Notification of early decision is sent December 15; regular decision, on a rolling basis. There are early decision and early admissions plans.

About 12 early decision candidates were accepted for the 1993–94 class.

Transfer: About 89 transfer students enrolled in 1993–94. Applicants must take the SAT I or ACT and submit transcripts. An interview is recommended. A minimum GPA of 2.5 is required in college work. A total of 30 credits out of 120 must be completed at Keuka.

Visiting: There are regularly scheduled orientations for prospective students. Open houses are held in October, November, and February, when students can speak with faculty, student affairs, financial aid representatives, and current students. There are guides for informal visits and visitors may sit in on classes and stay overnight at the school. To arrange for a visit, contact the Admissions Office at (800) 54-KEUKA.

Financial Aid: In 1993–94, 98% of all current freshmen and 95% of continuing students received some form of financial aid. About 90% of freshmen and 82% of continuing students received need-based aid. The average freshman award was $9400. Of that total, scholarships or need-based grants averaged $2600 ($9100 maximum); loans averaged $2200 ($2625 maximum); and work contracts averaged $1200 ($1500 maximum). Seventy-five percent of undergraduate students work part-time. The average financial indebtedness of the 1992–93 graduate was $10,500. Keuka is a member of CSS. The college's own financial statement and FAFSA are required. The deadline for financial aid applications is March 15.

International Students: There are currently 5 international students enrolled. They must take the TOEFL and achieve a minimum score of 550.

Computers: The college provides computer facilities for student use. The mainframe is a DEC 11/34A. Two fully equipped microcomputer laboratories, with some access to the mainframe, provide students with word processing, graphics, spreadsheet, and other academic support functions. All students may access the system. There are no time limits on using the system and no fees.

Graduates: In a recent year 103 bachelor's degrees were awarded. The most popular majors among graduates were occupational therapy (27%), elementary special education (26%), and management (13%).

Admissions Contact: Robert J. Iannuzzo, Dean of Admissions and Financial Aid.

KING'S COLLEGE

D-5

Briarcliff Manor, NY 10510　　　(914) 944-5650; (800) 344-4926

Full-time: 80 men, 141 women　　　Faculty: 26
Part-time: 9 men, 9 women　　　Ph.D.s: 46%
Graduate: none　　　Student/Faculty: 9 to 1
Year: semesters, summer session　　　Tuition: $8440
Application Deadline: open　　　Room & Board: $3920
Freshman Class: 256 applied, 233 accepted, 72 enrolled
SAT I Verbal/Math: 442/465　　　ACT: 25　　　**LESS COMPETITIVE**

King's College, founded in 1938, is a private Christian college offering instruction in liberal arts. The library contains 100,000 volumes and 11,067 microform items, and subscribes to 600 periodicals. Computerized library sources and services include the card catalog, interlibrary loans, and database searching. Special learning facilities include a learning resource center and a technological learning center. The 80-acre campus is in a suburban area 30 miles north of New York City. Including residence halls, there are 10 buildings on campus.

Student Life: About 55% of undergraduates are from out-of-state, mostly the Northeast. Students come from 15 states, 3 foreign countries, and Canada. Forty percent are from public schools; 60% from private. Eighty-one percent are white; 12% African American. Most are Protestant. The average age of freshmen is 18; all undergraduates, 21. Twenty-four percent drop out by the end of their first year; 45% remain to graduate.

Housing: A total of 580 students can be accommodated in college housing. College-sponsored living facilities include single-sex dormitories. On-campus housing is guaranteed for all 4 years. Ninety-seven percent of students live on campus; of those, 50% remain on campus on weekends. Alcohol is not permitted. All students may keep cars on campus.

Activities: There are no fraternities or sororities on campus. There are 20 groups on campus, including cheerleading, choir, chorus, drama, honors, international, jazz band, literary magazine, musical theater, orchestra, pep band, political, professional, religious, social, social service, and student government. Popular campus events include the King's College Tourney, Homecoming, and Parents Day.

Sports: There are 3 intercollegiate sports for men and 4 for women, and 4 intramural sports for men and 3 for women. Athletic and recreation facilities include an outdoor track; soccer, baseball, and softball fields; tennis courts; a field house; and a game room.

Disabled Students: Sixty-five percent of the campus is accessible to disabled students. The following facilities are available: wheelchair ramps, elevators, special parking, and specially equipped rest rooms.

Services: In addition to many counseling and information services, tutoring is available in every subject. There is also remedial math, reading, and writing.

Campus Safety and Security: Campus safety and security measures include 24-hour foot and vehicle patrol, informal discussions, and lighted pathways and sidewalks.

Programs of Study: King's awards the B.A. and B.S. degrees. Associate degrees also are awarded. Bachelor's degrees are awarded in BIOLOGICAL SCIENCE (biology/biological science), BUSINESS (accounting and business administration and management), COMMUNICATIONS AND THE ARTS (English, French, music, and Spanish), COMPUTER AND PHYSICAL SCIENCE (chemistry, computer science, and mathematics), EDUCATION (elementary, music, and physical), HEALTH PROFESSIONS (medical laboratory technology, nursing, and premedicine), SOCIAL SCIENCE (prelaw, psychology, religion, and sociology). Sciences, music, business, and elementary education are the strongest academically. Business and elementary education have the largest enrollments.

Required: All students must take 53 credits in the core curriculum, including courses in the Bible, English, ethics, history, foreign language, physical education, literature, social science, and natural science. A total of 130 credits is required to graduate, with 30 to 72 in the major, and a minimum GPA of 2.0 must be maintained. A comprehensive examination is required in all disciplines.

Special: There are co-op programs in nursing and business/accounting, and cross-registration with Pace University. There are internships in business, communications, and sociology, and study abroad in France, Spain, Germany, England, and the Dominican Republic. The Washington semester is part of the American Studies program. Work-study programs are available with NBC, the March of Dimes, and other companies. Nondegree study and pass/fail options are available.

Faculty/Classroom: Twenty-two percent of faculty are male; 78%, female. All teach undergraduates and 75% do research.

Admissions: About 91% of the 1993–94 applicants were accepted. The SAT scores for the 1993–94 freshman class were as follows: Verbal—76% below 500, 19% between 500 and 599, and 6% between 600 and 700; Math—67% below 500, 21% between 500 and 599, and 12% between 600 and 700. About 24% of the current freshmen were in the top fifth of their class; 40% were in the top two fifths. Five freshmen graduated first in their class.

Requirements: King's requires a minimum grade average of B-. The SAT I or ACT is required. Applicants should graduate from an accredited secondary school or have a GED. A total of 16 Carnegie units is required, including 3 or more units of English, and 6 from the subject areas of science, mathematics, and language. An essay and an interview are recommended. Students must audition for the music program. AP and CLEP credits are accepted. Important factors used in the admissions decision are advanced placement or honor courses, personality, intangible qualities, leadership record, evidence of special talent, and extracurricular activities record.

Procedure: Freshmen are admitted to all sessions. Entrance exams should be taken in the junior or senior year. The application deadlines are open. Application fee is $20. Notification is sent on a rolling basis. There are early admissions and deferred admissions plans.

Transfer: Some 17 transfer students enrolled in 1993–94. Transfer applicants must submit a college transcript, or high school transcript if there are fewer than 30 hours of college credit, and 2 recommendations, 1 from a pastor. A minimum 2.0 GPA is required. The SAT I or ACT is recommended. A total of 30 credits out of 130 must be completed at King's.

Visiting: There are regularly scheduled orientations for prospective students, including a campus tour; meetings with a financial aid officer, a faculty member, and an admissions officer; and attendance at chapel and a class. There are guides for informal visits and visitors may sit in on classes and stay overnight at the school. To arrange for a visit, contact the Office of Admissions at (800) 344-4926.

Financial Aid: In 1993–94 89% of all current freshmen and 85% of continuing students received some form of financial aid. About 93% of freshmen and 95% of continuing students received need-based aid. The average freshman award was $9885. Of that total, scholarships or need-based grants averaged $2500 ($5000 maximum); loans averaged $2550 ($4875 maximum); and work contracts averaged $1300 ($1500 maximum). Seventy-two percent of undergraduate students work part-time. Average earnings from campus work for the school year are $1350. The average financial indebtedness of the 1992–93 graduate was $12,000. King's is a member of CSS. The FAF, the college's own financial statement, income tax forms, and FAFSA are required. The deadline for financial aid applications is August 1.

International Students: The school actively recruits these students. They must take the TOEFL and achieve a minimum score of 450. The student must also take the SAT I or the ACT, achieving a minimum composite score of 800 or 18, respectively.

Computers: The college provides computer facilities for student use. The mainframe is a DEC VAX 11/750. There are also 50 Apple II, Apple Macintosh, and IBM-compatible microcomputers available in the computer center. Those students in a class for which access is required and those students majoring in mathematical or computer science may access the system. There are no time limits on using the system and no fees.

Graduates: In 1992–93 116 bachelor's degrees were awarded.

Admissions Contact: Cheryl L. Burdick, Director of Admissions.

LABORATORY INSTITUTE OF
MERCHANDISING   D-5

New York, NY 10022–5268   (212) 752–1530; (800) 677–1323

Full-time: 9 men, 161 women	Faculty: 7
Part-time: 3 women	Ph.D.s: 3%
Graduate: none	Student/Faculty: 24 to 1
Year: 4–1–4, summer session	Tuition: $9800
Application Deadline: open	Room & Board: n/app
Freshman Class: 151 applied, 109 accepted, 69 enrolled	
SAT I or ACT: required	SPECIAL

The Laboratory Institute of Merchandising, founded in 1939, is a private college offering programs in fashion merchandising and visual merchandising. The library contains 9660 volumes, 63 microform items, and 350 audiovisual forms, and subscribes to 110 periodicals. Special learning facilities include a learning resource center. The campus is in midtown Manhattan. There is 1 building on campus. There are no residence halls.

Student Life: About 52% of undergraduates are from out-of-state, mostly the Middle Atlantic. Students come from 18 states, 7 foreign countries, and Canada. Sixty-five percent are from public schools; 35% from private. Fifty-three percent are white; 25% African American; 20% Hispanic. The average age of freshmen is 18; all undergraduates, 20. About 89% of freshmen remain to graduate.

Housing: There are no residence halls. Alcohol is not permitted.

Activities: There are no fraternities or sororities on campus. There are some groups and organizations, including ethnic, film, student government, and yearbook. Popular campus events include the Annual Fashion Show.

Sports: There is no sports program at LIM.

Disabled Students: Elevators are available for disabled students.

Services: In addition to many counseling and information services, tutoring is available in some subjects. There is also remedial math, reading, and writing.

Campus Safety and Security: Campus safety and security measures include informal discussions and pamphlets, posters, and films.

Programs of Study: LIM awards the B.P.S. in fashion merchandising and visual merchandising. Associate degrees also are awarded. Bachelor's degrees are awarded in BUSINESS (apparel and accessories marketing and fashion merchandising).

Required: Students must complete 33 credits in the liberal arts and a minimum of 70 in fashion/business courses. Freshmen and sophomores must successfully complete a 3-credit work project each year. Seniors must complete a 13-credit, semester-long co-op program. A total of 128 credits and a GPA of 2.0 are required to graduate.

Special: There is cross-registration with Fordham University and Marymount College. Internships are required in the first, second, and fourth years. Study abroad is available in London and Paris. There are co-op programs as well as work-study programs with major department stores and specialty shops, manufacturers, showrooms, magazine publishers, and cosmetics companies.

Faculty/Classroom: Forty-eight percent of faculty are male; 52%, female. The average class size in an introductory lecture is 25.

Admissions: About 72% of the 1993–94 applicants were accepted.

Requirements: The SAT I or the ACT is required, as are an essay and interview. Applicants should be high school graduates or hold the GED. AP and CLEP credits are accepted. Important factors used in the admissions decision are personality, intangible qualities, leadership record, extracurricular activities record, recommendations by school officials, and recommendations by alumni.

Procedure: Freshmen are admitted fall and spring. Application deadlines are open. The application fee is $35. Notification is sent on a rolling basis.

Transfer: Some 34 transfer students enrolled in 1993–94. Applicants for the upper division (junior or senior year) must have a GPA of 2.5 in at least 60 college credits, submit 2 letters of recommendation (1 educational and 1 professional), and have 2 interviews at the college (1 with Admissions and 1 with Placement). A total of 46 credits out of 128 must be completed at LIM.

Visiting: There are regularly scheduled orientations for prospective students. The Student for a Day program includes classroom visits, a financial aid presentation, lunch, interviews, and a scholarship exam, and is held approximately twice a month. There are guides for informal visits and visitors may sit in on classes. To arrange for a visit, contact the Admissions Office at (212) 752–1530 or (800) 677–1323.

Financial Aid: In 1993–94 65% of all students received some form of financial aid. The average financial indebtedness of the 1992–93 graduate was $12,000. LIM is a member of CSS. The FAF, the college's own financial statement, and FAFSA are required. The deadline for financial aid applications is April 1.

International Students: There are currently 6 international students enrolled. They must take the TOEFL and achieve a minimum score of 550. The student must also take the college's own entrance exam.

Computers: The college provides computer facilities for student use. All students may access the system. There are no time limits on using the system and no fees.

Graduates: In 1992–93 38 bachelor's degrees were awarded. Within an average freshman class, 89% graduate in 4 years. In the 1992 graduating class, 98% of all students found employment within 6 months of graduation.

Admissions Contact: Sandy Joseph, Acting Director of Admission.

LE MOYNE COLLEGE   C-3

Syracuse, NY 13214   (315) 445–4300; (800) 333–4733 (out-of-state)

Full-time: 831 men, 1011 women	Faculty: 119; IIB, +$
Part-time: 227 men, 333 women	Ph.D.s: 92%
Graduate: 58 men, 82 women	Student/Faculty: 15 to 1
Year: semesters, summer session	Tuition: $10,640
Application Deadline: March 15	Room & Board: $4540
Freshman Class: 1470 applied, 1199 accepted, 425 enrolled	
SAT I or ACT: required	COMPETITIVE

Le Moyne College, founded in 1946, is a coeducational liberal arts college in the Jesuit tradition. The library contains 205,464 volumes, 30,363 microform items, and 5348 audiovisual forms, and subscribes to 1734 periodicals. Computerized library sources and services include the card catalog, interlibrary loans, and database searching. Special learning facilities include a learning resource center, art gallery, and radio station. The 150-acre campus is in a suburban area on the eastern edge of the city of Syracuse. Including residence halls, there are 20 buildings on campus.

Student Life: About 92% of undergraduates are from New York. Students come from 17 states, 5 foreign countries, and Canada. Sixty-five percent are from public schools; 35% from private. Eighty-nine percent are white. Eighty-five percent are Catholic; 14% Protestant. The average age of freshmen is 18; all undergraduates, 20. Eight percent drop out by the end of their first year; 73% remain to graduate.

Housing: A total of 1400 students can be accommodated in college housing. College-sponsored living facilities include single-sex and coed dormitories and on-campus apartments. In addition, there are special interest housing. On-campus housing is guaranteed for all 4 years. Seventy-three percent of students live on campus; of those, 80% remain on campus on weekends. All students may keep cars on campus.

Activities: There are no fraternities or sororities on campus. There are 65 groups on campus, including art, cheerleading, chess, chorus, computers, drama, ethnic, honors, international, literary magazine, musical theater, newspaper, opera, pep band, photography, political, professional, radio and TV, religious, social, social service, student government, and yearbook. Popular campus events include Winter/ Spring Olympics, Model UN, student theatrical productions, Women's Week Programs, Winter Formal, ethnic celebrations, concerts, films, and a comedian series.

Sports: There are 8 intercollegiate sports for men and 8 for women, and 6 intramural sports for men and 5 for women. Athletic and recreation facilities include a 2500-seat athletic center, a multipurpose recreation center, indoor and outdoor tennis courts, grass playing fields for varsity and intramural events, on-campus cross-country trails, a 6-lane, 25-yd. indoor swimming pool, 4 racquetball courts, an indoor running track, and exercise equipment.

Disabled Students: Ninety-five percent of the campus is accessible to disabled students. The following facilities are available: wheelchair ramps, elevators, special parking, specially equipped rest rooms, lowered drinking fountains, and lowered telephones.

Services: In addition to many counseling and information services, tutoring is available in every subject. There is also remedial math and writing.

Campus Safety and Security: Campus safety and security measures include 24-hour foot and vehicle patrol, self-defense education, escort service, and informal discussions. In addition, there are pamphlets, posters, and films, emergency telephones, lighted pathways and sidewalks, and a campus watch program.

Programs of Study: Le Moyne awards the B.A. and B.S. degrees. Master's degrees are also awarded. Bachelor's degrees are awarded in BIOLOGICAL SCIENCE (biology/biological science), BUSINESS (accounting, business administration and management, industrial relations and human resource management, marketing/retailing/ merchandising, and operations research), COMMUNICATIONS

AND THE ARTS (communications, dramatic arts, English, and foreign languages and literature), COMPUTER AND PHYSICAL SCIENCE (actuarial science, chemistry, computer science, mathematics, multiple sciences, physics, and statistics), EDUCATION (business, elementary, foreign languages, science, secondary, and special), ENGINEERING AND ENVIRONMENTAL DESIGN (preengineering), HEALTH PROFESSIONS (predentistry and premedicine), SOCIAL SCIENCE (criminal justice, economics, history, philosophy, political science/government, prelaw, psychology, religious studies, and sociology). Business, biology, psychology, and accounting have the largest enrollments.

Required: A core curriculum of 14 courses in the humanities is required. Students must earn a GPA of 2.0 and 120 credit hours to graduate.

Special: Internships are available with businesses, government offices, social service agencies, and poverty programs. A campus work-study program, study abroad in a variety of countries, dual majors, and a Washington semester are offered. A 3–2 engineering degree is available with several other institutions and there are early assurance medical and dental programs. Some pass/fail options are possible. There is a freshman honors program on campus, as well as 10 national honor societies. Most departments have honors programs.

Faculty/Classroom: Sixty-six percent of faculty are male; 34%, female. All teach and do research. No introductory courses are taught by graduate students. The average class size in an introductory lecture is 23; in a laboratory, 16; and in a regular course offering, 19.

Admissions: About 82% of the 1993–94 applicants were accepted. The SAT scores for the 1993–94 freshman class were as follows: Verbal—66% below 500, 29% between 500 and 599, and 5% between 600 and 700; Math—31% below 500, 46% between 500 and 599, 20% between 600 and 700, and 3% above 700. The ACT scores were 14% below 21, 24% between 21 and 23, 30% between 24 and 26, 16% between 27 and 28, and 16% above 28. About 46% of the current freshmen were in the top fifth of their class; 77% were in the top two fifths. There were 50 National Merit semifinalists. Ten freshmen graduated first in their class.

Requirements: The SAT I or ACT is required. Students should graduate from an accredited high school. A total of 16 academic units is required: 4 in English, 3 in foreign language, and 3 to 4 each in mathematics, science, and social studies. An essay is required. AP and CLEP credits are accepted. Important factors used in the admissions decision are recommendations by school officials, extracurricular activities record, leadership record, parents or siblings attending the school, and geographic diversity.

Procedure: Freshmen are admitted fall and spring. Entrance exams should be taken in the spring of the junior year or fall of the senior year. Early decision applications should be filed by December 1; regular applications, by March 15 for fall entry and December 1 for spring entry, along with an application fee of $25. Notification of early decision is sent December 15; regular decision, on a rolling basis beginning January 2. There are early decision, early admissions, and deferred admissions plans. Twenty-three early decision candidates were accepted for the 1993–94 class.

Transfer: Some 170 transfer students enrolled in 1993–94. A 2.6 GPA is usually required for admission. A total of 30 credits out of 120 must be completed at Le Moyne.

Visiting: There are regularly scheduled orientations for prospective students, including a campus tour and an interview with admissions counselors. Accepted students are invited to attend class and stay overnight in a dormitory. There are guides for informal visits and visitors may sit in on classes and stay overnight at the school. To arrange for a visit, contact the Admissions Office at (315) 445–4300 or (800) 333–4733.

Financial Aid: In 1993–94 95% of all current freshmen and 90% of continuing students received some form of financial aid. About 66% of freshmen and 65% of continuing students received need-based aid. The average freshman award was $10,000. Of that total, scholarships or need-based grants averaged $6500 ($14,880 maximum); loans averaged $2625 ($4000 maximum); and work contracts averaged $1000 (maximum). Ninety percent of undergraduate students work part-time. Average earnings from campus work for the school year are $1200. The average financial indebtedness of the 1992–93 graduate was $10,936. Le Moyne is a member of CSS. The FAF and the FAFSA, and the college's own financial statement are required. The deadline for financial aid applications is February 15.

International Students: There are currently 25 international students enrolled. The school actively recruits these students. They must take the TOEFL and achieve a minimum score of 550. The student should, if possible, also take the SAT I or the ACT.

Computers: The college provides computer facilities for student use. The mainframe is a DEC VAX 3100–80. Approximately 35 terminals provide public access to the VAX. Dial-in lines and department terminals are also available. There are, in addition, 84 microcomputers in public and departmental laboratories. Available applications include language compilers, statistical packages, curriculum-specific programs, and local and wide-area E-mail. All students may access the system. It may be used 24 hours a day. There are no time limits on using the system and no fees.

Graduates: In 1992–93 515 bachelor's degrees were awarded. The most popular majors among graduates were business administration (25%), accounting (18%), and English and psychology (12%). Within an average freshman class, 70% graduate in 4 years, 75% in 5 years, and 76% in 6 years. Some 63 companies recruited on campus in 1992–93. In the 1992 graduating class, 32% of all students were enrolled in graduate school within 6 months of graduation; 64% had found employment.

Admissions Contact: Edwin B. Harris, Director of Admissions.

LONG ISLAND UNIVERSITY

The Long Island University, established in 1886, is a private system in New York. It is governed by a board of trustees, whose chief administrator is the president. The primary goal of the system is to provide Long Island's communities with a high-quality higher education. The main priorities are teaching in the liberal arts and professions, extending higher education to underrepresented populations, and providing every student with opportunities for cooperative education placements in a field related to his or her major. The total enrollment in a recent year of all 6 campuses was 22,937; there were 1440 faculty members. Altogether there are 179 baccalaureate, 148 master's, and 2 doctoral programs offered at Long Island University. Four-year campuses are located in Brooklyn, Brookville, and Southampton. Profiles of the 4-year campuses are included in this chapter in alphabetical order with other New York schools.

LONG ISLAND UNIVERSITY
(See Brooklyn Campus of Long Island University)

LONG ISLAND UNIVERSITY
(See Long Island University/C. W. Post Campus)

LONG ISLAND UNIVERSITY
(See Long Island University/Southampton Campus)

LONG ISLAND UNIVERSITY
C. W. POST CAMPUS
Brookville, NY 11548

D-5

(516) 299–2413
(800) LIU-PLAN (out-of-state)

Full-time: 1652 men, 2038 women	Faculty: 320; IIA, +$
Part-time: 362 men, 705 women	Ph.D.s: 87%
Graduate: 1186 men, 2167 women	Student/Faculty: 12 to 1
Year: semesters, summer session	Tuition: $11,590
Application Deadline: open	Room & Board: $5280
Freshman Class: 3129 applied, 2665 accepted, 778 enrolled	
SAT I Verbal/Math: 479/547	COMPETITIVE

Long Island University/C.W. Post Campus, founded in 1954 as part of the private Long Island University system, offers 82 undergraduate and 64 graduate majors in liberal arts and sciences, accounting, business, public service, health professions, visual and performing arts, education, and library information science. There are 5 undergraduate and 6 graduate schools. In addition to regional accreditation, C.W. Post has baccalaureate program accreditation with ADA, ASLA, CAHEA, and NLN. The library contains 2,169,157 volumes, 913,544 microform items, and 38,478 audiovisual forms, and subscribes to 8042 periodicals. Computerized library sources and services include the card catalog, interlibrary loans, and database searching. Special learning facilities include a learning resource center, art gallery, radio station, and an art museum, a tax institute, a speech and hearing center, a center for business research, a federal depository, a center for the performing arts, a visual and performing arts computer center, a center for excellence in communications and learning, and an early childhood development center. The 305-acre campus is in a suburban area 25 miles east of New York City, on the former estate of Marjorie Merriweather Post. Including residence halls, there are 48 buildings on campus.

Student Life: About 66% of undergraduates are from New York. Students come from 24 states and Canada. Seventy-one percent are from public schools; 29% from private. Seventy-six percent are white. The average age of freshmen is 18; all undergraduates, 21. Nine percent drop out by the end of their first year; 39% remain to graduate.

Housing: A total of 2100 students can be accommodated in college housing. College-sponsored living facilities include single-sex and coed dormitories, on-campus apartments, and married-student housing. In addition there are quiet dorms, and all-female dorms. On-campus housing is guaranteed for the freshman year only, is available on a first-come, first-served basis, and is available on a lottery system

for upperclassmen. Priority is given to out-of-town students. Sixty percent of students commute. All students may keep cars on campus.

Activities: About 6% of men and 1% of women belong to 1 local and 9 national fraternities; about 4% of women belong to 1 local and 9 national sororities. There are 104 groups on campus, including art, band, cheerleading, chess, choir, chorale, chorus, computers, dance, drama, drill team, ethnic, film, gay, honors, international, jazz band, literary magazine, musical theater, newspaper, orchestra, photography, political, professional, radio and TV, religious, social, social service, student government, and yearbook. Popular campus events include Homecoming, Senior Week, Spring Week, Renaissance Fair, Science Expo, Greek Olympiad, International Student Dinner, Winter Week, Senior Week, and rock concerts in the Tilles Center.

Sports: There are 7 intercollegiate sports for men and 7 for women, and 4 intramural sports for men and 2 for women. Athletic and recreation facilities include a 6000-seat football stadium, a 700-seat indoor gymnasium, an equestrian center, tennis courts, a fitness center, and soccer, baseball, and softball fields.

Disabled Students: Seventy-five percent of the campus is accessible to disabled students. The following facilities are available: wheelchair ramps, elevators, special parking, specially equipped rest rooms, lowered drinking fountains, and electric doors.

Services: In addition to many counseling and information services, tutoring is available in most subjects. There is also a reader service for the blind; remedial math, reading, and writing; and an academic resource center for the learning disabled.

Campus Safety and Security: Campus safety and security measures include 24-hour foot and vehicle patrol, self defense education, escort service, and shuttle buses. In addition, there are informal discussions, pamphlets, posters, and films, emergency telephones, lighted pathways and sidewalks, restricted night access to campus, dormitory security staff, women and safety conferences, and Alcohol Awareness Week.

Programs of Study: C.W. Post awards the B.A., B.S., B.S.Ed., B.F.A., and B.P.S. degrees. Associate, master's, and doctoral degrees also are awarded. Bachelor's degrees are awarded in AGRICULTURE (conservation and regulation), BIOLOGICAL SCIENCE (biology/biological science, molecular biology, and nutrition), BUSINESS (accounting, banking and finance, business administration and management, and marketing/retailing/merchandising), COMMUNICATIONS AND THE ARTS (arts administration/management, broadcasting, communications, dramatic arts, English, film arts, fine arts, French, German, Italian, journalism, music, photography, public relations, and Spanish), COMPUTER AND PHYSICAL SCIENCE (chemistry, computer science, geology, mathematics, physics, and radiological technology), EDUCATION (art, early childhood, elementary, English, foreign languages, health, music, science, and secondary), ENGINEERING AND ENVIRONMENTAL DESIGN (preengineering), HEALTH PROFESSIONS (art therapy, biomedical science, health care administration, medical laboratory technology, medical records administration/services, nursing, predentistry, premedicine, prepharmacy, and speech pathology/audiology), SOCIAL SCIENCE (criminal justice, economics, geography, history, international studies, philosophy, political science/government, prelaw, psychology, and public administration). Accounting, nursing, radiologic technology are the strongest academically. Accounting, business, education, and political science have the largest enrollments.

Required: Core requirements include 8 credits of laboratory science, 9 each of history and philosophy, 6 each of language and literature, arts, political science and economics, sociology, psychology, geography, or anthropology, and 3 of mathematics. A minimum of 128 credits is required to graduate. GPA requirements range from 2.0 to 2.5 in most departments, 3.0 in interdisciplinary studies. Students must demonstrate competency in writing, quantitative skills, computer skills, oral communications, and library use.

Special: There is cross-registration with several other Long Island colleges. C.W. Post offers co-op programs in all majors, internships, study abroad in 11 countries, work-study in most departments, accelerated degree programs, and a Washington semester for outstanding criminal justice students. Dual majors and student designed majors are available. There is a 3–2 engineering degree with Polytechnic University and Pratt Institute, and credit is available for life, military, and work experience. Nondegree study is available, as are pass/fail options. There is a freshman honors program on campus, as well as 19 national honor societies. Sixteen departments have honors programs.

Faculty/Classroom: Thirty-nine percent of faculty are male; 61%, female. No introductory courses are taught by graduate students. The average class size in an introductory lecture is 26; in a laboratory, 20; and in a regular course offering, 17.

Admissions: About 85% of the 1993–94 applicants were accepted. The SAT scores for the 1993–94 freshman class were as follows: Verbal—60% below 500, 31% between 500 and 599, and 10% between 600 and 700; Math—28% below 500, 41% between 500 and 599, 27% between 600 and 700, and 4% above 700. About 48% of the

current freshmen were in the top fifth of their class; 75% were in the top two fifths.

Requirements: The SAT I or ACT is required, with a minimum score of 900 on the SAT I or 20 on the ACT. Applicants should be graduates of an accredited secondary school or have a GED. Preparatory work should include 4 years of English, 3 of social science, 2 each of foreign language and college-preparatory mathematics, and 1 of laboratory science. AP and CLEP credits are accepted. Important factors used in the admissions decision are advanced placement or honor courses, recommendations by school officials, recommendations by alumni, personality, intangible qualities, and extracurricular activities record.

Procedure: Freshmen are admitted to all sessions. Entrance exams should be taken from May of the junior year through December of the senior year. Application deadlines are open. Notification is sent on a rolling basis. The application fee is $30. There are early admissions and deferred admissions plans.

Transfer: Some 743 transfer students enrolled in 1993–94. Applicants should have appropriate high school credentials and a minimum college GPA of 2.25. A total of 32 credits out of 128 must be completed at C.W. Post.

Visiting: There are regularly scheduled orientations for prospective students, including an admissions interview and a student-guided campus tour. There are guides for informal visits and visitors may sit in on classes. To arrange for a visit, contact the Office of Admissions at (516) 299–2413.

Financial Aid: In 1993–94 70% of all current freshmen and 75% of continuing students received some form of financial aid. About 55% of freshmen and 65% of continuing students received need-based aid. The average freshman award was $6500. Of that total, scholarships or need-based grants averaged $3000 ($11,060 maximum); loans averaged $2000 ($2625 maximum); and work contracts averaged $1500 ($2000 maximum). Thirty-one percent of undergraduate students work part-time. Average earnings from campus work for the school year are $900. The average financial indebtedness of the 1992–93 graduate was $12,000. C.W. Post is a member of CSS. The FAF and FAFSA are required. The deadline for financial aid applications is May 15.

International Students: There are currently 296 international students enrolled. The school actively recruits these students. They must take the TOEFL (with a minimum score of 500) and the SAT I or ACT.

Computers: The college provides computer facilities for student use. The mainframes are a DEC VAX 6210, 7500, and 8600 in the academic computing center. There are advanced Omega and Macintosh computer laboratories in the School of Visual and Performing Arts. More than 200 IBM, Apple, and other microcomputers are available in various other campus locations, including dormitories and academic buildings. Dial-up capabilities allow students access from home, office, or dormitory. All dormitory rooms are equipped with phone, cable, and computer services connections. All students may access the system. It may be used Monday to Thursday, 8 A.M. to 11 P.M., and Friday to Sunday, 9 A.M. to 10 P.M. Dial-up capability is available 24 hours a day. There are no time limits on using the system and no fees.

Graduates: In 1992–93, 958 bachelor's degrees were awarded. The most popular majors among graduates were business and accounting (38%), education (14%), and political science (9%). Within an average freshman class, 4% graduate in 3 years, 63% in 4 years, 31% in 5 years, and 3% in 6 years. Some 500 companies recruited on campus in 1992–93. In the 1992 graduating class, 62% were enrolled in graduate school and 56% had found employment within 6 months of graduating.

Admissions Contact: Christine Natali, Director of Admissions.

LONG ISLAND UNIVERSITY
SOUTHAMPTON CAMPUS
E-5
(Formerly Southampton Campus of Long Island University)
Southampton, NY 11968

(516) 283–4000, ext. 200
(800) LIU-PLAN (548–7526)

Full-time: 483 men, 737 women	Faculty: 74; IIA, +$
Part-time: 38 men, 84 women	Ph.D.s: 86%
Graduate: 16 men, 95 women	Student/Faculty: 16 to 1
Year: semesters, summer session	Tuition: $11,630
Application Deadline: open	Room & Board: $5650
Freshman Class: 1124 applied, 991 accepted, 318 enrolled	
SAT I Verbal/Math: 468/495	ACT: 27 COMPETITIVE

Long Island University/Southampton Campus, established in 1963, is a private liberal arts institution offering undergraduate and graduate programs in the arts and sciences, business, and education. There are 6 undergraduate and 2 graduate schools. The library contains 1 million volumes, 1000 microform items, and 500 audiovisual forms, and subscribes to 690 periodicals. Computerized library sources and services include the card catalog, interlibrary loans, and database searching. Special learning facilities include a learning resource cen-

ter, art gallery, radio station, on-campus marine station, seawater laboratories, and research vessels. The 110-acre campus is in a rural area 90 miles east of New York City. Including residence halls, there are 33 buildings on campus.

Student Life: About 60% of undergraduates are from New York. Students come from 20 states and 5 foreign countries. Eighty-five percent are from public schools; 15% from private. Eighty-two percent are white. Most are Catholic. The average age of freshmen is 18; all undergraduates, 21. Ten percent drop out by the end of their first year; 78% remain to graduate.

Housing: A total of 710 students can be accommodated in college housing. College-sponsored living facilities include single-sex and coed dormitories. In addition, there are honors houses, quiet-study dormitories, and an all-women dormitory. On-campus housing is guaranteed for all 4 years. Eighty-five percent of students live on campus; of those, 50% remain on campus on weekends. All students may keep cars on campus.

Activities: There are no fraternities or sororities on campus. There are 50 groups on campus, including art, cheerleading, choir, drama, ethnic, film, honors, jazz band, literary magazine, musical theater, newspaper, photography, political, professional, radio and TV, recycling, religious, social, social service, student government, and yearbook. Popular campus events include Ray Boston Beach Party, Oktoberfest, and Spring Fest.

Sports: There are 4 intercollegiate sports for men and 4 for women, and 4 intramural sports for men and 4 for women. Athletic and recreation facilities include a gymnasium, swimming pool, basketball and volleyball courts, a weight room, and a fitness trail.

Disabled Students: Fifteen percent of the campus is accessible to disabled students. The following facilities are available: wheelchair ramps and special parking.

Services: In addition to many counseling and information services, tutoring is available in most subjects. There is also remedial math, reading, and writing, and a drop-in study center that offers support for most courses.

Campus Safety and Security: Campus safety and security measures include 24-hour foot and vehicle patrol, self-defense education, shuttle buses, and informal discussions. In addition, there are pamphlets, posters, and films, and emergency telephones. The college also conducts an alcohol awareness week and date-rape seminars.

Programs of Study: Southampton awards the B.A., B.S., and B.F.A. degrees. Master's degrees also are awarded. Bachelor's degrees are awarded in BIOLOGICAL SCIENCE (biology/biological science and marine science), COMMUNICATIONS AND THE ARTS (communications, English, fine arts, and graphic design), COMPUTER AND PHYSICAL SCIENCE (chemistry and geology), EDUCATION (art and elementary), SOCIAL SCIENCE (history, political science/government, prelaw, psychology, social science, and sociology). Marine science and art are the strongest academically. Marine science, business, and art have the largest enrollments.

Required: In order to graduate, students must complete 128 credits with an overall 2.0 GPA and a 2.25 GPA in the major. The required core courses must include 3 courses in English, 2 each in humanities, social science, and science/mathematics, and 1 in fine arts. Forty-five to 88 hours must be completed in the major.

Special: Cross-registration is permitted with the C.W. Post and Brooklyn campuses of Long Island University, and the Friends World Program. Opportunities are provided for internships, in science research, legislative offices, and the Smithsonian Institution. Study abroad, work-study programs, B.A.-B.S. degrees, dual majors, credit by examination, credit for life experience, nondegree study, and pass/fail options are also available. Students in the Friends World Program receive credit based on experiential education, fieldwork, and overseas travel. There is a freshman honors program on campus, as well as 2 national honor societies.

Faculty/Classroom: Seventy-nine percent of faculty are male; 21%, female. All teach undergraduates. No introductory courses are taught by graduate students. The average class size in an introductory lecture is 20; in a laboratory and a regular course offering, 15.

Admissions: About 88% of the 1993-94 applicants were accepted. The SAT scores for the 1993-94 freshman class were as follows: Verbal—65% below 500, 26% between 500 and 599, 8% between 600 and 700, and 1% above 700. About 26% of the current freshmen were in the top fifth of their class; 46% were in the top two fifths. Six freshmen graduated first in their class.

Requirements: A minimum GPA of 75 is required. The SAT I or ACT is required. A minimum composite score of 900 (450 verbal and 450 math) is required on the SAT I and a score of 20 is required on the ACT. Graduation from an accredited secondary school is required; the GED will be accepted. The academic record should include 4 credits in English, 3 each in history and social studies, 2 each in mathematics and science, and 1 in art. An essay, portfolio, audition, or interview may be recommended. AP and CLEP credits are accepted. Important factors used in the admissions decision are advanced placement or honor courses, personality, intangible qualities, evidence of special talent, leadership record, and extracurricular activities record.

Procedure: Freshmen are admitted fall and spring. Entrance exams should be taken during the junior year. Application deadlines are open. The application fee is $30. Notification is sent on a rolling basis. There are early admissions and deferred admissions plans.

Transfer: Some 150 transfer students enrolled in 1993-94. Applicants must have a 2.0 GPA in previous college work. An interview is recommended. High school grades and SAT scores are required if the transfer has fewer than 30 college credits. A total of 32 credits out of 128 must be completed at Southampton College.

Visiting: There are regularly scheduled orientations for prospective students, including an interview, a tour, and lunch or dinner. Students may also attend a class, meet with a coach, and attend a cooperative education meeting. There are guides for informal visits and visitors may sit in on classes and stay overnight at the school. To arrange for a visit, contact the Admissions Office at (516) 283-4000, ext. 200.

Financial Aid: In a recent year, 75% of all students received some form of financial aid. About 57% of freshmen and 60% of continuing students received need-based aid. The average freshman award was $8600. Of that total, scholarships or need-based grants averaged $5000 ($10,050 maximum); loans averaged $2500 ($3625 maximum); and work contracts averaged $1100 ($1300 maximum). Thirty percent of undergraduate students worked part-time. Average annual earnings from campus work were $1100. The average financial indebtedness of a recent graduate was $6000. Southampton College is a member of CSS. The FAF is required. The deadline for financial aid applications is June 1.

International Students: There are currently 22 international students enrolled. They must take the TOEFL, SAT I, or ACT, and achieve a minimum score on the TOEFL of 500.

Computers: The college provides computer facilities for student use. The mainframes are a DEC VAX 750, 8600, and 6210 and an IBM 520. The Long Island University Network is connected to Internet, which gives students access to computers and institutions worldwide. There are 120 microcomputers located at 6 campus locations and there are in-room PC hookups. The student-to-computer ratio is 12 to 1. All students may access the system. It may be used 24 hours a day. There are no time limits on using the system and no fees. If students are interested in bringing a personal computer for in-room dormitory use, an IBM or compatible is recommended.

Graduates: In a recent year, 203 bachelor's degrees were awarded. The most popular majors among graduates were business (26%), science (24%), and psychology (14%). Within an average freshman class, 1% graduate in 3 years, 39% in 4 years, and 10% in 5 years. Some 30 companies recruited on campus that year. In a recent graduating class, 30% of all students were enrolled in graduate school within 6 months of graduation; 81% of the men and 79% of the women had found employment.

Admissions Contact: Carol Gilbert, Director of Admissions.

MANHATTAN COLLEGE D-5
New York, NY 10471 (212) 920-0200
(800) MC2-XCEL (out-of-state)

Full-time: 1492 men, 1088 women	**Faculty:** 194
Part-time: 147 men, 107 women	**Ph.D.s:** 89%
Graduate: 402 men, 238 women	**Student/Faculty:** 13 to 1
Year: semesters, summer session	**Tuition:** $12,500
Application Deadline: March 1	**Room & Board:** $6500
Freshman Class: 2432 applied, 1678 accepted, 559 enrolled	
SAT I Verbal/Math: 467/539	**COMPETITIVE**

Manhattan College, founded in 1853, is a private, coeducational institution affiliated with the Christian Brothers of the Catholic Church. It offers degree programs in the arts, science, education and human services, business, and engineering. There are 5 undergraduate and 3 graduate schools. In addition to regional accreditation, Manhattan has baccalaureate program accreditation with ABET, AHEA, and CAHEA. The 3 libraries contain 250,000 volumes, 331,461 microform items, and 3244 audiovisual forms, and subscribe to 1500 periodicals. Computerized library sources and services include the card catalog, interlibrary loans, and database searching. Special learning facilities include a learning resource center, radio station, and a nuclear reactor laboratory, and a media center. The 47-acre campus is in a suburban area 12 miles north of midtown Manhattan. Including residence halls, there are 28 buildings on campus.

Student Life: About 82% of undergraduates are from New York. Students come from 36 states, 13 foreign countries, and Canada. Thirty-seven percent are from public schools; 63% from private. Seventy-six percent are white; 12% Hispanic. Eighty percent are Catholic; 15% Protestant. The average age of freshmen is 18; all undergraduates, 20. Fourteen percent drop out by the end of their first year; 81% remain to graduate.

Housing: A total of 1617 students can be accommodated in college housing. College-sponsored living facilities include coed dormitories and off-campus apartments. On-campus housing is guaranteed for all 4 years. Fifty-six percent of students commute. Alcohol is not permitted. All students may keep cars on campus.

Activities: About 2% of men belong to 3 local and 1 national fraternities; about 1% of women belong to 4 local sororities. There are 70 groups on campus, including bagpipe band, cheerleading, choir, chorus, computers, drama, ethnic, honors, international, jazz band, literary magazine, musical theater, newspaper, pep band, political, professional, radio and TV, religious, social, social service, student government, and yearbook. Popular campus events include Annual Springfest, Special Olympics, and Jasper Jingle.

Sports: There are 9 intercollegiate sports for men and 9 for women, and 10 intramural sports for men and 10 for women. Athletic and recreation facilities include 5 full basketball courts, which can also be used for volleyball and tennis, an indoor track, a weight room, a swimming pool, and a Nautilus center.

Disabled Students: Ninety-five percent of the campus is accessible to disabled students. The following facilities are available: wheelchair ramps, elevators, special parking, specially equipped rest rooms, lowered drinking fountains, and lowered telephones.

Services: In addition to many counseling and information services, tutoring is available in every subject.

Campus Safety and Security: Campus safety and security measures include 24-hour foot and vehicle patrol, escort service, pamphlets, posters, and films, and lighted pathways and sidewalks.

Programs of Study: Manhattan awards the B.A. and B.S. degrees. Associate's and master's degrees also are awarded. Bachelor's degrees are awarded in BIOLOGICAL SCIENCE (biochemistry and biology/biological science), BUSINESS (accounting, banking and finance, business economics, international business management, and marketing/retailing/merchandising), COMMUNICATIONS AND THE ARTS (communications, English, fine arts, French, and Spanish), COMPUTER AND PHYSICAL SCIENCE (chemistry, computer science, information sciences and systems, mathematics, and physics), EDUCATION (early childhood, elementary, foreign languages, health, middle school, physical, science, secondary, and special), ENGINEERING AND ENVIRONMENTAL DESIGN (chemical engineering, civil engineering, electrical/electronics engineering, environmental engineering, and mechanical engineering), HEALTH PROFESSIONS (predentistry, premedicine, and radiological science), SOCIAL SCIENCE (economics, history, international studies, peace studies, philosophy, political science/government, prelaw, psychology, religion, social science, social work, sociology, and urban studies). Engineering and business are the strongest academically. Engineering, business, and science have the largest enrollments.

Required: All students must take courses in English composition and literature, religious studies, philosophy, humanities, social science, science, and mathematics. About 130 credit hours are required for graduation, with about 36 in the major. The minimum GPA is 2.0.

Special: Manhattan offers co-op programs in 11 majors, cross-registration with the college of Mount St. Vincent, and off-campus internships in business, industry, government, and social or cultural organizations. Student may study abroad in 10 countries and enter work-study programs with major U.S. corporations, Montefiore Hospital, or the Bronx Museum of the Arts. General studies degree, a 3–2 engineering degree, credit by exam, and nondegree study are also available. There is a freshman honors program on campus, as well as 22 national honor societies, including Phi Beta Kappa.

Faculty/Classroom: Seventy-seven percent of faculty are male; 23%, female. All teach undergraduates. No introductory courses are taught by graduate students. The average class size in an introductory lecture is 15 and in a regular course offering, 22.

Admissions: About 69% of the 1993–94 applicants were accepted. The SAT I scores for the 1993–94 freshman class were as follows: Verbal—59% below 500, 34% between 500 and 599, and 7% between 600 and 700; Math—38% below 500, 41% between 500 and 599, 20% between 600 and 700, and 1% above 700. About 39% of the current freshmen were in the top fifth of their class; 63% were in the top two fifths. There were 3 National Merit semifinalists. About 12 freshmen graduated first in their class.

Requirements: A minimum GPA of 2.8 is required. The SAT I is required. Applicants must graduate from an accredited secondary school with a GPA of 2.8. The GED is accepted. Sixteen academic units are required, including 4 of English, 3 each of history, mathematics, and science, and 2 of foreign language. An essay is required and an interview is recommended. AP and CLEP credits are accepted. Important factors used in the admissions decision are recommendations by school officials, advanced placement or honor courses, parents or siblings attending the school, recommendations by alumni, and extracurricular activities record.

Procedure: Freshmen are admitted fall and spring. Entrance exams should be taken in the spring of the junior year or the fall of the senior year. Early decision applications should be filed by December 1; reg-

ular applications, by March 1 for fall entry and December 1 for spring entry, along with an application fee of $25. Notification of early decision is sent December 15; regular decision, February 1. There are early decision and deferred admissions plans. About 30 early decision candidates were accepted for the 1993–94 class.

Transfer: About 270 transfer students enrolled in 1993–94. Applicants must have a GPA of 2.5 and meet subject course requirements according to their course of study. They must submit transcripts from colleges and high schools attended. An interview is recommended. A total of 66 credits out of 130 must be completed at Manhattan.

Visiting: There are regularly scheduled orientations for prospective students, during 2 days in the summer, which include scheduling, parent workshops, loan seminars, and English and math testing. There are guides for informal visits and visitors may sit in on classes and stay overnight at the school. To arrange for a visit, contact the Admission Center at (800) MC2-XCEL.

Financial Aid: In 1993–94 84% of all current freshmen and 89% of continuing students received some form of financial aid. About 79% of freshmen and 76% of continuing students received need-based aid. The average freshman award was $10,428. Of that total, scholarships or need-based grants averaged $4084 ($20,185 maximum); loans averaged $1596 ($2625 maximum); and work contracts averaged $927 ($1500 maximum). Eleven percent of undergraduate students work part-time. Average earnings from campus work for the school year are $1640. The average financial indebtedness of the 1992–93 graduate was $13,250. Manhattan is a member of CSS. The FAF, FFS or SFS , the college's own financial statement, and the FAFSA are required. The deadline for financial aid applications is February 1.

International Students: There are currently 186 international students enrolled. The school actively recruits these students. They must take the TOEFL and achieve a minimum score of 520.

Computers: The college provides computer facilities for student use. The mainframe is a DEC VAX 8350. Terminals and microcomputers are located in the computer center and in engineering laboratories. All students may access the system. It may be used 13 hours a day in the laboratories and 24 hours a day by modem. There are no time limits on using the system and no fees.

Graduates: In 1992–93 672 bachelor's degrees were awarded. The most popular majors among graduates were business (32%), arts and science (28%), and engineering (25%). Within an average freshman class, 60% graduate in 4 years and 78% in 5 years. Some 229 companies recruited on campus in 1992–93. In the 1992 graduating class, 24% were enrolled in graduate school within 6 months of graduation; 46% had found employment.

Admissions Contact: John Brennan, Dean of Admissions.

MANHATTAN SCHOOL OF MUSIC   D-5
New York, NY 10027   (212) 749-2802, ext. 2

Full-time: 204 men, 213 women	**Faculty:** 20
Part-time: 4 men, 5 women	**Ph.D:s:** 60%
Graduate: 188 men, 238 women	**Student/Faculty:** 21 to 1
Year: semesters, summer session	**Tuition:** $12,000
Application Deadline: see profile	**Room & Board:** n/app
Freshman Class: 351 applied, 161 accepted, 69 enrolled	
SAT I or ACT: recommended	**SPECIAL**

The Manhattan School of Music, founded in 1917, is a private institution offering professional undergraduate and graduate degrees in music performance and composition. There is one graduate school. The library contains 61,000 volumes and 21,000 audiovisual forms, and subscribes to 125 periodicals. Special learning facilities include 2 electronic music studios and a recording studio. The 1-acre campus is in an urban area and consists of 1 building.

Student Life: About 70% of undergraduates are from out-of-state, mostly the Northeast. Students come from 41 states, 37 foreign countries, and Canada. Forty-two percent are white; 41% foreign nationals. The average age of freshmen is 19; all undergraduates, 21. Thirteen percent drop out by the end of their first year; 65% remain to graduate.

Housing: A total of 90 students can be accommodated in coed off-campus apartments, which are available on a first-come, first-served basis. Priority is given to out-of-town students. Ninety percent of students commute. Alcohol is not permitted. All students may keep cars on campus.

Activities: There are no fraternities or sororities on campus. Groups on campus, include band, chess, choir, chorale, chorus, ethnic, gay, international, jazz band, opera, orchestra, and symphony. Popular campus events include a Halloween party, square dancing, and a Christmas/Chanukah party.

Sports: There is no sports program at Manhattan.

Disabled Students: Seventy percent of the campus is accessible to disabled students. The following facilities are available: wheelchair ramps, elevators, specially equipped rest rooms, and special class scheduling.

Services: In addition to many counseling and information services, tutoring is available in most subjects, including English, music theory, music history, and humanities courses. There is also a reader service for the blind.

Campus Safety and Security: Campus safety and security measures include 24-hour foot and vehicle patrol, informal discussions, and lighted pathways and sidewalks.

Programs of Study: Manhattan awards the B.Mus. degree. Master's and doctoral degrees also are awarded. Bachelor's degrees are awarded in COMMUNICATIONS AND THE ARTS (jazz/commercial music, music, music performance, music theory and composition, and voice). Classical piano, classical voice, and jazz/commercial music have the largest enrollments.

Required: All students must take a 4-course core curriculum in the humanities and 4 elective humanities courses, and perform a final, senior-year recital. Composition majors must complete an original work. To graduate, all students must earn 120 to 130 credit hours, including 90 in the major, with a minimum GPA of 2.0.

Special: There is cross-registration with Barnard College. Credit by examination in theory and music history, and nondegree study are available.

Faculty/Classroom: Seventy percent of faculty are male; 30%, female. All teach undergraduates. Graduate students teach 1% of introductory courses. The average class size in an introductory lecture is 30 and in a regular course offering, 11.

Admissions: About 46% of the 1993–94 applicants were accepted.

Requirements: A minimum GPA of 2.0 is required. The SAT I or ACT is recommended. Applicants should graduate from an accredited high school. The GED is accepted. Admission is based on the results of a performance audition, evaluation of prior scholastic achievements, and available openings in the major field. AP and CLEP credits are accepted. Important factors used in the admissions decision are evidence of special talent, extracurricular activities record, advanced placement or honor courses, leadership record, and geographic diversity.

Procedure: Freshmen are admitted fall and spring. Application deadlines are December 1 for January auditions, January 15 for March auditions, and April 15 for May auditions. The application fee is $85. Notification is sent 3 weeks after the audition. A waiting list is an active part of the admissions procedure, with about 3% of applicants on the list.

Transfer: Some 71 transfer students enrolled in 1993–94. Applicants must audition and submit college transcripts. A total of 60 to 70 credits out of 120 to 130 must be completed at Manhattan.

Visiting: There are regularly scheduled orientations for prospective students. There are guides for informal visits and visitors may sit in on classes. To arrange for a visit, contact the Admission Office at (212) 749-2802, ext. 2.

Financial Aid: In 1993–94 68% of all current freshmen and 71% of continuing students received some form of financial aid. About 61% of freshmen and 64% of continuing students received need-based aid. Scholarships or need-based grants averaged $5000 ($11,700 maximum); loans averaged $2500 ($2625 maximum); and work contracts averaged $1000 ($1500 maximum). Sixty percent of undergraduate students work part-time. Average earnings from campus work for the school year are $1000. The average financial indebtedness of the 1992–93 graduate was $15,000. Manhattan is a member of CSS. The FAF, the college's own financial statement, and FAFSA are required. The deadline for financial aid applications is April 15.

International Students: There are currently 364 international students enrolled. The school actively recruits these students. They must take the TOEFL and achieve a minimum score of 450.

Graduates: In 1992–93 107 bachelor's degrees were awarded. The most popular majors among graduates were piano (21%), voice (14%), and jazz/commercial music (13%). Within an average freshman class, 50% graduate in 4 years, 58% in 5 years, and 65% in 6 years.

Admissions Contact: James Gandre, Dean of Admission.

MANHATTANVILLE COLLEGE D-5

Purchase, NY 10577   (914) 694-2200, ext. 464; (800) 328-4553

Full-time: 266 men, 564 women	Faculty: 79; IIB, +$
Part-time: 38 men, 112 women	Ph.D.s: 85%
Graduate: 67 men, 523 women	Student/Faculty: 11 to 1
Year: semesters, summer session	Tuition: $13,900
Application Deadline: March 15	Room & Board: $6550
Freshman Class: 850 applied, 750 accepted, 260 enrolled	
SAT I Verbal/Math: 413/471	**LESS COMPETITIVE**

Manhattanville College, founded in 1841, is an independent, coeducational institution offering programs in liberal and fine arts, business, health science, and teacher preparation. There are 2 graduate schools. In addition to regional accreditation, Manhattanville has baccalaureate program accreditation with NASM. The library contains 260,000 volumes, 3500 microform items, and 4000 audiovisual

forms, and subscribes to 1600 periodicals. Computerized library sources and services include the card catalog, interlibrary loans, and database searching. Special learning facilities include a learning resource center, art gallery, and radio station. The 100-acre campus is in a suburban area 25 miles north of New York City. Including residence halls, there are 20 buildings on campus.

Student Life: About 53% of undergraduates are from New York. Students come from 20 states and 18 foreign countries. Fifty-four percent are from public schools; 46% from private. Sixty-nine percent are white; 12% foreign nationals. Sixty-three percent are Catholic; 22% Protestant. The average age of freshmen is 18; all undergraduates, 20. Seven percent drop out by the end of their first year; 75% remain to graduate.

Housing: A total of 900 students can be accommodated in college housing. College-sponsored living facilities include single-sex and coed dormitories. In addition, there are language houses, special interest houses, and an intercultural residence hall. On-campus housing is guaranteed for all 4 years. Eighty-two percent of students live on campus; of those, 75% remain on campus on weekends. All students may keep cars on campus.

Activities: There are no fraternities or sororities on campus. There are 60 groups on campus, including art, band, choir, chorale, chorus, computers, dance, drama, ethnic, film, honors, international, jazz band, literary magazine, musical theater, newspaper, orchestra, photography, political, professional, religious, social, social service, student government, and yearbook. Popular campus events include Black History Month, Convocation, Founders Day, Christmas Concert, and Renaissance Dinner.

Sports: There are 5 intercollegiate sports for men and 7 for women, and 5 intramural sports for men and 5 for women. Athletic and recreation facilities include a 1000-seat gymnasium; baseball, lacrosse, field hockey, and softball fields; a 25-yard indoor pool; 6 deco-turf tennis courts; and a healthworks-wellness center.

Disabled Students: The entire campus is accessible to disabled students. The following facilities are available: wheelchair ramps, elevators, special parking, specially equipped rest rooms, and special class scheduling.

Services: In addition to many counseling and information services, tutoring is available in every subject.

Campus Safety and Security: Campus safety and security measures include 24-hour foot and vehicle patrol, escort service, informal discussions, and pamphlets, posters, and films. In addition, there are emergency telephones and lighted pathways and sidewalks.

Programs of Study: Manhattanville awards the B.A., B.F., and B.Mus. degrees. Master's degrees also are awarded. Bachelor's degrees are awarded in BIOLOGICAL SCIENCE (biochemistry and biology/biological science), BUSINESS (management science), COMMUNICATIONS AND THE ARTS (art history and appreciation, dance, design, dramatic arts, English, fine arts, French, German, music, photography, and Spanish), COMPUTER AND PHYSICAL SCIENCE (chemistry, computer science, mathematics, and physics), EDUCATION (art, early childhood, elementary, middle school, music, science, secondary, and special), ENGINEERING AND ENVIRONMENTAL DESIGN (environmental science), HEALTH PROFESSIONS (predentistry and premedicine), SOCIAL SCIENCE (American studies, Asian/Oriental studies, economics, history, international relations, medieval studies, philosophy, political science/government, prelaw, psychology, religion, Russian and Slavic studies, and sociology). Art, education, English, psychology, political science, economics, and management have the largest enrollments.

Required: Distribution requirements include 18 credits in social sciences and humanities, and either a major or minor in foreign language or 18 credits in Western and non-Western courses, 8 credits in mathematics and natural sciences, and 6 in the arts. A year-long freshman humanities course, courses in library skills, writing, and global perspective, and a preceptorial are required. A total of 120 credit hours and a minimum GPA of 2.0 are needed to graduate.

Special: Manhattanville offers cross-registration with SUNY Purchase; internships in management, international studies, and economics; and study abroad in 10 countries. A 3–2 engineering program with Clarkson University, dual, student-designed, and interdisciplinary majors, and pass/fail options are also available. Under the portfolio degree plan, students develop an individualized program combining both academic and nonacademic training. There is a freshman honors program on campus, as well as 3 national honor societies. Sixteen departments have honors programs.

Faculty/Classroom: Fifty percent of faculty are male; 50%, female. Ninety-five percent teach undergraduates. No introductory courses are taught by graduate students. The average class size in an introductory lecture is 20; in a laboratory, 15; and in a regular course offering, 15.

Admissions: About 88% of the 1993–94 applicants were accepted. The SAT scores for the 1993–94 freshman class were as follows: Verbal—77% below 500, 18% between 500 and 599, and 5% between 600 and 700; Math—59% below 500, 32% between 500 and 599,

9% between 600 and 700, and 1% above 700. About 31% of the current freshmen were in the top fifth of their class; 56% were in the top two fifths. There was 1 National Merit finalist and 14 semifinalists. Five freshmen graduated first in their class.

Requirements: Manhattanville requires applicants to be in the upper 50% of their class. A minimum GPA of 2.5 is required. The SAT I or ACT is required. Under an alternative admissions plan, students may submit a substantial piece of writing plus SAT II: Subject tests in writing and mathematics in lieu of SAT I or ACT scores. Applicants should graduate with 4 years of English, 3 each of history, mathematics, and science, including 2 of laboratory science, and a 1/2 year each of art and music. The GED is accepted. An essay is required, and an interview is strongly encouraged. Art applicants must submit a portfolio; music applicants must audition. AP and CLEP credits are accepted. Important factors used in the admissions decision are advanced placement or honor courses, recommendations by school officials, evidence of special talent, extracurricular activities record, and leadership record.

Procedure: Freshmen are admitted fall and spring. Entrance exams should be taken in the spring of the junior or fall of the senior year. SAT II: Subject tests should be taken no later than December of the senior year. Early decision applications should be filed by January 15; regular applications, by March 15 for fall entry and December 15 for spring entry, along with an application fee of $35. Notification of early decision is sent February 1; regular decision, on a rolling basis. There are early admissions and deferred admissions plans. Six early decision candidates were accepted for the 1993–94 class.

Transfer: Some 46 transfer students enrolled in a recent year. Applicants must submit college transcripts, recommendations from a dean and 2 professors, a secondary school transcript, a counselor recommendation, and results from standardized testing. A minimum GPA of 2.5 is required. A total of 60 credits out of 120 must be completed at Manhattanville.

Visiting: There are regularly scheduled orientations for prospective students. There are guides for informal visits and visitors may sit in on classes and stay overnight at the school. To arrange for a visit, contact the Office of Admissions and Financial Aid at (914) 694–2200, ext. 464, or (800) 328–4553.

Financial Aid: In a recent year, 68% of all freshmen and 58% of continuing students received some form of financial aid. Scholarships or need-based grants averaged $7200 ($15,000 maximum); loans averaged $2800 ($5000 maximum); and work contracts averaged $1500 ($2200 maximum). Thirty-one percent of undergraduate students worked part-time. Average earnings from campus work for the school year were $1700. The average financial indebtedness of a recent graduate was $13,000. Manhattanville is a member of CSS. The FAF, the college's own financial statement, and FAFSA are required. The deadline for financial aid applications is March 15.

International Students: There are currently 121 international students enrolled. The school actively recruits these students. They must take the TOEFL and achieve a minimum score of 550.

Computers: The college provides computer facilities for student use. The mainframe is a DEC PDP 11/44 minicomputer. Students may access the mainframe through the computer centers on campus. All students may access the system. It may be used for 65 to 70 hours throughout the week. There are no time limits on using the system and no fees.

Graduates: In 1992–93 230 bachelor's degrees were awarded. Within an average freshman class, 3% graduate in 3 years, 68% in 4 years, 85% in 5 years, and 95% in 6 years. Some 100 companies recruited on campus in 1992–93.

Admissions Contact: Barry W. Ward, Dean of Admissions and Financial Planning.

MANNES COLLEGE OF MUSIC D-5
New York, NY 10024 (212) 580–0210; (800) 292–3040

Full-time: 51 men, 58 women	**Faculty:** 25
Part-time: 1 woman	**Ph.D.s:** 10%
Graduate: 59 men, 87 women	**Student/Faculty:** 4 to 1
Year: semesters	**Tuition:** $12,000
Application Deadline: see profile	**Room:** $5200
Freshman Class: 261 applied, 89 accepted, 41 enrolled	
SAT I or ACT: not required	**SPECIAL**

Mannes College of Music, founded in 1916 and today part of the New School for Social Research, is a private institution offering instruction in music. There is one graduate school. The library contains 28,000 volumes and 2600 audiovisual forms, and subscribes to 50 periodicals. Special learning facilities include 2 concert/recital halls, a recording studio, and an electronic music studio. The campus is in an urban area in Manhattan and consists of 1 building.

Student Life: About 40% of undergraduates are from New York. Students come from 27 foreign countries and Canada. Forty-four percent are foreign nationals; 41% white; 10% Asian American. The av-

erage age of freshmen is 19; all undergraduates, 21. Fifteen percent drop out by the end of their first year; 60% remain to graduate.

Housing: A total of 30 students can be accommodated in college housing. College-sponsored living facilities include coed dormitories. On-campus housing is available on a first-come, first-served basis. Priority is given to out-of-town students. Alcohol is not permitted.

Activities: There are no fraternities or sororities on campus. There are some groups and organizations on campus, including choir, chorus, jazz band, opera, orchestra, and symphony. Popular campus events include orchestra/chorus concerts, Christmas parties, recitals, seminars, and master classes.

Sports: There is no sports program at Mannes.

Disabled Students: The entire campus is accessible to disabled students. Elevators are available for these students.

Services: In addition to many counseling and information services, tutoring is available in most subjects.

Campus Safety and Security: There is a security guard 24 hours a day at the front entrance of the dormitory and from 8 A.M. to 11 P.M. at the front desk of the college lobby.

Programs of Study: Mannes awards the B.S. and B.Mus. degrees. Master's degrees also are awarded. Bachelor's degrees are awarded in COMMUNICATIONS AND THE ARTS (music, music performance, music theory and composition, and voice). Voice, piano, and violin have the largest enrollments.

Required: The required core curriculum includes courses in English, Western civilization, art history, and literature. Students majoring in all instruments and voice must participate in various ensemble classes. Courses are also required in techniques and history of music. To graduate, performance majors must perform before a faculty jury, and composition majors must submit 5 original pieces for juried consideration.

Special: Mannes offers cross-registration with Hunter College, Marymount Manhattan, and the New School for Social Research. There are some dual majors by permission.

Faculty/Classroom: No introductory courses are taught by graduate students. The average class size in a regular course offering is 10 to 12.

Admissions: About 34% of the 1993–94 applicants were accepted.

Requirements: The SAT I or ACT is not required. Applicants must be graduates of an accredited secondary school or have a GED certificate. An audition, an interview, a letter of recommendation, and a written test in music theory and musicianship are required. Important factors used in the admissions decision are evidence of special talent, personality, intangible qualities, advanced placement or honor courses, recommendations by school officials, and recommendations by alumni.

Procedure: Freshmen are admitted in the fall. There are rolling deadlines. The application fee is $60. Notification is sent on a rolling basis. There are early admissions and deferred admissions plans.

Transfer: Some 23 transfer students enrolled in 1993–94. Transfer applicants must complete the same procedures as entering freshmen and submit transcripts from all secondary schools and colleges attended.

Visiting: There are guides for informal visits and visitors may sit in on classes. To arrange for a visit, contact Marilyn Groves, Director of Admissions at (212) 580–0210.

Financial Aid: In 1993–94, 78% of all current freshmen and 83% of continuing students received some form of financial aid. About 50% of all students received need-based aid. Scholarships or need-based grants averaged $3014 ($11,850 maximum); loans averaged $2000 ($5000 maximum). Thirty-five percent of undergraduate students work part-time. Average earnings from campus work for the school year are $1200. The average financial indebtedness of the 1992–93 graduate was $5600. Mannes is a member of CSS. The FAF, the college's own financial statement, and FAFSA are required. There are rolling deadlines for financial aid applications.

International Students: There are currently 108 international students enrolled. They must take the TOEFL and achieve a minimum score of 500. The student must also take the college's own entrance exam.

Graduates: In 1992–93 19 bachelor's degrees were awarded. The most popular majors among graduates were voice (32%), composition (16%), and piano (16%).

Admissions Contact: Marilyn Groves, Director of Admissions.

MARIST COLLEGE
Poughkeepsie, NY 12601

D-4

(914) 575-3226

Full-time: 1433 men, 1611 women
Part-time: 300 men, 321 women
Graduate: 293 men, 226 women
Year: semesters, summer session
Application Deadline: March 1
Freshman Class: 4732 applied, 3171 accepted, 845 enrolled
SAT I or ACT: required

Faculty: 154; IIB, av$
Ph.D.s: 75%
Student/Faculty: 20 to 1
Tuition: $10,532
Room & Board: $5874

COMPETITIVE

Marist College, founded in 1946, is an independent liberal arts college with a Catholic tradition. There is one graduate school. The library contains 150,000 volumes, 53,154 microform items, and 21,750 audiovisual forms, and subscribes to 1500 periodicals. Computerized library sources and services include interlibrary loans and database searching. Special learning facilities include a learning resource center, art gallery, radio station, TV station, an aquarium, a gallery of memorabilia from Lowell Thomas's career, an estuarine and environment studies laboratory, and a public opinion institute. The 150-acre campus is in a suburban area 75 miles north of New York City. Including residence halls, there are 21 buildings on campus.

Student Life: About 51% of undergraduates are from out-of-state, mostly the Northeast. Students come from 23 states, 14 foreign countries, and Canada. Seventy percent are from public schools. Eighty-six percent are white. Sixty percent are Catholic; 20% Protestant; 13% claim no religious affiliation. The average age of freshmen is 18; all undergraduates, 19.8. Ten percent drop out by the end of their first year; 63% remain to graduate.

Housing: A total of 2400 students can be accommodated in college housing. College-sponsored living facilities include coed dormitories, on-campus apartments, and off-campus apartments. In addition there are language houses. On-campus housing is guaranteed for the freshman year only and is available on a lottery system for upperclassmen. Sixty-five percent of students live on campus; of those, 70% remain on campus on weekends. Alcohol is not permitted. Upperclassmen may keep cars on campus.

Activities: About 6% of men belong to 3 local and 1 national fraternities; about 9% of women belong to 1 local and 1 national sorority. There are 70 groups on campus, including art, cheerleading, chess, choir, chorale, chorus, computers, dance, drama, ethnic, film, gay, honors, international, jazz band, literary magazine, musical theater, newspaper, pep band, political, radio and TV, religious, social, social service, student government, and yearbook. Popular campus events include President's Cup Regatta, Parents Weekend, Senior Week, Spring Weekend, Community Unity, Foxfest, Medieval Banquet, and formal dances.

Sports: There are 12 intercollegiate sports for men and 9 for women, and 9 intramural sports for men and 7 for women. Athletic and recreation facilities include 2 boat houses, a 4000-seat basketball arena, a 3000-seat stadium, 6 outdoor tennis courts, playing fields, a field house, a swimming pool, a diving tank, racquetball courts, a dance and aerobics studio, a weight room, and rowing tanks.

Disabled Students: The entire campus is accessible to disabled students. The following facilities are available: wheelchair ramps, elevators, special parking, specially equipped rest rooms, special class scheduling, lowered drinking fountains, and lowered telephones.

Services: In addition to many counseling and information services, tutoring is available in every subject. There is a reader service for the blind, and remedial math, reading, and writing.

Campus Safety and Security: Campus safety and security measures include 24-hour foot and vehicle patrol, escort service, shuttle buses, and informal discussions. In addition, there are pamphlets, posters, and films, emergency telephones, lighted pathways and sidewalks, and security personnel in residence halls.

Programs of Study: Marist awards the B.A., B.S., and B.P.S. degrees. Master's degrees also are awarded. Bachelor's degrees are awarded in BIOLOGICAL SCIENCE (biochemistry and biology/biological science), BUSINESS (accounting, business administration and management, business economics, and fashion merchandising), COMMUNICATIONS AND THE ARTS (communications, English, film arts, fine arts, French, journalism, Russian, and Spanish), COMPUTER AND PHYSICAL SCIENCE (chemistry, computer science, information sciences and systems, and mathematics), EDUCATION (elementary, science, secondary, and special), ENGINEERING AND ENVIRONMENTAL DESIGN (environmental science), HEALTH PROFESSIONS (medical laboratory technology, predentistry, premedicine, and speech pathology/audiology), SOCIAL SCIENCE (American studies, criminal justice, economics, fashion design and technology, history, interdisciplinary studies, political science/government, prelaw, psychology, and social work). Computer science, computer information systems, natural sciences, environmental science, and psychology are the strongest academically. Business administration and communications have the largest enrollments.

Required: To graduate, students must maintain a GPA of 2.0 in the major while taking 120 credits. A 30-credit core curriculum and 30 to 36 credits in a major field are required. Distribution requirements include 6 credits each in natural sciences, social sciences, history, literature, and mathematics, 3 credits each in fine arts and philosophy/religious studies, and up to 12 credits in foreign language and culture. Specific course requirements include English writing skills and foundation courses.

Special: Study abroad in Europe, Africa, Latin America, Central America, and the Far East, and a 3–2 engineering degree with the University of Detroit are offered. A 3-year bachelor's degree, work-study programs, a B.A.-B.S. degree, dual and student-designed majors, a 5-year program in psychology, and nondegree study are also available. There are internships available with over 250 organizations. There is one national honor society on campus.

Faculty/Classroom: Sixty-five percent of faculty are male; 35%, female. All teach undergraduates, 20% do research, and 20% do both. No introductory courses are taught by graduate students. The average class size in an introductory lecture is 35; in a laboratory, 15; and in a regular course offering, 25.

Admissions: About 67% of the 1993–94 applicants were accepted. The SAT scores for the 1993–94 freshman class were as follows: Verbal—57% below 500, 39% between 500 and 599, and 4% between 600 and 700; Math—49% below 500, 43% between 500 and 599, 6% between 600 and 700, and 2% above 700. About 29% of the current freshmen were in the top fifth of their class; 66% were in the top two fifths. There were 6 National Merit semifinalists.

Requirements: Marist requires applicants to be in the upper 50% of their class. A minimum average of 80% is required. The SAT I or ACT is required. Applicants should have 18 academic credits, including a recommended 4 each in English, science, and social studies, 3 each in mathematics and history, and 1 each in art and music. An essay and interview are recommended. AP and CLEP credits are accepted. Important factors used in the admissions decision are recommendations by school officials, advanced placement or honor courses, leadership record, extracurricular activities record, and evidence of special talent.

Procedure: Freshmen are admitted fall and spring. Entrance exams should be taken during the fall of the senior year. Early decision applications should be filed by December 1; regular applications, by March 1 for fall entry and December 1 for spring entry, along with an application fee of $30. Notification of early decision is sent December 15; regular decision, on a rolling basis. There are early decision and early admissions plans. About 514 early decision candidates were accepted for the 1993–94 class. A waiting list is an active part of the admissions procedure, with about 10% of applicants on the list.

Transfer: About 126 transfer students enrolled in 1993–94. Applicants must have at least a 2.0 GPA (depending on the college and major programs) in at least 30 college credits. Students with fewer than 25 credits will be treated as freshmen. Grades of C or better transfer. A total of 30 credits out of 120 must be completed at Marist.

Visiting: There are regularly scheduled orientations for prospective students. There are guides for informal visits and visitors may sit in on classes and stay overnight at the school. To arrange for a visit, contact Carol Mulqueen, Admissions Office at (914) 575-3226.

Financial Aid: In 1993–94, 78% of all current freshmen received some form of financial aid. About 66% of freshmen and 60% of continuing students received need-based aid. The average freshman award was $9200. Of that total, scholarships or need-based grants averaged $3800; loans averaged $2500; and work contracts averaged $1000. Thirty percent of undergraduate students work part-time. Average earnings from campus work for the school year are $1200. The average financial indebtedness of the 1992–93 graduate was $9600. Marist is a member of CSS. The FAF and the FAFSA are required. The deadline for financial aid applications is February 15.

International Students: There are currently 56 international students enrolled. The school actively recruits these students. They must take the TOEFL and achieve a minimum score of 550.

Computers: The college provides computer facilities for student use. The mainframe is an IBM 3090 200 E series. The campus center has a drop-in laboratory available to all students from 8 A.M. to midnight during the week and longer on weekends. All dormitory rooms are equipped with datajacks allowing students to hookup PCs with the mainframe and to access library files. Overall, there are 5 areas on campus providing more than 200 terminals for student use, as well as 150 microcomputers and numerous printers. All students may access the system. There are no time limits on using the system and no fees.

Graduates: In 1992–93 742 bachelor's degrees were awarded. The most popular majors among graduates were communications (33%), business (28%), and psychology (10%). Within an average freshman class, 61% graduate in 4 years and 63% in 5 years. Some 140 companies recruited on campus in 1992–93.

Admissions Contact: Sean Kaylor, Associate Director of Admissions.

MARYMOUNT COLLEGE TARRYTOWN

D-5

Tarrytown, NY 10591

(914) 332–8295; (800) 724–4312

Full-time: 40 men, 691 women
Part-time: 67 men, 303 women
Graduate: none
Year: semesters, weekend summer session
Application Deadline: May 1
Freshman Class: 478 applied, 327 accepted, 117 enrolled
SAT I Verbal/Math: 460/460

Faculty: 56; IIB, av$
Ph.D.s: 86%
Student/Faculty: 13 to 1
Tuition: $11,150
Room & Board: $6200

COMPETITIVE

Marymount College/Tarrytown, founded in 1907, is an independent undergraduate institution in the Catholic tradition. The college offers programs in liberal arts and teacher preparation. In addition to regional accreditation, the college has baccalaureate program accreditation with CSWE. The library contains 117,000 volumes, 85,000 microform items, and 160 audiovisual forms, and subscribes to 800 periodicals. Computerized library sources and services include the card catalog and database searching. Special learning facilities include a learning resource center. The 25-acre campus is in a suburban area 30 miles north of New York City. Including residence halls, there are 12 buildings on campus.

Student Life: About 77% of undergraduates are from New York. Students come from 25 states and 15 foreign countries. Seventy-one percent are from public schools; 29% from private. Sixty percent are white; 16% African American; 14% Hispanic. Fifty-five percent are Catholic; 21% Protestant; 13% claim no religious affiliation; the remaining 10% are Eastern Orthodox, Quaker, and Muslim. The average age of freshmen is 20.4; all undergraduates, 22.5. Five percent drop out by the end of their first year; 63% remain to graduate.

Housing: A total of 638 students can be accommodated in college housing. College-sponsored living facilities include dormitories. On-campus housing is guaranteed for all 4 years. Eighty-five percent of students live on campus. Alcohol is not permitted. All students may keep cars on campus.

Activities: There are no fraternities or sororities on campus. There are 25 groups on campus, including art, chorale, computers, dance, drama, environmental, ethnic, honors, international, literary magazine, newspaper, photography, political, professional, social, social service, student government, video, and yearbook. Popular campus events include Talent Show, Fashion Show and Competition, Women's Day, Oktoberfest, and Springfest.

Sports: There are 6 intercollegiate and 2 intramural sports for women. Athletic and recreation facilities include 2 tennis courts and an athletic field. The campus stadium seats 350, the indoor gymnasium 375.

Disabled Students: Eighty-five percent of the campus is accessible to disabled students. The following facilities are available: wheelchair ramps, elevators, special parking, specially equipped rest rooms, special class scheduling, automatic door openers, and paid notetakers.

Services: In addition to many counseling and information services, tutoring is available in every subject. There is also remedial math, reading, and writing, and writing and mathematics laboratories.

Campus Safety and Security: Campus safety and security measures include 24-hour foot and vehicle patrol, self-defense education, informal discussions, and pamphlets, posters, and films. In addition, there are emergency telephones and lighted pathways and sidewalks.

Programs of Study: The college awards the B.A., B.S., and B.S.W. degrees. Bachelor's degrees are awarded in BIOLOGICAL SCIENCE (biology/biological science), BUSINESS (accounting, banking and finance, business administration and management, business economics, corporate training, fashion merchandising, international business management, and marketing/retailing/merchandising), COMMUNICATIONS AND THE ARTS (art history, communications, dramatic arts, English, fine arts, French, journalism, and Spanish), COMPUTER AND PHYSICAL SCIENCE (chemistry, information systems, and mathematics), EDUCATION (art, early childhood, elementary, foreign languages, home economics, middle school, science, secondary, and special), ENGINEERING AND ENVIRONMENTAL DESIGN (interior design), SOCIAL SCIENCE (American studies, economics, fashion design, foods and nutrition, history, home economics, individualized interdisciplinary, international studies, area studies, philosophy, political science/government, psychology, social work, and sociology).

Required: All students must take 3 semesters of English composition, 2 of mathematics, 4 of physical education, and a computer course. Humanities courses are also required. Distribution requirements include 2 semesters each of natural science and foreign language, and 1 each of social science, fine arts, and religious studies. A total of 120 credits is required for graduation, as is a minimum GPA of 2.0.

Special: Juniors and seniors in all disciplines may receive up to 12 credits for on-site internships. There is study abroad in 7 countries. The college offers a Washington semester, work-study programs, dual and student-designed majors, credit by examination, nondegree study, and pass/fail options. There are 3–2 business and education programs with Fordham University and 3–2 programs in speech pathology and occupational therapy with New York University. There is a Weekend College for working men and women. Marymount's summer session is held on weekends. There is a freshman honors program on campus, as well as 3 national honor societies.

Faculty/Classroom: Forty-eight percent of faculty are male; 52% female. All both teach and do research. The average class size in an introductory lecture is 25; in a laboratory, 16; and in a regular course offering, 15.

Admissions: About 68% of the 1993–94 applicants were accepted. The SAT scores for the 1993–94 freshman class were as follows: Verbal—77% below 500, 20% between 500 and 599, and 3% between 600 and 700; Math—73% below 500, 20% between 500 and 599, and 7% between 600 and 700. About 23% of the current freshmen were in the top fifth of their class; 51% were in the top two fifths. One freshman graduated first in their class.

Requirements: A minimum GPA of 2.0 is required. SAT I scores are required, but ACT scores may be submitted instead. Applicants must complete 16 academic credits, including 4 years of English, and 3 years each of foreign language, mathematics, science, and history or social studies. The GED is accepted. An essay is required, and an interview recommended. AP and CLEP credits are accepted. Important factors used in the admissions decision are recommendations by school officials, extracurricular activities record, leadership record, advanced placement or honor courses, and personality, intangible qualities.

Procedure: Freshmen are admitted fall and spring. Entrance exams should be taken in the fall of the year preceding enrollment. Applications should be filed by May 1 for fall entry and January 10 for spring entry, along with an application fee of $25. Notification is sent on a rolling basis. There are early admissions and deferred admissions plans.

Transfer: Some 57 transfer students enrolled in a recent year. Applicants with fewer than 24 college credits must submit SAT I scores and a high school transcript. A GPA of at least 2.2 is required. All students must submit a recommendation from an instructor or a dean at the last school attended. A total of 45 credits out of 120 must be completed at the college.

Visiting: There are regularly scheduled orientations for prospective students. There are guides for informal visits and visitors may sit in on classes and stay overnight at the school. To arrange for a visit, contact Gina Campbell, Director of Admissions, at (914) 631–3200, ext. 295.

Financial Aid: In 1993–94 87% of all current freshmen and 80% of continuing students received some form of financial aid. About 87% of freshmen and 78% of continuing students received need-based aid. The average freshman award was $13,400. Of that total, scholarships or need-based grants averaged $9500 ($13,875 maximum); loans averaged $3825 ($4425 maximum); and work contracts averaged $1200 (maximum). Fifty percent of undergraduate students work part-time. Average earnings from campus work for the school year are $1000. The average financial indebtedness of the 1992–93 graduate was $18,925. the college is a member of CSS. The FAF and FAFSA, and the college's own financial statement are required. The deadline for financial aid applications is May 1.

International Students: There are currently 40 international students enrolled. The school actively recruits these students. They must take the TOEFL and achieve a minimum score of 500.

Computers: The college provides computer facilities for student use. The mainframe is a DEC VAX. There are 45 microcomputers available to students in classroom, graphics, and drop-in laboratories on campus. Available software includes word processing, spreadsheets, database, statistical packages, graphics, and programming languages. All students may access the system. It may be used 7 days a week and there are no time limits or fees.

Graduates: In 1992–93 224 bachelor's degrees were awarded. The most popular majors among graduates were business (17%), education (16%), and psychology (11%). Within an average freshman class, 2% graduate in 3 years, 61% in 4 years, and 1% in 6 years. Some 57 companies recruited on campus in 1992–93. In the 1992 graduating class, 15% of the women were enrolled in graduate school within 6 months of graduation; 80% of the women had found employment.

Admissions Contact: Gina Campbell, Director of Admissions.

MARYMOUNT MANHATTAN COLLEGE

D-5

New York, NY 10021

(212) 517-0555

(800) MARYMOUNT (out-of-state)

Full-time: 190 men, 778 women	Faculty: 62; IIB, -$
Part-time: 80 men, 711 women	Ph.D.s: 75%
Graduate: none	Student/Faculty: 16 to 1
Year: 4-1-4, summer session	Tuition: $10,450
Application Deadline: open	Room & Board: $5000
Freshman Class: 695 applied, 600 accepted, 239 enrolled	
SAT I Verbal/Math: 460/500	**COMPETITIVE**

Marymount Manhattan College, founded in 1961, is an independent college offering programs in liberal arts, fine arts, business, and teacher preparation. The library contains 100,535 volumes, 70 microform items, and 1643 audiovisual forms, and subscribes to 855 periodicals. Computerized library sources and services include the card catalog and database searching. Special learning facilities include a learning resource center, an art gallery, a radio station, and a TV station. The 1-acre campus is in an urban area in Manhattan. Including residence halls, there are 2 buildings on campus.

Student Life: About 70% of undergraduates are from New York. Students come from 27 states, 24 foreign countries, and Canada. Fifty percent are from public schools; 30% from private. Fifty-four percent are white; 20% African American; 17% Hispanic. The average age of freshmen is 19; all undergraduates, 31. About 65% of freshmen remain to graduate.

Housing: A total of 130 students can be accommodated in college housing. College-sponsored living facilities include single-sex and coed dormitories and off-campus apartments. On-campus housing is available on a first-come, first-served basis and is available on a lottery system for upperclassmen. Priority is given to out-of-town students. Eighty-five percent of students commute. Alcohol is not permitted. All students may keep cars on campus.

Activities: About 3% of women belong to 1 national sorority. There are no fraternities on campus. There are 30 groups on campus, including art, choir, computers, dance, drama, ethnic, film, gay, honors, international, literary magazine, musical theater, newspaper, photography, political, professional, radio and TV, religious, social, social service, student government, and yearbook. Popular campus events include Octoberfest, Strawberry Festival, International Day, and Holiday Soiree.

Sports: There is no sports program at MMC. Athletic and recreation facilities include an Olympic-sized pool and a 300-seat auditorium.

Disabled Students: All of the campus is accessible to disabled students. The following facilities are available: wheelchair ramps, elevators, specially equipped rest rooms, special class scheduling, and lowered drinking fountains.

Services: In addition to many counseling and information services, tutoring is available in every subject, including reading, writing, and study skills. There is also remedial math.

Campus Safety and Security: Campus safety and security measures include 24-hour foot and vehicle patrol, informal discussions, pamphlets, posters, films, and lighted pathways and sidewalks. In addition, there are security cameras and photo ID check-in.

Programs of Study: MMC awards the B.A., B.S., and B.F.A. degrees. Bachelor's degrees are awarded in BIOLOGICAL SCIENCE (biology/biological science), BUSINESS (accounting, business administration and management, and international business management), COMMUNICATIONS AND THE ARTS (communications, dance, dramatic arts, English, and fine arts), EDUCATION (early childhood, elementary, secondary, and special), HEALTH PROFESSIONS (premedicine and speech pathology/audiology), SOCIAL SCIENCE (history, international studies, liberal arts/general studies, political science/government, psychology, and sociology). Premedicine, English, and liberal arts are the strongest academically. Theater and dance have the largest enrollments.

Required: To graduate, students must complete 120 credit hours, including 37 to 56 in the major, with a minimum GPA of 2.5. The core curriculum totals 36 credits in the areas of critical thinking, psychology and philosophy, quantitative reasoning and science, the modern world, communications/language, and the arts.

Special: MMC offers study abroad, interdisciplinary courses, pass/fail options, nondegree study, credit for life experience, and some 250 internships in industry, government, and the media. Cooperative programs in business and finance, dance, music, languages, nursing, and urban education are offered in conjunction with local colleges and institutes. There is a freshman honors program on campus, as well as 2 national honor societies.

Faculty/Classroom: Fifty percent of faculty are male; 50%, female. The average class size in an introductory lecture is 25; in a laboratory, 6; and in a regular course offering, 16.

Admissions: About 86% of the 1993-94 applicants were accepted. The SAT scores for the freshman class were as follows: Verbal—69% below 500, 20% between 500 and 599, 10% between 600 and 700,

and 1% above 700; Math—60% below 500, 29% between 500 and 599, and 11% between 600 and 700. About 45% of the current freshmen were in the top fifth of their class; 60% were in the top two fifths.

Requirements: A minimum GPA of 2.5 is required. The SAT I or ACT is required. Applicants should be graduates of an accredited secondary school or have a GED certificate. MMC recommends completion of 16 academic units, including 4 each in English and electives, and 3 each in language, mathematics, social science, and science. Recommendations are required and an interview is strongly advised. Applicants to the dance and acting programs must audition. AP and CLEP credits are accepted. Important factors used in the admissions decision are personality, intangible qualities, evidence of special talent, leadership record, advanced placement or honor courses, and recommendations by school officials.

Procedure: Freshmen are admitted to all sessions. Entrance exams should be taken as early as possible. Application deadlines are open and the fee is $30. Notification is sent on a rolling basis. There are early decision, early admissions, and deferred admissions plans.

Transfer: About 120 transfer students enrolled in 1993-94. Applicants who have graduated from high school since 1989 must meet standard freshman requirements and all must submit official transcripts from all colleges attended. A total of 30 credits out of 120 must be completed at MMC.

Visiting: There are regularly scheduled orientations for prospective students, including an interview with an admissions counselor, a tour of the school and dorms, and a meeting with a financial aid advisor. There are guides for informal visits and visitors may sit in on classes and stay overnight at the school. To arrange for a visit, contact the Admissions Office at (212) 517-0555.

Financial Aid: In 1993-94, 83% of continuing students received some form of financial aid. The average freshman award was $18,000. Of that total, scholarships or need-based grants averaged $5100 ($10,200 maximum); loans averaged $2625; and work contracts averaged $1000 ($2000 maximum). The average financial indebtedness of the 1992-93 graduate was $20,000. MMC is a member of CSS. The FAFSA financial statement is required. The deadline for financial aid applications is February 25.

International Students: There are currently 70 international students enrolled. The school actively recruits these students. They must take the TOEFL and achieve a minimum score of 550.

Computers: The college provides computer facilities for student use. There are Apple IIe and IBM PC microcomputers in the Computer Laboratory, as well as a Commodore Amiga 2000 for graphics work. All students may access the system. There are no time limits on using the system and no fees.

Graduates: The most popular majors among graduates were business (17%), theater (13%), and psychology (12%). Within an average freshman class, 65% graduate in 4 years.

Admissions Contact: Dina Colandro, Assistant Director of Admissions.

MEDAILLE COLLEGE

A-3

Buffalo, NY 14214

(716) 884-3281

Full-time: 399 men, 511 women	Faculty: 46; IIB, --$
Part-time: 55 men, 181 women	Ph.D.s: 66%
Graduate: none	Student/Faculty: 20 to 1
Year: semesters, summer session	Tuition: $8350
Application Deadline: August 15	Room & Board: $4300
Freshman Class: 384 applied, 223 accepted, 143 enrolled	
SAT I or ACT: not required	**COMPETITIVE**

Medaille College, founded in 1875, is a private, nonsectarian institution offering undergraduate programs in liberal arts, education, business, and humanities to a primarily commuter student body. The library contains 48,761 volumes, 22,925 microform items, and 1236 audiovisual forms, and subscribes to 346 periodicals. Special learning facilities include a learning resource center, radio station, and TV station. The 13-acre campus is in an urban area in Buffalo. Including residence halls, there are 7 buildings on campus.

Student Life: About 99% of undergraduates are from New York. Students also come from Canada. Seventy-three percent are white; 22% African American. The average age of freshmen is 20; all undergraduates, 28.

Housing: A total of 50 students can be accommodated in college housing. College-sponsored living facilities include single-sex on-campus apartments and off-campus apartments. On-campus housing is guaranteed for all 4 years. Ninety-nine percent of students commute. Alcohol is not permitted. All students may keep cars on campus.

Activities: There are no fraternities or sororities on campus. There are 17 groups on campus, including chorus, computers, drama, ethnic, honors, literary magazine, musical theater, newspaper, photography, radio and TV, social, social service, student government, and yearbook. Popular campus events include Founders Day, Silent Auction, and Honors Convocation.

Sports: There is an intramural sports program. Athletic and recreation facilities include an NCAA regulation gymnasium located in the student center.

Disabled Students: The entire campus is accessible to disabled students. The following facilities are available: wheelchair ramps, elevators, special parking, specially equipped rest rooms, lowered drinking fountains, and lowered telephones.

Services: In addition to many counseling and information services, tutoring is available in most subjects. There is also a reader service for the blind, and remedial math, reading, and writing.

Campus Safety and Security: Campus safety and security measures include escort service, shuttle buses, informal discussions, and pamphlets, posters, and films. In addition, there are emergency telephones and lighted pathways and sidewalks.

Programs of Study: Medaille awards the B.A. and B.S. degrees. Associate degrees also are awarded. Bachelor's degrees are awarded in BUSINESS (business administration and management and human resources), EDUCATION (elementary), SOCIAL SCIENCE (human services, humanities, liberal arts/general studies, and social science). Business and education are the strongest academically. Business and education have the largest enrollments.

Required: The bachelor's degree requires successful completion of 120 credit hours, or 128 for elementary education majors. In addition to specific course requirements for each major, students must maintain a minimum GPA of 2.0. All degree programs require internships.

Special: Cross-registration is available with colleges in the Western New York Consortium. Opportunities are provided for student-designed majors, credit by examination, pass/fail options, and credit for work experience. A modular program of evening courses and another of Saturday classes enable students to maintain full-time status by attending classes either 2 nights a week or on weekends. There is a freshman honors program on campus, as well as 1 national honor society.

Faculty/Classroom: The average class size in an introductory lecture is 20; in a laboratory, 10; and in a regular course offering, 15.

Admissions: About 58% of the 1993–94 applicants were accepted.

Requirements: The SAT I or ACT is not required. Applicants must be graduates of an accredited secondary school or hold the GED. An essay and an interview are required. AP and CLEP credits are accepted. Important factors used in the admissions decision are advanced placement or honor courses, personality, intangible qualities, leadership record, evidence of special talent, and recommendations by school officials.

Procedure: Freshmen are admitted to all sessions. Applications should be filed by August 15 for fall entry, January 15 for spring entry, and June 15 for summer entry, along with an application fee of $25. Notification is sent on a rolling basis. There is a deferred admissions plan.

Transfer: Some 235 transfer students enrolled in 1993–94. Transfer applicants must have a minimum GPA of 2.0 in their previous college work. An interview and recommendations are required. A total of 30 credits out of 120 or 128, depending on the degree, must be completed at Medaille.

Visiting: There are regularly scheduled orientations for prospective students. There are guides for informal visits and visitors may sit in on classes and stay overnight at the school. To arrange for a visit, contact Jacqueline S. Matheny, Director of Enrollment Management, at (716) 884–3281.

Financial Aid: In 1993–94 70% of all current freshmen and 66% of continuing students received some form of financial aid. About 76% of freshmen and 75% of continuing students received need-based aid. The average freshman award was $7846. Of that total, scholarships or need-based grants averaged $500 ($2000 maximum); loans averaged $2000 ($6000 maximum); and work contracts averaged $1200 ($1500 maximum). Thirteen percent of undergraduate students work part-time. Average earnings from campus work for the school year are $1500. The average financial indebtedness of the 1992–93 graduate was $12,000. Medaille is a member of CSS. The FAF is required. The deadline for financial aid applications is March 15.

International Students: They must take the TOEFL and achieve a minimum score of 550.

Computers: The college provides computer facilities for student use. There are 40 IBM and Apple microcomputers available for academic use. All students may access the system. There are no time limits on using the system and no fees.

Graduates: In 1992–93 158 bachelor's degrees were awarded. The most popular majors among graduates are elementary education, veterinary technology, and business administration. In the 1992 graduating class, 16% of all students were enrolled in graduate school within 6 months of graduation.

Admissions Contact: Jacqueline S. Matheny, Director of Enrollment Management.

MERCY COLLEGE   D-5
Dobbs Ferry, NY 10522–1189   (914) 693–7600
                                  (800) MERCY NY (in-state)

Full-time: 1748 men, 2519 women	**Faculty:** 128; IIB, av$
Part-time: 573 men, 1238 women	**Ph.D.s:** 60%
Graduate: 164 men and women	**Student/Faculty:** 33 to 1
Year: semesters, summer session	**Tuition:** $7380
Application Deadline: open	**Room & Board:** $3800
Freshman Class: 3329 accepted, 2044 enrolled	
SAT I or ACT: required	**NONCOMPETITIVE**

Mercy College, founded in 1950, is an independent commuter institution offering programs in liberal arts, fine arts, business, and health science. In addition to regional accreditation, Mercy has baccalaureate program accreditation with CSWE and NLN. The library contains 312,000 volumes, and subscribes to 1170 periodicals. Computerized library sources and services include the card catalog, interlibrary loans, and database searching. Special learning facilities include a learning resource center, an art gallery, and a radio station. The 40-acre campus is in a suburban area 12 miles north of New York City. Including residence halls, there are 12 buildings on campus.

Student Life: About 97% of undergraduates are from New York. Students come from 14 states and 10 foreign countries. Ninety-five percent are from public schools; 5% from private. Sixty percent are white; 20% African American; 19% Hispanic. The average age of freshmen is 19; all undergraduates, 28. Twenty-five percent drop out by the end of their first year; 60% remain to graduate.

Housing: College-sponsored living facilities include dormitories. In addition, Mercy maintains a dormitory located at Manhattan College in Riverdale. Ninety-nine percent of students commute. All students may keep cars on campus.

Activities: There are no fraternities or sororities on campus. There are many groups and organizations on campus, including art, cheerleading, chess, choir, chorale, chorus, computers, dance, drama, ethnic, film, honors, international, jazz band, literary magazine, musical theater, newspaper, orchestra, political, professional, radio and TV, religious, social, social service, student government, and yearbook. Popular campus events include plays and special honors programs.

Sports: Athletic and recreation facilities include a 200-seat gymnasium, a soccer/baseball field, a swimming pool, tennis courts, and a track.

Disabled Students: Seventy-five percent of the campus is accessible to disabled students. The following facilities are available: wheelchair ramps, elevators, special parking, specially equipped rest rooms, lowered drinking fountains, and lowered telephones.

Services: In addition to many counseling and information services, tutoring is available in every subject. There is also a reader service for the blind, and remedial math, reading, and writing.

Programs of Study: Mercy awards the B.A., B.S., and B.F.A. degrees. Associate and master's degrees are also awarded. Bachelor's degrees are awarded in AGRICULTURE (animal science), BIOLOGICAL SCIENCE (biology/biological science), BUSINESS (accounting, banking and finance, business administration and management, hotel/motel and restaurant management, and marketing/retailing/merchandising), COMMUNICATIONS AND THE ARTS (broadcasting, communications, English, French, graphic design, Italian, journalism, music, Spanish, and speech/debate/rhetoric), COMPUTER AND PHYSICAL SCIENCE (actuarial science, computer programming, computer science, information sciences and systems, and mathematics), EDUCATION (art, early childhood, education of the deaf and hearing impaired, elementary, foreign languages, middle school, music, science, secondary, special, and teaching English as a second language/foreign language), HEALTH PROFESSIONS (chiropractic, medical laboratory technology, nursing, predentistry, premedicine, prepharmacy, speech pathology/audiology, and veterinary science), SOCIAL SCIENCE (behavioral science, criminal justice, history, interdisciplinary studies, political science/government, prelaw, psychology, social science, social work, sociology, and urban studies). The health professions programs are the strongest academically. Business has the largest enrollment.

Required: To graduate, students must complete 120 semester hours with a minimum GPA of 2.0 overall and in the major. Distribution requirements include 12 credits each of mathematics/natural science and philosophy/language/fine arts, 9 of social science, 6 each of English and history, and 3 of speech.

Special: Mercy offers internships in each major, work-study programs through the Westchester Employee Association, study abroad, dual majors and degrees, credit for life experience, nondegree study, and pass/fail options. There is a freshman honors program on campus, as well as 14 national honor societies, including Phi Beta Kappa. Fourteen departments have honors programs.

Faculty/Classroom: Ninety-five percent teach undergraduates and 5% do research. No introductory courses are taught by graduate students. The average class size in an introductory lecture is 15; in a laboratory, 12; and in a regular course offering, 14.

Requirements: The SAT I or ACT is required. Applicants must be graduates of an accredited secondary school or have a GED certificate. They should have completed at least 16 academic units. An interview is encouraged and a letter of recommendation from the high school counselor or principal is required. Art students must submit a portfolio; music students must audition. AP and CLEP credits are accepted. Important factors used in the admissions decision are personality, intangible qualities, recommendations by school officials, leadership record, extracurricular activities record, and evidence of special talent.

Procedure: Entrance exams should be taken between October and January of the senior year. Application deadlines are open. The application fee is $20. Notification is sent on a rolling basis. There are early admissions and deferred admissions plans.

Transfer: About 634 transfer students enrolled in a recent year. Applicants must submit official transcripts from all colleges attended. Students with fewer than 15 college credits must also submit their high school transcript. An interview is encouraged. A total of 30 credits out of 120 must be completed at Mercy.

Visiting: There are regularly scheduled orientations for prospective students. Visitors may sit in on classes. To arrange for a visit, contact the Admissions Office at (914) 693-7600.

Financial Aid: In a recent year, 85% of all current freshmen received some form of financial aid. The average freshman award was $7750. Mercy is a member of CSS. The FAF is required. The deadline for financial aid applications is February 1.

International Students: There are currently 125 international students enrolled. They must take the college's own test.

Computers: The college provides computer facilities for student use. The mainframe is an IBM 4381. There are also 250 IBM and Apple microcomputers, as well as graphics workstations with IBM XTs and Vectrix graphics boards. All students may access the system. There are no time limits on using the system. The fees are $35.

Graduates: Within an average freshman class, 20% graduate in 4 years, 50% in 5 years, and 30% in 6 years. Some 100 companies recruited on campus in an earlier year.

Admissions Contact: Joy Colelli, Acting Director of Admissions.

MOLLOY COLLEGE
Rockville Centre, NY 11570

D-5

(516) 678-5000, ext. 240
(800) 229-1020 (in-state)

Full-time: 248 men, 1154 women
Part-time: 88 men, 491 women
Graduate: 94 women
Year: 4-1-4, summer session
Application Deadline: open
Freshman Class: 481 applied, 401 accepted, 185 enrolled
SAT I Verbal/Math: 396/416

Faculty: 88; IIB, -$
Ph.D.s: 42%
Student/Faculty: 16 to 1
Tuition: $8580
Room & Board: n/app

ACT: 19   **LESS COMPETITIVE**

Molloy College, founded in 1955, is a private primarily women's commuter college affiliated with the Catholic Church. It offers programs in art, business, health science, liberal arts, music, and teacher preparation. The library contains 100,700 volumes and 1508 microform items, and subscribes to 911 periodicals. Computerized library sources and services include the card catalog, interlibrary loans, and database searching. Special learning facilities include a learning resource center and a radio station. The 25-acre campus is in a suburban area 20 miles east of New York City. There are 3 buildings on campus.

Student Life: About 99% of undergraduates are from New York. Twenty-three percent are from public schools; 77% from private. Seventy-eight percent are white; 16% African American. The average age of freshmen is 18. Sixteen percent drop out by the end of their first year; 95% remain to graduate.

Housing: There are no residence halls. All students commute.

Activities: There are no fraternities or sororities on campus. There are 20 groups on campus, including cheerleading, choir, dance, drama, ethnic, honors, international, literary magazine, musical theater, newspaper, orchestra, political, religious, social, student government, and yearbook. Popular campus events include Tree Trimming Party, Senior 55 Nights Party, Junior Ring Night, and Graduate Champagne Brunch.

Sports: Athletic and recreation facilities include a gymnasium, a dance studio, a weight room, sports fields, and basketball and tennis courts.

Disabled Students: The entire campus is accessible to disabled students. The following facilities are available: wheelchair ramps, elevators, special parking, specially equipped rest rooms, special class scheduling, and lowered drinking fountains.

Services: In addition to many counseling and information services, tutoring is available in every subject. There is also remedial math, reading, and writing.

Campus Safety and Security: Campus safety and security measures include a 24-hour foot and vehicle patrol and a Campus Concerns Committee.

Programs of Study: Molloy awards the B.A. and B.S. degrees. Associate and master's degrees are also awarded. Bachelor's degrees are awarded in BIOLOGICAL SCIENCE (biology/biological science), BUSINESS (accounting and business administration and management), COMMUNICATIONS AND THE ARTS (communications, English, music, and speech/debate/rhetoric), COMPUTER AND PHYSICAL SCIENCE (computer science and mathematics), EDUCATION (art, elementary, foreign languages, secondary, and special), HEALTH PROFESSIONS (music therapy, nursing, predentistry, and premedicine), SOCIAL SCIENCE (history, interdisciplinary studies, philosophy, prelaw, psychology, religion, social work, and sociology). Nursing and cardiorespiratory science are the strongest programs academically. Nursing, business, psychology, and education have the largest enrollments.

Required: Core requirements consist of 9 credits of philosophy and theology, 6 each of English and modern language, 1 of physical education, and courses in art and music history, speech, history, political science, psychology, sociology, mathematics, and science. A total of 128 credit hours is required for graduation.

Special: Students may cross-register with 16 area colleges. The college offers internships, a Washington semester, and dual and student-designed majors. Credit by examination and for life, military, and work experience, nondegree study, and pass/fail options are available. There is a freshman honors program on campus, as well as 16 national honor societies.

Faculty/Classroom: Twenty-five percent of faculty are male; 75%, female. All teach undergraduates and 25% also do research. No introductory courses are taught by graduate students. The average class size in an introductory lecture is 30; in a laboratory, 18; and in a regular course offering, 30.

Admissions: About 83% of the 1993-94 applicants were accepted. About 16% of the current freshmen were in the top fifth of their class; 53% were in the top two fifths. Two freshmen graduated first in their class.

Requirements: Molloy requires applicants to be in the upper 60% of their class. A minimum GPA of 75 is required. The SAT I or ACT is required, with a minimum composite score of 800 on the SAT I. Applicants should be graduates of a secondary school or have a GED. Preparation should include 4 years of English, 3 each of mathematics and history, and 2 each of foreign language and science. An essay is required, and an interview is recommended. AP and CLEP credits are accepted. Important factors used in the admissions decision are leadership record, recommendations by school officials, evidence of special talent, advanced placement or honor courses, and extracurricular activities record.

Procedure: Freshmen are admitted in the fall and spring. Entrance exams should be taken in the fall of the senior year. The application deadlines are open. Application fee is $25. Notification is sent on a rolling basis. There are early decision, early admissions, and deferred admissions plans. About 120 early decision candidates were accepted for the 1993-94 class.

Transfer: About 231 transfer students enrolled in a recent year. A minimum college GPA of 2.0 is required, and an interview is recommended. A total of 30 credits out of 128 must be completed at Molloy.

Visiting: There are regularly scheduled orientations for prospective students, including 2 open houses each year. There are guides for informal visits and visitors may sit in on classes. To arrange for a visit, contact the Admissions Office at (516) 678-5000, ext. 240.

Financial Aid: In a recent year, 93% of all freshmen and 80% of continuing students received some form of financial aid. About 76% of freshmen received need-based aid. The average freshman award was $3906. Of that total, scholarships or need-based grants averaged $4000 ($6700 maximum); loans averaged $1000 ($2600 maximum); and work contracts averaged $1440. All undergraduate students work part-time. The average financial indebtedness of the 1992-93 graduate was $10,000. Molloy is a member of CSS. The FAF and the college's own financial statement is required. The deadline for financial aid applications is February 15.

International Students: There were recently 9 international students enrolled. The school actively recruits these students. They must take the TOEFL or the college's own test and achieve a minimum score on the TOEFL of 500.

Computers: The college provides computer facilities for student use. There are 68 microcomputers available to students in 4 campus laboratories. Additional microcomputers are available within individual departments. There are no time limits and no fees.

Graduates: In a recent year, 253 bachelor's degrees were awarded. Within an average freshman class, 50% graduate in 4 years, 60% in 5 years, and 62% in 6 years.

Admissions Contact: Wayne F. James, Director of Admissions.

MOUNT SAINT MARY COLLEGE D-4
Newburgh, NY 12550 (914) 569–3248; (800) 558–0942 (in-state)

Full-time: 445 men, 725 women	Faculty: 68; IIB, av$
Part-time: 159 men, 270 women	Ph.D.s: 73%
Graduate: 97 men, 306 women	Student/Faculty: 17 to 1
Year: semesters	Tuition: $8060
Application Deadline: open	Room & Board: $4850
Freshman Class: 1055 applied, 700 accepted	
ACT: 20	COMPETITIVE

Mount Saint Mary College, founded in 1960, is a private, nonsectarian, coeducational institution offering programs in the liberal arts. There are 2 graduate schools. In addition to regional accreditation, The Mount has baccalaureate program accreditation with NLN. The library contains 115,000 volumes, 33,000 microform items, and 5300 audiovisual forms, and subscribes to 660 periodicals. Computerized library sources and services include interlibrary loans and database searching. Special learning facilities include a learning resource center, an elementary school, and a TV production studio. The 36-acre campus is in a suburban area 58 miles north of New York City. Including residence halls, there are 31 buildings on campus.

Student Life: About 72% of undergraduates are from New York. Students come from 17 states and 11 foreign countries. Fifty percent are from public schools; 50% from private. Eighty-six percent are white. Seventy-five percent are Catholic; 23% Protestant. The average age of freshmen is 18; all undergraduates, 24. Thirteen percent drop out by the end of their first year; 68% remain to graduate.

Housing: A total of 800 students can be accommodated in college housing. College-sponsored living facilities include single-sex dormitories. In addition there are on-campus town houses. On-campus housing is guaranteed for all 4 years. Seventy-three percent of students live on campus; of those, 78% remain on campus on weekends. All students may keep cars on campus.

Activities: There are no fraternities or sororities on campus. There are 30 groups on campus, including art, band, cheerleading, choir, computers, drama, ethnic, honors, literary magazine, musical theater, newspaper, photography, political, professional, radio and TV, religious, social, student government, and yearbook. Popular campus events include Octoberfest, Block Party Weekend, Parents Weekend, lecture series, and a cultural series.

Sports: There are 4 intercollegiate sports for men and 5 for women, and 15 intramural sports for men and 15 for women. Athletic and recreation facilities include a gymnasium, a weight room, tennis and handball courts, an indoor running track, a swimming pool, a Nautilus room, a game room, and an aerobics/dance studio.

Disabled Students: The entire campus is accessible to disabled students. The following facilities are available: wheelchair ramps, elevators, special parking, specially equipped rest rooms, and lowered telephones.

Services: In addition to many counseling and information services, tutoring is available in every subject. There is remedial math, reading, and writing.

Campus Safety and Security: Campus safety and security measures include 24-hour foot and vehicle patrol, self defense education, escort service, and informal discussions. In addition, there are pamphlets, posters, and films and lighted pathways and sidewalks.

Programs of Study: The Mount awards the B.A., B.S., B.S.Ed., and B.S.N degrees. Master's degrees also are awarded. Bachelor's degrees are awarded in BIOLOGICAL SCIENCE (biology/biological science), BUSINESS (accounting and business administration and management), COMMUNICATIONS AND THE ARTS (communications, English, and public relations), COMPUTER AND PHYSICAL SCIENCE (chemistry, computer science, and mathematics), EDUCATION (elementary, secondary, and special), HEALTH PROFESSIONS (medical laboratory technology, nursing, predentistry, premedicine, and preveterinary science), SOCIAL SCIENCE (Hispanic American studies, history, human services, interdisciplinary studies, international studies, political science/government, prelaw, psychology, social science, and sociology). Nursing and education are the strongest academically. Education has the largest enrollment.

Required: The required core curriculum includes 39 credits in natural sciences, mathematics, computer science, philosophy/religion, arts and letters, and social sciences. A total of 120 credit hours is required for the B.A. or B.S., with 24 to 40 in the major and a minimum GPA of 2.0. Overall requirements are higher for nursing, medical technology, and education students. All students must achieve computer literacy before graduation.

Special: Co-op programs and internships are available in all majors. There is cross-registration with the associated colleges of the mid-Hudson area as well as accelerated degree programs in business, ac-

counting, nursing, computer science, and public relations. The college also offers study abroad in more than 22 countries, a Washington semester, work-study, and dual and student-designed majors. Credit by exam, life, military, work experience, nondegree study, and pass/fail options are available. There is a freshman honors program on campus, as well as 6 national honor societies, including Phi Beta Kappa. Five departments have honors programs.

Faculty/Classroom: Forty-eight percent of faculty are male; 52%, female. All teach undergraduates, 40% do research, and 40% do both. No introductory courses are taught by graduate students. The average class size in an introductory lecture is 30; in a laboratory, 10; and in a regular course offering, 24.

Admissions: About 66% of the 1993–94 applicants were accepted. There were 3 National Merit semifinalists. One freshman graduated first in their class.

Requirements: A minimum GPA of 2.0 and the SAT I or ACT is required. Students should be graduates of an accredited secondary school. The GED is accepted. Applicants should prepare with 4 years each of English and history, and at least 3 each of mathematics and science and 2 of foreign language. An essay and an interview are recommended. AP and CLEP credits are accepted. Important factors used in the admissions decision are advanced placement or honor courses, personality, intangible qualities, recommendations by school officials, leadership record, and evidence of special talent.

Procedure: Freshmen are admitted to all sessions. Entrance exams should be taken as early as possible. Application deadlines are open. The application fee is $20. Notification of early decision is sent immediately; regular decision, on a rolling basis. There are early decision, early admissions, and deferred admissions plans. About 10 early decision candidates were accepted for the 1993–94 class.

Transfer: About 107 transfer students enrolled in 1993–94. Applicants must have a GPA of at least 2.0 in all college work. The SAT I or ACT, an associate degree, and an interview are recommended. A total of 30 credits out of 120 must be completed at The Mount.

Visiting: There are regularly scheduled orientations for prospective students, including 6 open houses per year, a 4-day fall orientation program, and a Spend a Day with a Current Student program in the spring. There are guides for informal visits and visitors may sit in on classes and stay overnight at the school. To arrange for a visit, contact Admissions at (914) 569–3248 or (800) 558–0942 (in state).

Financial Aid: In a recent year 85% of all current freshmen and 80% of continuing students received some form of financial aid. About 73% of freshmen and 70% of continuing students received need-based aid. The average freshman award was $4500. Of that total, scholarships or need-based grants averaged $1500 ($4050 maximum); loans averaged $2200 ($4000 maximum); and work contracts averaged $800 ($1200 maximum). Twenty percent of undergraduate students work part-time. Average earnings from campus work for the school year are $900. The average financial indebtedness of the 1992–93 graduate was $7000. The Mount is a member of CSS. The FAF is required. The deadline for financial aid applications is March 15.

International Students: There are currently 17 international students enrolled. They must take the TOEFL and achieve a minimum score of 525. The student must also take the SAT I or the ACT.

Computers: The college provides computer facilities for student use. The mainframe is an Intel 310 Super-Microcomputer Network. The student-computer ratio is 14 to 1. Microcomputers are located in the main computer center, laboratories, some classrooms, and the library. All students may access the system. It may be used weekdays from 10 A.M. to 11 P.M., and weekends from 10 A.M. to 5 P.M. There are no time limits on using the system and no fees.

Graduates: In 1992–93 230 bachelor's degrees were awarded. The most popular majors among graduates were education (24%), business (15%), and nursing (14%). Within an average freshman class, 70% graduate in 4 years, 27% in 5 years, and 3% in 6 years. Some 10 companies recruited on campus in 1992–93. In a recent graduating class, 7% of the men and 8% of the women were enrolled in graduate school within 6 months of graduation; 90% of the graduates had found employment.

Admissions Contact: J. Randall Ognibene, Director of Admissions.

NAZARETH COLLEGE OF ROCHESTER B-3
Rochester, NY 14618–3790 (716) 586–2525, ext. 265
(800) 462–3944

Full-time: 341 men, 962 women	Faculty: 110; IIB, +$
Part-time: 91 men, 344 women	Ph.D.s: 92%
Graduate: 141 men, 794 women	Student/Faculty: 12 to 1
Year: semesters, summer session	Tuition: $10,480
Application Deadline: June 1	Room & Board: $4830
Freshman Class: 942 applied, 793 accepted, 275 enrolled	
SAT I Verbal/Math: 494/540	ACT: 24 COMPETITIVE +

Nazareth College of Rochester, founded in 1924, is an independent coeducational institution offering programs in the liberal arts. There is

one graduate school. In addition to regional accreditation, Nazareth has baccalaureate program accreditation with CSWE, NASM, and NLN. The library contains 256,516 volumes, 285,144 microform items, and 15,420 audiovisual forms, and subscribes to 1620 periodicals. Computerized library sources and services include the card catalog, interlibrary loans, and database searching. Special learning facilities include a learning resource center, art gallery, and radio station. The 75-acre campus is in a suburban area 7 miles east of Rochester. Including residence halls, there are 13 buildings on campus.

Student Life: About 94% of undergraduates are from New York. Students come from 25 states, 6 foreign countries, and Canada. Eighty-eight percent are from public schools; 12% from private. Ninety-two percent are white. The average age of freshmen is 18; all undergraduates, 21. Eighteen percent drop out by the end of their first year; 57% remain to graduate.

Housing: A total of 825 students can be accommodated in college housing. College-sponsored living facilities include single-sex and coed dormitories. In addition, there are honors houses and language houses. On-campus housing is guaranteed for all 4 years. Sixty-one percent of students live on campus; of those, 75% remain on campus on weekends. All students may keep cars on campus.

Activities: There are no fraternities or sororities on campus. There are 30 groups on campus, including art, band, cheerleading, choir, computers, dance, drama, ethnic, gay, honors, jazz band, literary magazine, musical theater, newspaper, political, religious, student government, and yearbook. Popular campus events include Springfest, Fall Formal Dance, Parents Weekend, and Alumni Weekend.

Sports: There are 6 intercollegiate sports for men and 6 for women, and 20 intramural sports for men and 20 for women. Athletic and recreation facilities include a gymnasium, a pool, soccer and lacrosse fields, tennis courts, a fitness center, racquetball courts, and a sauna.

Disabled Students: The entire campus is accessible to disabled students. The following facilities are available: wheelchair ramps, elevators, special parking, specially equipped rest rooms, and special class scheduling.

Services: In addition to many counseling and information services, tutoring is available in every subject.

Campus Safety and Security: Campus safety and security measures include 24-hour foot and vehicle patrol, escort service, informal discussions, and emergency telephones. In addition, there are lighted pathways and sidewalks.

Programs of Study: Nazareth awards the B.A., B.S., and B.Mus. degrees. Master's degrees are also are awarded. Bachelor's degrees are awarded in BIOLOGICAL SCIENCE (biochemistry and biology/biological science), BUSINESS (accounting and business administration and management), COMMUNICATIONS AND THE ARTS (English, fine arts, French, German, Italian, music, and Spanish), COMPUTER AND PHYSICAL SCIENCE (chemistry, computer science, and mathematics), EDUCATION (art, business, elementary, foreign languages, middle school, and music), HEALTH PROFESSIONS (nursing and speech pathology/audiology), SOCIAL SCIENCE (anthropology, economics, history, international studies, philosophy, political science/government, psychology, religion, social science, social work, and sociology). English, psychology, foreign languages, and art are the strongest academically. Art, psychology, and music have the largest enrollments.

Required: All students must take courses in English, mathematics, laboratory science, philosophy, social science, history, and religious studies. Two semesters of physical education, a course in computer literacy, and a writing competency examination in the junior year are required. Other requirements vary according to the major with a total of anywhere from 30 to 75 upper-division credits needed. A total of 120 credit hours is required to graduate. The minimum GPA is 2.0.

Special: There is cross-registration with members of the Rochester Area Colleges Consortium. Internships in political science and law as well as specific internship opportunities in all other majors; a Washington semester; college-sponsored study abroad in France and Spain; a 3–2 chemical engineering degree with Clarkson University; and nondegree study are also available. There is a freshman honors program on campus, as well as 11 national honor societies. Ten departments have honors programs.

Faculty/Classroom: Fifty-two percent of faculty are male; 48%, female. All teach undergraduates. No introductory courses are taught by graduate students. The average class size in an introductory lecture is 25; in a laboratory, 15; and in a regular course offering, 24.

Admissions: About 84% of the 1993–94 applicants were accepted. The SAT scores for the 1993–94 freshman class were as follows: Verbal—52% below 500, 35% between 500 and 599, 12% between 600 and 700, and 2% above 700; Math—28% below 500, 49% between 500 and 599, 20% between 600 and 700, and 3% above 700. There were 10 National Merit semifinalists. Six freshmen graduated first in their class.

Requirements: The SAT I, with minimum scores of 420 verbal and 430 math, or the ACT, with a minimum score of 20, is required. Applicants should graduate from an accredited secondary school or have a GED. A total of 17 academic credits is required, including 4 years each of English and social studies, and 3 each of foreign language, mathematics, and science. An essay is required, as are an audition for music students and a portfolio for art students. An interview is recommended. AP and CLEP credits are accepted. Important factors used in the admissions decision are advanced placement or honor courses, leadership record, evidence of special talent, extracurricular activities record, and recommendations by alumni.

Procedure: Freshmen are admitted fall and spring. Entrance exams should be taken by December of the senior year. Applications should be filed by June 1 for fall entry and January 15 for spring entry, along with an application fee of $25. Notification is sent on a rolling basis. There are early admissions and deferred admissions plans. A waiting list is an active part of the admissions procedure, with about 5% of applicants on the list.

Transfer: Some 160 transfer students enrolled in 1993–94. Applicants must have a college GPA of 2.5. Those with fewer than 30 credits must submit high school transcripts. An associate degree and an interview are recommended. A total of 30 credits out of 120 must be completed at Nazareth.

Visiting: There are regularly scheduled orientations for prospective students. There are guides for informal visits and visitors may sit in on classes and stay overnight at the school. To arrange for a visit, contact the Admissions Office at (800) 462–3944.

Financial Aid: In 1993–94 78% of all current freshmen and 83% of continuing students received some form of financial aid. About 69% of freshmen and 72% of continuing students received need-based aid. The average freshman award was $8730. Of that total, scholarships or need-based grants averaged $5810 ($10,240 maximum); loans averaged $2440 ($4125 maximum); and work contracts averaged $735 ($1400 maximum). Sixty-nine percent of undergraduate students work part-time. Average earnings from campus work for the school year are $1014. The average financial indebtedness of the 1992–93 graduate was $9976. Nazareth is a member of CSS. The FAF and FAFSA are required. The deadline for financial aid applications is March 31.

International Students: There are currently 8 international students enrolled. The school actively recruits these students. They must take the TOEFL and achieve a minimum score of 550.

Computers: The college provides computer facilities for student use. The mainframe is a DEC VAX 5810. There are 100 microcomputers available for academic use in 5 laboratories. Two of these laboratories are open 24 hours a day. All students may access the system. There are no time limits on using the system and no fees.

Graduates: In 1992–93 463 bachelor's degrees were awarded. The most popular majors among graduates were education certification (30%), business administration (30%), and social sciences (28%). Some 70 companies recruited on campus in 1992–93.

Admissions Contact: Thomas DaRin, Director of Admissions.

NEW SCHOOL FOR SOCIAL RESEARCH
(See Eugene Lang College of the New School for Social Researc)

NEW YORK INSTITUTE OF TECHNOLOGY
OLD WESTBURY
Old Westbury, NY 11568

D-5
(516) 686–7520
(800) 345-NYIT (out-of-state)

Full-time: 3377 men, 1353 women	Faculty: 170; IIA, av$
Part-time: 1387 men, 620 women	Ph.Ds: 29%
Graduate: 910 men, 522 women	Student/Faculty: 28 to 1
Year: semesters, summer session	Tuition: $8650
Application Deadline: open	Room & Board: $5264
Freshman Class: 2541 applied, 1977 accepted, 1509 enrolled	
SAT I or ACT: see profile	LESS COMPETITIVE

The New York Institute of Technology, founded in 1955, is a private institution offering programs in architecture, engineering, technology, management, hotel administration, culinary arts, and the arts and sciences. NYIT has additional campuses in Central Islip on Long Island, and in Manhattan. There are 7 undergraduate and 6 graduate schools. In addition to regional accreditation, NYIT has baccalaureate program accreditation with ABET, FIDER, and NAAB. The library contains 198,000 volumes, 377,100 microform items, and 4458 audiovisual forms, and subscribes to 3300 periodicals. Computerized library sources and services include interlibrary loans and database searching. Special learning facilities include a learning resource center, radio station, and TV studios. The 750-acre campus is in a suburban area 25 miles east of New York City. Including residence halls, there are 25 buildings on campus.

Student Life: About 94% of undergraduates are from New York. Students come from 36 states, more than 70 foreign countries, and Canada. Fifty-seven percent are white; 14% foreign nationals; 14% African American. The average age of freshmen is 18; all undergraduates, 22. Thirty-five percent drop out by the end of their first year; 21% remain to graduate.

Housing: On-campus housing is guaranteed for all 4 years. Eighty-eight percent of students commute. Alcohol is not permitted. All students may keep cars on campus.

Activities: There are some groups and organizations on campus, including international, newspaper, professional, radio and TV, religious, student government, and yearbook.

Sports: There are 7 intercollegiate sports for men and 7 for women, and 5 intramural sports for men and 6 for women. Athletic and recreation facilities include a gymnasium and soccer fields, a track, and courts for tennis, handball, and basketball.

Disabled Students: The following facilities are available: wheelchair ramps, elevators, special parking, and specially equipped rest rooms.

Services: In addition to many counseling and information services, tutoring is available in every subject. In addition, there is remedial math, reading, and writing.

Programs of Study: NYIT awards the B.A., B.S., B.Arch., B.F.A., B.P.S., and B.Tech. degrees. Associate and master's degrees are also awarded. Bachelor's degrees are awarded in BIOLOGICAL SCIENCE (biology/biological science), BUSINESS (accounting, banking and finance, business administration and management, business economics, hotel/motel and restaurant management, and marketing/retailing/merchandising), COMMUNICATIONS AND THE ARTS (advertising, communications, fine arts, journalism, and telecommunications), COMPUTER AND PHYSICAL SCIENCE (chemistry, computer science, mathematics, and physics), EDUCATION (art, business, health, and secondary), ENGINEERING AND ENVIRONMENTAL DESIGN (aeronautical engineering, architecture, electrical/electronics engineering, engineering technology, industrial engineering, and mechanical engineering), HEALTH PROFESSIONS (medical laboratory technology), SOCIAL SCIENCE (political science/government and sociology). Architecture is the strongest academically. Business has the largest enrollment.

Required: All students take a core curriculum, sequenced over 8 semesters, that includes 42 credits in English, speech, behavioral and natural science, social science, philosophy, economics, and 2 capstone courses in the major field. A total of 120 to 138 credits and a minimum GPA of 2.0, both overall and in the major, are required for graduation.

Special: NYIT offers cooperative programs, cross-registration with the C. W. Post campus of Long Island University, summer study abroad, internships, student-designed majors, a general studies degree, and nondegree study. There are 5 national honor societies on campus. Six departments have honors programs.

Faculty/Classroom: Seventy-seven percent of faculty are male; 23%, female. No introductory courses are taught by graduate students. The average class size in an introductory lecture is 20; in a laboratory, 15; and in a regular course offering, 17.

Admissions: About 78% of the 1993–94 applicants were accepted.

Requirements: The SAT I is required for the engineering and architecture programs; it is recommended for all other programs. Engineering programs require a minimum SAT I composite score of 900, with 500 in mathematics; students failing to meet these standards may enter preengineering and transfer later. Architecture programs require an 830 composite SAT I score. Applicants must be graduates of an accredited secondary school or have a GED certificate. Completion of 16 academic units is required, but the specific courses needed vary by degree program. AP and CLEP credits are accepted.

Procedure: Freshmen are admitted to all sessions. Application deadlines are open. Application fee is $30. Notification is sent on a rolling basis.

Transfer: Applicants must submit official transcripts from all colleges attended. Engineering applicants must have a 2.3 GPA in mathematics, physics, and engineering courses. A total of 30 credits out of 120 to 138 must be completed at NYIT.

Visiting: There are regularly scheduled orientations for prospective students. There are guides for informal visits and visitors may sit in on classes. To arrange for a visit, contact the Admissions Office at (516) 686–7520 or (800) 345-NYIT.

Financial Aid: Ten percent of undergraduate students work part-time. NYIT is a member of CSS. The FAF is required.

International Students: The school actively recruits these students. They must take the TOEFL and achieve a minimum score of 450.

Computers: The college provides computer facilities for student use. The mainframes are DEC VAX 8700 and 11/7800 models. There are also 12 rooms equipped with Zenith, Commodore PC-40, Apple, IBM, and DEC microcomputers, and a laboratory with equipment for computer-aided design. All students may access the system. There are no time limits on using the system and no fees.

Admissions Contact: Beverly Tota, Director, Undergraduate Admissions.

NEW YORK UNIVERSITY D-5

New York, NY 10011 (212) 998–4500

Undergraduate: 6437 men, 8788 women	Faculty: 1226; I, +$
	Ph.D.s: 94%
Graduate: 6485 men, 8759 women	Student/Faculty: 10 to 1
Year: semesters, summer session	Tuition: $17,640
Application Deadline: February 1	Room & Board: $7065
Freshman Class: 13,594 applied, 7244 accepted, 2505 enrolled	
SAT I or ACT: required	VERY COMPETITIVE +

New York University, founded in 1831, is a private liberal arts institution offering programs in arts and sciences, business, education, health, nursing, and social work. There are 7 undergraduate and 7 graduate schools. In addition to regional accreditation, NYU has baccalaureate program accreditation with AACSB, ABET, ADA, APTA, CSWE, FIDER, NAAB, NASAD, NASM, NCATE, and NLN. The 6 libraries contain more than 3,000,000 volumes and 20,000 audiovisual forms, and subscribe to 15,936 periodicals. Computerized library sources and services include the card catalog, interlibrary loans, and database searching. Special learning facilities include a learning resource center, art gallery, radio station, TV station, and audiology laboratory. The 28-acre campus is in an urban area in New York City's Greenwich Village. Including residence halls, there are 109 buildings on campus.

Student Life: About 60% of undergraduates are from New York. Students come from 50 states, 120 foreign countries, and Canada. Fifty-one percent are white; 18% Asian American. Fifteen percent drop out by the end of their first year; 66% remain to graduate.

Housing: A total of 4500 students can be accommodated in college housing. College-sponsored living facilities include coed dormitories, on-campus apartments, and fraternity houses. In addition, there are special-interest houses. On-campus housing is guaranteed for all 4 years. Sixty percent of students commute. All students may keep cars on campus.

Activities: About 7% of men and about 6% of women belong to 11 national fraternities; about 5% of women belong to 7 local and 3 national sororities. There are 230 groups on campus, including bagpipe band, band, cheerleading, chess, choir, chorale, chorus, computers, dance, drama, ethnic, film, gay, honors, international, jazz band, literary magazine, musical theater, newspaper, orchestra, pep band, photography, political, professional, radio and TV, religious, social, social service, student government, symphony, and yearbook. Popular campus events include Spring Strawberry Festival, Greek Olympics, Annual Club Fair, and Winter Festival.

Sports: There are 11 intercollegiate sports for men and 8 for women, and 19 intramural sports for men and 16 for women. Athletic and recreation facilities include a sports and recreation center that includes a pool, tennis courts, a track, a dance studio, an exercise prescription facility, a weight room, handball, racquetball, and squash courts, a fencing area, and multipurpose courts.

Disabled Students: Ninety-five percent of the campus is accessible to disabled students. The following facilities are available: wheelchair ramps, elevators, special parking, specially equipped rest rooms, lowered drinking fountains, and lowered telephones.

Services: In addition to many counseling and information services, tutoring is available in every subject. There is also a reader service for the blind as well as services for the hearing-impaired and the terminally ill.

Campus Safety and Security: Campus safety and security measures include self-defense education, escort service, shuttle buses, and informal discussions. In addition, there are pamphlets, posters, films, emergency telephones, lighted pathways and sidewalks, vehicle patrol, 24-hour security in residence halls, and a neighborhood-merchant emergency help service.

Programs of Study: NYU awards the B.A., B.S., B.B.A., B.F.A., and B.S./B.E. degrees. Associate, master's, and doctoral degrees also are awarded. Bachelor's degrees are awarded in BIOLOGICAL SCIENCE (biochemistry and biology/biological science), BUSINESS (accounting, banking and finance, business administration and management, business economics, hotel/motel and restaurant management, and marketing/retailing/merchandising), COMMUNICATIONS AND THE ARTS (broadcasting, communications, creative writing, dance, dramatic arts, English, film arts, fine arts, French, German, Greek, Hebrew, Italian, journalism, languages, Latin, music, music business management, photography, Portuguese, Russian, Spanish, and speech/debate/rhetoric), COMPUTER AND PHYSICAL SCIENCE (actuarial science, chemistry, computer science, mathematics, physics, and statistics), EDUCATION (art, early childhood, music, science, secondary, and special), ENGINEERING AND ENVIRONMENTAL DESIGN (engineering technology), HEALTH PROFESSIONS (nursing, physical therapy, predentistry, premedicine, and speech pathology/audiology), SOCIAL SCIENCE (anthropology, dietetics,

economics, history, international relations, philosophy, political science/government, prelaw, psychology, public administration, social science, social work, sociology, and urban studies). Business, biology, psychology, film and TV, political science, accounting, and journalism have the largest enrollments.

Required: All students must complete a minimum of 128 credit hours and maintain a minimum GPA of 2.0. A course in expository writing is required. Students must complete a core liberal arts curriculum in addition to major and elective credit.

Special: A 3–2 engineering degree is available with the Stevens Institute of Technology in New Jersey. Opportunities are provided for internships, study abroad in more than 20 countries, a B.A.-B.S. degree, accelerated degrees, dual and student-designed majors, credit by examination, and pass/fail options. A Washington semester is available to political science majors. There is a freshman honors program on campus.

Faculty/Classroom: No introductory courses are taught by graduate students. The average class size in an introductory lecture is 50; in a laboratory, 20; and in a regular course offering, 30.

Admissions: About 53% of the 1993–94 applicants were accepted. The SAT scores for the 1993–94 freshman class were as follows: Verbal—22% below 500, 48% between 500 and 599, 26% between 600 and 700, and 4% above 700; Math—12% below 500, 34% between 500 and 599, 41% between 600 and 700, and 13% above 700. There were 18 National Merit finalists.

Requirements: A minimum GPA of 3.0 is required. The SAT I or ACT is required. Applicants must graduate from an accredited secondary school. The GED is accepted. Students must present at least 16 Carnegie units, including 4 in English. Some majors require an essay, an audition, submission of a creative portfolio, or an interview. AP and CLEP credits are accepted. Important factors used in the admissions decision are advanced placement or honor courses, leadership record, evidence of special talent, recommendations by school officials, and extracurricular activities record.

Procedure: Freshmen are admitted to all sessions. Entrance exams should be taken by November of the senior year. There are early decision, early admissions, and deferred admissions plans. Early decision applications should be filed by December 15; regular applications, by February 1 for fall entry, December 1 for spring entry, and May 1 for summer entry, along with an application fee of $45. Notification of early decision is sent January 15; regular decision, April 1. About 560 early decision candidates were accepted for the 1993–94 class. A waiting list is an active part of the admissions procedure.

Transfer: About 1120 transfer students enrolled in 1993–94. Applicants must submit a minimum GPA of 2.5 if transferring from a 4-year college, or 3.0 from a 2-year college. The SAT I or ACT is recommended. At least 32 credits out of 128 must be completed at NYU.

Visiting: There are regularly scheduled orientations for prospective students, including campus tours and weekday information sessions by appointment. There are guides for informal visits, and visitors may sit in on classes. To arrange for a visit, contact the Admissions Office at (212) 998–4524.

Financial Aid: In 1993–94, 97% of all current freshmen and 66% of continuing students received some form of financial aid. About 66% of continuing students received need-based aid. The average freshman award was $11,300. Of that total, scholarships or need-based grants averaged $8894; loans averaged $5305; and work contracts averaged $3000. Average earnings from campus work for the school year are $3000. NYU is a member of CSS. The FAFSA financial statement is required. The deadline for financial aid applications is February 15.

International Students: There are currently 937 international students enrolled. The school actively recruits these students. They must take the TOEFL or the college's own test. They must also take the SAT I, ACT, or the college's own entrance exam.

Computers: The college provides computer facilities for student use. The mainframes are a CDC CYBER 180/830a; an IBM 4381; DEC VAX Models 11/785, 11/750, 8350/2, 8600, and 8650; and a SUN 4/280s. There are also IBM PS/2, IBM PC, and Apple Macintosh Plus microcomputers available in the computing center and in several departments. Those with course requirements to use the system may access the system 24 hours a day, 7 days a week in some cases. The fees are $2 per hour.

Graduates: In 1992–93, 2927 bachelor's degrees were awarded. The most popular majors among graduates were arts and humanities (21%), business (16%), and social sciences (10%). Within an average freshman class, 66% graduate in 5 years. Some 400 companies recruited on campus in 1992–93. In the 1992 graduating class, 73% of all graduates were enrolled in graduate school within 6 months of graduation; 90% had found employment.

Admissions Contact: Office of Undergraduate Admissions.

NIAGARA UNIVERSITY A-3
Niagara University, NY 14109   (716) 286–8700, 8721
(800) 462–2111 (out-of-state)

Full-time: 767 men, 1152 women	Faculty: 112; IIA, -$
Part-time: 99 men, 235 women	Ph.D.s: 83%
Graduate: 224 men, 359 women	Student/Faculty: 17 to 1
Year: semesters, summer session	Tuition: $10,070
Application Deadline: August 15	Room & Board: $4482
Freshman Class: 2220 applied, 1796 accepted, 467 enrolled	
SAT I or ACT: required	COMPETITIVE

Niagara University, founded in 1856 by the Vincentian fathers and brothers, is today a private, nonsectarian institution rooted in a Roman Catholic tradition. Programs offered include those in liberal arts, business, education, nursing, and travel, hotel, and restaurant administration. There are 6 undergraduate and 3 graduate schools. In addition to regional accreditation, Niagara has baccalaureate program accreditation with ACCE, CSWE, NCATE, and NLN. The library contains 284,647 volumes and 73,456 microform items, and subscribes to 1272 periodicals. Computerized library sources and services include the card catalog, interlibrary loans, and database searching. Special learning facilities include a learning resource center, art gallery, radio station, TV station, 2 theaters, and greenhouse. The 160-acre campus is in a suburban area 4 miles north of Niagara Falls, overlooking the Niagara River gorge and 20 miles north of Buffalo. Including residence halls, there are 25 buildings on campus.

Student Life: About 91% of undergraduates are from New York. Students come from 25 states, 20 foreign countries, and Canada. Seventy-five percent are from public schools; 25% from private. Eighty-six percent are white. Most are Catholic. The average age of freshmen is 18; all undergraduates, 20. Twenty-five percent drop out by the end of their first year; 58% remain to graduate.

Housing: A total of 1314 students can be accommodated in college housing. College-sponsored living facilities include single-sex and coed dormitories. In addition, there is honors, international, and special interest housing. On-campus housing is guaranteed for all 4 years. Fifty-five percent of students live on campus; of those, 75% remain on campus on weekends. Alcohol is not permitted. All students may keep cars on campus.

Activities: About 2% of men and women belong to 2 national fraternities. There are no sororities on campus. There are 78 groups on campus, including art, cheerleading, choir, chorale, computers, drama, drill team, ethnic, film, honors, international, musical theater, newspaper, pep band, political, professional, radio and TV, religious, social, social service, student government, and yearbook. Popular campus events include Orientation, CARE, University Ball, Parents Weekend, Alumni Weekend, Fall and Spring weekends, class weekends, university theater productions, art museum events, job and activities fairs, and guest speakers.

Sports: There are 7 intercollegiate sports for men and 6 for women, and 25 intramural sports for men and 25 for women. Athletic and recreation facilities include a 3400-seat gymnasium, a 6-lane swimming and diving pool, exercise and weight rooms, saunas and dance areas, outdoor tennis courts, baseball and soccer fields, basketball and racquetball courts, and multipurpose courts with indoor track. Hiking and biking trails are nearby.

Disabled Students: Most of the campus is accessible to disabled students. The following facilities are available: wheelchair ramps, elevators, special parking, specially equipped rest rooms, special class scheduling, and campus accommodation for the vision-impaired.

Services: In addition to many counseling and information services, tutoring is available in most subjects. In addition, there is a reader service for the blind, and remedial math, reading, and writing. Study skills development, note taking, and escort-assistance services are available, as are educational assistant services for the vision-impaired, educational/classroom services and machines for the hearing-impaired, and services for the learning-disabled.

Campus Safety and Security: Campus safety and security measures include 24-hour foot and vehicle patrol, self defense education, escort service, and informal discussions. In addition, there are pamphlets, posters, and films, emergency telephones, lighted pathways and sidewalks, and a campus security advisory board.

Programs of Study: Niagara awards the B.A., B.S., B.B.A., and B.F.A. degrees. Associate and master's degrees also are awarded. Bachelor's degrees are awarded in BIOLOGICAL SCIENCE (biochemistry, biology/biological science, and life science), BUSINESS (accounting, business administration and management, business economics, hotel/motel and restaurant management, human resources, marketing/retailing/merchandising, transportation management, and travel/tourism), COMMUNICATIONS AND THE ARTS (communications, dramatic arts, English, French, and Spanish), COMPUTER AND PHYSICAL SCIENCE (chemistry, computer science, information sciences and systems, and mathematics), EDUCATION (elementary, English, foreign languages, mathematics, science, secondary, and so-

cial studies), ENGINEERING AND ENVIRONMENTAL DESIGN (pre-engineering), HEALTH PROFESSIONS (nursing, predentistry, and premedicine), SOCIAL SCIENCE (criminal justice, history, international studies, philosophy, political science/government, prelaw, psychology, religion, social science, social work, and sociology). Business, social sciences, education, and natural sciences are the strongest programs academically. Business administration, travel and tourism, and social services have the largest enrollments.

Required: To graduate, students must earn 120 to 126 credit hours and a GPA of at least 2.0; 60 to 66 such hours are required in the major, 20 in specific disciplines, and 20 in liberal arts classes.

Special: Niagara offers a Washington semester, a semester at the state capitol in Albany, on-campus work-study, internships in most majors with such companies as the Big 6 accounting firms and Walt Disney World, and co-op programs in all areas except nursing, education, and social work. Students may study abroad in 4 countries and cross-register through the Western New York Consortium. Accelerated degree programs in most majors, B.A.-B.S. degrees, dual majors, a 2–3 engineering program with the University of Detroit, nondegree study, credit for life, military, and work experience, pass/fail options, and research are also available. There is also an academic exploration program for undeclared majors. There is a freshman honors program on campus, as well as 14 national honor societies. There is a universitywide honors program.

Faculty/Classroom: Sixty-three percent of faculty are male; 37%, female. All teach undergraduates. No introductory courses are taught by graduate students. The average class size in an introductory lecture is 25 and in a regular course offering, 20.

Admissions: About 81% of the 1993–94 applicants were accepted. About 32% of the current freshmen were in the top fifth of their class; 65% were in the top two fifths.

Requirements: A minimum grade average of 80% to 85% is required. The SAT I or ACT is required. In addition, applicants should be graduates of an accredited high school. The GED is accepted. The high school program should include 16 academic credits, with 4 in English and 2 each in foreign language, history, mathematics, science, social studies, as well as academic electives. Science, mathematics, and computer majors should have 3 credits each in mathematics and science. AP and CLEP credits are accepted. Important factors used in the admissions decision are advanced placement or honor courses, parents or siblings attending the school, recommendations by school officials, recommendations by alumni, and extracurricular activities record.

Procedure: Freshmen are admitted to all sessions. Entrance exams should be taken in the junior year or fall of the senior year. Early decision applications should be filed by August 15; regular applications, by August 15 for fall entry and January 10 for spring entry, along with an application fee of $25. Notification is sent on a rolling basis. There are early decision, early admissions, and deferred admissions plans.

Transfer: About 213 transfer students enrolled in 1993–94. Applicants must have a minimum GPA of 2.0 in travel, hotel, and restaurant administration, arts and sciences, and academic exploration (except for 2.25 in business and 2.5 for nursing and education majors) and submit all high school and college transcripts. The SAT I or ACT is recommended. A total of 30 credits out of 120 to 126 must be completed at Niagara.

Visiting: There are regularly scheduled orientations for prospective students, including individual interviews and campus tours. Other arrangements can be made individually, such as to attend a class, eat in the student cafeteria, and/or speak with a faculty member. There are guides for informal visits and visitors may sit in on classes and stay overnight at the school. To arrange for a visit, contact the Admissions Office appointment desk at (716) 286–8700 or (800) 462–2111.

Financial Aid: In 1993–94 85% of all current freshmen and 80% of continuing students received some form of financial aid. About 75% of freshmen and 75% of continuing students received need-based aid. The average freshman award was $10,000. Of that total, scholarships or need-based grants averaged $4100 ($15,000 maximum); loans averaged $4800 ($5100 maximum); and work contracts averaged $1600 ($2100 maximum). Twenty-six percent of undergraduate students work part-time. Average earnings from campus work for the school year are $1300. Niagara is a member of CSS. The FAF and FAFSA are required. The deadline for financial aid applications is February 15.

International Students: There are currently 71 international students enrolled. The school actively recruits these students. They must take the TOEFL and achieve a minimum score of 500.

Computers: The college provides computer facilities for student use. The mainframe is a DEC MicroVAX 3800. There are 150 terminals/PCs available to students in several academic computing laboratories and in the academic computing center. All dormitories are networked, and some rooms are tied in so students can access the system. All students may access the system. It may be used from 9 A.M. to 11 P.M. Monday to Thursday, 9 A.M. to 5 P.M. Friday, noon to 5

P.M. Saturday, and 3 P.M. to 10 P.M. Sunday. There are no time limits on using the system and no fees.

Graduates: In 1992–93 498 bachelor's degrees were awarded. The most popular majors among graduates were commerce and accounting (29%), travel and tourism/and hotel and restaurant management (14%), and social services (10%). Within an average freshman class, 47% graduate in 4 years, 56% in 5 years, and 75% in 6 years. Some 139 companies recruited on campus in 1992–93. In the 1992 graduating class, 11% of all students were enrolled in graduate school within 6 months of graduation; 86% of the men and 89% of the women had found employment.

Admissions Contact: George C. Pachter, Dean of Admissions and Records.

NYACK COLLEGE D-5

Nyack, NY 10960 (914) 358–1710; (800) 336–9225 (out-of-state)

Full-time and part-time: 600 men and women	**Faculty:** 62
	Ph.D.s: 50%
Graduate: none	**Student/Faculty:** 10 to 1
Year: semesters, summer session	**Tuition:** $8400
Application Deadline: open	**Room & Board:** $3810
Freshman Class: n/av	
SAT I or ACT: required	**LESS COMPETITIVE**

Nyack College, founded in 1882, is a private liberal arts institution affiliated with the Christian and Missionary Alliance. There are 2 undergraduate schools and one graduate school. In addition to regional accreditation, Nyack has baccalaureate program accreditation with NASM. The 2 libraries contain 76,000 volumes and 420 microform items, and subscribe to 614 periodicals. Special learning facilities include a learning resource center and radio station. The 63-acre campus is in a suburban area 20 miles north of New York City. Including residence halls, there are 6 buildings on campus.

Student Life: Students come from 20 states. Fifty-eight percent are white; 16% Hispanic; 16% Asian American; 10% African American. Twenty-two percent drop out by the end of their first year.

Housing: College-sponsored living facilities include single-sex dormitories and married-student housing. On-campus housing is guaranteed for all 4 years. Alcohol is not permitted. All students may keep cars on campus.

Activities: There are no fraternities or sororities on campus. There are many groups and organizations on campus, including band, cheerleading, chorale, drama, ethnic, literary magazine, newspaper, orchestra, radio and TV, religious, student government, and yearbook. Popular campus events include music festivals and the Cultural Events Series.

Sports: There are 3 intercollegiate sports for men and 3 for women. There is also an intramural sports program.

Disabled Students: The following facilities are available: elevators and special parking.

Services: In addition to many counseling and information services, tutoring is available in every subject.

Campus Safety and Security: Campus safety and security measures include 24-hour foot and vehicle patrol.

Programs of Study: Nyack awards the B.A., B.S., B.Mus., and S.M.B. degrees. Associate degrees also are awarded. Bachelor's degrees are awarded in BUSINESS (business administration and management), COMMUNICATIONS AND THE ARTS (communications, English, music, music theory and composition, piano/organ, and voice), EDUCATION (early childhood, elementary, and secondary), SOCIAL SCIENCE (biblical studies, crosscultural studies, history, interdisciplinary studies, ministries, missions, pastoral studies, philosophy, psychology, religion, religious education, religious music, social science, and sociology).

Required: To graduate, students must complete 128 to 148 credits with a minimum GPA of 2.0, or 2.3 for education majors. General education and major requirements vary by degree program. Students must adhere to the college's standards of Christian living and behavior.

Special: Nyack offers internships, cooperative programs with other schools, study abroad, a semester in Hollywood for cinema communications majors, dual and student-designed majors, independent study, nondegree study, and pass/fail options.

Faculty/Classroom: The average class size in a regular course offering is 25.

Requirements: The SAT I or ACT is required. Applicants must be graduates of an accredited secondary school or have the GED. Completion of 16 academic credits is required and should include 4 units of English, 2 of a foreign language, 3 of history or social science, 3 of any combination of mathematics and science, and 4 of electives. Students must demonstrate sound Christian character through personal testimony and recommendations. An interview may be required. AP and CLEP credits are accepted.

Procedure: Application deadlines are open. Application fee is $15. Notification is sent on a rolling basis.

Transfer: A total of 30 credits out of 128 to 148 must be completed at Nyack.

Visiting: There are regularly scheduled orientations for prospective students. There are guides for informal visits and visitors may sit in on classes and stay overnight at the school. To arrange for a visit, contact the Office of Admissions at (914) 358-1710.

Financial Aid: In 1993-94, 87% of all current freshmen received some form of financial aid. The FAF, the college's own financial statement, and parent and student tax returns are required. The deadline for financial aid applications is May 1.

International Students: Students whose native language is other than English must take the TOEFL and obtain a minimum score of 550.

Admissions Contact: Miguel Sanchez, Director of Admissions.

PACE UNIVERSITY

New York, NY 10038

D-5

Full-time: 2268 men, 3541 women
Part-time: 1521 men, 2858 women
Graduate: 2460 men, 2260 women
Year: semesters, summer session
Application Deadline: July 15
Freshman Class: 3883 applied, 2981 accepted, 1006 enrolled
SAT I Verbal/Math: 441/517

(212) 346-1225; (800) 874-PACE
Faculty: 339; IIA, +$
Ph.D.s: 87%
Student/Faculty: 17 to 1
Tuition: $10,780
Room & Board: $4760

COMPETITIVE

Pace University, founded in 1906, is a private institution offering programs in arts and sciences, business, nursing, education, and computer and information science. There are 5 undergraduate and 6 graduate schools. In addition to regional accreditation, Pace has baccalaureate program accreditation with NLN. The 4 libraries contain 825,000 volumes, 655,000 microform items, and 5900 audiovisual forms, and subscribe to 7300 periodicals. Computerized library sources and services include the card catalog, interlibrary loans, and database searching. Special learning facilities include a learning resource center, a radio station, a TV station, 2 art galleries, a performing arts center, biological research laboratories, and an environmental center. The New York City campus occupies 1 city block in an urban area; the Pleasantville/Briarcliff campus is located on 200 acres in a small town. Including residence halls, there are 41 buildings on the campuses.

Student Life: About 87% of undergraduates are from New York. Students come from 24 states, 61 foreign countries, and Canada. Forty-seven percent are from public schools; 53% from private. Fifty-five percent are white; 14% African American; 12% Hispanic; 10% foreign nationals. Forty percent are Catholic; 30% Protestant. The average age of freshmen is 18; all undergraduates, 20. Twenty percent drop out by the end of their first year; 60% remain to graduate.

Housing: A total of 2150 students can be accommodated in college housing. College-sponsored living facilities include coed dormitories. In addition, there are honors houses. On-campus housing is guaranteed for all 4 years. Sixty-three percent of students commute. Alcohol is not permitted. All students may keep cars on campus.

Activities: About 10% of men belong to 2 local and 6 national fraternities; about 10% of women belong to 10 local and 2 national sororities. There are 100 groups on campus, including art, cheerleading, chorus, computers, dance, drama, ethnic, film, gay, honors, international, literary magazine, musical theater, newspaper, photography, political, professional, radio and TV, religious, social, social service, student government, and yearbook. Popular campus events include Homecoming, talent shows, concerts, and Picnic.

Sports: There are 7 intercollegiate sports for men and 6 for women, and 6 intramural sports each for men and women. Athletic and recreation facilities include the Civic Center Gym in New York City and gymnasiums, tennis courts, and playing fields at the Pleasantville campus.

Disabled Students: Seventy percent of the campus is accessible to disabled students. The following facilities are available: wheelchair ramps, elevators, special parking, specially equipped rest rooms, special class scheduling, lowered drinking fountains, and lowered telephones. There is a coordinator of all services for disabled students.

Services: In addition to many counseling and information services, tutoring is available in every subject. There is also remedial math, reading, and writing and an academic skills center.

Campus Safety and Security: Campus safety and security measures include 24-hour foot and vehicle patrol, escort service, shuttle buses, and informal discussions. In addition, there are pamphlets, posters, films, emergency telephones, and lighted pathways and sidewalks.

Programs of Study: Pace awards the B.A., B.S., B.B.A., and B.F.A., and B.S.N. degrees. Associate, master's, and doctoral degrees are also awarded. Bachelor's degrees are awarded in BIOLOGICAL SCIENCE (biology/biological science), BUSINESS (accounting, banking and finance, business administration and management, business economics, international business management, marketing/retailing/merchandising, and real estate), COMMUNICATIONS AND THE

ARTS (communications, dramatic arts, English, fine arts, French, journalism, Spanish, and theater design), COMPUTER AND PHYSICAL SCIENCE (chemistry, computer science, information sciences and systems, mathematics, and physics), EDUCATION (business, early childhood, elementary, and secondary), ENGINEERING AND ENVIRONMENTAL DESIGN (chemical engineering, electrical/electronics engineering, and industrial administration/management), HEALTH PROFESSIONS (medical laboratory technology, nursing, predentistry, premedicine, and speech pathology/audiology), SOCIAL SCIENCE (anthropology, criminal justice, economics, history, political science/government, psychology, social science, and sociology). Business administration has the largest enrollment.

Required: To graduate, students must complete at least 128 credit hours, including 32 to 50 in the major, with a minimum GPA of 2.0. A core curriculum of 60 credits and an introductory computer science course are required.

Special: Internships, study abroad, a Washington semester, and a cooperative education program in all majors are available. Pace also offers accelerated degree programs, B.A.-B.S. degrees, dual majors, general studies degrees, and 3-2 engineering degrees, with Manhattan College and Rensselaer Polytechnic Institute. Credit for life, military, and work experience, nondegree study, and pass/fail options are available. There is a freshman honors program on campus, as well as 15 national honor societies.

Faculty/Classroom: Fifty-nine percent of faculty are male; 41%, female. Eighty-four percent teach undergraduates. No introductory courses are taught by graduate students. The average class size in an introductory lecture is 35; in a laboratory, 10; and in a regular course offering, 23.

Admissions: About 77% of the 1993-94 applicants were accepted. The SAT scores for the 1993-94 freshman class were as follows: Verbal—74% below 500, 22% between 500 and 599, 3% between 600 and 700, and 1% above 700; Math—41% below 500, 38% between 500 and 599, 19% between 600 and 700, and 2% above 700. About 50% of the current freshmen were in the top fifth of their class; 50% were in the top two fifths. Ten freshmen graduated first in their class.

Requirements: Pace requires applicants to be in the upper 50% of their class. A minimum high school average of 80% is required. The SAT I or ACT is required. Applicants should be graduates of an accredited secondary school, with 16 to 18 academic credits, including 4 in English, 3 to 4 each in mathematics, science, and history, and 2 to 3 in foreign language. The GED is accepted. An essay and an interview are recommended. AP and CLEP credits are accepted. Important factors used in the admissions decision are recommendations by school officials, recommendations by alumni, advanced placement or honor courses, leadership record, and extracurricular activities record.

Procedure: Freshmen are admitted fall and spring. Early action applications should be filed by November 1; regular applications, by July 15 for fall entry and November 15 for spring entry, along with an application fee of $25. Notification of early action is sent December 15; regular decision, on a rolling basis. There is a deferred admission plan.

Transfer: About 720 transfer students enrolled in 1993-94. Applicants are admitted in the fall or spring. A college GPA of 2.5 is required. Grades of C or better transfer for credit. A maximum of 68 credits will be accepted from a 2-year school. A total of 32 credits out of 128 must be completed at Pace.

Visiting: There are regularly scheduled orientations with invitations extended to prospective students. There are guides for informal visits and visitors may sit in on classes and stay overnight at the school. To arrange for a visit, contact the Office of Undergraduate Admission at (212) 346-1225 (New York City campus) or (914) 773-3746 (Pleasantville campus).

Financial Aid: In 1993-94, 67% of all current freshmen and 61% of continuing students received some form of financial aid. About 64% of freshmen and 60% of continuing students received need-based aid. The average freshman award was $4830 ($10,000 maximum). Ninety-five percent of undergraduate students work part-time. Average earnings from campus work for the school year are $3600. The average financial indebtedness of the 1992-93 graduate was $10,000. Pace is a member of CSS. The FAFSA financial statement is required. The deadline for financial aid applications is February 8.

International Students: There are currently 1051 international students enrolled. The school actively recruits these students. They must take the TOEFL (and achieve a minimum score of 550) or the college's own test.

Computers: The college provides computer facilities for student use. The mainframe is an IBM 4381/P13. There are about 850 terminals on both campuses and at the midtown center. All students may access the system. It may be used 24 hours a day. There are no time limits on using the system and no fees.

Graduates: In 1992-93, 1798 bachelor's degrees were awarded. The most popular majors among graduates were business and management (69%), education (6%), and social science (6%). Within an

average freshman class, 37% graduate in 4 years, 21% in 5 years, and 4% in 6 years. Some 450 companies recruited on campus in 1992–93. In the 1992 graduating class, 70% of graduates had found employment within 6 months of graduation.

Admissions Contact: Richard P. Alvarez (NYC) or Christine G. Richard (Pleasantville).

PARSONS SCHOOL OF DESIGN
D-5

New York, NY 10011   (212) 229–8910; (800) 252–0852 (in-state)

Full-time: 504 men, 1123 women	Faculty: 41
Part-time: 24 men, 36 women	Ph.D.s: 6%
Graduate: 45 men, 92 women	Student/Faculty: 40 to 1
Year: semesters	Tuition: $14,210
Application Deadline: open	Room & Board: $7200
Freshman Class: 932 applied, 694 accepted, 370 enrolled	
SAT I or ACT: required	**SPECIAL**

Parsons School of Design, founded in 1896, is a private, coeducational professional art school and is part of the New School for Social Research. There is one graduate school. In addition to regional accreditation, Parsons has baccalaureate program accreditation with NASAD. The 2 libraries contain 177,000 volumes and 5000 audiovisual forms, and subscribe to 230 periodicals. Computerized library sources and services include the card catalog and database searching. Special learning facilities include an art gallery. The 2-acre campus is in an urban area in the northern section of Manhattan's Greenwich Village. Including residence halls, there are 8 buildings on campus.

Student Life: About 72% of undergraduates are from out-of-state, mostly the Middle Atlantic. Students come from 49 states, 70 foreign countries, and Canada. Eighty percent are from public schools; 20% from private. Seventy-two percent are white; 12% Asian American. The average age of freshmen is 18; all undergraduates, 20. Four percent drop out by the end of their first year; 69% remain to graduate.

Housing: A total of 700 students can be accommodated in college housing. College-sponsored living facilities include coed dormitories and off-campus apartments. On-campus housing is available on a first-come, first-served basis and is available on a lottery system for upperclassmen. Priority is given to out-of-town students. Alcohol is not permitted. All students may keep cars on campus.

Activities: There are no fraternities or sororities on campus. There are some groups and organizations on campus, including ethnic, gay, international, literary magazine, political, religious, social, and student government. Popular campus events include the Fashion Critics Award Show, and annual senior shows.

Sports: There is no sports program at Parsons.

Disabled Students: All of the campus is accessible to disabled students. The following facilities are available: wheelchair ramps, elevators, and specially equipped rest rooms.

Services: In addition to many counseling and information services, tutoring is available in some subjects, including English and art history.

Campus Safety and Security: Campus safety and security measures include informal discussions and pamphlets, posters, and films.

Programs of Study: Parsons awards the B.A.-B.F.A., B.F.A., and B.B.A. degrees. Associate and master's degrees also are awarded. Bachelor's degrees are awarded in BUSINESS (business administration and management), COMMUNICATIONS AND THE ARTS (advertising, design, fine arts, illustration, photography, and studio art), ENGINEERING AND ENVIRONMENTAL DESIGN (interior design), SOCIAL SCIENCE (fashion design and technology). Communication design, illustration, and fashion design have the largest enrollments.

Required: To graduate, students must complete 134 credit hours, including 97 in the major, with a minimum GPA of 2.0. Parsons requires a minimum of 30 credits in liberal arts and 12 in art history.

Special: Students may cross-register at the New School for Social Research, Cooper Union, and Pratt Institute. Internships are required for some majors. Students may study abroad at the Parsons campus in Paris or in 4 other countries. The 5-year combined B.A.-B.F.A. degree requires 180 credits for graduation. A mobility semester or year at any AICAD school is available and interdisciplinary majors, including architecture and environmental design and design marketing, are possible.

Faculty/Classroom: Sixty percent of faculty are male; 40%, female. The average class size in an introductory lecture is 30 and in a regular course offering, 18.

Admissions: About 74% of the 1993–94 applicants were accepted. About 30% of the current freshmen were in the top fifth of their class; 56% were in the top two fifths. About 20 freshmen graduated first in their class.

Requirements: A minimum GPA of 2.0 is required. The SAT I or the ACT is required. Applicants must be graduates of an accredited secondary school. The GED is accepted. Applicants should have completed 4 years each of art, English, history, and social studies. A portfolio and home exam are required and an interview is recommended.

AP credits are accepted. Important factors used in the admissions decision are evidence of special talent, advanced placement or honor courses, leadership record, personality, intangible qualities, and extracurricular activities record.

Procedure: Freshmen are admitted fall and spring. Entrance exams should be taken spring of junior year. Application deadlines are open. Application fee is $30. Notification is sent on a rolling basis. There is an early admissions plan. A waiting list is an active part of the admissions procedure, with about 15% of applicants on the list.

Transfer: About 280 transfer students enrolled in an earlier year. Applicants will receive credit for grade C work or better in college courses that are similar in content, purpose, and standards to the courses offered at Parsons. A high school transcript is required for undergraduates, and SAT I or ACT is recommended. All students must present a portfolio and home exam. Transfers are admitted in the fall or spring. A total of 67 credits out of 134 must be completed at Parsons.

Visiting: There are guides for informal visits. To arrange for a visit, contact the Office of Admissions at (212) 229–8910 or (800) 252–0852 (in-state).

Financial Aid: In 1993–94, 80% of all current freshmen and 80% of continuing students received some form of financial aid. About 80% of freshmen and 80% of continuing students received need-based aid. Scholarships or need-based grants averaged $3950 ($10,000 maximum); loans averaged $2625 ($4125 maximum); and work contracts averaged $2000. Eleven percent of undergraduate students work part-time. Average earnings from campus work for the school year are $1035. The average financial indebtedness of the 1992–93 graduate was $8000. Parsons is a member of CSS. The FAF or FFS and the college's own financial statement are required. The deadline for financial aid applications is March 1.

International Students: There are currently 600 international students enrolled. The school actively recruits these students.

Computers: The college provides computer facilities for student use. The Parsons computer graphics laboratory has 8 MS-DOS computers as well as 64 Macintosh II work stations, supported by peripherals and software for 2-D and 3-D applications. The general New School computer facility, with a range of word processors and graphic programs, is also available to all students. All students enrolled in computer classes and all upperclassmen may access the system. There are no time limits on using the system and no fees.

Graduates: In a recent year, 460 bachelor's degrees were awarded. Some 100 companies recruited on campus in 1992–93. In the 1992 graduating class, 3% of the men and 5% of the women were enrolled in graduate school within 6 months of graduation; 85% of the men and 80% of the women had found employment.

Admissions Contact: Nadine M. Bourgeois, Director of Admissions.

POLYTECHNIC UNIVERSITY
BROOKLYN
D-5

Brooklyn, NY 11201-2999   (718) 260–3100 or (516) 755–4200
                                (800) POLYTEC (in-state)

Full-time: 873 men, 156 women	Faculty: 150
Part-time: 148 men, 22 women	Ph.D.s: 90%
Graduate: 968 men, 148 women	Student/Faculty: 7 to 1
Year: semesters, summer session	Tuition: $15,700
Application Deadline: open	Room & Board: $4000
Freshman Class: 759 applied, 558 accepted, 203 enrolled	
SAT I Verbal/Math: 460/630	**HIGHLY COMPETITIVE**

Polytechnic University, founded in 1854, is a private, multicampus university offering undergraduate and graduate programs through the divisions of arts and sciences, engineering, and management. There are 3 undergraduate and 3 graduate schools. In addition to regional accreditation, Polytechnic has baccalaureate program accreditation with ABET. The library contains 366,890 volumes and 32,921 microform items, and subscribes to 2200 periodicals. Computerized library sources and services include the card catalog, interlibrary loans, and database searching. Special learning facilities include a learning resource center. The 3-acre campus is in an urban area 5 minutes from downtown Manhattan. Including residence halls, there are 4 buildings on campus.

Student Life: About 92% of undergraduates are from New York. Students come from 11 states and 21 foreign countries. Seventy percent are from public schools; 30% from private. Thirty-seven percent are Asian American; 35% white; 13% African American. The average age of freshmen is 18; all undergraduates, 21. Twenty percent drop out by the end of their first year; 66% remain to graduate.

Housing: A total of 300 students can be accommodated in college housing. College-sponsored living facilities include coed dormitories and fraternity houses. On-campus housing is available on a first-come, first-served basis. Priority is given to out-of-town students. Eighty-eight percent of students commute. Alcohol is not permitted. All students may keep cars on campus.

Activities: About 12% of men and about 3% of women belong to 2 local and 2 national fraternities. There are no sororities on campus. There are 52 groups on campus, including chess, computers, ethnic, honors, international, jazz band, newspaper, photography, professional, religious, social, social service, student government, and yearbook. Popular campus events include Chinese New Year, International Food Fair, Indian-Pakistan dinner, barbecues, Comedy Night, ski trips, and dances.

Sports: There are 6 intercollegiate sports for men and 1 for women, and 13 intramural sports for men and 10 for women. Athletic and recreation facilities include soccer, lacrosse, and baseball fields, a gymnasium, and 2 student centers.

Disabled Students: Seventy percent of the campus is accessible to disabled students. The following facilities are available: wheelchair ramps, elevators, special parking, specially equipped rest rooms, lowered drinking fountains, and lowered telephones.

Services: In addition to many counseling and information services, tutoring is available in every subject. In addition, there is remedial writing.

Campus Safety and Security: Campus safety and security measures include 24-hour foot and vehicle patrol, informal discussions, pamphlets, posters, and films, and emergency telephones. In addition, there are lighted pathways and sidewalks.

Programs of Study: Polytechnic awards the B.S. degree. Master's and doctoral degrees also are awarded. Bachelor's degrees are awarded in COMMUNICATIONS AND THE ARTS (journalism and technical and business writing), COMPUTER AND PHYSICAL SCIENCE (chemistry, computer science, information sciences and systems, mathematics, and physics), ENGINEERING AND ENVIRONMENTAL DESIGN (aeronautical engineering, chemical engineering, civil engineering, computer engineering, electrical/electronics engineering, engineering, environmental engineering, mechanical engineering, and metallurgical engineering), SOCIAL SCIENCE (humanities and social science). Engineering, management, and arts and sciences are the strongest programs academically. Electrical engineering, computer engineering, aerospace engineering, and computer science have the largest enrollments.

Required: Students must complete all university and departmental course requirements, earn 126 to 136 credits, and maintain a minimum GPA of 2.0 in order to graduate.

Special: Cooperative programs are available in all majors. Cross-registration is permitted through a consortium of Long Island colleges. Opportunities are provided for internships, work-study programs, study abroad, accelerated degree programs in engineering and computer science, dual majors, student-designed majors, and nondegree study. There is a freshman honors program on campus, as well as 5 national honor societies. Three departments have honors programs.

Faculty/Classroom: Ninety-one percent of faculty are male; 9%, female. Seventy percent teach undergraduates, 40% do research, and 25% do both. No introductory courses are taught by graduate students. The average class size in an introductory lecture is 30; in a laboratory, 15; and in a regular course offering, 25.

Admissions: About 74% of the 1993–94 applicants were accepted. The SAT scores for the 1993–94 freshman class were as follows: Verbal—71% below 500, 22% between 500 and 599, and 7% between 600 and 700; Math—3% below 500, 31% between 500 and 599, 46% between 600 and 700, and 20% above 700. About 83% of the current freshmen were in the top fifth of their class; 96% were in the top two fifths.

Requirements: The SAT I or the ACT is required. In addition, graduation from an accredited secondary school is required; a GED will be accepted. Applicants must submit a minimum of 16 credit hours, including 4 each in English, mathematics, and science, and 1 each in foreign language, art, music, and social studies. SAT II: Subject tests in writing, mathematics I or II, and chemistry or physics are recommended. An essay and an interview are recommended. AP credit is accepted. Important factors used in the admissions decision are leadership record, evidence of special talent, advanced placement or honor courses, recommendations by school officials, and recommendations by alumni.

Procedure: Freshmen are admitted to all sessions. Entrance exams should be taken by November of the senior year. Early admission applications should be filed by November 1; regular application deadlines are open. Application fee is $40. Notification of early decision is sent December 1; regular decision, on a rolling basis. There are early decision, early admissions, and deferred admissions plans. Twelve early decision candidates were accepted for the 1993–94 class.

Transfer: About 107 transfer students enrolled in 1993–94. Transfer applicants must have a 2.8 cumulative GPA. A total of 36 credits out of 126 to 136 must be completed at Polytechnic.

Visiting: There are regularly scheduled orientations for prospective students, including a keynote speaker, major presentations, financial aid and scholarship sessions, and student life and career services ses-

sions. There are guides for informal visits and visitors may sit in on classes and stay overnight at the school. To arrange for a visit, contact the Director of Admissions at (718) 260–3100 or (800) POLYTEC (in-state).

Financial Aid: In 1993–94 88% of all current freshmen and 85% of continuing students received some form of financial aid. About 85% of freshmen and 85% of continuing students received need-based aid. The average freshman award was $6758. Of that total, scholarships or need-based grants averaged $6000 ($15,300 maximum); and loans averaged $2600 ($5500 maximum). Sixteen percent of undergraduate students work part-time. Average earnings from campus work for the school year are $1500. The average indebtedness of the 1992–93 graduate was $10,835. Polytechnic is a member of CSS. The FAF and the college's own financial statement are required. The deadline for financial aid applications is March 1.

International Students: There are currently 135 international students enrolled. The school actively recruits these students. They must take the TOEFL and achieve a minimum score of 500. The student must also take the SAT I or the ACT.

Computers: The college provides computer facilities for student use. The mainframes are an IBM 4381 and an IBM 4341. There are also 100 IBM microcomputers, 100 SUN workstations, and 62 X-Window workstations available throughout the campus. All students may access the system 24 hours a day. There are no time limits on using the system and no fees.

Graduates: In 1992–93 197 bachelor's degrees were awarded. The most popular majors among graduates were electrical engineering (45%), mechanical engineering (11%), and industrial engineering (9%). Within an average freshman class, 30% graduate in 4 years, 48% in 5 years, and 51% in 6 years. Some 250 companies recruited on campus in 1992–93. In the 1992 graduating class, 83% of all graduates had found employment within 6 months of graduation.

Admissions Contact: Dean of Admissions.

POLYTECHNIC UNIVERSITY FARMINGDALE

Farmingdale, NY 11735	**D-5**
Full-time: 313 men, 37 women	(516) 755–4200; (800) POLYTEC
Part-time: 42 men, 2 women	**Faculty:** 150
Graduate: 273 men, 38 women	**Ph.D.s:** 90%
Year: semesters, summer session	**Student/Faculty:** 2 to 1
Application Deadline: open	**Tuition:** $15,700
Freshman Class: 373 applied, 289 accepted, 99 enrolled	**Room & Board:** $5000
SAT I Verbal/Math: 490/630	**VERY COMPETITIVE**

Polytechnic University, founded in 1854, is a private university offering undergraduate and graduate programs through the divisions of arts and sciences, engineering, and management. There are 3 undergraduate and 3 graduate schools. In addition to regional accreditation, Polytechnic University/Farmingdale has baccalaureate program accreditation with ABET. The library contains 366,890 volumes and 32,921 microform items, and subscribes to 2200 periodicals. Computerized library sources and services include the card catalog, interlibrary loans, and database searching. Special learning facilities include a learning resource center. The 25-acre campus is in a suburban area in the center of Long Island, on the border of Nassau and Suffolk counties. Including residence halls, there are 5 buildings on campus.

Student Life: About 95% of undergraduates are from New York. Students come from 8 states and 7 foreign countries. Seventy percent are from public schools; 30% from private. Sixty-six percent are white; 20% Asian American. The average age of freshmen is 18; all undergraduates, 21. Twenty percent drop out by the end of their first year; 66% remain to graduate.

Housing: A total of 100 students can be accommodated in college housing. College-sponsored living facilities include coed dormitories and fraternity houses. On-campus housing is available on a first-come, first-served basis. Priority is given to out-of-town students. Eighty percent of students commute. Alcohol is not permitted. All students may keep cars on campus.

Activities: About 12% of men and about 3% of women belong to 2 local and 2 national fraternities. There are no sororities on campus. There are 52 groups on campus, including chess, computers, ethnic, honors, international, jazz band, newspaper, photography, professional, religious, social, social service, student government, and yearbook. Popular campus events include Chinese New Year, International Food Fair, Indian-Pakistan dinner, barbecues, Comedy Night, ski trips, and dances.

Sports: There are 6 intercollegiate sports for men and 1 for women, and 13 intramural sports for men and 10 for women. Athletic and recreation facilities include soccer, lacrosse, and baseball fields, a gymnasium, and 2 student centers.

Disabled Students: Seventy percent of the campus is accessible to disabled students. The following facilities are available: wheelchair ramps, elevators, special parking, specially equipped rest rooms, lowered drinking fountains, and lowered telephones.

Services: In addition to many counseling and information services, tutoring is available in every subject. In addition, there is remedial writing.

Campus Safety and Security: Campus safety and security measures include 24-hour foot and vehicle patrol, informal discussions, pamphlets, posters, and films, and emergency telephones. In addition, there are lighted pathways and sidewalks.

Programs of Study: Polytechnic University/Farmingdale awards the B.S. degree. Master's and doctoral degrees also are awarded. Bachelor's degrees are awarded in COMMUNICATIONS AND THE ARTS (journalism and technical and business writing), COMPUTER AND PHYSICAL SCIENCE (chemistry, computer science, information sciences and systems, mathematics, and physics), ENGINEERING AND ENVIRONMENTAL DESIGN (aeronautical engineering, chemical engineering, civil engineering, computer engineering, electrical/electronics engineering, engineering, environmental engineering, mechanical engineering, and metallurgical engineering), SOCIAL SCIENCE (social science). Engineering, management, and arts and sciences are the strongest academically. Computer science and electrical, computer, and aerospace engineering have the largest enrollments.

Required: Students must complete all university and departmental course requirements, earn 126 to 136 credits, and maintain a minimum GPA of 2.0 to graduate.

Special: Cross-registration is permitted through a consortium of Long Island colleges. Opportunities are provided for internships, work-study programs, study abroad, an accelerated degree program in engineering, dual and student-designed majors, and nondegree study. There is a freshman honors program on campus, as well as 5 national honor societies. Three departments have honors programs.

Faculty/Classroom: Ninety-one percent of faculty are male; 9%, female. Seventy-five percent teach undergraduates, 40% do research, and 25% do both. No introductory courses are taught by graduate students. The average class size in an introductory lecture is 30; in a laboratory, 15; and in a regular course offering, 20.

Admissions: About 77% of the 1993–94 applicants were accepted. The SAT scores for the 1993–94 freshman class were as follows: Verbal—52% below 500, 36% between 500 and 599, and 12% between 600 and 700; Math—2% below 500, 31% between 500 and 599, 52% between 600 and 700, and 15% above 700. About 86% of the current freshmen were in the top fifth of their class; 90% were in the top two fifths.

Requirements: The SAT I or ACT is required; a minimum ACT score of 24 may be substituted for SAT I results. Graduation from an accredited secondary school is required; a GED will be accepted. Applicants must submit a minimum of 16 credit hours, including 4 each in English, mathematics, and science, and 1 each in foreign language, art, music, and social studies. SAT II: Subject tests in writing, mathematics I or II, and chemistry or physics are recommended. An essay and an interview are also recommended. AP credits are accepted. Important factors used in the admissions decision are leadership record, evidence of special talent, advanced placement or honor courses, recommendations by school officials, and recommendations by alumni.

Procedure: Freshmen are admitted to all sessions. Entrance exams should be taken by November of the senior year. Application deadlines are open. The application fee is $40. Notification of early decision is sent December 1; regular decision, on a rolling basis. There are early decision, early admissions, and deferred admissions plans. About 12 early decision candidates were accepted for the 1993–94 class.

Transfer: About 27 transfer students enrolled in 1993–94. Transfer applicants must have a 2.75 cumulative GPA. A total of 36 credits out of 126 to 136 must be completed at Polytechnic University/Farmingdale.

Visiting: There are regularly scheduled orientations for prospective students, including a keynote speaker, major presentations, financial aid and scholarship sessions, and student life and career services sessions. There are guides for informal visits, and visitors may sit in on classes and stay overnight at the school. To arrange for a visit, contact the Director of Admissions at (516) 755–4200.

Financial Aid: In 1993–94 88% of all current freshmen and 85% of continuing students received some form of financial aid. About 85% of freshmen and 85% of continuing students received need-based aid. The average freshman award was $6758. Of that total, scholarships or need-based grants averaged $6000 ($15,300 maximum); and loans averaged $2600 ($5500 maximum). Sixteen percent of undergraduate students work part-time. Average earnings from campus work for the school year are $1500. The average financial indebtedness of the 1992–93 graduate was $10,835. Polytechnic University/Farmingdale is a member of CSS. The FAF and the college's own financial statement are required. The deadline for financial aid applications is March 1.

International Students: There are currently 135 international students enrolled. The school actively recruits these students. They must take the TOEFL and achieve a minimum score of 500. The student must also take the college's own entrance exam.

Computers: The college provides computer facilities for student use. The mainframes are an IBM 4381 and 4341. There are also 22 IBM 486 and 19 IBM 386 microcomputers, 1 IBM 286 microcomputer, 20 X-Window workstations, plus additional facilities available as part of the Engineering 101 laboratory. All students may access the system. It may be used 24 hours a day. There are no time limits on using the system and no fees.

Graduates: In 1992–93 197 bachelor's degrees were awarded. The most popular majors among graduates were electrical engineering (45%), mechanical engineering (11%), and industrial engineering (9%). Within an average freshman class, 30% graduate in 4 years, 48% in 5 years, and 51% in 6 years. Some 250 companies recruited on campus in 1992–93. In the 1992 graduating class, 83% of all students had found employment within 6 months of graduation.

Admissions Contact: Peter Jordan, Dean of Admissions.

PRATT INSTITUTE
D-5

Brooklyn, NY 11205   (718) 636–3669; (800) 331–0834 (out-of-state)

Full-time: 1050 men, 606 women	Faculty: 110
Part-time: 123 men, 69 women	Ph.D.s: 51%
Graduate: 644 men, 815 women	Student/Faculty: 15 to 1
Year: semesters, summer session	Tuition: $13,140
Application Deadline: February 1	Room & Board: $6380
Freshman Class: 1127 applied, 879 accepted, 304 enrolled	
SAT I Verbal/Math: 460/520	COMPETITIVE

Pratt Institute, founded in 1887, is a private, coeducational institution offering undergraduate and graduate programs in architecture, art and design education, industrial design, fine arts, and professional studies. There are 3 undergraduate and 3 graduate schools. In addition to regional accreditation, Pratt has baccalaureate program accreditation with FIDER, NAAB, and NASAD. The library contains 203,790 volumes, 43,835 microform items, and 1371 audiovisual forms, and subscribes to 823 periodicals. Computerized library sources and services include the card catalog and database searching. Special learning facilities include a learning resource center, art gallery, and radio station. The 25-acre campus is in an urban area 25 miles east of downtown Manhattan. Including residence halls, there are 23 buildings on campus.

Student Life: About 54% of undergraduates are from New York. Students come from 44 states, 52 foreign countries, and Canada. Eighty-one percent are from public schools; 19% from private. Fifty-five percent are white; 13% Asian American; 10% African American. The average age of freshmen is 19; all undergraduates, 23. Ten percent drop out by the end of their first year; 65% remain to graduate.

Housing: A total of 1175 students can be accommodated in college housing. College-sponsored living facilities include single-sex and coed on-campus apartments and married-student housing. On-campus housing is guaranteed for all 4 years. Fifty-five percent of students live on campus; of those, 80% remain on campus on weekends. All students may keep cars on campus.

Activities: About 3% of men belong to 1 local and 1 national fraternity; about 1% of women belong to 1 local sorority. There are 60 groups on campus, including art, chess, drama, ethnic, film, gay, honors, international, literary magazine, musical theater, newspaper, professional, radio and TV, religious, social, student government, and yearbook. Popular campus events include Springfest, International Food Fair, Holiday Ball, Thursday Night Comedy, and film and concert series.

Sports: There are 6 intercollegiate sports for men and 4 for women, and 3 intramural sports for men and 1 for women. Athletic and recreation facilities include an activities resource center with 5 indoor tennis courts, a 200-meter indoor track, volleyball and basketball courts, a weight room, and 2 dance studios.

Disabled Students: Seventy-five percent of the campus is accessible to disabled students. The following facilities are available: wheelchair ramps, elevators, special parking, specially equipped rest rooms, and specially equipped residence hall spaces.

Services: In addition to many counseling and information services, tutoring is available in some subjects, including mathematics, English, science, social science, and art history. There is a reader service for the blind. Individual tutoring and testing services are also available.

Campus Safety and Security: Campus safety and security measures include 24-hour foot and vehicle patrol, escort service, shuttle buses, and informal discussions. In addition, there are pamphlets, posters, and films, emergency telephones, lighted pathways and sidewalks, and trained security officers.

Programs of Study: Pratt awards the B.S., B.E., B.F.A., B.I.D., B.P.S., and B.Arch. degrees. Associate and master's degrees also are awarded. Bachelor's degrees are awarded in BUSINESS (fashion merchandising), COMMUNICATIONS AND THE ARTS (art history and appreciation, communications, film arts, fine arts, industrial design, and photography), EDUCATION (art), ENGINEERING AND ENVIRONMENTAL DESIGN (architecture, computer graphics, construction management, and interior design), SOCIAL SCIENCE (fashion design and technology). Fine arts, industrial design, communications design, and architecture are the strongest academically. Architecture and communications design have the largest enrollments.

Required: The number of credits needed for graduation varies with the major, but a minimum of 132 is required, one-quarter of which must be in liberal arts. Undergraduates must maintain a GPA of 2.0. All students must take 6 credits each of social sciences or philosophy, English, and cultural history, and 3 credits of science.

Special: Pratt offers co-op programs with the East Coast Consortium (art and design schools) and cross-registration with St. John's College and Queen's College. Internships, study abroad in 4 countries, work-study programs, dual majors, credit for work experience, nondegree study, and pass/fail options are available. There are 4 national honor societies on campus.

Faculty/Classroom: Sixty percent of faculty are male; 40%, female. Ninety-two percent teach undergraduates and 1% do research. No introductory courses are taught by graduate students. The average class size in an introductory lecture is 22; in a laboratory, 20; and in a regular course offering, 15.

Admissions: About 78% of the 1993–94 applicants were accepted. The SAT scores for the 1993–94 freshman class were as follows: Verbal—77% below 500, 16% between 500 and 599, and 7% between 600 and 700; Math—60% below 500, 24% between 500 and 599, 14% between 600 and 700, and 2% above 700. About 40% of the current freshmen were in the top fifth of their class; 93% were in the top two fifths.

Requirements: Pratt requires applicants to be in the upper 20% of their class. A minimum GPA of 2.8 is required. The SAT I or ACT is required. SAT II: writing and mathematics I or II are recommended for architecture applicants. Applicants must be graduates of an accredited secondary school. The GED is accepted. Students should have completed 4 years of English, 3 of mathematics, and 2 each of science, social studies, and history. A portfolio is required, as is an interview for all applicants who live within 100 miles of Pratt. An essay is recommended for all students. AP and CLEP credits are accepted. Important factors used in the admissions decision are evidence of special talent, advanced placement or honor courses, recommendations by school officials, recommendations by alumni, and extracurricular activities record.

Procedure: Freshmen are admitted fall and spring. Entrance exams should be taken by November of the senior year. Applications should be filed by February 1 for fall entry and November 1 for spring entry, along with an application fee of $30. Notification is sent on a rolling basis. There are early admissions and deferred admissions plans. A waiting list is an active part of the admissions procedure, with about 5% of applicants on the list.

Transfer: About 220 transfer students enrolled in 1993–94. Applicants should present college transcripts and recommendations. Students with fewer than 30 college credits must submit SAT I or ACT scores and high school transcripts. A portfolio is required for architecture and art and design students. An essay and an interview are recommended. A total of 48 credits out of 132 must be completed at Pratt.

Visiting: There are regularly scheduled orientations for prospective students, including a campus tour, schoolwide presentations, departmental presentations, and financial-aid workshops. There are guides for informal visits and visitors may sit in on classes and stay overnight at the school. To arrange for a visit, contact the Office of Admissions at (718) 636-3669 or (800) 331-0834.

Financial Aid: In 1993–94, 79% of all current freshmen and 71% of continuing students received some form of financial aid. About 75% of all students received need-based aid. The average freshman award was $9105. Of that total, scholarships or need-based grants averaged $6385 ($13,500 maximum); loans averaged $620 ($2625 maximum); and work contracts averaged $2100 ($3000 maximum). Thirty-two percent of undergraduate students work part-time. Average earnings from campus work for the school year are $2100. Pratt is a member of CSS. The FAF, the college's own financial statement, the FAFSA, and parents' and student's tax returns are required. The deadline for financial aid applications is March 1.

International Students: There are currently 506 international students enrolled. They must take the TOEFL or the college's own test and achieve a minimum score on the TOEFL of 500.

Computers: The college provides computer facilities for student use. The mainframe is a DEC VAX 6210. The mainframe may be reached via 12 VT340 terminals in the engineering laboratory or by dial-up modem. All students may access the system. It may be used 24-hours 7 days a week. There are no time limits on using the system and no fees.

Graduates: In 1992–93 482 bachelor's degrees were awarded. The most popular majors among graduates were architecture (25%), communications design (13%), and fine arts (12%). Within an average freshman class, 55% graduate in 5 years. Some 23 companies recruited on campus in 1992–93. In the 1992 graduating class, 4% of the graduates were enrolled in graduate school within 6 months of graduation; 87% of the men and 82% of the women had found employment.

Admissions Contact: Judith Aaron, Dean of Admissions.

RENSSELAER POLYTECHNIC INSTITUTE   D-3
Troy, NY 12180–3590

(518) 276-6216
(800) 448-6562 (out-of-state)

Full-time: 3427 men, 864 women	Faculty: 394
Part-time: 10 men, 6 women	Ph.D.s: 94%
Graduate: 1760 men, 456 women	Student/Faculty: 11 to 1
Year: semesters	Tuition: $17,325
Application Deadline: January 15	Room & Board: $5742
Freshman Class: 4996 applied, 4166 accepted, 936 enrolled	
SAT I or ACT: required	**HIGHLY COMPETITIVE**

Rensselaer Polytechnic Institute, founded in 1824, is a private, coeducational institution that emphasizes science and engineering technology but also offers programs in architecture, management, the humanities, and social sciences. There are 5 undergraduate and 5 graduate schools. In addition to regional accreditation, RPI has baccalaureate program accreditation with AACSB and ABET. The 2 libraries contain 538,000 volumes, 754,565 microform items, and 2023 audiovisual forms, and subscribe to 5175 periodicals. Computerized library sources and services include the card catalog, interlibrary loans, and database searching. Special learning facilities include a learning resource center, art gallery, radio station, and observatory. The 276-acre campus is in an urban area 10 miles north of Albany. Including residence halls, there are 190 buildings on campus.

Student Life: About 59% of undergraduates are from out-of-state, mostly the Northeast. Students come from 50 states, 39 foreign countries, and Canada. Seventy-eight percent are from public schools; 22% from private. Eighty percent are white; 13% Asian American. The average age of freshmen is 18; all undergraduates, 21. Fourteen percent drop out by the end of their first year; 72% remain to graduate.

Housing: A total of 2923 students can be accommodated in college housing. College-sponsored living facilities include single-sex and coed dormitories, on-campus apartments, married-student housing, fraternity houses, and sorority houses. In addition, there is a wellness house and a black cultural center. On-campus housing is guaranteed for the freshman year only, is available on a first-come, first-served basis, and is available on a lottery system for upperclassmen. Sixty-one percent of students live on campus; of those, 98% remain on campus on weekends. Alcohol is not permitted. All students may keep cars on campus.

Activities: About 33% of men belong to 2 local and 27 national fraternities; about 25% of women belong to 2 local and 3 national sororities. There are 125 groups on campus, including art, cheerleading, chess, chorale, chorus, computers, dance, drama, drill team, ethnic, gay, honors, international, jazz band, literary magazine, musical theater, newspaper, orchestra, pep band, photography, political, professional, radio and TV, religious, social, social service, student government, symphony, and yearbook. Popular campus events include Grand Marshall Week, Rite of Spring Week, International Festival, Activities Fair, Career-athalon, Black History Month, and Black Awareness Week.

Sports: There are 12 intercollegiate sports for men and 7 for women, and 21 intramural sports for men and 8 for women. Athletic and recreation facilities include a field house, 2 pools, a stadium, 2 gymnasiums, a sports and recreation center, several playing fields, 2 weight rooms, and 6 tennis courts.

Disabled Students: Fifty-two percent of the campus is accessible to disabled students. The following facilities are available: wheelchair ramps, elevators, special parking, specially equipped rest rooms, special class scheduling, lowered drinking fountains, and lowered telephones.

Services: In addition to many counseling and information services, tutoring is available in every subject. There is a writing center.

Campus Safety and Security: Campus safety and security measures include 24-hour foot and vehicle patrol, self defense education, escort service, and shuttle buses. In addition, there are informal discussions, pamphlets, posters, and films, emergency telephones, lighted pathways and sidewalks, locked residence halls, on-campus bicycle patrol, and a student volunteer program.

Programs of Study: RPI awards the B.S. and B.Arch. degrees. Master's and doctoral degrees also are awarded. Bachelor's degrees are awarded in BIOLOGICAL SCIENCE (biology/biological science),

BUSINESS (management information systems and management science), COMMUNICATIONS AND THE ARTS (communications), COMPUTER AND PHYSICAL SCIENCE (chemistry, computer science, geology, mathematics, physics, and science technology), ENGINEERING AND ENVIRONMENTAL DESIGN (aeronautical engineering, architecture, biomedical engineering, chemical engineering, civil engineering, computer engineering, electrical/electronics engineering, engineering, engineering physics, environmental engineering, industrial engineering, materials engineering, mechanical engineering, and nuclear engineering), HEALTH PROFESSIONS (predentistry and premedicine), SOCIAL SCIENCE (economics, interdisciplinary studies, philosophy, prelaw, and psychology). Engineering, physical sciences, architecture, management, humanities, and social sciences are the strongest programs academically. Engineering and science have the largest enrollments.

Required: For graduation, students must earn at least 124 credits for the B.S. degree and 168 credits for the B.Arch., including 24 credits in physical, life, and engineering sciences and 24 credits in humanities and social sciences. Students must maintain a minimum GPA of 1.8 and must pass a writing assessment or take a writing course. Physical education and 4 lifetime activities courses are required.

Special: RPI offers an exchange program with Williams and Harvey Mudd colleges and cross-registration with the Hudson Mohawk Association of Colleges and Universities. Co-op programs, internships, study abroad in more than 10 countries, work-study programs, and pass/fail options are available. Students may pursue an accelerated 4-year B.S.-M.S. degree in engineering as well as a 3-2 engineering degree. Continuing education programs are broadcast via TV satellite to various industrial locations. There is a freshman honors program on campus, as well as 14 national honor societies. Three departments have honors programs.

Faculty/Classroom: Ninety percent of faculty are male; 10%, female. The average class size in an introductory lecture is 350; in a laboratory, 25; and in a regular course offering, 24.

Admissions: About 83% of the 1993-94 applicants were accepted. The SAT scores for the 1993-94 freshman class were as follows: Verbal—29% below 500, 45% between 500 and 599, 22% between 600 and 700, and 3% above 700; Math—2% below 500, 15% between 500 and 599, 51% between 600 and 700, and 32% above 700. About 76% of the current freshmen were in the top fifth of their class. There were 17 National Merit finalists. About 57 freshmen graduated first in their class.

Requirements: The SAT I or ACT is required. In addition, SAT II: Subject tests in writing, mathematics (level I or II), and chemistry or physics are recommended. Applicants must be graduates of an accredited secondary school. High school preparation should include 4 years each of English and mathematics, and 3 years each of science and social studies. An essay is required for most programs, and an interview is recommended. Architecture applicants must submit a portfolio. AP credit is accepted. Important factors used in the admissions decision are advanced placement or honor courses, recommendations by school officials, leadership record, extracurricular activities record, and evidence of special talent.

Procedure: Freshmen are admitted in the fall and spring. Entrance exams should be taken in the junior and/or senior year. Early decision applications should be filed by January 1; regular applications, by January 15 for fall entry and December 1 for spring entry, along with an application fee of $35. Notification of early decision is sent 3 weeks after the application is received; regular decision, March 15. There are early decision, early admissions, and deferred admissions plans. About 140 early decision candidates were accepted for the 1993-94 class. A waiting list is an active part of the admissions procedure, with about 5% of applicants on the list.

Transfer: About 174 transfer students enrolled in 1993-94. The SAT I or ACT is required for applicants with fewer than 2 years of college, and is recommended for all other applicants. All students are advised to have an interview and to present faculty recommendations. Grades of C or better transfer for credit. A total of 30 credits out of 124 must be completed at RPI.

Visiting: There are regularly scheduled orientations for prospective students. There are guides for informal visits and visitors may sit in on classes and stay overnight at the school. To arrange for a visit, contact the Admissions Office at (800) 448-6562.

Financial Aid: In a recent year, 75% of all freshmen and 75% of continuing students received some form of financial aid. About 73% of freshmen and 73% of continuing students received need-based aid. The average freshman award in a recent year was $13,150. Of that total, scholarships or need-based grants averaged $9995 ($21,000 maximum); loans averaged $3750 ($6800 maximum); and work contracts averaged $1400. The average financial indebtedness of a recent year's graduate was $15,000. RPI is a member of CSS. The FAF and FAFSA are required. The deadline for financial aid applications is February 15.

International Students: There are currently 137 international students enrolled. The school actively recruits these students. They must take the TOEFL and achieve a minimum score of 550. The student must also take the SAT I or the ACT. SAT II: Subject tests in writing, mathematics, and physics or chemistry are recommended.

Computers: The college provides computer facilities for student use. The mainframe is an IBM 3090-200S. There are several microcomputer laboratories on campus. All students may access the system. There are no time limits on using the system and no fees.

Graduates: In a recent year, 1040 bachelor's degrees were awarded. Within an average freshman class, 72% graduate in 5 years. Some 472 companies recruited on campus in a recent year.

Admissions Contact: Dean of Admissions.

ROBERTS WESLEYAN COLLEGE B-3
Rochester, NY 14624-1997

(716) 594-6400
(800) 777-4RWC (out-of-state)

Full-time: 365 men, 567 women	**Faculty:** 51
Part-time: 37 men, 70 women	**Ph.Ds:** 45%
Graduate: 17 men, 59 women	**Student/Faculty:** 18 to 1
Year: semesters, summer session	**Tuition:** $9951
Application Deadline: August 1	**Room & Board:** $3366
Freshman Class: 459 applied, 422 accepted, 212 enrolled	
SAT I Verbal/Math: 464/503	**ACT:** 23 **COMPETITIVE**

Roberts Wesleyan College, founded in 1866, is a private coeducational institution affiliated with the Free Methodist Church. The curriculum offers a liberal arts education in the Christian tradition. In addition to regional accreditation, Roberts has baccalaureate program accreditation with CSWE, NASAD, NASM, and NLN. The library contains 99,869 volumes, 50,419 microform items, and 2702 audiovisual forms, and subscribes to 678 periodicals. Computerized library sources and services include the card catalog, interlibrary loans, and database searching. Special learning facilities include a learning resource center. The 75-acre campus is in a suburban area 8 miles southwest of Rochester. Including residence halls, there are 31 buildings on campus.

Student Life: About 84% of undergraduates are from New York. Students come from 22 states, 14 foreign countries, and Canada. Eighty-five percent are white. Seventy-eight percent are Protestant; 15% claim no religious affiliation. About 50% of freshmen remain to graduate.

Housing: A total of 675 students can be accommodated in college housing. College-sponsored living facilities include single-sex dormitories, on-campus apartments, and off-campus apartments. On-campus housing is guaranteed for all 4 years. Priority is given to out-of-town students. Sixty-seven percent of students live on campus; of those, 50% remain on campus on weekends. Alcohol is not permitted. All students may keep cars on campus.

Activities: There are no fraternities or sororities on campus. There are a number of groups and organizations on campus, including band, cheerleading, choir, chorale, drama, ethnic, international, musical theater, newspaper, orchestra, pep band, religious, social, social service, student government, and yearbook. Popular campus events include Winter Weekend, Junior-Senior Banquet, Homecoming, Parents and Friends Weekend, a lecture series, and musical stage performances.

Sports: There are 4 intercollegiate sports for men and 4 for women, and 20 intramural sports for men and 21 for women. Athletic and recreation facilities include a fitness center, which provides facilities for basketball, volleyball, tennis, badminton, track, soccer, weight lifting, walleyball, racquetball, swimming, and diving.

Disabled Students: Seventy-five percent of the campus is accessible to disabled students. The following facilities are available: wheelchair ramps, elevators, special parking, specially equipped rest rooms, special class scheduling, lowered drinking fountains, and lowered telephones.

Services: In addition to many counseling and information services, tutoring is available in every subject. There is a reader service for the blind, and remedial math, reading, and writing.

Campus Safety and Security: Campus safety and security measures include 24-hour foot and vehicle patrol, self defense education, escort service, and informal discussions. In addition, there are pamphlets, posters, films, emergency telephones, lighted pathways and sidewalks, and personal-safety education programs.

Programs of Study: Roberts awards the B.A. and B.S. degrees. Associate and master's degrees also are awarded. Bachelor's degrees are awarded in BIOLOGICAL SCIENCE (biochemistry and biology/biological science), BUSINESS (accounting, business administration and management, and human resources), COMMUNICATIONS AND THE ARTS (communications, English, fine arts, and music), COMPUTER AND PHYSICAL SCIENCE (chemistry, computer science, mathematics, and physics), EDUCATION (art, elementary, and music), HEALTH PROFESSIONS (nursing, premedicine, prepharmacy, and preveterinary science), SOCIAL SCIENCE (criminal justice,

gerontology, history, prelaw, psychology, social work, and sociology). Nursing and engineering are the strongest programs academically. Elementary education and management of human resources have the largest enrollments.

Required: To graduate, students must complete 124 to 126 credit hours, with a minimum of 30 hours in the major and a GPA of 2.0. Required courses include freshman seminar, physical education, modern technology, world issues, speech, writing, history, and philosophy.

Special: Students may cross-register with members of the Rochester Area Colleges consortium. Internships, study abroad in 5 countries, a Washington semester, co-op programs, a B.A.-B.S. degree in natural science and mathematics, dual majors, and 3–2 engineering degrees with Clarkson University, Rensselaer Polytechnic Institute, and Rochester Institute of Technology are available. Nondegree study, pass/fail options, and credit for life, military, and work experience also are offered. The Management of Human Resources program, geared to adults, consists of 4-hour weekly sessions with reliance on out-of-class work. There is a freshman honors program on campus.

Faculty/Classroom: Fifty-four percent of faculty are male; 46%, female. All teach undergraduates. No classes are taught by graduate students. The average class size in an introductory lecture is 38; in a laboratory, 15; and in a regular course offering, 23.

Admissions: About 92% of the 1993–94 applicants were accepted. The SAT scores for the 1993–94 freshman class were as follows: Verbal—69% below 500, 27% between 500 and 599, and 4% between 600 and 700; Math—47% below 500, 39% between 500 and 599, 13% between 600 and 700, and 1% above 700. The ACT scores were 33% below 21, 27% between 21 and 23, 27% between 24 and 26, 6% between 27 and 28, and 6% above 28. About 36% of the current freshmen were in the top fifth of their class; 76% were in the top two fifths. Nine freshmen graduated first in their class.

Requirements: A minimum GPA of 2.0 is required. The SAT I or ACT is required. In addition, applicants must be graduates of an accredited secondary school. The GED is accepted. At least 12 academic credits are required, including 4 years of English and 2 years each of mathematics and science. A foreign language and 3 years of social studies are recommended. The chosen major may modify requirements. An essay is required and an interview is recommended for all students. AP and CLEP credits are accepted. Important factors used in the admissions decision are advanced placement or honor courses, personality, intangible qualities, extracurricular activities record, leadership record, and evidence of special talent.

Procedure: Freshmen are admitted to all sessions. Applications should be filed by August 1 for fall entry and December 1 for spring entry, along with an application fee of $25. Notification is sent on a rolling basis. There are early admissions and deferred admissions plans.

Transfer: About 82 transfer students enrolled in 1993–94. Applicants must submit transcripts from all previous institutions attended. Credit is usually accepted for courses with grade C or better. A total of 30 credits out of 124 to 126 must be completed at Roberts.

Visiting: There are regularly scheduled orientations for prospective students, including a campus tour, class visits, admissions and departmental interviews, and a financial aid presentation. Visitors may sit in on classes and stay overnight at the school. To arrange for a visit, contact the Admissions Office at (716) 594–6400 or (800) 777–4RWC.

Financial Aid: In 1993–94 91% of all current freshmen and 86% of continuing students received some form of financial aid. About 91% of freshmen and 82% of continuing students received need-based aid. The average freshman award was $7499. Of that total, scholarships or need-based grants averaged $3290; loans averaged $3534 ($3625 maximum); and work contracts averaged $1000 ($1500 maximum). Seventy percent of undergraduate students work part-time. Average earnings from campus work for the school year are $780. The average financial indebtedness of the 1992–93 graduate was $13,860. Roberts is a member of CSS. The FAF, FFS, or SFS and the college's own financial statement are required. The deadline for financial aid applications is July 1.

International Students: There are currently 58 international students enrolled. They must take the TOEFL and achieve a minimum score of 550. The student must also take the Nelson-Denny.

Computers: The college provides computer facilities for student use. Apple Macintosh, Apple IIe, and IBM-compatible microcomputers are available to students for academic or personal use in the science center, for about 90 hours per week, and in the library learning center, for about 48 hours per week. All students may access the system. There are no time limits on using the system and no fees.

Graduates: In 1992–93 269 bachelor's degrees were awarded. The most popular majors among graduates were management of human resources (30%), elementary education (11%), and nursing (8%). Within an average freshman class, 60% graduate in 3 years and 43% in 4 years. Some 120 companies recruited on campus in 1992–93. In the 1992 graduating class, 40% of the men and 26% of the women were enrolled in graduate school within 6 months of graduation; 85%

of the men and 87% of the women had found employment.
Admissions Contact: Linda Kurtz, Director of Admissions.

ROCHESTER INSTITUTE OF TECHNOLOGY
B-3
Rochester, NY 14623 (716) 475–6631

Full-time: 5349 men, 2408 women	Faculty: 638; IIA, av$
Part-time: 1668 men, 910 women	Ph.D.s: 70%
Graduate: 1165 men, 711 women	Student/Faculty: 12 to 1
Year: quarters, summer session	Tuition: $13,515
Application Deadline: open	Room & Board: $5439
Freshman Class: 4704 applied, 3797 accepted, 1385 enrolled	
SAT I or ACT: required	**VERY COMPETITIVE**

Rochester Institute of Technology, founded in 1829, offers programs in science, computer science, allied health, engineering, fine arts, business, hotel management, graphic arts, and photography, as well as liberal arts, and includes the National Technical Institute for the Deaf. Most programs include a cooperative education component, which provides full-time work experience to complement classroom studies. There are 12 undergraduate and 7 graduate schools. In addition to regional accreditation, RIT has baccalaureate program accreditation with AACSB, ABET, and NASAD. The library contains 324,000 volumes, 4803 microform items, and 4016 audiovisual forms, and subscribes to 6394 periodicals. Computerized library sources and services include the card catalog, interlibrary loans, and database searching. Special learning facilities include a learning resource center, art gallery, radio station, and a computer chip manufacturing facility, a student-operated restaurant, an electronic prepress laboratory, and an imaging science facility. The 1300-acre campus is in a suburban area 5 miles south of Rochester. Including residence halls, there are 80 buildings on campus.

Student Life: About 65% of undergraduates are from New York. Students come from 50 states, 80 foreign countries, and Canada. Ninety percent are from public schools; 10% from private. Eighty-one percent are white. The average age of freshmen is 18; all undergraduates, 21. Fifteen percent drop out by the end of their first year; 62% remain to graduate.

Housing: A total of 5500 students can be accommodated in college housing. College-sponsored living facilities include single-sex and coed dormitories, on-campus apartments, married-student housing, fraternity houses, and sorority houses. In addition there are special interest houses. On-campus housing is guaranteed for all 4 years. Sixty-five percent of students live on campus; of those, 90% remain on campus on weekends. All students may keep cars on campus.

Activities: About 10% of men belong to 13 national fraternities; about 5% of women belong to 3 national sororities. There are 75 groups on campus, including art, band, cheerleading, choir, chorale, chorus, computers, dance, drama, ethnic, film, gay, honors, international, jazz band, literary magazine, newspaper, orchestra, pep band, photography, political, professional, radio and TV, religious, social, social service, student government, and yearbook. Popular campus events include Fall, Spring, and Winter Weekends and Martin Luther King, Jr. Celebration.

Sports: There are 11 intercollegiate sports for men and 9 for women, and 22 intramural sports for men and 15 for women. Athletic and recreation facilities include 3 gymnasiums, 1 with seating for 2300, an ice rink, a pool, 12 tennis courts, a fitness trail, many athletic fields, and a student life center with 8 racquetball courts, dance facilities, weight training facilities, and an indoor track.

Disabled Students: Ninety-five percent of the campus is accessible to disabled students. The following facilities are available: wheelchair ramps, elevators, special parking, specially equipped rest rooms, lowered drinking fountains, lowered telephones, and special fire alarm systems to accommodate the needs of deaf students.

Services: In addition to many counseling and information services, tutoring is available in most subjects. In addition, there is a reader service for the blind, remedial math, reading, and writing, and comprehensive support services for students with physical or learning disabilities and for first-generation college students.

Campus Safety and Security: Campus safety and security measures include 24-hour foot and vehicle patrol, self defense education, escort service, and shuttle buses. In addition, there are informal discussions, pamphlets, posters, and films, emergency telephones, and lighted pathways and sidewalks.

Programs of Study: RIT awards the B.S., B.F.A., and B.Tech. degrees. Associate, master's, and doctoral degrees also are awarded. Bachelor's degrees are awarded in BIOLOGICAL SCIENCE (biology/biological science), BUSINESS (accounting, banking and finance, business administration and management, hotel/motel and restaurant management, international business management, management science, and marketing management), COMMUNICATIONS AND THE ARTS (communications, crafts, design, film arts, fine arts, industrial design, photography, printmaking, and telecommunications), COMPUTER AND PHYSICAL SCIENCE (chemistry, computer science, mathematics, physics, polymer science, and statistics), EN-

GINEERING AND ENVIRONMENTAL DESIGN (Aerospace Studies, civil engineering technology, computer engineering, computer technology, electrical/electronics engineering, electrical/electronics engineering technology, engineering technology, environmental engineering technology, graphic and printing production, industrial administration/management, industrial engineering, interior design, mechanical engineering, mechanical engineering technology, printing technology, and woodworking), HEALTH PROFESSIONS (medical laboratory technology, nuclear medical technology, physician's assistant, and ultrasound technology), SOCIAL SCIENCE (criminal justice, dietetics, economics, food production/management/services, and social work). Engineering, computer science, photography, crafts, and imaging science are the strongest academically. Engineering, computer science, art and design, and photography have the largest enrollments.

Required: Students must have a GPA of 2.0 and have completed 180 quarter credit hours to graduate. Distribution requirements include English composition, social sciences, science, and humanities; specific courses include English composition, computer science, senior seminar, and physical education. B.S. programs require a minimum of 20 quarter credit hours in science or mathematics. There are no general science or mathematics requirements for the B.F.A. programs in art, design, or photography.

Special: RIT offers many internships and work-study programs; cooperative education is required or recommended in most programs and provides full-time paid work experience. Cross-registration with Rochester-area colleges is available. There are accelerated degree programs in science, mathematics, and business. The school grants credit for life, military, and work experience. Students may study abroad in England or Japan, and student-designed majors are permitted in applied arts and sciences. There are 6 national honor societies on campus.

Faculty/Classroom: Eighty-five percent of faculty are male; 15%, female. All teach undergraduates. No introductory courses are taught by graduate students. The average class size in an introductory lecture is 30; in a laboratory, 16; and in a regular course offering, 19.

Admissions: About 81% of the 1993–94 applicants were accepted. The SAT scores for the 1993–94 freshman class were as follows: Verbal—54% below 500, 34% between 500 and 599, 11% between 600 and 700, and 1% above 700; Math—21% below 500, 37% between 500 and 599, 32% between 600 and 700, and 10% above 700. The ACT scores were 20% below 21, 21% between 21 and 23, 19% between 24 and 26, 25% between 27 and 28, and 15% above 28. About 51% of the current freshmen were in the top fifth of their class; 67% were in the top two fifths.

Requirements: RIT requires applicants to be in the upper 70% of their class. A minimum GPA of 2.5 is required. The SAT I or ACT is required. Applicants must be high school graduates or show a GED certificate. Applicants are required to submit an essay, and an interview is recommended. The School of Art and Design emphasizes a required portfolio of artwork. Required high school mathematics and science credits vary by program, with 3 years in each area generally acceptable. AP and CLEP credits are accepted. Important factors used in the admissions decision are advanced placement or honor courses, evidence of special talent, leadership record, recommendations by school officials, and parents or siblings attending the school.

Procedure: Freshmen are admitted to all sessions. Entrance exams should be taken during the junior and/or senior year. Early decision applications should be filed by December 15, along with an application fee of $35. Notification of early decision is sent January 1; regular decision, on a rolling basis. There are early decision, early admissions, and deferred admissions plans. About 230 early decision candidates were accepted for the 1993–94 class.

Transfer: About 950 transfer students enrolled in 1993–94. Transfer students must have a GPA of 2.5 for admission to most programs; those with fewer than 30 college credits must supply SAT I or ACT scores. Other requirements vary by program. A total of 45 quarter credits out of 180 must be completed at RIT.

Visiting: There are regularly scheduled orientations for prospective students, including academic advising and information on housing and student services. There are guides for informal visits and visitors may sit in on classes and stay overnight at the school. To arrange for a visit, contact Mary Menard at (716) 475-6736.

Financial Aid: In 1993–94, 70% of all current freshmen and 65% of continuing students received some form of financial aid. About 65% of freshmen and 63% of continuing students received need-based aid. The average freshman award was $13,200. Of that total, scholarships or need-based grants averaged $6000 ($9000 maximum); loans averaged $3700 ($7375 maximum); and work contracts averaged $1600 ($2200 maximum). Seventy percent of undergraduate students work part-time. Average earnings from campus work for the school year are $1400. RIT is a member of CSS. The FAF, FFS, SFS, or the college's own financial statement and the FAFSA are required. The deadline for financial aid applications is March 15.

International Students: There are currently 335 international students enrolled. The school actively recruits these students. They must take the TOEFL or the University of Michigan Language Test and achieve a minimum score on the TOEFL of 525. The student must also take the SAT I or the ACT.

Computers: The college provides computer facilities for student use. The mainframes are a VMS cluster of 5 DEC VAX Models 6000–620, 6000–430, and 6000–520, and 4 Digital VAXstation 4000–90 Models. RIT has 14 computer centers on campus for student use. There are more than 300 mainframe terminals available, as well as hundreds of microcomputers. Students may link their terminals or personal computers to the mainframe system from individual dormitory rooms or from off-campus locations and access to the Internet is available. All students may access the system. It may be used 7 days per week, from 8 A.M. to 1 A.M. There are no time limits on using the system and no fees.

Graduates: In 1992–93, 1820 bachelor's degrees were awarded. The most popular majors among graduates were business administration (17%), engineering (13%), and engineering technology (13%). Within an average freshman class, 62% graduate in 6 years. Some 600 companies recruited on campus in a recent year. In a recent graduating class, 8% of the students were enrolled in graduate school within 6 months of graduation; 91% had found employment.

Admissions Contact: Daniel Shelley, Director of Admissions.

RUSSELL SAGE COLLEGE

D-3

Troy, NY 12180   (518) 270-2217; (800) 999-3RSC (out-of-state)

Full-time: 1009 women	Faculty: 120; IIA, --$
Part-time: 119 women	Ph.D.s: 86%
Graduate: none	Student/Faculty: 8 to 1
Year: semesters, summer session	Tuition: $11,930
Application Deadline: August 1	Room & Board: $4860
Freshman Class: 550 applied, 510 accepted, 185 enrolled	
SAT I Verbal/Math: 446/483	COMPETITIVE

Russell Sage College, established in 1916, is a private women's college offering undergraduate degrees in the liberal arts, business, health science, and teacher preparation. It is one of 4 colleges comprising the Sage Colleges, which are coeducational. In addition to regional accreditation, Russell Sage has baccalaureate program accreditation with APTA and NLN. The library contains 197,500 volumes, 12,000 microform items, and 3000 audiovisual forms, and subscribes to 1050 periodicals. Computerized library sources and services include the card catalog, interlibrary loans, and database searching. Special learning facilities include a learning resource center and art gallery. The 8-acre campus is in an urban area 10 miles from Albany, on the Hudson River in the center of Troy. Including residence halls, there are 38 buildings on campus.

Student Life: About 85% of undergraduates are from New York. Students come from 21 states, 1 foreign country, and Canada. Eighty-two percent are white. The average age of freshmen is 18; all undergraduates, 22. Eleven percent drop out by the end of their first year; 60% remain to graduate.

Housing: A total of 802 students can be accommodated in college housing. College-sponsored living facilities include dormitories. In addition, there are language houses and special interest houses, and quiet housing and substance-free/wellness housing is available. On-campus housing is guaranteed for all 4 years. Sixty-six percent of students live on campus; of those, 85% remain on campus on weekends. Upperclassmen may keep cars on campus.

Activities: There are no sororities on campus. There are 40 groups on campus, including art, band, chorale, chorus, computers, dance, drama, ethnic, gay, honors, international, literary magazine, musical theater, newspaper, professional, religious, social, social service, student government, and yearbook. Popular campus events include Rally Day, Sage Fest, Parents Weekend, Secret Sophomores, and class dinners.

Sports: There are 5 intercollegiate sports and 12 intramural sports. Athletic and recreation facilities include athletic and weight-training rooms, a human performance laboratory, a dance studio, a swimming pool, tennis courts, bowling lanes, a practice field, a 1200-seat auditorium, and 2 gymnasiums, one of which seats 500.

Disabled Students: Twenty percent of the campus is accessible to disabled students. The following facilities are available: wheelchair ramps, elevators, special parking, specially equipped rest rooms, and special class scheduling.

Services: In addition to many counseling and information services, tutoring is available in every subject. In addition, there is remedial math, reading, and writing.

Campus Safety and Security: Campus safety and security measures include 24-hour foot and vehicle patrol, self defense education, escort service, and shuttle buses. In addition, there are informal discussions, pamphlets, posters, and films, emergency telephones, and lighted pathways and sidewalks.

Programs of Study: Russell Sage awards the B.A. and B.S. degrees. Associate and master's degrees are awarded by the other Sage Colleges. Bachelor's degrees are awarded in BIOLOGICAL SCIENCE (biochemistry, biology/biological science, and nutrition), BUSINESS (accounting and management science), COMMUNICATIONS AND THE ARTS (arts administration/management, communications, English, French, and Spanish), COMPUTER AND PHYSICAL SCIENCE (chemistry, computer science, and mathematics), EDUCATION (elementary, physical, science, and secondary), HEALTH PROFESSIONS (art therapy, nursing, occupational therapy, physical therapy, predentistry, and premedicine), SOCIAL SCIENCE (criminal justice, economics, human services, interdisciplinary studies, international studies, psychology, and sociology). Physical therapy is the strongest program academically and has the largest enrollment.

Required: To graduate, students must complete 120 credits with a 2.0 GPA. At least 30 credits and a 2.2 GPA are required in the major. B.A. candidates must earn 90 credits in the arts and sciences and B.S. candidates must earn 60. General education requirements of 39 credits include 12 credits each in humanities and the arts, natural and social sciences, and analytic, quantitative, and communication skills, and a 3-credit course in values and consequences.

Special: Students may cross-register with the 14 area schools of the Hudson-Mohawk Association of Colleges. Study abroad in England and Spain, a Washington semester at Mount Vernon College, and work-study programs are available. There is an accelerated 5-year program, a 6-year program with Albany Law School, and a 3–2 engineering degree with Rensselaer Polytechnic Institute. The college confers credit for life, military, or work experience. Nondegree study, student-designed majors, cooperative programs, internships, and pass/fail options are available. There is a freshman honors program on campus, as well as 7 national honor societies.

Faculty/Classroom: Forty-two percent of faculty are male; 58%, female. Ninety-seven percent teach undergraduates and 20% both teach and do research. The average class size in an introductory lecture is 18; in a laboratory, 9; and in a regular course offering, 18.

Admissions: About 93% of the 1993–94 applicants were accepted. The SAT scores for the 1993–94 freshman class were as follows: Verbal—75% below 500, 22% between 500 and 599, and 3% between 600 and 700; Math—55% below 500, 40% between 500 and 599, and 5% between 600 and 700. About 38% of the current freshmen were in the top fifth of their class; 64% were in the top two fifths. Two freshmen graduated first in their class.

Requirements: Russell Sage requires applicants to be in the upper 50% of their class. A minimum average of C is required. The SAT I or ACT is required. Applicants must be graduates of an accredited secondary school or have a GED. Sixteen academic units are required, including courses in English, social sciences, natural sciences, and foreign languages. An essay is required and an interview is recommended for all applicants. AP and CLEP credits are accepted. Important factors used in the admissions decision are recommendations by school officials, personality, intangible qualities, parents or siblings attending the school, leadership record, and advanced placement or honor courses.

Procedure: Freshmen are admitted to all sessions. Entrance exams should be taken during the spring of the junior year or the fall of the senior year. Early decision applications should be filed by November 1; regular applications, by August 1 for fall entry and December 15 for spring entry, along with an application fee of $20. Notification of early decision is sent November 15; regular decision, on a rolling basis. There are early decision, early admissions, and deferred admissions plans. About 25 early decision candidates were accepted for the 1993–94 class.

Transfer: About 159 transfer students enrolled in 1993–94. Applicants must have a minimum GPA of 2.5. Interviews are strongly encouraged and may be required in some instances. A total of 45 credits out of 120 must be completed at Russell Sage.

Visiting: There are regularly scheduled orientations for prospective students, including meetings with faculty, a campus tour, and a financial aid session, in addition to an admission interview. There are guides for informal visits and visitors may sit in on classes and stay overnight at the school. To arrange for a visit, contact the Office of Admission at (518) 270–2217 or (800) 999–3772.

Financial Aid: In 1993–94 98% of all current freshmen and 90% of continuing students received some form of financial aid. About 87% of freshmen and 74% of continuing students received need-based aid. The average freshman award was $11,900. Of that total, scholarships or need-based grants averaged $7400 ($7800 maximum); loans averaged $3500 ($4200 maximum); and work contracts averaged $1000 (maximum). Thirty-five percent of undergraduate students work part-time. Average earnings from campus work for the school year are $1000. The average financial indebtedness of the 1992–93 graduate was $13,500. Russell Sage is a member of CSS. The FAF is required. The deadline for financial aid applications is March 1.

International Students: There are currently 5 international students enrolled. The school actively recruits these students. They must take the TOEFL and achieve a minimum score of 550. The SAT I or ACT is required for international applicants with English as their native language.

Computers: The college provides computer facilities for student use. The mainframe is a Prime 9955 II. Students have access to mainframe computers at Rensselaer Polytechnic Institute and at the State University of New York at Albany. The college campus has 11 terminals and a total of 34 microcomputers in the computer laboratory. There is access to about 10 terminals in various academic departments, and additional PCs in department laboratores. All students may access the system. It may be used 17 hours per day. There are no time limits on using the system and no fees.

Graduates: In 1992–93 357 bachelor's degrees were awarded. The most popular majors among graduates were physical therapy (16%), nursing (15%), and psychology (11%). Within an average freshman class, 55% graduate in 4 years, 60% in 5 years, and 62% in 6 years. Some 75 companies recruited on campus in 1992–93. In the 1992 graduating class, 13% of all graduates were enrolled in graduate school within 6 months of graduation; 68% of all graduates had found employment.

Admissions Contact: Patrice M. Tate, Director of Admission.

SAINT BONAVENTURE UNIVERSITY

A-3
St. Bonaventure, NY 14778–2284

(716) 375–2400
(800) 848–1181

Full-time: 877 men, 867 women	**Faculty:** 155; IIA, -$
Part-time: 68 men, 83 women	**Ph.D.s:** 98%
Graduate: 330 men, 354 women	**Student/Faculty:** 11 to 1
Year: semesters, summer session	**Tuition:** $10,026
Application Deadline: April 15	**Room & Board:** $4736
Freshman Class: 1490 applied, 374 enrolled	
SAT I Verbal/Math: 473/525	**ACT:** 23 **COMPETITIVE**

Saint Bonaventure University, founded in 1858, is a private, Roman Catholic institution operated by the Franciscans, which offers programs in the liberal arts and sciences, education, and business. There are 3 undergraduate schools and one graduate school. The library contains 241,000 volumes, 97,000 microform items, and 7000 audiovisual forms, and subscribes to 1500 periodicals. Computerized library sources and services include the card catalog, interlibrary loans, and database searching. Special learning facilities include a learning resource center, art gallery, radio station, and observatory. The 600-acre campus is in a rural area 70 miles southeast of Buffalo. Including residence halls, there are 16 buildings on campus.

Student Life: About 75% of undergraduates are from New York. Students come from 31 states, 16 foreign countries, and Canada. Sixty percent are from public schools; 40% from private. Ninety-two percent are white. The average age of freshmen is 18; all undergraduates, 20. Twelve percent drop out by the end of their first year; 67% remain to graduate.

Housing: A total of 1860 students can be accommodated in college housing. College-sponsored living facilities include single-sex and coed dormitories and on-campus apartments. On-campus housing is guaranteed for all 4 years. Seventy-five percent of students live on campus; of those, 90% remain on campus on weekends. All students may keep cars on campus.

Activities: There are no fraternities or sororities on campus. There are 73 groups on campus, including art, band, cheerleading, choir, chorale, chorus, computers, drama, ethnic, honors, international, jazz band, literary magazine, newspaper, orchestra, pep band, photography, political, professional, radio and TV, religious, social, social service, student government, and yearbook. Popular campus events include Family Weekend, Spring and Winter Weekends, and Oktoberfest.

Sports: There are 7 intercollegiate sports for men and 7 for women, and 10 intramural sports for men and 9 for women. Athletic and recreation facilities include a 6000-seat gymnasium with basketball and volleyball courts, an indoor swimming pool, a golf course, universal weight facilities and free weights, and a fitness center with racquetball courts, Nautilus equipment, and an aerobics room. There is also a 77-acre area on campus with soccer, baseball, softball, rugby, and intramural fields.

Disabled Students: Ninety percent of the campus is accessible to disabled students. The following facilities are available: wheelchair ramps, elevators, special parking, specially equipped rest rooms, and a coordinator for disabled services.

Services: In addition to many counseling and information services, tutoring is available in some subjects. There is also remedial math, reading, and writing.

Campus Safety and Security: Campus safety and security measures include 24-hour foot and vehicle patrol, self-defense education, shuttle buses, and informal discussions. In addition, there are pam-

phlets, posters, films, emergency telephones, and lighted pathways and sidewalks.

Programs of Study: SBU awards the B.A., B.S., B.B.A., and B.S.Ed. degrees. Master's degrees also are awarded. Bachelor's degrees are awarded in BIOLOGICAL SCIENCE (biology/biological science), BUSINESS (accounting, banking and finance, business economics, management science, and marketing/retailing/merchandising), COMMUNICATIONS AND THE ARTS (classics, English, French, German, journalism, and Spanish), COMPUTER AND PHYSICAL SCIENCE (chemistry, computer science, mathematics, and physics), EDUCATION (elementary, physical, and secondary), HEALTH PROFESSIONS (medical laboratory technology and premedicine), SOCIAL SCIENCE (economics, history, philosophy, political science/government, prelaw, psychology, public administration, religion, social science, social work, sociology, and theological studies). Psychology, accounting, biology, and elementary education are the strongest academically. Mass communication, elementary education, and accounting have the largest enrollments.

Required: In order to graduate, students must complete 129 credit hours, 30 of them in the major, with a minimum GPA of 2.0. The school requires 12 hours each in culture and civilization, mathematics and natural sciences, and social and behavioral sciences. Students must also complete 9 credits each in theology and philosophy. A thesis or comprehensive exam is required in all majors.

Special: Cross-registration can be arranged almost anywhere in the United States through the Visiting Student Program. Internships are available in business, mass communication, political science, psychology, and social science. Study abroad in 18 countries, B.A.-B.S. degrees, accelerated degree programs, dual and student-designed majors, a Washington semester with American University, and pass/fail options are offered. Students may complete a 2–2 or 2–3 engineering degree with the University of Detroit or a 2–3 engineering degree with Clarkson University. There is a freshman honors program on campus, as well as 10 national honor societies. Nine departments have honors programs.

Faculty/Classroom: Eighty percent of faculty are male; 20%, female. All teach undergraduates. Graduate students teach 5% of introductory courses. The average class size in an introductory lecture is 30; in a laboratory, 20; and in a regular course offering, 30.

Admissions: The SAT scores for the 1993–94 freshman class were as follows: Verbal—63% below 500, 28% between 500 and 599, and 9% between 600 and 700; Math—35% below 500, 44% between 500 and 599, 21% between 600 and 700, and 2% above 700. The ACT scores were 23% below 21, 31% between 21 and 23, 26% between 24 and 26, 10% between 27 and 28, and 10% above 28. About 38% of the current freshmen were in the top fifth of their class; 70% were in the top two fifths. Seven freshmen graduated first in their class.

Requirements: SBU requires applicants to be in the upper 60% of their class. A minimum average of 83% is required. The SAT I or ACT is required, with minimum composite scores of 1000 on the SAT I (500 verbal, 500 mathematics) and 24 on the ACT. Applicants must be graduates of an accredited secondary school. The GED is accepted. Sixteen academic credits are required, including 4 years each of English and social studies, 3 each of mathematics and science, and 2 of a foreign language. An essay and an interview are recommended. AP and CLEP credits are accepted. Important factors used in the admissions decision are recommendations by school officials, advanced placement or honor courses, extracurricular activities record, leadership record, and parents or siblings attending the school.

Procedure: Freshmen are admitted in the fall, spring, and summer. Entrance exams should be taken during the spring of the junior year or the fall of the senior year. Applications should be filed by April 15 for fall entry, along with an application fee of $30. Notification is sent on a rolling basis. There are early admissions and deferred admissions plans.

Transfer: About 80 transfer students enrolled in 1993–94. Applicants must have a minimum 2.5 GPA and a minimum SAT score of 1000 or a minimum ACT score of 24. Grades of D or better transfer for credit except in the major. At least 36 credits out of 129 must be completed at SBU.

Visiting: There are regularly scheduled orientations for prospective students, including interviews, tours, class visits, and meeting with professors. There are guides for informal visits, and visitors may sit in on classes. To arrange for a visit, contact the Admissions Office at (716) 375-2400 or (800) 848-1181.

Financial Aid: In an earlier year, 80% of all freshmen and 75% of continuing students received some form of financial aid. Scholarships or need-based grants averaged $2300 ($7500 maximum); loans averaged $2500 ($4800 maximum); and work contracts averaged $500 ($1000 maximum). The average financial indebtedness of an earlier graduate was $9500. SBU is a member of CSS. The FAF is required. The deadline for financial aid applications is March 1.

International Students: They must take the TOEFL and achieve a minimum score of 550.

Computers: The college provides computer facilities, including 4 PC and 2 Macintosh laboratories for student use. There are 80 386SX machines and 20 Apple Macintosh computers connected to a campuswide network. The computer science laboratory is equipped with 5 Sun workstations and provides a UNIX environment that is used to support upper-division courses in computer science. All students may access the system Monday through Thursday, 8 A.M. to 12 noon; Friday, 8 A.M. to 5 P.M.; and Saturday and Sunday, noon to 10 P.M. There are no time limits on using the system and no fees.

Graduates: In a recent class, 532 bachelor's degrees were awarded. The most popular majors among graduates were elementary education (15%), accounting (13%), and marketing (11%). Within an average freshman class, 64% graduate in 3 years and 70% in 4 years. Some 44 companies recruited on campus in a recent year.

Admissions Contact: June Solan, Director of Admissions.

SAINT FRANCIS COLLEGE D-5
Brooklyn, NY 11201 (718) 522-2300, ext. 200
Full-time: 666 men, 909 women Faculty: 57; IIB, +$
Part-time: 273 men, 408 women Ph.Ds: 64%
Graduate: none Student/Faculty: 28 to 1
Year: semesters, summer session Tuition: $6710
Application Deadline: open Room & Board: n/app
Freshman Class: 1013 applied, 916 accepted, 401 enrolled
SAT I: required **LESS COMPETITIVE**

Saint Francis College, chartered in 1884 by the Franciscan Brothers, is an independent commuter institution conferring degrees in the arts, sciences, business, and health sciences. The library contains 160,849 volumes, 12,500 microform items, and 2223 audiovisual forms, and subscribes to 700 periodicals. Computerized library sources and services include interlibrary loans and database searching. Special learning facilities include a learning resource center and a greenhouse. The 1-acre campus is in an urban area. There are 5 buildings on campus.

Student Life: Nearly all undergraduates are from New York. Students come from 42 foreign countries and Canada. Forty-three percent are from public schools; 57% from private. Fifty-four percent are white; 23% African American; 15% Hispanic. The average age of freshmen is 18; all undergraduates, 21. Twenty-four percent drop out by the end of their first year; 35% remain to graduate.

Housing: There are no residence halls. All students commute.

Activities: About 5% of men and about 2% of women belong to 2 local fraternities; about 5% of women belong to 1 local sorority. There are 27 groups on campus, including art, cheerleading, chess, chorus, computers, drama, ethnic, gay, international, literary magazine, newspaper, political, professional, religious, social, social service, student government, and yearbook. Popular campus events include Charter Day, Brooklyn Accents, and personal issues and public interest lecture series.

Sports: There are 9 intercollegiate sports for men and 8 for women, and 6 intramural sports for men and 6 for women. Athletic and recreation facilities include a 1100-seat gymnasium, an Olympic-size swimming pool, a weight training room, and a roof recreation area.

Disabled Students: Eighty-five percent of the campus is accessible to disabled students. The following facilities are available: wheelchair ramps, elevators, specially equipped rest rooms, lowered drinking fountains, and lowered telephones.

Services: In addition to many counseling and information services, tutoring is available in most subjects, including accounting, math, economics, English, history, and the sciences. There is a reader service for the blind, and remedial math, reading, and writing. In addition, there are workshops in academic skills such as note- and test-taking techniques and study skills.

Campus Safety and Security: Campus safety and security measures include self defense education, informal discussions, pamphlets, posters, and films. There is 1 entrance building security guard on duty at all times when the college is open.

Programs of Study: The college awards the B.A., and B.S. degrees. Associate degrees also are awarded. Bachelor's degrees are awarded in BIOLOGICAL SCIENCE (biology/biological science), BUSINESS (accounting), COMMUNICATIONS AND THE ARTS (communications and English), COMPUTER AND PHYSICAL SCIENCE (mathematics), EDUCATION (elementary, middle school, secondary, and special), ENGINEERING AND ENVIRONMENTAL DESIGN (aviation administration/management), HEALTH PROFESSIONS (health care administration, health science, medical laboratory technology, and premedicine), SOCIAL SCIENCE (economics, history, political science/government, psychology, social studies, and sociology). Management, education, and communications have the largest enrollments.

Required: The core curriculum varies according to the major, but all baccalaureate degree programs require courses in communications, English, fine arts, history, philosophy, sociology, and science or math-

ematics. A minimum 2.0 GPA and 128 credit hours are required to graduate.

Special: There is an FAA co-op program for aviation students. A variety of internships are available in such areas as industrial and public accounting, and with the NYC Transit Authority, Public Interest Research, the NYS Assembly, and the Urban Fellow Program. Study abroad, dual majors, pass/fail options, and credit for life experience are possible. There is a freshman honors program on campus, as well as 15 national honor societies.

Faculty/Classroom: Sixty-six percent of faculty are male; 34%, female. All teach undergraduates, 15% do research, and 15% do both. The average class size in an introductory lecture is 23; in a laboratory, 19; and in a regular course offering, 23.

Admissions: About 90% of the 1993-94 applicants were accepted. There was 1 National Merit semifinalist. One freshman graduated first in their class.

Requirements: The SAT I is required. Applicants should graduate from an accredited secondary school or have a GED. An entrance essay is required. AP and CLEP credits are accepted. Important factors used in the admissions decision are recommendations by school officials, leadership record, recommendations by alumni, extracurricular activities record, and evidence of special talent.

Procedure: Freshmen are admitted to all sessions. Application deadlines are open. The application fee is $20. Notification is sent on a rolling basis.

Transfer: About 97 transfer students enrolled in 1993-94. A minimum 2.0 GPA is required in order to transfer. A total of 30 credits out of 128 must be completed at the college.

Visiting: There are regularly scheduled orientations for prospective students, and visits of all types, including meeting with faculty, can be arranged. There are guides for informal visits and visitors may sit in on classes. To arrange for a visit, contact the Office of Admissions at (718) 522-2300, ext. 200.

Financial Aid: In 1993-94 83% of all current freshmen and 69% of continuing students received some form of financial aid. About 73% of freshmen and 68% of continuing students received need-based aid. The average freshman award was $4360. Of that total, scholarships or need-based grants averaged $4500 ($6400 maximum); and loans averaged $1250 ($2625 maximum). Five percent of undergraduate students work part-time. Average earnings from campus work for the school year are $1350. The average financial indebtedness of the 1992-93 graduate was $5913. The college is a member of CSS. The FAF, FAFSA, and NY State TAP application are required. The deadline for financial aid applications is February 15.

International Students: There are currently 105 international students enrolled. The school actively recruits these students. They must take the TOEFL and achieve a minimum score of 500.

Computers: The college provides computer facilities for student use. A microcomputer center is available to students. It has 40 microcomputers that are connected to a Local Area Network (LAN). All students may access the system. There are no time limits on using the system. The fees are $35 per course, included in tuition.

Graduates: In 1992-93 297 bachelor's degrees were awarded. The most popular majors among graduates were management (23%), special studies (14%), and accounting (11%). Within an average freshman class, 1% graduate in 3 years, 15% in 4 years, 30% in 5 years, and 35% in 6 years. Some 51 companies recruited on campus in 1992-93.

Admissions Contact: Brother George Larkin, O.S.F., Dean of Admissions.

SAINT JOHN FISHER COLLEGE   B-3

Rochester, NY 14618   (716) 385-8064; (800) 444-4640 (in-state)

Full-time: 744 men, 943 women	Faculty: 106; IIB, +$
Part-time: 1190 men, 1992 women	Ph.D.s: 86%
Graduate: 115 men, 165 women	Student/Faculty: 16 to 1
Year: semesters	Tuition: $10,275
Application Deadline: open	Room & Board: $5140
Freshman Class: 1368 applied, 1064 accepted, 354 enrolled	
SAT I Verbal/Math: (mean) 465/525	ACT: (mean) 22 COMPETITIVE

Saint John Fisher College, established in 1948, is a private institution affiliated with the Roman Catholic Church. It offers degrees through its divisions of liberal arts, business/accounting, education, and nursing. There are 2 graduate schools. The library contains 170,000 volumes, 85,000 microform items, and 30,000 audiovisual forms, and subscribes to 975 periodicals. Computerized library sources and services include the card catalog, interlibrary loans, and database searching. Special learning facilities include a learning resource center, radio station, multimedia center, greenhouse, modern language laboratories, and biology, chemistry, physics, and psychology laboratories. The 125-acre campus is in a suburban area 12 miles southeast of Rochester. Including residence halls, there are 16 buildings on campus.

Student Life: About 96% of undergraduates are from New York. Students come from 17 states, 8 foreign countries, and Canada. Sixty-five percent are from public schools; 35% from private. Eighty-five percent are white. Sixty-five percent are Catholic; 30% Protestant. The average age of freshmen is 18; all undergraduates, 21. Eighteen percent drop out by the end of their first year; 64% remain to graduate.

Housing: A total of 894 students can be accommodated in college housing. College-sponsored living facilities include single-sex and coed dormitories. In addition there are residence halls providing a year-long freshman wellness program. On-campus housing is guaranteed for all 4 years. Priority is given to out-of-town students. Fifty-five percent of students live on campus; of those, 85% remain on campus on weekends. All students may keep cars on campus.

Activities: There are no fraternities or sororities on campus. There are 35 groups on campus, including cheerleading, chess, choir, computers, drama, ethnic, honors, international, literary magazine, musical theater, newspaper, pep band, photography, political, professional, radio and TV, religious, social, social service, student government, and yearbook. Popular campus events include Dorm Muter Day, Senior Week, Winter Olympics, Winter Snow Ball, Senior Week, a 24-hour dance marathon for charity, Homecoming, and Family Weekend.

Sports: There are 7 intercollegiate sports for men and 7 for women, and 7 intramural sports for men and 7 for women. Athletic and recreation facilities include football, soccer, and softball fields, indoor and outdoor tracks, a 9-hole golf course, a weight/exercise room, a sauna, a game room, indoor and outdoor tennis courts, racquetball and volleyball courts, and 2 gymnasiums for basketball.

Disabled Students: Seventy-five percent of the campus is accessible to disabled students. The following facilities are available: wheelchair ramps, elevators, special parking, specially equipped rest rooms, special class scheduling, lowered drinking fountains, and lowered telephones.

Services: In addition to many counseling and information services, tutoring is available in most subjects. There is also remedial math and writing as well as mathematics and writing centers that provide help to students at all skill levels.

Campus Safety and Security: Campus safety and security measures include 24-hour foot and vehicle patrol, self-defense education, escort service, and informal discussions. In addition, there are pamphlets, posters, films, emergency telephones, and lighted pathways and sidewalks.

Programs of Study: The college awards the B.A., B.S., B.B.A., and B.S.N. degrees. Master's degrees also are awarded. Bachelor's degrees are awarded in BIOLOGICAL SCIENCE (biology/biological science), BUSINESS (accounting, business administration and management, and marketing/retailing/merchandising), COMMUNICATIONS AND THE ARTS (communications, English, French, German, Italian, journalism, and Spanish), COMPUTER AND PHYSICAL SCIENCE (chemistry, computer science, mathematics, and physics), EDUCATION (elementary, science, and secondary), ENGINEERING AND ENVIRONMENTAL DESIGN (preengineering), HEALTH PROFESSIONS (nursing, predentistry, premedicine, and prepharmacy), SOCIAL SCIENCE (anthropology, economics, history, interdisciplinary studies, international studies, philosophy, political science/government, prelaw, psychology, religion, and sociology). Accounting, biology, management, communications/journalism, history, chemistry, and nursing are the strongest academically. Management, accounting, communications/journalism, biology, psychology, and nursing have the largest enrollments.

Required: To graduate, students must complete at least 120 credit hours, including at least 30 in the major, and maintain a 2.0 minimum GPA. Required core curriculum courses include 4 each in literature/language, social science, and religious studies/philosophy, and 3 in mathematics/natural science.

Special: College credit may be earned in selected Rochester high schools through the Step Ahead Program. The college has cooperative programs with the University of Rochester in public policy, and with the Pennsylvania College of Optometry. Students may cross-register with 8 Rochester area colleges. Study abroad may be pursued in many countries. The college offers internships in 15 majors, independent research in 16 majors, Washington, state, and local government semesters, dual and student-designed majors, and degrees in interdisciplinary studies or liberal studies. A 3-2 engineering degree is offered in conjunction with the State University of New York at Buffalo, Clarkson University, and Manhattan College, a 2-2 engineering program with the University of Detroit, and a 4-2 program with Columbia University. Credit for life, military, and work experience, nondegree study, and pass/fail options are possible. There is a V.O.V.E. grant for collaborative research program between physics and chemistry students, and faculty and scientists at NASA's Goddard Space Center and Marshal Space Center. A new modern optics concentration (physics) and African American studies concentration (international studies) are offered. There is a freshman honors pro-

gram on campus, as well as 9 national honor societies. Seven departments have honors programs.

Faculty/Classroom: Seventy-three percent of faculty are male; 27%, female. All teach undergraduates and 65% both teach and do research. No introductory courses are taught by graduate students. The average class size in an introductory lecture is 35; in a laboratory, 14; and in a regular course offering, 28.

Admissions: About 78% of the 1993–94 applicants were accepted. The SAT scores for the 1993–94 freshman class were as follows: Verbal—70% below 500, 25% between 500 and 599, and 5% between 600 and 700; Math—40% below 500, 40% between 500 and 599, 19% between 600 and 700, and 1% above 700. The ACT scores were 32% below 21, 36% between 21 and 23, 20% between 24 and 26, 8% between 27 and 28, and 4% above 28. About 43% of the current freshmen were in the top fifth of their class; 64% were in the top two fifths. Four freshmen graduated first in their class.

Requirements: A minimum GPA of 80% is required. The SAT I or ACT is required. Applicants must be graduates of an accredited secondary school. Sixteen academic credits are required, including 4 years each in English, history, and social studies, 3 years each in mathematics and science, and 2 years in a foreign language. Essays are required and interviews recommended. AP and CLEP credits are accepted. Important factors used in the admissions decision are advanced placement or honor courses, leadership record, evidence of special talent, recommendations by school officials, and extracurricular activities record.

Procedure: Freshmen are admitted to all sessions. Entrance exams should be taken in the spring of the junior year or the fall of the senior year. There are early decision, early admissions, and deferred admissions plans. Early decision applications should be filed by November 15; regular applications are open. The application fee is $25. Notification of early decision is sent in November; regular decision, on a rolling basis.

Transfer: About 210 transfer students enrolled in 1993–94. Applicants must have a minimum GPA of 2.0 to be considered (mean GPA is 2.7). A high school transcript is required for students with fewer than 12 college credits. Interviews are recommended. At least the last 30 credits out of 120 and half the major credits must be completed at the college.

Visiting: There are regularly scheduled orientations for prospective students, including a tour, an interview, and meetings with faculty and coaches. There are guides for informal visits, and visitors may sit in on classes and stay overnight at the school. To arrange for a visit, contact the Admissions Office at (800) 444–4640 (in-state) or (716) 385–8064.

Financial Aid: In 1993–94, 91% of all current freshmen and 96% of continuing students received some form of financial aid. About 82% of freshmen and 84% of continuing students received need-based aid. The average freshman award was $9670. Of that total, scholarships or need-based grants averaged $5090 ($9890 maximum); loans averaged $3480 ($4125 maximum); and work contracts averaged $1100 ($1200 maximum). Twenty-one percent of undergraduate students work part-time. Average earnings from campus work for the school year are $764. The average financial indebtedness of the 1992–93 graduate was $6690. The FAFSA and the TAP Application for N.Y. State residents financial statement are required. The deadline for financial aid applications is March 1.

International Students: There are currently 23 international students enrolled. They must take the TOEFL or the University of Michigan Language Test and achieve a minimum score on the TOEFL of 525.

Computers: The college provides computer facilities for student use. The mainframe is a DEC Station 5000/260. A variety of programming languages are utilized by the DEC system, including BASIC, COBOL, Pascal, and FORTRAN. Facilities include Apple Macintosh, Sun computer, and 2 PC laboratories in the academic computing center. There is a 35-station PC laboratory in the library. The DEC Station can be accessed from terminals in 2 terminal laboratories and from all computers in the academic computing center. All students may access the system 24 hours daily. There are no time limits on using the system. The fees are $90.

Graduates: In 1992–93, 443 bachelor's degrees were awarded. The most popular majors among graduates were business and management (40%), social sciences (22%), and communications/journalism (11%). Within an average freshman class, 56% graduate in 4 years, 5% in 5 years, and 3% in 6 years. Some 134 companies recruited on campus in 1992–93. In the 1992 graduating class, 6% of the men and 7% of the women were enrolled in graduate school within 6 months of graduation.

Admissions Contact: Peter E. Lindsey, Dean of Admissions.

SAINT JOHN'S UNIVERSITY   D-5
Jamaica, NY 11439   (718) 990–6114; (800) 232–4-SJU (out-of-state)

Full-time: 5472 men, 5866 women	Faculty: 637
Part-time: 715 men, 920 women	Ph.D.s: 81%
Graduate: 2403 men, 2840 women	Student/Faculty: 18 to 1
Year: , early semesters, summer session	Tuition: $8980
	Room & Board: n/app

Application Deadline: open
Freshman Class: 7775 applied, 2836 accepted, 2412 enrolled
SAT I Verbal/Math: 430/500   **COMPETITIVE +**

Saint John's University, founded in 1870 by the Vincentian fathers, is a private Roman Catholic institution offering programs in the arts and sciences, education, business, theology, pharmacy and allied health professions, and other professional training. The main campus is in the borough of Queens; a branch campus is on Staten Island. There are 6 undergraduate and 5 graduate schools. In addition to regional accreditation, Saint John's has baccalaureate program accreditation with AACSB and ACPE. The 3 libraries contain 1.3 million volumes, 1.8 millon microform items, and 43,271 audiovisual forms, and subscribe to 6753 periodicals. Computerized library sources and services include the card catalog, interlibrary loans, and database searching. Special learning facilities include a learning resource center, an art gallery, a radio station, a TV station, a health education resource center, a model pharmacy, a speech and hearing clinic, a psychological services center, and an instructional materials center. The 100-acre campus is in a suburban area New York City. There are 17 buildings on the Queens and 8 on the Staten Island campus.

Student Life: About 93% of undergraduates are from New York. Students come from 17 states, 101 foreign countries, and Canada. Sixty-one percent are white; 12% Hispanic; 12% African American; 11% Asian American. Sixty-one percent are Catholic; 16% claim no religious affiliation. The average age of freshmen is 18; all undergraduates, 21. Seventeen percent drop out by the end of their first year; 67% remain to graduate.

Housing: There are no residence halls. One-hundred percent of students commute. All students may keep cars on campus.

Activities: About 8% of men belong to 9 local and 11 national fraternities; about 6% of women belong to 12 local and 6 national sororities. There are 140 groups on campus, including art, cheerleading, choir, chorus, computers, dance, drama, ethnic, film, honors, international, jazz band, literary magazine, musical theater, newspaper, pep band, photography, political, professional, radio and TV, religious, social, social service, student government, and yearbook. Popular campus events include Harmony Week, Culture Week, organization and recognition banquets, and annual outdoor festivals.

Sports: There are 15 intercollegiate sports for men and 10 for women, and 15 intramural sports for men and 11 for women. Athletic and recreation facilities include gymnasiums, a swimming pool, squash and tennis courts, weight and exercise rooms, baseball and softball diamonds, and fields for football, lacrosse, and soccer.

Disabled Students: All of the campus is accessible to disabled students. The following facilities are available: wheelchair ramps, elevators, special parking, specially equipped rest rooms, special class scheduling, lowered drinking fountains, and lowered telephones.

Services: There is remedial math, reading, and writing are available.

Campus Safety and Security: Campus safety and security measures include a 24-hour foot and vehicle patrol, an escort service, informal discussions, and pamphlets, posters, and films. In addition, there are emergency telephones and lighted pathways and sidewalks.

Programs of Study: Saint John's awards the B.A., B.S., B.F.A., B.S.Ed., B.S.Med.Tech., and B.S.Pharm. degrees. Associate, master's, and doctoral degrees also are awarded. Bachelor's degrees are awarded in BIOLOGICAL SCIENCE (biology/biological science and toxicology), BUSINESS (accounting, banking and finance, business administration and management, business economics, business systems analysis, management science, and transportation management), COMMUNICATIONS AND THE ARTS (communications, English, fine arts, French, German, Italian, journalism, photography, Spanish, and speech/debate/rhetoric), COMPUTER AND PHYSICAL SCIENCE (chemistry, computer programming, computer science, mathematics, physical sciences, physics, and statistics), EDUCATION (art, early childhood, education of the deaf and hearing impaired, elementary, foreign languages, middle school, science, secondary, and special), ENGINEERING AND ENVIRONMENTAL DESIGN (environmental science and preengineering), HEALTH PROFESSIONS (health care administration, medical laboratory technology, pharmacy, physician's assistant, predentistry, premedicine, and speech pathology/audiology), SOCIAL SCIENCE (American studies, anthropology, criminal justice, economics, ethnic studies, history, human services, paralegal studies, philosophy, political science/government, prelaw, psychology, public administration, religion, safety management, social science, and sociology). Pharmacy is the

strongest program academically. Pharmacy, accounting, and government and politics/political science have the largest enrollments.

Required: To graduate, students must complete at least 126 credit hours, including core courses in liberal arts, with a minimum GPA of 2.0 overall and in the major. Other requirements vary by program.

Special: Saint John's offers internships, study abroad in Hungary and Ireland, an accelerated degree program in many majors, B.A.-B.S. degrees, dual majors and combined programs, pass/fail options, and some credit for life, military, and work experience. There are cooperative programs in nursing with Niagara University, in dentistry with Columbia University, in photography with the Germaine School, and in funeral service administration with the McAllister Institute, as well as a 3–2 engineering program with Pratt Institute and Polytechnic University. There are 25 national honor societies on campus.

Faculty/Classroom: Sixty-five percent of faculty are male; 35%, female. Nearly all faculty both teach undergraduates and do research. No introductory courses are taught by graduate students. The average class size in an introductory lecture is 28.

Admissions: About 36% of the 1993–94 applicants were accepted.

Requirements: A minimum GPA of 3.0 is required. The SAT I or ACT is required. A minimum GPA of 3.0 or an SAT I composite score of 1000 is required. Applicants must be high school graduates of an accredited secondary school or have a GED certificate. For most programs, they should have completed 16 units including 4 of English, 3 of history, 2 of mathematics, 1 science, and 6 electives, 3 of them academic. An interview may be required. Portfolios are required for art students. Admissions requirements for the pharmacy program students are significantly higher. AP and CLEP credits are accepted.

Procedure: Freshmen are admitted to all sessions. Entrance exams should be taken late in the junior year or early in the senior year. Application deadlines are open. The application fee is $20. Notification is sent on a rolling basis. There are early admissions and deferred admissions plans.

Transfer: About 2518 transfer students enrolled in 1993–94. Applicants must present official transcripts of high school and college work, as well as a list of courses in progress. If the student has been out of school a semester or more, a letter of explanation is also required. Admissions requirements for transfer students to the pharmacy program are stricter and few places are available. A minimum of 30 credits out of 126 must be completed at Saint John's.

Visiting: There are regularly scheduled orientations for prospective students. There are guides for informal visits and visitors may sit in on classes. To arrange for a visit, contact Jeanne Umland, Associate Vice President, Admissions.

Financial Aid: In 1993–94, 65% of all current freshmen and 75% of continuing students received some form of financial aid. About 90% of all students received need-based aid. The average freshman award was $6198. Of that total, scholarships or need-based grants averaged $4142 ($7850 maximum); and loans averaged $1958 ($4000 maximum). Eighty percent of undergraduate students work part-time. Average earnings from campus work for the school year are $5304. The average financial indebtedness of a recent graduate was $10,189. Saint John's is a member of CSS. The FAF and the FAFSA are required. The deadline for financial aid applications is April 1.

International Students: There are currently 792 international students enrolled. The school actively recruits these students. They must take the TOEFL and achieve a minimum score of 500. The student must also take the SAT I, or ACT. This requirement may be waived for international students with a high school GPA of 3.0.

Computers: The college provides computer facilities for student use. The mainframe is an IBM 4381 Model 22. There are also hundreds of IBM PS/2 Model 50Z and Apple Macintosh IIcx microcomputers available. All students may access the system. There are no time limits on using the system. A fee is charged for enrollment and system use for computer courses.

Graduates: In 1992–93, 2691 bachelor's degrees were awarded. The most popular majors among graduates were pharmacy (12%), accounting (9%), and management (8%). Within an average freshman class, 2% graduate in 3 years, 62% in 4 years, 28% in 5 years, and 5% in 6 years. Some 165 companies recruited on campus in 1992–93.

Admissions Contact: Jeanne Umland, Associate Vice President and Executive Director of Admissions.

SAINT JOSEPH'S COLLEGE

D-5

Brooklyn, NY 11205

(718) 636-6868

Full-time: 85 men, 327 women	**Faculty:** 43
Part-time: 185 men, 547 women	**Ph.D.s:** 60%
Graduate: none	**Student/Faculty:** 10 to 1
Year: semesters, summer session	**Tuition:** $7322
Application Deadline: open	**Room & Board:** n/app
Freshman Class: 268 applied, 163 accepted, 73 enrolled	
SAT I Verbal/Math: 426/460	**COMPETITIVE**

Saint Joseph's College, established in 1916, is a private, multicampus, commuter institution offering undergraduate degrees in arts and sciences, child study, business, accounting, health professions, and nursing. There is a branch campus in Patchogue, Long Island. There are 2 undergraduate schools. In addition to regional accreditation, Saint Joseph's has baccalaureate program accreditation with NLN. The library contains 116,505 volumes, 265 microform items, and 3042 audiovisual forms, and subscribes to 431 periodicals. Computerized library sources and services include database searching. Special learning facilities include a laboratory preschool. The 3-acre campus is in an urban area 1 mile east of Manhattan. There are 5 buildings on campus.

Student Life: About 99% of undergraduates are from New York. Students come from 2 states and Canada. Twenty percent are from public schools; 80% from private. Forty-nine percent are white; 38% African American. The average age of freshmen is 18; all undergraduates, 32. Fifteen percent drop out by the end of their first year; 75% remain to graduate.

Housing: There are no residence halls. All students commute. Alcohol is not permitted. All students may keep cars on campus.

Activities: About 15% of men belong to 1 local fraternity; about 10% of women belong to 1 local sorority. There are 24 groups on campus, including art, cheerleading, chorus, computers, dance, drama, ethnic, honors, newspaper, photography, political, professional, religious, social, social service, student government, and yearbook. Popular campus events include the annual dinner dance, Junior Class Night, Christmas party, costume party, '101 Nights', and Theater Night.

Sports: There is 1 intercollegiate sport for men and 1 for women, and 4 intramural sports for men and 4 for women. Athletic and recreation facilities include a gymnasium, a handball court, an outdoor mall, and recreation rooms.

Disabled Students: Twenty percent of the campus is accessible to disabled students. The following facilities are available: wheelchair ramps and elevators.

Services: In addition to many counseling and information services, tutoring is available in most subjects, including mathematics, languages, philosophy, speech, business, English, psychology, child study, biology, and chemistry.

Campus Safety and Security: Campus safety and security measures include self defense education, escort service, informal discussions, and pamphlets, posters, and films. In addition, there are lighted pathways and sidewalks.

Programs of Study: Saint Joseph's awards the B.A. and B.S. degrees. Bachelor's degrees are awarded in BIOLOGICAL SCIENCE (biology/biological science), BUSINESS (accounting and business administration and management), COMMUNICATIONS AND THE ARTS (English, French, Spanish, and speech/debate/rhetoric), COMPUTER AND PHYSICAL SCIENCE (chemistry and mathematics), EDUCATION (early childhood, elementary, secondary, and special), HEALTH PROFESSIONS (community health work, health care administration, and nursing), SOCIAL SCIENCE (history, psychology, and social science). Child study, biology, and social sciences have the largest enrollments.

Required: To graduate, students must complete a 51-credit core curriculum requirement consisting of 8 courses in humanities, 3 in social science and mathematics/science, and 1 in English composition. The minimum GPA is 2.0. Students must earn 128 credits, with 30 to 36 credits in the major. All students are required to take an English composition class. Most majors require a thesis.

Special: The college offers internship programs in history, political science, social work, speech, and business/accounting, and an interdisciplinary major in human relations. Adult students may pursue a general studies degree in which the college allows credit for life, military, and work experience. Nondegree study and a pass/fail grading option are available. There is a freshman honors program on campus, as well as 4 national honor societies.

Faculty/Classroom: Thirty-eight percent of faculty are male; 62%, female. All teach undergraduates and 10% also do research. The average class size in an introductory lecture is 15; in a laboratory, 15; and in a regular course offering, 12.

Admissions: About 61% of the 1993–94 applicants were accepted. The SAT scores for the 1993–94 freshman class were as follows: Verbal—77% below 500, 19% between 500 and 599, and 3% between

600 and 700; Math—61% below 500, 34% between 500 and 599, and 4% between 600 and 700. About 79% of the current freshmen were in the top fifth of their class; 89% were in the top two fifths. One freshman graduated first in his/her class.

Requirements: A minimum GPA of 3.0 is required. The SAT I is required, with a minimum required composite score of 800. Applicants must graduate from an accredited secondary school or earn a GED. Sixteen Carnegie units are required, including 4 units of English, 2 each of languages and mathematics, 1 each of American history and science, and 6 elective units. Interviews are recommended. AP and CLEP credits are accepted. Important factors used in the admissions decision are advanced placement or honor courses, recommendations by school officials, evidence of special talent, personality, intangible qualities, and extracurricular activities record.

Procedure: Freshmen are admitted in the fall and spring. Application deadlines are open. Application fee is $25. Notification is sent on a rolling basis. There are early decision, early admissions, and deferred admissions plans.

Transfer: About 29 transfer students enrolled in 1993–94. Transfer applicants must have a minimum GPA of 2.0. If fewer than 30 credits have been earned, the SAT I is required with a minimum composite score of 800. A total of 48 credits out of 128 must be completed at Saint Joseph's.

Visiting: There are guides for informal visits and visitors may sit in on classes. To arrange for a visit, contact the Admissions Office at (718) 636–6868.

Financial Aid: In 1993–94 90% of all current freshmen and 85% of continuing students received some form of financial aid. About 60% of freshmen and 65% of continuing students received need-based aid. The average freshman award was $6000. Of that total, scholarships or need-based grants averaged $3000 ($7000 maximum); loans averaged $1500 ($2625 maximum); and work contracts averaged $1500 ($2500 maximum). Four percent of undergraduate students work part-time. Average earnings from campus work for the school year are $1000. The average financial indebtedness of the 1992–93 graduate was $5000. The college's own financial statement and the FAFSA are required. The deadline for financial aid applications is February 25.

International Students: There are currently 4 international students enrolled. The school actively recruits these students. They must take the TOEFL or the SAT I and achieve a minimum score on the TOEFL of 500.

Computers: The college provides computer facilities for student use. Microcomputers are available to students in the computer laboratory and in department offices. All students may access the system. There are no time limits on using the system and no fees.

Graduates: In 1992–93 202 bachelor's degrees were awarded. The most popular majors among graduates were health administration (34%), child study (18%), and community health (12%). Within an average freshman class, 1% graduate in 3 years, 72% in 4 years, 75% in 5 years, and 75% in 6 years. Some 30 companies recruited on campus in 1992–93. In the 1992 graduating class, 40% of all graduates were enrolled in graduate school within 6 months of graduation; 25% of all graduates had found employment.

Admissions Contact: Geraldine Foudy, Director of Admissions.

SAINT LAWRENCE UNIVERSITY
C-2

Canton, NY 13617   (315) 379–5261; (800) 285–1856 (out-of-state)

Full-time: 942 men, 987 women   Faculty: 152; IIB, +$
Part-time: 20 men, 29 women   Ph.D.s: 94%
Graduate: 33 men, 57 women   Student/Faculty: 13 to 1
Year: semesters, summer session   Tuition: $17,890
Application Deadline: February 1   Room & Board: $5530
Freshman Class: 2757 applied, 1822 accepted, 505 enrolled
SAT I Verbal/Math: 510/560   **VERY COMPETITIVE**

St. Lawrence University, established in 1856, is a private liberal arts institution. The library contains 428,345 volumes and 380,000 microform items, and subscribes to 2371 periodicals. Computerized library sources and services include the card catalog, interlibrary loans, and database searching. Special learning facilities include a learning resource center, art gallery, and radio station. The 1000-acre campus is in a rural area 80 miles south of Ottawa, Canada. Including residence halls, there are 30 buildings on campus.

Student Life: About 51% of undergraduates are from New York. Students come from 43 states, 18 foreign countries, and Canada. Sixty-four percent are from public schools; 36% from private. Ninety-one percent are white. The average age of freshmen is 18; all undergraduates, 20. Eight percent drop out by the end of their first year; 81% remain to graduate.

Housing: A total of 1770 students can be accommodated in college housing. College-sponsored living facilities include single-sex and coed dormitories, fraternity houses, and sorority houses. In addition there are special interest houses and theme cottages, such as Habitat for Humanity theme cottage. On-campus housing is guaranteed for all

4 years. Ninety-five percent of students live on campus. All students may keep cars on campus.

Activities: About 35% of men belong to 7 national fraternities; about 35% of women belong to 1 local and 4 national sororities. There are 75 groups on campus, including cheerleading, chess, choir, chorus, dance, drama, ethnic, gay, honors, international, literary magazine, musical theater, newspaper, orchestra, pep band, photography, political, professional, radio and TV, religious, social service, student government, and yearbook. Popular campus events include St. Lawrence Festival of the Arts, Black History Week, Holiday Candlelight Service, Festival of Nations, and Moving Up Day.

Sports: There are 13 intercollegiate sports for men and 12 for women, and 12 intramural sports for men and 9 for women. Athletic and recreation facilities include basketball, squash, and tennis courts, a pool, and weight, Nautilus, and wrestling rooms. There is also a field house, an arena, an artificial ice rink, an 18-hole golf course, riding stables, and jogging and cross-country ski trails.

Disabled Students: Seventy-five percent of the campus is accessible to disabled students. The following facilities are available: wheelchair ramps, elevators, special parking, specially equipped rest rooms, and special class scheduling.

Services: In addition to many counseling and information services, tutoring is available in every subject. There is also a writing center and science and technology counseling. In addition, there is a reader service for the blind and remedial writing.

Campus Safety and Security: Campus safety and security measures include 24-hour foot and vehicle patrol, self defense education, escort service, and shuttle buses. In addition, there are informal discussions, pamphlets, posters, and films, emergency telephones, and lighted pathways and sidewalks.

Programs of Study: St. Lawrence awards the B.A. and B.S. degrees. Master's degrees also are awarded. Bachelor's degrees are awarded in BIOLOGICAL SCIENCE (biology/biological science), COMMUNICATIONS AND THE ARTS (English, fine arts, French, German, music, and Spanish), COMPUTER AND PHYSICAL SCIENCE (chemistry, computer science, geology, mathematics, and physics), EDUCATION (art), ENGINEERING AND ENVIRONMENTAL DESIGN (environmental science and preengineering), SOCIAL SCIENCE (anthropology, Asian/Oriental studies, Canadian studies, economics, history, philosophy, political science/government, psychology, religion, and sociology). Environmental studies, government, and economics are the strongest academically. Economics, government, English, psychology, sociology, and biology have the largest enrollments.

Required: To graduate, students must maintain a minimum GPA of 2.0 and complete 34 units, with 8 to 12 units in the major. Freshmen must take First-Year Program, a 2-semester team-taught course. Distribution requirements must be fulfilled in natural science, social science, and humanities. Students must also complete 1 course in non-Western or Third World topics and 1 course each from 2 of the following areas: mathematics or symbolic logic, arts or forms of expression, and foreign languages, as well as 1 year of physical education.

Special: Students may cross-register with the Associated Colleges of the St. Lawrence Valley, Clarkson University, and the State University of New York Colleges at Potsdam and Canton. Internships are available through the sociology, psychology, and English departments. Study-abroad in 11 countries, a Washington semester, and a semester at sea are offered. Dual majors and student-designed majors can be arranged. Students may earn 3–2 engineering degrees in conjunction with 7 engineering schools. A 3–2 nursing degree program is available with Columbia University or the University of Rochester. Early assurance, early decision, and deferred entrance agreements may be made with the Syracuse University College of Medicine. Non-degree study and pass/fail options are available. There are 19 national honor societies on campus, including Phi Beta Kappa. Seventeen departments have honors programs.

Faculty/Classroom: Seventy-five percent of faculty are male; 25%, female. Ninety-nine percent teach undergraduates, 100% do research, and 99% do both. No introductory courses are taught by graduate students. The average class size in an introductory lecture is 30; in a laboratory, 20; and in a regular course offering, 15.

Admissions: About 66% of the 1993–94 applicants were accepted. The SAT scores for the 1993–94 freshman class were as follows: Verbal—42% below 500, 45% between 500 and 599, 13% between 600 and 700, and 1% above 700; Math—11% below 500, 54% between 500 and 599, 31% between 600 and 700, and 4% above 700. About 48% of the current freshmen were in the top fifth of their class; 74% were in the top two fifths. There were 5 National Merit finalists. About 18 freshmen graduated first in their class.

Requirements: The SAT I or the ACT is required. If the SAT I is taken, the SAT II writing test is required; 2 other subject tests are recommended. Applicants must be graduates of an accredited high school. Sixteen or more academic credits are required, including 4 years of English and 3 years each of foreign languages, mathematics, science,

and social studies. Essays are required and interviews are recommended for all applicants. AP and CLEP credits are accepted.

Procedure: Freshmen are admitted fall, spring, and summer. Entrance exams should be taken during the spring of the junior or fall of the senior year. Applications should be filed by February 1 for fall entry and December 1 for spring entry, along with an application fee of $40. Notification is sent March 15. There are early decision and deferred admissions plans. About 120 early decision candidates were accepted for the 1993–94 class. A waiting list is an active part of the admissions procedure, with about 14% of applicants on the list.

Transfer: About 40 transfer students enrolled in 1993–94. Applicants must have a 3.0 GPA and a minimum of 4 courses must have been completed. The high school transcript and SAT I scores will be evaluated, but college work is more important. Interviews and high school and college recommendations are required. A total of 16 units out of 34 must be completed at St. Lawrence.

Visiting: There are guides for informal visits and visitors may sit in on classes and stay overnight at the school. To arrange for a visit, contact the Admissions Office at (315) 379–5261 or (800) 258–1856.

Financial Aid: In 1993–94 66% of all current freshmen and 60% of continuing students received some form of financial aid. About 65% of freshmen and 59% of continuing students received need-based aid. The average freshman award was $14,747. Of that total, scholarships or need-based grants averaged $12,546 ($23,800 maximum); loans averaged $2117 ($5600 maximum); and work contracts averaged $872 ($1700 maximum). Thirty-seven percent of undergraduate students work part-time. Average earnings from campus work for the school year are $1000. The average financial indebtedness of the 1992–93 graduate was $7500. St. Lawrence is a member of CSS. The FAF is required. The deadline for financial aid applications is February 15.

International Students: There are currently 66 international students enrolled. The school actively recruits these students.

Computers: The college provides computer facilities for student use. The mainframe is an IBM 4381 (Model 13). Six hundred personal computers are linked to the mainframe and card catalog. Word processing and spreadsheet software, and electronic mail, calendars, and bulletin boards are available. Computer laboratories are located in all residence halls and most academic buildings. All students may access the system. It may be used 24 hours per day. There are no time limits on using the system and no fees.

Graduates: In 1992–93 542 bachelor's degrees were awarded. The most popular majors among graduates were English (15%), government (13%), and psychology (12%). Within an average freshman class, 1% graduate in 3 years, 76% in 4 years, 81% in 5 years, and 81% in 6 years. Some 40 companies recruited on campus in 1992–93. About 27% of graduates enrolled in graduate school within 6 months of graduation and 67% found employment within 6 months of graduation.

Admissions Contact: Joel R. Wincowski.

SAINT THOMAS AQUINAS COLLEGE D-5

Sparkill, NY 10976   (914) 398–4100; (800) 999-STAC

Full-time: 467 men, 650 women	Faculty: 86; IIB, av$
Part-time: 302 men, 513 women	Ph.D.s: 90%
Graduate: 31 men, 119 women	Student/Faculty: 13 to 1
Year: 4–1–4, summer session	Tuition: $8150
Application Deadline: open	Room & Board: $5400
Freshman Class: 861 applied, 615 accepted, 238 enrolled	
SAT I or ACT: required	**COMPETITIVE**

Saint Thomas Aquinas College, founded in 1952, is an independent, coeducational liberal arts institution. There is one graduate school. The library contains 102,943 volumes and 45,900 microform items, and subscribes to 108 periodicals. Computerized library sources and services include the card catalog, interlibrary loans, and database searching. Special learning facilities include a learning resource center, radio station, and TV station. The 42-acre campus is in a suburban area 13 miles north of New York City. Including residence halls, there are 12 buildings on campus.

Student Life: About 75% of undergraduates are from New York. Students come from 6 states, 8 foreign countries, and Canada. Eighty percent are from public schools; 20% from private. Eighty-four percent are white. Sixty-two percent are Catholic; 23% Protestant. The average age of freshmen is 18; all undergraduates, 22. Six percent drop out by the end of their first year; 86% remain to graduate.

Housing: A total of 450 students can be accommodated in college housing. College-sponsored living facilities include single-sex dormitories and on-campus apartments. On-campus housing is guaranteed for all 4 years. Seventy-five percent of students commute. Alcohol is not permitted. All students may keep cars on campus.

Activities: There are no fraternities or sororities on campus. There are 10 groups on campus, including chorus, drama, honors, literary magazine, newspaper, professional, radio and TV, social service, stu-

dent government, and yearbook. Popular campus events include trips to Broadway shows and Halloween and Christmas mixers.

Sports: There are 4 intercollegiate sports for men and 4 for women, and 3 intramural sports for men and 3 for women. Athletic and recreation facilities include an auditorium, a 750-seat gymnasium, a weight room, and basketball and tennis courts.

Disabled Students: Ninety percent of the campus is accessible to disabled students. The following facilities are available: wheelchair ramps, elevators, special parking, specially equipped rest rooms, special class scheduling, and lowered telephones.

Services: In addition to many counseling and information services, tutoring is available in most subjects. There is also remedial math and writing.

Campus Safety and Security: Campus safety and security measures include 24-hour foot and vehicle patrol, escort service, pamphlets, posters, films, and emergency telephones. In addition, there are lighted pathways and sidewalks.

Programs of Study: STAC awards the B.A., B.S., and B.S.E. degrees. Master's degrees also are awarded. Bachelor's degrees are awarded in BUSINESS (accounting, banking and finance, business administration and management, marketing/retailing/merchandising, and recreation and leisure services), COMMUNICATIONS AND THE ARTS (communications, English, fine arts, romance languages, and Spanish), EDUCATION (art, bilingual/bicultural, early childhood, elementary, foreign languages, middle school, science, secondary, and special), ENGINEERING AND ENVIRONMENTAL DESIGN (commercial art), HEALTH PROFESSIONS (medical laboratory technology and premedicine), SOCIAL SCIENCE (criminal justice, history, philosophy, prelaw, psychology, religion, and social science). Education is the strongest academically. Business administration has the largest enrollment.

Required: To graduate, all students must complete a total of 120 credit hours, with 36 to 54 in the major. Students must have a minimum GPA of 2.0. A core curriculum of 51 credits in liberal arts courses is required.

Special: STAC offers internships in business, criminal justice, commercial design, recreation and leisure, and communications. Study abroad in England, a 3–2 engineering degree with George Washington University and Manhattan College, and work-study programs are available. Nondegree study and pass/fail options are possible. There is a freshman honors program on campus, as well as 7 national honor societies.

Faculty/Classroom: Fifty-five percent of faculty are male; 45%, female. All teach undergraduates. No introductory courses are taught by graduate students. The average class size in an introductory lecture is 35; in a laboratory, 15; and in a regular course offering, 25.

Admissions: About 71% of the 1993–94 applicants were accepted. About 12% of the current freshmen were in the top fifth of their class; 43% were in the top two fifths. Two freshmen graduated first in their class.

Requirements: A minimum GPA of 78% is required. The SAT I or ACT is required. Applicants must be graduates of an accredited secondary school or have a GED certificate. Sixteen Carnegie units are required, including 4 years of English, 2 years each of mathematics and science, and 1 year each of foreign language and history. An interview is recommended. AP and CLEP credits are accepted. Important factors used in the admissions decision are advanced placement or honor courses, extracurricular activities record, leadership record, evidence of special talent, and recommendations by school officials.

Procedure: Freshmen are admitted in the fall and spring. Entrance exams should be taken by the spring of the junior year. Application deadlines are open. Application fee is $25. Notification is sent on a rolling basis. There are early admissions and deferred admissions plans.

Transfer: About 200 transfer students enrolled in 1993–94. Applicants must have a minimum 2.0 GPA from the previous school. At least 30 credits out of 120 must be completed at STAC.

Visiting: There are guides for informal visits, and visitors may sit in on classes. To arrange for a visit, contact the Admissions Office at (914) 398–4100 or (800) 999-STAC.

Financial Aid: In 1993–94, 75% of all current freshmen and 60% of continuing students received some form of financial aid. The average freshman award was $6300. Of that total, scholarships or need-based grants averaged $1500 ($6600 maximum); loans averaged $2000 ($2625 maximum); and work contracts averaged $1120 ($1500 maximum). Eighty-five percent of undergraduate students work part-time. Average earnings from campus work for the school year are $1200. The average financial indebtedness of the 1992–93 graduate was $10,000. STAC is a member of CSS. The FAF and the college's own financial statement are required. The deadline for financial aid applications is April.

International Students: There are currently 18 international students enrolled. They must take the TOEFL and achieve a minimum score of 450.

Computers: The college provides computer facilities for student use. The mainframe is an HP3000. There are also 50 IBM, Zenith, Apple, and HP microcomputers available throughout campus. Those enrolled in programming courses may access the system 8:30 A.M. to 5 P.M. Monday through Thursday and 4 hours on Friday, Saturday, and Sunday. Students may access the system 1 hour per session per half day. The fees are $35.

Graduates: In a recent year, 350 bachelor's degrees were awarded. The most popular majors among graduates were business (27%), education (22%), and psychology (12%). Within an average freshman class, 1% graduate in 3 years, 56% in 4 years, and 5% in 5 years. Some 24 companies recruited on campus in 1992–93. In the 1992 graduating class, 24% of the men and 24% of all graduates were enrolled in graduate school within 6 months of graduation; 95% had found employment.

Admissions Contact: Andrea Kraeft, Director of Admissions.

SARAH LAWRENCE COLLEGE
Bronxville, NY 10708

D-5

(914) 395-2510
(800) 888-2858 (out-of-state)

Full-time: 233 men, 699 women
Part-time: 5 men, 83 women
Graduate: 26 men, 196 women
Year: semesters
Application Deadline: February 1
Freshman Class: 1380 applied, 768 accepted, 263 enrolled
SAT I Verbal/Math: 590/560

Faculty: 163; IIB, + +$
Ph.Ds: 92%
Student/Faculty: 6 to 1
Tuition: $18,460
Room & Board: $6515

HIGHLY COMPETITIVE

Sarah Lawrence College, established in 1926, is an independent, co-educational institution conferring liberal arts degrees. The academic structure is based on the British don system. Students meet biweekly with professors in tutorials and are enrolled in small seminars. There are no formal majors. The 3 libraries contain 210,250 volumes and 13,530 microform items, and subscribe to 1190 periodicals. Computerized library sources and services include the card catalog, interlibrary loans, and database searching. Special learning facilities include a greenhouse, an environmental theater, and an early childhood center. The 40-acre campus is in a suburban area 15 miles north of New York City. Including residence halls, there are 50 buildings on campus.

Student Life: About 80% of undergraduates are from out-of-state, mostly the Northeast. Students come from 44 states, 19 foreign countries, and Canada. Fifty-five percent are from public schools; 45% from private. Seventy-eight percent are white. The average age of freshmen is 18; all undergraduates, 21. Between 4% and 8% percent drop out by the end of their first year; 80% remain to graduate.

Housing: A total of 732 students can be accommodated in college housing. College-sponsored living facilities include single-sex and coed dormitories and on-campus apartments. On-campus housing is guaranteed for all 4 years. Ninety percent of students live on campus. Upperclassmen may keep cars on campus.

Activities: There are no fraternities or sororities on campus. There are 40 groups on campus, including art, band, chess, choir, chorale, chorus, computers, dance, drama, ethnic, film, gay, international, jazz band, literary magazine, musical theater, newspaper, opera, orchestra, photography, political, radio and TV, religious, social, social service, student government, and yearbook. Popular campus events include Octoberfest, Mayfair, Winter Wonder Week, Dance-a-thon, and a student scholarship fundraising auction.

Sports: There are 3 intercollegiate sports for men and 4 for women, and 5 intramural sports for men and 5 for women. Athletic and recreation facilities include a fitness center, a weight room, billiards tables, tennis courts, and a number of open fields and lawns. Off-campus, the college has the use of a boat house, stables, and a swimming pool.

Disabled Students: Fifty percent of the campus is accessible to disabled students. The following facilities are available: wheelchair ramps, special parking, specially equipped rest rooms, special class scheduling, lowered drinking fountains, and lowered telephones.

Campus Safety and Security: Campus safety and security measures include 24-hour foot and vehicle patrol, self-defense education, escort service, and shuttle buses. In addition, there are informal discussions, pamphlets, posters, and films, emergency telephones, and lighted pathways and sidewalks.

Programs of Study: Sarah Lawrence awards the B.A. degree. Master's degrees also are awarded. Bachelor's degrees are awarded in BIOLOGICAL SCIENCE (biology/biological science), COMMUNICATIONS AND THE ARTS (creative writing, dance, dramatic arts, English, film arts, fine arts, French, German, Greek, Italian, Latin, music, photography, Russian, and Spanish), COMPUTER AND PHYSICAL SCIENCE (chemistry, computer science, earth science, geology, mathematics, physics, and statistics), EDUCATION (early childhood), HEALTH PROFESSIONS (premedicine), SOCIAL SCIENCE (anthropology, Asian/Oriental studies, economics, history, international relations, philosophy, political science/government, prelaw, psychology, religion, Russian and Slavic studies, sociology, urban studies, and wo-

men's studies). Literature, history, creative writing, psychology, and theater have the largest enrollments.

Required: To graduate, students must meet distribution requirements in 3 of 4 academic areas, including history and social sciences, creative and performing arts, natural science and mathematics, and humanities, and they must complete 120 credit hours. Students must fulfill first year studies requirement in one of 18 areas, and meet a physical education requirement. Students must also fulfill a 2-year lecture requirement or the equivalent.

Special: Internships are available in a variety of fields, with close proximity to New York City art galleries and agencies. Study abroad in 4 countries, work-study programs, and a general degree may be pursued. All majors are self-designed and can be combined.

Faculty/Classroom: Fifty percent of faculty are male; 50%, female. All teach undergraduates. No introductory courses are taught by graduate students. The average class size in a regular course offering is 11.

Admissions: About 56% of the 1993–94 applicants were accepted. The SAT scores for the 1993–94 freshman class were as follows: Verbal—17% below 500, 37% between 500 and 599, 39% between 600 and 700, and 7% above 700; Math—26% below 500, 42% between 500 and 599, 28% between 600 and 700, and 4% above 700. About 71% of the current freshmen were in the top fifth of their class; 89% were in the top two fifths.

Requirements: The SAT I, ACT, or 3 SAT II: Subject tests is required. Applicants must graduate from an accredited secondary school or have a GED. The number of academic credits required depends on the high school attended. The college recommends completion of 4 years of English, 3 years each of mathematics, science, social studies, and a foreign language, 2 to 3 years of history, and 1 year each of art and music. Three essays are required. An interview is recommended. AP credits are accepted. Important factors used in the admissions decision are advanced placement or honor courses, personality, intangible qualities, evidence of special talent, recommendations by school officials, and extracurricular activities record.

Procedure: Freshmen are admitted fall and spring. Early decision applications should be filed by November 15; regular applications, by February 1 for fall entry and December 1 for spring entry, along with an application fee of $45. Notification of early decision is sent December 15; regular decision, April 1. There are early decision, early admissions, and deferred admissions plans. About 65 early decision candidates were accepted for the 1993–94 class. A waiting list is an active part of the admissions procedure, with about 10% of applicants on the list.

Transfer: About 60 transfer students enrolled in 1993–94. Transfer applicants must submit the Application for Admission (Form A); the common application is not accepted. They must also submit the College Report form, high school and college transcripts, 2 teacher evaluations, and a dean's report. A GPA of 3.0 is recommended. Students must have completed 1 full year of college. Sarah Lawrence has a 2-year residency requirement. An interview is highly recommeded. A total of 60 credits out of 120 must be completed at Sarah Lawrence.

Visiting: There are regularly scheduled orientations for prospective students, consisting of a full day of faculty and student panels, lectures, tours, and discussion with admissions officers, offered twice per year during the fall. There are guides for informal visits and visitors may sit in on classes and stay overnight at the school. To arrange for a visit, contact Linda Bloom, Receptionist, Admissions Office at (914) 395-2510 or (800) 888-2858, Monday through Thursday.

Financial Aid: In 1993–94, 64% of all current freshmen and 50% of continuing students received some form of financial aid. About 52% of freshmen and 47% of continuing students received need-based aid. The average freshman award was $12,197. Fifty percent of undergraduate students work part-time. Average earnings from campus work for the school year are $1400. Sarah Lawrence is a member of CSS. The FAF, the college's own financial statement and the FAFSA are required. The deadline for financial aid applications is February 1.

International Students: There are currently 80 international students enrolled. The school actively recruits these students. They must take the TOEFL and achieve a minimum score of 550. The student must also take the SAT I.

Computers: The college provides computer facilities for student use. There are 40 stand-alone PCs, Macintosh microcomputers, and laserprinters located in the student computer center, available 24 hours. All students may access the system. It may be used 24 hours. There are no time limits on using the system and no fees.

Graduates: In a recent year, 205 bachelor's degrees were awarded. The most popular majors among graduates were literature (25%), history (20%), and psychology (15%). Within an average freshman class, 75% graduate in 4 years and 80% in 5 years.

Admissions Contact: Barbara Friend, Dean of Admissions.

SCHOOL OF VISUAL ARTS
D-5

New York, NY 10010–3994   (212) 592–2100

Full-time: 1413 men, 888 women	Faculty: 46
Part-time: 1051 men, 1407 women	Ph.D.s: n/av
Graduate: 135 men, 164 women	Student/Faculty: 50 to 1
Year: semesters, summer session	Tuition: $11,750
Application Deadline: open	Room & Board: $5370
Freshman Class: 1600 applied, 1200 accepted, 600 enrolled	**SPECIAL**

The School of Visual Arts, established in 1947, is a private, coeducational institution conferring the bachelor of fine arts degree. There are 7 undergraduate and 4 graduate schools. In addition to regional accreditation, SVA has baccalaureate program accreditation with NASAD. The library contains 62,000 volumes, 750 microform items, and 1500 audiovisual forms, and subscribes to 255 periodicals. Computerized library sources and services include the card catalog. Special learning facilities include a learning resource center, art gallery, radio station, 5 student galleries, 2 media arts workshops, 7 computer rooms, 2 video studios, and 2 animation studios. The campus is in an urban area in the middle of Manhattan. Including residence halls, there are 5 buildings on campus.

Student Life: About 60% of undergraduates are from New York. Students come from 39 states, 24 foreign countries, and Canada. Eighty-five percent are from public schools; 15% from private. Seventy-three percent are white; 12% foreign nationals. The average age of freshmen is 18. Fourteen percent drop out by the end of their first year; 60% remain to graduate.

Housing: A total of 500 students can be accommodated in college housing. College-sponsored living facilities include single-sex and coed dormitories and off-campus apartments. On-campus housing is available on a first-come, first-served basis. Ninety percent of students commute. Alcohol is not permitted. All students may keep cars on campus.

Activities: There are no fraternities or sororities on campus. There are numerous groups and organizations on campus, including art, computers, drama, ethnic, film, gay, honors, international, literary magazine, newspaper, photography, political, professional, radio and TV, religious, social, social service, student government, and yearbook. Popular campus events include 4 annual illustration exhibitions, 3 annual advertising exhibitions, 86 annual fine art and photography exhibitions, 2 art therapy exhibitions, 2 art education exhibitions, lectures, symposia, panel discussions, and numerous visiting lecture talks.

Sports: There is an intramural sports program at SVA.

Disabled Students: All of the campus is accessible to disabled students. The following facilities are available: wheelchair ramps, elevators, specially equipped rest rooms, and lowered telephones.

Services: In addition to some counseling and information services, there is remedial reading and writing.

Campus Safety and Security: Campus safety and security measures include 24-hour patrol, informal discussions, pamphlets, posters, and films, and emergency telephones.

Programs of Study: SVA awards the B.F.A. degree. Master's degrees also are awarded. Bachelor's degrees are awarded in COMMUNICATIONS AND THE ARTS (advertising, film arts, fine arts, graphic design, illustration, photography, and video), ENGINEERING AND ENVIRONMENTAL DESIGN (computer graphics and interior design). Graphic design and fine arts have the largest enrollments.

Required: To graduate, students must complete 128 credits, including at least 70 in the major. Distribution requirements include 1 upper-level course each in history, literature, and science. The minimum GPA is 2.0.

Special: Study abroad in France, Italy, Spain, Portugal, Greece, Israel, and England and a pass/fail option are offered. A summer internship with Walt Disney Studios is possible for illustration/cartooning majors. A certificate in art education or art therapy is offered in combination with fine arts.

Faculty/Classroom: The studio faculty are professional and exhibiting artists who teach part time.

Admissions: About 75% of the 1993–94 applicants were accepted.

Requirements: A minimum GPA of 2.0 is required. The SAT I or ACT is required. Applicants must graduate from an accredited secondary school or have a GED. A personal interview is required of all students living within a 250-mile radius of the school. An essay is required. A portfolio is also required, except for film applicants. AP credit is accepted. Important factors used in the admissions decision are evidence of special talent, personality, intangible qualities, leadership record, extracurricular activities record, and recommendations by school officials.

Procedure: Freshmen are admitted to all sessions. Application deadlines are open. Application fee is $30. Notification is sent on a rolling basis. There are early decision and deferred admissions plans.

Transfer: About 258 transfer students enrolled in a recent year. A total of 64 credits out of 128 must be completed at SVA.

Visiting: There are regularly scheduled orientations for prospective students, including 6 Saturday Open House receptions and weekly tours. There are guides for informal visits. To arrange for a visit, contact the Office of Admissions at (212) 592–2100.

Financial Aid: In 1993–94 73% of all current freshmen received some form of financial aid. About 71% of freshmen and 71% of continuing students received need-based aid. Scholarships or need-based grants averaged $2500 ($10,500 maximum); loans averaged $3125 ($3625 maximum); and work contracts averaged $1000 ($3000 maximum). The average financial indebtedness of the 1992–93 graduate was $14,000. SVA is a member of CSS. The FAF and the college's own financial statement are required. The deadline for financial aid applications is September 15.

International Students: There are currently 200 international students enrolled. The school actively recruits these students. They must take the TOEFL and achieve a minimum score of 500.

Computers: The college provides computer facilities for student use. There are 140 microcomputers available. To access the system, students must book the time ahead of usage. There are no fees.

Graduates: In 1992–93 394 bachelor's degrees were awarded. The most popular majors among graduates were graphic design/advertising (30%), illistration/cartooning (25%), and fine arts (20%). Within an average freshman class, 42% graduate in 4 years, 46% in 5 years, and 48% in 6 years. Some 53 companies recruited on campus in 1992–93.

Admissions Contact: Paul Marro, Assistant to the Director of Admissions.

SIENA COLLEGE
D-3

Loudonville, NY 12211–1462   (518) 783–2423

(800) 45 SIENA (out-of-state)

Full-time: 1296 men, 1374 women	Faculty: 169; IIB, av$
Part-time: 410 men, 412 women	Ph.D.s: 79%
Graduate: none	Student/Faculty: 16 to 1
Year: semesters, summer session	Tuition: $10,505
Application Deadline: March 1	Room & Board: $4905
Freshman Class: 2961 applied, 1932 accepted, 628 enrolled	
SAT I Verbal/Math: 491/560	**VERY COMPETITIVE**

Siena College, established in 1937, is an independent, coeducational liberal arts college operating within the Franciscan Tradition. The college confers undergraduate degrees in liberal arts, business, and science, and provides continuing education programs for the surrounding community. In addition to regional accreditation, Siena has baccalaureate program accreditation with CSWE. The library contains 244,564 volumes, 29,613 microform items, and 2133 audiovisual forms, and subscribes to 1412 periodicals. Computerized library sources and services include interlibrary loans and database searching. Special learning facilities include a radio station. The 162-acre campus is in a suburban area 2 miles north of Albany. Including residence halls, there are 24 buildings on campus.

Student Life: About 85% of undergraduates are from New York. Students come from 22 states, 10 foreign countries, and Canada. Seventy percent are from public schools; 30% from private. Ninety-four percent are white. The average age of freshmen is 18; all undergraduates, 20. Five percent drop out by the end of their first year; 82% remain to graduate.

Housing: A total of 1796 students can be accommodated in college housing. College-sponsored living facilities include coed dormitories and on-campus townhouse/apartment complexes. On-campus housing is guaranteed for all 4 years. Sixty-seven percent of students live on campus; of those, 90% remain on campus on weekends. Upperclassmen may keep cars on campus.

Activities: There are no fraternities or sororities on campus. There are 60 groups on campus, including art, cheerleading, choir, chorus, computers, drama, ethnic, honors, international, literary magazine, musical theater, newspaper, pep band, political, professional, radio and TV, religious, social, social service, student government, and yearbook. Popular campus events include Spring Weekend, Parents Weekend, Winter Weekend, Sibling Weekend, Junior/Senior Formal, Black History Month, and cultural dinners.

Sports: There are 9 intercollegiate sports for men and 8 for women, and 10 intramural sports for men, 10 for women, and 2 for both men and women. Athletic and recreation facilities include an athletic complex, with free weights, a training facility, an indoor track, an 8-lane 25-meter pool, fitness equipment, life cycles, 4 multipurpose courts, 6 outdoor tennis courts, 5 outdoor fields, 2 squash courts, and 2 racquetball courts.

Disabled Students: The entire campus is accessible to disabled students. The following facilities are available: wheelchair ramps, elevators, special parking, specially equipped rest rooms, and special class scheduling.

Services: In addition to many counseling and information services, tutoring is available in most subjects. In addition, there is a reader service for the blind and remedial math and writing.

Campus Safety and Security: Campus safety and security measures include 24-hour foot and vehicle patrol, escort service, informal discussions, and pamphlets, posters, and films. In addition, there are emergency telephones and lighted pathways and sidewalks.

Programs of Study: Siena awards the B.A., B.S., and B.B.A. degrees. Bachelor's degrees are awarded in BIOLOGICAL SCIENCE (biology/biological science), BUSINESS (accounting, banking and finance, business economics, and marketing management), COMMUNICATIONS AND THE ARTS (classical languages, English, French, and Spanish), COMPUTER AND PHYSICAL SCIENCE (chemistry, computer science, mathematics, and physics), SOCIAL SCIENCE (American studies, economics, history, philosophy, political science/government, psychology, religion, social work, and sociology). Biology, premedical programs, political science, and accounting are the strongest programs academically. Accounting, marketing/management, and biology have the largest enrollments.

Required: To graduate, students must earn 120 credits, including 30 to 39 in the major, with a 2.0 GPA. The required core curriculum of 39 credits must include 2 courses each in English, history, social science, philosophy, religious studies, and mathematics/science, and 1 course in fine arts.

Special: The college offers a cooperative 4–1 business program with Clarkson University, and a cooperative 2–2 program in environmental science and forestry with Syracuse University. Cross-registration with the Hudson-Mohawk Association and a Washington semester with American University are possible. Domestic and international internships, dual majors, B.A.-B.S. degrees, study abroad in 15 countries, and pass/fail options are available. Students may earn 3–2 engineering degrees with Clarkson and Catholic universities, Manhattan College, Western New England College, SUNY at Binghamton, and Rensselaer Polytechnic Institute. Sienna also offers a 4–4 early assurance program with the Columbia University School of Dental and Oral Surgery and a 4–4 medical program with Albany Medical College. There is a freshman honors program on campus, as well as 7 national honor societies. Two departments have honors programs.

Faculty/Classroom: Seventy-two percent of faculty are male; 28%, female. All both teach and do research. The average class size in an introductory lecture is 30; in a laboratory, 20; and in a regular course offering, 22.

Admissions: About 65% of the 1993–94 applicants were accepted. The SAT scores for the 1993–94 freshman class were as follows: Verbal—58% below 500, 36% between 500 and 599, and 6% between 600 and 700; Math—21% below 500, 51% between 500 and 599, 25% between 600 and 700, and 3% above 700. The ACT scores were 14% below 21, 33% between 21 and 23, 34% between 24 and 26, 9% between 27 and 28, and 10% above 28. About 49% of the current freshmen were in the top fifth of their class; 82% were in the top two fifths. Six freshmen graduated first in their class.

Requirements: The SAT I or ACT is required. Applicants must be graduates of an accredited secondary school or have a GED. Sixteen academic credits are required, including 4 years each of English and history, 3 to 4 years each of mathematics and science, and a recommended 3 years of foreign language study. All applicants must submit an essay; an interview is recommended. AP and CLEP credits are accepted. Important factors used in the admissions decision are leadership record, advanced placement or honor courses, evidence of special talent, recommendations by school officials, and recommendations by alumni.

Procedure: Freshmen are admitted in the fall and spring. Entrance exams should be taken during May of the junior year or November of the senior year. Early decision applications should be filed by December 1; regular applications, by March 1 for fall entry, December 1 for spring entry, and January 1 for summer entry, along with an application fee of $40. Notification of early decision is sent January 15; regular decision, March 15. There are early decision, early admissions, and deferred admissions plans. About 251 early decision candidates were accepted for the 1993–94 class. A waiting list is an active part of the admissions procedure, with about 10% of applicants on the list.

Transfer: About 199 transfer students enrolled in 1993–94. Applicants must have a minimum 2.8 GPA. An interview is recommended. A total of 30 credits out of 120 must be completed at Siena.

Visiting: There are regularly scheduled orientations for prospective students. There are guides for informal visits and visitors may sit in on classes and stay overnight at the school. To arrange for a visit, contact the Admissions Office at (518) 783-2423 or (800) 45 SIENA.

Financial Aid: In 1993–94 82% of all current freshmen and 79% of continuing students received some form of financial aid. About 77% of freshmen and 60% of continuing students received need-based aid. The average freshman award was $6025. Of that total, scholarships or need-based grants averaged $2710 ($15,985 maximum); loans averaged $2480 ($6125 maximum); and work contracts averaged $800 ($1000 maximum). Fifteen percent of undergraduate students work part-time. Average earnings from campus work for the school year are $800. The average financial indebtedness of the

1992–93 graduate was $9002. Siena is a member of CSS. The college's own financial statement, the FAFSA, and the TAP application are required. The deadline for financial aid applications is February 1.

International Students: There are currently 12 international students enrolled. The school actively recruits these students. They must take the TOEFL and achieve a minimum score of 500.

Computers: The college provides computer facilities for student use. The mainframes include a DEC VAX 6210, 8200, and 8250. Students obtain a student access number from the computer center to use terminals available at various locations throughout the campus. IBM-compatible and Apple Macintosh workstations are also available. All students may access the system 24 hours per day. There are no time limits on using the system and no fees.

Graduates: In 1992–93 752 bachelor's degrees were awarded. The most popular majors among graduates were marketing/management (21%), accounting (20%), and finance (13%). Within an average freshman class, 75% graduate in 4 years, 80% in 5 years, and 82% in 6 years. Some 105 companies recruited on campus in 1992–93. In the 1992 graduating class, 24% of the men and women were enrolled in graduate school within 6 months of graduation; 74% of the men and women had found employment.

Admissions Contact: Katherine McCarthy, Dean of Admissions.

SKIDMORE COLLEGE
Saratoga Springs, NY 12866–1632

	D-3
	(518) 581-7400, ext. 2213
Full-time: 834 men, 1269 women	Faculty: 195; IIB, +$
Part-time: 25 men and women	Ph.D.s: 95%
Graduate: 19 men and women	Student/Faculty: 11 to 1
Year: semesters, summer session	Tuition: $17,775
Application Deadline: February 1	Room & Board: $5455
Freshman Class: 4293 applied, 2728 accepted, 591 enrolled	
SAT I or ACT: required	HIGHLY COMPETITITVE

Skidmore College, established in 1903, is an independent, coeducational institution offering undergraduate programs in liberal arts and sciences, as well as business, social work, education, studio art, dance, and theater. In addition to regional accreditation, Skidmore has baccalaureate program accreditation with CSWE and NASAD. The library contains 400,000 volumes, 245,000 microform items, and 9800 audiovisual forms, and subscribes to 1700 periodicals. Computerized library sources and services include database searching and networking. Special learning facilities include a learning resource center, an art gallery and studio, a radio station, a TV station, an electronic music studio, a theater teaching facility, an anthropology laboratory, and special biological habitats. The 850-acre campus is in a small town 30 miles north of Albany. Including residence halls, there are 49 buildings on campus.

Student Life: About 65% of undergraduates are from out-of-state, mostly the Northeast. Students come from 48 states, 20 foreign countries, and Canada. Sixty-one percent are from public schools; 39% from private. Eighty-four percent are white. Thirty-three percent claim no religious affiliation; 22% are Catholic; 18% Protestant; 17% Jewish. The average age of freshmen is 18; all undergraduates, 20. Nine percent drop out by the end of their first year; 81% remain to graduate.

Housing: A total of 1800 students can be accommodated in college housing. College-sponsored living facilities include coed dormitories and on-campus apartments. In addition there are language houses and special interest houses. On-campus housing is guaranteed for all 4 years and is available on a lottery system for upperclassmen. Eighty-two percent of students live on campus; of those, 90% remain on campus on weekends. All students may keep cars on campus.

Activities: There are no fraternities or sororities on campus. There are 80 groups on campus, including art, chorale, chorus, computers, dance, drama, ethnic, film, gay, honors, international, jazz band, literary magazine, musical theater, newspaper, orchestra, photography, political, professional, radio and TV, religious, social, social service, student government, and yearbook. Popular campus events include Martin Luther King Week, Oktoberfest, Spring Fling, Parents Weekend, Winter Carnival, Homecoming, various cultural/ethnic observances such as Black History Month and Native American Week, Women's Festival, Senior Art Show, and basketball games with Hamilton and Union.

Sports: There are 10 intercollegiate sports each for men and women, and 15 intramural sports for men and 13 for women. Athletic and recreation facilities include a fitness center; an indoor swimming and diving pool; 2 gymnasiums with 4 basketball courts; an indoor jogging track; a weight room; fields for baseball and other sports; dance studios; cross-country ski trails; a riding center; courts for tennis, handball, racquetball, and squash; and an outdoor facility with a synthetic surface soccer/lacrosse field, an all-weather, 400-meter track, lights, and permanent stands.

Disabled Students: Seventy-five percent of the campus is accessible to disabled students. The following facilities are available: wheelchair ramps, elevators, special parking, specially equipped rest rooms, and lowered drinking fountains.

Services: In addition to many counseling and information services, tutoring is available in most subjects. There is a reader service for the blind. Diagnostic services, note takers, and books on tape are also offered.

Campus Safety and Security: Campus safety and security measures include 24-hour foot and vehicle patrol, escort service, shuttle buses, and informal discussions. In addition, there are pamphlets, posters, and films, emergency telephones, lighted pathways and sidewalks, a special security alert system, rigorous fire response procedures, and a lock system on dormitory entrances after 8 P.M.

Programs of Study: Skidmore awards the B.A. and B.S. degrees. Master's degrees are also awarded. Bachelor's degrees are awarded in BIOLOGICAL SCIENCE (biochemistry and biology/biological science), BUSINESS (business administration and management and business economics), COMMUNICATIONS AND THE ARTS (art history and appreciation, classics, dance, dramatic arts, English, fine arts, French, German, music, and Spanish), COMPUTER AND PHYSICAL SCIENCE (chemistry, computer science, geology, mathematics, and physics), EDUCATION (art, elementary, and physical), SOCIAL SCIENCE (American studies, anthropology, economics, history, philosophy, political science/government, psychology, social work, and sociology). English, business, psychology, government, and art have the largest enrollments.

Required: To graduate, students must complete 120 credits, including at least 24 of 300-level courses, with a minimum GPA of 2.0 overall and in the major. They must fulfill foundation requirements in writing and quantitative reasoning; meet a liberal studies requirement that includes 1 course each in the human experience, cultural traditions and social change, artistic forms and critical concepts, and science and human values; and complete distribution requirements in laboratory science, foreign language, non-Western culture, and creative expression in the arts.

Special: Skidmore offers cross-registration with the Hudson-Mohawk Consortium, individually designed internships, various study-abroad programs, a Washington semester in conjunction with American University, dual and student-designed majors, credit for life and experience, and pass/fail options, as well as a nondegree study program for senior citizens. There are cooperative programs in engineering with Dartmouth College and Clarkson University, in business with Clarkson and Rensselaer Polytechnic Institute, in education with Union College, and in law with the Benjamin Cardozo Law School. There is a 6-week internship period available at the end of the spring term. There are 9 national honor societies on campus, including Phi Beta Kappa.

Faculty/Classroom: Sixty-nine percent of faculty are male; 31%, female. Ten percent teach undergraduates and 90% both teach and do research. No introductory courses are taught by graduate students. The average class size in a laboratory is 16 and in a regular course offering, 19.

Admissions: About 64% of the 1993-94 applicants were accepted. The SAT scores for the 1993-94 freshman class were as follows: Verbal—29% below 500, 46% between 500 and 599, 24% between 600 and 700, and 2% above 700; Math—10% below 500, 40% between 500 and 599, 40% between 600 and 700, and 8% above 700. About 59% of the current freshmen were in the top fifth of their class; 88% were in the top two fifths. Ten freshmen graduated first in their class.

Requirements: The SAT I or ACT is required. Skidmore recommends SAT II: Subject tests in writing, a foreign language, and 1 other subject. Applicants must be graduates of an accredited secondary school or have the GED. They must complete 16 academic units, including 4 years of English, 2 or more of laboratory science, and 3 each of mathematics, social science, and a foreign language. An essay is required and interviews are recommended. Applicants to creative arts programs may want to submit representations of their work. AP and CLEP credits are accepted. Important factors used in the admissions decision are advanced placement or honor courses, recommendations by school officials, evidence of special talent, leadership record, and extracurricular activities record.

Procedure: Freshmen are admitted fall and spring. Entrance exams should be taken by December of the senior year. Early decision applications should be filed by December 1; regular applications, by February 1 for fall entry and November 15 for spring entry, along with an application fee of $40. Notification of early decision is sent January 1; regular decision, April 1. There are early decision, early admissions, and deferred admissions plans. About 240 early decision candidates were accepted for the 1993-94 class. A waiting list is an active part of the admissions procedure, with about 8% of applicants on the list.

Transfer: About 30 transfer students enrolled in 1993-94. Applicants must submit SAT I or ACT scores, a high school transcript, and official transcripts from all colleges attended. A dean's report and 2 recommendations by professors are also required. A total of 60 credits out of 120 must be completed at Skidmore.

Visiting: There are regularly scheduled orientations for prospective students, including full open-house day programs. There are guides for informal visits and visitors may sit in on classes and stay overnight at the school. To arrange for a visit, contact the Admissions Office Overnight Host Coordinator at (518) 581-7400, ext 2721.

Financial Aid: In 1993-94, 50% of all students received some form of financial aid. About 35% of freshmen and 37% of continuing students received need-based aid. The average freshman award was $16,900. Of that total, scholarships or need-based grants averaged $13,100 ($20,500 maximum); loans averaged $2600 (maximum); and work contracts averaged $1200 (maximum). Forty-seven percent of undergraduate students work part-time. Average earnings from campus work for the school year are $850. The average financial indebtedness of the 1992-93 graduate was $12,500. Skidmore is a member of CSS. The FAF, the college's own financial statement, and the FAFSA are required. The deadline for financial aid applications is February 1.

International Students: There are currently 57 international students enrolled. The school actively recruits these students. They must take the TOEFL and achieve a minimum score of 580. The student must also take the SAT I or the ACT.

Computers: The college provides computer facilities for student use. The mainframe is a DEC VAX 11/780. There are 200 microcomputers available in 3 major computing clusters, with networking capabilities throughout campus and through Internet and Bitnet. A computer graphics laboratory and teaching facility is available. A cluster of 9 Sun computers provides the backbone for time-shared computing, providing access to E-mail, electronic bulletin boards, and compilers. Statistical analysis software, free services, and technical support are provided. Students may connect to central computing facilities through personal computers via modem capabilities in each dormitory room. All students may access the system. It may be used 24 hours per day. There are no time limits on using the system and no fees.

Graduates: In 1992-93, 531 bachelor's degrees were awarded. The most popular majors among graduates were business (15%), English (14%), and government (12%). Within an average freshman class, 75% graduate in 4 years, 80% in 5 years, and 81% in 6 years. Some 65 companies recruited on campus in 1992-93. In the 1992 graduating class, 26% of graduates were enrolled in graduate school within 6 months of graduation; 64% had found employment.

Admissions Contact: Mary Lou Bates, Director of Admissions.

SOUTHAMPTON CAMPUS OF LONG ISLAND UNIVERSITY
(See Long Island University/Southampton Campus)

STATE UNIVERSITY OF NEW YORK

The State University of New York, established in 1948, is 1 of 2 public university systems in New York. It is governed by a board of trustees, whose chief administrator is the chancellor. The primary goals of the university are teaching, research, and public service. Its main priorities are to educate the largest number of people possible at the highest level, including educationally and financially disadvantaged groups; to provide students with enhanced educational skills and techniques; and to improve the quality of life for all New Yorkers. With 64 campuses located across the state, the university's total enrollment in a recent year reached 404,065 students and its faculty numbered 27,095 members. Altogether, the university offers 1,504 baccalaureate, 499 master's, and 307 doctoral programs. Profiles of the 20 4-year campuses are included in this chapter in alphabetical order with other New York colleges and universities.

STATE UNIVERSITY OF NEW YORK AT ALBANY
D-3
Albany, NY 12222   **(518) 442-5435**

Full-time: 5500 men, 5300 women	Faculty: 671; I, av$
Part-time: 530 men, 670 women	Ph.D.s: 95%
Graduate: 2110 men, 2960 women	Student/Faculty: 16 to 1
Year: semesters, summer session	Tuition: $2884 ($6784)
Application Deadline: February 15	Room & Board: $4136
Freshman Class: n/av	
SAT I or ACT: required	**VERY COMPETITIVE**

The State University of New York at Albany, established in 1844, is a public institution conferring undergraduate degrees in humanities and fine arts, science and mathematics, social and behavioral sciences, business, and social welfare. There are 5 undergraduate and 3

graduate schools. In addition to regional accreditation, SUNY at Albany has baccalaureate program accreditation with AACSB and CSWE. The 2 libraries contain 1.3 million volumes, 6100 microform items, and 5000 audiovisual forms, and subscribe to 7000 periodicals. Computerized library sources and services include the card catalog, interlibrary loans, and database searching. Special learning facilities include a learning resource center, an art gallery, a radio station, a linear accelerator, a highly sophisticated weather data system, and a national lightning detection system. The 515-acre campus is in a suburban area. Including residence halls, there are 90 buildings on campus.

Student Life: About 97% of undergraduates are from New York. Students come from 19 states, 25 foreign countries, and Canada. Sixty-nine percent are white. The average age of freshmen is 18; all undergraduates, 21. Ten percent drop out by the end of their first year; 66% remain to graduate.

Housing: A total of 6373 students can be accommodated in college housing. College-sponsored living facilities include single-sex and coed dormitories and on-campus apartments. In addition, there are honors houses and special interest houses. On-campus housing is guaranteed for the freshman year only, is available on a first-come, first-served basis, and is available on a lottery system for upperclassmen. Fifty percent of students live on campus. Alcohol is not permitted. Upperclassmen may keep cars on campus.

Activities: About 20% of men belong to 4 local and 13 national fraternities; about 10% of women belong to 6 local and 4 national sororities. There are 160 groups on campus, including band, cheerleading, chess, chorale, computers, dance, drama, ethnic, honors, international, literary magazine, newspaper, orchestra, photography, political, professional, radio and TV, religious, social, social service, student government, and yearbook. Popular campus events include the week-long Rites of Spring and outdoor concerts.

Sports: There are 11 intercollegiate sports for men and 10 for women, and 13 intramural sports for men and 9 for women. Athletic and recreation facilities include a gymnasium with an Olympic-size pool; an ancillary gymnasium with a quarter-mile track; football, softball, soccer, and practice fields; and a 5000-seat recreation and convocation center.

Disabled Students: The entire campus is accessible to disabled students. The following facilities are available: wheelchair ramps, elevators, special parking, specially equipped rest rooms, lowered drinking fountains, and lowered telephones.

Services: In addition to many counseling and information services, tutoring is available in every subject. In addition, there is remedial math, reading, and writing.

Campus Safety and Security: Campus safety and security measures include escort service, shuttle buses, pamphlets, posters, and films, and emergency telephones.

Programs of Study: SUNY at Albany awards the B.A. and B.S. degrees. Master's and doctoral degrees also are awarded. Bachelor's degrees are awarded in BIOLOGICAL SCIENCE (biochemistry, biology/biological science, and molecular biology), BUSINESS (accounting and business administration and management), COMMUNICATIONS AND THE ARTS (Chinese, communications, English, fine arts, French, German, Greek, Hebrew, Italian, Latin, linguistics, music, Portuguese, Russian, and Spanish), COMPUTER AND PHYSICAL SCIENCE (applied mathematics, chemistry, computer science, geology, information sciences and systems, mathematics, and physics), EDUCATION (elementary, foreign languages, middle school, music, science, secondary, special, and teaching English as a second language/foreign language), HEALTH PROFESSIONS (medical laboratory technology, predentistry, and premedicine), SOCIAL SCIENCE (African American studies, African studies, anthropology, Caribbean studies, classical/ancient civilization, criminal justice, economics, geography, history, Latin American studies, medieval studies, philosophy, political science/government, prelaw, psychology, religion, social work, sociology, and women's studies). Business and accounting, political science, and criminal justice are the strongest academically. Psychology, English, and political science have the largest enrollments.

Required: To graduate, students must complete a total of 120 credits with a 2.0 GPA, including 30 to 36 credits required in the major for a B.A. degree and 30 to 42 credits for a B.S. degree. B.A. degree candidates must complete 90 credits in liberal arts courses and B.S. candidates must complete 60. All students must complete a writing requirement and a general education core consisting of 6 credits each in literature and fine arts, natural science, social science, symbolics, values, and world cultures.

Special: Cross-registration is available with Rensselaer Polytechnic Institute, Albany Law School, and Union, Siena, and Russell Sage Colleges. Internships may by arranged with state government agencies and private organizations. Study abroad in many countries, work-study programs, B.A.-B.S. degrees in biology, mathematics, and economics, and a 3–2 engineering degree with Rensselaer Polytechnic Institute and Clarkson University are offered. Dual and student-designed majors, nondegree study, and pass/fail grading options are available. There is a freshman honors program on campus, as well as 14 national honor societies, including Phi Beta Kappa. Twenty departments have honors programs.

Faculty/Classroom: Seventy-nine percent of faculty are male; 21%, female. Ninety-eight percent teach undergraduates and 75% do research. Graduate students teach 10% of introductory courses. The average class size in an introductory lecture is 60; in a laboratory, 20; and in a regular course offering, 30.

Requirements: The SAT I or ACT is required. Applicants must be graduates of an accredited secondary school or have a GED. Eighteen academic credits are required, including 2 to 3 units of mathematics and 2 units of laboratory sciences. Foreign language study is also recommended. AP credits are accepted. Important factors used in the admissions decision are advanced placement or honor courses, evidence of special talent, recommendations by school officials, leadership record, and extracurricular activities record.

Procedure: Freshmen are admitted to all sessions. Applications should be filed by February 15 for fall entry, November 15 for spring entry, and February 15 for summer entry, along with an application fee of $25. Notification is sent on a rolling basis. There is an early admissions plan. A waiting list is an active part of the admissions procedure.

Transfer: About 1025 transfer students enrolled in an earlier year. Applicants must have a minimum GPA of C. Students will be admitted to programs according to availability of space and degree of competitiveness. SAT I or ACT requirements will be determined upon application. A total of 30 credits out of 120 must be completed at SUNY at Albany.

Visiting: There are regularly scheduled orientations for prospective students. There are guides for informal visits and visitors may sit in on classes. To arrange for a visit, contact the Undergraduate Admissions Office at (518) 442-5435.

Financial Aid: In a recent year, 76% of all freshmen and 74% of continuing students received some form of financial aid. SUNY at Albany is a member of CSS. The FAF is required. The deadline for financial aid applications is April 25.

International Students: There are currently 700 international students enrolled. The school actively recruits these students. They must take the TOEFL.

Computers: The college provides computer facilities for student use. The mainframe is an IBM 3081, a Sperry 7000, and a VAX minicomputer and VAX cluster. The Computing Services Center networks provide electronic mail facilities and contact with computers throughout the world. Computer access rooms, terminals in residence halls, as well as phone hookups provide 24-hour access to mainframe computing facilities. All students may access the system. There are no time limits on using the system and no fees.

Graduates: In a recent year, 2534 bachelor's degrees were awarded. The most popular majors among graduates were psychology (15%), English (12%), and business administration (11%). Within an average freshman class, 1% graduate in 3 years, 56% in 4 years, 66% in 5 years, and 68% in 6 years. Some 100 companies recruited on campus in a recent year.

Admissions Contact: Dr. Micheleen Tredwell, Director of Admissions.

STATE UNIVERSITY OF NEW YORK AT BINGHAMTON
C-4

Binghamton, NY 13901–6001 (607) 777-2171

Full-time: 3875 men, 4669 women	Faculty: 492; I, av$
Part-time: 322 men, 349 women	Ph.D.s: 84%
Graduate: 1473 men, 1309 women	Student/Faculty: 17 to 1
Year: semesters, summer session	Tuition: $2961 ($6861)
Application Deadline: January 15	Room & Board: $4960
Freshman Class: 14,463 applied, 6166 accepted, 1764 enrolled	
SAT I Verbal/Math: 530/620	ACT: 26 HIGHLY COMPETITIVE

State University of New York at Binghamton, founded in 1946, is part of the State University of New York System. The university offers programs through the Harpur College of Arts and Sciences, the School of Education and Human Development, the Decker School of Nursing, the School of Management, and the Thomas J. Watson School of Engineering and Applied Science. There are 5 undergraduate and 5 graduate schools. In addition to regional accreditation, Binghamton has baccalaureate program accreditation with AACSB, ABET, and NLN. The 6 libraries contain 1,471,424 volumes, 1,321,894 microform items, and 81,569 audiovisual forms, and subscribe to 9595 periodicals. Computerized library sources and services include the card catalog, interlibrary loans, and database searching. Special learning facilities include a learning resource center, art gallery, radio station, TV station, and a nature preserve, and a four-climate greenhouse. The 606-acre campus is in a suburban area 1 mile west of Binghamton. Including residence halls, there are 61 buildings on campus.

Student Life: About 93% of undergraduates are from New York. Students come from 31 states, 35 foreign countries, and Canada. Eighty-seven percent are from public schools; 13% from private. Seventy-seven percent are white; 11% Asian American. Thirty-six percent are Catholic; 28% Jewish; 21% Protestant. The average age of freshmen is 18; all undergraduates, 21. Seven percent drop out by the end of their first year; 78% remain to graduate.

Housing: A total of 5087 students can be accommodated in college housing. College-sponsored living facilities include coed dormitories, on-campus apartments, off-campus apartments, and married-student housing. In addition there are language houses and special interest houses. On-campus housing is guaranteed for all 4 years. Fifty-seven percent of students live on campus; of those, 95% remain on campus on weekends. All students may keep cars on campus.

Activities: About 15% of men belong to 4 local and 17 national fraternities; about 15% of women belong to 3 local and 11 national sororities. There are 150 groups on campus, including art, band, cheerleading, chess, choir, chorale, chorus, computers, dance, drama, ethnic, film, gay, honors, international, jazz band, literary magazine, musical theater, newspaper, orchestra, pep band, photography, political, professional, radio and TV, religious, social, social service, student government, symphony, and yearbook. Popular campus events include Martin Luther King, Jr. Day, Spring Carnival, Fall Fest, theater productions, and concerts.

Sports: There are 10 intercollegiate sports for men and 9 for women, and 20 intramural sports for men and 18 for women. Athletic and recreation facilities include 2 gymnasiums with swimming pools, an indoor track, dance and karate studios, basketball, volleyball, racquetball and tennis courts, a weight room, batting and driving cages, a fitness trail, a cross-country course, a new fitness center, a 400-meter track and soccer complex, plus many playing fields. The larger gymnasium seats 2600.

Disabled Students: Ninety percent of the campus is accessible to disabled students. The following facilities are available: wheelchair ramps, elevators, special parking, specially equipped rest rooms, special class scheduling, lowered drinking fountains, and lowered telephones.

Services: In addition to many counseling and information services, tutoring is available in most subjects. In addition, there is a reader service for the blind.

Campus Safety and Security: Campus safety and security measures include 24-hour foot and vehicle patrol, self defense education, escort service, and shuttle buses. In addition, there are informal discussions, pamphlets, posters, and films, emergency telephones, lighted pathways and sidewalks, and public safety officers, and monitored entrance to campus with proper identification between 12 midnight and 6 A.M.

Programs of Study: Binghamton awards the B.A., B.S., B.F.A., and B.Mus. degrees. Master's and doctoral degrees also are awarded. Bachelor's degrees are awarded in BIOLOGICAL SCIENCE (biochemistry and biology/biological science), BUSINESS (accounting and business administration and management), COMMUNICATIONS AND THE ARTS (Arabic, art, art history and appreciation, classics, comparative literature, dramatic arts, English, film arts, fine arts, French, German, Hebrew, Italian, music, and Spanish), COMPUTER AND PHYSICAL SCIENCE (chemistry, computer science, geology, geophysics and seismology, mathematics, and physics), ENGINEERING AND ENVIRONMENTAL DESIGN (electrical/electronics engineering and mechanical engineering), HEALTH PROFESSIONS (nursing), SOCIAL SCIENCE (African American studies, anthropology, Caribbean studies, classical/ancient civilization, economics, geography, history, human ecology, Judaic studies, Latin American studies, medieval studies, philosophy, political science/government, psychobiology, psychology, social science, and sociology). Psychology, English, management, accounting, biology, history, and political science have the largest enrollments.

Required: In order to graduate, all students must complete 120 to 132 total credit hours, with 36 to 72 in the major, and a minimum GPA of 2.0. Most schools require courses in humanities, social science, science/mathematics, writing, and physical education. Other requirements vary by school.

Special: The University offers cross-registration with Broome Community and Empire State Colleges, internships with nonprofit agencies in Albany and in Washington, D.C. through the political science department, and study abroad in 100 countries. A Washington semester, on- and off-campus work-study programs, B.A.-B.S. degrees in 28 departments in arts and sciences and in the professional schools, and dual and student-designed majors are available. The 3–2 engineering degree is possible with SUNY at Buffalo, SUNY at Stony Brook, Columbia University, Rochester Institute of Technology, University of Rochester, and Clarkson University. Independent study and pass/fail options are offered. There are 8 national honor societies on campus, including Phi Beta Kappa. Thirty-two departments have honors programs.

Faculty/Classroom: Seventy-four percent of faculty are male; 26%, female. All teach undergraduates, 80% do research, and 80% do both. Graduate students teach 10% of introductory courses.

Admissions: About 43% of the 1993–94 applicants were accepted. The SAT scores for the 1993–94 freshman class were as follows: Verbal—29% below 500, 51% between 500 and 599, 18% between 600 and 700, and 2% above 700; Math—6% below 500, 32% between 500 and 599, 49% between 600 and 700, and 13% above 700. The ACT scores were 5% below 22, 39% between 22 and 25, 45% between 26 and 29, and 11% above 30. About 91% of the current freshmen were in the top fifth of their class; 99% were in the top two fifths. About 23 freshmen graduated first in their class.

Requirements: The SAT I or ACT is required. Applicants must be graduates of an accredited secondary school or have a GED certificate, and complete 16 academic credits. These include 4 units of English, 2 1/2 of mathematics, 2 each of science and social studies, and 3 units of 1 foreign language or 2 units each of 2 foreign languages. Students may submit slides of artwork, request an audition for music, prepare a videotape for dance or theater, or share athletic achievements. An essay is required. AP and CLEP credits are accepted. Important factors used in the admissions decision are advanced placement or honor courses, extracurricular activities record, evidence of special talent, leadership record, and personality and intangible qualities.

Procedure: Freshmen are admitted fall and spring. Entrance exams should be taken in the spring of the junior year or the fall of the senior year. Early decision applications should be filed by November 1; regular applications, by January 15 for fall entry and November 15 for spring entry, along with an application fee of $25. Notification of early decision is sent December 31; regular decision, March 15. There are early decision, early admissions, and deferred admissions plans. About 147 early decision candidates were accepted for the 1993–94 class. A waiting list is an active part of the admissions procedure.

Transfer: About 800 transfer students enrolled in 1993–94. Transfer students must submit college transcripts. Transfer students who wish to transfer after their first year of college must also submit their high school transcripts. An associate degree or equivalent is required for some programs. The SAT I and an interview are recommended, but not required. A total of 30 credits out of 120 to 132 must be completed at Binghamton.

Visiting: There are regularly scheduled orientations for prospective students. An information session and a tour of campus may be scheduled a week in advance of a visit. Visitors may sit in on classes. To arrange for a visit, contact the Office of Undergraduate Admissions at (607) 777-2171.

Financial Aid: In 1993–94, 92% of all current freshmen and 56% of continuing students received some form of financial aid. About 53% of freshmen and 48% of continuing students received need-based aid. The average freshman award was $4120. Of that total, scholarships or need-based grants averaged $3802 ($7105 maximum); loans averaged $1284 ($2625 maximum); and work contracts averaged $899 ($2200 maximum). Ten percent of undergraduate students work part-time. Average earnings from campus work for the school year are $850. Binghamton is a member of CSS. The FAFSA financial statement is required. The deadline for financial aid applications is February 15.

International Students: There are currently 536 international students enrolled. The school actively recruits these students. They must take the TOEFL and achieve a minimum score of 550. The TOEFL replaces the SAT I or ACT for non-native speakers of English.

Computers: The college provides computer facilities for student use. The mainframes are an IBM 9000/500 and 4831, and 2 DEC VAX 6440s. Each student is given a computer account. Terminals and microcomputers are available in libraries, some academic areas, and some residential halls. All students may access the system. It may be used 24 hours per day, and the limit on the amount of time each student may access the system varies by course. There are no fees.

Graduates: In 1992–93, 2169 bachelor's degrees were awarded. The most popular majors among graduates were management/accounting (13%), English and English literature (12%), and psychology (10%). Within an average freshman class, 68% graduate in 4 years and 77% in 5 years. Some 175 companies recruited on campus in 1992–93.

Admissions Contact: Geoffrey D. Gould, Director of Undergraduate Admissions.

STATE UNIVERSITY OF NEW YORK AT BUFFALO

A-3

Buffalo, NY 14260 (716) 645-6136

Full-time: 8066 men, 5897 women
Part-time: 1516 men, 1608 women
Graduate: 4512 men, 4036 women
Year: semesters, summer session
Application Deadline: January 5
Freshman Class: 15,039 applied, 9649 accepted, 3087 enrolled
SAT I Verbal/Math: 480/575

Faculty: 1000; IIA, av$
Ph.D.s: 97%
Student/Faculty: 14 to 1
Tuition: $3074 ($6974)
Room & Board: $4822

ACT: 24   VERY COMPETITIVE

The State University of New York at Buffalo, established in 1846, is a public institution offering undergraduate degrees in liberal arts and sciences, architecture and planning, engineering, health-related professions, medicine, and management. There are 11 undergraduate and 16 graduate schools. In addition to regional accreditation, UB has baccalaureate program accreditation with AACSB, ABET, ACPE, ADA, APTA, ASLA, CAHEA, CSWE, NAAB, NASAD, NASM, and NLN. The 7 libraries contain 2,724,222 volumes, 4,093,112 microform items, and 116,700 audiovisual forms, and subscribe to 23,292 periodicals. Computerized library sources and services include the card catalog, interlibrary loans, and database searching. Special learning facilities include a learning resource center, art gallery, radio station, anthropology research museum, observatory, concert hall, theater, nature preserve, and nuclear reactor. The 1350-acre campus is in a suburban area 3 miles north of Buffalo. Including residence halls, there are 78 buildings on campus.

Student Life: About 97% of undergraduates are from New York. Students come from 34 states, 49 foreign countries, and Canada. Seventy-eight percent are white. The average age of freshmen is 18; all undergraduates, 22. Three percent drop out by the end of their first year; 55% remain to graduate.

Housing: A total of 5200 students can be accommodated in college housing. College-sponsored living facilities include coed dormitories. In addition there are honors houses, special-interest houses, and freshman-only and transfer-only residence halls. On-campus housing is guaranteed for the freshman year only and is available on a first-come, first-served basis thereafter. Alcohol is not permitted. All students may keep cars on campus.

Activities: About 7% of students belong to 4 local and 18 national fraternities and 3 local and 6 national sororities. There are 150 groups on campus, including art, band, cheerleading, chess, choir, chorale, chorus, computers, dance, drama, ethnic, film, gay, honors, international, jazz band, literary magazine, musical theater, newspaper, opera, orchestra, pep band, photography, political, professional, radio and TV, religious, social, social service, student government, symphony, and yearbook. Popular campus events include Fall Fest, September Welcome, Spring Fest, and Greek Week.

Sports: There are 9 intercollegiate sports for men and 8 for women, and 25 intramural sports for men and 21 for women. Athletic and recreation facilities include racquetball, squash, tennis, basketball, volleyball, badminton, and handball courts; baseball, soccer, hockey, and multipurpose fields; a football, track, and field stadium; an indoor jogging track; an Olympic-size pool and diving well; a triple gymnasium; weight-training and wrestling rooms; a gymnastics arena; and dance studios.

Disabled Students: Ninety-five percent of the campus is accessible to disabled students. The following facilities are available: wheelchair ramps, elevators, special parking, specially equipped rest rooms, lowered drinking fountains, and lowered telephones. Additional services include pool accessibility, wheelchair vans for transport, and specially equipped rooms in residence halls.

Services: In addition to many counseling and information services, tutoring is available in most subjects. There is also a reader service for the blind, and remedial math, reading, and writing.

Campus Safety and Security: Campus safety and security measures include 24-hour foot and vehicle patrol, self-defense education, escort service, and shuttle buses. In addition, there are informal discussions, pamphlets, posters, films, emergency telephones, and lighted pathways and sidewalks.

Programs of Study: UB awards the B.A., B.S., B.F.A., B.P.S., B.S.Pharm., and Mus.B. degrees. Master's and doctoral degrees also are awarded. Bachelor's degrees are awarded in BIOLOGICAL SCIENCE (biochemistry, biology/biological science, and biophysics), BUSINESS (accounting and business administration and management), COMMUNICATIONS AND THE ARTS (art history and appreciation, communications, design, dramatic arts, English, fine arts, French, German, Italian, linguistics, media arts, music, music performance, Spanish, and studio art), COMPUTER AND PHYSICAL SCIENCE (chemistry, computer science, geology, mathematics, physics, and statistics), EDUCATION (foreign languages, music, science, and secondary), ENGINEERING AND ENVIRONMENTAL DESIGN (aeronautical engineering, architectural engineering, chemical engineering, civil engineering, electrical/electronics engineering, engineer-

ing physics, environmental design, industrial engineering, and mechanical engineering), HEALTH PROFESSIONS (medical laboratory technology, nuclear medical technology, nursing, occupational therapy, pharmacy, physical therapy, and speech pathology/audiology), SOCIAL SCIENCE (African American studies, anthropology, community services, economics, geography, history, international relations, philosophy, physical fitness/movement, political science/government, psychology, social science, sociology, urban studies, and women's studies). Business administration, engineering, and psychology have the largest enrollments.

Required: In order to graduate, students must complete 128 semester hours with a minimum GPA of 2.0. General education requirements include writing and library skills, mathematics or computer science, and courses in world civilization, literature, and social and natural sciences.

Special: Students may cross-register with the Western New York consortium. Internships are available. Students may study abroad in 13 countries. UB offers a Washington semester, B.A.-B.S. degrees, dual and student-designed and interdisciplinary majors, including biochemical pharmacology and medicinal chemistry, nondegree study, and credit for military experience. A 3–2 engineering degree can be pursued. Students may choose a successful/unsuccessful (S/U) grading option for selected courses. There is an early assurance of admission program to medical school for students who have completed 3 semesters with a GPA of 3.5. There is a freshman honors program on campus, as well as 17 national honor societies, including Phi Beta Kappa.

Faculty/Classroom: Seventy-seven percent of faculty are male; 23%, female. Seventy-three percent teach undergraduates, 100% do research, and 73% do both. The average class size in a laboratory is 15 and in a regular course offering, 20.

Admissions: About 64% of the 1993–94 applicants were accepted. The SAT scores for the 1993–94 freshman class were as follows: Verbal—59% below 500, 33% between 500 and 599, 7% between 600 and 700, and 1% above 700; Math—17% below 500, 44% between 500 and 599, 31% between 600 and 700, and 8% above 700. About 50% of the current freshmen were in the top fifth of their class; 91% were in the top two fifths. There were 14 National Merit finalists.

Requirements: The SAT I or ACT is required. Applicants must be graduates of an accredited secondary school or have a GED. Applicants must submit a portfolio; music applicants must audition. AP and CLEP credits are accepted. Advanced placement or honor courses is an important factor used in the admission decision.

Procedure: Freshmen are admitted in the fall and spring. Entrance exams should be taken during the spring of the junior year or the fall of the senior year. Applications should be filed by January 5 for fall entry and December 1 for spring entry, along with an application fee of $25. Notification is sent February 15. There is an early admissions plan.

Transfer: About 1960 transfer students enrolled in 1993–94. Applicants must have a minimum GPA of 2.5 with 24 semester hours completed at time of application. Students with an associate degree will be considered with a GPA of 2.0 or higher. Students with fewer than 24 semester hours will be evaluated according to both college and high school work, and SAT I or ACT scores. At least 32 credits out of 128 must be completed at UB.

Visiting: There are regularly scheduled orientations for prospective students, consisting of information sessions and tours. To arrange for a visit, contact the Office of Admissions at (716) 645-6900.

Financial Aid: In 1993–94 60% of all students received need-based aid. The average freshman award was $4440. Of that total, scholarships or need-based grants averaged $1337 ($4800 maximum); loans averaged $2625 (maximum); and work contracts averaged $478 ($1000 maximum). Eighty percent of undergraduate students work part-time. Average earnings from campus work for the school year are $1200. The average financial indebtedness of the 1992–93 graduate was $10,000. The FAFSA financial statement is required. The deadline for financial aid applications is April 1.

International Students: There are currently 1710 international students enrolled. They must take the TOEFL and achieve a minimum score of 550 and must also take the SAT I or the ACT.

Computers: The college provides computer facilities for student use. The mainframes are an IBM 3084QX, a DEC VAX 8800, 8650, and 6520, and a Solbourne 5/803 (UNIX). Students have access through 300 public terminals and 450 microcomputers and workstations. Dial-up access is also available. All students may access the system anytime. There are no time limits on using the system. The fees are $25 per year.

Graduates: In 1992–93, 3225 bachelor's degrees were awarded. The most popular majors among graduates were business administration (13%), social science interdisciplinary (11%), and psychology (8%). Within an average freshman class, 28% graduate in 4 years, 50% in 5 years, and 55% in 6 years. Some 350 companies recruited on campus in 1992–93.

Admissions Contact: Kevin Durkin, Director of Admissions.

STATE UNIVERSITY OF NEW YORK AT STONY BROOK

Stony Brook, NY 11794   **(516) 632-6866**

Full-time: 4875 men, 4869 women	Faculty: 1284; I, av$
Part-time: 600 men, 751 women	Ph.D.s: 95%
Graduate: 2883 men, 3227 women	Student/Faculty: 8 to 1
Year: semesters, summer session	Tuition: $2946 ($6846)
Application Deadline: July 15	Room & Board: $4712
Freshman Class: 12,512 applied, 6969 accepted, 1724 enrolled	
SAT I Verbal/Math: 469/537	**VERY COMPETITIVE**

The State University of New York at Stony Brook, founded in 1957, offers undergraduate and graduate degrees in arts and sciences, engineering and applied sciences, management and policy, nursing, health technology and management, and social welfare. There are 6 undergraduate and 9 graduate schools. In addition to regional accreditation, Stony Brook has baccalaureate program accreditation with ABET, APTA, CAHEA, CSWE, and NLN. The 7 libraries contain 1,807,481 volumes and 3,073,549 microform items. Special learning facilities include an art gallery, radio station, the Museum of Long Island Natural Sciences, and the Fine Arts Center, which includes a 1100-seat theater, a 400-seat recital hall, and 3 experimental theaters. The 1100-acre campus is in a suburban area on Long Island, 60 miles from New York City. Including residence halls, there are 113 buildings on campus.

Student Life: About 96% of undergraduates are from New York. Students come from 30 states, 90 foreign countries, and Canada. Fifty-one percent are white; 17% Asian American. Forty-three percent are Catholic; 19% claim no religious affiliation; 14% Protestant. The average age of freshmen is 19; all undergraduates, 21. Seventeen percent drop out by the end of their first year; 56% remain to graduate.

Housing: A total of 7430 students can be accommodated in college housing. College-sponsored living facilities include coed dormitories, on-campus apartments, and married-student housing. In addition, there are special- interest houses and and 5 living/learning centers that integrate academic experience with living environments. On-campus housing is guaranteed for all 4 years. Fifty-three percent of students commute. Alcohol is not permitted. Upperclassmen may keep cars on campus.

Activities: There are 3 local and 9 national fraternities and 3 local and 8 national sororities. There are 140 groups on campus, including band, cheerleading, chorale, drama, ethnic, film, international, literary magazine, newspaper, orchestra, political, radio and TV, religious, student government, and yearbook. Popular campus events include Fall Fest, Homecoming Weekend, Opening Week Activities, and Caribbean Weekend.

Sports: There are 11 intercollegiate sports for men and 9 for women, and 50 intramural sports for men and 50 for women. Athletic and recreation facilities include a gymnasium complex housing a swimming pool, 4 squash and 4 racquetball courts, a dance studio, and exercise and Universal gym rooms. There are also 18 tennis courts, a 400-meter track, 2 sand volleyball courts, 2 outdoor basketball courts, and separate fields for baseball, soccer, football, lacrosse, and intramural football. An additional facility contains a 5000-seat arena, an indoor track, and a squash court. The stadium seats 3000, and the indoor gymnasium seats 1900.

Disabled Students: Seventy-five percent of the campus is accessible to disabled students. The following facilities are available: wheelchair ramps, special parking, specially equipped rest rooms, lowered drinking fountains, lowered telephones, automatic door openers, and specially equipped living accommodations.

Services: There is remedial math and writing.

Campus Safety and Security: Campus safety and security measures include 24-hour foot and vehicle patrol, shuttle buses, pamphlets, posters, films, and emergency telephones. In addition, there are lighted pathways and sidewalks.

Programs of Study: Stony Brook awards the B.A., B.S., and B.E. degrees. Master's and doctoral degrees also are awarded. Bachelor's degrees are awarded in BIOLOGICAL SCIENCE (biochemistry and biology/biological science), BUSINESS (business administration and management), COMMUNICATIONS AND THE ARTS (art history and appreciation, comparative literature, English, French, German, Italian, linguistics, music, Russian, Spanish, and studio art), COMPUTER AND PHYSICAL SCIENCE (applied mathematics, astronomy, atmospheric sciences and meteorology, chemistry, computer science, earth science, geology, information sciences and systems, mathematics, physics, and planetary and space science), ENGINEERING AND ENVIRONMENTAL DESIGN (electrical/electronics engineering, engineering and applied science, and mechanical engineering), HEALTH PROFESSIONS (medical laboratory technology, nursing, physical therapy, and physician's assistant), SOCIAL SCIENCE (African studies, anthropology, economics, history, humanities, liberal arts/general studies, philosophy, political science/government, psy-

chology, religion, social science, social work, and sociology). Business management, physical therapy, biology, English, mathematics, biochemistry, clinical psychology, physics, computer science, physical anthropology, philosophy, chemistry, and electrical engineering are the strongest academically. Psychology, biology, multidisciplinary studies, English, social sciences, and electrical engineering have the largest enrollments.

Required: To graduate, students must have a minimum 2.0 GPA. B.A. and B.S. degree candidates need a total of 120 credit hours, B.E. degree candidates, 128. The required number of hours in the major varies. At least 39 credits must be earned in upper-division courses. Students must take 13 courses to satisfy the 11 general education requirements. These cover writing and quantitative reasoning skills, literary and philosophic analysis, exposure to the arts, disciplinary diversity, the interrelationship of science and society, and three culminating multicultural requirements. Arts and sciences majors must fulfill a foreign language requirement, unless they completed the requirement through advanced high-school study. Other requirements vary by school.

Special: Cross-registration may be arranged through the Long Island Regional Advisory Council for Higher Education. The college offers a Washington semester and internships with a variety of government, legal, and social agencies, with hospitals and clinics, and in business and industry. Study abroad in 7 countries, B.A.-B.S. degrees in chemistry, earth and space science, and psychology, and pass/fail options are available. The Federated Learning Communities enables students to concentrate on a major issue each year, and the URECA Program allows undergraduates to work with faculty on research and creative projects. There is a freshman honors program on campus, as well as 4 national honor societies, including Phi Beta Kappa. Twenty-two departments have honors programs.

Faculty/Classroom: Seventy-four percent of faculty are male; 26%, female. Eighty percent teach undergraduates, 90% do research, and 70% do both. Graduate students teach 40% of introductory courses. The average class size in an introductory lecture is 75; in a laboratory, 25; and in a regular course offering, 45.

Admissions: About 56% of the 1993–94 applicants were accepted. The SAT scores for the 1993–94 freshman class were as follows: Verbal—63% below 500, 31% between 500 and 599, and 6% between 600 and 700; Math—28% below 500, 45% between 500 and 599, 22% between 600 and 700, and 5% above 700. About 57% of the current freshmen were in the top fifth of their class; 87% were in the top two fifths.

Requirements: Stony Brook requires applicants to be in the upper 20% of their class. A minimum GPA of B+ is required. The SAT I is required. Applicants must be graduates of an accredited secondary school or have a GED certificate. Sixteen or 17 academic credits are required, including 4 years of English, 3 or 4 years of mathematics, 3 years each of science and social studies, and 2 years of a foreign language. SAT II: Subject tests, an essay, and an interview are recommended. AP and CLEP credits are accepted. Important factors used in the admissions decision are advanced placement or honor courses, extracurricular activities record, evidence of special talent, leadership record, and recommendations by school officials.

Procedure: Freshmen are admitted to all sessions. Entrance exams should be taken during the junior year in high school. Applications should be filed by July 15 for fall entry, along with an application fee of $25. Notification is sent on a rolling basis. There are early admissions and deferred admissions plans.

Transfer: About 1325 transfer students enrolled in 1993–94. Transfer applicants must have a minimum 2.5 GPA. An associate degree and an interview are recommended. Other requirements vary by program. After the fifty-seventh credit, at least 36 credits must be earned at Stony Brook.

Visiting: There are regularly scheduled orientations for prospective students, during which students may confer with faculty, register for classes, and take placement exams for English and mathematics. There are guides for informal visits, and visitors may sit in on classes. To arrange for a visit, contact the Admissions Office at (516) 632-6868.

Financial Aid: In 1993–94, 70% of all students received some form of financial aid. About 45% of students received need-based aid. The average freshman award was $5500. Of that total, scholarships or need-based grants averaged $2000 ($3000 maximum); loans averaged $3000 ($4000 maximum); and work contracts averaged $1200. Ten percent of undergraduate students work part-time. Average earnings from campus work for the school year are $1350. Stony Brook is a member of CSS. The FAFSA financial statement is required. The deadline for financial aid applications is March 1.

International Students: There are currently 1420 international students enrolled. They must take the TOEFL and achieve a minimum score of 550.

Computers: The college provides computer facilities for student use. The mainframes are an IBM 3090 180E and a DEC VAX 8600, 8350, and 6410. There are also IBM, Apple, and DEC-PRO 350 microcom-

puters throughout the campus. All students may access the system 24 hours per day. There are no time limits on using the system and no fees.

Graduates: In 1992–93, 2298 bachelor's degrees were awarded. The most popular majors among graduates were psychology (12%), liberal arts (12%), and social sciences (9%). Within an average freshman class, 56% graduate in 6 years. In the 1992 graduating class, 55% of all graduates were enrolled in graduate school within 6 months of graduation.

Admissions Contact: Michael J. McHale, Associate Director.

STATE UNIVERSITY OF NEW YORK COLLEGE OF ENVIRONMENTAL SCIENCE AND FORESTRY
Syracuse, NY 13210–2779

C-3

(315) 470–6600
(800) 7777-ESF (out-of-state)

Full-time: 711 men, 303 women	Faculty: 117; IIA, +$
Part-time: 107 men, 76 women	Ph.D.s: 90%
Graduate: 428 men, 246 women	Student/Faculty: 9 to 1
Year: semesters	Tuition: $2937 ($6837)
Application Deadline: open	Room & Board: $6320
Freshman Class: 750 applied, 167 accepted, 102 enrolled	
SAT I Verbal/Math: 519/584	HIGHLY COMPETITIVE +

The College of Environmental Science and Forestry, founded in 1911 and located adjacent to the campus of Syracuse University, is one of the colleges of the State University of New York, specializing in undergraduate and graduate degrees in agricultural, biological, environmental, health, and physical sciences, landscape architecture, and engineering. Students have access to the academic, cultural, and social life at Syracuse University. There is one graduate school. In addition to regional accreditation, ESF has baccalaureate program accreditation with ABET, ASLA, and SAF. The library contains 94,000 volumes. Computerized library sources and services include the card catalog, interlibrary loans, and database searching. Special learning facilities include a learning resource center, an art gallery, a radio station, and a TV station. The 12-acre campus is in Syracuse. Including residence halls, there are 7 buildings on campus.

Student Life: About 85% of undergraduates are from New York. Students come from 17 states, 5 foreign countries, and Canada. Eighty-nine percent are from public schools; 11% from private. Eighty-six percent are white; 11% foreign nationals. The average age of freshmen is 18; all undergraduates, 22. Three percent drop out by the end of their first year; 90% remain to graduate.

Housing: A total of 9000 students can be accommodated in college housing. College-sponsored living facilities include single-sex and coed dormitories, on-campus apartments, married-student housing, fraternity houses, and sorority houses. In addition, there are special interest houses, substance-free floors, quiet lifestyle floors, and a global living center. On-campus housing is guaranteed for the freshman year only, is available on a first-come, first-served basis, and is available on a lottery system for upperclassmen. Sixty percent of students live on campus; of those, 90% remain on campus on weekends. Alcohol is not permitted. Upperclassmen may keep cars on campus.

Activities: About 5% of men belong to 1 local fraternity and 27 national fraternities; about 5% of women belong to 1 local sorority and 21 national sororities. There are many groups and organizations on campus, including art, band, cheerleading, choir, chorale, chorus, computers, dance, drama, drum and bugle corps, ethnic, film, honors, international, jazz band, marching band, musical theater, newspaper, orchestra, pep band, photography, professional, radio and TV, religious, student government, symphony, and yearbook. Popular campus events include Charter Day (Homecoming), Activities Fair, December Soiree, Winter Weekend, Earth Day, and Awards Banquet.

Sports: There are 21 intercollegiate sports each for men and women, and 30 intramural sports each for men and women. Athletic and recreational facilities are contracted through Syracuse University.

Disabled Students: Ninety percent of the campus is accessible to disabled students. The following facilities are available: wheelchair ramps, elevators, special parking, specially equipped rest rooms, and lowered drinking fountains and telephones.

Services: There is a reader service for the blind and remedial math.

Campus Safety and Security: Campus safety and security measures include 24-hour foot and vehicle patrol, shuttle buses, informal discussions, pamphlets, posters, and films. In addition, there are emergency telephones and lighted pathways and sidewalks.

Programs of Study: ESF awards the B.S. and B.L.A. degrees. Associate, master's, and doctoral degrees also are awarded. Bachelor's degrees are awarded in AGRICULTURE (animal science, forest engineering, forestry and related sciences, natural resource management, plant science, and soil science), BIOLOGICAL SCIENCE (biology/biological science, botany, ecology, entomology, environmental biology, microbiology, molecular biology, plant genetics, and plant phys-

iology), COMPUTER AND PHYSICAL SCIENCE (chemistry and polymer science), EDUCATION (environmental and science), ENGINEERING AND ENVIRONMENTAL DESIGN (chemical engineering, construction management, environmental design, environmental engineering, environmental science, landscape architecture/design, paper and pulp science, paper engineering, and survey and mapping technology), HEALTH PROFESSIONS (predentistry, premedicine, and prepharmacy), SOCIAL SCIENCE (prelaw). Engineering, chemistry, and biology are the strongest programs academically. Environmental and forest biology and environmental studies have the largest enrollments.

Required: Students must complete 121 to 130 credit hours for the B.S. (160 for the B.L.A.), including 60 in the major, with a minimum 2.0 GPA. Courses in chemistry, English, mathematics, and botany are required.

Special: Cross-registration is offered with Syracuse University. Co-op programs, accelerated degrees in biology and landscape architecture, and dual options in biology and forestry are available. There is one national honor society on campus.

Faculty/Classroom: Ninety-three percent of faculty are male; 7%, female. All teach and also do research. No introductory courses are taught by graduate students. The average class size in an introductory lecture and regular course offering is 25; in a laboratory, 12.

Admissions: About 22% of the 1993–94 applicants were accepted. The SAT scores for the 1993–94 freshman class were as follows: Verbal—36% below 500, 48% between 500 and 599, 15% between 600 and 700, and 1% above 700; Math—11% below 500, 41% between 500 and 599, 41% between 600 and 700, and 7% above 700. About 77% of the current freshmen were in the top fifth of their class; 23% were in the top two fifths. There were 2 National Merit semifinalists. Four freshmen graduated first in their class.

Requirements: ESF requires applicants to be in the upper 30% of their class. A minimum grade average of 86 is required. The SAT I or ACT is required. Applicants are required to have a minimum of 4 years of mathematics and science, including chemistry, in a college preparatory curriculum. An essay is required and an interview, letters of recommendation, and a personal portfolio or resume are recommended. AP and CLEP credits are accepted. Important factors used in the admissions decision are advanced placement or honor courses, leadership record, personality, intangible qualities, extracurricular activities record, and parents or siblings attending the school.

Procedure: Freshmen are admitted in the fall. Application deadlines are open. Application fee is $25. There are early decision and deferred admissions plans. Notification of early decision is sent December 15; regular decision, on a rolling basis. About 23 early decision candidates were accepted for the 1993–94 class. A waiting list is an active part of the admissions procedure.

Transfer: Transfer requirements vary by major. Students must successfully complete prerequisite course work and should have a 2.5 or higher GPA.

Visiting: There are regularly scheduled orientations for prospective students, including a fall open house, with campus tours, faculty sessions, an activities fair, and student affairs presentations. There are guides for informal visits and visitors may sit in on classes. To arrange for a visit, contact the Admissions Office at (800) 7777-ESF.

Financial Aid: In 1993–94, 80% of all current freshmen and 85% of continuing students received some form of financial aid. About 70% of freshmen and 80% of continuing students received need-based aid. The average freshman award was $4000. Of that total, scholarships or need-based grants averaged $600; loans averaged $2600; and work contracts averaged $800. Forty-five percent of undergraduate students work part-time. Average earnings from campus work for the school year are $1200. The average financial indebtedness of the 1992–93 graduate was $3450. The college's own financial statement and the FAFSA are required. The deadline for financial aid applications is March 15.

International Students: There are currently 69 international students enrolled. They must take the TOEFL and achieve a minimum score of 550.

Computers: The college provides computer facilities for student use. The mainframes are a Macintosh and IBM. There are several laboratories at ESF and Syracuse University. All students may access the system. There are no time limits and no fees.

Graduates: In 1992–93, 319 bachelor's degrees were awarded. The most popular majors among graduates were environmental studies (26%), environmental and forestry biology (23%), and landscape architecture (12%). Within an average freshman class, 10% graduate in 3 years, 90% in 4 years, and 92% in 5 years. Some 28 companies recruited on campus in 1992–93. In the 1992 graduating class, 23% of all graduates were enrolled in graduate school within 6 months of graduation; 70% had found employment.

Admissions Contact: Dennis O. Stratton, Director of Admissions and Inter-Institutional Relations.

STATE UNIVERSITY OF NEW YORK
COLLEGE AT BROCKPORT

B-3

Brockport, NY 14420-2915   (716) 395-2751

Full-time: 2685 men, 3073 women	Faculty: 275; IIA, av$
Part-time: 545 men, 818 women	Ph.D.s: 81%
Graduate: 654 men, 1231 women	Student/Faculty: 21 to 1
Year: semesters, summer session	Tuition: $2940 ($6840)
Application Deadline: March 1	Room & Board: $4280
Freshman Class: 7291 applied, 3562 accepted, 987 enrolled	
SAT I: 449/504	ACT: 22 COMPETITIVE +

The State University of New York/College at Brockport, established in 1867, is a public institution offering 39 undergraduate programs in liberal arts, sciences, business, and teacher preparation. There are 4 undergraduate schools and one graduate school. In addition to regional accreditation, Brockport has baccalaureate program accreditation with CSWE, NLN, and NRPA. The library contains 520,000 volumes, 1,900,000 microform items, and 9000 audiovisual forms, and subscribes to 2300 periodicals. Computerized library sources and services include the card catalog, interlibrary loans, and database searching. Special learning facilities include a learning resource center, art gallery, planetarium, radio station, and TV station. The 597-acre campus is in a small town 16 miles west of Rochester. Including residence halls, there are 37 buildings on campus.

Student Life: About 98% of undergraduates are from New York. Students come from 22 states, 16 foreign countries, and Canada. Ninety-four percent are from public schools; 6% from private. Ninety-one percent are white. Forty-six percent are Catholic; 27% Protestant; 18% claim no religious affiliation. The average age of freshmen is 18; all undergraduates, 24. Twenty-three percent drop out by the end of their first year; 43% remain to graduate.

Housing: A total of 2540 students can be accommodated in college housing. College-sponsored living facilities include single-sex and coed dormitories. In addition, there are special interest houses and special living facilities for transfer and first year students. Other facilities offer wellness programs and international living/ year-round housing. On-campus housing is guaranteed for all 4 years. All students may keep cars on campus.

Activities: About 3% of men belong to 9 national fraternities; about 3% of women belong to 7 national sororities. There are 75 groups on campus, including art, cheerleading, choir, computers, dance, drama, ethnic, gay, honors, international, literary magazine, newspaper, pep band, political, professional, radio and TV, religious, social, cial service, student government, symphony, and yearbook. Popular campus events include Afro-American Week, Homecoming/Parents and Family Weekend, Midnite Merry Madness, Kwanza, AIDS Awareness Week, Scholar's Day, Honors Convocation, Winter Weekend, Greek Week, Greek Olympics, and concerts, lectures, and dances.

Sports: There are 10 intercollegiate sports for men and 11 for women, and 57 intramural sports for men and 57 for women. Athletic and recreation facilities include field hockey and softball fields, 2 swimming pools, 6 gymnasiums, a gymnastics area, wrestling and weight rooms, handball, squash, and racquetball courts, and a special olympics stadium with an 8-lane, all-weather track.

Disabled Students: The following facilities are available: wheelchair ramps, elevators, special parking, specially equipped rest rooms, special class scheduling, lowered drinking fountains, lowered telephones, and classroom accomodations.

Services: In addition to many counseling and information services, tutoring is available in most subjects. There is remedial math and writing. Study skills support is available to all students.

Campus Safety and Security: Campus safety and security measures include 24-hour foot and vehicle patrol, self defense education, escort service, and shuttle buses. In addition, there are informal discussions, pamphlets, posters, and films, emergency telephones, lighted pathways and sidewalks, a community policing program, and a crime prevention team.

Programs of Study: Brockport awards the B.A., B.S., B.F.A., and B.S.N. degrees. Master's degrees also are awarded. Bachelor's degrees are awarded in BIOLOGICAL SCIENCE (biology/biological science), BUSINESS (accounting, business administration and management, international business management, and recreation and leisure services), COMMUNICATIONS AND THE ARTS (art history and appreciation, communications, dance, dramatic arts, English, fine arts, French, Spanish, speech/debate/rhetoric, and studio art), COMPUTER AND PHYSICAL SCIENCE (atmospheric sciences and meteorology, chemistry, computer science, earth science, geology, mathematics, and physics), EDUCATION (physical and secondary), HEALTH PROFESSIONS (health science and nursing), SOCIAL SCIENCE (African American studies, African studies, American studies, anthropology, criminal justice, economics, history, international studies, liberal arts/general studies, philosophy, political science/government, psychology, social work, sociology, and water resources). English, politi-

cal science, international business, physics, chemistry, and biological sciences are the strongest academically. Business administration, psychology, physical education and sports, criminal justice, communications, nursing, English, biological sciences, health science, and social work have the largest enrollments.

Required: To graduate, students must complete a total of 120 credits, including 30 to 38 credits in the major with a 2.0 GPA. The core curriculum must include 6 credits each in fine arts, humanities, social science, natural science, and mathematics. All students must take courses in computer literacy, contemporary issues, perspectives on women, comparative culture, quantitative skills, and composition skills. An academic planning seminar is also required.

Special: Co-op programs are offered in the sciences, business, communications, criminal justice, and computer science. Internships in all subjects and work-study programs in education are available. Brockport offers cross-registration with Rochester area colleges, a Washington semester, study abroad in 11 countries, accelerated degree programs, student-designed majors, and an interdisciplinary major in arts for children, emphasizing art, dance, music, and theater. The college confers numerous B.A.-B.S. degrees and a general studies degree. The 3-2 engineering degree is offered with SUNY-Binghamton, SUNY-Buffalo, and Clarkson, Case Western Reserve, and Syracuse universities. Credit for life, military, and work experience, nondegree study, and pass/fail grading options are available. There is a freshman honors program on campus, as well as 11 national honor societies. Three departments have honors programs.

Faculty/Classroom: Sixty-seven percent of faculty are male; 33%, female. Ninety-five percent teach undergraduates, 70% do research, and 68% do both. Graduate students teach 1% of introductory courses. The average class size in an introductory lecture is 35; in a laboratory, 15; and in a regular course offering, 25.

Admissions: About 49% of the 1993-94 applicants were accepted. The SAT scores for the 1993-94 freshman class were as follows: Verbal—79% below 500, 18% between 500 and 599, and 3% between 600 and 700; Math—48% below 500, 41% between 500 and 599, and 11% between 600 and 700. The ACT scores were 27% below 21, 48% between 21 and 23, 14% between 24 and 26, and 11% between 27 and 28. About 27% of the current freshmen were in the top fifth of their class; 78% were in the top two fifths. There were 7 National Merit semifinalists. Eleven freshmen graduated first in their class.

Requirements: Brockport requires applicants to be in the upper 60% of their class. The SAT I or the ACT is required, with recommended composite scores of 800 on the SAT I and 18 on the ACT. Applicants must be graduates of an accredited school or have a GED. Requirements include 17 Carnegie units or academic credits, including 4 years each in English and history and 2 years each in mathematics and science. Portfolios and auditions are recommended when appropriate. AP and CLEP credits are accepted. Important factors used in the admissions decision are recommendations by school officials, advanced placement or honor courses, leadership record, extracurricular activities record, and evidence of special talent.

Procedure: Freshmen are admitted in the fall. Entrance exams should be taken during the fall of the senior year. Early decision applications should be filed by November 15; regular applications, by March 1 for fall entry and December 1 for winter entry, along with an application fee of $25. Notification of early decision is sent December 6; regular decision, on a rolling basis. There are early decision, early admissions, and deferred admissions plans. Ten early decision candidates were accepted for the 1993-94 class.

Transfer: About 1188 transfer students enrolled in 1993-94. The applicant must have a minimum GPA of 2.25. Many departments specify prerequisite courses and a higher GPA. Brockport recommends that transfer applicants have an associate degree or 54 credit hours. Preference is given to holders of associate degrees. A total of 24 credits out of 120 must be completed at Brockport.

Visiting: There are regularly scheduled orientations for prospective students, including group information sessions conducted Mondays, Thursdays, and Fridays at 1 P.M., and campus tours conducted daily at 11:30 A.M. and 2 P.M. Visits may also be arranged on selected Saturdays and holidays. There are guides for informal visits and visitors may sit in on classes and stay overnight at the school. To arrange for a visit, contact the Thompson Conference Center at (716) 395-2275.

Financial Aid: In 1993-94 70% of all current freshmen and 49% of continuing students received some form of financial aid. About 70% of freshmen and 80% of continuing students received need-based aid. The average freshman award was $4471. Of that total, scholarships or need-based grants averaged $1463 ($2300 maximum); loans averaged $1844 ($3625 maximum); and work contracts averaged $1222 ($1500 maximum). Eighty percent of undergraduate students work part-time. Average earnings from campus work for the school year are $600. The average financial indebtedness of the 1992-93 graduate was $6914. The FFS and the college's own financial statement are required, and a financial aid transcript is required

for transfers only. The deadline for financial aid applications is May 1.

International Students: There are currently 47 international students enrolled. They must take the TOEFL or the University of Michigan Language Test and achieve a minimum score on the TOEFL of 520.

Computers: The college provides computer facilities for student use. The mainframes are a Prime 6650 and an IBM 9221 Model 150. There are more than 50 terminals available in central laboratories for student class projects. There are 425 PCs available for student use. All students may access the system. It may be used 24 hours per day. There are no time limits on using the system and no fees.

Graduates: In 1992–93 1612 bachelor's degrees were awarded. The most popular majors among graduates were business administration (16%), psychology (10%), and criminal justice (10%). Within an average freshman class, 2% graduate in 3 years, 24% in 4 years, 41% in 5 years, and 42% in 6 years. Some 275 companies recruited on campus in 1992–93. In the 1992 graduating class, 11% of the men and 14% of the women were enrolled in graduate school within 6 months of graduation; 40% of the men and 47% of the women had found employment.

Admissions Contact: James R. Cook, Acting Director of Admissions.

STATE UNIVERSITY OF NEW YORK COLLEGE AT BUFFALO

A-3

Buffalo, NY 14222 (716) 878–4017

Full-time: 9848 men and women	Faculty: 430; IIA, av$
Part-time: none	Ph.D.s: 90%
Graduate: 1810 men and women	Student/Faculty: 19 to 1
Year: semesters, summer session	Tuition: $2835 ($6685)
Application Deadline: none	Room & Board: $4200
Freshman Class: 6500 applied, 3472 accepted, 1044 enrolled	
SAT I or ACT: not required	**VERY COMPETITIVE**

The State University of New York/College at Buffalo, established in 1867, is a public institution conferring undergraduate liberal arts degrees. In addition to regional accreditation, Buffalo State has baccalaureate program accreditation with ABET, ADA, CSWE, and NCATE. The library contains 578,377 volumes, 726,811 microform items, and 9274 audiovisual forms, and subscribes to 2087 periodicals. Computerized library sources and services include the card catalog and database searching. Special learning facilities include a learning resource center, an art gallery, a planetarium, a radio station, a speech, language, and hearing clinic, and a center for performing arts. The 115-acre campus is in an urban area in Buffalo. Including residence halls, there are 36 buildings on campus.

Student Life: About 99% of undergraduates are from New York. Students come from 16 states, 39 foreign countries, and Canada. Eighty-five percent are white. The average age of freshmen is 18; all undergraduates, 23. Twenty-nine percent drop out by the end of their first year; 36% remain to graduate.

Housing: A total of 2086 students can be accommodated in college housing. College-sponsored living facilities include coed dormitories and an international student dormitory. On-campus housing is available on a first-come, first-served basis. Eighty-three percent of students commute. All students may keep cars on campus.

Activities: There are 1 local fraternity and 9 national fraternities and 3 local and 7 national sororities. There are 75 groups on campus, including art, cheerleading, choir, chorus, computers, dance, drama, ethnic, honors, international, jazz band, literary magazine, musical theater, newspaper, orchestra, political, professional, radio and TV, religious, social, social service, student government, and yearbook. Popular campus events include Homecoming and Commuter Daze.

Sports: There are 13 intercollegiate sports for men and 10 for women, and 5 intramural sports for men and 3 for women. Athletic and recreation facilities include a gymnasium, an athletic bubble, a natatorium, and an arena.

Disabled Students: Ninety percent of the campus is accessible to disabled students. The following facilities are available: wheelchair ramps, elevators, special parking, specially equipped rest rooms, special class scheduling, lowered drinking fountains, lowered telephones, and special dormitory accommodations.

Services: In addition to many counseling and information services, tutoring is available in every subject. There is also a reader service for the blind, and remedial math, reading, and writing. Tutors for visually impaired and hearing-impaired students are also available.

Campus Safety and Security: Campus safety and security measures include an escort service, emergency telephones, and lighted pathways and sidewalks.

Programs of Study: Buffalo State awards the B.A., B.S., B.F.A., B.S.Ed., and B.T. degrees. Master's degrees also are awarded. Bachelor's degrees are awarded in BIOLOGICAL SCIENCE (biology/biological science), BUSINESS (business administration and manage-

ment and office supervision and management), COMMUNICATIONS AND THE ARTS (broadcasting, communications, design, dramatic arts, English, fine arts, French, Italian, journalism, music, photography, Spanish, and speech/debate/rhetoric), COMPUTER AND PHYSICAL SCIENCE (chemistry, geology, information sciences and systems, mathematics, and physics), EDUCATION (art, business, elementary, foreign languages, industrial arts, science, secondary, and special), ENGINEERING AND ENVIRONMENTAL DESIGN (engineering technology and industrial engineering technology), HEALTH PROFESSIONS (speech pathology/audiology), SOCIAL SCIENCE (anthropology, child psychology/development, criminal justice, dietetics, economics, family/consumer studies, food production/management/services, geography, history, humanities, philosophy, political science/government, psychology, social work, sociology, and urban studies). Elementary education, psychology, design, business studies, and exceptional education have the largest enrollments.

Required: To graduate, students must complete a 60-hour general education requirement consisting of 42 core credits in applied science and education, arts, humanities, mathematics and science, and social science, and 18 hours of electives. Students must earn 123 credits with a minimum GPA of 2.0. The number of hours in the major varies. All students are required to complete 2 hours of physical education.

Special: Students may cross-register with the Western New York Consortium and the National Student Exchange. Internships, a Washington semester, study abroad in 5 countries, dual majors, and a general studies degree are offered. Students may earn 3–2 engineering degrees in association with the State University of New York centers at Buffalo and Binghamton, and Clarkson University. Credit for life, military, and work experience, nondegree study, and pass/fail grading options are available. There is a freshman honors program on campus. Thirteen departments have honors programs.

Faculty/Classroom: Seventy-three percent of faculty are male; 27%, female. Ninety-five percent teach undergraduates. No introductory courses are taught by graduate students.

Admissions: About 53% of the 1993–94 applicants were accepted. Sixty-five percent of the current freshmen were in the top fifth of their class.

Requirements: The SAT I or ACT is not required. Students must graduate from an accredited secondary school or have a GED. They must complete 4 years of English, 3 years each of mathematics, science, and social studies, and 2 years of a foreign language. A portfolio is required for fine arts applicants. AP and CLEP credits are accepted. Important factors used in the admissions decision are advanced placement or honor courses, evidence of special talent, recommendations by school officials, extracurricular activities record, personality, and intangible qualities.

Procedure: Freshmen are admitted to all sessions. Entrance exams should be taken during the junior and senior years. Early decision applications should be filed by November 1, along with an application fee of $30. Notification is sent on a rolling basis. There are early admissions and deferred admissions plans. A waiting list is an active part of the admissions procedure, with about 10% of applicants on the list.

Transfer: About 1166 transfer students enrolled in a recent year. Transfer applicants must have a minimum GPA of 2.0. An associate degree is recommended, and a minimum of 15 credit hours must have been earned. A total of 32 credits out of 123 must be completed at Buffalo State.

Visiting: There are regularly scheduled orientations for prospective students. There are guides for informal visits and visitors may sit in on classes. To arrange for a visit, contact the Admissions Office at (716) 878–4017.

Financial Aid: Buffalo State is a member of CSS. The FAF or FFS is required. The deadline for financial aid applications is March 1.

International Students: There were recently 113 international students enrolled. The school actively recruits these students. They must take the TOEFL and achieve a minimum score of 500.

Computers: The college provides computer facilities for student use. The mainframe is a DEC VAX 6340. Access to the mainframe is through the campus local area network. Approximately 350 terminals and microcomputers are available at various campus sites including the library, classrooms, Computing Services' remote computing facilities, and departmental micro/terminal laboratories. All students may access the system during site hours. Dial-in access is available 24 hours per day. There are no time limits and no fees.

Graduates: In a recent year, 1776 bachelor's degrees were awarded. The most popular majors among graduates were business studies (13%), elementary education (13%), and social work (6%). Within an average freshman class, 1% graduate in 3 years, 16% in 4 years, 32% in 5 years, and 36% in 6 years. Some 47 companies recruited on campus in a recent year.

Admissions Contact: Paul T. Collyer, Associate Director of Admissions.

STATE UNIVERSITY OF NEW YORK
COLLEGE AT CORTLAND
C-5

Cortland, NY 13045   (607) 753–4711

Full-time: 2217 men, 2799 women	Faculty: 243; IIA, -$
Part-time: 159 men, 184 women	Ph.D.s: 82%
Graduate: 384 men, 974 women	Student/Faculty: 21 to 1
Year: semesters, summer session	Tuition: $2926 ($6826)
Application Deadline: February 1	Room & Board: $4400

Freshman Class: 7888 applied, 3598 accepted, 1036 enrolled

SAT I Verbal/Math: 460/524   ACT: 24   **COMPETITIVE +**

The State University of New York College at Cortland, founded in 1868, is a public, coeducational institution offering programs in liberal arts and professional studies. There are 2 undergraduate schools and one graduate school. The library contains 375,000 volumes, 533,060 microform items, and 9527 audiovisual forms, and subscribes to 1507 periodicals. Computerized library sources and services include the card catalog and interlibrary loans. Special learning facilities include a learning resource center, art gallery, natural history museum, planetarium, radio station, TV station, and anthropology, cartography, archaeology, and journalism laboratories; a natural science museum, and a center for speech and hearing disorders. The 191-acre campus is in a small town 18 miles north of Ithaca. Including residence halls, there are 34 buildings on campus.

Student Life: About 97% of undergraduates are from New York. Students come from 19 states, 11 foreign countries, and Canada. Ninety-one percent are from public schools; 9% from private. Ninety-four percent are white. The average age of freshmen is 18; all undergraduates, 20. Twenty-four percent drop out by the end of their first year; 50% remain to graduate.

Housing: A total of 2693 students can be accommodated in college housing. College-sponsored living facilities include coed dormitories, off-campus apartments, fraternity houses, and sorority houses. In addition there are special interest houses and a residence for Americans majoring in international studies and/or studying abroad. On-campus housing is guaranteed for all 4 years. Sixty percent of students live on campus; of those, 95% remain on campus on weekends. Upperclassmen may keep cars on campus.

Activities: About 10% of men belong to 5 national fraternities; about 10% of women belong to 4 national sororities. There are 100 groups on campus, including art, band, cheerleading, choir, chorale, chorus, computers, dance, drama, ethnic, gay, honors, international, jazz band, literary magazine, musical theater, newspaper, orchestra, political, professional, radio and TV, religious, social, social service, student government, symphony, and yearbook. Popular campus events include Spring Picnic, annual Cortland-Ithaca College football game, and Black Solidarity Week.

Sports: There are 11 intercollegiate sports for men and 12 for women, and 13 intramural sports for men and 13 for women. Athletic and recreation facilities include an Olympic-sized pool, a 3600-seat gymnasium, an ice arena, a gymnastics arena, wrestling and weight rooms, a dance studio, handball/racquetball courts, squash courts, an athletic training facility, fully equipped fitness centers, a free-swimming pool, a track, a baseball field, a football/lacrosse/track field seating 4000, a lighted soccer field, and 50 acres of athletic fields.

Disabled Students: All of the campus is accessible to disabled students. The following facilities are available: wheelchair ramps, elevators, special parking, specially equipped rest rooms, and special class scheduling.

Services: In addition to many counseling and information services, tutoring is available in some subjects, including There is a fully staffed skills center for writing, mathematics, study, and organizational/skill support, with peer tutors. There is also a reader service for the blind.

Campus Safety and Security: Campus safety and security measures include 24-hour foot and vehicle patrol, self defense education, escort service, and shuttle buses. In addition, there are informal discussions, pamphlets, posters, films, emergency telephones, and lighted pathways and sidewalks.

Programs of Study: Cortland College awards the B.A., B.S., and B.S.E. degrees. Master's degrees also are awarded. Bachelor's degrees are awarded in BIOLOGICAL SCIENCE (biology/biological science), BUSINESS (management science), COMMUNICATIONS AND THE ARTS (broadcasting, communications, dramatic arts, English, fine arts, languages, music, and speech/debate/rhetoric), COMPUTER AND PHYSICAL SCIENCE (chemistry, geochemistry, geology, mathematics, and physics), EDUCATION (art, early childhood, elementary, foreign languages, health, middle school, science, and secondary), HEALTH PROFESSIONS (health care administration, predentistry, premedicine, recreation therapy, and speech pathology/audiology), SOCIAL SCIENCE (anthropology, economics, geography, history, international studies, parks and recreation management, philosophy, political science/government, prelaw, psychology, public administration, social science, and sociology). Biolo-

gy, political science, sociology, psychology, elementary education, and physical education are the strongest academically. Elementary education, physical education, communications, and management science have the largest enrollments.

Required: To graduate, students must complete specific course work in English, mathematics, and a foreign language. A general education requirement includes courses in American institutions, analysis of values, contrasting cultures, fine arts, history, literature, modern Western thought, natural science, human affairs, and prejudice and discrimination. Students must maintain a GPA of 2.0, and they must complete 128 credits, with 36 credits in the major.

Special: Cortland has cooperative programs with the State University of New York College of Environmental Science and Forestry, and Centers at Binghamton and Buffalo, and Cornell and Case Western Reserve Universities. Students may study abroad in 8 countries, and they may enroll in a Washington semester. Work-study programs are available. The college confers a general studies degree. Student-designed majors can be arranged. Students may pursue a 3–2 engineering degree in conjunction with Alfred, Case Western Reserve, and Clarkson universities, and the State University of New York Centers at Binghamton, Buffalo, and Stony Brook. Credit may be granted for military and work experience. Cortland offers nondegree study programs. There is a freshman honors program on campus, as well as 15 national honor societies. Three departments have honors programs.

Faculty/Classroom: Fifty-seven percent of faculty are male; 43%, female. All teach undergraduates. No introductory courses are taught by graduate students. The average class size in an introductory lecture is 40 and in a regular course offering, 25.

Admissions: About 46% of the 1993–94 applicants were accepted. The SAT scores for the 1993–94 freshman class were as follows: Verbal—82% below 500, 17% between 500 and 599, and 1% between 600 and 700; Math—43% below 500, 49% between 500 and 599, and 9% between 600 and 700. The ACT scores were 11% below 21, 38% between 21 and 23, 39% between 24 and 26, 10% between 27 and 28, and 2% above 28. About 23% of the current freshmen were in the top fifth of their class; 68% were in the top two fifths. There were 2 National Merit finalists.

Requirements: The SAT I or the ACT is required. Applicants must graduate from an accredited secondary school or have a GED. They must have earned 16 Carnegie units and 16 to 20 academic credits, including 4 units each in English, history, and social studies; 2 each, or preferably 3 each, in mathematics and science, as well as course work in a foreign language. Essays and recommendations are required, and in some cases auditions as well. Interviews are strongly recommended. AP and CLEP credits are accepted. Important factors used in the admissions decision are advanced placement or honor courses, extracurricular activities record, recommendations by school officials, leadership record, and personality and intangible qualities.

Procedure: Freshmen are admitted fall and spring. Entrance exams should be taken during the spring or fall. Early decision applications should be filed by November 15; regular applications, by February 1 for fall entry and December 1 for spring entry, along with an application fee of $25. Notification of early decision is sent December 15; regular decision, February 1. There are early decision, early admissions, and deferred admissions plans. About 48 early decision candidates were accepted for the 1993–94 class. A waiting list is an active part of the admissions procedure, with about 7% of applicants on the list.

Transfer: About 800 transfer students enrolled in 1993–94. Transfer applicants must have a minimum GPA of 2.5. Essays and recommendations are required. Interviews are strongly encouraged. A total of 45 credits out of 128 must be completed at Cortland College.

Visiting: There are regularly scheduled orientations for prospective students, including Autumn Preview Days for prospective students and Spring Open House for accepted students. There are guides for informal visits and visitors may sit in on classes. To arrange for a visit, contact the Admission Office at (607) 753–4711.

Financial Aid: In an earlier year, 75% of all current freshmen and 80% of continuing students received some form of financial aid. Loans averaged $1700 ($2700 maximum); and work contracts averaged $800 ($1000 maximum). Cortland College is a member of CSS. The college's own financial statement and FAFSA are required. The deadline for financial aid applications is May 1.

International Students: There are currently 33 international students enrolled. They must take the TOEFL and achieve a minimum score of 550.

Computers: The college provides computer facilities for student use. The mainframes are a Burroughs 810, a Unisys 810, and a DEC VAX 11/750. There are also 323 IBM, Apple, Zenith, Tandy, AT&T, and IBM-compatible microcomputers available throughout the campus. All students may access the system. It may be used 24 hours per day. There are no time limits on using the system and no fees.

Graduates: In 1992–93, 1317 bachelor's degrees were awarded. The most popular majors among graduates were elementary education (21%), physical education (13%), and sociology (7%). Within an average freshman class, 1% graduate in 3 years, 42% in 4 years, and 9% in 5 years. Some 157 companies recruited on campus in 1992–93.

Admissions Contact: Michael K. McKeon, Director of Admission.

STATE UNIVERSITY OF NEW YORK
COLLEGE AT FREDONIA
A-4

Fredonia, NY 14063   (716) 673-3251; (800) 252-1212 (in-state)

Full-time: 1857 men, 2267 women	Faculty: 234; IIA, av$
Part-time: 107 men, 191 women	Ph.Ds: 90%
Graduate: 102 men, 314 women	Student/Faculty: 18 to 1
Year: semesters, summer session	Tuition: $2959 ($6859)
Application Deadline: March 1	Room & Board: $4200

Freshman Class: 4877 applied, 2798 accepted, 885 enrolled

ACT: 23   VERY COMPETITIVE

The State University of New York at Fredonia, established in 1826, is a public institution offering undergraduate programs in the arts and sciences, business and professional curricula, teacher preparation, and music. In addition to regional accreditation, Fredonia has baccalaureate program accreditation with NASAD and NASM. The library contains 381,405 volumes, 932,635 microform items, and 16,569 audiovisual forms, and subscribes to 1936 periodicals. Computerized library sources and services include the card catalog, interlibrary loans, and database searching. Special learning facilities include a learning resource center, art gallery, planetarium, radio station, and TV station. The 266-acre campus is in a small town 50 miles south of Buffalo. Including residence halls, there are 24 buildings on campus.
Student Life: About 98% of undergraduates are from New York. Students come from 21 states, 12 foreign countries, and Canada. Sixty-five percent are from public schools; 35% from private. Ninety-three percent are white. The average age of freshmen is 18. Fourteen percent drop out by the end of their first year; 60% remain to graduate.
Housing: A total of 2621 students can be accommodated in college housing. College-sponsored living facilities include single-sex and coed dormitories and on-campus apartments. Living space for fraternities and sororities is available in residence halls. In addition, there are special interest houses for computer and athletics students and quiet-hour centers. On-campus housing is guaranteed for all 4 years. Fifty-five percent of students live on campus; of those, 80% remain on campus on weekends. Alcohol is not permitted. All students may keep cars on campus.
Activities: About 5% of men belong to 3 national fraternities; about 3% of women belong to 2 national sororities. There are 160 groups on campus, including art, band, cheerleading, chorale, chorus, computers, dance, drama, drill team, ethnic, gay, honors, international, jazz band, literary magazine, musical theater, newspaper, opera, orchestra, pep band, photography, political, professional, radio and TV, religious, social, social service, student government, symphony, and yearbook. Popular campus events include various Art Center presentations.
Sports: There are 7 intercollegiate sports for men and 5 for women, and 6 intramural sports for men and 6 for women. Athletic and recreation facilities include a basketball arena, an ice rink, a swimming pool, a gymnasium, a weight room, dance studios, soccer fields, indoor and outdoor tracks, and racquetball, tennis, and volleyball courts.
Disabled Students: Forty-five percent of the campus is accessible to disabled students. The following facilities are available: wheelchair ramps, elevators, special parking, specially equipped rest rooms, lowered drinking fountains, and lowered telephones.
Services: In addition to many counseling and information services, tutoring is available in most subjects. There is also a reader service for the blind and a language laboratory.
Campus Safety and Security: Campus safety and security measures include 24-hour foot and vehicle patrol, escort service, shuttle buses, and informal discussions. In addition, there are pamphlets, posters, and films, emergency telephones, and lighted pathways and sidewalks.
Programs of Study: Fredonia awards the B.A., B.S., B.A.S.S., B.F.A., B.S.Ed., B.S.S.S., and Mus.B. degrees. Master's degrees also are awarded. Bachelor's degrees are awarded in BIOLOGICAL SCIENCE (biology/biological science), BUSINESS (accounting, business administration and management, and business economics), COMMUNICATIONS AND THE ARTS (communication, design, dramatic arts, English, fine arts, French, German, music, and Spanish), COMPUTER AND PHYSICAL SCIENCE (chemistry, computer science, earth science, geology, mathematics, and physics), EDUCATION (early childhood, elementary, foreign languages, middle school, music, science, and secondary), HEALTH PROFESSIONS (medical laboratory technology, predentistry, premedicine, and speech pathology/

audiology), SOCIAL SCIENCE (philosophy, political science/government, psychology, and sociology). Business, education, music, psychology, and communication have the largest enrollments.
Required: To graduate, students must complete 120 hours, including 33 to 45 in the major, with a 2.0 GPA. Students must take specific courses in English and mathematics and complete 36 hours of general education courses, including writing, statistical/quantitative abilities, oral communication, natural and social sciences, humanities, and arts.
Special: Cooperative programs are available with many other institutions. Students may cross-register with colleges in the Western New York Consortium. Fredonia offers a variety of internships, study-abroad programs in more than 90 countries, and a Washington semester. Accelerated degrees, a general studies degree, dual and student-designed majors, a 3–2 engineering degree program, nondegree study, and pass/fail grading options are available. There is a freshman honors program on campus, as well as 17 national honor societies. Seventeen departments have honors programs.
Faculty/Classroom: Seventy-three percent of faculty are male; 27%, female. All teach undergraduates. Graduate students teach 1% of introductory courses. The average class size in an introductory lecture is 100; in a laboratory, 18; and in a regular course offering, 24.
Admissions: About 57% of the 1993–94 applicants were accepted. The SAT scores for the 1993–94 freshman class were as follows: Verbal—69% below 500, 27% between 500 and 599, and 4% between 600 and 700; Math—35% below 500, 48% between 500 and 599, 15% between 600 and 700, and 1% above 700. The ACT scores were 20% below 21, 42% between 21 and 23, 27% between 24 and 26, 8% between 27 and 28, and 3% above 28. About 37% of the current freshmen were in the top fifth of their class; 84% were in the top two fifths. About 21 freshmen graduated first in their class.
Requirements: Fredonia requires applicants to be in the upper 50% of their class. A minimum GPA of 2.5 is required. The SAT I or ACT is required, with a minimum composite score of 900 on SAT I or 18 on the ACT. Applicants must be graduates of an accredited secondary school or have a GED. Sixteen academic credits are required, including 4 credits each in English and social studies, 3 each in mathematics and science, and 2 in a foreign language. Four years of mathematics and science may be substituted for a foreign language. Essays and interviews are recommended, and, where applicable, an audition is required. AP and CLEP credits are accepted. Important factors used in the admissions decision are advanced placement or honor courses, evidence of special talent, recommendations by school officials, leadership record, and parents or siblings attending the school.
Procedure: Freshmen are admitted fall and spring. Entrance exams should be taken during the spring of the junior year or fall of the senior year. Applications should be filed by March 1 for fall entry and November 1 for spring entry, along with an application fee of $25. Notification is sent on a rolling basis. There are early admissions and deferred admissions plans. A waiting list is an active part of the admissions procedure, with about 5% of applicants on the list.
Transfer: About 458 transfer students enrolled in 1993–94. Applicants should have earned at least 30 credit hours with a minimum GPA of 2.5. Students without an associate degree or 45 credit hours of upper-division study must meet the requirements of incoming freshmen. An interview is recommended. A total of 45 credits out of 120 must be completed at Fredonia.
Visiting: There are regularly scheduled orientations for prospective students. Visitors may sit in on classes and stay overnight at the school. To arrange for a visit, contact the Office of Admissions at (716) 673-3251.
Financial Aid: In 1993–94 67% of all current freshmen and 61% of continuing students received some form of financial aid. About 64% of freshmen and 59% of continuing students received need-based aid. The average freshman award was $4302. Of that total, scholarships or need-based grants averaged $1438 ($4900 maximum); loans averaged $3120 ($3625 maximum); and work contracts averaged $1000. Average earnings from campus work for the school year are $950. The average financial indebtedness of the 1992–93 graduate was $5926. Fredonia is a member of CSS. The FAFSA and TAP financial statement are required. The deadline for financial aid applications is February 28.
International Students: There are currently 15 international students enrolled. The school actively recruits these students. They must take the TOEFL and achieve a minimum score of 500.
Computers: The college provides computer facilities for student use. The mainframe is a Unisys A12T. There are 500 terminals connected to the mainframe. Apple, Commodore, and Compaq microcomputers, a Sun microsystems 4/470 server, and a DEC MicroVAX II are available. All students may access the system. There are no time limits on using the system and no fees.
Graduates: In 1992–93 1107 bachelor's degrees were awarded. The most popular majors among graduates were elementary education (17%), business administration (16%), and English (8%). Within

an average freshman class, 45% graduate in 4 years, 55% in 5 years, and 60% in 6 years. Some 27 companies recruited on campus in 1992–93.

Admissions Contact: William S. Clark, Director of Admissions and Enrollment.

STATE UNIVERSITY OF NEW YORK
COLLEGE AT GENESEO
Geneseo, NY 14454

B-3

(716) 245–5571

Full-time: 5007 men and women	Faculty: 237; IIA, -$
Part-time: 155 men and women	Ph.D.s: 87%
Graduate: 426 men and women	Student/Faculty: 21 to 1
Year: semesters, summer session	Tuition: $2955 ($6855)
Application Deadline: January 15	Room & Board: $3994
Freshman Class: 8598 applied, 4562 accepted, 1143 enrolled	
SAT I Verbal/Math: 541/608	ACT: 25 HIGHLY COMPETITIVE

The State University of New York/College at Geneseo, founded in 1867, and opened to students in 1871, offers liberal arts, business and accounting programs, and teacher certification. There is one graduate school. In addition to regional accreditation, Geneseo has baccalaureate program accreditation with ASLA. The library contains 421,000 volumes, 1,000,000 microform items, and 3813 audiovisual forms, and subscribes to 3179 periodicals. Computerized library sources and services include interlibrary loans and database searching. Special learning facilities include a learning resource center, art gallery, planetarium, radio station, TV station, and 3 theaters. The 220-acre campus is in a small town 30 miles south of Rochester. Including residence halls, there are 37 buildings on campus.

Student Life: About 98% of undergraduates are from New York. Students come from 10 states, 5 foreign countries, and Canada. Eighty-three percent are from public schools; 17% from private. Eighty-six percent are white. Fifty-five percent are Catholic; 27% Protestant. The average age of freshmen is 18; all undergraduates, 20. Eight percent drop out by the end of their first year; 70% remain to graduate.

Housing: A total of 3100 students can be accommodated in college housing. College-sponsored living facilities include single-sex and coed dormitories. In addition, there are special-interest houses including science and mathematics houses. On-campus housing is guaranteed for all 4 years. Sixty percent of students live on campus. Alcohol is not permitted. All students may keep cars on campus.

Activities: About 19% of men belong to 4 local and 4 national fraternities; about 15% of women belong to 4 local and 6 national sororities. There are 154 groups on campus, including art, band, cheerleading, choir, chorale, chorus, computers, dance, drama, ethnic, gay, honors, international, jazz band, literary magazine, musical theater, newspaper, orchestra, political, professional, radio and TV, religious, social, social service, student government, symphony, and yearbook. Popular campus events include Homecoming, Siblings Weekend, Parents Weekend, and Spring Weekend.

Sports: There are 8 intercollegiate sports for men and 8 for women, and 24 intramural sports for men and 24 for women. Athletic and recreation facilities include an ice arena, 2 swimming pools, 3 gymnasiums, 8 squash and 8 tennis courts, an outdoor track and field stadium, bowling alleys, Nautilus and weight rooms, and a sauna. The stadium, indoor gymnasium, and largest auditorium/arena each seat 3000.

Disabled Students: Ninety percent of the campus is accessible to disabled students. The following facilities are available: wheelchair ramps, elevators, special parking, specially equipped rest rooms, special class scheduling, lowered drinking fountains, lowered telephones, and fire alarms for the deaf.

Services: In addition to many counseling and information services, tutoring is available in every subject. There is also a reader service for the blind.

Campus Safety and Security: Campus safety and security measures include 24-hour foot and vehicle patrol, escort service, informal discussions, pamphlets, posters, and films. In addition, there are emergency telephones and lighted pathways and sidewalks.

Programs of Study: Geneseo awards the B.A., B.S., and B.S.Ed. degrees. Master's degrees also are awarded. Bachelor's degrees are awarded in BIOLOGICAL SCIENCE (biochemistry, biology/biological science, and biophysics), BUSINESS (accounting, business administration and management, business economics, international business management, marketing/retailing/merchandising, and personnel management), COMMUNICATIONS AND THE ARTS (broadcasting, communications, dramatic arts, English, fine arts, French, music, and Spanish), COMPUTER AND PHYSICAL SCIENCE (chemistry, computer science, earth science, geochemistry, geology, geoscience, mathematics, and physics), EDUCATION (early childhood, elementary, foreign languages, science, secondary, and special), HEALTH PROFESSIONS (medical laboratory technology, predentistry, premedicine, and speech pathology/audiology), SOCIAL SCIENCE (anthropology, economics, geography, history, international relations, philosophy, political science/government, prelaw,

psychology, public administration, and sociology). Biology, management, accounting, psychology, and education have the largest enrollments.

Required: To graduate, students must complete 120 credit hours with a 2.0 minimum GPA. The total number of hours in the major varies. The required core curriculum includes 2 courses each in humanities, fine arts, social science, natural science, and critical reasoning. All students must fulfill a physical education requirement.

Special: The college offers a cooperative 3–2 engineering degree with Alfred, Case Western Reserve, Clarkson, Columbia, Ohio State, and Syracuse universities, Rochester Institute of Technology, SUNY at Binghamton and Buffalo, and the University of Rochester. Cross-registration is available with the Rochester Area Colleges Consortium. The college offers internships in all majors, study abroad through more than 95 programs, and a Washington semester. Dual majors, credit for military experience, and pass/fail options are offered. There is a freshman honors program on campus, as well as 8 national honor societies. Three departments have honors programs.

Faculty/Classroom: Seventy percent of faculty are male; 30%, female. All both teach and do research. No introductory courses are taught by graduate students. The average class size in an introductory lecture is 50; in a laboratory, 24; and in a regular course offering, 25.

Admissions: About 53% of the 1993–94 applicants were accepted. The SAT scores for the 1993–94 freshman class were as follows: Verbal—27% below 500, 53% between 500 and 599, 19% between 600 and 700, and 1% above 700; Math—4% below 500, 38% between 500 and 599, 48% between 600 and 700, and 10% above 700. The ACT scores were 4% below 21, 5% between 21 and 23, 30% between 24 and 26, 48% between 27 and 28, and 13% above 28. About 89% of the current freshmen were in the top fifth of their class; 99% were in the top two fifths. About 35 freshmen graduated first in their class.

Requirements: Geneseo requires applicants to be in the upper 50% of their class and to have a B + minimum average. The SAT I or ACT is required. Applicants must be graduates of an accredited secondary school or have a GED certificate. The academic program must have included 4 years each of English, mathematics, science, and social studies, and 3 years of a foreign language. An essay is required. A portfolio or audition for certain programs and an interview are recommended. AP and CLEP credits are accepted. Important factors used in the admissions decision are advanced placement or honor courses, personality, intangible qualities, extracurricular activities record, recommendations by school officials, and leadership record.

Procedure: Freshmen are admitted in the fall and spring. Entrance exams should be taken during the spring of the junior year. There are early decision, early admissions, and deferred admissions plans. Early decision applications should be filed by November 15; regular applications, by January 15 for fall entry and November 1 for spring entry, along with an application fee of $25. Notification of early decision is sent December 15; regular decision, on a rolling basis beginning February 15. About 170 early decision candidates were accepted for the 1993–94 class. A waiting list is an active part of the admissions procedure, with about 10% of applicants on the list.

Transfer: About 340 transfer students enrolled in 1993–94. Applicants must provide transcripts from all previously attended colleges. A minimum 2.0 GPA is required. Students with fewer than 24 credit hours must submit SAT I or ACT scores. An essay is required and an interview is recommended. At least 32 credits out of 120 must be completed at Geneseo.

Visiting: There are regularly scheduled orientations for prospective students, including a day and a half summer program consisting of academic advisement and registration. There are guides for informal visits, and visitors may sit in on classes and stay overnight at the school. To arrange for a visit, contact the Office of Admissions at (716) 245–5571.

Financial Aid: In 1993–94, 70% of all current freshmen and 75% of continuing students received some form of financial aid. About 65% of freshmen and 70% of continuing students received need-based aid. The average freshman award was $2830. Of that total, scholarships or need-based grants averaged $2000 ($6900 maximum); loans averaged $2135 ($4000 maximum); and work contracts averaged $1005 ($3500 maximum). Sixty-eight percent of undergraduate students work part-time. Geneseo is a member of CSS. The FAFSA financial statement is required. The deadline for financial aid applications is February 15.

International Students: There are currently 9 international students enrolled. They must take the TOEFL and achieve a minimum score of 530.

Computers: The college provides computer facilities for student use. The mainframes are a DEC VAX 6000–510 and an 8530. A variety of PCs are located throughout the campus. All students may access the system. There are no time limits on using the system and no fees.

Graduates: In 1992–93, 1280 bachelor's degrees were awarded. The most popular majors among graduates were education (19%), business (10%), and psychology (10%). Within an average freshman

class, 2% graduate in 3 years, 53% in 4 years, 14% in 5 years, and 1% in 6 years. Some 41 companies recruited on campus in 1992–93.
Admissions Contact: Jill Conlon, Director of Admissions.

STATE UNIVERSITY OF NEW YORK COLLEGE AT NEW PALTZ
New Paltz, NY 12561-2499 **D-4**
(914) 257-3200

Full-time: 1985 men, 2761 women	Faculty: 289; IIA, av$
Part-time: 541 men, 888 women	Ph.D.s: 78%
Graduate: 456 men, 1310 women	Student/Faculty: 16 to 1
Year: semesters, summer session	Tuition: $2650 ($6550)
Application Deadline: May 1	Room & Board: $4240
Freshman Class: 8399 applied, 3609 accepted, 798 enrolled	
SAT I Verbal/Math: 479/537	ACT: 24 VERY COMPETITIVE

State University of New York/College at New Paltz, founded in 1828, is a state-supported liberal arts college offering undergraduate and graduate programs in the arts and sciences, business, education, engineering, and the health professions. There is one graduate school. In addition to regional accreditation, The College at New Paltz has baccalaureate program accreditation with ABET, NASM, and NLN. The library contains 397,699 volumes and 929,681 microform items, and subscribes to 1385 periodicals. Computerized library sources and services include the card catalog, interlibrary loans, and database searching. Special learning facilities include a learning resource center, art gallery, planetarium, radio station, TV station, a greenhouse, a robotics laboratory, an electron microscope, a speech and hearing clinic, and a music therapy training facility. The 216-acre campus is in a rural area 96 miles north of New York City and 65 miles south of Albany. Including residence halls, there are 55 buildings on campus.
Student Life: About 94% of undergraduates are from New York. Students come from 46 states and 55 foreign countries. Ninety-five percent are from public schools; 5% from private. Seventy-three percent are white; 10% African American. Thirty-nine percent are Catholic; 21% claim no religious affiliation; 16% Jewish; 13% Protestant. The average age of freshmen is 18; all undergraduates, 25. Twenty-two percent drop out by the end of their first year; 45% remain to graduate.
Housing: A total of 2269 students can be accommodated in college housing. College-sponsored living facilities include coed dormitories. On-campus housing is guaranteed for all 4 years. Fifty-one percent of students live on campus; of those, 90% remain on campus on weekends. All students may keep cars on campus.
Activities: About 3% of men belong to 6 local and 9 national fraternities; about 3% of women belong to 2 local and 6 national sororities. There are 152 groups on campus, including art, band, cheerleading, choir, chorale, chorus, computers, dance, drama, ethnic, gay, honors, international, jazz band, literary magazine, musical theater, newspaper, orchestra, photography, political, professional, radio and TV, religious, social, social service, student government, and yearbook. Popular campus events include Spirit Weekend, Family Weekend, Rainbow Month, Greek Weekend, Welcome Week, New Paltz Summer Repertory Theatre, and the Music in the Mountains summer concert series.
Sports: There are 8 intercollegiate sports for men and 7 for women, and 20 intramural sports for men and 15 for women. Athletic and recreation facilities include a gymnasium, numerous playing fields, and a 35,000-square-foot air-supported structure for tennis, jogging, volleyball, and basketball.
Disabled Students: Ninety percent of the campus is accessible to disabled students. The following facilities are available: wheelchair ramps, elevators, special parking, specially equipped rest rooms, special class scheduling, lowered drinking fountains, lowered telephones, and some specially equipped residence halls.
Services: In addition to many counseling and information services, tutoring is available in most subjects. In addition, there is a reader service for the blind, and remedial math, reading, and writing.
Campus Safety and Security: Campus safety and security measures include 24-hour foot and vehicle patrol, escort service, informal discussions, and pamphlets, posters, and films. In addition, there are emergency telephones, lighted pathways and sidewalks, and a bicycle patrol.
Programs of Study: The College at New Paltz awards the B.A., B.S., B.F.A., B.S.E.E., and B.S.N. degrees. Master's degrees also are awarded. Bachelor's degrees are awarded in BIOLOGICAL SCIENCE (biology/biological science), BUSINESS (accounting, banking and finance, business administration and management, and marketing/retailing/merchandising), COMMUNICATIONS AND THE ARTS (broadcasting, communications, design, dramatic arts, English, fine arts, French, German, journalism, music, photography, Spanish, and speech/debate/rhetoric), COMPUTER AND PHYSICAL SCIENCE (chemistry, computer science, geology, mathematics, and physics), EDUCATION (art, early childhood, elementary, foreign languages, middle school, science, and secondary), ENGINEERING AND ENVI-

RONMENTAL DESIGN (computer engineering and electrical/electronics engineering), HEALTH PROFESSIONS (premedicine and speech pathology/audiology), SOCIAL SCIENCE (anthropology, economics, geography, history, international relations, philosophy, political science/government, psychology, social science, and sociology). Business administration, communications, education, and psychology have the largest enrollments.
Required: To graduate, students must complete 120 credits with a 2.0 GPA. The number of credits required in the major varies. Other requirements include 45 credits in liberal arts and sciences, including courses in English, analytical skills, history, and physical education, and 60 credits in upper-division courses.
Special: There is cross-registration with the mid-Hudson Consortium of Colleges. The college offers co-op programs in most majors, internships in Albany and New York City, work-study programs, student-designed and dual majors, and B.A.-B.S. degrees. Students may study abroad in 11 countries. A 3–2 degree in geological engineering is offered with the New Mexico Institute of Mining and Technology. There is a freshman honors program and several honor societes on campus.
Faculty/Classroom: Sixty-six percent of faculty are male; 34%, female. The average class size in an introductory lecture is 25; in a laboratory, 10; and in a regular course offering, 25.
Admissions: About 43% of the 1993–94 applicants were accepted. The SAT scores for the 1993–94 freshman class were as follows: Verbal—62% below 500, 31% between 500 and 599, 6% between 600 and 700, and 1% above 700; Math—32% below 500, 48% between 500 and 599, 20% between 600 and 700, and 2% above 700. About 41% of the current freshmen were in the top fifth of their class; 84% were in the top two fifths.
Requirements: The SAT I or ACT is required, with a recommended minimum composite score of 950 on the SAT I or 22 on the ACT. Graduation from an accredited secondary school is required; a GED will be accepted. The applicant's academic record must include 4 years each of English and social studies, and 3 years each of a foreign language, mathematics, and science. Where required, a portfolio and an audition are used for placement purposes only. AP and CLEP credits are accepted. Important factors used in the admissions decision are advanced placement or honor courses, extracurricular activities record, leadership record, evidence of special talent, and recommendations by school officials.
Procedure: Freshmen are admitted fall and spring. Early decision applications should be filed by November 1; regular applications, by May 1 for fall entry and December 1 for spring entry, along with an application fee of $25. Notification of early decision is sent December 15; regular decision, on a rolling basis. There are early decision, early admissions, and deferred admissions plans. A waiting list is an active part of the admissions procedure, with about 2% of applicants on the list.
Transfer: About 1184 transfer students enrolled in 1993–94. To be considered, applicants must have maintained a minimum GPA of 2.5 in colleges previously attended. Some programs require a 3.0 GPA. A total of 30 credits out of 120 must be completed at The College at New Paltz.
Visiting: There are regularly scheduled orientations for prospective students, including 4 to 5 sessions scheduled by appointment on Mondays, Wednesdays, and Fridays during the summer. An open house and Saturday sessions are conducted during the fall. Visitors may sit in on classes. To arrange for a visit, contact the Office of Undergraduate Admissions at (914) 257–3200.
Financial Aid: In 1993–94 75% of all current freshmen and 80% of continuing students received some form of financial aid. About 70% of freshmen and 75% of continuing students received need-based aid. The average freshman award was $2862. Of that total, scholarships or need-based grants averaged $1000 ($5900 maximum); loans averaged $1500 ($2625 maximum); and work contracts averaged $800 ($1200 maximum). Thirty-five percent of undergraduate students work part-time. Average earnings from campus work for the school year are $800. The average financial indebtedness of the 1992–93 graduate was $10,000. The college's own financial statement and FAFSA are required. The deadline for financial aid applications is April 1.
International Students: There are currently 450 international students enrolled. The school actively recruits these students. They must take the TOEFL and achieve a minimum score of 525. The SAT I or ACT is required if the TOEFL has not been taken.
Computers: The college provides computer facilities for student use. The mainframe is an IBM 4381. Students have access to 35 terminals in residence halls, the humanities building, administration buildings, and the library. In addition, there are some 160 microcomputers in general access areas, departmental areas, and laboratories. All students may access the system. It may be used during those hours that the buildings are open. There are no time limits on using the system and no fees.

Graduates: In 1992–93 1460 bachelor's degrees were awarded. The most popular majors among graduates were elementary education (14%), psychology (9%), and business administration (9%). Within an average freshman class, 22% graduate in 4 years, 19% in 5 years, and 3% in 6 years. Some 419 companies recruited on campus in 1992–93.

Admissions Contact: Robert J. Seaman, Dean of Admissions.

STATE UNIVERSITY OF NEW YORK COLLEGE AT OLD WESTBURY

D-5

Westbury, NY 11568–0210 (516) 876-3073

Full-time: 1273 men, 1575 women	Faculty: 133; IIB, +$
Part-time: 470 men, 629 women	Ph.Ds: 75%
Graduate: none	Student/Faculty: 21 to 1
Year: semesters, summer session	Tuition: $2928 ($6828)
Application Deadline: June 1	Room & Board: $4200
Freshman Class: n/av	
SAT I or ACT: recommended	**LESS COMPETITIVE**

The State University of New York/College at Old Westbury, founded in 1968, is a public institution offering degree programs in the arts and sciences, business, education, fine arts, health science, and music. The library contains 242,176 volumes, 187,834 microform items, and 12,000 audiovisual forms, and subscribes to 1059 periodicals. Computerized library sources and services include interlibrary loans and database searching. Special learning facilities include a learning resource center, an art gallery, and a radio station. The 605-acre campus is in a suburban area 20 miles east of New York City. Including residence halls, there are 14 buildings on campus.

Student Life: About 97% of undergraduates are from New York. Students come from 8 states and 28 foreign countries. Fifty-one percent are white; 28% African American; 12% Hispanic. The average age of freshmen is 19; all undergraduates, 25.8. Thirty percent drop out by the end of their first year; 25% remain to graduate.

Housing: A total of 792 students can be accommodated in college housing. College-sponsored living facilities include coed dormitories and honors houses. On-campus housing is available on a first-come, first-served basis. Priority is given to out-of-town students. Eighty percent of students commute. Alcohol is not permitted. All students may keep cars on campus.

Activities: There are 4 national fraternities and 4 national sororities. There are 25 groups on campus, including art, cheerleading, choir, computers, dance, drama, ethnic, jazz band, newspaper, political, professional, radio and TV, religious, social, social service, student government, and yearbook. Popular campus events include Welcome Back Festival, Spring Fling, May Festival, Thanksgiving Festival, Christmas Ball, Black History Month, Women's History Month, and Latin History Week.

Sports: There are 5 intercollegiate sports for men and 4 for women, and 10 intramural sports for men and 11 for women. Athletic and recreation facilities include a 3000-seat gymnasium, an auxiliary gymnasium, playing fields, a swimming pool, a fitness center, a weight room, jogging trails, and courts for tennis, paddleball, handball, racquetball, and squash.

Disabled Students: The entire of the campus is accessible to disabled students. The following facilities are available: wheelchair ramps, elevators, special parking, specially equipped rest rooms, lowered drinking fountains, lowered telephones, and and limited volunteer transportation.

Services: In addition to many counseling and information services, tutoring is available in most subjects. There is also a reader service for the blind, and remedial math, reading, and writing.

Campus Safety and Security: Campus safety and security measures include a 24-hour foot and vehicle patrol, an escort service, shuttle buses, and informal discussions. In addition, there are pamphlets, posters, films, emergency telephones, and lighted pathways and sidewalks.

Programs of Study: SUNY Old Westbury awards the B.A., B.S., and B.P.S. degrees. Bachelor's degrees are awarded in BIOLOGICAL SCIENCE (biology/biological science), BUSINESS (accounting, banking and finance, business administration and management, management information systems, and marketing/retailing/merchandising), COMMUNICATIONS AND THE ARTS (media arts, musical theater, Spanish, and visual arts), COMPUTER AND PHYSICAL SCIENCE (chemistry, computer science, and mathematics), EDUCATION (bilingual/bicultural, elementary, foreign languages, mathematics, science, secondary, and special), HEALTH PROFESSIONS (community health work), SOCIAL SCIENCE (American studies, criminology, economics, humanities, international studies, philosophy, political science/government, psychology, and sociology). Teacher education is the strongest program academically. Business has the largest enrollment.

Required: To graduate, students must maintain a GPA of 2.0 in 120 semester credits; accounting and special education majors require 128 credits. General education requirements include courses in writing and reasoning skills, creative arts, ideas and ideology, cross-cultural perspectives, U.S. society and history, physical or life science, and foreign language.

Special: SUNY Old Westbury offers cross-registration with SUNY Empire State, Lirache, and colleges in Nassau County, internships in teacher education, study abroad, a B.A.-B.S. in biological science, dual majors, a 3–2 engineering degree with SUNY at Stony Brook, credit for military and life experience, nondegree study, and pass/fail options.

Faculty/Classroom: Fifty-two percent of faculty are male; 48%, female. All teach undergraduates. The average class size in an introductory lecture is 35; in a laboratory, 13; and in a regular course offering, 23.

Admissions: Two freshmen graduated first in their class.

Requirements: The SAT I or ACT is recommended. Applicants must be graduates of an accredited secondary school or have the GED. An essay, portfolio, and interview also are recommended. Students are evaluated according to qualifying categories of academic achievement, special knowledge and creative ability, paid work experience, and social or personal experience. AP and CLEP credits are accepted. Important factors used in the admissions decision are leadership record, evidence of special talent, recommendations by school officials, extracurricular activities record, and geographic diversity.

Procedure: Freshmen are admitted in the fall and spring. Applications should be filed by June 1 for fall entry and November 1 for spring entry, along with an application fee of $25. Notification is sent on a rolling basis. There is a deferred admissions plan.

Transfer: About 757 transfer students enrolled in 1993–94. Applicants must submit official transcripts from all colleges attended. Those students with fewer than 24 college credits must also submit a high school transcript. A total of 48 semester credits out of 120 to 128 must be completed at SUNY Old Westbury.

Visiting: There are regularly scheduled orientations for prospective students. There are guides for informal visits and visitors may sit in on classes and stay overnight at the school. To arrange for a visit, contact the Admissions Office at (516) 876–3073.

Financial Aid: In an earlier year, 57% of all freshmen and 43% of continuing students received some form of financial aid. Scholarships or need-based grants averaged $1000 ($1500 maximum); loans averaged $1850 ($2625 maximum); and work contracts averaged $1390 ($2520 maximum). Twenty-eight percent of undergraduate students work part-time. The average financial indebtedness of an earlier graduate was $8500. SUNY Old Westbury is a member of CSS. The FAF, the college's own financial statement and a Singlefile Form are required. The deadline for financial aid applications is April.

International Students: There are currently 83 international students enrolled. They must take the TOEFL.

Computers: The college provides computer facilities for student use. The mainframes are a Unisys A10F, a DEC MicroVAX II, and 2 Motorola machines. The Educational Technology Center houses 3 laboratories with 35 Apple Macintosh Plus, 16 Apple IIe, and 25 Zenith 150 microcomputers. All students may access the system 24 hours daily. There are no time limits and no fees.

Graduates: In 1992–93, 938 bachelor's degrees were awarded. The most popular majors among graduates were teacher education, and business and management (23%), and accounting (13%). Within an average freshman class, 29% graduate in 4 years, 32% in 5 years, and 36% in 6 years. Some 25 companies recruited on campus in 1992–93.

Admissions Contact: Admissions Officer.

STATE UNIVERSITY OF NEW YORK COLLEGE AT ONEONTA

D-3

Oneonta, NY 13820 (607) 436-2524

Full-time: 1859 men, 2786 women	Faculty: 260; IIA, -$
Part-time: 164 men, 323 women	Ph.Ds: 70%
Graduate: 182 men, 413 women	Student/Faculty: 18 to 1
Year: semesters, summer session	Tuition: $2926 ($6826)
Application Deadline: April 1	Room & Board: $4952
Freshman Class: 7500 applied, 4350 accepted, 872 enrolled	
SAT I Verbal/Math: 463/509	ACT: 22 **COMPETITIVE**

The State University of New York/College at Oneonta, founded in 1889, is a state-supported institution offering undergraduate and graduate programs in the arts and sciences. There is one undergraduate and one graduate school. In addition to regional accreditation, Oneonta has baccalaureate program accreditation with ADA and AHEA. The library contains 525,215 volumes, 721,766 microform items, and 13,332 audiovisual forms, and subscribes to 2752 periodicals. Computerized library sources and services include the card catalog, interlibrary loans, and database searching. Special learning facilities include a learning resource center, natural history museum, planetarium, radio station, observatory, science discovery center, col-

lege camp, and off-campus biological field station. The 250-acre campus is in a rural area 75 miles southwest of Albany and 55 miles northeast of Binghamton. Including residence halls, there are 40 buildings on campus.

Student Life: About 98% of undergraduates are from New York. Students come from 14 states and 13 foreign countries. Ninety-three percent are white. The average age of all undergraduates is 20. Nineteen percent drop out by the end of their first year; 57% remain to graduate.

Housing: A total of 2900 students can be accommodated in college housing. College-sponsored living facilities include single-sex and coed dormitories. In addition there are a mathematics and science wing, an international wing, all-freshman housing, and other special interest groupings. On-campus housing is available on a first-come, first-served basis and is available on a lottery system for upperclassmen. Fifty-three percent of students live on campus; of those, 53% remain on campus on weekends. Alcohol is not permitted. Upperclassmen may keep cars on campus.

Activities: Ther are 7 local and 6 national fraternities and 3 local and 5 national sororities. There are 25 groups on campus, including art, band, cheerleading, choir, chorale, computers, dance, drama, ethnic, film, gay, honors, international, musical theater, newspaper, orchestra, pep band, photography, political, professional, religious, social, social service, student government, and yearbook.

Sports: There are 7 intercollegiate sports for men and 9 for women, and 17 intramural sports for men and 17 for women. Athletic and recreation facilities include a field house, a dance studio, weight rooms, and bowling alleys.

Disabled Students: The following facilities are available: wheelchair ramps, elevators, special parking, specially equipped rest rooms, special class scheduling, and lowered drinking fountains.

Services: In addition to many counseling and information services, tutoring is available in most subjects. There is a reader service for the blind, and remedial math, reading, and writing.

Campus Safety and Security: Campus safety and security measures include self defense education, escort service, shuttle buses, and informal discussions. In addition, there are pamphlets, posters, and films, lighted pathways and sidewalks, 24-hour vehicle patrol, and formal workshops.

Programs of Study: Oneonta awards the B.A. and B.S. degrees. Master's degrees also are awarded. Bachelor's degrees are awarded in BIOLOGICAL SCIENCE (biology/biological science), BUSINESS (accounting, business economics, and fashion merchandising), COMMUNICATIONS AND THE ARTS (dramatic arts, English, fine arts, French, music, Spanish, and speech/debate/rhetoric), COMPUTER AND PHYSICAL SCIENCE (chemistry, computer science, earth science, geology, mathematics, physics, and statistics), EDUCATION (art, business, elementary, foreign languages, home economics, middle school, science, and secondary), ENGINEERING AND ENVIRONMENTAL DESIGN (environmental science), HEALTH PROFESSIONS (predentistry and premedicine), SOCIAL SCIENCE (anthropology, child care/child and family studies, dietetics, economics, geography, gerontology, history, home economics, international studies, philosophy, political science/government, prelaw, psychology, and sociology). Business economics, home economics, and physical and natural sciences are the strongest academically. Business economics, education, and psychology have the largest enrollments.

Required: Students must complete 122 semester hours, with at least 48 hours in upper-division courses and 30 to 36 hours in the major. A minimum GPA of 2.0 (2.5 for education majors) must be maintained. In addition, students must complete core curriculum requirements in the fine arts, social and behavioral sciences, natural and mathematical sciences, and foreign language, as well as pass writing and speech proficiency examinations.

Special: Oneonta offers limited cross-registration with Hartwick College, internships in many fields, study abroad in 13 countries, a Washington semester, work-study programs, and dual majors. A 3-2 engineering degree is offered with Alfred, Clarkson, and Syracuse universities, SUNY at Buffalo and Binghamton, Georgia Institute of Technology, and Polytechnic University. Other cooperative programs include a 3-4 in optometry, a 3-2 in management, a 3-1 in fashion, and a 2-2 in physical therapy, medical technology, respiratory care, cytotechnology, or forestry. Credit for life experience, nondegree study, and pass/fail options are available. There is a chapter of Phi Beta Kappa on campus.

Faculty/Classroom: No introductory courses are taught by graduate students.

Admissions: About 58% of the 1993-94 freshman class were accepted. The SAT scores for the 1993-94 freshman class were as follows: Verbal—68% below 500, 30% between 500 and 599, and 2% between 600 and 700; Math—33% below 500, 53% between 500 and 599, and 14% between 600 and 700. The ACT scores were 25% below 21, 50% between 21 and 23, and 25% between 24 and 26.

Requirements: Oneonta requires applicants to be in the upper 50% of their class. The SAT I or ACT is required. Applicants should be graduates of an accredited secondary school and have 16 academic credits, including 4 years each of English and history, and 8 years combined of foreign language, mathematics, and science, with at least 2 years in each of these 3 broad areas. The GED is accepted. AP and CLEP credits are accepted. Important factors used in the admissions decision are advanced placement or honor courses, leadership record, evidence of special talent, extracurricular activities record, and recommendations by school officials.

Procedure: Freshmen are admitted fall and spring. Entrance exams should be taken in the spring of the junior year or the fall of the senior year. Applications should be filed by April 1 for fall entry and November 15 for spring entry, along with an application fee of $25. Notification is sent on a rolling basis. There are early admissions and deferred admissions plans.

Transfer: About 678 transfer students enrolled in 1993-94. Official transcripts of all previous college work must be submitted. A minimum of 15 semester hours of transferable credit and a minimum GPA of 2.5 are required. A total of 45 credits out of 122 must be completed at Oneonta.

Visiting: There are regularly scheduled orientations for prospective students, including 2 fall open houses, individual appointments, and group information sessions. There are guides for informal visits and visitors may sit in on classes. To arrange for a visit, contact the Admissions Office at (607) 436-2524.

Financial Aid: In 1993-94, 67% of all current freshmen and 82% of continuing students received some form of financial aid. About 67% of freshmen and 68% of continuing students received need-based aid. The average freshman award was $2200. Forty percent of undergraduate students work part-time. Average earnings from campus work for the school year are $1200. Oneonta is a member of CSS. The FAFSA financial statement is required. The deadline for financial aid applications is April 15.

International Students: There are currently 60 international students enrolled. The school actively recruits these students. They must take the TOEFL and achieve a minimum score of 500.

Computers: The college provides computer facilities for student use. The mainframe is a DEC VAX. More than 200 microcomputers and terminals are available on campus. Students have access to electronic mail on Bitnet and Internet and to multimedia, graphics, and other specialized laboratories within departments. There is also a token ring network for education and service training courses. All students may access the system. There are no time limits on using the system and no fees.

Graduates: In 1992-93 1340 bachelor's degrees were awarded. The most popular majors among graduates were elementary education (27%), business economics (20%), and psychology (6%). Within an average freshman class, 1% graduate in 3 years, 45% in 4 years, 55% in 5 years, and 57% in 6 years.

Admissions Contact: Richard H. Burr, Director of Admissions.

STATE UNIVERSITY OF NEW YORK COLLEGE AT OSWEGO

C-3

Oswego, NY 13126 (315) 341-2250

Full-time: 3000 men, 3600 women	Faculty: 326; IIA, av$
Part-time: 468 men, 537 women	Ph.D.s: 72%
Graduate: 351 men, 778 women	Student/Faculty: 20 to 1
Year: semesters, summer session	Tuition: $2930 ($6830)
Application Deadline: see profile	Room & Board: $4400
Freshman Class: 7500 applied, 4500 accepted, 1450 enrolled	
SAT I Verbal/Math: 480/550	ACT: 23 **VERY COMPETITIVE**

The State University of New York/College at Oswego, founded in 1861, is a liberal arts institution with regional centers for vocational technical education in Albany and Syracuse. There is one graduate school. In addition to regional accreditation, Oswego has baccalaureate program accreditation with NASM. The library contains 409,000 volumes, 1.6 microform items, and 55,000 audiovisual forms, and subscribes to 1726 periodicals. Computerized library sources and services include the card catalog and interlibrary loans. Special learning facilities include a learning resource center, art gallery, planetarium, radio station, TV station, and biological field station. The 696-acre campus is in a small town on the southeast shore of Lake Ontario, 35 miles north of Syracuse. Including residence halls, there are 45 buildings on campus.

Student Life: About 98% of undergraduates are from New York. Students come from 12 states, 15 foreign countries, and Canada. Ninety percent are from public schools; 10% from private. Ninety percent are white. Forty-three percent are Catholic; 42% Protestant; 15% Jewish; 10% claim no religious affiliation. The average age of freshmen is 18; all undergraduates, 21. Ten percent drop out by the end of their first year; 54% remain to graduate.

Housing: A total of 3900 students can be accommodated in college housing. College-sponsored living facilities include single-sex and coed dormitories. In addition, there are honors houses and language houses. On-campus housing is guaranteed for all 4 years. Sixty-seven percent of students live on campus; of those, 90% remain on campus on weekends. All students may keep cars on campus.

Activities: About 15% of men belong to 9 local and 9 national fraternities; about 15% of women belong to 8 local and 6 national sororities. There are 125 groups on campus, including art, band, cheerleading, choir, chorale, chorus, computers, dance, drama, ethnic, gay, honors, international, jazz band, musical theater, newspaper, opera, orchestra, photography, political, professional, radio and TV, religious, ROTC (Army), social, social service, student government, and yearbook. Popular campus events include Honors Convocations and Quest, Alumni Weekend, Parents Weekend, and College Open House.

Sports: There are 9 intercollegiate sports for men and 8 for women, and 14 intramural sports for men and 20 for women. Athletic and recreation facilities include an ice hockey rink, a field house with an artificial-grass practice area, 23 tennis courts, an outdoor track, 3 soccer and 3 lacrosse fields, baseball and softball fields, 3 basketball courts, and handball, racquetball, and squash courts. The indoor gymnasium seats 1500, and the largest auditorium/arena seats 4200.

Disabled Students: Almost all the campus is accessible to disabled students. The following facilities are available: elevators, special parking, specially equipped rest rooms, lowered drinking fountains, and and a student support group.

Services: In addition to many counseling and information services, tutoring is available in some subjects, including English, mathematics, and college skills. There is also a reader service for the blind, and remedial math, reading, and writing. The Office of Learning Support Services provides general foundation support.

Campus Safety and Security: Campus safety and security measures include 24-hour foot and vehicle patrol, escort service, shuttle buses, and informal discussions. In addition, there are emergency telephones, lighted pathways and sidewalks, a campus police force, and on safety issues and alcohol education programs.

Programs of Study: Oswego awards the B.A., B.S., and B.F.A. degrees. Master's degrees also are awarded. Bachelor's degrees are awarded in BIOLOGICAL SCIENCE (biology/biological science and zoology), BUSINESS (accounting, business administration and management, and marketing/retailing/merchandising), COMMUNICATIONS AND THE ARTS (broadcasting, communications, dramatic arts, English, fine arts, French, German, linguistics, music, Russian, and Spanish), COMPUTER AND PHYSICAL SCIENCE (atmospheric sciences and meteorology, chemistry, computer science, earth science, geochemistry, geology, information sciences and systems, mathematics, and physics), EDUCATION (business, elementary, foreign languages, industrial arts, secondary, and vocational), HEALTH PROFESSIONS (predentistry and premedicine), SOCIAL SCIENCE (American studies, anthropology, economics, history, philosophy, political science/government, prelaw, psychology, and sociology). Chemistry, accounting, English, psychology, and theater are the strongest academically. Business administration, accounting, communications, elementary/secondary education, psychology, and biology have the largest enrollments.

Required: To graduate, all students must complete 42 to 48 general education credits, including 6 credits each in expository writing and mathematics, 9 credits each in social/behavioral sciences, natural sciences, and humanities and fine arts, and a 3-credit human diversity course. Students must have a minimum 2.0 GPA and complete 122 total credit hours (126 hours for technology education and vocational education students). The total number of hours in the major varies from 30 to 78.

Special: Oswego offers cross-registration with ACUSNY-Visiting Student Program. More than 600 internships are available with business and social, cultural, and government agencies. The college also offers a Washington semester, study abroad in more than 80 programs, accelerated degree, dual majors, B.A.-B.S. degrees, a general studies degree, credit for military experience, nondegree study, and pass/fail options. A 3-2 engineering degree is offered with Clarkson University, SUNY at Binghamton, and Case Western Reserve University. There is a freshman honors program on campus, as well as 21 national honor societies. Nine departments have honors programs.

Faculty/Classroom: Seventy percent of faculty are male; 30%, female. Ninety-seven percent teach undergraduates, 91% do research, and 91% do both. The average class size in an introductory lecture is 80; in a laboratory, 13; and in a regular course offering, 24.

Admissions: About 60% of the 1993–94 applicants were accepted. The SAT scores for the 1993–94 freshman class were as follows: Verbal—66% below 500, 29% between 500 and 599, and 5% between 600 and 700; Math—24% below 500, 55% between 500 and 599, 20% between 600 and 700, and 1% above 700. The ACT scores were 14% below 21, 39% between 21 and 23, 28% between 24 and 26, 14% between 27 and 28, and 5% above 28. About 39% of the

current freshmen were in the top fifth of their class; 86% were in the top two fifths. Eight freshmen graduated first in their class.

Requirements: The SAT I or ACT is required. Applicants must be graduates of an accredited secondary school or have a GED certificate. Eighteen academic credits are required, including 4 years each of English and social studies, 3 years each of mathematics and science, and 2 years of a foreign language. An essay and interview are recommended. AP and CLEP credits are accepted. Important factors used in the admissions decision are advanced placement or honor courses, recommendations by school officials, leadership record, extracurricular activities record, and evidence of special talent.

Procedure: Freshmen are admitted fall and spring. Entrance exams should be taken during the spring of the junior year or fall of the senior year. The priority dates for filing applications are January 15 for fall entry and October 15 for spring entry; the application fee is $25. Notification is sent on a rolling basis beginning February 1. There is a deferred admissions plan.

Transfer: Some 850 transfer students enrolled in 1993–94. Applicants must submit official transcripts from previously attended colleges. A minimum 2.5 GPA is generally required. SUNY associate-degree holders are given preference. Secondary school records may be required for 1-year transfers. A total of 30 credits out of 122 or 126, depending on the degree, must be completed at Oswego.

Visiting: There are regularly scheduled orientations for prospective students, usually including a campus tour and a meeting with a counselor. There are guides for informal visits and visitors may sit in on classes and stay overnight at the school. To arrange for a visit, contact the Office of Admissions at (315) 341–2250.

Financial Aid: In a recent year, 80% of all freshmen and 78% of continuing students received some form of financial aid. About 52% of freshmen and 60% of continuing students received need-based aid. The average freshman award was $2366. Of that total, scholarships or need-based grants averaged $931 ($2900 maximum); loans averaged $2135 ($3825 maximum); and work contracts averaged $987 ($1200 maximum). Thirty-five percent of undergraduate students worked part-time. Average earnings from campus work for the school year were $1000. The average financial indebtedness of a recent graduate was $6286. Oswego is a member of CSS. The FAF or FAFSA is required. The deadline for financial aid applications is March 1.

International Students: There are currently 45 international students enrolled. The school actively recruits these students. They must take the TOEFL and achieve a minimum score of 550.

Computers: The college provides computer facilities for student use. The mainframes include a DEC VAX 6000–520 and 6000–320, a Sun 4/280, 2 Sun Sparc servers, 15 Sun or DEC VAX workstations, and a DEC MicroVAX II. There are more than 250 personal computers available for student access. Microcomputer laboratories are located throughout the campus for general access and in support of departmental programs. There is an instructional computing center. All students may access the system. There are no time limits on using the system and no fees.

Graduates: In 1992–93 1937 bachelor's degrees were awarded. The most popular majors among graduates were elementary education (10%), business administration (10%), and communications (7%). Within an average freshman class, 1% graduate in 3 years, 40% in 4 years, 56% in 5 years, and 59% in 6 years. Some 60 companies recruited on campus in 1992–93. In the 1992 graduating class, 26% of all students were enrolled in graduate school within 6 months of graduation; 87% had found employment.

Admissions Contact: Joseph F. Grant, Jr., Dean of Admissions.

STATE UNIVERSITY OF NEW YORK COLLEGE AT PLATTSBURGH

Plattsburgh, NY 12901   D-2
                                                (518) 564–2040

Full-time: 2219 men, 2852 women	Faculty: 265; IIA, -$
Part-time: 188 men, 276 women	Ph.Ds: 80%
Graduate: 190 men, 528 women	Student/Faculty: 19 to 1
Year: semesters, summer session	Tuition: $3105 ($7005)
Application Deadline: March 15	Room & Board: $3812
Freshman Class: 4618 applied, 3583 accepted, 846 enrolled	
SAT I Verbal/Math: 450/540	ACT: 23 COMPETITIVE

The State University of New York/College at Plattsburgh, founded in 1889, is a public institution offering degree programs in the liberal arts. There is one graduate school. In addition to regional accreditation, SUNY Plattsburgh has baccalaureate program accreditation with ADA and NLN. The library contains 354,299 volumes, 801,551 microform items, and 17,161 audiovisual forms, and subscribes to 1447 periodicals. Computerized library sources and services include the card catalog, interlibrary loans, and database searching. Special learning facilities include a learning resource center, art gallery, planetarium, radio station, and TV station. The 300-acre campus is in a suburban area 150 miles north of Albany and 65 miles south of Mont-

real, Canada. Including residence halls, there are 35 buildings on campus.

Student Life: About 96% of undergraduates are from New York. Students come from 32 states, 19 foreign countries, and Canada. Ninety-eight percent are from public schools; 2% from private. Eighty-two percent are white. The average age of freshmen is 19; all undergraduates, 22. Thirteen percent drop out by the end of their first year; 60% remain to graduate.

Housing: A total of 2900 students can be accommodated in college housing. College-sponsored living facilities include coed dormitories. In addition, there are special-interest houses and adult student halls/floors. On-campus housing is guaranteed for all 4 years. Upperclassmen may keep cars on campus.

Activities: About 9% of men belong to 4 local and 5 national fraternities; about 9% of women belong to 7 local and 2 national sororities. There are 90 groups on campus, including art, band, cheerleading, choir, chorale, chorus, computers, drama, ethnic, film, gay, honors, international, jazz band, literary magazine, musical theater, newspaper, orchestra, photography, political, professional, radio and TV, religious, social, social service, student government, symphony, and yearbook. Popular campus events include Canada Day, Homecoming, Family Weekend, Arts and Crafts Fair, Black History Month, Women's History Month, Multicultural Awareness Week, and the Showcase student/faculty research presentation.

Sports: There are 6 intercollegiate sports for men and 7 for women, and 13 intramural sports for men and 12 for women. Athletic and recreation facilities include a 3000-seat ice arena, a 2000-seat gymnasium, an indoor track, soccer and volleyball areas, an indoor swimming pool, a bowling alley, exercise and weight rooms, and racquetball and tennis courts.

Disabled Students: Fifty percent of the campus is accessible to disabled students. The following facilities are available: wheelchair ramps, elevators, special parking, specially equipped rest rooms, special class scheduling, lowered drinking fountains, and lowered telephones.

Services: In addition to many counseling and information services, tutoring is available in every subject. There is also a reader service for the blind, and remedial math, reading, and writing.

Campus Safety and Security: Campus safety and security measures include 24-hour foot and vehicle patrol, escort service, shuttle buses, and informal discussions. In addition, there are pamphlets, posters, films, emergency telephones, lighted pathways and sidewalks, combination locks on student rooms, and a computerized keyless entry system for residence hall access.

Programs of Study: SUNY Plattsburgh awards the B.A., B.S., and B.S.Ed. degrees. Master's degrees also are awarded. Bachelor's degrees are awarded in BIOLOGICAL SCIENCE (biochemistry and biology/biological science), BUSINESS (accounting, business economics, hotel/motel and restaurant management, international business management, management science, and marketing/retailing/merchandising), COMMUNICATIONS AND THE ARTS (art history and appreciation, broadcasting, communications, dramatic arts, English, French, journalism, Spanish, speech/debate/rhetoric, and studio art), COMPUTER AND PHYSICAL SCIENCE (chemistry, computer programming, computer science, earth science, geology, mathematics, and physics), EDUCATION (education of the deaf and hearing impaired, elementary, English, foreign languages, mathematics, science, secondary, and special), ENGINEERING AND ENVIRONMENTAL DESIGN (chemical engineering, civil engineering, computer engineering, engineering physics, environmental science, and mechanical engineering), HEALTH PROFESSIONS (medical laboratory technology, nursing, predentistry, premedicine, and speech pathology/audiology), SOCIAL SCIENCE (anthropology, Canadian studies, community services, criminal justice, dietetics, economics, family and community services, food science, geography, history, human services, international relations, Latin American studies, philosophy, political science/government, prelaw, psychology, social science, social work, and sociology). Biochemistry, nursing, business, education, and social work are the strongest academically. Business, economics, education, and social sciences have the largest enrollments.

Required: To graduate, students must have a 2.0 minimum GPA and complete 125 to 128 semester hours. General education courses total 41 to 42 credits, including 7 or 8 credits in natural science, 6 in social science, 3 or 4 in mathematics, 3 each in English literature or philosophy, history, fine arts, foreign culture and language, and critical thinking/reading/speaking, and 1 in library skills, as well as 6 in upper-division, liberal arts courses. All students must demonstrate proficiency in writing by examination or course work.

Special: The college offers cross-registration with Clinton Community College, internships, study abroad in more than 50 countries, cooperative programs with a variety of employers, B.A.-B.S. degrees, dual and student-designed majors, and an accelerated degree program in any major except nursing. A 3-2 engineering degrees is offered with Clarkson University, SUNY Stony Brook and Binghamton, Syracuse

and McGill universities, and the University of Vermont. Credit for military experience, nondegree study if space is available, and limited pass/fail options are possible. There is a freshman honors program on campus, as well as 18 national honor societies. Fifteen departments have honors programs.

Faculty/Classroom: Seventy-one percent of faculty are male; 29%, female. All both teach and do research. No introductory courses are taught by graduate students. The average class size in an introductory lecture is 30; in a laboratory, 13; and in a regular course offering, 25.

Admissions: About 78% of the 1993-94 applicants were accepted. The SAT scores for the 1993-94 freshman class were as follows: Verbal—72% below 500, 26% between 500 and 599, and 2% between 600 and 700; Math—37% below 500, 50% between 500 and 599, and 13% between 600 and 700. The ACT scores were 27% below 21, 41% between 21 and 23, 23% between 24 and 26, 6% between 27 and 28, and 3% above 28. About 29% of the current freshmen were in the top fifth of their class; 71% were in the top two fifths. Two freshmen graduated first in their class.

Requirements: SUNY Plattsburgh requires applicants to be in the upper 30% of their class. A minimum grade average of 82% is required. The SAT I or ACT is required. Applicants must have at least 12 academic credits, including 4 years of English, 5 combined years of mathematics and science, and 3 years of social studies. An essay, portfolio, audition, and interview are recommended in some programs. The GED is accepted. AP and CLEP credits are accepted. Important factors used in the admissions decision are advanced placement or honor courses, leadership record, extracurricular activities record, evidence of special talent, personality, and intangible qualities.

Procedure: Freshmen are admitted in the fall and spring. Entrance exams should be taken during the junior year. Recommended filing dates are March 15 for fall entry and November 1 for spring entry. The application fee is $25. Notification is sent on a rolling basis. There are early admissions and deferred admissions plans.

Transfer: About 790 transfer students enrolled in 1993-94. Most academic programs require a 2.5 minimum GPA. At least 36 credits out of 125 must be completed at SUNY Plattsburgh.

Visiting: There are regularly scheduled orientations for prospective students, which include a student-led tour and an interview. Special overnight events for accepted freshmen include meals with students and faculty, classroom visits, discussions with faculty, and special workshops. There are guides for informal visits, and visitors may sit in on classes and stay overnight at the school. To arrange for a visit, contact the Admissions Office at (518) 564-2040.

Financial Aid: In a recent year, 50% of all students received some form of financial aid. About 60% of freshmen and 50% of continuing students received need-based aid. The average freshman award was $3750. Of that total, scholarships or need-based grants averaged $1100 ($2400 maximum); loans averaged $1630 ($2625 maximum); and work contracts averaged $1020. Thirty-two percent of undergraduate students work part-time. Average earnings from campus work for the school year are $900. The average financial indebtedness of the 1992-93 graduate was $6700. SUNY Plattsburgh is a member of CSS. The FAFSA and federal and state income tax returns are required; in-state students must also file the TAP application. The deadline for financial aid applications is April 15.

International Students: There are currently 70 international students enrolled. They must take the TOEFL and achieve a minimum score of 500.

Computers: The college provides computer facilities for student use. The mainframe is a DEC VAX 6000/320. There are also 130 IBM PC and compatibles, Zenith, and Apple Macintosh Plus and SE microcomputers available in the microlaboratory and the academic computing center. All students may access the system. There are no time limits on using the system and no fees.

Graduates: In 1992-93, 1325 bachelor's degrees were awarded. The most popular majors among graduates were business and economics (17%), education (13%), and social sciences (11%). Within an average freshman class, 37% graduate in 4 years, 57% in 5 years, and 60% in 6 years. Some 150 companies recruited on campus in 1992-93. In the 1992 graduating class, 33% of all graduates were enrolled in graduate school within 6 months of graduation; 92% had found employment.

Admissions Contact: Richard Higgins, Director of Admissions.

STATE UNIVERSITY OF NEW YORK
COLLEGE AT PURCHASE

Purchase, NY 10577-1400 D-5
(914) 251-6300

Full-time: 1126 men, 1354 women	Faculty: 129; IIB, +$
Part-time: 949 men, 498 women	Ph.D.s: 67%
Graduate: 29 men, 28 women	Student/Faculty: 19 to 1
Year: semesters, summer session	Tuition: $3030 ($6930)
Application Deadline: August 1	Room & Board: $4294
Freshman Class: 2119 applied, 1264 accepted, 391 enrolled	
SAT I Verbal/Math: 470/490	COMPETITIVE

The State University of New York/College at Purchase, founded in 1967, is a liberal arts institution that offers programs in visual arts, music, acting, dance, film, theater/stage design technology, natural science, social science, and humanities. There are 2 undergraduate schools. The library contains 220,000 volumes, and subscribes to 1500 periodicals. Special learning facilities include a learning resource center, an art gallery, a listening and viewing center, science and photography laboratories, music practice rooms and instruments, multitrack synthesizers, an experimental stage, typesetting and computer graphics laboratories, a performing arts complex, and an electron microscope. The 500-acre campus is in a suburban area 35 miles north of midtown Manhattan. Including residence halls, there are 40 buildings on campus.

Student Life: About 87% of undergraduates are from New York. Students come from 32 states and Canada. Seventy-eight percent are white. The average age of freshmen is 18.4; all undergraduates, 23.5. Twenty-seven percent drop out by the end of their first year; 35% remain to graduate.

Housing: A total of 1800 students can be accommodated in college housing. College-sponsored living facilities include single-sex and coed dormitories, on-campus apartments, and married-student housing. In addition, there are units for nonsmokers, freshmen, those interested in health and exercise, and other interests. On-campus housing is guaranteed for all 4 years. Sixty-one percent of students live on campus; of those, 60% remain on campus on weekends. Alcohol is not permitted. All students may keep cars on campus.

Activities: There are no fraternities or sororities. There are 40 groups on campus, including art, band, book publication, cheerleading, choir, chorale, chorus, computers, dance, drama, ethnic, film, gay, international, jazz band, literary magazine, newspaper, opera, orchestra, photography, political, professional, religious, social, social service, student government, symphony, and typesetting. Popular campus events include April Showers Weekend, Family Day, Alcohol Awareness Week; film programs, art exhibits, and music, theater, and dance.

Sports: There are 4 intercollegiate sports for men and 3 for women, and 9 intramural sports for men and 9 for women. Athletic and recreation facilities include a state-of-the-art gymnasium, weight rooms, racquetball and tennis courts, an Olympic-size swimming pool, and playing fields.

Disabled Students: The entire campus is accessible to disabled students. The following facilities are available: wheelchair ramps, special parking, and specially equipped rest rooms.

Services: In addition to many counseling and information services, tutoring is available in every subject. There is also a reader service for the blind, and remedial math, reading, and writing.

Campus Safety and Security: Campus safety and security measures include 24-hour foot and vehicle patrol, escort service, informal discussions, and pamphlets, posters, and films. In addition, there are emergency telephones and lighted pathways and sidewalks.

Programs of Study: SUNY Purchase awards the B.A., B.S., and B.F.A. degrees. Master's degrees also are awarded. Bachelor's degrees are awarded in BIOLOGICAL SCIENCE (biology/biological science), COMMUNICATIONS AND THE ARTS (art history and appreciation, dance, design, dramatic arts, film arts, fine arts, French, Italian, literature, music, photography, and Spanish), COMPUTER AND PHYSICAL SCIENCE (chemistry, mathematics, and physics), ENGINEERING AND ENVIRONMENTAL DESIGN (environmental science), SOCIAL SCIENCE (anthropology, economics, history, philosophy, political science/government, psychology, and sociology). Literature, environmental and natural sciences, and psychology are the strongest academically. Literature and psychology have the largest enrollments.

Required: To graduate, students must prove proficiency in writing, mathematics, and language. A minimum 2.0 GPA is required in 120 total credit hours. Arts majors need 90 hours in the major and 30 hours in liberal arts. Letters and science majors need a minimum of 30 hours in the major. Students in the College of Letters and Science must complete the freshman seminar and the core curriculum, which includes 1 course each in origins of Western culture, structures of the modern world, social and behavioral analysis, literature and literary analysis, quantitative or symbolic analysis, physical or biological science, fine or performing art, non-Western culture, and focus on race

and gender, plus 2 credits of physical education. A senior thesis is required of all students.

Special: SUNY Purchase offers cross-registration with Manhattanville and Empire State Colleges, internships with corporations, newspapers, and local agencies, student-designed majors, dual majors, study abroad, work-study, nondegree study, and pass/fail options. There is also an arts conservatory program. There is a freshman honors program on campus.

Faculty/Classroom: All faculty teach undergraduates. The average class size in an introductory lecture is 25; in a laboratory and in a regular course offering, 20.

Admissions: About 60% of the 1993-94 applicants were accepted. The SAT scores for the 1993-94 freshman class were as follows: Verbal—60% below 500, 31% between 500 and 599, 9% between 600 and 700, and 1% above 700; Math—51% below 500, 36% between 500 and 599, and 13% between 600 and 700. About 25% of the current freshmen were in the top fifth of their class; 57% were in the top two fifths. There were 2 National Merit semifinalists. Nine freshmen graduated first in their class.

Requirements: SUNY Purchase requires applicants to be in the upper 20% of their class. The SAT I or ACT is required. Minimum composite scores are 1000 on the SAT I or 19 on the ACT. Applicants must be graduates of an accredited secondary school or have a GED. Sixteen academic credits, 16 Carnegie units, and official high school transcripts are required. Visual arts students must submit an essay and portfolio and have an interview, film students need an essay and interview, design technology students need a portfolio and an interview, performing arts students must audition. AP and CLEP credits are accepted. Important factors used in the admissions decision are evidence of special talent, personality, intangible qualities, recommendations by school officials, recommendations by alumni, and extracurricular activities record.

Procedure: Freshmen are admitted fall and spring. Entrance exams should be taken in the fall of the senior year or earlier. Applications should be filed by August 1 for fall entry and December 1 for spring entry, along with an application fee of $25. Notification is sent on a rolling basis. There is a deferred admissions plan. A waiting list is an active part of the admissions procedure, with about 5% of applicants on the list.

Transfer: Some 476 transfer students enrolled in 1993-94. Students transferring to the School of Arts with 60 earned credits may transfer only those courses with a minimum 2.0 GPA. Students with fewer than 30 earned credits need a minimum 2.5 GPA and must submit a high school transcript. To transfer into the visual or performing arts, students must pass an audition or portfolio review. The SAT I or ACT, with minimum composite scores of 1000 or 19, respectively, and a minimum 30 credit hours earned are required. A total of 30 credits out of 120 must be completed at SUNY Purchase.

Visiting: There are regularly scheduled orientations for prospective students. There are guides for informal visits and visitors may sit in on classes and stay overnight at the school. To arrange for a visit, contact the Office of Campus and Residence Life or Campus Center North at (914) 251-6335.

Financial Aid: In 1993-94 80% of all current freshmen and 50% of continuing students received some form of financial aid. About 70% of freshmen and 50% of continuing students received need-based aid. The average freshman award was $3800. Of that total, scholarships or need-based grants averaged $1410 ($5000 maximum); loans averaged $3020 ($6000 maximum); and work contracts averaged $970 ($1200 maximum). Eighty-five percent of undergraduate students work part-time. Average earnings from campus work for the school year are $1000. The average financial indebtedness of the 1992-93 graduate was $8000. SUNY Purchase is a member of CSS. The college's own financial statement and the FAFSA are required. The deadline for financial aid applications is March 15.

International Students: There are currently 49 international students enrolled. The school actively recruits these students. They must take the TOEFL and achieve a minimum score of 550. The student must also take the SAT I or the ACT, with minimum composite scores of 1000 or 19, respectively.

Computers: The college provides computer facilities for student use. The mainframe is a Prime 750. IBM PCs are available for student use in the computer center in the social sciences building. The natural sciences building houses PCs as well. Only students taking computer courses may access the system. It may be used when the computer center is open. There are no time limits on using the system and no fees.

Graduates: In 1992-93 about 400 bachelor's degrees were awarded. The most popular majors among graduates were liberal arts (18%), visual arts (18%), and literature (11%). Within an average freshman class, 22% graduate in 4 years, 32% in 5 years, and 36% in 6 years. Some 50 companies recruited on campus in 1992-93.

Admissions Contact: Betsy Immergut, Director of Admissions.

STATE UNIVERSITY OF NEW YORK COLLEGE OF AGRICULTURE AND TECHNOLOGY AT COBLESKILL

D-3

Cobleskill, NY 12043

(518) 234-5525

Full-time: 1344 men, 1176 women	Faculty: 140; III, av$
Part-time: 72 men, 105 women	Ph.D.s: 16%
Graduate: none	Student/Faculty: 18 to 1
Year: semesters	Tuition: $2195 ($5245)
Application Deadline: open	Room & Board: $3450
Freshman Class: 4082 applied, 2987 accepted, 1564 enrolled	
ACT: 19	**LESS COMPETITIVE**

The State University of New York/College of Agriculture and Technology at Cobleskill, established in 1916, is a public institution conferring the Bachelor of Technology in Agriculture degree. There are 5 graduate schools. The library contains 86,000 volumes and 55,000 audiovisual forms, and subscribes to 1000 periodicals. Special learning facilities include a learning resource center, art gallery, radio station, arboretum, greenhouses, and plant nursery. The 750-acre campus is in a rural area 35 miles south of Albany. Including residence halls, there are 53 buildings on campus.

Student Life: About 93% of undergraduates are from New York. Students come from 14 states and 5 foreign countries. Ninety-eight percent are from public schools; 2% from private. Ninety-two percent are white. The average age of freshmen is 18; all undergraduates, 19.5. Twenty percent drop out by the end of their first year; 50% remain to graduate.

Housing: College-sponsored living facilities include single-sex and coed dormitories. In addition there are special interest floors in residence halls. On-campus housing is guaranteed for the freshman year only and is available on a lottery system for upperclassmen. Eighty percent of students live on campus; of those, 90% remain on campus on weekends. Alcohol is not permitted. All students may keep cars on campus.

Activities: There are no fraternities or sororities on campus. There are 50 groups on campus, including cheerleading, choir, chorus, computers, ethnic, honors, jazz band, musical theater, newspaper, professional, religious, social service, student government, and yearbook. Popular campus events include Parents Weekend and Alumni Weekend.

Sports: There are 10 intercollegiate sports for men and 9 for women, and 11 intramural sports for men and 10 for women. Athletic and recreation facilities include tennis courts, playing fields, a gymnasium, a swimming pool, bowling lanes, a field house, a ski center, and a fitness trail.

Disabled Students: Twenty percent of the campus is accessible to disabled students. The following facilities are available: wheelchair ramps, elevators, special parking, specially equipped rest rooms, lowered drinking fountains, and lowered telephones.

Services: In addition to many counseling and information services, tutoring is available in some subjects, including biology, intermediate algebra, and chemistry. There is a reader service for the blind, and remedial math, reading, and writing. There is also an academic skills center.

Campus Safety and Security: Campus safety and security measures include 24-hour foot and vehicle patrol, informal discussions, pamphlets, posters, films, and emergency telephones. In addition, there are lighted pathways and sidewalks.

Programs of Study: SUNY Cobleskill awards the Bachelor of Technology in Agriculture degree. Associate degrees also are awarded.

Required: Degree requirements include completion of 126 credit hours, with 30 to 32 upper-division credits in the major, 11 credits of technical electives, and 7 to 15 credits in other electives. Students must maintain a minimum 2.0 GPA.

Special: The college sponsors internship programs. Students may study abroad at Thomas Danby and South Fields colleges in England. There is a freshman honors program on campus as well as one national honor society. One department has an honors program.

Faculty/Classroom: Seventy percent of faculty are male; 30%, female. All teach undergraduates and 40% both teach and do research. The average class size in an introductory lecture is 33; in a laboratory, 15; and in a regular course offering, 30.

Admissions: About 73% of the 1993–94 applicants were accepted. About 12% of the current freshmen were in the top fifth of their class; 48% were in the top two fifths.

Requirements: The SAT I or ACT is recommended. Applicants must have graduated from an accredited secondary school or earned a GED, and are encouraged to have completed college-preparatory courses. Students planning to enter the agricultural program should also take vocational agricultural courses. Applicants are required to visit the campus. AP and CLEP credits are accepted. Important factors used in the admissions decision are evidence of special talent, advanced placement or honor courses, leadership record, recommendations by school officials, and geographic diversity.

Procedure: Freshmen are admitted in the fall and spring. Application deadlines are open. Notification is sent on a rolling basis. There are early admissions and deferred admissions plans. The application fee is $25. A waiting list is an active part of the admissions procedure.

Transfer: A total of 167 transfer students enrolled in 1993–94. Transfer applicants must have a minimum GPA of 2.0. At least 30 credits out of 126 must be completed at SUNY Cobleskill.

Visiting: There are regularly scheduled orientations for prospective students. To arrange for a visit, contact the Office of Admissions at (518) 234–5525.

Financial Aid: In a recent year, 70% of all students received some form of financial aid. Scholarships or need-based grants averaged $600 ($1000 maximum); loans averaged $1160 ($2625 maximum); and work contracts averaged $370 ($700 maximum). Fifteen percent of undergraduate students work part-time. The average financial indebtedness of a recent graduate was $2308. SUNY Cobleskill is a member of CSS. The FAF or FFS and the college's own financial statement are required. The deadline for financial aid applications is March 1.

International Students: There are currently 14 international students enrolled. The school actively recruits these students. They must take the TOEFL and achieve a minimum score of 500.

Computers: The college provides computer facilities for student use. The mainframe is a DEC. There are 3 open-access computer laboratories, as well as network access in all residence halls. All students may access the system during computer center hours. There are no time limits on using the system and no fees.

Graduates: In 1992–93, 48 bachelor's degrees were awarded. Within an average freshman class, 54% graduate in 3 years and 60% in 4 years. Some 77 companies recruited on campus in a recent year.

Admissions Contact: Henry Geerken, Acting Director of Admissions and Enrollment Management.

STATE UNIVERSITY OF NEW YORK EMPIRE STATE COLLEGE

D-3

Saratoga Springs, NY 12866-4391

(518) 587-2100
(800) 847-3000 (in-state)

Full-time: 631 men, 965 women	Faculty: 124; IIB, +$
Part-time: 2021 men, 2312 women	Ph.D.s: 85%
Graduate: 152 men, 168 women	Student/Faculty: 1:1
Year: see profile	Tuition: $2687 ($6587)
Application Deadline: open	Room & Board: n/app
Freshman Class: n/av	
SAT I or ACT: not required	**NONCOMPETITIVE**

Empire State College, founded in 1971 as part of the State University of New York, offers degree programs in the arts and sciences through its statewide network of more than 40 regional centers and units. Students study on their own with guidance from faculty advisors or mentors, with whom they develop learning contracts. The college maintains year-round operation and students study on flexible schedules. The college's headquarters as well as a regional center is in Saratoga Springs; other regional centers are in Buffalo, Rochester, Albany, Hartsdale in Westchester County, Old Westbury on Long Island, and in New York City with the college's School of Labor Studies. Students gain access through the regional center to other schools as well as businesses, government agencies, and other organizations. There is one graduate school. Students have access to library resources through cooperative programs with SUNY, CUNY, and public libraries statewide. Computerized library sources and services include the card catalog and interlibrary loans. Special learning facilities include a learning resource center.

Student Life: About 98% of undergraduates are from New York. Students come from 15 states and 10 foreign countries. Eighty-five percent are white. The average age of all undergraduates is 37.

Housing: There are no residence halls. All students commute. Alcohol is not permitted on campus.

Activities: There are no fraternities or sororities on campus. There are 17 groups on campus, including student government. Popular campus events include regional centers sponsor events and outside speakers throughout the year.

Sports: There is no sports program at Empire State.

Services: In addition to many counseling and information services, tutoring is available in most subjects.

Programs of Study: Empire State awards the B.A., B.S., and B.P.S. degrees. Associate and master's degrees also are awarded. Bachelor's degrees are awarded in BUSINESS (business administration and management and management science), COMPUTER AND PHYSICAL SCIENCE (mathematics and science), EDUCATION (education), SOCIAL SCIENCE (community services, economics, history, human development, humanities and social science, interdisciplinary studies, liberal arts/general studies, and sociology). Business, management, and economics have the largest enrollments.

Required: Students must earn 128 credits to graduate.

Special: Empire State uses a range of teaching methods, including learning contracts, study groups, and residencies, as well as distance learning in which students confer with faculty by mail and telephone. Students can cross-register with any SUNY or CUNY school and some private institutions, and may study abroad in England, Denmark, Cyprus, and Israel. Accelerated degree programs, student-designed majors, nondegree study, and credit for life, military, and work experience are possible.

Faculty/Classroom: Fifty-six percent of faculty are male; 44%, female. Most work is done on an independent-study basis, with a 1-to-1 student-mentor interaction.

Requirements: The SAT I or ACT is not required. Applicants must be high school graduates, have a GED, or show ability to succeed at the college level. Empire State also considers the ability of a learning location to meet individual needs. AP and CLEP credits are accepted.

Procedure: Application deadlines are open. However, students are admitted to each regional location in order of application. Freshmen are admitted any month except August. The application fee is $30. The college accepts all applicants. Notification is sent on a rolling basis. A waiting list is an active part of the admissions procedure.

Transfer: Empire State offers maximum flexibility to transfer applicants, who must provide official transcripts from previous colleges attended. A total of 32 credits out of 128 must be completed at Empire State.

Visiting: There are regularly scheduled orientations for prospective students. There are guides for informal visits. To arrange for a visit, contact the deans of the individual regional center.

Financial Aid: In an earlier year, 35% of continuing students received some form of financial aid. Empire State is a member of CSS. The FAF and the college's own financial statement are required.

International Students: There are currently 33 international students enrolled.

Computers: The college provides computer facilities for student use. The mainframe is a DEC VAX 11/750. There are also 400 microcomputers, primarily IBM and IBM-compatible models, distributed among the college's branches. It may be used 24 hours a day. There are no time limits on using the system and no fees.

Graduates: In an earlier year, 919 bachelor's degrees were awarded.

Admissions Contact: Martin N. Thorsland, Director of Admissions and Educational Assessment.

STATE UNIVERSITY OF NEW YORK
MARITIME COLLEGE

Throgs Neck, NY 10465   D-5
                                                        (718) 409-7220
                                          (800) 642-1874 (Northeast only)

Full-time: 617 men, 65 women	Faculty: 65; IIB, +$
Part-time: 40 men, 1 women	Ph.D.s: 49%
Graduate: 165 men, 22 women	Student/Faculty: 10 to 1
Year: semesters, summer session	Tuition: $2806 ($6706)
Application Deadline: open	Room & Board: $4364

Freshman Class: 763 applied, 405 accepted, 217 enrolled
SAT I Verbal/Math: 500/550   **COMPETITIVE**

The Maritime College of the State University of New York, founded in 1874, prepares students for the U.S. Merchant Marine officers' license and for bachelor degrees in engineering, naval architecture, science, and marine transportation/business administration. The college curriculum includes 3 summer semesters at sea aboard the training ship Empire State VI. There is one undergraduate and one graduate school. In addition to regional accreditation, New York Maritime has baccalaureate program accreditation with ABET. The library contains 75,643 volumes, 25,462 microform items, and 12,500 audiovisual forms, and subscribes to 484 periodicals. Computerized library sources and services include interlibrary loans and database searching. Special learning facilities include a learning resource center, planetarium, and a 17,000-ton training ship, a tug, a barge, and a training tanker center for marine operations and simulation. The 55-acre campus is in a suburban area on the peninsula where the Long Island Sound meets the East River. Including residence halls, there are 27 buildings on campus.

Student Life: About 72% of undergraduates are from New York. Students come from 18 states and 22 foreign countries. Fifty-four percent are from public schools; 46% from private. Seventy-nine percent are white. The average age of freshmen is 18; all undergraduates, 20. Twelve percent drop out by the end of their first year; 69% remain to graduate.

Housing: A total of 800 students can be accommodated in college housing. College-sponsored living facilities include dormitories. On-campus housing is guaranteed for all 4 years. Ninety-seven percent of students live on campus; of those, 68% remain on campus on weekends. Alcohol is not permitted. Upperclassmen may keep cars on campus.

Activities: There are no fraternities or sororities on campus. There are 38 groups on campus, including band, cheerleading, chess, chorus, computers, drill team, ethnic, honors, international, marching band, newspaper, political, professional, religious, social, social service, student government, and yearbook. Popular campus events include spring formal, Friday night mixers, regattas, and Admiral's Ball.

Sports: There are 11 intercollegiate sports for men and 7 for women, and 11 intramural sports for men and 6 for women. Athletic and recreation facilities include a 2000-seat gymnasium, a swimming pool, a sailing center, and baseball, lacrosse, and soccer fields.

Disabled Students: Ninety percent of the campus is accessible to disabled students. The following facilities are available: wheelchair ramps, elevators, special parking, and specially equipped rest rooms.

Services: In addition to many counseling and information services, tutoring is available in every subject.

Campus Safety and Security: Campus safety and security measures include 24-hour foot and vehicle patrol, informal discussions, emergency telephones, and lighted pathways and sidewalks.

Programs of Study: New York Maritime awards the B.S. and B.E. degrees. Master's degrees also are awarded. Bachelor's degrees are awarded in COMPUTER AND PHYSICAL SCIENCE (atmospheric sciences and meteorology and oceanography), ENGINEERING AND ENVIRONMENTAL DESIGN (computer engineering, electrical/electronics engineering, engineering, mechanical engineering, and naval architecture and marine engineering), SOCIAL SCIENCE (humanities). Engineering, naval architecture, and marine transportation/business administration are the strongest academically. Marine transportation/business administration has the largest enrollment.

Required: To graduate, students must complete the U.S. Merchant Marine officers license program. Students must earn 160 credit hours, with a GPA of 2.0. Distribution requirements and the number of hours required in major varies. All students must spend 3 summer semesters at sea acquiring hands-on experience aboard the college's training vessel.

Special: The college offers co-op programs in engineering and an accelerated degree program in marine transportation/transportation management. There are 2 national honor societies on campus. Two departments have honors programs.

Faculty/Classroom: All teach undergraduates, 12% do research, and 12% do both. The average class size in an introductory lecture is 25; in a laboratory, 15; and in a regular course offering, 20.

Admissions: About 53% of the 1993-94 applicants were accepted. The SAT scores for the 1993-94 freshman class were as follows: Verbal—68% below 500, 22% between 500 and 599, and 10% between 600 and 700; Math—30% below 500, 46% between 500 and 599, 20% between 600 and 700, and 2% above 700. About 27% of the current freshmen were in the top fifth of their class; 60% were in the top two fifths. There were 11 National Merit semifinalists.

Requirements: The SAT I is required. SAT II: Subject tests are recommended. Applicants must be high-school graduates, or hold a GED. Sixteen Carnegie units are required, including 4 years each of English and history, 3 years of mathematics (4 years are preferred), and 2 years of laboratory science. An essay is required and an interview recommended. AP credits are accepted. Important factors used in the admissions decision are advanced placement or honor courses, leadership record, extracurricular activities record, recommendations by school officials, and parents or siblings attending the school.

Procedure: Freshmen are admitted in the fall. Entrance exams should be taken during the junior or senior year. Application deadlines are open. The application fee is $25. Notification is sent on a rolling basis. There are early decision, early admissions, and deferred admissions plans. About 28 early decision candidates were accepted for the 1993-94 class.

Transfer: About 41 transfer students enrolled in a recent year. Transfer students must have a 2.5 GPA. Students having fewer than 30 credits must supply SAT I or ACT scores.

Visiting: There are regularly scheduled orientations for prospective students. There are guides for informal visits and visitors may sit in on classes and stay overnight at the school. To arrange for a visit, contact the Admissions Office at (718) 409-7220.

Financial Aid: In 1993-94, 52% of all current freshmen received some form of financial aid. About 41% of freshmen and 58% of continuing students received need-based aid. The average freshman award was $2700. Of that total, scholarships or need-based grants averaged $844 ($1300 maximum); loans averaged $2238; and work contracts averaged $600 ($1100 maximum). Seventy percent of undergraduate students work part-time. Average earnings from campus work for the school year are $500. The average financial indebtedness of the 1992-93 graduate was $8000. New York Maritime is a member of CSS. The FAF is required. The deadline for financial aid applications is May 1.

International Students: There are currently 41 international students enrolled. The school actively recruits these students. They must take the TOEFL and achieve a minimum score of 500. The student must also take the SAT I or the ACT.

Computers: The college provides computer facilities for student use. The mainframe is a Prime 4050. Students have access from 8:30 A.M. to 11 P.M. to 27 terminals, 8 CAD stations, and 58 microcomputers. The computer center stays open after 11 P.M. when there is sufficient demand. All students may access the system. There are no time limits on using the system and no fees.

Graduates: In a recent year 139 bachelor's degrees were awarded. The most popular majors among graduates were marine transportation (35%), marine engineering (25%), and electrical engineering (10%). Within an average freshman class, 4% graduate in 3 years. Some 50 companies recruited on campus in a recent year. In the 1992 graduating class, 90% of the men and 100% of the women had found employment within 6 months of graduation.

Admissions Contact: Peter Cooney, Director of Admissions and Financial Aid.

STATE UNIVERSITY OF NEW YORK
POTSDAM COLLEGE
C-2

Potsdam, NY 13676   (315) 267–2180; (800) 433–3154 (in-state)

Full-time: 1452 men, 2162 women   Faculty: 234; IIA, -$

Part-time: 90 men, 150 women   Ph.D.s: 68%

Graduate: 134 men, 435 women   Student/Faculty: 15 to 1

Year: semesters, summer session   Tuition: $2916 ($6816)

Application Deadline: April 1   Room & Board: $3990

Freshman Class: 3066 applied, 2163 accepted, 650 enrolled

SAT I: Verbal/Math 480/520   COMPETITIVE

Potsdam College, founded in 1816 by early settlers of New York State's North Country, joined the State University system in 1948. It offers liberal arts and teachers programs, and includes the Crane School of Music. There are 3 undergraduate schools and one graduate school. In addition to regional accreditation, Potsdam has baccalaureate program accreditation with NASM. The 2 libraries contain 393,819 volumes, 605,863 microform items, and 24,000 audiovisual forms, and subscribe to 1417 periodicals. Computerized library sources and services include interlibrary loans and database searching. Special learning facilities include a learning resource center, art gallery, natural history museum, planetarium, radio station, electronic music and recording studios, and a seismographic laboratory. The 240-acre campus is in a rural area 140 miles northeast of Syracuse. Including residence halls, there are 31 buildings on campus.

Student Life: About 97% of undergraduates are from New York. Students come from 20 states, 11 foreign countries, and Canada. Ninety-eight percent are from public schools; 2% from private. Eighty-two percent are white. The average age of freshmen is 18; all undergraduates, 22. Thirteen percent drop out by the end of their first year; 50% remain to graduate.

Housing: A total of 2555 students can be accommodated in college housing. College-sponsored living facilities include single-sex and coed dormitories and on-campus apartments. In addition there are language houses, special interest houses, a wellness house, international house, and first-year experience housing. On-campus housing is guaranteed for all 4 years. Sixty percent of students live on campus; of those, 85% remain on campus on weekends. Alcohol is not permitted. All students may keep cars on campus.

Activities: About 10% of men belong to 4 local and 2 national fraternities; about 15% of women belong to 7 local and 1 national sororities. There are 88 groups on campus, including art, band, cheerleading, chess, choir, chorale, chorus, computers, dance, drama, ethnic, environmental awareness, gay, honors, international, jazz band, literary magazine, musical theater, newspaper, opera, orchestra, pep band, photography, political, professional, radio and TV, religious, social, social service, student government, symphony, and yearbook. Popular campus events include Potsdam Pride Day, Harvest Ball, Ice Carnival, campus picnic, Alcohol Awareness Week, and Parents Weekend.

Sports: There are 6 intercollegiate sports for men and 6 for women, and 8 intramural sports for men and 5 for women. Athletic and recreation facilities include a 2400-seat ice arena, an Olympic-size pool, a 3000-seat gymnasium, a field house; tennis, squash, handball, and basketball courts, a weight room, a wrestling room, and a dance studio. Potsdam's Star Lake Campus provides a recreational setting amidst the Adirondack Mountains wilderness.

Disabled Students: Eighty-five percent of the campus is accessible to disabled students. The following facilities are available: wheelchair ramps, elevators, special parking, specially equipped rest rooms, special class scheduling, lowered drinking fountains, and lowered telephones.

Services: In addition to many counseling and information services, tutoring is available in some subjects. There is also a reader service for the blind, a mathematics laboratory, writing center, language laboratory, reading clinic, and the Educational Opportunity Summer Program.

Campus Safety and Security: Campus safety and security measures include 24-hour foot and vehicle patrol, self defense education, escort service, and shuttle buses. In addition, there are informal discussions, pamphlets, posters, and films, emergency telephones, and lighted pathways and sidewalks.

Programs of Study: Potsdam awards the B.A. and B.M. degrees. Master's degrees also are awarded. Bachelor's degrees are awarded in BIOLOGICAL SCIENCE (biology/biological science), COMMUNICATIONS AND THE ARTS (art history and appreciation, dance, dramatic arts, English, fine arts, French, music, music performance, Spanish, speech/debate/rhetoric, and studio art), COMPUTER AND PHYSICAL SCIENCE (chemistry, computer science, geology, mathematics, and physics), EDUCATION (art, early childhood, elementary, foreign languages, middle school, music, science, secondary, and special), ENGINEERING AND ENVIRONMENTAL DESIGN (industrial administration/management), SOCIAL SCIENCE (anthropology, economics, history, interdisciplinary studies, philosophy, political science/government, psychology, and sociology). Mathematics, education, music education, and physics are the strongest academically. Music education, elementary education, psychology, mathematics, and English have the largest enrollments.

Required: To graduate, students must earn 124 credit hours, with 30 to 33 in the major, and a minimum GPA of 2.0. They must fulfill the school's general education requirements, demonstrate foreign language proficiency, and take 4 credits of physical education.

Special: Cross-registration is offered with Clarkson University, St. Lawrence University, and Canton College of Technology. Political science internships in Albany, as well as others, or an art apprenticeship in New York City are possible. Work-study opportunities, co-op programs in premedicine, prelaw, and optometry, a 3–2 engineering degree with Clarkson University, and study abroad in more than 4 countries are offered. Accelerated degree programs in mathematics, English, and education, as well as 3–2 management and accounting degrees, student-designed majors, and dual majors in interdisciplinary natural science are available. Nondegree study and pass/fail options are offered. There is a freshman honors program on campus, as well as 21 national honor societies. Fifteen departments have honors programs.

Faculty/Classroom: Sixty-six percent of faculty are male; 33%, female. No introductory courses are taught by graduate students. The average class size in an introductory lecture is 40; in a laboratory, 18; and in a regular course offering, 29.

Admissions: About 71% of the 1993–94 applicants were accepted. The SAT scores for the 1993–94 freshman class were as follows: Verbal—68% below 500, 28% between 500 and 599, and 4% between 600 and 700; Math—35% below 500, 51% between 500 and 599, 12% between 600 and 700, and 2% above 700. About 32% of the current freshmen were in the top fifth of their class; 70% were in the top two fifths.

Requirements: Potsdam requires applicants to be in the upper 50% of their class. A minimum GPA of 80% is required. The SAT I or ACT is required. In addition, applicants must be high school graduates in a college preparatory program or hold a GED. Students should have earned 16 academic credits. An interview is recommended; an audition, when appropriate, is required. AP and CLEP credits are accepted. Important factors used in the admissions decision are advanced placement or honor courses, evidence of special talents, leadership record, extracurricular activities record, and recommendations by school officials.

Procedure: Freshmen are admitted fall and spring. Entrance exams should be taken in the junior year or early senior year. Applications should be filed by April 1 for fall entry and December 1 for spring entry, along with an application fee of $25. Notification is sent on a rolling basis beginning January 15. There are early admissions and deferred admissions plans.

Transfer: About 408 transfer students enrolled in 1993–94. Transfer applicants must have earned 12 hours of college credit. Transfers with fewer than 24 credit hours must submit a high school transcript showing a minimum 2.0 GPA. An interview is recommended, as are supplemental recommendations. A total of 30 credits out of 124 must be completed at Potsdam.

Visiting: There are regularly scheduled orientations for prospective students, including open houses, off-campus interviews by faculty, and alumni receptions. There are guides for informal visits and visitors may sit in on classes and stay overnight at the school. To arrange for a visit, contact the Admissions Office at (800) 433–3154 (in-state).

Financial Aid: In a recent year 80% of all students received some form of financial aid. About 75% of all students received need-based aid. The average freshman award was $5500. Of that total, scholarships or need-based grants averaged $1000 ($5150 maximum); loans averaged $3500 ($5125 maximum); and work contracts averaged $800 (maximum). Fifty percent of undergraduate students work part-time. Average earnings from campus work for the school year are $900. The average financial indebtedness of the 1992–93 gradu-

ate was $7500. The FAFSA financial statement is required. The deadline for financial aid applications is March 1.

International Students: There are currently 44 international students enrolled. The school actively recruits these students. They must take the TOEFL and achieve a minimum score of 500.

Computers: The college provides computer facilities for student use. The mainframes are a DEC VAX 6410 and a DEC MicroVAX. There are about 250 Apple Macintosh and MS-DOS microcomputers networked and connected to all campus buildings and residence hall computer laboratories. About 40 terminals are networked to a VAX minicomputer. All students may access the system. It may be used 7 days a week; schedules are flexible. There are no time limits and no fees.

Graduates: In 1992–93 904 bachelor's degrees were awarded. The most popular majors among graduates were psychology (19%), music and music education (11%), and English (10%). Within an average freshman class, 1% graduate in 3 years, 35% in 4 years, 52% in 5 years, and 55% in 6 years. Some 12 companies recruited on campus in 1992–93. In the 1992 graduating class, 25% of all students enrolled in graduate school within 6 months of graduating, 57% found employment within 6 months of graduating.

Admissions Contact: Mary Lou Retelle, Director of Enrollment Management.

SYRACUSE UNIVERSITY

C-3

Syracuse, NY 13244

(315) 443–3611

Full-time: 5027 men, 5115 women	Faculty: 897; I, -$
Part-time: 71 men, 46 women	Ph.D.s: 84%
Graduate: 4484 men and women	Student/Faculty: 11 to 1
Year: semesters, summer session	Tuition: $14,705
Application Deadline: February 1	Room & Board: $6600
Freshman Class: 10,477 applied, 7260 accepted, 2442 enrolled	
SAT I or ACT: required	HIGHLY COMPETITIVE

Syracuse University, founded in 1870, is a private, coeducational institution. Its 11 undergraduate colleges offer programs in liberal arts and sciences, architecture, public communications, education, engineering, management, human development, information studies, nursing, social work, visual and performing arts, engineering, and computer science. There are 11 undergraduate and 13 graduate schools. In addition to regional accreditation, Syracuse has baccalaureate program accreditation with AACSB, ABET, ACEJMC, ADA, ASLA, CAHEA, CSWE, FIDER, NAAB, NASAD, NASM, NCATE, and NLN. The 5 libraries contain 2,300,000 volumes, 4,300,000 microform items, and 26,000 audiovisual forms, and subscribe to 16,559 periodicals. Computerized library sources and services include the card catalog, interlibrary loans, and database searching. Special learning facilities include a learning resource center, art gallery, radio station, TV station, a gerontology center, a speech and hearing clinic, and audio archives. The 200-acre campus is in an urban area 270 miles northwest of New York City. Including residence halls, there are 170 buildings on campus.

Student Life: About 61% of undergraduates are from out-of-state, mostly the Northeast. Students come from 49 states, 62 foreign countries, and Canada. Seventy-five percent are from public schools; 25% from private. Seventy-eight percent are white; 10% African American. The average age of freshmen is 18; all undergraduates, 20. Twelve percent drop out by the end of their first year; 65% remain to graduate.

Housing: A total of 6833 students can be accommodated in college housing. College-sponsored living facilities include single-sex and coed dormitories, on-campus apartments, married-student housing, fraternity houses, and sorority houses. In addition there are language houses, and special interest houses, including theme and language units in Shaw Living/Learning Center. On-campus housing is guaranteed for all 4 years and is available on a lottery system for upperclassmen. Seventy-five percent of students live on campus; of those, 85% remain on campus on weekends. Alcohol is not permitted. Upperclassmen may keep cars on campus.

Activities: About 24% of men belong to 1 local and 29 national fraternities; about 33% of women belong to 2 local and 20 national sororities. There are 250 groups on campus, including art, band, cheerleading, chess, choir, chorale, computers, dance, drama, ethnic, film, gay, honors, international, jazz band, literary magazine, marching band, musical theater, newspaper, pep band, photography, political, professional, radio and TV, religious, social, social service, student government, and yearbook. Popular campus events include Homecoming and Parents Weekend.

Sports: There are 11 intercollegiate sports for men and 9 for women, and 25 intramural sports for men and 19 for women. Athletic and recreation facilities include 3 gymnasiums, 2 swimming pools, weight rooms, exercise rooms, a dance studio, courts for racquet sports, an indoor track, and playing fields. The multipurpose domed stadium seats 50,000 for football and 30,000 for basketball.

Disabled Students: The following facilities are available: wheelchair ramps, elevators, special parking, specially equipped rest rooms, special class scheduling, lowered drinking fountains, and lowered telephones.

Services: In addition to many counseling and information services, tutoring is available in most subjects. There is a reader service for the blind, and remedial math, reading, and writing. There are also special supportive services for the learning disabled.

Campus Safety and Security: Campus safety and security measures include 24-hour foot and vehicle patrol, self defense education, escort service, and shuttle buses. In addition, there are informal discussions, pamphlets, posters, films, lighted pathways and sidewalks. Other services include a blue light security system that enables students to have an immediate link to security throughout the campus in case of an emergency, and a card-key access system in university residence halls.

Programs of Study: Syracuse awards the A.B., B.S., B. Arch., B.F.A, B.I.D., and B.Mus. degrees. Master's and doctoral degrees also are awarded. Bachelor's degrees are awarded in BIOLOGICAL SCIENCE (biology/biological science and nutrition), BUSINESS (accounting, banking and finance, business administration and management, management information systems, management science, marketing management, marketing/retailing/merchandising, and transportation management), COMMUNICATIONS AND THE ARTS (advertising, art history and appreciation, broadcasting, classics, communications technology, comparative literature, design, dramatic arts, English, English literature, fiber/textiles/weaving, film arts, fine arts, French, German, illustration, industrial design, Italian, journalism, Latin, linguistics, metal/jewelry, music, music business management, music performance, music theory and composition, painting, photography, printmaking, public relations, publishing, Russian, sculpture, Spanish, and speech/debate/rhetoric), COMPUTER AND PHYSICAL SCIENCE (chemistry, computer science, geology, information sciences and systems, mathematics, physics, and statistics), EDUCATION (art, early childhood, elementary, foreign languages, mathematics, middle school, music, physical, science, secondary, social studies, and special), ENGINEERING AND ENVIRONMENTAL DESIGN (aeronautical engineering, architecture, bioengineering, ceramic science, chemical engineering, civil engineering, computer engineering, computer graphics, electrical/electronics engineering, engineering physics, environmental design, environmental engineering, industrial administration/management, interior design, manufacturing engineering, and mechanical engineering), HEALTH PROFESSIONS (nursing, predentistry, premedicine, and rehabilitation therapy), SOCIAL SCIENCE (African American studies, American studies, anthropology, child care/child and family studies, classical/ancient civilization, dietetics, economics, family and community services, family/consumer studies, fashion design and technology, food production/management/services, geography, history, international relations, Latin American studies, medieval studies, peace studies, philosophy, political science/government, prelaw, psychology, public administration, public affairs, religion, Russian and Slavic studies, social science, social work, sociology, and textiles and clothing). Communications, social sciences, management, engineering, sciences, and architecture are the strongest academically. Communications, social sciences, management, engineering, sciences, and visual and performing arts have the largest enrollments.

Required: A minimum of 120 credits with a minimum GPA of 2.0 is required in order to graduate. All students must take freshman English and core requirements. Distribution requirements vary according to college and major.

Special: The Community Internship Program places students in off-campus field positions related to their major. Cooperative education programs are available in engineering and retailing. Cross-registration is offered with SUNY College of Environmental Science and Forestry. Study abroad in 7 countries, B.A.-B.S. degrees, dual and student-designed majors, work-study programs, a general studies degree, and pass/fail options are offered. Nondegree study is possible. There is a freshman honors program on campus

Faculty/Classroom: Seventy-six percent of faculty are male, 24% are female; 99% teach undergraduates and 1% do research. The average class size in an introductory lecture is 40; in a laboratory, 15; and in a regular course offering, 20.

Admissions: About 69% of the 1993–94 applicants were accepted. The SAT scores for the 1993–94 freshman class were as follows: Verbal—32% below 500, 54% between 500 and 599, 12% between 600 and 700, and 2% above 700; Math—13% below 500, 51% between 500 and 599, 29% between 600 and 700, and 7% above 700. About 63% of the current freshmen were in the top fifth of their class; 86% were in the top two fifths. Twenty-seven freshmen graduated first in their class.

Requirements: The SAT I (preferred) or ACT is required. SAT II: Subject tests are recommended. Applicants should be graduates of an accredited secondary school, or have a GED equivalent, with 24 credit hours of college preparatory course work. An essay is required.

A portfolio is required for art and architecture majors, and an audition for music and drama majors. AP and CLEP credits are accepted. Important factors used in the admissions decision are advanced placement or honor courses, recommendations by school officials, extracurricular activities record, leadership record, and evidence of special talent.

Procedure: Freshmen are admitted fall and spring. Entrance exams should be taken prior to February 1 of the senior year. Early decision applications should be filed by November 15; regular applications, by February 1 for fall entry, along with an application fee of $40. Notification is sent mid December to mid January for early decision; March 15 for regular decision. There are early decision, early admissions, and deferred admissions plans. About 366 early decision candidates were accepted for the 1993–94 class.

Transfer: About 387 transfer students enrolled in 1993–94. Requirements vary by college. SAT I or ACT scores and secondary school and college transcripts are required for transfer applicants with fewer than 24 credit hours. A total of 30 credits out of a minimum 120 must be completed at Syracuse.

Visiting: There are regularly scheduled orientations for prospective students, including information programs and a campus tour. There are guides for informal visits. To arrange for a visit, contact the Admissions Office at (315) 443–3611.

Financial Aid: In 1993–94 69% of all current freshmen and 62% of continuing students received some form of financial aid. About 64% of freshmen and 55% of continuing students received need-based aid. The average freshman award was $12,600. Of that total, scholarships or need-based grants averaged $7400 ($14,360 maximum); loans averaged $3300 ($4625 maximum); and work contracts averaged $1900 ($2000 maximum). Forty-five percent of undergraduate students work part-time. Average earnings from campus work for the school year are $1500. The average financial indebtedness of the 1992–93 graduate was $14,000. Syracuse is a member of CSS. The FAF and FAFSA are required. The deadline for financial aid applications is March 1.

International Students: There are currently 1610 international students enrolled. The school actively recruits these students. They must take the TOEFL and achieve a minimum score of 500. The student must also take the SAT I.

Computers: The college provides computer facilities for student use. The mainframes are an IBM 3090, a DEC VAX 8820, and a Sun 6/670. Students have access to 400 IBM or IBM-compatible, Apple Macintosh, and Sun microcomputers located in several locations throughout the campus. All students may access the system. It may be used 24 hours per day. There are no time limits and no fees.

Graduates: In 1992–93 2879 bachelor's degrees were awarded. The most popular majors among graduates were management (17%), social sciences (16%), and communications (14%). Within an average freshman class, 64% graduate in 5 years and 64% in 6 years. More than 300 companies recruited on campus in 1992–93. In the 1992 graduating class, 19% of all graduates were enrolled in graduate school within 6 months of graduation; 71% had found employment.

Admissions Contact: David C. Smith, Dean of Admissions.

TOURO COLLEGE
D-5

New York, NY 10010   (212) 463–0400, ext. 400

Full-time: 2925 men, 5034 women	Faculty: 160
Part-time: 173 men, 250 women	Ph.D.s: 65%
Graduate: 667 men, 512 women	Student/Faculty: 50 to 1
Year: semesters, summer session	Tuition: $7130
Application Deadline: open	Room: $4800
Freshman Class: 3686 applied, 2921 accepted, 1149 enrolled	
SAT I or ACT: recommended	COMPETITIVE

Touro College, founded in 1971, is a private institution offering undergraduate programs through the College of Liberal Arts and Sciences and the schools of General Studies and Health Sciences. Campuses are in midtown Manhattan and in Brooklyn. There are 3 undergraduate and 2 graduate schools. In addition to regional accreditation, Touro College has baccalaureate program accreditation with APTA and CAHEA. The library contains 140,000 volumes, and subscribes to 750 periodicals. The campus is in an urban area.

Student Life: Sixty-five percent of undergraduates are from New York.

Housing: College-sponsored living facilities include single-sex dormitories. Housing is limited. Alcohol is not permitted. All students may keep cars on campus.

Activities: There are no fraternities or sororities on campus. There are some groups and organizations on campus, including literary magazine, newspaper, student government, and yearbook. Popular campus events include a student-sponsored lecture series and student-faculty social events.

Sports: There are 2 intramural sports each for men and women.

Disabled Students: The following facilities are available: Some facilities, including elevators, are available for physically disabled persons.

Services: In addition to many counseling and information services, tutoring is available in some subjects, including accounting, mathematics, and English.

Programs of Study: Touro College awards the B.A. and B.S. degrees. Associate and master's degrees also are awarded. Bachelor's degrees are awarded in BIOLOGICAL SCIENCE (biology/biological science), BUSINESS (accounting, business administration and management, and marketing/retailing/merchandising), COMPUTER AND PHYSICAL SCIENCE (chemistry, computer science, mathematics, and physics), EDUCATION (elementary), HEALTH PROFESSIONS (occupational therapy, physical therapy, predentistry, and premedicine), SOCIAL SCIENCE (economics, history, political science/government, prelaw, psychology, social science, and sociology).

Required: To graduate, all students must complete at least 120 credit hours, with 30 to 67 in the major. A minimum 2.0 GPA is required.

Special: The college offers cross-registration, internships, study abroad in Israel, work-study programs, credit for life, military, and work experience, and pass/fail options. There is a freshman honors program on campus.

Faculty/Classroom: Sixty percent of faculty are male; 40%, female. No introductory courses are taught by graduate students.

Admissions: Seventy-nine percent of the 1993–94 applicants were accepted.

Requirements: The SAT I, 500 verbal and 500 mathematics, or the ACT is recommended for some programs. Applicants must be graduates of an accredited secondary school or have a GED certificate. AP and CLEP credits are accepted. Important factors used in the admissions decision are leadership record, advanced placement or honor courses, extracurricular activities record, recommendations by alumni, and recommendations by school officials.

Procedure: Freshmen are admitted to all sessions. Application deadlines are open. The application fee is $35. Notification is sent on a rolling basis. There are early admissions and deferred admissions plans.

Transfer: A 2.5 GPA is required. A total of 30 credits out of 120 must be completed at Touro College.

Visiting: There are regularly scheduled orientations for prospective students. There are guides for informal visits and visitors may sit in on classes and stay overnight at the school. To arrange for a visit, contact Admissions at (212) 463–0400, ext. 400.

Financial Aid: Touro College is a member of CSS. The FAF is required.

International Students: International students must take the TOEFL and achieve a minimum score of 525.

Computers: The college provides computer facilities for student use. The mainframe is an IBM System/36. Microcomputers are also available in the Manhattan computing center. Students in computer clubs may access the system. There are no time limits on using the system. The fees are $40.

Admissions Contact: Jack Abramowitz, Director of Admissions.

UNION COLLEGE
D-3

Schenectady, NY 12308   (518) 388–6112

Full-time: 1059 men, 854 women	Faculty: 183; IIA, +$
Part-time: 77 men, 25 women	Ph.D.s: 95%
Graduate: 231 men, 135 women	Student/Faculty: 10 to 1
Year: trimesters, summer session	Tuition: $17,877
Application Deadline: February 1	Room & Board: $5940
Freshman Class: 3495 applied, 1712 accepted, 529 enrolled	
ACT: 28	HIGHLY COMPETITIVE

Union College, founded in 1795, is an independent, coeducational liberal arts and engineering college. There is one undergraduate and one graduate school. In addition to regional accreditation, Union has baccalaureate program accreditation with ABET. The library contains 489,504 volumes, 554,877 microform items, and 4582 audiovisual forms, and subscribes to 2123 periodicals. Computerized library sources and services include the card catalog, interlibrary loans, and database searching. Special learning facilities include a radio station and writing center. The 100-acre campus is in a small town 15 miles west of Albany. Including residence halls, there are 65 buildings on campus.

Student Life: About 52% of undergraduates are from New York. Students come from 34 states, 11 foreign countries, and Canada. Seventy percent are from public schools; 30% from private. Eighty-five percent are white. The average age of freshmen is 18. Five percent drop out by the end of their first year; 86% remain to graduate.

Housing: A total of 1380 students can be accommodated in college housing. College-sponsored living facilities include single-sex and coed dormitories, fraternity houses, and sorority houses. In addition there are special interest houses, an international house, a cultural unity house, a substance-free house, and an interdisciplinary house.

Eighty percent of students live on campus. Students must reside on campus through their junior year. Upperclassmen may keep cars on campus.

Activities: About 45% of men belong to 17 national fraternities; about 25% of women belong to 4 national sororities. There are 86 groups on campus, including band, cheerleading, choir, dance, drama, ethnic, gay, international, jazz band, literary magazine, newspaper, orchestra, photography, political, radio and TV, religious, social service, student government, and yearbook. Popular campus events include Homecoming Weekend, Parents Weekend, Fitz Hugh Ludlow Day, Women's Week, Black History Month, and Asian Awareness Week.

Sports: There are 12 intercollegiate sports for men and 11 for women, and 17 intramural sports for men and 17 for women. Athletic and recreation facilities include a field house for volleyball, basketball, and track; fields for soccer, football, lacrosse, and field hockey; an ice rink; a gymnasium; a swimming pool; weight rooms; and racquetball/squash courts.

Disabled Students: Sixty percent of the campus is accessible to disabled students. The following facilities are available: wheelchair ramps, elevators, special parking, specially equipped rest rooms, and lowered drinking fountains.

Services: There is remedial math and writing. There is a writing center.

Campus Safety and Security: Campus safety and security measures include 24-hour foot and vehicle patrol, escort service, informal discussions, and pamphlets, posters, and films. In addition, there are emergency telephones, lighted pathways and sidewalks, 24-hour locked residence halls, and security assistants on duty in most residence halls from late evening to early morning.

Programs of Study: Union awards the B.A., B.S., B.S.C.E., B.S.E.E., and B.S.M.E. degrees. Master's and doctoral degrees also are awarded. Bachelor's degrees are awarded in BIOLOGICAL SCIENCE (biology/biological science), COMMUNICATIONS AND THE ARTS (classics, English, fine arts, and modern language), COMPUTER AND PHYSICAL SCIENCE (chemistry, computer science, geology, mathematics, and physics), ENGINEERING AND ENVIRONMENTAL DESIGN (civil engineering, electrical/electronics engineering, environmental science, and mechanical engineering), SOCIAL SCIENCE (American studies, East Asian studies, economics, history, interdisciplinary studies, Latin American studies, philosophy, political science/government, psychology, sociology, and women's studies). Mathematics, chemistry, political science, psychology, classics, history, biology, and electrical engineering are the strongest academically. Biology, political science, psychology, economics, and English have the largest enrollments.

Required: Students must complete a minimum of 36 courses and must maintain a minimum GPA of 1.8 overall and 2.0 in the major. Students must also meet the requirements of the freshman preceptorial and the general education program, which includes courses distributed in 4 areas: history, literature, and civilization; social or behavioral science; mathematics and natural science; and foreign langauges and non-Western studies.

Special: Cross-registration is permitted with the Hudson Mohawk Consortium. Opportunities are provided for legislative internships in Albany and Washington, D.C. Union also offers pass/fail options, dual and student-designed majors, a Washington semester, accelerated degree programs in law and medicine, and study abroad in 20 countries. There are 12 national honor societies on campus, including Phi Beta Kappa. All departments have honors programs.

Faculty/Classroom: Seventy-two percent of faculty are male; 28%, female. All teach and do research. The average class size in an introductory lecture is 35 to 50; in a laboratory, 12 to 18; and in a regular course offering, 25.

Admissions: About 49% of the 1993–94 applicants were accepted. About 74% of the current freshmen were in the top fifth of their class; 95% were in the top two fifths.

Requirements: While the SAT I is optional, the ACT or 3 SAT II: Subject tests, including writing is required. Graduation from an accredited secondary school is required. Applicants must submit a minimum of 16 full-year credits, distributed as follows: 4 years of English, 2 of a foreign language, 2 1/2 to 3 1/2 years of mathematics, 2 years each of science and social studies, and the remainder in college-preparatory courses. Engineering and mathematics majors are expected to have completed additional mathematics and science courses beyond the minimum requirements. An essay is also required, and an interview recommended. AP credits are accepted. Important factors used in the admissions decision are advanced placement or honor courses, recommendations by school officials, extracurricular activities record, leadership record, and personality, intangible qualities.

Procedure: Freshmen are admitted in the fall. Entrance exams should be taken before February 1. Early decision applications should be filed by February 1; regular applications, by February 1 for fall entry, along with an application fee of $40. Notification is sent by April 1.

There are early decision, early admissions, and deferred admissions plans. About 178 early decision candidates were accepted for the 1993–94 class. A waiting list is an active part of the admissions procedure, with about 17% of applicants on the list.

Transfer: About 29 transfer students enrolled in 1993–94. A 3.0 GPA and 1 full year of college academic work are required. Transfer students must study at Union for at least 2 years. The SAT I is optional. A total of 18 credits out of 36 must be completed at Union.

Visiting: There are regularly scheduled orientations for prospective students, including interviews and a tour of the campus. There are guides for informal visits and visitors may sit in on classes and stay overnight at the school. To arrange for a visit, contact the Admissions Office, Becker Hall at (518) 388-6112.

Financial Aid: In 1993–94, 61% of all current freshmen and 51% of continuing students received some form of financial aid. About 59% of freshmen and 49% of continuing students received need-based aid. The average freshman award was $16,200. Of that total, scholarships or need-based grants averaged $12,000 ($21,475 maximum); loans averaged $3000; and work contracts averaged $1200. Thirty-eight percent of undergraduate students work part-time. Average earnings from campus work for the school year are $815. The average financial indebtedness of the 1992–93 graduate was $11,200. Union is a member of CSS. The FAF, the college's own financial statement, and the FAFSA are required. The deadline for financial aid applications is February 1.

International Students: There are currently 75 international students enrolled. The school actively recruits these students. They must take the TOEFL and achieve a minimum score of 550. For most applicants, the college requires the ACT or 3 SAT II: Subject tests. This requirement is subject to availability for international students.

Computers: The college provides computer facilities for student use. The mainframes are 4 DEC VAX computers and a DEC System 5000/200. All dormitory rooms are connected to the central systems. There are about 175 personal computers plus another 50 terminals available for student use throughout the campus in general-purpose and departmental computer laboratories. All students may access the system. It may be used 24 hours per day, 7 days a week. There are no time limits on using the system and no fees.

Graduates: In 1992–93 496 bachelor's degrees were awarded. The most popular majors among graduates were political science (11%), biological science (9%), and history (9%). Within an average freshman class, 80% graduate in 4 years, 87% in 5 years, and 88% in 6 years. Some 75 companies recruited on campus in 1992–93. In the 1992 graduating class, 28% of the men and 36% of the women were enrolled in graduate school within 6 months of graduation; 64% of the men and 59% of the women had found employment.

Admissions Contact: Daniel Lundquist, Director of Admissions and Financial Aid.

UNITED STATES MERCHANT MARINE ACADEMY
D-5
Kings Point, NY 11024

(516) 773-5391
(800) 732-6267 (out-of-state)

Full-time: 892 men, 95 women	Faculty: 74
Part-time: none	Ph.D.s: 85%
Graduate: none	Student/Faculty: 13 to 1
Year: quarters	Tuition: see profile
Application Deadline: March 1	Room & Board: see profile
Freshman Class: 942 applied, 356 accepted, 283 enrolled	
SAT I Verbal/Math: 530/590	**HIGHLY COMPETITIVE**

The United States Merchant Marine Academy, founded in 1943, is a publicly supported institution offering maritime, military, and engineering programs for the purpose of training officers for the U.S. Merchant Marines and the maritime industry. Students make no conventional tuition and board payments. Earnings at sea cover basic expenses at the academy. Cash deposits/fees required total $4090. In addition to regional accreditation, Kings Point has baccalaureate program accreditation with ABET. The library contains 228,806 volumes, 109,694 microform items, and 1872 audiovisual forms, and subscribes to 918 periodicals. Special learning facilities include a maritime museum. The 80-acre campus is in a suburban area 19 miles east of New York City. Including residence halls, there are 28 buildings on campus.

Student Life: About 86% of undergraduates are from out-of-state, mostly the Middle Atlantic. Students come from 48 states and 6 foreign countries. Ninety-two percent are white. The average age of freshmen is 17; all undergraduates, 20. Twenty percent drop out by the end of their first year; 65% remain to graduate.

Housing: A total of 732 students can be accommodated in college housing. College-sponsored living facilities include coed dormitories. On-campus housing is guaranteed for all 4 years. All students live on campus; of those, 75% remain on campus on weekends. Alcohol is not permitted. Upperclassmen may keep cars on campus.

Activities: There are no fraternities or sororities on campus. There are 45 groups on campus, including band, cheerleading, choir, computers, drill team, drum and bugle corps, ethnic, jazz band, marching band, newspaper, photography, professional, radio and TV, religious, social, student government, and yearbook. Popular campus events include Homecoming, Parents Weekend, Christmas Ball, and Graduation Ball.

Sports: There are 17 intercollegiate sports for men and 7 for women, and 4 intramural sports for men and 2 for women. Athletic and recreation facilities include a 4000-seat stadium, a 1000-seat gymnasium, athletic fields, and extensive sailing facilities.

Services: In addition to many counseling and information services, tutoring is available in most subjects, including calculus, chemistry, and physics.

Campus Safety and Security: Campus safety and security measures include 24-hour foot and vehicle patrol and lighted pathways and sidewalks.

Programs of Study: Kings Point awards the B.S. degree. Bachelor's degrees are awarded in BUSINESS (transportation management), ENGINEERING AND ENVIRONMENTAL DESIGN (engineering and marine engineering). Marine engineering systems is the strongest academically. Marine engineering has the largest enrollment.

Required: To graduate, students must complete 160 credit hours with a 2.0 minimum GPA. The required core curriculum includes courses in mathematics, science, English, humanities and history, naval science, physical education and ship's medicine, and computer science. Students must spend 5 months during their junior and senior years at sea on U.S. flagships. All students must pass resident and sea project courses, the U.S. Coast Guard licensing examination and all required certificates, and the academy physical fitness test. Students must apply for and accept, if offered, a commission in the U.S. Naval Reserve.

Special: The college offers internships in the maritime industry and work-study programs with U.S. shipping companies.

Faculty/Classroom: Ninety-one percent of faculty are male; 9%, female. All teach undergraduates. The average class size in an introductory lecture is 25 and in a laboratory, 15.

Admissions: About 38% of the 1993–94 applicants were accepted. The SAT scores for the 1993–94 freshman class were as follows: Verbal—35% below 500, 39% between 500 and 599, 19% between 600 and 700, and 7% above 700; Math—1% below 500, 56% between 500 and 599, 39% between 600 and 700, and 4% above 700. About 61% of the current freshmen were in the top fifth of their class; 96% were in the top two fifths.

Requirements: Kings Point requires applicants to be in the upper 40% of their class. The SAT I is required. SAT II: Subject tests are recommended. Candidates for admission to the academy must be nominated by a member of the U.S. Congress. They must be between the ages of 17 and 25, U.S. citizens (except by special arrangement), and in excellent physical condition. Applicants should be graduates of an accredited secondary school or have a GED equivalent. Fifteen academic credits are required, including 3 credits each in English and mathematics, 1 credit in laboratory science, and 8 credits in electives. An essay is required. Important factors used in the admissions decision are advanced placement or honor courses, leadership record, extracurricular activities record, recommendations by school officials, and evidence of special talent.

Procedure: Freshmen are admitted in the spring. Entrance exams should be taken by the first test date of the year of requested admission. Applications should be filed by March 1 for fall entry. Notification is sent on a rolling basis. There is an early decision plan. About 72 early decision candidates were accepted for the 1993–94 class. A waiting list is an active part of the admissions procedure, with about 50% of applicants on the list.

Transfer: All students must spend 4 years at the academy.

Visiting: There are guides for informal visits, and visitors may sit in on classes and stay overnight at the school. To arrange for a visit, contact the Admissions Office at (516) 773–5391 or (800) 732–6267 (out-of-state).

Financial Aid: In 1993–94, 28% of all current freshmen and 17% of continuing students received some form of financial aid. The average freshman award was $3339. Of that total, scholarships or need-based grants averaged $3339. One percent of undergraduate students work part-time. Kings Point is a member of CSS. The FAFSA financial statement is required.

International Students: There are currently 33 international students enrolled. They must take the TOEFL and achieve a minimum score of 500 and must also take the SAT I.

Computers: The college provides computer facilities for student use. The mainframes are a DEC VAX 8600, an IBM 4381, and a Honeywell GPS. There are also 1200 IBM-compatible and Apple Macintosh microcomputers available in dormitories and laboratories. All students may access the system 24 hours per day. There are no time limits on using the system and no fees.

Graduates: In 1992–93, 203 bachelor's degrees were awarded. The most popular majors among graduates were marine transportation (32%), marine engineering systems (32%), and marine engineering (24%). Within an average freshman class, 65% graduate in 4 years, 71% in 5 years, and 72% in 6 years. Some 20 companies recruited on campus in 1992–93. In the 1992 graduating class, 4% of all graduates were enrolled in graduate school within 6 months of graduation; 85% had found employment.

Admissions Contact: Comdr. Joseph A. Gebhard, Admissions.

UNITED STATES MILITARY ACADEMY   D-4
West Point, NY 10996–1797   (914) 938–4041

Full-time: 3777 men, 496 women	Faculty: 483
Part-time: none	Ph.D.s: 26%
Graduate: none	Student/Faculty: 9 to 1
Year: semesters, summer session	Tuition: see profile
Application Deadline: see profile	Room & Board: n/app
Freshman Class: 10,464 applied, 1610 accepted, 1212 enrolled	
SAT I: Verbal/Math 558/653	ACT: 28 MOST COMPETITIVE

The United States Military Academy, founded in 1802, offers military, engineering, and comprehensive arts and sciences programs leading to a bachelor's degree and a commission as a Second Lieutenant in the U.S. Army, with a 6-year active duty service obligation. All students receive free tuition and room and board as well as an annual salary of more than $6500. An initial deposit of $1500 is required. In addition to regional accreditation, West Point has baccalaureate program accreditation with ABET. The 2 libraries contain 414,711 volumes, 718,666 microform items, and 13,158 audiovisual forms, and subscribe to 2400 periodicals. Computerized library sources and services include the card catalog, interlibrary loans, and database searching. Special learning facilities include a learning resource center and a radio station. Cadets may conduct research in conjunction with the academic departments through the Operations Research Cell, the Photonics Research Center, and the Office of Artificial Intelligence and Analysis. The 16,080-acre campus is in a small town 56 miles north of New York City. Including residence halls, there are 901 buildings on campus.

Student Life: About 82% of undergraduates are from out-of-state, mostly the Northeast. Students come from 50 states and 20 foreign countries. Eighty-three percent are white. Forty-nine percent are Protestant; 36% Catholic; 13% claim no religious affiliation. The average age of freshmen is 18; all undergraduates, 20. Six percent drop out by the end of their first year; 82% remain to graduate.

Housing: A total of 4500 students can be accommodated in college housing. College-sponsored housing is coed. All cadets live in cadet barracks. On-campus housing is guaranteed for all 4 years. Upperclassmen may keep cars on campus.

Activities: There are no fraternities or sororities on campus. There are 104 groups on campus, including bagpipe band, cheerleading, chess, choir, chorale, chorus, computers, drama, drill team, drum and bugle corps, ethnic, honors, international, literary magazine, musical theater, pep band, photography, professional, radio and TV, religious, social, social service, student government, and yearbook. Popular campus events include Ring Weekend and 100th Night for Seniors, Homecoming, 500th Night for Juniors, Yearling Winter Weekend for Sophomores, Plebe-Parent Weekend for Freshman, and graduation week activities.

Sports: There are 18 intercollegiate sports for men and 9 for women, and 16 intramural sports for men and 12 for women. Athletic and recreation facilities include a 40,000-seat football stadium, baseball fields, a 2500-seat gymnasium, an ice rink, courts for squash, handball, tennis and racquetball, 3 swimming pools, workout areas, indoor/outdoor tracks, a golf course and a ski slope, and hunting, fishing, and boating facilities.

Disabled Students: Because cadets must meet physical and medical prerequisites, the campus is not designed for physically disabled students. The following facilities, however, are available: wheelchair ramps, elevators, special parking, specially equipped rest rooms, lowered drinking fountains, and lowered telephones.

Services: In addition to many counseling and information services, tutoring is available in every subject.

Campus Safety and Security: Campus safety and security measures include 24-hour foot and vehicle patrol, self defense education, shuttle buses, and lighted pathways and sidewalks.

Programs of Study: West Point awards the B.S. degree. Bachelor's degrees are awarded in BIOLOGICAL SCIENCE (life science), BUSINESS (management science and operations research), COMMUNICATIONS AND THE ARTS (languages and literature), COMPUTER AND PHYSICAL SCIENCE (chemistry, computer science, mathematics, and physics), ENGINEERING AND ENVIRONMENTAL DESIGN (chemical engineering, civil engineering, computer engineering, electrical/electronics engineering, engineering management, engineering physics, environmental engineering, environmental science, mechanical engineering, military science, nuclear

engineering, and systems engineering), SOCIAL SCIENCE (American studies, area studies, behavioral science, economics, geography, history, law, philosophy, and political science/government). Engineering, geography, and management have the largest enrollments.

Required: All cadets must complete a core of 31 courses and 9 academic electives pertinent to their field of study. The major requires an additional 1 to 3 electives in the field. In addition, all cadets must complete 4 courses each in physical education and military science. A total of 140 credits, including 127 academic, 6 military, and 7 physical, is required to graduate.

Special: There is a freshman honors program on campus, as well as 7 national honor societies, including Phi Beta Kappa. Five departments have honors programs.

Faculty/Classroom: Ninety-three percent of faculty are male; 7%, female. All teach undergraduates and 1% do research. The average class size in an introductory lecture is 15 to 18; in a laboratory, 15; and in a regular course offering, 15.

Admissions: About 15% of the 1993–94 applicants were accepted. The SAT I scores for the 1993–94 freshman class were as follows: Verbal—20% below 500, 51% between 500 and 599, 26% between 600 and 700, and 3% above 700; Math—19% between 500 and 599, 52% between 600 and 700, and 29% above 700. About 82% of the current freshmen were in the top fifth of their class; 95% were in the top two fifths. There were 33 National Merit finalists and 29 semifinalists. About 81 freshmen graduated first in their class.

Requirements: The SAT I and ACT are recommended. Applicants must be qualified academically, physically, and medically. Candidates must be nominated for admission by members of the U.S. Congress or executive sources. Applicants must have 4 years each of English and mathematics, 2 years each of foreign language and laboratory science, such as chemistry and physics, and 1 year of U.S. history. Courses in geography, government, and economics are also suggested. An essay is required and an interview is recommended. The GED is accepted. Applicants must be 17 to 22 years old, a U.S. citizen at the time of enrollment (except by agreement with another country), unmarried, and not pregnant or legally obligated to support children. AP credits are accepted. Important factors used in the admissions decision are leadership record, extracurricular activities record, advanced placement or honor courses, evidence of special talent, and recommendations by school officials.

Procedure: Freshmen are admitted in the summer. Entrance exams should be taken spring of the junior year and not later than the fall of the senior year. Early action admission applications should be filed by October 25; regular applications, by March 1 for summer entry. Notification of early action admission is sent beginning January 15; regular decision, on a rolling basis, beginning mid-April. There is an early action admission plan. About 594 early action admission candidates were accepted for the 1993–94 class. A waiting list is an active part of the admissions procedure, with about 5% of applicants on the list.

Transfer: All applicants must enter as freshmen. A total of 140 credits out of 140 must be completed at West Point.

Visiting: There are regularly scheduled orientations for prospective students. Candidates will be escorted by a cadet, will attend class, have lunch with the Corps of Cadets, and talk with cadets about all phases of West Point life. There are guides for informal visits and visitors may sit in on classes and stay overnight at the school. To arrange for a visit, contact the Admissions Office at (914) 938–4041.

International Students: There are currently 36 international students enrolled. They must take the TOEFL. The student must also take the SAT I or the ACT.

Computers: The college provides computer facilities for student use. The mainframe is a Unisys 2200/425. Each cadet is issued a personal computer that is connected to all other users and the campus mainframe through a state-of-the-art local area network. All students may access the system. It may be used 24 hours daily. There are no time limits on using the system and no fees.

Graduates: In 1992–93, 1009 bachelor's degrees were awarded. The most popular majors among graduates were engineering (25%), management (15%), and political science (11%). Within an average freshman class, 81% graduate in 4 years and 1% in 5 years.

Admissions Contact: Col. Pierce A. Rushton, Jr., Director of Admissions.

UNIVERSITY OF ROCHESTER
Rochester, NY 14627

B-3
(716) 275–3221

Full-time: 2694 men, 2382 women	**Faculty:** 505; I, +$
Part-time: 66 men, 128 women	**Ph.D.s:** 99%
Graduate: 1840 men, 1291 women	**Student/Faculty:** 10 to 1
Year: semesters	**Tuition:** $17,400
Application Deadline: January 15	**Room & Board:** $6296
Freshman Class: 8777 applied, 5498 accepted, 1243 enrolled	
SAT I: required	**HIGHLY COMPETITIVE**

The University of Rochester, founded in 1850, is a private, coeducational institution offering programs in the arts and sciences, engineer-

ing and applied science, nursing, medicine and dentistry, business administration, music, and education. There are 4 undergraduate and 7 graduate schools. In addition to regional accreditation, the university has baccalaureate program accreditation with AACSB, ABET, ACPE, NASM, and NLN. The 7 libraries contain 2,812,892 volumes, 3,781,757 microform items, and 59,757 audiovisual forms, and subscribe to 13,849 periodicals. Computerized library sources and services include the card catalog, interlibrary loans, and database searching. Special learning facilities include a learning resource center, art gallery, radio station, laboratories for nuclear structure research and laser energetics, center for visual science, Strong Memorial Hospital, art center, observatory, and Institute of Optics. The 534-acre campus is in a suburban area 2 miles south of downtown Rochester. Including residence halls, there are 151 buildings on campus.

Student Life: About 55% of undergraduates are from out-of-state, mostly the Middle Atlantic. Students come from 50 states, 58 foreign countries, and Canada. Seventy percent are white; 10% Asian American. Thirty-two percent are Catholic; 27% Protestant; 17% Jewish; 14% claim no religious affiliation. Eight percent drop out by the end of their first year; 78% remain to graduate.

Housing: A total of 3705 students can be accommodated in college housing. College-sponsored living facilities include single-sex and coed dormitories, on-campus apartments, married-student housing, and fraternity houses. In addition, there are language houses, special interest houses, drama and medieval houses, and faculty-in-residence housing. On-campus housing is guaranteed for the freshman year only and is available on a lottery system for upperclassmen. Eighty-two percent of students live on campus; of those, 90% remain on campus on weekends. All students may keep cars on campus.

Activities: About 24% of men belong to 16 national fraternities; about 19% of women belong to 10 national sororities. There are 139 groups on campus, including art, band, cheerleading, choir, chorale, chorus, computers, dance, drama, ethnic, film, gay, honors, international, jazz band, literary magazine, musical theater, newspaper, opera, orchestra, pep band, photography, political, professional, radio and TV, religious, social, social service, student government, symphony, and yearbook. Popular campus events include Yellowjacket Day, Boar's Head Dinner, Dandelion Day, and University Day.

Sports: There are 22 intercollegiate sports for men and 20 for women, and 14 intramural sports for men and 13 for women. Athletic and recreation facilities include a sports center, 5000-seat stadium, a 3000-seat gymnasium, a field house, an ice rink, courts for handball, racquetball, squash, and tennis, an indoor track, a fitness center and weight room, and a jogging path.

Disabled Students: Sixty-three percent of the campus is accessible to disabled students. The following facilities are available: wheelchair ramps, elevators, special parking, specially equipped rest rooms, special class scheduling, lowered drinking fountains, lowered telephones, and pushers for wheelchairs.

Services: In addition to many counseling and information services, tutoring is available in every subject. In addition, there is a reader service for the blind.

Campus Safety and Security: Campus safety and security measures include 24-hour foot and vehicle patrol, self defense education, escort service, and shuttle buses. In addition, there are informal discussions, pamphlets, posters, and films, emergency telephones, and lighted pathways and sidewalks.

Programs of Study: The university awards the B.A., B.S., and B.M. degrees. Master's and doctoral degrees also are awarded. Bachelor's degrees are awarded in BIOLOGICAL SCIENCE (biochemistry, biology/biological science, cell biology, ecology, microbiology, and neurosciences), COMMUNICATIONS AND THE ARTS (art history and appreciation, Chinese, classics, comparative literature, English, film arts, fine arts, French, German, Japanese, linguistics, music, Russian, Spanish, and studio art), COMPUTER AND PHYSICAL SCIENCE (applied mathematics, chemistry, computer science, geology, mathematics, optics, physics, and statistics), ENGINEERING AND ENVIRONMENTAL DESIGN (chemical engineering, electrical/electronics engineering, engineering and applied science, geological engineering, and mechanical engineering), HEALTH PROFESSIONS (nursing), SOCIAL SCIENCE (anthropology, cognitive science, economics, history, philosophy, political science/government, psychology, religion, and women's studies). Psychology, political science, biology, biological sciences, and applied music have the largest enrollments.

Required: A total of 128 credit hours with a minimum GPA of 2.0 is required in order to graduate. College of Arts and Science students must complete 1 primary and 2 upper-level writing courses, 2 courses each in social sciences, humanities, and natural sciences, and 1 course in formal reasoning. They must also demonstrate proficiency in a foreign language.

Special: Cross-registration is offered with other Rochester area colleges. A 3–2 engineering degree is offered with Colby College, Denison University, Earlham University, SUNY College at Geneseo, Hamilton College, Hobart and William Smith College, Middlebury College,

Mansfield University, Morgan State University, and St. Lawrence University. Internships, a Washington semester, B.A.-B.S. degrees, dual and student-designed majors, nondegree study, and pass/fail options are available. Study abroad is possible in Australia, China, Japan, Egypt, Israel, and the former Soviet Union, and in several European countries. Other options include Take Five, a fifth year of courses tuition-free, Freshman Ventures, an integrated course sequence, a management studies certificate, and music lessons for credit at the Eastman School of Music. Qualified freshmen may obtain early assurance of admission to the university's medical school through the Rochester Early Medical Scholars program. There are 5 national honor societies on campus, including Phi Beta Kappa. Thirteen departments have honors programs.

Faculty/Classroom: Seventy-eight percent of faculty are male; 22%, female. All both teach and do research. Graduate students teach 7% of introductory courses. The average class size in an introductory lecture is 75; in a laboratory, 20; and in a regular course offering, 35.

Admissions: About 63% of the 1993–94 applicants were accepted. The SAT scores for the 1993–94 freshman class were as follows: Verbal—37% below 500, 41% between 500 and 599, 19% between 600 and 700, and 3% above 700; Math—12% below 500, 30% between 500 and 599, 42% between 600 and 700, and 16% above 700. The ACT scores were 6% below 21, 20% between 21 and 23, 24% between 24 and 26, 20% between 27 and 28, and 30% above 28. About 75% of the current freshmen were in the top fifth of their class; 92% were in the top two fifths. About 70 freshmen graduated first in their class.

Requirements: The SAT I is required. SAT II: Subject tests are recommended. Applicants should be graduates of an accredited secondary school or have a GED equivalent. An essay is required and an interview is recommended. An audition is required for music majors. AP credit is accepted. Important factors used in the admissions decision are advanced placement or honor courses, recommendations by school officials, leadership record, personality, intangible qualities, and evidence of special talent.

Procedure: Freshmen are admitted to all sessions. Entrance exams should be taken by February of the senior year. Early decision applications should be filed by November 15; regular applications, by January 15 for fall entry and November 15 for spring entry, along with an application fee of $50. Notification of early decision is sent December 15; regular decision, between late March and mid-April for fall entry. There are early decision, early admissions, and deferred admissions plans. About 167 early decision candidates were accepted for the 1993–94 class. A waiting list is an active part of the admissions procedure, with about 6% of applicants on the list.

Transfer: About 178 transfer students enrolled in 1993–94. The most important criterion is an applicant's college record. Transfers are accepted on a rolling admissions basis. A total of 32 credits out of 128 must be completed at the university.

Visiting: There are guides for informal visits and visitors may sit in on classes and stay overnight at the school. To arrange for a visit, contact the Admissions Office Receptionist at (716) 725–3221.

Financial Aid: In 1993–94 73% of all current freshmen and 87% of continuing students received some form of financial aid. About 68% of freshmen and 62% of continuing students received need-based aid. The average freshman award was $18,575. Of that total, scholarships or need-based grants averaged $11,225 ($17,950 maximum); loans averaged $3475 ($4625 maximum); work contracts averaged $1475 ($2000 maximum); and external grants averaged $2400 (variable maximum). Fifty-five percent of undergraduate students work part-time. Average earnings from campus work for the school year are $1400. The average financial indebtedness of the 1992–93 graduate was $14,425. The university is a member of CSS. The FAF or FFS and the college's own financial statement are required. The deadline for financial aid applications is January 31.

International Students: There are currently 468 international students enrolled. The school actively recruits these students. They must take the TOEFL and achieve a minimum score of 600. The student must also take the SAT I or ACT.

Computers: The college provides computer facilities for student use. The mainframes include an IBM 4381, DEC VAX systems, SUN systems, and a Solbourne computer. Students have access to hundreds of PCs, workstations, printers, and terminals in the libraries, classrooms, laboratories, and resource centers on campus. Most residence hall rooms have lines accessing the mainframe computers. All students may access the system 24 hours every day. There are no time limits on using the system and no fees.

Graduates: In 1992–93 1203 bachelor's degrees were awarded. The most popular majors among graduates were economics (13%), psychology (13%), and political science (10%). Within an average freshman class, 65% graduate in 4 years, 75% in 5 years, and 78% in 6 years. Some 87 companies recruited on campus in 1992–93. In the 1992 graduating class, 17% of the men and 18% of the women were enrolled in graduate school within 6 months of graduation; 18%

of the men and 13% of the women had found employment.

Admissions Contact: Wayne A. Locust, Director of Admissions.

UNIVERSITY OF THE STATE OF NEW YORK REGENTS COLLEGE DEGREES

D-3

Albany, NY 12205   (518) 474–3703

Full-time: none	Faculty: n/app
Part-time: 6655 men, 8645 women	Ph.D.s: n/app
Graduate: none	Student/Faculty: n/app
Year: see profile	Tuition: $510
Application Deadline: open	Room & Board: n/app
Freshman Class: 9308 enrolled	NONCOMPETITIVE

Regents College, founded in 1971, is an external degree, noninstructional institution that is part of the state-affiliated University of the State of New York. Students earn undergraduate degrees without attending classes. Credit is given through various sources, including Regents College Examinations, known as ACT-PEP nationally, college-level proficiency examinations such as CLEP, course credit from accredited colleges, course credit sponsored by business, government, or industry, and evaluated by PONSI, military service school courses evaluated by ACE, and special assessment tests and nursing performance examinations where existing proficiency examinations are inappropriate or unavailable. In addition to regional accreditation, Regents College has baccalaureate program accreditation with NLN. There are no residence halls.

Student Life: About 85% of undergraduates are from out-of-state, mostly the South. Students come from 50 states, more than 30 foreign countries, and Canada. Seventy-nine percent are white; 11% African American. The average age of all undergraduates is 37.

Housing: There are no residence halls. Alcohol is not permitted.

Activities: There are no fraternities or sororities on campus.

Sports: There is no sports program at Regents College.

Disabled Students: The following facilities are available: elevators, special parking, and specially equipped rest rooms.

Programs of Study: Regents College awards the B.A., B.S., B.S.Bus., B.S.Comp.Soft., B.S.Comp.Tech., B.S.Elect.T., B.S.N., B.S.Nuc.T., and B.S.Tech. degrees. Associate degrees also are awarded. Bachelor's degrees are awarded in BUSINESS (business administration and management), COMPUTER AND PHYSICAL SCIENCE (computer programming and nuclear technology), ENGINEERING AND ENVIRONMENTAL DESIGN (computer technology and electrical/electronics engineering technology), HEALTH PROFESSIONS (nursing), SOCIAL SCIENCE (liberal arts/general studies). Nursing has the largest enrollment.

Required: To graduate, students must complete 120 credits with a 2.0 GPA. At least 50% of course work must be in the arts and science. The required core courses must include 6 to 12 credits each in humanities, mathematics/science, and social science/history. The nursing program requires a different set of core courses as well as the nursing performance examinations. All students must fulfill a written English requirement.

Special: B.A. or B.S. candidates may major in liberal studies or in most traditional academic disciplines. Faculty consultants design curricula, create examinations, and assess student learning. They do not offer instruction. Students receive academic advising by phone, letter, or in-person. The flexibility of this alternate program enables adults to pursue an undergraduate degree independently. Examinations are available. Pass/fail options are possible.

Requirements: There are no admissions requirements. Applicants need not be residents of New York State. Students without a high school diploma or equivalent are admitted as special students. AP and CLEP credits are accepted.

Procedure: Application deadlines are open. The college accepts all applicants. Notification is sent on a rolling basis.

Financial Aid: In 1993–94, 10% of continuing students received some form of financial aid. The FFS and the college's own financial statement are required. The deadline for financial aid applications is July 1.

International Students: There are currently 250 international students enrolled.

Computers: The mainframe is a DEC Ultrix 5700. There are no time limits on using the system and no fees.

Graduates: In 1992–93 2579 bachelor's degrees were awarded. The most popular majors among graduates were liberal arts (78%), business (10%), and nursing (7%). Within an average freshman class, 52% graduate in 6 years. In the 1992 graduating class, 38% of the graduates were enrolled in graduate school within 6 months of graduation.

Admissions Contact: Louise Koroluk, Dean, Enrollment Services and Records.

UTICA COLLEGE OF SYRACUSE UNIVERSITY C-3

Utica, NY 13502

Full-time: 228 men, 313 women	(315) 792-3006; (800) 782-8884
Part-time: 268 men, 499 women	Faculty: 111; IIB, av$
Graduate: none	Ph.D.s: 85%
Year: semesters, summer session	Student/Faculty: 5 to 1
Application Deadline: open	Tuition: $11,980
Freshman Class: 1278 applied, 978 accepted, 256 enrolled	Room & Board: $4734
SAT I or ACT: recommended	**LESS COMPETITIVE**

Utica College of Syracuse University, a private liberal arts institution founded in 1946, is one of the academic divisions of Syracuse University. There are 5 undergraduate schools. The library contains 154,000 volumes and 49,000 microform items, and subscribes to 1300 periodicals. Computerized library sources and services include the card catalog, interlibrary loans, and database searching. Special learning facilities include an art gallery, a radio station, a TV station, and an early childhood education laboratory. The 185-acre campus is in a suburban area 50 miles east of Syracuse. Including residence halls, there are 12 buildings on campus.

Student Life: About 78% of undergraduates are from New York. Students come from 28 states, 12 foreign countries, and Canada. Eighty percent are from public schools. Eighty percent are white; 18% African American. The average age of freshmen is 18; all undergraduates, 22. Eighteen percent drop out by the end of their first year; 72% remain to graduate.

Housing: A total of 860 students can be accommodated in college housing. College-sponsored living facilities include single-sex and coed dormitories and on-campus apartments. On-campus housing is guaranteed for all 4 years. Seventy percent of students live on campus; of those, 98% remain on campus on weekends. All students may keep cars on campus.

Activities: About 5% of men belong to 2 local and 12 national fraternities; about 2% of women belong to 4 local and 4 national sororities. There are 73 groups on campus, including art, band, cheerleading, choir, chorus, computers, drama, ethnic, film, gay, honors, international, jazz band, literary magazine, musical theater, newspaper, pep band, photography, political, professional, radio and TV, religious, social, social service, student government, and yearbook. Popular campus events include outdoor concerts, mock elections, air and band competitions, Winter Weekend, and Family Weekend.

Sports: There are 7 intercollegiate sports each for men and women, and 23 intramural sports for men and 22 for women. Athletic and recreation facilities include a 2200-seat gymnasium, a competition-size swimming pool, tennis, racquetball, handball, and squash courts, a sauna, Nautilus and weight rooms, dance and aerobic rooms, and a variety of playing fields.

Disabled Students: Eighty percent of the campus is accessible to disabled students. The following facilities are available: wheelchair ramps, elevators, special parking, specially equipped rest rooms, and lowered drinking fountains.

Services: In addition to many counseling and information services, tutoring is available in most subjects. In addition, there is a reader service for the blind, and remedial math, reading, and writing.

Campus Safety and Security: Campus safety and security measures include 24-hour foot and vehicle patrol, escort service, informal discussions and pamphlets, posters, and films. In addition, there are lighted pathways and sidewalks.

Programs of Study: UC awards the B.A. and B.S. degrees. Bachelor's degrees are awarded in BIOLOGICAL SCIENCE (biology/ biological science), BUSINESS (accounting, business administration and management, and business economics), COMMUNICATIONS AND THE ARTS (communications, dramatic arts, English, fine arts, journalism, public relations, and speech/debate/rhetoric), COMPUTER AND PHYSICAL SCIENCE (actuarial science, chemistry, computer science, mathematics, and physics), ENGINEERING AND ENVIRONMENTAL DESIGN (construction management and electrical/ electronics engineering), HEALTH PROFESSIONS (nursing, occupational therapy, physical therapy, predentistry, premedicine, and recreation therapy), SOCIAL SCIENCE (anthropology, child psychology/development, criminal justice, economics, history, international relations, philosophy, political science/government, prelaw, psychology, social science, and sociology). Occupational therapy, criminal justice, and journalism are the strongest academically. Business administration has the largest enrollment.

Required: To graduate, students must complete a total of 120 hours with a minimum 2.0 GPA. There is a required core curriculum of 30 credits distributed in 3 areas: humanities, social science, and natural science. All students must take a proficiency examination in English.

Special: UC offers internships and work-study programs in all majors. Study abroad may be arranged in 8 countries. There is a freshman honors program on campus, as well as 5 national honor societies.

Faculty/Classroom: Sixty-two percent of faculty are male; 38%, female. All teach undergraduates and do research. The average class size in a regular course offering is 18.

Admissions: About 77% of the 1993-94 applicants were accepted. The SAT scores for the 1993-94 freshman class were as follows: Verbal—80% below 500, 17% between 500 and 599, and 3% between 600 and 700; Math—52% below 500, 36% between 500 and 599, 11% between 600 and 700, and 1% above 700. About 27% of the current freshmen were in the top fifth of their class; 26% were in the top two fifths.

Requirements: The SAT I or ACT is recommended. Graduation from an accredited secondary school or satisfactory scores on the GED are required. Recommended high school courses include 4 years of English, 3 years each of mathematics and social studies, and 2 years each of foreign language and science. An essay and an interview are also recommended. AP and CLEP credits are accepted. Important factors used in the admissions decision are personality, intangible qualities, advanced placement or honor courses, leadership record, extracurricular activities record, and recommendations by school officials.

Procedure: Freshmen are admitted fall and spring. Entrance exams should be taken during the junior year. Early decision applications should be filed by December 1, along with an application fee of $25. Notification of early decision is sent December 15; regular decision, on a rolling basis. There are early decision, early admissions, and deferred admissions plans.

Transfer: About 270 transfer students enrolled in 1993-94. Applicants must have a minimum 2.5 GPA. A total of 30 credits out of 120 must be completed at UC.

Visiting: There are regularly scheduled orientations for prospective students, including an interview, financial aid information, and a tour of the campus. There are guides for informal visits and visitors may sit in on classes and stay overnight at the school. To arrange for a visit, contact the Admissions Office at (800) 782-8884.

Financial Aid: In 1993-94, 90% of all current freshmen and 88% of continuing students received some form of financial aid. About 86% of freshmen and 88% of continuing students received need-based aid. The average freshman award was $11,000. Of that total, scholarships or need-based grants averaged $2820 ($4500 maximum); loans averaged $2282 ($2625 maximum); and work contracts averaged $1095 ($1300 maximum). Forty-five percent of undergraduate students work part-time. Average earnings from campus work for the school year are $1095. The average financial indebtedness of the 1992-93 graduate was $11,000. UC is a member of CSS. The FAF is required. The deadline for financial aid applications is March 15.

International Students: There are currently 25 international students enrolled. They must take the TOEFL and achieve a minimum score of 500.

Computers: The college provides computer facilities for student use. The mainframe is a Prime 750. There are also 85 IBM and Apple microcomputers available in 4 laboratories. All students may access the system during posted hours. Time limits are imposed only during peak hours. There are no fees.

Graduates: In 1992-93, 491 bachelor's degrees were awarded. Within an average freshman class, 68% graduate in 4 years. Some 500 companies recruited on campus in a recent year. In a recent graduating class, 11% of the men and 10% of the women were enrolled in graduate school within 6 months of graduation; 84% of the men and 87% of the women had found employment.

Admissions Contact: Leslie North, Director of Admissions.

VASSAR COLLEGE D-4

Poughkeepsie, NY 12601

	(914) 437-7300
Full-time: 841 men, 1323 women	Faculty: 202; IIB, ++$
Part-time: 23 men, 54 women	Ph.D.s: 90%
Graduate: none	Student/Faculty: 11 to 1
Year: semesters	Tuition: $18,456
Application Deadline: January 15	Room & Board: $5750
Freshman Class: 3550 applied, 1887 accepted, 653 enrolled	
SAT I Verbal/Math: 600/620	**HIGHLY COMPETITIVE**

Vassar College, founded in 1861, is a private, independent liberal arts college offering programs in the arts, sciences, education, and multicultural studies. The 2 libraries contain 716,921 volumes, 350,000 microform items, and 27,000 audiovisual forms, and subscribe to 3900 periodicals. Computerized library sources and services include the card catalog, interlibrary loans, and database searching. Special learning facilities include a learning resource center, an art gallery, a radio station, a geological museum, a satellite hook-up to receive television from Russia, an observatory, 3 theaters, an environmental field station, and an intercultural center. The 1000-acre campus is in a suburban area 75 miles north of New York City. Including residence halls, there are 100 buildings on campus.

Student Life: About 68% of undergraduates are from out-of-state, mostly the Middle Atlantic. Students come from 45 states, 36 foreign countries, and Canada. Sixty percent are from public schools; 30% from private. Seventy-five percent are white. The average age of freshmen is 18; all undergraduates, 20. Two percent drop out by the end of their first year; 88% remain to graduate.

Housing: A total of 2250 students can be accommodated in college housing. College-sponsored living facilities include single-sex and coed dormitories, on-campus apartments, off-campus apartments, and married-student housing. In addition, there is 1 all-women residence hall and one cooperative living unit. On-campus housing is guaranteed for all 4 years. Ninety-eight percent of students live on campus; of those, 90% remain on campus on weekends. All students may keep cars on campus.

Activities: There are no fraternities or sororities on campus. There are 85 groups on campus, including art, band, chess, choir, chorale, chorus, computers, dance, drama, ethnic, film, gay, jazz band, literary magazine, newspaper, opera, orchestra, radio, religious, social service, student government, and yearbook. Popular campus events include Founders Day, fall and spring convocations, serenading, spring and fall formals, All Parents Weekend, and Freshman Parents Weekend.

Sports: There are 10 intercollegiate sports for men and 10 for women, and 11 intramural sports for men and 10 for women. Athletic and recreation facilities include a field house with swimming pool, 5 indoor tennis courts, a weight and conditioning room, a gymnasium with squash and racquetball courts and basketball facilities, a 9-hole golf course, 13 outdoor tennis courts, an all-weather track, 2 soccer fields, a baseball diamond, a rugby field, and various club and intramural fields.

Disabled Students: Thirty percent of the campus is accessible to disabled students. The following facilities are available: wheelchair ramps, elevators, special parking, specially equipped rest rooms, and lowered drinking fountains.

Services: In addition to many counseling and information services, tutoring is available in most subjects. There is also a reader service for the blind, and remedial math, reading, and writing.

Campus Safety and Security: Campus safety and security measures include 24-hour foot and vehicle patrol, escort service, informal discussions, and emergency telephones. In addition, there are lighted pathways and sidewalks.

Programs of Study: Vassar awards the A.B. degree. Master's degrees also are awarded. Bachelor's degrees are awarded in BIOLOGICAL SCIENCE (biochemistry and biology/biological science), COMMUNICATIONS AND THE ARTS (art, dramatic arts, English, film arts, fine arts, languages, and music), COMPUTER AND PHYSICAL SCIENCE (chemistry, computer science, geology, mathematics, and physics), EDUCATION (foreign languages), ENGINEERING AND ENVIRONMENTAL DESIGN (engineering and environmental science), HEALTH PROFESSIONS (premedicine), SOCIAL SCIENCE (African studies, American studies, anthropology, Asian/Oriental studies, economics, geography, history, international studies, philosophy, political science/government, prelaw, psychobiology, psychology, religion, social studies, sociology, urban studies, and women's studies). English, political science, and psychology have the largest enrollments.

Required: In order to graduate, students must have a total of 34 units equivalent to 120 credit hours, with a minimum GPA of 2.0. Of this total, no more than 17 units may be in a single field of concentration and 8 1/2 units must be outside the major field. Entering freshmen must take the freshman course. All students must meet the foreign language proficiency requirement and must take a quantitative skills course before their third year.

Special: The school offers field work in social agencies and schools, a Washington semester, dual majors, independent majors, and pass/fail options. Study abroad programs may be arranged in 8 countries. A 3–2 engineering degree with Dartmouth College is offered. There is a chapter of Phi Beta Kappa on campus.

Faculty/Classroom: Sixty percent of faculty are male; 40%, female. All teach and do research. The average class size in an introductory lecture is 50; in a laboratory, 7; and in a regular course offering, 20.

Admissions: About 53% of the 1993–94 applicants were accepted. The SAT I scores for the 1993–94 freshman class were as follows: Verbal—9% below 500, 40% between 500 and 599, 47% between 600 and 700, and 4% above 700; Math—7% below 500, 31% between 500 and 599, 51% between 600 and 700, and 11% above 700. About 79% of the current freshmen were in the top fifth of their class; 97% were in the top two fifths. There was 1 National Merit finalist and 22 semifinalists. Eighteen freshmen graduated first in their class.

Requirements: The SAT I plus 3 SAT II: Subject tests, preferably 1 in writing, or the ACT is required. In addition, graduation from an accredited secondary school or satisfactory scores on the GED are required for admission. The high school program should typically include 4 years of English, 3 or more years of a foreign language, 3 or

4 years of social studies, 3 years of mathematics, and 2 or 3 years of science. An essay and a writing sample are required. AP and CLEP credits are accepted. Important factors used in the admissions decision are advanced placement or honor courses, leadership record, recommendations by school officials, extracurricular activities record, personality, and intangible qualities.

Procedure: Freshmen are admitted in the fall. Entrance exams should be taken as early as possible, but no later than December of the senior year. There are early decision, early admissions, and deferred admissions plans. Early decision applications should be filed by December 1 and January 15; regular applications, by January 15 for fall entry, along with an application fee of $60. Notification is sent early April. About 175 early decision candidates were accepted for the 1993–94 class. A waiting list is an active part of the admissions procedure.

Transfer: About 30 transfer students enrolled in 1993–94. Transfer students must have at least 1 year of liberal arts course work with a minimum GPA of 3.0. At least 17 credits out of 34 must be completed at Vassar.

Visiting: There are regularly scheduled orientations for prospective students, including a campus tour, an information session, a class visit, and an interview, if desired. There are guides for informal visits, and visitors may sit in on classes and stay overnight at the school. To arrange for a visit, contact the Admissions Office at (914) 437–7300.

Financial Aid: In 1993–94, 53% of all current freshmen and 58% of continuing students received some form of financial aid. About 52% of freshmen and 51% of continuing students received need-based aid. The average freshman award was $17,233. Of that total, scholarships or need-based grants averaged $13,948 ($21,016 maximum); loans averaged $2185 ($2625 maximum); and work contracts averaged $1100 ($1150 maximum). Sixty percent of undergraduate students work part-time. Average earnings from campus work for the school year were $800. The average financial indebtedness of the 1992–93 graduate was $12,250. Vassar is a member of CSS. The FAF and the college's own financial statement are required. The deadline for financial aid applications is January 15.

International Students: There are currently 92 international students enrolled. The school actively recruits these students. They must take the TOEFL and achieve a minimum score of 600 and must also take the SAT I and SAT II: Subject tests.

Computers: The college provides computer facilities for student use. The mainframes are a DEC VAX 6200, an 11/780, an 11/750, and a MicroVAX II. There are also 350 Apple Macintosh and IBM microcomputers available throughout the campus. All students may access the system 24 hours per day. There are no time limits on using the system and no fees.

Graduates: In 1992–93, 583 bachelor's degrees were awarded. The most popular majors among graduates were English (16%), political science (8%), and psychology (7%). Within an average freshman class, 1% graduate in 3 years, 78% in 4 years, 86% in 5 years, and 87% in 6 years. Some 14 companies recruited on campus in 1992–93. In the 1992 graduating class, 24% of all graduates were enrolled in graduate school within 6 months of graduation; 60% had found employment.

Admissions Contact: Thomas Matos, Director of Admissions.

WAGNER COLLEGE

D-5

Staten Island, NY 10301   (718) 390–3411; (800) 221–1010

Full-time: 582 men, 742 women	**Faculty:** 76; IIB, -$
Part-time: 33 men, 84 women	**Ph.D.s:** 85%
Graduate: 99 men, 289 women	**Student/Faculty:** 17 to 1
Year: semesters, summer session	**Tuition:** $12,500
Application Deadline: February 15	**Room & Board:** $5450
Freshman Class: 1411 applied, 1015 accepted, 416 enrolled	
SAT I Verbal/Math: 480/510	**COMPETITIVE**

Wagner College, founded in 1883, is a private liberal arts institution. There is one graduate school. In addition to regional accreditation, Wagner has baccalaureate program accreditation with NLN. The library contains 300,000 volumes and 225,000 microform items, and subscribes to 1000 periodicals. Computerized library sources and services include interlibrary loans and database searching. Special learning facilities include an art gallery, planetarium, and radio station. The 110-acre campus is in an urban area 10 miles from Manhattan. Including residence halls, there are 18 buildings on campus.

Student Life: About 71% of undergraduates are from New York. Students come from 23 states, 28 foreign countries, and Canada. Sixty-one percent are from public schools; 39% from private. Eighty-seven percent are white. Seventy-six percent claim no religious affiliation; 17% Catholic. The average age of freshmen is 18; all undergraduates, 20. Eighteen percent drop out by the end of their first year; 68% remain to graduate.

Housing: A total of 1315 students can be accommodated in college housing. College-sponsored living facilities include coed dormitories. In addition, there are fraternity/sorority floors in dormitories and quiet

floors. On-campus housing is guaranteed for all 4 years. Sixty-five percent of students live on campus; of those, 75% remain on campus on weekends. Alcohol is not permitted. Upperclassmen may keep cars on campus.

Activities: About 30% of men belong to 4 local and 4 national fraternities; about 20% of women belong to 1 local and 2 national sororities. There are 70 groups on campus, including art, band, cheerleading, chess, choir, chorale, computers, dance, drama, ethnic, gay, honors, international, jazz band, musical theater, newspaper, pep band, political, professional, radio and TV, religious, social service, student government, symphony, and yearbook. Popular campus events include Songfest, Homecoming, and Community Chest.

Sports: There are 7 intercollegiate sports for men and 6 for women, and 8 intramural sports for men and 5 for women. Athletic and recreation facilities include a football stadium, a gymnasium, a fitness center, a track, and a basketball stadium.

Disabled Students: Twenty-five percent of the campus is accessible to disabled students. The following facilities are available: wheelchair ramps, elevators, special parking, specially equipped rest rooms, and special class scheduling.

Services: In addition to many counseling and information services, tutoring is available in every subject. There is also a reader service for the blind, and remedial math, reading, and writing.

Campus Safety and Security: Campus safety and security measures include 24-hour foot and vehicle patrol, escort service, shuttle buses, and informal discussions. In addition, there are emergency telephones and lighted pathways and sidewalks.

Programs of Study: Wagner awards the B.A. and B.S. degrees. Master's degrees also are awarded. Bachelor's degrees are awarded in BIOLOGICAL SCIENCE (biology/biological science and microbiology), BUSINESS (accounting, banking and finance, business administration and management, business economics, and marketing/retailing/merchandising), COMMUNICATIONS AND THE ARTS (arts administration/management, dramatic arts, fine arts, music, and speech/debate/rhetoric), COMPUTER AND PHYSICAL SCIENCE (chemistry, computer science, mathematics, and physics), EDUCATION (elementary, middle school, and secondary), HEALTH PROFESSIONS (medical laboratory technology, nursing, physician's assistant, predentistry, and premedicine), SOCIAL SCIENCE (anthropology, gerontology, history, philosophy, political science/government, prelaw, psychology, public administration, religion, social science, social work, and sociology). Natural sciences is the strongest academically. Business and economics have the largest enrollments.

Required: In order to graduate, students must complete a total of 128 credit hours with a minimum GPA of 2.0. Sixty hours are required in the major for a B.A. (75 for a B.S.). All students must take courses in English, mathematics, and interdisciplinary studies. In addition, students must fulfill distribution requirements in physical science, life science, mathematics and computers, history, literature, philosophy and religion, foreign culture, aesthetics, and human behavior.

Special: Internships are required for business and English majors and recommended for all majors. Students may earn B.A.-B.S. degrees in mathematics, physics, and psychology. Student-designed and dual majors, credit for life experience, nondegree study, and pass/fail options are available. Study abroad in most countries of Asia and Europe is possible. There is a freshman honors program on campus, as well as 9 national honor societies.

Faculty/Classroom: Fifty-two percent of faculty are male; 48%, female. All teach undergraduates. No introductory courses are taught by graduate students. The average class size in an introductory lecture is 35; in a laboratory, 15; and in a regular course offering, 20.

Admissions: About 72% of the 1993–94 applicants were accepted. The SAT scores for the 1993–94 freshman class were as follows: Verbal—52% below 500, 37% between 500 and 599, 9% between 600 and 700, and 1% above 700; Math—36% below 500, 47% between 500 and 599, 12% between 600 and 700, and 3% above 700. About 27% of the current freshmen were in the top fifth of their class; 27% were in the top two fifths. Three freshmen graduated first in their class.

Requirements: Wagner requires applicants to be in the upper 50% of their class. A minimum average of 80% is required. The SAT I or ACT is required. For the SAT I, the required minimum scores are 430 for the verbal section and 450 for the mathematics. A composite score of 21 is required on the ACT. Graduation from an accredited secondary school or satisfactory scores on the GED are required for admission. Sixteen academic credits or Carnegie units are required, including 4 years of English, 2 years each of a foreign language, history, mathematics, science, and social studies, and 1 year each of art and music. An essay and an interview are recommended. Auditions are required for music and theater applicants. AP and CLEP credits are accepted. Important factors used in the admissions decision are extracurricular activities record, leadership record, evidence of special talent, advanced placement or honor courses, and recommendations by school officials.

Procedure: Freshmen are admitted in the fall and spring. Entrance exams should be taken by December of the senior year. There are early decision, early admissions, and deferred admissions plans. Early decision applications should be filed by December 15; regular applications, by February 15 for fall entry and December 1 for spring entry, along with an application fee of $35. Notification of early decision is sent January 15; regular decision, on a rolling basis. About 35 early decision candidates were accepted for the 1993–94 class. A waiting list is an active part of the admissions procedure, with about 8% of applicants on the list.

Transfer: About 80 transfer students enrolled in 1993–94. The school recommends that transfer students have a minimum of 30 credit hours earned with a minimum GPA of 2.5. Applicants must submit all college and high school transcripts, a letter of recommendation, and a personal statement. An interview is recommended. SAT I or ACT scores taken within the last 5 years may be submitted. At least 30 credits out of 128 must be completed at Wagner.

Visiting: There are guides for informal visits, and visitors may sit in on classes and stay overnight at the school. To arrange for a visit, contact the Admissions Office at (718) 390–3411 or (800) 221–1010.

Financial Aid: In a recent year, 75% of all freshmen and 70% of continuing students received some form of financial aid. About 70% of freshmen and 65% of continuing students received need-based aid. Scholarships or need-based grants averaged $4225 ($6500 maximum); loans averaged $2625; and work contracts averaged $800 ($1200 maximum). Wagner is a member of CSS. The FAF, the college's own financial statement and the FAFSA are required. The deadline for financial aid applications is April 1.

International Students: There are currently 70 international students enrolled. The school actively recruits these students. They must take the TOEFL and achieve a minimum score of 550.

Computers: The college provides computer facilities for student use. The mainframe is a DEC VAX. There are 75 IBM PS/s microcomputers in the computer center that are connected to the mainframe. There are an additional 52 IBM microcomputers available for student use. Printers include 4 HP LaserJet, 2 Epson LQ dot-matrix, and 1 HP PaintJet. All students may access the system Monday through Thursday, 9 A.M. to 10 P.M.; Friday, 9 A.M. to 6 P.M.; and Saturday and Sunday, 11 A.M. to 5 P.M. There are no time limits on using the system and no fees.

Graduates: In 1992–93, 283 bachelor's degrees were awarded. The most popular majors among graduates were education (17%), business administration (16%), and biological sciences (10%). Within an average freshman class, 60% graduate in 4 years and 7% in 5 years. Some 43 companies recruited on campus in 1992–93. In the 1992 graduating class, 20% of all graduates were enrolled in graduate school within 6 months of graduation; 90% had found employment.

Admissions Contact: Joseph Foneke, Dean of Admissions and Financial Aid.

WEBB INSTITUTE OF NAVAL ARCHITECTURE   D-5
Glen Cove, NY 11542   **(516) 671-2213**

Full-time: 66 men, 17 women	Faculty: 10
Part-time: none	Ph.D.s: 50%
Graduate: none	Student/Faculty: 8 to 1
Year: semesters	Tuition: none
Application Deadline: February 15	Room & Board: $4800
Freshman Class: 77 applied, 28 accepted, 25 enrolled	
SAT I Verbal/Math: 620/700	**MOST COMPETITIVE**

The Webb Institute of Naval Architecture, founded in 1889, is a private, primarily men's engineering school devoted to professional knowledge of ship construction, design, and motive power. In addition to regional accreditation, Webb has baccalaureate program accreditation with ABET. The library contains 46,737 volumes, 1516 microform items, and 1159 audiovisual forms, and subscribes to 197 periodicals. Special learning facilities include a marine engineering laboratory and a ship model testing/towing tank. The 26-acre campus is in a suburban area 24 miles east of New York City. Including residence halls, there are 11 buildings on campus.

Student Life: About 80% of undergraduates are from out-of-state, mostly the Northeast. Students come from 18 states and 1 foreign country. Eighty percent are from public schools; 20% from private. Ninety-four percent are white. The average age of freshmen is 18; all undergraduates, 20. Four percent drop out by the end of their first year; 75% remain to graduate.

Housing: A total of 90 students can be accommodated in college housing. College-sponsored living facilities include single-sex dormitories. On-campus housing is guaranteed for all 4 years. All students live on campus; of those, 70% remain on campus on weekends. All students may keep cars on campus.

Activities: There are no fraternities or sororities on campus. There are some groups and organizations on campus, including marching band, orchestra, professional, social, student government, and year-

book. Popular campus events include Homecoming, Parents Day, and Webbstock.

Sports: There are 6 intercollegiate sports for men and 6 for women, and 2 intramural sports for men and 2 for women. Athletic and recreation facilities include a 60-seat gymnasium, tennis courts, an athletic field, a boat house, and a beach-front dock.

Disabled Students: Ninety percent of the campus is accessible to disabled students. Elevators and special parking are available.

Services: In addition to many counseling and information services, tutoring is available in some subjects.

Campus Safety and Security: Campus safety and security measures include informal discussions, pamphlets, posters, and films. There are also student and professional security services.

Programs of Study: Webb awards the B.S. degree. Bachelor's degrees are awarded in ENGINEERING AND ENVIRONMENTAL DESIGN (naval architecture and marine engineering).

Required: The curriculum is prescribed, with all students taking the same courses in each of the 4 years. The Webb program has 4 practical 8-week paid work periods: freshman year, a helper mechanic in a shipyard; sophomore year, a cadet in the engine room of a ship; and junior and senior years, a draftsman or junior engineer in a design office. All students must complete a senior seminar and thesis and technical reports, as well as make engineering inspection visits. A total of 146 1/2 credits with a minimum passing grade of 70% is required in order to graduate.

Special: All students are employed 2 months each year through co-op programs.

Faculty/Classroom: Ninety-three percent of faculty are male; 7%, female. All teach undergraduates and 40% both teach and do research. The average class size in an introductory lecture is 25; in a laboratory, 9; and in a regular course offering, 25.

Admissions: About 36% of the 1993–94 applicants were accepted. The SAT scores for the 1993–94 freshman class were as follows: Verbal—44% between 500 and 599, 48% between 600 and 700, and 8% above 700; Math—48% between 600 and 700 and 52% above 700. About 96% of the current freshmen were in the top fifth of their class; all were in the top two fifths. There was 1 National Merit finalist. Three freshmen graduated first in their class.

Requirements: A minimum GPA of 3.2 is required. The SAT I is required. Minimum SAT I scores of 500 verbal and 650 mathematics are required. Applicants should be graduates of an accredited secondary school with 16 academic credits completed, including 4 each in English and mathematics, 2 each in history and science, 1 in foreign language, and 3 in electives. Three SAT II: Subject tests in writing, mathematics level I or II, and physics or chemistry are required, as is an interview. Candidates must be U.S. citizens. Important factors used in the admissions decision are advanced placement or honor courses, personality, intangible qualities, leadership record, recommendations by school officials, and evidence of special talent.

Procedure: Freshmen are admitted in the fall. Entrance exams should be taken by January of the senior year. There is an early decision plan. Early decision applications should be filed by October 15; regular applications, by February 15 for fall entry, along with an application fee of $15. Notification of early decision is sent December 10; regular decision, April 15. One early decision candidate was accepted for the 1993–94 class.

Transfer: Three transfer students enrolled in a recent year. Transfers must enter as freshmen. A 3.2 GPA is required. SAT I scores and an interview are required. All credits of the required 146 1/2 must be completed at Webb.

Visiting: There are guides for informal visits, and visitors may sit in on classes and stay overnight at the school. To arrange for a visit, contact the Director of Admissions at (516) 671–2213.

Financial Aid: In 1993–94, 24% of all current freshmen and 20% of continuing students received some form of financial aid. About 20% all students received need-based aid. The average freshman award was $4125. Of that total, scholarships or need-based grants averaged $1000 ($2000 maximum); and loans averaged $3125. The average financial indebtedness of the 1992–93 graduate was $2000. Webb is a member of CSS. The FAF, the college's own financial statement, and FAFSA are required. The deadline for financial aid applications is July 1.

Computers: The college provides computer facilities for student use. There are 20 microcomputers available on campus. All students may access the system 24 hours per day. There are no time limits and no fees.

Graduates: In 1992–93, 18 bachelor's degrees were awarded. Within an average freshman class, 75% graduate in 4 years. Some 10 companies recruited on campus in an earlier year. In the 1992 graduating class, 11% of the men and 17% of the women were enrolled in graduate school within 6 months of graduation; 89% of the men and 83% of the women had found employment.

Admissions Contact: William G. Murray, Director of Admissions.

WELLS COLLEGE   C-3

Aurora, NY 13026   (315) 364–3264; (800) 952–9355 (out-of-state)

Full-time: 415 women	Faculty: 48; IIB, av$
Part-time: none	Ph.D.s: 96%
Graduate: none	Student/Faculty: 9 to 1
Year: semesters	Tuition: $14,160
Application Deadline: March 1	Room & Board: $5300
Freshman Class: 314 applied, 262 accepted, 130 enrolled	
SAT I or ACT: required	COMPETITIVE +

Wells College, founded in 1868, is a private liberal arts college for women offering programs in the humanities, social sciences, natural sciences, arts, and preprofessional areas. The library contains 230,000 volumes, 8000 microform items, and 920 audiovisual forms, and subscribes to 644 periodicals. Computerized library sources and services include interlibrary loans and database searching. Special learning facilities include a learning resource center and art gallery. The 360-acre campus is in a small town 25 miles north of Ithaca and 40 miles southeast of Syracuse on Cayuga Lake. Including residence halls, there are 22 buildings on campus.

Student Life: About 60% of undergraduates are from New York. Students come from 38 states and 4 foreign countries. Eighty-five percent are from public schools; 15% from private. Eighty-three percent are white. The average age of freshmen is 18; all undergraduates, 20.3. Fifteen percent drop out by the end of their first year; 75% remain to graduate.

Housing: A total of 500 students can be accommodated in college housing. College-sponsored living facilities include dormitories. In addition, there is nontraditional-age housing. On-campus housing is guaranteed for all 4 years. Ninety-nine percent of students live on campus; of those, 80% remain on campus on weekends. Alcohol is not permitted. All students may keep cars on campus.

Activities: There are no sororities on campus. There are 36 groups, including choir, chorale, dance, drama, ethnic, gay, international, jazz band, literary magazine, musical theater, newspaper, orchestra, photography, political, professional, religious, social, social service, student government, and yearbook. Popular campus events include the Odd-Even Basketball Game, Spring Weekend, Junior Blast, 100 Days for Seniors, Mothers Weekend, Fathers Weekend, and Leadership Week.

Sports: Athletic and recreation facilities include a competition-sized swimming pool, a gymnasium, a weight room, indoor tennis courts/practice space, 4-lane bowling, a 9-hole golf course, 4 all-weather tennis courts, and a boat house and dock with canoes and sailboats.

Disabled Students: Seventy percent of the campus is accessible to disabled students. The following facilities are available: elevators, special parking, specially equipped rest rooms, special class scheduling, and lowered drinking fountains.

Services: In addition to many counseling and information services, tutoring is available in every subject. In addition, there is remedial writing. Personal and psychological counseling is available.

Campus Safety and Security: Campus safety and security measures include 24-hour foot and vehicle patrol, self defense education, escort service, and shuttle buses. In addition, there are informal discussions, pamphlets, posters, and films, emergency telephones, and lighted pathways and sidewalks.

Programs of Study: Wells awards the B.A. degree. Bachelor's degrees are awarded in BIOLOGICAL SCIENCE (biochemistry and biology/biological science), COMMUNICATIONS AND THE ARTS (dance, dramatic arts, English, fine arts, French, German, Italian, music, Russian, and Spanish), COMPUTER AND PHYSICAL SCIENCE (chemistry, computer science, and mathematics), EDUCATION (art, elementary, foreign languages, music, science, and secondary), ENGINEERING AND ENVIRONMENTAL DESIGN (environmental science), HEALTH PROFESSIONS (predentistry, premedicine, and preveterinary science), SOCIAL SCIENCE (American studies, economics, ethics, politics, and social policy, history, international studies, philosophy, political science/government, prelaw, psychology, public affairs, religion, sociology, and women's studies). Biology, chemistry, premedicine, prelaw, English, and sociology are the strongest programs academically. Psychology, sociology, English, biology, and economics have the largest enrollments.

Required: In order to graduate, students must complete a total of 120 credit hours (36 courses) with a minimum GPA of 2.0. A total of 40 credit hours, depending on the major, and a minimum GPA of 2.0 are required in the major. All students must fulfill core requirements in English, formal reasoning, and a modern foreign language. In addition, all students must take 4 courses in physical education and wellness. A comprehensive examination and a thesis or project must be completed.

Special: Wells offers cross-registration with Cornell University and a Washington semester with American University. Internships are available with companies such as American Express, Dunn & Bradstreet, and Working Woman. Study abroad in 7 countries is permitted. A

3–2 engineering degree is available with Washington University in St. Louis and Columbia, Clarkson, Texas Agricultural and Mechanical, and Cornell universities. Students may also earn 3–2 degrees in business and community health. Student-designed majors and pass-fail options are available. There is 1 national honor society on campus, Phi Beta Kappa.

Faculty/Classroom: Fifty percent of faculty are male; 50%, female. All teach undergraduates. The average class size in an introductory lecture is 15; in a laboratory, 15; and in a regular course offering, 12.

Admissions: About 83% of the 1993–94 applicants were accepted. About 55% of the current freshmen were in the top fifth of their class; 79% were in the top two fifths. There were 7 National Merit semifinalists. Three freshmen graduated first in their class.

Requirements: Wells requires applicants to be in the upper 50% of their class. A minimum GPA of 2.0 is required. The SAT I or ACT is required, along with graduation from an accredited secondary school. Sixteen academic credits or Carnegie units are required. High school courses must include 4 years each of English and history or social studies, 3 years each of a foreign language and mathematics, and 2 years of science. An essay is required and an interview is strongly recommended. AP credits are accepted. Important factors used in the admissions decision are advanced placement or honor courses, recommendations by school officials, leadership record, extracurricular activities record, and parents or siblings attending the school.

Procedure: Freshmen are admitted in the fall. Entrance exams should be taken prior to application. Early decision applications should be filed by December 15; regular applications, by March 1 for fall entry, along with an application fee of $25. Notification of early decision is sent January 15; regular decision, April 1. There are early decision, early admissions, and deferred admissions plans. About 40 early decision candidates were accepted for the 1993–94 class.

Transfer: About 31 transfer students enrolled in 1993–94. Transfer students must be in good standing at the institution last attended. A minimum GPA of 2.5 is required. The school recommends composite scores of 1000 on the SAT I and 24 on the ACT. There is a 2-year residency requirement. A total of 60 credits out of 120 must be completed at Wells.

Visiting: There are regularly scheduled orientations for prospective students, including tours, interviews, and presentations, an overnight hostess program, and class attendance. There are guides for informal visits and visitors may sit in on classes and stay overnight at the school. To arrange for a visit, contact the Admissions Office at (800) 952-9355.

Financial Aid: In 1993–94 84% of all current freshmen and 78% of continuing students received some form of financial aid. About 80% of freshmen and 82% of continuing students received need-based aid. The average freshman award was $8853. Of that total, scholarships or need-based grants averaged $8852 ($12,750 maximum); loans averaged $2000 ($2625 maximum); and work contracts averaged $1000 ($1500 maximum). Ninety percent of undergraduate students work part-time. Average earnings from campus work for the school year are $1000. The average financial indebtedness of the 1992–93 graduate was $10,500. Wells is a member of CSS. The FAF or FFS is required. The deadline for financial aid applications is February 15.

International Students: There are currently 7 international students enrolled. They must take the TOEFL and achieve a minimum score of 550.

Computers: The college provides computer facilities for student use. The mainframe is an IBM System 36. There are also Apple and IBM microcomputers available in academic buildings. There are no time limits on using the system and no fees.

Graduates: In 1992–93 93 bachelor's degrees were awarded. The most popular majors among graduates were English (15%), psychology (15%), and biology and political science (9%). Within an average freshman class, 75% graduate in 4 years and 78% in 5 years. In the 1992 graduating class, 41% of the women were enrolled in graduate school within 6 months of graduation; 60% of the women had found employment.

Admissions Contact: Mary Ann Kalbaugh, Dean of Admissions.

YESHIVA UNIVERSITY
New York, NY 10033–3201

D-5

(212) 960-5277

Full-time: 1029 men, 919 women	Faculty: 120
Part-time: 23 men, 19 women	Ph.D.s: 79%
Graduate: 1374 men, 1625 women	Student/Faculty: 16 to 1
Year: semesters	Tuition: $12,400
Application Deadline: February 15	Room & Board: $5800

Freshman Class: 1374 applied, 1152 accepted, 806 enrolled

SAT I Verbal/Math: 559/629

VERY COMPETITIVE

Yeshiva University, founded in 1886, is an independent liberal arts institution offering undergraduate programs through Yeshiva College, its undergraduate college for men; Stern College for Women;

and Sy Syms School of Business. There are 3 undergraduate and 7 graduate schools. In addition to regional accreditation, YU has baccalaureate program accreditation with CSWE. The 7 libraries contain 900,000 volumes, 759,000 microform items, and 980 audiovisual forms, and subscribe to 7790 periodicals. Computerized library sources and services include the card catalog, interlibrary loans, and database searching. Special learning facilities include an art gallery, a radio station, and a museum. The 26-acre campus is in an urban area in New York City.

Student Life: About 48% of undergraduates are from New York. Students come from 31 states, 16 foreign countries, and Canada. Fourteen percent are from public schools; 86% from private. The average age of freshmen is 17; all undergraduates, 19. Eight percent drop out by the end of their first year; 90% remain to graduate.

Housing: A total of 1600 students can be accommodated in college housing. College-sponsored living facilities include single-sex dormitories and off-campus apartments. On-campus housing is guaranteed for all 4 years and is available on a first-come, first-served basis. Priority is given to out-of-town students. Eighty-five percent of students live on campus. Alcohol is not permitted. All students may keep cars on campus.

Activities: There are no fraternities or sororities on campus. There are 70 groups on campus, including art, choir, computers, drama, honors, international, jazz band, literary magazine, musical theater, newspaper, political, professional, religious, social service, student government, and yearbook. Popular campus events include holiday and dramatic presentations and Parents Day.

Sports: There are 8 intercollegiate sports for men and 2 for women, and 5 intramural sports for men and 4 for women. The athletic center at Yeshiva College houses a variety of facilities, including a 1000-seat gymnasium.

Disabled Students: Ninety-five percent of the campus is accessible to disabled students. The following facilities are available: wheelchair ramps and elevators.

Services: In addition to many counseling and information services, there is remedial reading and writing. There is also a writing center, which helps students with composition and verbal skills.

Campus Safety and Security: Campus safety and security measures include a 24-hour foot and vehicle patrol, an escort service, shuttle buses, and informal discussions. In addition, there are pamphlets, posters, films, lighted pathways and sidewalks, ID cards, vulnerability surveys, fire drills, alarm systems, emergency telephone numbers, and transportation for routine and special events.

Programs of Study: YU awards the B.A. and B.S. degrees. Associate degrees also are awarded. Bachelor's degrees are awarded in BIOLOGICAL SCIENCE (biology/biological science), BUSINESS (accounting, business administration and management, and marketing/retailing/merchandising), COMMUNICATIONS AND THE ARTS (classical languages, communications, English, French, Hebrew, music, and speech/debate/rhetoric), COMPUTER AND PHYSICAL SCIENCE (chemistry, computer science, and mathematics), ENGINEERING AND ENVIRONMENTAL DESIGN (preengineering), HEALTH PROFESSIONS (health science), SOCIAL SCIENCE (economics, history, philosophy, political science/government, psychology, religion, and sociology). The dual program of liberal arts and Jewish studies are the strongest academically. Accounting, psychology, economics, political science, and prehealth have the largest enrollments.

Required: In order to graduate, students must complete a total of 128 credit hours. Under the Dual Program, students pursue a liberal arts or business curriculum together with courses in Hebrew language, literature, and culture. Courses in Jewish learning are geared to the student's level of preparation.

Special: YU offers a 3–2 degree in occupational therapy with Columbia and New York Universities; a 3–4 degree in podiatry with the New York College of Podiatric Medicine; and a 3–2 or 4–2 degree in engineering with Columbia University. Stern College students may take courses in advertising, photography, and design at the Fashion Institute of Technology. Study abroad programs may be arranged in Israel. The school offers independent study options and an optional pass/no credit system. There are 9 national honor societies on campus. Twenty departments have honors programs.

Faculty/Classroom: Seventy-three percent of faculty are male; 27%, female. Fifty-eight percent teach undergraduates, 60% do research, and 28% do both. No introductory courses are taught by graduate students. The average class size in an introductory lecture is 38; in a laboratory, 15; and in a regular course offering, 18.

Admissions: About 84% of the 1993–94 applicants were accepted. The SAT scores for the 1993–94 freshman class were as follows: Verbal—35% below 500, 39% between 500 and 599, 19% between 600 and 700, and 7% above 700; Math—18% below 500, 37% between 500 and 599, 31% between 600 and 700, and 14% above 700. There were 3 National Merit finalists.

Requirements: A minimum GPA of 3.3 is required. The SAT I or ACT is required. In addition, graduation from an accredited secondary school with 16 academic credits are required for admission. The GED is accepted under limited and specific circumstances. The SAT II: Subject test in Hebrew is recommended for placement purposes. An interview and an essay are required. AP and CLEP credits are accepted. Important factors used in the admissions decision are extracurricular activities record, personality, intangible qualities, evidence of special talent, leadership record, and parents or siblings attending the school.

Procedure: Freshmen are admitted to all sessions. Applications should be filed by February 15 for fall entry, along with an application fee of $35. Notification is sent on a rolling basis. There are early admissions and deferred admissions plans. A waiting list is an active part of the admissions procedure, with about 25% of applicants on the list.

Transfer: About 88 transfer students enrolled in a recent year. A total of 95 credits out of 128 must be completed at YU.

Visiting: There are regularly scheduled orientations for prospective students; YU holds open houses for high school students. There are guides for informal visits and visitors may sit in on classes and stay overnight at the school. To arrange for a visit, contact the Office of Admissions at (212) 960–5277.

Financial Aid: In an earlier year, 75% of all students received some form of financial aid. Scholarships or need-based grants averaged $3000 ($4000 maximum); loans averaged $2500; and work contracts averaged $1600. Twenty-five percent of undergraduate students work part-time. Average earnings from campus work for the school year were $750. The average financial indebtedness of a recent graduate was $15,000. YU is a member of CSS. The FAF and the college's own financial statement are required. The deadline for financial aid applications is April 15.

International Students: There are currently 110 international students enrolled. The school actively recruits these students. They must take the TOEFL and achieve a minimum score of 500. The student must also take the SAT I or the ACT.

Computers: The college provides computer facilities for student use. The mainframe is an IBM RS 6000. There are more than 200 networked and stand-alone IBM-compatible microcomputers and workstations at 4 academic centers; there are additional facilities at university libraries. All students may access the system 24 hours per day via modem or when buildings are open. There are no time limits on using the system. The fees are $50 per course and specific uses per semester; otherwise there is no charge for general, non-course-related use.

Graduates: In a recent year, 393 bachelor's degrees were awarded. The most popular majors among graduates were social sciences (25%), psychology (13%), and accounting (10%). Some 75 companies recruited on campus in an earlier year. In a recent graduating class, 37% of the men and 15% of the women were enrolled in graduate school within 6 months of graduation; 19% of the men and 11% of the women had found employment.

Admissions Contact: Michael Kranzler, Associate Director of Admissions.

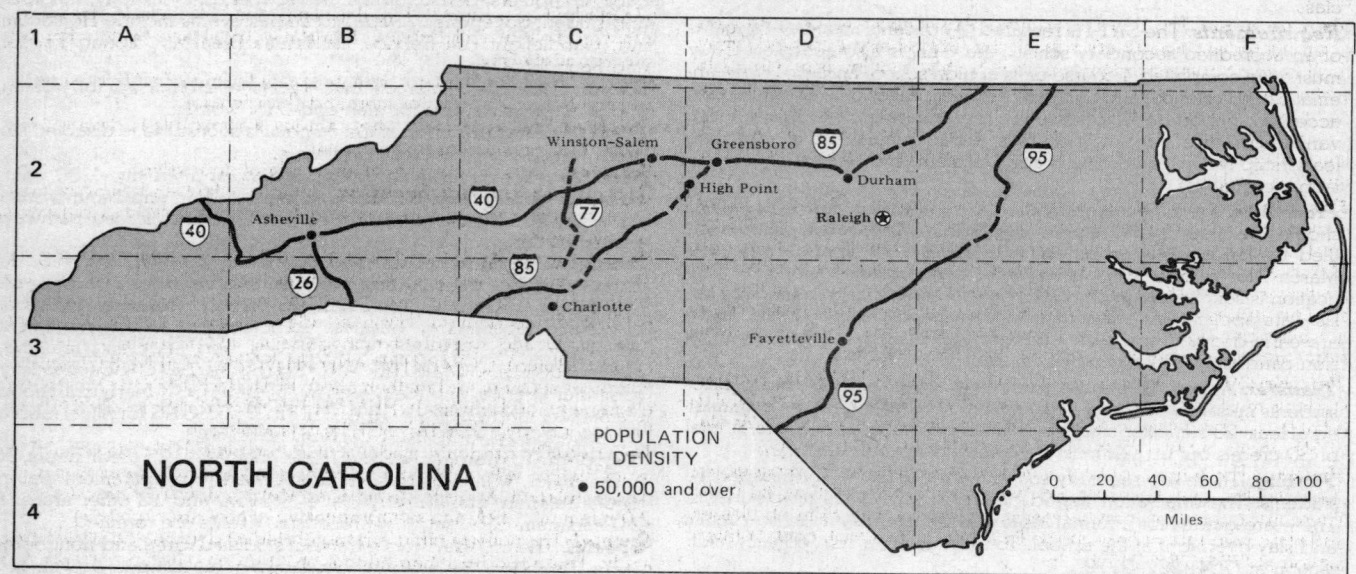

NORTH CAROLINA

POPULATION DENSITY
● 50,000 and over

0 20 40 60 80 100
Miles

APPALACHIAN STATE UNIVERSITY

B-2

Boone, NC 28608
(704) 262-2120

Full-time: 4841 men, 5073 women	Faculty: 535; IIA, -$
Part-time: 365 men, 414 women	Ph.D.s: 86%
Graduate: 371 men, 577 women	Student/Faculty: 19 to 1
Year: semesters, summer session	Tuition: $1555 ($7621)
Application Deadline: January 31	Room & Board: $2540
Freshman Class: 7313 applied, 4664 accepted, 1910 enrolled	
SAT I: Verbal/Math 471/519	ACT: 22 COMPETITIVE

Appalachian State University, founded in 1899 and a member of the University of North Carolina system, is a liberal arts institution that offers undergraduate programs in the arts and sciences, business, teacher education, fine and applied arts, and music. There are 5 undergraduate schools and one graduate school. The 2 libraries contain 629,576 volumes and 1,115,245 microform items, and subscribe to 3789 periodicals. Computerized library sources and services include the card catalog, interlibrary loans, and database searching. Special learning facilities include a learning resource center, radio station, TV station, and an Appalachian cultural center. The 255-acre campus is in a small town 90 miles northwest of Winston/Salem. Including residence halls, there are 70 buildings on campus.

Student Life: About 90% of undergraduates are from North Carolina. Students come from 39 states, 29 foreign countries, and Canada. Ninety-seven percent are from public schools; 3% from private. Ninety-four percent are white. The average age of freshmen is 19; all undergraduates, 24. Fourteen percent drop out by the end of their first year; 59% remain to graduate.

Housing: A total of 4600 students can be accommodated in college housing. College-sponsored living facilities include single-sex and coed dormitories and on-campus apartments. In addition there are honors houses and language houses. On-campus housing is guaranteed for the freshman year only and is available on a lottery system for upperclassmen. Sixty percent of students commute. Alcohol is not permitted. All students may keep cars on campus.

Activities: About 5% of men belong to 11 local and 11 national fraternities; about 2% of women belong to 7 local and 7 national sororities. There are many groups on campus, including art, band, cheerleading, chess, choir, chorale, chorus, computers, dance, drama, drill team, ethnic, gay, honors, international, jazz band, marching band, newspaper, orchestra, pep band, political, professional, religious, social, social service, student government, symphony, and yearbook. Popular campus events include Appalachian Summer.

Sports: There are 10 intercollegiate sports for men and 8 for women, and 18 intramural sports for men and 16 for women. Approximately 80% of undergraduates participate. Athletic and recreation facilities include a 7000-seat varsity gymnasium, an 18,000-seat stadium, an athletic center, facilities for football, soccer, field hockey, basketball, volleyball, wrestling, indoor and outdoor track, golf, baseball, and tennis, and a 2000-seat auditorium.

Disabled Students: Seventy percent of the campus is accessible to disabled students. The following facilities are available: wheelchair ramps, elevators, special parking, specially equipped rest rooms, spe-

cial class scheduling, lowered drinking fountains, and lowered telephones.

Services: In addition to many counseling and information services, tutoring is available in most subjects. There is also a reader service for the blind, and remedial math, reading, and writing.

Campus Safety and Security: Campus safety and security measures include 24-hour foot and vehicle patrol, escort service, shuttle buses, and informal discussions. In addition, there are pamphlets, posters, and films, emergency telephones, and lighted pathways and sidewalks.

Programs of Study: Appalachian awards the B.A., B.S., B.M., B.S.B.A., B.S.C.J., B.S.Ed., and B.T. degrees. Master's and doctoral degrees also are awarded. Bachelor's degrees are awarded in BIOLOGICAL SCIENCE (biology/biological science), BUSINESS (accounting, banking and finance, business administration and management, business economics, hotel/motel and restaurant management, international business management, and marketing/retailing/merchandising), COMMUNICATIONS AND THE ARTS (advertising, broadcasting, communications, dramatic arts, English, fine arts, French, journalism, music, Spanish, and speech/debate/rhetoric), COMPUTER AND PHYSICAL SCIENCE (chemistry, computer programming, computer science, geology, information sciences and systems, mathematics, and physics), EDUCATION (art, business, early childhood, elementary, foreign languages, home economics, industrial arts, middle school, music, science, secondary, and special), ENGINEERING AND ENVIRONMENTAL DESIGN (preengineering), HEALTH PROFESSIONS (medical laboratory technology, predentistry, premedicine, prepharmacy, and speech pathology/audiology), SOCIAL SCIENCE (anthropology, criminal justice, economics, geography, history, parks and recreation management, philosophy, political science/government, prelaw, psychology, public administration, religion, social science, social work, and sociology). Education and business are the strongest academically. Business has the largest enrollment.

Required: To graduate, students must complete 122 credit hours for most programs, including 60 in the major, with a minimum 2.0 GPA. General education requirements include courses in mathematics, science, history, physical education, English, social sciences, and humanities.

Special: Appalachian offers co-op programs with Auburn University, Wake Forest University, and the University of North Carolina/Greensboro; student-designed internships and majors, study abroad in Europe, China, and Costa Rica, and work-study programs. A B.A.-B.S. degree, dual majors, and a general studies degree are available. Credit for life/military/work experience, nondegree study, and a pass/fail option are permitted. There is a freshman honors program on campus, as well as 15 national honor societies. Six departments have honors programs.

Faculty/Classroom: Seventy-three percent of faculty are male; 27%, female.

Admissions: About 64% of the 1993–94 applicants were accepted. The SAT scores for the 1993–94 freshman class were as follows: Verbal—67% below 500, 26% between 500 and 599, 6% between 600 and 700, and 1% above 700; Math—41% below 500, 44% between

500 and 599, 14% between 600 and 700, and 2% above 700. About 47% of the current freshmen were in the top fifth of their class; 45% were in the top two fifths. Eighteen freshmen graduated first in their class.

Requirements: The SAT I is required. Applicants must be graduates of an accredited secondary school; the GED is also accepted. They must have completed 4 course units in high school English, 3 in mathematics and science, and 2 in social studies. AP and CLEP credits are accepted. Important factors used in the admissions decision are advanced placement or honor courses, extracurricular activities record, leadership record, evidence of special talent, and personality and intangible qualities.

Procedure: Freshmen are admitted to all sessions. Entrance exams should be taken by November, if possible. Applications should be filed by January 31 for fall entry, October 1 for spring entry, and March 1 for summer entry, along with an application fee of $25. Notification is sent beginning in October and continues on a monthly basis. Late applications are accepted on a space-available basis. There are early decision and early admissions plans. About 50 early decision candidates were accepted for the 1993–94 class.

Transfer: About 828 transfer students enrolled in 1993–94. Transfer students must have earned a minimum 2.0 GPA and have accumulated at least 28 semester credits for transfer, or 42 quarter hours. A total of 30 credits out of 122 must be completed at Appalachian.

Visiting: There are regularly scheduled orientations for prospective students. The orientation period begins in July for all new students. There are guides for informal visits and visitors may sit in on classes and stay overnight at the school. To arrange for a visit, contact Information at (704) 262–2179.

Financial Aid: In 1993–94, 44% of all current freshmen and 58% of continuing students received some form of financial aid. The average freshman award was $2260. Of that total, scholarships or need-based grants averaged $2260 ($11,000 maximum); loans averaged $2600 ($11,500 maximum); and work contracts averaged $1400. Sixteen percent of undergraduate students work part-time. Appalachian is a member of CSS. The FAF or FFS and the college's own financial statement are required. The deadline for financial aid applications is March 15.

International Students: There are currently 50 international students enrolled. The school actively recruits these students. They must take the TOEFL and achieve a minimum score of 500.

Computers: The college provides computer facilities for student use. The mainframes are clustered VAX machines, a DEC VAX 8550, 8650 and 6310; and an IBM 9370. There are also more than 500 IBM-compatible and Macintosh microcomputers in classroom buildings and residence halls. Those students who pay the $5 service charge may access the system. It may be used whenever the student signs a request for usage. There are no time limits on using the system. The fees are $15 per semester.

Graduates: In an earlier year, 1798 bachelor's degrees were awarded. Within an average freshman class, 59% graduate in 5 years. Some 272 companies recruited on campus in 1992–93. In the 1992 graduating class, 15% of the students were enrolled in graduate school within 6 months of graduation; 94% had found employment.

Admissions Contact: Joe Watts, Director of Enrollment Services.

BARBER-SCOTIA COLLEGE
C-3
Concord, NC 28025   (704) 786–5171, ext. 451; (800) 610–0778

Full-time: 379 men, 338 women	Faculty: 49; IIB, --$
Part-time: 5 men, 10 women	Ph.D.s: 52%
Graduate: none	Student/Faculty: 15 to 1
Year: semesters, summer session	Tuition: $4045
Application Deadline: open	Room & Board: $2795
Freshman Class: 1143 applied, 458 accepted, 344 enrolled	
SAT I Verbal/Math: 280/310	**NONCOMPETITIVE**

Barber-Scotia College, founded in 1867, is a liberal arts institution affiliated with the United Presbyterian Church. The library contains 14,135 volumes and 5927 microform items, and subscribes to 268 periodicals. Special learning facilities include a learning resource center. The 40-acre campus is in a suburban area 20 miles from Charlotte. Including residence halls, there are 24 buildings on campus.

Student Life: About 55% of undergraduates are from North Carolina. Ninety-eight percent are from public schools; 2% from private. Ninety-eight percent are African American. The average age of freshmen is 19; all undergraduates, 21. Thirteen percent drop out by the end of their first year; 56% remain to graduate.

Housing: A total of 650 students can be accommodated in college housing. College-sponsored living facilities include single-sex dormitories and off-campus apartments. On-campus housing is guaranteed for the freshman year only. Ninety percent of students live on campus; of those, 85% remain on campus on weekends. Alcohol is not permitted. Upperclassmen may keep cars on campus.

Activities: About 25% of men belong to 4 national fraternities; about 35% of women belong to 4 national sororities. There are many groups and organizations on campus, including art, cheerleading, choir, computers, dance, drama, newspaper, photography, religious, and student government. Popular campus events include Homecoming, Candlelight Fall Service, Christmas Breakfast, Spring Formal, and Founders Day.

Sports: There are 5 intercollegiate sports for men and 5 for women, and 9 intramural sports for men and 8 for women.

Disabled Students: Half of the campus is accessible to disabled students. Wheelchair ramps are available.

Services: There is remedial math, reading, and writing.

Campus Safety and Security: Campus safety and security measures include 24-hour foot and vehicle patrol and lighted pathways and sidewalks.

Programs of Study: Barber-Scotia awards the B.A. and B.S. degrees. Associate degrees also are awarded. Bachelor's degrees are awarded in BIOLOGICAL SCIENCE (biology/biological science), BUSINESS (accounting, business administration and management, hotel/motel and restaurant management, and marketing/retailing/merchandising), COMPUTER AND PHYSICAL SCIENCE (chemistry, computer science, and mathematics), EDUCATION (early childhood, elementary, and physical), HEALTH PROFESSIONS (medical laboratory technology), SOCIAL SCIENCE (sociology).

Required: To graduate, students must complete 125 credit hours, 36 in the major, with a 55-hour general education requirement that includes religion, English, physical education, and 13 other areas. A 2.0 minimum GPA and comprehensive exams are required.

Special: The college offers a general studies degree and nondegree study. There is a freshman honors program on campus, as well as 3 national honor societies, including Phi Beta Kappa.

Faculty/Classroom: All faculty teach undergraduates.

Admissions: About 40% of the 1993–94 applicants were accepted.

Requirements: The SAT I or the ACT is required.

Procedure: Application deadlines are open. The application fee is $10. The college accepts all applicants. There is a deferred admissions plan.

Transfer: Applicants for transfer should have a 2.0 minimum GPA. At least 30 credits out of 125 must be completed at Barber-Scotia.

Visiting: There are guides for informal visits, and visitors may sit in on classes and stay overnight at the school.

Financial Aid: In a recent year, 93% of all freshmen and 95% of continuing students received some form of financial aid. About 92% of freshmen and 93% of continuing students received need-based aid. The average freshman award was $5500. Of that total, scholarships or need-based grants averaged $2000 ($2480 maximum); loans averaged $2434 ($4000 maximum); and work contracts averaged $400. All students work part-time. Average earnings from campus work for the school year are $500. The average financial indebtedness of a recent year graduate was $7000. Barber-Scotia is a member of CSS. The FAF, FFS, or SFS, and FAFSA are required. The deadline for financial aid applications is June 30.

International Students: They must take the TOEFL and the SAT I or the ACT.

Computers: The college provides computer facilities for student use. The mainframe is a DEC PDP 4/34. All students may access the system from 8:30 A.M. to 5 P.M. There are no time limits and no fees.

Admissions Contact: Abbie L. Butler, Director of Admissions/Recruitment.

BARTON COLLEGE
E-2
Wilson, NC 27893   (919) 399–6300; (800) 345–4973

Full-time: 376 men, 733 women	Faculty: 84; IIB, --$
Part-time: 154 men, 351 women	Ph.D.s: 61%
Graduate: none	Student/Faculty: 13 to 1
Year: semesters, summer session	Tuition: $7363
Application Deadline: July 31	Room & Board: $3326
Freshman Class: 709 applied, 642 accepted, 232 enrolled	
SAT I Verbal/Math: 396/444	**LESS COMPETITIVE**

Barton College, founded in 1902, is a private, nonprofit liberal arts college affiliated with the Christian Church-Disciples of Christ. In addition to regional accreditation, Barton has baccalaureate program accreditation with NLN. The library contains 160,993 volumes, 195,343 microform items, and 6896 audiovisual forms, and subscribes to 981 periodicals. Computerized library sources and services include interlibrary loans and database searching. Special learning facilities include an art gallery, writing center, and TV studio. The 62-acre campus is in a suburban area 45 miles east of Raleigh. Including residence halls, there are 23 buildings on campus.

Student Life: About 76% of undergraduates are from North Carolina. Students come from 19 states, 15 foreign countries, and Canada. Eighty percent are from public schools; 20% from private. Eighty-four percent are white; 11% African American. Seventy-three percent are Protestant; 17% claim no religious affiliation. The average age of

freshmen is 19; all undergraduates, 20. Seven percent drop out by the end of their first year; 71% remain to graduate.

Housing: A total of 718 students can be accommodated in college housing. College-sponsored living facilities include single-sex and coed dormitories. In addition, there are honors houses and a global-living residence hall. On-campus housing is available on a first-come, first-served basis. Fifty percent of students live on campus; of those, 35% remain on campus on weekends. Alcohol is not permitted. All students may keep cars on campus.

Activities: About 6% of men belong to 4 national fraternities; about 6% of women belong to 3 national sororities. There are 40 groups on campus, including art, band, cheerleading, choir, chorus, computers, drama, ethnic, film, honors, international, jazz band, literary magazine, newspaper, pep band, photography, political, professional, radio and TV, religious, social, social service, student government, symphony, and yearbook. Popular campus events include Fall Fling, Greek Sing, Pre-exam Jam, Lighting of the Luminaries Christmas Celebration, and Global Focus.

Sports: There are 5 intercollegiate sports for men and 5 for women, and 12 intramural sports for men and 12 for women. Athletic and recreation facilities include a gymnasium, tennis complex, baseball, softball, and soccer fields, and community parks for intramural activities.

Disabled Students: Eighty-two percent of the campus is accessible to disabled students. The following facilities are available: wheelchair ramps, elevators, special parking, specially equipped rest rooms, and special class scheduling.

Services: In addition to many counseling and information services, tutoring is available in some subjects, including mathematics, English, and the sciences. There is also a reader service for the blind.

Campus Safety and Security: Campus safety and security measures include 24-hour foot and vehicle patrol, escort service, informal discussions, pamphlets, posters, and films. In addition, there are emergency telephones, lighted pathways and sidewalks, campus-wide surveillance cameras, and peephole doors to residence rooms.

Programs of Study: Barton awards the B.A., B.S., B.F.A., B.L.S., B.S.N., and B.S.W. degrees. Bachelor's degrees are awarded in BIOLOGICAL SCIENCE (biology/biological science and cell biology), BUSINESS (accounting, business administration and management, organizational behavior, and sports management), COMMUNICATIONS AND THE ARTS (audio technology, ceramic art and design, communications, drawing, English, French, music, painting, photography, printmaking, sculpture, Spanish, and studio art), COMPUTER AND PHYSICAL SCIENCE (chemistry, mathematics, and science), EDUCATION (art, education of the deaf and hearing impaired, elementary, mathematics, middle school, music, physical, and science), ENGINEERING AND ENVIRONMENTAL DESIGN (commercial art and environmental science), HEALTH PROFESSIONS (medical laboratory technology, nursing, and sports medicine), SOCIAL SCIENCE (American studies, history, international studies, political science/government, psychology, religion, social studies, social work, and sociology). Nursing and education of the deaf and hard of hearing are the strongest academically. Business, nursing, and education have the largest enrollments.

Required: All students must complete a minimum of 126 credit hours, including 36 in the major, with a minimum GPA of 2.0. Core requirements include 15 semester hours in humanities and fine arts, 6 in social sciences, 11 in natural science/mathematics, 6 to 9 each in writing proficiency and global and cross-cultural perspective, 3 to 4 in computational proficiency, 2 in sports science, and 2 in the Barton College Seminar.

Special: Barton offers internships, a Washington semester, a general studies degree, dual majors, and credit by examination in entry-level courses. The Weekend College trimester program is offered through the Office of Lifelong Education. There is a freshman honors program on campus, as well as 4 national honor societies. Eleven departments have honors programs.

Faculty/Classroom: Fifty-two percent of faculty are male; 48%, female. All teach undergraduates. The average class size in an introductory lecture is 30; in a laboratory, 20; and in a regular course offering, 20.

Admissions: About 91% of the 1993–94 applicants were accepted. The SAT scores for the 1993–94 freshman class were as follows: Verbal—92% below 500 and 8% between 500 and 599; Math—75% below 500, 20% between 500 and 599, and 5% between 600 and 700. About 25% of the current freshmen were in the top fifth of their class; 45% were in the top two fifths. There were 6 National Merit semifinalists. Twelve freshmen graduated first in their class.

Requirements: Barton requires applicants to be in the upper 60% of their class. A minimum GPA of 2.0 is required. The SAT I or ACT is required. AP and CLEP credits are accepted. Important factors used in the admissions decision are advanced placement or honor courses, evidence of special talent, leadership record, extracurricular activities record, and geographic diversity.

Procedure: Freshmen are admitted to all sessions. Applications should be filed by July 31 for fall entry and November 30 for spring entry, along with an application fee of $20. Notification is sent on a rolling basis. There is a deferred admissions plan.

Transfer: About 225 transfer students enrolled in 1993–94. Applicants must have a minimum college GPA of 2.0. Students with fewer than 12 transferable credits must submit SAT I scores. At least 45 credits out of 126 must be completed at Barton.

Visiting: There are regularly scheduled orientations for prospective students, including meetings with the president of the college, admissions director, faculty, and students; visiting classes; financial aid and freshman advising workshops; and tours of the campus. There are guides for informal visits and visitors may stay overnight at the school. To arrange for a visit, contact Kathy Daugherty, Associate Director of Admissions, at (800) 345–4973.

Financial Aid: In 1993–94, 87% of all current freshmen and 81% of continuing students received some form of financial aid. About 82% of freshmen and 78% of continuing students received need-based aid. The average freshman award was $6475. Of that total, scholarships or need-based grants averaged $1451 ($6000 maximum); loans averaged $2551 ($8000 maximum); and work contracts averaged $1200 ($3000 maximum). Thirty-two percent of undergraduate students work part-time. Average earnings from campus work for the school year are $1200. The average financial indebtedness of the 1992–93 graduate was $9000. The FFS and FAFSA are required. The deadline for financial aid applications is July 1.

International Students: There are currently 20 international students enrolled. The school actively recruits these students. They must take the TOEFL and achieve a minimum score of 525.

Computers: The college provides computer facilities for student use. There is a connecting network system, which all students may access. There are no time limits on using the system. The fees are $15 per semester.

Graduates: In 1992–93, 321 bachelor's degrees were awarded. The most popular majors among graduates were business (32%), nursing (15%), and education (13%). In the 1992 graduating class, 8% of the men and 12% of the women were enrolled in graduate school within 6 months of graduation.

Admissions Contact: Anthony C. Britt, Director of Admissions.

BELMONT ABBEY COLLEGE   C-3
Belmont, NC 28012   (704) 825–6665; (800) 523–2355 (out-of-state)

Full-time: 334 men, 375 women	Faculty: 46; IIB, --$
Part-time: 59 men, 99 women	Ph.D.s: 85%
Graduate: 9 men, 49 women	Student/Faculty: 15 to 1
Year: semesters	Tuition: $8684
Application Deadline: open	Room & Board: $4506
Freshman Class: 632 applied, 494 accepted, 129 enrolled	
SAT I Verbal/Math: 449/499	**COMPETITIVE**

Belmont Abbey College, founded in 1876, is a private, coeducational, nonprofit liberal arts college affiliated with the Roman Catholic Church. In addition to regional accreditation, Belmont Abbey has baccalaureate program accreditation with NCATE. The library contains 110,050 volumes, 59,000 microform items, and 2042 audiovisual forms, and subscribes to 609 periodicals. Special learning facilities include a learning resource center and radio station. The 650-acre campus is in a suburban area 12 miles southwest of Charlotte. Including residence halls, there are 20 buildings on campus.

Student Life: About 63% of undergraduates are from North Carolina. Students come from 27 states, 16 foreign countries, and Canada. Eighty-seven percent are white. Thirty-six percent are Catholic. The average age of freshmen is 18; all undergraduates, 23. Thirty percent drop out by the end of their first year; 35% remain to graduate.

Housing: A total of 600 students can be accommodated in college housing. College-sponsored living facilities include single-sex and coed dormitories and on-campus apartments. In addition there are special interest houses and a quiet residence hall. Single occupancy housing is available for all students. On-campus housing is guaranteed for all 4 years. Fifty-five percent of students commute. Alcohol is not permitted. All students may keep cars on campus.

Activities: About 30% of men belong to 5 national fraternities; about 30% of women belong to 4 national sororities. There are 34 groups on campus, including cheerleading, chorus, drama, honors, international, literary magazine, newspaper, political, professional, radio and TV, religious, social, social service, student government, and yearbook. Popular campus events include Homecoming, Spring Weekend, Special Olympics, and Greek Week.

Sports: There are 6 intercollegiate sports for men and 4 for women, and 13 intramural sports for men and 13 for women. Athletic and recreation facilities include a center for physical education, which contains an indoor gymnasium seating 1200, and a college union, which has a 225-seat auditorium.

Disabled Students: Sixty percent of the campus is accessible to disabled students. The following facilities are available: wheelchair ramps, elevators, special parking, specially equipped rest rooms, special class scheduling, and lowered drinking fountains.

Services: In addition to many counseling and information services, tutoring is available in some subjects, including mathematics, English, and foreign language. There is a Learning Disability program for students with learning disabilities, attention deficit disorders, and traumatic brain injury.

Campus Safety and Security: Campus safety and security measures include 24-hour foot and vehicle patrol, informal discussions, and lighted pathways and sidewalks.

Programs of Study: Belmont Abbey awards the B.A. and B.S. degrees. Master's degrees also are awarded. Bachelor's degrees are awarded in BIOLOGICAL SCIENCE (biology/biological science), BUSINESS (accounting, business administration and management, and sports management), COMMUNICATIONS AND THE ARTS (English), COMPUTER AND PHYSICAL SCIENCE (chemistry and mathematics), EDUCATION (education, elementary, secondary, and special), ENGINEERING AND ENVIRONMENTAL DESIGN (preengineering), HEALTH PROFESSIONS (medical laboratory technology, predentistry, premedicine, prepharmacy, and recreation therapy), SOCIAL SCIENCE (economics, history, liberal arts/general studies, parks and recreation management, philosophy, political science/government, prelaw, psychology, sociology, and theological studies). Natural and physical sciences, mathematics, preengineering, and English are the strongest academically. Business and natural sciences have the largest enrollments.

Required: All students must complete a minimum of 130 credits, which includes 65 credits of core curriculum and 30 upper-level credits in the major. Among the core requirements are history, mathematics, natural sciences, theology, foreign language, philosophy, English, and Great Books Seminar. A 2.0 GPA must be maintained.

Special: The college is 1 of 12 members of the Charlotte Area Educational Consortium. Study abroad is available in Japan and Europe. Also offered are internships in many majors, including required internships in recreational studies and therapeutic recreation. There are work-study programs on campus, nondegree study, 3–2 engineering degrees with Clemson University and Georgia Institute of Technology, an accelerated Adult Degree Program in accounting, business, computer studies, and liberal studies, and limited pass/fail options. College placement exams and credit for life, military, and work experience are accepted. There is a freshman honors program on campus, as well as 5 national honor societies.

Faculty/Classroom: Sixty percent of faculty are male; 40%, female. All teach undergraduates and 60% do research. No introductory courses are taught by graduate students. The average class size in an introductory lecture is 25; in a laboratory, 18; and in a regular course offering, 17.

Admissions: About 78% of the 1993–94 applicants were accepted. The SAT scores for the 1993–94 freshman class were as follows: Verbal—84% below 500, 14% between 500 and 599, and 2% between 600 and 700; Math—70% below 500, 24% between 500 and 599, and 6% between 600 and 700. About 18% of the current freshmen were in the top fifth of their class; 50% were in the top two fifths.

Requirements: A minimum GPA of 2.3 is required. The SAT I is required, with a minimum verbal score of 350. Candidates must be graduates of an accredited secondary school. A minimum of 16 academic credits must be completed, including 4 in English, 3 each in mathematics and electives, and 2 each in a foreign language, history, and science. An interview is recommended. AP and CLEP credits are accepted. Important factors used in the admissions decision are advanced placement or honor courses, evidence of special talent, leadership record, extracurricular activities record, and recommendations by school officials.

Procedure: Freshmen are admitted fall and spring. Entrance exams should be taken by October of the senior year. Application deadlines are open. The application fee is $25. Notification is sent on a rolling basis. There are early decision, early admissions, and deferred admissions plans.

Transfer: About 96 transfer students enrolled in 1993–94. Students with 24 or more credit hours must submit all college transcripts, and those with less than 24 credit hours must also submit a high school transcript and SAT I scores. All candidates must have a minimum 2.0 GPA and they must be eligible to return to the last college attended. An interview is recommended. A total of 30 credits out of 130 must be completed at Belmont Abbey.

Visiting: There are regularly scheduled orientations for prospective students, including meetings with a financial aid advisor, faculty, and students, and a campus tour. There are guides for informal visits and visitors may sit in on classes and stay overnight at the school. To arrange for a visit, contact the Admissions Office at (800) 532-2355.

Financial Aid: In 1993–94, 85% of all current freshmen and 80% of continuing students received some form of financial aid. About 75% of all students received need-based aid. The average freshman

award was $6900. Of that total, scholarships or need-based grants averaged $3900; loans averaged $2600 ($2625 maximum); and work contracts averaged $1400 ($1800 maximum). Twenty-five percent of undergraduate students work part-time. Average earnings from campus work for the school year are $1400. The average financial indebtedness of the 1992–93 graduate was $9500. Belmont Abbey is a member of CSS. The FAF and the FAFSA are required. The deadline for financial aid applications is March 1.

International Students: There are currently 32 international students enrolled. They must take the TOEFL and achieve a minimum score of 500.

Computers: The college provides computer facilities for student use. There are 39 AT&T 6300, IBM PS/2 Models 50 and 60, and Western Digital 286 microcomputers available in academic buildings. All students may access the system. It may be used anytime. There are no time limits on using the system. There is a $25 laboratory fee for computer science courses only.

Graduates: In 1992–93 216 bachelor's degrees were awarded. The most popular majors among graduates were business management (45%), accounting (6%), and biology (5%). Within an average freshman class, 28% graduate in 4 years, 34% in 5 years, and 36% in 6 years. Some 81 companies recruited on campus in 1992–93.

Admissions Contact: Laurie W. Taylor, Dean of Admissions.

BENNETT COLLEGE
D-2

Greensboro, NC 27401-3239   (910) 370–8624; (800) 338-BENN

Full-time: 650 women	Faculty: 52; IIB, --$
Part-time: 13 women	Ph.D.s: 51%
Graduate: none	Student/Faculty: 13 to 1
Year: semesters	Tuition: $6010
Application Deadline: open	Room & Board: $2910
Freshman Class: 774 applied, 542 accepted, 193 enrolled	
SAT I: 385/395	ACT: 17 **LESS COMPETITIVE**

Bennett College, founded in 1873, is a private, liberal arts women's institution affiliated with the United Methodist Church. In addition to regional accreditation, Bennett has baccalaureate program accreditation with ADA and CSWE. The library contains 92,000 volumes, 300 microform items, and 1490 audiovisual forms, and subscribes to 259 periodicals. Computerized library sources and services include interlibrary loans and database searching. Special learning facilities include a learning resource center. The 55-acre campus is in an urban area 1 mile from downtown Greensboro.

Student Life: About 67% of undergraduates are from out-of-state, mostly the Northeast. Students come from 30 states. Eighty-eight percent are from public schools; 12% from private. Ninety-six percent are African American. Most are Protestant. The average age of freshmen is 18; all undergraduates, 21. Twenty percent drop out by the end of their first year; 58% remain to graduate.

Housing: A total of 602 students can be accommodated in college housing. College-sponsored living facilities include dormitories. In addition, there are honors houses. On-campus housing is guaranteed for all 4 years. Eighty-three percent of students live on campus; of those, 50% remain on campus on weekends. Alcohol is not permitted. All students may keep cars on campus.

Activities: About 18% of women belong to 4 national sororities. There are 22 groups on campus, including cheerleading, choir, dance, drama, honors, international, newspaper, professional, religious, student government, and yearbook. Popular campus events include the Christmas Concert, the President's Ball, White Breakfast, and Founders Day.

Sports: Athletic and recreation facilities include a gymnasium, a pool, exercise and gymnastic facilities, an athletic field, and basketball and tennis courts.

Disabled Students: Twenty-five percent of the campus is accessible to disabled students. The following facilities are available: wheelchair ramps, elevators, special parking, and specially equipped rest rooms. Facilities are available in most campus buildings.

Services: In addition to many counseling and information services, tutoring is available in every subject. There is also remedial math, reading, and writing.

Campus Safety and Security: Campus safety and security measures include 24-hour foot and vehicle patrol, self defense education, escort service, and informal discussions. In addition, there are pamphlets, posters, and films and lighted pathways and sidewalks.

Programs of Study: Bennett awards the B.A., B.S., and B.A.S.I.S. degrees. Bachelor's degrees are awarded in BIOLOGICAL SCIENCE (biology/biological science and nutrition), BUSINESS (accounting, business administration and management, and fashion merchandising), COMMUNICATIONS AND THE ARTS (English and visual and performing arts), COMPUTER AND PHYSICAL SCIENCE (chemistry, computer science, and mathematics), EDUCATION (early childhood, elementary, English, mathematics, middle school, science, and secondary), HEALTH PROFESSIONS (predentistry and premedicine), SOCIAL SCIENCE (dietetics, political science/government,

psychology, social work, and sociology). Biology, mathematics, and education are the strongest academically. Business administration/accounting and biology have the largest enrollments.

Required: All students must take 54 to 64 semester hours of general education courses in communication, humanities, mathematics, natural science, reading, history, foreign language, philosophy, physical education, religion, and women's studies. A total of 124 semester hours, with 60 to 64 in the major, and at least a 2.0 GPA are required for graduation. Comprehensive examinations in mathematics and English are required.

Special: Students may cross-register at member colleges of the Greensboro Regional Consortium, study off-campus through exchange programs, take a Washington semester, and study abroad. Bennett offers student-designed majors, dual majors in engineering and nursing, nondegree study, a 3-1 nursing program, a B.A.-B.S. degree in interdisciplinary studies, and a 3-2 engineering degree with North Carolina Agricultural and Technical State University. There are 6 national honor societies on campus.

Faculty/Classroom: Forty-two percent of faculty are male; 58%, female. All faculty teach undergraduates. The average class size in an introductory lecture is 25 and in a laboratory, 30.

Admissions: About 70% of the 1993-94 applicants were accepted. The ACT scores for the 1993-94 freshman class were as follows: 90% below 21, 5% between 21 and 23, and 5% between 27 and 28. About 16% of the current freshmen were in the top fifth of their class; 37% were in the top two fifths.

Requirements: A minimum GPA of 2.0 is required. The SAT I or ACT is required. Applicants must be graduates of accredited high schools or have earned the GED. Secondary preparation should include 4 years each of English and other academic courses, 2 of mathematics, and 1 each of science and social studies. A personal essay is required and an interview is recommended. AP and CLEP credits are accepted. Important factors used in the admissions decision are recommendations by school officials, parents or siblings attending the school, evidence of special talent, advanced placement or honor courses, and recommendations by alumni.

Procedure: Freshmen are admitted in the fall and spring. Entrance exams should be taken prior to enrollment, preferably during the senior year. Application deadlines are open. The application fee is $20. Notification is sent on a rolling basis. There are early decision, early admissions, and deferred admissions plans.

Transfer: About 20 transfer students enrolled in a recent year. A total of 64 semester hours out of 124 must be completed at Bennett.

Visiting: There are regularly scheduled orientations for prospective students, including a campus tour and meetings with a financial aid officer and an academic program director. There are guides for informal visits and visitors may sit in on classes and stay overnight at the school. To arrange for a visit, contact Yolanda Johnson, Senior Admissions Counselor, at (910) 370-8624.

Financial Aid: Bennett is a member of CSS. The FAF or FFS is required. The deadline for financial aid applications is March 15.

International Students: There are currently 18 international students enrolled. The school actively recruits these students. They must take the TOEFL and achieve a minimum score of 500. The student must also take the SAT I or the ACT.

Computers: The college provides computer facilities for student use. The mainframes are an IBM System 34 and an HP. There are also microcomputers available for academic use in various departments. All students may access the system from 8 A.M. to 10:30 P.M. There are no time limits on using the system and no fees.

Graduates: In a recent year, 65 bachelor's degrees were awarded. The most popular majors among graduates were business administration (25%), biology (17%), and interdisciplinary (14%). Within an average freshman class, 20% graduate in 4 years, 28% in 5 years, and 30% in 6 years. Some 50 companies recruited on campus in a recent year.

Admissions Contact: Yolanda Johnson, Senior Admissions Counselor.

CAMPBELL UNIVERSITY
D-3

Buies Creek, NC 27506

(800) 334-4111, ext. 1320

Full-time: 905 men, 1139 women	Faculty: 88
Part-time: 75 men, 64 women	Ph.D.s: 77%
Graduate: 523 men, 507 women	Student/Faculty: 23 to 1
Year: semesters, summer session	Tuition: $8024
Application Deadline: open	Room & Board: $2600
Freshman Class: 2087 applied, 1339 accepted, 610 enrolled	
SAT I Verbal/Math: 439/476	COMPETITIVE

Campbell University, founded in 1887, is a private, nonsectarian, coeducational institution affiliated with the North Carolina Baptist Convention offering undergraduate and graduate programs in liberal arts and sciences, business, and education. There are 5 undergraduate and 4 graduate schools. In addition to regional accreditation, Campbell has baccalaureate program accreditation with ACPE and

NCATE. The library contains 256,000 volumes, 300,000 microform items, and 4200 audiovisual forms, and subscribes to 1006 periodicals. Special learning facilities include a radio station and a drug information center for the School of Pharmacy. The 850-acre campus is in a rural area 28 miles south of Raleigh. Including residence halls, there are 47 buildings on campus.

Student Life: About 63% of undergraduates are from North Carolina. Students come from 50 states, 41 foreign countries, and Canada. Ninety percent are from public schools; 10% from private. Eighty-six percent are white. Fifty-seven percent are Baptist; 28% Protestant; 12% Catholic. The average age of freshmen is 18; all undergraduates, 21.

Housing: A total of 1507 students can be accommodated in college housing. College-sponsored living facilities include single-sex dormitories, on-campus apartments, and married-student housing. In addition, there is graduate student housing. On-campus housing is guaranteed for all 4 years and is available on a first-come, first-served basis. Sixty-four percent of students live on campus. Alcohol is not permitted. All students may keep cars on campus.

Activities: There are no fraternities or sororities on campus. There are 44 groups on campus, including art, band, cheerleading, choir, chorale, chorus, computers, drama, honors, international, jazz band, literary magazine, musical theater, newspaper, orchestra, pep band, political, professional, radio and TV, religious, social, social service, student government, and yearbook. Popular campus events include Staley Lecture Series, Beach Day, Parents Day, Homecoming, and Spring and Christmas Formals.

Sports: There are 7 intercollegiate sports for men and 7 for women, and 23 intramural sports for men and 18 for women. Athletic and recreation facilities include a 2000-seat gymnasium, an athletic complex, a lake, a coffee house, a concert hall, a theater, and a nature trail.

Disabled Students: Seventy-five percent of the campus is accessible to disabled students. The following facilities are available: wheelchair ramps, elevators, special parking, specially equipped rest rooms, special class scheduling, lowered drinking fountains, and lowered telephones.

Campus Safety and Security: Campus safety and security measures include 24-hour foot and vehicle patrol, self defense education, escort service, and informal discussions. In addition, there are pamphlets, posters, and films, emergency telephones, and lighted pathways and sidewalks.

Programs of Study: Campbell awards the B.A., B.S., B.Applied.Sci., B.B.A., and B.H.S. degrees. Associate, master's, and doctoral degrees also are awarded. Bachelor's degrees are awarded in BIOLOGICAL SCIENCE (biology/biological science), BUSINESS (accounting, business administration and management, and business economics), COMMUNICATIONS AND THE ARTS (broadcasting, communications, dramatic arts, English, French, journalism, music, and Spanish), COMPUTER AND PHYSICAL SCIENCE (chemistry, computer science, and mathematics), EDUCATION (elementary and middle school), ENGINEERING AND ENVIRONMENTAL DESIGN (military science), HEALTH PROFESSIONS (medical laboratory technology), SOCIAL SCIENCE (history, political science/government, psychology, religion, and social work). Prelaw, prepharmacy, and trust management are the strongest programs academically. Prepharmacy, government, mass communications, and business have the largest enrollments.

Required: To graduate, students must complete 128 credit hours with a minimum GPA of 2.0 overall and in the major. All students must take English, mathematics, science, education, fine arts, physical education, and the Cultural Enrichment Program.

Special: Campbell offers co-op programs, cross-registration with Central Carolina Community College, internships, study abroad, a Washington semester, numerous apprenticeships, a 3-3 law program, a 3-2 business program, B.A.-B.S. degrees, dual majors, and a general studies degree. There is credit for life, military, and work experience. There are 5 national honor societies on campus. Nine departments have honors programs.

Faculty/Classroom: Sixty-seven percent of faculty are male; 33%, female. All teach undergraduates, 40% do research, and 40% do both. No introductory courses are taught by graduate students. The average class size in an introductory lecture is 30; in a laboratory, 25; and in a regular course offering, 12.

Admissions: About 64% of the 1993-94 applicants were accepted. The SAT scores for the 1993-94 freshman class were as follows: Verbal—75% below 500, 20% between 500 and 599, 4% between 600 and 700, and 1% above 700; Math—59% below 500, 29% between 500 and 599, 11% between 600 and 700, and 1% above 700. About 31% of the current freshmen were in the top fifth of their class; 57% were in the top two fifths. About 49 freshmen graduated first in their class.

Requirements: Campbell requires applicants to be in the upper 50% of their class. A minimum GPA of 2.0 is required. The SAT I with a minimum recommended composite score of 850, or the ACT is required. Applicants for admission should have completed 12 high

school academic credits, including 4 credits of English, 3 credits of mathematics, and 2 credits each of history or social studies, science, and foreign language. An essay, an interview, and a portfolio are recommended. An audition is required for some majors. AP and CLEP credits are accepted. Important factors used in the admissions decision are personality, intangible qualities, leadership record, extracurricular activities record, advanced placement or honor courses, and recommendations by school officials.

Procedure: Freshmen are admitted to all sessions. Entrance exams should be taken during junior year or fall of senior year. Application deadlines are open. Application fee is $15. Notification is sent on a rolling basis. There are early decision, early admissions, and deferred admissions plans. One early decision candidate was accepted for the 1993–94 class.

Transfer: About 283 transfer students enrolled in 1993–94. Applicants for transfer should have a minimum GPA of 2.0. A total of 32 credits out of 128 must be completed at Campbell.

Visiting: There are regularly scheduled orientations for prospective students. There are guides for informal visits and visitors may sit in on classes and stay overnight at the school. To arrange for a visit, contact the Admissions Office at (800) 334-4111.

Financial Aid: In 1993–94 88% of all current freshmen and 80% of continuing students received some form of financial aid. About 80% of freshmen and 78% of continuing students received need-based aid. The average freshman award was $6800. Of that total, scholarships or need-based grants averaged $1900 ($3750 maximum); loans averaged $2625; and work contracts averaged $800 ($2000 maximum). Thirty percent of undergraduate students work part-time. Average earnings from campus work for the school year are $523. The average financial indebtedness of the 1992–93 graduate was $13,250. Campbell is a member of CSS. The FAFSA is preferred. The deadline for financial aid applications is March 15.

International Students: There are currently 139 international students enrolled. The school actively recruits these students. They must take the TOEFL and achieve a minimum score of 500.

Computers: The college provides computer facilities for student use. The mainframe is an IBM System/36. There are 36 computer terminals in a centralized academic computer center. All students may access the system. It may be used during posted students hours; generally, Monday through Thursday, 8 A.M. to 11 P.M., with extended hours Friday through Sunday. There are no time limits on using the system and no fees.

Graduates: In a recent year, 403 bachelor's degrees were awarded. The most popular majors among graduates were business administration (30%), prepharmacy (17%), and government (10%). Within an average freshman class, 5% graduate in 3 years, 55% in 4 years, 35% in 5 years, and 5% in 6 years. Some 56 companies recruited on campus in a recent year. In a recent year's graduating class, 10% of the men and 9% of the women were enrolled in graduate school within 6 months of graduation; 84% of the men and 85% of the women had found employment.

Admissions Contact: Herbert V. Kerner, Dean.

CATAWBA COLLEGE
C-2
Salisbury, NC 28144
(704) 637-4402
(800) CATAWBA (out-of-state)

Full-time: 482 men, 433 women	Faculty: 63; IIB, --$
Part-time: 27 men, 53 women	Ph.D.s: 85%
Graduate: 7 women	Student/Faculty: 15 to 1
Year: semesters	Tuition: $9000
Application Deadline: open	Room & Board: $3950
Freshman Class: 1083 applied, 880 accepted, 291 enrolled	
SAT I Verbal/Math: 420/480	**COMPETITIVE**

Catawba College, founded in 1851, is a private, coeducational institution affiliated with the United Church of Christ and offering undergraduate programs in the arts and sciences, business, education, performing arts, forestry and environmental science, and preprofessional fields. There are 8 undergraduate schools and one graduate school. In addition to regional accreditation, Catawba has baccalaureate program accreditation with NCATE. The library contains 178,000 volumes, 398,000 microform items, and 10,500 audiovisual forms, and subscribes to 1200 periodicals. Computerized library sources and services include interlibrary loans and database searching. Special learning facilities include a curriculum materials center. The 210-acre campus is in a small town 40 miles northeast of Charlotte. Including residence halls, there are 28 buildings on campus.

Student Life: About 51% of undergraduates are from North Carolina. Students come from 27 states, 8 foreign countries, and Canada. Eighty-seven percent are from public schools; 13% from private. Eighty-nine percent are white. Seventy-three percent are Protestant; 16% Catholic. The average age of freshmen is 18; all undergraduates, 20. Thirty percent drop out by the end of their first year; 42% remain to graduate.

Housing: A total of 696 students can be accommodated in college housing. College-sponsored living facilities include single-sex and coed dormitories. In addition there are honors houses. On-campus housing is guaranteed for all 4 years. Sixty-five percent of students live on campus; of those, 70% remain on campus on weekends. All students may keep cars on campus.

Activities: There are no fraternities or sororities on campus. There are 25 groups on campus, including art, band, cheerleading, chess, choir, chorale, chorus, computers, dance, drama, ethnic, honors, jazz band, literary magazine, musical theater, newspaper, orchestra, pep band, political, professional, religious, social, social service, student government, symphony, and yearbook. Popular campus events include Homecoming, Winterfest, May Day, Inaugural Ball, Parents Weekend, Hall of Fame, and Spring Fling.

Sports: There are 8 intercollegiate sports for men and 8 for women, and 4 intramural sports for men and 4 for women. Athletic and recreation facilities include those for football, baseball, basketball, soccer, tennis, softball, field hockey, racquetball, weightlifting, swimming, and other sports, including a 5000-seat stadium and a 300-seat gymnasium.

Disabled Students: The following facilities are available: wheelchair ramps and special parking.

Services: In addition to many counseling and information services, tutoring is available in every subject.

Campus Safety and Security: Campus safety and security measures include 24-hour foot and vehicle patrol, self defense education, escort service, and informal discussions. In addition, there are pamphlets, posters, and films, emergency telephones, and lighted pathways and sidewalks.

Programs of Study: Catawba awards the B.A. degree. Master's degrees also are awarded. Bachelor's degrees are awarded in AGRICULTURE (forestry and related sciences), BIOLOGICAL SCIENCE (biology/biological science), BUSINESS (accounting, business administration and management, international business management, and recreation and leisure services), COMMUNICATIONS AND THE ARTS (arts administration/management, communications, dramatic arts, English, French, music, Spanish, and speech/debate/rhetoric), COMPUTER AND PHYSICAL SCIENCE (chemistry, computer science, information sciences and systems, and mathematics), EDUCATION (education, elementary, middle school, music, physical, and special), HEALTH PROFESSIONS (medical technology, predentistry, premedicine, recreation therapy, and sports medicine), SOCIAL SCIENCE (history, philosophy, political science/government, prelaw, psychology, religion, and sociology). Premedicine, predentistry, law, theater arts, and education are the strongest academically. Business, health professions, and communications/arts have the largest enrollments.

Required: To graduate, students must complete at least 128 credit hours, including up to 54 in the major, with a minimum GPA of 2.0. General education requirements include up to 12 hours in a foreign language, 9 in humanities, 7 in natural science, 2 in fitness and nutrition, and 6 each in social science, fine arts, and quantitative skills.

Special: There are cooperative programs in deaf education with Appalachian State University, forestry and environmental science with Duke University, and physician assistant and medical technician training with Wake Forest University. Catawba also offers internships, study abroad in London, a Washington semester, work-study programs, accelerated degree programs, dual majors, a general studies degree, pass/fail options, and student-designed majors. The freshman Educare program emphasizes study skills and personal development through exploration of ancient philosophies. There is a freshman honors program on campus, as well as 4 national honor societies.

Faculty/Classroom: Sixty-five percent of faculty are male; 35%, female. All teach undergraduates and 40% do research. No introductory courses are taught by graduate students. The average class size in an introductory lecture is 55; in a laboratory, 30; and in a regular course offering, 25.

Admissions: About 81% of the 1993–94 applicants were accepted. The SAT scores for the 1993–94 freshman class were as follows: Verbal—78% below 500, 19% between 500 and 599, and 3% between 600 and 700; Math—57% below 500, 32% between 500 and 599, and 11% between 600 and 700. About 27% of the current freshmen were in the top fifth of their class; 53% were in the top two fifths.

Requirements: A minimum GPA of 2.0 is required. The SAT I is required; the ACT may be substituted. A minimum SAT composite score of 800 or ACT score of 21 is required. Applicants must be graduates of an accredited secondary school or have a GED. They must have completed 16 academic credits, of which 12 must be Carnegie units. An essay is required and an interview is encouraged for all students, with a portfolio recommended for the marginal student. An audition is required for music and drama scholarships. AP and CLEP credits are accepted. Important factors used in the admissions decision are advanced placement or honor courses, leadership rec-

ord, recommendations by alumni, recommendations by school officials, and extracurricular activities record.

Procedure: Freshmen are admitted to all sessions. Entrance exams should be taken by December of the senior year. The application deadlines are open. Application fee is $25. Notification is sent on a rolling basis. There are early admissions and deferred admissions plans.

Transfer: About 54 transfer students enrolled in 1993–94. Applicants must present at least 12 semester hours, a GPA of 2.0 or better, and a minimum SAT I score of 800 or ACT score of 21. Students out of high school for 5 or more years are exempt from the SAT I/ACT requirement. A total of 30 credits out of 128 must be completed at Catawba.

Visiting: There are regularly scheduled orientations for prospective students, including a campus tour, lunch, meetings with faculty, and financial aid and athletic workshops. There are guides for informal visits and visitors may sit in on classes.

Financial Aid: In 1993–94 85% of all students received some form of financial aid. About 49% of freshmen and 44% of continuing students received need-based aid. The average freshman award was $6082. Of that total, scholarships or need-based grants averaged $2049 ($12,950 maximum); loans averaged $2634 ($5625 maximum); and work contracts averaged $995 ($1500 maximum). Thirty-six percent of undergraduate students work part-time. Average earnings from campus work for the school year are $594. The average financial indebtedness of the 1992–93 graduate was $6691. Catawba is a member of CSS. The college's own financial statement and FAFSA are required. The deadline for financial aid applications is March 15.

International Students: There are currently 11 international students enrolled. They must take the TOEFL and achieve a minimum score of 525.

Computers: The college provides computer facilities for student use. The mainframe is a DEC VAX 3400. All students have access to a 32-station PC network in Ketner Hall as well as to 40 PCs in the library. Computer science students also have access to a DEC Micro VAX II. All students may access the system. There are no time limits on using the system and no fees.

Graduates: In 1992–93 170 bachelor's degrees were awarded. The most popular majors among graduates were business and accounting (38%), education (13%), and communication arts (8%). Within an average freshman class, 32% graduate in 4 years and 44% in 5 years. Some 15 companies recruited on campus in 1992–93. In the 1992 graduating class, 5% of the men and 7% of the women were enrolled in graduate school within 6 months of graduation; 32% of the men and 31% of the women had found employment.

Admissions Contact: Robert W. Bennett, Director of Admissions.

DAVIDSON COLLEGE
C-3

Davidson, NC 28036   (704) 892–2230; (800) 768–0380

Full-time: 865 men, 736 women	Faculty: 130; IIB, + +$
Part-time: 2 men, 4 women	Ph.Ds: 97%
Graduate: none	Student/Faculty: 12 to 1
Year: semesters	Tuition: $16,263
Application Deadline: February 1	Room & Board: $4774
Freshman Class: 2373 applied, 956 accepted, 452 enrolled	
SAT I Verbal/Math: 580/650	ACT: 29 **MOST COMPETITIVE**

Davidson College, founded in 1837, is a private, coeducational liberal arts institution affiliated with the Presbyterian Church (USA). In addition to regional accreditation, Davidson has baccalaureate program accreditation with NCATE. The library contains 396,454 volumes and 355,923 microform items, and subscribes to 1897 periodicals. Computerized library sources and services include the card catalog, interlibrary loans, and database searching. Special learning facilities include a learning resource center, an art gallery, a radio station, and an arboretum. The 450-acre campus is in a suburban area 19 miles north of Charlotte. Including residence halls, there are 60 buildings on campus.

Student Life: About 75% of undergraduates are from out-of-state, mostly the South. Students come from 46 states, 39 foreign countries, and Canada. Sixty percent are from public schools; 40% from private. Eighty-nine percent are white. Seventy percent are Protestant; 12% Catholic. The average age of freshmen is 18; all undergraduates, 19. Four percent drop out by the end of their first year; 91% remain to graduate.

Housing: A total of 1397 students can be accommodated in college housing. College-sponsored living facilities include single-sex and coed dormitories and on-campus apartments. On-campus housing is guaranteed for the freshman year only and is available on a lottery system for upperclassmen. Eighty-nine percent of students live on campus. All students may keep cars on campus.

Activities: About 65% of men belong to 6 national fraternities. While there are no sororities on campus, 70% of women belong to 4 local dining houses. There are 100 groups on campus, including art,

cheerleading, choir, chorale, chorus, computers, dance, drama, ethnic, gay, honors, international, jazz band, literary magazine, musical theater, newspaper, opera, orchestra, pep band, political, professional, radio and TV, religious, social, social service, student government, and yearbook. Popular campus events include Solidarity Week, Homecoming, convocations, Alumni Weekend, and International Festival.

Sports: There are 11 intercollegiate sports for men and 10 for women, and 6 intramural sports each for men and women. Athletic and recreation facilities include indoor and outdoor tennis courts, a natatorium, a Nautilus room, a gymnasium, and facilities for sailing, swimming, water skiing, and canoeing at the Pine Lake campus.

Disabled Students: Seventy percent of the campus is accessible to disabled students. The following facilities are available: wheelchair ramps, elevators, special parking, specially equipped rest rooms, special class scheduling, lowered drinking fountains, and lowered telephones.

Services: In addition to many counseling and information services, tutoring is available in every subject. There is also a reader service for the blind.

Campus Safety and Security: Campus safety and security measures include 24-hour foot and vehicle patrol, self-defense education, escort service, and informal discussions. In addition, there are pamphlets, posters, and films, emergency telephones, and lighted pathways and sidewalks.

Programs of Study: Davidson awards the B.A. and B.S. degrees. Bachelor's degrees are awarded in BIOLOGICAL SCIENCE (biology/biological science), COMMUNICATIONS AND THE ARTS (art, classics, English, French, German, music, performing arts, Russian, and Spanish), COMPUTER AND PHYSICAL SCIENCE (chemistry, mathematics, and physics), SOCIAL SCIENCE (anthropology, economics, history, interdisciplinary studies, philosophy, political science/government, psychology, religion, and sociology).

Required: Students must complete 32 courses, 10 to 12 in the major, with a 2.0 GPA in order to graduate. Core curriculum requirements include courses in literature, fine arts, history, religion and philosophy, natural sciences, mathematics, and social sciences. In addition, students must meet foreign language, composition, cultural diversity, and physical education requirements. Comprehensive examinations and a thesis are required in some majors.

Special: Davidson offers interdisciplinary, international, and Asian studies programs and study abroad in 9 countries. A 3–2 engineering program may be arranged with Columbia, Duke, Georgia Institute of Technology, North Carolina State, and Washington Universities. Students may design their own majors, cross-register with any college in the Charlotte Area Educational Consortium, enroll in a Washington, D.C. or Philadelphia semester, or undertake independent study. There are 12 national honor societies on campus, including Phi Beta Kappa. Twenty-one departments have honors programs.

Faculty/Classroom: Seventy-five percent of faculty are male; 25%, female. All both teach and do research. The average class size in an introductory lecture is 30; in a laboratory, 10; and in a regular course offering, 20.

Admissions: About 40% of the 1993–94 applicants were accepted. The SAT scores for the 1993–94 freshman class were as follows: Verbal—12% below 500, 41% between 500 and 599, 41% between 600 and 700, and 6% above 700; Math—3% below 500, 20% between 500 and 599, 52% between 600 and 700, and 25% above 700. About 90% of the current freshmen were in the top fifth of their class; all were in the top two fifths. About 50 freshmen graduated first in their class.

Requirements: The SAT I or ACT is required. SAT II: Subject tests in writing, mathematics level I or II, and 1 other subject are strongly recommended. Applicants should be high school graduates who have taken a strong academic program, including at least 4 years of English, 2 years each of intermediate mathematics and a single foreign language, and 1 year each of plane geometry and history. The third and fourth year of a foreign language are recommended. A personal interview and campus visit are recommended. AP credits are accepted. Important factors used in the admissions decision are advanced placement or honor courses, recommendations by school officials, leadership record, evidence of special talent, and extracurricular activities record.

Procedure: Freshmen are admitted in the fall. Entrance exams should be taken by January of the senior year. Early decision applications should be filed by December 1; regular applications, by February 1 for fall entry, along with an application fee of $45. Notification of early decision is sent December 15; regular decision, April 1. There are early decision, early admissions, and deferred admissions plans. About 165 early decision candidates were accepted for the 1993–94 class. A waiting list is an active part of the admissions procedure.

Transfer: Eight transfer students enrolled in 1993–94. Applicants must have at least 1 full year of college work, generally with a 3.0 GPA. A total of 16 courses out of 32 must be completed at Davidson.

Visiting: There are guides for informal visits and visitors may sit in on classes and stay overnight at the school. To arrange for a visit, contact the Admissions Office at (800) 768–0380 or (704) 892–2230.

Financial Aid: In 1993–94, 65% of all current freshmen and 62% of continuing students received some form of financial aid. About 34% of freshmen and 31% of continuing students received need-based aid. The average freshman award was $9000. Of that total, scholarships or need-based grants ranged from $200 to $21,547; loans ranged from $400 to $5500; and work contracts averaged $1200. Forty percent of undergraduate students work part-time. Average earnings from campus work for the school year are $1200. The average financial indebtedness of the 1992–93 graduate was $8500. Davidson is a member of CSS. The FAF and the college's own financial statement are required. The deadline for financial aid applications is February 15.

International Students: There are currently 66 international students enrolled. The school actively recruits these students. They must take the TOEFL and achieve a minimum score of 600. The student must also take the SAT I or the ACT.

Computers: The college provides computer facilities for student use. The mainframes are a DEC VAX 8530, an HP, and a Prime. Students may use the host computer and microcomputer network for word processing; for computation and graphics (Mathematica, Quattro); for statistics (SAS, SPSS, Minitab); and for electronic Internet mail. Access is available from 40 terminals and 138 networked microcomputers in academic buildings and the college library. All students may access the system. It may be used 24 hours per day. There are no time limits on using the system and no fees.

Graduates: In 1992–93, 367 bachelor's degrees were awarded. The most popular majors among graduates were history (17%), English (14%), and psychology (11%). Within an average freshman class, 91% graduate in 4 years and 88% in 5 years. Some 39 companies recruited on campus in 1992–93.

Admissions Contact: Dr. Nancy Cable Wells, Dean of Admissions and Financial Aid.

DUKE UNIVERSITY
D-2

Durham, NC 27706

(919) 684–3214

Full-time: 3323 men, 2758 women	Faculty: 738; I, + +$
Part-time: 17 men, 37 women	Ph.D.s: 97%
Graduate: 2987 men, 1949 women	Student/Faculty: 8 to 1
Year: semesters	Tuition: $16,121
Application Deadline: January 2	Room & Board: $5150
Freshman Class: 13,789 applied, 3893 accepted, 1583 enrolled	
SAT I Verbal/Math: 620/700	MOST COMPETITIVE

Duke University, founded in 1838, is a private, coeducational institution affiliated with the United Methodist Church and offering undergraduate programs in arts and sciences and engineering. There are 2 undergraduate and 8 graduate schools. In addition to regional accreditation, Duke has baccalaureate program accreditation with AACSB, ABET, ACPE, APTA, NLN, and SAF. The 12 libraries contain 4,239,000 volumes and 113,963 microform items, and subscribe to 35,554 periodicals. Computerized library sources and services include the card catalog, interlibrary loans, and database searching. Special learning facilities include a learning resource center; an art gallery; a radio station; a TV station; a marine laboratory at Beaufort; a primate center; a center for international studies; the Institutes of the Arts, Statistics and Decision Sciences, and Policy Sciences and Public Affairs; a nuclear laboratory; and a free electron laser. The 8500-acre campus is in a suburban area 285 miles southwest of Washington, D.C. Including residence halls, there are 230 buildings on campus.

Student Life: About 85% of undergraduates are from out-of-state, mostly the Northeast. Students come from 50 states, 81 foreign countries, and Canada. Sixty-seven percent are from public schools; 33% from private. Seventy-five percent are white. Thirty-seven percent are Protestant; 35% claim no religious affiliation; 18% are Catholic. The average age of freshmen is 18; all undergraduates, 20. One percent drop out by the end of their first year; 94% remain to graduate.

Housing: A total of 5400 students can be accommodated in college housing. College-sponsored living facilities include single-sex and coed dormitories, on-campus apartments, and married-student housing. In addition, there are language houses, special interest houses, and theme houses in women's studies, the arts, and community service (APO). On-campus housing is guaranteed for all 4 years. Ninety-one percent of students live on campus. All students may keep cars on campus.

Activities: About 40% of men belong to 21 national fraternities; about 25% of women belong to 12 national sororities. There are 350 groups on campus, including art, band, cheerleading, chess, choir, chorale, chorus, computers, dance, drama, drill team, ethnic, film, gay, honors, international, jazz band, literary magazine, marching band, musical theater, newspaper, opera, orchestra, pep band, photography, political, professional, radio and TV, religious, social, social service, student government, symphony, and yearbook. Popular cam-

pus events include College Bowl, football and basketball games, Oktoberfest, Springfest, Delta Sigma Phi Reggae Fest, Sigma Chi Derby Day, Parents Weekend and Homecoming, holiday tree lighting, and Viennese Ball.

Sports: There are 12 intercollegiate sports for men and 11 for women, and 15 intramural sports for men and 13 for women. Athletic and recreation facilities include stadiums for baseball, basketball/volleyball, football, and soccer/lacrosse; squash, racquetball, and tennis courts; an aquatic center; training and weight rooms; a golf course; cross-country and jogging trails; and practice and intramural sport club fields. One stadium seats 33,941 and the largest arena seats 8564.

Disabled Students: The following facilities are available: wheelchair ramps, elevators, special parking, specially equipped rest rooms, special class scheduling, lowered drinking fountains, lowered telephones, and and accessible housing arrangements. In addition, activities such as concerts can be moved to accessible facilities upon request.

Services: In addition to many counseling and information services, tutoring is available in every subject. In addition, there is a reader service for the blind.

Campus Safety and Security: Campus safety and security measures include 24-hour foot and vehicle patrol, self-defense education, escort service, and shuttle buses. In addition, there are informal discussions, pamphlets, posters, and films, emergency telephones, lighted pathways and sidewalks, and a crime prevention program.

Programs of Study: Duke awards the A.B., B.S., and B.S.E. degrees. Master's and doctoral degrees also are awarded. Bachelor's degrees are awarded in BIOLOGICAL SCIENCE (anatomy and biology/biological science), COMMUNICATIONS AND THE ARTS (art history and appreciation, design, English, French, German, Greek, Italian, Latin, literature, music, Slavic languages, and Spanish), COMPUTER AND PHYSICAL SCIENCE (chemistry, computer science, geology, mathematics, and physics), ENGINEERING AND ENVIRONMENTAL DESIGN (biomedical engineering, civil engineering, electrical/electronics engineering, environmental science, materials science, and mechanical engineering), SOCIAL SCIENCE (African American studies, anthropology, classical/ancient civilization, economics, history, medieval studies, philosophy, political science/government, psychology, public affairs, religion, and sociology). The sciences, public policy studies, political science, comparative area studies, English, literature, and psychology are the strongest academically. Political science, psychology, and history have the largest enrollments.

Required: A minimum of 34 course credits is required for graduation. Students pursue a general course of study, including a writing course and courses in arts and literature, civilizations, foreign languages, natural sciences, quantitative reasoning, and social sciences. No more than 17 course credits are allowed in a major for the B.A., and no more than 19 for the B.S. At least 12 courses must be at or above the 100 level. At least 3 courses designed as seminars, tutorials, independent study, or thesis are required. Computer proficiency must be demonstrated by engineering students.

Special: Duke offers cross-registration with the University of North Carolina/Chapel Hill and North Carolina State and North Carolina Central Universities. Also available are internships through the Career Development Center, study abroad, and a Washington semester. An accelerated degree program is possible, achieving graduation in 3 years or combining the senior year with the first graduate year of the law, business, or environment schools. Dual majors of any combination and student-designed majors are available. The 3–2 engineering degree is offered with Salem, Davidson, Whitman, Randolph-Macon, and Allegheny Colleges. Several 3–2 and 4–1 medical technology programs (degree completed at Duke) are available. Project Calc, an innovative program in calculus, is also offered. Nondegree study and pass/fail options are possible. There are 3 national honor societies on campus, including Phi Beta Kappa.

Faculty/Classroom: Seventy-eight percent of faculty are male; 22%, female. All faculty both teach undergraduates and do research. The average class size in an introductory lecture is 150; in a laboratory, 24; and in a regular course offering, 41.

Admissions: About 28% of the 1993–94 applicants were accepted. The SAT scores for the 1993–94 freshman class were as follows: Verbal—7% below 500, 28% between 500 and 599, 51% between 600 and 700, and 14% above 700; Math—2% below 500, 10% between 500 and 599, 36% between 600 and 700, and 52% above 700. About 97% of the current freshmen were in the top fifth of their class; 99% were in the top two fifths.

Requirements: The SAT I (with 3 SAT II: Subject tests, including writing) or ACT is required. In addition, applicants must be graduates of an accredited secondary school and have completed 15 academic credits; 4 in English are required; 3 each in mathematics, science, and foreign language, and 2 in social studies or history are recommended. Engineering students must have 4 credit units in mathematics and 1 in physics or chemistry. An essay is required, and an inter-

view recommended. A portfolio or audition are advised in appropriate instances. AP credits are accepted. Important factors used in the admissions decision are advanced placement or honor courses, evidence of special talent, recommendations by school officials, leadership record, and extracurricular activities record.

Procedure: Freshmen are admitted to all sessions. Entrance exams should be taken in June of the junior year for early decision applicants and by January for an April decision. Early decision applications should be filed by November 1; regular applications, by January 2 for fall entry and October 15 for spring entry, along with an application fee of $50. Notification of early decision is sent December 15; regular decision, April 15. There are early decision, early admissions, and deferred admissions plans. About 536 early decision candidates were accepted for the 1993–94 class. A waiting list is an active part of the admissions procedure.

Transfer: About 20 transfer students enrolled in 1993–94. A minimum 3.6 GPA is recommended. The SAT I plus 3 SAT II: Subject tests, or the ACT is required. A total of 17 course credits out of 34 must be completed at Duke.

Visiting: There are regularly scheduled orientations for prospective students, including student-led tours, counselor-led group information sessions, class visits, and lunch with students. There are guides for informal visits and visitors may sit in on classes and stay overnight at the school. To arrange for a visit, contact Undergraduate Admissions at (919) 684-3214.

Financial Aid: In 1993–94, 41% of all students received some form of financial aid. About 40% received need-based aid. The average freshman award was $15,669. Of that total, scholarships or need-based grants averaged $11,437; loans averaged $2532; and work contracts averaged $1700. Twenty-eight percent of undergraduate students work part-time. Average earnings from campus work for the school year are $1400. The average financial indebtedness of the 1992–93 graduate was $7965. Duke is a member of CSS. The FAF is required. The deadline for financial aid applications is February 1.

International Students: There are currently 106 international students enrolled. The school actively recruits these students. They must take the TOEFL and the SAT I with 3 SAT II: Subject tests or the ACT.

Computers: The college provides computer facilities for student use. The mainframe is an IBM ES/9000. Access to the mainframe system varies by specific course requirements or project. Students may access a number of computer clusters located throughout the campus. These clusters provide access to networked and nonnetworked PCs and to workstations. About 450 terminals/PCs are available for general student use. The system may be used 24 hours a day, 7 days a week. Individual limits on length of time students may access the system varies by course or project. There are no fees.

Graduates: In 1992–93, 1456 bachelor's degrees were awarded. The most popular majors among graduates were biology (11%), English (10%), and political science (10%). Within an average freshman class, 9% graduate in 3 years, 83% in 4 years, and 2% in 5 years. Some 220 companies recruited on campus in a recent year.

Admissions Contact: Director, Office of Undergraduate Admissions.

EAST CAROLINA UNIVERSITY
E-2

Greenville, NC 27858-4353   (919) 757-6640

Full-time: 5877 men, 7293 women	Faculty: IIA, -$
Part-time: 711 men, 895 women	Ph.D.s: n/av
Graduate: 1099 men, 1853 women	Student/Faculty: 15 to 1
Year: semesters, summer session	Tuition: $1348 ($7414)
Application Deadline: March 15	Room & Board: $3150

Freshman Class: 9703 applied, 5947 accepted, 2477 enrolled
SAT I Verbal/Math: 434/487   **COMPETITIVE**

East Carolina University, founded in 1907, is a state-supported institution offering degree programs in the arts and sciences, art, music, business, education, health sciences, and applied technology. ECU also maintains the Brody Medical Science Complex for its medicine and allied health programs. There are 12 undergraduate and 2 graduate schools. In addition to regional accreditation, ECU has baccalaureate program accreditation with AACSB, ADA, AHEA, APTA, CSWE, NASAD, NASM, NCATE, NLN, and NRPA. The 2 libraries contain 835,000 volumes, 1 million microform items, and 37,000 audiovisual forms, and subscribe to 5600 periodicals. Computerized library sources and services include the card catalog. Special learning facilities include a learning resource center, art gallery, and radio station. The 370-acre campus is in a suburban area 85 miles from Raleigh. Including residence halls, there are 72 buildings on campus.

Student Life: About 84% of undergraduates are from North Carolina. Students come from 47 states, 42 foreign countries, and Canada. Eighty-eight percent are white. Fifty-nine percent are Protestant; 10% Catholic. The average age of freshmen is 18. Eighteen percent drop out by the end of their first year; 55% remain to graduate.

Housing: A total of 5400 students can be accommodated in college housing. College-sponsored living facilities include single-sex and coed dormitories, off-campus apartments, fraternity houses, and sorority houses. In addition, there are honors houses and an international house. On-campus housing is guaranteed for the freshman year only and is available on a first-come, first-served basis. Alcohol is not permitted. All students may keep cars on campus.

Activities: There are many groups and organizations on campus, including art, band, cheerleading, choir, chorale, chorus, computers, dance, drama, ethnic, honors, international, jazz band, literary magazine, marching band, musical theater, newspaper, opera, orchestra, pep band, photography, political, professional, radio and TV, religious, social, social service, student government, symphony, and yearbook. Popular campus events include Homecoming, Parents Weekend, Purple and Gold Nights, Madrigal Dinners, and Barefoot on the Mall Day.

Sports: Athletic and recreation facilities include a 35,000-seat stadium, a basketball coliseum, a gymnasium, a weight room, a track, a natatorium, playing fields, and courts for tennis, racquetball, and volleyball.

Disabled Students: The following facilities are available: wheelchair ramps, elevators, special parking, specially equipped rest rooms, special class scheduling, lowered drinking fountains, and lowered telephones.

Services: Tutoring and remedial instruction are available. In addition, there is a reader service for the blind.

Campus Safety and Security: Campus safety and security measures include 24-hour foot and vehicle patrol, escort service, shuttle buses, and informal discussions. In addition, there are pamphlets, posters, and films, emergency telephones, and lighted pathways and sidewalks.

Programs of Study: ECU awards the B.A., B.S., B.F.A., B.M., B.S.A., B.S.A.P., B.S.B., B.S.B.A., B.S.B.E., B.S.N., B.S.O.T., and B.S.P.T. degrees. Master's and doctoral degrees also are awarded. Bachelor's degrees are awarded in BIOLOGICAL SCIENCE (biochemistry and biology/biological science), BUSINESS (accounting, banking and finance, and business administration and management), COMMUNICATIONS AND THE ARTS (broadcasting, communications, design, English, French, German, music, and Spanish), COMPUTER AND PHYSICAL SCIENCE (chemistry, computer science, geology, mathematics, and physics), EDUCATION (art, business, early childhood, elementary, home economics, middle school, secondary, and special), HEALTH PROFESSIONS (nursing, occupational therapy, and physical therapy), SOCIAL SCIENCE (anthropology, criminal justice, economics, geography, history, home economics, philosophy, psychology, public administration, social work, and sociology). Allied health is the strongest academically.

Required: To graduate, students must complete 120 to 126 semester hours with a minimum GPA of 2.0 overall and in the major. General education requirements include 13 hours of social science, 10 of humanities and fine arts, 8 of science, 6 of English, 3 each of mathematics and health/physical education, and 1 of library science.

Special: ECU offers cooperative programs, internships, study abroad programs, dual majors, a 3–2 engineering degree, credit by examination, and nondegree study. There is a freshman honors program on campus, as well as 19 national honor societies.

Admissions: About 61% of the 1993–94 applicants were accepted. The SAT I scores for the 1993–94 freshman class were as follows: Verbal—82% below 500, 15% between 500 and 599, and 3% between 600 and 700; Math—57% below 500, 35% between 500 and 599, 7% between 600 and 700, and 1% above 700. About 32% of the current freshmen were in the top fifth of their class; 82% were in the top two fifths.

Requirements: ECU requires applicants to be in the upper 50% of their class. A minimum GPA of 2.0 is required. The SAT I or ACT is required. Applicants must be graduates of an accredited secondary school or have a GED certificate. They must have completed 20 academic units including 4 in English, 3 in mathematics, 3 in science with 1 laboratory course, and 2 in social studies with 1 in U.S. history; also recommended are 2 units in a foreign language and completion of 1 unit each in foreign language and mathematics in the senior year. AP and CLEP credits are accepted.

Procedure: Freshmen are admitted to all sessions. Applications should be filed by March 15 for fall entry, December 1 for spring entry, and April 30 for summer entry, along with an application fee of $35. Notification is sent on a rolling basis. There are early admissions and deferred admissions plans.

Transfer: A total of 1654 transfer students enrolled in 1993–94. Applicants must submit official transcripts from all colleges attended and have a satisfactory GPA in courses attempted. A total of 30 credits out of 120 to 126 must be completed at ECU.

Visiting: There are regularly scheduled orientations for prospective students. There are guides for informal visits. To arrange for a visit, contact the Admissions Office at (919) 757-6640.

Financial Aid: The FAF or FFS financial statement is required. The deadline for financial aid applications is April 15.

International Students: There are currently 101 international students enrolled. They must take the TOEFL and achieve a minimum score of 550.

Computers: The university provides computer facilities for student use. The mainframes are an IBM 4381, an AT&T 3B2/400, and a DEC MicroVAX II. There are also more than 600 IBM and Apple microcomputers. There are no time limits on using the system and no fees.

Admissions Contact: Thomas E. Powell, Jr., Director of Admissions.

ELIZABETH CITY STATE UNIVERSITY   F-2
Elizabeth City, NC 27909   (919) 335–3304

Full-time: 778 men, 1195 women	**Faculty:** 98; IIB, av$
Part-time: 51 men, 106 women	**Ph.D.s:** n/av
Graduate: none	**Student/Faculty:** 20 to 1
Year: semesters, summer session	**Tuition:** $1242 ($6606)
Application Deadline: August 1	**Room & Board:** $3012
Freshman Class: 1106 applied, 807 accepted, 461 enrolled	
SAT I Verbal/Math: 360/410	**LESS COMPETITIVE**

Elizabeth City State University, founded in 1891 as part of the University of North Carolina System, is a public coeducational institution offering undergraduate programs in liberal arts and sciences, education, and business. The library contains 128,000 volumes and 41,783 microform items, and subscribes to 1592 periodicals. Special learning facilities include a radio station and a farm, and a 639-acre educational research tract. The 829-acre campus is in a small town 55 miles from Norfolk, Virginia.

Student Life: Eight percent of undergraduates are from North Carolina. About 50% of freshmen remain to graduate.

Housing: College-sponsored living facilities include single-sex on-campus apartments, and honors houses. On-campus housing is guaranteed for all 4 years.

Activities: There are 4 national fraternities and 4 national sororities. There are some groups and organizations on campus, including band, choir, dance, drama, jazz band, newspaper, religious, social, student government, and yearbook.

Sports: Athletic and recreation facilities include a 4500-seat gymnasium, a 3500-seat stadium, an all-weather track, a golf range, an Olympic pool, a weight room, 8 tennis courts, dance and exercise studios, handball and racquetball courts, and playing fields.

Disabled Students: The following facilities are available: wheelchair ramps, elevators, special parking, specially equipped rest rooms, and lowered drinking fountains.

Services: In addition to vocational counseling services, tutoring is available.

Campus Safety and Security: ECSO has its own police department on campus.

Programs of Study: ECSU awards the B.A., B.S., and B.S.Ed. degrees. Bachelor's degrees are awarded in BIOLOGICAL SCIENCE (biology/biological science), BUSINESS (accounting and business administration and management), COMMUNICATIONS AND THE ARTS (English, fine arts, and music), COMPUTER AND PHYSICAL SCIENCE (chemistry, computer science, geology, mathematics, and physics), EDUCATION (art, business, early childhood, elementary, industrial arts, middle school, physical, science, secondary, and special), ENGINEERING AND ENVIRONMENTAL DESIGN (industrial engineering technology and military science), SOCIAL SCIENCE (criminal justice, history, political science/government, psychology, social science, social work, and sociology).

Required: Students must have maintained a minimum GPA of 2.0, fulfilled a major, and completed the requirements of general education courses in the fields of grammar, composition, and literature.

Special: Opportunities are provided for internships, dual majors, weekend/evening degree completion programs, work-study, and credit by examination and for military service. There are 5 national honor societies on campus.

Admissions: About 73% of the 1993–94 applicants were accepted. The SAT scores for the 1993–94 freshman class were as follows: Verbal—94% below 500 and 6% between 500 and 599; Math—85% below 500, 14% between 500 and 599, and 1% between 600 and 700. About 27% of the current freshmen were in the top two fifths of their class.

Requirements: ECSU requires applicants to be in the upper 64% of their class. A minimum GPA of 2.0 is required. The SAT I or ACT is required. Minimum composite scores are 650 on the SAT I for in-state and 750 for out-of-state residents, and 13 on the ACT for in-state and 16 for out-of-state residents. Graduation from an accredited secondary school is required; the GED is accepted. Applicants should submit an academic record with 4 courses in English, 8 in electives including 2 in a foreign language, 3 each in mathematics and science, and 1 each in history and social sciences. Students must also pass the

---

NC Competency Examination or its equivalent. AP and CLEP credits are accepted.

Procedure: Freshmen are admitted to all sessions. Entrance exams should be taken as early as possible. Applications should be filed by August 1 for fall entry and December 1 for spring entry, along with an application fee of $15. Notification is sent on a rolling basis. There are early admissions and deferred admissions plans.

Transfer: Transfer students must have a minimum college GPA of 2.0 and submit high school and college transcripts. Those with fewer than 30 credit hours must meet both freshman and transfer admission requirements. A total of 30 credits must be completed at ECSU.

Visiting: There are regularly scheduled orientations for prospective students. To arrange for a visit, contact the Admissions Office at (919) 335–3304.

Financial Aid: The FAF or FFS, the college's own financial statement and the FAFSA, and income tax forms are required. The deadline for financial aid applications is May 1.

Computers: The college provides computer facilities for student use. The mainframe is a DEC VAX 11/780 with an IBM PC network. The Academic Computing Center houses a computer laboratory that provides access to the state's major computer network and other systems through LINCNET and BITNET. Students in computer-related courses may access the system.

Admissions Contact: Erthel Hines, Coordinator of Admissions.

ELON COLLEGE   D-2
Elon College, NC 27244–2010   (919) 584–2370
                                    (800) 334–8448 (out-of-state)

Full-time: 1295 men, 1638 women	**Faculty:** 138; IIB, -$
Part-time: 89 men, 119 women	**Ph.D.s:** 75%
Graduate: 76 men, 62 women	**Student/Faculty:** 21 to 1
Year: 4–1–4, summer session	**Tuition:** $8630
Application Deadline: open	**Room & Board:** $3660
Freshman Class: 3624 applied, 2786 accepted, 858 enrolled	
SAT I Verbal/Math: 439/483	**LESS COMPETITIVE**

Elon College, founded in 1889, is a private, coeducational institution affiliated with the United Church of Christ and offering programs in the arts and sciences, education, business, and professional and pre-professional studies. There are 2 graduate schools. In addition to regional accreditation, Elon has baccalaureate program accreditation with CAHEA and NCATE. The library contains 179,222 volumes, 509,427 microform items, and 4434 audiovisual forms, and subscribes to 1700 periodicals. Computerized library sources and services include database searching. Special learning facilities include a learning resource center, radio station, and TV station. The 330-acre campus is in a small town adjacent to Burlington 17 miles east of Greensboro. Including residence halls, there are 47 buildings on campus.

Student Life: About 62% of undergraduates are from out-of-state, mostly Middle Atlantic and the South. Students come from 37 states, 21 foreign countries, and Canada. Eighty-five percent are from public schools; 15% from private. Ninety-three percent are white. Fifty-two percent are Protestant; 24% Catholic. The average age of freshmen is 18; all undergraduates, 20. Twenty percent drop out by the end of their first year; 54% remain to graduate.

Housing: A total of 1812 students can be accommodated in college housing. College-sponsored living facilities include single-sex dormitories, off-campus apartments, fraternity houses, and sorority houses. In addition, there are honors houses, special interest houses, and theme suites. On-campus housing is guaranteed for the freshman year only, is available on a first-come, first-served basis, and is available on a lottery system for upperclassmen. Fifty-eight percent of students live on campus; of those, 50% remain on campus on weekends. All students may keep cars on campus.

Activities: About 23% of men belong to 11 national fraternities; about 29% of women belong to 9 national sororities. There are 90 groups on campus, including art, band, cheerleading, choir, chorale, chorus, computers, dance, drama, drill team, ethnic, film, honors, international, jazz band, literary magazine, musical theater, newspaper, orchestra, pep band, photography, political, professional, radio and TV, religious, social, social service, student government, symphony, and yearbook. Popular campus events include Family Weekend, Homecoming, Spring Fling, Greek Week, music theater productions, art exhibits, recitals, concerts, and guest lectures.

Sports: There are 8 intercollegiate sports for men and 6 for women, and 27 intramural and campus recreation activities for both men and women. Athletic and recreation facilities include a 10,000-seat stadium, handball courts, lighted tennis courts, a baseball stadium, a field house, and 7 athletic fields. A newly renovated athletic center has racquetball courts, aerobic rooms, a human performance laboratory, a weight room, a fitness center, 2 gymnasiums, and an indoor pool.

Disabled Students: Seventy percent of the campus is accessible to disabled students. The following facilities are available: wheelchair ramps, elevators, special parking, specially equipped rest rooms, spe-

cial class scheduling, lowered drinking fountains, lowered telephones, special housing assignments, and special class locations.

Services: In addition to many counseling and information services, tutoring is available in most subjects, including many lower-level courses. In addition, there is a reader service for the blind, and remedial math, reading, and writing. A writing center is available.

Campus Safety and Security: Campus safety and security measures include 24-hour foot and vehicle patrol, self defense education, escort service, and informal discussions. In addition, there are pamphlets, posters, and films, emergency telephones, and lighted pathways and sidewalks.

Programs of Study: Elon awards the B.A. and B.S. degrees. Master's degrees also are awarded. Bachelor's degrees are awarded in BIOLOGICAL SCIENCE (biology/biological science), BUSINESS (accounting, business administration and management, and sports management), COMMUNICATIONS AND THE ARTS (broadcast communications, corporate communications, dramatic arts, English, French, journalism, music, music performance, musical theater, Spanish, and theater arts), COMPUTER AND PHYSICAL SCIENCE (chemistry, computer science, mathematics, and physics), EDUCATION (elementary, health, middle school, music, physical, science, and secondary), HEALTH PROFESSIONS (medical laboratory technology and sports medicine), SOCIAL SCIENCE (economics, history, human services, philosophy, political science/government, psychology, public administration, religious studies, social science, and sociology). Business, education, communications, chemistry, computer science, and psychology are the strongest programs academically. Business, education, communications, psychology, biology, sports medicine, political science, and history have the largest enrollments.

Required: To graduate, students must complete 126 semester hours, including 35 to 58 in the major, with a minimum GPA of 2.0. Distribution requirements total 54 hours in English, mathematics, fine arts, science, religion/philosophy, social science, history, and physical education, including Foundation of Physical Activity. Students must also complete a 2-semester writing course and a comprehensive examination in the major.

Special: Elon offers co-op programs in most majors, dual majors, cross-registration with 7 state schools, part- or full-time internships, study abroad in 10 countries, a Washington semester, pass/fail options, and 3–2 engineering degree programs with North Carolina Agricultural and Technical State University, the University of North Carolina at Charlotte, and North Carolina State University. There is a freshman honors program on campus, as well as 5 national honor societies. Many departments have honors courses.

Faculty/Classroom: Sixty-four percent of faculty are male; 36%, female. All teach undergraduates. No introductory courses are taught by graduate students. The average class size in an introductory lecture is 24; in a laboratory, 20; and in a regular course offering, 23.

Admissions: About 77% of the 1993–94 applicants were accepted. The SAT I scores for the 1993–94 freshman class were as follows: Verbal—80% below 500, 17% between 500 and 599, and 3% between 600 and 700; Math—57% below 500, 35% between 500 and 599, 7% between 600 and 700, and 1% above 700. About 25% of the current freshmen were in the top fifth of their class; 53% were in the top two fifths. Three freshmen graduated first in their class.

Requirements: The SAT I or ACT is required. In addition, students must be graduates of an accredited secondary school or have a GED certificate. They should have completed 4 credits in English, 2 in a foreign language, 2 or more in science, including at least 1 laboratory science, 2 or more in social studies, including U.S. history, and 3 in mathematics. An interview is recommended. AP and CLEP credits are accepted. Important factors used in the admissions decision are advanced placement or honor courses, leadership record, extracurricular activities record, evidence of special talent, and parents or siblings attending the school.

Procedure: Freshmen are admitted to all sessions. Entrance exams should be taken in the spring of the junior year or the fall of the senior year. Early decision applications should be filed by December 1; the deadline for regular application is open. The application fee is $25. Notification of early decision is sent December 15; regular decision, on a rolling basis. There are early decision and deferred admissions plans. About 149 early decision candidates were accepted for the 1993–94 class.

Transfer: About 125 transfer students enrolled in 1993–94. Applicants must present a high school transcript and a minimum GPA of 2.25 in college course work. An interview is recommended. A total of 32 credits out of 126 must be completed at Elon.

Visiting: There are regularly scheduled orientations for prospective students, including a general session, meetings with faculty to discuss majors, a campus tour, student panel discussions, and information sessions regarding study abroad, athletics, and financial planning. There are guides for informal visits and visitors may sit in on classes and stay overnight at the school. To arrange for a visit, contact the Admissions Office at (919) 584–2370 or (800) 334–8448.

Financial Aid: In 1993–94 61% of all current freshmen and 49% of continuing students received some form of financial aid. About 39% of freshmen and 45% of continuing students received need-based aid. The average freshman award was $6897. Of that total, scholarships or need-based grants averaged $3648 ($12,290 maximum); loans averaged $4761 ($12,000 maximum); and work contracts averaged $1597 ($2500 maximum). Twenty-six percent of undergraduate students work part-time. Average earnings from campus work for the school year are $835. The average financial indebtedness of the 1992–93 graduate was $5919. Elon is a member of CSS. The FAF, the college's own financial statement, and the FAFSA are required. The deadline for financial aid applications is April 1.

International Students: There are currently 50 international students enrolled. They must take the TOEFL and achieve a minimum score of 500.

Computers: The college provides computer facilities for student use. The mainframes are a DEC VAX 8350 and an HP 857-S/Series 9000. The computer laboratories have 120 microcomputer workstations connected to both the VAX mainframe and 3 Novell networks to the library and to Internet. Apple Macintosh and IBM-compatible microcomputers also are available. All students may access the system 24 hours a day via modem. There are no time limits on using the system and no fees.

Graduates: In 1992–93 614 bachelor's degrees were awarded. The most popular majors among graduates were business (18%), communications/journalism (17%), and psychology (10%). Within an average freshman class, 45% graduate in 4 years, 54% in 5 years, and 57% in 6 years. Some 70 companies recruited on campus in 1992–93. In the 1992 graduating class, 23% of the men and 23% of the women were enrolled in graduate school within 6 months of graduation; 77% of the men and 77% of the women had found employment.

Admissions Contact: Nan P. Perkins, Dean of Admissions and Financial Planning.

FAYETTEVILLE STATE UNIVERSITY
Fayetteville, NC 28301-4298

D-3

(910) 486–1371
(800) 222–2594 (out-of-state)

Full-time: 976 men, 1656 women	**Faculty:** 182; IIA, --$
Part-time: 169 men, 448 women	**Ph.D.s:** 74%
Graduate: 233 men, 550 women	**Student/Faculty:** 14 to 1
Year: semesters, summer session	**Tuition:** $1376 ($7442)
Application Deadline: open	**Room & Board:** $2550
Freshman Class: 1455 applied, 1064 accepted, 452 enrolled	
SAT I Verbal/Math: 390/426	**LESS COMPETITIVE**

Fayetteville State University, founded in 1867 and today part of the University of North Carolina, is a public institution offering degree programs in the arts and sciences, business, and teacher preparation. There are 3 undergraduate schools and one graduate school. In addition to regional accreditation, FSU has baccalaureate program accreditation with NCATE. The library contains 174,971 volumes, 478,375 microform items, and 6414 audiovisual forms, and subscribes to 3314 periodicals. Computerized library sources and services include the card catalog, interlibrary loans, and database searching. Special learning facilities include a planetarium and radio station. The 156-acre campus is in an urban area 60 miles south of Raleigh. Including residence halls, there are 40 buildings on campus.

Student Life: About 93% of undergraduates are from North Carolina. Sixty-seven percent are African American; 29% white. The average age of freshmen is 18; all undergraduates, 25. Twenty percent drop out by the end of their first year; 30% remain to graduate.

Housing: A total of 1003 students can be accommodated in college housing. College-sponsored living facilities include single-sex dormitories. On-campus housing is available on a first-come, first-served basis. Seventy percent of students commute. Alcohol is not permitted. All students may keep cars on campus.

Activities: About 5% of men belong to 5 local and 4 national fraternities; about 5% of women belong to 4 national sororities. There are more than 20 groups on campus, including band, cheerleading, choir, chorus, dance, drama, film, honors, international, jazz band, literary magazine, marching band, newspaper, pep band, political, radio and TV, religious, social service, student government, and yearbook. Popular campus events include the Lyceum, Homecoming, Martin Luther King Day, and Black History Month.

Sports: There are 6 intercollegiate sports for men and 7 for women, and 4 intramural sports for men and 2 for women. Athletic and recreation facilities include 2 gymnasiums, a stadium, tennis courts, a bowling alley, a dance studio, a swimming pool, and playing fields.

Disabled Students: Seventy-five percent of the campus is accessible to disabled students. The following facilities are available: wheelchair ramps, elevators, special parking, specially equipped rest rooms, and lowered drinking fountains.

Services: In addition to many counseling and information services, tutoring is available in some subjects. There is remedial math, reading, and writing.

Campus Safety and Security: Campus safety and security measures include 24-hour foot and vehicle patrol, escort service, and lighted pathways and sidewalks.

Programs of Study: FSU awards the B.A., B.S., and B.S.M.T. degrees. Associate and master's degrees also are awarded. Bachelor's degrees are awarded in BIOLOGICAL SCIENCE (biology/ biological science), BUSINESS (accounting, banking and finance, business administration and management, business economics, marketing/retailing/merchandising, and office supervision and management), COMMUNICATIONS AND THE ARTS (dramatic arts, English, Spanish, speech/debate/rhetoric, and visual and performing arts), COMPUTER AND PHYSICAL SCIENCE (chemistry and mathematics), EDUCATION (business, early childhood, elementary, middle school, music, and secondary), HEALTH PROFESSIONS (medical laboratory technology and nursing), SOCIAL SCIENCE (criminal justice, economics, geography, history, political science/government, psychology, public administration, social science, and sociology).

Required: To graduate, students must complete 120 credit hours with a minimum GPA of 2.0 overall and in the major. The core curriculum includes 8 to 11 credits in natural science, 6 to 15 in humanities, 6 to 7 in mathematics, 3 to 9 in social science, 3 each in critical thinking and speech, and 2 each in physical education/health and university seminar.

Special: FSU offers cooperative programs in business, mathematics, and biological and physical sciences with North Carolina State University, internships, B.A.-B.S. degrees, dual majors, 3–2 engineering degree programs, credit for military experience, and nondegree study. There is a freshman honors program on campus as well as 10 national honor societies. Seven departments have honors programs.

Faculty/Classroom: Seventy-two percent of faculty are male; 28%, female. No introductory courses are taught by graduate students. The average class size in a regular course offering is 20.

Admissions: About 73% of the 1993–94 applicants were accepted. The SAT scores for the 1993–94 freshman class were as follows: Verbal—88% below 500, 11% between 500 and 599, and 1% between 600 and 700; Math—79% below 500, 18% between 500 and 599, 2% between 600 and 700, and 1% above 700. About 25% of the current freshmen were in the top fifth of their class; 50% were in the top two fifths.

Requirements: A minimum GPA of 2.0 is required. The SAT I or ACT is required. Successful scores are also required on the North Carolina Competency Examination. Applicants must be graduates of an accredited secondary school or hold the GED. They should have completed 4 academic units of English, 3 each of mathematics and science with 1 laboratory course, and 2 of social studies; also recommended are 2 units of a foreign language and completion of 1 unit each of foreign language and mathematics in the senior year. AP and CLEP credits are accepted. Important factors used in the admissions decision are advanced placement or honor courses, recommendations by school officials, leadership record, extracurricular activities record, and evidence of special talent.

Procedure: Freshmen are admitted to all sessions. Entrance exams should be taken in November. Application deadlines are open. Application fee is $15. Notification is sent on a rolling basis. There are early decision, early admissions, and deferred admissions plans.

Transfer: More than 400 transfer students enrolled in 1993–94. Applicants must submit official transcripts from all colleges attended, have a minimum GPA of 2.0, and be eligible to return to their previous institution. A total of 30 credits out of 120 must be completed at FSU.

Visiting: There are regularly scheduled orientations for prospective students, including a campus tour, recreational activity, placement tests, preregistration, and orientation to FSU services. There are guides for informal visits and visitors may sit in on classes and stay overnight at the school. To arrange for a visit, contact James Scurry, Director of Enrollment Management, at (910) 486–1371, (800) 672–6667 (in-state), or (800) 222–2594 (out-of-state).

Financial Aid: Scholarships or need-based grants averaged $650, loans averaged $500, and work contracts averaged $850 in a recent year. FSU is a member of CSS. The FAF or FFS is required. The priority deadline for financial aid applications is April 1.

International Students: They must take the TOEFL and achieve a minimum score of 550. The student must also take the SAT I or the ACT.

Computers: The college provides computer facilities for student use. The mainframes are a DEC VAX 8530 and 6000–320 and a Sequent Balance. Microcomputers are available in academic and administrative units. There are PC laboratories available to students, as well as teaching laboratories. All students may access the system 24 hours a day. There are no time limits and no fees.

Graduates: In 1992–93, 428 bachelor's degrees were awarded. The most popular majors among graduates were business administration (24%), criminal justice (16%), and elementary education (9%). Within an average freshman class, 1% graduate in 3 years, 12% in 4 years, and 32% in 5 years.

Admissions Contact: James Scurry, Director, Enrollment Management.

GARDNER-WEBB COLLEGE
(See Gardner-Webb University)

GARDNER-WEBB UNIVERSITY   C-3
(Formerly Gardner-Webb College)
Boiling Springs, NC 28017

(704) 434-4491
(800) 253-6472 (in-state)

Full-time: 740 men, 863 women	Faculty: 83; IIB, --$
Part-time: 86 men, 288 women	Ph.D.s: 70%
Graduate: 112 men, 184 women	Student/Faculty: 19 to 1
Year: semesters, summer session	Tuition: $7680
Application Deadline: August 1	Room & Board: $4270
Freshman Class: 1100 applied, 930 accepted, 338 enrolled	
SAT I: 400/445	ACT: 18 LESS COMPETITIVE

Gardner-Webb University, founded in 1905, is an independent, coeducational institution affiliated with the Baptist Church and offering undergraduate programs in the arts and sciences, business, education, nursing, and preprofessional studies. There are 4 graduate schools. In addition to regional accreditation, the university has baccalaureate program accreditation with NASM, NCATE, and NLN. The library contains 188,380 volumes, 413,691 microform items, and 7114 audiovisual forms, and subscribes to 542 periodicals. Computerized library sources and services include interlibrary loans and database searching. Special learning facilities include a learning resource center, radio station, and observatory. The 250-acre campus is in a small town 50 miles west of Charlotte. Including residence halls, there are 30 buildings on campus.

Student Life: About 76% of undergraduates are from North Carolina. Students come from 19 states and 16 foreign countries. Eighty-eight percent are white; 11% African American. Seventy-eight percent are Protestant; 15% Catholic. The average age of freshmen is 19; all undergraduates, 24. Thirty percent drop out by the end of their first year; 50% remain to graduate.

Housing: A total of 875 students can be accommodated in college housing. College-sponsored living facilities include single-sex dormitories, off-campus apartments, and married-student housing. On-campus housing is guaranteed for all 4 years. Sixty-five percent of students live on campus; of those, 30% remain on campus on weekends. Alcohol is not permitted. All students may keep cars on campus.

Activities: There are no fraternities or sororities on campus. There are 43 groups on campus, including band, cheerleading, choir, chorale, chorus, dance, drama, honors, international, jazz band, literary magazine, musical theater, newspaper, opera, orchestra, pep band, photography, radio and TV, religious, student government, symphony, and yearbook. Popular campus events include Homecoming, Parents Weekend, Spring Jubilee, and Alumni Day.

Sports: There are 7 intercollegiate sports for men and 4 for women, and 12 intramural sports for men and 12 for women. Athletic and recreation facilities include a 5000-seat stadium, a gymnasium, tennis and racquetball courts, a weight room, a swimming pool, and playing fields for softball, soccer, football, and baseball.

Disabled Students: All of the campus is accessible to disabled students. The following facilities are available: wheelchair ramps, elevators, special parking, specially equipped rest rooms, special class scheduling, and lowered drinking fountains.

Services: In addition to many counseling and information services, tutoring is available in every subject. In addition, there is a reader service for the blind, and remedial math, reading, and writing.

Campus Safety and Security: Campus safety and security measures include 24-hour foot and vehicle patrol, escort service, informal discussions, and pamphlets, posters, and films. In addition, there are emergency telephones and a foot patrol inside the dormitories.

Programs of Study: The university awards the B.A., B.S., and B.S.N. degrees. Associate and master's degrees also are awarded. Bachelor's degrees are awarded in BIOLOGICAL SCIENCE (biology/ biological science), BUSINESS (accounting and business administration and management), COMMUNICATIONS AND THE ARTS (communications, English, and music), COMPUTER AND PHYSICAL SCIENCE (chemistry, computer science, information sciences and systems, and mathematics), EDUCATION (elementary, foreign languages, health, middle school, music, and secondary), ENGINEERING AND ENVIRONMENTAL DESIGN (industrial administration/ management), HEALTH PROFESSIONS (nursing), SOCIAL SCIENCE (history, psychology, religion, social science, and sociology).

Preengineering, computer science, premedicine, and prelaw are the strongest programs academically. Business has the largest enrollment.

Required: To graduate, students must complete 128 credit hours, including 24 to 32 in the major, with a minimum GPA of 2.0. The required core curriculum includes courses in English, history, religion, fine arts, foreign language, natural science, and mathematics.

Special: The college offers work-study programs, internships, study abroad in 18 countries, a 3–2 engineering degree with Auburn University and Wake Forest University, and both cooperative programs and dual majors in the fields of engineering and physician's assistant. Independent study is encouraged. There is a freshman honors program on campus, as well as 2 national honor societies. Three departments have honors programs.

Faculty/Classroom: Fifty-eight percent of faculty are male; 43%, female. All teach undergraduates. No introductory courses are taught by graduate students. The average class size in an introductory lecture is 30; in a laboratory, 9; and in a regular course offering, 18.

Admissions: About 85% of the 1993–94 applicants were accepted. The SAT scores for the 1993–94 freshman class were as follows: Verbal—66% below 500, 33% between 500 and 599, and 1% between 600 and 700; Math—66% below 500, 33% between 500 and 599, and 1% between 600 and 700. The ACT scores were 65% below 21, 25% between 21 and 23, and 10% between 24 and 26. About 35% of the current freshmen were in the top fifth of their class; 50% were in the top two fifths.

Requirements: The college requires applicants to be in the upper 50% of their class. A minimum GPA of 2.0 is required. The SAT I or ACT is required. Candidates should be graduates of an accredited secondary school or have a GED certificate. An interview is recommended. AP and CLEP credits are accepted. Important factors used in the admissions decision are leadership record, advanced placement or honor courses, evidence of special talent, recommendations by school officials, and extracurricular activities record.

Procedure: Freshmen are admitted to all sessions. Entrance exams should be taken in the senior year. Applications should be filed by August 1 for fall entry and December 1 for spring entry, along with an application fee of $20. Notification is sent on a rolling basis. There are early admissions and deferred admissions plans.

Transfer: About 379 transfer students enrolled in 1993–94. Applicants must submit the standard application and fee, official high school and college transcripts, and SAT I or ACT scores. A total of 30 credits out of 128 must be completed at the university.

Visiting: There are regularly scheduled orientations for prospective students. There are guides for informal visits and visitors may sit in on classes and stay overnight at the school. To arrange for a visit, contact the Admissions Office at (704) 434–4491 or (800) 253–6472 (in state).

Financial Aid: In a recent year, 88% of all freshmen and 63% of continuing students received some form of financial aid. The average freshman award was $6000. Of that total, scholarships or need-based grants averaged $2500 ($4485 maximum); loans averaged $3000 ($4000 maximum); and work contracts averaged $1300 ($2000 maximum). The average financial indebtedness of a recent year's graduate was $9000. The university is a member of CSS. The FAF is required. The deadline for financial aid applications is April 1.

International Students: There are currently 26 international students enrolled. The school actively recruits these students. They must take the TOEFL and achieve a minimum score of 500.

Computers: The college provides computer facilities for student use. The mainframe is an IBM/34. There are IBM microcomputers available in the Belk Ellis Computer Laboratory, located in the library. All students may access the system. It may be used from 7 A.M. to 11 P.M. except when a class is in process. There are no time limits on using the system and no fees.

Admissions Contact: Ray M. Hardee, Director of Admissions.

GREENSBORO COLLEGE

D-2

Greensboro, NC 27401-1875

(919) 272-7102; (800) 346-8226

Full-time: 297 men, 352 women	Faculty: 47; IIB, --$
Part-time: 89 men, 225 women	Ph.D.s: 75%
Graduate: none	Student/Faculty: 14 to 1
Year: semesters, summer session	Tuition: $7816
Application Deadline: open	Room & Board: $3680
Freshman Class: 608 applied, 494 accepted, 176 enrolled	
SAT I Verbal/Math: 430/460	COMPETITIVE

Greensboro College, founded in 1838, is a private, coeducational institution affiliated with the United Methodist Church, offering undergraduate programs in the arts and sciences, business, education, health sciences, and preprofessional studies. The library contains 90,000 volumes and 3247 microform items, and subscribes to 450 periodicals. Computerized library sources and services include the card catalog, interlibrary loans, and database searching. Special learning facilities include an art gallery, a natural history museum, and a greenhouse. The 30-acre campus is in an urban area in Greensboro. Including residence halls, there are 12 buildings on campus.

Student Life: About 54% of undergraduates are from out-of-state, mostly the Middle Atlantic. Students come from 20 states and 5 foreign countries. Eighty-six percent are from public schools; 14% from private. Eighty-one percent are white; 12% African American. Sixty percent are Protestant; 20% Catholic. The average age of freshmen is 18; all undergraduates, 21. Twenty percent drop out by the end of their first year; 35% remain to graduate.

Housing: A total of 540 students can be accommodated in college housing. College-sponsored living facilities include single-sex and coed dormitories. On-campus housing is guaranteed for the freshman year only and is available on a first-come, first-served basis thereafter. Sixty percent of students live on campus. All students may keep cars on campus.

Activities: There are no fraternities or sororities on campus. There are 40 groups on campus, including band, cheerleading, choir, chorale, drama, honors, international, jazz band, literary magazine, musical theater, newspaper, pep band, political, professional, religious, social, social service, student government, and yearbook. Popular campus events include Homecoming, Winter Rose Affair, Spring Fling, and Cap and Gown.

Sports: There are 7 intercollegiate sports for men and 5 for women, and 35 intramural sports for men and 35 for women. Athletic and recreation facilities include an athletic field for soccer and lacrosse, tennis and basketball courts, and a gymnasium with indoor swimming pool and weight room.

Disabled Students: Eighty percent of the campus is accessible to disabled students. The following facilities are available: wheelchair ramps, elevators, and special parking.

Services: In addition to many counseling and information services, tutoring is available in most subjects.

Campus Safety and Security: Campus safety and security measures include 24-hour foot and vehicle patrol, self-defense education, escort service, and informal discussions. In addition, there are pamphlets, posters, films, lighted pathways and sidewalks, and security entrances to residence halls.

Programs of Study: Greensboro awards the B.A. and B.S. degrees. Bachelor's degrees are awarded in BIOLOGICAL SCIENCE (biology/biological science), BUSINESS (accounting and business administration and management), COMMUNICATIONS AND THE ARTS (art, dramatic arts, English, French, music, and Spanish), COMPUTER AND PHYSICAL SCIENCE (chemistry and mathematics), EDUCATION (elementary, middle school, physical, secondary, and special), SOCIAL SCIENCE (history, political science/government, psychology, religion, and sociology). Education, business, biology, music, theater, and psychology are the strongest academically. Business and education have the largest enrollments.

Required: To graduate, students must complete 124 credit hours, including 65 to 71 in the major, depending upon the program. They must take courses in social science, fine arts, laboratory science, leadership, English, religion, history, physical education, mathematics, literature, and foreign language. A minimum GPA of 1.6 is required at the end of the freshman year, and 2.0 thereafter.

Special: The college offers cross-registration with members of the Greater Greensboro Consortium and Piedmont Independent College Association, internships in all areas, a B.A.-B.S. degree in 20 majors, work-study programs, study abroad, student-designed majors, pass/fail options, and credit for life, military, and work experience. There is a freshman honors program on campus, as well as 2 national honor societies. One department has an honors program.

Faculty/Classroom: Fifty-seven percent of faculty are male; 43%, female. All teach undergraduates, 40% do research, and 40% do both. The average class size in a regular course offering is 18.

Admissions: About 81% of the 1993–94 applicants were accepted. The SAT scores for the 1993–94 freshman class were as follows: Verbal—81% below 500, 17% between 500 and 599, and 2% between 600 and 700; Math—66% below 500, 28% between 500 and 599, 5% between 600 and 700, and 1% above 700. About 22% of the current freshmen were in the top fifth of their class; 45% in the top two fifths. Two freshmen graduated first in their class.

Requirements: Greensboro requires applicants to be in the upper 60% of their class. A minimum GPA of 2.0 is required. The SAT I or ACT is required. Applicants must be graduates of an accredited secondary school or have a GED certificate. An essay is required and an interview is recommended. AP and CLEP credits are accepted. Important factors used in the admissions decision are advanced placement or honor courses, leadership record, evidence of special talent, extracurricular activities record, and recommendations by school officials.

Procedure: Freshmen are admitted in the fall and spring. Entrance exams should be taken in the spring of the junior year. Application deadlines are open. Application fee is $20. Notification is sent on a rolling basis. There are early admissions and deferred admissions

plans. A waiting list is an active part of the admissions procedure, with about 5% of applicants on the list.

Transfer: About 55 transfer students enrolled in 1993–94. The SAT I is required of applicants with fewer than 30 semester hours. An associate degree and an interview are recommended. At least 31 credits out of 124 must be completed at Greensboro.

Visiting: There are regularly scheduled orientations for prospective students, including an interview, a campus tour, and meetings with faculty and students. There are guides for informal visits, and visitors may sit in on classes. To arrange for a visit, contact the Admissions Office at (800) 346–8226.

Financial Aid: In a recent year, 65% of all freshmen and 50% of continuing students received some form of financial aid. About 52% of freshmen and 39% of continuing students received need-based aid. The average freshman award was $5357. Of that total, scholarships or need-based grants averaged $3261 ($6000 maximum); loans averaged $1296 ($2625 maximum); and work contracts averaged $800. Seventy percent of undergraduate students work part-time. Average earnings from campus work for the school year are $800. The average financial indebtedness of a recent graduate was $6029. Greensboro is a member of CSS. The FAF is required. The deadline for financial aid applications is March 1.

International Students: There are currently 4 international students enrolled. They must take the TOEFL and must also take the SAT I or the ACT.

Computers: The college provides computer facilities for student use. There are 36 microcomputers located in Cowan Humanities Building, with assistance available at all times. All students may access the system 90 hours per week. There are no time limits on using the system and no fees.

Graduates: In 1992–93, 171 bachelor's degrees were awarded. The most popular majors among graduates were business (27%), elementary education (13%), and biology (11%). Within an average freshman class, 2% graduate in 3 years, 25% in 4 years, 38% in 5 years, and 43% in 6 years. Some 30 companies recruited on campus in 1992–93. In a recent graduating class, 6% of the men and 8% of the women were enrolled in graduate school within 6 months of graduation.

Admissions Contact: Martha Bunch, Director of Admissions.

GUILFORD COLLEGE

D-2

Greensboro, NC 27410

(910) 316–2100
(800) 992–7759 (out-of-state)

Full-time: 580 men, 628 women	Faculty: 88; IIB, av$
Part-time: 9 men, 8 women	Ph.D.s: 88%
Graduate: none	Student/Faculty: 14 to 1
Year: semesters, summer session	Tuition: $12,610
Application Deadline: March 1	Room & Board: $5070
Freshman Class: 1202 applied, 1054 accepted, 326 enrolled	
SAT I Verbal/Math: 498/531	COMPETITIVE

Guilford College, founded in 1837, is a private liberal arts and sciences institution affiliated with the Religious Society of Friends (Quakers). In addition to regional accreditation, Guilford College has baccalaureate program accreditation with NCATE. The library contains 226,000 volumes, 15,500 microform items, and 4700 audiovisual forms, and subscribes to 1150 periodicals. Computerized library sources and services include the card catalog, interlibrary loans, and database searching. Special learning facilities include a learning resource center, art gallery, radio station, and observatory. The 300-acre campus is in a suburban area on 300 wooded acres in northwest Greensboro. Including residence halls, there are 70 buildings on campus.

Student Life: About 62% of undergraduates are from out-of-state, mostly the Middle Atlantic. Students come from 38 states, 64 foreign countries, and Canada. Sixty-four percent are from public schools; 36% from private. Eighty-nine percent are white. Sixty percent are Protestant; 17% claim no religious affiliation; 13% Catholic. The average age of freshmen is 18; all undergraduates, 20. Nineteen percent drop out by the end of their first year; 62% remain to graduate.

Housing: A total of 961 students can be accommodated in college housing. College-sponsored living facilities include single-sex and coed dormitories, on-campus apartments, and married-student housing. In addition, there are language houses and special interest houses. On-campus housing is guaranteed for all 4 years. Seventy-eight percent of students live on campus; of those, 95% remain on campus on weekends. All students may keep cars on campus.

Activities: There are no fraternities or sororities on campus. There are 58 groups on campus, including art, band, cheerleading, chess, choir, chorale, chorus, drama, film, gay, honors, international, literary magazine, musical theater, newspaper, pep band, photography, professional, radio and TV, religious, social, social service, student government, symphony, and yearbook. Popular campus events include Spring Fling, Christmas Choir Concert, and International Dinner.

Sports: There are 7 intercollegiate sports for men and 5 for women, and 12 intramural sports for men, 12 for women, and 3 for both men and women. Athletic and recreation facilities include a 3500-seat stadium, a 2500-seat gymnasium, a field house, basketball courts, a swimming pool and diving tank, playing fields, and courts for tennis, badminton, and volleyball.

Disabled Students: Seventy-five percent of the campus is accessible to disabled students. The following facilities are available: wheelchair ramps, elevators, special parking, specially equipped rest rooms, and special class scheduling.

Services: In addition to many counseling and information services, tutoring is available in most subjects. In addition, there is remedial math, reading, and writing.

Campus Safety and Security: Campus safety and security measures include 24-hour foot and vehicle patrol, self defense education, escort service, and informal discussions. In addition, there are pamphlets, posters, and films, emergency telephones, and lighted pathways and sidewalks.

Programs of Study: Guilford College awards the A.B., B.S., B.A.S., and B.F.A. degrees. Associate degrees also are awarded. Bachelor's degrees are awarded in BIOLOGICAL SCIENCE (biology/biological science), BUSINESS (accounting, business administration and management, and sports management), COMMUNICATIONS AND THE ARTS (dramatic arts, English, fine arts, French, German, music, and Spanish), COMPUTER AND PHYSICAL SCIENCE (chemistry, geology, mathematics, and physics), EDUCATION (elementary, physical, and secondary), HEALTH PROFESSIONS (sports medicine), SOCIAL SCIENCE (criminal justice, economics, history, humanistic studies, international studies, philosophy, political science/government, psychology, religion, and sociology/anthropology). Physics and psychology are the strongest programs academically. Management and psychology have the largest enrollments.

Required: To graduate, students are required to complete 128 semester hours, including a minimum of 32 in the major, with a minimum GPA of 2.0. Distribution requirements include courses in social science, humanities, creative arts, laboratory and nonlaboratory science, history, and a foreign language. Core requirements include First-Year Seminar, English, Senior Interdisciplinary Seminar, and Intercultural Studies.

Special: There are 3–2 degree programs available in engineering with Georgia Institute of Technology, in forestry and environmental studies with Duke University, and in medical technology and physician assistant training with Bowman Gray School of Medicine at Wake Forest University. Guilford also offers many internships, a Washington semester, work-study programs, dual majors, the B.A.-B.S. degree, student-designed majors, study abroad in 8 countries, pass/fail options, and cross-registration with members of the Greater Greensboro Consortium (8 colleges/universities). There is a freshman honors program on campus, as well as 2 national honor societies. All departments have honor programs.

Faculty/Classroom: Sixty-seven percent of faculty are male; 33%, female. Seventy-five percent teach as well as do research. The average class size in an introductory lecture is 25; in a laboratory, 23; and in a regular course offering, 20.

Admissions: About 88% of the 1993–94 applicants were accepted. The SAT scores for the 1993–94 freshman class were as follows: Verbal—54% below 500, 31% between 500 and 599, 12% between 600 and 700, and 2% above 700; Math—30% below 500, 45% between 500 and 599, 21% between 600 and 700, and 4% above 700. About 38% of the current freshmen were in the top fifth of their class; 71% were in the top two fifths. Nine freshmen graduated first in their class.

Requirements: A minimum GPA of 2.0 is required. The SAT I is required. A minimum SAT composite score of 1000 or ACT score of 22 is recommended. Applicants should have completed 20 Carnegie units, including 4 in English, 2 each in foreign language and science, and 1 each in history and social studies. The GED is accepted. An essay is required and an interview is recommended. AP and CLEP credits are accepted. Important factors used in the admissions decision are advanced placement or honor courses, evidence of special talent, leadership record, personality, intangible qualities, and recommendations by school officials.

Procedure: Freshmen are admitted fall and spring. Early decision applications should be filed by December 1; regular applications, by March 1 for fall entry and November 15 for spring entry, along with an application fee of $25. Notification of early decision is sent December 15; regular decision, April 1. There are early decision, early admissions, and deferred admissions plans. About 23 early decision candidates were accepted for the 1993–94 class. A waiting list is an active part of the admissions procedure, with about 5% of applicants on the list.

Transfer: About 58 transfer students enrolled in 1993–94. Applicants must have a minimum GPA of 2.5 in at least 12 credit hours, submit either SAT or ACT scores, and provide a letter from the academic adviser or dean of the previous school. An interview and an as-

sociate degree are recommended. A total of 24 credits out of 128 must be completed at Guilford College.

Visiting: There are regularly scheduled orientations for prospective students, including forums, a campus tour, and presentations by faculty, administrators, and students. There are guides for informal visits and visitors may sit in on classes and stay overnight at the school. To arrange for a visit, contact the Admission Office at (910) 316–2100 or (800) 992–7759.

Financial Aid: In 1993–94 78% of all current freshmen and 67% of continuing students received some form of financial aid. About 53% of freshmen and 49% of continuing students received need-based aid. The average freshman award was $12,043. Of that total, scholarships or need-based grants averaged $7010 ($10,000 maximum); loans averaged $3630 ($5125 maximum); and work contracts averaged $1400 ($1750 maximum). Forty-one percent of undergraduate students work part-time. Average earnings from campus work for the school year are $825. The average financial indebtedness of the 1992–93 graduate was $9825. Guilford College is a member of CSS. The college's own financial statement is required. The deadline for financial aid applications is March 1.

International Students: There are currently 62 international students enrolled. The school actively recruits these students. They must take the TOEFL and achieve a minimum score of 550.

Computers: The college provides computer facilities for student use. The mainframe is a DEC VAX 8350. There are also 120 terminals and PCs in the central laboratory and classroom building, with access from other buildings through the campus network. All students may access the system. There are no time limits on using the system and no fees.

Graduates: In 1992–93 328 bachelor's degrees were awarded. The most popular majors among graduates were management (13%), justice and policy studies (9%), and psychology (9%). Within an average freshman class, 1% graduate in 3 years, 49% in 4 years, 61% in 5 years, and 62% in 6 years. Some 82 companies recruited on campus in 1992–93. In the 1992 graduating class, 19% of the men and women were enrolled in graduate school within 6 months of graduation; 26% of the men and women had found employment.

Admissions Contact: Larry M. West, Director of Admission.

HIGH POINT UNIVERSITY

D-2

High Point, NC 27262–3598

(919) 841–9216; (800) 345–6993

Full-time: 831 men, 1214 women	Faculty: 90; IIB, --$
Part-time: 140 men, 214 women	Ph.D.s: 60%
Graduate: 11 men, 14 women	Student/Faculty: 23 to 1
Year: semesters, summer session	Tuition: $8300
Application Deadline: open	Room & Board: $4050
Freshman Class: 1358 applied, 1149 accepted, 341 enrolled	
SAT I Verbal/Math: 420/450	**LESS COMPETITIVE**

High Point University, founded in 1924, is a private institution affiliated with the United Methodist Church. The university offers degree programs in the arts and science, business, and education both on its main campus and on its Winston-Salem campus, which accommodates evening students. There is one graduate school. In addition to regional accreditation, High Point has baccalaureate program accreditation with NCATE. The library contains 141,937 volumes, 468 microform items, and 294 audiovisual forms, and subscribes to 1400 periodicals. Computerized library sources and services include the card catalog, interlibrary loans, and database searching. Special learning facilities include a learning resource center, radio station, and TV station. The 77-acre campus is in a suburban area 15 miles southeast of Winston-Salem and 12 miles southwest of Greensboro. Including residence halls, there are 17 buildings on campus.

Student Life: About 55% of undergraduates are from out-of-state, mostly the Middle Atlantic. Students come from 32 states, 27 foreign countries, and Canada. Eighty-eight percent are from public schools; 12% from private. Ninety percent are white. Seventy-six percent are Protestant; 15% Catholic; 14% claim no religious affiliation. The average age of freshmen is 18; all undergraduates, 20. Thirty percent drop out by the end of their first year; 47% remain to graduate.

Housing: A total of 856 students can be accommodated in college housing. College-sponsored living facilities include single-sex and coed dormitories, on-campus apartments, fraternity houses, and sorority houses. In addition there are special interest houses and a quiet house. On-campus housing is guaranteed for all 4 years. Sixty-two percent of students live on campus; of those, 80% remain on campus on weekends. All students may keep cars on campus.

Activities: About 38% of men and about 1% of women belong to 5 national fraternities; about 37% of women belong to 1 local and 4 national sororities. There are 51 groups on campus, including cheerleading, choir, chorale, chorus, computers, dance, drama, ethnic, film, honors, international, literary magazine, musical theater, newspaper, political, professional, radio and TV, religious, social, social service, student government, and yearbook. Popular campus events include Senior Send-Off, Homecoming, and Greek Week.

Sports: There are 7 intercollegiate sports for men and 6 for women, and 12 intramural sports for men and 10 for women. Athletic and recreation facilities include intramural fields, tennis courts, 3 gymnasiums, and a new recreation center featuring a swimming pool, racquetball courts, aerobics equipment, a weight room, and a 2500-seat basketball arena.

Disabled Students: Fifty percent of the campus is accessible to disabled students. The following facilities are available: wheelchair ramps, elevators, special parking, specially equipped rest rooms, and lowered drinking fountains.

Services: In addition to many counseling and information services, tutoring is available in every subject. There is also remedial math and writing.

Campus Safety and Security: Campus safety and security measures include 24-hour foot and vehicle patrol, escort service, informal discussions, pamphlets, posters, and films. In addition, there are emergency telephones and lighted pathways and sidewalks.

Programs of Study: High Point awards the B.A. and B.S. degrees. Master's degrees also are awarded. Bachelor's degrees are awarded in AGRICULTURE (forestry and related sciences), BIOLOGICAL SCIENCE (biology/biological science), BUSINESS (accounting, business economics, and international business management), COMMUNICATIONS AND THE ARTS (art, dramatic arts, English, fine arts, French, and Spanish), COMPUTER AND PHYSICAL SCIENCE (chemistry, information sciences and systems, and mathematics), EDUCATION (art, elementary, middle school, physical, secondary, and special), HEALTH PROFESSIONS (medical laboratory technology and sports medicine), SOCIAL SCIENCE (history, industrial and organizational psychology, international studies, philosophy, political science/government, psychology, religion, and sociology). Business administration has the largest enrollment.

Required: To graduate, students must complete 124 credit hours, including up to 60 in the major, with a minimum GPA of 2.0. The core curriculum consists of 2 courses each in Western Civilization, social science, physical education, and a modern foreign language, as well as 1 course each in mathematics, laboratory science, English, literature, ethics, and world affairs.

Special: There is cross-registration with the University of North Carolina at Greensboro, North Carolina A & T State University, and Greensboro, Elon, Guilford, and Bennett colleges. High Point also offers study abroad in Europe, the Student Career Internship Program, a dual major in chemistry/business, B.A.-B.S. degrees in home furnishings marketing and human relations, student-designed majors, a 3–2 forestry program with Duke University, credit for life experience, and pass/fail options. There is a freshman honors program on campus, as well as one national honor society. Two departments have honors programs.

Faculty/Classroom: Seventy-seven percent of faculty are male; 23%, female. All teach undergraduates. No introductory courses are taught by graduate students. The average class size in an introductory lecture is 25; in a laboratory, 20; and in a regular course offering, 24.

Admissions: About 85% of the 1993–94 applicants were accepted. The SAT scores for the 1993–94 freshman class were as follows: Verbal—83% below 500, 15% between 500 and 599, and 2% between 600 and 700; Math—65% below 500, 28% between 500 and 599, and 7% between 600 and 700. About 27% of the current freshmen were in the top fifth of their class; 49% were in the top two fifths. There were 2 National Merit semifinalists. Three freshmen graduated first in their class.

Requirements: The SAT I is required. Applicants should be graduates from an accredited secondary school or have a GED certificate. They should have completed 16 academic units, including 4 in English, 3 each in mathematics and history, and 2 each in science, social studies, and a foreign language. AP and CLEP credits are accepted. Important factors used in the admissions decision are advanced placement or honor courses, parents or siblings attending the school, leadership record, evidence of special talent, and recommendations by alumni.

Procedure: Freshmen are admitted to all sessions. Entrance exams should be taken prior to high school graduation. Application deadlines are open. Application fee is $20. Notification is sent on a rolling basis. There are early decision and deferred admissions plans.

Transfer: About 150 transfer students enrolled in 1993–94. Generally, a minimum GPA of 2.0 is required. At least 31 credits out of 124 must be completed at High Point.

Visiting: There are regularly scheduled orientations for prospective students. There are guides for informal visits, and visitors may sit in on classes. To arrange for a visit, contact the Admissions Office at (800) 345–6993.

Financial Aid: In 1993–94, 70% of all current freshmen and 66% of continuing students received some form of financial aid. About 48% of freshmen and 60% of continuing students received need-based aid. The average freshman award was $5827. Of that total, scholarships or need-based grants averaged $2501 ($7700 maximum); loans averaged $2240 ($2625 maximum); and work contracts

averaged $900 ($2000 maximum). Twenty-two percent of undergraduate students work part-time. Average earnings from campus work for the school year are $1075. The average financial indebtedness of the 1992–93 graduate was $10,200. High Point is a member of CSS. The FAF is required. The deadline for financial aid applications is March 1.

International Students: There are currently 52 international students enrolled. They must take the TOEFL, the University of Michigan Language Test, the Comprehensive English Language Test, or the college's own test. The SAT I is required of students who wish to play on varsity athletic teams.

Computers: The college provides computer facilities for student use. The mainframes are a Data General Avion (1992) minisystem and a Data General 10000. There are 3 computer laboratories on campus with more than 100 PCs, most of which are 486 DOS. Internet service is available to all students and accessed from more than 30 terminals on campus. All students may access the system up to 80 hours per week. There are no time limits on using the system and no fees.

Graduates: In 1992–93, 525 bachelor's degrees were awarded. The most popular majors among graduates were business administration (34%), accounting (13%), and computer information systems (10%). Within an average freshman class, 1% graduate in 3 years, 32% in 4 years, and 14% in 5 years. Some 30 companies recruited on campus in 1992–93. In the 1992 graduating class, 20% of all graduates were enrolled in graduate school within 6 months of graduation; 94% of the men and 98% of the women had found employment.

Admissions Contact: Jim Schlimmer, Dean of Admissions.

JOHNSON C. SMITH UNIVERSITY   C-3

Charlotte, NC 28216   (704) 378-1010; (800) 782-7303 (in-state)

Full-time: 527 men, 785 women	Faculty: 74; IIB, --$
Part-time: 31 men, 50 women	Ph.D.s: 73%
Graduate: none	Student/Faculty: 18 to 1
Year: semesters, summer session	Tuition: $6338
Application Deadline: July 1	Room & Board: $2578
Freshman Class: n/av	
SAT I Verbal/Math: 339/362	**LESS COMPETITIVE**

Johnson C. Smith University, founded in 1867, is a progressive, historically black private institution offering a liberal arts education. In addition to regional accreditation, JCSU has baccalaureate program accreditation with CSWE and NCATE. The library contains 112,477 volumes, 26,991 microform items, and 5714 audiovisual forms, and subscribes to 673 periodicals. Computerized library sources and services include the card catalog, interlibrary loans, and database searching. Special learning facilities include a learning resource center and radio station. The 105-acre campus is in an urban area. Including residence halls, there are 32 buildings on campus.

Student Life: About 83% of undergraduates are from out-of-state, mostly the Northeast. Students come from 33 states. Ninety percent are from public schools; 10% from private. All are African American. The average age of freshmen is 18; all undergraduates, 20. Thirty percent drop out by the end of their first year; 35% remain to graduate.

Housing: A total of 1174 students can be accommodated in college housing. College-sponsored living facilities include single-sex dormitories. In addition there are honors houses. On-campus housing is available on a first-come, first-served basis. Seventy-two percent of students live on campus; of those, 75% remain on campus on weekends. Alcohol is not permitted. Upperclassmen may keep cars on campus.

Activities: About 10% of men and about 15% of women belong to 2 local and 4 national fraternities; about 15% of women belong to 2 local and 4 national sororities. There are 40 groups on campus, including art, band, cheerleading, chess, choir, chorus, computers, dance, drama, ethnic, film, honors, jazz band, literary magazine, marching band, newspaper, pep band, photography, political, radio and TV, religious, social service, student government, and yearbook. Popular campus events include Founders Day, West Fest, and Homecoming.

Sports: There are 6 intercollegiate sports for men and 5 for women, and 5 intramural sports for men and 6 for women. Athletic and recreation facilities include 2 gymnasiums, of which the larger seats 3200, a pool, tennis and basketball courts, and an off-campus city-owned stadium seating 25,000.

Disabled Students: Ten percent of the campus is accessible to disabled students. The following facilities are available: wheelchair ramps and special parking.

Services: In addition to many counseling and information services, tutoring is available in every subject.

Campus Safety and Security: Campus safety and security measures include 24-hour foot and vehicle patrol, lighted pathways and sidewalks, and emergency stations.

Programs of Study: JCSU awards the B.A., B.S., and B.S.W degrees. Bachelor's degrees are awarded in BIOLOGICAL SCIENCE (biology/biological science), BUSINESS (business administration and management and business economics), COMMUNICATIONS AND THE ARTS (communications, English, music, and music business management), COMPUTER AND PHYSICAL SCIENCE (chemistry, computer science, mathematics, and physics), EDUCATION (elementary, health, middle school, physical, science, secondary, and social studies), ENGINEERING AND ENVIRONMENTAL DESIGN (preengineering), HEALTH PROFESSIONS (predentistry and premedicine), SOCIAL SCIENCE (economics, history, political science/government, prelaw, psychology, social science, social work, and sociology). Business and mathematics are the strongest academically. Business and communication arts have the largest enrollments.

Required: To graduate, students must complete 122 credit hours, including 30 to 59 in the major, with a minimum GPA of 2.0. Distribution requirements include courses in English, composition, the humanities, social science, health and physical education, mathematics, and natural science.

Special: JCSU offers cooperative programs with the University of North Carolina at Charlotte and Central Piedmont Community College, 3–2 engineering degrees with UNCC and Florida A & M University, cross-registration with the Charlotte area educational consortium, internships with local businesses, study abroad in Europe, a summer Washington semster, and a B.A.-B.S. degree in all majors. Nondegree study in continuing education and pass/fail options are available. There are 9 national honor societies on campus.

Faculty/Classroom: Sixty-four percent of faculty are male; 36%, female. All teach undergraduates, and 2% also do research. The average class size in an introductory lecture is 30; in a laboratory, 15; and in a regular course offering, 25.

Admissions: There were 6 National Merit finalists. About 11 freshmen graduated first in their class.

Requirements: The SAT I or ACT is required. A minimum SAT I composite score of 600 or ACT score of 10 is recommended. Applicants should have completed 16 Carnegie units, including 4 in English, 2 each in mathematics and social science, 1 in science, and 7 in electives. The GED is accepted. An essay and an interview are suggested. AP credits are accepted. Important factors used in the admissions decision are evidence of special talent, advanced placement or honor courses, leadership record, extracurricular activities record, and recommendations by school officials.

Procedure: Freshmen are admitted fall and spring. Entrance exams should be taken prior to application. Applications should be filed by July 1 for fall entry and December 1 for spring entry, along with an application fee of $20. Notification is sent on a rolling basis. There are early admissions and deferred admissions plans.

Transfer: About 30 transfer students enrolled in 1993–94. Applicants need a minimum GPA of 2.0. The SAT I or ACT is recommended. A total of 32 credits out of 122 must be completed at JCSU.

Visiting: There are regularly scheduled orientations for prospective students. There are guides for informal visits and visitors may sit in on classes and stay overnight at the school. To arrange for a visit, contact the Director of Admissions at (704) 378-1010.

Financial Aid: In 1993–94 94% of all current freshmen and 87% of continuing students received some form of financial aid. About 95% of freshmen and 82% of continuing students received need-based aid. The average freshman award was $5500. Of that total, scholarships or need-based grants averaged $2816 ($9103 maximum); loans averaged $2229 ($2625 maximum); and work contracts averaged $2000. Twenty-two percent of undergraduate students work part-time. Average earnings from campus work for the school year are $1500. The average financial indebtedness of the 1992–93 graduate was $9961. JCSU is a member of CSS. The FAFSA financial statement is required. The deadline for financial aid applications is April 15.

International Students: The school actively recruits these students. They must take the TOEFL. The student must also take the SAT I or the ACT.

Computers: The college provides computer facilities for student use. The mainframe is an AS 400. More than 100 PCs and printers are located throughout the campus, including some residence halls. All students may access the system. It may be used 8:15 A.M. to 10 P.M. There are no time limits on using the system and no fees.

Graduates: In 1992–93 155 bachelor's degrees were awarded. The most popular majors among graduates were business administration (34%), communications arts (17%), and computer science (5%). Within an average freshman class, 1% graduate in 3 years, 18% in 4 years, 26% in 5 years, and 33% in 6 years. Some 75 companies recruited on campus in 1992–93. In the 1992 graduating class, 10% were enrolled in graduate school within 6 months of graduation; 35% had found employment.

Admissions Contact: Marvin Dunlap, Director of Admissions.

LEES-MCRAE COLLEGE

B-2

Banner Elk, NC 28604   (800) 280-4562

Full-time: 400 men, 220 women	Faculty: 53; III, --$
Part-time: 23 men, 16 women	Ph.D.s: 50%
Graduate: none	Student/Faculty: 12 to 1
Year: semesters, summer session	Tuition: $6948
Application Deadline: March 15	Room & Board: $2902
Freshman Class: 577 applied, 529 accepted, 216 enrolled	
SAT I: required	**LESS COMPETITIVE**

Lees-McRae College, founded in 1900, is an independent, nonprofit liberal arts institution affiliated with the Presbyterian Church USA. In addition to regional accreditation, Lees-McRae has baccalaureate program accreditation with NCATE. The 3 libraries contain 79,900 volumes, 5025 microform items, and 1315 audiovisual forms, and subscribe to 453 periodicals. Computerized library sources and services include interlibrary loans. Special learning facilities include a learning resource center and academic advancement center. The 400-acre campus is in a rural area 100 miles northwest of Charlotte. Including residence halls, there are 33 buildings on campus.

Student Life: About 60% of undergraduates are from North Carolina. Students come from 16 states, 3 foreign countries, and Canada. Ninety-five percent are from public schools; 5% from private. Ninety percent are white. Eighty-nine percent are Protestant; 11% Catholic. The average age of freshmen is 18; all undergraduates, 20. Twenty-nine percent drop out by the end of their first year.

Housing: A total of 714 students can be accommodated in college housing. College-sponsored living facilities include single-sex dormitories. In addition, there are honors houses. On-campus housing is guaranteed for all 4 years. Seventy percent of students live on campus; of those, 75% remain on campus on weekends. Alcohol is not permitted. All students may keep cars on campus.

Activities: There are no fraternities or sororities on campus. There are 13 groups on campus, including cheerleading, chorus, computers, dance, drama, ethnic, honors, musical theater, newspaper, photography, religious, student government, and yearbook. Popular campus events include Black History Month, Staley Distinguished Lectureship, Martin Luther King Day, Spring Fling, Homecoming, and theater and Christmas performances.

Sports: There are 4 intercollegiate sports for men and 5 for women, and 17 intramural sports for men and 17 for women. Athletic and recreation facilities include a 1200-seat playing arena, indoor tennis courts, an Olympic-size swimming pool, soccer fields, a field house, a weight-training room, basketball courts, and a student recreation center.

Disabled Students: Fifty percent of the campus is accessible to disabled students. The following facilities are available: wheelchair ramps, elevators, special parking, and specially equipped rest rooms.

Services: In addition to many counseling and information services, tutoring is available in every subject. There is also remedial math, reading, and writing.

Campus Safety and Security: Campus safety and security measures include 24-hour foot and vehicle patrol, escort service, informal discussions, pamphlets, posters, and films. In addition, there are emergency telephones and lighted pathways and sidewalks.

Programs of Study: Lees-McRae awards the B.A. and B.S. degrees. Bachelor's degrees are awarded in BIOLOGICAL SCIENCE (biology/biological science), BUSINESS (business administration and management), COMMUNICATIONS AND THE ARTS (communications, dance, dramatic arts, English, and musical theater), COMPUTER AND PHYSICAL SCIENCE (mathematics), SOCIAL SCIENCE (criminal justice, history, humanities, interdisciplinary studies, religion, and social studies). Business, criminal justice, and communications have the largest enrollments.

Required: To graduate, students must complete at least 126 credit hours, including 57 in the major, with a minimum GPA of 2.0. Core requirements include courses in English, religion, history, the sciences, mathematics, computer science, physical education, and senior seminar.

Special: The college has work-study programs and student-designed majors in the interdisciplinary studies program. The teacher education program provides preparation for certification in elementary, middle school, and secondary education. There is a freshman honors program on campus, as well as one national honor society. One department has an honors program.

Faculty/Classroom: Sixty-one percent of faculty are male; 39%, female. All teach undergraduates. The average class size in an introductory lecture is 18; in a laboratory, 20; and in a regular course offering, 25.

Admissions: About 92% of the 1993-94 applicants were accepted.

Requirements: Lees-McRae requires applicants to be in the upper 50% of their class. A minimum GPA of 2.0 is required. The SAT I is required. AP and CLEP credits are accepted. Important factors used in the admissions decision are recommendations by school officials, personality, intangible qualities, leadership record, evidence of special talent, and advanced placement or honor courses.

Procedure: Freshmen are admitted to all sessions. Entrance exams should be taken in the fall of the senior year. Applications should be filed by March 15 for fall entry, along with an application fee of $15. Notification is sent on a rolling basis. There are early decision, early admissions, and deferred admissions plans.

Transfer: About 45 transfer students enrolled in 1993-94. Applicants must submit a minimum college GPA of 2.0 and be in good standing at the previous or current institution. At least 30 credits out of 126 must be completed at Lees-McRae.

Visiting: There are regularly scheduled orientations for prospective students in June and July. There are guides for informal visits, and visitors may sit in on classes and stay overnight at the school. To arrange for a visit, contact the Director of Admissions at (800) 280-4562.

Financial Aid: In 1993-94, 82% of all current freshmen and 76% of continuing students received some form of financial aid. About 43% of freshmen and 31% of continuing students received need-based aid. The average freshman award was $5000. Of that total, scholarships or need-based grants averaged $500 ($4000 maximum); loans averaged $1000 ($2625 maximum); and work contracts averaged $1000 ($1500 maximum). Twenty-six percent of undergraduate students work part-time. Average earnings from campus work for the school year are $1000. The average financial indebtedness of the 1992-93 graduate was $2000. Lees-McRae is a member of CSS. The FAF and the college's own financial statement are required. The deadline for financial aid applications is April 1.

International Students: There are currently 6 international students enrolled. The school actively recruits these students. They must take the TOEFL and achieve a minimum score of 500 and must also take the SAT I or the ACT.

Computers: The college provides computer facilities for student use. The mainframes are a DEC VAX 4000 and an IBM System/36. Students have access to the VAX system from 50 PCs on campus for use in electronic mail, word processing, spreadsheets, and programming languages. A local area network allows access to PC applications such as WordPerfect, Lotus 123, Pagemaker, Dbase, and various graphics packages. A full Internet connection allows access to thousands of computers worldwide from any PC on the network. All students may access the system Monday to Friday from 7 A.M. to 10 P.M., Sunday from 5 P.M. to 10 P.M., and 24 hours a day by dial-up modem. There are no time limits on using the system. The fee is $50.

Graduates: In 1992-93, 82 bachelor's degrees were awarded. The most popular majors among graduates were business administration (37%), history (14%), and interdisciplinary studies (11%). In the 1992 graduating class, 1% of all graduates were enrolled in graduate school within 6 months of graduation; 85% had found employment.

Admissions Contact: Michael Andrews, Director of Admissions.

LENOIR-RHYNE COLLEGE

C-2

Hickory, NC 28603   (704) 328-7300

Full-time: 477 men, 696 women	Faculty: 95; IIB, -$
Part-time: 59 men, 107 women	Ph.D.s: 71%
Graduate: 14 men, 72 women	Student/Faculty: 12 to 1
Year: semesters, summer session	Tuition: $10,220
Application Deadline: open	Room & Board: $3848
Freshman Class: 868 applied, 701 accepted, 254 enrolled	
SAT I Verbal/Math: 451/496	ACT: 21 **COMPETITIVE**

Lenoir-Rhyne College, founded in 1891, is a private institution affiliated with the Lutheran Church, offering liberal arts programs that focus on business and education. There is one graduate school. In addition to regional accreditation, Lenoir-Rhyne has baccalaureate program accreditation with NCATE and NLN. The library contains 130,000 volumes and 250,000 microform items, and subscribes to 1000 periodicals. Computerized library sources and services include the card catalog, interlibrary loans, and database searching. Special learning facilities include a learning resource center, a radio station, a TV station, and an observatory. The 100-acre campus is in a small town 55 miles north of Charlotte. Including residence halls, there are 22 buildings on campus.

Student Life: About 60% of undergraduates are from North Carolina. Students come from 28 states and 7 foreign countries. Eighty percent are from public schools; 20% from private. Ninety-five percent are white. Ninety percent are Protestant; 10% Catholic. The average age of freshmen is 18; all undergraduates, 20. Eighteen percent drop out by the end of their first year; 55% remain to graduate.

Housing: A total of 881 students can be accommodated in college housing. College-sponsored living facilities include single-sex and coed dormitories and on-campus apartments. On-campus housing is guaranteed for all 4 years. Sixty percent of students live on campus; of those, 70% remain on campus on weekends. Alcohol is not permitted. All students may keep cars on campus.

Activities: About 30% of men belong to 4 national fraternities; about 35% of women belong to 4 national sororities. There are 40 groups on campus, including art, band, cheerleading, choir, chorus, computers, dance, drama, ethnic, honors, international, jazz band, literary magazine, marching band, musical theater, newspaper, political, professional, radio and TV, religious, social, social service, student government, and yearbook. Popular campus events include Spring Fling, Homecoming, and Advent Candlelight Service.

Sports: There are 8 intercollegiate sports for men and 6 for women, and 14 intramural sports for men and 14 for women. Athletic and recreation facilities include an 8500-seat football stadium, a 3600-seat gymnasium, practice fields, a track, tennis and racquetball courts, weight rooms, a sauna, and a swimming pool.

Disabled Students: The entire campus is accessible to disabled students. The following facilities are available: wheelchair ramps, elevators, special parking, and specially equipped rest rooms.

Services: In addition to many counseling and information services, tutoring is available in most subjects. There is also remedial math and writing.

Campus Safety and Security: Campus safety and security measures include 24-hour foot and vehicle patrol, informal discussions, pamphlets, posters, films, and lighted pathways and sidewalks.

Programs of Study: Lenoir-Rhyne awards the B.A., B.S., and B.Mus.Ed. degrees. Master's degrees also are awarded. Bachelor's degrees are awarded in BIOLOGICAL SCIENCE (biology/biological science), BUSINESS (business administration and management and international business management), COMMUNICATIONS AND THE ARTS (applied music, classics, communications, dramatic arts, English, French, German, music, and Spanish), COMPUTER AND PHYSICAL SCIENCE (chemistry, computer science, mathematics, and physics), EDUCATION (art, business, early childhood, education of the deaf and hearing impaired, elementary, foreign languages, guidance, health, middle school, science, and secondary), HEALTH PROFESSIONS (medical laboratory technology, nursing, physician's assistant, predentistry, and premedicine), SOCIAL SCIENCE (economics, history, philosophy, political science/government, prelaw, psychology, religious education, sociology, and theological studies). Business and education have the largest enrollments.

Required: To graduate, students must complete 128 credit hours, including 53 in liberal arts courses, with a minimum GPA of 2.0. The total number of hours in a major varies by program.

Special: Lenoir-Rhyne offers cross-registration in design courses at area schools, study abroad in 19 countries, a Washington semester at American University, internships in most majors, dual majors, a general studies degree, work-study programs, a 3-2 engineering degree, pass/fail options, and auditing for most courses. In addition, the Broyhill Institute for Business Leadership offers programs to promote understanding of the business community. The college uses the Dartmouth method in foreign language. There is a freshman honors program on campus, as well as 7 national honor societies. Eighteen departments have honors programs.

Faculty/Classroom: Sixty-four percent of faculty are male; 36%, female. All teach undergraduates. The average class size in an introductory lecture is 30; in a laboratory, 12; and in a regular course offering, 19.

Admissions: About 81% of the 1993-94 applicants were accepted. The SAT scores for the 1993-94 freshman class were as follows: Verbal—77% below 500, 19% between 500 and 599, and 4% between 600 and 700; Math—61% below 500, 28% between 500 and 599, 10% between 600 and 700, and 1% above 700. The ACT scores were 10% below 21, 79% between 21 and 23, 3% between 24 and 26, 5% between 27 and 28, and 3% above 28. About 39% of the current freshmen were in the top fifth of their class; 68% were in the top two fifths. Nine freshmen graduated first in their class.

Requirements: Lenoir-Rhyne requires applicants to be in the upper 50% of their class. A minimum GPA of 2.5 is required. The SAT I or ACT is required. Applicants need 16 academic credits and should have 4 units in English, 3 in mathematics, 2 in foreign language, and 1 each in American history and a laboratory science. An essay is required and an interview is recommended for all students. Music majors must also audition. AP and CLEP credits are accepted. Important factors used in the admissions decision are advanced placement or honor courses, personality, intangible qualities, leadership record, parents or siblings attending the school, and evidence of special talent.

Procedure: Freshmen are admitted to all sessions. Entrance exams should be taken in the spring of the junior year. Application deadlines are open. Application fee is $25. Notification is sent on a rolling basis. There are early admissions and deferred admissions plans.

Transfer: About 145 transfer students enrolled in 1993-94. Transfer applicants with more than 30 semester hours need a 2.0 minimum GPA in general studies programs or a 2.5 minimum GPA in nursing or education programs. Those with fewer than 30 semester hours must meet freshman entrance criteria. At least 30 credits out of 128 must be completed at Lenoir-Rhyne.

Visiting: There are regularly scheduled orientations for prospective students. There are guides for informal visits, and visitors may sit in on classes and stay overnight at the school. To arrange for a visit, contact the Admissions Office at (704) 328-7300.

Financial Aid: In 1993-94, 63% of all students received some form of financial aid. About 45% of all students received need-based aid. Scholarships or need-based grants averaged $2100 ($9710 maximum); loans averaged $2625 ($6625 maximum); and work contracts averaged $1000 ($1200 maximum). Sixty-five percent of undergraduate students work part-time. Average earnings from campus work for the school year are $1000. The average financial indebtedness of the 1992-93 graduate was $10,000. Lenoir-Rhyne is a member of CSS. The FAF, FFS, or SFS and the FAFSA are required. The deadline for financial aid applications is March 15.

International Students: There are currently 11 international students enrolled. They must take the TOEFL and achieve a minimum score of 500. They must also take the SAT I or the ACT.

Computers: The college provides computer facilities for student use. The mainframe is a DEC PDP 11/34A. There are also 30 IBM, Samsung, and Apple Macintosh microcomputers available in the library. All students may access the system 24 hours per day via modem. There are no time limits on using the system and no fees.

Graduates: In a recent year, 326 bachelor's degrees were awarded. The most popular majors among graduates were business (30%), education (20%), and psychology (8%). Within an average freshman class, 1% graduate in 3 years, 55% in 4 years, and 65% in 5 years. In the 1992 graduating class, 40% of all graduates were enrolled in graduate school within 6 months of graduation; 50% had found employment.

Admissions Contact: Timothy L. Jackson, Director of Admissions.

LIVINGSTONE COLLEGE
C-2
Salisbury, NC 28144   (704) 638-5502; (800) 835-3435 (out-of-state)

Full-time: 623 men and women	Faculty: 50; IIB, --$
Part-time: 5	Ph.D.s: 55%
Graduate: 49 men and women	Student/Faculty: 13 to 1
Year: semesters, summer session	Tuition: $5200
Application Deadline: April 30	Room & Board: $3400
Freshman Class: 556 applied, 473 accepted, 217 enrolled	
SAT I Verbal/Math: 304/340	LESS COMPETITIVE

Livingstone College, founded in 1879, is a private undergraduate institution affiliated with the African Methodist Episcopal Zion Church, offering programs in business, engineering, liberal arts, music, and professional and religious training. In addition to regional accreditation, LC has baccalaureate program accreditation with CSWE. The library contains 80,000 volumes and 1000 microform items, and subscribes to 423 periodicals. Special learning facilities include a learning resource center and a natural history museum. The 272-acre campus is in a small town between Greensboro and Charlotte. Including residence halls, there are 22 buildings on campus.

Student Life: About 54% of undergraduates are from North Carolina. Students come from 22 states and 7 foreign countries. Ninety percent are from public schools; 10% from private. Ninety-six percent are African American. The average age of freshmen is 18; all undergraduates, 19.

Housing: A total of 650 students can be accommodated in college housing. College-sponsored living facilities include single-sex dormitories and honors houses. On-campus housing is guaranteed for all 4 years and is available on a first-come, first-served basis. Eighty-eight percent of students live on campus; of those, 50% remain on campus on weekends. Alcohol is not permitted. All students may keep cars on campus.

Activities: Twenty percent of men belong to 4 national fraternities; about 30% of women belong to 3 national sororities. There are many groups and organizations on campus, including band, cheerleading, choir, chorus, computers, drama, honors, jazz band, marching band, newspaper, pep band, religious, student government, and yearbook.

Sports: There are 4 intercollegiate sports each for men and women, and 5 intramural sports for men and 4 for women. Athletic and recreation facilities include a gymnasium and a 4000-seat stadium.

Disabled Students: The following facilities are available: special parking and special class scheduling.

Services: In addition to many counseling and information services, tutoring is available in every subject. There is also remedial reading and writing.

Campus Safety and Security: Campus safety and security measures include a 24-hour foot and vehicle patrol.

Programs of Study: LC awards the B.A., B.S., and B.S.W. degrees. Bachelor's degrees are awarded in BIOLOGICAL SCIENCE (biology/biological science), BUSINESS (accounting and business administration and management), COMMUNICATIONS AND THE ARTS (English and music), COMPUTER AND PHYSICAL SCIENCE (chemistry, computer science, and mathematics), EDUCATION (early childhood, elementary, music, science, and secondary), HEALTH

PROFESSIONS (predentistry and premedicine), SOCIAL SCIENCE (history, political science/government, prelaw, psychology, social work, and sociology).

Required: A total of at least 126 semester hours with a GPA of at least 2.0 are required for graduation. Required courses include Freshman English and Religion, 2 semesters each of foreign language and physical education, 8 hours each of natural science, mathematics, and social science, and a minimum of 9 hours chosen from offerings in art, literature, music, and philosophy.

Special: Upperclassmen are eligible for a cooperative education program. The college offers internships and 3–2 engineering programs with Georgia Institute of Technology and Clemson University, and a 3–3 law program with Saint John's University. There are 2 national honor societies on campus.

Faculty/Classroom: Forty percent of faculty are male; 60%, female.

Admissions: About 85% of the 1993–94 applicants were accepted. The SAT scores for the 1993–94 freshman class were as follows: Verbal—98% below 500 and 2% between 500 and 599; Math—98% below 500 and 2% between 500 and 599. The ACT scores were 100% below 21.

Requirements: A minimum GPA of 2.0 is required. The SAT I or ACT is required. Applicants should be high school graduates or have earned the GED. Secondary preparation should include 4 academic credits in English, 2 each in history, mathematics, and music, and 1 each in social studies, science, and art. AP and CLEP credits are accepted. Important factors used in the admissions decision are evidence of special talent, leadership record, extracurricular activities record, personality, intangible qualities, and recommendations by school officials.

Procedure: Freshmen are admitted in the fall and spring. Entrance exams should be taken as early as possible. Early decision applications should be filed by February 1; regular applications, by April 30 for fall entry and December 1 for spring entry, along with an application fee of $15. Notification is sent on a rolling basis. There is an early decision plan. One-hundred early decision candidates were accepted for a recent class. A waiting list is an active part of the admissions procedure.

Transfer: Transfers should have at least a 2.0 GPA in 30 hours of previous college work. Those with fewer hours must meet freshman requirements. A total of 45 credits out of 126 must be completed at LC.

Visiting: There are regularly scheduled orientations for prospective students. There are guides for informal visits and visitors may sit in on classes and stay overnight at the school. To arrange for a visit, contact Grady Deese, Director of Admissions at (704) 638–5530 or (800) 422–5430 (out-of-state).

Financial Aid: In a recent year, 90% of all students received some form of financial aid. About 82% of freshmen received need-based aid. The average freshman award was $2100. Of that total, scholarships or need-based grants averaged $2100; loans averaged $2625; and work contracts averaged $1200. Fifty percent of undergraduate students work part-time. Average earnings from campus work for the school year are $1200. LC is a member of CSS. The FFS is required. The deadline for financial aid applications is August 15.

International Students: There are currently 10 international students enrolled. The school actively recruits these students. They must take the TOEFL and achieve a minimum score of 500. The student must also take the SAT I or the ACT.

Computers: The college provides computer facilities for student use. The mainframe is an IBM 34. There are also microcomputers available. All students may access the system. There are no time limits and no fees.

Graduates: In a recent year, 90 bachelor's degrees were awarded. The most popular majors among graduates were business administration (40%), education (20%), and computer science (20%). Within an average freshman class, 60% graduate in 4 years. In a recent graduating class, 15% of the men and 25% of the women were enrolled in graduate school within 6 months of graduation; 30% of the men and 40% of the women had found employment.

Admissions Contact: Charles M. Alexander, Enrollment Management Specialist.

MARS HILL COLLEGE
B-2

Mars Hill, NC 28754   (704) 689–1201; (800) 543–1514 (out-of-state)

Full-time: 486 men, 517 women	Faculty: 80; IIB, --$
Part-time: 18 men, 3 women	Ph.D.s: 70%
Graduate: none	Student/Faculty: 13 to 1
Year: semesters, summer session	Tuition: $7500
Application Deadline: open	Room & Board: $3550
Freshman Class: 1056 applied, 873 accepted, 385 enrolled	
SAT I Verbal/Math: 406/442	COMPETITIVE

Mars Hill College, founded in 1856, is a private institution affiliated with the Baptist Church and offering undergraduate programs in the arts and sciences, business, education, and preprofessional studies. In addition to regional accreditation, Mars Hill has baccalaureate program accreditation with CSWE, NASM, and NCATE. The 2 libraries contain 98,150 volumes, 1050 microform items, and 6180 audiovisual forms, and subscribe to 650 periodicals. Computerized library sources and services include interlibrary loans and database searching. Special learning facilities include an art gallery, radio station, the Southern Appalachian Center of regional history and culture, and the Rural Life Museum. The 180-acre campus is in a rural area 18 miles north of Asheville. Including residence halls, there are 47 buildings on campus.

Student Life: About 60% of undergraduates are from North Carolina. Students come from 25 states, 22 foreign countries, and Canada. Ninety-one percent are white. Eighty-one percent are Protestant; 13% claim no religious affiliation. The average age of freshmen is 18; all undergraduates, 21. Twenty-nine percent drop out by the end of their first year; 40% remain to graduate.

Housing: College-sponsored living facilities include single-sex dormitories, on-campus apartments, and married-student housing. In addition, there are honors houses. On-campus housing is guaranteed for all 4 years. Sixty-eight percent of students live on campus; of those, 33% remain on campus on weekends. Alcohol is not permitted. All students may keep cars on campus.

Activities: About 30% of men belong to 4 local and 2 national fraternities; about 12% of women belong to 5 local sororities and 1 national sorority. There are 60 groups on campus, including art, band, cheerleading, choir, chorale, chorus, dance, drama, ethnic, honors, international, jazz band, literary magazine, marching band, musical theater, newspaper, photography, political, professional, radio and TV, religious, social, social service, student government, and yearbook. Popular campus events include Culturefest, Homecoming, Spring Fling, and the Bascom Lamar Lunsford Festival.

Sports: There are 7 intercollegiate sports for men and 5 for women, and 10 intramural sports for men and 10 for women. Athletic and recreation facilities include a 5000-seat stadium, a 3500-seat gymnasium, an Olympic-size pool, and a 10-acre complex that has a track, baseball diamond, soccer field, all-purpose playing field, and 6 tennis courts.

Disabled Students: Forty-one percent of the campus is accessible to disabled students. The following facilities are available: wheelchair ramps, elevators, special parking, and specially equipped rest rooms.

Services: In addition to many counseling and information services, tutoring is available in every subject. In addition, there is remedial math, reading, and writing.

Campus Safety and Security: Campus safety and security measures include 24-hour foot and vehicle patrol, self defense education, escort service, and informal discussions. In addition, there are emergency telephones and lighted pathways and sidewalks.

Programs of Study: Mars Hill awards the B.A., B.S., B.F.A., B.M., and B.S.W. degrees. Bachelor's degrees are awarded in BIOLOGICAL SCIENCE (biology/biological science, botany, and zoology), BUSINESS (accounting, business administration and management, fashion merchandising, and recreation and leisure services), COMMUNICATIONS AND THE ARTS (art history and appreciation, communications, dramatic arts, English, fine arts, music, music performance, Spanish, and studio art), COMPUTER AND PHYSICAL SCIENCE (chemistry, information sciences and systems, and mathematics), EDUCATION (art, elementary, foreign languages, home economics, middle school, music, physical, science, and secondary), HEALTH PROFESSIONS (allied health, medical laboratory technology, physician's assistant, predentistry, and premedicine), SOCIAL SCIENCE (history, home economics, international studies, political science/government, prelaw, psychology, religion, religious music, social work, and sociology). Business, music, history, and education are the strongest academically. Business has the largest enrollment.

Required: To graduate, students must complete at least 128 semester hours with a minimum GPA of 2.0. Distribution requirements include courses in fine arts, literature, American culture, foreign culture, mathematics, natural science, social/behavioral science, ethics, and physical education.

Special: Mars Hill offers cooperative programs with the Bowman Gray School of Medicine at Wake Forest, internships, study abroad, B.A.-B.S. degrees, dual majors, student-designed majors, and credit for life experience. The Community Life program promotes student involvement in culture and community activities. There is a freshman honors program on campus, as well as 4 national honor societies.

Faculty/Classroom: Fifty-eight percent of faculty are male; 42%, female. All teach undergraduates. The average class size in an introductory lecture is 20; in a laboratory, 15; and in a regular course offering, 15.

Admissions: About 83% of the 1993–94 applicants were accepted. The SAT scores for the 1993–94 freshman class were as follows: Verbal—66% below 500, 28% between 500 and 599, 5% between 600 and 700, and 1% above 700; Math—51% below 500, 38% between 500 and 599, 10% between 600 and 700, and 1% above 700. About

28% of the current freshmen were in the top fifth of their class; 58% were in the top two fifths. Eight freshmen graduated first in their class.

Requirements: Mars Hill requires applicants to be in the upper 50% of their class. A minimum GPA of 2.0 is required. The SAT I or ACT is required. In addition, applicants need at least 18 credits, including 4 in English, 3 in mathematics, and 2 each in history, science, and foreign language, with 2 additional units of foreign language or 1 of computer science recommended. The GED is accepted. An essay and an interview are recommended. AP and CLEP credits are accepted. Important factors used in the admissions decision are advanced placement or honor courses, leadership record, extracurricular activities record, personality, intangible qualities, and recommendations by school officials.

Procedure: Freshmen are admitted to all sessions. Application deadlines are open. Application fee is $15. Notification is sent on a rolling basis. There are early decision and early admissions plans. Three early decision candidates were accepted for the 1993–94 class.

Transfer: Transfer applicants must be eligible to return to their previous college or have been out of school for at least 1 semester. They must have a minimum GPA of 2.0 and submit SAT I or ACT scores, a high school transcript, transcripts from each previous institution, and a recommendation from the last school attended. An interview is recommended. A total of 30 credits out of 128 must be completed at Mars Hill.

Visiting: There are regularly scheduled orientations for prospective students. Two days in the fall and spring are set aside for prospective students during which a variety of special programs are offered. Individual students and their families may visit anytime throughout the year. There are guides for informal visits and visitors may sit in on classes and stay overnight at the school. To arrange for a visit, contact the Admissions Office at (800) 543–1514.

Financial Aid: In 1993–94, 80% of all current freshmen and 75% of continuing students received some form of financial aid. About 80% of students received need-based aid. The average freshman award was $7000. Of that total, scholarships or need-based grants averaged $2500 ($5300 maximum); loans averaged $2000 ($2625 maximum); and work contracts averaged $1000. Thirty-five percent of undergraduate students work part-time. Average earnings from campus work for the school year are $1000. The average financial indebtedness of the 1992–93 graduate was $7500. Mars Hill is a member of CSS. The FAFSA financial statement is required. The deadline for financial aid applications is May 1.

International Students: There are currently 25 international students enrolled. The school actively recruits these students. They must take the TOEFL and achieve a minimum score of 500.

Computers: The college provides computer facilities for student use. The mainframe is a Wang V565. There are also 90 IBM PC, Leading Edge, Apple gs, and Compaq microcomputers available. Only those students taking COBOL and upper-level programming classes may access the mainframe system, but all students may use the microcomputers. The system may be used 8 A.M. to 4 P.M. and 5 P.M. to 9 P.M. Monday through Friday for 2 hours at a time. There are no fees.

Graduates: In a recent year, 201 bachelor's degrees were awarded. The most popular majors among graduates were business administration (14%), elementary education (11%), and physical education (11%). Within an average freshman class, 1% graduate in 3 years, 40% in 4 years, and 48% in 5 years. Some 35 companies recruited on campus in a recent year.

Admissions Contact: Office of Admissions.

MEREDITH COLLEGE
Raleigh, NC 27607-5298

D-2

(919) 829-8581
(800) MEREDITH (out-of-state)

Full-time: 1720 women	Faculty: 103; IIB, -$
Part-time: 470 women	Ph.D.s: 75%
Graduate: 154 women	Student/Faculty: 17 to 1
Year: semesters, summer session	Tuition: $6340
Application Deadline: February 15	Room & Board: $3100
Freshman Class: 899 applied, 772 accepted, 376 enrolled	
SAT I Verbal/Math: 440/480	**COMPETITIVE**

Meredith College, founded in 1891 by North Carolina Baptists, is a private school for women offering degree programs in the arts and sciences, business, and professional training. There is one undergraduate and one graduate school. In addition to regional accreditation, Meredith has baccalaureate program accreditation with CSWE, NASM, and NCATE. The library contains 144,000 volumes, 76,800 microform items, and 9200 audiovisual forms, and subscribes to 770 periodicals. Computerized library sources and services include the card catalog, interlibrary loans, and database searching. Special learning facilities include a learning resource center, an art gallery, a child-care laboratory, a greenhouse, experimental and clinical psychology laboratories, and an astronomy observation deck. The 225-acre campus is in a suburban area in the city of Raleigh. Including residence halls, there are 28 buildings on campus.

Student Life: About 84% of undergraduates are from North Carolina. Students come from 26 states, 17 foreign countries, and Canada. Eighty-six percent are from public schools; 14% from private. Ninety-two percent are white. Seventy-eight percent are Protestant; 14% claim no religious affiliation. The average age of freshmen is 18; all undergraduates, 20.5. Six percent drop out by the end of their first year; 68% remain to graduate.

Housing: A total of 1231 students can be accommodated in college housing. College-sponsored living facilities include single-sex dormitories. In addition, there is an international house and nonsmoking halls. On-campus housing is guaranteed for all 4 years. Fifty-four percent of students live on campus. Alcohol is not permitted. Sophomores, juniors, and seniors may keep cars on campus.

Activities: There are no sororities on campus. There are 70 groups on campus, including art, band, chorale, chorus, dance, drama, ethnic, honors, international, literary magazine, marching band, musical theater, newspaper, orchestra, photography, political, professional, religious, social service, student government, symphony, and yearbook. Popular campus events include Cornhuskin', Spring Fling, Pops in the Park, Fall Fest, Stunt, holiday dinner and caroling, convocation series, leadership awards day, academic awards day, class day, black emphasis month activities, international week activities, religious emphasis week, rush week for service clubs, White Iris Ball, and Fletcher School of Performing Arts performances.

Sports: There are 5 intercollegiate sports and 5 intramural sports. Athletic and recreation facilities include an indoor swimming pool, a dance studio, a weight room, an archery range, a putting green and driving range, a softball diamond, a gymnasium with basketball, volleyball, and badminton courts, tennis courts, and a soccer field.

Disabled Students: Ninety percent of the campus is accessible to disabled students. The following facilities are available: wheelchair ramps, elevators, special parking, specially equipped rest rooms, special class scheduling, some specially equipped residence hall rooms, and a handicap lift in the swimming pool.

Services: In addition to many counseling and information services, tutoring is available in some subjects, including mathematics, computer laboratories, foreign language, and psychology/statistics. In addition, there is a reader service for the blind and a writing center providing assistance with any type of writing.

Campus Safety and Security: Campus safety and security measures include 24-hour foot and vehicle patrol, self defense education, informal discussions, and pamphlets, posters, and films. In addition, there are emergency telephones, lighted pathways and sidewalks, and controlled campus access at night.

Programs of Study: Meredith awards the B.A., B.S., and B.M. degrees. Master's degrees are also awarded. Bachelor's degrees are awarded in BIOLOGICAL SCIENCE (biology/biological science and nutrition), BUSINESS (business administration and management and fashion merchandising), COMMUNICATIONS AND THE ARTS (applied music, dance, dramatic arts, English, fine arts, French, music, Spanish, and speech/communications), COMPUTER AND PHYSICAL SCIENCE (chemistry, computer science, and mathematics), EDUCATION (music), ENGINEERING AND ENVIRONMENTAL DESIGN (interior design), HEALTH PROFESSIONS (health science and medical laboratory technology), SOCIAL SCIENCE (American studies, child psychology/development, economics, history, home economics, international studies, political science/government, psychology, religion, social work, and sociology). Business, psychology, and child development have the largest enrollments.

Required: To graduate, students must complete a total of 124 credit hours, including an average of 36 hours in the major, with a minimum GPA of 2.0. Distribution requirements include 27 to 30 credit hours in the humanities and fine arts, 13 in mathematics and science, 12 in social and behavioral sciences, and 4 to 6 in physical education. Specific course requirements include English Composition, British Authors, Introduction to Biblical History and Literature, and Western Civilization.

Special: Meredith offers cooperative programs, cross-registration with cooperating Raleigh colleges, internships, study abroad in Europe and the Orient, a Washington semester at American University, a U.N. semester at Drew University, and work-study programs on campus. Dual majors, interdisciplinary and student-designed majors, and pass/fail options are available. Second-degree programs in engineering with North Carolina State University and B.A.-B.S. degrees in biology, chemistry, and mathematics are available. There is a freshman honors program on campus, as well as 12 national honor societies. All departments have honors programs.

Faculty/Classroom: Thirty-five percent of faculty are male; 65%, female. All teach undergraduates. No introductory courses are taught by graduate students. The average class size in an introductory lecture is 30; in a laboratory, 15; and in a regular course offering, 20.

Admissions: About 86% of the 1993–94 applicants were accepted. About 49% of the current freshmen were in the top fifth of their class; 80% were in the top two fifths. There was 1 National Merit semifinalist. Three freshmen graduated first in their class.

Requirements: Meredith requires applicants to be in the upper 50% of their class. The SAT I or ACT is required. Applicants must have a minimum of 16 units of credit, with at least 13 chosen from academic subjects including 4 in English, 3 in mathematics, and 1 in foreign language. Grades in academic subjects are very important. An interview may be requested as part of the evaluation process. AP and CLEP credits are accepted. Important factors used in the admissions decision are recommendations by school officials, advanced placement or honor courses, evidence of special talent, personality, intangible qualities, and geographic diversity.

Procedure: Freshmen are admitted in the fall and spring. Entrance exams should be taken by January of the senior year. Early decision applications should be filed by October 15; regular applications, by February 15 for fall entry and December 1 for spring entry, along with an application fee of $25. Notification of early decision is sent November 1; regular decision, on a rolling basis. There are early decision, early admissions, and deferred admissions plans. About 77 early decision candidates were accepted for the 1993–94 class.

Transfer: About 201 transfer students enrolled in 1993–94. Applicants must have a minimum GPA of 2.0, be eligible to return to the last college attended, and be recommended by college officials. Those students with fewer than 30 hours of credit must also meet freshman admission requirements. An interview is recommended for all applicants. A total of 30 credits out of 124 must be completed at Meredith.

Visiting: There are regularly scheduled orientations for prospective students, including 'Open Days' information sessions for students and parents, class visitation, informal conversations with students and faculty/staff, and campus tours. 'Experience Meredith!' for accepted students and parents includes various 'go-to-college' information sessions, an academic fair, a student activities fair, and campus tours. Individual visitors typically have a conference with an admissions counselor and a campus tour. There are guides for informal visits and visitors may sit in on classes. To arrange for a visit, contact the Admissions Office at (919) 829–8581 or (800) MEREDITH.

Financial Aid: In 1993–94 57% of all current freshmen and 42% of continuing students received some form of financial aid. About 38% of freshmen and 32% of continuing students received need-based aid. The average freshman award was $6667. Of that total, scholarships or need-based grants averaged $4706 ($9440 maximum); loans averaged $2576 ($3000 maximum); and work contracts averaged $1116 ($1200 maximum). Twenty-two percent of undergraduate students work part-time. Average earnings from campus work for the school year are $850. The average financial indebtedness of the 1992–93 graduate was $4746. Meredith is a member of CSS. The college's own financial statement and the FAFSA are required. The deadline for financial aid applications is October 15 for early decision and February 15 for regular decision.

International Students: There are currently 55 international students enrolled. The school actively recruits these students. They must take the TOEFL and achieve a minimum score of 500. If English is the student's native language or primary language of instruction, the SAT I should be taken instead of the TOEFL.

Computers: The college provides computer facilities for student use. Some 45 microcomputers are located in student laboratories, 8 microcomputers are located in residence halls, and there is also a library on-line system with 8 terminals. All students may access the system 24 hours per day in residence halls; 7 A.M. to 1 A.M. in laboratories. There are no time limits on using the system and no fees.

Graduates: In 1992–93, 461 bachelor's degrees were awarded. The most popular majors among graduates were business administration (22%), child development (12%), and psychology (10%). Within an average freshman class, 62% graduate in 4 years and 68% in 5 years. Some 77 companies recruited on campus in 1992–93. In the 1992 graduating class, 17% of all graduates were enrolled in graduate school within 6 months of graduation; 97% of all graduates had found employment.

Admissions Contact: Sue E. Kearney, Director of Admissions.

METHODIST COLLEGE
Fayetteville, NC 28311–1420

D-3

(919) 630–7027

(800) 488–7110 (out-of-state)

Full-time: 590 men, 524 women	Faculty: 53; IIB, --$
Part-time: 200 men, 194 women	Ph.D.s: 68%
Graduate: none	Student/Faculty: 21 to 1
Year: 4–1–4, summer session	Tuition: $8850
Application Deadline: open	Room & Board: $3550
Freshman Class: 1100 applied, 776 accepted, 307 enrolled	
SAT I Verbal/Math: 398/459	ACT: 20	**COMPETITIVE**

Methodist College, founded in 1956, is a private institution affiliated with the United Methodist Church. The college offers programs in the arts and sciences, education, business, and professional training. There are 2 undergraduate schools. The library contains 81,382 volumes, 8172 microform items, and 12,121 audiovisual forms, and sub-

scribes to 577 periodicals. Computerized library sources and services include the card catalog and interlibrary loans. Special learning facilities include an art gallery and a professional golf and tennis management house. The 600-acre campus is in a suburban area 5 miles north of Fayetteville. Including residence halls, there are 20 buildings on campus.

Student Life: About 66% of undergraduates are from North Carolina. Students come from 24 states, 18 foreign countries, and Canada. Eighty-eight percent are from public schools; 12%, from private. Eighty-one percent are white; 10%, African American. Twenty-nine percent are Protestant; 16%, Catholic. The average age of freshmen is 18; all undergraduates, 21.

Housing: A total of 600 students can be accommodated in college housing. College-sponsored living facilities include single-sex and coed dormitories and on-campus apartments. In addition there are honors houses. On-campus housing is guaranteed for all 4 years. Fifty-two percent of students commute. Alcohol is not permitted. All students may keep cars on campus.

Activities: There are no fraternities or sororities on campus. There are 33 groups on campus, including art, band, cheerleading, chess, choir, chorale, chorus, computers, dance, drama, film, honors, international, literary magazine, musical theater, newspaper, orchestra, pep band, photography, political, professional, religious, social service, student government, and yearbook. Popular campus events include Show You Care Day, Homecoming, Spring Fest, and Southern Writers Symposium.

Sports: There are 8 intercollegiate sports for men and 8 for women, and 7 intramural sports for men and 4 for women. Athletic and recreation facilities include a 4000-seat stadium, a 1500-seat gymnasium, a golf course, a track and field area, tennis courts, and fields for baseball, softball, and soccer.

Disabled Students: One percent of the campus is accessible to disabled students. The following facilities are available: wheelchair ramps and special parking.

Services: In addition to many counseling and information services, tutoring is available in most subjects. In addition, there is remedial math, reading, and writing.

Campus Safety and Security: Campus safety and security measures include 24-hour foot and vehicle patrol, escort service, informal discussions, and pamphlets, posters, and films. In addition, there are emergency telephones and lighted pathways and sidewalks.

Programs of Study: Methodist awards the B.A., B.S., B.A.S., B. Applied Sc., and B.M. degrees. Associate degrees are also awarded. Bachelor's degrees are awarded in BIOLOGICAL SCIENCE (biology/biological science), BUSINESS (accounting, business administration and management, and business economics), COMMUNICATIONS AND THE ARTS (applied music, arts administration/management, communications, creative writing, dramatic arts, English, fine arts, French, music, music business management, Spanish, and speech/debate/rhetoric), COMPUTER AND PHYSICAL SCIENCE (chemistry, computer science, mathematics, and science), EDUCATION (art, early childhood, elementary, foreign languages, middle school, music, physical, science, secondary, special, and teaching English as a second language/foreign language), HEALTH PROFESSIONS (predentistry and prepharmacy), SOCIAL SCIENCE (history, liberal arts/general studies, political science/government, prelaw, psychology, religion, social science, social work, and sociology). Business administration, biology, music, and education are the strongest academically. Business administration, education, and sociology have the largest enrollments.

Required: To graduate, students must complete at least 124 semester hours, including core requirements, with a minimum GPA of 2.0.

Special: Methodist offers internships in political science and social work, study abroad in 2 countries, a Washington semester, a general studies degree, a 3–2 engineering degree with North Carolina State University, pass/fail options, and nondegree study. The business administration major offers concentrations in professional golf and tennis management with specialized facilities and co-op programs. There is a freshman honors program on campus, as well as 7 national honor societies. Three departments have honors programs.

Faculty/Classroom: Sixty-seven percent of faculty are male; 33%, female. All teach undergraduates. The average class size in an introductory lecture is 25; in a laboratory, 20; and in a regular course offering, 20.

Admissions: About 71% of the 1993–94 applicants were accepted. The SAT scores for the 1993–94 freshman class were as follows: Verbal—93% below 500, 5% between 500 and 599, and 2% between 600 and 700; Math—81% below 500, 15% between 500 and 599, 3% between 600 and 700, and 1% above 700. The ACT scores were 46% below 21, 40% between 21 and 23, 6% between 24 and 26, and 8% between 27 and 28. About 22% of the current freshmen were in the top fifth of their class; 46% were in the top two fifths. Four freshmen graduated first in their class.

Requirements: Methodist requires applicants to be in the upper 75% of their class. A minimum GPA of 2.0 is required. The SAT I or ACT is required. Applicants should be graduates of an accredited secondary school or have a GED certificate. They must have 18 academic credits, including 4 in English and 2 each in history, mathematics, science, and social studies. An essay and interview are recommended. AP and CLEP credits are accepted. Important factors used in the admissions decision are advanced placement or honor courses, evidence of special talent, personality, intangible qualities, leadership record, and parents or siblings attending the school.

Procedure: Freshmen are admitted in the fall and spring. Entrance exams should be taken by June of the junior year. Application deadlines are open. Notification is sent on a rolling basis. The application fee is $20. There is a deferred admissions plan.

Transfer: In 1993–94, 223 transfer students enrolled. Applicants must have a minimum GPA of 2.0. Those with fewer than 32 semester hours must also submit a high school transcript and SAT I or ACT scores. A total of 30 credits out of 124 must be completed at Methodist.

Visiting: There are guides for informal visits, and visitors may sit in on classes and stay overnight at the school. To arrange for a visit, contact the Admissions or Athletic Office at (800) 488–7110 or (919) 630–7027.

Financial Aid: In 1993–94, 87% of all current freshmen and 86% of continuing students received some form of financial aid. About 71% of freshmen and 76% of continuing students received need-based aid. The average freshman award was $6178. Of that total, scholarships or need-based grants averaged $4037 ($8850 maximum); loans averaged $2140 ($2625 maximum); and work contracts averaged $1000 ($1500 maximum). Forty-six percent of undergraduate students work part-time. Average earnings from campus work for the school year are $1500. The average financial indebtedness of the 1992–93 graduate was $13,250. The FAF is required. The deadline for financial aid applications is May 1.

International Students: There are currently 38 international students enrolled. The school actively recruits these students. They must take the TOEFL. The student may take the SAT I or ACT in place of the TOEFL if English proficiency is demonstrated.

Computers: The college provides computer facilities for student use. The mainframe is an IBM. There are also 60 IBM, AT&T, and Leading Edge PCs available in various laboratories. All students may access the system. It may be used during specified hours. There are no time limits on using the system. There are no fees.

Graduates: In 1992–93, 263 bachelor's degrees were awarded. The most popular majors among graduates were business (39%), education (14%), and sociology (9%). Some 15 companies recruited on campus in 1992–93.

Admissions Contact: J. Alan Coheley, Vice President for Enrollment Services.

MONTREAT-ANDERSON COLLEGE

Montreat, NC 28757   (704) 669–8011; (800) 622–6968 (out-of-state)

Full-time: 179 men, 157 women	Faculty: 26; IIB, --$
Part-time: 11 men, 9 women	Ph.D.s: n/av
Graduate: none	Student/Faculty: 13 to 1
Year: semesters, summer session	Tuition: $7600
Application Deadline: open	Room & Board: $3372
Freshman Class: 263 applied, 223 accepted, 103 enrolled	
SAT I Verbal/Math: 372/401	LESS COMPETITIVE

Montreat-Anderson College, founded in 1916, is a private, coeducational, liberal arts institution affiliated with the Presbyterian Church, USA, and committed to the integration of faith and learning. The library contains 60,500 volumes, 2888 microform items, and 230 audiovisual forms, and subscribes to 391 periodicals. Special learning facilities include a learning resource center and the Presbyterian Church USA Historical Foundation. The 100-acre campus is in a rural area 15 miles east of Asheville. Including residence halls, there are 12 buildings on campus.

Student Life: About 60% of undergraduates are from North Carolina. Students come from 21 states and 12 foreign countries. Ninety-five percent are white.

Housing: A total of 392 students can be accommodated in college housing. College-sponsored living facilities include single-sex dormitories. On-campus housing is guaranteed for all 4 years. Seventy-seven percent of students live on campus. Alcohol is not permitted. All students may keep cars on campus.

Activities: There are no fraternities or sororities on campus. There are some groups and organizations on campus, including cheerleading, choir, chorus, drama, honors, newspaper, professional, religious, student government, and yearbook.

Sports: There are 4 intercollegiate sports for men and 4 for women. Athletic and recreation facilities include standard athletic facilities complemented by opportunities for outdoor recreation activities, such as skiing, whitewater sports, mountain climbing, and camping.

Disabled Students: One percent of the campus is accessible to disabled students.

Services: In addition to many counseling and information services, tutoring is available in most subjects, including all academic areas. In addition, there is remedial math, reading, and writing.

Campus Safety and Security: Campus safety and security measures include 24-hour foot and vehicle patrol, lighted pathways and sidewalks, and a closed campus.

Programs of Study: Montreat-Anderson awards the B.A. and B.S. degrees. Associate degrees also are awarded. Bachelor's degrees are awarded in BUSINESS (business administration and management and recreation and leisure services), COMMUNICATIONS AND THE ARTS (English), EDUCATION (English, secondary, and social studies), SOCIAL SCIENCE (crosscultural studies, history, and liberal arts/general studies). English is the strongest program academically. Business has the largest enrollment.

Required: To graduate, students must complete 126 credit hours with a minimum GPA of 2.0. They must pass a comprehensive exam covering mathematics, computation, oral expression, reading, and writing. A thesis is required for some majors.

Special: Montreat-Anderson offers internships in all majors, study abroad, a Washington semester, and dual majors. There is a freshman honors program on campus, as well as 2 national honor societies. Three departments have honors programs.

Faculty/Classroom: All faculty teach undergraduates. The average class size in an introductory lecture is 30; in a laboratory, 15; and in a regular course offering, 10.

Admissions: About 85% of the 1993–94 applicants were accepted.

Requirements: A minimum GPA of 2.25 is required. The SAT I or ACT is required. Important factors used in the admissions decision are advanced placement or honor courses, extracurricular activities record, evidence of special talent, personality, intangible qualities, and recommendations by school officials.

Procedure: Freshmen are admitted to all sessions. Application deadlines are open. Application fee is $15. Notification is sent on a rolling basis.

Transfer: About 49 transfer students enrolled in a recent year. Applicants must have completed at least 12 semester hours of college credit with a minimum GPA of 2.0. A total of 12 credits out of 126 must be completed at Montreat-Anderson.

Visiting: There are regularly scheduled orientations for prospective students, including a campus tour, faculty introduction, and student program. There are guides for informal visits and visitors may sit in on classes and stay overnight at the school. To arrange for a visit, contact the Admissions Office at (800) 622–6968.

Financial Aid: In a recent year, 70% of all freshmen and 73% of continuing students received some form of financial aid. About 66% of freshmen and 68% of continuing students received need-based aid. The average freshman award was $7197. Sixty-two percent of undergraduate students work part-time. Average earnings from campus work for the school year are $1000. The average financial indebtedness of a recent year's graduate was $12,000. Montreat-Anderson is a member of CSS. The FAF, the college's own financial statement, and FAFSA are required. The deadline for financial aid applications is April 15.

International Students: There are currently 15 international students enrolled. The school actively recruits these students. They must take the TOEFL and achieve a minimum score of 500.

Graduates: In a recent year, 29 bachelor's degrees were awarded.

Admissions Contact: David Walters, Director of Admissions.

MOUNT OLIVE COLLEGE

Mount Olive, NC 28365   (919) 658–2502
(800) 653–0854 (out-of-state)

Full-time: 210 men, 218 women	Faculty: 35; IIB, --$
Part-time: 244 men, 191 women	Ph.D.s: 40%
Graduate: none	Student/Faculty: 12 to 1
Year: semesters, summer session	Tuition: $7100
Application Deadline: open	Room & Board: $2550
Freshman Class: 407 applied, 335 accepted, 138 enrolled	
SAT I Verbal/Math: 370/430	LESS COMPETITIVE

Mount Olive College, founded in 1951, is a private liberal arts institution affiliated with the Original Free Will Baptist Church. The library contains 55,000 volumes, 300 microform items, and 350 audiovisual forms, and subscribes to 360 periodicals. Computerized library sources and services include interlibrary loans and database searching. Special learning facilities include an art gallery and a church archives collection. The 110-acre campus is in a small town 65 miles southeast of Raleigh. Including residence halls, there are 16 buildings on campus.

Student Life: About 94% of undergraduates are from North Carolina. Students come from 12 states and 1 foreign country. Ninety-five percent are from public schools; 5% from private. Seventy-eight percent are white; 19% African American. Most are Protestant. The aver-

age age of freshmen is 18; all undergraduates, 27. Forty percent drop out by the end of their first year; 20% remain to graduate.

Housing: A total of 275 students can be accommodated in college housing. College-sponsored living facilities include single-sex dormitories and on-campus apartments. On-campus housing is guaranteed for all 4 years. Sixty-five percent of students commute. Alcohol is not permitted. All students may keep cars on campus.

Activities: There are no fraternities or sororities on campus. There are 20 groups on campus, including art, cheerleading, choir, chorale, chorus, drama, honors, international, literary magazine, newspaper, orchestra, photography, political, professional, religious, student government, and yearbook. Popular campus events include Founders Day, Pickle Classic Weekend, and the North Carolina Pickle Festival.

Sports: There are 5 intercollegiate sports for men and 4 for women, and 5 intramural sports for men and 5 for women. Athletic and recreation facilities include a 2000-seat gymnasium, racquetball and tennis courts, a track, wrestling/gymnastics and weight rooms, an outdoor education center for camping and canoeing, an athletic field, outdoor basketball areas, and a student center.

Disabled Students: Ninety percent of the campus is accessible to disabled students. The following facilities are available: wheelchair ramps, elevators, special parking, specially equipped rest rooms, and special class scheduling.

Services: In addition to many counseling and information services, tutoring is available in most subjects, including mathematics, English, and science. In addition, there is remedial math and reading.

Campus Safety and Security: Campus safety and security measures include 24-hour foot and vehicle patrol, informal discussions, pamphlets, posters, and films, and lighted pathways and sidewalks.

Programs of Study: Mount Olive awards the B.A., B.S., and B.Applied Sc. degrees. Associate degrees also are awarded. Bachelor's degrees are awarded in BIOLOGICAL SCIENCE (biology/biological science), BUSINESS (accounting, business administration and management, and recreation and leisure services), COMMUNICATIONS AND THE ARTS (English and fine arts), COMPUTER AND PHYSICAL SCIENCE (computer management), SOCIAL SCIENCE (history, liberal arts/general studies, ministries, psychology, and religion). Business, accounting, psychology, and recreation liberal arts are the strongest programs academically. Business, psychology, and recreation have the largest enrollments.

Required: To graduate, students must have a minimum 2.0 overall GPA in 63 credit hours for the B.S. or B.A., or in 53 hours for the B.Applied Sc. Distribution requirements include 30 to 36 hours in humanities, 18 in science/mathematics, and 12 in social science. Specific course work includes 6 hours of religion, 4 of physical education, and 3 of data processing.

Special: Mount Olive offers co-op programs and internships in all majors, work-study, B.A.-B.S. degrees, dual majors, and accelerated degree programs in business, industrial management, and accounting. Cross-registration with James Sprunt Community College, study abroad, and credit for life, military, and work experience are also possible. There is a freshman honors program on campus, as well as 1 national honor society.

Faculty/Classroom: Fifty-nine percent of faculty are male; 41%, female. All teach undergraduates, 14% do research, and 86% do both. The average class size in an introductory lecture is 20; in a laboratory, 18; and in a regular course offering, 25.

Admissions: About 82% of the 1993-94 applicants were accepted. The SAT scores for the 1993-94 freshman class were as follows: Verbal—91% below 500, 8% between 500 and 599, 1% between 600 and 700, and 1% above 700; Math—76% below 500, 18% between 500 and 599, and 6% between 600 and 700. About 21% of the current freshmen were in the top fifth of their class; 50% were in the top two fifths. One freshman graduated first in her/his class.

Requirements: The SAT I is required, but the ACT may be substituted. A minimum SAT I composite score of 700 or ACT score of 16 is recommended. Applicants must be graduates of an accredited secondary school or have a GED certificate. They must have completed 4 units of English, 3 each of mathematics and science, and 2 of history. An essay and interview are suggested. AP and CLEP credits are accepted.

Procedure: Freshmen are admitted to all sessions. Entrance exams should be taken in the junior or senior year. Application deadlines are open. Application fee is $15. Notification is sent on a rolling basis. There are early admissions and deferred admissions plans.

Transfer: About 58 transfer students enrolled in 1993-94. Applicants must have a minimum GPA of 2.0 and submit a dean's evaluation from the previous institution and an official transcript. An interview may be required. A total of 30 credits out of 126 must be completed at Mount Olive.

Visiting: There are regularly scheduled orientations for prospective students, consisting of 2 days of advising, sports, and entertainment. There are guides for informal visits and visitors may sit in on classes. To arrange for a visit, contact the Admissions Office at (919) 658-2502, ext. 3009, or (800) 653-0854.

Financial Aid: In 1993-94 95% of all current freshmen and 95% of continuing students received some form of financial aid. About 45% of freshmen and 60% of continuing students received need-based aid. The average freshman award was $5200. Thirty-five percent of undergraduate students work part-time. Average earnings from campus work for the school year are $600. The average financial indebtedness of the 1992-93 graduate was $2100. Mount Olive is a member of CSS. The college's own financial statement and the FAFSA are required. The deadline for financial aid applications is March 1.

International Students: There are currently 6 international students enrolled. They must take the TOEFL and achieve a minimum score of 500. The student must also take the SAT I or the ACT.

Computers: The college provides computer facilities for student use. The mainframe is an IBM System/36. The NSF/Internet System may be accessed via IBM, IBM-compatible, and Apple IIe and Macintosh microcomputers located in 2 PC laboratories, with software and assistance also available. Those students enrolled in specific courses may access the system. It may be used from 8 A.M. to 10 P.M. Monday through Friday and during scheduled hours on the weekend. There are no fees.

Graduates: In 1992-93 149 bachelor's degrees were awarded. The most popular majors among graduates were business (62%), recreation (10%), and psychology (8%). Within an average freshman class, 1% graduate in 3 years, 13% in 4 years, and 9% in 5 years. Some 12 companies recruited on campus in 1992-93. In the 1992 graduating class, 10% all graduates were enrolled in graduate school within 6 months of graduation; 50% of all graduates had found employment.

Admissions Contact: Director of Admissions.

NORTH CAROLINA AGRICULTURAL AND TECHNICAL STATE UNIVERSITY

D-2

Greensboro, NC 27411   (919) 334-7946; (800) 443-8964 (in-state)

Full-time: 2985 men, 3177 women	Faculty: 338; IIA, -$
Part-time: 451 men, 420 women	Ph.D.s: 59%
Graduate: 449 men, 491 women	Student/Faculty: 18 to 1
Year: semesters	Tuition: $1367 ($7433)
Application Deadline: June 1	Room & Board: $3110
Freshman Class: 4809 applied, 3089 accepted, 1444 enrolled	
SAT I Verbal/Math: 384/441	**LESS COMPETITIVE**

North Carolina Agricultural and Technical State University, founded in 1891, is a public institution within the University of North Carolina System. A & T offers programs in arts and sciences, education, business and economics, agriculture, nursing, engineering, and technology. There are 7 undergraduate schools and one graduate school. In addition to regional accreditation, A & T has baccalaureate program accreditation with AACSB, ABET, CSWE, NCATE, and NLN. Computerized library sources and services include the card catalog, interlibrary loans, and database searching. Special learning facilities include an art gallery, planetarium, radio station, and African Heritage Center. The 181-acre campus is in an urban area 90 miles northeast of Charlotte. Including residence halls, there are 68 buildings on campus.

Student Life: About 74% of undergraduates are from North Carolina. Students come from 39 states and 27 foreign countries. Eighty-six percent are African American; 11% white. The average age of freshmen is 18; all undergraduates, 21. Fourteen percent drop out by the end of their first year; 86% remain to graduate.

Housing: A total of 2890 students can be accommodated in college housing. College-sponsored living facilities include single-sex dormitories. In addition, there are honors houses. On-campus housing is available on a first-come, first-served basis and is available on a lottery system for upperclassmen. Fifty-nine percent of students commute. Alcohol is not permitted. All students may keep cars on campus.

Activities: About 1% of men belong to 4 national fraternities; about 1% of women belong to 4 national sororities. There are 152 groups on campus, including art, band, cheerleading, choir, chorus, computers, dance, drama, drill team, ethnic, film, honors, international, marching band, newspaper, orchestra, pep band, photography, political, professional, radio and TV, religious, social, social service, student government, symphony, and yearbook. Popular campus events include Spring Fest, Homecoming, and the annual picnic.

Sports: There are 8 intercollegiate sports for men and 5 for women, and 17 intramural sports for men and 17 for women. Athletic and recreation facilities include a gymnasium, a sports center, a stadium, tennis courts, and a student union.

Disabled Students: Eighty percent of the campus is accessible to disabled students. The following facilities are available: wheelchair ramps, elevators, special parking, specially equipped rest rooms, special class scheduling, and lowered drinking fountains.

Services: In addition to many counseling and information services, tutoring is available in every subject. In addition, there is a reader service for the blind, and remedial math, reading, and writing.

Campus Safety and Security: Campus safety and security measures include 24-hour foot and vehicle patrol, escort service, shuttle buses, and pamphlets, posters, and films. In addition, there are emergency telephones and lighted pathways and sidewalks.

Programs of Study: A & T awards the B.A., B.S., B.F.A., B.S.I.E., B.S.M.E., B.S.N., and B.S.W. degrees. Master's degrees also are awarded. Bachelor's degrees are awarded in AGRICULTURE (agricultural economics, agriculture, and animal science), BIOLOGICAL SCIENCE (biology/biological science), BUSINESS (accounting and business administration and management), COMMUNICATIONS AND THE ARTS (communications, dramatic arts, English, French, music, and speech/debate/rhetoric), COMPUTER AND PHYSICAL SCIENCE (chemistry, computer science, mathematics, and physics), EDUCATION (agricultural, art, business, driver and safety, early childhood, English, home economics, industrial arts, mathematics, music, physical, science, social science, and special), ENGINEERING AND ENVIRONMENTAL DESIGN (architectural engineering, chemical engineering, civil engineering, electrical/electronics engineering, engineering physics, industrial engineering, landscape architecture/design, mechanical engineering, and occupational safety and health), HEALTH PROFESSIONS (nursing), SOCIAL SCIENCE (child psychology/development, clothing and textiles management/production/services, economics, history, political science/government, psychology, social work, and sociology). Business, engineering, and industrial technology are the strongest programs academically. Business, engineering, and arts and sciences have the largest enrollments.

Required: To graduate, students must complete a minimum of 124 credit hours, including at least 80 in the major, with an overall GPA of 2.0 or better. Specific course work is required in English, mathematics, natural science, social science, humanities, and health or physical education.

Special: A & T offers cross-registration with the Greensboro Regional Consortium, internships, B.A.-B.S. degrees, and cooperative programs in business, engineering, industrial technology, and computer science. There is a freshman honors program on campus, as well as 14 national honor societies. Ten departments have honors programs.

Faculty/Classroom: Sixty percent of faculty are male; 40%, female. The average class size in an introductory lecture is 25; in a laboratory, 32; and in a regular course offering, 30.

Admissions: About 64% of the 1993–94 applicants were accepted. About 40% of the current freshmen were in the top fifth of their class; 65% were in the top two fifths.

Requirements: A minimum GPA of 2.0 is required. The SAT I, with a minimum composite score of 750, or ACT, with a minimum score of 17, is required. Applicants must be graduates of an accredited secondary school or have a GED certificate. They must have completed at least 16 academic credits, including 4 in English and 2 each in history, mathematics, music, science, social studies, and a foreign language. An audition is required of fine arts majors, and a portfolio is recommended. An interview is suggested for all applicants. AP and CLEP credits are accepted. Important factors used in the admissions decision are geographic diversity, advanced placement or honor courses, personality, intangible qualities, parents or siblings attending the school, and evidence of special talent.

Procedure: Freshmen are admitted to all sessions. Applications should be filed by June 1 for fall entry and December 1 for spring entry, along with an application fee of $25. Notification is sent on a rolling basis. There is an early decision plan. A waiting list is an active part of the admissions procedure.

Transfer: About 433 transfer students enrolled in 1993–94. Applicants must have a minimum GPA of 2.0 in at least 62 credit hours and be in good standing at their previous school. A total of 62 credits out of 124 must be completed at A & T.

Visiting: There are regularly scheduled orientations for prospective students. There are guides for informal visits and visitors may sit in on classes. To arrange for a visit, contact the Admissions Office at (919) 334-7946.

Financial Aid: In a recent year 64% of all freshmen received some form of financial aid. The average freshman award was $2400. Average earnings from campus work for the school year are $2400. The FAF or FFS is required. The deadline for financial aid applications is May 15.

International Students: There are currently 151 international students enrolled. They must take the TOEFL and achieve a minimum score of 550.

Computers: The college provides computer facilities for student use. The mainframes include a DEC VAX 6320 and a DEC VAX 11/785. There are also Apple Macintosh microcomputers. All students may access the system. There are no time limits on using the system and no fees.

Graduates: In 1992–93, 863 bachelor's degrees were awarded. The most popular majors among graduates were business administration (15%), industrial technology (10%), and accounting (9%). Within an average freshman class, 14% graduate in 4 years, 36% in 5 years,

and 37% in 6 years. Some 710 companies recruited on campus in 1992–93.

Admissions Contact: John Smith, Admissions.

NORTH CAROLINA CENTRAL UNIVERSITY D-2
Durham, NC 27707 (919) 560-6298

Full-time: 1355 men, 2224 women	Faculty: 254; IIA, -$
Part-time: 314 men, 425 women	Ph.D.s: 64%
Graduate: 450 men, 867 women	Student/Faculty: 14 to 1
Year: semesters, summer session	Tuition: $1338 ($7404)
Application Deadline: July 1	Room & Board: $3009
Freshman Class: 2707 applied, 2015 accepted, 855 enrolled	
SAT I: 371/410	ACT: 21 LESS COMPETITIVE

North Carolina Central University, founded in 1909, is a publicly funded liberal arts institution in the University of North Carolina system. There are 3 undergraduate and 2 graduate schools. In addition to regional accreditation, NCCU has baccalaureate program accreditation with NCATE and NLN. The 6 libraries contain 588,168 volumes, 5017 microform items, and 1569 audiovisual forms, and subscribe to 3911 periodicals. Computerized library sources and services include the card catalog and database searching. Special learning facilities include a learning resource center and an art gallery. The 103-acre campus is in an urban area 2 miles from the center of Durham. Including residence halls, there are 56 buildings on campus.

Student Life: About 82% of undergraduates are from North Carolina. Students come from 32 states. Eighty-three percent are African American; 15% white. The average age of freshmen is 18; all undergraduates, 20. Fifteen percent drop out by the end of their first year; 35% remain to graduate.

Housing: A total of 2002 students can be accommodated in college housing. College-sponsored living facilities include single-sex and coed dormitories and on-campus apartments. In addition there are honors houses. On-campus housing is available on a first-come, first-served basis. Sixty-three percent of students commute. Alcohol is not permitted. All students may keep cars on campus.

Activities: There are 4 national fraternities and 3 national sororities. There are 50 groups on campus, including art, band, cheerleading, chess, choir, computers, dance, drama, drill team, ethnic, honors, international, jazz band, literary magazine, marching band, newspaper, political, professional, religious, social, social service, student government, symphony, and yearbook.

Sports: There are 4 intercollegiate sports for men and 3 for women, and 1 intramural sport each for men and women. Athletic and recreation facilities include a 12,000-seat stadium, a 4500-seat gymnasium, a swimming pool, handball and tennis courts, a track, a bowling alley, dance studios, and a weight room.

Disabled Students: The following facilities are available: wheelchair ramps, elevators, special parking, and specially equipped rest rooms.

Services: In addition to many counseling and informational services, there is a reader service for the blind, and remedial math, reading, and writing.

Campus Safety and Security: Campus safety and security measures include informal discussions and lighted pathways and sidewalks.

Programs of Study: NCCU awards the B.A. and B.S. degrees. Master's degrees also are awarded. Bachelor's degrees are awarded in BIOLOGICAL SCIENCE (biology/biological science), BUSINESS (accounting, business administration and management, and business economics), COMMUNICATIONS AND THE ARTS (dramatic arts, English, fine arts, French, music, and Spanish), COMPUTER AND PHYSICAL SCIENCE (chemistry, computer science, mathematics, and physics), EDUCATION (business, elementary, health, middle school, physical, and special), HEALTH PROFESSIONS (nursing), SOCIAL SCIENCE (criminal justice, geography, history, parks and recreation management, philosophy, political science/government, psychology, social science, and sociology). Social sciences and biology are the strongest programs academically. Business, political science, and criminal justice have the largest enrollments.

Required: To graduate, students must complete 124 semester hours, including 30 in the major, with a minimum GPA of 2.0. Core requirements include courses in communications, mathematics and natural science, social science, humanities, and health and physical education.

Special: NCCU offers internships, work-study programs, dual majors, and nondegree study. There is a freshman honors program on campus, as well as 2 national honor societies. Ten departments have honors programs.

Faculty/Classroom: Fifty-seven percent of faculty are male; 43%, female. All teach undergraduates and 20% also do research. No introductory courses are taught by graduate students. The average class size in an introductory lecture is 40.

Admissions: About 74% of the 1993–94 applicants were accepted. The SAT scores for the 1993–94 freshman class were as follows: Math—89% below 500, 9% between 500 and 599, and 2% between 600 and 700. About 25% of the current freshmen were in the top fifth of their class; 52% were in the top two fifths.

Requirements: The SAT I or ACT is required. Applicants must be graduates of an accredited secondary school or have a GED certificate. They must have completed 11 academic credits, based on 4 years of English, 3 each of mathematics and science, and 2 each of a foreign language and social studies. Music applicants must audition. AP and CLEP credits are accepted. Important factors used in the admissions decision are advanced placement or honor courses, leadership record, evidence of special talent, parents or siblings attending the school, and recommendations by school officials.

Procedure: Entrance exams should be taken in the spring of the junior year. Applications should be filed by July 1 for fall entry and November 1 for spring entry, along with an application fee of $15. Notification is sent as early as possible after receipt of the completed application.

Transfer: Applicants must have a minimum GPA of 2.0 in all college-level courses. A total of 30 credits out of 124 must be completed at NCCU.

Visiting: There are regularly scheduled orientations for prospective students. There are guides for informal visits and visitors may sit in on classes and stay overnight at the school. To arrange for a visit, contact LuAnn Harris at (919) 560-6066.

Financial Aid: NCCU is a member of CSS. The FFS or SFS is required. The deadline for financial aid applications is May 1.

International Students: There were 12 international students enrolled in an earlier year. They must take the TOEFL and achieve a minimum score of 500. The student must also take the SAT I, ACT, or unless these tests are not administered in their country..

Computers: The college provides computer facilities for student use. The mainframe is a Data General MV/15000. All students may access the system from 9 A.M. to 5 P.M. Monday through Friday. The computing center also has dial-in service. There are no time limits and no fees.

Graduates: In a recent year, 506 bachelor's degrees were awarded. The most popular majors among graduates were political science (22%), business administration (15%), and law enforcement (10%). Within an average freshman class, 11% graduate in 4 years, 25% in 5 years, and 30% in 6 years.

Admissions Contact: Nancy Rowland, Director of Admissions.

NORTH CAROLINA SCHOOL OF THE ARTS   C-2
Winston-Salem, NC 27117   (919) 770-3399

Full-time: 300 men, 350 women	Faculty: 81
Part-time: 20 men, 20 women	Ph.D.s: n/av
Graduate: 20 men, 10 women	Student/Faculty: 8 to 1
Year: trimesters, summer session	Tuition: $1889 ($8807)
Application Deadline: April 1	Room & Board: $3486
Freshman Class: 500 applied, 200 accepted, 100 enrolled	
SAT I or ACT: required	SPECIAL

North Carolina School of the Arts, founded in 1963 and now part of the University of North Carolina system, is a public institution offering professional training in the performing arts. There are 4 undergraduate schools. The library contains 93,000 volumes, 17 microform items, 34,000 musical scores, and 33,000 audiovisual forms, and subscribes to 450 periodicals. Computerized library sources and services include the card catalog, interlibrary loans, and database searching. The 30-acre campus is in an urban area. Including residence halls, there are 11 buildings on campus.

Student Life: About 40% of undergraduates are from North Carolina. Students come from 45 states and 12 foreign countries. Ninety percent are from public schools. The average age of freshmen is 19; all undergraduates, 21.

Housing: A total of 300 students can be accommodated in college housing. College-sponsored living facilities include coed dormitories and on-campus apartments. Priority for on-campus housing is given to out-of-town students. Eighty-five percent of students live on campus; of those, 90% remain on campus on weekends. Alcohol is not permitted. All students may keep cars on campus.

Activities: There are no fraternities or sororities on campus. There are some groups and organizations on campus, including band, dance, drama, film, jazz band, musical theater, newspaper, opera, orchestra, and radio and TV.

Sports: There is no sports program at NCSA. Athletic and recreation facilities include a gymnasium, fitness and weight rooms, a swimming pool, a soccer/touch-football field, a par course, and courts for tennis, basketball, and volleyball.

Disabled Students: Fifty percent of the campus is accessible to disabled students. The following facilities are available: wheelchair ramps, special parking, and elevators in 2 buildings.

Services: In addition to many counseling and information services, tutoring is available in every subject. There is also remedial math, reading, and writing. Private tutoring is also offered on a fee basis.

Programs of Study: NCSA awards the B.F.A. and B.M. degrees. Master's degrees also are awarded. Bachelor's degrees are awarded in COMMUNICATIONS AND THE ARTS (dance, dramatic arts, film arts, music, performing arts, and theater design and production).

Required: To earn a bachelor's degree, students must demonstrate satisfactory skills in reading, writing, oral communication, and mathematics, take courses in foundations of Western thought, complete studies in the areas of fine arts/humanities, social/behavioral sciences, and mathematics/natural science, and meet all requirements in their arts major.

Special: NCSA offers work-study programs, a general studies major, independent study, and design and production apprenticeships. An accelerated degree program is available to high school students in the areas of dance, drama, music, and visual arts.

Admissions: About 40% of the 1993–94 applicants were accepted. About 14% of the current freshmen were in the top fifth of their class; 31% were in the top two fifths.

Requirements: The SAT I or ACT is required. A minimum composite score of 800 on the SAT I or 19 on the ACT is required. Applicants must be graduates of an accredited secondary school or have a GED certificate. They should have completed 4 units in English, 3 in mathematics, 3 in science with 1 in a laboratory course, and 2 in social studies with 1 in U.S. history. Also recommended are 2 units in a foreign language and completion of 1 unit each in foreign language and mathematics in the senior year. An audition/interview demonstrating evidence of a special talent is the primary admissions criterion. Applicants to the School of Design and Production must submit a portfolio. CLEP credit is accepted.

Procedure: Freshmen are admitted to all sessions. Applications should be filed by April 1 for fall entry, along with an application fee of $25. Notification is sent on a rolling basis.

Transfer: Evidence of special talent and good academic standing are required. Placement is based on ability and experience, prior courses, and interviews.

Visiting: To arrange for a visit, contact the Admissions Office at (919) 770-3399.

Financial Aid: In an earlier year, 68% of all freshmen received some form of financial aid. The average freshman award was $1600. NCSA is a member of CSS. The FAF or FFS is required. The deadline for financial aid applications is April 1.

International Students: They must take the TOEFL.

Computers: There are no time limits on using the system and no fees.

Admissions Contact: Carol Palm, Director of Enrollment and Admissions.

NORTH CAROLINA STATE UNIVERSITY   D-2
Raleigh, NC 27695-7103   (919) 515-2434

Full-time: 10,269 men, 6187 women	Faculty: 1307; I, -$
Part-time: 2891 men, 2061 women	Ph.D.s: 88%
Graduate: 3272 men, 2490 women	Student/Faculty: 13 to 1
Year: semesters, summer session	Tuition: $1584 ($8498)
Application Deadline: February 1	Room & Board: $3400
Freshman Class: 10,678 applied, 7059 accepted, 3176 enrolled	
SAT I Verbal/Math: 493/578	VERY COMPETITIVE

North Carolina State University, founded in 1887, is a member of the University of North Carolina System. Its degree programs emphasize the arts and sciences, agriculture, business, education, engineering, and professional training. There are 9 undergraduate and 2 graduate schools. In addition to regional accreditation, NC State has baccalaureate program accreditation with ABET, CSWE, NAAB, NCATE, NRPA, and SAF. The 5 libraries contain 2,000,000 volumes, 3,700,000 microform items, and 128,000 audiovisual forms, and subscribe to 18,086 periodicals. Computerized library sources and services include interlibrary loans and database searching. Special learning facilities include a learning resource center, an art gallery, a radio station, a TV station, a nuclear reactor, a phytotron, electron microscope facilities, the Materials Research Center, the Integrated Manufacturing Systems Engineering Institute, Japan Center, and the Precision Engineering Center. The 1640-acre campus is in an urban area in Raleigh. Including residence halls, there are 150 buildings on campus.

Student Life: About 86% of undergraduates are from North Carolina. Students come from 50 states, 93 foreign countries, and Canada. Eighty-eight percent are from public schools; 12% from private. Eighty-two percent are white. Forty-four percent are Protestant. The average age of freshmen is 18; all undergraduates, 22. Ten percent drop out by the end of their first year; 64% remain to graduate.

Housing: A total of 6600 students can be accommodated in college housing. College-sponsored living facilities include single-sex and coed dormitories, married-student housing, fraternity houses, and sorority houses. In addition, there are honors houses, special-interest

houses, and International, Arts and Creative Living, Computer theme, and First-Year Experience Halls. On-campus housing is guaranteed for the freshman year only and is available on a lottery system for upperclassmen. Fifty-nine percent of students commute. Alcohol is not permitted. Upperclassmen may keep cars on campus.

Activities: About 15% of men belong to 24 national fraternities; about 15% of women belong to 10 national sororities. There are 350 groups on campus, including art, bagpipe band, band, cheerleading, chess, choir, chorale, chorus, computers, dance, drama, drill team, drum and bugle corps, ethnic, film, gay, honors, international, jazz band, literary magazine, marching band, musical theater, newspaper, orchestra, pep band, photography, political, professional, radio and TV, religious, social, social service, student government, symphony, and yearbook. Popular campus events include Homecoming, Pan African Festival, Wolfstock, and Greek Week.

Sports: There are 19 intercollegiate sports for men and 14 for women, and 28 intramural sports for men and 28 for women. Athletic and recreation facilities include a 55,000-seat football stadium, 5000-seat soccer stadium, baseball stadium, 12,500-seat basketball gymnasium, tennis complex, and areas for track.

Disabled Students: Seventy-eight percent of the campus is accessible to disabled students. The following facilities are available: wheelchair ramps, elevators, special parking, specially equipped rest rooms, special class scheduling, lowered drinking fountains, lowered telephones, and van transportation.

Services: In addition to many counseling and information services, tutoring is available in most subjects. There is also a reader service for the blind, and remedial math, reading, and writing.

Campus Safety and Security: Campus safety and security measures include 24-hour foot and vehicle patrol, self-defense education, escort service, and shuttle buses. In addition, there are informal discussions, pamphlets, posters, films, emergency telephones, lighted pathways and sidewalks, and bicycle and mounted horse patrol.

Programs of Study: NC State awards the B.A., B.S., B.Arch., B.E.D., and B.S.W. degrees. Associate, master's, and doctoral degrees also are awarded. Bachelor's degrees are awarded in AGRICULTURE (agricultural business management, agricultural economics, agriculture, animal science, conservation and regulation, fishing and fisheries, forestry and related sciences, horticulture, natural resource management, poultry science, soil science, and wood science), BIOLOGICAL SCIENCE (biochemistry, biology/biological science, botany, microbiology, and zoology), BUSINESS (accounting, business administration and management, business economics, and recreation and leisure services), COMMUNICATIONS AND THE ARTS (communications, design, English, French, graphic design, industrial design, and Spanish), COMPUTER AND PHYSICAL SCIENCE (atmospheric sciences and meteorology, chemistry, computer science, earth science, geology, mathematics, physics, and statistics), EDUCATION (agricultural, education, foreign languages, industrial arts, marketing and distribution, mathematics, middle school, science, secondary, social studies, technical, and vocational), ENGINEERING AND ENVIRONMENTAL DESIGN (aeronautical engineering, agricultural engineering, architecture, chemical engineering, civil engineering, computer engineering, construction management, electrical/electronics engineering, engineering, environmental design, environmental engineering, environmental science, furniture design, industrial engineering, landscape architecture/design, materials science, mechanical engineering, nuclear engineering, paper and pulp science, and textile engineering), HEALTH PROFESSIONS (medical laboratory technology, predentistry, premedicine, preveterinary science, and speech pathology/audiology), SOCIAL SCIENCE (clothing and textiles management/production/services, criminal justice, economics, food science, history, interdisciplinary studies, parks and recreation management, philosophy, political science/government, prelaw, psychology, religion, social science, social work, sociology, and textiles and clothing). Electrical engineering, chemical engineering, and architecture are the strongest academically. Business management has the largest enrollment.

Required: To graduate, students must complete 120 to 142 semester hours, including 60 to 70 in the major, with a minimum GPA of 2.0. Distribution requirements include 6 semester hours of English composition, 6 to 8 each in mathematics and science, and 12 to 18 in humanities and social sciences. Four semester hours of physical education are also required.

Special: NC State offers cross-registration within the Cooperating Raleigh Colleges network, study abroad in more than 90 countries, internships, work-study programs, an accelerated degree plan, dual majors within any program, a general studies degree in education, a 3-2 engineering degree, student-designed majors, credit by examination, nondegree study, and pass/fail options. There is a freshman honors program on campus, as well as 15 national honor societies. Forty-four departments have honors programs.

Faculty/Classroom: Seventy-eight percent of faculty are male; 22%, female. All teach undergraduates and do research. Graduate students teach 6% of introductory courses. The average class size in

an introductory lecture is 35; in a laboratory, 20; and in a regular course offering, 30.

Admissions: About 66% of the 1993-94 applicants were accepted. The SAT scores for the 1993-94 freshman class were as follows: Verbal—55% below 500, 34% between 500 and 599, 10% between 600 and 700, and 1% above 700; Math—15% below 500, 44% between 500 and 599, 30% between 600 and 700, and 10% above 700. About 68% of the current freshmen were in the top fifth of their class; 96% were in the top two fifths. There were 18 National Merit finalists.

Requirements: The SAT I or ACT is required. An SAT II: Subject test in mathematics is recommended. Applicants must be graduates of an accredited secondary school or have a GED certificate. They must have completed 20 academic credits, including 4 units of English, 3 each of science and mathematics, 2 of social studies, 1 of history, and 2 of foreign language. 4 units of mathematics are advised. An essay is recommended for all applicants. A portfolio and interview are required for the School of Design. AP and CLEP credits are accepted. Important factors used in the admissions decision are advanced placement or honor courses, leadership record, geographic diversity, extracurricular activities record, and evidence of special talent.

Procedure: Freshmen are admitted to all sessions. Entrance exams should be taken in the spring of the junior year and the fall of the senior year. Early decision applications should be filed by November 1; regular applications, by February 1 for fall entry, November 1 for spring entry, and February 1 for summer entry, along with an application fee of $45. Notification of early decision is sent December 15; regular decision, on a rolling basis. There is a deferred admissions plan. A waiting list is an active part of the admissions procedure, with about 3% of applicants on the list.

Transfer: About 1320 transfer students enrolled in 1993-94. Applicants must have completed 28 semester hours of college-level work with a minimum GPA of 2.0. Priority is given to students who have completed 60 hours of relevant course work. An associate degree and an interview are recommended. Applicants must have mathematics, English, and foreign language proficiency. At least 30 credits out of 120 must be completed at NC State.

Visiting: There are regularly scheduled orientations for prospective students, consisting of admissions information sessions. There are guides for informal visits, and visitors may sit in on classes. To arrange for a visit, contact the Admissions Office at (919) 515-2434.

Financial Aid: In 1993-94, 62% of all current freshmen and 42% of continuing students received some form of financial aid. About 44% of freshmen and 42% of continuing students received need-based aid. The average freshman award was $1218. Of that total, scholarships or need-based grants averaged $740 ($7122 maximum); and loans averaged $1095. Thirty-five percent of undergraduate students work part-time. Average earnings from campus work for the school year are $1200. The average financial indebtedness of the 1992-93 graduate was $10,200. NC State is a member of CSS. The FAF is required. The deadline for financial aid applications is March 1.

International Students: There are currently 1050 international students enrolled. The school actively recruits these students. They must take the TOEFL and achieve a minimum score of 550 and must also take the SAT I, or ACT, if it is available to students in their country.

Computers: The college provides computer facilities for student use. The mainframes are an IBM 3081, an IBM 4381/P12, and a DEC VAX 8700. There are also 3200 computer stations located campuswide. Several departments have additional stations available for their majors only. All students may access the system. The fees are $100.

Graduates: In 1992-93, 3922 bachelor's degrees were awarded. The most popular majors among graduates were engineering (26%), business management (23%), and computer science (10%). Within an average freshman class, 1% graduate in 3 years, 25% in 4 years, 58% in 5 years, and 64% in 6 years. Some 625 companies recruited on campus in an earlier year. In the 1992 graduating class, 65% of all graduates had found employment within 6 months of graduation.

Admissions Contact: Dr. George R. Dixon, Director of Admissions.

NORTH CAROLINA WESLEYAN COLLEGE   E-2
Rocky Mount, NC 27804   (919) 985-5201
                                                (800) 488-NCWC (in-state)

Full-time: 309 men, 337 women	**Faculty:** 43; IIB, --$
Part-time: 33 men, 51 women	**Ph.D.s:** 68%
Graduate: none	**Student/Faculty:** 15 to 1
Year: semesters, summer session	**Tuition:** $8350
Application Deadline: July 15	**Room & Board:** $4130
Freshman Class: 750 applied, 680 accepted, 195 enrolled	
SAT I Verbal/Math: 420/430	**ACT:** 21 **LESS COMPETITIVE**

North Carolina Wesleyan College, founded in 1956, is a private liberal arts institution affiliated with the United Methodist Church. In addition to regional accreditation, NCWC has baccalaureate program

accreditation with NCATE. The library contains 77,500 volumes, 20,000 microform items, and 4107 audiovisual forms, and subscribes to 743 periodicals. Computerized library sources and services include the card catalog, interlibrary loans, and database searching. Special learning facilities include a learning resource center and radio station. The 200-acre campus is in a suburban area 57 miles east of Raleigh. Including residence halls, there are 14 buildings on campus.

Student Life: About 51% of undergraduates are from out-of-state, mostly the Middle Atlantic. Students come from 24 states and 8 foreign countries. Seventy percent are from public schools; 30% from private. Seventy-eight percent are white; 18% African American. Seventy percent are Protestant; 16% Catholic; 14% claim no religious affiliation. The average age of freshmen is 18; all undergraduates, 21. Fifty-two percent drop out by the end of their first year; 37% remain to graduate.

Housing: A total of 467 students can be accommodated in college housing. College-sponsored living facilities include single-sex and coed dormitories. On-campus housing is guaranteed for all 4 years. Sixty-six percent of students live on campus; of those, 60% remain on campus on weekends. Alcohol is not permitted. All students may keep cars on campus.

Activities: About 5% of men belong to 1 local and 2 national fraternities; about 4% of women belong to 3 local sororities. There are 23 groups on campus, including band, cheerleading, choir, chorus, computers, drama, ethnic, honors, international, jazz band, literary magazine, newspaper, pep band, political, professional, radio, religious, social, social service, student government, and yearbook. Popular campus events include Homecoming, Spring Fling, Parents Weekend, and Alumni Weekend.

Sports: There are 4 intercollegiate sports for men and 4 for women, and 38 intramural sports for men and 38 for women. Athletic and recreation facilities include a 1,200-seat gymnasium with areas for basketball, volleyball, and indoor soccer matches. There are also tennis courts, a skeet range, and intramural and practice fields for baseball, softball, and soccer.

Disabled Students: Eighty-five percent of the campus is accessible to disabled students. The following facilities are available: wheelchair ramps, elevators, special parking, and lowered drinking fountains.

Services: In addition to many counseling and information services, tutoring is available in some subjects. There is also remedial math, reading, and writing.

Campus Safety and Security: Campus safety and security measures include escort service, informal discussions, pamphlets, posters, films, and lighted pathways and sidewalks.

Programs of Study: NCWC awards the B.A. and B.S. degrees. Bachelor's degrees are awarded in BIOLOGICAL SCIENCE (biology/biological science), BUSINESS (accounting, business administration and management, and hotel/motel and restaurant management), COMMUNICATIONS AND THE ARTS (English and music), COMPUTER AND PHYSICAL SCIENCE (chemistry, computer programming, and mathematics), EDUCATION (elementary, middle school, and physical), ENGINEERING AND ENVIRONMENTAL DESIGN (environmental science), SOCIAL SCIENCE (anthropology, criminal justice, history, philosophy, psychology, religion, and sociology). Business administration, justice and public policy, and computer information systems have the largest enrollments.

Required: To graduate, students must complete 124 semester hours with a minimum GPA of 2.0. Distribution requirements consist of 6 semester hours each of English composition and foreign language; 3 each of ethics, non-Western culture, mathematics, history, social science, psychology or sociology, religion, literature and fine arts; 4 each of biolgical and physical science; and 2 of physical education.

Special: NCWC offers cooperative programs in all majors except religion, internships, work-study programs through the college offices, study abroad at Sorbonne University in Paris, credit for military experience, nondegree study, and pass/fail options. There is a freshman honors program on campus, as well as 5 national honor societies.

Faculty/Classroom: Sixty-seven percent of faculty are male; 33%, female. All teach undergraduates. The average class size in an introductory lecture is 23; in a laboratory, 15; and in a regular course offering, 17.

Admissions: About 91% of the 1993–94 applicants were accepted. The SAT scores for the 1993–94 freshman class were as follows: Verbal—87% below 500, 11% between 500 and 599, and 2% between 600 and 700; Math—83% below 500, 13% between 500 and 599, and 4% between 600 and 700. About 25% of the current freshmen were in the top fifth of their class.

Requirements: A minimum GPA of 2.0 is required. The SAT I or ACT is required. A minimum SAT I composite score of 800 or ACT score of 19 is recommended. Applicants should be graduates of an accredited secondary school or have a GED certificate. They should have completed 16 credit hours, including 4 in English and 2 each in foreign language and social studies. NCWC also recommends that students have 2 hours in mathematics and 2 to 3 in science. An essay

and interview are advised. AP and CLEP credits are accepted. Important factors used in the admissions decision are advanced placement or honor courses, extracurricular activities record, leadership record, evidence of special talent, and recommendations by school officials.

Procedure: Freshmen are admitted fall and spring. Entrance exams should be taken prior to or at orientation. Applications should be filed by July 15 for fall entry, December 15 for spring entry, and June 1 for summer entry, along with an application fee of $25. Notification is sent on a rolling basis. There are early admissions and deferred admissions plans.

Transfer: About 40 transfer students enrolled in 1993–94. Applicants must have a minimum GPA of 2.0 in their college courses. They must submit transcripts of all high school and college work, along with proof of high school graduation. A total of 30 credits out of 124 must be completed at NCWC.

Visiting: There are regularly scheduled orientations for prospective students, including an individual campus tour, interview, financial aid session, and meeting with faculty. There are guides for informal visits and visitors may sit in on classes and stay overnight at the school. To arrange for a visit, contact the Admissions Office at (919) 985–5201 or (800) 488–6292 (in-state).

Financial Aid: In 1993–94 67% of all current freshmen and 70% of continuing students received some form of financial aid. About 52% of all students received need-based aid. The average freshman award was $5600. Of that total, scholarships or need-based grants averaged $2688 ($2400 maximum); loans averaged $2128 ($2625 maximum); and work contracts averaged $784 ($800 maximum). Fifty-two percent of undergraduate students work part-time. Average earnings from campus work for the school year are $800. The average financial indebtedness of a recent year's graduate was $13,000. NCWC is a member of CSS. The FAF and FAFSA are required. The deadline for financial aid applications is March 1.

International Students: There are currently 10 international students enrolled. They must take the TOEFL and achieve a minimum score of 500. The student must also take the college's own entrance exam.

Computers: The college provides computer facilities for student use. The mainframe is an IBM/36. There are also 41 microcomputers located in the computer laboratory, residence halls, tutoring center, and library. All students may access the system. It may be used on a sign-up basis in the computer laboratory or as available at other locations. There are no time limits and no fees.

Graduates: In a recent year, 203 bachelor's degrees were awarded. The most popular majors among graduates were business administration (35%), justice and public policy (15%), and computer information systems (15%). Within an average freshman class, 37% graduate in 5 years. About 20 companies usually recruit on campus. In the 1992 graduating class, 15% of all graduates were enrolled in graduate school within 6 months of graduation; 90% had found employment.

Admissions Contact: Patricia Cerjan, Vice President of Admissions/Financial Aid.

PEMBROKE STATE UNIVERSITY D-3

Pembroke, NC 28372   (919) 521–6000; (800) 634–2984 (in-state)

Full-time: 980 men, 1194 women	Faculty: 148; IIA, -$
Part-time: 168 men, 361 women	Ph.Ds: 77%
Graduate: 84 men, 258 women	Student/Faculty: 15 to 1
Year: semesters, summer session	Tuition: $1078 ($6442)
Application Deadline: July 15	Room & Board: $2460
Freshman Class: 944 applied, 774 accepted, 440 enrolled	
SAT I Verbal/Math: 380/430	**LESS COMPETITIVE**

Pembroke State University, founded in 1887, is part of the University of North Carolina state-supported system. It provides a liberal arts education that includes art, business, health sciences, music, teacher preparation, and preprofessional studies. There is one graduate school. In addition to regional accreditation, PSU has baccalaureate program accreditation with CSWE, NASM, and NCATE. The 2 libraries contain 177,000 volumes and 277,000 microform items, and subscribe to 1439 periodicals. Computerized library sources and services include the card catalog, interlibrary loans, and database searching. Special learning facilities include a learning resource center, art gallery, TV station, and a Native American resource center. The 108-acre campus is in a small town 30 miles south of Fayetteville. Including residence halls, there are 38 buildings on campus.

Student Life: About 97% of undergraduates are from North Carolina. Students come from 31 states, 4 foreign countries, and Canada. Sixty-three percent are white; 23% Native American/Eskimo; 12% African American. The average age of freshmen is 19; all undergraduates, 25. Twenty-five percent drop out by the end of their first year.

Housing: A total of 834 students can be accommodated in college housing. College-sponsored living facilities include single-sex dormitories. On-campus housing is available on a first-come, first-served basis. Seventy-two percent of students commute. All students may keep cars on campus.

Activities: About 3% of men belong to 1 local and 7 national fraternities; about 3% of women belong to 1 local and 5 national sororities. There are 61 groups on campus, including art, band, cheerleading, choir, chorale, chorus, dance, drama, ethnic, gay, honors, international, jazz band, literary magazine, musical theater, newspaper, pep band, political, professional, radio and TV, religious, social, social service, student government, and yearbook. Popular campus events include the Performing Arts Cultural Series, Miss PSU Scholarship Pageant, and Pembroke Day.

Sports: There are 7 intercollegiate sports for men and 4 for women, and 12 intramural sports for men and 12 for women. Athletic and recreation facilities include the 3200-seat main gymnasium, auxiliary gymnasium, a track, tennis courts, a natatorium, weight rooms, a bowling alley, a 1700-seat auditorium, and fields for soccer, baseball, and softball.

Disabled Students: Ninety-eight percent of the campus is accessible to disabled students. The following facilities are available: wheelchair ramps, elevators, special parking, specially equipped rest rooms, special class scheduling, lowered drinking fountains, and lowered telephones.

Services: In addition to many counseling and information services, tutoring is available in every subject. There is also remedial math and writing.

Campus Safety and Security: Campus safety and security measures include 24-hour foot and vehicle patrol, self defense education, escort service, pamphlets, posters, and films. In addition, there are emergency telephones and lighted pathways and sidewalks.

Programs of Study: PSU awards the B.A., B.S., B.M., B.S.A.S., B.S.N., and B.S.W. degrees. Master's degrees also are awarded. Bachelor's degrees are awarded in BIOLOGICAL SCIENCE (biochemistry and biology/biological science), BUSINESS (accounting, business administration and management, business economics, management science, office supervision and management, and recreational facilities management), COMMUNICATIONS AND THE ARTS (arts administration/management, broadcasting, communications, English, fine arts, journalism, and music), COMPUTER AND PHYSICAL SCIENCE (chemistry, computer science, and mathematics), EDUCATION (art, business, early childhood, elementary, English, mathematics, middle school, music, physical, science, secondary, social studies, and special), HEALTH PROFESSIONS (medical laboratory technology, predentistry, and premedicine), SOCIAL SCIENCE (American Indian studies, criminal justice, economics, history, parks and recreation management, philosophy, political science/government, prelaw, psychology, public administration, social work, and sociology). Education is the strongest academically. Education, business, and social science have the largest enrollments.

Required: All students are required to complete 128 total credits, which include 50 semester hours of general education courses, 39 to 69 hours in a major, and a university orientation class before entrance. A minimum GPA of 2.0 must be maintained.

Special: Co-op programs, cross-registration, internships, study abroad, a Washington semester and work-study programs are available. A 3–1 degree program is offered in medical technology. The B.A.-B.S. degree is available in American Indian studies, broadcasting, or with the B.S.A.S. degree. In addition, dual majors, credit for military experience, and nondegree study are offered. There is a freshman honors program on campus, as well as 7 national honor societies. Seven departments have honors programs.

Faculty/Classroom: Seventy-four percent of faculty are male; 26%, female. No introductory courses are taught by graduate students. The average class size in an introductory lecture is 30; in a laboratory, 15; and in a regular course offering, 20.

Admissions: About 82% of the 1993–94 applicants were accepted. The SAT scores for the 1993–94 freshman class were as follows: Verbal—92% below 500, 6% between 500 and 599, 1% between 600 and 700, and 1% above 700; Math—81% below 500, 17% between 500 and 599, and 2% between 600 and 700. About 26% of the current freshmen were in the top fifth of their class; 54% were in the top two fifths.

Requirements: The SAT I is required. Applicants are required to have graduated from an accredited secondary school and to have 20 credits, including 4 courses in English, 3 each in mathematics and science, and 2 in history. An essay and an interview are recommended. Students also must submit an official high school transcript that shows their class rank and GPA. The College Opportunity Program is designed to admit a limited number of students who meet most, but not all, of the regular admission standards. Students who receive the GED should consult an admissions counselor. AP and CLEP credits are accepted. Important factors used in the admissions decision are advanced placement or honor courses, recommendations by school officials, extracurricular activities record, leadership record, and evidence of special talent.

Procedure: Freshmen are admitted to all sessions. Entrance exams should be taken during junior and senior years. Applications should be filed by July 15 for fall entry, December 1 for spring entry, and

May 15 for summer entry, along with an application fee of $25. Notification is sent on a rolling basis. There is a deferred admissions plan.

Transfer: About 301 transfer students enrolled in 1993–94. Transfer applicants must have a minimum GPA of 2.0, submit transcripts from high school and from all previous colleges, and be eligible to return to the last institution attended. The SAT I and an interview are recommended. A total of 30 credits out of 128 must be completed at PSU.

Visiting: There are regularly scheduled orientations for prospective students, including an open house in the fall. There are guides for informal visits and visitors may sit in on classes and stay overnight at the school. To arrange for a visit, contact the Admissions Office at (919) 521–6262.

Financial Aid: In 1993–94 46% of all current freshmen and 38% of continuing students received some form of financial aid. About 45% of freshmen and 37% of continuing students received need-based aid. The average freshman award was $1110. Of that total, scholarships or need-based grants averaged $1234 ($4666 maximum); loans averaged $1012 ($5500 maximum); and work contracts averaged $702 ($1912 maximum). Ten percent of undergraduate students work part-time. Average earnings from campus work for the school year are $809. PSU is a member of CSS. The FAFSA financial statement is required. The deadline for financial aid applications is April 15.

International Students: There are currently 10 international students enrolled. They must take the TOEFL and achieve a minimum score of 500.

Computers: The college provides computer facilities for student use. The mainframe is a DEC VAX Station 4000 and a DEC VAX 6310. There are also PCs available in the computer center and in classrooms. All students may access the system. Students may access the system 1 hour at a time. There are no fees.

Graduates: In 1992–93 432 bachelor's degrees were awarded. The most popular majors among graduates were education (31%), business (18%), and social sciences (16%). Within an average freshman class, 33% graduate in 5 years. Some 300 companies recruited on campus in an earlier year.

Admissions Contact: Anthony Locklear, Director of Admissions.

PFEIFFER COLLEGE
C-2
Misenheimer, NC 28109
(704) 463–1360, ext. 2060
(800) 338–2060

Full-time: 321 men, 334 women	Faculty: 47; IIB, --$
Part-time: 65 men, 95 women	Ph.Ds: 57%
Graduate: 95 men, 94 women	Student/Faculty: 14 to 1
Year: semesters, summer session	Tuition: $8190
Application Deadline: open	Room & Board: $3480
Freshman Class: 838 applied, 586 accepted, 159 enrolled	
SAT I Verbal/Math: 390/441	**LESS COMPETITIVE**

Pfeiffer College, founded in 1885, is a private, coeducational institution of liberal arts and sciences affiliated with the United Methodist Church. There are 2 graduate schools. In addition to regional accreditation, Pfeiffer has baccalaureate program accreditation with NASM. The library contains 113,984 volumes, 21,480 microform items, and 2343 audiovisual forms, and subscribes to 380 periodicals. Computerized library sources and services include database searching. Special learning facilities include a learning resource center, art gallery, and radio station. The 300-acre campus is in a rural area 35 miles east of Charlotte. Including residence halls, there are 28 buildings on campus.

Student Life: About 66% of undergraduates are from North Carolina. Students come from 23 states, 13 foreign countries, and Canada. Eighty-six percent are white; 10% African American. Fifty-one percent are Protestant; 10% Catholic. The average age of freshmen is 18.2; all undergraduates, 23.4. Thirty-five percent drop out by the end of their first year; 42% remain to graduate.

Housing: A total of 650 students can be accommodated in college housing. College-sponsored living facilities include single-sex dormitories, on-campus apartments, and married-student housing. On-campus housing is guaranteed for all 4 years. Fifty-four percent of students live on campus; of those, 60% remain on campus on weekends. All students may keep cars on campus.

Activities: There are no fraternities or sororities on campus. There are 41 groups on campus, including band, cheerleading, chess, choir, chorale, chorus, drama, ethnic, honors, international, jazz band, literary magazine, newspaper, pep band, political, professional, religious, social, social service, student government, and yearbook. Popular campus events include Homecoming, Winterfest, and Aprilfest.

Sports: There are 7 intercollegiate sports for men and 7 for women, and 21 intramural sports for men and 21 for women. Athletic and recreation facilities include an 1800-seat gymnasium, an indoor pool, exercise rooms, training facilities, and weight rooms. The campus also has 6 tennis courts, fields for baseball, softball, lacrosse, and soccer, areas for golf practice and volleyball, and an indoor batting cage.

Disabled Students: Seventy-five percent of the campus is accessible to disabled students. The following facilities are available: wheelchair ramps, elevators, special parking, specially equipped rest rooms, special class scheduling, and lowered telephones.

Services: In addition to many counseling and information services, tutoring is available in most subjects. There is also remedial math, reading, and writing.

Campus Safety and Security: Campus safety and security measures include 24-hour foot and vehicle patrol, informal discussions, and lighted pathways and sidewalks.

Programs of Study: Pfeiffer awards the A.B. and B.S. degrees. Master's degrees also are awarded. Bachelor's degrees are awarded in BIOLOGICAL SCIENCE (biology/biological science), BUSINESS (accounting, business administration and management, and sports management), COMMUNICATIONS AND THE ARTS (arts administration/management, communications, dramatic arts, English literature, and music), COMPUTER AND PHYSICAL SCIENCE (chemistry, computer management, and mathematics), EDUCATION (elementary, music, physical, science, secondary, and special), ENGINEERING AND ENVIRONMENTAL DESIGN (preengineering), HEALTH PROFESSIONS (premedicine and sports medicine), SOCIAL SCIENCE (criminal justice, economics, history, prelaw, psychology, religion, religious education, religious music, social studies, and sociology). Chemistry, music, sports medicine and management, criminal justice, and premedicine are the strongest academically. Business administration, criminal justice, elementary education, and sociology have the largest enrollments.

Required: All students must complete 120 to 124 semester hours, including 60 credits in writing, language and literature, history/political science, music/art/theater, natural science, mathematics, economics/psychology/sociology, religion, and physical education. Students must maintain a minimum GPA of 2.0 and complete 42 to 72 hours in the major.

Special: A 3-2 program in engineering with Auburn University and Georgia Institute of Technology, many internships in business, education, and physical education, work-study programs with the federal government, study abroad in Germany and Japan, and interdisciplinary majors are offered. There is a freshman honors program on campus. Three departments have honors programs.

Faculty/Classroom: Sixty percent of faculty are male; 40%, female. All teach undergraduates, and 20% also do research. No introductory courses are taught by graduate students. The average class size in an introductory lecture is 35; in a laboratory, 22; and in a regular course offering, 17.

Admissions: About 70% of the 1993-94 applicants were accepted. The SAT scores for the 1993-94 freshman class were as follows: Verbal—90% below 500, 7% between 500 and 599, and 1% between 600 and 700; Math—71% below 500, 19% between 500 and 599, 6% between 600 and 700, and 1% above 700. About 21% of the current freshmen were in the top fifth of their class; 41% were in the top two fifths.

Requirements: The SAT I or ACT is required. In addition, all applicants are required to have completed 4 years of English and 3 years of mathematics, including Algebra I. The GED is accepted. AP and CLEP credits are accepted. Important factors used in the admissions decision are advanced placement or honor courses, leadership record, extracurricular activities record, recommendations by school officials, and evidence of special talent.

Procedure: Freshmen are admitted to all sessions. Entrance exams should be taken by January of the senior year. Application deadlines are open. Application fee is $20. Notification is sent on a rolling basis. There are early admissions and deferred admissions plans.

Transfer: About 75 transfer students enrolled in 1993-94. Transfer applicants should be eligible for readmission to, or should have graduated from, the last college attended, and have a minimum GPA of 2.0. At least 45 credits out of 120 must be completed at Pfeiffer.

Visiting: There are regularly scheduled orientations for prospective students, including meetings with faculty/staff, a question-and-answer session, a tour, and lunch. There are guides for informal visits, and visitors may sit in on classes and stay overnight at the school. To arrange for a visit, contact the Admission Office at (800) 338-2060.

Financial Aid: In 1993-94, 90% of all current freshmen and 85% of continuing students received some form of financial aid. About 68% of freshmen and 57% of continuing students received need-based aid. The average freshman award was $7380. Of that total, scholarships or need-based grants averaged $4213 ($9470 maximum); loans averaged $3924 ($7625 maximum); and work contracts averaged $770 ($1912 maximum). Twenty-two percent of undergraduate students work part-time. Average earnings from campus work for the school year are $965. The average financial indebtedness of the 1992-93 graduate was $9795. Pfeiffer is a member of CSS. The FAF or FFS is required. The deadline for financial aid applications is open.

International Students: There are currently 19 international students enrolled. They must take the TOEFL or the University of Michigan Language Test and achieve a minimum score on the TOEFL of 500. They must also take the SAT I or the ACT.

Computers: The college provides computer facilities for student use. The mainframe is a Prime 2755. There are 7 terminals and 54 microcomputers available to students on a flexible schedule, including early mornings and late evenings. All students may access the system. There are no time limits on using the system and no fees.

Graduates: In 1992-93, 148 bachelor's degrees were awarded. The most popular majors among graduates were business administration (20%), criminal justice (14%), and elementary education (12%). Within an average freshman class, 25% graduate in 4 years, 37% in 5 years, and 41% in 6 years.

Admissions Contact: David Maltby, Dean of Admissions and Financial Aid.

QUEENS COLLEGE
C-3

Charlotte, NC 28274   (704) 337-2212; (800) 849-0202 (out-of-state)

Full-time: 165 men, 465 women	Faculty: 65; IIB, -$
Part-time: 96 men, 453 women	Ph.D.s: 74%
Graduate: 161 men, 209 women	Student/Faculty: 10 to 1
Year: semesters, summer session	Tuition: $10,400
Application Deadline: August 20	Room & Board: $4550
Freshman Class: 516 applied, 395 accepted, 154 enrolled	
SAT I Verbal/Math: 500/510	ACT: 25 COMPETITIVE

Queens College, founded in 1857, is a private, coeducational liberal arts institution affiliated with the Presbyterian Church. Undergraduate programs are offered through the College of Arts and Sciences and the New College, a division offering courses in the evening and on Saturday. There are 2 undergraduate schools and one graduate school. In addition to regional accreditation, Queens has baccalaureate program accreditation with ACBSP, NASM, NCATE, and NLN. The library contains 115,879 volumes, 42,300 microform items, and 430 audiovisual forms, and subscribes to 593 periodicals. Computerized library sources and services include the card catalog, interlibrary loans, and database searching. Special learning facilities include a learning resource center, art gallery, McEwen Liberal Learning Center, rare books and archival collection, photographic laboratory, ceramics studio, and recital hall. The 25-acre campus is in a suburban area 2 miles south of downtown Charlotte. Including residence halls, there are 29 buildings on campus.

Student Life: About 67% of undergraduates are from North Carolina. Students come from 28 states and 19 foreign countries. Eighty-two percent are from public schools; 18% from private. Eighty-two percent are white. Sixty-four percent are Protestant; 11% Catholic. The average age of freshmen is 18; all undergraduates, 20.5. Ten percent drop out by the end of their first year; 56% remain to graduate.

Housing: A total of 600 students can be accommodated in college housing. College-sponsored living facilities include single-sex and coed dormitories. On-campus housing is guaranteed for all 4 years. Seventy-five percent of students live on campus; of those, 75% remain on campus on weekends. All students may keep cars on campus.

Activities: About 35% of men belong to 2 national fraternities; about 45% of women belong to 5 national sororities. There are 42 groups on campus, including art, cheerleading, choir, chorale, chorus, computers, dance, drama, drill team, ethnic, honors, international, jazz band, literary magazine, musical theater, newspaper, orchestra, political, professional, religious, social, social service, student government, symphony, and yearbook. Popular campus events include Oktoberfest, Casino Party, Boar's Head Banquet, Moravian Lovefeast, Mardi Gras Festival, International Symposium, and May Day.

Sports: There are 4 intercollegiate sports for men and 5 for women, and 10 intramural sports for men and 10 for women. Athletic and recreation facilities include Ovens Athletic Center with a gymnasium, classrooms, dance studios, weight room, training room, and swimming pool. There are also 6 tennis courts (4 lighted) and a soccer/softball complex. In addition, the Trexler College Center offers various recreational opportunities.

Disabled Students: Thirty percent of the campus is accessible to disabled students. The following facilities are available: wheelchair ramps, elevators, special parking, specially equipped rest rooms, and special class scheduling.

Services: In addition to many counseling and information services, tutoring is available in every subject. There is also remedial math, reading, writing, and English.

Campus Safety and Security: Campus safety and security measures include 24-hour foot and vehicle patrol, self defense education, escort service, and informal discussions. In addition, there are pamphlets, posters, films, emergency telephones, and lighted pathways and sidewalks.

Programs of Study: Queens awards the B.A., B.S., B.Mus., and B.S.N. degrees. Master's degrees also are awarded. Bachelor's degrees are awarded in BIOLOGICAL SCIENCE (biochemistry and

biology/biological science), BUSINESS (accounting and business administration and management), COMMUNICATIONS AND THE ARTS (communications, dramatic arts, English, fine arts, French, music, and Spanish), COMPUTER AND PHYSICAL SCIENCE (mathematics), EDUCATION (elementary, English, foreign languages, mathematics, science, secondary, and social studies), HEALTH PROFESSIONS (nursing, predentistry, premedicine, and preveterinary science), SOCIAL SCIENCE (history, political science/ government, prelaw, psychology, and sociology). Liberal arts and sciences are the strongest programs academically. Business and communications have the largest enrollments.

Required: In order to graduate, students must complete a total of 122 credit hours with a minimum GPA of 2.0. For the B.A., between 30 and 40 hours are required in the student's major. For the B.S., 32 are required. All students must take a sequence of 6 courses in the Foundations of Liberal Learning Program. In addition, 2 courses in English composition, 2 in physical education, and 1 laboratory science course are required. If entering freshmen do not pass placement examinations given in mathematics and a foreign language, additional courses will be required. Some majors require a thesis or research project.

Special: Internships in all majors, cross-registration with colleges of the Charlotte Area Educational Consortium, dual majors, nondegree study, and pass/fail options are available. The school offers a Washington semester. A study tour in Europe and Asia (included in the cost of tuition) may be arranged through the school's International Experience Program. There are 4 national honor societies on campus.

Faculty/Classroom: Fifty-two percent of faculty are male; 48%, female. All teach undergraduates. No introductory courses are taught by graduate students. The average class size in an introductory lecture is 25; in a laboratory, 20; and in a regular course offering, 17.

Admissions: About 77% of the 1993–94 applicants were accepted. The SAT scores for the 1993–94 freshman class were as follows: Verbal—62% below 500, 24% between 500 and 599, and 11% between 600 and 700; Math—46% below 500, 38% between 500 and 599, and 13% between 600 and 700. About 50% of the current freshmen were in the top fifth of their class; 80% were in the top two fifths. Four freshmen graduated first in their class.

Requirements: The SAT I or the ACT is required. SAT II: Subject tests in writing and mathematics level 1 are recommended. Applicants should have a college preparatory background in an accredited secondary school. The GED is accepted. High school courses should include 4 years of English, 2 years each of social studies and a foreign language, 3 years of mathematics, and 1 year of laboratory science. An essay is required and an interview is recommended. An audition or portfolio is recommended for art and music students. AP and CLEP credits are accepted. Important factors used in the admissions decision are advanced placement or honor courses, recommendations by school officials, evidence of special talent, and leadership record.

Procedure: Freshmen are admitted in the fall and spring. Entrance exams should be taken in the junior year or as early as possible in the senior year. Applications should be filed by August 20 for fall entry and January 6 for spring entry, along with an application fee of $25 (waived if the student visits campus). Notification is sent on a rolling basis.

Transfer: About 209 transfer students enrolled in 1993–94. Transfer students are accepted in all but the senior class. A GPA of 2.0 is required for all previous college-level work. A total of 45 credits out of 122 must be completed at Queens.

Visiting: There are regularly scheduled orientations for prospective students, including a sampling of classes, campus tours, a college overview, a tour of Charlotte, and a question/answer segment. There are guides for informal visits and visitors may sit in on classes and stay overnight at the school. To arrange for a visit, contact the Admissions Office at (704) 337-2212 or (800) 849-0202.

Financial Aid: In 1993–94 85% of all current freshmen and 92% of continuing students received some form of financial aid. About 65% of freshmen and 83% of continuing students received need-based aid. The average freshman award was $11,800. Of that total, scholarships or need-based grants averaged $7400 ($10,400 maximum); loans averaged $2625 (maximum); and work contracts averaged $1500 (maximum). Forty percent of undergraduate students work part-time. Average earnings from campus work for the school year are $1150. The average financial indebtedness of the 1992–93 graduate was $11,500. Queens is a member of CSS. The FAF, the college's own financial statement, and the FAFSA are required. The deadline for financial aid applications is March 1.

International Students: There are currently 30 international students enrolled. The school actively recruits these students. They must take the TOEFL and achieve a minimum score of 550. The student must also take the SAT I or the ACT.

Computers: The college provides computer facilities for student use. The mainframe is a DEC MicroVAX. IBM-compatible microcomputers are available for student use in the computer center, the library, and the residence halls. All students may access the system. There are no time limits on using the system and no fees.

Graduates: In a recent year, 128 bachelor's degrees were awarded. The most popular majors among graduates were business (20%), nursing (9%), and communications (9%). Within an average freshman class, 55% graduate in 4 years. Some 50 companies recruited on campus in a recent year. In the 1992 graduating class, 24% of all graduates were enrolled in graduate school within 6 months of graduation; 70% of all graduates had found employment.

Admissions Contact: Dr. D. Stephen Cloniger, Director of Admissions.

SAINT ANDREWS PRESBYTERIAN COLLEGE D-3

Laurinburg, NC 28352

(919) 277-5555; (800) 763-0198

Full-time: 286 men, 326 women	**Faculty:** 51; IIB, --$
Part-time: 57 men, 92 women	**Ph.D.s:** 80%
Graduate: none	**Student/Faculty:** 12 to 1
Year: 4-1-4, summer session	**Tuition:** $9880
Application Deadline: open	**Room & Board:** $4360
Freshman Class: 460 applied, 440 accepted, 160 enrolled	
SAT I or ACT: required	**LESS COMPETITIVE**

Saint Andrews Presbyterian College, founded in 1958, is a private liberal arts institution affiliated with the Presbyterian Church. The library contains 104,852 volumes, 66,127 microform items, and 2986 audiovisual forms, and subscribes to 399 periodicals. Computerized library sources and services include the card catalog, interlibrary loans, and database searching. Special learning facilities include an art gallery, a 20,000-square-foot science laboratory, and an artronics laboratory. The 600-acre campus is in a small town 40 miles southwest of Fayetteville. Including residence halls, there are 17 buildings on campus.

Student Life: About 64% of undergraduates are from out-of-state, mostly the South. Students come from 39 states, 19 foreign countries, and Canada. Eighty-two percent are white; 10% African American. Sixty-six percent are Protestant; 17% claim no religious affiliation; 15% Catholic. The average age of freshmen is 18; all undergraduates, 22. Thirty-eight percent drop out by the end of their first year; 55% remain to graduate.

Housing: A total of 770 students can be accommodated in college housing. College-sponsored living facilities include single-sex and coed dormitories. On-campus housing is guaranteed for all 4 years. Eighty-one percent of students live on campus; of those, 90% remain on campus on weekends. All students may keep cars on campus.

Activities: There are no fraternities or sororities on campus. There are 30 groups on campus, including art, bagpipe band, cheerleading, choir, chorale, drama, ethnic, honors, literary magazine, newspaper, political, professional, radio and TV, religious, social, social service, student government, and yearbook. Popular campus events include Writers' Forum, Monday Night in the Arts, and Extravaganza spring beach party.

Sports: There are 7 intercollegiate sports for men and 6 for women, and 6 intramural sports for men and 6 for women. Athletic and recreation facilities include a basketball and volleyball arena, a pool, and soccer, baseball, and softball fields.

Disabled Students: The entire campus is accessible to disabled students. The following facilities are available: wheelchair ramps, elevators, special parking, specially equipped rest rooms, lowered drinking fountains, and lowered telephones.

Services: In addition to many counseling and information services, tutoring is available in most subjects. There is also remedial writing.

Campus Safety and Security: Campus safety and security measures include 24-hour foot and vehicle patrol, escort service, informal discussions, pamphlets, posters, and films. In addition, there are emergency telephones and lighted pathways and sidewalks.

Programs of Study: Saint Andrews awards the B.A. and B.S. degrees. Bachelor's degrees are awarded in BIOLOGICAL SCIENCE (biochemistry and biology/biological science), BUSINESS (business administration and management and business economics), COMMUNICATIONS AND THE ARTS (communications, dramatic arts, English, fine arts, French, languages, literature, and music), COMPUTER AND PHYSICAL SCIENCE (chemistry, mathematics, and physics), EDUCATION (elementary and physical), HEALTH PROFESSIONS (allied health), SOCIAL SCIENCE (history, philosophy, political science/government, psychology, and religion). Business is the strongest academically and has the largest enrollment.

Required: In order to graduate, students must complete a total of 120 hours with a minimum GPA of 2.0. Between 10 and 15 courses are required in the student's major. All students must complete 6 hours in the interdisciplinary SAGE program. In addition, students must satisfy breadth requirements in the arts, humanities, laboratory sciences, social and behavioral sciences, and physical education.

Special: Saint Andrews offers student-designed majors for contract and thematic majors, credit for life experience, nondegree study, on-campus work-study, and pass/fail options. Students may study

abroad in 11 countries. A B.A.-B.S. degree, a 3-2 engineering degree with Georgia Institute of Technology and North Carolina State University, and an accounting program with the University of Georgia are available. There are year-long, semester-long, and winter-term internships in all majors. There is a freshman honors program on campus. Eight departments have honors programs.

Faculty/Classroom: Sixty-eight percent of faculty are male; 32%, female. The average class size in a regular course offering is 20.

Admissions: About 96% of the 1993–94 applicants were accepted. There were 3 National Merit finalists.

Requirements: The SAT I, with a minimum score of 400 on each section, or the ACT is required. Graduation from an accredited secondary school or the GED is required for admission. High school courses should include 4 credits of English, 2 each of science and a foreign language, 3 of mathematics, and 1 each of history and social studies. AP and CLEP credits are accepted. Important factors used in the admissions decision are recommendations by school officials, advanced placement or honor courses, leadership record, personality, intangible qualities, and evidence of special talent.

Procedure: Freshmen are admitted to all sessions. Entrance exams should be taken as early as possible. Application deadlines are open; the fee is $25. Notification is sent on a rolling basis. There are early admissions and deferred admissions plans.

Transfer: About 60 transfer students enrolled in an earlier year. Transfer students must have a minimum GPA of 2.0. Up to 65 semester or 97 quarter hours may be transferred from a 2-year college and 90 semester or 135 quarter hours from a 4-year college. At least 60 credits out of 120 must be completed at Saint Andrews.

Visiting: There are regularly scheduled orientations for prospective students, including open houses with activities, fairs, and information sessions. There are guides for informal visits, and visitors may sit in on classes and stay overnight at the school. To arrange for a visit, contact the Admissions Office at (800) 763-0198.

Financial Aid: In an earlier year, 90% of all freshmen and 85% of continuing students received some form of financial aid. Thirty-six percent of undergraduate students work part-time. The average financial indebtedness of an earlier graduate was $2935. Saint Andrews is a member of CSS. The FAF is preferred, but the FFS and SFS are accepted.

International Students: There are currently 42 international students enrolled. The school actively recruits these students. They must take the TOEFL and achieve a minimum score of 500.

Computers: The college provides computer facilities for student use. The mainframe is a DEC PDP 11/44. Microcomputers are also available in the computer laboratory. All students may access the system up to 100 hours per week. There are no time limits on using the system and no fees.

Graduates: In an earlier year, 158 bachelor's degrees were awarded. The most popular majors among graduates were business/economics (21%), English (14%), and biology (9%). Some 25 companies recruited on campus in 1992–93. In an earlier graduating class, 15% of all graduates were enrolled in graduate school within 6 months of graduation; 21% of the men and 19% of the women had found employment.

Admissions Contact: Admissions Office.

SAINT AUGUSTINE'S COLLEGE

Raleigh, NC 27610-2298
D-2
(919) 828-4451

Full-time: 668 men, 926 women	Faculty: 110
Part-time: 56 men, 75 women	Ph.D.s: 42%
Graduate: none	Student/Faculty: 15 to 1
Year: semesters, summer session	Tuition: $5700
Application Deadline: August 10	Room & Board: $3600
Freshman Class: 3113 applied, 1786 accepted, 457 enrolled	
SAT I Verbal/Math: 530/510	COMPETITIVE +

Saint Augustine's College, founded in 1867, is a historically black liberal arts institution affiliated with the Episcopal Church. The library contains 145,000 volumes, and subscribes to 500 periodicals. Special learning facilities include a learning resource center. The 125-acre campus is in an urban area. Including residence halls, there are 36 buildings on campus.

Student Life: About 61% of undergraduates are from North Carolina. Students come from 30 states and 20 foreign countries. About 50% of freshmen remain to graduate.

Housing: College-sponsored living facilities include single-sex dormitories and honors houses. On-campus housing is guaranteed for all 4 years.

Activities: Two percent of men belong to 6 local fraternities; two percent of women belong to 4 local sororities. There are many groups and organizations on campus, including band, chorus, dance, drama, ethnic, newspaper, radio and TV, religious, social service, student government, and yearbook.

Sports: There are 8 intramural sports for men and 5 for women. Athletic and recreation facilities include a 1700-seat gymnasium, a track, baseball fields, and tennis and basketball courts.

Services: In addition to many counseling and information services, there is remedial math, reading, and writing. Help with writing and test-taking skills is also available.

Programs of Study: The college awards the B.A. and B.S. degrees. Bachelor's degrees are awarded in BIOLOGICAL SCIENCE (biology/biological science), BUSINESS (accounting, business administration and management, and office supervision and management), COMMUNICATIONS AND THE ARTS (communications, English, fine arts, French, music, and Spanish), COMPUTER AND PHYSICAL SCIENCE (chemistry, computer science, mathematics, and physics), EDUCATION (business, early childhood, elementary, middle school, and physical), ENGINEERING AND ENVIRONMENTAL DESIGN (aeronautical engineering, agricultural engineering, chemical engineering, civil engineering, electrical/electronics engineering, industrial administration/management, industrial engineering, materials engineering, and mechanical engineering), HEALTH PROFESSIONS (medical laboratory technology, physical therapy, and premedicine), SOCIAL SCIENCE (criminal justice, economics, history, political science/government, prelaw, psychology, social studies, sociology, and urban studies).

Required: Students must complete at least 120 hours with a minimum 2.0 GPA for graduation. A 51-credit core curriculum includes courses in reading and communication, foreign language, science, mathematics, philosophy, ethics, humanities, world civilization, psychology, and physical education. Juniors must pass a written examination in English composition; seniors, written and oral examinations in their major fields.

Special: Students may cross-register at any of 5 area colleges, study abroad, or pursue a combined B.A.-B.S. degree or a 3–2 engineering program. An interdisciplinary recreation studies program, field experience programs, nondegree study, internships, work-study, cooperative programs, and credit for military service are offered. There are 13 national honor societies on campus.

Admissions: About 57% of the 1993–94 applicants were accepted. The SAT scores for the 1993–94 freshman class were as follows: Verbal—20% below 500, 50% between 500 and 599, 25% between 600 and 700, and 5% above 700; Math—15% below 500, 55% between 500 and 599, 24% between 600 and 700, and 6% above 700. Fifteen percent of the current freshmen were in the top fifth of their class; 30% were in the top two fifths.

Requirements: The college requires applicants to be in the upper 70% of their class. A minimum GPA of 2.0 is required. The SAT I or ACT is required. In addition, applicants must be graduates of an accredited secondary school with a C + average in at least 18 academic units, including 4 in English, 2 each in social studies and science, and 3 in mathematics.

Procedure: Early decision applications should be filed by April 5; regular applications, by August 10 for fall entry, December 1 for spring entry, and June 1 for summer entry, along with an application fee of $25.

Transfer: Transfers must submit high school and college transcripts and must be eligible to reenter the last institution attended. A total of 30 credits out of 120 must be completed at the college.

Financial Aid: In a recent year, 85% of all freshmen received some form of financial aid. The FAF or FFS is required; the FAF is preferred. The deadline for financial aid applications is March 15.

International Students: There were 100 international students enrolled in an earlier year. They must take the TOEFL. These students must also take the SAT I.

Computers: The college provides computer facilities for student use. The mainframe is an NCR 84–50. PCs are available for students enrolled in computer classes. There are no fees.

Admissions Contact: Wanzo Hendrix, Director of Admissions and Recruitment.

SALEM COLLEGE

Winston-Salem, NC 27108
C-2
(910) 721-2621; (800) 327-2536

Full-time: 9 men, 490 women	Faculty: 47; IIB, --$
Part-time: 25 men, 233 women	Ph.D.s: 82%
Graduate: 4 men, 76 women	Student/Faculty: 11 to 1
Year: 4-1-4, summer session	Tuition: $10,000
Application Deadline: open	Room & Board: $6025
Freshman Class: 377 applied, 260 accepted, 114 enrolled	
SAT I or ACT: required	COMPETITIVE

Salem College, founded in 1890, traces its roots back to 1772, when it was founded as a school for girls by the Moravians, an early Protestant denomination. Today the college, which retains a historical relationship with the church, offers a liberal arts education primarily for women. In addition to regional accreditation, Salem has baccalaureate program accreditation with NASM and NCATE. The 2 libraries contain 113,000 volumes, 20,430 microform items, and 7551 audio-

visual forms, and subscribe to 540 periodicals. Computerized library sources and services include the card catalog, interlibrary loans, and database searching. Special learning facilities include a learning resource center, art gallery, and radio station. The 57-acre campus is in an urban area in the center of Old Salem, a restored 18th-century village. Including residence halls, there are 17 buildings on campus.

Student Life: About 78% of undergraduates are from North Carolina. Students come from 24 states, 7 foreign countries, and Canada. Sixty-one percent are from public schools; 39% from private. Eighty-seven percent are white; 10% African American. The average age of freshmen is 18; all undergraduates, 28. Nineteen percent drop out by the end of their first year; 55% remain to graduate.

Housing: A total of 470 students can be accommodated in college housing. College-sponsored living facilities include single-sex dormitories. On-campus housing is guaranteed for all 4 years. Ninety-one percent of students live on campus; of those, 55% remain on campus on weekends. All students may keep cars on campus.

Activities: There are no fraternities or sororities on campus. There are 41 groups on campus, including chorale, chorus, dance, drama, ethnic, honors, international, literary magazine, musical theater, newspaper, political, professional, radio, religious, social, social service, student government, and yearbook. Popular campus events include Fall Fest, a Christian candlelight service, a sophomore-senior banquet, April Arts, and the On the Town series.

Sports: There are 7 intercollegiate and 7 intramural sports for women. Athletic and recreation facilities include 2 athletic fields, an archery range, a swimming pool, 2 basketball/volleyball and tennis courts, 2 dance studios, and a universal weight room.

Disabled Students: Seventy-five percent of the campus is accessible to disabled students. The following facilities are available: wheelchair ramps, elevators, special parking, specially equipped rest rooms, and special class scheduling.

Services: In addition to many counseling and information services, tutoring is available in every subject. There is also remedial reading and writing.

Campus Safety and Security: Campus safety and security measures include 24-hour foot and vehicle patrol, escort service, emergency telephones, and lighted pathways and sidewalks.

Programs of Study: Salem awards the B.A., B.S., B.M., and B.S.B.A. degrees. Master's degrees also are awarded. Bachelor's degrees are awarded in BIOLOGICAL SCIENCE (biology/biological science), BUSINESS (accounting, business administration and management, and management science), COMMUNICATIONS AND THE ARTS (art history and appreciation, arts administration/management, communications, English, French, German, music, Spanish, and studio art), COMPUTER AND PHYSICAL SCIENCE (chemistry and mathematics), ENGINEERING AND ENVIRONMENTAL DESIGN (interior design), HEALTH PROFESSIONS (medical laboratory technology and physician's assistant), SOCIAL SCIENCE (American studies, economics, history, international relations, philosophy, psychology, religion, and sociology). Sociology, communications, psychology, English, and the combined B.S.-B.A. program have the largest enrollments.

Required: To graduate, students must complete a total of 36 courses, or 144 semester hours, with a minimum GPA of 2.0. A minimum of 7 courses, or 28 semester hours, is required in the student's major. All students must take 1 year of English and 4 terms of physical education. They must also complete 1 course each in laboratory science, mathematics, fine arts, and philosophy/religion, 2 courses each in social science and history, and 3 courses in a modern foreign language, as well as 4 January-term courses.

Special: The school offers an extensive internship program in all majors and a cooperative program in medical technology with Bowman Gray School of Medicine, Forsyth Memorial Hospital, and Duke University. Cross-registration is available with Wake Forest University. Students may study abroad in London, Paris, and Guadalajara, Mexico. A Washington semester, student-designed majors, a B.A.-B.S. degree, nondegree study, and pass/fail options during the January term are available. Dual majors are offered in arts management and foreign language management. A 3-2 engineering degree is available with Duke and Vanderbilt universities. Students may participate in a model U.N. program directed by Drew University in Madison, New Jersey. There are 9 national honor societies on campus.

Faculty/Classroom: Fifty-five percent of faculty are male; 45%, female. Ninety-four percent teach undergraduates. No introductory courses are taught by graduate students. The average class size in an introductory lecture, in a laboratory, and in a regular course offering is 15.

Admissions: About 69% of the 1993-94 applicants were accepted. About 22% of the current freshmen were in the top fifth of their class; 26% were in the top two fifths. One freshman graduated first in the class.

Requirements: A minimum GPA of 2.0 is required. The SAT I or ACT is required. In addition, graduation from an accredited secondary school or the GED is needed for admission. Students must have

12 academic credits plus electives, including 4 years of high school English, 2 each of a foreign language and history, 3 of mathematics, and 1 of laboratory science. An essay is required for all students. Music students must audition. AP and CLEP credits are accepted. Important factors used in the admissions decision are advanced placement or honor courses, leadership record, evidence of special talent, recommendations by school officials, and extracurricular activities record.

Procedure: Freshmen are admitted in the fall and spring. Entrance exams should be taken by January of the senior year. Application deadlines are open. The application fee is $25. Notification is sent on a rolling basis. There are early admissions and deferred admissions plans.

Transfer: About 22 transfer students enrolled in 1993-94. Transfer students must have a minimum GPA of 2.0 in all previous college work. Applicants must also submit a statement of good standing from the dean of students of the college previously attended, 2 letters of recommendation from teachers, and a transcript and catalog from each college attended. SAT I or ACT scores may be required on an individual basis. An interview is recommended. A total of 36 credits out of 144 must be completed at Salem.

Visiting: There are regularly scheduled orientations for prospective students. There are guides for informal visits and visitors may sit in on classes and stay overnight at the school. To arrange for a visit, contact the Admissions Office at (800) 327-2536.

Financial Aid: In 1993-94, 70% of all current freshmen and 61% of continuing students received some form of financial aid. About 61% of freshmen and 60% of continuing students received need-based aid. Scholarships or need-based grants averaged $7038 ($11,930 maximum); loans averaged $2578 ($2625 maximum); and work contracts averaged $1380 ($2550 maximum). Fifty percent of undergraduate students work part-time. The average financial indebtedness of the 1992-93 graduate was $13,250. Salem is a member of CSS. The college's own financial statement and the FAFSA are required.

International Students: There are currently 15 international students enrolled. The school actively recruits these students. They must take the TOEFL and achieve a minimum score of 550.

Computers: The college provides computer facilities for student use. The mainframe is an AT&T 3B15. There are also microcomputers available in the science building, library, and main hall. All students may access the system. It may be used when school is in session. There are no time limits on using the system and no fees.

Graduates: In 1992-93, 142 bachelor's degrees were awarded. The most popular majors among graduates were communications (15%), English (10%), and psychology (8%). Within an average freshman class, 53% graduate in 4 years and 55% in 5 years. In an earlier year's graduating class, 11% of the women were enrolled in graduate school within 6 months of graduation; 89% of the women had found employment.

Admissions Contact: Katherine Knapp, Director of Admissions.

SHAW UNIVERSITY
D-2
Raleigh, NC 27601
(919) 755-4803

Full-time: 999 men, 1361 women	Faculty: IIB, --$
Part-time: 47 men, 97 women	Ph.D.s: n/av
Graduate: none	Student/Faculty: n/av
Year: semesters, summer session	Tuition: $5562
Application Deadline: July 15	Room & Board: $3374
Freshman Class: 2533 applied, 937 accepted, 620 enrolled	
SAT I or ACT: required	COMPETITIVE +

Shaw University, founded in 1865, is a private liberal arts university affiliated with the Baptist Church. There are 5 undergraduate schools. In addition to regional accreditation, Shaw has baccalaureate program accreditation with NCATE. The library contains 80,000 volumes and 15,000 microform items, and subscribes to 428 periodicals. Special learning facilities include a learning resource center and radio station. The 18-acre campus is in an urban area in downtown Raleigh, the capital of North Carolina. Including residence halls, there are 26 buildings on campus.

Student Life: About 67% of undergraduates are from North Carolina.

Housing: A total of 815 students can be accommodated in college housing. College-sponsored living facilities include single-sex dormitories. On-campus housing is available on a first-come, first-served basis. Alcohol is not permitted.

Activities: There are no fraternities or sororities on campus.

Sports: There are intercollegiate and intramural sports programs at Shaw.

Services: In addition to some counseling and information services, there is remedial math, reading, and writing.

Programs of Study: Shaw awards the B.A. and B.S. degrees. Associate degrees also are awarded. Bachelor's degrees are awarded in BIOLOGICAL SCIENCE (biology/biological science), BUSINESS

(accounting and business administration and management), COMMUNICATIONS AND THE ARTS (broadcasting, dramatic arts, English, music, and speech/debate/rhetoric), COMPUTER AND PHYSICAL SCIENCE (chemistry, computer programming, computer science, and mathematics), EDUCATION (early childhood, elementary, physical, and secondary), ENGINEERING AND ENVIRONMENTAL DESIGN (preengineering), HEALTH PROFESSIONS (predentistry, premedicine, and speech pathology/audiology), SOCIAL SCIENCE (behavioral science, criminal justice, gerontology, international relations, ministries, public administration, and religion).

Required: To graduate, students must earn 120 credits, maintain a minimum GPA of 2.0, and successfully complete competency examinations in mathematics and English. The general core curriculum includes a total of 51 credits in English, mathematics, humanities, natural sciences, social sciences, and a core seminar.

Special: Shaw offers cooperative programs with 5 other North Carolina colleges, a combined B.A.-B.S. degree in engineering in conjunction with North Carolina State University, dual majors, independent study, and an external degree program for working adults.

Admissions: About 37% of the 1993–94 applicants were accepted.

Requirements: A minimum GPA of 2.0 is required. The SAT I or ACT is required. Applicants must be graduates of an accredited secondary school or have a GED certificate. They should have completed 3 units of English, 2 each of mathematics, natural science (with 1 in a laboratory course), and social science, and 4 of academic electives. Admission to the Teacher Education Program follows separate guidelines. CLEP credit is accepted.

Procedure: Applications should be filed by July 15 for fall entry and December 10 for spring entry, along with an application fee of $25.

Transfer: Applicants must submit official transcripts from all colleges attended. Credits from unaccredited institutions are accepted only after completion of 15 credits at Shaw with at least a 2.5 GPA. A total of 30 credits out of 120 must be completed at Shaw.

Visiting: There are guides for informal visits. To arrange for a visit, contact the Admissions Office at (919) 755–4803.

Financial Aid: Shaw is a member of CSS. The FAF or FFS is required. The deadline for financial aid applications is May 15.

Admissions Contact: Alfonza Carter, Director of Admissions and Recruitment.

UNIVERSITY OF NORTH CAROLINA AT ASHEVILLE

Asheville, NC 28804–3299

B-2

(704) 251–6481
(800) 531–9842 (in-state)

Full-time: 958 men, 1075 women	Faculty: 144; IIB, av$
Part-time: 446 men, 632 women	Ph.D.s: 84%
Graduate: 29 men, 25 women	Student/Faculty: 14 to 1
Year: semesters, summer session	Tuition: $1476 ($6840)
Application Deadline: April 1	Room & Board: $3315
Freshman Class: 1757 applied, 979 accepted, 397 enrolled	
SAT I Verbal/Math: 500/540	ACT: 24 VERY COMPETITIVE

The University of North Carolina at Asheville, founded in 1927, is a publicly assisted liberal arts institution in the University of North Carolina system. There is one graduate school. In addition to regional accreditation, UNCA has baccalaureate program accreditation with NCATE. The library contains 213,919 volumes, 610,672 microform items, and 12,400 audiovisual forms, and subscribes to 2043 periodicals. Computerized library sources and services include the card catalog, interlibrary loans, and database searching. Special learning facilities include a learning resource center, art gallery, the Southern Highlands Research Center, the Environmental Quality Institute, a statewide microwave telecommunication network, and a simulation laboratory. The 265-acre campus is in a suburban area 130 miles west of Charlotte and 200 miles from Atlanta, Georgia. Including residence halls, there are 24 buildings on campus.

Student Life: About 90% of undergraduates are from North Carolina. Students come from 36 states, 32 foreign countries, and Canada. Eighty-five percent are from public schools; 15% from private. Ninety-three percent are white. The average age of freshmen is 18; all undergraduates, 26. Twenty-two percent drop out by the end of their first year; 37% remain to graduate.

Housing: A total of 850 students can be accommodated in college housing. College-sponsored living facilities include single-sex and coed dormitories and off-campus apartments. In addition there are honors houses. On-campus housing is guaranteed for the freshman year only and is available on a first-come, first-served basis. Priority is given to out-of-town students. Fifty-eight percent of students commute and all students may keep cars on campus.

Activities: About 8% of men belong to 4 national fraternities; about 6% of women belong to 1 local and 2 national sororities. There are 70 groups on campus, including art, band, cheerleading, chess, choir, chorus, computers, drama, ethnic, gay, honors, international, jazz band, literary magazine, newspaper, pep band, political, professional, religious, social, social service, and student government. Popular campus events include Homecoming, Family Day, summer concerts, the Second Sunday at 4 concert series, UNCAMONT (spring student activity), monthly 'Big Weekend,' International Student Day, art exhibits, campus theater, Cultural Arts Series, Folkmoot, Greek Weekend, annual Undergraduate Research Symposium, Health Fair, Greenfest, and World Affairs Series.

Sports: There are 8 intercollegiate sports for men and 7 for women, and 13 intramural sports for men and 11 for women. Athletic and recreation facilities include a sports, health, and physical education center, which includes a weight room, a basketball court, a track, tennis courts, a soccer field, a dance studio, and an Olympic swimming pool.

Disabled Students: Eighty-five percent of the campus is accessible to disabled students. The following facilities are available: wheelchair ramps, elevators, special parking, specially equipped rest rooms, lowered drinking fountains, and lowered telephones.

Services: In addition to many counseling and information services, tutoring is available in most subjects. A mathematics, reading, and writing resource center is available and there is also a reader service for the blind.

Campus Safety and Security: Campus safety and security measures include 24-hour foot and vehicle patrol, self defense education, escort service, and informal discussions. In addition, there are pamphlets, posters, films, and lighted pathways and sidewalks.

Programs of Study: UNCA awards the B.A., B.S., and B.F.A. degrees. Master's degrees also are awarded. Bachelor's degrees are awarded in BIOLOGICAL SCIENCE (biology/biological science), BUSINESS (accounting, business administration and management, and personnel management), COMMUNICATIONS AND THE ARTS (classics, communications, dramatic arts, English, fine arts, French, German, music, and Spanish), COMPUTER AND PHYSICAL SCIENCE (atmospheric sciences and meteorology, chemistry, computer science, mathematics, and physics), ENGINEERING AND ENVIRONMENTAL DESIGN (environmental science), SOCIAL SCIENCE (economics, history, philosophy, political science/government, psychology, and sociology). Management, psychology, environmental science, and history have the largest enrollments.

Required: Graduation requirements for all students include completion of a minimum of 120 credit hours, including 30 to 36 in the major, with a senior capstone experience consisting of undergraduate research, an examination, or a seminar. The student must complete a core curriculum of 16 semester hours of humanities, 8 of natural science, including laboratory, 6 of social science, 4 each of arts and mathematics, 3 to 6 each of English and foreign language, 2 of health and fitness, and 1 of library research.

Special: Students may participate in cooperative programs in nursing, forestry, and textile chemistry, and there is cross-registration with a number of North Carolina universities and colleges. Study-abroad programs are available in 7 countries. The school offers dual majors, student-designed majors, and a 2–2 engineering degree with North Carolina State University. There is a Washington semester. Nondegree study is available. UNCA participates in a consortium with Warren Wilson and Mars Hill Colleges. There is a freshman honors program on campus, as well as 11 national honor societies. All departments have honors programs.

Faculty/Classroom: Sixty-eight percent of faculty are male; 32%, female. All teach undergraduates. No introductory courses are taught by graduate students. The average class size in an introductory lecture is 21; in a laboratory, 19; and in a regular course offering, 21.

Admissions: About 56% of the 1993–94 applicants were accepted. The SAT scores for the 1993–94 freshman class were as follows: Verbal—48% below 500, 38% between 500 and 599, 13% between 600 and 700, and 1% above 700; Math—24% below 500, 46% between 500 and 599, 27% between 600 and 700, and 3% above 700. The ACT scores were 46% between 21 and 23, 39% between 24 and 26, and 15% between 27 and 28. About 64% of the current freshmen were in the top fifth of their class; 95% were in the top two fifths. There were 6 National Merit finalists and 25 semifinalists. Ten freshmen graduated first in their class.

Requirements: UNCA requires applicants to be in the upper 50% of their class. The SAT I or ACT is required. In addition, graduation from an accredited secondary school or the GED is required. UNCA requires 16 high school academic units, including 4 credits of English, 3 each of mathematics and science, to include 2 of biology and 1 of physical science, and 2 each of a foreign language and social studies/history. Applicants are evaluated primarily upon SAT I or ACT scores and school achievement record. AP and CLEP credits are accepted. Important factors used in the admissions decision are advanced placement or honor courses, leadership record, recommendations by school officials, extracurricular activities record, and evidence of special talent.

Procedure: Freshmen are admitted to all sessions. Entrance exams should be taken at the end of the junior year or the beginning of the senior year. Early decision applications should be filed by October

15; regular applications, by April 1 for fall entry and December 1 for spring entry, along with an application fee of $25. Notification is sent on a rolling basis. There are early decision, early admissions, and deferred admissions plans.

Transfer: About 301 transfer students enrolled in 1993–94. A total of 30 credits out of 120 must be completed at UNCA.

Visiting: There are regularly scheduled orientations for prospective students, including meetings with faculty and with student organizations, as well as an information session for students and families and a campus tour. There are guides for informal visits and visitors may sit in on classes. To arrange for a visit, contact the Admissions Office at (704) 251–6481 or (800) 531–9842 (in-state).

Financial Aid: In 1993–94 59% of all current freshmen and 32% of continuing students received some form of financial aid. About 22% of freshmen and 20% of continuing students received need-based aid. The average freshman award was $2341. Of that total, scholarships or need-based grants averaged $1838 ($7300 maximum); loans averaged $2671 ($7590 maximum); and work contracts averaged $1000 (5000 maximum). Fifteen percent of undergraduate students work part-time. Average earnings from campus work for the school year are $1000. UNCA is a member of CSS. The FAFSA financial statement is required. The deadline for financial aid applications is March 1.

International Students: There are currently 28 international students enrolled. They must take the TOEFL and achieve a minimum score of 600. The student must also take the SAT I or the ACT.

Computers: The college provides computer facilities for student use. The mainframe is a DEC VAX 4000 and a DEC VAX 6000. Students may access the mainframe from 16 text-based terminals, from 7 dial-in modems, or from over 40 networked personal computers. The terminals and computers with mainframe access are contained in 5 of the 7 computer laboratories on campus. They contain a total of over 100 PCs and Apple Macintoshes, and offer a wide variety of personal productivity software and course-specific software for both platforms. All students may access the system. It may be used 24 hours per day. There are no time limits and no fees.

Graduates: In 1992–93 435 bachelor's degrees were awarded. The most popular majors among graduates were management (24%), psychology (11%), and sociology (7%). Within an average freshman class, 16% graduate in 4 years, 34% in 5 years, and 34% in 6 years. Some 10 companies recruited on campus in 1992–93.

Admissions Contact: John W. White, Director of Admissions.

UNIVERSITY OF NORTH CAROLINA AT CHAPEL HILL
D-2

Chapel Hill, NC 27599–2200   (919) 966–3621

Full-time: 5756 men, 8853 women	Faculty: 2249; I, av$
Part-time: 470 men, 630 women	Ph.D.s: 94%
Graduate: 4068 men, 4537 women	Student/Faculty: 6 to 1
Year: semesters, summer session	Tuition: $1454 ($8496)
Application Deadline: January 15	Room & Board: $3876
Freshman Class: 15,041 applied, 5977 accepted, 3331 enrolled	
SAT I Verbal/Math: 527/594	**HIGHLY COMPETITIVE**

The University of North Carolina at Chapel Hill, founded in 1789, offers undergraduate programs in arts and sciences, social sciences, business, health professions, and teacher certification. There are 13 undergraduate and 12 graduate schools. The 4 libraries contain 3,956,338 volumes and 3,463,005 microform items, and subscribe to 39,044 periodicals. Special learning facilities include an art gallery, planetarium, radio station, and TV station. The 1200-acre campus is in a small town 30 miles west of Raleigh. Including residence halls, there are 127 buildings on campus.

Student Life: About 82% of undergraduates are from North Carolina. Eighty-six percent are from public schools; 14% from private. Eighty-two percent are white. The average age of freshmen is 18; all undergraduates, 19.9. Ten percent drop out by the end of their first year; 76% remain to graduate.

Housing: A total of 7078 students can be accommodated in college housing. College-sponsored living facilities include single-sex and coed dormitories, married-student housing, fraternity houses, and sorority houses. On-campus housing is guaranteed for the freshman and sophomore years only and is available on a lottery system for upperclassmen. Fifty-six percent of students commute. Alcohol is not permitted. Upperclassmen may keep cars on campus.

Activities: About 20% of men belong to 30 national fraternities; about 20% of women belong to 15 national sororities. There are many groups and organizations on campus, including art, band, cheerleading, chess, choir, chorus, dance, drama, ethnic, gay, honors, international, jazz band, literary magazine, marching band, musical theater, newspaper, orchestra, pep band, photography, political, professional, radio and TV, religious, social, social service, student government, and yearbook. Popular campus events include University Day, HRC Springfest, Homecoming, and Black Greek Council Step-show.

Sports: There are 13 intercollegiate sports for men and 13 for women, and 18 intramural sports for men and 15 for women. Athletic and recreation facilities include a 50,000-seat stadium, 3 swimming pools, a 21,000-seat sports arena, tennis courts, gym facilities, and softball fields.

Disabled Students: The following facilities are available: wheelchair ramps, elevators, special parking, specially equipped rest rooms, special class scheduling, lowered drinking fountains, lowered telephones, and a dormitory specially modified for the handicapped.

Services: In addition to many counseling and information services, tutoring is available in every subject. There is also a reader service for the blind and remedial math.

Campus Safety and Security: Campus safety and security measures include 24-hour foot and vehicle patrol, self defense education, escort service, and shuttle buses. In addition, there are informal discussions, pamphlets, posters, films, emergency telephones, and lighted pathways and sidewalks.

Programs of Study: UNC at Chapel Hill awards the B.A., B.S., B.A.Ed., B.F.A., B.M., B.Med., B.S.B.A., B.S.N., and B.S.S.T. degrees. Master's and doctoral degrees also are awarded. Bachelor's degrees are awarded in BIOLOGICAL SCIENCE (biology/biological science and botany), BUSINESS (business administration and management and recreation and leisure services), COMMUNICATIONS AND THE ARTS (art history and appreciation, broadcasting, classical languages, classics, comparative literature, dramatic arts, English, French, German, Greek, Italian, journalism, Latin, linguistics, music, Portuguese, Russian, Slavic languages, Spanish, speech/debate/rhetoric, and studio art), COMPUTER AND PHYSICAL SCIENCE (astronomy, chemistry, geology, mathematics, physics, science, and statistics), EDUCATION (art, early childhood, education, elementary, foreign languages, middle school, music, science, and secondary), ENGINEERING AND ENVIRONMENTAL DESIGN (industrial administration/management), HEALTH PROFESSIONS (dental hygiene, medical laboratory technology, nursing, pharmacy, physical therapy, public health, and radiological science), SOCIAL SCIENCE (African American studies, African studies, American studies, anthropology, criminal justice, East Asian studies, economics, geography, history, international studies, Latin American studies, liberal arts/general studies, peace studies, philosophy, political science/government, psychology, public affairs, religion, Russian and Slavic studies, sociology, and women's studies).

Required: To graduate, students must complete 120 credits with a 2.0 GPA. All students must take liberal arts courses in their first two years, including English, social sciences, history, philosophy, fine arts, foreign language, mathematics, and physical education.

Special: Students may participate in joint programs with Duke University and North Carolina State University. Internships, study abroad, work-study programs, B.A.-B.S. degrees, and student-designed majors are available. The university offers a 2–2 engineering operations program with North Carolina State. There are pass/fail options and nondegree study. There is a freshman honors program on campus. All departments have honors programs.

Faculty/Classroom: Seventy-three percent of faculty are male; 27%, female.

Admissions: About 40% of the 1993–94 applicants were accepted. About 92% of the current freshmen were in the top fifth of their class; 99% were in the top two fifths.

Requirements: The SAT I or ACT is required. In addition, applicants must be graduates of an accredited secondary school. They should complete 16 high school academic credits, including 4 in English, 3 each in mathematics (2 in algebra and 1 in geometry) and science (including at least 1 in a physical science and 1 laboratory course), and 2 each in a single foreign language, history, and social studies. An essay, portfolio, and audition are recommended. AP and CLEP credits are accepted. Important factors used in the admissions decision are advanced placement or honor courses, extracurricular activities record, leadership record, evidence of special talent, and parents or siblings attending the school.

Procedure: Freshmen are admitted in the fall. Entrance exams should be taken in the junior and senior years. Applications should be filed by January 15 for fall entry, along with an application fee of $45. Notification is sent on a rolling basis. There is an early admissions plan. A waiting list is an active part of the admissions procedure, with about 5% of applicants on the list.

Transfer: About 685 transfer students enrolled in a recent year. Transfers are admitted for the junior year only. Applicants for transfer should have a minimum GPA of 2.0 before seeking admission. At least 30 semester hours in the major, out of 120 must be completed at UNC at Chapel Hill.

Visiting: There are regularly scheduled orientations for prospective students, including campus tours and information sessions, offered twice each day. There are guides for informal visits and visitors may

sit in on classes. To arrange for a visit, contact the Office of Undergraduate Admissions at (919) 966-3621.

Financial Aid: In 1993-94 35% of all current freshmen and 33% of continuing students received some form of financial aid. About 30% of all students received need-based aid. UNC at Chapel Hill is a member of CSS. The FAF and FAFSA are required. The deadline for financial aid applications is March 1.

International Students: There are currently 825 international students enrolled. They must take the TOEFL and achieve a minimum score of 600. The student must also take the SAT I or the ACT.

Computers: The university provides computer facilities for student use. The mainframes are 3 IBM mainframe computers, and a CONVEX Supercomputer. Microcomputers are available for student use. All students may access the system. It may be used 24 hours a day. There are no time limits and no fees.

Graduates: Within an average freshman class, 59% graduate in 4 years, 76% in 5 years, and 78% in 6 years. In the 1992 graduating class, 19% of all graduates were enrolled in graduate school within 6 months of graduation; 71% had found employment.

Admissions Contact: Undergraduate Admissions.

UNIVERSITY OF NORTH CAROLINA AT CHARLOTTE

C-3

Charlotte, NC 28223

(704) 547-2213

Full-time: 5100 men, 4999 women	Faculty: 608; IIA, -$
Part-time: 1559 men, 1558 women	Ph.D.s: 79%
Graduate: 1020 men, 1409 women	Student/Faculty: 17 to 1
Year: semesters	Tuition: $1385 ($7451)
Application Deadline: July 1	Room & Board: $3212
Freshman Class: 5803 applied, 4441 accepted, 1730 enrolled	
SAT I Verbal/Math: 435/491	**COMPETITIVE**

The University of North Carolina at Charlotte, founded in 1946, is a publicly funded institution in the University of North Carolina System. There are 6 undergraduate schools and one graduate school. In addition to regional accreditation, UNCC has baccalaureate program accreditation with AACSB, ABET, NAAB, NCATE, and NLN. The library contains 557,729 volumes, 385,135 microform items, and 8808 audiovisual forms, and subscribes to 5032 periodicals. Computerized library sources and services include the card catalog, interlibrary loans, and database searching. Special learning facilities include a learning resource center, art gallery, radio station, TV station, on-line teleconferencing facility, high-tech research center in engineering, and botanical garden and greenhouse complex that includes a tropical rain forest. The 1000-acre campus is in an urban area 8 miles northeast of the center of Charlotte. Including residence halls, there are 75 buildings on campus.

Student Life: About 88% of undergraduates are from North Carolina. Students come from 45 states, 70 foreign countries, and Canada. Seventy-nine percent are white; 13% African American. Forty-four percent are Protestant; 42% claim no religious affiliation. The average age of freshmen is 18.2; all undergraduates, 23.3. Sixteen percent drop out by the end of their first year; 46% remain to graduate.

Housing: A total of 3826 students can be accommodated in college housing. College-sponsored living facilities include coed dormitories and on-campus apartments. In addition, there are honors houses, special interest houses, and international and sorority floors. On-campus housing is available on a first-come, first-served basis. Seventy-six percent of students commute. All students may keep cars on campus.

Activities: About 11% of men belong to 12 national fraternities; about 9% of women belong to 8 national sororities. There are 135 groups on campus, including art, cheerleading, choir, chorale, chorus, computers, dance, drama, ethnic, gay, honors, international, jazz band, literary magazine, newspaper, opera, pep band, photography, political, professional, radio and TV, religious, social, social service, student government, and yearbook. Popular campus events include Greek Week, Miss 49er Pageant, International Festival, University City Fest, and Homecoming.

Sports: There are 8 intercollegiate sports for men and 7 for women, and 18 intramural sports for men and 18 for women. Athletic and recreation facilities include an Olympic-size pool; basketball, tennis, and racquetball courts; fitness trail; track; weight room; and training room.

Disabled Students: Ninety percent of the campus is accessible to disabled students. The following facilities are available: wheelchair ramps, elevators, special parking, specially equipped rest rooms, special class scheduling, lowered drinking fountains, and lowered telephones. The Disability Services Office assists students with all academic and physical accommodations.

Services: In addition to many counseling and information services, tutoring is available in some subjects, including mathematics, science, foreign language, and introductory courses. In addition, there is a reader service for the blind.

Campus Safety and Security: Campus safety and security measures include 24-hour foot and vehicle patrol, self defense education, escort service, and informal discussions. In addition, there are pamphlets, posters, and films, emergency telephones, and lighted pathways and sidewalks.

Programs of Study: UNCC awards the B.A., B.S., B.Arch., B.C.A., B.S.B.A., B.S.C.E., B.S.E.E., B.S.E.T., B.S.M.E., B.S.N., and B.S.W. degrees. Master's and doctoral degrees also are awarded. Bachelor's degrees are awarded in BIOLOGICAL SCIENCE (biology/biological science), BUSINESS (accounting, banking and finance, business administration and management, international business management, management information systems, and marketing/retailing/merchandising), COMMUNICATIONS AND THE ARTS (dance, dramatic arts, English, fine arts, French, German, music, and Spanish), COMPUTER AND PHYSICAL SCIENCE (chemistry, computer science, earth science, mathematics, and physics), EDUCATION (elementary, middle school, and special), ENGINEERING AND ENVIRONMENTAL DESIGN (architecture, civil engineering, electrical/electronics engineering, engineering technology, industrial administration/management, and mechanical engineering), HEALTH PROFESSIONS (nursing), SOCIAL SCIENCE (African American studies, anthropology, child care/child and family studies, criminal justice, economics, geography, history, human services, philosophy, political science/government, psychology, religion, social work, and sociology). Architecture, business administration, geography and earth science, history, mathematics, psychology, nursing, and engineering are the strongest programs academically. Business administration, psychology, accounting, biology, elementary education, and English have the largest enrollments.

Required: In order to graduate, students must complete a minimum of 120 credit hours with an overall minimum GPA of 2.0. Between 30 and 42 hours are required in the major, with a minimum GPA of 2.0 in major and minor courses. All students must complete core requirements in the 6 interrelated areas of communication, problem solving, values, science and technology, arts, literature, and ideas, and the individual, society, and culture.

Special: Cross-registration is available through the Charlotte Area Education Consortium. Also available are cooperative programs in numerous majors, and internships of 1 semester arranged with public and private community organizations. Study abroad, B.A.-B.S. degrees, dual majors, and nondegree study are available. Pass/fail options are limited to 1 course per academic year. There is a freshman honors program on campus, as well as 17 national honor societies. Nine departments have honors programs.

Faculty/Classroom: Sixty-eight percent of faculty are male; 32%, female. Ninety-four percent teach undergraduates, 30% do research, and 30% do both. No introductory courses are taught by graduate students. The average class size in a laboratory is 20 and in a regular course offering, 32.

Admissions: About 77% of the 1993-94 applicants were accepted. The SAT scores for the 1993-94 freshman class were as follows: Verbal—79% below 500, 18% between 500 and 599, 2% between 600 and 700, and 1% above 700; Math—51% below 500, 38% between 500 and 599, 10% between 600 and 700, and 1% above 700. About 47% of the current freshmen were in the top fifth of their class; 90% were in the top two fifths. About 15 freshmen graduated first in their class.

Requirements: UNCC requires applicants to be in the upper 50% of their class. A minimum GPA of 2.0 is required. The SAT I or ACT is required. In addition, graduation from an accredited secondary school or the GED is required. The school requires 14 academic credits including 4 years of English, 2 of a foreign language, 3 each of mathematics and of science (including 1 physical science and 1 biological science), and 2 of social studies, including 1 of U.S. history. Priority is given to students whose senior-year courses include a foreign language, mathematics, world history, and health education. A portfolio and interview are required for architecture students only. Class rank is weighted twice as important as test scores. AP and CLEP credits are accepted. Important factors used in the admissions decision are advanced placement or honor courses, evidence of special talent, recommendations by school officials, leadership record, and extracurricular activities record.

Procedure: Freshmen are admitted to all sessions. Entrance exams should be taken at the end of the junior year or by December of the senior year. Applications should be filed by July 1 for fall entry, November 15 for spring entry, and May 1 for summer entry, along with an application fee of $25. Notification is sent December 15, February 1, and March 15. There are early admissions and deferred admissions plans. A waiting list is an active part of the admissions procedure, with about 8% of applicants on the list.

Transfer: About 1645 transfer students enrolled in 1993-94. Transfer students must have a minimum GPA of 2.0 on all college courses attempted. Certain majors have limited space and require a higher GPA and/or prerequisites. Applicants with fewer than 24 hours of transferable credit must meet both transfer and freshman admissions

requirements. An interview is required only for architecture students. A total of 30 credits out of 120 must be completed at UNCC.

Visiting: There are regularly scheduled orientations for prospective students, including scheduled tours. There are guides for informal visits and visitors may sit in on classes and stay overnight at the school. To arrange for a visit, contact the Admissions Office at (704) 547-2213.

Financial Aid: In 1993–94 45% of all current freshmen and 42% of continuing students received some form of financial aid. About 40% of freshmen and 39% of continuing students received need-based aid. The average freshman award was $3150. Of that total, scholarships or need-based grants averaged $1100 ($3500 maximum); loans averaged $1300 ($2625 maximum); and work contracts averaged $750 ($1600 maximum). Seventeen percent of undergraduate students work part-time. Average earnings from campus work for the school year are $1500. The average financial indebtedness of the 1992–93 graduate was $8300. UNCC is a member of CSS. The FAFSA is required. The deadline for financial aid applications is April 1.

International Students: There are currently 276 international students enrolled. They must take the TOEFL or the University of Michigan Language Test and achieve a minimum score on the TOEFL of 500.

Computers: The college provides computer facilities for student use. The mainframes include an IBM 4381 and a DEC VAX 8530 and 6210. Approximately 650 microcomputers are located at various laboratories on campus. Students can access Internet and Bitnet. Students needing a computer to complete a class assignment may access the system. It may be used 24 hours per day. There are no time limits on using the system and no fees.

Graduates: In 1992–93 2326 bachelor's degrees were awarded. The most popular majors among graduates were business administration (19%), education (10%), and engineering (8%). Within an average freshman class, 1% graduate in 3 years, 25% in 4 years, 46% in 5 years, and 49% in 6 years. Some 145 companies recruited on campus in 1992–93.

Admissions Contact: Kathi M. Baucom, Director of Admissions.

UNIVERSITY OF NORTH CAROLINA AT GREENSBORO

D-2

Greensboro, NC 27412

(910) 334-5243

Full-time: 2683 men, 4849 women	Faculty: 613; I, --$
Part-time: 735 men, 1112 women	Ph.D.s: 72%
Graduate: 899 men, 1836 women	Student/Faculty: 12 to 1
Year: semesters, summer session	Tuition: $1717 ($8759)
Application Deadline: August 1	Room & Board: $3475
Freshman Class: 5191 applied, 4134 accepted, 1525 enrolled	
SAT I Verbal/Math: 450/490	COMPETITIVE

The University of North Carolina at Greensboro, founded in 1891, is a publicly funded liberal arts institution in the University of North Carolina System. There are 7 undergraduate and 7 graduate schools. In addition to regional accreditation, UNCG has baccalaureate program accreditation with AACSB, ADA, AHEA, CSWE, FIDER, NASM, NCATE, and NLN. The 2 libraries contain 850,098 volumes, 874,988 microform items, and 13,352 audiovisual forms, and subscribe to 5525 periodicals. Computerized library sources and services include the card catalog, interlibrary loans, and database searching. Special learning facilities include a learning resource center, art gallery, planetarium, radio station, and TV station. The 178-acre campus is in an urban area in Greensboro. Including residence halls, there are 74 buildings on campus.

Student Life: About 87% of undergraduates are from North Carolina. Students come from 43 states, 53 foreign countries, and Canada. Ninety-five percent are from public schools; 5% from private. Eighty-four percent are white; 11% African American. The average age of freshmen is 18; all undergraduates, 23. Twenty-two percent drop out by the end of their first year; 51% remain to graduate.

Housing: A total of 3688 students can be accommodated in college housing. College-sponsored living facilities include single-sex and coed dormitories and on-campus apartments. In addition, there are special interest houses, an international house, and the Residential College program. On-campus housing is available on a first-come, first-served basis. Priority is given to out-of-town students. Fifty-nine percent of students commute and upperclassmen may keep cars on campus.

Activities: About 15% of men belong to 8 national fraternities; about 15% of women belong to 8 national sororities. There are 143 groups on campus, including art, band, choir, chorale, chorus, dance, drama, ethnic, film, gay, honors, international, jazz band, literary magazine, musical theater, newspaper, opera, orchestra, pep band, photography, political, professional, radio and TV, religious, social, social service, student government, symphony, and yearbook. Popular campus events include Spring Fling, Fall Kickoff, Homecoming, and Founders Day.

Sports: There are 6 intercollegiate sports for men and 6 for women, and 12 intramural sports for men and 12 for women. Athletic and recreation facilities include a physical activities complex and the 44-acre Piney Lake Field Campus, which includes 2 lakes for swimming, boating, and fishing.

Disabled Students: Eighty percent of the campus is accessible to disabled students. The following facilities are available: wheelchair ramps, elevators, special parking, specially equipped rest rooms, special class scheduling, and lowered drinking fountains.

Services: In addition to many counseling and information services, tutoring is available in every subject. There is a reader service for the blind and remedial math.

Campus Safety and Security: Campus safety and security measures include 24-hour foot and vehicle patrol, self defense education, escort service, and shuttle buses. In addition, there are informal discussions, pamphlets, posters, films, emergency telephones, and lighted pathways and sidewalks.

Programs of Study: UNCG awards the B.A., B.S., B.F.A., B.M., B.S.H.E., and B.S.N. degrees. Master's and doctoral degrees also are awarded. Bachelor's degrees are awarded in BIOLOGICAL SCIENCE (biology/biological science), BUSINESS (accounting, banking and finance, business administration and management, business economics, hotel/motel and restaurant management, marketing/retailing/merchandising, and personnel management), COMMUNICATIONS AND THE ARTS (broadcasting, communications, dance, design, dramatic arts, English, film arts, fine arts, French, German, Greek, Latin, music, Spanish, and speech/debate/rhetoric), COMPUTER AND PHYSICAL SCIENCE (chemistry, earth science, information sciences and systems, mathematics, physics, and statistics), EDUCATION (art, business, early childhood, elementary, foreign languages, health, home economics, middle school, music, and science), HEALTH PROFESSIONS (medical laboratory technology, nursing, predentistry, premedicine, public health, and speech pathology/audiology), SOCIAL SCIENCE (anthropology, child care/child and family studies, dietetics, economics, geography, history, parks and recreation management, philosophy, political science/government, prelaw, psychology, public administration, religion, social science, social work, and sociology). Psychology, business, teacher education, and fine and performing arts are the strongest programs academically and have the largest enrollments.

Required: In order to graduate, students must complete a minimum of 122 credit hours with a GPA of at least 2.0. Major requirements vary. The liberal education curriculum for all students requires 45 credit hours chosen from specified courses in the humanities, mathematics and physical sciences, social and behavioral sciences, and a foreign language.

Special: Cooperative programs, internships, accelerated degree programs, and a B.A.-B.S. degree can be arranged in all majors. Cross-registration is offered with the Greater Greensboro Consortium. Students may study abroad in more than 30 countries, including Spain, where UNCG sponsors a semester of study in Madrid. A Washington semester and student-designed majors are also available. The Residential College, a 2-year program for freshmen and sophomores, offers an interdisciplinary curriculum, with faculty and students living in the same residence. Students in this program participate in independent study, community work, and workshops. There is a freshman honors program on campus, as well as 20 national honor societies, including Phi Beta Kappa. Sixteen departments have honors programs.

Faculty/Classroom: Fifty-eight percent of faculty are male; 42%, female.

Admissions: About 80% of the 1993–94 applicants were accepted. The SAT scores for the 1993–94 freshman class were as follows: Verbal—72% below 500, 21% between 500 and 599, 6% between 600 and 700, and 1% above 700; Math—51% below 500, 38% between 500 and 599, 9% between 600 and 700, and 2% above 700. About 35% of the current freshmen were in the top fifth of their class; 66% were in the top two fifths.

Requirements: The SAT I is required. Graduation from an accredited secondary school or the GED is required. High school courses must include 4 credits of English, 2 of a foreign language, 1 of U.S. history, 3 each of mathematics and science, and 1 of social studies. An interview is recommended, and a portfolio or audition is required of art and music students. AP and CLEP credits are accepted. Important factors used in the admissions decision are advanced placement or honor courses, leadership record, evidence of special talent, personality, intangible qualities, and recommendations by alumni.

Procedure: Freshmen are admitted in the fall and spring. Entrance exams should be taken in June of the junior year or in the fall of the senior year. Applications should be filed by August 1 for fall entry and December 1 for spring entry, along with an application fee of $35. Notification is sent on a rolling basis. There are early decision and early admissions plans. A waiting list is an active part of the admissions procedure.

Transfer: About 959 transfer students enrolled in 1993–94. Transfer students must have a minimum GPA of 2.0. Students having fewer than 24 semester hours must meet the freshman entrance requirements, including satisfactory scores on the SAT I. A total of 30 credits out of 122 must be completed at UNCG.

Visiting: There are regularly scheduled orientations for prospective students. There are guides for informal visits and visitors may sit in on classes and stay overnight at the school. To arrange for a visit, contact the Office of Undergraduate Admissions at (910) 334–5243.

Financial Aid: In 1993–94 41% of all current freshmen and 24% of continuing students received some form of financial aid. The average freshman award was $3500. Nineteen percent of undergraduate students work part-time. Average earnings from campus work for the school year are $1058. UNCG is a member of CSS. The FAF is required. The deadline for financial aid applications is March 1.

International Students: International students must take the TOEFL and achieve a minimum score of 550. The student must also take the SAT I.

Computers: The college provides computer facilities for student use. The mainframes are a DEC VAX 8700 and a DEC VAX 11/780. Microcomputers and terminals to the mainframe are in laboratories in most classroom buildings and in the student center. All students may access the system. It may be used until late night hours in laboratories and 24 hours a day via personal modem. There are no time limits on using the system and no fees.

Graduates: In 1992–93 1679 bachelor's degrees were awarded. The most popular majors among graduates were business management (11%), teacher education (9%), and speech debate (8%). Within an average freshman class, 1% graduate in 3 years, 31% in 4 years, 46% in 5 years, and 52% in 6 years. Some 77 companies recruited on campus in 1992–93.

Admissions Contact: Director of Undergraduate Admissions.

UNIVERSITY OF NORTH CAROLINA AT WILMINGTON

Wilmington, NC 28403–3297   E-4

    (919) 395–3243

Full-time: 2750 men, 3885 women	Faculty: 321; IIA, -$
Part-time: 468 men, 677 women	Ph.D.s: 68%
Graduate: 161 men, 216 women	Student/Faculty: 21 to 1
Year: semesters, summer session	Tuition: $1492 ($7558)
Application Deadline: February 15	Room & Board: $3680

Freshman Class: 6071 applied, 3856 accepted, 1449 enrolled
SAT I Verbal/Math: 441/494   ACT: 22   **COMPETITIVE**

The University of North Carolina at Wilmington, founded in 1947, is a publicly funded institution offering programs in the liberal arts and sciences, education, and business. It is a part of the University of North Carolina System. There are 4 undergraduate schools and one graduate school. In addition to regional accreditation, UNC at Wilmington has baccalaureate program accreditation with NCATE and NLN. The library contains 376,273 volumes, 622,383 microform items, and 7523 audiovisual forms, and subscribes to 4981 periodicals. Special learning facilities include a radio station and the Herbert Bluethenthal Memorial Wildflower Preserve, the Museum of World Cultures, and the research vessel Seahawk, used for a marine biology laboratory and for research. The 650-acre campus is in a suburban area 125 miles southeast of Raleigh. Including residence halls, there are 55 buildings on campus.

Student Life: About 87% of undergraduates are from North Carolina. Students come from 40 states, 29 foreign countries, and Canada. Ninety-one percent are white. The average age of freshmen is 19; all undergraduates, 22. Twenty-one percent drop out by the end of their first year; 40% remain to graduate.

Housing: A total of 1933 students can be accommodated in college housing. College-sponsored living facilities include single-sex and coed dormitories and on-campus apartments. On-campus housing is available on a first-come, first-served basis. Seventy-six percent of students commute. All students may keep cars on campus.

Activities: About 14% of men belong to 13 national fraternities; about 9% of women belong to 11 national sororities. There are 95 groups on campus, including art, cheerleading, chorale, computers, dance, drama, ethnic, film, honors, international, jazz band, literary magazine, musical theater, newspaper, pep band, political, radio and TV, religious, social, social service, student government, and symphony. Popular campus events include Business Week, Homecoming, Greek Week, Spring Week, LivWell, Club Fair, and Special Olympics.

Sports: There are 8 intercollegiate sports for men and 8 for women, and 11 intramural sports for men and 11 for women. Athletic and recreation facilities include a 6000-seat coliseum, an Olympic-size swimming pool and separate diving tank, a track and field complex, and basketball, tennis, and racquetball courts.

Disabled Students: Ninety-five percent of the campus is accessible to disabled students. The following facilities are available: wheelchair ramps, elevators, special parking, specially equipped rest rooms, special class scheduling, and lowered drinking fountains.

Services: There is a reader service for the blind, and remedial math, reading, and writing.

Campus Safety and Security: Campus safety and security measures include 24-hour foot and vehicle patrol, self-defense education, escort service, and informal discussions. In addition, there are pamphlets, posters, films, emergency telephones, and lighted pathways and sidewalks.

Programs of Study: UNC at Wilmington awards the B.A., B.S., and B.S.W. degrees. Master's degrees also are awarded. Bachelor's degrees are awarded in BIOLOGICAL SCIENCE (biology/biological science and marine biology), BUSINESS (accounting, business administration and management, business economics, and marketing/retailing/merchandising), COMMUNICATIONS AND THE ARTS (English, fine arts, French, Spanish, and speech/debate/rhetoric), COMPUTER AND PHYSICAL SCIENCE (chemistry, computer science, geology, mathematics, and physics), EDUCATION (elementary, middle school, music, physical, secondary, and special), ENGINEERING AND ENVIRONMENTAL DESIGN (environmental science), HEALTH PROFESSIONS (medical laboratory technology and nursing), SOCIAL SCIENCE (anthropology, criminal justice, geography, history, parks and recreation management, political science/government, psychology, religion, social science, social work, and sociology). Business, education, social sciences, and marine biology are the strongest academically. Psychology has the largest enrollment.

Required: In order to graduate, students must complete a total of 124 semester hours, with 45 semester hours distributed as follows: 6 hours of English composition, 2 hours of physical education, 9 to 15 hours of humanities, 3 to 6 hours of creative arts, 10 to 15 hours of natural and mathematical science, and 3 to 9 hours of behavioral science.

Special: UNC at Wilmington offers short-term internships and work study programs. Dual majors may be pursued if requirements are met, and credit is given for military experience. There is a freshman honors program on campus, as well as 4 national honor societies. Thirty departments have honors programs.

Faculty/Classroom: Sixty-two percent of faculty are male; 38%, female. Ninety-three percent teach undergraduates and 3% do research. The average class size in an introductory lecture is 31; in a laboratory, 26; and in a regular course offering, 24.

Admissions: About 64% of the 1993–94 applicants were accepted. The SAT scores for the 1993–94 freshman class were as follows: Verbal—78% below 500, 18% between 500 and 599, 3% between 600 and 700, and 1% above 700; Math—49% below 500, 41% between 500 and 599, 9% between 600 and 700, and 1% above 700. The ACT scores were 26% below 21, 48% between 21 and 23, and 26% between 24 and 26. About 41% of the current freshmen were in the top fifth of their class; 83% were in the top two fifths.

Requirements: A minimum GPA of 2.0 is required. The SAT I or ACT is required. The SAT I is preferred. The required minimum composite scores are 800 for the SAT I and 18 for the ACT. Graduation from an accredited secondary school or the GED is required for admission. High school courses must include 4 years of English, 3 years of mathematics, 1 year each of biology, physical science, and a laboratory course, 2 years of social studies including 1 year of U.S. history, and 2 years of a foreign language. Students meeting all requirements except that for foreign language will be accepted with a deficiency and will be required to complete a foreign language sequence before receiving a degree. An essay is not required. AP and CLEP credits are accepted.

Procedure: Freshmen are admitted to all sessions. Entrance exams should be taken during the junior or senior year. Applications should be filed by February 15 for fall entry, December 1 for spring entry, and May 1 for summer entry, along with an application fee of $25. Notification is sent on a rolling basis. A waiting list is an active part of the admissions procedure.

Transfer: About 843 transfer students enrolled in 1993–94. Transfer students must have a minimum GPA of 2.0 and be eligible to return to the institution last attended. Applicants with fewer than 24 semester hours or 36 quarter hours of transferable credit must also meet the freshman entrance requirements. Prior to admission, transfer applicants must have successfully completed 1 year of freshman-level English and 1 unit of college-level mathematics. One unit of life sciences is also recommended. A total of 30 credits out of 124 must be completed at UNC at Wilmington.

Visiting: There are regularly scheduled orientations for prospective students. There are guides for informal visits. To arrange for a visit, contact the Admissions Office at (919) 395–3243.

Financial Aid: In 1993–94 40% of all current freshmen and 48% of continuing students received some form of financial aid. About 37% of freshmen and 33% of continuing students received need-based aid. The average freshman award was $4342. Of that total, scholar-

ships or need-based grants averaged $2046 ($4700 maximum); loans averaged $2668; and work contracts averaged $1300. Eighty-one percent of undergraduate students work part-time. Average earnings from campus work for the school year are $1300. The average financial indebtedness of the 1992–93 graduate was $10,000. UNC at Wilmington is a member of CSS. The FAF is required. The deadline for financial aid applications is March 15.

International Students: There are currently 40 international students enrolled. They must take the TOEFL and achieve a minimum score of 550.

Computers: The college provides computer facilities for student use. The mainframes are a DEC VAX 11/785 and a DEC VAX 6000/420. Microcomputers are available in academic and administrative departments. All students may access the system. It may be used from 8 A.M. to 11 P.M. at on-campus clusters, and 24-hours daily via modems. There are no time limits on using the system and no fees.

Graduates: In 1992–93, 1400 bachelor's degrees were awarded. The most popular majors among graduates were marketing (11%), elementary education (9%), and psychology (7%). Within an average freshman class, 20% graduate in 4 years, 38% in 5 years, and 41% in 6 years. Some 78 companies recruited on campus in 1992–93.

Admissions Contact: Director of Undergraduate Admissions.

WAKE FOREST UNIVERSITY
Winston-Salem, NC 27109

C-2
(919) 759-5201

Full-time: 1804 men, 1754 women	**Faculty:** 272; IIA, +$
Part-time: 83 men, 52 women	**Ph.D.s:** 85%
Graduate: 1139 men, 744 women	**Student/Faculty:** 13 to 1
Year: semesters, summer session	**Tuition:** $13,000
Application Deadline: January 15	**Room & Board:** $4280

Freshman Class: 5664 applied, 2392 accepted, 903 enrolled
SAT I: required

MOST COMPETITIVE

Wake Forest University, established in 1834, is a private institution offering undergraduate programs in the liberal arts and sciences, business, education, and preprofessional fields. The school maintains a fraternal relationship with the North Carolina Baptist Convention. There are 2 undergraduate and 4 graduate schools. In addition to regional accreditation, Wake Forest has baccalaureate program accreditation with AACSB. The 4 libraries contain 1,337,142 volumes, 1,231,634 microform items, and 4794 audiovisual forms, and subscribe to 18,678 periodicals. Computerized library sources and services include the card catalog, interlibrary loans, and database searching. Special learning facilities include a learning resource center, art gallery, radio station, fine arts center, anthropology museum, primate research station, computer center, and laser research facility. The 490-acre campus is in a suburban area 4 miles northwest of Winston-Salem. Including residence halls, there are 44 buildings on campus.

Student Life: About 67% of undergraduates are from out-of-state, mostly the South. Students come from 49 states, 27 foreign countries, and Canada. Seventy-five percent are from public schools; 25% from private. Eighty-nine percent are white. Sixty-four percent are Protestant; 19% Catholic; 10% claim no religious affiliation. The average age of freshmen is 18; all undergraduates, 20. Two percent drop out by the end of their first year; 87% remain to graduate.

Housing: A total of 2857 students can be accommodated in college housing. College-sponsored living facilities include single-sex and coed dormitories, on-campus apartments, and married-student housing. In addition, there are honors houses, language houses, and special interest houses. On-campus housing is guaranteed for all 4 years. Eighty-three percent of students live on campus; of those, 85% remain on campus on weekends. All students may keep cars on campus.

Activities: About 42% of men belong to 14 national fraternities; about 52% of women belong to 10 national sororities. There are 90 groups on campus, including art, band, cheerleading, chess, choir, chorale, chorus, computers, dance, drama, drill team, ethnic, film, gay, honors, international, jazz band, literary magazine, marching band, musical theater, newspaper, orchestra, pep band, photography, political, professional, radio and TV, religious, social, social service, student government, symphony, and yearbook. Popular campus events include Convocation, Moravian Christmas Love Feast, Parents Weekend, Homecoming, and Spring Fest.

Sports: There are 9 intercollegiate sports for men and 7 for women, and 19 intramural sports for men and 19 for women. Athletic and recreation facilities include 6 playing fields, 4 indoor basketball courts, a swimming pool, a track, racquetball and tennis courts, an exercise room and weight room, an indoor tennis center, a fitness center, a soccer complex, a golf practice complex, and a cross-country course.

Disabled Students: All of the campus is accessible to disabled students. The following facilities are available: wheelchair ramps, elevators, special parking, specially equipped rest rooms, special class scheduling, lowered drinking fountains, and lowered telephones.

Services: In addition to many counseling and information services, tutoring is available in most subjects. In addition, there is a reader service for the blind and remedial reading and writing.

Campus Safety and Security: Campus safety and security measures include 24-hour foot and vehicle patrol, self defense education, escort service, and shuttle buses. In addition, there are informal discussions, pamphlets, posters, and films, emergency telephones, and lighted pathways and sidewalks.

Programs of Study: Wake Forest awards the B.A. and B.S. degrees. Master's and doctoral degrees also are awarded. Bachelor's degrees are awarded in BIOLOGICAL SCIENCE (biology/biological science), BUSINESS (accounting and business administration and management), COMMUNICATIONS AND THE ARTS (art, broadcasting, communications, dramatic arts, English, film arts, French, German, music, Spanish, and speech/debate/rhetoric), COMPUTER AND PHYSICAL SCIENCE (chemistry, computer science, mathematics, and physics), EDUCATION (education), SOCIAL SCIENCE (anthropology, economics, history, philosophy, political science/government, psychology, religion, and sociology). Biology, psychology, business, English, and history have the largest enrollments.

Required: To graduate, students must complete a total of 144 credits with a GPA of 2.0. The number of hours required in the major varies. All students must take 1 semester of English composition and 2 each of a foreign language and health and sports science. In addition, students must complete 3 courses in each of 4 basic divisions: English literature, foreign literature, and fine arts; natural sciences and mathematics and computer science; social and behavioral sciences; and history, religion, and philosophy.

Special: The school offers cooperative programs in forestry with Duke University. Cross-registration with Salem College is available. The school sponsors study-abroad programs in 9 countries. A Washington semester, internships, work-study programs, dual majors, a 3–2 engineering degree with North Carolina State University, a B.A.-B.S. degree in chemistry/physics, and pass/fail options are available. Accelerated degree programs may be arranged in law, dentistry, and medical technology. Interdisciplinary honors courses and the Open Curriculum program are available for selected students. Wake Forest owns residences in London and Venice where students and professors may attend semester-long courses in a variety of disciplines. There is a freshman honors program on campus, as well as 16 national honor societies, including Phi Beta Kappa. Twenty-one departments have honors programs.

Faculty/Classroom: Seventy-three percent of faculty are male; 27%, female. All teach undergraduates. No introductory courses are taught by graduate students. The average class size in an introductory lecture is 33; in a laboratory, 27; and in a regular course offering, 25.

Admissions: About 42% of the 1993–94 applicants were accepted. The SAT scores for the 1993–94 freshman class were as follows: Verbal—17% below 500, 48% between 500 and 599, 32% between 600 and 700, and 3% above 700; Math—5% below 500, 24% between 500 and 599, 49% between 600 and 700, and 22% above 700. About 84% of the current freshmen were in the top fifth of their class; 97% were in the top two fifths. Fifty-two freshmen graduated first in their class.

Requirements: The SAT I is required and the ACT is recommended. Three SAT II: Subject tests, including writing and mathematics, are recommended. Graduation from an accredited secondary school or the GED is required. The school requires 16 academic credits, including 4 credits of English, 2 each of a foreign language, history, and social studies, 3 of mathematics, and 1 of science. One credit each of art and music is recommended. All students must submit an essay. AP and CLEP credits are accepted. Important factors used in the admissions decision are advanced placement or honor courses, leadership record, evidence of special talent, recommendations by school officials, and personality, intangible qualities.

Procedure: Freshmen are admitted in the fall and spring. Entrance exams should be taken during the junior year, and at least one SAT II: Subject test should be taken during the senior year. Early decision applications should be filed by November 15; regular applications by January 15 for fall entry and November 1 for spring entry, along with an application fee of $25. Notification is sent April 1. There are early decision and deferred admissions plans. About 165 early decision candidates were accepted for the 1993–94 class. A waiting list is an active part of the admissions procedure, with about 8% of applicants on the list.

Transfer: About 69 transfer students enrolled in 1993–94. Transfer students must have a minimum GPA of 2.0 on all college work attempted. The SAT I is required. A total of 72 credits out of 144 must be completed at Wake Forest.

Visiting: There are regularly scheduled orientations for prospective students, including group information sessions and tours by appointment. There are guides for informal visits, and visitors may sit in on classes and stay overnight at the school. To arrange for a visit, contact the Admissions Office at (919) 759-5201.

Financial Aid: In 1993–94, 72% of all current freshmen and 60% of continuing students received some form of financial aid. About 31% of freshmen and 25% of continuing students received need-based aid. The average freshman award was $8040. Of that total, scholarships or need-based grants averaged $5300 ($17,430 maximum); loans averaged $1250 ($19,030 maximum); and work contracts averaged $1400 (maximum). Twenty-five percent of undergraduate students work part-time. Average earnings from campus work for the school year are $1200. Wake Forest is a member of CSS. The FAF, the college's own financial statement, and the SAR are required. The deadline for financial aid applications is March 1.

International Students: There are currently 46 international students enrolled. They must take the TOEFL. The student must also take the SAT I.

Computers: The college provides computer facilities for student use. The mainframe is an HP 852. In addition to the mainframe used for academic computing and library automation, there are Macintosh systems for word processing. These systems are available in 5 student microcomputer laboratories, university departments, 2 terminal rooms, and a graphic workstation. All students may access the system 24 hours per day. There are no time limits on using the system and no fees.

Graduates: In 1992–93, 769 bachelor's degrees were awarded. The most popular majors among graduates were English (12%), business (11%), and biology (11%). Within an average freshman class, 87% graduate in 5 years. Some 150 companies recruited on campus in 1992–93. In the 1992 graduating class, 35% of all graduates were enrolled in graduate school within 6 months of graduation; 65% of all graduates had found employment.

Admissions Contact: William G. Starling, Director of Admissions and Financial Aid.

WARREN WILSON COLLEGE

B-2

Asheville, NC 28815   (704) 298–3325; (800) 934–3536 (out-of-state)

Full-time: 238 men, 246 women	**Faculty:** 40; IIB, --$
Part-time: 5 men and women	**Ph.D.s:** 65%
Graduate: 65 men and women	**Student/Faculty:** 12 to 1
Year: terms	**Tuition:** $10,065
Application Deadline: March 15	**Room & Board:** see profile
Freshman Class: 440 applied, 306 accepted, 113 enrolled	
SAT I or ACT: required	**COMPETITIVE**

Warren Wilson College, founded in 1894, is a coeducational liberal arts institution affiliated with the Presbyterian Church. All students work 15 hours per week in jobs related to the operation and maintenance of the college. In exchange, room and board costs $812 per year. There is one graduate school. In addition to regional accreditation, Warren Wilson College has baccalaureate program accreditation with CSWE and NCATE. The library contains 90,000 volumes, 25,000 microform items, and 5000 audiovisual forms, and subscribes to 530 periodicals. Computerized library sources and services include the card catalog, interlibrary loans, and database searching. Special learning facilities include a learning resource center, art gallery, and radio station. The 1100-acre campus is in a small town 10 miles east of Asheville. Including residence halls, there are 25 buildings on campus.

Student Life: About 68% of undergraduates are from out-of-state, mostly the South. Students come from 38 states, 27 foreign countries, and Canada. Eighty-four percent are white. The average age of freshmen is 19; all undergraduates, 21. Eighteen percent drop out by the end of their first year; 60% remain to graduate.

Housing: A total of 506 students can be accommodated in college housing. College-sponsored living facilities include single-sex and coed dormitories and married-student housing. On-campus housing is guaranteed for all 4 years. Priority is given to out-of-town students. Ninety-three percent of students live on campus; of those, 95% remain on campus on weekends. All students may keep cars on campus.

Activities: There are no fraternities or sororities on campus. There are many groups and organizations on campus, including art, cheerleading, chess, choir, chorale, computers, dance, drama, ethnic, film, gay, honors, international, literary magazine, musical theater, newspaper, photography, political, professional, radio and TV, religious, social, social service, student government, and yearbook. Popular campus events include Career Fair, Homecoming, Human Rights Festival, Harvest Festival, International Fair, Halloween, and Spring Festival.

Sports: There are 2 intercollegiate sports for men and 2 for women, and 8 intramural sports for men and 8 for women. Athletic and recreation facilities include a gymnasium, an aquatic center, weight and fitness rooms, tennis courts, a swimming pool, playing fields, whitewater kayaking course, and 25 miles of hiking/biking trails.

Disabled Students: Twenty-five percent of the campus is accessible to disabled students. The following facilities are available: wheelchair ramps, elevators, special parking, specially equipped rest rooms, and special class scheduling.

Services: Tutoring is arranged through the Peer Assistance Center.

Campus Safety and Security: Campus safety and security measures include 24-hour foot and vehicle patrol, self-defense education, and informal discussions.

Programs of Study: Warren Wilson College awards the B.A. degree. Master's degrees also are awarded. Bachelor's degrees are awarded in BIOLOGICAL SCIENCE (biology/biological science), COMMUNICATIONS AND THE ARTS (English), COMPUTER AND PHYSICAL SCIENCE (chemistry and mathematics), EDUCATION (elementary and middle school), ENGINEERING AND ENVIRONMENTAL DESIGN (environmental science), SOCIAL SCIENCE (economics, history, humanities, parks and recreation management, psychology, and social work). Biology is the strongest academically. Environmental studies, biology, and education have the largest enrollments.

Required: In order to graduate, students must complete a total of 128 semester hours with a minimum GPA of 2.0. Between 32 and 40 hours are required in the student's major. All students must complete 36 hours in the core curriculum and also complete 20 hours of community service each year.

Special: Cross-registration is offered with Appalachian State University. Internships related to the major may be arranged. Study-abroad programs in South America and India are available. The college offers an accelerated degree program in education, a general studies degree, student-designed majors, credit for life experience, nondegree study, and pass/fail options. There are dual majors in history/political science and English/theater arts. Cooperative programs are available in engineering with Washington University in St. Louis, and in nursing with Western Carolina University. Three departments have honors programs.

Faculty/Classroom: Sixty-eight percent of faculty are male; 32%, female. All teach undergraduates. No introductory courses are taught by graduate students. The average class size in an introductory lecture is 13; in a laboratory, 13; and in a regular course offering, 11.

Admissions: About 70% of the 1993–94 applicants were accepted. The SAT scores for the 1993–94 freshman class were as follows: Verbal—40% below 500, 38% between 500 and 599, 20% between 600 and 700, and 2% above 700; Math—40% below 500, 38% between 500 and 599, 21% between 600 and 700, and 1% above 700. The ACT scores were 30% below 21, 20% between 21 and 23, 30% between 24 and 26, 7% between 27 and 28, and 13% above 28. About 31% of the current freshmen were in the top fifth of their class; 60% were in the top two fifths. There was 1 National Merit finalist and 1 semifinalist. Three freshmen graduated first in their class.

Requirements: A minimum GPA of 2.0 is required. The SAT I, with a score of 400 on each section, or the ACT, with a composite score of 17, is required. Graduation from an accredited secondary school or the GED is required. Applicants should have a total of 12 academic credits. An essay and an interview are recommended. AP credits are accepted. Important factors used in the admissions decision are advanced placement or honor courses, evidence of special talent, recommendations by school officials, leadership record, and extracurricular activities record.

Procedure: Freshmen are admitted fall and winter. Entrance exams should be taken by March 15 of senior year. Applications should be filed by March 15 for fall entry and December 15 for winter entry. Notification is sent on a rolling basis. There are early admissions and deferred admissions plans. A waiting list is an active part of the admissions procedure, with about 5% of applicants on the list.

Transfer: About 40 transfer students enrolled in 1993–94. Transfer students must have a minimum GPA of 2.0. A year of residence at Warren Wilson is required for graduation. Applicants must be eligible to return to previous institutions. A total of 32 credits out of 128 must be completed at Warren Wilson College.

Visiting: There are guides for informal visits and visitors may sit in on classes and stay overnight at the school. To arrange for a visit, contact Nina Bell, Assistant Director of Admission at (704) 298–3325 or (800) 934–3536.

Financial Aid: In an earlier year, 75% of all current freshmen received some form of financial aid. The FAF or FFS is required. The deadline for financial aid applications is May 1.

International Students: There are currently 37 international students enrolled. They must take the TOEFL and achieve a minimum score of 500.

Computers: The college provides computer facilities for student use. The mainframe is a McDonnel/Douglas Spirit 6000. There are IBM-compatible and Apple microcomputers available for student use in academic buildings and the library. All students may access the system. There are no time limits on using the system and no fees.

Admissions Contact: Tom Weede, Dean of Admission.

WESTERN CAROLINA UNIVERSITY

B-3

Cullowhee, NC 28723 (704) 227-7317

Full-time: 2554 men, 2446 women	Faculty: 320; IIA, -$
Part-time: 203 men, 314 women	Ph.D.s: 69%
Graduate: 317 men, 534 women	Student/Faculty: 16 to 1
Year: semesters, summer session	Tuition: $1391 ($7457)
Application Deadline: open	Room & Board: $2420
Freshman Class: 3646 applied, 2519 accepted, 1057 enrolled	
SAT I Verbal/Math: 400/450	**COMPETITIVE**

Western Carolina University, founded in 1889, is a publicly funded institution in the University of North Carolina system. There are 4 undergraduate schools and one graduate school. In addition to regional accreditation, WCU has baccalaureate program accreditation with AACSB, ADA, CSWE, NASM, NCATE, and NLN. The library contains 420,923 volumes, 1,124,547 microform items, and 2304 audiovisual forms, and subscribes to 2119 periodicals. Computerized library sources and services include the card catalog, interlibrary loans, and database searching. Special learning facilities include a learning resource center, art gallery, natural history museum, and radio station. The 265-acre campus is in a rural area 160 miles northeast of Atlanta, Georgia, and 50 miles west of Asheville. Including residence halls, there are 88 buildings on campus.

Student Life: About 92% of undergraduates are from North Carolina. Students come from 35 states, 24 foreign countries, and Canada. Ninety-five percent are from public schools; 5% from private. Ninety-three percent are white. The average age of freshmen is 18; all undergraduates, 20. Twenty-eight percent drop out by the end of their first year; 44% remain to graduate.

Housing: A total of 2878 students can be accommodated in college housing. College-sponsored living facilities include single-sex dormitories, on-campus apartments, and married-student housing. In addition there are houses houses. On-campus housing is available on a first-come, first-served basis. Fifty-seven percent of students live on campus; of those, 50% remain on campus on weekends. Alcohol is not permitted. All students may keep cars on campus.

Activities: About 25% of men belong to 15 national fraternities; about 12% of women belong to 9 national sororities. There are 130 groups on campus, including art, band, cheerleading, choir, chorale, chorus, computers, dance, drama, drill team, ethnic, honors, international, literary magazine, marching band, musical theater, newspaper, pep band, photography, political, professional, radio and TV, religious, social, social service, student government, and yearbook. Popular campus events include Mountain Heritage Day, Homecoming Weekend, Parents Day, Greek Week, Madrigal Christmas Dinners, Black History Week, and Cullowhee Music Festival.

Sports: There are 7 intercollegiate sports for men and 6 for women, and 30 intramural sports for men and 30 for women. Athletic and recreation facilities include 6 intramural softball and football fields, 5 gymnasiums, a field house, a rifle range, jogging trails, picnic areas, game rooms, an archery range, a golf driving range, and a golf putting green.

Disabled Students: Ninety percent of the campus is accessible to disabled students. The following facilities are available: wheelchair ramps, elevators, special parking, specially equipped rest rooms, special class scheduling, lowered drinking fountains, and lowered telephones.

Services: In addition to many counseling and information services, tutoring is available in most subjects. There is also a reader service for the blind, and remedial math, reading, and writing.

Campus Safety and Security: Campus safety and security measures include 24-hour foot and vehicle patrol, informal discussions, pamphlets, posters, films, and emergency telephones. In addition, there are lighted pathways and sidewalks and crime-prevention education programs.

Programs of Study: WCU awards the B.A., B.S., B.F.A., B.S.B.A., B.S.Ed., and B.S.N. degrees. Master's degrees also are awarded. Bachelor's degrees are awarded in AGRICULTURE (natural resource management), BIOLOGICAL SCIENCE (biology/biological science and nutrition), BUSINESS (accounting, banking and finance, business economics, business law, management science, marketing/retailing/merchandising, and office supervision and management), COMMUNICATIONS AND THE ARTS (art, broadcasting, dramatic arts, English, fine arts, French, German, music, and Spanish), COMPUTER AND PHYSICAL SCIENCE (chemistry, computer science, earth science, geology, mathematics, and physics), EDUCATION (art, business, early childhood, elementary, foreign languages, health, home economics, middle school, music, physical, science, secondary, special, and speech correction), ENGINEERING AND ENVIRONMENTAL DESIGN (electrical/electronics engineering technology, emergency/disaster science, engineering technology, and interior design), HEALTH PROFESSIONS (clinical science, environmental health science, health care administration, medical records administration/services, and nursing), SOCIAL SCIENCE (anthropology, child care/child and family studies, clothing and textiles management/production/services, criminal justice, dietetics, economics, food production/management/services, geography, history, home economics, parks and recreation management, political science/government, psychology, social science, social work, and sociology). Elementary education, marketing, nursing, and criminal justice have the largest enrollments.

Required: In order to graduate, students must complete a total of 128 credit hours with a minimum GPA of 2.0. Between 30 and 64 hours are required in the major. All students must fulfill general education requirements in English composition, computer literacy, leisure and fitness, social sciences, physical and biological sciences, mathematics, humanistic experience, comparative culture, and human past.

Special: The school offers cooperative education programs, internships, work-study programs, accelerated degree programs, B.A.-B.S. degrees, dual majors, a general studies degree, nondegree study, pass/fail options in designated courses, and credit for life experience. Cross-registration is available with the University of North Carolina at Asheville. Study-abroad programs may be arranged in several countries. There is a freshman honors program on campus, as well as 14 national honor societies.

Faculty/Classroom: Sixty-one percent of faculty are male; 39%, female. Ninety-five percent teach undergraduates, 80% do research, and 75% do both. Graduate students teach 5% of introductory courses. The average class size in an introductory lecture is 25; in a laboratory, 20; and in a regular course offering, 25.

Admissions: About 69% of the 1993-94 applicants were accepted. The SAT scores for the 1993-94 freshman class were as follows: Verbal—87% below 500, 11% between 500 and 599, 2% between 600 and 700, and 1% above 700; Math—70% below 500, 24% between 500 and 599, 5% between 600 and 700, and 1% above 700. About 23% of the current freshmen were in the top fifth of their class; 56% were in the top two fifths.

Requirements: WCU requires applicants to be in the upper 50% of their class. A minimum GPA of 2.0 is required. The SAT I (preferred) or ACT is required. Graduation from an accredited secondary school or the GED is required. High school courses must include 4 units of English, 3 each of mathematics and science, and 2 of social studies, including 1 of U.S. history. Two units of a foreign language are recommended. AP and CLEP credits are accepted. Important factors used in the admissions decision are recommendations by school officials, evidence of special talent, advanced placement or honor courses, leadership record, and extracurricular activities record.

Procedure: Freshmen are admitted to all sessions. Entrance exams should be taken during the spring of the junior year or the fall of the senior year. Application deadlines are open. The application fee is $20. Notification is sent on a rolling basis. There is a deferred admissions plan.

Transfer: About 500 transfer students enrolled in 1993-94. Tranfer students must have a minimum GPA of 2.0 and meet freshman admissions requirements. A total of 30 credits out of 128 must be completed at WCU.

Visiting: There are regularly scheduled orientations for prospective students, open houses, 1 in fall; 1 in spring, include registration, a visit to the department of choice, a campus tour, and an athletic event. There are guides for informal visits and visitors may sit in on classes and stay overnight at the school. To arrange for a visit, contact the Admissions Office at (704) 227-7317.

Financial Aid: In 1993-94 46% of all current freshmen and 45% of continuing students received some form of financial aid. About 40% of freshmen and 32% of continuing students received need-based aid. The average freshman award was $1510. Of that total, scholarships or need-based grants averaged $1050 ($3100 maximum); loans averaged $1850 ($2625 maximum); and work contracts averaged $1150 ($1910 maximum). Nine percent of undergraduate students work part-time. Average earnings from campus work for the school year are $1000. The average financial indebtedness of the 1992-93 graduate was $7000. WCU is a member of CSS. The FAFSA financial statement is required. The deadline for financial aid applications is April 1.

International Students: There are currently 67 international students enrolled. The school actively recruits these students. They must take the TOEFL and achieve a minimum score of 550. The student must also take the SAT I.

Computers: The college provides computer facilities for student use. The mainframes are a VAX 4000/500 and a VAX 4000/300. Computer terminals connected to a mainframe are available for student use in 4 classroom buildings. There are also more than 400 microcomputers in computer laboratories, the library, the learning centers, and various other locations. All students may access the system. It may be used 8 A.M. to 10 P.M. Monday through Friday; some weekend hours are available. There are no time limits and no fees.

Graduates: In 1992-93 1071 bachelor's degrees were awarded. The most popular majors among graduates were marketing (9%), criminal justice (7%), and early childhood education (6%). Within an

average freshman class, 2% graduate in 3 years, 25% in 4 years, 40% in 5 years, and 44% in 6 years. Some 172 companies recruited on campus in 1992–93. In a recent graduating class, 10% of the men and 12% of the women were enrolled in graduate school within 6 months of graduation; 85% of the men and 80% of the women had found employment.

Admissions Contact: Drumont I. Bowman, Director of Admissions.

WINGATE COLLEGE
C-3

Wingate, NC 28174   (704) 233–8201; (800) 755–5550 (out-of-state)

Full-time: 637 men, 599 women	Faculty: 78; IIB, --$
Part-time: 38 men, 119 women	Ph.D.s: 71%
Graduate: 33 men, 35 women	Student/Faculty: 16 to 1
Year: semesters, summer session	Tuition: $7410
Application Deadline: August 15	Room & Board: $3200
Freshman Class: 1239 applied, 1017 accepted, 389 enrolled	
SAT I Verbal/Math: 398/444	**COMPETITIVE**

Wingate College, founded in 1896, is a private liberal arts institution affiliated with the Baptist Church. There are 2 graduate schools. In addition to regional accreditation, Wingate has baccalaureate program accreditation with NASM and NLN. The library contains 110,000 volumes, 20,000 microform items, and 5600 audiovisual forms, and subscribes to 670 periodicals. Special learning facilities include a learning resource center, art gallery, and TV station. The 330-acre campus is in a small town 25 miles east of Charlotte. Including residence halls, there are 35 buildings on campus.

Student Life: About 60% of undergraduates are from North Carolina. Students come from 24 states and 7 foreign countries. Ninety percent are from public schools; 10% from private. Eighty-seven percent are white. Eighty-eight percent are Protestant; 11% Catholic. The average age of freshmen is 18; all undergraduates, 20. Thirteen percent drop out by the end of their first year; 66% remain to graduate.

Housing: A total of 1200 students can be accommodated in college housing. College-sponsored living facilities include single-sex dormitories and on-campus apartments. In addition there are honors houses. On-campus housing is guaranteed for all 4 years. Seventy percent of students live on campus; of those, 70% remain on campus on weekends. Alcohol is not permitted. All students may keep cars on campus.

Activities: About 15% of men belong to 3 national fraternities; about 11% of women belong to 2 national sororities. There are 40 groups on campus, including art, band, cheerleading, choir, chorale, computers, dance, drama, ethnic, honors, international, jazz band, literary magazine, marching band, newspaper, pep band, photography, political, professional, radio and TV, religious, social, social service, student government, and yearbook. Popular campus events include Homecoming, Spring Fling and Fall Festival at campus lake, and name-band concerts.

Sports: There are 7 intercollegiate sports for men and 6 for women, and 17 intramural sports for men and 17 for women. Athletic and recreation facilities include an athletic complex with a gymnasium, swimming pool, racquetball courts, weight room, and tennis courts, and a student center with bowling, table tennis, pool, and a game room.

Disabled Students: Ninety-five percent of the campus is accessible to disabled students. The following facilities are available: wheelchair ramps, elevators, special parking, specially equipped rest rooms, and special class scheduling.

Services: In addition to many counseling and information services, tutoring is available in every subject. Additional academic support is available for students with learning disabilities.

Campus Safety and Security: Campus safety and security measures include 24-hour foot and vehicle patrol, escort service, informal discussions, and pamphlets, posters, and films. In addition, there are lighted pathways and sidewalks.

Programs of Study: Wingate awards the B.A., B.S., B.G.S., B.M., B.M.Ed., B.S. in All. Health, B.S.N., and B.T. degrees. Associate and master's degrees also are awarded. Bachelor's degrees are awarded in BIOLOGICAL SCIENCE (biology/biological science), BUSINESS (accounting, business administration and management, business economics, and sports management), COMMUNICATIONS AND THE ARTS (art, communications, English, music, and music business management), COMPUTER AND PHYSICAL SCIENCE (applied mathematics, chemistry, information sciences and systems, and mathematics), EDUCATION (art, elementary, English, mathematics, middle school, music, and science), ENGINEERING AND ENVIRONMENTAL DESIGN (preengineering), HEALTH PROFESSIONS (allied health, predentistry, premedicine, prepharmacy, preveterinary science, and sports medicine), SOCIAL SCIENCE (American studies, history, human services, liberal arts/general studies, parks and recreation management, prelaw, psychology, religion, religious education, and sociology). Biological sciences, history, and religious studies are the strongest academically. Business, education, and communications have the largest enrollments.

Required: In order to graduate, students must complete a minimum of 125 credit hours with a GPA of 2.0. At least 30 hours must be completed in the student's major. All students must take core courses in English composition, literature, religion, life issues, fine arts, history, social sciences, foreign language, mathematics, laboratory science, fitness and wellness, physical education, and freshman experience.

Special: Cross-registration through the Charlotte Area Education Consortium, internships, on-campus work-study programs, a general studies degree, and nondegree study are available. A 3–2 engineering degree is offered with North Carolina State University, Clemson University, and Virginia Polytechnic Institute. Wingate conducts a study abroad semester in London. The school also sponsors Winternational, a semester seminar with a 10-day trip to a foreign country for which students earn academic credit, at little personal cost. There are double majors offered, including biology and education, history and education, chemistry and business, and music and communications. There is a freshman honors program on campus, as well as 8 national honor societies.

Faculty/Classroom: Sixty percent of faculty are male; 40%, female. All teach undergraduates. No introductory courses are taught by graduate students. The average class size in an introductory lecture is 26; in a laboratory, 15; and in a regular course offering, 13.

Admissions: About 82% of the 1993–94 applicants were accepted. The SAT scores for the 1993–94 freshman class were as follows: Verbal—89% below 500, 9% between 500 and 599, and 2% between 600 and 700; Math—74% below 500, 19% between 500 and 599, and 7% between 600 and 700. About 23% of the current freshmen were in the top fifth of their class; 39% were in the top two fifths. Six freshmen graduated first in their class.

Requirements: Wingate requires applicants to be in the upper 50% of their class. A minimum GPA of 2.0 is required. The SAT I or ACT is required. Graduation from an accredited secondary school or the GED is required. High school curriculum must include 4 courses in English, 2 each in history and science, 3 in mathematics, and 1 in social studies. Two courses in a foreign language are recommended. An essay is required of all applicants, and an interview is recommended in some cases. AP and CLEP credits are accepted. Important factors used in the admissions decision are advanced placement or honor courses, leadership record, recommendations by school officials, personality, intangible qualities, and evidence of special talent.

Procedure: Freshmen are admitted to all sessions. Entrance exams should be taken in spring of the junior year or fall of the senior year. Applications should be filed by August 15 for fall entry and December 27 for spring entry, along with an application fee of $20. Notification is sent on a rolling basis.

Transfer: About 89 transfer students enrolled in 1993–94. Transfer students must have a minimum GPA of 2.0 and must be eligible to return to the institution last attended. The SAT I or ACT is required if a student has been out of high school for less than 5 years. An interview may be recommended in some cases. A total of 30 credits out of 125 must be completed at Wingate.

Visiting: There are regularly scheduled orientations for prospective students, including Saturday Preview Day 4 times a year, campus tours and presentations of travel programs, academic life, athletics, and student life. There are guides for informal visits and visitors may sit in on classes. To arrange for a visit, contact the Admissions Office at (704) 233–8201 or (800) 755–5550.

Financial Aid: In 1993–94 91% of all current freshmen and 92% of continuing students received some form of financial aid. About 87% of freshmen and 85% of continuing students received need-based aid. The average freshman award was $6700. Of that total, scholarships or need-based grants averaged $3000 ($7000 maximum); loans averaged $2500 ($2625 maximum); and work contracts averaged $1100 ($1200 maximum). Fifteen percent of undergraduate students work part-time. Average earnings from campus work for the school year are $1000. The average financial indebtedness of the 1992–93 graduate was $2500. Wingate is a member of CSS. The college's own financial statement and the FAFSA are required. The deadline for financial aid applications is March 1.

International Students: There are currently 10 international students enrolled. They must take the TOEFL and achieve a minimum score of 550.

Computers: The college provides computer facilities for student use. The mainframe is an HP 3000. Microcomputers are avaiable in laboratories and offices. All students may access the system. It may be used during library hours. There are no time limits and no fees.

Graduates: In 1992–93 212 bachelor's degrees were awarded. Some 45 companies usually recruit on campus. In an earlier graduating class, 9% of the men and 7% of the women were enrolled in graduate school within 6 months of graduation.

Admissions Contact: Christopher J. Keller, Director of Admissions.

WINSTON-SALEM STATE UNIVERSITY

C-2

Winston-Salem, NC 27110
(910) 750-2070

Full-time: 776 men, 1293 women
Part-time: 274 men, 474 women
Graduate: none
Year: semesters, summer session
Application Deadline: open
Freshman Class: 1065 applied, 801 accepted, 385 enrolled
SAT I Verbal/Math: 369/405

Faculty: 145; IIB, av$
Ph.D.s: 74%
Student/Faculty: 14 to 1
Tuition: $1242 ($6606)
Room & Board: $2900

LESS COMPETITIVE

Winston-Salem State University, founded in 1892, is a state-supported liberal arts institution offering undergraduate programs through divisions of arts and sciences, business and economics, education, and nursing and allied health. There are 4 undergraduate schools. In addition to regional accreditation, WSSU has baccalaureate program accreditation with NASM, NCATE, and NLN. The library contains 162,358 volumes, 98,185 microform items, and 17,805 audiovisual forms, and subscribes to 1125 periodicals. Computerized library sources and services include the card catalog, interlibrary loans, and database searching. Special learning facilities include a learning resource center, an art gallery, a radio station, a TV station, the Plato laboratory, and an enrichment center. The 31-acre campus is in a suburban area in Winston-Salem. Including residence halls, there are 30 buildings on campus.

Student Life: About 93% of undergraduates are from North Carolina. Students come from 30 states. Seventy-eight percent are African American; 21% white. The average age of all undergraduates is 25. Twenty-eight percent drop out by the end of their first year; 13% remain to graduate.

Housing: A total of 1263 students can be accommodated in college housing. College-sponsored living facilities include single-sex and coed dormitories. On-campus housing is guaranteed for the freshman year only and is available on a first-come, first-served basis. Sixty-five percent of students commute. Alcohol is not permitted. All students may keep cars on campus.

Activities: There are 70 groups on campus, including art, band, cheerleading, choir, computers, dance, drama, drill team, ethnic, honors, international, jazz band, marching band, newspaper, photography, political, radio and TV, social, student government, and yearbook. Popular campus events include Open House, Homecoming, Founders Day, and International Day.

Sports: There are 4 intercollegiate sports for men and 5 for 2 women. Athletic and recreation facilities include 2 gymnasiums, tennis courts, an indoor swimming pool, and a track.

Disabled Students: The following facilities are available: wheelchair ramps, elevators, special parking, and specially equipped rest rooms.

Services: In addition to many counseling and information services, tutoring is available in most subjects. In addition, there is remedial math, reading, and writing.

Campus Safety and Security: Campus safety and security measures include 24-hour foot and vehicle patrol, informal discussions, pamphlets, posters, and films, and lighted pathways and sidewalks.

Programs of Study: WSSU awards the B.A., B.S., and B.S. in Applied Science degrees. Master's and doctoral degrees also are awarded. Bachelor's degrees are awarded in BIOLOGICAL SCIENCE (biology/biological science), BUSINESS (accounting, business administration and management, management information systems, and sports management), COMMUNICATIONS AND THE ARTS (communications, English, fine arts, and Spanish), COMPUTER AND PHYSICAL SCIENCE (chemistry, computer science, mathematics, and physical sciences), EDUCATION (art, business, early childhood, elementary, middle school, music, physical, and special), ENGINEERING AND ENVIRONMENTAL DESIGN (environmental science), HEALTH PROFESSIONS (medical laboratory technology, nursing, physical therapy, and recreation therapy), SOCIAL SCIENCE (history, political science/government, psychology, public administration, sociology, and urban studies). Physical education, computer science, mathematics, nursing, education, and business are the strongest programs academically. Nursing, business administration, and education have the largest enrollments.

Required: Students must complete a minimum of 127 semester hours, with 40 of these hours in upper-level courses, and must maintain an overall minimum GPA of 2.0. All students must also complete the general education core requirement, which includes courses in English composition, social sciences, mathematics and natural sciences, humanities, and physical education or military science.

Special: Opportunities are provided for cooperative programs, internships, work-study programs, a B.A.-B.S. degree, a general studies degree, and credit for military experience. The nursing division offers flexible scheduling for employed RNs. There is a freshman honors program on campus.

Faculty/Classroom: Fifty-four percent of faculty are male; 46%, female. All teach undergraduates.

Admissions: About 75% of the 1993–94 applicants were accepted. The SAT scores for the 1993–94 freshman class were as follows: Verbal—96% below 500, 3% between 500 and 599, and 1% between 600 and 700; Math—93% below 500, 6% between 500 and 599, and 1% between 600 and 700. About 13% of the current freshmen were in the top fifth of their class; 37% were in the top two fifths.

Requirements: A minimum GPA of 2.0 is required. The SAT I is required, with a minimum composite score of 700 recommended. Graduation from an accredited secondary school is required; a GED will be accepted. Applicants should submit an academic record including 4 credits in English, 3 each in mathematics and science, 1 each in U.S. history, social studies, and physical education and health, and 2 in a foreign language. AP and CLEP credits are accepted. Important factors used in the admissions decision are advanced placement or honor courses, leadership record, recommendations by school officials, evidence of special talent, and extracurricular activities record.

Procedure: Freshmen are admitted to all sessions. Entrance exams should be taken in the summer or early fall of the senior year. Application deadlines are open. Application fee is $15. Notification is sent on a rolling basis. There are early admissions and deferred admissions plans.

Transfer: About 346 transfer students enrolled in 1993–94. Transfer applicants must submit official transcripts from all colleges previously attended, showing no grade lower than C. No more than 64 semester hours (96 quarter hours) will be accepted for transfer. Those applicants transferring fewer than 29 credits will be admitted as freshmen and must meet all freshman admission requirements. A total of 30 credits out of 127 must be completed at WSSU.

Visiting: There are regularly scheduled orientations for prospective students, including summer and fall orientation. There are guides for informal visits and visitors may sit in on classes. To arrange for a visit, contact Robert Callaway or Jackie Humphrey at (910) 750–2070.

Financial Aid: In 1993–94, 46% of all current freshmen and 62% of continuing students received some form of financial aid. About 40% of freshmen and 57% of continuing students received need-based aid. The average freshman award was $5300. Of that total, scholarships or need-based grants averaged $2300 ($3300 maximum); loans averaged $1000 ($2625 maximum); and work contracts averaged $1000 ($2000 maximum). Twenty-eight percent of undergraduate students work part-time. Average earnings from campus work for the school year are $1125. The FAF or FFS and the college's own financial statement are required. The deadline for financial aid applications is June 30.

International Students: There are currently 10 international students enrolled. They must take the TOEFL and achieve a minimum score of 540.

Computers: The college provides computer facilities for student use. The academic computer center maintains a DEC VAX 11/750 with 20 terminals and 2 on-line printers. There are no time limits on using the system. The fees are $20.

Graduates: In 1992–93, 438 bachelor's degrees were awarded. The most popular majors among graduates were business administration (28%), nursing (8%), and accounting (7%). Within an average freshman class, 13% graduate in 4 years, 30% in 5 years, and 35% in 6 years.

Admissions Contact: Van C. Wilson, Director of Admissions.

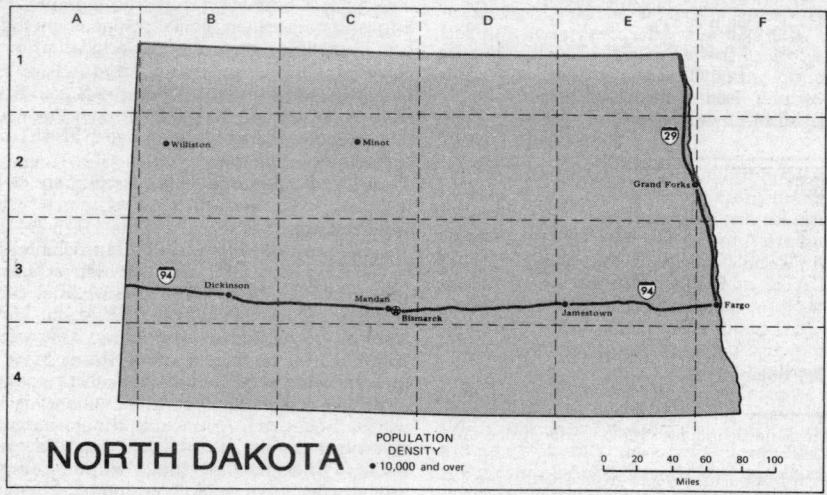

NORTH DAKOTA

POPULATION DENSITY
• 10,000 and over

0 20 40 60 80 100
Miles

DICKINSON STATE UNIVERSITY

B-3

Dickinson, ND 58601   (701) 227–2175; (800) 472–2608 (in-state)

Full-time: 589 men, 787 women	**Faculty:** 60; IIB, --$
Part-time: 60 men, 177 women	**Ph.D.s:** 40%
Graduate: none	**Student/Faculty:** 23 to 1
Year: semesters, summer session	**Tuition:** $1782 ($4462)
Application Deadline: August 15	**Room & Board:** $2010
Freshman Class: 459 applied, 459 accepted, 319 enrolled	
ACT: 20	**NONCOMPETITIVE**

Dickinson State University, founded in 1918, is a public coeducational institution offering undergraduate programs in arts and sciences; business, education, health sciences, physical education and recreation, and psychology; and applied science and technology. There are 4 undergraduate schools. In addition to regional accreditation, DSU has baccalaureate program accreditation with NLN. The library contains 157,242 volumes, 9048 microform items, and 2161 audiovisual forms, and subscribes to 1157 periodicals. Special learning facilities include a learning resource center and art gallery. The 100-acre campus is in a rural area 100 miles west of Bismarck. Including residence halls, there are 15 buildings on campus.

Student Life: About 86% of undergraduates are from North Dakota. Students come from 17 states, 5 foreign countries, and Canada. Ninety-five percent are from public schools; 5% from private. Ninety-nine percent are white. Fifty percent are Protestant; 50% Catholic. The average age of freshmen is 19; all undergraduates, 22. Two percent drop out by the end of their first year; 45% remain to graduate.

Housing: A total of 440 students can be accommodated in college housing. College-sponsored living facilities include single-sex and coed dormitories and married-student housing. On-campus housing is guaranteed for the freshman year only and is available on a first-come, first-served basis. Seventy percent of students commute. Alcohol is not permitted. All students may keep cars on campus.

Activities: There are 40 groups on campus, including art, band, cheerleading, choir, chorus, computers, drama, honors, international, jazz band, literary magazine, marching band, musical theater, newspaper, pep band, political, student government, and yearbook. Popular campus events include Homecoming, Winter Week, and Spring Week.

Sports: There are 8 intercollegiate sports for men and 5 for women, and 3 intramural sports for men and 2 for women. Athletic and recreation facilities include a gymnasium, hall, and stadium.

Disabled Students: Ninety percent of the campus is accessible to disabled students. The following facilities are available: wheelchair ramps, elevators, special parking, specially equipped rest rooms, and special class scheduling.

Services: In addition to many counseling and information services, tutoring is available in every subject. There is a reader service for the blind, and remedial math, reading, and writing.

Campus Safety and Security: Campus safety and security measures include pamphlets, posters, and films, lighted pathways and sidewalks, and 10-hour-a-day security.

Programs of Study: DSU awards the B.A. and B.S. degrees. Associate degrees also are awarded. Bachelor's degrees are awarded in AGRICULTURE (agricultural business management), BIOLOGICAL SCIENCE (biology/biological science), BUSINESS (accounting, business administration and management, and personnel management), COMMUNICATIONS AND THE ARTS (communications, English, fine arts, journalism, music, Spanish, and speech/debate/rhetoric), COMPUTER AND PHYSICAL SCIENCE (chemistry, computer programming, computer science, earth science, and mathematics), EDUCATION (art, business, early childhood, elementary, middle school, music, science, and secondary), HEALTH PROFESSIONS (nursing), SOCIAL SCIENCE (geography, history, political science/government, social work, and sociology). Elementary education, mathematics, and business are the strongest academically. Education and business have the largest enrollments.

Required: To graduate, students must complete 128 semester hours, 36 in the major, with a minimum GPA of 2.0. General education requirements include 10 hours in scientific inquiry, including 1 computer science course, 9 hours each in expressions of human civilizations, understanding human civilization, and communication, and 2 hours in physical education.

Special: DSU offers a co-op program in social work with the University of North Dakota. Internships in business and social work, credit for life experience, and pass/fail options are available. Student-designed majors are possible through the Bachelor of College Studies program. There is a chapter of Phi Beta Kappa on campus.

Faculty/Classroom: Seventy-five percent of faculty are male; 25%, female. The average class size in an introductory lecture is 40; in a laboratory, 25; and in a regular course offering, 20.

Admissions: All 1993–94 applicants were accepted. The ACT scores for the 1993–94 freshman class were as follows: 69% below 21, 13% between 21 and 23, 13% between 24 and 26, 2% between 27 and 28, and 3% above 28. About 19% of the current freshmen were in the top fifth of their class; 47% were in the top two fifths.

Requirements: DSU requires applicants to be in the upper 50% of their class. A minimum GPA of 2.0 is required. An entrance examination is required; the ACT is preferred, but applicants may submit SAT I or SAT II: Subject tests scores. Graduation from an accredited secondary school is recommended. The GED is accepted. Students must have 20 academic credits. An essay is not required. AP and CLEP credits are accepted.

Procedure: Freshmen are admitted to all sessions. Applications should be filed by August 15 for fall entry, January 1 for spring entry, and May 15 for summer entry, along with an application fee of $20. Notification is sent on a rolling basis.

Transfer: About 134 transfer students enrolled in a recent year. Transfer students must have a minimum GPA of 2.0. The ACT is preferred, but applicants may submit SAT I scores. A total of 32 credits out of 128 must be completed at DSU.

Visiting: There are guides for informal visits, and visitors may sit in on classes and stay overnight at the school. To arrange for a visit, contact the Admissions Office at (800) 279–4295 or (701) 227–2175.

Financial Aid: In an earlier year, 75% of all current freshmen and 75% of continuing students received some form of financial aid. Fifty-eight percent of undergraduate students work part-time. The average financial indebtedness of an earlier year's graduate was $6000. The FFS is required.

International Students: There are currently 17 international students enrolled. The school actively recruits these students. They must take the TOEFL and achieve a minimum score of 525.

Computers: The college provides computer facilities for student use. The mainframe is an IBM AS 400. There are 100 IBM and Epson PCs available in May Hall. Those students taking a programming course may access the system. There are no time limits on using the system.
Graduates: In a recent year, 209 bachelor's degrees were awarded. In a recent graduating class, 1% of the men and 1% of the women were enrolled in graduate school within 6 months of graduation; 30% of the men and 30% of the women had found employment.
Admissions Contact: Marshall Melbye, Director of Admissions and Registrar.

JAMESTOWN COLLEGE
Jamestown, ND 58401

E-3

(701) 252-3467
(800) 336-2554 (out-of-state)

Full-time: 486 men, 509 women	Faculty: 53; IIB, --$
Part-time: 23 men, 48 women	Ph.D.s: 51%
Graduate: none	Student/Faculty: 19 to 1
Year: semesters	Tuition: $7270
Application Deadline: open	Room & Board: $2980
Freshman Class: 472 applied, 400 accepted, 262 enrolled	
ACT: 22	COMPETITIVE

Jamestown College, founded in 1883, is a private, nonprofit, coeducational institution affiliated with the Presbyterian Church. Its emphases are on the liberal arts, business, arts, health science, music, religious studies, and teacher preparation. In addition to regional accreditation, Jamestown College has baccalaureate program accreditation with NLN. The library contains 83,000 volumes, 200 microform items, and 1500 audiovisual forms, and subscribes to 370 periodicals. Computerized library sources and services include the card catalog, interlibrary loans, and database searching. Special learning facilities include a learning resource center and art gallery. The 107-acre campus is in a small town 100 miles west of Fargo. Including residence halls, there are 38 buildings on campus.
Student Life: About 59% of undergraduates are from North Dakota. Students come from 20 states, 12 foreign countries, and Canada. Ninety-eight percent are from public schools; 2% from private. Ninety-six percent are white. Sixty percent are Protestant; 29% claim no religious affiliation; 25% Catholic. The average age of freshmen is 18; all undergraduates, 22. Twenty percent drop out by the end of their first year; 50% remain to graduate.
Housing: A total of 730 students can be accommodated in college housing. College-sponsored living facilities include single-sex and coed dormitories, off-campus apartments, and married-student housing. On-campus housing is guaranteed for all 4 years. Seventy-one percent of students live on campus; of those, 75% remain on campus on weekends. Alcohol is not permitted. All students may keep cars on campus.
Activities: There are no fraternities or sororities on campus. There are 25 groups on campus, including band, cheerleading, choir, chorale, drama, honors, international, jazz band, literary magazine, newspaper, pep band, political, professional, religious, social, social service, student government, and yearbook. Popular campus events include Foreign Language Week, Homecoming, Family Weekend, Winter Carnival, and Jimmie Jive Week.
Sports: There are 7 intercollegiate sports for men and 5 for women, and 4 intramural sports for men and 4 for women. Athletic and recreation facilities include a sports center-YMCA, ice arena, and a stadium, as well as a municipal golf course and a civic arena.
Disabled Students: Thirty percent of the campus is accessible to disabled students. The following facilities are available: wheelchair ramps, elevators, special parking, specially equipped rest rooms, special class scheduling, and lowered drinking fountains.
Services: In addition to many counseling and information services, tutoring is available in most subjects. There is also remedial math, reading, and writing.
Campus Safety and Security: Campus safety and security measures include informal discussions, pamphlets, posters, films, and lighted pathways and sidewalks.
Programs of Study: Jamestown College awards the B.A. degree. Bachelor's degrees are awarded in BIOLOGICAL SCIENCE (biology/biological science), BUSINESS (accounting, business administration and management, and business economics), COMMUNICATIONS AND THE ARTS (dramatic arts, English, fine arts, and music), COMPUTER AND PHYSICAL SCIENCE (actuarial science, chemistry, computer science, information sciences and systems, and mathematics), EDUCATION (elementary, middle school, and secondary), HEALTH PROFESSIONS (nursing, predentistry, and premedicine), SOCIAL SCIENCE (history, philosophy, political science/government, prelaw, psychology, and religion). Business, nursing, physical sciences, and education are the strongest academically. Business and nursing have the largest enrollments.
Required: In order to graduate, students must have a minimum of 128 semester credits, at least 48 of which must be upper-division level, with an average of 48 semester credits in the major, and maintain

at least a 2.0 GPA. General education requirements include 42 semester credits of cultural heritage/values.
Special: Special academic programs include cooperative programs in business and nursing, on-campus work-study, internships, study abroad, and dual majors with any of the 25 concentrations. A 3–2 engineering program is offered with North Dakota State University, as are nondegree study, pass/fail options, and credit for life, military, and work experience. Directed study is also possible. There are 2 national honor societies on campus. Ten departments have honors programs.
Faculty/Classroom: Sixty-six percent of faculty are male; 34%, female. All teach undergraduates. The average class size in an introductory lecture is 40; in a laboratory, 30; and in a regular course offering, 25.
Admissions: About 85% of the 1993–94 applicants were accepted. The ACT scores for the 1993–94 freshman class were as follows: 39% below 21, 31% between 21 and 23, 20% between 24 and 26, 5% between 27 and 28, and 5% above 28. About 29% of the current freshmen were in the top fifth of their class; 55% were in the top two fifths. Sixteen freshmen graduated first in their class.
Requirements: Jamestown College requires applicants to be in the upper 50% of their class. A minimum GPA of 2.5 is required. The ACT is recommended. Other admissions requirements include graduation from an accredited secondary school; the GED is also accepted. An interview is highly recommended. AP and CLEP credits are accepted. Important factors used in the admissions decision are evidence of special talent, extracurricular activities record, leadership record, advanced placement or honor courses, and geographic diversity.
Procedure: Freshmen are admitted fall and spring. Entrance exams should be taken in the fall of the senior year. Application deadlines are open. The application fee is $20. Notification is sent on a rolling basis. There are early admissions and deferred admissions plans.
Transfer: About 77 transfer students enrolled in 1993–94. Transfer students must have at least a 2.5 GPA and be in good standing with their previous college; if suspended, the student must allow 1 semester to elapse before applying for probationary admission. A total of 35 credits out of 128 must be completed at Jamestown College.
Visiting: There are guides for informal visits and visitors may sit in on classes and stay overnight at the school. To arrange for a visit, contact the Admissions Office at (701) 252-3467 or (800) 336-2554.
Financial Aid: In 1993–94, all current freshmen and nearly all continuing students received some form of financial aid. Scholarships or need-based grants averaged $4500 ($7220 maximum); loans averaged $2000 ($3000 maximum); and work contracts averaged $700 ($1000 maximum). Sixty-four percent of undergraduate students work part-time. Average earnings from campus work for the school year are $750. The average financial indebtedness of a recent graduate was $7500. Jamestown College is a member of CSS. The FAF, FFS or SFS and the FAFSA are required. The deadline for financial aid applications is August 1.
International Students: There are currently 79 international students enrolled. They must take the TOEFL and achieve a minimum score of 500.
Computers: The college provides computer facilities for student use. The mainframe is a DEC MicroVAX II. There are also microcomputers available in the computer center, laboratories, and faculty offices. All students may access the system. It may be used 24 hours a day. There are no time limits and no fees.
Graduates: In 1992–93 131 bachelor's degrees were awarded. The most popular majors among graduates were business (30%), nursing (19%), and history/political science (18%). Within an average freshman class, 2% graduate in 3 years, 40% in 4 years, and 8% in 5 years. In a recent graduating class, 99% of the men and 97% of the women had found employment.
Admissions Contact: Carol Schmeichel, Director of Admissions.

MAYVILLE STATE UNIVERSITY
Mayville, ND 58257-1299

E-3

(701) 786-4873
(800) 437-4104 (out-of-state)

Full-time: 351 men, 307 women	Faculty: IIB, -$
Part-time: 17 men, 41 women	Ph.D.s: 61%
Graduate: none	Student/Faculty: 18 to 1
Year: semesters, summer session	Tuition: $1828 ($4511)
Application Deadline: open	Room & Board: $2444
Freshman Class: 233 applied, 233 accepted, 153 enrolled	
SAT I or ACT: required	NONCOMPETITIVE

Mayville State University, founded in 1889, is a public institution that emphasizes teacher education and business. There are 6 divisions within the university. In addition to regional accreditation, Mayville State has baccalaureate program accreditation with NCATE. The library contains 75,000 volumes and 350 microform items, and subscribes to 600 periodicals. Special learning facilities include a learning resource center and a learning services center. The 55-acre

campus is in a rural area 58 miles north of Fargo and 42 miles south of Grand Forks. Including residence halls, there are 19 buildings on campus.

Student Life: About 74% of undergraduates are from North Dakota. Students come from 12 states, 2 foreign countries, and Canada. Ninety-five percent are from public schools. Eighty-eight percent are white. Seventy-five percent are Lutheran; 25% Catholic. The average age of freshmen is 17. Twenty percent drop out by the end of their first year; 50% remain to graduate.

Housing: A total of 450 students can be accommodated in college housing. College-sponsored living facilities include single-sex and coed dormitories, on-campus apartments, and married-student housing. On-campus housing is guaranteed for the freshman year only and is available on a first-come, first-served basis. Fifty-six percent of students commute. Alcohol is not permitted. All students may keep cars on campus.

Activities: About 5% of men belong to 1 local fraternity; about 5% of women belong to 1 local sorority. There are many groups and organizations on campus, including band, cheerleading, chorus, dance, drama, film, musical theater, newspaper, pep band, political, religious, student government, and yearbook. Popular campus events include Homecoming, Winterfest, Springfest, and 'We Are the World' (international cultural program).

Sports: There are 4 intercollegiate sports for men and 3 for women, and 10 intramural sports for men and 9 for women. Athletic and recreation facilities include a 4500-seat football stadium, a track and practice field, a baseball diamond, tennis courts, a swimming pool, and handball and racquetball courts.

Disabled Students: Ten percent of the campus is accessible to disabled students. The following facilities are available: elevators, special parking, and special class scheduling. Although facilities for the physically disabled are limited, there are 2 special counselors and 3 assistants to provide help.

Services: In addition to many counseling and information services, tutoring is available in some subjects, including writing, mathematics, reading, and study skills.

Campus Safety and Security: Campus safety and security measures include informal discussions, pamphlets, posters, and films, lighted pathways and sidewalks, and nighttime foot patrol.

Programs of Study: Mayville State awards the B.A., B.S., B.G.S., and B.S.Ed. degrees. Associate degrees also are awarded. Bachelor's degrees are awarded in BIOLOGICAL SCIENCE (biology/biological science), BUSINESS (business administration and management), COMMUNICATIONS AND THE ARTS (English), COMPUTER AND PHYSICAL SCIENCE (chemistry, computer programming, mathematics, physical sciences, and science), EDUCATION (business, elementary, science, and secondary), SOCIAL SCIENCE (liberal arts/general studies and social science). Business administration, computer information science, and elementary education are the strongest programs academically. Business administration and elementary education have the largest enrollments.

Required: To graduate, students must complete 128 semester hours with a minimum overall GPA of 2.0 in most programs and 2.5 in education. General requirements include 8 to 10 quarter hours of science, 9 each of humanities and social science, 6 of English, up to 3 of mathematics, and 3 each of computer information systems, psychology, speech, and physical education.

Special: Through a reciprocity program, residents of all contiguous states and Canadian provinces pay a considerably reduced out-of-state fee. Mayville State also offers preprofessional programs, internships, work-study programs, B.A.-B.S. degrees, dual majors, a general studies degree, credit for life experience, nondegree study, and pass/fail options. Co-op programs are available, including a certified education program for all subject areas. There is also a K-8 mathematics specialist program.

Faculty/Classroom: All faculty teach undergraduates. The average class size in an introductory lecture is 35; in a laboratory, 20; and in a regular course offering, 20.

Admissions: All of the 1993–94 applicants were accepted. The ACT scores for the 1993–94 freshman class were as follows: 61% below 21, 23% between 21 and 23, 13% between 24 and 26, and 3% between 27 and 28. About 12% of the current freshmen were in the top fifth of their class; 32% were in the top two fifths.

Requirements: A minimum GPA of 2.0 is required. The SAT I or ACT is required. Applicants must be graduates of an accredited secondary school or have a GED certificate. Those who graduated in 1993 and thereafter must have the following core courses completed: 4 English, 3 mathematics (Algebra I or higher), and 3 social sciences. AP and CLEP credits are accepted.

Procedure: Freshmen are admitted to all sessions. Entrance exams should be taken during the senior year. Application deadlines are open. Application fee is $20. The college accepts all applicants. Notification is sent on a rolling basis. There is an early decision plan.

Transfer: Applicants must submit official transcripts from all colleges attended and should have a minimum GPA of 2.0, with scores on the SAT I or ACT also recommended. A total of 45 credits out of 128 must be completed at Mayville State.

Visiting: There are regularly scheduled orientations for prospective students, including a campus tour, meetings with faculty in fields of interest, and meetings with the financial aid director if needed. There are guides for informal visits and visitors may sit in on classes and stay overnight at the school. To arrange for a visit, contact the Office of Admissions at (701) 786–4873.

Financial Aid: In a recent year, 75% of continuing students received some form of financial aid. Mayville State is a member of CSS. The FAFSA is required. The deadline for financial aid applications is April 15.

International Students: There are currently 36 international students enrolled. They must take the TOEFL and achieve a minimum score of 525. The SAT I or ACT is recommended.

Computers: The college provides computer facilities for student use. All students may access the system. There are no time limits on using the system and no fees.

Admissions Contact: Ronald G. Brown, Director of Admissions.

MINOT STATE UNIVERSITY
C-2

Minot, ND 58707
(701) 857–3350

Full-time: 1354 men, 1945 women	Faculty: 171; IIA, --$
Part-time: 241 men, 361 women	Ph.D.s: 53%
Graduate: 24 men, 101 women	Student/Faculty: 19 to 1
Year: semesters, summer session	Tuition: $1836 ($4600)
Application Deadline: open	Room & Board: $1912
Freshman Class: n/av	
SAT I or ACT: required	NONCOMPETITIVE

Minot State University, founded in 1913, is a public institution offering undergraduate and graduate programs in art, fine arts, health science, liberal arts, music, and teacher preparation. There are 5 undergraduate schools and one graduate school. In addition to regional accreditation, MSU has baccalaureate program accreditation with CSWE, NASM, NCATE, and NLN. The library contains 226,933 volumes, 40,676 microform items, and 9664 audiovisual forms, and subscribes to 850 periodicals. Computerized library sources and services include the card catalog, interlibrary loans, and database searching. Special learning facilities include a learning resource center, art gallery, natural history museum, and radio station. The 103-acre campus is in a small town located in Minot. Including residence halls, there are 19 buildings on campus.

Student Life: About 79% of undergraduates are from North Dakota. Students come from 6 states, 2 foreign countries, and Canada. Seventy-eight percent are white; 16% foreign nationals. The average age of freshmen is 19; all undergraduates, 20. Eighteen percent drop out by the end of their first year; 24% remain to graduate.

Housing: A total of 817 students can be accommodated in college housing. College-sponsored living facilities include single-sex and coed dormitories, on-campus apartments, and married-student housing. In addition, there are special interest houses. On-campus housing is guaranteed for all 4 years. Alcohol is not permitted. All students may keep cars on campus.

Activities: There are 42 groups on campus, including band, cheerleading, choir, chorale, chorus, drama, honors, jazz band, marching band, musical theater, newspaper, orchestra, radio and TV, religious, social service, student government, symphony, and yearbook.

Sports: There are 7 intercollegiate sports for men and 6 for women, and 4 intramural sports for men and 4 for women. Athletic and recreation facilities include a campus field house seating 10,000.

Disabled Students: The following facilities are available: wheelchair ramps, elevators, special parking, specially equipped rest rooms, special class scheduling, lowered drinking fountains, lowered telephones, and some dormitory rooms specially designed for disabled students.

Services: In addition to many counseling and information services, tutoring is available in every subject.

Programs of Study: MSU awards the B.A., B.S., B.S.Ed., B.S.N., and B.S.W. degrees. Associate and master's degrees also are awarded. Bachelor's degrees are awarded in BIOLOGICAL SCIENCE (biology/biological science), BUSINESS (accounting, business administration and management, and marketing/retailing/merchandising), COMMUNICATIONS AND THE ARTS (broadcasting, fine arts, French, German, and music), COMPUTER AND PHYSICAL SCIENCE (chemistry, computer science, earth science, physics, and radiological technology), EDUCATION (art, business, education of the deaf and hearing impaired, elementary, foreign languages, and music), HEALTH PROFESSIONS (medical laboratory technology, nursing, and speech pathology/audiology), SOCIAL SCIENCE (criminal justice, economics, history, psychology, social science, social work, and sociology).

Required: Students must take a number of general education courses in humanities, communication, natural sciences, social and behavorial sciences, and leisure-time education. They must complete 128 semester hours, with 30 to 37 in the major and a minimum GPA of 2.0.

Special: A general studies degree, independent research, and unique programs such as one teaching vocal music to rural and grade schools by radio are available. Cross-registration with several community colleges, combined B.A.-B.S. degrees, dual majors, work-study programs, internships, and pass/fail options also are offered. There is a freshman honors program on campus.

Faculty/Classroom: Sixty-three percent of faculty are male; 37%, female. All teach undergraduates, 20% do research, and 20% do both. Graduate students teach 5% of introductory courses.

Requirements: The SAT I or ACT (preferred) is required as part of a study of the state's open-admission policy. The GED is accepted. CLEP credit is accepted.

Procedure: Freshmen are admitted to all sessions. Entrance exams can be taken anytime. Application deadlines are open. Application fee is $20. The college accepts all applicants. Notification is sent on a rolling basis.

Transfer: About 458 transfer students enrolled in 1993–94. Transfers must submit transcripts from each college attended as well as ACT scores. A total of 30 credits out of 128 must be completed at MSU.

Visiting: There are regularly scheduled orientations for prospective students. There are guides for informal visits, and visitors may sit in on classes and stay overnight at the school. To arrange for a visit, contact Enrollment Services at (701) 857-3350.

Financial Aid: In 1993–94, 72% of all students received some form of financial aid, including need-based aid. The average freshman award was $3519. Of that total, scholarships or need-based grants averaged $1427 ($3300 maximum); loans averaged $1736 ($3625 maximum); and work contracts averaged $53 ($2400 maximum). One percent of undergraduate students work part-time. Average earnings from campus work for the school year are $700. The average financial indebtedness of the 1992–93 graduate was $11,300. MSU is a member of CSS. The FAF, FFS, or SFS is required. The deadline for financial aid applications is October 15.

International Students: There are currently 10 international students enrolled. They must take the TOEFL and achieve a minimum score of 525. The student must also take the SAT I or the ACT.

Computers: The college provides computer facilities for student use. Microcomputers are available throughout the campus. Network access to Bitnet, NWNET, and Internet is available through a campus Ethernet backbone. All students may access the system 24 hours daily. There are no time limits on using the system and no fees.

Graduates: In 1992–93, 518 bachelor's degrees were awarded. The most popular majors among graduates were elementary education (16%), business administration (9%), and social work (8%).

Admissions Contact: Angela Kirchmeier, Admissions Counselor.

NORTH DAKOTA STATE UNIVERSITY OF AGRICULTURE AND APPLIED SCIENCE

F-3

Fargo, ND 58105-5596

(701) 237-8643
(800) 488-NDSU (out-of-state)

Full-time: 4434 men, 2989 women	Faculty: 464; IIA, --$
Part-time: 582 men, 491 women	Ph.D.s: 87%
Graduate: 589 men, 375 women	Student/Faculty: 16 to 1
Year: semesters	Tuition: $2184 ($5498)
Application Deadline: open	Room & Board: $2590
Freshman Class: 3041 applied, 2246 accepted, 1710 enrolled	
ACT: 23	VERY COMPETITIVE

North Dakota State University, founded in 1890, is a comprehensive, public, coeducational land-grant institution. Its undergraduate and graduate programs emphasize the liberal arts and sciences, agricultural and technical studies, architecture, business, engineering, teacher preparation, and pharmaceutical studies. There are 8 undergraduate schools and one graduate school. In addition to regional accreditation, NDSU has baccalaureate program accreditation with ABET, ACPE, ADA, AHEA, NAAB, NASM, NCATE, and NLN. The 4 libraries contain 455,338 volumes, 220,119 microform items, and 1912 audiovisual forms, and subscribe to 4265 periodicals. Computerized library sources and services include the card catalog, interlibrary loans, and database searching. Special learning facilities include an art gallery and radio station. The 2100-acre campus is in an urban area in Fargo. Including residence halls, there are 84 buildings on campus.

Student Life: About 58% of undergraduates are from North Dakota. Students come from 43 states, 39 foreign countries, and Canada. Ninety-three percent are from public schools; 7% from private. Ninety-six percent are white. Sixty-one percent are Protestant; 32% Catholic. The average age of freshmen is 19; all undergraduates, 23. Thirty

percent drop out by the end of their first year; 70% remain to graduate.

Housing: A total of 3431 students can be accommodated in college housing. College-sponsored living facilities include single-sex and coed dormitories, on-campus apartments, married-student housing, fraternity houses, and sorority houses. On-campus housing is guaranteed for all 4 years. Sixty-one percent of students commute. Alcohol is not permitted. All students may keep cars on campus.

Activities: About 10% of men belong to 11 national fraternities; about 10% of women belong to 5 national sororities. There are 200 groups on campus, including art, band, cheerleading, chess, choir, chorus, computers, dance, drama, drill team, ethnic, gay, honors, international, jazz band, marching band, musical theater, newspaper, pep band, political, professional, radio and TV, religious, social, social service, and student government. Popular campus events include Homecoming, Little International, Career Days, International Students' Week, Women's Week, Spring Blast, and Native American Week.

Sports: There are 8 intercollegiate sports for men and 6 for women, and 15 intramural sports for men and 13 for women. Athletic and recreation facilities include a sports arena, indoor and outdoor tracks, volleyball, tennis, basketball, and racquetball courts, baseball and softball fields, a pool, wrestling and weight rooms, and a multipurpose fitness room.

Disabled Students: The entire campus is accessible to disabled students. The following facilities are available: wheelchair ramps, elevators, special parking, specially equipped rest rooms, special class scheduling, lowered drinking fountains, lowered telephones, and special transportation.

Services: In addition to many counseling and information services, tutoring is available in most subjects. In addition, there is a reader service for the blind, remedial math, reading, and writing, note takers, and reader services.

Campus Safety and Security: Campus safety and security measures include 24-hour foot and vehicle patrol, self defense education, escort service, and shuttle buses. In addition, there are informal discussions, pamphlets, posters, and films, and lighted pathways and sidewalks.

Programs of Study: NDSU awards the B.A., B.S., B.F.A. in Theater Arts, and B.Univ.Studies degrees. Master's and doctoral degrees also are awarded. Bachelor's degrees are awarded in AGRICULTURE (agricultural economics, agricultural mechanics, agriculture, animal science, horticulture, range/farm management, and soil science), BIOLOGICAL SCIENCE (biology/biological science, biotechnology, botany, entomology, microbiology, plant pathology, and zoology), BUSINESS (accounting, business administration and management, hotel/motel and restaurant management, and recreation and leisure services), COMMUNICATIONS AND THE ARTS (communications, design, dramatic arts, English, fine arts, French, German, music, and Spanish), COMPUTER AND PHYSICAL SCIENCE (chemistry, computer science, earth science, mathematics, physics, and statistics), EDUCATION (agricultural, home economics, physical, and secondary), ENGINEERING AND ENVIRONMENTAL DESIGN (agricultural engineering, architecture, civil engineering, construction engineering, construction management, construction technology, electrical/electronics engineering, engineering physics, food services technology, industrial administration/management, interior design, landscape architecture/design, mechanical engineering, and transportation engineering), HEALTH PROFESSIONS (medical laboratory technology, nursing, pharmacy, and veterinary science), SOCIAL SCIENCE (child care/child and family studies, economics, family/consumer resource management, food science, history, home economics, humanities, physical fitness/movement, political science/government, psychology, social science, sociology, and textiles and clothing). Sciences, engineering, and business have the largest enrollments.

Required: Students must complete at least 122 semester credits, with at least 24 in the major, and maintain a minimum GPA of 2.0. General education requirements include 6 credits in written/oral communication, with at least 1 course in writing; 12 credits in the humanities/social sciences and behavioral sciences; 6 credits in mathematics/science, with at least 1 course in mathematics, statistics, or computer science; and a minimum of 2 credits of physical education.

Special: Special academic programs include cooperative work programs and internships. There is cross-registration with the Tri-college Consortium. Student-designed and dual majors, a B.A.-B.S. degree, credit for life, military, and work experience, nondegree study, and pass/fail options are possible. There is a freshman honors program on campus, as well as 20 national honor societies.

Faculty/Classroom: Seventy-eight percent of faculty are male; 22%, female. Graduate students teach 5% of introductory courses. The average class size in an introductory lecture is 100; in a laboratory, 25; and in a regular course offering, 37.

Admissions: About 74% of the 1993–94 applicants were accepted. The ACT scores for the 1993–94 freshman class were as follows: 30% below 21, 45% between 21 and 25, 20% between 26 and 29, and

5% above 29. There were 10 National Merit finalists and 6 semifinalists. About 57 freshmen graduated first in their class.

Requirements: NDSU requires applicants to be in the upper 50% of their class. A minimum GPA of 2.5 is required. The SAT I or ACT is required, as are 4 units of English, and 3 each of mathematics, natural science, and social science. The GED is accepted, with a minimum score of 40. AP and CLEP credits are accepted.

Procedure: Freshmen are admitted to all sessions. Entrance exams should be taken in the fall of the senior year. Application deadlines are open. The application fee is $20. Notification is sent on a rolling basis. There are early admissions and deferred admissions plans.

Transfer: About 868 transfer students enrolled in 1993–94. Transfer students must have a minimum GPA of 2.0; ACT or SAT I scores are required if the applicant has less than 1 year of college credit. A total of 30 credits out of 122 must be completed at NDSU.

Visiting: There are regularly scheduled orientations for prospective students, including a tour of the campus, an academic appointment, and a meeting with an admissions counselor. There are guides for informal visits and visitors may sit in on classes. To arrange for a visit, contact the Office of Admission at (710) 237-8643 or (800) 488-NDSU.

Financial Aid: In a recent year, 70% of all freshmen and 60% of continuing students received some form of financial aid. About 65% of freshmen and 55% of continuing students received need-based aid. The average freshman award in a recent year was $4100. Of that total, scholarships or need-based grants averaged $1500 ($2500 maximum); loans averaged $2000 ($4000 maximum); and work contracts averaged $600 ($1200 maximum). Seventeen percent of undergraduate students work part-time. Average earnings from campus work for the school year are $750. The average financial indebtedness of a recent year's graduate was $9100. NDSU is a member of CSS. The FFS is required. The deadline for financial aid applications is April 15.

International Students: The school actively recruits these students. They must take the TOEFL and achieve a minimum score of 525. The student must also take the ACT.

Computers: The college provides computer facilities for student use. The mainframe is an IBM ES-9000. Students access the system from various terminal clusters across campus as well as from their living areas via modem. Microcomputers are also available throughout the campus. All students may access the system 24 hours a day or as posted. There are no time limits on using the system and no fees.

Graduates: In a recent year, 1326 bachelor's degrees were awarded. The most popular majors among a recent year's graduates were electrical and electronics engineering (9%), business administration (9%), and pharmacy (6%). Some 195 companies recruited on campus in an earlier year.

Admissions Contact: Carolyn Schnell, Interim Director of Admission.

UNIVERSITY OF MARY
C-3

Bismarck, ND 58504   (701) 255-7500; (800) 288-6279 (out-of-state)

Full-time: 538 men, 938 women	Faculty: 75
Part-time: 86 men, 196 women	Ph.D.s: 30%
Graduate: 45 men, 90 women	Student/Faculty: 20 to 1
Year: 4-4-1, summer session	Tuition: $6340
Application Deadline: see profile	Room & Board: $2570
Freshman Class: 674 applied, 654 accepted, 350 enrolled	
ACT: 21	LESS COMPETITIVE

The University of Mary, founded in 1959, is a private coeducational institution affiliated with the Roman Catholic Church. The emphases of its undergraduate and graduate programs are on liberal arts, humanities, social sciences, business, health science, music, professional training, philosophy and religious studies, and teacher preparation. There are 7 undergraduate and 3 graduate schools. In addition to regional accreditation, Mary has baccalaureate program accreditation with CSWE and NLN. The library contains 50,000 volumes, 2500 microform items, and 7200 audiovisual forms, and subscribes to 500 periodicals. Computerized library sources and services include the card catalog, interlibrary loans, and database searching. Special learning facilities include a learning resource center, art gallery, radio station, and TV station. The 107-acre campus is in a suburban area 7 miles south of Bismarck. Including residence halls, there are 10 buildings on campus.

Student Life: About 70% of undergraduates are from North Dakota. Students come from 15 states and 3 foreign countries. Ninety-five percent are from public schools. Ninety-six percent are white. Sixty percent are Catholic; 30% Protestant. The average age of freshmen is 18; all undergraduates, 23. Twenty-nine percent drop out by the end of their first year; 40% remain to graduate.

Housing: A total of 600 students can be accommodated in college housing. College-sponsored living facilities include single-sex and coed dormitories and on-campus apartments. On-campus housing is

guaranteed for all 4 years. Fifty percent of students commute. Alcohol is not permitted. All students may keep cars on campus.

Activities: There are no fraternities or sororities on campus. There are 20 groups on campus, including band, cheerleading, choir, chorale, chorus, computers, drama, jazz band, musical theater, newspaper, orchestra, pep band, photography, radio and TV, religious, social, social service, student government, symphony, and yearbook. Popular campus events include Homecoming, Parents Day, and Cultural Day.

Sports: There are 6 intercollegiate sports for men and 6 for women, and 10 intramural sports for men and 10 for women. Athletic and recreation facilities include an activity center housing a 1200-seat gymnasium, basketball and racquetball courts, wrestling and weight rooms, and a pool; there are also track/football, intramural, and softball fields, tennis courts, and a 1200-seat stadium.

Disabled Students: The entire campus is accessible to disabled students. The following facilities are available: wheelchair ramps, elevators, special parking, specially equipped rest rooms, and lowered telephones.

Services: In addition to many counseling and information services, tutoring is available in every subject. In addition, there is remedial math, reading, and writing. Tutoring is free of charge.

Campus Safety and Security: Campus safety and security measures include escort service, shuttle buses, emergency telephones, and lighted pathways and sidewalks.

Programs of Study: Mary awards the B.A., B.S., and B.Univ.Studies degrees. Master's degrees also are awarded. Bachelor's degrees are awarded in BIOLOGICAL SCIENCE (biology/biological science), BUSINESS (accounting and business administration and management), COMMUNICATIONS AND THE ARTS (communications, English, and music), COMPUTER AND PHYSICAL SCIENCE (computer programming and radiological technology), EDUCATION (early childhood, elementary, music, physical, science, and secondary), HEALTH PROFESSIONS (medical laboratory technology, nursing, premedicine, and respiratory therapy), SOCIAL SCIENCE (addiction studies, behavioral science, prelaw, religion, social science, and social work). Business administration, accounting, nursing, and education are the strongest programs academically. Business, nursing, and elementary education have the largest enrollments.

Required: To graduate, students must complete 128 semester hours, with 32 to 56 in the major and 44 at the 300/400 level, and have a minimum GPA of 2.0. At least 60 semester hours must be in liberal arts courses. A B.A. degree additionally requires 16 semester hours of a foreign language or 20 semester hours of philosophy/theology, with 12 such hours at the 300/400 level.

Special: Special academic programs include internships, study abroad in France, Germany, and Spain, on-campus work-study, and a general studies degree. Dual majors include those in elementary education/early childhood, elementary education/special education, athletic training/biology, athletic training/physical education, business/accounting, and business/computer. There are 3 national honor societies on campus.

Faculty/Classroom: Fifty percent of faculty are male; 50%, female. All teach undergraduates. No introductory courses are taught by graduate students. The average class size in an introductory lecture is 30; in a laboratory, 20; and in a regular course offering, 20.

Admissions: About 97% of the 1993–94 applicants were accepted. The ACT scores for the 1993–94 freshman class were as follows: 50% below 21, 26% between 21 and 23, 18% between 24 and 26, 4% between 27 and 28, and 2% above 28. About 25% of the current freshmen were in the top fifth of their class; 54% were in the top two fifths. There was 1 National Merit finalist and 5 semifinalists. About 20 freshmen graduated first in their class.

Requirements: Mary requires applicants to be in the upper 50% of their class. A minimum GPA of 2.5 is required. The SAT I or ACT is recommended. In addition, applicants should be graduates of an accredited secondary school; the GED is accepted. For automatic acceptance, 3 requirements must be met: a minimum 2.5 GPA; an 18 or higher on the ACT; and rank in the upper half of the graduating class. The school's own testing can also be used to determine acceptance. A recommendation from a school counselor, teacher, or employer is requested. An interview is advised. AP and CLEP credits are accepted.

Procedure: Freshmen are admitted in the fall and spring. Entrance exams should be taken in the fall of the senior year. Regular applications should be filed by the first day of class. Application fee is $15. Notification is sent on a rolling basis. There is a deferred admissions plan.

Transfer: About 209 transfer students enrolled in 1993–94. Transfer students should have close to a 2.0 minimum GPA and should present a recommendation from a school counselor, instructor, or employer. A total of 32 credits out of 128 must be completed at Mary.

Visiting: There are regularly scheduled orientations for prospective students, including a campus tour and meetings with individual professors, coaches, students, and music instructors. There are guides for

informal visits and visitors may sit in on classes and stay overnight at the school. To arrange for a visit, contact the Admissions Office at (800) 288–6279.

Financial Aid: In 1993–94, 91% of all current freshmen and 85% of continuing students received some form of financial aid. Scholarships or need-based grants averaged $1500 ($6190 maximum); loans averaged $2800 ($3800 maximum); and work contracts averaged $900 ($1500 maximum). Seventy percent of undergraduate students work part-time. The FAF or FFS, or FAFSA are required. The deadline for financial aid applications is August 15.

International Students: There are currently 18 international students enrolled. They must take the TOEFL and achieve a minimum score of 500.

Computers: The college provides computer facilities for student use. The mainframe is an IBM 5360 System/36. There are 4 workstations connected to the mainframe that are located in the laboratory and 25 microcomputers located throughout the university. Students taking program languages may access the system. It may be used 24 hours a day. There are no time limits on using the system. The fees are $20 per semester.

Graduates: In 1992–93, 314 bachelor's degrees were awarded. Within an average freshman class, 40% graduate in 4 years. Some 8 companies recruited on campus in 1992–93. In the 1992 graduating class, 5% of all graduates were enrolled in graduate school within 6 months of graduation; 90% of all graduates had found employment.

Admissions Contact: Steph Storey, Director of Admissions.

UNIVERSITY OF NORTH DAKOTA

Grand Forks, ND 58202

E-2

(701) 777–3367

Full-time: 4466 men, 3868 women	Faculty: 595; I, --$
Part-time: 630 men, 805 women	Ph.D.s: 78%
Graduate: 902 men, 964 women	Student/Faculty: 14 to 1
Year: semesters, summer session	Tuition: $2298 ($5612)
Application Deadline: July	Room & Board: $2604

Freshman Class: 2777 applied, 2249 accepted, 1652 enrolled

SAT I Verbal/Math: 465/535

NONCOMPETITIVE

The University of North Dakota, established in 1883, is a state-supported comprehensive institution. Its undergraduate and graduate programs emphasize the liberal arts, fine arts, engineering, medicine, aviation, human resources, professional training, business and public health administration, health science, and teacher preparation. There are 10 undergraduate schools and one graduate school. In addition to regional accreditation, UND has baccalaureate program accreditation with AACSB, ABET, ADA, AHEA, APTA, CSWE, NASAD, NASM, NCATE, and NLN. The 3 libraries contain 1,872,663 volumes, 2,257,965 microform items, and 6375 audiovisual forms, and subscribe to 8673 periodicals. Computerized library sources and services include the card catalog, interlibrary loans, and database searching. Special learning facilities include a learning resource center, art gallery, natural history museum, radio station, TV station, and atmospherium. The 570-acre campus is in an urban area. Including residence halls, there are 270 buildings on campus.

Student Life: About 57% of undergraduates are from North Dakota. Students come from 50 states, 44 foreign countries, and Canada. Ninety-two percent are from public schools; 2% from private. Ninety-two percent are white. Fifty-seven percent are Protestant; 34% Catholic. The average age of freshmen is 18; all undergraduates, 25. Twenty-one percent drop out by the end of their first year; 50% remain to graduate.

Housing: A total of 3900 students can be accommodated in college housing. College-sponsored living facilities include single-sex and coed dormitories, on-campus apartments, married-student housing, fraternity houses, and sorority houses. On-campus housing is guaranteed for all 4 years. Sixty-five percent of students commute. Alcohol is not permitted. All students may keep cars on campus.

Activities: About 12% of men belong to 14 national fraternities; about 10% of women belong to 7 national sororities. There are 200 groups on campus, including art, band, cheerleading, chess, choir, chorale, chorus, computers, dance, drama, drill team, ethnic, film, gay, honors, international, jazz band, literary magazine, marching band, musical theater, newspaper, orchestra, pep band, photography, political, professional, radio and TV, religious, social, social service, student government, and symphony. Popular campus events include Homecoming, Honors Day, Founders Day, Native American Week, and Potato Bowl.

Sports: There are 13 intercollegiate sports for men and 9 for women, and 22 intramural sports for men and 21 for women. Athletic and recreation facilities include a sports center/field house with racquetball and basketball courts, pools, and weight rooms; an ice arena; a golf course; a 15,000-seat stadium; a 6000-seat hockey arena; and a 6100-seat basketball center.

Disabled Students: Ninety-seven percent of the campus is accessible to disabled students. The following facilities are available: wheelchair ramps, elevators, special parking, specially equipped rest rooms, special class scheduling, lowered drinking fountains, lowered telephones, accessible transportation, housing, and academic and personal support services.

Services: In addition to many counseling and information services, tutoring is available in every subject. There is a reader service for the blind.

Campus Safety and Security: Campus safety and security measures include 24-hour foot and vehicle patrol, self defense education, escort service, and shuttle buses. In addition, there are informal discussions, pamphlets, posters, films, emergency telephones, and lighted pathways and sidewalks.

Programs of Study: UND awards the B.A., B.S., B.Acc., B.B.A., B.F.A., B.Mus., B.S.Ed., B.S.N., and B.S.P.A. degrees. Master's and doctoral degrees also are awarded. Bachelor's degrees are awarded in AGRICULTURE (wildlife management), BIOLOGICAL SCIENCE (biology/biological science and zoology), BUSINESS (accounting, banking and finance, business administration and management, business economics, marketing/retailing/merchandising, and retailing), COMMUNICATIONS AND THE ARTS (advertising, broadcasting, communications, dramatic arts, English, fine arts, French, German, journalism, Latin, music, public relations, Scandinavian languages, Spanish, speech/debate/rhetoric, and visual and performing arts), COMPUTER AND PHYSICAL SCIENCE (atmospheric sciences and meteorology, chemistry, computer science, earth science, geology, information sciences and systems, mathematics, meteorological studies, natural sciences, physical sciences, and physics), EDUCATION (business, early childhood, elementary, health, home economics, industrial arts, library science, middle school, and music), ENGINEERING AND ENVIRONMENTAL DESIGN (aeronautical science, aviation administration/management, chemical engineering, civil engineering, electrical/electronics engineering, geological engineering, and mechanical engineering), HEALTH PROFESSIONS (communications disorders, cytotechnology, medical laboratory technology, nursing, occupational therapy, physical therapy, premedicine, and speech pathology/audiology), SOCIAL SCIENCE (American studies, anthropology, criminal justice, dietetics, economics, geography, history, humanities, parks and recreation management, philosophy, physical fitness/movement, political science/government, prelaw, psychology, public administration, religion, social science, social work, and sociology). Engineering and the health professions are the strongest programs academically. Business, liberal arts, and aviation have the largest enrollments.

Required: In order to graduate, students must complete at least 125 credit hours, 30 in the major, with a minimum GPA of 2.0. Distribution requirements include 5 credits of English composition, 9 of social sciences, 12 each of art and humanities, and mathematics, science, and technology.

Special: Special academic programs include cooperative programs, accelerated degree programs in most majors, internships in many majors, study abroad in at least 40 countries, work-study, and dual majors in all areas. Also offered are a general studies degree, student-designed majors, nondegree study, and pass/fail options. Alternative academic programs include the Division of Continuing Education's correspondence study, the Integrated Studies Program, which offers a means of fulfilling general education requirements by a semester of related course work, and study via telecommunications. There is a freshman honors program on campus, as well as 26 national honor societies, including Phi Beta Kappa. One department has an honors program.

Faculty/Classroom: Sixty-six percent of faculty are male; 34%, female. All teach undergraduates.

Admissions: About 81% of the 1993–94 applicants were accepted. The SAT scores for the 1993–94 freshman class were as follows: Verbal—68% below 500, 22% between 500 and 599, 7% between 600 and 700, and 3% above 700. The ACT scores were 15% between 12 and 21, 27% between 19 and 21, 41% between 22 and 26, and 17% between 27 and 36. About 54% of the current freshmen were in the top quarter of their class; 87% were in the top half. There were 10 National Merit finalists and 25 semifinalists.

Requirements: The ACT is required, but the SAT I will be accepted. Applicants must be graduates of an accredited secondary school; the GED is accepted. All North Dakota residents who are high school graduates are eligible for admission. Nonresidents must have a GPA of at least 2.0. AP and CLEP credits are accepted.

Procedure: Freshmen are admitted to all sessions. Entrance exams should be taken in the spring of the junior year or the fall of the senior year. Applications should be filed by July for fall entry, December 1 for spring entry, and April 1 for summer entry, along with an application fee of $25. The college accepts all in-state residents who apply. Notification is sent on a rolling basis. There is an early decision plan.

Transfer: About 762 transfer students enrolled in 1993–94. Transfer students must have a minimum GPA of 2.0 and be in good academic standing. A total of 30 credits out of 125 must be completed at UND.

Visiting: There are regularly scheduled orientations for prospective students, including a visit with an admissions counselor, a campus tour, an academic appointment, and an athletic appointment (if applicable). There are guides for informal visits and visitors may sit in on classes and stay overnight at the school. To arrange for a visit, contact Enrollment Services at (701) 777-3304.

Financial Aid: In 1993–94, 55% of all current freshmen and 82% of continuing students received some form of financial aid. About 52% of freshmen and 46% of continuing students received need-based aid. The average freshman award was $3800. Of that total, scholarships or need-based grants averaged $250 ($2250 maximum); loans averaged $1200 ($1500 maximum); and work contracts averaged $1000 ($1500 maximum). Forty-five percent of undergraduate students work part-time. The average financial indebtedness of the 1992–93 graduate was $8500. UND is a member of CSS. The FFS is required; other financial statements are also accepted. The deadline for financial aid applications is March 15.

International Students: There are currently 476 international students enrolled. They must take the TOEFL and achieve a minimum score of 525. The student must also take the SAT I or the ACT.

Computers: The college provides computer facilities for student use. The mainframes include an IBM ES/9000 480, a DEC VAX 8530, and a Unisys 2200–401. Access to the mainframe is available via modems. More than 2000 microcomputers are located campuswide and include DEC VAX 785s and 8530s, IBMs and IBM AS/r00s, Apples, and Solbourne 5/802s. Token-ring, Ethernet, and Appletalk networks are available. All students may access the system 24 hours a day. There are no time limits on using the system and no fees.

Graduates: In 1992–93, 1773 bachelor's degrees were awarded. The most popular majors among graduates were aerospace sciences (6%), business administration (6%), and accounting (6%). Within an average freshman class, 40% graduate in 5 years. Some 253 companies recruited on campus in 1992–93.

Admissions Contact: Gerald Hamerlik, Dean of Enrollment Services.

VALLEY CITY STATE UNIVERSITY
Valley City, ND 58072

E-3

(701) 845–7101
(800) 532–8641 (out-of-state)

Full-time: 440 men, 423 women	Faculty: 54; IIB, --$
Part-time: 50 men, 139 women	Ph.Ds: 40%
Graduate: none	Student/Faculty: 16 to 1
Year: semesters, summer session	Tuition: $1815 ($4495)
Application Deadline: open	Room & Board: $2570
Freshman Class: 368 applied, 350 accepted, 212 enrolled	
ACT: 21	**LESS COMPETITIVE**

Valley City State University, founded in 1890, is a state-supported institution offering degree programs in the arts and sciences, business, and education. In addition to regional accreditation, VCSU has baccalaureate program accreditation with NCATE. The library contains 87,164 volumes, 29,159 microform items, and 4787 audiovisual forms, and subscribes to 428 periodicals. Computerized library sources and services include the card catalog and database searching. Special learning facilities include a learning resource center and planetarium. The 55-acre campus is in a small town 58 miles west of Fargo. Including residence halls, there are 24 buildings on campus.

Student Life: About 89% of undergraduates are from North Dakota. Students come from 19 states, 3 foreign countries, and Canada. Ninety-nine percent are from public schools. Ninety-two percent are white. Sixty-eight percent are Protestant; 31% Catholic. The average age of freshmen is 19; all undergraduates, 23. Twenty-nine percent drop out by the end of their first year; 31% remain to graduate.

Housing: A total of 592 students can be accommodated in college housing. College-sponsored living facilities include single-sex and coed dormitories and married-student housing. On-campus housing is guaranteed for all 4 years. Sixty-six percent of students commute. Alcohol is not permitted. All students may keep cars on campus.

Activities: About 10% of men belong to 2 local fraternities; about 10% of women belong to 2 local sororities. There are more than 15 groups on campus, including art, band, cheerleading, choir, chorus, computers, dance, drama, honors, jazz band, musical theater, newspaper, pep band, photography, political, religious, social, student government, and yearbook. Popular campus events include Homecoming, Sno-Daze, and EBC-Hit Parade.

Sports: There are 8 intercollegiate sports for men and 6 for women, and 4 intramural sports for men and 4 for women. Athletic and recreation facilities include a 2500-seat football stadium with an all-weather track, a 2500-seat arena, an indoor pool, a field house, tennis and racquetball courts, a cross-country course, softball and baseball fields, a golf course, wrestling and weight rooms, and a fitness room.

Disabled Students: Ninety percent of the campus is accessible to disabled students. The following facilities are available: wheelchair ramps, elevators, special parking, specially equipped rest rooms, lowered drinking fountains, and lowered telephones.

Services: In addition to many counseling and information services, tutoring is available in most subjects. There is remedial math, reading, and writing.

Campus Safety and Security: Campus safety and security measures include informal discussions, pamphlets, posters, films, and lighted pathways and sidewalks.

Programs of Study: VCSU awards the B.A., B.S., B.S.Ed., and B.University Studies degrees. Bachelor's degrees are awarded in BIOLOGICAL SCIENCE (biology/biological science), BUSINESS (business administration and management), COMMUNICATIONS AND THE ARTS (communications, English, fine arts, music, Spanish, and speech/debate/rhetoric), COMPUTER AND PHYSICAL SCIENCE (chemistry, computer science, earth science, and mathematics), EDUCATION (art, business, elementary, foreign languages, health, industrial arts, middle school, music, science, secondary, and teaching English as a second language/foreign language), ENGINEERING AND ENVIRONMENTAL DESIGN (industrial engineering technology), HEALTH PROFESSIONS (premedicine), SOCIAL SCIENCE (history). Education and business are the strongest programs academically. Elementary education and business have the largest enrollments.

Required: To graduate, students must complete at least 128 semester hours with a minimum GPA of 2.0, or 2.5 for a B.S.Ed. degree. Except for those pursuing the Bachelor of University Studies degree, all students must complete the foundation studies curriculum, which includes 8 hours each in communication and science, 6 each in humanities and social science, 3 each in technology, physical education, computer science, mathematics, and psychology, and 2 in technology.

Special: VCSU offers internships, on-campus work-study, a 3–1–3 program with Northwestern College of Chiropractic in Minnesota, a B.A.-B.S. degree, a dual major in business administration/management, pass/fail options for some courses, and credit for life, military, and work experience. There are 6 national honor societies on campus. Five departments have honors programs.

Faculty/Classroom: Sixty-six percent of faculty are male; 34%, female. All teach undergraduates and 10% both teach and do research. The average class size in an introductory lecture is 40; in a laboratory, 20; and in a regular course offering, 25.

Admissions: About 95% of the 1993–94 applicants were accepted.

Requirements: The SAT I or ACT is required. Applicants must be graduates of an accredited secondary school or have a GED certificate. Core curriculum requirements include 4 units of English and 3 units each of mathematics, laboratory science, and social science. CLEP credit is accepted. Important factors used in the admissions decision are evidence of special talent, advanced placement or honor courses, leadership record, parents or siblings attending the school, and personality, intangible qualities.

Procedure: Freshmen are admitted to all sessions. Entrance exams should be taken in the fall or spring of the junior year. Application deadlines are open. Application fee is $20. Notification is sent on a rolling basis. There is an early admissions plan.

Transfer: About 75 transfer students enrolled in 1993–94. Applicants must be in good academic standing and eligible to return to their previous institution. Official transcripts from all colleges attended are required. A total of 24 credits out of 128 must be completed at VCSU.

Visiting: There are regularly scheduled orientations for prospective students. There are guides for informal visits and visitors may sit in on classes and stay overnight at the school. To arrange for a visit, contact the Office of Admissions at (701) 845–7101 or (800) 532–8641.

Financial Aid: In an earlier year, 70% of all freshmen and 60% of continuing students received some form of financial aid. Scholarships or need-based grants averaged $1027 ($2300 maximum); loans averaged $2286 ($3625 maximum); and work contracts averaged $1613 ($2000 maximum). Fifty percent of undergraduate students work part-time. The average financial indebtedness of an earlier year's graduate was $4000. VCSU is a member of CSS. The FAF or FFS is required. The deadline for financial aid applications is April 15.

International Students: There are currently 49 international students enrolled. They must take the TOEFL and achieve a minimum score of 500.

Computers: The college provides computer facilities for student use. About 70 Apple, IBM PS/2, and IBM-compatible microcomputers are available throughout the campus. All students may access the system. It may be used from 8 A.M. to 9 P.M. There are no time limits on using the system and no fees.

Graduates: In 1992–93 174 bachelor's degrees were awarded. The most popular majors among graduates were elementary education (27%), business administration (20%), and human resources (9%). Within an average freshman class, 18% graduate in 4 years, 27% in 5 years, and 31% in 6 years.

Admissions Contact: Monte H. Johnson, Director of Admissions.

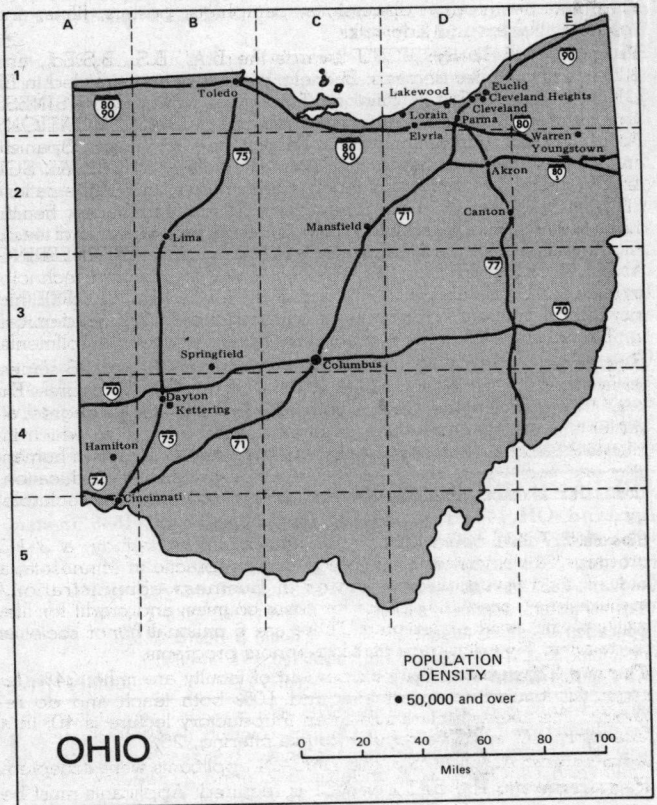

POPULATION DENSITY

● 50,000 and over

OHIO

0   20   40   60   80   100
Miles

ANTIOCH COLLEGE
B-4

Yellow Springs, OH 45387

(513) 767-6400
(800) 543-9436 (out-of-state)

Full-time: 287 men, 468 women
Part-time: 12 men, 11 women
Graduate: none
Year: quarters
Application Deadline: February 1
Freshman Class: 571 applied, 534 accepted, 188 enrolled
SAT I Verbal/Math: 520/500

Faculty: 51; IIA, --$
Ph.D.s: 68%
Student/Faculty: 15 to 1
Tuition: $16,356
Room & Board: $3176

ACT: 24   **COMPETITIVE**

Antioch College, established in 1852, is an independent liberal arts institution where students alternate full-time study on campus with full-time related work experience off campus. The library contains 268,000 volumes, 45,123 microform items, and 4666 audiovisual forms, and subscribes to 1060 periodicals. Computerized library sources and services include interlibrary loans and database searching. Special learning facilities include an art gallery and radio station. The 100-acre campus is in a small town 18 miles east of Dayton. Including residence halls, there are 31 buildings on campus.

Student Life: About 80% of undergraduates are from out-of-state, mostly the Northeast. Students come from 45 states, 8 foreign countries, and Canada. Eighty-four percent are white. The average age of freshmen is 19; all undergraduates, 21. About 46% of freshmen remain to graduate.

Housing: A total of 592 students can be accommodated in college housing. College-sponsored living facilities include single-sex and coed dormitories and on-campus apartments. In addition, there are language houses and special interest houses. On-campus housing is guaranteed for all 4 years. Ninety-five percent of students live on campus; of those, 95% remain on campus on weekends. Alcohol is not permitted. All students may keep cars on campus.

Activities: There are no fraternities or sororities on campus. There are 27 groups on campus, including choir, ethnic, film, gay, international, literary magazine, newspaper, photography, political, radio and TV, social, social service, and student government.

Sports: There are 16 intramural sports for men and 16 for women.

Disabled Students: Ten percent of the campus is accessible to disabled students. The following facilities are available: wheelchair ramps, elevators, special parking, and specially equipped rest rooms.

Services: In addition to many counseling and information services, there is remedial math and writing.

Campus Safety and Security: Campus safety and security measures include 24-hour foot and vehicle patrol, escort service, informal discussions, and pamphlets, posters, and films. In addition, there are lighted pathways and sidewalks.

Programs of Study: Antioch awards the B.A. and B.S. degrees. Bachelor's degrees are awarded in BIOLOGICAL SCIENCE (biology/biological science), BUSINESS (business administration and management), COMMUNICATIONS AND THE ARTS (communications, creative writing, dance, dramatic arts, fine arts, journalism, literature, media arts, and music), COMPUTER AND PHYSICAL SCIENCE (chemistry, computer science, mathematics, and physics), EDUCATION (elementary and secondary), ENGINEERING AND ENVIRONMENTAL DESIGN (environmental studies), HEALTH PROFESSIONS (premedicine), SOCIAL SCIENCE (African and African American studies, anthropology, crosscultural studies, economics, history, international languages and cultures, international relations, peace studies, philosophy, political science/government, prelaw, psychology, public administration, social science, social work, sociology, and women's studies). Social sciences and environmental studies have the largest enrollments.

Required: In order to graduate, students must complete at least 160 academic credits, with 60 in the major, and 6 co-op experiences. The general education program consists of 12 5-credit courses. The core curriculum includes writing, mathematics, and foreign language. Distribution requirements include 64 credits in arts and humanities, social sciences, and natural sciences. Additionally, students must demonstrate proficiency in a foreign language and must successfully complete a work-study experience of at least 1 term in an international or cross-cultural setting.

Special: Special academic programs include an alternating work-study program that is required of all students; co-op jobs, normally 3 months long and resulting in 1 block of co-op credit, are individually arranged according to the needs, interests, and qualifications of each student. There is cross-registration with 17 higher education institutions in southwestern Ohio, and Antioch's membership in the Great Lakes Colleges Association allows for opportunities for special off-campus programs sponsored by several liberal arts colleges in the consortium. An extensive study-abroad program in 15 countries is based on student-designed majors and accelerated degree programs in all majors. Nondegree study is possible. All courses are graded on a credit/no credit basis and evaluated by faculty through narrative evaluations of each student's work.

Faculty/Classroom: Sixty-five percent of faculty are male; 35%, female. Eighty-nine percent teach undergraduates. The average class size in a regular course offering is 13.

Admissions: About 94% of the 1993–94 applicants were accepted. The SAT scores for the 1993–94 freshman class were as follows: Verbal—39% below 500, 40% between 500 and 599, 20% between 600 and 700, and 1% above 700; Math—44% below 500, 35% between 500 and 599, 20% between 600 and 700, and 1% above 700. The ACT scores were 22% below 21, 29% between 21 and 23, 27% between 24 and 26, 11% between 27 and 28, and 11% above 28. About 24% of the current freshmen were in the top fifth of their class; 48% were in the top two fifths.

Requirements: The SAT I or ACT is recommended. AP and CLEP credits are accepted. Important factors used in the admissions decision are recommendations by school officials, personality, intangible qualities, extracurricular activities record, leadership record, and evidence of special talent.

Procedure: Freshmen are admitted in the fall and winter. Early decision applications should be filed by November 15; regular applications, by February 1 for fall entry and November 15 for winter entry, along with an application fee of $25. Notification of early decision is sent December 15; regular decision, April 1. There are early decision, early admissions, and deferred admissions plans.

Transfer: About 63 transfer students enrolled in 1993–94. A total of 80 quarter credits out of 160, plus 6 co-op blocks, must be completed at Antioch.

Visiting: There are regularly scheduled orientations for prospective students, including admissions interviews, co-op presentations, tours, and special events. There are guides for informal visits and visitors may sit in on classes and stay overnight at the school. To arrange for a visit, contact the Admissions Office at (800) 543–9436, or in Ohio call collect: (513) 767–6400.

Financial Aid: In 1993–94 69% of all current freshmen and 73% of continuing students received some form of financial aid. About 61% of freshmen and 65% of continuing students received need-based aid. The average freshman award was $11,292. Of that total, scholarships or need-based grants averaged $6883 ($12,410 maximum); loans averaged $2932 ($4750 maximum); and work contracts averaged $1477 ($1850 maximum). Sixty-five percent of undergraduate

students work part-time. Average earnings from campus work for the school year was $1700. The average financial indebtedness of the 1992–93 graduate was $10,000. Antioch is a member of CSS. The FAF and FAFSA are required. The deadline for financial aid applications is February 15.

International Students: There are currently 16 international students enrolled. They must take the TOEFL and achieve a minimum score of 525.

Computers: The college provides computer facilities for student use. The mainframe is a DEC MicroVAX II. There are also 20 Apple IIe and Macintosh microcomputers and an IBM XT available in the academic computer center. All students may access the system. There are no time limits on using the system and no fees.

Graduates: In 1992–93 113 bachelor's degrees were awarded. The most popular majors among graduates were communications (17%), environmental science/biology (13%), and visual arts (10%). Within an average freshman class, 25% graduate in 4 years, 41% in 5 years, and 46% in 6 years.

Admissions Contact: James Williams, Dean of Admissions.

ART ACADEMY OF CINCINNATI   A-5

Cincinnati, OH 45202   (513) 562–8757; (800) 323–5692

Full-time: 97 men, 80 women	Faculty: 16; IIB, --$
Part-time: 12 men, 19 women	Ph.D.s: 99%
Graduate: none	Student/Faculty: 11 to 1
Year: semesters, summer session	Tuition: $8820
Application Deadline: September 1	Room & Board: n/app
Freshman Class: 144 applied, 84 accepted, 37 enrolled	
SAT I Verbal/Math: 425/420	ACT: 18 SPECIAL

The Art Academy of Cincinnati, founded in 1887, is a private art college offering degrees in fine art, communication design, and art history. In addition to regional accreditation, the academy has baccalaureate program accreditation with NASAD. The library contains 50,000 volumes. Special learning facilities include an art gallery and art museum. The 184-acre campus is in an urban area 2 miles northeast of downtown Cincinnati. There are 2 buildings on campus.

Student Life: About 80% of undergraduates are from Ohio. Students come from 10 states and 1 foreign country. Ninety-two percent are white. The average age of freshmen is 25; all undergraduates, 30. Twenty percent drop out by the end of their first year.

Housing: There are no residence halls. All students commute. Alcohol is not permitted.

Activities: There are no fraternities or sororities on campus. There are some groups and organizations on campus, including art, computers, and student government.

Sports: There is no sports program at the academy.

Services: In addition to many counseling and information services, tutoring is available in most subjects, including art history and English.

Programs of Study: The academy awards the B.F.A. degree. Associate degrees also are awarded. Bachelor's degrees are awarded in COMMUNICATIONS AND THE ARTS (art history and appreciation, graphic design, illustration, painting, photography, printmaking, and sculpture). Art history is the strongest academically. Graphic design has the largest enrollment.

Required: To graduate, students must complete 129 semester hours, including 30 to 42 in the major, with a minimum GPA of 2.0. The 21-credit foundation curriculum is required of all students, as are a computer workshop and a senior exhibition. Distribution requirements include 15 credits in art history and 6 each in English, social science, natural science, and humanities, as well as 3 each in a related art, aesthetics, and an elective.

Special: Students may cross-register with member institutions of the Greater Cincinnati Consortium. Co-op programs are available in graphic design, illustration, and art history. Art history majors may intern at the Cincinnati Art Museum.

Faculty/Classroom: Fifty percent of faculty are male; 50%, female.

Admissions: About 58% of the 1993–94 applicants were accepted. The SAT scores for the 1993–94 freshman class were as follows: Verbal—90% below 500 and 10% between 500 and 599; Math—90% below 500 and 10% between 500 and 599. The ACT scores were 90% below 21, 5% between 21 and 23, and 5% between 24 and 26.

Requirements: The SAT I or ACT is required. Applicants should be graduates of an accredited secondary school with a minimum GPA of 2.0. The GED is accepted. A portfolio review or interview is necessary. AP and CLEP credits are accepted. Evidence of special talent is an important factor used in the admission decision.

Procedure: Freshmen are admitted in the fall and spring. Applications should be filed by September 1 (March 15, priority) for fall entry and January 12 for spring entry, along with an application fee of $25. Notification is sent on a rolling basis. There is a deferred admissions plan.

Transfer: About 30 transfer students enrolled in 1993–94. Applicants must present academic transcripts and a portfolio. At least 65 credits out of 129 must be completed at the academy.

Visiting: There are guides for informal visits, and visitors may sit in on classes. To arrange for a visit, contact Douglas Dobbins at (800) 323–5692 or (513) 562–8757.

Financial Aid: In 1993–94, 95% of all current freshmen and 96% of continuing students received some form of financial aid. About 54% of freshmen and 61% of continuing students received need-based aid. The average freshman award was $2692. Of that total, scholarships or need-based grants averaged $915 ($2400 maximum); loans averaged $1608 ($6625 maximum); and work contracts averaged $116 ($2000 maximum). Twenty-one percent of undergraduate students work part-time. Average earnings from campus work for the school year are $1000. The academy is a member of CSS. The FAFSA financial statement is required. The deadline for financial aid applications is April 1.

International Students: There is currently 1 international student enrolled. International applicants must take the TOEFL and achieve a minimum score of 525.

Computers: Amiga and Macintosh microcomputers are available to students for art and design functions and word processing. All students may access the system. There are no time limits on using the system and no fees.

Admissions Contact: Douglas Dobbins, Director of Admissions.

ASHLAND UNIVERSITY   C-2

Ashland, OH 44805   (419) 289–5052; (800) 882–1548 (in-state)

Full-time: 827 men, 1047 women	Faculty: 195
Part-time: 226 men, 531 women	Ph.D.s: 50%
Graduate: 2952 men and women	Student/Faculty: 10 to 1
Year: semesters, summer session	Tuition: $10,988
Application Deadline: August 15	Room & Board: $4520
Freshman Class: 1454 applied, 1267 accepted, 426 enrolled	
SAT I Verbal/Math: 410/438	ACT: 21 COMPETITIVE

Ashland University, founded in 1878, is a private liberal arts institution affiliated with the Brethren Church, offering undergraduate and graduate programs in the arts and sciences, business, education, and health services. There are 5 undergraduate and 2 graduate schools. In addition to regional accreditation, Ashland has baccalaureate program accreditation with AACSB, AHEA, NASM, NCATE, and NLN. The 3 libraries contain 260,682 volumes, 250,000 microform items, and 8682 audiovisual forms, and subscribe to 1108 periodicals. Special learning facilities include an art gallery, radio station, TV station, writing center, media center, and theater. The 98-acre campus is in a small town midway between Cleveland and Columbus. Including residence halls, there are 35 buildings on campus.

Student Life: About 84% of undergraduates are from Ohio. Students come from 29 states and 26 foreign countries. Ninety-two percent are white. Forty-three percent claim no religious affiliation; 18% Catholic; 10% Protestant. The average age of freshmen is 18; all undergraduates, 20. Twenty-five percent drop out by the end of their first year; 51% remain to graduate.

Housing: A total of 1400 students can be accommodated in college housing. College-sponsored living facilities include single-sex and coed dormitories and fraternity houses. In addition, there is a home management house. On-campus housing is guaranteed for all 4 years and is available on a lottery system for upperclassmen. Eighty percent of students live on campus. Alcohol is not permitted. All students may keep cars on campus.

Activities: About 20% of men belong to 4 national fraternities; about 23% of women belong to 4 national sororities. There are 75 groups on campus, including band, cheerleading, choir, chorus, drama, drill team, ethnic, honors, international, jazz band, literary magazine, marching band, musical theater, newspaper, orchestra, pep band, political, radio and TV, religious, social, social service, student government, symphony, and yearbook. Popular campus events include Spectrum Series, Homecoming, and Parents Day.

Sports: There are 11 intercollegiate sports for men and 8 for women, and 10 intramural sports for men and 10 for women. Athletic and recreation facilities include a 5800-seat stadium, 3000-seat gymnasium, all-weather track, fieldhouse, weight-training center, 8-lane swimming pool with diving boards, saunas, exercise rooms, 3 basketball courts, 2 handball/racquetball courts, and playing fields.

Disabled Students: The following facilities are available: wheelchair ramps, elevators, special parking, specially equipped rest rooms, special class scheduling, and lowered drinking fountains.

Services: In addition to many counseling and information services, tutoring is available in most subjects.

Campus Safety and Security: Campus safety and security measures include 24-hour foot and vehicle patrol, escort service, informal discussions, and lighted pathways and sidewalks. In addition, there are encoded student identification cards and an electronic-access system in residence halls.

Programs of Study: Ashland awards the B.A., B.S., B.M., B.S.B.A., B.S.Ed., B.S.N., and B.S.W. degrees. Associate, master's, and doctoral degrees also are awarded. Bachelor's degrees are awarded in BIOLOGICAL SCIENCE (biology/biological science), BUSINESS (accounting, business administration and management, business economics, hotel/motel and restaurant management, and marketing/retailing/merchandising), COMMUNICATIONS AND THE ARTS (broadcasting, communications, English, journalism, music, and speech/debate/rhetoric), COMPUTER AND PHYSICAL SCIENCE (chemistry, computer science, geology, mathematics, and physics), EDUCATION (art, early childhood, elementary, foreign languages, home economics, music, science, and secondary), HEALTH PROFESSIONS (medical laboratory technology, nursing, predentistry, and premedicine), SOCIAL SCIENCE (criminal justice, history, philosophy, political science/government, prelaw, psychology, public administration, social science, social work, and sociology). Preprofessional science is the strongest academically. Business and teacher education have the largest enrollments.

Required: To graduate, students must complete at least 128 semester hours with a minimum GPA of 2.0 overall and 2.25 in the major. All students must complete 3 semester hours of freshman studies and 44 semester hours of interdisciplinary studies, including courses in English, physical education, religion, speech, business or economics, fine arts, humanities, science, and social science.

Special: Opportunities are provided for internships, work-study programs, dual majors, a 3–2 engineering degree with Washington University or University of Detroit, credit by examination, study abroad in 20 countries, a Washington semester, and pass/fail options. There is a freshman honors program on campus, as well as 14 national honor societies. Ten departments have honors programs.

Faculty/Classroom: All teach undergraduates. No introductory courses are taught by graduate students. The average class size in an introductory lecture is 23 and in a laboratory, 20.

Admissions: About 87% of the 1993–94 applicants were accepted. The SAT scores for the 1993–94 freshman class were as follows: Verbal—84% below 500, 13% between 500 and 599, and 2% between 600 and 700; Math—67% below 500, 22% between 500 and 599, and 10% between 600 and 700. The ACT scores were 22% below 21, 47% between 21 and 23, 4% between 24 and 26, 6% between 27 and 28, and 21% above 28. About 35% of the current freshmen were in the top fifth of their class; 52% were in the top two fifths.

Requirements: Ashland requires applicants to be in the upper 50% of their class. A minimum GPA of 2.5 is required. The SAT I or ACT is required. Applicants must be graduates of an accredited secondary school. The GED is accepted. The recommended preparatory program includes 4 units of English, 3 each of science, social studies, and mathematics, and 2 of foreign language. An interview is recommended. AP and CLEP credits are accepted. Important factors used in the admissions decision are advanced placement or honor courses, evidence of special talent, leadership record, personality, intangible qualities, and recommendations by school officials.

Procedure: Entrance exams should be taken in the spring of the junior year. Applications should be filed by August 15 for fall entry and January 2 for spring entry, along with an application fee of $15. There are early decision and deferred admissions plans.

Transfer: Official transcripts from all previous colleges, showing course credits and a minimum GPA of 2.0, must be submitted when applying for transfer. Generally, if the student has successfully completed a minimum of one year of college, the SAT I or ACT will not be required.

Visiting: There are regularly scheduled orientations for prospective students. There are guides for informal visits and visitors may sit in on classes and stay overnight at the school. To arrange for a visit, contact the Office of Admissions at (419) 289–5052.

Financial Aid: In 1993–94 97% of all current freshmen received some form of financial aid. The average freshman award was $6000. The FAF, the college's own financial statement, and FAFSA are required. The deadline for financial aid applications is March 15.

International Students: They must take the TOEFL and achieve a minimum score of 500.

Admissions Contact: Office of Admissions.

BALDWIN-WALLACE COLLEGE
Berea, OH 44017

D-1
(216) 826-2222

Full-time: 1092 men, 1626 women	Faculty: 149; IIB, +$
Part-time: 469 men, 991 women	Ph.D.s: 71%
Graduate: 289 men, 305 women	Student/Faculty: 18 to 1
Year: quarters, summer session	Tuition: $10,980
Application Deadline: July 1	Room & Board: $4230
Freshman Class: 1558 applied, 1359 accepted, 658 enrolled	
SAT I Verbal/Math: 460/530	ACT: 23 COMPETITIVE

Baldwin-Wallace College, established in 1845, is a private liberal arts institution affiliated with the United Methodist Church. There are 2 graduate schools. In addition to regional accreditation, B-W has bac-

calaureate program accreditation with NASM and NCATE. The 3 libraries contain 250,000 volumes, 103,000 microform items, and 18,500 audiovisual forms, and subscribe to 1000 periodicals. Computerized library sources and services include the card catalog, interlibrary loans, and database searching. Special learning facilities include a learning resource center, art gallery, and radio station. The 56-acre campus is in a suburban area 14 miles southwest of Cleveland. Including residence halls, there are 57 buildings on campus.

Student Life: About 90% of undergraduates are from Ohio. Students come from 29 states, 26 foreign countries, and Canada. Eighty-five percent are from public schools; 15% from private. Ninety-one percent are white. Forty-nine percent are Catholic; 44% Protestant. The average age of freshmen is 18; all undergraduates, 23. Ten percent drop out by the end of their first year; 62% remain to graduate.

Housing: A total of 1600 students can be accommodated in college housing. College-sponsored living facilities include single-sex and coed dormitories. In addition there are honors houses, special interest houses, and the Freshman Center. On-campus housing is guaranteed for all 4 years. Sixty percent of students live on campus; of those, 40% remain on campus on weekends. Upperclassmen may keep cars on campus.

Activities: About 13% of men belong to 5 national fraternities; about 15% of women belong to 7 national sororities. There are 40 groups on campus, including art, band, cheerleading, chess, choir, chorale, chorus, computers, dance, drama, drill team, ethnic, gay, honors, international, jazz band, literary magazine, musical theater, newspaper, opera, orchestra, pep band, political, professional, radio and TV, religious, social, social service, student government, symphony, and yearbook. Popular campus events include May Day Games, Homecoming, Greek Week, Black History Month, Founders Day, Little Sibs Weekend, and Women's Week.

Sports: There are 10 intercollegiate sports for men and 8 for women, and 12 intramural sports for men and 11 for women. Athletic and recreation facilities include an 8000-seat stadium with polyturf and all-weather track, a 3000-seat gymnasium, baseball fields, and a 6-court tennis complex. The recreation center houses a 200-meter track, a swimming pool, a dance studio, wrestling, gymnastic, and weight rooms, and facilities for basketball, racquetball, volleyball, bowling, and billiards.

Disabled Students: Fifty percent of the campus is accessible to disabled students. The following facilities are available: wheelchair ramps, elevators, special parking, specially equipped rest rooms, special class scheduling, and lowered telephones.

Services: In addition to many counseling and information services, tutoring is available in every subject. There is a reader service for the blind, and remedial math, reading, and writing.

Campus Safety and Security: Campus safety and security measures include 24-hour foot and vehicle patrol, escort service, shuttle buses, and informal discussions. In addition, there are pamphlets, posters, and films, emergency telephones, and lighted pathways and sidewalks.

Programs of Study: B-W awards the B.A., B.S., B.M., B.M.E, and B.S.Ed. degrees. Master's degrees are also awarded. Bachelor's degrees are awarded in BIOLOGICAL SCIENCE (biology/biological science), BUSINESS (accounting, banking and finance, business administration and management, marketing/retailing/merchandising, personnel management, and sports management), COMMUNICATIONS AND THE ARTS (broadcasting, communications, dance, dramatic arts, English, fine arts, French, German, music business management, music performance, Spanish, and speech/debate/rhetoric), COMPUTER AND PHYSICAL SCIENCE (chemistry, computer science, earth science, geology, mathematics, and physics), EDUCATION (art, elementary, foreign languages, health, home economics, music, science, secondary, social studies, and special), ENGINEERING AND ENVIRONMENTAL DESIGN (engineering), HEALTH PROFESSIONS (medical laboratory technology, music therapy, predentistry, premedicine, speech pathology/audiology, and sports medicine), SOCIAL SCIENCE (community services, criminal justice, economics, history, international relations, philosophy, physical fitness/movement, political science/government, prelaw, psychology, religion, and sociology). Business, music, education, biology, psychology, and speech communication have the largest enrollments.

Required: All students must complete 186 quarter hours, with a minimum of 45 and a maximum of 90 in the major, and must have at least a 2.0 GPA. A total of 68 quarter hours must be taken in the liberal arts core, which encompasses 5 divisions: humanities, natural science, social science, mathematics/computer science/statistics, and health and physical education. Comprehensive examinations are required in some majors.

Special: Special academic programs include internships, which can qualify for up to 18 credits; study abroad in Europe, India, Japan, Central America, and the Middle East; student teaching in England; and work-study programs. There is cross-registration with the Cleveland Commission on Higher Education, as well as a social work program with Case Western Reserve University, 3-2 programs with

Duke University in biology and engineering, and with Columbia, Washington, and Case Western Reserve universities in engineering; a 2–2 co-op allied health program is offered with local community colleges. B-W also offers the Consortium for Music Therapy, a general studies degree, a B.A.-B.S. degree, dual and student-designed majors, credit for life, military, and work experience, and pass/fail options. The Continuing Education Program offers degrees through evening and weekend colleges. There is a freshman honors program on campus, as well as 5 national honor societies. Eleven departments have honors programs.

Faculty/Classroom: Seventy-one percent of faculty are male; 29%, female. All teach, and do research. No introductory courses are taught by graduate students. The average class size in an introductory lecture is 24; in a laboratory, 20; and in a regular course offering, 24.

Admissions: About 87% of the 1993–94 applicants were accepted. The SAT scores for the 1993–94 freshman class were as follows: Verbal—62% below 500, 33% between 500 and 599, 5% between 600 and 700, and 1% above 700; Math—36% below 500, 39% between 500 and 599, 21% between 600 and 700, and 4% above 700. The ACT scores were 28% below 21, 31% between 21 and 23, 25% between 24 and 26, 8% between 27 and 28, and 7% above 28. About 52% of the current freshmen were in the top fifth of their class; 80% were in the top two fifths. There was 1 National Merit finalist and 13 freshmen graduated first in their class.

Requirements: B-W requires applicants to be in the upper 40% of their class. A minimum GPA of 2.5 is required. The SAT I or ACT is required. The recommended minimum score on the ACT is 20, and a composite score of 900 (450 each in verbal and mathematics) is recommended on SAT I. The scores are used to support data from the high school record; alternative scores are considered. Applicants must be graduates of an accredited secondary school. Sixteen academic credits are required, including 4 in English and 3 each in a foreign language, mathematics, science, and social studies; alternative distributions are considered. The GED is accepted. AP and CLEP credits are accepted. Important factors used in the admissions decision are leadership record, extracurricular activities record, recommendations by school officials, personality, intangible qualities, and geographic diversity.

Procedure: Freshmen are admitted to all sessions. Entrance exams should be taken late in the junior year or early in the senior year. Applications should be filed by July 1 for fall entry, January 1 for winter entry, March 15 for spring entry, and June 15 for summer entry, along with an application fee of $15. Notification is sent on a rolling basis. There is a deferred admissions plan.

Transfer: About 228 transfer students enrolled in 1993–94. Applicants must have a minimum 2.0 GPA from an accredited institution and be in good standing academically and socially. High school graduation is required. A total of 48 quarter hours out of 186 must be completed at B-W.

Visiting: There are regularly scheduled orientations for prospective students including an interview, a tour, and classroom visits. There are guides for informal visits and visitors may sit in on classes and stay overnight at the school. To arrange for a visit, contact the Admission Office at (216) 826–2222.

Financial Aid: In 1993–94, 96% of all current freshmen and 67% of continuing students received some form of financial aid. About 74% of freshmen received need-based aid. The average freshman award was $9300. Of that total, scholarships or need-based grants averaged $6737 ($15,391 maximum); loans averaged $2083 ($5625 maximum); and work contracts averaged $1369 ($2158 maximum). Eighty percent of undergraduate students work part-time. The average financial indebtedness of the 1992–93 graduate was $10,000. B-W is a member of CSS. The college's own financial statement and FAFSA are required. The deadline for financial aid applications is July 1.

International Students: There are currently 60 international students enrolled. The school actively recruits these students. They must take the TOEFL and achieve a minimum score of 500. The student must also take the SAT I or the ACT.

Computers: The college provides computer facilities for student use. The primary academic computer is an IBM RISC 6000 Model 350. The RISC 6000 is networked with approximately 50 microcomputers in the math and computer science building and may also be accessed via modem. Scores of microcomputers are available for student use throughout the campus. All students may access the system 24 hours a day. There are no time limits and no fees.

Graduates: In 1992–93, 633 bachelor's degrees were awarded. The most popular majors among graduates were business (45%), education (10%), and English (6%). Within an average freshman class, 1% graduate in 3 years, 56% in 4 years, 61% in 5 years, and 62% in 6 years. In the 1992 graduating class, 12% of all students were enrolled in graduate school within 6 months of graduation; 70% had found employment.

Admissions Contact: Juliann K. Baker; J. Edward Warner, Director of Undergraduate Admission; Dean of Enrollment Services.

BLUFFTON COLLEGE   B-2

Bluffton, OH 45817   (419) 358–3257; (800) 488–3257 (out-of-state)

Full-time: 760 men and women	**Faculty:** 45; IIB, --$
Part-time: 81 men and women	**Ph.D.s:** 69%
Graduate: none	**Student/Faculty:** 17 to 1
Year: quarters, summer session	**Tuition:** $9225
Application Deadline: August 15	**Room & Board:** $3726
Freshman Class: 568 applied, 514 accepted, 209 enrolled	
SAT I: 438/512	**ACT:** 22 **COMPETITIVE**

Bluffton College, founded in 1899, is a private, Christian, liberal arts institution affiliated with the General Conference Mennonite Church. In addition to regional accreditation, Bluffton College has baccalaureate program accreditation with ADA, CSWE, NASM, and NLN. The library contains 130,000 volumes, 65,000 microform items, and 650 audiovisual forms, and subscribes to 580 periodicals. Computerized library sources and services include interlibrary loans and database searching. Special learning facilities include a learning resource center, art gallery, radio station, and peace arts center. The 65-acre campus is in a small town 60 miles south of Toledo and 70 miles north of Dayton. Including residence halls, there are 18 buildings on campus.

Student Life: About 85% of undergraduates are from Ohio. Students come from 10 states and 19 foreign countries. Ninety-five percent are from public schools; 5% from private. Ninety-two percent are white. Eighty percent are Protestant; 13% Catholic. The average age of freshmen is 18; all undergraduates, 21. Twenty-eight percent drop out by the end of their first year; 55% remain to graduate.

Housing: A total of 700 students can be accommodated in college housing. College-sponsored living facilities include single-sex dormitories. All full-time students must live in residence halls unless commuting from home. On-campus housing is guaranteed for all 4 years. Seventy percent of students live on campus; of those, 50% remain on campus on weekends. Alcohol is not permitted. All students may keep cars on campus.

Activities: There are no fraternities or sororities on campus. There are more than 30 groups on campus, including art, band, cheerleading, choir, chorale, chorus, drama, drill team, ethnic, honors, international, jazz band, literary magazine, musical theater, newspaper, opera, pep band, photography, political, professional, radio, religious, social, social service, student government, and yearbook. Popular campus events include International Week, Black Emphasis, Service, Christian Emphasis Weeks, Artist Series, Forum Program, and Chapel.

Sports: There are 8 intercollegiate sports for men and 7 for women, and 10 intramural sports for men and 10 for women. Athletic and recreation facilities include 2 gymnasiums, an athletic complex, baseball/softball and football fields, an all-weather track, and a 2600-seat stadium.

Disabled Students: Thirty-three percent of the campus is accessible to disabled students. The following facilities are available: elevators, special parking, specially equipped rest rooms, special class scheduling, and lowered drinking fountains.

Services: In addition to many counseling and information services, tutoring is available for most students and classes at the student's request and/or faculty designation.

Campus Safety and Security: Campus safety and security measures include informal discussions, pamphlets, posters, and films, emergency telephones, and lighted pathways and sidewalks. In a town of only 3500, village police cruisers regularly patrol the campus during night hours. There is also a night watchman who can communicate directly with village police.

Programs of Study: Bluffton College awards the B.A. and B.S. degrees. Bachelor's degrees are awarded in BIOLOGICAL SCIENCE (biochemistry and biology/biological science), BUSINESS (accounting, banking and finance, business administration and management, business economics, marketing/retailing/merchandising, personnel management, recreational facilities management, and sports management), COMMUNICATIONS AND THE ARTS (communications, English, fine arts, music, and Spanish), COMPUTER AND PHYSICAL SCIENCE (chemistry, computer science, and mathematics), EDUCATION (art, business, early childhood, elementary, foreign languages, health, home economics, music, physical, science, and secondary), SOCIAL SCIENCE (child psychology/development, clothing and textiles management/production/services, criminal justice, dietetics, economics, food science, history, humanities, parks and recreation management, psychology, religion, social science, social work, and sociology). Business and elementary education have the largest enrollments.

Required: In order to graduate, students must complete 184 quarter hours, with 60 to 90 in the major, depending on the major, and have a minimum GPA of 2.0. The general education requirements must be met, and satisfactory achievement in departmental senior comprehensives demonstrated. Distribution requirements are approximately one

third for general education requirements and one third to one half for the major.

Special: Special arrangements include co-op programs in business, internships in business, recreation, social work, and education, a Washington semester through the Christian College Coalition, and study abroad, including Latin American exchange programs. Student-designed majors and independent study are possible, as is credit for prior learning and for learning in voluntary service. Nondegree study and pass/fail options are offered. There is a freshman honors program on campus.

Faculty/Classroom: Seventy-one percent of faculty are male; 29%, female. All teach undergraduates. The average class size in an introductory lecture is 30; in a laboratory, 10; and in a regular course offering, 17.

Admissions: About 90% of the 1993-94 applicants were accepted. The SAT scores for the 1993-94 freshman class were as follows: Verbal—69% below 500, 27% between 500 and 599, and 4% between 600 and 700; Math—44% below 500, 33% between 500 and 599, 17% between 600 and 700, and 6% above 700. The ACT scores were 42% below 22, 48% between 22 and 26, and 10% between 27 and 30. About 43% of the current freshmen were in the top fifth of their class; 67% were in the top two fifths. Four freshmen graduated first in their class.

Requirements: Bluffton College requires applicants to be in the upper 50% of their class. A minimum GPA of 2.3 is required. The ACT (preferred) or SAT I is required, with a required minimum of 19 on the ACT or 800 on the SAT I. Other admissions requirements include graduation from an accredited secondary school, with a recommended 4 units of English and 3 units each of mathematics, science, social studies, and a foreign language. The GED is accepted. An interview is recommended and music students must audition. AP and CLEP credits are accepted. Important factors used in the admissions decision are recommendations by school officials, leadership record, personality, intangible qualities, extracurricular activities record, and parents or siblings attending the school.

Procedure: Freshmen are admitted to all sessions. Entrance exams should be taken in spring of the junior year or fall of the senior year. Applications should be filed by August 15 for fall entry, along with an application fee of $20. Notification is sent on a rolling basis. There is a deferred admissions plan.

Transfer: About 46 transfer students enrolled in 1993-94. Transfer students must have a minimum GPA of 2.0, meet eligibility criteria from previous institutions, and have met their financial obligations at the former institution. A signed transfer recommendation from each college attended must be submitted. A total of 45 credits out of 184 must be completed at Bluffton College.

Visiting: There are regularly scheduled orientations for prospective students, including high school preview days on Saturdays and overnight visit programs; personal visits are arranged on a daily basis and are strongly encouraged. There are guides for informal visits and visitors may sit in on classes and stay overnight at the school. To arrange for a visit, contact the Office of Admission at (800) 488-3257.

Financial Aid: In 1993-94, all freshmen and 95% of continuing students received some form of financial aid. About 81% of freshmen and 76% of continuing students received need-based aid. The average freshman award was $7408. Of that total, scholarships or need-based grants averaged $3892 ($9225 maximum); loans averaged $2000 ($3625 maximum); and work contracts averaged $1100 (maximum). Seventy-two percent of undergraduate students work part-time. Average earnings from campus work for the school year are $1100. Bluffton College is a member of CSS. The FAF and FAFSA are required.

International Students: There are currently 35 international students enrolled. The school actively recruits these students. They must take the TOEFL and achieve a minimum score of 500. The SAT I is preferred for international students if possible, with a minimum composite score of 750.

Computers: The college provides computer facilities for student use. The mainframe is an IBM AS/400. Microcomputers are available to all students in a central laboratory and other various locations, including many academic departments. There are no time limits on using the system and no fees.

Graduates: In 1992-93, 161 bachelor's degrees were awarded. Within an average freshman class, 47% graduate in 4 years and 53% in 5 years. More than 200 companies recruited on campus in 1992-93.

Admissions Contact: Michael Hieronimus, Dean of Admission.

BOWLING GREEN STATE UNIVERSITY B-1
Bowling Green, OH 43403 (419) 372-2086

Full-time: 5767 men, 7871 women	Faculty: 675; I, --$
Part-time: 543 men, 632 women	Ph.D.s: 89%
Graduate: 1172 men, 1264 women	Student/Faculty: 20 to 1
Year: semesters, summer session	Tuition: $3553 ($7727)
Application Deadline: February 1	Room & Board: $3148
Freshman Class: 9251 applied, 7333 accepted, 3076 enrolled	
SAT I: 440/500	ACT: 22 COMPETITIVE

Bowling Green State University, founded in 1910, is a public, liberal arts institution offering more than 170 undergraduate and 75 graduate programs. There are 6 undergraduate schools and one graduate school. In addition to regional accreditation, Bowling Green has baccalaureate program accreditation with ACEJMC, ADA, APTA, ASLA, CAHEA, CSWE, NASAD, NCATE, and NLN. The 4 libraries contain 1,828,511 volumes, 1,716,275 microform items, and 667,282 audio-visual forms, and subscribe to 5414 periodicals. Computerized library sources and services include the card catalog, interlibrary loans, and database searching. Special learning facilities include a learning resource center, art gallery, planetarium, radio station, and TV station. The 1177-acre campus is in a small town 25 miles south of Toledo. Including residence halls, there are 114 buildings on campus.

Student Life: About 92% of undergraduates are from Ohio. Students come from 41 states, 67 foreign countries, and Canada. Ninety-three percent are white. The average age of freshmen is 18; all undergraduates, 20. Nineteen percent drop out by the end of their first year; 66% remain to graduate.

Housing: A total of 7030 students can be accommodated in college housing. College-sponsored living facilities include single-sex and coed dormitories, on-campus apartments, fraternity houses, and sorority houses. In addition, there are honors houses, language houses, and special interest houses, as well as a living learning center and accommodations for international students. On-campus housing is guaranteed for all 4 years. All students may keep cars on campus.

Activities: About 25% of men belong to 22 national fraternities; about 21% of women belong to 16 national sororities. There are 200 groups on campus, including band, cheerleading, chess, choir, chorale, chorus, computers, dance, drama, drill team, ethnic, film, gay, honors, international, jazz band, literary magazine, marching band, musical theater, newspaper, opera, orchestra, pep band, photography, political, professional, radio and TV, religious, social, social service, student government, symphony, and yearbook. Popular campus events include Homecoming, Parents Weekend, Greek Week, Black History Month, Alcohol Awareness Week, International Festival, and Hispanic Awareness Month.

Sports: There are 11 intercollegiate sports for men and 10 for women, and 17 intramural sports for men and 17 for women. Athletic and recreation facilities include 4 buildings, including a student recreation center and an intramural field house facility, a 30,000-seat football stadium, a 5000-seat gym, tennis courts, a golf course, basketball and ice arenas, and softball and intramural fields.

Disabled Students: Eighty percent of the campus is accessible to disabled students. The following facilities are available: wheelchair ramps, elevators, special parking, specially equipped rest rooms, special class scheduling, lowered drinking fountains, lowered telephones, and a shuttle van with lift capabilities.

Services: In addition to many counseling and information services, tutoring is available in writing, mathematics, and 100-level content area classes such as biology, chemistry and sociology. There is also a reader service for the blind, and remedial math, reading, and writing.

Campus Safety and Security: Campus safety and security measures include 24-hour foot and vehicle patrol, escort service, shuttle buses, and informal discussions. In addition, there are pamphlets, posters, and films, emergency telephones, lighted pathways and sidewalks, and a campus '911' number.

Programs of Study: Bowling Green awards the B.A., B.S., B.A.C., B.F.A. (Art), B.F.A. (Creative Writing), B.L.S., B.Mus., B.S. Applied Microbiology, B.S.A.Therapy, B.S.B.A., B.S. Child and Family Community Services, B.S.C.J., B.S. Communication, B.S. Communication Disorders, B.S.Diet, B.S. in Econ., B.S.Ed., B.S.E.H., B.S.G., B.S. (Health and Human Services), B.S.J., B.S. Medical Technology, B.S.N., B.S.P.T., B.S.S.W., and B.S.Tech. degrees. Associate, master's, and doctoral degrees also are awarded. Bachelor's degrees are awarded in BIOLOGICAL SCIENCE (biochemistry, biology/biological science, and microbiology), BUSINESS (accounting, banking and finance, business administration and management, business economics, hotel/motel and restaurant management, international business management, marketing/retailing/merchandising, and personnel management), COMMUNICATIONS AND THE ARTS (broadcasting, communications, dance, dramatic arts, English, film arts, fine arts, French, German, journalism, music, Russian, Spanish, and speech/

debate/rhetoric), COMPUTER AND PHYSICAL SCIENCE (chemistry, computer science, earth science, geology, mathematics, physics, and statistics), EDUCATION (art, business, early childhood, elementary, foreign languages, health, home economics, music, science, secondary, and special), ENGINEERING AND ENVIRONMENTAL DESIGN (construction technology, electrical/electronics engineering technology, and environmental science), HEALTH PROFESSIONS (art therapy, medical laboratory technology, nursing, physical therapy, predentistry, premedicine, and speech pathology/audiology), SOCIAL SCIENCE (criminal justice, dietetics, economics, food science, geography, gerontology, history, liberal arts/general studies, parks and recreation management, philosophy, political science/government, prelaw, psychology, public administration, social science, social work, and sociology). Elementary education, psychology, and marketing have the largest enrollments.

Required: To graduate, students must complete a minimum of 122 semester hours, including at least 30 in the major, depending on the major, and maintain a minimum 2.0 GPA. The 8-course mandatory general education core includes 2 courses each from natural sciences, social sciences, and humanities and the arts, 1 course from cultural diversity in the United States, and 1 additional course from among natural sciences, social sciences, humanities and the arts, and foreign languages and cultures. At least 1 of the courses in the social sciences or humanities and arts must be designated as foreign cultures or foreign language at the 200 level or above.

Special: Special academic programs include co-op programs in all majors with the National Student Exchange, internships, a Washington semester, work-study, and study or student exchange in 13 countries. Dual majors are available in all programs, and a B.A.-B.S. degree is offered in computer science, geology, mathematics, psychology, and statistics. Student-designed majors, independent study, credit for experience, nondegree study, and pass/fail options are possible. There is a freshman honors program on campus, as well as 30 national honor societies, including Phi Beta Kappa.

Faculty/Classroom: Seventy percent of faculty are male; 30%, female. Ninety percent teach undergraduates; 75% do research, and 75% do both. Graduate students teach 10% of introductory courses. The average class size in an introductory lecture is 200; in a laboratory, 20; and in a regular course offering, 30.

Admissions: About 79% of the 1993–94 applicants were accepted. The SAT scores for the 1993–94 freshman class were as follows: Verbal—73% below 500, 21% between 500 and 599, 5% between 600 and 700, and 1% above 700; Math—49% below 500, 36% between 500 and 599, 13% between 600 and 700, and 2% above 700. The ACT scores were 32% below 21, 37% between 21 and 23, 21% between 24 and 26, 6% between 27 and 28, and 4% above 28. About 34% of the current freshmen were in the top fifth of their class; 72% were in the top two fifths. There were 27 National Merit finalists and 1 semifinalist.

Requirements: A minimum GPA of 2.0 is required. The SAT I or ACT is required for all freshmen except those out of high school for 3 or more years; the minimum composite SAT score is 700, and the minimum ACT score, based on the enhanced ACT assessment, should be 17. Performance and test scores must be at minimum and above to be considered. There is no automatic admission. Special circumstances are reviewed as applicable. Other admissions requirements include graduation from an accredited secondary school, with a recommended 4 years of English, 3 years each of mathematics, science, and social studies/history, 2 years of a foreign language, and 1 year of art or music. The GED is accepted. Music students must audition. AP and CLEP credits are accepted.

Procedure: Freshmen are admitted to all sessions. Entrance exams should be taken in the junior year. Applications should be filed by February 1 for fall entry, December 1 for spring entry, and April 15 for summer entry, along with an application fee of $30. Notification is sent on a rolling basis. There is a deferred admissions plan.

Transfer: About 613 transfer students enrolled in 1993–94. Transfer students who have attempted 12 or more hours at a college are eligible. Applicants with 60 or more semester hours or an associate degree must have at least a 2.0 GPA; those with fewer hours need a minimum GPA of 2.5, but may petition for admission if it is lower. A total of 30 credits out of 122 must be completed at Bowling Green.

Visiting: There are regularly scheduled orientations for prospective students. There are guides for informal visits and visitors may sit in on classes and stay overnight at the school. To arrange for a visit, contact the Office of Admissions at (419) 372-2086.

Financial Aid: In an earlier year, 55% of all students received some form of financial aid. About 40% of freshmen and 45% of continuing students received need-based aid. The average freshman award was $3000. Of that total, scholarships or need-based grants averaged $600 ($4526 maximum); loans averaged $1200 ($3825 maximum); and work contracts averaged $1200 ($1500 maximum). Thirty percent of undergraduate students work part-time. Average earnings from campus work for the school year are $1000. The average financial indebtedness of the 1992–93 graduate was $6000. Bowling

Green is a member of CSS. The FAFSA financial statement is required. The deadline for financial aid applications is March 1.

International Students: There are currently 497 international students enrolled. The school actively recruits these students. They must take the TOEFL or the University of Michigan Language Test and achieve a minimum score on the TOEFL of 500.

Computers: The college provides computer facilities for student use. The mainframes are an IBM ES9000–320 and 4341, a DEC VAX 8650, and a DEC 6000. There are more than 800 terminals and microcomputers available in computer laboratories and in residence halls. Students are able to get accounts on university mainframes through specified classes. All students may access the system. It may be used during operating hours. There are no time limits on using the system and no fees.

Graduates: In 1992–93 3240 bachelor's degrees were awarded. The most popular majors among graduates were elementary education (9%), nursing (4%), marketing (4%), and biological sciences (4%). Within an average freshman class, 32% graduate in 4 years, 62% in 5 years, and 66% in 6 years. Some 366 companies recruited on campus in 1992–93.

Admissions Contact: John Martin, Director of Admissions.

CAPITAL UNIVERSITY

C-3

Columbus, OH 43209–2394   (614) 236-6101

(800) 289-6289 (out-of-state)

Full-time: 585 men, 960 women	Faculty: 107; IIA, -$
Part-time: 26 men, 34 women	Ph.D.s: 78%
Graduate: 725 men, 477 women	Student/Faculty: 14 to 1
Year: semesters, summer session	Tuition: $12,625
Application Deadline: August 1	Room & Board: $3910
Freshman Class: 1747 applied, 1382 accepted, 449 enrolled	
SAT I: 465/510	ACT: 23 VERY COMPETITIVE

Capital University, established in 1830, is a private coeducational institution affiliated with the Evangelical Lutheran Church in America. Its undergraduate and graduate programs emphasize the liberal arts and sciences, music, and nursing. There are 3 undergraduate and 2 graduate schools. In addition to regional accreditation, Capital has baccalaureate program accreditation with CSWE, NASM, NCATE, and NLN. The 2 libraries contain 199,150 volumes, 52,000 microform items, and 12,000 audiovisual forms, and subscribe to 850 periodicals. Computerized library sources and services include interlibrary loans and database searching. Special learning facilities include an art gallery and TV studio. The 42-acre campus is in an urban area 3 miles east of downtown Columbus. Including residence halls, there are 24 buildings on campus.

Student Life: About 90% of undergraduates are from Ohio. Students come from 23 states and 30 foreign countries. Ninety-seven percent are from public schools; 3% from private. Eighty-nine percent are white. Sixty-six percent are Protestant; 20% Catholic. The average age of freshmen is 18; all undergraduates, 20. Nineteen percent drop out by the end of their first year; 65% remain to graduate.

Housing: A total of 1000 students can be accommodated in college housing. College-sponsored living facilities include single-sex and coed dormitories. In addition, there are honors dormitories and special-interest floors. On-campus housing is guaranteed for all 4 years. Seventy percent of students live on campus; of those, 75% remain on campus on weekends. Alcohol is not permitted. Upperclassmen may keep cars on campus.

Activities: About 30% of men belong to 4 local and 2 national fraternities; about 30% of women belong to 3 local and 1 national sororities. There are 50 groups on campus, including art, band, cheerleading, choir, chorale, chorus, dance, drama, drill team, ethnic, gay, honors, international, jazz band, literary magazine, musical theater, newspaper, opera, orchestra, pep band, photography, political, professional, radio and TV, religious, social, social service, student government, symphony, and yearbook. Popular campus events include Homecoming and Spring Fling.

Sports: There are 7 intercollegiate sports for men and 4 for women, and 4 intramural sports for men and 4 for women. Athletic and recreation facilities include a 2500-seat football stadium, a 2400-seat gymnasium, tennis courts, and weight and game rooms. The recreation center offers bowling, billiards, and other game facilities.

Disabled Students: Thirty-five percent of the campus is accessible to disabled students. The following facilities are available: elevators, special parking, specially equipped rest rooms, and special class scheduling.

Services: In addition to many counseling and information services, tutoring is available in most subjects, including arts and sciences, music, and nursing. There is also remedial math.

Campus Safety and Security: Campus safety and security measures include 24-hour foot and vehicle patrol, escort service, and lighted pathways and sidewalks.

Programs of Study: Capital awards the B.A., B.F.A., B.G.S., B.M., B.S.N., and B.S.W. degrees. Master's degrees also are awarded. Bachelor's degrees are awarded in BIOLOGICAL SCIENCE (biology/biological science), BUSINESS (accounting and business administration and management), COMMUNICATIONS AND THE ARTS (communications, dramatic arts, English, fine arts, French, music, public relations, Spanish, and speech/debate/rhetoric), COMPUTER AND PHYSICAL SCIENCE (chemistry, computer science, and mathematics), EDUCATION (art, elementary, foreign languages, health, middle school, music, physical, science, and secondary), HEALTH PROFESSIONS (art therapy, nursing, predentistry, premedicine, and sports medicine), SOCIAL SCIENCE (criminal justice, economics, history, international relations, political science/government, prelaw, psychology, public administration, religion, social work, and sociology). Business, education, history, political science, music, and nursing have the largest enrollments.

Required: In order to graduate, all students must complete at least 124 semester hours, with a varying number of hours in the major, and maintain a minimum 2.0 GPA. The university core, 36 semester hours, must be followed in an ordered sequence throughout the 4 years; considered an assessment program, it includes specific courses in reading and writing, communication, health, art, science, social science, the humanities, ethics, and religion.

Special: Special academic programs include co-op programs available through the School of Nursing, cross-registration with the Higher Education Council of Columbus, 1-semester internships in most majors, and a Washington semester. Study abroad in 21 countries, including those in Europe, Asia, Africa, and South America, is possible, as are a general studies degree and student-designed majors. A 3–2 engineering degree is offered with Case Western Reserve University and Washington University in St. Louis. Credit for life, military, and work experience may be granted, and nondegree study and pass/fail options are offered. There is a freshman honors program on campus.

Faculty/Classroom: Sixty-five percent of faculty are male; 35%, female. All teach undergraduates. No introductory courses are taught by graduate students. The average class size in an introductory lecture is 25; in a laboratory, 15; and in a regular course offering, 20.

Admissions: About 79% of the 1993–94 applicants were accepted. The SAT scores for the 1993–94 freshman class were as follows: Verbal—64% below 500, 29% between 500 and 599, and 7% between 600 and 700; Math—44% below 500, 36% between 500 and 599, 15% between 600 and 700, and 5% above 700. The ACT scores were 23% below 21, 32% between 21 and 23, 26% between 24 and 26, 11% between 27 and 28, and 8% above 28. About 58% of the current freshmen were in the top fifth of their class; 86% were in the top two fifths. There was 1 National Merit finalist. Fifteen freshmen graduated first in their class.

Requirements: A minimum GPA of 2.5 is required. The SAT I or ACT is required. Other admissions requirements include graduation from an accredited secondary school, with 16 academic credits, including 4 units of English, 2 units of a foreign language, 3 each of mathematics, science, and social science, and 1 of electives; nursing applicants need chemistry. The GED is accepted. High school students must submit recommendations from their guidance counselor. An interview is recommended. Students must audition for entry to the Conservatory of Music. AP and CLEP credits are accepted. Important factors used in the admissions decision are advanced placement or honor courses, evidence of special talent, leadership record, recommendations by school officials, and extracurricular activities record.

Procedure: Freshmen are admitted to all sessions. Entrance exams should be taken by December of the senior year. Applications should be filed by August 1 for fall entry, December 1 for winter entry, and April 1 for summer entry, along with an application fee of $15. Notification is sent on a rolling basis. There is a deferred admissions plan.

Transfer: About 128 transfer students enrolled in 1993–94. Transfer students must have a minimum college GPA of 2.25. The SAT I or ACT is recommended, as is an interview. A total of 30 credits out of 124 must be completed at Capital.

Visiting: There are regularly scheduled orientations for prospective students, including an interview with a counselor and a campus tour. There are guides for informal visits and visitors may sit in on classes and stay overnight at the school. To arrange for a visit, contact the Admissions Office at (800) 289–6289 or (614) 236–6101.

Financial Aid: In 1993–94 82% of all current freshmen and 80% of continuing students received some form of financial aid. About 75% of freshmen and 80% of continuing students received need-based aid. The average freshman award was $11,051. Of that total, scholarships or need-based grants averaged $4300 ($9530 maximum); loans averaged $2625 ($4650 maximum); and work contracts averaged $1200 ($1500 maximum). Fifty percent of undergraduate students work part-time. Average earnings from campus work for the school year are $1000. The average financial indebtedness of the 1992–93 graduate was $12,000. Capital is a member of CSS. The college's own financial statement and the FAFSA are required. The deadline for financial aid applications is April 1.

International Students: There are currently 41 international students enrolled. The school actively recruits these students. They must take the TOEFL and achieve a minimum score of 500.

Computers: The college provides computer facilities for student use. The mainframe is a Prime 9755. There are also 60 IBM PS/2 Model 30 and Apple IIgs microcomputers available in the library. A SUN microsystem is also available. All students may access the system. It may be used during library hours. There are no time limits and no fees.

Graduates: In 1992–93 248 bachelor's degrees were awarded. The most popular majors among graduates were nursing (18%), business (17%), and music (11%). Some 40 companies recruited on campus in 1992–93. In the 1992 graduating class, 15% of all graduates were enrolled in graduate school within 6 months of graduation.

Admissions Contact: Dr. Dolphus E. Henry, Vice President for Enrollment Management.

CASE WESTERN RESERVE UNIVERSITY   D-1
Cleveland, OH 44106   (216) 368–4450

Full-time: 1823 men, 1228 women	Faculty: 451; I, av$
Part-time: 220 men, 293 women	Ph.D.s: 97%
Graduate: 2973 men, 2739 women	Student/Faculty: 7 to 1
Year: semesters, summer session	Tuition: $15,320
Application Deadline: February 15	Room & Board: $4590
Freshman Class: 3877 applied, 3156 accepted, 713 enrolled	
SAT I or ACT: required	**HIGHLY COMPETITIVE**

Case Western Reserve University, founded in 1826, is a private, coeducational institution offering undergraduate, graduate, and professional programs in arts and sciences, dentistry, engineering, law, management, medicine, nursing, and social work. There are 3 undergraduate and 7 graduate schools. In addition to regional accreditation, CWRU has baccalaureate program accreditation with AACSB, ABET, ADA, CAHEA, CSWE, NASM, and NLN. The 8 libraries contain 1,765,412 volumes, 2,016,248 microform items, and 15,431 audiovisual forms, and subscribe to 15,517 periodicals. Computerized library sources and services include the card catalog, interlibrary loans, and database searching. Special learning facilities include an art gallery, natural history museum, and radio station. The 128-acre campus is in an urban area 4 miles east of downtown Cleveland. Including residence halls, there are 85 buildings on campus.

Student Life: About 62% of undergraduates are from Ohio. Students come from 50 states, 49 foreign countries, and Canada. Seventy percent are from public schools; 30% from private. Sixty-eight percent are white; 10% Asian American. The average age of freshmen is 18; all undergraduates, 20. Nine percent drop out by the end of their first year; 70% remain to graduate.

Housing: A total of 1827 students can be accommodated in college housing. College-sponsored living facilities include single-sex and coed dormitories, fraternity houses, and sorority houses. On-campus housing is guaranteed for all 4 years. Seventy-four percent of students live on campus; of those, 85% remain on campus on weekends. All students may keep cars on campus.

Activities: About 40% of men belong to 18 national fraternities; about 20% of women belong to 1 local and 4 national sororities. There are 100 groups on campus, including art, cheerleading, chess, choir, chorale, computers, dance, drama, ethnic, film, gay, honors, international, jazz band, literary magazine, marching band, musical theater, newspaper, orchestra, photography, political, professional, radio, religious, social, social service, student government, and yearbook. Popular campus events include Hudson Relays, Greek Week, Homecoming Weekend, African American Heritage Celebration, Engineers Week, Fine Arts Week, Winter Carnival, and Spring Olympics.

Sports: There are 11 intercollegiate sports for men and 8 for women, and 30 intramural sports for men and 30 for women. Athletic and recreation facilities include football, baseball, and soccer fields, all-weather track, softball diamonds, swimming pool, weight room, basketball, badminton, volleyball, squash, tennis, and racquetball courts, rifle range, and archery range.

Disabled Students: The following facilities are available: wheelchair ramps, elevators, special parking, specially equipped rest rooms, special class scheduling, lowered drinking fountains, lowered telephones, and TDD.

Services: In addition to many counseling and information services, tutoring is available in every subject. There is also a reader service for the blind. Courses in developmental writing and reading, reading and learning strategies, test-taking strategies, and diagnostic testing are available.

Campus Safety and Security: Campus safety and security measures include 24-hour foot and vehicle patrol, self defense education, escort service, and shuttle buses. In addition, there are informal discussions, pamphlets, posters, films, emergency telephones, lighted pathways and sidewalks, and property crime prevention programs (bicycle lock rental, vehicle ID etching, equipment bolting).

Programs of Study: CWRU awards the B.A., B.S., B.S.E., and B.S.N. degrees. Master's and doctoral degrees also are awarded. Bachelor's degrees are awarded in BIOLOGICAL SCIENCE (biochemistry, biology/biological science, and nutrition), BUSINESS (accounting, business administration and management, and management science), COMMUNICATIONS AND THE ARTS (art history and appreciation, classics, communications, comparative literature, dramatic arts, English, French, German, literature, music, and Spanish), COMPUTER AND PHYSICAL SCIENCE (applied mathematics, astronomy, chemistry, computer science, fluid and thermal science, geology, mathematics, natural sciences, physics, polymer science, and statistics), EDUCATION (art and music), ENGINEERING AND ENVIRONMENTAL DESIGN (Aerospace Studies, architecture, biomedical engineering, chemical engineering, civil engineering, computer engineering, electrical/electronics engineering, engineering, industrial engineering, materials science, mechanical engineering, and systems engineering), HEALTH PROFESSIONS (medical laboratory technology, nursing, and speech pathology/audiology), SOCIAL SCIENCE (American studies, anthropology, Asian/Oriental studies, economics, German area studies, gerontology, history, history of science, international studies, philosophy, political science/government, psychology, religion, and sociology). Engineering, accounting, biology, chemistry, English, music, psychology, anthropology, nursing, art history, management, and physics are the strongest academically. Engineering, management, and psychology have the largest enrollments.

Required: To graduate, students must complete a minimum of 120 semester hours, with at least 30 hours in the major, and maintain a minimum GPA of 2.0. Students must take 1 of 3 core curricula as well as courses in English composition and physical education.

Special: CWRU offers co-op programs with more than 160 employers; students may alternate classroom study with full-time employment. Cross-registration with 13 institutions in the Cleveland area is available, as well as internships in government, corporations, and nonprofit agencies. Students may participate in study abroad, a Washington semester, work-study programs, and accelerated-degree programs. B.A.-B.S. degrees, dual majors, student-designed majors, 3–2 engineering degrees, nondegree study, and pass/fail options are possible. There are extensive opportunities for undergraduates to work with faculty on research projects. The LAMBDA (liberal arts/mathematics based) core curriculum combines liberal arts and computer and mathematics courses, with an emphasis on the latter two subjects. Interdisciplinary majors, such as environmental geology, and intradisciplinary majors, such as nutritional biochemistry and metabolism, are available. There are 4 national honor societies on campus, including Phi Beta Kappa.

Faculty/Classroom: Seventy-three percent of faculty are male; 27%, female. All do research, 25% teach undergraduates, and 25% do both. Graduate students teach 5% of introductory courses. The average class size in an introductory lecture is 33 and in a regular course offering, 27.

Admissions: About 81% of the 1993–94 applicants were accepted. The SAT scores for the 1993–94 freshman class were as follows: Verbal—21% below 500, 36% between 500 and 599, 34% between 600 and 700, and 9% above 700; Math—3% below 500, 17% between 500 and 599, 36% between 600 and 700, and 44% above 700. The ACT scores were 1% below 21, 6% between 21 and 23, 20% between 24 and 26, 20% between 27 and 28, and 53% above 28. About 89% of the current freshmen were in the top fifth of their class; 99% were in the top two fifths. There were 75 National Merit finalists. About 45 freshmen graduated first in their class.

Requirements: The SAT I or ACT is required. SAT II: Subject tests are strongly recommended for students who take the SAT I. The school specifies SAT II: Subject test in writing plus 2 others of the student's choice. Applicants must be graduates of an accredited secondary school. The GED is accepted. Sixteen high school academic credits are required, including 4 years of English, 3 of mathematics, (4 for science, mathematics, and engineering majors), and 1 of laboratory science (2 for science and mathematics majors and premedical students). Two to four years of foreign language are strongly recommended. Engineering, mathematics, and science students should take mathematics I or II and physics or chemistry. A writing sample of the student's choice is required and an interview is recommended. AP credits are accepted. Important factors used in the admissions decision are advanced placement or honor courses, leadership record, recommendations by school officials, extracurricular activities record, and evidence of special talent.

Procedure: Freshmen are admitted to all sessions. Entrance exams should be taken by the fall of the senior year; the school recommends also taking the test during the spring of the junior year. Early decision applications should be filed by January 15; regular applications, by February 15 for fall entry. Notification is sent within two weeks of receipt of application for early decision; regular decision April 1. There are early decision, early admissions, and deferred admissions plans. About 111 early decision candidates were accepted for the 1993–94

class. A waiting list is an active part of the admissions procedure, with about 3% of applicants on the list.

Transfer: About 132 transfer students enrolled in 1993–94. Transfer students should have a minimum GPA of 3.0 and meet all high school requirements. Grades of C or better transfer for credit. A total of 60 credits out of 120 must be completed at CWRU.

Visiting: There are regularly scheduled orientations for prospective students. There are guides for informal visits and visitors may sit in on classes and stay overnight at the school. To arrange for a visit, contact the Office of Undergraduate Admission at (216) 368–4450.

Financial Aid: In 1993–94 90% of all current freshmen and 84% of continuing students received some form of financial aid. About 69% of freshmen and 53% of continuing students received need-based aid. The average freshman award was $15,730. Eighty percent of undergraduate students work part-time. Average earnings from campus work for the school year are $1200. CWRU is a member of CSS. The FAF or FFS and FAFSA are required. The deadline for financial aid applications is February 1.

International Students: There are currently 1192 international students enrolled. The school actively recruits these students. They must take the TOEFL and achieve a minimum score of 550.

Computers: The college provides computer facilities for student use. The mainframe is an IBM 4381. CWRUnet, the university's high-speed fiber-optic network, connects every residence-hall room with academic departments, libraries, and laboratories on campus, giving students desktop access to information resources including a software library, public and commercial databases, regional and national networks, and the Ohio Supercomputer Center. Many students purchase networkable personal computers through special university purchase arrangements. There are also a number of open-access computer laboratories at various locations on campus with approximately 200 microcomputers for student use. All students may access the system. It may be used 24 hours a day. There are no time limits and no fees.

Graduates: In 1992–93 645 bachelor's degrees were awarded. The most popular majors among graduates were mechanical engineering (10%), nursing (9%), and psychology (9%). Within an average freshman class, 70% graduate in 5 years. Some 224 companies recruited on campus in 1992–93. In the 1992 graduating class, 39% of all graduates were enrolled in graduate school within 6 months of graduation; 41% had found employment.

Admissions Contact: Dean of Undergraduate Admission.

CEDARVILLE COLLEGE
Cedarville, OH 45314–0601

B-4

(513) 766–2211
(800) CEDARVILLE (out-of-state)

Full-time: 950 men, 1246 women	Faculty: 130; IIB, --$
Part-time: 30 men, 52 women	Ph.D.s: 51%
Graduate: none	Student/Faculty: 17 to 1
Year: quarters, summer session	Tuition: $6959
Application Deadline: open	Room & Board: $3756
Freshman Class: 1307 applied, 1090 accepted, 616 enrolled	
SAT I Verbal/Math: 480/520	ACT: 23 COMPETITIVE

Cedarville College, founded in 1887, is a private liberal arts college affiliated with the General Association of Regular Baptist Churches, offering programs in business, education, engineering, nursing, preprofessional studies, and social work. In addition to regional accreditation, the 'Ville has baccalaureate program accreditation with NLN. The library contains 122,220 volumes, 20,776 microform items, and 15,078 audiovisual forms, and subscribes to 1030 periodicals. Special learning facilities include a radio station and an observatory. The 100-acre campus is in a small town 12 miles south of Springfield. Including residence halls, there are 32 buildings on campus.

Student Life: About 65% of undergraduates are from out-of-state, mostly the Midwest. Students come from 48 states, 11 foreign countries, and Canada. Fifty-five percent are from public schools; 45% from private. Ninety-six percent are white. Most are Protestant. The average age of freshmen is 18; all undergraduates, 20. Seventy-six percent drop out by the end of their first year; 46% remain to graduate.

Housing: A total of 1788 students can be accommodated in college housing. College-sponsored living facilities include single-sex dormitories and married-student housing. On-campus housing is guaranteed for all 4 years. Eighty percent of students live on campus. Alcohol is not permitted. All students may keep cars on campus.

Activities: There are no fraternities or sororities on campus. There are 47 groups on campus, including band, cheerleading, choir, chorale, chorus, drama, ethnic, honors, international, jazz band, newspaper, orchestra, pep band, photography, political, professional, radio and TV, religious, social, social service, student government, and yearbook. Popular campus events include Cedar Day and Homecoming.

Sports: There are 7 intercollegiate sports for men and 6 for women, and 26 intramural sports for men and 23 for women. Athletic and recreation facilities include a 3000-seat gymnasium, 5 basketball courts,

an indoor track, 3 volleyball courts, 3 racquetball courts, 2 indoor tennis courts, badminton courts, a weight room, a wrestling room, a training room, 6 outdoor tennis courts, a 400m track and field, and soccer, baseball, softball, and intramural playing fields.

Disabled Students: Fifty percent of the campus is accessible to disabled students. The following facilities are available: wheelchair ramps, elevators, special parking, specially equipped rest rooms, special class scheduling, lowered drinking fountains, and lowered telephones.

Services: In addition to many counseling and information services, tutoring is available in some subjects. There is also remedial math and writing.

Campus Safety and Security: Campus safety and security measures include 24-hour foot and vehicle patrol, escort service, informal discussions, and pamphlets, posters, and films. In addition, there are emergency telephones and lighted pathways and sidewalks.

Programs of Study: The 'Ville awards the B.A., B.M.E., B.S.E.E., B.S.M.E., and B.S.N. degrees. Associate degrees also are awarded. Bachelor's degrees are awarded in BIOLOGICAL SCIENCE (biology/biological science), BUSINESS (accounting, banking and finance, business administration and management, international business management, and marketing/retailing/merchandising), COMMUNICATIONS AND THE ARTS (broadcasting, communications, communications technology, English, journalism, music, and Spanish), COMPUTER AND PHYSICAL SCIENCE (chemistry, information sciences and systems, mathematics, and science), EDUCATION (business, elementary, foreign languages, music, physical, science, secondary, and teaching English as a second language/foreign language), ENGINEERING AND ENVIRONMENTAL DESIGN (electrical/electronics engineering, mechanical engineering, and pre-engineering), HEALTH PROFESSIONS (medical science, nursing, optometry, physical therapy, predentistry, and premedicine), SOCIAL SCIENCE (American studies, behavioral science, biblical studies, criminal justice, history, missions, philosophy, political science/government, prelaw, psychology, public administration, religion, social science, social work, and sociology). Elementary education, business, nursing, science and mathematics, and engineering have the largest enrollments.

Required: To graduate, all students must maintain a minimum GPA of 2.0 while taking 192 quarter hours and completing 80 to 102 quarter hours of general education requirements that include 24 quarter hours of biblical education, English composition, fundamentals of speech, humanities, social sciences, and physical education. Students must demonstrate proficiency in English and have at least 2 years of high school foreign language or 1 year of college-level classical or modern foreign language.

Special: Internships, study abroad, dual majors, work-study programs with the college, and pass/fail options are available. There is a freshman honors program on campus

Faculty/Classroom: Seventy-two percent of faculty are male; 29%, female. All teach undergraduates.

Admissions: About 83% of the 1993–94 applicants were accepted. The SAT scores for the 1993–94 freshman class were as follows: Verbal—57% below 500, 30% between 500 and 599, 12% between 600 and 700, and 1% above 700; Math—41% below 500, 31% between 500 and 599, 23% between 600 and 700, and 4% above 700. The ACT scores were 19% below 21, 31% between 21 and 23, 26% between 24 and 26, 12% between 27 and 28, and 12% above 28. About 47% of the current freshmen were in the top fifth of their class; 76% were in the top two fifths. There were 6 National Merit finalists and 3 semifinalists. Fifty-six freshmen graduated first in their class.

Requirements: The 'Ville requires applicants to be in the upper 50% of their class. A minimum GPA of 2.8 is required. The SAT I or ACT is required, with scores above the national average recommended. The ACT is preferred. The college recommends that applicants have 4 years of English, 3 years each of social studies, mathematics, and science, and 2 years of foreign language. A GPA of 2.8 or better and ranking in the upper half of the high school class are preferred. The GED is accepted. Recommendations from a local pastor and a high school counselor are required. An interview is recommended. AP and CLEP credits are accepted. Important factors used in the admissions decision are advanced placement or honor courses, evidence of special talent, leadership record, extracurricular activities record, and recommendations by alumni.

Procedure: Freshmen are admitted to all sessions. Entrance exams should be taken by December of the senior year. Application deadlines are open. Application fee is $20. Notification is sent on a rolling basis. There are early admissions and deferred admissions plans. A waiting list is an active part of the admissions procedure.

Transfer: About 102 transfer students enrolled in 1993–94. Transfer students must have a minimum college GPA of 2.5. The SAT I or ACT is recommended. A total of 48 quarter hours out of 192 must be completed at The 'Ville.

Visiting: There are regularly scheduled orientations for prospective students, including campus tours, chapel services, class visits, and meetings with faculty, coaches, and admissions counselors. There are guides for informal visits and visitors may sit in on classes and stay overnight at the school. To arrange for a visit, contact the Admissions Office at (800) CEDARVILLE.

Financial Aid: In 1993–94 78% of all current freshmen and 73% of continuing students received some form of financial aid. About 54% of freshmen and 48% of continuing students received need-based aid. The average freshman award was $7725. Of that total, scholarships or need-based grants averaged $2300 ($3000 maximum); loans averaged $2625 (maximum); and work contracts averaged $1300 ($2600 maximum). Thirty-five percent of undergraduate students work part-time. Average earnings from campus work for the school year are $1300. The average financial indebtedness of the 1992–93 graduate was $9542. The college's own financial statement and FAFSA are required. The deadline for financial aid applications is March 1.

International Students: There are currently 24 international students enrolled. They must take the TOEFL and achieve a minimum score of 500. The student must also take the SAT I or the ACT.

Computers: The college provides computer facilities for student use. A network connects 4 public computer laboratories with more than 100 PCs and approximately 700 residence hall rooms, which are equipped with IBM or compatible 486 PC and printer. The network provides access to more than 100 software packages, library resources, E-mail, and Internet. All students may access the system. It may be used 8 A.M. to 10 P.M. Monday through Saturday. There are no time limits on using the system. The fees are $80/quarter.

Graduates: In 1992–93 362 bachelor's degrees were awarded. The most popular majors among graduates were education (18%), nursing (12%), and management (6%). Within an average freshman class, 14% graduate in 3 years, 74% in 4 years, 8% in 5 years, and 2% in 6 years. Some 115 companies recruited on campus in 1992–93. In the 1992 graduating class, 18% of the men and 18% of all graduates were enrolled in graduate school within 6 months of graduation; 80% had found employment.

Admissions Contact: Director of Admissions.

CENTRAL STATE UNIVERSITY
B-4
Wilberforce, OH 45384   (513) 376–6348; (800) 388-CSU1 (in-state)

Full-time: 1279 men, 1317 women	Faculty: 127; IIB, av$
Part-time: 170 men, 302 women	Ph.D.s: 46%
Graduate: 18 men and women	Student/Faculty: 20 to 1
Year: quarters, summer session	Tuition: $2811 ($6348)
Application Deadline: June 15	Room & Board: $4509
Freshman Class: 3556 applied, 2474 accepted, 706 enrolled	
ACT: required	NONCOMPETITIVE

Central State University, founded in 1887, is a public, coeducational institution offering programs in liberal arts, business, engineering, teacher preparation, and professional training. There are 3 undergraduate schools and one graduate school. In addition to regional accreditation, Central State has baccalaureate program accreditation with NASM. The library contains 155,643 volumes, 555,443 microform items, and 400 audiovisual forms, and subscribes to 890 periodicals. Computerized library sources and services include the card catalog, interlibrary loans, and database searching. Special learning facilities include a learning resource center, natural history museum, and radio station. The 60-acre campus is in a rural area 18 miles east of Dayton. Including residence halls, there are 39 buildings on campus.

Student Life: About 62% of undergraduates are from Ohio. Students come from 26 states and 18 foreign countries. Ninety percent are African American. The average age of freshmen is 18; all undergraduates, 20.

Housing: A total of 1395 students can be accommodated in college housing. College-sponsored living facilities include single-sex and coed dormitories. In addition, there are honors houses and a coed honors dormitory. On-campus housing is guaranteed for all 4 years. Priority is given to out-of-town students. Fifty percent of students live on campus. Alcohol is not permitted. All students may keep cars on campus.

Activities: About 3% of men belong to 4 local and 4 national fraternities; about 5% of women belong to 4 local and 4 national sororities. There are 40 groups on campus, including art, band, cheerleading, choir, chorale, chorus, drama, drill team, honors, jazz band, marching band, newspaper, pep band, photography, political, professional, radio and TV, social, student government, and yearbook. Popular campus events include Homecoming, Career Day, and May Weekend.

Sports: There are 4 intercollegiate sports for men and 3 for women, and 8 intramural sports for men and 7 for women. Athletic and recreation facilities include 2 gymnasiums, a swimming pool, a pool room, and tennis courts.

Disabled Students: The following facilities are available: wheelchair ramps, elevators, special parking, specially equipped rest rooms, lowered drinking fountains, and lowered telephones.

Services: In addition to many counseling and information services, tutoring is available in every subject. In addition, there is remedial math, reading, and writing.

Campus Safety and Security: Campus safety and security measures include 24-hour foot and vehicle patrol, emergency telephones, and lighted pathways and sidewalks.

Programs of Study: Central State awards the B.A., B.S., B.M., B.S.Ed., and B.S.M.E. degrees. Associate and master's degrees also are awarded. Bachelor's degrees are awarded in BIOLOGICAL SCIENCE (biology/biological science), BUSINESS (accounting, banking and finance, business administration and management, business economics, and marketing/retailing/merchandising), COMMUNICATIONS AND THE ARTS (advertising, broadcasting, communications, English, French, journalism, music, Spanish, and speech/debate/rhetoric), COMPUTER AND PHYSICAL SCIENCE (chemistry, computer science, information sciences and systems, mathematics, and physics), EDUCATION (art, business, elementary, health, industrial arts, music, secondary, and special), ENGINEERING AND ENVIRONMENTAL DESIGN (computer engineering and industrial engineering), HEALTH PROFESSIONS (predentistry and premedicine), SOCIAL SCIENCE (anthropology, economics, history, philosophy, political science/government, prelaw, psychology, public administration, social work, and sociology). Business administration has the largest enrollment.

Required: To graduate, students must complete 186 quarter credits, with a minimum GPA of 2.0. Required university core courses include 71 credits in English, mathematics, computer concepts, humanities, natural sciences, social sciences, and health and physical education.

Special: Central State offers co-op programs in all majors, cross-registration with 15 area colleges, study abroad in 3 countries, internships, on-campus work-study programs, B.A.-B.S. degrees, and non-degree study. There is a freshman honors program on campus.

Faculty/Classroom: All faculty teach undergraduates and 50% also do research. The average class size in an introductory lecture is 25; in a laboratory, 20; and in a regular course offering, 15.

Admissions: About 70% of the 1993–94 applicants were accepted.

Requirements: A minimum GPA of 2.0 is required. The ACT is required. Applicants must be graduates of an accredited secondary school. The GED is accepted. Students should have completed 4 years of high school English, 2 years of foreign language, and 3 years each of mathematics, science, and social studies. Central State follows an open admissions policy for Ohio applicants. AP credit is accepted.

Procedure: Freshmen are admitted to all sessions. Applications should be filed by June 15 for fall entry, October 15 for winter entry, February 15 for spring entry, and April 15 for summer entry, along with an application fee of $15. The college accepts all in-state residents who apply. Notification is sent on a rolling basis. There are early decision and early admissions plans.

Transfer: About 109 transfer students enrolled in 1993–94. Applicants should have a minimum college GPA of 2.0. Grades of C or better transfer for credit. Transfer students with fewer than 47 credit hours must submit ACT scores. Transfers are admitted every term.

Visiting: There are regularly scheduled orientations for prospective students. There are guides for informal visits and visitors may sit in on classes. To arrange for a visit, contact the Admissions Office at (513) 376-6348.

Financial Aid: Scholarships or need-based grants averaged $5000 ($8070 maximum); loans averaged $2625 (maximum); and work contracts averaged $1400 ($2211 maximum). Central State is a member of CSS. The FAF and the college's own financial statement are required. The deadline for financial aid applications is March 31.

International Students: There are currently 126 international students enrolled. They must take the TOEFL and achieve a minimum score of 500. The student must also take the ACT and achieve a minimum score of 15.

Computers: The college provides computer facilities for student use. Students can access the campus VAX system at various departmental locations. There are no time limits on using the system and no fees.

Graduates: In 1992–93 280 bachelor's degrees were awarded. The most popular majors among graduates were business administration (32%) and education (21%).

Admissions Contact: Robert E. Johnson, Director of Admissions.

CINCINNATI COLLEGE OF MORTUARY SCIENCE

A-4

Cincinnati, OH 45207–1033   (513) 745–3631

Full-time: 131 men, 40 women	**Faculty:** 7
Part-time: none	**Ph.D.s:** 33%
Graduate: none	**Student/Faculty:** 24 to 1
Year: quarters, summer session	**Tuition:** $7380
Application Deadline: October 1	**Room & Board:** n/app
Freshman Class: 108 applied, 101 accepted, 91 enrolled	
SAT I or ACT: required	**LESS COMPETITITVE**

The Cincinnati College of Mortuary Science, founded in 1882, is the only private mortuary college in the country that is regionally accredited at the bachelor's level. The curriculum encompasses the embalming sciences, funeral directing, and the liberal arts. In addition to regional accreditation, CCMS has baccalaureate program accreditation with ABFSE. The 2 libraries contain 6000 volumes. Special learning facilities include an art gallery and radio station. The 10-acre campus is in an urban area 5 miles from downtown Cincinnati. There are 45 buildings on campus.

Student Life: About 50% of undergraduates are from out-of-state, mostly the Midwest. Students come from 15 states, 2 foreign countries, and Canada. Ninety-three percent are white. The average age of all undergraduates is 23. Fifteen percent drop out by the end of their first year; 85% remain to graduate.

Housing: There are no residence halls. Alcohol is not permitted.

Activities: There are no fraternities or sororities on campus. There are some groups and organizations on campus, including student government and yearbook.

Sports: There are 2 intramural sports for men and 2 for women. Athletic and recreation facilities include CCMS has the use of Xavier University's sports center.

Disabled Students: The entire campus is accessible to disabled students. The following facilities are available: wheelchair ramps, elevators, special parking, and specially equipped rest rooms.

Campus Safety and Security: Campus safety and security measures include informal discussions, pamphlets, posters, films, emergency telephones, and lighted pathways and sidewalks.

Programs of Study: CCMS awards the Bachelor of Mortuary Science degree. Associate degrees also are awarded.

Required: Students must complete 180 quarter credit hours, with 90 in the major and a minimum GPA of 2.0. The general education core required of all students consists of 18 quarter hours each in the natural science/mathematics, social science, humanities/arts, and 12 each in English composition and literature, business, and free electives.

Special: Limited credit may be given for life, military, and work experience.

Faculty/Classroom: Eighty-seven percent of faculty are male; 13%, female. All teach undergraduates. The average class size in an introductory lecture is 50 and in a laboratory, 20.

Admissions: About 94% of the 1993–94 applicants were accepted. About 17% of the current freshmen were in the top fifth of their class; 50% were in the top two fifths.

Requirements: A minimum GPA of 2.0 is required. The SAT I, with a minimum composite score of 750, or the ACT, with a minimum composite score of 14, is required. Applicants must be graduates of an accredited secondary school. The GED is accepted. Students must complete 16 high school units, including 3 of English, 2 each of science and history, 1 of mathematics, and 8 of electives. An interview is recommended. AP and CLEP credits are accepted. Important factors used in the admissions decision are recommendations by alumni, leadership record, parents or siblings attending the school, and ability to finance college education.

Procedure: Freshmen are admitted fall and spring. Applications should be filed by October 1 for fall entry and April 1 for spring entry, along with an application fee of $25. Notification is sent on a rolling basis. There is an early admissions plan.

Transfer: Grades of D + or better transfer for credit if students have a GPA of 2.0. Transfers are admitted for the fall and spring terms. A total of 90 quarter credit hours out of 180 must be completed at CCMS.

Visiting: There are regularly scheduled orientations for prospective students, including an open house. There are guides for informal visits. To arrange for a visit, contact Patsy Leon at (513) 745–3632.

Financial Aid: In an earlier year, 49% of all current freshmen and 15% of continuing students received some form of financial aid. The average freshman award was $5000. Of that total, scholarships or need-based grants averaged $500 ($1000 maximum); and loans averaged $4000 ($5500 maximum). The average financial indebtedness of an earlier graduate was $4000. CCMS is a member of CSS. The FAF and FAFSA are required. The deadline for financial aid applications is September 15.

International Students: There is currently 1 international student enrolled.

Graduates: In an earlier year, 56 bachelor's degrees were awarded. In an earlier graduating class, all graduates had found employment within 6 months of graduation.

Admissions Contact: Director of Admissions.

CLEVELAND INSTITUTE OF ART   D-1
Cleveland, OH 44106 (216) 421–7418; (800) 223–4700 (out-of-state)

Full-time: 250 men, 225 women	Faculty: 48
Part-time: 14 men, 29 women	Ph.D.s: 90%
Graduate: none	Student/Faculty: 10 to 1
Year: semesters, summer session	Tuition: $11,370
Application Deadline: open	Room & Board: $4260
Freshman Class: 329 applied, 210 accepted, 99 enrolled	
SAT I Verbal/Math: 464/474	ACT: 22 SPECIAL

Cleveland Institute of Art, founded in 1882, is an independent, professional school of art offering a 5-year B.F.A. degree. In addition to regional accreditation, the institute has baccalaureate program accreditation with NASAD. The 3 libraries contain 40,000 volumes and 1600 audiovisual forms, and subscribe to 260 periodicals. Computerized library sources and services include the card catalog, interlibrary loans, and database searching. Special learning facilities include an art gallery and natural history museum. The 500-acre campus is in an urban area 4 miles east of downtown Cleveland, sharing a campus with Case Western Reserve University. Including residence halls, there are 3 buildings on campus.

Student Life: About 71% of undergraduates are from Ohio. Students come from 34 states and 6 foreign countries. Ninety-seven percent are from public schools; 3% from private. Eighty-six percent are white. Fifty percent are Protestant; 41% Catholic. The average age of freshmen is 20; all undergraduates, 25. Ten percent drop out by the end of their first year; 46% remain to graduate.

Housing: A total of 113 students can be accommodated in college housing. College-sponsored living facilities include single-sex and coed dormitories. On-campus housing is guaranteed for the freshman year only, is available on a first-come, first-served basis, and is available on a lottery system for upperclassmen. Priority is given to out-of-town students. Seventy-five percent of students commute. Alcohol is not permitted. All students may keep cars on campus.

Activities: About 1% of men belong to 6 national fraternities, and there are 6 national sororities. There are 6 groups on campus, including art, ethnic, international, literary magazine, professional, and student government. Popular campus events include museum trips, spring cookout, and student art exhibits.

Sports: There are 8 intramural sports for men and 8 for women. For a fee, students may use the recreation facilities of Case Western Reserve.

Disabled Students: Ninety percent of the campus is accessible to disabled students. The following facilities are available: wheelchair ramps, elevators, special parking, and specially equipped rest rooms.

Services: In addition to many counseling and information services, tutoring is available in most subjects.

Campus Safety and Security: Campus safety and security measures include 24-hour foot and vehicle patrol, escort service, shuttle buses, and informal discussions. In addition, there are pamphlets, posters, films, emergency telephones, and lighted pathways and sidewalks.

Programs of Study: The institute awards the B.F.A. degree. Bachelor's degrees are awarded in COMMUNICATIONS AND THE ARTS (advertising, applied art, design, graphic design, industrial design, painting, photography, and studio art), EDUCATION (art). Industrial design, painting, and metals are the strongest academically. Industrial design, graphic design, and painting have the largest enrollments.

Required: To graduate, students must complete 150 to 153 credit hours, with 42 to 51 in the major, and must maintain a minimum GPA of 2.0. Distribution requirements call for 105 studio credits and 48 academic credits. A thesis is required, which is encompassed in the B.F.A. show that each student mounts in the spring of the fifth year.

Special: Cross-registration with Case Western Reserve University and the Cleveland Commission on Higher Education, internships for 3rd-, 4th-, and 5th-year students with business and industry, and study abroad in 3 countries are available. There are joint programs with Case Western Reserve University in art education and medical illustration.

Faculty/Classroom: Seventy percent of faculty are male; 30%, female. All teach undergraduates. The average class size in an introductory lecture is 40 and in a regular course offering, 20.

Admissions: About 64% of the 1993–94 applicants were accepted. The SAT scores for the 1993–94 freshman class were as follows: Verbal—64% below 500, 24% between 500 and 599, 8% between 600 and 700, and 4% above 700; Math—53% below 500, 35% between 500 and 599, and 12% between 600 and 700. The ACT scores were 47% below 21, 16% between 21 and 23, 22% between 24 and 26, 14% between 27 and 28, and 1% above 28. About 31% of the current freshmen were in the top fifth of their class; 56% were in the top

two fifths. In an earlier year, there were 2 National Merit semifinalists. Two freshmen graduated first in their class.

Requirements: The institute requires applicants to be in the upper 75% of their class. A minimum GPA of 2.0 is required. The SAT I or ACT is recommended, with SAT I scores of 350 verbal and 350 mathematics or an ACT composite score of 15. Applicants must be graduates of an accredited secondary school. The GED is accepted. Students should have completed 4 units each of art, English, and mathematics; 2 each of history, science, and social studies; and 1 of a foreign language. An essay and a portfolio are required. An interview is strongly recommended. AP and CLEP credits are accepted.

Procedure: Freshmen are admitted in the fall and spring. Entrance exams should be taken during the junior year. Early decision applications should be filed by November 15, along with an application fee of $30. Notification is sent on a rolling basis. There are early decision, early admissions, and deferred admissions plans. A waiting list is an active part of the admissions procedure, with about 5% of the applicants on the list.

Transfer: Fifty-eight transfer students enrolled in 1993–94. Applicants must have a 2.0 GPA and must submit a portfolio. They are reviewed by department faculty if they have 30 to 36 credits in comparable studio courses or a strong portfolio. Grades of C or better transfer for credit. Transfers are admitted in the fall and spring. A total of 72 credits out of 150 must be completed at the institute.

Visiting: There are guides for informal visits, and visitors may sit in on classes and stay overnight at the school. To arrange for a visit, contact Thomas W. Steffen, Director of Admissions, at (216) 421–7418.

Financial Aid: In an earlier year, 60% of all current freshmen and 68% of continuing students received some form of financial aid. About 81% of freshmen and 70% of continuing students received need-based aid. The average freshman award was $7846. Of that total, scholarships or need-based grants averaged $2800 ($4000 maximum); loans averaged $2877 ($4000 maximum); and work contracts averaged $1187 ($1500 maximum). About 90% of undergraduate students work part-time. Average earnings from campus work for the school year are $2700. The average financial indebtedness of the graduate of an earlier year was $15,000. The institute is a member of CSS. The FAF and the college's own financial statement are required. The deadline for financial aid applications is July 1.

International Students: There are currently 11 international students enrolled. The school actively recruits these students. They must take the TOEFL and achieve a minimum score of 550.

Computers: The college provides computer facilities for student use. There are 20 Amiga PCs available in the computer laboratory and 15 Apple Macintosh microcomputers each in the industrial design/interior design laboratories and the graphic design/illustration labs. Students may access the system for up to 2 hours. There are no fees.

Graduates: In 1992–93, 94 bachelor's degrees were awarded. The most popular majors among graduates were industrial design (18%), graphic design (16%), and painting (15%). Within an average freshman class, 55% graduate in 5 years and 65% in 6 years. Some 6 companies recruited on campus in 1992–93.

Admissions Contact: Thomas W. Steffen, Director of Admissions.

CLEVELAND INSTITUTE OF MUSIC   D-1
Cleveland, OH 44106   (216) 795–3107

Full-time: 82 men, 99 women	Faculty: 29
Part-time: none	Ph.D.s: 18%
Graduate: 65 men, 101 women	Student/Faculty: 6 to 1
Year: semesters, summer session	Tuition: $13,407
Application Deadline: January 15	Room & Board: $4770
Freshman Class: 206 applied, 93 accepted, 45 enrolled	
SAT I Verbal/Math: 570/550	SPECIAL

Cleveland Institute of Music, founded in 1920, is a private music conservatory offering education and training in the arts of performance, composition, and related music programs. In addition to regional accreditation, CIM has baccalaureate program accreditation with NASM. The library contains 47,000 volumes and 16,000 audiovisual forms, and subscribes to 105 periodicals. Computerized library sources and services include the card catalog and interlibrary loans. Special learning facilities include 2 concert halls, an electronic music studio, a theater, an opera workshop, practice rooms, and a specially designed eurythmics studio. The 480-acre campus is in an urban area.

Student Life: About 63% of undergraduates are from out-of-state, mostly the Midwest. Students come from 42 states, 26 foreign countries, and Canada. Ninety-five percent are from public schools. Sixty-eight percent are white; 22% foreign nationals. The average age of freshmen is 19; all undergraduates, 21. Two percent drop out by the end of their first year; 73% remain to graduate.

Housing: College-sponsored housing is coed. Alcohol is not permitted. All students may keep cars on campus.

Activities: There are no fraternities or sororities on campus. There are some groups and organizations on campus, including chorale, chorus, jazz band, opera, orchestra, religious, student government, and symphony. Popular campus events include weekly concerts by the Cleveland Orchestra.

Sports: There is no sports program at CIM. Athletic and recreation facilities and a fitness center are available.

Disabled Students: The entire campus is accessible to disabled students. The following facilities are available: wheelchair ramps, elevators, special parking, specially equipped rest rooms, and lowered drinking fountains.

Services: In addition to many counseling and information services, tutoring is available in some subjects.

Campus Safety and Security: Campus safety and security measures include 24-hour foot and vehicle patrol, escort service, shuttle buses, and informal discussions. In addition, there are emergency telephones and lighted pathways and sidewalks.

Programs of Study: CIM awards the B.M.; B.A.Mus.Ed. and B.S.Mus.Ed. are offered in conjunction with Case Western Reserve University. degrees. Master's and doctoral degrees also are awarded. Bachelor's degrees are awarded in COMMUNICATIONS AND THE ARTS (music).

Required: CIM requires 126 credits with a minimum GPA of 2.0 for graduation. A core curriculum of liberal arts, music history, theory, and literature is required. Performance evaluation is based on jury examinations and recitals.

Special: Students may take a 5-year double major in performance/audio recording. Work-study and nondegree study are available. There are 2 national honor societies on campus.

Admissions: About 45% of the 1993–94 applicants were accepted.

Requirements: The SAT I or ACT is required. Applicants should have completed 16 Carnegie units. The GED is accepted. An audition and an interview are required. Freshmen applicants must complete a questionnaire pertaining to general knowledge of music and a diagnostic evaluation of rhythmic comprehension. All candidates will be tested in theory. Applicants majoring in composition should submit score and tapes. Other factors in the admissions decision are advanced placement or honors courses and recommendations. AP credits are accepted.

Procedure: Freshmen are admitted fall and spring. Entrance exams should be taken at the time of the entrance audition. Applications should be filed by January 15 for fall entry and November 1 for spring entry, along with an application fee of $50. Notification is sent April 1. There is an early admissions plan. A waiting list is an active part of the admissions procedure.

Transfer: About 10 transfer students enrolled in 1993–94. Applicants must meet the same criteria as entering freshmen and submit transcripts and letters of recommendation. A total of 24 credits out of 126 must be completed at CIM.

Visiting: There are guides for informal visits and visitors may sit in on classes. To arrange for a visit, contact the Admission Office at (216) 795–3107.

Financial Aid: In a recent year, 90% of all students received some form of financial aid. CIM is a member of CSS. The FAF and FAFSA are required. The deadline for financial aid applications is March 1.

International Students: There are currently 86 international students enrolled. They must take the TOEFL and achieve a minimum score of 500. The students must also audition.

Computers: The college provides computer facilities for student use. Each dormitory room is connected to CWRUnet, the university's fiber-optic computer network. Students are encouraged to bring their own personal computers for easy access to this extensive system. Computer facilities are available on the CWRU campus. All students may access the system. There are no time limits and no fees.

Graduates: In 1992–93, 39 bachelor's degrees were awarded. Within an average freshman class, 73% graduate in 5 years.

Admissions Contact: Admission Office.

CLEVELAND STATE UNIVERSITY   D-1
Cleveland, OH 44115-2403   (216) 687-3755

Full-time: 3887 men, 4051 women	Faculty: 561; IIA, +$
Part-time: 2028 men, 2000 women	Ph.D.s: 98%
Graduate: 2456 men, 2715 women	Student/Faculty: 14 to 1
Year: quarters, summer session	Tuition: $3126 ($6278)
Application Deadline: open	Room & Board: $4161
Freshman Class: 2285 applied, 2187 accepted, 1194 enrolled	
SAT I Verbal/Math: 410/430	ACT: 19 NONCOMPETITIVE

Cleveland State University, founded in 1964, is a primarily commuter public institution offering undergraduate programs through the colleges of arts and sciences, business administration, education, engineering, and urban affairs. There are 5 undergraduate and 2 graduate schools. In addition to regional accreditation, CSU has baccalaureate program accreditation with AACSB, ABET, CSWE, NCATE, and NLN. The 2 libraries contain 1.2 million volumes and 680,000 microform items, and subscribe to 7000 periodicals. Computerized library sources and services include database searching. Special learning facilities include a learning resource center, art gallery, and radio station. The 70-acre campus is in the heart of downtown Cleveland. Including residence halls, there are 33 buildings on campus.

Student Life: Seventy-six percent are white; 14% African American. The average age of freshmen is 20.2; all undergraduates, 25.6. Forty-seven percent drop out by the end of their first year; 34% remain to graduate.

Housing: A total of 550 students can be accommodated in college housing. College-sponsored living facilities include coed dormitories, off-campus apartments, married-student housing, fraternity houses, and sorority houses. In addition, there are graduate, law, quiet study, and first-year experience floors. Ninety-seven percent of students commute. All students may keep cars on campus.

Activities: About 1% of men belong to 2 local and 6 national fraternities; about 1% of women belong to 8 national sororities. There are 150 groups on campus, including art, cheerleading, chess, choir, chorale, chorus, computers, dance, drama, ethnic, honors, international, jazz band, literary magazine, musical theater, newspaper, opera, orchestra, pep band, photography, political, professional, radio and TV, religious, social, social service, student government, and symphony. Popular campus events include Black Aspiration Week, Homecoming, and Springfest.

Sports: There are 7 intercollegiate sports for men and 8 for women, and 34 intramural sports for men and 34 for women. Athletic and recreation facilities include a gymnasium, gymnastics and weight rooms, dance studio, swimming pool, fitness trail, indoor track, handball and squash courts, a 2500-seat soccer stadium, and a convocation center.

Disabled Students: Ninety-nine percent of the campus is accessible to disabled students. The following facilities are available: wheelchair ramps, elevators, special parking, specially equipped rest rooms, and lowered drinking fountains.

Services: In addition, there is a reader service for the blind, and remedial math, reading, and writing. Services for the physically handicapped are available through the Division of Special Studies. Students are assigned academic advisors and given physical and academic assistance until they graduate.

Campus Safety and Security: Campus safety and security measures include 24-hour foot and vehicle patrol, escort service, informal discussions, and pamphlets, posters, and films. In addition, there are emergency telephones and lighted pathways and sidewalks.

Programs of Study: CSU awards the B.A., B.S., B.B.A., B.C.E., B.Ch.E., B.E.E., B.M., B.M.E., B.S.C.I.S., B.S.Ed., B.S.I.E., B.S.N., and B.S.T. degrees. Master's and doctoral degrees also are awarded. Bachelor's degrees are awarded in BIOLOGICAL SCIENCE (biology/biological science), BUSINESS (accounting, banking and finance, business economics, labor studies, and marketing/retailing/merchandising), COMMUNICATIONS AND THE ARTS (classics, communications, dramatic arts, English, French, German, linguistics, music, and Spanish), COMPUTER AND PHYSICAL SCIENCE (chemistry, computer science, geology, information sciences and systems, mathematics, physics, and quantitative methods), EDUCATION (early childhood, elementary, health, physical, and special), ENGINEERING AND ENVIRONMENTAL DESIGN (chemical engineering, civil engineering, electrical/electronics engineering, electromechanical technology, engineering, environmental science, industrial engineering, and mechanical engineering), HEALTH PROFESSIONS (music therapy, nursing, occupational therapy, physical therapy, premedicine, and speech therapy), SOCIAL SCIENCE (anthropology, economics, history, international relations, liberal arts/general studies, philosophy, political science/government, psychology, religion, social science, social studies, social work, sociology, and urban studies). Physical therapy, occupational therapy, and nursing are the strongest programs academically. Accounting, communications, and psychology have the largest enrollments.

Required: Students must complete at least 192 quarter hours with a minimum 2.0 GPA for graduation. Requirements include a core curriculum containing courses in English composition, physical education, fine arts, humanities, social or behavioral science, natural sciences or mathematics, and contemporary social problems.

Special: CSU offers a developmental program for Ohio students not qualified for regular freshman admission. There are also cooperative education programs, nondegree study, work-study programs, internships, pass/fail options, and cross-registration at other Cleveland area colleges including the Cleveland Music Therapy Consortium and Baldwin-Wallace. Student-designed and dual majors, study abroad in England, Germany, Mexico, Poland, or Spain, and volunteer opportunites are available, as well as a combined liberal arts and engineering degree and a 3–2 engineering degree. There are 6 national honor societies on campus. Five departments have honors programs.

Faculty/Classroom: Seventy-five percent of faculty are male; 25%, female.

Admissions: About 96% of the 1993–94 applicants were accepted. The SAT scores for the 1993–94 freshman class were as follows: Verbal—82% below 500, 16% between 500 and 599, 2% between 600 and 700, and 1% above 700; Math—70% below 500, 20% between 500 and 599, 9% between 600 and 700, and 1% above 700. The ACT scores were 61% below 21, 23% between 21 and 23, 11% between 24 and 26, 3% between 27 and 28, and 2% above 28.

Requirements: The SAT I or ACT is required. The scores should meet the standards of the specific program for which the student is applying. Advanced placement and honors courses are considered in the admissions decision. AP and CLEP credits are accepted.

Procedure: Freshmen are admitted to all sessions. Entrance exams should be taken prior to application. Application deadlines are open. Application fee is $25. The college accepts all in-state residents who apply. Notification is sent on a rolling basis.

Transfer: About 1068 transfer students enrolled in 1993–94. Applicants must have a minimum GPA of 2.0. A total of 45 credits out of 192 must be completed at CSU.

Visiting: There are regularly scheduled orientations for prospective students, including general visitation days for the university (in the fall) and each of the colleges (in the spring). There are guides for informal visits and visitors may sit in on classes. To arrange for a visit, contact the Office of Undergraduate Admissions at (216) 687-3755.

Financial Aid: In 1993–94 51% of all current freshmen received some form of financial aid. About 51% of freshmen received need-based aid. The average freshman award was $3374. Of that total, scholarships or need-based grants averaged $2863 ($7671 maximum); and loans averaged $2466 ($7000 maximum). The FAF is required. The deadline for financial aid applications is April 15.

International Students: There are currently 513 international students enrolled. They must take the TOEFL and achieve a minimum score of 525.

Computers: The college provides computer facilities for student use. The mainframes include an IBM 3081K, 3 DEC VAX 750s, and a VAX 8600. The mainframes are accessible by modem, 24 hours per day, or during posted hours at the university's 10 stations across campus. PC services are available at several networked PC laboratories around the campus. Mainframe access is available to students in approved courses only. Hours vary by input center. There are no time limits on using the system and no fees.

Graduates: In 1992–93 1671 bachelor's degrees were awarded. The most popular majors among graduates were communication (10%), quantitative business analysis (7%), and accounting (7%). Within an average freshman class, 8% graduate in 3 years, 26% in 4 years, 34% in 5 years, and 38% in 6 years.

Admissions Contact: Dr. Ruth Ann Moyer, Acting Director of Admissions.

COLLEGE OF MOUNT SAINT JOSEPH
A-5
Cincinnati, OH 45233–1670

(513) 244–4531
(800) 654–9314 (in-state)

Full-time: 352 men, 761 women	Faculty: 95; IIB, -$
Part-time: 256 men, 1051 women	Ph.D.s: 46%
Graduate: 43 men, 131 women	Student/Faculty: 12 to 1
Year: semesters, summer session	Tuition: $9230
Application Deadline: open	Room & Board: $4042
Freshman Class: 798 applied, 620 accepted, 238 enrolled	
SAT I Verbal/Math: 440/480	ACT: 21 COMPETITIVE

The College of Mount St. Joseph, founded in 1920, is a private, liberal arts Catholic institution. There is one graduate school. In addition to regional accreditation, the Mount has baccalaureate program accreditation with ADA, NASM, NCATE, and NLN. The library contains 87,169 volumes, 205,059 microform items, and 9622 audiovisual forms, and subscribes to 710 periodicals. Computerized library sources and services include interlibrary loans and database searching. Special learning facilities include an art gallery and radio station. The 75-acre campus is in a suburban area 7 miles west of Cincinnati. Including residence halls, there are 6 buildings on campus.

Student Life: About 89% of undergraduates are from Ohio. Students come from 8 states and 17 foreign countries. Sixty percent are from public schools; 40% from private. Ninety-three percent are white. Sixty-five percent are Catholic; 30% Protestant. The average age of freshmen is 19; all undergraduates, 32. Twenty percent drop out by the end of their first year; 66% remain to graduate.

Housing: A total of 350 students can be accommodated in college housing. College-sponsored living facilities include coed dormitories. On-campus housing is guaranteed for all 4 years. Eighty-two percent of students commute. All students may keep cars on campus.

Activities: There are no fraternities or sororities on campus. There are 23 groups on campus, including art, band, cheerleading, choir, chorale, chorus, computers, drama, honors, international, literary magazine, musical theater, newspaper, orchestra, pep band, photography, radio, religious, social, and student government. Popular campus events include the Christmas gala, community Halloween events,

Career Exploration Day for African American High School Sophomores, Homecoming, and campus fair.

Sports: There are 4 intercollegiate sports for men and 4 for women, and 6 intramural sports for men and 6 for women. Athletic and recreation facilities include a gymnasium, a weight room, a hockey field, tennis courts, and a pool.

Disabled Students: Eighty percent of the campus is accessible to disabled students. The following facilities are available: wheelchair ramps, elevators, special parking, specially equipped rest rooms, special class scheduling, lowered drinking fountains, lowered telephones, and special door openings for wheelchair access.

Services: In addition to many counseling and information services, tutoring is available in most subjects. There is also remedial math, reading, writing and peer tutoring.

Campus Safety and Security: Campus safety and security measures include 24-hour foot and vehicle patrol, escort service, informal discussions, and lighted pathways and sidewalks.

Programs of Study: The Mount awards the B.A., B.S., B.F.A., and B.S.N. degrees. Associate and master's degrees also are awarded. Bachelor's degrees are awarded in BIOLOGICAL SCIENCE (biology/biological science), BUSINESS (business administration and management), COMMUNICATIONS AND THE ARTS (communications, English, fine arts, and music), COMPUTER AND PHYSICAL SCIENCE (chemistry, computer science, and mathematics), EDUCATION (art, elementary, music, science, and secondary), HEALTH PROFESSIONS (health care administration, medical laboratory technology, nursing, and premedicine), SOCIAL SCIENCE (gerontology, history, humanities, liberal arts/general studies, paralegal studies, prelaw, religion, social work, sociology, and women's studies). Nursing, biology, art, and humanities are the strongest academically. Business, education, nursing, art, and humanities have the largest enrollments.

Required: To graduate, students must complete 128 credits with an overall minimum GPA of 2.0. and 2.5 in the major. Forty-eight semester hours of liberal arts and sciences and 36 to 40 hours in the major are required. All students must take computer literacy and written and oral English.

Special: The college offers co-op programs in all majors, cross-registration with the Greater Consortium of Colleges and Universities of Ohio, internships, and study abroad in England, Germany, Spain, and Korea. Work-study programs, dual majors, a general studies degree, nondegree study, and pass/fail options are available. The Weekend College offers students an opportunity to earn a degree by enrolling in specially designed classes that meet only on weekends. There is a freshman honors program on campus, as well as one national honor society.

Faculty/Classroom: Forty-one percent of faculty are male; 59%, female. Ninety-five percent teach undergraduates and 25% both teach and do research. No introductory courses are taught by graduate students. The average class size in an introductory lecture is 25; in a laboratory, 14; and in a regular course offering, 25.

Admissions: About 78% of the 1993–94 applicants were accepted. The SAT scores for the 1993–94 freshman class were as follows: Verbal—70% below 500, 25% between 500 and 599, and 5% between 600 and 700; Math—55% below 500, 35% between 500 and 599, and 10% between 600 and 700. The ACT scores were 45% below 21, 27% between 21 and 23, 18% between 24 and 26, 6% between 27 and 28, and 4% above 28. About 38% of the current freshmen were in the top fifth of their class; 71% were in the top two fifths. There was 1 National Merit finalist and 1 semifinalist. Five freshmen graduated first in their class.

Requirements: The Mount requires applicants to be in the upper 60% of their class. A minimum GPA of 2.3 is required. The SAT I or ACT is required. Applicants must be graduates of an accredited secondary school. The GED (with scores in the top 75th percentile) is accepted. Students should have completed the following high school academic credits: 4 years of English, 2 each of mathematics (including algebra and geometry), social studies, and foreign language or 2 additional years of previously listed courses, and 1 each of laboratory science and fine arts. Letters of recommendation and a personal essay are required for those students not meeting 3 of the 4 following criteria: completion of above-listed high school core subject courses, class rank in upper three fifths, minimum GPA of 2.3, or minimum testing scores of 19 on the ACT or 400 on the SAT I Verbal and 440 on the SAT I Math. An audition is required of music students, and a portfolio is recommended for all students. AP and CLEP credits are accepted. Important factors used in the admissions decision are advanced placement or honor courses, personality, intangible qualities, evidence of special talent, extracurricular activities record, and leadership record.

Procedure: Freshmen are admitted to all sessions. Application deadlines are open. Application fee is $25. Notification is sent on a rolling basis. There is an early admissions plan.

Transfer: About 65 transfer students enrolled in 1993–94. Transfer students must meet freshman criteria or have a college GPA of 2.0 or better in a minimum of 12 semester or 18 quarter hours. A total of the final 27 credits of 128 or 45 of the last 54 credits must be completed at the Mount.

Visiting: There are regularly scheduled orientations for prospective students, including a meeting with an admissions counselor, a student-guided tour, a visit to financial aid, and a meeting with a faculty member if requested. There are guides for informal visits and visitors may sit in on classes and stay overnight at the school. To arrange for a visit, contact the Admissions Office at (513) 244–4531 or (800) 654–9314 (in-state).

Financial Aid: In an earlier year, 75% of all students received some form of financial aid. About 60% of all students received need-based aid. The average freshman award was $5500. Of that total, scholarships or need-based grants averaged $2200 ($4500 maximum); loans averaged $2000 ($4125 maximum); and work contracts averaged $700 ($1200 maximum). The average financial indebtedness of an earlier year's graduate was $9000. The Mount is a member of CSS. The FAF, the college's own financial statement and FAFSA are required. The deadline for financial aid applications is April 15.

International Students: There are currently 99 international students enrolled. The school actively recruits these students. They must take the TOEFL and achieve a minimum score of 500.

Computers: The college provides computer facilities for student use. The mainframes are a MicroVAX II and an HP 3000. The mainframe is used for programming classes. All students may access the system. It may be used 8 A.M. to 10:30 P.M. and 24 hours a day by modem. There are no time limits and no fees.

Graduates: In 1992–93, 324 bachelor's degrees were awarded. The most popular majors among graduates were business (31%), liberal arts (16%), and education (14%). Within an average freshman class, 1% graduate in 3 years, 66% in 4 years, 1% in 5 years, and 1% in 6 years. About 15 companies normally recruit on campus. In an earlier graduating class, 6% of the men and 7% of the women were enrolled in graduate school within 6 months of graduation.

Admissions Contact: Edward C. Eckel, Director of Admission.

COLLEGE OF WOOSTER
D-2

Wooster, OH 44691   (216) 263–2118; (800) 877–9905

Full-time: 830 men, 874 women   Faculty: 145; IIB, +$
Part-time: none   Ph.D.s: 95%
Graduate: none   Student/Faculty: 12 to 1
Year: semesters, summer session   Tuition: $15,425
Application Deadline: February 15   Room & Board: $4450
Freshman Class: 2100 applied, 1883 accepted, 553 enrolled
SAT I Verbal/Math: 520/560   ACT: 25   **VERY COMPETITIVE**

The College of Wooster, founded in 1866, is a coeducational liberal arts college. In addition to regional accreditation, Wooster has baccalaureate program accreditation with NASM. The library contains 650,538 volumes, 258,478 microform items, and 6745 audiovisual forms, and subscribes to 1254 periodicals. Computerized library sources and services include the card catalog. Special learning facilities include a learning resource center, art gallery, and radio station. The 320-acre campus is in a suburban area 54 miles south of Cleveland. Including residence halls, there are 35 buildings on campus.

Student Life: About 59% of undergraduates are from out-of-state, mostly the Midwest. Students come from 44 states, 32 foreign countries, and Canada. Seventy percent are from public schools; 27% from private. Eighty-three percent are white. The average age of freshmen is 18; all undergraduates, 21. Fourteen percent drop out by the end of their first year; 66% remain to graduate.

Housing: A total of 1800 students can be accommodated in college housing. College-sponsored living facilities include single-sex and coed dormitories. In addition, there are language houses, special interest houses, and almost three dozen small house residential options, most of which are associated with community service/volunteer programs. On-campus housing is guaranteed for all 4 years. Ninety-five percent of students live on campus; of those, 80% remain on campus on weekends. All students may keep cars on campus.

Activities: About 20% of men belong to 7 local fraternities; about 15% of women belong to 6 local sororities. There are 70 groups on campus, including art, bagpipe band, band, cheerleading, chess, choir, chorale, chorus, dance, drama, ethnic, gay, honors, international, jazz band, literary magazine, marching band, musical theater, newspaper, orchestra, pep band, photography, radio and TV, religious, social service, student government, symphony, and yearbook. Popular campus events include Party on the Green, Winter Gala, Scot Spirit Day, and Parents Weekend.

Sports: There are 11 intercollegiate sports for men and 10 for women, and 4 intramural sports for men and 3 for women. Athletic and recreation facilities include a physical education center, a stadium, a golf course, tennis courts, a track, a soccer field, and a hockey and lacrosse field.

Disabled Students: Ninety-five percent of the campus is accessible to disabled students. The following facilities are available: wheelchair ramps, elevators, special parking, specially equipped rest rooms, special class scheduling, and lowered drinking fountains.

Services: In addition to many counseling and information services, tutoring is available in every subject. There is a reader service for the blind, and remedial math, reading, and writing.

Campus Safety and Security: Campus safety and security measures include 24-hour foot and vehicle patrol, escort service, informal discussions, and pamphlets, posters, and films. In addition, there are emergency telephones and lighted pathways and sidewalks.

Programs of Study: Wooster awards the B.A., B.Mus., and B.Mus.Ed. degrees. Bachelor's degrees are awarded in BIOLOGICAL SCIENCE (biology/biological science), BUSINESS (business economics), COMMUNICATIONS AND THE ARTS (communications, dramatic arts, English, fine arts, French, German, Greek (classical), Latin, music, and Spanish), COMPUTER AND PHYSICAL SCIENCE (chemistry, computer science, geology, mathematics, and physics), SOCIAL SCIENCE (African American studies, economics, history, international relations, philosophy, political science/government, psychology, religion, sociology, urban studies, and women's studies). History, chemistry, and English are the strongest academically. History, English, and biology have the largest enrollments.

Required: To graduate, students must complete 32 course credits, with 9 to 13 courses in the major and a minimum GPA of 2.0. All students must take 3 courses each in science, social science, and humanities, and 1 course in religion, as well as a first-year seminar and departmental independent study.

Special: A 3–2 engineering degree is offered in conjunction with Case Western Reserve and Washington universities. A B.A.-B.S. is offered in music/music education. Cross-registration is possible with off-campus programs of the Great Lakes Colleges Association. Internships are available in American politics in Washington, D.C., the Ohio State Legislature, the U.S. State Department, as well as in professional theater and economics. Student-designed majors, double majors, study abroad, a Washington semester, nondegree study, and pass/fail options for a limited number of courses are available. All students participate in a 2-term independent-study project in the senior year that is related to the major. Topics are chosen by the student, who is guided by a faculty mentor and with whom the student works on a one-to-one basis. A sophomore research program is available to a number of students by application. There is a chapter of Phi Beta Kappa on campus.

Faculty/Classroom: Fifty-nine percent of faculty are male; 41%, female. All teach undergraduates and do research. The average class size in an introductory lecture is 23 and in a regular course offering, 21.

Admissions: About 90% of the 1993–94 applicants were accepted. The SAT scores for the 1993–94 freshman class were as follows: Verbal—39% below 500, 40% between 500 and 599, 18% between 600 and 700, and 3% above 700; Math—23% below 500, 44% between 500 and 599, 24% between 600 and 700, and 9% above 700. The ACT scores were 9% below 20, 37% between 20 and 24, 39% between 25 and 29, and 15% betweem 30 amd 36. About 57% of the current freshmen were in the top fifth of their class; 81% were in the top two fifths. Thirty freshmen graduated first in their class.

Requirements: The SAT I or ACT is required, with an SAT I minimum composite score of 900 (450 verbal, 450 mathematics) or an ACT minimum composite score of 20. In addition, applicants should be graduates of an accredited secondary school. The GED is accepted. Students should have completed 16 high school academic credits. The school also requires an essay and recommends an interview. AP credits are accepted. Important factors used in the admissions decision are advanced placement or honor courses, recommendations by school officials, leadership record, evidence of special talent, and extracurricular activities record.

Procedure: Freshmen are admitted fall and winter. Entrance exams should be taken in the fall of the senior year. Early decision applications should be filed by December 15; regular applications, by February 15 for fall entry, along with an application fee of $35. Notification of early decision is sent January 1; regular decision, April 1. There are early decision, early admissions, and deferred admissions plans. About 100 early decision candidates were accepted for the 1993–94 class. A waiting list is an active part of the admissions procedure, with about 10% of applicants on the list.

Transfer: About 21 transfer students enrolled in 1993–94. Applicants for transfer must have a minimum GPA of 2.5 and must submit either SAT I or ACT scores as well as a dean's reference and a high school transcript. An interview is recommended. Grades of C or better transfer for credit. Transfers are admitted every semester. A total of 16 course credits out of 32 must be completed at Wooster.

Visiting: There are regularly scheduled orientations for prospective students. There are guides for informal visits and visitors may sit in on classes and stay overnight at the school. To arrange for a visit, contact the Office of Admissions at (800) 877–9905.

Financial Aid: In 1993–94, 90% of all current freshmen and 80% of continuing students received some form of financial aid. The average freshman award was $10,000. Of that total, scholarships or need-based grants averaged $2128 ($8000 maximum); loans averaged $2000 ($3400 maximum); and work contracts averaged $946 ($1000 maximum). The average financial indebtedness of an earlier year's graduate was $8500. Wooster is a member of CSS. The FAF is required. The deadline for financial aid applications is February 15.

International Students: There are currently 134 international students enrolled. The school actively recruits these students. They must take the TOEFL or the University of Michigan Language Test and achieve a minimum score on the TOEFL of 550. The student must also take the SAT I or the ACT and obtain a minimum composite score of 900 on the SAT I.

Computers: The college provides computer facilities for student use. The mainframe is a DEC VAX 11/750. The Academic Computing Center includes a minicluster of DEC VAX 11/750s sharing nearly 1 billion characters of disk storage, file servers, laser printers, other minicomputers, and more than 100 personal computers on campus for student use. More than 500 personal computers have been linked to WoosterNet, which is the college's broadband local-area network linking this equipment to the library and to computers in faculty offices, residence halls, and classroom buildings and which provides computing capabilities 24 hours a day. Luce Residence Hall has a desktop publishing laboratory. All students may access the system any time. There are no time limits on using the system and no fees.

Graduates: In 1992–93 465 bachelor's degrees were awarded. Some 65 companies recruited on campus in 1992–93. In an earlier graduating class, 17% of the men and 22% of the women were enrolled in graduate school within 6 months of graduation; 26% of the men and 35% of the women had found employment.

Admissions Contact: Hayden Schilling, Dean of Admissions.

COLUMBUS COLLEGE OF ART AND DESIGN   C-3
Columbus, OH 43215   (614) 224–9101

Full-time: 724 men, 496 women	**Faculty:** 61
Part-time: 173 men, 302 women	**Ph.D.s:** 60%
Graduate: none	**Student/Faculty:** 20 to 1
Year: semesters, summer session	**Tuition:** $9350
Application Deadline: open	**Room & Board:** $5200
Freshman Class: 714 applied, 437 accepted, 300 enrolled	
SAT I Verbal/Math: 440/440	**ACT:** 21 **SPECIAL**

Columbus College of Art and Design, founded in 1879, is a private coeducational institution offering undergraduate programs in art and fine arts. In addition to regional accreditation, CCAD has baccalaureate program accreditation with NASAD. The library contains 36,387 volumes and 9119 microform items, and subscribes to 256 periodicals. Special learning facilities include a learning resource center and art gallery. The 14-acre campus is in an urban area in Columbus. Including residence halls, there are 15 buildings on campus.

Student Life: About 77% of undergraduates are from Ohio. Students come from 49 states, 36 foreign countries, and Canada. Eighty-seven percent are white. The average age of freshmen is 19; all undergraduates, 21. Twenty-two percent drop out by the end of their first year; 36% remain to graduate.

Housing: A total of 245 students can be accommodated in college housing. College-sponsored living facilities include coed dormitories and off-campus apartments. On-campus housing is guaranteed for the freshman year only and is available on a first-come, first-served basis. Priority is given to out-of-town students. Eighty-two percent of students commute. Alcohol is not permitted. All students may keep cars on campus.

Activities: There are no fraternities or sororities on campus. There are 7 groups on campus, including ethnic, international, literary magazine, newspaper, professional, religious, and student government. Popular campus events include biannual student art sales, International Reception, and International Students Holiday Brunch.

Disabled Students: Fifty percent of the campus is accessible to disabled students. The following facilities are available: wheelchair ramps, elevators, special parking, specially equipped rest rooms, special class scheduling, and lowered telephones.

Services: In addition to many counseling and information services, there is remedial reading and writing.

Campus Safety and Security: Campus safety and security measures include 24-hour foot and vehicle patrol, informal discussions, and lighted pathways and sidewalks.

Programs of Study: CCAD awards the B.F.A. degree. Bachelor's degrees are awarded in COMMUNICATIONS AND THE ARTS (advertising, design, fine arts, illustration, industrial design, and photography), ENGINEERING AND ENVIRONMENTAL DESIGN (interior design). Illustration and advertising design have the largest enrollments.

Required: All students must complete foundation studies, including 4 years of drawing and 3 years of design/color, and courses in English, sociology, psychology, business, art history, science, literature, painting, and physical education. A total of 145 credit hours, with 75 to 90 in the major, depending on the major, and a minimum GPA of 2.0 are required to graduate. A sophomore English examination must be passed. Students must complete a portfolio of professional caliber, and students in fine arts must have an individual showing of recent works.

Special: Cross-registration is offered with Franklin, Ohio State, and Capital universities, Ohio Dominican and Otterbein colleges, Pontifical College Josephinum, and DeVry Institute of Technology. Internships, including biannual opportunities with Walt Disney Studios, are available, as are on-campus work-study, dual majors, and nondegree study.

Faculty/Classroom: Seventy-one percent of faculty are male; 29%, female. All teach undergraduates. The average class size in an introductory lecture is 23; in a laboratory, 18; and in a regular course offering, 20.

Admissions: About 61% of the 1993–94 applicants were accepted. The SAT scores for the 1993–94 freshman class were as follows: Verbal—62% below 500, 30% between 500 and 599, and 8% between 600 and 700; Math—63% below 500, 28% between 500 and 599, and 9% between 600 and 700. The ACT scores were 46% below 21, 40% between 21 and 25, and 14% 26 and above. One freshman was first in a graduating class.

Requirements: A minimum GPA of 2.0 is required. The SAT I or ACT is recommended. Applicants should be graduates of an accredited secondary school or have the GED. A portfolio of artwork indicative of abilities must be submitted. An interview is advised. Important factors used in the admissions decision are evidence of special talent, recommendations by school officials, recommendations by alumni, parents or siblings attending the school, and ability to finance college education.

Procedure: Freshmen are admitted fall and winter. Application deadlines are open. The fee is $25. Notification is sent on a rolling basis.

Transfer: About 65 transfer students enrolled in 1993–94. Applicants must submit an acceptable portfolio of artwork as well as all high school and college transcripts. A minimum GPA of 2.0 is required. An interview is recommended. A total of 60 credits out of 145 must be completed at CCAD.

Visiting: There are regularly scheduled orientations for prospective students, including a tour, assembly, class registration, and an appointment for photo IDs. There are guides for informal visits. To arrange for a visit, contact the Admissions Office at (614) 224–9101.

Financial Aid: In 1993–94 88% of all students received some form of financial aid. About 70% of freshmen received need-based aid. The average freshman award was $4000. Scholarships or need-based grants averaged $10,000 ($30,000 maximum); loans averaged $2500 ($2650 maximum); and work contracts averaged $1500 ($2000 maximum). Average earnings from campus work for the school year are $1636. The average financial indebtedness of the 1992–93 graduate was $17,000. CCAD is a member of CSS. The FAF and the college's own financial statement are required. The deadline for financial aid applications is May 1.

International Students: There are currently 48 international students enrolled. They must take the TOEFL or the University of Michigan Language Test and achieve a minimum score on the TOEFL of 500.

Computers: The college provides computer facilities for student use. There are 63 computers available for student use. The 3 computer systems include Amiga, Macintosh Desktop Publishing, and Apple Macintosh CADD. All students may access the system. It may be used during scheduled laboratory hours and class time. There are no time limits on using the system. Laboratory fees vary.

Graduates: In a recent year, 164 bachelor's degrees were awarded. The most popular majors among graduates were advertising design (26%), illustration (26%), and fine arts (18%). Within an average freshman class, 13% graduate in 4 years, 28% in 5 years, and 36% in 6 years. Some 20 companies recruited on campus in an earlier year. In a recent graduating class, 5% of the men and 6% of the women were enrolled in graduate school within 6 months of graduation; 42% of the men and 37% of the women had found employment.

Admissions Contact: Thomas Green, Director of Admissions.

DEFIANCE COLLEGE   A-2
Defiance, OH 43512 (419) 784–4010; (800) (419) 783–2330 (collect)

Full-time: 339 men, 306 women	**Faculty:** 52; IIB, --$
Part-time: 110 men, 179 women	**Ph.D.s:** 58%
Graduate: 7 men, 35 women	**Student/Faculty:** 12 to 1
Year: semesters plus optional May	**Tuition:** $9950
term, summer	**Room & Board:** $3530

Application Deadline: August 15
Freshman Class: 489 applied, 466 accepted, 174 enrolled
SAT I Verbal/Math: 400/438   **ACT:** 21   **LESS COMPETITIVE**

Defiance College, chartered in 1850, is a small liberal arts institution affiliated with the United Church of Christ. In addition to regional accreditation, Defiance has baccalaureate program accreditation with CSWE. The library contains 100,000 volumes and 5000 microform items, and subscribes to 500 periodicals. Computerized library sources and services include the card catalog and interlibrary loans. Special learning facilities include an art gallery, a nature sanctuary, and a greenhouse. The 150-acre campus is in a small town 55 miles southwest of Toledo. Including residence halls, there are 23 buildings on campus.

Student Life: About 88% of undergraduates are from Ohio. Students come from 15 states and 14 foreign countries. Ninety percent are from public schools; 10% from private. Eighty-seven percent are white. Forty percent are Protestant; 29% Catholic. Seventy-five percent drop out by the end of their first year; 45% remain to graduate.

Housing: A total of 490 students can be accommodated in college housing. College-sponsored living facilities include single-sex dormitories, fraternity houses, and sorority houses. On-campus housing is guaranteed for all 4 years. Sixty percent of students commute. Alcohol is not permitted. All students may keep cars on campus.

Activities: About 14% of men belong to 3 national fraternities; about 13% of women belong to 2 local and 1 national sororities. There are 33 groups on campus, including art, band, cheerleading, chess, choir, chorale, drama, ethnic, honors, international, jazz band, literary magazine, musical theater, newspaper, professional, religious, social, social service, student government, and yearbook. Popular campus events include ArtsFest, Professor Appreciation Week, Homecoming, Spring Formal, Greek Week, Hispanic Awareness Week, and Black History Month.

Sports: There are 9 intercollegiate sports for men and 6 for women, and 12 intramural sports for men and 12 for women. Athletic and recreation facilities include a 4000-seat football stadium, baseball, softball, and soccer fields, a cross-country course, a recreation fitness center with a 5000-seat gymnasium, a racquetball court, an indoor track, a weight-lifting room, and basketball courts.

Disabled Students: Fifty percent of the campus is accessible to disabled students. The following facilities are available: wheelchair ramps, elevators, special parking, specially equipped rest rooms, special class scheduling, lowered drinking fountains, and lowered telephones.

Services: In addition to many counseling and information services, tutoring is available in every subject. There is also a reader service for the blind, and remedial math, reading, and writing.

Campus Safety and Security: Campus safety and security measures include 24-hour foot and vehicle patrol, escort service, informal discussions, and pamphlets, posters, and films. In addition, there are lighted pathways and sidewalks and 24-hour security guards in residence halls.

Programs of Study: Defiance awards the B.A. and B.S. degrees. Associate and master's degrees also are awarded. Bachelor's degrees are awarded in BIOLOGICAL SCIENCE (biology/biological science), BUSINESS (accounting, banking and finance, business administration and management, management science, marketing/retailing/merchandising, recreation and leisure services, and sports management), COMMUNICATIONS AND THE ARTS (communications, English, fine arts, music, and speech/debate/rhetoric), COMPUTER AND PHYSICAL SCIENCE (chemistry, computer science, mathematics, and physics), EDUCATION (art, business, elementary, mathematics, music, physical, science, secondary, and special), ENGINEERING AND ENVIRONMENTAL DESIGN (environmental science), HEALTH PROFESSIONS (medical laboratory technology, predentistry, premedicine, preveterinary science, recreation therapy, and sports medicine), SOCIAL SCIENCE (criminal justice, history, ministries, philosophy, prelaw, psychology, religion, religious education, social studies, and social work). Education is the strongest academically. Business has the largest enrollment.

Required: All students must fulfill general education requirements, including written and oral communications and foreign language, and distribution studies in sciences, social sciences, humanities, and fine arts. A freshman seminar, physical education course, interdisciplinary studies in Western civilization and contemporary world, as well as senior assessment in the major are also required. A total of

120 semester credits, with at least 30 in the major, and a minimum GPA of 2.0 is required to graduate.

Special: The optional May term provides opportunities for individual study or group projects on or off campus. The college offers a strong interdisciplinary emphasis, for example, a wellness and corporate fitness major is offered, and student-designed majors and courses as well as independent study are available. Work-study programs as well as dual and student-designed majors are available. Numerous cooperative education programs and internships are also offered. A B.A.-B.S. degree, limited pass/fail options, and some credit for life experience are available. There are 8 national honor societies on campus.

Faculty/Classroom: Seventy-one percent of faculty are male; 29%, female. All teach undergraduates and 20% do research. No introductory courses are taught by graduate students. The average class size in an introductory lecture is 25; in a laboratory, 18; and in a regular course offering, 16.

Admissions: About 95% of the 1993-94 applicants were accepted. The SAT scores for the 1993-94 freshman class were as follows: Verbal—91% below 500, 8% between 500 and 599, and 1% between 600 and 700; Math—68% below 500, 26% between 500 and 599, and 8% between 600 and 700. The ACT scores were 67% below 21, 10% between 21 and 23, 15% between 24 and 26, 7% between 27 and 28, and 1% above 28. About 21% of the current freshmen were in the top fifth of their class; 45% were in the top two fifths. Seven freshmen graduated first in their class.

Requirements: Defiance requires applicants to be in the upper 60% of their class. A minimum GPA of 2.0 is required. The SAT I or ACT is required. Applicants should be graduates of an accredited secondary school, or have GED equivalent, with 15 Carnegie units completed, including 4 in English, 3 each in mathematics, science, and social studies, and 2 in foreign language. An essay and an interview are recommended. AP and CLEP credits are accepted. Important factors used in the admissions decision are advanced placement or honor courses, personality, intangible qualities, leadership record, evidence of special talent, and extracurricular activities record.

Procedure: Freshmen are admitted to all sessions. Entrance exams should be taken in the spring of the junior year or the fall of the senior year. Applications should be filed by August 15 for fall entry, December 15 for spring entry, and May 1 for summer entry, along with an application fee of $25. Notification is sent on a rolling basis. There is a deferred admissions plan.

Transfer: About 57 transfer students enrolled in 1993-94. A minimum GPA of 2.0 is required and an interview recommended. A total of 35 credits out of 120 must be completed at Defiance.

Visiting: There are regularly scheduled orientations for prospective students, including admissions and financial aid sessions, a campus tour, a complimentary lunch, meetings with faculty, and observing a class in session. There are guides for informal visits and visitors may sit in on classes and stay overnight at the school. To arrange for a visit, contact the Office of Admission at (419) 783-2330 (collect).

Financial Aid: In a recent year, 92% of all current freshmen and 95% of continuing students received some form of financial aid. About 78% of students received need-based aid. The average freshman award was $8340. Of that total, scholarships or need-based grants averaged $4100 ($9000 maximum); loans averaged $2880 ($4625 maximum); and work contracts averaged $1360 ($2000 maximum). Eighty percent of undergraduate students work part-time. Average earnings from campus work for the school year are $800. The average financial indebtedness of a recent year's graduate was $7731. Defiance is a member of CSS. The FAF and FAFSA are required. The deadline for financial aid applications is March 1.

International Students: There are currently 12 international students enrolled. The school actively recruits these students. They must take the TOEFL and achieve a minimum score of 500.

Computers: The college provides computer facilities for student use. The mainframe is a DEC MicroVAX II. There are also 40 IBM-compatible and Apple IIe microcomputers available in computer laboratories and faculty offices. All students may access the system. It may be used 24 hours a day, every day. There are no time limits and no fees.

Graduates: In a recent year, bachelor's degrees were awarded. The most popular majors among graduates were business and management (34%), education (29%), and social sciences (13%). Within an average freshman class, 4% graduate in 3 years, 38% in 4 years, 18% in 5 years, and 9% in 6 years. Nearly 100 companies usually recruit on campus. In a recent graduating class, 6% of all graduates were enrolled in graduate school within 6 months of graduation; 68% of the men and 71% of the women had found employment.

Admissions Contact: Penny D. Bell, Director of Admission.

DENISON UNIVERSITY
Granville, OH 43023

C-3

(614) 587-6276
(800) DENISON (out-of-state)

Full-time: 889 men, 1026 women
Part-time: 8 men, 17 women
Graduate: none
Year: 4-4-1 (2 semesters and May term)
Application Deadline: February 1
Freshman Class: 2762 applied, 2279 accepted, 533 enrolled
SAT I Verbal/Math: 510/570

Faculty: 155; IIB, +$
Ph.D.s: 97%
Student/Faculty: 12 to 1
Tuition: $16,730
Room & Board: $4420

ACT: 27   VERY COMPETITIVE +

Denison University, founded in 1831, is a private independent institution of liberal arts and sciences. The library contains 313,202 volumes, 52,989 microform items, and 16,606 audiovisual forms, and subscribes to 1174 periodicals. Computerized library sources and services include interlibrary loans and database searching. Special learning facilities include a learning resource center, art gallery, radio station, TV station, and an observatory, and a 275-acre biological reserve. The 1200-acre campus is in a small town 30 miles east of Columbus. Including residence halls, there are 14 buildings on campus.

Student Life: About 62% of undergraduates are from out-of-state, mostly the Middle Atlantic. Students come from 44 states and 28 foreign countries. Sixty-five percent are from public schools; 21% from private. Ninety percent are white. Forty-nine percent are Protestant; 29% Catholic; 10% Buddhist, Muslim, and Orthodox; 11% claim no religious affiliation. The average age of freshmen is 18; all undergraduates, 20. Fourteen percent drop out by the end of their first year; 78% remain to graduate.

Housing: A total of 1631 students can be accommodated in college housing. College-sponsored living facilities include single-sex and coed dormitories and fraternity houses. In addition there are honors houses, special interest houses, a first-year center, substance-free dorms, quiet dorms, all-women dorms, and apartments for juniors and seniors with high GPA/leadership. On-campus housing is guaranteed for all 4 years and is available on a lottery system for upperclassmen. Ninety-seven percent of students live on campus; of those, 80% remain on campus on weekends. Upperclassmen may keep cars on campus.

Activities: About 56% of men belong to 11 national fraternities; about 58% of women belong to 8 national sororities. There are 110 groups on campus, including art, cheerleading, choir, chorale, chorus, computers, dance, drama, ethnic, film, gay, honors, international, jazz band, literary magazine, musical theater, newspaper, orchestra, pep band, photography, political, professional, radio and TV, religious, social, social service, student government, symphony, and yearbook. Popular campus events include community picnic and fair, Homecoming, All-Campus Gala, and Vail Cultural Series.

Sports: There are 11 intercollegiate sports for men and 10 for women, and 14 intramural sports for men and 13 for women. Athletic and recreation facilities include a 6000-seat stadium, a 1500-seat gymnasium, 14 outdoor tennis courts, squash courts, an 8-lane quarter-mile track, weight, aerobic, and fitness rooms, a field house with 200 meter track and 4 tennis courts, and baseball/softball fields.

Disabled Students: Sixty percent of the campus is accessible to disabled students. The following facilities are available: wheelchair ramps, elevators, special parking, specially equipped rest rooms, special class scheduling, lowered drinking fountains, and lowered telephones.

Services: In addition to many counseling and information services, tutoring is available in most subjects. A reading and writing center is available, as are study sessions for mathematics and chemistry.

Campus Safety and Security: Campus safety and security measures include 24-hour foot and vehicle patrol, self defense education, escort service, and informal discussions. In addition, there are pamphlets, posters, films, emergency telephones, and lighted pathways and sidewalks.

Programs of Study: Denison awards the B.A., B.S., and B.F.A. degrees. Bachelor's degrees are awarded in BIOLOGICAL SCIENCE (biochemistry and biology/biological science), COMMUNICATIONS AND THE ARTS (communications, dance, dramatic arts, English, film arts, fine arts, French, German, languages, Latin, music, Spanish, and speech/debate/rhetoric), COMPUTER AND PHYSICAL SCIENCE (chemistry, computer science, geology, mathematics, and physics), EDUCATION (physical), SOCIAL SCIENCE (African American studies, anthropology, classical/ancient civilization, East Asian studies, economics, history, Latin American studies, philosophy, political science/government, psychology, religion, and women's studies). Psychology, philosophy, physics, sociology/anthropology, and mathematics are the strongest academically. English, economics, history, psychology, communications, and biology have the largest enrollments.

Required: All students must fulfill aproximately 13 courses of the general education program, including freshman studies in textual, critical, social, scientific, and artistic inquiries, along with oral communication, minority/women's studies, and two other global studies requirements. A total of 127 semester hours with a minimum GPA of 2.0 is required in order to graduate.

Special: Cross-registration is possible through the Great Lakes Colleges Association. Work-study programs, a Washington semester, study-abroad programs, student-designed majors, a mathematics/economics dual major, a philosophy, political science, and economics interdisciplinary major, and pass/fail options are available. A 3-2 engineering program is offered with Rensselear Polytechnic Institute, Case Western Reserve, Columbia University, Washington universities. A B.A.-B.S. degree, accelerated degree programs, and nondegree study are possible. There is a freshman honors program on campus, as well as 15 national honor societies, including Phi Beta Kappa.

Faculty/Classroom: Sixty-six percent of faculty are male; 34%, female. All teach undergraduates and do research. The average class size in an introductory lecture is 20; in a laboratory, 20; and in a regular course offering, 18.

Admissions: About 83% of the 1993-94 applicants were accepted. The SAT scores for the 1993-94 freshman class were as follows: Verbal—54% below 500, 36% between 500 and 599, 9% between 600 and 700, and 1% above 700; Math—26% below 500, 45% between 500 and 599, 23% between 600 and 700, and 6% above 700. The ACT scores were 11% below 21, 27% between 21 and 23, 28% between 24 and 26, 15% between 27 and 28, and 19% above 28. About 48% of the current freshmen were in the top fifth of their class; 71% were in the top two fifths. There were 5 National Merit finalists. Twenty-two freshmen graduated first in their class.

Requirements: The SAT I is required. Applicants should have completed 16 Carnegie units, including 4 in English, 3 each in mathematics, social studies, and foreign language, 2 in science, and 1 in art. An essay is part of the application process. An interview is advised, and a portfolio or an audition is recommended for art or music majors, respectively. AP credits are accepted. Important factors used in the admissions decision are advanced placement or honor courses, leadership record, evidence of special talent, extracurricular activities record, and parents or siblings attending the school.

Procedure: Freshmen are admitted fall and winter. Entrance exams should be taken by December of the senior year. Early decision applications should be filed by January 1; regular applications, by February 1 for fall entry and December 1 for spring entry, along with an application fee of $35. Notification of early decision is sent January 1; regular decision, April 1. There are early decision, early admissions, and deferred admissions plans. About 77 early decision candidates were accepted for the 1993-94 class. A waiting list is an active part of the admissions procedure, with about 6% of applicants on the list.

Transfer: About 20 transfer students enrolled in 1993-94. A minimum GPA of 2.75 is required. SAT I or ACT scores should be submitted. An interview is recommended. A total of 60 credits out of 127 must be completed at Denison.

Visiting: There are regularly scheduled orientations for prospective students, including orientation, programs, class visits, tours, and interviews. There are guides for informal visits and visitors may sit in on classes and stay overnight at the school. To arrange for a visit, contact the Admissions Office at (800) DENISON (336-4766).

Financial Aid: In 1993-94 63% of all current freshmen and 61% of continuing students received some form of financial aid. About 47% of freshmen and 39% of continuing students received need-based aid. The average freshman award was $16,202. Of that total, scholarships or need-based grants averaged $11,851 ($15,950 maximum); loans averaged $2750 ($4125 maximum); and work contracts averaged $1600 (maximum). Forty percent of undergraduate students work part-time. Average earnings from campus work for the school year are $876. The average financial indebtedness of the 1992-93 graduate was $10,245. Denison is a member of CSS. The FAF and FAFSA are required. The deadline for financial aid applications is April 1.

International Students: There are currently 57 international students enrolled. The school actively recruits these students. They must take the TOEFL and achieve a minimum score of 550. The student must also take the SAT I or ACT.

Computers: The college provides computer facilities for student use. About half the 160 Apple Macintosh and DOS microcomputers and all the 36 terminals in student clusters and departmental laboratories are connected to the campus network, Bitnet, and Internet. Access to computers and software in departmental laboratories may be limited. Software for the DOS microcomputers includes WordPerfect and Quattro Pro, and Macintosh microcomputers software includes Microsoft Word and Excel. All students may access the system. It may be used 24 hours a day. There are no time limits and no fees.

Graduates: In 1992-93, 480 bachelor's degrees were awarded. The most popular majors among graduates were economics (18%), English (14%), and history (11%). Within an average freshman class,

75% graduate in 4 years, 77% in 5 years, and 79% in 6 years. Some 40 companies recruited on campus in 1992–93. In the 1992 graduating class, 15% of all graduates were enrolled in graduate school within 6 months of graduation; 85% had found employment.

Admissions Contact: Stuart Oremus, Director of Admissions.

DEVRY INSTITUTE OF TECHNOLOGY COLUMBUS
Columbus, OH 43209–2764

C-3

(614) 253–1525
(800) 426–2206 (out-of-state)

Full-time: 1827 men, 425 women	Faculty: 60
Part-time: 416 men, 130 women	Ph.D.s: n/av
Graduate: none	Student/Faculty: 38 to 1
Year: trimesters, summer session	Tuition: $5609
Application Deadline: open	Room & Board: n/app
Freshman Class: 1426 applied, 1295 accepted, 716 enrolled	
SAT I or ACT: see profile	**LESS COMPETITIVE**

DeVry Institute of Technology/Columbus, one of 11 DeVry Institutes in the United States and 2 in Canada, opened in 1952. The institute offers undergraduate degrees in business operations, electronics, computer information systems, and accounting. In addition to regional accreditation, DeVry has baccalaureate program accreditation with ABET. The library contains 14,858 volumes, 5 microform items, and 316 audiovisual forms, and subscribes to 186 periodicals. Computerized library sources and services include the card catalog, interlibrary loans, and database searching. Special learning facilities include a learning resource center and electronics and other laboratories. The 21-acre campus is in an urban area. There is one building on campus. There are no residence halls.

Student Life: About 60% of undergraduates are from Ohio. Students come from 11 foreign countries and Canada. Seventy-nine percent are white; 18% African American. The average age of all undergraduates is 23. Fifty-six percent drop out by the end of their first year; 37% remain to graduate.

Housing: There are no residence halls. College-sponsored living facilities include off-campus apartments. All students commute. Alcohol is not permitted. All students may keep cars on campus.

Activities: There are no fraternities or sororities on campus. There are 19 groups on campus, including band, chess, computers, ethnic, honors, newspaper, professional, radio and TV, religious, and student government. Popular campus events include weekly movie and weekly comedy series, Parents Weekend, midwinter beach party, and pig roast.

Sports: There are 5 intramural sports each for men and women.

Disabled Students: Ninety percent of the campus is accessible to disabled students. The following facilities are available: wheelchair ramps, elevators, special parking, specially equipped rest rooms, and special class scheduling.

Services: In addition to many counseling and information services, tutoring is available in every subject.

Campus Safety and Security: Campus safety and security measures include informal discussions, pamphlets, posters, and films, emergency telephones, and lighted pathways and sidewalks. In addition, daytime and evening security is provided until the building is closed. Security systems and motion detectors are used after business hours.

Programs of Study: DeVry awards the B.S. degree. Associate degrees also are awarded. Bachelor's degrees are awarded in BUSINESS (accounting and business administration and management), COMPUTER AND PHYSICAL SCIENCE (information sciences and systems), ENGINEERING AND ENVIRONMENTAL DESIGN (electrical/electronics engineering technology). Electronics has the largest enrollment.

Required: To graduate, students must complete between 143 and 158 credit hours with a 2.0 minimum GPA. Course requirements vary according to program. All first-semester students take courses in business organization, computer applications, algebra, psychology, and student success strategies.

Special: Nondegree study and evening classes are possible. There is 1 national honor society on campus. One department has an honors program.

Faculty/Classroom: Seventy-eight percent of faculty are male; 22%, female. All teach undergraduates. The average class size in an introductory lecture is 30; in a laboratory, 30; and in a regular course offering, 30.

Admissions: About 91% of the 1993–94 applicants were accepted.

Requirements: Admissions requirements include graduation from a secondary school; the GED is also accepted. Applicants must pass the DeVry entrance exam or present satisfactory ACT, SAT I, or WPCT scores. CLEP credit is accepted.

Procedure: Freshmen are admitted to all sessions. Application deadlines are open. The fee is $25. Notification is sent on a rolling basis. There are early decision and deferred admissions plans.

Transfer: At least 35% of the 143 to 158 total credits must be completed at DeVry.

Visiting: There are regularly scheduled orientations for prospective students. There are guides for informal visits and visitors may sit in on classes. To arrange for a visit, contact Frank Cordy, New Student Coordinator, at (614) 253–0851.

Financial Aid: In 1993–94, 81% of all students received some form of financial aid. About 81% of students received need-based aid. DeVry is a member of CSS. The FAFSA financial statement is required.

International Students: Applicants must take the TOEFL and achieve a minimum score of 550. The student must also take the college's own entrance exam; the ACT, SAT I, or WPCT may be accepted in lieu of the DeVry entrance exam.

Computers: The college provides computer facilities for student use. The mainframes are an IBM 3033 and an IBM System 36. Laboratory facilities include IBM and IBM-compatible PCs in stand-alone and network configurations, with access to the mainframe. LANs provide access to a wide range of applications software. Hard copy from the mainframes is provided through a local minicomputer and medium- and high-speed printers. Those in the computer information systems program may access the system. It may be used during laboratory hours. There are no fees.

Graduates: In 1992–93, 366 bachelor's degrees were awarded. The most popular majors among graduates were electronics technology (66%), business administration and management (17%), and computer information systems and sciences (17%). Within an average freshman class, 37% graduate in 5 years. Some 108 companies recruited on campus in 1992–93. In the 1992 graduating class, 89% of all students had found employment within 6 months of graduation.

Admissions Contact: Richard Rodman, Director of Admissions.

DYKE COLLEGE
Cleveland, OH 44115

D-1

(216) 696–9000

Full-time: 198 men, 525 women	Faculty: 18
Part-time: 253 men, 450 women	Ph.D.s: 17%
Graduate: none	Student/Faculty: 40 to 1
Year: 4-1-4, summer session	Tuition: $5200
Application Deadline: August 1	Room & Board: n/app
Freshman Class: 272 applied, 185 accepted, 140 enrolled	
SAT I or ACT: required	**COMPETITIVE**

Dyke College, founded in 1848, is a private coeducational institution offering undergraduate programs in business to commuting students. The library contains 14,000 volumes, 138 microform items, and 1811 audiovisual forms, and subscribes to 142 periodicals. Special learning facilities include a learning resource center. The 1-building, 2-acre campus is in an urban area.

Student Life: About 99% of undergraduates are from Ohio, with a few from foreign countries. Ninety-eight percent are from public schools; 2% from private. Fifty percent are white; 45% African American. The average age of freshmen is 28; all undergraduates, 34. Thirty percent drop out by the end of their first year; 50% remain to graduate.

Housing: There are no residence halls. All students commute. Alcohol is not permitted.

Activities: There is 1 local fraternity and no sororities on campus. There are 13 groups including chess, computers, honors, international, newspaper, professional, religious, student government, and yearbook. Popular campus events include lectures, movies, dances, and rap sessions with the college president.

Sports: Athletic and recreation facilities include a 500-seat gymnasium and a leased field house.

Disabled Students: All of the campus is accessible to disabled students. The following facilities are available: wheelchair ramps, elevators, specially equipped rest rooms, special class scheduling, and lowered drinking fountains and telephones.

Services: In addition to many counseling and information services, tutoring is available in most subjects. There is a reader service for the blind along with remedial math, reading, and writing.

Programs of Study: Dyke awards the B.S. degree. Associate degrees are also awarded. Bachelor's degrees are awarded in BUSINESS (accounting, business administration and management, marketing/retailing/merchandising, office supervision and management, real estate, retailing, and secretarial studies/office management), COMPUTER AND PHYSICAL SCIENCE (information sciences and systems), ENGINEERING AND ENVIRONMENTAL DESIGN (industrial administration/management), HEALTH PROFESSIONS (health care administration), SOCIAL SCIENCE (economics, paralegal studies, public administration, and social science).

Required: All students must complete 63 hours of general education requirements, 27 to 33 hours in the business core, plus major requirements and electives. A total of 126 semester hours with a minimum GPA of 2.0 is required in order to graduate.

Special: The external degree program enables working adults to earn a bachelor's degree in a nontraditional manner, including credit by examination and credit for life/work experience. Work-study programs, co-op programs in 7 majors, internships, dual majors, pass/fail options, and cross-registration with other area colleges are offered. Evening and Saturday classes and study are also available.

Faculty/Classroom: Fifty percent of faculty are male; 50%, female. All teach undergraduates. The average class size in an introductory lecture is 28 and in a regular course offering, 18.

Admissions: About 68% of the 1993–94 applicants were accepted.

Requirements: The SAT I or ACT is required. Applicants should have completed 19 Carnegie units, including 4 years of high school English, 3 of mathematics, and 2 each of science, social studies, and history. The GED is accepted. An interview is recommended. AP and CLEP credits are accepted. Important factors used in the admissions decision are ability to finance college education, advanced placement or honor courses, recommendations by school officials, leadership record, and evidence of special talent.

Procedure: Freshmen are admitted to all sessions. Entrance exams should be taken by March of the senior year. Applications should be filed by August 1 for fall entry, December 15 for winter entry, April 15 for spring entry, and June 15 for summer entry, along with an application fee of $25. Notification is sent on a rolling basis. There are early decision, early admissions, and deferred admissions plans.

Transfer: About 93 transfer students enrolled in 1993–94. Applicants should have a minimum GPA of 2.0 in 24 semester hours. An associate degree and an interview are recommended. A total of 33 credits out of 126 must be completed at Dyke.

Visiting: There are guides for informal visits and visitors may sit in on classes. To arrange for a visit, contact Admission Services at (216) 696-2000.

Financial Aid: Dyke is a member of CSS. The FAF is required.

International Students: They must take the TOEFL and achieve a minimum score of 500.

Computers: The college provides computer facilities for student use. The mainframe is a DEC VAX 4000/300. There are 20 IBM and HP PCs available in the computer laboratory.

Graduates: In 1992–93, 195 bachelor's degrees were awarded. The most popular majors among graduates were business management (43%), accounting (22%), and health services management (4%).

Admissions Contact: Director of Admission Services and Recruitment.

FRANCISCAN UNIVERSITY OF STEUBENVILLE

E-3

Steubenville, OH 43952

(614) 283-6226
(800) 282-8283 (out-of-state)

Full-time: 534 men, 767 women	Faculty: 70
Part-time: 85 men, 157 women	Ph.D.s: 64%
Graduate: 174 men, 184 women	Student/Faculty: 19 to 1
Year: semesters, summer session	Tuition: $9200
Application Deadline: July 31	Room & Board: $4200
Freshman Class: 553 applied, 452 accepted, 228 enrolled	
SAT I Verbal/Math: 488/516	ACT: 24 COMPETITIVE

The Franciscan University of Steubenville, founded in 1946 by the Franciscan Friars, is a private coeducational institution affiliated with the Roman Catholic Church, and known as a center for Christian renewal. In addition to regional accreditation, Franciscan University of Steubenville has baccalaureate program accreditation with NLN. The library contains 200,499 volumes, 105,802 microform items, and 3655 audiovisual forms, and subscribes to 800 periodicals. Computerized library sources and services include database searching. The 100-acre campus is in a suburban area 42 miles west of Pittsburgh, Pennsylvania. Including residence halls, there are 15 buildings on campus.

Student Life: About 63% of undergraduates are from out-of-state, mostly the Middle Atlantic. Students come from 50 states, 21 foreign countries, and Canada. Fifty-six percent are from public schools; 44% from private. Eighty-four percent are white. Most are Catholic. The average age of freshmen is 19; all undergraduates, 23. Eight percent drop out by the end of their first year; 68% remain to graduate.

Housing: A total of 769 students can be accommodated in college housing. College-sponsored living facilities include single-sex dormitories. In addition there are Christian faith households in residence halls. On-campus housing is available on a first-come, first-served basis. Priority is given to out-of-town students. Sixty-four percent of students live on campus; of those, 90% remain on campus on weekends. Upperclassmen may keep cars on campus.

Activities: About 2% of men belong to 1 national and 2 local fraternities; about 2% of women belong to 1 national and 2 local sororities. There are 25 groups on campus, including choir, chorus, computers, drama, ethnic, honors, international, literary magazine, newspaper, political, religious, social, social service, student government, and

yearbook. Popular campus events include the Feast of St. Francis and Pro-Life Rally.

Sports: There are 10 intramural sports for men and 9 for women. Athletic and recreation facilities include a campus athletic center, which houses 2 full-sized basketball courts, racquetball courts, saunas, whirlpools, and locker rooms, and provides indoor seating for 2,000. Outdoor athletic facilities include a basketball court, 4 tennis courts, 2 sand volleyball courts, and softball, flag football, and soccer fields.

Disabled Students: Sixty percent of the campus is accessible to disabled students. The following facilities are available: wheelchair ramps, elevators, special parking, specially equipped rest rooms, special class scheduling, lowered drinking fountains, and lowered telephones.

Services: In addition to many counseling and information services, tutoring is available in most subjects. In addition, there is a reader service for the blind. Counseling is available for learning-disabled students.

Campus Safety and Security: Campus safety and security measures include 24-hour foot and vehicle patrol, self-defense education, escort service, and informal discussions. In addition, there are pamphlets, posters, and films, emergency telephones, and lighted pathways and sidewalks.

Programs of Study: Franciscan University of Steubenville awards the B.A., B.S., and B.S.N. degrees. Associate and master's degrees also are awarded. Bachelor's degrees are awarded in BIOLOGICAL SCIENCE (biology/biological science), BUSINESS (accounting and business administration and management), COMMUNICATIONS AND THE ARTS (communications, English, French, and Spanish), COMPUTER AND PHYSICAL SCIENCE (chemistry, computer science, and mathematics), EDUCATION (elementary, secondary, and special), ENGINEERING AND ENVIRONMENTAL DESIGN (engineering), HEALTH PROFESSIONS (medical laboratory technology, mental health/human services, and nursing), SOCIAL SCIENCE (criminal justice, history, humanities and social science, philosophy, political science/government, psychology, sociology, and theological studies). Theology, psychology, education, and business are the strongest academically. Theology, education, business, and psychology have the largest enrollments.

Required: All students must complete core liberal arts courses, including 15 credits each in humanities and communications, and 6 each in theology, social science, and natural science. A 1-credit thesis is required in most majors. A total of 124 credit hours, with at least 30 in the major, and a minimum GPA of 2.0 are required in order to graduate.

Special: Dual majors and internships for up to 6 credit hours are available in most majors. There is a co-op program in engineering science. A humanities and Catholic culture major in Western tradition and minors in human life issues and anthropology are offered. Study abroad is possible; the university operates a campus in Gaming, Austria, where students spend a semester studying humanities while traveling through Europe. There is a freshman honors program on campus, as well as one national honor society. One department has an honors program.

Faculty/Classroom: Sixty-six percent of faculty are male; 34%, female. Ninety-four percent teach undergraduates. No introductory courses are taught by graduate students.

Admissions: About 82% of the 1993–94 applicants were accepted. The SAT scores for the 1993–94 freshman class were as follows: Verbal—51% below 500, 34% between 500 and 599, 14% between 600 and 700, and 1% above 700; Math—41% below 500, 34% between 500 and 599, 22% between 600 and 700, and 3% above 700. The ACT scores were 26% below 21, 27% between 21 and 23, 22% between 24 and 26, 13% between 27 and 28, and 12% above 28. About 44% of the current freshmen were in the top fifth of their class; 66% were in the top two fifths. Seven freshmen graduated first in their class.

Requirements: Franciscan University of Steubenville requires applicants to be in the upper 50% of their class. A minimum GPA of 2.4 is required. The SAT I or the ACT is required. Applicants should have completed 15 academic high school units, including 10 in English, foreign language, social science, and mathematics and natural sciences. The GED is accepted. An essay and an interview are recommended. AP and CLEP credits are accepted. Important factors used in the admissions decision are advanced placement or honor courses, evidence of special talent, leadership record, extracurricular activities record, and personality and intangible qualities.

Procedure: Freshmen are admitted fall and spring. Entrance exams should be taken in spring of the junior year or fall of the senior year. Applications should be filed by July 31 for fall entry and January 9 for spring entry, along with an application fee of $20. Notification of early decision and regular decision is on a rolling basis. There are early decision, early admissions, and deferred admissions plans.

Transfer: About 200 transfer students enrolled in 1993–94. A minimum 2.0 college GPA is required. High school and college transcripts must be submitted. An interview is recommended. A total of

30 credits out of 124 must be completed at Franciscan University of Steubenville.

Visiting: There are regularly scheduled orientations for prospective students, including a tour, interviews with professors and financial aid officers, and class visits. There are guides for informal visits and visitors may sit in on classes and stay overnight at the school. To arrange for a visit, contact the Admissions Office at (614) 283-6226.

Financial Aid: In 1993-94, 80% of all current freshmen and 82% of continuing students received some form of financial aid. About 78% of freshmen and 80% of continuing students received need-based aid. The average freshman award was $6000. Of that total, scholarships or need-based grants averaged $1500 ($4000 maximum); loans averaged $2625 ($4000 maximum); and work contracts averaged $1200 (maximum). Fifty percent of undergraduate students work part-time. Average earnings from campus work for the school year are $1200. The average financial indebtedness of the 1992-93 graduate was $12,000. Franciscan University of Steubenville is a member of CSS. The FAF is required. The deadline for financial aid applications is March 1.

International Students: There are currently 120 international students enrolled. The school actively recruits these students. They must take the TOEFL and achieve a minimum score of 500.

Computers: The college provides computer facilities for student use. The mainframes are an IBM System/36 and a DEC MicroVAX II. There are also 32 Apple II, Macintosh, and IBM PC microcomputers available in classroom computer laboratories. Students enrolled in certain classes may access the system. It may be used 9 A.M. to 11 P.M. Monday through Friday, 10 A.M. to 10 P.M. Saturday, and 1 to 11 P.M. Sunday. There are no time limits on using the system. The fees are $25 for courses requiring computer time.

Graduates: In 1992-93, 308 bachelor's degrees were awarded. The most popular majors among graduates were theology (23%), business (20%), and psychology (15%). Within an average freshman class, 5% graduate in 3 years, 53% in 4 years, and 11% in 5 years. Some 36 companies recruited on campus in 1992-93.

Admissions Contact: Margaret Weber, Director of Admissions.

FRANKLIN UNIVERSITY
Columbus, OH 43215-5399   C-3
                                 (614) 341-6237

Full-time: 605 men, 572 women	Faculty: 54; IIB, -$
Part-time: 1133 men, 1515 women	Ph.D.s: 32%
Graduate: 52 men, 38 women	Student/Faculty: 22 to 1
Year: trimesters	Tuition: $4621
Application Deadline: open	Room & Board: n/app
Freshman Class: n/av	
ACT: recommended	NONCOMPETITIVE

Franklin University, founded in 1902, is a private commuter institution offering undergraduate business and technical programs from its College of Arts and Sciences and College of Business and Technology. There are 2 undergraduate schools. In addition to regional accreditation, Franklin has baccalaureate program accreditation with AACSB, ABET, and NLN. The library contains 200,000 volumes, 124,000 microform items, and 650 audiovisual forms, and subscribes to 1200 periodicals. Computerized library sources and services include the card catalog, interlibrary loans, and database searching. Special learning facilities include a learning resource center and an art gallery. The 12-acre campus is in an urban area. There are 5 buildings on campus.

Student Life: About 98% of undergraduates are from Ohio. Students come from 4 states and 32 foreign countries. Eighty-five percent are from public schools. Eighty-two percent are white; 14% African American. The average age of freshmen is 20; all undergraduates, 27. Fifty percent drop out by the end of their first year; 25% remain to graduate.

Housing: There are no residence halls. One-hundred percent of students commute. Alcohol is not permitted. All students may keep cars on campus.

Activities: There are no fraternities or sororities on campus. There are some groups and organizations on campus, including computers, ethnic, international, newspaper, social, and student government.

Sports: Athletic and recreation facilities include men's intramural soccer and basketball which are held at city recreational facilities.

Disabled Students: The entire campus is accessible to disabled students. The following facilities are available: wheelchair ramps, elevators, special parking, specially equipped rest rooms, special class scheduling, lowered drinking fountains, and lowered telephones.

Services: In addition to many counseling and information services, tutoring is available in most subjects. There is also remedial math, reading, and writing.

Campus Safety and Security: There is a parking guard on duty in each lot and a city police officer on duty daily during class hours. All such personnel are connected by an emergency radio system.

Programs of Study: Franklin awards the B.S., B.S.N., and B.P.A. degrees. Associate degrees also are awarded. Bachelor's degrees are awarded in BUSINESS (accounting, banking and finance, business administration and management, management science, marketing/retailing/merchandising, personnel management, and real estate), COMMUNICATIONS AND THE ARTS (communications), COMPUTER AND PHYSICAL SCIENCE (computer management and computer science), ENGINEERING AND ENVIRONMENTAL DESIGN (electrical/electronics engineering technology and mechanical engineering technology), HEALTH PROFESSIONS (nursing), SOCIAL SCIENCE (public administration). Accounting and business management are the strongest programs academically and have the largest enrollments.

Required: Students must complete general education core requirements in communication, mathematics, humanities, socal and behavioral sciences, and science. A total of 120 to 132 semester hours with a minimum GPA of 2.0 (2.25 for some majors) is required in order to graduate.

Special: Cross-registration is possible with other area colleges and universities through the Higher Education Council of Columbus. Internships are available for accounting, finance, marketing, public administration, business management, employee assistance counseling, and applied communication majors. Study abroad at Richmond College, London, England, is possible through affiliation with the American Institute for Foreign Studies. Dual majors, work-study programs, and some pass/fail courses are offered. The Adult Degree Program gives credit for life/work experience through portfolio development and evaluation.

Faculty/Classroom: Seventy-five percent of faculty are male; 25%, female. All teach undergraduates and 10% also do research. The average class size in an introductory lecture is 22; in a laboratory, 15; and in a regular course offering, 22.

Requirements: The ACT is recommended. Applicants should be graduates of an accredited secondary school or have a GED. AP and CLEP credits are accepted.

Procedure: Freshmen are admitted in the fall, winter, and summer. Application deadlines are open. The college accepts all applicants Notification is sent on a rolling basis. There are early admissions and deferred admissions plans.

Transfer: About 551 transfer students enrolled in a recent year. The open admission policy applies to transfer students as well as freshmen. A total of 30 credits out of 120 to 132 must be completed at Franklin.

Visiting: There are regularly scheduled orientations for prospective students. There are guides for informal visits and visitors may sit in on classes. To arrange for a visit, contact the Admission Office at (614) 224-6231.

Financial Aid: In an earlier class, 25% of all freshmen and 35% of continuing students received some form of financial aid. Scholarships or need-based grants averaged $1500 ($3800 maximum); loans averaged $1000 ($2625 maximum); and work contracts averaged $2000 ($4000 maximum). The average financial indebtedness of a recent graduate was $6000. Franklin is a member of CSS. The FAF and the college's own financial statement are required. The deadline for financial aid applications is May 30.

International Students: There are currently 74 international students enrolled. They must take the TOEFL and achieve a minimum score of 550.

Computers: The college provides computer facilities for student use. The mainframe is an IBM System/3800. There are also 48 IBM microcomputers available in the computer center. There are no fees.

Graduates: In a recent year, 753 bachelor's degrees were awarded. The most popular majors among graduates were business management (30%), marketing (12%), and accounting (12%). Within an average freshman class, 26% graduate in 4 years, 30% in 5 years, and 33% in 6 years. Some 40 companies recruited on campus in a recent year.

Admissions Contact: Karen L. Greene, Director, Institutional Research.

HEIDELBERG COLLEGE
Tiffin, OH 44883-2434   C-2
                               (419) 448-2330
                               (800) HEIDELBERG (out-of-state)

Full-time: 510 men, 424 women	Faculty: 73; IIB, --$
Part-time: 60 men, 100 women	Ph.D.s: 72%
Graduate: 43 men, 105 women	Student/Faculty: 13 to 1
Year: semesters, summer session	Tuition: $13,000
Application Deadline: June 1	Room & Board: $4160
Freshman Class: 952 applied, 800 accepted, 247 enrolled	
SAT I Verbal/Math: 416/460	ACT: 21 COMPETITIVE

Heidelberg College, founded in 1850, is a private liberal arts institution affiliated with the United Church of Christ/Congregational. There are two graduate schools. In addition to regional accreditation, Heidelberg has baccalaureate program accreditation with NASM.

The library contains 193,205 volumes, 58,100 microform items, and 8300 audiovisual forms, and subscribes to 750 periodicals. Computerized library sources and services include interlibrary loans and database searching. Special learning facilities include a learning resource center, radio station, TV station, a media center, and an anthropology museum. The 110-acre campus is in a small town 50 miles south of Toledo. Including residence halls, there are 26 buildings on campus.

Student Life: About 78% of undergraduates are from Ohio. Students come from 24 states and 9 foreign countries. Sixty-three percent are from public schools; 37% from private. Eighty-six percent are white. Fifty-four percent are Protestant; 42% Catholic. The average age of freshmen is 19; all undergraduates, 24. Twenty-two percent drop out by the end of their first year; 55% remain to graduate.

Housing: A total of 854 students can be accommodated in college housing. College-sponsored living facilities include single-sex and coed dormitories. On-campus housing is guaranteed for all 4 years and is available on a lottery system for upperclassmen. Ninety-four percent of students live on campus; of those, 85% remain on campus on weekends. Alcohol is not permitted. All students may keep cars on campus.

Activities: About 32% of men belong to 4 local fraternities; about 36% of women belong to 5 local sororities. There are 65 groups on campus, including band, cheerleading, choir, chorale, chorus, computers, dance, drama, drill team, ethnic, honors, international, jazz band, literary magazine, marching band, musical theater, newspaper, opera, orchestra, pep band, political, professional, radio and TV, religious, social, social service, student government, symphony, and yearbook. Popular campus events include Parents Weekend, Greek Sing, Homecoming, Madrigal Dinner, Messiah, and Spring Fling Weekend.

Sports: There are 9 intercollegiate sports for men and 7 for women, and 9 intramural sports for men and 8 for women. Athletic and recreation facilities include a wrestling arena, indoor courts for volleyball, basketball, racquetball, and tennis; a sports medicine clinic; and outdoor tennis, soccer, lacrosse, and football facilities. A YMCA adjacent to college provides additional recreation options.

Disabled Students: Twenty percent of the campus is accessible to disabled students. The following facilities are available: wheelchair ramps, elevators, special parking, specially equipped rest rooms, and special class scheduling.

Services: In addition to many counseling and information services, tutoring is available in every subject.

Campus Safety and Security: Campus safety and security measures include 24-hour foot and vehicle patrol, escort service, informal discussions, and pamphlets, posters, and films. In addition, there are lighted pathways and sidewalks.

Programs of Study: Heidelberg awards the A.B., B.S., and B.Mus. degrees. Master's degrees also are awarded. Bachelor's degrees are awarded in BIOLOGICAL SCIENCE (biology/biological science), BUSINESS (accounting, business administration and management, business economics, international business management, management science, and marketing/retailing/merchandising), COMMUNICATIONS AND THE ARTS (broadcasting, communications, dramatic arts, English, German, music, public relations, and Spanish), COMPUTER AND PHYSICAL SCIENCE (chemistry, computer science, mathematics, and physics), EDUCATION (elementary, foreign languages, middle school, music, physical, science, and secondary), ENGINEERING AND ENVIRONMENTAL DESIGN (preengineering), HEALTH PROFESSIONS (predentistry, premedicine, and sports medicine), SOCIAL SCIENCE (anthropology, economics, geography, history, international studies, political science/government, prelaw, psychology, public administration, religion, and social science). Business administration, communications, and sciences are the strongest academically. Business administration, sciences, and psychology have the largest enrollments.

Required: Students must fulfill 40 semester hours of general education requirements, including English composition and public speaking, arts, languages and literature, civilization, religion and philosophy, social sciences, natural sciences, and mathematics, and 40 semester hours each in the major and electives. Four units of health and physical education are needed. A total of 120 semester hours with a minimum GPA of 2.0 overall and 2.5 in the major is required in order to graduate.

Special: There are co-op programs in preengineering, prenursing, and medical technician. A 3–2 engineering degree and a 3–3 nursing degree are offered in cooperation with Case Western Reserve University. Study abroad is possible at the University of Heidelberg, Germany and in Seville, Spain. A Washington semester is available at American University. Dual majors in any combination, student-designed majors, credit for life experience, and pass/fail options are possible. There is a freshman honors program on campus, as well as 10 national honor societies. Fifteen departments have honors programs.

Faculty/Classroom: Seventy-one percent of faculty are male; 29%, female. All teach undergraduates and 60% both teach and do research. No introductory courses are taught by graduate students. The average class size in an introductory lecture is 25; in a laboratory, 15; and in a regular course offering, 20.

Admissions: About 84% of the 1993–94 applicants were accepted. The SAT scores for the 1993–94 freshman class were as follows: Verbal—32% below 500, 50% between 500 and 599, 15% between 600 and 700, and 3% above 700; Math—25% below 500, 55% between 500 and 599, 15% between 600 and 700, and 5% above 700. The ACT scores were 27% below 21, 31% between 21 and 23, 17% between 24 and 26, 13% between 27 and 28, and 12% above 28. About 26% of the current freshmen were in the top fifth of their class; 64% were in the top two fifths. There were 4 National Merit finalists and 6 semifinalists. Twelve freshmen graduated first in their class.

Requirements: Heidelberg requires applicants to be in the upper 50% of their class. A minimum GPA of 2.0 is required. The SAT or ACT is required. Applicants should have completed 22 high school academic credits, including 4 years each of English and social studies, 3 each of mathematics and science, and 2 of foreign language. An audition is required for music majors. An essay and an interview are recommended. AP and CLEP credits are accepted. Important factors used in the admissions decision are recommendations by school officials, advanced placement or honor courses, personality, intangible qualities, leadership record, and evidence of special talent.

Procedure: Freshmen are admitted to all sessions. Entrance exams should be taken by the end of the junior year or the beginning of the senior year. Applications should be filed by June 1 for fall entry, December 1 for spring entry, and June 1 for summer entry, along with an application fee of $20. Notification is sent on a rolling basis. There is a deferred admissions plan.

Transfer: About 29 transfer students enrolled in 1993–94. A minimum GPA of 2.0 is required. A character reference from the institution most recently attended is required. A total of 30 credits out of 120 must be completed at Heidelberg.

Visiting: There are regularly scheduled orientations for prospective students, including coach and faculty sessions, academic overview, student panel, admissions and financial aid presentations, tour of the college, and lunch. There are guides for informal visits and visitors may sit in on classes and stay overnight at the school. To arrange for a visit, contact the Office of Admission at (800) HEIDELBERG.

Financial Aid: In a recent year, 65% of all current freshmen and 70% of continuing students received some form of financial aid. About 76% of freshmen and 93% of continuing students received need-based aid. The average freshman award was $10,000. Of that total, scholarships or need-based grants averaged $4200 ($7500 maximum); loans averaged $2142 ($3825 maximum); and work contracts averaged $919 ($1800 maximum). Forty-six percent of undergraduate students work part-time. Average earnings from campus work for the school year are $821. The average financial indebtedness of a recent year's graduate was $12,960. Heidelberg is a member of CSS. The FAF is required. The deadline for financial aid applications is May 1.

International Students: There are currently 128 international students enrolled. The school actively recruits these students. They must take the TOEFL or the University of Michigan Language Test and achieve a minimum score on the TOEFL of 450.

Computers: The college provides computer facilities for student use. The mainframe is a Prime 9955. Terminals are located in all residence halls. All Macintosh and IBM PCs are networked through the mainframe for use throughout the campus. Almost every department requires some knowledge of computers. Separate computer centers are located in the sciences complex, the library, and the administration building. All students may access the system. There are no time limits and no fees.

Graduates: In a recent year, 186 bachelor's degrees were awarded. The most popular majors among graduates were business administration (22%), elementary education (9%), and accounting and political science (7%). Within an average freshman class, 53% graduate in 4 years and 60% in 5 years. Some 50 companies recruited on campus in a recent year. In the 1992 graduating class, 16% all graduates were enrolled in graduate school within 6 months of graduation; 80% had found employment.

Admissions Contact: Stephen E. Eidson, Dean of Admission.

HIRAM COLLEGE
E-1

Hiram, OH 44234   (216) 569-5169; (800) 362-5280 (out-of-state)

Full-time: 408 men, 432 women	Faculty: 81; IIB, -$
Part-time: none	Ph.D.s: 95%
Graduate: none	Student/Faculty: 10 to 1
Year: 3-1-3-3	Tuition: $13,825
Application Deadline: April 15	Room & Board: $4515
Freshman Class: 922 applied, 729 accepted, 244 enrolled	
SAT I Verbal/Math: 510/540	ACT: 25 **VERY COMPETITIVE**

Hiram College, founded in 1850, is a private liberal arts institution affiliated with the Christian Church (Disciples of Christ). In addition to regional accreditation, Hiram has baccalaureate program accreditation with NASM and NCATE. The library contains 169,695 volumes, 76,597 microform items, and 663 audiovisual forms, and subscribes to 826 periodicals. Computerized library sources and services include the card catalog, interlibrary loans, and database searching. Special learning facilities include a learning resource center, art gallery, planetarium, radio station, and a 260-acre biological field station and a field station in the Upper Peninsula of Michigan. The 110-acre campus is in a rural area 35 miles southeast of Cleveland. Including residence halls, there are 25 buildings on campus.

Student Life: About 80% of undergraduates are from Ohio. Students come from 20 states and 6 foreign countries. Ninety percent are white. The average age of freshmen is 18. Seventeen percent drop out by the end of their first year; 70% remain to graduate.

Housing: A total of 1000 students can be accommodated in college housing. College-sponsored living facilities include single-sex and coed dormitories. On-campus housing is guaranteed for all 4 years. Ninety-three percent of students live on campus. All students may keep cars on campus.

Activities: There are no fraternities or sororities on campus. There are 50 groups on campus, including art, band, cheerleading, choir, chorale, chorus, computers, dance, drama, ethnic, gay, honors, international, jazz band, literary magazine, musical theater, newspaper, opera, orchestra, photography, political, professional, radio and TV, religious, social, social service, student government, and yearbook. Popular campus events include Homecoming, Campus Days, and Da-Bowery Dance.

Sports: There are 9 intercollegiate sports for men and 8 for women, and 14 intramural sports for men and 14 for women. Athletic and recreation facilities include a 4000-seat stadium, a gymnasium, sports fields, an all-weather track, a fitness room, a sauna, racquetball and tennis courts, an indoor swimming pool with diving area, an outdoor exercise and fitness trail, a cross-country ski trail, and a fully equipped athletic training facility.

Disabled Students: Forty percent of the campus is accessible to disabled students.

Campus Safety and Security: Campus safety and security measures include 24-hour foot and vehicle patrol, self defense education, escort service, and informal discussions. In addition, there are pamphlets, posters, and films, emergency telephones, and lighted pathways and sidewalks.

Programs of Study: Hiram awards the B.A. degree. Bachelor's degrees are awarded in BIOLOGICAL SCIENCE (biology/biological science), BUSINESS (international economics and management science), COMMUNICATIONS AND THE ARTS (art, art history and appreciation, classics, communications, dramatic arts, English, French, German, music, and Spanish), COMPUTER AND PHYSICAL SCIENCE (applied physics, chemistry, computer science, and mathematics), EDUCATION (elementary), SOCIAL SCIENCE (economics, history, philosophy, political science/government, psychobiology, psychology, religion, social science, and sociology).

Required: All students must complete distribution requirement courses in the fine arts, humanities, natural sciences, and social sciences; the Freshman Institute and Colloquium; a 2-course sequence in writing and speaking skills, a 2-course skills requirement in computer science, arts, foreign language, or reasoning and analysis; and 1 upper-division 3-course sequence. A total of 180 academic quarter units, plus 3 quarter credits of physical education wellness units, and a minimum GPA of 2.0 are required in order to graduate.

Special: There are cooperative programs in environmental management and forestry with Duke University, in business administration with Washington University, in engineering with Case Western Reserve University and Washington University, in public administration and international affairs with the University of Pittsburgh, in medical technology with Cleveland Clinic, in nursing and social work with Case Western Reserve University, and in physical therapy with Cleveland State University. There is a Washington semester and study abroad in many countries with courses taught by Hiram faculty. Double majors and individually arranged internships in all fields, student-designed majors, and pass/fail options are possible. The first-year seminar, a series of 3 courses taught by 2 or more faculty mem-

bers, provides an interdisciplinary approach on specific issues. There are 8 national honor societies on campus, including Phi Beta Kappa.

Faculty/Classroom: Sixty-three percent of faculty are male; 37%, female. All teach undergraduates. The average class size in an introductory lecture is 19; in a laboratory, 15; and in a regular course offering, 15.

Admissions: About 79% of the 1993-94 applicants were accepted. The SAT scores for the 1993-94 freshman class were as follows: Verbal—49% below 500, 37% between 500 and 599, and 14% between 600 and 700; Math—36% below 500, 44% between 500 and 599, 21% between 600 and 700, and 2% above 700. The ACT scores were 17% below 21, 26% between 21 and 23, 27% between 24 and 26, 16% between 27 and 28, and 14% above 28. About 56% of the current freshmen were in the top fifth of their class; 81% were in the top two fifths. About 7 freshmen graduated first in their class.

Requirements: The SAT I or ACT is required. SAT II: Subject tests in writing, mathematics, and 1 other academic area are required. Applicants should have completed 16 units or GED equivalent. An essay, portfolio, audition, and interview are recommended. AP and CLEP credits are accepted. Important factors used in the admissions decision are advanced placement or honor courses, leadership record, evidence of special talent, extracurricular activities record, and personality, intangible qualities.

Procedure: Entrance exams should be taken no later than fall of the senior year. Applications should be filed by April 15 for fall entry, December 1 for winter entry, and March 1 for spring entry, along with an application fee of $20. Notification is sent on a rolling basis. There is a deferred admissions plan.

Transfer: About 34 transfer students enrolled in 1993-94. Applicants should have at least a 2.5 GPA and be in good academic and social standing from the previous institution. An interview is recommended. A total of 90 quarter units out of 183 must be completed at Hiram.

Visiting: There are regularly scheduled orientations for prospective students, held weekdays except Wednesdays. There are guides for informal visits and visitors may sit in on classes and stay overnight at the school. To arrange for a visit, contact Admissions at (800) 362-5280 or (216) 569-5169.

Financial Aid: In 1993-94, 90% of all current freshmen and 90% of continuing students received some form of financial aid. About 85% of freshmen and 85% of continuing students received need-based aid. The average freshman award was $12,533. Of that total, scholarships or need-based grants averaged $9133 ($13,395 maximum); loans averaged $2200 ($2600 maximum); and work contracts averaged $1200 ($1400 maximum). Sixty-nine percent of undergraduate students work part-time. Average earnings from campus work for the school year are $1085. The average financial indebtedness of the 1992-93 graduate was $12,000. Hiram is a member of CSS. The FAF, the college's own financial statement, and the FAFSA are required. The deadline for financial aid applications is March 1.

International Students: There are currently 10 international students enrolled. The school actively recruits these students. They must take the TOEFL and achieve a minimum score of 550. The student must also take the SAT I or the ACT.

Computers: The college provides computer facilities for student use. The mainframes are a DEC VAX 6000-510 and 8350, and a DEC MicroVAX 3500. Students access the mainframes through terminals and PCs attached to the Ethernet network. There are terminal clusters with about 40 terminals each located in each dormitory and 3 classroom buildings. A VAXstation and 3 DECstations are available in the terminal cluster located in the science building. All students may access the system. It may be used 24 hours a day. There are no time limits on using the system and no fees.

Graduates: In 1992-93, 202 bachelor's degrees were awarded. Within an average freshman class, 95% graduate in 4 years, 98% in 5 years, and 100% in 6 years. In the 1992 graduating class, 30% of the students were enrolled in graduate school within 6 months of graduation; 70% had found employment.

Admissions Contact: Gary Craig, Dean of Admissions.

JOHN CARROLL UNIVERSITY
D-1

University Heights, OH 44118   (216) 397-4294

Full-time: 1583 men, 1585 women	Faculty: 206; IIA, av$
Part-time: 171 men, 221 women	Ph.D.s: 89%
Graduate: 318 men, 565 women	Student/Faculty: 15 to 1
Year: semesters, summer session	Tuition: $11,060
Application Deadline: June 1	Room & Board: $5450
Freshman Class: 2421 applied, 2110 accepted, 820 enrolled	
SAT I Verbal/Math: 502/561	ACT: 23 **COMPETITIVE**

John Carroll University, founded in 1886, is a private, coeducational Catholic institution operated by the Jesuits. It offers undergraduate degree programs in the arts, sciences, and business. There are 2 undergraduate schools and one graduate school. In addition to regional accreditation, Carroll has baccalaureate program accreditation with

AACSB and NCATE. The library contains 533,899 volumes, 164,737 microform items, and 7595 audiovisual forms, and subscribes to 1620 periodicals. Computerized library sources and services include the card catalog, interlibrary loans, and database searching. Special learning facilities include a radio station and TV station. The 61-acre campus is in a suburban area 10 miles east of Cleveland. Including residence halls, there are 26 buildings on campus.

Student Life: About 65% of undergraduates are from Ohio. Students come from 31 states and 15 foreign countries. Forty-eight percent are from public schools; 52% from private. Eighty-nine percent are white. Seventy percent are Catholic; 11% Protestant. The average age of freshmen is 18; all undergraduates, 20. Twelve percent drop out by the end of their first year; 76% remain to graduate.

Housing: A total of 2100 students can be accommodated in college housing. College-sponsored living facilities include single-sex and coed dormitories. On-campus housing is guaranteed for all 4 years. Sixty percent of students live on campus; of those, 85% remain on campus on weekends. Upperclassmen may keep cars on campus.

Activities: About 32% of men belong to 12 local fraternities; about 35% of women belong to 7 local sororities. There are 87 groups on campus, including band, cheerleading, chess, choir, chorale, chorus, computers, drama, drill team, ethnic, honors, international, jazz band, literary magazine, musical theater, newspaper, pep band, political, professional, radio and TV, religious, social, social service, student government, symphony, and yearbook. Popular campus events include Homecoming, Welcome Back Week, Christmas Formal, Little Siblings Weekend, Greek Week, Spring Fling, Senior Week, Parents Weekend, Dance Marathon, and Christmas caroling.

Sports: There are 10 intercollegiate sports for men and 8 for women, and 15 intramural sports for men and 12 for women. Athletic and recreation facilities include a swimming pool and diving well, a 3800-seat football stadium, a baseball field, an indoor track, tennis, volleyball, racquetball, squash, and basketball courts, a weight room, a fitness center, and a 33-acre off-campus student villa. Club sports include hockey, rugby, lacrosse, skiing, and sailing.

Disabled Students: Ninety-six percent of the campus is accessible to disabled students. The following facilities are available: wheelchair ramps, elevators, special parking, specially equipped rest rooms, special class scheduling, lowered drinking fountains, and lowered telephones.

Services: In addition to many counseling and information services, tutoring is available in every subject. There is also a reader service for the blind.

Campus Safety and Security: Campus safety and security measures include 24-hour foot and vehicle patrol, self defense education, escort service, and shuttle buses. In addition, there are informal discussions, pamphlets, posters, films, emergency telephones, and lighted pathways and sidewalks.

Programs of Study: Carroll awards the B.A., B.S., B.A. in Classics, and B.S. Econ. degrees. Master's degrees also are awarded. Bachelor's degrees are awarded in BIOLOGICAL SCIENCE (biology/biological science), BUSINESS (accounting, banking and finance, business administration and management, and marketing/retailing/merchandising), COMMUNICATIONS AND THE ARTS (art history and appreciation, communications, English, French, German, Greek, Latin, literature, and Spanish), COMPUTER AND PHYSICAL SCIENCE (chemistry, computer science, mathematics, and physics), EDUCATION (early childhood, elementary, mathematics, physical, and secondary), ENGINEERING AND ENVIRONMENTAL DESIGN (engineering physics), SOCIAL SCIENCE (economics, history, humanities, philosophy, political science/government, psychology, public administration, religion, and sociology). Business, sciences, humanities, English, and communications are the strongest academically. English, accounting, political science, psychology, marketing, and communications have the largest enrollments.

Required: All students must complete a liberal arts core curriculum, including 4 courses each in humanities and science and mathematics, 3 each in social sciences and philosophy, 2 in religious studies, and courses in English composition and rhetoric and speech communication. A total of 128 credit hours with a minimum GPA of 2.0 is required in order to graduate.

Special: Co-op programs are available, and cross-registration with 16 area colleges is offered through the Cleveland Consortium of Higher Education. Study abroad is possible in Europe, the Middle East, and in Japan. Joint engineering degrees are offered with Case Western Reserve University, University of Detroit, Mercy University, and Washington University in St. Louis. Work-study programs with local corporations, internships, a Washington semester, student-designed majors, and some pass/fail options are available. There is a freshman honors program on campus, as well as 13 national honor societies.

Faculty/Classroom: Sixty-nine percent of faculty are male; 31%, female. All teach undergraduates and 75% also do research. Graduate students teach 2% of introductory courses. The average class size in an introductory lecture is 25; in a laboratory, 15; and in a regular course offering, 20.

Admissions: About 87% of the 1993–94 applicants were accepted. The SAT scores for the 1993–94 freshman class were as follows: Verbal—46% below 500, 39% between 500 and 599, 14% between 600 and 700, and 1% above 700; Math—22% below 500, 42% between 500 and 599, 30% between 600 and 700, and 6% above 700. The ACT scores were 35% below 21, 22% between 21 and 23, 29% between 24 and 26, 9% between 27 and 28, and 5% above 28. About 58% of the current freshmen were in the top fifth of their class; 88% were in the top two fifths. There were 9 National Merit finalists and 7 semifinalists. Twenty-three freshmen graduated first in their class.

Requirements: The SAT I or ACT is required. Applicants should be graduates of an accredited secondary school with 16 academic credits, including 4 in English, 3 in mathematics, 2 each in foreign language, laboratory science, and social studies, and 3 in electives. An essay is part of the application process, and an interview is recommended. AP and CLEP credits are accepted. Important factors used in the admissions decision are advanced placement or honor courses, extracurricular activities record, geographic diversity, parents or siblings attending the school, and leadership record.

Procedure: Freshmen are admitted fall and spring. Entrance exams should be taken in the spring of the junior year or the fall of the senior year. Applications should be filed by June 1 for fall entry and January 1 for spring entry, along with an application fee of $25. Notification is sent on a rolling basis. There is a deferred admissions plan. A waiting list is an active part of the admissions procedure, with about 5% of applicants on the list.

Transfer: About 144 transfer students enrolled in 1993–94. Transfer students must be in good standing at the time of application. The most recent term average and the cumulative average at the home school must be 2.0 or better to be considered for admission, and the cumulative average for all schools attended must be 2.0 or better. A GPA of at least 2.5 is recommended. A total of 30 credits out of 128 must be completed at Carroll.

Visiting: There are regularly scheduled orientations for prospective students, including testing, guidance, and counseling sessions, class scheduling, and social events. There are guides for informal visits and visitors may sit in on classes and stay overnight at the school. To arrange for a visit, contact the Office of Admission at (216) 397-4294.

Financial Aid: In a recent year, 60% of all current freshmen and 55% of continuing students received some form of financial aid. About 56% of freshmen and 65% of continuing students received need-based aid. The average freshman award was $9900. Of that total, scholarships or need-based grants averaged $3700 ($8000 maximum); loans averaged $2500 ($5500 maximum); and work contracts averaged $1000 (maximum). Twenty-four percent of undergraduate students work part-time. Average earnings from campus work for the school year are $1000. The average financial indebtedness of a recent year's graduate was $10,000. Carroll is a member of CSS. The FAFSA financial statement is required. The deadline for financial aid applications is March 1.

International Students: There are currently 33 international students enrolled. They must take the TOEFL and achieve a minimum score of 550.

Computers: The college provides computer facilities for student use. The mainframes are a DEC VAX 8300, 8530, and 6000 Model 420. Any registered student may obtain a user code for the mainframe through 50 public-access terminals and 100 microcomputers in 6 different computer labs across campus. Stand-alone microcomputers are available in the science and mathematics laboratories. All students may access the system. It may be used 24 hours a day in some locations. There are no time limits and no fees.

Graduates: In 1992–93, 750 bachelor's degrees were awarded. The most popular majors among graduates were communications (13%), English (11%), and psychology (10%). Within an average freshman class, 1% graduate in 3 years, 59% in 4 years, 72% in 5 years, and 76% in 6 years. Some 182 companies recruited on campus in 1992–93. In the 1992 graduating class, 21% of all graduates were enrolled in graduate school within 6 months of graduation; 47% had found employment.

Admissions Contact: Laryn D. Runco, Director of Admission.

KENT STATE UNIVERSITY

D-2

Kent, OH 44242-0001   (216) 672-2444

Full-time: 6298 men, 8363 women   Faculty: 798; I, -$
Part-time: 1411 men, 1740 women   Ph.D.s: 85%
Graduate: 1843 men, 3045 women   Student/Faculty: 18 to 1
Year: semesters, summer session   Tuition: $3740 ($7480)
Application Deadline: March 15   Room & Board: $3000
Freshman Class: 8498 applied, 7368 accepted, 2760 enrolled
SAT I or ACT: recommended   **LESS COMPETITIVE**

Kent State University, founded in 1910, is a public, coeducational university offering degree programs in liberal and fine arts, business, health science, teacher and professional training, and aviation. There are 6 undergraduate and 3 graduate schools. In addition to regional accreditation, KSU has baccalaureate program accreditation with AACSB, ABET, ACEJMC, FIDER, NAAB, NASAD, NASM, NCATE, and NLN. The library contains 2,110,328 volumes, 1,414,912 microform items, and 27,901 audiovisual forms, and subscribes to 10,700 periodicals. Computerized library sources and services include the card catalog, interlibrary loans, and database searching. Special learning facilities include an art gallery, planetarium, radio station, TV station, a writing clinic, and a fashion museum. The 1200-acre campus is in a small town 45 miles southeast of Cleveland. Including residence halls, there are 110 buildings on campus.

Student Life: About 93% of undergraduates are from Ohio. Students come from 48 states, 64 foreign countries, and Canada. Eighty-four percent are from public schools; 16% from private. Ninety-one percent are white. The average age of freshmen is 20; all undergraduates, 22. Twenty-six percent drop out by the end of their first year; 45% remain to graduate.

Housing: A total of 7558 students can be accommodated in college housing. College-sponsored living facilities include single-sex and coed dormitories and married-student housing. In addition there are honors houses and special interest houses. On-campus housing is guaranteed for all 4 years. Seventy-five percent of students commute. Alcohol is not permitted. All students may keep cars on campus.

Activities: About 7% of men belong to 1 local and 19 national fraternities; about 6% of women belong to 3 local and 9 national sororities. There are 230 groups on campus, including art, band, cheerleading, chess, choir, chorale, chorus, computers, dance, drama, drill team, ethnic, film, gay, honors, international, jazz band, literary magazine, marching band, musical theater, newspaper, opera, orchestra, pep band, photography, political, professional, radio and TV, religious, social, social service, student government, and symphony. Popular campus events include Black Squirrel Festival, Homecoming, Greek Week, Black History Month, Folk Festival, Parents Day, and Yuletide Feast.

Sports: There are 10 intercollegiate sports for men and 8 for women, and 25 intramural sports for men and 24 for women. Athletic and recreation facilities include a gymnasium, a stadium, a field house, 2 fitness circuits, a golf course, a bowling alley, tennis courts, soccer, lacrosse, and rugby fields, an ice arena, a pool, and a weight room.

Disabled Students: Ninety percent of the campus is accessible to disabled students. The following facilities are available: wheelchair ramps, elevators, special parking, specially equipped rest rooms, special class scheduling, lowered drinking fountains, lowered telephones, and transportation services.

Services: In addition to many counseling and information services, tutoring is available in most subjects. There is also a reader service for the blind, and remedial math, reading, and writing.

Campus Safety and Security: Campus safety and security measures include 24-hour foot and vehicle patrol, escort service, pamphlets, posters, and films, and emergency telephones. In addition, there are lighted pathways and sidewalks and a 24-hour campus police department, overnight security guards, and a 2-key system for residence halls.

Programs of Study: KSU awards the B.A., B.S., B.Arch., B.B.A., B.F.A., B.G.S., B.Mus., B.Mus.Ed., B.S.Ed., and B.S.N. degrees. Master's and doctoral degrees also are awarded. Bachelor's degrees are awarded in AGRICULTURE (conservation and regulation), BIOLOGICAL SCIENCE (biology/biological science, botany, and zoology), BUSINESS (accounting, banking and finance, business administration and management, business economics, fashion merchandising, international economics, management science, marketing/retailing/merchandising, personnel management, and real estate), COMMUNICATIONS AND THE ARTS (advertising, art history and appreciation, broadcasting, communications, crafts, dance, design, dramatic arts, English, film arts, fine arts, French, German, graphic design, industrial design, journalism, Latin, music, photography, public relations, Russian, Spanish, speech/debate/rhetoric, and telecommunications), COMPUTER AND PHYSICAL SCIENCE (chemistry, computer science, earth science, geology, mathematics, and physics), EDUCATION (art, business, early childhood, education of the deaf and hearing impaired, education of the multiply handicapped, elementary, En-

glish, foreign languages, health, mathematics, music, physical, science, secondary, social studies, and special), ENGINEERING AND ENVIRONMENTAL DESIGN (aeronautical technology, aircraft mechanics, architectural engineering, aviation administration/management, aviation computer technology, engineering technology, food services technology, industrial administration/management, industrial engineering technology, and interior design), HEALTH PROFESSIONS (cytotechnology, medical laboratory technology, nursing, predentistry, premedicine, preveterinary science, and speech pathology/audiology), SOCIAL SCIENCE (African studies, American studies, anthropology, criminal justice, dietetics, Eastern European studies, economics, ethnic studies, fashion design and technology, geography, gerontology, history, international relations, Latin American studies, parks and recreation management, peace studies, philosophy, political science/government, psychology, Russian and Slavic studies, and sociology). Architecture, business, education, fashion design and merchandising, interior design, journalism, mass communication, nursing, and radio and TV are the strongest academically. Elementary education, marketing, and nursing have the largest enrollments.

Required: Students are required to complete 129 total credit hours, of which 42 must be upper division. Distribution requirements include 6 hours each in basic sciences, composition, mathematics, logic, and foreign languages, 9 hours in social science, and 12 hours in humanities and fine arts. Students must maintain an overall GPA of 2.0.

Special: A co-op program is available with the School of Technology. Work-study programs and internships are available. Study abroad in 8 countries, a Washington semester, B.A.-B.S. degrees, dual majors, a general studies degree, student-designed majors, possible credit for military education, nondegree study, and pass/fail options are also available. The Honors College provides honors coursework in all majors. There is a freshman honors program on campus, as well as 13 national honor societies, including Phi Beta Kappa.

Faculty/Classroom: Seventy-two percent of faculty are male; 28%, female. Graduate students teach 18% of introductory courses. The average class size in a regular course offering is 28.

Admissions: About 87% of the 1993–94 applicants were accepted. About 47% of the current freshmen were in the top two fifths of their class. About eleven freshmen graduated first in their class.

Requirements: The SAT I or ACT is recommended. Applicants must be graduates of an accredited secondary school. KSU strongly recommends a college preparatory program of art, 2 years of foreign language, 3 years each of mathematics, science, and social studies, and 4 years of English. AP and CLEP credits are accepted. Important factors used in the admissions decision are advanced placement or honor courses, evidence of special talent, and recommendations by school officials.

Procedure: Freshmen are admitted to all sessions. Entrance exams should be taken in the spring of the junior year or the fall of the senior year. Applications should be filed by March 15 for fall entry, December 15 for spring entry, and June 1 for summer entry, along with an application fee of $25. Notification is sent on a rolling basis. A waiting list is an active part of the admissions procedure.

Transfer: About 927 transfer students enrolled in a recent year. Applicants must present a minimum GPA of 2.0 on completed college coursework as recalculated by the university. For students with fewer than 24 semester hours or 36 quarter hours, a high school transcript and ACT or SAT I scores are also required. A total of 32 credits out of 129 must be completed at KSU.

Visiting: There are regularly scheduled orientations for prospective students. Visitors may sit in on classes. To arrange for a visit, contact the Admissions receptionist at (216) 672-2444.

Financial Aid: In an earlier year, 55% of all current freshmen and 50% of continuing students received some form of financial aid. The FAF and OIG for Ohio residents is required. The deadline for financial aid applications is April 1.

International Students: There are currently 430 international students enrolled. They must take the TOEFL and achieve a minimum score of 525.

Computers: The college provides computer facilities for student use. The mainframes are an IBM 4381 R-2, an IBM 3090/200 S, and a DEC VAX 11/780. Terminals and microcomputer facilities are available for student use in academic buildings and residence halls. Students with departmental authorization may access the system. It may be used 24 hours a day, 7 days a week. There are no time limits and no fees.

Graduates: In a recent year, 2813 bachelor's degrees were awarded. The most popular majors among graduates were elementary education (8%), marketing (7%), and nursing (5%). Within an average freshman class, 14% graduate in 4 years, 35% in 5 years, and 41% in 6 years. Some 400 companies normally recruit on campus.

Admissions Contact: Charles E. Rickard, Director of Admissions.

KENYON COLLEGE
Gambier, OH 43022–9623

C-3

(614) 427–5776
(800) 848–2468 (out-of-state)

Full-time: 685 men, 760 women	Faculty: 122; IIB, +$
Part-time: 4 men, 5 women	Ph.D.s: 96%
Graduate: none	Student/Faculty: 12 to 1
Year: semesters	Tuition: $18,730
Application Deadline: February 15	Room & Board: $3700
Freshman Class: 2212 applied, 1538 accepted, 408 enrolled	
SAT I Verbal/Math: 570/593 (mean)	ACT: 27 HIGHLY COMPETITIVE +

Kenyon College, founded in 1824, is a private, coeducational liberal arts and sciences college affiliated with the Episcopal Church. The library contains 368,090 volumes, 254,231 microform items, and 4742 audiovisual forms, and subscribes to 1360 periodicals. Special learning facilities include a learning resource center, art gallery, radio station, TV station, and observatory. The 800-acre campus is in a small town 50 miles northeast of Columbus. Including residence halls, there are 51 buildings on campus.

Student Life: About 76% of undergraduates are from out-of-state, mostly the Middle Atlantic. Students come from 48 states, 22 foreign countries, and Canada. Seventy percent are from public schools; 30% from private. Eighty-eight percent are white. Thirty-four percent are Protestant; 33% claim no religious affiliation; 19% Catholic. The average age of freshmen is 18; all undergraduates, 20. Six percent drop out by the end of their first year; 86% remain to graduate.

Housing: A total of 1524 students can be accommodated in college housing. College-sponsored living facilities include single-sex and coed dormitories and on-campus apartments. In addition, there are special interest floors. On-campus housing is guaranteed for all 4 years. All students live on campus; 98% remain on campus on weekends. All students may keep cars on campus.

Activities: About 25% of men belong to 2 local and 7 national fraternities; about 2% of women belong to 2 local sororities. There are 97 groups on campus, including art, band, chess, choir, chorale, chorus, dance, drama, ethnic, film, gay, international, jazz band, literary magazine, musical theater, newspaper, orchestra, pep band, photography, political, radio and TV, religious, social, social service, student government, symphony, and yearbook. Popular campus events include Gambier Folk Festival; Homecoming; dance, drama, music, and athletic events; and foreign and domestic film festivals.

Sports: There are 11 intercollegiate sports for men and 10 for women, and 16 intramural sports for men and 15 for women. Athletic and recreation facilities include 70 acres of playing, football, and soccer fields; a 50-yard pool; a field house; a Nautilus center; basketball, tennis, squash, and racquetball courts; and weight rooms.

Disabled Students: The following facilities are available: wheelchair ramps, elevators, special parking, specially equipped rest rooms, special class scheduling, lowered drinking fountains, and lowered telephones.

Services: In addition to many counseling and information services, tutoring is available in some subjects upon request. In addition, there is a reader service for the blind and remedial writing. There is a writing center available.

Campus Safety and Security: Campus safety and security measures include 24-hour foot and vehicle patrol, self defense education, escort service, and informal discussions. In addition, there are pamphlets, posters, and films, emergency telephones, and lighted pathways and sidewalks.

Programs of Study: Kenyon awards the B.A. and B.F.A. degrees. Bachelor's degrees are awarded in BIOLOGICAL SCIENCE (biology/biological science and neurosciences), COMMUNICATIONS AND THE ARTS (art history and appreciation, classics, dance, dramatic arts, English, fine arts, French, German, Greek, Latin, modern language, music, Spanish, and studio art), COMPUTER AND PHYSICAL SCIENCE (chemistry, mathematics, and physics), ENGINEERING AND ENVIRONMENTAL DESIGN (environmental science), SOCIAL SCIENCE (anthropology, Asian/Oriental studies, economics, history, international studies, philosophy, political science/government, psychology, religion, Russian and Slavic studies, sociology, and women's studies). Biology, chemistry, drama, economics, English, history, mathematics, philosophy, political science, psychology, religion, studio art, and international studies are the strongest programs academically. English, history, political science, psychology, biology, and economics have the largest enrollments.

Required: Students are required to complete a total of 16 units, including 4 to 7 units in the major and 1 unit in each of 4 divisions representing the arts, humanities, natural sciences, and social sciences. Students must maintain a minimum GPA of 2.0 and pass a comprehensive exam.

Special: Students may study abroad in a wide variety of countries. The college also offers dual majors, student-designed majors, pass/fail options, internships, a Washington semester consisting of apprenticeships in any of several U.S. programs, and a 3–2 engineering degree with Case Western and Rensselaer Polytech gram in Humane Studies human predicament. There including Phi Beta Kappa.

Faculty/Classroom: Sixty-male. All teach undergradua size in an introductory lecture lar course offering, 15.

Admissions: About 70% of the The SAT scores for the 1993–94 bal—24% below 500, 43% bet 600 and 700, and 6% above 70 tween 500 and 599, 34% between The ACT scores were 21% between 26, 23% between 27 and 28, and 2 current freshmen were in the top fifth top two fifths. There were 17 National ists. About 22 freshmen graduated firs.

Requirements: The SAT I or ACT is re graduates of an accredited secondary s 4 units each of English, foreign languag units each of science and social studies. C to exceed the minimum requirements, espe science, and to take advanced placement c 2 subjects. An essay and interview are impor sions decision. Talent in music, theater, art, given extra consideration. AP credit is accep used in the admissions decision are advanced courses, recommendations by school officials, e ties record, evidence of special talent, and leade

Procedure: Freshmen are admitted to all session should be taken in the fall of the senior year. Early tions should be filed by December 1; regular applic ary 15 for fall entry and November 15 for spring ent application fee of $45. Notification of early decision is 15; regular decision, April 1. There are early decisio sions, and deferred admissions plans. About 115 early didates were accepted for the 1993–94 class. A waiting tive part of the admissions procedure, with about 7% of a the list.

Transfer: About 17 transfer students enrolled in 1993–9 applicants must have a minimum college GPA of 3.0 ar school record suggesting ability and promise. A total of 8 fu gie units out of 16 must be completed at Kenyon.

Visiting: There are regularly scheduled orientations for pros students, consisting of interviews with staff, a campus tour, and visit. Students may also request to meet with faculty and coa There are guides for informal visits and visitors may sit in on cl and stay overnight at the school. To arrange for a visit, contact the missions Office at (800) 848–2468.

Financial Aid: In 1993–94, 40% of all current freshmen and 35 of continuing students received some form of financial aid. Abou 32% of freshmen and 34% of continuing students received need-based aid. The average freshman award was $11,420. Of that total, scholarships or need-based grants averaged $10,020 ($22,000 maximum); loans averaged $3400 ($4625 maximum); and work contracts averaged $650 ($900 maximum). Thirty-six percent of undergraduate students work part-time. Average earnings from campus work for the school year are $900. The average financial indebtedness of the 1992–93 graduate was $15,750. Kenyon is a member of CSS. The FAF and the FAFSA are required. The deadline for financial aid applications is February 15.

International Students: There are currently 40 international students enrolled. The school actively recruits these students. They must take the TOEFL and achieve a minimum score of 550. The student must also take the SAT I or the ACT.

Computers: The college provides computer facilities for student use. The mainframes include a DEC VAX 3100, VAX 4100, VAX 4200, VAX 4300, and VAX 4500. Students may access the campus network via 145 terminals and 50 microcomputers connected to the full campus network. Public access locations include residence halls, classrooms, laboratories, studios, the library, and public computing areas. For a small fee, students with personal computers may have personal network connections from their residence rooms. All students may access the system 24 hours a day. There are no time limits on using the system and no fees.

Graduates: In 1992–93 388 bachelor's degrees were awarded. The most popular majors among graduates were English (23%), history (12%), and political science (11%). Within an average freshman class, 82% graduate in 4 years and 86% in 5 years. Some 31 companies recruited on campus in 1992–93. In the 1992 graduating class, 29% of the men and 31% of the women were enrolled in graduate school within 6 months of graduation.

Admissions Contact: John W. Anderson, Dean of Admissions.

1172 OHIO

LAKE ERIE CO
Painesville, OH

Full-time: 93 men,
Part-time: 105 mer
Graduate: 59
Year: semesters,
Application Deadl
Freshman Class:
SAT I: 434/473

Lake Erie Colle
al arts college
The library
4469 audiov
learning faci
seum. The 5
land. Includ

Student L
dents come
percent ar
are white.
29.5.

Housing
housing.
coed do
first-serv
men. E
ted. Al

Activit
are 20
honor
gious
ular
tiona
Spri

Spo
Ath
cer

Di
ra
S
tr
r

227 women **Faculty:** 30
, 245 women **Ph.D.s:** 70%
69 women **Student/Faculty:** 11 to 1
ummer session **Tuition:** $9600
ne: open **Room & Board:** $4100
115 applied, 112 accepted, 45 enrolled
ACT: 21 **COMPETITIVE**

ge, founded in 1856, is a private, coeducational, liber-
. There is one undergraduate and 2 graduate schools.
ontains 89,232 volumes, 8091 microform items, and
sual forms, and subscribes to 767 periodicals. Special
ities include an art gallery and an American Indian Mu-
7-acre campus is in a small town 28 miles east of Cleve-
ing residence halls, there are 16 buildings on campus.

ife: About 88% of undergraduates are from Ohio. Stu-
e from 22 states, 6 foreign countries, and Canada. Ninety-
from public schools; 10% from private. Ninety-six percent
The average age of freshmen is 18; all undergraduates,

A total of 256 students can be accommodated in college
College-sponsored living facilities include single-sex and
rmitories. On-campus housing is available on a first-come,
ed basis and is available on a lottery system for upperclass-
ghty-two percent of students commute. Alcohol is not permit-
students may keep cars on campus.

ies: There are no fraternities or sororities on campus. There
groups on campus, including art, choir, chorus, dance, drama,
s, musical theater, pep band, photography, professional, reli-
social, social service, student government, and yearbook. Pop-
campus events include Prix de Ville of North America, interna-
l dinners, class dinners, Spirit Week, Mountain Weekend, and
g Formal.

rts: There are intercollegiate and intramural sports programs.
letic and recreation facilities include a gymnasium, an equestrian
ter, playing fields, and the Jane White Lincoln Center.

sabled Students: The following facilities are available: wheelchair
mps, elevators, special parking, and specially equipped rest rooms.

ervices: In addition to many counseling and information services,
toring is available in most subjects. There is also remedial math,
eading, and writing.

Campus Safety and Security: Campus safety and security measures include informal discussions, pamphlets, posters, and films,
emergency telephones, and lighted pathways and sidewalks. In addition, there is a 24-hour foot patrol.

Programs of Study: Lake Erie awards the B.A., B.S., and B.F.A. degrees. Master's degrees also are awarded. Bachelor's degrees are
awarded in AGRICULTURE (equestrian science), BIOLOGICAL SCI-
ENCE (biology/biological science), BUSINESS (accounting, business
administration and management, and international business management), COMMUNICATIONS AND THE ARTS (communications,
dance, English, fine arts, French, German, Italian, music, and Spanish), COMPUTER AND PHYSICAL SCIENCE (chemistry and mathematics), EDUCATION (elementary), ENGINEERING AND ENVIRON-
MENTAL DESIGN (environmental science), HEALTH PROFESSIONS
(health care administration), SOCIAL SCIENCE (paralegal studies,
psychology, and social science). Equestrian science, elementary education, and business have the largest enrollments.

Required: General education requirements include 2 semester hours
of public speaking; 4 hours each of mathematics, English, and either
a foreign language or mathematics with application; and 6 hours of
computers. There are specific core requirements for 25 additional semester hours. Students must complete 128 credits, including 64 in the
major, with a minimum GPA of 2.0.

Special: Students may choose either national or international internships or study abroad in the Netherlands, France, Germany, Spain,
England, and other countries. The college offers a general studies degree, accelerated degrees in business and accounting, B.A.-B.S. degrees, student-designed majors, nondegree study, and potential credit for life, military, or work experience. Cross-registration is available
with the Cleveland Commission on Higher Education. There is 1 national honor society on campus.

Faculty/Classroom: Sixty-three percent of faculty are male; 37%,
female. All teach undergraduates. The average class size in an introductory lecture is 20; in a laboratory, 10; and in a regular course offering, 10.

Admissions: About 97% of the 1993–94 applicants were accepted.
The ACT scores for the 1993–94 freshman class were as follows: 38%
below 21, 40% between 21 and 23, 9% between 24 and 26, 7% between 27 and 28, and 6% above 28.

Requirements: A minimum GPA of 2.8 is required. The SAT I or the
ACT is recommended. Applicants should be graduates of an accredited secondary school with a minimum GPA of 2.8. The high school
program should include 4 years each of English, mathematics, and
science (including 2 years of laboratory science), and 2 years each of
history and social studies. Two years of a foreign language are recommended. AP and CLEP credits are accepted. Important factors used
in the admissions decision are advanced placement or honor courses,
recommendations by school officials, leadership record, extracurricular activities record, and personality, intangible qualities.

Procedure: Freshmen are admitted to all sessions. Application deadlines are open. The fee is $20. Notification is sent on a rolling basis.
There are early admissions and deferred admissions plans.

Transfer: About 117 transfer students enrolled in 1993–94. Applicants should submit transcripts from all schools attended and show a
GPA of 2.0 in all college work. A letter of recommendation and an essay are recommended. A total of 32 credits out of 128 must be completed at Lake Erie.

Visiting: There are regularly scheduled orientations for prospective
students, including a campus tour, a financial aid information session,
an equestrian center tour, observation of classes, and faculty or department head interviews. There are guides for informal visits and visitors may sit in on classes and stay overnight at the school. To arrange
for a visit, contact the Office of Admissions at (216) 639–7879.

Financial Aid: In 1993–94 87% of all current freshmen and 56% of
continuing students received some form of financial aid. About 86%
of freshmen and 55% of continuing students received need-based
aid. The average freshman award was $9336. Of that total, scholar-
ships or need-based grants averaged $5542 ($10,000 maximum);
loans averaged $2794 ($4625 maximum); and work contracts averaged $1000 ($2000 maximum). The average financial indebtedness
of the 1992–93 graduate was $12,000. Lake Erie is a member of
CSS. The FAF and the college's own financial statement are required.
The deadline for financial aid applications is March 1.

International Students: There are currently 7 international students
enrolled. The school actively recruits these students. They must take
the TOEFL or the University of Michigan Language Test and achieve
a minimum score on the TOEFL of 500. The student must also take the
SAT I or the ACT.

Computers: The college provides computer facilities for student use.
Personal computers are available in residence halls, the center, and
the library for student use. There are no time limits on using the system and no fees.

Graduates: In a recent year, 134 bachelor's degrees were awarded.
The most popular majors among graduates were business (37%), education (13%), and accounting (10%).

Admissions Contact: Phyliss B. Hammerstrom, Director of Admissions.

LOURDES COLLEGE B-1

Sylvania, OH 43560 (419) 885–5291; (800) 878–3210
Full-time: 74 men, 356 women **Faculty:** 62; IIB, --$
Part-time: 162 men, 1013 women **Ph.D.s:** 18%
Graduate: none **Student/Faculty:** 7 to 1
Year: semesters, summer session **Tuition:** $6410
Application Deadline: August 10 **Room & Board:** n/app
Freshman Class: 57 applied, 55 accepted, 32 enrolled
ACT: 20 **LESS COMPETITIVE**

Lourdes College, founded in 1958, is a private liberal arts college affiliated with the Roman Catholic Church. In addition to regional accreditation, Lourdes has baccalaureate program accreditation with
CSWE and NLN. The library contains 53,214 volumes, 8624 microform items, and 1063 audiovisual forms, and subscribes to 375 periodicals. Computerized library sources and services include the card
catalog and interlibrary loans. Special learning facilities include a
learning resource center, art gallery, and planetarium. The 89-acre
campus is in a suburban area 10 miles west of Toledo. There are 8
buildings on campus. There are no residence halls.

Student Life: About 91% of undergraduates are from Ohio. Students come from 2 states and 6 foreign countries. Seventy-seven percent are from public schools; 23% from private. Ninety-two percent
are white. Sixty percent are Catholic; 38% Protestant. The average
age of freshmen is 29; all undergraduates, 32. Three percent drop
out by the end of their first year; 40% remain to graduate.

Housing: There are no residence halls. All students commute. All students may keep cars on campus.

Activities: About 2% of women belong to 1 national sorority. There
are no fraternities on campus. There are 15 groups on campus, including choir, chorus, honors, newspaper, political, professional, religious, social service, and student government. Popular campus
events include Founders Day, Humanities Lecture, Doyle Lecture,
and Arbor Day.

Sports: There is 1 intramural sport for men and 1 for women. Athletic
and recreation facilities include a gymnasium.

Disabled Students: Eighty percent of the campus is accessible to disabled students. The following facilities are available: wheelchair ramps, elevators, special parking, specially equipped rest rooms, special class scheduling, lowered drinking fountains, and lowered telephones.

Services: In addition to many counseling and information services, tutoring is available in some subjects, including the sciences and mathematics. In addition, there is a reader service for the blind, and remedial math, reading, and writing. Assistance in note writing and test taking is available.

Campus Safety and Security: Campus safety and security measures include escort service, pamphlets, posters, and films, and lighted pathways and sidewalks.

Programs of Study: Lourdes awards the B.A., B.A.R.S., B.I.S., and B.S.N. degrees. Associate degrees also are awarded. Bachelor's degrees are awarded in BUSINESS (business administration and management), COMMUNICATIONS AND THE ARTS (art, art history and appreciation, English, and fine arts), EDUCATION (early childhood), HEALTH PROFESSIONS (nursing), SOCIAL SCIENCE (gerontology, history, psychology, religious studies, social work, and sociology). Business, psychology, gerontology, early childhood, and nursing are the strongest academically. Business, psychology, and nursing have the largest enrollments.

Required: Students are required to maintain at least a 2.0 overall GPA, although most disciplines require 2.5. The total number of hours in the major varies from 36 to 59 semester hours depending on the major. Students must complete 128 credit hours, the requirements varying according to the degree sought. Most students will need courses in art/music, religious studies, composition, literature, physical education, and social science.

Special: The college offers field experience in certain disciplines, co-op programs in business, and work-study programs with various employers. Students may pursue dual majors, nondegree study, or select pass/fail options. The college gives credit for life, military, or work experience. There are 6 national honor societies on campus.

Faculty/Classroom: Twenty-seven percent of faculty are male; 73%, female. All teach undergraduates. The average class size in an introductory lecture is 20; in a laboratory, 14; and in a regular course offering, 15.

Admissions: About 96% of the 1993–94 applicants were accepted. The ACT scores for the 1993–94 freshman class were as follows: 66% below 21, 14% between 21 and 23, 10% between 24 and 26, and 10% between 27 and 28. About 41% of the current freshmen were in the top fifth of their class; 63% were in the top two fifths.

Requirements: A minimum GPA of 2.0 is required. The SAT I or ACT is required. Candidates for admission should have completed 4 units of English, 3 units of mathematics, 3 units of science, and 3 units of social studies. AP and CLEP credits are accepted.

Procedure: Freshmen are admitted to all sessions. Entrance exams should be taken at least 30 days prior to the beginning of the freshman year of college. Applications should be filed by August 10 for fall entry, January 10 for winter entry, and June 10 for summer entry, along with an application fee of $20. Notification is sent on a rolling basis.

Transfer: About 300 transfer students enrolled in 1993–94. Transfer students should submit official transcripts, completed application and fee, and placement tests when necessary. A total of 32 credits out of 128 must be completed at Lourdes.

Visiting: There are guides for informal visits, and visitors may sit in on classes. To arrange for a visit, contact Mary Ellen Briggs at (419) 885–5291 or (800) 878–3210.

Financial Aid: In 1993–94 30% of all current freshmen and 35% of continuing students received some form of financial aid. About 28% of freshmen and 33% of continuing students received need-based aid. The average freshman award was $3400. Of that total, scholarships or need-based grants averaged $500 ($1000 maximum); loans averaged $2500 ($4000 maximum); and work contracts averaged $1000 ($1500 maximum). Eighty-one percent of undergraduate students work part-time. Average earnings from campus work for the school year are $1100. The college's own financial statement and the FAFSA are required.

International Students: There are currently 9 international students enrolled. They must take the TOEFL and achieve a minimum score of 500.

Computers: The college provides computer facilities for student use. The mainframe is an IBM 5363. There are 37 IBM-compatible and 5 Apple Macintosh microcomputers available for student use.

Graduates: In 1992–93 108 bachelor's degrees were awarded. The most popular majors among graduates were business (35%) and nursing (22%).

Admissions Contact: Mary Ellen Briggs, Director of Admissions.

MALONE COLLEGE
D-2

Canton, OH 44709

(216) 471–8100; (800) 521–1146

Full-time: 490 men, 743 women	Faculty: 70; IIB, -$
Part-time: 61 men, 139 women	Ph.D.s: 45%
Graduate: 26 men, 100 women	Student/Faculty: 18 to 1
Year: semesters, summer session	Tuition: $9172
Application Deadline: July 1	Room & Board: $3400
Freshman Class: 1077 applied, 925 accepted, 559 enrolled	
SAT I: 430/466	ACT: 21 COMPETITIVE

Malone College, founded in 1892, is a private, coeducational liberal arts college affiliated with the Evangelical Friends Church. In addition to regional accreditation, Malone has baccalaureate program accreditation with CSWE. The library contains 128,079 volumes, 136,692 microform items, and 5715 audiovisual forms, and subscribes to 1123 periodicals. Computerized library sources and services include interlibrary loans and database searching. Special learning facilities include a learning resource center, radio station, and TV station. The 78-acre campus is in an urban area 56 miles southeast of Cleveland. Including residence halls, there are 13 buildings on campus.

Student Life: About 95% of undergraduates are from Ohio. Students come from 18 states, 10 foreign countries, and Canada. Ninety percent are from public schools; 10% from private. Ninety-five percent are white. Most are Protestant. The average age of freshmen is 19; all undergraduates, 25. Twelve percent drop out by the end of their first year; 44% remain to graduate.

Housing: A total of 906 students can be accommodated in college housing. College-sponsored living facilities include single-sex dormitories, off-campus apartments, and married-student housing. On-campus housing is guaranteed for the freshman year only, is available on a first-come, first-served basis, and is available on a lottery system for upperclassmen. Fifty-two percent of students commute. Alcohol is not permitted. All students may keep cars on campus.

Activities: There are no fraternities or sororities on campus. There are 41 groups on campus, including art, band, cheerleading, choir, chorale, chorus, computers, drama, ethnic, film, jazz band, literary magazine, marching band, musical theater, newspaper, pep band, photography, political, radio and TV, religious, social, social service, student government, and yearbook. Popular campus events include Homecoming, Gleaning, Little Sibs Weekend, Fall Fest, Staley Lecture, and Martin Luther King Day Celebrations.

Sports: There are 9 intercollegiate sports for men and 7 for women, and 6 intramural sports for men and 5 for women. Athletic and recreation facilities include a gymnasium and a Nautilus center.

Disabled Students: The entire campus is accessible to disabled students. The following facilities are available: wheelchair ramps, elevators, special parking, specially equipped rest rooms, special class scheduling, lowered drinking fountains, and lowered telephones.

Services: In addition to many counseling and information services, tutoring is available in every subject. There is also a reader service for the blind, and remedial math, reading, and writing.

Campus Safety and Security: Campus safety and security measures include 24-hour foot and vehicle patrol, self defense education, escort service, and shuttle buses. In addition, there are emergency telephones and lighted pathways and sidewalks.

Programs of Study: Malone awards the B.A., B.S.Ed., B.S.N., and B.S.W. degrees. Associate and master's degrees also are awarded. Bachelor's degrees are awarded in BIOLOGICAL SCIENCE (biology/biological science), BUSINESS (accounting, business administration and management, and management science), COMMUNICATIONS AND THE ARTS (communications, English, and music), COMPUTER AND PHYSICAL SCIENCE (chemistry, computer science, mathematics, and science), EDUCATION (elementary, music, physical, science, and secondary), HEALTH PROFESSIONS (allied health, medical laboratory technology, nursing, premedicine, and radiological science), SOCIAL SCIENCE (history, liberal arts/general studies, ministries, psychology, social science, and social work). Premedicine, education, business, and social work are the strongest programs academically. Business and education have the largest enrollments.

Required: Students must maintain a GPA of 2.0 overall and 2.25 in the major. At least 30 total hours in the major and 39 hours at the 300 or 400 level are required. To graduate, all students must complete at least 124 credit hours, including 13 to 17 hours in writing, physical education, and mathematics, 9 hours in religion, 7 to 8 hours in science, and 23 hours in humanities.

Special: Students may participate in co-op programs and internships in all majors and may cross-register within the Christian College Consortium. Malone offers study abroad in Hong Kong, Guatemala, Costa Rica, and Africa, Hollywood and Washington semesters, work-study programs, and an accelerated degree program in management. A general studies degree, a 3–2 engineering degree, dual and student-designed majors, and credit for life, military, or work experience are also available. The Malone College Management Program

offers degree completion for students age 25 or older who have the equivalent of 2 years of college. There are 2 national honor societies on campus.

Faculty/Classroom: Fifty-six percent of faculty are male; 44%, female. Ninety-nine percent teach undergraduates and also do research. No introductory courses are taught by graduate students. The average class size in an introductory lecture is 34; in a laboratory, 17; and in a regular course offering, 23.

Admissions: About 86% of the 1993–94 applicants were accepted. The SAT scores for the 1993–94 freshman class were as follows: Verbal—72% below 500, 20% between 500 and 599, and 8% between 600 and 700; Math—65% below 500, 17% between 500 and 599, and 18% between 600 and 700. The ACT scores were 51% below 21, 26% between 21 and 23, 15% between 24 and 26, 3% between 27 and 28, and 5% above 28. About 46% of the current freshmen were in the top fifth of their class; 78% were in the top two fifths. Twelve freshmen graduated first in their class.

Requirements: A minimum GPA of 2.5 is required. The SAT I is required for traditional students. Applicants should be graduates of an accredited secondary school with a minimum GPA of 2.5. The GED is accepted. AP and CLEP credits are accepted. Important factors used in the admissions decision are advanced placement or honor courses, leadership record, evidence of special talent, parents or siblings attending the school, and extracurricular activities record.

Procedure: Freshmen are admitted to all sessions. Entrance exams should be taken in the junior year. Applications should be filed by July 1 for fall entry, along with an application fee of $20. There are early admissions and deferred admissions plans. About 7 early decision candidates were accepted for the 1993–94 class.

Transfer: About 78 transfer students enrolled in 1993–94. Applicants must submit an official transcript and a financial aid transcript from each college attended and a transfer reference form from the most recent school. A total of 30 credits out of 124 must be completed at Malone.

Visiting: There are regularly scheduled orientations for prospective students. There are guides for informal visits and visitors may sit in on classes and stay overnight at the school. To arrange for a visit, contact the Admissions Office at (216) 471–8145.

Financial Aid: In 1993–94, 94% of all current freshmen and 79% of continuing students received some form of financial aid. About 84% of freshmen and 73% of continuing students received need-based aid. The average freshman award was $8112. Of that total, scholarships or need-based grants averaged $5020 ($7500 maximum); loans averaged $2450 ($2625 maximum); and work contracts averaged $1300 ($1400 maximum). Sixty-four percent of undergraduate students work part-time. Average earnings from campus work for the school year are $1300. The average financial indebtedness of the 1992–93 graduate was $12,759. Malone is a member of CSS. The college's own financial statement and the FAFSA are required. The deadline for financial aid applications is March 31.

International Students: There are currently 11 international students enrolled. They must take the TOEFL and achieve a minimum score of 520. The student must also take the SAT I or the ACT.

Computers: The college provides computer facilities for student use. The mainframe is a DEC MicroVAX II. All students may access the system. It may be used 7 A.M. to 9 P.M. Monday through Friday. There are no time limits on using the system and no fees.

Graduates: In 1992–93, 323 bachelor's degrees were awarded. The most popular majors among graduates were management (35%), elementary education (14%), and business administration (9%). Within an average freshman class, 29% graduate in 4 years, 13% in 5 years, and 3% in 6 years. Some 50 companies recruited on campus in an earlier year. In a recent graduating class, 7% of all students were enrolled in graduate school within 6 months of graduation; 31% of the men and 47% of the women had found employment.

Admissions Contact: Leland Sommers, Dean of Admissions.

MARIETTA COLLEGE
E-5

Marietta, OH 45750–4005

Full-time: 530 men, 470 women	(614) 374–4600; (800) 331–7896
Part-time: 90 men, 145 women	Faculty: 72; IIB, -$
Graduate: 15 men, 60 women	Ph.D.s: n/av
Year: semesters, summer session	Student/Faculty: 14 to 1
Application Deadline: open	Tuition: $13,170
Freshman Class: 1519 applied, 1030 accepted, 343 enrolled	Room & Board: $3770
SAT I: 500/540	ACT: 24 COMPETITIVE +

Marietta College, founded in 1835, is a private, liberal arts college. In addition to regional accreditation, Marietta has baccalaureate program accreditation with ABET. The library contains 250,600 volumes, 28,384 microform items, and 6179 audiovisual forms, and subscribes to 950 periodicals. Computerized library sources and services include interlibrary loans. Special learning facilities include a learning resource center, art gallery, radio station, TV station, observatory, and greenhouse. The 120-acre campus is in a small town 115 miles south-

east of Columbus. Including residence halls, there are 40 buildings on campus.

Student Life: About 54% of undergraduates are from Ohio. Students come from 34 states and 11 foreign countries. Ninety-four percent are white. The average age of freshmen is 19; all undergraduates, 20. Twenty-two percent drop out by the end of their first year; 60% remain to graduate.

Housing: A total of 1063 students can be accommodated in college housing. College-sponsored living facilities include single-sex and coed dormitories, fraternity houses, and sorority houses. In addition, there are honors houses. On-campus housing is guaranteed for all 4 years. Eighty percent of students live on campus; of those, 80% remain on campus on weekends. All students may keep cars on campus.

Activities: About 43% of men belong to 7 national fraternities; about 38% of women belong to 4 national sororities. There are 116 groups on campus, including art, band, cheerleading, chess, choir, chorale, chorus, computers, drama, ethnic, film, honors, international, jazz band, literary magazine, musical theater, newspaper, orchestra, pep band, photography, political, professional, radio and TV, religious, social, social service, student government, and yearbook. Popular campus events include DooDah Day, Homecoming, and Winter Weekend.

Sports: There are 8 intercollegiate sports for men and 6 for women, and 12 intramural sports for men and 10 for women. Athletic and recreation facilities include a field house, a field park, a pool, a Nautilus/Universal room, and an aerobic fitness center.

Disabled Students: Eighty percent of the campus is accessible to disabled students. The following facilities are available: wheelchair ramps, elevators, special parking, specially equipped rest rooms, and special class scheduling.

Services: In addition to many counseling and information services, tutoring is available in most subjects. There is remedial math and writing. Writing and mathematics laboratories are available.

Campus Safety and Security: Campus safety and security measures include 24-hour foot and vehicle patrol, escort service, informal discussions, and pamphlets, posters, and films. In addition, there are lighted pathways and sidewalks.

Programs of Study: Marietta awards the B.A., B.S., B.F.A., and B.S. in Petroleum Engineering degrees. Associate and master's degrees also are awarded. Bachelor's degrees are awarded in BIOLOGICAL SCIENCE (biochemistry and biology/biological science), BUSINESS (accounting, business administration and management, international business management, management science, marketing/retailing/merchandising, and personnel management), COMMUNICATIONS AND THE ARTS (advertising, broadcasting, communications, English, fine arts, French, journalism, music, public relations, Spanish, speech/debate/rhetoric, and telecommunications), COMPUTER AND PHYSICAL SCIENCE (chemistry, computer science, geology, information sciences and systems, mathematics, and physics), EDUCATION (art, elementary, middle school, music, science, and secondary), ENGINEERING AND ENVIRONMENTAL DESIGN (industrial engineering and petroleum/natural gas engineering), HEALTH PROFESSIONS (predentistry, premedicine, and sports medicine), SOCIAL SCIENCE (economics, history, philosophy, prelaw, psychology, and religion). Sports medicine, mass media, petroleum engineering, education, and accounting are the strongest academically. Business, education, and mass media have the largest enrollments.

Required: To graduate, students must complete at least 124 total credit hours, including 4 courses in humanities, fine arts, social science, and history, and 2 in natural science; English composition; speech 101; and mathematics. The minimum number of hours required for a major is 36. A minimum GPA of 2.0 must be maintained.

Special: There are binary programs with Case Western Reserve and Duke universities and the universities of Pennsylvania and Michigan. Students may take internships, study abroad in various countries, and participate in a Washington semester. Work-study programs, B.A.-B.S. degrees in 47 fields, student-designed majors, a 3–2 engineering degree, pass/fail options, and credit for life, military, and work experience are available. The freshman year program is designed to assist with the student's academic and social transition to college life. There is a freshman honors program on campus, as well as 12 national honor societies, including Phi Beta Kappa.

Faculty/Classroom: Sixty-seven percent of faculty are male; 33% female. All teach undergraduates. The average class size in an introductory lecture is 25; in a laboratory, 12; and in a regular course offering, 22.

Admissions: About 68% of the 1993–94 applicants were accepted. About 41% of the current freshmen were in the top fifth of their class; 73% were in the top two fifths.

Requirements: The SAT I or ACT is required. In addition, students seeking admission should have completed 4 years of English, 3 of history, mathematics, and science; 2 years of a foreign language are also recommended. AP and CLEP credits are accepted. Important factors used in the admissions decision are advanced placement or honor

courses, extracurricular activities record, parents or siblings attending the school, evidence of special talent, and leadership record.

Procedure: Freshmen are admitted fall and spring. Entrance exams should be taken no later than February of the senior year. Early decision applications should be filed by December 1; deadlines for regular applications are open. The application fee is $25. Notification of early decision is sent December 15; regular decision, on a rolling basis. There are early decision, early admissions, and deferred admissions plans.

Transfer: About 48 transfer students enrolled in 1993–94. A minimum GPA of 2.0, a recommendation, and an essay are required. A total of 30 credits out of 124 must be completed at Marietta.

Visiting: There are regularly scheduled orientations for prospective students, including fall and spring open houses, tours, and meetings with faculty, coaches, and financial aid representatives. There are guides for informal visits, and visitors may sit in on classes and stay overnight at the school. To arrange for a visit, contact the Office of Admissions at (800) 331–7896 or (614) 374–4600.

Financial Aid: In a recent year, 89% of all freshmen and 83% of continuing students received some form of financial aid. About 86% of freshmen and 81% of continuing students received need-based aid. The average freshman award was $9420. Fifty percent of undergraduate students work part-time. Average earnings from campus work for the school year are $975. Marietta is a member of CSS. The FAF is required. The deadline for financial aid applications is May 1.

International Students: There are currently 25 international students enrolled. The school actively recruits these students. They must take the TOEFL and achieve a minimum score of 525.

Computers: The college provides computer facilities for student use. The mainframe is a DEC VAX 11/750. There are also 150 IBM, Zenith, and Apple Macintosh PCs available in the computer laboratory, library, and academic buildings. All students may access the system. It may be used 8 A.M. to 12 midnight. There are no time limits on using the system and no fees.

Graduates: In a recent year, 222 bachelor's degrees were awarded. The most popular majors among graduates were economics, management, accounting (39%), communications (13%), and education (9%). Some 43 companies recruited on campus in an earlier year. In a recent graduating class, 13% of the men and 14% of the women were enrolled in graduate school within 6 months of graduation; 82% of the men and 80% of the women had found employment.

Admissions Contact: Dennis R. De Perro, Dean of Admission and Financial Aid.

MIAMI UNIVERSITY
A-4
Oxford, OH 45056
(513) 529–2531

Full-time: 6315 men, 7247 women
Part-time: 384 men, 433 women
Graduate: 687 men, 1167 women
Year: semesters, summer session
Application Deadline: January 31
Freshman Class: 9239 applied, 7788 accepted, 3351 enrolled
SAT I or ACT: required

Faculty: 743; I, --$
Ph.D.s: 88%
Student/Faculty: 18 to 1
Tuition: $4226 ($9098)
Room & Board: $3840

VERY COMPETITIVE

Miami University, founded in 1809, is a public, coeducational university offering a variety of programs in the liberal arts and professional-vocational fields. There are 6 undergraduate schools and one graduate school. In addition to regional accreditation, Miami University has baccalaureate program accreditation with AACSB, ABET, ADA, AHEA, ASLA, NAAB, NASAD, NASM, NCATE, and NLN. The 5 libraries contain 1,438,200 volumes, 214,800 microform items, and 16,200 audiovisual forms, and subscribe to 5000 periodicals. Computerized library sources and services include the card catalog, interlibrary loans, and database searching. Special learning facilities include a learning resource center, art gallery, natural history museum, radio station, and TV station. The 1921-acre campus is in a small town 35 miles northwest of Cincinnati. Including residence halls, there are 162 buildings on campus.

Student Life: About 73% of undergraduates are from Ohio. Students come from 49 states, 51 foreign countries, and Canada. Seventy-eight percent are from public schools; 22% from private. Ninety-three percent are white. The average age of freshmen is 18; all undergraduates, 20. Three percent drop out by the end of their first year; 83% remain to graduate.

Housing: A total of 7080 students can be accommodated in college housing. College-sponsored living facilities include single-sex and coed dormitories, married-student housing, and sorority suites. In addition, there are honors houses, language houses, and special interest houses. On-campus housing is guaranteed for the freshman year only and is available on a lottery system for upperclassmen. Fifty percent of students live on campus; of those, 90% to 95% remain on campus on weekends. Alcohol is not permitted.

Activities: About 33% of men belong to 28 national fraternities; about 39% of women belong to 22 national sororities. There are 325 groups on campus, including art, band, cheerleading, choir, chorale, chorus, dance, drama, drill team, ethnic, gay, honors, international, jazz band, literary magazine, marching band, musical theater, newspaper, opera, orchestra, pep band, political, professional, radio and TV, religious, social, social service, student government, symphony, and yearbook. Popular campus events include Parents Weekend, Kidsfest Weekend, Homecoming, Unity Fest, Task of the World, Asian Fest, Diwali, Holi, Bike Race, Greek Week, Women of Color Celebration, Martin Luther King Celebration Week, Black History Month, and Women's History Month.

Sports: There are 12 intercollegiate sports for men and 9 for women, and 25 intramural sports for men and 18 for women. Athletic and recreation facilities include a 25,000-seat football stadium, 70 acres of playing fields, 36 outdoor tennis courts, 10 indoor basketball courts, racquetball and squash courts, a climbing wall, equestrian stables and pressage course, 2 indoor swimming pools, jogging and park courses, sand volleyball courts, and aerobic and weight rooms.

Disabled Students: The entire campus is accessible to disabled students. The following facilities are available: wheelchair ramps, elevators, special parking, specially equipped rest rooms, special class scheduling, lowered drinking fountains, and lowered telephones.

Services: In addition to many counseling and information services, tutoring is available in most subjects. In addition, there is a reader service for the blind. Assistance in study skills is available.

Campus Safety and Security: Campus safety and security measures include 24-hour foot and vehicle patrol, self defense education, escort service, and shuttle buses. In addition, there are informal discussions, pamphlets, posters, and films, emergency telephones, and lighted pathways and sidewalks.

Programs of Study: Miami University awards the B.A., B.S., B.E.D., B.F.A., B.Mus., and B.Phil. degrees. Master's and doctoral degrees also are awarded. Bachelor's degrees are awarded in BIOLOGICAL SCIENCE (biology/biological science, botany, microbiology, and zoology), BUSINESS (accounting, banking and finance, business administration and management, business economics, management information systems, marketing/retailing/merchandising, personnel management, and sports management), COMMUNICATIONS AND THE ARTS (broadcasting, communications, dramatic arts, English, fine arts, French, German, Greek, Latin, music, Russian, Spanish, speech/debate/rhetoric, and telecommunications), COMPUTER AND PHYSICAL SCIENCE (chemistry, computer science, geology, mathematics, physics, and statistics), EDUCATION (art, early childhood, elementary, foreign languages, health, home economics, middle school, music, physical, science, secondary, and special), ENGINEERING AND ENVIRONMENTAL DESIGN (engineering, engineering management, engineering physics, environmental design, interior design, manufacturing engineering, and paper science and engineering), HEALTH PROFESSIONS (health, medical technology, premedicine, and speech pathology/audiology), SOCIAL SCIENCE (African American studies, American studies, anthropology, dietetics, economics, geography, history, interdisciplinary studies, international relations, philosophy, physical fitness/movement, political science/government, prelaw, psychology, public administration, religion, social science, sociology, and urban studies). Zoology, chemistry, accountancy, and microbiology are the strongest academically. Accountancy, elementary education, marketing, zoology, and finance have the largest enrollments.

Required: Students are required to complete 128 semester hours, with a minimum 2.0 GPA. A total of 36 of the 128 hours must include English composition, fine arts, humanities, social science, world cultures, natural science, mathematics, formal reasoning, and technology. A 3-hour Senior Capstone Experience, which integrates liberal learning and specialized knowledge, is also required.

Special: Students may cross-register with Cincinnati area colleges, and study abroad is possible in 15 countries. Co-op programs are available in the School of Applied Science. Internships in health and sport studies and science are possible. A 3–2 engineering degree with Case Western Reserve and Columbia universities and a 3–2 forestry degree with Duke University are available. Students may pursue student-designed majors through the School of Interdisciplinary Studies or interdisciplinary majors, including decision sciences and history of art and architecture. There is a freshman honors program on campus, as well as 15 national honor societies, including Phi Beta Kappa. Most departments have honors programs.

Faculty/Classroom: Seventy-two percent of faculty are male; 28% female. The average class size in a regular course offering is 28.

Admissions: About 84% of the 1993–94 applicants were accepted. The SAT scores for the 1993–94 freshman class were as follows: Verbal—41% below 500, 46% between 500 and 599, 12% between 600 and 700, and 1% above 700; Math—10% below 500, 43% between 500 and 599, 40% between 600 and 700, and 7% above 700. The ACT scores were 7% below 21, 24% between 21 and 23, 38% between 24 and 26, 18% between 27 and 28, and 13% above 28. About 64% of the current freshmen were in the top fifth of their class; 93% were in the top two fifths. There were 39 National Merit finalists. About 63 freshmen graduated first in their class.

Requirements: The SAT I or ACT is required. Candidates for admission must be graduates of accredited secondary schools or hold the GED and should have completed 4 units of English, 3 units each of mathematics, science, and social studies/history, 2 units of a foreign language, and 1 unit of fine arts. An audition, a portfolio, or an interview is required for direct admission to majors in the School of Fine Arts. AP and CLEP credits are accepted. Important factors used in the admissions decision are advanced placement or honor courses, evidence of special talent, extracurricular activities record, leadership record, and recommendations by school officials.

Procedure: Freshmen are admitted to all sessions. Entrance exams should be taken no later than February of the senior year of high school. Early decision applications should be filed by November 1; regular applications, by January 31 for fall entry and November 15 for winter entry, along with an application fee of $30. Notification of early decision is sent December 15; regular decision, March 15. There is an early decision plan. About 536 early decision candidates were accepted for the 1993–94 class. A waiting list is an active part of the admissions procedure, with about 1% of applicants on the list.

Transfer: About 387 transfer students enrolled in 1993–94. A limited number of transfer students can be accepted. Usually a GPA of 2.75 or higher is necessary. A total of 30 credits out of 128 must be completed at Miami University.

Visiting: There are regularly scheduled orientations for prospective students. There are guides for informal visits, and visitors may sit in on classes and stay overnight at the school. To arrange for a visit, contact the Office of Admissions at (513) 529–4632.

Financial Aid: In 1993–94 44% of all current freshmen and 28% of continuing students received some form of financial aid. About 40% of freshmen and 26% of continuing students received need-based aid. The average freshman award was $4543. Of that total, scholarships or need-based grants averaged $1001 ($15,106 maximum); loans averaged $227 ($15,106 maximum); and work contracts averaged $414 ($1360 maximum). Forty-three percent of undergraduate students work part-time. Average earnings from campus work for the school year are $843. Miami University is a member of CSS. The college's own financial statement and the FAFSA are required. The deadline for financial aid applications is January 31.

International Students: There are currently 313 international students enrolled. They must take the TOEFL and achieve a minimum score of 530. The student must also take the SAT I or the ACT.

Computers: The college provides computer facilities for student use. The mainframes are an IBM ES 9121 model 480 and a DEC VAX 640. Computer facilities include statistical analysis, database programming, and electronic mail, via student computing facilities in academic departments, residence halls, or dial-up. More than 500 microcomputers and terminals are available. All students may access the system. There are no time limits on using the system and no fees.

Graduates: In 1992–93 3481 bachelor's degrees were awarded. The most popular majors among graduates were accountancy (8%), marketing (8%), and elementary education (7%). Within an average freshman class, 2% graduate in 3 years, 75% in 4 years, 82% in 5 years, and 83% in 6 years. Some 345 companies recruited on campus in 1992–93. In the 1992 graduating class, 26% of all students were enrolled in graduate school within 6 months of graduation.

Admissions Contact: James S. McCoy, Assistant Vice President and Director of Admissions.

MOUNT UNION COLLEGE   E-2

Alliance, OH 44601   (216) 821–5320; (800) 992–6682 (in-state)

Full-time: 711 men, 642 women	Faculty: 78; IIB, av$
Part-time: 22 men, 32 women	Ph.D.s: 75%
Graduate: none	Student/Faculty: 17 to 1
Year: semesters, summer session	Tuition: $12,320
Application Deadline: open	Room & Board: $3530
Freshman Class: 1310 applied, 1086 accepted, 458 enrolled	
ACT: 23	COMPETITIVE

Mount Union College, founded in 1846, is a private, coeducational liberal arts college affiliated with the United Methodist Church. In addition to regional accreditation, Mount Union has baccalaureate program accreditation with NASM. The 3 libraries contain 215,507 volumes and 20,110 microform items, and subscribe to 799 periodicals. Computerized library sources and services include interlibrary loans and database searching. Special learning facilities include a learning resource center, art gallery, radio station, an astronomical observatory, a university theater, and a playhouse. The 72-acre campus is in a suburban area 20 miles east of Canton. Including residence halls, there are 25 buildings on campus.

Student Life: About 80% of undergraduates are from Ohio. Students come from 20 states and 20 foreign countries. Eighty-eight percent are from public schools; 12% from private. Eighty-five percent are white. Fifty percent are Protestant; 29% Catholic. The average age of freshmen is 18; all undergraduates, 20. Sixteen percent drop out by the end of their first year; 65% remain to graduate.

Housing: A total of 1184 students can be accommodated in college housing. College-sponsored living facilities include single-sex dormitories and fraternity houses. In addition, the college offers honors, special interest, and international houses. On-campus housing is guaranteed for all 4 years. Eighty percent of students live on campus; of those, 75% remain on campus on weekends. Alcohol is not permitted. All students may keep cars on campus.

Activities: About 40% of men belong to 5 national fraternities; about 40% of women belong to 1 local and 4 national sororities. There are 70 groups on campus, including art, band, cheerleading, chess, choir, chorale, chorus, computers, dance, drama, ethnic, honors, international, jazz band, literary magazine, marching band, newspaper, orchestra, pep band, political, professional, radio, religious, social, social service, student government, and yearbook. Popular campus events include Homecoming, Spring Fest, and Greek Week.

Sports: There are 11 intercollegiate sports for men and 9 for women, and 8 intramural sports for men and 8 for women. Athletic and recreation facilities include a gymnasium, a field house, a stadium, tennis courts, and the Hoover Price Campus Center.

Disabled Students: Seventy-five percent of the campus is accessible to disabled students. The following facilities are available: wheelchair ramps, elevators, special parking, specially equipped rest rooms, and lowered drinking fountains.

Services: In addition to many counseling and information services, tutoring is available in most subjects. There is also a reader service for the blind.

Campus Safety and Security: Campus safety and security measures include 24-hour foot and vehicle patrol, self defense education, informal discussions, and pamphlets, posters, and films. In addition, there are emergency telephones and lighted pathways and sidewalks.

Programs of Study: Mount Union awards the B.A., B.S., B.Mus., and B.Mus.Ed. degrees. Bachelor's degrees are awarded in BIOLOGICAL SCIENCE (biology/biological science), BUSINESS (accounting, business administration and management, business economics, international business management, and sports management), COMMUNICATIONS AND THE ARTS (communications, dramatic arts, English, fine arts, French, music, Spanish, and speech/debate/rhetoric), COMPUTER AND PHYSICAL SCIENCE (astronomy, chemistry, computer science, geology, information sciences and systems, mathematics, and physics), EDUCATION (elementary, foreign languages, health, music, and secondary), HEALTH PROFESSIONS (sports medicine), SOCIAL SCIENCE (American studies, crosscultural studies, economics, history, philosophy, political science/government, psychology, religion, social science, and sociology). Business and education have the largest enrollments.

Required: To graduate, students must complete a minimum of 120 semester hours, including 30 in upper-division courses and up to 48 in the major, with a minimum GPA of 2.0. General requirements include 36 to 39 hours in a core curriculum encompassing communication skills, analytical skills, religion/philosophy, international studies, Western history, literature, fine arts, physical education, and the freshmen liberal arts experience. Students must also complete a minor requirement and the senior year culminating experience.

Special: Mount Union offers internships for credit in many majors, co-op programs in business, work-study programs with various employers, student-designed majors, and pass/fail options. Adults in the nontraditional study program may receive credit for life, military, or work experience. There is a freshman honors program on campus, as well as 17 national honor societies.

Faculty/Classroom: Seventy-seven percent of faculty are male; 23%, female. All teach undergraduates. The average class size in an introductory lecture is 30; in a laboratory, 15; and in a regular course offering, 15.

Admissions: About 83% of the 1993–94 applicants were accepted. The ACT scores for the 1993–94 freshman class were as follows: 31% below 21, 28% between 21 and 23, 21% between 24 and 26, 13% between 27 and 28, and 7% above 28. About 47% of the current freshmen were in the top fifth of their class; 74% were in the top two fifths. About 12 freshmen graduated first in their class.

Requirements: The ACT is required. Preference is given to high school graduates who have completed a minimum of 15 academic units, including 4 in English, 3 each in mathematics, social science, laboratory science, and 2 in foreign language. AP and CLEP credits are accepted. Important factors used in the admissions decision are advanced placement or honor courses, recommendations by school officials, personality, intangible qualities, parents or siblings attending the school, and evidence of special talent.

Procedure: Freshmen are admitted fall and spring. Entrance exams should be taken for the first time in the spring of the junior year. Application deadlines are open, but there is a $20 application fee. There is a deferred admissions plan.

Transfer: About 43 transfer students enrolled in 1993–94. Applicants must have a college GPA of 2.0 and must submit a statement of honorable dismissal and an official transcript from the last college

attended. A personal statement must accompany the transfer application. A total of 45 credits out of 120 must be completed at Mount Union.

Visiting: There are regularly scheduled orientations for prospective students, including interviews, a campus tour, meetings with faculty, and classroom visits. There are guides for informal visits and visitors may sit in on classes and stay overnight at the school. To arrange for a visit, contact the Admissions Office at (800) 922-6682 or (216) 821-5320.

Financial Aid: In 1993-94 90% of all current freshmen and 92% of continuing students received some form of financial aid. The average freshman award was $9600. Of that total, scholarships or need-based grants averaged $5800 ($12,000 maximum); loans averaged $2600 ($3350 maximum); and work contracts averaged $1200 ($1500 maximum). Seventy-five percent of undergraduate students work part-time. Average earnings from campus work for the school year are $1000. Mount Union is a member of CSS. The FAF is required. The deadline for financial aid applications is August 1.

International Students: There are currently 70 international students enrolled. The school actively recruits these students. They must take the TOEFL and achieve a minimum score of 500.

Computers: The college provides computer facilities for student use. The mainframe is an HP 3000 series 70. There are 50 Epson IBM-compatible microcomputers available for student use in the computer laboratory. Macintosh computers are also available at various campus locations. All students may access the system. There are no time limits and no fees.

Graduates: In 1992-93 258 bachelor's degrees were awarded. The most popular majors among graduates were business administration (18%), education (11%), and accounting (8%). Within an average freshman class, 2% graduate in 3 years, 63% in 4 years, and 65% in 5 years. Some 95 companies usually recruit on campus. In a recent year's graduating class, 20% of all graduates were enrolled in graduate school within 6 months of graduation; 75% had found employment.

Admissions Contact: Greg King, Director of Admissions.

MOUNT VERNON NAZARENE COLLEGE
C-3
Mt. Vernon, OH 43050

(614) 397-1244
(800) 782-2435 (out-of-state)

Full-time: 479 men, 635 women	Faculty: 50; IIB, --$
Part-time: 55 men, 39 women	Ph.D.s: 56%
Graduate: 15 men	Student/Faculty: 22 to 1
Year: 4-1-4, summer session	Tuition: $7190
Application Deadline: August 1	Room & Board: $3200
Freshman Class: 510 applied, 485 accepted, 334 enrolled	
ACT: 22	COMPETITIVE

Mount Vernon Nazarene College, founded in 1964, is a private liberal arts college affiliated with the Church of the Nazarene. The library contains 86,762 volumes, 3600 microform items, and 2298 audiovisual forms, and subscribes to 526 periodicals. Computerized library sources and services include interlibrary loans. Special learning facilities include a learning resource center, art gallery, radio station, and nature center. The 210-acre campus is in a small town 50 miles northeast of Columbus. Including residence halls, there are 26 buildings on campus.

Student Life: About 81% of undergraduates are from Ohio. Students come from 31 states, 5 foreign countries, and Canada. Ninety-eight percent are white. Most are Protestant. The average age of freshmen is 18; all undergraduates, 20. Twenty-three percent drop out by the end of their first year; 50% remain to graduate.

Housing: A total of 786 students can be accommodated in college housing. College-sponsored living facilities include single-sex dormitories and on-campus apartments. On-campus housing is guaranteed for all 4 years. Sixty-eight percent of students live on campus; of those, 60% remain on campus on weekends. Alcohol is not permitted. All students may keep cars on campus.

Activities: There are no fraternities or sororities on campus. There are 27 groups on campus, including art, band, cheerleading, choir, chorale, chorus, drama, honors, international, jazz band, musical theater, newspaper, pep band, photography, professional, radio and TV, religious, social, social service, student government, and yearbook. Popular campus events include Homecoming, Blue-Green Day, Festival of Youth, concerts, banquets, and revivals.

Sports: There are 4 intercollegiate sports for men and 3 for women, and 9 intramural sports for men and 9 for women. Athletic and recreation facilities include a main gymnasium, an intramural/practice gymnasium, a weight room, 6 tennis courts, and intramural, baseball, softball, and soccer fields.

Disabled Students: Seventy-five percent of the campus is accessible to disabled students. The following facilities are available: wheelchair ramps, elevators, special parking, specially equipped rest rooms, special class scheduling, and lowered telephones.

Services: In addition to many counseling and information services, tutoring is available in most subjects. In addition, there is remedial math, reading, and writing. The College Experience Enhancement Program (CEEP) is available for underprepared students.

Campus Safety and Security: Campus safety and security measures include 24-hour foot and vehicle patrol, self defense education, and lighted pathways and sidewalks.

Programs of Study: MVNC awards the B.A., B.S., and B.B.A. degrees. Associate and master's degrees also are awarded. Bachelor's degrees are awarded in BIOLOGICAL SCIENCE (biology/biological science), BUSINESS (accounting, business administration and management, and office supervision and management), COMMUNICATIONS AND THE ARTS (communications, English, music, and Spanish), COMPUTER AND PHYSICAL SCIENCE (chemistry, computer science, and mathematics), EDUCATION (art, business, early childhood, elementary, home economics, music, physical, science, secondary, and special), SOCIAL SCIENCE (history, philosophy, psychology, religion, religious education, and sociology). Premedicine, teacher education, business, and religion are the strongest programs academically. Business, teacher education, psychology, and religion have the largest enrollments.

Required: Students must complete 124 semester hours, at least 40 to 60 hours in the major and 40 in upper-division courses, and maintain a minimum GPA of 2.0. The 40- to 47-hour B.A. general education core includes 9 to 14 hours of general requirements, 18 to 19 in the humanities, 7 to 8 in natural sciences, and 6 in social sciences. Students must also complete 1 semester of a foreign language (or 2 years of 1 language in high school), intermediate algebra (or 2 years of algebra and/or geometry in high school), and the Junior-Senior Testing Program.

Special: MVNC offers internships with local businesses/organizations, on-campus work-study programs, travel abroad during the January interim, dual majors, a general studies degree, and non-degree study. A 2-2 nursing degree in cooperation with Capital University also is available. There is a freshman honors program on campus, as well as 3 national honor societies, including Phi Beta Kappa.

Faculty/Classroom: Seventy-eight percent of faculty are male; 22%, female. All teach undergraduates and 5% both teach and do research. No introductory courses are taught by graduate students. The average class size in an introductory lecture is 35; in a laboratory, 16; and in a regular course offering, 23.

Admissions: About 95% of the 1993-94 applicants were accepted. The ACT scores for the 1993-94 freshman class were as follows: 44% below 21, 25% between 21 and 23, 20% between 24 and 26, 8% between 27 and 28, and 3% above 28. Eight freshmen graduated first in their class.

Requirements: A minimum GPA of 2.0 is required. The ACT is required, and a minimum score of 18 is recommended. Applicants should be graduates of an accredited high school and be in the upper two thirds of their class. Required preparatory courses include 3 units in English, 2 units each in mathematics (algebra I and II and geometry) and social studies, and 1 unit in science. Two units of 1 foreign language and a second science course are recommended. AP and CLEP credits are accepted. Important factors used in the admissions decision are recommendations by school officials, personality, intangible qualities, leadership record, advanced placement or honor courses, and evidence of special talent.

Procedure: Freshmen are admitted to all sessions. Applications should be filed by August 1 for fall entry, December 1 for winter entry, January 1 for spring entry, and May 1 for summer entry, along with an application fee of $20. Notification is sent on a rolling basis.

Transfer: About 74 transfer students enrolled in 1993-94. Transfer students must be in good standing academically and financially. Official transcripts from all colleges attended must be submitted. A total of 30 credits out of 124 must be completed at MVNC.

Visiting: There are regularly scheduled orientations for prospective students. Friday and Saturday overnight visits for students and their parents are possible. There are guides for informal visits and visitors may sit in on classes and stay overnight at the school. To arrange for a visit, contact the Admissions Office at (800) 782-2435.

Financial Aid: In 1993-94 97% of all current freshmen and 86% of continuing students received some form of financial aid. About 7% of freshmen and 60% of continuing students received need-based aid. The average freshman award was $6739. Of that total, scholarships or need-based grants averaged $2500 ($9256 maximum); loans averaged $2625 (maximum); and work contracts averaged $1200 ($2000 maximum). Twenty-five percent of undergraduate students work part-time. Average earnings from campus work for the school year are $1200. The average financial indebtedness of the 1992-93 graduate was $8500. MVNC is a member of CSS. The FAF and the college's own financial statement are required. The deadline for financial aid applications is May 30.

International Students: There are currently 9 international students enrolled. They must take the TOEFL and achieve a minimum score of 500.

Computers: The college provides computer facilities for student use. The mainframe is an HP 9000/800 G30. Six laboratories house HP, Macintosh, and IBM-compatible computers. All students may access the system from 10 A.M. to 5 P.M. Saturday and all day Monday through Friday. There are no time limits on using the system and no fees.

Graduates: In 1992–93 179 bachelor's degrees were awarded. The most popular majors among graduates were business (35%), social studies (21%), and education (16%). Some 7 companies recruited on campus in 1992–93.

Admissions Contact: Bruce Oldham, Director of Admissions and Enrollment Development.

MUSKINGUM COLLEGE
New Concord, OH 43762

D-3

(614) 826-8137
(800) 752-6082 (out-of-state)

Full-time: 577 men, 545 women	Faculty: 75; IIB, -$
Part-time: 29 men, 37 women	Ph.D.s: 88%
Graduate: 10 men, 32 women	Student/Faculty: 15 to 1
Year: semesters, summer session	Tuition: $12,910
Application Deadline: open	Room & Board: $3740
Freshman Class: 1109 applied, 922 accepted, 375 enrolled	
SAT I Verbal/Math: 430/500	ACT: 22 **COMPETITIVE**

Muskingum College, founded in 1837, is a private, coeducational liberal arts and sciences college affiliated with the Presbyterian Church, USA. There is one graduate school. The library contains 222,039 volumes, 164,501 microform items, and 5144 audiovisual forms, and subscribes to 647 periodicals. Computerized library sources and services include the card catalog, interlibrary loans, and database searching. Special learning facilities include a learning resource center, art gallery, radio station, and TV station. The 215-acre campus is in a small town 9 miles west of Cambridge and 50 miles east of Columbus. Including residence halls, there are 28 buildings on campus.

Student Life: About 84% of undergraduates are from Ohio. Students come from 26 states, 10 foreign countries, and Canada. Eighty-five percent are from public schools; 15% from private. Ninety-five percent are white. Forty-eight percent are Protestant; 25% claim no religious affiliation; 25% Catholic. The average age of freshmen is 18; all undergraduates, 21. Seventeen percent drop out by the end of their first year; 63% remain to graduate.

Housing: A total of 950 students can be accommodated in college housing. College-sponsored living facilities include single-sex and coed dormitories, fraternity houses, and sorority houses. In addition, there are language houses and special interest houses. On-campus housing is guaranteed for all 4 years. Eighty-five percent of students live on campus; of those, 65% remain on campus on weekends. All students may keep cars on campus.

Activities: About 50% of men belong to 2 local and 2 national fraternities; about 50% of women belong to 3 local and 1 national sororities. There are 60 groups on campus, including art, band, cheerleading, choir, chorus, computers, drama, honors, international, jazz band, literary magazine, musical theater, newspaper, orchestra, pep band, political, professional, radio and TV, religious, social, social service, student government, symphony, and yearbook. Popular campus events include Homecoming Weekend, Parents Weekend, Lil' Sibs Weekend, Greek Day, Migration Day, and Spring Fling.

Sports: There are 9 intercollegiate sports for men and 7 for women, and 5 intramural sports for men, 3 for women, and 5 for both men and women. Athletic and recreation facilities include football, baseball, and soccer fields, tennis, basketball, and racquetball courts, weightlifting/training rooms, a baseball batting cage, a swimming pool, a walking/jogging trail, and an all-weather track.

Disabled Students: Twenty-five percent of the campus is accessible to disabled students. The following facilities are available: wheelchair ramps, elevators, special parking, and lowered drinking fountains.

Services: In addition to many counseling and information services, tutoring is available in every subject. In addition, there is a reader service for the blind. The PLUS program is available for disabled students. The Center for the Advancement of Learning assists all students with study strategies.

Campus Safety and Security: Campus safety and security measures include 24-hour foot and vehicle patrol, escort service, informal discussions, and pamphlets, posters, and films. In addition, there are emergency telephones and lighted pathways and sidewalks.

Programs of Study: Muskingum awards the B.A. and B.S. degrees. Master's degrees also are awarded. Bachelor's degrees are awarded in BIOLOGICAL SCIENCE (biology/biological science and neuroscience), BUSINESS (accounting and international business management), COMMUNICATIONS AND THE ARTS (communications, dramatic arts, English, French, German, Spanish, and speech/debate/rhetoric), COMPUTER AND PHYSICAL SCIENCE (chemistry, computer science, geology, mathematics, and physics), EDUCATION (early childhood, elementary, foreign languages, music, physical, reading, science, secondary, and special), ENGINEERING AND EN-

VIRONMENTAL DESIGN (environmental science), SOCIAL SCIENCE (American studies, economics, history, international relations, philosophy, political science/government, psychology, public affairs, religion, religious education, social science, and sociology). Accounting, education, history, natural sciences, and psychology are the strongest programs academically. Education, business, speech communication, English, and history have the largest enrollments.

Required: To graduate, students must complete a minimum of 124 credit hours, at least 40 of which must be earned in upper-level courses. Students must maintain a GPA of at least 2.0. Students must also complete the 50 to 55 credit hours of Liberal Arts Essentials. A senior capstone experience is required in all areas.

Special: Internships, work-study programs, study abroad in 12 countries, and a Washington semester are possible. Students may earn a 3-2 engineering degree, a B.A.-B.S. degree, or a general studies degree, or they may pursue dual and student-designed majors. Nondegree study, pass/fail options, and credit for life, military, or work experience are also available. There are 12 national honor societies on campus.

Faculty/Classroom: Sixty-nine percent of faculty are male; 31%, female. All teach undergraduates and 90% also do research. No introductory courses are taught by graduate students. The average class size in an introductory lecture is 30; in a laboratory, 16; and in a regular course offering, 25.

Admissions: About 83% of the 1993–94 applicants were accepted. The SAT scores for the 1993–94 freshman class were as follows: Verbal—73% below 500, 22% between 500 and 599, 3% between 600 and 700, and 2% above 700; Math—45% below 500, 39% between 500 and 599, 15% between 600 and 700, and 1% above 700. The ACT scores were 45% below 21, 21% between 21 and 23, 20% between 24 and 26, 9% between 27 and 28, and 5% above 28. About 41% of the current freshmen were in the top fifth of their class; 70% were in the top two fifths. Ten freshmen graduated first in their class.

Requirements: A minimum GPA of 2.0 is required. The SAT I or ACT is required. Candidates for admission must have a high school diploma or its equivalent and should have 4 years of English, 3 years of college preparatory mathematics, and 2 years each of science, social science, and foreign language. AP and CLEP credits are accepted. Important factors used in the admissions decision are personality, intangible qualities, recommendations by school officials, advanced placement or honor courses, extracurricular activities record, and evidence of special talent.

Procedure: Freshmen are admitted in the fall and spring. Entrance exams should be taken in the junior year. Application deadlines are open. The application fee is $20. Notification is sent on a rolling basis. There are early admissions and deferred admissions plans.

Transfer: About 43 transfer students enrolled in 1993–94. Applicants must submit an official college transcript. A total of 48 credits out of 124 must be completed at Muskingum.

Visiting: There are regularly scheduled orientations for prospective students, consisting of general information and preliminary class scheduling. There are guides for informal visits and visitors may sit in on classes and stay overnight at the school. To arrange for a visit, contact the Admission Office at (800) 752–6082 or (614) 826–8137.

Financial Aid: In 1993–94 88% of all current freshmen and 86% of continuing students received some form of financial aid. About 83% of freshmen and 81% of continuing students received need-based aid. The average freshman award was $13,100. Of that total, scholarships or need-based grants averaged $9000 ($15,000 maximum); loans averaged $3300 ($3800 maximum); and work contracts averaged $800 (maximum). Fifty percent of undergraduate students work part-time. Average earnings from campus work for the school year are $800. The average financial indebtedness of the 1992–93 graduate was $12,300. Muskingum is a member of CSS. The FAFSA and either the FAF or the Muskingum Supplement are required. The deadline for financial aid applications is March 1.

International Students: There are currently 11 international students enrolled. The school actively recruits these students. They must take the TOEFL and achieve a minimum score of 550.

Computers: The college provides computer facilities for student use. The mainframe is a DEC Alpha Series. There are 3 primary computing laboratories, and residence hall rooms can access the network. All students may access the system 24 hours a day. There are no time limits on using the system and no fees.

Graduates: In 1992–93 228 bachelor's degrees were awarded. The most popular majors among graduates were business administration (20%), elementary education (14%), and speech communication (9%). Within an average freshman class, 1% graduate in 3 years, 58% in 4 years, and 4% in 5 years. Some 27 companies recruited on campus in 1992–93. In the 1992 graduating class, 10% of the men and women enrolled in graduate school within 6 months of graduation; 75% of the men and women had found employment.

Admissions Contact: Office of Admission.

NOTRE DAME COLLEGE OF OHIO
D-1
South Euclid, OH 44121   (216) 381-1680, ext. 239

Full-time: 377 women	Faculty: 33; IIB, --$
Part-time: 373 women	Ph.D.s: 61%
Graduate: 44 women	Student/Faculty: 11 to 1
Year: semesters, summer session	Tuition: $7680
Application Deadline: June 30	Room & Board: $3690
Freshman Class: 136 applied, 107 accepted, 42 enrolled	
SAT I Verbal/Math: 450/440	ACT: 19 COMPETITIVE

Notre Dame College, founded in 1922, is a private women's liberal arts and sciences college affiliated with the Roman Catholic Church. There is one undergraduate and one graduate school. In addition to regional accreditation, NDC has baccalaureate program accreditation with ADA. The library contains 88,476 volumes, 10,183 microform items, and 2502 audiovisual forms, and subscribes to 266 periodicals. Special learning facilities include a learning resource center. The 53-acre campus is in a suburban area 13 miles east of Cleveland. Including residence halls, there are 6 buildings on campus.

Student Life: About 99% of undergraduates are from Ohio. Students come from 4 states, 3 foreign countries, and Canada. Sixty-four percent are from public schools; 36% from private. Sixty-one percent are white; 27% African American. Forty-eight percent are Catholic; 17% Baptist and Muslim; 17% Protestant; 14% claim no religious affiliation. The average age of freshmen is 18. Thirty percent drop out by the end of their first year.

Housing: A total of 182 students can be accommodated in college housing. College-sponsored living facilities include dormitories. In addition, there are nonsmoking floors and quiet floors. Housing is available for weekend college students on WECO weekends. On-campus housing is guaranteed for all 4 years. Fifty-five percent of students live on campus. Alcohol is not permitted. All students may keep cars on campus.

Activities: There are no sororities on campus. There are 30 groups on campus, including choir, drama, ethnic, honors, international, literary magazine, newspaper, political, professional, religious, social, social service, and student government. Popular campus events include CAB Lecture Series, Catherine of Siena Lecture, Opening Convocation, Ring Ceremony, Academic Investiture, Family Day, Founders Weekend, All-College Luncheon, All-College Recognition Dinner, Christmas Happening, All College Formal, Cole Lecture Series, Farewell Banquet, Honors Convocation, Student Appreciation Day, and athletic home games.

Sports: There are 3 intercollegiate sports and 5 intramural sports. Athletic and recreation facilities include a 500-seat gymnasium, a pool, and a fitness center.

Disabled Students: Seventy-five percent of the campus is accessible to disabled students. The following facilities are available: wheelchair ramps, elevators, special parking, specially equipped rest rooms, lowered drinking fountains, and lowered telephones.

Services: In addition to many counseling and information services, tutoring is available in most subjects. In addition, there is remedial math, reading, and writing.

Campus Safety and Security: Campus safety and security measures include 24-hour foot and vehicle patrol, escort service, informal discussions, and pamphlets, posters, and films. In addition, there are emergency telephones and lighted pathways and sidewalks.

Programs of Study: NDC awards the B.A. and B.S. degrees. Associate and master's degrees also are awarded. Bachelor's degrees are awarded in BIOLOGICAL SCIENCE (biochemistry, biology/biological science, and nutrition), BUSINESS (accounting, business administration and management, human resources, international business management, and marketing/retailing/merchandising), COMMUNICATIONS AND THE ARTS (communications, English, fine arts, graphic design, Spanish, and studio art), COMPUTER AND PHYSICAL SCIENCE (chemistry and mathematics), EDUCATION (art, business, early childhood, elementary, foreign languages, science, and secondary), ENGINEERING AND ENVIRONMENTAL DESIGN (pre-engineering), HEALTH PROFESSIONS (medical laboratory technology, predentistry, and premedicine), SOCIAL SCIENCE (dietetics, history, political science/government, prelaw, psychology, religious education, social science, and sociology). Business, education, and science are the strongest programs academically. Business administration has the largest enrollment.

Required: To graduate, students must complete 128 semester hours with a minimum GPA of 2.0. Core requirements include English, speech, literature, fine arts, foreign language, health and physical education, mathematics, science, social or behavioral science, philosophy/theology, world civilization, and senior seminar.

Special: Students may cross-register with the Cleveland Institutes of Music and Art and with a number of Cleveland area universities and community colleges. The college offers co-op programs in most majors, internships with local businesses, a 3-2 engineering degree with Case Western Reserve, special degrees including a B.A. with a diplo-

ma in theology and interdisciplinary majors including visual arts management, credit by exam, nondegree study, and pass/fail options. NDC also offers Weekend College, a program designed for working women. There are 5 national honor societies on campus.

Faculty/Classroom: Forty-one percent of faculty are male; 59%, female. All teach undergraduates. No introductory courses are taught by graduate students. The average class size in an introductory lecture is 25; in a laboratory, 10; and in a regular course offering, 15.

Admissions: About 79% of the 1993-94 applicants were accepted. The SAT scores for the 1993-94 freshman class were as follows: Verbal—84% below 500 and 16% between 500 and 599; Math—84% below 500 and 16% between 500 and 599. The ACT scores were 58% below 21, 29% between 21 and 23, 10% between 24 and 26, and 3% above 28. About 31% of the current freshmen were in the top fifth of their class; 57% were in the top two fifths. One freshman graduated first in her class.

Requirements: A minimum GPA of 2.5 is required. The SAT I, with a minimum composite score of 850, or the ACT, with a minimum composite score of 20, is required. Applicants should be graduates of an accredited secondary school with 15 academic credits, including 4 of English, 2 each of foreign language, mathematics, and social studies, and 1 of science, plus 4 electives. The GED is accepted. An interview is recommended. AP and CLEP credits are accepted. Important factors used in the admissions decision are personality, intangible qualities, parents or siblings attending the school, leadership record, extracurricular activities record, and evidence of special talent.

Procedure: Freshmen are admitted in the fall and spring. Early decision applications should be filed by December 15; regular applications, by June 30 for fall entry and December 1 for spring entry, along with an application fee of $20. Notification of early decision is sent January 15; regular decision, on a rolling basis. There are early decision and early admissions plans.

Transfer: About 15 transfer students enrolled in 1993-94. Applicants must have a college GPA of at least 2.5. An interview is recommended. A total of 32 credits out of 128 must be completed at NDC.

Visiting: There are regularly scheduled orientations for prospective students, including placement testing, academic advising, scheduling, and an overview of student services. There are guides for informal visits and visitors may sit in on classes and stay overnight at the school. To arrange for a visit, contact the Admissions Office at (216) 381-1680, ext. 239.

Financial Aid: In 1993-94 95% of all current freshmen and 85% of continuing students received some form of financial aid. About 93% of freshmen and 85% of continuing students received need-based aid. The average freshman award was $7021. Of that total, scholarships or need-based grants averaged $3168 ($9270 maximum); loans averaged $1850 ($2625 maximum); and work contracts averaged $1088 (maximum). Twenty percent of undergraduate students work part-time. Average earnings from campus work for the school year are $1088. The average financial indebtedness of the 1992-93 graduate was $9601. NDC is a member of CSS. The college's own financial statement and FAFSA are required. The deadline for financial aid applications is April 15.

International Students: There are currently 5 international students enrolled. They must take the TOEFL or the ELS Proficiency Test 109 and achieve a minimum score on the TOEFL of 500.

Computers: The college provides computer facilities for student use. NDC has a UNISYS system and the students use individual PCs in the computer laboratory networked for classwork and homework. There are also 21 PCs located in education and writing laboratories and in dormitories and the learning center. There are no time limits on using the system and no fees.

Graduates: In 1992-93 128 bachelor's degrees were awarded. The most popular majors among graduates were business and industry (60%), education (12%), and communications (6%). Some 39 companies recruited on campus in 1992-93.

Admissions Contact: Karen Poelking, Dean of Admissions and Records.

OBERLIN COLLEGE
D-2
Oberlin, OH 44074   (216) 775-8411; (800) 622-OBIE (out-of-state)

Full-time: 1114 men, 1469 women	Faculty: 236; IIB, +$
Part-time: 48 men, 38 women	Ph.D.s: 95%
Graduate: 6 men, 10 women	Student/Faculty: 11 to 1
Year: 4-1-4	Tuition: $18,950
Application Deadline: January 15	Room & Board: $5620
Freshman Class: 3887 applied, 2472 accepted, 600 enrolled	
SAT I Verbal/Math: 610/630	ACT: 28 HIGHLY COMPETITIVE +

Oberlin College, founded in 1833, is an independent, coeducational institution offering degree programs in the liberal arts and sciences and music. There are 2 undergraduate schools. In addition to regional accreditation, Oberlin has baccalaureate program accreditation with NASM. The 4 libraries contain 1,074,526 volumes, 298,110 microform items, and 52,750 audiovisual forms, and subscribe to 2825

periodicals. Computerized library sources and services include the card catalog, interlibrary loans, and database searching. Special learning facilities include a learning resource center, art gallery, radio station, an observatory, and an art museum. The 440-acre campus is in a small town 35 miles southwest of Cleveland. Including residence halls, there are 65 buildings on campus.

Student Life: About 90% of undergraduates are from out-of-state, mostly the Middle Atlantic. Students come from 49 states, 51 foreign countries, and Canada. Sixty-six percent are from public schools; 34% from private. Seventy-three percent are white; 10% Asian American. The average age of freshmen is 18; all undergraduates, 20. Six percent drop out by the end of their first year; 84% remain to graduate.

Housing: A total of 2060 students can be accommodated in college housing. College-sponsored living facilities include single-sex and coed dormitories. In addition there are language houses, special interest houses, and co-ops. On-campus housing is guaranteed for all 4 years. Seventy-five percent of students live on campus; of those, 99% remain on campus on weekends. Upperclassmen may keep cars on campus.

Activities: There are no fraternities or sororities on campus. There are 100 groups on campus, including art, band, choir, chorale, chorus, computers, dance, drama, ethnic, film, gay, honors, international, jazz band, literary magazine, musical theater, newspaper, opera, orchestra, photography, political, professional, radio and TV, religious, social, social service, student government, symphony, and yearbook. Popular campus events include Mayfair, Octoberfest, Mardi Gras, and Campus Illumination.

Sports: Athletic and recreation facilities include a gymnasium, an enclosed and a semi-enclosed field house, a stadium, an indoor 6-lane, 200-meter track, an 8-lane outdoor track, 12 outdoor and 4 indoor tennis courts, a cross-country course, a fitness trail, 2 swimming pools, a Nautilus center, a free-weight room, 22 practice/play fields, and indoor space for football, soccer, and lacrosse practice.

Disabled Students: Sixty percent of the campus is accessible to disabled students. The following facilities are available: wheelchair ramps, elevators, special parking, specially equipped rest rooms, special class scheduling, lowered drinking fountains, lowered telephones, and an indoor/outdoor lift.

Services: In addition to many counseling and information services, tutoring is available in every subject. There is a reader service for the blind, and remedial math, reading, and writing. Computer-assisted services for hearing and visually impaired students and special tutoring and peer-counseling services for learning-disabled students are available.

Campus Safety and Security: Campus safety and security measures include 24-hour foot and vehicle patrol, self defense education, escort service, and informal discussions. In addition, there are pamphlets, posters, and films, emergency telephones, lighted pathways and sidewalks, and a full-time crime prevention officer, a 24-hour headquarters facility staffed by professional dispatchers, and an electronic card-access system in all dorms. All security officers are state-certified academy graduates.

Programs of Study: Oberlin awards the B.A. and B.Mus. degrees. Master's degrees also are awarded. Bachelor's degrees are awarded in BIOLOGICAL SCIENCE (biochemistry, biology/biological science, and neurosciences), COMMUNICATIONS AND THE ARTS (classics, comparative literature, creative writing, dance, dramatic arts, English, fine arts, French, German, music, Russian, and Spanish), COMPUTER AND PHYSICAL SCIENCE (chemistry, computer science, geology, mathematics, and physics), EDUCATION (music), ENGINEERING AND ENVIRONMENTAL DESIGN (environmental science), SOCIAL SCIENCE (African American studies, anthropology, archeology, East Asian studies, economics, history, Judaic studies, Latin American studies, law, Near Eastern studies, philosophy, political science/government, psychology, sociology, and women's studies). Sciences, art and humanities, and music are the strongest academically. English, government, history, biology, music performance, and psychology have the largest enrollments.

Required: Students are required to complete 112 to 124 total credit hours, including 9 hours each in arts/humanities, social/behavioral sciences, natural science/mathematics, and courses dealing with cultural diversity, and 3 winter term projects. In addition, they must earn writing and quantitative proficiency certification. A minimum of 24 credits is required for the major.

Special: Internships are available through the Business Initiatives Program. Students may study abroad in more than 25 countries. The college offers independent and dual majors, 3–2 engineering programs with three other institutions, nondegree study for special and visiting students, and a 5-year B.A.-B.Mus. double degree. Pass/no credit options are available to all students. There are 4 national honor societies on campus, including Phi Beta Kappa. Twenty-five departments have honors programs.

Faculty/Classroom: Seventy percent of faculty are male; 30%, female. All teach undergraduates, and all do research. The average class size in a laboratory is 25 and in a regular course offering, 21.

Admissions: About 64% of the 1993–94 applicants were accepted. The SAT scores for the 1993–94 freshman class were as follows: Verbal—10% below 500, 35% between 500 and 599, 48% between 600 and 700, and 8% above 700; Math—6% below 500, 27% between 500 and 599, 51% between 600 and 700, and 17% above 700. The ACT scores were 6% below 21, 9% between 21 and 23, 23% between 24 and 26, 18% between 27 and 28, and 47% above 28. About 79% of the current freshmen were in the top fifth of their class; 99% were in the top two fifths. There were 34 National Merit finalists. About 25 freshmen graduated first in their class.

Requirements: The SAT I or ACT is required. Candidates for admission should have completed 4 years each of English and mathematics, and 3 each of science, social studies, and 1 foreign language. AP credits are accepted. Important factors used in the admissions decision are advanced placement or honor courses, leadership record, evidence of special talent, personality, intangible qualities, and extracurricular activities record.

Procedure: Freshmen are admitted fall and spring. Entrance exams should be taken late in the junior year. Early decision I applications should be filed by November 15 and early decision II applications by January 2; regular applications, by January 15 for fall entry and November 15 for spring entry, along with an application fee of $45. There are early decision, early admissions, and deferred admissions plans. Notification of early decision I is sent December 10 and early decision II January 28; regular decision, April 1. About 162 early decision candidates were accepted for the 1993–94 class. A waiting list is an active part of the admissions procedure, with about 20% of applicants on the list.

Transfer: Fifty-three transfer students enrolled in 1993–94. Applicants should submit official transcripts of all college work completed, plus a list of current courses and midterm grades. An average of B or better should be presented. A high school transcript, recommendations, and standardized test scores are also required. A total of 56 credits out of 112 must be completed at Oberlin.

Visiting: There are regularly scheduled orientations for prospective students, including campus tours, class visits, an interview with an admissions officer, and an overnight stay in the dormitory. To arrange for a visit, contact the Admissions Office at (216) 775-8411.

Financial Aid: In 1993–94 69% of all current freshmen and 63% of continuing students received some form of financial aid. About 55% of freshmen and 52% of continuing students received need-based aid. The average freshman award was $16,474. Of that total, scholarships or need-based grants averaged $11,159 ($23,000 maximum); loans averaged $3886 ($5500 maximum); and work contracts averaged $1429 ($1500 maximum). Eighty-nine percent of undergraduate students work part-time. Average earnings from campus work for the school year are $715. The average financial indebtedness of the 1992–93 graduate was $12,798. Oberlin is a member of CSS. The FAF, the college's own financial statement, and the FAFSA are required. The deadline for financial aid applications is February 1.

International Students: There are currently 145 international students enrolled. The school actively recruits these students. They must take the TOEFL and achieve a minimum score of 600, and the SAT I.

Computers: The college provides computer facilities for student use. The mainframe is a DEC VAX 6410. There are 190 Macintosh, Zenith, and HP microcomputers and 47 terminals available for student use in the computing center, music conservatory, residence halls, and classrooms. All students may access the system. There are no time limits on using the system and no fees.

Graduates: In 1992–93 752 bachelor's degrees were awarded. The most popular majors among graduates were English (14%), biology (8%), and history (8%). Within an average freshman class, 3% graduate in 3 years, 74% in 4 years, 83% in 5 years, and 84% in 6 years. Some 47 companies recruited on campus in 1992–93.

Admissions Contact: Debra Chermonte, Director of Admissions.

OHIO DOMINICAN COLLEGE

Columbus, OH 43219

C-3

(614) 251-4505

(800) 955-6446 (out-of-state)

Full-time: 438 men, 626 women	Faculty: 53; IIB, -$
Part-time: 130 men, 400 women	Ph.D.s: 50%
Graduate: none	Student/Faculty: 20 to 1
Year: semesters, summer session	Tuition: $7730
Application Deadline: open	Room & Board: $4090
Freshman Class: 223 enrolled	
SAT I or ACT: required	LESS COMPETITIVE

Ohio Dominican College, founded in 1911, is a private, coeducational, liberal arts college affiliated with the Roman Catholic Church. The library contains 154,000 volumes, 5545 microform items, and 4921 audiovisual forms, and subscribes to 552 periodicals. Computerized

library sources and services include interlibrary loans and database searching. Special learning facilities include a learning resource center, art gallery, and radio station. The 54-acre campus is in a suburban area 5 miles from downtown Columbus. Including residence halls, there are 9 buildings on campus.

Student Life: About 83% of undergraduates are from Ohio. Students come from 9 states and 28 foreign countries. Fifty-eight percent are from public schools; 21% from private. Seventy-two percent are white; 13% African American; 11% foreign nationals. Thirty-seven percent are Catholic; 35% Protestant. The average age of freshmen is 19; all undergraduates, 27. About 46% of freshmen remain to graduate.

Housing: A total of 350 students can be accommodated in college housing. College-sponsored living facilities include single-sex and coed dormitories. On-campus housing is available on a first-come, first-served basis. Eighty percent of students commute. Alcohol is not permitted. All students may keep cars on campus.

Activities: There are no fraternities or sororities on campus. There are 22 groups on campus, including cheerleading, choir, ethnic, film, honors, literary magazine, professional, radio and TV, religious, social service, and student government. Popular campus events include Black History Week, International Student Week, and ODC Day in the Spring.

Sports: There are 3 intercollegiate sports each for men and women, and 10 intramural sports each. Athletic and recreation facilities include an athletic center, a gymnasium, a baseball and softball field, and tennis courts.

Disabled Students: Ninety percent of the campus is accessible to disabled students. The following facilities are available: wheelchair ramps, elevators, special parking, specially equipped rest rooms, and special class scheduling.

Services: In addition to many counseling and information services, tutoring is available in most subjects. There is also remedial math. The Academic Development Center offers workshops in study-related topics, provides professional and peer tutoring in a variety of subjects, and counsels students and faculty on learning and study problems.

Campus Safety and Security: Campus safety and security measures include 24-hour foot and vehicle patrol, self defense education, escort service, and informal discussions. In addition, there are pamphlets, posters, and films, emergency telephones, and lighted pathways and sidewalks.

Programs of Study: ODC awards the B.A., B.S., and B.S.Ed. degrees. Associate degrees also are awarded. Bachelor's degrees are awarded in BIOLOGICAL SCIENCE (biology/biological science), BUSINESS (accounting, business administration and management, fashion merchandising, and international business management), COMMUNICATIONS AND THE ARTS (communications, English, fine arts, public relations, and Spanish), COMPUTER AND PHYSICAL SCIENCE (chemistry, computer science, and mathematics), EDUCATION (art, elementary, library science, secondary, special, and teaching English as a second language/foreign language), HEALTH PROFESSIONS (health care administration), SOCIAL SCIENCE (criminal justice, economics, history, liberal arts/general studies, philosophy, political science/government, psychology, social science, social work, sociology, and theological studies). Business, education, communications, and criminal justice have the largest enrollments.

Required: Core curriculum requirements include 24 semester credits of humanities, with at least 8 in humanities and 8 in English, 4 each of fine arts (except for the B.S. degree), literature, mathematics, and science, 4 or 8 of language, 12 of philosophy/theology, 8 of behavioral science, and 1 of physical education. All students beyond the freshman year must maintain a GPA of 2.0. Students should complete 124 semester credits. The total number of hours for the major is set by the individual departments.

Special: Students may cross-register with members of the Higher Education Council of Columbus Consortium, study abroad in various countries, and participate in a Washington semester. Internships are required in some majors. The college offers dual and student-designed majors, a general studies degree, and pass/fail options in some courses. Credit for life, military, or work experience is available through the Acquire College Through Experiential Learning Program. Nondegree study is available through the Continuing Education Office. The Weekend College Program allows students to attend classes scheduled every other weekend. There is a freshman honors program on campus, as well as 4 national honor societies.

Faculty/Classroom: Forty-four percent of faculty are male; 56%, female. All teach undergraduates. The average class size in an introductory lecture is 19 and in a regular course offering, 19.

Requirements: A minimum GPA of 2.0 is required. The SAT I or ACT is required. Candidates for admission should have completed 4 units of English and 3 units each of a foreign language, mathematics, science, and social studies. An essay and an interview (in-state applicants) are required. AP and CLEP credits are accepted.

Procedure: Freshmen are admitted to all sessions. Application deadlines are open. Notification is sent on a rolling basis. There is a deferred admissions plan.

Transfer: About 220 transfer students enrolled in 1993–94. An interview and transcripts of all college work are required of transfer applicants. A total of 32 credits out of 124 must be completed at ODC.

Visiting: There are regularly scheduled orientations for prospective students. ODC has July and September orientations for fall entry and a January orientation for second semester. Individual appointments can be arranged. There are guides for informal visits, and visitors may sit in on classes and stay overnight at the school. To arrange for a visit, contact Kathleen Groskopf-Coons, Director of Admissions, at (614) 251–4500 or (800) 955–6446.

Financial Aid: In 1993–94, 98% of all current freshmen and 85% of continuing students received some form of financial aid. The average freshman award was $6750. Seventeen percent of undergraduate students work part-time. Average earnings from campus work for the school year was $1100. ODC is a member of CSS. The FAF is required. The deadline for financial aid applications is May 1.

International Students: There are currently 170 international students enrolled. The school actively recruits these students. They must take the University of Michigan Language Test.

Computers: The college provides computer facilities for student use. ODC has a Novell Network, with 20 computers. Also available are 12 Apple IIe and IIgs microcomputers. Both systems are located in the library and are available most of the time as an open laboratory. Software for word processing, spreadsheet, and database functions is provided, as well as languages for computer science courses. All students may access the system. There are no time limits on using the system and no fees.

Graduates: In 1992–93, 271 bachelor's degrees were awarded. The most popular majors among graduates were elementary education (19%), business administration (18%), and communication and public relations (8%).

Admissions Contact: Kathleen Groskopf-Coons, Director of Admissions.

OHIO NORTHERN UNIVERSITY B-2
Ada, OH 45810 (419) 772–2260

Full-time: 1352 men, 1150 women	Faculty: 156; IIB, +$
Part-time: 35 men, 32 women	Ph.D.s: 77%
Graduate: 274 men, 121 women	Student/Faculty: 16 to 1
Year: quarters, summer session	Tuition: $14,775
Application Deadline: open	Room & Board: $3885
Freshman Class: 2458 applied, 2138 accepted, 676 enrolled	
SAT I Verbal/Math: 441/509	ACT: 24 VERY COMPETITIVE

Ohio Northern University, founded in 1871, is a private, coeducational institution affiliated with the United Methodist Church. Undergraduate programs are offered in arts and sciences, business administration, engineering, and pharmacy. There are 4 undergraduate schools and one graduate school. In addition to regional accreditation, ONU has baccalaureate program accreditation with ABET, ACPE, and NASM. The 2 libraries contain 378,801 volumes, 268,907 microform items, and 8103 audiovisual forms, and subscribe to 4003 periodicals. Computerized library sources and services include the card catalog, interlibrary loans, and database searching. Special learning facilities include a learning resource center, art gallery, radio station, TV station, and an off-campus nature center. The 260-acre campus is in a small town 14 miles east of Lima. Including residence halls, there are 30 buildings on campus.

Student Life: About 88% of undergraduates are from Ohio. Students come from 31 states, 20 foreign countries, and Canada. Eighty-two percent are from public schools; 18% private. Ninety-five percent are white. Forty-seven percent are Protestant; 31% claim no religious affiliation; 22% Catholic. The average age of freshmen is 18; all undergraduates, 20. Twenty-six percent drop out by the end of their first year; 66% remain to graduate.

Housing: A total of 1590 students can be accommodated in college housing. College-sponsored living facilities include single-sex and coed dormitories, fraternity houses, and sorority houses. In addition there are honors houses and special interest houses. On-campus housing is guaranteed for all 4 years. Seventy percent of students live on campus; of those, 60% remain on campus on weekends. All students may keep cars on campus.

Activities: About 30% of men belong to 7 national fraternities; about 26% of women belong to 4 national sororities. There are 100 groups on campus, including art, band, cheerleading, chess, choir, chorale, chorus, computers, dance, drama, drill team, ethnic, honors, international, jazz band, literary magazine, marching band, musical theater, newspaper, pep band, political, professional, radio and TV, religious, social, social service, student government, symphony, and yearbook. Popular campus events include Homecoming, Tunes on the Tundra, TGIF Friday Night Party, International Week, Parents Weekend, and Little Sibs Weekend.

Sports: There are 11 intercollegiate sports for men and 9 for women, and 16 intramural sports for men and 10 for women. Athletic and recreation facilities include a pool, a wrestling room, weight rooms, tennis and basketball courts, a football stadium, a training room, bowling lanes, a billiards room, a dance room, a fitness laboratory, a 6-lane, 200-meter indoor track, and an 8-lane, 400-meter outdoor tack.

Disabled Students: Ninety percent of the campus is accessible to disabled students. The following facilities are available: wheelchair ramps, elevators, special parking, specially equipped rest rooms, special class scheduling, lowered drinking fountains, and lowered telephones.

Services: In addition to many counseling and information services, tutoring is available in most subjects.

Campus Safety and Security: Campus safety and security measures include 24-hour foot and vehicle patrol, self defense education, escort service, and informal discussions. In addition, there are pamphlets, posters, and films, emergency telephones, and lighted pathways and sidewalks.

Programs of Study: ONU awards the B.A., B.S., B.F.A., B.M., B.S.B.A., B.S.C.E., B.S.E.E., B.S.M.E., B.S.M.T., and B.S.Ph. degrees. Doctoral degrees also are awarded. Bachelor's degrees are awarded in BIOLOGICAL SCIENCE (biochemistry and biology/biological science), BUSINESS (accounting, banking and finance, business administration and management, business economics, management science, marketing/retailing/merchandising, and sports management), COMMUNICATIONS AND THE ARTS (broadcasting, ceramic art and design, communications, dramatic arts, English, fine arts, French, graphic design, music, music performance, painting, printmaking, public relations, sculpture, Spanish, and speech/debate/rhetoric), COMPUTER AND PHYSICAL SCIENCE (chemistry, computer science, mathematics, and physics), EDUCATION (elementary, health, music, and physical), ENGINEERING AND ENVIRONMENTAL DESIGN (civil engineering, industrial engineering technology, and mechanical engineering), HEALTH PROFESSIONS (environmental health science, medical laboratory technology, pharmacy, and sports medicine), SOCIAL SCIENCE (criminal justice, history, international studies, philosophy, political science/government, psychology, religion, and sociology). Chemistry, engineering, pharmacy, and political science are the strongest academically. Pharmacy and accounting have the largest enrollments.

Required: To graduate, students must complete 182 quarter hours, maintain a cumulative GPA of 2.0, and fulfill all departmental and core requirements.

Special: Students may take internships in pharmacy, engineering, and business, and may study abroad in Great Britain, France, Germany, or Spain. B.A.-B.S. degrees and dual majors are available in arts/engineering, arts/pharmacy, and arts/business. The university offers pass/fail options and a cooperative program in engineering. There are 6 national honor societies on campus. Fifteen departments have honors programs.

Faculty/Classroom: Seventy-five percent of faculty are male; 25%, female. Eighty-eight percent teach undergraduates. No introductory courses are taught by graduate students. The average class size in an introductory lecture is 29; in a laboratory, 14; and in a regular course offering, 21.

Admissions: About 87% of the 1993–94 applicants were accepted. The ACT scores for the 1993–94 freshman class were as follows: 24% below 21, 30% between 21 and 23, 26% between 24 and 26, 12% between 27 and 28, and 8% above 28. About 56% of the current freshmen were in the top fifth of their class; 82% were in the top two fifths. There were 2 National Merit finalists. About 40 freshmen graduated first in their class.

Requirements: ONU requires applicants to be in the upper 50% of their class. A minimum GPA of 2.5 is required. The SAT I or ACT is required. The preparatory program should include 4 years of English, 3 years of mathematics, and 2 years each of science, social studies, art, history, and music. Two years of foreign language are recommended. AP and CLEP credits are accepted. Important factors used in the admissions decision are recommendations by school officials, advanced placement or honor courses, leadership record, evidence of special talent, and recommendations by alumni.

Procedure: Freshmen are admitted to all sessions. Entrance exams should be taken in spring of the junior year or the fall of the senior year. Application deadlines are open. Notification is sent on a rolling basis. There are early decision and early admissions plans. The application fee is $30. Thirty early decision candidates were accepted for the 1993–94 class.

Transfer: About 125 transfer students enrolled in 1993–94. Applicants should have a minimum college GPA of 2.0 and submit official transcripts from all the schools they have attended. A total of 45 quarter hours out of 182 must be completed at ONU.

Visiting: There are regularly scheduled orientations for prospective students. There are guides for informal visits and visitors may sit in on classes and stay overnight at the school. To arrange for a visit, contact the Admissions Office at (419) 772-2260.

Financial Aid: In 1993–94 92% of all current freshmen and 90% of continuing students received some form of financial aid. About 81% of freshmen and 78% of continuing students received need-based aid. The average freshman award was $12,120. Of that total, scholarships or need-based grants averaged $6400 ($19,000 maximum); loans averaged $3300 ($4600 maximum); and work contracts averaged $1000 ($2000 maximum). Forty-nine percent of undergraduate students work part-time. Average earnings from campus work for the school year are $1000. The average financial indebtedness of the 1992–93 graduate was $12,500. ONU is a member of CSS. The FAF and the college's own financial statement are required. The deadline for financial aid applications is May 1.

International Students: There are currently 67 international students enrolled. The school actively recruits these students. They must take the TOEFL and achieve a minimum score of 500.

Computers: The college provides computer facilities for student use. The mainframe is a Data General MV/30000 and an AOS/VS 11 operating system. Personal computers are located in all academic buildings, with clusters for general use in Hill Building, Heterick Library, and Taggart Law Library. Smaller clusters of personal computers are located in 9 residence halls. PCs access the other computer hosts around campus via a network. Modem ports may be accessed through telephones on and off campus. All students may access the system. It may be used during building hours and 24 hours a day via modem. There are no time limits on using the system and no fees.

Graduates: In 1992–93 410 bachelor's degrees were awarded. The most popular majors among graduates were pharmacy (18%), mechanical engineering (7%), and industrial technology (6%). Within an average freshman class, 35% graduate in 4 years, 64% in 5 years, and 68% in 6 years. Some 125 companies recruited on campus in 1992–93.

Admissions Contact: Karen P. Condeni, Vice President, Admissions.

OHIO STATE UNIVERSITY

The Ohio State University, established in 1870, is a land-grant system in Ohio. It is governed by the Ohio Board of Regents, whose chief administrator is the president. The primary goal of the system is teaching, research, and public service. The main priorities are to provide a scholarly environment in which research inspires and informs teaching, as well as sharing creative and scholarly work with practitioners throughout the world. Four-year campuses are located in Columbus, Lima, Mansfield, Marion, and Newark. The total enrollment in a recent year of all 5 campuses was 58,585; there were 4461 faculty members. Altogether there are nearly 200 baccalaureate, 121 master's, and 99 doctoral programs offered in Ohio State University. Profiles of the 4-year campuses are included in this chapter in alphabetical order with other Ohio schools.

OHIO STATE UNIVERSITY

C-3

Columbus, OH 43210–1200 (614) 292-3980

Full-time: 16,418 men, 14,621 women	Faculty: 2968; I, av$
Part-time: 3234 men, 2771 women	Ph.D.s: 95%
Graduate: 6627 men, 6952 women	Student/Faculty: 10 to 1
Year: quarters, summer session	Tuition: $2940 ($8871)
Application Deadline: February 15	Room & Board: $4278

Freshman Class: 15,076 applied, 12,860 accepted, 6486 enrolled
SAT I or ACT: required LESS COMPETITIVE

Ohio State University, founded in 1870, is a public land-grant institution offering programs in agriculture, arts and sciences, business, education, engineering, nursing, pharmacy, social work, dental hygiene, and human ecology. The University College offers preprofessional training. There are 5 other campuses. There are 14 undergraduate schools and one graduate school. In addition to regional accreditation, Ohio State has baccalaureate program accreditation with AACSB, ABET, ACPE, ADA, APTA, ASLA, FIDER, NAAB, NASAD, NASM, NCATE, and NLN. The 30 libraries contain 4,693,081 volumes, 3,700,774 microform items, and 34,337 audiovisual forms, and subscribe to 33,010 periodicals. Computerized library sources and services include the card catalog, interlibrary loans, and database searching. Special learning facilities include a learning resource center, art gallery, planetarium, radio station, and TV station. The 3317-acre campus is in an urban area 4 miles north of downtown Columbus. Including residence halls, there are 339 buildings on campus.

Student Life: About 91% of undergraduates are from Ohio. Students come from 50 states, 84 foreign countries, and Canada. Seventy-nine percent are white. The average age of freshmen is 18.1; all undergraduates, 22. Nineteen percent drop out by the end of their first year; 55% remain to graduate.

Housing: A total of 9100 students can be accommodated in college housing. College-sponsored living facilities include single-sex and coed dormitories, on-campus apartments, and married-student hous-

ing. In addition, there are honors houses and special interest houses. On-campus housing is guaranteed for all 4 years. Eighty-five percent of students commute. Alcohol is not permitted. All students may keep cars on campus.

Activities: About 10% of men belong to 35 national fraternities; about 11% of women belong to 24 national sororities. There are 550 groups on campus, including art, band, cheerleading, chess, choir, chorale, chorus, computers, dance, drama, drill team, ethnic, film, gay, honors, international, jazz band, literary magazine, marching band, musical theater, newspaper, orchestra, pep band, photography, political, professional, radio and TV, religious, social, social service, student government, symphony, and yearbook. Popular campus events include Homecoming, United Black World Week, Medieval and Renaissance Festival, Greek Week, and Michigan Weekend.

Sports: There are 18 intercollegiate sports for men and 17 for women, and 70 intramural sports for men and 71 for women. Athletic and recreation facilities include a 90,000-seat stadium, a 13,000-seat gymnasium, weight rooms, a swimming pool, basketball, volleyball, and racquetball courts, field houses for tennis, volleyball, basketball, soccer, baseball, and softball fields, and a track.

Disabled Students: Ninety-nine percent of the campus is accessible to disabled students. The following facilities are available: wheelchair ramps, elevators, special parking, specially equipped rest rooms, special class scheduling, lowered drinking fountains, lowered telephones, accessible housing, and adaptive transportation.

Services: In addition to many counseling and information services, tutoring is available in most subjects. There is a reader service for the blind, and remedial math, reading, and writing.

Campus Safety and Security: Campus safety and security measures include 24-hour foot and vehicle patrol, self defense education, escort service, and informal discussions. In addition, there are pamphlets, posters, and films, emergency telephones, and lighted pathways and sidewalks.

Programs of Study: Ohio State awards the B.A., B.S., B.Mus., and B.Mus.Ed. degrees. Master's and doctoral degrees also are awarded. Bachelor's degrees are awarded in AGRICULTURE (agricultural economics, animal science, fish and game management, horticulture, and wildlife management), BIOLOGICAL SCIENCE (biochemistry, biology/biological science, entomology, microbiology, nutrition, plant pathology, and zoology), BUSINESS (accounting, banking and finance, hospitality management services, human resources, international business management, marketing and distribution, and transportation management), COMMUNICATIONS AND THE ARTS (Arabic, art, art history and appreciation, ceramic art and design, Chinese, classics, communications, dance, dramatic arts, drawing, English, fine arts, French, German, glass, Greek (modern), Hebrew, Italian, Japanese, jazz, journalism, linguistics, music, music theory and appreciation, music theory and composition, piano/organ, sculpture, Slavic languages, Spanish, and voice), COMPUTER AND PHYSICAL SCIENCE (actuarial science, astronomy, chemistry, geodetic science, geology, information sciences and systems, mathematics, physics, radiological technology, and statistics), EDUCATION (agricultural, art, business, elementary, English, environmental, health, home economics, music, physical, recreation, science, social studies, and trade and industrial), ENGINEERING AND ENVIRONMENTAL DESIGN (aeronautical engineering, agricultural engineering, architecture, ceramic engineering, chemical engineering, civil engineering, electrical/electronics engineering, engineering physics, industrial engineering, interior design, landscape architecture/design, mechanical engineering, metallurgical engineering, mining and mineral engineering, survey and mapping technology, and welding engineering), HEALTH PROFESSIONS (dental hygiene, medical technology, nursing, occupational therapy, pharmacy, physical therapy, and respiratory therapy), SOCIAL SCIENCE (anthropology, classical/ancient civilization, criminology, dietetics, economics, family/consumer resource management, food science, geography, history, international studies, Islamic studies, Judaic studies, medieval studies, parks and recreation management, philosophy, political science/government, psychology, religion, social work, sociology, textiles and clothing, and women's studies). Business and engineering have the largest enrollments.

Required: To graduate, students must complete 181 to 220 quarter hours, including 40 to 60 in the major, with a minimum GPA of 2.0. The core curriculum consists of courses in writing skills, quantitative and logical skills, foreign language, and social diversity. Distribution requirements include 4 to 5 courses in natural science, 3 in social science, and 5 in arts and humanities.

Special: Students may cross-register with all central Ohio colleges. OSU offers internships, co-op programs, extensive study abroad, work-study programs, dual and student-designed majors, a general degree, a B.A.-B.S. degree, a 3-2 engineering degree, credit by examination, nondegree study, and pass/fail options. There is a freshman honors program on campus, as well as 4 national honor societies, including Phi Beta Kappa. Twelve departments have honors

Faculty/Classroom: Seventy-two percent of faculty are male; 28%, female. The average class size in an introductory lecture is 100; in a laboratory, 30; and in a regular course offering, 20.

Admissions: About 85% of the 1993–94 applicants were accepted. The ACT scores for the 1993–94 freshman class were as follows: 30% below 21, 28% between 21 and 23, 21% between 24 and 26, 10% between 27 and 28, and 11% above 28. About 44% of the current freshmen were in the top fifth of their class; 72% were in the top two fifths. There were 101 National Merit finalists. About 149 freshmen graduated first in their class.

Requirements: The SAT I or ACT is required. Applicants must complete high school with at least 18 academic credits, including 4 in English, 3 in mathematics, 2 each in foreign language, science, and history/social studies, and 1 in art or music. The GED is accepted. AP and CLEP credits are accepted. Important factors used in the admissions decision are advanced placement or honor courses, leadership record, extracurricular activities record, evidence of special talent, and recommendations by school officials.

Procedure: Freshmen are admitted to all sessions. Entrance exams should be taken by October of the senior year. Applications should be filed by February 15 for fall entry, November 1 for winter entry, February 1 for spring entry, and February 15 for summer entry, along with an application fee of $30. Notification is sent on a rolling basis. There is an early decision plan. A waiting list is an active part of the admissions procedure, with about 3% of applicants on the list.

Transfer: About 1706 transfer students enrolled in 1993–94. High school graduates with 45 hours of college credit and a minimum GPA of 2.0 are admitted for transfer. Those with fewer than 23 hours apply on a competitive basis. A total of 45 quarter hours out of 181 to 220 must be completed at Ohio State.

Visiting: There are regularly scheduled orientations for prospective students, including campus tours, placement tests, course scheduling, and special sessions designed for parents. There are guides for informal visits, and visitors may sit in on classes.

Financial Aid: In an earlier year, 60% of all freshmen and continuing students received some form of financial aid. About 65% of freshmen and continuing students received need-based aid. Thirty percent of undergraduate students work part-time. Ohio State is a member of CSS. The FAF and the college's own financial statement are required. The deadline for financial aid applications is February 15.

International Students: There are currently 3612 international students enrolled. They must take the TOEFL or the University of Michigan Language Test and achieve a minimum score on the TOEFL of 500.

Computers: The college provides computer facilities for student use. The mainframes are an IBM 3081, an IBM 4381, an HP 9000, and a DEC VAX 20. More than 1000 microcomputers are available to students in the main computer center and in libraries, residence halls, laboratories, and student centers. All students may access the system. It may be used 24 hours a day. There are no time limits on using the system. A fee is assessed by certain colleges for use of their computing facilities.

Graduates: In 1992–93 7815 bachelor's degrees were awarded. Within an average freshman class, 1% graduate in 3 years, 19% in 4 years, 46% in 5 years, and 54% in 6 years. In the 1992 graduating class, 25% of all students were enrolled in graduate or professional school within 6 months of graduation; 38% of all graduates had found employment.

Admissions Contact: James J. Mager, Director of Admission and Financial Aid.

OHIO STATE UNIVERSITY AT LIMA
B-2

Lima, OH 45804   (419) 221-1641, ext. 264

Full-time: 380 men, 511 women	Faculty: 51; IIB, -$
Part-time: 129 men, 171 women	Ph.D.s: 90%
Graduate: 17 men, 140 women	Student/Faculty: 18 to 1
Year: quarters, summer session	Tuition: $2835 ($8766)
Application Deadline: July 1	Room & Board: n/app
Freshman Class: 537 applied, 526 accepted, 364 enrolled	
SAT I or ACT: recommended	NONCOMPETITIVE

Ohio State University at Lima, founded in 1960, is a regional, coeducational, commuter campus in the Ohio State University system. At Lima, students may earn a bachelor's degree in elementary education as well as 1 to 3 years of credit toward any degree conferred by OSU. The student may finish the degree at the Columbus campus or transfer to another institution. There are 19 undergraduate schools and one graduate school. In addition to regional accreditation, OSU Lima has baccalaureate program accreditation with NCATE. The library contains 82,054 volumes, 8703 microform items, and 2429 audiovisual forms, and subscribes to 584 periodicals. Special learning facilities include a radio station. The 565-acre campus is in a subur-

Student Life: Almost all undergraduates are from Ohio. Ninety-four percent are white. The average age of freshmen is 19.1; all undergraduates, 23.3.

Housing: All students commute. Alcohol is not permitted. All students may keep cars on campus.

Activities: There are no fraternities or sororities on campus. There are a number of groups on campus, including cheerleading, chess, chorus, computers, drama, ethnic, honors, newspaper, pep band, political, radio and TV, religious, social, social service, and student government. Popular campus events include May Week.

Sports: There are 17 intramural sports for men and 15 for women. Athletic and recreation facilities include a baseball diamond, tennis courts, a gynasium, and a weight room.

Disabled Students: The entire campus is accessible to disabled students. The following facilities are available: wheelchair ramps, elevators, special parking, specially equipped rest rooms, special class scheduling, and lowered drinking fountains.

Services: In addition to many counseling and information services, tutoring is available in most subjects. In addition, there is a reader service for the blind, and remedial math, reading, and writing. Developmental education, taped textbooks, oral testing, test readers and scribes, tape recorders, note takers, and a learning disabilities coordinator/counselor are available.

Campus Safety and Security: Campus safety and security measures include 24-hour foot and vehicle patrol, self defense education, escort service, and informal discussions. In addition, there are pamphlets, posters, and films, emergency telephones, and lighted pathways and sidewalks.

Programs of Study: OSU Lima awards the B.S.Ed. degree in elementary education. Associate degrees also are awarded.

Required: All students must complete 181 to 220 quarter hours, with a minimum GPA of 2.0 to graduate. There are general education curriculum requirements.

Special: Students may cross-register with Lima Technical College. Work-study programs, nondegree study, pass/fail options, and credit for life, military, or work experience are available. There is a freshman honors program on campus

Faculty/Classroom: The average class size in an introductory lecture is 35; in a laboratory, 25; and in a regular course offering, 20.

Admissions: About 98% of the 1993–94 applicants were accepted. The SAT scores for the 1993–94 freshman class were as follows: Verbal—75% below 500 and 25% between 500 and 599; Math—55% below 500, 35% between 500 and 599, and 10% between 600 and 700. The ACT scores were 52% below 21, 27% between 21 and 23, 14% between 24 and 26, 5% between 27 and 28, and 2% above 28. About 24% of the current freshmen were in the top fifth of their class; 50% were in the top two fifths.

Requirements: The SAT I or ACT is recommended. Candidates for admission should be high school graduates with 4 years of English, 3 years of mathematics, 2 years each of foreign language, science, and social studies, 1 year of visual or performing arts, and 2 additional years of any of the above subjects. OSU Lima follows an open admissions policy for Ohio residents.

Procedure: Freshmen are admitted to all sessions. Applications should be filed by July 1 for fall entry, December 1 for winter entry, March 1 for spring entry, and June 1 for summer entry, along with an application fee of $30. The university accepts all in-state residents who apply. Notification is sent on a rolling basis.

Transfer: A total of 131 transfer students enrolled in 1993–94. An overall GPA of 2.0 on all previous college work is required of transfer students. A total of 45 credits out of 181 to 220 must be completed at OSU Lima.

Visiting: There are regularly scheduled orientations for prospective students. There are guides for informal visits and visitors may sit in on classes. To arrange for a visit, contact the Admissions Office at (419) 221-1641, ext. 264.

Financial Aid: In 1993–94, 51% of all current freshmen and 58% of continuing students received some form of financial aid. OSU Lima is a member of CSS. The FAFSA financial statement is required. The deadline for financial aid applications is February 1.

International Students: International students must take the TOEFL and achieve a minimum score of 500.

Computers: The university provides computer facilities for student use. There are 77 microcomputers available in laboratories, the library, and the career center for student use. All students may access the system. There are no time limits on using the system and no fees.

Admissions Contact: Melissa Green, Assistant Director of Admissions.

OHIO STATE UNIVERSITY AT MANSFIELD   C-2

Mansfield, OH 44906   (419) 755-4011

Full-time: 369 men, 503 women	Faculty: 35; IIB, -$
Part-time: 154 men, 280 women	Ph.D.s: 85%
Graduate: 23 men, 83 women	Student/Faculty: 25 to 1
Year: quarters, summer session	Tuition: $2835 ($8766)
Application Deadline: July 1	Room & Board: n/app
Freshman Class: 575 applied, 554 accepted, 490 enrolled	
SAT I or ACT: recommended	NONCOMPETITIVE

Ohio State University at Mansfield, founded in 1958, is a regional commuter campus of the Ohio State University system. At Mansfield, students may earn an undergraduate degree in elementary education. There are 19 undergraduate schools and one graduate school. In addition to regional accreditation, OSU Mansfield has baccalaureate program accreditation with NCATE. The library contains 38,874 volumes, 17,559 microform items, and 2155 audiovisual forms, and subscribes to 410 periodicals. Special learning facilities include a learning resource center, art gallery, radio station, and TV station. The 600-acre campus is in a suburban area 2 miles from Mansfield. There are 7 buildings on campus.

Student Life: About 99% of undergraduates are from Ohio. Ninety-one percent are white. The average age of freshmen is 19; all undergraduates, 23.9.

Housing: All students commute. Alcohol is not permitted. All students may keep cars on campus.

Activities: There are no fraternities or sororities on campus. There are 50 groups on campus, including chorale, drama, ethnic, film, musical theater, newspaper, radio and TV, religious, social, social service, and student government. Popular campus events include May Day and Buckeye Week.

Sports: There are 12 intramural sports for men and 12 for women. Athletic and recreation facilities include a gymnasium and a weight room.

Disabled Students: The entire campus is accessible to disabled students. The following facilities are available: wheelchair ramps, elevators, special parking, specially equipped rest rooms, special class scheduling, lowered drinking fountains, and lowered telephones.

Services: In addition to many counseling and information services, tutoring is available in most subjects. In addition, there is a reader service for the blind, and remedial math, reading, and writing. Writing and mathematics laboratories are provided. Books on tape, test readers and scribes, and priority scheduling are available.

Campus Safety and Security: Campus safety and security measures include 24-hour foot and vehicle patrol, self defense education, escort service, and informal discussions. In addition, there are pamphlets, posters, and films, emergency telephones, and lighted pathways and sidewalks.

Programs of Study: OSU Mansfield awards the B.S. degree in Elem.Ed. Associate degrees also are awarded.

Required: To graduate, all students must complete 181 to 220 quarter hours, with a minimum GPA of 2.0. There are general education curriculum requirements.

Special: OSU Mansfield offers co-op programs, study abroad, internships, general studies degree (no major), nondegree study, pass/fail options, and work-study programs. Three national honor societies have chapters on campus. There is a freshman honors program on campus

Admissions: About 96% of the 1993–94 applicants were accepted. The SAT I scores for the 1993–94 freshman class were as follows: Verbal—72% below 500 and 28% between 500 and 599; Math—59% below 500, 31% between 500 and 599, 3% between 600 and 700, and 7% above 700. The ACT scores were 56% below 21, 27% between 21 and 23, 12% between 24 and 26, 3% between 27 and 28, and 2% above 28. About 20% of the current freshmen were in the top fifth of their class; 51% were in the top two fifths. Five freshmen graduated first in their class.

Requirements: The SAT I or ACT is recommended. The GED is accepted. OSU Mansfield follows an open admissions policy for in-state applicants. AP and CLEP credits are accepted.

Procedure: Freshmen are admitted to all sessions. Applications should be filed by July 1 for fall entry, December 1 for winter entry, March 1 for spring entry, and June 1 for summer entry, along with an application fee of $30. The university accepts all in-state residents who apply. Notification is sent on a rolling basis. There are early admissions and deferred admissions plans.

Transfer: About 165 transfer students enrolled in 1993–94. Transfer applicants must present a minimum 2.0 GPA on previous university course work. A total of 45 credits out of 181 to 220 must be completed at OSU Mansfield.

Visiting: There are regularly scheduled orientations for prospective students. There are guides for informal visits and visitors may sit in on classes. To arrange for a visit, contact Henry Thomas at (419) 755-4011.

Financial Aid: OSU Mansfield is a member of CSS. The FAFSA financial statement is required. The deadline for financial aid applications is April 1.

International Students: There is currently 1 international student enrolled. International students must take the TOEFL and achieve a minimum score of 500.

Computers: The university provides computer facilities for student use. The mainframe is an Amdahl V8. There are also 47 microcomputers in laboratories and the library. All students may access the system. There are no time limits on using the system and no fees.

Admissions Contact: Henry Thomas, Coordinator of Admissions.

OHIO STATE UNIVERSITY AT MARION

C-3

Marion, OH 43302   (614) 389-6786

Full-time: 381 men, 357 women	Faculty: 25; IIB, av$
Part-time: 105 men, 178 women	Ph.D.s: 90%
Graduate: 25 women	Student/Faculty: 30 to 1
Year: quarters, summer session	Tuition: $2835 ($8766)
Application Deadline: July 1	Room & Board: n/app
Freshman Class: 490 applied, 460 accepted, 293 enrolled	
SAT I or ACT: recommended	**NONCOMPETITIVE**

Ohio State University at Marion, founded in 1957, is a coeducational commuter campus of the Ohio State University system. At Marion, students may earn a bachelor's degree in elementary education as well as 1 to 3 years of credit applicable to any other degree, including 219 academic programs, conferred by OSU, provided the program is completed at the main campus in Columbus. In addition to regional accreditation, OSU Marion has baccalaureate program accreditation with NCATE. The library contains 36,764 volumes, 2906 microform items, and 7247 audiovisual forms, and subscribes to 322 periodicals. The 180-acre campus is in a rural area 60 miles north of Columbus.

Student Life: About 99% of undergraduates are from Ohio. Eighty-eight percent are white. The average age of freshmen is 20.2; all undergraduates, 24.5.

Housing: All students commute. Alcohol is not permitted. All students may keep cars on campus.

Activities: There are no fraternities or sororities on campus. There are a number of groups on campus, including chorale, newspaper, religious, social, social service, and student government. Popular campus events include Buckeye Week, May Day, and Learning Lunches.

Sports: There are 4 intercollegiate sports for men and 3 for women, and 5 intramural sports each for men and women. Athletic and recreation facilities include a 740-seat gymnasium, an outdoor fitness court, a weight room, and a game room.

Disabled Students: The entire campus is accessible to disabled students. The following facilities are available: wheelchair ramps, elevators, special parking, specially equipped rest rooms, lowered drinking fountains, and lowered telephones.

Services: In addition to many counseling and information services, tutoring is available in most subjects. In addition, there is remedial math, reading, and writing.

Campus Safety and Security: Campus safety and security measures include pamphlets, posters, and films, emergency telephones, and lighted pathways and sidewalks.

Programs of Study: OSU Marion awards the B.S.Ed. degree in elementary education. Associate degrees also are awarded.

Required: Between 181 and 220 credit hours are needed for graduation. Students must complete general education curriculum requirements and maintain a 2.0 GPA.

Special: OSU Marion offers cross-registration with Ohio State University Columbus, various co-op and work-study programs, nondegree study in continuing education, and pass/fail options. There is a freshman honors program on campus

Faculty/Classroom: The average class size in a regular course offering is 25.

Admissions: About 94% of the 1993-94 applicants were accepted. The SAT scores for the 1993-94 freshman class were as follows: Verbal—87% below 500, 10% between 500 and 599, and 3% between 600 and 700; Math—67% below 500, 23% between 500 and 599, and 10% between 600 and 700. The ACT scores were 59% below 21, 22% between 21 and 23, 14% between 24 and 26, 4% between 27 and 28, and 1% above 28. About 29% of the current freshmen were in the top fifth of their class; 49% were in the top two fifths.

Requirements: OSU Marion follows an open admissions policy for in-state students. Applicants should be high school graduates with 4 units of English, 3 of mathematics, 2 each of foreign language, history or social studies, and science, and 1 of art or music. The SAT I or the ACT is recommended. AP and CLEP credits are accepted.

Procedure: Freshmen are admitted to all sessions. Entrance exams should be taken before fall of the senior year in high school. Applications should be filed by July 1 for fall entry, December 1 for winter entry, March 1 for spring entry, and June 1 for summer entry, along with

an application fee of $30. The university accepts all in-state residents who apply. Notification is sent on a rolling basis.

Transfer: About 125 transfer students enrolled in 1993-94. A GPA of 2.0 is required. A total of 45 credits out of 181 to 220 must be completed at OSU Marion.

Visiting: There are regularly scheduled orientations for prospective students. There are guides for informal visits and visitors may sit in on classes. To arrange for a visit, contact Becky Vanderlind at (614) 389-6786.

Financial Aid: In 1993-94, 43% of all current freshmen and 42% of continuing students received some form of financial aid. The FAFSA financial statement is required. The deadline for financial aid applications is March 1.

International Students: International students must take the TOEFL and achieve a minimum score of 500.

Computers: The university provides computer facilities for student use. Some 174 microcomputers are available in a computer center and in laboratories. All students may access the system. There are no time limits on using the system and no fees.

Admissions Contact: Becky Vanderlind, Admissions Officer.

OHIO STATE UNIVERSITY AT NEWARK

C-3

Newark, OH 43055   (614) 366-9334

Full-time: 479 men, 658 women	Faculty: 49; IIB, av$
Part-time: 175 men, 275 women	Ph.D.s: 80%
Graduate: 7 men, 81 women	Student/Faculty: 23 to 1
Year: quarters, summer session	Tuition: $2835 ($8766)
Application Deadline: July 1	Room & Board: n/app
Freshman Class: 644 applied, 616 accepted, 370 enrolled	
SAT I Verbal/Math: 370/390	ACT: 18 **NONCOMPETITIVE**

Ohio State University at Newark, founded in 1957, is a regional, coeducational, commuter campus of the Ohio State University system. At Newark, students may earn a bachelor's degree in elementary education as well as 1 to 3 years of credit applicable to any other degree, including 219 academic programs, conferred by OSU, provided the program is completed at the main campus in Columbus. The library contains 46,388 volumes, 15,481 microform items, and 2909 audiovisual forms, and subscribes to 427 periodicals. Computerized library sources and services include the card catalog, interlibrary loans, and database searching. Special learning facilities include a learning resource center. The 150-acre campus is in a suburban area 40 miles east of Columbus. There are 5 buildings on campus.

Student Life: Almost all undergraduates are from Ohio. Ninety-three percent are white. The average age of freshmen is 19; all undergraduates, 24.1.

Housing: College-sponsored living facilities include coed on-campus apartments. Ninety percent of students commute. Alcohol is not permitted. All students may keep cars on campus.

Activities: There are no fraternities or sororities on campus. There are a number of groups on campus, including cheerleading, choir, chorale, chorus, drama, ethnic, honors, professional, religious, social service, and student government. Popular campus events include Ten Evenings on Campus and Christmas Chorale.

Sports: There are 5 intercollegiate sports for men and 3 for women, and 7 intramural sports for men, 6 for women, and 5 for both. Athletic and recreation facilities include a weight room, a gymnasium, and a vita course.

Disabled Students: The entire campus is accessible to disabled students. The following facilities are available: wheelchair ramps, elevators, special parking, specially equipped rest rooms, special class scheduling, lowered drinking fountains, and lowered telephones.

Services: In addition to many counseling and information services, tutoring is available in every subject. In addition, there is a reader service for the blind and remedial math and writing as well as books on tape, extended test time, readers, scribes, word processing assistance, and loans of specialized equipment.

Campus Safety and Security: Campus safety and security measures include 24-hour foot and vehicle patrol, self defense education, escort service, and informal discussions. In addition, there are pamphlets, posters, films, and emergency telephones.

Programs of Study: OSU Newark awards the B.S.Ed. degree in elementary education. Associate degrees also are awarded.

Required: Between 181 and 220 credit hours are necessary for graduation. General education requirements include courses in English, mathematics, natural sciences, social sciences, and humanities.

Special: Students may participate in co-op programs, cross-registration, and study abroad through the Columbus campus. Work-study programs, nondegree study, and pass/fail options are available. There is a freshman honors program on campus

Faculty/Classroom: The average class size in a regular course offering is 24.

Admissions: About 96% of the 1993-94 applicants were accepted. The SAT scores for the 1993-94 freshman class were as follows: Verbal—72% below 500, 25% between 500 and 599, and 3% between

600 and 700; Math—63% below 500, 27% between 500 and 599, 9% between 600 and 700, and 1% above 700. The ACT scores were 54% below 21, 24% between 21 and 23, 17% between 24 and 26, 3% between 27 and 28, and 2% above 28. About 15% of the current freshmen were in the top fifth of their class; 36% were in the top two fifths.

Requirements: The SAT I or ACT is recommended for placement and may be taken during freshman orientation. Candidates for admission should be high school graduates with 4 units of English, 3 units of mathematics, 2 units each of science, foreign language, and history or social studies, and 1 unit of visual or performing arts. OSU Newark follows an open admissions policy for Ohio applicants. AP and CLEP credits are accepted.

Procedure: Freshmen are admitted to all sessions. Applications should be filed by July 1 for fall entry, December 1 for winter entry, March 1 for spring entry, and June 1 for summer entry, along with an application fee of $30. The university accepts all in-state residents who apply. Notification is sent on a rolling basis.

Transfer: A total of 113 transfer students enrolled in 1993–94. A GPA of 2.0 is required. A total of 45 credits out of 181 to 220 must be completed at OSU Newark.

Visiting: There are regularly scheduled orientations for prospective students. There are guides for informal visits and visitors may sit in on classes and stay overnight at the school. To arrange for a visit, contact Admissions at (614) 366-9333.

Financial Aid: In 1993–94, 40% of all current freshmen and 60% of continuing students received some form of financial aid. OSU Newark is a member of CSS. The FAFSA financial statement is required. The deadline for financial aid applications is April 1.

International Students: There is currently 1 international student enrolled. International students must take the TOEFL and achieve a minimum score of 500.

Computers: The university provides computer facilities for student use. Some 36 microcomputers are available for academic use in computer laboratories. All students may access the system. There are no time limits and no fees.

Admissions Contact: Ann Donahue, Coordinator of Admissions.

OHIO UNIVERSITY

Athens, OH 45701

D-4

(614) 593-4100

Full-time: 6731 men, 7886 women	Faculty: 754; I, -$
Part-time: 273 men, 433 women	Ph.D.s: 91%
Graduate: 1654 men, 1271 women	Student/Faculty: 19 to 1
Year: quarters, summer session	Tuition: $3384 ($7266)
Application Deadline: March 1	Room & Board: $3957
Freshman Class: 11,457 applied, 8374 accepted, 3271 enrolled	
SAT I: 470/520	ACT: 23	COMPETITIVE

Ohio University, founded in 1804, is a public, coeducational university offering programs in liberal and fine arts, aviation, business, communication, engineering, health science, professional training, and teacher preparation. There are 9 undergraduate and 8 graduate schools. In addition to regional accreditation, OU has baccalaureate program accreditation with AACSB, ABET, ACEJMC, ADA, AHEA, APTA, CSWE, FIDER, NASAD, NASM, NCATE, and NLN. The 5 libraries contain 1,600,000 volumes, 2,000,000 microform items, and 355,000 audiovisual forms, and subscribe to 11,083 periodicals. Computerized library sources and services include the card catalog, interlibrary loans, and database searching. Special learning facilities include a learning resource center, art gallery, radio station, TV station, a daily newspaper, and a quarterly magazine. The 1300-acre campus is in a small town 75 miles southeast of Columbus. Including residence halls, there are 212 buildings on campus.

Student Life: About 85% of undergraduates are from Ohio. Students come from 50 states, 100 foreign countries, and Canada. Eighty-seven percent are from public schools; 13% from private. Ninety-one percent are white. Fifty-six percent are Protestant; 38% Catholic. The average age of freshmen is 18; all undergraduates, 21. Thirteen percent drop out by the end of their first year; 70% remain to graduate.

Housing: A total of 7000 students can be accommodated in college housing. College-sponsored living facilities include single-sex and coed dormitories, on-campus apartments, married-student housing, fraternity houses, and sorority houses. In addition there are honors houses, language houses, special interest houses, international houses, quiet halls, and engineering, business, and communication halls. On-campus housing is guaranteed for all 4 years. Alcohol is not permitted. Upperclassmen may keep cars on campus.

Activities: About 13% of men belong to 20 national fraternities; about 20% of women belong to 13 national sororities. There are 338 groups on campus, including art, band, cheerleading, chess, choir, chorale, chorus, computers, dance, drama, ethnic, film, gay, honors, international, jazz band, literary magazine, marching band, musical theater, newspaper, opera, orchestra, pep band, photography, political, professional, radio and TV, religious, social, social service, student government, symphony, and yearbook. Popular campus events include Homecoming, Parents Weekend, Siblings Weekend, Springfest, Athens Criterium International Bike Race, International Street Fair, and Communication Week.

Sports: There are 9 intercollegiate sports for men and 8 for women, and 25 intramural sports for men and 25 for women. Athletic and recreation facilities include a football stadium, basketball and convocation center, an aquatic center, an ice rink, tennis courts, a golf course, an intramural gymnasium, a running track, and a fitness and aerobics center.

Disabled Students: Sixty-five percent of the campus is accessible to disabled students. The following facilities are available: wheelchair ramps, elevators, special parking, specially equipped rest rooms, special class scheduling, lowered drinking fountains, and lowered telephones.

Services: In addition to many counseling and information services, tutoring is available in most subjects. There is a reader service for the blind, and remedial math, reading, and writing.

Campus Safety and Security: Campus safety and security measures include 24-hour foot and vehicle patrol, self defense education, escort service, pamphlets, posters, and films. In addition, there are emergency telephones and lighted pathways and sidewalks.

Programs of Study: OU awards the B.A., B.S., B.B.A., B.C.J., B.F.A., B.G.S., B.S.C., B.S.C.E., B.S.Ch.E., B.S.Ed., B.S.E.E., B.S.E.H., B.S.H., B.S.H.C.S., B.S.H.S.S., B.S.I.H., B.S.I.S.E., B.S.I.T., B.Mus., B.S.J., B.S.M.E., B.S.N., B.S.P.E., B.S.P.T., B.S.R.S., B.S.S.P.S., and B.S.V.C. degrees. Associate, master's, and doctoral degrees also are awarded. Bachelor's degrees are awarded in BIOLOGICAL SCIENCE (botany, microbiology, and zoology), BUSINESS (accounting, banking and finance, business administration and management, business economics, business law, international business management, marketing/retailing/merchandising, and personnel management), COMMUNICATIONS AND THE ARTS (advertising, broadcasting, communications, dance, design, dramatic arts, English, film arts, fine arts, journalism, languages, music, photography, speech/debate/rhetoric, and telecommunications), COMPUTER AND PHYSICAL SCIENCE (chemistry, computer science, geology, mathematics, and physics), EDUCATION (art, business, early childhood, elementary, foreign languages, health, home economics, industrial arts, middle school, music, science, secondary, and teaching English as a second language/foreign language), ENGINEERING AND ENVIRONMENTAL DESIGN (chemical engineering, civil engineering, computer engineering, electrical/electronics engineering, engineering technology, industrial engineering, and mechanical engineering), HEALTH PROFESSIONS (medical laboratory technology, nursing, physical therapy, predentistry, premedicine, and speech pathology/audiology), SOCIAL SCIENCE (anthropology, community services, criminal justice, dietetics, economics, food science, geography, history, international relations, parks and recreation management, philosophy, political science/government, prelaw, psychology, public administration, social science, social work, and sociology). Journalism, accounting, telecommunications, and engineering are the strongest academically. Biological sciences, journalism, and elementary education have the largest enrollments.

Required: To graduate, students must complete 192 quarter hours, including 45 to 55 in the major, with a minimum GPA of 2.0 in most departments. General education requirements include 2 courses in English composition plus 30 quarter hours in social sciences, natural sciences, humanities, and third-world cultures, and a minimum of 1 course in mathematics or quantitative skills.

Special: The university offers co-op programs in engineering and computer science, internships, study abroad, work-study programs, and an accelerated degree program for students in the Honors Tutorial College. Students may earn a B.A.-B.S. degree in most arts and sciences majors, or a general studies degree. Dual and student-designed majors, nondegree study, limited pass/fail options, and credit for life, military, or work experience are also available. There is a freshman honors program on campus, as well as 50 national honor societies, including Phi Beta Kappa.

Faculty/Classroom: Seventy-three percent of faculty are male; 27%, female. All teach undergraduates, and do research. Graduate students teach 15% of introductory courses. The average class size in an introductory lecture is 34; in a laboratory, 20; and in a regular course offering, 22.

Admissions: About 73% of the 1993–94 applicants were accepted. The SAT scores for the 1993–94 freshman class were as follows: Verbal—62% below 500, 30% between 500 and 599, 7% between 600 and 700, and 1% above 700; Math—40% below 500, 41% between 500 and 599, 17% between 600 and 700, and 2% above 700. The ACT scores were 17% below 21, 36% between 21 and 23, 29% between 24 and 26, 10% between 27 and 28, and 8% above 28. About 45% of the current freshmen were in the top fifth of their class; 83% were in the top two fifths. There were 8 National Merit finalists. About 68 freshmen graduated first in their class.

Requirements: OU requires applicants to be in the upper 50% of their class. A minimum GPA of 2.0 is recommended. The SAT I or ACT is required. Applicants should graduate with 4 units of English, 3 units each of mathematics, science, and social studies, 2 units of foreign language, and 1 unit each of history and visual or performing arts. AP and CLEP credits are accepted. Important factors used in the admissions decision are advanced placement or honor courses, recommendations by school officials, evidence of special talent, parents or siblings attending the school, and leadership record.

Procedure: Freshmen are admitted to all sessions. Entrance exams should be taken in the spring of the junior year or the fall of the senior year. Applications should be filed by March 1 for fall entry, December 1 for winter entry, February 1 for spring entry, and May 1 for summer entry, along with an application fee of $25. Notification is sent on a rolling basis.

Transfer: About 472 transfer students enrolled in a recent year. All transfer students are evaluated individually but must have a cumulative GPA of at least 2.5 and 30 quarter hours of transferrable college credit. Business and journalism majors usually require a GPA of 3.0 or higher. A total of 48 quarter hours out of 192 must be completed at OU.

Visiting: There are regularly scheduled orientations for prospective students, including information sessions and campus tours conducted daily Monday to Saturday. There are guides for informal visits and visitors may sit in on classes. To arrange for a visit, contact the Admissions Office at (614) 593-4100.

Financial Aid: In a recent year, 74% of all current freshmen and 56% of continuing students received some form of financial aid. About 74% of freshmen and 56% of continuing students received need-based aid. The average freshman award was $3837. Of that total, scholarships or need-based grants averaged $2200 ($6000 maximum); and loans averaged $2976 ($7825 maximum). Fifty percent of undergraduate students work part-time. Average earnings from campus work for the school year are $700. OU is a member of CSS. The FAFSA financial statement is required. The deadline for financial aid applications is April 1.

International Students: There are currently 1295 international students enrolled. They must take the TOEFL or the University of Michigan Language Test.

Computers: The college provides computer facilities for student use. The mainframes are 2 IBM 4381s, an IBM ES9000, and a VAX6000 Model 440. More than 1200 terminals linked to the mainframe and 800 microcomputers are available to students in various campus locations. All students may access the system. There are no time limits on using the system and no fees.

Graduates: In 1992–93 3474 bachelor's degrees were awarded. The most popular majors among graduates were journalism (6%), health and sport sciences (6%), and interpersonal communication (5%). Within an average freshman class, 53% graduate in 4 years, 66% in 5 years, and 70% in 6 years. Some 450 companies recruited on campus in 1992–93. In the 1992 graduating class, 29% of the men and 25% of the women were enrolled in graduate school within 6 months of graduation; 79% of the men and 74% of the women had found employment.

Admissions Contact: N. Kip Howard, Director of Admissions.

OHIO WESLEYAN UNIVERSITY

C-3

Delaware, OH 43015   (614) 368-3020; (800) 922-8953 (out-of-state)

Full-time: 871 men, 909 women	Faculty: 133; IIB, +$
Part-time: 15 men, 33 women	Ph.D.s: 95%
Graduate: none	Student/Faculty: 14 to 1
Year: semesters	Tuition: $15,726
Application Deadline: March 1	Room & Board: $5382
Freshman Class: 2190 applied, 1700 accepted, 458 enrolled	
SAT I: 523/580	ACT: 26 VERY COMPETITIVE +

Ohio Wesleyan University, founded in 1842, is an independent, coeducational liberal arts institution affiliated with the United Methodist Church. In addition to regional accreditation, Ohio Wesleyan has baccalaureate program accreditation with NASM. The 5 libraries contain 460,000 volumes, 3000 microform items, and 4200 audiovisual forms, and subscribe to 1190 periodicals. Special learning facilities include an art gallery, radio station, and TV station. The 200-acre campus is in a small town 20 miles north of Columbus. Including residence halls, there are 55 buildings on campus.

Student Life: About 57% of undergraduates are from out-of-state, mostly the Midwest. Students come from 44 states and 50 foreign countries. Seventy-two percent are from public schools; 28% from private. Eighty-four percent are white. Fifty percent are Protestant; 26% Catholic; 10% claim no religious affiliation. The average age of freshmen is 18; all undergraduates, 20. Sixteen percent drop out by the end of their first year; 74% remain to graduate.

Housing: A total of 1720 students can be accommodated in college housing. College-sponsored living facilities include single-sex and coed dormitories, fraternity houses, and sorority houses. In addition, there are honors houses, language houses, and special interest houses. Students are invited to submit theme proposals to run a residential house for 8 to 20 students. On-campus housing is guaranteed for all 4 years. Ninety-five percent of students live on campus; of those, 93% remain on campus on weekends. Alcohol is not permitted. Upperclassmen may keep cars on campus.

Activities: About 50% of men belong to 11 national fraternities; about 40% of women belong to 8 national sororities. There are 100 groups on campus, including art, cheerleading, choir, chorale, chorus, computers, dance, drama, ethnic, honors, international, jazz band, literary magazine, musical theater, newspaper, pep band, photography, political, professional, radio and TV, religious, social, social service, student government, symphony, and yearbook. Popular campus events include National Colloquium Day, Fallfest, and Monett Weekend.

Sports: There are 11 intercollegiate sports for men and 11 for women, and 17 intramural sports for men and 17 for women. Athletic and recreation facilities include a gymnasium, a football and lacrosse stadium, field hockey and soccer fields, practice fields, a weight room, indoor and outdoor tracks, handball and squash courts, and an indoor pool.

Disabled Students: Sixty percent of the campus is accessible to disabled students. The following facilities are available: wheelchair ramps, special parking, specially equipped rest rooms, and special class scheduling.

Services: In addition to many counseling and information services, tutoring is available in most subjects. Students with learning disabilities may receive special help in writing and organization.

Campus Safety and Security: Campus safety and security measures include 24-hour foot and vehicle patrol, self defense education, escort service, and informal discussions. In addition, there are pamphlets, posters, and films and lighted pathways and sidewalks.

Programs of Study: Ohio Wesleyan awards the B.A., B.F.A., and B.M. degrees. Bachelor's degrees are awarded in BIOLOGICAL SCIENCE (biochemistry, biology/biological science, botany, genetics, microbiology, and zoology), BUSINESS (accounting, business administration and management, business economics, and international business management), COMMUNICATIONS AND THE ARTS (broadcasting, dramatic arts, English, fine arts, French, German, Italian, journalism, music, photography, and Spanish), COMPUTER AND PHYSICAL SCIENCE (chemistry, computer science, earth science, geology, mathematics, and physics), EDUCATION (art, early childhood, elementary, foreign languages, middle school, music, physical, science, and secondary), ENGINEERING AND ENVIRONMENTAL DESIGN (environmental science), HEALTH PROFESSIONS (physical therapy, predentistry, premedicine, and preveterinary science), SOCIAL SCIENCE (African American studies, anthropology, economics, geography, history, international relations, philosophy, political science/government, prelaw, psychology, religion, social science, sociology, and women's studies). Psychology, political science and prelaw, biological sciences, English, and international studies are the strongest academically. Economics and business, biological sciences, political science and government, and international studies have the largest enrollments.

Required: Most students are required to complete at least 34 units, including 3 units each of humanities/English, social sciences, and science/mathematics and 1 unit of fine or performing arts. Each unit equals a full course and 3.25 semester hours. All students must also take 8 to 12 units in the major, maintain a minimum GPA of 2.0, and satisfy the university writing skills requirements.

Special: Cross-registration is available with members of the Great Lakes College Association. Students may study abroad in 20 countries or participate in a Washington semester, a departmental internship, or a work-study program. Students may also take dual majors in any combination, design their own majors, or pursue a 3–2 engineering degree in conjunction with 5 major universities. Nondegree study and pass/fail options are available. There is a freshman honors program on campus, as well as 23 national honor societies, including Phi Beta Kappa.

Faculty/Classroom: Sixty-two percent of faculty are male; 38%, female. All teach undergraduates, 90% do research, and 90% do both. The average class size in an introductory lecture is 22; in a laboratory, 15; and in a regular course offering, 12.

Admissions: About 78% of the 1993–94 applicants were accepted. The SAT scores for the 1993–94 freshman class were as follows: Verbal—39% below 500, 38% between 500 and 599, 22% between 600 and 700, and 1% above 700; Math—13% below 500, 43% between 500 and 599, 32% between 600 and 700, and 12% above 700. The ACT scores were 16% below 21, 18% between 21 and 23, 24% between 24 and 26, 16% between 27 and 28, and 26% above 28. About 54% of the current freshmen were in the top fifth of their class; 78% were in the top two fifths. There were 2 National Merit finalists and 3 semifinalists. About 20 freshmen graduated first in their class.

Requirements: The SAT I or ACT is recommended. Candidates for admission should have completed 4 units of English, 3 of mathematics, 2 each of foreign language, history, and science, and 3 more units in any of the aforementioned areas. AP credits are accepted. Important factors used in the admissions decision are advanced placement or honor courses, extracurricular activities record, recommendations by school officials, leadership record, and evidence of special talent.

Procedure: Freshmen are admitted fall and spring. Entrance exams should be taken in the spring of the junior year and the fall of the senior year. Early decision applications should be filed by December 31; regular applications, by March 1 for fall entry and November 1 for spring entry, along with an application fee of $30. Notification is sent in February. There are early decision and deferred admissions plans. About 201 early decision candidates were accepted for the 1993–94 class. A waiting list is an active part of the admissions procedure, with about 7% of applicants on the list.

Transfer: Applicants should have better than a 2.5 college GPA. Two years of courses must be completed at Ohio Wesleyan.

Visiting: There are regularly scheduled orientations for prospective students. There are guides for informal visits, and visitors may sit in on classes and stay overnight at the school. To arrange for a visit, contact the Office of Admissions at (614) 368–3020.

Financial Aid: In 1993–94, 68% of all current freshmen and continuing students received some form of financial aid. About 58% of freshmen and continuing students received need-based aid. The average freshman award was $13,500. Of that total, scholarships or need-based grants averaged $9600 ($16,600 maximum); loans averaged $2800 ($3800 maximum); and work contracts averaged $1100 ($1350 maximum). Fifty-three percent of undergraduate students work part-time. Average earnings from campus work for the school year are $1000. The average financial indebtedness of the 1992–93 graduate was $10,000. Ohio Wesleyan is a member of CSS. The FAF is required. The deadline for financial aid applications is March 15.

International Students: There are currently 148 international students enrolled. The school actively recruits these students. They must take the TOEFL and achieve a minimum score of 550. The student must also take the SAT I.

Computers: The college provides computer facilities for student use. The mainframes are a DEC VAX 11/750 and an IBM 4341 Model 2. More than 120 microcomputers are available for student use in 5 computer laboratories and in academic departments. Students with their own PCs may network the campus computer via modem. All students may access the system. It may be used 24 hours a day. There are no time limits on using the system and no fees.

Graduates: In 1992–93 420 bachelor's degrees were awarded. The most popular majors among graduates were biological (16%), economics and business (15%), and politics, government, and prelaw (14%). Within an average freshman class, 72% graduate in 4 years and 73% in 5 years. Some 20 companies recruited on campus in 1992–93. In the 1992 graduating class, 30% of all students were enrolled in graduate school within 6 months of graduation; 65% of all graduates had found employment.

Admissions Contact: Don Bishop, Dean of Enrollment and Admission.

OTTERBEIN COLLEGE
Westerville, OH 43081   C-3

Full-time: 649 men, 1041 women	Faculty: 130; IIB, -$
Part-time: 208 men, 567 women	Ph.D.s: 64%
Graduate: 16 men, 103 women	Student/Faculty: 13 to 1
Year: quarters, summer session	Tuition: $12,192
Application Deadline: April 20	Room & Board: $4314
Freshman Class: 1535 applied, 1417 accepted, 416 enrolled	
SAT I Verbal/Math: 430/430	ACT: 23 COMPETITIVE

(614) 823–1500; (800) 488–8144

Otterbein College, founded in 1847, is an independent, coeducational institution affiliated with the United Methodist Church. Degree programs are offered in the liberal and fine arts, business, health sciences, military science, religion, and teacher preparation. There is one undergraduate and one graduate school. In addition to regional accreditation, the college has baccalaureate program accreditation with NASM, NCATE, and NLN. The library contains 150,000 volumes, 65,000 microform items, and 7230 audiovisual forms, and subscribes to 927 periodicals. Computerized library sources and services include the card catalog, interlibrary loans, and database searching. Special learning facilities include a learning resource center, art gallery, radio station, and TV station. The 70-acre campus is in a suburban area 12 miles northeast of Columbus. Including residence halls, there are 25 buildings on campus.

Student Life: About 88% of undergraduates are from Ohio. Students come from 32 states, 24 foreign countries, and Canada. Ninety-two percent are white. Seventy-six percent are Protestant; 20% Catholic. The average age of freshmen is 18; all undergraduates, 22. Sev-

en percent drop out by the end of their first year; 74% remain to graduate.

Housing: A total of 758 students can be accommodated in college housing. College-sponsored living facilities include single-sex and coed dormitories, fraternity houses, and sorority houses. In addition, there are honors houses and special interest houses. On-campus housing is guaranteed for the freshman year only and is available on a first-come, first-served basis. Fifty-five percent of students live on campus; of those, 50% remain on campus on weekends. Alcohol is not permitted. All students may keep cars on campus.

Activities: About 50% of men belong to 6 local fraternities and 1 national fraternity; about 50% of women belong to 5 local sororities and 1 national sorority. There are 95 groups on campus, including art, bagpipe band, band, cheerleading, choir, chorale, chorus, dance, drama, drill team, ethnic, gay, honors, international, jazz band, literary magazine, marching band, musical theater, newspaper, opera, orchestra, pep band, photography, political, professional, radio and TV, religious, social, social service, student government, symphony, and yearbook. Popular campus events include Homecoming Weekend, Renaissance Festival, Winterfest, Greek Week, and Spring Unity Week.

Sports: There are 8 intercollegiate sports for men and 7 for women, and 15 intramural sports for men and 15 for women. Athletic and recreation facilities include a basketball and volleyball center, a football stadium, a soccer field, a weight room, and tennis courts.

Disabled Students: Eighty-one percent of the campus is accessible to disabled students. The following facilities are available: wheelchair ramps, elevators, special parking, specially equipped rest rooms, special class scheduling, lowered drinking fountains, and lowered telephones.

Services: In addition to many counseling and information services, tutoring is available in every subject. There is a reader service for the blind, and remedial math, reading, and writing.

Campus Safety and Security: Campus safety and security measures include 24-hour foot and vehicle patrol, self defense education, escort service, and informal discussions. In addition, there are pamphlets, posters, films, emergency telephones, and lighted pathways and sidewalks.

Programs of Study: The college awards the B.A., B.S., B.F.A., B.Mus.Ed., B.S. in Ed., and B.S.N. degrees. Master's degrees also are awarded. Bachelor's degrees are awarded in AGRICULTURE (equestrian science), BIOLOGICAL SCIENCE (biology/biological science), BUSINESS (accounting, banking and finance, business administration and management, international business management, and marketing/retailing/merchandising), COMMUNICATIONS AND THE ARTS (broadcasting, communications, dance, dramatic arts, English, fine arts, French, journalism, music, public relations, Spanish, and speech/debate/rhetoric), COMPUTER AND PHYSICAL SCIENCE (chemistry, computer science, mathematics, and physics), EDUCATION (art, early childhood, elementary, foreign languages, middle school, music, science, and secondary), HEALTH PROFESSIONS (nursing, predentistry, premedicine, and sports medicine), SOCIAL SCIENCE (economics, history, international relations, philosophy, political science/government, prelaw, psychology, religion, social science, and sociology). Sports medicine, life sciences, and chemistry are the strongest academically. Business and psychology have the largest enrollments.

Required: All students must complete 180 quarter hours, including 65 in the major, with a minimum GPA of 2.0. General education requirements include 15 hours in English composition and literature, 10 hours each in natural science, social science, and religion/philosophy, 5 hours in the arts, and 3 hours in physical education.

Special: Students may cross-register with members of the Higher Education Council of Columbus, study abroad in France or Spain, have an internship in any major, or participate in a Washington semester. A B.A.-B.S. degree, a 3–2 engineering degree, credit for military experience, student-designed majors, nondegree study, and limited pass/fail options are also available. There is a freshman honors program on campus, as well as 9 national honor societies.

Faculty/Classroom: Fifty-six percent of faculty are male; 44%, female. All teach undergraduates. No introductory courses are taught by graduate students. The average class size in an introductory lecture is 16; in a laboratory, 10; and in a regular course offering, 16.

Admissions: About 92% of the 1993–94 applicants were accepted. The SAT scores for the 1993–94 freshman class were as follows: Verbal—69% below 500, 23% between 500 and 599, 7% between 600 and 700, and 1% above 700; Math—44% below 500, 38% between 500 and 599, 14% between 600 and 700, and 4% above 700. About 80% of the current freshmen were in the top two fifths of their class.

Requirements: The college requires applicants to be in the upper 50% of their class. A minimum GPA of 2.5 is required. The SAT I or ACT is required. Applicants should be graduates of an accredited secondary school. The recommended preparatory program includes 4 units of English, 3 to 4 units each of mathematics, science, and social studies, 2 to 3 units of foreign language, and 1 to 2 units of per-

forming arts. A high school GPA of 2.5 or better is recommended. AP and CLEP credits are accepted. Important factors used in the admissions decision are advanced placement or honor courses, evidence of special talent, personality, intangible qualities, leadership record, and extracurricular activities record.

Procedure: Freshmen are admitted to all sessions. Entrance exams should be taken in the spring of the junior year. Applications should be filed by April 20 for fall entry, along with an application fee of $15. Notification is sent on a rolling basis. There is a deferred admissions plan.

Transfer: About 83 transfer students enrolled in 1993–94. Applicants should present a college GPA of 2.5. A total of 60 credits out of 180 must be completed at the college.

Visiting: There are regularly scheduled orientations for prospective students. There are guides for informal visits, and visitors may sit in on classes and stay overnight at the school. To arrange for a visit, contact Debbie Jamieson at (614) 823–1500 or (800) 488–8144.

Financial Aid: In 1993–94, 95% of all current freshmen and 93% of continuing students received some form of financial aid. About 75% of freshmen and 70% of continuing students received need-based aid. The average freshman award was $7500. Of that total, scholarships or need-based grants averaged $2600 ($6000 maximum); loans averaged $2600 ($3825 maximum); and work contracts averaged $1000 ($1500 maximum). Sixty percent of undergraduate students work part-time. Average earnings from campus work for the school year are $775. The average financial indebtedness of the 1992–93 graduate was $8300. The college is a member of CSS. The FAF is required. The deadline for financial aid applications is April 1.

International Students: There are currently 30 international students enrolled. The school actively recruits these students. They must take the TOEFL and achieve a minimum score of 500.

Computers: The college provides computer facilities for student use. The mainframe is a DEC VAX/VMS. Terminals and microcomputers are available in several campus locations. All students may access the system. There are no time limits on using the system and no fees.

Graduates: In 1992–93, 423 bachelor's degrees were awarded. The most popular majors among graduates were business administration (24%), elementary education (12%), and psychology (7%). Within an average freshman class, 4% graduate in 3 years, 69% in 4 years, and 77% in 5 years. Some 23 companies recruited on campus in 1992–93. In a recent graduating class, 7% of all students were enrolled in graduate school within 6 months of graduation; 33% of the men and 50% of the women had found employment.

Admissions Contact: Cass Johnson, Director of Admissions.

SHAWNEE STATE UNIVERSITY
C-5
Portsmouth, OH 45662   **(614) 355–3205**
        (800) 959–2778 (out-of-state)

Full-time: 960 men, 1576 women	Faculty: 106; IIB, +$
Part-time: 285 men, 491 women	Ph.D.s: n/av
Graduate: none	Student/Faculty: 24 to 1
Year: quarters, summer session	Tuition: $2529 ($4257)
Application Deadline: open	Room: $1850

Freshman Class: 803 applied, 803 accepted, 531 enrolled
SAT I or ACT: required   **NONCOMPETITIVE**

Shawnee State University, founded in 1975, is a public institution offering programs in arts and sciences, business, engineering, health sciences, and education. There are 4 undergraduate schools. The library contains 110,000 volumes, 7124 microform items, and 950 audiovisual forms, and subscribes to 915 periodicals. Special learning facilities include a learning resource center and a planetarium. The 50-acre campus is in a small town 90 miles south of Columbus. Including residence halls, there are 25 buildings on campus.

Student Life: About 91% of undergraduates are from Ohio. Students come from 7 foreign countries and Canada. Ninety-three percent are white.

Housing: A total of 120 students can be accommodated in college housing. College-sponsored housing is single-sex. On-campus housing is available on a first-come, first-served basis. Ninety-nine percent of students commute. All students may keep cars on campus. Alcohol is not permitted.

Activities: There is 1 local fraternity and 1 national fraternity. There are many groups and organizations on campus, including art, cheerleading, choir, chorus, computers, ethnic, honors, international, literary magazine, newspaper, pep band, photography, professional, social, and student government.

Sports: Athletic and recreation facilities include an activities center with basketball and volleyball courts, a sports center with racquetball courts, nautilus and weight rooms, a pool, a sauna, and whirl pool.

Disabled Students: The following facilities are available: wheelchair ramps, elevators, special parking, specially equipped rest rooms, lowered drinking fountains, and lowered telephones.

Services: In addition to many counseling and information services, tutoring is available in most subjects. There is a reader service for the blind, and remedial math, reading, and writing.

Campus Safety and Security: Campus safety and security measures include a 24-hour foot and vehicle patrol, pamphlets, posters, and films, and lighted pathways and sidewalks.

Programs of Study: Shawnee State awards the B.A. and B.S. degrees. Associate degrees are also awarded. Bachelor's degrees are awarded in BIOLOGICAL SCIENCE (biology/biological science), BUSINESS (business administration and management), COMMUNICATIONS AND THE ARTS (English), COMPUTER AND PHYSICAL SCIENCE (chemistry, mathematics, natural sciences, and physical sciences), EDUCATION (elementary), ENGINEERING AND ENVIRONMENTAL DESIGN (computer technology and plastics technology), HEALTH PROFESSIONS (premedicine and preveterinary science), SOCIAL SCIENCE (humanities, prelaw, and social science).

Required: To graduate, students must earn 180 to 190 quarter credit hours with a 2.0 GPA in all course work and in the major.

Special: Study abroad in Russia or Mexico, internships, and work-study programs are available. There is a freshman honors program on campus.

Faculty/Classroom: All teach undergraduates. The average class size in an introductory lecture is 25 and in a laboratory, 20.

Admissions: One hundred percent of the 1993–94 applicants were accepted. The ACT scores for the 1993–94 freshman class were as follows: 67% below 21, 23% between 21 and 23, 7% between 24 and 26, 2% between 27 and 28, and 1% above 28.

Requirements: The SAT I or ACT is required if applicant is under age 21. In addition, applicants must graduate from an accredited high school or have a GED. AP and CLEP credits are accepted.

Procedure: Freshmen are admitted to all sessions. Application deadlines are open. The application fee is $30. The college accepts all applicants. Notification is sent on a rolling basis.

Transfer: A total of 45 quarter credit hours out of 180 must be completed at Shawnee State.

Visiting: There are regularly scheduled orientations for prospective students, including fall and spring visitation days which consists of small sessions with deans and faculty, orientation by student affairs offices, and tours with current college students. There are guides for informal visits and visitors may sit in on classes. To arrange for a visit, contact the Office of Admissions at (614) 355–2221 or (800) 959–2778.

Financial Aid: In 1993–94, 82% of all current freshmen and 80% of continuing students received some form of financial aid. The FAFSA financial statement is required. The deadline for financial aid applications is June 15.

International Students: The school actively recruits international students. They must take the TOEFL or the college's own test and achieve a minimum score on the TOEFL of 500. The student must also take the SAT I or the ACT (ACT preferred).

Computers: The college provides computer facilities for student use. Microcomputers are available in College of Business and College of Engineering Technologies. There are no time limits on using the system and no fees.

Graduates: In 1992–93, 171 bachelor's degrees were awarded. Some 104 companies recruited on campus in 1992–93.

Admissions Contact: Director of Admissions.

TIFFIN UNIVERSITY
C-2
Tiffin, OH 44883   **(419) 447–6443; (800) 968–6446 (out-of-state)**

Full-time: 394 men, 268 women	Faculty: 27; IIB, -$
Part-time: 129 men, 222 women	Ph.D.s: 65%
Graduate: 34 men, 27 women	Student/Faculty: 25 to 1
Year: semesters, summer session	Tuition: $7100
Application Deadline: open	Room & Board: $3700

Freshman Class: 783 applied, 734 accepted, 254 enrolled
ACT: 19   **LESS COMPETITIVE**

Tiffin University, established in 1888, is a nonprofit, independent institution emphasizing degree programs in business and criminal justice. The library contains 15,971 volumes, 27,400 microform items, and 817 audiovisual forms, and subscribes to 105 periodicals. Computerized library sources and services include interlibrary loans and database searching. The 25-acre campus is in a small town 90 miles north of Columbus and 60 miles south of Toledo. Including residence halls, there are 22 buildings on campus.

Student Life: About 91% of undergraduates are from Ohio. Students come from 15 states, 13 foreign countries, and Canada. Eighty percent are from public schools; 20% from private. Eighty-six percent are white. The average age of freshmen is 18; all undergraduates, 25. Forty-five percent drop out by the end of their first year; 35% remain to graduate.

Housing: A total of 360 students can be accommodated in college housing. College-sponsored living facilities include single-sex and coed dormitories, on-campus apartments, fraternity houses, and soror-

ity houses. In addition there are special interest houses. On-campus housing is guaranteed for all 4 years. Sixty-five percent of students commute. All students may keep cars on campus.

Activities: About 2% of men belong to 1 local fraterintiy and 1 national fraternity; about 2% of women belong to 1 local sorority and 1 national sorority. There are 13 groups on campus, including cheerleading, computers, ethnic, international, newspaper, political, professional, social, social service, and student government. Popular campus events include Homecoming, Spring Formal Dance, Spring Fest, International Students Fair, Little Siblings Weekend, and Family Day.

Sports: There are 7 intercollegiate sports for men and 6 for women, and 5 intramural sports for men and 5 for women. Athletic and recreation facilities include a student center gymnasium, indoor batting cages, a weight room, tennis courts, and soccer, baseball, and softball fields.

Disabled Students: The following facilities are available: elevators, special parking, specially equipped rest rooms, and special class scheduling.

Services: In addition to many counseling and information services, tutoring is available in most subjects. There is remedial math, reading, and writing.

Campus Safety and Security: Campus safety and security measures include escort service, informal discussions, pamphlets, posters, films, and lighted pathways and sidewalks.

Programs of Study: TU awards the B.B.A. and B.Crim.Just. degrees. Associate and master's degrees also are awarded. Bachelor's degrees are awarded in BUSINESS (accounting, business administration and management, hotel/motel and restaurant management, marketing/retailing/merchandising, and personnel management), COMPUTER AND PHYSICAL SCIENCE (information sciences and systems), SOCIAL SCIENCE (corrections and law enforcement and corrections). Business administration and management and accounting are the strongest academically. Accounting and criminal justice have the largest enrollments.

Required: To graduate, all students must complete 120 semester hours, including 51 in the major, with a GPA of 2.0 cumulatively and 2.5 in the major. The 51-semester-hours general education program includes courses in computer systems, speech, finite mathematics, statistics, macroeconomics, psychology, sociology, English, and cultural heritage.

Special: Internships are recommended for all students. Work-study programs, a junior semester in England, nondegree study, and pass/fail options are also available. There is one national honor society on campus.

Faculty/Classroom: Fifty-five percent of faculty are male; 45%, female. All teach undergraduates and 30% do research. No introductory courses are taught by graduate students. The average class size in an introductory lecture is 36 and in a regular course offering, 19.

Admissions: About 94% of the 1993–94 applicants were accepted. The ACT scores for the 1993–94 freshman class were as follows: 78% below 21, 13% between 21 and 23, 6% between 24 and 26, 1% between 27 and 28, and 2% above 28. About 20% of the current freshmen were in the top fifth of their class; 51% were in the top two fifths. One freshman graduated first in her/his class.

Requirements: A minimum GPA of 2.0 is required. The ACT is recommended. Candidates should be graduates of an accredited secondary school, with 4 units of English, 3 of mathematics, 2 each of science and social studies, and 5 of electives. The GED is accepted. An interview is recommended. AP credits are accepted. Important factors used in the admissions decision are leadership record, recommendations by school officials, extracurricular activities record, advanced placement or honor courses, and evidence of special talent.

Procedure: Freshmen are admitted to all sessions. Application deadlines are open. Application fee is $20. Notification is sent on a rolling basis.

Transfer: A total of 94 transfer students enrolled in 1993–94. Applicants with 15 or more hours of credit must have a minimum college GPA of 2.0; applicants with fewer hours of credit need a minimum GPA of 1.8 to enter in good standing. The ACT and an interview are recommended. A total of 30 credits out of 120 must be completed at TU.

Visiting: There are regularly scheduled orientations for prospective students, consisting of welcoming remarks, placement testing, tours of the campus, lunch with advisors, and an appointment with an individual advisor to schedule fall classes. There are guides for informal visits and visitors may sit in on classes and stay overnight at the school. To arrange for a visit, contact the Admissions Office at (800) 968–6446.

Financial Aid: In 1993–94, 94% of all current freshmen and 80% of continuing students received some form of financial aid. About 77% of freshmen and 68% of continuing students received need-based aid. The average freshman award was $4100. Of that total, scholarships or need-based grants averaged $900 ($7100 maximum); loans averaged $2500 ($2625 maximum); and work contracts averaged $700 ($950 maximum). Five percent of undergraduate students work part-time. Average earnings from campus work for the

school year are $700. The average financial indebtedness of the 1992–93 graduate was $7507. TU is a member of CSS. The FAF or FFS, and FAFSA are required. The deadline for financial aid applications is August 1.

International Students: There are currently 29 international students enrolled. The school actively recruits these students. They must take the TOEFL and achieve a minimum score of 500.

Computers: The university provides computer facilities for student use. The computer system operates on a Novell network, with 60 PCs distributed among 3 computer laboratories in classroom buildings. All students may access the system. There are no time limits on using the system. The computer fee varies with coursework or project requirements.

Graduates: In 1992–93, 129 bachelor's degrees were awarded. The most popular majors among graduates were management (50%), accounting (28%), and law enforcement (6%). Within an average freshman class, 27% graduate in 4 years, 5% in 5 years, and 3% in 6 years. Some 8 companies recruited on campus in 1992–93. In the 1992 graduating class, 7% of the men and 3% of the women were enrolled in graduate school within 6 months of graduation; 96% of all graduates had found employment.

Admissions Contact: Kristine M. Boyle, Director of Admissions.

UNION INSTITUTE
Cincinnati, OH 45206–1947

A-5
(513) 861–6400
(800) 486–3116 (out-of-state)

Full-time: 164 men, 231 women	**Faculty:** 19
Part-time: 12 men, 5 women	**Ph.D.s:** 84%
Graduate: 464 men, 684 women	**Student/Faculty:** 21 to 1
Year: trimesters, summer session	**Tuition:** $6840
Application Deadline: October 15	**Room & Board:** n/app
Freshman Class: n/av	
SAT I or ACT: not required	**SPECIAL**

The Union Institute, established in 1969, serves the academic needs of midlife working adults seeking to earn or complete the B.A. or B.S. degree. In addition to the main Cincinnati campus, there are study centers in Miami, Los Angeles, San Diego, and Sacramento. The institute's Distant Learning Program enables adults living in remote locations to complete their educational requirements through conference calls, tutorial instruction, and teleconferencing. There are no residence halls.

Housing: There are no residence halls.

Programs of Study: The institute awards the B.A. and B.S. degrees. A doctoral degrees also are awarded.

Required: To graduate, students must complete a total of 180 quarter credits. Distribution requirements include a minimum of 20 quarter credits each in humanities and arts, social sciences, language and communications, and natural sciences and mathematics, plus 60 credits in the area of concentration, and 40 credits in electives. A senior project, including an oral presentation, is required

Special: All newly admitted undergraduates participate in an entrance colloquium that provides orientation, assistance in the development of a degree plan, and advice on arranging for experiential learning credit. The remaining course work is based on a system of group and individual learning contracts. All undergraduates, whether active or interim, are required to register at the beginning of each quarter.

Requirements: The SAT I or ACT is not required. Applicants must show evidence of college-level academic ability. They are also expected to be highly motivated, and to have the capacity for self-directed learning. No standardized tests are required. All applicants should present 3 letters of recommendation, a structural personal essay, and transcripts of any previous college work. An interview is usually required.

Procedure: Freshmen are admitted to all sessions. Applications should be filed by October 15 for fall entry, February 11 for winter entry, and June 15 for summer entry, along with an application fee of $50. Notification is sent on a rolling basis.

Transfer: Grades of C or better may be transferred to the institute. A total of 45 quarter hour credits out of 180 must be completed at the institute.

Financial Aid: The deadline for financial aid applications is 6 to 8 weeks before the start of each quarter.

Admissions Contact: Sueanne Mapes, Admissions Processor.

UNIVERSITY OF AKRON
D-2
Akron, OH 44325
(216) 972-7100

Full-time: 6228 men, 6259 women | Faculty: 837; I, --$
Part-time: 4224 men, 5071 women | Ph.D.s: 85%
Graduate: 2092 men, 2158 women | Student/Faculty: 15 to 1
Year: semesters, summer session | Tuition: $3039 ($7575)
Application Deadline: August 12 | Room & Board: $3660
Freshman Class: 6312 applied, 5992 accepted, 3211 enrolled
SAT I or ACT: required | **NONCOMPETITIVE**

The University of Akron, founded in 1870, is a public, primarily commuter institution emphasizing degree programs in the arts and sciences, business, engineering, preprofessional training, teacher preparation, and health science fields, including nursing. There are 7 undergraduate and 8 graduate schools. In addition to regional accreditation, UA has baccalaureate program accreditation with AACSB, ABET, ADA, ASLA, CAHEA, CSWE, NASAD, NASM, NCATE, and NLN. The 3 libraries contain 914,234 volumes, 1 million microform items, and 24,396 audiovisual forms, and subscribe to 13,323 periodicals. Computerized library sources and services include the card catalog and interlibrary loans. Special learning facilities include an art gallery, a radio station, a TV station, a nursing center, a speech and hearing center, a chemical laboratory, a dance institute, an institute of polymer science, and an educational media laboratory. The 166-acre campus is in an urban area 35 miles south of Cleveland. Including residence halls, there are 80 buildings on campus.

Student Life: Almost all undergraduates are from Ohio. Students come from 48 states, 83 foreign countries, and Canada. Eighty-six percent are white. The average age of freshmen is 18; all undergraduates, 22. Twenty-five percent drop out by the end of their first year; 75% remain to graduate.

Housing: A total of 2200 students can be accommodated in college housing. College-sponsored living facilities include single-sex and coed dormitories and on-campus apartments. In addition, there are special interest houses and and fraternity and sorority houses. On-campus housing is available on a first-come, first-served basis. Priority is given to out-of-town students. Ninety percent of students commute. Alcohol is not permitted. All students may keep cars on campus.

Activities: There are 15 national fraternities and 10 national sororities. There are 200 groups on campus, including art, cheerleading, chess, choir, chorale, chorus, computers, dance, drama, ethnic, gay, honors, international, jazz band, marching band, musical theater, newspaper, orchestra, pep band, photography, political, professional, radio and TV, religious, social, social service, student government, symphony, and yearbook. Popular campus events include Homecoming, May Day, Parents/Family Day, All Campus Leadership Conference, All Campus Recognition Dinner, and International Festival.

Sports: There are 9 intercollegiate sports for men and 7 for women, and 17 intramural sports for men and 15 for women. Athletic and recreation facilities include a 7000-seat gymnasium, a 35,000-seat stadium, an indoor pool, a student center, indoor and outdoor tracks, 9 racquetball courts, gymnastics and combatives areas, and weight training and fitness rooms.

Disabled Students: Ninety percent of the campus is accessible to disabled students. The following facilities are available: wheelchair ramps, elevators, special parking, specially equipped rest rooms, special class scheduling, lowered drinking fountains, and lowered telephones.

Services: In addition to many counseling and information services, tutoring is available in most subjects. There is a reader service for the blind, and remedial math, reading, and writing.

Campus Safety and Security: Campus safety and security measures include 24-hour foot and vehicle patrol, self-defense education, escort service, and informal discussions. In addition, there are emergency telephones and lighted pathways and sidewalks.

Programs of Study: UA awards the B.A., B.S., and B.F.A degrees. Associate, master's, and doctoral degrees are also awarded. Bachelor's degrees are awarded in BIOLOGICAL SCIENCE (biology/biological science, botany, microbiology, and zoology), BUSINESS (accounting, banking and finance, business administration and management, business economics, marketing/retailing/merchandising, and personnel management), COMMUNICATIONS AND THE ARTS (advertising, art, broadcasting, classics, communications, dance, design, dramatic arts, English, fine arts, French, German, music, photography, Russian, Spanish, and speech/debate/rhetoric), COMPUTER AND PHYSICAL SCIENCE (chemistry, computer science, earth science, geology, mathematics, natural sciences, physics, and statistics), EDUCATION (art, business, early childhood, elementary, foreign languages, health, home economics, music, science, secondary, and special), ENGINEERING AND ENVIRONMENTAL DESIGN (chemical engineering, civil engineering, computer engineering, electrical/electronics engineering, manufacturing technology, mechanical engineering, and mechanical engineering technology), HEALTH PROFESSIONS (medical laboratory technology, nursing, predentistry,

premedicine, prepharmacy, preveterinary science, and speech pathology/audiology), SOCIAL SCIENCE (anthropology, criminal justice, dietetics, economics, geography, history, home economics, humanities, philosophy, political science/government, prelaw, psychology, public administration, social science, social work, and sociology). Engineering, nursing, and business are the strongest academically. Arts and sciences, business, and engineering have the largest enrollments.

Required: To graduate, all students must complete 128 credits, with a varying number of hours in the major, and maintain a GPA of 2.0. Specific course requirements include English, mathematics, natural science, social science, speech, and physical education.

Special: UA offers co-op programs with local and out-of-state employers, study abroad in 9 countries, internships and work-study opportunities with community employers, a 6-year accelerated B.S.-M.D. program, a 3–2 engineering degree in survey and construction technology, B.A.-B.S. degrees in 10 majors, credit for military experience, nondegree study, and pass/fail options. There is a freshman honors program on campus, as well as 26 national honor societies.

Faculty/Classroom: Seventy-one percent of faculty are male; 29%, female. The average class size in a regular course offering is 30.

Admissions: Almost all of the 1993–94 applicants were accepted. There were 8 National Merit finalists.

Requirements: A minimum GPA of 2.3 is required. The SAT I or ACT is required. UA follows an open admissions policy. Applicants should be graduates of an accredited secondary school or hold the GED. Secondary school credits should include 4 of English, 3 each of mathematics, science, and social studies, and 2 of foreign language. A portfolio is recommended for art and graphic design students, an audition is required for music and dance students, and an interview is advised for nursing and engineering students. AP and CLEP credits are accepted. Important factors used in the admissions decision are recommendations by school officials, personality, intangible qualities, leadership record, extracurricular activities record, and advanced placement or honor courses.

Procedure: Freshmen are admitted to all sessions. Applications should be filed by August 12 for fall entry, December 31 for spring entry, and May 27 for summer entry, along with an application fee of $25. The college accepts all in-state residents who apply. Notification is sent on a rolling basis.

Transfer: About 870 transfer students enrolled in a recent year. In-state applicants should present a minimum college GPA of 2.0; out-of-state applicants, a GPA of 2.5. A total of 32 credits out of 128 must be completed at UA.

Visiting: There are regularly scheduled orientations for prospective students. There are guides for informal visits. To arrange for a visit, contact the Office of Undergraduate Admissions at (216) 972–7100.

Financial Aid: In a recent year, half of all current freshmen received some form of financial aid. Scholarships or need-based grants averaged $1000 ($2500 maximum); loans averaged $1500 ($4000 maximum); and work contracts averaged $1200 ($2500 maximum). The average financial indebtedness of the 1992–93 graduate was $1500. UA is a member of CSS. The FAFSA financial statement is required. The deadline for financial aid applications is March 15.

International Students: There are currently 900 international students enrolled. They must take the TOEFL and achieve a minimum score of 500.

Computers: The college provides computer facilities for student use. The mainframes are an IBM 3090, an IBM 4381, and a DEC system 5000/240. Workstations access the mainframes via ZIPnet and are connected with the statewide OARnet and worldwide Internet systems. All students may access the system. It may be used from 7 A.M. to 1 A.M. at the computer center. There are no time limits on using the system and no fees.

Graduates: In a recent year, 2700 bachelor's degrees were awarded. Some 539 companies recruited on campus in 1992–93.

Admissions Contact: Director of Admissions.

UNIVERSITY OF CINCINNATI
A-5
Cincinnati, OH 45221–0127
(513) 556–1100

Full-time: 5672 men, 5364 women | Faculty: 966; I, -$
Part-time: 1070 men, 941 women | Ph.D.s: 75%
Graduate: 2503 men, 2557 women | Student/Faculty: 11 to 1
Year: quarters, summer session | Tuition: $3558 ($8712)
Application Deadline: open | Room & Board: $4431
Freshman Class: 6855 applied, 5553 accepted, 2408 enrolled
SAT I Verbal/Math: 464/533 | ACT: 23 | **COMPETITIVE**

The University of Cincinnati, founded in 1819, is a state-supported coeducational institution offering undergraduate programs in art and architecture, business, engineering, health science, liberal arts and sciences, music, and technical training. There are 17 undergraduate and 10 graduate schools. In addition to regional accreditation, UC has baccalaureate program accreditation with AACSB and NCATE. The 18 libraries contain 1,948,000 volumes, 2,691,000 microform

items, and 21,000 audiovisual forms, and subscribe to 19,600 periodicals. Computerized library sources and services include the card catalog. Special learning facilities include a learning resource center, art gallery, and radio station. The 270-acre campus is in an urban area in downtown Cincinnati. Including residence halls, there are 90 buildings on campus.

Student Life: About 93% of undergraduates are from Ohio. Students come from 45 states and 78 foreign countries. Eighty-three percent are white. The average age of freshmen is 19; all undergraduates, 22. Twenty-four percent drop out by the end of their first year; 45% remain to graduate.

Housing: A total of 3200 students can be accommodated in college housing. College-sponsored living facilities include dormitories and on-campus apartments. On-campus housing is guaranteed for the freshman year only. Priority is given to out-of-town students. Alcohol is not permitted. All students may keep cars on campus.

Activities: About 11% of men belong to 24 local fraternities; about 10% of women belong to 11 local sororities. There are many groups and organizations on campus, including art, band, cheerleading, chess, choir, chorale, chorus, computers, dance, drama, ethnic, gay, honors, international, jazz band, literary magazine, marching band, musical theater, newspaper, opera, orchestra, pep band, photography, political, professional, radio and TV, religious, social, social service, student government, symphony, and yearbook. Popular campus events include Homecoming and College Conservatory of Music productions.

Sports: There are 32 intramural sports for men and 32 for women. Athletic and recreation facilities include a 30,000-seat stadium, a field house, a 13,000-seat gymnasium, indoor and outdoor tracks, a swimming pool, tennis courts, and athletic fields.

Disabled Students: Ninety-five percent of the campus is accessible to disabled students. The following facilities are available: wheelchair ramps, elevators, special parking, specially equipped rest rooms, special class scheduling, lowered drinking fountains, and lowered telephones.

Services: In addition to many counseling and information services, tutoring is available in most subjects. There is also remedial math, reading, and writing, note-taking and reading services for the blind, and interpreting services for the hearing-impaired.

Campus Safety and Security: Campus safety and security measures include escort service, shuttle buses, emergency telephones, and lighted pathways and sidewalks.

Programs of Study: UC awards the B.A., B.S., B.Arch., B.B.A., B.F.A., B.G.S., B.M., B.S.Des., B.S.E., B.S.I.M., B.S.N., B.S.Pharm., B.S.W, and B.U.P. degrees. Associate, master's, and doctoral degrees also are awarded. Bachelor's degrees are awarded in BIOLOGICAL SCIENCE (biochemistry and biology/biological science), BUSINESS (accounting, banking and finance, business administration and management, management science, marketing/retailing/merchandising, and real estate), COMMUNICATIONS AND THE ARTS (broadcasting, communications, comparative literature, dance, design, dramatic arts, English, fine arts, French, German, jazz, linguistics, music, music history and appreciation, music theory and composition, piano/organ, Spanish, theater design, and voice), COMPUTER AND PHYSICAL SCIENCE (chemistry, computer science, geology, information sciences and systems, mathematics, physics, and quantitative methods), EDUCATION (art, business, early childhood, elementary, foreign languages, guidance, health, industrial arts, middle school, music, nutrition, science, secondary, and special), ENGINEERING AND ENVIRONMENTAL DESIGN (aeronautical engineering, architectural engineering, architectural technology, chemical engineering, city/community/regional planning, civil engineering, computer engineering, construction management, electrical/electronics engineering, electrical/electronics engineering technology, engineering, engineering mechanics, engineering technology, industrial administration/management, industrial engineering technology, materials engineering, mechanical engineering, mechanical engineering technology, metallurgical engineering, and nuclear engineering), HEALTH PROFESSIONS (medical laboratory technology, nuclear medical technology, nursing, pharmacy, predentistry, premedicine, and speech pathology/audiology), SOCIAL SCIENCE (African American studies, anthropology, Asian/Oriental studies, classical/ancient civilization, criminal justice, economics, geography, history, international studies, Judaic studies, Latin American studies, philosophy, political science/government, prelaw, psychology, social science, social work, sociology, and urban studies). Engineering is the strongest academically. Arts and sciences have the largest enrollments.

Required: All students must complete English and humanities requirements. A minimum of 185 quarter credits is required for the baccalaureate degree.

Special: The Professional Practice Program, a 5-year cooperative plan offering alternate work in academic subjects and industry, is available for students in engineering, business, arts and sciences, and design, architecture, and art. Study abroad opportunities include a

winter quarter in Spain, an academic program in Paris, and a language/area studies work program in Germany. A general studies degree and nondegree study are available. There is a freshman honors program on campus.

Faculty/Classroom: Seventy-six percent of faculty are male; 24%, female.

Admissions: About 81% of the 1993–94 applicants were accepted. The SAT scores for the 1993–94 freshman class were as follows: Verbal—65% below 500, 28% between 500 and 599, and 7% between 600 and 700; Math—34% below 500, 36% between 500 and 599, and 30% between 600 and 700.

Requirements: A minimum GPA of 2.0 is required. The SAT I or ACT is required. Applicants should be graduates of an accredited secondary school with 4 units of high school English, 3 of mathematics, 2 each of science, social science, foreign language, and electives, and 1 of fine arts.

Procedure: Freshmen are admitted to all sessions. Entrance exams should be taken in May of the junior year or January or March of the senior year. Application deadlines are open. The fee is $30. Notification is sent on a rolling basis.

Transfer: About 1030 transfer students enrolled in 1993–94. A GPA of 2.0 is required to apply from a 4-year college, a GPA of 2.5 or an associate degree from a 2-year college.

Visiting: There are regularly scheduled orientations for prospective students. There are guides for informal visits, and visitors may sit in on classes and stay overnight at the school. To arrange for a visit, contact the Admissions Office at (513) 556–1100.

Financial Aid: The FAF is required. The deadline for financial aid applications is March 1.

International Students: There are currently 1192 international students enrolled. The school actively recruits these students. They must take the TOEFL and achieve a minimum score of 515.

Computers: The college provides computer facilities for student use. The mainframes are an Amdahl 5880 and 470, and a DEC VAX. There are also 350 Apple, IBM, and Zenith microcomputers available in all colleges and in the library. All students may access the system. There are no time limits on using the system and no fees.

Graduates: In 1992–93 2656 bachelor's degrees were awarded. Some 350 companies recruited on campus in a recent year.

Admissions Contact: Director of Admissions.

UNIVERSITY OF DAYTON

B-4

Dayton, OH 45469

Full-time: 3085 men, 2804 women	Faculty: 371; IIA, av$
Part-time: 391 men, 282 women	Ph.Ds: 83%
Graduate: 1805 men, 2273 women	Student/Faculty: 16 to 1
Year: semesters, summer session	Tuition: $11,090
Application Deadline: open	Room & Board: $4030

(513) 229–4411; (800) 837–7433

Freshman Class: 6361 applied, 5293 accepted, 1507 enrolled
SAT I Verbal/Math: 504/578 **ACT:** 25 **COMPETITIVE +**

The University of Dayton, founded in 1850, is a nonprofit, private, comprehensive coeducational institution affiliated with the Roman Catholic Church. Part of the Southwestern Council for Higher Education, it has undergraduate and graduate programs emphasizing the arts and sciences, business administration, engineering, education, and law. There are 4 undergraduate and 6 graduate schools. In addition to regional accreditation, UD has baccalaureate program accreditation with AACSB, ABET, ADA, NASM, and NCATE. The 2 libraries contain 1,302,522 volumes and 682,505 microform items, and subscribe to 2776 periodicals. Computerized library sources and services include the card catalog, interlibrary loans, and database searching. Special learning facilities include a learning resource center, art gallery, radio station, TV station, engineering and science research institute, information sciences center, and day-care facility that provides a learning environment for education majors. The 110-acre campus is in a suburban area 2 miles south of downtown Dayton. Including residence halls, there are 41 buildings on campus.

Student Life: About 59% of undergraduates are from Ohio. Students come from 45 states and 34 foreign countries. Fifty-four percent are from public schools; 46% from private. Eighty-nine percent are white. Seventy-one percent are Catholic; 14% Protestant. The average age of freshmen is 18; all undergraduates, 20. Fifteen percent drop out by the end of their first year; 67% remain to graduate.

Housing: A total of 5100 students can be accommodated in college housing. College-sponsored living facilities include single-sex and coed dormitories, on-campus apartments, off-campus apartments, fraternity houses, and sorority houses. In addition, there are honors houses, special interest houses, scholar floors and suites, and special interest floors. On-campus housing is guaranteed for all 4 years. Ninety-five percent of students live on campus; of those, 95% remain on campus on weekends. Upperclassmen may keep cars on campus.

Activities: About 18% of men belong to 5 local and 9 national fraternities; about 25% of women belong to 2 local and 8 national sororities. There are 160 groups on campus, including art, band, cheer-

leading, chess, choir, chorale, computers, dance, drama, drill team, ethnic, gay, honors, international, jazz band, literary magazine, marching band, musical theater, newspaper, orchestra, pep band, photography, political, professional, radio and TV, religious, social, social service, student government, and yearbook. Popular campus events include Christmas on Campus, Hands Across the Ghetto, Homecoming Weekend, Week in Solidarity with Homeless (WISH), and home football and basketball games.

Sports: There are 9 intercollegiate sports for men and 7 for women, and 25 intramural sports for men and 21 for women. Athletic and recreation facilities include a physical activities center, a field house, a 13,500-seat arena, a 12,000-seat football stadium, soccer and baseball fields, indoor and outdoor tennis courts, racquetball and squash courts, a swimming pool, a basketball court, weight rooms, and a fully equipped aerobic conditioning center.

Disabled Students: The following facilities are available: wheelchair ramps, elevators, special parking, specially equipped rest rooms, lowered drinking fountains, and lowered telephones.

Services: In addition to many counseling and information services, tutoring is available in most subjects. There is a reader service for the blind, and remedial math, reading, and writing.

Campus Safety and Security: Campus safety and security measures include self defense education, escort service, shuttle buses, and informal discussions. In addition, there are pamphlets, posters, films, emergency telephones, lighted pathways and sidewalks, and 24-hour vehicle patrol.

Programs of Study: UD awards the B.A., B.S., B.F.A., B.G.S., and B.M. degrees. Master's and doctoral degrees also are awarded. Bachelor's degrees are awarded in BIOLOGICAL SCIENCE (biochemistry, biology/biological science, and nutrition), BUSINESS (accounting, banking and finance, business economics, management information systems, management science, marketing/retailing/merchandising, and sports management), COMMUNICATIONS AND THE ARTS (broadcasting, communications, design, dramatic arts, English, fine arts, French, German, journalism, music, photography, public relations, and Spanish), COMPUTER AND PHYSICAL SCIENCE (chemical process technology, chemistry, computer science, geology, information sciences and systems, mathematics, physical sciences, and physics), EDUCATION (art, business, early childhood, elementary, health, music, secondary, and special), ENGINEERING AND ENVIRONMENTAL DESIGN (chemical engineering, civil engineering, electronic engineering, electrical/electronics engineering technology, engineering, engineering technology, environmental engineering technology, industrial engineering technology, manufacturing engineering technology, mechanical engineering, and mechanical engineering technology), HEALTH PROFESSIONS (music therapy, nuclear medical technology, predentistry, and premedicine), SOCIAL SCIENCE (American studies, criminal justice, dietetics, economics, history, international studies, philosophy, physical fitness/movement, political science/government, psychology, religion, and sociology). Engineering and business are the strongest academically. Communication arts has the largest enrollment.

Required: To graduate, all students must complete a minimum of 120 semester hours with at least 30 in the major, and maintain a minimum GPA of 2.0. The curricula must include general education requirements, including 4 classes in religious studies and philosophy, as well as basic skills requirements. Departmental requirements vary.

Special: Special academic programs include co-op and work-study programs, internships, summer study abroad at 3 European sites chosen each year, and cross-registration with the Miami Valley consortium. Some accelerated degree programs and many dual major programs are available, as is a B.A.-B.S. degree in geology, economics, chemistry, mathematics, and psychology. A 3-2 engineering degree is offered with Wilberforce University and Thomas More College. A general studies degree, student-designed majors, credit for life, military, or work experience, and pass/fail options are also available. There is a freshman honors program on campus, as well as 20 national honor societies. All departments have honors programs.

Faculty/Classroom: Seventy-nine percent of faculty are male; 21%, female. All teach undergraduates. The average class size in a regular course offering is 28.

Admissions: About 83% of the 1993–94 applicants were accepted. The SAT scores for the 1993–94 freshman class were as follows: Verbal—48% below 500, 38% between 500 and 599, 13% between 600 and 700, and 2% above 700; Math—17% below 500, 41% between 500 and 599, 32% between 600 and 700, and 11% above 700. The ACT scores were 8% below 20, 41% between 20 and 24, 39% between 25 and 29, and 13% between 30 and 36. About 42% of the current freshmen were in the top fifth of their class; 71% were in the top two fifths. There were 23 National Merit finalists. About 42 freshmen graduated first in their class.

Requirements: The SAT I or ACT is required. In addition, applicants should be graduates of an accredited secondary school with 18 academic credits or Carnegie units, including 4 units of English, 3 of

mathematics, 2 of foreign language, and 8 academic electives. Additional mathematics and science courses may be necessary for certain programs. The GED is accepted. High school transcripts and a letter of recommendation must be submitted. An essay is required, and an interview is recommended. Music students must audition. AP and CLEP credits are accepted. Important factors used in the admissions decision are advanced placement or honor courses, leadership record, extracurricular activities record, and recommendations by school officials.

Procedure: Freshmen are admitted to all sessions. Entrance exams should be taken by December of the senior year. Application deadlines are open. The fee is $20. Notification is sent beginning in November. There is a deferred admissions plan.

Transfer: About 190 transfer students enrolled in 1993–94. Applicants must submit transcripts from all colleges attended and must have a minimum GPA of 2.0; 2.5 is needed for selected programs. An interview is advised. A total of 30 credits out of at least 120 must be completed at UD.

Visiting: There are regularly scheduled orientations for prospective students, including an admissions interview, a campus and residence hall tour, meetings with faculty members, and a financial-aid discussion. Group visits are also arranged. There are guides for informal visits, and visitors may sit in on classes and stay overnight at the school. To arrange for a visit, contact Terri Bullman, Office of Admissions, at (513) 229–4411 or (800) 837–7433.

Financial Aid: In 1993–94 96% of all current freshmen and 93% of continuing students received some form of financial aid. About 63% of freshmen and 51% of continuing students received need-based aid. The average freshman award was $9438. Of that total, scholarships or need-based grants averaged $4130 ($8450 maximum); loans averaged $3226 ($5525 maximum); and work contracts averaged $2100 (maximum). Sixty-one percent of undergraduate students work part-time. Average earnings from campus work for the school year are $1200. The average financial indebtedness of the 1992–93 graduate was $14,900. UD is a member of CSS. The college's own financial statement and the FAFSA are required. The priority deadline for financial aid applications is March 31.

International Students: There are currently 209 international students enrolled. The school actively recruits these students. They must take the TOEFL and achieve a minimum score of 500.

Computers: The college provides computer facilities for student use. The mainframe is a DEC VAX minicomputer. There are 75 networked terminals, 200 networked microcomputers, and about 100 workstations available on campus. Students with their own computers may have access to a dataline from their dormitory. All students may access the system. It may be used 24 hours a day, 7 days a week. There are no time limits on using the system and no fees.

Graduates: In 1992–93 1544 bachelor's degrees were awarded. The most popular majors among graduates were business (20%), engineering (18%), and communication (14%). Within an average freshman class, 67% graduate in 5 years and 70% in 6 years. Some 200 companies recruited on campus in 1992–93.

Admissions Contact: Myron Achbach, Director of Admissions.

UNIVERSITY OF FINDLAY   B-2

Findlay, OH 45840   (419) 424–4540; (800) 548–0932 (out-of-state)

Full-time: 2178 men and women	Faculty: 115; IIB, --$
Part-time: 159 men and women	Ph.D.s: 50%
Graduate: 78 men and women	Student/Faculty: 19 to 1
Year: semesters, summer session	Tuition: $10,984
Application Deadline: August 15	Room & Board: $4780
Freshman Class: 2165 applied, 1783 accepted, 412 enrolled	
SAT I Verbal/Math: 439/473	ACT: 20 COMPETITIVE

The University of Findlay, founded in 1882, is a private, independent, coeducational institution affiliated with the Churches of God, General Conference, offering liberal arts and sciences and teacher preparation programs. There is one graduate school. In addition to regional accreditation, Findlay has baccalaureate program accreditation with NCATE. The library contains 122,000 volumes, 90,400 microform items, and 1200 audiovisual forms, and subscribes to 980 periodicals. Computerized library sources and services include interlibrary loans and database searching. Special learning facilities include a learning resource center, art gallery, planetarium, radio station, a university-owned farm, and an equine facility. The 25-acre main campus is in a small town 45 miles south of Toledo. Including residence halls, there are 21 buildings on campus.

Student Life: About 80% of undergraduates are from Ohio. Students come from 23 states, 23 foreign countries, and Canada. Eighty percent are from public schools; 20% from private. Ninety percent are white. Sixty percent are Protestant; 30% Catholic. The average age of freshmen is 18. Eleven percent drop out by the end of their first year; 40% remain to graduate.

Housing: A total of 900 students can be accommodated in college housing. College-sponsored living facilities include single-sex dormitories, fraternity houses, and sorority houses. On-campus housing is guaranteed for all 4 years. Sixty-five percent of students live on campus. Alcohol is not permitted. All students may keep cars on campus.

Activities: About 4% of men belong to 4 national fraternities; about 3% of women belong to 2 national sororities. There are 32 groups on campus, including art, band, cheerleading, chess, choir, chorale, computers, drama, ethnic, honors, international, jazz band, literary magazine, musical theater, newspaper, pep band, political, professional, radio and TV, religious, social, social service, student government, and yearbook. Popular campus events include Homecoming, Snowcoming, and Family Weekend.

Sports: Athletic and recreation facilities include a fitness center, a 7200-seat stadium, and a physical education center with a 3200-seat gymnasium.

Disabled Students: The following facilities are available: wheelchair ramps, elevators, special parking, specially equipped rest rooms, special class scheduling, and lowered drinking fountains.

Services: In addition to many counseling and information services, tutoring is available in every subject. There is also remedial math, reading, and writing. Other services include assistance with note taking, test taking, research papers, and study skills.

Campus Safety and Security: Campus safety and security measures include 24-hour foot and vehicle patrol, escort service, informal discussions, and emergency telephones. In addition, there are lighted pathways and sidewalks.

Programs of Study: Findlay awards the B.A. and B.S. degrees. Associate and master's degrees also are awarded. Bachelor's degrees are awarded in AGRICULTURE (equestrian science), BIOLOGICAL SCIENCE (biology/biological science), BUSINESS (accounting, banking and finance, business administration and management, business economics, business systems analysis, and marketing/retailing/merchandising), COMMUNICATIONS AND THE ARTS (broadcasting, communications, creative writing, dramatic arts, English, English as a second/foreign language, fine arts, German, Japanese, journalism, and Spanish) COMPUTER AND PHYSICAL SCIENCE (computer science, mathematics, and science), EDUCATION (art, bilingual/bicultural, business, education, elementary, foreign languages, and physical), ENGINEERING AND ENVIRONMENTAL DESIGN (environmental science), HEALTH PROFESSIONS (art therapy, medical technology, premedicine, and preveterinary science), SOCIAL SCIENCE (criminal justice, economics, history, philosophy, political science/government, psychology, religion, social work, and sociology). Business administration, preveterinary medicine, English writing, and environmental/hazardous materials management are the strongest academically. Business administration, equestrian studies, education, sciences, and environmental/hazardous materials management have the largest enrollments.

Required: All students must complete 33 semester hours of general education requirements, including fine arts, humanities, and natural science and/or mathematics and computer science, liberal arts electives, and religion or philosophy. There are competency requirements in library use, English and reading, and lifetime activities. A total of 124 semester hours with a minimum GPA of 2.0 is required in order to graduate.

Special: A co-op program is available in accounting. There is a 3–2 engineering program with the University of Toledo, Ohio Northern University, Case Western Reserve University, and Washington University. The field experience program provides up to 20 semester hours in field placement. Internships are available for business, business education, communication, hazardous materials management, and theater majors. Through the College Consortium for International Studies, study abroad is possible in 16 countries. A Washington semester, B.A.-B.S. degrees, dual and student-designed majors, a general studies degree, pass/fail options, and credit for life experience are offered. Nondegree study is possible. There is a freshman honors program on campus

Faculty/Classroom: Sixty percent of faculty are male; 40%, female. All teach undergraduates. No introductory courses are taught by graduate students. The average class size in an introductory lecture is 35; in a laboratory, 15; and in a regular course offering, 35.

Admissions: About 82% of the 1993–94 applicants were accepted. The SAT scores for the 1993–94 freshman class were as follows: Verbal—76% below 500, 16% between 500 and 599, and 8% between 600 and 700; Math—58% below 500, 25% between 500 and 599, 15% between 600 and 700, and 2% above 700. About 72% of the current freshmen were in the top two fifths of their class. Sixteen freshmen graduated first in their class.

Requirements: Findlay requires applicants to be in the upper 50% of their class. A minimum GPA of 2.3 is required. The SAT I or ACT is required. Applicants should have completed 16 high school credits or GED equivalents, including 4 years of English, 2 years of social studies/history, 3 to 4 mathematics courses, and 2 to 3 science courses. AP and CLEP credits are accepted. Important factors used in the admissions decision are advanced placement or honor courses, evidence of special talent, extracurricular activities record, leadership record, and personality, intangible qualities.

Procedure: Freshmen are admitted to all sessions. Entrance exams should be taken during fall of the senior year. Applications should be filed by August 15 for fall entry and December 15 for winter entry. Notification is sent on a rolling basis. There are early admissions and deferred admissions plans.

Transfer: About 80 transfer students enrolled in 1993–94. A minimum 2.0 GPA and eligibility to return to the current institution are required. An interview is recommended. A total of 30 credits out of 124 must be completed at Findlay.

Visiting: There are regularly scheduled orientations for prospective students, including a tour, interview, coach/faculty visits and lunch. There are guides for informal visits and visitors may sit in on classes and stay overnight at the school. To arrange for a visit, contact the Admissions Office at (800) 548–0932.

Financial Aid: In an earlier year, 85% of all current freshmen and 80% of continuing students received some form of financial aid. About 85% of all students received need-based aid. The average freshman award was $6300. Of that total, scholarships or need-based grants averaged $3300 ($7000 maximum); loans averaged $2200 ($2625 maximum); and work contracts averaged $800 ($1000 maximum). Forty percent of undergraduate students work part-time. Average earnings from campus work for the school year are $1000. The average financial indebtedness of an earlier year's graduate was $9000. Findlay is a member of CSS. The FAF and FAFSA are required. The deadline for financial aid applications is August 1.

International Students: There are currently 170 international students enrolled. The school actively recruits these students. They must take the TOEFL and achieve a minimum score of 500. The student must also take the SAT I or the ACT.

Computers: The college provides computer facilities for student use. The mainframe is an HP G-30. A PC laboratory with microcomputers is located in the library. There are 104 student workstations available. All students may access the system. There are no time limits and no fees.

Graduates: In a recent year, 178 bachelor's degrees were awarded. The most popular majors among graduates were business administration (22%), environmental/hazardous materials manage (14%), and accounting (13%). Within an average freshman class, 49% graduate in 4 years.

Admissions Contact: Mary Ellen Klein, Director of Admissions.

UNIVERSITY OF RIO GRANDE
D-5

Rio Grande, OH 45674   (614) 245-5353; (800) 282-7201 (in-state)

Full-time: 740 men, 1064 women	Faculty: 72; IIB, --$
Part-time: 94 men, 134 women	Ph.D.s: 22%
Graduate: 21 men, 117 women	Student/Faculty: 25 to 1
Year: quarters, summer session	Tuition: $2700 ($6252)
Application Deadline: August 1	Room & Board: $3600
Freshman Class: 925 applied, 889 accepted, 725 enrolled	
ACT: 19	NONCOMPETITIVE

The University of Rio Grande, founded in 1876, is a private, coeducational institution offering programs in the liberal arts and sciences, business, and education. There are 6 undergraduate schools and one graduate school. In addition to regional accreditation, Rio has baccalaureate program accreditation with NLN. The library contains 83,000 volumes, 14,076 microform items, and 1204 audiovisual forms, and subscribes to 590 periodicals. Special learning facilities include a learning resource center, art gallery, radio station, and TV station. The 270-acre campus is in a rural area 100 miles southeast of Columbus. Including residence halls, there are 19 buildings on campus.

Student Life: About 90% of undergraduates are from Ohio. Students come from 10 states, 14 foreign countries, and Canada. Eighty percent are from public schools; 20% from private. Eighty percent are white; 15% African American. Eighty percent are Protestant; 20% Catholic. Twenty percent drop out by the end of their first year; 60% remain to graduate.

Housing: A total of 630 students can be accommodated in college housing. College-sponsored living facilities include single-sex and coed dormitories. On-campus housing is guaranteed for all 4 years. Seventy percent of students commute. Alcohol is not permitted. All students may keep cars on campus.

Activities: About 20% of men belong to 2 local and 2 national fraternities; about 20% of women belong to 4 local and 1 national sororities. There are 25 groups on campus, including art, band, cheerleading, choir, chorale, chorus, drama, drill team, ethnic, gay, honors, international, jazz band, musical theater, newspaper, orchestra, pep band, photography, political, professional, radio and TV, religious, social, student government, and yearbook. Popular campus events include Homecoming, May Day, Parents Weekend, Greek Week, and Alumni Weekend.

Sports: There are 5 intercollegiate sports for men and 4 for women, and 7 intramural sports for men and 7 for women. Athletic and recreation facilities include tennis courts, an indoor Olympic-size pool, handball and sand volleyball courts, a fitness center, a cross-country track, and soccer, baseball, and softball fields.

Disabled Students: Seventy-five percent of the campus is accessible to disabled students. The following facilities are available: wheelchair ramps, elevators, special parking, specially equipped rest rooms, special class scheduling, lowered drinking fountains, and lowered telephones.

Services: In addition to many counseling and information services, tutoring is available in every subject. There is a reader service for the blind, and remedial math, reading, and writing. There is also a Special Needs Office.

Campus Safety and Security: Campus safety and security measures include 24-hour foot and vehicle patrol, informal discussions, pamphlets, posters, films, and emergency telephones. In addition, there are lighted pathways and sidewalks.

Programs of Study: Rio awards the B.S. degree. Associate and master's degrees also are awarded. Bachelor's degrees are awarded in BIOLOGICAL SCIENCE (biology/biological science), BUSINESS (accounting, business administration and management, and marketing/retailing/merchandising), COMMUNICATIONS AND THE ARTS (communications, English, fine arts, journalism, and music), COMPUTER AND PHYSICAL SCIENCE (chemistry, mathematics, and physics), EDUCATION (business, elementary, physical, and secondary), ENGINEERING AND ENVIRONMENTAL DESIGN (industrial engineering technology), SOCIAL SCIENCE (American studies, economics, history, humanities, social science, social work, and sociology). Education and business are the strongest academically. Education has the largest enrollment.

Required: Students must complete 190 to 198 credit hours, including 47 to 53 in the major, with a minimum GPA of 2.0. The required general studies program, for all but teacher certification and industrial technology majors, includes 13 credit hours in communication skills, 12 hours each in the humanities, mathematics, natural sciences, and social sciences, 3 hours in health and physical education, and 1 hour in liberal arts.

Special: Internships in social work, communications, and business, study abroad in Japan, and a Washington semester internship are available. Student-designed majors, limited pass/fail options, credit for life, military, or work experience, and nondegree study for a one-year certificate in secretarial science are also available. There is a freshman honors program on campus, as well as 3 national honor societies. One department has an honors program.

Faculty/Classroom: Sixty-six percent of faculty are male; 34%, female. All teach undergraduates. The average class size in an introductory lecture is 25; in a laboratory, 25; and in a regular course offering, 20.

Admissions: About 96% of the 1993–94 applicants were accepted. The ACT scores for the 1993–94 freshman class were as follows: 50% below 21, 25% between 21 and 23, 15% between 24 and 26, 7% between 27 and 28, and 3% above 28. About 15% of the current freshmen were in the top fifth of their class; 50% were in the top two fifths. There were 2 National Merit finalists and 5 semifinalists. About 5 freshmen graduated first in their class.

Requirements: A minimum GPA of 2.0 is required. The ACT is required. The university follows an open admissions policy for all applicants. A high school diploma is required. AP and CLEP credits are accepted. Important factors used in the admissions decision are advanced placement or honor courses, leadership record, evidence of special talent, parents or siblings attending the school, and personality, intangible qualities.

Procedure: Freshmen are admitted to all sessions. Applications should be filed by August 1 for fall entry, October 30 for winter entry, February 10 for spring entry, and May 1 for summer entry, along with an application fee of $15. The college accepts all applicants. Notification is sent on a rolling basis. There are early admissions and deferred admissions plans.

Transfer: About 98 transfer students enrolled in 1993–94. Candidates must submit a final transcript from the last school attended and a dean's evaluation form. A total of 50 quarter hours out of 190 must be completed at Rio.

Visiting: There are regularly scheduled orientations for prospective students. There are guides for informal visits and visitors may sit in on classes and stay overnight at the school. To arrange for a visit, contact the Admissions Office at (614) 245-5353 or (800) 282-7201 in-state.

Financial Aid: In 1993–94 68% of all current freshmen and 72% of continuing students received some form of financial aid. Scholarships or need-based grants averaged $988 ($5055 maximum); and loans averaged $1200 ($2625 maximum). Ten percent of undergraduate students work part-time. Average earnings from campus work for the school year are $1200. Rio is a member of CSS. The FAFSA financial statement is required. The deadline for financial aid applications is July 1.

International Students: There are currently 138 international students enrolled. The school actively recruits these students. They must take the TOEFL and achieve a minimum score of 400.

Computers: The college provides computer facilities for student use. The mainframe is an IBM System 34. All students may access the system. There are no fees.

Graduates: In a recent year, bachelor's degrees were awarded. The most popular majors among graduates were education (34%), mathematics (11%), and communications (10%). Within an average freshman class, 5% graduate in 3 years, 35% in 4 years, 50% in 5 years, and 10% in 6 years. Some 52 companies recruited on campus in a recent year. In the 1992 graduating class, 2% of the men and 2% of the women were enrolled in graduate school within 6 months of graduation; 80% of the men and 82% of the women had found employment.

Admissions Contact: Mark F. Abell, Executive Director of Admissions.

UNIVERSITY OF TOLEDO

B-1

Toledo, OH 43606-3398   (419) 537-2696

Full-time: 7652 men, 7776 women	Faculty: 565; I, --$
Part-time: 2488 men, 2882 women	Ph.D.s: 88%
Graduate: 1736 men, 1654 women	Student/Faculty: 27 to 1
Year: quarters	Tuition: $3236 ($7757)
Application Deadline: see profile	Room & Board: $3400
Freshman Class: 7131 applied, 7092 accepted, 3647 enrolled	
SAT I Verbal/Math: 440/510	ACT: 21 NONCOMPETITIVE

The University of Toledo, founded in 1872, is a public, comprehensive coeducational institution emphasizing undergraduate degree programs in the liberal arts and sciences, business, engineering, teacher preparation, and health professions. There are 7 undergraduate and 6 graduate schools. In addition to regional accreditation, Toledo has baccalaureate program accreditation with AACSB, ABET, ACPE, and NASM. The 3 libraries contain 1,558,864 volumes and 1,477,497 microform items, and subscribe to 7529 periodicals. Computerized library sources and services include the card catalog, interlibrary loans, and database searching. Special learning facilities include a learning resource center, art gallery, planetarium, and radio station. The 305-acre campus is in a suburban area 6 miles northwest of downtown Toledo. Including residence halls, there are more than 40 buildings on campus.

Student Life: About 89% of undergraduates are from Ohio. Students come from 42 states, 83 foreign countries, and Canada. Eighty-two percent are white. The average age of freshmen is 18.9; all undergraduates, 23.4. Twenty-nine percent drop out by the end of their first year; 71% remain to graduate.

Housing: A total of 2548 students can be accommodated in college housing. College-sponsored living facilities include single-sex and coed dormitories, fraternity houses, and sorority houses. In addition, there are honors houses. On-campus housing is available on a first-come, first-served basis. Eighty percent of students commute. All students may keep cars on campus.

Activities: About 10% of men belong to 15 national fraternities; about 10% of women belong to 2 local and 8 national sororities. There are 216 groups on campus, including art, band, cheerleading, chess, choir, chorale, chorus, computers, dance, drama, drill team, ethnic, film, gay, honors, international, jazz band, literary magazine, marching band, musical theater, newspaper, orchestra, pep band, photography, political, professional, radio, religious, social, social service, student government, and symphony. Popular campus events include Homecoming, All-Campus Beach Party, Songfest, Spring Release, Winter Week, Greek Week, Black History Month, Hispanic Awareness Week, Drug Awareness Week, National Alcohol Awareness Week, AIDS Awareness Week, Spring Week, Blue Jeans Day, and International Student Dinner.

Sports: There are 10 intercollegiate sports for men and 8 for women, and 53 intramural sports for men and 52 for women. Athletic and recreation facilities include a recreation center, a 25,000-seat stadium, a 9000-seat arena, a field house, 3 pools, 12 tennis courts, an indoor/outdoor track, a 4-field recreational softball complex, and recreational/sport club fields.

Disabled Students: Ninety-six percent of the campus is accessible to disabled students. The following facilities are available: wheelchair ramps, elevators, special parking, specially equipped rest rooms, special class scheduling, lowered drinking fountains, and lowered telephones.

Services: In addition to many counseling and information services, tutoring is available in every subject. There is a reader service for the blind, and remedial math, reading, and writing.

Campus Safety and Security: Campus safety and security measures include 24-hour foot and vehicle patrol, self defense education, escort service, and shuttle buses. In addition, there are informal discussions, pamphlets, posters, films, emergency telephones, lighted

pathways and sidewalks, and student patrols. All security officers are state-certified with full arrest authority.

Programs of Study: Toledo awards the B.A., B.S., B.B.A., B.Ed., B.in Eng., B.Eng.Tech., B.F.A., B.S.Admin.Serv., B.S. Criminal Justice, B.S. Exercise Science, B.S. Institutional Health Care, B.S.Med.Tech., B.S. in Nursing, B.S.Pharm., B.S. in Physical Therapy, and B.Voc.Ed. degrees. Associate, master's, and doctoral degrees also are awarded. Bachelor's degrees are awarded in BIOLOGICAL SCIENCE (biology/biological science), BUSINESS (accounting, banking and finance, business administration and management, business economics, international business management, marketing/retailing/merchandising, and personnel management), COMMUNICATIONS AND THE ARTS (broadcasting, communications, dance, dramatic arts, English, film arts, fine arts, French, German, journalism, music, Spanish, and speech/debate/rhetoric), COMPUTER AND PHYSICAL SCIENCE (chemistry, computer programming, computer science, geology, mathematics, and physics), EDUCATION (art, business, early childhood, elementary, foreign languages, health, middle school, music, science, secondary, and special), ENGINEERING AND ENVIRONMENTAL DESIGN (chemical engineering, civil engineering, computer engineering, electrical/electronics engineering, engineering, engineering technology, industrial engineering technology, and mechanical engineering), HEALTH PROFESSIONS (medical laboratory technology, nursing, pharmacy, physical therapy, predentistry, premedicine, and speech pathology/audiology), SOCIAL SCIENCE (anthropology, criminal justice, economics, geography, history, international relations, philosophy, physical fitness/movement, political science/government, prelaw, psychology, social work, sociology, urban studies, and women's studies). Engineering, pharmacy, business, education, and health professions are the strongest programs academically.

Required: To graduate, all students must complete 186 quarter hours of credit, with 60 in the major, and maintain a minimum GPA of 2.0.

Special: Special academic programs include internships in most majors, study abroad in 12 countries, and on-campus employment through the Financial Aid Office. There is a co-op program with the College of Engineering and cross-registration with Bowling Green State University. The B.A.-B.S. degree and dual majors are available in many areas of study. A general studies degree, student-designed majors, credit for life, military, and work experience, nondegree study, and pass/fail options are also offered. There is a freshman honors program on campus, as well as 56 national honor societies. There is a college-wide honors program.

Faculty/Classroom: Seventy-eight percent of faculty are male; 22%, female. All teach undergraduates, 64% do research, and 64% do both. The average class size in an introductory lecture is 28 and in a regular course offering, 25.

Admissions: About 99% of the 1993–94 applicants were accepted. The SAT scores for the 1993–94 freshman class were as follows: Verbal—67% below 500, 20% between 500 and 599, 10% between 600 and 700, and 3% above 700; Math—42% below 500, 29% between 500 and 599, 18% between 600 and 700, and 11% above 700. The ACT scores were 45% below 21, 25% between 21 and 23, 16% between 24 and 26, 6% between 27 and 28, and 8% above 28. There were 37 National Merit finalists.

Requirements: A minimum GPA of 2.0 is required. The SAT I or ACT is required. The university follows an open admissions policy for Ohio applicants. Students should be graduates of an accredited secondary school or hold the GED. The preparatory program should include 4 years of English, 2 years of a foreign language, and 3 years of mathematics; 3 years each of science and social studies are recommended, as is history for arts and sciences majors. An interview is advised. AP and CLEP credits are accepted. Important factors used in the admissions decision are evidence of special talent, recommendations by school officials, leadership record, extracurricular activities record, and parents or siblings attending the school.

Procedure: Freshmen are admitted to all sessions. Entrance exams should be taken late in the junior year or early in the senior year. The application deadline is 1 week prior to the beginning of each quarter. Application fee is $30. The college accepts all in-state residents who apply. Notification is sent on a rolling basis. There is a deferred admissions plan.

Transfer: About 1574 transfer students enrolled in 1993–94. Applicants must have a minimum of 12 quarter hour college credits or 8 semester hour college credits and a GPA of 2.0. An interview is recommended. A total of 45 quarter hours out of 186 must be completed at Toledo.

Visiting: There are regularly scheduled orientations for prospective students, including an interview with an admissions counselor and a student-guided campus tour. There are guides for informal visits and visitors may sit in on classes and stay overnight at the school. To arrange for a visit, contact the Office of Admissions at (419) 537-2696.

Financial Aid: In 1993–94, 33% of all current freshmen and 60% of continuing students received some form of financial aid. About 29% of freshmen and 48% of continuing students received need-based aid. The average freshman award was $3286. Of that total, scholarships or need-based grants averaged $1657; loans averaged $2570; and work contracts averaged $3093 ($3230 maximum). Fifty percent of undergraduate students work part-time. Average earnings from campus work for the school year are $2500. Toledo is a member of CSS. The college's own financial statement, a state grant form, and the FAFSA are required. The deadline for financial aid applications is April 1.

International Students: There are currently 1349 international students enrolled. The school actively recruits these students. They must take the TOEFL.

Computers: The college provides computer facilities for student use. The mainframes are an IBM-compatible, NAS 9080 and a DEC 6220. Mainframe terminals and networked microcomputers are available at many campus locations. Students with user accounts issued through course instructors may access the mainframe. It may be used 8:30 P.M. to 12 A.M. Monday through Friday, 8:30 A.M. to 5 P.M. Saturday, and 1 P.M. to 12 A.M. Sunday. Time limits on using the system depend on the course requiring computer use. There are no fees.

Graduates: In 1992–93 2369 bachelor's degrees were awarded. The most popular majors among graduates were communication (6%), marketing (5%), and finance (5%). Within an average freshman class, 3% graduate in 3 years, 19% in 4 years, and 32% in 5 years. Some 401 companies recruited on campus in 1992–93.

Admissions Contact: Richard J. Eastop, Dean of Admissions Services.

URBANA UNIVERSITY
B-3

Urbana, OH 43078-2091　　　　　　　(513) 652-1301, ext. 356

Full-time: 476 men, 269 women	Faculty: 32; IIB, --$
Part-time: 57 men, 109 women	Ph.D.s: 62%
Graduate: none	Student/Faculty: 23 to 1
Year: semesters, summer session	Tuition: $8396
Application Deadline: open	Room & Board: $4140
Freshman Class: 318 applied, 265 accepted, 132 enrolled	
ACT: 19	COMPETITIVE

Urbana University, founded in 1850, is a nonprofit, independent coeducational institution emphasizing programs in liberal arts, business, professional training, and teacher preparation. The library contains 63,000 volumes, 8176 microform items, and 2099 audiovisual forms, and subscribes to 328 periodicals. Computerized library sources and services include interlibrary loans and database searching. Special learning facilities include a learning resource center, TV station, and rare book room. The 128-acre campus is in a small town 40 miles west of Columbus and north of Dayton. Including residence halls, there are 23 buildings on campus.

Student Life: About 95% of undergraduates are from Ohio. Students come from 5 states, 5 foreign countries, and Canada. Ninety-five percent are from public schools; 5% from private. Seventy-two percent are white; 25% African American. The average age of freshmen is 20; all undergraduates, 24. Twenty-three percent drop out by the end of their first year; 35% remain to graduate.

Housing: A total of 265 students can be accommodated in college housing. College-sponsored living facilities include single-sex and coed dormitories. In addition, there are honors houses. On-campus housing is guaranteed for all 4 years. Fifty-eight percent of students commute. Alcohol is not permitted. All students may keep cars on campus.

Activities: There are no fraternities or sororities on campus. There are 15 groups on campus, including band, cheerleading, choir, chorus, drama, ethnic, international, literary magazine, musical theater, newspaper, pep band, professional, radio and TV, student government, and yearbook. Popular campus events include Homecoming, Spring Week, and convocations.

Sports: There are 6 intercollegiate sports for men and 5 for women, and 10 intramural sports for men and 8 for women. Athletic and recreation facilities include a community center with a 3500-seat gymnasium, a pool, handball and racquetball courts, and a weight room.

Disabled Students: Thirty percent of the campus is accessible to disabled students. The following facilities are available: wheelchair ramps, special parking, and special class scheduling.

Services: In addition to many counseling and information services, tutoring is available in most subjects. There is also remedial math, reading, and writing, as well as taped textbooks, reading and writing laboratories, and study skills seminars.

Campus Safety and Security: Campus safety and security measures include 24-hour foot and vehicle patrol, informal discussions, and lighted pathways and sidewalks.

Programs of Study: Urbana awards the B.A., B.S., and B.S.Ed. degrees. Associate degrees also are awarded. Bachelor's degrees are awarded in BIOLOGICAL SCIENCE (biology/biological science),

BUSINESS (accounting, banking and finance, business administration and management, business economics, marketing/retailing/merchandising, personnel management, and recreation and leisure services), COMMUNICATIONS AND THE ARTS (communications and English), COMPUTER AND PHYSICAL SCIENCE (chemistry and science), EDUCATION (elementary, middle school, physical, and secondary), HEALTH PROFESSIONS (premedicine and sports medicine), SOCIAL SCIENCE (community services, law enforcement and corrections, liberal arts/general studies, philosophy, prelaw, psychology, religion, social work, and sociology). Business and education are the strongest programs academically and have the largest enrollments.

Required: To graduate, all students must complete 126 semester hours, including 87 in the major, with a minimum overall GPA of 2.0 and 2.5 in the major. Distribution requirements include 9 hours each in humanities, social sciences, communications, and mathematics/science, and 2 hours in health and physical education.

Special: Special academic programs include internships, cross-registration with the Southwestern Ohio Council for Higher Education, and accelerated degree programs in teacher certification. B.A.-B.S. degrees, dual and student-designed majors, credit for life, military, and work experience, and nondegree study are also available. There is 1 national honor society on campus.

Faculty/Classroom: Eighty-four percent of faculty are male; 16%, female. All teach undergraduates and 13% both teach and do research. The average class size in an introductory lecture is 18; in a laboratory, 7; and in a regular course offering, 19.

Admissions: About 83% of the 1993–94 applicants were accepted. About 26% of the current freshmen were in the top fifth of their class; 54% were in the top two fifths. About 4 freshmen graduated first in their class.

Requirements: A minimum GPA of 2.2 is required. The SAT I or ACT is required of applicants under 21 years of age. The minimum SAT I score should be 700, and the minimum ACT score, 19. Applicants must be graduates of an accredited secondary school with a GPA of 2.2. The GED is accepted. An essay is required of all applicants, and an interview is recommended. CLEP credit is accepted. Important factors used in the admissions decision are advanced placement or honor courses, evidence of special talent, recommendations by school officials, personality, intangible qualities, and leadership record.

Procedure: Freshmen are admitted to all sessions. Entrance exams should be taken during the junior or senior years. Application deadlines are open. The fee is $10. Notification is sent on a rolling basis. There are early admissions and deferred admissions plans.

Transfer: About 109 transfer students enrolled in 1993–94. Applicants must be in good standing at their previous institution. A total of 30 credits out of 126 must be completed at Urbana.

Visiting: There are regularly scheduled orientations for prospective students. There are guides for informal visits, and visitors may sit in on classes and stay overnight at the school. To arrange for a visit, contact the Office of Admissions at (513) 652–1301, ext. 356.

Financial Aid: In a recent year, all freshmen and continuing students received some form of financial aid. About 80% of freshmen and continuing students received need-based aid. The average freshman award was $6500. Of that total, scholarships or need-based grants averaged $1600 ($7840 maximum); loans averaged $2625 (maximum); and work contracts averaged $1000 (maximum). Sixty percent of undergraduate students work part-time. Average earnings from campus work for the school year are $1000. The average financial indebtedness of a recent year's graduate was $4500. Urbana is a member of CSS. The FAF, FFS, or SFS is required. The deadline for financial aid applications is June 1.

International Students: There are currently 10 international students enrolled. The school actively recruits these students. They must take the TOEFL or the University of Michigan Language Test and achieve a minimum score on the TOEFL of 500.

Computers: The college provides computer facilities for student use. The mainframe is a DEC PDP 11/84. IBM and Apple Macintosh microcomputers are available for student use in the computer laboratory, the education department, and the library. There are no time limits on using the system and no fees.

Graduates: In a recent year, 101 bachelor's degrees were awarded. The most popular majors among graduates were business (40%), social services (22%), and education (18%). Some 21 companies recruited on campus in a recent year. In a recent graduating class, 3% of the men and 1% of the women were enrolled in graduate school within 6 months of graduation; 79% of the men and 73% of the women had found employment.

Admissions Contact: Lori Botkin-Carpenter, Director of Admissions.

URSULINE COLLEGE
D-1

Pepper Pike, OH 44124 (216) 449–4203

Full-time: 32 men, 667 women	Faculty: 68; IIB, --$
Part-time: 37 men, 680 women	Ph.D.s: 60%
Graduate: 12 men, 135 women	Student/Faculty: 10 to 1
Year: semesters, summer session	Tuition: $9180
Application Deadline: open	Room & Board: $4000
Freshman Class: 325 applied, 260 accepted, 86 enrolled	
SAT I Verbal/Math: 390/410	ACT: 20 LESS COMPETITIVE

Ursuline College, established in 1871, is a private, liberal arts, primarily women's college affiliated with the Roman Catholic Church. There are 5 undergraduate and 3 graduate schools. In addition to regional accreditation, Ursuline has baccalaureate program accreditation with NLN. The library contains 101,730 volumes and 37,000 audiovisual forms, and subscribes to 1189 periodicals. Computerized library sources and services include the card catalog, interlibrary loans, and database searching. Special learning facilities include an art gallery, a media center, and a curriculum library. The 115-acre campus is in a suburban area 20 miles east of Cleveland. Including residence halls, there are 12 buildings on campus.

Student Life: Almost all undergraduates are from Ohio. Students come from 3 states and 3 foreign countries. Sixty percent are from public schools; 40% from private. Eighty-four percent are white; 13% African American. Sixty-one percent are Catholic; 21% Protestant. The average age of freshmen is 29; all undergraduates, 33. Eight percent drop out by the end of their first year; 91% remain to graduate.

Housing: A total of 196 students can be accommodated in college housing. College-sponsored living facilities include single-sex dormitories. On-campus housing is guaranteed for all 4 years and is available on a first-come, first-served basis. Eighty-seven percent of students commute. Alcohol is not permitted. All students may keep cars on campus.

Activities: There are no fraternities or sororities on campus. There are 13 groups on campus, including art, ethnic, international, literary magazine, newspaper, photography, professional, religious, social, social service, student government, and yearbook. Popular campus events include All College Day, a Christmas semiformal dance, and charity benefits.

Sports: Athletic and recreation facilities include a swimming pool, a gymnasium, a campus center, and tennis courts.

Disabled Students: Eighty percent of the campus is accessible to disabled students. The following facilities are available: wheelchair ramps, elevators, special parking, and specially equipped rest rooms.

Services: In addition to many counseling and information services, tutoring is available in every subject. There is also remedial math, reading, and writing.

Campus Safety and Security: Campus safety and security measures include 24-hour foot and vehicle patrol, escort service, informal discussions, pamphlets, posters, and films. In addition, there are emergency telephones and lighted pathways and sidewalks.

Programs of Study: Ursuline awards the B.A. and B.S.N. degrees. Associate and master's degrees are also awarded. Bachelor's degrees are awarded in BIOLOGICAL SCIENCE (biology/biological science), BUSINESS (accounting, business administration and management, and fashion merchandising), COMMUNICATIONS AND THE ARTS (art, arts administration/management, English, and public relations), COMPUTER AND PHYSICAL SCIENCE (mathematics), EDUCATION (art, elementary, foreign languages, science, secondary, and social studies), ENGINEERING AND ENVIRONMENTAL DESIGN (interior design), HEALTH PROFESSIONS (art therapy, cytotechnology, health care administration, nursing, and premedicine), SOCIAL SCIENCE (American studies, behavioral science, child care/child and family studies, fashion design and technology, history, humanities, philosophy, prelaw, psychology, religion, social science, social work, and sociology). Nursing is the strongest academically. Nursing and business have the largest enrollments.

Required: To graduate, students must complete 128 semester hours for the B.A. and 129 for the B.S.N., with a minimum GPA of 2.0 (2.5 in education courses). All students must take 49 credits of general education courses, structured to develop progressive stages of learning.

Special: Ursuline offers co-op programs with the Cleveland College of Jewish Studies and cross-registration with the 8 area colleges in the Cleveland Commission of Higher Education. Internships, a general studies degree, dual and student-designed majors, and nondegree study are available. Students may receive credit for life, military, or work experience. There are pass/fail options and a continuing studies program for nontraditional students.

Faculty/Classroom: Five percent of faculty are male; 95%, female. All teach undergraduates. No introductory courses are taught by graduate students.

Admissions: About 80% of the 1993–94 applicants were accepted. The SAT scores for the 1993–94 freshman class were as follows: Verbal—82% below 500, 13% between 500 and 599, and 5% between

600 and 700; Math—68% below 500, 25% between 500 and 599, and 7% between 600 and 700. The ACT scores were 50% below 21, 29% between 21 and 23, 10% between 24 and 26, 6% between 27 and 28, and 5% above 28. About 36% of the current freshmen were in the top fifth of their class; 62% were in the top two fifths. There were 5 National Merit finalists and 12 semifinalists. About 5 freshmen graduated first in their class.

Requirements: The SAT I or ACT is required. Students should be graduates of an accredited secondary school and have a GPA of 2.5. Recommeded college preparatory courses include 4 units of English, 3 each of social studies, mathematics, and science, 2 of a foreign language, and 1 each of fine/performing arts and physical education/health. A recommendation from a teacher or counselor is required and an interview is encouraged. AP and CLEP credits are accepted. Important factors used in the admissions decision are advanced placement or honor courses, recommendations by school officials, leadership record, extracurricular activities record, and evidence of special talent.

Procedure: Freshmen are admitted to all sessions. Entrance exams should be taken in the junior year. Application deadlines are open. Application fee is $25. Notification is sent on a rolling basis.

Transfer: About 60 transfer students enrolled in a recent year. A total of 43 credits out of 128 of 129 must be completed at Ursuline.

Visiting: There are regularly scheduled orientations for prospective students. There are guides for informal visits and visitors may sit in on classes and stay overnight at the school. To arrange for a visit, contact Massi Hourihan at (216) 449-4203.

Financial Aid: In a recent year, 95% of all current freshmen and 53% of continuing students received some form of financial aid. About 80% of freshmen received need-based aid. The average freshman award was $6578. Ninety-seven percent of undergraduate students work part-time. Average earnings from campus work for the school year was $800. The average financial indebtedness of the 1992–93 graduate was $8000. Ursuline is a member of CSS. The FAF and the college's own financial statement are required. The deadline for financial aid applications is March 15.

International Students: Students must take the TOEFL and achieve a minimum score of 500.

Computers: The college provides computer facilities for student use. The mainframe is a Unisys. Computer laboratories in the science center house IBM-compatible HP microcomputers. All students may access the system. It may be used daily at designated hours. There are no time limits on using the system. The fees are $40.

Graduates: Within an average freshman class, 90% graduate in 4 years and 10% in 5 years. Some 50 companies recruited on campus in a recent year.

Admissions Contact: Dennis L. Giacomino, Director of Admission.

WALSH COLLEGE
(See Walsh University)

WALSH UNIVERSITY
D-2

(Formerly Walsh College)
North Canton, OH 44720

(216) 499-7090; (800) 362-9846

Full-time: 350 men, 506 women	Faculty: 65; IIB, --$
Part-time: 122 men, 378 women	Ph.D.s: 50%
Graduate: 76 men, 146 women	Student/Faculty: 13 to 1
Year: semesters, summer session	Tuition: $7710
Application Deadline: open	Room & Board: $3930
Freshman Class: 825 applied, 795 accepted, 456 enrolled	
ACT: 22	**COMPETITIVE**

Walsh University, founded in 1960, is a private institution affiliated with the Roman Catholic Church and operated by the Brothers of Christian Instruction. The college offers undergraduate and graduate programs in the liberal arts, business, professional training, counseling, teacher preparation, and religious studies. There is one undergraduate and 2 graduate schools. In addition to regional accreditation, Walsh has baccalaureate program accreditation with NLN. The library contains 105,000 volumes. Special learning facilities include a radio station. The 58-acre campus is in a small town 20 miles south of Akron. Including residence halls, there are 8 buildings on campus.

Student Life: About 90% of undergraduates are from Ohio. Students come from 5 states and 8 foreign countries. Eighty-nine percent are white. Fifty percent are Protestant; 50% Catholic. The average age of freshmen is 19; all undergraduates, 27.

Housing: A total of 380 students can be accommodated in college housing. College-sponsored living facilities include single-sex and coed dormitories. On-campus housing is guaranteed for all 4 years. Seventy-two percent of students commute. Alcohol is not permitted. All students may keep cars on campus.

Activities: There are no fraternities or sororities on campus. There are 25 groups on campus, including cheerleading, computers, drama, international, newspaper, political, professional, radio and TV, religious, social, social service, student government, and yearbook.

Sports: There are 7 intercollegiate sports for men and 7 for women, and 10 intramural sports for men and 10 for women. Athletic and recreation facilities include a 1200-seat gymnasium, tennis courts, a track, soccer and baseball fields, and an indoor swimming pool.

Disabled Students: The entire campus is accessible to disabled students. The following facilities are available: wheelchair ramps, elevators, special parking, and specially equipped rest rooms.

Services: In addition to many counseling and information services, tutoring is available in every subject. There is remedial math, reading, and writing.

Campus Safety and Security: Campus safety and security measures include 24-hour foot and vehicle patrol and lighted pathways and sidewalks.

Programs of Study: Walsh awards the B.A., B.S., and B.S.N. degrees. Associate and master's degrees also are awarded. Bachelor's degrees are awarded in BIOLOGICAL SCIENCE (biology/biological science), BUSINESS (accounting, banking and finance, business administration and management, and marketing/retailing/merchandising), COMMUNICATIONS AND THE ARTS (communications, English, French, and Spanish), COMPUTER AND PHYSICAL SCIENCE (chemistry, computer science, and mathematics), EDUCATION (early childhood, elementary, middle school, physical, secondary, and special), HEALTH PROFESSIONS (medical laboratory technology, nursing, predentistry, premedicine, and preveterinary science), SOCIAL SCIENCE (community services, history, international studies, philosophy, political science/government, prelaw, psychology, religion, and sociology). Business, psychology, nursing, and education are the strongest academically.

Required: To graduate, students must complete 130 semester hours with a 2.0 GPA. The number of hours required in the major is usually 36. A core curriculum of 65 to 67 hours is required, including courses in English, art and music appreciation, economics, social science, mathematics, science, humanities, physical education, theology, philosophy, and possibly a foreign language.

Special: Work-study programs are available to students having substantial financial need. A 3–2 program in natural resources, including forestry, conservation teaching, fisheries, and wildlife management, is offered with the University of Michigan. The college offers co-op programs in business, evening and continuing education programs, and credit for life experience. There is a chapter of Phi Beta Kappa on campus.

Faculty/Classroom: The average class size in an introductory lecture is 20; in a laboratory, 20; and in a regular course offering, 19.

Admissions: About 96% of the 1993–94 applicants were accepted. About 22% of the current freshmen were in the top fifth of their class; 60% were in the top two fifths.

Requirements: A minimum GPA of 2.3 is required. The SAT I or ACT is required. The applicant must be a graduate of an accredited secondary school; the GED is accepted. An essay and an interview are recommended. AP and CLEP credits are accepted. Important factors used in the admissions decision are recommendations by school officials, leadership record, personality, intangible qualities, extracurricular activities record, and recommendations by alumni.

Procedure: Freshmen are admitted to all sessions. Entrance exams should be taken during the junior year. Application deadlines are open. The fee is $15. Notification is sent on a rolling basis. There are early decision, early admissions, and deferred admissions plans. About 10 early decision candidates were accepted for the 1993–94 class.

Transfer: Applicants must have a minimum GPA of 2.0 from previous colleges attended. A total of 32 credits out of 130 must be completed at Walsh.

Visiting: There are regularly scheduled orientations for prospective students. There are guides for informal visits, and visitors may sit in on classes and stay overnight at the school. To arrange for a visit, contact the Admissions Office at (800) 362-9846 or (216) 499-7090.

Financial Aid: In a recent year, 85% of all freshmen and continuing students received some form of financial aid. Walsh is a member of CSS. The FAF is required. The deadline for financial aid applications is March 15.

International Students: There are currently 39 international students enrolled. The school actively recruits these students. They must take the TOEFL and achieve a minimum score of 550.

Computers: The college provides computer facilities for student use. The mainframe is an IBM. There are 24 terminals located in the computer laboratory in Hannon Center. All students may access the system. There are no time limits on using the system and no fees.

Graduates: In a recent year, 240 bachelor's degrees were awarded. The most popular majors among graduates were business (42%) and nursing (20%). Some 33 companies recruited on campus in a recent year. In a recent graduating class, 5% of all students were enrolled in

graduate school within 6 months of graduation; 85% of the men and 75% of the women had found employment.

Admissions Contact: Doug Swartz, Director of Admissions.

WILBERFORCE UNIVERSITY
B-4
Wilberforce, OH 45384-1091

(513) 376-2911
(800) 367-8568 (out-of-state)

Full-time: 302 men, 543 women	Faculty: 54
Part-time: none	Ph.Ds: 45%
Graduate: none	Student/Faculty: 16 to 1
Year: semesters, summer session	Tuition: $6926
Application Deadline: June 1	Room & Board: $3482
Freshman Class: 1179 applied, 1122 accepted, 388 enrolled	
ACT: 17	COMPETITIVE

Wilberforce University, founded in 1856, is a nonprofit, private coeducational institution operated under the auspices of the African Methodist Episcopal Church; it was the first black college in America. Its programs emphasize the liberal arts, business, art and fine arts, engineering, and music. The library contains 60,000 volumes, 12,000 microform items, and 200 audiovisual forms, and subscribes to 350 periodicals. Special learning facilities include a learning resource center, a radio station, and the nearby National Afro-American Museum. The 125-acre campus is in a rural area 20 miles east of Dayton. Including residence halls, there are 21 buildings on campus.

Student Life: About 64% of undergraduates are from out-of-state, mostly the Midwest. Students come from 32 states and 2 foreign countries. All are African American. The average age of freshmen is 18; all undergraduates, 20.

Housing: A total of 775 students can be accommodated in college housing. College-sponsored living facilities include dormitories and married-student housing. In addition there are honors houses. On-campus housing is guaranteed for all 4 years and is available on a first-come, first-served basis. Eighty-five percent of students live on campus; of those, 70% remain on campus on weekends. Alcohol is not permitted. All students may keep cars on campus.

Activities: Ten percent of men belong to 3 national fraternities; ten percent of women belong to 3 national sororities. There are 30 groups on campus, including choir, computers, dance, ethnic, honors, international, literary magazine, newspaper, political, religious, social, student government, and yearbook. Popular campus events include Fall Festival, Homecoming, and Dawn Dance.

Sports: There are 5 intercollegiate sports for men and 4 for women, and 4 intramural sports each for men and women. Athletic and recreation facilities include a 1500-seat gymnasium, outdoor and cross-country track, a softball field, and basketball, volleyball, and tennis courts.

Disabled Students: Fifty percent of the campus is accessible to disabled students. The following facilities are available: wheelchair ramps, special parking, specially equipped rest rooms, and and limited elevator service in classroom buildings only.

Services: In addition to many counseling and information services, tutoring is available in most subjects. There is also a reader service for the blind, and remedial math, reading, and writing.

Programs of Study: Wilberforce awards the B.A. and B.S. degrees. Bachelor's degrees are awarded in BIOLOGICAL SCIENCE (biology/biological science), BUSINESS (accounting, banking and finance, business administration and management, business economics, management science, and marketing/retailing/merchandising), COMMUNICATIONS AND THE ARTS (communications, fine arts, literature, and music), COMPUTER AND PHYSICAL SCIENCE (chemistry, information sciences and systems, mathematics, and science), ENGINEERING AND ENVIRONMENTAL DESIGN (preengineering), HEALTH PROFESSIONS (health care administration, predentistry, premedicine, and rehabilitation therapy), SOCIAL SCIENCE (criminal justice, economics, liberal arts/general studies, political science/government, prelaw, psychology, and social science). Business administration, accounting, and banking and finance are the strongest programs academically.

Required: To graduate, students must complete 126 credit hours with a minimum GPA of 2.0 and no grade in the major below a C. Core course requirements and distribution requirements across 5 divisions must be met. Basic mathematics credits, 2 credits of physical education, a composition course, and at least 2 successful cooperative education assignments must be completed.

Special: Wilberforce offers a co-op arrangement with St. John's University School of Law and cross-registration with the Southwestern Ohio Council for Higher Education. B.A.-B.S. degrees are available in all majors, and there are dual majors in engineering along with a 3–2 engineering degree with the University of Dayton. Credit is given for the mandatory co-op education program, in which students participate in paid work experience in their chosen field. Nondegree study is possible in military science. There is a freshman honors program on campus, as well as one national honor society, Phi Beta Kappa. Four departments have honors programs.

Faculty/Classroom: Fifty percent of faculty are male; 50%, female. The average class size in an introductory lecture is 12 and in a regular course offering, 18.

Admissions: About 95% of the 1993–94 applicants were accepted.

Requirements: A minimum GPA of 2.0 is required. The SAT I or ACT is required. Other admissions requirements include graduation from an accredited secondary school with a GPA of 2.0 and 15 Carnegie units, including 4 units of English; 2 to 3 of mathematics, including algebra; 2 to 3 of science, including 1 laboratory course; and 2 of social studies, including U.S. history. The GED is accepted with a score of 45 or better. SAT II: Subject tests are recommended. AP and CLEP credits are accepted. Important factors used in the admissions decision are recommendations by school officials, advanced placement or honor courses, evidence of special talent, leadership record, and recommendations by alumni.

Procedure: Freshmen are admitted in the fall and spring. Entrance exams should be taken by the fall of the senior year. Applications should be filed by June 1 for fall entry and November 15 for spring entry, along with an application fee of $20. Notification is sent on a rolling basis. There are early decision and early admissions plans. A waiting list is an active part of the admissions procedure.

Transfer: About 50 transfer students enrolled in a recent year. A minimum college GPA of 2.0 is required. A total of 36 credits out of 126 must be completed at Wilberforce.

Visiting: There are regularly scheduled orientations for prospective students. There are guides for informal visits. To arrange for a visit, contact Joel Robinson, Admissions Counselor, at (800) 367-8568 or (513) 376-2911.

Financial Aid: In a recent year, about 95% of all students received some form of financial aid. Scholarships or need-based grants averaged $600 ($2000 maximum); loans averaged $2000 ($2625 maximum); and work contracts averaged $2070 ($2400 maximum). The average financial indebtedness of an earlier graduate was $9000. Wilberforce is a member of CSS. The FAF, FFS or SFS is required. The deadline for financial aid applications is April 30.

International Students: There are currently 7 international students enrolled. They must take the TOEFL and achieve a minimum score of 500. The student must also take the SAT I or the ACT.

Computers: The college provides computer facilities for student use. The mainframe is an NCR Tower Series 32/650. There are also 85 NCR 710 microcomputers available in the computer center. Students enrolled in computer and engineering programs may access the system. There are no time limits on using the system.

Graduates: In an earlier graduating class, 6% of the men and 10% of the women were enrolled in graduate school within 6 months of graduation.

Admissions Contact: Wendell Webster, Director of Admissions.

WILMINGTON COLLEGE
B-4
Wilmington, OH 45177

(513) 382-6661; (800) 341-9318

Full-time: 405 men, 421 women	Faculty: 55; IIB, --$
Part-time: 31 men, 32 women	Ph.Ds: 55%
Graduate: none	Student/Faculty: 15 to 1
Year: semesters, summer session	Tuition: $9830
Application Deadline: open	Room & Board: $3870
Freshman Class: 750 applied, 650 accepted, 230 enrolled	
ACT: 21	LESS COMPETITIVE

Wilmington College, established in 1870, is a private institution sponsored by the Society of Friends. The college offers programs in the liberal arts, business, health science, teacher preparation, agricultural studies, religious studies, and athletic training. The library contains 100,000 volumes, 20,000 microform items, and 500 audiovisual forms, and subscribes to 405 periodicals. Special learning facilities include a learning resource center, an art gallery, the Peace Resource Center, a Quaker museum, an observatory, and a greenhouse. The 65-acre campus is in a small town 50 miles from Cincinnati and from Columbus. Including residence halls, there are 16 buildings on campus.

Student Life: About 96% of undergraduates are from Ohio. Students come from 13 states and 12 foreign countries. Ninety-seven percent are from public schools; 3% from private. Ninety-six percent are white. The average age of freshmen is 19. Thirty percent drop out by the end of their first year; 58% remain to graduate.

Housing: A total of 510 students can be accommodated in college housing. College-sponsored living facilities include single-sex and coed dormitories and fraternity houses. On-campus housing is guaranteed for all 4 years. Fifty-two percent of students live on campus. All students may keep cars on campus.

Activities: There are 3 local and 2 national fraternities and 4 local sororities. There are 19 groups on campus, including cheerleading, choir, chorale, drama, ethnic, honors, international, jazz band, literary magazine, musical theater, newspaper, orchestra, photography, political, religious, social, social service, student government, and year-

book. Popular campus events include Li'l Sibs Weekend and Homecoming.

Sports: There are 9 intercollegiate sports for men and 5 for women, and 8 intramural sports for men and 8 for women. Athletic and recreation facilities include an Olympic-size pool, a Nautilus weight-training room, an exercise room, and racquetball courts. There is also a 4500-seat gymnasium and a 3000-seat stadium.

Disabled Students: The following facilities are available: wheelchair ramps, elevators, special parking, specially equipped rest rooms, and special class scheduling.

Services: In addition to many counseling and information services, tutoring is available in every subject. There is also remedial math, reading, and writing.

Campus Safety and Security: Campus safety and security measures include 24-hour foot and vehicle patrol, escort service, informal discussions, and pamphlets, posters, and films. In addition, there are lighted pathways and sidewalks.

Programs of Study: Wilmington awards the B.A. and B.S. degrees. Bachelor's degrees are awarded in AGRICULTURE (agricultural business management and agriculture), BIOLOGICAL SCIENCE (biology/biological science), BUSINESS (accounting, business administration and management, and marketing/retailing/merchandising), COMMUNICATIONS AND THE ARTS (communications, dramatic arts, English, English literature, fine arts, French, journalism, and Spanish), COMPUTER AND PHYSICAL SCIENCE (chemistry, computer science, and mathematics), EDUCATION (agricultural, art, business, elementary, foreign languages, health, mathematics, music, physical, science, secondary, and vocational), HEALTH PROFESSIONS (occupational therapy, predentistry, premedicine, and preveterinary science), SOCIAL SCIENCE (community services, criminal justice, economics, history, prelaw, psychology, religion, social science, and sociology). Business/education and agriculture have the largest enrollments.

Required: In order to graduate, students must complete 124 semester hours, with no more than 60 hours in the major, and maintain a minimum GPA of 2.0. At least 40 of the 124 hours must be in upper-division work. General education requirements include courses in English and mathematics competence, international knowledge, basic areas of thought expression, and personal fitness.

Special: Special academic programs include internships, a Washington semester, and cross-registration with the Southwest Ohio Consortium. Study abroad may be arranged in Mexico, Austria, France, and other countries. Dual majors in any subject and student-designed majors are offered. Credit for experience, nondegree study, and pass/fail options are possible. There is 1 national honor society on campus.

Faculty/Classroom: Seventy-five percent of faculty are male; 25% female. All teach undergraduates. The average class size in an introductory lecture is 25 and in a regular course offering, 19.

Admissions: About 87% of the 1993–94 applicants were accepted. The ACT scores for the 1993–94 freshman class were as follows: 55% below 21, 21% between 21 and 23, 15% between 24 and 26, 6% between 27 and 28, and 3% above 28. About 30% of the current freshmen were in the top fifth of their class. Five freshmen graduated first in their class.

Requirements: A minimum GPA of 2.0 is required. The SAT I or ACT is required. Applicants must be graduates of an accredited secondary school, with 4 units of English, 2 units each of mathematics, science, and social studies, and a recommended 2 units of a foreign language. An additional 6 units is required in other areas. The GED is accepted. An interview is recommended. An essay may sometimes be required. AP and CLEP credits are accepted.

Procedure: Freshmen are admitted fall and spring. Entrance exams should be taken as early as possible. Application deadlines are open. The application fee is $15. Notification is sent on a rolling basis. There is an early decision plan.

Transfer: Some 70 transfer students enrolled in 1993–94. An applicant's college and high school transcripts will be evaluated on an individual basis. A total of 30 semester hours out of 124 must be completed at Wilmington.

Visiting: There are regularly scheduled orientations for prospective students, including meetings with faculty and a tour of the campus. There are guides for informal visits and visitors may sit in on classes and stay overnight at the school. To arrange for a visit, contact the Admissions Office at (513) 382–6661 or (800) 341–9318.

Financial Aid: In 1993–94 89% of all students received some form of financial aid. About 85% of all students received need-based aid. The average freshman award was $7142. Of that total, scholarships or need-based grants averaged $2743 ($5000 maximum); loans averaged $2705 ($4625 maximum); work contracts averaged $1200 ($1300 maximum); and Choice awards averaged $494 (maximum). Forty percent of undergraduate students work part-time. Average earnings from campus work for the school year are $700. The average financial indebtedness of the 1992–93 graduate was $6800. Wilmington is a member of CSS. The FAF and FAFSA are required. Financial applications should be filed as early as possible.

International Students: There are currently 20 international students enrolled. The school actively recruits these students. They must take the TOEFL and achieve a specified minimum score. Students who have been previously enrolled in a U.S. high school must also take the SAT I.

Computers: The college provides computer facilities for student use. The mainframe is an HP 9000. There are 40 IBM and IBM-compatible microcomputers available. All students may access the system. It may be used at any time. There are no time limits on using the system and no fees.

Graduates: In 1992–93 180 bachelor's degrees were awarded. The most popular majors among graduates were education (40%), business (25%), and agriculture (10%). Within an average freshman class, 49% graduate in 4 years, 57% in 5 years, and 59% in 6 years.

Admissions Contact: Larry Lesick, Director of Admissions.

WITTENBERG UNIVERSITY B-3
Springfield, OH 45501

(513) 327–6314; (800) 677–7558

Full-time: 973 men, 1096 women
Faculty: 144; IIB, +$
Part-time: 90 men, 58 women
Ph.D.s: 97%
Graduate: none
Student/Faculty: 14 to 1
Year: terms, summer session
Tuition: $15,726
Application Deadline: March 15
Room & Board: $4272
Freshman Class: 2203 applied, 1850 accepted, 580 enrolled
SAT I Verbal/Math: 522/575
ACT: 24
VERY COMPETITIVE

Wittenberg University, founded in 1845, is a private, liberal arts and sciences institution affiliated with the Evangelical Lutheran Church in America. The library contains 350,000 volumes, 65,000 microform items, and 23,594 audiovisual forms, and subscribes to 1703 periodicals. Computerized library sources and services include the card catalog, interlibrary loans, and database searching. Special learning facilities include a learning resource center, art gallery, radio station, and geology museum. The 71-acre campus is in a suburban area 25 miles east of Dayton and 40 miles west of Columbus. Including residence halls, there are 35 buildings on campus.

Student Life: About 52% of undergraduates are from Ohio. Students come from 43 states, 35 foreign countries, and Canada. Eighty percent are from public schools; 20% from private. Eighty-nine percent are white. Fifty-nine percent are Protestant; 22% Catholic; 15% claim no religious affiliation. The average age of freshmen is 18; all undergraduates, 20. Fourteen percent drop out by the end of their first year; 74% remain to graduate.

Housing: A total of 1300 students can be accommodated in college housing. College-sponsored living facilities include single-sex and coed dormitories, on-campus apartments, off-campus apartments, married-student housing, fraternity houses, and sorority houses. In addition there are honors houses, language houses, special interest houses, and a substance-free house. On-campus housing is guaranteed for all 4 years. Ninety-five percent of students live on campus; of those, 85% remain on campus on weekends. All students may keep cars on campus.

Activities: About 38% of men belong to 7 national fraternities; about 40% of women belong to 8 national sororities. There are 110 groups on campus, including art, band, cheerleading, chess, choir, chorale, chorus, computers, dance, drama, ethnic, gay, honors, international, jazz band, literary magazine, musical theater, newspaper, orchestra, pep band, photography, political, professional, radio and TV, religious, social, social service, student government, symphony, and yearbook. Popular campus events include the Wittenberg Series, speakers, cultural events, International Festival, and Professional Alumni Days.

Sports: There are 11 intercollegiate sports for men and 11 for women, and 15 intramural sports for men and 12 for women. Athletic and recreation facilities include a multipurpose field house, a swimming pool, 6 racquetball/handball courts, a fitness center, and sports medicine rooms. There is also a 6000-seat stadium, a 3200-seat gymnasium, a 3200-seat arena, and 12 acres of playing fields. The stadium includes an artificially lit playing field, a track, and tennis courts.

Disabled Students: One percent of the campus is accessible to disabled students. The following facilities are available: wheelchair ramps, elevators, special parking, specially equipped rest rooms, special class scheduling, lowered drinking fountains, and lowered telephones.

Services: In addition to many counseling and information services, tutoring is available in most subjects. There are also mathematics and writers' workshops.

Campus Safety and Security: Campus safety and security measures include 24-hour foot and vehicle patrol, escort service, informal discussions, and pamphlets, posters, and films. In addition, there are emergency telephones and lighted pathways and sidewalks. City police support campus police during the evening. There is also a student Eyes and Ears Program, and a campus security committee made up of students and faculty staff.

Programs of Study: Wittenberg awards the B.A., B.F.A., B.M., and B.M.E. degrees. Bachelor's degrees are awarded in BIOLOGICAL SCIENCE (biology/biological science), BUSINESS (business administration and management), COMMUNICATIONS AND THE ARTS (dramatic arts, English, fine arts, French, German, music, Russian, and Spanish), COMPUTER AND PHYSICAL SCIENCE (chemistry, computer science, earth science, geology, mathematics, and physics), EDUCATION (art, business, elementary, foreign languages, middle school, music, science, secondary, and special), HEALTH PROFESSIONS (predentistry and premedicine), SOCIAL SCIENCE (American studies, East Asian studies, economics, geography, history, international relations, philosophy, political science/government, prelaw, psychology, religion, and sociology). Political science, English, East Asian studies, business, education, and psychology are the strongest academically. Business, political science, biology, education, English, and psychology have the largest enrollments.

Required: To graduate, students must complete at least 150 to 155 credit hours. The required minimum GPA and number of hours in the major vary by department. The liberal arts core includes 13 courses distributed in various areas. All students must take a Common Learning course, and courses in writing proficiency, services, physical education, and mathematics/computer science. Comprehensive examinations are required in some departments. Sophomores must spend 30 hours in volunteer service.

Special: Special academic programs include internships, cross-registration through the Southwest Ohio Consortium, a Washington semester, work-study programs, study-abroad opportunities in many countries, accelerated degree programs, dual and student-designed majors, nondegree study, and pass/fail options. A liberal studies degree is available to adult students. A 3–2 engineering degree is offered through Washington, Columbia, and Case Western Reserve Universities and Georgia Institute of Technology. There is a freshman honors program on campus, as well as 4 national honor societies, including Phi Beta Kappa.

Faculty/Classroom: Sixty-six percent of faculty are male; 34%, female. All teach and do research. The average class size in an introductory lecture is 25; in a laboratory, 20; and in a regular course offering, 18.

Admissions: About 84% of the 1993–94 applicants were accepted. The SAT scores for the 1993–94 freshman class were as follows: Verbal—30% below 500, 50% between 500 and 599, 17% between 600 and 700, and 3% above 700; Math—16% below 500, 45% between 500 and 599, 33% between 600 and 700, and 6% above 700. The ACT scores were 8% below 21, 12% between 21 and 23, 37% between 24 and 26, 29% between 27 and 28, and 14% above 28. About 61% of the current freshmen were in the top fifth of their class; 85% were in the top two fifths. There were 6 National Merit finalists and 10 semifinalists. Twenty-five freshmen graduated first in their class.

Requirements: The SAT I or ACT is required. Students should have graduated from an accredited secondary school with 16 academic credits, including 4 units of English and 3 units each of a foreign language, mathematics, science, and social studies, which includes history. The SAT II: Writing test is recommended. An essay is required and an interview advised. Art students must present a portfolio, and music students must audition. AP credits are accepted. Important factors used in the admissions decision are advanced placement or honor courses, recommendations by school officials, leadership record, parents or siblings attending the school, and extracurricular activities record.

Procedure: Freshmen are admitted to all sessions. Entrance exams should be taken as early as possible, and no later than fall of the senior year. Early decision applications should be filed by December 15; regular applications, by March 15 for fall entry, November 15 for winter entry, February 15 for spring entry, and May 15 for summer entry, along with an application fee of $40. Notification of early decision is sent by February 1; regular decision, on a rolling basis. There are early decision, early admissions, and deferred admissions plans. Some 25 early decision candidates were accepted for the 1993–94 class. A waiting list is an active part of the admissions procedure, with about 2% of applicants on the list.

Transfer: Thirty-two transfer students enrolled in 1993–94. Transfer students should have a minimum GPA of 2.4 at an accredited college and be in good academic and social standing. High school transcripts are required in some cases. An interview is recommended. A total of 75 credit hours out of 150 to 155 must be completed at Wittenberg.

Visiting: There are regularly scheduled orientations for prospective students, including a fall, winter, and spring program. There are guides for informal visits and visitors may sit in on classes and stay overnight at the school. To arrange for a visit, contact the Admissions Office at (800) 677-7558.

Financial Aid: In 1993–94 70% of all current freshmen and 65% of continuing students received some form of financial aid. About 65% of freshmen and 60% of continuing students received need-based aid. The average freshman award was $14,000. Of that total, scholarships or need-based grants averaged $9100 ($14,904/full tuition maximum); loans averaged $2100 ($2500 maximum); work contracts averaged $1000 ($1275 maximum); and Ohio Choice Awards (for Ohio students attending Ohio private colleges) averaged $500 ($600 Maximum). Fifty-five percent of undergraduate students work part-time. Average earnings from campus work for the school year are $1000. The average financial indebtedness of the 1992–93 graduate was $7000. Wittenberg is a member of CSS. The FAF, FFS, or SFS, and FAFSA are required. The deadline for financial aid applications is March 15.

International Students: There are currently 105 international students enrolled. The school actively recruits these students. They must take the TOEFL and achieve a minimum score of 550. In some cases, SATs are required.

Computers: The college provides computer facilities for student use. The mainframe is a DEC VAX 11/750. There are 225 terminals and microcomputers located in dormitories and most academic buildings. All students may access the system. It may be used 24 hours a day. There are no time limits on using the system and no fees.

Graduates: In 1992–93 510 bachelor's degrees were awarded. The most popular majors among graduates were business (16%), biology (10%), and education (8%). Within an average freshman class, 1% graduate in 3 years, 68% in 4 years, 74% in 5 years, and 1% in 6 years. More than 100 companies recruited on campus in 1992–93. In the 1992 graduating class, 30% of the men and 25% of the women were enrolled in graduate school within 6 months of graduation; 85% of all students had found employment.

Admissions Contact: Kenneth G. Benne, Dean of Admissions.

WRIGHT STATE UNIVERSITY   B-4

Dayton, OH 45435   (513) 873-2211; (800) 247-1770 (in-state)

Full-time: 4508 men, 5035 women	Faculty: 708; IIA, av$
Part-time: 1532 men, 1652 women	Ph.D.s: 80%
Graduate: 1568 men, 2302 women	Student/Faculty: 13 to 1
Year: quarters	Tuition: $3084 ($6168)
Application Deadline: open	Room & Board: $3812
Freshman Class: 3944 applied, 3644 accepted, 1914 enrolled	
SAT I or ACT: required	**LESS COMPETITIVE**

Wright State University, founded in 1964, is a state-supported institution offering undergraduate programs in business administration, education and human services, engineering and computer science, liberal arts, mathematics and science, and nursing. There are 6 undergraduate and 3 graduate schools. In addition to regional accreditation, Wright State has baccalaureate program accreditation with AACSB, ABET, CSWE, NASM, NCATE, and NLN. The 2 libraries contain 460,000 volumes and 940,000 microform items, and subscribe to 4151 periodicals. Computerized library sources and services include the card catalog, interlibrary loans, and database searching. Special learning facilities include a learning resource center, art gallery, radio station, TV station, and a TV production studio. The Department of Archives and Special Collections houses one of the most complete depositories of information on the Wright Brothers in the world. The 645-acre campus is in a suburban area 8 miles northeast of Dayton. Including residence halls, there are 38 buildings on campus.

Student Life: About 98% of undergraduates are from Ohio. Students come from 43 states, 46 foreign countries, and Canada. Eighty-nine percent are white. The average age of all undergraduates is 24. Thirty percent drop out by the end of their first year.

Housing: A total of 1800 students can be accommodated in college housing. College-sponsored living facilities include coed dormitories, on-campus apartments, and married-student housing. On-campus housing is available on a first-come, first-served basis and is available on a lottery system for upperclassmen. Eighty-five percent of students commute. All students may keep cars on campus.

Activities: About 2% of men belong to 4 local and 5 national fraternities; about 2% of women belong to 5 local and 3 national sororities. There are 160 groups on campus, including band, cheerleading, chess, choir, chorus, computers, drill team, ethnic, film, honors, international, jazz band, literary magazine, newspaper, orchestra, pep band, political, professional, radio and TV, religious, social, social service, and student government. Popular campus events include October Daze, May Daze, and Madrigal Dinner.

Sports: There are 8 intercollegiate sports for men and 8 for women, and 12 intramural sports for men and 12 for women. Athletic and recreation facilities include a an arena seating over 10,000 spectators, weight rooms, break-off rooms, auxiliary gymnasiums, and baseball and practice fields. There is a natatorium in the physical education building.

Disabled Students: Ninety-nine percent of the campus is accessible to disabled students. The following facilities are available: wheelchair ramps, elevators, special parking, specially equipped rest rooms, lowered drinking fountains, lowered telephones, and specially equipped

on-campus housing. An underground tunnel system connects all buildings.

Services: In addition to many counseling and information services, tutoring is available in most subjects. There is also a reader service for the blind, and remedial math, reading, and writing.

Campus Safety and Security: Campus safety and security measures include 24-hour foot and vehicle patrol, self defense education, escort service, and shuttle buses. In addition, there are informal discussions, pamphlets, posters, films, emergency telephones, and lighted pathways and sidewalks.

Programs of Study: Wright State awards the B.A., B.S., B.F.A., B.Mus., B.S.B., B.S.Comp.Eng., B.S.E., B.S.Ed., B.S.M.T., and B.S.N. degrees. Master's and doctoral degrees also are awarded. Bachelor's degrees are awarded in BIOLOGICAL SCIENCE (biology/biological science), BUSINESS (accounting, banking and finance, business economics, management information systems, management science, and marketing/retailing/merchandising), COMMUNICATIONS AND THE ARTS (art history and appreciation, arts administration/management, classical languages, communications, dance, dramatic arts, English, film arts, fine arts, French, German, modern language, music, music history and appreciation, music theory and composition, Spanish, and theater design), COMPUTER AND PHYSICAL SCIENCE (chemistry, computer science, geology, geophysics and seismology, mathematics, and physics), EDUCATION (art, business, elementary, foreign languages, music, physical, science, secondary, and special), ENGINEERING AND ENVIRONMENTAL DESIGN (biomedical engineering, computer engineering, electrical/electronics engineering, engineering physics, materials engineering, mechanical engineering, systems engineering, and water and wastewater technology), HEALTH PROFESSIONS (environmental health science, medical laboratory technology, nursing, predentistry, premedicine, and rehabilitation therapy), SOCIAL SCIENCE (anthropology, economics, geography, history, humanities, international relations, philosophy, political science/government, prelaw, psychology, religion, social work, sociology, and urban studies). Education, theater arts, and engineering are the strongest academically. Elementary education, accounting, nursing, and psychology have the largest enrollments.

Required: All students are required to complete 57 credit hours of general education courses in 4 areas: communication and mathematical skills, the Western experience, the non-Western world, and understanding the contemporary world. In order to graduate, students must complete a minimum of 183 credits with a minimum 2.0 GPA.

Special: B.A.-B.S. degrees are offered in computer science, geography, urban affairs, biological sciences, chemistry, geological sciences, mathematics, and psychology. A dual major in social and industrial communications is offered. Cross-registration with other area colleges is available through the Southwestern Ohio Council for Higher Education. Co-op programs, internships, study abroad, work-study programs, student-designed majors, nondegree study, and credit for military experience are available. There is a freshman honors program on campus, as well as 13 national honor societies. Sixty-two departments have honors programs.

Faculty/Classroom: Seventy-five percent of faculty are male; 25%, female. The average class size in an introductory lecture is 150; in a laboratory, 35; and in a regular course offering, 40.

Admissions: About 92% of the 1993–94 applicants were accepted. About 25% of the current freshmen were in the top fifth of their class; 51% were in the top two fifths. There were 3 National Merit finalists. Fifty freshmen graduated first in their class.

Requirements: The SAT or ACT is required. Applicants should be graduates of an accredited secondary school and have 4 credits of English, 3 credits each of mathematics, science, and social studies, 2 credits in a foreign language, and 1 credit in art. A portfolio is required for art majors, an audition for theater and music. The GED is accepted. AP and CLEP credits are accepted.

Procedure: Freshmen are admitted to all sessions. Application deadlines are open. Application fee is $25. Notification is sent on a rolling basis. There is a deferred admissions plan.

Transfer: About 1500 transfer students enrolled in a recent year. Applicants must have a 2.0 GPA. A total of 45 credits out of 183 must be completed at Wright State.

Visiting: There are guides for informal visits. To arrange for a visit, contact the Office of Admissions at (513) 873–2211 or (800) 247–1770 (in-state).

Financial Aid: In a recent year, 64% of all current freshmen and 48% of continuing students received some form of financial aid. About 48% of freshmen and 42% of continuing students received need-based aid. The average freshman award was $2784. Average earnings from campus work for the school year are $1960. The average financial indebtedness of a recent graduate was $1696. Wright State is a member of CSS. The FAF, FFS, or SFS and the college's own financial statement are required. The deadline for financial aid applications is April 1.

International Students: There are currently 350 international students enrolled. They must take the TOEFL and achieve a minimum score of 500.

Computers: The university provides computer facilities for student use. The mainframes are an IBM 3090/190 and a DEC VAX 6420. There are also IBM-PC-compatible and Apple Macintosh microcomputers available throughout the campus. All students may access the system. There are no time limits on using the system and no fees.

Graduates: In 1992–93, 1797 bachelor's degrees were awarded. The most popular majors among graduates were business (27%), education (16%), and science and mathematics (13%). Within an average freshman class, 25% graduate in 5 years and 35% in 6 years. Some 200 companies recruited on campus in 1992–93.

Admissions Contact: Ken Davenport, Director of Undergraduate Admissions.

XAVIER UNIVERSITY
Cincinnati, OH 45207   A-5

Full-time: 1343 men, 1506 women	(513) 745–3301; (800) 344–4698
Part-time: 377 men, 730 women	Faculty: 199; IIA, av$
Graduate: 1114 men, 1209 women	Ph.D.s: 75%
Year: semesters, summer session	Student/Faculty: 14 to 1
Application Deadline: open	Tuition: $10,970
Freshman Class: 1959 applied, 1805 accepted, 695 enrolled	Room & Board: $4740
SAT I: 480/520	ACT: 24 COMPETITIVE +

Xavier University, founded in 1831, is a liberal arts Jesuit institution affiliated with the Roman Catholic Church. There are 3 undergraduate and 10 graduate schools. In addition to regional accreditation, Xavier has baccalaureate program accreditation with CAHEA, CSWE, and NLN. The 2 libraries contain 350,000 volumes, 450,744 microform items, and 5000 audiovisual forms, and subscribe to 1500 periodicals. Computerized library sources and services include the card catalog, interlibrary loans, and database searching. Special learning facilities include a learning resource center, art gallery, radio station, TV station, and observatory. The 100-acre campus is 5 miles northeast of the center of Cincinnati in a residential area. Including residence halls, there are 50 buildings on campus.

Student Life: About 70% of undergraduates are from Ohio. Students come from 42 states, 40 foreign countries, and Canada. Forty percent are from public schools; 60% from private. Seventy percent are white. Thirty-eight percent are Catholic. The average age of freshmen is 19; all undergraduates, 25. Eleven percent drop out by the end of their first year; 67% remain to graduate.

Housing: A total of 1372 students can be accommodated in college housing. College-sponsored living facilities include coed dormitories, on-campus apartments, and off-campus apartments. In addition, there are honors houses. On-campus housing is available on a first-come, first-served basis and is available on a lottery system for upperclassmen. Priority is given to out-of-town students. Fifty-two percent of students commute. All students may keep cars on campus.

Activities: There are no fraternities or sororities on campus. There are 75 groups on campus, including art, band, cheerleading, choir, chorale, chorus, computers, dance, drama, ethnic, film, honors, international, jazz band, literary magazine, musical theater, newspaper, orchestra, pep band, photography, political, professional, radio and TV, religious, social, social service, student government, and yearbook. Popular campus events include Homecoming, Family Weekend, Little Sibs Weekend, Spring Break Away, Welcome Week, Black History Month, Fitness Week, Mini Indy 500, Multi-Cultural Week, Wellness Week, Club Day, and International Week.

Sports: There are 8 intercollegiate sports for men and 8 for women, and 25 intramural sports for men and 25 for women. Athletic and recreation facilities include Schmidt Memorial Field, O'Connor Sports Center, Cincinnati gardens, and baseball, soccer, and softball fields.

Disabled Students: Seventy percent of the campus is accessible to disabled students. The following facilities are available: wheelchair ramps, elevators, special parking, specially equipped rest rooms, special class scheduling, and lowered drinking fountains.

Services: In addition to many counseling and information services, tutoring is available in most subjects. There are mathematics and writing laboratories and effective reading and study skill classes. There is also remedial math, reading, and writing.

Campus Safety and Security: Campus safety and security measures include 24-hour foot and vehicle patrol, self defense education, escort service, and informal discussions. In addition, there are pamphlets, posters, films, emergency telephones, and lighted pathways and sidewalks. There is also the Crime Prevention Program and Neighbors Helping Neighbors, a community-based program operated in conjunction with the university.

Programs of Study: Xavier awards the B.A., B.S., B.F.A., B.L.A., B.S.B.A., H.A.B., B.S.N., and B.S.W degrees. Associate and master's degrees also are awarded. Bachelor's degrees are awarded in BIOLOGICAL SCIENCE (biology/biological science), BUSINESS (accounting, business administration and management, business eco-

nomics, human resources, management science, marketing/retailing/merchandising, and sports management), COMMUNICATIONS AND THE ARTS (advertising, classics, communications, English, fine arts, French, German, music, public relations, and Spanish), COMPUTER AND PHYSICAL SCIENCE (chemistry, computer science, information sciences and systems, mathematics, natural sciences, and physics), EDUCATION (art, early childhood, elementary, health, music, science, secondary, and special), ENGINEERING AND ENVIRONMENTAL DESIGN (industrial administration/management), HEALTH PROFESSIONS (medical laboratory technology, nursing, occupational therapy, predentistry, premedicine, prepharmacy, and sports medicine), SOCIAL SCIENCE (criminal justice, economics, history, international relations, philosophy, political science/government, psychology, religion, social work, and sociology). Physics, Honors A.B., and University Scholars are the strongest programs academically. Business, communications, and education have the largest enrollments.

Required: To graduate, students must complete between 120 and 140 credit hours with a minimum GPA of 2.0. The total number of hours required in the major varies. All students must take core curriculum courses in English composition, cultural diversity, mathematics, science, social science, history, theology, philosophy, a foreign language, literature, and fine arts.

Special: Xavier offers internships related to the major and cross-registration through the Greater Cincinnati Consortium. Students may study abroad in Argentina, France, Germany, and Spain. A general studies degree, B.A.-B.S. degrees, an interdisciplinary major, sports marketing, dual majors, a Washington semester, and nondegree study are available. A 3–2 engineering degree is offered with the University of Cincinnati. There is a freshman honors program on campus, as well as 8 national honor societies.

Faculty/Classroom: Sixty-four percent of faculty are male; 36%, female. No introductory courses are taught by graduate students. The average class size in an introductory lecture is 28; in a laboratory, 15; and in a regular course offering, 22.

Admissions: About 92% of the 1993–94 applicants were accepted. The SAT scores for the 1993–94 freshman class were as follows: Verbal—59% below 500, 32% between 500 and 599, 8% between 600 and 700, and 1% above 700; Math—41% below 500, 33% between 500 and 599, 21% between 600 and 700, and 5% above 700. The ACT scores were 25% below 21, 23% between 21 and 23, 24% between 24 and 26, 14% between 27 and 28, and 14% above 28. About 45% of the current freshmen were in the top fifth of their class; 67% were in the top two fifths. There were 3 National Merit finalists. Twenty-one freshmen graduated first in their class.

Requirements: Xavier requires applicants to be in the upper 50% of their class. A minimum GPA of 2.4 is required. The SAT I or ACT is required, with minimum composite scores of 20 on the ACT or 800 on the SAT I. Graduation from an accredited secondary school or satisfactory scores on the GED are required for admission. The school requires 11 academic credits, including 4 years of English, 2 years each of mathematics and a foreign language, and 1 year each of history, science, and 1 other academic subject. Students may substitute additional history and/or science courses for the foreign language requirement. Xavier recommends an interview. AP and CLEP credits are accepted. Important factors used in the admissions decision are advanced placement or honor courses, leadership record, extracurricular activities record, evidence of special talent, and recommendations by school officials.

Procedure: Freshmen are admitted to all sessions. Entrance exams should be taken during the spring or summer before the senior year. Application deadlines are open. The fee is $25. Notification is sent on a rolling basis. There is a deferred admissions plan.

Transfer: About 180 transfer students enrolled in a recent year. Transfer students must have a minimum GPA of 2.0 in all college-level work. Minimum composite scores of 20 on the ACT or 800 on the SAT I are recommended. An interview is also recommended. A total of 30 credits out of 120 to 140 must be completed at Xavier.

Visiting: There are regularly scheduled orientations for prospective students, including an interview and a tour of the campus. There are guides for informal visits, and visitors may sit in on classes and stay overnight at the school. To arrange for a visit, contact the Admissions Office at (800) 344–4698 or (513) 745–3301.

Financial Aid: In 1993–94 80% of all current freshmen and 75% of continuing students received some form of financial aid. About 65% of freshmen and 63% of continuing students received need-based aid. The average freshman award was $7300. Of that total, scholarships or need-based grants averaged $3700 ($15,700 maximum); loans averaged $2625 ($6625 maximum); and work contracts averaged $1300 ($2000 maximum). Eighty-four percent of undergraduate students work part-time. Average earnings from campus work for the school year are $1100. Xavier is a member of CSS. The FAFSA financial statement is required. The deadline for financial aid applications is February 15.

International Students: There are currently 272 international students enrolled. The school actively recruits these students. They must take the TOEFL and achieve a minimum score of 525.

Computers: The college provides computer facilities for student use. The mainframe is a DEC VAX 8350. Students may create their own accounts on the mainframe from any of the 425 PC, Apple Macintosh, or VT terminal devices in the 3 academic computing laboratories. All students may access the system. It may be used 8 A.M. to 11 P.M. There are no time limits on using the system and no fees.

Graduates: In 1992–93 706 bachelor's degrees were awarded. The most popular majors among graduates were business (40%), education (17%), and communication arts (6%). Within an average freshman class, 1% graduate in 3 years, 52% in 4 years, 63% in 5 years, and 65% in 6 years. Some 100 companies recruited on campus in 1992–93.

Admissions Contact: John R. Leiendecker, Jr., Director of Admissions.

YOUNGSTOWN STATE UNIVERSITY
C-2

Youngstown, OH 44555–0001	(216) 742–3175; (800) 336–9YSU
Full-time: 4816 men, 4817 women	Faculty: 459; IIA, av$
Part-time: 1649 men, 2013 women	Ph.D.s: 71%
Graduate: 477 men, 729 women	Student/Faculty: 21 to 1
Year: quarters, summer session	Tuition: $2772 ($4680–5112)
Application Deadline: August 15	Room & Board: $3675
Freshman Class: 3297 applied, 2903 accepted, 2157 enrolled	
ACT: 19	LESS COMPETITIVE

Youngstown State University, founded in 1908, is a publicly funded, primarily commuter institution offering undergraduate programs in the liberal arts and sciences, education, business, engineering, fine and performing arts, and health and human services. There are 6 undergraduate schools and one graduate school. In addition to regional accreditation, YSU has baccalaureate program accreditation with ABET, ADA, CAHEA, CSWE, NASM, NCATE, and NLN. The library contains 615,796 volumes and 1,012,937 microform items, and subscribes to 3200 periodicals. Computerized library sources and services include the card catalog, interlibrary loans, and database searching. Special learning facilities include a learning resource center, art gallery, planetarium, radio station, and TV station. The 125-acre campus is in an urban area 65 miles southeast of Cleveland. Including residence halls, there are 32 buildings on campus.

Student Life: About 93% of undergraduates are from Ohio. Students come from 26 states, 58 foreign countries, and Canada. Eighty-eight percent are white. The average age of freshmen is 19; all undergraduates, 25. Thirty-three percent drop out by the end of their first year; 37% remain to graduate.

Housing: A total of 630 students can be accommodated in college housing. College-sponsored living facilities include single-sex and coed dormitories and on-campus apartments. In addition there are special interest houses, an international living-learning center, and off-campus fraternity and sorority houses. On-campus housing is guaranteed for all 4 years. Fifty percent of students commute. Alcohol is not permitted. All students may keep cars on campus.

Activities: About 3% of men belong to 1 local and 8 national fraternities; about 3% of women belong to 1 local and 5 national sororities. There are 120 groups on campus, including art, band, cheerleading, chess, choir, chorale, chorus, computers, dance, drama, ethnic, film, gay, honors, international, jazz band, literary magazine, marching band, musical theater, newspaper, opera, orchestra, pep band, photography, political, professional, radio and TV, religious, social, social service, student government, and symphony. Popular campus events include Homecoming, Hispanic Awareness Week, NCDAA Week, Mr. Wizzard Show, Black History Month, Organization 'S' Fair, NPHC Step Show, Greek Sing, Dating Game, Surfs-Up Spring Break, Fashion Show, Fun-in-Sun, Career Night, and 'Into-the-Streets' Community Clean-up.

Sports: There are 8 intercollegiate sports for men and 7 for women, and 35 intramural sports for men, 35 for women, and 20 for both. Athletic and recreation facilities include a sports complex with a 16,000-seat stadium, artificial turf field for football and soccer, racquetball courts, gymnasiums, weight rooms, all-weather 400-meter track, outdoor basketball, handball, and volleyball courts, and 10 lighted tennis courts. There is also a physical education center with a 7,000-spectator gymnasium, an Olympic-sized swimming pool, a dance studio, rifle range, fitness center, racquetball and squash courts, and separate gymnasiums for wrestling, weightlifting, gymnastics, and the handicapped.

Disabled Students: Ninety-five percent of the campus is accessible to disabled students. The following facilities are available: wheelchair ramps, elevators, special parking, specially equipped rest rooms, special class scheduling, lowered drinking fountains, lowered telephones, and an escort service.

Services: In addition to many counseling and information services, tutoring is available in some subjects, including basic entry-level subjects and some advanced courses, including the sciences, mathematics, economics, and business. There is also a reader service for the blind, and remedial math, reading, and writing, as well as student enrichment services and multicultural student services.

Campus Safety and Security: Campus safety and security measures include 24-hour foot and vehicle patrol, self defense education, escort service, and shuttle buses. In addition, there are informal discussions, pamphlets, posters, films, emergency telephones, lighted pathways and sidewalks, night security posts in dormitories, and concentrated security in parking and other critical areas.

Programs of Study: YSU awards the A.B., B.S., B.Eng., B.F.A., B.M., B.S.Appl.Sci., B.S.B.A., B.S.Ed., and B.S.N degrees. Associate, master's, and doctoral degrees also are awarded. Bachelor's degrees are awarded in AGRICULTURE (preforestry and related sciences), BIOLOGICAL SCIENCE (biology/biological science), BUSINESS (accounting, banking and finance, business administration and management, fashion merchandising, hotel/motel and restaurant management, labor studies, marketing and distribution, marketing management, and marketing/retailing/merchandising), COMMUNICATIONS AND THE ARTS (advertising, applied art, art history and appreciation, communications, dramatic arts, English, French, German, Italian, Latin, music, music history and appreciation, music performance, music theory and composition, Russian, Spanish, speech/debate/rhetoric, studio art, technical and business writing, and telecommunications), COMPUTER AND PHYSICAL SCIENCE (astronomy, chemistry, computer science, earth science, geology, mathematics, physics, and science), EDUCATION (art, business, early childhood, elementary, foreign languages, health, home economics, music, physical, science, secondary, and special), ENGINEERING AND ENVIRONMENTAL DESIGN (chemical engineering, civil engineering, computer technology, electrical/electronics engineering, engineering technology, industrial administration/management, industrial engineering, materials engineering, and mechanical engineering), HEALTH PROFESSIONS (allied health, health, medical laboratory technology, medical technology, nursing, predentistry, premedicine, preoptometry, preosteopathy, prepharmacy, and preveterinary science), SOCIAL SCIENCE (African American studies, American studies, anthropology, criminal justice, dietetics, economics, geography, history, home economics, philosophy, political science/government, prelaw, psychology, public administration, religion, social science, social work, and sociology). Elementary education, psychology, prebusiness accounting, and criminal justice have the largest enrollments.

Required: To graduate, students must complete between 186 and 212 quarter hours, depending on major. A minimum GPA of 2.0 is required. At least 45 quarter hours are required in the major. All students must fulfill core requirements in English composition, health/physical education, humanities, social studies, and science/mathematics.

Special: YSU offers co-op programs, internships, dual majors, credit for military experience, nondegree study, honors degree programs, and pass/fail options. Student-designed majors are available through the Individualized Curriculum Program. There is a freshman honors program on campus, as well as 4 national honor societies. Six departments have honors programs.

Faculty/Classroom: Seventy-one percent of faculty are male; 29%, female. Graduate students teach 3% of introductory courses. The average class size in an introductory lecture is 26 and in a laboratory, 13.

Admissions: About 88% of the 1993–94 applicants were accepted. The ACT scores for the 1993–94 freshman class were as follows: 61% below 21, 20% between 21 and 23, 10% between 24 and 26, 4% between 27 and 28, and 4% above 28. About 27% of the current freshmen were in the top fifth of their class; 48% were in the top two fifths. A total of 39 freshmen graduated first in their class.

Requirements: ACT or SAT I scores are required if the applicant has been out of high school for fewer than two years. Out-of-state applicants must rank in the upper two thirds of their class or have minimum composite scores of 700 on the SAT I or 15 on the ACT. Graduation from an accredited secondary school or satisfactory scores on the GED are required for admission for all applicants. High school courses must include 4 units of English, 3 units of mathematics, 2 units each of a foreign language, science, and social studies, and 1 unit each of history and of fine and performing arts. AP and CLEP credits are accepted.

Procedure: Freshmen are admitted to all sessions. Entrance exams should be taken in the spring of the junior year or fall of the senior year. Early decision applications should be filed by February 15 or June 15; regular applications, by August 15 for fall entry, November 15 for winter entry, February 15 for spring entry, and May 15 for summer entry, along with an application fee of $20. Notification is sent on a rolling basis. There are early decision, early admissions, and deferred admissions plans. About 600 early decision candidates were accepted for the 1993–94 class.

Transfer: About 650 transfer students enrolled in 1993–94. Transfer students must provide transcripts from all secondary schools and colleges attended. Ohio residents must have a minimum GPA of 2.0. Those with a lower GPA may be admitted if high school grades and test scores show potential. Nonresidents must have a minimum GPA of 2.0 and be in good standing at the last institution attended. A total of 45 quarter hours out of 186 to 212 must be completed at YSU.

Visiting: There are regularly scheduled orientations for prospective students. There are guides for informal visits and visitors may sit in on classes. To arrange for a visit, contact New Student Relations Office at (216) 742-2000.

Financial Aid: In 1993–94, 65% of all students received some form of financial aid. About 55% of students received need-based aid. The average freshman award was $2000. Of that total, scholarships or need-based grants averaged $1800 ($2400 maximum); loans averaged $1800 ($4000 maximum); and work contracts averaged $1500 ($3000 maximum). Eight percent of undergraduate students work part-time. Average earnings from campus work for the school year are $1500. The average financial indebtedness of the 1992–93 graduate was $2000. YSU is a member of CSS. The FAF, FFS, or SFS and the college's own financial statement are required. The deadline for financial aid applications is April 1.

International Students: There are currently 255 international students enrolled. The school actively recruits these students. They must take the TOEFL or the University of Michigan Language Test and achieve a minimum score on the TOEFL of 500.

Computers: The university provides computer facilities for student use. The mainframes are an Amdahl 5868 Multiprocessor and an Amdahl 5860 Uniprocessor. Terminals are located in various academic departments throughout the campus. The main facilities are located in Meshel Hall, which contains 7 classrooms and 12 laboratories dedicated to students use. Telephone lines are provided for remote access off-campus. A total of 225 IBM PCs are available on a local area network for instruction and research. An ethernet backbone connects the Amdahl 5860 with a UNIX-based parallel processor and a RISC System/6000 processor. All students may access the system. Students may access the system for 10 minutes of CPU-time, renewable upon request. There are no fees.

Graduates: In 1992–93, 1471 bachelor's degrees were awarded. The most popular majors among graduates were elementary education (8%), accounting (7%), and criminal justice (6%). Within an average freshman class, 2% graduate in 3 years, 9% in 4 years, 23% in 5 years, and 32% in 6 years. Some 200 companies recruited on campus in 1992–93.

Admissions Contact: Dr. Harold Yiannaki, Director of Enrollment Services.

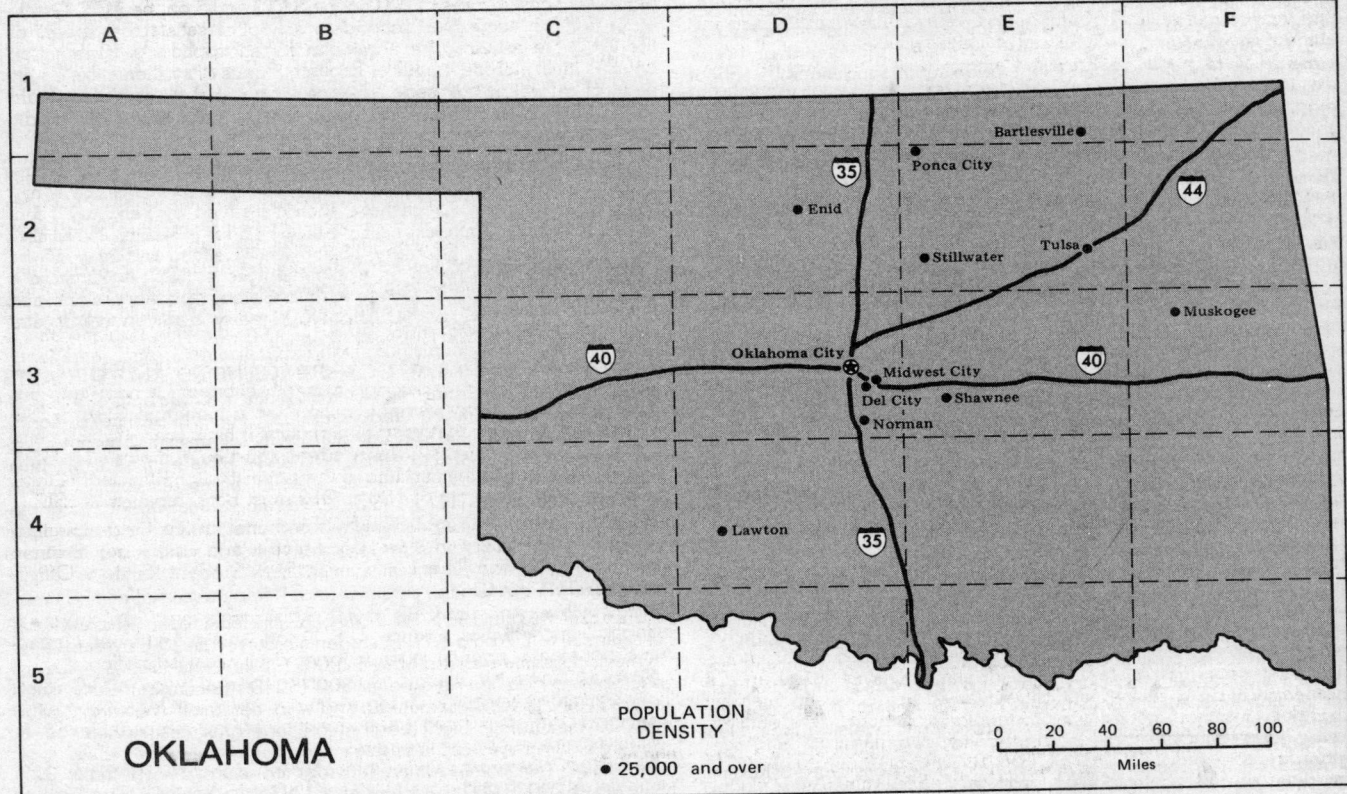

OKLAHOMA

POPULATION
DENSITY

● 25,000 and over

0 20 40 60 80 100

Miles

BARTLESVILLE WESLEYAN COLLEGE   E-1
Bartlesville, OK 74006   (918) 335-6219

Full-time: 335 men and women	**Faculty:** 34; IIB, --$
Part-time: 173 men and women	**Ph.D.s:** 51%
Graduate: none	**Student/Faculty:** 10 to 1
Year: semesters, summer session	**Tuition:** $6350
Application Deadline: open	**Room & Board:** $3050

Freshman Class: 147 applied, 111 accepted, 94 enrolled
ACT: 21   **COMPETITIVE**

Bartlesville Wesleyan College, founded in 1909, is a private liberal arts institution affiliated with the Wesleyan Church. The library contains 120,000 volumes, 20,000 microform items, and 500 audiovisual forms, and subscribes to 18,000 periodicals. Computerized library sources and services include the card catalog, interlibrary loans, and database searching. Special learning facilities include a learning resource center. The 101-acre campus is in a suburban area 40 miles north of Tulsa. Including residence halls, there are 15 buildings on campus.

Student Life: About 59% of undergraduates are from Oklahoma. Students come from 26 states and 9 foreign countries. Ninety percent are from public schools; 10% from private. Eighty-three percent are white. Forty-eight percent are Protestant. The average age of freshmen is 18; all undergraduates, 27. Five percent drop out by the end of their first year; 60% remain to graduate.

Housing: A total of 240 students can be accommodated in college housing. College-sponsored living facilities include single-sex dormitories. On-campus housing is guaranteed for all 4 years. Fifty-six percent of students commute. Alcohol is not permitted. All students may keep cars on campus.

Activities: There are no fraternities or sororities on campus. There are many groups on campus, including cheerleading, choir, chorale, chorus, computers, drama, ethnic, international, newspaper, pep band, photography, political, professional, religious, social service, student government, and yearbook. Popular campus events include Homecoming, Community Days, and Spiritual Emphasis Week.

Sports: There are 2 intercollegiate sports for men and 3 for women, and 10 intramural sports for men and 10 for women. Athletic and recreation facilities include an 1800-seat indoor gymnasium and an 8-acre athletic field.

Disabled Students: Seventy-three percent of the campus is accessible to disabled students. The following facilities are available: wheelchair ramps, elevators, special parking, and specially equipped rest rooms.

Services: In addition to many counseling and information services, tutoring is available in most subjects. There is also remedial math, reading, and writing.

Campus Safety and Security: Campus safety and security measures include informal discussions, lighted pathways and sidewalks, and an evening patrol by a security guard.

Programs of Study: BWC awards the B.A. and B.S. degrees. Associate degrees also are awarded. Bachelor's degrees are awarded in BUSINESS (accounting, business administration and management, and human resources), COMMUNICATIONS AND THE ARTS (communications and English), COMPUTER AND PHYSICAL SCIENCE (chemistry and mathematics), EDUCATION (art, business, elementary, English, mathematics, middle school, physical, science, and secondary), HEALTH PROFESSIONS (predentistry and premedicine), SOCIAL SCIENCE (behavioral science, history, political science/government, prelaw, religion, social science, and sociology). Business and education are the strongest programs academically and have the largest enrollments.

Required: In order to graduate, students must complete a total of 126 credit hours with a minimum GPA of 2.0. Approximately 30 hours are required in the major. All students must take 9 hours of religion and a writing proficiency examination.

Special: BWC offers cross-registration with Tri-County Tech, a Washington semester, a co-op program, internships, a general studies degree, credit for life experience, an accelerated degree program in management of human resources, and nondegree study. There is an accelerated program for adult learners.

Faculty/Classroom: Sixty percent of faculty are male; 40%, female. All teach undergraduates. The average class size in an introductory lecture, a laboratory, and in a regular course offering is 20.

Admissions: About 76% of the 1993–94 applicants were accepted. The ACT scores for the 1993–94 freshman class were as follows: 45% below 21, 23% between 21 and 23, 26% between 24 and 26, 5% between 27 and 28, and 2% above 28. About 20% of the current freshmen were in the top fifth of their class; 60% were in the top two fifths. Five freshmen graduated first in their class.

Requirements: BWC requires applicants to be in the upper 50% of their class. A minimum GPA of 2.0 is required. The ACT is required and the SAT I is recommended. Graduation from an accredited sec-

ondary school or satisfactory scores on the GED are required for admission. Eighteen academic credits must be completed, including 4 credits of English and 2 credits each of history, mathematics, science, and social studies. AP and CLEP credits are accepted. Important factors used in the admissions decision are extracurricular activities record, recommendations by alumni, advanced placement or honor courses, evidence of special talent, and recommendations by school officials.

Procedure: Freshmen are admitted to all sessions. Entrance exams should be taken during the senior year. Application deadlines are open. Application fee is $25. Notification is sent on a rolling basis.

Transfer: About 79 transfer students enrolled in 1993–94. Transfer students must have a minimum GPA of 2.0. A total of 24 credits out of 126 must be completed at BWC.

Visiting: There are regularly scheduled orientations for prospective students. There are guides for informal visits, and visitors may sit in on classes and stay overnight at the school. To arrange for a visit, contact the Enrollment Services Office at (918) 335-6219.

Financial Aid: In 1993–94, 90% of all students received some form of financial aid. About 80% of freshmen and 75% of continuing students received need-based aid. The average freshman award was $11,500. Of that total, scholarships or need-based grants averaged $3601 ($7000 maximum); loans averaged $6625 ($9600 maximum); and work contracts averaged $1274 ($1654 maximum). Twenty-two percent of undergraduate students work part-time. Average earnings from campus work for the school year are $1600. The average financial indebtedness of the 1992–93 graduate was $15,000. The college's own financial statement and the FAFSA are required. The deadline for financial aid applications is open.

International Students: There are currently 125 international students enrolled. The school actively recruits these students. They must take the TOEFL and achieve a minimum score of 500. The student must also take the college's own entrance exam and placement tests.

Computers: The college provides computer facilities for student use. There is a computer laboratory housing both IBM PCs and Macintosh microcomputers. All students may access the system. It may be used from 8 A.M. to 10 P.M. There are no time limits on using the system and no fees.

Graduates: In a recent year 86 bachelor's degrees were awarded. The most popular majors among graduates were business administration (22%), management of human resources (16%), and elementary education (12%). Some 5 companies recruited on campus in a recent year.

Admissions Contact: Bob Hubbard, Enrollment Services Administrator.

CAMERON UNIVERSITY
D-4

Lawton, OK 73505

(405) 581-2230

Full-time: 1496 men, 1940 women	Faculty: 213; IIB, --$
Part-time: 1029 men, 1149 women	Ph.D.s: 57%
Graduate: 134 men, 221 women	Student/Faculty: 16 to 1
Year: semesters, summer session	Tuition: $1400 ($3350)
Application Deadline: open	Room & Board: $2286
Freshman Class: 1288 applied, 1248 accepted, 912 enrolled	
ACT: 19	**LESS COMPETITIVE**

Cameron University, founded in 1908, is a publicly funded institution offering undergraduate programs in business, education and psychology, fine arts, liberal arts, and science, mathematics, and technology. There are 5 undergraduate and 3 graduate schools. In addition to regional accreditation, Cameron has baccalaureate program accreditation with NASM, NCATE, and NLN. The library contains 225,300 volumes and 365,458 microform items, and subscribes to 2956 periodicals. Computerized library sources and services include the card catalog, interlibrary loans, and database searching. Special learning facilities include a learning resource center, art gallery, and radio station. The 160-acre campus is in a small town 90 miles southwest of Oklahoma City. Including residence halls, there are 20 buildings on campus.

Student Life: About 92% of undergraduates are from Oklahoma. Students come from 29 states, 6 foreign countries, and Canada. Ninety-seven percent are from public schools; 3% from private. Seventy-two percent are white; 15% African American. The average age of freshmen is 24; all undergraduates, 27.

Housing: A total of 600 students can be accommodated in college housing. College-sponsored living facilities include single-sex dormitories. On-campus housing is guaranteed for all 4 years. Ninety-five percent of students commute. Alcohol is not permitted. All students may keep cars on campus.

Activities: About 4% of men belong to 2 national fraternities; about 6% of women belong to 1 local and 2 national sororities. There are 53 groups on campus, including art, band, cheerleading, chess, choir, computers, dance, drama, drill team, ethnic, honors, international, jazz band, literary magazine, marching band, musical theater, newspaper, opera, orchestra, pep band, political, professional, radio

and TV, religious, social, student government, and yearbook. Popular campus events include Homecoming and Spring Fling.

Sports: There are 4 intercollegiate sports for men and 4 for women, and 6 intramural sports for men and 6 for women. Athletic and recreation facilities include a 10,000-seat football stadium, an 1800-seat gymnasium, a 100-seat baseball park, a running track, Nautilus and free-weight rooms, an indoor swimming pool, and basketball, volleyball, and racquetball courts.

Disabled Students: Eighty percent of the campus is accessible to disabled students. The following facilities are available: wheelchair ramps, elevators, special parking, and specially equipped rest rooms.

Services: In addition to many counseling and information services, tutoring is available in most subjects, including writing, reading, accounting, mathematics, fine arts, and technology.

Programs of Study: Cameron awards the B.A., B.S., B.Acctg., and B.F.A. degrees. Associate and master's degrees also are awarded. Bachelor's degrees are awarded in BIOLOGICAL SCIENCE (biology/biological science), BUSINESS (accounting, banking and finance, business administration and management, and marketing/retailing/merchandising), COMMUNICATIONS AND THE ARTS (broadcasting, communications, dramatic arts, English, fine arts, journalism, music, romance languages, and speech/debate/rhetoric), COMPUTER AND PHYSICAL SCIENCE (chemistry, computer science, mathematics, and physics), EDUCATION (agricultural, art, business, early childhood, elementary, health, home economics, music, and science), HEALTH PROFESSIONS (medical laboratory technology and nursing), SOCIAL SCIENCE (criminal justice, history, political science/government, prelaw, psychology, and sociology). Business has the largest enrollment.

Required: To graduate, students must complete a total of 128 credit hours with a minimum GPA of 2.0. All students must take courses in English, mathematics, science, U.S. history and government, humanities, behavioral science, economics, and physical education.

Special: Cameron offers dual majors in several fields, an interdisciplinary studies degree, nondegree study, and credit for military experience. There are 13 national honor societies on campus. Eleven departments have honors programs.

Faculty/Classroom: Sixty-eight percent of faculty are male; 32%, female. All teach undergraduates and 50% do research. The average class size in an introductory lecture is 45; in a laboratory, 30; and in a regular course offering, 30.

Admissions: About 97% of the 1993–94 applicants were accepted. The ACT scores for the 1993–94 freshman class were as follows: 74% below 21, 17% between 21 and 23, 6% between 24 and 26, and 3% between 27 and 28.

Requirements: The SAT I or ACT is required, and applicants must score in the upper 55 percentile or rank in the top 55 percentile of their graduating class. High school courses must include 4 years of English, 3 years of mathematics (including algebra I and above), and 2 years each of history and of laboratory science. AP and CLEP credits are accepted.

Procedure: Freshmen are admitted to all sessions. Entrance exams should be taken late in the junior year or early in the senior year. Application deadlines are open. The application fee is $15. Notification is sent on a rolling basis. There is an early admissions plan.

Transfer: Some 112 transfer students enrolled in 1993–94. Transfer students must have a minimum GPA of 2.0 and be in good standing at the institution last attended. A total of 30 credit hours out of 128 must be completed at Cameron.

Visiting: There are regularly scheduled orientations for prospective students. There are guides for informal visits and visitors may sit in on classes and stay overnight at the school. To arrange for a visit, contact Cindy Zelbst, Admissions Counselor, at (405) 581-2230.

Financial Aid: In 1993–94 48% of all current freshmen and 52% of continuing students received some form of financial aid. About 30% of freshmen and 48% of continuing students received need-based aid. The average freshman award was $5250. Of that total, scholarships or need-based grants averaged $2250 ($5100 maximum); loans averaged $1500 ($2625 maximum); and work contracts averaged $1500 ($2000 maximum). Seventy-six percent of undergraduate students work part-time. Average earnings from campus work for the school year are $1500. The average financial indebtedness of the 1992–93 graduate was $6000. Cameron is a member of CSS. The FAF, FFS, or SFS is required; the FFS is preferred. The deadline for financial aid applications is July 15.

International Students: There are currently 20 international students enrolled. They must take the TOEFL and achieve a minimum score of 500. The student must also take the ACT.

Computers: The college provides computer facilities for student use. The mainframes are a DEC VAX 11/750–2 and an HP 3000/70–1. There are also 60 IBM microcomputers available in academic laboratories. Students enrolled in computer-based courses may access the system. It may be used 7 A.M. to 11 P.M. daily. There are no time limits on using the system and no fees.

Graduates: In 1992–93 606 bachelor's degrees were awarded. The most popular majors among graduates were education (25%), business (22%), and social science (20%). Some 41 companies recruited on campus in 1992–93.

Admissions Contact: Zoe Du Rant, Director of Admissions.

EAST CENTRAL UNIVERSITY

E-4

Ada, OK 74820   (405) 332–8000

Full-time: 1376 men, 1909 women   Faculty: 158; IIB, av$
Part-time: 217 men, 339 women   Ph.D.s: 64%
Graduate: 183 men, 394 women   Student/Faculty: 21 to 1
Year: semesters, summer session   Tuition: $1490 ($3553)
Application Deadline: open   Room & Board: $2068
Freshman Class: 638 applied, 600 accepted, 499 enrolled
ACT: 20   **COMPETITIVE**

East Central University, founded in 1909, is a publicly funded institution offering undergraduate programs in liberal arts and sciences, education, business, and health-related fields. There are 3 undergraduate schools and one graduate school. In addition to regional accreditation, ECU has baccalaureate program accreditation with CAHEA, CSWE, NCATE, and NLN. The library contains 203,301 volumes, 293,094 microform items, and 5131 audiovisual forms, and subscribes to 1300 periodicals. Computerized library sources and services include interlibrary loans and database searching. Special learning facilities include a learning resource center. The 140-acre campus is in a small town 90 miles south of Oklahoma City. Including residence halls, there are 26 buildings on campus.

Student Life: About 98% of undergraduates are from Oklahoma. Students come from 16 states and 9 foreign countries. Ninety-nine percent are from public schools; 1% from private. Eighty-six percent are white; 10% Native American/Eskimo. The average age of freshmen is 20; all undergraduates, 25. Forty percent drop out by the end of their first year.

Housing: A total of 1121 students can be accommodated in college housing. College-sponsored living facilities include single-sex and coed dormitories, on-campus apartments, and married-student housing. On-campus housing is available on a first-come, first-served basis. Alcohol is not permitted. All students may keep cars on campus.

Activities: About 8% of men belong to 4 national fraternities; about 8% of women belong to 3 national sororities. There are 20 groups on campus, including art, band, cheerleading, choir, chorale, drill team, ethnic, honors, jazz band, marching band, newspaper, pep band, political, social, student government, and yearbook. Popular campus events include Homecoming, Welcome Week, Don't Go Home This Weekend Weekend, Rush Weekend, and Christmas in the Eyes of a Child.

Sports: There are 6 intercollegiate sports for men and 2 for women, and 4 intramural sports for men and 4 for women. Athletic and recreation facilities include a swimming pool, tennis and basketball courts, a weight room, a football field, and indoor and outdoor tracks.

Disabled Students: The entire campus is accessible to disabled students. The following facilities are available: wheelchair ramps, elevators, special parking, specially equipped rest rooms, special class scheduling, lowered drinking fountains, lowered telephones, and adaptive swimming and weight training.

Services: In addition to many counseling and information services, tutoring is available in every subject. There is a reader service for the blind, and remedial math, reading, and writing. Other services include interpreters for the deaf, note taking/typing, and tape transcription for the disabled.

Campus Safety and Security: Campus safety and security measures include 24-hour foot and vehicle patrol and lighted pathways and sidewalks.

Programs of Study: ECU awards the B.A., B.S., B.M., B.S.Ed., and B.S.W. degrees. Master's degrees also are awarded. Bachelor's degrees are awarded in BIOLOGICAL SCIENCE (biology/biological science), BUSINESS (accounting, banking and finance, business administration and management, and marketing/retailing/merchandising), COMMUNICATIONS AND THE ARTS (English, journalism, music, and speech/debate/rhetoric), COMPUTER AND PHYSICAL SCIENCE (chemistry, computer science, mathematics, and physics), EDUCATION (art, business, early childhood, elementary, health, industrial arts, music, science, secondary, and special), ENGINEERING AND ENVIRONMENTAL DESIGN (cartography), HEALTH PROFESSIONS (medical laboratory technology, medical records administration/services, and nursing), SOCIAL SCIENCE (criminal justice, home economics, human services, prelaw, psychology, social work, and sociology). Business administration, accounting, elementary education, and nursing have the largest enrollments.

Required: To graduate, students must complete a minimum of 124 credit hours with a minimum GPA of 2.0. Between 45 and 55 hours must be completed in the major and 18 to 21 hours in a minor. All students must take 40 hours of upper-level courses, as well as 40 to 50 hours in general studies.

Special: The school offers co-op programs with Westfield (Massachusetts) State College and the Ardmore (Oklahoma) Higher Education Center. Internships are available in human resources, environmental science, government, and cartography. Students may participate in a work-study program with the Veterans Administration. Nondegree study and credit for military experience are available. The school offers special rates for nonresidents from approved states who wish to major in cartography. There is a freshman honors program on campus, as well as 1 national honor society, Phi Beta Kappa.

Faculty/Classroom: Seventy-two percent of faculty are male; 28%, female. The average class size in an introductory lecture is 30 and in a laboratory, 20.

Admissions: About 94% of the 1993–94 applicants were accepted. The ACT scores for the 1993–94 freshman class were as follows: 1% below 21, 61% between 21 and 23, 31% between 24 and 26, 6% between 27 and 28, and 1% above 28.

Requirements: ECU requires applicants to be in the upper 50% of their class. A minimum GPA of 2.7 is required. The ACT is required, with a minimum composite score of 19. A composite score of 720 on the SAT I will be accepted in place of the ACT. Applicants must be graduates of an accredited secondary school or have the GED. High school courses must include 4 years of English, 3 years of mathematics, and 2 years each of history and science. AP and CLEP credits are accepted.

Procedure: Freshmen are admitted to all sessions. Application deadlines are open. Notification is sent on a rolling basis. There is an early admissions plan.

Transfer: About 478 transfer students enrolled in a recent year. Applicants having fewer than 24 credit hours must meet the criteria for entering freshmen. The required minimum GPA for transfer students is determined annually by the Oklahoma State Regents for Higher Education. At least 30 credits out of 124 must be completed at ECU.

Visiting: There are regularly scheduled orientations for prospective students. There are guides for informal visits. To arrange for a visit, contact the Student Services Office at (405) 332–8000, ext. 208.

Financial Aid: In an earlier year, 51% of all freshmen received some form of financial aid. The average freshman award was $1300. Seven percent of undergraduate students work part-time. The FFS, the college's own financial statement, federal tax returns, and the state grant form are required. The deadline for financial aid applications is July 1.

International Students: Applicants must take the TOEFL and achieve a minimum score of 500. Students may also be required to take the ACT upon arrival.

Computers: The college provides computer facilities for student use. The mainframe is an HP 3000. There are also 20 microcomputers available in the library and in various departments. Computer science majors may access the system. It may be used 24 hours per day. There are no time limits on using the system and no fees.

Graduates: In a recent year, 608 bachelor's degrees were awarded. The most popular majors among graduates were elementary education (43%), health education (15%), and nursing (9%). Some 40 companies recruited on campus in a recent year.

Admissions Contact: Pamla Armstrong, Registrar.

LANGSTON UNIVERSITY

D-3

Langston, OK 73050   (405) 466–2231, ext. 2980

Full-time, part-time: 2100 men and women   Faculty: 77
    Ph.D.s: 38%
Graduate: none   Student/Faculty: 27 to 1
Year: semesters, summer session   Tuition: $1423 ($3485)
Application Deadline: open   Room & Board: $1484
Freshman Class: n/av
ACT: required   **LESS COMPETITIVE**

Langston University, founded in 1897 as the Colored Agricultural and Normal University, is today a multiracial public institution offering programs in liberal arts, business, allied health, and teacher preparation. In addition to regional accreditation, LU has baccalaureate program accreditation with ADA, APTA, NCATE, and NLN. Computerized library sources and services include the card catalog and interlibrary loans. Special learning facilities include a learning resource center, satellite teaching, a black heritage center, an institute for goat research, and a state research group in catfish production. The 40-acre campus is in a rural area 45 miles from Oklahoma City. Including residence halls, there are 20 buildings on campus.

Student Life: About 66% of undergraduates are from Oklahoma. Ninety-eight percent are from public schools. Fifty percent are African American; 50% white. About 65% of freshmen remain to graduate.

Housing: A total of 676 students can be accommodated in college housing. College-sponsored living facilities include dormitories and married-student housing. Alcohol is not permitted. All students may keep cars on campus.

Activities: About 25% of men belong to 4 national fraternities; about 30% of women belong to 4 national sororities. There are 30 groups on campus, including band, cheerleading, choir, drama, ethnic, international, jazz band, marching band, newspaper, professional, religious, social service, student government, and yearbook. Popular campus events include student theater productions and a performing arts series.

Sports: There are 4 intercollegiate sports for men and 2 for women, and 6 intramural sports for men and 5 for women. Athletic and recreation facilities include a gymnasium, tennis courts, a baseball field, and a track.

Disabled Students: Seventy percent of the campus is accessible to disabled students. The following facilities are available: wheelchair ramps, elevators, special parking, specially equipped rest rooms, and special class scheduling.

Services: In addition to many counseling and information services, tutoring is available in some subjects. There is remedial math, reading, and writing.

Campus Safety and Security: Campus safety and security measures include a PBX security system staffed 20 hours per day and emergency transportation services.

Programs of Study: LU awards the B.A., B.B.A., B.S., B.S.Ed., and B.S.N. degrees. Associate and master's degrees also are awarded. Bachelor's degrees are awarded in AGRICULTURE (agricultural economics and animal science), BIOLOGICAL SCIENCE (biology/biological science and nutrition), BUSINESS (accounting, business administration and management, and management science), COMMUNICATIONS AND THE ARTS (dramatic arts, English, music, and speech/debate/rhetoric), COMPUTER AND PHYSICAL SCIENCE (chemistry, computer science, and mathematics), EDUCATION (business, elementary, home economics, industrial arts, mathematics, physical, and science), ENGINEERING AND ENVIRONMENTAL DESIGN (industrial engineering technology), HEALTH PROFESSIONS (health care administration, medical laboratory technology, nursing, and physical therapy), SOCIAL SCIENCE (criminal justice, early childhood studies, economics, gerontology, history, home economics, psychology, social science, sociology, and urban studies).

Required: To graduate, students must complete a total of 124 semester hours, with a GPA of 2.0. The required general education core consists of 50 credits in English, mathematics, computer science, biological and physical sciences, social science, and health and physical education. Six credits are required in American history and government, and all students must complete an internship or field experience.

Special: Work-study programs, internships, and nondegree and noncredit study are available. There is a freshman honors program on campus, as well as 6 national honor societies.

Requirements: The ACT is required. SAT I scores are accepted. In general, test scores should place students in the upper 60 percent of Oklahoma high school seniors. Applicants should be graduates of accredited high schools with at least a C average (2.7 on a 4.0 scale) and rank in the upper 60 percent of their graduating classes. Required secondary preparation includes 4 years of English, 3 years of mathematics, and 2 years each of laboratory science and history, including 1 year of American history. Four additional academic units, including a foreign language, are strongly recommended. There are alternative admissions programs for students with varying backgrounds. AP and CLEP credits are accepted.

Procedure: Freshmen are admitted to all sessions. Application deadlines are open. Notification is sent on a rolling basis.

Transfer: Applicants should be in good standing and have earned at least a C average in previous college work. A total of 30 credits out of 124 must be completed at LU.

Visiting: There are regularly scheduled orientations for prospective students. There are guides for informal visits, and visitors may sit in on classes and stay overnight at the school. To arrange for a visit, contact the High School/College Relations Office at (405) 466–2231.

Financial Aid: The FAF, FFS, or SFS is required. The deadline for financial aid applications is March 1.

International Students: Applicants must take the TOEFL and achieve a minimum score of 500.

Computers: The college provides computer facilities for student use. The mainframes are a DEC VAX 11/750 and an IBM 34. There are also 40 microcomputers available in academic laboratories. There are no time limits on using the system and no fees.

Admissions Contact: Ronald K. Smith, Director of Admission.

NORTHEASTERN STATE UNIVERSITY F-3
Tahlequah, OK 74464

(918) 456–5511, ext. 2200
(800) 722–9614 (in-state)

Full-time: 2270 men, 2455 women	Faculty: 208; IIA, --$
Part-time: 970 men, 1050 women	Ph.D.s: n/av
Graduate: 615 men, 1270 women	Student/Faculty: 23 to 1
Year: semesters, summer session	Tuition: $3162 ($7500)
Application Deadline: open	Room & Board: $2088
Freshman Class: 2250 applied, 1700 accepted, 828 enrolled	
ACT: 20	COMPETITIVE

Northeastern State University, founded in 1846, is a coeducational public institution offering programs in arts and sciences, professional training, teacher preparation, and business. There are 5 undergraduate schools and one graduate school. In addition to regional accreditation, NSU has baccalaureate program accreditation with NCATE and NLN. The library contains 200,000 volumes, 300,000 microform items, and 3800 audiovisual forms, and subscribes to 2600 periodicals. Computerized library sources and services include the card catalog. Special learning facilities include a learning resource center. The 200-acre campus is in a small town 70 miles from Tulsa. Including residence halls, there are 25 buildings on campus.

Student Life: About 95% of undergraduates are from Oklahoma. Seventy-seven percent are white; 17% Native American/Eskimo. Sixty-eight percent are Protestant; 30% Catholic. The average age of freshmen is 19; all undergraduates, 26. Thirty percent drop out by the end of their first year.

Housing: College-sponsored living facilities include single-sex dormitories, married-student housing, and fraternity houses. In addition, there are rooming arrangements for special interest groups. On-campus housing is available on a first-come, first-served basis. Alcohol is not permitted. All students may keep cars on campus.

Activities: About 10% of men belong to 4 national fraternities; about 10% of women belong to 3 national sororities. There are 75 groups on campus, including band, cheerleading, choir, ethnic, honors, international, literary magazine, newspaper, social service, student government, and yearbook. Popular campus events include the Lyceum Series, Cherokee Seminaries, Homecoming, NSU Playhouse events, and NSU Jazz Labs.

Sports: There are 7 intercollegiate sports for men and 3 for women, and 4 intramural sports for men and 3 for women. Athletic and recreation facilities include a swimming pool, a softball/soccer complex, a weight room, basketball, handball, and racquetball courts, playing fields, and a 10,000-seat track and football stadium.

Disabled Students: Ninety-eight percent of the campus is accessible to disabled students. The following facilities are available: wheelchair ramps, elevators, special parking, and specially equipped rest rooms.

Services: In addition to personal, psychological, and vocational counseling, tutoring and remedial instruction are available.

Campus Safety and Security: Campus safety and security measures include 24-hour foot and vehicle patrol, escort service, shuttle buses, and informal discussions. In addition, there are emergency telephones and lighted pathways and sidewalks. There is a campus security police department.

Programs of Study: NSU awards the B.A., B.S., B.A.Ed., B.B.A., B.S.Ed., B.S.N., and B.S.W. degrees. Master's and doctoral degrees also are awarded. Bachelor's degrees are awarded in AGRICULTURE (horticulture), BIOLOGICAL SCIENCE (biology/biological science, botany, microbiology, and zoology), BUSINESS (accounting, banking and finance, business administration and management, business economics, hotel/motel and restaurant management, and marketing/retailing/merchandising), COMMUNICATIONS AND THE ARTS (advertising, broadcasting, communications, English, fine arts, journalism, music, Spanish, and speech/debate/rhetoric), COMPUTER AND PHYSICAL SCIENCE (chemistry, computer programming, computer science, geology, information sciences and systems, mathematics, and physics), EDUCATION (art, business, early childhood, elementary, health, home economics, industrial arts, music, science, secondary, and special), HEALTH PROFESSIONS (medical laboratory technology, nursing, predentistry, and premedicine), SOCIAL SCIENCE (criminal justice, geography, history, parks and recreation management, political science/government, prelaw, psychology, social science, social work, and sociology).

Required: To graduate, students must complete at least 124 credit hours, with 24 to 50 in the major. General education requirements include 40 hours in language arts, social science, natural science, humanities, and physical education. Freshman orientation and English proficiency are required.

Special: NSU offers educational tours for academic credit, B.A.-B.S. degrees, a weekend program, nondegree study, credit by examination or for military experience, and a pass/fail option.

Admissions: About 76% of the 1993–94 applicants were accepted. The ACT scores for the 1993–94 freshman class were as follows: 78% below 21, 15% between 21 and 23, 4% between 24 and 26, 2% be-

tween 27 and 28, and 1% above 28. About 25% of the current freshmen were in the top fifth of their class; 50% were in the top two fifths.

Requirements: NSU requires applicants to be in the upper 50% of their class. A minimum GPA of 2.7 is required. The SAT I or ACT is required, with a minimum composite score on the ACT of 20. Applicants should be high school graduates or have a GED. Students should have completed 4 years of English, 3 years of mathematics, and 2 years each of history and science. AP and CLEP credits are accepted.

Procedure: Freshmen are admitted to all sessions. Application deadlines are open. Notification is sent on a rolling basis. There are early decision and early admissions plans.

Transfer: Transfer applicants must have a minimum GPA of 2.0, with 24 transfer hours completed, and be in good standing at the last institution attended. A total of 30 credits out of 124 must be completed at NSU.

Visiting: There are regularly scheduled orientations for prospective students, including a general campus visit with highlights presented by trained tour guides. Visitors may sit in on classes and stay overnight at the school. To arrange for a visit, contact the University Relations Office at (918) 456–5511.

Financial Aid: In an earlier year, 65% of all freshmen received some form of financial aid. The FAF is required. The deadline for financial aid applications is April 1.

International Students: Applicants must take the TOEFL and achieve a minimum score of 500.

Computers: The college provides computer facilities for student use. The mainframe is an HP 6000. Apple and TRS 80 PCs are available in classrooms and laboratories. Students in computer classes may access the system. There are no time limits on using the system and no fees.

Admissions Contact: David J. Harbeck, Director of Admissions and Registrar.

NORTHWESTERN OKLAHOMA STATE UNIVERSITY

C-1

Alva, OK 73717   (405) 327–1700, ext. 213

Full-time: 576 men, 654 women	Faculty: 83; IIB, --$
Part-time: 148 men, 246 women	Ph.D.s: 42%
Graduate: 90 men, 183 women	Student/Faculty: 15 to 1
Year: semesters, summer session	Tuition: $1468 ($3668)
Application Deadline: open	Room & Board: $1956
Freshman Class: 306 applied, 289 accepted, 256 enrolled	
ACT: required	**COMPETITIVE**

Northwestern Oklahoma State University, founded in 1897, is a public institution offering programs in liberal and fine arts, agriculture, business, professional training, and teacher preparation. There is one graduate school. In addition to regional accreditation, Northwestern has baccalaureate program accreditation with NCATE and NLN. The library contains 135,000 volumes, 366,000 microform items, and 1100 audiovisual forms, and subscribes to 1480 periodicals. Computerized library sources and services include interlibrary loans and database searching. Special learning facilities include a learning resource center, natural history museum, radio station, TV station, and cable channel. The 70-acre campus is in a small town 150 miles northwest of Oklahoma City. Including residence halls, there are 35 buildings on campus.

Student Life: About 90% of undergraduates are from Oklahoma. Students come from 25 states, 7 foreign countries, and Canada. Ninety-three percent are white. The average age of freshmen is 22; all undergraduates, 25.

Housing: A total of 850 students can be accommodated in college housing. College-sponsored living facilities include single-sex dormitories. In addition, there is a dormitory with all private rooms for junior and senior women. On-campus housing is guaranteed for all 4 years. Alcohol is not permitted. All students may keep cars on campus.

Activities: About 1% of men belong to 1 national fraternity. There are 39 groups on campus, including art, band, cheerleading, choir, chorale, computers, drama, ethnic, honors, international, jazz band, marching band, musical theater, newspaper, pep band, photography, political, professional, radio and TV, religious, social, student government, and yearbook. Popular campus events include Homecoming, Foundation Scholarship Banquet, Alumni Banquet, Science Fair, speech and music contest, Parents Day, Bahama Breakaway, Cinderella Pageant, Cinderfella Contest, and Red Carpet Country Pageant.

Sports: There are 5 intercollegiate sports for men and 3 for women, and 7 intramural sports for men and 6 for women. Athletic and recreation facilities include a field house, playing fields, a basketball court, a pool, and racquetball and tennis courts.

Disabled Students: The entire campus is accessible to disabled students. The following facilities are available: wheelchair ramps, elevators, special parking, specially equipped rest rooms, special class

scheduling, and lowered drinking fountains. Northwestern works with disabled students to accommodate their special needs.

Services: In addition to many counseling and information services, tutoring is available in most subjects. There is remedial math, reading, and writing.

Campus Safety and Security: Campus safety and security measures include 24-hour foot and vehicle patrol and lighted pathways and sidewalks.

Programs of Study: Northwestern awards the B.A., B.S., B.A.Ed., B.S.Ed., and B.S.N. degrees. Master's degrees also are awarded. Bachelor's degrees are awarded in AGRICULTURE (agricultural business management, agriculture, and conservation and regulation), BIOLOGICAL SCIENCE (biology/biological science and zoology), BUSINESS (accounting, business administration and management, and office supervision and management), COMMUNICATIONS AND THE ARTS (broadcasting, dramatic arts, English, journalism, music, public relations, Spanish, and speech/debate/rhetoric), COMPUTER AND PHYSICAL SCIENCE (chemistry, computer science, mathematics, and physics), EDUCATION (business, early childhood, elementary, English, guidance, home economics, industrial arts, library science, mathematics, middle school, music, physical, science, secondary, and special), HEALTH PROFESSIONS (medical laboratory technology and nursing), SOCIAL SCIENCE (criminal justice, economics, history, political science/government, psychology, social science, social work, and sociology). Education, business, social science, health sciences, and nursing are the strongest academically. Education and business have the largest enrollments.

Required: A total of 124 credit hours is required, including at least 40 in the major, with a minimum GPA of 2.0. General education courses total 54 semester hours, including 19 hours in communication and humanities, 15 in social and behavioral science, 11 in mathematics and natural science, and 9 in physical education and other practical arts. This general sequence totals 50 hours for education majors and includes a computer science requirement.

Special: Northwestern offers credit by exam and for military experience. There are 4 national honor societies on campus.

Faculty/Classroom: Sixty-one percent of faculty are male; 39%, female. All teach undergraduates. No introductory courses are taught by graduate students. The average class size in an introductory lecture is 38; in a laboratory, 24; and in a regular course offering, 19.

Admissions: About 94% of the 1993–94 applicants were accepted. The ACT scores for the 1993–94 freshman class were as follows: 58% below 21, 25% between 21 and 23, 11% between 24 and 26, 5% between 27 and 28, and 1% above 28.

Requirements: Northwestern requires applicants to be in the upper 55% of their class. A minimum GPA of 2.7 is required. The ACT is required, with a minimum required score of 19. Applicants must be graduates of an accredited secondary school or have earned a GED. Northwestern requires 20 academic credits, including 4 in English, 3 in mathematics, and 2 each in history and laboratory science. CLEP credit is accepted.

Procedure: Freshmen are admitted to all sessions. Entrance exams should be taken in the junior or senior year. Application deadlines are open. Notification is sent on a rolling basis.

Transfer: About 218 transfer students enrolled in a recent year. Applicants must have a GPA of at least 2.0. A total of 40 credits out of 124 must be completed at Northwestern.

Visiting: There are regularly scheduled orientations for prospective students. In April, usually during 2 sessions, entering freshmen receive information, tour the campus, and enroll. There are guides for informal visits, and visitors may sit in on classes and stay overnight at the school. To arrange for a visit, contact the Pre-Admissions Office at (405) 327–1700, ext. 213.

Financial Aid: In 1993–94 70% of all current freshmen and continuing students received some form of financial aid. About 70% of freshmen and continuing students received need-based aid. The average freshman award was $2600. Of that total, scholarships or need-based grants averaged $700 ($1400 maximum); loans averaged $2600 ($2625 maximum); and work contracts averaged $1100 ($2040 maximum). Fifty-seven percent of undergraduate students work part-time. Average earnings from campus work for the school year are $2040. The average financial indebtedness of the 1992–93 graduate was $3500. The FAFSA financial statement is preferred.

International Students: There are currently 7 international students enrolled. The school actively recruits these students. They must take the TOEFL and achieve a minimum score of 500.

Computers: The college provides computer facilities for student use. The mainframe is a DEC VAX 4000 Model 300. There are also 120 terminals attached to the mainframe and 17 microcomputers networked to a 286 Novell. All students may access the system. It may be used 8 A.M. to 8 P.M. There are no time limits on using the system and no fees.

Graduates: In 1992–93 241 bachelor's degrees were awarded. The most popular majors among graduates were elementary education (16%), business administration (10%), and law enforcement (8%).

Some 29 companies recruited on campus in 1992–93.

Admissions Contact: S. L. White, Director of Pre-Admissions.

OKLAHOMA BAPTIST UNIVERSITY E-3
Shawnee, OK 74801 (405) 878–2033; (800) 654–3285

Full-time: 730 men, 981 women	Faculty: 107; IIB, --$
Part-time: 415 men, 286 women	Ph.D.s: 63%
Graduate: 11 men, 9 women	Student/Faculty: 16 to 1
Year: 4–1–4, summer session	Tuition: $5436
Application Deadline: open	Room & Board: $3050
Freshman Class: 717 applied, 681 accepted, 483 enrolled	
ACT: 23	**COMPETITIVE**

Oklahoma Baptist University, founded in 1910, is a liberal arts institution affiliated with the Southern Baptist Convention. OBU offers degrees in Christian service, business, nursing, fine arts, telecommunications, teacher education, and the traditional liberal arts areas. There are 5 undergraduate schools and one graduate school. In addition to regional accreditation, OBU has baccalaureate program accreditation with NASM, NCATE, and NLN. The library contains 200,000 volumes and 300,000 microform items, and subscribes to 600 periodicals. Computerized library sources and services include interlibrary loans and database searching. Special learning facilities include a learning resource center, planetarium, and TV station. The 125-acre campus is in a small town 35 miles east of Oklahoma City. Including residence halls, there are 25 buildings on campus.

Student Life: About 72% of undergraduates are from Oklahoma. Students come from 42 states, 28 foreign countries, and Canada. Eighty-five percent are from public schools; 15% from private. Eighty-nine percent are white. Most are Protestant. The average age of freshmen is 19; all undergraduates, 22. Twenty-one percent drop out by the end of their first year; 54% remain to graduate.

Housing: A total of 1268 students can be accommodated in college housing. College-sponsored living facilities include single-sex dormitories, on-campus apartments, and married-student housing. On-campus housing is guaranteed for all 4 years. Fifty percent of students live on campus; of those, 60% remain on campus on weekends. Alcohol is not permitted. All students may keep cars on campus.

Activities: About 18% of men belong to 5 local fraternities; about 16% of women belong to 5 local sororities. There are 60 groups on campus, including art, band, cheerleading, chorale, chorus, computers, drama, ethnic, film, honors, international, jazz band, literary magazine, musical theater, newspaper, opera, orchestra, pep band, photography, political, professional, radio and TV, religious, social, social service, student government, and yearbook. Popular campus events include Stampede of Stars, Homecoming, International Awareness Day, and Hanging of the Green.

Sports: There are 4 intercollegiate sports for men and 3 for women, and 10 intramural sports for men and 6 for women. Athletic and recreation facilities include the Noble Complex, which houses a 2500-seat arena, a swimming pool, tennis and racquetball courts, weight rooms, an all-weather track, and baseball, softball, and sand volleyball facilities.

Disabled Students: Ninety percent of the campus is accessible to disabled students. The following facilities are available: wheelchair ramps, elevators, special parking, specially equipped rest rooms, lowered drinking fountains, and lowered telephones.

Services: In addition to many counseling and information services, tutoring is available in most subjects. There is a reader service for the blind, and remedial math, reading, and writing.

Campus Safety and Security: Campus safety and security measures include 24-hour foot and vehicle patrol, escort service, emergency telephones, and lighted pathways and sidewalks.

Programs of Study: OBU awards the B.A., B.S., B.B.A., B.F.A., B.Hum., B.M., B.M.A., B.Mus.Ed., and B.S.E. degrees. Associate degrees also are awarded. Bachelor's degrees are awarded in BIOLOGICAL SCIENCE (biology/biological science), BUSINESS (accounting, banking and finance, business administration and management, and marketing/retailing/merchandising), COMMUNICATIONS AND THE ARTS (broadcasting, communications, dramatic arts, English, fine arts, French, German, journalism, music, Spanish, speech/debate/rhetoric, and telecommunications), COMPUTER AND PHYSICAL SCIENCE (computer science, information sciences and systems, mathematics, and physics), EDUCATION (art, business, early childhood, elementary, foreign languages, music, science, and secondary), HEALTH PROFESSIONS (nursing, physical therapy, predentistry, and premedicine), SOCIAL SCIENCE (history, political science/government, prelaw, psychology, religion, social science, social work, and sociology). Teacher education, biology, music, religion, telecommunications, and nursing are the strongest academically. Elementary education, management, accounting, biology, youth ministry, nursing, telecommunications, and psychology have the largest enrollments.

Required: To graduate, students must complete a total of 128 credit hours, including 30 to 48 hours in the major, with a 2.0 GPA. Students are also required to complete 6 credits each of English, literature, history, science, Bible, social sciences, and language, 3 each in mathematics, fine arts, and comparative civilization, 2 each in speech, philosophy, and physical education, and 1 in computer literacy.

Special: The school offers co-op programs in business, cross-registration with Saint Gregory's College, and a 3–2 engineering degree with Oklahoma State University. Students may study abroad in Europe, South America, Hungary, China, and Japan. Student-designed majors, including an interdisciplinary program in humanities, and pass/fail options are available. There is a freshman honors program on campus, as well as 4 national honor societies.

Faculty/Classroom: Sixty percent of faculty are male; 40%, female. All teach undergraduates. No introductory courses are taught by graduate students. The average class size in an introductory lecture is 22 and in a laboratory, 18.

Admissions: About 95% of the 1993–94 applicants were accepted. The ACT scores for the 1993–94 freshman class were as follows: 28% below 21, 24% between 21 and 23, 17% between 24 and 26, 19% between 27 and 28, and 12% above 28. About 49% of the current freshmen were in the top fifth of their class; 69% were in the top two fifths. There were 5 National Merit semifinalists. Twenty-three freshmen graduated first in their class.

Requirements: OBU requires applicants to be in the upper 50% of their class. A minimum GPA of 2.0 is required. The SAT I or ACT is required. Admission is granted to students with composite scores of 720 on the SAT I or 20 on the ACT, with a 2.0 GPA. Graduation from an accredited secondary school or satisfactory scores on the GED are required for admission. The recommended high school courses should include 4 units of English, 2 units each of social studies, laboratory science, and a foreign language, and 1 unit each of algebra and geometry. AP and CLEP credits are accepted. Important factors used in the admissions decision are advanced placement or honor courses, recommendations by school officials, leadership record, evidence of special talent, and extracurricular activities record.

Procedure: Freshmen are admitted to all sessions. Entrance exams should be taken during the spring of the junior year. Application deadlines are open. The fee is $25. Notification is sent on a rolling basis.

Transfer: About 154 transfer students enrolled in 1993–94. Transfer students must have a GPA of 2.0. A total of 30 credits out of 128 must be completed at OBU.

Visiting: There are regularly scheduled orientations for prospective students, including tours, faculty visits, and general information sessions. There are guides for informal visits, and visitors may sit in on classes and stay overnight at the school. To arrange for a visit, contact the Admissions Office at (800) 654–3285.

Financial Aid: In an earlier year, 85% of all freshmen and continuing students received some form of financial aid. About 53% of freshmen and 41% of continuing students received need-based aid. The average freshman award was $4500. Of that total, scholarships or need-based grants averaged $2450 ($4500 maximum); loans averaged $1200 ($4500 maximum); and work contracts averaged $850 ($2000 maximum). Eighty-five percent of undergraduate students work part-time. Average earnings from campus work for the school year are $1450. The FAFSA financial statement is required. The deadline for financial aid applications is April 15.

International Students: There are currently 25 international students enrolled. The school actively recruits these students. They must take the TOEFL and achieve a minimum score of 500.

Computers: The college provides computer facilities for student use. The mainframe is an HP 935. Students have access to about 120 networked microcomputers, including Everex, HP, and Zenith, in laboratories on campus. All students may access the system. It may be used 75 hours per week. There are no time limits on using the system. The fees are $10 per semester.

Graduates: In 1992–93 335 bachelor's degrees were awarded. The most popular majors among graduates were elementary education (15%), nursing (7%), and English (5%). Within an average freshman class, 1% graduate in 3 years, 34% in 4 years, 38% in 5 years, and 40% in 6 years.

Admissions Contact: Jody Johnson, Dean of Admissions.

OKLAHOMA CHRISTIAN UNIVERSITY OF SCIENCE AND ARTS
D-3
Oklahoma City, OK 73136-1100
(405) 425-5055
(800) 877-5010 (out-of-state)

Full-time: 733 men, 686 women	Faculty: 80; IIB, av$
Part-time: 111 men, 117 women	Ph.D.s: 59%
Graduate: 29 men	Student/Faculty: 18 to 1
Year: trimesters, summer session	Tuition: $5810
Application Deadline: open	Room & Board: $2980
Freshman Class: 765 applied, 754 accepted, 349 enrolled	
SAT I or ACT: required	**NONCOMPETITIVE**

Oklahoma Christian University of Science and Arts, founded in 1950, is a private liberal arts institution affiliated with the Church of Christ. There are 5 undergraduate schools and one graduate school. In addition to regional accreditation, OC has baccalaureate program accreditation with ABET, NASM, and NCATE. The library contains 110,000 volumes, 126,000 microform items, and 6447 audiovisual forms, and subscribes to 976 periodicals. Computerized library sources and services include the card catalog, interlibrary loans, and database searching. Special learning facilities include a learning resource center, radio station, studio, free enterprise museum, and journalism laboratory. The 200-acre campus is in a suburban area on the north side of Oklahoma City. Including residence halls, there are 33 buildings on campus.

Student Life: About 56% of undergraduates are from out-of-state, mostly the Midwest. Students come from 43 states, 33 foreign countries, and Canada. Eighty-seven percent are white. The average age of freshmen is 18. Thirty-three percent drop out by the end of their first year; 36% remain to graduate.

Housing: A total of 1440 students can be accommodated in college housing. College-sponsored living facilities include single-sex dormitories, on-campus apartments, and married-student housing. On-campus housing is guaranteed for all 4 years. Seventy percent of students live on campus. Alcohol is not permitted. All students may keep cars on campus.

Activities: There are no fraternities or sororities on campus. There are 22 groups on campus, including band, cheerleading, chorale, computers, drama, honors, international, jazz band, literary magazine, musical theater, newspaper, opera, pep band, photography, political, professional, radio and TV, religious, social service, student government, symphony, and yearbook. Popular campus events include Homecoming, High School Day, Spring Sing, and Special Olympics Banquet.

Sports: There are 8 intercollegiate sports for men and 5 for women, and 15 intramural sports for men and 15 for women. Athletic and recreation facilities include 2 gymnasiums, a swimming pool, 3 softball fields, 2 football fields, a soccer field, and a fitness center with weight training, stair, and bicycle machines.

Disabled Students: Ninety-eight percent of the campus is accessible to disabled students. The following facilities are available: wheelchair ramps, elevators, special parking, specially equipped rest rooms, special class scheduling, lowered drinking fountains, and lowered telephones. All buildings except one are ground level.

Services: In addition to many counseling and information services, tutoring is available in some subjects, including English, mathematics, speech, chemistry, physics, business, education, and computer science. In addition, there is remedial math, reading, and writing.

Campus Safety and Security: Campus safety and security measures include 24-hour foot and vehicle patrol, self defense education, escort service, and informal discussions. In addition, there are pamphlets, posters, and films, emergency telephones, lighted pathways and sidewalks, and security officers.

Programs of Study: OC awards the B.A., B.S., B.Mus.Ed., B.S.Ed., B.S.E.E., and B.S.M.E. degrees. Master's degrees also are awarded. Bachelor's degrees are awarded in BIOLOGICAL SCIENCE (biochemistry and biology/biological science), BUSINESS (accounting, banking and finance, business administration and management, marketing/retailing/merchandising, and office supervision and management), COMMUNICATIONS AND THE ARTS (advertising, broadcasting, communications, creative writing, design, English, journalism, music, Spanish, and speech/debate/rhetoric), COMPUTER AND PHYSICAL SCIENCE (chemistry, computer science, information sciences and systems, and mathematics), EDUCATION (art, business, early childhood, elementary, English, mathematics, middle school, music, physical, science, social studies, special, speech correction, and teaching English as a second language/foreign language), ENGINEERING AND ENVIRONMENTAL DESIGN (computer engineering, electrical/electronics engineering, engineering physics, interior design, and mechanical engineering), HEALTH PROFESSIONS (medical laboratory technology and premedicine), SOCIAL SCIENCE (biblical studies, child care/child and family studies, history, liberal arts/general studies, ministries, missions, prelaw, psychology, religion, religious education, social work, sociology, and youth minis-

try). Business, science and engineering, and communication and fine arts have the largest enrollments.

Required: To graduate, students must have a minimum of 126 credit hours, including 49 to 102 in the major, with a GPA of 2.0. All students must complete 60 to 61 hours in the general education program, which includes courses in Bible, English, speech, American studies, American government, mathematics, literature, fine arts, economics, biology, physical science, philosophy, Western civilization, physical education, personal development, and social science.

Special: OC offers cross-registration with University of Central Oklahoma, a liberal studies degree, internships in various majors, and credit for military experience. Students may study abroad in Austria, Japan, and Latin America. Major-minor combinations are offered in mass communication, family life, engineering, prelaw, advertising design, speech communication, English, music, education, and mathematics. There are 2 national honor societies on campus.

Faculty/Classroom: Seventy-six percent of faculty are male; 24%, female. All teach undergraduates and 10% both teach and do research. The average class size in an introductory lecture is 55; in a laboratory, 19; and in a regular course offering, 18.

Admissions: About 99% of the 1993-94 applicants were accepted. The ACT scores for the 1993-94 freshman class were as follows: 41% below 21, 21% between 21 and 23, 18% between 24 and 26, 7% between 27 and 28, and 13% above 28. There were 5 National Merit finalists.

Requirements: The SAT I or ACT is required. Graduation from an accredited secondary school or satisfactory scores on the GED are required for admission. AP and CLEP credits are accepted.

Procedure: Freshmen are admitted to all sessions. Application deadlines are open. Application fee is $10. The university accepts all qualified applicants. Notification is sent on a rolling basis. There are early admissions and deferred admissions plans.

Transfer: About 120 transfer students enrolled in 1993-94. Applicants must be eligible to return to the school from which they are transferring. A total of 30 credits out of 126 must be completed at OC.

Visiting: There are regularly scheduled orientations for prospective students, including High School Days in October and March. There are guides for informal visits and visitors may sit in on classes and stay overnight at the school. To arrange for a visit, contact the Admissions Office at (405) 425-5200 or (800) 877-5010 (out-of-state).

Financial Aid: In an earlier year, 80% of all students received some form of financial aid. About 50% of students received need-based aid. The average freshman award was $5515. Of that total, scholarships or need-based grants averaged $1512 ($4650 maximum); loans averaged $2400 ($2625 maximum); and work contracts averaged $1200. Fifty-five percent of undergraduate students work part-time. Average earnings from campus work for the school year are $1200. The average financial indebtedness of a recent graduate was $6700. The FFS financial statement is required. The deadline for financial aid applications is April 15.

International Students: There are currently 86 international students enrolled. The school actively recruits these students. They must take the TOEFL and achieve a minimum score of 500. The student must also take the SAT I or the ACT.

Computers: The university provides computer facilities for student use. The mainframes are a DEC MicroVAX 3400 and an AT&T 3B4000. More than 100 IBM, IBM-compatible, and Apple microcomputers are available for academic use. All students may access the system during building hours. There are no time limits on using the system. The fees are $10.

Graduates: In 1992-93, 284 bachelor's degrees were awarded. The most popular majors among graduates were science and engineering (18%), business (18%), and education (16%). Within an average freshman class, 33% graduate in 5 years. Some 52 companies recruited on campus in 1992-93. In an earlier graduating class, 40% of the men and women had found employment within 6 months of graduation.

Admissions Contact: Duane Eggleston, Director of Admissions.

OKLAHOMA CITY UNIVERSITY
D-3
Oklahoma City, OK 73106
(405) 521-5050
(800) 633-7242 (out-of-state)

Full-time: 741 men, 872 women	Faculty: 157; IIA, --$
Part-time: 263 men, 278 women	Ph.D.s: 55%
Graduate: 1282 men, 1045 women	Student/Faculty: 10 to 1
Year: semesters, summer session	Tuition: $6210
Application Deadline: open	Room & Board: $3630
Freshman Class: 940 applied, 653 accepted, 343 enrolled	
SAT I Verbal/Math: 501/531	ACT: 23 **COMPETITIVE**

Oklahoma City University, founded in 1904, is a private liberal arts institution affiliated with the Methodist Church, and offering undergraduate programs in arts and sciences, business, music and performing arts, nursing, and religion and church vocations. There are 6 un-

dergraduate and 5 graduate schools. In addition to regional accreditation, OCU has baccalaureate program accreditation with NASM and NLN. The 2 libraries contain 356,213 volumes, 149,251 microform items, and 11,364 audiovisual forms, and subscribe to 4036 periodicals. Computerized library sources and services include interlibrary loans and database searching. Special learning facilities include a learning resource center, art gallery, planetarium, radio station, and TV station. The 64-acre campus is in an urban area within Oklahoma City. Including residence halls, there are 26 buildings on campus.

Student Life: About 56% of undergraduates are from Oklahoma. Students come from 48 states, 61 foreign countries, and Canada. Fifty-six percent are white; 33% foreign nationals. Thirty-two percent are Protestant; 13% claim no religious affiliation; 11% Catholic. The average age of freshmen is 18; all undergraduates, 20. Thirty-three percent drop out by the end of their first year.

Housing: A total of 542 students can be accommodated in college housing. College-sponsored living facilities include single-sex dormitories, on-campus apartments, and fraternity houses. In addition, there are special interest houses. On-campus housing is guaranteed for all 4 years. Fifty-nine percent of students commute. Alcohol is not permitted. All students may keep cars on campus.

Activities: About 12% of men belong to 3 national fraternities; about 13% of women belong to 3 national sororities. There are 36 groups on campus, including art, band, cheerleading, choir, chorus, computers, dance, drama, ethnic, film, honors, international, jazz band, literary magazine, musical theater, newspaper, opera, orchestra, pep band, photography, political, professional, radio and TV, religious, social, student government, symphony, and yearbook. Popular campus events include Homecoming, and sports, theater, dance, and music programs.

Sports: There are 5 intercollegiate sports for men and 3 for women, and 21 intramural sports for men and 2 for women. Athletic and recreation facilities include a field house, tennis courts, and baseball, softball, and soccer fields.

Disabled Students: Ninety-six percent of the campus is accessible to disabled students. The following facilities are available: wheelchair ramps, elevators, special parking, specially equipped rest rooms, lowered drinking fountains, and lowered telephones.

Services: In addition to many counseling and information services, tutoring is available in most subjects. There is also remedial math, reading, and writing, and a learning enhancement center.

Campus Safety and Security: Campus safety and security measures include 24-hour foot and vehicle patrol, escort service, informal discussions, and pamphlets, posters, and films. In addition, there are emergency telephones, lighted pathways and sidewalks, and an inner-campus bicycle patrol.

Programs of Study: OCU awards the B.A., B.S., B.F.A., B.M., B.Perf.Arts, B.S.B., and B.S.N. degrees. Associate, master's, and doctoral degrees also are awarded. Bachelor's degrees are awarded in BIOLOGICAL SCIENCE (biology/biological science), BUSINESS (accounting, banking and finance, business administration and management, business economics, and marketing/retailing/merchandising), COMMUNICATIONS AND THE ARTS (advertising, broadcasting, communications, dance, dramatic arts, English, fine arts, French, German, journalism, music, Spanish, and speech/debate/rhetoric), COMPUTER AND PHYSICAL SCIENCE (chemistry, computer management, computer science, mathematics, physics, and science), EDUCATION (early childhood, elementary, foreign languages, health, music, science, and secondary), HEALTH PROFESSIONS (nursing and premedicine), SOCIAL SCIENCE (Asian/Oriental studies, corrections, criminal justice, economics, history, humanities, law enforcement and corrections, philosophy, political science/government, prelaw, psychology, religion, and sociology). Business, performing arts, nursing, mathematics, science, and computer science are the strongest academically. Business, performing arts, and liberal arts have the largest enrollments.

Required: To graduate, students must complete a total of 124 credit hours, including 30 to 80 in the major, with a minimum GPA of 2.0. Students must complete their last 15 hours, including the last 6 in the major, at OCU with a minimum GPA of 2.0. All students must take courses in the Foundation Curriculum as specified by their college or department.

Special: OCU offers internships, a Washington semester, work-study programs, a general studies degree, dual and student-designed majors, credit for life experience, nondegree study, and pass/fail options. Study-abroad programs are available in 6 countries. There is a freshman honors program on campus, as well as 8 national honor societies. Ten departments have honors programs.

Faculty/Classroom: Sixty-three percent of faculty are male; 37%, female. All teach undergraduates. The average class size in an introductory lecture is 25; in a laboratory, 8; and in a regular course offering, 18.

Admissions: About 69% of the 1993–94 applicants were accepted. The SAT scores for the 1993–94 freshman class were as follows: Verbal—44% below 500, 36% between 500 and 599, 16% between 600 and 700, and 4% above 700; Math—33% below 500, 33% between 500 and 599, 31% between 600 and 700, and 2% above 700. The ACT scores were 32% below 21, 24% between 21 and 23, 21% between 24 and 26, 12% between 27 and 28, and 11% above 28. About 46% of the current freshmen were in the top fifth of their class; 72% were in the top two fifths. There was 1 National Merit finalist and 4 semifinalists. Nine freshmen graduated first in their class.

Requirements: A minimum GPA of 2.0 is required. The SAT I, with a minimum composite score of 920 (450 verbal and 470 mathematics), or the ACT, with a minimum score of 20, is required. Graduation from an accredited secondary school or satisfactory scores on the GED are also required for admission. High school courses must include 4 units of English, 3 units each of science, social studies, and mathematics, and 2 units of a foreign language. Music students are required to have an audition. AP and CLEP credits are accepted. Important factors used in the admissions decision are ability to finance college education, leadership record, advanced placement or honor courses, extracurricular activities record, and evidence of special talent.

Procedure: Freshmen are admitted to all sessions. Application deadlines are open. Application fee is $20. Notification is sent on a rolling basis. There is an early admissions plan.

Transfer: A total of 218 transfer students enrolled in 1993–94. Applicants must submit a transcript from each college attended and must have a minimum GPA of 2.0 from an accredited institution. Applicants must submit a transcript from each college attended. Applicants having fewer than 26 credit hours must submit a high school transcript. Minimum composite scores of 900 on the SAT I and 20 on the ACT are required. A total of 30 credits out of 124 must be completed at OCU.

Visiting: There are guides for informal visits and visitors may sit in on classes and stay overnight at the school. To arrange for a visit, contact the Undergraduate Admissions Office at (800) 633–7242, ext. 5050, or (405) 521–5050.

Financial Aid: In 1993–94, 84% of all current freshmen and 58% of continuing students received some form of financial aid. About 55% of freshmen and 88% of continuing students received need-based aid. The average freshman award was $6032. Of that total, scholarships or need-based grants averaged $3711 ($11,209 maximum); loans averaged $3354 ($10,500 maximum); and work contracts averaged $1815 ($2720 maximum). Twenty percent of undergraduate students work part-time. Average earnings from campus work for the school year are $1386. The average financial indebtedness of the 1992–93 graduate was $9288. OCU is a member of CSS. The FAF, FFS, or SFS is required. The deadline for financial aid applications is March 1.

International Students: There are currently 1100 international students enrolled. The school actively recruits these students. They must take the TOEFL and achieve a minimum score of 500.

Computers: The university provides computer facilities for student use. The mainframe is a DEC VAX 6210. Students may access the system from dormitory rooms and from off campus. In addition, there are a number of open-access laboratories housing approximately 130 PCs and terminals. Only students enrolled in computer classes may access the system. It may be used 24 hours a day. There are no time limits on using the system. Off-campus students are charged $30 per semester. Dormitory students do not pay a fee.

Graduates: In 1992–93, 272 bachelor's degrees were awarded. The most popular majors among graduates were mass communications (12%), computer science (12%), and accounting (8%).

Admissions Contact: Undergraduate Admissions Office.

OKLAHOMA PANHANDLE STATE UNIVERSITY

B-2

(Formerly Panhandle State University)
Goodwell, OK 73939

(405) 349–2611, ext. 274

Full-time: 460 men, 479 women	Faculty: 54; IIB, -$
Part-time: 99 men, 159 women	Ph.D.s: 52%
Graduate: none	Student/Faculty: 17 to 1
Year: semesters, summer session	Tuition: $1355 ($3634)
Application Deadline: September 15	Room & Board: $1800
Freshman Class: n/av	
SAT I or ACT: required	**NONCOMPETITIVE**

Oklahoma Panhandle State University, founded in 1909, is a publicly funded institution offering undergraduate programs in the liberal arts, business, education, agriculture, and preprofessional training. There are 5 undergraduate schools. In addition to regional accreditation, Oklahoma Panhandle State University has baccalaureate program accreditation with NCATE. The library contains 94,372 volumes and 6918 microform items, and subscribes to 510 periodicals. Special

learning facilities include a natural history museum, planetarium, and radio station. The 120-acre campus is in a rural area 100 miles from Amarillo. Including residence halls, there are 26 buildings on campus.

Student Life: About 52% of undergraduates are from out-of-state, mostly the South. Ninety-eight percent are from public schools. Eighty-nine percent are white. The average age of freshmen is 18; all undergraduates, 24. Thirty-five percent drop out by the end of their first year; 10% remain to graduate.

Housing: A total of 292 students can be accommodated in college housing. College-sponsored living facilities include coed dormitories, on-campus apartments, off-campus apartments, and married-student housing. In addition there are honors houses. On-campus housing is guaranteed for all 4 years. Seventy percent of students commute and all students may keep cars on campus. Alcohol is not permitted.

Activities: There are no fraternities or sororities. There are 45 groups on campus, including art, band, cheerleading, choir, chorale, chorus, computers, dance, drama, drill team, ethnic, honors, jazz band, marching band, musical theater, newspaper, pep band, photography, professional, radio and TV, religious, social, and student government.

Sports: There are 4 intercollegiate sports for men and 3 for women, and 10 intramural sports for men and 9 for women.

Disabled Students: The following facilities are available: wheelchair ramps, elevators, and special parking.

Services: In addition to many counseling and information services, tutoring is available in most subjects. There is remedial math, reading, and writing. Free tutoring is provided through the peer counseling center.

Campus Safety and Security: Campus safety and security measures include 24-hour foot and vehicle patrol, emergency telephones, and lighted pathways and sidewalks.

Programs of Study: Oklahoma Panhandle State University awards the B.A., B.S., B.B.A., and B.M.E. degrees. Associate degrees are also awarded. Bachelor's degrees are awarded in AGRICULTURE (agricultural business management, animal science, forestry and related sciences, and horticulture), BIOLOGICAL SCIENCE (biology/biological science), BUSINESS (accounting and business administration and management), COMMUNICATIONS AND THE ARTS (communications, English, music, and speech/debate/rhetoric), COMPUTER AND PHYSICAL SCIENCE (chemistry, computer science, and mathematics), EDUCATION (business, elementary, home economics, industrial arts, music, science, and secondary), HEALTH PROFESSIONS (medical laboratory technology), SOCIAL SCIENCE (history and psychology). Business, agriculture, and education are the strongest academically. Education, agriculture, and business have the largest enrollments.

Required: To graduate, students must complete a total of 124 semester hours with a minimum GPA of 2.0. The number of hours required in a major varies. All students must complete 50 hours of general education courses, with at least 1 course at the upper-division level.

Special: Oklahoma Panhandle State University offers dual majors in most areas.

Faculty/Classroom: Fifty percent of faculty are male; 50%, female. All teach undergraduates. The average class size in an introductory lecture is 35; in a laboratory, 24; and in a regular course offering, 20.

Requirements: Oklahoma Panhandle State University requires applicants to be in the upper 50% of their class. The SAT I or the ACT, with a minimum composite score of 16, is required. Graduation from an accredited secondary school or satisfactory scores on the GED are required. High school courses must include 4 units of English, 3 units of mathematics, (beginning with algebra I), and 2 units each of history (including 1 unit of American history), and laboratory science. CLEP credit is accepted.

Procedure: Freshmen are admitted to all sessions. Applications should be filed by September 15 for fall entry. The college accepts all applicants

Transfer: A total of 30 credits out of 124 must be completed at Oklahoma Panhandle State University.

Visiting: There are regularly scheduled orientations for prospective students. There are guides for informal visits and visitors may sit in on classes and stay overnight at the school. To arrange for a visit, contact the Office of Admissions at (405) 349–2611, ext. 274.

Financial Aid: In 1993–94, 39% of all current freshmen and 61% of continuing students received some form of financial aid, including need-based aid. The average freshman award was $700. Of that total, scholarships or need-based grants averaged $400 ($5500 maximum); loans averaged $800 ($5500 maximum); and work contracts averaged $800 ($2000 maximum). Oklahoma Panhandle State University is a member of CSS. The FAF, FFS or SFS is required.

International Students: There are currently 5 international students enrolled. They must take the TOEFL and achieve a minimum score of 500. The student must also take the SAT I or the ACT.

Computers: The college provides computer facilities for student use. The mainframe is an HP 9000/8275. There are 40 Apple, IBM, and Compaq microcomputers available in laboratories. Students enrolled in computer information system classes may access the system. It may be used 5 A.M. to 11 P.M. There are no time limits and no fees.

Graduates: In a recent year, 155 bachelor's degrees were awarded.

Admissions Contact: Gin Manning, Admissions Counselor.

OKLAHOMA STATE SYSTEM OF HIGHER EDUCATION

The Oklahoma State System of Higher Education, established in 1941, is a public system in Oklahoma. It is governed by the Oklahoma State Regents for Higher Education, whose chief administrator is the chancellor. The primary goals of the system are teaching, research, and public service. The main priorities are student success, excellence, and system efficiency. The total enrollment of all 25 campuses is about 166,000, with more than 4000 faculty members. Altogether there are 679 baccalaureate, 274 master's, and 145 doctoral programs offered by the Oklahoma State System of Higher Education. Four-year campuses are located in Stillwater, Norman, Edmond, Ada, Tahlequah, Alva, Durant, Weatherford, Lawton, Langston, Goodwell, and Chickasha. Profiles of those campuses are included in this chapter in alphabetical order with other Oklahoma schools.

OKLAHOMA STATE UNIVERSITY
E-2

Stillwater, OK 74078 (405) 744–6858; (800) 852–1255 (out-of-state)

Full-time: 6981 men, 5849 women	Faculty: 609; I, --$
Part-time: 855 men, 803 women	Ph.D.s: 88%
Graduate: 2439 men, 1802 women	Student/Faculty: 21 to 1
Year: semesters, summer session	Tuition: $1882 ($5328)
Application Deadline: open	Room & Board: $3204
Freshman Class: 4102 applied, 3913 accepted, 2181 enrolled	
ACT: 23	**VERY COMPETITIVE**

Oklahoma State University, founded in 1890, is a publicly funded land-grant institution, offering undergraduate programs in agricultural sciences and natural resources, arts and sciences, business, education, engineering, architecture, technology, and human environmental resources. There are 6 undergraduate schools. In addition to regional accreditation, OSU has baccalaureate program accreditation with AACSB, ABET, ACEJMC, ADA, AHEA, ASLA, FIDER, NAAB, NASM, NRPA, and SAF. The 5 libraries contain 1,625,000 volumes, 2,620,000 microform items, and 2500 audiovisual forms, and subscribe to 14,500 periodicals. Computerized library sources and services include interlibrary loans. Special learning facilities include an art gallery, natural history museum, and radio station. The 415-acre campus is in a small town 65 miles north of Oklahoma City. Including residence halls, there are 200 buildings on campus.

Student Life: About 86% of undergraduates are from Oklahoma. Students come from 48 states, 92 foreign countries, and Canada. Eighty-two percent are white. The average age of freshmen is 19.7; all undergraduates, 22.3. Twenty-five percent drop out by the end of their first year; 47% remain to graduate.

Housing: A total of 5930 students can be accommodated in college housing. College-sponsored living facilities include single-sex and coed dormitories, on-campus apartments, off-campus apartments, married-student housing, fraternity houses, and sorority houses. In addition there are honors houses, language houses, special interest houses, and fine arts floors and engineering floors. On-campus housing is guaranteed for all 4 years. Alcohol is not permitted. All students may keep cars on campus.

Activities: About 18% of men belong to 25 national fraternities; about 16% of women belong to 14 national sororities. There are 265 groups on campus, including art, band, cheerleading, choir, chorale, chorus, computers, dance, drama, ethnic, gay, honors, international, jazz band, literary magazine, marching band, musical theater, newspaper, opera, orchestra, pep band, political, professional, radio and TV, religious, social, social service, student government, symphony, and yearbook. Popular campus events include Homecoming, Spring Sing, Freshmen Follies, and Special Olympics.

Sports: There are 9 intercollegiate sports for men and 7 for women, and 40 intramural sports for men, 40 for women, and 20 for both. Athletic and recreation facilities include a physical education center and a variety of intramural facilities and swimming pools.

Disabled Students: Ninety percent of the campus is accessible to disabled students. The following facilities are available: wheelchair ramps, elevators, special parking, specially equipped rest rooms, special class scheduling, lowered drinking fountains, and adaptive technology.

Services: In addition to many counseling and information services, tutoring is available in some subjects, including mathematics. Academic assessment and minority programs are also available.

Campus Safety and Security: Campus safety and security measures include 24-hour foot and vehicle patrol, self defense education, informal discussions, and pamphlets, posters, and films. In addition, there are emergency telephones and lighted pathways and sidewalks.

Programs of Study: OSU awards the B.A., B.S., B.F.A., B.Arch., B.Arch.Eng., B.Land.Arch., and B.M. degrees. Master's and doctoral degrees also are awarded. Bachelor's degrees are awarded in AGRICULTURE (agricultural business management, agricultural economics, agriculture, animal science, and horticulture), BIOLOGICAL SCIENCE (biochemistry, biology/biological science, botany, cell biology, microbiology, and zoology), BUSINESS (accounting, banking and finance, business administration and management, business economics, business law, hotel/motel and restaurant management, international business management, marketing/retailing/merchandising, and personnel management), COMMUNICATIONS AND THE ARTS (advertising, broadcasting, communications, design, English, fine arts, French, German, journalism, music, Russian, Spanish, and speech/debate/rhetoric), COMPUTER AND PHYSICAL SCIENCE (chemistry, computer programming, computer science, geology, information sciences and systems, mathematics, physics, and statistics), EDUCATION (agricultural, art, business, early childhood, elementary, English, foreign languages, health, industrial arts, middle school, science, secondary, and special), ENGINEERING AND ENVIRONMENTAL DESIGN (aeronautical engineering, aeronautical science, agricultural engineering, architecture, chemical engineering, civil engineering, computer engineering, construction management, electrical/electronics engineering, electrical/electronics engineering technology, engineering, engineering technology, industrial engineering, manufacturing technology, mechanical engineering, and mechanical engineering technology), HEALTH PROFESSIONS (premedicine, preveterinary science, and speech pathology/audiology), SOCIAL SCIENCE (dietetics, economics, fire control and safety technology, geography, history, international relations, philosophy, political science/government, prelaw, psychology, social work, and sociology). Engineering and business are the strongest academically. Business has the largest enrollment.

Required: To graduate, the student must have a minimum GPA of 2.0 and a total of 123 to 140 hours, including 65 to 75 in the major, for most programs. A higher GPA may be required in some majors. All students must take a minimum of 40 credit hours of core courses in English, mathematics, social studies, science, and humanities.

Special: OSU offers internships in medical technology, engineering, home economics, and arts and sciences. A B.A.-B.S. degree, dual majors, a general studies degree, a 3–2 engineering degree, credit for life experience, nondegree study, and pass/fail options are available. Students may study abroad in 7 countries. The school also sponsors Semester at Sea, a 1-semester program of study on a ship traveling to ports throughout the world. There is a freshman honors program on campus

Faculty/Classroom: Eighty percent of faculty are male; 20%, female. Sixty-seven percent teach undergraduates and 44% do research. Graduate students teach 25% of introductory courses. The average class size in an introductory lecture is 37.

Admissions: About 95% of the 1993–94 applicants were accepted. The ACT scores for the 1993–94 freshman class were as follows: 23% below 21, 30% between 21 and 23, 24% between 24 and 26, 12% between 27 and 28, and 12% above 28. About 48% of the current freshmen were in the top fifth of their class; 76% were in the top two fifths. There were 26 National Merit finalists and 30 semifinalists. A total of 256 freshmen graduated first in their class.

Requirements: OSU requires applicants to be in the upper 33% of their class. The SAT I or ACT is required. For admission in good standing, freshman applicants must have a cumulative high school GPA of 3.0 (4.0 scale) and rank in the upper third of their graduating class or achieve at least a 21 composite on the ACT or 990 on the SAT I. In addition, freshman applicants must have 11 specific curricular units from high school, including 4 years of English, 3 of mathematics (algebra I and above), 2 of history, and 2 years of laboratory science. AP and CLEP credits are accepted. Important factors used in the admissions decision are evidence of special talent and advanced placement or honor courses.

Procedure: Freshmen are admitted to all sessions. Application deadlines are open. Application fee is $15. Notification is sent on a rolling basis. There is an early admissions plan.

Transfer: A total of 1553 transfer students enrolled in 1993–94. Transfer students having fewer than 24 credit hours must meet the requirements for entering freshmen. Nonresidents must have a minimum GPA of 2.0 and a total of 24 credit hours. In-state applicants must meet the requirements on a scaled GPA. A total of 30 credits out of 123 to 140 must be completed at OSU.

Visiting: There are regularly scheduled orientations for prospective students. High School and College Relations conducts personal meetings and tours. Appointments are scheduled with other campus departments, as needed, to assist prospective students. There are guides

for informal visits and visitors may sit in on classes and stay overnight at the school. To arrange for a visit, contact High School and College Relations at (405) 744–5358 or (800) 852–1255 (out-of-state).

Financial Aid: In 1993–94, 88% of all current freshmen and 58% of continuing students received some form of financial aid. About 40% of freshmen and 39% of continuing students received need-based aid. The average freshman award was $5655. Of that total, scholarships or need-based grants averaged $1415; loans averaged $3035; and work contracts averaged $2027 ($2200 maximum). Six percent of undergraduate students work part-time. Average earnings from campus work for the school year are $1960. The average financial indebtedness of the 1992–93 graduate was $9486. The FAFSA financial statement is required. The deadline for financial aid applications is March 1.

International Students: There are currently 1745 international students enrolled. The school actively recruits these students. They must take the TOEFL and achieve a minimum score of 500.

Computers: The university provides computer facilities for student use. The mainframe is an IBM 3090–200S. There are 3000 to 4000 Apple, IBM, and IBM-compatible microcomputers available throughout the campus. All students may access the system. There are no time limits on using the system and no fees.

Graduates: In 1992–93, 2756 bachelor's degrees were awarded. The most popular majors among graduates were marketing (5%), elementary education (5%), and finance (4%). Some 458 companies recruited on campus in 1992–93.

Admissions Contact: Gordon L. Reese, Associate Director of Admissions.

ORAL ROBERTS UNIVERSITY E-2
Tulsa, OK 74171

Full-time: 1146 men, 1499 women	(918) 495–6518; (800) 678–8876
Part-time: 52 men, 90 women	Faculty: 133
Graduate: 227 men, 247 women	Ph.D.s: 57%
Year: semesters, summer session	Student/Faculty: 20 to 1
Application Deadline: March 1	Tuition: $6883
Freshman Class: 1886 applied, 1141 accepted, 580 enrolled	Room & Board: $3724
SAT I: 500/500	ACT: 24 COMPETITIVE +

Oral Roberts University, founded in 1963, is a private, coeducational liberal arts university committed to the Christian faith. There are 6 undergraduate and 3 graduate schools. In addition to regional accreditation, ORU has baccalaureate program accreditation with NASM and NLN. The library contains 750,000 volumes, 200,000 microform items, and 500,000 audiovisual forms, and subscribes to 2100 periodicals. Computerized library sources and services include the card catalog and database searching. Special learning facilities include a learning resource center, natural history museum, radio station, TV station, and TV production studio. The 400-acre campus is in a suburban area of Tulsa. Including residence halls, there are 22 buildings on campus.

Student Life: About 86% of undergraduates are from out-of-state, mostly the West. Students come from 50 states, 40 foreign countries, and Canada. Fifty percent are from public schools; 50% from private. Seventy percent are white; 21% African American. Most are Protestant. The average age of freshmen is 20. Fifteen percent drop out by the end of their first year; 42% remain to graduate.

Housing: A total of 3000 students can be accommodated in college housing. College-sponsored living facilities include single-sex dormitories, on-campus apartments, and married-student housing. On-campus housing is available on a first-come, first-served basis. Ninety-one percent of students live on campus; of those, 99% remain on campus on weekends. Alcohol is not permitted. All students may keep cars on campus.

Activities: There are no fraternities or sororities on campus. There are 60 groups on campus, including art, band, cheerleading, choir, chorale, chorus, computers, drama, ethnic, film, honors, international, jazz band, newspaper, opera, pep band, photography, political, professional, radio and TV, religious, social, social service, student government, symphony, and yearbook. Popular campus events include Fall Break.

Sports: There are 8 intercollegiate sports for men and 8 for women, and 20 intramural sports for men and 20 for women. Athletic and recreation facilities include a physical fitness center, a track, tennis, racquetball, squash, volleyball, and basketball courts, and baseball and soccer fields.

Disabled Students: Ninety percent of the campus is accessible to disabled students. The following facilities are available: wheelchair ramps, elevators, special parking, specially equipped rest rooms, special class scheduling, lowered drinking fountains, and lowered telephones.

Services: In addition to many counseling and information services, tutoring is available in most subjects. There is a reader service for the blind, and remedial math, reading, and writing.

Campus Safety and Security: Campus safety and security measures include 24-hour foot and vehicle patrol, self defense education, escort service, and shuttle buses. In addition, there are lighted pathways and sidewalks.

Programs of Study: ORU awards the B.A., B.S., B.M., B.Mus.Ed., and B.S.N. degrees. Master's and doctoral degrees also are awarded. Bachelor's degrees are awarded in BIOLOGICAL SCIENCE (biology/biological science), BUSINESS (accounting, business administration and management, management information systems, management science, and marketing/retailing/merchandising), COMMUNICATIONS AND THE ARTS (applied art, broadcasting, communications, dramatic arts, English, film arts, French, German, literature, music, music theory and composition, Spanish, and telecommunications), COMPUTER AND PHYSICAL SCIENCE (chemistry, computer science, mathematics, and physics), EDUCATION (art, business, elementary, health, music, and secondary), ENGINEERING AND ENVIRONMENTAL DESIGN (commercial art, electrical/ electronics engineering, engineering, engineering management, mechanical engineering, and preengineering), HEALTH PROFESSIONS (biomedical science, medical laboratory technology, nursing, optometry, predentistry, and premedicine), SOCIAL SCIENCE (history, ministries, philosophy, political science/government, prelaw, psychology, religion, religious education, religious music, and social work). All science programs, music, and theology are the strongest academically. Business has the largest enrollment.

Required: A minimum of 128 credit hours is required to graduate. All students must complete specific courses in the Bible, theology, and English, plus 12 hours in social sciences, 11 in biological, physical, and mathematical sciences, 6 to 7 in a modern foreign language, 3 in communication arts, and 2 in fine arts. One physical activity course is required per semester, along with regular, semiweekly chapel attendance. A senior paper must be completed in most majors.

Special: ORU offers combined B.A.-B.S. degrees, 3–2 programs, dual and student-designed majors, study abroad, nondegree study, and a liberal arts degree. Army ROTC is available through the University of Tulsa. There is a freshman honors program on campus, as well as 3 national honor societies. Seven departments have honors programs.

Faculty/Classroom: Sixty-eight percent of faculty are male; 32%, female. Seventy-seven percent both teach and do research. No introductory courses are taught by graduate students. The average class size in an introductory lecture is 30; in a laboratory, 20; and in a regular course offering, 20.

Admissions: About 60% of the 1993–94 applicants were accepted. The SAT scores for the 1993–94 freshman class were as follows: Verbal—68% below 500, 25% between 500 and 599, and 7% between 600 and 700; Math—54% below 500, 28% between 500 and 599, 16% between 600 and 700, and 2% above 700. The ACT scores were 45% below 21, 22% between 21 and 23, 17% between 24 and 26, 8% between 27 and 28, and 8% above 28. About 40% of the current freshmen were in the top fifth of their class.

Requirements: ORU requires applicants to be in the upper 40% of their class. A minimum GPA of 2.6 is required. The SAT I or ACT is required. Students should be graduates of an accredited secondary school or hold a GED. High school preparation should include 4 years of English, 2 years of mathematics, including algebra and geometry or 2 years of algebra, and 2 years each of foreign language, social studies, and science, including laboratory science. A recommendation from the student's minister is required. An academic recommendation and an interview are recommended. AP and CLEP credits are accepted.

Procedure: Freshmen are admitted to all sessions. Entrance exams should be taken during the last semester of the junior year or during the senior year. Early decision applications should be filed by October 1; regular applications, by March 1 for fall entry, October 1 for spring entry, and March 1 for summer entry, along with an application fee of $35. Notification of early decision is sent November 1; regular decision, on a rolling basis. There are early decision, early admissions, and deferred admissions plans. About 80 early decision candidates were accepted for the 1993–94 class.

Transfer: About 273 transfer students enrolled in 1993–94. A transcript showing honorable dismissal from each previous institution is required. The final 30 credit hours out of 128 must be completed at ORU.

Visiting: There are regularly scheduled orientations for prospective students, including College Weekend, which consists of visiting classes, meeting with faculty and staff, attending chapel services, and attending student life events. Visitors may sit in on classes and stay overnight at the school. To arrange for a visit, contact Rick Wyatt, Admissions Office, at (918) 495-6518.

Financial Aid: In 1993–94 80% of all current freshmen and continuing students received some form of financial aid. About 80% of freshmen and continuing students received need-based aid. The average freshman award was $8000. Of that total, scholarships or need-based grants averaged $2000; loans averaged $4200; and work contracts

averaged $1800. Almost all undergraduate students work part-time. Average earnings from campus work for the school year are $1800. The average financial indebtedness of the 1992–93 graduate was $12,000. The FAF and federal income tax return are required. The deadline for financial aid applications is April 1.

International Students: There are currently 270 international students enrolled. They must take the TOEFL and achieve a minimum score of 500. The student must also take the SAT I or ACT.

Computers: The college provides computer facilities for student use. The mainframe is an IBM. Students can access the library computer via a modem. Microcomputers are also available in a computer laboratory. Business students may access the system. There are no time limits on using the system. The fees are $10 per credit hour for each computer course.

Graduates: In 1992–93 496 bachelor's degrees were awarded. The most popular majors among graduates were telecommunications (11%), marketing (7%), and accounting (7%). Within an average freshman class, 60% graduate in 5 years. Some 45 companies recruited on campus in 1992–93.

Admissions Contact: Shawn Nichols, Director of Admissions.

PANHANDLE STATE UNIVERSITY
(See Oklahoma Panhandle State University)

PHILLIPS UNIVERSITY
D-2

Enid, OK 73701   (405) 548–2203; (800) 238–1185 (out-of-state)

Full-time: 292 men, 361 women	Faculty: 50; IIB, --$
Part-time: 30 men, 47 women	Ph.D.s: 70%
Graduate: 39 men, 35 women	Student/Faculty: 13 to 1
Year: semesters, summer session	Tuition: $9740
Application Deadline: August 23	Room & Board: $3004
Freshman Class: 690 applied, 574 accepted, 172 enrolled	
SAT I Verbal/Math: 430/470	ACT: 21 COMPETITIVE

Phillips University, founded in 1906, is a private, coeducational liberal arts institution affiliated with the Christian Church (Disciples of Christ). In addition to regional accreditation, Phillips has baccalaureate program accreditation with NASM. The 2 libraries contain 300,000 volumes, 30,000 microform items, and 8910 audiovisual forms, and subscribe to 733 periodicals. Computerized library sources and services include the card catalog, interlibrary loans, and database searching. Special learning facilities include an art gallery. The 35-acre campus is in a small town 80 miles north of Oklahoma City. Including residence halls, there are 18 buildings on campus.

Student Life: About 54% of undergraduates are from Oklahoma. Students come from 30 states, 25 foreign countries, and Canada. Seventy-one percent are white; 10% foreign nationals. Sixty-seven percent are Disciples of Christ, Baptist, Episcopal, Lutheran, Methodist, and other Protestant; 13% are Catholic.

Housing: A total of 340 students can be accommodated in college housing. College-sponsored living facilities include single-sex and coed dormitories, on-campus apartments, and married-student housing. In addition there are special interest houses. On-campus housing is available on a first-come, first-served basis. Priority is given to out-of-town students. Alcohol is not permitted. All students may keep cars on campus.

Activities: There are no fraternities or sororities on campus. There are 25 groups on campus, including art, band, cheerleading, choir, chorale, chorus, computers, drama, ethnic, honors, international, jazz band, musical theater, newspaper, orchestra, pep band, political, professional, religious, social, social service, student government, symphony, and yearbook. Popular campus events include Enid-Phillips Day, Homecoming, Spring Fling, and Parents Weekend.

Sports: There are 4 intercollegiate sports for men and 3 for women, and 5 intramural sports for men and 5 for women. Athletic and recreation facilities include a 2500-seat gymnasium, a field house, tennis and racquetball courts, a weight room, a swimming pool, a golf course, and baseball and soccer fields.

Disabled Students: Ninety percent of the campus is accessible to disabled students. The following facilities are available: wheelchair ramps, elevators, special parking, specially equipped rest rooms, lowered drinking fountains, and lowered telephones.

Services: In addition to many counseling and information services, tutoring is available in study skills and most subjects.

Campus Safety and Security: Campus safety and security measures include escort service, informal discussions, emergency telephones, and lighted pathways and sidewalks.

Programs of Study: Phillips awards the B.A., B.S., B.F.A., B.M.E., B.M.T., B.S.Bus.Admin., B.S.Ed., B.S.M., and B.S.Med.Tech. degrees. Associate and master's degrees also are awarded. Bachelor's degrees are awarded in BIOLOGICAL SCIENCE (biology/biological science), BUSINESS (accounting, banking and finance, business administration and management, business economics, management science, and marketing/retailing/merchandising), COMMUNICA-

TIONS AND THE ARTS (communications, dramatic arts, English, fine arts, German, music, and Spanish), COMPUTER AND PHYSICAL SCIENCE (chemistry, computer science, geology, and mathematics), EDUCATION (art, elementary, health, library science, music, physical, science, and secondary), ENGINEERING AND ENVIRONMENTAL DESIGN (aviation administration/management and preengineering), HEALTH PROFESSIONS (medical laboratory technology, nursing, optometry, physical therapy, predentistry, premedicine, prepharmacy, and preveterinary science), SOCIAL SCIENCE (American studies, European studies, history, philosophy, political science/government, prelaw, psychology, religion, social work, and sociology). Business and education have the largest enrollments.

Required: All students must complete the general studies program, including courses in English, religion, philosophy, history, science, mathematics, psychology, music or art, and physical fitness, as well as a senior project. A total of 128 semester hours with a minimum GPA of 2.0 is required for the baccalaureate degree.

Special: A 3–2 engineering degree is offered with Washington University in St. Louis. Study abroad is available at Phillips branches in Sweden and Japan. Internships, a Washington semester, student-designed majors, a general studies degree, credit for life experience, nondegree study, and pass/fail options are offered.

Faculty/Classroom: Seventy-four percent of faculty are male; 26%, female. No introductory courses are taught by graduate students. The average class size in a regular course offering is 18.

Admissions: About 83% of the 1993–94 applicants were accepted. The ACT scores for the 1993–94 freshman class were as follows: 42% below 21, 28% between 21 and 23, 17% between 24 and 26, 7% between 27 and 28, and 6% above 28.

Requirements: A minimum GPA of 2.8 is required. The SAT I or ACT is required. Applicants should be graduates of an accredited secondary school or hold the GED. High school preparation should include 3 years each of English, mathematics, and science, and 2 years of history or social studies. An essay and interview are recommended, as is an audition for music applicants. AP and CLEP credits are accepted. Important factors used in the admissions decision are advanced placement or honor courses, personality, intangible qualities, leadership record, extracurricular activities record, and evidence of special talent.

Procedure: Freshmen are admitted to all sessions. Entrance exams should be taken during the junior or senior year. Applications should be filed by August 23 for fall entry, January 4 for spring entry, and May 8 for summer entry. Notification is sent on a rolling basis. There are early decision and early admissions plans.

Transfer: About 50 transfer students enrolled in 1993–94. A transcript must be submitted from each college attended. Applicants with fewer than 15 semester hours of transferable credit must also present SAT I or ACT scores. An interview is recommended. A total of 32 credits out of 128 must be completed at Phillips.

Visiting: There are regularly scheduled orientations for prospective students. There are guides for informal visits and visitors may sit in on classes and stay overnight at the school. To arrange for a visit, contact the Admissions Office at (405) 237–4433 or (800) 238–1185.

Financial Aid: The average freshman award was $4003. Phillips is a member of CSS. The FAF or FFS and the college's own financial statement are required.

International Students: There are currently 79 international students enrolled. The school actively recruits these students. They must take the TOEFL and achieve a minimum score of 500.

Computers: The university provides computer facilities for student use. The mainframe is an HP 3000. There are also 64 IBM microcomputers available in academic laboratories. All students may access the system. It may be used during library hours from 8 A.M. to 11:30 P.M. There are no time limits on using the system.

Graduates: In 1992–93, 103 bachelor's degrees were awarded. The most popular majors among graduates were business (27%), education (21%), and social science (16%).

Admissions Contact: Leigh A. Smith, Director of Admission.

SOUTHEASTERN OKLAHOMA STATE UNIVERSITY

D-3

Durant, OK 74701

(405) 924–0121, ext. 240

Full-time: 1420 men, 1576 women	Faculty: 151; IIA, --$
Part-time: 263 men, 495 women	Ph.D.s: 48%
Graduate: 155 men, 293 women	Student/Faculty: 20 to 1
Year: semesters, summer session	Tuition: $1494 ($3665)
Application Deadline: open	Room & Board: $2100
Freshman Class: 616 enrolled	
ACT: 19	COMPETITIVE

Southeastern Oklahoma State University, founded in 1909, is a public institution offering programs in the arts and sciences, business, education, music, and technology to a primarily commuter student body. There are 4 undergraduate schools and one graduate school.

In addition to regional accreditation, Southeastern has baccalaureate program accreditation with NASM and NCATE. The library contains 160,000 volumes, 300,000 microform items, and 800 audiovisual forms, and subscribes to 1150 periodicals. Computerized library sources and services include the card catalog, interlibrary loans, and database searching. Special learning facilities include a learning resource center, radio station, and an herbarium. The 179-acre campus is in a rural area 90 miles north of Dallas, Texas. Including residence halls, there are 43 buildings on campus.

Student Life: About 88% of undergraduates are from Oklahoma. Students come from 27 states and 20 foreign countries. Ninety-nine percent are from public schools. Sixty-one percent are white; 31% Native American/Eskimo. The average age of freshmen is 22.5; all undergraduates, 25.2. Forty percent drop out by the end of their first year; 34% remain to graduate.

Housing: A total of 665 students can be accommodated in college housing. College-sponsored living facilities include single-sex and coed dormitories and married-student housing. On-campus housing is guaranteed for all 4 years and is available on a first-come, first-served basis. Priority is given to out-of-town students. Eighty percent of students commute. Alcohol is not permitted. All students may keep cars on campus.

Activities: About 3% of men belong to 2 local and 3 national fraternities and 2 national sororities. There are 74 groups on campus, including art, band, cheerleading, choir, chorale, computers, dance, drama, drill team, ethnic, honors, international, jazz band, marching band, musical theater, newspaper, opera, pep band, photography, political, professional, radio and TV, religious, social, social service, student government, and yearbook. Popular campus events include Springfest, Hokey Days, Parents Day, homecoming, candlelighting, and Greek Games.

Sports: There are 6 intercollegiate sports for men and 2 for women, and 7 intramural sports for men and 6 for women. Athletic and recreation facilities include a 4000-seat football stadium, a 2000-seat gymnasium, a baseball field, a track, tennis courts, playing fields, and a swimming pool.

Disabled Students: One percent of the campus is accessible to disabled students. The following facilities are available: wheelchair ramps, elevators, special parking, specially equipped rest rooms, special class scheduling, and lowered telephones.

Services: In addition to many counseling and information services, tutoring is available in every subject. In addition, there is remedial writing. and in study skills.

Campus Safety and Security: Campus safety and security measures include 24-hour foot and vehicle patrol and lighted pathways and sidewalks.

Programs of Study: Southeastern awards the B.A., B.S., B.A.Ed., B.S.Ed., B.M., and B.M.Ed. degrees. Master's degrees are also awarded. Bachelor's degrees are awarded in AGRICULTURE (conservation and regulation), BIOLOGICAL SCIENCE (biology/biological science), BUSINESS (accounting, business administration and management, recreation and leisure services, and secretarial studies/office management), COMMUNICATIONS AND THE ARTS (dramatic arts, English, fine arts, French, modern language, music, Spanish, and speech/debate/rhetoric), COMPUTER AND PHYSICAL SCIENCE (chemistry, computer science, information sciences and systems, mathematics, and physics), EDUCATION (art, business, early childhood, elementary, foreign languages, industrial arts, music, physical, science, and secondary), ENGINEERING AND ENVIRONMENTAL DESIGN (occupational safety and health), HEALTH PROFESSIONS (medical laboratory technology and physical therapy), SOCIAL SCIENCE (criminal justice, economics, gerontology, history, home economics, political science/government, psychology, social science, and sociology). Chemistry, history, music, and mathematics are the strongest academically. Management, elementary education, and accounting have the largest enrollments.

Required: A total of 124 credit hours with a minimum GPA of 2.0 (2.5 for teacher education majors) is required for graduation. All students must complete 50 semester hours of general education requirements, including 6 hours each of English and American history/government, and courses in humanities, arts, social and laboratory sciences, mathematics, communications, and health and physical education.

Special: Credit is given for military experience. Pass/fail options are available in some courses. Nondegree study is possible. There are 9 national honor societies on campus. Five departments have honors programs.

Faculty/Classroom: Sixty-five percent of faculty are male; 35%, female. Ninety percent teach undergraduates and 10% do research. The average class size in an introductory lecture is 28; in a laboratory, 23; and in a regular course offering, 21.

Admissions: The ACT scores for the 1993–94 freshman class were as follows: 62% below 21, 22% between 21 and 23, 10% between 24 and 26, 4% between 27 and 28, and 2% above 28. About 35% of the

current freshmen were in the top fifth of their class; 67% were in the top two fifths. Twenty-six freshmen graduated first in their class.

Requirements: Southeastern requires applicants to be in the upper 50% of their class. A minimum GPA of 2.7 is required. The ACT is required. Applicants should be graduates of an accredited secondary school or have earned a GED. High school courses must include 4 years of English, 3 of mathematics, and 2 each of laboratory science and history. AP and CLEP credits are accepted. Important factors used in the admissions decision are geographic diversity, ability to finance college education, personality, intangible qualities, advanced placement or honor courses, and leadership record.

Procedure: Entrance exams should be taken by the fall of the senior year. Application deadlines are open. Notification is sent on a rolling basis. A waiting list is an active part of the admissions procedure, with about 5% of applicants on the list.

Transfer: About 404 transfer students enrolled in a recent year. Out-of-state applicants must have a 2.0 GPA. In-state applicants must have a 1.7 GPA with 24 to 36 credit hours earned, 1.8 with 37 to 72 hours, and 2.0 with 73 or more hours. A total of 30 credits out of 124 must be completed at Southeastern.

Visiting: There are guides for informal visits and visitors may sit in on classes. To arrange for a visit, contact Rudy Manley, Director of High School Relations at (405) 924-0121, ext. 596.

Financial Aid: In a recent year, 60% of all current freshmen and 75% of continuing students received some form of financial aid; 54% of freshmen and 70% of continuing students received need-based aid. The average freshman award was $4000. Of that total, scholarships or need-based grants averaged $500 ($900 maximum); loans averaged $1500 ($2625 maximum); and work contracts averaged $1000 ($2000 maximum). Twenty percent of undergraduate students work part-time. Average earnings from campus work for the school year are $1200. The average financial indebtedness of a recent graduate was $5000. Southeastern is a member of CSS. The FFS is required. The deadline for financial aid applications is April 1.

International Students: There are currently 85 international students enrolled. They must take the TOEFL and achieve a minimum score of 500.

Computers: The college provides computer facilities for student use. The mainframe is a DEC VAX 3400. There are also 50 IBM PS/2s, Models 30 and 50, available in the Fine Arts and Morrison buildings. Computer science and information systems students may access the system. It may be used Monday through Friday, 8 A.M. to midnight, and Sunday, 1 P.M. to midnight. There are no time limits and no fees.

Graduates: In a recent year, 532 bachelor's degrees were awarded. The most popular majors among graduates were elementary education (26%), business administration (12%), and accounting (7%). Some 100 companies usually recruit on campus. In an earlier graduating class, 15% of the men and 10% of the women were enrolled in graduate school within 6 months of graduation; 80% of the men and 70% of the women had found employment.

Admissions Contact: Fred Stroup, Admissions.

SOUTHERN NAZARENE UNIVERSITY D-3
Bethany, OK 73008

(405) 789-6400, ext. 6324
(800) 648-9899 (out-of-state)

Full-time: 592 men, 732 women	**Faculty:** 51; IIB, --$
Part-time: 83 men, 129 women	**Ph.D.s:** 60%
Graduate: 95 men, 100 women	**Student/Faculty:** 26 to 1
Year: semesters, summer session	**Tuition:** $5644
Application Deadline: August 1	**Room & Board:** $3562
Freshman Class: 538 applied, 538 accepted, 319 enrolled	
ACT: 21	**NONCOMPETITIVE**

Southern Nazarene University, founded in 1899, is a private institution affiliated with the Church of the Nazarene. It offers programs in liberal arts and sciences, health fields, business, and education. There are 3 undergraduate schools and one graduate school. In addition to regional accreditation, SNU has baccalaureate program accreditation with NCATE and NLN. The library contains 112,673 volumes, 219,576 microform items, and 3543 audiovisual forms, and subscribes to 667 periodicals. Computerized library sources and services include the card catalog, interlibrary loans, and database searching. Special learning facilities include a learning resource center. The 40-acre campus is in a suburban area 10 miles northwest of Oklahoma City. Including residence halls, there are 19 buildings on campus.

Student Life: About 55% of undergraduates are from out-of-state, mostly the South. Students come from 31 states, 22 foreign countries, and Canada. Ninety percent are white. Most are Protestant. The average age of freshmen is 18; all undergraduates, 23. Ten percent drop out by the end of their first year; 45% remain to graduate.

Housing: A total of 938 students can be accommodated in college housing. College-sponsored living facilities include single-sex dormitories and married-student housing. On-campus housing is guaranteed for all 4 years. Fifty-five percent of students live on campus; of

those, 80% remain on campus on weekends. Alcohol is not permitted. All students may keep cars on campus.

Activities: There are no fraternities or sororities on campus. There are 40 groups on campus, including band, cheerleading, choir, chorale, chorus, computers, drama, drum and bugle corps, honors, international, jazz band, literary magazine, newspaper, orchestra, pep band, photography, political, professional, religious, social, social service, student government, and yearbook. Popular campus events include Homecoming, Valentine Banquet, Fall Fest, Yule Feast, and Lighting-of-the-Mall.

Sports: There are 3 intercollegiate sports for men and 5 for women, and 3 intramural sports for men and 3 for women. Athletic and recreation facilities include a 1824-seat physical education center, gymnasiums, a soccer complex, and tennis courts.

Disabled Students: Ninety-five percent of the campus is accessible to disabled students. The following facilities are available: wheelchair ramps, elevators, special parking, specially equipped rest rooms, special class scheduling, and lowered telephones. Dormitory rooms may be adapted for handicapped students.

Services: In addition to many counseling and information services, tutoring is available in most subjects. In addition, there is remedial math, reading, and writing. Services may be arranged for deaf or learning-disabled students.

Campus Safety and Security: Campus safety and security measures include 24-hour foot and vehicle patrol, escort service, informal discussions, and lighted pathways and sidewalks. In addition, there is 24-hour controlled access into dormitories.

Programs of Study: SNU awards the A.B., B.S., and B.Mus.Ed. degrees. Associate and master's degrees also are awarded. Bachelor's degrees are awarded in AGRICULTURE (agriculture), BIOLOGICAL SCIENCE (biology/biological science), BUSINESS (accounting, business administration and management, business economics, fashion merchandising, marketing/retailing/merchandising, and office supervision and management), COMMUNICATIONS AND THE ARTS (communications, creative writing, English, fine arts, French, German, journalism, music, music performance, piano/organ, Spanish, speech/debate/rhetoric, and voice), COMPUTER AND PHYSICAL SCIENCE (chemistry, computer science, mathematics, and physics), EDUCATION (art, business, early childhood, elementary, foreign languages, music, physical, and secondary), ENGINEERING AND ENVIRONMENTAL DESIGN (aviation administration/management, interior design, and preengineering), HEALTH PROFESSIONS (medical laboratory technology, nursing, predentistry, premedicine, and prepharmacy), SOCIAL SCIENCE (biblical languages, criminal justice, gerontology, history, international studies, philosophy, political science/government, prelaw, psychology, religion, religious education, social science, and sociology). Premedicine, physics, theology, and education are the strongest academically. Business has the largest enrollment.

Required: A total of 124 semester hours, including at least 32 hours in the major, with a minimum GPA of 2.0 is required to graduate. All students must complete 53 hours of general education requirements covering core areas of self and identity, faith and tradition, and service and society. Skills courses must be taken in computer science, composition, speech communication, mathematics, natural science, citizenship, foreign language, and physical education.

Special: Cross-registration and co-op programs are available through the Southwestern Colleges of Christian Ministry. Internships may be arranged in the major. A Washington semester, study abroad in Latin America, England, Russia, and the Middle East, work-study programs in sociology, and dual and student-designed majors are available. There is an accelerated degree program in management of human resources and family studies and gerontology. SNU offers nondegree study for life/military/work experience. A Hollywood semester may be arranged through the Christian College Coalition. There is a freshman honors program on campus, as well as 6 national honor societies, including Phi Beta Kappa.

Faculty/Classroom: Fifty-seven percent of faculty are male; 43%, female. All teach undergraduates and 15% do research. Graduate students teach 1% of introductory courses. The average class size in an introductory lecture is 20 and in a laboratory, 15.

Admissions: All of the 1993–94 applicants were accepted. The ACT scores for the 1993–94 freshman class were as follows: 43% below 21, 24% between 21 and 23, 17% between 24 and 26, 8% between 27 and 28, and 8% above 28. There were 3 National Merit finalists.

Requirements: SNU requires applicants to be in the upper 50% of their class. A minimum GPA of 2.5 is required. The SAT I or ACT is required. Applicants must be graduates of an accredited secondary school or have a GED. AP and CLEP credits are accepted. Important factors used in the admissions decision are advanced placement or honor courses, extracurricular activities record, leadership record, evidence of special talent, and parents or siblings attending the school.

Procedure: Freshmen are admitted fall and spring. Entrance exams should be taken by April of the senior year or at orientation prior to the beginning of classes. Applications should be filed by August 1 for fall entry and January 7 for spring entry, along with an application fee of $25. The university accepts all applicants. Notification is sent on a rolling basis. There are early admissions and deferred admissions plans.

Transfer: About 100 transfer students enrolled in 1993–94. Transfer applicants must have a 2.0 GPA and be in good standing at their previous college. A total of 30 credits out of 124 must be completed at SNU.

Visiting: There are regularly scheduled orientations for prospective students, including visits with faculty and students and seminars on financial aid. There are campus tours, group social activities, and small group mentoring throughout the fall semester. There are guides for informal visits and visitors may sit in on classes and stay overnight at the school. To arrange for a visit, contact the Office of Admission at (405) 491–6324 or (800) 648–9899.

Financial Aid: In 1993–94, 82% of all current freshmen and 78% of continuing students received some form of financial aid. About 55% of freshmen and 49% of continuing students received need-based aid. The average freshman award was $6184. Of that total, scholarships or need-based grants averaged $2472 ($9300 maximum); loans averaged $2822 ($11,856 maximum); and work contracts averaged $890 ($2000 maximum). Five percent of undergraduate students work part-time. Average earnings from campus work for the school year are $2000. The FAFSA financial statement is required. The deadline for financial aid applications is March 1.

International Students: International students must take the TOEFL.

Computers: The university provides computer facilities for student use. The mainframe is an IBM AS 400. Students have access to 45 network and 15 non-network computers. DOS-based students may access an IBM s/36 and a MicroVAX II. All students may access the system. It may be used Monday through Saturday. There are no time limits on using the system and no fees.

Graduates: In 1992–93, 392 bachelor's degrees were awarded. The most popular majors among graduates were business and management (38%), health professions (12%), and education (8%).

Admissions Contact: Jeff Williamson, Admissions Director.

SOUTHWESTERN OKLAHOMA STATE UNIVERSITY
D-3
Weatherford, OK 73096 (405) 774–3009

Full-time: 1815 men, 2022 women	Faculty: 207; IIA, --$
Part-time: 228 men, 358 women	Ph.D.s: 62%
Graduate: 187 men, 380 women	Student/Faculty: 19 to 1
Year: semesters, summer session	Tuition: $1392 ($3563)
Application Deadline: open	Room & Board: $1920
Freshman Class: 1041 applied, 969 accepted, 953 enrolled	
SAT I or ACT: required	COMPETITIVE

Southwestern Oklahoma State University, founded in 1901, is a public coeducational institution offering programs in education, arts and sciences, business, health sciences, and pharmacy. There are 4 undergraduate schools and one graduate school. In addition to regional accreditation, SWOSU has baccalaureate program accreditation with ABHES, ACPE, CAHEA, NASM, NCATE, and NLN. The library contains 242,406 volumes, 751,114 microform items, and 1760 audiovisual forms, and subscribes to 1518 periodicals. Computerized library sources and services include interlibrary loans and database searching. The 73-acre campus is in a small town 70 miles west of Oklahoma City. Including residence halls, there are 30 buildings on campus.

Student Life: About 89% of undergraduates are from Oklahoma. Students come from 35 states, 22 foreign countries, and Canada. Ninety-eight percent are from public schools; 2% from private. Ninety percent are white. The average age of freshmen is 20.7; all undergraduates, 23.4.

Housing: A total of 1540 students can be accommodated in college housing. College-sponsored living facilities include single-sex dormitories and married-student housing. On-campus housing is guaranteed for all 4 years. Seventy-six percent of students commute. Alcohol is not permitted. All students may keep cars on campus.

Activities: About 2% of men belong to 2 local fraternities and 1 national fraternity; about 2% of women belong to 3 local sororities. There are 82 groups on campus, including art, band, cheerleading, choir, chorus, computers, drama, drill team, ethnic, honors, international, jazz band, marching band, musical theater, newspaper, opera, orchestra, pep band, political, professional, religious, social, social service, student government, symphony, and yearbook. Popular campus events include Homecoming, Beach Bash, Howdy Week, Miss Southwestern Pageant, Greek Week, Spring Fling, and Panorama Series.

Sports: There are 6 intercollegiate sports for men and 3 for women, and 8 intramural sports for men and 8 for women. Athletic and recreation facilities include 2 gymnasiums, a weight room, an indoor pool, an outdoor track, tennis courts, an outdoor football field and outdoor baseball diamond, 2 football practice fields, a rodeo arena, and an exercise equipment room.

Disabled Students: Eighty-five percent of the campus is accessible to disabled students. The following facilities are available: wheelchair ramps, elevators, special parking, specially equipped rest rooms, special class scheduling, lowered drinking fountains, and lowered telephones.

Services: In addition to many counseling and information services, tutoring is available in some subjects, including mathematics, science, business, English, and social sciences. There is also remedial math, reading, and writing. A student development center offers counseling and tutoring on an individual basis.

Campus Safety and Security: Campus safety and security measures include 24-hour foot and vehicle patrol, self defense education, escort service, and informal discussions. In addition, there are pamphlets, posters, and films, emergency telephones, and lighted pathways and sidewalks.

Programs of Study: SWOSU awards the B.A., B.S., B.A.Ed., B.Art., B.Comm.Art, B.Gen.Tech., B.M., B.M.Ed., B.Rec., B.S.Ed., B.S.Eng.Tech., B.S.H.I.M., B.S.M.T., B.S.N., and B.S.P. degrees. Associate and master's degrees also are awarded. Bachelor's degrees are awarded in BIOLOGICAL SCIENCE (biology/biological science and biophysics), BUSINESS (accounting, banking and finance, business administration and management, business economics, management science, marketing/retailing/merchandising, and retailing), COMMUNICATIONS AND THE ARTS (dramatic arts, English, fine arts, music, and speech/debate/rhetoric), COMPUTER AND PHYSICAL SCIENCE (chemistry, computer programming, computer science, information sciences and systems, mathematics, and physics), EDUCATION (art, business, early childhood, elementary, English, health, home economics, industrial arts, library science, music, physical, recreation, science, secondary, social science, special, and vocational), ENGINEERING AND ENVIRONMENTAL DESIGN (commercial art, engineering physics, engineering technology, and industrial engineering technology), HEALTH PROFESSIONS (allied health, health care administration, medical laboratory technology, medical records administration/services, music therapy, nursing, pharmacy, predentistry, premedicine, and recreation therapy), SOCIAL SCIENCE (criminal justice, economics, geography, history, home economics, home furnishings and equipment management/production/services, political science/government, prelaw, psychology, social science, social work, and sociology). Pharmacy and chemistry are the strongest academically. Business, education, and pharmacy have the largest enrollments.

Required: To graduate, students must complete 124 semester hours (166 for pharmacy majors) with a minimum GPA of 2.0. Distribution requirements include 9 hours in history and social sciences, 6 in English composition, 4 each in physical education, biological science, and physical science, 3 each in American government, American history, and mathematics, and 15 in electives such as music, art, literature, psychology, and foreign language.

Special: SWOSU offers study abroad in France, Russia, and Belarus, work-study programs, and a program allowing high school seniors to earn college credits. There are 4 national honor societies on campus.

Faculty/Classroom: Sixty-nine percent of faculty are male; 31%, female. All teach undergraduates and 10% both teach and do research. Graduate students teach 2% of introductory courses. The average class size in an introductory lecture is 50; in a laboratory, 18; and in a regular course offering, 25.

Admissions: About 93% of the 1993–94 applicants were accepted.

Requirements: SWOSU requires applicants to be in the upper 50% of their class. A minimum GPA of 2.7 is required. The SAT I or the ACT, with a minimum composite score of 19, is required. Applicants should be graduates of an accredited secondary school. The GED is accepted. Students should present at least 11 academic credits, including 4 in English, 3 in mathematics, and 2 each in history and laboratory science. AP and CLEP credits are accepted. -- M6j6 A6 Q6 -- s. AP and CLEP credits are accepted.

Procedure: Freshmen are admitted to all sessions. Entrance exams should be taken during the senior year. Application deadlines are open. The fee is $15 starting in the spring of 1995. Notification is sent on a rolling basis. There is an early admissions plan.

Transfer: About 1538 transfer students enrolled in a recent year. Applicants must have a minimum college GPA of 2.0 and submit official transcripts from all institutions attended. A total of 30 semester hours out of 124 must be completed at SWOSU.

Visiting: There are regularly scheduled orientations for prospective students, including counseling sessions on careers, financial aid, social activities, and enrollment procedures. There are guides for informal visits, and visitors may sit in on classes and stay overnight at the

school. To arrange for a visit, contact the Director of High School and College Relations at (405) 774–3782.

Financial Aid: In 1993–94 50% of all current freshmen and continuing students received some form of financial aid. About 40% of freshmen and continuing students received need-based aid. The average freshman award was $2000. Of that total, scholarships or need-based grants averaged $900 ($3360 maximum); loans averaged $900 ($2625 maximum); and work contracts averaged $200 ($2000 maximum). Twelve percent of undergraduate students work part-time. Average earnings from campus work for the school year are $1200. The average financial indebtedness of the 1992–93 graduate was $6100. The college's own financial statement and the FAFSA are required.

International Students: There are currently 54 international students enrolled. They must take the TOEFL and achieve a minimum score of 500. The student must also take the ACT and achieve a minimum score of 19.

Computers: The college provides computer facilities for student use. The mainframe is a DEC VAX 6310. Terminals and Apple and IBM-compatible microcomputers are available in laboratories across campus. All students may access the system. It may be used from 8 A.M. to midnight Monday through Thursday, 8 A.M. to 5 P.M. Friday, 10 A.M. to 2 P.M. Saturday, and 2 P.M. to midnight Sunday. There are no time limits on using the system and no fees.

Graduates: In 1992–93 681 bachelor's degrees were awarded. The most popular majors among graduates were pharmacy (14%), elementary education (13%), and accounting (6%). Some 36 companies recruited on campus in 1992–93.

Admissions Contact: Bob Klaasseen, Director of Admissions.

UNIVERSITY OF CENTRAL OKLAHOMA
E-5

Edmond, OK 73034   (405) 341–2980

Full-time: 3463 men, 4293 women	Faculty: 395
Part-time: 1812 men, 2624 women	Ph.D.s: 66%
Graduate: 1381 men, 2328 women	Student/Faculty: 20 to 1
Year: semesters, summer session	Tuition: $1447 ($3559)
Application Deadline: August 15	Room & Board: $2150

Freshman Class: 3405 applied, 3199 accepted, 1296 enrolled

ACT: 20   **COMPETITIVE**

The University of Central Oklahoma, founded in 1890, is a state-supported institution offering undergraduate and graduate programs in the liberal arts and sciences, education, business, and music. There are 4 undergraduate schools and one graduate school. In addition to regional accreditation, UCO has baccalaureate program accreditation with NCATE and NLN. The library contains 250,463 volumes, 537,228 microform items, and 15,668 audiovisual forms, and subscribes to 2735 periodicals. Computerized library sources and services include the card catalog, interlibrary loans, and database searching. Special learning facilities include a learning resource center, art gallery, radio station, and TV station. The 200-acre campus is in a suburban area north of Oklahoma City. Including residence halls, there are 43 buildings on campus.

Student Life: About 92% of undergraduates are from Oklahoma. Students come from 44 states, 78 foreign countries, and Canada. Eighty-three percent are from public schools; 2% from private. Eighty-one percent are white. The average age of freshmen is 22; all undergraduates, 25. Forty-two percent drop out by the end of their first year; 23% remain to graduate.

Housing: A total of 1469 students can be accommodated in college housing. College-sponsored living facilities include single-sex dormitories, on-campus apartments, off-campus apartments, and married-student housing. On-campus housing is guaranteed for all 4 years. Ninety-two percent of students commute. Alcohol is not permitted. All students may keep cars on campus.

Activities: About 2% of men and women belong to 5 national fraternities and sororities. There are 93 groups on campus, including art, band, cheerleading, chess, choir, computers, dance, ethnic, gay, honors, international, jazz band, marching band, musical theater, newspaper, opera, orchestra, political, professional, radio and TV, religious, social, student government, and yearbook. Popular campus events include Homecoming, International Week, Black Heritage Week, Indian Heritage Week, and Miss UCO Pageant.

Sports: There are 6 intercollegiate sports for men and 6 for women, and 12 intramural sports for men and 11 for women. Athletic and recreation facilities include a field house with a gym, swimming pool, track, and weight room, and a stadium with a track and softball field.

Disabled Students: Sixty percent of the campus is accessible to disabled students. The following facilities are available: wheelchair ramps, elevators, special parking, specially equipped rest rooms, special class scheduling, and lowered drinking fountains.

Services: In addition to many counseling and information services, tutoring is available in some subjects. There is also remedial math.

Campus Safety and Security: Campus safety and security measures include 24-hour foot and vehicle patrol, escort service, and lighted pathways and sidewalks.

Programs of Study: UCO awards the B.A., B.S., B.A.Ed., B.B.A., B.S.Ed., B.M.Ed., and B.Mus. degrees. Master's degrees also are awarded. Bachelor's degrees are awarded in BIOLOGICAL SCIENCE (biology/biological science), BUSINESS (accounting, business administration and management, business economics, hotel/motel and restaurant management, and marketing/retailing/merchandising), COMMUNICATIONS AND THE ARTS (advertising, broadcasting, communications, dance, dramatic arts, English, fine arts, French, German, journalism, music, photography, Spanish, and speech/debate/rhetoric), COMPUTER AND PHYSICAL SCIENCE (actuarial science, chemistry, computer science, mathematics, and physics), EDUCATION (art, business, early childhood, elementary, foreign languages, guidance, health, home economics, industrial arts, music, science, and secondary), HEALTH PROFESSIONS (medical laboratory technology, nursing, and speech pathology/audiology), SOCIAL SCIENCE (criminal justice, dietetics, economics, geography, history, philosophy, political science/government, prelaw, psychology, public administration, and sociology). Accounting, elementary education, and business administration have the largest enrollments.

Required: Students must complete 124 semester hours with a 2.25 GPA. At least 15 hours in upper-division courses in the major are required. Students must also complete 12 semester hours in general education requirements, including physical education.

Special: Opportunities are provided for internships, B.A.-B.S. degree, dual majors, a general studies degree, credit by examination, nondegree study, and credit for military experience. Work-study programs may be arranged through the Federal College Work-Study Program.

Faculty/Classroom: Fifty-nine percent of faculty are male; 41%, female. All teach undergraduates.

Admissions: About 94% of the 1993–94 applicants were accepted. The ACT scores for the 1993–94 freshman class were as follows: 56% below 21, 25% between 21 and 23, 13% between 24 and 26, 5% between 27 and 28, and 1% above 28. About 6% of the current freshmen were in the top fifth of their class; 36% were in the top two fifths.

Requirements: UCO requires applicants to be in the upper 50% of their class. A minimum GPA of 2.7 is required. The ACT is required, with a minimum composite enhanced score of 19. Graduation from an accredited secondary school is required. A GED will be accepted for adult students. The applicant's academic record should include 4 years of English, 3 years of mathematics, first-year algebra and beyond, and 2 years each of laboratory science and history, of which 1 year must be in American history. AP and CLEP credits are accepted. Important factors used in the admissions decision are evidence of special talent, extracurricular activities record, leadership record, advanced placement or honor courses, and ability to finance college education.

Procedure: Freshmen are admitted to all sessions. Entrance exams should be taken within 30 days of submitting the application. Applications should be filed by August 15 for fall entry, January 2 for spring entry, and May 25 for summer entry, along with an application fee of $15. Notification is sent on a rolling basis. There is an early admissions plan.

Transfer: A total of 1497 transfer students enrolled in 1993–94. Applicants must submit official transcripts from previous colleges attended and have a minimum GPA of 2.0. Students who have completed fewer than 24 hours of transferable credit must meet the requirements of entering freshmen. A total of 30 credits out of 124 must be completed at UCO.

Visiting: There are regularly scheduled orientations for prospective students. There are guides for informal visits and visitors may sit in on classes. To arrange for a visit, contact High School/College Relations at (405) 341–2980.

Financial Aid: Average earnings from campus work for a recent school year were $2500. The FAF or FFS and the college's own financial statement are required. The deadline for financial aid applications is April 1.

International Students: There are currently 650 international students enrolled. The school actively recruits these students. They must take the TOEFL and achieve a minimum score of 500. The student must also take the ACT.

Computers: The university provides computer facilities for student use. The mainframe is a DEC VAX 4000. Students may access 139 terminals located in computer laboratories and in the library during scheduled hours. All students may access the system. There are no time limits on using the system and no fees.

Graduates: In 1992–93, 1990 bachelor's degrees were awarded. The most popular majors among graduates were business administration and management (12%), elementary education (11%), and accounting (9%). Within an average freshman class, 23% graduate in 6 years. Some 34 companies recruited on campus in 1992–93.

Admissions Contact: Paul Patrick, Acting Registrar.

UNIVERSITY OF OKLAHOMA
D-3

Norman, OK 73019 (405) 325–2251

Full-time: 6753 men, 5571 women Faculty: 764; I, --$
Part-time: 1348 men, 1160 women Ph.D.s: 83%
Graduate: 2613 men, 2235 women Student/Faculty: 16 to 1
Year: semesters, summer session Tuition: $1901 ($5348)
Application Deadline: open Room & Board: $3526
Freshman Class: 4743 applied, 3970 accepted, 2233 enrolled
ACT: 24 **VERY COMPETITIVE**

The University of Oklahoma, founded in 1890, is a comprehensive research university offering 160 areas for undergraduate study. There are 9 undergraduate and 9 graduate schools. In addition to regional accreditation, OU has baccalaureate program accreditation with AACSB, ABET, ACCE, ACEJMC, ADA, APTA, CSWE, FIDER, NAAB, NASM, and NCATE. The 8 libraries contain 2,425,086 volumes and 3,294,140 microform items, and subscribe to 17,440 periodicals. Computerized library sources and services include the card catalog, interlibrary loans, and database searching. Special learning facilities include a learning resource center, art gallery, natural history museum, radio station, and an observatory. The 3107-acre campus is in a suburban area 18 miles south of Oklahoma City. Including residence halls, there are 233 buildings on campus.

Student Life: About 80% of undergraduates are from Oklahoma. Students come from 50 states, 85 foreign countries, and Canada. Seventy-four percent are white. The average age of freshmen is 19; all undergraduates, 22.3. Twenty-three percent drop out by the end of their first year; 47% remain to graduate.

Housing: A total of 5000 students can be accommodated in college housing. College-sponsored living facilities include single-sex and coed dormitories, on-campus apartments, and married-student housing. In addition, there are honors houses and special interest houses. Intensive-study housing is also available. On-campus housing is guaranteed for all 4 years. Eighty-five percent of students commute. All students may keep cars on campus.

Activities: About 19% of men belong to 23 national fraternities; about 17% of women belong to 15 national sororities. There are 214 groups on campus, including art, band, cheerleading, chess, choir, chorale, chorus, dance, drama, drill team, ethnic, film, gay, honors, international, jazz band, literary magazine, marching band, musical theater, newspaper, opera, orchestra, pep band, political, professional, radio and TV, religious, social, social service, student government, and symphony. Popular campus events include Medieval Fair, Moms and Dads Days, Sooner Scandals, Theater Season, and University Sing.

Sports: There are 10 intercollegiate sports for men and 9 for women, and 19 intramural sports for men and 19 for women. Athletic and recreation facilities include a golf course, a field house, a gymnastics center, tennis courts, a swimming pool complex, and a fitness center.

Disabled Students: Ninety percent of the campus is accessible to disabled students. The following facilities are available: wheelchair ramps, elevators, special parking, specially equipped rest rooms, special class scheduling, lowered drinking fountains, lowered telephones, and a disabled student services office.

Services: In addition to many counseling and information services, tutoring is available in most subjects. In addition, there is a reader service for the blind, and remedial math, reading, and writing. There are also volunteer note takers, interpreter services for the deaf or hearing impaired, and special testing services.

Campus Safety and Security: Campus safety and security measures include 24-hour foot and vehicle patrol, self defense education, escort service, and shuttle buses. In addition, there are informal discussions, pamphlets, posters, and films, emergency telephones, and lighted pathways and sidewalks. There is also a modified 911 system and a bicycle patrol.

Programs of Study: OU awards the B.A., B.S., B.B.A. B.F.A., B.L.S., and B.S.Ed. degrees. Master's and doctoral degrees also are awarded. Bachelor's degrees are awarded in BIOLOGICAL SCIENCE (botany, microbiology, and zoology), BUSINESS (accounting, banking and finance, business administration and management, business economics, international business management, management information systems, marketing/retailing/merchandising, and real estate), COMMUNICATIONS AND THE ARTS (advertising, broadcasting, classics, communications, dance, dramatic arts, English, film arts, fine arts, French, German, journalism, linguistics, music, photography, Russian, Spanish, and video), COMPUTER AND PHYSICAL SCIENCE (astronomy, astrophysics, atmospheric sciences and meteorology, chemistry, computer science, geology, geophysics and seismology, geoscience, mathematics, and physics), EDUCATION (early childhood, elementary, foreign languages, health, mathematics, music, science, social studies, and special), ENGINEERING AND ENVIRONMENTAL DESIGN (aeronautical engineering, architecture, chemical engineering, civil engineering, construction engineering, electrical/electronics engineering, engineering, engineering physics,

environmental design, environmental science, geological engineering, industrial engineering, interior design, land use management and reclamation, mechanical engineering, and petroleum/natural gas engineering), HEALTH PROFESSIONS (medical laboratory technology), SOCIAL SCIENCE (African American studies, anthropology, Asian/Oriental studies, economics, European studies, geography, history, humanities and social science, Latin American studies, liberal arts/general studies, Native American studies, philosophy, political science/government, psychology, public affairs, religion, Russian and Slavic studies, social work, sociology, and women's studies). Chemistry and biochemistry, history of science, meteorology, botany and microbiology, physics and astronomy, civil engineering and environmental science, chemical engineering and materials science, accounting, petroleum engineering, music education, and dance are the strongest academically. Management, accounting, and electrical engineering have the largest enrollments.

Required: To graduate, students must have a minimum 2.0 GPA, depending on the major, and complete a minimum of 124 semester hours. The number of hours required in the major varies. General education core courses include arts and humanities, oral and symbolic communication, natural science, and social science. All students must take 6 hours each in English composition, American history, and government. Seniors must take a 3-credit hour capstone experience course integrating their undergraduate studies.

Special: Co-op programs are available in engineering. A variety of internships—from informal, voluntary arrangements to those that are formal and required—are available in more than 50 fields of study. OU offers study abroad in 27 countries, work-study programs, a general studies degree, dual and student-designed majors, nondegree study, pass/fail options, and credit for life experience. B.A.-B.S. degrees are offered in many subjects. There is a freshman honors program on campus, as well as 37 national honor societies, including Phi Beta Kappa.

Faculty/Classroom: Seventy-eight percent of faculty are male; 22%, female. Graduate students teach 30% of introductory courses.

Admissions: About 84% of the 1993–94 applicants were accepted. The ACT scores for the 1993–94 freshman class were as follows: 20% below 21, 31% between 21 and 23, 21% between 24 and 26, 11% between 27 and 28, and 16% above 28. About 53% of the current freshmen were in the top fifth of their class; 82% were in the top two fifths.

Requirements: OU requires applicants to be in the upper 33% of their class. A minimum GPA of 3.0 is required. The SAT I or ACT is required, with a minimum composite score of 990 on the SAT I or 21 on the ACT. Graduation from an accredited secondary school or a satisfactory score on the GED is required. Students must have a total of 11 curricular units, including 4 years of English, 3 of mathematics, and 2 each of history, science, and a foreign language. Alternative admission opportunities include summer provisional admission, adult admission, and an alternative admission program. AP and CLEP credits are accepted. Recommendations by school officials is an important factor used in the admission decision.

Procedure: Freshmen are admitted to all sessions. Entrance exams should be taken during the junior year. Application deadlines are open. Application fee is $25. Notification is sent on a rolling basis.

Transfer: A total of 1610 transfer students enrolled in 1993–94. Transfer applicants who are residents or have attended an Oklahoma college must have a minimum GPA of 1.7 in 7 to 30 semester hours (2.0 for 30 or more); nonresidents must be in good standing at the last institution attended and have a minimum GPA of 2.0. Applicants with fewer than 24 semester hours must meet freshman requirements. A total of 30 credits out of 124 must be completed at OU.

Visiting: There are regularly scheduled orientations for prospective students. There are guides for informal visits and visitors may sit in on classes and stay overnight at the school. To arrange for a visit, contact Leslie Baumert, Director of Prospective Student Services at (405) 325–2151 or (800) 234–6868.

Financial Aid: In 1993–94, 62% of all current freshmen and 51% of continuing students received some form of financial aid. About 27% of freshmen and 33% of continuing students received need-based aid. The average freshman award was $4154. Of that total, scholarships or need-based grants averaged $2373 ($4000 maximum) and loans averaged $1455 ($4000 maximum). Sixty-three percent of undergraduate students work part-time. Average earnings from campus work for the school year was $1818. The average financial indebtedness of the 1992–93 graduate was $15,014. OU is a member of CSS. The FAF, FFS, or SFS is required. The deadline for financial aid applications is July 1.

International Students: There are currently 1162 international students enrolled. They must take the TOEFL and achieve a minimum score of 550.

Computers: The university provides computer facilities for student use. The mainframes are an IBM 3081 Model K and a Unisys A1OH. Students have access to 350 microcomputers in 7 locations, and access to a DEC VAX 6610, an Alliant FX-8, and a DEC VAX 6520.

They can utilize the mainframes through a local network. All students may access the system. It may be used 24 hours per day. There are no time limits on using the system and no fees.

Graduates: In 1992–93, 2456 bachelor's degrees were awarded. The most popular majors among graduates were marketing (6%), accounting (6%), and management information systems (6%). Within an average freshman class, 1% graduate in 3 years, 16% in 4 years, 35% in 5 years, and 43% in 6 years. Some 174 companies recruited on campus in 1992–93.

Admissions Contact: Marc Borish, Director of Admissions.

UNIVERSITY OF SCIENCE AND ARTS OF OKLAHOMA
D-4

Chickasha, OK 73018–0001　　　　(405) 224–3140, ext. 205

Full-time: 395 men, 745 women	Faculty: 54; IIB, -$
Part-time: 158 men, 315 women	Ph.D.s: 72%
Graduate: none	Student/Faculty: 21 to 1
Year: trimesters, summer session	Tuition: $1384 ($3446)
Application Deadline: open	Room & Board: $1920

Freshman Class: 438 applied, 400 accepted, 208 enrolled
ACT: 19　　　　　　　　　　　　　　　　　　　　**COMPETITIVE**

The University of Science and Arts of Oklahoma, founded in 1908, is a publicly funded liberal arts institution. In addition to regional accreditation, USAO has baccalaureate program accreditation with NASM and NCATE. The library contains 90,000 volumes, 6000 microform items, and 1000 audiovisual forms, and subscribes to 600 periodicals. The 75-acre campus is in a small town 40 miles southwest of Oklahoma City. Including residence halls, there are 14 buildings on campus.

Student Life: About 96% of undergraduates are from Oklahoma. Students come from 13 states and 8 foreign countries. Ninety-nine percent are from public schools; 1% from private. Eighty-four percent are white; 10% Native American/Eskimo. The average age of freshmen is 20; all undergraduates, 29. Forty percent drop out by the end of their first year; 30% remain to graduate.

Housing: A total of 508 students can be accommodated in college housing. College-sponsored living facilities include single-sex dormitories. On-campus housing is available on a first-come, first-served basis. Eighty percent of students commute. Alcohol is not permitted. All students may keep cars on campus.

Activities: There are no fraternities or sororities on campus. There are 22 groups on campus, including art, band, cheerleading, choir, chorale, chorus, drama, ethnic, honors, international, jazz band, musical theater, newspaper, opera, orchestra, pep band, photography, political, professional, religious, social, and student government.

Sports: There are 3 intercollegiate sports for men and 3 for women, and 4 intramural sports for men and 4 for women. Athletic and recreation facilities include a field house, a 2000-seat gymnasium, and a 1000-seat auditorium.

Disabled Students: The entire campus is accessible to disabled students. The following facilities are available: wheelchair ramps, elevators, special parking, specially equipped rest rooms, special class scheduling, lowered drinking fountains, and lowered telephones.

Services: In addition to many counseling and information services, tutoring is available in some subjects, including mathematics, writing, and reading. In addition, there is remedial math, reading, and writing.

Campus Safety and Security: Campus safety and security measures include 24-hour foot and vehicle patrol, informal discussions, pamphlets, posters, and films, and lighted pathways and sidewalks.

Programs of Study: USAO awards the B.A. and B.S. degrees. Bachelor's degrees are awarded in BIOLOGICAL SCIENCE (biology/biological science), BUSINESS (accounting and business administration and management), COMMUNICATIONS AND THE ARTS (communications, dramatic arts, English, and music), COMPUTER AND PHYSICAL SCIENCE (chemistry, computer science, mathematics, and physics), EDUCATION (art, business, early childhood, elementary, home economics, music, and science), HEALTH PROFESSIONS (medical laboratory technology), SOCIAL SCIENCE (economics, history, political science/government, psychology, and sociology). Humanities, sciences, and social sciences are the strongest academically. Business, computer science, education, and art have the largest enrollments.

Required: To graduate, students must complete a total of 124 credit hours with a minimum GPA of 2.2. All students must take 52 hours of required core courses, more than half of which are interdisciplinary and team taught.

Special: USAO offers dual majors, accelerated degree programs in all majors, and a limited number of pass/fail options. There are 3 national honor societies on campus, including Phi Beta Kappa. One department has an honors program.

Faculty/Classroom: Sixty-five percent of faculty are male; 35%, female. All teach undergraduates and 40% both teach undergraduates and do research. The average class size in an introductory lecture is 40; in a laboratory, 20; and in a regular course offering, 30.

Admissions: About 91% of the 1993–94 applicants were accepted. The ACT scores for the 1993–94 freshman class were as follows: 58% below 21, 20% between 21 and 23, 14% between 24 and 26, 5% between 27 and 28, and 3% above 28. There were 3 National Merit semifinalists. Eighteen freshmen graduated first in their class.

Requirements: USAO requires applicants to be in the upper 50% of their class. A minimum GPA of 2.7 is required. The SAT I or ACT with a minimum composite score of 19, is required. Applicants must be graduates of an accredited secondary school or have a GED. They must complete 20 high school academic credits, including 4 years of English, 3 of mathematics, 2 of science, and 1 each of history and social studies. AP and CLEP credits are accepted. Important factors used in the admissions decision are recommendations by school officials, recommendations by alumni, personality, intangible qualities, parents or siblings attending the school, and leadership record.

Procedure: Freshmen are admitted to all sessions. Application deadlines are open. Notification is sent on a rolling basis.

Transfer: About 100 transfer students enrolled in a recent year. Transfer students must have a GPA of 2.0. A total of 30 credits out of 124 must be completed at USAO.

Visiting: There are guides for informal visits and visitors may sit in on classes. To arrange for a visit, contact School Relations at (405) 224–3140, ext. 338.

Financial Aid: In a recent year, 71% of all current freshmen and 60% of continuing students received some form of financial aid. About 75% of freshmen and 73% of continuing students received need-based aid. The average freshman award was $4200. Of that total, scholarships or need-based grants averaged $1975 ($2600 maximum); loans averaged $1500 ($4000 maximum); and work contracts averaged $1275. All undergraduate students work part-time. Average earnings from campus work for the school year are $1275. The average financial indebtedness of a recent graduate was $1911. The FFS is required. The deadline for financial aid applications is July 1.

International Students: There are currently 27 international students enrolled. The school actively recruits these students. They must take the TOEFL and achieve a minimum score of 500.

Computers: The university provides computer facilities for student use. The mainframe is a a DEC VAX 4000. IBM PCs are also available for academic use. All students may access the system. It may be used at any time. There are no time limits on using the system and no fees.

Graduates: In 1992–93, 151 bachelor's degrees were awarded. The most popular majors among graduates were business (30%), education (26%), and fine arts (13%). Within an average freshman class, 7% graduate in 3 years, 19% in 4 years, 25% in 5 years, and 35% in 6 years. In the 1992 graduating class, 14% of graduates were enrolled in graduate school within 6 months of graduation; 51% had found employment.

Admissions Contact: Dr. Tim McElroy, Director of Admissions.

UNIVERSITY OF TULSA
E-2

Tulsa, OK 74104–3189　　　　　　　(918) 631–2307
　　　　　　　　　　　　　　(800) 331–3050 (out-of-state)

Full-time: 1404 men, 1532 women	Faculty: 339; IIA, av$
Part-time: 163 men, 270 women	Ph.D.s: 93%
Graduate: 855 men, 585 women	Student/Faculty: 9 to 1
Year: semesters	Tuition: $9995
Application Deadline: open	Room & Board: $3800

Freshman Class: 1712 applied, 1557 accepted, 696 enrolled
SAT I Verbal/Math: 527/580　　ACT: 24　　**VERY COMPETITIVE**

The University of Tulsa, founded in 1894, is a private comprehensive coeducational institution offering more than 70 major areas of study through its programs in liberal arts and sciences, engineering and applied sciences, and business administration. There are 3 undergraduate and 2 graduate schools. In addition to regional accreditation, TU has baccalaureate program accreditation with AACSB, ABET, NASM, NCATE, and NLN. The 2 libraries contain 2,023,298 volumes, 1,592,700 microform items, and 9385 audiovisual forms, and subscribe to 3421 periodicals. Computerized library sources and services include the card catalog, interlibrary loans, and database searching. Special learning facilities include an art gallery, radio station, and TV station. The 75-acre campus is in an urban area in the city of Tulsa. Including residence halls, there are 75 buildings on campus.

Student Life: About 58% of undergraduates are from Oklahoma. Students come from 43 states, 63 foreign countries, and Canada. Eighty-five percent are from public schools; 15% from private. Seventy-four percent are white; 10% foreign nationals. Fifty-nine percent are Protestant; 15% Catholic. The average age of freshmen is 18;

all undergraduates, 23. Twenty-six percent drop out by the end of their first year; 44% remain to graduate.

Housing: A total of 1531 students can be accommodated in college housing. College-sponsored living facilities include single-sex and coed dormitories, on-campus apartments, off-campus apartments, married-student housing, fraternity houses, and sorority houses. In addition there are honors houses. On-campus housing is guaranteed for all 4 years. Sixty percent of students commute. All students may keep cars on campus.

Activities: About 23% of men belong to 7 national fraternities; about 21% of women belong to 7 national sororities. There are 140 groups on campus, including art, band, cheerleading, chess, choir, chorale, chorus, computers, dance, drama, drill team, ethnic, gay, honors, international, jazz band, literary magazine, marching band, musical theater, newspaper, opera, orchestra, pep band, photography, political, professional, radio and TV, religious, social, social service, student government, symphony, and yearbook. Popular campus events include Homecoming, Parents Weekend, Springfest, Black Heritage Month, Womens Heritage Month, Hispanic Folklore Show, Reggaefest, Airband, and Greek Week.

Sports: There are 6 intercollegiate sports each for men and women, and 30 intramural sports each for men and women. Athletic and recreation facilities include a 40,000-seat stadium, a gymnasium, an athletic field, indoor racquetball courts, basketball and tennis courts, an indoor swimming pool, a handball court, a weight room, and a dance studio.

Disabled Students: Eighty percent of the campus is accessible to disabled students. The following facilities are available: wheelchair ramps, elevators, special parking, specially equipped rest rooms, and lowered drinking fountains.

Services: In addition to many counseling and information services, tutoring is available in every subject. In addition, there is a reader service for the blind and remedial math and writing. Special laboratories are available to students in need of assistance in mathematics and writing, and study skills classes are available free of charge.

Campus Safety and Security: Campus safety and security measures include 24-hour foot and vehicle patrol, self defense education, escort service, and informal discussions. In addition, there are pamphlets, posters, and films, emergency telephones, and lighted pathways and sidewalks.

Programs of Study: TU awards the B.A., B.S., B.F.A, B.Mus., and B.Mus.Ed. degrees. Master's and doctoral degrees also are awarded. Bachelor's degrees are awarded in BIOLOGICAL SCIENCE (biology/biological science), BUSINESS (accounting, banking and finance, business economics, management information systems, management science, and marketing/retailing/merchandising), COMMUNICATIONS AND THE ARTS (advertising, broadcasting, design, dramatic arts, English, fine arts, French, journalism, music, and Spanish), COMPUTER AND PHYSICAL SCIENCE (chemistry, computer programming, computer science, earth science, geology, geoscience, mathematics, and physics), EDUCATION (art, education of the deaf and hearing impaired, elementary, foreign languages, middle school, music, science, and secondary), ENGINEERING AND ENVIRONMENTAL DESIGN (chemical engineering, electrical/electronics engineering, engineering physics, environmental science, mechanical engineering, and petroleum/natural gas engineering), HEALTH PROFESSIONS (nursing, predentistry, premedicine, preveterinary science, speech pathology/audiology, and sports medicine), SOCIAL SCIENCE (anthropology, economics, history, philosophy, political science/government, prelaw, psychology, and sociology). Petroleum engineering, psychology, English, anthropology, and accounting are the strongest academically. Mechanical engineering, accounting, communication, nursing, psychology, and chemical engineering have the largest enrollments.

Required: To graduate, students must complete 126 to 136 credit hours, including 24 to 39 in the major, with a minimum GPA of 2.0. Freshmen in liberal arts and business administration must complete the First Seminar. All students must complete the Tulsa curriculum, consisting of the core curriculum, which includes 3 writing courses and at least 1 course in mathematics. All students must also complete the general curriculum, which requires 9 courses in 5 categories (artistic imagination, social inquiry, cultural interpretation, scientific investigation, and contemporary and artistic experience). A foreign language requirement of 2 years for liberal arts and sciences students and 1 year for business majors must be completed.

Special: Internships are available in the Tulsa area during the school year and in cities throughout the United States during the summer. Students may participate in 40 study-abroad programs, most of them arranged through the Institute of European Studies. TU offers a Washington semester, B.A.-B.S. degrees, dual and student-designed majors, nondegree study, and pass/fail options. There is a freshman honors program on campus, as well as 37 national honor societies, including Phi Beta Kappa.

Faculty/Classroom: Sixty-seven percent of faculty are male; 33%, female. All teach undergraduates and do research. Graduate students teach 15% of introductory courses. The average class size in an introductory lecture is 25; in a laboratory, 25; and in a regular course offering, 25.

Admissions: About 91% of the 1993–94 applicants were accepted. The SAT scores for the 1993–94 freshman class were as follows: Verbal—34% below 500, 46% between 500 and 599, 18% between 600 and 700, and 3% above 700; Math—18% below 500, 39% between 500 and 599, 32% between 600 and 700, and 11% above 700. The ACT scores were 20% below 21, 25% between 21 and 23, 26% between 24 and 26, 14% between 27 and 28, and 15% above 28. About 59% of the current freshmen were in the top fifth of their class; 84% were in the top two fifths. There were 14 National Merit finalists. About 35 freshmen graduated first in their class.

Requirements: The SAT I or ACT is required. Graduation from an accredited secondary school or satisfactory scores on the GED are also required for admission. The school recommends a minimum of 15 academic credits, including 4 years of English, 3 to 4 years each of mathematics, science, and social studies (including history), and 2 years of a single foreign language. An essay and an interview are highly recommended. An audition or a portfolio is required for students applying for music, theater, or art scholarships. AP and CLEP credits are accepted. Important factors used in the admissions decision are advanced placement or honor courses, recommendations by school officials, evidence of special talent, leadership record, and extracurricular activites record.

Procedure: Freshmen are admitted fall and spring. Entrance exams should be taken during spring of the junior year or fall of the senior year. Application deadlines are open. Application fee is $25. Notification is sent on a rolling basis geginning in December. There is a deferred admissions plan.

Transfer: A total of 286 transfer students enrolled in 1993–94. Transfer students must submit official transcripts from all colleges attended and should have a minimum GPA of 2.5 for all college and high school work. Applicants with fewer than 30 credit hours must submit ACT or SAT I scores. Those with fewer than 60 credit hours must submit an official high school transcript. Applicants 25 years of age or older are exempt from submitting ACT or SAT I scores unless requested to do so by the Admission Office. A total of 30 credits out of 126 to 136 must be completed at TU.

Visiting: There are regularly scheduled orientations for prospective students, including 2-day overnight programs in the fall and spring. Students stay on campus and attend special information sessions. There are guides for informal visits and visitors may sit in on classes and stay overnight at the school. To arrange for a visit, contact the Office of Admission at (800) 331–3050 or (918) 631–2307.

Financial Aid: In 1993–94, 76% of all current freshmen and 75% of continuing students received some form of financial aid. About 51% of freshmen and 55% of continuing students received need-based aid. The average freshman award was $9400. Of that total, scholarships or need-based grants averaged $5069 ($13,800 maximum); loans averaged $3257 ($5625 maximum); and work contracts averaged $1080 ($2000 maximum). Forty percent of undergraduate students work part-time. Average earnings from campus work for the school year are $1225. The average financial indebtedness of the 1992–93 graduate was $7000. TU is a member of CSS. The college's own financial statement and FAFSA are required. The deadline for financial aid applications is April 1.

International Students: There are currently 523 international students enrolled. The school actively recruits these students. They must take the TOEFL and achieve a minimum score of 500.

Computers: The university provides computer facilities for student use. The mainframe is a DEC VAX 6320. There are also 250 IBM and Apple Macintosh microcomputers available. All students may access the system 24 hours per day. There are no time limits on using the system and no fees.

Graduates: In a recent year, 557 bachelor's degrees were awarded. The most popular majors among graduates were accounting (12%), marketing (8%), and finance (8%). Within an average freshman class, 50% graduate in 5 years and 44% in 6 years. Some 186 companies recruited on campus in 1992–93.

Admissions Contact: John C. Corso, Dean of Admission.

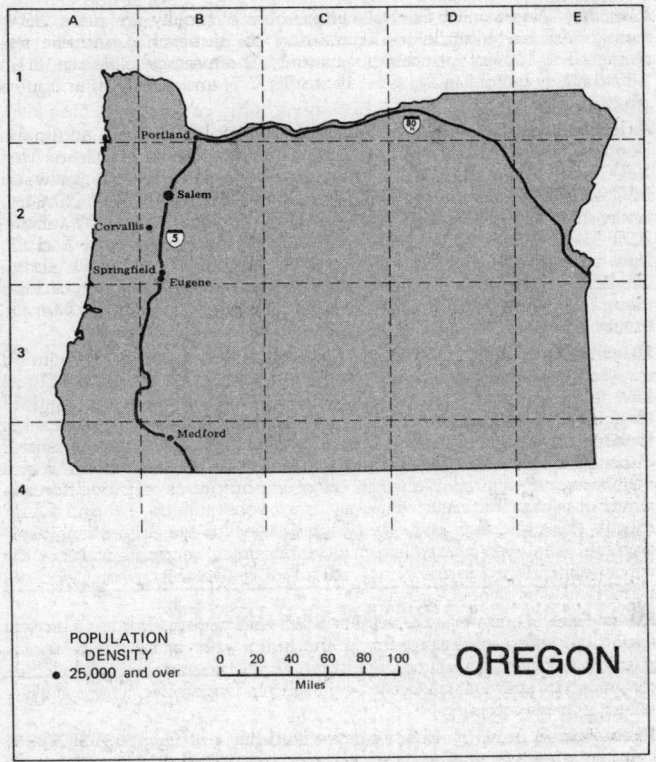

POPULATION
DENSITY
• 25,000 and over

0 20 40 60 80 100
Miles

OREGON

BASSIST COLLEGE

B-1

Portland, OR 97201   (503) 228–6528; (800) 547–0937 (in-state)

Full-time: 12 men, 138 women   **Faculty:** 9
Part-time: 4 men, 20 women   **Ph.D.s:** 11%
Graduate: none   **Student/Faculty:** 17 to 1
Year: quarters, summer session   **Tuition:** $8590
Application Deadline: September 1   **Room & Board:** $4000
Freshman Class: 123 applied, 123 accepted, 95 enrolled
SAT I or ACT: not required   **SPECIAL**

Bassist College, founded in 1963, is a private coeducational institution offering undergraduate programs in interior, apparel, and industrial design and retail management. Students spend 2 terms working in the field as part of their degree training. There are 4 undergraduate schools. The library contains 13,500 volumes and 60 audiovisual forms, and subscribes to 125 periodicals. Computerized library sources and services include interlibrary loans. Special learning facilities include an art gallery. The 1-acre campus is in an urban area in downtown Portland. Including residence halls, there are 3 buildings on campus.

Student Life: About 60% of undergraduates are from Oregon. Students come from 14 states, 7 foreign countries, and Canada. Ninety percent are from public schools; 10% from private. Ninety-two percent are white. The average age of freshmen is 25; all undergraduates, 28. About 73% of freshmen remain to graduate.

Housing: A total of 30 students can be accommodated in college housing. College-sponsored living facilities include coed dormitories. On-campus housing is available on a first-come, first-served basis. Priority is given to out-of-town students. Eighty percent of students commute. Alcohol is not permitted. All students may keep cars on campus.

Activities: There are no fraternities or sororities on campus. There are 3 groups on campus, including interior design, professional, and student government. Popular campus events include Costume Day, Valentine's Day, and Career Days.

Sports: There is no sports program at the college.

Disabled Students: Seventy-five percent of the campus is accessible to disabled students. The following facilities are available: elevators, special parking, specially equipped rest rooms, special class scheduling, lowered drinking fountains, and lowered telephones.

Services: In addition to many counseling and information services, tutoring is available in all classes. There is also remedial writing.

Campus Safety and Security: Campus safety and security measures include informal discussions, pamphlets, posters, and films, emergency telephones, and lighted pathways and sidewalks.

Programs of Study: The college awards the B.Apparel Design, B.Int.Design, B.Ind.Design, and B.Retail Management degrees. Associate degrees also are awarded. Bachelor's degrees are awarded in BUSINESS (retailing), COMMUNICATIONS AND THE ARTS (apparel design and industrial design), ENGINEERING AND ENVIRONMENTAL DESIGN (interior design). Industrial design is the strongest program academically. Interior design has the largest enrollment.

Required: To graduate, students must complete 190 quarter hours, including 70 to 78 in the major, with a minimum GPA of 2.0. Distribution requirements include 26 credits in humanities and arts, 20 in social sciences, 17 in communications, 6 in science, and 3 in quantitative reasoning. A senior paper or project is required. Two terms of internships in the field of study must be completed.

Special: College and community work-study programs, accelerated degrees in all majors, and field trips to Seattle and San Francisco are available.

Faculty/Classroom: Thirty-three percent of faculty are male; 67%, female. All teach undergraduates, and 10% also do research. The average class size in an introductory lecture is 25; in a laboratory, 15; and in a regular course offering, 25.

Admissions: All of the 1993–94 applicants were accepted.

Requirements: A minimum GPA of 2.25 is required. The SAT I or the ACT is not required. A high school diploma is required. The GED is also accepted, with a minimum score of 55 required. AP credits are accepted. Important factors used in the admissions decision are evidence of special talent, recommendations by school officials, ability to finance college education, recommendations by alumni, and parents or siblings attending the school.

Procedure: Freshmen are admitted in the fall. Early decision applications should be filed by April 1; regular applications, by September 1 for fall entry, along with an application fee of $200. Notification of early decision is sent by April 15; regular decision, September 5. There are early decision, early admissions, and deferred admissions plans. About 70 early decision candidates were accepted for a recent class. A waiting list is an active part of the admissions procedure, with about 2% of applicants on the list.

Transfer: About 64 transfer students enrolled in 1993–94. Requirements include a GPA of 2.0 in all previous college work and for applicants with fewer than 30 quarter credits of college, a high school GPA of 2.25. A total of 65 quarter credits out of 190 must be completed at the college.

Visiting: There are regularly scheduled orientations for prospective students, including college tours, mini class sessions, financial aid and financial planning meetings, and career assessment. There are guides for informal visits and visitors may stay overnight at the school. To arrange for a visit, contact Annamarie Whitaker at (503) 228–6528.

Financial Aid: In 1993–94, 68% of all current freshmen and 91% of continuing students received some form of financial aid. About 58% of freshmen and 79% of continuing students received need-based aid. The average freshman award was $9242. Of that total, scholarships or need-based grants averaged $1135 ($3300 maximum); and loans averaged $5800 ($12,850 maximum). Ten percent of undergraduate students work part-time. Average earnings from campus work for the school year are $325. The average financial indebtedness of the 1992–93 graduate was $6713. The college's own financial statement and the FAFSA are required. The deadline for financial aid applications is August 1.

International Students: There are currently 7 international students enrolled. The school actively recruits these students. They must take the TOEFL and achieve a minimum score of 550.

Computers: The college provides computer facilities for student use. Six IBM PCs and six CAD machines are available for student use during laboratory hours. Students that have been trained on the system may access it in the daytime during the week. There are no time limits on using the system. The fees are $5 per term.

Graduates: In 1992–93, 6 bachelor's degrees were awarded. The most popular majors among graduates were interior design (47%), apparel design (30%), and retail management (23%). Within an average freshman class, 73% graduate in 3 years and 75% in 4 years. Some 30 companies recruited on campus in 1992–93. In the 1992 graduating class, 1% of the men and 9% of the women were enrolled in graduate school within 6 months of graduation; 75% of the men and 80% of the women had found employment.

Admissions Contact: Annamarie Whitaker, Director of Admissions.

CASCADE COLLEGE B-2
(Formerly Columbia Christian College)
Portland, OR 97216–1515   (503) 255–7060; (800) 926–7678

Full-time: 95 men, 120 women	Faculty: 25
Part-time: 25 men, 35 women	Ph.D.s: 32%
Graduate: none	Student/Faculty: 9 to 1
Year: semesters, summer session	Tuition: $6600
Application Deadline: open	Room & Board: $3200
Freshman Class: n/av	
SAT I or ACT: recommended	**NONCOMPETITIVE**

Cascade College, founded in 1956 in affiliation with the Churches of Christ, offers an undergraduate liberal arts education in biblical studies, business, education, humanities, music, and natural and social sciences. The library contains 31,109 volumes, 20,000 microform items, and 4000 audiovisual forms, and subscribes to 207 periodicals. Computerized library sources and services include interlibrary loans. Special learning facilities include a learning resource center. The 12-acre campus is in an urban area 8 miles east of downtown Portland. Including residence halls, there are 16 buildings on campus.

Student Life: About 52% of undergraduates are from out-of-state, mostly the Northwest. Students come from 11 states, 10 foreign countries, and Canada. Ninety-one percent are white. Most are Protestant. The average age of freshmen is 18; all undergraduates, 21.

Housing: A total of 350 students can be accommodated in college housing. College-sponsored living facilities include single-sex dormitories. On-campus housing is guaranteed for all 4 years. Fifty-four percent of students live on campus; of those, 50% remain on campus on weekends. Alcohol is not permitted. All students may keep cars on campus.

Activities: About 47% of men belong to 2 national fraternities; about 51% of women belong to 2 national sororities. There are 18 groups on campus, including cheerleading, choir, chorale, international, jazz band, professional, religious, social, social service, student government, and yearbook. Popular campus events include a campus variety show, formal banquets, Chinook Court, and Critical Awareness Week.

Sports: There are 2 intercollegiate sports each for men and women, and 5 intramural sports each. Athletic and recreation facilities include a gymnasium, basketball, volleyball, and badminton courts, a weight room, a team room, and a soccer field.

Disabled Students: Seventy percent of the campus is accessible to disabled students. The following facilities are available: elevators, special parking, and specially equipped rest rooms.

Services: In addition to many counseling and information services, tutoring is available in most subjects. There is also remedial reading.

Campus Safety and Security: Campus safety and security measures include self-defense education, escort service, and lighted pathways and sidewalks.

Programs of Study: Cascade College awards the B.A. and B.S. degrees. Bachelor's degrees are awarded in BIOLOGICAL SCIENCE (biology/biological science), BUSINESS (business administration and management), COMMUNICATIONS AND THE ARTS (English and music), EDUCATION (physical), SOCIAL SCIENCE (American studies, biblical studies, history, liberal arts/general studies, ministries, and psychology). Education, music, and mathematics are the strongest programs academically. Education and music have the largest enrollments.

Required: To graduate, students must complete at least 127 semester hours, including 45 in upper-division courses, with a GPA of 2.0. In addition to biblical and religious curriculum requirements, students must take courses in English, mathematics, and computer science, and 1 year of foreign language. There is a comprehensive exam in the major field.

Special: Cascade College offers co-op programs for education majors, ministry internships, and student-designed majors in the liberal studies program. There is one national honor society on campus.

Faculty/Classroom: Fifty-nine percent of faculty are male; 41%, female. All teach undergraduates. No introductory courses are taught by graduate students. The average class size in an introductory lecture is 25; in a laboratory, 10; and in a regular course offering, 8.

Admissions: About 90% of a recent year's applicants were accepted. There were 2 National Merit finalists and 2 semifinalists.

Requirements: A minimum GPA of 2.0 is required. The SAT I or ACT is recommended. Applicants should be graduates of an accredited secondary school with a minimum GPA of 2.0. AP and CLEP credits are accepted. Important factors used in the admissions decision are recommendations by school officials, personality, intangible qualities, ability to finance college education, advanced placement or honor courses, and leadership record.

Procedure: Freshmen are admitted to all sessions. Entrance exams should be taken in December of the senior year. The application fee is $25. Notification is sent on a rolling basis.

Transfer: About 25 transfer students enrolled in a recent year. A total of 32 credits out of 127 must be completed at Cascade College.

Visiting: There are regularly scheduled orientations for prospective students, including a meeting with faculty members, a financial aid workshop, and a survey of college programs. There are guides for informal visits and visitors may sit in on classes and stay overnight at the school. To arrange for a visit, contact the Admissions Office at (503) 257–1202.

Financial Aid: In 1993–94, 80% of all students received some form of financial aid. About 72% of freshmen and 75% of continuing students received need-based aid. The average freshman award was $7000. Of that total, scholarships or need-based grants averaged $2750 ($4400 maximum); loans averaged $2750 ($4400 maximum); and work contracts averaged $1500 ($1800 maximum). Sixty-six percent of undergraduate students work part-time. Average earnings from campus work for the school year are $1500. The average financial indebtedness of the 1992–93 graduate was $9548. Cascade College is a member of CSS. The FAF is required. The deadline for financial aid applications is May 1.

International Students: There were recently 23 international students enrolled. The school actively recruits these students. They must take the TOEFL and achieve a minimum score of 525. The student must also take the SAT I.

Computers: The college provides computer facilities for student use. The mainframe is an AT&T 6386E. There are 15 stand-alone Epson microcomputers available in the computer laboratory. The mainframe is not networked for student use.

Graduates: In a recent year, 44 bachelor's degrees were awarded.

Admissions Contact: Brad Fisher, Director of Development.

COLUMBIA CHRISTIAN COLLEGE
(See Cascade College)

CONCORDIA COLLEGE B-1
Portland, OR 97211
Recognized candidate for accreditation   (503) 280–8501
(800) 321–9371 (out-of-state)

Full-time: 369 men, 442 women	Faculty: 37
Part-time: 66 men, 140 women	Ph.D.s: 52%
Graduate: none	Student/Faculty: 22 to 1
Year: quarters, summer session	Tuition: $9300
Application Deadline: open	Room & Board: $3000
Freshman Class: 299 applied, 206 accepted, 81 enrolled	
SAT I Verbal/Math: 434/466	ACT: 19 **COMPETITIVE**

Concordia College, founded in 1905, is a private liberal arts institution affiliated with the Lutheran Church Missouri Synod. The library contains 50,000 volumes, 47,000 microform items, and 2945 audiovisual forms, and subscribes to 426 periodicals. Computerized library sources and services include interlibrary loans and database searching. The 13-acre campus is in a suburban area in Portland. Including residence halls, there are 20 buildings on campus.

Student Life: About 72% of undergraduates are from Oregon. Students come from 17 states, 12 foreign countries, and Canada. The average age of all undergraduates is 26. Forty-five percent drop out by the end of their first year; 60% remain to graduate.

Housing: A total of 210 students can be accommodated in college housing. College-sponsored living facilities include single-sex and coed dormitories and married-student housing. On-campus housing is available on a first-come, first-served basis. Eighty percent of students commute. Alcohol is not permitted. All students may keep cars on campus.

Activities: There are no fraternities or sororities on campus. There are many groups and organizations on campus, including choir, chorus, computers, drama, ethnic, honors, international, musical theater, newspaper, pep band, professional, religious, social, social service, student government, and yearbook. Popular campus events include International Days and Lutheran Elementary School Tournament.

Sports: There are 3 intercollegiate sports each for men and women, and 3 intramural sports each for men and women. Athletic and recreation facilities include a weight room, a 1200-seat gymnasium, and a baseball field. The school's auditorium seats 2000.

Disabled Students: The following facilities are available: wheelchair ramps, elevators, special parking, and specially equipped rest rooms.

Services: In addition to many counseling and information services, tutoring is available in most subjects. In addition, there is remedial math, reading, and writing, and student supported individual help and media resources.

Campus Safety and Security: Campus safety and security measures include self defense education, escort service, informal discussions, and pamphlets, posters, and films. In addition, there are emergency telephones and lighted pathways and sidewalks.

Programs of Study: Concordia awards the B.A. and B.S. degrees. Associate degrees also are awarded. Bachelor's degrees are awarded in BIOLOGICAL SCIENCE (biology/biological science), BUSINESS (accounting and marketing/retailing/merchandising), COMMUNICATIONS AND THE ARTS (dramatic arts and fine arts), EDUCATION (early childhood, elementary, and secondary), HEALTH PROFESSIONS (health care administration), SOCIAL SCIENCE (behavioral science, humanities, religion, religious education, and social work). Business administration, health care administration, preseminary, and liberal arts are the strongest academically. Education and business have the largest enrollments.

Required: To graduate, students must complete a total of 185 quarter hours, including 60 in the major, with a minimum GPA of 2.0. General education requirements total 70 quarter hours. All students must take freshman composition and courses in mathematics, physical education, humanities, religion, science, and advanced writing.

Special: Cross-registration may be arranged through the Oregon Independent Colleges Association. There is also an accelerated degree program in business and a prime time program. There is one national honor society on campus. One department has an honors program.

Faculty/Classroom: Seventy-seven percent of faculty are male; 23%, female. All teach undergraduates and 5% both teach and do research. The average class size in an introductory lecture is 25; in a laboratory, 15; and in a regular course offering, 25.

Admissions: About 69% of the 1993–94 applicants were accepted. The SAT scores for the 1993–94 freshman class were as follows: Verbal—78% below 500, 13% between 500 and 599, 7% between 600 and 700, and 2% above 700; Math—65% below 500, 21% between 500 and 599, 10% between 600 and 700, and 4% above 700. The ACT scores were 50% below 21, 40% between 21 and 23, and 10% between 24 and 26. About 35% of the current freshmen were in the top fifth of their class; 56% were in the top two fifths. Three freshmen graduated first in their class.

Requirements: A minimum GPA of 2.5 is required. The SAT I or ACT is required. For the SAT I, a minimum verbal score of 400 is recommended. Graduation from an accredited secondary school or satisfactory scores on the GED are required. The school recommends that high school courses include 4 units of English, 3 units each of social studies, mathematics and science, 2 units of a foreign language, and 1 unit of art and music. An interview is recommended. AP and CLEP credits are accepted. Important factors used in the admissions decision are recommendations by school officials, leadership record, personality, intangible qualities, evidence of special talent, and advanced placement or honor courses.

Procedure: Freshmen are admitted to all sessions. Entrance exams should be taken during the junior year or early in the senior year. Application deadlines are open. Notification is sent on a rolling basis.

Transfer: About 200 transfer students enrolled in 1993–94. Transfer students must have a minimum GPA of 2.0. A total of 45 quarter hours out of 185 must be completed at Concordia.

Visiting: There are guides for informal visits and visitors may sit in on classes and stay overnight at the school. To arrange for a visit, contact the Admissions Office at (800) 321–9371.

Financial Aid: In 1993–94, 90% of all current freshmen and 80% of continuing students received some form of financial aid. About 90% of freshmen and 80% of continuing students received need-based aid. The average freshman award was $6000. Of that total, scholarships or need-based grants averaged $3500 ($4500 maximum); loans averaged $2625 ($4000 maximum); and work contracts averaged $800 ($1500 maximum). Forty percent of undergraduate students work part-time. The average financial indebtedness of the 1992–93 graduate was $8000. Concordia is a member of CSS. The FAF and the college's own financial statement are required.

International Students: There are currently 85 international students enrolled. The school actively recruits these students. They must take the TOEFL and achieve a minimum score of 500. The student must also take the SAT I. Placement examinations are administered upon arrival.

Computers: The college provides computer facilities for student use. The mainframe is a DEC VAX 4000. There is an IBM and Apple Macintosh laboratory, and terminals are located in the library and the main administration/classroom building. All students may access the system any time the library is open. There are no fees.

Graduates: In a recent year, 185 bachelor's degrees were awarded. The most popular majors among recent graduates were business administration (60%), education (30%), and health care (10%). Some 20 companies recruited on campus in 1992–93.

Admissions Contact: Admissions Office.

EASTERN OREGON STATE COLLEGE D-2
La Grande, OR 97850–2899

(503) 962–3393
(800) 452–8639 (in-state)

Full-time: 780 men, 810 women	Faculty: 127; IIB, -$
Part-time: 90 men, 140 women	Ph.D.s: 54%
Graduate: 20 men and women	Student/Faculty: 13 to 1
Year: terms, summer session	Tuition: $2595
Application Deadline: August 1	Room & Board: $3495
Freshman Class: n/av	
SAT I or ACT: required	**COMPETITIVE**

Eastern Oregon State College, founded in 1929, is a public, coeducational institution that is part of the Oregon State System of Higher Education. It offers programs in liberal and fine arts, agriculture, business, health science, and teacher preparation. There are 3 undergraduate schools and one graduate school. In addition to regional accreditation, Eastern has baccalaureate program accreditation with NCATE. The library contains 110,000 volumes and subscribes to 1025 periodicals. Computerized library sources and services include the card catalog, interlibrary loans, and database searching. Special learning facilities include a learning resource center, art gallery, natural history museum, and radio station. The 121-acre campus is in a rural area 250 miles east of Portland. Including residence halls, there are 12 buildings on campus.

Student Life: About 78% of undergraduates are from Oregon. Students come from 20 states, 24 foreign countries, and Canada. Ninety-six percent are from public schools; 4% from private. Eighty-seven percent are white. The average age of freshmen is 18; all undergraduates, 22. Fifty percent drop out by the end of their first year; 20% remain to graduate.

Housing: A total of 400 students can be accommodated in college housing. College-sponsored living facilities include single-sex and coed dormitories and married-student housing. On-campus housing is available on a first-come, first-served basis. Seventy-five percent of students commute. All students may keep cars on campus.

Activities: There are no fraternities or sororities on campus. There are 60 groups on campus, including art, band, cheerleading, choir, chorale, chorus, computers, dance, drama, ethnic, gay, international, jazz band, literary magazine, musical theater, newspaper, orchestra, pep band, photography, professional, radio and TV, religious, social, student government, and symphony. Popular campus events include Oktoberfest, Casino Night, Homecoming, and Spring Fling.

Sports: There are 7 intercollegiate sports for men and 6 for women, and 6 intramural sports for men and 6 for women. Athletic and recreation facilities include racquetball courts, a weight room, 3 gymnasiums, a swimming pool, aerobics facilities, a track, and indoor and outdoor tennis.

Disabled Students: Seventy-five percent of the campus is accessible to disabled students. The following facilities are available: wheelchair ramps, elevators, special parking, and specially equipped rest rooms.

Services: In addition to many counseling and information services, tutoring is available in most subjects. There is a reader service for the blind, and remedial math, reading, and writing.

Campus Safety and Security: Campus safety and security measures include 24-hour foot and vehicle patrol, self defense education, escort service, and informal discussions. In addition, there are pamphlets, posters, and films, emergency telephones, and lighted pathways and sidewalks.

Programs of Study: Eastern awards the B.A. and B.S degrees. Associate and master's degrees also are awarded. Bachelor's degrees are awarded in AGRICULTURE (agricultural business management, agriculture, and forestry and related sciences), BIOLOGICAL SCIENCE (biology/biological science), BUSINESS (accounting and business administration and management), COMMUNICATIONS AND THE ARTS (dramatic arts, English, and music), COMPUTER AND PHYSICAL SCIENCE (chemistry, mathematics, and physics), EDUCATION (education and physical), HEALTH PROFESSIONS (health, nursing, predentistry, premedicine, and preveterinary science), SOCIAL SCIENCE (anthropology, history, liberal arts/general studies, prelaw, psychology, and sociology). Sciences are the strongest academically. Business and education have the largest enrollments.

Required: Students must complete 186 credit hours, including 60 hours of general education courses, with a GPA of at least 2.0. They must demonstrate computer competency and pass a writing proficiency examination.

Special: There are cooperative and 3-2 engineering degree programs with Oregon State University. The college offers work-study, student-designed and dual majors, study abroad in 8 countries, a general studies degree, B.A.-B.S. degrees, a multidisciplinary degree, credit by examination and for life/military/work experience, external degrees, and pass/fail options. The college also serves students with course work via telecommunications and video, and with a weekend

college. There are 6 national honor societies on campus. Six departments have honors programs.

Faculty/Classroom: All faculty teach undergraduates and do research. No introductory courses are taught by graduate students. The average class size in an introductory lecture is 60; in a laboratory, 20; and in a regular course offering, 35.

Admissions: About 40 freshmen graduated first in their class.

Requirements: A minimum GPA of 2.5 is required. The SAT I or ACT is required. A GED is accepted. Applicants must complete 14 academic credits, including 4 years of English, 3 each of mathematics and social studies, and 2 of science. AP and CLEP credits are accepted. Important factors used in the admissions decision are geographic diversity, extracurricular activities record, evidence of special talent, advanced placement or honor courses, and leadership record.

Procedure: Freshmen are admitted to all sessions. Entrance exams should be taken in the senior year. Applications should be filed by August 1 for fall entry, along with an application fee of $50. Selection deadlines for out-of-state applicants are April 1, June 1, and August 1. There are early decision, early admissions, and deferred admissions plans. About 50 early decision candidates were accepted for the 1993–94 class.

Transfer: About 269 transfer students enrolled in a recent year. Transfer applicants must have 24 quarter hours of transferable academic work with a GPA of 2.0. A total of 45 quarter hours out of 186 must be completed at Eastern.

Visiting: There are regularly scheduled orientations for prospective students, including a campus tour, academic advising, and information sessions on financial aid and residence life. There are guides for informal visits, and visitors may sit in on classes and stay overnight at the school. To arrange for a visit, contact Admissions at (503) 962–3393 or (800) 452–8639 (in-state).

Financial Aid: In 1993–94 80% of all current freshmen and continuing students received some form of financial aid. About 71% of freshmen and continuing students received need-based aid. Twenty-five percent of undergraduate students work part-time. Average earnings from campus work for the school year are $1003. The average financial indebtedness of the 1992–93 graduate was $4300. Eastern is a member of CSS. The FAF, FFS, or SFS is required. The deadline for financial aid applications is February 1.

International Students: There are currently 54 international students enrolled. They must take the TOEFL and achieve a minimum score of 500. The student must also take the University of Michigan Language Test for placement.

Computers: The college provides computer facilities for student use. There is a Super Mini:Bull International minicomputer available. There are also some 36 microcomputers in the classroom computer center, 15 in the learning center, 30 in the library, and a number in the residence halls. All students may access the system. It may be used at various posted hours. There are no time limits on using the system and no fees.

Graduates: Within an average freshman class, 20% graduate in 4 years and 45% in 5 years. Some 30 companies recruited on campus in 1992–93.

Admissions Contact: Terral Schut, Director of Admissions/New Student Programs.

GEORGE FOX COLLEGE
B-2

Newberg, OR 97132   (503) 538–8383, ext. 235

Full-time: 524 men, 754 women	Faculty: 52; IIB, --$
Part-time: 18 men, 30 women	Ph.D.s: 71%
Graduate: 136 men, 95 women	Student/Faculty: 25 to 1
Year: semesters	Tuition: $11,750
Application Deadline: June 1	Room & Board: $3890
Freshman Class: 811 applied, 702 accepted, 350 enrolled	
SAT I Verbal/Math: 470/500	LESS COMPETITIVE

George Fox College, founded in 1891, is a private, coeducational school of liberal arts and sciences operated by the Northwest Yearly Meeting of Friends (Quaker). There are 3 undergraduate and 4 graduate schools. In addition to regional accreditation, George Fox has baccalaureate program accreditation with NASM. The library contains 93,658 volumes, 31,294 microform items, and 2331 audiovisual forms, and subscribes to 870 periodicals. Computerized library sources and services include the card catalog, interlibrary loans, and database searching. Special learning facilities include a learning resource center, art gallery, radio station, television production studio, and Quaker museum. The 65-acre campus is in a small town 23 miles southwest of Portland. Including residence halls, there are 53 buildings on campus.

Student Life: About 66% of undergraduates are from Oregon. Students come from 22 states, 12 foreign countries, and Canada. Ninety-two percent are from public schools; 8% from private. Ninety-one percent are white. Eighty-four percent are Protestant; 14% claim no religious affiliation. The average age of freshmen is 19; all undergradu-

ates, 23. Thirty-four percent drop out by the end of their first year; 45% remain to graduate.

Housing: A total of 900 students can be accommodated in college housing. College-sponsored living facilities include single-sex dormitories and on and off-campus apartments. On-campus housing is available on a first-come, first-served basis. Seventy-five percent of students live on campus; of those, 50% remain on campus on weekends. Alcohol is not permitted. All students may keep cars on campus.

Activities: There are no fraternities or sororities on campus. There are 27 groups on campus, including art, band, cheerleading, chess, choir, chorale, chorus, computers, drama, ethnic, honors, international, jazz band, literary magazine, musical theater, newspaper, orchestra, pep band, political, professional, radio and TV, religious, social, social service, student government, symphony, and yearbook. Popular campus events include Quaker Heritage Week, Homecoming, Christian Emphasis Week, and a raft race.

Sports: There are 5 intercollegiate sports for men and 6 for women, and 3 intramural sports for men and 2 for women. Athletic and recreation facilities include an all-weather track, baseball, softball, and soccer fields, a weight room, tennis and handball/racquetball courts, a 1200-seat stadium, and a 2500-seat gymnasium.

Disabled Students: Eighty percent of the campus is accessible to disabled students. The following facilities are available: wheelchair ramps, elevators, special parking, specially equipped rest rooms, and special class scheduling.

Services: In addition to many counseling and information services, tutoring is available in some subjects. There is a reader service for the blind, and remedial math, reading, and writing.

Campus Safety and Security: Campus safety and security measures include 24-hour foot and vehicle patrol, self-defense education, escort service, and informal discussions. In addition, there are emergency telephones and lighted pathways and sidewalks.

Programs of Study: George Fox awards the B.A. and B.S. degrees. Master's and doctoral degrees also are awarded. Bachelor's degrees are awarded in BIOLOGICAL SCIENCE (biology/biological science), BUSINESS (business economics and personnel management), COMMUNICATIONS AND THE ARTS (communications, literature, music, and telecommunications), COMPUTER AND PHYSICAL SCIENCE (chemistry, computer science, information sciences and systems, mathematics, and science), EDUCATION (elementary, health, home economics, mathematics, middle school, music, physical, science, secondary, and social studies), ENGINEERING AND ENVIRONMENTAL DESIGN (preengineering), HEALTH PROFESSIONS (predentistry, premedicine, and preveterinary science), SOCIAL SCIENCE (biblical studies, economics, history, home economics, international studies, ministries, prelaw, psychology, religion, social work, and sociology). Natural sciences is the strongest academically. Business has the largest enrollment.

Required: To graduate, all students must have a minimum 2.0 GPA and complete 126 semester hours, including 48 in the major. The required core curriculum of 52 semester hours includes 12 hours of history/literature, 10 of Bible/religious studies, 6 each in communication, mathematics/language, natural science, and social science, and 4 each in music/art and health/physical education.

Special: There is a 3–2 engineering degree with the University of Portland, Oregon State University, and Washington University in St. Louis, and cross-registration through the Oregon Independent College Association. George Fox also offers internships with area companies, study abroad in Kenya, England, Costa Rica, Russia, and Egypt, and a Washington semester through the Christian College Coalition. Work-study programs with the college, B.A.-B.S. degrees in all majors, dual and student-designed interdisciplinary majors, and pass/fail options in upper-division courses outside of the major also are offered. There is a freshman honors program on campus

Faculty/Classroom: Eighty percent of faculty are male; 20%, female. All teach undergraduates. The average class size in an introductory lecture is 50; in a laboratory, 20; and in a regular course offering, 20.

Admissions: About 87% of the 1993–94 applicants were accepted. The SAT scores for the 1993–94 freshman class were as follows: Verbal—59% below 500, 32% between 500 and 599, 8% between 600 and 700, and 1% above 700; Math—46% below 500, 30% between 500 and 599, 19% between 600 and 700, and 3% above 700. There were 3 National Merit semifinalists, and 1 finalist.

Requirements: The SAT I, with a recommended composite score of 800, or the ACT is required. Applicants need 16 academic credits or 14 Carnegie units, with 4 units of English and 2 units each of a foreign language, mathematics, science, and social studies recommended. An essay is required; a portfolio, audition, and interview are recommended in certain majors. AP and CLEP credits are accepted.

Procedure: Freshmen are admitted fall and spring. Entrance exams should be taken in fall or winter. Applications should be filed by June 1 for fall entry and December 1 for spring entry, along with an appli-

cation fee of $30. Notification is sent on a rolling basis. There are early admissions and deferred admissions plans.

Transfer: About 132 transfer students enrolled in 1993–94. Transfers must have a minimum 2.3 GPA and 14 earned credits from their previous college. A personal recommendation is required. A total of 20 semester hours out of 126 must be completed at George Fox.

Visiting: There are regularly scheduled orientations for prospective students. There are guides for informal visits and visitors may sit in on classes and stay overnight at the school. To arrange for a visit, contact Julie Manley, Office of Admissions, at (503) 538–8383, ext. 337.

Financial Aid: In 1993–94, 92% of all current freshmen and 88% of continuing students received some form of financial aid. About 60% of all students received need-based aid. The average freshman award was $6600. Of that total, scholarships or need-based grants averaged $2490 ($11,000 maximum); loans averaged $2400 ($4500 maximum); and work contracts averaged $1300 ($1700 maximum). Fifty-two percent of undergraduate students work part-time. Average earnings from campus work for the school year are $1800. The average financial indebtedness of the 1992–93 graduate was $7790. George Fox is a member of CSS. The FAF, FFS or SFS, and the FAFSA are required. The deadline for financial aid applications is August 1.

International Students: There are currently 52 international students enrolled. The school actively recruits these students.

Computers: The college provides computer facilities for student use. The mainframe is a DEC PDP 11. Computers Across the Curriculum provides each entering freshman with a computer to use while a student and to keep after graduation. Students also have access to a full computer resource area, including color monitors and printers and a training center. Those enrolled in computer programming courses may access the system. There are no time limits on using the system. The fees are $10 per semester.

Graduates: In 1992–93, 351 bachelor's degrees were awarded. The most popular majors among graduates were human resources (49%), education (12%), and business (9%). Within an average freshman class, 1% graduate in 3 years, 42% in 4 years, 1% in 5 years, and 1% in 6 years. Some 50 companies recruited on campus in 1992–93.

Admissions Contact: Randy Comfort, Director of Admissions.

LEWIS AND CLARK COLLEGE   B-1

Portland, OR 97219–7899   (503) 768–7040; (800) 444–4111

Full-time: 778 men, 961 women	Faculty: 110; IIA, av$
Part-time: 30 men, 26 women	Ph.D.s: 96%
Graduate: 596 men, 825 women	Student/Faculty: 16 to 1
Year: semesters	Tuition: $15,051
Application Deadline: February 1	Room & Board: $4929
Freshman Class: 2774 applied, 2092 accepted, 482 enrolled	
SAT I or ACT: required	**VERY COMPETITIVE**

Lewis and Clark College, founded in 1867, is an independent coeducational liberal arts and sciences institution with an international emphasis. There are 2 graduate schools. In addition to regional accreditation, the college has baccalaureate program accreditation with NASM and NCATE. The library contains 270,000 volumes, 222,000 microform items, and 12,000 audiovisual forms, and subscribes to 1880 periodicals. Computerized library sources and services include interlibrary loans and database searching. Special learning facilities include a learning resource center, art gallery, radio station, research astronomical observatory, and language laboratory. The 130-acre campus is in a suburban area 6 miles south of downtown Portland. Including residence halls, there are 30 buildings on campus.

Student Life: About 68% of undergraduates are from out-of-state, mostly the West. Students come from 47 states, 54 foreign countries, and Canada. Seventy-four percent are from public schools; 26% from private. Eighty-one percent are white. The average age of freshmen is 18; all undergraduates, 20. Seven percent drop out by the end of their first year; 67% remain to graduate.

Housing: A total of 939 students can be accommodated in college housing. College-sponsored living facilities include single-sex and coed dormitories. In addition there are language, wellness, community service, and international awareness floors. On-campus housing is guaranteed for all 4 years. Upperclassmen may keep cars on campus.

Activities: There is 1 national fraternity. There are no sororities on campus. There are about 55 groups on campus, including art, band, choir, chorale, chorus, computers, dance, drama, ethnic, film, gay, honors, international, jazz band, literary magazine, newspaper, opera, orchestra, pep band, photography, political, professional, radio and TV, religious, social, social service, student government, and yearbook. Popular campus events include International Students Week, Black History Month, Cinco de Mayo, Gender Studies Symposium, International Affairs Symposium, and Otto Sack Day.

Sports: There are 8 intercollegiate sports for men and 7 for women, and 11 coed intramural sports. Athletic and recreation facilities include indoor and outdoor swimming pools, 6 tennis courts, racquetball/squash courts, a football field, basketball/volleyball courts, softball and baseball fields, a track, and weight and aerobics rooms. There is also a 3700-seat stadium and a 2200-seat auditorium/ arena. The 2200-seat indoor gymnasium is the practice site of the NBA Portland Trailblazers.

Disabled Students: Thirty-two percent of the campus is accessible to disabled students. The following facilities are available: wheelchair ramps, elevators, special parking, specially equipped rest rooms, special class scheduling, lowered drinking fountains, and lowered telephones.

Services: In addition to many counseling and information services, tutoring is available in every subject. In addition, there is a reader service for the blind.

Campus Safety and Security: Campus safety and security measures include 24-hour foot and vehicle patrol, self defense education, escort service, and shuttle buses. In addition, there are informal discussions, pamphlets, posters, and films, emergency telephones, lighted pathways and sidewalks, and card key locks in all residence halls.

Programs of Study: The college awards the B.A. degree. Master's degrees also are awarded. Bachelor's degrees are awarded in BIOLOGICAL SCIENCE (biochemistry and biology/biological science), BUSINESS (business administration and management), COMMUNICATIONS AND THE ARTS (art history and appreciation, communications, dramatic arts, English, fine arts, French, German, languages, music, and studio art), COMPUTER AND PHYSICAL SCIENCE (chemistry, computer mathematics, computer science, mathematics, and physics), EDUCATION (social studies), SOCIAL SCIENCE (anthropology/sociology, economics, Hispanic American studies, history, interdisciplinary studies, international relations, philosophy, political science/government, psychology, religion, and sociology/ anthropology). Business, international affairs, English, psychology, biology, communications, and sociology/anthropology have the largest enrollments.

Required: To graduate, students must complete a total of 128 semester credit hours with a 2.0 GPA. A third of this total generally falls in the major program, a third in electives, and a third in the core program, which includes a required freshman course, 2 international studies courses, and requirements in foreign language, quantitative reasoning, and natural science. A course in physical education is also required.

Special: The college offers B.A. degrees in 26 majors, internships, one of the oldest and largest study abroad programs in the United States encompassing 57 countries, semesters in Washington and New York City, work-study programs, and dual and student-designed majors. A 3–2 engineering degree may be arranged with Columbia and Washington Universities, the University of Southern California, and the Oregon Graduate Institute. There is 1 national honor society on campus. Sixteen departments have honors programs.

Faculty/Classroom: Seventy percent of faculty are male; 30%, female. All both teach and do research. No introductory courses are taught by graduate students. The average class size in an introductory lecture is 23; in a laboratory, 12; and in a regular course offering, 18.

Admissions: About 75% of the 1993–94 applicants were accepted. The SAT scores for the 1993–94 freshman class were as follows: Verbal—29% below 500, 46% between 500 and 599, 21% between 600 and 700, and 4% above 700; Math—15% below 500, 45% between 500 and 599, 31% between 600 and 700, and 9% above 700. The ACT scores were 8% below 21, 18% between 21 and 23, 34% between 24 and 26, 22% between 27 and 28, and 18% above 28. About 56% of the current freshmen were in the top fifth of their class; 81% were in the top two fifths. There were 8 National Merit finalists. About 25 freshmen graduated first in their class.

Requirements: The SAT I or ACT is required. A GED may be accepted. It is recommended that applicants have 4 years each of English and mathematics, 3 to 4 years of science, 2 years of history and social studies, and 1 year of art and music. An essay is required and an interview recommended. The college also admits exceptional students through the Portfolio Path option. This allows students to create a portfolio of materials they feel best demonstrates the strengths of their academic program. AP credits are accepted. Important factors used in the admissions decision are advanced placement or honor courses, leadership record, recommendations by school officials, evidence of special talent, and extracurricular activities record.

Procedure: Freshmen are admitted fall and spring. Entrance exams should be taken during the spring of the junior year and the fall of the senior year. Early decision applications should be filed by November 15 and early action applications by December 15; regular applications, by February 1 for fall entry, December 1 for spring entry, and May 1 for summer entry, along with an application fee of $40. Notification of early decision is sent December 15 and early action, January 15; regular decision, April 1. There are early decision, early admissions, and deferred admissions plans. About 16 early decision candidates were accepted for the 1993–94 class. A waiting list is an active part of the admissions procedure, with about 10% of applicants on the list.

Transfer: A total of 92 transfer students enrolled in 1993–94. Applicants must submit high school and college transcripts, 2 essays, and SAT I or ACT scores, if they have fewer than 2 years of transferrable credit. A total of 60 credits out of 128 must be completed at the college.

Visiting: There are regularly scheduled orientations for prospective students, including a campus tour, class visits, interviews, special interest appointments, and an overnight stay in a residence hall. There are guides for informal visits and visitors may sit in on classes. To arrange for a visit, contact Laura Mathewson, Office of Admissions at (503) 768–7040 or (800) 444–4111.

Financial Aid: In 1993–94, 70% of all current freshmen and 71% of continuing students received some form of financial aid. About 57% of freshmen and 49% of continuing students received need-based aid. The average freshman award was $13,864. Of that total, scholarships or need-based grants averaged $9327 ($19,521 maximum); loans averaged $3213 ($4125 maximum); and work contracts averaged $1324 ($1375 maximum). Seventy-two percent of undergraduate students work part-time. Average earnings from campus work for the school year are $1505. The average financial indebtedness of the 1992–93 graduate was $14,890. The college is a member of CSS. The college's own financial statement and FAFSA are required. The deadline for financial aid applications is February 15.

International Students: There are currently 134 international students enrolled. The school actively recruits these students. They must take the TOEFL and achieve a minimum score of 550.

Computers: The college provides computer facilities for student use. The mainframes are a Sun 490 and a Sequent. The mainframes are networked with 5 DEC 3100 and 5000/200 workstations and 20 parallel processors. They run the UNIX operating system and are interconnected through Ethernet on campus with the library, residence halls, and academic buildings. Macintosh and IBM clusters are available 24 hours per day in the library and in residence halls. All students may access the system. There are no time limits on using the system and no fees.

Graduates: In 1992–93, 425 bachelor's degrees were awarded. The most popular majors among graduates were international affairs (11%), sociology/anthropolgy (10%), and psychology (10%). Within an average freshman class, 62% graduate in 4 years and 67% in 5 years. Some 31 companies recruited on campus in 1992–93. In the 1992 graduating class, 12% of the graduates were enrolled in graduate school within 6 months of graduation; 47% had found employment.

Admissions Contact: Michael B. Sexton, Dean of Admissions and Student Financial Services.

LINFIELD COLLEGE
McMinnville, OR 97128

B-2

(503) 472–4121, ext. 213

Full-time: 675 men, 886 women	Faculty: 122; IIB, -$
Part-time: 30 men, 41 women	Ph.Ds: 91%
Graduate: 18 men, 32 women	Student/Faculty: 13 to 1
Year: 4–1–4, summer session	Tuition: $12,700
Application Deadline: February 15	Room & Board: $3970
Freshman Class: 1561 applied, 1179 accepted, 458 enrolled	
SAT I: 495/556	ACT: 25 **VERY COMPETITIVE**

Linfield College, founded in 1849, is a private, coeducational liberal arts school affiliated with the American Baptist Church. In addition to regional accreditation, Linfield has baccalaureate program accreditation with NASM, NCATE, and NLN. The library contains 128,705 volumes, 116,363 microform items, and 6149 audiovisual forms, and subscribes to 1029 periodicals. Computerized library sources and services include the card catalog, interlibrary loans, and database searching. Special learning facilities include a learning resource center, art gallery, radio station, TV station, and an observatory. The 100-acre campus is in a small town 38 miles southwest of Portland. Including residence halls, there are 43 buildings on campus.

Student Life: About 63% of undergraduates are from Oregon. Students come from 21 states, 27 foreign countries, and Canada. Eighty-six percent are from public schools; 14% from private. Eighty-six percent are white. Forty-seven percent are Protestant; 23% Catholic; 17% claim no religious affiliation. The average age of freshmen is 18; all undergraduates, 20.9.

Housing: A total of 1036 students can be accommodated in college housing. College-sponsored living facilities include single-sex and coed dormitories, on-campus apartments, off-campus apartments, and fraternity houses. In addition, there are special interest houses. On-campus housing is guaranteed for all 4 years. Seventy percent of students live on campus; of those, 80% remain on campus on weekends. All students may keep cars on campus.

Activities: About 30% of men belong to 1 local and 3 national fraternities; about 30% of women belong to 1 local and 2 national sororities. There are 61 groups on campus, including art, band, cheerleading, chess, choir, chorale, chorus, computers, dance, drama, ethnic, honors, international, jazz band, literary magazine, musical theater,

newspaper, orchestra, pep band, photography, political, professional, radio and TV, religious, social, social service, student government, symphony, and yearbook. Popular campus events include Cultural Awareness Week, Oregon Nobel Laureate Symposium, Hawaiian Luau, Christmas Choral Concert, Parents Weekend, Homecoming, Lecture Series, January Term Special Events, and International Dinners.

Sports: There are 9 intercollegiate sports for men and 7 for women, and 8 intramural sports for men and 8 for women. Athletic and recreation facilities include a complex with a 2200-seat main gymnasium, 3 full-length basketball courts, a 25-yard swimming pool, racquetball courts, and a 3200-square foot weight room. There also are soccer and football fields, all-weather track, and additional basketball, tennis, and racquetball courts.

Disabled Students: Fifty percent of the campus is accessible to disabled students. The following facilities are available: wheelchair ramps, elevators, special parking, specially equipped rest rooms, special class scheduling, and lowered telephones.

Services: In addition to many counseling and information services, tutoring is available in every subject. In addition, there is a reader service for the blind, and remedial math, reading, and writing. There is also a writing laboratory.

Campus Safety and Security: Campus safety and security measures include 24-hour foot and vehicle patrol, escort service, informal discussions, and pamphlets, posters, and films. In addition, there are lighted pathways and sidewalks.

Programs of Study: Linfield awards the B.A., B.S., and B.S.N. degrees. Master's degrees also are awarded. Bachelor's degrees are awarded in BIOLOGICAL SCIENCE (biology/biological science), BUSINESS (accounting, banking and finance, business administration and management, business economics, and international business management), COMMUNICATIONS AND THE ARTS (arts administration/management, communications, creative writing, dramatic arts, English, fine arts, French, German, music, and Spanish), COMPUTER AND PHYSICAL SCIENCE (chemistry, computer science, mathematics, physics, and science), EDUCATION (art, early childhood, elementary, foreign languages, health, middle school, music, physical, science, and secondary), ENGINEERING AND ENVIRONMENTAL DESIGN (environmental science), HEALTH PROFESSIONS (medical laboratory technology, nursing, predentistry, and premedicine), SOCIAL SCIENCE (anthropology, economics, history, humanities, liberal arts/general studies, philosophy, political science/government, prelaw, psychology, religion, and sociology). Political science, biology, chemistry, modern languages, physics, computer science, mathematics, and history are the strongest academically. Economics/mathematics, communications, psychology, and education have the largest enrollments.

Required: To graduate, students must have a 2.0 GPA and complete 125 credit hours, including 35 to 45 in the major. Distribution requirements include courses from physical and biological science, literature, fine arts, religion or philosophy, culture, and social behavior. Students must also take courses in Western culture and effective writing.

Special: Students may study abroad in 6 countries. During the January term, programs may be arranged in such areas as New York City or New Zealand. Internships and work-study programs, a B.A.-B.S. degree in environmental science, accelerated degree programs, a liberal studies degree, dual and student-designed majors, nondegree study for special students, and pass/fail options are also offered. Credit for life experience may be obtained by written portfolio. A 3–2 engineering degree may be arranged with Oregon State and Washington State universities, and the University of Southern California. There is also a 3–2 forestry degree. There is a freshman honors program on campus, as well as 7 national honor societies. Fifteen departments have honors programs.

Faculty/Classroom: Sixty-one percent of faculty are male; 39%, female. All teach undergraduates and do research. No introductory courses are taught by graduate students. The average class size in an introductory lecture is 33; in a laboratory, 20; and in a regular course offering, 12.

Admissions: About 76% of the 1993–94 applicants were accepted. The SAT scores for the 1993–94 freshman class were as follows: Verbal—54% below 500, 30% between 500 and 599, 11% between 600 and 700, and 4% above 700; Math—24% below 500, 43% between 500 and 599, 26% between 600 and 700, and 7% above 700. The ACT scores were 7% below 21, 34% between 21 and 23, 23% between 24 and 26, 16% between 27 and 28, and 21% above 28. About 64% of the current freshmen were in the top fifth of their class; 91% were in the top two fifths. There were 11 National Merit finalists. About 35 freshmen graduated first in their class.

Requirements: Linfield requires applicants to be in the upper 40% of their class. A minimum GPA of 2.9 is required. The SAT I or ACT is required. Applicants must have 14 to 17 academic credits, including a recommended 4 years each in English and mathematics, 3 years in science, and 2 years each in foreign language, history, and

social studies. An essay is required and an interview is recommended. The GED is accepted. AP and CLEP credits are accepted. Important factors used in the admissions decision are recommendations by school officials, geographic diversity, evidence of special talent, advanced placement or honor courses, and extracurricular activities record.

Procedure: Freshmen are admitted fall and spring. Entrance exams should be taken during the fall of the senior year. Early decision applications should be filed by December 1; regular applications, by February 15 for fall entry and November 15 for spring entry, along with an application fee of $30. Notification of early decision is sent January 15; regular decision, April 1. There are early decision, early admissions, and deferred admissions plans. A waiting list is an active part of the admissions procedure, with about 2% of applicants on the list.

Transfer: A total of 55 transfer students enrolled in 1993–94. Applicants must have a 2.0 GPA from an accredited institution. An interview is also recommended. A total of 30 credits out of 125 must be completed at Linfield.

Visiting: There are regularly scheduled orientations for prospective students. Individual visits are encouraged and include tours, class visits, interviews, and overnight stays. There are guides for informal visits and visitors may sit in on classes and stay overnight at the school. To arrange for a visit, contact the Admissions Office at (503) 472–4121, ext. 213.

Financial Aid: In 1993–94, 95% of all current freshmen and 78% of continuing students received some form of financial aid. About 75% of freshmen and 65% of continuing students received need-based aid. The average freshman award was $9579. Of that total, scholarships or need-based grants averaged $5684 ($12,510 maximum); loans averaged $2198 ($5500 maximum); and work contracts averaged $1069 ($2000 maximum). Sixty-two percent of undergraduate students work part-time. Average earnings from campus work for the school year are $704. The average financial indebtedness of the 1992–93 graduate was $9874. Linfield is a member of CSS. The FAF, FFS, or SFS is required. The deadline for financial aid applications is February 1.

International Students: There are currently 83 international students enrolled. The school actively recruits these students. They must take the TOEFL and achieve a minimum score of 450.

Computers: The college provides computer facilities for student use. The mainframes are 2 Sequent S-27s. Programming classes in UNIX may be accessed on any of 30 terminals located around campus. In addition, an extensive microcomputer laboratory has Apple Macintosh and IBM computers connected to the mainframe. Students can also use approximately 60 networked micro-computers in 3 public, open access laboratories and several networked departmental laboratories. There is also connection to the Internet, file servers, and laser and dot matrix printers. All students may access the system. There are no time limits on using the system and no fees.

Graduates: In a recent year, 428 bachelor's degrees were awarded. The most popular majors among graduates were economics and business (37%), liberal arts and sciences (13%), and education (12%). Within an average freshman class, 7% graduate in 3 years, 52% in 4 years, 58% in 5 years, and 62% in 6 years. Some 34 companies recruited on campus in a recent year. In a recent graduating class, 11% of the men and 12% of the women were enrolled in graduate school within 6 months of graduation; 39% of the men and 38% of the women had found employment.

Admissions Contact: Dean of Admissions.

MARYLHURST COLLEGE
B-1

Marylhurst, OR 97036   (503) 636–8141, ext. 330; (800) 634–9982

Full-time: 57 men, 175 women	Faculty: 20
Part-time: 168 men, 635 women	Ph.D.s: 25%
Graduate: 64 men, 84 women	Student/Faculty: 12 to 1
Year: quarters, summer session	Tuition: $6486
Application Deadline: open	Room & Board: n/app
Freshman Class: n/av	
SAT I or ACT: not required	**NONCOMPETITIVE**

Marylhurst College, founded in 1893, is a private liberal arts institution affiliated with the Roman Catholic Church. The primary emphasis is on innovative programs such as the Weekend College for adult students. There are 3 graduate schools. In addition to regional accreditation, Marylhurst has baccalaureate program accreditation with NASM. The library contains 100,000 volumes, 638 microform items, and 926 audiovisual forms, and subscribes to 400 periodicals. Computerized library sources and services include the card catalog, interlibrary loans, and database searching. Special learning facilities include an art gallery. The 68-acre campus is in a suburban area 10 miles south of Portland. There are 14 buildings on campus.

Student Life: About 98% of undergraduates are from Oregon. Students come from 3 states, 6 foreign countries, and Canada. Eighty-five percent are white. The average age of freshmen is 34; all undergraduates, 38.

Housing: There are no residence halls; all students commute. Alcohol is not permitted. All students may keep cars on campus.

Activities: There are no fraternities or sororities on campus. There are 4 groups on campus, including art, chorale, orchestra, professional, social service, and symphony.

Sports: There is no sports program at Marylhurst.

Disabled Students: Seventy-five percent of the campus is accessible to disabled students. The following facilities are available: wheelchair ramps, elevators, special parking, and specially equipped rest rooms.

Services: In addition to many counseling and information services, tutoring is available in some subjects, including mathematics and writing. There is also a reader service for the blind.

Campus Safety and Security: Campus safety and security measures include 24-hour foot and vehicle patrol, self-defense education, escort service, and lighted pathways and sidewalks.

Programs of Study: Marylhurst awards the B.A., B.S., B.F.A., and B.M. degrees. Master's degrees are also awarded. Bachelor's degrees are awarded in BUSINESS (management science), COMMUNICATIONS AND THE ARTS (art, communications, fine arts, and music), COMPUTER AND PHYSICAL SCIENCE (science), SOCIAL SCIENCE (humanities, interdisciplinary studies, ministries, and social science). Art, management, social science, and communication have the largest enrollments.

Required: To graduate, students must have a minimum 2.0 GPA and complete 180 quarter credits, including 60 to 129 in the major. Distribution requirements vary according to major but include 12 credits each (10 for the B.M. degree) in communications, humanities, science/mathematics, and social science. An interdisciplinary seminar is also required, as are internships in some majors.

Special: Cross-registration may be arranged through the Oregon Independent College Association. Marylhurst offers work-study programs, B.A.-B.S. degrees, internships, an interdisciplinary studies degree, dual and student-designed majors, accelerated degree programs in all majors, credit for life experience, nondegree study, and pass/fail options.

Faculty/Classroom: Fifty percent of faculty are male; 50%, female. All teach undergraduates. No introductory courses are taught by graduate students. The average class size in an introductory lecture is 15 and in a regular course offering, 15.

Requirements: No entrance examinations are required. Applicants must be high school graduates or have the GED. Marylhurst accepts all who apply. CLEP credit is accepted.

Procedure: Freshmen are admitted to all sessions. Application deadlines are open. Application fee is $77. The college accepts all applicants. Notification is sent on a rolling basis.

Transfer: Almost all students are returning adults who have transferred prior college credit. Grades of C or better transfer for credit. A total of 45 quarter credits out of 180 must be completed at Marylhurst.

Visiting: There are regularly scheduled orientations for prospective students, including addressing registration and financial aid issues; academic advising; and use of the library, cafeteria, and bookstore. There are guides for informal visits and visitors may sit in on classes and stay overnight at the school. To arrange for a visit, contact the Dean of Student Services at (503) 636–8141, ext. 330.

Financial Aid: In a recent year, 65% of all students received need-based aid. The average freshman award was $9200. Of that total, loans averaged $2625 ($6625 maximum); and work contracts averaged $1500 ($3000 maximum). Eighty-nine percent of undergraduate students work part-time. Average earnings from campus work for the school year are $2000. The average financial indebtedness of the 1992–93 graduate was $13,700. The FAFSA financial statement is required.

International Students: There are currently 25 international students enrolled. They must take the TOEFL and achieve a minimum score of 550.

Computers: The college provides computer facilities for student use. Students may use independent PCs available in the computer center. There are no time limits on using the system and no fees.

Graduates: In a recent year, 130 bachelor's degrees were awarded. The most popular majors among graduates were management (25%), communication (22%), and social science (16%).

Admissions Contact: Ellen Sawyer and Janet Cleveland, Admissions Counselors.

OREGON INSTITUTE OF TECHNOLOGY
Klamath Falls, OR 97601–8801

B-4
(503) 885–1150
(800) 343–6653 (out-of-state)

Full-time: 1100 men, 800 women	Faculty: 155; IIB, av$
Part-time: 300 men, 300 women	Ph.D.s: 19%
Graduate: none	Student/Faculty: 12 to 1
Year: terms, summer session	Tuition: $2595 ($6678)
Application Deadline: July 1	Room & Board: $3390

Freshman Class: 1237 applied, 1203 accepted, 908 enrolled
SAT I Verbal/Math: 447/482   **COMPETITIVE**

The Oregon Institute of Technology, founded in 1947, is the polytechnical arm of the Oregon State System of Higher Education. There are 2 undergraduate schools. In addition to regional accreditation, Oregon Tech has baccalaureate program accreditation with ABET and NLN. The library contains 99,757 volumes, 24,230 microform items, and 2236 audiovisual forms, and subscribes to 1403 periodicals. Special learning facilities include a learning resource center, art gallery, and radio station. The 173-acre campus is in a small town in South Central Oregon, 60 miles east of Medford. Including residence halls, there are 12 buildings on campus.

Student Life: About 93% of undergraduates are from Oregon. Students come from 19 states, 15 foreign countries, and Canada. Ninety-five percent are from public schools; 5% from private. Eighty-nine percent are white. The average age of all undergraduates is 26. Twenty-six percent drop out by the end of their first year; 29% remain to graduate.

Housing: A total of 556 students can be accommodated in college housing. College-sponsored living facilities include coed dormitories, fraternity houses, and sorority houses. On-campus housing is guaranteed for all 4 years. Seventy-five percent of students commute. Alcohol is not permitted. All students may keep cars on campus.

Activities: About 3% of men belong to 1 local and 1 national fraternity; about 3% of women belong to 1 local and 1 national sorority. There are 37 groups on campus, including cheerleading, computers, ethnic, gay, honors, international, newspaper, pep band, political, professional, radio and TV, religious, social, social service, and student government. Popular campus events include Tech Challenge, Family Weekend Tech Fest, Twist, and a skills contest for business students.

Sports: There is 1 intercollegiate sport for men and 1 for women, and 3 intramural sports for men and 2 for women. Athletic and recreation facilities include a 3500-seat stadium, a 2250-seat gymnasium, football, baseball, and softball fields, free weights and aerobic areas, an indoor pool, a track, and tennis, volleyball, and badminton courts.

Disabled Students: Ninety percent of the campus is accessible to disabled students. The following facilities are available: wheelchair ramps, elevators, special parking, and specially equipped rest rooms.

Services: In addition to many counseling and information services, tutoring is available in every subject. There is remedial math, reading, and writing.

Campus Safety and Security: Campus safety and security measures include escort service and lighted pathways and sidewalks.

Programs of Study: Oregon Tech awards the B.S. degree. Associate degrees also are awarded. Bachelor's degrees are awarded in COMPUTER AND PHYSICAL SCIENCE (information technology management), ENGINEERING AND ENVIRONMENTAL DESIGN (civil engineering technology, computer engineering technology, electronics engineering technology, industrial management, laser optical engineering, manufacturing technology, mechanical engineering technology, software engineering technology, and surveying), HEALTH PROFESSIONS (dental hygiene, medical imaging technology, and nursing). Engineering technology programs have the largest enrollment.

Required: General education requirements include 9 hours each in communication, business, and humanities, and 12 hours in social science. Students must also take 9 hours in English composition and technical report writing. Completion of about 200 quarter hours, with a minimum GPA of 2.0, is required to graduate.

Special: Co-op programs are available in all engineering technologies. There are 2 national honor societies on campus.

Faculty/Classroom: Seventy-eight percent of faculty are male; 22%, female. All teach undergraduates. The average class size in an introductory lecture is 20 and in a laboratory, 20.

Admissions: About 97% of the 1993–94 applicants were accepted. The SAT scores for the 1993–94 freshman class were as follows: Verbal—79% below 500, 17% between 500 and 599, and 4% between 600 and 700; Math—60% below 500, 28% between 500 and 599, 10% between 600 and 700, and 2% above 700. About 18% of the current freshmen were in the top fifth of their class; 56% were in the top two fifths.

Requirements: A minimum GPA of 2.5 is required. The SAT I or ACT is recommended, with a suggested composite score of 890 on the SAT I or 21 on the ACT. Applicants must have 14 academic units,

including 4 years of English, 3 years each in mathematics and social studies, and 2 years each in science, history, and other college preparatory classes such as foreign language or computer science. The GED is accepted. AP and CLEP credits are accepted. Advanced placement or honor courses is an important factor used in the admission decision.

Procedure: Freshmen are admitted to all sessions. The SAT I/ACT should be taken during the senior year, and placement tests just prior to registration. Early decision applications should be filed by March 1; regular applications, by July 1 for fall entry, November 15 for winter entry, February 15 for spring entry, and June 1 for summer entry, along with an application fee of $50. Notification of early decision is sent in March; regular decision, July. There are early decision and early admissions plans. About 105 early decision candidates were accepted for the 1993–94 class.

Transfer: About 247 transfer students enrolled in 1993–94. Applicants must have a minimum GPA of 2.0 and at least 24 credit hours. An associate degree is recommended. A total of 55 quarter hours out of about 200 must be completed at Oregon Tech.

Visiting: There are regularly scheduled orientations for prospective students. There are guides for informal visits, and visitors may sit in on classes and stay overnight at the school. To arrange for a visit, contact the Admissions Office at (503) 885–1150, (800) 422–2017 (in-state), or (800) 343–6653 (out-of-state).

Financial Aid: In 1993–94 80% of all current freshmen and 85% of continuing students received some form of financial aid. About 77% of freshmen and 74% of continuing students received need-based aid. Oregon Tech is a member of CSS. The FAF and the college's own financial statement are required. The deadline for financial aid applications is May 1.

International Students: There are currently 37 international students enrolled. The school actively recruits these students. They must take the TOEFL and achieve a minimum score of 520.

Computers: The college provides computer facilities for student use. The mainframes are a Prime EXL-316, a DEC PDP 11/44, and a Sequent. More than 700 terminals and IBM-compatible microcomputers are available on campus. Modem access is available to students off campus. All students may access the system. It may be used 24 hours daily during the last 2 weeks of the quarter and 18 hours daily otherwise. There are no time limits on using the system and no fees.

Graduates: In 1992–93 607 bachelor's degrees were awarded. The most popular majors among graduates were industrial management (12%), electronics engineering technology (11%), and manufacturing engineering technology (9%). Some 32 companies recruited on campus in 1992–93.

Admissions Contact: Barbara Kratochvil, Director of Admissions.

OREGON STATE HIGHER EDUCATION SYSTEM

The Oregon State Higher Education system, established in 1929, is a public system in Oregon. It is governed by the Oregon State Board of Higher Education, whose chief administrator is the chancellor. The primary goals of the system include teaching at the undergraduate, graduate, and professional levels, both basic and applied research, and public service to the state and nation. The main priorities are to insure that students are liberally educated, to advance understanding in the areas of arts and sciences, and to be responsive to the particular circumstances of the people of Oregon. The total enrollment of all 8 campuses exceeds 68,000, with nearly 4000 faculty members. Altogether, there are 182 baccalaureate, 116 master's, and 63 doctoral programs offered in the system. Four-year campuses are located in Eugene, Corvallis, Portland, La Grande, Ashland, Klamath Falls, and Monmouth. Profiles of those campuses are included in this chapter.

OREGON STATE UNIVERSITY
Corvallis, OR 97331–2106

B-2
(503) 737–4411

Full-time: 10,580 men and women	Faculty: 2142; I, --$
Part-time: 850 men and women	Ph.D.s: 91%
Graduate: 2906 men and women	Student/Faculty: 5 to 1
Year: quarters, summer session	Tuition: $2877 ($7974)
Application Deadline: March 1	Room & Board: $3298

Freshman Class: 4966 applied, 4331 accepted, 1636 enrolled
SAT I Verbal/Math: 440/520   ACT: 22   **COMPETITIVE**

Oregon State University, founded in 1868, is the oldest institution in the Oregon state system, offering liberal arts and preprofessional programs. There are 10 undergraduate and 12 graduate schools. In addition to regional accreditation, OSU has baccalaureate program accreditation with AACSB, ABET, ACCE, ACEJMC, ACPE, AHEA, NASM, NCATE, and SAF. The 4 libraries contain 1.2 million volumes, 1.7 million microform items, and 13,515 audiovisual forms, and subscribe to 19,034 periodicals. Computerized library sources and services include the card catalog. Special learning facilities include an art gallery, a natural history museum, a radio station, a TV station, an arboretum, a wave research laboratory, a research farm, a research vessel, and the Linus Pauling Collection. The 400-acre campus is in

a small town 80 miles south of Portland. Including residence halls, there are 201 buildings on campus.

Student Life: About 77% of undergraduates are from Oregon. Students come from 50 states and 98 foreign countries. Ninety-five percent are from public schools; 5% from private. Eighty-nine percent are white. Twenty-four percent drop out by the end of their first year; 43% remain to graduate.

Housing: A total of 6421 students can be accommodated in college housing. College-sponsored living facilities include dormitories and married-student housing. In addition, there are special interest houses and cooperative houses. On-campus housing is guaranteed for the freshman year only and is available on a first-come, first-served basis. All students may keep cars on campus.

Activities: About 14% of men belong to 27 national fraternities; about 10% of women belong to 15 national sororities. There are 350 groups on campus, including art, band, cheerleading, chess, choir, chorale, chorus, computers, dance, drama, drill team, drum and bugle corps, ethnic, film, gay, honors, international, jazz band, literary magazine, marching band, musical theater, newspaper, orchestra, pep band, photography, political, professional, radio and TV, religious, social, social service, student government, symphony, and yearbook. Popular campus events include Homecoming, Renaissance Fair, and Native American Powwow.

Sports: There are 7 intercollegiate sports for men and 8 for women, and 19 intramural sports for men and 17 for women. Athletic and recreation facilities include 2 fitness centers, a 10,400-seat gymnasium, a 40,000-seat stadium, indoor and outdoor recreation centers, weight and exercise rooms, bowling alleys, and numerous courts and playing fields.

Disabled Students: Ninety-two percent of the campus is accessible to disabled students. The following facilities are available: wheelchair ramps, elevators, special parking, specially equipped rest rooms, special class scheduling, lowered drinking fountains and telephones. Note-takers and interpreters for the deaf, and visual-aid equipment and a reader service for the blind are also available.

Services: In addition to many counseling and information services, tutoring is available in most subjects, including chemistry, computer science, mathematics, psychology and counseling, and physics. In addition, there is remedial math, reading, and writing. Facilites include a communication skills center and a mathematical sciences learning center.

Programs of Study: OSU awards the B.A., B.S., and B.F.A. degrees. Master's and doctoral degrees also are awarded. Bachelor's degrees are awarded in AGRICULTURE (agricultural business management, agricultural economics, agriculture, animal science, fishing and fisheries, forest engineering, forestry and related sciences, forestry production and processing, horticulture, poultry science, range/farm management, and soil science), BIOLOGICAL SCIENCE (biochemistry, biology/biological science, biophysics, botany, entomology, microbiology, plant pathology, wildlife biology, and zoology), BUSINESS (accounting, banking and finance, business administration and management, hotel/motel and restaurant management, international business management, management information systems, management science, marketing management, and marketing/retailing/merchandising), COMMUNICATIONS AND THE ARTS (communications, dramatic arts, English, French, German, journalism, music, Spanish, speech/debate/rhetoric, and visual and performing arts), COMPUTER AND PHYSICAL SCIENCE (atmospheric sciences and meteorology, chemistry, computer science, geology, mathematics, physics, and science), EDUCATION (health), ENGINEERING AND ENVIRONMENTAL DESIGN (chemical engineering, civil engineering, computer engineering, construction management, engineering physics, industrial engineering technology, landscape architecture/design, mechanical engineering, nuclear engineering, and urban design), HEALTH PROFESSIONS (health, health care administration, medical laboratory technology, nursing, occupational therapy, pharmacy, physical therapy, predentistry, and premedicine), SOCIAL SCIENCE (American studies, anthropology, consumer services, dietetics, economics, family/consumer studies, fashion design and technology, food science, geography, history, home economics, human development, liberal arts/general studies, philosophy, political science/government, psychology, religion, sociology, and textiles and clothing). Engineering, biochemistry, and forestry are the strongest academically. Business, liberal arts, mechanical engineering, and psychology have the largest enrollments.

Required: To graduate, students must complete at least 192 quarter credits with a GPA of 2.0. The required core curriculum includes a total of 37 credits in writing and communications, mathematics, humanities and social studies, natural sciences, and fitness. Students must take a writing-intensive course in their major field and meet additional distribution requirements.

Special: OSU offers cooperative veterinary medicine programs with Washington State University and the University of Idaho; geological, metallurgical, and mining engineering programs with the University of Idaho; and an education program with the University of Oregon.

Students may cross-register at any college in the Oregon state system, at member colleges of the Western Interstate Commission, and with any member of the National Student Exchange. Study abroad is possible in any of 13 countries, including New Zealand and the former Soviet Union. There is a 5-year B.A.-B.S. program in civil engineering and forest engineering, and a 3–2 engineering program with the University of Oregon. Internships, a liberal studies degree, nondegree study, and pass/fail options are also available. There is a freshman honors program on campus, as well as 7 national honor societies. Twenty departments have honors programs.

Faculty/Classroom: Seventy-two percent of faculty are male; 28%, female. Thirty-nine percent teach undergraduates and 24% do research.

Admissions: About 87% of the 1993–94 applicants were accepted. The SAT scores for the 1993–94 freshman class were as follows: Verbal—65% below 500, 30% between 500 and 599, and 6% between 600 and 700; Math—38% below 500, 35% between 500 and 599, 22% between 600 and 700, and 4% above 700. The ACT scores were 34% below 21, 23% between 21 and 23, 21% between 24 and 26, 12% between 27 and 28, and 10% above 28. There were 3 National Merit finalists.

Requirements: A minimum GPA of 3.0 is required. The SAT I or ACT is required. Applicants should be high school graduates or hold the GED. Required high school preparation includes 4 years of English; 3 years of mathematics, including algebra I; 2 years of natural science; and 1 year each of U.S history, world history, and social science. Among electives, government and foreign language are strongly recommended. Some subject requirements may be fulfilled by test scores. AP and CLEP credits are accepted. Advanced placement or honor courses is an important factor used in the admission decision.

Procedure: Freshmen are admitted to all sessions. Entrance exams should be taken during the junior or senior year. Applications should be filed by March 1 for fall entry, December 3 for winter entry, February 24 for spring entry, and March 1 for summer entry, along with an application fee of $50. Notification is sent on a rolling basis. There is an early admissions plan.

Transfer: About 1940 transfer students enrolled in an earlier year. Applicants who are Oregon residents must present a GPA of at least 2.25 in previous college work; for nonresidents, a GPA of 2.5. Students should have completed at least 36 hours of college credit. Either SAT I or ACT scores must be submitted. A total of 45 quarter credits out of 192 must be completed at OSU.

Visiting: There are regularly scheduled orientations for prospective students. There are guides for informal visits and visitors may sit in on classes and stay overnight at the school. To arrange for a visit, contact the Office of New Student Programs.

Financial Aid: In an earlier year, 67% of all current freshmen and 45% of continuing students received some form of financial aid. Scholarships or need-based grants averaged $1172 ($4000 maximum); loans averaged $1900 ($2625 maximum); and work contracts averaged $1153 ($1800 maximum). OSU is a member of CSS. The FAF is required. The deadline for financial aid applications is March 1.

International Students: There were recently 1575 international students enrolled. The school actively recruits these students. They must take the TOEFL and achieve a minimum score of 550.

Computers: The college provides computer facilities for student use. The mainframe is an IBM 4381, a DEC VAX 11/780, and a CDC Cyber 960. There are more than 400 IBM, Apple Macintosh, Hewlett Packard, and Leading Edge microcomputer systems available to students in the computer laboratory, the library, and various academic buildings. All students may access the system. It may be used at any time. Students may access the system according to departmental allocation. There are no fees.

Graduates: In an earlier year, 2622 bachelor's degrees were awarded. Some 244 companies recruited on campus in 1992–93.

Admissions Contact: Kay Conrad, Director of Admissions.

PACIFIC NORTHWEST COLLEGE OF ART
Portland, OR 97205

B-1
(503) 226-0462

Full-time: 100 men, 124 women	Faculty: 17; IIB, --$
Part-time: 16 men, 24 women	Ph.D.s: 70%
Graduate: none	Student/Faculty: 13 to 1
Year: semesters	Tuition: $7700
Application Deadline: August 15	Room & Board: n/app
Freshman Class: 145 applied, 135 accepted, 76 enrolled	
SAT I or ACT: not required	SPECIAL

Pacific Northwest College of Art, founded in 1909, offers professional training in art in a liberal arts curriculum. PNCA is affiliated with the Portland Art Museum and the Northwest Film Center. In addition to regional accreditation, PNCA has baccalaureate program accreditation with NASAD. The library contains 22,000 volumes and subscribes to 73 periodicals. Special learning facilities include an art gal-

lery. The 1-acre campus is in an urban area in downtown Portland. There are 2 buildings on campus.

Student Life: About 71% of undergraduates are from Oregon. Students come from 21 states, 10 foreign countries, and Canada. Eighty-six percent are white. The average age of freshmen is 23; all undergraduates, 26. Thirty-four percent drop out by the end of their first year; 70% remain to graduate.

Housing: There are no residence halls; all students commute. Alcohol is not permitted.

Activities: There are no fraternities or sororities on campus. There are some groups and organizations on campus, including art and student government.

Sports: There is no sports program at PNCA.

Disabled Students: Ninety percent of the campus is accessible to disabled students. The following facilities are available: wheelchair ramps, elevators, and specially equipped rest rooms.

Campus Safety and Security: Campus safety and security measures include self defense education, emergency telephones, lighted pathways and sidewalks, and guards at building entrances.

Programs of Study: PNCA awards the B.F.A. degree. Bachelor's degrees are awarded in COMMUNICATIONS AND THE ARTS (ceramic art and design, crafts, drawing, graphic design, illustration, painting, photography, printmaking, and sculpture).

Required: A 2.0 GPA is required for both semesters of the senior year. All students must complete 122 credits, including 42 in liberal arts and sciences courses and 36 to 58 in studio courses. Of the studio requirements, 22 credits consist of required courses in visual elements, 3-dimensional design, drawing, art and ideas, and composition or literature. Between 36 and 58 hours are required in the major. All seniors must complete a thesis, which is critiqued by the faculty and later exhibited.

Special: A joint B.A./B.F.A. degree is offered with Reed College. Students may cross-register with members of the Oregon Independent Colleges Association. Students may study abroad in either Italy or England. Fourth-year graphic design majors may undertake a 1-semester professional internship. Nondegree study is possible. There is a Mobility Program for 1 semester or 1 year with member schools of the Association of Schools of Art and Design.

Faculty/Classroom: Sixty-eight percent of faculty are male; 32%, female. All teach undergraduates. The average class size in an introductory lecture is 19; in a laboratory, 20; and in a regular course offering, 17.

Admissions: About 93% of the 1993–94 applicants were accepted.

Requirements: Neither the SAT I nor ACT is required. Applicants should be high school graduates or have earned the GED. The application consists of high school transcripts, a personal statement about the applicant's decision to become an artist, 3 recommendations, and a portfolio of at least 12 pieces of artwork. The portfolio must consist of 6 drawings from life, the college's Home Exam or other artwork, and at least 6 additional pieces. Important factors used in the admissions decision are evidence of special talent and recommendations by school officials.

Procedure: Freshmen are admitted fall and spring. Applications should be filed by August 15 for fall entry and December 1 for spring entry, along with an application fee of $25. Notification is sent on a rolling basis. There is a deferred admissions plan.

Transfer: About 27 transfer students enrolled in 1993–94. Transfer applicants must submit college, and in some cases high school, transcripts. They may submit up to 40 slides, or up to 20 original pieces of artwork, at least 6 of which must be drawings. Potential graphic design majors must submit samples of their work. A minimum 2.0 GPA is required. A total of 48 credits out of 122 must be completed at PNCA.

Visiting: There are guides for informal visits, and visitors may sit in on classes. To arrange for a visit, contact the Admissions Office at (503) 226–0462.

Financial Aid: In 1993–94 all current freshmen and 76% of continuing students received some form of financial aid. All freshmen and 76% of continuing students received need-based aid. The average freshman award was $3300. Of that total, scholarships or need-based grants averaged $1170 ($3300 maximum); loans averaged $3000; and work contracts averaged $900 ($1200 maximum). Almost all undergraduate students work part-time. Average earnings from campus work for the school year are $1000. The average financial indebtedness of the 1992–93 graduate was $11,750. PNCA is a member of CSS. The FAF is required. The deadline for financial aid applications is April 1.

International Students: There are currently 16 international students enrolled. They must take the TOEFL and achieve a minimum score of 500.

Computers: The college provides computer facilities for student use. There are 17 Apple Macintosh SE, Mac II, and Mac Plus microcomputers available for academic use in the computer laboratory and library. All students may access the system. There are no fees.

Graduates: In 1992–93 26 bachelor's degrees were awarded. The most popular majors among graduates were painting (46%), graphic design/illustration (23%), and sculpture (12%). Within an average freshman class, 33% graduate in 6 years.

Admissions Contact: Colin Page, Director of Admissions.

PACIFIC UNIVERSITY
B-1

Forest Grove, OR 97116	(503) 359–2267; (800) 677–6712
Full-time: 405 men, 588 women	Faculty: 64; IIA, --$
Part-time: 13 men, 21 women	Ph.D.s: 84%
Graduate: 305 men, 455 women	Student/Faculty: 16 to 1
Year: 4–1–4	Tuition: $13,575
Application Deadline: March 1	Room & Board: $4294
Freshman Class: 1176 applied, 1041 accepted, 411 enrolled	
SAT I Verbal/Math: 480/530	ACT: 24 COMPETITIVE

Pacific University, founded in 1849, is an independent, coeducational institution affiliated with the Congregational Church (United Church of Christ), offering undergraduate programs in liberal arts, science, business, education, and health professions. There are 5 graduate schools. In addition to regional accreditation, Pacific has baccalaureate program accreditation with APTA and NASM. The library contains 229,055 volumes, 28,307 microform items, and 9695 audiovisual forms, and subscribes to 1022 periodicals. Computerized library sources and services include the card catalog, interlibrary loans, and database searching. Special learning facilities include a learning resource center, art gallery, radio station, and TV station. The 55-acre campus is in a small town 25 miles west of Portland. Including residence halls, there are 17 buildings on campus.

Student Life: About 53% of undergraduates are from out-of-state, mostly the West. Students come from 30 states, 19 foreign countries, and Canada. Eighty-eight percent are from public schools; 12% from private. Sixty-four percent are white; 10% Asian American. Twenty-eight percent drop out by the end of their first year; 45% remain to graduate.

Housing: A total of 566 students can be accommodated in college housing. College-sponsored living facilities include single-sex and coed dormitories, off-campus apartments, married-student housing, and fraternity houses. In addition, there are special interest houses. On-campus housing is guaranteed for the freshman year only, is available on a first-come, first-served basis, and is available on a lottery system for upperclassmen. Fifty-six percent of students live on campus; of those, 90% remain on campus on weekends. All students may keep cars on campus.

Activities: About 17% of men belong to 3 local fraternities; about 15% of women belong to 3 local sororities. There are 33 groups on campus, including art, band, cheerleading, choir, chorale, chorus, computers, dance, drama, ethnic, honors, international, jazz band, literary magazine, musical theater, newspaper, opera, orchestra, pep band, photography, political, professional, radio and TV, religious, social, social service, student government, and yearbook. Popular campus events include Springfest and Homecoming.

Sports: There are 7 intercollegiate sports for men and 6 for women, and 7 intramural sports for men and 7 for women. Athletic and recreation facilities include a gymnasium, various courts, a sauna, weight and wrestling rooms, a dance studio, and various outdoor playing fields.

Disabled Students: Eighty percent of the campus is accessible to disabled students. The following facilities are available: wheelchair ramps, elevators, special parking, specially equipped rest rooms, and lowered drinking fountains.

Services: In addition to many counseling and information services, tutoring is available in most subjects.

Campus Safety and Security: Campus safety and security measures include 24-hour foot and vehicle patrol, escort service, informal discussions, and pamphlets, posters, and films. In addition, there are emergency telephones and lighted pathways and sidewalks.

Programs of Study: Pacific awards the B.A., B.S., and B.M.E. degrees. Master's and doctoral degrees also are awarded. Bachelor's degrees are awarded in BIOLOGICAL SCIENCE (biology/biological science), BUSINESS (accounting, banking and finance, business administration and management, marketing/retailing/merchandising, and small business management), COMMUNICATIONS AND THE ARTS (creative writing, dramatic arts, French, German, Japanese, literature, music, and Spanish), COMPUTER AND PHYSICAL SCIENCE (chemistry, computer science, mathematics, physics, and science), EDUCATION (elementary and physical), SOCIAL SCIENCE (economics, history, humanities, philosophy, political science/government, psychology, social work, and sociology). Business administration and English have the largest enrollments.

Required: All students take a core curriculum that includes courses in writing, human heritage, foreign language, social and natural sciences, and art. Completion of 1 course in computer science and 2 semester hours of physical education is required. A cumulative GPA

Of 2.0 in 124 semester hours is required for graduation. The number of hours required in the major varies, depending on the discipline.

Special: Cross-registration is available with Lewis and Clark University and Oregon Graduate Institute. The university also offers cooperative programs with Washington University in St. Louis, Oregon Graduate Center, and Oregon Art Institute, as well as study abroad in 9 countries. Full-time, semester-long internships, including one in Washington D.C., are possible. Dual majors, a general studies degree in humanities, nondegree study, 3–2 engineering programs with Washington University (St. Louis) and Oregon Graduate Institute, and an interdisciplinary program in peace and conflict studies are available. There is a freshman honors program on campus, as well as 2 national honor societies.

Faculty/Classroom: Seventy percent of faculty are male; 30%, female. Fifty-six percent both teach and do research. No introductory courses are taught by graduate students. The average class size in an introductory lecture is 25; in a laboratory, 15; and in a regular course offering, 25.

Admissions: About 89% of the 1993–94 applicants were accepted. The SAT scores for the 1993–94 freshman class were as follows: Verbal—67% below 500, 28% between 500 and 599, 4% between 600 and 700, and 1% above 700; Math—37% below 500, 40% between 500 and 599, 21% between 600 and 700, and 2% above 700. The ACT scores were 21% below 21, 34% between 21 and 23, 25% between 24 and 26, 10% between 27 and 28, and 10% above 28. About 60% of the current freshmen were in the top fifth of their class; 82% were in the top two fifths. There were 3 National Merit finalists and 7 semifinalists. About 11 freshmen graduated first in their class.

Requirements: A minimum GPA of 3.0 is required. The SAT I or ACT is required. Applicants are expected to be high school graduates or to hold the GED. A personal essay is required, and an interview is recommended. AP and CLEP credits are accepted. Important factors used in the admissions decision are personality, intangible qualities, leadership record, evidence of special talent, advanced placement or honor courses, and recommendations by school officials.

Procedure: Freshmen are admitted to all sessions. Early decision applications should be filed by December 1; regular applications, by March 1 for fall entry, along with an application fee of $25. Notification of early decision is sent December 15; regular decision, on a rolling basis. There are early admissions and deferred admissions plans.

Transfer: About 123 transfer students enrolled in 1993–94. Transfer applicants must present at least a 2.8 GPA in previous college work; those with fewer than 30 college credits must also submit SAT I, ACT, or WPCT test scores and high school transcripts. A personal interview is strongly recommended. A total of 30 semester hours out of 124 must be completed at Pacific.

Visiting: There are regularly scheduled orientations for prospective students. There are guides for informal visits, and visitors may sit in on classes and stay overnight at the school. To arrange for a visit, contact the Office of Admissions at (800) 677–6712.

Financial Aid: In 1993–94 87% of all current freshmen and 90% of continuing students received some form of financial aid. About 75% of freshmen and 78% of continuing students received need-based aid. The average freshman award was $10,017. Of that total, scholarships or need-based grants averaged $7336 ($11,704 maximum); loans averaged $3768 ($5625 maximum); and work contracts averaged $1211 ($1800 maximum). Fifty-three percent of undergraduate students work part-time. Average earnings from campus work for the school year are $1005. The average financial indebtedness of the 1992–93 graduate was $12,900. Pacific is a member of CSS. The FAF is required. The deadline for financial aid applications is April 1.

International Students: There are currently 82 international students enrolled. The school actively recruits these students. They must take the TOEFL and achieve a minimum score of 550.

Computers: The college provides computer facilities for student use. There is an Apple Macintosh-based LAN with 45 student terminals, as well as 6 IBM student-use PCs, 18 Macintosh stand-alones in residence halls, a Sequent S-81, an Intel System 303 running UNIX System 5, and a Sun 3/80 workstation. All students may access the system. There are no time limits on using the system and no fees.

Graduates: In 1992–93 234 bachelor's degrees were awarded. The most popular majors among graduates were health professions (22%), business (12%), and psychology (9%).

Admissions Contact: Bart Howard, Dean of Admissions, Financial Aid, and Records.

PORTLAND STATE UNIVERSITY
B-1
Portland, OR 97207–0751

(503) 725–3511

(800) 547–8887 (out-of-state)

Full-time: 2889 men, 2879 women	Faculty: 493; I, --$
Part-time: 2115 men, 2394 women	Ph.D.s: 80%
Graduate: 1916 men, 2293 women	Student/Faculty: 12 to 1
Year: quarters, summer session	Tuition: $2826 ($7923)
Application Deadline: June 1	Room & Board: $4365
Freshman Class: 1639 applied, 1590 accepted, 817 enrolled	
SAT I Verbal/Math: 420/480	ACT: 22 COMPETITIVE

Portland State University, founded in 1946, is a comprehensive public institution serving a primarily commuter student body. Graduate and undergraduate degree programs are offered in liberal arts and sciences, business, education, engineering, extended studies, fine and performing arts, social work, and urban and public affairs. There are 5 undergraduate and 3 graduate schools. In addition to regional accreditation, PSU has baccalaureate program accreditation with AACSB, ABET, ASLA, CSWE, NASM, and NCATE. The library contains 930,693 volumes, 1,919,542 microform items, and 102,323 audiovisual forms, and subscribes to 11,132 periodicals. Computerized library sources and services include the card catalog, interlibrary loans, and database searching. Special learning facilities include a learning resource center and art gallery. The 49-acre campus is in an urban area in downtown Portland. Including residence halls, there are 39 buildings on campus.

Student Life: About 82% of undergraduates are from Oregon. Students come from 46 states, 71 foreign countries, and Canada. Sixty-six percent are white; 10% Asian American. The average age of freshmen is 19; all undergraduates, 27. Thirty-six percent drop out by the end of their first year; 30% remain to graduate.

Housing: A total of 1600 students can be accommodated in college housing. College-sponsored living facilities include coed dormitories, on-campus apartments, off-campus apartments, fraternity houses, and sorority houses. On-campus housing is available on a first-come, first-served basis. Priority is given to out-of-town students. Eighty-nine percent of students commute. All students may keep cars on campus.

Activities: About 2% of men belong to 5 national fraternities; about 2% of women belong to 1 local and 3 national sororities. There are 165 groups on campus, including art, band, cheerleading, chess, choir, chorale, chorus, computers, dance, drama, drill team, ethnic, film, gay, honors, international, jazz band, literary magazine, musical theater, newspaper, opera, orchestra, pep band, photography, political, professional, religious, social, social service, student government, and yearbook. Popular campus events include UISHE Powwow Salmon Bake, Association of African Students Cultural Day, and International Student Cultural Night.

Sports: There are 7 intercollegiate sports for men and 7 for women, and 7 intramural sports for men and 6 for women. Athletic and recreation facilities include a swimming pool, an all-weather tennis facility, gymnasiums, circuit training and weight rooms, a golf putting green, and racquetball, handball, and squash courts. Nearby Civic Stadium and Duniway Park provide football, baseball, and track and field facilities.

Disabled Students: Ninety-eight percent of the campus is accessible to disabled students. The following facilities are available: wheelchair ramps, elevators, special parking, specially equipped rest rooms, special class scheduling, lowered drinking fountains, lowered telephones, and several modified housing units.

Services: In addition to many counseling and information services, tutoring is available in every subject. In addition, there is a reader service for the blind, remedial math and writing, Student Support Services, and an Educational Opportunity Program that provides assistance to students who are low-income, who have a physical disability, or whose parents did not graduate from college.

Campus Safety and Security: Campus safety and security measures include 24-hour foot and vehicle patrol, self defense education, escort service, and informal discussions. In addition, there are pamphlets, posters, and films, emergency telephones, lighted pathways and sidewalks, a campus watch newsletter, information lectures, and community liaison.

Programs of Study: PSU awards the B.A., B.S., and B.M. degrees. Master's and doctoral degrees also are awarded. Bachelor's degrees are awarded in BIOLOGICAL SCIENCE (biology/biological science), BUSINESS (accounting, banking and finance, business administration and management, management science, marketing/retailing/merchandising, and personnel management), COMMUNICATIONS AND THE ARTS (advertising, dramatic arts, English, fine arts, French, German, Japanese, languages, linguistics, music, Russian, Spanish, and speech/debate/rhetoric), COMPUTER AND PHYSICAL SCIENCE (chemistry, computer science, geology, information sciences and systems, mathematics, physics, and science), EDUCATION (health), ENGINEERING AND ENVIRONMENTAL DESIGN (civil engineering, computer engineering, electrical/electronics

engineering, and mechanical engineering), SOCIAL SCIENCE (anthropology, criminal justice, economics, geography, history, international studies, philosophy, political science/government, psychology, social science, and sociology). Business administration, psychology, and marketing have the largest enrollments.

Required: All students must complete at least 186 quarter credits with a 2.0 GPA. Other requirements and the number of hours that must be completed in the major vary by degree program. Freshmen must complete three 5-credit freshman inquiry courses; sophomores, three 4-credit courses from different interdisciplinary programs or general education clusters; juniors and seniors, one interdisciplinary program or general education cluster (four 3-credit courses); and seniors must complete Capstone Experience.

Special: Students may cross-register with all colleges in the Oregon State System of Higher Education, and they may study abroad in 21 countries. Numerous internships, a Washington semester, and work-study programs are available. Most undergraduate programs may be taken on an accelerated basis, and students in all programs may undertake dual majors or design their own majors. A general studies program is available in arts and letters, science, or social science. Nondegree study and pass/fail grading options are possible. Students may enroll for 7 or fewer credits per term without formal admission. There is a freshman honors program on campus, as well as 15 national honor societies. A university honors program, limited to zoo students, is available to all undergraduate majors.

Faculty/Classroom: Sixty-six percent of faculty are male; 34%, female. The average class size in an introductory lecture is 35; in a laboratory, 21; and in a regular course offering, 23.

Admissions: About 97% of the 1993–94 applicants were accepted. The SAT scores for the 1993–94 freshman class were as follows: Verbal—78% below 500, 18% between 500 and 599, and 4% between 600 and 700; Math—57% below 500, 29% between 500 and 599, 12% between 600 and 700, and 2% above 700. The ACT scores were 34% below 21, 40% between 21 and 23, 14% between 24 and 26, 8% between 27 and 28, and 4% above 28.

Requirements: A minimum GPA of 2.5 is required. Either SAT I or ACT scores may be submitted; the university suggests a minimum composite SAT I score of 890 and a minimum composite ACT score of 21. Applicants should be high school graduates or have earned the GED. Secondary preparation should include 4 years of English, 3 years each of social studies and mathematics, and 2 years each of science and other college preparatory work. An interview is recommended. AP and CLEP credits are accepted.

Procedure: Freshmen are admitted to all sessions. Entrance exams should be taken as early as possible. Applications should be filed by June 1 for fall entry, October 1 for winter entry, and February 1 for spring entry, along with an application fee of $50. Notification is sent on a rolling basis. There are early admissions and deferred admissions plans.

Transfer: About 1417 transfer students enrolled in 1993–94. Applicants who are Oregon residents must have earned at least a 2.0 GPA in 30 college credits; those with 12 to 30 credits must meet freshman admission requirements and have a 2.0 GPA in all college work attempted. Nonresident applicants must have at least a 2.3 GPA in 30 hours of college work; those with 12 to 30 hours must meet freshman requirements and have a 2.3 GPA in all college work attempted. A total of 45 quarter credits out of 186 must be completed at PSU.

Visiting: There are regularly scheduled orientations for prospective students. There are guides for informal visits and visitors may sit in on classes and stay overnight at the school. To arrange for a visit, contact the Office of Admissions at (503) 725–3511.

Financial Aid: In 1993–94, 34% of all current freshmen and 53% of continuing students received some form of financial aid. About 31% of freshmen and 42% of continuing students received need-based aid. The average freshman award was $3529. Of that total, scholarships or need-based grants averaged $940 ($9639 maximum); loans averaged $2478 ($7171 maximum); and work contracts averaged $2071 ($4500 maximum). Eighty percent of undergraduate students work part-time. The average financial indebtedness of the 1992–93 graduate was $6230. PSU is a member of CSS. The FAF, FFS, or SFS, the college's own financial statement, and the FAFSA are required. The deadline for financial aid applications is June 15.

International Students: There are currently 468 international students enrolled. They must take the TOEFL and achieve a minimum score of 525.

Computers: The college provides computer facilities for student use. The mainframes include an IBM 4381 and a Sequent 581. Some 45 terminals are located in Shattuck Hall. The open-access microcomputer laboratories (63 MS/DOS and Apple Macintosh) are open to all students. Laboratories are available in SmithCenter, Shattuck Hall, and various departmental locations throughout the campus. Students taking computer-related classes may access the mainframe. It may be used 24 hours a day. There are no time limits on using the system and no fees.

Graduates: In 1992–93, 1804 bachelor's degrees were awarded. The most popular majors among graduates were psychology (10%), business administration (8%), and accounting (7%). Within an average freshman class, 1% graduate in 3 years, 6% in 4 years, 21% in 5 years, and 27% in 6 years. Some 152 companies recruited on campus in 1992–93. In the 1992 graduating class, 10% of all graduates were enrolled in graduate school within 6 months of graduation; 89% of all graduates had found employment.

Admissions Contact: Jesse Welch, Director of Admissions.

REED COLLEGE
B-1

Portland, OR 97202-8199

(503) 777-7511

(800) 547-4750 (out-of-state)

Full-time: 594 men, 605 women	Faculty: 92; IIB, +$
Part-time: 33 men, 28 women	Ph.D.s: 78%
Graduate: 6 men, 11 women	Student/Faculty: 13 to 1
Year: semesters	Tuition: $19,250
Application Deadline: February 1	Room & Board: $5230
Freshman Class: 1966 applied, 1436 accepted, 327 enrolled	
SAT I Verbal/Math: 610/640	**HIGHLY COMPETITIVE +**

Reed College, founded in 1909, is a private, nonsectarian institution offering programs in liberal arts and science, and emphasizing instruction through small conference-style classes. There is one undergraduate and one graduate school. The library contains 364,600 volumes and 177,144 microform items, and subscribes to 1615 periodicals. Computerized library sources and services include the card catalog, interlibrary loans, and database searching. Special learning facilities include a learning resource center, art gallery, and radio station. The 100-acre campus is in an urban area in Portland. Including residence halls, there are 36 buildings on campus.

Student Life: About 83% of undergraduates are from out-of-state, mostly the Northwest. Students come from 48 states, 11 foreign countries, and Canada. Seventy-one percent are from public schools; 29% from private. Eighty-two percent are white. The average age of freshmen is 18; all undergraduates, 20. Ten percent drop out by the end of their first year; 69% remain to graduate.

Housing: A total of 626 students can be accommodated in college housing. College-sponsored living facilities include coed dormitories and on-campus apartments. In addition, there are language houses. On-campus housing is guaranteed for the freshman year only, is available on a first-come, first-served basis, and is available on a lottery system for upperclassmen. Fifty-two percent of students commute. Alcohol is not permitted. All students may keep cars on campus.

Activities: There are no fraternities or sororities on campus. There are 65 groups on campus, including art, chess, choir, chorale, chorus, computers, dance, drama, ethnic, gay, international, literary magazine, newspaper, orchestra, photography, radio and TV, religious, social service, student government, and yearbook. Popular campus events include Performing Arts Festival, Campus Clean Up Day (Common Day), Renaissance Fair, and Reed Arts Week.

Sports: There are 6 intercollegiate sports for men and 4 for women, and 12 intramural sports for men and 12 for women. Athletic and recreation facilities include a sports center that houses 2 gymnasiums (1 seating 1200), an indoor pool, squash and racquetball courts, saunas, a weight room, an exercise room, and a dance studio. Outdoor facilities include a pool, tennis courts, a track, and areas for soccer, rugby, volleyball, and baseball.

Disabled Students: Two percent of the campus is accessible to disabled students. The following facilities are available: wheelchair ramps, special parking, specially equipped rest rooms, lowered drinking fountains, and lowered telephones.

Services: In addition to many counseling and information services, tutoring is available in most subjects. In addition, there is a reader service for the blind, and remedial math, reading, and writing.

Campus Safety and Security: Campus safety and security measures include 24-hour foot and vehicle patrol, self defense education, escort service, and shuttle buses. In addition, there are pamphlets, posters, and films and lighted pathways and sidewalks.

Programs of Study: Reed awards the B.A. degree. Master's degrees also are awarded. Bachelor's degrees are awarded in BIOLOGICAL SCIENCE (biology/biological science), COMMUNICATIONS AND THE ARTS (Chinese, classics, dance, dramatic arts, English, fine arts, French, German, linguistics, literature, music, Russian, and Spanish), COMPUTER AND PHYSICAL SCIENCE (chemistry, mathematics, and physics), SOCIAL SCIENCE (American studies, anthropology, economics, history, international studies, medieval studies, philosophy, political science/government, psychology, religion, and sociology). Biology has the largest enrollment.

Required: All students are required to maintain a C average while taking 120 semester hours. The liberal arts program also requires 1 year of humanities and 1 year for a senior research project, in addition to 1 year each from literature and the arts, history, social science, and psychology, natural science, mathematics, logic, foreign lan-

guages, and linguistics. Students also must take 3 semesters of physical education.

Special: Cross-registration is available through the Oregon Independent Colleges organization. Also available are 3–2 engineering degrees with California Institute of Technology, Columbia University, and Rensselaer Polytechnic Institute, combined 3–2 programs in science, programs with the Pacific Northwest College of Art, and business programs with the universities of Oregon and Chicago. Study abroad in 6 countries, a domestic exchange program with Howard University in Washington, D.C., accelerated degree programs, dual and student-designed majors, numerous interdisciplinary majors, non-degree study, and pass/fail options are also offered. There is a chapter of Phi Beta Kappa on campus.

Faculty/Classroom: Sixty-nine percent of faculty are male; 31%, female. All both teach and do research. No introductory courses are taught by graduate students. The average class size in a laboratory is 20 and in a regular course offering, 15.

Admissions: About 73% of the 1993–94 applicants were accepted. The SAT scores for the 1993–94 freshman class were as follows: Verbal—10% below 500, 30% between 500 and 599, 48% between 600 and 700, and 12% above 700; Math—6% below 500, 25% between 500 and 599, 44% between 600 and 700, and 25% above 700. About 68% of the current freshmen were in the top fifth of their class; 93% were in the top two fifths. Six freshmen graduated first in their class.

Requirements: The SAT I is required. The SAT II: Subject test in writing is recommended. Reed strongly recommends that applicants have 4 years of English, 3 each of mathematics and science, and 2 each of foreign language, history, and social studies. An essay is required, and an interview is recommended. The GED is accepted. AP credits are accepted. Important factors used in the admissions decision are advanced placement or honor courses, recommendations by school officials, recommendations by alumni, personality, intangible qualities, and parents or siblings attending the school.

Procedure: Freshmen are admitted fall and spring. Applications should be filed by February 1 for fall entry, along with an application fee of $45. Notification is sent April 1. There are early decision, early admissions, and deferred admissions plans. About 107 early decision candidates were accepted for the 1993–94 class. A waiting list is an active part of the admissions procedure.

Transfer: About 70 transfer students enrolled in 1993–94. Transfer students must have a GPA of 3.0. A total of 60 credits out of 120 must be completed at Reed.

Visiting: There are regularly scheduled orientations for prospective students. Visitors may sit in on classes and stay overnight at the school. To arrange for a visit, contact the Office of Admissions at (503) 777-7511.

Financial Aid: In 1993–94 40% of all current freshmen and 47% of continuing students received some form of financial aid. About 40% of freshmen and 47% of continuing students received need-based aid. The average freshman award was $16,300. Of that total, scholarships or need-based grants averaged $13,200 ($21,300 maximum); loans averaged $2500 (maximum); and work contracts averaged $600 ($1000 maximum). Sixty-five percent of undergraduate students work part-time. Average earnings from campus work for the school year are $730. The average financial indebtedness of the 1992–93 graduate was $7660. Reed is a member of CSS. The FAF, the college's own financial statement, and the FAFSA are required. The deadline for financial aid applications is March 1.

International Students: There are currently 21 international students enrolled. The school actively recruits these students. They must take the TOEFL and achieve a minimum score of 600. The student must also take the SAT I or the ACT. Students must take SAT II: Subject tests in writing and 2 others.

Computers: The college provides computer facilities for student use. The mainframe is a DEC System 5500. There are more than 800 Apple Macintosh PCs available and various laboratories and workstations as well as campus networking to residence hall rooms. All students may access the system. It may be used 24 hours daily. There are no time limits on using the system and no fees.

Graduates: In 1992–93 267 bachelor's degrees were awarded. The most popular majors among graduates were biology (15%), English (14%), and history (12%). Within an average freshman class, 42% graduate in 4 years, 61% in 5 years, and 69% in 6 years. Some 9 companies recruited on campus in 1992–93. In a recent graduating class, 33% of all students were enrolled in graduate school within 6 months of graduation; 40% of all graduates had found employment.

Admissions Contact: Robert Mansueto, Dean of Admission.

SOUTHERN OREGON STATE COLLEGE   B-4

Ashland, OR 97520   (503) 552-6411; (800) 552-7672 (in-state)

Full-time: 1568 men, 1647 women	Faculty: 188; IIA, --$
Part-time: 410 men, 537 women	Ph.D.s: 87%
Graduate: 140 men, 213 women	Student/Faculty: 17 to 1
Year: quarters, summer session	Tuition: $2628 ($6819)
Application Deadline: open	Room & Board: $3500
Freshman Class: 1237 applied, 1037 accepted, 768 enrolled	
SAT I Verbal/Math: 440/473	ACT: 21 COMPETITIVE

Southern Oregon State College, founded in 1926, is a public comprehensive school providing undergraduate and graduate programs in humanities, science, business, fine and performing arts, social sciences, and teacher education. There are 5 undergraduate schools and one graduate school. In addition to regional accreditation, Southern Oregon has baccalaureate program accreditation with NASM, NCATE, and NLN. The library contains 265,000 volumes, 650,000 microform items, and 2500 audiovisual forms, and subscribes to 2150 periodicals. Computerized library sources and services include interlibrary loans and database searching. Special learning facilities include a radio station, TV station, art museum, 3 art galleries, and wildlife forensics laboratory. The 175-acre campus is in a small town 10 miles southeast of Medford. Including residence halls, there are 36 buildings on campus.

Student Life: About 82% of undergraduates are from Oregon. Students come from 44 states, 36 foreign countries, and Canada. Eighty-five percent are from public schools; 15% from private. Eighty-three percent are white. The average age of all undergraduates is 25. Thirty-five percent drop out by the end of their first year; 30% remain to graduate.

Housing: A total of 1330 students can be accommodated in college housing. College-sponsored living facilities include coed dormitories and married-student housing. In addition, there are special interest houses, well halls, and 24-hour and 12-hour quiet halls. On-campus housing is guaranteed for all 4 years. Priority is given to out-of-town students. Seventy-five percent of students commute. All students may keep cars on campus.

Activities: There are no fraternities or sororities on campus. There are 55 groups on campus, including art, band, cheerleading, choir, drama, ethnic, gay, honors, international, jazz band, literary magazine, newspaper, pep band, political, professional, radio and TV, religious, student government, symphony, and yearbook. Popular campus events include Homecoming and Campus Day.

Sports: There are 9 intramural sports for men and 7 for women. Athletic and recreation facilities include an indoor swimming pool, 6 racquetball courts, 12 tennis courts, 4 gymnasiums, a climbing-wall gymnasium, a dance studio, wrestling and weight rooms, a sauna, and a football stadium.

Disabled Students: More than 90% of the campus is accessible to disabled students. The following facilities are available: wheelchair ramps, elevators, special parking, specially equipped rest rooms, special class scheduling, lowered drinking fountains, and individualized programming.

Services: In addition to many counseling and information services, tutoring is available in most subjects. In addition, there is a reader service for the blind and remedial math and writing. Program design is offered for students with learning disabilities. TDD is available for the hearing-impaired.

Campus Safety and Security: Campus safety and security measures include 24-hour foot and vehicle patrol, informal discussions, pamphlets, posters, and films, and lighted pathways and sidewalks.

Programs of Study: Southern Oregon awards the B.A., B.S., and B.F.A. degrees. Associate and master's degrees also are awarded. Bachelor's degrees are awarded in BIOLOGICAL SCIENCE (biology/biological science), BUSINESS (accounting, business administration and management, marketing/retailing/merchandising, personnel management, and purchasing/inventory management), COMMUNICATIONS AND THE ARTS (broadcasting, communications, dramatic arts, English, fine arts, music, music business management, and Spanish), COMPUTER AND PHYSICAL SCIENCE (chemistry, computer programming, computer science, geology, mathematics, and physics), EDUCATION (elementary), HEALTH PROFESSIONS (nursing and premedicine), SOCIAL SCIENCE (criminology, economics, geography, history, international studies, liberal arts/general studies, political science/government, prelaw, psychology, social science, and sociology). Business, criminology, sciences, and fine and performing arts are the strongest programs academically. Business and social sciences have the largest enrollments.

Required: Students need a minimum GPA of 2.0 earned over 186 quarter hours, with 50 to 100 in the major and at least 60 in upper-division course work. Competency in writing, speech, and mathematics must be demonstrated through course work or examination. Distribution requirements include 9 goals that provide skills for effective communication, critical judgment, and research, and give students

awareness of social, artistic, cultural, and scientific traditions of civilization. There is a required senior capstone experience.

Special: Cross-registration through the National Students Exchange, study abroad in 11 countries, and work-study programs are available. A general studies degree, student-designed majors, dual majors in business plus chemistry, mathematics, or music, credit for life experience, and pass/fail options in up to 1 course per quarter also are offered. Internships are possible with NASA in Houston, in which undergraduates may study raw space data. There is a freshman honors program on campus, as well as 7 national honor societies. Three departments have honors programs.

Faculty/Classroom: Sixty-five percent of faculty are male; 35%, female. All teach undergraduates. The average class size in an introductory lecture is 50; in a laboratory, 26; and in a regular course offering, 25.

Admissions: About 84% of the 1993–94 applicants were accepted.

Requirements: A minimum GPA of 2.75 is required. The SAT I or the ACT is required. A minimum composite score of 900 on the SAT I is needed if the high school GPA is less than 2.75. Applicants need 14 academic credits, including 4 years of English, 3 each of mathematics and social studies, 2 of science, and electives. SAT II: Subject test in writing, mathematics, and another area are needed if there is insufficient college-preparatory course work. The GED is accepted. AP and CLEP credits are accepted. Important factors used in the admissions decision are advanced placement or honor courses, evidence of special talent, and leadership record.

Procedure: Freshmen are admitted to all sessions. Entrance exams should be taken in the senior year. Application deadlines are open, but June 1 is the priority date for fall entry. Application fee is $50. Notification is sent on a rolling basis. There are early admissions and deferred admissions plans.

Transfer: About 450 transfer students enrolled in 1993–94. Transfer students need a minimum GPA of 2.25 and at least 24 quarter credits. A total of 45 quarter credits out of 186 must be completed at Southern Oregon.

Visiting: There are regularly scheduled orientations for prospective students, including tours of the campus and dormitories and meeting with an admissions representative; appointments with faculty and class visits can be arranged. There are guides for informal visits and visitors may sit in on classes and stay overnight at the school. To arrange for a visit, contact the Admissions Office at (503) 552–6411.

Financial Aid: In a recent year 65% of all freshmen and 65% of continuing students received some form of financial aid. About 49% of freshmen and 49% of continuing students received need-based aid. Scholarships or need-based grants averaged $1300 ($1574 maximum); loans averaged $1000 (maximum); and work contracts averaged $2000 (maximum). Forty-six percent of undergraduate students work part-time. The average financial indebtedness of a recent year's graduate was $7000. Southern Oregon is a member of CSS. The FAF is required. The deadline for financial aid applications is March 1.

International Students: There are currently 200 international students enrolled. They must take the TOEFL and achieve a minimum score of 520.

Computers: The college provides computer facilities for student use. The mainframe is a DEC VAX 4310. A new computing services center for students houses 130 PCs; 70 more will be added soon. Smaller laboratories house 65 computers, including Apple Macintosh and IBM-compatibles, for student use. All students may access the system. It may be accessed more than 75 hours a week and there are no individual time limits or fees.

Graduates: In a recent year 678 bachelor's degrees were awarded. Within an average freshman class, 1% graduate in 3 years, 14% in 4 years, 14% in 5 years, and 10% in 6 years. Some 90 companies recruited on campus in a recent year.

Admissions Contact: Al Blaszak, Director of Admissions.

UNIVERSITY OF OREGON B-2

Eugene, OR 97403 (503) 346–3201; (800) 232–3825 (in-state)

Full-time: 5433 men, 5944 women	Faculty: 902; I, --$
Part-time: 848 men, 849 women	Ph.D.s: 80%
Graduate: 1997 men, 1894 women	Student/Faculty: 13 to 1
Year: quarters, summer session	Tuition: $2916 ($9285)
Application Deadline: March 1	Room & Board: $3550
Freshman Class: 7159 applied, 5189 accepted, 2232 enrolled	
SAT I or ACT: required	VERY COMPETITIVE

The University of Oregon, founded in 1876, is a public, coeducational, liberal arts institution. There are 7 undergraduate and 6 graduate schools. In addition to regional accreditation, UO has baccalaureate program accreditation with AACSB, ACEJMC, ASLA, FIDER, NAAB, NASM, and NRPA. The 6 libraries contain 2 million volumes, and subscribe to 18,600 periodicals. Special learning facilities include an art gallery; a natural history museum; a radio station,; 13 specialized science institutes, including the Center for Volcanology, the Institute of

Neuroscience, the Oregon Insititute of Marine Biology, and Pine Mountain Observatory; 7 humanities and social science centers; and 12 other research facilities. The 250-acre campus is in a suburban area near downtown Eugene. Including residence halls, there are 98 buildings on campus.

Student Life: About 67% of undergraduates are from Oregon. Students come from 50 states, 85 foreign countries, and Canada. Ninety-one percent are from public schools. Seventy-four percent are white. The average age of freshmen is 19; all undergraduates, 22. Eight percent drop out by the end of their first year; 53% remain to graduate.

Housing: A total of 3200 students can be accommodated in college housing. College-sponsored living facilities include single-sex and coed dormitories and married-student housing. In addition, there are honors houses, language houses, special interest houses, and an international college. On-campus housing is available on a first-come, first-served basis. Eighty percent of students commute. Alcohol is not permitted. All students may keep cars on campus.

Activities: About 10% of men belong to 16 national fraternities; about 10% of women belong to 11 national sororities. There are 300 groups on campus, including art, band, cheerleading, choir, chorale, chorus, computers, dance, drama, ethnic, film, gay, honors, international, jazz band, literary magazine, marching band, musical theater, newspaper, opera, orchestra, pep band, photography, political, professional, radio and tv, religious, social, social service, student government, and symphony.

Sports: There are 7 intercollegiate sports each for men and women, and 21 intramural sports for men and 19 for women. Athletic and recreation facilities include a 41,000-seat stadium, a 10,000-seat arena, a swimming pool, several gymnasiums, 15 tennis courts, running tracks, and fields for outdoor sports.

Disabled Students: Sixty percent of the campus is accessible to disabled students. The following facilities are available: wheelchair ramps, elevators, special parking, specially equipped rest rooms, special class scheduling, lowered drinking fountains, and lowered telephones.

Services: In addition, there is a reader service for the blind and remedial writing.

Campus Safety and Security: Campus safety and security measures include 24-hour foot and vehicle patrol, self-defense education, escort service, and shuttle buses. In addition, there are pamphlets, posters, and films, emergency telephones, and lighted pathways and sidewalks.

Programs of Study: UO awards the B.A., B.S., B.Arch., B.Ed., B.F.A., B.Int.Arch., B.Land.Arch., and B.Mus. degrees. Master's and doctoral degrees also are awarded. Bachelor's degrees are awarded in BIOLOGICAL SCIENCE (biology/biological science), BUSINESS (accounting, banking and finance, business administration and management, management science, marketing/retailing/merchandising, and recreation and leisure services), COMMUNICATIONS AND THE ARTS (art history and appreciation, ceramic art and design, Chinese, classics, comparative literature, dance, English, fine arts, French, German, Greek, Italian, Japanese, journalism, languages, Latin, linguistics, metal/jewelry, music, painting, printmaking, romance languages, Russian, sculpture, Spanish, and speech/debate/rhetoric), COMPUTER AND PHYSICAL SCIENCE (chemistry, computer science, geology, mathematics, and physics), ENGINEERING AND ENVIRONMENTAL DESIGN (landscape architecture/design and preengineering), SOCIAL SCIENCE (American studies, anthropology, Asian/Oriental studies, classical/ancient civilization, economics, geography, history, international studies, philosophy, political science/government, psychology, religion, and sociology). Architecture, journalism, business, psychology, economics, and Asian languages are the strongest academically.

Required: At least 186 quarter credits are required of all students, with a minimum GPA of 2.0. A minimum of 42 credits must be in the major, including 24 in upper-division work. Basic courses vary by major, but all students must take 2 courses in written English and 1 course each in race, gender, and non European-Western areas.

Special: The university offers study abroad, preengineering in conjunction with Lane Community College, an engineering/physics program with Oregon State University, and internships. A B.A.-B.S. degree, dual majors, 3–2 engineering, and pass/fail options are available. There is a freshman honors program on campus, as well as 24 national honor societies, including Phi Beta Kappa. Fifty-four departments have honors programs.

Faculty/Classroom: Sixty-three percent of faculty are male; 37%, female. The average class size in a regular course offering is 33.

Admissions: About 72% of the 1993–94 applicants were accepted. About 35% of the current freshmen were in the top fifth of their class; 63% were in the top two fifths.

Requirements: A minimum GPA of 3.0 is required. The SAT I or ACT is required. Students should be graduates from standard or accredited high schools, have completed specific subject requirements, and obtained a score of 30 on the TSWE or 12 on the English portion of the ACT. A high school GPA of 3.0 or better is required. The GED

is accepted. Specific subject requirements include 4 years of English, 3 years each of mathematics and social studies, 2 years of science, and 2 years of other college preparatory work. AP and CLEP credits are accepted. Important factors used in the admissions decision are advanced placement or honor courses, evidence of special talent, leadership record, geographic diversity, and extracurricular activities record.

Procedure: Freshmen are admitted to all sessions. Entrance exams should be taken before March of the senior year. Applications should be filed by March 1 for fall entry, October 15 for winter entry, January 24 for spring entry, and March 1 for summer entry, along with an application fee of $50. Notification is sent on a rolling basis. There is an early admissions plan.

Transfer: About 1250 transfer students enrolled in 1993–94. Students who have completed 36 or more quarter credits with a minimum 2.3 GPA for residents and 2.5 for nonresidents, and whose college record includes 1 college level course each in writing and mathematics passed with a C or better, may be admitted as transfer students. An official transcript from each college and university attended must be submitted. A total of 45 of the last 60 quarter credits out of 186 must be completed at UO.

Visiting: There are regularly scheduled orientations for prospective students, including 2-day programs scheduled for late July that include both advising and telephone registration. There are guides for informal visits and visitors may sit in on classes. To arrange for a visit, contact the Office of Admissions at (503) 346–3201 or (800) BE-A-DUCK (in-state).

Financial Aid: In 1993–94, 45% of all current freshmen and 45% of continuing students received some form of financial aid. About 40% of freshmen and 40% of continuing students received need-based aid. The average freshman award was $5700. The FAFSA financial statement is required. The deadline for financial aid applications is March 1.

International Students: There are currently 1602 international students enrolled. The school actively recruits these students. They must take the TOEFL and achieve a minimum score of 500.

Computers: The college provides computer facilities for student use. The mainframe is a DEC VAX 8800 cluster and a SUN computer server. There are approximately 300 networked microcomputers and terminals available on campus in 6 instructional and open laboratories, the student union, and various academic departments. All students may access the system. It may be used 24 hours a day. There are no time limits on using the system. The fees are $10 a term for microlaboratories only.

Graduates: In 1992–93, 2934 bachelor's degrees were awarded. The most popular majors among graduates were psychology (12%), marketing (9%), and journalism (8%). Within an average freshman class, 1% graduate in 3 years, 32% in 4 years, 50% in 5 years, and 54% in 6 years. In the 1992 graduating class, 21% of all graduates were enrolled in graduate school within 6 months of graduation; 80% had found employment.

Admissions Contact: Mentha Hynes, Senior Assistant Director.

UNIVERSITY OF PORTLAND

B-1

Portland, OR 97203

(503) 283–7147; (800) 227–4568

Full-time: 904 men, 1137 women	Faculty: 120; IIA, -$
Part-time: 78 men, 94 women	Ph.D.s: 93%
Graduate: 210 men, 267 women	Student/Faculty: 17 to 1
Year: semesters, summer session	Tuition: $11,504
Application Deadline: open	Room & Board: $4060
Freshman Class: 1758 applied, 1485 accepted, 427 enrolled	
SAT I Verbal/Math: 470/530	COMPETITIVE

The University of Portland, founded in 1901, is an independent institution affiliated with the Roman Catholic Church and offering degree programs in the arts and sciences, business administration, education, engineering, and nursing. There are 5 undergraduate schools and one graduate school. In addition to regional accreditation, the university has baccalaureate program accreditation with AACSB, ABET, and NLN. The library contains 310,000 volumes, 210,000 microform items, and 3863 audiovisual forms, and subscribes to 2200 periodicals. Computerized library sources and services include interlibrary loans and database searching. Special learning facilities include an art gallery, radio station, and an observatory. The 92-acre campus is in a suburban area 10 miles north of Portland. Including residence halls, there are 26 buildings on campus.

Student Life: About 58% of undergraduates are from Oregon. Students come from 35 states, 43 foreign countries, and Canada. Seventy percent are from public schools; 30% from private. Seventy-seven percent are white; 10% foreign nationals. Forty-five percent are Catholic; 34% Protestant. The average age of freshmen is 19; all undergraduates, 24. Twenty-five percent drop out by the end of their first year; 62% remain to graduate.

Housing: A total of 1100 students can be accommodated in college housing. College-sponsored living facilities include single-sex and coed dormitories. On-campus housing is guaranteed for all 4 years. Fifty-five percent of students commute. Upperclassmen and commuting freshmen may keep cars on campus.

Activities: There are no fraternities or sororities on campus. There are 50 groups on campus, including band, cheerleading, choir, chorus, drama, ethnic, honors, international, jazz band, literary magazine, newspaper, orchestra, pep band, political, professional, radio and TV, religious, social, social service, student government, and yearbook. Popular campus events include a coffee house, Christmas in April, Casino Night, Luau, volunteer services, and intercollegiate sports events.

Sports: There are 7 intercollegiate sports for men and 6 for women, and 17 intramural sports for men and 14 for women. Athletic and recreation facilities include weight rooms, a track, a gymnasium, a swimming pool, and a 5000-seat athletic and convocation center with rental equipment available for biking and camping activities.

Disabled Students: Ninety percent of the campus is accessible to disabled students. The following facilities are available: wheelchair ramps, elevators, special parking, specially equipped rest rooms, special class scheduling, lowered drinking fountains, and lowered telephones.

Services: In addition to many counseling and information services, tutoring is available in most subjects, including English and mathematics. The faculty is available for individual assistance.

Campus Safety and Security: Campus safety and security measures include 24-hour foot and vehicle patrol, escort service, informal discussions, and pamphlets, posters, and films. In addition, there are emergency telephones and lighted pathways and sidewalks.

Programs of Study: The university awards the B.A., B.S., B.A.E.Ed., B.A.M., B.A.S.Ed., B.B.A., B.M.Ed., B.S.C.E., B.S.E.E., B.S.E.M., B.S.E.S., and B.S.M.E. degrees. Master's degrees also are awarded. Bachelor's degrees are awarded in BIOLOGICAL SCIENCE (biology/biological science), BUSINESS (accounting, banking and finance, management science, and marketing/retailing/merchandising), COMMUNICATIONS AND THE ARTS (communications, dramatic arts, English, French, German, journalism, modern language, music, Spanish, and theater management), COMPUTER AND PHYSICAL SCIENCE (chemistry, computer management, computer science, mathematics, and physics), EDUCATION (elementary, music, and secondary), ENGINEERING AND ENVIRONMENTAL DESIGN (civil engineering, electrical/electronics engineering, engineering, engineering and applied science, engineering management, and mechanical engineering), HEALTH PROFESSIONS (allied health, nursing, predentistry, premedicine, prepharmacy, and preveterinary science), SOCIAL SCIENCE (criminal justice, history, interdisciplinary studies, philosophy, political science/government, prelaw, psychology, social work, sociology, and theological studies). Engineering, premedical fields, and business are the strongest academically. Engineering, business, and science have the largest enrollments.

Required: To graduate, students must complete 120 credit hours, including 24 in the major, with a minimum GPA of 2.0. Required courses include 9 hours each of philosophy and theology; 6 each of science, social sciences, and electives, and 3 each of fine arts, history, mathematics, and literature.

Special: The university offers internships through individual departments, cross-registration with members of the Oregon Independent College Association, B.A.-B.S. degrees, dual and interdisciplinary majors, including engineering chemistry and organizational communications, and pass/fail options. Study abroad may be arranged in Austria, England, Japan, France, Spain, and Germany. There is a freshman honors program on campus, as well as 9 national honor societies.

Faculty/Classroom: Fifty-five percent of faculty are male; 45%, female. All teach undergraduates. No introductory courses are taught by graduate students. The average class size in an introductory lecture is 30; in a laboratory, 20; and in a regular course offering, 20.

Admissions: About 84% of the 1993–94 applicants were accepted. About 46% of the current freshmen were in the top fifth of their class; 74% were in the top two fifths.

Requirements: A minimum GPA of 2.7 is required. The SAT I or ACT are required. The required minimum scores are 400 for each section of the SAT I and a composite score of 17 on the ACT. Graduation from an accredited secondary school or satisfactory scores on the GED are required. The high school curriculum should include courses in English composition, mathematics, social studies, science, and a foreign language. Two essays are required. AP and CLEP credits are accepted. Important factors used in the admissions decision are advanced placement or honor courses, recommendations by school officials, leadership record, extracurricular activities record, and evidence of special talent.

Procedure: Freshmen are admitted to all sessions. Entrance exams should be taken before March 15 of the senior year. Application deadlines are open. Application fee is $30. Notification is sent on a rolling basis. There are early admissions and deferred admissions plans.

Transfer: A total of 193 transfer students enrolled in 1993–94. Applicants must have a minimum GPA of 2.5. A total of 30 credits out of 120 must be completed at the university.

Visiting: There are regularly scheduled orientations for prospective students. There are guides for informal visits and visitors may sit in on classes and stay overnight at the school. To arrange for a visit, contact the Office of Admissions at (800) 227–4568 or (503) 283–7147.

Financial Aid: In 1993–94, 80% of all current freshmen and 75% of continuing students received some form of financial aid. The average freshman award was $7687. Of that total, scholarships or need-based grants averaged $4427; loans averaged $3260; and work contracts averaged $1180. Thirty-seven percent of undergraduate students work part-time. Average earnings from campus work for the school year are $1180. The average financial indebtedness of the 1992–93 graduate was $10,030. The university is a member of CSS. The college's own financial statement and the FAFSA are required. The deadline for financial aid applications is March 15.

International Students: There are currently 276 international students enrolled. The school actively recruits these students. They must take the TOEFL or the college's own test and achieve a minimum score on the TOEFL of 500.

Computers: The university provides computer facilities for student use. The mainframe is a DEC VAX 11/780. All students may utilize more than 85 microcomputers for various projects, with additional terminals designated specifically for certain computer-intensive majors such as computer science, engineering, and education. There are no time limits on using the system and no fees.

Graduates: In a recent year, 461 bachelor's degrees were awarded. The most popular majors among graduates were business (13%), engineering (8%), and communication (7%). Within an average freshman class, 62% graduate in 5 years. Some 100 companies recruited on campus in a recent year. In a recent graduating class, 90% of graduates had found employment within 6 months of graduation.

Admissions Contact: Daniel B. Reilly, Director of Admissions.

WARNER PACIFIC COLLEGE
Portland, OR 97215

B-1

(503) 775–4366, ext. 530
(800) 582–7885 (out-of-state)

Full-time: 198 men, 320 women	Faculty: 26
Part-time: 54 men, 68 women	Ph.D.s: 41%
Graduate: 10 men, 1 woman	Student/Faculty: 20 to 1
Year: semesters, summer session	Tuition: $8112
Application Deadline: August 15	Room & Board: $4000
Freshman Class: 112 applied, 87 accepted, 53 enrolled	
SAT I or ACT: required	COMPETITIVE

Warner Pacific College, founded in 1937, is a private, coeducational, liberal arts college affiliated with the Church of God. There is one undergraduate school. The library contains 42,210 volumes, 1155 microform items, and 1110 audiovisual forms, and subscribes to 233 periodicals. Computerized library sources and services include interlibrary loans and database searching. Special learning facilities include a learning resource center, an art gallery, 2 electron microscopes, and a childhood early learning center. The 14-acre campus is in an urban area 5 miles east of downtown Portland. Including residence halls, there are 30 buildings on campus.

Student Life: About 74% of undergraduates are from Oregon. Students come from 18 states, 12 foreign countries, and Canada. Seventy-eight percent are from public schools; 22% from private. Eighty-three percent are white. Fifty-one percent claim no religious affiliation; 42% are Protestant. The average age of freshmen is 21.8; all undergraduates, 28. Thirty-seven percent drop out by the end of their first year; 30% remain to graduate.

Housing: A total of 250 students can be accommodated in college housing. College-sponsored living facilities include single-sex dormitories, on-campus apartments, and married-student housing. In addition, there are language houses and special interest houses. On-campus housing is guaranteed for all 4 years. Seventy-seven percent of students commute. Alcohol is not permitted. All students may keep cars on campus.

Activities: There are no fraternities or sororities on campus. There are many groups and organizations on campus, including art, band, choir, chorale, chorus, drama, ethnic, international, jazz band, newspaper, photography, religious, social service, student government, and yearbook. Popular campus events include campus days and annual touring volleyball.

Sports: There are 10 intramural sports for men and 10 for women. Athletic and recreation facilities include a gymnasium, a weight training room, and hiking trails.

Disabled Students: Seventy-five percent of the campus is accessible to disabled students. The following facilities are available: wheelchair ramps, special parking, specially equipped rest rooms, special class scheduling, and personalized care and services.

Services: In addition to many counseling and information services, tutoring is available in most subjects. In addition, there is remedial math, reading, and writing, and testing and study skills workshops are offered.

Campus Safety and Security: Campus safety and security measures include 24-hour foot and vehicle patrol, self-defense education, escort service, and informal discussions. In addition, there are pamphlets, posters, and films and lighted pathways and sidewalks.

Programs of Study: Warner Pacific awards the B.A., and B.S degrees. Associate and master's degrees also are awarded. Bachelor's degrees are awarded in BIOLOGICAL SCIENCE (biology/biological science), BUSINESS (business administration and management), COMMUNICATIONS AND THE ARTS (English and music), COMPUTER AND PHYSICAL SCIENCE (mathematics, physical sciences, and science), EDUCATION (elementary, health, middle school, music, science, and secondary), SOCIAL SCIENCE (American studies, history, human development, liberal arts/general studies, ministries, psychology, religion, social science, social work, and sociology). Biological science, business administration, and education are the strongest academically. Business administration, human development, and music education have the largest enrollments.

Required: To graduate, students must complete 124 credits with a minimum GPA of 2.0. All students must take a core curriculum of 42 credits consisting of 9 hours in communications, 15 in humanities, and 3 each in religion, mathematics, science, fine arts, health, and physical education. A thesis also is required.

Special: Cross-registration with local consortium schools, accelerated degree programs in human development and business administration, and study abroad through the Christian College Coalition are offered. Internships, work-study programs, double majors, individualized majors, independent study credit for life and military experience, and pass/fail options are available. There is a freshman honors program on campus, as well as 2 national honor societies. Three departments have honors programs.

Faculty/Classroom: Forty-one percent of faculty are male; 59%, female. All faculty both teach undergraduates and do research. No introductory courses are taught by graduate students. The average class size in an introductory lecture is 15; in a laboratory, 10; and in a regular course offering, 15.

Admissions: About 78% of the 1993–94 applicants were accepted. The SAT scores for the 1993–94 freshman class were as follows: Verbal—86% below 500, 7% between 500 and 599, and 7% between 600 and 700; Math—57% below 500, 39% between 500 and 599, and 4% between 600 and 700. The ACT scores were 50% below 21, 40% between 21 and 23, and 10% between 24 and 26.

Requirements: A minimum GPA of 2.0 is required. The SAT I, with a recommended minimum composite score of 750, or the ACT, with a minimum composite score of 18, is required. Applicants must be graduates of an accredited secondary school. The GED is accepted. AP and CLEP credits are accepted. Important factors used in the admissions decision are evidence of special talent, leadership record, advanced placement or honor courses, personality, intangible qualities, and extracurricular activities record.

Procedure: Freshmen are admitted to all sessions. Early decision applications should be filed by January 15; regular applications, by August 15 for fall entry and December 15 for spring entry, along with an application fee of $50. Notification is sent on a rolling basis. There are early decision, early admissions, and deferred admissions plans.

Transfer: About 100 transfer students enrolled in 1993–94. Applicants for transfer must provide transcripts from their previous college. A minimum GPA of 2.0 is required. A total of 30 credits out of 124 must be completed at Warner Pacific.

Visiting: There are regularly scheduled orientations for prospective students, including 3 visitation weekends, academic fairs, scholarship days, attending a sampling of classes and student activities, and a retreat. There are guides for informal visits and visitors may sit in on classes and stay overnight at the school. To arrange for a visit, contact June Ensey at (503) 775–4366, ext. 491.

Financial Aid: In a recent year, 58% of all current freshmen and 75% of continuing students received some form of financial aid. About 49% of freshmen and 63% of continuing students received need-based aid. The average freshman award was $6489. Of that total, scholarships or need-based grants averaged $2400 ($3000 maximum); loans averaged $1541 ($4000 maximum); and work contracts averaged $1519 ($2000 maximum). Twenty-two percent of undergraduate students work part-time. Average earnings from campus work for the school year are $1722. The average financial indebtedness of the 1992–93 graduate was $12,500. Warner Pacific is a member of CSS. The FAF, FFS or SFS and the college's own financial statement are required. The deadline for financial aid applications is May 1.

International Students: There are currently 50 international students enrolled. The school actively recruits these students. They must take the TOEFL, the University of Michigan Language Test, the Comprehensive English Language Test, or the college's own test.

Computers: The college provides computer facilities for student use. Departmental computers are located in student government offices. All students may access the system. It may be used during hours posted by the computer laboratory. There are no time limits on using the system.

Graduates: In 1992–93, 120 bachelor's degrees were awarded. The most popular majors among graduates were business administration (32%), human development (23%), and music education (8%). Within an average freshman class, 1% graduate in 3 years, 17% in 4 years, 12% in 5 years, and 3% in 6 years.

Admissions Contact: John Barber, Director of Admissions.

WESTERN BAPTIST COLLEGE   2B

Salem, OR 97301-9392   (503) 581-8600; (800) 845-3005 (in-state)

Full-time: 229 men, 284 women	Faculty: 22; IIB, --$
Part-time: 10 men, 13 women	Ph.D.s: 22%
Graduate: none	Student/Faculty: 23 to 1
Year: semesters	Tuition: $8700
Application Deadline: open	Room & Board: $3700

Freshman Class: 259 applied, 219 accepted, 118 enrolled

SAT I Verbal/Math: 404/429   **LESS COMPETITIVE**

Western Baptist College is a coeducational, Christian liberal arts institution offering degrees in biblical-theological studies, business administration, education, humanities, mathematics, physical education, social sciences, psychology, intercultural studies, and youth work. The library contains 63,014 volumes, 1347 microform items, and 2818 audiovisual forms, and subscribes to 385 periodicals. Computerized library sources and services include interlibrary loans. The 107-acre campus is in an urban area in Salem. Including residence halls, there are 20 buildings on campus.

Student Life: About 58% of undergraduates are from Oregon. Students come from 25 states, 5 foreign countries, and Canada. Fifty-six percent are from public schools; 25% from private. Eighty-eight percent are white. Most are Protestant. The average age of freshmen is 18. Ten percent drop out by the end of their first year; 45% remain to graduate.

Housing: A total of 360 students can be accommodated in college housing. College-sponsored living facilities include single-sex dormitories. On-campus housing is guaranteed for the freshman year only and is available on a first-come, first-served basis. Priority is given to out-of-town students. Fifty-one percent of students live on campus. Alcohol is not permitted. All students may keep cars on campus.

Activities: There are no fraternities or sororities on campus. There are 11 groups on campus, including cheerleading, choir, chorale, chorus, drama, pep band, social, student government, and yearbook. Popular campus events include Charter Day (Homecoming), Christmas Alive, and Western Daze.

Sports: There is no sports program at Western. There are 3 intercollegiate sports each for men and women, and 3 intramural sports each. Athletic and recreation facilities include a sports center with a gymnasium, soccer and baseball fields, archery, and a tennis court.

Disabled Students: Elevators are available.

Services: In addition to many counseling and information services, tutoring is available in some subjects, as needed.

Campus Safety and Security: Campus safety and security measures include informal discussions and lighted pathways and sidewalks.

Programs of Study: Western awards the B.A., B.S., and Th.B. degrees. Associate degrees are also awarded. Bachelor's degrees are awarded in BUSINESS (business administration and management), COMPUTER AND PHYSICAL SCIENCE (mathematics), EDUCATION (education and physical), SOCIAL SCIENCE (biblical studies, crosscultural studies, humanities, psychology, and social science). Education, psychology, and business have the largest enrollments.

Required: To graduate, students must complete 128 credits, with 25 to 50 in the major. The minimum required GPA is 2.0 for most programs; the education major requires a 3.0 GPA. The general education core consists of 45 credits. Courses must be taken in the Bible, humanities, social sciences, mathematics, science, and physical education. A computer literacy/competency course is also required.

Special: Western offers a preseminary co-op program, cross-registration with Oregon Independent Colleges, internships with the approval of a program advisor, accelerated programs in management and communication and in family studies, and B.A.-B.S. degrees. There is a freshman honors program on campus. Three departments have honors programs.

Faculty/Classroom: Seventy-one percent of faculty are male; 29%, female. The average class size in an introductory lecture is 50 and in a laboratory, 15.

Admissions: About 85% of the 1993–94 applicants were accepted. The SAT scores for the 1993–94 freshman class were as follows: Verbal—78% below 500, 18% between 500 and 599, and 4% between 600 and 700; Math—62% below 500, 34% between 500 and 599, and 4% between 600 and 700.

Requirements: A minimum GPA of 2.5 is required. The SAT I or ACT is required, as is an essay. AP and CLEP credits are accepted. Important factors used in the admissions decision are extracurricular activities record, leadership record, evidence of special talent, advanced placement or honor courses, and recommendations by alumni.

Procedure: Freshmen are admitted fall and spring. Application deadlines are open. Application fee is $25. Notification is sent on a rolling basis.

Transfer: About 100 transfer students enrolled in 1993–94. Transfer applicants are required to have a minimum 2.0 cumulative college GPA and submit the college transcript and 3 references. A total of 30 credits out of 128 must be completed at Western.

Visiting: There are regularly scheduled orientations for prospective students, including scheduled weekend visits and Western Daze. There are guides for informal visits and visitors may sit in on classes and stay overnight at the school. To arrange for a visit, contact the Admissions Office at (503) 581-8600.

International Students: There are currently 5 international students enrolled. They must take the TOEFL and achieve a minimum score of 500.

Computers: The college provides computer facilities for student use. The microcomputer laboratory contains 12 PCs. All students may access the system. There are no fees.

Graduates: In a recent year, 103 bachelor's degrees were awarded. The most popular majors among graduates were management and communication (28%), education (20%), and psychology (12%). Within an average freshman class, 34% graduate in 4 years, 43% in 5 years, and 49% in 6 years.

Admissions Contact: Palmer Muntz, Director of Admissions and Financial Aid.

WESTERN OREGON STATE COLLEGE   B-2

Monmouth, OR 97361   (503) 838-8211

Full-time, part-time: 3715	Faculty: 136; IIA, --$
Graduate: 116 men, 168 women	Ph.D.s: 85%
Year: quarters, summer session	Student/Faculty: 24 to 1
Application Deadline: April 15	Tuition: $2640 ($6810)
	Room & Board: $3540

Freshman Class: 1438 applied, 1279 accepted, 695 enrolled

SAT I or ACT: required   **COMPETITIVE**

Western Oregon State College, founded in 1856, is a publicly funded institution and a member of the Oregon State System of Higher Education. Western offers undergraduate programs in education and arts and sciences. There are 2 undergraduate schools and 1 graduate school. In addition to regional accreditation, WOSC has baccalaureate program accreditation with NASM and NCATE. The library contains 180,000 volumes and 307,000 microform items, and subscribes to 1630 periodicals. Computerized library sources and services include the card catalog, interlibrary loans, and database searching. Special learning facilities include a learning resource center, an art gallery, a tv station, and the Paul Jensen Arctic Museum. The 134-acre campus is in a rural area 15 miles west of Salem. Including residence halls, there are 34 buildings on campus.

Student Life: About 94% of undergraduates are from Oregon. Students come from 20 foreign countries and Canada. Ninety-two percent are white. The average age of all undergraduates is 22. Thirty-seven percent drop out by the end of their first year.

Housing: A total of 1050 students can be accommodated in college housing. College-sponsored living facilities include coed dormitories, on-campus apartments, and married-student housing. In addition, there are special interest floors. On-campus housing is guaranteed for all 4 years. Alcohol is not permitted. All students may keep cars on campus.

Activities: There are no fraternities or sororities on campus. There are 50 groups on campus, including art, band, cheerleading, chess, choir, chorale, chorus, computers, dance, drama, ethnic, gay, honors, international, jazz band, literary magazine, marching band, musical theater, newspaper, orchestra, political, tv, religious, social, social service, student government, and yearbook. Popular campus events include Homecoming, Annual Christmas Tree Lighting, Alcohol Awareness Week, and Family Day.

Sports: There are 5 intercollegiate sports each for men and women, and 25 intramural sports each for men and women. Athletic and recreation facilities include a sports field, a physical education building, a swimming pool, a weight room, indoor/outdoor tennis courts, handball and racquetball courts, a dance studio, archery facilities, and baseball, softball, and soccer fields.

Disabled Students: Ninety percent of the campus is accessible to disabled students. The following facilities are available: wheelchair ramps, elevators, special parking, specially equipped rest rooms, special class scheduling, lowered drinking fountains, lowered telephones, and the Regional Resource Center of Deafness.

Services: In addition to many counseling and information services, tutoring is available in most subjects. In addition, there is a reader service for the blind, and remedial math, reading, and writing. There is a student support and services program for first-generation, low income, and physically disabled students.

Campus Safety and Security: Campus safety and security measures include 24-hour foot and vehicle patrol, self-defense education, escort service, and informal discussions. In addition, there are pamphlets, posters, and films, emergency telephones, and lighted pathways and sidewalks.

Programs of Study: WOSC awards the B.A. and B.S. degrees. Associate and master's degrees also are awarded. Bachelor's degrees are awarded in BIOLOGICAL SCIENCE (biology/biological science), BUSINESS (business administration and management), COMMUNICATIONS AND THE ARTS (English, fine arts, languages, music, Spanish, and speech/debate/rhetoric), COMPUTER AND PHYSICAL SCIENCE (chemistry, computer science, mathematics, natural sciences, and science), EDUCATION (elementary, foreign languages, health, mathematics, physical, science, secondary, and social studies), SOCIAL SCIENCE (corrections, economics, fire protection, geography, history, humanities, interdisciplinary studies, international studies, interpreter for the deaf, law enforcement and corrections, political science/government, psychology, public affairs, and social science). Education, business, and psychology are the strongest academically. Education, criminal justice, business, and psychology have the largest enrollments.

Required: To graduate, students must complete a total of 192 quarter hours with a minimum GPA of 2.0. Between 45 and 72 hours are required in major. All students must fulfill the requirements of the liberal arts core curriculum. In addition, they must take 5 hours of physical education and 2 hours of computer literacy.

Special: Most academic majors in liberal arts and sciences offer a B.A.-B.S degree option. Dual majors, study abroad through the Oregon State System of Higher Education, and student-designed majors in interdisciplinary studies are available. Nondegree study and pass/fail options are possible. There is a freshman honors program on campus, as well as 4 national honor societies, including Phi Beta Kappa.

Faculty/Classroom: Seventy percent of faculty are male; 30%, female. All teach undergraduates. No introductory courses are taught by graduate students. The average class size in an introductory lecture is 50; in a laboratory, 15; and in a regular course offering, 25.

Admissions: About 89% of the 1993–94 applicants were accepted.

Requirements: A minimum GPA of 2.8 is required. The SAT I, with a minimum composite score of 890, or the ACT, with a minimum composite score of 21, is required. Graduation from an accredited secondary school or satisfactory scores on the GED are required. Students must have 14 academic credits or Carnegie units. High school courses must include 4 years of English, 3 years each of science and social studies, 2 years of mathematics, and 2 years of electives in college preparatory courses. AP and CLEP credits are accepted.

Procedure: Freshmen are admitted to all sessions. Entrance exams should be taken during the junior or senior year. Applications should be filed by April 15 for fall entry, October 15 for winter entry, and January 15 for spring entry, along with an application fee of $50. Notification is sent on a rolling basis. A waiting list is an active part of the admissions procedure, with about 15% of applicants on the list.

Transfer: About 650 transfer students enrolled in 1993–94. Transfer students must have a minimum GPA of 2.0. Applicants with fewer than 24 quarter hours must also meet freshman admission requirements. A total of 60 quarter credits, with 45 of the last 60 on campus, out of 192 must be completed at WOSC.

Visiting: There are regularly scheduled orientations for prospective students, consisting of a 1 day program for students and a parent program; all admitted students must make arrangements to register during orientation in July to reserve their enrollment slot. There are guides for informal visits and visitors may sit in on classes. To arrange for a visit, contact the Admissions Office at (503) 838–8211.

Financial Aid: In a recent year, 65% of all current freshmen and 55% of continuing students received some form of financial aid. About 95% of freshmen and 90% of continuing students received need-based aid. Scholarships or need-based grants averaged $1526 ($3000 maximum); loans averaged $1473 ($2625 maximum); and work contracts averaged $361 ($1000 maximum). Fifty percent of undergraduate students work part-time. Average earnings from campus work for the school year are $500. The average financial indebtedness of the 1992–93 graduate was $13,000. WOSC is a member of CSS. The FAFSA financial statement is required. The deadline for financial aid applications is March 1.

International Students: There are currently 100 international students enrolled. They must take the TOEFL or the University of Michigan Language Test and achieve a minimum score on the TOEFL of 500.

Computers: The college provides computer facilities for student use. The mainframes are a DEC VAX 2850 and a Sequent. There are IBM/Macintosh PCs available in the Instructional Technology Center. All students may access the system. There are no time limits on using the system and no fees.

Graduates: In a recent year, 771 bachelor's degrees were awarded. The most popular majors among graduates were education (42%), business (14%), and psychology (12%). Some 27 companies recruited on campus in 1992–93. In the 1992 graduating class, 9% of all graduates were enrolled in graduate school within 6 months of graduation; 51% had found employment.

Admissions Contact: Craig Kolins, Admissions.

WILLAMETTE UNIVERSITY
B-2
Salem, OR 97301 (503) 370–6303

Full-time: 712 men, 883 women	Faculty: 108; IIB, +$
Part-time: 13 men, 30 women	Ph.D.s: 90%
Graduate: 429 men, 268 women	Student/Faculty: 15 to 1
Year: semesters	Tuition: $13,575
Application Deadline: February 1	Room & Board: $4420
Freshman Class: 1658 applied, 1314 accepted, 396 enrolled	
SAT I Verbal/Math: 520/580	ACT: 26 VERY COMPETITIVE

Willamette University, founded in 1842, is an independent, coeducational, liberal arts institution. There are 3 graduate schools. In addition to regional accreditation, Willamette has baccalaureate program accreditation with NASM. The 2 libraries contain 225,000 volumes, 7000 microform items, and 3800 audiovisual forms, and subscribe to 1395 periodicals. Computerized library sources and services include the card catalog, interlibrary loans, and database searching. Special learning facilities include a learning resource center, art gallery, natural history museum, radio station, and botanical and Japanese gardens. The 72-acre campus is in a suburban area 45 minutes south of Portland. Including residence halls, there are 42 buildings on campus.

Student Life: About 55% of undergraduates are from out-of-state, mostly the West. Students come from 36 states, 11 foreign countries, and Canada. Eighty-five percent are from public schools; 15% from private. Eighty-eight percent are white. Forty-four percent are Protestant; 28% claim no religious affiliation; 17% Catholic. The average age of freshmen is 18; all undergraduates, 21. Ten percent drop out by the end of their first year; 73% remain to graduate.

Housing: A total of 1140 students can be accommodated in college housing. College-sponsored living facilities include single-sex and coed dormitories, off-campus apartments, fraternity houses, and sorority houses. In addition, there are language houses and special interest houses. On-campus housing is guaranteed for all 4 years. Seventy percent of students live on campus; of those, 85% remain on campus on weekends. All students may keep cars on campus.

Activities: About 35% of men belong to 6 national fraternities; about 35% of women belong to 3 national sororities. There are 80 groups on campus, including art, band, cheerleading, chess, choir, chorale, chorus, computers, dance, drama, ethnic, film, gay, honors, international, jazz band, literary magazine, musical theater, newspaper, opera, orchestra, pep band, photography, political, professional, radio, religious, social, social service, student government, symphony, and yearbook. Popular campus events include Freshman Glee, International Extravaganza, and Understanding Gender Perspectives.

Sports: There are 12 intercollegiate sports for men and 10 for women, and 15 intramural sports for men and 15 for women. Athletic and recreation facilities include a physical education and recreation center, a new 4000-seat football stadium, a 3000-seat indoor gymnasium, a 1200-seat auditorium, a new baseball stadium, a soccer field, a new all-weather track, a new track building, 2 other gymnasiums, a mini-Olympic indoor swimming pool, an outdoor swimming pool, 3 indoor and 10 outdoor tennis courts, handball/racquetball courts, weight training facilities, and other practice fields.

Disabled Students: Ninety percent of the campus is accessible to disabled students. The following facilities are available: wheelchair ramps, elevators, special parking, specially equipped rest rooms, special class scheduling, lowered drinking fountains, lowered telephones, special equipment, and readers.

Services: In addition to many counseling and information services, tutoring is available in most subjects. In addition, there is a reader service for the blind. Three full-time therapists are available for students on an individual need basis.

Campus Safety and Security: Campus safety and security measures include 24-hour foot and vehicle patrol, self defense education, escort service, and informal discussions. In addition, there are pamphlets, posters, and films, emergency telephones, lighted pathways

and sidewalks, formal programs and education, and a weekly published campus safety report.

Programs of Study: Willamette awards the B.A., B.S., B.M., B.Mus.Ed., and B.M.T. degrees. Master's and doctoral degrees also are awarded. Bachelor's degrees are awarded in BIOLOGICAL SCIENCE (biology/biological science), BUSINESS (business economics), COMMUNICATIONS AND THE ARTS (dramatic arts, English, fine arts, French, German, music, Spanish, and speech/debate/rhetoric), COMPUTER AND PHYSICAL SCIENCE (chemistry, computer science, mathematics, and physics), ENGINEERING AND ENVIRONMENTAL DESIGN (environmental science), HEALTH PROFESSIONS (predentistry and premedicine), SOCIAL SCIENCE (economics, history, humanities, international relations, philosophy, political science/government, prelaw, psychology, religion, and sociology). Social sciences and physical science are the strongest academically. Social sciences have the largest enrollment.

Required: To graduate, students must complete a total of 124 semester hours, including a minimum of 32 in the major, with a minimum GPA of 2.0. All students must complete general education requirements in fine arts, humanities, literature, interdisciplinary courses, natural sciences, and social sciences, and meet mathematics and English proficiency levels. Freshmen are required to take a World Views seminar. Seniors are required to complete a senior thesis or other project in their major.

Special: Willamette offers internships with the state and city government, a Washington semester, and a 3–2 engineering degree with Washington University, University of Southern California, and Columbia University. Nondegree study, B.A.-B.S. degrees, dual majors, work-study programs with numerous employers in the Salem area and at the university, and pass/fail options are also available. Study-abroad programs are available in 9 countries. There are 3–2 degrees in management, forestry, and computer science. There are 15 national honor societies on campus.

Faculty/Classroom: Sixty-three percent of faculty are male; 37%, female. All both teach undergraduates and do research. No introductory courses are taught by graduate students. The average class size in an introductory lecture is 35; in a laboratory, 20; and in a regular course offering, 15.

Admissions: About 79% of the 1993–94 applicants were accepted. The SAT scores for the 1993–94 freshman class were as follows: Verbal—36% below 500, 42% between 500 and 599, 18% between 600 and 700, and 3% above 700; Math—16% below 500, 40% between 500 and 599, 34% between 600 and 700, and 9% above 700. The ACT scores were 6% below 21, 23% between 21 and 23, 33% between 24 and 26, 19% between 27 and 28, and 16% above 28. About 73% of the current freshmen were in the top fifth of their class; 92% were in the top two fifths. There were 15 National Merit finalists and 28 semifinalists. About 24 freshmen graduated first in their class.

Requirements: Willamette requires applicants to be in the upper 50% of their class. A minimum GPA of 2.0 is required. The SAT I or ACT is required. Graduation from an accredited secondary school or satisfactory scores on the GED are required. Students must have 14 academic credits, including a minimum of 4 years of English, 3 years each of mathematics, social studies, or history, and 2 years of a foreign language. Two essays are required, and an interview is recommended. Portfolios or auditions are recommended for art and music students. AP credits are accepted. Important factors used in the admissions decision are advanced placement or honor courses, leadership record, evidence of special talent, extracurricular activities record, and personality, intangible qualities.

Procedure: Freshmen are admitted fall and spring. Entrance exams should be taken in November. Early decision applications should be filed by December 1; regular applications, by February 1 for fall entry and November 1 for spring entry, along with an application fee of $35. Notification of early decision is sent January 1; regular decision, April 1. There are early decision, early admissions, and deferred admissions plans. About 90 early decision candidates were accepted for the 1993–94 class. A waiting list is an active part of the admissions procedure, with about 4% of applicants on the list.

Transfer: About 100 transfer students enrolled in 1993–94. Transfer students must submit transcripts for all college and high school courses. A minimum GPA of 2.0 is required. A total of 60 credits out of 124 must be completed at Willamette.

Visiting: There are regularly scheduled orientations for prospective students, consisting of fall and spring campus preview days, tours, and faculty and student presentations. There are guides for informal visits, and visitors may sit in on classes and stay overnight at the school. To arrange for a visit, contact Martha Cripe at (503) 370–6303.

Financial Aid: In 1993–94 75% of all current freshmen and 77% of continuing students received some form of financial aid. About 70% of freshmen and 72% of continuing students received need-based aid. The average freshman award was $12,300. Of that total, scholarships or need-based grants averaged $6950 ($13,575 maximum); loans averaged $4200 ($4875 maximum); and work contracts averaged $1000 ($2000 maximum). Seventy-five percent of undergraduate students work part-time. Average earnings from campus work for the school year are $1200. The average financial indebtedness of the 1992–93 graduate was $12,500. Willamette is a member of CSS. The FAFSA financial statement is required. The deadline for financial aid applications is February 1.

International Students: There are currently 67 international students enrolled. The school actively recruits these students. They must take the TOEFL and achieve a minimum score of 550. The student must also take the SAT I or the ACT.

Computers: The college provides computer facilities for student use. The mainframe is a Sun SPARC 4/470. More than 100 IBM and Apple Macintosh microcomputers are available for student use in the computer laboratory, library, and science building. Students may access the mainframe from their residence hall rooms through telephone lines. All students may access the system. It may be used 24 hours per day. There are no time limits on using the system and no fees.

Graduates: In 1992–93 389 bachelor's degrees were awarded. The most popular majors among graduates were economics (19%), psychology (16%), and politics (11%). Within an average freshman class, 68% graduate in 4 years and 73% in 5 years. Some 35 companies recruited on campus in 1992–93. In the 1992 graduating class, 20% of the men and 10% of the women were enrolled in graduate school within 6 months of graduation; 60% of all graduates had found employment.

Admissions Contact: James M. Sumner, Dean of University Admissions.

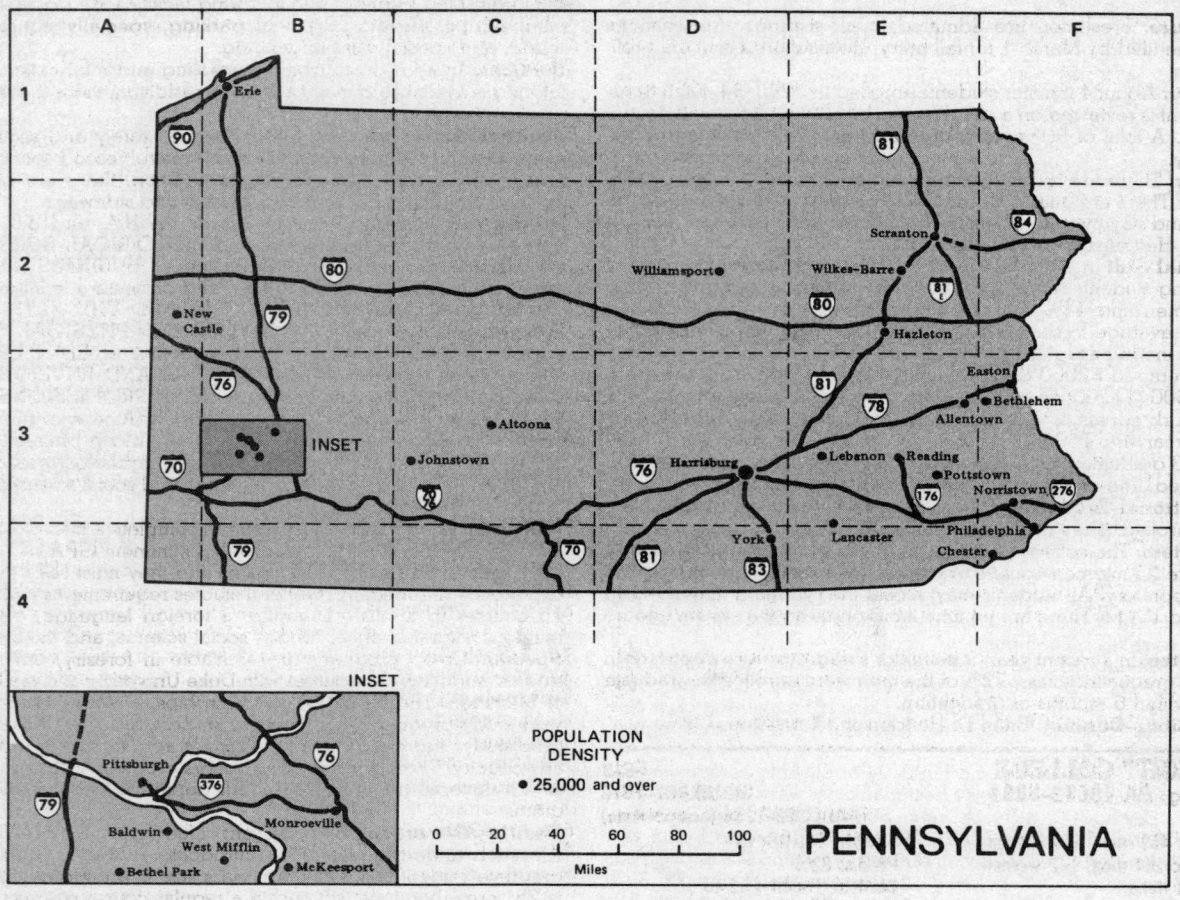

POPULATION DENSITY

● 25,000 and over

0 20 40 60 80 100
Miles

PENNSYLVANIA

ACADEMY OF THE NEW CHURCH

Bryn Athyn, PA 19009

F-3

(215) 938-2511

Full-time: 54 men, 51 women
Part-time: 5 men, 15 women
Graduate: 5 men
Year: trimesters
Application Deadline: March 1
Freshman Class: 58 applied, 58 accepted, 51 enrolled
SAT I Verbal/Math: 500/530

Faculty: 20; IIB, +$
Ph.D.s: 30%
Student/Faculty: 5 to 1
Tuition: $3990
Room & Board: $3351

NONCOMPETITIVE

Academy of the New Church, founded in 1877, is an independent, coeducational liberal arts institution affiliated with the General Church of the New Jerusalem. There is one graduate school. The 2 libraries contain 95,000 volumes, 1400 microform items, and 493 audiovisual forms, and subscribe to 270 periodicals. Special learning facilities include the Glencairn Museum. The 170-acre campus is in a suburban area 15 miles north of Philadelphia. Including residence halls, there are 12 buildings on campus.

Student Life: About 51% of undergraduates are from out-of-state, mostly the Midwest. Students come from 8 states, 12 foreign countries, and Canada. Twenty-five percent are from public schools; 75% from private. Twenty-eight percent are foreign nationals. Most students have been baptized into the Church of the New Jerusalem. The average age of freshmen is 18; all undergraduates, 21. Five percent drop out by the end of their first year.

Housing: A total of 103 students can be accommodated in college housing. College-sponsored living facilities include single-sex dormitories and off-campus apartments. On-campus housing is guaranteed for all 4 years. Seventy percent of students live on campus; of those, all remain on campus on weekends. Alcohol is not permitted. All students may keep cars on campus.

Activities: There are no fraternities or sororities on campus. There are 9 groups on campus, including chorale, dance, drama, political, religious, social, social service, student government, and yearbook. Popular campus events include Charter Day (Homecoming) and the annual college trip.

Sports: There are 3 intercollegiate sports for men and 4 for women, and 6 intramural sports for men and 6 for women. Athletic and recreation facilities include a field house, a 500-seat gymnasium, an outdoor skating rink, soccer and field hockey fields, and tennis courts.

Disabled Students: Seventy-five percent of the campus is accessible to disabled students. The following facilities are available: wheelchair ramps and special parking.

Services: In addition to many counseling and information services, tutoring is available in some subjects, including English and mathematics.

Campus Safety and Security: Campus safety and security measures include emergency telephones, lighted pathways and sidewalks, and an 18-hour foot and vehicle patrol.

Programs of Study: The academy awards the B.A. and B.S. degrees. Associate and master's degrees also are awarded. Bachelor's degrees are awarded in EDUCATION (education), SOCIAL SCIENCE (interdisciplinary studies and religion).

Required: To graduate, students must complete a total of 136 credit hours with a minimum GPA of 1.9. All students must take required courses in religion, English composition, introduction to literature, and philosophy.

Special: Cross-registration is available with Holy Family College. Also available are co-op interdisciplinary programs, a general studies degree, student-designed majors, nondegree study, and study abroad in Scotland and England in association with Beaver College.

Faculty/Classroom: Eighty percent of faculty are male; 20%, female. All teach undergraduates. No introductory courses are taught by graduate students. The average class size in an introductory lecture is 20 and in a laboratory, 15.

Admissions: All 1993–94 applicants were accepted. The SAT scores for the 1993–94 freshman class were as follows: Verbal—48% below 500, 28% between 500 and 599, 21% between 600 and 700, and 3% above 700; Math—41% below 500, 33% between 500 and 599, 23% between 600 and 700, and 3% above 700. There was 1 National Merit finalist. About 2 freshmen graduated first in their class.

Requirements: The SAT I is required. Graduation from an accredited secondary school or satisfactory scores on the GED are required. An interview is recommended. AP and CLEP credits are accepted.

Important factors used in the admissions decision are personality, intangible qualities, advanced placement or honor courses, evidence of special talent, leadership record, and recommendations by school officials.

Procedure: Freshmen are admitted to all sessions. Applications should be filed by March 1 for fall entry. Notification is sent on a rolling basis.

Transfer: About 4 transfer students enrolled in 1993–94. Each transfer student is reviewed on a case-by-case basis. An interview is recommended. A total of 30 credits out of 136 must be completed at the academy.

Visiting: There are regularly scheduled orientations for prospective students. There are guides for informal visits, and visitors may sit in on classes and stay overnight at the school. To arrange for a visit, contact Brian D. Henderson at (215) 938–2511.

Financial Aid: In 1993–94 43% of all current freshmen and 44% of continuing students received some form of financial aid. About 43% of freshmen and 44% of continuing students received need-based aid. The average freshman award was $3611. Of that total, scholarships or need-based grants averaged $1600 ($5200 maximum); loans averaged $2000 ($5200 maximum); and work contracts averaged $600 ($1200 maximum). Thirty percent of undergraduate students work part-time. Average earnings from campus work for the school year are $560. The average financial indebtedness of the 1992–93 graduate was $2370. The college's own financial statement is required. The deadline for financial aid applications is April 1.

International Students: There are currently 40 international students enrolled. They must take the TOEFL.

Computers: The college provides computer facilities for student use. There are 25 microcomputers available for academic use in the computer laboratory. All students may access the system. It may be used 8 A.M. to 1 A.M. There are no time limits on using the system and no fees.

Graduates: In a recent year, 9 bachelor's degrees were awarded. In a recent graduating class, 22% of the men were enrolled in graduate school within 6 months of graduation.

Admissions Contact: Brian D. Henderson, Admissions Office.

ALBRIGHT COLLEGE
Reading, PA 19612–5234

E-3

(215) 921–7512
(800) 252–1856 (out-of-state)

Full-time: 459 men, 514 women	Faculty: 79; IIB, av$
Part-time: 164 men, 142 women	Ph.Ds: 82%
Graduate: none	Student/Faculty: 12 to 1
Year: 4-1-4, summer session	Tuition: $15,010
Application Deadline: February 15	Room & Board: $4250
Freshman Class: 1041 applied, 841 accepted, 235 enrolled	
SAT I Verbal/Math: 480/540	ACT: 22 COMPETITIVE

Albright College, founded in 1856, is a private, coeducational liberal arts institution affiliated with the United Methodist Church. The 2 libraries contain 175,000 volumes, 9000 microform items, and 6800 audiovisual forms, and subscribe to 1002 periodicals. Computerized library sources and services include interlibrary loans and database searching. Special learning facilities include an art gallery, a radio station, a multicultural center, and centers for women and child development and psychological testing. The 110-acre campus is in a suburban area 55 miles west of Philadelphia. Including residence halls, there are 36 buildings on campus.

Student Life: About 57% of undergraduates are from Pennsylvania. Students come from 28 states and 23 foreign countries. Seventy-seven percent are from public schools; 23% from private. Eighty-seven percent are white. Thirty-five percent are Protestant; 34% Catholic; 24% claim no religious affiliation. The average age of freshmen is 18; all undergraduates, 20. Thirteen percent drop out by the end of their first year; 75% remain to graduate.

Housing: A total of 1085 students can be accommodated in college housing. College-sponsored living facilities include single-sex and coed dormitories and on-campus apartments. In addition, there are honors houses, language houses, and special interest houses. On-campus housing is guaranteed for all 4 years. Eighty-nine percent of students live on campus; of those, 95% remain on campus on weekends. Upperclassmen may keep cars on campus.

Activities: About 25% of men belong to 6 national fraternities; about 27% of women belong to 4 national sororities. There are 70 groups on campus, including band, cheerleading, chess, choir, chorus, computers, drama, ethnic, film, gay, honors, international, jazz band, literary magazine, musical theater, newspaper, photography, political, professional, radio and TV, religious, social, social service, student government, and yearbook. Popular campus events include MDA Dance Marathon, Greek Weekend, Homecoming, Spring Fever Weekend, and Alumni Weekend.

Sports: There are 10 intercollegiate sports for men and 9 for women, and 3 intramural sports for men and 4 for women. Athletic and recreation facilities include a 6000-seat stadium, baseball and soccer fields, indoor and outdoor tracks, a bowling alley, a swimming pool, and racquetball courts.

Disabled Students: Seventy-five percent of the campus is accessible to disabled students. The following facilities are available: wheelchair ramps, elevators, special parking, specially equipped rest rooms, and special class scheduling.

Services: In addition to many counseling and information services, tutoring is available in every subject. In addition, there is a reader service for the blind.

Campus Safety and Security: Campus safety and security measures include 24-hour foot and vehicle patrol, escort service, shuttle buses, and informal discussions. In addition, there are pamphlets, posters, and films and lighted pathways and sidewalks.

Programs of Study: Albright awards the B.A. and B.S. degrees. Bachelor's degrees are awarded in BIOLOGICAL SCIENCE (biochemistry and biology/biological science), BUSINESS (accounting, apparel and accessories marketing, and business administration and management), COMMUNICATIONS AND THE ARTS (English, French, and Spanish), COMPUTER AND PHYSICAL SCIENCE (chemistry, computer science, and mathematics), EDUCATION (elementary and secondary), ENGINEERING AND ENVIRONMENTAL DESIGN (environmental science), HEALTH PROFESSIONS (medical laboratory technology), SOCIAL SCIENCE (American studies, child care/child and family studies, economics, history, philosophy, political science/government, psychobiology, psychology, religion, and textiles and clothing). Business, sciences, and social sciences have the largest enrollments.

Required: To graduate, students must complete a total of 32 courses, including 13 to 14 in the major, with a minimum GPA of 2.0. All students take 1 interdisciplinary course and they must fulfill the cultural experience requirement. General studies requirements include 11 to 15 courses in English, literature, a foreign language, philosophy/religion, natural science, history, social science, and the arts.

Special: Co-op programs are available in forestry, environmental studies, and natural resources with Duke University and the University of Michigan. The school offers internships, a Washington semester, work-study programs, dual majors, student-designed majors, nondegree study, and pass/fail options. Study abroad may be arranged in any country. There is a freshman honors program on campus, as well as 11 national honor societies. All departments have honors programs.

Faculty/Classroom: Sixty percent of faculty are male; 40%, female. All teach undergraduates. No introductory courses are taught by graduate students. The average class size in an introductory lecture is 25; in a laboratory, 15; and in a regular course offering, 15.

Admissions: About 81% of the 1993–94 applicants were accepted. About 51% of the current freshmen were in the top fifth of their class; 80% were in the top two fifths.

Requirements: The SAT I or ACT is required. SAT II: Subject tests in writing, mathematics, and a foreign language are recommended for placement purposes. Graduation from an accredited secondary school or satisfactory scores on the GED are required for admission. Students must have a total of 15 Carnegie units including 4 years of English, 2 years each of a foreign language, mathematics, science, and social studies, and 3 electives in college preparatory subjects. An essay is required, and an interview highly recommended. AP and CLEP credits are accepted. Important factors used in the admissions decision are advanced placement or honor courses, evidence of special talent, leadership record, personality, intangible qualities, and extracurricular activities record.

Procedure: Freshmen are admitted fall and spring. Entrance exams should be taken during the spring of the junior year or the fall of the senior year. Applications should be filed by February 15 for fall entry and December 15 for spring entry, along with an application fee of $25. Notification is sent on a rolling basis. There are early admissions and deferred admissions plans.

Transfer: About 30 transfer students enrolled in 1993–94. Transfer students must have a minimum GPA of 2.5. A total of 16 course units out of 32 must be completed at Albright.

Visiting: There are regularly scheduled orientations for prospective students, including an interview with a counselor and a tour of the campus with a currently enrolled student. There are guides for informal visits and visitors may sit in on classes and stay overnight at the school. To arrange for a visit, contact the Admissions Office at (800) 252–1856.

Financial Aid: In 1993–94, 90% of all current freshmen received some form of financial aid. About 65% of freshmen and 60% of continuing students received need-based aid. The average freshman award was $4600. Of that total, scholarships or need-based grants averaged $6700 ($10,000 maximum); loans averaged $2340 ($4600 maximum); and work contracts averaged $400 ($2000 maximum). Nearly all undergraduate students work part-time. Average earnings from campus work for the school year was $670. The average financial indebtedness of the 1992–93 graduate was $9600. Albright is a member of CSS. The FAF and the Pennsylvania grant form

for state residents are required. The deadline for financial aid applications is April 1.

International Students: There are currently 48 international students enrolled. The school actively recruits these students. They must take the TOEFL and achieve a minimum score of 550.

Computers: The college provides computer facilities for student use. The mainframe is a DEC MicroVAX II. The Center for Computing and Mathematics houses 3 IBM-compatible and 2 Macintosh microcomputers in 5 laboratories and 75 workstations, as well as 2 Sun workstations. All terminals are networked. All students may access the system. It may be used 24 hours per day. There are no time limits on using the system and no fees.

Graduates: In 1992–93, 290 bachelor's degrees were awarded. The most popular majors among graduates were business administration (14%), psychology/psychobiology (8%), and biology/biochemistry (8%). Within an average freshman class, 70% graduate in 4 years and 75% in 5 years. Some 60 companies recruited on campus in 1992–93. In the 1992 graduating class, 40% of all graduates were enrolled in graduate school within 6 months of graduation; 45% had found employment.

Admissions Contact: Dr. William J. Stahler, Dean of Admissions and Financial Aid.

ALLEGHENY COLLEGE
B-1
Meadville, PA 16335 — (814) 332–4351; (800) 521–5293

Full-time: 848 men, 898 women	Faculty: 161; IIB, av$
Part-time: 17 men, 27 women	Ph.D.s: 91%
Graduate: none	Student/Faculty: 11 to 1
Year: semesters, summer session	Tuition: $16,700
Application Deadline: February 15	Room & Board: $4320
Freshman Class: 2652 applied, 1900 accepted, 487 enrolled	
SAT I or ACT: required	**VERY COMPETITIVE**

Allegheny College, founded in 1815, is an independent, coeducational liberal arts institution affiliated with the United Methodist Church. The 3 libraries contain 570,609 volumes, 176,510 microform items, and 3222 audiovisual forms, and subscribe to 1065 periodicals. Computerized library sources and services include the card catalog, interlibrary loans, and database searching. Special learning facilities include a learning resource center, art gallery, planetarium, radio station, TV studio, observatory, and a 283-acre experimental forest. The 254-acre campus is in a small town 90 miles north of Pittsburgh. Including residence halls, there are 33 buildings on campus.

Student Life: About 53% of undergraduates are from Pennsylvania. Students come from 36 states and 28 foreign countries. Eighty percent are from public schools; 20% from private. Ninety-one percent are white. Forty-one percent are Catholic; 35% Protestant; 13% claim no religious affiliation. The average age of freshmen is 18.5; all undergraduates, 20.2. Five percent drop out by the end of their first year; 74% remain to graduate.

Housing: A total of 1352 students can be accommodated in college housing. College-sponsored living facilities include single-sex and coed dormitories, on-campus apartments, off-campus apartments, and fraternity houses. In addition, there are language houses, special interest houses, and a black cultural residence. On-campus housing is guaranteed for all 4 years. Seventy-two percent of students live on campus; of those, 90% remain on campus on weekends. All students may keep cars on campus.

Activities: About 25% of men belong to 5 national fraternities; about 30% of women belong to 5 national sororities. There are 110 groups on campus, including art, band, cheerleading, chess, choir, chorale, chorus, computers, dance, drama, ethnic, film, gay, honors, international, jazz band, literary magazine, musical theater, newspaper, opera, orchestra, pep band, photography, political, professional, radio and TV, religious, social, social service, student government, symphony, and yearbook. Popular campus events include Winter Carnival, Centerstage Series (arts and lecture), Homecoming, Black History Month, and Latin Culture Week.

Sports: There are 10 intercollegiate sports for men and 10 for women, and 14 intramural sports for men and 13 for women. Athletic and recreation facilities include a 2500-seat gymnasium and field house, a natatorium, and a field complex with a stadium and 8 fields. In addition, there are 102 wooded acres for cross-country skiing.

Disabled Students: Seventy-five percent of the campus is accessible to disabled students. The following facilities are available: wheelchair ramps, elevators, special parking, specially equipped rest rooms, special class scheduling, lowered drinking fountains, and lowered telephones.

Services: In addition to many counseling and information services, tutoring is available in most subjects. There is a reader service for the blind, and remedial math, reading, and writing.

Campus Safety and Security: Campus safety and security measures include 24-hour foot and vehicle patrol, self defense education, escort service, and informal discussions. In addition, there are pamphlets, posters, and films, emergency telephones, and lighted pathways and sidewalks.

Programs of Study: Allegheny awards the B.A. and B.S. degrees. Bachelor's degrees are awarded in BIOLOGICAL SCIENCE (biochemistry and biology/biological science), COMMUNICATIONS AND THE ARTS (art history and appreciation, classical languages, classics, communications, dramatic arts, English, French, German, Greek (classical), Latin, music, Russian, Spanish, speech/debate/rhetoric, and studio art), COMPUTER AND PHYSICAL SCIENCE (chemistry, computer science, geology, mathematics, and physics), EDUCATION (elementary and secondary), ENGINEERING AND ENVIRONMENTAL DESIGN (environmental science), HEALTH PROFESSIONS (predentistry and premedicine), SOCIAL SCIENCE (economics, history, human ecology, international studies, philosophy, political science/government, prelaw, psychology, religion, and sociology). Physical and biological sciences, English, premedicine, and prelaw are the strongest academically. Economics, psychology, political science, English, and biology have the largest enrollments.

Required: To graduate, students must complete a total of 128 credit hours with a minimum GPA of 2.0. Between 32 and 48 hours are required in the major, including the junior seminar and senior project. All students must fulfill liberal studies requirements in arts and humanities, natural sciences, and social sciences. The liberal studies program extends through all 4 years and promotes breadth at both introductory and advanced levels of study. Additional required courses include the freshman seminar, sophomore writing course, and junior-senior concentration in a topic outside the major. The school also requires noncredit courses in physical education.

Special: Allegheny offers cross-registration with Chatham College, a Washington semester, internships, dual and student-designed majors, study abroad in 30 countries, nondegree study, and pass/fail options. A 3–2 engineering degree is available with Case Western Reserve, Columbia, Duke, Pittsburgh, and Washington universities. There are 3–2 forestry programs available with Duke and Michigan and a 3–2 environmental management program available with Duke. Other cooperative arrangements are available in allied health fields, nursing, and physical therapy. B.A.-B.S. degrees are possible in geology and psychology. There are 6 national honor societies on campus, including Phi Beta Kappa.

Faculty/Classroom: Seventy percent of faculty are male; 30%, female. All both teach and do research. The average class size in an introductory lecture is 18; in a laboratory, 15; and in a regular course offering, 16.

Admissions: About 72% of the 1993–94 applicants were accepted. The SAT scores for the 1993–94 freshman class were as follows: Verbal—43% below 500, 43% between 500 and 599, 13% between 600 and 700, and 1% above 700; Math—14% below 500, 48% between 500 and 599, 32% between 600 and 700, and 6% above 700. The ACT scores were 13% below 21, 20% between 21 and 23, 31% between 24 and 26, 23% between 27 and 28, and 13% above 28. About 70% of the current freshmen were in the top fifth of their class; 91% were in the top two fifths. There were 4 National Merit finalists. About 11 freshmen graduated first in their class.

Requirements: The SAT I or ACT is required. SAT II: Subject tests are recommended in writing and in the student's expected major. Graduation from an accredited secondary school is required for admission. Students must have 16 Carnegie units, including 4 years of English, 3 years each of mathematics, science, and social studies, and 2 years of a foreign language. An essay is required, and an interview is recommended. AP and CLEP credits are accepted. Important factors used in the admissions decision are advanced placement or honor courses, personality, intangible qualities, leadership record, extracurricular activities record, and recommendations by school officials.

Procedure: Freshmen are admitted fall and winter. Entrance exams should be taken by December of the senior year. Early decision applications should be filed by November 30 and January 15; regular applications, by February 15 for fall entry and November 1 for winter entry, along with an application fee of $30. Notification of early decision is sent December 15 and February 1; regular decision, April 1. There are early decision, early admissions, and deferred admissions plans. About 147 early decision candidates were accepted for the 1993–94 class. A waiting list is an active part of the admissions procedure, with 2% to 3% of applicants on the list.

Transfer: About 15 transfer students enrolled in 1993–94. Transfer applicants must submit a transcript of all college courses and a letter describing reasons for transfer, and have a minimum GPA of 2.0 (3.0 recommended). A total of 64 credits out of 128 must be completed at Allegheny.

Visiting: There are regularly scheduled orientations for prospective students, consisting of tours, panels, and presentations on academic programs, student life, admissions, and financial aid. There are guides for informal visits, and visitors may sit in on classes and stay overnight at the school. To arrange for a visit, contact the Office of Admissions at (800) 521–5293 or (814) 332–4351.

Financial Aid: In 1993–94 91% of all current freshmen and 85% of continuing students received some form of financial aid. About 78% of freshmen and 72% of continuing students received need-based aid. The average freshman award was $16,072. Of that total, scholarships or need-based grants averaged $11,221 ($16,900 maximum); loans averaged $2294 ($4625 maximum); and work contracts averaged $1012 ($1300 maximum). Seventy percent of undergraduate students work part-time. Average earnings from campus work for the school year are $1012. The average financial indebtedness of the 1992–93 graduate was $10,500. Allegheny is a member of CSS. The FAF and IRS 1040 for verification and the FAFS are required. The deadline for financial aid applications is February 15.

International Students: There are currently 57 international students enrolled. The school actively recruits these students. They must take the TOEFL and achieve a minimum score of 550. The student must also take the SAT I or the ACT.

Computers: The college provides computer facilities for student use. The mainframe is an IBM 4341 Model 2. More than 250 UNIX workstations and microcomputers are available to students in the library and all academic buildings. All students may access the system. It may be used 24 hours per day. There are no time limits on using the system and no fees.

Graduates: In 1992–93 395 bachelor's degrees were awarded. The most popular majors among graduates were psychology (17%), English (14%), and economics (12%). Within an average freshman class, 65% graduate in 4 years, 69% in 5 years, and 70% in 6 years. Some 25 companies recruited on campus in 1992–93. In the 1992 graduating class, 29% of all students were enrolled in graduate school within 6 months of graduation; 67% of all graduates had found employment.

Admissions Contact: Gayle W. Pollock, Director of Admissions.

ALLENTOWN COLLEGE OF SAINT FRANCIS DE SALES

E-3

Center Valley, PA 18034–9568   (215) 282–1100; (800) 228–5114

Full-time: 436 men, 503 women	Faculty: 67; IIB, -$
Part-time: 435 men, 657 women	Ph.D.s: 72%
Graduate: 152 men, 205 women	Student/Faculty: 14 to 1
Year: semesters, summer session	Tuition: $9330
Application Deadline: August 1	Room & Board: $4150

Freshman Class: 1179 applied, 780 accepted, 290 enrolled
SAT I Verbal/Math: 460/510   **COMPETITIVE**

Allentown College of Saint Francis de Sales, founded in 1964, is a private, coeducational, liberal arts institution affiliated with the Roman Catholic Church. There is one undergraduate and 4 graduate schools. In addition to regional accreditation, Allentown College has baccalaureate program accreditation with NLN. The library contains 150,000 volumes, 114,000 microform items, and 4000 audiovisual forms, and subscribes to 1000 periodicals. Computerized library sources and services include the card catalog, interlibrary loans, and database searching. Special learning facilities include a learning resource center and radio station. The 300-acre campus is in a rural area 50 miles north of Philadelphia. Including residence halls, there are 18 buildings on campus.

Student Life: About 65% of undergraduates are from Pennsylvania. Students come from 14 states and 9 foreign countries. Thirty-nine percent are from public schools; 61% from private. Ninety-six percent are white. Eighty-five percent are Catholic; 14% Protestant. The average age of freshmen is 19; all undergraduates, 23. Twelve percent drop out by the end of their first year; 62% remain to graduate.

Housing: A total of 775 students can be accommodated in college housing. College-sponsored living facilities include single-sex dormitories and on-campus apartments. In addition, there are special interest houses. On-campus housing is guaranteed for all 4 years. Eighty percent of students live on campus; of those, 68% remain on campus on weekends. All students may keep cars on campus.

Activities: About 8% of women belong to 1 local sorority. There are no fraternities on campus. There are 38 groups on campus, including cheerleading, chorale, dance, drama, honors, international, literary magazine, musical theater, newspaper, orchestra, political, professional, radio and TV, religious, social, social service, student government, and yearbook. Popular campus events include Furphy Lecture Series, Act One Plays, Marcon Lecture Series, Founders Day, and a dance recital.

Sports: There are 7 intercollegiate sports for men and 6 for women, and 9 intramural sports for men and 8 for women. There are athletic facilities for soccer, baseball, softball, tennis, basketball, volleyball, and weight lifting.

Disabled Students: Eighty percent of the campus is accessible to disabled students. The following facilities are available: wheelchair ramps, elevators, special parking, and specially equipped rest rooms.

Services: In addition to many counseling and information services, tutoring is available in every subject.

Campus Safety and Security: Campus safety and security measures include 24-hour foot and vehicle patrol, escort service, and lighted pathways and sidewalks.

Programs of Study: Allentown College awards the B.A., B.S., and B.S.N. degrees. Master's degrees also are awarded. Bachelor's degrees are awarded in BIOLOGICAL SCIENCE (biology/biological science), BUSINESS (accounting, banking and finance, business administration and management, marketing/retailing/merchandising, and sports management), COMMUNICATIONS AND THE ARTS (dance, dramatic arts, English, French, Spanish, and technical and business writing), COMPUTER AND PHYSICAL SCIENCE (chemistry, computer science, and mathematics), HEALTH PROFESSIONS (nursing), SOCIAL SCIENCE (criminal justice, liberal arts/general studies, political science/government, psychology, and theological studies). Business, theater, dance, and nursing are the strongest academically. Business, theater, and criminal justice have the largest enrollments.

Required: For graduation, students must complete 120 credit hours, including 48 in the major, with a minimum GPA of 2.0. Liberal arts distribution requirements consist of 12 to 16 courses, including cultural literacy, modes of thinking, and Christian values, as well as 3 units in physical education. Internships are required for degrees in business communications and sports administration.

Special: Students may cross-register with schools in the Lehigh Valley Association of Independent Colleges. Internships are strongly encouraged in all majors. Study abroad in many countries and a Washington semester are available. Dual majors, pass/fail options, and credit for life, military, and work experience are offered. There is a freshman honors program on campus, as well as 9 national honor societies.

Faculty/Classroom: Sixty percent of faculty are male; 40%, female. Ninety-eight percent teach undergraduates. No introductory courses are taught by graduate students. The average class size in an introductory lecture is 22; in a laboratory, 13; and in a regular course offering, 18.

Admissions: About 66% of the 1993–94 applicants were accepted. The SAT scores for the 1993–94 freshman class were as follows: Verbal—65% below 500, 26% between 500 and 599, 8% between 600 and 700, and 1% above 700; Math—44% below 500, 37% between 500 and 599, 17% between 600 and 700, and 2% above 700. About 39% of the current freshmen were in the top fifth of their class; 68% were in the top two fifths. One freshman was first in a graduating class.

Requirements: Allentown College requires applicants to be in the upper 50% of their class. A minimum GPA of 2.5 is required. The SAT I or ACT is required. Applicants must be graduates of an accredited secondary school. The GED is accepted. Applicants should have completed 17 college preparatory courses, including 4 years each of English, history, and mathematics, 3 years of science, and 2 years of foreign language. The school recommends an essay, an interview, and, for theater and dance students, an audition. AP credits are accepted. Important factors used in the admissions decision are advanced placement or honor courses, leadership record, recommendations by school officials, and evidence of special talent.

Procedure: Freshmen are admitted in the fall and the spring. Entrance exams should be taken during the junior or senior year. Applications should be filed by August 1 for fall entry and December 1 for spring entry, along with an application fee of $25. Notification is sent on a rolling basis. There is an early admissions plan. A waiting list is an active part of the admissions procedure, with about 15% of applicants on the list.

Transfer: About 47 transfer students enrolled in 1993–94. Applicants for transfer must have completed a minimum of 12 college credit hours with a GPA of 2.5. An interview is recommended. A total of 60 credits out of 120 must be completed at Allentown College.

Visiting: There are regularly scheduled orientations for prospective students. Visitors should schedule classes with a faculty adviser, complete a writing sample, and plan to engage in social activities. There are guides for informal visits, and visitors may sit in on classes and stay overnight at the school. To arrange for a visit, contact the Admissions Office at (215) 282–1100, ext. 1277 or (800) 228–5114.

Financial Aid: In 1993–94 90% of all current freshmen and 90% of continuing students received some form of financial aid. About 50% of freshmen and 50% of continuing students received need-based aid. The average freshman award was $3500. Of that total, scholarships or need-based grants averaged $3000 ($9270 maximum); loans averaged $1450 ($2625 maximum); and work contracts averaged $800 ($1000 maximum). Sixty percent of undergraduate students work part-time. Average earnings from campus work for the school year are $800. The average financial indebtedness of the 1992–93 graduate was $8000. Allentown College is a member of CSS. The FAF, the college's own financial statement, and the PHEAA are required. The deadline for financial aid applications is March 15.

International Students: There are currently 10 international students enrolled. They must take the TOEFL and achieve a minimum score of 500. The student must also take the SAT I or the ACT.

Computers: The college provides computer facilities for student use. The mainframe is a DEC VAX 11. There are also 60 IBM and Apple Macintosh microcomputers available for students in the academic building and the library. All students may access the system. It may be used 8 A.M. to 11 P.M. Students may access the system 1 hour when a line is present. The fees are $25 a year.

Graduates: In 1992–93 319 bachelor's degrees were awarded. The most popular majors among graduates were management (14%), accounting (13%), and marketing (10%). Within an average freshman class, 53% graduate in 4 years, 7% in 5 years, and 1% in 6 years. In the 1992 graduating class, 10% of all students were enrolled in graduate school within 6 months of graduation; 86% of all graduates had found employment.

Admissions Contact: Kathleen H. Link, Director of Admissions.

ALVERNIA COLLEGE
E-3
Reading, PA 19607   (610) 796-8220

Full-time: 291 men, 504 women	Faculty: 57; IIB, --$
Part-time: 131 men, 335 women	Ph.D.s: 30%
Graduate: none	Student/Faculty: 14 to 1
Year: semesters, summer session	Tuition: $8950
Application Deadline: open	Room & Board: $4200
Freshman Class: n/av	
SAT I: required	**LESS COMPETITIVE**

Alvernia College, established in 1958, is a Roman Catholic liberal arts institution. In addition to regional accreditation, Alvernia has baccalaureate program accreditation with AACSB and NLN. The library contains 66,000 volumes and 15,400 microform items, and subscribes to 1500 periodicals. Special learning facilities include a radio station. The 85-acre campus is in a suburban area 3 miles outside Reading. Including residence halls, there are 8 buildings on campus.

Student Life: About 90% of undergraduates are from Pennsylvania. Seventy-five percent are from public schools. Most are Catholic. Ten percent drop out by the end of their first year; 87% remain to graduate.

Housing: College-sponsored living facilities include a coed dormitory and on-campus townhouses. On-campus housing is guaranteed for the freshman year only and is available on a lottery system for upperclassmen. All students may keep cars on campus.

Activities: There are no fraternities or sororities on campus. There are 15 groups on campus, including chorale, drama, honors, international, literary magazine, musical theater, newspaper, professional, religious, and student government. Popular campus events include Charter Week, Homecoming, Harvest Weekend, and Parents Weekend.

Sports: There are 3 intercollegiate sports for men and 5 for women, and 6 intramural sports for men and 7 for women. Athletic and recreation facilities include a gymnasium, a physical fitness and recreation center, playing fields, and outdoor tennis, basketball, and volleyball courts.

Disabled Students: Alverina has limited access for disabled students. The following facilities are available: elevators, special parking, and specially equipped rest rooms.

Services: In addition to many counseling and information services, tutoring is available in every subject. Facilities include a writing center and a mathematics tutorial laboratory.

Campus Safety and Security: Campus safety and security measures include photo ID cards that must be worn by students.

Programs of Study: Alvernia awards the B.A. and B.S. degrees. Associate degrees are also awarded. Bachelor's degrees are awarded in BIOLOGICAL SCIENCE (biochemistry and biology/biological science), BUSINESS (accounting, banking and finance, and business administration and management), COMMUNICATIONS AND THE ARTS (communications, English, and Spanish), COMPUTER AND PHYSICAL SCIENCE (chemistry, information sciences and systems, mathematics, and science), EDUCATION (elementary and secondary), HEALTH PROFESSIONS (medical laboratory technology, nursing, predentistry, premedicine, and preveterinary science), SOCIAL SCIENCE (addiction studies, criminal justice, history, liberal arts/general studies, philosophy, political science/government, prelaw, psychology, social studies, social work, and theological studies). Biology, chemistry, computer science, and education are the strongest academically. Accounting, banking and finance, addiction studies, and criminal justice have the largest enrollments.

Required: To graduate, all students must complete at least 123 credit hours with a minimum GPA of 2.0 overall and in the major (2.5 for elementary education and nursing majors). Requirements include 40 credits in a liberal arts core, consisting of 15 credits of theology and philosophy, 6 each of fine arts, foreign language, and social science, and 3 each of communications, composition and research, contemporary American culture, human wellness, literature, mathematics, and

science. All students also must perform 40 clock hours of service to others before graduation, complete course work in college success skills and in human diversity, and demonstrate computer proficiency.

Special: The college offers internships, study abroad, a Washington semester, dual majors, campus work-study, a general studies degree, nondegree study, and B.A.-B.S. degrees in biology, psychology, and chemistry.

Faculty/Classroom: Forty-six percent of faculty are male; 54%, female.

Requirements: The SAT I is required. Nursing candidates must submit results of the NLN prenursing test. All applicants must be graduates of an accredited secondary school or have a GED certificate. They should have completed at least 16 academic units, including 4 in English and electives, and 2 each in mathematics, foreign language, science, and social studies. An interview is required for physical therapist assistant and nursing applicants and strongly recommended for all others. Nursing candidates also must submit results of the NLN prenursing test, and physical therapist assistant candidates must meet specific program requirements. AP and CLEP credits are accepted. Important factors used in the admissions decision are advanced placement or honor courses, recommendations by school officials, and extracurricular activities record.

Procedure: Freshmen are admitted fall and spring. Application deadlines are open. Application fee is $25. Notification is sent on a rolling basis. There are early admissions and deferred admissions plans.

Transfer: Applicants must have a college GPA of 2.0 or better. At least 30 of the last 36 degree credits out of 123 must be completed at Alvernia.

Visiting: There are guides for informal visits and visitors may sit in on classes and stay overnight at the school. To arrange for a visit, contact the Admissions Office.

Financial Aid: In an earlier year, 90% of all students received some form of financial aid. Alvernia is a member of CSS. The FAF and Pennsylvania state grant application are required. The deadline for financial aid applications is July 1.

International Students: They must take the TOEFL.

Computers: The college provides computer facilities for student use. The mainframe is an IBM System/38. DEC MicroVAX, Apple Macintosh, and IBM microcomputers are available to students in the science and mathematics building. Computer science students may access the system. The fees are $37 per course.

Admissions Contact: Karin Allmendinger, Director of Admission.

BEAVER COLLEGE
F-3
Glenside, PA 19038   (215) 572-2910; (800) 776-BEAVER (2328)

Full-time: 222 men, 650 women	Faculty: 59; IIA, --$
Part-time: 161 men, 365 women	Ph.D.s: 85%
Graduate: 242 men, 747 women	Student/Faculty: 15 to 1
Year: semesters, summer session	Tuition: $12,510
Application Deadline: open	Room & Board: $5150
Freshman Class: 1163 applied, 850 accepted, 348 enrolled	
SAT I Verbal/Math: 460/505	**COMPETITIVE**

Beaver College, founded in 1853, is a private institution affiliated with the Presbyterian Church offering undergraduate and graduate programs in the fine arts, the sciences, business, education, and preprofessional fields. There is one graduate school. In addition to regional accreditation, Beaver has baccalaureate program accreditation with APTA and NASAD. The library contains 143,469 volumes, 109,790 microform items, and 2421 audiovisual forms, and subscribes to 699 periodicals. Special learning facilities include a learning resource center, art gallery, radio station, an observatory, a theater, and computer graphics and communication laboratories. The 55-acre campus is in a suburban area 10 miles north of Philadelphia. Including residence halls, there are 13 buildings on campus.

Student Life: About 78% of undergraduates are from Pennsylvania. Students come from 21 states and 11 foreign countries. Seventy percent are from public schools; 30% from private. Eighty-six percent are white. Thirty-five percent are Catholic; 29% Protestant; 23% claim no religious affiliation. The average age of freshmen is 19; all undergraduates, 23. Fifteen percent drop out by the end of their first year; 71% remain to graduate.

Housing: A total of 522 students can be accommodated in college housing. College-sponsored living facilities include single-sex and coed dormitories. On-campus housing is guaranteed for all 4 years. Seventy-five percent of students live on campus; of those, 75% remain on campus on weekends. Upperclassmen may keep cars on campus.

Activities: There are no fraternities or sororities on campus. There are 48 groups on campus, including art, cheerleading, choir, chorale, chorus, computers, dance, drama, ethnic, gay, honors, international, literary magazine, musical theater, newspaper, photography, political, professional, radio and TV, religious, social, social service, student government, and yearbook. Popular campus events include Alcohol Awareness Week, Black History Month, Danish Exchange Program,

Red Cross Blood Drives, Woodstock Weekend, Parents Weekend, Black and White Formals, Homecoming, and International Festival.

Sports: There are 6 intercollegiate sports for men and 10 for women, and 5 intramural sports for men and 5 for women. Athletic and recreation facilities include a new softball field, outdoor tennis and basketball courts, field hockey and soccer/lacrosse fields, and an athletic and recreation center, which includes a 1500-seat gymnasium for basketball and volleyball, an indoor track, an indoor NCAA regulation swimming pool, an aerobics and dance studio, and fitness and training rooms.

Disabled Students: Sixty percent of the campus is accessible to disabled students. The following facilities are available: wheelchair ramps, elevators, special parking, specially equipped rest rooms, special class scheduling, and lowered telephones.

Services: In addition to many counseling and information services, tutoring is available in every subject. In addition, there is a reader service for the blind, and remedial math, reading, and writing.

Campus Safety and Security: Campus safety and security measures include 24-hour foot and vehicle patrol, escort service, informal discussions, and pamphlets, posters, and films. In addition, there are emergency telephones, lighted pathways and sidewalks, alarmed doors, and night receptionists.

Programs of Study: Beaver awards the B.A., B.S., and B.F.A. degrees. Associate and master's degrees also are awarded. Bachelor's degrees are awarded in BIOLOGICAL SCIENCE (biology/ biological science), BUSINESS (accounting, banking and finance, business administration and management, marketing/retailing/ merchandising, and personnel management), COMMUNICATIONS AND THE ARTS (communications, design, dramatic arts, English, fine arts, graphic design, and photography), COMPUTER AND PHYSICAL SCIENCE (chemistry, computer science, mathematics, and science), EDUCATION (art, early childhood, elementary, secondary, and special), ENGINEERING AND ENVIRONMENTAL DESIGN (interior design), HEALTH PROFESSIONS (art therapy, health care administration, predentistry, premedicine, and prephysical therapy), SOCIAL SCIENCE (history, philosophy, political science/ government, prelaw, psychobiology, psychology, and sociology). Education, psychology, chemistry, and prehealth professions are the strongest academically. Fine arts, business, biology, and education have the largest enrollments.

Required: Students must take English composition, mathematics, 1 semester of computer science, and 2 semesters each of a laboratory science, a foreign language, and physical education. They must also fulfill 24 credits of distribution requirements in the arts, humanities, and social sciences; core courses in American pluralism and non-Western cultures; and a final project or thesis. To graduate, completion of 128 credit hours is required, including 40 or more in the major with a minimum GPA of 2.0.

Special: Internships are encouraged in all majors. There are study-abroad programs in 11 countries and co-op programs in business, computer science, chemistry, actuarial science, and accounting. There is a 3-2 engineering program with Columbia University, a 3-4 optometry program with the Pennsylvania College of Optometry, and a 4-2 physical therapy program. Beaver also offers a Washington semester, work-study, student-designed majors, a dual major in chemistry and business, interdisciplinary majors in artificial intelligence and science illustration, credit by exam and for life/military/work experience, and nondegree study. There is a freshman honors program on campus, as well as 1 national honor society.

Faculty/Classroom: Fifty-one percent of faculty are male; 49%, female. Seventy-two percent teach undergraduates. No introductory courses are taught by graduate students. The average class size in an introductory lecture is 28; in a laboratory, 20; and in a regular course offering, 16.

Admissions: About 73% of the 1993-94 applicants were accepted. The SAT scores for the 1993-94 freshman class were as follows: Verbal—71% below 500, 27% between 500 and 599, 2% between 600 and 700, and 1% above 700; Math—42% below 500, 42% between 500 and 599, 13% between 600 and 700, and 3% above 700. About 43% of the current freshmen were in the top fifth of their class; 80% were in the top two fifths.

Requirements: The SAT I is required. Applicants must be graduates of an accredited secondary school or have a GED. A total of 16 academic credits is required, including 4 years of English, 3 each of mathematics and social studies, and 2 each of a foreign language and science. An essay is required. Science illustration majors must submit a portfolio. AP and CLEP credits are accepted. Important factors used in the admissions decision are advanced placement or honor courses, recommendations by school officials, leadership record, evidence of special talent, and extracurricular activities record.

Procedure: Freshmen are admitted fall and spring. Early decision applications should be filed by November 1, along with an application fee of $25. Notification of early decision is sent December 1; regular decision, on a rolling basis. There are early decision, early admis-

sions, and deferred admissions plans. About 16 early decision candidates were accepted for the 1993-94 class.

Transfer: A total of 123 transfer students enrolled in 1993-94. Applicants must have a GPA of 2.5. Art majors must submit a portfolio. The SAT I or ACT is required if the student has earned less than 1 year of college credit. An interview is encouraged. A total of 32 credits out of 128 must be completed at Beaver.

Visiting: There are regularly scheduled orientations for prospective students, including personal interviews Monday through Saturday, open houses, and opportunities to dine on campus and to meet with faculty, financial aid officers, and current students. There are guides for informal visits and visitors may sit in on classes and stay overnight at the school. To arrange for a visit, contact the Office of Admissions at (800) 776-BEAVER (2328).

Financial Aid: In 1993-94, 73% of all current freshmen and 64% of continuing students received some form of financial aid. About 69% of freshmen and 58% of continuing students received need-based aid. The average freshman award was $11,042. Of that total, scholarships or need-based grants averaged $6748 ($9000 maximum); loans averaged $2625; and work contracts averaged $800 ($1000 maximum). Thirty-three percent of undergraduate students work part-time. Average earnings from campus work for the school year are $920. The average financial indebtedness of the 1992-93 graduate was $13,250. Beaver is a member of CSS. The FAFSA, PHEAA, and parent and student tax returns are required. The deadline for financial aid applications is March 15.

International Students: There are currently 27 international students enrolled. The school actively recruits these students. They must take the TOEFL and achieve a minimum score of 500.

Computers: The college provides computer facilities for student use. The mainframes are a DEC VAX 8250 and a DEC VAX 4000/500. There are also IBM, Zenith, and Apple IIg microcomputers available in the library and in academic buildings linking with Novell network and Internet systems. All students may access the system. There are no time limits on using the system and no fees.

Graduates: In 1992-93, 215 bachelor's degrees were awarded. The most popular majors among graduates were education (17%), business administration (17%), and fine arts (13%). Within an average freshman class, 1% graduate in 3 years, 67% in 4 years, 2% in 5 years, and 1% in 6 years. Some 25 companies recruited on campus in 1992-93. In the 1992 graduating class, 15% of the men and 17% of the women were enrolled in graduate school within 6 months of graduation; 90% of graduates had found employment.

Admissions Contact: Dennis L. Nostrand, Vice President for Enrollment Management.

BLOOMSBURG UNIVERSITY OF PENNSYLVANIA
E-2

Bloomsburg, PA 17815
(717) 389-4316

Full-time: 2249 men, 3599 women	Faculty: 369; IIA, av$
Part-time: 347 men, 598 women	Ph.D.s: 60%
Graduate: 157 men, 425 women	Student/Faculty: 16 to 1
Year: semesters, summer session	Tuition: $3458 ($7856)
Application Deadline: open	Room & Board: $2854

Freshman Class: 6773 applied, 3028 accepted, 1025 enrolled
SAT I Verbal/Math: 459/520
COMPETITIVE +

Bloomsburg University of Pennsylvania, founded in 1839, is a public, coeducational institution offering undergraduate programs in the liberal arts and sciences, business, and teacher education. There are 5 undergraduate schools and one graduate school. In addition to regional accreditation, BU has baccalaureate program accreditation with CSWE, NCATE, and NLN. The library contains 341,402 volumes, 1,751,790 microform items, and 6836 audiovisual forms, and subscribes to 1745 periodicals. Computerized library sources and services include the card catalog, interlibrary loans, and database searching. Special learning facilities include a learning resource center, art gallery, radio station, and TV station. The 192-acre campus is in a small town 80 miles northeast of Harrisburg. Including residence halls, there are 54 buildings on campus.

Student Life: About 90% of undergraduates are from Pennsylvania. Students come from 26 states and 16 foreign countries. Eighty-six percent are from public schools; 14% from private. Ninety-four percent are white. Twenty percent are Catholic; 17% Protestant. The average age of freshmen is 18.5; all undergraduates, 22.1. Sixteen percent drop out by the end of their first year; 66% remain to graduate.

Housing: A total of 2698 students can be accommodated in college housing. College-sponsored living facilities include single-sex and coed dormitories and on-campus apartments. On-campus housing is guaranteed for the freshman year only and is available on a lottery system for upperclassmen. Alcohol is not permitted. Upperclassmen may keep cars on campus.

Activities: About 12% of men belong to 3 local and 7 national fraternities; about 15% of women belong to 5 local and 5 national sororities. There are 124 groups on campus, including art, band, cheerleading, chess, choir, chorale, chorus, computers, drama, drill team, ethnic, film, gay, honors, international, literary magazine, marching band, musical theater, newspaper, orchestra, pep band, political, professional, radio and TV, religious, social, social service, student government, and yearbook. Popular campus events include Parents Weekend, Renaissance Jamboree, Siblings and Childrens Weekend, and Homecoming.

Sports: There are 9 intercollegiate sports for men and 9 for women, and 25 intramural sports for men and women. Athletic and recreation facilities include a 5000-seat stadium, 2 gymnasiums, an athletic field, an indoor track, a 6-lane swimming pool, 9 practice fields, and 18 Grasstex tennis courts.

Disabled Students: Seventy percent of the campus is accessible to disabled students. The following facilities are available: wheelchair ramps, elevators, special parking, specially equipped rest rooms, special class scheduling, lowered drinking fountains, and lowered telephones.

Services: In addition to many counseling and information services, tutoring is available in some subjects. In addition, there is a reader service for the blind, and remedial math, reading, and writing.

Campus Safety and Security: Campus safety and security measures include 24-hour foot and vehicle patrol, escort service, shuttle buses, and emergency telephones. In addition, there are lighted pathways and sidewalks, monitored surveillance cameras, and strict residence hall security.

Programs of Study: BU awards the B.A., B.S., B.S.Ed., B.S.N., and B.S.O.A. degrees. Associate and master's degrees also are awarded. Bachelor's degrees are awarded in BIOLOGICAL SCIENCE (biology/biological science), BUSINESS (accounting, business administration and management, business economics, and office supervision and management), COMMUNICATIONS AND THE ARTS (art history and appreciation, communications, dramatic arts, English, French, German, music, Spanish, speech/debate/rhetoric, and studio art), COMPUTER AND PHYSICAL SCIENCE (chemistry, computer science, earth science, geology, mathematics, natural sciences, physics, and radiological technology), EDUCATION (business, early childhood, elementary, science, secondary, social studies, and special), HEALTH PROFESSIONS (dental hygiene, health, medical laboratory technology, nursing, and speech pathology/audiology), SOCIAL SCIENCE (anthropology, economics, ethics, politics, and social policy, geography, history, humanities, interpreter for the deaf, philosophy, political science/government, psychology, social science, social work, and sociology). Business and education have the largest enrollments.

Required: To graduate, students must complete 128 credit hours with a minimum GPA of 2.0. The university requires 12 semester hours each in humanities, social sciences, natural sciences, and mathematics. There are specific course requirements in communication, quantitative/analytical reasoning, values, ethics, responsible decision making, and survival, fitness, and recreational skills.

Special: Internships for upperclassmen, study abroad in more than 11 countries, work-study programs, and dual majors are available. BU offers a 3–2 engineering degree with Pennsylvania State and Wilkes universities. There is nondegree study, pass/fail options, and credit for life, military, and work experience. The school utilizes telecourses and interactive video. There is a freshman honors program on campus, as well as 9 national honor societies.

Faculty/Classroom: Sixty-five percent of faculty are male; 35%, female. All teach undergraduates. No introductory courses are taught by graduate students. The average class size in a regular course offering is 28.

Admissions: About 45% of the 1993–94 applicants were accepted. The SAT scores for the 1993–94 freshman class were as follows: Verbal—69% below 500, 28% between 500 and 599, and 3% between 600 and 700; Math—34% below 500, 51% between 500 and 599, 14% between 600 and 700, and 1% above 700. About 40% of the current freshmen were in the top fifth of their class; 85% were in the top two fifths. Five freshmen graduated first in their class.

Requirements: The SAT I is required, with a minimum composite score of 850. Applicants must be graduates of an accredited secondary school. To be competitive, a student should also rank in the top 30% of the high school class with a B average. The GED is accepted. Applicants should complete 4 years each of English and social studies, 3 years each of mathematics and science, and 2 years of a foreign language. An interview is recommended. AP and CLEP credits are accepted.

Procedure: Freshmen are admitted to all sessions. Entrance exams should be taken during the junior year. Application deadlines are open. Application fee is $25. Notification is sent on a rolling basis. There is an early admissions plan. A waiting list is an active part of the admissions procedure.

Transfer: A total of 313 transfer students enrolled in 1993–94. Applicants for transfer must have a minimum GPA of 2.0. Either the SAT I or ACT is required from applicants who have completed fewer than 24 semester hours of college credits. An official secondary school transcript or a GED and official transcripts from any post-secondary school attended are also required. Applicants must be in good standing at the college last attended. Those who have completed 30 semester hours must select a major upon entering the university. A total of 32 credits out of 128 must be completed at BU.

Visiting: There are regularly scheduled orientations for prospective students, consisting of a general meeting with admissions staff, a question and answer session, a campus tour, lunch, and meetings with faculty from various academic departments. There are guides for informal visits. To arrange for a visit, contact the Office of Admissions at (717) 389–4316.

Financial Aid: In 1993–94, 80% of all students received some form of financial aid. Twenty-eight percent of undergraduate students work part-time. Average earnings from campus work for the school year are $2500. BU is a member of CSS. The FAFSA and PHEAA Aid Information Request (PAIR) financial statement are required. The deadline for financial aid applications is March 15.

International Students: There are currently 27 international students enrolled. They must take the TOEFL and achieve a minimum score of 500.

Computers: The university provides computer facilities for student use. The mainframes are Unisys 2200/402 and a Unisys U6000 UNIX System. Terminal direct attachment to the mainframe is provided in several laboratories throughout the campus for use in instruction and research. Students can access the mainframes through a modem over Ethernet lines on a selected service basis. There are no time limits on using the system and no fees.

Graduates: In 1992–93, 1347 bachelor's degrees were awarded. The most popular majors among graduates were business administration and management (17%), elementary education (14%), and accounting (8%). Within an average freshman class, 43% graduate in 4 years, 64% in 5 years, and 66% in 6 years. Some 154 companies recruited on campus in 1992–93. In the 1992 graduating class, 14% of the men and 15% of the women were enrolled in graduate school within 6 months of graduation; 74% of the men and 73% of the women had found employment.

Admissions Contact: Bernie Vinovrski, Director of Admissions.

BRYN MAWR COLLEGE

F-3

Bryn Mawr, PA 19010–2899

(610) 526–5152
(800) 262–1885 (out-of-state)

Full-time: 40 men, 1166 women	Faculty: 137; IIA, +$
Part-time: 103 women	Ph.D.s: 99%
Graduate: 540 men and women	Student/Faculty: 9 to 1
Year: semesters, summer session	Tuition: $17,660
Application Deadline: January 15	Room & Board: $6450
Freshman Class: n/av	
SAT I: required	**MOST COMPETITIVE**

Bryn Mawr College, founded in 1885, is an independent liberal arts institution, primarily for women. There are 2 graduate schools. The 3 libraries contain 926,464 volumes and 108,724 microform items, and subscribe to 1958 periodicals. Computerized library sources and services include the card catalog, interlibrary loans, and database searching. Special learning facilities include a radio station, an archaelogical museum, and a language learning center with audio, video, and computer technology. The 135-acre campus is in a suburban area 10 miles west of Philadelphia. Including residence halls, there are 57 buildings on campus.

Student Life: About 89% of undergraduates are from out-of-state, mostly the Middle Atlantic. Students come from 48 states, 51 foreign countries, and Canada. Sixty-five percent are from public schools; 35% from private. Sixty-eight percent are white; 15% Asian American; 11% foreign nationals. The average age of freshmen is 18; all undergraduates, 20. Three percent drop out by the end of their first year; 86% remain to graduate.

Housing: A total of 1180 students can be accommodated in college housing. College-sponsored living facilities include single-sex and coed dormitories and off-campus apartments. In addition there are language houses, special interest houses, and an African American culture center. On-campus housing is guaranteed for all 4 years. Ninety-five percent of students live on campus; of those, 80% remain on campus on weekends. Alcohol is not permitted. Upperclassmen may keep cars on campus.

Activities: There are no fraternities or sororities on campus. There are more than 100 groups on campus, including art, chess, choir, chorale, chorus, computers, dance, drama, ethnic, gay, honors, international, jazz band, literary magazine, musical theater, newspaper, orchestra, photography, political, professional, radio and TV, religious, social, social service, student government, and yearbook. Popular campus events include May Day, Lantern Night, and Fall Frolic.

Sports: There are 8 intercollegiate sports for women and 6 intramural sports for women. Athletic and recreation facilities include a gymnasium with an Olympic-size pool and diving well; basketball, badminton, and volleyball courts; a gymnastics room and dance floor; a weight-training room; a 1000-seat auditorium; and a student center.

Disabled Students: Sixty percent of the campus is accessible to disabled students. The following facilities are available: wheelchair ramps, elevators, special parking, specially equipped rest rooms, and special class scheduling.

Services: In addition to many counseling and information services, tutoring is available in most subjects. There is a reader service for the blind and remedial math.

Campus Safety and Security: Campus safety and security measures include 24-hour foot and vehicle patrol, self-defense education, escort service, and shuttle buses. In addition, there are informal discussions, pamphlets, posters, films, emergency telephones, and lighted pathways and sidewalks.

Programs of Study: Bryn Mawr awards the A.B. degree. Master's and doctoral degrees also are awarded. Bachelor's degrees are awarded in BIOLOGICAL SCIENCE (biochemistry, biology/biological science, and neurosciences), BUSINESS (international economics), COMMUNICATIONS AND THE ARTS (art history and appreciation, classical languages, comparative literature, English, fine arts, French, German, Greek, Italian, Latin, music, romance languages, Russian, and Spanish), COMPUTER AND PHYSICAL SCIENCE (astronomy, chemistry, computer science, geology, mathematics, and physics), SOCIAL SCIENCE (African studies, anthropology, archeology, East Asian studies, economics, history, history of philosophy, peace studies, philosophy, political science/government, psychology, sociology, and urban studies). English, anthropology, political science, biology, economics, chemistry, history, and psychology have the largest enrollments.

Required: To graduate, students must complete 32 semester courses, 8 to 12 in the major. There are distribution requirements in social sciences, humanities, and laboratory sciences. Students must take foreign language, mathematics, and English composition.

Special: Students may cross-register with Haverford and Swarthmore colleges and the University of Pennsylvania. Bryn Mawr offers study abroad, student-designed and dual majors, pass/fail options, work-study, and a 3–2 engineering degree with California Institute of Technology and the University of Pennsylvania.

Faculty/Classroom: Forty-six percent of faculty are male; 54%, female. Ninety-four percent teach undergraduates. No introductory courses are taught by graduate students. The average class size in an introductory lecture is 80; in a laboratory, 15; and in a regular course offering, 20.

Admissions: Thirty-six freshmen graduated first in their class.

Requirements: The SAT I is required; the ACT may be substituted. SAT II: Subject tests in writing and 2 other areas are required. Applicants must be graduates of an accredited secondary school. The GED is accepted. Applicants should complete 4 years of English, at least 3 years of foreign language, 3 years of mathematics, and 1 year each of science, social studies, and history. An essay and an interview are required. AP credits are accepted. Important factors used in the admissions decision are advanced placement or honor courses, recommendations by school officials, personality, intangible qualities, evidence of special talent, and leadership record.

Procedure: Freshmen are admitted in the fall. Entrance exams should be taken in spring of the junior year or fall of the senior year. Early decision applications should be filed by November 15; regular applications, by January 15 for fall entry, along with an application fee of $40. There are early decision, early admissions, and deferred admissions plans. Notification of early decision is sent December 15; regular decision, April 10. About 85 early decision candidates were accepted for the 1993–94 class. A waiting list is an active part of the admissions procedure, with about 10% of the applicants on the list.

Transfer: Twenty transfer students enrolled in an earlier year. Applicants for transfer must have a minimum GPA of 3.0. SAT I and recommendations from both college and high school are required. A total of 16 semester courses out of 32 must be completed at Bryn Mawr.

Visiting: There are regularly scheduled orientations for prospective students. Student-guided campus tours and interviews can be arranged. There are guides for informal visits and visitors may sit in on classes and stay overnight at the school. To arrange for a visit, contact the Office of Admissions at (610) 526–5152.

Financial Aid: In 1993–94, 48% of all current freshmen and 50% of continuing students received some form of financial aid. About 48% of freshmen and 50% of continuing students received need-based aid. Scholarships or need-based grants averaged $11,642 ($20,000 maximum); loans averaged $2900 (maximum); and work contracts averaged $1200 ($1400 maximum). Seventy-five percent of undergraduate students work part-time. Average earnings from campus work for the school year are $1200. The average financial indebtedness of the 1992–93 graduate was $9000. Bryn Mawr is a

member of CSS. The FAF, the college's own financial statement, and the FAFSA are required. The application deadline is January 15.

International Students: There are currently 120 international students enrolled. The school actively recruits these students. They must take the TOEFL and achieve a minimum score of 600. The student must also take the SAT I.

Computers: The college provides computer facilities for student use. The mainframes are a DEC VAX 8200 and a DEC MicroVAX II. The computing center, libraries, and some classrooms are equipped with terminals and/or microcomputers, including more than 100 IBM, Apple Macintosh, and other models. All students may access the system. It may be used every day. Students may access the system in 2-hour blocks, which can be renewed. There are no fees.

Graduates: In 1992–93, 295 bachelor's degrees were awarded. The most popular majors among graduates were English (15%), political science (9%), and biology (8%). Within an average freshman class, 85% graduate within 5 years and 86% within 6 years. More than 50 companies recruited on campus in 1992–93. In the 1992 graduating class, half of the women were enrolled in graduate school and half had found employment within 6 months of graduation.

Admissions Contact: Elizabeth G. Vermey, Director of Admissions.

BUCKNELL UNIVERSITY

D-2

Lewisburg, PA 17837   (717) 524–1101

Full-time: 1730 men, 1596 women	**Faculty:** 241; IIA, +$
Part-time: 8 men, 23 women	**Ph.D.s:** 96%
Graduate: 128 men, 115 women	**Student/Faculty:** 14 to 1
Year: semesters, summer session	**Tuition:** $17,730
Application Deadline: January 1	**Room & Board:** $4590
Freshman Class: 6548 applied, 3813 accepted, 862 enrolled	
SAT I or ACT: required	**HIGHLY COMPETITIVE**

Bucknell University, established in 1846, is an independent, coeducational institution offering undergraduate and graduate programs in arts, music, education, humanities, management, and engineering. There are 2 undergraduate schools and one graduate school. In addition to regional accreditation, Bucknell University has baccalaureate program accreditation with ABET and NASM. The library contains 562,800 volumes, 562,083 microform items, and 2020 audiovisual forms, and subscribes to 2336 periodicals. Computerized library sources and services include the card catalog, interlibrary loans, and database searching. Special learning facilities include an art gallery, radio station, outdoor natural area, greenhouse, primate facility, observatory, photography laboratory, craft center, women's resource center, library resources training laboratory, and multicultural center. The 320-acre campus is in a small town 60 miles north of Harrisburg. Including residence halls, there are 71 buildings on campus.

Student Life: About 67% of undergraduates are from out-of-state, mostly the Middle Atlantic. Students come from 46 states, 39 foreign countries, and Canada. Seventy-two percent are from public schools; 28% from private. Eighty-nine percent are white. Thirty-eight percent are Protestant; 34% Catholic; 21% claim no religious affiliation. The average age of freshmen is 18; all undergraduates, 20. Five percent drop out by the end of their first year; 88% remain to graduate.

Housing: A total of 2600 students can be accommodated in college housing. College-sponsored living facilities include single-sex and coed dormitories, on-campus apartments, fraternity houses, and special interest houses. There are 5 residential colleges for the first year (arts, environmental, humanities, international, and social justice). On-campus housing is guaranteed for all 4 years. Eighty-two percent of students live on campus; of those, 85% remain on campus on weekends. Upperclassmen may keep cars on campus.

Activities: About 52% of men belong to 12 national fraternities; about 58% of women belong to 1 local and 7 national sororities. There are 48 groups on campus, including art, band, cheerleading, chess, choir, chorale, chorus, computers, dance, drama, drill team, ethnic, gay, honors, international, jazz band, literary magazine, musical theater, newspaper, opera, orchestra, pep band, photography, political, professional, radio and TV, religious, social, social service, student government, symphony, and yearbook. Popular campus events include Homecoming, Spring Weekend, Greek Weekend, Special Olympics, Christmas Candelight Service, Kwaanza, Poetry Symposium, and Celebration for the Arts.

Sports: There are 14 intercollegiate sports for men and 12 for women, and 30 intramural sports for men and 25 for women. Athletic and recreation facilities include a field house with a 6-lane track, weight and wrestling rooms, a basketball arena, a dance studio, a gymnasium with a 6-lane pool, a 14,000-seat stadium, a golf course, a jogging course, tennis courts, soccer and lacrosse fields, and handball, racquetball, and squash courts.

Disabled Students: Eighty-five percent of the campus is accessible to disabled students. The following facilities are available: wheelchair ramps, elevators, special parking, specially equipped rest rooms, lowered drinking fountains, and lowered telephones. Individual arrangements may be made with faculty for students with disabilities.

Services: In addition to many counseling and information services, tutoring is available in most subjects including writing, computer, and library skills. There is a writing center.

Campus Safety and Security: Campus safety and security measures include 24-hour foot and vehicle patrol, self defense education, escort service, and informal discussions. In addition, there are pamphlets, posters, and films, emergency telephones, and lighted pathways and sidewalks.

Programs of Study: Bucknell University awards the B.A., B.S., B.Mus., B.S.B.A., B.S.CH.E., B.S.C.E., B.S.Ed., B.S.E.E., and B.S.M.E. degrees. Master's degrees also are awarded. Bachelor's degrees are awarded in AGRICULTURE (animal science), BIOLOGICAL SCIENCE (biochemistry, biology/biological science, and cell biology), BUSINESS (accounting and business administration and management), COMMUNICATIONS AND THE ARTS (classics, dramatic arts, English, fine arts, French, German, Greek, Japanese, Latin, music, Russian, and Spanish), COMPUTER AND PHYSICAL SCIENCE (chemistry, computer science, geology, mathematics, and physics), EDUCATION (early childhood, educational statistics and research, elementary, music, and secondary), ENGINEERING AND ENVIRONMENTAL DESIGN (chemical engineering, civil engineering, computer engineering, electrical/electronics engineering, engineering, environmental studies, and mechanical engineering), SOCIAL SCIENCE (anthropology, East Asian studies, economics, geography, history, international relations, Latin American studies, philosophy, political science/government, psychology, religion, sociology, and women's studies). Engineering, natural science, psychology, English, music, management, and geology are the strongest academically. Economics, management, political science/international relations, English, and biology have the largest enrollments.

Required: All students enrolled in the College of Arts and Sciences will complete a foundation seminar during the freshman year; distribution requirements which require 4 humanities courses, 2 social science courses, and 3 courses in natural science and mathematics; perspectives for the 21st Century, consisting of 1 course each in natural and fabricated worlds and human diversity; departmental, college, or interdepartmental majors; and a capstone seminar or experience during the senior year. In addition, Bucknell requires a minimum writing competency for graduation. All students enrolled in the College of Engineering have a common first semester and must complete Exploring Engineering (EG 100). A total of 128 credits, or 32 courses (34 courses for engineering), and a minimum GPA of 2.0 are required to graduate.

Special: The university offers internships, study abroad in 15 countries, a Washington semester, a 5-year B.A.-B.S. degree in arts and engineering, and dual and student-designed majors. Nondegree study is possible and a pass/fail grading option is offered in some courses. The Residential College program offers opportunities for an academic-residential mix and faculty-student collaborative learning. Undergraduate research opportunities are available in the humanities/social sciences and the sciences and engineering. There are 21 national honor societies on campus, including Phi Beta Kappa. Twenty-four departments have honors programs.

Faculty/Classroom: Seventy-two percent of faculty are male; 28%, female. All teach undergraduates and do research. No introductory courses are taught by graduate students. The average class size in an introductory lecture is 55; in a laboratory, 21; and in a regular course offering, 20.

Admissions: About 58% of the 1993–94 applicants were accepted. The SAT scores for the 1993–94 freshman class were as follows: Verbal—25% below 500, 52% between 500 and 599, 21% between 600 and 700, and 1% above 700; Math—4% below 500, 31% between 500 and 599, 47% between 600 and 700, and 18% above 700. About 79% of the current freshmen were in the top fifth of their class; 96% were in the top two fifths. About 40 freshmen graduated first in their class.

Requirements: The SAT I or ACT is required. Applicants must graduate from an accredited secondary school or have a GED. Sixteen Carnegie units must be earned, including 4 courses in English, 3 in mathematics, and 2 each in history, science, social studies, and a foreign language. An essay is required, and an interview is recommended. Music applicants are required to audition. A portfolio is recommended for art applicants. AP credits are accepted. Important factors used in the admissions decision are advanced placement or honor courses, recommendations by school officials, evidence of special talent, leadership record, and extracurricular activities record.

Procedure: Freshmen are admitted in the fall. Entrance exams should be taken before January 1. Early decision applications should be filed by December 1; regular applications, by January 1 for fall entry and December 1 for spring entry, along with an application fee of $35. Notification of early decision is sent December 20; regular decision, by April 1. There are early decision, early admissions, and deferred admissions plans. About 290 early decision candidates were accepted for the 1993–94 class. A waiting list is an active part of the admissions procedure, with about 16% of applicants on the list.

Transfer: A total of 46 transfer students enrolled in 1993–94. Transfer students must have a minimum GPA of 2.5 in courses comparable to those offered at Bucknell. The SAT I or ACT is required. A minimum of 16 credit hours must have been earned; 32 are recommended. Students are accepted on a space-available basis. An interview is recommended. A total of 48 credits out of 128 must be completed at Bucknell University.

Visiting: There are regularly scheduled orientations for prospective students. There are guides for informal visits and visitors may sit in on classes and stay overnight at the school. To arrange for a visit, contact the Office of Admissions at (717) 524–1101.

Financial Aid: In 1993–94, 50% of all current freshmen and 59% of continuing students received some form of financial aid. About 45% of freshmen and 47% of continuing students received need-based aid. The average freshman award was $11,840. Of that total, scholarships or need-based grants averaged $12,038 ($23,600 maximum); loans averaged $3391 ($4025 maximum); and work contracts averaged $1222 ($1500 maximum). Forty-two percent of undergraduate students work part-time. Average earnings from campus work for the school year are $1500. The average financial indebtedness of the 1992–93 graduate was $13,564. Bucknell University is a member of CSS. The FAF and parent and student tax returns are required. The deadline for financial aid applications is February 15.

International Students: There are currently 90 international students enrolled. The school actively recruits these students. They must take the TOEFL and achieve a minimum score of 550.

Computers: The university provides computer facilities for student use. The mainframe is a DEC System 5000 Model 240. There are more than 450 microcomputers available in 15 student access sites, as well as more than 400 microcomputers on student and faculty desks. Access to the mainframe is possible through terminals, microcomputers, and dial up from residence hall room phone using a modem adapter. There are 50 SUN engineering workstations. All students may access the system 24 hours per day, 7 days per week. There are no time limits on using the system and no fees.

Graduates: In 1992–93, 828 bachelor's degrees were awarded. The most popular majors among graduates were business administration (13%), economics (12%), and biology (8%). Within an average freshman class, 86% graduate in 4 years and 88% in 5 years. Some 140 companies recruited on campus in 1992–93. In the 1992 graduating class, 26% of the men and 24% of the women were enrolled in graduate school within 6 months of graduation; 69% of the men and 68% of the women had found employment.

Admissions Contact: Mark D. Davies, Director of Admissions.

CABRINI COLLEGE   F-4
Radnor, PA 19087–3699

Full-time: 267 men, 554 women	(610) 971–8552; (800) 848–1003
Part-time: 298 men, 344 women	Faculty: 40; IIB, av$
Graduate: 46 men, 378 women	Ph.D.s: 73%
Year: semesters, summer session	Student/Faculty: 21 to 1
Application Deadline: August 15	Tuition: $10,222
Freshman Class: 599 applied, 494 accepted, 224 enrolled	Room & Board: $5790
SAT I Verbal/Math: 448/468	**COMPETITIVE**

Cabrini College, founded in 1957, is a private, coeducational, liberal arts college affiliated with the Roman Catholic Church and operated by the Missionary Sisters of the Sacred Heart. There is one graduate school. The library contains 98,530 volumes, including microform items, audiovisual forms, and periodicals. Computerized library sources and services include interlibrary loans and database searching. Special learning facilities include a learning resource center, art gallery, radio station, TV station, communications laboratory, and children's school. The 110-acre campus is in a suburban area 20 miles west of Philadelphia. Including residence halls, there are 18 buildings on campus.

Student Life: About 74% of undergraduates are from Pennsylvania. Students come from 10 states, 11 foreign countries, and Canada. Forty-two percent are from public schools; 58% from private. Ninety-two percent are white. Seventy-three percent are Catholic; 11% Protestant. The average age of freshmen is 18; all undergraduates, 29. Twenty-one percent drop out by the end of their first year; 59% remain to graduate.

Housing: A total of 394 students can be accommodated in college housing. College-sponsored living facilities include single-sex and coed dormitories. In addition there are honors houses, language houses, and special interest houses. On-campus housing is available on a first-come, first-served basis and is available on a lottery system for upperclassmen. Fifty percent of students live on campus; of those, 50% remain on campus on weekends. All students may keep cars on campus.

Activities: There are no fraternities or sororities on campus. There are 38 groups on campus, including cheerleading, chess, chorus, computers, dance, drama, ethnic, honors, international, jazz band, literary magazine, newspaper, photography, political, professional, ra-

dio and TV, religious, social, social service, student government, and yearbook. Popular campus events include Mother Cabrini Feast Day, Yule Log, Superthon, fall and spring concerts, and drama presentations.

Sports: There are 7 intercollegiate sports for men and 8 for women, and 2 intramural sports for men and 2 for women. Athletic and recreation facilities include a weight room, athletic fields, a game room, a 700-seat gymnasium, and tennis courts.

Disabled Students: Ninety percent of the campus is accessible to disabled students. The following facilities are available: wheelchair ramps, elevators, special parking, specially equipped rest rooms, and special class scheduling.

Services: In addition to many counseling and information services, tutoring is available in most subjects. Students may enroll in a study skills course or participate in individual counseling to acquire learning skills.

Campus Safety and Security: Campus safety and security measures include 24-hour foot and vehicle patrol, self defense education, escort service, and informal discussions. In addition, there are pamphlets, posters, and films, emergency telephones, and lighted pathways and sidewalks.

Programs of Study: Cabrini awards the B.A., B.S., B.S.W., and B.S.Ed. degrees. Master's degrees also are awarded. Bachelor's degrees are awarded in BIOLOGICAL SCIENCE (biology/biological science), BUSINESS (accounting, business administration and management, human resources, marketing, and office supervision and management), COMMUNICATIONS AND THE ARTS (arts administration/management, communications, English, French, Spanish, and visual and performing arts), COMPUTER AND PHYSICAL SCIENCE (chemistry, computer science, and mathematics), EDUCATION (education), HEALTH PROFESSIONS (medical laboratory technology), SOCIAL SCIENCE (American studies, history, liberal arts/general studies, philosophy, political science, psychology, religion, social work, and sociology). Education and English/communications are the strongest academically. Business, education and English/communications have the largest enrollments.

Required: Students must complete a minimum of 123 credits to graduate, with an average of 45 in the major, and a minimum GPA of 2.0. All students must complete a core curriculum, which includes English, mathematics, foreign language, computers, physical education, an interdisiplinary seminar in self-understanding, and a junior seminar exploring the common good. Distribution requirements cover science, heritage, cultural diversity, values, the individual and society, contemporary issues, and creativity. A thesis is required in some majors, and a volunteer project is part of the junior seminar.

Special: Cabrini offers cooperative programs, internships, study abroad, work-study programs, and cross-registration with Eastern and Rosemont Colleges and Villanova University. B.A.-B.S. degrees, dual majors, a general studies degree, and student-designed majors are available, as well as an accelerated interdisciplinary degree program in organizational management. Credit by examination, credit for life/military/work experience, nondegree study, and pass/fail options are also offered. There is a freshman honors program on campus, as well as 10 national honor societies, including Phi Beta Kappa. Ten departments have honors programs.

Faculty/Classroom: Forty-six percent of faculty are male; 54%, female. Ninety-eight percent teach undergraduates and 49% both teach and do research. No introductory courses are taught by graduate students. The average class size in an introductory lecture is 20; in a laboratory, 16; and in a regular course offering, 19.

Admissions: About 82% of the 1993–94 applicants were accepted. The SAT scores for the 1993–94 freshman class were as follows: Verbal—76% below 500, 18% between 500 and 599, and 6% between 600 and 700; Math—65% below 500, 28% between 500 and 599, 6% between 600 and 700, and 1% above 700. About 28% of the current freshmen were in the top fifth of their class; 50% were in the top two fifths.

Requirements: Cabrini requires applicants to be in the upper 50% of their class. A minimum GPA of 2.5 is required. The SAT I, with a minimum score of 400 each on the verbal and math or a composite score of 900, or the ACT is required. All students must be graduates of an accredited secondary school or hold a GED certificate. A minimum of 17 Carnegie units are required, consisting of 4 in English, 3 each in mathematics, science, and social studies, 2 in a foreign language, and the rest in electives. A letter of recommendation from a guidance counselor or academic subject teacher and an essay are required. An interview is recommended. AP and CLEP credits are accepted. Important factors used in the admissions decision are recommendations by school officials, advanced placement or honor courses, evidence of special talent, personality, intangible qualities, and leadership record.

Procedure: Freshmen are admitted fall and spring. Entrance exams should be taken before December of the senior year. Applications should be filed by August 15 for fall entry and December 15 for spring entry, along with an application fee of $25. Notification is sent

on a rolling basis. There are early admissions and deferred admissions plans. A waiting list is an active part of the admissions procedure, with about 5% of applicants on the list.

Transfer: A total of 154 transfer students enrolled in 1993–94. A mimimum of 15 credit hours with at least a GPA of 2.2 overall is required. A 2.5 GPA is preferred. Some programs may have higher requirements. A total of 45 credits out of 123 must be completed at Cabrini.

Visiting: There are regularly scheduled orientations for prospective students. Fall enrollees may choose from 3 summer 1 1/2-day preview programs during which they register for classes. Fall and spring orientations are held 2 to 3 days before classes begin. There are guides for informal visits and visitors may sit in on classes and stay overnight at the school. To arrange for a visit, contact the Admissions Office at (610) 971–8552 or (800) 848–1003.

Financial Aid: In 1993–94, 71% of all current freshmen and 70% of continuing students received some form of financial aid. About 68% of freshmen and 70% of continuing students received need-based aid. The average freshman award was $8825. Of that total, scholarships or need-based grants averaged $3500 ($10,100 maximum); loans averaged $3225 ($4125 maximum); and work contracts averaged $1000 ($1500 maximum). Thirty percent of undergraduate students work part-time. Average earnings from campus work for the school year are $1000. The average financial indebtedness of the 1992–93 graduate was $14,750. The college's own financial statement and FAFSA, PHEAA, and income tax forms are required. The deadline for financial aid applications is February 15.

International Students: There are currently 13 international students enrolled. The school actively recruits these students. They must take the TOEFL and achieve a minimum score of 550. The student must also take the SAT I or ACT; optional for a student whose native language is not English.

Computers: The college provides computer facilities for student use. There are 35 networked IBM microcomputers and a 15-unit Apple educational laboratory. All students may access the system more than 80 hours a week. There are no time limits on using the system and no fees.

Graduates: In 1992–93, 288 bachelor's degrees were awarded. The most popular majors among graduates were education (25%), business administration (24%), and communications (19%). Within an average freshman class, 1% graduate in 3 years, 55% in 4 years, 61% in 5 years, and 62% in 6 years. Some 22 companies recruited on campus in 1992–93.

Admissions Contact: Nancy Gardner, Executive Director of Admissions and Financial Aid.

CALIFORNIA UNIVERSITY OF PENNSYLVANIA

B-3

California, PA 15419–1394	(412) 938–4404
Full-time: 2391 men, 2176 women	Faculty: 306; IIA, +$
Part-time: 315 men, 501 women	Ph.D.s: 45%
Graduate: 360 men, 587 women	Student/Faculty: 15 to 1
Year: semesters, summer session	Tuition: $3760 ($8158)
Application Deadline: August 1	Room & Board: $3610
Freshman Class: 2594 applied, 1987 accepted, 1006 enrolled	
SAT I Verbal/Math: 409/449	**COMPETITIVE**

California University of Pennsylvania, founded in 1852, is a state-supported institution offering degree programs in the arts and sciences, engineering, and education. There are 3 undergraduate schools and one graduate school. In addition to regional accreditation, the university has baccalaureate program accreditation with CSWE, NCATE, and NLN. The library contains 330,728 volumes, 408,677 microform items, and 11,814 audiovisual forms, and subscribes to 1492 periodicals. Computerized library sources and services include the card catalog, interlibrary loans, and database searching. Special learning facilities include a learning resource center, an art gallery, a radio station, and a TV station. The 148-acre campus is in a small town 35 miles south of Pittsburgh. Including residence halls, there are 38 buildings on campus.

Student Life: About 94% of undergraduates are from Pennsylvania. Students come from 38 states, 25 foreign countries, and Canada. Ninety-four percent are white. The average age of freshmen is 19; all undergraduates, 23. Twenty percent drop out by the end of their first year; 50% remain to graduate.

Housing: A total of 1500 students can be accommodated in college housing. College-sponsored living facilities include single-sex and coed dormitories. On-campus housing is available on a first-come, first-served basis. Alcohol is not permitted. All students may keep cars on campus.

Activities: There are many groups and organizations on campus, including band, cheerleading, chess, choir, chorale, chorus, computers, drama, drill team, ethnic, honors, international, marching band,

newspaper, pep band, professional, radio and TV, student government, and yearbook.

Sports: Athletic and recreation facilities include tennis and basketball courts, an all-weather track, a swimming pool, and a 4500-seat stadium.

Disabled Students: The following facilities are available: wheelchair ramps, elevators, special parking, specially equipped rest rooms, special class scheduling, and lowered drinking fountains.

Services: In addition to many counseling and information services, tutoring is available in most subjects. In addition, there is a reader service for the blind, and remedial math, reading, and writing.

Programs of Study: The university awards the B.A., B.S., and B.S.Ed. degrees. Associate's and master's degrees also are awarded. Bachelor's degrees are awarded in BIOLOGICAL SCIENCE (biology/biological science), BUSINESS (business administration and management and business economics), COMMUNICATIONS AND THE ARTS (broadcasting, communications, dramatic arts, English, fine arts, French, German, Spanish, and speech/debate/rhetoric), COMPUTER AND PHYSICAL SCIENCE (chemistry, computer science, earth science, geology, mathematics, natural sciences, and physics), EDUCATION (early childhood, education of the mentally handicapped, education of the physically handicapped, elementary, English, foreign languages, industrial arts, mathematics, science, secondary, social science, special, and technical), ENGINEERING AND ENVIRONMENTAL DESIGN (electrical/electronics engineering technology, environmental science, graphic arts technology, manufacturing technology, and mining and petroleum technology), HEALTH PROFESSIONS (medical laboratory technology, nursing, predentistry, premedicine, and speech pathology/audiology), SOCIAL SCIENCE (anthropology, economics, geography, gerontology, history, parks and recreation management, philosophy, physical fitness/movement, political science/government, psychology, social science, social work, sociology, and urban studies).

Required: Students must complete a minimum of 128 semester credits and must maintain a minimum GPA of 2.5 in teacher education curricula, 2.3 in the student's area of concentration, and 2.0 overall.

Special: Cooperative programs are available with Pennsylvania State University and the University of Pittsburgh. Opportunities are provided for internships, study abroad, work-study programs, a B.A.-B.S. degree, a general studies degree, a 3–2 engineering degree, credit by examination, nondegree study, and pass/fail options. There is a freshman honors program on campus.

Faculty/Classroom: Seventy-five percent of faculty are male; 25% female. All teach undergraduates.

Admissions: About 77% of the 1993–94 applicants were accepted. About 15% of the current freshmen were in the top fifth of their class; 40% were in the top two fifths. About 18 freshmen graduated first in their class.

Requirements: The university requires applicants to be in the upper 60% of their class. A minimum GPA of 2.3 is required. The SAT I or ACT is required, with minimum composite scores of 800 (400 verbal, 400 mathematics) on the SAT I and 20 on the ACT recommended with a minimum score of 20. Graduation from an accredited secondary school is required; a GED will be accepted. Applicants should submit an academic record including 4 credits each in English and history, 3 each in mathematics and academic electives, 2 in science, and 1 each in social studies and a foreign language. An essay and an interview are recommended. AP and CLEP credits are accepted. Important factors used in the admissions decision are advanced placement or honor courses, evidence of special talent, leadership record, parents or siblings attending the school, and recommendations by school officials.

Procedure: Freshmen are admitted to all sessions. Entrance exams should be taken during the senior year. Early decision applications should be filed by December 1; regular applications, by August 1 for fall entry, January 1 for winter entry, and May 1 for summer entry, along with an application fee of $25. Notification of early decision is sent December 1; regular decision, on a rolling basis. There are early decision, early admissions, and deferred admissions plans. About 35 early decision candidates were accepted for the 1993–94 class.

Transfer: About 480 transfer students enrolled in 1993–94. Applicants must submit official transcripts from all previous colleges attended. If fewer than 30 transferable credits are submitted, applicants must also include a high school transcript and standardized test score. Grades of D are not transferable. A total of 38 credits out of 128 must be completed at the university.

Visiting: There are regularly scheduled orientations for prospective students. There are guides for informal visits and visitors may sit in on classes and stay overnight at the school. To arrange for a visit, contact the Admissions Office at (412) 938-4404.

Financial Aid: In a recent year, 74% of all current freshmen and 69% of continuing students received some form of financial aid. About 65% of freshmen and 61% of continuing students received need-based aid. The average freshman award was $4500. Of that total, scholarships or need-based grants averaged $1500 ($6778 maxi-

mum); loans averaged $2000 ($5800 maximum); and work contracts averaged $1000. Twenty-one percent of undergraduate students work part-time. Average earnings from campus work for the school year are $920. The average financial indebtedness of a recent graduate was $6260. The Pennsylvania State Grant and Federal Financial Aid Application financial statement is required. The deadline for financial aid applications is April 1.

International Students: There are currently 97 international students enrolled. The school actively recruits these students. They must take the TOEFL and achieve a minimum score of 450.

Computers: The college provides computer facilities for student use. The mainframe is a DEC VAX 11/780. Approximately 350 access points (terminal/PCs) are available for the mainframe. In addition, there are approximately 700 IBM, IBM-compatible, and Apple PCs on campus in various laboratories and offices. All students may access the system. There are no time limits on using the system and no fees.

Graduates: In 1992–93, 976 bachelor's degrees were awarded. The most popular majors among graduates were early childhood education (12%), elementary education (9%), and accounting (4%). Within an average freshman class, 30% graduate in 4 years, 40% in 5 years, and 30% in 6 years. In the 1992 graduating class, 8% of the men and 9% of the women were enrolled in graduate school within 6 months of graduation; 37% of the men and 38% of the women had found employment.

Admissions Contact: Norman G. Hasbrouck, Dean for Enrollment Management and Academic Services.

CARLOW COLLEGE
B-3
Pittsburgh, PA 15213

(412) 578-6059
(800) 333-CARLOW (out-of-state)

Full-time: 74 men, 733 women	**Faculty:** 57; IIB, -$
Part-time: 75 men, 938 women	**Ph.D.s:** 65%
Graduate: 43 women	**Student/Faculty:** 14 to 1
Year: semesters, summer session	**Tuition:** $9650
Application Deadline: open	**Room & Board:** $4264
Freshman Class: 376 applied, 306 accepted, 160 enrolled	
SAT I or ACT: required	**COMPETITIVE**

Carlow College, founded in 1929, is a private, primarily women's college, affiliated with the Roman Catholic Church, offering programs in liberal and fine arts, business, health science, professional training, and teacher preparation. There is one undergraduate and one graduate school. In addition to regional accreditation, Carlow has baccalaureate program accreditation with NLN. The library contains 93,781 volumes, 11,154 microform items, and 6437 audiovisual forms, and subscribes to 441 periodicals. Computerized library sources and services include the card catalog, interlibrary loans, and database searching. Special learning facilities include a learning resource center. The 13-acre campus is in an urban area in Pittsburgh. Including residence halls, there are 11 buildings on campus.

Student Life: About 97% of undergraduates are from Pennsylvania. Students come from 11 states and 15 foreign countries. Eighty-six percent are from public schools; 3% from private. Eighty-eight percent are white; 10% African American. The average age of freshmen is 18; all undergraduates, 31. Thirty percent drop out by the end of their first year; 55% remain to graduate.

Housing: A total of 380 students can be accommodated in college housing. College-sponsored living facilities include single-sex dormitories. On-campus housing is guaranteed for all 4 years. Fifty-nine percent of students live on campus; of those, 50% remain on campus on weekends. Alcohol is not permitted.

Activities: There are no fraternities or sororities on campus. There are 28 groups on campus, including choir, ethnic, honors, international, professional, religious, social, social service, and student government. Popular campus events include Homecoming, Founder Day, Christmas Concert, Saint Patrick's Day Celebration and Parade, International Festival, Black History Month, Women's History Month, Focus on Women Lecture Series, and drama productions.

Sports: There are 3 intercollegiate sports for women and 2 intramural sports for women. Athletic and recreation facilities include a gymnasium, a pool, and a weight room.

Disabled Students: The following facilities are available: wheelchair ramps, elevators, special parking, specially equipped rest rooms, special class scheduling, lowered drinking fountains, and lowered telephones.

Services: In addition to many counseling and information services, tutoring is available in some subjects, including study skills, mathematics, and sciences. In addition, there is a reader service for the blind, and remedial math, reading, and writing.

Campus Safety and Security: Campus safety and security measures include 24-hour foot and vehicle patrol, self-defense education, escort service, and informal discussions. In addition, there are pamphlets, posters, and films, emergency telephones, and lighted pathways and sidewalks.

Programs of Study: Carlow awards the B.A., B.S., and B.S.M. degrees. Master's degrees also are awarded. Bachelor's degrees are awarded in BIOLOGICAL SCIENCE (biology/biological science), BUSINESS (accounting and business administration and management), COMMUNICATIONS AND THE ARTS (art, art history and appreciation, communications, creative writing, and English), COMPUTER AND PHYSICAL SCIENCE (computer mathematics, information sciences and systems, and mathematics), EDUCATION (art, early childhood, elementary, and special), HEALTH PROFESSIONS (health science and nursing), SOCIAL SCIENCE (history, liberal arts/general studies, philosophy, psychology, and theological studies). Nursing and biology are the strongest academically. Nursing and business management have the largest enrollments.

Required: A total of 120 credit hours (125 for nursing students), including 27 to 44 in the major, is required to graduate. Credits must be earned in history, literature, art, music or drama, mathematics or logic, philosophy, anthropology, psychology or sociology, biology, chemistry or physics, and women's studies. A minimum GPA of 2.0 is required.

Special: Carlow offers cross-registration, internships, study abroad, work-study programs, accelerated degree programs, dual majors, interdisciplinary majors, including communication/business management, English/business management, medical marketing, and sociology and anthropology, student-designed majors, a weekend college, and nondegree study. Students may elect pass/fail options and receive credit for life, military, or work experience. There is a freshman honors program on campus, as well as 3 national honor societies.

Faculty/Classroom: Twenty-eight percent of faculty are male; 72%, female.

Admissions: About 81% of the 1993–94 applicants were accepted.

Requirements: Carlow requires applicants to have a minimum B average and to be in the upper 40% of their class. The SAT I or ACT is required. The minimum scores depend on the major selected. Admission candidates must be graduates of an accredited secondary school. Eighteen Carnegie units are required, including 4 each in English and arts/humanities, 3 each in mathematics and science, and 4 in electives. The GED is accepted. An essay is required and an interview is recommended. Art majors must have a portfolio. AP and CLEP credits are accepted. Important factors used in the admissions decision are advanced placement or honor courses, leadership record, personality, intangible qualities, recommendations by school officials, and extracurricular activities record.

Procedure: Freshmen are admitted fall and spring. Entrance exams should be taken early in the senior year. Application deadlines are open. Application fee is $20. Notification of early decision is sent October 30; regular decision, on a rolling basis. There are early decision, early admissions, and deferred admissions plans.

Transfer: About 35 transfer students enrolled in 1993–94. Transfer students must have a minimum GPA of 2.0 and submit high school and college transcripts. Minimum SAT I and ACT scores depend on the major. The minimum credit hours required are 3, but 12 are recommended for scholarship consideration. An interview is also recommended. A total of 32 credits out of 120 to 125 must be completed at Carlow.

Visiting: There are regularly scheduled orientations for prospective students. There are guides for informal visits and visitors may sit in on classes and stay overnight at the school. To arrange for a visit, contact the Admissions Office at (800) 333-CARLOW.

Financial Aid: In 1993–94 94% of all current freshmen and 87% of continuing students received some form of financial aid. About 72% of freshmen and 77% of continuing students received need-based aid. Scholarships or need-based grants averaged $6236 ($11,900 maximum); loans averaged $2956 ($6625 maximum); and work contracts averaged $731 ($1000 maximum). Thirty percent of undergraduate students work part-time. Average earnings from campus work for the school year are $630. Carlow is a member of CSS. The college's own financial statement and the FAFSA are required. The deadline for financial aid applications is May 1.

International Students: There are currently 15 international students enrolled. The school actively recruits these students. They must take the TOEFL and achieve a minimum score of 500.

Computers: The college provides computer facilities for student use. There are 35 computer terminals/PCs available on campus for student use in a computer center and the Apple laboratory. All students may access the system. There are no time limits on using the system. The fees are $50.

Graduates: In 1992–93, 261 bachelor's degrees were awarded. The most popular majors among graduates were nursing (33%), communication/business management (12%), and business management (12%). Within an average freshman class, 41% graduate in 4 years, 52% in 5 years, and 54% in 6 years. Ten companies recruited on campus in 1992–93.

Admissions Contact: Carol Descak, Director of Admissions.

CARNEGIE MELLON UNIVERSITY B-3
Pittsburgh, PA 15213 (412) 268-2082

Full-time: 2960 men, 1305 women	Faculty: 548; I, +$
Part-time: 183 men, 108 women	Ph.Ds: 91%
Graduate: 1890 men, 813 women	Student/Faculty: 8 to 1
Year: semesters, summer session	Tuition: $17,060
Application Deadline: February 1	Room & Board: $5500
Freshman Class: 8728 applied, 5201 accepted, 1191 enrolled	
SAT I: required	HIGHLY COMPETITIVE +

Carnegie Mellon University, established in 1900, is a private, coeducational nonsectarian institution offering undergraduate programs in liberal arts and science and professional technology. There are 6 undergraduate and 8 graduate schools. In addition to regional accreditation, Carnegie Mellon has baccalaureate program accreditation with AACSB, ABET, NAAB, NASAD, and NASM. The 3 libraries contain 828,109 volumes, 717,355 microform items, and 20,601 audiovisual items, and subscribe to 3727 periodicals. Computerized library sources and services include the card catalog, interlibrary loans, and database searching. Special learning facilities include a learning resource center, an art gallery, and a radio station. The 103-acre campus is in a suburban area 5 miles from Pittsburgh. Including residence halls, there are 58 buildings on campus.

Student Life: About 70% of undergraduates are from out-of-state, mostly the Middle Atlantic. Students come from 50 states, 36 foreign countries, and Canada. Seventy percent are from public schools; 30% from private. Fifty-six percent are white; 24% foreign nationals; 13% Asian American. The average age of freshmen is 18; all undergraduates, 20. Twelve percent drop out by the end of their first year; 71% remain to graduate.

Housing: A total of 3296 students can be accommodated in college housing. College-sponsored living facilities include single-sex and coed dormitories, on-campus apartments, off-campus apartments, fraternity houses, and sorority houses. In addition, there are honors houses, language houses, and special interest houses. On-campus housing is guaranteed for all 4 years. Seventy-four percent of students live on campus; of those, 90% remain on campus on weekends. Alcohol is not permitted. All students may keep cars on campus.

Activities: About 25% of men belong to 12 national fraternities; about 14% of women belong to 4 national sororities. There are 118 groups on campus, including art, bagpipe band, band, cheerleading, chess, choir, chorale, chorus, computers, drama, ethnic, gay, honors, international, jazz band, literary magazine, marching band, musical theater, newspaper, orchestra, pep band, political, professional, radio and tv, religious, social, social service, student government, symphony, and yearbook. Popular campus events include Spring Carnival, Homecoming, and International Festival.

Sports: There are 9 intercollegiate sports for men and 8 for women, and 22 intramural sports for men and 16 for women. Athletic and recreation facilities include a gymnasium, a stadium, athletic fields, tennis courts, and a pool.

Disabled Students: Almost the entire campus is accessible to disabled students. The following facilities are available: wheelchair ramps, elevators, special parking, specially equipped rest rooms, special class scheduling, lowered drinking fountains, and lowered telephones.

Services: In addition to many counseling and information services, tutoring is available in most subjects. In addition, there is a reader service for the blind.

Campus Safety and Security: Campus safety and security measures include 24-hour foot and vehicle patrol, escort service, shuttle buses, and informal discussions. In addition, there are pamphlets, posters, and films, emergency telephones, lighted pathways and sidewalks, and a SafeWalk Program.

Programs of Study: Carnegie Mellon awards the B.A., B.S., B.A.H., B.Arch., and B.F.A. degrees. Master's and doctoral degrees also are awarded. Bachelor's degrees are awarded in BIOLOGICAL SCIENCE (biology/biological science), BUSINESS (business administration and management, business economics, and marketing/retailing/merchandising), COMMUNICATIONS AND THE ARTS (communications, design, dramatic arts, English, fine arts, French, German, journalism, languages, music, and Spanish), COMPUTER AND PHYSICAL SCIENCE (chemistry, computer programming, computer science, information sciences and systems, mathematics, physics, and statistics), EDUCATION (music), ENGINEERING AND ENVIRONMENTAL DESIGN (chemical engineering, civil engineering, computer engineering, electrical/electronics engineering, engineering, and mechanical engineering), SOCIAL SCIENCE (economics, history, philosophy, political science/government, psychology, public administration, social science, and urban studies). Electrical and computer engineering are the strongest programs academically and have the largest enrollments.

Required: To graduate, students must complete requirements in English, history, and computing skills, and they must have a GPA of 2.0. Distribution requirements, the number of credits needed to graduate, and the number of credits required in the major vary by college.

Special: Students may cross-register with the Pittsburgh Council of Higher Education. Also available are internships, work-study programs, study abroad in Switzerland and Japan, a Washington semester, accelerated degrees, B.A.-B.S. degrees, and co-op programs in metallurgical engineering and materials science. Dual majors are available in biomedical engineering/engineering and public policy and European study/foreign languages. There is a freshman honors program on campus, as well as 10 national honor societies.

Faculty/Classroom: Eighty-four percent of faculty are male; 16%, female. All faculty both teach and do research. Graduate students teach 34% of introductory courses. The average class size in an introductory lecture is 80; in a laboratory, 19; and in a regular course offering, 21.

Admissions: About 60% of the 1993–94 applicants were accepted.

Requirements: The SAT I is required. SAT II: Subject tests in writing and mathematics are required for all applicants. Engineering applicants must take the chemistry or physics test. Science applicants may take either of these or the biology test. Business and liberal arts applicants must take a third test of their choice. Applicants must graduate from an accredited secondary school or have a GED. They must earn 16 Carnegie units. All applicants must have completed 4 years of English. Applicants to the Carnegie Institute of Technology and the Mellon College of Science must take 4 years of mathematics and 1 year each of biology, chemistry, and physics. Essays are required, and interviews are recommended. Art and design applicants are required to submit a portfolio. Drama and music applicants are required to audition. AP credits are accepted. Important factors used in the admissions decision are advanced placement or honor courses, leadership record, evidence of special talent, recommendations by school officials, and extracurricular activities record.

Procedure: Freshmen are admitted in the fall. Entrance exams should be taken by February 1. Early decision applications should be filed by December 1; regular applications, by February 1 for fall entry, along with an application fee of $50. Notification of early decision is sent January 15; regular decision, April 15. There are early decision, early admissions, and deferred admissions plans. About 180 early decision candidates were accepted for the 1993–94 class. A waiting list is an active part of the admissions procedure, with about 10% of applicants on the list.

Transfer: About 65 transfer students enrolled in 1993–94. Transfer students must maintain a minimum GPA of 3.3. One academic year must be completed at Carnegie Mellon.

Visiting: There are regularly scheduled orientations for prospective students, including Saturday group sessions in September, October, November, and April. There are guides for informal visits and visitors may sit in on classes and stay overnight at the school. To arrange for a visit, contact the Admissions Office at (412) 268-2082.

Financial Aid: In 1993–94, 74% of all current freshmen and 70% of continuing students received some form of financial aid. About 68% of freshmen and 68% of continuing students received need-based aid. The average freshman award was $15,832. Of that total, scholarships or need-based grants averaged $11,254 ($24,280 maximum); loans averaged $3139 ($5625 maximum); and work contracts averaged $1385 ($2495 maximum). Seventy percent of undergraduate students work part-time. Average earnings from campus work for the school year are $1400. The average financial indebtedness of the 1992–93 graduate was $14,000. Carnegie Mellon is a member of CSS. The FAF, the college's own financial statement, federal tax returns and W-2 forms of parents and student, and the FAFSA are required. The deadline for financial aid applications is February 15.

International Students: There are currently 416 international students enrolled. The school actively recruits these students. They must take the TOEFL or the University of Michigan Language Test and achieve a minimum score on the TOEFL of 600. The student must also take the SAT I or the ACT and SAT II: Subject tests in writing and mathematics I or II.

Computers: The college provides computer facilities for student use. The mainframes are a DEC VAX 6320, 6330, 11/780, and a SUN 3280. The campuswide computer network extends to every office and dormitory room, connecting hundreds of personal computers and advanced workstations. All students may access the system. It may be used 24 hours per day. There are no time limits on using the system and no fees.

Graduates: In 1992–93, 962 bachelor's degrees were awarded. The most popular majors among graduates were electrical and computer engineering (9%), industrial management (7%), and mathematics (4%). Within an average freshman class, 56% graduate in 4 years, 70% in 5 years, and 71% in 6 years.

Admissions Contact: Michael Steidel, Director of Admissions.

CEDAR CREST COLLEGE   E-3

Allentown, PA 18104   (215) 740-3780; (800) 360-1222 (out-of-state)

Full-time: 18 men, 773 women	Faculty: 64; IIB, -$
Part-time: 74 men, 680 women	Ph.D.s: 78%
Graduate: none	Student/Faculty: 12 to 1
Year: semesters, summer session	Tuition: $13,720
Application Deadline: open	Room & Board: $5210
Freshman Class: 667 applied, 633 accepted, 198 enrolled	
SAT I Verbal/Math: 469/489	**COMPETITIVE**

Cedar Crest College, founded in 1867, is a private, liberal arts college for women affiliated with the United Church of Christ. In addition to regional accreditation, Cedar Crest has baccalaureate program accreditation with CAHEA, CSWE, and NLN. The library contains 318,887 volumes, 30,344 microform items, and 5684 audiovisual forms, and subscribes to 1274 periodicals. Computerized library sources and services include the card catalog, interlibrary loans, and database searching. Special learning facilities include a learning resource center, art gallery, arboretum, and a theater. The 84-acre campus is in a suburban area 55 miles north of Philadelphia and 90 miles west of New York City. Including residence halls, there are 15 buildings on campus.

Student Life: About 83% of undergraduates are from Pennsylvania. Students come from 23 states, 20 foreign countries, and Canada. Eighty-eight percent are from public schools; 12% from private. Ninety-six percent are white. Eighty percent claim no religious affiliation; 10% Catholic. The average age of freshmen is 18; all undergraduates, 24. Eighteen percent drop out by the end of their first year; 56% remain to graduate.

Housing: A total of 500 students can be accommodated in college housing. College-sponsored living facilities include single-sex dormitories. On-campus housing is available on a first-come, first-served basis and is available on a lottery system for upperclassmen. Priority is given to out-of-town students. Eighty-five percent of students live on campus; of those, 70% remain on campus on weekends. All students may keep cars on campus.

Activities: There are no fraternities on campus. There are 46 groups on campus, including art, choir, chorus, computers, dance, drama, ethnic, honors, international, literary magazine, musical theater, newspaper, political, professional, religious, social, social service, student government, and yearbook. Popular campus events include Song Contest, Junior Ring Ceremony, Student Faculty Frolic, Move-Up-Day, International Week, Midnight Breakfast, and Ambassador lecture series.

Sports: Athletic and recreation facilities include 5 tennis courts, field hockey and lacrosse fields, a cross-country course, a gymnasium with basketball, volleyball, and badminton courts, dance and aerobics studios, and weight and training rooms.

Disabled Students: Thirty percent of the campus is accessible to disabled students. The following facilities are available: wheelchair ramps, elevators, special parking, two specially equipped rest rooms, and special class scheduling.

Services: In addition to many counseling and information services, tutoring is available in every subject. The Academic Support Center is available to all students and coordinates individual and group tutoring. There is also remedial math and writing.

Campus Safety and Security: Campus safety and security measures include 24-hour foot and vehicle patrol, self defense education, escort service, and informal discussions. In addition, there are pamphlets, posters, and films, emergency telephones, lighted pathways and sidewalks. Residence halls are equipped with fire/intrusion alarms which are monitored 24 hours a day.

Programs of Study: Cedar Crest awards the B.A. and B.S. degrees. Bachelor's degrees are awarded in BIOLOGICAL SCIENCE (biochemistry, biology/biological science, and genetics), BUSINESS (accounting and business administration and management), COMMUNICATIONS AND THE ARTS (art, communications, comparative literature, dramatic arts, English, fine arts, French, German, languages, music, Spanish, and speech/debate/rhetoric), COMPUTER AND PHYSICAL SCIENCE (chemistry, computer science, and mathematics), EDUCATION (elementary, middle school, science, and secondary), ENGINEERING AND ENVIRONMENTAL DESIGN (bioengineering), HEALTH PROFESSIONS (medical laboratory technology, nuclear medical technology, and nursing), SOCIAL SCIENCE (history, paralegal studies, philosophy/religion, political science/government, psychology, public administration, social work, and sociology). Health professions, sciences, and genetic engineering are the strongest academically. Business, nursing, and education have the largest enrollments.

Required: For graduation, students must complete 120 credit hours (125 for nursing) with a minimum GPA of 2.0. Distribution requirements include 44 credits in 8 departments, including English composition, junior seminar, foreign language, science literacy, humanities,

aesthetic views and appreciation, historical and societal perspectives, and quantitative reasoning.

Special: Cross-registration is available with Lehigh Valley Association of Independent Colleges. Also available are internships, a Washington semester, work-study programs, dual majors, student-designed majors, co-op programs in business and psychology, 3–2 engineering degrees, pass/fail options, and credit for life, military, and work experience. There is a freshman honors program on campus, as well as 6 national honor societies. One department has an honors program.

Faculty/Classroom: Thirty-nine percent of faculty are male; 61%, female. All teach undergraduates. The average class size in an introductory lecture is 22; in a laboratory, 12; and in a regular course offering, 19.

Admissions: About 95% of the 1993–94 applicants were accepted. The SAT scores for the 1993–94 freshman class were as follows: Verbal—67% below 500, 25% between 500 and 599, 7% between 600 and 700, and 1% above 700; Math—58% below 500, 35% between 500 and 599, 5% between 600 and 700, and 2% above 700. About 40% of the current freshmen were in the top fifth of their class; 70% were in the top two fifths. About 4 freshmen graduated first in their class.

Requirements: Cedar Crest requires applicants to be in the upper 50% of their class. A minimum GPA of 2.0 is required. The SAT I or ACT is required. Applicants must be graduates of an accredited secondary school. The GED is accepted. Students should have completed 16 high school academic credits, including 4 years of English, 3 years of mathematics, 2 years each of science, history, and foreign language, and 1 year each of art, music, and social studies. An essay and interview are required. A portfolio is recommended for art students and an audition for music students. AP and CLEP credits are accepted. Important factors used in the admissions decision are advanced placement or honor courses, leadership record, evidence of special talent, extracurricular activities record, personality, and intangible qualities.

Procedure: Freshmen are admitted fall and spring. Entrance exams should be taken in the junior year or early senior year. Application deadlines are open. Application fee is $30. Notification is sent on a rolling basis. There are early admissions and deferred admissions plans.

Transfer: About 67 transfer students enrolled in 1993–94. Applicants for transfer should have a minimum GPA of 2.0. An interview is required. A total of 30 credits out of 120 must be completed at Cedar Crest.

Visiting: There are regularly scheduled orientations for prospective students. There are guides for informal visits and visitors may sit in on classes and stay overnight at the school. To arrange for a visit, contact the Admissions Office at (800) 360–1222 or (215) 740–3780.

Financial Aid: In 1993–94 90% of all current freshmen and 84% of continuing students received some form of financial aid. About 80% of freshmen and 78% of continuing students received need-based aid. The average freshman award was $12,484. Of that total, scholarships or need-based grants averaged $7200 ($12,000 maximum); loans averaged $3984 ($5125 maximum); and work contracts averaged $1300. Forty-two percent of undergraduate students work part-time. Average earnings from campus work for the school year are $1100. The average financial indebtedness of the 1992–93 graduate was $12,000. Cedar Crest is a member of CSS. The FAF, the college's own financial statement, and the FAFSA are required.

International Students: There are currently 47 international students enrolled. The school actively recruits these students. They must take the TOEFL and achieve a minimum score of 500. The applicant must also take the SAT I or the ACT.

Computers: The college provides computer facilities for student use. A total of 62 microcomputers are available in 4 computer laboratories and 4 dormitories. All students may access the system. There are no time limits on using the system and no fees.

Graduates: In 1992–93 181 bachelor's degrees were awarded. The most popular majors among graduates were nursing (23%), psychology (14%), and business administration (14%). Within an average freshman class, 59% graduate in 4 years and 61% in 5 years. Some 12 companies recruited on campus in 1992–93. In the 1992 graduating class, 15% of the women were enrolled in graduate school within 6 months of graduation; 80% had found employment.

Admissions Contact: Cynthia Phillips, Director of Admissions.

CHATHAM COLLEGE
Pittsburgh, PA 15232

B-3
(412) 365–1290
(800) 837–1290 (out-of-state)

Full-time: 471 women	Faculty: 43
Part-time: 150 women	Ph.D.s: 93%
Graduate: 4 women	Student/Faculty: 11 to 1
Year: 4–1–4, summer session	Tuition: $12,780
Application Deadline: open	Room & Board: $5230
Freshman Class: 393 applied, 357 accepted, 194 enrolled	
SAT I Verbal/Math: 491/481	ACT: 22

COMPETITIVE

Chatham College, founded in 1869, is a private women's college offering undergraduate degree programs in the arts and sciences, business, and education. The library contains 130,000 volumes, 500 microform items, and 4300 audiovisual forms, and subscribes to 600 periodicals. Special learning facilities include a learning resource center, art gallery, radio station, 285-seat theater, and a media center. The 34-acre campus is in an urban area 8 miles east of downtown Pittsburgh. Including residence halls, there are 30 buildings on campus.

Student Life: About 86% of undergraduates are from Pennsylvania. Students come from 22 states, 9 foreign countries, and Canada. Eighty-two percent are from public schools; 18% from private. Eighty-seven percent are white. The average age of freshmen is 18; all undergraduates, 21. Twenty-four percent drop out by the end of their first year; 46% remain to graduate.

Housing: A total of 340 students can be accommodated in college housing. College-sponsored living facilities include dormitories and on-campus apartments. In addition there are special interest houses, a residence hall for adult students, and an intercultural residence hall. On-campus housing is guaranteed for all 4 years. Eighty-five percent of students live on campus; of those, 75% remain on campus on weekends. Alcohol is not permitted. Upperclassmen may keep cars on campus.

Activities: There are 32 groups on campus, including choir, computers, dance, drama, ethnic, film, honors, international, literary magazine, musical theater, newspaper, photography, political, professional, radio and TV, religious, social service, student government, and yearbook. Popular campus events include Fall Festival, Spring Fling, Air Band Contest, Activities Fair, Halloween Party and Haunted House, Fickes Eggnog Party, Candlelight Holiday Concert, and Senior Faculty Dinner.

Sports: Athletic and recreation facilities include a swimming pool, tennis and platform tennis courts, conditioning rooms, Nautilus equipment, a gymnasium, a dance studio, an athletic field, and bowling alleys.

Disabled Students: Seventy-five percent of the campus is accessible to disabled students. The following facilities are available: wheelchair ramps, elevators, special parking, specially equipped rest rooms, and special class scheduling.

Services: In addition to many counseling and information services, tutoring is available in every subject, including student peer tutoring and organized study groups.

Campus Safety and Security: Campus safety and security measures include 24-hour foot and vehicle patrol, self-defense education, escort service, and shuttle buses. In addition, there are informal discussions, pamphlets, posters, films, emergency telephones, and lighted pathways and sidewalks.

Programs of Study: Chatham awards the B.A. and B.S. degrees. Master's degrees also are awarded. Bachelor's degrees are awarded in BIOLOGICAL SCIENCE (biology/biological science), BUSINESS (accounting, international business management, and management science), COMMUNICATIONS AND THE ARTS (art history and appreciation, communications, dramatic arts, English, French, music, Spanish, and visual and performing arts), COMPUTER AND PHYSICAL SCIENCE (chemistry, information sciences and systems, and mathematics), EDUCATION (early childhood, elementary, and secondary), ENGINEERING AND ENVIRONMENTAL DESIGN (environmental science), HEALTH PROFESSIONS (premedicine), SOCIAL SCIENCE (criminal justice, economics, European studies, history, human services, international relations, international studies, philosophy, political science/government, prelaw, psychology, and women's studies). Economics, management, English, information science, psychology, and communications are the strongest academically. Communications, education, psychology, economics, and management have the largest enrollments.

Required: For graduation, students must complete 36 units, including a general education curriculum of 7 courses and a senior tutorial. A minimum GPA of 1.8 for freshmen and 2.0 for upperclassmen is required. Computer literacy along with writing, language, mathematical, reading, and vocabulary skills, are required proficiencies.

Special: Chatham offers a study-abroad program in 4 countries for juniors, cross-registration with other Pittsburgh Council on Higher Education institutions, internships in the public and private sectors, and

a Washington semester in conjunction with American University and the Public Leadership Education Network. Accelerated degree programs, work-study, combined B.A.-B.S. degrees, and dual and student-designed majors are possible. Chatham students may complete a 3-2 engineering program with one of 3 partner institutions, gain early admission to the Medical College of Pennsylvania, or combine teacher certification with a master's degree from Carnegie Mellon University. There are 3 national honor societies on campus, including Phi Beta Kappa.

Faculty/Classroom: Forty percent of faculty are male; 60%, female. All faculty members both teach and do research. No introductory courses are taught by graduate students. The average class size in an introductory lecture is 19; in a laboratory and in a regular course offering, 10.

Admissions: About 91% of the 1993-94 applicants were accepted. The SAT scores for the 1993-94 freshman class were as follows: Verbal—56% below 500, 28% between 500 and 599, and 16% between 600 and 700; Math—50% below 500, 34% between 500 and 599, 10% between 600 and 700, and 6% above 700. The ACT scores were 37% below 21, 33% between 21 and 23, 11% between 24 and 26, 15% between 27 and 28, and 4% above 28. About 54% of the current freshmen were in the top fifth of their class; 80% were in the top two fifths. There were 4 National Merit semifinalists.

Requirements: Chatham requires applicants to be in the upper 40% of their class. A minimum GPA of 2.5 is required. The SAT I or ACT is required. Applicants must be graduates of an accredited secondary school or have earned the GED. Students should have completed 4 years of high school English and 2 years each of mathematics, science, and social studies. A foreign language is recommended. An essay and an interview are required. An audition is required for the RUDD Scholarship. AP and CLEP credits are accepted. Important factors used in the admissions decision are leadership record, advanced placement or honor courses, extracurricular activities record, recommendations by school officials, and evidence of special talent.

Procedure: Freshmen are admitted to all sessions. Entrance exams should be taken by fall of the senior year. Application deadlines are open. The application fee is $25. Notification is sent on a rolling basis. There are early decision, early admissions, and deferred admissions plans. About 22 early decision candidates were accepted for the 1993-94 class.

Transfer: About 60 transfer students enrolled in 1993-94. Applicants must present high school and college transcripts and 3 recommendations. The SAT I or ACT and an interview are required. A total of 14 units out of 36 must be completed at Chatham.

Visiting: There are regularly scheduled orientations for prospective students as well as guides for informal visits. Visitors may sit in on classes and stay overnight at the school. To arrange for a visit, contact the Admissions Office at (412) 365-1290 or (800) 837-1290.

Financial Aid: In 1993-94 87% of all current freshmen and 85% of continuing students received some form of financial aid. About 73% of freshmen and 60% of continuing students received need-based aid. The average freshman award was $13,330. Of that total, scholarships or need-based grants averaged $8843 ($13,142 maximum); loans averaged $3220 ($4625 maximum); and work contracts averaged $1738 ($1800 maximum). Fifty-six percent of undergraduate students work part-time. Average earnings from campus work for the school year are $1800. The average financial indebtedness of the 1992-93 graduate was $13,500. Chatham is a member of CSS. The college's own financial statement and the FAFSA are required. The deadline for financial aid applications is May 1.

International Students: There are currently 15 international students enrolled. The school actively recruits these students. They must take the TOEFL or the University of Michigan Language Test and achieve a minimum score on the TOEFL of 500.

Computers: The college provides computer facilities for student use. The mainframe is a DEC VAX Model 300 minicomputer. There are also 30 IBM PC and 25 Apple Macintosh microcomputers available in the student computer laboratory and the communications laboratory. All students may access the system. It may be used 85 hours per week during normal operating hours of the student laboratory. There are no time limits on using the system and no fees.

Graduates: In 1992-93 121 bachelor's degrees were awarded. The most popular majors among graduates were communications (17%), psychology (13%), and history (8%). Within an average freshman class, 44% graduate in 4 years, 48% in 5 years, and 49% in 6 years. Ten companies recruited on campus in 1992-93. In the 1992 graduating class, 30% of the women were enrolled in graduate school within 6 months of graduation; 50% of the women had found employment.

Admissions Contact: Suellen Ofe, Dean of Admissions and Financial Aid.

CHESTNUT HILL COLLEGE
F-3

Philadelphia, PA 19118-2695

(215) 248-7004

(800) 248-0052 (out-of-state)

Full-time: 518 women	Faculty: 66; IIB, --$
Part-time: 44 men, 253 women	Ph.D.s: 71%
Graduate: 64 men, 334 women	Student/Faculty: 8 to 1
Year: semesters, summer session	Tuition: $9750
Application Deadline: March 15	Room & Board: $4775
Freshman Class: 342 applied, 254 accepted, 126 enrolled	
SAT I Verbal/Math: 495/483	**COMPETITIVE**

Chestnut Hill College, founded in 1924, is a private, liberal arts, primarily women's institution, affiliated with the Roman Catholic Church. Men over the age of 23 may matriculate part-time through the Continuing Education Division (undergraduate) and the Graduate Division. There is one graduate school. In addition to regional accreditation, the college has baccalaureate program accreditation with ACS. The library contains 135,554 volumes, 1427 microform items, and 1939 audiovisual forms, and subscribes to 1220 periodicals. Computerized library sources and services include the card catalog, interlibrary loans, and database searching. Special learning facilities include a planetarium, an equipped, rotating observatory, and a technology center. The 45-acre campus is in a suburban area 25 miles northwest of downtown Philadelphia. Including residence halls, there are 13 buildings on campus.

Student Life: About 81% of undergraduates are from Pennsylvania. Students come from 16 states and 8 foreign countries. Forty-one percent are from public schools; 59% from private. Seventy-seven percent are white; 10% African American. Fifty-nine percent are Catholic; 26% claim no religious affiliation; 11% are Protestant. The average age of freshmen is 18; all undergraduates, 20. Fifteen percent drop out by the end of their first year; 65% remain to graduate.

Housing: A total of 400 students can be accommodated in college housing. College-sponsored living facilities include single-sex dormitories. On-campus housing is guaranteed for all 4 years. Sixty-seven percent of students live on campus; of those, 60% remain on campus on weekends. Alcohol is not permitted. All students may keep cars on campus.

Activities: There are no fraternities or sororities on campus. There are 32 groups on campus, including art, chorus, drama, ethnic, honors, international, jazz band, literary magazine, newspaper, opera, orchestra, political, professional, religious, social, social service, student government, and yearbook. Popular campus events include Opening Convocation, Honors Convocation, International Gourmet Day, Peace Net, Road Rally, and Intramural One-Act Play Night.

Sports: There are 6 intercollegiate sports for women and 6 intramural sports for women. Athletic and recreation facilities include a gymnasium; softball, lacrosse, and hockey fields; 8 tennis courts; an indoor pool; neighboring stables; an archery range; and a weight and fitness center.

Disabled Students: Ninety percent of the campus is accessible to disabled students. The following facilities are available: wheelchair ramps, elevators, special parking, specially equipped rest rooms, and a shower area in residence halls.

Services: In addition to many counseling and information services, tutoring is available in most subjects. There is remedial math and writing.

Campus Safety and Security: Campus safety and security measures include 24-hour foot and vehicle patrol, self-defense education, informal discussions, pamphlets, posters, films, and lighted pathways and sidewalks. Doors are locked after 6 P.M. and on weekends and are monitored by cameras. Escorted shuttle carts to parking lots are available in the evenings.

Programs of Study: The college awards the B.A. and B.S. degrees. Associate and master's degrees also are awarded. Bachelor's degrees are awarded in BIOLOGICAL SCIENCE (biochemistry, biology/biological science, and molecular biology), BUSINESS (accounting, business administration and management, management science, and marketing/retailing/merchandising), COMMUNICATIONS AND THE ARTS (art history and appreciation, English, French, German, music, Spanish, and studio art), COMPUTER AND PHYSICAL SCIENCE (chemistry, computer science, and mathematics), EDUCATION (early childhood, elementary, and music), SOCIAL SCIENCE (economics, history, political science/government, psychology, and sociology). Biological/computer/physical sciences, humanities, and social sciences are the strongest academically. Education, social sciences, and humanities have the largest enrollments.

Required: To graduate, students must complete 120 credit hours, including 30 to 45 in the major, with a GPA of 2.0 overall and in the major. Among the course requirements are 21 hours in the humanities, 11 in the natural and laboratory sciences, 9 in social sciences, 6 in religious studies, 6 beyond elementary level in foreign language, 3 in writing, and a senior seminar. All students must complete a senior research paper prepared on a computer and defend it orally. Physi-

cal education and a first-year college experience seminar are required. All students must pass a swimming test.

Special: Cross-registration is available with LaSalle University and at the 10 colleges in the Sisters of St. Joseph College Consortium Student Exchange Program. The college offers internships, study abroad in England, Spain, Italy, and Austria, work-study programs, accelerated degree programs, interdisciplinary majors, including communications and technology and fine arts and technology, and dual and student-designed majors. Up to 6 credits may be given for life experience. Nondegree study and pass/fail options are available. The school offers unique career preparation programs in communications, international studies, and women in management. There is a freshman honors program on campus, as well as 4 national honor societies. All departments have honors programs.

Faculty/Classroom: Twenty-three percent of faculty are male; 77%, female. All teach undergraduates and 8% both teach and do research. No introductory courses are taught by graduate students. The average class size in an introductory lecture is 20; in a laboratory, 12; and in a regular course offering, 15.

Admissions: About 74% of the 1993–94 applicants were accepted. The SAT scores for the 1993–94 freshman class were as follows: Verbal—46% below 500, 44% between 500 and 599, and 10% between 600 and 700; Math—45% below 500, 42% between 500 and 599, and 13% between 600 and 700. About 51% of the current freshmen were in the top fifth of their class; 79% were in the top two fifths. One freshman graduated first in her class.

Requirements: The college requires applicants to be in the upper 40% of their class. A minimum GPA of 2.5 is required. The SAT I or ACT is required, with a recommended minimum composite score on the SAT I of 900 to 1000. Applicants must be graduates of an accredited secondary school. Sixteen Carnegie units are required, with a recommended 4 units each of English, mathematics, science, and social studies, and 3 of foreign language. An interview is recommended for all students, an audition is required for music students, and a portfolio is recommended for art studio majors. An essay is required. AP and CLEP credits are accepted. Important factors used in the admissions decision are advanced placement or honor courses, recommendations by school officials, leadership record, extracurricular activities record, personality, and intangible qualities.

Procedure: Freshmen are admitted fall and spring. Entrance exams should be taken early in the senior year. Applications should be filed by March 15 for fall entry, along with an application fee of $35. Notification is sent on a rolling basis. There are early admissions and deferred admissions plans.

Transfer: Twelve transfer students enrolled in 1993–94. Applicants for transfer must have a minimum GPA of 2.0; a 2.5 is recommended. A total of 60 credits out of 120 must be completed at the college.

Visiting: There are regularly scheduled orientations for prospective students, including faculty presentations and workshops on specific issues. There are guides for informal visits and visitors may sit in on classes and stay overnight at the school. To arrange for a visit, contact the Director of Admissions at (215) 248–7004.

Financial Aid: In 1993–94, 65% of all current freshmen and 68% of continuing students received some form of financial aid, including need-based aid. The average freshman award was $4000. Of that total, scholarships or need-based grants averaged $2100; loans averaged $1250 ($2625 maximum); and work contracts averaged $700. Twenty-five percent of undergraduate students work part-time. Average earnings from campus work for the school year are $700. The average financial indebtedness of the 1992–93 graduate was $6000. the college is a member of CSS. The college's own financial statement and PHEAA are required. The deadline for financial aid applications is March 15.

International Students: There are currently 16 international students enrolled. The school actively recruits these students. They must take the TOEFL and achieve a minimum score of 550.

Computers: The college provides computer facilities for student use. Students use Apple, Macintosh, and IBM PCs in the technology center, other computer laboratories, and dormitories. All students may access the system. Students may access the system during published schedules of operating times regulated by reservations. There are no fees.

Graduates: In 1992–93, 142 bachelor's degrees were awarded. The most popular majors among graduates were elementary education (14%), early childhood education (13%), and English (13%). Within an average freshman class, 65% graduate in 4 years and 4% in 5 years. Some 25 companies recruited on campus in 1992–93. In the 1992 graduating class, 20% of the women were enrolled in graduate school within 6 months of graduation; 71% had found employment.

Admissions Contact: Sr. Margaret Anne Birtwistle, SSJ, Director of Admissions.

CHEYNEY UNIVERSITY OF PENNSYLVANIA F-4

Cheyney, PA 19319　　(215) 399–2275; (800) 223–3608 (out-of-state)

Full-time: 568 men, 562 women	Faculty: 89; IIA, +$
Part-time: 23 men, 42 women	Ph.D.s: 52%
Graduate: 98 men, 226 women	Student/Faculty: 13 to 1
Year: semesters, summer session	Tuition: $3319 ($7717)
Application Deadline: June 30	Room & Board: $3686
Freshman Class: 1104 applied, 767 accepted, 287 enrolled	
SAT I or ACT: required	COMPETITIVE

Cheyney University of Pennsylvania, founded in 1837, is a public, coeducational, liberal arts institution offering programs in art, business, engineering, music, and teacher preparation. There are 2 undergraduate schools and one graduate school. In addition to regional accreditation, Cheyney has baccalaureate program accreditation with NCATE. The library contains 237,780 volumes, 517,955 microform items, and 3573 audiovisual forms, and subscribes to 655 periodicals. Computerized library sources and services include the card catalog. Special learning facilities include a planetarium, a radio station, a TV station, a weather station, a world cultures center, and a theater arts center. The 275-acre campus is in a suburban area 24 miles west of Philadelphia. Including residence halls, there are 33 buildings on campus.

Student Life: About 79% of undergraduates are from Pennsylvania. Students come from 17 states and 7 foreign countries. Eighty-five percent are from public schools; 15% from private. Ninety-seven percent are African American. The average age of freshmen is 20; all undergraduates, 21.

Housing: A total of 1300 students can be accommodated in college housing. College-sponsored living facilities include single-sex dormitories. On-campus housing is available on a first-come, first-served basis. Sixty-five percent of students live on campus. Alcohol is not permitted. All students may keep cars on campus.

Activities: About 6% of men belong to 4 national fraternities; about 6% of women belong to 4 national sororities. There are 47 groups on campus, including art, cheerleading, chess, choir, computers, drama, ethnic, honors, international, newspaper, political, professional, radio and TV, religious, social, social service, student government, and yearbook. Popular campus events include Founders Day, Founders Day Ball, Wade Wilson Football Classic, and Black College Convention.

Sports: There are 7 intercollegiate sports for men and 5 for women, and 10 intramural sports for men and 10 for women. Athletic and recreation facilities include a track, tennis courts, outdoor and indoor basketball courts, a pool, a men's gymnasium, a women's gymnasium, a weight room, and a field house.

Disabled Students: Eighty-six percent of the campus is accessible to disabled students. The following facilities are available: wheelchair ramps, elevators, special parking, specially equipped rest rooms, lowered drinking fountains, and lowered telephones.

Services: In addition to many counseling and information services, tutoring is available in most subjects. In addition, there is remedial math, reading, and writing. Both peers and professionals serve as tutors.

Campus Safety and Security: Campus safety and security measures include 24-hour foot and vehicle patrol, shuttle buses, informal discussions, and pamphlets, posters, and films. In addition, there are lighted pathways and sidewalks.

Programs of Study: Cheyney awards the B.A., B.S., and B.S.Ed. degrees. Master's degrees are also awarded. Bachelor's degrees are awarded in BIOLOGICAL SCIENCE (biology/biological science), BUSINESS (business administration and management and hotel/motel and restaurant management), COMMUNICATIONS AND THE ARTS (communications, dramatic arts, English, fine arts, music, and telecommunications), COMPUTER AND PHYSICAL SCIENCE (chemistry, computer science, mathematics, and science), EDUCATION (early childhood, elementary, home economics, secondary, and special), ENGINEERING AND ENVIRONMENTAL DESIGN (industrial administration/management and industrial engineering technology), HEALTH PROFESSIONS (medical laboratory technology), SOCIAL SCIENCE (clothing and textiles management/production/services, dietetics, economics, geography, history, parks and recreation management, political science/government, psychology, and social science). Psychology, political science, and social relations are the strongest academically. Business administration and social relations have the largest enrollments.

Required: To graduate, students must complete at least 128 credit hours, with 30 in the major and a minimum GPA of 2.0. Distribution requirements include 6 credits each in communications, humanities, science, and social science, 4 credits in health and physical education, and 3 credits in mathematics.

Special: Students may participate in a co-op program and cross-register with West Chester University of Pennsylvania. Internships, study abroad, work-study programs, a chemistry-biology dual degree,

nondegree study, pass/fail options, and credit for life, military, and work experience are available. There is a freshman honors program on campus, as well as 9 national honor societies.

Faculty/Classroom: Sixty percent of faculty are male; 40%, female. Ninety-six percent teach undergraduates and 7% both teach and do research. No introductory courses are taught by graduate students. The average class size in an introductory lecture is 25; in a laboratory, 16; and in a regular course offering, 20.

Admissions: About 69% of the 1993–94 applicants were accepted.

Requirements: The SAT I (preferred) or ACT is required. Applicants must be graduates of an accredited secondary school or hold a GED. An interview is recommended. CLEP credit is accepted. Important factors used in the admissions decision are ability to finance college education, extracurricular activities record, geographic diversity, recommendations by alumni, and recommendations by school officials.

Procedure: Freshmen are admitted fall and spring. Entrance exams should be taken during the junior or senior year. Early decision applications should be filed by November 30; regular applications, by June 30 for fall entry and November 15 for spring entry, along with an application fee of $20. Notification is sent on a rolling basis. There are early decision and early admissions plans. A waiting list is an active part of the admissions procedure, with about 10% of applicants on the list.

Transfer: About 60 transfer students enrolled in 1993–94. Transfer applicants must have a C average from an accredited postsecondary institution; others may be admitted on probation. Students with fewer than 30 credits must submit a high school transcript. A total of 30 credits out of 128 must be completed at Cheyney.

Visiting: There are regularly scheduled orientations for prospective students. There are guides for informal visits and visitors may sit in on classes. To arrange for a visit, contact Shawn Jeffrey at (800) CHEYNEY or (215) 399–2055.

Financial Aid: In 1993–94, 85% of all current freshmen and 88% of continuing students received some form of financial aid. About 81% of freshmen and 84% of continuing students received need-based aid. The average freshman award was $5600. Of that total, scholarships or need-based grants averaged $4000 ($4960 maximum); loans averaged $2625; and work contracts averaged $1000. Thirty-five percent of undergraduate students work part-time. Average earnings from campus work for the school year are $967. The average financial indebtedness of the 1992–93 graduate was $14,500. Cheyney is a member of CSS. The FAF, FFS, SFS, or AFSA, and the combined Application for PA State Grant and Federal Student Aid are required. The deadline for financial aid applications is April 15.

International Students: There are currently 50 international students enrolled. The school actively recruits these students. They must take the TOEFL.

Computers: The college provides computer facilities for student use. The mainframe is a Unisys A-5. About 150 Apple, Macintosh, and IBM microcomputers are available in the library and departmental offices. Only authorized terminal operators may access the system. It may be used 24 hours a day. There are no time limits on using the system and no fees.

Graduates: In 1992–93, 151 bachelor's degrees were awarded. The most popular majors among graduates were business administration (25%), elementary education (13%), and social relations (13%). Some 25 companies recruited on campus in 1992–93. In the 1992 graduating class, 4% of the men and 3% of the women were enrolled in graduate school within 6 months of graduation; 32% of the men and 37% of the women had found employment.

Admissions Contact: William A.T. Byrd, Director of Admissions.

CLARION UNIVERSITY OF PENNSYLVANIA   B-2

Clarion, PA 16214   (814) 226–2306; (800) 672–7171 (in-state)

Full-time: 2098 men, 2886 women	**Faculty:** 341; IIA, +$
Part-time: 183 men, 524 women	**Ph.D.s:** 65%
Graduate: 148 men, 320 women	**Student/Faculty:** 15 to 1
Year: semesters, summer session	**Tuition:** $3710 ($8108)
Application Deadline: April 1	**Room & Board:** $2808
Freshman Class: 4244 applied, 2720 accepted, 1190 enrolled	
SAT I Verbal/Math: 429/474	**COMPETITIVE**

Clarion University of Pennsylvania, founded in 1867, is a public coeducational institute. There are 5 undergraduate and 4 graduate schools. In addition to regional accreditation, the university has baccalaureate program accreditation with NCATE and NLN. The library contains 365,000 volumes, and subscribes to 2000 periodicals. Special learning facilities include an art gallery, planetarium, radio station, and TV station. The 99-acre campus is in a small town 85 miles northeast of Pittsburgh. Including residence halls, there are 43 buildings on campus.

Student Life: About 92% of undergraduates are from Pennsylvania. Students come from 31 states, 37 foreign countries, and Canada. Ninety-five percent are white. The average age of freshmen is 19; all

undergraduates, 23. Twenty-three percent drop out by the end of their first year; 77% remain to graduate.

Housing: A total of 2045 students can be accommodated in college housing. College-sponsored living facilities include single-sex and coed dormitories. In addition there are honors houses. On-campus housing is guaranteed for the freshman year only, is available on a first-come, first-served basis, and is available on a lottery system for upperclassmen. Priority is given to out-of-town students. Alcohol is not permitted. All students may keep cars on campus.

Activities: About 12% of men belong to 2 local and 9 national fraternities; about 12% of women belong to 1 local and 8 national sororities. There are 125 groups on campus, including band, cheerleading, chess, choir, chorus, computers, dance, drama, drill team, ethnic, honors, international, jazz band, literary magazine, marching band, musical theater, newspaper, orchestra, political, professional, radio and TV, religious, social, social service, student government, symphony, and yearbook. Popular campus events include Autumn Leaf Festival, Homecoming Week, Family Weekend, Spring Festival of the Arts, Celebration of Black Heritage Week, and Welcome Freshmen Week.

Sports: There are 8 intercollegiate sports for men and 7 for women, and 20 intramural sports for men and 20 for women. Athletic and recreation facilities include a 5000-seat stadium, a gymnasium with physical fitness center and recreation swimming, and a natatorium.

Disabled Students: Eighty-five percent of the campus is accessible to disabled students. The following facilities are available: wheelchair ramps, elevators, special parking, specially equipped rest rooms, lowered drinking fountains, and lowered telephones.

Services: In addition to many counseling and information services, tutoring is available in every subject. There is a reader service for the blind, and remedial math, reading, and writing.

Campus Safety and Security: Campus safety and security measures include 24-hour foot and vehicle patrol, self defense education, escort service, and shuttle buses. In addition, there are informal discussions, pamphlets, posters, and films, emergency telephones, and lighted pathways and sidewalks.

Programs of Study: The university awards the B.A., B.S., B.F.A., B.Mus., B.S.B.A., and B.S.E. degrees. Associate and master's degrees also are awarded. Bachelor's degrees are awarded in BIOLOGICAL SCIENCE (biology/biological science), BUSINESS (accounting, banking and finance, business administration and management, business economics, and marketing/retailing/merchandising), COMMUNICATIONS AND THE ARTS (communications, dramatic arts, English, fine arts, French, German, music, Spanish, and speech/debate/rhetoric), COMPUTER AND PHYSICAL SCIENCE (chemistry, computer programming, computer science, earth science, geology, information sciences and systems, mathematics, and physics), EDUCATION (early childhood, elementary, foreign languages, music, secondary, and special), ENGINEERING AND ENVIRONMENTAL DESIGN (industrial administration/management), HEALTH PROFESSIONS (medical laboratory technology, nursing, and speech pathology/audiology), SOCIAL SCIENCE (anthropology, economics, geography, history, philosophy, political science/government, psychology, social science, and sociology). Sciences, psychology, and business are the strongest academically. Business, education, and communication have the largest enrollments.

Required: For graduation, students must complete a minimum of 128 semester hours, with a GPA of at least 2.5 in education, business, and communication, and 2.0 for other programs. Distribution requirements include at least 12 credits in modes of communication and 9 credits each of natural sciences and mathematics, humanities, and personal development and life skills. Students must take physical education, English composition, and computer science courses.

Special: Co-op programs are available with the University of Pittsburgh, Case Western Reserve, and Akron University. The school offers internships in all majors, study abroad all over the world, work-study programs, accelerated degree programs, B.A.-B.S. degrees, dual majors, a Washington semester at the Deaf Institute, general studies programs, and student-designed majors. Students may take a 3–2 engineering degree with the University of Pittsburgh and Case Western Reserve. Credit may be given for military experience. There are pass/fail options and nondegree study. There is a freshman honors program on campus, as well as 18 national honor societies.

Faculty/Classroom: Sixty-one percent of faculty are male; 39%, female. All teach undergraduates. No introductory courses are taught by graduate students.

Admissions: About 64% of the 1993–94 applicants were accepted. About 30% of the current freshmen were in the top fifth of their class; 63% were in the top two fifths. There were 2 National Merit semifinalists. About 30 freshmen graduated first in their class.

Requirements: A minimum GPA of 2.5 is required. The SAT I or ACT is required, with recommended minimum composite scores of 850 on the SAT I (at least 400 verbal and 400 mathematics) and 19 on the ACT. Applicants must be graduates of an accredited secondary school. The GED is accepted. Students should have completed 4

years each of English and social studies, and 2 years each of mathematics, science, and foreign language. An essay and interview are recommended. AP and CLEP credits are accepted. Important factors used in the admissions decision are advanced placement or honor courses, recommendations by school officials, extracurricular activities record, evidence of special talent, and leadership record.

Procedure: Freshmen are admitted fall and spring. Entrance exams should be taken in the spring of junior year and early fall of the senior year. Early decision applications should be filed by October 15; regular applications, by April 1 for fall entry and November 1 for spring entry, along with an application fee of $15. Notification of early decision is sent November 1; regular decision, on a rolling basis. There are early decision, early admissions, and deferred admissions plans. A waiting list is an active part of the admissions procedure.

Transfer: About 412 transfer students enrolled in a recent year. Applicants for transfer should have completed at least 12 college credit hours with a GPA of 2.5 for business and education majors and 2.0 for other programs. An associate degree is recommended. An audition is required for music majors and an interview for nursing. A total of 45 credits out of 128 must be completed at Clarion.

Visiting: There are regularly scheduled orientations for prospective students, including a 1 1/2-day summer program. There are guides for informal visits. To arrange for a visit, contact the Admissions Office at (814) 226-2306.

Financial Aid: In 1993–94 83% of all current freshmen and 60% of continuing students received some form of financial aid. About 78% of freshmen and 67% of continuing students received need-based aid. The average freshman award was $2044. Of that total, scholarships or need-based grants averaged $634 ($6511 maximum); loans averaged $940 ($2625 maximum); and work contracts averaged $470 ($1100 maximum). Thirty-two percent of undergraduate students work part-time. Average earnings from campus work for the school year are $1020. The average financial indebtedness of the 1992–93 graduate was $9100. The university is a member of CSS. The PHEAA and FAFSA financial statement are required. The deadline for financial aid applications is May 1.

International Students: There are currently 115 international students enrolled. The school actively recruits these students. They must take the TOEFL and achieve a minimum score of 550.

Computers: The college provides computer facilities for student use. The mainframe is a DEC VAX 8810. There are also 200 IBM and Apple IIe microcomputers available in student laboratories. All students may access the system. There are no time limits on using the system and no fees.

Graduates: In 1992–93 972 bachelor's degrees were awarded. The most popular majors among graduates were education (28%), communications (11%), and marketing (8%). Within an average freshman class, 36% graduate in 4 years and 59% in 5 years. Some 132 companies recruited on campus in 1992–93. In the 1992 graduating class, 11% enrolled in graduate school within six months of graduation; 83% had found employment.

Admissions Contact: John Shropshire, Dean of Enrollment Management and Academic Records.

COLLEGE MISERICORDIA
B-2

Dallas, PA 18612   (717) 674–6400; (800) 852–7675 (in-state)

Full-time: 277 men, 844 women	Faculty: 81; IIB, -$
Part-time: 104 men, 389 women	Ph.D.s: 57%
Graduate: 30 men, 135 women	Student/Faculty: 14 to 1
Year: semesters	Tuition: $10,460
Application Deadline: open	Room & Board: $5360

Freshman Class: 1432 applied, 888 accepted, 317 enrolled

SAT I Verbal/Math: 460/480   **COMPETITIVE**

College Misericordia, established in 1924 and sponsored by the Religious Sisters of Mercy, is a liberal arts institution affiliated with the Roman Catholic Church. There are 4 graduate programs. In addition to regional accreditation, College Misericordia has baccalaureate program accreditation with CAHEA, CSWE, and NLN. The library contains 73,043 volumes, 369 microform items, and 11,445 audiovisual forms, and subscribes to 652 periodicals. Computerized library sources and services include interlibrary loans and database searching. Special learning facilities include a learning resource center and art gallery. The 100-acre campus is in a small town 9 miles south of Wilkes-Barre. Including residence halls, there are 16 buildings on campus.

Student Life: About 70% of undergraduates are from Pennsylvania. Students come from 10 states and 3 foreign countries. Forty-five percent are from public schools; 55% from private. Ninety-five percent are white. Sixty-five percent are Catholic; 32% Protestant. The average age of freshmen is 18; all undergraduates, 21. Ten percent drop out by the end of their first year; 90% remain to graduate.

Housing: A total of 650 students can be accommodated in college housing. College-sponsored living facilities include single-sex and coed dormitories and on-campus apartments. In addition there are

special interest houses. On-campus housing is guaranteed for all 4 years and is available on a lottery system for upperclassmen. Fifty-four percent of students live on campus; of those, 70% remain on campus on weekends. Upperclassmen may keep cars on campus.

Activities: About 10% of men belong to 2 local fraternities; about 5% of women belong to 1 local sorority. There are 25 groups on campus, including cheerleading, choir, chorus, computers, drama, ethnic, honors, international, literary magazine, musical theater, newspaper, political, professional, religious, social service, student government, and yearbook. Popular campus events include Homecoming, Spring Fling, Winter Weekend, and Junior Ring Day.

Sports: There are 4 intercollegiate sports for men and 6 for women, and 10 intramural sports for men and 10 for women. Athletic and recreation facilities include a sports-health center and athletic fields.

Disabled Students: Eighty-five percent of the campus is accessible to disabled students. The following facilities are available: wheelchair ramps, elevators, special parking, specially equipped rest rooms, and special class scheduling.

Services: In addition to many counseling and information services, tutoring is available in every subject. There is remedial math and reading.

Campus Safety and Security: Campus safety and security measures include 24-hour foot and vehicle patrol, informal discussions, pamphlets, posters, and films, and lighted pathways and sidewalks.

Programs of Study: College Misericordia awards the B.A., B.S., B.S.N., and B.S.W. degrees. Associate and master's degrees also are awarded. Bachelor's degrees are awarded in BIOLOGICAL SCIENCE (biology/biological science), BUSINESS (accounting, business administration and management, and marketing/retailing/merchandising), COMMUNICATIONS AND THE ARTS (English), COMPUTER AND PHYSICAL SCIENCE (chemistry, computer science, information sciences and systems, and mathematics), EDUCATION (early childhood, elementary, secondary, and special), HEALTH PROFESSIONS (medical laboratory technology, nursing, occupational therapy, predentistry, and premedicine), SOCIAL SCIENCE (history, liberal arts/general studies, prelaw, and social work). Occupational therapy and physical therapy are the strongest programs academically and have the largest enrollments.

Required: To graduate, students must earn 128 credits, with 60 credits in the major. The required 54-credit core curriculum includes courses in anthropology, English composition and literature, fine arts, history, mathematics, philosophy, political science, psychology, religious studies, and science. A minimum GPA of 2.0 is required.

Special: Students may cross-register with King's College. The college offers accounting and business administration, co-op programs, internships in social work and psychology, work-study programs, study abroad in England, an accelerated degree program in business and nursing for adult students, student-designed majors, dual majors in elementary and early childhood education, and in mathematics and computer science. Credit may be granted for life, military, and work experience. Nondegree study is also available. The college offers an alternative learner's project, which accepts a limited number of learning disabled students each year. There is a freshman honors program on campus, as well as one national honor society.

Faculty/Classroom: Fifty percent of faculty are male; 50%, female. All teach undergraduates and 45% both teach and do research. No introductory courses are taught by graduate students. The average class size in an introductory lecture is 30; in a laboratory, 20; and in a regular course offering, 25.

Admissions: About 62% of the 1993–94 applicants were accepted. The SAT scores for the 1993–94 freshman class were as follows: Verbal—23% below 500, 67% between 500 and 599, and 10% between 600 and 700; Math—20% below 500, 65% between 500 and 599, and 15% between 600 and 700. About 36% of the current freshmen were in the top fifth of their class; 63% were in the top two fifths. About 8 freshmen graduated first in their class.

Requirements: A minimum GPA of 2.0 is required. The ACT or SAT I with a minimum composite score of 800 (400 mathematics, 400 verbal) is required. Applicants must graduate from an accredited secondary school or have a GED. Sixteen Carnegie units must be earned, and students must complete 3 years each in English, mathematics, history, and science, and 2 to 3 years in social studies. Radiography applicants must take physics. Physical therapy students must take calculus. AP and CLEP credits are accepted. Important factors used in the admissions decision are advanced placement or honor courses, personality, intangible qualities, leadership record, extracurricular activities record, and evidence of special talent.

Procedure: Freshmen are admitted fall and spring. Entrance exams should be taken during junior year. Application deadlines are open. Application fee is $15. Notification is sent on a rolling basis. There are early decision, early admissions, and deferred admissions plans. Two early decision candidates were accepted for the 1993–94 class. A waiting list is an active part of the admissions procedure, with about 5% of applicants on the list.

Transfer: About 118 transfer students enrolled in 1993–94. Transfer students must have a minimum GPA of 2.5. The college recommends a minimum of 60 credits, and encourages an admissions interview. A total of 70 credits out of 128 must be completed at College Misericordia.

Visiting: There are regularly scheduled orientations for prospective students, including a meeting with an admissions counselor, a tour of the campus, and a meeting with a financial aid counselor. There are guides for informal visits and visitors may sit in on classes and stay overnight at the school. To arrange for a visit, contact the Admissions Office at (800) 852–7675.

Financial Aid: In 1993–94 92% of all current freshmen and 95% of continuing students received some form of financial aid. About 80% of all students received need-based aid. Scholarships or need-based grants averaged $2800 ($6000 maximum); loans averaged $2500 ($5000 maximum); and work contracts averaged $600 ($900 maximum). One-hundred percent of undergraduate students work part-time. Average earnings from campus work for the school year are $900. College Misericordia is a member of CSS. The FAF and PHEAA are required. The deadline for financial aid applications is March 1.

International Students: There are currently 20 international students enrolled. They must take the TOEFL and achieve a minimum score of 500.

Computers: The college provides computer facilities for student use. The mainframe is a DEC VAX. Microcomputers are available. All students may access the system. There are no time limits on using the system and no fees.

Graduates: In 1992–93 280 bachelor's degrees were awarded. The most popular majors among graduates were business (21%), occupational therapy (19%), and education (18%). Within an average freshman class, 70% graduate in 4 years and 5% in 5 years. Some 40 companies recruited on campus in 1992–93. Of the 1992 graduating class, 5% were enrolled in graduate school within 6 months of graduation; 96% of the men and 98% of the women had found employment.

Admissions Contact: Michael Joseph, Dean of Enrollment Management.

CURTIS INSTITUTE OF MUSIC

F-3

Philadelphia, PA 19103   (215) 893–5262

Full-time: 40 men, 80 women	Faculty: 87
Part-time: none	Ph.D.s: n/av
Graduate: 10 men, 10 women	Student/Faculty: n/av
Year: semesters	Tuition: see profile
Application Deadline: January 15	Room & Board: n/app
Freshman Class: n/av	
SAT I: required	SPECIAL

Curtis Institute of Music, founded in 1924, is a private, coeducational conservatory offering undergraduate, graduate, and professional programs in music. The institution serves an entirely commuter student body. All applicants are accepted on full-tuition scholarships. However, they must pay $655 in fees and provide all their living expenses. There are 2 graduate schools. In addition to regional accreditation, Curtis has baccalaureate program accreditation with NASM. The library contains 60,000 volumes, 100 microform items, and 10,000 audiovisual forms, and subscribes to 40 periodicals. Special learning facilities include The Leonard Stolowski Collection. The campus is in an urban area. There are 3 buildings on campus.

Student Life: About 92% of undergraduates are from out-of-state, mostly the Northeast. Students come from 30 states, 21 foreign countries, and Canada. Ninety percent are from public schools; 10% from private. Sixty-two percent are white. The average age of freshmen is 18. Two percent drop out by the end of their first year; 98% remain to graduate.

Housing: There are no residence halls; all students commute. Alcohol is not permitted.

Activities: There are no fraternities or sororities on campus. There are some groups and organizations on campus, including student government.

Sports: There is no sports program at Curtis.

Disabled Students: Elevators and specially equipped rest rooms are available.

Services: In addition to many counseling and information services, tutoring is available on an individual basis in every subject.

Campus Safety and Security: Campus safety and security measures include informal discussions, 24-hour security guards in the main building, and buzzer entry to other buildings.

Programs of Study: Curtis awards the B.M. degree. Master's degrees are also awarded. Bachelor's degrees are awarded in COMMUNICATIONS AND THE ARTS (music).

Required: To graduate, students must complete 131 semester hours, including 48 in applied music, with a minimum GPA of 2.0. General music requirements include courses in applied music, theory, solfege,

techniques of 20th century music, music, history, and elements of conducting. Academic requirements include courses in English composition, literature, and history of Western civilization.

Special: Curtis maintains a co-op program with the University of Pennsylvania and offers pass/fail options.

Faculty/Classroom: Seventy percent of faculty are male; 30%, female. The average class size in an introductory lecture is 15 and in a regular course offering, 10.

Requirements: The SAT I is required. Applicant must be a graduate of an accredited secondary school or have earned a GED. Confidential letters of recommendation from two qualified musicians are required. Admission is based primarily on evidence of the applicant's special talent. An audition is required. AP and CLEP credits are accepted.

Procedure: Freshmen are admitted in the fall. Entrance exams should be taken by March of the senior year. Applications should be filed by January 15 for fall entry, along with an application fee of $60. Notification is sent 2 weeks after the applicant's audition.

Transfer: Ten transfer students enrolled in an earlier year. A total of 97 credits out of 131 must be completed at Curtis.

Financial Aid: Forty percent of undergraduate students work part-time. Average earnings from campus work for the school year are $400. The average financial indebtedness of the recent graduate was $9000. Curtis is a member of CSS. The FAF and the college's own financial statement are required. The deadline for financial aid applications is June 1.

International Students: There are currently 60 international students enrolled. They must take the TOEFL. The student must also take the SAT I.

Computers: The college provides computer facilities for student use. All students may access the system.

Graduates: In a recent year, 21 bachelor's degrees were awarded. In an earlier year's graduating class, 35% of the men and 12% of the women were enrolled in graduate school within 6 months of graduation; 30% of the men and 13% of the women had found employment.

Admissions Contact: Judi L. Gattone, Director of Admissions.

DELAWARE VALLEY COLLEGE

F-3

Doylestown, PA 18901–2697   (215) 345–1500, ext. 2211
                                       (800) 2-DELVAL (in-state)

Full-time: 759 men, 621 women	Faculty: 74; IIB, av$
Part-time: 44 men, 44 women	Ph.D.s: 57%
Graduate: none	Student/Faculty: 19 to 1
Year: semesters, summer session	Tuition: $11,645
Application Deadline: open	Room & Board: $4420
Freshman Class: 1383 applied, 1199 accepted, 435 enrolled	
SAT I Verbal/Math: 440/470	LESS COMPETITIVE

Delaware Valley College, founded in 1896, is a private institution offering undergraduate programs in specialized fields of agriculture, business administration, English, the sciences, mathematics, criminal justice administration, and secondary education. The library contains 73,110 volumes, 50,554 microform items, and 950 audiovisual forms, and subscribes to 630 periodicals. Computerized library services and services include interlibrary loans and database searching. Special learning facilities include a learning resource center, radio station, a dairy science center, a livestock farm, horse facilities, an apiary, a small animal laboratory, an arboretum, a tissue culture laboratory, and greenhouses. The 600-acre campus is in a suburban area 20 miles north of Philadelphia. Including residence halls, there are 36 buildings on campus.

Student Life: About 68% of undergraduates are from Pennsylvania. Students come from 15 states and 6 foreign countries. Eighty-seven percent are from public schools; 13% from private. Ninety-six percent are white. Thirty-seven percent are Catholic; 29% Protestant; 21% claim no religious affiliation. The average age of freshmen is 18.8; all undergraduates, 20. Twenty-seven percent drop out by the end of their first year; 57% remain to graduate.

Housing: A total of 807 students can be accommodated in college housing. College-sponsored living facilities include single-sex and coed dormitories. In addition there are honors houses. On-campus housing is guaranteed for the freshman year only, is available on a first-come, first-served basis, and is available on a lottery system for upperclassmen. Priority is given to out-of-town students. Seventy percent of students live on campus; of those, 50% remain on campus on weekends. All students may keep cars on campus.

Activities: There are no fraternities or sororities on campus. There are 40 groups on campus, including art, band, cheerleading, chess, choir, chorale, computers, dance, drama, ethnic, honors, international, literary magazine, newspaper, pep band, photography, professional, radio, religious, social, social service, student government, and yearbook. Popular campus events include A-Day, Homecoming, and Parents Day.

Sports: There are 8 intercollegiate sports for men and 7 for women, and 9 intramural sports for men and 9 for women. Athletic and recreation facilities include 2 gymnasiums, tennis courts, outdoor playing courts and fields, a football stadium, a running track, a small lake, a video game room, picnic areas, nature walks, riding trails, and indoor and outdoor equine facilities.

Disabled Students: Sixty-five percent of the campus is accessible to disabled students. The following facilities are available: wheelchair ramps, elevators, special parking, specially equipped rest rooms, special class scheduling, and lowered drinking fountains.

Services: In addition to many counseling and information services, tutoring is available in most subjects. In addition, there is a reader service for the blind, and remedial math, reading, and writing.

Campus Safety and Security: Campus safety and security measures include 24-hour foot and vehicle patrol, self defense education, escort service, and shuttle buses. In addition, there are informal discussions, pamphlets, posters, and films, emergency telephones, and lighted pathways and sidewalks.

Programs of Study: DVC awards the B.A. and B.S. degrees. Associate degrees also are awarded. Bachelor's degrees are awarded in AGRICULTURE (agriculture, animal science, dairy science, and horticulture), BIOLOGICAL SCIENCE (biology/biological science), BUSINESS (accounting, business administration and management, and marketing/retailing/merchandising), COMMUNICATIONS AND THE ARTS (English), COMPUTER AND PHYSICAL SCIENCE (chemistry, computer science, mathematics, and statistics), EDUCATION (secondary), ENGINEERING AND ENVIRONMENTAL DESIGN (food services technology), HEALTH PROFESSIONS (premedicine), SOCIAL SCIENCE (criminal justice, food production/management/services, and food science). Science is the strongest academically. Business administration and animal science have the largest enrollments.

Required: The bachelor's degree requires completion of at least 128 credits, including 48 in the major, with a minimum GPA of 2.0. The core curriculum consists of 48 credits of liberal arts courses, including cultural enrichment, physical education, and an introduction to computers. Students must also fulfill employment program requirements.

Special: DVC offers a specialized methods and techniques program that enables students to learn laboratory techniques and gain experience in the practical aspects of their majors. There are co-op programs, internships, and work-study programs in a wide variety of employment and research settings. Nondegree study is possible, and pass/fail options are available. There is a freshman honors program on campus, as well as 3 national honor societies.

Faculty/Classroom: Seventy-two percent of faculty are male; 28%, female. All teach undergraduates. The average class size in an introductory lecture is 40; in a laboratory, 20; and in a regular course offering, 22.

Admissions: About 87% of the 1993–94 applicants were accepted. The SAT scores for the 1993–94 freshman class were as follows: Verbal—78% below 500, 19% between 500 and 599, 3% between 600 and 700, and 1% above 700; Math—59% below 500, 31% between 500 and 599, 8% between 600 and 700, and 1% above 700. About 27% of the current freshmen were in the top fifth of their class; 57% were in the top two fifths. There were 6 National Merit semifinalists. Three freshmen graduated first in their class.

Requirements: The SAT I is required. Applicants must be graduates of accredited secondary schools or have earned a GED. The college requires 15 academic units, including 3 in English, 2 each in mathematics, science, and social studies, and the remaining 6 in electives. An interview is recommended. AP and CLEP credits are accepted. Important factors used in the admissions decision are personality, intangible qualities, leadership record, advanced placement or honor courses, extracurricular activities record, and evidence of special talent.

Procedure: Freshmen are admitted fall and spring. Entrance exams should be taken in the junior or senior year. Application deadlines are open. Application fee is $35. Notification is sent on a rolling basis. There is an early admissions plan.

Transfer: About 114 transfer students enrolled in 1993–94. Applicants must have a minimum GPA of 2.0 and must submit SAT I scores. An interview is recommended. A total of 48 credits out of 128 must be completed at DVC.

Visiting: There are regularly scheduled orientations for prospective students, consisting of a student panel, meetings with department chairs, and general information sessions. There are guides for informal visits and visitors may sit in on classes and stay overnight at the school. To arrange for a visit, contact the Admissions Department at (215) 345-1500 or (800) 2-DELVAL (in-state).

Financial Aid: In 1993–94, 84% of all current freshmen and 74% of continuing students received some form of financial aid; 71% of freshmen and 69% of continuing students received need-based aid. The average freshman award was $8860. Of that total, scholarships or need-based grants averaged $4230 ($17,000 maximum); loans averaged $2600 ($3600 maximum); and work contracts averaged

$1500 ($2000 maximum). Twenty-two percent of undergraduate students work part-time. Average earnings from campus work for the school year are $1500. The average financial indebtedness of the 1992–93 graduate was $7800. DVC is a member of CSS. The FAFSA, the Pennsylvania State Grant, and Federal Grant Application financial statement are required. The deadline for financial aid applications is May 1.

International Students: There are currently 8 international students enrolled. They must take the TOEFL and achieve a minimum score of 500.

Computers: The college provides computer facilities for student use. The mainframe is a Motorola 8125. There are also 52 microcomputers on system in the computer center, library, and tutoring center. Those students who are computer majors or in work-study programs may access the system. There are no time limits on using the system and no fees.

Graduates: In 1992–93 231 bachelor's degrees were awarded. The most popular majors among graduates were business administration (34%), ornamental horticulture (16%), and animal science (10%). Within an average freshman class, 48% graduate in 4 years, 52% in 5 years, and 55% in 6 years. Some 111 companies recruited on campus in 1992–93. In the 1992 graduating class, 12% of all graduates were enrolled in graduate school within 6 months of graduation; 73% had found employment.

Admissions Contact: Stephen W. Zenko, Director of Admissions.

DICKINSON COLLEGE
D-3

Carlisle, PA 17013 (717) 245-1231

Full-time: 795 men, 1076 women	Faculty: 174; IIB, +$
Part-time: 30 men, 50 women	Ph.D.s: 99%
Graduate: none	Student/Faculty: 11 to 1
Year: semesters, summer session	Tuition: $17,775
Application Deadline: February 20	Room & Board: $4930
Freshman Class: 3014 applied, 2039 accepted, 487 enrolled	
SAT I or ACT: required	**HIGHLY COMPETITIVE**

Dickinson College, founded in 1773, offers liberal arts curriculum including international education and science. The library contains 540,463 volumes, 157,411 microform items, and 9766 audiovisual forms, and subscribes to 1699 periodicals. Computerized library sources and services include the card catalog, interlibrary loans, and database searching. Special learning facilities include a learning resource center, art gallery, planetarium, radio station, fiber optic and satellite telecommunications networks, telescope observatory, and an archival collection. The 87-acre campus is in a suburban area 2 1/2 hours from Washington DC, Philadelphia, and Baltimore. Including residence halls, there are 105 buildings on campus.

Student Life: About 59% of undergraduates are from out-of-state, mostly the Middle Atlantic. Students come from 43 states, 20 foreign countries, and Canada. Sixty-eight percent are from public schools; 32% from private. Ninety-three percent are white. Thirty-eight percent are Protestant; 28% Catholic; 18% claim no religious affiliation; 12% Jewish. The average age of freshmen is 18; all undergraduates, 20. Seven percent drop out by the end of their first year; 86% remain to graduate.

Housing: A total of 1700 students can be accommodated in college housing. College-sponsored living facilities include single-sex and coed dormitories, on-campus apartments, off-campus apartments, fraternity houses, and sorority houses. In addition there are language houses, special interest houses, and including arts, environmental, Hillel, Asian, African American/West Indian, and multicultural. On-campus housing is guaranteed for all 4 years and is available on a lottery system for upperclassmen. Ninety percent of students live on campus; of those, 85% remain on campus on weekends. All students may keep cars on campus.

Activities: About 30% of men belong to 1 local and 8 national fraternities; about 40% of women belong to 1 local and 4 national sororities. There are 118 groups on campus, including art, band, cheerleading, chess, choir, chorale, chorus, computers, dance, drama, ethnic, film, gay, honors, international, jazz band, literary magazine, musical theater, newspaper, orchestra, pep band, photography, political, professional, radio and TV, religious, social, social service, student government, symphony, and yearbook. Popular campus events include Dickinson Follies, the Common Hour, Fall Fest, Spring Fest, Parents Weekend, Siblings Weekend, Homecoming, public affairs symposium, Black Arts Festival, and multicultural fair.

Sports: There are 11 intercollegiate sports for men and 11 for women, and 49 intramural sports for men and 46 for women. Athletic and recreation facilities include an indoor 86,000-square-foot sports facility, including a basketball court, swimming pool, squash and handball courts, and an indoor track, tennis courts, a varsity football field plus 4 other fields, an outdoor track, and a 19-acre recreational park with a jogging trail.

Disabled Students: More than 75% percent of the campus is accessible to disabled students. The following facilities are available: wheelchair ramps, elevators, special parking, specially equipped rest rooms, special class scheduling, lowered drinking fountains, and telephone access.

Services: In addition to many counseling and information services, tutoring is available in most subjects. Services are provided as necessary on a case-by-case basis. There is remedial writing, language, mathematics, and science. There is also a writing center.

Campus Safety and Security: Campus safety and security measures include 24-hour foot and vehicle patrol, escort service, informal discussions, and pamphlets, posters, and films. In addition, there are emergency telephones and lighted pathways and sidewalks.

Programs of Study: Dickinson awards the B.A. and B.S. degrees. Bachelor's degrees are awarded in BIOLOGICAL SCIENCE (biology/biological science), COMMUNICATIONS AND THE ARTS (dramatic arts, English, fine arts, French, German, Greek, Latin, music, Russian, and Spanish), COMPUTER AND PHYSICAL SCIENCE (chemistry, computer science, geology, mathematics, and physics), SOCIAL SCIENCE (American studies, anthropology, East Asian studies, economics, ethics, politics, and social policy, history, international studies, Italian studies, Judaic studies, philosophy, political science/government, psychology, religion, Russian and area studies, and sociology). International education/foreign languages, natural sciences, premedicine, prelaw, and business are the strongest academically. Political science, English, economics, history, biology, and foreign languages have the largest enrollments.

Required: To graduate, students must complete 34 courses, 9 to 10 of them in the major, with a minimum GPA of 2.0. The school requires 3 courses each in humanities, social sciences, and natural and mathematical sciences. A freshman seminar, crosscultural studies, and physical education activities are required.

Special: Students may cross-register with Central Pennsylvania Consortium Colleges. Also available are internships, study abroad in 9 countries, a Washington semester, work-study programs, accelerated degree programs, dual majors, student-designed majors, nondegree study, and pass/fail options. There are 3–2 engineering degrees offered with the University of Pennsylvania, Case Western Reserve University, and Rensselaer Polytechnic Institute. Instruction in 11 languages is available. There are certification programs in environmental studies, Latin American studies, and women's studies. Linkage programs are available with 3 graduate programs in business at the Monterey Institute, the Thunderbird School, and Rutgers University. There is a freshman honors program on campus, as well as 12 national honor societies, including Phi Beta Kappa. All departments have honors programs.

Faculty/Classroom: Sixty-two percent of faculty are male; 38%, female. All teach undergraduates and do research. The average class size in an introductory lecture is 25; in a laboratory, 17; and in a regular course offering, 18.

Admissions: About 68% of the 1993–94 applicants were accepted. The SAT scores for the 1993–94 freshman class were as follows: Verbal—41% below 500, 44% between 500 and 599, 14% between 600 and 700, and 1% above 700; Math—23% below 500, 46% between 500 and 599, 29% between 600 and 700, and 2% above 700. About 58% of the current freshmen were in the top fifth of their class; 91% were in the top two fifths.

Requirements: Dickinson requires applicants to be in the upper 15% of their class. The SAT I or ACT is required and SAT II: Subject tests are recommended. Applicants must be graduates of an accredited secondary school. The GED is accepted. Applicants should have completed 16 academic credits, including 4 years of English, 3 years each of mathematics and science, 2 years each of foreign language and social studies, and 2 additional courses drawn from the above areas. An essay is required and an interview is recommended. AP credits are accepted. Important factors used in the admissions decision are advanced placement or honor courses, personality, intangible qualities, recommendations by school officials, extracurricular activities record, and leadership record.

Procedure: Freshmen are admitted fall and spring. Entrance exams should be taken in the spring of the junior year or the fall of the senior year. There are early decision, early admissions, and deferred admissions plans. Early decision applications should be filed by December 15; regular applications, by February 20 for fall entry and December 1 for spring entry, along with an application fee of $35. Notification of early decision is sent February 15; regular decision, by March 25. About 153 early decision candidates were accepted for the 1993–94 class. A waiting list is an active part of the admissions procedure.

Transfer: About 65 transfer students enrolled in 1993–94. Applicants for transfer must have a minimum GPA of 2.5. Either the SAT I or ACT is required. A total of 17 courses out of 34 must be completed at Dickinson.

Visiting: There are regularly scheduled orientations for prospective students, including campus tours, individual and/or group interviews, class visits, and overnight stays in residence halls. There are guides for informal visits. To arrange for a visit, contact the Admissions Office at (717) 245–1231.

Financial Aid: In 1993–94 57% of all current freshmen and 61% of continuing students received some form of financial aid. About 56% of freshmen and 59% of continuing students received need-based aid. The average freshman award was $13,030. Of that total, scholarships or need-based grants averaged $9228 ($17,660 maximum); loans averaged $2694 ($4625 maximum); and work contracts averaged $1107 ($1300 maximum). Sixty-three percent of undergraduate students work part-time. Average earnings from campus work for the school year are $710. The average financial indebtedness of the 1992–93 graduate was $13,000. Dickinson is a member of CSS. The FAF is required. The deadline for financial aid applications is February 15.

International Students: There are currently 47 international students enrolled. The school actively recruits these students. They must take the TOEFL. The student must also take the SAT I or the ACT.

Computers: The college provides computer facilities for student use. The mainframe is a DEC VAX 6340. A fiber optics network enables students to have private personal computer hook-up to the mainframe from their residence hall rooms. All students are assigned VAX accounts. There are more than 175 microcomputers and 60 terminals located in the library, student union, and classroom buildings. All students may access the system. There are no time limits on using the system and no fees.

Graduates: In 1992–93 542 bachelor's degrees were awarded. The most popular majors among graduates were foreign languages (17%), political science (14%), and English (13%). Within an average freshman class, 83% graduate in 4 years, 84% in 5 years, and 86% in 6 years. Some 31 companies recruited on campus in 1992–93.

Admissions Contact: J. Larry Mench, Dean.

DREXEL UNIVERSITY

F-3

Philadelphia, PA 19104

(215) 895–2400

(800) 2 DREXEL (out-of-state)

Full-time: 3588 men, 1734 women	Faculty: 393; I, av$
Part-time: 1390 men, 560 women	Ph.D.s: 97%
Graduate: 1876 men, 1024 women	Student/Faculty: 14 to 1
Year: quarters, summer session	Tuition: $12,426
Application Deadline: March 1	Room & Board: $3544
Freshman Class: 3504 applied, 2960 accepted, 1131 enrolled	
SAT I Verbal/Math: 460/550	COMPETITIVE

Drexel University, established in 1891, is a private, nonsectarian coeducational institution, with undergraduate programs in business and administration, engineering, information studies, design arts, and arts and science. There are 6 undergraduate and 5 graduate schools. In addition to regional accreditation, Drexel has baccalaureate program accreditation with AACSB, ABET, ADA, and NAAB. The library contains 500,000 volumes and 740,000 microform items, and subscribes to 4800 periodicals. Computerized library sources and services include the card catalog, interlibrary loans, and database searching. Special learning facilities include a learning resource center, art gallery, radio station, and TV station. The 38-acre campus is in an urban area near the center of Philadelphia. Including residence halls, there are 34 buildings on campus.

Student Life: About 66% of undergraduates are from Pennsylvania. Students come from 41 states, 75 foreign countries, and Canada. Seventy-one percent are white; 11% Asian American. The average age of freshmen is 18.4; all undergraduates, 23. Twenty-five percent drop out by the end of their first year; 59% remain to graduate.

Housing: A total of 1600 students can be accommodated in college housing. College-sponsored living facilities include coed dormitories. In addition there is an international house. On-campus housing is guaranteed for the freshman year only, is available on a first-come, first-served basis, and is available on a lottery system for upperclassmen. Priority is given to out-of-town students. All students may keep cars on campus.

Activities: About 23% of men belong to 13 national fraternities; about 22% of women belong to 5 national sororities. There are 78 groups on campus, including art, band, cheerleading, chess, choir, chorus, computers, dance, drama, ethnic, film, gay, honors, international, jazz band, literary magazine, musical theater, newspaper, orchestra, pep band, photography, political, professional, radio and TV, religious, social, social service, student government, and yearbook. Popular campus events include Annual Greek Block Party, and an ongoing program of musical, cultural, and art events.

Sports: There are 12 intercollegiate sports for men and 9 for women, and more than 10 intramural sports for men and for women. Athletic and recreation facilities include a physical education center with 3 gymnasiums, 6 squash courts, swimming pool, diving well, wrestling room, dance studio, fencing room, Nautilus weight training rooms, special exercise rooms, a field house, a bowling alley and game room with billiards, table tennis, and arcade games, volleyball courts, and a 22-acre lodge outside of the city.

Disabled Students: The following facilities are available: wheelchair ramps, elevators, special parking, specially equipped rest rooms, special class scheduling, lowered drinking fountains, and lowered telephones.

Services: In addition to many counseling and information services, tutoring is available in most subjects. There is also remedial math, reading, and writing and a resident tutor program.

Campus Safety and Security: Campus safety and security measures include 24-hour foot and vehicle patrol, escort service, shuttle buses, and pamphlets, posters, and films. In addition, there are emergency telephones and lighted pathways and sidewalks.

Programs of Study: Drexel awards the B.S. and B.Architecture degrees. Master's and doctoral degrees also are awarded. Bachelor's degrees are awarded in BIOLOGICAL SCIENCE (biology/biological science and nutrition), BUSINESS (accounting, banking and finance, business administration and management, business economics, fashion merchandising, hotel/motel and restaurant management, human resources, international business management, and marketing/retailing/merchandising), COMMUNICATIONS AND THE ARTS (communications, design, literature, music, and photography), COMPUTER AND PHYSICAL SCIENCE (chemistry, computer science, mathematics, physics, and science), EDUCATION (education), ENGINEERING AND ENVIRONMENTAL DESIGN (architecture, chemical engineering, civil engineering, computer engineering, electrical/electronics engineering, materials engineering, and mechanical engineering), HEALTH PROFESSIONS (predentistry and premedicine), SOCIAL SCIENCE (dietetics, fashion design and technology, humanities, international studies, political science/government, prelaw, and sociology). Engineering, business, design arts, computer science, and information studies are the strongest academically. Electrical and computer engineering, business, architecture, computer science, and information sciences have the largest enrollments.

Required: To graduate, students must complete 180 to 192 term credits with a minimum GPA of 2.0. There are requirements in mathematics, English, laboratory science, social science, history, and physical education.

Special: The Drexel Plan of Cooperative Education enables students to alternate periods of full-time classroom studies and full-time employment with university-approved employers. The student's participation in cooperative education is mandatory, except for a small percentage of students in the business and administration program. Cross-registration is available with Eastern Mennonite College, Indiana University of Pennsylvania, and Lincoln University. The university offers study abroad, a general studies degree, 3–3 engineering degrees, nondegree study, credit/no credit options, and a Sea Education Association semester. There is a freshman honors program on campus.

Faculty/Classroom: Eighty percent of faculty are male; 20%, female. Eighty-seven percent teach undergraduates. The average class size in a laboratory is 30 and in a regular course offering, 37.

Admissions: About 84% of the 1993–94 applicants were accepted. The SAT scores for the 1993–94 freshman class were as follows: Verbal—66% below 500, 26% between 500 and 599, 7% between 600 and 700, and 1% above 700; Math—30% below 500, 38% between 500 and 599, 25% between 600 and 700, and 7% above 700. About 40% of the current freshmen were in the top fifth of their class; 72% were in the top two fifths. There were 26 National Merit finalists. Fifteen freshmen graduated first in their class.

Requirements: The SAT I or ACT is required. Applicants must be graduates of an accredited secondary school. The GED is accepted. An essay is required and an interview is recommended. AP and CLEP credits are accepted. Important factors used in the admissions decision are advanced placement or honor courses, evidence of special talent, recommendations by school officials, leadership record, and extracurricular activities record.

Procedure: Freshmen are admitted in the fall. Entrance exams should be taken by January 15 of the senior year. Early decision applications should be filed by November 15; regular applications, by March 1 for fall entry, along with an application fee of $35. Notification of early decision is sent December 15; regular decision, on a rolling basis. There are early decision, early admissions, and deferred admissions plans. About 145 early decision candidates were accepted for the 1993–94 class. A waiting list is an active part of the admissions procedure, with about 1% of applicants on the list.

Transfer: About 256 transfer students enrolled in 1993–94. Applicants for transfer must have a minimum GPA of 2.5. Other requirements vary among the individual colleges within the university. A total of 45 quarter-term credits out of 192 must be completed at Drexel.

Visiting: There are regularly scheduled orientations for prospective students, consisting of a 2-day program for new freshmen and their parents in late July. There are guides for informal visits and visitors may sit in on classes and stay overnight at the school. To arrange for a visit, contact the Admissions Office at (215) 895-6727.

Financial Aid: In 1993–94, 80% of all current freshmen and 75% of continuing students received some form of financial aid. About 67% of freshmen and 64% of continuing students received need-based aid. The average freshman award was $8651. Of that total, scholarships or need-based grants averaged $5026; loans averaged $1744 ($2625 maximum); and work contracts averaged $600. Eleven percent of undergraduate students work part-time. Average earnings from campus work for the school year are $600. The average financial indebtedness of the 1992–93 graduate was $13,400. Drexel is a member of CSS. The PHEAA form financial statement is required. The deadline for financial aid applications is May 1.

International Students: There are currently 296 international students enrolled. The school actively recruits these students. They must take the TOEFL and achieve a minimum score of 510. Freshmen applicants must also take the SAT I or the ACT.

Computers: The college provides computer facilities for student use. The mainframes are an IBM 9121–320 and a Sun Server 670. All students may access the mainframes, the library, and the Internet through Macintosh microcomputers in dormitories or residences. There are also 150 networked public computers available. It may be used 24 hours a day. There are no time limits on using the system and no fees. It is recommended that students in all programs have personal computers; an Apple Macintosh is preferred.

Graduates: In 1992–93 1328 bachelor's degrees were awarded. The most popular majors among graduates were electrical and computer engineering (13%), marketing (11%), and accounting (10%). Within an average freshman class, 5% graduate in 3 years, 15% in 4 years, 52% in 5 years, and 58% in 6 years. Some 275 companies recruited on campus in 1992–93.

Admissions Contact: Donald Dickason, Vice Provost, Enrollment Management.

DUQUESNE UNIVERSITY

Pittsburgh, PA 15282–0201   B-3

(412) 396-6000; (800) 456-0590

Full-time: 1836 men, 2425 women	Faculty: 216; IIA, av$
Part-time: 395 men, 523 women	Ph.D.s: 89%
Graduate: 1482 men, 1963 women	Student/Faculty: 20 to 1
Year: semesters, summer session	Tuition: $11,320
Application Deadline: July 1	Room & Board: $5114
Freshman Class: n/av	
SAT I Verbal/Math: 490/520	ACT: 24 VERY COMPETITIVE

Duquesne University, founded in 1878, is a private institution affiliated with the Roman Catholic Church, offering programs in the arts and sciences, nursing, pharmacy, business, music, teacher preparation, and preprofessional training. There are 7 undergraduate and 8 graduate schools. In addition to regional accreditation, Duquesne has baccalaureate program accreditation with AACSB, ACPE, NASM, and NLN. The 3 libraries contain 479,390 volumes, 63,484 microform items, and 6550 audiovisual forms, and subscribe to 2223 periodicals. Computerized library sources and services include the card catalog, interlibrary loans, and database searching. Special learning facilities include a learning resource center, an art gallery, a radio station, and a TV station. The 39-acre campus is in an urban area. Including residence halls, there are 22 buildings on campus.

Student Life: About 85% of undergraduates are from Pennsylvania. Students come from 41 states, 66 foreign countries, and Canada. Ninety-five percent are white. Eighty percent are Catholic; 16% Protestant. The average age of freshmen is 18; all undergraduates, 22.

Housing: A total of 2540 students can be accommodated in college housing. College-sponsored living facilities include single-sex and coed dormitories. On-campus housing is guaranteed for all 4 years. Fifty-four percent of students live on campus; of those, 40% remain on campus on weekends. All students may keep cars on campus.

Activities: About 15% of men belong to 3 local and 6 national fraternities; about 15% of women belong to 2 local and 6 national sororities. There are 95 groups on campus, including band, cheerleading, choir, chorale, chorus, computers, dance, drama, ethnic, film, honors, international, jazz band, literary magazine, marching band, musical theater, newspaper, opera, orchestra, pep band, photography, political, professional, radio and TV, religious, social, social service, student government, symphony, and yearbook. Popular campus events include Carnival, Greek Week, Spring Fling, Valentine Ball, Dance Marathon, and freshman orientation activities.

Sports: There are 13 intercollegiate sports for men and 11 for women, and 9 intramural sports for men and 7 for women. Athletic and recreation facilities include the A. J. Palumbo Center and the Duquesne Union.

Disabled Students: Fifty percent of the campus is accessible to disabled students. The following facilities are available: wheelchair ramps, elevators, special parking, specially equipped rest rooms, special class scheduling, lowered drinking fountains, and lowered telephones.

Services: In addition to many counseling and information services, tutoring is available in every subject. In addition, there is a reader service for the blind, and remedial math, reading, and writing.

Campus Safety and Security: Campus safety and security measures include 24-hour foot and vehicle patrol, self-defense education, escort service, and shuttle buses. In addition, there are informal discussions, pamphlets, posters, and films, emergency telephones, and lighted pathways and sidewalks.

Programs of Study: Duquesne awards the B.A., B.S., B.S.Ed., B.S.M., B.S.M.E., and B.S.N. degrees. Master's and doctoral degrees also are awarded. Bachelor's degrees are awarded in BIOLOGICAL SCIENCE (biochemistry, biology/biological science, and microbiology), BUSINESS (accounting, banking and finance, business administration and management, business economics, business law, international business management, marketing/retailing/merchandising, and personnel management), COMMUNICATIONS AND THE ARTS (advertising, broadcasting, communications, English, French, German, Greek, journalism, Latin, music, and speech/debate/rhetoric), COMPUTER AND PHYSICAL SCIENCE (chemistry, computer science, information sciences and systems, mathematics, and physics), EDUCATION (early childhood, elementary, foreign languages, middle school, music, science, secondary, and special), HEALTH PROFESSIONS (nursing, pharmacy, predentistry, and premedicine), SOCIAL SCIENCE (criminal justice, economics, history, international relations, philosophy, political science/government, prelaw, psychology, religion, social science, and sociology). Pharmacy, business, and education are the strongest academically. Communications, business, and pharmacy have the largest enrollments.

Required: Students are required to complete at least 120 credit hours, including 27 in the major, with a minimum 2.0 GPA. General requirements vary by department, but there is a 27-credit liberal arts core curriculum.

Special: The university offers co-op programs in business, communications, and pharmacy, cross-registration through the Pittsburgh Council of Higher Education, internships, study abroad in 5 countries, work-study programs, and a Washington semester. Also available are B.A.-B.S. degrees, a general studies degree, an accelerated degree program, dual and student-designed majors, 3–2 engineering programs with Case Western Reserve University and Florida Institute of Technology, pass/fail options, and credit for life, military, and work experience. There is a freshman honors program on campus, as well as 4 national honor societies.

Faculty/Classroom: Seventy percent of faculty are male; 30%, female. Seventy percent teach undergraduates. The average class size in an introductory lecture is 40; in a laboratory, 20; and in a regular course offering, 18.

Admissions: The SAT scores for the 1993–94 freshman class were as follows: Math—40% below 500, 40% between 500 and 599, 17% between 600 and 700, and 3% above 700. The ACT scores were 11% below 21, 47% between 21 and 23, 35% between 24 and 26, and 6% above 28. About 47% of the current freshmen were in the top fifth of their class; 73% were in the top two fifths. About 22 freshmen graduated first in their class.

Requirements: The SAT I or ACT is required. Students should have either a high school diploma or the GED. Applicants are required to have 16 academic credits, including 4 each in English and academic electives, and 8 combined in social studies, language, mathematics, and/or science. An audition is required for music majors. An essay and interview are recommended. AP and CLEP credits are accepted. Important factors used in the admissions decision are evidence of special talent, parents or siblings attending the school, leadership record, extracurricular activities record, and recommendations by school officials.

Procedure: Freshmen are admitted to all sessions. Early decision applications should be filed by November 15; regular applications, by July 1 for fall entry, December 15 for spring entry, and April 1 for summer entry, along with an application fee of $40. Notification of early decision is sent December 15; regular decision, on a rolling basis, beginning in January. There are early decision, early admissions, and deferred admissions plans. A waiting list is an active part of the admissions procedure.

Transfer: About 450 transfer students enrolled in a recent year. Applicants must submit complete high school and college transcripts. Students should have a minimum GPA of 2.0 for the university, but some schools require a higher average. A minimum of 12 credits earned is required and an interview is recommended. A total of 30 credits out of 120 must be completed at Duquesne.

Visiting: There are regularly scheduled orientations for prospective students. There are guides for informal visits and visitors may sit in on classes and stay overnight at the school. To arrange for a visit, contact the Student Admissions Advisors at (412) 434–6222.

Financial Aid: In an earlier year, 78% of all students received some form of financial aid. Scholarhips or need-based grant averaged $2900 ($3000 maximum); loans averaged $3130 ($4125 maximum); and work contracts averaged $1666. Six percent of undergraduate students work part-time. Average earnings from campus work for the school year is $1900. Duquesne is a member of CSS. The FAF and PHEAA are required. The deadline for financial aid applications is May 1.

International Students: There are currently 330 international students enrolled. The school actively recruits these students. They must take the TOEFL, the University of Michigan Language Test, the Comprehensive English Language Test, or the college's own test.

Computers: The college provides computer facilities for student use. The mainframes are a Unisys 1100/70, a DEC systems 5810 and 5500, and DEC VAX 8200 and 8550 units. There are also microcomputers available in laboratories throughout the campus. All students may access the system. It may be used 24 hours a day, 7 days a week. There are no time limits on using the system. The fees are $25.

Graduates: In a recent year, 915 bachelor's degrees were awarded. The most popular majors among graduates were business and management (26%), education (18%), and pharmacy (14%). Within an average freshman class, 66% graduate in 4 years, 68% in 5 years, and 70% in 6 years. In the 1992 graduating class, 10% of all graduates were enrolled in graduate school within 6 months of graduation; 90% found employment.

Admissions Contact: Veronica White, Admissions Counselor.

EAST STROUDSBURG UNIVERSITY   F-2

East Stroudsburg, PA 18301   (717) 424–3542

Full-time: 1726 men, 2218 women	Faculty: 239; IIA, +$
Part-time: 287 men, 338 women	Ph.Ds: 62%
Graduate: 313 men, 528 women	Student/Faculty: 17 to 1
Year: semesters, summer session	Tuition: $3664 ($8602)
Application Deadline: March 1	Room & Board: $3222
Freshman Class: 3812 applied, 2227 accepted, 825 enrolled	
SAT I Verbal/Math: 421/475	**COMPETITIVE**

East Stroudsburg University, founded in 1893, is a part of the Pennsylvania State System of Higher Education and offers programs in arts and science, health sciences and physical education, and professional studies. There are 3 undergraduate schools and one graduate school. In addition to regional accreditation, East Stroudsburg has baccalaureate program accreditation with NCATE and NLN. The library contains 390,000 volumes, 1,004,000 microform items, and 7650 audiovisual forms, and subscribes to 2200 periodicals. Computerized library sources and services include the card catalog. Special learning facilities include a learning resource center, art gallery, radio station, and a wildlife museum. The 183-acre campus is in a small town 75 miles west of New York City. Including residence halls, there are 39 buildings on campus.

Student Life: About 79% of undergraduates are from Pennsylvania. Students come from 22 states, 25 foreign countries, and Canada. Ninety-three percent are white. The average age of freshmen is 18; all undergraduates, 2. Seventeen percent drop out by the end of their first year; 60% remain to graduate.

Housing: A total of 2140 students can be accommodated in college housing. College-sponsored living facilities include single-sex and coed dormitories and on-campus apartments. In addition there are honors floors. On-campus housing is guaranteed for all 4 years. Fifty-three percent of students commute. Alcohol is not permitted. Upperclassmen may keep cars on campus.

Activities: About 12% of men belong to 8 national fraternities; about 15% of women belong to 2 local and 6 national sororities. There are 76 groups on campus, including art, band, cheerleading, chess, choir, computers, dance, drama, ethnic, gay, honors, international, jazz band, literary magazine, musical theater, newspaper, pep band, political, professional, radio and TV, religious, social, social service, student government, and yearbook. Popular campus events include concerts, Spring Music Festival, and International Celebrations.

Sports: There are 9 intercollegiate sports for men and 9 for women, and 12 intramural sports for men and women. Athletic and recreation facilities include a 5000-seat stadium, a 2600-seat gymnasium, another gymnasium, 8 athletic fields, 12 outdoor tennis courts, 1 indoor tennis court, a swimming pool, indoor and outdoor tracks, and a weight room.

Disabled Students: Ninety-eight percent of the campus is accessible to disabled students. The following facilities are available: wheelchair ramps, elevators, special parking, specially equipped rest rooms, special class scheduling, lowered drinking fountains, lowered telephones, and visual fire alarms for hearing impaired persons.

Services: In addition to many counseling and information services, tutoring is available in every subject. In addition, there is remedial math, reading, and writing.

Campus Safety and Security: Campus safety and security measures include 24-hour foot and vehicle patrol, self defense education, escort service, and informal discussions. In addition, there are pamphlets, posters, and films, emergency telephones, lighted pathways and sidewalks, a campus escort service, and a police bicycle patrol.

Programs of Study: East Stroudsburg awards the B.A. and B.S. degrees. Master's degrees also are awarded. Bachelor's degrees are awarded in BIOLOGICAL SCIENCE (biochemistry, biology/biological science, and marine science), BUSINESS (business administration and management and hotel/motel and restaurant management), COMMUNICATIONS AND THE ARTS (communications, communications technology, dramatic arts, English, fine arts, French, German, media arts, Spanish, and speech/debate/rhetoric), COMPUTER AND PHYSICAL SCIENCE (chemistry, computer science, earth science, mathematics, physical sciences, and science), EDUCATION (early childhood, elementary, foreign languages, physical, science, secondary, and special), ENGINEERING AND ENVIRONMENTAL DESIGN (engineering), HEALTH PROFESSIONS (allied health, medical laboratory technology, nursing, premedicine, public health, rehabilitation therapy, and speech pathology/audiology), SOCIAL SCIENCE (anthropology, economics, geography, history, parks and recreation management, philosophy, political science/government, psychology, social science, and sociology). Computer science, nursing, mathematics and science are the strongest academically. Education, hospitality management, physical education, and management have the largest enrollments.

Required: All students must maintain a GPA of at least 2.0 while taking 128 semester hours, including 27 to 83 hours in the major. General education courses total 60 credits, with English composition and physical education required courses. Distribution requirements include 15 hours in arts and letters, science, and social science.

Special: Internships in most programs, B.A.-B.S. degrees, dual majors for most fields, 3–2 engineering degrees with Pennsylvania State University or the University of Pittsburgh, nondegree study, study abroad, and cross-registration through the National Student Exchange are available. There is a freshman honors program on campus, as well as 16 national honor societies.

Faculty/Classroom: Sixty-two percent of faculty are male; 38%, female. Ninety-four percent teach undergraduates and 35% do research. No introductory courses are taught by graduate students. The average class size in an introductory lecture is 40; in a laboratory, 25; and in a regular course offering, 25.

Admissions: About 58% of the 1993–94 applicants were accepted. The SAT scores for the 1993–94 freshman class were as follows: Verbal—88% below 500, 11% between 500 and 599, and 1% between 600 and 700; Math—63% below 500, 31% between 500 and 599, 5% between 600 and 700, and 1% above 700. About 20% of the current freshmen were in the top fifth of their class; 64% were in the top two fifths. Two freshmen graduated first in their class.

Requirements: The SAT I or the ACT is required, but the SAT I is preferred. Applicant must be a graduate of an accredited secondary school. The GED is accepted. AP and CLEP credits are accepted. Important factors used in the admissions decision are advanced placement or honor courses, evidence of special talent, leadership record, recommendations by school officials, and extracurricular activities record.

Procedure: Freshmen are admitted in the fall. Entrance exams should be taken during the fall of the senior year. Applications should be filed by March 1 for fall entry, along with an application fee of $25. Notification is sent March 1.

Transfer: A total of 473 transfer students enrolled in 1993–94. Transfer students must have a 2.3 GPA earned over at least 24 credit hours. A total of 32 credits out of 128 must be completed at East Stroudsburg.

Visiting: There are regularly scheduled orientations for prospective students. There are guides for informal visits and visitors may sit in on classes. To arrange for a visit, contact the Admissions Office at (717) 424-3542.

Financial Aid: In 1993–94, 79% of all current freshmen and 75% of continuing students received need-based aid. East Stroudsburg is a member of CSS. The college's own financial statement and the FAFSA are required. The deadline for financial aid applications is March 15.

International Students: There are currently 51 international students enrolled. They must take the TOEFL and achieve a minimum score of 500.

Computers: The university provides computer facilities for student use. The mainframe is a Unisys A-11. There is a DEC file server with 75 DEC workstations, and 51 PCs comprising an academic network. Additionally, there are 28 PCs and 70 Apple MacIntosh (primarily LCs) available for student use in general purpose laboratories. All students may access the system. Most computers are available 7 A.M. to 10 P.M., some are available on a 24-hour basis. There are no time limits on using the system and no fees.

Graduates: In 1993–94, 864 bachelor's degrees were awarded. The most popular majors among graduates were elementary education (16%), physical education (12%), and management (9%). Within an average freshman class, 1% graduate in 3 years, 25% in 4 years, 45% in 5 years, and 50% in 6 years. Some 75 companies recruited on campus in 1993–94. In the 1992 graduating class, 11% of all graduates were enrolled in graduate school within 6 months of graduation; 75% had found employment.

Admissions Contact: Alan T. Chesterton, Director of Admissions.

EASTERN COLLEGE

F-3

St. Davids, PA 19087–3696 (215) 341-5967

Full-time: 423 men, 634 women	**Faculty:** 56; IIA, --$
Part-time: 93 men, 262 women	**Ph.D.s:** 70%
Graduate: 187 men, 243 women	**Student/Faculty:** 19 to 1
Year: semesters, summer session	**Tuition:** $10,620
Application Deadline: open	**Room & Board:** $4530
Freshman Class: 690 applied, 342 accepted, 250 enrolled	
SAT I Verbal/Math: 450/476	**ACT:** 23 COMPETITIVE +

Eastern College, founded in 1932, is a private, coeducational liberal arts institution affiliated with the American Baptist Church. There is one graduate school. In addition to regional accreditation, Eastern has baccalaureate program accreditation with CSWE and NLN. The 2 libraries contain 111,416 volumes, 257,618 microform items, and 2681 audiovisual forms, and subscribe to 969 periodicals. Computerized library sources and services include interlibrary loans and database searching. Special learning facilities include a planetarium and radio station. The 100-acre campus is in a small town 20 miles northwest of Philadelphia. Including residence halls, there are 26 buildings on campus.

Student Life: About 69% of undergraduates are from Pennsylvania. Students come from 35 states, 20 foreign countries, and Canada. Eighty-three percent are white; 11% African American. Thirty-one percent are Protestant; 17% claim no religious affiliation; 17% Catholic. The average age of freshmen is 20; all undergraduates, 26. Twenty-eight percent drop out by the end of their first year; 50% remain to graduate.

Housing: A total of 567 students can be accommodated in college housing. College-sponsored living facilities include coed dormitories and on-campus apartments. In addition there are honors houses, language houses, and special interest houses. On-campus housing is guaranteed for all 4 years. Sixty-one percent of students commute. Alcohol is not permitted. All students may keep cars on campus.

Activities: There are no fraternities or sororities on campus. There are more than 60 groups on campus, including art, band, cheerleading, chess, choir, chorale, chorus, computers, dance, drama, ethnic, honors, international, jazz band, literary magazine, musical theater, newspaper, orchestra, pep band, photography, political, radio, religious, social, social service, student government, and yearbook. Popular campus events include Black History Week, Homecoming, and Christmas Celebration, dances, coffee houses, and chapel.

Sports: There are 6 intercollegiate sports for men and 8 for women, and 6 intramural sports for men and 5 for women. Athletic and recreation facilities include a gymnasium, a game room, a soccer pitch, a baseball field, and a weight room.

Disabled Students: Ninety percent of the campus is accessible to disabled students. The following facilities are available: wheelchair ramps, elevators, special parking, specially equipped rest rooms, special class scheduling, lowered drinking fountains, lowered telephones, and special residence hall spaces.

Services: In addition to many counseling and information services, tutoring is available in every subject. There is a reader service for the blind, and remedial math, reading, and writing, as well as a summer skills workshop.

Campus Safety and Security: Campus safety and security measures include 24-hour foot and vehicle patrol, escort service, informal discussions, and pamphlets, posters, and films. In addition, there are emergency telephones and lighted pathways and sidewalks.

Programs of Study: Eastern awards the B.A., B.S., B.S.N., and B.S.W. degrees. Associate and master's degrees also are awarded. Bachelor's degrees are awarded in BIOLOGICAL SCIENCE (biology/biological science), BUSINESS (business administration and management and organizational behavior), COMMUNICATIONS AND THE ARTS (art history and appreciation, communications, creative writing, English literature, French, music, Spanish, and studio art), COMPUTER AND PHYSICAL SCIENCE (astronomy, chemistry, and mathematics), EDUCATION (elementary, English, health, and secondary), HEALTH PROFESSIONS (medical laboratory technology and nursing), SOCIAL SCIENCE (biblical studies, history, philosophy, political science/government, psychology, social work, sociology, and youth ministry). Biology, elementary education, pychology, biblical studies, and Englsih literature are the strongest academically. Elementary education, business, youth ministries, and health and physical education have the largest enrollments.

Required: To graduate, all students must complete at least 127 credit hours with a minimum 2.0 GPA. The required hours in the major vary. Students must take courses in biblical foundations, theological and philosophical foundations, mathematics, writing, health, symbolic languages, literature and the arts, cross-cultural learning, our heri-

tage, government and economics, the individual and social systems, natural science, and capstone.

Special: Eastern offers cross-registration with Cabrini and Rosement Colleges, study abroad, internships, a Washington semester in American studies through the Christian College Coalition, and student-designed majors. Also available are an accelerated degree program in organizational management, credit for experience, nondegree study, and pass/fail options. Eastern also has an interim winter session. There is a freshman honors program on campus, as well as 9 national honor societies.

Faculty/Classroom: Fifty-four percent of faculty are male; 47%, female. Eighty-eight percent teach undergraduates. No introductory courses are taught by graduate students. The average class size in an introductory lecture is 50; in a laboratory, 20; and in a regular course offering, 30.

Admissions: About 50% of the 1993–94 applicants were accepted. The SAT scores for the 1993–94 freshman class were as follows: Verbal—68% below 500, 27% between 500 and 599, 5% between 600 and 700, and 1% above 700; Math—56% below 500, 30% between 500 and 599, 13% between 600 and 700, and 1% above 700. The ACT scores were 20% below 21, 40% between 21 and 23, and 40% between 27 and 28. About 29% of the current freshmen were in the top fifth of their class; 54% were in the top two fifths. Two freshmen graduated first in their class.

Requirements: A minimum GPA of 2.0 is required. The SAT I is required. The college applies an admissions formula that emphasizes class rank over test results. Interviews are encouraged, but not required. AP and CLEP credits are accepted. Important factors used in the admissions decision are leadership record, extracurricular activities record, advanced placement or honor courses, recommendations by school officials, and parents or siblings attending the school.

Procedure: Freshmen are admitted to all sessions. Entrance exams should be taken as soon as possible. Application deadlines are open. Application fee is $25. Notification is sent on a rolling basis. There are early admissions and deferred admissions plans.

Transfer: About 82 transfer students enrolled in 1993–94. Transfer students must have a 2.0 GPA and must be in good standing at their previous institution. A total of 30 credits out of 127 must be completed at Eastern.

Visiting: There are regularly scheduled orientations for prospective students, including 2 orientations in the fall and 1 in the spring. There are guides for informal visits and visitors may sit in on classes and stay overnight at the school. To arrange for a visit, contact the Admissions Office at (215) 341–5967.

Financial Aid: In 1993–94, 58% of all current freshmen and 85% of continuing students received some form of financial aid. Scholarships averaged $5500 (maximum); loans $2625 (maximum); and work contracts $1500 (maximum). Average earnings from campus work for the school year are $900. Eastern is a member of CSS. The FAF or FFS, the college's own financial statement and the PHEAA, AFSA, and income tax forms are required.

International Students: There are currently 24 international students enrolled. The school actively recruits these students. They must take the TOEFL and achieve a minimum score of 550. The student must also take the SAT I or the ACT.

Computers: The college provides computer facilities for student use. Microcomputers are available for all students. All students may access the system. There are no time limits on using the system. There are fees for using the laser printer.

Graduates: In 1992–93, 296 bachelor's degrees were awarded. The most popular majors among graduates were organizational management (40%), elementary education (8%), and nursing (7%). Within an average freshman class, 50% graduate in 5 years. Some 15 companies recruited on campus in 1992–93. In the 1992 graduating class, 9% of all graduates were enrolled in graduate school within 6 months of graduation; 93% had found employment.

Admissions Contact: Stephen Mark Seymour, Director of Admissions.

EDINBORO UNIVERSITY OF PENNSYLVANIA   B-1

Edinboro, PA 16444   (814) 732–2761; (800) 626–2203 (in-state)

Full-time: 2751 men, 3567 women	Faculty: 370; IIA, av$
Part-time: 290 men, 527 women	Ph.D.s: 56%
Graduate: 147 men, 448 women	Student/Faculty: 17 to 1
Year: semesters, summer session	Tuition: $3531 ($7929)
Application Deadline: open	Room & Board: $3650
Freshman Class: 4419 applied, 3074 accepted, 1349 enrolled	
SAT I or ACT: required	COMPETITIVE

Edinboro University of Pennsylvania, founded in 1857, is a public, coeducational institution and a member of the Pennsylvania State System of Higher Education. The university offers programs in fine and liberal arts, business, engineering, health science, and teacher preparation. There are 3 undergraduate schools and one graduate school. In addition to regional accreditation, The university has baccalaure-

ate program accreditation with ADA, CSWE, and NLN. The 2 libraries contain 412,081 volumes and 1,234,416 microform items, and subscribe to 2175 periodicals. Computerized library sources and services include the card catalog, interlibrary loans, and database searching. Special learning facilities include an art gallery, planetarium, radio station, and TV studio. The 585-acre campus is in a small town 20 miles south of Erie. Including residence halls, there are 42 buildings on campus.

Student Life: About 87% of undergraduates are from Pennsylvania. Students come from 29 states and 38 foreign countries. Ninety-two percent are white. The average age of freshmen is 19; all undergraduates, 23. Twenty-eight percent drop out by the end of their first year; 49% remain to graduate.

Housing: A total of 2604 students can be accommodated in college housing. College-sponsored living facilities include single-sex and coed dormitories. In addition there are honors houses. On-campus housing is guaranteed for the freshman year only and is available on a first-come, first-served basis. Alcohol is not permitted. Upperclassmen may keep cars on campus.

Activities: About 10% of men belong to 7 national fraternities; about 15% of women belong to 5 national sororities. There are 85 groups on campus, including art, band, cheerleading, chess, choir, chorale, chorus, computers, dance, drama, drill team, ethnic, film, gay, honors, international, jazz band, literary magazine, marching band, newspaper, opera, orchestra, photography, political, professional, radio and tv, religious, social, social service, student government, symphony, and yearbook. Popular campus events include Academic Festival, Black History, and a cultural arts series.

Sports: There are 9 intramural sports for men and 8 for women. Athletic and recreation facilities include a field house, a stadium, a gymnasium, and a pool.

Disabled Students: Ninety-five percent of the campus is accessible to disabled students. The following facilities are available: wheelchair ramps, elevators, special parking, specially equipped rest rooms, special class scheduling, lowered drinking fountains, and lowered telephones. The university also offers special residence halls, computer facilities, and transportation services for the physically and learning disabled.

Services: In addition to many counseling and information services, tutoring is available in every subject. There is a reader service for the blind, and remedial math, reading, and writing.

Campus Safety and Security: Campus safety and security measures include 24-hour foot and vehicle patrol, informal discussions, pamphlets, posters, and films, and emergency telephones. In addition, there are lighted pathways and sidewalks and a commissioned police force.

Programs of Study: The university awards the B.A., B.S., B.S.Ed., and B.F.A. degrees. Associate and master's degrees also are awarded. Bachelor's degrees are awarded in BIOLOGICAL SCIENCE (biochemistry, biology/biological science, and nutrition), BUSINESS (accounting, business administration and management, and business economics), COMMUNICATIONS AND THE ARTS (art history and appreciation, ceramic art and design, communications, creative writing, dramatic arts, drawing, English, English literature, fiber/textiles/weaving, film arts, fine arts, French, German, graphic design, media arts, metal/jewelry, music, painting, photography, printmaking, Russian, sculpture, and Spanish), COMPUTER AND PHYSICAL SCIENCE (chemistry, computer science, earth science, geology, mathematics, natural sciences, and physics), EDUCATION (art, early childhood, elementary, English, foreign languages, health, music, science, secondary, and special), ENGINEERING AND ENVIRONMENTAL DESIGN (environmental science and industrial administration/management), HEALTH PROFESSIONS (medical laboratory technology, nuclear medical technology, nursing, predentistry, premedicine, prepharmacy, preveterinary science, and speech pathology/audiology), SOCIAL SCIENCE (African American studies, anthropology, criminal justice, economics, geography, history, humanities, liberal arts/general studies, philosophy, political science/government, prelaw, psychology, social science, social work, sociology, and textiles and clothing). Elementary education, business, psychology, speech communication, and criminal justice have the largest enrollments.

Required: To graduate, students must complete 128 credits, including 60 hours in general education and 3 hours of physical education, with a minimum GPA of 2.0.

Special: Edinboro University offers cross-registration with Merchurst College and Gannon University, internships in many majors, a general studies degree, student-designed majors, a 3–2 engineering degree, study abroad in 8 countries, and nondegree study. Students may select pass/fail options and receive credit for life, military, and work experience. There is a freshman honors program on campus, as well as 11 national honor societies.

Faculty/Classroom: Sixty-six percent of faculty are male; 34%, female. All teach undergraduates. No introductory courses are taught by graduate students. The average class size in a regular course offering is 27.

Admissions: About 70% of the 1993–94 applicants were accepted.

Requirements: The SAT I or ACT is required. Candidates for admission should be graduates of an accredited secondary school. The GED is accepted. A portfolio is recommended for art students and an audition for music students. An interview is recommended for all. Admissions decisions are based upon high school curriculum, grades, GPA, class rank, SAT I or ACT scores, and extracurricular activities record. AP and CLEP credits are accepted.

Procedure: Freshmen are admitted fall and spring. Entrance exams should be taken in the junior year or early in the senior year. Application deadlines are open. Application fee is $20. Notification is sent on a rolling basis. There is a deferred admissions plan. A waiting list is an active part of the admissions procedure, with about 5% of applicants on the list.

Transfer: About 409 transfer students enrolled in 1993–94. Either the SAT I or the ACT is required, and interview is recommended. The applicant must have a 2.0 GPA and must submit transcripts from high school and all previous colleges. A total of 32 credits out of 128 must be completed at Edinboro.

Visiting: There are regularly scheduled orientations for prospective students. There are guides for informal visits and visitors may sit in on classes. To arrange for a visit, contact the Admissions Office at (814) 732–2761 or (800) 626–2203 (in-state).

Financial Aid: In 1993–94, 80% of all students received some form of financial aid, including need-based aid. The average freshman award was $4140. Of that total, scholarships or need-based grants averaged $2600 ($4800 maximum); and loans averaged $2506 ($3025 maximum). Fifty percent of undergraduate students work part-time. Average earnings from campus work for the school year are $1200. The average financial indebtedness of the 1992–93 graduate was $9000. The university is a member of CSS. The FAFSA financial statement is required. The deadline for financial aid applications is May 1.

International Students: The school actively recruits these students. They must take the TOEFL or the University of Michigan Language Test after arrival at the college and must achieve a minimum score on the TOEFL of 450.

Computers: The college provides computer facilities for student use. The mainframe is a DEC VAX. More than 200 IBM, Apple, Macintosh, Zenith, Tandy, and other microcomputers are available to students in locations across campus. All students may access the system. There are no time limits on using the system and no fees.

Graduates: In 1992–93 1230 bachelor's degrees were awarded. The most popular majors among graduates were education (34%), business (12%), and speech and communication (8%). Some 150 companies recruited on campus in 1992–93.

Admissions Contact: Terrence Carlin, Assistant Vice President for Admissions.

ELIZABETHTOWN COLLEGE

	D-3
Elizabethtown, PA 17022	(717) 361–1400

Full-time: 504 men, 981 women	Faculty: 105; IIB, +$
Part-time: 126 men, 177 women	Ph.D.s: 70%
Graduate: none	Student/Faculty: 14 to 1
Year: semesters, summer session	Tuition: $13,600
Application Deadline: see profile	Room & Board: $4250
Freshman Class: 2417 applied, 1843 accepted, 426 enrolled	
SAT I Verbal/Math: 490/540	**VERY COMPETITIVE**

Elizabethtown College, founded in 1899, is a private institution affiliated with the Church of the Brethren and offering undergraduate degrees in liberal arts, sciences, and preprofessional programs. In addition to regional accreditation, E-town has baccalaureate program accreditation with ACBSP, CSWE, ACS, AOTA, NAMT and NASM. The library contains 180,000 volumes, 100,485 microform items, and 29,031 audiovisual forms, and subscribes to 1100 periodicals. Computerized library sources and services include the card catalog, interlibrary loans, and database searching. Special learning facilities include a learning resource center, art gallery, radio station, tv station, and a meeting house for the study of Anabaptist and Pietist groups. The 180-acre campus is in a small town 20 miles southeast of Harrisburg. Including residence halls, there are 23 buildings on campus.

Student Life: About 62% of undergraduates are from Pennsylvania. Students come from 21 states and 19 foreign countries. Ninety-five percent are white. Forty-nine percent are Protestant; 34% Catholic. The average age of freshmen is 18; all undergraduates, 20. Twenty percent drop out by the end of their first year; 65% remain to graduate.

Housing: A total of 1300 students can be accommodated in college housing. College-sponsored living facilities include single-sex and coed dormitories and on-campus apartments. In addition there are special interest houses. On-campus housing is guaranteed for all 4 years. Ninety percent of students live on campus; of those, 80% remain on campus on weekends. All students may keep cars on campus.

Activities: There are no fraternities or sororities on campus. There are more than 50 groups on campus, including art, band, cheerleading, choir, chorale, chorus, computers, drama, ethnic, gay, international, jazz band, literary magazine, musical theater, newspaper, orchestra, photography, political, professional, radio and TV, religious, social, social service, student government, and yearbook. Popular campus events include Parents Weekend, Homecoming, Thank God It's Spring Weekend, theme weekends, Spring Arts Festival, Annual Symposia, and Thanksgiving Dinner served by faculty and administration.

Sports: There are 8 intercollegiate sports for men and 8 for women, and 9 intramural sports for men and 9 for women. Athletic and recreation facilities include a swimming pool, 70 acres of playing fields, weight training rooms, a 1200-seat soccer complex, a 2400-seat gymnasium, racquetball and tennis courts, basketball courts, sand volleyball courts, aerobic classes, and a fitness center.

Disabled Students: Eighty percent of the campus is accessible to disabled students. The following facilities are available: wheelchair ramps, elevators, special parking, specially equipped rest rooms, special class scheduling, lowered drinking fountains, and lowered telephones.

Services: In addition to many counseling and information services, tutoring is available in most subjects. There is remedial math and writing. Workshops and individual help with study skills are also available.

Campus Safety and Security: Campus safety and security measures include 24-hour foot and vehicle patrol, self defense education, escort service, and informal discussions. In addition, there are pamphlets, posters, and films, emergency telephones, lighted pathways and sidewalks, limited shuttle bus service, a student patrol, and a crime prevention program.

Programs of Study: E-town awards the B.A. and B.S. degrees. Bachelor's degrees are awarded in BIOLOGICAL SCIENCE (biochemistry and biology/biological science), BUSINESS (accounting, business administration and management, and international business management), COMMUNICATIONS AND THE ARTS (communications, English, French, German, music, and Spanish), COMPUTER AND PHYSICAL SCIENCE (chemistry, computer science, mathematics, physical chemistry, physics, science, and science and management), EDUCATION (early childhood, elementary, music, and secondary), ENGINEERING AND ENVIRONMENTAL DESIGN (computer engineering, engineering, engineering physics, environmental science, and industrial engineering); HEALTH PROFESSIONS (medical laboratory technology, music therapy, and occupational therapy), SOCIAL SCIENCE (economics, history, philosophy, political science/government, psychology, religion, social studies, and social work). Sciences, occupational therapy, international business, and music therapy are the strongest academically. Business administration, communications, elementary and early childhood education, and occupational therapy have the largest enrollments.

Required: The core curriculum includes a freshman seminar, a junior/senior coloquium, and courses in foreign cultures and international studies, mathematics analysis, the power of language, creative expression, cultural heritage, physical well-being, the natural and social worlds, and values and choice. Distribution requirements include 37 to 39 hours in 9 areas of understanding. Students must complete 125 credit hours, with at least 30 in the major, and maintain a GPA of 2.0 overall and in the major.

Special: Work-study programs, internships, study abroad in 8 countries, and dual majors are available. A 3–2 engineering degree with Pennsylvania State University, a 2–2 allied health degree and a 2–3 physical therapy degree with Thomas Jefferson University, and a 3–2 forestry or environmental management degree with Duke University are also offered. There are 13 national honor societies on campus.

Faculty/Classroom: Seventy-five percent of faculty are male; 25%, female. All teach undergraduates and 33% both teach and do research. The average class size in an introductory lecture is 28; in a laboratory, 20; and in a regular course offering, 25.

Admissions: About 76% of the 1993–94 applicants were accepted. The SAT scores for the 1993–94 freshman class were as follows: Verbal—54% below 500, 38% between 500 and 599, 8% between 600 and 700, and 1% above 700; Math—27% below 500, 46% between 500 and 599, 22% between 600 and 700, and 5% above 700. About 61% of the current freshmen were in the top fifth of their class; 85% were in the top two fifths. About 8 freshmen graduated first in their class.

Requirements: Recommended composite scores for the SAT I range from 960 to 1130; for the ACT, 23 to 27. Applicants must be graduates of an accredited secondary school or have earned a GED. The college encourages completion of 18 academic credits, based on 4 years of English, 3 of mathematics, 2 each of laboratory science,

social studies, and consecutive foreign language, and 5 additional college preparatory units. An audition is required for music majors and an interview is required for occupational therapy majors. AP and CLEP credits are accepted. Important factors used in the admissions decision are advanced placement or honor courses, leadership record, evidence of special talent, extracurricular activities record, and recommendations by school officials.

Procedure: Freshmen are admitted to all sessions. Entrance exams should be taken in the spring of the junior year or the fall of the senior year. The application deadline for occupational therapy majors is December 15. For all others, deadlines are open. The application fee is $20. Notification is sent on a rolling basis beginning in mid-November. There is a deferred admissions plan.

Transfer: About 34 transfer students enrolled in 1993–94. Applicants should present a minimum GPA of 3.0 in at least 15 credit hours earned from a community college, or 2.5 from a 4-year institution. A total of 30 credits out of 125 must be completed at E-town.

Visiting: There are regularly scheduled orientations for prospective students, including 6 open houses and weekday appointments throughout the year, with Saturday interviews available during the academic year. There are guides for informal visits and visitors may sit in on classes and stay overnight at the school. To arrange for a visit, contact the Admissions Office at (717) 361-1400.

Financial Aid: In 1993–94, 91% of all current freshmen and 82% of continuing students received some form of financial aid. About 85% of freshmen and 73% of continuing students received need-based aid. The average freshman award was $11,550. Of that total, scholarships or need-based grants averaged $8000 ($14,000 maximum); loans averaged $3600 ($3625 maximum); and work contracts averaged $1375 ($1500 maximum). Sixty-five percent of undergraduate students work part-time. Average earnings from campus work for the school year are $763. The average financial indebtedness of the 1992–93 graduate was $13,250. E-town is a member of CSS. The college's own financial statement and the FAFSA are required. The deadline for financial aid applications is April 1.

International Students: There are currently 34 international students enrolled. The school actively recruits these students. They must take the TOEFL and achieve a minimum score of 525.

Computers: The college provides computer facilities for student use. The mainframes are a DEC VAX 11/780, and a DEC MicroVAX 3100. A 24-hour terminal room allows student access to the mainframes. Several laboratories house a total of 40 Apple Macintosh and 43 IBM and IBM-compatible microcomputers, 15 of which are networked to the mainframe and provide access to the Internet system. All students may access the system. It may be used Monday through Friday, 8 A.M. to midnight; Saturday and Sunday, noon to midnight. There are no time limits on using the system and no fees.

Graduates: In a recent year, 350 bachelor's degrees were awarded. The most popular majors among graduates were business (23%), education (16%), and communications (10%). Within an average freshman class, 53% graduate in 4 years, 62% in 5 years, and 65% in 6 years. About 65 companies have recruited on campus in recent years. In the 1992 graduating class, 15% of all graduates were enrolled in graduate school within 6 months of graduation; 70% had found employment.

Admissions Contact: Ronald Potier, Director of Admissions.

FRANKLIN AND MARSHALL COLLEGE   E-3
Lancaster, PA 17604–3003   (717) 291–3951

Full-time: 972 men, 836 women	Faculty: 147; IIB, +$
Part-time: 18 men, 18 women	Ph.D.s: 95%
Graduate: none	Student/Faculty: 12 to 1
Year: semesters, summer session	Tuition: Tuition,
Application Deadline: February 1	Room & Board: 23,655
Freshman Class: 3270 applied, 2119 accepted, 510 enrolled	
SAT I: required	**HIGHLY COMPETITIVE**

Franklin and Marshall College, founded in 1787, is a private, coeducational liberal arts institution. The 2 libraries contain 345,000 volumes, 250,000 microform items, and 8500 audiovisual forms, and subscribe to 1703 periodicals. Computerized library sources and services include the card catalog, interlibrary loans, and database searching. Special learning facilities include a learning resource center, art gallery, natural history museum, planetarium, radio station, tv station, and instructional media services. The 125-acre campus is in a suburban area 60 miles west of Philadelphia. Including residence halls, there are 44 buildings on campus.

Student Life: About 67% of undergraduates are from out-of-state, mostly the Middle Atlantic. Students come from 40 states, 50 foreign countries, and Canada. Fifty-eight percent are from public schools; 42% from private. Eighty percent are white. Thirty percent are Protestant; 30% Catholic, 11% Jewish, 17% claim no religious affiliation. The average age of freshmen is 18; all undergraduates, 19.5. Five percent drop out by the end of their first year; 85% remain to graduate.

Housing: A total of 1320 students can be accommodated in college housing. College-sponsored living facilities include coed dormitories and off-campus apartments. In addition there are language houses, special interest houses, an arts house, a co-op house, and an international living center. On-campus housing is guaranteed for freshmen and sophomores only and is available on a lottery system for upperclassmen. Seventy-four percent of students live on campus; of those, 80% remain on campus on weekends. All students may keep cars on campus.

Activities: About 40% of men belong to fraternities; about 30% of women belong to sororities. There are 110 groups on campus, including art, band, cheerleading, chess, choir, chorale, chorus, computers, dance, drama, ethnic, film, gay, honors, international, jazz band, literary magazine, musical theater, newspaper, opera, orchestra, pep band, photography, political, professional, radio and tv, religious, social, social service, student government, symphony, and yearbook. Popular campus events include Spring and Fall Arts Weekends.

Sports: Athletic and recreation facilities include a 3000-seat gymnasium, a steam room, a swimming pool, 4 squash courts, a wrestling room, an ice rink, 54 acres of playing fields, a 400-meter all-weather track, a wellness/aerobic center, a strength training center, and tennis courts.

Disabled Students: Seventy percent of the campus is accessible to disabled students. The following facilities are available: wheelchair ramps, elevators, special parking, specially equipped rest rooms, special class scheduling, lowered drinking fountains, and lowered telephones.

Services: In addition to many counseling and information services, tutoring is available in every subject.

Campus Safety and Security: Campus safety and security measures include 24-hour foot and vehicle patrol, self defense education, escort service, and informal discussions. In addition, there are pamphlets, posters, and films, emergency telephones, lighted pathways and sidewalks, and regular fire safety drills are held in residence halls and academic buildings.

Programs of Study: F & M awards the B.A. degree. Bachelor's degrees are awarded in BIOLOGICAL SCIENCE (biology/biological science), BUSINESS (accounting and business administration and management), COMMUNICATIONS AND THE ARTS (classics, dramatic arts, English, fine arts, French, German, Greek, Latin, music, and Spanish), COMPUTER AND PHYSICAL SCIENCE (chemistry, geology, mathematics, and physics), SOCIAL SCIENCE (American studies, anthropology, economics, history, philosophy, political science/government, psychology, religion, and sociology). Biological and physical science and social sciences are the strongest academically. Government, business administration, and English have the largest enrollments.

Required: Students must complete 11 college studies courses from 8 areas of study, including scientific inquiry, social analysis, arts, foreign cultures, historical studies, literature, systems of knowledge and belief, and language studies. They must also demonstrate writing proficiency. The bachelor's degree requires completion of at least 32 courses, including a minimum of 8 in the major, with a minimum GPA of 2.0.

Special: There is a 3–2 degree program in forestry and environmental studies with Duke University as well as 3–2 degree programs in engineering with the University of Pennsylvania, Columbia University, Rensselaer Polytechnic Institute, Case Western Reserve, Georgia Institute of Technology, and Washington University at St. Louis. Cross-registration with the Central Pennsylvania Consortium allows students to study at nearby Dickinson College or Gettysburg College. Students may also study architecture and urban planning at Columbia University, studio art at the School of Visual Arts in New York City, theater in Connecticut, oceanography in Massachusetts, and American studies at American University. There are study abroad programs in England, Greece, Italy, Denmark, India, the Orient, and other locations. F & M also offers internships, an accelerated degree program, dual majors, student-designed majors, independent study, interdisciplinary studies, optional freshman seminars, pass/fail options, and nondegree study. There are 12 national honor societies on campus, including Phi Beta Kappa.

Faculty/Classroom: Seventy percent of faculty are male; 30%, female. All faculty members both teach and do research. The average class size in a laboratory is 18 and in a regular course offering, 19.

Admissions: About 65% of the 1993–94 applicants were accepted. The SAT scores for the 1993–94 freshman class were as follows: Verbal—22% below 500, 51% between 500 and 599, 25% between 600 and 700, and 2% above 700; Math—5% below 500, 36% between 500 and 599, 44% between 600 and 700, and 15% above 700. About 70% of the current freshmen were in the top fifth of their class; 93% were in the top two fifths. There were 19 National Merit semifinalists. About 22 freshmen graduated first in their class.

Requirements: The SAT I is required. Standardized tests are optional for students in the top 10% of their class. The SAT II: Subject test in writing is required. Applicants must be graduates of accredited

secondary schools. Recommended college preparatory study includes 4 years each of English and mathematics, 3 or 4 of foreign language, 3 each of laboratory science and history/social studies, and 1 or 2 courses in art or music. All students must also submit their high school transcripts, recommendations from a teacher and a counselor, and a personal essay. An interview is recommended. AP and CLEP credits are accepted. Important factors used in the admissions decision are advanced placement or honor courses, recommendations by school officials, leadership record, extracurricular activities record, and evidence of special talent.

Procedure: Freshmen are admitted in the fall. Entrance exams should be taken by December of the senior year. Early decision applications should be filed by January 15; regular applications, by February 1 for fall entry, along with an application fee of $35. Notification is sent on or before April 1. There are early decision, early admissions, and deferred admissions plans. Early decision notification is sent within one month after receipt of application and supporting documentation. About 124 early decision candidates were accepted for the 1993–94 class. A waiting list is an active part of the admissions procedure, with about 20% of applicants on the list.

Transfer: About 10 transfer students enrolled in 1993–94. Applicants must present a minimum GPA of 3.0 in course work completed at an accredited college. An interview, SAT I or ACT scores, college and secondary school transcripts, a dean's form, recommendations from 2 professors, and a letter explaining the reason for transfer are also required. An associate degree is recommended. A total of 16 courses out of 32 must be completed at F & M.

Visiting: There are regularly scheduled orientations for prospective students, including a campus tour, interview, class visit, and overnight stay. There are guides for informal visits and visitors may sit in on classes and stay overnight at the school. To arrange for a visit, contact the Admissions Office at (717) 291–3951.

Financial Aid: In 1993–94, 60% of all students received some form of financial aid. About 42% of freshmen and 41% of continuing students received need-based aid. The average freshman award was $19,442. Of that total, scholarships or need-based grants averaged $15,647 ($23,250 maximum); loans averaged $2625; and work contracts averaged $1350. Forty-two percent of undergraduate students work part-time. Average earnings from campus work for the school year are $1350. The average financial indebtedness of the 1992–93 graduate was $13,250. F & M is a member of CSS. The FAF and FAFSA are required. The deadline for financial aid applications is February 1.

International Students: There are currently 106 international students enrolled. The school actively recruits these students. They must take the TOEFL and achieve a minimum score of 600. The student must also take the SAT I or the ACT.

Computers: The college provides computer facilities for student use. The mainframe is a DEC MicroVAX 3800. There is a computer workroom housing 32 Apple Macintosh computers, 6 Apple LaserWriter printers, 1 Apple Image Writer, and 1 HP Laser printer, which is directly connected to the mainframe. All of the Apple Macintosh computers are on the campus-wide network for access to file servers and the academic VAX. A team of 25 student computing consultants is available for computing support and problem-solving assistance. All students may access the system. It may be used 16 hours on weekdays and 13 hours on weekends. There are no time limits on using the system and no fees.

Graduates: In 1992–93, 400 bachelor's degrees were awarded. The most popular majors among graduates were government (18%), business (accounting and management) (13%), and English (8%). Within an average freshman class, 75% graduate in 4 years, 83% in 5 years, and 84% in 6 years. Some 190 companies recruited on campus in 1992–93. In the 1992 graduating class, 39% of the men and 37% of the women were enrolled in graduate school within 6 months of graduation; 53% of the men and 60% of the women had found employment.

Admissions Contact: Peter Van Buskirk, Dean of Admissions.

GANNON UNIVERSITY
B-1

Erie, PA 16541   (814) 871-7407; (800) GANNON U (out-of-state)

Full-time: 1299 men, 1394 women	Faculty: 204; IIA, --$
Part-time: 275 men, 416 women	Ph.D.s: 52%
Graduate: 228 men, 369 women	Student/Faculty: 13 to 1
Year: semesters, summer session	Tuition: $9760-$10,250
Application Deadline: open	Room & Board: $4540
Freshman Class: 2464 applied, 1908 accepted, 678 enrolled	
SAT I: 450/510	ACT: 23 COMPETITIVE

Gannon University, founded in 1925, is a private, coeducational liberal arts and teacher preparation university affiliated with the Roman Catholic Church. There are 5 undergraduate schools. In addition to regional accreditation, Gannon has baccalaureate program accreditation with ABET, ADA, CAHEA, CSWE, and NLN. The library contains 215,024 volumes, 343,073 microform items, and 2291 audiovi-

sual forms, and subscribes to 1283 periodicals. Computerized library sources and services include interlibrary loans and database searching. Special learning facilities include a learning resource center, art gallery, planetarium, radio station, tv station, and a historical museum. The 13-acre campus is in an urban area 135 miles north of Pittsburgh. Including residence halls, there are 29 buildings on campus.

Student Life: About 82% of undergraduates are from Pennsylvania. Students come from 34 states, 17 foreign countries, and Canada. Forty-five percent are from public schools. Ninety-three percent are white. Fifty-nine percent are Catholic; 24% Protestant; 17% Buddhist, Hindu, Muslim, and other. The average age of freshmen is 19.3; all undergraduates, 21.4. Twenty-one percent drop out by the end of their first year; 60% remain to graduate.

Housing: A total of 1200 students can be accommodated in college housing. College-sponsored living facilities include single-sex and coed dormitories and on-campus apartments. On-campus housing is guaranteed for all 4 years. Fifty-two percent of students live on campus. Alcohol is not permitted. Upperclassmen may keep cars on campus.

Activities: About 20% of men belong to 7 national fraternities; about 5% of women belong to 5 national sororities. There are 60 groups on campus, including cheerleading, computers, drama, ethnic, honors, international, literary magazine, newspaper, pep band, political, professional, radio and TV, social, social service, student government, and yearbook. Popular campus events include the Dance Marathon, dances, the Homecoming Parade, the Yearly Concert, and Greek Festival.

Sports: There are 9 intercollegiate sports for men and 7 for women, and 18 intramural sports for men and 9 for women. Athletic and recreation facilities include a pool, a gymnasium, a track, a weight room, racquetball courts, an outdoor recreation field, outdoor tennis courts, and a 3000-seat basketball and volleyball venue.

Disabled Students: Eighty-five percent of the campus is accessible to disabled students. The following facilities are available: wheelchair ramps, elevators, specially equipped rest rooms, special class scheduling, lowered drinking fountains and telephones, and special drop-off points.

Services: In addition to many counseling and information services, tutoring is available in some subjects. There are mathematics, writing, and advising centers.

Campus Safety and Security: Campus safety and security measures include 24-hour foot and vehicle patrol, escort service, informal discussions, and pamphlets, posters, and films. In addition, there are emergency telephones, lighted pathways and sidewalks, and security cameras in some buildings.

Programs of Study: Gannon awards the B.A., B.S., B.E.E., B.M.E., B.E.T., and B.S.N. degrees. Associate and master's degrees also are awarded. Bachelor's degrees are awarded in BIOLOGICAL SCIENCE (biology/biological science), BUSINESS (accounting, banking and finance, business administration and management, business economics, international business management, marketing/retailing/merchandising, and trade and industrial supervision and management), COMMUNICATIONS AND THE ARTS (communications and English), COMPUTER AND PHYSICAL SCIENCE (chemistry, computer science, earth science, information sciences and systems, mathematics, and physics), EDUCATION (early childhood, elementary, secondary, and special), ENGINEERING AND ENVIRONMENTAL DESIGN (chemical engineering, electrical/electronics engineering, engineering technology, industrial administration/management, and industrial engineering technology), HEALTH PROFESSIONS (medical laboratory technology, mental health/human services, nursing, occupational therapy, physical therapy, physician's assistant, predentistry, premedicine, prepharmacy, prephysical therapy, preveterinary science, recreation therapy, and respiratory therapy), SOCIAL SCIENCE (anthropology, criminal justice, dietetics, history, international relations, international studies, paralegal studies, philosophy, political science/government, prelaw, psychology, religion, social science, social work, and sociology). Engineering and preprofessional programs are the strongest academically. Nursing, biology, criminal justice, physician's assistant, prephysical therapy, and engineering have the largest enrollments.

Required: Students must complete at least 128 hours of academic work. Each academic program has specific course requirements. Students must have a cumulative GPA of at least 2.0 overall and in the area of concentration.

Special: Gannon offers study abroad in more than 5 countries, co-op programs, summer internships, cross-registration with Mercyhurst College, pass/fail options, work-study programs, a general studies program, an accelerated degree program, a combined B.A.-B.S. degree, student-designed majors, a 3–2 engineering degree with the universities of Akron, Pittsburgh, and Detroit, and nondegree study. The B.S. in mortuary science program consists of 2 or 3 years of study at Gannon with degree completion at a school of mortuary science. There is a freshman honors program on campus, as well as 13 national honor societies.

Faculty/Classroom: Sixty-one percent of faculty are male; 39%, female. Ninety-one percent teach undergraduates and 6% do research. No introductory courses are taught by graduate students. The average class size in a laboratory is 20 and in a regular course offering, 18.

Admissions: About 77% of the 1993–94 applicants were accepted. The SAT scores for the 1993–94 freshman class were as follows: Verbal—66% below 500, 28% between 500 and 599, 5% between 600 and 700, and 1% above 700; Math—40% below 500, 41% between 500 and 599, 17% between 600 and 700, and 2% above 700. The ACT scores were 31% below 21, 30% between 21 and 23, 27% between 24 and 26, 5% between 27 and 28, and 7% above 28. About 47% of the current freshmen were in the top fifth of their class; 82% were in the top two fifths. Twelve freshmen graduated first in their class.

Requirements: Gannon requires applicants to be in the upper 50% of their class. A minimum GPA of 2.5 is required. The SAT I or ACT is required. Candidates should have completed 16 academic units including 4 in English and 12 in social sciences, foreign languages, mathematics, and science, depending on the degree sought. Specific courses in mathematics and science are required for some majors in health sciences and engineering. AP and CLEP credits are accepted. Important factors used in the admissions decision are advanced placement or honor courses, leadership record, recommendations by school officials, extracurricular activities record, and evidence of special talent.

Procedure: Freshmen are admitted to all sessions. Entrance exams should be taken at the end of junior year or the beginning of senior year. The application deadlines are open. Application fee is $25. Notification is sent on a rolling basis. There are early admissions and deferred admissions plans.

Transfer: About 141 transfer students enrolled in 1993–94. Transfer students should be in good standing at their previous institution with at least a 2.0 GPA. They must submit a college clearance from the college most recently attended and all transcripts. A high school transcript is required from transfer students with fewer than 60 credits. Several health science programs are not designed to accomodate transfers. A total of 30 credits out of 128 must be completed at Gannon.

Visiting: There are regularly scheduled orientations for prospective students, consisting of open houses for prospective students in the fall and spring. Students may meet with faculty, tour the campus, and attend a variety of presentations. There are guides for informal visits and visitors may sit in on classes and stay overnight at the school. To arrange for a visit, contact the Admissions Office at (814) 871–7240 or (800) GANNON U.

Financial Aid: In 1993–94, 92% of all current freshmen and 90% of continuing students received some form of financial aid. About 72% of freshmen and 70% of continuing students received need-based aid. The average freshman award was $6936. Of that total, scholarships or need-based grants averaged $3236 ($9670 maximum); loans averaged $2500 ($2625 maximum); and work contracts averaged $1200. Eighty-two percent of undergraduate students work part-time. Average earnings from campus work for the school year are $1200. The average financial indebtedness of the 1992–93 graduate was $15,600. Gannon is a member of CSS. The college's own financial statement and the PHEAA/Federal Aid are required. The deadline for financial aid applications is March 1.

International Students: There are currently 34 international students enrolled. The school actively recruits these students. They must take the TOEFL and achieve a minimum score of 500.

Computers: The college provides computer facilities for student use. The mainframe consists of a DEC VAX 6000–410 cluster and 2 DEC VAX 6410 clusters. There is 1 mainframe laboratory and 2 personal computer laboratories with about 20 personal computers in each laboratory. The engineering department has a designated laboratory containing 12 PCs and the school of education has 16 Apple computers. All students may access the system. It may be used Monday through Friday 9 A.M. to midnight; Saturday noon-6 P.M.; Sunday noon-midnight. There are no time limits on using the system. The VAX computer lab fees vary per course. There is no fee for use of the PC computer laboratory.

Graduates: In 1992–93 524 bachelor's degrees were awarded. The most popular majors among graduates were biology (8%), professional nursing (8%), and marketing (7%). Five companies recruited on campus in 1992–93.

Admissions Contact: Joyce Scheid-Gilman, Director of Freshman Admissions.

GENEVA COLLEGE
A-3
Beaver Falls, PA 15010

(412) 847–6500
(800) 847–8255 (out-of-state)

Full-time: 606 men, 605 women	Faculty: 50; IIB, -$
Part-time: 76 men, 60 women	Ph.D.s: 63%
Graduate: 24 men, 47 women	Student/Faculty: 24 to 1
Year: semesters, summer session	Tuition: $8810
Application Deadline: open	Room & Board: $4220
Freshman Class: 624 applied, 534 accepted, 237 enrolled	
SAT I Verbal/Math: 460/490	ACT: 22 COMPETITIVE

Geneva College, founded in 1848, is a private, coeducational institution affiliated with the Reformed Presbyterian Church of North America. The college offers undergraduate programs in the arts and sciences, business education, health science, biblical and religious studies, engineering, and professional training. The library contains 149,482 volumes, 77,717 microform items, and 21,900 audiovisual forms, and subscribes to 737 periodicals. Computerized library sources and services include the card catalog, interlibrary loans, and database searching. Special learning facilities include a radio and tv station. The 50-acre campus is in a small town 35 miles north of Pittsburgh. Including residence halls, there are 30 buildings on campus.

Student Life: About 78% of undergraduates are from Pennsylvania. Students come from 34 states, 17 foreign countries, and Canada. Eighty-seven percent are from public schools; 13% from private. Eighty-seven percent are white; 10% African American. Seventy-four percent are Protestant; 19% Catholic. The average age of freshmen is 18; all undergraduates, 22. Twenty-three percent drop out by the end of their first year; 55% remain to graduate.

Housing: A total of 773 students can be accommodated in college housing. College-sponsored living facilities include single-sex dormitories and on-campus apartments. In addition, there is Discipleship House for those interested in structural growth opportunities. On-campus housing is guaranteed for all 4 years. Fifty-nine percent of students live on campus. Alcohol is not permitted. All students may keep cars on campus.

Activities: There are no fraternities or sororities on campus. There are many groups and organizations on campus, including band, cheerleading, choir, chorus, computers, drama, drill team, ethnic, honors, international, jazz band, literary magazine, marching band, musical theater, newspaper, pep band, photography, radio and TV, religious, social, student government, and yearbook. Popular campus events include Parents Weekend and Homecoming.

Sports: There are 7 intercollegiate sports for men and 7 for women, and 4 intramural sports for men and 3 for women. Athletic and recreation facilities include a 5600-seat stadium, a field house, a 3200-seat gymnasium, a practice gymnasium, track, athletic fields, racquetball and tennis courts, and weight training rooms.

Disabled Students: The following facilities are available: wheelchair ramps, elevators, special parking, specially equipped rest rooms, and special class scheduling.

Services: In addition to many counseling and information services, tutoring is available in most subjects. There is also remedial math, reading, and writing.

Campus Safety and Security: Campus safety and security measures include self defense education and informal discussions.

Programs of Study: Geneva awards the B.A., B.S., B.S.B.A., B.S.Ed., and B.S.E. degrees. Associate and master's degrees also are awarded. Bachelor's degrees are awarded in BIOLOGICAL SCIENCE (biology/biological science), BUSINESS (accounting, business administration and management, and human resources), COMMUNICATIONS AND THE ARTS (applied music, broadcasting, communications, creative writing, English, music, music business management, Spanish, speech/debate/rhetoric, and technical and business writing), COMPUTER AND PHYSICAL SCIENCE (applied mathematics, chemistry, computer science, physics, and science), EDUCATION (business, elementary, mathematics, and music), ENGINEERING AND ENVIRONMENTAL DESIGN (aviation administration/management, chemical engineering, civil engineering, electrical/electronics engineering, engineering, industrial engineering, and mechanical engineering), HEALTH PROFESSIONS (medical laboratory technology, nursing, premedicine, and speech pathology/audiology), SOCIAL SCIENCE (biblical studies, counseling psychology, history, ministries, philosophy, political science/government, prelaw, psychology, and sociology). Engineering and business administration are the strongest academically. Elementary education and business administration have the largest enrollments.

Required: The core curriculum includes 12 hours of humanities, 9 each of biblical studies and social science, 8 to 10 of natural science, 2 of physical education, 6 of communications and the 1-hour Freshman Experience course. To graduate, students must complete 126 to 138 semester hours, including those required for a major, with a minimum GPA of 2.0.

Special: Cross-registration is offered in conjunction with Pennsylvania State University/Beaver Campus and Community College of Beaver County. There are 2–2 and 3–2 degree programs in nursing with the University of Rochester, a 3–1 degree program in cardiovascular technology, an accelerated degree program in human resource management, and prelaw and premedical programs. Off-campus study includes programs at centers for urban biblical studies, a Washington semester, and a summer program at AuSable Trails Institute of Environmental Studies in Michigan. Geneva also offers internships, independent study, and credit by proficiency exam. Nondegree study is available through adult education programs. There is a freshman honors program on campus, as well as one national honor society.

Faculty/Classroom: Eighty-five percent of faculty are male; 15%, female. All teach undergraduates. No introductory courses are taught by graduate students.

Admissions: About 86% of the 1993–94 applicants were accepted. The SAT scores for the 1993–94 freshman class were as follows: Verbal—68% below 500, 25% between 500 and 599, and 7% between 600 and 700; Math—52% below 500, 30% between 500 and 599, 17% between 600 and 700, and 2% above 700. About 34% of the current freshmen were in the top fifth of their class; 64% were in the top two fifths. There were 2 National Merit semifinalists. Four freshmen graduated first in their class.

Requirements: Geneva requires applicants to be in the upper 50% of their class. A minimum GPA of 2.0 is required. The SAT I or ACT is required. Applicants must be graduates of accredited secondary schools or have earned a GED. The college requires 16 academic credits, based on 1 year of science, 2 each of mathematics and foreign language, 3 of social studies, and 4 each of English and electives. An essay is required, and an interview is recommended. AP and CLEP credits are accepted. Important factors used in the admissions decision are recommendations by school officials, advanced placement or honor courses, leadership record, personality, intangible qualities, and evidence of special talent.

Procedure: Freshmen are admitted to all sessions. Entrance exams should be taken during the junior or senior year. Application deadlines are open. The application fee is $15. Notification is sent on a rolling basis. There is an early admissions plan.

Transfer: About 107 transfer students enrolled in 1993–94. A total of 48 credits out of 126 must be completed at Geneva.

Visiting: There are regularly scheduled orientations for prospective students, including meetings with financial aid, faculty, class admissions, and a campus tour. There are guides for informal visits and visitors may sit in on classes and stay overnight at the school. To arrange for a visit, contact the Admissions Office, Campus Visit Coordinator at (412) 847-6500.

Financial Aid: In 1993–94, 93% of all current freshmen and 90% of continuing students received some form of financial aid. About 73% of freshmen and 65% of continuing students received need-based aid. The average freshman award was $6390. Of that total, scholarships or need-based grants averaged $4124 ($5000 maximum); loans averaged $1486 ($2625 maximum); and work contracts averaged $750 ($1000 maximum). Sixty-five percent of undergraduate students work part-time. Average earnings from campus work for the school year are $800. The average financial indebtedness of the 1992–93 graduate was $9000. Geneva is a member of CSS. The FAF, the college's own financial statement, the PHEAA, and FAFSA are required. The deadline for financial aid applications is March 1.

International Students: There are currently 33 international students enrolled. The school actively recruits these students. They must take the TOEFL and achieve a minimum score of 500.

Computers: The college provides computer facilities for student use. The mainframes are a DEC VAX 11/780 and an AS 400. A DEC VAX-12 is used for classroom work. Computer science students may access the system. It may be used during supervised laboratory hours. There are no time limits on using the system and no fees.

Graduates: In 1992–93, 429 bachelor's degrees were awarded. The most popular majors among graduates were business administration (19%), elementary education (16%), and secondary education (8%). Within an average freshman class, 1% graduate in 3 years, 46% in 4 years, 59% in 5 years, and 64% in 6 years. Some 30 companies recruited on campus in 1992–93. Twenty percent of the 1992 graduates were enrolled in graduate school within 6 months of graduation; 88% had found employment.

Admissions Contact: William J. Katip, Vice President for Enrollment Management.

GETTYSBURG COLLEGE

D-4

Gettysburg, PA 17325   (717) 337–6100; (800) 431–0803 (in-state)

Full-time: 975 men, 975 women	Faculty: 154; IIB, +$
Part-time: 10 men, 25 women	Ph.D.s: 95%
Graduate: none	Student/Faculty: 13 to 1
Year: semesters	Tuition: $18,870
Application Deadline: February 15	Room & Board: $4090
Freshman Class: 3596 applied, 2420 accepted, 586 enrolled	
SAT I or ACT: required	**HIGHLY COMPETITIVE**

Gettysburg College, founded in 1832, is an independent college affiliated with the Lutheran Church. It offers programs in the liberal arts. The library contains 345,000 volumes, 35,000 microform items, and 40,000 audiovisual forms, and subscribes to 1400 periodicals. Computerized library sources and services include the card catalog, interlibrary loans, and database searching. Special learning facilities include a learning resource center, an art gallery, a planetarium, a radio station, and fine arts facilities. The 200-acre campus is in a small town 30 miles south of Harrisburg and 50 miles from Baltimore. Including residence halls, there are 60 buildings on campus.

Student Life: About 75% of undergraduates are from out-of-state, mostly the Middle Atlantic. Students come from 40 states, 25 foreign countries, and Canada. Seventy-five percent are from public schools; 25% from private. Eighty-nine percent are white. Thirty-eight percent are Protestant; 33% Catholic. The average age of freshmen is 18; all undergraduates, 20. Ten percent drop out by the end of their first year; 80% remain to graduate.

Housing: A total of 1750 students can be accommodated in college housing. College-sponsored living facilities include single-sex and coed dormitories, on-campus apartments, off-campus apartments, and fraternity houses. In addition, there are language houses and special interest houses. On-campus housing is guaranteed for all 4 years. Ninety percent of students live on campus; of those, 90% remain on campus on weekends. All students may keep cars on campus.

Activities: About 55% of men belong to 11 national fraternities; about 45% of women belong to 7 national sororities. There are 65 groups on campus, including art, band, cheerleading, chess, choir, chorale, chorus, computers, dance, drama, drill team, ethnic, gay, honors, international, jazz band, literary magazine, marching band, musical theater, newspaper, opera, orchestra, pep band, photography, political, professional, radio and TV, religious, social, social service, student government, symphony, and yearbook. Popular campus events include Christmas Concert and Lighting of the Cupola, International Festival, all-campus picnics and talent shows, parents weekends, Get Acquainted Day, and Homecoming.

Sports: There are 11 intercollegiate sports each for men and women, and 15 intramural sports each for men and women. Athletic and recreation facilities include 7 basketball courts, indoor and outdoor tennis courts, a pool, and several tracks and fields.

Disabled Students: Ninety percent of the campus is accessible to disabled students. The following facilities are available: wheelchair ramps, elevators, special parking, specially equipped rest rooms, and special class scheduling.

Services: In addition to many counseling and information services, tutoring is available in most subjects. There is also a writing center available.

Campus Safety and Security: Campus safety and security measures include 24-hour foot and vehicle patrol, self-defense education, escort service, and informal discussions. In addition, there are pamphlets, posters, and films, emergency telephones, and lighted pathways and sidewalks.

Programs of Study: Gettysburg awards the B.A., and B.S. degrees. Bachelor's degrees are awarded in BIOLOGICAL SCIENCE (biology/biological science), BUSINESS (business administration and management), COMMUNICATIONS AND THE ARTS (classics, dramatic arts, English, fine arts, French, German, Greek, Latin, music, and Spanish), COMPUTER AND PHYSICAL SCIENCE (chemistry, computer science, mathematics, and physics), EDUCATION (elementary, foreign languages, music, science, and secondary), HEALTH PROFESSIONS (predentistry and premedicine), SOCIAL SCIENCE (economics, history, international relations, philosophy, political science/government, prelaw, psychology, religion, and sociology). Management, political science, psychology, English, and biology are the strongest academically and have the largest enrollments.

Required: All students must take a freshman colloquy, demonstrate proficiency in written English, take 3 courses in physical education, and fulfill distribution requirements consisting of 2 natural science courses, 1 to 4 foreign language courses, and 1 course each in the arts, history/philosophy, literature, social science, religion, and non-Western culture. A total of 35 course units is required, with 8 to 12 in the major. The minimum GPA is 2.0.

Special: The college offers study abroad and has special centers in 8 countries. There are summer internships and a Washington semester with American University. Cross-registration is possible with mem-

bers of the Central Pennsylvania Consortium. There is a United Nations semester at Drew University, and a 3-2 engineering program with Columbia University, Rensselaer Polytechnic, and Washington University in St. Louis. There are also joint programs in optometry, with the Pennsylvania College of Optometry, and Forestry and Environmental Studies with Duke University. The college also offers dual majors, student-designed majors, and B.A.-B.S. degrees in biology, mathematics, chemistry, physics, and biochemistry. There are 16 national honor societies on campus, including Phi Beta Kappa.

Faculty/Classroom: Sixty-five percent of faculty are male; 35%, female. All faculty both teach undergraduates and do research. The average class size in an introductory lecture is 25; in a laboratory, 15; and in a regular course offering, 20.

Admissions: About 67% of the 1993-94 applicants were accepted. The SAT scores for the 1993-94 freshman class were as follows: Verbal—24% below 500, 59% between 500 and 599, 15% between 600 and 700, and 2% above 700; Math—9% below 500, 51% between 500 and 599, 35% between 600 and 700, and 5% above 700. The ACT scores were 21% between 21 and 23, 24% between 24 and 26, 35% between 27 and 28, and 20% above 28. About 74% of the current freshmen were in the top fifth of their class; 99% were in the top two fifths. About 15 freshmen graduated first in their class.

Requirements: Gettysburg requires applicants to have a minimum B average and to be in the upper 40% of their class. The SAT I or ACT is required. The GED is accepted. An essay is required. Art students need to submit a portfolio and music students need an audition. An interview and SAT II: Subject tests are recommended. AP credits are accepted. Important factors used in the admissions decision are advanced placement or honor courses, recommendations by school officials, leadership record, evidence of special talent, and recommendations by alumni.

Procedure: Freshmen are admitted fall and spring. Entrance exams should be taken by the January testing date of the senior year. Early decision applications should be filed by February 1; regular applications, by February 15 for fall entry and December 1 for spring entry, along with an application fee of $35. Notification is sent about 2 to 3 weeks after application for early decision and by early April for regular decision. There are early decision, early admissions, and deferred admissions plans. About 135 early decision candidates were accepted for the 1993-94 class. A waiting list is an active part of the admissions procedure, with about 5% of applicants on the list.

Transfer: About 35 transfer students enrolled in 1993-94. Transfer applicants must have a GPA of at least 2.0. An interview is required. The high school record and test scores are also considered. A total of 9 course units out of 35 must be completed at Gettysburg.

Visiting: There are regularly scheduled orientations for prospective students, including interviews, tours, and special programs. There are guides for informal visits and visitors may sit in on classes and stay overnight at the school. To arrange for a visit, contact the Admissions Office at (800) 431-0803.

Financial Aid: In 1993-94, 55% of all current freshmen and 47% of continuing students received some form of financial aid. About 50% of freshmen and 45% of continuing students received need-based aid. The average freshman award was $14,750. Of that total, scholarships or need-based grants averaged $11,000 ($18,900 maximum); loans averaged $2460 ($3200 maximum); and work contracts averaged $1290 ($1400 maximum). Thirty-eight percent of undergraduate students work part-time. Average earnings from campus work for the school year are $1290. The average financial indebtedness of the 1992-93 graduate was $8755. Gettysburg is a member of CSS. The FAF is required. The deadline for financial aid applications is February 1.

International Students: There are currently 49 international students enrolled. The school actively recruits these students. They must take the TOEFL and achieve a minimum score of 550. The student must also take the SAT I or the ACT.

Computers: The college provides computer facilities for student use. The mainframes are 4 100+ mips multiprocessor Sun servers, 2 VAX/VMS computers, a MicroVAX II, and a VAX II/750. There is a campuswide network with connections to Internet and Bitnet. Microcomputers are available in laboratories and other locations throughout the campus. All students may access the system. It may be used 24 hours a day. There are no time limits on using the system and no fees.

Graduates: In 1992-93, 470 bachelor's degrees were awarded. The most popular majors among graduates were management (18%), political science (17%), and psychology (10%). Within an average freshman class, 1% graduate in 3 years, 75% in 4 years, 80% in 5 years, and 81% in 6 years. Some 95 companies recruited on campus in 1992-93. In the 1992 graduating class, 35% of all graduates were enrolled in graduate school within 6 months of graduation; 62% had found employment.

Admissions Contact: Delwin Gustafson, Dean of Admissions.

GRATZ COLLEGE
F-3

Melrose Park, PA 19126   (215) 635-7300

Full-time: 2 men, 6 women	**Faculty:** 9
Part-time: 15 men, 55 women	**Ph.D.s:** 86%
Graduate: 27 men, 115 women	**Student/Faculty:** 4 to 1
Year: semesters, summer session	**Tuition:** $4620
Application Deadline: open	**Room & Board:** n/app
Freshman Class: 7 applied, 7 accepted, 7 enrolled	
SAT I or ACT: not required	**NONCOMPETITIVE**

Gratz College, founded in 1895, is an independent, nosectarian college offering undergraduate and graduate programs in Jewish, Hebraic, and Middle Eastern studies and in Jewish education. There is one graduate school. The library contains 100,000 volumes, 250 microform items, and 2500 audiovisual forms, and subscribes to 145 periodicals. Computerized library sources and services include the card catalog, interlibrary loans, and database searching. Special learning facilities include a Holocaust oral history archive, and a music library. The 28-acre campus is in a suburban area 4 miles north of Philadelphia. There are 6 buildings on campus. There are no residence halls.

Student Life: About 80% of undergraduates are from Pennsylvania. Students come from 3 states, 3 foreign countries, and Canada. Ninety-three percent are white. Most are Jewish.

Housing: There are no residence halls. All students commute. All students may keep cars on campus.

Activities: There are no fraternities or sororities on campus. There are some groups and organizations on campus, including chorus, dance, professional, religious, and student government.

Sports: There is no sports program at Gratz.

Disabled Students: The entire campus is accessible to disabled students. The following facilities are available: wheelchair ramps, elevators, special parking, and specially equipped rest rooms.

Services: In addition to many counseling and information services, tutoring is available in most subjects.

Campus Safety and Security: Campus safety and security measures include 24-hour foot and vehicle patrol and lighted pathways and sidewalks.

Programs of Study: Gratz awards the B.A.J.S. degree. Master's degrees also are awarded. Bachelor's degrees are awarded in SOCIAL SCIENCE (Judaic studies and religion). Jewish studies is the strongest academically. Jewish studies has the largest enrollment.

Required: All students must complete 120 semester hours including 78 in the major. Distribution requirements include biblical studies, history, Jewish literature, music and the arts, rabbinics, Jewish social science, Jewish thought, and electives. In addition, 15 hours are needed in the Hebrew language.

Special: Study abroad in Israel is available. A B.A.-B.S. degree in Jewish studies, dual majors, nondegree study, and pass/fail options for transfer students also are possible.

Faculty/Classroom: Fifty percent of faculty are male; 50%, female. All teach undergraduates. No introductory courses are taught by graduate students. The average class size in an introductory lecture is 13 and in a regular course offering, 13.

Admissions: All of the 1993-94 applicants were accepted.

Requirements: The SAT I or ACT is not required. Gratz follows an open admissions policy for all applicants who are graduates of an accredited high school or Jewish secondary day school. An essay is required for admission. The GED is accepted and students may take a series of proficiency examinations for credit. AP credits are accepted. Important factors used in the admissions decision are personality, intangible qualities, extracurricular activities record, evidence of special talent, advanced placement or honor courses, and leadership record.

Procedure: Freshmen are admitted fall and winter. Application deadlines are open. The application fee is $50. The college accepts all applicants. Notification is sent on a rolling basis. There is a deferred admissions plan.

Transfer: A total of 39 credits out of 120 must be completed at Gratz.

Visiting: There are guides for informal visits and visitors may sit in on classes. To arrange for a visit, contact the Office of Enrollment Management at (215) 635-7300.

Financial Aid: Scholarships or need-based grants averaged $875 ($1200 maximum). Ten percent of undergraduate students work part-time. The college's own financial statement is required. The deadline for financial aid applications is September 11.

International Students: There are currently 13 international students enrolled. They must take the TOEFL.

Graduates: In 1992-93 6 bachelor's degrees were awarded. The most popular major among graduates was Jewish studies (100%). Seven percent of a recent year's graduates were enrolled in graduate school within 6 months of graduation.

Admissions Contact: Naomi Zvirman, Director of Enrollment Management.

GROVE CITY COLLEGE
Grove City, PA 16127-2104

B-2

(412) 458-2100

Full-time: 1123 men, 1090 women   **Faculty:** 111
Part-time: 16 men, 19 women   **Ph.D.s:** 66%
Graduate: none   **Student/Faculty:** 20 to 1
Year: semesters   **Tuition:** $4976
Application Deadline: February 15   **Room & Board:** $2894
Freshman Class: 2491 applied, 1109 accepted, 573 enrolled
SAT I Verbal/Math: 537/607   **ACT:** 27   **HIGHLY COMPETITIVE**

Grove City College, founded in 1876, is a private, coeducational, liberal arts college affiliated with the United Presbyterian Church, USA. In addition to regional accreditation, Grove City has baccalaureate program accreditation with ABET. The library contains 169,000 volumes, 244,000 microform items, and 520 audiovisual forms, and subscribes to 1200 periodicals. Computerized library sources and services include the card catalog, interlibrary loans, and database searching. Special learning facilities include a learning resource center, art gallery, and radio station. The 150-acre campus is in a small town 60 miles north of Pittsburgh. Including residence halls, there are 27 buildings on campus.

Student Life: About 64% of undergraduates are from Pennsylvania. Students come from 37 states and 16 foreign countries. Ninety percent are from public schools; 10% from private. Ninety-seven percent are white. Seventy-seven percent are Protestant; 19% Catholic. The average age of freshmen is 17; all undergraduates, 20. Four percent drop out by the end of their first year; 80% remain to graduate.

Housing: A total of 1984 students can be accommodated in college housing. College-sponsored living facilities include single-sex dormitories. On-campus housing is guaranteed for all 4 years and is available on a lottery system for upperclassmen. Eighty-eight percent of students live on campus; of those, 90% remain on campus on weekends. Alcohol is not permitted. Upperclassmen may keep cars on campus.

Activities: About 25% of men belong to 6 local fraternities; about 50% of women belong to 9 local sororities. There are more than 100 groups on campus, including band, cheerleading, choir, chorale, chorus, computers, dance, drama, drill team, ethnic, film, honors, international, jazz band, literary magazine, marching band, musical theater, newspaper, orchestra, pep band, photography, political, professional, radio and tv, religious, social, social service, student government, symphony, and yearbook. Popular campus events include Homecoming, Parents Weekend, Christmas Candlelight Service, talent shows, and Faculty Follies.

Sports: There are 9 intercollegiate sports for men and 8 for women, and 4 intramural sports for men and 11 for women. Athletic and recreation facilities include a field house, a recreation building, 2 indoor pools, an indoor running track, 4 basketball, volleyball, or tennis courts, 8 racquetball courts, bowling lanes, a weight room, 10 outdoor tennis courts, a football stadium with a track, baseball, soccer, and softball fields, and a basketball arena.

Disabled Students: Most of the campus is accessible to disabled students. The following facilities are available: wheelchair ramps, elevators, special parking, specially equipped rest rooms, special class scheduling, lowered drinking fountains, and lowered telephones.

Services: In addition to many counseling and information services, tutoring is available in most subjects. A student tutoring program is available for a small fee.

Campus Safety and Security: Campus safety and security measures include 24-hour foot and vehicle patrol, escort service, pamphlets, posters, and films, and emergency telephones. In addition, there are lighted pathways and sidewalks.

Programs of Study: Grove City awards the B.A., B.S., B.Mus., B.S.E.E., and B.S.M.E. degrees. Bachelor's degrees are awarded in BIOLOGICAL SCIENCE (biochemistry and biology/biological science), BUSINESS (accounting, banking and finance, business administration and management, international business management, management information systems, and marketing/retailing/merchandising), COMMUNICATIONS AND THE ARTS (communications, English, French, music, music business management, music performance, and Spanish), COMPUTER AND PHYSICAL SCIENCE (chemistry, computer science, mathematics, and physics), EDUCATION (elementary, music, science, and secondary), ENGINEERING AND ENVIRONMENTAL DESIGN (electrical/electronics engineering, industrial administration/management, and mechanical engineering), HEALTH PROFESSIONS (predentistry and premedicine), SOCIAL SCIENCE (economics, history, philosophy, political science/government, prelaw, psychology, religion, and religious music). Business, engineering, accounting, and education are the strongest programs academically and have the largest enrollments.

Required: Students are required to complete a minimum of 128 credit hours (136 for engineering students). All students must complete the 38 semester-hour general education curriculum, which includes 18 hours of humanities, 8 of natural science, and 6 each of social science and quantitative and logical reasoning, 2 hours in physical education, and 4 chapel credits. A minimum GPA of 2.0 is required.

Special: Grove City offers study abroad, summer internships, 3 accelerated degree programs, student-designed interdisciplinary majors, nondegree study for special students, and a Washington semester. There are 9 national honor societies on campus. Sixteen departments have honors programs.

Faculty/Classroom: Seventy-five percent of faculty are male; 25%, female. All teach undergraduates and 20% both teach and do research. The average class size in an introductory lecture is 65; in a laboratory, 35; and in a regular course offering, 35.

Admissions: About 45% of the 1993–94 applicants were accepted. The SAT scores for the 1993–94 freshman class were as follows: Verbal—28% below 500, 52% between 500 and 599, 18% between 600 and 700, and 2% above 700; Math—7% below 500, 35% between 500 and 599, 45% between 600 and 700, and 13% above 700. The ACT scores were 4% below 21, 16% between 21 and 23, 28% between 24 and 26, 22% between 27 and 28, and 30% above 28. About 81% of the current freshmen were in the top fifth of their class; 92% were in the top two fifths. There were 9 National Merit finalists. About 47 freshmen graduated first in their class.

Requirements: The SAT I or ACT is required. The academic or college preparatory course is highly recommended, including 4 units each of English, history, mathematics, science, and a foreign language. An essay is required of all applicants, and an audition is required of music students. An interview is recommended. AP and CLEP credits are accepted. Important factors used in the admissions decision are advanced placement or honor courses, leadership record, extracurricular activities record, evidence of special talent, and parents or siblings attending the school.

Procedure: Freshmen are admitted fall and spring. Entrance exams should be taken in the spring of the junior year or the fall of the senior year. Early decision applications should be filed by November 15; regular applications, by February 15 for fall entry and January 1 for spring entry, along with an application fee of $20. Notification of early decision is sent December 10; regular decision, March 15. There are early decision, early admissions, and deferred admissions plans. About 322 early decision candidates were accepted for the 1993–94 class. A waiting list is an active part of the admissions procedure, with about 37% of applicants on the list.

Transfer: About 36 transfer students enrolled in 1993–94. Transfer students should have a minimum of 17 credit hours earned with a 2.0 minimum GPA. Either the SAT I or the ACT is recommended, as is an interview. A total of 32 credits out of 128 must be completed at Grove City.

Visiting: There are regularly scheduled orientations for prospective students, consisting of daily interviews and tours, 3 high school visitation days in the fall, and a career day in the spring. There are science and engineering open houses in the fall and spring. There are guides for informal visits and visitors may sit in on classes and stay overnight at the school. To arrange for a visit, contact the Admissions Office at (412) 458-2100.

Financial Aid: In 1993–94 54% of all current freshmen and 49% of continuing students received some form of financial aid. About 38% of freshmen and 35% of continuing students received need-based aid. The average freshman award was $3994. Of that total, scholarships or need-based grants averaged $2328 ($9700 maximum); loans averaged $3208 ($7870 maximum); and work contracts averaged $500 ($1000 maximum). Thirty-five percent of undergraduate students work part-time. Average earnings from campus work for the school year was $534. The average financial indebtedness of the 1992–93 graduate was $9399. Grove City is a member of CSS. The FAF, the college's own financial statement, and FAFSA are required. The deadline for financial aid applications is May 1.

International Students: There are currently 28 international students enrolled. The school actively recruits these students. They must take the TOEFL and achieve a minimum score of 550. If the TOEFL is not available, either the SAT I or the ACT is required.

Computers: The college provides computer facilities for student use. The mainframe is a DEC VAX 6250. The technological learning center houses 135 microcomputers and terminal stations, and a room for the mainframe. All students may access the system. It may be used open 7:45 A.M. to 11 P.M., Monday through Friday; 7:45 A.M. to 5 P.M., Saturday; and 2 P.M. to 11 P.M., Sunday. There are no time limits on using the system and no fees.

Graduates: In 1992–93 454 bachelor's degrees were awarded. The most popular majors among graduates were business administration (14%), elementary education (11%), and engineering, electrical/mechanical (11%). Within an average freshman class, 71% graduate in 4 years, 78% in 5 years, and 79% in 6 years. Some 59 companies

recruited on campus in 1992–93. In the 1992 graduating class, 14% of the graduates were enrolled in graduate school within 6 months of graduation; 67% had found employment.

Admissions Contact: Jeffrey C. Mincey, Director of Admissions.

GWYNEDD-MERCY COLLEGE
F-4
Gwynedd Valley, PA 19437
(215) 641-5510
(800) DIAL-GMC (out-of-state)

Full-time: 136 men, 580 women	**Faculty:** 86; IIB, --$
Part-time: 215 men, 893 women	**Ph.D.s:** 29%
Graduate: 10 men, 152 women	**Student/Faculty:** 8 to 1
Year: semesters, summer session	**Tuition:** $10,200
Application Deadline: open	**Room & Board:** $5250
Freshman Class: 491 applied, 247 accepted, 104 enrolled	
SAT I Verbal/Math: 470/500	**COMPETITIVE**

Gwynedd-Mercy College, founded in 1948, is a private, coeducational liberal arts and sciences college affiliated with the Roman Catholic Church. There are 9 undergraduate and 2 graduate schools. In addition to regional accreditation, Gwynedd-Mercy has baccalaureate program accreditation with CAHEA and NLN. The library contains 91,000 volumes, 84 microform items, and 5918 audiovisual forms, and subscribes to 798 periodicals. Special learning facilities include a center for creative studies and a laboratory school for education majors. The 170-acre campus is in a suburban area 20 miles northwest of Philadelphia. Including residence halls, there are 15 buildings on campus.

Student Life: About 94% of undergraduates are from Pennsylvania. Students come from 5 states, 23 foreign countries, and Canada. Forty-five percent are from public schools; 55% from private. Ninety percent are white. Fifty-nine percent are Catholic; 22% Protestant. The average age of freshmen is 24; all undergraduates, 29. About 85% of freshmen remain to graduate.

Housing: A total of 164 students can be accommodated in college housing. College-sponsored living facilities include coed dormitories. On-campus housing is available on a first-come, first-served basis. Ninety-two percent of students commute. Alcohol is not permitted. All students may keep cars on campus.

Activities: There are no fraternities or sororities on campus. There are 21 groups on campus, including choir, chorus, drama, honors, international, literary magazine, newspaper, professional, religious, social, social service, student government, and yearbook. Popular campus events include Family Day, Carol Night, and International Night.

Sports: There are 4 intercollegiate sports for men and 6 for women, and 2 intramural sports each for men and women. Athletic and recreation facilities include a wellness recreation center/gymnasium, including a racquetball court, a weight room, an aerobics room, an outdoor pool, and a jogging trail.

Disabled Students: The entire campus is accessible to disabled students. The following facilities are available: wheelchair ramps, elevators, special parking, specially equipped rest rooms, and special class scheduling.

Services: In addition to many counseling and information services, tutoring is available in some subjects, including sciences. In addition, there is remedial math, reading, and writing. Tutoring is made available in conjunction with student needs.

Campus Safety and Security: Campus safety and security measures include 24-hour foot and vehicle patrol, emergency telephones, and lighted pathways and sidewalks.

Programs of Study: Gwynedd-Mercy awards the B.A., B.S., and B.H.S. degrees. Associate and master's degrees also are awarded. Bachelor's degrees are awarded in BIOLOGICAL SCIENCE (biology/biological science), BUSINESS (accounting and business administration and management), COMMUNICATIONS AND THE ARTS (English), COMPUTER AND PHYSICAL SCIENCE (computer mathematics, information sciences and systems, and mathematics), EDUCATION (business, early childhood, elementary, English, mathematics, science, secondary, social studies, and special), HEALTH PROFESSIONS (health science, medical laboratory technology, nursing, and premedicine), SOCIAL SCIENCE (gerontology, history, psychology, and sociology). Nursing, biology, medical technology, and education are the strongest academically. Nursing, business, and education have the largest enrollments.

Required: All students must complete at least 125 credit hours, including courses in language, literature and fine arts, behavioral and social sciences, humanities, and natural science. Specific courses in English composition, literature, philosophy, and religious studies are required. The total number of hours required in the major is 60. Students must maintain a minimum GPA of 2.0.

Special: The college offers internships, dual majors, B.A.-B.S. degrees, and pass/fail options. All programs require or have the option for hands-on experiences. There is a 3–1 program in medical technology available. There are 4 national honor societies on campus. Three departments have honors programs.

Faculty/Classroom: Twenty-seven percent of faculty are male; 73%, female. Ninety-three percent teach undergraduates. The average class size in an introductory lecture is 25; in a laboratory, 15; and in a regular course offering, 25.

Admissions: About 50% of the 1993–94 applicants were accepted. The SAT scores for the 1993–94 freshman class were as follows: Verbal—69% below 500, 23% between 500 and 599, 7% between 600 and 700, and 1% above 700; Math—57% below 500, 32% between 500 and 599, 10% between 600 and 700, and 1% above 700. About 38% of the current freshmen were in the top fifth of their class; 82% were in the top two fifths.

Requirements: Gwynedd-Mercy requires applicants to be in the upper 50% of their class. A minimum GPA of 2.0 is required. The SAT I or ACT is required. Candidates for admission must be graduates of accredited secondary schools and have completed 16 academic credits/Carnegie units, including 4 credits in English, 2 in a foreign language, 1 in history, and 3 each in mathematics, science, and college preparatory electives. The GED is accepted. An interview is recommended for all candidates and is required for some programs. AP and CLEP credits are accepted. Important factors used in the admissions decision are advanced placement or honor courses, parents or siblings attending the school, recommendations by alumni, recommendations by school officials, and leadership record.

Procedure: Freshmen are admitted fall and spring. Entrance exams should be taken in the spring of the junior year or the fall of the senior year. Application deadlines are open. Application fee is $25. Notification is sent on a rolling basis. There is a deferred admissions plan. A waiting list is an active part of the admissions procedure, with about 10% of applicants on the list.

Transfer: About 430 transfer students enrolled in 1993–94. Neither the SAT I nor the ACT is required for transfer students out of high school for 2 or more years. A minimum GPA of 2.0 is necessary; some programs require a higher GPA. An interview is recommended. A total of 60 credits out of 125 must be completed at Gwynedd-Mercy.

Visiting: There are regularly scheduled orientations for prospective students, consisting of open houses with formal presentations, campus tours, and class days with class visitations. There are guides for informal visits and visitors may stay overnight at the school. To arrange for a visit, contact the Admissions Office at (215) 641–5510.

Financial Aid: In 1993–94 75% of all current freshmen and 88% of continuing students received some form of financial aid. About 65% of freshmen and 68% of continuing students received need-based aid. The average freshman award was $11,225. Of that total, scholarships or need-based grants averaged $7600 ($12,060 maximum); loans averaged $2625 ($5125 maximum); and work contracts averaged $1000 ($1300 maximum). Almost all undergraduate students work part-time. Average earnings from campus work for the school year are $873. The average financial indebtedness of the 1992–93 graduate was $8167. Gwynedd-Mercy is a member of CSS. The FAF, the college's own financial statement, and the FAFSA are required. The deadline for financial aid applications is March 15.

International Students: There are currently 52 international students enrolled. They must take the TOEFL or the University of Michigan Language Test and achieve a minimum score on the TOEFL of 500.

Computers: The college provides computer facilities for student use. There are 12 IBM PS/2 Model 25s networked to an IBM PS/2 Model 80. Students use the networked system in the computer laboratory for BASIC, COBOL, Assembler, and other applications programs. Those students enrolled in computer laboratory courses. may access the system. It may be accessed more than 75 hours a week. There are no time limits on using the system. The fees are $40 per course for the computer laboratory.

Graduates: In 1992–93, 218 bachelor's degrees were awarded. The most popular majors among graduates were nursing (33%), business administration (17%), and elementary education (12%). Within an average freshman class, 68% graduate in 4 years and 80% in 5 years. Some 50 companies recruited on campus in 1992–93.

Admissions Contact: Marjorie S. DeSimone, Dean of Admissions.

HAVERFORD COLLEGE
E-4
Haverford, PA 19041-1392
(610) 896-1350

Full-time: 563 men, 521 women	**Faculty:** 97; IIB, + +$
Part-time: none	**Ph.D.s:** 97%
Graduate: none	**Student/Faculty:** 11 to 1
Year: semesters	**Tuition:** $18,000
Application Deadline: January 15	**Room & Board:** $5950
Freshman Class: 2128 applied, 927 accepted, 294 enrolled	
SAT I: required	**MOST COMPETITIVE**

Haverford College, founded in 1833, is a private, coeducational liberal arts college. The 5 libraries contain 425,000 volumes, 67,000 microform items, and 6600 audiovisual forms, and subscribe to 1383 periodicals. Computerized library sources and services include the card catalog, interlibrary loans, and database searching. Special

learning facilities include an art gallery, radio station, observatory, and arboretum. The 216-acre campus is in a suburban area 10 miles west of Philadelphia. Including residence halls, there are 70 buildings on campus.

Student Life: About 84% of undergraduates are from out-of-state, mostly the Middle Atlantic. Students come from 44 states, 17 foreign countries, and Canada. Sixty percent are from public schools; 40% from private. Eighty-two percent are white. The average age of all undergraduates is 19. Two percent drop out by the end of their first year; 91% remain to graduate.

Housing: A total of 1100 students can be accommodated in college housing. College-sponsored living facilities include single-sex and coed dormitories and on-campus apartments. In addition there are language houses, special interest houses, and Haverford students may live at Bryn Mawr College through a dormitory exchange program. On-campus housing is guaranteed for all 4 years. Ninety-six percent of students live on campus; of those, 90% remain on campus on weekends. Upperclassmen may keep cars on campus.

Activities: There are no fraternities or sororities. There are more than 75 groups on campus, including chorale, dance, drama, ethnic, gay, international, jazz band, literary magazine, musical theater, newspaper, orchestra, political, radio and tv, religious, social service, student government, and yearbook. Popular campus events include Swarthmore Weekend, LaFiesta, Haverfest, and Snowball.

Sports: There are 11 intercollegiate sports for men and women, and 6 co-ed intramural sports. Athletic and recreation facilities include a field house with an indoor track, tennis, squash, and basketball courts, extensive outdoor fields, and a new 400-meter, 8-lane, all-weather track.

Disabled Students: Thirty percent of the campus is accessible to disabled students. The following facilities are available: wheelchair ramps, elevators, special parking, specially equipped rest rooms, special class scheduling, and reasonable accomodation.

Services: In addition to many counseling and information services, tutoring is available in every subject.

Campus Safety and Security: Campus safety and security measures include 24-hour foot and vehicle patrol, escort service, shuttle buses, and informal discussions. In addition, there are pamphlets, posters, and films, emergency telephones, lighted pathways and sidewalks, and a fire safety program.

Programs of Study: Haverford awards the B.A. and B.S. degrees. Bachelor's degrees are awarded in BIOLOGICAL SCIENCE (biology/biological science), COMMUNICATIONS AND THE ARTS (art history and appreciation, classics, comparative literature, English, fine arts, French, German, Italian, music, Russian, and Spanish), COMPUTER AND PHYSICAL SCIENCE (astronomy, chemistry, geology, mathematics, and physics), SOCIAL SCIENCE (anthropology, archeology, East Asian studies, economics, history, philosophy, political science/government, psychology, religion, sociology, and urban studies). Natural and physical sciences are the strongest academically. History, English, biology, economics, political science, and psychology have the largest enrollments.

Required: All students must take a minimum of 32 course credits, including freshman writing and 3 courses each in social science, natural science, and the humanities. One of the distribution courses must be quantitative and 1 must meet the social justice requirement. Students must also take 3 semesters of physical education and demonstrate proficiency in a foreign language. Students must take a minimum of 6 courses in the major and 6 in related fields. Each major includes a capstone experience (a comprehensive examination, thesis, or advanced project, a specially-designed course, or some combination), which varies by department.

Special: Haverford offers internship programs, cross-registration with Bryn Mawr College, Swarthmore College, and the University of Pennsylvania, study abroad in 29 countries, dual majors, student-designed majors, and a 3–2 engineering degree with the University of Pennsylvania. Pass/fail options are limited to 4 in 4 years. There is a chapter of Phi Beta Kappa on campus. Twenty-seven departments have honors programs.

Faculty/Classroom: Sixty percent of faculty are male; 40%, female. All teach undergraduates, and most do research. The average class size in an introductory lecture is 35; in a laboratory, 16; and in a regular course offering, 17.

Admissions: About 44% of the 1993–94 applicants were accepted. The SAT scores for the 1993–94 freshman class were as follows: Verbal—5% below 500, 24% between 500 and 599, 58% between 600 and 700, and 13% above 700; Math—3% below 500, 11% between 500 and 599, 47% between 600 and 700, and 39% above 700. About 97% of the current freshmen were in the top fifth of their class; 100% were in the top two fifths.

Requirements: The SAT I is required. The SAT II: Writing test plus 2 others are also required. Candidates for admission must be graduates of an accredited secondary school and have taken 4 courses in English, 3 each in a foreign language, and mathematics, and 1 each in science and history. The GED is accepted. An essay is required

and an interview is recommended. AP credits are accepted. Important factors used in the admissions decision are advanced placement or honor courses, leadership record, recommendations by school officials, personality, intangible qualities, and evidence of special talent.

Procedure: Freshmen are admitted in the fall. Entrance exams should be taken before January 15. Early decision applications should be filed by November 15; regular applications, by January 15 for fall entry, along with an application fee of $45. Notification of early decision is sent December 15; regular decision, by April 15. There are early decision, early admissions, and deferred admissions plans. About 59 early decision candidates were accepted for the 1993–94 class. A waiting list is an active part of the admissions procedure, with about 15% of applicants on the list.

Transfer: Two transfer students enrolled in 1993–94. Transfer students must be able to enter the sophomore or junior class. Admission depends mainly on college grades. A minimum GPA of 3.0 is necessary and the SAT I is recommended. Thirty minimum credit hours or the equivalent of 1 year of courses must have been earned. A liberal arts curriculum is also recommended. A total of 16 credits out of 32 must be completed at Haverford.

Visiting: There are guides for informal visits and visitors may sit in on classes and stay overnight at the school. To arrange for a visit, contact the Admissions Office at (610) 896–1350.

Financial Aid: In 1993–94, 45% of all students received some form of financial aid, including need-based aid. The average freshman award was $16,197. Of that total, scholarships or need-based grants averaged $11,480; loans averaged $2126; and work contracts averaged $1226. Haverford is a member of CSS. The FAF, the college's own financial statement, and FAFSA are required. The deadline for financial aid applications is January 31.

International Students: There are currently 28 international students enrolled. The school actively recruits these students. They must take the TOEFL and achieve a minimum score of 600. The student must also take the SAT I.

Computers: The college provides computer facilities for student use. The mainframe is a Sun SPARCstation with distributed servers. There are approximately 80 publicly accessible Macintosh and IBM-compatible PCs available in 3 computer laboratories and in the library. There are special-purpose computing laboratories available to students in the physical sciences, biology, psychology, and mathematics/computer science. Every student has a Unix that allows use of the Unix systems on campus and the Internet. All publicly-accessible computers are networked, as are some of the dormitory rooms. All students may access the system. There are no time limits on using the system and no fees.

Graduates: In 1992–93, 298 bachelor's degrees were awarded. The most popular majors among graduates were political science (13%), biology (13%), and English (12%). Within an average freshman class, 89% graduate in 4 years, and 5% in 5 or 6 years. Some 34 companies recruited on campus in 1992–93. In the 1992 graduating class, 29% of the students were enrolled in graduate school within 6 months of graduation; 58% had found employment.

Admissions Contact: Delsie Z. Phillips, Director of Admissions.

HOLY FAMILY COLLEGE

F-3

Philadelphia, PA 19114   **(215) 637–3050**

Full-time: 282 men, 863 women	**Faculty:** 83; IIB, -$
Part-time: 261 men, 798 women	**Ph.D.s:** 42%
Graduate: 58 men, 194 women	**Student/Faculty:** 14 to 1
Year: semesters, summer session	**Tuition:** $8300
Application Deadline: July 1	**Room & Board:** n/app
Freshman Class: 622 applied, 354 accepted, 169 enrolled	
SAT I Verbal/Math: 427/456	**COMPETITIVE**

Holy Family College, established in 1954, is a private, nonresidential liberal arts institution affiliated with the Roman Catholic Church. In addition to regional accreditation, Holy Family has baccalaureate program accreditation with AACSB, CSWE, and NLN. The library contains 110,332 volumes and 1273 microform items, and subscribes to 509 periodicals. Computerized library sources and services include database searching. Special learning facilities include a radio station. The 46-acre campus is in a suburban area. There are 7 buildings on campus. There are no residence halls.

Student Life: About 96% of undergraduates are from Pennsylvania. Students come from 4 states and 8 foreign countries. Twenty-one percent are from public schools; 79% from private. Ninety-four percent are white. The average age of freshmen is 19; all undergraduates, 22. Sixteen percent drop out by the end of their first year; 55% remain to graduate.

Housing: There are no residence halls. All students commute. Alcohol is not permitted. All students may keep cars on campus.

Activities: There are no fraternities or sororities on campus. There are many groups and organizations on campus, including cheerleading, choir, drama, honors, international, newspaper, professional, religious, social service, student government, and yearbook.

Sports: There are 2 intercollegiate sports for men and 2 for women, and 3 intramural sports for men and 3 for women. Athletic and recreation facilities include a gymnasium, a weight room, and racquetball courts.

Disabled Students: The entire campus is accessible to disabled students. The following facilities are available: wheelchair ramps, elevators, special parking, specially equipped rest rooms, lowered drinking fountains, and lowered telephones.

Services: In addition to many counseling and information services, tutoring is available in some subjects. There is remedial math and writing.

Campus Safety and Security: Campus safety and security measures include 24-hour foot and vehicle patrol and lighted pathways and sidewalks.

Programs of Study: Holy Family awards the B.A., B.S., and B.S.N. degrees. Associate and master's degrees also are offered. Bachelor's degrees are awarded in BIOLOGICAL SCIENCE (biochemistry and biology/biological science), BUSINESS (accounting, business administration and management, international business management, and marketing/retailing/merchandising), COMMUNICATIONS AND THE ARTS (communications, English, fine arts, French, and Spanish), COMPUTER AND PHYSICAL SCIENCE (chemistry, information sciences and systems, and mathematics), EDUCATION (early childhood, elementary, foreign languages, science, secondary, and special), HEALTH PROFESSIONS (medical laboratory technology, nursing, predentistry, and premedicine), SOCIAL SCIENCE (criminal justice, economics, history, philosophy, prelaw, psychology, religion, social science, social work, and sociology). Nursing, elementary education, and accounting are the strongest academically. Nursing, education, and business have the largest enrollments.

Required: Students must complete 120 to 130 semester hours, including at least 30 in the major, with a minimum GPA of 2.0. Nursing, medical technology, and education majors must maintain a GPA of 2.5. Specific discipline requirements include English, science, mathematics, and philosophy. A core curriculum of communication, quantification, philosophy, humanities, and social science must be fulfilled. All majors require satisfactory performance on a comprehensive examination.

Special: Opportunities are provided for co-op programs in business and criminal justice, internships in English and social sciences, study abroad, work-study programs with 11 companies, a B.A.-B.S. degree, an accelerated degree program, credit by examination, nondegree study, and pass/fail options. Students may pursue dual majors in business and French, business and Spanish, and elementary and special education. There is a freshman honors program on campus, as well as 10 national honor societies. Two departments have honors programs.

Faculty/Classroom: Thirty-four percent of faculty are male; 66%, female. All teach undergraduates and 33% both teach and do research. No introductory courses are taught by graduate students. The average class size in an introductory lecture is 25; in a laboratory, 16; and in a regular course offering, 21.

Admissions: About 57% of the 1993–94 applicants were accepted. About 26% of the current freshmen were in the top fifth of their class; 63% were in the top two fifths. Four freshmen graduated first in their class.

Requirements: The SAT I or ACT is required. Graduation from an accredited secondary school is required; a GED will be accepted. Applicants must submit 16 academic credits, including 4 courses in English, 3 in history, 2 each in mathematics, a foreign language, and science, 1 in social studies, and the remainder in other academic electives. AP and CLEP credits are accepted. Important factors used in the admissions decision are recommendations by school officials, recommendations by alumni, personality, intangible qualities, geographic diversity, and leadership record.

Procedure: Freshmen are admitted to all sessions. Entrance exams should be taken by October or November of the senior year. Early decision applications should be filed by December 1; regular applications, by July 1 for fall entry and January 2 for spring entry, along with an application fee of $25. Notification of early decision is sent January 7; regular decision, on a rolling basis. There are early decision, early admissions, and deferred admissions plans. About 18 early decision candidates were accepted for the 1993–94 class.

Transfer: About 163 transfer students enrolled in 1993–94. Applicants must submit official transcripts from all previous colleges. Grades of D are not transferable. A maximum of 75 credits will be accepted for transfer. A total of 45 credits out of 120 must be completed at Holy Family.

Visiting: There are regularly scheduled orientations for prospective students, consisting of an interview and a tour. There are guides for informal visits and visitors may sit in on classes. To arrange for a visit, contact the Office of Admissions at (215) 637-3050.

Financial Aid: In 1993–94, about 84% of all students received some form of financial aid, including need-based aid. The average freshman award was $2650. Of that total, scholarships or need-based grants averaged $500 ($4000 maximum); loans averaged $2625; and work contracts averaged $200 ($1000 maximum). All undergraduate students work part-time. Average earnings from campus work for the school year are $200. The average financial indebtedness of the 1992–93 graduate was $7000. Holy Family is a member of CSS. The deadline for financial aid applications is May 1.

International Students: There are currently 9 international students enrolled. They must take the TOEFL and achieve a minimum score of 530.

Computers: The college provides computer facilities for student use. There are 60 microcomputers in 3 laboratories available for student use. All students may access the system. It may be used weekdays, 8:30 A.M. to 9 P.M., Saturday and Sunday, noon to 5 P.M. There are no time limits on using the system and no fees.

Graduates: In 1992–93 301 bachelor's degrees were awarded. The most popular majors among graduates were elementary (21%), nursing (21%), and management (9%). Within an average freshman class, 11% graduate in 3 years, 55% in 4 years, 67% in 5 years, and 71% in 6 years. Some 92 companies recruited on campus in 1992–93. In the 1992 graduating class, 7% of the men and 11% of the women were enrolled in graduate school within 6 months of graduation; 51% of the men and 62% of the women had found employment.

Admissions Contact: Dr. Mott R. Linn, Director of Admissions.

IMMACULATA COLLEGE
E-4
Immaculata, PA 19345 (610) 647-4400, ext. 3015

Full-time: 15 men, 479 women	Faculty: 58; IIB, av$
Part-time: 201 men, 1104 women	Ph.D.s: 59%
Graduate: 80 men, 467 women	Student/Faculty: 9 to 1
Year: semesters, summer session	Tuition: $9610
Application Deadline: May 1	Room & Board: $5010
Freshman Class: 268 applied, 253 accepted, 101 enrolled	
SAT I Verbal/Math: 440/450	**COMPETITIVE**

Immaculata College, founded in 1920, is a private, primarily women's liberal arts and teacher preparation college affiliated with the Roman Catholic Church. There is one undergraduate and one graduate school. In addition to regional accreditation, Immaculata has baccalaureate program accreditation with ADA, AHEA, NASM, and NLN. The library contains 160,000 volumes, 6500 microform items, and 3100 audiovisual forms, and subscribes to 650 periodicals. Computerized library sources and services include the card catalog, interlibrary loans, and database searching. The 400-acre campus is in a suburban area 20 miles west of Philadelphia. Including residence halls, there are 13 buildings on campus.

Student Life: About 87% of undergraduates are from Pennsylvania. Students come from 15 states and 26 foreign countries. Seventy-five percent are from public schools; 25% from private. Ninety percent are white. Seventy-seven percent are Catholic; 15% Protestant. The average age of freshmen is 18; all undergraduates, 26. Twelve percent drop out by the end of their first year; 72% remain to graduate.

Housing: A total of 500 students can be accommodated in college housing. College-sponsored living facilities include single-sex dormitories. On-campus housing is guaranteed for all 4 years. Seventy-nine percent of students commute. Alcohol is not permitted. All students may keep cars on campus.

Activities: There are no fraternities or sororities on campus. There are 30 groups on campus, including art, choir, chorale, chorus, computers, dance, drama, ethnic, honors, international, literary magazine, musical theater, newspaper, orchestra, photography, political, professional, religious, social, social service, student government, and yearbook. Popular campus events include Rose Arbor Dinner, Investiture, college orchestra and chorus performances, Friday's Pub, Variety show, Ring Dance, plays, Christmas dance, and Carol Night.

Sports: There are 5 intercollegiate sports for women and 10 intramural sports for women. Athletic and recreation facilities include Tennis courts, a full gymnasium, a handball gymnasium, an Olympic-size swimming pool, hockey and softball fields, and a weight room.

Disabled Students: Ninety-five percent of the campus is accessible to disabled students. The following facilities are available: wheelchair ramps, elevators, special parking, specially equipped rest rooms, special class scheduling, lowered drinking fountains, and lowered telephones.

Services: In addition to many counseling and information services, tutoring is available in most subjects. In addition, there is a reader service for the blind, and remedial math, reading, and writing.

Campus Safety and Security: Campus safety and security measures include 24-hour foot and vehicle patrol, self-defense education, informal discussions, and pamphlets, posters, and films. In addition, there are lighted pathways and sidewalks.

Programs of Study: Immaculata awards the B.A., B.S., B.Mus., and B.S.N. degrees. Associate, master's, and doctoral degrees also are awarded. Bachelor's degrees are awarded in BIOLOGICAL SCIENCE (biochemistry and biology/biological science), BUSINESS (accounting, business administration and management, and fashion mer-

chandising), COMMUNICATIONS AND THE ARTS (English, French, German, music, and Spanish), COMPUTER AND PHYSICAL SCIENCE (chemistry, information sciences and systems, and mathematics), EDUCATION (early childhood, elementary, foreign languages, home economics, middle school, music, science, and secondary), HEALTH PROFESSIONS (nursing and premedicine), SOCIAL SCIENCE (dietetics, economics, food science, history, international relations, prelaw, psychology, social science, and sociology).

Required: To graduate, all students must complete 54 credits in liberal arts, including distribution requirements in humanities, social sciences, and sciences. Students must take a minimum of 126 credits, including 36 to 52 in the major. Six credits of physical education are also required. The college requires a minimum GPA of 2.0. A thesis, which is the outcome of a required senior seminar, is also required. Internships are required for dietetics, music therapy, and education.

Special: All majors offer opportunities for internships, and most require them. Students may study abroad in 6 countries. The college offers dual-major combinations, student-designed majors, nondegree study, and pass/fail options. There is a freshman honors program on campus, as well as 14 national honor societies. Twelve departments have honors programs.

Faculty/Classroom: Thirty-two percent of faculty are male; 68%, female. Eighty-six percent teach undergraduates and 4% both teach and do research. No introductory courses are taught by graduate students. The average class size in an introductory lecture is 35; in a laboratory, 16; and in a regular course offering, 20.

Admissions: About 94% of the 1993–94 applicants were accepted. About 31% of the current freshmen were in the top fifth of their class; 59% were in the top two fifths. About 20 freshmen graduated first in their class.

Requirements: A minimum GPA of 2.3 is required. The SAT I is required, with a minimum composite score of 800, 400 verbal and 400 mathematics. Candidates for admissions should be graduates of an accredited secondary school with a minimum of 16 academic credits, including 4 in English, 2 each in a foreign language, mathematics, science, and social studies, 1 in history, and 3 more in college preparatory courses. The GED is accepted. An audition is required for music students and an essay and an interview are recommended for all. AP and CLEP credits are accepted. Important factors used in the admissions decision are recommendations by school officials, leadership record, geographic diversity, extracurricular activities record, and advanced placement or honor courses.

Procedure: Freshmen are admitted fall and spring. Entrance exams should be taken in the spring of the junior year. Early decision applications should be filed by November 1; regular applications, by May 1 for fall entry and November 1 for spring entry, along with an application fee of $25. Notification of early decision is sent December 1; regular decision, on a rolling basis. There are early decision, early admissions, and deferred admissions plans. About 40 early decision candidates were accepted for the 1993–94 class.

Transfer: About 55 transfer students enrolled in a recent year. In addition to high school credentials, transfer applicants must present college transcripts. Courses in which the student has achieved a C or better are accepted if they are comparable to Immaculata's courses. A minimum composite score of 800 in the SAT I is required, as is an interview. Students must have a minimum GPA of 2.0. A total of 36 credits out of 126 must be completed at Immaculata.

Visiting: There are regularly scheduled orientations for prospective students, including an open house and class visitation. There are guides for informal visits and visitors may sit in on classes and stay overnight at the school. To arrange for a visit, contact the Office of Admission at (610) 647–4400.

Financial Aid: In a recent year, 82% of all current freshmen and 79% of continuing students received some form of financial aid. About 81% of freshmen and 77% of continuing students received need-based aid. The average freshman award was $4100. Of that total, scholarships or need-based grants averaged $2900 ($6000 maximum); loans averaged $2500 ($4000 maximum); and work contracts averaged $750 ($1000 maximum). Most undergraduate students work part-time. Average earnings from campus work for the school year are $1000. The average financial indebtedness of the recent year's graduate was $9000. Immaculata is a member of CSS. The PHEAA financial statement is required. The deadline for financial aid applications is April 1.

International Students: There are currently 81 international students enrolled. The school actively recruits these students. They must take the TOEFL and achieve a minimum score of 550.

Computers: The college provides computer facilities for student use. The mainframe is an HP. Students may use the networked computer terminals in the administrative offices, computer center, and library. Those students assisting in offices may access the system. It may be used during office hours. There are no time limits on using the system and no fees.

Graduates: In 1992–93, 191 bachelor's degrees were awarded. The most popular majors among graduates were psychology (17%), English (15%), and economics (12%). Within an average freshman class, 1% graduate in 3 years, 71% in 4 years, 3% in 5 years, and 4% in 6 years. Some 23 companies recruited on campus in 1992–93. In a recent graduating class, 2% of the men and 26% of the women were enrolled in graduate school within 6 months of graduation; 95% of the men and 77% of the women had found employment.

Admissions Contact: James P. Sullivan, Director of Admission.

INDIANA UNIVERSITY OF PENNSYLVANIA   B-3

Indiana, PA 15705	(412) 357–2230; (800) 357–2230 (in-state)
Full-time: 5041 men, 6334 women	Faculty: 649; IIA, +$
Part-time: 488 men, 644 women	Ph.D.s: 76%
Graduate: 594 men, 961 women	Student/Faculty: 18 to 1
Year: semesters, summer session	Tuition: $3539 ($7937)
Application Deadline: December 31	Room & Board: $2834
Freshman Class: 6373 applied, 3264 accepted, 1625 enrolled	
SAT I Verbal/Math: 444/495	COMPETITIVE

Indiana University of Pennsylvania, founded in 1875, is a public, coeducational member of the Pennsylvania State System of Higher Education offering programs in liberal and fine arts, business, preengineering, health science, military science, teacher preparation, basic and applied science, social science and humanities, criminology, and safety science. There are 6 undergraduate schools and one graduate school. In addition to regional accreditation, IUP has baccalaureate program accreditation with AHEA, CAHEA, NASM, NCATE, and NLN. The library contains 731,871 volumes, and subscribes to 4500 periodicals. Computerized library sources and services include the card catalog, interlibrary loans, and database searching. Special learning facilities include a learning resource center, an art gallery, a planetarium, a radio station, and a TV station. The 200-acre campus is in a small town 50 miles northeast of Pittsburgh. Including residence halls, there are 75 buildings on campus.

Student Life: About 96% of undergraduates are from Pennsylvania. Students come from 36 states, 69 foreign countries, and Canada. Ninety-one percent are from public schools. Ninety percent are white. The average age of freshmen is 18; all undergraduates, 20. Thirteen percent drop out by the end of their first year; 75% remain to graduate.

Housing: A total of 4300 students can be accommodated in college housing. College-sponsored living facilities include single-sex and coed dormitories and on-campus apartments. In addition, there are honors houses and honors floors, 24-hour intensified study floors, and an international house. On-campus housing is guaranteed for the freshman year only and is available on a lottery system for upperclassmen. Sixty-seven percent of students commute. Alcohol is not permitted.

Activities: About 20% of men belong to 5 local and 17 national fraternities; about 15% of women belong to 3 local and 13 national sororities. There are 180 groups on campus, including band, cheerleading, choir, chorale, chorus, computers, dance, drama, ethnic, film, gay, honors, international, jazz band, marching band, musical theater, newspaper, opera, orchestra, pep band, political, professional, radio and TV, religious, social, social service, student government, symphony, and yearbook. Popular campus events include Homecoming, Parents Weekend, Artist Series, and Diversity Day.

Sports: There are 9 intercollegiate sports each for men and women, and 25 intramural sports for men and 20 for women. Athletic and recreation facilities include a 7600-seat stadium, swimming pools, a fitness trail, softball fields, and courts for tennis, badminton, handball/racquetball, basketball, and volleyball.

Disabled Students: Fifty-five percent of the campus is accessible to disabled students. The following facilities are available: wheelchair ramps, elevators, special parking, specially equipped rest rooms, special class scheduling, and lowered drinking fountains.

Services: In addition to many counseling and information services, tutoring is available in some subjects. In addition, there is a reader service for the blind, and remedial math, reading, and writing.

Campus Safety and Security: Campus safety and security measures include 24-hour foot and vehicle patrol, escort service, informal discussions, and pamphlets, posters, and films. In addition, there are emergency telephones and lighted pathways and sidewalks.

Programs of Study: IUP awards the B.A., B.S., B.F.A., and B.S.Ed. degrees. Associate, master's, and doctoral degrees also are awarded. Bachelor's degrees are awarded in BIOLOGICAL SCIENCE (biology/biological science), BUSINESS (business administration and management, hotel/motel and restaurant management, and marketing/retailing/merchandising), COMMUNICATIONS AND THE ARTS (communications, dramatic arts, dramatic arts, English, fine arts, French, German, journalism, music, and Spanish), COMPUTER AND PHYSICAL SCIENCE (chemistry, computer science, earth science, geology, geoscience, mathematics, and physics), EDUCATION (art, business, early childhood, education, elementary, health, home

economics, marketing and distribution, mathematics, music, nutrition, science, secondary, social science, and special), HEALTH PROFESSIONS (medical laboratory technology, nursing, premedicine, preveterinary science, and respiratory therapy), SOCIAL SCIENCE (anthropology, criminal justice, economics, food science, geography, history, philosophy, political science/government, prelaw, psychology, religion, social science, and sociology). Elementary education, criminology, accounting, and nursing have the largest enrollments.

Required: All candidates for graduation must have completed approximately 124 credits, including 53 credits in the liberal studies core, with a minimum GPA of 2.0. The total number of hours in the major varies.

Special: The university offers various co-op programs, cross-registration through the National Student Exchange Consortium, a 3–2 engineering degree with the University of Pittsburgh and Drexel University, and a B.A.-B.S. degree. Internships and dual and student-designed majors are available. Students may study abroad in 30 countries. Also available are work-study programs, a Washington semester, and an accelerated degree program. The university offers credit for military experience. There are 15 national honor societies on campus.

Faculty/Classroom: Sixty-three percent of faculty are male; 37%, female. No introductory courses are taught by graduate students. The average class size in a laboratory is 16 and in a regular course offering, 25.

Admissions: About 51% of the 1993–94 applicants were accepted. About 30% of the current freshmen were in the top fifth of their class; 67% were in the top two fifths.

Requirements: The SAT I is required. Candidates for admission should be graduates of an accredited secondary school. There are no specific course requirements. Art majors must have a portfolio and music majors must audition. AP and CLEP credits are accepted. Important factors used in the admissions decision are extracurricular activities record and recommendations by school officials.

Procedure: Freshmen are admitted fall and spring. Entrance exams should be taken by December of the preceding year. Early decision applications should be filed by October 15; regular applications, by December 31 for fall entry and November 1 for spring entry, along with an application fee of $20. Notification of early decision is sent November 30; regular decision, on a rolling basis. There are early decision, early admissions, and deferred admissions plans.

Transfer: About 700 transfer students enrolled in 1993–94. Transfer students must have a minimum GPA of 2.0 for all subjects; a 2.4 GPA is required for business and a 2.5 for education students. A minimum of 12 credit hours are required. A total of 45 credits out of 124 must be completed at IUP.

Visiting: There are regularly scheduled orientations for prospective students. There are guides for informal visits and visitors may sit in on classes. To arrange for a visit, contact the Admissions Office at (412) 357-2230.

Financial Aid: In 1993–94, 85% of all current freshmen and 85% of continuing students received some form of financial aid. About 85% of freshmen received need-based aid. Scholarships or need-based grants averaged $6613; and loans averaged $2930. Twenty percent of undergraduate students work part-time. The average financial indebtedness of the 1992–93 graduate was $8800. IUP is a member of CSS. The Pennsylvania State Grant and Federal Student Aid Application form is required. The deadline for financial aid applications is May 1.

International Students: There are currently 386 international students enrolled. They must take the TOEFL and achieve a minimum score of 500.

Computers: The college provides computer facilities for student use. The mainframe is a DEC VAX cluster. There are also 500 IBM, Zenith, and Apple Macintosh microcomputers available throughout the campus for student use in teaching facilities. There are more than 3000 microcomputers on campus. All students may access the system. Computer facilities are open more than 120 hours a week and the system may be accessed 24 hours a day from external modems. There are no time limits on using the system and no fees.

Graduates: In 1992–93, 2319 bachelor's degrees were awarded. The most popular majors among graduates were elementary education (10%), accounting (7%), and criminology (6%). Within an average freshman class, 61% graduate in 5 years. Some 134 companies recruited on campus in 1992–93. In the 1992 graduating class, 14% of all graduates were enrolled in graduate school within 6 months of graduation; 63% had found employment.

Admissions Contact: William Nunn, Dean of Admissions.

JUNIATA COLLEGE
Huntingdon, PA 16652

C-3

(814) 643–4310, ext. 420
(800) 526–1970 (in-state)

Full-time: 495 men, 650 women	Faculty: 75; IIB, av$
Part-time: 136	Ph.D.s: 92%
Graduate: 150 men and women	Student/Faculty: 15 to 1
Year: semesters, summer session	Tuition: $14,150
Application Deadline: March 1	Room & Board: $4240
Freshman Class: 1004 applied, 857 accepted, 299 enrolled	
SAT I Verbal/Math: 510/560	COMPETITIVE +

Juniata College, founded in 1876, is an independent, private, coeducational liberal arts college. In addition to regional accreditation, Juniata has baccalaureate program accreditation with CSWE. The library contains 129,809 volumes, 9435 microform items, and 650 audiovisual forms, and subscribes to 950 periodicals. Computerized library sources and services include the card catalog, interlibrary loans, and database searching. Special learning facilities include an art gallery, radio station, and an observatory. The 100-acre campus is in a small town 32 miles east of Altoona. Including residence halls, there are 32 buildings on campus.

Student Life: About 72% of undergraduates are from Pennsylvania. Students come from 25 states and 12 foreign countries. Eighty-five percent are from public schools; 15% from private. Ninety-two percent are white. Sixty-two percent are Protestant; 30% Catholic. The average age of freshmen is 18; all undergraduates, 20. Eight percent drop out by the end of their first year; 71% remain to graduate.

Housing: A total of 1041 students can be accommodated in college housing. College-sponsored living facilities include single-sex and coed dormitories, on-campus apartments, and off-campus apartments. On-campus housing is guaranteed for all 4 years and is available on a lottery system for upperclassmen. Ninety-two percent of students live on campus; of those, 80% remain on campus on weekends. All students may keep cars on campus.

Activities: There are no fraternities or sororities on campus. There are more than 50 groups on campus, including band, cheerleading, choir, chorale, chorus, color guard, computers, dance, departmental, ethnic, honors, international, jazz band, literary magazine, majorettes, marching band, musical theater, newspaper, orchestra, pep band, photography, political, professional, radio and tv, religious, social, social service, student government, and yearbook. Popular campus events include Mountain Day, Madrigal Dinner, Spring Fest, All Class Night, Homecoming, Parents Weekend, Presidential Ball, and International Week.

Sports: There are 11 intercollegiate sports for men and 8 for women, and 9 intramural sports for men and 8 for women. Athletic and recreation facilities include 2 gymnasiums, a swimming pool, 3 weight rooms, a wrestling room, 4 racquetball courts, a multi-purpose room, a sauna; varsity football field and stadium, baseball, soccer, and hockey fields; an outdoor running track, 7 tennis courts, and an outdoor basketball court.

Disabled Students: Eighty percent of the campus is accessible to disabled students. The following facilities are available: wheelchair ramps, elevators, special parking, specially equipped rest rooms, and wide doors.

Services: In addition to many counseling and information services, tutoring is available in most subjects. There is also a reader service for the blind available. Juniata also offers courses and/or workshops in study skills, reading skills, and writing skills.

Campus Safety and Security: Campus safety and security measures include 24-hour foot and vehicle patrol, escort service, pamphlets, posters, films, and emergency telephones. In addition, there are lighted pathways and sidewalks.

Programs of Study: Juniata awards the B.A. and B.S. degrees. Bachelor's degrees are awarded in BIOLOGICAL SCIENCE (biochemistry and biology/biological science), BUSINESS (accounting, banking and finance, business administration and management, business economics, marketing/retailing/merchandising, and personnel management), COMMUNICATIONS AND THE ARTS (communications, English, fine arts, French, German, music, Russian, and Spanish), COMPUTER AND PHYSICAL SCIENCE (chemistry, computer programming, computer science, earth science, geology, information sciences and systems, mathematics, and physics), EDUCATION (early childhood, elementary, foreign languages, science, and secondary), ENGINEERING AND ENVIRONMENTAL DESIGN (environmental science and preengineering), HEALTH PROFESSIONS (medical laboratory technology, nursing, occupational therapy, physical therapy, predentistry, premedicine, and preveterinary science), SOCIAL SCIENCE (anthropology, economics, history, international relations, peace studies, philosophy, political science/government, prelaw, psychology, public administration, religion, social science, social work, and sociology). Preprofessional programs, chemistry, biology, economics, business administration, education, and international stud-

ies are the strongest academically. Biology, business, education, and communications have the largest enrollments.

Required: Students are required to complete a minimum of 120 credit hours, including courses in the 4 areas of fine arts, international studies, social sciences, and humanities and natural sciences, as well as freshman English, a 200-level general education course, senior value studies, and computer literacy. The total number of hours required for the major varies from 45 to 60. Students must have a minimum GPA of 2.0.

Special: The college offers co-op programs, internships, study abroad in 9 countries, a Washington semester, a Philadelphia Urban semester, nondegree study, and an accelerated degree program in premedicine. There are 3–2 engineering degrees with Columbia, Clarkson, and Pennsylvania State Universities, Georgia Institute of Technology, and Washington University at St. Louis. A 3–2 forestry degree is offered with Pennsylvania State University. With the assistance of 2 faculty advisers, all students design their own majors to meet their individual goals. There are 2 national honor societies on campus.

Faculty/Classroom: Sixty-nine percent of faculty are male; 31%, female. All teach undergraduates, 2% do research, and 65% do both. No introductory courses are taught by graduate students. The average class size in an introductory lecture is 28; in a laboratory, 14; and in a regular course offering, 12.

Admissions: About 85% of the 1993–94 applicants were accepted. Ninety percent of the current freshmen were in the top two fifths of their class. About 10 freshmen graduated first in their class.

Requirements: A minimum GPA of 2.0 is required. The SAT I is required. Candidates for admission should be graduates of an accredited secondary school and have completed 16 academic credits, including 4 in English, 2 in a foreign language, and a combination of 10 in mathematics, social studies, and laboratory science. The GED is accepted. An essay is required and an interview is recommended. AP credits are accepted. Important factors used in the admissions decision are advanced placement or honor courses, leadership record, evidence of special talent, personality, intangible qualities, and extracurricular activities record.

Procedure: Freshmen are admitted fall and spring. Entrance exams should be taken in the junior and/or senior years. Applications should be filed by March 1 for fall entry, along with an application fee of $30. Notification is sent on a rolling basis. There are early decision, early admissions, and deferred admissions plans. About 62 early decision candidates were accepted for the 1993–94 class.

Transfer: About 31 transfer students enrolled in 1993–94. A GPA of 2.0 and SAT I scores are required. A total of 30 credits out of 120 must be completed at Juniata.

Visiting: There are regularly scheduled orientations for prospective students, including a campus tour and an interview. There are guides for informal visits and visitors may sit in on classes and stay overnight at the school. To arrange for a visit, contact Nancy Erisman, Campus Visit Coordinator at (800) 526–1970.

Financial Aid: In 1993–94, 91% of all current freshmen and 83% of continuing students received some form of financial aid. About 83% of freshmen and 80% of continuing students received need-based aid. The average freshman award was $13,553. Of that total, scholarships or need-based grants averaged $8871 ($13,000 maximum); loans averaged $3782 ($4425 maximum); and work contracts averaged $1100 ($1200 maximum). Fifty-five percent of undergraduate students work part-time. Average earnings from campus work for the school year are $700. The average financial indebtedness of the 1992–93 graduate was $14,000. Juniata is a member of CSS. The FAF, the PHEAA grant application, and FAFSA are required. The deadline for financial aid applications is March 1.

International Students: There are currently 32 international students enrolled. The school actively recruits these students. They must take the TOEFL and achieve a minimum score of 550.

Computers: The college provides computer facilities for student use. The mainframe is a DEC VAX 11/80. There are 50 terminals and 50 microcomputers located throughout the academic buildings. Students have access to all locations and are provided with a personal account. All students may access the system. It may be used 80 hours per week, usually 7 A.M. to 1:30 A.M. There are no time limits and no fees.

Graduates: In a recent year, 250 bachelor's degrees were awarded. The most popular majors among graduates were business management (18%), education (13%), and natural science (10%). Within an average freshman class, 70% graduate in 4 years. Some 35 companies recruited on campus in 1992–93. In an earlier year's graduating class, 34% of all students were enrolled in graduate school within 6 months of graduation; 64% of all students had found employment.

Admissions Contact: Carlton Surbeck, Director of Admissions.

KING'S COLLEGE
E-2

Wilkes Barre, PA 18711 (717) 826–5858
(800) 955–5777 (out-of-state)

Full-time: 916 men, 855 women	**Faculty:** 97; IIB, av$
Part-time: 181 men, 305 women	**Ph.D.s:** 68%
Graduate: 28 men, 24 women	**Student/Faculty:** 18 to 1
Year: semesters, summer session	**Tuition:** $10,600
Application Deadline: August 1	**Room & Board:** $4820
Freshman Class: 1456 applied, 1053 accepted, 381 enrolled	
SAT I or ACT: required	**COMPETITIVE**

King's College, founded in 1946, is a private, coeducational institution affiliated with the Roman Catholic Church. The college offers undergraduate programs in humanities, the natural and social sciences, and specialized programs in business and other professions. The library contains 145,481 volumes, 432,580 microform items, and 5224 audiovisual forms, and subscribes to 760 periodicals. Computerized library sources and services include the card catalog and database searching. Special learning facilities include a learning resource center, art gallery, radio station, and TV station. The 48-acre campus is in an urban area 90 miles north of Philadelphia. Including residence halls, there are 18 buildings on campus.

Student Life: About 72% of undergraduates are from Pennsylvania. Students come from 17 states and 1 foreign country. Ninety-six percent are white. Seventy-five percent are Catholic; 14% Protestant. The average age of freshmen is 18.5; all undergraduates, 20.5. Fifteen percent drop out by the end of their first year; 69% remain to graduate.

Housing: A total of 748 students can be accommodated in college housing. College-sponsored living facilities include single-sex dormitories and on-campus apartments. On-campus housing is guaranteed for all 4 years. Sixty-one percent of students commute. Alcohol is not permitted. All students may keep cars on campus.

Activities: There are no fraternities or sororities. There are 56 groups on campus, including art, cheerleading, choir, chorale, chorus, computers, dance, drama, ethnic, film, honors, international, jazz band, literary magazine, musical theater, newspaper, photography, political, professional, radio and TV, religious, social, social service, student government, and yearbook. Popular campus events include Spring Fling, visual and performing arts events, Parents Weekend, Homecoming Weekend, All College Ball, Student Activities Fair, Christmas Fair, Christmas Tree Lighting Ceremony, King's Players, theater productions, and comedy nights.

Sports: There are 10 intercollegiate sports for men and 9 for women, and 9 intramural sports for men and 10 for women. Athletic and recreation facilities include a physical education center, outdoor basketball courts, a fitness center, a wrestling room, racquetball courts, a swimming pool, a multipurpose area, a 3200-seat gymnasium, a free weight-lifting area, an outdoor athletic complex with a field house, a football stadium, and baseball, field hockey, softball, and soccer fields.

Disabled Students: Nearly all of the campus is accessible to disabled students. The following facilities are available: wheelchair ramps, elevators, special parking, specially equipped rest rooms, special class scheduling, lowered drinking fountains, and lowered telephones.

Services: In addition to many counseling and information services, tutoring is available in every subject. The academic skills center provides a writing center, learning skills workshops, and a tutoring program.

Campus Safety and Security: Campus safety and security measures include 24-hour foot and vehicle patrol, self defense education, escort service, and informal discussions. In addition, there are pamphlets, posters, and films, emergency telephones, and lighted pathways and sidewalks.

Programs of Study: King's awards the B.A. and B.S. degrees. Associate and master's degrees also are awarded. Bachelor's degrees are awarded in BIOLOGICAL SCIENCE (biology/biological science), BUSINESS (accounting, banking and finance, business administration and management, business economics, international business management, marketing/retailing/merchandising, and personnel management), COMMUNICATIONS AND THE ARTS (communications, dramatic arts, English, French, languages, and Spanish), COMPUTER AND PHYSICAL SCIENCE (chemistry, computer programming, computer science, information sciences and systems, mathematics, physics, and science), EDUCATION (elementary, foreign languages, middle school, science, and secondary), HEALTH PROFESSIONS (health care administration, medical laboratory technology, physician's assistant, predentistry, and premedicine), SOCIAL SCIENCE (criminal justice, economics, gerontology, history, philosophy, political science/government, prelaw, psychology, sociology, and theological studies). Accounting, English, biology, and psychology are the strongest academically. Accounting, business administration, education, biology, and criminal justice have the largest enrollments.

Required: All students must earn a minimum of 120 credits and maintain a minimum GPA of 2.0. The core requirements represent 51 credits. The major comprises a maximum of 60 credits, of which a maximum of 40 credits can be specified in the major department with the balance in related fields.

Special: Co-op programs in early childhood and special education and cross-registration with Wilkes University and College Misericordia are offered. The Experiential Learning Program provides internship opportunities with a variety of employers. King's also offers study abroad in 3 countries, a Washington semester, work-study programs, B.A.-B.S. degrees, dual and student-designed majors, credit for life experience, and pass/fail options. There is a freshman honors program on campus, as well as 9 national honor societies.

Faculty/Classroom: Seventy-seven percent of faculty are male; 23%, female. All teach undergraduates. No introductory courses are taught by graduate students. The average class size in an introductory lecture is 24; in a laboratory, 18; and in a regular course offering, 20.

Admissions: About 72% of the 1993–94 applicants were accepted. About 40% of the current freshmen were in the top fifth of their class; 73% were in the top two fifths. There was 1 National Merit finalist and 3 semifinalists. About 7 freshmen graduated first in their class.

Requirements: The SAT I or ACT is required. King's requires 15 academic credits, including 4 in English, 3 each in mathematics, science, and history, 2 in foreign language, and 1 in social studies. AP and CLEP credits are accepted. Important factors used in the admissions decision are advanced placement or honor courses, extracurricular activities record, leadership record, personality, intangible qualities, and evidence of special talent.

Procedure: Freshmen are admitted to all sessions. Entrance exams should be taken before December of the senior year. Applications should be filed by August 1 for fall entry, December 1 for spring entry, and May 1 for summer entry, along with an application fee of $30. Notification is sent on a rolling basis. There are early admissions and deferred admissions plans. A waiting list is an active part of the admissions procedure, with about 20% of applicants on the list.

Transfer: About 135 transfer students enrolled in 1993–94. Applicants planning to major in the sciences or business must present a minimum GPA of 2.5; all others must present a 2.0. Students must have earned at least 3 credit hours at another college. An interview is recommended. A total of 60 credits out of 120 must be completed at King's.

Visiting: There are regularly scheduled orientations for prospective students. There are guides for informal visits and visitors may sit in on classes and stay overnight at the school. To arrange for a visit, contact the Admissions Office at (717) 826-5858 or (800) 955-5777.

Financial Aid: In 1993–94, 90% of all current freshmen and 83% of continuing students received some form of financial aid. About 86% of freshmen and 84% of continuing students received need-based aid. The average freshman award was $8450. Of that total, scholarships or need-based grants averaged $5280 ($10,600 maximum); loans averaged $3100 ($4625 maximum); and work contracts averaged $1000 ($1100 maximum). Sixty percent of undergraduate students work part-time. Average earnings from campus work for the school year are $1020. The average financial indebtedness of the 1992–93 graduate was $11,500. King's is a member of CSS. All students seeking financial aid must submit the FAFSA and the college's own financial statement. The deadline for financial aid applications is March 1.

International Students: There are currently 9 international students enrolled. The school actively recruits these students. They must take the TOEFL and achieve a minimum score of 500.

Computers: The college provides computer facilities for student use. The mainframes are an IBM AS/400 F45 and an IBM RS/6000 570. Students taking programming courses in CICS, C, RPG, COBOL, Pascal, and PL/1 and statistical research and course work in SAS and SPSS utilize the mainframe computer with access provided through dial-in lines and 100 networked IBM PS/2 computers. Software packages include Windows, EXCEL, Word for Windows, and Foxpro for Windows. Two networked Macintosh laboratories containing 62 Macintosh computers and a computer science/graphics laboratory containing 40 MS-DOS computers are available for student use. All students may access the system. A small 24-hour networked laboratory exists. Other laboratories are available Monday through Friday, 8 A.M. to 11 P.M.; Saturday, 9 A.M. to 6 P.M.; and Sunday 1 P.M. to 12 A.M. There are no time limits and no fees.

Graduates: In 1992–93 460 bachelor's degrees were awarded. The most popular majors among graduates were accounting (15%), communications (10%), and criminal justice (9%). Within an average freshman class, 66% graduate in 4 years, 68% in 5 years, and 69% in 6 years. Some 77 companies recruited on campus in 1992–93. In the 1992 graduating class, 4% of the men and 8% of the women were enrolled in graduate school within 6 months of graduation; 38% of the men and 45% of the women had found employment.

Admissions Contact: Daniel Conry, Dean of Admissions.

KUTZTOWN UNIVERSITY   E-3

Kutztown, PA 19530   (215) 683-4060

Full-time: 2594 men, 3367 women	Faculty: 318; IIA, av$
Part-time: 275 men, 621 women	Ph.D.s: 50%
Graduate: 233 men, 674 women	Student/Faculty: 19 to 1
Year: semesters, summer session	Tuition: $3558 ($8286)
Application Deadline: open	Room & Board: $2970
Freshman Class: 5095 applied, 3033 accepted, 1304 enrolled	
SAT I or ACT: required	**COMPETITIVE**

Kutztown University, founded in 1866, is a public, coeducational institution within the Pennsylvania state system of higher education. The university offers undergraduate programs in the arts and sciences, business, education, and visual and performing arts. There are 4 undergraduate schools and one graduate school. In addition to regional accreditation, KU has baccalaureate program accreditation with NCATE and NLN. The library contains 409,432 volumes, 1,138,515 microform items, and 5419 audiovisual forms, and subscribes to 2015 periodicals. Computerized library sources and services include the card catalog, interlibrary loans, and database searching. Special learning facilities include a learning resource center, art gallery, planetarium, radio station, tv station, a women's center, and a cartography laboratory. The 325-acre campus is in a rural area 90 miles north of Philadelphia. Including residence halls, there are 42 buildings on campus.

Student Life: About 86% of undergraduates are from Pennsylvania. Students come from 21 states and 30 foreign countries. Ninety-six percent are from public schools. Ninety-three percent are white. The average age of freshmen is 18; all undergraduates, 20. Twenty-three percent drop out by the end of their first year; 50% remain to graduate.

Housing: A total of 2848 students can be accommodated in college housing. College-sponsored living facilities include single-sex and coed dormitories. In addition there are language houses and special interest houses. On-campus housing is available on a first-come, first-served basis and is available on a lottery system for upperclassmen. Fifty percent of students live on campus; of those, 60% remain on campus on weekends. Alcohol is not permitted. Upperclassmen may keep cars on campus.

Activities: About 4% of men belong to 2 local and 6 national fraternities; about 4% of women belong to 2 local and 4 national sororities. There are 90 groups on campus, including art, band, cheerleading, choir, chorus, computers, dance, drama, ethnic, honors, international, jazz band, literary magazine, marching band, musical theater, newspaper, orchestra, political, professional, radio and tv, religious, social, social service, student government, and yearbook. Popular campus events include Homecoming, Alumni Day, Academic Festival, International Animated Film Festival, and Family Day.

Sports: There are 9 intercollegiate sports for men and 9 for women, and 22 intramural sports for men and 19 for women. Athletic and recreation facilities include a 7500-seat stadium, a field house, a swimming pool, tennis courts, a 4700-seat arena, a 4000-seat gymnasium, and athletic fields.

Disabled Students: Seventy percent of the campus is accessible to disabled students. The following facilities are available: wheelchair ramps, elevators, special parking, specially equipped rest rooms, special class scheduling, lowered drinking fountains, and lowered telephones. All programs can be made accessible to physically disabled persons.

Services: In addition to many counseling and information services, tutoring is available in some subjects. In addition, there is a reader service for the blind and remedial math and reading.

Campus Safety and Security: Campus safety and security measures include 24-hour foot and vehicle patrol, escort service, informal discussions, and pamphlets, posters, and films. In addition, there are emergency telephones and lighted pathways and sidewalks.

Programs of Study: KU awards the B.A., B.S., B.F.A., B.S.B.A, B.S.Ed., and B.S.N. degrees. Master's degrees also are awarded. Bachelor's degrees are awarded in BIOLOGICAL SCIENCE (biology/biological science and marine science), BUSINESS (accounting, business administration and management, business economics, international business management, marketing/retailing/merchandising, and personnel management), COMMUNICATIONS AND THE ARTS (communications, crafts, design, dramatic arts, English, fine arts, French, German, music, Russian, Spanish, speech/debate/rhetoric, and telecommunications), COMPUTER AND PHYSICAL SCIENCE (chemistry, geology, mathematics, and physics), EDUCATION (art, early childhood, elementary, library science, secondary, and special), ENGINEERING AND ENVIRONMENTAL DESIGN (environmental science), HEALTH PROFESSIONS (medical laboratory technology, nursing, and speech pathology/audiology), SOCIAL SCIENCE (American studies, anthropology, criminal justice, economics, geography, history, philosophy, political science/government, psychology, public administration, social work, and sociology). Com-

munications and design are the strongest academically. Education and business have the largest enrollments.

Required: General education requirements vary by program, but all students must take physical education, speech 10, English composition, or introduction to dance. Distribution requirements also include courses in humanities, social sciences, natural sciences, and mathematics. To graduate, students must complete at least 128 semester hours, including 33 to 80 in a major field, with a minimum GPA of 2.0. Students in the College of Liberal Arts and Sciences must take a comprehensive exam.

Special: Students may study abroad in 7 countries. There is a 3–2 engineering degree program with Pennsylvania State University. KU also offers internships, several student-designed majors, and a general studies degree. Nondegree study is possible. There is a freshman honors program on campus, as well as 20 national honor societies. Thirteen departments have honors programs.

Faculty/Classroom: Sixty-seven percent of faculty are male; 33%, female. Ninety-five percent teach undergraduates and 100% do research.

Admissions: About 60% of the 1993–94 applicants were accepted. About 22% of the current freshmen were in the top fifth of their class; 58% were in the top two fifths.

Requirements: KU requires applicants to be in the upper 50% of their class. A minimum GPA of 3.0 is required. The SAT I or ACT is required. Applicants must be graduates of accredited secondary schools or have earned a GED. Admission to a special curriculum may require additional proof of ability. AP and CLEP credits are accepted. Important factors used in the admissions decision are advanced placement or honor courses, evidence of special talent, leadership record, recommendations by school officials, and extracurricular activities record.

Procedure: Freshmen are admitted fall and spring. Entrance exams should be taken in the fall of the senior year. Application deadlines are open. Application fee is $25. Notification is sent on a rolling basis. There are early admissions and deferred admissions plans. A waiting list is an active part of the admissions procedure, with about 5% of applicants on the list.

Transfer: About 573 transfer students enrolled in 1993–94. Applicants must present a GPA of 2.0 and official transcripts from all colleges and secondary schools previously attended. Students transferring fewer than 30 credit hours must also submit SAT I or ACT scores. A total of 33 credits out of 128 must be completed at KU.

Visiting: There are regularly scheduled orientations for prospective students, including 2 Fall Preview Days, and 4 Spring Visitations. There are guides for informal visits. To arrange for a visit, contact the Admissions Office at (215) 683–4060.

Financial Aid: In 1993–94, 75% of all current freshmen and 80% of continuing students received some form of financial aid. About 50% of freshmen and 60% of continuing students received need-based aid. The average freshman award was $4000. Of that total, scholarships or need-based grants averaged $575 ($1000 maximum); loans averaged $2625; and work contracts averaged $800 ($3000 maximum). Forty percent of undergraduate students work part-time. Average earnings from campus work for the school year are $1600. The average financial indebtedness of the 1992–93 graduate was $13,000. All students must submit the Pennsylvania State Grant and federal Student Aid Application (PHEAA). The deadline for financial aid applications is March 15.

International Students: There are currently 135 international students enrolled. They must take the TOEFL and achieve a minimum score of 500.

Computers: The college provides computer facilities for student use. The mainframe is a Unisys A-11, 2200, and U6000. The Unisys U6000 is a parallel processor, UNIX-based system used exclusively by students and faculty. The Unisys 2200 supports library automation. A number of hardwired and dial-up lines are available. All students may access the system. There are no time limits on using the system and no fees.

Graduates: In 1992–93 1440 bachelor's degrees were awarded. The most popular majors among graduates were elementary education (17%), secondary education (9%), and telecommunications, communication design, and marketing (6%). Within an average freshman class, 25% graduate in 4 years, 50% in 5 years, and 52% in 6 years. Some 25 companies recruited on campus in 1992–93.

Admissions Contact: George McKinley, Director of Admissions.

LA ROCHE COLLEGE

B-3

Pittsburgh, PA 15237 (412) 367-9240

Full-time: 258 men, 392 women	Faculty: 44; IIB, -$
Part-time: 196 men, 623 women	Ph.D.s: 70%
Graduate: 71 men, 273 women	Student/Faculty: 15 to 1
Year: semesters, summer session	Tuition: $8422
Application Deadline: open	Room & Board: $4555
Freshman Class: 361 applied, 349 accepted, 185 enrolled	
SAT I Verbal/Math: 420/420	LESS COMPETITIVE

La Roche College, founded in 1963, is a private, coeducational Catholic institution offering undergraduate programs in the arts and sciences, business, graphic art and design, health science, upper-level nursing, professional training, and religious studies. There are 6 undergraduate and 3 graduate schools. In addition to regional accreditation, La Roche has baccalaureate program accreditation with FIDER, NASAD, and NLN. The library contains 66,000 volumes, 125 microform items, and 973 audiovisual forms, and subscribes to 700 periodicals. Computerized library sources and services include interlibrary loans and database searching. Special learning facilities include a learning resource center, an art gallery, and interior and graphic design studios. The 100-acre campus is in a suburban area 10 miles north of Pittsburgh. Including residence halls, there are 11 buildings on campus.

Student Life: About 93% of undergraduates are from Pennsylvania. Students come from 17 states and 7 foreign countries. Ninety-three percent are white. Fifty-six percent are Catholic; 27% Protestant. The average age of freshmen is 19; all undergraduates, 29. Twenty-three percent drop out by the end of their first year; 40% remain to graduate.

Housing: A total of 300 students can be accommodated in college housing. College-sponsored living facilities include coed dormitories, on-campus apartments, and off-campus apartments. On-campus housing is guaranteed for all 4 years. Fifty-four percent of students commute. All students may keep cars on campus.

Activities: About 10% of women belong to 1 local sorority. There are no fraternities on campus. There are 25 groups on campus, including art, cheerleading, chorus, computers, drama, ethnic, honors, international, literary magazine, newspaper, pep band, photography, political, professional, religious, social, social service, student government, and yearbook. Popular campus events include Campus Visit Days, Campus Picnic, Martin Luther King Day, Thanksgiving Interfaith Forum, Parents Day, a literary series, a performing arts series, gallery exhibits, Fall Semiformal Dinner Dance, Spring Semiformal River Cruise, Parents Weekend, Alumni Weekend, Spring Carnival, Battle of the Bands, Madrigal Dinner, and Day and Night at LaRoche.

Sports: There are 3 intercollegiate sports each for men and women, and 10 intramural sports each for men and women. Athletic and recreation facilities include soccer and baseball fields, a gymnasium, hiking trails, a new fitness/sports center that houses a gymnasium, racquetball courts, an indoor track, an aerobics room, a weight room, and a nearby county park with tennis courts and a swimming pool.

Disabled Students: Eighty percent of the campus is accessible to disabled students. The following facilities are available: wheelchair ramps, elevators, special parking, specially equipped rest rooms, lowered drinking fountains, and lowered telephones.

Services: In addition to many counseling and information services, tutoring is available in every subject. In addition, there is remedial math, reading, and writing.

Campus Safety and Security: Campus safety and security measures include 24-hour foot and vehicle patrol, escort service, informal discussions, and pamphlets, posters, and films. In addition, there are emergency telephones, lighted pathways and sidewalks, an intercom security system, and residence halls locked 24 hours a day.

Programs of Study: La Roche awards the B.A., B.S., and B.S.N. degrees. Master's degrees are also awarded. Bachelor's degrees are awarded in BIOLOGICAL SCIENCE (biology/biological science), BUSINESS (accounting, banking and finance, business administration and management, international business management, and sports management), COMMUNICATIONS AND THE ARTS (communications, English, and graphic design), COMPUTER AND PHYSICAL SCIENCE (chemistry, computer programming, and natural sciences), EDUCATION (science), ENGINEERING AND ENVIRONMENTAL DESIGN (interior design), HEALTH PROFESSIONS (medical laboratory technology, medical technology, nursing, radiograph medical technology, and respiratory therapy), SOCIAL SCIENCE (history, human services, psychobiology, psychology, religion, religious education, and sociology). Graphic design, interior design, professional writing, and accounting are the strongest academically. Administration and management, design areas, and nursing have the largest enrollments.

Required: Students are required to complete 18 credits in basic skill areas, including writing, mathematics, computer applications, communication, and critical thinking, and 24 credits in the following liberal arts areas: ethical and spiritual values, aesthetics, imaginative litera-

ture, wellness, natural world, social systems, historical perspective, and global awareness. A minimum of 120 credit hours and a minimum GPA of 2.0 are requirements for graduation. A senior seminar is also required in most majors.

Special: There is cross-registration with members of the Pittsburgh Council of Higher Education. Internships for which students may receive up to 6 credits are available for juniors and seniors with numerous employers in the Pittsburgh area. LaRoche also offers study abroad, a Washington semester, dual majors, credit for life experience, directed research, honors programs, independent study, and pass/fail options.

Faculty/Classroom: Fifty percent of faculty are male; 50%, female. All teach undergraduates and 40% do research. No introductory courses are taught by graduate students. The average class size in an introductory lecture is 30; in a laboratory, 15; and in a regular course offering, 20.

Admissions: About 97% of the 1993–94 applicants were accepted. The SAT scores for the 1993–94 freshman class were as follows: Verbal—89% below 500 and 11% between 500 and 599; Math—85% below 500, 14% between 500 and 599, and 1% between 600 and 700. About 19% of the current freshmen were in the top fifth of their class; 40% were in the top two fifths.

Requirements: La Roche requires applicants to be in the upper 60% of their class. A minimum GPA of 2.0 is required. The SAT I or ACT is required. In addition, applicants must be graduates of accredited secondary schools or have earned a GED. An interview is recommended for all applicants. AP and CLEP credits are accepted. Important factors used in the admissions decision are advanced placement or honor courses, recommendations by school officials, evidence of special talent, and extracurricular activities record.

Procedure: Freshmen are admitted to all sessions. Entrance exams should be taken by fall of the senior year. Application deadlines are open. Application fee is $25. Notification is sent on a rolling basis. There is an early admissions plan.

Transfer: About 100 transfer students enrolled in 1993–94. Transfer design students may be required to submit a portfolio and must have a 2.0 GPA. A total of 30 credits out of a minimum of 120 must be completed at La Roche.

Visiting: There are regularly scheduled orientations for prospective students, including an overnight stay, information sessions and interactive sessions, class attendance, and meeting with faculty. There are also 1-day visits on Saturday and guides for informal visits. To arrange for a visit, contact the Admissions Office at (412) 367-9241.

Financial Aid: In 1993–94, 76% of all current freshmen and 72% of continuing students received some form of financial aid. About 75% of freshmen and 71% of continuing students received need-based aid. The average freshman award was $10,000. Of that total, scholarships or need-based grants averaged $6000 ($7000 maximum); loans averaged $2800 ($3625 maximum); and work contracts averaged $1200. Twenty-four percent of undergraduate students work part-time. Average earnings from campus work for the school year are $1200. The average financial indebtedness of the 1992–93 graduate was $7500. La Roche is a member of CSS. The FAFSA financial statement is required. The deadline for financial aid applications is May 1.

International Students: There are currently 30 international students enrolled. The school actively recruits these students. They must take the TOEFL and achieve a minimum score of 550. Students must take SAT II: Subject tests for college placement.

Computers: The college provides computer facilities for student use. Students have access to 40 microcomputers, including IBM, IBM-compatible, Apple and Apple Macintosh, which are part of a local area network. Students may access Dialog. The Macintosh computer laboratory offers software for illustration, Postscript, animation, dimensional design, and desktop publishing. All students may access the system. Student access time to the PCs varies by course, as does the fee for computer use, which ranges from $5 to $35.

Graduates: In 1992–93, 278 bachelor's degrees were awarded. The most popular majors among graduates were administration and management (23%), nursing (12%), and graphic design (10%). Within an average freshman class, 60% graduate in 4 years and 90% in 5 years. Some 20 companies recruited on campus in a recent year. In the 1992 graduating class, 77% of all graduates had found employment within 6 months of graduation.

Admissions Contact: Barry Duerr, Director of Admissions.

LA SALLE UNIVERSITY

F-3

Philadelphia, PA 19141–1199

(215) 951–1500

(800) 328–1910 (out-of-state)

Full-time: 1540 men, 1529 women	Faculty: 228; IIA, av$
Part-time: 480 men, 1158 women	Ph.D.s: 87%
Graduate: 706 men, 676 women	Student/Faculty: 14 to 1
Year: semesters, summer session	Tuition: $11,510
Application Deadline: August 15	Room & Board: $5430
Freshman Class: 2798 applied, 1719 accepted, 664 enrolled	
SAT I Verbal/Math: 500/560	**VERY COMPETITIVE**

La Salle University, founded in 1863, is a private, coeducational institution conducted under the auspices of the Christian Brothers of the Roman Catholic Church. The university offers undergraduate programs in the arts and sciences, business, education, health science, fine arts, religious studies, and nursing. There are 4 undergraduate and 6 graduate schools. In addition to regional accreditation, La Salle has baccalaureate program accreditation with CSWE and NLN. The library contains 362,000 volumes, 19,687 microform items, and 2725 audiovisual forms, and subscribes to 1710 periodicals. Computerized library sources and services include the card catalog, interlibrary loans, and database searching. Special learning facilities include a learning resource center, art gallery, radio station, tv station, and a Japanese tea ceremony house. The 120-acre campus is in an urban area 8 miles northwest of the center of Philadelphia. Including residence halls, there are 56 buildings on campus.

Student Life: About 64% of undergraduates are from Pennsylvania. Students come from 28 states, 10 foreign countries, and Canada. Forty-seven percent are from public schools; 53% from private. Eighty-nine percent are white. Seventy-four percent are Catholic; 16% Protestant. The average age of freshmen is 18; all undergraduates, 20. Nine percent drop out by the end of their first year; 73% remain to graduate.

Housing: A total of 1880 students can be accommodated in college housing. College-sponsored living facilities include single-sex and coed dormitories and on-campus apartments. In addition, there are honors houses and special interest houses for which student groups may submit proposals for use. Townhouses are available to juniors and seniors. On-campus housing is guaranteed for all 4 years. Fifty-eight percent of students live on campus; of those, 80% remain on campus on weekends. All students may keep cars on campus.

Activities: About 13% of men belong to 1 local and 7 national fraternities; about 12% of women belong to 1 local and 6 national sororities. There are 106 groups on campus, including band, cheerleading, choir, chorale, chorus, computers, dance, drama, drill team, ethnic, film, honors, international, jazz band, literary magazine, musical theater, newspaper, orchestra, pep band, political, professional, radio and tv, religious, social, social service, student government, and yearbook. Popular campus events include Open House, Spring Fling, Oktoberfest, First Tuesday, Comedy Hour, and Parents Weekend.

Sports: There are 11 intercollegiate sports for men and 10 for women, and 14 intramural sports for men and 14 for women. Athletic and recreation facilities include a 7000-seat stadium, a 1500-seat gymnasium, a 2000-seat auditorium, 4 playing fields, 6 tennis courts, a fully equipped athletic and exercise facility, wrestling rooms, a sauna, racquetball and squash courts, indoor and outdoor tracks, basketball and volleyball courts, and an indoor swimming pool.

Disabled Students: Ninety-five percent of the campus is accessible to disabled students. The following facilities are available: wheelchair ramps, elevators, special parking, specially equipped rest rooms, special class scheduling, and lowered drinking fountains.

Services: In addition to many counseling and information services, tutoring is available in some subjects. A writing center is also available.

Campus Safety and Security: Campus safety and security measures include 24-hour foot and vehicle patrol, escort service, shuttle buses, and emergency telephones. In addition, there are lighted pathways and sidewalks.

Programs of Study: La Salle awards the B.A., B.S., B.S.W., and B.S.N. degrees. Associate and master's degrees also are awarded. Bachelor's degrees are awarded in BIOLOGICAL SCIENCE (biochemistry and biology/biological science), BUSINESS (accounting, banking and finance, business administration and management, management information systems, marketing/retailing/merchandising, organizational behavior, and personnel management), COMMUNICATIONS AND THE ARTS (classics, communications, English, fine arts, French, German, Italian, music, Russian, and Spanish), COMPUTER AND PHYSICAL SCIENCE (chemistry, computer science, geology, mathematics, physics, quantitative methods, and statistics), EDUCATION (early childhood, elementary, foreign languages, science, secondary, social studies, and special), HEALTH PROFESSIONS (predentistry and premedicine), SOCIAL SCIENCE (criminal justice, economics, history, philosophy, political science/government, prelaw, psychology, public administration, religion, social work, and so-

ciology). Chemistry, premedicine, English, prelaw, communication arts, computer science, biology, accounting, finance, and nursing are the strongest academically. Accounting, finance, communication arts, and nursing have the largest enrollments.

Required: Students must first complete 9 foundation courses in English, philosophy, religion, social science, history, science, and computer science, and then complete 8 core courses in religion/ philosophy and selected subjects. To graduate, students must complete at least 120 credit hours, including 45 in a major field, with a minimum GPA of 2.0; 38 of the courses must be 3 credits in value.

Special: Students may study abroad in Switzerland and Spain. Cross-registration is offered in conjunction with Chestnut Hill College, and there is a 2 +2 program with Thomas Jefferson University Hospital. La Salle also offers work-study programs, internships for communication and business majors, accelerated degree programs, dual and student-designed majors, B.A.-B.S. degrees, and pass/fail options. There is a freshman honors program on campus, as well as 12 national honor societies. Four departments have honors programs.

Faculty/Classroom: Seventy percent of faculty are male; 30%, female. All teach undergraduates and 45% do research. No introductory courses are taught by graduate students. The average class size in an introductory lecture is 20; in a laboratory, 14; and in a regular course offering, 19.

Admissions: About 61% of the 1993–94 applicants were accepted. The SAT scores for the 1993–94 freshman class were as follows: Verbal—40% below 500, 41% between 500 and 599, 10% between 600 and 700, and 9% above 700; Math—20% below 500, 50% between 500 and 599, 20% between 600 and 700, and 10% above 700. About 47% of the current freshmen were in the top fifth of their class; 86% were in the top two fifths. There were 5 National Merit finalists and 30 semifinalists. About 28 freshmen graduated first in their class.

Requirements: La Salle requires applicants to be in the upper 50% of their class. The SAT I is required. The SAT II: Writing and Mathematics tests recommended. Applicants must be graduates of accredited secondary schools or have earned a GED. The university requires 16 academic units, based on 4 years of English, 3 of mathematics, 2 of foreign language, and 1 of history, with the remaining 5 units in academic electives; science and mathematics majors must have an additional one-half unit of mathematics. An essay is required. An interview is recommended. AP and CLEP credits are accepted. Important factors used in the admissions decision are advanced placement or honor courses, leadership record, parents or siblings attending the school, personality, intangible qualities, and evidence of special talent.

Procedure: Freshmen are admitted fall and spring. Entrance exams should be taken before February of the senior year. Applications should be filed by August 15 for fall entry, December 15 for spring entry, and May 15 for summer entry, along with an application fee of $30. Notification is sent on a rolling basis. There are early admissions and deferred admissions plans.

Transfer: About 258 transfer students enrolled in 1993–94. A total of 50 credits out of 120 must be completed at La Salle.

Visiting: There are regularly scheduled orientations for prospective students. There are guides for informal visits and visitors may sit in on classes and stay overnight at the school. To arrange for a visit, contact the Admissions Office at (800) 328–1910 or (215) 951–1500.

Financial Aid: In 1993–94, 85% of all students received some form of financial aid. About 70% received need-based aid. The average freshman award was $10,200. Of that total, scholarships or need-based grants averaged $5500 ($11,510 maximum); loans averaged $3500 ($5500 maximum); and work contracts averaged $1800. The average financial indebtedness of the 1992–93 graduate was $10,000. La Salle is a member of CSS. Pennsylvania residents must submit the PHEAA and the FAFSA; out-of-state applicants may submit either the PHEAA or the FAF. The deadline for financial aid applications is February 15.

International Students: There are currently 82 international students enrolled. The school actively recruits these students. They must take the TOEFL and achieve a minimum score of 500.

Computers: The college provides computer facilities for student use. The mainframe is an HP 9000/Model 8355E. The university provides 320 IBM and IBM-compatible microcomputers. A LAN is available for student use. The mainframe is used for computer science majors. All students may access the system. It may be used from 7 A.M. to 11 P.M. There are no time limits on using the system and no fees.

Graduates: In 1992–93 986 bachelor's degrees were awarded. The most popular majors among graduates were business and management (45%), health sciences (10%), and social sciences (8%). Within an average freshman class, 2% graduate in 3 years, 70% in 4 years, and 14% in 5 years. Some 190 companies recruited on campus in 1992–93. In the 1992 graduating class, 16% of the men and 14% of the women were enrolled in graduate school within 6 months of graduation; 78% of the men and 80% of the women had found employment.

Admissions Contact: Br. Gerald Fitzgerald, F.S.C., Director of Admissions.

LAFAYETTE COLLEGE F-3
Easton, PA 18042 (215) 250-5100

Full-time: 1116 men, 902 women	**Faculty:** 175; IIB, +$
Part-time: 176 men, 50 women	**Ph.D.s:** 92%
Graduate: none	**Student/Faculty:** 12 to 1
Year: semesters, summer session	**Tuition:** $17,950
Application Deadline: January 15	**Room & Board:** $5500

Freshman Class: 4010 applied, 2402 accepted, 572 enrolled
SAT I: required **HIGHLY COMPETITIVE**

Lafayette College, founded in 1826 and affiliated with the Presbyterian Church of the U.S.A., is a coeducational, private, undergraduate, liberal arts institution that emphasizes the liberal arts and engineering. In addition to regional accreditation, Lafayette has baccalaureate program accreditation with ABET. The 2 libraries contain 438,911 volumes and 105,949 microform items, and subscribe to 1807 periodicals. Computerized library sources and services include the card catalog, interlibrary loans, and database searching. Special learning facilities include a learning resource center, art gallery, radio station, a geological museum, a foreign languages laboratory, and a calculus laboratory. The 112-acre campus is in a residential area 70 miles west of New York City. Including residence halls, there are 64 buildings on campus.

Student Life: About 75% of undergraduates are from out-of-state, mostly the Middle Atlantic. Students come from 39 states, 45 foreign countries, and Canada. Seventy percent are from public schools; 30% from private. Eighty-four percent are white. Thirty-eight percent are Catholic; 30% Protestant; 15% claim no religious affiliation; 10% Jewish. The average age of freshmen is 18; all undergraduates, 20. Six percent drop out by the end of their first year; 92% remain to graduate.

Housing: A total of 1965 students can be accommodated in college housing. College-sponsored living facilities include single-sex and coed dormitories, on-campus apartments, off-campus apartments, fraternity houses, and sorority houses. In addition, there are honors houses, special interest houses, diversity-oriented houses, arts houses, a black cultural center, and language and special interest floors. On-campus housing is guaranteed for all 4 years. Ninety-eight percent of students live on campus; of those, 95% remain on campus on weekends. Upperclassmen may keep cars on campus.

Activities: About 50% of men belong to 12 national fraternities; about 70% of women belong to 6 national sororities. There are 100 groups on campus, including art, band, cheerleading, choir, chorale, chorus, computers, dance, drama, ethnic, film, gay, honors, international, jazz band, literary magazine, musical theater, newspaper, orchestra, pep band, photography, political, professional, radio and TV, religious, social, social service, student government, and yearbook. Popular campus events include Black History Month, All College Day, Earth Day, International Extravaganza, Family Weekend, Women's History Month, and Winterfest.

Sports: There are 11 intercollegiate sports for men and 11 for women, and 22 intramural sports for men and 22 for women. Athletic and recreation facilities include a 13,000-seat stadium, a 3500-seat gymnasium, a field house, a varsity house, a natatorium, a weight training room, an outdoor track, an indoor track, 9 tennis courts, and an 80-acre field complex for lacrosse, field hockey, soccer, and baseball.

Disabled Students: Ninety percent of the campus is accessible to disabled students. The following facilities are available: wheelchair ramps, elevators, special parking, specially equipped rest rooms, special class scheduling, lowered drinking fountains, and lowered telephones.

Services: In addition to many counseling and information services, tutoring is available in most subjects, including most 100-level and many 200-level classes. Assistance is available for students in the use of textbooks for the blind.

Campus Safety and Security: Campus safety and security measures include 24-hour foot and vehicle patrol, self defense education, escort service, and informal discussions. In addition, there are pamphlets, posters, films, emergency telephones, lighted pathways and sidewalks, and resident advisors in all residence halls. Residence halls are locked from 8 P.M. to 7 A.M. and are accessible by residents' room keys and outside telephones.

Programs of Study: Lafayette awards the A.B., B.S., and B.S.Eng. degrees. Bachelor's degrees are awarded in BIOLOGICAL SCIENCE (biochemistry and biology/biological science), BUSINESS (business economics), COMMUNICATIONS AND THE ARTS (English, fine arts, French, German, music history and appreciation, music theory and composition, and Spanish), COMPUTER AND PHYSICAL SCIENCE (chemistry, computer science, geology, mathematics, and physics), ENGINEERING AND ENVIRONMENTAL DESIGN (chemical engineering, civil engineering, electrical/electronics engi-

neering, and mechanical engineering), HEALTH PROFESSIONS (predentistry), SOCIAL SCIENCE (American studies, anthropology, economics, history, interdisciplinary studies, international relations, philosophy, political science/government, prelaw, psychology, religion, Russian studies, and sociology). Engineering, government and law, psychology, English, biology, and economics and business are the strongest academically. Economics and business, engineering, biology, and psychology have the largest enrollments.

Required: All students must maintain a minimum GPA of 1.8 and must complete a minimum of 120 semester hours. The common course of study, designed to build a background in the liberal arts and sciences in the first 2 years, includes interdisciplinary seminars, 4 courses in liberal arts and 4 in mathematics/science, as well as knowledge of foreign culture.

Special: Cross-registration through the Lehigh Valley Association of Independent Colleges, internships in all academic departments, study abroad in 3 countries, as well as through other individually arranged plans, a Washington semester at American University, and work-study programs with area employers are possible. An accelerated degree plan in all majors, dual and student-designed majors, and pass/fail options in any nonmajor subject also are available. Five-year, 2-degree programs are also offered. There are 12 national honor societies on campus, including Phi Beta Kappa. Twenty-four departments have honors programs.

Faculty/Classroom: Seventy-four percent of faculty are male; 26%, female. All both teach and do research. The average class size in a laboratory is 15 and in a regular course offering, 19.

Admissions: About 60% of the 1993–94 applicants were accepted. The SAT scores for the 1993–94 freshman class were as follows: Verbal—29% below 500, 50% between 500 and 599, 20% between 600 and 700, and 1% above 700; Math—4% below 500, 32% between 500 and 599, 49% between 600 and 700, and 16% above 700. About 59% of the current freshmen were in the top fifth of their class; 94% were in the top two fifths.

Requirements: The SAT I is required. Applicants need 4 years of English, 3 years of mathematics (4 for science or engineering majors), 2 years each of foreign language and science (with physics and chemistry for science or engineering students), and an additional 5 to 8 units. An essay is required and an interview recommended. The GED is accepted. AP credits are accepted. Important factors used in the admissions decision are advanced placement or honor courses, evidence of special talent, personality, intangible qualities, extracurricular activities record, and leadership record.

Procedure: Freshmen are admitted in the fall. Entrance exams should be taken by January of the senior year. Early decision applications should be filed by January 15; regular applications, by January 15 for fall entry, along with an application fee of $40. Notification of early decision is sent within 30 days; regular decision, mid-March. There are early decision, early admissions, and deferred admissions plans. A total of 138 early decision candidates were accepted for the 1993–94 class. A waiting list is an active part of the admissions procedure.

Transfer: Fourteen transfer students enrolled in 1993–94. Acceptance of transfer students usually depends on college-level performance and achievements. An interview is required if the student lives within 200 miles of the college. No minimum GPA is required and the SAT I or ACT are not required. The number of credit hours required varies with the program, but usually enough for freshmen status with advanced standing is needed. A total of 60 credits out of 120 must be completed at Lafayette.

Visiting: There are regularly scheduled orientations for prospective students, including student/faculty panel discussions, tours, and departmental open houses. There are guides for informal visits and visitors may sit in on classes and stay overnight at the school. To arrange for a visit, contact the Admissions Office at (215) 250-5100.

Financial Aid: In 1993–94, 60% of all current freshmen and 66% of continuing students received some form of financial aid. About 50% of freshmen and 48% of continuing students received need-based aid. The average freshman award was $15,697. Of that total, scholarships or need-based grants averaged $11,833 ($24,338 maximum); loans averaged $3158 ($6625 maximum); and work contracts averaged $1232 ($2000 maximum). Fifty-four percent of undergraduate students work part-time. Average earnings from campus work for the school year are $850. The average financial indebtedness of the 1992–93 graduate was $10,676. Lafayette is a member of CSS. The FAF and FAFSA, the college's own financial statement, and the Business/Farm supplement and the Divorce/Separation parent statement, if applicable, are required. The deadline for financial aid applications is February 15.

International Students: There are currently 140 international students enrolled. The school actively recruits these students. They must take the TOEFL and achieve a minimum score of 550. The student must also take the SAT I.

Computers: The college provides computer facilities for student use. The mainframes are a DEC VAX 6310, an ARIX, and an IBM 9375. Students have unlimited 24-hour access to the campus network, PCs, and multiuser systems. More than 200 computers are available for student use; all residence hall rooms are connected to the campus network. All students may access the system 24 hours daily. There are no time limits on using the system and no fees.

Graduates: In 1992–93, 485 bachelor's degrees were awarded. The most popular majors among graduates were economics and business (14%), government and law (10%), and English (8%). Within an average freshman class, 1% graduate in 3 years, 87% in 4 years, and 4% in 5 years. Some 100 companies recruited on campus in 1992–93.

Admissions Contact: Dr. G. Gary Ripple, Director of Admissions.

LEBANON VALLEY COLLEGE OF PENNSYLVANIA
E-3
Annville, PA 17003   (717) 867-6181; (800) 445-6181 (in-state)

Full-time: 498 men, 467 women	Faculty: 66; IIB, av$
Part-time: 158 men, 344 women	Ph.D.s: 80%
Graduate: 138 men, 75 women	Student/Faculty: 15 to 1
Year: semesters, summer session	Tuition: $13,700
Application Deadline: open	Room & Board: $4600
Freshman Class: 1548 applied, 1169 accepted, 372 enrolled	
SAT I Verbal/Math: 467/521	COMPETITIVE

Lebanon Valley College of Pennsylvania, founded in 1866, is a private, coeducational institution affiliated with the United Methodist Church. The college offers undergraduate programs in the arts and sciences, business, health science, professional training, and religious studies. In addition to regional accreditation, LVC has baccalaureate program accreditation with NASM. The library contains 140,426 volumes, 16,749 microform items, and 5767 audiovisual forms, and subscribes to 730 periodicals. Special learning facilities include a learning resource center and radio station. The 200-acre campus is in a rural area 7 miles east of Hershey. Including residence halls, there are 26 buildings on campus.

Student Life: About 82% of undergraduates are from Pennsylvania. Students come from 12 states and 10 foreign countries. Ninety-five percent are from public schools. Ninety-four percent are white. Seventy-four percent are Protestant; 27% claim no religious affiliation; 23% Catholic. The average age of freshmen is 18; all undergraduates, 20. Twenty percent drop out by the end of their first year; 68% remain to graduate.

Housing: A total of 832 students can be accommodated in college housing. College-sponsored living facilities include single-sex and coed dormitories and on-campus apartments. In addition there are special interest houses. On-campus housing is guaranteed for all 4 years. Eighty-one percent of students live on campus; of those, 70% remain on campus on weekends. Alcohol is not permitted. All students may keep cars on campus.

Activities: About 25% of men belong to 3 local and 2 national fraternities; about 23% of women belong to 2 local sororities and 1 national sorority. There are 48 groups on campus, including band, cheerleading, choir, chorus, computers, drama, drill team, ethnic, honors, jazz band, literary magazine, marching band, musical theater, newspaper, orchestra, photography, political, professional, radio and TV, religious, social, social service, student government, and yearbook. Popular campus events include Homecoming, Parents Weekend, Christmas at the Valley, and Spring Arts Festival.

Sports: There are 9 intercollegiate sports for men and 7 for women, and 10 intramural sports for men and 7 for women. Athletic and recreation facilities include a 3000-seat stadium, a sports center, athletic fields, indoor and outdoor tracks, a gymnasium, and playing courts for basketball, handball, squash, and tennis.

Disabled Students: Sixty-five percent of the campus is accessible to disabled students. The following facilities are available: wheelchair ramps, elevators, special parking, specially equipped rest rooms, and special class scheduling.

Services: In addition to many counseling and information services, tutoring is available in every subject.

Campus Safety and Security: Campus safety and security measures include 24-hour foot and vehicle patrol, pamphlets, posters, films, and lighted pathways and sidewalks.

Programs of Study: LVC awards the B.A., B.S., B.M., B.S.Ch., B.S.Med.Tech., and B.S.Ed. degrees. Associate and master's degrees also are awarded. Bachelor's degrees are awarded in BIOLOGICAL SCIENCE (biochemistry and biology/biological science), BUSINESS (accounting, hotel/motel and restaurant management, and international business management), COMMUNICATIONS AND THE ARTS (communications technology, English, French, German, music, music performance, and Spanish), COMPUTER AND PHYSICAL SCIENCE (actuarial science, chemistry, computer programming, computer science, mathematics, and physics), EDUCATION (elementary, music, and secondary), ENGINEERING AND ENVIRONMENTAL DESIGN

(engineering), HEALTH PROFESSIONS (medical laboratory technology, nursing, occupational therapy, physical therapy, predentistry, premedicine, prepharmacy, and preveterinary science), SOCIAL SCIENCE (American studies, economics, history, philosophy, political science/government, prelaw, psychobiology, psychology, religion, and sociology). Actuarial science, natural sciences, and education are the strongest academically. Mathematics, management, and natural sciences have the largest enrollments.

Required: The general education program consists of a course in leadership studies, distribution requirements in the liberal arts and physical education, and core courses in Western cultural heritage, aesthetics, and human behavior. To graduate, students must complete at least 122 credit hours, including those required in the major, with a minimum GPA of 2.0.

Special: The Freshman Experience Program assigns each entering freshman to a faculty member to facilitate student adjustment to college. Study abroad is available to students through the college's affiliation with the International Student Exchange Program and the LVC College in Cologne Program. LVC is also affiliated with Regents College in London and Anglia Polytechnic University in Cambridge, England. There are 3-2 degree programs in engineering with the University of Pennsylvania, in forestry with Duke University, and in medical technology with Hahnemann University. There is also a 2-2 degree program in allied health sciences with Thomas Jefferson University. LVC also offers internships, a Washington semester, work-study programs, an accelerated degree program, B.A.-B.S. degrees, student-designed majors, and nondegree study. Students can earn up to 12 credit hours for life experience and may select pass/fail options in 6 courses. There is a freshman honors program on campus, as well as 7 national honor societies. Four departments have honors programs.

Faculty/Classroom: Seventy-seven percent of faculty are male; 23%, female. All teach undergraduates. No introductory courses are taught by graduate students. The average class size in an introductory lecture is 25; in a laboratory, 16; and in a regular course offering, 25.

Admissions: About 76% of the 1993-94 applicants were accepted. The SAT scores for the 1993-94 freshman class were as follows: Verbal—65% below 500, 28% between 500 and 599, and 7% between 600 and 700; Math—42% below 500, 39% between 500 and 599, 15% between 600 and 700, and 4% above 700. About 52% of the current freshmen were in the top fifth of their class; 79% were in the top two fifths. There were 5 National Merit finalists. Ten freshmen graduated first in their class.

Requirements: The SAT I is required. Applicants must be graduates of accredited secondary schools or have earned a GED. LVC requires 16 academic units or 16 Carnegie units, including 4 in English, 2 each in mathematics and foreign language, and 1 each in science and social studies. An interview is recommended. Students applying as music majors must also present an audition. AP and CLEP credits are accepted. Important factors used in the admissions decision are advanced placement or honor courses, recommendations by school officials, leadership record, personality, intangible qualities, and geographic diversity.

Procedure: Freshmen are admitted fall and spring. Entrance exams should be taken in the spring of the junior year. Application deadlines are open. Application fee is $25. Notification is sent on a rolling basis. There are early decision, early admissions, and deferred admissions plans.

Transfer: About 50 transfer students enrolled in 1993-94. Requirements for transfer applicants include a minimum GPA of 2.0, SAT I scores, and an interview. An associate degree is recommended. A total of 30 credits out of 122 must be completed at LVC.

Visiting: There are regularly scheduled orientations for prospective students, including a tour, an interview, and possibly a meeting with a professor. There are guides for informal visits and visitors may sit in on classes and stay overnight at the school. To arrange for a visit, contact Susan Borelli, Admission Counselor at (717) 867-6181 or (800) 445-6181.

Financial Aid: In 1993-94, 80% of all students received some form of financial aid. About 75% of students received need-based aid. The average freshman award was $10,083. Of that total, scholarships or need-based grants averaged $5700 ($10,000 maximum); loans averaged $3133 ($4125 maximum); and work contracts averaged $1250. Forty-seven percent of undergraduate students work part-time. Average earnings from campus work for the school year are $700. The average financial indebtedness of the 1992-93 graduate was $7495. LVC is a member of CSS. The PHEAA financial statement is required. The deadline for financial aid applications is March 1.

International Students: There are currently 19 international students enrolled. The school actively recruits these students. They must take the TOEFL and achieve a minimum score of 500. The student must also take the SAT I.

Computers: The college provides computer facilities for student use. The mainframes are a DEC VAX 8200 and a DEC System 5810. The mainframes can be accessed through 30 workstations and 40 micro-computers in computer laboratories. The mainframes can also be accessed via 16 modems. All students may access the system. There are no time limits and no fees.

Graduates: About 60 companies recruited on campus in a recent year. In the 1992 graduating class, 9% of the men and 9% of the women were enrolled in graduate school within 6 months of graduation.

Admissions Contact: Dean of Enrollment Management Services.

LEHIGH UNIVERSITY
Bethlehem, PA 18015

F-3
(215) 758-3100

Full-time: 2749 men, 1549 women	Faculty: 396; I, +$
Part-time: 104 men, 81 women	Ph.D.s: 99%
Graduate: 2013 men and women	Student/Faculty: 11 to 1
Year: semesters, summer session	Tuition: $17,750
Application Deadline: February 15	Room & Board: $5500
Freshman Class: 6397 applied, 4424 accepted, 1095 enrolled	
SAT I or ACT: required	**HIGHLY COMPETITIVE**

Lehigh University, founded in 1865, is a private, coeducational university offering programs in liberal arts, and science, engineering, and business. There are 3 undergraduate and 2 graduate schools. In addition to regional accreditation, Lehigh has baccalaureate program accreditation with AACSB, ABET, and NCATE. The 3 libraries contain 1,027,455 volumes, 1,750,000 microform items, and 24,500 audiovisual forms, and subscribe to 9700 periodicals. Computerized library sources and services include the card catalog, interlibrary loans, and database searching. Special learning facilities include a learning resource center, art gallery, and radio station. The 1600-acre campus is in a suburban area 60 miles north of Philadelphia and 80 miles southwest of Manhatten. Including residence halls, there are 131 buildings on campus.

Student Life: About 71% of undergraduates are from out-of-state, mostly the Middle Atlantic. Students come from 41 states, 43 foreign countries, and Canada. Seventy percent are from public schools; 30% from private. Eighty-nine percent are white. The average age of freshmen is 18; all undergraduates, 20. Five percent drop out by the end of their first year; 88% remain to graduate.

Housing: A total of 3410 students can be accommodated in college housing. College-sponsored living facilities include single-sex and coed dormitories, on-campus apartments, married-student housing, fraternity houses, and sorority houses. In addition there are language houses, special interest houses, a community service volunteer house, a students-of-color house, an international house, and a creative arts house. On-campus housing is guaranteed for the freshman year only and is available on a lottery system for upperclassmen. Seventy-five percent of students live on campus; of those, 75% remain on campus on weekends. Upperclassmen may keep cars on campus.

Activities: About 48% of men belong to 28 national fraternities; about 45% of women belong to 8 national sororities. There are 200 groups on campus, including art, band, cheerleading, chess, choir, chorale, chorus, computers, dance, drama, ethnic, gay, honors, international, jazz band, literary magazine, marching band, musical theater, newspaper, orchestra, photography, political, professional, radio and TV, religious, social, social service, student government, and yearbook. Popular campus events include Greek Week, Spring Fest, South Side Alive (carnival with the community), the Lehigh-Lafayette football game, Bach Festival, Christmas Vespers, Annual Pops Concert, and Musikfest.

Sports: There are 12 intercollegiate sports for men and 11 for women, and 23 intramural sports for men and 22 for women. Athletic and recreation facilities include a 17,000-seat stadium, a 6,500-seat arena, a gymnasium, a champion cross-country course, a field house with basketball and tennis courts, swimming pools, a track, indoor squash courts, weight rooms, a fitness center, and playing fields for field hockey, football, lacrosse, and soccer.

Disabled Students: The following facilities are available: wheelchair ramps, elevators, special parking, specially equipped rest rooms, special class scheduling, lowered drinking fountains, and lowered telephones.

Services: In addition to many counseling and information services, tutoring is available in most subjects, including calculus, physics, and English. Tutoring in other courses is available on request.

Campus Safety and Security: Campus safety and security measures include 24-hour foot and vehicle patrol, self defense education, escort service, and shuttle buses. In addition, there are informal discussions, pamphlets, posters, films, emergency telephones, and lighted pathways and sidewalks.

Programs of Study: Lehigh awards the B.A., B.S., B.S.B.A., and B.S.E. degrees. Master's and doctoral degrees also are awarded. Bachelor's degrees are awarded in BIOLOGICAL SCIENCE (biochemistry, biology/biological science, and molecular biology), BUSINESS (accounting, banking and finance, business economics, management science, and marketing/retailing/merchandising), COMMUNICATIONS AND THE ARTS (classics, dramatic arts, English, fine arts, French, German, journalism, music, and Spanish),

COMPUTER AND PHYSICAL SCIENCE (actuarial science, chemistry, computer science, earth science, geology, geophysics and seismology, mathematics, and physics), ENGINEERING AND ENVIRONMENTAL DESIGN (architectural engineering, architecture, chemical engineering, civil engineering, computer engineering, electrical/electronics engineering, engineering mechanics, engineering physics, environmental science, industrial engineering, materials engineering, and mechanical engineering), HEALTH PROFESSIONS (predentistry and premedicine), SOCIAL SCIENCE (American studies, anthropology, behavioral science, cognitive science, East Asian studies, economics, history, international relations, philosophy, political science/government, prelaw, psychology, religion, Russian and Slavic studies, social science, sociology, and urban studies). Architecture, accounting, mechanical engineering, and psychology have the largest enrollments.

Required: Graduation requirements vary by degree sought, but all students must complete 2 semesters of English. Students must also maintain a minimum GPA of 2.0.

Special: The university offers co-op programs through the Colleges of Engineering and Applied Science and Business and Economics, cross-registration with the Lehigh Valley Association of Independent Colleges, study abroad in 50 countries, internships, a Washington semester, several work-study programs, accelerated degree programs in medicine and dentistry, student-designed majors, many combinations of dual majors, a B.A.-B.S. degree, a 3–2 engineering degree, and pass/fail options. There is a freshman honors program on campus, as well as 16 national honor societies, including Phi Beta Kappa. Sixty departments have honors programs.

Faculty/Classroom: Eighty-two percent of faculty are male; 18%, female. All both teach and do research. No introductory courses are taught by graduate students. The average class size in an introductory lecture is 150 and in a regular course offering, 29.

Admissions: About 69% of the 1993–94 applicants were accepted. The SAT scores for the 1993–94 freshman class were as follows: Verbal—37% below 500, 47% between 500 and 599, 15% between 600 and 700, and 1% above 700; Math—5% below 500, 29% between 500 and 599, 53% between 600 and 700, and 13% above 700. About 67% of the current freshmen were in the top fifth of their class; 90% were in the top two fifths. There were 7 National Merit finalists and 7 semifinalists.

Requirements: The SAT I or ACT is required. Candidates for admission should have completed at least 1 year each of art and music, 4 years of English, and 2 years each of a foreign language, history, mathematics, science, and social science. Most students present 4 years each of science, mathematics, and English. A graded writing sample is required. An on-campus interview is recommended. AP credits are accepted. Important factors used in the admissions decision are advanced placement or honor courses, evidence of special talent, leadership record, geographic diversity, and extracurricular activities record.

Procedure: Freshmen are admitted fall and spring. Entrance exams should be taken by the January test date. Early decision applications should be filed by December 1; regular applications, by February 15 for fall entry and November 15 for spring entry, along with an application fee of $40. Notification of early decision is sent December 15; regular decision, by April 1. About 253 early decision candidates were accepted for the 1993–94 class. A waiting list is an active part of the admissions procedure, with about 12% of applicants on the list.

Transfer: About 100 transfer students enrolled in 1993–94. Transfer candidates should have a minimum GPA of 2.8. An interview is recommended. A total of 30 credits out of 121 must be completed at Lehigh.

Visiting: There are regularly scheduled orientations for prospective students, consisting of interviews scheduled Monday through Friday, 9 A.M. to 5 P.M.; tours scheduled Monday through Friday, 10:15 A.M., 11:15 A.M., 1 P.M., 2 P.M., and 3 P.M., and interviews and tours also available on some Saturdays. There are guides for informal visits and visitors may sit in on classes and stay overnight at the school. To arrange for a visit, contact Jay Hipps, Admission Counselor at (215) 758-3100.

Financial Aid: In 1993–94, 57% of all current freshmen and 52% of continuing students received some form of financial aid. About 55% of freshmen and 47% of continuing students received need-based aid. The average freshman award was $16,078. Of that total, scholarships or need-based grants averaged $11,693 ($24,000 maximum); loans averaged $3405 ($6000 maximum); and work contracts averaged $980 ($1500 maximum). Eighteen percent of undergraduate students work part-time. Average earnings from campus work for the school year are $774. The average financial indebtedness of the 1992–93 graduate was $11,733. Lehigh is a member of CSS. The FAF and the college's own financial statement are required. The deadline for financial aid applications is February 7.

International Students: There are currently 129 international students enrolled. The school actively recruits these students. They must take the TOEFL and achieve a minimum score of 550. The student must also take the SAT I or the ACT.

Computers: The university provides computer facilities for student use. There are clusters of high-speed IBM RS/6000 computers, with more than 115 workstations in public sites. There are also more than 400 microcomputers available for student use in libraries, academic buildings, and computer centers. There are computer ports in all classrooms, dormitories, and offices. Many LANs and a high-speed fiber-optic network are available. All students may access the system 24 hours per day, 7 days per week. There are no time limits on using the system and no fees.

Graduates: In 1992–93, 1045 bachelor's degrees were awarded. The most popular majors among graduates were accounting (10%), civil engineering (8%), and government (4%). Within an average freshman class, 75% graduate in 4 years and 88% in 5 years. Some 313 companies recruited on campus in 1992–93.

Admissions Contact: Patricia G. Boig, Director of Admissions.

LINCOLN UNIVERSITY

E-4

Lincoln University, PA 19352   (215) 932-8300, ext. 205

Full-time: 500 men, 700 women	**Faculty:** 90; IIB, -$
Part-time: 20 men, 40 women	**Ph.D.s:** 71%
Graduate: 50 men, 135 women	**Student/Faculty:** 13 to 1
Year: semesters	**Tuition:** n/av
Application Deadline: January 1	**Room & Board:** n/app
Freshman Class: n/av	
SAT I Verbal/Math: 360/380	**LESS COMPETITIVE**

Lincoln University, founded in 1854, is a public, coeducational institution offering programs in liberal arts and teacher preparation. The library contains 167,438 volumes, 196,600 microform items, and 1419 audiovisual forms, and subscribes to 752 periodicals. Special learning facilities include an art gallery and radio station. The 422-acre campus is in a rural area 45 miles southwest of Philadelphia. Including residence halls, there are 28 buildings on campus.

Student Life: About 53% of undergraduates are from out-of-state, mostly the Middle Atlantic. Students come from 26 states and 14 foreign countries. Ninety-five percent are from public schools; 5% from private. Eighty-nine percent are African American. Fifty percent are Protestant. The average age of freshmen is 18; all undergraduates, 19. Thirty percent drop out by the end of their first year; 36% remain to graduate.

Housing: A total of 1300 students can be accommodated in college housing. College-sponsored living facilities include single-sex and coed dormitories. In addition, there are honors houses and language houses. On-campus housing is guaranteed for the freshman year only and is available on a first-come, first-served basis. Eighty-nine percent of students live on campus; of those, 90% remain on campus on weekends. Alcohol is not permitted. Upperclassmen may keep cars on campus.

Activities: About 10% of men belong to 4 national fraternities; about 20% of women belong to 3 national sororities. There are 60 groups on campus, including art, band, cheerleading, choir, chorale, computers, dance, drama, honors, international, jazz band, newspaper, pep band, political, radio and TV, religious, social, social service, student government, and yearbook. Popular campus events include Homecoming, Commencement, lectures and recitals, Black History Month, and convocations.

Sports: There are 9 intercollegiate sports for men and 6 for women, and 11 intramural sports each. Athletic and recreation facilities include a 2000-seat gymnasium, tennis courts, softball and track fields, a fitness trail, a swimming pool, and a bowling alley.

Disabled Students: All of the campus is accessible to disabled students. The following facilities are available: wheelchair ramps, elevators, special parking, and specially equipped rest rooms.

Services: In addition to many counseling and information services, tutoring is available in every subject. There is remedial math, reading, and writing.

Campus Safety and Security: Campus safety and security measures include 24-hour foot and vehicle patrol, self-defense education, escort service, and shuttle buses. In addition, there are informal discussions, pamphlets, posters, films, emergency telephones, and lighted pathways and sidewalks.

Programs of Study: Lincoln awards the B.A. and B.S. degrees. Master's degrees also are awarded. Bachelor's degrees are awarded in BIOLOGICAL SCIENCE (biology/biological science), BUSINESS (accounting, banking and finance, business administration and management, and recreation and leisure services), COMMUNICATIONS AND THE ARTS (communications, English, French, journalism, music, and Russian), COMPUTER AND PHYSICAL SCIENCE (actuarial science, chemistry, computer science, mathematics, and physics), EDUCATION (art, early childhood, elementary, English, foreign languages, health, mathematics, music, science, secondary, and social

studies), ENGINEERING AND ENVIRONMENTAL DESIGN (preengineering), HEALTH PROFESSIONS (recreation therapy), SOCIAL SCIENCE (criminal justice, economics, history, human services, international relations, philosophy, political science/government, psychology, public affairs, religion, and sociology). Physics, chemistry, and biology are the strongest academically. Business administration has the largest enrollment.

Required: Required courses include 9 to 12 hours of social science, 2 courses each of speech, writing, and critical thinking, a freshman seminar, world literature, music, art, philosophy, and religion. All students must take Integrative Themes in the Liberal Arts. Students must pass a writing proficiency and a comprehensive exam. A total of 120 to 128 semester hours is required, along with a GPA of 2.0.

Special: Lincoln offers co-op programs, internships, study abroad in 9 countries, work-study, and pass/fail options. There are 3–2 engineering degrees offered with Drexel and Pennsylvania State Universities, Lafayette College, and New Jersey Institute of Technology. There is a freshman honors program on campus, as well as 4 national honor societies. One department has an honors program.

Faculty/Classroom: Sixty-one percent of faculty are male; 39%, female. Eighty-four percent teach undergraduates. No introductory courses are taught by graduate students. The average class size is 15.

Admissions: About 21% of the current freshmen were in the top fifth of their class; 27% were in the top two fifths.

Requirements: Lincoln requires applicants to be in the upper 50% of their class. A minimum GPA of 2.0 is required. The SAT I or ACT is required. A GED is accepted. Applicants should complete 21 credit hours, including 4 credits in English, 3 each in mathematics, science, and social studies, 2 in art, and 1 in physical education. An essay and an interview are required. Important factors used in the admissions decision are advanced placement or honor courses, evidence of special talent, leadership record, ability to finance college education, and personality.

Procedure: Freshmen are admitted to all sessions. Entrance exams should be taken prior to admission. Applications should be filed by January 1 for fall entry and December 1 for spring entry, along with an application fee of $10. Notification is sent on a rolling basis. A waiting list is an active part of the admissions procedure.

Transfer: About 40 transfer students enrolled in a recent year. Transfer applicants must submit certificates of honorable dismissal, good moral character, and sound health, and transcripts. They must have a GPA of at least 2.0. A total of 60 credits out of 120 must be completed at Lincoln.

Visiting: There are regularly scheduled orientations for prospective students. There are guides for informal visits and visitors may sit in on classes and stay overnight at the school. To arrange for a visit, contact Jimmy Arrington, Director of Admissions at (215) 932–8300.

Financial Aid: In a recent year, 98% of all students received some form of financial aid. About 95% received need-based aid. The average freshman award was $5500. Of that total, scholarships or need-based grants averaged $1200 ($2400 maximum); loans averaged $1500 ($2625 maximum); and work contracts averaged $1000 ($2025 maximum). Thirty-five percent of undergraduate students work part-time. Average earnings from campus work for the school year are $1250. The average financial indebtedness of a recent year's graduate was $9500. Lincoln is a member of CSS. The FAF and PHEAA are required. The deadline for financial aid applications is March 1.

International Students: There are currently 14 international students enrolled. The school actively recruits these students. They must take the TOEFL.

Computers: The college provides computer facilities for student use. The mainframe is a DEC VAX 11/750. There are also 115 IBM, Apple, and Apple Macintosh microcomputers available for student use in the library and in computer laboratories. All students may access the system. There are no time limits on using the system and no fees.

Graduates: In a recent year, 208 bachelor's degrees were awarded. The most popular majors among graduates were business administration (26%), sociology (8%), and psychology (8%). Some 70 companies recruited on campus in 1992–93. In the 1992 graduating class, 20% of the men and 40% of the women were enrolled in graduate school within 6 months of graduation; 70% of the men and 50% of the women had found employment.

Admissions Contact: Jimmy Arrington, Director of Admissions.

LOCK HAVEN UNIVERSITY OF PENNSYLVANIA
D-2

Lock Haven, PA 17745

(717) 893–2027
(800) 233–8978 (out-of-state)

Full-time: 1633 men, 2054 women	Faculty: 185; IIB, +$
Part-time: 101 men, 107 women	Ph.D.s: 54%
Graduate: 1 man, 2 women	Student/Faculty: 20 to 1
Year: semesters, summer session	Tuition: $3508
Application Deadline: June 1	Room & Board: $3620
Freshman Class: 3300 applied, 2215 accepted, 651 enrolled	
SAT I Verbal/Math: 460/520	COMPETITIVE

Lock Haven University, established in 1870, is an independent, coeducational institution offering undergraduate degrees in arts and sciences, education, and human services. There are 2 undergraduate schools. In addition to regional accreditation, Lock Haven has baccalaureate program accreditation with CSWE and NCATE. The library contains 344,716 volumes, 13,574 microform items, and 508,122 audiovisual forms, and subscribes to 1598 periodicals. Computerized library sources and services include the card catalog and interlibrary loans. Special learning facilities include a learning resource center, an art gallery, a planetarium, a radio station, a TV station, and primate and human performance laboratories. The 135-acre campus is in a small town 30 miles west of Williamsport. Including residence halls, there are 28 buildings on campus.

Student Life: About 80% of undergraduates are from Pennsylvania. Students come from 35 states, 40 foreign countries, and Canada. Ninety-five percent are white. The average age of freshmen is 18; all undergraduates, 21. Fifteen percent drop out by the end of their first year; 60% remain to graduate.

Housing: A total of 1600 students can be accommodated in college housing. College-sponsored living facilities include single-sex and coed dormitories. On-campus housing is guaranteed for all 4 years. Fifty-eight percent of students commute. Upperclassmen may keep cars on campus. Alcohol is not permitted.

Activities: About 11% of men belong to 7 national fraternities; about 8% of women belong to 4 national sororities. There are 69 groups on campus, including art, band, cheerleading, choir, chorale, chorus, computers, dance, drama, ethnic, gay, honors, international, jazz band, literary magazine, marching band, musical theater, newspaper, orchestra, pep band, photography, political, professional, radio and TV, religious, social, social service, student government, and symphony. Popular campus events include Homecoming and Parents Weekend.

Sports: There are 7 intercollegiate sports for men and 9 for women, and 19 intramural sports for men and 18 for women. Athletic and recreation facilities include a 5000-seat stadium containing a football field and an all-weather track, a 2500-seat field house, a gymnasium used for intramurals, a weight training room, and a gymnasium that houses a swimming pool.

Disabled Students: The entire campus is accessible to disabled students. The following facilities are available: wheelchair ramps, elevators, special parking, specially equipped rest rooms, special class scheduling, and lowered drinking fountains and telephones.

Services: In addition to many counseling and information services, tutoring is available in most subjects, including reader services for the blind. There are also writing and mathematics centers.

Campus Safety and Security: Campus safety and security measures include a 24-hour foot and vehicle patrol, informal discussions, pamphlets, posters, films, emergency telephones, and lighted pathways and sidewalks.

Programs of Study: Lock Haven awards the B.A., B.S., and B.S.Ed. degrees. Associate and master's degrees are also awarded. Bachelor's degrees are awarded in BIOLOGICAL SCIENCE (biology/biological science and environmental biology), BUSINESS (business administration and management), COMMUNICATIONS AND THE ARTS (communications, English, fine arts, French, German, journalism, music, Spanish, and speech/debate/rhetoric), COMPUTER AND PHYSICAL SCIENCE (chemistry, computer science, earth science, geology, information sciences and systems, mathematics, and physics), EDUCATION (early childhood, elementary, foreign languages, health, library science, physical, science, secondary, and special), HEALTH PROFESSIONS (medical laboratory technology), SOCIAL SCIENCE (economics, geography, history, humanities and social science, Latin American studies, liberal arts/general studies, philosophy, political science/government, psychology, social science, social work, and sociology). Health science is the strongest program academically. Education, health science, and business management science have the largest enrollments.

Required: Students must complete 60 hours of general education, including 18 hours of humanities, 12 hours of social behavioral sciences, 9 hours of mathematics and science, and 18 hours of electives, and they must maintain a GPA of 2.0. A total of 128 credit hours is

required, with 68 credits earned in major and elective course work. All students must fulfill a 3-credit health and physical requirement.

Special: Lock Haven offers cooperative programs in music education and engineering, internships (which are required in some majors), an extensive study-abroad program in 18 countries, and many work-study options. An accelerated degree program for honor students and a general studies major are also offered. A 3–2 engineering degree is available with Pennsylvania State University. Pass/fail grading options are limited to 1 course outside the major per semester, not to exceed 12 credit hours. There is a freshman honors program on campus, as well as 9 national honor societies. Six departments have honors programs.

Faculty/Classroom: The average class size in a laboratory is 20 and in a regular course offering, 21.

Admissions: About 67% of the 1993–94 applicants were accepted. The SAT scores for the 1993–94 freshman class were as follows: Verbal—72% below 500, 26% between 500 and 599, and 2% between 600 and 700; Math—41% below 500, 45% between 500 and 599, 13% between 600 and 700, and 1% above 700. About 40% of the current freshmen were in the top fifth of their class; 81% were in the top two fifths. Three freshmen graduated first in their class.

Requirements: Lock Haven requires applicants to be in the upper 60% of their class. A minimum GPA of B- is required. The SAT I or ACT is required. Applicants must graduate from an accredited secondary school or have a GED. Sixteen academic credits are required, and a college preparatory course is recommended. AP and CLEP credits are accepted. Important factors used in the admissions decision are leadership record, advanced placement or honor courses, evidence of special talent, recommendations by school officials, and recommendations by alumni.

Procedure: Freshmen are admitted to all sessions. Entrance exams should be taken during the spring of the junior year or the fall of the senior year. Applications should be filed by June 1 for fall entry, along with an application fee of $25. Notification is sent on a rolling basis. There are early decision, early admissions, and deferred admissions plans.

Transfer: About 220 transfer students enrolled in a recent year. Transfer applicants must have completed 24 transfer credits. A minimum GPA of 2.0 is required, and a composite SAT I score of 970 is recommended. A total of 32 credits out of 128 must be completed at Lock Haven.

Visiting: There are regularly scheduled orientations for prospective students, consisting of an introduction to the administration, sessions with faculty, and an information arena/departmental showcase. There are guides for informal visits and visitors may sit in on classes. To arrange for a visit, contact the Admissions Office at (717) 893-2027 or (800) 332-8900 (in-state) or (800) 233-8998 (out-of-state).

Financial Aid: In a recent year, 80% of all students received some form of financial aid. About 78% of freshmen and 82% of continuing students received need-based aid. The average freshman award was $4250. Of that total, scholarships or need-based grants averaged $1700 ($3800 maximum); loans averaged $2000 ($2625 maximum); and work contracts averaged $550 ($900 maximum). Twenty-five percent of undergraduate students work part-time. Average earnings from campus work for the school year are $900. The average financial indebtedness of a recent graduate was $8556. Lock Haven is a member of CSS. The FAF and PHEAA are required. The deadline for financial aid applications is April 1.

International Students: There are currently 62 international students enrolled. They must take the TOEFL and achieve a minimum score of 550. The SAT I or the ACT is also required.

Computers: Lock Haven provides computer facilities for student use. The mainframe is an IBM 4381. More than 100 microcomputers are available for student use in computer laboratories and residence halls. The library's card catalog is also accessible from all on-campus computers hooked up to the mainframe. All students may access the system anytime. There are no fees.

Graduates: In 1992–93, 578 bachelor's degrees were awarded.

Admissions Contact: Joseph Coldren, Director of Admissions.

LYCOMING COLLEGE
D-2
Williamsport, PA 17701-5192 (800) 345-3920

Full-time: 642 men, 721 women	Faculty: 94; IIB, av$
Part-time: 23 men, 67 women	Ph.D.s: 80%
Graduate: none	Student/Faculty: 15 to 1
Year: 4-4-1, summer session	Tuition: $13,000
Application Deadline: April 1	Room & Board: $42,000
Freshman Class: 1286 applied, 1005 accepted, 363 enrolled	
SAT I Verbal/Math: 470/520	LESS COMPETITIVE

Lycoming College, established in 1812, is a private, nonprofit, coeducational liberal arts institution affiliated with the Methodist Church. The library contains 160,000 volumes, and subscribes to 1069 periodicals. Computerized library sources and services include the card catalog, interlibrary loans, and database searching. Special learning facilities include a learning resource center, art gallery, planetarium, radio station, and a nursing skills laboratory. The 34-acre campus is in a small town 94 miles north of Harrisburg. Including residence halls, there are 23 buildings on campus.

Student Life: About 71% of undergraduates are from Pennsylvania. Students come from 20 states, 12 foreign countries, and Canada. Seventy-five percent are from public schools; 25% from private. Ninety-five percent are white. Forty-nine percent are Protestant; 31% Catholic. The average age of freshmen is 18.3; all undergraduates, 21.6. Twenty percent drop out by the end of their first year; 59% remain to graduate.

Housing: A total of 1110 students can be accommodated in college housing. College-sponsored living facilities include single-sex and coed dormitories. In addition there are special interest, nonsmoking, and contract study floors. On-campus housing is guaranteed for all 4 years. Seventy-five percent of students live on campus; of those, 65% remain on campus on weekends. All students may keep cars on campus.

Activities: About 31% of men belong to 5 national fraternities; about 27% of women belong to 3 local sororities and 1 national sorority. There are 52 groups on campus, including art, band, cheerleading, choir, chorus, computers, drama, ethnic, film, honors, international, literary magazine, musical theater, newspaper, photography, professional, religious, social, social service, student government, and yearbook. Popular campus events include Campus Carnival, Christmas Party, Christmas Choir Concert, Homecoming, and Parents Weekend.

Sports: There are 9 intercollegiate sports for men and 9 for women, and 9 intramural sports for men, 9 for women, and 2 for both. Athletic and recreation facilities include an outdoor softball, football, soccer, and field hockey complex, indoor basketball courts, intramural fields, and tennis courts.

Disabled Students: Eighty-five percent of the campus is accessible to disabled students. The following facilities are available: wheelchair ramps, elevators, special parking, specially equipped rest rooms, special class scheduling, lowered drinking fountains, lowered telephones, and specially designed residence hall rooms.

Services: In addition to many counseling and information services, tutoring is available in most subjects, including mathematics, languages, sciences, and accounting. There is remedial math, reading, and writing.

Campus Safety and Security: Campus safety and security measures include 24-hour foot and vehicle patrol, escort service, informal discussions, pamphlets, posters, and films. In addition, there are emergency telephones and lighted pathways and sidewalks.

Programs of Study: Lycoming awards the B.A., B.F.A., and B.S.N. degrees. Bachelor's degrees are awarded in BIOLOGICAL SCIENCE (biology/biological science), BUSINESS (accounting and business administration and management), COMMUNICATIONS AND THE ARTS (art history and appreciation, communications, dramatic arts, English, French, German, literature, music, sculpture, Spanish, and studio art), COMPUTER AND PHYSICAL SCIENCE (astronomy, chemistry, computer science, mathematics, and physics), HEALTH PROFESSIONS (medical laboratory technology and nursing), SOCIAL SCIENCE (anthropology, archeology, criminal justice, economics, history, international relations, philosophy, political science/government, psychology, religion, and sociology). Business, psychology, nursing, and biology have the largest enrollments.

Required: To graduate, students must complete distribution requirements in English, a foreign language or mathematics, religion or philosophy, fine arts, natural science, and history and social science. A total of 128 credits, with a minimum GPA of 2.0 is required. The number of hours required in the major varies. Students must also complete 2 semesters of physical education and achieve competency in swimming, and they must prove competency in writing and take 2 writing-intensive courses.

Special: Cooperative programs are available with the Ohio and Pennsylvania Colleges of Podiatric Medicine, Johnson Atelier Technical Institute of Sculpture, Pennsylvania College of Optometry, and Pennsylvania State and Duke universities. Cross-registration is available with the Pennsylvania College of Technology. Teacher and other internship programs, study abroad in 4 countries, and a Washington semester are available. Lycoming offers work-study programs, dual and student-designed majors, and an accelerated degree program in conjunction with the college's Scholar Program. There is a 3–2 engineering degree program with Pennsylvania State University. Nondegree study and pass/fail grading options are available. There is a freshman honors program on campus, as well as 12 national honor societies. Eleven departments have honors programs.

Faculty/Classroom: Seventy-one percent of faculty are male; 29%, female. All teach undergraduates. The average class size in an introductory lecture is 30; in a laboratory, 15; and in a regular course offering, 18.

Admissions: About 78% of the 1993–94 applicants were accepted. The SAT scores for the 1993–94 freshman class were as follows: Verbal—72% below 500, 22% between 500 and 599, and 6% between 600 and 700; Math—52% below 500, 35% between 500 and 599, 12% between 600 and 700, and 2% above 700. About 26% of the current freshmen were in the top fifth of their class; 56% were in the top two fifths. There were 2 National Merit finalists and 2 semifinalists. Eleven freshmen graduated first in their class.

Requirements: The SAT I, with a minimum score of 400 on each section, or the ACT is required. Applicants must graduate from an accredited secondary school or have a GED. They must have earned 16 academic or Carnegie units, and completed 4 years in English, 3 years each in history, mathematics, and social studies, and 2 years each in science and a foreign language. An essay is optional, and an interview is recommended. Portfolios and auditions may be required for students seeking scholarships. AP and CLEP credits are accepted. Important factors used in the admissions decision are advanced placement or honor courses, recommendations by school officials, leadership record, evidence of special talent, and extracurricular activities record.

Procedure: Freshmen are admitted fall and spring. Entrance exams should be taken during the junior or senior year. Applications should be filed by April 1 for fall entry and December 1 for spring entry, along with an application fee of $25. Notification is sent on a rolling basis. There are early admissions and deferred admissions plans.

Transfer: A total of 64 transfer students enrolled in 1993–94. Transfer applicants must submit appropriate transcripts, and have a minimum GPA of 2.0 in transferable courses. Students who have completed 24 transferable semester hours are not required to submit SAT I or ACT results. A total of 32 credits out of 128 must be completed at Lycoming.

Visiting: There are regularly scheduled orientations for prospective students. There are guides for informal visits and visitors may sit in on classes and stay overnight at the school. To arrange for a visit, contact the Admissions House at (800) 345–3920.

Financial Aid: In 1993–94, 83% of all current freshmen and 84% of continuing students received some form of financial aid. About 80% of freshmen and 77% of continuing students received need-based aid. The average freshman award was $10,786. Of that total, scholarships or need-based grants averaged $5600 ($13,000 maximum); loans averaged $3049 ($3625 maximum); and work contracts averaged $600 ($1500 maximum). Thirty-five percent of undergraduate students work part-time. Average earnings from campus work for the school year are $750. The average financial indebtedness of the 1992–93 graduate was $9360. Lycoming is a member of CSS. Pennsylvania residents must submit the PHEAA and the FAFSA. Out-of-state applicants should submit the FAF and the college's own financial statement. The deadline for financial aid applications is April 1.

International Students: There are currently 20 international students enrolled. They must take the TOEFL and achieve a minimum score of 500. The student must also take the SAT I or ACT. This requirement may be waived, however.

Computers: The college provides computer facilities for student use. The mainframes are a DEC MicroVAX 3600, an HP Model 8275, and a Prime-Exl 316. Students may access the mainframe through various computer laboratories. There are also 150 terminals and microcomputers available to students. All students may access the system 8 A.M. to 12 midnight. There are no time limits on using the system and no fees.

Graduates: In 1992–93, 256 bachelor's degrees were awarded. The most popular majors among graduates were business (17%), psychology (11%), and biology (9%). Within an average freshman class, 1% graduate in 3 years, 47% in 4 years, and 53% in 5 years. Some 25 companies recruited on campus in 1992–93.

Admissions Contact: James Spencer, Dean of Admissions and Financial Aid.

MANSFIELD UNIVERSITY
Mansfield, PA 16933

D-1

(717) 662-4243

Full-time: 1171 men, 1505 women	Faculty: 195; IIB, +$
Part-time: 77 men, 138 women	Ph.D.s: 47%
Graduate: 74 men, 258 women	Student/Faculty: 14 to 1
Year: semesters, summer session	Tuition: $3224 ($7652)
Application Deadline: July 1	Room & Board: $3124

Freshman Class: 3614 applied, 2148 accepted, 887 enrolled
SAT I Verbal/Math: 421/461

COMPETITIVE

Mansfield University, founded in 1857, is a public university that is part of the Pennsylvania State System of Higher Education. It offers programs in professional studies and the arts and sciences. There is one graduate school. In addition to regional accreditation, Mansfield has baccalaureate program accreditation with CAHEA, CSWE, NASM, and NCATE. The 3 libraries contain 210,662 volumes, 994,649 microform items, and 16,993 audiovisual forms, and subscribe to 1952 periodicals. Computerized library sources and ser-

vices include the card catalog, interlibrary loans, and database searching. Special learning facilities include a learning resource center, a natural history museum, a planetarium, a radio station, a TV station, and a high-tech lecture laboratory. The 175-acre campus is in a rural area 28 miles south of Corning/Elmira, NY, and 58 miles north of Williamsport. Including residence halls, there are 38 buildings on campus.

Student Life: About 77% of undergraduates are from Pennsylvania. Students come from 20 states, 18 foreign countries, and Canada. Ninety-three percent are white. The average age of freshmen is 19; all undergraduates, 22. Twenty-two percent drop out by the end of their first year; 50% remain to graduate.

Housing: A total of 1864 students can be accommodated in college housing. College-sponsored living facilities include single-sex and coed dormitories and sorority houses. On-campus housing is guaranteed for all 4 years. Sixty-seven percent of students live on campus. Alcohol is not permitted. All students may keep cars on campus.

Activities: About 22% of men belong to 6 national fraternities; about 16% of women belong to 4 national sororities. There are more than 80 groups on campus, including band, cheerleading, choir, chorus, computers, drama, ethnic, honors, international, jazz band, literary magazine, marching band, musical theater, newspaper, orchestra, photography, political, professional, radio and TV, religious, social, social service, student government, symphony, and yearbook. Popular campus events include Homecoming, Parents Weekend Faculty Lecture Series, Black History Month, Fabulous 1890's Weekend, Alcohol Awareness Week, and Northern Appalachian Story Telling Festival.

Sports: There are 6 intercollegiate sports each for men and women, and 13 intramural sports each for men and women. Athletic and recreation facilities include football, baseball, and hockey fields, a gymnasium, a track, a recreation center, a 4000-seat stadium, a 2500-seat indoor gymnasium, and a 2500-seat auditorium.

Disabled Students: Eighty percent of the campus is accessible to disabled students. The following facilities are available: wheelchair ramps, elevators, special parking, specially equipped rest rooms, special class scheduling, lowered drinking fountains and telephones, and a wheelchair lift.

Services: In addition to many counseling and information services, tutoring is available in most subjects. There is remedial math, reading, and writing.

Campus Safety and Security: Campus safety and security measures include a 24-hour foot and vehicle patrol, escort service, shuttle buses, emergency telephones, and lighted pathways and sidewalks.

Programs of Study: Mansfield awards the B.A., B.S., B.M., B.M.E., B.S.Ed. B.S.N., and B.S.W. degrees. Associate and master's degrees are also awarded. Bachelor's degrees are awarded in AGRICULTURE (fishing and fisheries), BIOLOGICAL SCIENCE (biology/biological science), BUSINESS (accounting, business administration and management, business economics, fashion merchandising, marketing/retailing/merchandising, personnel management, and tourism), COMMUNICATIONS AND THE ARTS (art history and appreciation, broadcasting, dramatic arts, English, French, German, journalism, music, music business management, public relations, Spanish, and studio art), COMPUTER AND PHYSICAL SCIENCE (actuarial science, chemistry, computer science, geology, information sciences and systems, mathematics, and physics), EDUCATION (art, early childhood, elementary, English, foreign languages, mathematics, music, science, secondary, social studies, and special), ENGINEERING AND ENVIRONMENTAL DESIGN (city/community/regional planning, environmental science, and preengineering), HEALTH PROFESSIONS (medical laboratory technology, music therapy, nursing, and respiratory therapy), SOCIAL SCIENCE (anthropology, criminal justice, economics, geography, history, international studies, liberal arts/general studies, philosophy, political science/government, psychology, social science, social work, and sociology). Music, physical sciences, social sciences, and education are the strongest programs academically. Education, music, and social sciences have the largest enrollments.

Required: Students must complete 128 credit hours with a 2.0 GPA in core courses and satisfy distribution requirements, general education electives, and major requirements.

Special: There is study abroad in England, Spain, and Germany. There is a 3–2 engineering program with Pennsylvania State, George Washington University, the Georgia Institute of Technology, the University of Pittsburgh, and the University of Rochester. The university offers work-study, dual majors, a general studies degree, credit by examination, credit for military experience, nondegree study, and pass/fail options. There is a freshman honors program on campus.

Faculty/Classroom: Sixty-two percent of faculty are male; 38%, female. Ninety-eight percent teach undergraduates and 2% do research. No introductory courses are taught by graduate students. The average class size in an introductory lecture is 35; in a laboratory, 20; and in a regular course offering, 25.

Admissions: About 59% of the 1993–94 applicants were accepted. The SAT scores for the 1993–94 freshman class were as follows: Verbal—83% below 500, 16% between 500 and 599, and 1% between 600 and 700; Math—66% below 500, 26% between 500 and 599, 7% between 600 and 700, and 1% above 700. About 31% of the current freshmen were in the top fifth of their class; 66% were in the top two fifths. Two freshmen graduated first in their class.

Requirements: Mansfield requires applicants to be in the upper 60% of their class. A minimum GPA of 2.5 is required. The SAT I or ACT is required, with a minimum composite SAT I score of 800, or a minimum ACT score of 19. A GED is accepted. Applicants should prepare with 4 credits of English, 3 each of history, mathematics, science, and social studies, 2 of foreign language, and 6 of additional academic electives. Art students must submit a portfolio; music students must audition. AP and CLEP credits are accepted. Ability to finance college education is an important factor used in the admission decision.

Procedure: Freshmen are admitted in the fall and spring. Entrance exams should be taken by the junior or senior year of high school. Early decision applications should be filed by July 1; regular applications, by July 1 for fall entry and December 15 for spring entry, along with an application fee of $25. There are early decision, early admissions, and deferred admissions plans. Two early decision candidates were accepted for the 1993–94 class. A waiting list is an active part of the admissions procedure.

Transfer: About 250 transfer students enrolled in 1993–94. Transfer applicants must have a GPA of at least 2.0. A total of 32 credits out of 128 must be completed at Mansfield.

Visiting: There are regularly scheduled orientations for prospective students. There are guides for informal visits and visitors may sit in on classes. To arrange for a visit, contact the Admissions Office at (717) 662-4243.

Financial Aid: In 1993–94, 75% of all students received some form of financial aid. About 35% of students received need-based aid. The average freshman award was $3100. Of that total, scholarships or need-based grants averaged $1000 ($7352 maximum); loans averaged $2500 ($5500 maximum); and work contracts averaged $900 ($1400 maximum). The average financial indebtedness of the 1992–93 graduate was $5000. Mansfield is a member of CSS. The Pennsylvania Higher Education Agency Form (PHEAA) financial statement is required. The deadline for financial aid applications is April 15.

International Students: There are currently 37 international students enrolled. The school actively recruits these students. They must take the TOEFL and achieve a minimum score of 550. The student must also take the SAT I or the ACT.

Computers: The college provides computer facilities for student use. The mainframe is an IBM 4381 Model 23. There are also 70 Apple IIe and IIgs, IBM ATs, and PC microcomputers available. All students may access the system anytime. There are no fees.

Graduates: In a recent year, 436 bachelor's degrees were awarded. In the 1992 graduating class, about 5% of the students were enrolled in graduate school within 6 months of graduation; 45% had found employment.

Admissions Contact: John J. Abplanalp, Director of Enrollment Services.

MARYWOOD COLLEGE
Scranton, PA 18509   **E-2**

(717) 348-6234; (800) 346-5014 (in-state)

Full-time: 287 men, 1165 women	Faculty: 102; IIA, --$
Part-time: 117 men, 285 women	Ph.D.s: 79%
Graduate: 291 men, 872 women	Student/Faculty: 14 to 1
Year: semesters, summer session	Tuition: $10,590
Application Deadline: open	Room & Board: $4300
Freshman Class: 1064 applied, 826 accepted, 323 enrolled	
SAT I Verbal/Math: 440/460	ACT: 24 **COMPETITIVE**

Marywood College, established in 1915, is a private, coeducational nonprofit institution affiliated with the Roman Catholic Church, offering undergraduate degrees in the arts, business, professional training, liberal arts, religious studies, and teacher preparation. There are 2 graduate schools. In addition to regional accreditation, Marywood has baccalaureate program accreditation with ADA, CSWE, NASAD, NASM, NCATE, and NLN. The library contains 198,425 volumes, 213,881 microform items, and 40,269 audiovisual forms, and subscribes to 1114 periodicals. Computerized library sources and services include the card catalog, interlibrary loans, and database searching. Special learning facilities include a learning resource center, art gallery, radio station, TV station, a communication disorders clinic, an on-campus preschool and day care center, a psychology/education research laboratory, a science multi-media laboratory, and a language laboratory. The 152-acre campus is in a suburban area 120 miles west of New York City and 115 miles north of Philadelphia. Including residence halls, there are 29 buildings on campus.

Student Life: About 80% of undergraduates are from Pennsylvania. Students come from 24 states, 10 foreign countries, and Canada. Eighty-two percent are from public schools; 18% from private. Ninety-six percent are white. Seventy-two percent are Catholic; 12% Protestant. The average age of freshmen is 19; all undergraduates, 23. Nineteen percent drop out by the end of their first year; 63% remain to graduate.

Housing: A total of 557 students can be accommodated in college housing. College-sponsored living facilities include single-sex dormitories and on-campus apartments. In addition there are honors houses and a separate study-oriented residence. On-campus housing is guaranteed for all 4 years. Sixty-nine percent of students commute. Alcohol is not permitted. All students may keep cars on campus.

Activities: There are no fraternities or sororities on campus. There are 60 groups on campus, including art, choir, chorus, computers, drama, ethnic, film, honors, international, jazz band, literary magazine, musical theater, newspaper, orchestra, photography, professional, radio and TV, social, social service, student government, symphony, and yearbook. Popular campus events include New Student Orientation, Orientation Week, Family Weekend, Halloween Haunted House, Thanksgiving Celebration, Christmas Tree Lighting and Dinner, and Wednesdays in the coffee house.

Sports: There are 2 intercollegiate sports for men and 5 for women, and 20 intramural sports for men and 20 for women. Athletic and recreation facilities include an Olympic-sized pool, a human performance laboratory, a gymnasium, athletic training rooms, an athletic field, tennis and racquetball courts, a dance studio, a game room, a hockey field, picnic grounds, and weight rooms.

Disabled Students: Seventy-five percent of the campus is accessible to disabled students. The following facilities are available: wheelchair ramps, elevators, special parking, specially equipped rest rooms, lowered drinking fountains, and lowered telephones.

Services: In addition to many counseling and information services, tutoring is available in every subject. There is a reader service for the blind, and remedial math, reading, and writing. Remedial study skills and nonremedial tutoring, oral tests, note taking, tutors, and tape recorders are available, for physically challenged students.

Campus Safety and Security: Campus safety and security measures include 24-hour foot and vehicle patrol, self defense education, escort service, and informal discussions. In addition, there are pamphlets, posters, films and lighted pathways and sidewalks.

Programs of Study: Marywood awards the B.A., B.S., B.M., B.S.W., B.S.N., and B.F.A. degrees. Master's degrees also are awarded. Bachelor's degrees are awarded in BIOLOGICAL SCIENCE (biology/biological science), BUSINESS (accounting, business administration and management, fashion merchandising, hotel/motel and restaurant management, and international business management), COMMUNICATIONS AND THE ARTS (advertising, arts administration/management, communications, design, dramatic arts, English, French, music, performing arts, radio/television technology, Spanish, and studio art), COMPUTER AND PHYSICAL SCIENCE (information sciences and systems and mathematics), EDUCATION (art, early childhood, elementary, music, physical, science, secondary, and special), HEALTH PROFESSIONS (health care administration, medical laboratory technology, music therapy, nursing, and speech pathology/audiology), SOCIAL SCIENCE (clinical psychology, dietetics, home economics, human ecology, paralegal studies, religion, religious music, social science, social work, and sociology). Communication disorders, art, education, dietetics, psychology, nursing, and music are the strongest academically. Business administration, design, psychology, accounting, nursing, elementary education (ECE), art, social sciences, and human ecology have the largest enrollments.

Required: To graduate, students must complete a liberal arts requirement consisting of religious studies, philosophy, mathematics, science, psychology, history, social science, world literature, foreign language, and fine arts. Additional course requirements include speech, writing, and physical education. Students must have a GPA of 2.0, with a 2.5 in the major. A minimum of 126 credits must be earned, with the number of credits required in the major varying.

Special: Marywood offers student-designed and dual majors. Internships, student teaching, and study abroad and study at other institutions in the United States are available. There are accelerated degree programs in dietetics and social work and opportunities for semester experience at a fashion institute. Credit for life, military, and work experience, an off-campus degree program, nondegree study, and a pass/fail grading option are also available. There is a freshman honors program on campus, as well as 17 national honor societies. All departments have honors programs.

Faculty/Classroom: Forty-four percent of faculty are male; 56%, female. Seventy-eight percent teach undergraduates, 95% do research, and 70% do both. No introductory courses are taught by graduate students. The average class size in an introductory lecture is 25; in a laboratory, 14; and in a regular course offering, 16.

Admissions: About 78% of the 1993–94 applicants were accepted. The SAT scores for the 1993–94 freshman class were as follows: Verbal—64% below 500, 29% between 500 and 599, and 7% between 600 and 700; Math—75% below 500, 21% between 500 and 599, and 4% between 600 and 700. About 31% of the current freshmen were in the top fifth of their class; 60% were in the top two fifths. One freshman graduated first in class.

Requirements: Marywood requires applicants to be in the upper 50% of their class. A minimum GPA of 2.5 is required. The SAT I or ACT is required. Applicants must be graduates of an accredited secondary school or have the GED. A minimum of 16 academic credits is required, including 4 in English, 3 in social studies, 2 in mathematics, and a science course. A letter of support is required. In selected majors, a portfolio or an audition is also required. A personal interview is strongly recommended. AP and CLEP credits are accepted. Important factors used in the admissions decision are advanced placement or honor courses, recommendations by school officials, extracurricular activities record, leadership record, and evidence of special talent.

Procedure: Entrance exams should be taken by May 1. Application deadlines are open. Application fee is $20. Notification is sent on a rolling basis. There are early admissions and deferred admissions plans.

Transfer: A total of 165 transfer students enrolled in 1993–94. SAT I or ACT scores are required of transfer applicants with 18 credits; both secondary school and college transcripts are required. Transfer students are required to have earned a minimum GPA of 2.5 at the most recent college. A grade of C is the minimum requirement for transfer of academic credit. A total of 60 credits out of 126 must be completed at Marywood.

Visiting: There are regularly scheduled orientations for prospective students, including a campus tour, individual visits with admissions counselors, an appointment with a professor, and a financial aid appointment. There are guides for informal visits and visitors may sit in on classes and stay overnight at the school. To arrange for a visit, contact the Admissions Office at (717) 348–6234.

Financial Aid: In 1993–94, 90% of all current freshmen and 80% of continuing students received some form of financial aid. About 71% of freshmen and 70% of continuing students received need-based aid. The average freshman award was $9000. Of that total, scholarships or need-based grants averaged $5000 ($10,000 maximum); loans averaged $2625 ($4000 maximum); and work contracts averaged $800 ($1000 maximum). Twenty-four percent of undergraduate students work part-time. Average earnings from campus work for the school year are $900. The average financial indebtedness of the 1992–93 graduate was $8900. Marywood is a member of CSS. The FAF and FAFSA and the college's own financial statement are required. The deadline for financial aid applications is February 15.

International Students: There are currently 18 international students enrolled. The school actively recruits these students. They must take the TOEFL and achieve a minimum score of 500. The student must also take the SAT I or ACT, if available.

Computers: The college provides computer facilities for student use. The mainframes are a DEC VAX cluster with 3 mainframes, a DEC 5000 for the on-line library, a DEC MicroVAX 9100 for the academic network, and a DEC VAX 4000 for research. The computer facilities consist of an art laboratory, a psychology laboratory, 2 access laboratories with Apple Macintoshes, a science laboratory with interactive video, 3 IBM-compatible laboratories, and a DEC laboratory with 20 DEC terminals. Approximately 300 computers are available for student use in class laboratories, drop-in facilities, and dorms. All students may access the system 24 hours per day. There are no time limits on using the system and no fees.

Graduates: In 1992–93, 364 bachelor's degrees were awarded. The most popular majors among graduates were elementary education (12%), business administration (8%), and accounting (7%). Within an average freshman class, 38% graduate in 4 years, 56% in 5 years, and 63% in 6 years. Some 58 companies recruited on campus in 1992–93.

Admissions Contact: Fred Brooks, Admissions Officer.

MERCYHURST COLLEGE   B-1

Erie, PA 16546   (814) 824–2241; (800) 825–1926

Full-time: 764 men, 1066 women	Faculty: 93; IIB, --$
Part-time: 171 men, 237 women	Ph.D.s: 55%
Graduate: 33 men, 46 women	Student/Faculty: 20 to 1
Year: trimesters, summer session	Tuition: $9838
Application Deadline: open	Room & Board: $3650
Freshman Class: 1545 applied, 1043 accepted, 397 enrolled	
SAT I Verbal/Math: 450/570	ACT: 23 COMPETITIVE

Mercyhurst College, established in 1926, is a private, coeducational, nonprofit institution affiliated with the Roman Catholic Church, offering undergraduate degrees in the arts, business, health science, liberal arts, religious studies, and teacher preparation. The college also offers a degree-directed program for the learning disabled. In addition to regional accreditation, Mercyhurst has baccalaureate program accreditation with ADA. The library contains 136,436 volumes, 9500 microform items, and 1645 audiovisual forms, and subscribes to 807 periodicals. Computerized library sources and services include interlibrary loans and database searching. Special learning facilities include an art gallery, planetarium, radio station, northwestern Pennsylvania historical archives, and an archeological institute. The 88-acre campus is in a suburban area in Erie. Including residence halls, there are 25 buildings on campus.

Student Life: About 70% of undergraduates are from Pennsylvania. Students come from 37 states, 9 foreign countries, and Canada. Sixty-three percent are from public schools; 37% from private. Eighty-nine percent are white. Sixty-one percent are Catholic; 27% Protestant. The average age of freshmen is 18; all undergraduates, 24. Twenty-two percent drop out by the end of their first year; 68% remain to graduate.

Housing: A total of 1268 students can be accommodated in college housing. College-sponsored living facilities include single-sex and coed dormitories and on-campus apartments. On-campus housing is guaranteed for all 4 years. Fifty-six percent of students live on campus; of those, 90% remain on campus on weekends. Alcohol is not permitted. All students may keep cars on campus.

Activities: There are no fraternities or sororities on campus. There are 36 groups on campus, including art, band, cheerleading, choir, chorus, computers, dance, drama, ethnic, film, honors, international, jazz band, literary magazine, musical theater, newspaper, opera, orchestra, pep band, photography, political, professional, radio and TV, religious, social, social service, student government, and yearbook. Popular campus events include Activities Day, Parents Weekend, Homecoming, winter and spring formals, Academic Celebration, and D'Angelo Young Artist Competition.

Sports: There are 9 intercollegiate sports for men and 7 for women, and 3 intramural sports for men and 3 for women. Athletic and recreation facilities include indoor crew tanks, football and soccer fields, an ice hockey rink/arena, Nautilus facilities, a free weight room, a baseball/softball complex, and a training room.

Disabled Students: Ninety percent of the campus is accessible to disabled students. The following facilities are available: wheelchair ramps, elevators, and special parking.

Services: In addition to many counseling and information services, tutoring is available in every subject. There is remedial math, reading, and writing.

Campus Safety and Security: Campus safety and security measures include 24-hour foot and vehicle patrol, self defense education, shuttle buses, and informal discussions. In addition, there are emergency telephones, lighted pathways and sidewalks, and a 24-hour security camera surveillance system.

Programs of Study: Mercyhurst awards the B.A., B.S., and B.M. degrees. Associate and master's degrees also are awarded. Bachelor's degrees are awarded in BIOLOGICAL SCIENCE (biology/biological science), BUSINESS (accounting, banking and finance, business administration and management, fashion merchandising, hotel/motel and restaurant management, insurance and risk management, management information systems, and marketing/retailing/merchandising), COMMUNICATIONS AND THE ARTS (broadcasting, communications, dance, English, graphic design, journalism, music, and studio art), COMPUTER AND PHYSICAL SCIENCE (chemistry, earth science, geology, and mathematics), EDUCATION (art, business, early childhood, elementary, home economics, mathematics, music, science, secondary, social science, and special), ENGINEERING AND ENVIRONMENTAL DESIGN (environmental science and interior design), HEALTH PROFESSIONS (art therapy, medical laboratory technology, predentistry, premedicine, prepharmacy, and preveterinary science), SOCIAL SCIENCE (anthropology, archeology, criminal justice, dietetics, family/consumer studies, history, political science/government, prelaw, psychology, religious education, social work, and sociology). Education, hotel, restaurant and institutional management, sciences, business, history, archeology/anthropology, and sports medicine are the strongest academically. Business, education, and sports medicine have the largest enrollments.

Required: To graduate, students must take specified courses in English, mathematics, science, religion, philosophy, history, microcomputer systems, art, and music. They must complete 17 general education courses, 15 courses in the major, and 8 electives. A minimum GPA of 2.0 is required, with a 2.5 in the major, and a total minimum number of 120 credit hours to graduate. The number of credit hours in the major varies, with a minimum of 45. A thesis is necessary for history and English majors.

Special: Mercyhurst offers cross-registration with Gannon University. Internships are available in all majors through the co-op office, and students may study abroad in London and Dublin. Dual and student-designed majors, credit for life, military, or work experience, nondegree study, a pass/fail grading option, and a 3–2 engineering degree

with Pennsylvania State and University of Pennsylvania are also available. There is a freshman honors program on campus, as well as 7 national honor societies. Four departments have honors programs.

Faculty/Classroom: Sixty-two percent of faculty are male; 38%, female. All teach undergraduates, 15% do research, and 15% do both. No introductory courses are taught by graduate students. The average class size in an introductory lecture is 40; in a laboratory, 15; and in a regular course offering, 30.

Admissions: About 68% of the 1993–94 applicants were accepted. The SAT scores for the 1993–94 freshman class were as follows: Verbal—46% below 500, 38% between 500 and 599, and 16% between 600 and 700; Math—41% below 500, 43% between 500 and 599, 15% between 600 and 700, and 1% above 700. The ACT scores were 19% below 21, 48% between 21 and 23, 29% between 24 and 26, 3% between 27 and 28, and 1% above 28. About 42% of the current freshmen were in the top fifth of their class; 73% were in the top two fifths. Seventeen freshmen graduated first in their class.

Requirements: The SAT I or the ACT is required, with a recommended minimum composite score of 800 on the SAT, 400 on each section, or 18 on the ACT. Applicants must graduate from an accredited secondary school or have a GED. Sixteen academic credits are required, including 4 years of English, 3 years each of mathematics and social studies, and 2 years each of history, science, and a foreign language. Interviews are recommended. Art applicants must submit portfolios; auditions are required of music applicants. AP and CLEP credits are accepted. Important factors used in the admissions decision are leadership record, evidence of special talent, personality, intangible qualities, extracurricular activities record, and geographic diversity.

Procedure: Freshmen are admitted to all sessions. Entrance exams should be taken during the spring of the junior year. Application deadlines are open. Application fee is $25. Notification is sent on a rolling basis. There are early admissions and deferred admissions plans.

Transfer: A total of 116 transfer students enrolled in 1993–94. A minimum GPA of 2.0 on previous college work is required. A total of 45 credits out of 120 must be completed at Mercyhurst.

Visiting: There are regularly scheduled orientations for prospective students, including a tour, a class visit, faculty meeting, and interviews with financial aid and an admissions counselor. There are guides for informal visits and visitors may sit in on classes and stay overnight at the school. To arrange for a visit, contact the Admissions Office at (814) 824–2200.

Financial Aid: In 1993–94, 87% of all current freshmen and 85% of continuing students received some form of financial aid. About 78% of freshmen and 73% of continuing students received need-based aid. The average freshman award was $6500. Of that total, scholarships or need-based grants averaged $2650 ($8265 maximum); loans averaged $2100 ($4000 maximum); and work contracts averaged $750 ($1000 maximum). Eighty-eight percent of undergraduate students work part-time. Average earnings from campus work for the school year are $650. The average financial indebtedness of the 1992–93 graduate was $8000. Mercyhurst is a member of CSS. The college's own financial statement and PHEAA are required. The deadline for financial aid applications is May 1.

International Students: There are currently 72 international students enrolled. The school actively recruits these students. They must take the TOEFL and achieve a minimum score of 550. The student must also take the SAT I or the ACT.

Computers: The college provides computer facilities for student use. The mainframe is an HP 3000/Series 70. Students may access the mainframe through over 100 terminals in various buildings. In addition, there is a personal computer laboratory for students with over 40 terminals, plus another 100 terminals and personal computers in academic departments for student use. All students may access the system during set lab hours. There are no time limits on using the system and no fees.

Graduates: In 1992–93, 281 bachelor's degrees were awarded. The most popular majors among graduates were business (13%), education (9%), and hotel/restaurant management (8%). Within an average freshman class, 2% graduate in 3 years, 68% in 4 years, 74% in 5 years, and 81% in 6 years. Some 137 companies recruited on campus in 1992–93. In the 1992 graduating class, 6% of the men and 7% of the women were enrolled in graduate school within 6 months of graduation; 91% of the men and women had found employment.

Admissions Contact: Andrew Roth, Dean of Enrollment.

MESSIAH COLLEGE
D-3

Grantham, PA 17027 (717) 691–6000; (800) 233–4220 (out-of-state)

Full-time: 911 men, 1347 women	Faculty: 146; IIB, av$
Part-time: 28 men, 45 women	Ph.D.s: 66%
Graduate: none	Student/Faculty: 15 to 1
Year: 4–1–4, summer session	Tuition: $9804
Application Deadline: April 1	Room & Board: $4860
Freshman Class: 1742 applied, 1382 accepted, 607 enrolled	
SAT I Verbal/Math: 509/555	ACT: 24 **VERY COMPETITIVE**

Messiah College, founded in 1909, is a coeducational Christian liberal arts college affiliated with the Brethren in Christ Church. In addition to regional accreditation, Messiah has baccalaureate program accreditation with ADA and NLN. The library contains 180,000 volumes, 5000 microform items, and 5500 audiovisual forms, and subscribes to 1000 periodicals. Computerized library sources and services include the card catalog, interlibrary loans, and database searching. Special learning facilities include a learning resource center, an art gallery, and a radio station. The 310-acre campus is in a small town 10 miles south of Harrisburg. Including residence halls, there are 23 buildings on campus.

Student Life: About 51% of undergraduates are from out-of-state. Students come from 34 states, 26 foreign countries, and Canada. Seventy-six percent are from public schools; 24% from private. Ninety percent are white. Most are Protestant. The average age of freshmen is 18; all undergraduates, 20. Fourteen percent drop out by the end of their first year; 70% remain to graduate.

Housing: A total of 2110 students can be accommodated in college housing. College-sponsored living facilities include single-sex dormitories, on-campus apartments, and special interest houses. On-campus housing is guaranteed for all 4 years. Ninety-four percent of students live on campus; of those, 65% remain on campus on weekends. Alcohol is not permitted. All students may keep cars on campus.

Activities: There are no fraternities or sororities on campus. There are many groups and organizations on campus, including art, band, cheerleading, chess, choir, chorale, chorus, computers, drama, ethnic, film, honors, international, jazz band, literary magazine, musical theater, newspaper, orchestra, pep band, photography, political, professional, radio and TV, religious, social, social service, student government, symphony, and yearbook. Popular campus events include a speaker series, Christian rock concerts, Homecoming, and Family Weekend.

Sports: There are 7 intercollegiate sports each for men and women, and 10 intramural sports for men and 8 for women. Athletic and recreation facilities include indoor and outdoor tracks, a pool with separate diving well, wrestling and gymnastics areas, numerous playing fields, and courts for racquetball, basketball, and tennis. The campus center provides additional recreational facilities.

Disabled Students: Ninety-five percent of the campus is accessible to disabled students. The following facilities are available: wheelchair ramps, elevators, special parking, specially equipped rest rooms, and special class scheduling.

Services: There is a reader service for the blind and remedial reading.

Campus Safety and Security: Campus safety and security measures include a 24-hour foot and vehicle patrol, an escort service, informal discussions, pamphlets, posters, and films. In addition, there are emergency telephones and lighted pathways and sidewalks.

Programs of Study: Messiah awards the B.A. and B.S. degrees. Bachelor's degrees are awarded in BIOLOGICAL SCIENCE (biochemistry and biology/biological science), BUSINESS (accounting, business administration and management, international business management, marketing/retailing/merchandising, and personnel management), COMMUNICATIONS AND THE ARTS (applied music, art history and appreciation, communications, dramatic arts, English, fine arts, French, German, journalism, music, and Spanish), COMPUTER AND PHYSICAL SCIENCE (chemistry, computer science, mathematics, natural sciences, and physics), EDUCATION (art, early childhood, elementary, health, home economics, mathematics, music, physical, science, secondary, and social studies), ENGINEERING AND ENVIRONMENTAL DESIGN (civil engineering, electrical/electronics engineering, and mechanical engineering), HEALTH PROFESSIONS (medical laboratory technology, nursing, predentistry, premedicine, prepharmacy, preveterinary science, and sports medicine), SOCIAL SCIENCE (behavioral science, biblical studies, dietetics, economics, family/consumer studies, history, home economics, humanities, ministries, political science/government, prelaw, psychology, religion, religious education, social work, and sociology). Science, English, mathematics, business education, political science, and nursing are the strongest programs academically. Business, mathematics, and education have the largest enrollments.

Required: All students must complete at least 123 credits with a 2.0 GPA. While the number of credits in each area varies, both B.A. and B.S. candidates are required to take credits in integrated studies (including ethics), Bible courses, 3 credits in physical education, 2 credits each in oral communication and art and music studio, and 1 course each in life science, physical science, and mathematics. All students must also meet a foreign language requirement and attend chapel twice a week.

Special: Students may cross-register at Temple University in Philadephia. Off-campus study is available in Washington, D.C., Costa Rica, and Jerusalem, and at any member colleges of the Christian College Consortium. Through the Consortium and the Brethren Colleges Abroad program, students may spend a semester or a year in any of 12 countries. Numerous internships, practical, and ministry opportunities are available. Individualized interdisciplinary majors and combined B.S.-B.A. degree programs are possible. There are some pass/fail options. There is a freshman honors program on campus, as well as one national honor society. Four departments have honors programs.

Faculty/Classroom: Sixty-nine percent of faculty are male; 31%, female. All teach undergraduates. The average class size in an introductory lecture is 25; in a laboratory, 18; and in a regular course offering, 30.

Admissions: About 79% of the 1993–94 applicants were accepted. The SAT scores for the 1993–94 freshman class were as follows: Verbal—46% below 500, 41% between 500 and 599, 12% between 600 and 700, and 1% above 700; Math—26% below 500, 43% between 500 and 599, 24% between 600 and 700, and 7% above 700. The ACT scores were 14% below 21, 48% between 21 and 23, 19% between 24 and 26, 12% between 27 and 28, and 7% above 28. About 68% of the current freshmen were in the top fifth of their class; 95% were in the top two fifths. There were 4 National Merit finalists and 16 semifinalists. About 40 freshmen graduated first in their class.

Requirements: Messiah requires applicants to be in the upper 50% of their class. A minimum GPA of 2.5 is required. The SAT I or ACT is required. Minimum composite scores of 850 on the SAT I and 19 on the ACT are recommended. Applicants must have graduated from an accredited high school or the equivalent. Secondary preparation should include at least 4 units in English, and 2 each in mathematics, natural science, social studies, and a foreign language. An interview is strongly recommended. Potential music majors must audition. AP and CLEP credits are accepted. Important factors used in the admissions decision are advanced placement or honor courses, recommendations by school officials, leadership record, evidence of special talent, personality, and intangible qualities.

Procedure: Freshmen are admitted in the fall, spring, and summer. Entrance exams should be taken in the spring of the junior year. Applications should be filed by April 1 for fall entry, December 1 for spring entry, and May 1 for summer entry, along with an application fee of $15. Notification is sent on a rolling basis. There are early admissions and deferred admissions plans. A waiting list is an active part of the admissions procedure, with about 10% of applicants on the list.

Transfer: About 114 transfer students enrolled in 1993–94. Transfer applicants should have earned a 2.5 GPA in at least 30 college credits. The college recommends that applicants also have composite SAT I scores of at least 900 or composite ACT scores of at least 20, and that they seek a personal interview. A total of 60 credits out of 123 must be completed at Messiah.

Visiting: There are regularly scheduled orientations for prospective students, including a campus tour, academic and career advising, and a financial aid information session. There are guides for informal visits and visitors may sit in on classes and stay overnight at the school. To arrange for a visit, contact the Admissions Office at (800) 233–4220 or (800) 382–1349 (in-state).

Financial Aid: In 1993–94, 86% of all students received some form of financial aid. About 57% of freshmen and 58% of continuing students received need-based aid. The average freshman award was $7526. Of that total, scholarships or need-based grants averaged $1500 ($5000 maximum); loans averaged $2500 ($3500 maximum); and work contracts averaged $900 ($1500 maximum). Sixty-four percent of undergraduate students work part-time. Average earnings from campus work for the school year are $1250. The average financial indebtedness of the 1992–93 graduate was $8000. Messiah is a member of CSS. The FAF and PHEAA for Pennsylvania residents are required. The deadline for financial aid applications is April 1.

International Students: There are currently 41 international students enrolled. They must take the TOEFL and achieve a minimum score of 550.

Computers: The college provides computer facilities for student use. The mainframe is a DEC VAX 750. There are 7 computer laboratories throughout the campus. Students enrolled in certain courses may access the system 24 hours a day. There are no time limits or fees on using the system.

Graduates: In a recent year, 462 bachelor's degrees were awarded. The most popular majors among graduates were business (16%), sciences (15%), and behavioral sciences (10%). Within an average freshman class, 1% graduate in 3 years and 70% in 5 years. Some 85 companies recruited on campus in a recent year. In a recent graduating class, 27% of the men and 22% of the women were enrolled in graduate school within 6 months of graduation; 92% of the men and 86% of the women had found employment.

Admissions Contact: Ron Long, Vice President for Admissions.

MILLERSVILLE UNIVERSITY OF PENNSYLVANIA
E-4
Millersville, PA 17551–0302   (717) 872–3371

Full-time: 2131 men, 3015 women	Faculty: 309; IIA, +$
Part-time: 510 men, 1022 women	Ph.D.s: 75%
Graduate: 166 men, 538 women	Student/Faculty: 17 to 1
Year: 4–1–4, summer session	Tuition: $3750 ($8148)
Application Deadline: open	Room & Board: $3620
Freshman Class: 6011 applied, 3075 accepted, 960 enrolled	
SAT I or ACT: required	VERY COMPETITIVE

Millersville University, founded as Lancaster County Normal School in 1855, is a public coeducational institution offering undergraduate and graduate programs in liberal arts and sciences and education. There are 3 undergraduate schools. In addition to regional accreditation, Millersville has baccalaureate program accreditation with CAHEA, CSWE, NASM, NCATE, and NLN. The library contains 463,033 volumes, 420,717 microform items, and 5513 audiovisual forms, and subscribes to 2728 periodicals. Computerized library sources and services include the card catalog, interlibrary loans, and database searching. Special learning facilities include a learning resource center, an art gallery, a radio station, an early childhood center, and a foreign language laboratory. The 245-acre campus is in a small town 5 miles west of Lancaster. Including residence halls, there are 77 buildings on campus.

Student Life: About 93% of undergraduates are from Pennsylvania. Students come from 32 foreign countries and Canada. Eighty-nine percent are white. The average age of freshmen is 18; all undergraduates, 21. Seventeen percent drop out by the end of their first year; 67% remain to graduate.

Housing: A total of 2440 students can be accommodated in college housing. College-sponsored living facilities include single-sex and coed dormitories and off-campus housing. In addition, there are honors houses, language houses, and special interest houses. On-campus housing is guaranteed for the freshman year only and is available on a first-come, first-served basis. Sixty-one percent of students commute. Upperclassmen may keep cars on campus. Alcohol is not permitted.

Activities: Eleven percent of men belong to 1 local fraternity and 12 national fraternities; about 9% of women belong to 3 local and 9 national sororities. There are about 100 groups on campus, including art, band, cheerleading, choir, chorale, chorus, dance, drama, ethnic, honors, international, jazz band, literary magazine, marching band, musical theater, newspaper, orchestra, pep band, political, professional, radio and TV, religious, social, social service, student government, symphony, and yearbook. Popular campus events include Homecoming, Parents Day, Wellness Week, International Week, Black History Celebration, and Latino Celebration.

Sports: There are 9 intercollegiate sports each for men and women, and 20 intramural sports for men and 19 for women. Athletic and recreation facilities include 2 pools, 2 gymnasiums, a fitness center, wrestling and weight rooms, basketball, volleyball, tennis, and badminton courts, and various playing fields.

Disabled Students: Fifty-five percent of the campus is accessible to disabled students. The following facilities are available: wheelchair ramps, elevators, special parking, specially equipped rest rooms, special class scheduling, and lowered drinking fountains and telephones.

Services: In addition to many counseling and information services, tutoring is available in most subjects. There is a reader service for the blind, and remedial math, reading, and writing. Every effort is made to tailor a tutoring program to individual needs.

Campus Safety and Security: Campus safety and security measures include a 24-hour foot and vehicle patrol, an escort service, informal discussions, pamphlets, posters, and films. In addition, there are lighted pathways and sidewalks, and monthly crime awareness programs.

Programs of Study: Millersville awards the B.A., B.S., B.F.A., B.S.Ed., and B.S.N. degrees. Associate and master's degrees are also awarded. Bachelor's degrees are awarded in BIOLOGICAL SCIENCE (biochemistry, biology/biological science, biotechnology, environmental biology, marine biology, and molecular biology), BUSINESS (accounting, banking and finance, business administration and management, and marketing/retailing/merchandising), COMMUNICATIONS AND THE ARTS (broadcasting, communications, comparative literature, English, French, German, Greek, journalism, Latin, linguistics, music, public relations, Russian, Spanish, and speech/

debate/rhetoric), COMPUTER AND PHYSICAL SCIENCE (atmospheric sciences and meteorology, chemistry, computer science, earth science, geology, mathematics, oceanography, and physics), EDUCATION (art, early childhood, elementary, music, social studies, special, and teaching English as a second language/foreign language), ENGINEERING AND ENVIRONMENTAL DESIGN (commercial art, computer engineering, industrial engineering technology, and occupational safety and health), HEALTH PROFESSIONS (medical laboratory technology, nuclear medical technology, nursing, and respiratory therapy), SOCIAL SCIENCE (anthropology, economics, geography, history, international studies, philosophy, political science/government, psychology, social work, and sociology). Physical sciences and teacher education are the strongest programs academically. Business administration, elementary education, biology, and psychology have the largest enrollments.

Required: All students must complete at least 120 hours, including 30 in the major, with a minimum 2.0 GPA. Courses are required in humanities, science and mathematics, social sciences, and perspectives as part of a core curriculum. Specific courses required include writing, speech, and physical education, all part of an overall general education requirement.

Special: Numerous co-op and internship programs, including student teaching opportunities, are available. Millersville has exchange agreements with Franklin and Marshall College and Lancaster Theological Seminary, and 3–2 engineering programs with Pennsylvania State University and the University of Pennsylvania for chemistry and physics majors. Study abroad is offered in Germany, England, and Japan and at teachers' colleges in Taiwan. Dual majors are possible in all disciplines; accelerated degrees and B.A.-B.S. degrees are available in most. Nondegree study is offered, and there are limited pass/fail options. There is a university-wide honors program, including a freshman honors program, as well as 8 national honor societies on campus.

Faculty/Classroom: Sixty-six percent of faculty are male; 34%, female. Ninety-six percent teach undergraduates. No introductory courses are taught by graduate students.

Admissions: About 51% of the 1993–94 applicants were accepted. The SAT scores for the 1993–94 freshman class were as follows: Verbal—61% below 500, 33% between 500 and 599, and 6% between 600 and 700; Math—26% below 500, 53% between 500 and 599, 19% between 600 and 700, and 2% above 700. About 50% of the current freshmen were in the top fifth of their class; 89% were in the top two fifths. Seventeen freshmen graduated first in their class.

Requirements: Millersville requires applicants to be in the upper 35% of their class. The SAT I or ACT is required, with minimum composite scores of 930 or 21, respectively. Applicants must be graduates of approved secondary schools or hold a GED. Secondary preparation should include 4 credits each in English and social studies, 3 credits in mathematics, and 2 credits in science. Music program applicants must audition. An interview is recommended for all applicants. AP and CLEP credits are accepted. Important factors used in the admissions decision are advanced placement or honor courses, evidence of special talent, recommendations by school officials, extracurricular activities record, and leadership record.

Procedure: Freshmen are admitted to all sessions. Entrance exams should be taken in the spring of the junior year. Application deadlines are open. The application fee is $20. Notification is sent on a rolling basis. There are early admissions and deferred admissions plans.

Transfer: About 270 transfer students enrolled in 1993–94. Transfer applicants with fewer than 18 college credits must submit high school as well as college transcripts. Graduates of state community colleges are given preference over applicants with fewer than 2 and more than 5 semesters of previous college work. Applicants must have at least a 2.5 GPA. A personal interview is recommended. A total of 30 credits out of 120 must be completed at Millersville.

Visiting: There are regularly scheduled orientations for prospective students, including a president's welcome and admissions, financial aid, student organization, and department conferences. There are guides for informal visits and visitors may sit in on classes. To arrange for a visit, contact the Admissions Office at (717) 872–3371.

Financial Aid: In 1993–94, 73% of all current freshmen and 70% of continuing students received some form of financial aid. About 41% of freshmen and 39% of continuing students received need-based aid. The average freshman award was $3577. Of that total, scholarships or need-based grants averaged $1605 ($6000 maximum); loans averaged $1730 ($4526 maximum); and work contracts averaged $242 ($2400 maximum). Thirty-four percent of undergraduate students work part-time. Average earnings from campus work for the school year are $1100. The average financial indebtedness of the 1992–93 graduate was $8089. Millersville is a member of CSS. The college's own financial statement, PHEAA state grant, and FAFSA are required. The deadline for financial aid applications is May 1.

International Students: There are currently 93 international students enrolled. The school actively recruits these students. They must take the TOEFL and achieve a minimum score of 500. The student must also take the SAT I.

Computers: The college provides computer facilities for student use. The mainframes are an IBM 4381, a DEC VAX 3600, and a DEC VAX 4000. Approved students have accounts to access the mainframes, mostly for course work. Internet is available via the mainframes. There are 15 general purpose computer laboratories on campus housing IBM and Apple Macintosh microcomputers. Some microcomputer laboratories are local area networks. All students may access the system anytime. There are no fees.

Graduates: In 1992–93, 1298 bachelor's degrees were awarded. The most popular majors among graduates were elementary education (18%), business administration (12%), and psychology (7%). Within an average freshman class, 1% graduate in 3 years, 39% in 4 years, 62% in 5 years, and 67% in 6 years. Some 221 companies recruited on campus in 1992–93.

Admissions Contact: Director of Admissions, Darrell Davis.

MOORE COLLEGE OF ART AND DESIGN   F-3
Philadelphia, PA 19103   (215) 568–4515
                                 (800) 523–2025 (out-of-state)

Full-time: 320 women	**Faculty:** 40
Part-time: 60 women	**Ph.D.s:** 10%
Graduate: none	**Student/Faculty:** 8 to 1
Year: semesters	**Tuition:** $12,804
Application Deadline: see profile	**Room & Board:** $5143
Freshman Class: 289 applied, 200 accepted, 117 enrolled	
SAT I or ACT: required	**SPECIAL**

Moore College of Art and Design, founded in 1844, is the oldest professional and fine arts college for women in the country. In addition to regional accreditation, Moore has baccalaureate program accreditation with FIDER and NASAD. The library contains 34,000 volumes and subscribes to 250 periodicals. Special learning facilities include 2 art galleries. The 4-acre campus is in an urban area in Philadelphia. Including residence halls, there are 3 buildings on campus.

Student Life: About 60% of undergraduates are from Pennsylvania. Students come from 20 states, 8 foreign countries, and Canada. Sixty percent are from public schools; 40% from private. Eighty-five percent are white. The average age of freshmen is 18; all undergraduates, 20.

Housing: A total of 200 students can be accommodated in college housing. College-sponsored living facilities include dormitories and on-campus apartments. On-campus housing is guaranteed for all 4 years. Fifty percent of students live on campus; of those, 75% remain on campus on weekends. Alcohol is not permitted. All students may keep cars on campus.

Activities: There are 12 groups on campus, including computers, environmental action, ethnic, film, gay, international, newspaper, professional, religious, social service, student government, and yearbook. Popular campus events include Family Day, Spring Fling, Convocation, student art shows, and openings at the college gallery.

Sports: There is no sports program at Moore.

Disabled Students: The entire campus is accessible to disabled students. The following facilities are available: wheelchair ramps, elevators, special parking, and lowered telephones.

Services: In addition to many counseling and information services, tutoring is available in most subjects.

Campus Safety and Security: Campus safety and security measures include 24-hour foot and vehicle patrol, self-defense education, escort service, and informal discussions. In addition, there are pamphlets, posters, and films and lighted pathways and sidewalks.

Programs of Study: Moore awards the B.F.A. degree. Bachelor's degrees are awarded in COMMUNICATIONS AND THE ARTS (drawing, fine arts, graphic design, illustration, metal/jewelry, painting, printmaking, and sculpture), EDUCATION (art), ENGINEERING AND ENVIRONMENTAL DESIGN (interior design), SOCIAL SCIENCE (fashion design and technology and textiles and clothing). Interior design is the strongest academically. Graphic design has the largest enrollment.

Required: All students take 31 credits in basic arts, including design, drawing, color, and art history, and a liberal arts core in history, humanities, and social science. A total of 124 to 127 credits, with a 2.0 minimum GPA, is required for graduation.

Special: Moore has long established cooperative relationships with various employers who provide training to supplement academic studies in all majors. Dual majors, an individualized interdisciplinary major, nondegree study, and continuing education programs are offered.

Faculty/Classroom: Fifty percent of faculty are male; 50%, female. All teach undergraduates. The average class size in an introductory lecture is 20 and in a regular course offering, 10.

Admissions: About 69% of the 1993–94 applicants were accepted. The SAT I scores for the 1993–94 freshman class were as follows: Verbal—80% below 500; Math—80% below 500. The ACT scores were: 80% below 21. About 30% of the current freshmen were in the top fifth of their class. There were 2 National Merit finalists.

Requirements: A minimum GPA of 2.3 is required. The SAT I or ACT is required. Applicants should be graduates of accredited high schools or the equivalent, having taken 4 years of English and 2 years each of social studies, science, and mathematics. At least 2 years of art study are also recommended. The most important part of the application is the portfolio of 8 to 12 original pieces, 6 of which should be drawings from observation. In addition, Moore strongly recommends a personal interview. AP and CLEP credits are accepted. Important factors used in the admissions decision are evidence of special talent, personality, intangible qualities, extracurricular activities record, leadership record, and advanced placement or honor courses.

Procedure: Freshmen are admitted in the fall. Early decision applications should be filed by December 15; regular applications, by November 15 for spring entry, along with an application fee of $35. Notification of early decision is sent January 1; regular decision, on a rolling basis. There are early decision, early admissions, and deferred admissions plans. Some 35 early decision candidates were accepted for the 1993–94 class.

Transfer: Thirty-five transfer students enrolled in 1993–94. Transfer applicants from non-art programs must meet freshman admission requirements. Others must submit a portfolio for review. Applicants should have at least a 2.0 GPA in previous college work and submit composite SAT I scores of at least 800. A personal interview is required. A total of 62 credits out of 124 to 127 must be completed at Moore.

Visiting: There are regularly scheduled orientations for prospective students, including an open house in November. There are guides for informal visits and visitors may sit in on classes and stay overnight at the school. To arrange for a visit, contact the Admissions Office at (215) 568–4515, ext. 1105.

Financial Aid: In 1993–94, 80% of all students received some form of financial aid. About 70% of all students received need-based aid. Of the average freshman award, scholarships or need-based grants averaged $2827 ($5000 maximum); loans averaged $2731 (maximum); work contracts averaged $400 ($600 maximum); and state and federal grants average $1263 ($6000 maximum). Forty percent of undergraduate students work part-time. Average earnings from campus work for the school year are $500. The average financial indebtedness of the 1992–93 graduate was $10,000. Moore is a member of CSS. The FAF, the college's own financial statement, and FAFSA are required. The deadline for financial aid applications is April 1.

International Students: There are currently 40 international students enrolled. The school actively recruits these students. They must take the TOEFL and achieve a minimum score of 500.

Computers: The college provides computer facilities for student use. Apple IIe, Commodore Amiga, and Apple Macintosh PCs are available in the computer graphics laboratory. There are no time limits on using the system and no fees.

Graduates: In 1992–93, 140 bachelor's degrees were awarded. The most popular majors among graduates were graphic design (17%), interior design (12%), and 2D fine arts (11%). Within an average freshman class, 80% graduate in 4 years. Some 20 companies recruited on campus in 1992–93. In the 1992 graduating class, 10% of the women were enrolled in graduate school within 6 months of graduation; 87% of the women had found employment.

Admissions Contact: Claire E. Gallicano, Director of Admissions.

MORAVIAN COLLEGE

F-3

Bethlehem, PA 18018   (215) 861–1320

Full-time: 576 men, 595 women	Faculty: 79; IIB, av$
Part-time: 17 men, 16 women	Ph.D.s: 92%
Graduate: 123 men, 48 women	Student/Faculty: 15 to 1
Year: semesters, summer session	Tuition: $14,490
Application Deadline: March 1	Room & Board: $4470
Freshman Class: 1232 applied, 955 accepted, 303 enrolled	
ACT: 23	**VERY COMPETITIVE**

Moravian College, established in 1742, is a private, coeducational liberal arts institution affiliated with the Moravian Church. In addition to regional accreditation, Moravian has baccalaureate program accreditation with CAHEA. The library contains 220,000 volumes, 3500 microform items, and 5000 audiovisual forms, and subscribes to 1349 periodicals. Computerized library sources and services include the card catalog, interlibrary loans, and database searching. Special learning facilities include an art gallery and radio station. The 70-acre campus is in a suburban area 60 miles north of Philadelphia. Including residence halls, there are 55 buildings on campus.

Student Life: About 52% of undergraduates are from Pennsylvania. Students come from 23 states and 14 foreign countries. Seventy-five percent are from public schools; 25% from private. Ninety-two percent are white. Forty-four percent are Catholic; 31% Protestant; 19% claim no religious affiliation. The average age of freshmen is 18; all undergraduates, 21. Thirteen percent drop out by the end of their first year; 75% remain to graduate.

Housing: A total of 950 students can be accommodated in college housing. College-sponsored living facilities include single-sex and coed dormitories, on-campus apartments, off-campus apartments, fraternity houses, and sorority houses. In addition, there are special interest houses. On-campus housing is guaranteed for all 4 years. Ninety percent of students live on campus; of those, 75% remain on campus on weekends. All students may keep cars on campus.

Activities: About 20% of men belong to 1 national and 2 local fraternities; about 20% of women belong to 4 local sororities. There are 65 groups on campus, including art, band, cheerleading, choir, chorus, computers, dance, drama, ethnic, honors, international, jazz band, literary magazine, newspaper, orchestra, pep band, political, professional, religious, social, social service, student government, and yearbook. Popular campus events include arts and lecture series, Christmas vesper services, foreign film series, and Homecoming.

Sports: There are 9 intercollegiate sports for men and 7 for women, and 14 intramural sports for men and 14 for women. Athletic and recreation facilities include football, baseball, and soccer fields; a softball diamond, an all-weather track, tennis courts, and a field house.

Disabled Students: Thirty percent of the campus is accessible to disabled students. The following facilities are available: wheelchair ramps, elevators, special parking, specially equipped rest rooms, special class scheduling, and lowered drinking fountains.

Services: In addition to many counseling and information services, tutoring is available in most subjects. There is also a reader service for the blind.

Campus Safety and Security: Campus safety and security measures include 24-hour foot and vehicle patrol, escort service, shuttle buses, and informal discussions. In addition, there are pamphlets, posters, and films, lighted pathways and sidewalks, and ongoing crime prevention programming supervised by a crime prevention officer.

Programs of Study: Moravian awards the B.A., B.S., and B.Mus. degrees. Master's degree also are awarded. Bachelor's degrees are awarded in BIOLOGICAL SCIENCE (biology/biological science), BUSINESS (accounting, business economics, international business management, and management science), COMMUNICATIONS AND THE ARTS (art history and appreciation, art history and critisicm, dramatic arts, English, French, German, graphic design, Greek, journalism, Latin, music, Spanish, and studio art), COMPUTER AND PHYSICAL SCIENCE (chemistry, computer science, geology, information sciences and systems, mathematics, and physics), EDUCATION (elementary, music, and secondary), HEALTH PROFESSIONS (medical laboratory technology), SOCIAL SCIENCE (criminal justice, economics, history, philosophy, political science/government, prelaw, psychology, religion, social science, and sociology). Education, biology, music, art, psychology, management, and accounting are the strongest academically. Business, biology, education and psychology have the largest enrollments.

Required: To graduate, students must complete distribution requirements in natural science, communication, a foreign language, mathematics, social science, and humanities. They must maintain a minimum GPA of 1.8 and complete 32 courses equivalent to 128 credits. The number of hours required in the major varies. A physical education requirement must be met.

Special: Moravian offers cooperative programs in engineering, allied health, and geology with the University of Pennsylvania and Lehigh, Duke, Thomas Jefferson, and Washington Universities. Cross-registration is available with Lehigh University and Lafayette, Muhlenberg, Cedar Crest, and Allentown Colleges. Internships, study abroad in 4 countries, a Washington semester, dual majors, and student-designed majors may be pursued. The college offers 3–2 engineering degrees in conjunction with Lafayette College, the University of Pennsylvania, and Washington University. Students have a pass/fail grading option. They may also enroll in a core program comprised of 7 courses that offer an integrated introduction to college study. There are 10 national honor societies on campus.

Faculty/Classroom: Seventy-five percent of faculty are male; 25%, female. All teach undergraduates. No introductory courses are taught by graduate students. The average class size in an introductory lecture is 30; in a laboratory, 15; and in a regular course offering, 22.

Admissions: About 78% of the 1993–94 applicants were accepted. The SAT scores for the 1993–94 freshman class were as follows: Verbal—55% below 500, 35% between 500 and 599, and 10% between 600 and 700; Math—30% below 500, 48% between 500 and 599, 20% between 600 and 700, and 2% above 700. The ACT scores were 8% below 21, 46% between 21 and 23, and 46% between 24 and 26. About 50% of the current freshmen were in the top fifth of

their class; 83% were in the top two fifths. About 3 freshmen graduated first in their class.

Requirements: The SAT I or ACT is required with a composite score of 1000 (500 verbal and 500 math) recommended on the SAT I. Applicants must graduate from an accredited secondary school or have a GED. Sixteen Carnegie units are required. High school work should include 4 years of English, 3 years of mathematics, and 2 years each of science, history, social studies, and a foreign language. Essays are required and interviews are recommended. In appropriate cases, auditions are required and portfolios are recommended. AP and CLEP credits are accepted. Important factors used in the admissions decision are advanced placement or honor courses, leadership record, evidence of special talent, recommendations by school officials, and personality, intangible qualities.

Procedure: Freshmen are admitted fall and spring. Entrance exams should be taken prior to January of the senior year. Early decision applications should be filed by December 15; regular applications, by March 1 for fall entry and December 1 for spring entry, along with an application fee of $30. Notification of early decision is sent January 15; regular decision, March 15. There are early decision, early admissions, and deferred admissions plans. About 64 early decision candidates were accepted for the 1993–94 class. A waiting list is an active part of the admissions procedure, with about 15% of applicants on the list.

Transfer: About 83 transfer students enrolled in 1993–94. Transfer applicants must have a minimum GPA of 2.5, and are required to submit recommendations. A total of 32 credits out of 128 must be completed at Moravian.

Visiting: There are regularly scheduled orientations for prospective students, including tours and meetings with faculty. There are guides for informal visits and visitors may sit in on classes and stay overnight at the school. To arrange for a visit, contact the Office of Admissions at (215) 861–1320.

Financial Aid: In 1993–94, 86% of all current freshmen and 84% of continuing students received some form of financial aid. About 78% of freshmen and 76% of continuing students received need-based aid. The average freshman award was $11,425. Of that total, scholarships or need-based grants averaged $8091 (maximum); loans averaged $3101 ($5625 maximum); and work contracts averaged $1212 ($1300 maximum). Forty-six percent of undergraduate students work part-time. Average earnings from campus work for the school year are $784. The average financial indebtedness of the 1992–93 graduate was $11,235. Moravian is a member of CSS. The FAF, the college's own financial statement, the state grant applications, and FAFSA are required. The deadline for financial aid applications is March 15.

International Students: There are currently 20 international students enrolled. The school actively recruits these students. They must take the TOEFL and achieve a minimum score of 550. The student must also take the SAT I.

Computers: The college provides computer facilities for student use. The mainframe is a Sun 3 and Sun 4. Moravian has 24-hour student access to several computer networks, including a UNIX-based network of 16 Sun workstations, 25 networked IBM-compatible microcomputers, and 6 Macintosh PCs. All students may access the system. There are no time limits and no fees.

Graduates: In 1992–93, 316 bachelor's degrees were awarded. The most popular majors among graduates were management (20%), psychology (14%), and accounting (6%). Within an average freshman class, 68% graduate in 4 years, 75% in 5 years, and 76% in 6 years. Some 40 companies recruited on campus in 1992–93. In the 1992 graduating class, 13% of all students were enrolled in graduate school within 6 months of graduation; 82% had found employment.

Admissions Contact: Bernard J. Story, Director of Admissions.

MUHLENBERG COLLEGE E-3
Allentown, PA 18104 (215) 821-3200

Full-time: 736 men, 918 women	**Faculty:** 131; IIB, +$
Part-time: 167 men, 185 women	**Ph.D:s:** 86%
Graduate: none	**Student/Faculty:** 13 to 1
Year: semesters, summer session	**Tuition:** $16,385
Application Deadline: February 15	**Room & Board:** $4410
Freshman Class: 2518 applied, 1838 accepted, 464 enrolled	
SAT I Verbal/Math: 506/565	**ACT:** 25 **VERY COMPETITIVE**

Muhlenberg College, established in 1848, is a private, coeducational liberal arts institution affiliated with the Lutheran Church. The library contains 290,014 volumes, 19,453 microform items, and 4600 audiovisual forms, and subscribes to 1483 periodicals. Computerized library sources and services include the card catalog, interlibrary loans, and database searching. Special learning facilities include a learning resource center, art gallery, natural history museum, and radio station. The 75-acre campus is in a suburban area in west Allentown. Including residence halls, there are 30 buildings on campus.

Student Life: About 69% of undergraduates are from out-of-state, mostly the Northeast. Students come from 32 states, 16 foreign countries, and Canada. Sixty-nine percent are from public schools; 31% from private. Ninety-one percent are white. Forty percent are Protestant; 30% Catholic; 25% Jewish. The average age of freshmen is 18; all undergraduates, 20. Eight percent drop out by the end of their first year; 80% remain to graduate.

Housing: A total of 1368 students can be accommodated in college housing. College-sponsored living facilities include single-sex and coed dormitories, on-campus apartments, fraternity houses, and sorority houses. In addition, there are language houses and special interest houses. On-campus housing is guaranteed for all 4 years. Ninety-eight percent of students live on campus; of those, 80% remain on campus on weekends. Upperclassmen may keep cars on campus.

Activities: About 50% of men belong to 6 national fraternities; about 40% of women belong to 4 national sororities. There are 82 groups on campus, including art, band, cheerleading, chess, choir, chorale, chorus, computers, dance, drama, ethnic, gay, honors, international, jazz band, literary magazine, musical theater, newspaper, opera, orchestra, pep band, photography, political, professional, radio and TV, religious, social, social service, student government, and yearbook. Popular campus events include Spring Fling Weekend, Homecoming, Valentine Birthday Party, Community Service Weekend, and Candlelight Christmas Concert.

Sports: There are 9 intercollegiate sports for men and 9 for women, and 15 intramural sports for men and 14 for women. Athletic and recreation facilities include a sports center, which contains a 6-lane swimming pool, racquetball and squash courts, wrestling and weight training rooms, and a multipurpose field house with indoor tennis courts.

Disabled Students: Ninety percent of the campus is accessible to disabled students. The following facilities are available: wheelchair ramps, elevators, special parking, specially equipped rest rooms, special class scheduling, lowered drinking fountains, and lowered telephones.

Services: In addition to many counseling and information services, tutoring is available in every subject. There is also a reader service for the blind. A writing center is available.

Campus Safety and Security: Campus safety and security measures include 24-hour foot and vehicle patrol, escort service, informal discussions, and pamphlets, posters, and films. In addition, there are emergency telephones and lighted pathways and sidewalks.

Programs of Study: Muhlenberg awards the B.A. and B.S. degrees. Bachelor's degrees are awarded in BIOLOGICAL SCIENCE (biology/biological science), BUSINESS (accounting and business administration and management), COMMUNICATIONS AND THE ARTS (communications, dramatic arts, English, fine arts, French, German, Greek, Latin, music, and Spanish), COMPUTER AND PHYSICAL SCIENCE (chemistry, computer science, information sciences and systems, mathematics, and physics), SOCIAL SCIENCE (economics, history, philosophy, political science/government, psychology, religion, social science, social work, and sociology). Sciences, drama, English, history, psychology, and philosophy are the strongest academically. Physical sciences, business administration, English, and communications have the largest enrollments.

Required: To graduate, students must complete requirements in literature and the arts, religion or philosophy, human behavior and social institutions, historical studies, physical and life sciences, and other cultures. They must have a minimum GPA of 2.0 in a total of 34 course units, with 10 to 14 units in the major. All students must take 4 quarters of physical education, including 2 wellness courses, as well as English composition, and freshman and senior seminars.

Special: Muhlenberg offers cooperative programs with Hahnemann University School of Medicine, Columbia and Washington Universities, and the University of Pennsylvania. Students may cross-register with Lehigh, Lafayette, Cedar Crest, Moravian, and Allentown Colleges. Internships, work-study programs, study abroad in Asia, Latin America, the Soviet Union, and Europe, and a Washington semester are available. Dual majors, student-designed majors, and accelerated degrees in engineering or forestry may be pursued. A 3–2 engineering degree is available in cooperation with Columbia and Washington Universities. Nondegree study and a pass/fail grading option are also offered. There is a freshman honors program on campus, as well as 12 national honor societies, including Phi Beta Kappa. Nine departments have honors programs.

Faculty/Classroom: Sixty-nine percent of faculty are male; 31%, female. All teach undergraduates. The average class size in an introductory lecture is 25; in a laboratory, 20; and in a regular course offering, 23.

Admissions: About 73% of the 1993–94 applicants were accepted. The SAT scores for the 1993–94 freshman class were as follows: Verbal—44% below 500, 46% between 500 and 599, 9% between 600 and 700, and 1% above 700; Math—16% below 500, 51% between 500 and 599, 29% between 600 and 700, and 4% above 700. The ACT scores were 4% below 21, 41% between 21 and 23, 46% between 24 and 26, 7% between 27 and 28, and 2% above 28. About

52% of the current freshmen were in the top fifth of their class; 81% were in the top two fifths. There were 7 National Merit semifinalists. Twelve freshmen graduated first in their class.

Requirements: The SAT I or ACT is required. SAT II: Subject tests in writing and mathematics are also required. Applicants must graduate from an accredited secondary school or have a GED. Sixteen Carnegie units are required, and students must complete 4 courses in English, 3 in mathematics, and 2 each in history, science, and a foreign language. All students must submit essays. Interviews are recommended. AP and CLEP credits are accepted. Important factors used in the admissions decision are advanced placement or honor courses, leadership record, evidence of special talent, extracurricular activities record, and personality, intangible qualities.

Procedure: Freshmen are admitted fall and spring. Entrance exams should be taken during the junior or senior year. Early decision applications should be filed by January 15; regular applications, by February 15 for fall entry, along with an application fee of $30. Notification of early decision is sent February 1; regular decision, April 1. There are early decision, early admissions, and deferred admissions plans. Some 141 early decision candidates were accepted for the 1993–94 class. A waiting list is an active part of the admissions procedure, with about 10% of applicants on the list.

Transfer: Fifteen transfer students enrolled in 1993–94. A minimum GPA of 2.5 and an interview are required. A total of 17 units out of 34 must be completed at Muhlenberg.

Visiting: There are regularly scheduled orientations for prospective students, consisting of a tour of the campus and a personal interview. There are 2 open houses in the fall, and 1 in the spring. There are guides for informal visits and visitors may sit in on classes and stay overnight at the school. To arrange for a visit, contact Melissa Abramson at (215) 821–3200.

Financial Aid: In 1993–94, 60% of all current freshmen and 58% of continuing students received some form of financial aid. About 52% of freshmen and 50% of continuing students received need-based aid. The average freshman award was $11,857. Of that total, scholarships or need-based grants averaged $8371 ($14,250 maximum); loans averaged $2476 ($3625 maximum); and work contracts averaged $1000 (maximum). Thirty-eight percent of undergraduate students work part-time. Average earnings from campus work for the school year are $1000. The average financial indebtedness of the 1992–93 graduate was $8640. Muhlenberg is a member of CSS. The FAF, the college's own financial statement, and the FAFSA are required. The deadline for financial aid applications is February 15.

International Students: There are currently 25 international students enrolled. They must take the TOEFL and achieve a minimum score of 550.

Computers: The college provides computer facilities for student use. The mainframe is an HP 3000/Series 70. Students may access the mainframe from the computer laboratories. There are over 100 personal computers available to students. All students may access the system. It may be used 9 A.M. to midnight Monday through Thursday, 9 A.M. to 5 P.M. Friday, 1 P.M. to 5 P.M. Saturday, and 1 P.M. to midnight Sunday. There are no time limits on using the system and no fees.

Graduates: In 1992–93 433 bachelor's degrees were awarded. The most popular majors among graduates were biology (12%), business (12%), and psychology (11%). Within an average freshman class, 80% graduate in 4 years and 81% in 5 years. Some 42 companies recruited on campus in 1992–93. In the 1992 graduating class, 38% of all students were enrolled in graduate school within 6 months of graduation; 60% had found employment.

Admissions Contact: Christopher Hooker-Haring, Director of Admissions.

NEUMANN COLLEGE   E-4

Aston, PA 19014   **(215) 558-5616**

Full-time: 112 men, 384 women	Faculty: 46; IIB, --$
Part-time: 139 men, 607 women	Ph.D.s: 43%
Graduate: 16 men, 46 women	Student/Faculty: 11 to 1
Year: semesters, summer session	Tuition: $9950
Application Deadline: open	Room & Board: n/app
Freshman Class: 236 applied, 201 accepted, 84 enrolled	
SAT I Verbal/Math: 410/440	**LESS COMPETITIVE**

Neumann College, founded in 1965 by the Sisters of St. Francis, is a private, coeducational, nonresidential liberal arts institution affiliated with the Roman Catholic Church. There are 3 graduate schools. In addition to regional accreditation, Neumann has baccalaureate program accreditation with CAHEA and NLN. The library contains 83,000 volumes and 11,970 audiovisual forms, and subscribes to 600 periodicals. Computerized library sources and services include database searching. Special learning facilities include a learning resource center. The 14-acre campus is in a small town 12 miles southwest of Philadelphia. There are 4 buildings on campus.

Student Life: About 78% of undergraduates are from Pennsylvania. Students come from 3 states. Eighty-nine percent are white. Seventy percent are Catholic; 16% Protestant. The average age of freshmen is 18; all undergraduates, 29. Ten percent drop out by the end of their first year.

Housing: There are no residence halls. All students commute. Alcohol is not permitted.

Activities: There is 1 national fraternity. There are no sororities on campus. There are some groups on campus, including cheerleading, drama, honors, newspaper, political, student government, and yearbook. Popular campus events include dinner dances, Spring Fling, and charity fund raising.

Sports: Athletic and recreation facilities include a 350-seat gymnasium, weight and fitness rooms, tennis courts, video games, and a theater.

Disabled Students: The entire campus is accessible to disabled students. Elevators, special parking, and specially equipped rest rooms are available.

Services: In addition to many counseling and information services, tutoring is available in most subjects. In addition, there is remedial math, reading, and writing.

Campus Safety and Security: Campus safety and security measures include 24-hour foot and vehicle patrol, emergency telephones, and lighted pathways and sidewalks.

Programs of Study: Neumann awards the B.A. and B.S. degrees. Associate and master's degrees also are awarded. Bachelor's degrees are awarded in BIOLOGICAL SCIENCE (biology/biological science), BUSINESS (accounting and business administration and management), COMMUNICATIONS AND THE ARTS (communications and English), COMPUTER AND PHYSICAL SCIENCE (computer science and information sciences and systems), EDUCATION (early childhood and elementary), HEALTH PROFESSIONS (medical laboratory technology and nursing), SOCIAL SCIENCE (political science/government, prelaw, psychology, and religion). Nursing is the strongest academically. Nursing and education have the largest enrollments.

Required: To graduate, all students must complete 121 to 130 credits, depending on the major. A minimum 2.0 GPA is required.

Special: The college offers co-op programs in all majors, internships, work-study programs, dual majors, and a general studies degrees. Credit for life, work, and military experience, nondegree study, and pass/fail options are available. There is a freshman honors program on campus

Faculty/Classroom: Forty-one percent of faculty are male; 59%, female. All teach undergraduates. No introductory courses are taught by graduate students.

Admissions: About 85% of the 1993–94 applicants were accepted. The SAT scores for the 1993–94 freshman class were as follows: Verbal—86% below 500, 12% between 500 and 599, and 2% between 600 and 700; Math—75% below 500, 20% between 500 and 599, and 5% between 600 and 700. About 27% of the current freshmen were in the top fifth of their class; 54% were in the top two fifths.

Requirements: Neumann requires applicants to be in the upper 60% of their class. A minimum GPA of 2.0 is required. The SAT I or ACT is required. Applicants must be graduates of an accredited secondary school or have a GED. High school courses must include 4 years of English and 2 years each of a foreign language, history, and science. An interview is recommended. CLEP credit is accepted. Important factors used in the admissions decision are recommendations by school officials, extracurricular activities record, leadership record, recommendations by alumni, and evidence of special talent.

Procedure: Freshmen are admitted fall and spring. Entrance exams should be taken by December of the senior year. Application deadlines are open. Application fee is $25. Notification is sent on a rolling basis. There is an early admissions plan.

Transfer: About 90 transfer students enrolled in a recent year. A total of 30 credits out of 121 to 130 must be completed at Neumann.

Visiting: There are regularly scheduled orientations for prospective students, including class visits and informal meetings with faculty. There are guides for informal visits and visitors may sit in on classes. To arrange for a visit, contact the Admissions Office at (215) 558–5616.

Financial Aid: In 1993–94, 85% of all current freshmen and 65% of continuing students received some form of financial aid. About 70% of freshmen and 65% of continuing students received need-based aid. Loans averaged $2625 (maximum) and work contracts averaged $550 ($600 maximum). Four percent of undergraduate students work part-time. Average earnings from campus work for the school year are $600. The average financial indebtedness of the 1992–93 graduate was $10,300. The college's own financial statement and FAFSA are required. The deadline for financial aid applications is March 15.

International Students: International students must take the TOEFL and achieve a minimum score of 500.

Computers: The college provides computer facilities for student use. About 50 microcomputers and terminals are available in the computer laboratory and in the library. All students may access the system. There are no time limits on using the system and no fees.

Graduates: In 1992–93, 173 bachelor's degrees were awarded. The most popular majors among graduates were nursing (29%), liberal studies (29%), and business administration (12%). Some 55 companies recruited on campus in 1992–93. In the 1992 graduating class, 4% of the men and women were enrolled in graduate school within 6 months of graduation; 92% had found employment.

Admissions Contact: Mark Osborn, Director of Admissions.

PENN STATE UNIVERSITY AT ERIE
BEHREND COLLEGE
B-1

Erie, PA 16563 (814) 898–6100

Full-time: 1510 men, 844 women	Faculty: 134
Part-time: 502 men, 225 women	Ph.D.s: 85%
Graduate: 95 men, 64 women	Student/Faculty: 18 to 1
Year: semesters, summer session	Tuition: $4822 ($10,170)
Application Deadline: open	Room & Board: $3930
Freshman Class: 2902 applied, 2048 accepted, 544 enrolled	
SAT I Verbal/Math: 446/510	**COMPETITIVE**

Penn State University at Erie/Behrend College, founded in 1948, offers 21 baccalaureate programs as well as the first 2 years of most Penn State University Park baccalaureate programs. It offers courses in business, humanities, social sciences, science, engineering technology, and engineering. There are 2 undergraduate schools and 2 divisions. In addition to regional accreditation, Behrend has baccalaureate program accreditation with ABET. The library contains 73,325 volumes, 33,460 microform items, and 1670 audiovisual forms, and subscribes to 950 periodicals. Computerized library sources and services include the card catalog, interlibrary loans, and database searching. Special learning facilities include a learning resource center, a radio station, a TV studio, and an engineering workstation laboratory. The 700-acre campus is in a suburban area 5 miles east of Erie. Including residence halls, there are 39 buildings on campus.

Student Life: About 94% of undergraduates are from Pennsylvania. Students come from 27 states. Ninety-two percent are white. The average age of freshmen is 18; all undergraduates, 22. Sixteen percent drop out by the end of their first year; 61% remain to graduate.

Housing: A total of 1099 students can be accommodated in college housing. College-sponsored living facilities include single-sex dormitories, on-campus apartments, and honors houses. On-campus housing is available on a first-come, first-served basis. Sixty-four percent of students commute. All students may keep cars on campus. Alcohol is not permitted.

Activities: About 10% of men belong to 1 local fraternity and 5 national fraternities; about 8% of women belong to 1 local sorority and 3 national sororities. There are 70 groups on campus, including cheerleading, chess, choir, computers, drama, ethnic, gay, honors, literary magazine, newspaper, pep band, political, professional, radio and TV, religious, social service, student government, and yearbook. Popular campus events include speaker series, parents events, black cultural awareness month, winter carnival, Logan Music at Noon Series, leadership conference, Homecoming, and Martin Luther King, Jr. Birthday Celebration Week.

Sports: There are 5 intercollegiate sports for men and 4 for women, and 18 intramural sports each for men and women. Athletic and recreation facilities include an arena seating 265, tennis courts, a weight room, a fitness trail, basketball courts, and baseball, softball, and soccer playing fields.

Disabled Students: Ninety percent of the campus is accessible to disabled students. The following facilities are available: wheelchair ramps, elevators, special parking, specially equipped rest rooms, and special class scheduling.

Services: In addition to many counseling and information services, tutoring is available in most subjects. There is a reader service for the blind, and remedial math, reading, and writing.

Campus Safety and Security: Campus safety and security measures include a 24-hour foot and vehicle patrol, self defense education, an escort service, informal discussions, pamphlets, posters, films, emergency telephones, and lighted pathways and sidewalks.

Programs of Study: Behrend awards the B.A. and B.S. degrees. Associate and master's degrees are also awarded. Bachelor's degrees are awarded in BIOLOGICAL SCIENCE (biology/biological science), BUSINESS (accounting, business administration and management, business economics, and management information systems), COMMUNICATIONS AND THE ARTS (communications and English), COMPUTER AND PHYSICAL SCIENCE (chemistry, mathematics, physics, and science), ENGINEERING AND ENVIRONMENTAL DESIGN (engineering, engineering technology, mechanical engineering technology, and plastics engineering technology), SOCIAL SCIENCE (economics, history, political science/government, and

psychology). Management information systems, psychology, mathematics, plastics engineering technology, mechanical engineering technology, and political science are the strongest programs academically. Business, engineering, and engineering technology have the largest enrollments.

Required: All baccalaureate degree candidates must take 46 general education credits, including 27 in arts, humanities, natural science, and social and behavioral sciences, including a cultural diversity course, 15 in quantification and communication skills (with a writing intensive course), and 4 in health and physical education. All students must complete a minimum of 120 credit hours with a GPA of 2.0. Further requirements vary by degree program.

Special: Internships, study abroad in 14 countries, and work-study programs are available. In addition, B.A.-B.S. degrees in communications, history, and psychology, dual majors, a general studies degree, and student-designed majors in business and behavioral sciences are offered. Nondegree study and up to 12 credits of pass/fail options are possible. There is a freshman honors program on campus, as well as 3 national honor societies.

Faculty/Classroom: Seventy-four percent of faculty are male; 26%, female. All teach undergraduates. No introductory courses are taught by graduate students. The average class size in an introductory lecture is 35; in a laboratory, 18; and in a regular course offering, 29.

Admissions: About 71% of the 1993–94 applicants were accepted. The SAT scores for the 1993–94 freshman class were as follows: Verbal—76% below 500, 21% between 500 and 599, and 3% between 600 and 700; Math—43% below 500, 38% between 500 and 599, 18% between 600 and 700, and 1% above 700. About 40% of the current freshmen were in the top fifth of their class; 80% were in the top two fifths.

Requirements: The SAT I or ACT is required. Candidates for admission must have 15 academic credits or 15 Carnegie units, including 5 years in social studies, 4 in English, 3 each in mathematics and science, and 2 in foreign language (for some majors). The GED is accepted. AP and CLEP credits are accepted. Important factors used in the admissions decision are advanced placement or honor courses and evidence of special talent.

Procedure: Freshmen are admitted to all sessions. Entrance exams should be taken during the junior year. Application deadlines are open. The application fee is $35. Notification is sent on a rolling basis.

Transfer: About 67 transfer students enrolled in the fall of 1993. Transfer candidates need a minimum GPA of 2.0, good academic standing, and 18 or more credits from a regionally accredited college or institution at the college level. A total of 36 credits out of a minimum of 120 must be completed at Behrend.

Visiting: There are regularly scheduled orientations for prospective students, including meetings with a counselor and faculty, a campus tour, and a class visit. There are guides for informal visits. Visitors may sit in on classes and stay overnight at the school during the summer. To arrange for a visit, contact the Admissions Office at (814) 898–6100.

Financial Aid: In 1993–94, 70% of all current freshmen and 84% of continuing students received some form of financial aid. The average freshman award was $4909. Of that total, scholarships or need-based grants averaged $442; loans averaged $2405; and work contracts averaged $148. Average earnings from campus work for the school year are $1044. The FAF and the Application for Pennsylvania State Grant are required. The deadline for financial aid applications is February 15.

International Students: There is currently 1 international student enrolled. International students must take the TOEFL and achieve a minimum score of 550. Students whose native language is English must submit SAT I or ACT scores.

Computers: The college provides computer facilities for student use. The mainframe is an IBM ES/3090–600S. A variety of computer laboratories are available; access is possible to all university computering facilities. A total of 220 computers are available in the computer center and laboratories in the library and engineering buildings. All students may access the system at posted hours or 24 hours by modem. There are no time limits and no fees.

Graduates: In 1992–93, 385 bachelor's degrees were awarded. The most popular majors among graduates were management (15%), accounting (12%), and engineering (11%). Within an average freshman class, 33% graduate in 4 years, 58% in 5 years, and 61% in 6 years. Some 20 companies recruited on campus in 1992–93.

Admissions Contact: Mary-Ellen Madigan, Director of Admissions.

PENN STATE UNIVERSITY
UNIVERSITY PARK CAMPUS   C-3
University Park, PA 16802   (814) 865-5471

Full-time: 16,253 men, 12,685 women	Faculty: 2365; I, -$
Part-time: 1113 men, 912 women	Ph.D.s: 88%
Graduate: 3810 men, 2921 women	Student/Faculty: 12 to 1
Year: semesters, summer session	Tuition: $4822 ($10,170)
Application Deadline: November 30	Room & Board: $3930
Freshman Class: 19,315 applied, 10,344 accepted, 3450 enrolled	
SAT I Verbal/Math: 506/591	**HIGHLY COMPETITIVE**

Penn State University/University Park Campus, founded in 1855, is the oldest and largest of 22 campuses in the Penn State system, offering undergraduate and graduate degrees in agricultural science, arts and architecture, business administration, earth and mineral sciences, education, engineering, health and human development, liberal arts, science, and communications. There are 10 undergraduate schools and one graduate school. In addition to regional accreditation, Penn State has baccalaureate program accreditation with AACSB, ABET, ACEJMC, ADA, ASLA, CSWE, NAAB, NASAD, NASM, NCATE, NLN, NRPA, and SAF. The 10 libraries contain 2,452,370 volumes, 1,917,033 microform items, and 38,931 audiovisual forms, and subscribe to 26,157 periodicals. Computerized library sources and services include the card catalog, interlibrary loans, and database searching. Special learning facilities include a learning resource center, an art gallery, a radio station, a TV station, museums of art, anthropology, and earth and mineral sciences, an observatory, and a nuclear reactor. The 5013-acre campus is in a suburban area 90 miles west of Harrisburg. Including residence halls, there are 358 buildings on campus.

Student Life: About 82% of undergraduates are from Pennsylvania. Students come from 53 states and Canada. Eighty-six percent are white. The average age of freshmen is 18; all undergraduates, 21. Sixteen percent drop out by the end of their first year; 61% remain to graduate.

Housing: A total of 12,854 students can be accommodated in college housing. College-sponsored living facilities include single-sex dormitories, on-campus apartments, and married-student housing. In addition, there are honors houses, language houses, and special interest houses. On-campus housing is guaranteed for the freshman year only and is available on a lottery system for upperclassmen. Sixty percent of students commute. All students may keep cars on campus. Alcohol is not permitted.

Activities: About 15% of men belong to 55 national fraternities; about 17% of women belong to 25 national sororities. There are more than 400 groups on campus, including art, band, cheerleading, chess, choir, chorale, chorus, computers, dance, drama, drill team, ethnic, film, gay, honors, international, jazz band, literary magazine, marching band, musical theater, newspaper, orchestra, pep band, photography, political, professional, radio and TV, religious, social, social service, student government, symphony, and yearbook. Popular campus events include Penn State Artists' Series, Central Pennsylvania Festival of the Arts, Sy Barash Regatta, Homecoming, Martin Luther King Convocation, Asylum, several film series, and Colloquy speaker series.

Sports: There are 15 intercollegiate sports for men and 13 for women, and 17 intramural sports each for men and women. Athletic and recreation facilities include 6 gymnasiums, 5 pools, indoor and outdoor tracks, 2 golf courses, a jogging course, a rink, 2 rifle ranges, 32 acres of practice fields, and numerous courts for tennis, handball, squash, and paddleball.

Disabled Students: Most of the campus is accessible to disabled students. The following facilities are available: wheelchair ramps, elevators, special parking, specially equipped rest rooms, special class scheduling, and lowered drinking fountains and telephones.

Services: In addition to many counseling and information services, tutoring is available in most subjects. There is a reader service for the blind, and remedial math, reading, and writing.

Campus Safety and Security: Campus safety and security measures include a 24-hour foot and vehicle patrol, self defense education, an escort service, shuttle buses, informal discussions, pamphlets, posters, films, emergency telephones, and lighted pathways and sidewalks.

Programs of Study: Penn State awards the B.A., B.S., B.Arch., B.Arch.Eng., B.F.A., B.M., and B.Ph. degrees. Associate, master's, and doctoral degrees are also awarded. Bachelor's degrees are awarded in AGRICULTURE (agricultural business management, agricultural economics, agricultural mechanics, agriculture, animal science, fishing and fisheries, forestry and related sciences, forestry production and processing, horticulture, natural resource management, and soil science), BIOLOGICAL SCIENCE (biochemistry, biology/biological science, botany, entomology, microbiology, molecular biology, nutrition, and wildlife biology), BUSINESS (accounting, banking and finance, business administration and management, business economics, hotel/motel and restaurant management, insurance, international business management, labor studies, management information systems, management science, marketing/retailing/merchandising, real estate, and recreation and leisure services), COMMUNICATIONS AND THE ARTS (advertising, art history and appreciation, broadcasting, classics, communications, comparative literature, English, film arts, fine arts, French, German, Italian, journalism, literature, music, Russian, Spanish, speech/debate/rhetoric, and telecommunications), COMPUTER AND PHYSICAL SCIENCE (actuarial science, astronomy, atmospheric sciences and meteorology, chemistry, computer science, earth science, geoscience, mathematics, metallurgy, physics, polymer science, and quantitative methods), EDUCATION (agricultural, art, early childhood, elementary, health, home economics, industrial arts, music, secondary, and special), ENGINEERING AND ENVIRONMENTAL DESIGN (aeronautical engineering, agricultural engineering, architectural engineering, ceramic engineering, ceramic science, chemical engineering, civil engineering, computer engineering, electrical/electronics engineering, engineering, environmental science, industrial engineering technology, landscape architecture/design, mechanical engineering, mining and mineral engineering, and nuclear engineering), HEALTH PROFESSIONS (health care administration, nursing, premedicine, rehabilitation therapy, and speech pathology/audiology), SOCIAL SCIENCE (American studies, anthropology, criminal justice, East Asian studies, economics, food science, geography, history, international relations, Latin American studies, liberal arts/general studies, medieval studies, philosophy, physical fitness/movement, political science/government, prelaw, psychology, religion, and sociology). Agriculture, architecture, meteorology, graphic design, geography, engineering, and communications are the strongest programs academically. Electrical engineering, education, and accounting have the largest enrollments.

Required: All bachelor's degree candidates must take 46 general education credits, including 15 in quantitative and communication skills, 9 in natural sciences, 6 each in arts, humanities, and social and behavioral sciences, and 4 in health sciences and physical education. Further requirements vary by degree program.

Special: Programs in African American studies, marine sciences, national security affairs, and science, technology, and society, as well as the B.Ph. program, are offered by faculty from several university colleges. There are internships available in many disciplines. Study abroad is possible through more than 30 programs in 14 countries. Dual and student-designed majors, a general studies degree in arts and sciences, and dual degrees in liberal arts and either earth/natural sciences or engineering are offered with 26 other institutions, as well as a 3-2 engineering program. Co-op programs are available in most engineering majors. There are limited pass/fail options, and nondegree study is possible. There is a freshman honors program on campus, in addition to 45 national honor societies, including Phi Beta Kappa. Most departments have honors programs.

Faculty/Classroom: Seventy-four percent of faculty are male; 26%, female. All both teach and do research. The average class size in a regular course offering is 26.

Admissions: About 54% of the 1993-94 applicants were accepted. The SAT scores for the 1993-94 freshman class were as follows: Verbal—45% below 500, 40% between 500 and 599, 13% between 600 and 700, and 2% above 700; Math—14% below 500, 37% between 500 and 599, 37% between 600 and 700, and 12% above 700. About 78% of the current freshmen were in the top fifth of their class; 96% were in the top two fifths. There were 163 National Merit finalists. About 130 freshmen graduated first in their class.

Requirements: The SAT I is required. Applicants should be graduates of accredited high schools or have earned the GED. Generally, all applicants should have 5 years in arts, humanities, and social sciences, 4 of English, and 3 each of science and mathematics. Two years of the same foreign language are required for the College of Liberal Arts and School of Communications, and recommended for all other programs. AP and CLEP credits are accepted. Important factors used in the admissions decision are advanced placement or honor courses and evidence of special talent.

Procedure: Freshmen are admitted to all sessions. Entrance exams should be taken in the junior year. Applications should be filed by November 30 for fall entry, along with an application fee of $35. Notification is sent on a rolling basis.

Transfer: About 383 transfer students enrolled in 1993. Transfer applicants need a minimum GPA of 2.0, good academic standing, and 18 or more credits from any regionally accredited college or institution at the college level. A total of 36 credits out of a minimum of 120 must be completed at Penn State.

Visiting: There are regularly scheduled orientations for prospective students. There are guides for informal visits and visitors may sit in on classes and stay overnight at the school. To arrange for a visit, contact the Undergraduate Admissions Office at (814) 865-5471.

Financial Aid: In 1993–94, 57% of all current freshmen and 76% of continuing students received some form of financial aid. The average freshman award was $4548. Of that total, scholarships or need-based grants averaged $1000; loans averaged $2001; and work contracts averaged $183. Average earnings from campus work for the school year are $1119. The FAF and application for Pennsylvania State Grant are required. The deadline for financial aid applications is February 15.

International Students: There are currently 1429 international students enrolled. They must take the TOEFL and achieve a minimum score of 550. Students whose native language is English must submit SAT I or ACT scores; others submit TOEFL.

Computers: The college provides computer facilities for student use. The mainframe is an IBM ES/3090–600s. The Center for Academic Computing is connected to a wide variety of academic facilities, the library, other Penn State campuses, the National Science Foundation network, Bitnet/CREN, and more than a thousand other organizations worldwide. Microcomputer classrooms and laboratories are available throughout the campus, and special facilities for graphics applications and desktop publishing are available. All students may access the system 24 hours a day. There are no fees.

Graduates: In 1992–93, 8307 bachelor's degrees were awarded. The most popular majors among graduates were elementary education (6%), accounting (4%), and administration of justice (3%). Within an average freshman class, 33% graduate in 4 years, 58% in 5 years, and 61% in 6 years. Some 106 companies recruited on campus in 1992–93.

Admissions Contact: Director of Admissions.

PENNSYLVANIA STATE SYSTEM OF HIGHER EDUCATION

The Pennsylvania State System of Higher Education, established in 1983, is a public system. It is governed by a board of governors, whose chief administrator is the chancellor. The primary goal of the system is to provide high-quality, liberal arts education at an affordable cost, with a central mission of teaching and service. The main priorities are capital facilities, matters of maintenance and funding, social equity, and tuition stabilization through appropriate funding. The total enrollment of all 14 campuses is about 99,000, with more than 5200 faculty members. Altogether, there are 217 baccalaureate, 107 master's, and 6 doctoral programs offered in the system. Four-year campuses are located in Bloomsburg, California, Cheyney, Clarion, East Stroudsberg, Edinboro, Indiana, Kutztown, Lock Haven, Mansfield, Millersville, Shippensburg, Slippery Rock, and West Chester. Profiles of the 4-year campuses are included in this chapter in alphabetical order with other Pennsylvania schools.

PHILADELPHIA COLLEGE OF BIBLE   F-3

Langhorne, PA 19047–2990	(215) 752–5800; (800) 366–0049
Full-time: 711 men and women	Faculty: 30
Part-time: 169 men and women	Ph.D.s: 30%
Graduate: 160 men and women	Student/Faculty: 24 to 1
Year: semesters, summer session	Tuition: $7140
Application Deadline: open	Room & Board: $3870
Freshman Class: 699 applied, 475 accepted, 302 enrolled	
SAT I Verbal/Math: 460/468	ACT: 21 COMPETITIVE

Philadelphia College of Bible, founded in 1913, is a private coeducational institution offering instruction in the Scriptures, liberal arts, and professional theory. Other campuses include the Wisconsin Wilderness Campus and the New Jersey Campus. There is one graduate school. In addition to regional accreditation, PCB has baccalaureate program accreditation with CSWE and NASM. The library contains 105,000 volumes, 17,000 microform items, and 4676 audiovisual forms, and subscribes to 469 periodicals. Computerized library sources and services include the card catalog and database searching. Special learning facilities include a learning resource center. The 105-acre campus is in a suburban area 30 miles north of Philadelphia. Including residence halls, there are 11 buildings on campus.

Student Life: About 60% of undergraduates are from Pennsylvania. Students come from 30 states, 40 foreign countries, and Canada. Seventy-three percent are from public schools; 25% from private. Seventy-eight percent are white; 11% African American. Most are Protestant. The average age of freshmen is 18; all undergraduates, 20. Thirty percent drop out by the end of their first year; 37% remain to graduate.

Housing: A total of 372 students can be accommodated in college housing. College-sponsored living facilities include single-sex dormitories. On-campus housing is guaranteed for all 4 years. Fifty-one percent of students commute. Alcohol is not permitted. All students may keep cars on campus.

Activities: There are no fraternities or sororities on campus. There are many groups and organizations on campus, including art, band, cheerleading, choir, chorale, chorus, computers, drama, ethnic, inter-

national, newspaper, orchestra, pep band, professional, religious, social, student government, symphony, and yearbook. Popular campus events include Charter Day (Homecoming), Late Skates, Christmas and Valentine socials, and Spring Formal.

Sports: There are 5 intercollegiate sports for men and 5 for women, and 4 intramural sports for men and 4 for women. Athletic and recreation facilities include a gymnasium, baseball diamond, soccer field, hockey field, and sand volleyball court.

Disabled Students: The entire campus is accessible to disabled students. The following facilities are available: wheelchair ramps, elevators, special parking, and lowered drinking fountains.

Services: The AIMS Program provides academic support for freshmen that need it.

Campus Safety and Security: Campus safety and security measures include 24-hour foot and vehicle patrol, shuttle buses, informal discussions, pamphlets, posters, and films. In addition, there are emergency telephones and lighted pathways and sidewalks.

Programs of Study: PCB awards the B.S., B.Mus., B.S.Ed., and B.S.W. degrees. Associate and master's degrees also are awarded. Bachelor's degrees are awarded in COMMUNICATIONS AND THE ARTS (music), EDUCATION (education), SOCIAL SCIENCE (biblical studies and social work). Bible is the strongest academically. Teacher education and Bible have the largest enrollments.

Required: Students must complete 51 credits in Bible, 48 in general education, and 27 in professional studies. A total of 126 credits, with a minimum GPA of 2.0, is required. Three credits in physical education must be taken. The number of hours in the major varies: 57 in Bible, 80 in music, 43 in social work, and 47 in education.

Special: PCB offers co-op programs in accounting, business administration, computer science, and office administration; cross-registration with Bucks County Community College; various church ministries, education, social work, and music internships; and study abroad in Israel. There are dual majors in social work, music, and education, and a B.A.-B.S. degree in Bible. Student-designed interdisciplinary majors are possible.

Faculty/Classroom: Seventy-seven percent of faculty are male; 23%, female. Ninety percent teach undergraduates.

Admissions: About 68% of the 1993–94 applicants were accepted. The SAT scores for the 1993–94 freshman class were as follows: Verbal—70% below 500, 23% between 500 and 599, and 7% between 600 and 700; Math—63% below 500, 26% between 500 and 599, 10% between 600 and 700, and 1% above 700. The ACT scores were 32% below 21, 26% between 21 and 23, 30% between 24 and 26, 11% between 27 and 28, and 1% above 28. About 26% of the current freshmen were in the top fifth of their class; 61% were in the top two fifths.

Requirements: PCB requires applicants to be in the upper 50% of their class. A minimum GPA of 2.0 is required. The SAT I or ACT is required, with minimum scores of 800 and 19, respectively. A high school diploma or the GED is needed. An essay and a pastor's reference are required. AP and CLEP credits are accepted. Important factors used in the admissions decision are advanced placement or honor courses, personality, intangible qualities, leadership record, evidence of special talent, and recommendations by school officials.

Procedure: Freshmen are admitted to all sessions. Entrance exams should be taken in the junior or senior year of high school. Application deadlines are open. Application fee is $15. Notification is sent on a rolling basis. There are early admissions and deferred admissions plans.

Transfer: About 400 transfer students enrolled in 1993–94. Tranfers must submit a pastor's reference, college transcripts, and a health form. SAT I and high school transcripts are required if the student has fewer than 60 college credit hours. At least 60 credits out of 126 must be completed at PCB.

Visiting: There are regularly scheduled orientations for prospective students, including chapel, class visits, a meal in the dining room, and an interview with a counselor. There are guides for informal visits, and visitors may sit in on classes and stay overnight at the school. To arrange for a visit, contact the Admissions Department at (800) 366–0049 or (215) 752–5800.

Financial Aid: In 1993–94, 95% of all current freshmen and 83% of continuing students received some form of financial aid. About 61% of freshmen and 66% of continuing students received need-based aid. The average freshman award was $3514. Of that total, scholarships or need-based grants averaged $1238 ($10,800 maximum); loans averaged $1640 ($2625 maximum); and work contracts averaged $636 ($1500 maximum). Twenty-eight percent of undergraduate students work part-time. Average earnings from campus work for the school year are $1200. PCB is a member of CSS.

International Students: There are currently 64 international students enrolled. The school actively recruits these students. They must take the TOEFL and achieve a minimum score of 550.

Computers: Twenty PCs are located in computer laboratories. All students may access the system anytime the library is open. There are no time limits on using the system.

Graduates: In 1992–93, 135 bachelor's degrees were awarded. The most popular majors among graduates were Bible (100%), and, in double-degree programs, education (18%), and music (12%). Within an average freshman class, 42% graduate in 5 years.

Admissions Contact: Mrs. Fran Emmons, Director of Admissions and Financial Aid.

PHILADELPHIA COLLEGE OF PHARMACY AND SCIENCE
F-3

Philadelphia, PA 19104–4495   (215) 596–8810

Full-time: 671 men, 1046 women	Faculty: 158; IIB, +$
Part-time: 4 men, 8 women	Ph.D.s: 64%
Graduate: 57 men, 96 women	Student/Faculty: 11 to 1
Year: semesters, summer session	Tuition: $10,750
Application Deadline: open	Room & Board: $4000
Freshman Class: 1374 applied, 843 accepted, 392 enrolled	
SAT I Verbal/Math: 470/570	**VERY COMPETITIVE**

Philadelphia College of Pharmacy and Science, founded in 1821 and coeducational since 1876, is a private, professional institution offering undergraduate and graduate programs in pharmacy and health related sciences. There is one graduate school. In addition to regional accreditation, PCPS has baccalaureate program accreditation with ACPE and APTA. The library contains 55,000 volumes and 30,500 microform items, and subscribes to 800 periodicals. Computerized library sources and services include the card catalog, interlibrary loans, and database searching. Special learning facilities include a learning resource center, the pharmacology and toxicology center, and a model pharmacy. The 15-acre campus is in an urban area in Philadelphia. Including residence halls, there are 14 buildings on campus.

Student Life: About 73% of undergraduates are from Pennsylvania. Students come from 12 states, 8 foreign countries, and Canada. Seventy-two percent are from public schools; 28% from private. Seventy-eight percent are white; 17% Asian American. The average age of freshmen is 19; all undergraduates, 20. Nine percent drop out by the end of their first year; 82% remain to graduate.

Housing: A total of 680 students can be accommodated in college housing. College-sponsored living facilities include coed dormitories and fraternity houses. In addition there are honors houses. On-campus housing is guaranteed for the freshman year only, is available on a first-come, first-served basis, and is available on a lottery system for upperclassmen. Priority is given to out-of-town students. Alcohol is not permitted. Upperclassmen may keep cars on campus.

Activities: About 20% of men belong to 4 local fraternities and 1 national fraternity; about 17% of women belong to 2 local sororities and 1 national sorority. There are 28 groups on campus, including cheerleading, chess, chorus, computers, drama, ethnic, honors, international, literary magazine, musical theater, newspaper, professional, religious, social, social service, student government, and yearbook. Popular campus events include Greek Week and Student Appreciation Days.

Sports: There are 7 intercollegiate sports for men and 8 for women, and 19 intramural sports for men and 19 for women. Athletic and recreation facilities include a gymnasium, a rifle range, and recreational areas in the residence halls.

Disabled Students: Ten percent of the campus is accessible to disabled students. The following facilities are available: wheelchair ramps, elevators, and specially equipped rest rooms.

Services: In addition to many counseling and information services, tutoring is available in every subject. In addition, there is remedial math and writing.

Campus Safety and Security: Campus safety and security measures include 24-hour foot and vehicle patrol, self defense education, escort service, and shuttle buses. In addition, there are pamphlets, posters, and films, emergency telephones, and lighted pathways and sidewalks.

Programs of Study: PCPS awards the B.S. degree. Master's and doctoral degrees also are awarded. Bachelor's degrees are awarded in BIOLOGICAL SCIENCE (biochemistry, biology/biological science, microbiology, and toxicology), COMPUTER AND PHYSICAL SCIENCE (chemical technology and chemistry), HEALTH PROFESSIONS (medical laboratory technology and pharmacy). Health and basic science are the strongest academically. Health science has the largest enrollment.

Required: Requirements vary by major program. However, all students must take 3 English courses, introductory courses in psychology and sociology, a computer course, and physical education. They must pass a writing proficiency examination. In all programs, the first year courses are required. Total credits required range from 98 to 187, depending on the major. A 2.0 GPA is required for graduation.

Special: PCPS offers a 5-year B.S. in pharmacy and a 5-year integrated professional program in physical therapy. Internships are available in all disciplines. An open major is offered, as is a program of curriculum and advisement to prepare students to enter medical

school. Students may elect a minor in communications, economics, psychology, or sociology. There are 4 national honor societies on campus.

Faculty/Classroom: No introductory courses are taught by graduate students. The average class size in an introductory lecture is 200; in a laboratory, 20; and in a regular course offering, 25.

Admissions: About 61% of the 1993–94 applicants were accepted. The SAT scores for the 1993–94 freshman class were as follows: Verbal—61% below 500, 32% between 500 and 599, 6% between 600 and 700, and 1% above 700; Math—19% below 500, 51% between 500 and 599, 27% between 600 and 700, and 3% above 700. About 59% of the current freshmen were in the top fifth of their class; 85% were in the top two fifths.

Requirements: PCPS requires applicants to be in the upper 50% of their class. A minimum GPA of 3.0 is required. The SAT I is required and the ACT is recommended. A composite score of 1000 on the SAT is recommended. SAT II: writing and mathematics I are required. Applicants must be high school graduates or hold the GED. Minimum academic requirements include 4 credits in English, 1 credit each in American history and social science, and 4 credits in academic electives. Mathematics requirements include 2 years of algebra and 1 year of plane geometry. The college strongly recommends an additional year of higher-level mathematics, such as calculus. Three science credits are required; strongly recommended are 1 credit each in biology, chemistry, and physics. All applicants must submit a personal essay, and an interview is recommended. Applicants to the 5-year physical therapy program must present evidence of at least 20 hours of experience in a clinical setting and participate in an interview with the faculty. AP and CLEP credits are accepted. Important factors used in the admissions decision are advanced placement or honor courses, personality, intangible qualities, geographic diversity, leadership record, and recommendations by school officials.

Procedure: Freshmen are admitted in the fall. Entrance exams should be taken by the end of the junior year or fall of the senior year. Application deadlines are open. Application fee is $25. Notification is sent on a rolling basis. There are early admissions and deferred admissions plans.

Transfer: A total of 46 transfer students enrolled in a recent year. PCPS has transfer agreements with Trenton State and Rowan colleges in New Jersey, which allow students to complete the nonprofessional part of either the pharmacy or physical therapy program at those institutions. Other transfer applicants must present a GPA of 2.7 to 3.0, depending on the program for which they apply, a composite SAT I score of at least 950, and at least 9 credits of previous college work. Applicants to the physical therapy program must also meet freshman requirements for admission to that program. A total of 90 credits out of 98 to 187 must be completed at PCPS.

Visiting: There are guides for informal visits and visitors may sit in on classes and stay overnight at the school. To arrange for a visit, contact the Director of Admissions at (215) 596–8810.

Financial Aid: In a recent year, 70% of continuing students received some form of financial aid. About 80% of freshmen and 50% of continuing students received need-based aid. All undergraduate students work part-time. Average earnings from campus work for the school year are $1000. The average financial indebtedness of a recent graduate was $31,000. The college's own financial statement and PHEAA are required. The deadline for financial aid applications is March 15.

International Students: There are currently 45 international students enrolled. They must take the TOEFL and achieve a minimum score of 550.

Computers: The college provides computer facilities for student use. There are 34 IBM and Apple microcomputers available in the computer center. All students may access the system. There are no time limits on using the system and no fees.

Graduates: In 1992–93, 252 bachelor's degrees were awarded. The most popular majors among graduates were pharmacy (70%), biology (38%), and physical therapy (12%). Within an average freshman class, 82% graduate in 5 years. In a recent graduating class, 2% of the men and 1% of the women were enrolled in graduate school within 6 months of graduation; all of the men and women had found employment.

Admissions Contact: Louis L. Hegyes, Director of Admissions.

PHILADELPHIA COLLEGE OF TEXTILES AND SCIENCE

Philadelphia, PA 19144-5497

F-3

(215) 951-2800

Full-time: 587 men, 1077 women	Faculty: 95; IIB, av$
Part-time: 326 men, 716 women	Ph.D.s: n/av
Graduate: 335 men, 256 women	Student/Faculty: 18 to 1
Year: semesters, summer session	Tuition: $10,914
Application Deadline: open	Room & Board: $4982
Freshman Class: 1539 applied, 1359 accepted, 441 enrolled	
SAT I Verbal/Math: 455/520	COMPETITIVE

Philadelphia College of Textiles and Science, founded in 1884, is a private, coeducational institution offering preprofessional programs in architecture, design, business, the sciences, premedicine, prelaw, textiles, and engineering. There are 3 undergraduate and 3 graduate schools. In addition to regional accreditation, Textile has baccalaureate program accreditation with FIDER. The library contains 80,000 volumes and 5500 microform items, and subscribes to 1800 periodicals. Computerized library sources and services include the card catalog, interlibrary loans, and database searching. Special learning facilities include a learning resource center, art gallery, radio station, and the Paley Design Center. The 100-acre campus is in a suburban area 10 minutes west of metropolitan Philadelphia. Including residence halls, there are 56 buildings on campus.

Student Life: About 60% of undergraduates are from Pennsylvania. Students come from 35 states, 46 foreign countries, and Canada. Sixty-five percent are from public schools; 35% from private. Seventynine percent are white; 11% African American. The average age of freshmen is 18; all undergraduates, 20. Thirty percent drop out by the end of their first year; 60% remain to graduate.

Housing: A total of 900 students can be accommodated in college housing. College-sponsored living facilities include single-sex and coed dormitories, on-campus apartments, and off-campus apartments. On-campus housing is guaranteed for all 4 years. Fifty-three percent of students commute. Alcohol is not permitted. All students may keep cars on campus.

Activities: About 8% of men belong to 2 national fraternities; about 4% of women belong to 2 national sororities. There are 45 groups on campus, including cheerleading, choir, computers, dance, drama, ethnic, honors, international, literary magazine, newspaper, professional, radio, religious, social, social service, student government, and yearbook. Popular campus events include an annual fashion show and design competition, Welcome Week, and Special Olympics.

Sports: There are 5 intercollegiate sports for men and 6 for women, and 4 intramural sports for men and 4 for women. Athletic and recreation facilities include 2 gymnasiums, a fitness center and exercise facility, tennis courts, athletic fields, and a student center recreation room.

Disabled Students: Ninety percent of the campus is accessible to disabled students. The following facilities are available: wheelchair ramps, elevators, special parking, specially equipped rest rooms, special class scheduling, and lowered telephones.

Services: In addition to many counseling and information services, tutoring is available in most subjects. In addition, there is remedial math, reading, and writing.

Campus Safety and Security: Campus safety and security measures include 24-hour foot and vehicle patrol, self defense education, escort service, and shuttle buses. In addition, there are informal discussions, pamphlets, posters, and films, emergency telephones, and lighted pathways and sidewalks.

Programs of Study: Textile awards the B.S. degree. Associate and master's degrees also are awarded. Bachelor's degrees are awarded in BIOLOGICAL SCIENCE (biochemistry and biology/biological science), BUSINESS (accounting, banking and finance, fashion merchandising, international business management, management science, marketing/retailing/merchandising, and retailing), COMMUNICATIONS AND THE ARTS (graphic design), COMPUTER AND PHYSICAL SCIENCE (applied mathematics, chemistry, computer science, information sciences and systems, and polymer science), ENGINEERING AND ENVIRONMENTAL DESIGN (architecture, environmental science, interior design, textile engineering, and textile technology), HEALTH PROFESSIONS (premedicine), SOCIAL SCIENCE (fashion design and technology, prelaw, psychology, and textiles and clothing). Interior design, accounting, and fashion apparel management are the strongest academically. Fashion merchandising, marketing, and architecture have the largest enrollments.

Required: All students are required to complete a 60-credit residency with courses in mathematics, science, social science, and the humanities, 2 semesters of physical education, and a professional studies core curriculum, which differs by major program. A number of requirements may be satisfied and elective credits earned by proficiency examination. A total of 121 to 146 credits is required with an overall GPA of 2.0.

Special: Textile offers special B.S. degree programs for registered nurses and allied health professionals. Work-study programs are available locally and in New York, Boston, Washington D.C., and London, England. Students may undertake independent study in 1 discipline for 1 semester. Cooperative programs in all academic majors, summer internships, a dual major in international business, and an integrated major in business and science are available. There is a freshman honors program on campus. Twenty-six departments have honors programs.

Faculty/Classroom: Seventy percent of faculty are male; 30%, female. All teach undergraduates. The average class size in an introductory lecture is 30; in a laboratory, 18; and in a regular course offering, 25.

Admissions: About 88% of the 1993-94 applicants were accepted. About 26% of the current freshmen were in the top fifth of their class; 48% were in the top two fifths. There were 6 National Merit semifinalists. One freshman graduated first in the class.

Requirements: Textile requires applicants to be in the upper 50% of their class. A minimum GPA of 2.5 is required. The SAT I or ACT is required. Applicants should be high school graduates or have earned the GED. Recommended secondary preparation includes 4 years each of English and history, 3 years of mathematics, and 2 years of science. Potential science majors are strongly urged to take 4 years of mathematics. AP and CLEP credits are accepted. Important factors used in the admissions decision are evidence of special talent, advanced placement or honor courses, personality, intangible qualities, leadership record, and extracurricular activities record.

Procedure: Freshmen are admitted fall and spring. Application deadlines are open. Application fee is $20. Notification is sent on a rolling basis. There is a deferred admissions plan.

Transfer: A total of 139 transfer students enrolled in 1993-94. Applicants usually need a 2.5 GPA. A total of 60 credits out of 121 to 146 must be completed at Textile.

Visiting: There are regularly scheduled orientations for prospective students during the summer. There are guides for informal visits and visitors may sit in on classes and stay overnight at the school. To arrange for a visit, contact the Admissions Office at (215) 951-2800.

Financial Aid: In 1993-94, 80% of all current freshmen and 76% of continuing students received some form of financial aid. About 65% of freshmen and 61% of continuing students received need-based aid. The average freshman award was $9228. Of that total, scholarships or need-based grants averaged $5141 ($14,236 maximum); loans averaged $844 ($1500 maximum); and work contracts averaged $836 ($1200 maximum). Twenty-eight percent of undergraduate students work part-time. Average earnings from campus work for the school year are $746. The average financial indebtedness of the 1992-93 graduate was $10,841. Textile is a member of CSS. The college's own financial statement and PHEAA are required. The deadline for financial aid applications is April 15.

International Students: There are currently 215 international students enrolled. The school actively recruits these students. They must take the TOEFL and achieve a minimum score of 500.

Computers: The college provides computer facilities for student use. The mainframes are a DEC VAX 11/780, 6410, and 8250. There are also 50 IBM, Zenith, and Apple Macintosh microcomputers available in the computer center and design laboratories (with CAD and plotter facilities). All students may access the system 7 days a week. There are no time limits on using the system and no fees.

Graduates: In 1992-93, 466 bachelor's degrees were awarded. The most popular majors among graduates were marketing (18%), fashion design (12%), and fashion merchandising (12%). Within an average freshman class, 40% graduate in 4 years. Some 129 companies recruited on campus in 1992-93. In the 1992 graduating class, 93% of men and women had found employment within 6 months of graduation.

Admissions Contact: David B. Conway, Dean of Admissions.

POINT PARK COLLEGE

Pittsburgh, PA 15222

B-3

(412) 392-3430; (800) 321-0129 (in-state)

Full-time: 494 men, 679 women	Faculty: 72; IIB, -$
Part-time: 779 men, 623 women	Ph.D.s: 44%
Graduate: 43 men, 51 women	Student/Faculty: 16 to 1
Year: semesters, summer session	Tuition: $9312
Application Deadline: open	Room & Board: $4610
Freshman Class: 875 applied, 744 accepted, 207 enrolled	
SAT I Verbal/Math: 418/424	ACT: 21 LESS COMPETITIVE

Point Park College, founded in 1960, is an independent, coeducational institution offering programs in liberal arts, fine arts, business, engineering, health science, professional training, and teacher preparation. There are 2 graduate schools. In addition to regional accreditation, Point Park College has baccalaureate program accreditation with ABET. The library contains 124,371 volumes, 27,734 microform items, and 2432 audiovisual forms, and subscribes to 571 periodicals. Computerized library sources and services include the card cat-

alog, interlibrary loans, and database searching. Special learning facilities include a radio station, TV station, and theaters and dance studios. The campus is in an urban area in downtown Pittsburgh. Including residence halls, there are 5 buildings on campus.

Student Life: About 88% of undergraduates are from Pennsylvania. Students come from 16 states, 32 foreign countries, and Canada. Eighty-four percent are white. Forty-four percent are Catholic; 33% Protestant; 12% claim no religious affiliation. The average age of freshmen is 18; all undergraduates, 28. Twenty-eight percent drop out by the end of their first year; 55% remain to graduate.

Housing: A total of 650 students can be accommodated in college housing. College-sponsored living facilities include single-sex and coed dormitories. On-campus housing is guaranteed for all 4 years. Sixty-nine percent of students commute.

Activities: About 8% of men belong to 2 local fraternities; about 7% of women belong to 4 local sororities. There are 25 groups on campus, including cheerleading, choir, computers, dance, drama, ethnic, film, honors, international, literary magazine, musical theater, newspaper, photography, political, professional, radio and TV, religious, social, social service, and student government. Popular campus events include Snowball (Christmas) Dance, Spring Fling (spring dance), and performances at the Playhouse Theatre Company, Student Dance Company, Playhouse Junior, and Point Park College Theatre Company.

Sports: There are 3 intercollegiate sports for men and 3 for women, and 7 intramural sports for men and 7 for women. There is a recreation center. The auditorium seats 130.

Disabled Students: Ninety-eight percent of the campus is accessible to disabled students. The following facilities are available: wheelchair ramps, elevators, specially equipped rest rooms, special class scheduling, lowered drinking fountains, and lowered telephones.

Services: In addition to many counseling and information services, tutoring is available in most subjects. Learning-disabled services are available on a case-by-case basis. In addition, there is a reader service for the blind, and remedial math, reading, and writing.

Campus Safety and Security: Campus safety and security measures include 24-hour foot and vehicle patrol, informal discussions, pamphlets, posters, and films, and emergency telephones. In addition, there are lighted pathways and sidewalks.

Programs of Study: Point Park College awards the B.A., B.S., and B.F.A. degrees. Associate and master's degrees also are awarded. Bachelor's degrees are awarded in BIOLOGICAL SCIENCE (biology/biological science), BUSINESS (accounting, business administration and management, fashion merchandising, human resources, and management science), COMMUNICATIONS AND THE ARTS (applied art, arts administration/management, communications, dance, dramatic arts, English, journalism, and video), COMPUTER AND PHYSICAL SCIENCE (computer science and mathematics), EDUCATION (early childhood, elementary, and secondary), ENGINEERING AND ENVIRONMENTAL DESIGN (civil engineering technology, electrical/electronics engineering technology, environmental science, and mechanical engineering technology), HEALTH PROFESSIONS (health care administration), SOCIAL SCIENCE (behavioral science, history, international studies, liberal arts/general studies, paralegal studies, political science/government, psychology, and public administration). Education, history, journalism and communications, political science, English, biological science, theater arts, business, and engineering technology are the strongest academically. Electrical engineering technology, business management, performing arts, and journalism and communications have the largest enrollments.

Required: All majors leading to a baccalaureate degree require a minimum of 120 credits. The basic distribution requirement is 30 or more credits in the liberal arts and sciences, with a minimum of 12 credits in English and humanities and 6 credits each in human, natural, and social sciences. A minimum GPA of 2.0 is required.

Special: There is cross-registration with the Pittsburgh Council of Higher Education, and cooperative programs with the Art Institute of Pittsburgh. Internships exist in journalism and communications, legal studies, and business management. The college offers a Washington semester, work-study, dual and student-designed majors, credit by examination and for life/military/work experience, nondegree study, and pass/fail options. Capstone programs are available for students with associate degrees in legal studies. Other Capstone programs available to third and fourth-year students include management services, applied arts, international studies, general studies, human resources management, health services, and specialized professional studies-funeral service. CollegeFAST!, a 3-year baccalaureate program, is also offered. There are 2 national honor societies on campus.

Faculty/Classroom: Sixty-four percent of faculty are male; 36%, female. All teach undergraduates. The average class size in an introductory lecture is 40; in a laboratory, 12; and in a regular course offering, 25.

Admissions: About 85% of the 1993–94 applicants were accepted. The SAT scores for the 1993–94 freshman class were as follows: Verbal—84% below 500, 15% between 500 and 599, and 1% between 600 and 700; Math—78% below 500, 20% between 500 and 599, and 2% between 600 and 700. About 25% of the current freshmen were in the top fifth of their class; 49% were in the top two fifths.

Requirements: A minimum GPA of 2.0 is required. The SAT I or ACT is required. A GED is accepted in lieu of a high school diploma. Students should have completed 12 academic credits or 16 Carnegie units consisting of 4 in English and history, 3 in science, and 2 in mathematics. Theater and dance students must audition, and an interview is required for all candidates. AP and CLEP credits are accepted. Important factors used in the admissions decision are personality, intangible qualities, leadership record, extracurricular activities record, recommendations by school officials, and advanced placement or honor courses.

Procedure: Freshmen are admitted to all sessions. Entrance exams should be taken in the junior or senior year. Application deadlines are open. Application fee is $20. Notification is sent on a rolling basis. There are early admissions and deferred admissions plans.

Transfer: A total of 184 transfer students enrolled in 1993–94. Transfer applicants must have completed 12 credit hours with at least a 2.0 GPA. The SAT I or ACT, an associate degree, and an interview are recommended. A total of 30 credits out of 120 must be completed at Point Park College.

Visiting: There are regularly scheduled orientations for prospective students. There are guides for informal visits and visitors may sit in on classes and stay overnight at the school. To arrange for a visit, contact the Office of Admissions at (412) 392-3439.

Financial Aid: In 1993–94, 93% of all current freshmen received some form of financial aid. About 89% of freshmen received need-based aid. The average freshman award was $8900. Of that total, scholarships or need-based grants averaged $2030 ($13,622 maximum); loans averaged $2021 ($3625 maximum); and work contracts averaged $1028 ($1600 maximum). All undergraduate students work part-time. Average earnings from campus work for the school year are $1200. Point Park College is a member of CSS. The college's own financial statement and PHEAA are required.

International Students: There are currently 130 international students enrolled. The school actively recruits these students. They must take the TOEFL and achieve a minimum score of 500.

Computers: The college provides computer facilities for student use. The mainframe is an HP 9000/825. There are 82 PCs and terminals for student use. Access to the mainframe is limited to computer science and engineering technology majors. PC laboratories are available to all students, with special facilities open to journalism students only. Laboratory hours vary by facility. The fees are $60 per term.

Graduates: In 1992–93, 433 bachelor's degrees were awarded. The most popular majors among graduates were business management (11%), electrical engineering technology (11%), and journalism and communications (10%). Within an average freshman class, 2% graduate in 3 years and 55% in 6 years. Some 12 companies recruited on campus in 1992–93.

Admissions Contact: Terrence R. Kizina, Director of Admissions.

ROBERT MORRIS COLLEGE
Coraopolis, PA 15108

B-3

(412) 262-8463
(800) 762-0097 (out-of-state)

Full-time: 1371 men, 1250 women	Faculty: 129
Part-time: 683 men, 1125 women	Ph.D.s: 58%
Graduate: 595 men, 321 women	Student/Faculty: 20 to 1
Year: semesters, summer session	Tuition: $6300
Application Deadline: open	Room & Board: $4106
Freshman Class: 907 applied, 771 accepted, 387 enrolled	
SAT I Verbal/Math: 396/451	**LESS COMPETITIVE**

Robert Morris College, founded in 1921, is an independent, coeducational, nonprofit institution offering programs in business administration, English, and communications. There is also a campus in Pittsburgh. There are 3 undergraduate and 3 graduate schools. In addition to regional accreditation, the college has baccalaureate program accreditation with CAHEA. The 2 libraries contain 120,832 volumes, 276,525 microform items, and 23,170 audiovisual forms, and subscribe to 836 periodicals. Computerized library sources and services include the card catalog and database searching. Special learning facilities include a learning resource center and TV station. The 230-acre campus is in a suburban area 17 miles northwest of Pittsburgh. Including residence halls, there are 26 buildings on campus.

Student Life: About 95% of undergraduates are from Pennsylvania. Students come from 24 states, 14 foreign countries, and Canada. Ninety-three percent are white. The average age of freshmen is 18; all undergraduates, 23. Eighteen percent drop out by the end of their first year; 55% remain to graduate.

Housing: A total of 883 students can be accommodated in college housing. College-sponsored living facilities include single-sex dormitories. On-campus housing is guaranteed for all 4 years. Seventy percent of students commute. Alcohol is not permitted. All students may keep cars on campus.

Activities: About 15% of men belong to 4 national fraternities; about 5% of women belong to 2 local and 4 national sororities. There are 30 groups on campus, including band, cheerleading, chorale, computers, dance, drama, drill team, ethnic, film, honors, international, literary magazine, musical theater, newspaper, pep band, photography, professional, radio and TV, religious, social, social service, student government, and yearbook. Popular campus events include Muscular Dystrophy Dance-a-Thon, Spring Carnival, Snow Ball, Luninaire, ski trips, Winterfest, National Shakespeare Company, and Air Band Competition.

Sports: There are 6 intercollegiate sports for men and 6 for women, and 11 intramural sports for men and 9 for women. Athletic and recreation facilities include the Sewall Center and the John Jay Center, which houses a student union, a weight room, and indoor and outdoor swimming pools. There is a 700-seat gymnasium and a 300-seat arena.

Disabled Students: Thirty-five percent of the campus is accessible to disabled students. The following facilities are available: wheelchair ramps, elevators, special parking, specially equipped rest rooms, and special class scheduling.

Services: In addition to many counseling and information services, tutoring is available in most subjects. In addition, there is a reader service for the blind, and remedial math, reading, and writing.

Campus Safety and Security: Campus safety and security measures include 24-hour foot and vehicle patrol, escort service, shuttle buses, and informal discussions. In addition, there are pamphlets, posters, and films, emergency telephones, and lighted pathways and sidewalks.

Programs of Study: The college awards the B.A. and B.S.B.A. degrees. Associate and master's degrees also are awarded. Bachelor's degrees are awarded in BUSINESS (accounting, banking and finance, business administration and management, human resources, management science, marketing/retailing/merchandising, sports management, and transportation management), COMMUNICATIONS AND THE ARTS (communications and English), EDUCATION (business), HEALTH PROFESSIONS (health care administration), SOCIAL SCIENCE (economics). Accounting, radiologic technology, computer information systems, and communications management are the strongest academically. Accounting, management, and marketing have the largest enrollments.

Required: All candidates must complete 120 to 124 credit hours, including 18 to 39 in the major, with a 2.0 GPA overall and a 2.5 in the major. There is a core curriculum that varies with each major, consisting of liberal arts or business components. All students must have 2 credits in physical education and demonstrate competency in computer software applications.

Special: The college offers cooperative programs in all majors, cross-registration with the 9 schools of the Pittsburgh Council of Higher Education, internships in 2 majors, work-study programs, dual majors, and nondegree study. Credit by exam and pass/fail options are available. There is a B.A.-B.S. degree in business administration, and study abroad in Australia for sports management majors. There are 2 national honor societies on campus.

Faculty/Classroom: Sixty-nine percent of faculty are male; 31%, female. All teach undergraduates. No introductory courses are taught by graduate students. The average class size in an introductory lecture is 50 and in a regular course offering, 25.

Admissions: About 85% of the 1993–94 applicants were accepted. The SAT scores for the 1993–94 freshman class were as follows: Verbal—90% below 500, 7% between 500 and 599, 2% between 600 and 700, and 1% above 700; Math—66% below 500, 27% between 500 and 599, 5% between 600 and 700, and 2% above 700. About 24% of the current freshmen were in the top fifth of their class; 52% were in the top two fifths. One freshman graduated first in the class.

Requirements: The college requires applicants to be in the upper 60% of their class. A minimum GPA of 2.0 is required. The SAT I or ACT is required. Candidates should be graduates of an accredited secondary school or hold a GED diploma. They must have completed 16 Carnegie units, including 4 in English, 2 each in mathematics and social studies, and 1 each in history and science. An interview is required for some and recommended for all others. AP and CLEP credits are accepted. Important factors used in the admissions decision are advanced placement or honor courses, leadership record, personality, intangible qualities, extracurricular activities record, and geographic diversity.

Procedure: Freshmen are admitted to all sessions. Entrance exams should be taken by fall or late winter of the senior year. Application deadlines are open. Application fee is $20. Notification is sent on a rolling basis. There are early admissions and deferred admissions plans.

Transfer: About 500 transfer students enrolled in 1993–94. Students must have a minimum 2.0 GPA in nondevelopmental academic courses. Those with fewer than 30 earned credits must also submit an official high school transcript and test results of the SAT I or ACT. An interview is recommended. A total of 30 credits out of 120 to 124 must be completed at the college.

Visiting: There are guides for informal visits and visitors may sit in on classes and stay overnight at the school. To arrange for a visit, contact the Office of Admissions at (412) 262–8206 or (800) 762–0097.

Financial Aid: In a recent year, 82% of all current freshmen and 73% of continuing students received some form of financial aid. About 66% of freshmen and 60% of continuing students received need-based aid. The average freshman award was $4750. Of that total, scholarships or need-based grants averaged $1742 ($3000 maximum) and loans averaged $2118 ($8000 maximum). Eight percent of undergraduate students work part-time. Average earnings from campus work for the school year are $1040. the college is a member of CSS. The college's own financial statement and PHEAA are required. The deadline for financial aid applications is May 1.

International Students: There are currently 36 international students enrolled. They must take the TOEFL and achieve a minimum score of 500.

Computers: The college provides computer facilities for student use. The mainframes are a Prime 5370, an IBM 9370/90, and an IBM 9370/25. Students have access to 350 microcomputers at computer laboratories at each campus and 4 computerized classrooms. Students can also access mainframe systems with dial-up facilities. All students may access the system from 8 A.M. to 12 midnight Monday through Thursday, 8 A.M. to 9 P.M. Friday, 9 A.M. to 4 P.M. Saturday, and 9 A.M. to 11 P.M. Sunday. There are no time limits on using the system and no fees.

Graduates: In 1992–93, 727 bachelor's degrees were awarded. The most popular majors among graduates were accounting (23%), management (21%), and marketing (17%). Within an average freshman class, 32% graduate in 4 years, 19% in 5 years, and 4% in 6 years. Some 58 companies recruited on campus in 1992–93.

Admissions Contact: Jim Welsh, Dean of Enrollment.

ROSEMONT COLLEGE

Rosemont, PA 19010–1699

F-4

(215) 526–2966

(800) 331–0708 (out-of-state)

Full-time: 500 women	Faculty: 43; IIB, -$
Part-time: 5 men, 125 women	Ph.D.s: 75%
Graduate: 26 men, 62 women	Student/Faculty: 12 to 1
Year: semesters, summer session	Tuition: $11,075
Application Deadline: open	Room & Board: $5700
Freshman Class: 350 applied, 250 accepted, 121 enrolled	
SAT I Verbal/Math: 505/502	COMPETITIVE

Rosemont College, founded in 1921, is a private women's college affiliated with the Roman Catholic Church, offering programs in liberal and fine arts, and business. There is one graduate school. The library contains 154,626 volumes, 24,677 microform items, and 9879 audiovisual forms, and subscribes to 550 periodicals. Computerized library sources and services include the card catalog, interlibrary loans, and database searching. Special learning facilities include a learning resource center and art gallery. The 56-acre campus is in a suburban area 11 miles west of Philadelphia. Including residence halls, there are 15 buildings on campus.

Student Life: About 50% of undergraduates are from out-of-state, mostly the Middle Atlantic. Students come from 17 states and 6 foreign countries. Forty percent are from public schools; 60% from private. Ninety percent are white. Sixty percent are Catholic; 17% Protestant. The average age of freshmen is 18; all undergraduates, 22. Fifteen percent drop out by the end of their first year; 70% remain to graduate.

Housing: College-sponsored living facilities include dormitories. On-campus housing is guaranteed for all 4 years. Eighty-five percent of students live on campus; of those, 50% remain on campus on weekends. All students may keep cars on campus.

Activities: There are 25 groups on campus, including art, chorus, drama, ethnic, international, literary magazine, newspaper, photography, political, religious, social service, student government, and yearbook. Popular campus events include Oktoberfest, Founders Day, 100 Days Party, Winter Luncheon, Spring Luncheon, and Family Weekend.

Sports: There are 6 intercollegiate sports. Athletic and recreation facilities include those for indoor basketball, badminton, and volleyball; hockey and softball fields; tennis courts; and a 500-seat auditorium.

Disabled Students: The following facilities are available: wheelchair ramps, elevators, special parking, special class scheduling, and lowered telephones.

Services: In addition to many counseling and information services, tutoring is available in every subject.

Campus Safety and Security: Campus safety and security measures include 24-hour foot and vehicle patrol, informal discussions, emergency telephones, and lighted pathways and sidewalks.

Programs of Study: Rosemont awards the B.A., B.S., and B.F.A. degrees. Master's degrees also are awarded. Bachelor's degrees are awarded in BIOLOGICAL SCIENCE (biology/biological science), BUSINESS (accounting and business administration and management), COMMUNICATIONS AND THE ARTS (English, fine arts, French, German, and Spanish), COMPUTER AND PHYSICAL SCIENCE (chemistry and mathematics), EDUCATION (art, elementary, foreign languages, and secondary), HEALTH PROFESSIONS (predentistry and premedicine), SOCIAL SCIENCE (American studies, economics, history, Italian studies, liberal arts, philosophy, political science/government, prelaw, psychology, religion, social science, and sociology). Psychology and English have the largest enrollments.

Required: All students take classes in rhetoric, literature, religious studies, foreign language, philosophy, history, calculus or natural science, social science, and physical education. A total of 120 credits is required for graduation, with 33 to 36 in the major, and a minimum GPA of 2.0.

Special: There is cross-registration with Villanova, Cabrini College, and the Eastern Art Institute, and a joint admission program with Hahnemann Medical School. Dual and student-designed majors are available, as well as various internships, a Washington semester, and study abroad. There is a freshman honors program on campus, as well as 4 national honor societies. Seven departments have honors programs.

Faculty/Classroom: Forty percent of faculty are male; 60%, female. Ninety-seven percent teach undergraduates. No introductory courses are taught by graduate students. The average class size in an introductory lecture is 20; in a laboratory, 10; and in a regular course offering, 15.

Admissions: About 71% of the 1993–94 applicants were accepted. About 30% of the current freshmen were in the top fifth of their class; 65% were in the top two fifths.

Requirements: A minimum GPA of 2.5 is required. The SAT I is required. A GED is accepted. Applicants must complete 16 academic credits, including 4 in English and 2 each in foreign language, history, mathematics, and science. An interview is recommended. AP and CLEP credits are accepted. Important factors used in the admissions decision are personality, intangible qualities, leadership record, extracurricular activities record, recommendations by school officials, and advanced placement or honor courses.

Procedure: Freshmen are admitted fall and spring. Application deadlines are open. The application fee is $35.

Transfer: Some 35 transfer students enrolled in 1993–94. Transfer applicants should submit transcripts from each college attended, a letter of good standing from the dean at the last college attended, and catalogs from the colleges from which the student wishes to transfer credits. Students with fewer than 30 credits are required to submit high school transcripts and SAT I scores. The minimum GPA is 2.0. An associate degree and interview are recommended. A total of 60 credits out of 120 must be completed at Rosemont.

Visiting: There are regularly scheduled orientations for prospective students, including campus visit days, overnight visits, and class visits. There are guides for informal visits and visitors may sit in on classes and stay overnight at the school. To arrange for a visit, contact Judy Gallagher, Admissions, at (215) 526–2966.

Financial Aid: In 1993–94, 65% of all students received some form of financial aid. About 50% of all students received need-based aid. The average freshman award was $8500. Of that total, scholarships or need-based grants averaged $6500 ($10,700 maximum); loans averaged $2500 ($4625 maximum); and work contracts averaged $800 ($1500 maximum). Thirty percent of undergraduate students work part-time. Average earnings from campus work for the school year are $700. The average financial indebtedness of the 1992–93 graduate was $8560. Rosemont is a member of CSS. The FAF and FAFSA are required and Pennsylvania residents must submit the PHEAA. The deadline for financial aid applications is February 15.

International Students: There are currently 16 international students enrolled. The school actively recruits these students. They must take the TOEFL and achieve a minimum score of 500.

Computers: The college provides computer facilities for student use. The mainframe is an IBM/36. There are 75 Apple and IBM microcomputers available to all students in the library and the continuing education laboratory. There are no time limits on using the system and no fees.

Graduates: In a recent year, 120 bachelor's degrees were awarded. Within an average freshman class, 65% graduate in 4 years and 68% in 5 years. Twenty companies recruited on campus in a recent year. In the 1992 graduating class, 20% of the women were enrolled in graduate school within 6 months of graduation; 90% of the women had found employment.

Admissions Contact: Dr. Linda de Simone, Director of Enrollment Management.

SAINT FRANCIS COLLEGE C-3

Loretto, PA 15940 (814) 472–3100; (800) 342–5732

Full-time: 606 men, 617 women	**Faculty:** 66; IIB, -$
Part-time: 155 men, 296 women	**Ph.D.s:** 65%
Graduate: 177 men, 219 women	**Student/Faculty:** 19 to 1
Year: semesters, summer session	**Tuition:** $11,024
Application Deadline: open	**Room & Board:** $4720

Freshman Class: 1046 applied, 824 accepted, 284 enrolled

SAT I or ACT: required **LESS COMPETITIVE**

Saint Francis College, founded in 1847, is a private, coeducational Franciscan institution affiliated with the Roman Catholic Church. It offers programs in business, education, humanities, sciences, social science, and preprofessional programs. There is one graduate school. In addition to regional accreditation, Saint Francis has baccalaureate program accreditation with CAHEA, CSWE, and NLN. The library contains 179,017 volumes, 48 microform items, and 108 audiovisual forms, and subscribes to 616 periodicals. Computerized library sources and services include the card catalog, interlibrary loans, and database searching. Special learning facilities include a learning resource center, an art gallery, a radio station, classroom satellite hookup, a TV studio, and an art studio. The 600-acre campus is in a rural area 85 miles east of Pittsburgh. Including residence halls, there are 23 buildings on campus.

Student Life: About 84% of undergraduates are from Pennsylvania. Students come from 33 states, 6 foreign countries, and Canada. Sixty-six percent are from public schools; 34% from private. Ninety-five percent are white. The average age of freshmen is 18.8; all undergraduates, 22.1. Eighteen percent drop out by the end of their first year; 70% remain to graduate.

Housing: A total of 833 students can be accommodated in college housing. College-sponsored living facilities include single-sex dormitories, on-campus apartments, off-campus apartments, and married-student housing. In addition, there are intensive study floors. On-campus housing is guaranteed for all 4 years. Sixty-three percent of students live on campus; of those, 80% remain on campus on weekends. Alcohol is not permitted. Upperclassmen may keep cars on campus.

Activities: About 10% of men belong to 2 national fraternities; about 17% of women belong to 1 local sorority and 2 national sororities. There are 63 groups on campus, including art, cheerleading, choir, computers, drama, ethnic, honors, international, literary magazine, newspaper, pep band, photography, political, professional, radio and TV, religious, social, social service, student government, and yearbook. Popular campus events include a weekend movie program, soft rock cafe, Mock Democratic Presidential Nominating Convention, Springfest, and Homecoming.

Sports: There are 8 intercollegiate sports each for men and women, and 12 intramural sports each for men and women. Athletic and recreation facilities include a physical education building, with a pool for competition, racquetball courts, a suspended running track, a weight room, a 4000-seat gymnasium, and a multipurpose gymnasium for intramurals. Outdoor facilities include tennis and basketball courts, soccer, softball, and football facilities, a 9-hole golf course, a lake, and volleyball pits.

Disabled Students: Twenty percent of the campus is accessible to disabled students. The following facilities are available: wheelchair ramps, elevators, special parking, and lowered telephones.

Services: In addition to many counseling and information services, tutoring is available in most subjects. There is remedial math, reading, and writing.

Campus Safety and Security: Campus safety and security measures include a 24-hour foot and vehicle patrol, an escort service, informal discussions, pamphlets, posters, films, emergency telephones, and lighted pathways and sidewalks.

Programs of Study: Saint Francis awards the B.A., B.S., B.S.N., and B.S.W. degrees. Master's degrees are also awarded. Bachelor's degrees are awarded in BIOLOGICAL SCIENCE (biology/biological science), BUSINESS (accounting, human resources, management information systems, management science, and organizational behavior), COMMUNICATIONS AND THE ARTS (communications, English, French, modern language, and Spanish), COMPUTER AND PHYSICAL SCIENCE (chemistry, computer science, and mathematics), EDUCATION (elementary and secondary), ENGINEERING AND ENVIRONMENTAL DESIGN (engineering), HEALTH PROFESSIONS (medical laboratory technology, nursing, physical therapy, and physician's assistant), SOCIAL SCIENCE (American studies, anthropology, criminal justice, economics, history, international studies, philosophy, political science/government, psychology, public administration, religion, social work, and sociology). Business, allied health, sciences, and education have the largest enrollments.

Required: Students must complete 128 credits, with at least 36 in the major, while maintaining a 2.0 GPA. The core curriculum, totaling 58 credits, includes writing, public speaking, fine arts, foreign language,

history, philosophy, religious studies (with required service component), psychology, sociology, political science, and economics. A word processing and research workshop is required in the freshman year.

Special: The college offers internships, co-op programs, study abroad, a Washington semester, work-study programs, and nondegree study. Student-designed majors and 3–2 engineering degrees with Pennsylvania State and Clarkson universities, and the University of Pittsburgh are available. There is a dual major available in international business/modern languages. Credit by exam and pass/fail options are also offered. There is a freshman honors program on campus, as well as 8 national honor societies.

Faculty/Classroom: Sixty-eight percent of faculty are male; 32%, female. All teach undergraduates. The average class size in an introductory lecture is 25; in a laboratory, 20; and in a regular course offering, 16.

Admissions: About 79% of the 1993–94 applicants were accepted. The SAT scores for the 1993–94 freshman class were as follows: Verbal—79% below 500, 15% between 500 and 599, and 4% between 600 and 700; Math—57% below 500, 30% between 500 and 599, 10% between 600 and 700, and 2% above 700. About 35% of the current freshmen were in the top fifth of their class; 66% were in the top two fifths. Five freshmen graduated first in their class.

Requirements: The SAT I or ACT is required. Applicants must be graduates of an accredited secondary school or have earned a GED certificate. All applicants must have completed 16 Carnegie units, consisting of 4 years of English, 2 each of mathematics and social science, 1 laboratory science, and 7 academic electives. Applicants to biology and allied health majors need an addiitonal unit of science. Chemistry, computer science, engineering and mathematics applicants need 4 mathematics units and 2 science units. Physical therapy applicants must have 4 units of mathematics and 4 of science. AP and CLEP credits are accepted. Important factors used in the admissions decision are advanced placement or honor courses, recommendations by school officials, extracurricular activities record, personality, intangible qualities, and parents or siblings attending the school.

Procedure: Freshmen are admitted to all sessions. Entrance exams should be taken in the spring of the junior year and the fall of the senior year. Application deadlines are open. The application fee is $25. Notification is sent on a rolling basis. There are early admissions and deferred admissions plans.

Transfer: About 97 transfer students enrolled in 1993–94. Applicants must have a minimum GPA of 2.0 for consideration, 2.5 for nursing majors, and 2.75 for physician assistant majors. A total of 64 credits out of 128 must be completed at Saint Francis.

Visiting: There are regularly scheduled orientations for prospective students, consisting of a campus tour, an admission interview, a financial aid interview, and class attendance. There are guides for informal visits and visitors may sit in on classes and stay overnight at the school. To arrange for a visit, contact the Admissions Office at (814) 472–3100 or (800) 457–6300 (in-state), or (800) 342–5732 (mid-Atlantic).

Financial Aid: In 1993–94, 90% of all current freshmen and 84% of continuing students received some form of financial aid. About 83% of freshmen and 78% of continuing students received need-based aid. The average freshman award was $11,678. Of that total, scholarships or need-based grants averaged $8068 ($15,150 maximum); loans averaged $2620 ($3625 maximum); and work contracts averaged $990 ($1000 maximum). Fifty-one percent of undergraduate students work part-time. Average earnings from campus work for the school year are $1010. The average financial indebtedness of the 1992–93 graduate was $14,000. Saint Francis is a member of CSS. The college's own financial statement and FAFSA are required. The deadline for financial aid applications is May 1.

International Students: There are currently 4 international students enrolled. They must take the TOEFL and achieve a minimum score of 500. The SAT I or the ACT is also required.

Computers: The college provides computer facilities for student use. The mainframe is a DEC VAX 4000. Mainframe access is limited to computer science majors, who may gain access through only one of 3 computer laboratories. The microcomputer network of about 46 IBM PC, XT, AT, and compatible PCs is available to all students. There are no time limits on using the system and no fees.

Graduates: In 1992–93, 192 bachelor's degrees were awarded. The most popular majors among graduates were management (23%), accounting (16%), elementary education (9%), and physician's assistant (9%). Within an average freshman class, 13% graduate in 3 years, 44% in 4 years, 11% in 5 years, and 2% in 6 years. Some 52 companies recruited on campus in 1992–93. In the 1992 graduating class, 96% of graduates had found employment within 6 months of graduation.

Admissions Contact: Gerard J. Rooney, Dean of Admissions.

SAINT JOSEPH'S UNIVERSITY
F-3
Philadelphia, PA 19131
(215) 660–1300

Full-time: 1159 men, 1318 women	Faculty: 154; IIA, av$
Part-time: 512 men, 804 women	Ph.D.s: 90%
Graduate: 1417 men, 1705 women	Student/Faculty: 16 to 1
Year: semesters, summer session	Tuition: $12,100
Application Deadline: open	Room & Board: $5700
Freshman Class: 2502 applied, 1945 accepted, 708 enrolled	
SAT I Verbal/Math: 500/540	**VERY COMPETITIVE**

Saint Joseph's University, founded in 1851, is a private, coeducational college affiliated with the Jesuit sect of the Catholic Church. It offers undergraduate programs in arts and sciences, and business administration. There are 3 undergraduate and 2 graduate schools. In addition to regional accreditation, Saint Joseph's has baccalaureate program accreditation with NCATE. The 2 libraries contain 313,000 volumes, 700,000 microform items, and 1800 audiovisual forms, and subscribe to 1800 periodicals. Computerized library sources and services include the card catalog, interlibrary loans, and database searching. Special learning facilities include a learning resource center, an art gallery, a radio station, an instructional media center, and foreign language laboratories. The 52-acre campus is in a suburban area in lower Merion. Including residence halls, there are 47 buildings on campus.

Student Life: About 58% of undergraduates are from Pennsylvania. Students come from 30 states, 31 foreign countries, and Canada. Thirty percent are from public schools; 68% from private. Eighty-five percent are white. Eighty-two percent are Catholic; 15% Protestant. The average age of freshmen is 18; all undergraduates, 20. Fourteen percent drop out by the end of their first year; 79% remain to graduate.

Housing: A total of 1400 students can be accommodated in college housing. College-sponsored living facilities include single-sex and coed dormitories, on-campus apartments, and off-campus apartments. In addition, there are honors houses and special interest houses. On-campus housing is guaranteed for all 4 years. Fifty-four percent of students live on campus; of those, 65% remain on campus on weekends. Upperclassmen may keep cars on campus.

Activities: About 25% of men belong to 4 national fraternities; about 25% of women belong to 3 national sororities. There are 57 groups on campus, including art, cheerleading, choir, chorus, computers, dance, drama, ethnic, film, honors, international, jazz band, literary magazine, musical theater, newspaper, pep band, photography, political, professional, radio and TV, religious social, social service, student government, and yearbook. Popular campus events include Hawktoberfest, Parents Weekend, Hand in Hand, Black Cultural Week, Hawkmania, Thanksgiving Dinner Dance, Spring Fling, and St. Joseph's Day.

Sports: There are 10 intercollegiate sports for men and 9 for women, and 17 intramural sports for men and 14 for women. Athletic and recreation facilities include a gymnasium, fields, 4 multipurpose courts, an indoor and an outdoor track, 4 racquetball courts, a pool, Nautilus equipment, and tennis courts.

Disabled Students: Ninety percent of the campus is accessible to disabled students. The following facilities are available: wheelchair ramps, elevators, special parking, specially equipped rest rooms, special class scheduling, lowered drinking fountains, lowered telephones, and automatic eye doors.

Services: In addition to many counseling and information services, tutoring is available in most subjects, as well as services for persons with learning disabilities.

Campus Safety and Security: Campus safety and security measures include a 24-hour foot and vehicle patrol, self defense education, an escort service, and shuttle buses. In addition, there are informal discussions, pamphlets, posters, films, emergency telephones, and lighted pathways and sidewalks.

Programs of Study: Saint Joseph's awards the B.A. and B.S. degrees. Associate and master's degrees also are awarded. Bachelor's degrees are awarded in BIOLOGICAL SCIENCE (biology/biological science), BUSINESS (accounting, banking and finance, business administration and management, labor studies, management science, and marketing/retailing/merchandising), COMMUNICATIONS AND THE ARTS (English, fine arts, French, German, and Spanish), COMPUTER AND PHYSICAL SCIENCE (chemistry, computer science, information sciences and systems, mathematics, and physics), EDUCATION (elementary and secondary), HEALTH PROFESSIONS (health care administration), SOCIAL SCIENCE (criminal justice, economics, history, human services, humanities, industrial and organizational psychology, international relations, philosophy, political science/government, psychology, public administration, religion, social studies, and sociology). Social sciences, natural sciences, English, marketing, and accounting are the strongest programs academically. Biolgy, psychology, English, and food marketing have the largest enrollments.

Required: All students must take general education common courses in language, theology, philosophy, and history. Distribution requirements include 2 courses of foreign language at the intermediate level, art or literature, 2 courses each of mathematics, natural sciences, and theology, 3 courses in social/behavioral sciences, and a philosophy course. A total of 120 credit hours is required for graduation, with 21 to 54 in the major. A GPA of 2.0 is required.

Special: There is an exchange with a Japanese university and study abroad in 5 countries. The college offers internships, a Washington semester, dual majors, minor concentrations, and special studies programs in American, Latin American, European, and medieval studies. There is a co-op program for food marketing majors and an interdisciplinary major in pharmaceutical marketing. All departments have honors programs. There is a freshman honors program on campus, as well as 10 national honor societies.

Faculty/Classroom: Seventy-five percent of faculty are male; 25%, female. Ninety-eight percent teach undergraduates and 85% also do research. No introductory courses are taught by graduate students. The average class size in an introductory lecture is 27; in a laboratory, 20; and in a regular course offering, 30.

Admissions: About 78% of the 1993–94 applicants were accepted. The SAT scores for the 1993–94 freshman class were as follows: Verbal—50% below 500, 38% between 500 and 599, 11% between 600 and 700, and 1% above 700; Math—24% below 500, 51% between 500 and 599, 20% between 600 and 700, and 5% above 700. About 56% of the current freshmen were in the top fifth of their class; 85% were in the top two fifths. Four freshmen graduated first in their class.

Requirements: The SAT I or ACT is required. The SAT II: Subject test in writing is also recommended. Applicants must graduate from an accredited secondary school and prepare with 4 years of English, 3 of mathematics, 2 each of foreign language and science, and 1 each of history and social studies. Preference is given to students with 3 to 4 years of foreign language and natural science and 4 years of mathematics. An interview is recommended. AP and CLEP credits are accepted. Important factors used in the admissions decision are advanced placement or honor courses, evidence of special talent, recommendations by school officials, leadership record, and parents or siblings attending the school.

Procedure: Freshmen are admitted in the fall and spring. Entrance exams should be taken in the spring of the junior year or the fall of the senior year. Application deadlines are open. The application fee is $30. Notification is sent on a rolling basis. There is a deferred admissions plan. A waiting list is an active part of the admissions procedure, with about 10% of applicants on the list.

Transfer: About 78 transfer students enrolled in 1993–94. Transfer applicants must have a GPA of at least 2.5, and submit former test scores and high school and college transcripts. An interview is recommended. A total of 60 credits out of 120 must be completed at Saint Joseph's.

Visiting: There are regularly scheduled orientations for prospective students, including formal interviews, tours, and faculty visits. There are guides for informal visits and visitors may sit in on classes and stay overnight at the school. To arrange for a visit, contact the Admissions Office at (215) 660–1300.

Financial Aid: In a recent year, 82% of all current freshmen and 79% of continuing students received some form of financial aid. About 75% of all students received need-based aid. The average freshman award was $7725. Of that total, scholarships or need-based grants averaged $3648 ($10,330 maximum); loans averaged $2850 ($3625 maximum); and work contracts averaged $903 ($1000 maximum). Forty percent of undergraduate students work part-time. Average earnings from campus work for the school year are $1000. The average financial indebtedness of a recent graduate was $11,500. Saint Joseph's is a member of CSS. The FAF and PHEAA are required. The deadline for financial aid applications is March 1.

International Students: There are currently 224 international students enrolled. The school actively recruits these students. They must take the TOEFL and achieve a minimum score of 500. The student must also take the SAT I or the ACT.

Computers: The college provides computer facilities for student use. The mainframes are a Sun 4/490, a Sun 3/150, and a GEAC library system. The Sun 4/490 minicomputer acts as the hub of the campuswide area network which links 5 minicomputers, 5 Macintosh networks, 2 local area networks, 9 Ethernet subnets, and more than 200 microcomputers in several buildings of classrooms and offices, including a residence hall. All students may access the system whenever the laboratory is open (approximately 90 hours per week) or anytime if they are connected in their dormitory rooms. There are no time limits on using the system and no fees.

Graduates: In a recent year, 769 bachelor's degrees were awarded. The most popular majors among graduates were marketing (13%), food marketing (12%), and English (10%). Within an average freshman class, 72% graduate in 4 years, 78% in 5 years, and 79% in 6

years. Some 96 companies recruited on campus in a recent year.

Admissions Contact: John M. Sullivan, Director of Admissions.

SAINT VINCENT COLLEGE
Latrobe, PA 15650

B-2

(412) 537–4540

Full-time: 533 men, 502 women	Faculty: 75; IIB, -$
Part-time: 73 men, 109 women	Ph.D.s: 68%
Graduate: none	Student/Faculty: 14 to 1
Year: semesters	Tuition: $10,168
Application Deadline: May 1	Room & Board: $3766

Freshman Class: 700 applied, 595 accepted, 278 enrolled
SAT I or ACT: required

LESS COMPETITIVE

Saint Vincent College, founded in 1846, is a Catholic college of liberal arts and sciences sponsored by Benedictine monks. There is one graduate school. The library contains 247,034 volumes, 98,476 microform items, and 3227 audiovisual forms, and subscribes to 856 periodicals. Computerized library sources and services include interlibrary loans and database searching. Special learning facilities include a learning resource center, art gallery, planetarium, radio station, observatory, radio telescope, small business development center, and drug and alcohol prevention center. The 100-acre campus is in a small town 35 miles east of Pittsburgh. Including residence halls, there are 20 buildings on campus.

Student Life: About 89% of undergraduates are from Pennsylvania. Students come from 30 states and 8 foreign countries. Sixty-eight percent are from public schools; 32% from private. Ninety-five percent are white. Seventy-two percent are Catholic; 19% Protestant. The average age of freshmen is 18; all undergraduates, 20. Thirteen percent drop out by the end of their first year; 70% remain to graduate.

Housing: A total of 834 students can be accommodated in college housing. College-sponsored living facilities include coed dormitories. In addition, there is a 24-hour quiet, private study dormitory. On-campus housing is guaranteed for all 4 years. Eighty percent of students live on campus; of those, 80% remain on campus on weekends. Alcohol is not permitted. All students may keep cars on campus.

Activities: There are 25 groups on campus, including art, choir, chorale, chorus, computers, dance, drama, ethnic, honors, international, jazz band, literary magazine, musical theater, newspaper, orchestra, political, professional, radio and tv, religious, social, social service, student government, symphony, and yearbook. Popular campus events include the annual indoor beach party, Threshold lecture series, summer theater, Pittsburgh Steeler training camp, Challenge Program, Sports Friendship Day, and Gold Concert series.

Sports: There are 6 intercollegiate sports for men and 5 for women, and 4 intramural sports for men and 4 for women. Athletic and recreation facilities include a 2400-seat gymnasium, basketball and volleyball facilities, a weight and exercise room, an indoor pool, tennis courts, baseball, soccer, and football fields, a mini movie theater, a mini bowling alley, and a 999-seat auditorium/arena.

Disabled Students: Ninety percent of the campus is accessible to disabled students. The following facilities are available: wheelchair ramps, elevators, special parking, and specially equipped rest rooms.

Services: In addition to many counseling and information services, tutoring is available in every subject. There is also remedial math, reading, and writing. An opportunity office provides individual counseling and freshman study skills class.

Campus Safety and Security: Campus safety and security measures include 24-hour foot and vehicle patrol, informal discussions, pamphlets, posters, and films, and lighted pathways and sidewalks.

Programs of Study: Saint Vincent awards the B.A., B.S., and B.F.A. degrees. Master's degrees also are awarded. Bachelor's degrees are awarded in BIOLOGICAL SCIENCE (biochemistry and biology/biological science), BUSINESS (accounting, banking and finance, business administration and management, fashion merchandising, marketing/retailing/merchandising, and retailing), COMMUNICATIONS AND THE ARTS (communications, design, dramatic arts, English, fine arts, French, graphic design, music, music performance, photography, Spanish, studio art, and visual and performing arts), COMPUTER AND PHYSICAL SCIENCE (chemistry, computer science, information sciences and systems, mathematics, and physics), EDUCATION (art, foreign languages, home economics, and music), ENGINEERING AND ENVIRONMENTAL DESIGN (environmental science and interior design), HEALTH PROFESSIONS (medical laboratory technology, predentistry, premedicine, prepharmacy, and preveterinary science), SOCIAL SCIENCE (dietetics, economics, food production/management/services, history, philosophy, political science/government, prelaw, psychology, religion, social work, and sociology). Biology, accounting, chemistry, mathematics, and economics are the strongest academically. Accounting, biology, management, and education have the largest enrollments.

Required: All students are required to take Language and Rhetoric, Exploring Religious Meaning, and Philosophy I. The core curriculum includes 12 credits of social science, 9 each of English, history, philosophy and religion, 8 of natural sciences, 6 of a foreign language, and

3 of mathematics. Some majors require comprehensive examinations, and all majors except English and business require a thesis. Students must complete 124 credits and achieve a minimum GPA of 2.0.

Special: There are co-op programs and cross-registration with Seton Hill College. The college offers internships, study abroad in Europe and Asia, a Washington semester, work-study program, dual majors, a general studies degree, credit by examination and for life/military/work experience, nondegree study and pass/fail options. There is an accelerated degree engineering program, and a 3–2 engineering option with Boston and Pennsylvania State Universities, and the University of Pittsburgh. The college offers teacher certificate programs in early childhood, elementary, and secondary education. There is a freshman honors program on campus, as well as 2 national honor societies, including Phi Beta Kappa.

Faculty/Classroom: Seventy-five percent of faculty are male; 25%, female. All faculty teach and do research. The average class size in an introductory lecture is 24; in a laboratory, 12; and in a regular course offering, 16.

Admissions: About 85% of the 1993–94 applicants were accepted. The SAT scores for the 1993–94 freshman class were as follows: Verbal—64% below 500, 28% between 500 and 599, and 8% between 600 and 700; Math—45% below 500, 35% between 500 and 599, 17% between 600 and 700, and 3% above 700. About 39% of the current freshmen were in the top fifth of their class; 67% were in the top two fifths. Six freshmen graduated first in their class.

Requirements: The SAT I or ACT is required. Applicants must complete 15 academic credits, including 4 of English, 3 of social studies, 2 each of foreign language and mathematics, and 1 of a laboratory science. Art students must submit a portfolio, and music and theater students must audition. An essay is required. A GED is accepted. AP and CLEP credits are accepted. Important factors used in the admissions decision are advanced placement or honor courses, recommendations by school officials, leadership record, evidence of special talent, and extracurricular activities record.

Procedure: Freshmen are admitted fall and spring. Entrance exams should be taken at the end of the junior year or beginning of the senior year. Applications should be filed by May 1 for fall entry and January 1 for spring entry, along with an application fee of $20. Notification is sent on a rolling basis. There are early admissions and deferred admissions plans.

Transfer: Some 48 transfer students enrolled in 1993–94. Transfer applicants must submit transcripts from postsecondary schools attended and a catalog describing courses taken. A total of 34 credits out of 124 must be completed at Saint Vincent.

Visiting: There are regularly scheduled orientations for prospective students, consisting of a general information session, an informal meeting with faculty, and campus tours. There are guides for informal visits and visitors may sit in on classes and stay overnight at the school. To arrange for a visit, contact the Admission and Financial Aid Office at (412) 537-4540.

Financial Aid: In 1993–94, 83% of all current freshmen and 80% of continuing students received some form of financial aid. About 75% of freshmen and 78% of continuing students received need-based aid. The average freshman award was $8368. Of that total, scholarships or need-based grants averaged $2000 ($9494 maximum); loans averaged $1000 ($3950 maximum); and work contracts averaged $1542 ($2104 maximum). Twenty-seven percent of undergraduate students work part-time. Average earnings from campus work for the school year are $1086. The average financial indebtedness of the 1992–93 graduate was $16,000. Saint Vincent is a member of CSS. The FAFSA is required.

International Students: There are currently 9 international students enrolled. They must take the TOEFL and achieve a minimum score of 525.

Computers: The college provides computer facilities for student use. The mainframe is an HP 9000/Series 800 G50. Two large computer terminal centers on campus can accommodate between 25 to 40 students each. In addition, there are 3 smaller computer centers located in various areas throughout the campus. All students may access the system. It may be used during computer laboratory hours. Students may access the system 30 minutes if someone is waiting. There are no fees.

Graduates: In 1992–93, 222 bachelor's degrees were awarded. The most popular majors among graduates were psychology (13%), accounting (12%), and political science (9%). Within an average freshman class, 56% graduate in 4 years and 14% in 5 years. Some 53 companies recruited on campus in 1992–93. In the 1992 graduating class, 23% of the men and 23% of the women were enrolled in graduate school within 6 months of graduation; 72% of all students had found employment.

Admissions Contact: Admission and Financial Aid Office.

SETON HILL COLLEGE
Greensburg, PA 15601

B-4

Full-time: 47 men, 705 women	(412) 838-4255; (800) 826-6234
Part-time: 23 men, 187 women	Faculty: 55; IIB, -$
Graduate: none	Ph.D.s: 67%
Year: semesters, summer session	Student/Faculty: 14 to 1
Application Deadline: open	Tuition: $10,340
Freshman Class: n/av	Room & Board: $3980
SAT I or ACT: required	COMPETITIVE

Seton Hill College, founded in 1883, is a private, primarily women's college affiliated with the Catholic Church. It offers programs in liberal arts. In addition to regional accreditation, Seton Hill has baccalaureate program accreditation with ADA and NASM. The library contains 101,000 volumes, 4600 microform items, and 3900 audiovisual forms, and subscribes to 465 periodicals. Computerized library sources and services include the card catalog and database searching. Special learning facilities include an art gallery, 2 theaters, a nursery school and kindergarten that function as laboratory schools for education students, and a performance hall. The 200-acre campus is in a small town 35 miles east of Pittsburgh. Including residence halls, there are 17 buildings on campus.

Student Life: About 80% of undergraduates are from Pennsylvania. Students come from 21 states and 7 foreign countries. Eighty percent are from public schools; 20% from private. Eighty-five percent are white. The average age of freshmen is 18; all undergraduates, 21. Twenty-two percent drop out by the end of their first year; 58% remain to graduate.

Housing: A total of 550 students can be accommodated in college housing. College-sponsored living facilities include single-sex dormitories. On-campus housing is guaranteed for all 4 years. Seventy percent of students live on campus. Alcohol is not permitted. All students may keep cars on campus.

Activities: There are no fraternities or sororities on campus. There are 30 groups on campus, including cheerleading, choir, chorale, chorus, drama, ethnic, honors, literary magazine, newspaper, orchestra, political, professional, radio and TV, religious, social, social service, student government, symphony, and yearbook. Popular campus events include Christmas on the Hill, Family Weekend, Clipper Dance, Crib Ceremony, Senior Dinner Dance, and President's Reception.

Sports: Athletic and recreation facilities include a gymnasium and pool, soccer field, tennis courts, softball field, weight room, jacuzzi, sauna, and fitness trail. The indoor gymnasium seats 650, the largest auditorium/arena 300.

Disabled Students: Ninety-five percent of the campus is accessible to disabled students. The following facilities are available: wheelchair ramps, elevators, special parking, specially equipped rest rooms, special class scheduling, lowered drinking fountains, and lowered telephones.

Services: In addition to many counseling and information services, tutoring is available in most subjects. In addition, there is a reader service for the blind and remedial math and writing.

Campus Safety and Security: Campus safety and security measures include 24-hour foot and vehicle patrol, self defense education, escort service, and shuttle buses. In addition, there are informal discussions, pamphlets, posters, and films, emergency telephones, and lighted pathways and sidewalks.

Programs of Study: Seton Hill awards the B.A., B.S., B.F.A., B.S.Med.Tech., B.Mus., and B.S.W. degrees. Bachelor's degrees are awarded in BIOLOGICAL SCIENCE (biochemistry and biology/biological science), BUSINESS (accounting, banking and finance, business administration and management, business economics, fashion merchandising, international business management, marketing/retailing/merchandising, and personnel management), COMMUNICATIONS AND THE ARTS (communications, design, dramatic arts, English, fine arts, French, journalism, music, performing arts, photography, Spanish, and studio art), COMPUTER AND PHYSICAL SCIENCE (actuarial science, chemistry, computer science, mathematics, and physics), EDUCATION (art, early childhood, elementary, home economics, music, and secondary), HEALTH PROFESSIONS (art therapy, medical laboratory technology, nursing, predentistry, premedicine, and preveterinary science), SOCIAL SCIENCE (dietetics, economics, family/consumer studies, food production/management/services, history, human ecology, philosophy, political science/government, prelaw, psychology, religion, religious music, social work, and sociology). Psychology, biology, art, management, sociology/social work, and education have the largest enrollments.

Required: All students must take a freshman seminar, senior seminars, and a course in Western cultural traditions. A total of 128 credit hours is required for graduation, as is a minimum GPA of 2.0.

Special: There are cooperative programs in all majors and cross-registration with Saint Vincent College, the University of Pittsburgh at Greensburg, and Westmoreland County Community College. Intern-

ships are encouraged. The college offers study abroad, a Washington semester, work-study, dual and student-designed majors, a 3–2 engineering program with Pennsylvania State University and Georgia Institute of Technology, a 2–2 nursing program with Catholic University of America, and a 3–2 or 3–1 medical technology program with area hospitals. Also offered are credit by examination and for life/military/work experience, nondegree study, and pass/fail options. There is a freshman honors program on campus, as well as 5 national honor societies. All departments have honors programs.

Faculty/Classroom: Thirty-eight percent of faculty are male; 62%, female. All teach undergraduates and 4% both teach and do research. The average class size in an introductory lecture is 25; in a laboratory, 16; and in a regular course offering, 18.

Admissions: About 47% of the current freshmen were in the top fifth of their class; 72% were in the top two fifths. Two freshmen graduated first in their class.

Requirements: The SAT I or ACT is required. A total of 15 Carnegie units is required, including 4 years of English, 2 years each of mathematics, social studies, and foreign language, and 1 year of a laboratory science. Art students must submit a portfolio; music and theater students must audition. An interview is recommended. The GED is accepted with supporting recommendations. AP and CLEP credits are accepted. Important factors used in the admissions decision are advanced placement or honor courses, evidence of special talent, leadership record, recommendations by school officials, and personality, intangible qualities.

Procedure: Freshmen are admitted fall and spring. Entrance exams should be taken in spring of the junior year or fall of the senior year. Application deadlines are open. Application fee is $20. Notification is sent on a rolling basis. There is a deferred admissions plan.

Transfer: About 75 transfer students enrolled in 1993–94. Transfer applicants must submit college transcripts and have a GPA of at least 2.0. An interview is recommended, as are supporting letters. A total of 48 credits out of 128 must be completed at Seton Hill.

Visiting: There are regularly scheduled orientations for prospective students, consisting of an introduction, an address by the president or dean, an open reception with faculty, a financial aid session, a student panel, a campus tour, and an overnight visit. There are guides for informal visits and visitors may sit in on classes. To arrange for a visit, contact the Director of Admissions at (412) 838–4255 or (800) 826–6234.

Financial Aid: In 1993–94, 96% of all current freshmen and 90% of continuing students received some form of financial aid. About 90% of freshmen and 80% of continuing students received need-based aid. The average freshman award was $9805. Of that total, scholarships or need-based grants averaged $4000 ($10,800 maximum); loans averaged $2700 ($4125 maximum); and work contracts averaged $750 ($1148 maximum). Forty-seven percent of undergraduate students work part-time. Average earnings from campus work for the school year are $900. The average financial indebtedness of the 1992–93 graduate was $9938. Seton Hill is a member of CSS. The FAF and FAFSA, and the college's own financial statement are required. The PHEAA form may be used in place of the FAF. The deadline for financial aid applications is July 1.

International Students: There are currently 17 international students enrolled. The school actively recruits these students. They must take the TOEFL and achieve a minimum score of 550.

Computers: The college provides computer facilities for student use. The mainframe is a DEC VAX. Students have access to 80 microcomputers on campus, including IBM and Apple units. All students may access the system. There are no time limits on using the system. The fees are $1 per credit.

Graduates: In 1992–93, 150 bachelor's degrees were awarded. The most popular majors among graduates were human ecology (13%), psychology (13%), and management (12%). Within an average freshman class, 50% graduate in 4 years, 55% in 5 years, and 58% in 6 years. Some 20 companies recruited on campus in 1992–93. In a recent graduating class, 22% of the women were enrolled in graduate school within 6 months of graduation; 85% of the men had found employment.

Admissions Contact: Director of Admissions.

SHIPPENSBURG UNIVERSITY OF PENNSYLVANIA
C-4

Shippensburg, PA 17257–2299

(717) 532–1231
(800) 822–8028 (in-state)

Full-time: 2462 men, 2797 women
Part-time: 137 men, 161 women
Graduate: 410 men, 520 women
Year: semesters, summer session
Application Deadline: open
Freshman Class: 5818 applied, 3281 accepted, 1144 enrolled
SAT I Verbal/Math: 460/520

Faculty: 307; IIA, +$
Ph.D.s: 80%
Student/Faculty: 17 to 1
Tuition: $3710 ($8108)
Room & Board: $3348

COMPETITIVE

Shippensburg University, founded in 1871, is a public university that is part of the Pennsylvania State System of Higher Education. It offers programs in liberal arts, business, and teacher preparation. There are 3 undergraduate schools and one graduate school. In addition to regional accreditation, Shippensburg has baccalaureate program accreditation with AACSB, CSWE, and NCATE. The library contains 425,325 volumes, 1,399,329 microform items, and 9839 audiovisual forms, and subscribes to 1727 periodicals. Special learning facilities include a learning resource center, art gallery, planetarium, radio station, closed-circuit television, a fashion archives center, a vertebrate museum, a women's center, and a learning assistance center. The 200-acre campus is in a rural area 40 miles southwest of Harrisburg. Including residence halls, there are 35 buildings on campus.

Student Life: About 91% of undergraduates are from Pennsylvania. Students come from 22 states and 22 foreign countries. Ninety-seven percent are from public schools; 3% from private. Ninety-five percent are white. The average age of freshmen is 18; all undergraduates, 20. Seventeen percent drop out by the end of their first year; 65% remain to graduate.

Housing: A total of 2400 students can be accommodated in college housing. College-sponsored living facilities include single-sex and coed dormitories and on-campus apartments. In addition there are honors houses and a designated quiet hall. On-campus housing is guaranteed for all 4 years. Fifty-seven percent of students commute. Alcohol is not permitted. All students may keep cars on campus.

Activities: About 15% of men belong to 1 local and 12 national fraternities; about 15% of women belong to 3 local and 8 national sororities. There are 100 groups on campus, including art, band, cheerleading, choir, chorus, computers, dance, drama, ethnic, film, gay, honors, international, jazz band, literary magazine, marching band, musical theater, newspaper, orchestra, political, professional, radio and TV, religious, social, social service, student government, and yearbook. Popular campus events include Homecoming, Parents Day, planetarium shows, Senior Olympics, Summer Music Festival, and Elderhostel.

Sports: There are 8 intercollegiate sports for men and 9 for women, and 14 intramural sports for men and 9 for women. Athletic and recreation facilities include athletic fields, practice areas, a 9-hole golf course, an 8000-seat stadium, a gymnasium, a field house, 2 swimming pools, racquetball and squash courts, a rehabilitation center, and a fitness center.

Disabled Students: Eighty-four percent of the campus is accessible to disabled students. The following facilities are available: wheelchair ramps, elevators, special parking, specially equipped rest rooms, special class scheduling, lowered drinking fountains, and lowered telephones.

Services: In addition to many counseling and information services, tutoring is available in most subjects. In addition, there is a reader service for the blind, and remedial math, reading, and writing. The Learning Assistance Center provides tutoring in mathematics, writing, geography, algebra, reading study skills, some basic sciences, and some business subjects. Departmental tutoring is available.

Campus Safety and Security: Campus safety and security measures include 24-hour foot and vehicle patrol, escort service, pamphlets, posters, and films, and emergency telephones. In addition, there are lighted pathways and sidewalks.

Programs of Study: Shippensburg awards the B.A., B.S., B.S.B.A., and B.S.Ed. degrees. Master's degrees also are awarded. Bachelor's degrees are awarded in BIOLOGICAL SCIENCE (biology/biological science), BUSINESS (accounting, management science, marketing management, office supervision and management, and real estate), COMMUNICATIONS AND THE ARTS (communications, English, French, German, and Spanish), COMPUTER AND PHYSICAL SCIENCE (chemistry, computer science, earth science, mathematics, and physics), EDUCATION (business and elementary), HEALTH PROFESSIONS (medical laboratory technology), SOCIAL SCIENCE (criminal justice, economics, geography, history, psychology, public administration, social work, sociology, and urban studies). Elementary education, marketing, accounting, criminal justice, psychology, and communication/journalism have the largest enrollments.

Required: General education courses include English composition, mathematics, and history, as well as courses in language and numbers for rational thinking; literary, artistic, and cultural traditions; laboratory science; biological and physical science; political, economic, and geographic sciences; and social and behavioral sciences. The core curriculum varies for degree programs. Most degree programs require 120 credit hours, with 22 to 30 hours in the major, and a 2.0 GPA for graduation.

Special: The university offers internships, study abroad at Humberside College, England, and a 3–2 engineering degree with Pennsylvania State University and the University of Maryland. There is a cooperative art program with design schools in Pennsylvania and 6 other states. There is a freshman honors program on campus, as well as 21 national honor societies.

Faculty/Classroom: Seventy-three percent of faculty are male; 27%, female. Ninety-five percent teach undergraduates, 33% do research, and 33% do both. No introductory courses are taught by graduate students. The average class size in an introductory lecture is 30; in a laboratory, 18; and in a regular course offering, 18.

Admissions: About 56% of the 1993–94 applicants were accepted. The SAT scores for the 1993–94 freshman class were as follows: Verbal—68% below 500, 29% between 500 and 599, and 3% between 600 and 700; Math—31% below 500, 54% between 500 and 599, 15% between 600 and 700, and 1% above 700. About 38% of the current freshmen were in the top fifth of their class; 75% were in the top two fifths.

Requirements: Shippensburg requires applicants to be in the upper 40% of their class. A minimum GPA of 3.0 is required. The SAT I is required. Although the university does not require specific numbers and types of high school courses, it strongly urges students to pursue a typical college preparatory program, which should include 4 years of English, 3 years each of social sciences, sequential mathematics, and laboratory science, and 2 years of one foreign language. A GED is accepted. AP and CLEP credits are accepted. Important factors used in the admissions decision are advanced placement or honor courses, recommendations by school officials, leadership record, evidence of special talent, and extracurricular activities record.

Procedure: Freshmen are admitted fall and spring. Entrance exams should be taken in the junior year and no later than fall of the senior year. Application deadlines are open, with March 1 recommended for fall entry and November 1 for spring entry. Application fee is $20. Notification is sent on a rolling basis 4 to 6 weeks after the completed file is received by the Admissions Office. There are early admissions and deferred admissions plans.

Transfer: About 400 transfer students enrolled in 1993–94. To be considered primarily on one's college, a candidate must have completed 30 semester hours of college-level work. GPA requirements vary by major. A total of 45 credits out of at least 120 must be completed at Shippensburg.

Visiting: There are regularly scheduled orientations for prospective students, including academic department group meetings; book discussion; workshops on study skills, time management, and reading textbooks; and a campus tour. There are guides for informal visits and visitors may sit in on classes. To arrange for a visit, contact the Admissions Office at (717) 532–1231 or (800) 822–8028 (in-state).

Financial Aid: In a recent year, 65% of all current freshmen and 55% of continuing students received some form of financial aid. About 50% of students received need-based aid. The average freshman award was $4200. Of that total, scholarships or need-based grants averaged $1200 ($5250 maximum); loans averaged $2625 (maximum); and work contracts averaged $1200 ($1500 maximum). Twenty-five percent of undergraduate students work part-time. Average earnings from campus work for the school year are $1200. The average financial indebtedness of a recent graduate was $2600. Shippensburg is a member of CSS. The FAF and PHEAA are required. The deadline for financial aid applications is May 1.

International Students: There are currently 76 international students enrolled. They must take the TOEFL and achieve a minimum score of 550. The student must also take the SAT I or the ACT.

Computers: The university provides computer facilities for student use. The mainframe is a Unisys 2200/422. Terminals are located throughout the campus, and dial-in telephone lines give access to the mainframe. Student instruction and faculty research is also supported on a DEC MicroVAX 3800. Access to the SAS statistical package, Internet, and instruction in the use of the ORACLE relational database are via this system. Shippen, library, and Horton Hall microlaboratories contain 44 MS DOS, 5 Apple Macintosh Plus, 8 Apple II GS, and 34 Apple Macintosh LC microcomputers. Various departmental laboratories are also available. All students may access the system. There are no time limits on using the system and no fees. It is recommended that students in computer science and accounting have personal computers.

Graduates: In 1992–93, 1139 bachelor's degrees were awarded. The most popular majors among graduates were teacher education (11%), management (7%), and criminal justice (7%). Within an aver-

age freshman class, 48% graduate in 4 years, 64% in 5 years, and 65% in 6 years. Some 140 companies recruited on campus in 1992–93.

Admissions Contact: Joseph G. Cretella, Dean of Admissions.

SLIPPERY ROCK UNIVERSITY   B-2
Slippery Rock, PA 16057   (412) 738–2015; (800) 662–1102

Full-time: 2698 men, 3266 women	**Faculty:** 392; IIA, av$
Part-time: 310 men, 645 women	**Ph.D.s:** 66%
Graduate: 261 men, 497 women	**Student/Faculty:** 15 to 1
Year: semesters, summer session	**Tuition:** $3547 ($7945)
Application Deadline: April 1	**Room & Board:** $3256
Freshman Class: 4677 applied, 2890 accepted, 1247 enrolled	
SAT I or ACT: recommended	**COMPETITIVE**

Slippery Rock University, founded in 1889, is a public institution that is part of the Pennsylvania State System of Higher Education. It offers programs in liberal arts and sciences, education, health and human services, and information science and business administration. There are 4 undergraduate schools and one graduate school. In addition to regional accreditation, The Rock has baccalaureate program accreditation with APTA, CSWE, NCATE, and NLN. The library contains 767,220 volumes, 1.1 million microform items, and 16,000 audiovisual forms, and subscribes to 1649 periodicals. Special learning facilities include a learning resource center, art gallery, natural history museum, planetarium, radio station, TV station, and a wellness center. The 600-acre campus is in a small town 50 miles north of Pittsburgh. Including residence halls, there are 60 buildings on campus.

Student Life: About 88% of undergraduates are from Pennsylvania. Students come from 43 states, 64 foreign countries, and Canada. Seventy percent are from public schools; 30% from private. Ninety-three percent are white. The average age of freshmen is 19; all undergraduates, 21. Twenty-two percent drop out by the end of their first year; 54% remain to graduate.

Housing: A total of 2800 students can be accommodated in college housing. College-sponsored living facilities include single-sex and coed dormitories. In addition there are honors houses and special interest houses. On-campus housing is guaranteed for all 4 years. Fifty-six percent of students live on campus; of those, 75% remain on campus on weekends. Alcohol is not permitted. All students may keep cars on campus.

Activities: About 10% of men belong to 10 national fraternities; about 10% of women belong to 8 national sororities. There are 120 groups on campus, including art, band, cheerleading, chess, choir, chorale, chorus, computers, dance, drama, ethnic, film, gay, honors, international, jazz band, literary magazine, marching band, musical theater, newspaper, orchestra, pep band, photography, political, professional, radio and TV, religious, social, social service, student government, symphony, and yearbook. Popular campus events include Homecoming and Spring Weekend.

Sports: There are 12 intercollegiate sports for men and 12 for women, and 7 intramural sports for men and 7 for women. Athletic and recreation facilities include a field house, gymnasium, and fitness center. The campus stadium seats 10,000, the indoor gymnasium seats 3000, and the largest auditorium/arena seats 7500.

Disabled Students: Ninety-two percent of the campus is accessible to disabled students. The following facilities are available: wheelchair ramps, elevators, special parking, specially equipped rest rooms, special class scheduling, lowered drinking fountains, and lowered telephones.

Services: In addition to many counseling and information services, tutoring is available in some subjects, including about 60 introductory-level general liberal studies courses. In addition, there is a reader service for the blind and remedial math and writing.

Campus Safety and Security: Campus safety and security measures include 24-hour foot and vehicle patrol, escort service, informal discussions, and pamphlets, posters, and films. In addition, there are lighted pathways and sidewalks. The university maintains its own police department, with officers having the same powers as municipal police.

Programs of Study: The Rock awards the B.A., B.S., B.B.A., B.F.A., B.Mus., B.Mus.Ed., and B.S.N. degrees. Master's degrees also are awarded. Bachelor's degrees are awarded in BIOLOGICAL SCIENCE (biology/biological science), BUSINESS (accounting, business administration and management, business economics, international business management, and marketing/retailing/merchandising), COMMUNICATIONS AND THE ARTS (communications, dance, English, fine arts, French, German, music, and Spanish), COMPUTER AND PHYSICAL SCIENCE (chemistry, computer science, earth science, geology, information sciences and systems, mathematics, and physics), EDUCATION (early childhood, elementary, foreign languages, health, music, science, and secondary), HEALTH PROFESSIONS (community health work, medical laboratory technology, and nursing), SOCIAL SCIENCE (anthropology, economics, geography, history, parks and recreation management, philosophy, political

science/government, psychology, public administration, social science, social work, and sociology). Business, education, and health science have the largest enrollments.

Required: B.A. students must demonstrate proficiency in a foreign language, and all must complete 42 to 53 credits in a 7-part liberal studies program, including basic competencies, arts, cultural diversity/global perspective, human institutions, science and mathematics, natural experience, and modern age. Specific requirements include public speaking, college writing, algebra, and physical education. A minimum of 128 credit hours, with at least 30 in the major, is required for graduation.

Special: Study abroad is available in 15 countries. Internships are available in all majors, and international internships are available in Scotland and England. There is a 3–2 engineering program with Pennsylvania State University. The dual major is an option, and credit is given for military experience. Pass/fail options also are available. There is a freshman honors program on campus, as well as 26 national honor societies. Thirty-three departments have honors programs.

Faculty/Classroom: Fifty-four percent of faculty are male; 46%, female. All teach undergraduates. No introductory courses are taught by graduate students. The average class size in an introductory lecture is 35; in a laboratory, 15; and in a regular course offering, 25.

Admissions: About 62% of the 1993–94 applicants were accepted. The ACT scores for the 1993–94 freshman class were as follows: 18% below 21, 40% between 21 and 23, 38% between 24 and 26, 3% between 27 and 28, and 1% above 28. About 34% of the current freshmen were in the top fifth of their class. There were 3 National Merit finalists and 11 semifinalists. A total of 28 freshmen graduated first in their class.

Requirements: The Rock requires applicants to be in the upper 60% of their class. A minimum GPA of 2.5 is required. The SAT I or ACT is recommended. Students should graduate from an accredited secondary school or have a GED. A total of 16 academic credits is required, and a college preparatory program, including 4 years of English and social studies, 3 each of science and mathematics, and 2 years of a foreign language is recommended. An interview is recommended. AP and CLEP credits are accepted. Important factors used in the admissions decision are advanced placement or honor courses, geographic diversity, recommendations by school officials, recommendations by alumni, and extracurricular activities record.

Procedure: Freshmen are admitted to all sessions. Entrance exams should be taken in the junior year or fall of the senior year. Applications should be filed by April 1 for fall entry, November 1 for spring entry, and April 1 for summer entry, along with an application fee of $25. Notification is sent on a rolling basis. There are early admissions and deferred admissions plans.

Transfer: About 500 transfer students enrolled in 1993–94. Transfer applicants should have completed at least 24 credit hours with a GPA of 2.5. The SAT I or ACT and an interview are recommended. A total of 36 credits out of 128 must be completed at The Rock.

Visiting: There are regularly scheduled orientations for prospective students, including a meeting with faculty, an information fair, and a campus tour. There are guides for informal visits and visitors may sit in on classes and stay overnight at the school. To arrange for a visit, contact Admissions at (800) 662-1102.

Financial Aid: In a recent year, 80% of all current freshmen and 83% of continuing students received some form of financial aid. About 70% of freshmen and 73% of continuing students received need-based aid. The average freshman award was $3000. Of that total, scholarships or need-based grants averaged $1300 ($4150 maximum); loans averaged $2000 ($2625 maximum); and work contracts averaged $800 ($2720 maximum). Fifteen percent of undergraduate students work part-time. Average earnings from campus work for the school year are $800. The average financial indebtedness of a recent graduate was $9000. The Rock is a member of CSS. The PHEAA financial statement is required. The deadline for financial aid applications is May 1.

International Students: There are currently 212 international students enrolled. The school actively recruits these students. They must take the TOEFL and achieve a minimum score of 500.

Computers: The university provides computer facilities for student use. The mainframe is an IBM ES 9000. About 100 public-use terminals are available for students and faculty, along with 200 microcomputers in 8 public areas. Networked microcomputers also have access to the mainframe and its gateway to BITNET and Internet. All students may access the mainframe system 24 hours a day. Campus terminal and microcomputer laboratories are generally open about 90 hours per week. There are no time limits on using the system and no fees.

Graduates: In a recent year, 1046 bachelor's degrees were awarded. The most popular majors among graduates were elementary education (18%), physical education (10%), and communications (8%). Within an average freshman class, 27% graduate in 4 years, 45% in 5 years, and 50% in 6 years. Some 385 companies recruited on campus in a recent year. In a recent graduating class, 25% of the men and 27% of the women had found employment within 6 months of

graduation.

Admissions Contact: David A. Collins, Director of Admissions.

SUSQUEHANNA UNIVERSITY
Selinsgrove, PA 17870

D-3

(717) 372-4260

(800) 326-9672 (out-of-state)

Full-time: 713 men, 738 women	Faculty: 97; IIB, +$
Part-time: 13 men, 57 women	Ph.D.s: 87%
Graduate: none	Student/Faculty: 15 to 1
Year: semesters, summer session	Tuition: $15,580
Application Deadline: March 15	Room & Board: $4370
Freshman Class: 2096 applied, 1512 accepted, 465 enrolled	
SAT I: required	**VERY COMPETITIVE**

Susquehanna University, founded in 1858, is an independent, coeducational institution affiliated with the Lutheran Church. It offers programs through schools of arts and sciences, fine arts and communications, and business. There are 3 undergraduate schools. In addition to regional accreditation, S.U. has baccalaureate program accreditation with AACSB and NASM. The library contains 212,000 volumes, 83,700 microform items, and 9400 audiovisual forms, and subscribes to 1400 periodicals. Computerized library sources and services include the card catalog, interlibrary loans, and database searching. Special learning facilities include a learning resource center; an art gallery; a radio station; a TV station; a campuswide voice and data telecommunications network, including residence hall connections, satellite dishes and distribution system for foreign language broadcasts; an ecological field station; a 28-inch reflecting telescope and observatory; a greenhouse; a child development center; and a new 450-seat theater. The 190-acre campus is in a small town 50 miles north of Harrisburg. Including residence halls, there are 50 buildings on campus.

Student Life: About 57% of undergraduates are from Pennsylvania. Students come from 25 states and 12 foreign countries. Eighty-five percent are from public schools; 15% from private. Ninety-five percent are white. Fifty-six percent are Protestant; 38% Catholic. The average age of freshmen is 18; all undergraduates, 20. Ten percent drop out by the end of their first year; 75% remain to graduate.

Housing: A total of 1130 students can be accommodated in college housing. College-sponsored living facilities include single-sex and coed dormitories, fraternity houses, and sorority houses. In addition, there are honors houses, and special interest houses. Volunteer project groups may reside in former private homes adjacent to the university with suite-type accommodations. On-campus housing is guaranteed for all 4 years. Eighty-five percent of students live on campus; of those, 87% remain on campus on weekends. All students may keep cars on campus.

Activities: About 28% of men belong to 4 national fraternities; about 28% of women belong to 4 national sororities. There are 100 groups on campus, including art, band, cheerleading, choir, chorale, chorus, computers, drama, ethnic, film, gay, honors, international, jazz band, literary magazine, marching band, musical theater, newspaper, opera, pep band, photography, political, professional, radio and TV, religious, social, social service, student government, and yearbook. Popular campus events include concerts and plays, Cultural Awareness Month, Homecoming, Spring Weekend, Candlelight Christmas Service, Parents Weekend, student musical, family-style Thanksgiving dinner served by faculty and staff, football and other sports events, tubing on the Susquehanna River, and Senior Convocation.

Sports: There are 11 intercollegiate sports for men and 11 for women, and 14 intramural sports for men and 7 for women. Athletic and recreation facilities include football, soccer, baseball, and hockey fields, basketball courts, tennis courts, a swimming pool, an all-weather track, paddleball courts, a weight training room, and a sauna. The campus stadium seats 4600, and the indoor gymnasium, 1800. The nearby Susquehanna River supports crew.

Disabled Students: Ninety percent of the campus is accessible to disabled students. The following facilities are available: wheelchair ramps, elevators, special parking, specially equipped rest rooms, special class scheduling, lowered drinking fountains, and lowered telephones.

Services: In addition to many counseling and information services, tutoring is available in some subjects, including writing, mathematics, foreign languages, computer science, and reading.

Campus Safety and Security: Campus safety and security measures include 24-hour foot and vehicle patrol, self-defense education, escort service, and informal discussions. In addition, there are pamphlets, posters, films, and lighted pathways and sidewalks.

Programs of Study: S.U. awards the B.A., B.S., B.Mu. degrees. Associate degrees also are awarded. Bachelor's degrees are awarded in BIOLOGICAL SCIENCE (biochemistry and biology/biological science), BUSINESS (accounting, business administration and management, and business economics), COMMUNICATIONS AND THE ARTS (art, art history and appreciation, communications, English, French, German, Greek, Latin, music, music performance, and Span-

ish), COMPUTER AND PHYSICAL SCIENCE (chemistry, computer science, geoscience, information sciences and systems, mathematics, and physics), EDUCATION (elementary, music, and secondary), ENGINEERING AND ENVIRONMENTAL DESIGN (environmental science), HEALTH PROFESSIONS (predentistry, premedicine, and preveterinary science), SOCIAL SCIENCE (economics, history, international studies, philosophy, political science/government, prelaw, psychology, religion, religious music, and sociology). Natural sciences, business administration, psychology, English, and political science are the strongest academically. Business administration, communications and theater arts, psychology, biology, and music have the largest enrollments.

Required: All students must complete a 3-part core curriculum of about 40 semester hours, including academic requirements in history, fine arts, literature, science, social science, philosophy, and religion or psychology; skills in computers, mathematics/logic, and foreign language; and noncredit personal-development courses in academic skills, library research, wellness/fitness, and career development. A total of 128 hours are required, with 36 to 44 hours in the major. A minimum GPA of 2.0 is also required to graduate.

Special: There is cross-registration with Bucknell University. Extensive programs include internships in almost all majors and study abroad in many countries. There is a Washington semester at American University and the Washington Center, a United Nations semester through Drew, and an Appalachian semester in Kentucky. The college offers dual and student-designed majors, work-study programs, credit by examination, nondegree study, and pass/fail options. The B.A.-B.S. degree is available in several majors, and there are 3–2 engineering programs with the University of Pennsylvania and Pennsylvania State University, a 3–2 program in forestry with Duke University, and a 2–2 program in allied health with Thomas Jefferson University. Susquehanna participates in the Philadelphia Center Program sponsored by the Great Lakes Colleges Association. There is a freshman honors program on campus, as well as 17 national honor societies. Thirteen departments have honors programs.

Faculty/Classroom: Sixty-seven percent of faculty are male; 33%, female. All teach undergraduates, and 50% do research. The average class size in an introductory lecture is 25; in a laboratory, 15; and in a regular course offering, 20.

Admissions: About 72% of the 1993–94 applicants were accepted. The SAT scores for the 1993–94 freshman class were as follows: Verbal—56% below 500, 33% between 500 and 599, 10% between 600 and 700, and 1% above 700; Math—25% below 500, 50% between 500 and 599, 22% between 600 and 700, and 3% above 700. About 53% of the current freshmen were in the top fifth of their class; 81% were in the top two fifths. There was 1 National Merit finalist and 5 semifinalists. Twelve freshmen graduated first in their class.

Requirements: The SAT I is required, except for students with a cumulative class rank in the top 20% in a strong college preparatory program. Such students have the option of submitting either the SAT I or 2 graded writing samples. Students need to graduate from an accredited high school. Preparation should include 4 years of English and mathematics, 3 to 4 years of science, and 2 to 3 years each of social studies and foreign language. In addition, 1 unit of art or music is recommended. Three SAT II: Subject tests are recommended, including writing and mathematics. An essay is required, and, for relevant fields, an art portfolio or a music audition. An interview is strongly recommended. AP and CLEP credits are accepted. Important factors used in the admissions decision are advanced placement or honor courses, recommendations by school officials, evidence of special talent, leadership record, and extracurricular activities record.

Procedure: Freshmen are admitted fall and spring. Entrance exams should be taken by January of the senior year. Early decision applications should be filed by December 15; regular applications, by March 15 for fall entry and December 1 for spring entry, along with an application fee of $25. Notification is sent on a rolling basis after Deceember 1 for early decision, and January 15 for regular decision. There are early decision, early admissions, and deferred admissions plans. About 93 early decision candidates were accepted for the 1993–94 class. A waiting list is an active part of the admissions procedure, with about 5% of applicants on the list.

Transfer: About 30 transfer students enrolled in 1993–94. Transfer applicants must submit transcripts, test scores, and a recommendation from a dean. An interview is strongly recommended. A total of 64 credits out of 128 must be completed at S.U.

Visiting: There are regularly scheduled orientations for prospective students, including special visiting days held in the spring and fall. These visiting days consist of sessions with faculty and admissions, financial aid, and placement staff, and tours of the campus. There are guides for informal visits and visitors may sit in on classes and stay overnight at the school. To arrange for a visit, contact the Office of Admissions at (717) 372-4260 or (800) 326-9672.

Financial Aid: In 1993–94, 80% of all current freshmen and 75% of continuing students received some form of financial aid. About 70% of freshmen and 60% of continuing students received need-based aid. The average freshman award was $12,950. Of that total, scholarships or need-based grants averaged $8985 ($17,510 maximum); loans averaged $2625 ($4125 maximum); and work contracts averaged $1460 ($1500 maximum). Sixty percent of undergraduate students work part-time. Average earnings from campus work for the school year are $1000. The average financial indebtedness of the 1992–93 graduate was $10,300. S.U. is a member of CSS. The FAF and federal tax return are required. The deadline for financial aid applications is May 1, but March 15 is recommended.

International Students: There are currently 22 international students enrolled. The school actively recruits these students. They must take the TOEFL and achieve a minimum score of 550. The student must also take the SAT I. SAT II: Subject tests in writing, mathematics, and one other subject are recommended.

Computers: The college provides computer facilities for student use. The mainframe is an HP 3000 series 947. Students have access to 106 microcomputers in 4 computer laboratories. Available software packages include WordPerfect, Lotus 1-2-3, FoxPro, SAS, Word, Excel, and Pagemaker. Students have worldwide access through Internet. All students may access the system. It may be used 24 hours a day from multiple locations on campus, including residence halls. There are no time limits on using the system and no fees.

Graduates: In 1992–93, 337 bachelor's degrees were awarded. The most popular majors among graduates were business administration (20%), communications and theater arts (15%), and English (9%). Within an average freshman class, 70% graduate in 4 years, 75% in 5 years, and 75% in 6 years. Some 52 companies recruited on campus in 1992–93. In the 1992 graduating class, 18% of all graduates were enrolled in graduate school within 6 months of graduation; 72% had found employment.

Admissions Contact: J. Richard Ziegler, Director of Admissions.

SWARTHMORE COLLEGE
F-4

Swarthmore, PA 19081
(215) 328-8300

Full-time: 695 men, 692 women	Faculty: 146; IIB, +$
Part-time: 1 man	Ph.D.s: 80%
Graduate: none	Student/Faculty: 10 to 1
Year: semesters	Tuition: $18,292
Application Deadline: February 1	Room & Board: $5844
Freshman Class: 3203 applied, 1255 accepted, 413 enrolled	
SAT I or ACT: required	**MOST COMPETITIVE**

Swarthmore College, established in 1864, is a private, nonprofit institution offering undergraduate courses in engineering and liberal arts. The library contains 776,000 volumes and subscribes to 2400 periodicals. Special learning facilities include an art gallery, radio station, observatory, and performing arts center. The 330-acre campus is in a suburban area 10 miles southwest of Philadelphia. Including residence halls, there are 40 buildings on campus.

Student Life: About 90% of undergraduates are from out-of-state, mostly the Middle Atlantic. Students come from 50 states, 40 foreign countries, and Canada. Sixty-five percent are from public schools; 35% from private. Seventy-five percent are white; 11% Asian American. Two percent drop out by the end of their first year; 93% remain to graduate.

Housing: College-sponsored living facilities include single-sex and coed dormitories. In addition, there are language houses and special interest houses. On-campus housing is guaranteed for the freshman year only and is available on a lottery system for upperclassmen. Ninety-three percent of students live on campus; all remain on campus on weekends. Upperclassmen may keep cars on campus.

Activities: About 5% of men belong to 1 local and 1 national fraternity. There are no sororities on campus. There are more than 100 groups on campus, including art, band, cheerleading, chess, choir, chorus, computers, dance, drama, ethnic, gay, international, jazz band, literary magazine, musical theater, newspaper, orchestra, pep band, political, radio and TV, religious, social, social service, student government, and yearbook. Popular campus events include Fall Weekend (Homecoming), Spring Fling, Fall and Spring Formals, McCabe Mile (race in the library basement), and Crum Regatta Worthstock (all-day music festival).

Sports: There are 11 intercollegiate sports for men and 11 for women, and 7 intramural sports for men and 7 for women. Athletic and recreation facilities include a field house, a 3000-seat stadium, a 500-seat gymnasium, a 1200-seat auditorium, squash courts, a pool, a track, an indoor pavilion, a variety of playing fields, and tennis courts.

Disabled Students: Seventy-five percent of the campus is accessible to disabled students. The following facilities are available: wheelchair ramps, elevators, special parking, specially equipped rest rooms, special class scheduling, and lowered drinking fountains.

Services: In addition to many counseling and information services, tutoring is available in most subjects. In addition, there is a reader service for the blind.

Campus Safety and Security: Campus safety and security measures include 24-hour foot and vehicle patrol, self defense education, escort service, and shuttle buses. In addition, there are informal discussions, pamphlets, posters, and films, emergency telephones, and lighted pathways and sidewalks.

Programs of Study: Swarthmore awards the B.A. and B.S. degrees. Bachelor's degrees are awarded in BIOLOGICAL SCIENCE (biology/biological science), COMMUNICATIONS AND THE ARTS (English, fine arts, French, German, Greek, Latin, music, Russian, and Spanish), COMPUTER AND PHYSICAL SCIENCE (chemistry, computer science, mathematics, and physics), ENGINEERING AND ENVIRONMENTAL DESIGN (civil engineering, computer engineering, electrical/electronics engineering, engineering, and mechanical engineering), SOCIAL SCIENCE (anthropology, economics, history, international relations, philosophy, political science/government, psychology, religion, and sociology). English, biology, history, economics, and political science have the largest enrollments.

Required: To graduate, students must complete 3 courses in each of 3 divisions consisting of humanities, natural sciences and engineering, and social sciences. They must have completed 32 courses or the equivalent, with a minimum of 20 credits earned outside the major. They must have a GPA of 2.0. Students must meet both a foreign language and a physical education requirement.

Special: Students may cross-register with Haverford and Bryn Mawr colleges and the University of Pennsylvania. They may study abroad in their country of choice. Dual and student-designed majors and a 4-year program leading to a B.A.-B.S. degree in engineering and liberal arts are available. Swarthmore offers an honors program of independent study. There are 2 national honor societies on campus, including Phi Beta Kappa.

Faculty/Classroom: Sixty-five percent of faculty are male; 35%, female. All teach undergraduates. The average class size in an introductory lecture is 40; in a laboratory, 12; and in a regular course offering, 20.

Admissions: About 39% of the 1993–94 applicants were accepted. The SAT scores for the 1993–94 freshman class were as follows: Verbal—7% below 500, 22% between 500 and 599, 49% between 600 and 700, and 23% above 700; Math—2% below 500, 12% between 500 and 599, 41% between 600 and 700, and 45% above 700. About 97% of the current freshmen were in the top fifth of their class; all were in the top two fifths. About 49 freshmen graduated first in their class.

Requirements: The SAT I or ACT is required. Applicants must graduate from an accredited secondary school. Swarthmore does not require a specific high school curricula. It does, however, recommend the inclusion of English, mathematics, 1 or 2 foreign languages, history and social studies, literature, art, and music, and the sciences. Interviews are strongly recommended. An essay, 2 teacher recommendations, and a counselor recommendation are required. AP credit is accepted. Important factors used in the admissions decision are evidence of special talent, extracurricular activities record, advanced placement or honor courses, parents or siblings attending the school, personality, and intangible qualities.

Procedure: Freshmen are admitted in the fall. Entrance exams should be taken in spring of the junior year or fall of the senior year. Application deadlines for the early decision plans are November 15 and January 1. Regular applications should be filed by February 1 for fall entry. The application fee is $45. Notification for the early decision plans is sent December 15 and February 1; for regular entry, April 1. There are early decision and deferred admissions plans. About 103 early decision candidates were accepted for the 1993–94 class. A waiting list is an active part of the admissions procedure.

Transfer: About 16 transfer students enrolled in 1993–94. Students considered for transfer must have a GPA of 3.0. The SAT I is required if not taken previously. An essay is required. A total of 16 course credits out of 32 must be completed at Swarthmore.

Visiting: There are guides for informal visits and visitors may sit in on classes and stay overnight at the school. To arrange for a visit, contact the Admissions Receptionist at (215) 328–8300.

Financial Aid: In 1993–94, 60% of all students received some form of financial aid; 45% received need-based aid. The average freshman award was $17,120. Of that total, scholarships or need-based grants averaged $13,500 ($26,000 maximum); loans averaged $2460 (maximum); and work contracts averaged $1160 (maximum). Seventy-seven percent of undergraduate students work part-time. Average earnings from campus work for the school year are $1160. The average financial indebtedness of the 1992–93 graduate was $9000. Swarthmore is a member of CSS. The FAF, the college's own financial statement, and the tax return are required. The deadline for financial aid applications is February 1.

International Students: There are currently 85 international students enrolled. The student must take the SAT I or the ACT. Students must take SAT II: Subject tests in writing and 2 other subjects.

Computers: The college provides computer facilities for student use. Several DEC AXP 3000/4000 servers run the OSF/1 UNIX operating system. There are also microcomputers available throughout the campus. Residence halls are fully hooked up to the network. All students may access the system. There are no time limits on using the system and no fees.

Graduates: In 1992–93 322 bachelor's degrees were awarded. The most popular majors among graduates were English (17%), biology (10%), and economics (9%). Within an average freshman class, 1% graduate in 3 years, 85% in 4 years, and 91% in 5 years. Some 50 companies recruited on campus in 1992–93. In the 1992 graduating class, 28% of the men and 21% of the women were enrolled in graduate school within 6 months of graduation; 62% of the men and 66% of the women had found employment.

Admissions Contact: O. Carl Wartenburg, Dean of Admissions.

TEMPLE UNIVERSITY
F-3

Philadelphia, PA 19122–1803   (215) 204–7200

Full-time: 8755 men, 9484 women	Faculty: 1732; I, av$
Part-time: 3200 men, 3500 women	Ph.D.s: 86%
Graduate: 4900 men, 5100 women	Student/Faculty: 11 to 1
Year: semesters, summer session	Tuition: $5151 ($9727)
Application Deadline: June 15	Room & Board: $5130
Freshman Class: 8848 applied, 5680 accepted, 2491 enrolled	
SAT I Verbal/Math: 455/508	COMPETITIVE

Temple University, founded in 1884, is part of the Commonwealth System of Higher Education in Pennsylvania. It offers programs in arts and sciences, allied health professions, education, engineering, computer sciences, architecture, health, physical education, recreation and dance, art, business and management, communications and theater, landscape architecture and horticulture, music, pharmacy, and social administration. Temple has 6 other campuses, including one in Rome and one in Tokyo. There are 11 undergraduate schools. In addition to regional accreditation, Temple has baccalaureate program accreditation with AACSB, ABET, ACEJMC, ACPE, ADA, APTA, CAHEA, CSWE, NAAB, NASAD, NASM, NCATE, NLN, and NRPA. The 3 libraries contain 2 million volumes. Special learning facilities include an art gallery, a radio station, a dance laboratory theater, a media learning center for the study of critical languages, and a multimedia laboratory for teacher education in music. The 82-acre campus is in an urban area 1 mile north of center city Philadelphia. Other area campuses are located in Montgomery. Including residence halls, there are 100 buildings on campus.

Student Life: About 93% of undergraduates are from Pennsylvania. Students come from 50 states and 60 foreign countries. Sixty-three percent are white; 22% African American; 10% Asian American.

Housing: A total of 3000 students can be accommodated in college housing. College-sponsored living facilities include dormitories, on-campus apartments, off-campus apartments, fraternity houses, and sorority houses. On-campus housing is guaranteed for all 4 years. Eighty percent of students commute. All students may keep cars on campus. Alcohol is not permitted.

Activities: About 10% of men belong to 12 local fraternities; about 10% of women belong to 11 local sororities. There are 125 groups on campus, including art, band, cheerleading, chess, choir, chorus, computers, dance, drama, drill team, ethnic, film, honors, international, jazz band, literary magazine, marching band, musical theater, newspaper, orchestra, pep band, photography, political, professional, radio and TV, religious, social, social service, student government, and yearbook. Popular campus events include Spring Fling.

Sports: There are 13 intercollegiate sports each for men and women, and 15 intramural sports for men and 12 for women. Athletic and recreation facilities include 2 Olympic-size swimming pools, a diving well, several gymnasiums, weight-training rooms, 10 bowling lanes, racquetball courts, an 8-lane 400-meter track, and playing fields. The campus stadium seats 65,000, the indoor gymnasium 2000, and the largest auditorium/arena 600.

Disabled Students: All of the campus is accessible to disabled students. The following facilities are available: wheelchair ramps, elevators, special parking, specially equipped rest rooms, special class scheduling, lowered drinking fountains, and lowered telephones. Additional services may be arranged through the Disabled Student Services Office.

Services: In addition to many counseling and information services, tutoring is available in most subjects. There is a reader service for the blind, and remedial math, reading, and writing.

Campus Safety and Security: Campus safety and security measures include a 24-hour foot and vehicle patrol, an escort service, shuttle buses, and informal discussions. In addition, there are pamphlets, posters, films, lighted pathways and sidewalks, and 24-hour access-controlled security in residence halls.

Programs of Study: Temple awards the B.A., B.S., B.Ar., B.B.A., B.F.A., B.M., B.S.Ar., B.S.E., B.S.Ed., B.S.E.E., B.S.N., and B.S.W. degrees. Associate, master's, and doctoral degrees also are awarded

Bachelor's degrees are awarded in AGRICULTURE (horticulture), BIOLOGICAL SCIENCE (biochemistry and biology/biological science), BUSINESS (accounting, banking and finance, business administration and management, business economics, business law, human resources, international business management, management science, marketing/retailing/merchandising, personnel management, real estate, and sports management), COMMUNICATIONS AND THE ARTS (art, art history and appreciation, broadcasting, Chinese, classics, communications, dance, English, film arts, fine arts, French, Germanic languages and literature, Greek, guitar, Hebrew, Italian, jazz, journalism, Latin, linguistics, music, music history and appreciation, music performance, music theory and composition, percussion, performing arts, photography, piano/organ, Portuguese, Russian, Spanish, speech/debate/rhetoric, strings, telecommunications, voice, and winds), COMPUTER AND PHYSICAL SCIENCE (actuarial science, chemistry, computer science, geology, mathematics, physics, and statistics), EDUCATION (art, business, early childhood, education, elementary, English, foreign languages, health, home economics, industrial arts, marketing and distribution, mathematics, middle school, music, physical, science, secondary, and social studies), ENGINEERING AND ENVIRONMENTAL DESIGN (architectural engineering, architecture, biomedical engineering, civil engineering, electrical/electronics engineering, electrical/electronics engineering technology, engineering, engineering technology, environmental engineering technology, landscape architecture/design, mechanical engineering, and mechanical engineering technology), HEALTH PROFESSIONS (health care administration, music therapy, nursing, occupational therapy, pharmacy, physical therapy, predentistry, and premedicine), SOCIAL SCIENCE (African American studies, American studies, anthropology, Asian/Oriental studies, community services, criminal justice, economics, geography, history, international relations, parks and recreation management, philosophy, political science/government, prelaw, psychology, public administration, religion, social science, social work, sociology, urban studies, and women's studies).

Required: The required core curriculum includes English composition, intellectual heritage, American culture, the arts, the individual and society, foreign language/international studies, mathematics/statistics/logic, and science and technology. A minimum 2.0 GPA and a total of 128 credit hours are required for graduation, including 24 credits in the major.

Special: The university offers study abroad, work-study programs, and up to 30 credits for life/military/work experience. There is a 5-year accelerated engineering technology program. There is a university-wide and a freshman honors program on campus.

Admissions: About 64% of the 1993–94 applicants were accepted. About 34% of the current freshmen were in the top fifth of their class; 63% were in the top two fifths.

Requirements: Temple requires applicants to be in the upper 50% of their class. A minimum GPA of 2.0 is required. The SAT I or ACT is required. In addition, applicants should complete 16 academic credits/Carnegie units, including 4 years of English, 2 each of mathematics and a foreign language, and 1 each of history and a laboratory science. A GED is accepted. A portfolio and audition are required in relevant fields. AP and CLEP credits are accepted. Important factors used in the admissions decision are advanced placement or honor courses, recommendations by school officials, parents or siblings attending the school, personality, intangible qualities, and extracurricular activities record.

Procedure: Freshmen are admitted in the fall and spring. Entrance exams should be taken by March of the junior year or April of the senior year. Applications should be filed by June 15 for fall entry and November 15 for spring entry, along with an application fee of $30. Notification is sent on a rolling basis.

Transfer: About 2300 transfer students enrolled in 1993–94. Transfer applicants must have earned at least 15 college credit hours with at least a 2.0 GPA and must submit official high school and college transcripts. A total of 30 credits out of 128 must be completed at Temple.

Visiting: There are regularly scheduled orientations for prospective students. There are guides for informal visits and visitors may sit in on classes. To arrange for a visit, contact the Office of Undergraduate Admissions at (215) 204-7200.

Financial Aid: Temple is a member of CSS. The FAF, the college's own financial statement, the FAFSA, and PHEAA (Pennsylvania residents) are required. The deadline for financial aid applications is March 31.

International Students: International students must take the TOEFL and achieve a minimum score of 500. The SAT I or the ACT is also required.

Computers: The college provides computer facilities for student use. The mainframes are a CDC Cyber 860 and 2 IBM 4381 VM/CMS. Students may access computer facilities through workstations distributed throughout the campus. Networked microcomputer laboratories and software libraries are available for student use. All students may access the system 24 hours per day. There are no time limits on using the system and no fees.

Graduates: In an earlier year, 3437 bachelor's degrees were awarded. Some 333 companies recruited on campus in an earlier year.

Admissions Contact: Admissions Counselor.

THIEL COLLEGE
Greenville, PA 16125

A-2
(412) 589-2345
(800) 24-THIEL (out-of-state)

Full-time: 371 men, 420 women
Part-time: 44 men, 96 women
Graduate: none
Year: 2 summer terms, summer session
Application Deadline: open
Freshman Class: 1154 applied, 951 accepted, 253 enrolled
SAT I Verbal Math: 418/444

Faculty: 59; IIB, -$
Ph.D.s: 71%
Student/Faculty: 13 to 1
Tuition: $11,312
Room & Board: $4970

ACT: 20   COMPETITIVE

Thiel College, founded in 1866, is an independent, coeducational college affiliated with the Lutheran Church. It offers programs in liberal arts, business, engineering, nursing, religion, teacher preparation, and professional programs. In addition to regional accreditation, Thiel has baccalaureate program accreditation with NLN. The library contains 135,000 volumes, 170 microform items, and 3300 audiovisual forms, and subscribes to 700 periodicals. Computerized library sources and services include interlibrary loans. Special learning facilities include a learning resource center, an art gallery, a radio station, and a wildlife sanctuary. The 135-acre campus is in a rural area 75 miles north of Pittsburgh and 75 miles southeast of Cleveland. Including residence halls, there are 21 buildings on campus.

Student Life: About 84% of undergraduates are from Pennsylvania. Students come from 15 states and 9 foreign countries. Ninety percent are from public schools; 10% from private. Ninety percent are white. Thirty-eight percent are Protestant; 27% Catholic; 11% claim no religious affiliation. The average age of freshmen is 18; all undergraduates, 20. Twenty-two percent drop out by the end of their first year; 50% remain to graduate.

Housing: A total of 1076 students can be accommodated in college housing. College-sponsored living facilities include single-sex and coed dormitories, fraternity houses, and an honors residence hall. On-campus housing is guaranteed for all 4 years. Eighty percent of students live on campus; of those, 60% remain on campus on weekends. All students may keep cars on campus.

Activities: About 20% of men belong to 1 local fraternity and 2 national fraternities; about 30% of women belong to 5 national sororities. There are 35 groups on campus, including band, cheerleading, choir, chorus, computers, dance, drama, ethnic, honors, international, literary magazine, musical theater, newspaper, pep band, political, professional, radio, religious, social, student government, symphony, and yearbook. Popular campus events include Homecoming, Spring Weekend, Greek Week, theatrical productions, events sponsored by student government, and weekly movies and shows.

Sports: There are 8 intercollegiate sports for men and 6 for women, and 5 intramural sports each for men and women. Athletic and recreation facilities include a 1200-seat gymnasium, basketball and handball courts, a swimming pool, and playing fields.

Disabled Students: Seventy-five percent of the campus is accessible to disabled students. The following facilities are available: wheelchair ramps, elevators, special parking, specially equipped rest rooms, and special class scheduling.

Services: In addition to many counseling and information services, tutoring is available in every subject. There is remedial math, reading, and writing.

Campus Safety and Security: Campus safety and security measures include a 24-hour foot and vehicle patrol, an escort service, pamphlets, posters, and films, and emergency telephones. In addition, there are lighted pathways and sidewalks.

Programs of Study: Thiel awards the B.A. and B.S.N. degrees. Associate degrees are also awarded. Bachelor's degrees are awarded in BIOLOGICAL SCIENCE (biology/biological science), BUSINESS (accounting, business administration and management, and international business management), COMMUNICATIONS AND THE ARTS (art, communications, English, French, and Spanish), COMPUTER AND PHYSICAL SCIENCE (actuarial science, chemistry, computer science, geology, mathematics, and physics), EDUCATION (elementary and secondary), ENGINEERING AND ENVIRONMENTAL DESIGN (environmental science and preengineering), HEALTH PROFESSIONS (cytotechnology, medical laboratory technology, mortuary science, nursing, physical therapy, predentistry, premedicine, prepharmacy, preveterinary science, respiratory therapy, and speech pathology/audiology), SOCIAL SCIENCE (history, philosophy, political science/government, prelaw, psychology, religion, religious education, and sociology). Nursing and engineering are the strongest programs academically. Accounting, business administration, nursing, and education have the largest enrollments.

Required: To graduate, students must complete a total of 124 credit hours, with 35 to 36 in the major, and a minimum GPA of 2.0. Distribution requirements, for all except nursing students, include 14 to 15 hours of Western heritage, 9 of Christianity, 6 to 8 of science, 3 to 10 of cultural studies, and 4 of health.

Special: Students may spend a semester at Argonne National Laboratories, the Art Institute of Pittsburgh, or Drew University. Special programs inlcude a UN semester, a Washington semester, an Appalachian semester, study at Pittsburgh Institute of Mortuary Science, and a forestry and environmental management semester at Duke University. There is a 3–2 engineering program with Case Western Reserve and the University of Pittsburgh. Internships, study abroad, work-study, dual majors, nondegree study, credit by examination, and credit for life, military, and work experience, are also available. There is a freshman honors program on campus, as well as 11 national honor societies.

Faculty/Classroom: Sixty-seven percent of faculty are male; 33%, female. All teach undergraduates. The average class size in an introductory lecture is 25; in a laboratory, 15; and in a regular course offering, 12.

Admissions: About 82% of the 1993–94 applicants were accepted. About 24% of the current freshmen were in the top fifth of their class; 53% were in the top two fifths.

Requirements: The SAT I or ACT is required. In some cases test scores may be required for admission. Applicants should be high school graduates who have completed 16 academic units, including 4 years of English, 3 of social science, and 2 each of foreign language, mathematics, and science. The GED is accepted. An essay and an interview are recommended. AP and CLEP credits are accepted. Important factors used in the admissions decision are advanced placement or honor courses, evidence of special talent, leadership record, extracurricular activities record, and parents or siblings attending the school.

Procedure: Freshmen are admitted to all sessions. Application deadlines are open. The application fee is $25. Notification of early decision is sent October 15; regular decision, on a rolling basis. There are early decision and deferred admissions plans.

Transfer: About 80 transfer students enrolled in 1993–94. Applicants should meet the same criteria as entering freshmen and should submit official transcripts and statements of good standing from all previous colleges attended. Students must have a 2.0 GPA to transfer and must complete financial aid transcripts and transfer forms from all schools previously attended. A total of 30 credits out of 124 must be completed at Thiel.

Visiting: There are regularly scheduled orientations for prospective students, including orientation sessions scheduled for students enrolling for the fall semester and monthly sessions beginning in February. There are guides for informal visits and visitors may sit in on classes and stay overnight at the school. To arrange for a visit, contact the Admissions Office at (412) 589-2345 or (800) 24-THIEL.

Financial Aid: In 1993–94, 95% of all students received some form of financial aid. About 79% of freshmen received need-based aid. The average freshman award was $7842. Of that total, scholarships or need-based grants averaged $3500 ($6000 maximum); loans averaged $3025 ($4600 maximum); and work contracts averaged $1224. Forty-four percent of undergraduate students work part-time. Average earnings from campus work for the school year are $1224. The average financial indebtedness of the 1992–93 graduate was $13,500. Thiel is a member of CSS. The FAF, FFS, or SFS and PHEAA (preferred) for Pennsylvania residents are required.

International Students: There are currently 32 international students enrolled. The school actively recruits these students. They must take the TOEFL and achieve a minimum score of 450.

Computers: The college provides computer facilities for student use. The mainframe is a DEC PDP 11/44. There are a number of computer systems in operation on campus, serving both administrative and academic applications. They are accessible to student workers and to other students for completing course assignments. There are no time limits on using the system and no fees.

Graduates: In an earlier year, 153 bachelor's degrees were awarded. The most popular majors among graduates were business (30%), health sciences (14%), and social science (14%). Some 40 companies recruited on campus in an earlier year. In a recent graduating class, 7% of the men and 8% of the women were enrolled in graduate school within 6 months of graduation; 40% of the men and 54% of the women had found employment.

Admissions Contact: David J. Rhodes, Director of Admissions.

UNIVERSITY OF PENNSYLVANIA

F-3

Philadelphia, PA 19104   (215) 898-7507

Full-time: 5313 men, 4125 women	Faculty: 1902; I, ++$
Part-time: 899 men, 1111 women	Ph.D.s: 99%
Graduate: 5689 men, 5332 women	Student/Faculty: 5 to 1
Year: semesters, summer session	Tuition: $17,838
Application Deadline: January 1	Room & Board: $6400
Freshman Class: 12,394 applied, 5232 accepted, 2464 enrolled	
SAT I Verbal/Math: 599/670	ACT: 29 **MOST COMPETITIVE**

The University of Pennsylvania, founded in 1740, is a private institution offering undergraduate and graduate degrees in arts and sciences, business, engineering and applied science, and nursing. There are 4 undergraduate and 12 graduate schools. In addition to regional accreditation, Penn has baccalaureate program accreditation with AACSB, ABET, NAAB, NCATE, and NLN. The 14 libraries contain 4,099,648 volumes, 3,600,000 microform items, and 33,906 audiovisual forms, and subscribe to 33,024 periodicals. Special learning facilities include an art gallery, natural history museum, planetarium, radio station, TV station, arboretum, animal research center, primate research center, language laboratory, center for performing arts, institute for contemporary art, wind tunnel, and electron microscope. The 260-acre campus is in an urban area in Philadelphia. Including residence halls, there are 119 buildings on campus.

Student Life: About 83% of undergraduates are from out-of-state, mostly the Middle Atlantic. Students come from 50 states, 100 foreign countries, and Canada. Sixty-five percent are from public schools; 35% from private. Sixty-eight percent are white; 14% Asian American. The average age of freshmen is 18; all undergraduates, 20. Four percent drop out by the end of their first year; 90% remain to graduate.

Housing: A total of 7400 students can be accommodated in college housing. College-sponsored living facilities include coed dormitories, on-campus apartments, married-student housing, fraternity houses, and sorority houses. In addition, there are honors houses, language houses, and special interest houses. On-campus housing is guaranteed for the freshman year only, is available on a first-come, first-served basis, and is available on a lottery system for upperclassmen. Seventy-one percent of students live on campus; of those, 90% remain on campus on weekends. Alcohol is not permitted. All students may keep cars on campus.

Activities: About 33% of men belong to 29 national fraternities; about 32% of women belong to 14 national sororities. There are 250 groups on campus, including art, band, cheerleading, chess, choir, chorale, chorus, computers, dance, drama, ethnic, gay, honors, international, jazz band, literary magazine, marching band, musical theater, newspaper, opera, orchestra, political, professional, radio and TV, religious, social, social service, student government, symphony, and yearbook. Popular campus events include Spring Fling, festival in April, Mask and Wig Show, and Franklin's Birthday.

Sports: There are 16 intercollegiate sports for men and 14 for women, and 16 intramural sports for men and 16 for women. Athletic and recreation facilities include 3 gymnasiums, a tennis pavilion, 2 swimming pools, squash courts, indoor/outdoor tennis courts, playing fields, an indoor ice rink, rowing tanks, saunas, and a weight room.

Disabled Students: Eighty percent of the campus is accessible to disabled students. The following facilities are available: wheelchair ramps, elevators, special parking, specially equipped rest rooms, special class scheduling, lowered drinking fountains, lowered telephones, TDD, accessible housing, and an accessible van shuttle.

Services: In addition to many counseling and information services, tutoring is available in every subject. In addition, there is a reader service for the blind.

Campus Safety and Security: Campus safety and security measures include 24-hour foot and vehicle patrol, self defense education, escort service, and shuttle buses. In addition, there are informal discussions, pamphlets, posters, films, emergency telephones, lighted pathways and sidewalks, 100 commissioned police officers, victim support/special services, Students Together Against Acquaintance Rape, Penn Watch, and Student Walking Escort.

Programs of Study: Penn awards the B.A., B.S., B.Applied Sc., B.S. in Econ., B.S.E., and B.S.N. degrees. Associate, master's, and doctoral degrees also are awarded. Bachelor's degrees are awarded in BIOLOGICAL SCIENCE (biochemistry, biology/biological science, and biophysics), BUSINESS (accounting, banking and finance, business administration and management, international business management, marketing/retailing/merchandising, organizational behavior, real estate, small business management, and transportation management), COMMUNICATIONS AND THE ARTS (art history and appreciation, communications, dramatic arts, English, German, languages, linguistics, music, romance languages, and Slavic languages), COMPUTER AND PHYSICAL SCIENCE (actuarial science, astronomy, chemistry, computer science, geology, mathematics, and physics), EDUCATION (education and elementary), ENGINEERING AND ENVIRONMEN-

TAL DESIGN (bioengineering, chemical engineering, civil engineering, electrical/electronics engineering, engineering, environmental design, environmental science, materials engineering, and mechanical engineering), HEALTH PROFESSIONS (hospital administration and nursing), SOCIAL SCIENCE (American studies, anthropology, area studies, behavioral science, economics, history, humanities, international relations, law, liberal arts/general studies, philosophy, political science/government, psychology, public affairs, religion, social science, sociology, urban studies, and women's studies).

Required: The bachelor's degree requires completion of 32 to 40 course units, depending on the student's major, with 12 to 18 of these units in the major and a GPA of 2.0. Students must also complete 10 courses from 6 areas of study in the humanities, science, and mathematics.

Special: Cross-registration is permitted with Haverford, Swarthmore, and Bryn Mawr colleges. Opportunities are provided for internships, a Washington semester, accelerated degree programs, B.A.-B.S. degrees, dual and student-designed majors, a 3–2 engineering degree, credit by examination, nondegree study, limited pass/fail options, and study abroad in 14 countries. Through the 'one university' concept, students in 1 undergraduate school may study in any of the other 3. There is a freshman honors program on campus, as well as 10 national honor societies, including Phi Beta Kappa.

Faculty/Classroom: Eighty-two percent of faculty are male; 18%, female. The average class size in an introductory lecture is 17; in a laboratory, 25; and in a regular course offering, 35.

Admissions: About 42% of the 1993–94 applicants were accepted. The SAT scores for the 1993–94 freshman class were as follows: Verbal—11% below 500, 34% between 500 and 599, 47% between 600 and 700, and 8% above 700; Math—2% below 500, 11% between 500 and 599, 40% between 600 and 700, and 47% above 700. About 94% of the current freshmen were in the top fifth of their class; 99% were in the top two fifths.

Requirements: The SAT I or ACT is required. Graduation from an accredited secondary school is required. Recommended preparation includes 4 years of high school English, 3 or 4 each of a foreign language and mathematics, and 3 each of history and science. An essay is required. A portfolio and an audition are recommended for prospective art and music majors, respectively. AP credit is accepted. Important factors used in the admissions decision are advanced placement or honor courses, leadership record, recommendations by school officials, extracurricular activities record, and geographic diversity.

Procedure: Freshmen are admitted in the fall. Entrance exams should be taken by January of the senior year. Early decision applications should be filed by November 1; regular applications, by January 1 for fall entry, along with an application fee of $55. Notification of early decision is sent mid-December; regular decision, early April. There are early decision, early admissions, and deferred admissions plans. Nearly 900 early decision candidates were accepted for the 1993–94 class. A waiting list is an active part of the admissions procedure, with about 5% of applicants on the list.

Transfer: About 250 transfer students enrolled in 1993–94. Transfer applicants must provide college and high school transcripts, essays, and 2 recommendations. They must pass a standardized test and meet the course credit requirements of the admitting school. A minimum 3.0 GPA is recommended. A total of 20 course units out of 32 to 40 must be completed at Penn.

Visiting: There are regularly scheduled orientations for prospective students. There are guides for informal visits and visitors may sit in on classes and stay overnight at the school. To arrange for a visit, contact the Admissions Office at (215) 898–7507.

Financial Aid: In 1993–94, 46% of all current freshmen and 44% of continuing students received some form of financial aid. About 46% of freshmen and 44% of continuing students received need-based aid. The average freshman award was $12,930. Of that total, scholarships or need-based grants averaged $12,930 ($22,500 maximum); loans averaged $3473 ($5625 maximum); and work contracts averaged $1270. Forty-seven percent of undergraduate students work part-time. Average earnings from campus work for the school year are $1270. The average financial indebtedness of the 1992–93 graduate was $11,850. Penn is a member of CSS. The FAF and the college's own financial statement are required. The deadline for financial aid applications is January 1.

International Students: There are currently 886 international students enrolled. The school actively recruits these students. They must take the TOEFL or the University of Michigan Language Test and achieve a minimum score on the TOEFL of 550. The student must also take the SAT I or the ACT. Students must take SAT II: Subject tests in writing and mathematics (for business and engineering).

Computers: The college provides computer facilities for student use. The mainframe is an IBM 3090. Students can use the 500 networked microcomputers to access information sources, including the on-line library catalog, a campuswide information system (Penn Info), and

worldwide resources via Internet. All students may access the system. There are no time limits on using the system and no fees.

Graduates: In 1992–93, 2802 bachelor's degrees were awarded. The most popular majors among graduates were banking and finance (11%), history (10%), and English (7%). Within an average freshman class, 2% graduate in 3 years, 82% in 4 years, 90% in 5 years, and 90% in 6 years. Some 500 companies recruited on campus in a recent year.

Admissions Contact: Willis J. Stetson, Jr., Dean of Admissions.

UNIVERSITY OF PITTSBURGH

The University of Pittsburgh, established in 1787, is a public research university system in Pennsylvania. It is governed by the board of trustees of the University of Pittsburgh, whose chief administrator is the president. The primary goal of the system is enhancing educational opportunities for the citizens of Pennsylvania and contributing to the state's social, intellectual, and economic development. The main priorities are to engage in research, artistic, and scholarly activities;, to provide high-quality undergraduate, graduate, and professional programs; and, and to offer expertise and educational services to meet the needs of the region and state. The total enrollment in fall 1993 of all 5 campuses was 33,756; there were 3772 faculty members. Altogether there are 183 baccalaureate, 120 master's, 84 doctoral, and 4 first-professional degree programs offered in University of Pittsburgh. Four-year campuses are located in Pittsburgh,, Bradford, Greensburg, and Johnstown. Profiles of the 4-year campuses are included in this chapter in alphabetical order with other Pennsylvania schools.

UNIVERSITY OF PITTSBURGH
Pittsburgh, PA 15260

B-3
(412) 624-PITT

Full-time: 6741 men, 6577 women	Faculty: 2817; I, av$
Part-time: 2113 men, 2176 women	Ph.D.s: 90%
Graduate: 4936 men, 4985 women	Student/Faculty: n/av
Year: semesters, summer session	Tuition: $5186 ($10,708)
Application Deadline: see profile	Room & Board: $4286
Freshman Class: 8301 applied, 6299 accepted, 2257 enrolled	
SAT I Verbal/Math: 480/540	COMPETITIVE

The University of Pittsburgh, founded in 1787, is a state-related, coeducational, public research university with programs in liberal arts and sciences, education, engineering, social work, business, and health fields. There are 11 schools with undergraduate programs and 14 graduate schools. In addition to regional accreditation, Pitt has baccalaureate program accreditation with AACSB, ABET, ACPE, ADA, APTA, CAHEA, CSWE, NAST, and NLN. The 25 libraries contain 3,123,745 volumes and 2,933,537 microform items, and subscribe to 23,119 periodicals. Computerized library sources and services include the card catalog, interlibrary loans, and database searching. Special learning facilities include a learning resource center, an art gallery, and a radio station. The Carnegie Museum of Natural History, Museum of Arts, and Music Hall is adjacent to the main campus, and the Allegheny Observatory is located off-campus. The Nationality Rooms, 23 classrooms representing various nationalities, are located in the 42-story Cathedral of Learning at the main campus. The 132-acre campus is in an urban area 3 miles east of downtown Pittsburgh. Including residence halls, there are more than 90 buildings on campus.

Student Life: About 90% of full-time undergraduates are from Pennsylvania. Students come from 48 states, 53 foreign countries, and Canada. Eighty-six percent are white. The average age of all undergraduates is 23. Fourteen percent drop out by the end of their first year; 64% remain to graduate.

Housing: A total of 5000 students can be accommodated in college housing. College-sponsored living facilities include single-sex and coed dormitories, off-campus apartments, and fraternity houses. On-campus housing is guaranteed for the freshman year only, is available on a first-come, first-served basis, and is available on a lottery system for upperclassmen. About 40% of full-time students live in university-wide housing. All students may keep cars on campus.

Activities: About 11% of men belong to 22 national fraternities; about 9% of women belong to 14 national sororities. There are 340 groups on campus, including art, band, cheerleading, chess, chorale, chorus, dance, drama, ethnic, gay, honors, international, jazz band, literary magazine, marching band, newspaper, political, professional, religious, social, social service, student government, and yearbook. Popular campus events include football games, university plays, Jazz Seminar, Black Week, and Greek Week.

Sports: There are 11 intercollegiate sports for men and 8 for women, and 16 intramural sports for men and 15 for women. Athletic and recreation facilities include a 56,500-seat stadium for football, and track; a 6750-seat field house for basketball, and track; a sports center that converts from a regulation football field to 9 tennis courts; and a hall for pool and racquetball. Recreation facilities are available in the union, and include billiard tables, table tennis, and video games.

Disabled Students: Ninety percent of the campus is accessible to disabled students. The following facilities are available: wheelchair ramps, elevators, special parking, specially equipped rest rooms, special class scheduling, lowered drinking fountains, lowered telephones, and transportation.

Services: In addition to many counseling and information services, tutoring is available in some subjects, including many lower-level undergraduate science and humanities courses. There is also a reader service for the blind, and remedial math, reading, and writing.

Campus Safety and Security: Campus safety and security measures include 24-hour foot and vehicle patrol, self-defense education, escort service, and shuttle buses. In addition, there are informal discussions, pamphlets, posters, and films, emergency telephones, lighted pathways and sidewalks, taxi service, and crime alerts are distributed.

Programs of Study: Pitt awards the B.A., B.S., B.A.S.W., B.Phil., B.S.E., B.S.N., and B.S.Phr. degrees. Master's and doctoral degrees also are awarded. Bachelor's degrees are awarded in BIOLOGICAL SCIENCE (microbiology, neurosciences, and nutrition), COMMUNICATIONS AND THE ARTS (Chinese, classics, communications, English literature, film arts, fine arts, French, German, Italian, Japanese, linguistics, music, Russian, Spanish, speech/debate/rhetoric, and studio art), COMPUTER AND PHYSICAL SCIENCE (astronomy, chemistry, computer science, geology, mathematics, natural sciences, physics, and statistics), EDUCATION (vocational), ENGINEERING AND ENVIRONMENTAL DESIGN (architecture, chemical engineering, civil engineering, electrical/electronics engineering, engineering physics, industrial engineering, materials science, mechanical engineering, and metallurgical engineering), HEALTH PROFESSIONS (medical laboratory technology, medical records administration/services, nursing, occupational therapy, and pharmacy), SOCIAL SCIENCE (African American studies, anthropology, child psychology/development, economics, history, humanities, liberal arts/general studies, philosophy, political science/government, psychology, public administration, religion, social work, sociology, urban studies, and women's studies). Philosophy, history and philosophy of science, anthropology, chemistry, microbiology, physics, psychology, statistics, and Spanish are the strongest academically. Engineering, psychology, and communications have the largest enrollments.

Required: All students in the College of Arts and Sciences must take a minimum of 120 credits, including at least 1 course in literature, music or art, creative expression, philosophy, social science, history, public policy, natural sciences, foreign culture, and non-Western culture. A minimum of 24 credits in the major and a 2.0 GPA are required. Requirements for other schools may vary.

Special: Students may cross-register with 10 member colleges and universities of the Pittsburgh Council on Higher Education Consortium. Internships, study abroad and a semester at sea, a Washington semester, work-study programs, a dual major in business and any other subject in arts and sciences, and student-designed majors are available. There are freshman seminars and a 5-year joint degree in liberal arts/engineering. Nondegree study is available in a wide range of subjects. Two summer sessions are offered. There is a freshman honors program on campus, as well as 28 national honor societies, including Phi Beta Kappa.

Faculty/Classroom: Seventy-two percent of faculty are male; 28%, female.

Admissions: About 76% of the 1993–94 applicants were accepted. The SAT scores for the 1993–94 freshman class were as follows: Verbal—57% below 500, 32% between 500 and 599, 10% between 600 and 700, and 1% above 700; Math—27% below 500, 46% between 500 and 599, 23% between 600 and 700, and 4% above 700. About 50% of the current freshmen were in the top fifth of their class; 87% were in the top two fifths.

Requirements: The SAT I or ACT is required. For admission to the College of Arts and Sciences, students must be graduates of an accredited secondary school. The GED is accepted. Students must have 15 high school academic credits, including 4 units of English, 3 each of mathematics, a laboratory science, and 1 of social studies, plus 4 units in academic electives. Pitt recommends that the student have 3 or more years of a single foreign language. An essay is recommended if the student is seeking scholarship consideration, and music students must have an audition. Requirements for schools other than Arts and Sciences may vary. AP and CLEP credits are accepted. Important factors used in the admissions decision are advanced placement or honor courses, recommendations by school officials, recommendations by alumni, personality and other intangible qualities, and leadership record.

Procedure: Freshmen are admitted to all sessions. Placement tests are given in writing, quantitative and formal reasoning, and foreign languages. They are administered frequently, during the summer, and at Freshman Orientation. Applications are accepted on a rolling basis. However, if applying for financial aid, freshmen should apply by March 1. Application fee is $30. Notification is sent on a rolling basis. There are early admissions and deferred admissions plans.

Transfer: About 700 transfer students enrolled in 1993–94. Applicants for transfer to the College of Arts and Sciences must supply transcripts of all secondary school and college course work and have a minimum GPA of 2.5. An interview is recommended. Grades of C or better transfer for credit. Application deadlines vary by school. The last 30 credits out of 120 must be completed at Pitt.

Visiting: There are regularly scheduled orientations for prospective students. There are guides for informal visits and visitors may sit in on classes and stay overnight at the school. To arrange for a visit, contact the Office of Admissions and Financial Aid at (412) 624-PITT.

Financial Aid: In 1993–94, 60% of continuing students received some form of financial aid. About 58% of continuing students received need-based aid. The average freshman award was $5000. Of that total, scholarships or need-based grants averaged $2500 ($15,000 maximum); loans averaged $2000 ($8000 maximum); and work contracts averaged $1000 ($1500 maximum). Twenty percent of undergraduate students work part-time. Average earnings from campus work for the school year are $900. The average financial indebtedness of the 1992–93 graduate was $9000. Pitt is a member of CSS. The FAF, the college's own financial statement, and the FAFSA are required. The deadline for financial aid applications is March 1.

International Students: There are currently 202 international students enrolled. They must take the TOEFL and achieve a minimum score of 500. The SAT I or ACT may be required.

Computers: The college provides computer facilities for student use. There are 2 computing systems based on DEC VAX mainframes; linked by Pitt Net, they serve the entire university. Seven public computing laboratories, with more than 600 personal computers and workstations, provide access to a variety of software, printers, and graphic plotters. All students may access the system. There are no time limits on using the system. There is a computing and network services fee of $220 per year charged to all full-time students.

Graduates: In 1992–93, 3253 bachelor's degrees were awarded. The most popular majors among graduates were engineering (10%), communications (8%), and psychology (8%). Within an average freshman class, 40% graduate in 4 years, 59% in 5 years, and 64% in 6 years. Some 700 companies recruited on campus in 1992–93.

Admissions Contact: Dr. Betsy A. Porter, Director, Office of Admissions and Financial Aid.

UNIVERSITY OF PITTSBURGH AT BRADFORD
Bradford, PA 16701-2898

C-2
(814) 362-7555
(800) UPB-1787 (out-of-state)

Full-time: 372 men, 464 women	Faculty: 64; IIB, -$
Part-time: 178 men, 247 women	Ph.D.s: 80%
Graduate: none	Student/Faculty: 13 to 1
Year: semesters, summer session	Tuition: $5150 ($10,672)
Application Deadline: July 1	Room & Board: $3900
Freshman Class: 687 applied, 620 accepted, 345 enrolled	
SAT I Verbal/Math: 440/487	**COMPETITIVE**

The University of Pittsburgh at Bradford, established in 1963, is a private, state-related, coeducational liberal arts institution. The library contains 100,000 volumes, 25,000 microform items, and 1700 audiovisual forms, and subscribes to 601 periodicals. Computerized library sources and services include the card catalog, interlibrary loans, and database searching. Special learning facilities include a learning resource center, art gallery, radio station, and sports medicine and rehabilitative therapy clinic. The 165-acre campus is in a small town 160 miles northeast of Pittsburgh and 80 miles south of Buffalo, New York. Including residence halls, there are 26 buildings on campus.

Student Life: About 90% of undergraduates are from Pennsylvania. Students come from 13 states and 2 foreign countries. Eighty-eight percent are white. The average age of freshmen is 19. Twenty percent drop out by the end of their first year; 77% remain to graduate.

Housing: A total of 579 students can be accommodated in college housing. College-sponsored living facilities include single-sex on-campus apartments. On-campus housing is guaranteed for all 4 years. Fifty percent of students live on campus; of those, 70% remain on campus on weekends. All students may keep cars on campus.

Activities: About 5% of men belong to 4 local and 1 national fraternities; about 8% of women belong to 3 local sororities. There are 40 groups on campus, including band, cheerleading, chess, choir, chorus, computers, drama, ethnic, jazz band, literary magazine, newspaper, photography, political, professional, radio and TV, religious, social, social service, student government, and yearbook. Popular campus events include Winter Weekend, Spring Fling, and Alumni Weekend.

Sports: There are 4 intercollegiate sports each for men and women, and 16 intramural sports each. Athletic and recreation facilities include a sports complex with a 1500-seat gymnasium, a weight/fitness center, a soccer field, intramural fields, basketball and tennis courts, and a sand volleyball court.

Disabled Students: The following facilities are available: elevators, special parking, specially equipped rest rooms, lowered drinking fountains, lowered telephones, and specially equipped dormitory space.

Services: In addition to many counseling and information services, tutoring is available in some subjects. There is a writing laboratory.

Campus Safety and Security: Campus safety and security measures include 24-hour foot and vehicle patrol, informal discussions, pamphlets, posters, and films, and lighted pathways and sidewalks.

Programs of Study: Pitt-Bradford awards the B.A. and B.S. degrees. Associate degrees also are awarded. Bachelor's degrees are awarded in BIOLOGICAL SCIENCE (biology/biological science), BUSINESS (business administration and management), COMMUNICATIONS AND THE ARTS (broadcasting, communications, and English), COMPUTER AND PHYSICAL SCIENCE (chemistry, computer programming, computer science, geology, and mathematics), EDUCATION (elementary and secondary), HEALTH PROFESSIONS (predentistry and premedicine), SOCIAL SCIENCE (economics, history, prelaw, psychology, and sociology). Computer science, business, and nursing are the strongest programs academically. Business administration, prehealth-related, and psychology have the largest enrollments.

Required: To graduate, students must complete 120 credits, with 24 to 45 in the major, and maintain a minimum GPA of 2.0. Distribution requirements include 16 credits in humanities, up to 12 in natural sciences and 12 in social sciences, plus 7 in English composition, 3 each in mathematics and computer science, and 1 in freshman seminar.

Special: Students may cross-register with colleges in the University of Pittsburgh system. Internships are required or strongly recommended for all majors. The school offers study abroad, a Washington semester, cooperative programs in engineering, dual majors, nondegree study, and pass/fail options. There are 4 national honor societies on campus.

Faculty/Classroom: Sixty-two percent of faculty are male; 38%, female. All teach undergraduates and 15% also do research. The average class size in an introductory lecture is 35; in a laboratory, 15; and in a regular course offering, 20.

Admissions: About 90% of the 1993–94 applicants were accepted. About 34% of the current freshmen were in the top fifth of their class; 60% were in the top two fifths. There was 1 National Merit semifinalist. Four freshmen graduated first in their class.

Requirements: A minimum GPA of 2.0 is required. The SAT I, with a minimum composite score of 800 (400 verbal and 400 mathematics), or the ACT, with a minimum composite score of 19, is required. Students must be graduates of an accredited secondary school with 16 Carnegie units, including 4 each in English and social studies, 3 each in science and mathematics, and 2 in foreign language. The GED is accepted. An essay is required, and an interview is recommended. AP and CLEP credits are accepted. Important factors used in the admissions decision are advanced placement or honor courses, extracurricular activities record, leadership record, recommendations by school officials, and recommendations by alumni.

Procedure: Freshmen are admitted to all sessions. Entrance exams should be taken during the junior year. Applications should be filed by July 1 for fall entry, December 1 for spring entry, and May 1 for summer entry, along with an application fee of $30. Notification is sent on a rolling basis. There are early decision, early admissions, and deferred admissions plans.

Transfer: About 98 transfer students enrolled in 1993–94. No more than 60 credits from 2-year institutions and no more than half the credits in a student's major or minor may be transferred. Grades of C or better are accepted for credit.

Visiting: There are regularly scheduled orientations for prospective students. There are guides for informal visits and visitors may sit in on classes and stay overnight at the school. To arrange for a visit, contact the Admissions Office at (800) UPB-1787.

Financial Aid: In 1993–94, 69% of all current freshmen received some form of financial aid. About 66% of freshmen received need-based aid. The average freshman award was $6253. Of that total, scholarships or need-based grants averaged $3062; and loans and work contracts averaged $3191. Twenty percent of undergraduate students work part-time. Average earnings from campus work for the school year are $1000. Pitt-Bradford is a member of CSS. The FAFSA is required. The deadline for financial aid applications is March 1.

International Students: International students must take the TOEFL and achieve a minimum score of 550.

Computers: The college provides computer facilities for student use. The mainframes are a DEC VAX 11/780 and a DEC VAX 8350. The campus features 50 computer stations, with 25 linked to the mainframe. All students may access the system. There are no time limits on using the system. The fees are $55 full-time; $15 part-time.

Graduates: Some 31 companies recruited on campus in an earlier year. In an earlier year's graduating class, 8% of the men and 9% of the women were enrolled in graduate school within 6 months of graduation; 90% of the men and 89% of the women had found employment.

Admissions Contact: Philip J. Alletto, Director of Admissions and Financial Aid.

UNIVERSITY OF PITTSBURGH AT GREENSBURG
B-3

Greensburg, PA 15601–5898 (412) 836–9880

Full-time: 522 men, 543 women	Faculty: 56; IIB, -$
Part-time: 187 men, 195 women	Ph.D.s: 77%
Graduate: none	Student/Faculty: 19 to 1
Year: trimesters, summer session	Tuition: $5090 ($10,612)
Application Deadline: open	Room & Board: $3570
Freshman Class: 906 applied, 718 accepted, 328 enrolled	
SAT I Verbal/Math: 422/474	COMPETITIVE

The University of Pittsburgh at Greensburg, established in 1963, is a private, state-related, coeducational institution, offering 13 undergraduate majors that can be completed at Pitt-Greensburg, as well as relocation programs that are begun at Greensburg and completed at another Pitt campus. The library contains 69,103 volumes, 7693 microform items, and 1247 audiovisual forms, and subscribes to 401 periodicals. Computerized library sources and services include the card catalog, interlibrary loans, and database searching. The 165-acre campus is in a suburban area 30 miles east of Pittsburgh. Including residence halls, there are 11 buildings on campus.

Student Life: About 99% of undergraduates are from Pennsylvania. Students come from 7 states. Ninety-three percent are from public schools; 7% from private. Ninety-eight percent are white. Fifty percent are Catholic; 34% Protestant; 10% claim no religious affiliation. The average age of freshmen is 17; all undergraduates, 28. Twenty-eight percent drop out by the end of their first year; 50% remain to graduate.

Housing: A total of 220 students can be accommodated in college housing. College-sponsored living facilities include coed dormitories and on-campus apartments. On-campus housing is guaranteed for all 4 years. Seventy percent of students commute. Alcohol is not permitted. All students may keep cars on campus.

Activities: There are no fraternities or sororities on campus. There are 21 groups on campus, including chess, drama, ethnic, honors, literary magazine, newspaper, social service, and student government. Popular campus events include Humanities Day.

Sports: There are 8 intramural sports for men and 2 for women. Athletic and recreation facilities include a gymnasium, a weight room, playing fields, and tennis and racquetball courts.

Disabled Students: Ninety percent of the campus is accessible to disabled students. The following facilities are available: wheelchair ramps, elevators, special parking, specially equipped rest rooms, lowered drinking fountains, and lowered telephones.

Services: In addition to many counseling and information services, tutoring is available in some subjects, including mathematics and computer science. In addition, there is remedial math, reading, and writing.

Campus Safety and Security: Campus safety and security measures include 24-hour foot and vehicle patrol, escort service, informal discussions, and pamphlets, posters, and films. In addition, there are emergency telephones and lighted pathways and sidewalks.

Programs of Study: Pitt-Greensburg awards the B.A. and B.S. degrees. Bachelor's degrees are awarded in BIOLOGICAL SCIENCE (biology/biological science), BUSINESS (accounting and management science), COMMUNICATIONS AND THE ARTS (creative writing and English literature), COMPUTER AND PHYSICAL SCIENCE (information sciences and systems, mathematics, and natural sciences), SOCIAL SCIENCE (criminal justice, humanities, political science/government, psychology, and social science). Management and psychology are the strongest programs academically. Management has the largest enrollment.

Required: To graduate, students must complete 120 to 126 hours, with 24 to 36 in the major, and maintain a minimum cumulative GPA of 2.0. Five courses each in humanities, social sciences, and natural sciences are required, along with 2 writing courses, 1 speech course, 1 mathematics course, and a critical reasoning course.

Special: Pitt-Greensburg offers cross-registration with the Pittsburgh and Johnstown campuses and with Seton Hill College. Internships are available in all majors and are required for English, writing and criminology. Double majors, student-designed majors, a Washington semester, nondegree study, and pass/fail options are available. There are 2 national honor societies on campus.

Faculty/Classroom: Fifty-six percent of faculty are male; 44%, female. All teach undergraduates and 50% also do research. The average class size in an introductory lecture is 50; in a laboratory, 24; and in a regular course offering, 28.

Admissions: About 79% of the 1993–94 applicants were accepted. The SAT scores for the 1993–94 freshman class were as follows: Verbal—72% below 500, 26% between 500 and 599, and 2% between

600 and 700; Math—59% below 500, 29% between 500 and 599, 10% between 600 and 700, and 2% above 700. About 25% of the current freshmen were in the top fifth of their class; 53% were in the top two fifths. Two freshmen graduated first in their class.

Requirements: Pitt-Greensburg requires applicants to be in the upper 60% of their class. A minimum GPA of 2.0 is required. The SAT I or ACT is required. Students must be graduates of an accredited secondary school. The GED is accepted. Students must complete 15 high school units, including 4 years each of English and social studies and 2 years each of mathematics and science. Three years of foreign language and additional mathematics and science are recommended. An essay is optional; an interview is recommended. AP and CLEP credits are accepted. Important factors used in the admissions decision are advanced placement or honor courses, recommendations by school officials, leadership record, personality, intangible qualities, and parents or siblings attending the school.

Procedure: Freshmen are admitted in the fall, winter, and spring. Entrance exams should be taken by December of the senior year. Application deadlines are open. Application fee is $30. Notification is sent on a rolling basis. There are early admissions and deferred admissions plans.

Transfer: About 100 transfer students enrolled in 1993–94. Transfer applicants must have a minimum GPA of 2.0. The SAT I, at least 15 credits, and an interview are recommended. Grades of C in comparable courses transfer for credit. A total of 30 credits out of 120 to 126 must be completed at Pitt-Greensburg.

Visiting: There are guides for informal visits and visitors may sit in on classes. To arrange for a visit, contact the Admissions Office at (412) 836–9880.

Financial Aid: In 1993–94, 65% of all current freshmen and 55% of continuing students received some form of financial aid. About 65% of freshmen and 55% of continuing students received need-based aid. The average freshman award was $5190. Of that total, scholarships or need-based grants averaged $450 ($500 maximum); loans averaged $1600 ($2250 maximum); and work contracts averaged $1300 (maximum). Fifty-six percent of undergraduate students work part-time. Average earnings from campus work for the school year are $1300. The average financial indebtedness of the 1992–93 graduate was $9000. Pitt-Greensburg is a member of CSS. The college's own financial statement and the FAFSA are required. The deadline for financial aid applications is April 1.

International Students: International students must take the TOEFL and achieve a minimum score of 550.

Computers: The college provides computer facilities for student use. The mainframes include a DEC VAX 9000 in a VAX cluster, a VAX 8800, and a DEC System 5000. All computers are networked locally and through wide-area networks to VMS and UNIX mainframe services. There are 30 DOS, 15 UNIX, and Apple Macintosh computers in the computer center. All students may access the system. There are no time limits on using the system and no fees.

Graduates: In a recent year 205 bachelor's degrees were awarded. The most popular majors among graduates in a recent year were management (23%), psychology (21%), and accounting (15%). Within an average freshman class, 46% graduate in 4 years, 52% in 5 years, and 2% in 6 years.

Admissions Contact: Larry J. Whatule, Director of Admissions.

UNIVERSITY OF PITTSBURGH AT JOHNSTOWN

Johnstown, PA 15904

C-3

(814) 269–7050
(800) 765–4875 (out-of-state)

Full-time: 1264 men, 1240 women	Faculty: 127; IIB, av$
Part-time: 213 men, 291 women	Ph.D.s: 68%
Graduate: none	Student/Faculty: 20 to 1
Year: Modified trimester	Tuition: $5212 ($10,734)
Application Deadline: open	Room & Board: $3702
Freshman Class: 1767 applied, 1229 accepted, 612 enrolled	
SAT I or ACT: required	**VERY COMPETITIVE**

The University of Pittsburgh at Johnstown is a 4-year, coeducational institution offering programs in arts and sciences, education, and engineering technology. In addition to regional accreditation, UPJ has baccalaureate program accreditation with ABET. The library contains 130,173 volumes, 16,249 microform items, and 5710 audiovisual forms, and subscribes to 638 periodicals. Computerized library sources and services include the card catalog, interlibrary loans, and database searching. Special learning facilities include a learning resource center, an art gallery, and a radio station. The 650-acre campus is in a suburban area 70 miles east of Pittsburgh. Including residence halls, there are 28 buildings on campus.

Student Life: Almost all undergraduates are from Pennsylvania. Students come from 12 states. Eighty-nine percent are from public schools; 11% from private. Ninety-five percent are white. Forty-eight percent are Protestant; 47% Catholic. The average age of freshmen

is 18; all undergraduates, 19. Nine percent drop out by the end of their first year; 70% remain to graduate.

Housing: A total of 1400 students can be accommodated in college housing. College-sponsored living facilities include single-sex dormitories, on-campus apartments, off-campus apartments, fraternity houses, and sorority houses. In addition there are special interest houses and fraternities, sororities, clubs, and organizations. On-campus housing is guaranteed for all 4 years. Sixty-two percent of students live on campus; of those, 70% remain on campus on weekends. All students may keep cars on campus.

Activities: About 15% of men belong to 1 local fraternity and 4 national fraternities; about 16% of women belong to 1 local sorority and 4 national sororities. There are 70 groups on campus, including band, cheerleading, chess, choir, chorus, computers, dance, drama, ethnic, honors, literary magazine, musical theater, newspaper, pep band, political, professional, radio and TV, religious, social, social service, student government, symphony, and yearbook. Popular campus events include Homecoming, Ethnic Festival, Greek Week, Engineer Week, Winter Carnival, and Welcome Back Week.

Sports: There are 4 intercollegiate sports each for men and women, and 32 intramural sports for men and 21 for women. Athletic and recreation facilities include a 2300-seat gymnasium, a pool, a dance studio, a weight room, a sauna, a cross-country track, tennis and basketball courts, and a nature area.

Disabled Students: Eighty percent of the campus is accessible to disabled students. The following facilities are available: elevators, special parking, specially equipped rest rooms, and special class scheduling.

Services: In addition to many counseling and information services, tutoring is available in most subjects.

Campus Safety and Security: Campus safety and security measures include 24-hour foot and vehicle patrol, informal discussions, and lighted pathways and sidewalks.

Programs of Study: UPJ awards the B.A. and B.S. degrees. Associate degrees also are awarded. Bachelor's degrees are awarded in BIOLOGICAL SCIENCE (biology/biological science), BUSINESS (accounting, banking and finance, business administration and management, and business economics), COMMUNICATIONS AND THE ARTS (communications, creative writing, dramatic arts, English, and journalism), COMPUTER AND PHYSICAL SCIENCE (chemistry, computer science, geology, and mathematics), EDUCATION (elementary, English, mathematics, science, and secondary), ENGINEERING AND ENVIRONMENTAL DESIGN (civil engineering technology, electrical/electronics engineering technology, and mechanical engineering technology), HEALTH PROFESSIONS (medical laboratory technology, predentistry, and premedicine), SOCIAL SCIENCE (economics, geography, history, political science/government, prelaw, psychology, social science, and sociology). Business economics, biology, education, and engineering technology have the largest enrollments.

Required: For graduation, students must complete 120 to 139 credits, with 30 to 36 credits in the major and a minimum GPA of 2.0. The school requires 12 credits each in humanities, natural sciences, and social sciences.

Special: Students may cross-register with schools in the Pittsburgh Council for Higher Education. Internships are available both on and off campus for credit, pay, or both. The school offers study abroad, a Washington semester, work-study programs, accelerated degree programs, dual majors, student-designed majors, nondegree study, and pass/fail options. There are 6 national honor societies on campus.

Faculty/Classroom: Seventy-five percent of faculty are male; 25%, female. Ninety-three percent teach undergraduates and 70% do research. The average class size in an introductory lecture is 30; in a laboratory, 18; and in a regular course offering, 25.

Admissions: About 70% of the 1993–94 applicants were accepted. About 50% of the current freshmen were in the top fifth of their class; 80% were in the top two fifths. Ten freshmen graduated first in their class.

Requirements: A minimum GPA of 2.0 is required. The SAT I or ACT is required. Applicants must be graduates of an accredited secondary school. The GED is accepted. For admission to freshman standing, 15 academic credits are required, including 4 each of English and history, 3 each of social studies and mathematics (2 of algebra, 1 of geometry preferred), 2 of foreign language, and 1 to 2 of laboratory science. Engineering students must have completed chemistry, physics, and trigonometry. An interview is recommended and an essay is required. AP credits are accepted. Important factors used in the admissions decision are advanced placement or honor courses, leadership record, recommendations by school officials, evidence of special talent, and extracurricular activities record.

Procedure: Freshmen are admitted to all sessions. Entrance exams should be taken in April to June of the junior year or by November of the senior year. Application deadlines are open. The application fee is $35. Notification is sent on a rolling basis. There are early admissions and deferred admissions plans.

Transfer: About 213 transfer students enrolled in 1993–94. Students wishing to transfer must have a minimum GPA of 2.5 and a minimum of 15 credit hours earned. Either the SAT I or ACT is required. Grades of C or better transfer for credit. A total of 30 credits out of 120 to 139 must be completed at UPJ.

Visiting: There are regularly scheduled open houses for prospective students, including 2 programs held on Saturdays in the fall. There are guides for informal visits, and visitors may sit in on classes. To arrange for a visit, contact the Office of Admissions at (814) 269–7050.

Financial Aid: In 1993–94, 84% of all current freshmen and 86% of continuing students received some form of financial aid. About 80% of students received need-based aid. The average freshman award was $3145. Of that total, scholarships or need-based grants averaged $1547 ($5300 maximum); loans averaged $2328 ($3425 maximum); and work contracts averaged $1210 ($1275 maximum). Ten percent of undergraduate students work part-time. Average earnings from campus work for the school year are $1275. The average financial indebtedness of an earlier graduate was $13,250. The PHEAA Application, State Grant, and FAFSA financial statement are required. The deadline for financial aid applications is April 1.

International Students: There is currently 1 international student enrolled. A student must take the TOEFL and achieve a minimum score of 550.

Computers: The university provides computer facilities for student use. The mainframe is a DEC VAX cluster. In addition, 130 microcomputers are available for student use, including Macintosh, IBM, AT&T, and others. Some laboratories have restricted use for education, engineering technology, or computer science majors. Others are open to all students. All students may access the system. There are no time limits on using the system. The fees are $110 per semester.

Graduates: In an earlier year, 583 bachelor's degrees were awarded. The most popular majors among graduates were business economics (23%), elementary education (17%), and biology (8%). Within an average freshman class, 70% graduate in 4 years. In the 1992 graduating class, 9% of the men and women were enrolled in graduate school within 6 months of graduation; 73% of the students had found employment.

Admissions Contact: Thomas J. Wonders, Director of Admissions.

UNIVERSITY OF SCRANTON
E-2

Scranton, PA 18510–4699   (717) 941–7540

Full-time: 1720 men, 1954 women	Faculty: 238; IIA, av$
Part-time: 223 men, 270 women	Ph.D.s: 78%
Graduate: 309 men, 441 women	Student/Faculty: 15 to 1
Year: 4-1-4, summer session	Tuition: $11,615
Application Deadline: March 1	Room & Board: $5456

Freshman Class: 4471 applied, 2942 accepted, 910 enrolled
SAT I Verbal/Math: 509/561   **VERY COMPETITIVE**

The University of Scranton, founded in 1888, is a private, coeducational institution operated by the Jesuit order of the Roman Catholic Church. It offers programs in arts and sciences, management, and health, education, and human resources. There are 4 undergraduate schools and one graduate school. In addition to regional accreditation, the university has baccalaureate program accreditation with APTA, NCATE, and NLN. The library contains 310,910 volumes, 280,802 microform items, and 9054 audiovisual forms, and subscribes to 2022 periodicals. Computerized library sources and services include the card catalog and database searching. Special learning facilities include a learning resource center, art gallery, radio station, TV station, satellite dish for telecommunication reception, music center, language laboratory, and greenhouse. The 50-acre campus is in an urban area 125 miles north of Philadelphia. Including residence halls, there are 68 buildings on campus.

Student Life: About 52% of undergraduates are from out-of-state, mostly the Middle Atlantic. Students come from 29 states, 10 foreign countries, and Canada. Fifty-one percent are from public schools; 49% from private. Ninety-four percent are white. Eighty-four percent are Catholic; 10% Protestant. The average age of freshmen is 18; all undergraduates, 20. Eight percent drop out by the end of their first year; 85% remain to graduate.

Housing: A total of 1875 students can be accommodated in college housing. College-sponsored living facilities include single-sex and coed dormitories and on-campus apartments. In addition, there are language houses, special interest houses, an international house, a residential college, a Spanish house, a French house, a performing arts house, an education house, and a volunteer/service house. On-campus housing is guaranteed for all 4 years. Eighty percent of students live on campus; of those, 75% remain on campus on weekends. Alcohol is not permitted. Upperclassmen may keep cars on campus.

Activities: There are no fraternities or sororities on campus. There are 60 groups on campus, including art, band, cheerleading, chess, choir, chorale, chorus, computers, drama, drill team, ethnic, film, honors, international, jazz band, literary magazine, musical theater, newspaper, orchestra, pep band, photography, political, professional, ra-

dio and TV, religious, social, social service, student government, and yearbook. Popular campus events include Fall Review, Noel Night, Trustee Day (interaction between students and board), O'Hara Day, Spring Band Concert, Parents Day, and Hand-in-Hand Carnival.

Sports: There are 12 intercollegiate sports for men and 8 for women, and 11 intramural sports for men and 8 for women. Athletic and recreation facilities include a 3000-seat gymnasium, basketball courts, wrestling and weight rooms, handball/racquetball and tennis courts, a sand volleyball court, a soccer/lacrosse field, a softball field, a swimming pool, a physical therapy room, and a sauna.

Disabled Students: The entire campus is accessible to disabled students. The following facilities are available: wheelchair ramps, elevators, special parking, specially equipped rest rooms, special class scheduling, lowered drinking fountains, and lowered telephones.

Services: In addition to many counseling and information services, tutoring is available in most subjects. In addition, there is a reader service for the blind, word-processing training, and study skills seminars.

Campus Safety and Security: Campus safety and security measures include 24-hour foot and vehicle patrol, self defense education, escort service, and informal discussions. In addition, there are pamphlets, posters, and films, emergency telephones, and lighted pathways and sidewalks.

Programs of Study: The university awards the B.A. and B.S. degrees. Associate and master's degrees also are awarded. Bachelor's degrees are awarded in BIOLOGICAL SCIENCE (biochemistry, biology/biological science, biophysics, and neurosciences), BUSINESS (accounting, banking and finance, business administration and management, business economics, marketing/retailing/merchandising, and operations research), COMMUNICATIONS AND THE ARTS (advertising, communications, English, French, German, Greek, Latin, and Spanish), COMPUTER AND PHYSICAL SCIENCE (chemistry, computer management, computer science, mathematics, and physics), EDUCATION (elementary, science, and secondary), ENGINEERING AND ENVIRONMENTAL DESIGN (electrical/electronics engineering and preengineering), HEALTH PROFESSIONS (health care administration, medical laboratory technology, nursing, occupational therapy, physical therapy, predentistry, and premedicine), SOCIAL SCIENCE (criminal justice, economics, gerontology, history, human services, international relations, philosophy, political science/government, prelaw, psychology, public administration, sociology, and theological studies). Chemistry, biology, physical therapy, nursing, business, premedicine, prelaw, English, and computer science are the strongest programs academically. Biology, accounting, communication, nursing, physical therapy, and psychology have the largest enrollments.

Required: Students take distribution requirements according to their general area of study. All are required to take philosophy/theology, physical education, English composition, and speech. A total of 127 to 150 credit hours is required for graduation, with 36 in the major. The minimum GPA is 2.0.

Special: There are cooperative programs with the University of Detroit/Mercy and Widener University, and cross-registration with 27 other Jesuit colleges. Internships are available in all career-oriented majors, and study abroad is offered in many countries. There is a Washington semester for history and political science majors. Students may earn a B.A.-B.S. degree in economics and accelerated degrees in history, chemistry, and biochemistry. The university also offers dual, student-designed, and interdisciplinary majors, including chemistry-business, chemistry-computers, electronics-business, and international language-business, credit by examination and for life/military/work experience, nondegree study, and pass/fail options. There is also a special Jesuit-oriented general education program. There is a freshman honors program on campus, as well as 26 national honor societies. Two departments have honors programs.

Faculty/Classroom: Seventy-three percent of faculty are male; 27%, female. Ninety-seven percent teach undergraduates and 80% do research. No introductory courses are taught by graduate students. The average class size in an introductory lecture is 25; in a laboratory, 12; and in a regular course offering, 25.

Admissions: About 66% of the 1993–94 applicants were accepted. The SAT scores for the 1993–94 freshman class were as follows: Verbal—44% below 500, 44% between 500 and 599, 11% between 600 and 700, and 1% above 700; Math—15% below 500, 56% between 500 and 599, 26% between 600 and 700, and 4% above 700. About 48% of the current freshmen were in the top fifth of their class; 75% were in the top two fifths. There were 5 National Merit finalists and 5 semifinalists. Eleven freshmen graduated first in their class.

Requirements: The SAT I or ACT is required. In addition, applicants should be graduates of an accredited secondary school, though in some cases a GED may be accepted. They should complete 18 academic or Carnegie units, including 4 years of high school English, 3 each of mathematics, science, history, and social studies, and 2 of foreign language. Two letters of reference/recommendation are required. Essays are not required, but for some students the additional information can be of assistance. Interviews are recommended but

are not a factor in admissions. AP and CLEP credits are accepted. Important factors used in the admissions decision are leadership record, advanced placement or honor courses, extracurricular activities record, evidence of special talent, and parents or siblings attending the school.

Procedure: Freshmen are admitted in the fall and spring. Entrance exams should be taken by fall of the senior year. Applications should be filed by March 1 for fall entry, December 15 for spring entry, and May 1 for summer entry, along with an application fee of $30. Notification of early decision is sent December 1; regular decision, on a rolling basis. There are early decision, early admissions, and deferred admissions plans. About 235 early decision candidates were accepted for the 1993–94 class.

Transfer: More than 100 transfer students enrolled in 1993–94. Transfer applicants should have earned at least 15 credit hours with a GPA of at least 2.5. A total of 63 credits out of 127 to 150 must be completed at the university.

Visiting: There are regularly scheduled orientations for prospective students, including private interviews conducted Monday through Friday throughout the school year. Group information sessions are offered on Saturdays and holidays in the fall and spring and during the week in the summer. There are guides for informal visits and visitors may sit in on classes and stay overnight at the school. To arrange for a visit, contact the Office of Admissions at (717) 941-7540.

Financial Aid: In 1993–94, 80% of all current freshmen and 80% of continuing students received some form of financial aid. About 57% of freshmen and 52% of continuing students received need-based aid. The average freshman award was $9275. Of that total, scholarships or need-based grants averaged $4300 ($11,725 maximum); loans averaged $3300 ($3625 maximum); and work contracts averaged $1200 ($1500 maximum). Sixteen percent of undergraduate students work part-time. Average earnings from campus work for the school year are $800. The average financial indebtedness of the 1992–93 graduate was $9500. The college's own financial statement, the FAFSA, and the PHEAA for Pennsylvania residents are required. The deadline for financial aid applications is February 15.

International Students: There are currently 170 international students enrolled. They must take the TOEFL and achieve a minimum score of 525.

Computers: The college provides computer facilities for student use. The mainframe is a DEC VAX 6610. There are more than 300 PCs and terminals on campus available for student use in the library, academic buildings, and residence halls. The campus is completely networked. All students may access the system 24 hours a day. There are no time limits on using the system and no fees.

Graduates: In 1992–93, 899 bachelor's degrees were awarded. The most popular majors among graduates were accounting (10%), communication (7%), and biology (7%). Within an average freshman class, 75% graduate in 4 years and 10% in 5 years. Some 100 companies recruited on campus in 1992–93. In the 1992 graduating class, 31% of the men and 22% of the women were enrolled in graduate school within 6 months of graduation; 63% of the men and 74% of the women had found employment.

Admissions Contact: Rev. Bernard R. McIlhenny, S.J.

UNIVERSITY OF THE ARTS
F-3

Philadelphia, PA 19102

(215) 875-4808

(800) 272-3790 (out-of-state)

Full-time: 543 men, 602 women	Faculty: 91; IIB, -$
Part-time: 19 men, 20 women	Ph.Ds: 48%
Graduate: 35 men, 83 women	Student/Faculty: 13 to 1
Year: semesters, summer session	Tuition: $12,400
Application Deadline: open	Room: $3750
Freshman Class: 938 applied, 821 accepted, 291 enrolled	
SAT I Verbal/Math: 443/452	SPECIAL

University of the Arts, founded in 1870, is a private, nonprofit institution offering education and professional training in visual and performing arts, with an emphasis on the humanities and interdisciplinary exploration. There are 2 undergraduate and 2 graduate schools. In addition to regional accreditation, UArts has baccalaureate program accreditation with NASAD and NASM. The 3 libraries contain 100,674 volumes, 788 microform items, and 12,396 audiovisual forms, and subscribe to 267 periodicals. Computerized library sources and services include database searching. Special learning facilities include an art gallery, several theaters, and music, animation, and recording studios. The campus is in an urban area in Philadelphia. Including residence halls, there are 8 buildings on campus.

Student Life: About 56% of undergraduates are from out-of-state, mostly the Middle Atlantic. Students come from 37 states, 24 foreign countries, and Canada. Seventy-nine percent are white. The average age of freshmen is 18; all undergraduates, 21. Twenty-three percent drop out by the end of their first year; 47% remain to graduate.

Housing: A total of 262 students can be accommodated in college housing. College-sponsored living facilities include coed on-campus apartments. On-campus housing is guaranteed for the freshman year only and is available on a first-come, first-served basis. Priority is given to out-of-town students. Seventy-nine percent of students commute. Alcohol is not permitted.

Activities: There are no fraternities or sororities on campus. There are 20 groups on campus, including band, choir, chorale, chorus, dance, drama, ethnic, jazz band, musical theater, opera, orchestra, religious, student government, and symphony. Popular campus events include exhibitions, performances, and international visual and performing arts seminars.

Sports: There is 1 intramural sport each for men and women. Athletic facilities are available at the YM/YWHA adjacent to the campus, for which the university provides free membership.

Disabled Students: All of the campus is accessible to disabled students. The following facilities are available: wheelchair ramps, elevators, specially equipped rest rooms, lowered drinking fountains, and lowered telephones.

Services: In addition to many counseling and information services, tutoring is available in every subject. In addition, there is remedial math, reading, and writing, and assistance with study skills.

Campus Safety and Security: Campus safety and security measures include 24-hour foot and vehicle patrol, self defense education, escort service, and informal discussions. In addition, there are pamphlets, posters, films, and lighted pathways and sidewalks.

Programs of Study: UArts awards the B.S., B.F.A., B.F.A. in Dance Education, and B.M. degrees. Associate and master's degrees also are awarded. Bachelor's degrees are awarded in COMMUNICATIONS AND THE ARTS (ceramic art and design, dance, fiber/textiles/weaving, film arts, graphic design, illustration, industrial design, jazz, metal/jewelry, music performance, music theory and composition, painting, performing arts, photography, printmaking, and sculpture), ENGINEERING AND ENVIRONMENTAL DESIGN (architecture). Dance, music performance, illustration, and theater have the largest enrollments.

Required: All students must complete a core program consisting of humanities courses in language and expression, literature, arts history and social studies, philosophy and science, and related arts. A GPA of 2.0 overall for 125 to 143 credits, with 24 to 45 in the major depending on the curriculum, must be achieved for graduation.

Special: UArts offers cross-registration with the 10-member Consortium East Coast Art Schools as well as with the Pennsylvania Academy of Fine Arts and Philadelphia College of Textiles and Sciences. Internships may be arranged, and there are extensive summer programs and opportunities to study abroad.

Faculty/Classroom: Sixty percent of faculty are male; 40%, female. All faculty both teach and do research. No introductory courses are taught by graduate students. The average class size in an introductory lecture is 25 and in a regular course offering, 30.

Admissions: About 88% of the 1993–94 applicants were accepted. The SAT scores for the 1993–94 freshman class were as follows: Verbal—74% below 500, 20% between 500 and 599, and 6% between 600 and 700; Math—66% below 500, 24% between 500 and 599, and 10% between 600 and 700. About 42% of the current freshmen were in the top fifth of their class; 60% were in the top two fifths.

Requirements: The SAT I or ACT is required. Students must have graduated from an accredited secondary school or hold a GED certificate. A minimum of 16 academic credits consisting of 4 each in English and mathematics, and 2 each in music or art and history are recommended. An essay and either a portfolio or an audition are required of all applicants. An interview is recommeded. AP and CLEP credits are accepted. Important factors used in the admissions decision are evidence of special talent, advanced placement or honor courses, personality, intangible qualities, recommendations by alumni, and recommendations by school officials.

Procedure: Freshmen are admitted fall and spring. Entrance exams should be taken late in the junior year or early in the senior year. Application deadlines are open. Application fee is $30. Notification is sent on a rolling basis. There are early admissions and deferred admissions plans.

Transfer: About 120 transfer students enrolled in 1993–94. Candidates must have a minimum 2.0 GPA overall. An interview is recommended, as well as test scores for either the SAT I or ACT if English composition has not been completed. A total of 48 credits out of 125 to 143 must be completed at UArts.

Visiting: There are regularly scheduled orientations for prospective students, including a spring and fall open house. There are guides for informal visits and visitors may sit in on classes and stay overnight at the school. To arrange for a visit, contact the Office of Admissions at (215) 875-4808.

Financial Aid: In a recent year, 90% of all current freshmen and 80% of continuing students received some form of financial aid. About 68% of freshmen and 79% of continuing students received need-based aid. The average freshman award was $3250. Of that to-

tal, scholarships or need-based grants averaged $3250 ($4000 maximum); loans averaged $2625 (maximum); and work contracts averaged $1500 ($2000 maximum). Twenty-eight percent of undergraduate students work part-time. Average earnings from campus work for the school year are $1500. The average financial indebtedness of a recent graduate was $16,250. UArts is a member of CSS. The FAF and AFSGFSA are required. The deadline for financial aid applications is February 15.

International Students: There are currently 80 international students enrolled. The school actively recruits these students. They must take the TOEFL. The student must also take the SAT I or the ACT.

Computers: The mainframe is a DEC PDP 11. Students have access to 82 nonnetworked personal computers located in residence halls, student services, electronic media centers, and departmental laboratories. None may access the system. There are no fees.

Graduates: In a recent class, 278 bachelor's degrees were awarded. The most popular majors among graduates were illustration (25%), dance (23%), and theater (11%). Within an average freshman class, 47% graduate in 4 years, 52% in 5 years, and 53% in 6 years.

Admissions Contact: Barbara Elliott, Director of Admissions.

URSINUS COLLEGE
Collegeville, PA 19426

E-3

(215) 489-4111

Full-time: 553 men, 578 women	Faculty: 93; IIB, +$
Part-time: 7 men, 10 women	Ph.D.s: 91%
Graduate: none	Student/Faculty: 12 to 1
Year: semesters, summer session	Tuition: $14,265
Application Deadline: February 15	Room & Board: $4900
Freshman Class: 1399 applied, 1026 accepted, 308 enrolled	
SAT I or ACT: required	VERY COMPETITIVE

Ursinus College, founded in 1869, is a private college affiliated with the United Church of Christ. It offers programs in the liberal arts. The library contains 185,000 volumes, 155,000 microform items, and 17,500 audiovisual forms, and subscribes to 900 periodicals. Computerized library sources and services include the card catalog, interlibrary loans, and database searching. Special learning facilities include an art gallery, a radio station, and a TV station. The 140-acre campus is in a suburban area 30 miles west of Philadelphia. Including residence halls, there are 48 buildings on campus.

Student Life: About 65% of undergraduates are from Pennsylvania. Students come from 23 states and 13 foreign countries. Seventy-five percent are from public schools; 25% from private. Eighty-eight percent are white. Forty percent are Catholic; 21% claim no religious affiliation. The average age of freshmen is 18; all undergraduates, 20. Eight percent drop out by the end of their first year; 76% remain to graduate.

Housing: A total of 1100 students can be accommodated in college housing. College-sponsored living facilities include single-sex and coed dormitories and on-campus apartments. In addition there are honors houses, language houses, and special interest houses. On-campus housing is guaranteed for all 4 years. Ninety percent of students live on campus; of those, 80% remain on campus on weekends. All students may keep cars on campus.

Activities: About 40% of men belong to 8 local fraternities and 1 national fraternity; about 40% of women belong to 5 local sororities. There are 41 groups on campus, including art, band, cheerleading, chess, choir, chorale, chorus, computers, dance, drama, ethnic, film, gay, honors, international, jazz band, literary magazine, musical theater, newspaper, orchestra, pep band, political, professional, radio and TV, religious, social, social service, student government, and yearbook. Popular campus events include Homecoming, Parents Day, Founders Day, and Air Band competition.

Sports: There are 10 intercollegiate sports each for men and women, and 14 intramural sports for men and 12 for women. Athletic and recreation facilities include a gymnasium, racquetball and squash courts, a weight room, dance rooms, tennis courts, and all types of playing fields.

Disabled Students: Most of the campus is accessible to disabled students. The following facilities are available: wheelchair ramps, elevators, special parking, specially equipped rest rooms, special class scheduling, and lowered drinking fountains and telephones.

Services: In addition to many counseling and information services, tutoring is available in every subject.

Campus Safety and Security: Campus safety and security measures include 24-hour foot and vehicle patrol, escort service, pamphlets, posters, films, and lighted pathways and sidewalks.

Programs of Study: Ursinus awards the B.A. and B.S. degrees. Bachelor's degrees are awarded in BIOLOGICAL SCIENCE (biology/biological science), BUSINESS (accounting, business administration and management, and business economics), COMMUNICATIONS AND THE ARTS (communications, English, French, German, music, and Spanish), COMPUTER AND PHYSICAL SCIENCE (chemistry, computer science, mathematics, and physics), EDUCATION (secondary), HEALTH PROFESSIONS (premedicine), SOCIAL

SCIENCE (anthropology, economics, history, international relations, political science/government, prelaw, psychology, religion, and sociology). Sciences, English, and foreign language are the strongest academically. Economics, business administration, sciences, and psychology have the largest enrollments.

Required: All students must fulfill requirements in English composition, speech, mathematics or logic, foreign language, humanities, natural and social science, and physical education. A total of 128 semester hours, with 32 to 40 in the major, is required with a GPA of 2.0.

Special: The college offers study abroad, student-designed majors, internships, a Washington semester, a Harrisburg and Philadelphia semester, dual majors, and a 3–2 engineering degree. There are 14 national honor societies on campus, including Phi Beta Kappa.

Faculty/Classroom: Fifty-seven percent of faculty are male; 43%, female. All faculty both teach and do research. The average class size in a regular course offering is 20.

Admissions: About 75% of the 1993–94 applicants were accepted. The SAT I scores for the freshman class were as follows: Verbal—42% below 500, 45% between 500 and 599, 12% between 600 and 700, and 1% above 700; Math—14% below 500, 48% between 500 and 599, 35% between 600 and 700, and 3% above 700. About 68% of the current freshmen were in the top fifth of their class; 92% were in the top two fifths.

Requirements: The SAT I, with a minimum score of 450 verbal, 500 mathematics, or ACT is required. SAT II: Subject tests are recommended. A GED is accepted. Applicants should prepare with 16 academic credits, including 4 years of English, 3 years of mathematics, 2 years of foreign language, and 1 year each of science and social studies. An interview is recommended. AP and CLEP credits are accepted. Important factors used in the admissions decision are advanced placement or honor courses, recommendations by school officials, leadership record, evidence of special talent, and extracurricular activities record.

Procedure: Freshmen are admitted fall and spring. Entrance exams should be taken in the junior or senior year. Early decision applications should be filed by December 15; regular applications, by February 15 for fall entry and December 1 for spring entry, along with an application fee of $30. Notification of early decision is sent January 1; regular decision, April 1. There are early decision, early admissions, and deferred admissions plans. Some 80 early decision candidates were accepted for the 1993–94 class. A waiting list is an active part of the admissions procedure, with about 5% of applicants on the list.

Transfer: About 15 transfer students enrolled in 1993–94. Transfer applicants must submit transcripts from all institutions attended. A dean's letter is recommended, as is a listing of courses taken. A total of 64 credits out of 128 must be completed at Ursinus.

Visiting: There are regularly scheduled orientations for prospective students, including a campus interview and a tour. There are guides for informal visits, and visitors may sit in on classes and stay overnight at the school. To arrange for a visit, contact the Admissions Office at (215) 489-4111.

Financial Aid: In 1993–94, 88% of all current freshmen and 80% of continuing students received some form of financial aid. About 79% of freshmen and 65% of continuing students received need-based aid. The average freshman award was $13,569. Of that total, scholarships or need-based grants averaged $9059 ($14,100 maximum); loans averaged $3512 ($4125 maximum); and work contracts averaged $998 ($2000 maximum). Fifty percent of undergraduate students work part-time. The average financial indebtedness of a graduate was $12,000. Ursinus is a member of CSS. The FAF and FAFSA are required. The deadline for financial aid applications is February 15.

International Students: There are currently 23 international students enrolled. The school actively recruits these students. They must take the TOEFL and achieve a minimum score of 550.

Computers: The college provides computer facilities for student use. The mainframe is a DEC VAX. Microcomputers are available for student use. All students may access the system about 102 hours per week. There are no time limits and no fees.

Graduates: In 1992–93, 323 bachelor's degrees were awarded. The most popular majors among graduates were social sciences (17%), economics (15%), and biological sciences (12%). Within an average freshman class, 76% graduate in 4 years and 78% in 5 years. In the 1992 graduating class, 21% of the men and women were enrolled in graduate school within 6 months of graduation; 72% had found employment.

Admissions Contact: Richard G. DiFeliciantonio, Director of Admissions.

VILLANOVA UNIVERSITY
Villanova, PA 19085-1672

F-4

(610) 519-4000
(800) 338-7927 (out-of-state)

Full-time: 3052 men, 3102 women
Part-time: 744 men, 745 women
Graduate: 1282 men, 1217 women
Year: semesters, summer session
Application Deadline: January 15
Freshman Class: 7042 applied, 5588 accepted, 1478 enrolled
SAT I or ACT: required

Faculty: 522; IIA, +$
Ph.D.s: 90%
Student/Faculty: 12 to 1
Tuition: $15,200
Room & Board: $6200

HIGHLY COMPETITIVE

Villanova University, founded in 1842, is a coeducational college affiliated with the Catholic Church. It offers undergraduate programs in arts and sciences, commerce and finance, engineering, and nursing. There are 4 undergraduate and 5 graduate schools. In addition to regional accreditation, Villanova has baccalaureate program accreditation with AACSB, ABET, and NLN. The library contains 590,000 volumes, 1,060,000 microform items, and 25,800 audiovisual forms, and subscribes to 2900 periodicals. Computerized library sources and services include the card catalog, interlibrary loans, and database searching. Special learning facilities include an art gallery, a planetarium, a radio station, and 2 observatories. The 222-acre campus is in a suburban area 12 miles west of Philadelphia. Including residence halls, there are 55 buildings on campus.

Student Life: About 70% of undergraduates are from out-of-state, mostly the Middle Atlantic. Students come from 48 states, 52 foreign countries, and Canada. Fifty percent are from public schools; 50% from private. Ninety percent are white. Most are Catholic. The average age of freshmen is 18; all undergraduates, 20. Six percent drop out by the end of their first year; 87% remain to graduate.

Housing: A total of 3850 students can be accommodated in college housing. College-sponsored living facilities include single-sex and coed dormitories and on-campus apartments. On-campus housing is available on a lottery system for seniors only. Sixty-five percent of students live on campus; of those, 90% remain on campus on weekends. Alcohol is not permitted. Upperclassmen may keep cars on campus.

Activities: About 30% of men belong to 1 local fraternity and 13 national fraternities; about 48% of women belong to 7 national sororities. There are 150 groups on campus, including art, band, cheerleading, choir, chorale, chorus, computers, dance, drama, drill team, ethnic, honors, international, jazz band, literary magazine, marching band, musical theater, newspaper, pep band, photography, political, professional, radio, religious, social, social service, student government, and yearbook. Popular campus events include Spring Fever Week, Merry Christmas Villanova Week, Balloon Day, Sibling Weekend, International Studies Week, Parents Weekend, Homecoming, Fall Festival, Special Olympics, and Honors Week.

Sports: There are 12 intercollegiate sports for men and 9 for women, and 11 intramural sports each for men and women. Athletic and recreation facilities include a 200-meter indoor track, a swimming pool, basketball, volleyball, and tennis courts, weight rooms, and a field house. The football stadium seats 11,800; the gymnasium, 6500.

Disabled Students: All of the campus is accessible to disabled students. The following facilities are available: wheelchair ramps, elevators, special parking, specially equipped rest rooms, special class scheduling, and lowered drinking fountains and telephones.

Services: In addition to many counseling and information services, tutoring is available in every subject.

Campus Safety and Security: Campus safety and security measures include 24-hour foot and vehicle patrol, escort service, shuttle buses, and informal discussions. In addition, there are pamphlets, posters, films, emergency telephones, lighted pathways and sidewalks, public safety officers on duty all night in women's residence halls, and a card-access system to all residence halls.

Programs of Study: Villanova awards the B.A. and B.S. degrees. Associate, master's, and doctoral degrees also are awarded. Bachelor's degrees are awarded in BIOLOGICAL SCIENCE (biology/biological science), BUSINESS (accounting, banking and finance, business administration and management, business economics, and marketing/retailing/merchandising), COMMUNICATIONS AND THE ARTS (classics, communications, English, French, German, and Spanish), COMPUTER AND PHYSICAL SCIENCE (astronomy, astrophysics, chemistry, computer science, mathematics, and physics), EDUCATION (elementary, secondary, and special), ENGINEERING AND ENVIRONMENTAL DESIGN (chemical engineering, civil engineering, electrical/electronics engineering, and mechanical engineering), HEALTH PROFESSIONS (nursing, optometry, physical therapy, and premedicine), SOCIAL SCIENCE (economics, ethnic studies, geography, history, human services, international studies, Islamic studies, peace studies, philosophy, political science/government, psychology, religion, and sociology). Sciences, engineering, and liberal arts are the strongest academically. Liberal arts, commerce, and finance have the largest enrollments.

Required: All students are required to take core courses in English, history, religious studies, sciences, philosophy, and mathematics. Students must complete a total of 122 credit hours with a 2.0 overall GPA and a 2.2 GPA in the major.

Special: There is a co-op program in elementary education with Rosemont College and one in special education with Cabrini College. Internships are available in the Philadelphia area as well as in New York City and Washington. Students may study abroad in the British Isles, the Pacific Rim, East Africa, the former Soviet Union, and the Caribbean. The college offers a Washington semester, dual majors, a general studies degree, and credit by examination. There is a freshman honors program on campus, as well as 28 national honor societies, including Phi Beta Kappa. Two departments have honors programs.

Faculty/Classroom: Seventy-four percent of faculty are male; 26%, female. All teach undergraduates and 8% both teach and do research. No introductory courses are taught by graduate students. The average class size in an introductory lecture is 24; in a laboratory, 17; and in a regular course offering, 24.

Admissions: About 79% of the 1993-94 applicants were accepted. The SAT scores for the freshman class were as follows: Verbal—35% below 500, 49% between 500 and 599, 14% between 600 and 700, and 1% above 700; Math—8% below 500, 45% between 500 and 599, 37% between 600 and 700, and 10% above 700. About 57% of the current freshmen were in the top fifth of their class; 89% were in the top two fifths. There were 12 National Merit finalists. Twenty-three freshmen graduated first in their class.

Requirements: The SAT I or ACT is required. The applicant must be a graduate of an accredited secondary school and should have completed 16 academic units. The specific courses required vary according to college. A GED is accepted. Applicants to the College of Arts and Sciences must also take SAT II: Subject test in foreign language. An essay is required. AP and CLEP credits are accepted. Important factors used in the admissions decision are advanced placement or honor courses, recommendations by school officials, parents or siblings attending the school, geographic diversity, and leadership record.

Procedure: Freshmen are admitted in the fall. Entrance exams should be taken by December of the senior year. Early decision applications should be filed by December 1; regular applications, by January 15 for fall entry, along with an application fee of $40. Notification of early action is sent January 15; regular decision, April 1. There are early action, early admissions, and deferred admissions plans. About 100 early action candidates were accepted for the 1993-94 class. A waiting list is an active part of the admissions procedure, with about 18% of applicants on the list.

Transfer: About 110 transfer students enrolled in 1993-94. Applicants must be sophomores or upperclassmen who have completed at least 30 credit hours and have a GPA of at least 3.0 for the College of Arts and Sciences, and 2.5 for the colleges of Nursing, Engineering, and Commerce and Finance. A total of 60 credits out of 122 must be completed at Villanova.

Visiting: There are regularly scheduled orientations for prospective students, including campus tours and information sessions conducted several times daily and on selected Saturdays throughout the academic year. There are guides for informal visits and visitors may sit in on classes and stay overnight at the school. To arrange for a visit, contact the Office of Undergraduate Admission at (610) 519-4000 or (800) 338-7927.

Financial Aid: In 1993-94, 62% of all current freshmen and 57% of continuing students received some form of financial aid. About 58% of freshmen and 46% of continuing students received need-based aid. The average freshman award was $11,543. Of that total, scholarships or need-based grants averaged $7933 ($10,000 maximum); loans averaged $4154 ($20,965 maximum); and work contracts averaged $1742 ($2000 maximum). Twenty-two percent of undergraduate students work part-time. The average financial indebtedness of a recent graduate was $10,000. Villanova is a member of CSS. The FAF, FFS or SFS, the college's own financial statement and the parent and student federal income tax return are required. The deadline for financial aid applications is March 15.

International Students: There are currently 280 international students enrolled. The school actively recruits these students. They must take the TOEFL and achieve a minimum score of 550.

Computers: The college provides computer facilities for student use. The mainframes are an IBM 4381-13 and a DEC VAX 11/780, 11/785, and 8200. There are also 150 IBM, Zenith, and Apple microcomputers available in 4 classroom buildings. Students also have access to microcomputers in academic offices. All students may access the system. There are no time limits and no fees.

Graduates: In 1992-93, 1843 bachelor's degrees were awarded. The most popular majors among graduates were business administration (17%), accounting (14%), and political science (9%). Within an average freshman class, 84% graduate in 4 years and 87% in 5 years. Some 236 companies recruited on campus in 1992-93. In the 1992

graduating class, 13% of the graduates were enrolled in graduate school within 6 months of graduation.

Admissions Contact: Stephen R. Merritt, Undergraduate Admission.

WASHINGTON AND JEFFERSON COLLEGE   A-3
Washington, PA 15301   (412) 223-6025

Full-time: 603 men, 507 women	Faculty: 85; IIB, +$
Part-time: 10 men, 9 women	Ph.D.s: 73%
Graduate: none	Student/Faculty: 13 to 1
Year: 4-1-4, summer session	Tuition: $15,620
Application Deadline: March 1	Room & Board: $3740
Freshman Class: 1308 applied, 1100 accepted, 332 enrolled	
SAT I or ACT: required	COMPETITIVE

Washington and Jefferson College, founded in 1781, is a private, co-educational institution offering instruction in liberal arts. The library contains 195,000 volumes, 5400 microform items, and 2950 audiovisual forms, and subscribes to 715 periodicals. Computerized library sources and services include the card catalog, interlibrary loans, and database searching. Special learning facilities include an art gallery, radio station, and biological field station. The 35-acre campus is in a small town 25 miles south of Pittsburgh. Including residence halls, there are 36 buildings on campus.

Student Life: About 65% of undergraduates are from Pennsylvania. Students come from 30 states, 7 foreign countries, and Canada. Seventy percent are from public schools; 30% from private. Ninety percent are white. Fifty-five percent are Catholic; 30% Protestant. The average age of freshmen is 18; all undergraduates, 20. Seven percent drop out by the end of their first year; 84% remain to graduate.

Housing: A total of 950 students can be accommodated in college housing. College-sponsored living facilities include single-sex and coed dormitories and fraternity houses. On-campus housing is guaranteed for all 4 years. Eighty-five percent of students live on campus; of those, 90% remain on campus on weekends. Alcohol is not permitted. All students may keep cars on campus.

Activities: About 55% of men belong to 10 national fraternities; about 65% of women belong to 4 national sororities. There are 77 groups on campus, including art, cheerleading, choir, chorale, chorus, computers, drama, jazz band, literary magazine, newspaper, orchestra, pep band, political, professional, radio and TV, religious, social, social service, student government, and yearbook. Popular campus events include Homecoming, Carnival, Bluegrass, and Greek Week.

Sports: There are 10 intercollegiate sports for men and 6 for women, and 8 intramural sports for men and 7 for women. Athletic and recreation facilities include swimming and diving pools, a track, a weight room, football, baseball, and soccer fields, and basketball, volleyball, squash, and racquetball courts. The stadium seats 4000, the largest auditorium/arena, 3500.

Disabled Students: The following facilities are available: special class scheduling.

Services: In addition to many counseling and information services, tutoring is available in most subjects. In addition, there is a reader service for the blind, and remedial math, reading, and writing.

Campus Safety and Security: Campus safety and security measures include 24-hour foot and vehicle patrol, escort service, informal discussions, and pamphlets, posters, and films. In addition, there are emergency telephones and lighted pathways and sidewalks.

Programs of Study: Washington and Jefferson awards the B.A. degree. Bachelor's degrees are awarded in BIOLOGICAL SCIENCE (biology/biological science), BUSINESS (accounting and business administration and management), COMMUNICATIONS AND THE ARTS (English, French, German, and Spanish), COMPUTER AND PHYSICAL SCIENCE (chemistry, computer science, mathematics, and physics), EDUCATION (art, foreign languages, and secondary), HEALTH PROFESSIONS (medical laboratory technology, predentistry, and premedicine), SOCIAL SCIENCE (economics, history, philosophy, political science/government, prelaw, psychology, and sociology). Prelaw and premedicine are the strongest programs academically. Business, English, psychology, and biology have the largest enrollments.

Required: Students are required to take a core of 14 courses (56 credit hours) in history/philosophy/religion, art/music, language, literature, science/mathematics, economics/business, political science, and biology. Other requirements include physical education, freshman English, and freshman forum. A total of 36 courses (144 credit hours), with 8 to 10 courses in the major, is required for graduation, as is a minimum 2.0 GPA.

Special: Washington and Jefferson offers study abroad, internships in all majors, a Washington semester with American University, dual and student-designed majors, credit by examination, and pass/fail options. There is a 3-2 engineering program with Case Western Reserve University and Washington University in St. Louis. The college offers special human resources management and entrepreneurial

studies programs. There is also a 3-4 podiatry program with Pennsylvania College of Podiatry and a 3-4 optometry program with Pennsylvania College of Optometry. There are 11 national honor societies on campus, including Phi Beta Kappa.

Faculty/Classroom: Seventy-five percent of faculty are male; 25%, female. All teach undergraduates. The average class size in an introductory lecture is 30; in a laboratory, 16; and in a regular course offering, 24.

Admissions: About 84% of the 1993-94 applicants were accepted. The SAT scores for the 1993-94 freshman class were as follows: Verbal—44% below 500, 47% between 500 and 599, 7% between 600 and 700, and 2% above 700; Math—35% below 500, 43% between 500 and 599, 18% between 600 and 700, and 4% above 700. About 56% of the current freshmen were in the top fifth of their class; 84% were in the top two fifths. There were 4 National Merit semifinalists. About 32 freshmen graduated first in their class.

Requirements: Washington and Jefferson requires applicants to be in the upper 40% of their class. The SAT I or ACT is required, plus SAT II: Subject tests in writing and 2 other subjects if submitting the SAT I. A GED is accepted. Applicants must complete 15 academic credits or Carnegie units, including 3 credits each of English and mathematics, 2 of foreign language, and 1 of science. An essay and interview are recommended. AP and CLEP credits are accepted. Important factors used in the admissions decision are advanced placement or honor courses, leadership record, recommendations by school officials, evidence of special talent, and personality, intangible qualities.

Procedure: Freshmen are admitted in the fall, winter, and spring. Entrance exams should be taken in the junior or senior year. Early decision applications should be filed by November 1; regular applications, by March 1 for fall entry, January 1 for winter entry, February 1 for spring entry, and June 1 for summer entry, along with an application fee of $25. Notification of early decision is sent November 15; regular decision, February 1. There are early decision, early admissions, and deferred admissions plans. About 38 early decision candidates were accepted for the 1993-94 class. A waiting list is an active part of the admissions procedure, with about 7% of applicants on the list.

Transfer: About 20 transfer students enrolled in 1993-94. Transfer applicants must have a GPA of at least 2.5 and must take the SAT I or ACT. A total of 18 courses (72 credit hours) out of 36 must be completed at Washington and Jefferson.

Visiting: There are regularly scheduled orientations for prospective students. There are guides for informal visits and visitors may sit in on classes and stay overnight at the school. To arrange for a visit, contact the Admission Office at (412) 223-6025.

Financial Aid: In 1993-94 70% of all current freshmen and 70% of continuing students received some form of financial aid. About 70% of freshmen and 70% of continuing students received need-based aid. The average freshman award was $13,000. Of that total, scholarships or need-based grants averaged $5700; loans averaged $2625 ($4125 maximum); and work contracts averaged $1000 (maximum). Fifteen percent of undergraduate students work part-time. Average earnings from campus work for the school year are $1000. Washington and Jefferson is a member of CSS. The FAF and the state scholarship application are required. The deadline for financial aid applications is March 15.

International Students: There are currently 7 international students enrolled. They must take the TOEFL and achieve a minimum score of 500.

Computers: The college provides computer facilities for student use. The mainframes are a DEC VAX 3800 and a PDP 11/44. Some 200 terminals and microcomputers, including IBM PS/2, IBM-compatible, Apple II, and Macintosh, are located in the computer center and classrooms. All students may access the system as needed. There are no time limits on using the system and no fees.

Graduates: In 1992-93 299 bachelor's degrees were awarded. The most popular majors among graduates were business administration (23%), accounting (13%), and English (12%). Within an average freshman class, 84% graduate in 4 years. Some 50 companies recruited on campus in 1992-93.

Admissions Contact: Thomas O'Connor, Director of Admission.

WAYNESBURG COLLEGE

B-4

Waynesburg, PA 15370

(412) 852-3248
(800) 225-7393 (out-of-state)

Full-time: 552 men, 728 women
Part-time: 22 men, 40 women
Graduate: 22 men, 14 women
Year: semesters, summer session
Application Deadline: open
Freshman Class: 1190 applied, 978 accepted, 324 enrolled
SAT I or ACT: recommended

Faculty: 67; IIB, --$
Ph.D.s: n/av
Student/Faculty: 19 to 1
Tuition: $8580
Room & Board: $3380

COMPETITIVE

Waynesburg College, founded in 1849, is a private, liberal arts institution affiliated with the Presbyterian Church (USA). There is one undergraduate and one graduate school. In addition to regional accreditation, Waynesburg has baccalaureate program accreditation with NLN. The library contains 120,000 volumes and 5327 microform items, and subscribes to 483 periodicals. Computerized library sources and services include the card catalog, interlibrary loans, and database searching. Special learning facilities include a learning resource center, natural history museum, radio station, and TV station. The 30-acre campus is in a small town 50 miles south of Pittsburgh. Including residence halls, there are 15 buildings on campus.

Student Life: About 89% of undergraduates are from Pennsylvania. Students come from 16 states and 8 foreign countries. Ninety-four percent are from public schools; 6% from private. Ninety-four percent are white. Fifty-three percent are Protestant; 28% Catholic. The average age of freshmen is 18; all undergraduates, 21. Twenty-two percent drop out by the end of their first year; 55% remain to graduate.

Housing: A total of 600 students can be accommodated in college housing. College-sponsored living facilities include single-sex and coed dormitories. In addition, there are special interest houses and a community service house. On-campus housing is guaranteed for all 4 years. Priority is given to out-of-town students. Alcohol is not permitted. Upperclassmen may keep cars on campus.

Activities: About 9% of men belong to 4 national fraternities; about 11% of women belong to 3 national sororities. There are 25 groups on campus, including band, cheerleading, chorale, dance, drama, drill team, ethnic, film, honors, international, jazz band, literary magazine, marching band, musical theater, newspaper, orchestra, pep band, photography, professional, radio and TV, religious, social, social service, student government, and yearbook. Popular campus events include Homecoming, Greek Week, Spring Weekend Formal, VIP Forum, Fine Arts Services, GNP-Alumni Concert, and Poetry Festival.

Sports: There are 7 intercollegiate sports for men and 5 for women, and 15 intramural sports for men and 12 for women. Athletic and recreation facilities include table tennis, billiards, bridge, basketball courts, a wrestling room, weight room facilities, racquetball courts, a golf driving net, and a gymnasium. The campus stadium seats 1500, the indoor gymnasium 1500, and the largest auditorium/arena 450.

Disabled Students: Eighty-five percent of the campus is accessible to disabled students. The following facilities are available: wheelchair ramps, elevators, special parking, specially equipped rest rooms, special class scheduling, and lowered drinking fountains.

Services: In addition to many counseling and information services, tutoring is available in every subject. In addition, there is remedial math and writing.

Campus Safety and Security: Campus safety and security measures include 24-hour foot and vehicle patrol, self defense education, escort service, and informal discussions. In addition, there are pamphlets, posters, and films, lighted pathways and sidewalks, and 24-hour security access.

Programs of Study: Waynesburg awards the B.A., B.S., B.S.B.A., and B.S.N. degrees. Associate and master's degrees also are awarded. Bachelor's degrees are awarded in BIOLOGICAL SCIENCE (biology/biological science), BUSINESS (accounting, business administration and management, management science, marketing/retailing/merchandising, and small business management), COMMUNICATIONS AND THE ARTS (English), COMPUTER AND PHYSICAL SCIENCE (chemistry, computer science, and mathematics), EDUCATION (elementary, mathematics, and secondary), ENGINEERING AND ENVIRONMENTAL DESIGN (commercial art), HEALTH PROFESSIONS (community health work, medical laboratory technology, nursing, predentistry, premedicine, and sports medicine), SOCIAL SCIENCE (criminal justice, economics, history, political science/government, prelaw, psychology, public administration, social science, and sociology). Nursing, business, education, and liberal arts are the strongest programs academically. Business administration, education, and nursing have the largest enrollments.

Required: To graduate, all students must complete a minimum of 124 semester hours, with at least 30 hours in the major. A minimum 2.0 GPA and courses in life skills and computer sciences are required. Other requirements include 9 credits of English/communications, 3 of mathematics, 8 of natural and physical sciences, 6 of literature and the arts, and 15 of humanities and social and behavioral sciences. Students must also pass an English usage and written competency test.

Special: The college offers internships, dual majors, credit for experience, nondegree study, and pass/fail options. There is a 3-2 engineering degree program with Case Western Reserve, Washington, and Pennsylvania State universities. There is a freshman honors program on campus, as well as 12 national honor societies. Ten departments have honors programs.

Faculty/Classroom: Fifty-five percent of faculty are male; 45%, female. All teach undergraduates. No introductory courses are taught by graduate students. The average class size in an introductory lecture is 30; in a laboratory, 10; and in a regular course offering, 18.

Admissions: About 82% of the 1993-94 applicants were accepted.

Requirements: Waynesburg requires applicants to be in the upper 60% of their class. A minimum GPA of 2.5 is required. The SAT I or ACT is recommended, and some applicants may be requested to submit scores to further validate academic potential. In addition, applicants must be graduates of an accredited secondary school or have a GED certificate and have completed 16 academic credits, including 4 in English and 2 each in mathematics, sciences, and history or social studies. An essay, interview, or enrollment in the summer Step Ahead Program may be required. AP and CLEP credits are accepted. Important factors used in the admissions decision are advanced placement or honor courses, recommendations by school officials, extracurricular activities record, leadership record, and personality, intangible qualities.

Procedure: Freshmen are admitted to all sessions. Entrance exams should be taken in April of the junior year or December of the senior year. Application deadlines are open. Application fee is $15. Notification is sent on a rolling basis.

Transfer: About 80 transfer students enrolled in 1993-94. Students must submit a high school transcript and complete grade transcripts from all colleges previously attended. A total of 30 credits out of 124 must be completed at Waynesburg.

Visiting: There are regularly scheduled orientations for prospective students, including visits with faculty, students, administrators, and financial aid officers, and a tour of the campus. There are guides for informal visits and visitors may sit in on classes and stay overnight at the school. To arrange for a visit, contact Robin L. Moore, Admissions Office, at (412) 852-3248 or (800) 225-7393.

Financial Aid: In 1993-94, 90% of all current freshmen and 89% of continuing students received some form of financial aid. About 90% of freshmen and 87% of continuing students received need-based aid. The average freshman award was $8523. Of that total, scholarships or need-based grants averaged $5740 ($12,410 maximum); loans averaged $2267 ($3625 maximum); and work contracts averaged $700 ($1000 maximum). Seventeen percent of undergraduate students work part-time. Average earnings from campus work for the school year are $700. The average financial indebtedness of the 1992-93 graduate was $7000. Waynesburg is a member of CSS. The FAF, FFS, or SFS, the college's own financial statement, the appropriate state grant applications, and the FAFSA are required. The deadline for financial aid applications is March 15.

International Students: There are currently 8 international students enrolled. The school actively recruits these students. They must take the TOEFL and achieve a minimum score of 550. The student must also take the SAT I or the ACT. Students must take SAT II: Subject tests in mathematics and writing.

Computers: The college provides computer facilities for student use. The mainframes are a DEC PDP 11/70 and a DEC VAX for administrative use. A number of microcomputers, including IBM, Macintosh, Apple II, and Amiga, are available for student use. All students may access the system. There are no time limits on using the system and no fees.

Graduates: In 1992-93, 247 bachelor's degrees were awarded. The most popular majors among graduates were business (25%), nursing (23%), and education (15%). Within an average freshman class, 4% graduate in 3 years, 44% in 4 years, 54% in 5 years, and 54% in 6 years. Some 30 companies recruited on campus in 1992-93. In the 1992 graduating class, 10% of the men and 8% of the women were enrolled in graduate school within 6 months of graduation; 80% of the men and 83% of the women had found employment.

Admissions Contact: Robin L. Moore, Director of Admissions.

WEST CHESTER UNIVERSITY OF PENNSYLVANIA

F-4

West Chester, PA 19383 (215) 436-3411

Full-time: 2920 men, 4763 women	Faculty: 548; IIA, av$
Part-time: 406 men, 1193 women	Ph.D.s: 67%
Graduate: 671 men, 1353 women	Student/Faculty: 14 to 1
Year: semesters, summer session	Tuition: $3504 ($7902)
Application Deadline: November 15	Room & Board: $3988
Freshman Class: 6502 applied, 3539 accepted, 1391 enrolled	
SAT I Verbal/Math: 450/500	COMPETITIVE

West Chester University, founded in 1871, is a public institution that is part of the Pennsylvania State System of Higher Education. It offers programs through the College of Arts and Sciences and the schools of business and public affairs, education, health sciences, and music. The Exton Center campus offers credit and noncredit classes geared to nontraditional populations. There are 5 undergraduate and 5 graduate schools. In addition to regional accreditation, the university has baccalaureate program accreditation with CSWE, NASM, NCATE, and NLN. The 3 libraries contain 450,000 volumes, 350,000 microform items, and 21,000 audiovisual forms, and subscribe to 2800 periodicals. Computerized library sources and services include the card catalog, interlibrary loans, and database searching. Special learning facilities include a learning resource center, art gallery, planetarium, radio station, herbarium, speech and hearing clinic, center for government and community affairs, and natural area for environmental studies. The 388-acre campus is in a small town 25 miles west of Philadelphia. Including residence halls, there are 61 buildings on campus.

Student Life: About 82% of undergraduates are from Pennsylvania. Students come from 32 states, 53 foreign countries, and Canada. Seventy-nine percent are from public schools; 21% from private. Ninety-one percent are white. Forty-six percent are Catholic; 34% Protestant; 11% claim no religious affiliation. The average age of freshmen is 18.1; all undergraduates, 23. Sixteen percent drop out by the end of their first year; 51% remain to graduate.

Housing: A total of 3500 students can be accommodated in college housing. College-sponsored living facilities include single-sex and coed dormitories and on-campus apartments. In addition, there are honors and international student sections. On-campus housing is guaranteed for all 4 years. Priority is given to out-of-town students. Fifty-six percent of students commute. Alcohol is not permitted. Upperclassmen may keep cars on campus.

Activities: About 10% of men belong to 15 national fraternities; about 7% of women belong to 10 national sororities. There are 184 groups on campus, including art, band, cheerleading, chess, choir, chorale, chorus, computers, dance, drama, drill team, drum and bugle corps, ethnic, film, gay, honors, international, jazz band, literary magazine, marching band, musical theater, newspaper, orchestra, photography, political, professional, radio and TV, religious, social, social service, student government, symphony, and yearbook. Popular campus events include International Day, Alcohol Awareness Week, Sexual Assault Prevention Week, African American History Month, Homecoming, Spring Weekend, Greek Week, El Milagro (Latino Heritage) Week, Lesbian, Gay, Bisexual Week, and Women's History Month.

Sports: There are 11 intercollegiate sports for men and 12 for women, and 11 intramural sports for men and 7 for women. Athletic and recreation facilities include a field house, practice fields, a stadium, indoor and outdoor tracks, swimming pools, a training room, and tennis and basketball courts. The campus stadium seats 8000, the indoor gymnasium 2000, and the largest auditorium/arena 1800.

Disabled Students: Ninety percent of the campus is accessible to disabled students. The following facilities are available: wheelchair ramps, elevators, special parking, specially equipped rest rooms, special class scheduling, lowered drinking fountains, and lowered telephones.

Services: In addition to many counseling and information services, tutoring is available in every subject. In addition, there is remedial math, reading, and writing.

Campus Safety and Security: Campus safety and security measures include 24-hour foot and vehicle patrol, self defense education, escort service, and shuttle buses. In addition, there are informal discussions, pamphlets, posters, and films, emergency telephones, and lighted pathways and sidewalks.

Programs of Study: The university awards the B.A., B.S., B.F.A., B.Mu., B.S.Ed., and B.S.N. degrees. Associate and master's degrees also are awarded. Bachelor's degrees are awarded in BIOLOGICAL SCIENCE (biochemistry, biology/biological science, and microbiology), BUSINESS (accounting, business administration and management, business economics, and marketing/retailing/merchandising), COMMUNICATIONS AND THE ARTS (communications, dramatic arts, English, fine arts, French, German, Latin, music, Russian, Spanish, and speech/debate/rhetoric), COMPUTER AND PHYSICAL SCI-

ENCE (chemistry, computer science, earth science, geology, mathematics, and physics), EDUCATION (early childhood, elementary, foreign languages, health, music, secondary, and special), HEALTH PROFESSIONS (health, nursing, predentistry, premedicine, public health, and speech pathology/audiology), SOCIAL SCIENCE (anthropology, criminal justice, economics, geography, history, philosophy, political science/government, prelaw, psychology, public administration, religion, social work, and sociology). Premedicine is the strongest program academically. Physical education, elementary/early childhood education, business management, and psychology have the largest enrollments.

Required: All students must satisfy requirements in English composition, mathematics, interdisciplinary study, and physical education. Distribution requirements include 9 hours each of science, behavioral and social science, and humanities, and 3 hours in the arts. A total of 128 credit hours and a 2.0 GPA are required.

Special: There is cross-registration with Cheyney University and a 3-2 engineering program with Pennsylvania State University. The university offers internships in most majors, study abroad in France, Austria, and Wales, a Washington semester, work-study, some student-designed majors, credit by examination and for life, military, and work experience, and pass/fail options. There is a freshman honors program on campus, as well as 23 national honor societies. Ten departments have honors programs.

Faculty/Classroom: Sixty percent of faculty are male; 40%, female. All teach undergraduates and 48% both teach and do research. No introductory courses are taught by graduate students. The average class size in an introductory lecture is 35; in a laboratory, 24; and in a regular course offering, 30.

Admissions: About 54% of the 1993-94 applicants were accepted. The SAT scores for the 1993-94 freshman class were as follows: Verbal—76% below 500, 21% between 500 and 599, 2% between 600 and 700, and 1% above 700; Math—50% below 500, 40% between 500 and 599, 9% between 600 and 700, and 1% above 700. About 33% of the current freshmen were in the top fifth of their class; 72% were in the top two fifths.

Requirements: The university requires applicants to be in the upper 50% of their class. A minimum GPA of 2.0 is required. The SAT I is required, with a recommended minimum composite score of 900. In addition, applicants should graduate from an accredited secondary school or have a GED. A total of 16 academic credits is required, including 4 years of English, 3 each of history, mathematics, and social studies, and 2 of science. An essay is required; music students need to audition. AP and CLEP credits are accepted. Important factors used in the admissions decision are advanced placement or honor courses, recommendations by school officials, evidence of special talent, personality, intangible qualities, and leadership record.

Procedure: Freshmen are admitted in the fall and spring. Entrance exams should be taken in spring of the junior year or fall of the senior year. Applications should be filed by November 15 for fall entry and October 1 for spring entry, along with an application fee of $25. Notification is sent on a rolling basis. There are early admissions and deferred admissions plans. A waiting list is an active part of the admissions procedure, with about 5% of applicants on the list.

Transfer: About 847 transfer students enrolled in 1993-94. Transfer applicants should have earned at least 30 credits; the minimum recommended GPA is 2.5. Some departments require a higher GPA and specific course requirements. Transfers who have earned fewer than 30 credits must take the SAT I. A total of 30 credits out of 128 must be completed at the university.

Visiting: There are regularly scheduled orientations for prospective students. These are 2-day events, including academic advising, scheduling, and social events. There are guides for informal visits and visitors may sit in on classes and stay overnight at the school. To arrange for a visit, contact the Office of Admissions at (215) 436-3411.

Financial Aid: In 1993-94, 44% of all current freshmen and 44% of continuing students received some form of financial aid. About 44% of freshmen and 44% of continuing students received need-based aid. The average freshman award was $3708. Of that total, scholarships or need-based grants averaged $1325 ($5000 maximum); loans averaged $2112 ($5625 maximum); and work contracts averaged $271 ($2137 maximum). Six percent of undergraduate students work part-time. Average earnings from campus work for the school year are $1520. The average financial indebtedness of the 1992-93 graduate was about $8500. The university is a member of CSS. The FAFSA is required. The deadline for financial aid applications is March 15.

International Students: There are currently 202 international students enrolled. They must take the TOEFL and achieve a minimum score of 550. The SAT I is recommended.

Computers: The college provides computer facilities for student use. The mainframe is an IBM 4381. More than 250 microcomputers are available in computer laboratories, classrooms, and residence halls. All students may access the system. There are no time limits on using the system and no fees.

Graduates: In 1992–93, 1718 bachelor's degrees were awarded. The most popular majors among graduates were elementary education (15%), physical education (7%), and criminal justice (7%). Within an average freshman class, 25% graduate in 4 years, 46% in 5 years, and 51% in 6 years. Some 30 companies recruited on campus in 1992–93. In the 1992 graduating class, 15% of the men and 21% of the women were enrolled in graduate school within 6 months of graduation; 81% of the men and 74% of the women had found employment.

Admissions Contact: Director of Admissions.

WESTMINSTER COLLEGE
A-2

New Wilmington, PA 16172

(412) 946-7100

(800) 942-8033 (in-state)

Full-time: 616 men, 795 women | Faculty: 94; IIB, av$
Part-time: 44 men, 28 women | Ph.D.s: 77%
Graduate: 27 men, 65 women | Student/Faculty: 15 to 1
Year: 4–1–4, summer session | Tuition: $11,770
Application Deadline: open | Room & Board: $3430
Freshman Class: 995 applied, 868 accepted, 377 enrolled
SAT I: 470/520 | ACT: 24 | **COMPETITIVE**

Westminster College, founded in 1852, is a private, coeducational liberal arts institution related to the Presbyterian Church (USA). In addition to regional accreditation, Westminster has baccalaureate program accreditation with NASM. The 2 libraries contain 220,000 volumes and subscribe to 1000 periodicals. Computerized library sources and services include interlibrary loans. Special learning facilities include a learning resource center, art gallery, planetarium, radio station, TV station, and electron microscope laboratories in the science center. The 300-acre campus is in a rural area 60 miles north of Pittsburgh. Including residence halls, there are 22 buildings on campus.

Student Life: About 76% of undergraduates are from Pennsylvania. Students come from 23 states and 1 foreign country. Ninety percent are from public schools; 10% from private. Ninety-seven percent are white. Fifty-six percent are Protestant; 34% Catholic; 10% claim no religious affiliation. The average age of freshmen is 18; all undergraduates, 20. One percent drop out by the end of their first year; 78% remain to graduate.

Housing: A total of 1120 students can be accommodated in college housing. College-sponsored living facilities include single-sex dormitories and fraternity houses. In addition, some residence hall floors have 24-hour weekend visitation. On-campus housing is guaranteed for all 4 years. Ninety percent of students live on campus. Alcohol is not permitted. All students may keep cars on campus.

Activities: About 29% of men belong to 5 national fraternities; about 30% of women belong to 5 national sororities. There are 85 groups on campus, including band, cheerleading, choir, chorus, dance, drama, drill team, ethnic, honors, jazz band, literary magazine, marching band, newspaper, orchestra, pep band, political, radio and TV, religious, social, social service, student government, and yearbook. Popular campus events include mock conventions, liberal arts forum, dances, and films.

Sports: There are 9 intercollegiate sports for men and 8 for women, and 7 intramural sports for men and 6 for women. Athletic and recreation facilities include a natatorium, racquetball, tennis, and basketball courts, a track, and weight and aerobics rooms.

Disabled Students: The following facilities are available: wheelchair ramps, elevators, special parking, specially equipped rest rooms, and special class scheduling.

Services: In addition to many counseling and information services, tutoring is available in most subjects. In addition, there is remedial reading and writing.

Campus Safety and Security: Campus safety and security measures include 24-hour foot and vehicle patrol, escort service, informal discussions, and pamphlets, posters, and films. In addition, there are emergency telephones and lighted pathways and sidewalks.

Programs of Study: Westminster awards the B.A., B.S., and B.M. degrees. Master's degrees also are awarded. Bachelor's degrees are awarded in BIOLOGICAL SCIENCE (biology/biological science), BUSINESS (accounting, banking and finance, business administration and management, international business management, and marketing/retailing/merchandising), COMMUNICATIONS AND THE ARTS (broadcasting, communications, English, fine arts, French, German, Latin, music, and Spanish), COMPUTER AND PHYSICAL SCIENCE (chemistry, computer science, mathematics, and physics), EDUCATION (elementary, guidance, music, and secondary), HEALTH PROFESSIONS (predentistry and premedicine), SOCIAL SCIENCE (criminal justice, economics, history, international relations, philosophy, political science/government, prelaw, psychology, religion, social science, and sociology). Sciences, business, education, and humanities are the strongest programs academically. Business, sciences, and education have the largest enrollments.

Required: To graduate, all students must complete 36 courses and 4 terms of physical education, with 9 to 15 courses in the major, for a total of 126 credit hours. Distribution requirements include 1 course each in writing, religion, literature, communications, computer science, and fine arts; 2 courses each in social science, natural science and mathematics, and humanities; and 2 to 4 in foreign language. A minimum GPA of 2.0 is required.

Special: Westminister offers internships, study abroad in many countries, a Washington semester, various dual and student-designed majors, a 3–2 engineering degree with Case Western Reserve, Pennsylvania State, and Washington universities, and nondegree study. There is a freshman honors program on campus, as well as 12 national honor societies.

Faculty/Classroom: Seventy-three percent of faculty are male; 22%, female. All teach undergraduates. No introductory courses are taught by graduate students. The average class size in a regular course offering is 25.

Admissions: About 87% of the 1993–94 applicants were accepted.

Requirements: Westminster requires applicants to be in the upper 50% of their class. A minimum GPA of 2.5 is required. The SAT I or ACT is required, with a minimum recommended composite score of 900 on the SAT I or 20 on the ACT. Applicants must be graduates of an accredited secondary school or have the GED; (minimum composite score 270) a minimum of 16 academic credits, including 4 units in English, 3 in mathematics, and 2 each in foreign language, science, and social studies is required. A portfolio, audition, and interview are recommended. An essay is required. AP and CLEP credits are accepted. Important factors used in the admissions decision are advanced placement or honor courses, leadership record, recommendations by school officials, personality, intangible qualities, and parents or siblings attending the school.

Procedure: Freshmen are admitted in the fall, winter, and spring. Entrance exams should be taken during the junior year. Application deadlines are open. Application fee is $20. Notification is sent on a rolling basis. There is a deferred admissions plan.

Transfer: About 40 transfer students enrolled in a recent year. Transfer students must have a college GPA of 2.0 or better.

Visiting: There are regularly scheduled orientations for prospective students, consisting of an introduction, a student panel, a financial aid workshop, a campus tour, a faculty fair, and lunch. Optional activities include a tour of residence halls and radio and TV stations and a football game. There are 2 visitation days in the fall and 2 in the spring. There are guides for informal visits and visitors may sit in on classes and stay overnight at the school. To arrange for a visit, contact the Office of Admissions at (412) 946-7100.

Financial Aid: In 1993–94, 75% of all current freshmen and 74% of continuing students received some form of financial aid. About 72% of freshmen and 72% of continuing students received need-based aid. The average freshman award was $8618. Of that total, scholarships or need-based grants averaged $5618 ($6000 maximum); loans averaged $3500 (maximum); and work contracts averaged $1300 (maximum). Twenty-six percent of undergraduate students work part-time. Average earnings from campus work for the school year are $1300. The average financial indebtedness of the 1992–93 graduate was $13,500. Westminster is a member of CSS. The FAF and the college's own financial statement are required. The deadline for financial aid applications is March 15.

International Students: There is currently 1 international student enrolled. International students must take the TOEFL or the University of Michigan Language Test and achieve a minimum score on the TOEFL of 550. The student must also take the SAT I or the ACT if the country of origin is English-speaking. The minimum required composite score on the SAT I is 900.

Computers: The college provides computer facilities for student use. The mainframe is a DEC VAX 11/85. Microcomputers are available throughout the campus. All students may access the system. There are no time limits on using the system and no fees.

Graduates: In 1992–93, 335 bachelor's degrees were awarded. The most popular majors among graduates were business (21%), elementary education (14%), and history (7%). Within an average freshman class, 74% graduate in 4 years, 75% in 5 years, and 76% in 6 years. Some 50 companies recruited on campus in 1992–93.

Admissions Contact: Richard Dana Paul, Director of Admissions.

WIDENER UNIVERSITY

F-4

Chester, PA 19013

(610) 499-4126

Full-time: 1010 men, 929 women	Faculty: 146; IIA, +$
Part-time: 100 men, 86 women	Ph.D.s: 92%
Graduate: 873 men, 1226 women	Student/Faculty: 13 to 1
Year: semesters, summer session	Tuition: $11,740
Application Deadline: April 1	Room & Board: $5100
Freshman Class: 2040 applied, 1279 accepted, 502 enrolled	
SAT I Verbal/Math: 466/491	**COMPETITIVE**

Widener University, founded in 1821, is a private, coeducational liberal arts institution offering undergraduate programs in the arts and sciences, business management, engineering, nursing, and hotel and restaurant management. Other campuses are in Harrisburg and Wilmington, Delaware. There are 7 undergraduate and 5 graduate schools. In addition to regional accreditation, Widener has baccalaureate program accreditation with ABET, ACCE, ACE, ACEHSA, AICE, APA, CSWE, NCATE, and NLN. The library contains 211,237 volumes, 106,791 microform items, and 7998 audiovisual forms, and subscribes to 2310 periodicals. Computerized library sources and services include the card catalog, interlibrary loans, and database searching. Special learning facilities include a learning resource center, art gallery, radio station, and child development center. The 105-acre campus is in a suburban area 15 miles south of Philadelphia. Including residence halls, there are 72 buildings on campus.

Student Life: About 51% of undergraduates are from out-of-state, mostly the Middle Atlantic. Students come from 32 states, 42 foreign countries, and Canada. Fifty-one percent are from public schools; 49% from private. Seventy-nine percent are white; 11% African American. Forty-five percent are Catholic; 44% Protestant. The average age of freshmen is 18; all undergraduates, 21. Nine percent drop out by the end of their first year; 56% remain to graduate.

Housing: A total of 1400 students can be accommodated in college housing. College-sponsored living facilities include single-sex and coed dormitories, on-campus apartments, fraternity houses, and sorority houses. In addition, there are special interest houses, a music house, and an international house. On-campus housing is guaranteed for all 4 years. Sixty percent of students live on campus; of those, 75% remain on campus on weekends. All students may keep cars on campus.

Activities: About 28% of men belong to 8 national fraternities; about 18% of women belong to 4 national sororities. There are 92 groups on campus, including art, band, cheerleading, chess, chorale, chorus, computers, drama, ethnic, environmental, honors, international, jazz band, literary magazine, model UN, musical theater, newspaper, pep band, photography, political, professional, radio, religious, social, social service, student government, video, and yearbook. Popular campus events include Greek Week, Homecoming, Hundredth Night, and Honors Week.

Sports: There are 12 intercollegiate sports for men and 10 for women, and 6 intramural sports for men and 3 for women. Athletic and recreation facilities include a 4000-seat stadium, an 1800-seat basketball gymnasium, a field house, a championship pool, a weight training room, an exercise room, squash and tennis courts, outdoor game and practice fields, and an 8-lane, all-weather championship track.

Disabled Students: Ninety-five percent of the campus is accessible to disabled students. The following facilities are available: wheelchair ramps, elevators, special parking, specially equipped rest rooms, special class scheduling, lowered drinking fountains, and lowered telephones.

Services: In addition to many counseling and information services, tutoring is available in most subjects. In addition, there is a reader service for the blind, and remedial math, reading, and writing.

Campus Safety and Security: Campus safety and security measures include 24-hour foot and vehicle patrol, self defense education, escort service, and informal discussions. In addition, there are pamphlets, posters, and films, lighted pathways and sidewalks, and residence hall briefings on personal safety, housing security, and enforcement procedures.

Programs of Study: Widener awards the B.A., B.S., B.S.B.A., B.S.C.E., B.S.Ch.E., B.S.E.E., B.S. in H.R.M., B.S.M.E., B.S.N., and B.S.W. degrees. Master's and doctoral degrees also are awarded. Bachelor's degrees are awarded in BIOLOGICAL SCIENCE (biochemistry and biology/biological science), BUSINESS (accounting, banking and finance, business administration and management, business economics, hotel/motel and restaurant management, and international business management), COMMUNICATIONS AND THE ARTS (communications, English, and modern language), COMPUTER AND PHYSICAL SCIENCE (chemistry, computer science, information sciences and systems, mathematics, and physics), EDUCATION (early childhood, elementary, foreign languages, science, and secondary), ENGINEERING AND ENVIRONMENTAL DESIGN (chemical engineering, civil engineering, electrical/electronics engineering, environmental science, and mechanical engineering), HEALTH PRO-FESSIONS (nursing, predentistry, and premedicine), SOCIAL SCIENCE (behavioral science, criminal justice, economics, history, humanities, international relations, political science/government, prelaw, psychology, social science, social work, and sociology). Engineering, chemistry, management, and biology are the strongest programs academically. Nursing, engineering, business, biology, and psychology have the largest enrollments.

Required: All students must complete 12 credits each in humanities, social sciences, and science/mathematics, and 1 credit in physical education. For graduation, students must have 121 credit hours and a GPA of 2.0. Hours in the major vary by program.

Special: Widener offers internships, study abroad in 6 countries, a Washington semester, accelerated degree programs, dual, student-designed, and interdisciplinary majors, including chemistry management, nondegree study, and pass/fail options. Cooperative education programs are available in management, engineering, and computer science and are required in hotel/restaurant management. There is also cross-registration with Swarthmore College and American University, a 3–2 engineering degree, and B.A.-B.S. degrees. There is a freshman honors program on campus, as well as 12 national honor societies. Eight departments have honors programs.

Faculty/Classroom: Fifty-six percent of faculty are male; 44%, female. Sixty-six percent teach undergraduates, 60% do research, and 65% do both. No introductory courses are taught by graduate students. The average class size in an introductory lecture is 32; in a laboratory, 16; and in a regular course offering, 22.

Admissions: About 63% of the 1993–94 applicants were accepted. The SAT scores for the 1993–94 freshman class were as follows: Verbal—68% below 500, 24% between 500 and 599, 7% between 600 and 700, and 1% above 700; Math—49% below 500, 32% between 500 and 599, 15% between 600 and 700, and 4% above 700. About 31% of the current freshmen were in the top fifth of their class; 77% were in the top two fifths. There were 11 National Merit semifinalists. About 36 freshmen graduated first in their class.

Requirements: Widener requires applicants to be in the upper 50% of their class. A minimum GPA of 2.5 is required. The SAT I is required, with a minimum composite score of 1000. Applicants must be graduates of an accredited secondary school and have completed 4 units each of English and social studies, 3 units each of mathematics and science, and 1 unit each of art, history, and music. The GED is accepted under limited circumstances. An interview is recommended. AP and CLEP credits are accepted. Important factors used in the admissions decision are advanced placement or honor courses, recommendations by school officials, leadership record, personality, intangible qualities, and evidence of special talent.

Procedure: Freshmen are admitted in the fall and spring. Entrance exams should be taken in the junior year and in November or December of the senior year. Applications should be filed by April 1 for fall entry and December 15 for spring entry, along with an application fee of $25. Notification is sent on a rolling basis. There are early decision, early admissions, and deferred admissions plans. About 70 early decision candidates were accepted for the 1993–94 class.

Transfer: About 300 transfer students enrolled in a recent year. Applicants must have at least 12 college credits with a minimum GPA of 2.2. An associate degree and an interview are recommended. A total of 45 credits out of 121 must be completed at Widener.

Visiting: There are regularly scheduled orientations for prospective students. There are guides for informal visits and visitors may sit in on classes and stay overnight at the school. To arrange for a visit, contact the Admissions Office at (610) 499-4126.

Financial Aid: In 1993–94 76% of all current freshmen and 64% of continuing students received some form of financial aid. About 73% of freshmen and 61% of continuing students received need-based aid. The average freshman award was $5200. Of that total, scholarships or need-based grants averaged $5000 ($7000 maximum); loans averaged $3443 ($3625 maximum); and work contracts averaged $1200 (maximum). Thirty-five percent of undergraduate students work part-time. Average earnings from campus work for the school year are $750. The average financial indebtedness of the 1992–93 graduate was $15,780. Widener is a member of CSS. The college's own financial statement and the FAFSA are required. The deadline for financial aid applications is March 1.

International Students: There are currently 96 international students enrolled. The school actively recruits these students. They must take the TOEFL and achieve a minimum score of 500. The student must also take the SAT I or the ACT; SAT I is preferred.

Computers: The college provides computer facilities for student use. The mainframes are a CYBER 932 and CDC 4680. The mainframes are accessed through IBM PS/2 computer laboratories throughout the university or from remote dial-in sites. There are 187 terminals on campus. All students may access the system. It may be used from 8 A.M. to midnight; longer during examination periods. There are no time limits on using the system and no fees.

Graduates: In 1992–93 690 bachelor's degrees were awarded. The most popular majors among graduates were nursing (18%), management (16%), and hotel/restaurant management (15%). Within an average freshman class, 1% graduate in 3 years, 4% in 4 years, 55% in 5 years, and 56% in 6 years. Some 65 companies recruited on campus in 1992–93. In the 1992 graduating class, 16% of all graduates were enrolled in graduate school within 6 months of graduation; 83% of all graduates had found employment.

Admissions Contact: Dr. Michael L. Mahoney, Director of Undergraduate Admissions.

WILKES UNIVERSITY
Wilkes Barre, PA 18766

E-2

(717) 831–4400
(800) WILKESU (945–5378)

Full-time: 979 men, 824 women	Faculty: 137; IIA, -$
Part-time: 250 men, 353 women	Ph.D.s: 85%
Graduate: 306 men, 545 women	Student/Faculty: 13 to 1
Year: semesters, summer session	Tuition: $10,898
Application Deadline: open	Room & Board: $4830
Freshman Class: 1631 applied, 1431 accepted, 434 enrolled	
SAT I Verbal/Math: 420/470	**LESS COMPETITIVE**

Wilkes University, founded in 1933, is a an independent, comprehensive, private university offering undergraduate programs in 36 fields, including the arts and sciences, business, and engineering. There are 3 undergraduate schools and one graduate school. In addition to regional accreditation, Wilkes has baccalaureate program accreditation with ABET and NLN. The library contains 200,000 volumes, 620,000 microform items, and 2500 audiovisual forms, and subscribes to 1150 periodicals. Computerized library sources and services include the card catalog, interlibrary loans, and database searching. Special learning facilities include a learning resource center, an art gallery, a radio station, and a TV station. The 25-acre campus is in an urban area 120 miles west of New York City. Including residence halls, there are 50 buildings on campus.

Student Life: About 70% of undergraduates are from Pennsylvania. Students come from 17 states, 13 foreign countries, and Canada. Eighty percent are from public schools; 20% from private. Ninety-six percent are white. Fifty-four percent are Catholic; 30% Protestant; 12% claim no religious affiliation. The average age of freshmen is 18; all undergraduates, 21. Eighteen percent drop out by the end of their first year; 63% remain to graduate.

Housing: A total of 800 students can be accommodated in college housing. College-sponsored living facilities include single-sex and coed dormitories. On-campus housing is guaranteed for all 4 years. Alcohol is not permitted. All students may keep cars on campus.

Activities: There are no fraternities or sororities on campus. There are 65 groups on campus, including art, band, cheerleading, choir, chorus, computers, drama, ethnic, gay, honors, international, jazz band, literary magazine, musical theater, newspaper, orchestra, pep band, political, professional, radio and TV, religious, social, social service, student government, and yearbook. Popular campus events include Casino Night, Junior-Senior Dinner Dance, Homecoming, Winter Weekend, Club Day, Cherry Blossom Festival, and Community Service Day.

Sports: There are 8 intercollegiate sports for men and 6 for women, and 10 intramural sports for men and 6 for women. Athletic and recreation facilities include tennis courts, a 5000-seat stadium, a 3500-seat gymnasium, a game room, and weight and exercise rooms.

Disabled Students: The entire campus is accessible to disabled students. The following facilities are available: wheelchair ramps, elevators, special parking, specially equipped rest rooms, special class scheduling, lowered drinking fountains, and lowered telephones.

Services: In addition to many counseling and information services, tutoring is available in every subject. There is remedial math, reading, and writing. The Learning Center also provides individual tutoring, group study sessions, and small-group supplemental instruction seminars.

Campus Safety and Security: Campus safety and security measures include 24-hour foot and vehicle patrol, escort service, informal discussions, and pamphlets, posters, and films. In addition, there are lighted pathways and sidewalks, Operation Alert, which provides personal alarm devices for students who wish to carry one, and Operation Identification, which allows students to engrave belongings with identifying information.

Programs of Study: Wilkes awards the B.A., B.S., B.B.A., B.F.A., and B.M. degrees. Master's and doctoral degrees are also awarded. Bachelor's degrees are awarded in BIOLOGICAL SCIENCE (biochemistry and biology/biological science), BUSINESS (accounting and business administration and management), COMMUNICATIONS AND THE ARTS (communications, dramatic arts, English, fine arts, French, German, music, and Spanish), COMPUTER AND PHYSICAL SCIENCE (chemistry, computer science, earth science, information sciences and systems, mathematics, and physics), EDUCATION (art, early childhood, elementary, foreign languages, music, science,

and secondary), ENGINEERING AND ENVIRONMENTAL DESIGN (electrical/electronics engineering, engineering and applied science, engineering management, environmental engineering, materials engineering, and mechanical engineering), HEALTH PROFESSIONS (medical laboratory technology, medical records administration/services, nursing, predentistry, and premedicine), SOCIAL SCIENCE (economics, history, international studies, philosophy, political science/government, prelaw, psychology, and sociology). Engineering and biology are the strongest academically. Business administration, psychology, communication, and accounting have the largest enrollments.

Required: To graduate, all students must complete at least 120 credit hours, with a minimum of 30 in the major, and a cumulative GPA of at least 2.0 overall and in the major. Students must demonstrate competency in written expression, computer literacy, oral expression, and mathematics, and complete 2 semesters of physical education. Distribution of studies requirements must also be met.

Special: Wilkes offers co-op programs with the College of Podiatric Medicine, Pennsylvania College of Optometry, College of Osteopathic Medicine, and Temple University Schools of Dentistry and Physical Therapy, and cross-registration with King's College. Also available are internships (required for accounting and communications majors), study abroad, dual majors in all disciplines, credit for military experience, and nondegree study. A mandatory research program is required for engineering majors. There is a freshman honors program on campus, as well as 9 national honor societies. Five departments have honors programs.

Faculty/Classroom: Sixty-six percent of faculty are male; 34%, female. Nearly all teach undergraduates. No introductory courses are taught by graduate students. The average class size in an introductory lecture is 26; in a laboratory, 13; and in a regular course offering, 20.

Admissions: About 88% of the 1993–94 applicants were accepted. The SAT scores for the 1993–94 freshman class were as follows: Verbal—77% below 500, 16% between 500 and 599, and 6% between 600 and 700; Math—59% below 500, 26% between 500 and 599, 11% between 600 and 700, and 3% above 700. About 29% of the current freshmen were in the top fifth of their class; 50% were in the top two fifths. Eleven freshmen graduated first in their class.

Requirements: Wilkes requires applicants to be in the upper 60% of their class. The SAT I or ACT is required, with minimum composite scores of 800 or 18, respectively; the SAT I is preferred. Applicants must be graduates of an accredited secondary school or have the GED. Sixteen academic credits are required, including 4 years of English, 3 years of mathematics, 2 years each of science and foreign language, and 1 year of history. Art majors must submit a portfolio, and music majors and theater arts majors must audition. An interview is recommended. AP and CLEP credits are accepted. Important factors used in the admissions decision are recommendations by school officials, advanced placement or honor courses, leadership record, parents or siblings attending the school, and extracurricular activities record.

Procedure: Freshmen are admitted to all sessions. Application deadlines are open. Application fee is $30. Notification is sent on a rolling basis. There are early admissions and deferred admissions plans. A waiting list is an active part of the admissions procedure.

Transfer: About 180 transfer students enrolled in 1993–94. Transfer applicants must have a minimum college GPA of 2.0 and at least 30 earned credits. A GPA of 2.5 is required for engineering majors. Students with fewer than 30 credits must submit official high school transcripts. An interview is recommended. A total of 60 credits out of 120 (for most programs) must be completed at Wilkes.

Visiting: There are regularly scheduled orientations for prospective students, including a general orientation session, a tour of the campus, and a meeting with faculty from the department of the student's intended majors. There are guides for informal visits and visitors may sit in on classes and stay overnight at the school. To arrange for a visit, contact the Admissions Office at (717) 831–4400 or (800) WILKESU (945–5378).

Financial Aid: In 1993–94, 80% of all students received some form of financial aid. About 77% received need-based aid. The average freshman award was $9050. Of that total, scholarships or need-based grants averaged $4900 ($10,900 maximum); loans averaged $3200 ($5125 maximum); and work contracts averaged $950 ($2000 maximum). Twenty-five percent of undergraduate students work part-time. Average earnings from campus work for the school year are $700. The average financial indebtedness of the 1992–93 graduate was $6636. Wilkes is a member of CSS. The PHEAA financial statement is required.

International Students: There are currently 35 international students enrolled. The school actively recruits these students. They must take the TOEFL and achieve a minimum score of 500. The student must also take the SAT I or ACT; SAT I is preferred.

Computers: The college provides computer facilities for student use. The mainframes are a DEC VAX 6310 and a DEC VAX 3500. There are also 120 IBM, 20 Apple, and 100 Apple Macintosh microcom-

puters available throughout the campus. All students may access the system. It may be used 24 hours daily. There are no time limits on using the system and no fees.

Graduates: In 1992–93, 544 bachelor's degrees were awarded. The most popular majors among graduates were business administration (23%), psychology (10%), and accounting (8%). Within an average freshman class, 40% graduate in 4 years, 55% in 5 years, and 63% in 6 years. Some 120 companies recruited on campus in 1992–93. In the 1992 graduating class, 27% of all students were enrolled in graduate school within 6 months of graduation; 86% had found employment.

Admissions Contact: Emory P. Guffrovich, Jr., Dean of Admissions.

WILSON COLLEGE
D-4

Chambersburg, PA 17201–1285

(717) 264–4141, ext. 223, 225
(800) 421–8402 (out-of-state)

Full-time: 160 women	Faculty: 33; IIB, --$
Part-time: 33 women	Ph.D.s: 77%
Graduate: none	Student/Faculty: 5 to 1
Year: 4–1–4, summer session	Tuition: $11,546
Application Deadline: August 1	Room & Board: $5084
Freshman Class: 134 applied, 111 accepted, 39 enrolled	
SAT I Verbal/Math: 465/500	**COMPETITIVE**

Wilson College, founded in 1869, is an independent, primarily women's liberal arts institution affiliated with the Presbyterian Church. The library contains 159,846 volumes, 11,703 microform items, and 1303 audiovisual forms, and subscribes to 393 periodicals. Special learning facilities include a learning resource center, an art gallery, a natural history museum, a radio station, a veterinary technology suite, an electron microscope, a classics collection, and an indoor riding arena. The 262-acre campus is in a small town 90 miles north of Washington, D.C. Including residence halls, there are 34 buildings on campus.

Student Life: About 60% of undergraduates are from Pennsylvania. Students come from 7 states and 2 foreign countries. Eighty-four percent are from public schools; 16% from private. Eighty-eight percent are white. Forty-nine percent are Protestant; 18% Catholic. The average age of freshmen is 18; all undergraduates, 20. Ten percent drop out by the end of their first year; 70% remain to graduate.

Housing: A total of 500 students can be accommodated in college housing. College-sponsored living facilities include dormitories. On-campus housing is guaranteed for all 4 years. Sixty-five percent of students live on campus; of those, 50% remain on campus on weekends. All students may keep cars on campus.

Activities: There are no fraternities on campus. There are 22 groups on campus, including art, choir, chorale, dance, drama, ethnic, gay, international, literary magazine, newspaper, photography, political, professional, religious, social, social service, student government, and yearbook. Popular campus events include May Weekend, Thanksgiving Dinner, White Dinner (Christmas), and Muhibbah Dinner.

Sports: Athletic and recreation facilities include a 400-seat gymnasium, a field house, a pool, a gymnastics area, a weight room, an archery range, a hockey field, tennis courts, a 2-lane bowling alley, and an equestrian center (indoor and outdoor arena).

Disabled Students: Thirty-five percent of the campus is accessible to disabled students. The following facilities are available: wheelchair ramps, elevators, special parking, specially equipped rest rooms, and special class scheduling.

Services: In addition to many counseling and information services, tutoring is available in every subject.

Campus Safety and Security: Campus safety and security measures include 24-hour foot and vehicle patrol, self defense education, informal discussions, pamphlets, posters, and films. In addition, there are emergency telephones and lighted pathways and sidewalks.

Programs of Study: Wilson awards the B.A. and B.S. degrees. Associate degrees also are awarded. Bachelor's degrees are awarded in AGRICULTURE (equestrian science), BIOLOGICAL SCIENCE (biology/biological science), BUSINESS (business economics), COMMUNICATIONS AND THE ARTS (communications, English, fine arts, and languages), COMPUTER AND PHYSICAL SCIENCE (chemistry and mathematics), EDUCATION (elementary), HEALTH PROFESSIONS (veterinary science), SOCIAL SCIENCE (behavioral science, international studies, and psychobiology). Business and economics, equestrian studies, veterinary medical technology, and physical and life sciences have the largest enrollments.

Required: A total of 36 course credits is required for graduation, with 10 to 15 credits in the major and a minimum GPA of 2.0. Proficiency in English must be established. Students are also required to take 4 core courses, as well as a computer course, a quantitative skills course, 2 physical education courses, a course in women's studies, and 3 electives (one from each of the academic divisions).

Special: Cross-registration is available with Shippenburg University and Gettysburg College. Wilson offers internships, a Washington semester, student-designed majors, credit by exam, pass/fail options,

and credit for noncollegiate learning. There are interdisciplinary majors in history and political science, and philosophy and religion. Students may participate in study-abroad programs sponsored by other colleges.

Faculty/Classroom: Fifty-seven percent of faculty are male; 43%, female. All teach undergraduates. The average class size in a regular course offering is 8.

Admissions: About 80% of the 1993–94 applicants were accepted. The SAT I scores for the freshman class were as follows: Verbal—67% below 500, 22% between 500 and 599, and 11% between 600 and 700; Math—49% below 500, 35% between 500 and 599, and 16% between 600 and 700. About 30% of the current freshmen were in the top fifth of their class; 65% were in the top two fifths. There was 1 National Merit semifinalist.

Requirements: Wilson requires applicants to be in the upper 50% of their class. A minimum GPA of 2.5 is required. The SAT I or ACT is required, with a minimum recommended score of 900 composite on the SAT I or 21 on the ACT. In addition, applicants should prepare with 4 years each of English and social studies/history, 3 of mathematics, and 2 of science. An essay is required, and an interview is recommended. AP and CLEP credits are accepted. Important factors used in the admissions decision are advanced placement or honor courses, personality, intangible qualities, leadership record, extracurricular activities record, and recommendations by alumni.

Procedure: Freshmen are admitted in the fall and spring. Entrance exams should be taken in the spring of the junior year. Applications should be filed by August 1 for fall entry and January 1 for spring entry, along with an application fee of $20. Notification of early decision is sent November 15; regular decision, on a rolling basis. There are early decision, early admissions, and deferred admissions plans.

Transfer: About 10 transfer students enrolled in 1993–94. Applicants must have a college GPA of at least 2.0. Either the SAT I or ACT is recommended, with a minimum composite score of 900 on the SAT I or a minimum ACT score of 21. A total of 14 course credits out of 36 must be completed at Wilson.

Visiting: There are regularly scheduled orientations for prospective students, consisting of a campus tour and meetings with various faculty members or administration, if requested. There are guides for informal visits, and visitors may sit in on classes and stay overnight at the school. To arrange for a visit, contact the Office of Admissions at (717) 264–4141, ext. 223, 225, 226, or 227.

Financial Aid: In 1993–94, 82% of all current freshmen and 81% of continuing students received some form of financial aid. About 70% of freshmen and 70% of continuing students received need-based aid. The average freshman award was $10,690. Of that total, scholarships or need-based grants averaged $5780 ($12,545 maximum); loans averaged $3805 ($4680 maximum); and work contracts averaged $1105. Forty-nine percent of undergraduate students work part-time. Average earnings from campus work for the school year are $812. The average financial indebtedness of the 1992–93 graduate was $7901. Wilson is a member of CSS. The college's own financial statement, the student's home-state grant application, and the FAFSA are required. The deadline for financial aid applications is April 30.

International Students: There are currently 3 international students enrolled. The school actively recruits these students. They must take the TOEFL and achieve a minimum score of 550.

Computers: The college provides computer facilities for student use. IBM-compatible computers are available for student use throughout the campus. All students may access the system. There are no time limits and no fees.

Graduates: In 1992–93, 40 bachelor's degrees were awarded. The most popular majors among graduates were equestrian studies (25%), business and economics (15%), and veterinary medical technology (15%). Within an average freshman class, 60% graduate in 4 years. In the 1992 graduating class, 23% of graduates were enrolled in graduate school within 6 months of graduation; 30% had found employment.

Admissions Contact: Karen Jewell, Director of Admissions.

YORK COLLEGE OF PENNSYLVANIA
D-4

York, PA 17405–7199

(717) 849–1600

Full-time: 1254 men, 1734 women	Faculty: 130; IIB, +$
Part-time: 649 men, 1077 women	Ph.D.s: 75%
Graduate: 67 men, 36 women	Student/Faculty: 23 to 1
Year: semesters, summer session	Tuition: $4995
Application Deadline: open	Room & Board: $3350
Freshman Class: 2989 applied, 1855 accepted, 691 enrolled	
SAT I Verbal/Math: 469/517	**COMPETITIVE**

York College of Pennsylvania, founded in 1787, is a private, coeducational institution offering undergraduate programs in the liberal arts and sciences, business, education, and nursing. There are 3 undergraduate schools and one graduate school. In addition to regional accreditation, YCP has baccalaureate program accreditation with NLN.

The library contains 300,000 volumes, 500,000 microform items, and 50,000 audiovisual forms, and subscribes to 1500 periodicals. Computerized library sources and services include interlibrary loans and database searching. Special learning facilities include a learning resource center, an art gallery, a radio station, a TV station, and a telecommunications center. The 80-acre campus is in a suburban area 45 miles north of Baltimore, Maryland. Including residence halls, there are 28 buildings on campus.

Student Life: About 60% of undergraduates are from Pennsylvania. Students come from 30 states, 19 foreign countries, and Canada. Eighty-two percent are from public schools; 18% from private. Ninety-five percent are white. Forty-one percent are Protestant; 36% Catholic. The average age of freshmen is 19; all undergraduates, 25. Nineteen percent drop out by the end of their first year; 78% remain to graduate.

Housing: A total of 1275 students can be accommodated in college housing. College-sponsored living facilities include single-sex and coed dormitories, on-campus apartments, fraternity houses, and sorority houses. On-campus housing is guaranteed for the freshman year only and is available on a first-come, first-served basis. Alcohol is not permitted. All students may keep cars on campus.

Activities: About 25% of men belong to 5 local and 5 national fraternities; about 20% of women belong to 4 local and 5 national sororities. There are 70 groups on campus, including band, cheerleading, chess, choir, chorale, chorus, computers, drama, ethnic, film, honors, international, jazz band, literary magazine, musical theater, newspaper, orchestra, photography, political, professional, radio and TV, religious, social, social service, student government, symphony, and yearbook. Popular campus events include Parents Weekend, Spring Weekend Festival, a cultural series, major contemporary concerts and lectures, weekly movies, dances, and live Sports Den performers.

Sports: There are 9 intercollegiate sports for men and 6 for women, and 9 intramural sports each for men and women. Athletic and recreation facilities include 2 gymnasiums, a track, a swimming pool, a game room, weight training rooms, tennis courts, and soccer, hockey, baseball, softball, and intramural fields.

Disabled Students: Sixty percent of the campus is accessible to disabled students. The following facilities are available: wheelchair ramps, elevators, special parking, specially equipped rest rooms, special class scheduling, lowered drinking fountains, and lowered telephones.

Services: In addition to many counseling and information services, tutoring is available in most subjects. In addition, there is remedial math and writing.

Campus Safety and Security: Campus safety and security measures include self-defense education, escort service, informal discussions, and pamphlets, posters, and films. In addition, there are emergency telephones, lighted pathways and sidewalks, and 24-hour foot patrol, safety seminars, crime prevention speakers, a desk monitor in residence halls, and a personal property engraving program.

Programs of Study: YCP awards the B.A. and B.S. degrees. Associate and master's degrees also are awarded. Bachelor's degrees are awarded in BIOLOGICAL SCIENCE (biology/biological science), BUSINESS (accounting, banking and finance, management science, marketing/retailing/merchandising, and office supervision and management), COMMUNICATIONS AND THE ARTS (broadcasting, English, fine arts, music, and speech/debate/rhetoric), COMPUTER AND PHYSICAL SCIENCE (chemistry, computer programming, mathematics, and physical sciences), EDUCATION (business, elementary, science, and secondary), ENGINEERING AND ENVIRONMENTAL DESIGN (engineering management), HEALTH PROFESSIONS (health care administration, medical laboratory technology, medical records administration/services, nuclear medical technology, nursing, premedicine, and respiratory therapy), SOCIAL SCIENCE (behavioral science, criminal justice, history, humanities, Latin American studies, parks and recreation management, political science/government, prelaw, psychology, and sociology). Business, health professions, education, and social sciences are the strongest programs academically and have the largest enrollments.

Required: To graduate, all students must complete at least 124 credit hours, with 60 to 80 in the major. The required core curriculum includes 12 credits each in foreign language and culture, and social and behavioral sciences, 9 each in English and speech, and humanities and fine arts, 6 each in mathematics and laboratory science, 4 in physical education, and 3 in American civilization. A minimum GPA of 2.0 is required.

Special: YCP offers internships for upper-division students, a Washington semester at American University, an exchange program with the College of Ripon and York St. John, York, England, dual majors in any combination, a 3–2 engineering degree with Columbia University, nondegree study, and pass/fail options. There are 2 national honor societies on campus.

Faculty/Classroom: Sixty-three percent of faculty are male; 37%, female. All teach undergraduates. No introductory courses are taught by graduate students. The average class size in an introductory lecture is 40; in a laboratory, 20; and in a regular course offering, 30.

Admissions: About 62% of the 1993–94 applicants were accepted. About 39% of the current freshmen were in the top fifth of their class; 76% were in the top two fifths. Four freshmen graduated first in their class.

Requirements: YCP requires applicants to be in the upper 60% of their class. A minimum GPA of 2.5 is required. The SAT I or ACT is required, with a minimum composite score of 870 on the SAT or 21 on the ACT. In addition, applicants must be graduates of an accredited secondary school or have a GED certificate. Fifteen academic credits are required, including 4 units in English, 3 or 4 in mathematics, 2 or 3 in science, 2 in history, and 1 in social studies. Music students must audition. AP and CLEP credits are accepted. Important factors used in the admissions decision are advanced placement or honor courses, leadership record, extracurricular activities record, personality, intangible qualities, and evidence of special talent.

Procedure: Freshmen are admitted fall and spring. Entrance exams should be taken in the spring of the junior year or the fall of the senior year. Application deadlines are open. Application fee is $20. Notification is sent on a rolling basis. There is a deferred admissions plan. A waiting list is an active part of the admissions procedure.

Transfer: About 180 transfer students enrolled in 1993–94. Applicants must have a minimum GPA of 2.5 from a regionally accredited institution. Students with fewer than 30 credit hours must submit a high school transcript. An interview is recommended. A total of 30 credits out of 124 must be completed at YCP.

Visiting: There are regularly scheduled orientations for prospective students, including Senior Saturday, which is the last Saturday in October. It consists of a general orientation, academic and support services sessions, and campus tours. There are guides for informal visits and visitors may sit in on classes. To arrange for a visit, contact the Admissions Office at (717) 849–1600.

Financial Aid: In 1993–94, 66% of all current freshmen and 69% of continuing students received some form of financial aid. About 45% of freshmen and 43% of continuing students received need-based aid. The average freshman award was $4386. Of that total, scholarships or need-based grants averaged $2681 ($8000 maximum); loans averaged $2363 ($2625 maximum); and work contracts averaged $1500 ($2000 maximum). Fifty-three percent of undergraduate students work part-time. Average earnings from campus work for the school year are $1500. The average financial indebtedness of the 1992–93 graduate was $10,000. YCP is a member of CSS. The FAF, the college's own financial statement, and the PHEAA are required. The deadline for financial aid applications is April 15.

International Students: There are currently 29 international students enrolled. They must take the TOEFL and achieve a minimum score of 500. The student must also take the SAT I or the ACT.

Computers: The college provides computer facilities for student use. The mainframes are a DEC VAX 6000–310 and a DEC VAX 4000–4400. Mainframe terminals and Apple IIe, IBM-compatible, and Apple Macintosh microcomputers plus English composition facilities and numerous software packages are available to students 120 hours a week in the academic computer center. All students may access the system. There are no time limits on using the system and no fees.

Graduates: In 1992–93, 668 bachelor's degrees were awarded. The most popular majors among graduates were elementary education (13%), nursing (12%), and management (10%). Within an average freshman class, 15% graduate in 3 years, 65% in 4 years, 72% in 5 years, and 79% in 6 years. Some 33 companies recruited on campus in 1992–93. In the 1992 graduating class, 31% of the men and 26% of the women were enrolled in graduate school within 6 months of graduation; 93% of the men and 91% of the women had found employment.

Admissions Contact: Director of Admissions.

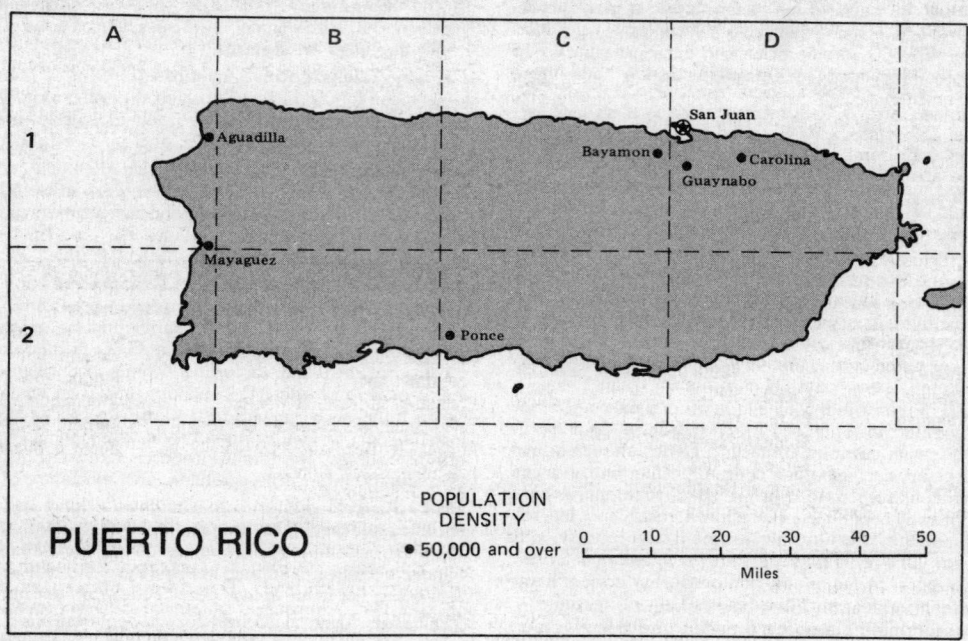

A   B   C   D

1

Aguadilla

San Juan
Bayamon • Carolina
Guaynabo

Mayaguez

2

Ponce

POPULATION
DENSITY
• 50,000 and over

0 10 20 30 40 50
Miles

PUERTO RICO

ANTILLIAN COLLEGE
(See Universidad Adventista de las Antillas)

BAYAMON CENTRAL UNIVERSITY
(See Central University of Bayamon)

BAYAMON TECHNOLOGICAL UNIVERSITY COLLEGE

A-1

Bayamon, PR 00959–1919   (809) 786–2885, ext. 259

Full-time: 1402 men, 1865 women	Faculty: 158; IIB, --$
Part-time: 403 men, 612 women	Ph.D.s: 17%
Graduate: none	Student/Faculty: 21 to 1
Year: semesters, summer session	Tuition: $1600 ($3000)
Application Deadline: December 20	Room & Board: n/app
Freshman Class: n/av	
CEEB, SAT I, or ACT: required	

Bayamon Technological University College, a coeducational commuter institution founded in 1971, is part of the University of Puerto Rico system. The college offers undergraduate business, education, and technical programs. There are 18 undergraduate schools. The library contains 56,654 volumes, 21,880 microform items, and 2871 audiovisual forms, and subscribes to 675 periodicals. Computerized library sources and services include the card catalog and database searching. Special learning facilities include a learning resource center. The 70-acre campus is in a suburban area 9 miles west of San Juan. There are 20 buildings on campus. There are no residence halls.

Student Life: Nearly all of undergraduates are from Puerto Rico. Students come from 3 foreign countries. Sixty-six percent are from public schools; 34% from private. All are Hispanic. The average age of freshmen is 18; all undergraduates, 20. Thirty-two percent drop out by the end of their first year; 75% remain to graduate.

Housing: There are no residence halls. All students commute. Alcohol is not permitted.

Activities: There are no fraternities or sororities on campus. There are 16 groups on campus, including art, band, chess, choir, chorale, computers, dance, drama, drill team, honors, professional, religious, social, social service, and student government. Popular campus events include an annual sports tournament, recognition of distinguished athletes, the college anniversary, arts and crafts fair, annual song festival, and annual drama festival.

Sports: There are 9 intercollegiate sports for men and 7 for women, and 14 intramural sports for men and 9 for women. Athletic and recreation facilities include a basketball/volleyball court, a tennis court, a track and field site, an exercise gymnasium, and a recreation room with table tennis, electronic games, and pool tables.

Disabled Students: Ninety percent of the campus is accessible to disabled students. The following facilities are available: wheelchair ramps, special parking, specially equipped rest rooms, lowered drinking fountains, and lowered telephones.

Services: In addition to many counseling and information services, tutoring is available in some subjects, including in English, mathematics, Spanish, and physics for engineering and electronics students. In addition, there is a reader service for the blind and remedial math.

Campus Safety and Security: Campus safety and security measures include 24-hour foot and vehicle patrol and pamphlets, posters, and films.

Programs of Study: CUTB awards the B.A. degree. Associate degrees are also awarded. Bachelor's degrees are awarded in BUSINESS (accounting, business administration and management, and marketing/retailing/merchandising), COMPUTER AND PHYSICAL SCIENCE (computer science), EDUCATION (early childhood and elementary). Electronics is the strongest academically. Business administration has the largest enrollment.

Required: General education requirements include courses in Spanish, English, mathematics, social sciences or humanities, and biological or physical sciences. To graduate, students must complete 130 to 135 credits, including 29 to 34 in the major, with a minimum GPA of 2.0.

Special: Students may cross-register with any campus in the University of Puerto Rico system. Co-op programs, work-study programs, dual majors, pass/fail options, and a 3–2 engineering degree with the Mayaguez campus are also available. There is a freshman honors program on campus.

Faculty/Classroom: Forty-nine percent of faculty are male; 51%, female. All teach undergraduates. The average class size in an introductory lecture is 23 and in a laboratory, 20.

Requirements: The SAT I or the ACT is required, or the CEEB Spanish version, along with SAT II: Subject tests in Spanish, writing, and mathematics. Applicants must be graduates of accredited secondary schools. The GED is accepted.

Procedure: Freshmen are admitted in the fall. Entrance exams should be taken by October of the senior year. Applications should be filed by December 20 for fall entry and September 15 for spring entry, along with an application fee of $15. Notification is sent by May 1.

Transfer: About 385 transfer students enrolled in a recent year. Applicants must present an associate degree or at least 30 college credits and a minimum GPA of 2.5. A total of 28 credits out of 130 to 135 must be completed at CUTB.

Visiting: There are regularly scheduled orientations for prospective students. To arrange for a visit, contact Pedro Martinez, Director of Admissions at (809) 786–6615.

Financial Aid: In a recent year, 75% of all current freshmen and 56% of continuing students received some form of financial aid. Scholarships or need-based grants averaged $829; loans averaged $1435; and work contracts averaged $1003. Applicants must submit the FAF, the college's own financial statement, income tax forms,

medical receipts, and social security information. The deadline for financial aid applications is May 1.

International Students: There are currently 4 international students enrolled. The student must take the SAT I or the Spanish equivalent version of the SAT I. Students must take SAT II: Subject tests in Spanish, writing, and mathematics.

Computers: The college provides computer facilities for student use. The mainframe is a DEC VAX 11/780. There are also 80 IBM PCs and PS/2, Apple Macintosh, and ITT microcomputers available in departmental laboratories. Those students enrolled in computer-related courses may access the mainframe. Students may access the system 2 hours per day. There are no fees.

Graduates: In a recent year, 385 bachelor's degrees were awarded. The most popular majors among graduates were accounting (21%), secretarial sciences (13%), and electronics (13%). Within an average freshman class, 10% graduate in 4 years, 26% in 5 years, and 17% in 6 years. Some 27 companies recruited on campus in a recent year.

Admissions Contact: Pedro Martinez, Director of Admissions.

CARIBBEAN UNIVERSITY

C-1

Bayamon, PR 00621–0493

(809) 780–0070, ext. 326

Full-time: 562 men, 982 women

Part-time: 547 men, 950 women

Graduate: none

Year: trimesters

Application Deadline: August 31

Freshman Class: 800 applied, 700 accepted, 590 enrolled

SAT I: required

Faculty: IIB

Ph.D.s: n/av

Student/Faculty: 32 to 1

Tuition: $2400

Room & Board: n/app

Caribbean University, founded in 1969, is an independent, commuter institution offering undergraduate programs in business, engineering, health science and liberal arts. There are extension centers in Vega Baja, Carolina, and Ponce. There are 6 undergraduate schools. The library contains 26,240 volumes, 1157 microform items, and 215 audiovisual forms, and subscribes to 371 periodicals. Special learning facilities include a learning resource center. The 21-acre campus is in an urban area. There are 8 buildings on campus. There are no residence halls.

Student Life: About 90% of undergraduates are from Puerto Rico.

Housing: There are no residence halls; all students commute.

Activities: There are 10 groups on campus, including chess, professional, social, and student government.

Sports: There are 6 intramural sports for men and 6 for women. Athletic and recreation facilities include basketball and tennis courts and a track and field arena.

Disabled Students: All of the campus is accessible to disabled students. The following facilities are available: wheelchair ramps, elevators, special parking, specially equipped rest rooms, and special counseling is provided.

Services: In addition to many counseling and information services, tutoring is available in every subject. In addition, there is remedial math, reading, and writing.

Campus Safety and Security: Campus safety and security measures include campus security guards, student ID cards, and regular fire drills.

Programs of Study: CU awards the B.A., B.S., B.A.E., B.B.A., B.S.C.E., B.S.I.E., B.S.N., and B.Secretarial Science degrees. Associate degrees also are awarded. Bachelor's degrees are awarded in BIOLOGICAL SCIENCE (biology/biological science), BUSINESS (accounting, banking and finance, business administration and management, and marketing/retailing/merchandising), COMPUTER AND PHYSICAL SCIENCE (computer programming, computer science, and mathematics), EDUCATION (business, elementary, middle school, science, secondary, special, and teaching English as a second language/foreign language), ENGINEERING AND ENVIRONMENTAL DESIGN (civil engineering, engineering, engineering technology, and industrial engineering technology), HEALTH PROFESSIONS (nursing and premedicine), SOCIAL SCIENCE (criminal justice, prelaw, social science, and social work).

Required: To graduate, all students must complete 135 to 140 credits, with a minimum GPA of 2.0. There are core curriculum requirements in English, Spanish, humanities, social sciences, biology, science, mathematics, and history.

Faculty/Classroom: Sixty-five percent of faculty are male; 35%, female.

Admissions: About 88% of the 1993–94 applicants were accepted.

Requirements: A minimum GPA of 2.0 is required. The SAT I is required, with a recommended minimum score of 400 in each component. Applicants must be graduates of an accredited secondary school with a GPA of 2.0. The GED is accepted. High school preparation should include 3 years each of art, English, Spanish, and social studies, 2 years each of history and mathematics, and 1 year of science.

Procedure: Freshmen are admitted to all sessions. Entrance exams should be taken in the junior or senior year. Applications should be filed by August 31 for fall entry, December 31 for winter entry, and April 30 for summer entry, along with an application fee of $15. The college accepts all applicants. Notification is sent on a rolling basis.

Transfer: A minimum college GPA of 2.0 is recommended. Applicants should submit two official transcripts and a catalog from each previous college attended, along with a written recommendation from the dean at the last institution. A total of 30 credits must be completed at CU.

Visiting: There are regularly scheduled orientations for prospective students. To arrange for a visit, contact Director of Admissions at (809) 780–0070, ext. 326.

Financial Aid: In 1993–94 85% of all current freshmen received some form of financial aid. CU is a member of CSS. The FAF and income tax returns is required. The deadline for financial aid applications is August 31.

Computers: CU provides microcomputers for the academic use of all students. It may be used during school hours.

Admissions Contact: Angie Diaz, Director of Admissions.

CENTRAL UNIVERSITY OF BAYAMON

C-1

(Formerly Bayamon Central University)

Bayamon, PR 00960–1725

(809) 786–3030, ext. 202

Full-time: 290 men, 515 women

Part-time: none

Graduate: 40 men, 39 women

Year: semesters, summer session

Application Deadline: April 15

Freshman Class: n/av

SAT I: required

Faculty: 69

Ph.D.s: 15%

Student/Faculty: 12 to 1

Tuition: $2430

Room & Board: n/app

Central University of Bayamon, founded in 1970, is a private Catholic institution offering degree programs in the arts and sciences, business, education, nursing, and religious studies and serving an entirely commuter student body. There are 4 undergraduate and 3 graduate schools. The 2 libraries contain 51,500 volumes and 40 microform items, and subscribe to 370 periodicals. The 55-acre campus is in an urban area 4 miles west of Bayamon. There are 13 buildings on campus.

Student Life: All undergraduates are from Puerto Rico. Ninety percent are from public schools; 10% from private. All are Hispanic. The average age of freshmen is 17; all undergraduates, 20.

Housing: There are no residence halls; all students commute and may keep cars on campus. Alcohol is not permitted.

Activities: There are no fraternities or sororities on campus. There are 13 groups on campus, including computers, literary magazine, professional, religious, social service, and student government.

Sports: Athletic and recreation facilities include a 400-seat gymnasium, basketball and volleyball courts, a swimming pool, and a weight-training room.

Disabled Students: All of the campus is accessible to disabled students. The following facilities are available: wheelchair ramps, elevators, special parking, specially equipped rest rooms, special class scheduling, lowered drinking fountains, and lowered telephones.

Services: In addition to many counseling and information services, tutoring is available in some subjects, including English, Spanish, philosophy, accounting, mathematics, biology, and computer science. There is also a reader service for the blind, and remedial math, reading, and writing.

Campus Safety and Security: Campus safety and security measures include 24-hour foot and vehicle patrol.

Programs of Study: Central University of Bayamon awards the B.A., B.S., B.B.A., B.S.N., and B.S.S. degrees. Associate and master's degrees also are awarded. Bachelor's degrees are awarded in BIOLOGICAL SCIENCE (biology/biological science), BUSINESS (accounting, business administration and management, and marketing/retailing/merchandising), COMMUNICATIONS AND THE ARTS (journalism and Spanish), COMPUTER AND PHYSICAL SCIENCE (chemistry and computer science), EDUCATION (elementary, English, science, and secondary), HEALTH PROFESSIONS (nursing and premedicine), SOCIAL SCIENCE (philosophy, psychology, religion, social work, and sociology). Business administration is the strongest academically and has the largest enrollment.

Required: Students must complete 48 credits distributed among specific courses in theology, philosophy, Spanish, English, humanities, social science, mathematics, science, and physical education. The bachelor's degree requires completion of 124 to 141 credits, including 33 to 43 in the major, with a minimum GPA of 2.0.

Special: The university offers limited pass/fail options, work-study programs, and nondegree study.

Faculty/Classroom: All teach undergraduates. The average class size in an introductory lecture is 35; in a laboratory, 20; and in a regular course offering, 35.

Requirements: A minimum GPA of 2.0 is required. The SAT I or the CEEB Spanish equivalent version is required. Spanish equivalent version. Applicants must be graduates of accredited secondary schools or have earned a GED. They must speak Spanish and have a good knowledge of English. The university requires 15 1/2 academic credits, including 1 credit each in social studies and electives, 1 1/2 in history, and 3 each in English, Spanish, mathematics, and science. An interview is recommended. CLEP credit is accepted. Important factors used in the admissions decision are recommendations by school

officials, personality, intangible qualities, ability to finance college education, leadership record, and extracurricular activities record.

Procedure: Freshmen are admitted to all sessions. Entrance exams should be taken by October of the senior year. Applications should be filed by April 15 for fall entry, November 15 for winter entry, and April 30 for summer entry, along with an application fee of $15. Notification is sent beginning in March.

Transfer: About 150 transfer students enrolled in a recent year. A minimum GPA of 2.0 is required. A total of 30 credits out of 124 to 141 must be completed at Central University of Bayamon.

Visiting: There are regularly scheduled orientations for prospective students. There are guides for informal visits and visitors may sit in on classes. To arrange for a visit, contact the Admissions Office at (809) 786-3030, ext. 202.

Financial Aid: In an earlier year, scholarships or need-based grants averaged $450 ($1600 maximum); loans averaged $2625 ($4000 maximum); and work contracts averaged $603 ($804 maximum). The average financial indebtedness of an earlier graduate was $1095. The college's own financial statement is required. The deadline for financial aid applications is July.

International Students: Recently, there were 9 international students enrolled.

Computers: The college provides computer facilities for student use. The mainframe is a Wang VS 45. Those students registered with the computer laboratory may access the mainframe from 9 A.M. to 7 P.M. Monday through Thursday and from 9 A.M. to noon on Friday. Students may access the system 2 hours per week. The fee is $30.

Admissions Contact: Christine M. Hernandez, Director of Admissions.

CONSERVATORY OF MUSIC OF PUERTO RICO   D-1
Hato Rey, PR 00918   (809) 751-0160, ext. 32

Full-time: 140 men, 52 women	Faculty: 30
Part-time: 59 men, 32 women	Ph.D.s: 2%
Graduate: none	Student/Faculty: 6 to 1
Year: semesters	Tuition: $715
Application Deadline: April 15	Room & Board: n/app
Freshman Class: 97 applied, 57 accepted, 43 enrolled	
CEEB or SAT I: required	

The Conservatory of Music of Puerto Rico, founded in 1959, is a specialized commuter school supported by the Commonwealth of Puerto Rico, offering 4- and 5-year degree programs. The library contains 23,608 volumes, 11 microform items, and 5000 audiovisual forms, and subscribes to 2 periodicals. Special learning facilities include a learning resource center and a computer-based ear-training laboratory. The 3-acre campus is in an urban area in the Hato Rey section of San Juan. There are 3 buildings on campus.

Student Life: About 98% of undergraduates are from Puerto Rico. Students come from 5 foreign countries. Sixty percent are from public schools; 40% from private. All are Hispanic. The average age of freshmen is 19; all undergraduates, 23. Four percent drop out by the end of their first year; 96% remain to graduate.

Housing: There are no residence halls. All students commute. Alcohol is not permitted.

Activities: There are no fraternities or sororities on campus. There are many groups and organizations on campus, including band, choir, chorale, chorus, jazz band, newspaper, opera, orchestra, religious, student government, and symphony. Popular campus events include Annual Open House, semester-closing concerts, Sanroma Piano Competition, and Sunday family concerts.

Sports: There is no sports program at the conservatory.

Disabled Students: The entire campus is accessible to disabled students. The following facilities are available: wheelchair ramps, special parking, specially equipped rest rooms, and lowered drinking fountains.

Campus Safety and Security: Campus safety and security measures include 24-hour foot and vehicle patrol, informal discussions, emergency telephones, and lighted pathways and sidewalks.

Programs of Study: The conservatory awards the B.F.A., B.M., and B.Perf.Arts degrees.

Required: To graduate, students must complete 142 credit hours (158 for music education) with a minimum GPA of 2.0. Requirements include 4 years of courses in the principal instrument and specific courses in music theory, including solfege, harmony, and counterpoint. All students must present a graduation recital.

Special: A dual major is available in the principal instrument and music education.

Faculty/Classroom: Seventy percent of faculty are male; 30%, female. All teach undergraduates.

Admissions: About 59% of the 1993–94 applicants were accepted. The SAT scores for the 1993–94 freshman class were as follows: Verbal—10% below 500 and 90% between 500 and 599; Math—60% below 500, 35% between 500 and 599, and 5% between 600 and 700. About 10% of the current freshmen were in the top fifth of their class; 90% were in the top two fifths.

Requirements: A minimum GPA of 2.0 is required. The SAT I is required, or the CEEB's Spanish version. Applicants must be graduates of an accredited secondary school. An interview and audition are required. AP credits are accepted. Important factors used in the admissions decision are evidence of special talent, recommendations by school officials, geographic diversity, personality, intangible qualities, and recommendations by alumni.

Procedure: Freshmen are admitted to all sessions. Entrance exams should be taken in May of the junior year or December of the senior year. Applications should be filed by April 15 for fall entry and November 15 for spring entry, along with an application fee of $25. Notification is sent by June 30. There is an early admissions plan. A waiting list is an active part of the admissions procedure.

Transfer: About 20 transfer students enrolled in a recent year. A total of 100 credits out of 142 must be completed at the conservatory.

Visiting: There are regularly scheduled orientations for prospective students. To arrange for a visit, contact Pilar Ruibal, Counselor, or Zulma Palos, Admissions Director, at (809) 751-0160, ext. 51 or 32.

Financial Aid: In 1993–94, 90% of all current freshmen and 50% of continuing students received some form of financial aid. About 90% of freshmen and 60% of continuing students received need-based aid. The average freshman award was $1540. Fifteen percent of undergraduate students work part-time. Average earnings from campus work for the school year are $850. The conservatory is a member of CSS. The FAF is required. The deadline for financial aid applications is July 30.

Graduates: In 1992–93, 22 bachelor's degrees were awarded. The most popular majors among graduates are instrument/voice (80%) and music education (20%). Within an average freshman class, 2% graduate in 4 years, 83% in 5 years, and 15% in 6 years. In the 1992 graduating class, 2% of all graduates were enrolled in graduate school within 6 months of graduation; 80% of the men and 90% of the women had found employment.

Admissions Contact: Zulma Palos, Admissions Director.

ESCUELA DE ARTES PLASTICAS   D-1
San Juan, PR 00902–1112   (809) 725-8120, ext. 234

Full-time: 95 men, 97 women	Faculty: 9
Part-time: none	Ph.D.s: n/av
Graduate: none	Student/Faculty: 21 to 1
Year: semesters	Tuition: $1524
Application Deadline: May 16	Room & Board: $2500
Freshman Class: 107 applied, 67 accepted, 62 enrolled	
CEEB: required	

Escuela de Artes Plasticas, founded in 1966, is a public institution considered to be the National Art School of Puerto Rico. The library contains 12,429 volumes, 10,000 microform items, and 300 audiovisual forms, and subscribes to 40 periodicals. Special learning facilities include a learning resource center and an art gallery. The 1-acre campus is in an urban area in Old San Juan. There are 3 buildings on campus.

Student Life: About 99% of undergraduates are from Puerto Rico. Students come from 6 foreign countries. Eighty-five percent are from public schools; 15% from private. Ninety-nine percent are Hispanic. The average age of freshmen is 18; all undergraduates, 25. Five percent drop out by the end of their first year; 20% remain to graduate.

Housing: There are no residence halls; all students commute. Alcohol is not permitted.

Activities: There are no fraternities or sororities on campus. There are some groups on campus, including art, dance, jazz band, literary magazine, newspaper, and student government. Popular campus events include Student Day, open house, and art fairs.

Sports: There is no sports program at Escuela de Artes Plasticas.

Disabled Students: Twenty-five percent of the campus is accessible to disabled students. The following facilities are available: wheelchair ramps and special class scheduling.

Services: In addition to many counseling and information services, tutoring is available in some subjects, including English and various art workshops. There is also remedial writing.

Campus Safety and Security: Campus safety and security measures include 24-hour foot and vehicle patrol, pamphlets, posters, films, and emergency telephones.

Programs of Study: Escuela de Artes Plasticas awards the B.A. degree. Bachelor's degrees are awarded in COMMUNICATIONS AND THE ARTS (graphic design, painting, and sculpture) and EDUCATION (art). Painting has the largest enrollment.

Required: To graduate, students must maintain a minimum GPA of 2.0 in 144 credits, including 33 in art fundamentals and 51 in general education courses.

Faculty/Classroom: Seventy percent of faculty are male; 30%, female. Sixty percent teach undergraduates and 40% do research. The average class size in an introductory lecture is 25 and in a laboratory, 18.

Admissions: About 63% of the 1993–94 applicants were accepted.

Requirements: A minimum GPA of 2.0 is required. The CEEB Spanish equivalent of the SAT I is required. Applicants must be graduates of an accredited secondary school or have earned a GED. A portfolio

and interview are required, with an essay recommended. Important factors used in the admissions decision are evidence of special talent, recommendations by school officials, personality, intangible qualities, recommendations by alumni, and extracurricular activities record.

Procedure: Freshmen are admitted in the fall. Applications should be filed by May 16 for fall entry, along with an application fee of $20. Notification is sent on a rolling basis.

Transfer: About 22 transfer students enrolled in a recent year.

Visiting: There are regularly scheduled orientations for prospective students. There are guides for informal visits. To arrange for a visit, contact the Student Affairs Office at (809) 725-8120.

Financial Aid: In 1993–94, 43% of all current freshmen and 62% of continuing students received some form of financial aid. The average freshman award was $2300. Of that total, scholarships or need-based grants averaged $200 ($300 maximum); and work contracts averaged $100 ($1000 maximum). Eight percent of undergraduate students work part-time. The FAF is required.

International Students: There are currently 6 international students enrolled. The school actively recruits these students. The student must take the CEEB English or Spanish SAT I.

Graduates: In an earlier year, 17 bachelor's degrees were awarded. Four companies recruited on campus in 1992–93. In the 1992 graduating class, 20% of the men and 10% of the women were enrolled in graduate school within 6 months of graduation; 40% of the men and 10% of the women had found employment.

Admissions Contact: Ivette Munoz Mercado, Professional Counselor.

INTER AMERICAN UNIVERSITY OF PUERTO RICO
AGUADILLA REGIONAL COLLEGE

A-1

Aguadilla, PR 00605   (809) 891-0925

Full-time, part-time: 3426 men and women	Faculty: IIA, --$
	Ph.D.s: n/av
Graduate: none	Student/Faculty: n/av
Year: semesters, summer session	Tuition: $2290
Application Deadline: May 1	Room & Board: n/app
Freshman Class: n/av	
SAT I: required	

Inter American Univeristy of Puerto Rico/Aguadilla regional College, a private, nonsectariam coeducational institution, was founded in 1912 and is a part of the Inter American University of Puerto Rico. Programs offered include undergraduate and graduate study in business, fine and liberal arts, health sciences, and teacher preparation. In addition to regional accreditation, Inter American at Aguadilla has baccalaureate program accreditation with CSWE. Computerized library sources and services include the card catalog. Special learning facilities include an audiovisual center, an instructional development center, and a publication center. The campus is in an urban area in a small city.

Housing: There are no residence halls.

Activities: There are some groups and organizations on campus, including chorale, professional, religious, and social.

Services: Professional advisers provide counseling and guidance services.

Programs of Study: Inter American at Aguadilla awards the B.A., B.S., and B.B.A. degrees. Associate, master's, and doctoral degrees are also awarded. Bachelor's degrees are awarded in BIOLOGICAL SCIENCE (biology/biological science), BUSINESS (accounting, banking and finance, business administration and management, insurance, management information systems, marketing/retailing/merchandising, and secretarial studies/office management), COMMUNICATIONS AND THE ARTS (applied music, Spanish, and visual and performing arts), COMPUTER AND PHYSICAL SCIENCE (chemical technology, chemistry, computer science, and mathematics), EDUCATION (early childhood, elementary, music, secondary, and special), ENGINEERING AND ENVIRONMENTAL DESIGN (electrical/electronics engineering technology), HEALTH PROFESSIONS (medical technology and nursing), SOCIAL SCIENCE (criminal justice, history, political science/government, psychology, public administration, social work, and sociology).

Required: To graduate, students must fulfill 50 general education credits as follows: 18 in communication skills; 12 in historical cultural heritage; 11 in ability to integrate, apply, and create; 8 in reasoning skills; 6 in methods of interpreting reality; and 2 nonacademic credits each in health/physical education/recreational and Introduction to University Life. A total of 120 credit hours is required; the number required in the major varies. A 2.0 GPA overall and in the major is required.

Special: Co-op programs in engineering and earth and mineral sciences with Pennsylvania State University, internship and work-study programs, cross-registration, and adult and continuing education programs are available.

Requirements: A minimum GPA of 2.0 is required. The SAT I is required. Native Spanish speakers may take the Spanish version of the SAT. The SAT II: writing is also required. Applicants must be gradu-

ates of an accredited secondary school. An interview may be required. AP credits are accepted.

Procedure: Applications should be filed by May 1 for fall entry, November 15 for spring entry, and April 15 for summer entry, along with an application fee of $15. Notification is sent on a rolling basis. There is an early admissions plan.

Transfer: Transfer applicants must submit all college transcripts and must be in good standing at their previous intitution. A minimum of 15 transferable credits with a grade of at least C must have been completed.

Financial Aid: The college's own financial statement and the Federal Student Aid form are required. The deadline for financial aid applications is April 28.

Computers: The college provides computer facilities for student use.

Admissions Contact: Director of Admissions, (809) 891-0925.

INTER AMERICAN UNIVERSITY OF PUERTO RICO
BAYAMON UNIVERSITY COLLEGE

C-1

Bayamon, PR 00619   (809) 780-4040

Full-time, part-time: 4,427 men and woment	Faculty: IIA, --$
	Ph.D.s: n/av
Graduate: none	Student/Faculty: n/av
Year: semesters, summer session	Tuition: $2300
Application Deadline: May 1	Room & Board: n/app
Freshman Class: n/av	
SAT I: required	

Inter American University of Puerto Rico/Bayamon University College, a private, nonsectarian, coeducational institution, was founded in 1912 and is a part of the Inter American University of Puerto Rico. Students may pursue undergraduate and graduate study in business, health sciences, liberal and fine arts, and teacher preparation. In addition to regional accreditation, Inter American at Bayamon has baccalaureate program accreditation with CSWE. Computerized library sources and services include the card catalog. Special learning facilities include an audiovisual center, an instructional development center, and a publicaton center. The campus is in an urban area in a medium-size city.

Activities: There are some groups and organizations on campus, including chorale, professional, religious, and social.

Services: Professional advisers are available for counseling and guidance.

Programs of Study: Inter American at Bayamon awards the B.A., B.S., and B.B.A. degrees. Associate, master's, and doctoral degrees are also awarded. Bachelor's degrees are awarded in BIOLOGICAL SCIENCE (biology/biological science), BUSINESS (accounting, banking and finance, business administration and management, insurance, management information systems, marketing/retailing/merchandising, and secretarial studies/office management), COMMUNICATIONS AND THE ARTS (applied music, Spanish, and visual and performing arts), COMPUTER AND PHYSICAL SCIENCE (chemical technology, chemistry, computer science, and mathematics), EDUCATION (early childhood, elementary, music, secondary, and special), ENGINEERING AND ENVIRONMENTAL DESIGN (electrical/electronics engineering technology), HEALTH PROFESSIONS (medical technology and nursing), SOCIAL SCIENCE (criminal justice, history, political science/government, psychology, public administration, social work, and sociology).

Required: All students must complete 59 general education credits as follows: 18 in communication skills; 12 in historical-cultural heritage; 11 in ability to integrate, apply, and create; 8 in reasoning skills; 6 in methods of interpreting reality; and 2 nonacademic credits each in health/physical education/recreation and introduction to university life. A total of 120 credit hours must be completed, with a variable number in the major, and a minimum 2.0 GPA overall and in the major must be maintained.

Special: Co-op programs in engineering and earth and mineral sciences with Pennsylvania State University, cross-registration, internship and work-study programs, and adult and continuing education programs are available.

Requirements: A minimum GPA of 2.0 is required. The SAT I is required. Students whose first language is Spanish may take the Spanish version of the SAT. The SAT II: writing is also required. Applicants must be graduates of an accredited secondary school. An interview may be required. AP credits are accepted.

Procedure: Applications should be filed by May 1 for fall entry, November 15 for spring entry, and April 15 for summer entry, along with an application fee of $15. Notification is sent on a rolling basis. There is an early admissions plan.

Transfer: Transfer applicants must have at least 15 transferable semester credits with a minimum grade of C and must be in good standing at their previous institution. All college transcripts must be submitted.

Financial Aid: The college's own financial statement and the Federal Student Aid form are required. The deadline for financial aid applications is April 28.

Computers: The college provides computer facilities for student use.

Admissions Contact: Director of Admissions.

INTER AMERICAN UNIVERSITY OF PUERTO RICO
METROPOLITAN CAMPUS

Hato Rey, PR 00919   (809) 758-8000

Full-time, part-time: 12,670 men and women	Faculty: IIA, --$
	Ph.D.s: n/av
Graduate: none	Tuition: $2340 ($2340)
Year: semesters, summer session	Room & Board: n/app
Application Deadline: May 1	
Freshman Class: n/av	
SAT I: required	

Inter American University of Puerto Rico/Metropolitan Campus, a private nonsectarian, coeducational institution, was founded in 1912 and is a unit of the Inter American University of Puerto Rico. Students may pursue undergraduate and graduate study in business, fine and liberal arts, health sciences, and teacher preparation. In addition to regional accreditation, Inter American Metro has baccalaureate program accreditation with CSWE. Computerized library sources and services include the card catalog. Special learning facilities include an audiovisual center, an instructional development center, and a publication center.

Housing: There are no residence halls.

Activities: There are some groups and organizations on campus, including chorale, drama, newspaper, orchestra, professional, religious, and social.

Services: Guidance and counseling services are available.

Programs of Study: Inter American Metro awards the B.A., B.S., and B.B.A. degrees. Associate, master's, and doctoral degrees are also awarded. Bachelor's degrees are awarded in BIOLOGICAL SCIENCE (biology/biological science), BUSINESS (accounting, banking and finance, business administration and management, insurance, management information systems, marketing/retailing/merchandising, and secretarial studies/office management), COMMUNICATIONS AND THE ARTS (applied music, Spanish, and visual and performing arts), COMPUTER AND PHYSICAL SCIENCE (chemical technology, chemistry, computer science, and mathematics), EDUCATION (early childhood, elementary, music, secondary, and special), ENGINEERING AND ENVIRONMENTAL DESIGN (electrical/electronics engineering technology), HEALTH PROFESSIONS (medical technology and nursing), SOCIAL SCIENCE (criminal justice, history, political science/government, psychology, public administration, social work, and sociology).

Required: To graduate, students must complete the 59 general education credits: 18 in communications skills; 12 in historical-cultural heritage, 11 in ability to integrate, apply, and create, 8 in reasoning skills, 6 in methods of interpreting reality, 2 nonacademic credits each in helath/physical education/recreation and Introduction to University Life. A total of 120 credit hours must be completed; the number in the major varies. A minimum 2.0 GPA overall and in the major is required.

Special: Special academic programs include co-op programs in engineering and earth and mineral sciences with Pennsylvania State University, cross-registration, internship and work-study programs, and adult and continuing education programs. There are 2 national honor societies on campus.

Requirements: A minimum GPA of 2.0 is required. The SAT I is required. Students whose first langauge is Spanish may take the Spanish version of the SAT. The SAT II: writing is also required. Applicant must be graduate of an accredited secondary school. An interview may be required. AP credits are accepted.

Procedure: Applications should be filed by May 1 for fall entry, November 15 for spring entry, and April 15 for summer entry. Notification is sent on a rolling basis. There is an early admissions plan.

Transfer: At least 15 semester credits must have been earned, with a minimum grade of C. Students must present transcripts from all colleges attended and must be in good standing at their previous institution.

Financial Aid: The college's own financial statement and the Federal Student Aid form are required. The deadline for financial aid applications is April 28.

Computers: The college provides computer facilities for student use.

INTER AMERICAN UNIVERSITY OF PUERTO RICO
PONCE REGIONAL COLLEGE   C-2

Ponce, PR 00715-2201   (809) 840-9090

Full-time: 3379	Faculty: IIA, --$
Part-time: none	Ph.D.s: n/av
Graduate: none	Student/Faculty: n/av
Year: semesters, summer session	Tuition: $2300 ($2300)
Application Deadline: May 1	Room & Board: n/app
Freshman Class: n/av	
SAT I: required	

Inter American University of Puerto Rico Ponce Regional College, founded in 1912 and a unit of the Inter American University of Puerto Rico, is a private, nonsectarian, coeducational institution offering undergraduate and graduate programs in business, liberal and fine arts, health sciences, and teacher preparation. In addition to regional accreditation, Inter American at Ponce has baccalaureate program accreditation with CSWE. Computerized library sources and services include the card catalog. Special learning facilities include an audiovisual center, an instructional development center, and a publication center. The campus is in an urban area in a medium-size city.

Housing: There are no residence halls.

Activities: There are some groups and organizations on campus, including chorale, professional, religious, social, and student government.

Services: Professional advisers are available for guidance and counseling services.

Programs of Study: Inter American at Ponce awards the B.A., B.S., and B.B.A. degrees. Associate, master's, and doctoral degrees are awarded. Bachelor's degrees are awarded in BIOLOGICAL SCIENCE (biology/biological science), BUSINESS (accounting, banking and finance, business administration and management, insurance, management information systems, marketing/retailing/merchandising, and secretarial studies/office management), COMMUNICATIONS AND THE ARTS (applied music, Spanish, and visual and performing arts), COMPUTER AND PHYSICAL SCIENCE (chemical technology, chemistry, computer science, and mathematics), EDUCATION (early childhood, elementary, music, secondary, and special), ENGINEERING AND ENVIRONMENTAL DESIGN (electrical/electronics engineering technology), HEALTH PROFESSIONS (medical technology and nursing), SOCIAL SCIENCE (criminal justice, history, political science/government, psychology, public administration, social work, and sociology).

Required: To graduate, students must fulfill general education requirements as follows: 18 credits in communications skills; 12 in historical-cultural heritage; 11 in ability to integrate, apply, and create; 8 in reasoning skills; 6 in methods of interpreting reality; and 2 nonacademic credits each in Introduction to University Life and health/physical education/recreation. All students must complete 120 credit hours, with a variable number in the major, and maintain a minimum 2.0 GPA overall and in the major.

Special: Special academic programs include co-op programs in engineering and earth and mineral sciences with Pennsylvania State University, cross-registration, internships, work-study, and adult and continuing education programs.

Requirements: A minimum GPA of 2.0 is required. The SAT I is required. Students whose first language is Spanish may take the Spanish version of the SAT I. The SAT II: Subject test in writing also is required. Applicants must be graduates of an accredited secondary school. An interview may be required. AP credits are accepted.

Procedure: Applications should be filed by May 1 for fall entry, November 15 for spring entry, and April 15 for summer entry, along with an application fee of $15. Notification is sent on a rolling basis. There is an early admissions plan.

Transfer: At least 15 transferable semester credits must have been completed, with a minimum grade of C. Students must be in good standing at their previous institution and must submit all college transcripts.

Financial Aid: The college's own financial statement and the Federal Student Aid form are required. The deadline for financial aid applications is April 28.

Computers: The college provides computer facilities for student use.

Admissions Contact: Director of Admissions.

INTER AMERICAN UNIVERSITY
ARECIBO CAMPUS
B-1

(Formerly Inter-American University/College of Arecibo)
Arecibo, PR 00614-4050   (809) 878-5195

Full-time: 1086 men, 2346 women | Faculty: 94
Part-time: 342 men, 605 women | Ph.Ds: 14%
Graduate: none | Student/Faculty: 37 to 1
Year: semesters, summer session | Tuition: $2750
Application Deadline: May 1 | Room & Board: n/app
Freshman Class: 1397 applied, 1299 accepted, 1032 enrolled
SAT I: required

Arecibo College, founded in 1957, is a private, nonsectarian unit of the Inter-American University of Puerto Rico. The college offers programs in business, health sciences, liberal arts, and teacher preparation. The library contains 69,839 volumes and 26,929 audiovisual forms, and subscribes to 426 periodicals. Computerized library sources and services include interlibrary loans and database searching. Special learning facilities include a learning resource center. The 20-acre campus is in a suburban area 50 miles west of San Juan. There are 9 buildings on campus.

Student Life: Almost all undergraduates are from Puerto Rico. Some 93% are from public schools; 7% from private. All are Hispanic. The average age of freshmen is 18; all undergraduates, 24. About 11% drop out by the end of their first year.

Housing: There are no residence halls. Alcohol is not permitted. All students may keep cars on campus.

Activities: There are 7 local fraternities and 2 local sororities. There are 21 groups on campus, including drama, film, honors, newspaper, professional, religious, social, and student government. Popular campus events include Open House, the Talents Festival, sports events, and concerts.

Sports: There are 8 intercollegiate sports for men and 8 for women, and 9 intramural sports for men and 9 for women.

Disabled Students: The following facilities are available: wheelchair ramps, elevators, special parking, specially equipped rest rooms, lowered drinking fountains, and lowered telephones.

Services: In addition to many counseling and information services, tutoring is available in some subjects, including accounting, secretarial sciences, and mathematics. There is also a reader service for the blind and remedial math.

Campus Safety and Security: Campus safety and security measures include 24-hour foot and vehicle patrol, pamphlets, posters, films, and lighted pathways and sidewalks.

Programs of Study: The college awards the B.A. and B.S. degrees. Associate degrees also are awarded. Bachelor's degrees are awarded in BIOLOGICAL SCIENCE (biology/biological science and microbiology), BUSINESS (accounting, business administration and management, and marketing and distribution), COMPUTER AND PHYSICAL SCIENCE (chemical technology, chemistry, and computer science), EDUCATION (elementary, secondary, special, and teaching English as a second language/foreign language), HEALTH PROFESSIONS (nursing), SOCIAL SCIENCE (criminal justice and social work). Business administration has the largest enrollment.

Required: To graduate, all students must complete at least 130 credits with a GPA of 2.0. General education requirements include 55 credits in Spanish, English, mathematics, logic, computers, Puerto Rican history, humanities, health, social studies, environment, and religion. Noncredit courses are required in physical education and orientation.

Special: The college offers 3-2 programs with Pennsylvania State University in engineering and earth and mineral sciences, and with Universidad Catolica Madre y Maestra of the Dominican Republic in medicine. Independent research, work-study, and independent study programs are available. Professional certificate programs are offered in nurse anesthetist and intensive nursing care. There is a freshman honors program on campus.

Faculty/Classroom: Some 52% of faculty are male; 48%, female. All teach undergraduates. The average class size in an introductory lecture is 27 and in a laboratory, 25.

Admissions: About 93% of the 1993-94 applicants were accepted.

Requirements: A minimum GPA of 2.0 is required. The SAT I is required or the CEEB's Spanish equivalent. The SAT II: writing test is also required. In addition, applicants should be graduates of an accredited high school. The GED is accepted. Secondary school preparation should include 15 to 30 academic credits. Some applicants may be required to schedule an interview. Important factors used in the admissions decision are advanced placement or honor courses, evidence of special talent, leadership record, ability to finance college education, and recommendations by alumni.

Procedure: Freshmen are admitted to all sessions. Entrance exams should be taken in October or February of the senior year. Early decision applications should be filed by April 15; regular applications, by May 1 for fall entry, November 15 for spring entry, and April 15 for summer entry, along with an application fee of $15. Notification of early decision is sent April 30; regular decision, on a rolling basis. There is an early decision plan.

Transfer: Transfers should present a C average in at least 15 college credits. Those with fewer transferable credits must meet freshman requirements.

Visiting: There are regularly scheduled orientations for prospective students. There are guides for informal visits. To arrange for a visit, contact the Admissions Office at (809) 878-5195.

Financial Aid: In 1993-94, 98% of all current freshmen and 96% of continuing students received some form of financial aid. Scholarships or need-based grants averaged $300 ($400 maximum); loans averaged $400 ($500 maximum); and work contracts averaged $400 ($500 maximum). Some 30% of undergraduate students work part-time. Average earnings from campus work for the school year are $400. The college is a member of CSS. The FAF and the college's own financial statement are required. The deadline for financial aid applications is April 29.

International Students: They must take the TOEFL.

Computers: The college provides computer facilities for student use. All students may access the system. There are no time limits on using the system. The fees are $30.

Graduates: In 1992-93, 491 bachelor's degrees were awarded. The most popular majors among graduates were business administration (21%), criminal justice (11%), and social work (10%).

Admissions Contact: Provi Montalvo, Director of Admissions.

INTER-AMERICAN UNIVERSITY OF PUERTO RICO SYSTEM

The Inter-American University of Puerto Rico System, established in 1912, is a private system in Puerto Rico. It is governed by a board of trustees, whose chief administrator is the president. The primary goal of the system is teaching. The main priorities are to provide quality education, public service, and devote attention to students' needs. The total enrollment in fall 1991 of all 10 campuses was 42,968; there were 862 faculty members. Altogether there are 35 baccalaureate, 28 master's, and 1 doctoral program offered in Inter-American University of Puerto Rico System. Four-year campuses are located in San Juan and San German. Profiles of the 4-year campuses are included in this chapter.

INTER-AMERICAN UNIVERSITY OF PUERTO RICO
BARRANQUITAS REGIONAL COLLEGE
C-2

Barranquitas, PR 00794   (809) 857-3600, ext. 222

Full-time: 477 men, 898 women | Faculty: 38; IIA, --$
Part-time: 76 men, 167 women | Ph.Ds: 2%
Graduate: none | Student/Faculty: 36 to 1
Year: semesters, summer session | Tuition: $2730
Application Deadline: open | Room & Board: n/app
Freshman Class: 435 applied, 435 accepted, 413 enrolled
SAT I or ACT: recommended

Inter-American University of Puerto Rico/Barranquitas Regional College, founded in 1957, is a private coeducational college that is part of the Inter-American University system. The primary focus of the college is teacher education. There are 6 undergraduate schools. The library contains 32,275 volumes, 23,657 microform items, and 926 audiovisual forms, and subscribes to 223 periodicals. Computerized library sources and services include the card catalog and interlibrary loans. Special learning facilities include a learning resource center. The 36-acre campus is in a small town. There are 5 buildings on campus.

Student Life: All undergraduates are from Puerto Rico. All are Hispanic. The average age of freshmen is 18; all undergraduates, 22.5. Four percent drop out by the end of their first year; 96% remain to graduate.

Housing: All students commute. All students may keep cars on campus. Alcohol is not permitted.

Activities: There are no fraternities or sororities on campus. There are 9 groups on campus, including chorus, dance, honors, religious, social, and student government. Popular campus events include Competencias LAI y LIDE, Health Fair, and Open House.

Sports: There are 8 intercollegiate sports for men and 7 for women, and 7 intramural sports for men and 6 for women. Athletic and recreation facilities include a student center, a gymnasium, volleyball and basketball courts, and a softball park.

Disabled Students: One percent of the campus is accessible to disabled students. The following facilities are available: wheelchair ramps and special parking.

Services: In addition to many counseling and information services, tutoring is available in some subjects, including Spanish, English, and mathematics. There is also a reader service for the blind, and remedial math, reading, and writing.

Campus Safety and Security: Campus safety and security measures include a 24-hour foot and vehicle patrol, pamphlets, posters, films, emergency telephones, and lighted pathways and sidewalks.

Programs of Study: Inter-American at Barranquitas awards the B.A. and B.B.A. degrees. Associate degrees are also awarded. Bachelor's degrees are awarded in BUSINESS (accounting, business administration and management, and secretarial studies/office management), EDUCATION (early childhood, elementary, and secondary), SOCIAL SCIENCE (criminal justice). Preschool education, business administration, secretarial studies, accounting, elementary education, and secondary education are the strongest programs academically.

Required: In order to graduate, students must complete 120 to 132 credit hours with a minimum GPA of 2.0.

Special: Internships are available in education, secretarial studies, and criminal justice. There is one national honor society on campus.

Admissions: One hundred percent of the 1993–94 applicants were accepted.

Requirements: Inter-American at Barranquitas requires applicants to be in the upper 70% of their class. A minimum GPA of 2.0 is required. The SAT I or ACT is recommended. SAT II: Subject tests are required. AP credits are accepted. Important factors used in the admissions decision are geographic diversity, recommendations by alumni, recommendations by school officials, extracurricular activities record, and parents or siblings attending the school.

Procedure: Freshmen are admitted in the fall, winter, and summer. Entrance exams should be taken in October, February, or June. Application deadlines are open. The application fee is $15. The college accepts all applicants. Notification is sent on a rolling basis. There is an early admissions plan.

Transfer: Transfer applicants must submit a university transcript, dean's recommendation, and financial aid transcript. A total of 36 credits out of 120 to 132 must be completed at Inter-American at Barranquitas.

Visiting: There are regularly scheduled orientations for prospective students. There are guides for informal visits. To arrange for a visit, contact the Admissions Director at (809) 857–3600, ext. 222 or (809) 857–4097.

Financial Aid: In a recent year, 96% of all current freshmen and 4% of continuing students received some form of financial aid. About 85% of freshmen and 15% of continuing students received need-based aid. The average freshman award was $2840. Of that total, scholarships or need-based grants averaged $400 ($800 maximum); loans averaged $100 ($600 maximum); and work contracts averaged $204 ($425 maximum). Forty-five percent of undergraduate students work part-time. Average earnings from campus work for a recent school year were $3000. Inter-American at Barranquitas is a member of CSS. The deadline for financial aid applications is April 15.

International Students: International students must take the college's own test. The student must also take SAT II: Subject tests.

Graduates: In a recent year, 110 bachelor's degrees were awarded. The most popular majors among graduates were elementary education (40%), secondary education (30%), and business administration (30%).

Admissions Contact: Maribel Diaz Pena, Director of Admissions.

INTER-AMERICAN UNIVERSITY OF PUERTO RICO
FAJARDO REGIONAL COLLEGE

Fajardo, PR 00738	**D-1**
	(809) 860–3100
Full-time: 500 men, 1083 women	Faculty: 46; IIA, --$
Part-time: 262 men, 129 women	Ph.D.s: n/av
Graduate: none	Student/Faculty: 34 to 1
Year: semesters, summer session	Tuition: $2732
Application Deadline: May 15	Room & Board: n/app
Freshman Class: 699 applied, 583 accepted, 501 enrolled	
CEEB or SAT I: required	

Inter-American University of Puerto Rico/Fajardo Regional College, founded in 1912 and a unit of the Inter-American University of Puerto Rico, is a private, coeducational, nonsectarian college offering graduate and undergraduate degrees in business, fine and liberal arts, health sciences, and teacher preparation. In addition to regional accreditation, Inter-American at Fajardo has baccalaureate program accreditation with CSWE. Computerized library sources and services include the card catalog. Special learning facilities include an audiovisual center, a publication center, and an instructional development center. The campus is in an urban area in a small city.

Housing: There are no residence halls. Alcohol is not permitted.

Activities: There are some groups and organizations on campus, including chorale, professional, religious, and social.

Services: Guidance and counseling services are available.

Programs of Study: Inter-American at Fajardo awards the B.A., B.S., and B.B.A. degrees. Associate, master's, and doctoral degrees are also awarded. Bachelor's degrees are awarded in BIOLOGICAL SCIENCE (biology/biological science), BUSINESS (accounting, banking and finance, business administration and management, insurance, management information systems, marketing/retailing/merchandising, and secretarial studies/office management), COMMUNICATIONS AND THE ARTS (applied music, Spanish, and visual and performing arts), COMPUTER AND PHYSICAL SCIENCE (chemical technology, chemistry, computer science, and mathematics), ED-

UCATION (early childhood, elementary, music, secondary, and special), ENGINEERING AND ENVIRONMENTAL DESIGN (electrical/electronics engineering technology), HEALTH PROFESSIONS (medical technology and nursing), SOCIAL SCIENCE (criminal justice, history, political science/government, psychology, public administration, social work, and sociology).

Required: Students must complete 59 credits in general education, including 18 credits in communication skills, 12 in historical-cultural heritage, 11 in ability to integrate, apply, and create, 8 in reasoning skills, 6 in methods of interpreting reality, and 2 nonacademic credits each in Introduction to University Life and health/physical education/recreation. A total of 120 credit hours is required; the number required in the major varies. A 2.0 minimum GPA must be maintained overall and in the major.

Special: Co-op programs in engineering and earth and mineral sciences with Pennsylvania State University, cross-registration, internships, work-study, and adult and continuing education programs are available.

Admissions: About 83% of the 1993–94 applicants were accepted.

Requirements: A minimum GPA of 2.0 is required. The SAT I is required. Native Spanish-speaking students may take the Spanish version of the SAT I. The SAT II: Writing test is also required. Students must have graduated from an accredited secondary school. An interview may be required. AP credits are accepted.

Procedure: Early decision applications should be filed by May 15; regular applications, by May 15 for fall entry, November 15 for winter entry, and April 15 for summer entry, along with an application fee of $15. Notification is sent on a rolling basis. There is an early admissions plan.

Transfer: Transfer applicants must have completed at least 15 transferable semester credits with a minimum grade of C and must be in good standing at their previous institution. All college transcripts must be submitted.

Financial Aid: The college's own financial statement and the Federal Student Aid form are required. The deadline for financial aid applications is April 28.

Computers: The college provides computer facilities for student use.

Admissions Contact: Evelyn Rivera Collazo, Admissions Director.

INTER-AMERICAN UNIVERSITY OF PUERTO RICO
SAN GERMAN

San German, PR 00683	**B-2**
	(809) 892–3090 or (809) 264–1912
Full-time: 1783 men, 2607 women	Faculty: 142; IIA, --$
Part-time: 340 men, 431 women	Ph.D.s: 35%
Graduate: 237 men, 489 women	Student/Faculty: 31 to 1
Year: semesters, summer session	Tuition: $2560
Application Deadline: May 15	Room & Board: $2060
Freshman Class: 1435 applied, 1435 accepted, 1130 enrolled	
SAT I Verbal/Math: 487/509	

Inter-American San German, founded in 1912, is a private institution that is part of the Inter-American University of Puerto Rico system. It offers programs in fine and liberal arts, business, health science, and teacher preparation. There are 3 graduate schools. The library contains 127,033 volumes, and subscribes to 2375 periodicals. Computerized library sources and services include interlibrary loans. Special learning facilities include a learning resource center and natural history museum. The 260-acre campus is in a rural area 14 miles from Mayaguez. Including residence halls, there are 63 buildings on campus.

Student Life: Almost all undergraduates are from Puerto Rico. Eighty percent are from public schools; 20% from private. Ninety-nine percent are Hispanic. The average age of freshmen is 18. Thirty-three percent drop out by the end of their first year.

Housing: A total of 795 students can be accommodated in college housing. College-sponsored living facilities include single-sex dormitories, on-campus apartments, and married-student housing. On-campus housing is guaranteed for all 4 years. Eighty-nine percent of students commute. Alcohol is not permitted. All students may keep cars on campus.

Activities: About 5% of men belong to 5 local and 4 national fraternities; about 5% of women belong to 3 local and 3 national sororities. There are 57 groups on campus, including art, band, choir, chorale, computers, dance, drama, ethnic, honors, international, jazz band, marching band, musical theater, orchestra, political, professional, religious, social, social service, and student government. Popular campus events include Beach Party, Haunted House, Feria Tipica, Christmas Concert, Broadway musicals, Justas Interuniversitarias, Founders Day, and Homecoming.

Sports: Athletic and recreation facilities include a gymnasium, a dirt track, a tartan track, tennis courts, a jogging course, table tennis, a billiards room, table games, aerobics areas, and small gyms in residence halls.

Disabled Students: The following facilities are available: wheelchair ramps, special parking, specially equipped rest rooms, special class scheduling, lowered drinking fountains, and lowered telephones.

Services: In addition to many counseling and information services, tutoring is available in some subjects, including Spanish, English, mathematics, and computer science.

Campus Safety and Security: Campus safety and security measures include 24-hour foot and vehicle patrol.

Programs of Study: The university awards the B.A., B.S., and B.B.A. degrees. Associate and master's degrees are also awarded. Bachelor's degrees are awarded in BIOLOGICAL SCIENCE (biology/biological science), BUSINESS (accounting, banking and finance, business administration and management, business economics, marketing/retailing/merchandising, and secretarial studies/office management), COMMUNICATIONS AND THE ARTS (English, fine arts, music, and Spanish), COMPUTER AND PHYSICAL SCIENCE (chemistry, computer science, and mathematics), EDUCATION (art, early childhood, elementary, health, music, science, secondary, special, and teaching English as a second language/foreign language), HEALTH PROFESSIONS (medical laboratory technology, nursing, and premedicine), SOCIAL SCIENCE (economics, history, political science/government, psychology, public administration, and sociology). Business administration and medical technology are the strongest academically. Computer science, business administration, and biology have the largest enrollments.

Required: To graduate, students must complete at least 124 credits, with a minimum GPA of 2.0. General education requirements include courses in Spanish, English, mathematical reasoning, logical and critical reasoning, introduction to computers, and history of Puerto Rico. In addition, students must take 1 credit each in art, music, ethics, and Puerto Rican culture, 2 in physical education, and 6 in methods of interpreting reality.

Special: The university offers internships, credit by examination, and nondegree study. A 3-2 engineering degree is available with Pennsylvania State University. There is a freshman honors program on campus, as well as 2 national honor societies.

Faculty/Classroom: Fifty-four percent of faculty are male; 46%, female. The average class size is 25.

Admissions: All of the 1993–94 applicants were accepted.

Requirements: A minimum GPA of 2.5 is required. The SAT I, or the CEEB Spanish equivalent version, is required. Applicants must be high school graduates and have completed 15 credits, including 3 each in Spanish, English, and electives, and 2 each in mathematics and science. AP and CLEP credits are accepted.

Procedure: Freshmen are admitted to all sessions. Entrance exams should be taken in the first or second semester of the senior year. Applications should be filed by May 15 for fall entry, November 15 for spring entry, and April 15 for summer entry, along with an application fee of $15. Notification is sent on a rolling basis. There are early admissions and deferred admissions plans.

Transfer: About 100 transfer students enrolled in a recent year. Applicants should have at least 15 college credits with a minimum GPA of 2.5. The SAT I, or the CEEB Spanish version, is required, as is a letter of recommendation from the dean of students. A total of 30 credits out of 124 must be completed at the university.

Visiting: There are regularly scheduled orientations for prospective students. There are guides for informal visits and visitors may sit in on classes and stay overnight at the school. To arrange for a visit, contact the Admissions Office at (809) 264–1912, ext. 213.

Financial Aid: In a recent year, 80% of all current freshmen and 90% of continuing students received need-based aid. The average freshman award was $3000. Of that total, work contracts averaged $380 ($532 maximum). The college's own financial statement and the application for Federal Student Aid (Pell Grant) are required. The deadline for financial aid applications is April 30.

International Students: There are currently about 85 international students enrolled. The student must take the English or Spanish SAT I.

Computers: The college provides computer facilities for student use. The mainframe is a DEC PDP 11/24. There are also 55 IBM, Apple, and Commodore PCs. Students enrolled in computer courses with laboratory may access the system. It may be used daily at designated hours. Students may access the system 3 hours a day, with a reservation. The fees are $20 per laboratory.

Graduates: In a recent class, 755 bachelor's degrees were awarded. The most popular majors among graduates were business administration (18%), biology (9%), and accounting (7%).

Admissions Contact: Mildred Camacho, Director of Admissions.

INTER-AMERICAN UNIVERSITY COLLEGE OF ARECIBO
(See Inter American University/Arecibo Campus)

PONTIFICAL CATHOLIC UNIVERSITY OF PUERTO RICO
PONCE
C-2

Ponce, PR 00732   (809) 841–2000, ext. 426

Full-time: 3123 men, 5838 women	Faculty: 385
Part-time: 753 men, 1377 women	Ph.D.s: 16%
Graduate: 466 men, 694 women	Student/Faculty: 23 to 1
Year: semesters, summer session	Tuition: $3129
Application Deadline: July 15	Room & Board: $2678

Freshman Class: 3390 applied, 2762 accepted, 2096 enrolled
SAT I Verbal/Math: 453/490

Pontifical Catholic University of Puerto Rico, founded in 1948, is a private, coeducational institution affiliated with the Catholic Church of Puerto Rico. The school offers undergraduate programs in liberal arts, the sciences, education, and business. There are 4 undergraduate and 5 graduate schools. In addition to regional accreditation, the university has baccalaureate program accreditation with CAHEA, CSWE, and NLN. The 2 libraries contain 321,801 volumes, 99,159 microform items, and 750 audiovisual forms, and subscribe to 2957 periodicals. Special learning facilities include a learning resource center, a radio station, and a TV station. The 120-acre campus is in an urban area 35 miles south of San Juan. Including residence halls, there are 43 buildings on campus.

Student Life: About 99% of undergraduates are from Puerto Rico. Students come from 23 foreign countries. Sixty-six percent are from public schools; 21% from private. Ninety-nine percent are Hispanic. Most are Catholic. The average age of freshmen is 20; all undergraduates, 20. Four percent drop out by the end of their first year; 84% remain to graduate.

Housing: A total of 296 students can be accommodated in college housing. College-sponsored living facilities include single-sex dormitories and on-campus apartments. Priority for on-campus housing is given to out-of-town students. Ninety-six percent of students commute. Alcohol is not permitted. All students may keep cars on campus.

Activities: About 12% of men belong to 17 local fraternities; about 10% of women belong to 10 local sororities. There are 60 groups on campus, including art, band, chess, choir, computers, dance, drama, ethnic, film, honors, musical theater, newspaper, pep band, photography, professional, radio and TV, religious, social service, student government, and yearbook. Popular campus events include freshmen activities at the beginning of the academic year, religious and social activities celebrated on Thanksgiving, Christmas, and Holy Week, and Puerto Rican Culture Week.

Sports: There are 13 intercollegiate sports for men and 11 for women, and 12 intramural sports for men and 11 for women. Athletic and recreation facilities include a gymnasium, a 6000-seat arena, a pool, and facilities for tennis, baseball, basketball, volleyball, and track and field.

Disabled Students: Most of the campus is accessible to disabled students. The following facilities are available: wheelchair ramps, elevators, special parking, special class scheduling, lowered drinking fountains, and lowered telephones.

Services: In addition to many counseling and information services, tutoring is available in mathematics, chemistry, physics, and English. There is also remedial math, reading, and writing.

Campus Safety and Security: Campus safety and security measures include 24-hour foot and vehicle patrol, informal discussions, pamphlets, posters, films, and emergency telephones. In addition, there are lighted pathways and sidewalks.

Programs of Study: The university awards the B.A., B.S., B.B.A., and B.S.Ed. degrees. Associate and master's degrees are also awarded. Bachelor's degrees are awarded in BIOLOGICAL SCIENCE (biology/biological science), BUSINESS (accounting, banking and finance, business administration and management, business economics, and marketing/retailing/merchandising), COMMUNICATIONS AND THE ARTS (communications, English, fine arts, public relations, and Spanish), COMPUTER AND PHYSICAL SCIENCE (chemistry, computer programming, mathematics, and physics), EDUCATION (art, business, elementary, home economics, mathematics, music, physical, science, secondary, social studies, special, and teaching English as a second language/foreign language), HEALTH PROFESSIONS (medical laboratory technology and nursing), SOCIAL SCIENCE (criminology, gerontology, history, philosophy, political science/government, psychology, public administration, religion, social science, social work, sociology, and theological studies). Physical sciences are the strongest academically. Accounting has the largest enrollment.

Required: Bachelor's candidates must complete a 136-credit program in not-more-than twice the usual number of years and maintain a GPA of 2.0. Required courses include theology, philosophy, hu-

manities, English, Spanish, mathematics, science, and physical education.

Special: The university offers science and pharmacy co-op programs with the Massachusetts College of Pharmacy, cross-registration with Seton Hall University, and a 3–2 engineering degree with Case Western Reserve University. A Washington semester, work-study programs within the university, nondegree study, and pass/fail options in elective courses are also available. There is a freshman honors program on campus, as well as 10 national honor societies. One department has an honors program.

Faculty/Classroom: Fifty-one percent of faculty are male; 49%, female. Ninety-nine percent teach undergraduates and 1% do research. The average class size in an introductory lecture is 35; in a laboratory, 32; and in a regular course offering, 35.

Admissions: About 81% of the 1993–94 applicants were accepted. The SAT scores for the 1993–94 freshman class were as follows: Verbal—71% below 500, 24% between 500 and 599, and 5% between 600 and 700; Math—68% below 500, 27% between 500 and 599, and 5% between 600 and 700. About 60% of the current freshmen were in the top fifth of their class; 40% were in the top two fifths.

Requirements: A minimum GPA of 2.0 is required. The SAT I is required, along with SAT II: Subject tests in mathematics, Spanish, and English as a second language. In addition, applicants must be high school graduates or hold a GED. Students from 3-year senior high schools should have earned 10 units, consisting of 3 each of English and Spanish, 2 of mathematics, and 1 each of science and history. Students from 4-year high schools should have earned 15 units, consisting of 4 each of English and Spanish, 3 of mathematics, and 2 each of science and history. Students from outside Puerto Rico may substitute 2 years of another foreign language for the Spanish requirement. An interview is required for special programs. AP and CLEP credits are accepted. Important factors used in the admissions decision are advanced placement or honor courses, evidence of special talent, leadership record, ability to finance college education, and recommendations by school officials.

Procedure: Freshmen are admitted to all sessions. Applications should be filed by July 15 for fall entry, October 15 for spring entry, and April 15 for summer entry, along with an application fee of $15. Notification is sent on a rolling basis.

Transfer: About 250 transfer students enrolled in 1993–94. Applicants must supply a college transcript. A GPA of 2.0 and 30 credit hours are required. An associate degree is recommended. A total of 30 credits out of 136 must be completed at the university.

Visiting: There are guides for informal visits and visitors may sit in on classes. To arrange for a visit, contact Caridad C. Frau at (809) 841–2000, ext. 426.

Financial Aid: In 1993–94, 90% of all current freshmen and 85% of continuing students received some form of financial aid. About 90% of freshmen and 83% of continuing students received need-based aid. The average freshman award was $1400. Of that total, scholarships or need-based grants averaged $300 ($800 maximum); loans averaged $850 ($1600 maximum); and work contracts averaged $850 ($1000 maximum). Eleven percent of undergraduate students work part-time. Average earnings from campus work for the school year are $1158. The average financial indebtedness of the 1992–93 graduate was $2796. The university is a member of CSS. The college's own financial statement, the ASFA, and income certification documents are required. The deadline for financial aid applications is June 15.

International Students: There are currently 11 international students enrolled. The school actively recruits these students. They must take the TOEFL.

Computers: The college provides computer facilities for student use. The mainframe is an IBM 4341. There are also IBM, PC, XT, AT, and compatible microcomputers available throughout the campus. Students taking computer or computer-related courses may access the system. It may be used 8 A.M. to 10 P.M. Monday through Friday, and 8 A.M. to 5 P.M. Saturday. There are no time limits on using the system. Students are charged an average fee of $25.

Graduates: In 1992–93, 1169 bachelor's degrees were awarded. The most popular majors among graduates were management and accounting (30%), education (12%), and nursing (9%). Within an average freshman class, 14% graduate in 4 years and 15% in 5 years. Some 20 companies recruited on campus in 1992–93.

Admissions Contact: Admissions Office.

TURABO UNIVERSITY
D-1

Gurabo, PR 00658   (809) 746–3009

Full-time: 7400 men and women	Faculty: n/av
Part-time: 7400 men and women	Ph.D.s: n/av
Graduate: 1200 men and women	Student/Faculty: n/av
Year: semesters, summer session	Tuition: $2670 ($2670)
Application Deadline: open	Room & Board: n/app
Freshman Class: n/av	
SAT I: required	

Turabo University, founded in 1972, is a private nonsectarian institution offering undergraduate programs in business administration, education, Spanish, social sciences, natural sciences and technology,

and English and communications, and graduate programs in business administration and education. There are 2 graduate schools. Computerized library sources and services include the card catalog and database searching. Special learning facilities include a learning resource center and an archeological-folkloric museum. The 116-acre campus is 15 miles south of San Juan.

Housing: There are no residence halls. All students may keep cars on campus.

Activities: There are no fraternities or sororities on campus. There are some groups and organizations on campus, including choir, computers, drama, musical theater, professional, and student government. Popular campus events include Student Government Assembly, dances, films, and theater productions.

Sports: Athletic and recreation facilities include 2 basketball courts, a gymnasium, and softball and baseball parks.

Services: In addition to some counseling and information services, tutoring is available in Spanish, English, and mathematics.

Programs of Study: The university awards the B.A., B.S., and B.B.A. degrees. Associate and master's degrees also are awarded. Bachelor's degrees are awarded in BIOLOGICAL SCIENCE (biology/biological science), BUSINESS (accounting, business administration and management, management science, marketing/retailing/merchandising, and secretarial studies/office management), COMMUNICATIONS AND THE ARTS (English and Spanish), COMPUTER AND PHYSICAL SCIENCE (chemistry, computer programming, mathematics, and natural sciences), EDUCATION (elementary, English, foreign languages, mathematics, physical, science, secondary, social science, and special), SOCIAL SCIENCE (criminology, economics, history, humanities, psychology, public administration, social science, and sociology).

Required: To graduate, students must complete at least 139 credit hours with a minimum 2.0 GPA overall and 2.5 in the major. Course requirements must be satisfied.

Special: The university offers a general studies degree, graduate-level night courses in business and education, work-study, and nondegree study. One department has an honors program.

Requirements: A minimum GPA of 2.0 is required. The SAT I is required. Applicants must be graduates of an accredited secondary school or have an equivalent certificate. Students must submit official secondary school transcripts, and a good-conduct certificate from the Puerto Rico Police Department showing that the applicant has not committed felonies or misdemeanors within the last 3 months. An interview may be required.

Procedure: Application deadlines are open. Application fee is $15. The college accepts all applicants

Transfer: Transfer students must submit official transcripts from previously attended accredited universities. Those studying outside Puerto Rico must also submit a catalog from the university. Students must have completed at least 15 college credits and meet residency requirements. Other freshman requirements apply.

Financial Aid: The deadline for financial aid applications is May 30.

Admissions Contact: Maritza Garcia, Admissions Office Director.

UNIVERSIDAD ADVENTISTA DE LAS ANTILLAS
A-1

(Formerly Antillian College)

Mayaguez, PR 00709   (809) 834–9595, ext. 2261, 2208

Full-time: 242 men, 439 women	Faculty: 48
Part-time: 45 men, 69 women	Ph.D.s: 20%
Graduate: none	Student/Faculty: 14 to 1
Year: semesters, summer session	Tuition: $2850
Application Deadline: July 15	Room & Board: $2150
Freshman Class: 258 applied, 213 accepted, 160 enrolled	
SAT I or ACT: required	

Universidad Adventista de las Antillas, formerly Antillian college, established in 1961 and affiliated with the Seventh-day Adventist Church, offers undergraduate programs in business administration, sciences and computers, education and psychology, nursing and allied health, music and fine arts, religion, and humanities. There are 7 undergraduate schools. The library contains 87,226 volumes, 1500 microform items, and 1717 audiovisual forms, and subscribes to 392 periodicals. Computerized library sources and services include the card catalog. The 284-acre campus is in a small town on the west coast of Puerto Rico. Including residence halls, there are 6 buildings on campus.

Student Life: About 84% of undergraduates are from Puerto Rico. Students come from 8 states and 116 foreign countries. Sixty-one percent are from public schools; 39% from private. Ninety-seven percent are Hispanic; 15% foreign nationals. Sixty-eight percent are Seventh-day Adventist; 15% Catholic. The average age of freshmen is 19; all undergraduates, 23. Forty-one percent drop out by the end of their first year; 59% remain to graduate.

Housing: A total of 252 students can be accommodated in college housing. College-sponsored living facilities include single-sex dormitories, on-campus apartments, and married-student housing. On-campus housing is guaranteed for all 4 years. Seventy-five percent of

students commute. Alcohol is not permitted. All students may keep cars on campus.

Activities: About 75% of men belong to 1 local fraternity; about 80% of women belong to 1 local sorority. There are some 20 groups on campus, including band, choir, chorale, chorus, drama, film, literary magazine, newspaper, orchestra, photography, professional, religious, social, social service, student government, and yearbook. Popular campus events include International Fair, Columbus Day, Discovering Puerto Rico, Christmas programs, and Spiritual Emphasis Week.

Sports: There are 4 intramural sports for men and 3 for women. Athletic and recreation facilities include a gymnasium and a swimming pool.

Disabled Students: Ninety percent of the campus is accessible to disabled students. The following facilities are available: wheelchair ramps, special parking, specially equipped rest rooms, lowered drinking fountains, and lowered telephones.

Services: In addition to many counseling and information services, tutoring is available in some subjects. In addition, there is remedial math, reading, and writing.

Campus Safety and Security: Campus safety and security measures include 24-hour foot and vehicle patrol.

Programs of Study: Universidad Adventista de las Antillas awards the B.A. and B.S. degrees. Associate degrees are also awarded. Bachelor's degrees are awarded in BIOLOGICAL SCIENCE (biology/biological science), BUSINESS (business administration and management), COMMUNICATIONS AND THE ARTS (music and Spanish), COMPUTER AND PHYSICAL SCIENCE (chemistry and computer science), EDUCATION (elementary, music, and secondary), HEALTH PROFESSIONS (nursing), SOCIAL SCIENCE (history, pastoral studies, religion, and theological studies). Business administration, nursing, computer science, and education are the strongest academically. Nursing has the largest enrollment.

Required: Students must complete 128 credits, with 44 to 64 in the student's major, and must maintain a minimum GPA of 2.0. General education requirements must be met, and also requirements for the major and professional concentration. Requirements include courses in religion, music or art, mathematics, physical education, computer science, Spanish, English, philosophy of education, and biological and physical sciences.

Special: Work-study programs, B.A.-B.S. degrees, credit by examination, and pass/fail options are available.

Faculty/Classroom: Sixty-two percent of faculty are male; 38%, female. All teach undergraduates. The average class size in an introductory lecture is 25; in a laboratory, 40; and in a regular course offering, 25.

Admissions: About 83% of the 1993-94 applicants were accepted. Ten freshmen graduated first in their class.

Requirements: A minimum GPA of 1.8 is required. The SAT I or ACT is required, with a minimum composite score on the SAT I of 640, 320 verbal and 320 mathematics, recommended. In addition, graduation from an accredited secondary school is required; a GED will be accepted. Applicants must submit 12 to 15 academic credits, including 3 each in English and a foreign language, 2 each in history, mathematics, science, and social studies, and 1 to 2 in other electives. An interview is recommended. AP and CLEP credits are accepted. Important factors used in the admissions decision are advanced placement or honor courses, geographic diversity, parents or siblings attending the school, evidence of special talent, and extracurricular activities record.

Procedure: Freshmen are admitted to all sessions. Applications should be filed by July 15 for fall entry, December 15 for winter entry, and May 15 for summer entry, along with an application fee of $15. Notification is sent on a rolling basis. A waiting list is an active part of the admissions procedure.

Transfer: About 40 transfer students enrolled in 1993-94. Transfer students must be in good standing from the previous institution and have at least a 2.0 GPA. Official transcripts of high school and college credit, and an official report of the CEEB Spanish equivalent of the SAT I must be provided if the transfer student has completed fewer than 24 semester credits. A total of 30 credits out of 128 must be completed at Universidad Adventista de las Antillas.

Visiting: There are regularly scheduled orientations for prospective students. There are guides for informal visits and visitors may sit in on classes and stay overnight at the school. To arrange for a visit, contact Dr. Wilma Gonzalez at (809) 834-9595, ext. 2208, 2261.

Financial Aid: In 1993-94, 50% of all current freshmen and 75% of continuing students received some form of financial aid. About 85% of freshmen and 71% of continuing students received need-based aid. The average freshman award was $1100. Of that total, scholarships or need-based grants averaged $1100 ($2500 maximum); loans averaged $2500 ($5500 maximum); and work contracts averaged $600 ($1200 maximum). Twenty-nine percent of undergraduate students work part-time. Average earnings from campus work for the school year are $1100. The average financial indebtedness of the 1992-93 graduate was $1509. The college's own financial statement is required.

International Students: There are currently 114 international students enrolled. The student must take the CEEB Spanish equivalent of the SAT I.

Computers: The college provides computer facilities for student use. The mainframes are a DEC Vaxmate and a DEC MicroVAX II. There are also IBM-compatible microcomputers available and an IBM 386 Server. All students may access the system. Students may access the system 7:30 A.M. to 10 P.M.

Graduates: In 1992-93, 82 bachelor's degrees were awarded. The most popular majors among graduates were nursing (30%), office administration (10%), and elementary education (2%). Within an average freshman class, 1% graduate in 3 years, 45% in 4 years, 35% in 5 years, and 11% in 6 years. Some 10 companies recruited on campus in 1992-93.

Admissions Contact: Dr. Wilma Gonzalez, Director of Admissions.

UNIVERSIDAD METROPOLITANA   D-1
Rio Piedras, PR 00928   (809)765-6262

Full-time: n/av	Faculty: n/av
Part-time: n/av	Ph.Ds: n/av
Graduate: n/av	Student/Faculty: 45 to 1
Year: semesters, summer session	Tuition: $2650
Application Deadline: open	Room & Board: n/app
Freshman Class: n/av	
SAT I: required	

Universidad Metropolitana, founded in 1980, is a private, coeducational commuter institution offering undergraduate programs in the liberal arts and sciences, business, nursing, and education. There are 6 undergraduate schools. In addition to regional accreditation, UMET has baccalaureate program accreditation with NLN. The library contains 34,445 volumes and 5000 microform items. Special learning facilities include a learning resource center and TV station. The campus is in an urban area. There are 11 buildings on campus.

Student Life: The average age of freshmen is 18.

Housing: There are no residence halls.

Activities: There are no fraternities or sororities on campus. There are some groups and organizations on campus, including chess, chorale, dance, musical theater, religious, and social service. Popular campus events include a film series and a performing arts series.

Sports: There are 5 intercollegiate sports for men and 5 for women, and 4 intramural sports for men and 4 for women. Athletic and recreation facilities include basketball, volleyball, and tennis courts, a cross-country track, a softball field, and weight and exercise rooms.

Disabled Students: Special parking and special transportation are available.

Services: In addition to many counseling and information services, tutoring is available in most subjects. There is also a reader service for the blind and interpreters.

Programs of Study: UMET awards the B.A., B.S., B.B.A., and B.S.N. degrees. Associate and master's degrees also are awarded. Bachelor's degrees are awarded in BUSINESS (accounting, business administration and management, and management science), COMPUTER AND PHYSICAL SCIENCE (natural sciences), EDUCATION (elementary and secondary), ENGINEERING AND ENVIRONMENTAL DESIGN (surveying engineering), HEALTH PROFESSIONS (nursing), SOCIAL SCIENCE (humanities, psychology, social science, and sociology). Business is the strongest academically. Education and natural sciences have the largest enrollments.

Required: To graduate, students must complete an average of 135 credits, including at least 30 in the major field. Specific GPA requirements vary by department. All students must take a computer course and complete a general education core.

Special: UMET offers work-study programs, B.A.-B.S. degrees, and an honors program in the natural sciences. The Televised Education Center (CET) offers students an opportunity for independent study. One department has an honors program.

Faculty/Classroom: Forty percent of faculty are male; 60%, female.

Admissions: About 76% of the 1993-94 applicants were accepted.

Requirements: The SAT I is required. Applicants must be graduates of an accredited secondary school with a GPA of 2.0. Some programs have higher GPA requirements.

Procedure: Freshmen are admitted to all sessions. Application deadlines are open. Application fee is $15. Notification is sent on a rolling basis.

Transfer: All applicants must meet the GPA requirements of the program they wish to enter. Students should submit transcripts from all previous colleges attended as well as letter of recommendation from the dean of the most recent institution. Grades of C or better transfer for credit.

Financial Aid: The college's own financial statement is required.

Admissions Contact: Office of Admissions.

UNIVERSIDAD POLITECNICA DE PUERTO RICO
D-1

Hato Rey, PR 00918   (809) 754-8000, ext. 240

Full-time: 2937 men, 649 women	Faculty: 80
Part-time: 1202 men, 199 women	Ph.D.s: 6%
Graduate: none	Student/Faculty: 45 to 1
Year: quarters, summer session	Tuition: $3300
Application Deadline: July 30	Room & Board: n/app

Freshman Class: 1495 applied, 1258 accepted, 1088 enrolled
SAT II: Subject tests: required

Universidad Politecnica de Puerto Rico, is a private, coeducational institution offering undergraduate programs in engineering and business administration and a graduate program in engineering management. The library contains 26,366 volumes, 1213 microform items, and 882 audiovisual forms, and subscribes to 437 periodicals. Computerized library sources and services include the card catalog. The 8-acre campus is in an urban area in the Hato Rey section of San Juan. There are 8 buildings on campus.

Student Life: All undergraduates are from Puerto Rico. Most are Catholic. The average age of freshmen is 19; all undergraduates, 22.

Housing: There are no residence halls. Alcohol is not permitted. All students may keep cars on campus.

Activities: There is 1 local fraternity. There are no sororities on campus. There are 8 groups on campus, including honors, newspaper, professional, religious, and student government. Popular campus events include Student Night, Library Week, Education Weeks, Ernesto Vazquez Torres Marathon, and Honor Night.

Sports: There are 8 intercollegiate sports for men and 8 for women, and 10 intramural sports for men and 10 for women. Athletic and recreation facilities include basketball and volleyball courts and a game room.

Disabled Students: The following facilities are available: wheelchair ramps, elevators, special parking, specially equipped rest rooms, and special class scheduling.

Services: In addition to many counseling and information services, tutoring is available in some subjects, including Spanish, English, and mathematics. There is also remedial math.

Campus Safety and Security: Campus safety and security measures include 24-hour foot and vehicle patrol, informal discussions, pamphlets, posters, and films, and lighted pathways and sidewalks.

Programs of Study: The university awards the B.B.A. and B.S.E. degrees. Master's degrees also are awarded. Bachelor's degrees are awarded in BUSINESS (business administration and management), ENGINEERING AND ENVIRONMENTAL DESIGN (civil engineering, electrical/electronics engineering, industrial administration/management, industrial engineering, mechanical engineering, and surveying engineering). Electrical and industrial engineering are the strongest academically and have the largest enrollments.

Required: All graduating students must complete 128 to 176 quarter credits, with a minimum GPA of 2.0. There are distribution requirements in Spanish, English, humanities, social sciences, and mathematics, and within the chosen field. All students must take 6 credits in computer science. All majors require a practicum course before graduation.

Special: Co-op programs are available in all majors.

Faculty/Classroom: Twenty-two percent of faculty are male; 78%, female. All teach undergraduates. The average class size in an introductory lecture is 30; in a laboratory, 20; and in a regular course offering, 22.

Admissions: About 84% of the 1993–94 applicants were accepted.

Requirements: A minimum GPA of 2.5 is required. SAT II: Subject tests are required. Applicants must be graduates of an accredited secondary school, with 15 high school academic credits. An interview is recommended.

Procedure: Freshmen are admitted to all sessions. Applications should be filed by July 30 for fall entry, October 13 for winter entry, February 26 for spring entry, and April 30 for summer entry, along with an application fee of $30. Notification is sent on a rolling basis. There is an early admissions plan. Four hundred early decision candidates were accepted for the 1993–94 class.

Transfer: Some 334 transfer students enrolled in 1993–94. Applicants must present an official transcript and letters of recommendation.

Visiting: There are regularly scheduled orientations for prospective students.

Financial Aid: In 1993–94, 75% of all current freshmen and 85% of continuing students received some form of financial aid. About 75% of freshmen and 85% of continuing students received need-based aid. The average freshman award was $2000. Of that total, scholarships or need-based grants averaged $2000 ($3100 maximum); loans averaged $2000 ($2625 maximum); and work contracts averaged $1872 ($3740 maximum). Five percent of undergraduate students work part-time. Average earnings from campus work for the school year are $2047. The average financial indebtedness of the 1992–93 graduate was $6844. The university is a member of CSS.

The college's own financial statement and the FAFSA are required. The deadline for financial aid applications is July 30.

International Students: There are currently 84 international students enrolled.

Computers: The college provides computer facilities for student use. The mainframe is a PC Limited 386, System (Unix) Xenix. There are also 60 IBM-compatible PCs available in campus laboratories. All students may access the system. It may be used daily. There are no time limits on using the system and no fees.

Graduates: In 1992–93, 186 bachelor's degrees were awarded. The most popular majors among graduates were civil engineering (28%), electrical engineering (24%), and industrial engineering (23%). Within an average freshman class, 47% graduate in 4 years, 45% in 5 years, and 46% in 6 years.

Admissions Contact: Teresa Cardona, Director of Admissions.

UNIVERSITY OF PUERTO RICO SYSTEM

The University of Puerto Rico System, established in 1903, is a public system. It is governed by the Puerto Rico Council on Higher Education, whose chief administrator is the president. The primary goal of the system is to serve as a center for scholarly research, to develop academic excellence, and to capitalize on its location as a focal point of the Caribbean region and the international community by developing programs germane to the residents of the region. The main priorities are to improve academic programs in key areas, to strengthen research and research training, and to upgrade physical facilities. The total enrollment in fall 1991 of all 11 campuses was 55,523; there were 4344 faculty members. Altogether there are 194 baccalaureate, 97 master's, and 15 doctoral programs offered in University of Puerto Rico System. Four-year campuses are located in Cayey, Humacao, Mayaguez, Rio Piedras, Arecibo, Bayamon, Ponce, and San Juan. Profiles of the 4-year campuses follow.

UNIVERSITY OF PUERTO RICO ARECIBO TECHNOLOGICAL UNIVERSITY COLLEGE
B-1

Arecibo, PR 00613   (809) 878-2830

Full-time: 909 men, 2041 women	Faculty: 165
Part-time: 199 men, 388 women	Ph.D.s: 14%
Graduate: none	Student/Faculty: 18 to 1
Year: semesters, summer session	Tuition: $1302 ($2752)
Application Deadline: December 15	Room & Board: n/app

Freshman Class: 1728 applied, 1066 accepted, 830 enrolled
SAT I: required

Arecibo Technological University College, founded in 1967, offers undergraduate programs in business administration, health sciences, natural sciences, and education. The college is part of the University of Puerto Rico system. In addition to regional accreditation, CUTA has baccalaureate program accreditation with NLN. The library contains 64,544 volumes, 5659 microform items, and 1606 audiovisual forms, and subscribes to 1100 periodicals. Special learning facilities include a learning resource center, an art gallery, and a TV station. The 49-acre campus is in a suburban area 40 miles west of San Juan. There is one building on campus.

Student Life: All undergraduates are from Puerto Rico. Ninety percent are from public schools; 10% from private. All are Hispanic. The average age of freshmen is 23; all undergraduates, 20. Seventeen percent drop out by the end of their first year; 83% remain to graduate.

Housing: There are no residence halls. Alcohol is not permitted. All students may keep cars on campus.

Activities: About 7% of men belong to 7 local fraternities; about 5% of women belong to 5 local sororities. There are 34 groups on campus, including art, band, chorus, dance, drama, film, newspaper, photography, political, professional, radio and TV, religious, social, social service, and student government. Popular campus events include fairs, plays, concerts, dances, art exhibits, and conferences.

Sports: There are 10 intercollegiate sports for men and 8 for women, and 5 intramural sports for men and 3 for women. Athletic and recreation facilities include basketball and tennis courts, a gymnasium, and an activity room.

Disabled Students: Ninety percent of the campus is accessible to disabled students. The following facilities are available: wheelchair ramps, special parking, specially equipped rest rooms, lowered drinking fountains, and lowered telephones.

Services: In addition to many counseling and information services, tutoring is available in most subjects. There is also remedial math, reading, and writing.

Campus Safety and Security: Campus safety and security measures include 24-hour foot and vehicle patrol, pamphlets, posters, films, and lighted pathways and sidewalks.

Programs of Study: CUTA awards the B.A. and B.S. degrees. Associate degrees also are awarded. Bachelor's degrees are awarded in BIOLOGICAL SCIENCE (microbiology), BUSINESS (business administration and management and secretarial studies/office management), COMMUNICATIONS AND THE ARTS (communications),

COMPUTER AND PHYSICAL SCIENCE (chemical technology), EDUCATION (elementary), HEALTH PROFESSIONS (nursing). Natural sciences is the strongest academically. Business administration has the largest enrollment.

Required: In order to graduate, students must have a 2.0 minimum GPA. The total number of credit hours required varies according to major. The core curriculum includes 2 semesters each of English, Spanish, mathematics, and social sciences or humanities.

Special: The college offers B.A.-B.S. degrees in all majors.

Faculty/Classroom: Fifty percent of faculty are male; 50%, female. All teach undergraduates. The average class size in an introductory lecture is 28; in a laboratory, 18; and in a regular course offering, 25.

Admissions: About 62% of the 1993–94 applicants were accepted.

Requirements: A minimum GPA of 2.0 is required. The SAT I is required.

Procedure: Freshmen are admitted in the fall. Entrance exams should be taken in October. Applications should be filed by December 15, along with an application fee of $15. Notification is sent in April.

Transfer: About 40 transfer students enrolled in 1993–94. Applicant should have a minimum of 24 credits with a 2.5 minimum GPA. Fifty percent of the required credits must be completed at CUTA.

Visiting: To arrange for a visit, contact the Dean of Student Affairs at (809) 878–2830.

Financial Aid: In 1993–94, 87% of freshmen and 55% of continuing students received need-based aid. The average freshman award was $3206. Of that total, scholarships or need-based grants averaged $3206 ($3906 maximum); and loans averaged $2625 ($4000 maximum). Thirteen percent of undergraduate students work part-time. Average earnings from campus work for the school year are $1000. CUTA is a member of CSS. The college's own financial statement is required. The deadline for financial aid applications is June 15.

Computers: The college provides computer facilities for student use. The mainframe is a DEC VAX 4000–300. Qualified personnel are available to offer instructions to users of the computer facilities. All students may access the system. There are no time limits on using the system and no fees.

Graduates: In 1992–93, 615 bachelor's degrees were awarded. The most popular majors among graduates were business administration (18%), nursing (14%), and secretarial sciences (11%). Within an average freshman class, 18% graduate in 4 years, 39% in 5 years, and 14% in 6 years.

Admissions Contact: Margarita Saez, Admissions Director.

UNIVERSITY OF PUERTO RICO
CAYEY UNIVERSITY COLLEGE
C-2
Cayey, PR 00633   (809) 738–2161

Full-time: 898 men, 1894 women	Faculty: 160
Part-time: 129 men, 211 women	Ph.Ds: 34%
Graduate: none	Student/Faculty: 17 to 1
Year: semesters, summer session	Tuition: $900 ($2400)
Application Deadline: December 15	Room & Board: n/app
Freshman Class: 2902 applied, 868 accepted, 694 enrolled	
CEEB: required	

Cayey University College, founded in 1967, is a public, coeducational liberal arts institution, and part of the University of Puerto Rico. Computerized library sources and services include the card catalog and interlibrary loans. Special learning facilities include a learning resource center and the Ramon Frade Museum. The 164-acre campus is in an urban area 30 miles south of San Juan. There are 54 buildings on campus.

Student Life: All undergraduates are from Puerto Rico. Eighty-five percent are from public schools; 15% from private. All are Hispanic. The average age of freshmen is 18; all undergraduates, 22. Twenty-two percent drop out by the end of their first year; 50% remain to graduate.

Housing: There are no residence halls. Alcohol is not permitted. All students may keep cars on campus.

Activities: About 1% of men belong to 1 local fraternity. There are no sororities on campus. There are 17 groups on campus, including band, cheerleading, chorus, drama, honors, religious, and student government. Popular campus events include Student Day.

Sports: There are 10 intercollegiate sports for men and 6 for women, and 9 intramural sports for men and 8 for women. Athletic and recreation facilities include a gymnasium, a pool, and tennis, basketball, and volleyball courts.

Disabled Students: The entire campus is accessible to disabled students. The following facilities are available: wheelchair ramps, elevators, special parking, specially equipped rest rooms, lowered drinking fountains, and lowered telephones.

Services: There is a reader service for the blind, and remedial math, reading, and writing.

Campus Safety and Security: Campus safety and security measures include 24-hour foot and vehicle patrol and lighted pathways and sidewalks.

Programs of Study: Cayey University College awards the B.A., B.S., B.B.A., and B.Ed. degrees. Associate degrees are also awarded. Bachelor's degrees are awarded in BIOLOGICAL SCIENCE

(biology/biological science), BUSINESS (accounting, business administration and management, and management science), COMMUNICATIONS AND THE ARTS (English), COMPUTER AND PHYSICAL SCIENCE (chemistry, mathematics, and natural sciences), EDUCATION (elementary and secondary), SOCIAL SCIENCE (economics, Hispanic American studies, history, humanities, psychology, social science, and sociology). Natural science is the strongest academically.

Required: To graduate, students must complete 129 to 135 credits, with 28 credits in the major and a minimum GPA of 2.0. There are requirements in humanities, social science, Spanish, English, and natural science. All students must take 2 courses in physical education.

Special: The university offers cross-registration through the National Student Exchange, study abroad in Toledo, Spain, and a Washington semester. There is a freshman honors program on campus, as well as one national honor society, Phi Beta Kappa.

Faculty/Classroom: Fifty-two percent of faculty are male; 48%, female. Ninety-nine percent teach undergraduates and 1% do research. The average class size in an introductory lecture is 30; in a laboratory, 20; and in a regular course offering, 30.

Admissions: About 30% of the 1993–94 applicants were accepted.

Requirements: A minimum GPA of 2.0 is required. The SAT I or the CEEB Spanish equivalent of the SAT I is required. Applicants must be graduates of an accredited secondary school. The GED is accepted. Students should complete 3 high school courses each in English, Spanish, mathematics, science, and social studies. CLEP credit is accepted.

Procedure: Freshmen are admitted in the fall. Entrance exams should be taken in October. Applications should be filed by December 15 for fall entry, along with an application fee of $15. Notification is sent May 1.

Transfer: About 15 transfer students enrolled in 1993–94. Applicants should have 48 approved credit hours toward the program they are entering. A total of 28 credits out of 129 to 135 must be completed at Cayey University College.

Visiting: Visitors may sit in on classes. To arrange for a visit, contact Maria Montalvo at (809) 738–2161, ext. 2053.

Financial Aid: In 1993–94, 77% of all current freshmen and 9% of continuing students received some form of financial aid. About 77% of freshmen and 9% of continuing students received need-based aid. The average freshman award was $2700. Of that total, scholarships or need-based grants averaged $2300; loans averaged $500 ($2625 maximum); and work contracts averaged $544 ($1088 maximum). Three percent of undergraduate students work part-time. Cayey University College is a member of CSS. The FAF is required. The deadline for financial aid applications is May 29.

International Students: The student must take the SAT I, ACT, or the CEEB Spanish equivalent of the SAT I.

Computers: The college provides computer facilities for student use. The mainframe is a DEC MicroVAX 3300. There are 3 computer laboratories integrated in Nonell LANS. All students may access the system. It may be used from 7 P.M. to 9 P.M. Monday through Thursday, and Friday from 7 A.M. to 4:30 P.M. Students may access the system 2 hours per student per week. There are no fees.

Graduates: In 1992–93, 387 bachelor's degrees were awarded.

Admissions Contact: Josefina Hernandez, Admissions Office.

UNIVERSITY OF PUERTO RICO
HUMACAO UNIVERSITY COLLEGE
D-2
Humacao, PR 00791   (809) 850–0000, ext. 9301

Full-time: 1066 men, 2076 women	Faculty: 214; IIB, --$
Part-time: 248 men, 435 women	Ph.Ds: 31%
Graduate: none	Student/Faculty: 15 to 1
Year: semesters, summer session	Tuition: see profile
Application Deadline: December 15	Room & Board: n/app
Freshman Class: 2724 applied, 971 accepted, 799 enrolled	
SAT I: see profile	

The University of Puerto Rico/Humacao University College, founded in 1962, is a public, coeducational institution offering undergraduate programs in the arts and sciences, business, education, and nursing to an entirely commuter student body. Tuition and fees for Puerto Rican residents total $1495 per year; nonresident U.S. citizens pay an amount equal to the nonresident rate at a state university in their home state. In addition to regional accreditation, the college has baccalaureate program accreditation with AOTA, APTA, CSWE, and NLN. The library contains 72,311 volumes, 4853 microform items, and 864 audiovisual forms, and subscribes to 684 periodicals. Special learning facilities include a learning resource center, a museum, an observatory, and a census data center. The 62-acre campus is in a suburban area 30 miles southeast of San Juan. There are 24 buildings on campus.

Student Life: Almost all undergraduates are from Puerto Rico. Eighty-one percent are from public schools; 19% from private. All are Hispanic. The average age of freshmen is 18; all undergraduates, 19. Sixteen percent drop out by the end of their first year; 84% remain to graduate.

Housing: There are no residence halls. All students commute. Alcohol is not permitted. Upperclassmen may keep cars on campus.

Activities: About 1% of men belong to 2 national fraternities. There are no sororities on campus. There are 21 groups on campus, including chess, chorus, computers, drama, honors, literary magazine, pep band, photography, professional, religious, social service, and student government. Popular campus events include Student Day, Humanities Week, Shakespeare Festival, Sound and Image Festival, Voice and Song Festival, Women's Week, Education Week, and Puerto Rican Culture Week.

Sports: There are 11 intercollegiate sports for men and 8 for women, and 4 intramural sports each for men and women. Athletic and recreation facilities include a 1000-seat gymnasium, a track, 2 tennis courts, a softball field, a swimming pool, wrestling mats, and a student center.

Disabled Students: Almost the entire campus is accessible to disabled students. The following facilities are available: wheelchair ramps, elevators, special parking, specially equipped rest rooms, lowered drinking fountains, and lowered telephones.

Services: In addition to many counseling and information services, tutoring is available in some subjects, including English, Spanish, and mathematics. There is a also a reader service for the blind and remedial math.

Campus Safety and Security: Campus safety and security measures include 24-hour foot and vehicle patrol, pamphlets, emergency telephones, and lighted pathways and sidewalks.

Programs of Study: The college awards the B.A., B.S., and B.B.A. degrees. Associate degrees also are awarded. Bachelor's degrees are awarded in BIOLOGICAL SCIENCE (biology/biological science, marine biology, and microbiology), BUSINESS (accounting, business administration and management, management science, personnel management, and secretarial studies/office management), COMMUNICATIONS AND THE ARTS (English), COMPUTER AND PHYSICAL SCIENCE (chemistry, mathematics, and physics), EDUCATION (elementary), HEALTH PROFESSIONS (nursing), SOCIAL SCIENCE (social work). Natural sciences is the strongest academically. Business administration has the largest enrollment.

Required: To graduate, students must complete 127 to 136 credit hours, including 21 to 51 in a major field, with a minimum GPA of 2.0. General education requirements include 33 to 73 liberal arts credits, with 6 credits in Spanish and 6 in English, humanities, and social sciences. Other distribution requirements vary by program.

Special: Students may study abroad through the National Student Exchange program. There are also co-op programs, internships in accounting, work-study programs, credit for work experience, and pass/fail options in remedial courses. Nondegree study is available through the Division of Continuing Education. The college offers programs in coastal marine biology, industrial microbiology, and industrial chemistry, and sponsors its Puerto Rican plain pigeon conservation project. There is a freshman honors program on campus, as well as 1 national honor society. Four departments have honors programs.

Faculty/Classroom: Forty-seven percent of faculty are male; 53%, female. Ninety-four percent teach undergraduates and 1% do research. The average class size in an introductory lecture is 25; in a laboratory, 18; and in a regular course offering, 30.

Admissions: About 36% of the 1993–94 applicants were accepted. The CEEB scores for the 1993–94 freshman class were as follows: Verbal—23% below 500, 58% between 500 and 599, and 20% between 600 and 700; Math—17% below 500, 51% between 500 and 599, 29% between 600 and 700, and 3% above 700.

Requirements: A minimum GPA of 2.0 is required. The SAT I is required, or the CEEB's Spanish equivalent, as well as SAT II: Subject tests in writing, Spanish, and mathematics. Applicants must be graduates of an accredited secondary school or have earned the GED. College preparatory study should include 1 credit in social studies, 2 in history, and 3 each in English, Spanish, and mathematics. All courses are conducted in Spanish only. Non-native speakers of Spanish are required to prove fluency through institutional examination interviews. AP credits are accepted.

Procedure: Freshmen are admitted in the fall. Entrance exams should be taken by October of the senior year. Applications should be filed by December 15 for fall entry, along with an application fee of $15. Notification is sent April 1. There are early decision and early admissions plans. Three early decision candidates were accepted for the 1993–94 class.

Transfer: Some 30 transfer students enrolled in 1993–94. Applicants must have at least 30 college credits with a minimum GPA of 3.0 and must be in good standing at their previous institution. A total of 30 credits out of 127 to 136 must be completed at the college.

Visiting: To arrange for a visit, contact the Student Affairs Office at (809) 850–0000, ext. 9328.

Financial Aid: In 1993–94 82% of all current freshmen and 75% of continuing students received some form of financial aid. About 82% of freshmen and 75% of continuing students received need-based aid. The average freshman award was $2539. Of that total, scholarships or need-based grants averaged $500 ($700 maximum); loans averaged $1500 ($4000 maximum); and work contracts averaged $800 ($1000 maximum). Twelve percent of undergraduate students work part-time. Average earnings from campus work for the school

year are $800. The AFSA is required. The deadline for financial aid applications is June 30.

International Students: The student must take the SAT I or CEEB.

Computers: The college provides computer facilities for student use. The mainframes are a DEC VAX 4300 and 4500. There are 51 terminals available in various departments and 108 microcomputers in 5 campus laboratories. All students may access the system. It may be used 24 hours a day. There are no time limits on using the system and no fees.

Graduates: In 1992–93 410 bachelor's degrees were awarded. The most popular majors among graduates were accounting (20%), business management (16%), and secretarial sciences (3%). Within an average freshman class, 10% graduate in 4 years, 25% in 5 years, and 8% in 6 years. Some 4 companies recruited on campus in 1992–93.

Admissions Contact: Inara Ferrer, Director of Admissions.

UNIVERSITY OF PUERTO RICO MAYAGUEZ

A-1

Mayaguez, PR 00681–5000   (809) 265–3811

Full-time: 4890 men, 4700 women	Faculty: 626
Part-time: 349 men, 383 women	Ph.D.s: 52%
Graduate: 376 men, 244 women	Student/Faculty: 15 to 1
Year: 4-1-4, summer session	Tuition: see profile
Application Deadline: December 18	Room & Board: n/app
Freshman Class: 2985 applied, 2460 accepted, 2006 enrolled	
SAT I: see profile	

The University of Puerto Rico at Mayaguez, founded in 1911, is a bilingual land-grant institution offering undergraduate programs in arts and sciences, business administration, agricultural sciences, and engineering. Tuition and fees for Puerto Rican residents total $1300 per year; nonresident U.S. citizens pay $30 per credit plus the equivalent nonresident rate at a state university in their home state. There are 4 undergraduate and 4 graduate schools. In addition to regional accreditation, the university has baccalaureate program accreditation with ABET and NLN. The library contains 783,905 volumes, 345,052 microform items, and 43,610 audiovisual forms, and subscribes to 2171 periodicals. Computerized library sources and services include database searching. Special learning facilities include a learning resource center, art gallery, natural history museum, planetarium, sea grant program, and resource center for science and engineering. The 520-acre campus is in an urban area 70 miles west of San Juan. There are 56 buildings on campus.

Student Life: About 97% of undergraduates are from Puerto Rico. Students come from 33 foreign countries and Canada. Sixty-one percent are from public schools; 39% from private. Ninety-nine percent are Hispanic. The average age of freshmen is 18; all undergraduates, 21. Ten percent drop out by the end of their first year; 66% remain to graduate.

Housing: There are no residence halls. Alcohol is not permitted. All students may keep cars on campus.

Activities: About 5% of men belong to 10 local fraternities and 1 national fraternity; about 2% of women belong to 5 local sororities. There are 100 groups on campus, including band, cheerleading, chess, choir, chorale, chorus, computers, dance, drama, drill team, drum and bugle corps, ethnic, honors, international, jazz band, literary magazine, marching band, newspaper, orchestra, photography, political, professional, religious, social, social service, student government, and yearbook. Popular campus events include an open house, fairs, concerts, and dances.

Sports: There are 12 intercollegiate sports for men and 9 for women, and 15 intramural sports for men and 11 for women. Athletic and recreation facilities include a gymnasium, a coliseum, a swimming pool, and 2 playing fields.

Disabled Students: Ninety percent of the campus is accessible to disabled students. The following facilities are available: wheelchair ramps, elevators, special parking, specially equipped rest rooms, lowered drinking fountains, and lowered telephones.

Services: In addition to many counseling and information services, tutoring is available in most subjects. There is also a reader service for the blind and remedial math.

Campus Safety and Security: Campus safety and security measures include 24-hour foot and vehicle patrol, informal discussions, and lighted pathways and sidewalks.

Programs of Study: The university awards the B.A., B.S., B.B.A., and B.S.A. degrees. Associate, master's, and doctoral degrees also are awarded. Bachelor's degrees are awarded in AGRICULTURE (animal science and horticulture), BIOLOGICAL SCIENCE (biochemistry, biology/biological science, biotechnology, and microbiology), BUSINESS (accounting, banking and finance, business administration and management, business economics, and marketing/retailing/merchandising), COMMUNICATIONS AND THE ARTS (English, fine arts, and French), COMPUTER AND PHYSICAL SCIENCE (chemistry, computer science, geology, information sciences and systems, mathematics, and physics), EDUCATION (foreign languages and teaching English as a second language/foreign language), ENGINEERING AND ENVIRONMENTAL DESIGN (chemical engineering, civil engineering, computer engineering, electrical/electronics engi-

neering, engineering, industrial engineering, mechanical engineering, and surveying engineering), HEALTH PROFESSIONS (nursing and premedicine), SOCIAL SCIENCE (economics, history, philosophy, political science/government, psychology, social science, and sociology). Engineering, business administration, and agricultural science are the strongest academically. Electrical, chemical, and civil engineering have the largest enrollments.

Required: To graduate, students must complete 172 credit hours with a GPA of 2.0. Required disciplines include humanities, English, Spanish, physical science, biology, social science, mathematics, and physical education.

Special: The university offers co-op programs in engineering, business, and nursing, as well as some study abroad. There is a freshman honors program on campus, as well as 1 national honor society.

Faculty/Classroom: Sixty-six percent of faculty are male; 34%, female. Twenty-three percent do research. The average class size in an introductory lecture is 30; in a laboratory, 20; and in a regular course offering, 30.

Admissions: About 82% of the 1993–94 applicants were accepted. The SAT scores for the 1993–94 freshman class were as follows: Verbal—63% between 600 and 700 and 37% above 700; Math—40% between 600 and 700 and 60% above 700. About 60% of the current freshmen were in the top fifth of their class; 95% were in the top two fifths.

Requirements: The university requires applicants to be in the upper 25% of their class. A minimum GPA of 3.0 is needed. The SAT I is required, or the CEEB's Spanish equivalent, along with SAT II: Subject tests in writing, composition, Spanish and Spanish reading, and mathematics level I. Applicants must be high school graduates or hold the GED. CLEP credit is accepted.

Procedure: Freshmen are admitted in the fall. Entrance exams should be taken during the first semester of the senior year. Applications should be filed by December 18 for fall entry, along with an application fee of $15. Notification is sent in May. There is an early admissions plan.

Transfer: Some 115 transfer students enrolled in an earlier class. Applicants must have 48 college credits with a GPA of 2.0.

Financial Aid: In an earlier year, 70% of all freshmen and 72% of continuing students received some form of financial aid. Scholarships or need-based grants averaged $600 ($800 maximum); and loans averaged $1500 ($2600 maximum). The average financial indebtedness of an earlier graduate was $4200. The university is a member of CSS. The college's own financial statement is required. The deadline for financial aid applications is July 15.

International Students: There are currently 205 international students enrolled.

Computers: The college provides computer facilities for student use. The mainframes are a DEC VAX 8700, 6320, and 11/750. There are also 100 IBM-compatible, DEC, and Apple PCs available in laboratories and the computer center. All students may access the system. It may be used 24 hours a day. There are no fees.

Graduates: In 1992–93, 1441 bachelor's degrees were awarded. The most popular majors among graduates were chemical engineering (9%), electrical engineering (7%), and civil engineering (7%). Some 113 companies recruited on campus in 1992–93.

Admissions Contact: Ivonne Ramirez-Serna, Director of Admissions.

UNIVERSITY OF PUERTO RICO
RIO PIEDRAS
D-1
Rio Piedras, PR 00931-3300   (809) 763-6888

Full-time: 3900 men, 8900 women	Faculty: 1292
Part-time: 1450 men, 2460 women	Ph.Ds: 36%
Graduate: 1225 men, 2325 women	Student/Faculty: 10 to 1
Year: semesters, summer session	Tuition: see profile
Application Deadline: December 15	Room & Board: n/app
Freshman Class: n/av	
CEEB or SAT I: required	

The University of Puerto Rico at Rio Piedras, founded in 1903, is a public, coeducational institution, offering undergraduate programs in arts and sciences, business, and education. Tuition and fees for Puerto Rican residents total $1606 per year; nonresident U.S. citizens pay tuition equal to what they would pay in their home states. There are 8 undergraduate and 30 graduate schools. In addition to regional accreditation, the university has baccalaureate program accreditation with ADA, CSWE, NAAB, and NCATE. The 10 libraries contain 24,131 audiovisual forms, and subscribe to 4950 periodicals. Computerized library sources and services include the card catalog. Special learning facilities include a learning resource center, an art gallery, a natural history museum, a radio station, audiovisual services, and television production facilities. The 271-acre campus is in an urban area in the Rio Piedras section of San Juan. Including residence halls, there are 133 buildings on campus.

Student Life: About 99% of undergraduates are from Puerto Rico. Students come from 2 states and 21 foreign countries. Fifty-nine percent are from public schools; 41% from private. All are Hispanic. The

average age of freshmen is 18. Five percent drop out by the end of their first year.

Housing: A total of 783 students can be accommodated in college housing. College-sponsored living facilities include coed dormitories. On-campus housing is available on a first-come, first-served basis and is available on a lottery system for upperclassmen. Priority is given to out-of-town students. Alcohol is not permitted. All students may keep cars on campus.

Activities: There are no fraternities or sororities on campus. There are 60 groups on campus, including art, band, chorus, drama, honors, international, literary magazine, newspaper, pep band, political, professional, radio and TV, religious, social, social service, and student government. Popular campus events include sports events, and spring and Christmas concerts.

Sports: There are 12 intercollegiate sports for men and 8 for women, and 15 intramural sports for men and 10 for women. Athletic and recreation facilities include a sports complex with a swimming pool, tennis, basketball, and volleyball courts, a gymnasium, and track and field areas.

Disabled Students: Eighty percent of the campus is accessible to disabled students. The following facilities are available: wheelchair ramps, elevators, special parking, specially equipped rest rooms, special class scheduling, lowered drinking fountains, and lowered telephones.

Services: There is a reader service for the blind, and remedial math, reading, and writing.

Campus Safety and Security: Campus safety and security measures include 24-hour foot and vehicle patrol, shuttle buses, pamphlets, posters, films, and lighted pathways and sidewalks.

Programs of Study: The university awards the B.A., B.S., B.B.A., B.E.D., and B. in Secretarial Science degrees. Associate, master's, and doctoral degrees are also awarded. Bachelor's degrees are awarded in AGRICULTURE (equestrian science), BIOLOGICAL SCIENCE (biology/biological science), BUSINESS (accounting, banking and finance, business administration and management, business economics, business statistics, labor studies, marketing/retailing/merchandising, personnel management, and secretarial studies/office management), COMMUNICATIONS AND THE ARTS (art history and appreciation, communications, dramatic arts, English, fine arts, French, music, Spanish, and speech/debate/rhetoric), COMPUTER AND PHYSICAL SCIENCE (chemistry, computer science, mathematics, physics, and quantitative methods), EDUCATION (art, business, early childhood, elementary, foreign languages, home economics, industrial arts, music, science, secondary, special, and teaching English as a second language/foreign language), ENGINEERING AND ENVIRONMENTAL DESIGN (architecture), SOCIAL SCIENCE (anthropology, dietetics, economics, geography, history, philosophy, political science/government, prelaw, psychology, social science, social work, and sociology). Natural sciences are the strongest programs academically. Business administration and accounting have the largest enrollments.

Required: To graduate, students must complete 117 to 147 credits, with a minimum GPA of 2.0. All students must take basic courses in biological sciences, physical sciences, social sciences, Spanish, humanities, and English. Spanish is the language of instruction in most courses, but students are required to have a working knowledge of English.

Special: The university offers internships at local government and private agencies, study abroad in 5 countries, a Washington semester, a general studies degree, and nondegree study. There is one national honor society on campus.

Faculty/Classroom: Fifty percent of faculty are male; 50%, female. No introductory courses are taught by graduate students. The average class size in an introductory lecture is 27; in a laboratory, 20; and in a regular course offering, 23.

Requirements: The SAT I or the CEEB's Spanish equivalent is required. Applicants must be graduates of an accredited secondary school. The GED is accepted. Students should have completed 3 courses each of English and Spanish, 2 each of mathematics and science, and 3 electives. AP credits are accepted. Important factors used in the admissions decision are recommendations by school officials, recommendations by alumni, personality, intangible qualities, parents or siblings attending the school, and leadership record.

Procedure: Freshmen are admitted in the fall. Entrance exams should be taken in November or February of the senior year. Applications should be filed by December 15 for fall entry, along with an application fee of $15. Notification is sent in April.

Transfer: Applicants for transfer should have a minimum of 45 college credits with a GPA of 2.5.

Visiting: To arrange for a visit, contact the Dean of Students at (809) 764-0000, ext. 5540 or 5541.

Financial Aid: Nine percent of undergraduate students work part-time. The university is a member of CSS. The Puerto Rico Income Tax Revenue Report and the FAF (Spanish version for Puerto Rico) financial statement are required. The deadline for financial aid applications is April.

International Students: There are currently 76 international students enrolled. The school actively recruits these students. The student must take the Spanish or English SAT I.

Computers: The college provides computer facilities for student use. The mainframe is an IBM 4381. Terminals and microcomputer facilities are available in the main computer center, the library, and various academic departments. All students may access the system. Schedules are provided during the semester. There are no time limits on using the system and no fees.

Graduates: In a recent year, 2297 bachelor's degrees were awarded. The most popular majors among graduates were business administration (29%), social science (22%), and education (18%). Within an average freshman class, 11% graduate in 4 years and 22% in 5 years.

Admissions Contact: Maria M. Rosado, Admissions Director.

UNIVERSITY OF THE SACRED HEART

Santurce, PR 00914

D-1

(809) 727-5500

Full-time: 1353 men, 2874 women	**Faculty:** 169
Part-time: 419 men, 758 women	**Ph.D.s:** 15%
Graduate: 86 men, 162 women	**Student/Faculty:** 25 to 1
Year: 2 + 2 summer sessions (June and July)	**Tuition:** $2690
	Room & Board: $1200
Application Deadline: June 30	
Freshman Class: n/av	
SAT I: required	

University of the Sacred Heart, founded in 1935, is a private, coeducational Catholic institution offering degree programs in arts and sciences, business, education, and nursing. Instructional models in English, French, biology, mathematics and other subjects are unique to the university. There are 6 undergraduate and 3 graduate schools. The library contains 68,835 volumes, 34,755 microform items, and 8128 audiovisual forms, and subscribes to 981 periodicals. Special learning facilities include a learning resource center, natural history museum, communication center, and secretarial, human performance, and art laboratories. The 33-acre campus is in an urban area in San Juan. Including residence halls, there are 14 buildings on campus.

Student Life: Thirty-seven percent are from public schools; 59% from private. All are Hispanic. The average age of freshmen is 21.

Housing: A total of 154 students can be accommodated in college housing. College-sponsored living facilities include single-sex dormitories. On-campus housing is available on a first-come, first-served basis. Priority is given to out-of-town students. Alcohol is not permitted. All students may keep cars on campus.

Activities: There are no fraternities or sororities on campus. There are 18 groups on campus, including art, cheerleading, choir, computers, drama, film, honors, literary magazine, newspaper, photography, radio and TV, religious, social service, and student government. Popular campus events include Library, Language, and Education Week, Intercollegiate Theater Festival, LAI Athletic Competition, and Crafts Fair.

Sports: There are 9 intercollegiate sports for men and 6 for women, and 9 intramural sports for men and 8 for women. Athletic and recreation facilities include basketball and volleyball courts, a swimming pool, a softball field, a jumps field, 4 tennis courts, Nautilis and free weight rooms, and a recreation room with pool and Ping-Pong tables.

Disabled Students: Ninety percent of the campus is accessible to disabled students. The following facilities are available: wheelchair ramps, elevators, special parking, specially equipped rest rooms, special class scheduling, and lowered drinking fountains.

Services: In addition to many counseling and information services, tutoring is available in most subjects. There is also remedial math, reading, and writing, an English and Spanish reader service for the blind, and notetaking services for the hearing-impaired.

Programs of Study: The university awards the B.A., B.S., B.B.A., B.S.S., B.S.N., B.A.C., and B.Ed. degrees. Associate and master's degrees also are awarded. Bachelor's degrees are awarded in BIOLOGICAL SCIENCE (biology/biological science), BUSINESS (accounting, business administration and management, management information systems, marketing/retailing/merchandising, personnel management, secretarial studies/office management, and tourism), COMMUNICATIONS AND THE ARTS (advertising, communications, journalism, telecommunications, and visual and performing arts), COMPUTER AND PHYSICAL SCIENCE (chemistry, computer science, and mathematics), EDUCATION (elementary and physical), HEALTH PROFESSIONS (nursing), SOCIAL SCIENCE (criminal justice, psychology, social work, and urban studies). Communications and business administration have the largest enrollments.

Required: To graduate, students must complete between 133 and 145 credits, including 22 to 45 in the major, with a minimum GPA of 2.1 in the major and 2.0 overall. All students must take 12 credits of English, 9 credits of Spanish, 6 credits each of theology, humanities, social sciences, and biology, and 3 credits each of logic and philosophy, arts, computer science, and physical fitness. Some programs require a field work practicum.

Special: The university offers co-op programs with Seton Hall and Marquette Universities, cross-registration with Manhattan college, work-study programs with local employers, and a political semester in Spain or Washington, D.C. Credit is granted for advanced placement in the English language. There is one national honor society on campus.

Faculty/Classroom: Forty-seven percent of faculty are male; 53% female.

Requirements: The SAT I or the CEEB's Spanish equivalent is required, along with SAT II: Subject tests in Spanish, writing, and mathematics. Applicants must be graduates of an accredited secondary school. The GED is accepted. The admissions formula is based on GPA (x 600) + CEEB (verbal + mathematics + English). Applicants whose index is 3300 will be admitted to the university. Those who comply with only 1 (GPA or CEEB) will be considered individually by the evaluation committee. AP credits are accepted.

Procedure: Entrance exams should be taken in October of the senior year. Applications should be filed by June 30 for fall entry and December 15 for spring entry, along with an application fee of $15. Notification is sent on a rolling basis. There are early decision and early admissions plans. About 427 early decision candidates were accepted for the 1993–94 class.

Transfer: About 88 transfer students enrolled in 1993–94. Applicants with at least 30 college credits and a high school and college GPA of 2.5 are eligible for transfer. Students must submit CEEB scores and a letter of recommendation. Three-quarters of the credits needed in the major must be taken at the university.

Visiting: There are regularly scheduled orientations for prospective students. Visitors may sit in on classes. To arrange for a visit, contact the Admission, Promotion, and Recruitment Office at (809) 728–1602.

Financial Aid: Scholarships or need-based grants averaged $383 ($23,600 maximum); and loans averaged $287 ($2250 maximum). The average financial indebtedness of the 1992–93 graduate was $3125. The university is a member of CSS. The FAF, the college's own financial statement and the AFSA is required. The deadline for financial aid applications is June.

International Students: There are currently 43 international students enrolled. The student must take the CEEB or SAT I.

Computers: The college provides computer facilities for student use. The mainframe is a DEC MicroVAX 3400 and 3100. There are 32 terminals as well as microcomputer facilities in the computer laboratory and in 5 computer classrooms. All students may access the system. There are no time limits on using the system. The fees are $25 to 75. It is recommended that students in IBM Education Product Coordinator Program have personal computers.

Graduates: In 1992–93 627 bachelor's degrees were awarded. The most popular majors among graduates were publicity (13%), telecommunications (12%), and tourism (9%).

Admissions Contact: Melvin Rosario, Director.

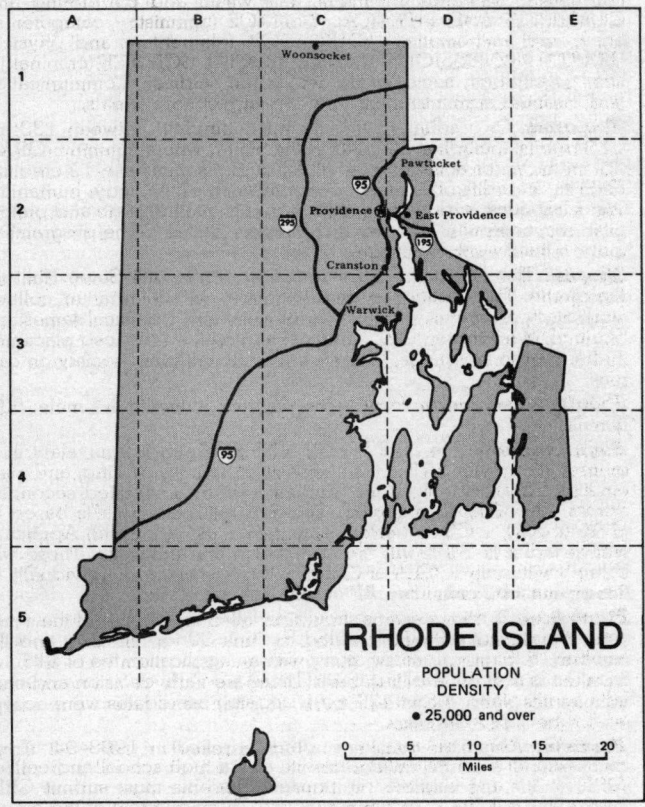

RHODE ISLAND

POPULATION
DENSITY

● 25,000 and over

0   5   10   15   20
Miles

ter, newspaper, orchestra, photography, political, professional, radio and TV, religious, social, social service, student government, and yearbook. Popular campus events include Commencement, Spring Weekend, Homecoming, and Parents Weekend.

Sports: There are 17 intercollegiate sports each for men and women, and 15 intramural sports each for men and women. Athletic and recreation facilities include a 25,000-seat stadium, an Olympic-size pool, a 200-meter, 6-lane track, a hockey rink, playing fields, and courts for squash, handball, racquetball, tennis, basketball, and volleyball.

Disabled Students: The following facilities are available: wheelchair ramps, elevators, and special parking.

Services: In addition to many counseling and information services, tutoring is available in most subjects, and there is a reader service for the blind. Other services include class note-taking, books on tape, diagnostic testing service, oral tests, tutors, and untimed tests.

Campus Safety and Security: Campus safety and security measures include 24-hour foot and vehicle patrol, self-defense education, escort service, and shuttle buses. In addition, there are informal discussions, pamphlets, posters, films, emergency telephones, lighted pathways and sidewalks, and the Safe Walk program.

Programs of Study: Brown awards the A.B. and Sc.B. degrees. Master's and doctoral degrees also are awarded. Bachelor's degrees are awarded in BIOLOGICAL SCIENCE (biochemistry, biology/biological science, biophysics, and neurosciences), BUSINESS (organizational behavior), COMMUNICATIONS AND THE ARTS (American literature, art history and appreciation, classics, comparative literature, English, French, German, Italian, linguistics, music, performing arts, and Slavic languages), COMPUTER AND PHYSICAL SCIENCE (applied mathematics, chemistry, computer science, geology, mathematics, and physics), EDUCATION (education), ENGINEERING AND ENVIRONMENTAL DESIGN (architectural technology, engineering, and environmental science), HEALTH PROFESSIONS (biomedical science), SOCIAL SCIENCE (African American studies, anthropology, cognitive science, East Asian studies, economics, Hispanic American studies, history, international relations, Judaic studies, Latin American studies, medieval studies, philosophy, political science/government, psychology, Russian and Slavic studies, sociology, South Asian studies, urban studies, and women's studies). Biological sciences, history, engineering, international relations, English and American literature, psychology, and political science have the largest enrollments.

Required: Students must pass 30 of 32 courses in order to graduate. There are no distribution requirements or specific required courses.

Special: Students may cross-register with Rhode Island School of Design, or study abroad in any of 21 programs in 18 countries. A combined B.A.-B.S. degree is possible in any major field with 5 years of study. Dual and student-designed majors, community internships, and pass/fail options are available. Students may pursue 5-year programs in the arts or sciences, or the 8-year program in liberal medical education continuum. There is a freshman honors program on campus. All departments have honors programs.

Faculty/Classroom: All faculty teach undergraduates and also do research. Graduate students teach 13% of introductory courses. The average class size in an introductory lecture is 40; in a laboratory, 20; and in a regular course offering, 45.

Admissions: About 26% of the 1993–94 applicants were accepted. The SAT scores for the 1993–94 freshman class were as follows: Verbal—7% below 500, 26% between 500 and 599, 51% between 600 and 700, and 16% above 700; Math—2% below 500, 11% between 500 and 599, 41% between 600 and 700, and 46% above 700. The ACT scores were 3% below 21, 23% between 21 and 25, 46% between 26 and 29, and 28% above 30. About 90% of the current freshmen were in the top fifth of their class; 98% were in the top two fifths. There were 150 National Merit finalists and 75 semifinalists.

Requirements: The SAT I or ACT is required, along with any 3 SAT II: Subject tests. Applicants must be graduates of accredited high schools. Secondary preparation is expected to include courses in English, foreign language, mathematics, science, and history. A personal essay is required. The high school transcript is a most important criterion for admission. AP credits are accepted. Important factors used in the admissions decision are advanced placement or honor courses, evidence of special talent, leadership record, recommendations by school officials, and extracurricular activities record.

Procedure: Freshmen are admitted fall and spring. Entrance exams should be taken in the junior or senior year. Early decision applications should be filed by November 1; regular applications, by January 1 for fall entry, along with an application fee of $55. Notification of early decision is sent December 15; regular decision, April 1. There are early decision, early admissions, and deferred admissions plans.

BROWN UNIVERSITY

Providence, RI 02912

C-2

(401) 863-2378

Full-time: 2762 men, 2881 women	**Faculty:** 551; I, +$
Part-time: 140 men, 209 women	**Ph.D.s:** 98%
Graduate: 935 men, 728 women	**Student/Faculty:** 10 to 1
Year: semesters, summer session	**Tuition:** $19,528
Application Deadline: January 1	**Room & Board:** $5926
Freshman Class: 12,587 applied, 3239 accepted, 1466 enrolled	
SAT I Verbal/Math: 620/680	**ACT:** 31 **MOST COMPETITIVE**

Brown University, founded in 1764, is a coeducational liberal arts institution and one of the Ivy League schools. There is one graduate school. In addition to regional accreditation, Brown has baccalaureate program accreditation with ABET. The 6 libraries contain 2.5 million volumes, 1 million microform items, and 26,342 audiovisual forms, and subscribe to 15,090 periodicals. Computerized library sources and services include the card catalog, interlibrary loans, and database searching. Special learning facilities include a learning resource center, an art gallery, a planetarium, a radio station, a TV station, and an anthropology museum. The 140-acre campus is in an urban area 45 miles south of Boston. Including residence halls, there are 243 buildings on campus.

Student Life: About 97% of undergraduates are from out-of-state, mostly the Middle Atlantic. Students come from 50 states, 63 foreign countries, and Canada. Eighty percent are from public schools; 20% from private. Sixty-seven percent are white; 14% Asian American. The average age of freshmen is 18; all undergraduates, 20. Four percent drop out by the end of their first year; 96% remain to graduate.

Housing: A total of 4331 students can be accommodated in college housing. College-sponsored living facilities include single-sex and coed dormitories, on-campus apartments, off-campus apartments, fraternity houses, and sorority houses. In addition, there are language houses and special interest houses. On-campus housing is guaranteed for all 4 years. Eighty-five percent of students live on campus; of those, 90% remain on campus on weekends. Upperclassmen may keep cars on campus.

Activities: About 12% of men belong to 11 national fraternities; about 2% of women belong to 2 national sororities. There are 240 groups on campus, including band, cheerleading, chess, choir, chorale, chorus, computers, dance, drama, ethnic, film, gay, honors, international, jazz band, literary magazine, marching band, musical thea-

About 540 early decision candidates were accepted for the 1993–94 class. A waiting list is an active part of the admissions procedure, with about 3% of applicants on the list.

Transfer: About 125 transfer students enrolled in 1993–94. Transfer applicants must submit high school and college transcripts, 2 recommendations from college professors, scores on the SAT I and 3 SAT II: Subject tests, a letter of good standing, and a personal essay. A total of 15 courses out of 30 must be completed at Brown.

Visiting: There are regularly scheduled orientations for prospective students, Monday through Friday at 2 P.M., and at 10 A.M. from mid-April through November, at 2 P.M. from December to April, and on Saturday mornings from mid-September to mid-November. There are guides for informal visits and visitors may sit in on classes and stay overnight at the school. To arrange for a visit, contact the Admission Office receptionist at (401) 863–2378.

Financial Aid: In 1993–94, 32% of all current freshmen received some form of financial aid. About 40% of freshmen and 39% of continuing students received need-based aid. The average freshman award was $14,025. Of that total, scholarships or need-based grants averaged $10,000; loans averaged $2795; and work contracts averaged $1215. Average earnings from campus work for the school year are $1360. The average financial indebtedness of the 1992–93 graduate was $12,000. Brown is a member of CSS. The FAF, the college's own financial statement, and some state forms are required. The deadline for financial aid applications is January 1.

International Students: There are currently 415 international students enrolled. The school actively recruits these students. They must take the TOEFL and achieve a minimum score of 600. The student must also take the SAT I or the ACT and any 3 SAT II: Subject tests.

Computers: The college provides computer facilities for student use. There are more than 300 workstations in several campus locations equipped with Macintosh and IBM microcomputers. Students may also access the mainframe from dormitory rooms. The main computer center is open 18 hours a day and around the clock during examination periods. All students may access the system. There are no time limits on using the system and no fees.

Graduates: In 1992–93, 1422 bachelor's degrees were awarded. The most popular majors among graduates were biological sciences (10%), history (8%), and engineering (7%). Within an average freshman class, 80% graduate in 4 years, 92% in 5 years, and 94% in 6 years. Some 300 companies recruited on campus in 1992–93. In the 1992 graduating class, 30% of all graduates were enrolled in graduate school within 6 months of graduation; 37% had found employment.

Admissions Contact: Eric Widmer, Dean of Admission and Financial Aid.

BRYANT COLLEGE
C-2

Smithfield, RI 02917–1284

Full-time: 1474 men, 1084 women
Part-time: 379 men, 631 women
Graduate: 405 men, 265 women
Year: semesters, summer session
Application Deadline: open
Freshman Class: 2221 applied, 1775 accepted, 632 enrolled
SAT I Verbal/Math: 450/540

(401) 232–6100; (800) 622–7001
Faculty: 135; IIB, + +$
Ph.D.s: 84%
Student/Faculty: 19 to 1
Tuition: $12,120
Room & Board: $6215

COMPETITIVE

Bryant College, founded in 1863, is a private, primarily residential institution that offers degrees in business and liberal arts. There is one graduate school. The library contains 129,249 volumes, 16,606 microform items, and 686 audiovisual forms, and subscribes to 1376 periodicals. Computerized library sources and services include the card catalog, interlibrary loans, and database searching. Special learning facilities include a learning resource center, a radio station, the Koffler Technology Center, and a language laboratory. The 397-acre campus is in a suburban area 12 miles northwest of Providence. Including residence halls, there are 42 buildings on campus.

Student Life: About 84% of undergraduates are from out-of-state, mostly the Northeast. Students come from 30 states and 24 foreign countries. Seventy-seven percent are from public schools; 23% from private. Ninety-one percent are white. Sixty percent are Catholic; 18% Protestant; 12% claim no religious affiliation. The average age of freshmen is 18; all undergraduates, 20. Twelve percent drop out by the end of their first year; 76% remain to graduate.

Housing: A total of 2484 students can be accommodated in college housing. College-sponsored living facilities include single-sex and coed dormitories and on-campus apartments. In addition, there are special interest houses and individual fraternities and sororities may live as a group within a dormitory. On-campus housing is guaranteed for all 4 years. Eighty percent of students live on campus; of those, 75% remain on campus on weekends. All students may keep cars on campus.

Activities: About 20% of men belong to 2 local and 7 national fraternities; about 19% of women belong to 5 national sororities. There are 62 groups on campus, including cheerleading, chess, chorus, computers, dance, drama, ethnic, honors, international, newspaper, political, professional, radio and TV, religious, student government, and yearbook. Popular campus events include Parents Weekend, Special Olympics Weekend, Spring Weekend, a performing arts series, Unhomecoming, and the Alcohol Awareness Road Race.

Sports: There are 7 intercollegiate sports for men and 7 for women, and 12 intramural sports for men and 11 for women. Athletic and recreation facilities include a 2700-seat gymnasium, a Nautilus fitness center, basketball, volleyball, tennis, racquetball, and multipurpose courts, a 400-meter all-weather track, a cross-country course, and playing fields for baseball, football, softball, rugby, lacrosse, and field hockey.

Disabled Students: Ninety percent of the campus is accessible to disabled students. The following facilities are available: wheelchair ramps, elevators, special parking, specially equipped rest rooms, special class scheduling, lowered drinking fountains, and lowered telephones.

Services: In addition to many counseling and information services, tutoring is available in most subjects. There is also a reader service for the blind, and remedial math, reading, and writing. A range of support services are available for the physically challenged and learning disabled.

Campus Safety and Security: Campus safety and security measures include 24-hour foot and vehicle patrol, escort service, informal discussions, and pamphlets, posters, and films. In addition, there are emergency telephones, lighted pathways and sidewalks, a 24-hour manned-entry control station, parking-lot cameras, and intrusion alarms sounded at the campus security office. In addition, grounds are patrolled on bicycle during the warmer months.

Programs of Study: Bryant awards the B.A. and B.S.B.A. degrees. Associate and master's degrees are also awarded. Bachelor's degrees are awarded in BUSINESS (accounting, banking and finance, business administration and management, and marketing/retailing/merchandising), COMMUNICATIONS AND THE ARTS (communications and English), COMPUTER AND PHYSICAL SCIENCE (actuarial science and information sciences and systems), SOCIAL SCIENCE (economics, history, and international studies). Applied actuarial mathematics, accounting, marketing, finance, and management are the strongest academically. Accounting and management have the largest enrollments.

Required: To graduate, all students must complete 55 semester hours of liberal arts, 54 hours of business, and 12 hours of electives (none for accounting majors), for a total of 121 hours, with 18 to 24 hours in the major. A GPA of 2.0, overall and in the major, must be maintained. Required courses include English composition, business, economics, mathematics, humanities, computer, and management.

Special: Bryant offers full- and part-time internships, study abroad in 21 countries, on-campus work-study programs, accelerated business programs, B.A.-B.S. degrees, dual and student-designed majors, credit for military experience, and nondegree study. There is a freshman honors program on campus, as well as one national honor society. Five departments have honors programs.

Faculty/Classroom: Seventy-three percent of faculty are male; 27%, female. All teach undergraduates, and 75% do research. No introductory courses are taught by graduate students. The average class size in an introductory lecture is 30; in a laboratory, 22; and in a regular course offering, 33.

Admissions: About 80% of the 1993–94 applicants were accepted. The SAT scores for the 1993–94 freshman class were as follows: Verbal—78% below 500, 20% between 500 and 599, and 2% between 600 and 700; Math—31% below 500, 48% between 500 and 599, 18% between 600 and 700, and 3% above 700. About 31% of the current freshmen were in the top fifth of their class; 65% were in the top two fifths. There were 5 National Merit semifinalists. Four freshmen graduated first in their class.

Requirements: The SAT I or ACT is required, along with SAT II: Subject tests and an essay. Applicants must be graduates of an accredited secondary school or have a GED certificate. A total of 16 Carnegie units is required, including 4 years of English, 2 years each of mathematics (minimum algebra I and II) and social studies, and 1 year of laboratory science. An interview is recommended. AP and CLEP credits are accepted. Important factors used in the admissions decision are advanced placement or honor courses, recommendations by school officials, leadership record, geographic diversity, and extracurricular activities record.

Procedure: Freshmen are admitted fall and spring. Entrance exams should be taken before January of the senior year. Application deadlines are open. Application fee is $20. Notification of early decision is sent December 20; regular decision, on a rolling basis. There are early decision, early admissions, and deferred admissions plans. About 75 early decision candidates were accepted for the 1993–94 class. A waiting list is an active part of the admissions procedure, with about 5% of applicants on the list.

Transfer: About 150 transfer students enrolled in 1993–94. Applicants must have a minimum GPA of 2.0, although a 3.0 is recommended, as is an interview. A total of 30 credits out of 121 must be completed at Bryant.

Visiting: There are regularly scheduled orientations for prospective students, including campus tours, a student aid presentation, and a student activities presentation. There are guides for informal visits and visitors may sit in on classes and stay overnight at the school. To arrange for a visit, contact the Admissions Office at (401) 232–6100 or (800) 622–7001.

Financial Aid: In 1993–94, 68% of all current freshmen and 58% of continuing students received some form of financial aid. About 68% of freshmen and 58% of continuing students received need-based aid. The average freshman award was $10,647. Of that total, scholarships or need-based grants averaged $6745 ($8000 maximum); loans averaged $2625 ($4125 maximum); and work contracts averaged $1200. Forty-three percent of undergraduate students work part-time. Average earnings from campus work for the school year are $1057. The average financial indebtedness of the 1992–93 graduate was $12,500. Bryant is a member of CSS. The FAF and the college's own financial statement are required. The deadline for financial aid applications is February 15.

International Students: There are currently 34 international students enrolled. The school actively recruits these students. They must take the TOEFL and achieve a minimum score of 550. The student must also take the SAT I or the ACT.

Computers: The college provides computer facilities for student use. The mainframe is a DEC Station 5000 Model 240. There are 90 terminals, in 3 campus locations, directly connected to the mainframe. Students with classes requiring access receive accounts. E-mail and user accounts are available to other students on request. All students may access the system. It may be used when the technology center is open. There are no time limits on using the system and no fees.

Graduates: In 1992–93, 875 bachelor's degrees were awarded. The most popular majors among graduates were management (26%), accounting (24%), and finance (20%). Within an average freshman class, 75% graduate in 4 years and 78% in 5 years. Some 154 companies recruited on campus in 1992–93. In the 1992 graduating class, 5% of all graduates were enrolled in graduate school within 6 months of graduation; 88% had found employment.

Admissions Contact: Roy A. Nelson, Director of Admission.

JOHNSON AND WALES UNIVERSITY

C-2

Providence, RI 02903

Full-time: 4246 men, 3351 women
Part-time: 598 men, 689 women
Graduate: 253 men, 199 women
Year: trimesters, summer session
Application Deadline: August 1

(401) 598–4664; (800) 343–2565

Faculty: 217
Ph.D.s: 20%
Student/Faculty: 35 to 1
Tuition: $9510 (see profile)
Room & Board: $4485 (see profile)

Freshman Class: 14,545 applied, 12,403 accepted, 2497 enrolled
SAT I or ACT: recommended   **LESS COMPETITIVE**

Johnson and Wales University, founded in 1914, is a private institution emphasizing business programs. Tuition at the Charleston, South Carolina campus is $7,572; room only is $2,685. There are 4 undergraduate schools and one graduate school. The 4 libraries contain 70,000 volumes, 170,000 microform items, and 2300 audiovisual forms, and subscribe to 1230 periodicals. Computerized library sources and services include the card catalog, interlibrary loans, and database searching. Special learning facilities include a learning resource center and culinary archives, and a museum. The 80-acre campus is in an urban area of Providence, with facilities in Warwick, Cranston, and Seekonk. There are also facilities in Charleston, South Carolina, and in Worchester, Massachusetts. Including residence halls, there are 60 buildings on campus.

Student Life: About 90% of undergraduates are from out-of-state, mostly the Northeast. Students come from 50 states, 75 foreign countries, and Canada. Eighty-two percent are from public schools; 18% from private. Seventy-nine percent are white. The average age of freshmen is 19; all undergraduates, 21. Twenty-two percent drop out by the end of their first year; 71% remain to graduate.

Housing: A total of 3955 students can be accommodated in college housing. College-sponsored living facilities include single-sex and coed dormitories, on-campus apartments, and married-student housing. In addition, there are special interest houses and international housing, national student organization housing, honors floors, and wellness housing available. On-campus housing is guaranteed for all 4 years. Fifty-one percent of students live on campus; of those, 75% remain on campus on weekends. Alcohol is not permitted. All students may keep cars on campus.

Activities: About 15% of men belong to 3 local and 12 national fraternities; about 15% of women belong to 2 local and 10 national sororities. There are 75 groups on campus, including cheerleading, chess, choir, chorale, computers, dance, drama, ethnic, gay, honors,

international, literary magazine, musical theater, newspaper, political, professional, religious, social, social service, student government, and yearbook. Popular campus events include Spring Weekend, Family Weekend, and SnoBall Dance.

Sports: There are 8 intercollegiate sports for men and 7 for women, and 7 intramural sports each. Athletic and recreation facilities include two gymnasiums, two weight rooms, two fitness centers, a swimming pool, hockey rinks, and athletic fields.

Disabled Students: Sixty percent of the campus is accessible to disabled students. The following facilities are available: wheelchair ramps, elevators, special parking, specially equipped rest rooms, special class scheduling, lowered drinking fountains, lowered telephones, lowered fire alarms, emergency lighting, audio-visual fire alarms in public bathrooms, and a lowering chair for the swimming pool.

Services: In addition to many counseling and information services, tutoring is available in every subject. There is also a reader service for the blind and remedial math and writing. Workshops in stress and time management, wellness, and learning strategies are offered. Special scheduling of courses and exams as well as taping are available to accommodate special needs.

Campus Safety and Security: Campus safety and security measures include 24-hour foot and vehicle patrol, self-defense education, escort service, and shuttle buses. In addition, there are informal discussions, pamphlets, posters, films, emergency telephones, lighted pathways and sidewalks, 24-hour dorm coverage, a phone hot-line for campus emergencies, and crime alerts in the student weekly newspaper.

Programs of Study: Johnson and Wales University awards the B.S. degree. Associate and master's degrees also are awarded. Bachelor's degrees are awarded in AGRICULTURE (equestrian science), BUSINESS (accounting, business administration and management, court reporting, fashion merchandising, hospitality management services, hotel/motel and restaurant management, institutional management, international business management, management information systems, management science, marketing and distribution, marketing management, marketing/retailing/merchandising, office supervision and management, recreation and leisure services, recreational facilities management, retailing, secretarial studies/office management, small business management, sports management, tourism, and transportation and travel marketing), COMMUNICATIONS AND THE ARTS (advertising and communications), COMPUTER AND PHYSICAL SCIENCE (computer management, computer science, and systems analysis), EDUCATION (marketing and distribution), ENGINEERING AND ENVIRONMENTAL DESIGN (food services technology), HEALTH PROFESSIONS (health care administration), SOCIAL SCIENCE (clothing and textiles management/production/services, food production/management/services, paralegal studies, parks and recreation management, and systems science). Culinary arts, hotel-restaurant management, marketing, and accounting are the strongest academically. Culinary arts, hotel-restaurant management, and accounting have the largest enrollments.

Required: To graduate, students must complete 124 credit hours, with a minimum of 24 in the major. Required courses include English, mathematics, history, psychology, and sociology

Special: Co-op programs, ROTC with Providence College, study abroad, and work study are available. There are required 11-week internships in culinary arts, hotel-restaurant management, and retail merchandising management. Accelerated degrees and dual majors are possible. There is a freshman honors program on campus, as well as one national honor society. Five departments have honors programs.

Faculty/Classroom: Sixty-three percent of faculty are male; 37%, female. All teach undergraduates. No introductory courses are taught by graduate students. The average class size in an introductory lecture is 30; in a laboratory, 18; and in a regular course offering, 30.

Admissions: About 85% of the 1993–94 applicants were accepted. About 15% of the current freshmen were in the top fifth of their class; 40% were in the top two fifths. Three freshmen graduated first in their class.

Requirements: Johnson and Wales University requires applicants to be in the upper 67% of their class. A minimum GPA of 2.0 is required. The SAT I or ACT is recommended. Graduation from high school or an equivalent credential is required. AP and CLEP credits are accepted. Important factors used in the admissions decision are leadership record, evidence of special talent, advanced placement or honor courses, recommendations by school officials, and extracurricular activities record.

Procedure: Freshmen are admitted to all sessions. Applications should be filed by August 1 for fall entry, November 1 for winter entry, February 1 for spring entry, and May 1 for summer entry. Notification is sent on a rolling basis. There are early admissions and deferred admissions plans.

Transfer: About 490 transfer students enrolled in 1993–94. Transfer students are required to submit official high school and college transcripts and must have earned a minimum college GPA of 2.0. A total of 30 credits out of 124 must be completed at Johnson and Wales University.

Visiting: There are regularly scheduled orientations for prospective students, including parent/student orientation, financial services, student testing, academic orientation, preparation for September registration, and parent-to-parent orientation. There are guides for informal visits and visitors may sit in on classes and stay overnight at the school. To arrange for a visit, contact the Admissions Office at (800) 343–2565.

Financial Aid: In 1993–94, 76% of all current freshmen and 78% of continuing students received some form of financial aid. About 70% of freshmen and 66% of continuing students received need-based aid. The average freshman award was $8026. Of that total, scholarships or need-based grants averaged $1801 ($9216 maximum); loans averaged $2376 ($4625 maximum); and work contracts averaged $1625 ($1800 maximum). Fifty-five percent of undergraduate students work part-time. Average earnings from campus work for the school year are $528. The average financial indebtedness of the 1992–93 graduate was $8441. The college's own financial statement and FAFSA are required. The deadline for financial aid applications is August 1.

International Students: There are currently 628 international students enrolled. The school actively recruits these students. They must take the TOEFL and achieve a minimum score of 550.

Computers: The college provides computer facilities for student use. There are 400 personal computers dedicated to student use, including 25 networked workstations for hospitality students. All students may access the system. It may be used daily, a total of 82 hours per week. There are no time limits on using the system and no fees.

Graduates: In 1992–93, 1107 bachelor's degrees were awarded. The most popular majors among graduates were food service management (26%), hospitality management (20%), and hotel-restaurant institutional management (12%). Within an average freshman class, 24% graduate in 3 years, 75% in 4 years, and 1% in 5 years. Some 219 companies recruited on campus in 1992–93. In the 1992 graduating class, 10% of all students were enrolled in graduate school within 6 months of graduation; 98% found employment.

Admissions Contact: Mark Burke, Director of Enrollment Management.

PROVIDENCE COLLEGE
C-2

Providence, RI 02918   (401) 865-2535

Full-time: 1648 men, 1964 women	**Faculty:** 257; IIA, av$
Part-time: 1687 men and women	**Ph.D.s:** 82%
Graduate: 804 men and women	**Student/Faculty:** 14 to 1
Year: semesters, summer session	**Tuition:** $13,850
Application Deadline: February 1	**Room & Board:** $5900
Freshman Class: 5138 applied, 3346 accepted, 973 enrolled	
SAT I Verbal/Math: 499/559	**ACT:** 25 **VERY COMPETITIVE**

Providence College, founded in 1917, is a liberal arts and sciences institution operated by the Dominican order of the Catholic Church. There is one graduate school. In addition to regional accreditation, Providence has baccalaureate program accreditation with AACSB, CSWE, and NCATE. The library contains 301,067 volumes, 25,709 microform items, and 1113 audiovisual forms, and subscribes to 1877 periodicals. Computerized library sources and services include interlibrary loans and database searching. Special learning facilities include a learning resource center, art gallery, radio station, and Blackfriars Theatre. The 105-acre campus is in an urban area 50 miles south of Boston. Including residence halls, there are 37 buildings on campus.

Student Life: About 86% of undergraduates are from out-of-state, mostly the Northeast. Students come from 41 states, 16 foreign countries, and Canada. Sixty-one percent are from public schools; 39% from private. Ninety-two percent are white. Most are Catholic. The average age of freshmen is 18; all undergraduates, 20. Seven percent drop out by the end of their first year; 89% remain to graduate.

Housing: A total of 2796 students can be accommodated in college housing. College-sponsored living facilities include single-sex and coed dormitories and on-campus apartments. In addition there are honors floors, living and learning floors, and international floors. On-campus housing is guaranteed for the freshman and sophomore years, is available on a first-come, first-served basis, and is available on a lottery system for upperclassmen. Priority is given to out-of-town students. Sixty-five percent of students live on campus; of those, 80% remain on campus on weekends. All students may keep cars on campus.

Activities: There are no fraternities or sororities on campus. There are 67 groups on campus, including art, band, cheerleading, choir, chorale, computers, dance, drama, ethnic, honors, international, jazz band, literary magazine, musical theater, newspaper, pep band, photography, political, professional, radio and tv, religious, social, social service, student government, and yearbook. Popular campus events include Junior Ring Weekend, Parents Weekend, Black History Month, Supersports Competition, Commencement Week, Multicultural Awareness Week, 'Done With Civ' Party, Harvest Fest, and Blind Date Balls.

Sports: There are 10 intercollegiate sports for men and 10 for women, and 30 intramural sports for men and 27 for women. Athletic and recreation facilities include an ice arena, indoor and outdoor tracks, courts for tennis, racquetball, handball, squash, basketball, and volleyball, a pool, a Nautilus program, facilities for weight lifting, aerobics, and ballet, a soccer field, and a baseball field.

Disabled Students: Seventy percent of the campus is accessible to disabled students. The following facilities are available: wheelchair ramps, elevators, special parking, specially equipped rest rooms, special class scheduling, lowered drinking fountains, lowered telephones, and specially equipped dormitory rooms for full-time day students.

Services: In addition to many counseling and information services, tutoring is available in most subjects. There is also a reader service for the blind and academic support services, including evaluation of learning-disabled students.

Campus Safety and Security: Campus safety and security measures include 24-hour foot and vehicle patrol, self-defense education, escort service, and shuttle buses. In addition, there are informal discussions, pamphlets, posters, and films, emergency telephones, lighted pathways and sidewalks, and a campus wide computerized card access system for entry into all dormitories and apartment buildings.

Programs of Study: Providence awards the B.A. and B.S. degrees. Master's and doctoral degrees also are awarded. Bachelor's degrees are awarded in BIOLOGICAL SCIENCE (biology/biological science), BUSINESS (accounting, banking and finance, business administration and management, business economics, and marketing/retailing/merchandising), COMMUNICATIONS AND THE ARTS (art history and appreciation, dramatic arts, English, fine arts, French, Italian, music, and Spanish), COMPUTER AND PHYSICAL SCIENCE (chemistry, computer science, and mathematics), EDUCATION (elementary, secondary, and special), ENGINEERING AND ENVIRONMENTAL DESIGN (engineering), HEALTH PROFESSIONS (health care administration), SOCIAL SCIENCE (American studies, economics, history, humanities, Latin American studies, philosophy, political science/government, psychology, religion, social science, social work, sociology, systems science, and theology). Biology, chemistry, business, political science, and English are the strongest academically. Business, political science, English, and psychology have the largest enrollments.

Required: To graduate, all students must complete at least 116 credit hours, with 24 upper-division hours in the major, and maintain a GPA of 2.0. Students must also meet an English proficiency requirement, complete courses in Western civilization, and fulfill the 30-credit core curriculum, including 6 credits each in natural science, social science, philosophy, and religion, and 3 each in mathematics and fine arts.

Special: Providence offers cross-registration with Rhode Island School of Design, internships in politics, broadcasting, journalism, and business, and study abroad in Europe and Japan and through the New England-Quebec Exchange Program. Also available are B.A.-B.S. degrees in science majors, dual and student-designed majors, a 3–2 engineering degree with Columbia University or Washington University in St. Louis, nondegree study, and pass/fail options. There is a freshman honors program on campus, as well as 11 national honor societies.

Faculty/Classroom: Seventy-one percent of faculty are male; 29%, female. All teach undergraduates. No introductory courses are taught by graduate students. The average class size in an introductory lecture is 30; in a laboratory, 7; and in a regular course offering, 25.

Admissions: About 65% of the 1993–94 applicants were accepted. The SAT scores for the 1993–94 freshman class were as follows: Verbal—54% below 500, 39% between 500 and 599, and 7% between 600 and 700; Math—25% below 500, 50% between 500 and 599, 23% between 600 and 700, and 2% above 700. About 46% of the current freshmen were in the top fifth of their class; 79% were in the top two fifths. There were 3 National Merit finalists and 32 semifinalists. Fourteen freshmen graduated first in their class.

Requirements: The SAT I or ACT is required. SAT II: Subject tests in writing and 2 others of the applicant's choice are recommended. Applicants must be graduates of an accredited secondary school or have a GED certificate. A GPA of 3.0 is recommended. High school preparation should include 4 years of English, 3 years each of foreign language and mathematics, and 2 years each of history, science, and social studies. An essay is required. AP and CLEP credits are accepted. Important factors used in the admissions decision are advanced placement or honor courses, extracurricular activities record, leadership record, evidence of special talent, and personality, intangible qualities.

Procedure: Freshmen are admitted fall and spring. Entrance exams should be taken in the junior or senior year. Early decision applications should be filed by December 15; regular applications, by February 1 for fall entry and November 1 for spring entry, along with an application fee of $30. Notification of early decision is sent January 1; regular decision, April 1. There are early decision, early admissions, and deferred admissions plans. Some 274 early decision candidates were accepted for the 1993–94 class. A waiting list is an active part of the admissions procedure, with about 11% of applicants on the list.

Transfer: Seventy-six transfer students enrolled in 1993–94. Applicants should have a minimum college GPA of 3.0 in a strong liberal arts program with a recommended 24 credit hours. The SAT I or ACT is required, and an interview is recommended. A total of 60 credits out of 116 must be completed at Providence.

Visiting: There are regularly scheduled orientations for prospective students, including campus tours and group information sessions. There are guides for informal visits and visitors may sit in on classes and stay overnight at the school. To arrange for a visit, contact the Admissions Office at (401) 865–2535.

Financial Aid: In 1993–94, 65% of all current freshmen and 60% of continuing students received some form of financial aid. About 61% of freshmen and 60% of continuing students received need-based aid. The average freshman award was $10,400. Of that total, scholarships or need-based grants averaged $5100 ($15,000 maximum); loans averaged $2625 ($3625 maximum); work contracts averaged $1600 ($2000 maximum); and federal grants averaged $2500 ($6300 maximum). Sixty-six percent of undergraduate students work part-time. Average earnings from campus work for the school year are $1525. The average financial indebtedness of the 1992–93 graduate was $14,000. Providence is a member of CSS. The FAF and FAFSA are required. The deadline for financial aid applications is February 15.

International Students: There are currently 45 international students enrolled. The school actively recruits these students. They must take the TOEFL and achieve a minimum score of 550. The student must also take the SAT I or the ACT.

Computers: The college provides computer facilities for student use. There are 79 Wang PC-240s and IBM PS/2 Models 30, 50, and 60 available in computer laboratories. Students enrolled in computer courses may access the mainframe at Brown University on a limited basis. There are no time limits on using the system and no fees.

Graduates: In 1992–93, 1012 bachelor's degrees were awarded. The most popular majors among graduates were business (32%), English (10%), and history/political science (8% each). Within an average freshman class, 95% graduate in 4 years and 96% in 5 years. Some 136 companies recruited on campus in 1992–93.

Admissions Contact: Michael G. Backes, Dean of Admissions.

RHODE ISLAND COLLEGE
C-2
Providence, RI 02908   (401) 456–8234

Full-time: 5338 men and women	Faculty: 363; IIA, -$
Part-time: 1523 men and women	Ph.D.s: 68%
Graduate: 1087 men and women	Student/Faculty: 15 to 1
Year: semesters, summer session	Tuition: $2701 ($6839)
Application Deadline: May 1	Room & Board: $5200
Freshman Class: 2310 applied, 1767 accepted, 950 enrolled	
SAT I Verbal/Math: 411/441	**LESS COMPETITIVE**

Rhode Island College, founded in 1854, is a state-supported liberal arts institution offering undergraduate and graduate programs in the liberal arts and sciences, social work, education, and human development. There are 3 undergraduate schools and one graduate school. In addition to regional accreditation, The college has baccalaureate program accreditation with NASAD, NASM, NCATE, and NLN. The library contains 335,000 volumes, and subscribes to 2100 periodicals. Special learning facilities include an art gallery and radio station. The 125-acre campus is in a suburban area 50 miles southwest of Boston. Including residence halls, there are 26 buildings on campus.

Student Life: About 90% of undergraduates are from Rhode Island. Ninety-one percent are white. Sixty-eight percent are Catholic; 16% Protestant. The average age of freshmen is 18; all undergraduates, 21.

Housing: A total of 850 students can be accommodated in college housing. College-sponsored living facilities include single-sex and coed dormitories. In addition there are honors houses. On-campus housing is available on a first-come, first-served basis. Priority is given to out-of-town students. Eighty percent of students commute. Alcohol is not permitted. All students may keep cars on campus.

Activities: There are 3 national sororities and 1 national fraternity. There are 64 groups on campus, including art, band, cheerleading, chess, chorale, chorus, dance, drama, ethnic, gay, honors, international, literary magazine, musical theater, newspaper, orchestra, political, professional, radio and TV, religious, social, social service, student government, symphony, and yearbook. Popular campus events

include a fine and performing arts calendar, chess tournaments, and campus center activities.

Sports: Athletic and recreation facilities include playing fields, an athletic center, and a recreation center.

Disabled Students: The entire campus is accessible to disabled students. The following facilities are available: wheelchair ramps, elevators, special parking, specially equipped rest rooms, special class scheduling, and a peer advisor is available to assist disabled students.

Services: In addition to many counseling and information services, tutoring is available in most subjects. There is also a reader service for the blind, remedial math, reading, and writing, and services for learning disabled students and any student needing academic assistance.

Campus Safety and Security: Campus safety and security measures include 24-hour foot and vehicle patrol, self defense education, escort service, and informal discussions. In addition, there are pamphlets, posters, and films, emergency telephones, and lighted pathways and sidewalks.

Programs of Study: The college awards the B.A., B.S., B.F.A., B.M., B.S.N., and B.S.W. degrees. Master's degrees also are awarded. Bachelor's degrees are awarded in BIOLOGICAL SCIENCE (biology/biological science), BUSINESS (accounting, business administration and management, business economics, marketing/retailing/merchandising, and personnel management), COMMUNICATIONS AND THE ARTS (communications, dramatic arts, English, film arts, fine arts, French, music, photography, and Spanish), COMPUTER AND PHYSICAL SCIENCE (chemistry, computer programming, computer science, information sciences and systems, mathematics, and physics), EDUCATION (art, early childhood, elementary, foreign languages, health, industrial arts, middle school, music, science, secondary, and special), ENGINEERING AND ENVIRONMENTAL DESIGN (industrial engineering technology), HEALTH PROFESSIONS (medical laboratory technology and nursing), SOCIAL SCIENCE (anthropology, economics, geography, history, philosophy, political science/government, prelaw, psychology, public administration, social science, social work, sociology, and urban studies). Education, management, and psychology have the largest enrollments.

Required: To graduate, students must complete 120 credits and maintain a minimum GPA of 2.0. All students must complete courses in Western civilization and literature and fulfill 9 distribution requirements.

Special: Cross-registration is available with other Rhode Island schools. The college offers internships, a general studies degree, dual and student-designed majors, credit by examination, credit for prior learning, and pass/fail options. There is a freshman honors program on campus, as well as 6 national honor societies. Twenty-one departments have honors programs.

Faculty/Classroom: Sixty percent of faculty are male; 40%, female. Ninety-eight percent both teach and do research. No introductory courses are taught by graduate students. The average class size in an introductory lecture is 30; in a laboratory, 14; and in a regular course offering, 30.

Admissions: About 76% of the 1993–94 applicants were accepted. The SAT scores for the 1993–94 freshman class were as follows: Verbal—83% below 500, 12% between 500 and 599, and 5% between 600 and 700; Math—72% below 500, 23% between 500 and 599, and 5% between 600 and 700. About 29% of the current freshmen were in the top fifth of their class; 62% were in the top two fifths.

Requirements: The SAT I is required. ACT scores will be accepted. Applicants should be graduates of an accredited secondary school with 18 academic credits, including 4 in English, 3 in mathematics, 2 each in foreign languages, science, and social studies, one-half credit in either art or music, one-half credit in computer literacy, and the remainder in academic electives. The GED is accepted. An essay is required along with a portfolio for art students and an audition for music students. AP and CLEP credits are accepted. Important factors used in the admissions decision are advanced placement or honor courses, evidence of special talent, leadership record, extracurricular activities record, and personality, intangible qualities.

Procedure: Freshmen are admitted fall and spring. Entrance exams should be taken by December of the senior year. Applications should be filed by May 1 for fall entry and November 15 for spring entry, along with an application fee of $25. Notification is sent on a rolling basis. There are early admissions and deferred admissions plans.

Transfer: About 600 transfer students enrolled in an earlier year. Applicants must submit at least 30 college credits and a minimum GPA of 2.0. A total of 30 credits out of 120 must be completed at the college.

Visiting: There are regularly scheduled orientations for prospective students. There are guides for informal visits and visitors may sit in on classes and stay overnight at the school. To arrange for a visit, contact the Admissions Office at (401) 456–8234.

Financial Aid: In 1993–94, 60% of all students received some form of financial aid, including need-based aid. The average freshman award was $2000. The college is a member of CSS. The FAF, the col-

lege's own financial statement, and the AFSA are required. The deadline for financial aid applications is March 1.

International Students: They must take the TOEFL and achieve a minimum score of 550.

Computers: The college provides computer facilities for student use. The mainframe is a DEC VAX 11/780. Apple Macintosh and IBM computer laboratories are available for student use. All students may access the system. There are no time limits on using the system and no fees.

Graduates: In a recent year, 990 bachelor's degrees were awarded. The most popular majors among graduates were management (16%), psychology (11%), and elementary education (9%). Some 42 companies recruited on campus in a recent year.

Admissions Contact: William H. Hurry, Jr., Dean of Admissions and Financial Aid.

RHODE ISLAND SCHOOL OF DESIGN   C-2
Providence, RI 02903   (401) 454-6300

Full-time: 840 men, 1004 women	Faculty: 122; IIB, +$
Part-time: none	Ph.D.s: 71%
Graduate: 64 men, 82 women	Student/Faculty: 15 to 1
Year: 4-1-4	Tuition: $15,900
Application Deadline: February 15	Room & Board: $6415
Freshman Class: 1412 applied, 842 accepted, 379 enrolled	
SAT I or ACT: required	**SPECIAL**

Rhode Island School of Design, a private institution founded in 1877, offers bachelor's degree programs in fine arts, design, and architecture. In addition to regional accreditation, RISD has baccalaureate program accreditation with ASLA, FIDER, NAAB, and NASAD. The library contains 80,000 volumes and 780 audiovisual forms, and subscribes to 360 periodicals. Computerized library sources and services include interlibrary loans and database searching. Special learning facilities include an art gallery, a nature laboratory, and an art museum. The 13-acre campus is in an urban area 50 miles south of Boston. Including residence halls, there are 40 buildings on campus.

Student Life: About 92% of undergraduates are from out-of-state, mostly the Northeast. Students come from 50 states, 48 foreign countries, and Canada. Sixty percent are from public schools; 40% from private. Sixty-five percent are white; 19% foreign nationals. The average age of freshmen is 18; all undergraduates, 23. Seven percent drop out by the end of their first year; 85% remain to graduate.

Housing: A total of 606 students can be accommodated in college housing. College-sponsored living facilities include coed dormitories and on-campus apartments. There is choice housing for freshmen participating in health-related programs within a chemical-free living space. On-campus housing is guaranteed for all 4 years. Sixty-five percent of students commute. Alcohol is not permitted.

Activities: There are no fraternities or sororities on campus. There are 60 groups on campus, including art, computers, dance, drama, ethnic, film, gay, international, literary magazine, newspaper, photography, political, professional, religious, social, social service, student government, and yearbook. Popular campus events include Talent Show, Halloween Ball, Artists Ball, student/alumni art sales, student film festival, and 'Collection' (apparel design student showcase).

Sports: Athletic and recreation facilities include a student center with dance, aerobics, weight lifting, and Nautilus and other exercise equipment, and Tillinghast Farm, a retreat on Narragansett Bay, 15 minutes from campus. Students may also use Brown University's athletic complex, and enroll in activity classes.

Disabled Students: The following facilities are available: wheelchair ramps, elevators, special parking, and specially equipped rest rooms.

Services: A writing program for learning-disabled students, access to taped lectures/note takers, and alternative test-taking procedures are available.

Campus Safety and Security: Campus safety and security measures include 24-hour foot and vehicle patrol, escort service, shuttle buses, and informal discussions. In addition, there are pamphlets, posters, films, emergency telephones, lighted pathways and sidewalks, evening studio monitors, and studio access keys.

Programs of Study: RISD awards the B.Arch., B.F.A., B.G.D., B.I.D., B.Int.Arch., and B.Land.Arch. degrees. Master's degrees are also awarded. Bachelor's degrees are awarded in COMMUNICATIONS AND THE ARTS (ceramic art and design, design, film arts, glass, graphic design, illustration, industrial design, metal/jewelry, painting, photography, printmaking, and sculpture), ENGINEERING AND ENVIRONMENTAL DESIGN (architecture, interior design, and landscape architecture/design), SOCIAL SCIENCE (textiles and clothing). Illustration, graphic design, and architecture have the largest enrollments.

Required: To graduate, all students must complete at least 126 credit hours, including 18 hours in freshmen foundation program, 42 in liberal arts, 12 in nonmajor electives, and 54 in the major. Liberal arts credits must include 12 in art/architectural history, 9 each in English and history/philosophy/social science, and 4 electives. A minimum 2

years' residency and completion of the final-year project are required.

Special: RISD offers cross-registration with Brown University and the Art Schools Mobility Consortium. Six-week internships during the midyear winter session, study abroad through the senior year European Honors Programs in Rome, and various 3- to 6-week travel courses are also available.

Faculty/Classroom: Sixty percent of faculty are male; 40%, female. All teach undergraduates. The average class size in an introductory lecture is 20 and in a laboratory, 17.

Admissions: About 60% of the 1993-94 applicants were accepted. The SAT scores for the 1993-94 freshman class were as follows: Verbal—47% below 500, 39% between 500 and 599, 12% between 600 and 700, and 2% above 700; Math—28% below 500, 39% between 500 and 599, 24% between 600 and 700, and 10% above 700. About 37% of the current freshmen were in the top fifth of their class; 70% were in the top two fifths.

Requirements: The SAT I or ACT is required. Applicants must be graduates of an accredited secondary school or have a GED certificate. An essay, assigned drawings, and a portfolio (optional for architecture majors) are also required. AP credits are accepted. Important factors used in the admissions decision are evidence of special talent, advanced placement or honor courses, personality, intangible qualities, recommendations by school officials, and leadership record.

Procedure: Freshmen are admitted fall and spring. Entrance exams should be taken at least 6 weeks before the application deadline. Applications should be filed by February 15 for fall entry and November 25 for spring entry, along with an application fee of $35. Notification is sent by April 1. There are early admissions and deferred admissions plans. A waiting list is an active part of the admissions procedure.

Transfer: About 160 transfer students enrolled in 1993-94. Applicants must have at least 27 college credits and should submit an essay along with academic transcripts from the previous 3 years. The SAT I or ACT is required for architecture applicants; others must submit a portfolio. Letters of recommendation are encouraged. Two years must be completed in residence at RISD. A total of 66 credits out of a minimum of 126 must be completed at RISD.

Visiting: There are regularly scheduled orientations for prospective students, including a presentation by the admissions staff and a campus tour. Visitors may sit in on classes. To arrange for a visit, contact the Admissions Office at (401) 454-6300.

Financial Aid: In 1993-94, 57% of all current freshmen and 63% of continuing students received some form of financial aid. About 56% of freshmen and 61% of continuing students received need-based aid. The average freshman award was $11,937. Of that total, scholarships or need-based grants averaged $8212 ($16,000 maximum); loans averaged $2625 (maximum); and work contracts averaged $1100 (maximum). Fifty-seven percent of undergraduate students work part-time. Average earnings from campus work for the school year are $1100. The average financial indebtedness of the 1992-93 graduate was $1400. RISD is a member of CSS. The FAF is required. The deadline for financial aid applications is February 15.

International Students: There are currently 355 international students enrolled. They must take the TOEFL and achieve a minimum score of 550. The student must also take the SAT I or the ACT.

Computers: The college provides computer facilities for student use. There are 163 Apple Macintosh, IBM, IBM-compatible, and Amiga PCs for student use. They are located in the computer center and various departments. All students may access the system. There are no time limits on using the system and no fees.

Graduates: In 1992-93, 500 bachelor's degrees were awarded. The most popular majors among graduates were architecture (25%), illustration (15%), and graphic design (12%). Within an average freshman class, 85% graduate in 5 years. Some 25 companies recruited on campus in 1992-93. In the 1992 graduating class, 5% of all graduates were enrolled in graduate school within 6 months of graduation.

Admissions Contact: Edward Newhall, Director of Admissions.

ROGER WILLIAMS COLLEGE
(See Roger Williams University)

ROGER WILLIAMS UNIVERSITY
(Formerly Roger Williams College)
Bristol, RI 02809-2921

D-3

(401) 254-3500
(800) 458-7144 (out-of-state)

Full-time: 1150 men, 950 women	Faculty: 109; IIB, +$
Part-time: none	Ph.D.s: 38%
Graduate: none	Student/Faculty: 19 to 1
Year: 4-1-4, summer session	Tuition: $11,750
Application Deadline: open	Room & Board: $5000

Freshman Class: 3126 applied, 2551 accepted, 672 enrolled
SAT I Verbal/Math: 414/458   **COMPETITIVE**

Roger Williams University, founded in 1919, is a liberal arts institution that offers programs in the arts and sciences, professional studies, architecture, and law. There are 8 undergraduate schools and one graduate school. In addition to regional accreditation, RWU has baccalaureate program accreditation with NAAB and NCATE. The 2 libraries contain 302,680 volumes, 27,135 microform items, and 3179 audiovisual forms, and subscribe to 1037 periodicals. Special learning facilities include a learning resource center, an art gallery, and a radio station. The 120-acre campus is in a small town 18 miles southeast of Providence, and 14 miles south of Newport. Including residence halls, there are 18 buildings on campus.

Student Life: About 85% of undergraduates are from out-of-state, mostly the Northeast. Students come from 32 states and 48 foreign countries. Seventy-five percent are from public schools; 25% from private. Ninety-five percent are white. Sixty-five percent are Catholic; 20% Protestant; 15% Jewish. The average age of freshmen is 18; all undergraduates, 20. Twenty percent drop out by the end of their first year; 60% remain to graduate.

Housing: A total of 1400 students can be accommodated in college housing. College-sponsored living facilities include single-sex and coed dormitories, on-campus apartments, and off-campus apartments. In addition, there are honors houses and special interest houses. On-campus housing is guaranteed for all 4 years. Seventy-two percent of students live on campus; of those, 70% remain on campus on weekends. Alcohol is not permitted. All students may keep cars on campus.

Activities: There are no fraternities or sororities on campus. There are 28 groups on campus, including art, band, cheerleading, choir, dance, drama, ethnic, film, gay, honors, international, jazz band, literary magazine, musical theater, newspaper, orchestra, photography, political, professional, radio and TV, religious, social service, student government, and yearbook.

Sports: There are 8 intercollegiate sports each for men and women, and 6 intramural sports each for men and women. Athletic and recreation facilities include a 2500-seat gymnasium, exercise and weight rooms, jogging facilities, and tennis, volleyball, and basketball courts.

Disabled Students: Eighty percent of the campus is accessible to disabled students. The following facilities are available: wheelchair ramps, elevators, special parking, specially equipped rest rooms, and special class scheduling.

Services: In addition to many counseling and information services, tutoring is available in every subject. There is also a reader service for the blind, and remedial math, reading, and writing.

Campus Safety and Security: Campus safety and security measures include 24-hour foot and vehicle patrol and lighted pathways and sidewalks.

Programs of Study: RWU awards the B.A., B.S., B.Arch., and B.F.A. degrees. Master's degrees are also awarded. Bachelor's degrees are awarded in BIOLOGICAL SCIENCE (biology/biological science and marine biology), BUSINESS (accounting, business administration and management, management science, and marketing/retailing/merchandising), COMMUNICATIONS AND THE ARTS (communications, creative writing, dance, dramatic arts, English, fine arts, and historic preservation), COMPUTER AND PHYSICAL SCIENCE (chemistry, computer programming, computer science, and mathematics), ENGINEERING AND ENVIRONMENTAL DESIGN (architectural engineering, architecture, and engineering), SOCIAL SCIENCE (corrections, history, paralegal studies, philosophy, political science/government, prelaw, and psychology). Architecture, sciences, engineering, and law are the strongest academically. Business has the largest enrollment.

Required: To graduate, all students must complete skills courses in composition, mathematics, and public speaking, and 9 general education courses. A minimum of 120 credit hours, with 30 to 66 hours in the major and a GPA of 2.0, is required.

Special: The university offers co-op programs, internships, study abroad in London and Europe, student-designed majors, and credit for life, military, and work experience. There is a freshman honors program on campus, as well as one national honor society.

Faculty/Classroom: Eighty-two percent of faculty are male; 18%, female. The average class size in an introductory lecture is 20; in a laboratory, 12; and in a regular course offering, 28.

Admissions: About 82% of the 1993-94 applicants were accepted.

Requirements: A minimum GPA of 2.0 is required. The SAT I is required. Applicants should be graduates of an accredited secondary school with a minimum GPA of 2.0. The GED is accepted. Students should have 4 years of English, 3 of mathematics, 2 each of social and natural sciences, and 4 to 6 electives, for a total of 16 Carnegie units. Art and architecture students must submit portfolios. An essay and an interview are recommended. AP and CLEP credits are accepted. Important factors used in the admissions decision are advanced placement or honor courses, leadership record, evidence of special talent, recommendations by school officials, and extracurricular activities record.

Procedure: Freshmen are admitted fall and spring. Entrance exams should be taken in November or December of the senior year. Application deadlines are open; the fee is $35. Notification is sent between February 1 and April 15. There are early admissions and deferred admissions plans.

Transfer: About 100 transfer students enrolled in 1993-94. Transfer applicants need a minimum college GPA of 2.4. The SAT I is recommended. A total of 30 credits out of 120 must be completed at RWU.

Visiting: There are regularly scheduled orientations for prospective students. There are guides for informal visits and visitors may sit in on classes.

Financial Aid: In an earlier year, 71% of all current freshmen and 50% of continuing students received some form of financial aid. Scholarships or need-based grants averaged $3000 ($8300 maximum); loans averaged $2500 ($6000 maximum); and work contracts averaged $1000 ($1800 maximum). The average financial indebtedness of the 1992-93 graduate was $13,000. RWU is a member of CSS. The FAF and the college's own financial statement are required. The deadline for financial aid applications is March 1.

International Students: There are currently 120 international students enrolled. The school actively recruits these students. They must take the University of Michigan Language Test or the college's own test.

Computers: The college provides computer facilities for student use. The mainframe is a Data General MU/15000. All students may access the system. It may be used 100 hours per week. There are no time limits on using the system and no fees.

Graduates: In an earlier year, 507 bachelor's degrees were awarded. Some 21 companies recruited on campus in 1992-93. In the 1992 graduating class, 3% of the men and 2% of the women were enrolled in graduate school within 6 months of graduation; 85% of the men and 90% of the women had found employment.

Admissions Contact: William B. Galloway, Dean of Admissions.

SALVE REGINA UNIVERSITY
Newport, RI 02840-4192

D-4

(401) 847-6650
(800) 321-7124 (out-of-state)

Full-time: 468 men, 935 women	Faculty: 105; IIA, --$
Part-time: 75 men, 211 women	Ph.D.s: 80%
Graduate: 260 men, 314 women	Student/Faculty: 13 to 1
Year: semesters, summer session	Tuition: $13,800
Application Deadline: August 8	Room & Board: $6300

Freshman Class: 1411 applied, 1257 accepted, 362 enrolled
SAT I or ACT: recommended   **LESS COMPETITIVE**

Salve Regina University, founded in 1947 and sponsored by the Sisters of Mercy, is an independent, coeducational institution affiliated with the Roman Catholic Church. The university offers programs in liberal arts, business, health science, and professional training. There is one graduate school. In addition to regional accreditation, Salve has baccalaureate program accreditation with CSWE, NASAD, and NLN. The library contains 71,771 volumes, 10,094 microform items, and 4294 audiovisual forms, and subscribes to 1250 periodicals. Computerized library sources and services include the card catalog, interlibrary loans, and database searching. Special learning facilities include a learning resource center, an art gallery, and information systems and computer science laboratories. The 70-acre campus is in a suburban area on Newport's waterfront, 60 miles south of Boston. Including residence halls, there are 35 buildings on campus.

Student Life: About 78% of undergraduates are from out-of-state, mostly the Northeast. Students come from 40 states, 28 foreign countries, and Canada. Forty percent are from public schools; 60% from private. Ninety-six percent are white. The average age of freshmen is 18; all undergraduates, 21. Twenty percent drop out by the end of their first year; 75% remain to graduate.

Housing: A total of 750 students can be accommodated in college housing. College-sponsored living facilities include single-sex dormitories and off-campus apartments. There is also a language house during summer session. On-campus housing is guaranteed for all 4 years. Fifty-one percent of students live on campus; of those, 50% remain on campus on weekends. Alcohol is not permitted. Upperclassmen may keep cars on campus.

Activities: There are no fraternities or sororities on campus. There are 43 groups on campus, including art, band, cheerleading, choir, chorale, chorus, computers, dance, drama, ethnic, honors, international, jazz band, literary magazine, musical theater, newspaper, orchestra, pep band, photography, political, professional, religious, social, social service, student government, and yearbook. Popular campus events include Octoberfest Weekend, New Year's Eve Ball, Homecoming, Christmas in Newport, Cotillion, and Alumni Weekend.

Sports: There are 9 intercollegiate sports for men and 8 for women, and 10 intramural sports each for men and women. Athletic and recreation facilities include soccer, baseball, and softball fields, tennis courts, outdoor basketball courts, an indoor track, a yacht club, a weight room, and a fitness center.

Disabled Students: Fifteen percent of the campus is accessible to disabled students. The following facilities are available: wheelchair ramps, elevators, special parking, specially equipped rest rooms, lowered drinking fountains, and lowered telephones.

Services: In addition to many counseling and information services, tutoring is available in most subjects.

Campus Safety and Security: Campus safety and security measures include 24-hour foot and vehicle patrol, self-defense education, shuttle buses, and informal discussions. In addition, there are pamphlets, posters, and films, emergency telephones, and lighted pathways and sidewalks.

Programs of Study: Salve awards the B.A., B.S., and B.A.S. degrees. Associate, master's, and doctoral degrees are also awarded. Bachelor's degrees are awarded in BIOLOGICAL SCIENCE (biology/biological science), BUSINESS (accounting and management science), COMMUNICATIONS AND THE ARTS (dramatic arts, English, fine arts, French, music, Spanish, and studio art), COMPUTER AND PHYSICAL SCIENCE (chemistry, information sciences and systems, and mathematics), EDUCATION (elementary, music, secondary, and special), HEALTH PROFESSIONS (medical laboratory technology and nursing), SOCIAL SCIENCE (American studies, anthropology, criminal justice, economics, history, philosophy, political science/government, psychology, religion, social science, social work, and sociology). Accounting, psychology, politics, chemistry, English, administration of justice, nursing, and medical technology are the strongest academically. Management, administration of justice, elementary education, and nursing have the largest enrollments.

Required: To graduate, students must have 128 credit hours, consisting of about 36 in the major, 44 in electives, and 48 in general distribution requirements. Required credits include 9 in religious studies, 6 each in English, science, and foreign language, and 3 each in logic, mathematics, philosophy, fine arts, social science, economics or geography, and history or politics. Computer literacy is also required. Students must maintain a minimum GPA of 2.0.

Special: Salve has a co-op program in ROTC with the University of Rhode Island, and offers internships in most academic disciplines as well as work-study programs on campus. Study abroad, B.A.-B.S. degrees, dual majors in all programs, and accelerated degree programs in administration of justice, health services administration, business, and international relations are available. A liberal studies degree, 5-year bachelor's and master's programs, credit for life, military, and work experience, nondegree study, and pass/fail options are also offered. There are 8 national honor societies on campus. Six departments have honors programs.

Faculty/Classroom: Fifty-one percent of faculty are male; 49%, female. Seventy-eight percent teach undergraduates, 5% do research, and 5% do both. No introductory courses are taught by graduate students. The average class size in an introductory lecture is 20; in a laboratory, 20; and in a regular course offering, 16.

Admissions: About 89% of the 1993–94 applicants were accepted.

Requirements: The SAT I or ACT is recommended. Applicants must be high school graduates or hold a GED. Students should have 16 Carnegie units, consisting of 4 in English, 3 in mathematics, 2 each in science and foreign language, 1 in history, and 4 in electives. An essay is required; an interview is recommended. AP and CLEP credits are accepted. Important factors used in the admissions decision are advanced placement or honor courses, leadership record, personality, intangible qualities, extracurricular activities record, and evidence of special talent.

Procedure: Freshmen are admitted fall and spring. Entrance exams should be taken as early as possible. Applications should be filed by August 8 for fall entry and January 1 for spring entry, along with an application fee of $25. Notification of early decision is sent December 10; regular decision, on a rolling basis. There are early decision, ear-

ly admissions, and deferred admissions plans. About 6 early decision candidates were accepted for the 1993–94 class. A waiting list is an active part of the admissions procedure, with about 2% of applicants on the list.

Transfer: About 90 transfer students enrolled in 1993–94. Applicants must have a college GPA of 2.5. An interview is recommended. A total of 36 credits out of 128 must be completed at Salve.

Visiting: There are regularly scheduled orientations for prospective students, including an introduction to the academic experience, history and visions for the university, a library orientation, student life expectations, a semiformal dinner with the president, social activities, residence hall orientation, preregistration for courses, a cook-out, and meetings with faculty, advisors, and administrators. There are guides for informal visits and visitors may sit in on classes. To arrange for a visit, contact the Admissions Office at (401) 847-6650 or (800) 321-7124 (out-of-state).

Financial Aid: In 1993–94, 78% of all current freshmen and 61% of continuing students received some form of financial aid. About 78% of freshmen and 61% of continuing students received need-based aid. The average freshman award was $11,800. Of that total, scholarships or need-based grants averaged $6700 ($13,000 maximum); loans averaged $4300 ($5125 maximum); and work contracts averaged $1300 ($2000 maximum). Thirty-one percent of undergraduate students work part-time. Average earnings from campus work for the school year are $1200. The average financial indebtedness of the 1992–93 graduate was $16,050. Salve is a member of CSS. The FAF is required. The deadline for financial aid applications is March 1.

International Students: There are currently 28 international students enrolled. They must take the TOEFL and achieve a minimum score of 450.

Computers: The university provides computer facilities for student use. The mainframe is an IBM 4381. There are also 148 IBM PS/2 microcomputers available in computer laboratories, faculty offices, and science laboratories for undergraduate use. All students may access the system. It may be used 16 hours per day. There are no time limits on using the system and no fees.

Graduates: In a recent year, 348 bachelor's degrees were awarded. The most popular majors among graduates were management (17%), administration of justice (16%), and elementary education (15%). Within an average freshman class, 1% graduate in 3 years, 70% in 4 years, 2% in 5 years, and 1% in 6 years. Some 80 companies recruited on campus in 1992–93. In the 1992 graduating class, 56% of all students were enrolled in graduate school within 6 months of graduation; 58% had found employment.

Admissions Contact: Roselina McKillop, Dean of Admissions.

UNIVERSITY OF RHODE ISLAND
C-4
Kingston, RI 02881 (401) 792-9800

Full-time: 4232 men, 4662 women	Faculty: 648; I, -$
Part-time: 1012 men, 1444 women	Ph.D.s: 87%
Graduate: 1599 men, 1976 women	Student/Faculty: 14 to 1
Year: semesters, summer session	Tuition: $3882 ($10,606)
Application Deadline: March 1	Room & Board: $5323
Freshman Class: 9642 applied, 7751 accepted, 1968 enrolled	
SAT I Verbal/Math: 440/510	COMPETITIVE

The University of Rhode Island, founded in 1892, is a land-grant, coeducational institution offering programs in liberal arts, business, engineering, human services, nursing, and pharmacy. Located near the ocean and the bay, the university has strong marine programs. There are 3 other campuses. There are 9 undergraduate and 3 graduate schools. In addition to regional accreditation, URI has baccalaureate program accreditation with AACSB, ABET, ACPE, ADA, APTA, NASM, NCATE, and NLN. The 3 libraries contain 1,019,000 volumes and 1,313,000 microform items, and subscribe to 8713 periodicals. Computerized library sources and services include the card catalog, interlibrary loans, and database searching. Special learning facilities include an art gallery, planetarium, radio station, TV station, historic textile collection, and early childhood education center. The 1248-acre campus is in a small town 30 miles south of Providence. Including residence halls, there are 314 buildings on campus.

Student Life: About 63% of undergraduates are from Rhode Island. Students come from 50 states, 74 foreign countries, and Canada. Seventy-nine percent are white. The average age of freshmen is 18; all undergraduates, 19.5. Twenty-five percent drop out by the end of their first year; 60% remain to graduate.

Housing: A total of 4100 students can be accommodated in college housing. College-sponsored living facilities include single-sex and coed dormitories and married-student housing. In addition, there are special interest houses, a freshman dormitory, and a wellness dormitory. On-campus housing is guaranteed for all 4 years. Fifty-three percent of students live on campus; of those, 75% remain on campus on weekends. Alcohol is not permitted. All students may keep cars on campus.

Activities: About 21% of men belong to 17 national fraternities; about 14% of women belong to 8 national sororities. There are 90 groups on campus, including band, cheerleading, chess, choir, chorus, dance, drama, ethnic, gay, honors, international, jazz band, literary magazine, marching band, musical theater, newspaper, pep band, photography, political, professional, radio and TV, religious, social, social service, student government, and yearbook. Popular campus events include Winterfest, Martin Luther King Week, International Week, Spring Fest, Homecoming, Greek Week, Diversity Week, and Welcome Week.

Sports: There are 10 intercollegiate sports for men and 11 for women, and 18 intramural sports for men and 18 for women. Athletic and recreation facilities include 3 gymnasiums, 3 pools, 3 weight rooms, and a multipurpose field house with an indoor track, indoor tennis courts, and a fitness room. The campus stadium seats 10,000, the gymnasium 4,000.

Disabled Students: Almost all of the campus is accessible to disabled students. The following facilities are available: wheelchair ramps, elevators, special parking, specially equipped rest rooms, special class scheduling, lowered drinking fountains, lowered telephones, and special transportation around campus.

Services: In addition to many counseling and information services, tutoring is available in some subjects, including ESL. There is a reader service for the blind, and remedial math, reading, and writing.

Campus Safety and Security: Campus safety and security measures include 24-hour foot and vehicle patrol, self-defense education, escort service, and shuttle buses. In addition, there are informal discussions, pamphlets, posters, films, emergency telephones, and lighted pathways and sidewalks.

Programs of Study: URI awards the B.A., B.S., B.F.A., B.L.A., B.M., and B.G.S. degrees. Master's and doctoral degrees also are awarded. Bachelor's degrees are awarded in AGRICULTURE (animal science, fishing and fisheries, horticulture, and wildlife management), BIOLOGICAL SCIENCE (biology/biological science, botany, marine science, microbiology, and zoology), BUSINESS (accounting, banking and finance, business administration and management, management information systems, management science, and marketing/retailing/merchandising), COMMUNICATIONS AND THE ARTS (comparative literature, dramatic arts, English, fine arts, French, German, Italian, journalism, linguistics, literature, music, Russian, Spanish, and speech/debate/rhetoric), COMPUTER AND PHYSICAL SCIENCE (chemistry, computer science, geology, mathematics, oceanography, physics, and statistics), EDUCATION (elementary, music, physical, and secondary), ENGINEERING AND ENVIRONMENTAL DESIGN (chemical engineering, civil engineering, computer engineering, electrical/electronics engineering, environmental science, industrial engineering, landscape architecture/design, materials engineering, and mechanical engineering), HEALTH PROFESSIONS (dental hygiene, medical laboratory technology, nursing, and pharmacy), SOCIAL SCIENCE (anthropology, dietetics, economics, food science, geography, history, home economics, Latin American studies, philosophy, political science/government, psychology, sociology, textiles and clothing, urban studies, water resources, and women's studies). Pharmacy, engineering, biology, and marine affairs are the strongest academically. Psychology, pharmacy, engineering, and biology education have the largest enrollments.

Required: To graduate, the student must earn 120 to 150 credit hours, at least 30 in the major, with a minimum GPA of 2.0. Distribution requirements include 6 credits each in English communication, fine arts and literature, foreign language or culture, letters, natural sciences, and social sciences, as well as 3 credits in mathematics.

Special: Cross-registration is available with Rhode Island College and Community College of Rhode Island. A Washington semester is offered, as well as semester-long internships with businesses and state agencies and an international internship as part of URI's engineering program. Study abroad in 6 countries, a B.A.-B.S. degree in German and engineering and in languages and business, a general studies degree, and dual majors are offered. Credit for life, military, and work experience, and pass/fail options are available. There is a freshman

honors program on campus, as well as 30 national honor societies, including Phi Beta Kappa. All departments have honors programs.

Faculty/Classroom: Seventy percent of faculty are male; 30%, female. All teach undergraduates and do research. Graduate students teach 6% of introductory courses. The average class size in an introductory lecture is 28; in a laboratory, 12; and in a regular course offering, 19.

Admissions: About 80% of the 1993–94 applicants were accepted. The SAT scores for the 1993–94 freshman class were as follows: Verbal—77% below 500, 19% between 500 and 599, 3% between 600 and 700, and 1% above 700; Math—41% below 500, 44% between 500 and 599, 14% between 600 and 700, and 1% above 700. About 31% of the current freshmen were in the top fifth of their class; 61% were in the top two fifths. About 30 freshmen graduated first in their class.

Requirements: URI requires applicants to be in the upper 30% of their class. The SAT I or ACT is required. In addition, applicants should be high school graduates and should have completed 18 courses, including 4 of English; 3 of mathematics; and 2 each of science, foreign language, and history or social studies. Remaining units should be college preparatory. AP and CLEP credits are accepted. Important factors used in the admissions decision are advanced placement or honor courses, evidence of special talent, recommendations by school officials, personality, intangible qualities, and leadership record.

Procedure: Freshmen are admitted in the fall and spring. Entrance exams should be taken during the spring of the junior year and the fall of the senior year. Applications should be filed by March 1 for fall entry and December 1 for spring entry, along with an application fee of $30 for in-state applicants and $45 for those from out-of-state. Notification is sent on a rolling basis. There is an early admissions plan.

Transfer: About 503 transfer students enrolled in a recent year. Transfer applicants must submit transcripts from high school and all colleges or universities attended. A minimum GPA of 2.5 is required; many programs require higher. At least 24 credits out of 120 must be completed at URI.

Visiting: There are regularly scheduled orientations for prospective students, including open house programs in October and campus tours. There are guides for informal visits, and visitors may sit in on classes. To arrange for a visit, contact the Admissions Office at (401)-792–9800.

Financial Aid: In 1993–94, 66% of all current freshmen and 63% of continuing students received some form of financial aid. About 60% of freshmen and 58% of continuing students received need-based aid. The average freshman award was $4200. Of that total, scholarships or need-based grants averaged $2000 ($6000 maximum); loans averaged $1400 ($3500 maximum); and work contracts averaged $1000. Twenty percent of undergraduate students work part-time. Average earnings from campus work for the school year are $1200. URI is a member of CSS. The FAF is required. The deadline for financial aid applications is March 1.

International Students: There are currently 388 international students enrolled. The school actively recruits these students. They must take the TOEFL and achieve a minimum score of 550 and must also take SAT I or the ACT.

Computers: The college provides computer facilities for student use. The mainframes are an IBM ES/9000–210VF and a Prime 6350. Students may access the mainframes through more than 200 on-site and remote terminals. There are also 350 IBM-compatible and Apple Macintosh microcomputers available at various locations. All students may access the system 24 hours per day. There are no time limits on using the system and no fees.

Graduates: In 1992–93, 2156 bachelor's degrees were awarded. The most popular majors among graduates were psychology (7%), political science (5%), and speech communications (5%). Within an average freshman class, 46% graduate in 4 years and 60% in 5 years. Some 300 companies recruited on campus in an earlier year.

Admissions Contact: David Taggart, Dean of Admissions.

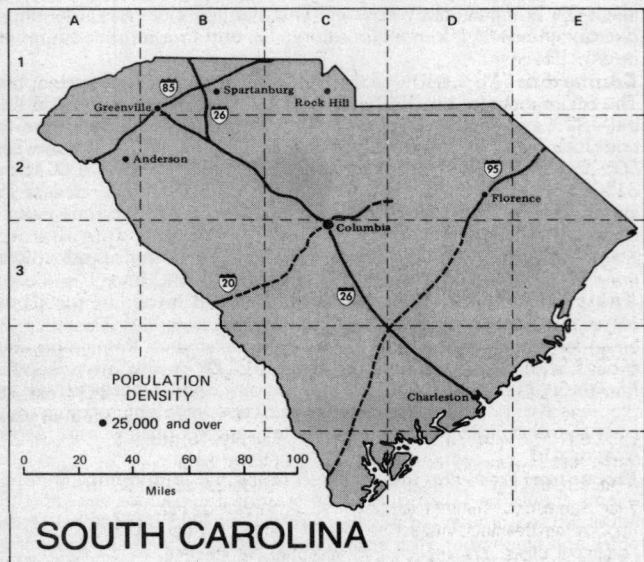

SOUTH CAROLINA

POPULATION DENSITY

● 25,000 and over

0 20 40 60 80 100
Miles

ALLEN UNIVERSITY
C-3
Columbia, SC 29204 (803) 376–5716

Full-time: 138 men, 145 women	Faculty: 35
Part-time: 14 men, 11 women	Ph.D.s: n/av
Graduate: none	Student/Faculty: 8 to 1
Year: semesters, summer session	Tuition: $4750
Application Deadline: open	Room & Board: $1955
Freshman Class: 250 accepted, 180 enrolled	
SAT I or ACT: recommended	**NONCOMPETITIVE**

Allen University, founded in 1870, is a small private institution affiliated with the African Methodist Episcopal (A.M.E.) Church offering undergraduate programs in liberal arts and sciences, business, and social work. The library contains 40,558 volumes, 2883 microform items, and 2527 audiovisual forms, and subscribes to 106 periodicals. Special learning facilities include a learning resource center. The 4-acre campus is in a small town. Including residence halls, there are 84 buildings on campus.

Student Life: About 70% of undergraduates are from South Carolina. Students come from 20 states and 9 foreign countries. Ninety-five percent are from public schools. Ninety-nine percent are African American. Most are Protestant. The average age of freshmen is 18; all undergraduates, 24. Twenty percent drop out by the end of their first year.

Housing: A total of 405 students can be accommodated in college housing. College-sponsored living facilities include single-sex dormitories and off-campus apartments. On-campus housing is guaranteed for all 4 years. Ninety-five percent of students live on campus. Alcohol is not permitted. All students may keep cars on campus.

Activities: About 8% of men belong to 4 national fraternities; about 6% of women belong to 4 national sororities. There are 20 groups on campus, including art, band, cheerleading, choir, chorus, drama, honors, international, newspaper, religious, social service, student government, and yearbook. Popular campus events include Homecoming, Cultural, Academic, and Religious Series (CARS), International Day, Black History Month, Founders Day, Fall Convocation, and Academic Awards Day.

Sports: There are 2 intercollegiate sports for men, and 1 intramural sport each for men and women.

Disabled Students: Special parking is available.

Services: In addition to many counseling and information services, tutoring is available in most subjects. In addition, there is remedial math, reading, and writing. There are mathematics, science, reading, and writing laboratories.

Campus Safety and Security: Campus safety and security measures include 24-hour foot and vehicle patrol, self-defense education, escort service, and pamphlets, posters, and films. In addition, there are emergency telephones and lighted pathways and sidewalks.

Programs of Study: Allen awards the B.A., and B.S. degrees. Associate degrees are also awarded. Bachelor's degrees are awarded in BIOLOGICAL SCIENCE (biology/biological science), BUSINESS (business administration and management), COMMUNICATIONS AND THE ARTS (English and music), COMPUTER AND PHYSICAL SCIENCE (mathematics), SOCIAL SCIENCE (history, political science/government, and sociology). Sociology/social work and business administration have the largest enrollments.

Required: To graduate, all students must complete 120 credit hours with a minimum 2.0 GPA. Students must demonstrate competence in reading, composition, speech, and fundamental mathematical skills.

Special: Allen offers internships with businesses and federal, state, and local agencies, and work-study with the Columbia Housing Authority. A certificate in gerontology is possible. There is one national honor society on campus. All departments have honors programs.

Admissions: There were 8 National Merit semifinalists. One freshman graduated first in his class.

Requirements: The SAT I or ACT is recommended. Applicants should be graduates of accredited high schools or have earned the GED. Secondary preparation should total 20 academic credits. The university recommends that applicants schedule a personal interview. Important factors used in the admissions decision are leadership record, evidence of special talent, advanced placement or honor courses, recommendations by school officials, and recommendations by alumni.

Procedure: Freshmen are admitted to all sessions. Entrance exams should be taken in the spring. Application deadlines are open. Application fee is $10. The college accepts all applicants. Notification of early decision is sent April 10; regular decision, June 10. There is an early decision plan. About 5 early decision candidates were accepted for the 1993–94 class.

Transfer: About 25 transfer students enrolled in 1993–94. An official transcript from each school attended is required at least one month prior to the beginning of the semester in which admission is desired. The last of 30 credits out of 120 must be completed at Allen.

Visiting: There are regularly scheduled orientations for prospective students. There are guides for informal visits and visitors may sit in on classes. To arrange for a visit, contact Dr. John Waddell, Dean of Student Development Services at (803) 376–5741.

Financial Aid: In 1993–94, all current freshmen and 93% of continuing students received some form of financial aid. About 97% of freshmen and 90% of continuing students received need-based aid. The average freshman award was $6000. Of that total, scholarships or need-based grants averaged $2500 ($3500 maximum); loans averaged $2500 ($2625 maximum); and work contracts averaged $1200 ($2000 maximum). Ninety-five percent of undergraduate students work part-time. Average earnings from campus work for the school year are $1200. The average financial indebtedness of the 1992–93 graduate was $900. Allen is a member of CSS. The FAF and the college's own financial statement are required. The deadline for financial aid applications is May 20.

International Students: There are currently 76 international students enrolled. The school actively recruits these students.

Computers: The college provides computer facilities for student use. The mainframe is an IBM. A computer laboratory is available. All students may access the system. There are no time limits on using the system and no fees.

Graduates: In 1992–93, 21 bachelor's degrees were awarded. The most popular majors among graduates were sociology (38%) and business administration (34%). Within an average freshman class, 40% graduate in 4 years and 20% in 5 years. Some 10 companies recruited on campus in 1992–93.

Admissions Contact: Glenn Prince, Director, Enrollment Management.

BENEDICT COLLEGE
C-3
Columbia, SC 29204 (803) 253–5147; (800) 868–6598

Full-time: 461 men, 742 women	Faculty: 90; IIB, --$
Part-time: 21 men, 42 women	Ph.D.s: 34%
Graduate: none	Student/Faculty: 13 to 1
Year: semesters, summer session	Tuition: $5484
Application Deadline: open	Room & Board: $2892
Freshman Class: 1893 applied, 1678 accepted, 459 enrolled	
SAT I or ACT: required	**LESS COMPETITIVE**

Benedict College, founded in 1870, is a private liberal arts institution affiliated with the Baptist Church. In addition to regional accreditation, Benedict has baccalaureate program accreditation with CSWE. The library contains 122,220 volumes, 3163 microform items, and 5140 audiovisual forms, and subscribes to 323 periodicals. Computerized library sources and services include database searching. Special learning facilities include a learning resource center and art gallery. The 20-acre campus is in an urban area 90 miles south of Charlotte, North Carolina. Including residence halls, there are 15 buildings on campus.

Student Life: About 82% of undergraduates are from South Carolina. Students come from 24 states and 10 foreign countries. Most are from public schools. Almost all are African American. The average age of freshmen is 19; all undergraduates, 20. Fifty percent drop out by the end of their first year; 20% remain to graduate.

Housing: A total of 1090 students can be accommodated in college housing. College-sponsored living facilities include single-sex dormitories. On-campus housing is available on a first-come, first-served basis. Priority is given to out-of-town students. Seventy-seven percent of students live on campus. Alcohol is not permitted. Upperclassmen may keep cars on campus.

Activities: About 2% of men belong to 4 local and 4 national fraternities; about 5% of women belong to 4 local and 4 national sororities. There are 50 groups on campus, including art, cheerleading, choir, chorus, dance, drama, drill team, international, newspaper, photography, religious, student government, and yearbook. Popular campus events include Fall Convocation, Crowning of Miss Benedict, Religion Emphasis Week, Homecoming, and Commencement.

Sports: There are 5 intercollegiate sports each for men and women, and 10 intramural sports for men and 9 for women. Athletic and recreation facilities include a gymnasium and student center.

Disabled Students: The following facilities are available: wheelchair ramps, elevators, and special parking.

Services: In addition to many counseling and information services, tutoring is available in every subject. There is also remedial math, reading, and writing.

Campus Safety and Security: Campus safety and security measures include 24-hour foot and vehicle patrol, informal discussions, pamphlets, posters, films, and lighted pathways and sidewalks.

Programs of Study: Benedict awards the B.A., B.S., and B.S.W. degrees. Bachelor's degrees are awarded in BIOLOGICAL SCIENCE (biology/biological science), BUSINESS (accounting and business administration and management), COMMUNICATIONS AND THE ARTS (English, journalism, and music), COMPUTER AND PHYSICAL SCIENCE (chemistry, computer science, mathematics, and physics), EDUCATION (early childhood and elementary), HEALTH PROFESSIONS (environmental health science), SOCIAL SCIENCE (criminal justice, philosophy, religion, social science, and social work). Business administration has the largest enrollment.

Required: Students must complete 125 credit hours, including 24 to 32 in the major, with a minimum GPA of 2.0; some degrees require a higher GPA. The 57-hour general education requirements include 15 hours of English, 9 of social science, 8 of natural science, 6 each of mathematics and a foreign language, 4 of humanities, and 2 each of health education, freshman seminar, physical education, and religion.

Special: Benedict offers Air Force ROTC through the University of South Carolina, work-study programs, a physics/engineering dual major, internships, a B.A./B.S. degree, and preprofessional programs in dentistry, engineering, law, and medicine.

Faculty/Classroom: Fifty-seven percent of faculty are male; 43%, female. All teach undergraduates, and 1% also do research. The average class size in an introductory lecture is 39; in a laboratory, 33; and in a regular course offering, 30.

Admissions: About 90% of the 1993–94 applicants were accepted.

Requirements: The SAT I or ACT is required. Students should have taken 4 secondary school units of English, 3 each of mathematics and social science, 2 of natural science, 7 of electives, and 1 of physical education or ROTC. The GED is accepted. AP and CLEP credits are accepted.

Procedure: Entrance exams should be taken prior to registration. Application deadlines are open. Application fee is $25. Notification is sent on a rolling basis. There are early admissions and deferred admissions plans.

Transfer: About 70 transfer students enrolled in a recent year. Applicants must submit transcripts from previous institutions attended plus evidence of honorable withdrawal. The SAT is required. Only courses in which a C or better was earned will be considered for credit. A total of 30 credits out of 125 must be completed at Benedict.

Visiting: There are regularly scheduled orientations for prospective students. There are guides for informal visits and visitors may sit in on classes. To arrange for a visit, contact the Admissions Office at (800) 868-6598 or (803) 253-5143.

Financial Aid: In a recent year, 67% of all current freshmen and 81% of continuing students received some form of financial aid. About 55% of freshmen and 63% of continuing students received need-based aid. The average freshman award was $6077. Of that total, scholarships or need-based grants averaged $3227 ($4200 maximum); loans averaged $2040 ($2625 maximum); and work contracts averaged $800. Fifty percent of undergraduate students work part-time. Average earnings from campus work for the school year are $1600. The average financial indebtedness of the 1992–93 graduate was $5258. Benedict is a member of CSS. The FAF, the college's own financial statement, and the South Carolina Tuition Grant applications are required. The deadline for financial aid applications is March 31.

International Students: There are currently about 45 international students enrolled. They must take the TOEFL or the college's own test and achieve a minimum score on the TOEFL of 500. The student must also take the SAT I, and some students may be required to complete an ESL program.

Computers: The college provides computer facilities for student use. The mainframes are a DEC PDP 11/70 and DEC VAX 11/785 and 11/780. Students use the mainframe for all programming courses, for computer graphic classes, to create a text file, and to access the Test Data Bank for General and Principles of Biology. There are 36 terminals housed in Room 106, Alumni Hall. All students may access the system. There are no time limits on using the system and no fees.

Graduates: In a recent year, 163 bachelor's degrees were awarded. The most popular majors among graduates were business administration (26%), criminal justice (12%), and social work (8%).

Admissions Contact: Dr. LeRoy R. Brown, Director of Enrollment Management.

CENTRAL WESLEYAN COLLEGE
A-2
Central, SC 29630-1020

(803) 639-2453, ext. 326

(800) 289-1CWC (289-1292) (out-of-state)

Full-time: 513 men, 731 women	Faculty: 40; IIB, --$
Part-time: 14 men, 19 women	Ph.D.s: 64%
Graduate: 57 men, 43 women	Student/Faculty: 31 to 1
Year: semesters, summer session	Tuition: $8100
Application Deadline: August 10	Room & Board: $1540
Freshman Class: 177 applied, 145 accepted, 98 enrolled	
SAT I or ACT: required	COMPETITIVE

Central Wesleyan College, founded in 1906, is a private, coeducational liberal arts college affiliated with the Wesleyan Church. The library contains 70,772 volumes, 345 microform items, and 2578 audiovisual forms, and subscribes to 427 periodicals. Computerized library sources and services include interlibrary loans. The 137-acre campus is in a rural area 30 miles southwest of Greenville. Including residence halls, there are 11 buildings on campus.

Student Life: About 81% of undergraduates are from South Carolina. Students come from 12 states, 4 foreign countries, and Canada. Ninety-eight percent are from public schools. Eighty-six percent are white; 12% African American. Most are Protestant. The average age of freshmen is 19; all undergraduates, 22. Thirty-five percent drop out by the end of their first year; 37% remain to graduate.

Housing: A total of 286 students can be accommodated in college housing. College-sponsored living facilities include single-sex dormitories. On-campus housing is guaranteed for all 4 years. Sixty-three percent of students commute. Alcohol is not permitted. All students may keep cars on campus.

Activities: There are no fraternities or sororities on campus. There are 20 groups on campus, including cheerleading, choir, computers, drama, ethnic, honors, literary magazine, newspaper, pep band, photography, professional, religious, social, social service, student government, and yearbook.

Sports: There are 4 intercollegiate sports for men and 3 for women, and 5 intramural sports each for men and women. Athletic and recreation facilities include a gymnasium, a soccer and softball field, a baseball field, and tennis courts.

Disabled Students: Seventy-five percent of the campus is accessible to disabled students. The following facilities are available: wheelchair ramps, elevators, special parking, specially equipped rest rooms, and special class scheduling.

Services: In addition to many counseling and information services, tutoring is available in some subjects. There is also remedial math and reading.

Campus Safety and Security: Campus safety and security measures include pamphlets, posters, and films, lighted pathways and sidewalks, and night security.

Programs of Study: CWC awards the B.A. and B.S. degrees. Associate and master's degrees also are awarded. Bachelor's degrees are awarded in BIOLOGICAL SCIENCE (biology/biological science), BUSINESS (accounting, business administration and management, and personnel management), COMMUNICATIONS AND THE ARTS (English and music), COMPUTER AND PHYSICAL SCIENCE (chemistry and mathematics), EDUCATION (elementary, music, physical, and special), HEALTH PROFESSIONS (medical laboratory technology), SOCIAL SCIENCE (history, psychology, religion, and social science). Education, business, and religion are the strongest programs academically and have the largest enrollments.

Required: To graduate, students must complete 128 credit hours with a minimum GPA of 2.0. All students must take 12 hours each of English and religion, 6 of history, 3 of social sciences, and 3 of mathematics or statistics, plus 2 science laboratory courses. Specific required courses include aesthetics, introduction to computer science, physical education, and interdisciplinary seminars.

Special: A co-op program in nursing is offered with Clemson University. Study abroad in 2 countries and internships in psychology, English, and business are available. A Washington semester with the Christian College Coalition and dual majors are available. The Leadership Education for the Adult Professional Program offers degrees for working professionals. There is one national honor society on campus. Five departments have honors programs.

Faculty/Classroom: Seventy-two percent of faculty are male; 28%, female. All teach and also do research. The average class size in an introductory lecture is 25; in a laboratory, 15; and in a regular course offering, 20.

Admissions: About 82% of the 1993–94 applicants were accepted.

Requirements: CWC requires applicants to be in the upper 50% of their class. A minimum GPA of 2.0 is required. The SAT I or ACT is required, with a recommended minimum composite score of 740 on the SAT I or 19 on the ACT. Applicants must be graduates of an accredited secondary school. The GED is accepted. Students should complete 16 Carnegie units, including 4 credits of English and 2 each of mathematics, science, and social studies, as well as 6 electives. AP and CLEP credits are accepted. Important factors used in the admissions decision are leadership record, advanced placement or honor courses, personality, intangible qualities, evidence of special talent, and recommendations by school officials.

Procedure: Freshmen are admitted in the fall and spring. Entrance exams should be taken prior to application. Applications should be filed by August 10 for fall entry, January 5 for spring entry, and May 30 for summer entry, along with an application fee of $15. Notification is sent on a rolling basis. There are early decision, early admissions, and deferred admissions plans.

Transfer: About 52 transfer students enrolled in a recent year. CWC recommends that transfer applicants have a minimum GPA of 2.0 in at least 29 credit hours. A total of 32 credits out of 128 must be completed at CWC.

Visiting: There are regularly scheduled orientations for prospective students. There are guides for informal visits and visitors may sit in on classes and stay overnight at the school. To arrange for a visit, contact the Admissions Office at (803) 639–2453, ext. 326.

Financial Aid: In a recent year, 92% of all students received some form of financial aid. About 70% of students received need-based aid. The average freshman award was $4648. Of that total, scholarships or need-based grants averaged $1358; loans averaged $2800 ($4000 maximum); and work contracts averaged $490 ($1000 maximum). Twenty-seven percent of undergraduate students work part-time. Average earnings from campus work for the school year were $490. The average financial indebtedness of a recent graduate was $6000. CWC is a member of CSS. The FAF, FFS or SFS and the college's own financial statement are required. The deadline for financial aid applications is April 15.

International Students: There are currently 7 international students enrolled. They must take the TOEFL and achieve a minimum score of 500. The student must also take the SAT I or the ACT.

Computers: The college provides computer facilities for student use. The mainframe is a Data General MU/2500. There are 2 computer laboratories with MS-DOS and Apple Macintosh microcomputers for student use. All students may access the system. There are no time limits on using the system. There is a $50 laboratory fee.

Graduates: In a recent year, 165 bachelor's degrees were awarded. Within an average freshman class, 35% graduate in 4 years and 2% in 5 years.

Admissions Contact: Tim Wilkerson, Dean of Enrollment Management.

CHARLESTON SOUTHERN UNIVERSITY   D-4

Charleston, SC 29423–8087   (803) 863–7050; (800) 947–7474

Full-time: 684 men, 849 women	Faculty: 70; IIB, --$
Part-time: 313 men, 421 women	Ph.D.s: 50%
Graduate: 87 men, 131 women	Student/Faculty: 22 to 1
Year: 4-1-4, summer session	Tuition: $7292
Application Deadline: open	Room & Board: $2990
Freshman Class: 1199 applied, 904 accepted, 397 enrolled	
SAT I or ACT: required	LESS COMPETITIVE

Charleston Southern University, founded in 1960, is a private liberal arts institution affiliated with the South Carolina Baptist Convention. In addition to regional accreditation, CSU has baccalaureate program accreditation with NASM. The library contains 70,000 volumes, and subscribes to 750 periodicals. Special learning facilities include an earthquake education center and a field physics laboratory. The 500-acre campus is in a suburban area 20 miles west of Charleston. Including residence halls, there are 11 buildings on campus.

Student Life: About 70% of undergraduates are from South Carolina. Eighty-five percent are from public schools; 15% from private. Seventy-eight percent are white; 21% African American. The average age of all undergraduates is 26. Forty-seven percent drop out by the end of their first year.

Housing: College-sponsored living facilities include single-sex and coed dormitories, on-campus apartments, and married-student housing. On-campus housing is available on a first-come, first-served basis. Alcohol is not permitted. All students may keep cars on campus.

Activities: There are many groups on campus, including art, band, cheerleading, choir, chorus, computers, drama, honors, literary magazine, newspaper, religious, social service, student government, and yearbook.

Sports: Athletic and recreation facilities include a gymnasium, tennis courts, a track center, football and soccer fields, a baseball diamond, training and weight rooms, and a 3-hole golf course with driving range.

Disabled Students: ALl of the campus is accessible to disabled students. The following facilities are available: wheelchair ramps, elevators, special parking, and specially equipped rest rooms.

Services: In addition to many counseling and information services, tutoring is available in most subjects. There is also remedial math, reading, and writing.

Programs of Study: CSU awards the B.A., B.S., and B.Tech. degrees. Associate and master's degrees are also awarded. Bachelor's degrees are awarded in BIOLOGICAL SCIENCE (biology/biological science), BUSINESS (business administration and management), COMMUNICATIONS AND THE ARTS (dramatic arts, English, fine arts, music, Spanish, and speech/debate/rhetoric), COMPUTER AND PHYSICAL SCIENCE (chemistry, computer science, geology, mathematics, natural sciences, and physics), EDUCATION (early childhood, elementary, mathematics, physical, and science), SOCIAL SCIENCE (criminal justice, economics, geography, history, humanities, political science/government, psychology, religion, social science, and sociology).

Required: To graduate, students must complete 125 credit hours, including all core curriculum, major, and minor requirements, with a GPA of 2.0. Core courses include 24 hours of communications and fine arts, 9 of social studies, and 11 of natural science/mathematics.

Special: CSU offers internships, work-study programs, dual majors, and nondegree study. Nonmajor preprofessional programs are available in dentistry, engineering, law, medicine, and ministry. There is a 6-year combined B.A./B.S.-J.D. program. Each major and minor offers honors study.

Faculty/Classroom: Sixty-three percent of faculty are male; 37%, female.

Admissions: About 75% of the 1993–94 applicants were accepted.

Requirements: The SAT I or ACT is required. Applicants must be graduates of an accredited secondary school. The GED is accepted. Character references are required, as is an English proficiency examination for all entering students. AP and CLEP credits are accepted.

Procedure: Freshmen are admitted to all sessions. Entrance exams should be taken any time before filing for admission. Application deadlines are open; the fee is $25. Notification is sent on a rolling basis. There is an early admissions plan.

Transfer: Applicants must submit official transcripts from all previous colleges attended. Accepted transfers must take an English proficiency examination. A total of 30 credits out of 125 must be completed at CSU.

Visiting: To arrange for a visit, contact the Admissions Office at (803) 863–7050.

Financial Aid: CSU is a member of CSS. Financial aid is available through scholarships, grants, loans, and work contracts. The FAF is required. The deadline for financial aid applications is May 1.

Computers: The college provides computer facilities for student use. The mainframe is an IBM System/36. Apple and IBM PCs are available in 5 computer laboratories and in the library. Students enrolled in computer courses may access the system. There are no time limits on using the system and no fees. CSU offers computers at discount prices for student purchase.

Graduates: In an earlier year, 239 bachelor's degrees were awarded.

Admissions Contact: Melinda Mitchum, Director of Admissions.

CLAFLIN COLLEGE   C-3

Orangeburg, SC 29115   (803) 534–2710

Full-time: 320 men, 500 women	Faculty: IIB, --$
Part-time: 30 men and women	Ph.D.s: n/av
Graduate: none	Student/Faculty: 13 to 1
Year: semesters, summer session	Tuition: n/av
Application Deadline: open	Room & Board: n/av
Freshman Class: n/av	
SAT I or ACT: required	LESS COMPETITIVE

Claffin College, established in 1869 and affiliated with the United Methodist Church, is a small, private, liberal arts institution offering undergraduate programs in education, humanities, natural sciences, mathematics, and social sciences. The library contains 130,849 volumes and 23,867 microform items, and subscribes to 519 periodicals. The 29-acre campus is in a suburban area near the business dis-

trict of Orangeburg. Including residence halls, there are 18 buildings on campus.

Student Life: About 90% of undergraduates are from South Carolina. Forty-eight percent drop out by the end of their first year.

Housing: A total of 590 students can be accommodated in college housing. College-sponsored living facilities include single-sex dormitories. All students may keep cars on campus.

Activities: There are some groups and organizations on campus, including dance, drama, honors, international, religious, social, social service, and student government.

Sports: Athletic and recreation facilities include a health and physical education center with a 2000-seat arena, a basketball gymnasium, running tracks, and tennis courts.

Services: Tutoring and remedial instruction are provided.

Programs of Study: Claflin awards the B.A. and B.S. degrees. Bachelor's degrees are awarded in BIOLOGICAL SCIENCE (biology/biological science), BUSINESS (business administration and management), COMMUNICATIONS AND THE ARTS (English, fine arts, and music), COMPUTER AND PHYSICAL SCIENCE (chemistry, computer science, and mathematics), EDUCATION (art, elementary, music, physical, and secondary), HEALTH PROFESSIONS (predentistry), SOCIAL SCIENCE (history, ministries, political science/government, prelaw, religion, social science, and sociology).

Required: To graduate, all students must complete 120 to 136 semester hours. General education requirements include courses in education, English, humanities, mathematics, physical education, natural science, computer science, and analytical reasoning. Liberal arts majors must also fulfill a foreign language requirement.

Special: Claflin offers co-op and accelerated degree programs in all majors, as well as Army or Air Force ROTC through South Carolina State College. There is a freshman honors program on campus, as well as 2 national honor societies.

Faculty/Classroom: Sixty-one percent of faculty are male; 39%, female.

Requirements: The SAT I or ACT is required. Applicants should be high school graduates who have completed 16 to 18 units, including 4 units in English, 2 in mathematics, and 1 each in social studies and natural science. Admissions decisions are based on the following criteria; the secondary school record, test scores, recommendations from the secondary school, personal qualities, and health record. AP and CLEP credits are accepted.

Procedure: Application deadlines are open; the fee is $10. Notification is sent on a rolling basis. There are early decision and early admissions plans.

Transfer: Applicants with fewer than 60 semester hours of college credit must submit test scores and meet the other criteria for entering freshmen. Official transcripts of all colleges attended are required.

Visiting: To arrange for a visit, contact the Admissions Office.

Financial Aid: In an earlier year, 97% of continuing students received some form of financial aid. Thirty-five percent of undergraduate students work part-time. Claflin is a member of CSS. The FAF and the student aid report (SAR) are required. The deadline for financial aid applications is June 1.

Computers: The college provides computer facilities for student use.

Admissions Contact: George Lee, Director of Admissions.

CLEMSON UNIVERSITY
A-2

Clemson, SC 29631-5124   (803) 656-2287

Full-time: 6599 men, 5156 women	Faculty: 1101; I, --$
Part-time: 476 men, 294 women	Ph.D.s: 83%
Graduate: 2179 men, 792 women	Student/Faculty: 11 to 1
Year: semesters, summer session	Tuition: $2954 ($7896)
Application Deadline: open	Room & Board: $3610
Freshman Class: 8065 applied, 5257 accepted, 2301 enrolled	
SAT I Verbal/Math: 470/550	**VERY COMPETITIVE**

Clemson University, founded in 1889, is a public, coeducational institution, with programs in agriculture, architecture, commerce and industry, education, engineering, forest and recreation resources, liberal arts, nursing, and sciences. There are 9 undergraduate schools and one graduate school. In addition to regional accreditation, Clemson has baccalaureate program accreditation with AACSB, ABET, NAAB, NCATE, NLN, and NRPA. The library contains 1,435,333 volumes and 1,715,200 microform items, and subscribes to 6611 periodicals. Computerized library sources and services include the card catalog, interlibrary loans, and database searching. Special learning facilities include an art gallery, planetarium, and radio station. The 1400-acre campus is in a small town 32 miles west of Greenville. Including residence halls, there are 626 buildings on campus.

Student Life: About 73% of undergraduates are from South Carolina. Students come from 46 states, 75 foreign countries, and Canada. Eighty percent are from public schools; 20% from private. Eighty-eight percent are white. The average age of freshmen is 18; all undergraduates, 21. Thirteen percent drop out by the end of their first year; 67% remain to graduate.

Housing: A total of 7000 students can be accommodated in college housing. College-sponsored living facilities include single-sex and coed dormitories, on-campus apartments, off-campus apartments, and married-student housing. In addition there are honors houses. On-campus housing is guaranteed for all 4 years. Fifty-two percent of students live on campus. All students may keep cars on campus.

Activities: About 15% of men belong to 20 national fraternities; about 25% of women belong to 14 national sororities. There are 260 groups on campus, including band, cheerleading, choir, chorus, computers, dance, drama, drill team, ethnic, gay, honors, international, jazz band, literary magazine, marching band, musical theater, newspaper, orchestra, pep band, photography, political, professional, radio and TV, religious, social, social service, student government, and yearbook. Popular campus events include Spirit Blitz, Homecoming, and First Friday.

Sports: There are 11 intercollegiate sports for men and 8 for women, and 23 intramural sports for men and 21 for women. Athletic and recreation facilities include a recreation center, an 80,000-seat stadium, and a 12,000-seat coliseum.

Disabled Students: The following facilities are available: wheelchair ramps, elevators, special parking, specially equipped rest rooms, special class scheduling, lowered drinking fountains, and lowered telephones.

Services: In addition to many counseling and information services, tutoring is available in some subjects. There is also a reader service for the blind.

Campus Safety and Security: Campus safety and security measures include 24-hour foot and vehicle patrol, self-defense education, escort service, and shuttle buses. In addition, there are informal discussions, pamphlets, posters, films, emergency telephones, and lighted pathways and sidewalks.

Programs of Study: Clemson awards the B.A., B.S., B.F.A, and B.L.A. degrees. Master's and doctoral degrees also are awarded. Bachelor's degrees are awarded in AGRICULTURE (agriculture, forestry and related sciences, forestry production and processing, and horticulture), BIOLOGICAL SCIENCE (biochemistry, biology/biological science, entomology, microbiology, and plant pathology), BUSINESS (accounting, banking and finance, business administration and management, and marketing/retailing/merchandising), COMMUNICATIONS AND THE ARTS (communications, design, English, French, German, and Spanish), COMPUTER AND PHYSICAL SCIENCE (chemistry, computer science, geology, information sciences and systems, mathematics, and physics), EDUCATION (agricultural, early childhood, elementary, industrial arts, secondary, and special), ENGINEERING AND ENVIRONMENTAL DESIGN (agricultural engineering, ceramic engineering, chemical engineering, civil engineering, computer engineering, construction management, electrical/electronics engineering, industrial administration/management, industrial engineering, mechanical engineering, and textile technology), HEALTH PROFESSIONS (medical laboratory technology, nursing, predentistry, premedicine, prepharmacy, and preveterinary science), SOCIAL SCIENCE (economics, food science, history, parks and recreation management, philosophy, political science/government, prelaw, psychology, and sociology). Engineering and architecture are the strongest academically. Nursing has the largest enrollment.

Required: To graduate, students must complete 132 credit hours, including 89 to 108 hours in the major, with a minimum GPA of 2.0. Courses are required in English, humanities, mathematics, science, and social science.

Special: Co-op programs in all majors except nursing, work-study programs, and study abroad in 38 countries are offered. There is a freshman honors program on campus, as well as 30 national honor societies. Forty departments have honors programs.

Faculty/Classroom: Seventy-two percent of faculty are male; 28%, female. Graduate students teach 9% of introductory courses. The average class size in an introductory lecture is 35; in a laboratory, 20; and in a regular course offering, 40.

Admissions: About 65% of the 1993–94 applicants were accepted. The SAT scores for the 1993–94 freshman class were as follows: Verbal—57% below 500, 35% between 500 and 599, 8% between 600 and 700, and 1% above 700; Math—19% below 500, 47% between 500 and 599, 28% between 600 and 700, and 6% above 700. About 64% of the current freshmen were in the top fifth of their class; 90% were in the top two fifths. There were 24 National Merit finalists. Eighty-eight freshmen graduated first in their class.

Requirements: The SAT I or ACT is required. In addition, applicants should be graduates of an accredited secondary school. The GED is accepted. AP and CLEP credits are accepted. Important factors used in the admissions decision are advanced placement or honor courses, recommendations by school officials, parents or siblings attending the school, geographic diversity, and recommendations by alumni.

Procedure: Freshmen are admitted to all sessions. Entrance exams should be taken during the spring of the junior year or fall of the senior year. Application deadlines are open. Notification is sent on a rolling basis. There are early admissions and deferred admissions plans. A waiting list is an active part of the admissions procedure, with about 10% of applicants on the list.

Transfer: A total of 469 transfer students enrolled in 1993–94. Transfer applicants must have completed at least 30 semester hours with a 2.5 minimum GPA. At least 30 credits must be completed at Clemson.

Visiting: There are regularly scheduled orientations for prospective students, including a series of 2-day summer programs of advisement, student services presentations, and registration for the fall semester. There are guides for informal visits. To arrange for a visit, contact the Visitor's Center at (803) 656–4789.

Financial Aid: In 1993–94, 59% of all current freshmen and 55% of continuing students received some form of financial aid. About 42% of freshmen and 40% of continuing students received need-based aid. The average freshman award was $3300. Of that total, scholarships or need-based grants averaged $1950 ($7700 maximum); loans averaged $950 ($3800 maximum); and work contracts averaged $1000 ($1200 maximum). Fifty-five percent of undergraduate students work part-time. Average earnings from campus work for the school year are $1050. The average financial indebtedness of the 1992–93 graduate was $6759. The FAF, FFS, or SFS is required. The deadline for financial aid applications is March 1.

International Students: There are currently 692 international students enrolled. They must take the TOEFL and achieve a minimum score of 550 and must also take the SAT I or the ACT.

Computers: The college provides computer facilities for student use. The mainframe is an HDS AS/EX-80. There are also 600 microcomputers available. All students may access the system. There are no time limits on using the system and no fees.

Graduates: In 1992–93, 2776 bachelor's degrees were awarded. The most popular majors among graduates were management (8%), financial management (6%), and marketing (5%). Within an average freshman class, 1% graduate in 3 years, 39% in 4 years, 66% in 5 years, and 71% in 6 years. Some 330 companies recruited on campus in 1992–93.

Admissions Contact: Michael R. Heintze, Director of Admissions.

COASTAL CAROLINA UNIVERSITY   E-3
(Formerly Univ of South Carolina/Coastal Carolina College)
Myrtle Beach, SC 29578   (803) 349–2026
(800) 277–7000 (out-of-state)

Full-time: 1513 men, 1690 women	Faculty: 168; IIB, -$
Part-time: 312 men, 644 women	Ph.D.s: 70%
Graduate: 25 men, 232 women	Student/Faculty: 19 to 1
Year: semesters, summer session	Tuition: $2470 ($6280)
Application Deadline: August 15	Room & Board: $3540
Freshman Class: 1854 applied, 1391 accepted, 755 enrolled	
SAT I or ACT: required	LESS COMPETITIVE

Coastal Carolina University, established in 1954, is a public coeducational liberal arts institution offering undergraduate programs through the schools of business administration, natural and applied sciences, education, and humanities and fine arts. There are 4 undergraduate schools and one graduate school. The library contains 138,953 volumes, 25,327 microform items, 8675 audiovisual forms, and subscribes to 1000 periodicals. Computerized library sources and services include the card catalog, interlibrary loans, and database searching. Special learning facilities include a learning resource center. The 242-acre campus is in a suburban area 9 miles west of Myrtle Beach. Including residence halls, there are 26 buildings on campus.

Student Life: About 80% of undergraduates are from South Carolina. Students come from 40 states, 23 foreign countries, and Canada. Almost 90% are from public schools; 10% from private. Nearly 90% are white. Most claim no religious affiliation. The average age of freshmen is 18; all undergraduates, 21. About 35% drop out by the end of their first year; 39% remain to graduate.

Housing: A total of 600 students can be accommodated in college housing. College-sponsored living facilities include coed dormitories and off-campus apartments. On-campus housing is available on a first-come, first-served basis. Some 86% of students commute. Alcohol is not permitted. All students may keep cars on campus.

Activities: About 5% of men belong to 2 local and 1 national fraternities; about 6% of women belong to 6 local sororities. There are 50 groups on campus, including art, cheerleading, chess, choir, chorus, computers, drama, ethnic, honors, international, jazz band, literary magazine, musical theater, newspaper, pep band, political, professional, religious, social, social service, student government, and yearbook. Popular campus events include CINO Day, Christmas formal, sports events, Welcome-back Dance, Homecoming, Lip Sync, and Ms. Coastal.

Sports: There are 7 intercollegiate sports for men and 7 for women, and 11 intramural sports for men and 7 for women. Athletic and recreation facilities include a gymnasium, baseball, soccer, and softball fields, tennis, basketball, volleyball, and racquetball courts, a swimming pool, an aerobic dance room, and a weight room. A new facility for outdoor sports including offices, dressing facilities, and a new weight room is under construction.

Disabled Students: About 95% of the campus is accessible to disabled students. The following facilities are available: wheelchair ramps, elevators, special parking, specially equipped rest rooms, special class scheduling, and lowered drinking fountains.

Services: In addition to many counseling and information services, tutoring is available in some subjects, including English, foreign languages, mathematics, and statistics. There are also a reader service for the blind, remedial math, reading, and writing and a program for learning disabled students.

Campus Safety and Security: Campus safety and security measures include 24-hour foot and vehicle patrol, escort service, informal discussions, pamphlets, posters, and films. In addition, there are lighted pathways and sidewalks.

Programs of Study: Coastal Carolina awards the B.A., B.S., B.A.Ed., B.S.B.A., and B.S.Ed. degrees. Associate degrees also are awarded. Bachelor's degrees are awarded in BIOLOGICAL SCIENCE (biology/biological science and marine science), BUSINESS (accounting, banking and finance, business administration and management, marketing/retailing/merchandising, and real estate), COMMUNICATIONS AND THE ARTS (English and fine arts), COMPUTER AND PHYSICAL SCIENCE (computer science and mathematics), EDUCATION (art, early childhood, elementary, English, mathematics, music, physical, secondary, and social studies), HEALTH PROFESSIONS (predentistry and premedicine), SOCIAL SCIENCE (history, political science/government, prelaw, psychology, and sociology). Accounting, finance, management, marketing, marine science, and biology are the strongest programs academically. Accounting, early childhood education, elementary education, management, marine science, and psychology have the largest enrollments.

Required: Students must successfully complete a minimum of 120 credits, varying with major department requirements, and must maintain a minimum GPA of 2.0. A 4-year core curriculum is required for proficiency in the broad areas of writing, library research, a foreign language, and computer usage.

Special: Internships are offered in art, sociology, education, and business. Study abroad at Oxford and through the International Student Exchange Program, work-study programs, dual majors, B.A.-B.S. degrees, and student-designed majors are offered. A general studies degree, credit by examination, and pass/fail options are possible. There is a freshman honors program on campus, as well as 6 national honor societies, including Phi Beta Kappa.

Faculty/Classroom: Some 67% of faculty are male; 33%, female. About 67% teach undergraduates and 33% both teach and do research. No introductory courses are taught by graduate students. The average class size in an introductory lecture is 35; in a laboratory, 20; and in a regular course offering, 23.

Admissions: About 75% of the 1993–94 applicants were accepted.

Requirements: The SAT I or ACT is required, with a minimum composite score of 650 to 700 on the SAT I or 18 on the ACT. Graduation from an accredited secondary school is required; a GED will be accepted. Applicants are required to submit 16 academic credits, including 4 years of high school English, 2 each of science, social studies, and a foreign language, 3 of mathematics, 1 each of history and physical education, and 1 from world geography, world history, computer science, or advanced mathematics. An interview is recommended. AP and CLEP credits are accepted. Important factors used in the admissions decision are advanced placement or honor courses, recommendations by school officials, evidence of special talent, leadership record, and recommendations by alumni.

Procedure: Freshmen are admitted to all sessions. Entrance exams should be taken in the spring of the junior year or the fall of the senior year. Applications should be filed by August 15 for fall entry and December 15 for spring entry, along with an application fee of $25. Notification is sent on a rolling basis. There are early admissions and deferred admissions plans.

Transfer: About 310 transfer students enrolled in a recent year. A minimum GPA of 2.0 is required. However, applicants with a lower GPA but in good academic standing at the previous college will be reviewed by the Admissions Committee for possible admission. A total of 30 credits out of 120 must be completed at Coastal Carolina.

Visiting: There are regularly scheduled orientations for prospective students. There are guides for informal visits and visitors may sit in on classes. To arrange for a visit, contact the Admissions Office at (803) 349–2026.

Financial Aid: In a recent year, 60% of all current freshmen and 52% of continuing students received some form of financial aid. Nearly 81% of undergraduate students work part-time. Average earnings from campus work for the school year are $2000. Coastal Carolina is

a member of CSS. The FAF is required. The deadline for financial aid applications is February 1.

International Students: There are currently 73 international students enrolled. They must take the TOEFL and achieve a minimum score of 500.

Computers: The college provides computer facilities for student use. The mainframe is an IBM 3081. Student computer laboratories are located in the School of Business and Computer Science and in the Academic Center. There are 109 terminals for student use. They may be used Monday, Wednesday, and Friday from 9:30 A.M. to 9:30 P.M., and Thursday from 8:30 A.M. to 9:30 P.M. There are no time limits on using the system and no fees.

Graduates: In a recent year, 432 bachelor's degrees were awarded. The most popular majors among graduates were early childhood education (11%), management (11%), and marketing (9%). Within an average freshman class, 39% graduate in 6 years. Some 60 companies recruited on campus in 1992–93.

Admissions Contact: Timothy J. McCormick, Director of Admissions.

COKER COLLEGE
Hartsville, SC 29550   (803) 383-8050; (800) 950-1908 (out-of-state)

Full-time: 284 men, 406 women	Faculty: 47; IIB, -$
Part-time: 116 men, 106 women	Ph.D.s: 76%
Graduate: none	Student/Faculty: 15 to 1
Year: semesters, summer session	Tuition: $9510
Application Deadline: August 1	Room & Board: $4280
Freshman Class: 374 applied, 277 accepted, 169 enrolled	
SAT I Verbal/Math: 431/469	COMPETITIVE

Coker College, founded in 1908, is a private coeducational institution offering undergraduate programs in business, education, and liberal arts. In addition to regional accreditation, Coker has baccalaureate program accreditation with NASM. The library contains 60,000 volumes, 1204 microform items, 4000 audiovisual forms, and subscribes to 327 periodicals. Computerized library sources and services include interlibrary loans. Special learning facilities include a learning resource center, art gallery, and botanical garden. The 15-acre campus is in a small town 25 miles west of Florence. Including residence halls, there are 17 buildings on campus.

Student Life: About 70% of undergraduates are from South Carolina. Students come from 22 states, 11 foreign countries, and Canada. Some 85% are from public schools; 15% from private. About 66% are white; 31%, African American. The average age of all undergraduates is 27. About 21% drop out by the end of their first year; 51% remain to graduate.

Housing: A total of 300 students can be accommodated in college housing. College-sponsored living facilities include coed dormitories. On-campus housing is guaranteed for all 4 years. About 67% of students commute. All students may keep cars on campus.

Activities: There are no fraternities or sororities. There are 25 groups on campus, including art, cheerleading, chess, choir, chorale, chorus, computers, dance, drama, ethnic, honors, international, newspaper, opera, photography, professional, radio and TV, religious, social, social service, student government, and yearbook. Popular campus events include Homecoming, May Day, Cow Day, (Coker Olympics of Winter), Christmas Dance, Spring Formal, drama productions, and a song contest.

Sports: There are 5 intercollegiate sports for men and 5 for women, and 18 intramural sports for men and 18 for women. Athletic and recreation facilities include a gymnasium, soccer and softball fields, tennis courts, an indoor pool, a boathouse with sailboats and canoes, and access to a golf course. The largest arena seats 600.

Disabled Students: About 30% of the campus is accessible to disabled students. The following facilities are available: wheelchair ramps, elevators, special parking, specially equipped rest rooms, special class scheduling, and lowered drinking fountains.

Services: In addition to many counseling and information services, tutoring is available in most subjects, including English and mathematics. There is also a writing laboratory.

Campus Safety and Security: Campus safety and security measures include 24-hour foot and vehicle patrol, self defense education, informal discussions, and pamphlets, posters, and films. In addition, there are lighted pathways and sidewalks.

Programs of Study: Coker awards the B.A. and B.S. degrees. Bachelor's degrees are awarded in BIOLOGICAL SCIENCE (biology/biological science), BUSINESS (business administration and management), COMMUNICATIONS AND THE ARTS (art, communications, dance, dramatic arts, English, French, graphic design, music, photography, and Spanish), COMPUTER AND PHYSICAL SCIENCE (chemistry and mathematics), EDUCATION (art, early childhood, education, elementary, English, mathematics, music, physical, and secondary), HEALTH PROFESSIONS (medical laboratory technology), SOCIAL SCIENCE (history, political science/government, psychology, religion, social science, and sociology). Art and education are the strong-

est programs academically. Business, education, and social sciences have the largest enrollments.

Required: Distribution requirements include 9 hours in humanities, 7 in science, 6 each in the arts, behavioral science, oral and written rhetoric, and nonnative language, and 3 in mathematics and physical education. A total of 120 credit hours, with 30 to 45 in the major, and a minimum 2.0 GPA are required to graduate.

Special: Co-op programs in all majors, internships, study abroad in 8 countries, on-campus work-study programs, B.A.-B.S. degrees, cross-registration with Central College, and dual and student-designed majors are offered. A 3–1 in medical technology with McCleod Regional Medical Center is possible. Also available are credit for military experience, nondegree study, and pass/fail options. The college's 'dialogical approach' to teaching allows students and professors to discuss topics and research in small, round-table settings. There are 2 national honor societies on campus. Two departments have honors programs.

Faculty/Classroom: Some 72% of faculty are male; 28%, female. All teach undergraduates and 60% both teach and do research. The average class size in an introductory lecture is 16; in a laboratory, 12; and in a regular course offering, 9.

Admissions: About 74% of the 1993–94 applicants were accepted. The SAT scores for the 1993–94 freshman class were as follows: Verbal—78% below 500, 13% between 500 and 599, and 8% between 600 and 700; Math—61% below 500, 33% between 500 and 599, and 5% between 600 and 700. About 31% of the current freshmen were in the top fifth of their class; 55% were in the top two fifths. There was 1 National Merit finalist. Two freshmen graduated first in their class.

Requirements: Coker requires applicants to be in the upper 50% of their class. A minimum GPA of 2.0 is required. The SAT I or ACT is required. Applicants must be graduates of an accredited secondary school or have a GED. An essay is required and an interview is recommended. An audition is recommended for music, dance, art, and drama students. AP and CLEP credits are accepted. Important factors used in the admissions decision are leadership record, advanced placement or honor courses, extracurricular activities record, personality, intangible qualities, and parents or siblings attending the school.

Procedure: Freshmen are admitted to all sessions. Entrance exams should be taken during the junior year or the first part of the senior year. Applications should be filed by August 1 for fall entry and December 1 for spring entry, along with an application fee of $15. Notification is sent on a rolling basis. There is an early admissions plan. A waiting list is an active part of the admissions procedure, with about 1% of applicants on the list.

Transfer: About 15 transfer students enrolled in 1993–94. Transfer applicants with fewer than 30 semester hours must submit high school transcripts and SAT I scores. A minimum 2.0 GPA is required. An interview is recommended. A total of 30 credits out of 120 must be completed at Coker.

Visiting: There are regularly scheduled orientations for prospective students, consisting of orientation, a meal, campus tours, and discussions with faculty and a student panel. There are guides for informal visits and visitors may sit in on classes and stay overnight at the school. To arrange for a visit, contact the Admissions Office at (803) 383–8050 or (800) 950–1908.

Financial Aid: In 1993–94, 90% of all students received some form of financial aid. About 70% of freshmen and 75% of continuing students received need-based aid. The average freshman award was $8300. Of that total, scholarships or need-based grants averaged $5518 ($13,500 maximum); loans averaged $2151 ($6625 maximum); and work contracts averaged $631 ($1500 maximum). Some 11% of undergraduate students work part-time. Average earnings from campus work for the school year are $1200. The average financial indebtedness of the 1992–93 graduate was $8190. Coker is a member of CSS. The FAF is required.

International Students: There are currently 11 international students enrolled. The school actively recruits these students. They must take the TOEFL and achieve a minimum score of 500.

Computers: The college provides computer facilities for student use. The mainframe is a DEC VAX 3600 accessed by a network of 25 microcomputers, and there are other independent computers on campus. All students may access the system. It may be used during regular hours. There are no time limits on using the system and no fees.

Graduates: In 1992–93, 156 bachelor's degrees were awarded. The most popular majors among graduates were business (35%), education (23%), and social sciences (22%). Within an average freshman class, 51% graduate in 5 years. Some 40 companies recruited on campus in 1992–93. In a recent graduating class, 30% of the men and 35% of the women were enrolled in graduate school within 6 months of graduation; 65% of the men and 60% of the women had found employment.

Admissions Contact: Dr. Stephen B. Terry, Vice President for Enrollment Management.

COLLEGE OF CHARLESTON

C-3

Charleston, SC 29424

(803) 953-5670

Full-time: 2585 men, 4266 women
Part-time: 537 men, 663 women
Graduate: 197 men, 2318 women
Year: semesters, summer session
Application Deadline: June 1
Freshman Class: 4772 applied, 3140 accepted, 1265 enrolled
SAT I Verbal/Math: 489/532

Faculty: 356; IIB, av$
Ph.D.s: 86%
Student/Faculty: 19 to 1
Tuition: $2950 ($5900)
Room & Board: $3300

ACT: 20   COMPETITIVE

The College of Charleston, founded in 1770, is a state-assisted, coeducational institution offering liberal arts programs, including business and education. There are 5 undergraduate schools and one graduate school. In addition to regional accreditation, the college has baccalaureate program accreditation with AACSB. The 2 libraries contain 464,698 volumes, 570,575 microform items, and 1849 audiovisual forms, and subscribe to 2667 periodicals. Computerized library sources and services include the card catalog, interlibrary loans, and database searching. Special learning facilities include a learning resource center, art gallery, an observatory, a communications museum, a marine laboratory, an African American research center, and a bronze sculpture foundry. The 52-acre campus is in the heart of historic Charleston, approximately 260 miles from Atlanta. Including residence halls, there are 100 buildings on campus.

Student Life: About 77% of undergraduates are from South Carolina. Students come from 46 states, 61 foreign countries, and Canada. Seventy-two percent are from public schools; 28% from private. Eighty-eight percent are white. Sixty-seven percent are Protestant; 16% Catholic; 10% claim no religious affiliation. The average age of freshmen is 19; all undergraduates, 22. Nineteen percent drop out by the end of their first year; 81% remain to graduate.

Housing: A total of 1891 students can be accommodated in college housing. College-sponsored living facilities include single-sex and coed dormitories, fraternity houses, and sorority houses. In addition there are honors houses, language houses, and special interest houses. On-campus housing is available on a first-come, first-served basis. Seventy-five percent of students commute. Alcohol is not permitted. All students may keep cars on campus.

Activities: About 18% of men belong to 11 national fraternities; about 18% of women belong to 10 national sororities. There are 65 groups on campus, including art, band, cheerleading, chess, choir, chorale, computers, dance, drama, ethnic, film, gay, honors, international, jazz band, literary magazine, musical theater, newspaper, opera, orchestra, pep band, political, professional, radio and TV, religious, social, social service, student government, symphony, and yearbook. Popular campus events include Sports Rally, Homecoming, Thursday Entertainment and Food Specials, Black History Month, Women's History Month, International Fair, Career Fair, Family Weekend, On-campus Spoleto festival events, Roach-a-thon, and Food for Thought lunch lecture series.

Sports: There are 8 intercollegiate sports for men and 7 for women, and 17 intramural sports for men and 17 for women. Athletic and recreation facilities include a physical education center with racquetball courts and a weight and workout room, a pool, an outdoor recreation center with baseball and soccer fields, tennis courts, a sailing marina, and a student center with a movie theater, a game room, meeting facilities, a ballroom, and a garden.

Disabled Students: Eighty percent of the campus is accessible to disabled students. The following facilities are available: wheelchair ramps, elevators, special parking, specially equipped rest rooms, special class scheduling, lowered drinking fountains, and telephones.

Services: In addition to many counseling and information services, tutoring is available in every subject. There is remedial math, reading, writing, a learning strategies course, study skills seminars, and supplemental instruction provided by tutors in group sessions.

Campus Safety and Security: Campus safety and security measures include 24-hour foot and vehicle patrol, self defense education, escort service, and informal discussions. In addition, there are pamphlets, posters, and films, emergency telephones, and lighted pathways and sidewalks.

Programs of Study: The college awards the B.A., B.S., A.B. and master's degrees. Bachelor's degrees are awarded in BIOLOGICAL SCIENCE (biochemistry, biology/biological science, and marine biology), BUSINESS (accounting and business administration and management), COMMUNICATIONS AND THE ARTS (art history and appreciation, communications, dramatic arts, English, French, German, music, Spanish, and studio art), COMPUTER AND PHYSICAL SCIENCE (chemistry, computer science, geology, mathematics, and physics), EDUCATION (early childhood, elementary, physical, and special), ENGINEERING AND ENVIRONMENTAL DESIGN (preengineering), HEALTH PROFESSIONS (predentistry and premedicine), SOCIAL SCIENCE (anthropology, economics, history, philosophy, political science/government, psychology, sociology, and urban

studies). Sciences and business are the strongest academically. Business and education have the largest enrollments.

Required: All students must complete a core curriculum, including English and history courses, 12 hours each of language and humanities, 8 hours of laboratory science, and 6 hours each of mathematics or logic and social science. A total of 122 credit hours, including 24 to 43 in the major, with a minimum overall GPA of 2.0 (2.5 in some majors) is required to graduate.

Special: Cross-registration is possible with the Medical University of South Carolina, Trident Technical College, The Citadel, and Charleston Southern University. Co-op programs and internships in all majors, a Washington semester, study abroad in about 36 countries, work-study programs, B.A.-B.S. degrees, and dual majors are offered. A 3-2 engineering degree is available with Case Western Reserve University, Clemson University, Georgia Institute of Technology, University of South Carolina, and Washington University of St. Louis. A 2-2 program in allied health, biometry, or nursing is offered with the Medical University of South Carolina. The college's 3-week Maymester session offers unconventional courses and programs using alternative methods of instruction. There is an interdisciplinary honors program, available to talented students. There is a freshman honors program on campus, as well as 10 national honor societies.

Faculty/Classroom: Sixty-six percent of faculty are male; 34%, female. All teach undergraduates, 90% do research, and 90% do both. No introductory courses are taught by graduate students. The average class size in an introductory lecture is 30; in a laboratory, 20; and in a regular course offering, 25.

Admissions: About 66% of the 1993-94 applicants were accepted. The SAT scores for the 1993-94 freshman class were as follows: Verbal—59% below 500, 32% between 500 and 599, and 9% between 600 and 700; Math—41% below 500, 45% between 500 and 599, 13% between 600 and 700, and 1% above 700. The ACT scores were 41% below 21, 51% between 21 and 23, and 8% between 24 and 26. About 44% of the current freshmen were in the top fifth of their class; 79% were in the top two fifths. About 34 freshmen graduated first in their class.

Requirements: The SAT I or ACT is required. In addition, applicants should have completed 4 units of high school English, 3 of mathematics, 2 to 3 of social studies, including 1/2 unit each of economics and government, 2 years each of laboratory science and foreign language, and 1 year of U.S. history. In addition, students should have 1 unit of advanced mathematics or computer science or a combination of these, or 1 unit of world history, world geography, or Western civilization. The GED is accepted, and interview is recommended. AP and CLEP credits are also accepted. Important factors used in the admissions decision are advanced placement or honor courses, leadership record, evidence of special talent, extracurricular activities record, and recommendations by school officials.

Procedure: Freshmen are admitted fall and spring. Entrance exams should be taken by March 1 or earlier. Applications should be filed by June 1 for fall entry and November 15 for spring entry, along with an application fee of $25. Notification is sent on a rolling basis. There are early admissions and deferred admissions plans.

Transfer: About 880 transfer students enrolled in 1993-94. Transfer applicants must be eligible to return to the last institution attended. Students with fewer than 60 hours must have a 2.3 GPA; all others must have a 2.0 GPA. A total of 36 credits out of 122 must be completed at the college.

Visiting: There are regularly scheduled orientations for prospective students, consisting of 1-day open houses throughout the year and 6 2-day orientation sessions throughout the summer, including a family session. Academic requirements and expectations, services offered, placement testing, individual academic advising, registration, and introduction to residence life and cultural offerings are included. There are guides for informal visits and visitors may sit in on classes and stay overnight at the school. To arrange for a visit, contact the Admissions Office at (803) 953-5670.

Financial Aid: In 1993-94, 62% of continuing students received some form of financial aid. About 62% of freshmen and 62% of continuing students received need-based aid. The average freshman award was $5797. Of that total, scholarships or need-based grants averaged $1800 ($2800 maximum); loans averaged $1950 ($2625 maximum); and work contracts averaged $847 ($1200 maximum). Forty-seven percent of undergraduate students work part-time. Average earnings from campus work for the school year are $1791. The average financial indebtedness of the 1992-93 graduate was $6800. The college is a member of CSS. The FAFSA financial statement is required. The deadline for financial aid applications is April 15.

International Students: There are currently 180 international students enrolled. The school actively recruits these students. They must take the TOEFL and achieve a minimum score of 550.

Computers: The college provides computer facilities for student use. The mainframe is a DEC VAX 6510. Dial-in capability, 2 large centers with about 90 personal computers in each, and 4 networked classrooms with a computer station for each student also are available.

Software includes word processing, spreadsheets, database, statistical, and specialized disciplines. All students may access the system. It may be used 24 hours a day. There are no time limits on using the system. The fees are $25 per semester.

Graduates: In 1992–93, 1285 bachelor's degrees were awarded. The most popular majors among graduates were business administration (21%), elementary education (12%), and political science (9%). Within an average freshman class, 4% graduate in 3 years, 40% in 4 years, and 53% in 5 years. In the 1992 graduating class, 30% of grduates were enrolled in graduate school within 6 months of graduation; 80% of the graduates had found employment.

Admissions Contact: Donald Burkard, Dean of Admissions.

COLUMBIA COLLEGE
Columbia, SC 29203

C-3

(803) 786–3871 (Call collect)
(800) 277–1301 (out-of-state)

Full-time: 968 women	Faculty: 70; IIB, -$
Part-time: 241 women	Ph.D.s: 62%
Graduate: 28 women	Student/Faculty: 14 to 1
Year: semesters, summer session	Tuition: $9750
Application Deadline: open	Room & Board: $3770
Freshman Class: 737 applied, 614 accepted, 242 enrolled	
SAT I or ACT: required	**LESS COMPETITIVE**

Columbia College, founded in 1854, is a private women's liberal arts college, affiliated with the United Methodist Church. In addition to regional accreditation, the college has baccalaureate program accreditation with CSWE, NASM, and NCATE. The library contains 132,321 volumes, 11,435 microform items, and 17,249 audiovisual forms, and subscribes to 651 periodicals. Computerized library sources and services include interlibrary loans and database searching. Special learning facilities include a learning resource center, art gallery, and radio station. The 33-acre campus is in an urban area in Columbia. Including residence halls, there are 26 buildings on campus.

Student Life: About 93% of undergraduates are from South Carolina. Students come from 22 states and 4 foreign countries. Seventy-nine percent are white; 20% African American. Eighty-one percent are Protestant; 11% claim no religious affiliation. The average age of freshmen is 18; all undergraduates, 23. Twenty-seven percent drop out by the end of their first year; 55% remain to graduate.

Housing: A total of 650 students can be accommodated in college housing. College-sponsored living facilities include dormitories. On-campus housing is guaranteed for all 4 years. Sixty percent of all students live on campus. Alcohol is not permitted. All students may keep cars on campus.

Activities: There are 57 groups on campus, including art, band, choir, chorus, computers, dance, drama, ethnic, honors, international, literary magazine, musical theater, newspaper, opera, photography, political, professional, radio and TV, religious, social, social service, student government, and yearbook. Popular campus events include Fine Arts Series, Follies, May Day, Moms Day, Dads Day, and Convocation.

Sports: Athletic and recreation facilities include an athletic field, tennis courts, a gymnasium, an Olympic-size pool, a fitness laboratory, and a dance studio.

Disabled Students: The following facilities are available: wheelchair ramps, elevators, special parking, specially equipped rest rooms, and special class scheduling.

Services: Counseling and information services are available.

Campus Safety and Security: Campus safety and security measures include 24-hour foot and vehicle patrol, self-defense education, escort service, and informal discussions. In addition, there are pamphlets, posters, films, emergency telephones, and lighted pathways and sidewalks.

Programs of Study: The college awards the B.A., B.F.A., and B.Mus. degrees. Master's degrees also are awarded. Bachelor's degrees are awarded in BIOLOGICAL SCIENCE (biology/biological science), BUSINESS (accounting and business administration and management), COMMUNICATIONS AND THE ARTS (communications, dance, dramatic arts, English, French, languages, music, music performance, performing arts, piano/organ, Spanish, and studio art), COMPUTER AND PHYSICAL SCIENCE (chemistry and mathematics), EDUCATION (Christian Education, dance, early childhood, elementary, music, physical, special, and speech correction), HEALTH PROFESSIONS (medical laboratory technology), SOCIAL SCIENCE (history, political science/government, psychology, public affairs, religion, religious music, social work, and sociology). Education, business, and performing arts have the largest enrollments.

Required: To graduate, students must complete 127 semester hours, with a minimum GPA of 2.5 in the major and 2.0 overall. General education requirements for the B.A. degree include 15 hours of communication skills, 12 of social science, 9 of aesthetics, 8 of natural science, 6 of religion, and 3 each of mathematics and physical education. Students also must satisfy proficiency requirements in English and mathematics.

Special: The Center for Contractual Studies allows qualified students to pursue individualized programs based on independent study, practicums, and a senior project. The college also offers internships, study abroad, dual majors, and credit for life, military, and work experience. Nondegree study and pass/fail options are available. There is a freshman honors program on campus.

Faculty/Classroom: Forty-five percent of faculty are male; 55%, female. No introductory courses are taught by graduate students. The average class size in an introductory lecture is 20 and in a laboratory, 20.

Admissions: About 83% of the 1993–94 applicants were accepted. About 41% of the current freshmen were in the top fifth of their class; 70% were in the top two fifths.

Requirements: The SAT I or ACT is required. Applicants must be graduates of an accredited secondary school or have earned a GED. They should complete 16 Carnegie units, including 4 years of English, 3 of mathematics, and 2 each of foreign language and laboratory science, as well as courses in history and social studies. An essay and an interview are recommended, as is a portfolio or audition for fine and performing arts students. AP and CLEP credits are accepted. Important factors used in the admissions decision are recommendations by school officials, personality, intangible qualities, leadership record, advanced placement or honor courses, and evidence of special talent.

Procedure: Entrance exams should be taken near the end of the junior year or by December of the senior year. Application deadlines are open. Application fee is $20. Notification is sent on a rolling basis.

Transfer: Nearly 100 transfer students enrolled in a recent year. An interview is recommended for transfer students. Applicants with fewer than 24 semester hours must present ACT or SAT I scores and high school transcripts. Grades of C or better transfer for credit. At least 30 credits out of 127 must be completed at the college.

Visiting: There are regularly scheduled orientations for prospective students, consisting of meetings with faculty advisors, classroom visits, campus tours, lunch, and student life and financial aid presentations. There are guides for informal visits and visitors may sit in on classes and stay overnight at the school. To arrange for a visit, contact the Admissions Office at (803) 786–3871 or (800) 277–1301.

Financial Aid: In 1993–94, 91% of all current freshmen and 77% of continuing students received some form of financial aid. About 87% of freshmen and 74% of continuing students received need-based aid. The average freshman award was $9126. Of that total, scholarships or need-based grants averaged $5685 ($6000 maximum); loans averaged $2703 ($5625 maximum); and work contracts averaged $500 ($700 maximum). Thirty-four percent of undergraduate students work part-time. Average earnings from campus work for the school year are $700. The average financial indebtedness of the 1992–93 graduate was $12,000. the college is a member of CSS. The FAFSA financial statement is required. The deadline for financial aid applications is May 1.

International Students: There are currently 7 international students enrolled. They must take the TOEFL and achieve a minimum score of 550.

Computers: The college provides computer facilities for student use. The mainframe is a DEC 5500 running UNIX. There are no time limits on using the system and no fees.

Graduates: In 1992–93, 218 bachelor's degrees were awarded. The most popular majors among graduates were business administration (14%), elementary education (11%), and speech/language pathology (7%). Within an average freshman class, 52% graduate in 4 years, 55% in 5 years, and 57% in 6 years.

Admissions Contact: Charlotte S. Broome, Director of Freshman Admissions.

CONVERSE COLLEGE
Spartanburg, SC 29302

B-1

(803) 596–9040; (800) 766–1125 (in-state)

Full-time: 635 women	Faculty: 84; IIB, av$
Part-time: 103 women	Ph.D.s: 75%
Graduate: 57 men, 349 women	Student/Faculty: 8 to 1
Year: 4-1-4	Tuition: $12,050
Application Deadline: April 1	Room & Board: $3700
Freshman Class: 440 applied, 391 accepted, 149 enrolled	
SAT I or ACT: required	**COMPETITIVE**

Converse College, founded in 1889, is a private, women's liberal arts college. Men are admitted to the graduate programs. There are 2 undergraduate and 2 graduate schools. In addition to regional accreditation, Converse College has baccalaureate program accreditation with FIDER and NASM. The library contains 150,000 volumes, 310 microform items, and 12,000 audiovisual forms, and subscribes to 700 periodicals. Computerized library sources and services include interlibrary loans and database searching. Special learning facilities include a learning resource center and art gallery. The 72-acre campus is in an urban area 80 miles southwest of Charlotte. Including residence halls, there are 27 buildings on campus.

Student Life: About 55% of undergraduates are from out-of-state, mostly the South. Students come from 25 states, 10 foreign countries, and Canada. Seventy percent are from public schools; 30% from private. Ninety percent are white. The average age of freshmen is 18; all undergraduates, 20. Twenty percent drop out by the end of their first year; 60% remain to graduate.

Housing: A total of 700 students can be accommodated in college housing. College-sponsored living facilities include dormitories. On-campus housing is guaranteed for all 4 years. Seventy-five percent of students live on campus; of those, 40% remain on campus on weekends. Alcohol is not permitted. All students may keep cars on campus.

Activities: There are no fraternities on campus. There are 50 groups on campus, including art, cheerleading, choir, chorale, chorus, computers, dance, drama, ethnic, honors, international, literary magazine, musical theater, newspaper, opera, orchestra, photography, political, professional, religious, social service, student government, symphony, and yearbook. Popular campus events include Probe and 1889 Day.

Sports: Athletic and recreation facilities include a gymnasium, a pool, a dance studio, a weight room, tennis courts, and bowling lanes.

Disabled Students: The following facilities are available: wheelchair ramps, elevators, special parking, and specially equipped rest rooms.

Services: In addition to many counseling and information services, tutoring is available in every subject.

Campus Safety and Security: Campus safety and security measures include 24-hour foot and vehicle patrol, self defense education, escort service, and informal discussions. In addition, there are pamphlets, posters, and films, emergency telephones, and lighted pathways and sidewalks.

Programs of Study: Converse College awards the B.A., B.F.A., and B.Mus. Master's degrees are also awarded. Bachelor's degrees are awarded in BIOLOGICAL SCIENCE (biology/biological science), BUSINESS (accounting and business administration and management), COMMUNICATIONS AND THE ARTS (design, English, fine arts, French, languages, modern language, music, and Spanish), COMPUTER AND PHYSICAL SCIENCE (chemistry, computer science, and mathematics), EDUCATION (art, early childhood, elementary, foreign languages, music, science, and secondary), HEALTH PROFESSIONS (predentistry and premedicine), SOCIAL SCIENCE (economics, history, political science/government, prelaw, psychology, religion, and sociology). English, politics, and chemistry are the strongest academically. Education, business, and interior design have the largest enrollments.

Required: To graduate, students must complete 120 semester hours, including 52 hours across the liberal arts discipline, with a minimum GPA of 2.0.

Special: There are co-op programs and cross-registration with Wofford College. Internships, study abroad, accelerated degree programs, B.A.-B.S. degrees, and dual majors are offered. There is a freshman honors program on campus, as well as 10 national honor societies. All departments have honors programs.

Faculty/Classroom: Fifty-five percent of faculty are male; 45%, female. All teach undergraduates. No introductory courses are taught by graduate students. The average class size in an introductory lecture is 20; in a laboratory, 15; and in a regular course offering, 11.

Admissions: About 89% of the 1993-94 applicants were accepted. There were 8 National Merit semifinalists. About 12 freshmen graduated first in their class.

Requirements: Converse College requires applicants to be in the upper 50% of their class. A minimum GPA of 2.0 is required. The SAT I or ACT is required. Applicants should be graduates of an accredited secondary school, having completed 20 Carnegie units, including 4 years of English, 3 of mathematics, 2 each of foreign language, science, and social studies, and 1 of history. The GED is accepted. An interview is recommended for all students and an audition is recommended for music students. AP and CLEP credits are accepted. Important factors used in the admissions decision are advanced placement or honor courses, recommendations by school officials, leadership record, extracurricular activities record, and evidence of special talent.

Procedure: Freshmen are admitted to all sessions. Entrance exams should be taken by the senior year of high school. Applications should be filed by April 1 for fall entry, October 1 for winter entry, October 1 for spring entry, and May 1 for summer entry, along with an application fee of $25. Notification is sent on a rolling basis.

Transfer: About 16 transfer students enrolled in 1993-94. Transfer applicants should have a minimum GPA of 2.0. A total of 42 credits out of 120 must be completed at Converse College.

Visiting: There are regularly scheduled orientations for prospective students, consisting of faculty meetings, panel discussions, and campus tours. There are guides for informal visits and visitors may sit in on classes and stay overnight at the school. To arrange for a visit, contact the Admissions Office at (803) 596-9040.

Financial Aid: In 1993-94, 80% of all current freshmen and 80% of continuing students received some form of financial aid. Thirty-three percent of undergraduate students work part-time. Converse College is a member of CSS, and the FAF is required. The deadline for financial aid applications is March 15.

International Students: There are currently 25 international students enrolled. The school actively recruits these students. They must take the TOEFL and achieve a minimum score of 550.

Computers: The college provides computer facilities for student use. The mainframe is a DEC VAX. There are also 2 microcomputer laboratories as well as microcomputers in the library and dormitories. All students may access the system. There are no time limits on using the system and no fees.

Graduates: In 1992-93, 166 bachelor's degrees were awarded. The most popular majors among graduates were business (21%), education (17%), and art (10%). Within an average freshman class, 2% graduate in 3 years, 64% in 4 years, and 65% in 5 years. Some 125 companies recruited on campus in 1992-93. In the 1992 graduating class, 25% of the women were enrolled in graduate school within 6 months of graduation; 70% of the women had found employment.

Admissions Contact: Director of Admissions.

ERSKINE COLLEGE

B-2

Due West, SC 29639 (803) 379-8830

Full-time: 228 men, 304 women	**Faculty:** 40; IIB, --$
Part-time: 20 men, 15 women	**Ph.D.s:** 83%
Graduate: 145 men, 8 women	**Student/Faculty:** 13 to 1
Year: 4-1-4, summer session	**Tuition:** $10,630
Application Deadline: open	**Room & Board:** $3680
Freshman Class: 659 applied, 557 accepted, 168 enrolled	
SAT I Verbal/Math: 482/532	**COMPETITIVE**

Erskine College, founded in 1839, is a private, coeducational liberal arts college, affiliated with the Associate Reformed Presbyterian Church. The library contains 215,000 volumes, 74,938 microform items, and 1053 audiovisual forms, and subscribes to 1065 periodicals. Computerized library sources and services include the card catalog and database searching. Special learning facilities include a TV station. The 85-acre campus is in a rural area 40 miles south of Greenville. Including residence halls, there are 22 buildings on campus.

Student Life: About 75% of undergraduates are from South Carolina. Students come from 17 states, 5 foreign countries, and Canada. Ninety percent are from public schools; 10% from private. Ninety-four percent are white. Most are Protestant. The average age of freshmen is 18; all undergraduates, 20. Fourteen percent drop out by the end of their first year; 69% remain to graduate.

Housing: A total of 634 students can be accommodated in college housing. College-sponsored living facilities include single-sex dormitories. On-campus housing is guaranteed for all 4 years. Ninety percent of students live on campus; of those, 50% remain on campus on weekends. All students may keep cars on campus.

Activities: About 40% of men belong to 3 local fraternities; about 40% of women belong to 5 local sororities. There are 45 groups on campus, including cheerleading, choir, chorale, chorus, computers, dance, drama, ethnic, honors, international, jazz band, literary magazine, newspaper, pep band, political, professional, radio and TV, religious, social, social service, student government, and yearbook. Popular campus events include Homecoming, Spring Fling, Back to School Bash, and Fall Fest.

Sports: There are 6 intercollegiate sports for men and 5 for women, and 3 intramural sports for men and 3 for women. Athletic and recreation facilities include a physical activities center, 2 gymnasiums, racquetball courts, soccer and baseball fields, tennis and basketball courts, an outdoor pavilion, an outdoor pool, and a sand volleyball court.

Disabled Students: Eighty percent of the campus is accessible to disabled students. The following facilities are available: wheelchair ramps, elevators, special parking, and special class scheduling.

Services: In addition to many counseling and information services, tutoring is available in most subjects. There is a reader service for the blind.

Campus Safety and Security: Campus safety and security measures include 24-hour foot and vehicle patrol, escort service, informal discussions, pamphlets, posters, and films. In addition, there are lighted pathways and sidewalks.

Programs of Study: Erskine awards the A.B. and B.S. degrees. Master's and doctoral degrees also are awarded. Bachelor's degrees are awarded in BIOLOGICAL SCIENCE (biology/biological science), BUSINESS (business administration and management), COMMUNICATIONS AND THE ARTS (English and music), COMPUTER AND PHYSICAL SCIENCE (chemistry, mathematics, natural sciences, and physics), EDUCATION (early childhood, elementary, foreign languages, music, physical, secondary, and special), HEALTH PROFESSIONS (medical laboratory technology, predentistry, and premedi-

cine), SOCIAL SCIENCE (behavioral science, history, psychology, and religion). Business administration has the largest enrollment.

Required: Students must complete 124 semester hours with an average of 27 credits in a major and a minimum GPA of 2.0. A basic curriculum of arts and letters, humanities, natural science and mathematics, social sciences, and physical education is required.

Special: Internships are available during the January term. Study abroad in 3 countries, a 3-2 engineering degree with Georgia Institute of Technology and Clemson University, and pass/fail options are offered. There are 5 national honor societies on campus. Three departments have honors programs.

Faculty/Classroom: Seventy-two percent of faculty are male; 28%, female. All teach undergraduates. No introductory courses are taught by graduate students. The average class size in an introductory lecture is 26; in a laboratory, 20; and in a regular course offering, 13.

Admissions: About 85% of the 1993-94 applicants were accepted. The SAT scores for the 1993-94 freshman class were as follows: Verbal—58% below 500, 27% between 500 and 599, 14% between 600 and 700, and 1% above 700; Math—38% below 500, 39% between 500 and 599, 21% between 600 and 700, and 2% above 700. About 74% of the current freshmen were in the top fifth of their class; 90% were in the top two fifths. There were 3 National Merit finalists. Six freshmen graduated first in their class.

Requirements: The SAT I is required, but grades from college preparatory courses are weighed twice as heavily as SAT I scores. Applicants must be graduates of an accredited secondary school. The GED is accepted. Applicants should have 14 high school academic credits, including 4 credits of English and 2 credits each of mathematics, science, and history, with 2 credits of foreign language recommended. An interview is recommended. AP credits are accepted. Important factors used in the admissions decision are advanced placement or honor courses, recommendations by school officials, parents or siblings attending the school, recommendations by alumni, and evidence of special talent.

Procedure: Freshmen are admitted to all sessions. Entrance exams should be taken during the spring of the junior year or the fall of the senior year. Application deadlines are open. The application fee is $20. Notification is sent on a rolling basis.

Transfer: Eighteen transfer students enrolled in 1993-94. Transfer applicants should have a minimum GPA of 2.0. An interview is recommended. At least 30 credits out of 124 must be completed at Erskine.

Visiting: There are regularly scheduled orientations for prospective students. There are guides for informal visits, and visitors may sit in on classes and stay overnight at the school. To arrange for a visit, contact Dot Carter, Director of Admissions and Financial Aid, at (800) 241-8721.

Financial Aid: In 1993-94, 92% of all current freshmen and 97% of continuing students received some form of financial aid. About 80% of freshmen and 75% of continuing students received need-based aid. The average freshman award was $9600. Of that total, scholarships or need-based grants averaged $7700 ($14,310 maximum); loans averaged $1560 ($3000 maximum); and work contracts averaged $340 ($900 maximum). Sixty-five percent of undergraduate students work part-time. Average earnings from campus work for the school year are $900. The average financial indebtedness of a recent graduate was $7500. Erskine is a member of CSS. The college's own financial statement and FAFSA are required. The deadline for financial aid applications is August 1.

International Students: There are currently 10 international students enrolled. They must take the TOEFL and achieve a minimum score of 600 and must also take the SAT I if it is available in their country.

Computers: The college provides computer facilities for student use. The mainframe is a DEC PDP 11/84. There are also 60 Apple Macintosh and IBM microcomputers available across campus. All students may access the system from 7 A.M. to 1 A.M. Monday through Saturday, and from 1 P.M. to 1 A.M. Sunday. There are no time limits on using the system. The fee is $15 a year.

Graduates: In 1992-93, 91 bachelor's degrees were awarded. The most popular majors among graduates were business (19%), history (16%), and biology (13%). Within an average freshman class, 61% graduate in 4 years, 62% in 5 years, and 62% in 6 years. Some 27 companies recruited on campus in an earlier year. In the 1992 graduating class, 18% of the men and 21% of the women were enrolled in graduate school within 6 months of graduation; 25% of the men and 35% of the women had found employment.

Admissions Contact: Dot Carter, Director of Admissions and Financial Aid.

FRANCIS MARION COLLEGE
(See Francis Marion University)

FRANCIS MARION UNIVERSITY
D-2
(Formerly Francis Marion College)
Florence, SC 29501-0547

(803) 661-1231

Full-time: 1463 men, 1758 women	**Faculty:** 166; IIB, av$
Part-time: 191 men, 248 women	**Ph.D.s:** 79%
Graduate: 87 men, 356 women	**Student/Faculty:** 19 to 1
Year: semesters, summer session	**Tuition:** $2800 ($5600)
Application Deadline: open	**Room & Board:** $3078
Freshman Class: 1801 applied, 1655 accepted, 819 enrolled	
SAT I Verbal/Math: 396/441	**LESS COMPETITIVE**

Francis Marion University, founded in 1970, is a state-supported, co-educational liberal arts, business, and teachers college. There are 2 undergraduate and 3 graduate schools. The library contains 245,173 volumes, 78,175 microform items, and 31,196 audiovisual forms, and subscribes to 1743 periodicals. Computerized library sources and services include the card catalog, interlibrary loans, and database searching. Special learning facilities include a learning resource center and planetarium. The 309-acre campus is in a rural area 8 miles east of Florence. Including residence halls, there are 34 buildings on campus.

Student Life: About 95% of undergraduates are from South Carolina. Students come from 29 states, 18 foreign countries, and Canada. Eighty-five percent are from public schools; 15% from private. Seventy-six percent are white; 22% African American. The average age of freshmen is 18; all undergraduates, 22.

Housing: A total of 1158 students can be accommodated in college housing. College-sponsored living facilities include coed dormitories and on-campus apartments. On-campus housing is available on a first-come, first-served basis. Sixty-nine percent of students commute. Alcohol is not permitted. All students may keep cars on campus.

Activities: About 13% of men belong to 1 local and 7 national fraternities; about 9% of women belong to 6 national sororities. There are 60 groups on campus, including cheerleading, choir, drama, ethnic, honors, international, literary magazine, newspaper, political, professional, religious, social, social service, and student government. Popular campus events include Freshman Fest, Back to School Dance, Christmas Party, Homecoming, and Greek Week.

Sports: There are 7 intercollegiate sports for men and 4 for women, and 16 intramural sports for men and 16 for women. Athletic and recreation facilities include a 3200-seat gymnasium; an Olympic-size pool; baseball, softball, and soccer fields; tennis and racquetball courts; a track; and weight, fitness, and game rooms.

Disabled Students: The entire campus is accessible to disabled students. The following facilities are available: wheelchair ramps, elevators, special parking, specially equipped rest rooms, special class scheduling, and lowered drinking fountains.

Services: In addition, there is a reader service for the blind, and remedial math, reading, and writing.

Campus Safety and Security: Campus safety and security measures include 24-hour foot and vehicle patrol, pamphlets, posters, films, emergency telephones, and lighted pathways and sidewalks.

Programs of Study: The university awards the B.A., B.S., B.B.A., and B.G.S degrees. Master's degrees also are awarded. Bachelor's degrees are awarded in BIOLOGICAL SCIENCE (biology/biological science), BUSINESS (accounting, banking and finance, business administration and management, business economics, management science, and marketing/retailing/merchandising), COMMUNICATIONS AND THE ARTS (communications, dramatic arts, English, fine arts, French, and Spanish), COMPUTER AND PHYSICAL SCIENCE (chemistry, computer science, information sciences and systems, mathematics, and physics), EDUCATION (early childhood and elementary), ENGINEERING AND ENVIRONMENTAL DESIGN (engineering technology), HEALTH PROFESSIONS (medical laboratory technology), SOCIAL SCIENCE (economics, geography, history, political science/government, psychology, and sociology). Premedicine, predentistry, health physics, and business are the strongest academically. Business, education, and biology have the largest enrollments.

Required: Students must complete from 120 to 132 credit hours, including 30 to 60 in the major, with a minimum GPA of 2.0. Distribution requirements include 15 hours of humanities, 12 each of sciences and basic communications (6 of English composition and 6 of mathematics and/or logic), 9 of social sciences, and 12 of a foreign language.

Special: There are co-op programs in civil engineering technology and electronic engineering technology with Florence Darlington Technical College, in geography with the University of South Carolina, in engineering and forest management with Clemson University, in nursing with the Medical University of South Carolina, and in medi-

cal technology with the McLeod Regional Medical Center. Internships are required in the communications and health physics programs. Students may join the school's Studycade in Summer, which visits different foreign lands every year. Accelerated degree programs and dual majors are possible. Nondegree study is permitted. Self-paced courses are offered in mathematics and French. There is a freshman honors program on campus, as well as 9 national honor societies.

Faculty/Classroom: Seventy-five percent of faculty are male; 25%, female.

Admissions: About 92% of the 1993–94 applicants were accepted. The SAT scores for the 1993–94 freshman class were as follows: Verbal—91% below 500, 8% between 500 and 599, and 2% between 600 and 700; Math—75% below 500, 20% between 500 and 599, and 5% between 600 and 700. About 30% of the current freshmen were in the top fifth of their class; 57% were in the top two fifths. Thirteen freshmen graduated first in their class.

Requirements: The SAT I is required, with a recommended minimum composite score of 900. Applicants should be high school graduates or hold a GED. Students should have earned 16 credits, consisting of 4 in English; 3 in mathematics (including algebra I and II); 2 each in social studies, foreign language, and laboratory science (including 1 each in biology, and either chemistry or physics); and 1 each in American history, physical education or ROTC, and either advanced mathematics, computer science, world history, Western civilization, or world geography. An interview is recommended. AP and CLEP credits are accepted.

Procedure: Freshmen are admitted to all sessions. Entrance exams should be taken in the fall of the senior year. Application deadlines are open. Notification is sent on a rolling basis. There is a deferred admissions plan.

Transfer: A total of 260 transfer students enrolled in 1993–94. Transfer students should have earned 30 hours of college credit, with a GPA of at least 2.0. At least 30 credits out of 120 must be completed at the university.

Visiting: There are regularly scheduled orientations for prospective students, including 3 open houses each year. There are guides for informal visits, and visitors may sit in on classes. To arrange for a visit, contact the Admissions Office at (803) 661-1231.

Financial Aid: In 1993–94, 51% of continuing students received some form of financial aid. Thirteen percent of undergraduate students work part-time. Average earnings from campus work for the school year are $705. The average financial indebtedness of a recent graduate was $6002. The college's own financial statement and FAFSA are required. The deadline for financial aid applications is March 1.

International Students: There are currently 32 international students enrolled. They must take the TOEFL and achieve a minimum score of 500 and must also take the SAT I or the ACT.

Computers: The college provides computer facilities for student use. The mainframes are an IBM System/36 and a DEC 3000. There are also 130 IBM PC and PS/2 microcomputers available in the computer center. All students may access the system from 8 A.M. to 11 P.M. A 90-minute time limit takes effect when there is a waiting list. There are no fees.

Graduates: In 1992–93, 486 bachelor's degrees were awarded. The most popular majors among graduates were business administration (23%), education (16%), and political science (11%). Some 86 companies recruited on campus in a recent year.

Admissions Contact: Marvin Lynch, Director of Admissions.

FURMAN UNIVERSITY
B-1

Greenville, SC 29613 (803) 294-2034

Full-time: 1078 men, 1293 women	Faculty: 185; IIB, +$
Part-time: 93 men, 82 women	Ph.D.s: 92%
Graduate: 65 men, 230 women	Student/Faculty: 13 to 1
Year: 3-2-3, summer session	Tuition: $12,605
Application Deadline: February 1	Room & Board: $3952
Freshman Class: 2161 applied, 1951 accepted, 687 enrolled	
SAT I or ACT: required	**VERY COMPETITIVE**

Founded in 1826, Furman University is an independent coeducational liberal arts college. There is one graduate school. In addition to regional accreditation, Furman has baccalaureate program accreditation with NASM. The library contains 350,289 volumes, 556,924 microform items, 1648 audiovisual forms, and subscribes to 2464 periodicals. Computerized library sources and services include the card catalog, interlibrary loans, and database searching. Special learning facilities include a learning resource center, art gallery, radio station, an observatory, and cable TV with on-campus broadcasting. The 750-acre campus is in a suburban area 5 miles north of Greenville. Including residence halls, there are 27 buildings on campus.

Student Life: About 67% of undergraduates are from out-of-state, mostly the South. Students come from 41 states and 20 foreign countries. Nearly 75% are from public schools; 25% from private. About

95% are white. Some 81% are Protestant; 12% Catholic. The average age of freshmen is 18; all undergraduates, 20. About 8% drop out by the end of their first year; 82% remain to graduate.

Housing: A total of 1512 students can be accommodated in college housing. College-sponsored living facilities include single-sex and coed dormitories. In addition there are lakeside cabins and on-campus apartments available through a lottery. On-campus housing is available on a first-come, first-served basis and is available on a lottery system for upperclassmen. Some 58% of students live on campus; of those, 75% remain on campus on weekends. Alcohol is not permitted. All students may keep cars on campus.

Activities: About 32% of men belong to 1 local and 7 national fraternities; about 30% of women belong to 7 local sororities. There are 121 groups on campus, including art, band, cheerleading, chess, choir, chorale, chorus, computers, dance, drama, drill team, ethnic, gay, international, jazz band, literary magazine, marching band, musical theater, newspaper, opera, orchestra, pep band, photography, political, professional, radio and TV, religious, social, social service, student government, symphony, and yearbook. Popular campus events include Homecoming, Parents Weekend, Beach Weekend, and Mountain Weekend.

Sports: There are 8 intercollegiate sports for men and 9 for women, and 36 intramural sports for men and 35 for women. Athletic and recreation facilities include a 16,500-seat stadium, a 2000-seat arena, a 500-seat gymnasium, a pool, an 18-hole golf course, 24 tennis courts, soccer facilities, 12 playing fields, a varsity softball field, and a baseball stadium. The gymnasium includes 6 racquetball courts and a fitness center.

Disabled Students: Nearly 99% of the campus is accessible to disabled students. The following facilities are available: wheelchair ramps, elevators, special parking, specially equipped rest rooms, special class scheduling, lowered drinking fountains, lowered telephones, and designated dormitory rooms.

Services: In addition to many counseling and information services, tutoring is available in every subject. There is also a reader service for the blind.

Campus Safety and Security: Campus safety and security measures include 24-hour foot and vehicle patrol, self defense education, escort service, and shuttle buses. In addition, there are informal discussions, pamphlets, posters, films, and lighted pathways and sidewalks.

Programs of Study: Furman awards the B.A., B.S., B.G.S., and B.M. degrees. Master's degrees also are awarded. Bachelor's degrees are awarded in BIOLOGICAL SCIENCE (biology/biological science), BUSINESS (accounting and business administration and management), COMMUNICATIONS AND THE ARTS (art, dramatic arts, English, French, German, Greek, Latin, music, music performance, music theory and composition, piano/organ, and Spanish), COMPUTER AND PHYSICAL SCIENCE (chemistry, computer science, geology, mathematics, and physics), EDUCATION (education, elementary, and music), ENGINEERING AND ENVIRONMENTAL DESIGN (pre-engineering), HEALTH PROFESSIONS (health science), SOCIAL SCIENCE (Asian/Oriental studies, economics, history, philosophy, political science/government, psychology, religion, religious music, sociology, and urban studies). Sciences, music, and psychology are the strongest programs academically. Business administration, political science, and history have the largest enrollments.

Required: To graduate, students must complete 128 credit hours, including 24 to 44 in the major, with a GPA of 2.0. Distribution requirements include 64 hours of general education courses in English composition, foreign language, religion, Western civilization, health and exercise science, natural sciences, social sciences, mathematics, and upper level humanities. Students must attend 36 cultural events before graduation.

Special: A 3-2 engineering degree is offered with Georgia Institute of Technology, Clemson, North Carolina State, and Auburn universities. Internships, study abroad in at least 15 countries, a Washington semester with an internship in a government agency or political organization, and work-study programs are offered. A B.A.-B.S. degree in biology, dual majors, interdisciplinary majors such as computer science-mathematics and computing-business, and student-designed majors are available. A general studies degree is granted in the evening division. Nondegree study and pass/fail options are possible. Furman features student/faculty research programs. There are 20 national honor societies on campus, including Phi Beta Kappa.

Faculty/Classroom: Some 74% of faculty are male; 26%, female. All teach undergraduates. No introductory courses are taught by graduate students. The average class size in an introductory lecture is 20; in a laboratory, 15; and in a regular course offering, 20.

Admissions: About 90% of the 1993–94 applicants were accepted. The SAT scores for the 1993–94 freshman class were as follows: Verbal—39% below 500, 38% between 500 and 599, 19% between 600 and 700, and 4% above 700; Math—16% below 500, 40% between 500 and 599, 33% between 600 and 700, and 11% above 700. The ACT scores were 7% below 21, 25% between 21 and 23,

36% between 24 and 26, 14% between 27 and 28, and 18% above 28. About 57% of the current freshmen were in the top fifth of their class; 71% were in the top two fifths. There were 31 National Merit finalists and 45 semifinalists. About 38 freshmen graduated first in their class.

Requirements: The SAT I or ACT is required. Applicants must be high school graduates or hold a GED. Students should have earned 20 units in high school, including 4 of English, 3 each of history, mathematics, and science, and 2 each of social studies and foreign language. An essay is required. A portfolio or an audition, where appropriate, is recommended. AP credits are accepted. Important factors used in the admissions decision are advanced placement or honor courses, evidence of special talent, parents or siblings attending the school, geographic diversity, and recommendations by school officials.

Procedure: Freshmen are admitted in the fall. Early decision applications should be filed by December 1; regular applications, by February 1 for fall entry, December 1 for winter entry, and February 1 for spring and summer entry, along with an application fee of $25. Notification of early decision is sent January 1; regular decision, March 15. There are early decision and early admissions plans. About 367 early decision candidates were accepted for the 1993–94 class. A waiting list is an active part of the admissions procedure.

Transfer: About 46 transfer students enrolled in 1993–94. Transfer students should complete at least 1 year elsewhere before seeking admission. Admission is competitive. A total of 96 credits out of 128 must be completed at Furman.

Visiting: There are guides for informal visits and visitors may sit in on classes and stay overnight at the school. To arrange for a visit, contact the Admissions Office at (803) 294-2034.

Financial Aid: In 1993–94, 56% of all current freshmen and 70% of continuing students received some form of financial aid. About 47% of freshmen and 68% of continuing students received need-based aid. The average freshman award was $8500. Of that total, scholarships or need-based grants averaged $4500 ($16,557 maximum); loans averaged $2000 ($4000 maximum); and work contracts averaged $1500 ($2000 maximum). About 53% percent of undergraduate students work part-time. Average earnings from campus work for the school year are $1200. The average financial indebtedness of the 1992–93 graduate was $7700. Furman is a member of CSS. The FAF, the college's own financial statement, and FAFSA is required. The deadline for financial aid applications is February 1.

International Students: There are currently 34 international students enrolled. They must take the TOEFL and achieve a minimum score of 570. The student must also take the SAT I or the ACT.

Computers: The college provides computer facilities for student use. The mainframe is an HP 3000/Series 957. There are 7 laboratories on campus containing a total of 80 HP Vectra personal computers. The computer science laboratory has 25 Apple Macintosh computers; other departments have their own computer laboratories. From all laboratories, students have access to the campus network including the library and the Internet. All students may access the system. It may be used 8 A.M. to 11 P.M. daily. There are no time limits on using the system and no fees.

Graduates: In 1992–93, 561 bachelor's degrees were awarded. The most popular majors among graduates were political science (10%), business administration (10%), and education (8%). Within an average freshman class, 1% graduate in 3 years, 82% graduate in 4 years and 84% in 5 years. Some 77 companies recruited on campus in 1992–93. In the 1992 graduating class, 40% of all graduates were enrolled in graduate school within 6 months of graduation; 47% of the men and 54% of the women had found employment.

Admissions Contact: J. Carey Thompson, Director of Admissions.

LANDER COLLEGE
(See Lander University)

LANDER UNIVERSITY   B-2
(Formerly Lander College)
Greenwood, SC 29649   (803) 229–8307; (800) 768–3600 (in-state)

Full-time: 736 men, 1339 women	Faculty: 122; IIB, av$
Part-time: 122 men, 366 women	Ph.D.s: 66%
Graduate: 12 men, 135 women	Student/Faculty: 17 to 1
Year: semesters, summer session	Tuition: $3220 ($4598)
Application Deadline: August 7	Room & Board: $2960
Freshman Class: 1166 applied, 1009 accepted, 510 enrolled	
SAT I: required	**LESS COMPETITIVE**

Lander University, founded in 1872, is a state-supported, coeducational institution offering undergraduate programs in liberal arts, science and mathematics, business, education, nursing, and physical education and exercise studies. In addition to regional accreditation, Lander has baccalaureate program accreditation with AACSB and NLN. The library contains 232,371 volumes, 79,146 microform items,

and 1408 audiovisual forms, and subscribes to 1067 periodicals. Computerized library sources and services include the card catalog, interlibrary loans, and database searching. Special learning facilities include a learning resource center, art gallery, and a media center. The 75-acre campus is in a small town 75 miles west of Columbia. Including residence halls, there are 37 buildings on campus.

Student Life: About 94% of undergraduates are from South Carolina. Students come from 24 states, 18 foreign countries, and Canada. Seventy-seven percent are white; 16% African American. The average age of freshmen is 20; all undergraduates, 22.

Housing: A total of 1046 students can be accommodated in college housing. College-sponsored living facilities include dormitories and on-campus apartments. On-campus housing is available on a first-come, first-served basis. Alcohol is not permitted. All students may keep cars on campus.

Activities: About 20% of men belong to 5 national fraternities; about 30% of women belong to 6 national sororities. There are 45 groups on campus, including art, band, cheerleading, choir, chorale, chorus, computers, dance, drama, honors, international, jazz band, literary magazine, musical theater, newspaper, orchestra, pep band, political, professional, religious, social, social service, and student government. Popular campus events include Autumnfest and the Greenwood Performing Arts Series.

Sports: There are 4 intercollegiate sports for men and 4 for women, and 6 intramural sports for men and 6 for women. Athletic and recreation facilities include a gymnasium, basketball courts, a weight room, a softball field, tennis courts, an indoor pool, and an indoor suspended track.

Disabled Students: Ninety percent of the campus is accessible to disabled students. The following facilities are available: wheelchair ramps, elevators, special parking, specially equipped rest rooms, special class scheduling, lowered drinking fountains, and lowered telephones.

Services: In addition to many counseling and information services, tutoring is available in most subjects. There is also a reader service for the blind, and remedial math, reading, and writing.

Campus Safety and Security: Campus safety and security measures include escort service, emergency telephones, and lighted pathways and sidewalks.

Programs of Study: Lander awards the B.A., B.S., and B.M.Ed. degrees. Master's degrees also are awarded. Bachelor's degrees are awarded in BIOLOGICAL SCIENCE (biology/biological science), COMMUNICATIONS AND THE ARTS (dramatic arts, English, music, speech/debate/rhetoric, and visual and performing arts), COMPUTER AND PHYSICAL SCIENCE (chemistry, computer science, and mathematics), EDUCATION (art, early childhood, elementary, music, physical, science, and special), HEALTH PROFESSIONS (medical laboratory technology, nursing, predentistry, and premedicine), SOCIAL SCIENCE (history, interdisciplinary studies, political science/government, prelaw, psychology, and sociology). Premedical and dual engineering are the strongest academically. Business administration, education, and sciences have the largest enrollments.

Required: To graduate, students must complete 125 semester hours, including 36 in the major, with a minimum GPA of 2.0.

Special: Lander offers internships, co-op and work-study programs, accelerated degrees, B.A.-B.S. degrees, a dual engineering degree with Clemson University, student-designed majors in interdisciplinary studies, credit for military experience, and nondegree study. Students in the Honors International Program study abroad in England for one semester during their sophomore year. There is a freshman honors program on campus, as well as 6 national honor societies.

Faculty/Classroom: Fifty-seven percent of faculty are male; 43%, female. Ninety-six percent teach undergraduates, and 53% both teach and do research. The average class size in a regular course offering is 20.

Admissions: About 87% of the 1993–94 applicants were accepted. Four freshmen graduated first in their class.

Requirements: Lander requires applicants to be in the upper 50% of their class. The SAT I is required. Applicants must be high school graduates with 20 credits, including 4 of English; 3 of mathematics; 2 each of laboratory science, foreign language, and social studies; and 1 each of American history and physical education. An interview and a portfolio or an audition, if appropriate, are recommended. AP and CLEP credits are accepted.

Procedure: Freshmen are admitted to all sessions. Entrance exams should be taken in the junior year. Applications should be filed by August 7 for fall entry and December 8 for spring entry, along with an application fee of $15. Notification is sent on a rolling basis. There are early decision, early admissions, and deferred admissions plans.

Transfer: A total of 202 transfer students enrolled in a recent year. Applicants must have a minimum college GPA of 2.0. Others may be considered on the strength of military or work experience. Transcripts from every school attended should be submitted. Students under 21 with fewer than 30 semester credits must submit high school tran-

scripts and SAT I or ACT results as well. An interview is recommended. At least 30 credits out of 125 must be completed at Lander.

Visiting: There are regularly scheduled orientations for prospective students. There are guides for informal visits, and visitors may sit in on classes. To arrange for a visit, contact the Admissions Office at (803) 229–8307 or (800) 768–3600 (in-state).

Financial Aid: In 1993–94, 53% of all current freshmen and 58% of continuing students received some form of financial aid. About 42% of freshmen and 51% of continuing students received need-based aid. The average freshman award was $4851. Of that total, scholarships or need-based grants averaged $1911 ($3220 maximum); loans averaged $2040 ($2625 maximum); and work contracts averaged $900 ($2000 maximum). Twelve percent of undergraduate students work part-time. Average earnings from campus work for the school year are $900. The average financial indebtedness of the 1992–93 graduate was $8800. Lander is a member of CSS. The FAFSA financial statement is required. The deadline for financial aid applications is April 15.

International Students: There are currently 37 international students enrolled. The school actively recruits these students. They must take the TOEFL and achieve a minimum score of 550 and must also take the SAT I or the ACT.

Computers: The college provides computer facilities for student use. The mainframe is an IBM AS/400. A cluster of networked terminals passes through to the mainframe at Clemson University. Laboratories available for general academic use have 26 networked terminals and 120 stand-alone microcomputers. Students may use the mainframe only if their course requires it. It may be used from 8 A.M. to 11 P.M. There are no time limits on using the system. The fee is $10.

Graduates: In 1992–93, 367 bachelor's degrees were awarded. The most popular majors among graduates were business administration (25%), elementary and early childhood education (14%), and art (8%). Some 60 companies recruited on campus in 1992–93.

Admissions Contact: Director of Admissions.

LIMESTONE COLLEGE
B-1

Gaffney, SC 29340   (803) 489–7151; (800) 795–7151 (out-of-state)

Full-time: 169 men, 141 women	Faculty: 28; IIB, --$
Part-time: 7 men, 7 women	Ph.D.s: 44%
Graduate: none	Student/Faculty: 11 to 1
Year: semesters, summer session	Tuition: $7200
Application Deadline: open	Room & Board: $3500
Freshman Class: 424 applied, 313 accepted, 136 enrolled	
SAT I Verbal/Math: 420/380	ACT: 19 **LESS COMPETITIVE**

Limestone College, founded in 1845, is an independent, coeducational institution offering programs in liberal arts, business, and teacher preparation. In addition to regional accreditation, the college has baccalaureate program accreditation with NASM. The library contains 91,804 volumes, 731 microform items, and 5012 audiovisual forms, and subscribes to 533 periodicals. Computerized library sources and services include the card catalog, interlibrary loans, and database searching. Special learning facilities include a learning resource center and planetarium. The 115-acre campus is in an urban area 45 miles south of Charlotte, North Carolina. Including residence halls, there are 15 buildings on campus.

Student Life: About 60% of undergraduates are from South Carolina. Students come from 20 states, 5 foreign countries, and Canada. Ninety percent are from public schools; 10% from private. Seventy-eight percent are white; 20% African American. The average age of freshmen is 18; all undergraduates, 20.

Housing: A total of 350 students can be accommodated in college housing. College-sponsored living facilities include single-sex dormitories. On-campus housing is guaranteed for all 4 years. Priority is given to out-of-town students. Seventy-five percent of students live on campus. Alcohol is not permitted. All students may keep cars on campus.

Activities: About 40% of men belong to 2 local fraternities; about 30% of women belong to 3 local sororities. There are 17 groups on campus, including art, band, cheerleading, choir, chorus, computers, drama, ethnic, honors, jazz band, literary magazine, newspaper, pep band, religious, social, social service, student government, and yearbook. Popular campus events include May Day, Christmas Luminaries, Field Day, and Luau.

Sports: Athletic and recreation facilities include an 1800-seat gymnasium, a health club, an indoor pool, a track, lighted tennis courts, a racquetball court, and baseball, softball, soccer, and lacrosse fields.

Disabled Students: Seventy-five percent of the campus is accessible to disabled students. The following facilities are available: wheelchair ramps, elevators, special parking, and specially equipped rest rooms.

Services: In addition to many counseling and information services, tutoring is available in some subjects. There is also remedial math, reading, and writing.

Campus Safety and Security: Campus safety and security measures include 24-hour foot and vehicle patrol and lighted pathways and sidewalks.

Programs of Study: The college awards the B.A. and B.S. degrees. Bachelor's degrees are awarded in BIOLOGICAL SCIENCE (biology/biological science), BUSINESS (business administration and management), COMMUNICATIONS AND THE ARTS (English, fine arts, music, and studio art), COMPUTER AND PHYSICAL SCIENCE (chemistry, computer science, and mathematics), EDUCATION (art, early childhood, elementary, music, and science), HEALTH PROFESSIONS (predentistry and premedicine), SOCIAL SCIENCE (history, human services, physical fitness/movement, prelaw, psychology, social studies, and social work). Music and education are the strongest academically. Business administration has the largest enrollment.

Required: To graduate, students must complete 120 semester hours with 30 to 48 hours in the major and a minimum GPA of 2.0. The required core curriculum includes 9 hours of social sciences; 8 of laboratory sciences; 6 of history; 3 each of religion/philosophy, English composition, literature, fine arts, mathematics, and computer science; 2 of physical education; and 1 of life skills.

Special: The college offers internships in social work, counseling, teacher education, and athletic training, as well as a work-study program and off-campus evening courses. Students may have divisional and multidisciplinary dual majors. The college confers a general studies degree and grants credit for life, military, and work experience. There is a freshman honors program on campus, as well as one national honor society. Five departments have honors programs.

Faculty/Classroom: Seventy percent of faculty are male; 30%, female. The average class size in an introductory lecture is 12; in a laboratory, 15; and in a regular course offering, 12.

Admissions: About 74% of the 1993–94 applicants were accepted.

Requirements: The college requires applicants to be in the upper 50% of their class. The SAT I is required, with a minimum composite score of 700. Applicants must be high school graduates with a minimum GPA of 2.0. The GED is accepted. The college recommends that students present 4 units of English, 3 of mathematics, and 2 each of laboratory science and social science. An interview is recommended. AP and CLEP credits are accepted. Important factors used in the admissions decision are advanced placement or honor courses, leadership record, evidence of special talent, extracurricular activities record, and recommendations by school officials.

Procedure: Freshmen are admitted in the fall and spring. Entrance exams should be taken during the fall of the senior year of high school. Application deadlines are open. Notification is sent on a rolling basis. The application fee is $15. There is a deferred admissions plan.

Transfer: A total of 32 transfer students enrolled in 1993–94. Applicants must have 30 hours of college credit with a minimum GPA of 2.0, and must be in good standing at their previous school. At least 30 credits out of 120 must be completed at the college.

Visiting: There are regularly scheduled orientations for prospective students. There are guides for informal visits, and visitors may sit in on classes and stay overnight at the school. To arrange for a visit, contact the Admissions Office at (803) 489–7151 or (800) 795–7151 (out-of-state).

Financial Aid: In 1993–94, 98% of all current freshmen and 90% of continuing students received some form of financial aid. Scholarships or need-based grants averaged $1675; loans averaged $1586; and work contracts averaged $1000. the college is a member of CSS. The FAF, FFS, or SFS is required.

International Students: There are currently 9 international students enrolled. They must take the TOEFL and achieve a minimum score of 500 and must also take the SAT I, with a minimum score of 700, or the ACT.

Computers: The college provides computer facilities for student use. The mainframe is a DEC VAX 11/7580. There are also IBM and Samsung PCs available in computer laboratories. All students may access the system from 8 A.M. to 11 P.M., Monday through Friday; 3 P.M. to 11 P.M. Sunday. There are no time limits on using the system and no fees.

Graduates: In a recent year, 178 bachelor's degrees were awarded.

Admissions Contact: Sherri R. Horton, Director of Admissions.

MORRIS COLLEGE
D-3

Sumter, SC 29150–3599   (803) 775–9371

Full-time: 329 men, 597 women	Faculty: 46; IIB, --$
Part-time: 5 men, 7 women	Ph.D.s: 50%
Graduate: none	Student/Faculty: 20 to 1
Year: semesters, summer session	Tuition: $4405
Application Deadline: open	Room & Board: $2475
Freshman Class: 882 applied, 730 accepted, 330 enrolled	
SAT I or ACT: recommended	**LESS COMPETITIVE**

Morris College, founded in 1908, is a private, coeducational liberal arts institution affiliated with the Baptist Church. The college offers

majors in biology, business administration, health, criminal justice, education, English, fine arts, history, liberal studies, and sociology. The library contains 90,610 volumes, 136,633 microform items, and 2116 audiovisual forms, and subscribes to 697 periodicals. Computerized library sources and services include the card catalog, interlibrary loans, and database searching. Special learning facilities include a learning resource center and radio station. The 34-acre campus is in a small town 40 miles east of Columbia. Including residence halls, there are 16 buildings on campus.

Student Life: About 91% of undergraduates are from South Carolina. Students come from 19 states. Ninety-eight percent are from public schools; 2% from private. Almost all are African American. The average age of freshmen is 18.6; all undergraduates, 21.5. Forty-three percent drop out by the end of their first year; 40% remain to graduate.

Housing: A total of 583 students can be accommodated in college housing. College-sponsored living facilities include single-sex dormitories. On-campus housing is guaranteed for the freshman year only. Seventy-four percent of students live on campus; of those, 50% remain on campus on weekends. Alcohol is not permitted. Upperclassmen may keep cars on campus.

Activities: About 5% of men belong to 4 national fraternities; about 5% of women belong to 4 national sororities. There are 33 groups on campus, including cheerleading, chess, choir, chorale, dance, drama, honors, literary magazine, newspaper, photography, professional, radio and TV, religious, social, social service, student government, and yearbook. Popular campus events include Coronation of Miss Morris College, Christmas and gospel choir concerts, Martin Luther King Observance, Black History Month Celebration, American Education Week, Constitution Day, Fine Arts Festival, and Science in Action Week.

Sports: There are 3 intercollegiate sports for men and 3 for women, and 5 intramural sports for men and 5 for women. Athletic and recreation facilities include a weight room, an athletic field complex, a 1700-seat gymnasium, and a 600-seat auditorium.

Disabled Students: Two percent of the campus is accessible to disabled students. The following facilities are available: wheelchair ramps, elevators, special parking, specially equipped rest rooms, and lowered drinking fountains.

Services: In addition to many counseling and information services, tutoring is available in every subject. In addition, there is remedial math, reading, and writing.

Campus Safety and Security: Campus safety and security measures include 24-hour foot and vehicle patrol, informal discussions, and lighted pathways and sidewalks.

Programs of Study: Morris awards the B.A., B.S., B.F.A., and B.S.Ed. degrees. Bachelor's degrees are awarded in BIOLOGICAL SCIENCE (biology/biological science), BUSINESS (business administration and management and recreation and leisure services), COMMUNICATIONS AND THE ARTS (English and fine arts), COMPUTER AND PHYSICAL SCIENCE (mathematics), EDUCATION (early childhood, elementary, English, mathematics, and social studies), HEALTH PROFESSIONS (community health work), SOCIAL SCIENCE (criminal justice, history, political science/government, religious education, social studies, and sociology). English, mathematics, and biology are the strongest academically. Business administration, biology, and elementary education have the largest enrollments.

Required: All students must complete 124 to 141 credit hours with a minimum 2.0 GPA. General education requirements, with a core curriculum of 21 to 51 credits, include 12 to 15 in English, 12 in social sciences, 8 in natural sciences, 6 in religion, 3 to 9 in mathematics, 4 in fine arts, 2 to 3 each in philosophy and speech, and 2 each in education and health education. A comprehensive examination in the major is required prior to graduation.

Special: Internships, co-op programs, and work-study programs are offered. B.A.-B.S. degrees are available. Credit by examination and credit for military experience are possible. There is a freshman honors program on campus, as well as one national honor society. One department has an honors program.

Faculty/Classroom: Sixty-one percent of faculty are male; 39%, female. All teach undergraduates. The average class size in an introductory lecture is 35; in a laboratory, 25; and in a regular course offering, 25.

Admissions: About 83% of the 1993–94 applicants were accepted. About 6% of the current freshmen were in the top fifth of their class; 26% were in the top two fifths.

Requirements: The SAT I or ACT is recommended. In addition, candidates should be graduates of an accredited secondary school or have the GED. They must have completed 20 Carnegie units, consisting of 4 in high school English, 2 each in natural and social sciences, 3 in mathematics, 1 in U.S. history, 1 in physical education, and 7 in electives. CLEP credit is accepted.

Procedure: Freshmen are admitted to all sessions. Application deadlines are open. The application fee is $10. Notification is sent on a rolling basis.

Transfer: Sixty-three transfer students enrolled in 1993–94. Applicants must submit transcripts and evidence of honorable release. A minimum GPA of 2.0 is required. At least 30 credits out of 124 must be completed at Morris.

Visiting: There are regularly scheduled orientations for prospective students, consisting of a campus tour, visits with division chairs and faculty members to discuss majors, scheduled activities, and lunch. There are guides for informal visits. To arrange for a visit, contact Queen W. Spann at (803) 775–9371, ext. 225.

Financial Aid: In 1993–94, 95% of all current freshmen and 93% of continuing students received some form of financial aid. About 95% of freshmen and 93% of continuing students received need-based aid. The average freshman award was $6500. Of that total, scholarships or need-based grants averaged $1000 ($4000 maximum); loans averaged $1700 ($2625 maximum); and work contracts averaged $1200 ($1800 maximum). Forty percent of undergraduate students work part-time. Average earnings from campus work for the school year are $1500. The average financial indebtedness of the 1992–93 graduate was $7000. Morris is a member of CSS. The FAF is required. The deadline for financial aid applications is April 30.

International Students: They must take the TOEFL.

Computers: The college provides computer facilities for student use. The mainframe is a DEC VAX 11/750. Some 121 terminals and microcomputers are located in the media center, science building, and various other locations. Students who take computer-related courses may access the system 78 hours per week. There are no time limits on using the system. The fee is $25 to $40.

Graduates: In 1992–93, 130 bachelor's degrees were awarded. The most popular majors among graduates were business administration (25%), sociology (19%), and liberal studies (12%). Within an average freshman class, 20% graduate in 4 years, 20% in 5 years, and 2% in 6 years. Some 67 companies recruited on campus in 1992–93. In the 1992 graduating class, 3% of the men and 4% of the women were enrolled in graduate school within 6 months of graduation; 14% of the men and 33% of the women had found employment.

Admissions Contact: Queen W. Spann, Director of Admissions and Records.

NEWBERRY COLLEGE   B-2
Newberry, SC 29108   (803) 321–5131; (800) 845–4955 (out-of-state)

Full-time: 315 men, 300 women	Faculty: 43; IIB, --$
Part-time: 13 men, 23 women	Ph.D.s: 60%
Graduate: none	Student/Faculty: 14 to 1
Year: semesters, summer session	Tuition: $8894
Application Deadline: open	Room & Board: $3100
Freshman Class: 872 applied, 701 accepted, 199 enrolled	
SAT I Verbal/Math: 431/452	ACT: 21 LESS COMPETITIVE

Newberry College, founded in 1856, is a private, coeducational institution affiliated with the Evangelical Lutheran Church in America. In addition to regional accreditation, Newberry has baccalaureate program accreditation with NASM and NCATE. The library contains 80,000 volumes, and subscribes to 359 periodicals. Computerized library sources and services include interlibrary loans and database searching. Special learning facilities include a TV station. The 60-acre campus is in a small town 40 miles northwest of Columbia. Including residence halls, there are 21 buildings on campus.

Student Life: About 85% of undergraduates are from South Carolina. Students come from 15 states and 1 foreign country. About 90% are from public schools; 10% from private. Some 82% are white; 17%, African American. Most are Protestant. The average age of freshmen is 18; all undergraduates, 20. Some 27% drop out by the end of their first year; 42% remain to graduate.

Housing: A total of 450 students can be accommodated in college housing. College-sponsored living facilities include single-sex and coed dormitories. On-campus housing is guaranteed for the freshman year only. About 65% of students live on campus; of those, 65% remain on campus on weekends. All students may keep cars on campus.

Activities: About 33% of men belong to 5 national fraternities; about 34% of women belong to 2 national sororities. There are 40 groups on campus, including band, cheerleading, choir, chorale, drama, jazz band, literary magazine, marching band, newspaper, pep band, professional, religious, social, student government, and yearbook.

Sports: There are 4 intercollegiate sports for men and 3 for women, and 6 intramural sports for men and 5 for women. Athletic and recreation facilities include a 7000-seat stadium, a physical education complex, a gymnasium, a pool, playing fields, and tennis courts.

Disabled Students: About 90% of the campus is accessible to disabled students. The following facilities are available: wheelchair ramps, elevators, special parking, specially equipped rest rooms, and special class scheduling.

Services: In addition to many counseling and information services, tutoring is available in every subject.

Campus Safety and Security: Campus safety and security measures include 24-hour foot and vehicle patrol.

Programs of Study: Newberry awards the B.A. and B.S. degrees. Bachelor's degrees are awarded in BIOLOGICAL SCIENCE (biology/biological science), BUSINESS (accounting and business administration and management), COMMUNICATIONS AND THE ARTS (dramatic arts, English, French, music, and Spanish), COMPUTER AND PHYSICAL SCIENCE (chemistry, computer science, and mathematics), EDUCATION (early childhood, elementary, and music), HEALTH PROFESSIONS (predentistry and premedicine), SOCIAL SCIENCE (economics, history, philosophy, political science/government, prelaw, religion, and sociology). Business administration has the largest enrollment.

Required: To graduate, students must complete 126 semester hours, with a minimum GPA of 2.0 overall and in the major. Distribution requirements include courses in communication skills, foreign language, mathematics, religion, humanities, natural science, social science, and physical education. There is also a 24-event fine arts and lectures requirement.

Special: Internships, dual majors, B.A.-B.S. degrees, study abroad, work-study programs, independent study, and cooperative education are offered. A 3-2 engineering degree program with Georgia Institute of Technology and Clemson University and a 3-2 forestry program with Duke University are available. Nondegree study is possible.

Faculty/Classroom: Some 76% of faculty are male; 24%, female. The average class size in an introductory lecture is 30; in a laboratory, 30; and in a regular course offering, 25.

Admissions: About 80% of the 1993-94 applicants were accepted. The SAT scores for the 1993-94 freshman class were as follows: Verbal—61% below 500, 22% between 500 and 599, 12% between 600 and 700, and 5% above 700; Math—57% below 500, 27% between 500 and 599, 14% between 600 and 700, and 2% above 700. The ACT scores were 67% below 21, 17% between 21 and 23, 10% between 24 and 26, 4% between 27 and 28, and 2% above 28. About 21% of the current freshmen were in the top fifth of their class; 52% were in the top two fifths.

Requirements: The SAT I or ACT is required. Applicants should have completed 18 high school academic units. The GED is accepted. An essay is recommended. AP and CLEP credits are accepted.

Procedure: Freshmen are admitted to all sessions. Entrance exams should be taken as early as possible in the spring of the junior year or the fall of the senior year. Application deadlines are open. The application fee is $15. Notification is sent on a rolling basis. There are early decision and early admissions plans.

Transfer: About 50 transfer students enrolled in a recent year. Transfer applicants must be eligible to return to their previous school. A 2.0 GPA is recommended. A total of 30 credits out of 126 must be completed at Newberry.

Visiting: There are guides for informal visits, and visitors may sit in on classes and stay overnight at the school. To arrange for a visit, contact the Admissions Office at (800) 845-4955.

Financial Aid: In a recent year, 90% of all students received some form of financial aid. The average freshman award was $5000. About 25% of undergraduate students work part-time. Average earnings from campus work for the school year are $600. Newberry is a member of CSS. The FAF and the college's own financial statement are required. The deadline for financial aid applications is June 1.

International Students: The school actively recruits these students. They must take the TOEFL.

Computers: The college provides computer facilities for student use. The mainframe is an IBM System/36 for administration use. There are 4 PCs, and word processing equipment is available for student use. There are no time limits on using the system. The fees are $50.

Graduates: In an earlier year, 100 bachelor's degrees were awarded.

Admissions Contact: John Ryder, Director of Admissions.

PRESBYTERIAN COLLEGE

	B-2
Clinton, SC 29325	(803) 833-8230; (800) 476-7272 (in-state)
Full-time: 581 men, 582 women	Faculty: 75; IIB, av$
Part-time: 8 men, 9 women	Ph.D.s: 90%
Graduate: none	Student/Faculty: 16 to 1
Year: semesters, summer session	Tuition: $11,984
Application Deadline: open	Room & Board: $3416
Freshman Class: 1083 applied, 831 accepted, 302 enrolled	
SAT I Verbal/Math: 530/570	ACT: 27 VERY COMPETITIVE

Presbyterian College, founded in 1880, is a private, coeducational liberal arts institution affiliated with the Presbyterian Church (USA). In addition to regional accreditation, PC has baccalaureate program accreditation with AACSB. The library contains 140,000 volumes and 2500 audiovisual forms, and subscribes to 750 periodicals. Computerized library sources and services include interlibrary loans and database searching. Special learning facilities include a learning re-

source center, art gallery, and radio station. The 212-acre campus is in a small town 40 miles south of Greenville. Including residence halls, there are 41 buildings on campus.

Student Life: About 51% of undergraduates are from South Carolina. Students come from 30 states and 8 foreign countries. Sixty percent are from public schools; 40% from private. Ninety-three percent are white. Most are Protestant. The average age of freshmen is 18; all undergraduates, 19. Ten percent drop out by the end of their first year; 79% remain to graduate.

Housing: A total of 1008 students can be accommodated in college housing. College-sponsored living facilities include single-sex dormitories, off-campus apartments, married-student housing, and fraternity houses. On-campus housing is guaranteed for all 4 years. Eighty-eight percent of students live on campus; of those, 75% remain on campus on weekends. All students may keep cars on campus.

Activities: About 44% of men belong to 6 national fraternities; about 41% of women belong to 3 national sororities. There are 30 groups on campus, including art, band, cheerleading, chess, choir, chorale, computers, drama, drill team, ethnic, honors, international, jazz band, literary magazine, newspaper, pep band, photography, political, professional, radio and TV, religious, social, social service, student government, and yearbook. Popular campus events include Spring Fling, Arnold Symposium, Shagfest, Black History Month, Fall Fling, Greek Day, and Band Blast.

Sports: There are 7 intercollegiate sports for men and 4 for women, and 8 intramural sports for men and 8 for women. Athletic and recreation facilities include a 5,000-seat football stadium, baseball, soccer, and intramural fields, tennis courts, weight rooms, a sauna, a basketball arena, a 3000-seat gymnasium, an outdoor amphitheater, a lighted running trail, an indoor swimming pool, table tennis and pool tables, and an intramural park with a driving range and putting green.

Disabled Students: Ninety percent of the campus is accessible to disabled students. The following facilities are available: wheelchair ramps, elevators, special parking, specially equipped rest rooms, special class scheduling, and lowered drinking fountains.

Services: In addition to many counseling and information services, tutoring is available in every subject. There is a reader service for the blind.

Campus Safety and Security: Campus safety and security measures include 24-hour foot and vehicle patrol, escort service, shuttle buses, and informal discussions. In addition, there are pamphlets, posters, films, emergency telephones, lighted pathways and sidewalks, and key-card dormitory locks.

Programs of Study: PC awards the B.A. and B.S degrees. Bachelor's degrees are awarded in BIOLOGICAL SCIENCE (biology/biological science), BUSINESS (accounting and business administration and management), COMMUNICATIONS AND THE ARTS (dramatic arts, English, fine arts, French, German, languages, music, Spanish, and visual and performing arts), COMPUTER AND PHYSICAL SCIENCE (chemistry, mathematics, and physics), EDUCATION (elementary, music, secondary, and special), SOCIAL SCIENCE (economics, history, political science/government, psychology, religion, social science, and sociology). Business, psychology, biology, economics, and English have the largest enrollments.

Required: To graduate, students must complete a minimum of 122 semester hours, including 24 to 48 in the major, with a minimum GPA of 2.0. General education requirements of 46 to 55 credits include 8 hours of laboratory science; 16 hours of foreign language; 6 each of religion, English, world history, and social science; 3 to 4 of mathematics; 3 of fine arts; and 2 of physical education.

Special: Educational internships, study abroad, and a Washington semester are available. Dual majors, accelerated degree programs, B.A.-B.S. degrees, and a 3-2 engineering degree with Auburn, Clemson, Vanderbilt, and Mercer universities are offered. Credit for life, military, or work experience, auditing courses, and pass/fail options are possible. There is a freshman honors program on campus, as well as 8 national honor societies. All departments have honors programs.

Faculty/Classroom: Eighty percent of faculty are male; 20%, female. All teach undergraduates, and 50% both teach and do research. The average class size in an introductory lecture is 16; in a laboratory, 16; and in a regular course offering, 16.

Admissions: About 77% of the 1993-94 applicants were accepted. The SAT scores for the 1993-94 freshman class were as follows: Verbal—30% below 500, 48% between 500 and 599, 18% between 600 and 700, and 4% above 700; Math—10% below 500, 57% between 500 and 599, 26% between 600 and 700, and 7% above 700. The ACT scores were 10% below 21, 16% between 21 and 23, 40% between 24 and 26, 22% between 27 and 28, and 12% above 28. About 68% of the current freshmen were in the top fifth of their class; 94% were in the top two fifths. There were 8 National Merit finalists and 32 semifinalists. About 25 freshmen graduated first in their class.

Requirements: A minimum GPA of 2.3 is required. The SAT I or ACT is required. In addition, applicants must be graduates of an accredited secondary school. The GED is accepted. Applicants should have completed 18 academic credits, including 4 years of high

school English; 3 years of mathematics; and 2 or more years each of foreign language, history, science, and social studies. An essay is required. For music scholarships, an audition is necessary. AP and CLEP credits are accepted. Important factors used in the admissions decision are advanced placement or honor courses, recommendations by school officials, extracurricular activities record, evidence of special talent, and personality and intangible qualities.

Procedure: Freshmen are admitted to all sessions. Entrance exams should be taken during the spring of the junior year. Application deadlines are open. Notification is sent on a rolling basis. The application fee is $30. There are early admissions and deferred admissions plans.

Transfer: Twenty-two transfer students enrolled in 1993–94. Transfer applicants must have a minimum GPA of 2.5. At least 57 credits out of 122 must be completed at PC.

Visiting: There are regularly scheduled orientations for prospective students, including academic, activity, and financial aid information sessions; tours; and lunch. There are guides for informal visits, and visitors may sit in on classes and stay overnight at the school. To arrange for a visit, contact the Office of Admissions at (803) 833–8230 or (800) 476–7272 (in-state).

Financial Aid: In 1993–94, 78% of all current freshmen and 75% of continuing students received some form of financial aid. About 43% of freshmen and 42% of continuing students received need-based aid. The average freshman award was $8119. Of that total, scholarships or need-based grants averaged $8000; loans averaged $2876 ($3000 maximum); and work contracts averaged $800 ($1000 maximum). Twenty-five percent of undergraduate students work part-time. Average earnings from campus work for the school year are $900. The average financial indebtedness of the 1992–93 graduate was $12,000. PC is a member of CSS. The college's own financial statement and FAFSA are required. The deadline for financial aid applications is March 1.

International Students: There are currently 8 international students enrolled. They must take the TOEFL and achieve a minimum score of 550.

Computers: The college provides computer facilities for student use. The mainframes are a Prime 2755 and a Data General Aviion. There are 100 microcomputers in 3 laboratories, including IBM and Apple Macintosh units. Software and printers, including laser printers, are available. Computer assistance is provided during open hours. All academic buildings, classrooms, laboratories, and faculty offices are networked through the Internet/BitNet and other national and international networks. All students may access the system from 7 A.M. to 12 A.M. weekdays and from 1 P.M. to 12 A.M. weekends. There are no time limits on using the system and no fees.

Graduates: In a recent year, 230 bachelor's degrees were awarded. The most popular majors among graduates were economics/business administration (30%), biology (13%), and English (11%). Within an average freshman class, 78% graduate in 4 years and 79% in 5 years. Some 45 companies recruited on campus in 1992–93. In the 1992 graduating class, 40% of all students were enrolled in graduate school within 6 months of graduation; 85% had found employment.

Admissions Contact: Margaret Williamson, Vice President for Enrollment and Dean of Admissions.

SOUTH CAROLINA STATE COLLEGE
(See South Carolina State University)

SOUTH CAROLINA STATE UNIVERSITY
(Formerly South Carolina State College)
Orangeburg, SC 29117

C-3

(803) 536–7185

Full-time: 1810 men, 2343 women	Faculty: IIB, -$
Part-time: 134 men, 339 women	Ph.D.s: n/av
Graduate: 123 men, 322 women	Student/Faculty: n/av
Year: semesters, summer session	Tuition: $2500 ($4980)
Application Deadline: July 31	Room & Board: $2924
Freshman Class: n/av	
SAT I Verbal/Math: 340/384	ACT: 17 **LESS COMPETITIVE**

South Carolina State University, an historically black, land-grant institution founded in 1895, offers undergraduate programs in liberal arts and sciences, business, education, engineering technology, and human sciences. There are 5 undergraduate schools and one graduate school. In addition to regional accreditation, SCSU has baccalaureate program accreditation with NCATE. The library contains 245,692 volumes and 395,569 microform items, and subscribes to 1032 periodicals. Computerized library sources and services include the card catalog, interlibrary loans, and database searching. Special learning facilities include a planetarium, radio station, and an instructional media center. The 160-acre campus is in a small town 40 miles east of Columbia. Including residence halls, there are 60 buildings on campus.

Student Life: About 94% of undergraduates are from South Carolina. Nearly 95% are African American. The average age of freshmen is 18; all undergraduates, 19. Some 22% drop out by the end of their first year; 32% remain to graduate.

Housing: College-sponsored living facilities include single-sex dormitories and married-student housing. On-campus housing is available on a first-come, first-served basis. About 80% of students live on campus. Alcohol is not permitted. All students may keep cars on campus.

Activities: There are 4 national fraternities and 4 national sororities. There are many groups and organizations on campus, including chorus, dance, jazz band, marching band, newspaper, orchestra, pep band, religious, social, social service, student government, and yearbook. Popular campus events include Colloquium Series, game nights, Halloween Haunt, and Leadership Training.

Sports: There are 8 intercollegiate sports for men and 4 for women, and 8 intramural sports for men and 7 for women. Athletic and recreation facilities include a student center with a game room and bowling alley, a gymnasium, tennis courts, and a 12,000-seat stadium.

Disabled Students: About 60% of the campus is accessible to disabled students. The following facilities are available: wheelchair ramps, elevators, special parking, specially equipped rest rooms, lowered drinking fountains, and lowered telephones.

Services: Free counseling, tutoring, and remedial instruction in mathematics, reading, and writing are available.

Campus Safety and Security: Campus safety and security measures include 24-hour foot and vehicle patrol, lighted pathways and sidewalks, and a campus police department with 25 safety and security officers.

Programs of Study: SCSU awards the B.A. and B.S. degrees. Master's and doctoral degrees also are awarded. Bachelor's degrees are awarded in AGRICULTURE (agricultural business management), BIOLOGICAL SCIENCE (biology/biological science and nutrition), BUSINESS (accounting, business administration and management, business economics, marketing/retailing/merchandising, and office supervision and management), COMMUNICATIONS AND THE ARTS (dramatic arts, English, fine arts, French, music business management, and Spanish), COMPUTER AND PHYSICAL SCIENCE (chemistry, computer science, mathematics, and physics), EDUCATION (art, business, early childhood, elementary, guidance, health, home economics, industrial arts, music, physical, reading, and special), ENGINEERING AND ENVIRONMENTAL DESIGN (civil engineering, electrical/electronics engineering technology, engineering technology, and mechanical engineering technology), HEALTH PROFESSIONS (nursing and speech pathology/audiology), SOCIAL SCIENCE (criminal justice, food science, history, human services, political science/government, psychology, social studies, social work, and sociology).

Required: To graduate, all students must complete at least 128 credit hours with a minimum GPA of 2.0. Students must attend the freshman orientation program, take a general education examination in their sophomore year, satisfy the general education program requirements, and pass an English proficiency test.

Special: The college offers co-op education and work-study programs, cross-registration with Claflin College, internships, combined B.A.-B.S. degrees, credit for educational and work experience, non-degree study, and pass/fail options for juniors and seniors. Also available are an electrical engineering technology program at Midlands, Greenville, and Trident Technical colleges, an evening school program, and a program for educationally disadvantaged students who do not meet traditional entrance requirements. There is a freshman honors program on campus.

Requirements: The SAT I or ACT is required. Applicants must rank in the upper half of their graduating class at an accredited secondary school. The GED is accepted. High school preparation should include 4 units of English, 3 of mathematics, 2 each of foreign language and laboratory science, and 1 each of history, social studies, and physical education or ROTC, plus 1/2 unit each in economics and government. AP and CLEP credits are accepted.

Procedure: Freshmen are admitted in the fall and spring. Entrance exams should be taken before filing an application. Applications should be filed by July 31 for fall entry and November 20 for spring entry, along with an application fee of $10. Notification is sent within 2 weeks after completed applications have been received.

Transfer: Transfer applicants should have a college GPA of 2.0. Students with fewer than 30 credit hours must submit high school and college transcripts and SAT I or ACT scores. A total of 30 credits out of 128 must be completed at SCSU.

Visiting: There are regularly scheduled orientations for prospective students. There are guides for informal visits, and visitors may sit in on classes. To arrange for a visit, contact the Office of Enrollment Management at (803) 536–7185.

Financial Aid: SCSU is a member of CSS. The FAF is required. The deadline for financial aid applications is June 1.

International Students: Applicants must take the TOEFL and either the SAT I, or the ACT. The application deadlines are May 30 for fall entry or September 30 for the spring entry.

Computers: The mainframe is a DEC VAX 11/780. Apple Macintosh microcomputers and one-on-one tutorial assistance are available to all students at the campus writing center. There are no time limits on using the system and no fees.

Admissions Contact: Office of Enrollment Management.

THE CITADEL
Charleston, SC 29409

D-4

(803) 953-5230
(800) 868-1842 (out-of-state)

Full-time: 2000 men	Faculty: 160; IIA, -$
Part-time: none	Ph.D.s: 95%
Graduate: none	Student/Faculty: 13 to 1
Year: semesters, summer session	Tuition: $6619 ($10,618)
Application Deadline: open	Room & Board: n/app
Freshman Class: 1500 applied, 1240 accepted, 611 enrolled	
SAT I Verbal/Math: 460/520	**COMPETITIVE**

The Citadel, established in 1842 by the South Carolina legislature, is an all-male liberal arts military college supported by the state. In addition to regional accreditation, the college has baccalaureate program accreditation with ABET and NCATE. The 2 libraries contain 220,000 volumes, 762,000 microform items, and 1500 audiovisual forms, and subscribe to 1600 periodicals. Computerized library sources and services include the card catalog, interlibrary loans, and database searching. Special learning facilities include a military museum and archives. The 100-acre campus is in a suburban area in a suburban section of Charleston. Including residence halls, there are 30 buildings on campus.

Student Life: About 50% of undergraduates are from out-of-state, mostly the South. Students come from 44 states, 12 foreign countries, and Canada. Seventy percent are from public schools; 30% from private. Eighty-nine percent are white. Seventy-two percent are Protestant; 25% Catholic. The average age of freshmen is 19; all undergraduates, 21. Twenty percent drop out by the end of their first year; 69% remain to graduate.

Housing: All cadets live in barracks on campus. On-campus housing is guaranteed for all 4 years. All cadets remain on campus on weekends. Alcohol is not permitted. Upperclassmen may keep cars on campus.

Activities: There are no sororities on campus. There are many groups and organizations on campus, including bagpipe band, band, cheerleading, choir, chorale, computers, drama, drill team, ethnic, honors, literary magazine, marching band, newspaper, orchestra, pep band, political, professional, religious, social, social service, student government, and yearbook. Popular campus events include Parents Weekend, Homecoming, and Corps Day.

Sports: Athletic and recreation facilities include a 22,000-seat stadium, a 6000-seat field house, fitness centers, weight and wrestling rooms, tennis courts, an all-weather track, and playing fields. The boating center and beach club are within a half-hour drive of the college.

Disabled Students: The following facilities are available: wheelchair ramps, elevators, special parking, and specially equipped rest rooms.

Services: In addition to many counseling and information services, tutoring is available in every subject. There is also a writing center.

Campus Safety and Security: Campus safety and security measures include 24-hour foot and vehicle patrol.

Programs of Study: The college awards the B.A., B.S., B.S.B.A., B.S.C.E., and B.S.E.E. degrees. Bachelor's degrees are awarded in BIOLOGICAL SCIENCE (biology/biological science), BUSINESS (business administration and management), COMMUNICATIONS AND THE ARTS (English, French, German, and Spanish), COMPUTER AND PHYSICAL SCIENCE (chemistry, computer science, mathematics, and physics), EDUCATION (health, physical, and secondary), ENGINEERING AND ENVIRONMENTAL DESIGN (civil engineering and electrical/electronics engineering), HEALTH PROFESSIONS (predentistry and premedicine), SOCIAL SCIENCE (history, political science/government, and psychology).

Required: To graduate, students must complete 121 to 139 credit hours, depending on the major, with an overall GPA of 2.0 (2.5 for education majors). The required core curriculum for all majors includes study in 5 areas: English, history, mathematics, science, and social sciences. Specific course requirements include 8 semesters of ROTC, 4 of English, and 4 of physical education. In addition, cadets must satisfy disciplinary requirements and observe the honor system.

Special: Students may earn a combined B.A.-B.S. degree, design their own majors, and take a 3-2 program in engineering. Work-study programs, independent study, study abroad, and pass/fail options are also available. There is a freshman honors program on campus, as well as 7 national honor societies, including Phi Beta Kappa. Seven departments have honors programs.

Faculty/Classroom: Ninety-one percent of faculty are male; 9%, female. Ninety-five percent teach undergraduates. The average class size in an introductory lecture is 25 and in a regular course offering, 20.

Admissions: About 83% of the 1993–94 applicants were accepted.

Requirements: The college requires applicants to be in the upper 50% of their class. A minimum GPA of 2.0 is required. The SAT I or ACT is required. The SAT II: Subject test in mathematics, level II, is strongly recommended for engineering, science, and mathematics applicants. Also required are recommendations from high school principals or guidance counselors. Applicants must be between 16 and 22, male, and unmarried, and must meet certain physical requirements. High school preparation should include 4 units in English; 3 in mathematics, including algebra I and II; 2 in laboratory science, biology, chemistry, or physics; 2 each in foreign language and social science; 1 in physical education or ROTC; and 1 other academic unit. AP and CLEP credits are accepted. Important factors used in the admissions decision are advanced placement or honor courses, extracurricular activities record, leadership record, recommendations by school officials, and recommendations by alumni.

Procedure: Freshmen are admitted in the fall. Entrance exams should be taken by February of the senior year. Application deadlines are open; the fee is $25. Notification is sent on a rolling basis.

Transfer: Applicants must meet freshmen entrance requirements and submit official transcripts from all previous colleges attended. A full year of course work, including half the required hours in the major, must be completed at The Citadel.

Visiting: There are regularly scheduled orientations for prospective students. There are guides for informal visits and visitors may sit in on classes and stay overnight at the school. To arrange for a visit, contact the Admissions Office at (800) 868-1842.

Financial Aid: In an earlier year, 70% of all students received some form of financial aid. Scholarships or need-based grants averaged $1500; loans averaged $900; and work contracts averaged $500. Fifteen percent of undergraduate students work part-time. The college is a member of CSS. The FAF is required. The deadline for financial aid applications is February 1.

International Students: There are currently 20 international students enrolled. They must take the TOEFL and achieve a minimum score of 500.

Computers: The college provides computer facilities for student use. The mainframe is a DEC VAX. There are 2 VAX terminal laboratories and 7 Macintosh and/or IBM PS/2 laboratories, some networked and some stand-alone, open to all students 7 days a week. There are no time limits on using the system and no fees.

Graduates: In 1992–93, 342 bachelor's degrees were awarded. The most popular majors among graduates were business administration (41%), political science (17%), and history (8%). Within an average freshman class, 68% graduate in 4 years and 70% in 5 years. Some 95 companies recruited on campus in 1992–93. In the 1992 graduating class, 20% of the men were enrolled in graduate school within 6 months of graduation; 80% had found employment.

Admissions Contact: Lt. Col. Wallace I. West, Director of Admissions and Recruiting.

UNIV OF SOUTH CAROLINA COASTAL CAROLINA COLLEGE
(See Coastal Carolina University)

UNIVERSITY OF SOUTH CAROLINA

The University of South Carolina, established in 1801, is a public system in South Carolina. It is governed by a board of trustees, whose chief administrator is the president. The primary goal of the system is to prepare informed and productive citizens in order to adapt to an increasingly complex environment. The main priorities are to foster excellence in undergraduate and graduate education, research, and service programs. Four-year campuses are located in Columbia, Aiken, Conway, and Spartanburg. The total enrollment in fall 1993 of all 8 campuses was 43,027; there were 1996 faculty members. Altogether there are 142 baccalaureate, 164 master's, and 63 doctoral programs offered in University of South Carolina. Four-year campuses are located in Columbia, Aiken, Conway, and Spartanburg. Profiles of the 4-year campuses are included in this chapter in alphabetical order with other South Carolina schools.

UNIVERSITY OF SOUTH CAROLINA
Columbia, SC 29208   (803) 777-7700; (800) 868-5872 (out-of-state)   C-3

Full-time: 6267 men, 6852 women	Faculty: 1104; I, --$
Part-time: 1116 men, 1567 women	Ph.D.s: 83%
Graduate: 3990 men, 5647 women	Student/Faculty: 12 to 1
Year: semesters, summer session	Tuition: $3090 ($7808)
Application Deadline: open	Room & Board: $3068
Freshman Class: 7693 applied, 5813 accepted, 2328 enrolled	
SAT I Verbal/Math: 460/510	ACT: 22 COMPETITIVE

The University of South Carolina, founded in 1801, is the main campus of the state system offering courses through its schools of applied professional sciences, business administration, criminal justice, engineering, public health, humanities and social sciences, journalism and mass communications, nursing, pharmacy, and science and mathematics. There are 11 undergraduate and 15 graduate schools. In addition to regional accreditation, USC has baccalaureate program accreditation with AACSB, ABET, ACEJMC, ACPE, CSWE, NASM, NCATE, and NLN. The 7 libraries contain 2,526,408 volumes, 3,777,699 microform items, 10,190 audiovisual forms, and subscribe to 20,722 periodicals. Computerized library sources and services include the card catalog and database searching. Special learning facilities include a learning resource center, art gallery, and radio station. The 242-acre campus is in an urban environment area in the downtown area of Columbia. Including residence halls, there are 202 buildings on campus.

Student Life: About 86% of undergraduates are from South Carolina. Students come from 50 states, 116 foreign countries, and Canada. Some 79% are white; 14%, African American. The average age of freshmen is 18; all undergraduates, 22. About 20% drop out by the end of their first year; 62% remain to graduate.

Housing: A total of 6992 students can be accommodated in college housing. College-sponsored living facilities include single-sex and coed dormitories, on-campus apartments, married-student housing, fraternity houses, and sorority houses. In addition, there are honors houses. On-campus housing is guaranteed for all 4 years. Some 58% of students commute. Alcohol is not permitted. All students may keep cars on campus.

Activities: About 17% of men belong to 20 national fraternities; about 17% of women belong to 14 national sororities. There are 240 groups on campus, including art, band, cheerleading, chess, choir, chorale, chorus, computers, dance, drama, ethnic, gay, honors, international, jazz band, literary magazine, marching band, musical theater, newspaper, opera, orchestra, pep band, political, professional, radio and TV, religious, social, social service, student government, symphony, and yearbook. Popular campus events include Greek Rush, Homecoming, Tigerburn, Cockfest, CPU Cultural Series, Black History Month, Women's History Month, Carolina Cares Community Service Week, Spring Fling, and Greek Week.

Sports: There are 9 intercollegiate sports for men and 7 for women, and 33 intramural sports for men and 33 for women. Athletic and recreation facilities include a 72,400-seat football stadium, a 12,000-seat gymnasium, a track with stands for 2500, a 4000-seat baseball stadium, a 2000-seat tennis center, nearby golf courses, a weight room, an Olympic-sized swimming pool, racquetball, squash, basketball, volleyball, and badminton courts, and playing fields.

Disabled Students: About 80% of the campus is accessible to disabled students. The following facilities are available: wheelchair ramps, elevators, special parking, specially equipped rest rooms, special class scheduling, adapted housing, transportation, and computers.

Services: In addition to many counseling and information services, tutoring is provided in every subject for a fee. There is also a reader service for the blind, and remedial math, reading, and writing.

Campus Safety and Security: Campus safety and security measures include 24-hour foot and vehicle patrol, escort service, shuttle buses, and pamphlets, posters, and films. In addition, there are emergency telephones and lighted pathways and sidewalks.

Programs of Study: USC awards the B.A., B.S., A.B.J., B.Ar.Sc., B.F.A., B.M., B.S.B.A., B.S.Chem., B.S.C.S., B.S. in Eng., B.S.Med.Tech., B.S.N., B.S.P.E., and B.S.Pharm. degrees. Master's and doctoral degrees also are awarded. Bachelor's degrees are awarded in BIOLOGICAL SCIENCE (biology/biological science and marine science), BUSINESS (accounting, banking and finance, business administration and management, business economics, hotel/motel and restaurant management, insurance, management science, marketing/retailing/merchandising, office supervision and management, real estate, retailing, and sports management), COMMUNICATIONS AND THE ARTS (advertising, art history and appreciation, broadcasting, classics, dramatic arts, English, fine arts, French, German, Greek, Italian, journalism, Latin, media arts, music, music performance, music theory and composition, public relations, Spanish, and speech/debate/rhetoric), COMPUTER AND PHYSICAL SCIENCE (chemistry, computer science, geology, mathematics, physics, and statistics), EDUCATION (art, music, and physical), ENGINEERING AND ENVIRONMENTAL DESIGN (chemical engineering, civil engineering, computer engineering, electrical/electronics engineering, and mechanical engineering), HEALTH PROFESSIONS (medical laboratory technology, nursing, and pharmacy), SOCIAL SCIENCE (African American studies, anthropology, criminal justice, economics, European studies, geography, history, interdisciplinary studies, international relations, Latin American studies, philosophy, political science/government, psychology, public administration, religion, and sociology). Business administration, engineering, computer science, journalism, and political science have the largest enrollments.

Required: All students must maintain a GPA of 2.0 in 120 semester hours, including 24 in their major. Distribution requirements include 6 hours in English, 6 in numerical and analytical reasoning, 12 in humanities and social science, 7 in natural science, and a demonstrated ability in foreign languages.

Special: USC transmits live interactive televised instruction to more than 20 locations in the state. Cross-registration is offered with the National Technological University in engineering and through the National Student Exchange. Internships in many fields, study abroad in many countries through the Byrnes International Center, co-op programs, and work-study programs are available. Double majors through the colleges of humanities and social sciences and science and mathematics, student-designed majors, an interdisciplinary studies degree, and a 3-2 engineering degree with the College of Charleston are offered. Credit for military experience, nondegree study, and pass/fail options also are possible. There is a freshman honors program on campus, as well as 24 national honor societies, including Phi Beta Kappa.

Faculty/Classroom: Some 75% of faculty are male; 25%, female. About 89% teach undergraduates.

Admissions: About 76% of the 1993–94 applicants were accepted. The SAT scores for the 1993–94 freshman class were as follows: Verbal—65% below 500, 26% between 500 and 599, 8% between 600 and 700, and 1% above 700; Math—40% below 500, 39% between 500 and 599, 18% between 600 and 700, and 3% above 700. The ACT scores were 32% below 21, 29% between 21 and 23, 23% between 24 and 26, 10% between 27 and 28, and 7% above 28. About 55% of the current freshmen were in the top fifth of their class; 89% were in the top two fifths. There were 17 National Merit finalists. About 57 freshmen graduated first in their class.

Requirements: USC requires applicants to be in the upper 75% of their class. A minimum GPA of 2.0 is required. The SAT I or ACT is required, with the SAT I preferred. Applicants must have 15 academic credits, including 4 in high school English, 3 each in mathematics and social studies, 2 each in foreign language and laboratory science, and 1 elective. The GED is accepted. AP and CLEP credits are accepted. Important factors used in the admissions decision are advanced placement or honor courses, recommendations by school officials, evidence of special talent, personality, intangible qualities, and extracurricular activities record.

Procedure: Freshmen are admitted to all sessions. Entrance exams should be taken during the spring of the junior year and the fall of the senior year, if necessary. Application deadlines are open. The application fee is $25. Notification is sent on a rolling basis.

Transfer: About 944 transfer students enrolled in 1993–94. Transfer students must have a 2.0 GPA from a 4-year college, and a 2.5 GPA from a 2-year program. The SAT I or ACT is required for transfers who have attempted fewer than 30 semester hours of college credit. These students must meet both freshman and transfer requirements. Test scores are required for all business and engineering applicants. Requirements are higher for some majors. A total of 30 credits out of 120 must be completed at USC.

Visiting: There are guides for informal visits, and visitors may sit in on classes. To arrange for a visit, contact the Office of Admissions at (803) 777-7700 or (800) 868-8572 (out-of-state).

Financial Aid: In 1993–94, 50% of all current freshmen and 45% of continuing students received some form of financial aid. About 50% of freshmen and 40% of continuing students received need-based aid. The average freshman award was $6925. Of that total, scholarships or need-based grants averaged $1500 ($7000 maximum); loans averaged $1500 ($2625 maximum); and work contracts averaged $1363 ($2000 maximum). Some 55% of undergraduate students work part-time. Average earnings from campus work for the school year are $1288. The average financial indebtedness of the 1992–93 graduate was $10,968. USC is a member of CSS. The FAFSA financial statement is required. The deadline for financial aid applications is April 15.

International Students: There are currently 252 international students enrolled. The school actively recruits these students. They must take the TOEFL and achieve a minimum score of 550.

Computers: The college provides computer facilities for student use. The mainframes are an IBM 3090/400E and an IBM 4381/92E. Terminals are located at various locations on campus. Access is also available by modem. All students may access the system although in

some laboratories, use is restricted or priority given to that college's students. Each laboratory has its own hours. Access is usually possible from 8 A.M. to 12 A.M. Monday through Thursday, from 8 A.M. to 8 P.M. Fridays, from 10 A.M. to 10 P.M. Saturdays, and from 2 P.M. to 12 A.M. Sundays. There are no time limits on using the system, although some laboratories restrict use to 2-hour blocks. There are no fees.

Graduates: In 1992–93, 3219 bachelor's degrees were awarded. The most popular majors among graduates were marketing (9%), psychology (6%), and political science (5%). Within an average freshman class, 34% graduate in 4 years, 56% in 5 years, and 60% in 6 years. Some 428 companies recruited on campus in 1992–93.

Admissions Contact: Director of Admissions.

UNIVERSITY OF SOUTH CAROLINA AT AIKEN   C-3
Aiken, SC 29801   (803) 648–6851

Full-time: 759 men, 1193 women	Faculty: 110; IIB, av$
Part-time: 423 men, 909 women	Ph.D.s: 68%
Graduate: 438 men and women	Student/Faculty: 18 to 1
Year: semesters, summer session	Tuition: $2320 ($5800)
Application Deadline: August 1	Room & Board: $3066
Freshman Class: 864 applied, 560 accepted, 377 enrolled	
SAT I Verbal/Math: 413/473	COMPETITIVE

The University of South Carolina at Aiken, established in 1961, is a state-supported coeducational institution offering undergraduate and graduate programs in humanities and social sciences, health sciences, education, business administration and economics, and nursing. There are 6 undergraduate and 3 graduate schools. In addition to regional accreditation, USCA has baccalaureate program accreditation with NLN. The library contains 120,444 volumes, 19,180 microform items, 626 audiovisual forms, and subscribes to 1418 periodicals. Computerized library sources and services include the card catalog, interlibrary loans, and database searching. Special learning facilities include a learning resource center, art gallery, radio station, and a science education center. The 144-acre campus is in a small town. Including residence halls, there are 9 buildings on campus.

Student Life: About 86% of undergraduates are from South Carolina. Students come from 27 states, 8 foreign countries, and Canada. Nearly 98% are from public schools; 2% from private. Some 82% are white; 15%, African American. The average age of freshmen is 18; all undergraduates, 26.

Housing: A total of 368 students can be accommodated in college housing. College-sponsored living facilities include coed on-campus apartments. On-campus housing is available on a first-come, first-served basis. About 88% of students commute. Alcohol is not permitted. All students may keep cars on campus.

Activities: About 1% of men belong to 2 national fraternities; about 1% of women belong to 3 national sororities. There are 40 groups on campus, including cheerleading, choir, chorus, computers, drama, ethnic, honors, international, literary magazine, musical theater, newspaper, pep band, photography, political, professional, radio and TV, religious, social, social service, student government, and yearbook. Popular campus events include Halloween Dance and Alcohol Awareness.

Sports: There are 5 intercollegiate sports for men and 4 for women, and 13 intramural sports for men and 12 for women. Athletic and recreation facilities include an activities center, a baseball field, and a soccer/intramural/softball field.

Disabled Students: The entire campus is accessible to disabled students. The following facilities are available: wheelchair ramps, elevators, special parking, and specially equipped rest rooms.

Services: In addition to many counseling and information services, tutoring is available in some subjects, including mathematics and writing. There are also remedial math, reading, and writing.

Campus Safety and Security: Campus safety and security measures include 24-hour foot and vehicle patrol, self defense education, escort service, and informal discussions. In addition, there are pamphlets, posters, films, emergency telephones, and lighted pathways and sidewalks.

Programs of Study: USCA awards the B.A., B.S., and B.I.S. degrees. Associate and master's degrees also are awarded. Bachelor's degrees are awarded in BIOLOGICAL SCIENCE (biology/biological science), BUSINESS (accounting), COMMUNICATIONS AND THE ARTS (English), COMPUTER AND PHYSICAL SCIENCE (chemistry and computer mathematics), EDUCATION (early childhood, elementary, science, and secondary), HEALTH PROFESSIONS (nursing, predentistry, and premedicine), SOCIAL SCIENCE (economics, history, interdisciplinary studies, political science/government, prelaw, psychology, and sociology). The sciences, English, history, and political science are the strongest programs academically. Business, education, and nursing have the largest enrollments.

Required: Students must complete a minimum of 120 credit hours, with at least a 2.0 GPA. General education requirements include courses in English, political science, psychology, history, sociology, and interdisciplinary studies.

Special: Cross-registration is permitted with other schools in the University of South Carolina system. Co-op programs in engineering and business, business internships, student-designed majors, and work-study programs are offered. B.A.-B.S. degrees in psychology and education, a general studies degree, nondegree study, and pass/fail options are possible. There is a freshman honors program on campus, as well as 2 national honor societies. All departments have honors programs.

Faculty/Classroom: Some 54% of faculty are male; 46%, female. All teach undergraduates. No introductory courses are taught by graduate students. The average class size in an introductory lecture is 24; in a laboratory, 18; and in a regular course offering, 15.

Admissions: About 65% of the 1993–94 applicants were accepted. The SAT scores for the 1993–94 freshman class were as follows: Verbal—88% below 500, 9% between 500 and 599, and 2% between 600 and 700; Math—62% below 500, 28% between 500 and 599, 8% between 600 and 700, and 1% above 700. About 31% of the current freshmen were in the top fifth of their class; 63% were in the top two fifths. Three freshmen graduated first in their class.

Requirements: The SAT I or ACT is required, with a minimum of 350 verbal and 350 mathematics on the SAT I or 19 on the ACT. Those with 300 verbal and 300 mathematics on the SAT I or 15 on the ACT may be admitted on a provisional basis. Admission is based on a combination of an applicant's scores on college entrance examinations and high school GPA. Applicants are required to submit 16 academic credits, including 4 years of high school English, 3 each of mathematics and social studies, 2 each of a foreign language and a laboratory science, 1 of history, and 1 year of either physical education or ROTC. AP and CLEP credits are accepted. Important factors used in the admissions decision are advanced placement or honor courses, recommendations by school officials, leadership record, extracurricular activities record, and evidence of special talent.

Procedure: Freshmen are admitted to all sessions. Entrance exams should be taken by the fall of the senior year. Applications should be filed by August 1 for fall entry and December 1 for spring entry, along with an application fee of $25. Notification is sent on a rolling basis. There are early admissions and deferred admissions plans.

Transfer: About 257 transfer students enrolled in 1993–94. A total of 30 credits out of 120 must be completed at USCA.

Visiting: There are regularly scheduled 3-day orientations for prospective students, guides for informal visits, and visitors may sit in on classes. To arrange for a visit, contact the Admissions Office at (803) 641–3366.

Financial Aid: In 1993–94, 44% of all current freshmen and 48% of continuing students received some form of financial aid. About 41% of freshmen and 44% of continuing students received need-based aid. The average freshman award was $3000. Of that total, scholarships or need-based grants averaged $1750; loans averaged $2625; and work contracts averaged $1500. The average financial indebtedness of the 1992–93 graduate was $5379. USCA is a member of CSS. The FAF, the colleges own financial statement, and the FAFSA are required. The deadline for financial aid applications is March 15.

International Students: There are currently 12 international students enrolled. They must take the TOEFL and achieve a minimum score of 550. The student must also take the SAT I, and achieve a minimum composite score of 700.

Computers: The college provides computer facilities for student use. The mainframe is an IBM 3081D. There are more than 100 microcomputers for student use throughout the campus. Students enrolled in courses requiring mainframe work may access the system. It may be used 24 hours a day, 7 days a week. There are no time limits on using the system and no fees.

Graduates: In 1992–93, 473 bachelor's degrees were awarded. The most popular majors among graduates were business administration (34%), education (19%), and nursing (17%). Some 100 companies recruited on campus in 1992–93.

Admissions Contact: Randy R. Duckett, Associate Dean of Students.

UNIVERSITY OF SOUTH CAROLINA AT SPARTANBURG
B-1

Spartanburg, SC 29303   (803) 599-2280

Full-time: 831 men, 1376 women

Part-time: 386 men, 672 women

Graduate: none

Year: semesters, summer session

Application Deadline: open

Freshman Class: 885 applied, 553 accepted, 381 enrolled

SAT I Verbal/Math: 400/450

Faculty: 162; IIB, -$

Ph.D.s: 59%

Student/Faculty: 14 to 1

Tuition: $2320 ($5800)

Room & Board: n/app

COMPETITIVE

The University of South Carolina at Spartanburg, established in 1967, is a public coeducational institution offering undergraduate programs in the liberal arts and sciences, business administration, education, and nursing. There are 4 undergraduate schools. In addition to regional accreditation, USCS has baccalaureate program accreditation with NLN. The library contains 107,905 volumes, 18,518 microform items, and 3172 audiovisual forms, and subscribes to 1200 periodicals. Special learning facilities include an art gallery, TV station, and a greenhouse. The 298-acre campus is in an urban area 100 miles north of Columbia. There are 7 buildings on campus.

Student Life: About 95% of undergraduates are from South Carolina. Students come from 28 states, 15 foreign countries, and Canada. About 85% are white; 12%, African American. The average age of freshmen is 23.1; all undergraduates, 24.6.

Housing: There are no residence halls. Privately owned 2-bedroom apartments can accommodate 400 students on campus. On-campus housing is available on a first-come, first-served basis. Some 88% of students commute. Alcohol is not permitted. All students may keep cars on campus.

Activities: About 4% of men belong to 2 national fraternities; about 5% of women belong to 2 local sororities. There are 46 groups on campus, including cheerleading, choir, chorale, chorus, computers, dance, drama, ethnic, honors, international, literary magazine, newspaper, pep band, photography, political, professional, religious, social, social service, student government, and yearbook. Popular campus events include Homecoming, RIOTS, Wet and Wild Day, and intramural tournaments.

Sports: There are 6 intercollegiate sports for men and 4 for women, and 13 intramural sports for men and 12 for women. Athletic and recreation facilities include a soccer field, tennis courts, baseball fields, a basketball gymnasium, racquetball courts, and an auxiliary gymnasium.

Disabled Students: About 80% of the campus is accessible to disabled students. The following facilities are available: wheelchair ramps, elevators, special parking, specially equipped rest rooms, special class scheduling, and lowered drinking fountains.

Services: In addition to many counseling and information services, tutoring is available in most subjects, including mathematics, English, foreign languages, psychology, statistics, and natural sciences. There are also remedial math, reading, and writing programs.

Campus Safety and Security: Campus safety and security measures include 24-hour foot and vehicle patrol, self defense education, pamphlets, posters, films, and emergency telephones. In addition, there are lighted pathways and sidewalks.

Programs of Study: USCS awards the B.A., B.S., and B.S.N. degrees. Associate degrees also are awarded. Bachelor's degrees are awarded in BIOLOGICAL SCIENCE (biology/biological science), BUSINESS (business administration and management), COMMUNICATIONS AND THE ARTS (communications, English, French, and Spanish), COMPUTER AND PHYSICAL SCIENCE (chemistry, computer science, and mathematics), EDUCATION (early childhood, elementary, physical, and secondary), HEALTH PROFESSIONS (nursing and premedicine), SOCIAL SCIENCE (criminal justice, history, political science/government, prelaw, psychology, and sociology). Business administration has the largest enrollment.

Required: Students must complete 120 to 136 credits, including 69 to 82 in the major, with a minimum GPA of 2.0. General education requirements include courses in communications, mathematics, arts and humanities, social and behavioral sciences, natural science, foreign culture, computer studies, and a senior seminar.

Special: Cross-registration is permitted within the University of South Carolina system and with Wofford College and Greenville Technical College. Opportunities are provided for B.A.-B.S. degrees, student-designed majors, a 3-2 engineering degree, nondegree study, credit for military service, and study abroad in Mexico, France, and Germany. There are 5 national honor societies on campus, including Phi Beta Kappa.

Faculty/Classroom: Some 47% of faculty are male; 53%, female. About 91% teach undergraduates and 9% both teach and do research. The average class size in an introductory lecture is 22; in a laboratory, 20; and in a regular course offering, 15.

Admissions: About 62% of the 1993-94 applicants were accepted. The SAT scores for the 1993-94 freshman class were as follows: Verbal—86% below 500, 12% between 500 and 599, and 2% between 600 and 700; Math—69% below 500, 26% between 500 and 599, and 5% between 600 and 700. About 30% of the current freshmen were in the top fifth of their class; 60% were in the top two fifths. Three freshmen graduated first in their class.

Requirements: A minimum GPA of 2.0 is required. The SAT I or ACT is required, with a minimum composite score of 700 on the SAT I or 18 on the ACT. Graduation from an accredited secondary school with a GPA of 2.0 is required. The GED is accepted. Applicants must submit 20 academic credits, distributed as follows: 4 years of English, 3 of mathematics, 2 each of laboratory science, foreign language, and social studies, 1 each of history and physical education or ROTC, and the remainder in electives. AP and CLEP credits are accepted.

Procedure: Entrance exams should be taken at the beginning of the senior year. Application deadlines are open. The application fee is $25. Notification is sent on a rolling basis.

Transfer: About 408 transfer students enrolled in 1993-94. Applicants must have a minimum college GPA of 2.0 and submit final transcripts from all schools attended. Students transferring with fewer than 30 semester credits must submit a minimum SAT I score of 700 or ACT score of 18 and meet other freshmen requirements. A total of 30 credits out of 120 to 136 must be completed at USCS.

Visiting: There are regularly scheduled orientations for prospective students. There are guides for informal visits, and visitors may sit in on classes. To arrange for a visit, contact the Admissions Office at (803) 599-2280.

Financial Aid: In 1993-94, 43% of all current freshmen and 45% of continuing students received some form of financial aid. About 34% of freshmen and 35% of continuing students received need-based aid. USCS is a member of CSS. The FAF, FFS or SFS is required.

International Students: There are currently 51 international students enrolled. They must take the TOEFL and achieve a minimum score of 500.

Computers: The college provides computer facilities for student use. The mainframe is an IBM 9375. There are also 70 Apple, IBM, and IBM-compatible microcomputers available to students in several campus laboratories. All students may access the system. It may be used during school hours. There are no time limits on using the system and no fees.

Graduates: In 1992-93, 561 bachelor's degrees were awarded. The most popular majors among graduates were business (32%), education (21%), and social science (13%). Within an average freshman class, 10% graduate in 4 years, 24% in 5 years, and 31% in 6 years.

Admissions Contact: Donette Stewart, Director of Admissions.

VOORHEES COLLEGE

Denmark, SC 29042   (803) 793-3351

Full-time: 405 men, 298 women

Part-time: 7 men, 13 women

Graduate: none

Year: semesters, summer session

Application Deadline: open

Freshman Class: 1465 applied, 1006 accepted, 242 enrolled

SAT I Verbal/Math: 326/330

Faculty: 31; IIB, --$

Ph.D.s: 35%

Student/Faculty: 23 to 1

Tuition: $4250

Room & Board: $2522

ACT: 15   **LESS COMPETITIVE**

Voorhees College, founded in 1897, is a historically black liberal arts college affiliated with the Protestant Episcopal Church. Undergraduate programs are offered in accounting, biology, business administration, English, health and recreation, political science, sociology, criminal justice, computer science, and mathematics. The library contains 111,057 volumes, 23,387 microform items, 238 audiovisual forms, and subscribes to 417 periodicals. Special learning facilities include a learning resource center. The 350-acre campus is in a rural area 50 miles south of Columbia. Including residence halls, there are 21 buildings on campus.

Student Life: About 70% of undergraduates are from South Carolina. Students come from 20 states and 2 foreign countries. All are from public schools. Almost 99% are African American. Most are Protestant. The average age of freshmen is 17; all undergraduates, 23. Some 40% drop out by the end of their first year; 50% remain to graduate.

Housing: A total of 521 students can be accommodated in college housing. College-sponsored living facilities include single-sex dormitories. On-campus housing is guaranteed for all 4 years. About 75% of students live on campus; of those, 50% remain on campus on weekends. Alcohol is not permitted. Upperclassmen may keep cars on campus.

Activities: About 10% of men belong to 1 local and 5 national fraternities; about 10% of women belong to 4 national sororities. There are 20 groups on campus, including cheerleading, choir, computers, dance, drama, honors, newspaper, pep band, political, professional, religious, social, student government, and yearbook. Popular campus

events include Homecoming, Drug Awareness Week, Career Awareness Week, Black History Month, Science Fair, Religious Emphasis Week, and Coronation of Miss Voorhees.

Sports: There are 3 intercollegiate sports for men and 4 for women, and 4 intramural sports for men and 4 for women. Athletic and recreation facilities include a gymnasium, tennis courts, baseball and softball fields, a weight room, a dance studio, and a student center.

Disabled Students: About 80% of the campus is accessible to disabled students. The following facilities are available: wheelchair ramps, elevators, special parking, specially equipped rest rooms, and lowered drinking fountains.

Services: In addition to many counseling and information services, tutoring is available in most subjects. There are also remedial math, reading, and writing programs.

Campus Safety and Security: Campus safety and security measures include 24-hour foot and vehicle patrol, informal discussions, and lighted pathways and sidewalks.

Programs of Study: Voorhees awards the B.A. and B.S. degrees. Bachelor's degrees are awarded in BIOLOGICAL SCIENCE (biology/biological science), BUSINESS (accounting and business administration and management), COMMUNICATIONS AND THE ARTS (English), COMPUTER AND PHYSICAL SCIENCE (computer science and mathematics), SOCIAL SCIENCE (criminal justice, political science/government, and sociology). Biology is the strongest program academically. Business has the largest enrollment.

Required: To graduate, students must earn at least 122 credit hours, with at least 30 in the major, and have a minimum GPA of 2.0. The 55-hour general education requirement includes 13 hours of humanities, 9 of English, 6 each of social science, natural science, mathematics, and foreign language, 3 of computer science, 2 of physical education, and 1 of freshmen orientation. A number of free electives, a senior seminar, computer science, and physical education are also required. An English proficiency exam and an exit exam must also be passed.

Special: Voorhees offers cooperative education, internships in some programs, work-study, an evening/Saturday program, off-campus summer study, credit by exam, and a degree completion program. Cross-registration with Denmark Technical College and interdisciplinary majors, such as health and recreation, are possible. There are 2 national honor societies on campus.

Faculty/Classroom: Some 69% of faculty are male; 31%, female. All teach undergraduates. The average class size in an introductory lecture is 30; in a laboratory, 20; and in a regular course offering, 25.

Admissions: About 69% of the 1993–94 applicants were accepted. The SAT scores for the 1993–94 freshman class were as follows: Verbal—99% below 500 and 1% between 500 and 599; Math—99% below 500 and 1% between 500 and 599. About 10% of the current freshmen were in the top fifth of their class; 25% were in the top two fifths.

Requirements: A minimum GPA of 2.0 is required. The SAT I or ACT is required. Recommended minimum scores are 600 on the SAT I or 16 on the ACT. Applicants must be high school graduates or hold a GED. Students should have earned 20 academic credits in high school, including 4 of English, 3 of mathematics, 2 each of science and foreign language (optional), and 1 each of history, social studies, economics/government, and physical education. Letters of recommendation and a campus visit are advised. AP and CLEP credits are accepted. Important factors used in the admissions decision are advanced placement or honor courses, recommendations by school officials, recommendations by alumni, parents or siblings attending the school, and ability to finance college education.

Procedure: Freshmen are admitted to all sessions. Entrance exams should be taken in the senior year. Application deadlines are open. The application fee is $10. Notification is sent on a rolling basis. There is a deferred admissions plan.

Transfer: About 33 transfer students enrolled in 1993–94. Transfer students must submit complete records, including a confidential report from each college attended. The confidential report form is provided by the Office of Admission and Recruitment. Students with fewer than 30 semester hours must submit their high school record with rank in class and GPA. The SAT I is recommended; a minimum composite score of 600 is expected. An interview is advised. A total of 30 credits out of 122 must be completed at Voorhees.

Visiting: There are regularly scheduled orientations for prospective students, including senior visitation days which are held in January through April. There are guides for informal visits and visitors may sit in on classes and stay overnight at the school. To arrange for a visit, contact Dr. Timothy Autry, Vice President for Student Affairs at (803) 793-3351.

Financial Aid: In 1993–94, 99% of all current freshmen and 98% of continuing students received some form of financial aid. About 99% of freshmen received need-based aid. The average freshman award was $6272. Of that total, scholarships or need-based grants averaged $2300 ($3000 maximum); loans averaged $2500 ($2625 maximum); and work contracts averaged $1292. About 5% of under-

graduate students work part-time. The average financial indebtedness of the 1992–93 graduate was $3000. Voorhees is a member of CSS. The FAF, FFS, or SAR is required; the FAF is preferred. The deadline for financial aid applications is April 1.

International Students: There are currently 2 international students enrolled. They must take the TOEFL and achieve a minimum score of 500. The student must also take the SAT I or the ACT.

Computers: The college provides computer facilities for student use. The mainframe is an IBM 4361. There are also 50 IBM PS/2 Models 25 and 30 available in a social science laboratory and an instructional laboratory. Among additional computer facilities, there is a science laboratory with 20 Apple Macintosh computers. All students may access the system. There are no time limits on using the system and no fees.

Graduates: In 1992–93, 56 bachelor's degrees were awarded. The most popular majors among graduates were criminal justice (21%), business administration (21%), and biology (14%). Within an average freshman class, 25% graduate in 4 years, 27% in 5 years, and 2% in 6 years. Some 20 companies recruited on campus in 1992–93. In the 1992 graduating class, 3% of all graduates were enrolled in graduate school within 6 months of graduation; 30% of the men and 40% of the women had found employment.

Admissions Contact: Samuel Blackwell, Director of Admissions and Recruitment.

WINTHROP COLLEGE
(See Winthrop University)

WINTHROP UNIVERSITY
C-1
(Formerly Winthrop College)
Rock Hill, SC 29733   (803) 323–2191; (800) 763–0230 (in-state)

Full-time: 1094 men, 2301 women	Faculty: 297; IIA, --$
Part-time: 261 men, 409 women	Ph.D.s: 78%
Graduate: 307 men, 735 women	Student/Faculty: 11 to 1
Year: semesters, summer session	Tuition: $3470 ($6110)
Application Deadline: May 1	Room & Board: $3280
Freshman Class: 2320 applied, 1805 accepted, 769 enrolled	
SAT I Verbal/Math: 460/510	ACT: 18 COMPETITIVE

Winthrop University, founded in 1886, is a state-supported coeducational institution offering undergraduate and graduate programs in liberal arts and sciences, business administration, education, and visual and performing arts. There are 4 undergraduate schools. In addition to regional accreditation, Winthrop has baccalaureate program accreditation with AACSB, ADA, CSAB, CSWE, FIDER, NASAD, NASM, and NCATE. The library contains 357,110 volumes, 1,026,572 microform items, 1755 audiovisual forms, and subscribes to 70,037 periodicals. Computerized library sources and services include interlibrary loans and database searching. Special learning facilities include an art gallery, TV station, and an audio recording studio. The 100-acre campus is in a small town 23 miles south of Charlotte, North Carolina. Including residence halls, there are 40 buildings on campus.

Student Life: About 86% of undergraduates are from South Carolina. Students come from 35 states, 47 foreign countries, and Canada. Nearly 77% are white; 18%, African American. The average age of freshmen is 18; all undergraduates, 21.8. About 25% drop out by the end of their first year; 50% remain to graduate.

Housing: A total of 2421 students can be accommodated in college housing. College-sponsored living facilities include single-sex and coed dormitories, on-campus apartments, and married-student housing. In addition there are independent, off-campus fraternity and sorority houses. On-campus housing is guaranteed for all 4 years. Some 53% of students commute. All students may keep cars on campus.

Activities: About 14% of men belong to 10 national fraternities; about 16% of women belong to 9 national sororities. There are 120 groups on campus, including art, band, cheerleading, choir, chorale, chorus, dance, drama, ethnic, gay, honors, international, jazz band, literary magazine, musical theater, newspaper, opera, orchestra, pep band, political, professional, religious, social, social service, student government, symphony, and yearbook. Popular campus events include convocation, Fall Fest, and Homecoming.

Sports: There are 7 intercollegiate sports for men and 7 for women, and 44 intramural sports for men and 44 for women. Athletic and recreation facilities include baseball, softball, and soccer fields, a golf course, a coliseum, a swimming pool, a cross-country course, tennis courts, racquetball courts, a weight room, and a training room.

Disabled Students: The following facilities are available: wheelchair ramps, elevators, special parking, specially equipped rest rooms, special class scheduling, lowered drinking fountains, lowered telephones, and adapted campus housing.

Campus Safety and Security: Campus safety and security measures include 24-hour foot and vehicle patrol, self defense education, informal discussions, pamphlets, posters, and films. In addition, there are emergency telephones and lighted pathways and sidewalks.

Programs of Study: Winthrop awards the B.A., B.S., B.F.A., B.M., B.M.E., and B.S.W. degrees. Master's degrees also are awarded. Bachelor's degrees are awarded in BIOLOGICAL SCIENCE (biology/biological science), BUSINESS (business administration and management), COMMUNICATIONS AND THE ARTS (art, art history and appreciation, communications, dance, dramatic arts, English, fine arts, French, music, Spanish, and speech/debate/rhetoric), COMPUTER AND PHYSICAL SCIENCE (chemistry, computer science, and mathematics), EDUCATION (business, early childhood, education, elementary, home economics, music, physical, secondary, and special), HEALTH PROFESSIONS (medical laboratory technology), SOCIAL SCIENCE (food science, history, home economics, philosophy, political science/government, psychology, religion, social work, and sociology). Business administration, elementary education, and biology have the largest enrollments.

Required: Students must complete a minimum of 124 semester hours, including a 59-hour general education distribution requirement, and maintain a minimum GPA of 2.0. Specific courses in writing, oral communication, computer information systems, critical issues, and the American Constitution are required.

Special: Cross-registration is permitted with the Charlotte Area Educational Consortium. Co-op programs and internships in most professional areas, study abroad in 14 countries, and on-campus work-study programs are offered. Interdisciplinary majors such as science communication, nondegree study, and pass/fail options are possible. There is a freshman honors program on campus, as well as 3 national honor societies. Some 18 departments have honors programs.

Faculty/Classroom: About 55% of faculty are male; 45%, female. No introductory courses are taught by graduate students.

Admissions: About 78% of the 1993–94 applicants were accepted. The SAT scores for the 1993–94 freshman class were as follows: Verbal—65% below 500, 26% between 500 and 599, 8% between 600 and 700, and 1% above 700; Math—42% below 500, 40% between 500 and 599, 15% between 600 and 700, and 3% above 700. The ACT scores were 78% below 21, 21% between 21 and 23, and 1% between 24 and 26. About 49% of the current freshmen were in the top fifth of their class; 80% were in the top two fifths. About 15 freshmen graduated first in their class.

Requirements: Winthrop requires applicants to be in the upper 50% of their class. A minimum GPA of 2.5 is required. The SAT I or ACT is required. Graduation from an accredited secondary school is also required; a GED will be accepted. Applicants must have successfully completed 4 credits in high school English, 3 in mathematics, 2 each in laboratory science, social studies, and a foreign language, 1 in United States history, and 1 in physical education or ROTC. AP and CLEP credits are accepted. Important factors used in the admissions decision are advanced placement or honor courses, leadership record, recommendations by school officials, evidence of special talent, and extracurricular activities record.

Procedure: Freshmen are admitted to all sessions. Applications should be filed by May 1 for fall entry and January 2 for spring entry, along with an application fee of $35. Notification is sent monthly. A waiting list is an active part of the admissions procedure, with about 10% of applicants on the list.

Transfer: About 359 transfer students enrolled in 1993–94. Transfer applicants must have completed at least 30 credits with a minimum grade of C and a cumulative GPA of at least 2.2. They must be eligible to return to the previous institution. A total of 30 credits out of 124 must be completed at Winthrop.

Visiting: There are regularly scheduled orientations for prospective students, consisting of the Winthrop Festival, with all academic areas and student life areas represented, a general session, minisessions, and a campus tour. There are guides for informal visits and visitors may sit in on classes. To arrange for a visit, contact the Admissions Office at (803) 323–2191 or (800) 763–0230 (in-state).

Financial Aid: In a recent year, 68% of all current freshmen and 47% of continuing students received some form of financial aid. About 51% of freshmen and 40% of continuing students received need-based aid. The average freshman award was $3703. Of that total, scholarships or need-based grants averaged $2661 ($9270 maximum); loans averaged $1371 ($3625 maximum); and work contracts averaged $164 ($1200 maximum). About 20% of undergraduate students work part-time. Average earnings from campus work for the school year are $818. Winthrop is a member of CSS. The college's own financial statement or the FAFSA is required. The deadline for financial aid applications is May 1.

International Students: There are currently 165 international students enrolled. They must take the TOEFL and achieve a minimum score of 520.

Computers: The college provides computer facilities for student use. The mainframe is a DEC VAX 6000–510(2). Approximately 250 microcomputers are available for students in various locations across campus. Many are networked. All students may access the system. It may be used 84 hours a week, weekdays until 11 P.M. There are no time limits on using the system and no fees.

Graduates: In 1992–93, 807 bachelor's degrees were awarded. Within an average freshman class, 1% graduate in 3 years, 26% in 4 years, 43% in 5 years, and 49% in 6 years. Some 53 companies recruited on campus in 1992–93.

Admissions Contact: Deborah Barber, Admissions Office.

WOFFORD COLLEGE
B-1

Spartanburg, SC 29303–3663 (803) 597–4130

Full-time: 627 men, 432 women	Faculty: 64; IIB, +$
Part-time: 29 men, 20 women	Ph.D.s: 92%
Graduate: none	Student/Faculty: 17 to 1
Year: 4–1–4, summer session	Tuition: $11,480
Application Deadline: February 1	Room & Board: $4150
Freshman Class: 1119 applied, 935 accepted, 273 enrolled	
ACT: 24	VERY COMPETITIVE

Wofford College, founded in 1854, is a private, coeducational institution, affiliated with the United Methodist Church, offering programs in liberal arts and preprofessional studies. The library contains 165,676 volumes and 60,354 microform items, and subscribes to 641 periodicals. Computerized library sources and services include the card catalog, interlibrary loans, and database searching. Special learning facilities include a learning resource center, art gallery, planetarium, foreign language center, satellite earth station, and international studies center with simultaneous translation capabilities. The 110-acre campus is in an urban area 65 miles southeast of Charlotte. Including residence halls, there are 31 buildings on campus.

Student Life: About 70% of undergraduates are from South Carolina. Students come from 28 states and 8 foreign countries. Eighty-one percent are from public schools; 19% from private. Eighty-nine percent are white. Seventy-three percent are Protestant; 10% claim no religious affiliation. The average age of freshmen is 18.5; all undergraduates, 21. Nine percent drop out by the end of their first year; 70% remain to graduate.

Housing: A total of 962 students can be accommodated in college housing. College-sponsored living facilities include single-sex dormitories, on-campus apartments, and fraternity houses. On-campus housing is guaranteed for all 4 years. Eighty-one percent of students live on campus. All students may keep cars on campus.

Activities: About 50% of men belong to 8 national fraternities; about 58% of women belong to 3 national sororities. There are 51 groups on campus, including adventurers, art, cheerleading, choir, chorale, chorus, computers, debate, drama, ethnic, honors, international, literary magazine, newspaper, pep band, photography, political, professional, religious, social, social service, student government, and yearbook. Popular campus events include Homecoming, Phi Beta Kappa Day, Christmas Concert, all football weekends, and Spring Weekend/Greek games.

Sports: There are 7 intercollegiate sports for men and 5 for women, and 7 intramural sports for men and 5 for women. Athletic and recreation facilities include an 8000-seat campus stadium, a 3500-seat arena, a tennis complex, and a soccer field.

Disabled Students: The entire campus is accessible to disabled students. The following facilities are available: wheelchair ramps, elevators, special parking, specially equipped rest rooms, special class scheduling, lowered drinking fountains, and lowered telephones.

Services: In addition to many counseling and information services, tutoring is available in every subject. There is also a reader service for the blind.

Campus Safety and Security: Campus safety and security measures include 24-hour foot and vehicle patrol, self-defense education, escort service, and informal discussions. In addition, there are pamphlets, posters, and films and lighted pathways and sidewalks.

Programs of Study: Wofford awards the B.A. and B.S. degrees. Bachelor's degrees are awarded in BIOLOGICAL SCIENCE (biology/biological science), BUSINESS (accounting, banking and finance, and business economics), COMMUNICATIONS AND THE ARTS (art history and appreciation, English, French, German, and Spanish), COMPUTER AND PHYSICAL SCIENCE (chemistry, computer mathematics, and physics), SOCIAL SCIENCE (economics, history, humanities, philosophy, political science/government, prelaw, psychology, religion, and sociology). Biology, premedicine, history, English, finance, computer science/mathematics, and foreign languages are the strongest academically. Economics, business/economics, biology, premedicine, and English have the largest enrollments.

Required: To graduate, students must complete 124 credits, with 21 to 38 credits in the major and a minimum GPA of 2.0. General education requirements include 12 credits of history/philosophy/religion, 8

of natural sciences, 6 of English, 3 each of fine arts and mathematics, and 2 of physical education. Students must complete 3 interim projects and take a freshman humanities seminar.

Special: There is limited cross-registration with Converse College. Internships, study abroad in 21 countries, work-study programs, dual majors in all fields, and interdisciplinary majors in humanities, intercultural studies, and political economy and philosophy are available. A 3–2 engineering degree with Georgia Institute of Technology and Columbia University and a 3–2 nursing program with Emory University are offered. The 1-month winter interim session permits students to concentrate on a single study project. There are 9 national honor societies on campus, including Phi Beta Kappa.

Faculty/Classroom: Eighty-four percent of faculty are male; 16%, female. All teach undergraduates. The average class size in an introductory lecture is 20; in a laboratory, 15; and in a regular course offering, 10.

Admissions: About 84% of the 1993–94 applicants were accepted. The SAT scores for the 1993–94 freshman class were as follows: Verbal—47% below 500, 34% between 500 and 599, 16% between 600 and 700, and 3% above 700; Math—19% below 500, 45% between 500 and 599, 30% between 600 and 700, and 6% above 700. About 77% of the current freshmen were in the top fifth of their class; 96% were in the top two fifths. There were 6 National Merit finalists. Eleven freshmen graduated first in their class.

Requirements: The SAT I or ACT is required, and SAT II: Subject tests are recommended. Applicants must be graduates of an accredited secondary school. The GED is accepted. Students should have completed 4 years each of high school English and mathematics, 3 of laboratory science, and 2 each of a foreign language and social studies. An essay is required and an interview is strongly recommended. AP and CLEP credits are accepted. Important factors used in the admissions decision are advanced placement or honor courses, leadership record, personality, intangible qualities, evidence of special talent, and recommendations by school officials.

Procedure: Freshmen are admitted fall, spring, and summer. Entrance exams should be taken in the spring of the junior year or the fall of the senior year. Applications should be filed by February 1 for fall entry, along with an application fee of $25. Notification is sent March 15. There are early admissions and deferred admissions plans.

Transfer: Some 26 transfer students enrolled in 1993–94. Transfers should have a minimum GPA of 2.5 from a 4-year college or 3.0 from a 2-year college, or they may submit ACT or SAT I scores. An interview is recommended. A total of 30 credits out of 124 must be completed at Wofford.

Visiting: There are regularly scheduled orientations for prospective students. There are guides for informal visits and visitors may sit in on classes and stay overnight at the school. To arrange for a visit, contact the Director of Admissions at (803) 597–4130.

Financial Aid: In 1993–94 78% of all current freshmen and 69% of continuing students received some form of financial aid. About 54% of freshmen and 51% of continuing students received need-based aid. The average freshman award was $9824. Of that total, scholarships or need-based grants averaged $7356 ($15,640 maximum); loans averaged $2188 ($5625 maximum); and work contracts averaged $280 ($1200 maximum). Thirty-five percent of undergraduate students work part-time. Average earnings from campus work for the school year are $1200. The average financial indebtedness of the 1992–93 graduate was $12,260. Wofford is a member of CSS. The FAF and FAFSA, and the college's own financial statement are required. The deadline for financial aid applications is March 15.

International Students: There are currently 8 international students enrolled. They must take the TOEFL and achieve a minimum score of 500.

Computers: The college provides computer facilities for student use. The mainframe is a DEC VAX cluster with a DEC MicroVAX 3800 and 3100. All students may access the system. There are no time limits on using the system and no fees.

Graduates: In 1992–93 241 bachelor's degrees were awarded. The most popular majors among graduates were biology (16%), English (15%), and business economics (12%). Within an average freshman class, 2% graduate in 3 years, 69% in 4 years, 70% in 5 years, and 73% in 6 years. In the 1992 graduating class, 39% of all students were enrolled in graduate school within 6 months of graduation; 54% had found employment.

Admissions Contact: Charles H. Gray, Director of Admissions.

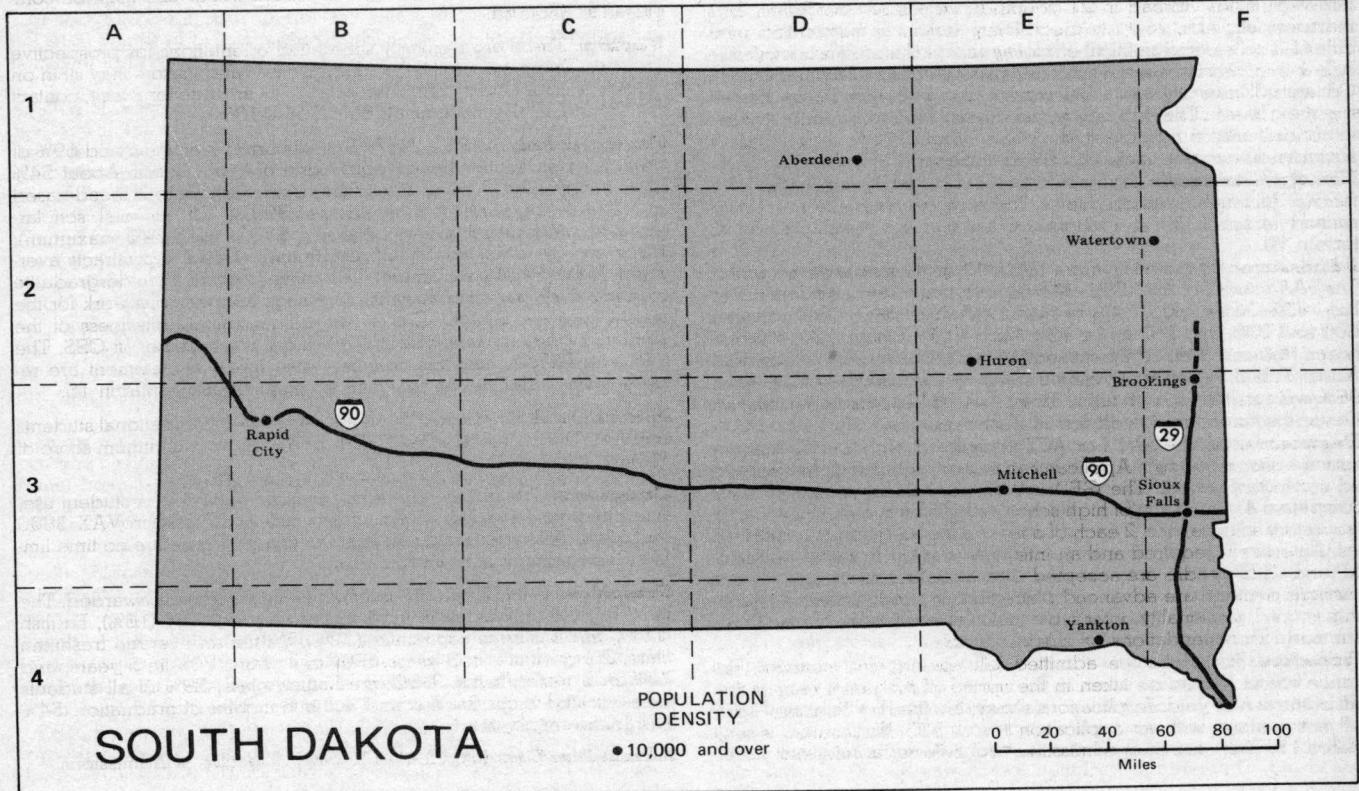

SOUTH DAKOTA

POPULATION DENSITY
• 10,000 and over

0 20 40 60 80 100
Miles

AUGUSTANA COLLEGE

Sioux Falls, SD 57197

F-3

(605) 336–5516
(800) 727–2844 (out-of-state)

Full-time: 485 men, 855 women
Part-time: 133 men, 219 women
Graduate: 17 men, 38 women
Year: 4–1–4, summer session
Application Deadline: August 15
Freshman Class: 761 applied, 726 accepted, 306 enrolled
SAT I or ACT: recommended

Faculty: 107; IIB, -$
Ph.D.s: 51%
Student/Faculty: 13 to 1
Tuition: $10,300
Room & Board: $3120

COMPETITIVE

Augustana College, founded in 1860, is a private, coeducational liberal arts institution affiliated with the Evangelical Lutheran Church in America. In addition to regional accreditation, Augustana has baccalaureate program accreditation with CSWE, NASM, and NCATE. The library contains 231,000 volumes, 54,449 microform items, and 5134 audiovisual forms, and subscribes to 1072 periodicals. Computerized library sources and services include interlibrary loans. Special learning facilities include an art gallery, natural history museum, and radio station. The 100-acre campus is in a suburban area 150 miles north of Omaha, Nebraska. Including residence halls, there are 17 buildings on campus.

Student Life: About 50% of undergraduates are from South Dakota. Students come from 33 states, 12 foreign countries, and Canada. Ninety-five percent are from public schools; 5% from private. Ninety-eight percent are white. Seventy-six percent are Protestant; 17% Catholic. The average age of freshmen is 18; all undergraduates, 20. Twenty percent drop out by the end of their first year; 57% remain to graduate.

Housing: A total of 1292 students can be accommodated in college housing. College-sponsored living facilities include coed dormitories. In addition there are independent student housing. On-campus housing is guaranteed for all 4 years and is available on a first-come, first-served basis. Sixty-five percent of students live on campus; of those, 80% remain on campus on weekends. Alcohol is not permitted. All students may keep cars on campus.

Activities: There are no fraternities or sororities on campus. There are 90 groups on campus, including art, band, cheerleading, choir, chorale, chorus, computers, dance, drama, international, jazz band, literary magazine, musical theater, newspaper, opera, pep band, photography, political, professional, radio and TV, religious, social, social

service, student government, and yearbook. Popular campus events include Viking Days, Homecoming, and Christmas Vespers.

Sports: There are 7 intercollegiate sports for men and 6 for women, and 32 intramural sports for men and 32 for women. Athletic and recreation facilities include a 3600-seat gymnasium and a health, physical education, and recreation center.

Disabled Students: Fifty percent of the campus is accessible to disabled students. The following facilities are available: wheelchair ramps, elevators, special parking, specially equipped rest rooms, special class scheduling, and lowered telephones.

Services: In addition to many counseling and information services, tutoring is available in some subjects. In addition, there is remedial math and writing.

Campus Safety and Security: Campus safety and security measures include 24-hour foot and vehicle patrol, escort service, informal discussions, and pamphlets, posters, and films. In addition, there are emergency telephones, lighted pathways and sidewalks, and key card access to residence halls.

Programs of Study: Augustana awards the B.A. degree. Associate and master's degrees also are awarded. Bachelor's degrees are awarded in BIOLOGICAL SCIENCE (biology/biological science), BUSINESS (accounting and business administration and management), COMMUNICATIONS AND THE ARTS (communications, English, fine arts, journalism, music, and speech/debate/rhetoric), COMPUTER AND PHYSICAL SCIENCE (chemistry, computer programming, computer science, earth science, information sciences and systems, mathematics, physics, and science), EDUCATION (art, early childhood, elementary, foreign languages, music, secondary, and special), HEALTH PROFESSIONS (medical laboratory technology, nursing, predentistry, and premedicine), SOCIAL SCIENCE (economics, geography, history, philosophy, political science/government, prelaw, psychology, religion, social science, social work, and sociology). Biology, chemistry, government, English, nursing, and education are the strongest academically. Business, education, special education, and biology have the largest enrollments.

Required: Students must complete 130 semester hours, with 43 in the major, and must maintain a minimum GPA of 2.0. General education requirements total 58 to 60 semester hours.

Special: Internships, study abroad in many countries, and a 3–2 engineering degree with Columbia University or Washington University in St. Louis are offered. Credit for life experience is possible. There are 16 national honor societies on campus. Eleven departments have honors classes.

Faculty/Classroom: Sixty-nine percent of faculty are male; 31%, female. All teach undergraduates and 100% both teach and do research. No introductory courses are taught by graduate students. The average class size in an introductory lecture is 30; in a laboratory, 18; and in a regular course offering, 20.

Admissions: About 95% of the 1993–94 applicants were accepted. The ACT scores for the 1993–94 freshman class were as follows: 30% below 21, 29% between 21 and 23, 18% between 24 and 26, 13% between 27 and 28, and 10% above 28. About 46% of the current freshmen were in the top fifth of their class; 70% were in the top two fifths. There were 3 National Merit finalists.

Requirements: Augustana requires applicants to be in the upper 50% of their class. A minimum GPA of 2.5 is required. The SAT I or ACT is recommended. In addition, graduation from an accredited secondary school is required. A GED will be accepted. Applicants should have completed 4 years of high school English, 3 each of mathematics and science, and 2 each of a foreign language and history. An essay and an interview are recommended. AP and CLEP credits are accepted. Important factors used in the admissions decision are recommendations by school officials, advanced placement or honor courses, leadership record, extracurricular activities record, and personality, intangible qualities.

Procedure: Freshmen are admitted fall, spring, and summer. Entrance exams should be taken in the spring of the junior year. Applications should be filed by August 15 for fall entry and January 15 for spring entry, along with an application fee of $25. Notification is sent on a rolling basis. There are early and deferred admissions plans.

Transfer: About 96 transfer students enrolled in 1993–94. Transfer applicants must have a 2.0 GPA in previous college work. If only 1 semester or 1 quarter has been completed, and applicant has just graduated from high school, then Augustana requires a high school transcript. A total of 30 credits out of 130 must be completed at Augustana.

Visiting: There are guides for informal visits and visitors may sit in on classes and stay overnight at the school. To arrange for a visit, contact the Office of Admission at (800) 727–2844.

Financial Aid: In 1993–94, 93% of all current freshmen and 90% of continuing students received some form of financial aid. About 75% of freshmen and 72% of continuing students received need-based aid. The average freshman award was $8500. Of that total, scholarships or need-based grants averaged $3500; loans averaged $3200; and work contracts averaged $1000. One-hundred-twenty percent of undergraduate students work part-time. Average earnings from campus work for the school year are $850. Augustana is a member of CSS. The FAFSA financial statement is required. The priority deadline for financial aid applications is March.

International Students: There are currently 50 international students enrolled. The school actively recruits these students. They must take the TOEFL and achieve a minimum score of 550.

Computers: The college provides computer facilities for student use. The mainframe is an Encore 310. All students may access the system. There are no time limits on using the system and no fees.

Graduates: In 1992–93, 378 bachelor's degrees were awarded. The most popular majors among graduates were business administration (16%), nursing (8%), and elementary education (7%). Within an average freshman class, 44% graduate in 4 years, 53% in 5 years, and 55% in 6 years. Some 60 companies recruited on campus in 1992–93. In the 1992 graduating class, 20% of the men and 20% of the women were enrolled in graduate school within 6 months of graduation; 90% of the men and 90% of the women had found employment.

Admissions Contact: Robert A. Preloger, Assistant to the President and Dean of Enrollment.

BLACK HILLS STATE UNIVERSITY

A-2

Spearfish, SD 57799-9502

Full-time: 1171 men, 1632 women	(605) 642-6343; (800) 255-2478
Part-time: none	**Faculty:** 103; IIB, --$
Graduate: 67 men and women	**Ph.D.s:** 63%
Year: semesters, summer session	**Student/Faculty:** 27 to 1
Application Deadline: open	**Tuition:** $2220 ($3892)
Freshman Class: 1908 applied, 1908 accepted, 1216 enrolled	**Room & Board:** $2611
ACT: 19	**NONCOMPETITIVE**

Black Hills State University, founded in 1883, is a public, coeducational institution offering undergraduate programs in applied science and technology, arts and humanities, business and public affairs, and education and human resources development. There are 4 undergraduate schools and 1 graduate school. In addition to regional accreditation, Black Hills State University has baccalaureate program accreditation with NCATE. The library contains 141,513 volumes, 355,000 microform items, and 137 audiovisual forms, and subscribes to 598 periodicals. Computerized library sources and services include the card catalog, interlibrary loans, and database searching. Special learning facilities include a learning resource center, art gal-

lery, radio station, and TV station. The 123-acre campus is in a small town 45 miles northwest of Rapid City. Including residence halls, there are 13 buildings on campus.

Student Life: About 72% of undergraduates are from South Dakota. Students come from 39 states, 11 foreign countries, and Canada. Ninety-two percent are white. The average age of freshmen is 19; all undergraduates, 28. Forty percent drop out by the end of their first year; 55% remain to graduate.

Housing: A total of 610 students can be accommodated in college housing. College-sponsored living facilities include single-sex and coed dormitories, on-campus apartments, and married-student housing. On-campus housing is guaranteed for the freshman year only and is available on a first-come, first-served basis. Alcohol is not permitted. All students may keep cars on campus.

Activities: About 2% of men belong to 1 local and 1 national fraternity; about 2% of women belong to 1 local and 1 national sorority. There are 55 groups on campus, including art, band, cheerleading, choir, chorale, chorus, computers, dance, debate, drama, drill team, ethnic, honors, international, jazz band, musical theater, newspaper, pep band, photography, political, professional, radio and TV, religious, social, social service, student government, and yearbook. Popular campus events include Swarm Week (Homecoming) and Big 100 Week.

Sports: There are 4 intercollegiate sports for men and 4 for women, and 20 intramural sports for men and 20 for women. Athletic and recreation facilities include a stadium, a sport and fitness center, tennis courts, swimming pools, a track, a gymnasium, a golf course, and a baseball and softball complex.

Disabled Students: Seventy-five percent of the campus is accessible to disabled students. The following facilities are available: wheelchair ramps, elevators, special parking, specially equipped rest rooms, and lowered drinking fountains.

Services: In addition to many counseling and information services, tutoring is available in most subjects. There is also remedial math.

Campus Safety and Security: Campus safety and security measures include escort service and lighted pathways and sidewalks.

Programs of Study: Black Hills State University awards the B.A., B.S., and B.S.E.D. degrees. Associate and master's degrees also are awarded. Bachelor's degrees are awarded in BIOLOGICAL SCIENCE (biology/biological science), BUSINESS (accounting, business administration and management, hotel/motel and restaurant management, and office supervision and management), COMMUNICATIONS AND THE ARTS (broadcasting, communications, communications technology, dramatic arts, English, fine arts, journalism, music, Spanish, and speech/debate/rhetoric), COMPUTER AND PHYSICAL SCIENCE (chemistry, mathematics, and technology), EDUCATION (art, business, elementary, health, industrial arts, music, science, secondary, and special), SOCIAL SCIENCE (community services, gerontology, history, physical fitness/movement, political science/government, prelaw, psychology, social science, and sociology). Education and business are the strongest academically and have the largest enrollments.

Required: Students must successfully complete 128 credits, with at least 36 in the major, and must maintain a minimum GPA of 2.0. Core curriculum requirements include courses in English, speech, psychology, mathematics, science, non-Western cultures, and physical education. All students must pass an English proficiency examination.

Special: The university offers a co-op program in social work, cross-registration with the University of South Dakota, internships, work-study programs, a B.A.-B.S. degree, dual majors, a general studies degree, credit by examination, credit for military service, nondegree study, and pass/fail options. Composite majors offered include marketing, environmental physical science, outdoor education, tourism, and wellness management. A library media major is possible in conjunction with a second major. There are 5 national honor societies on campus.

Faculty/Classroom: Seventy-six percent of faculty are male; 24%, female. No introductory courses are taught by graduate students. The average class size in an introductory lecture is 120; in a laboratory, 20; and in a regular course offering, 30.

Admissions: All the 1993–94 applicants were accepted. The ACT scores for the 1993–94 freshman class were as follows: 68% below 21, 20% between 21 and 23, 9% between 24 and 26, 2% between 27 and 28, and 1% above 28. About 17% of the current freshmen were in the top fifth of their class; 40% were in the top two fifths. Three freshmen graduated first in their class.

Requirements: The university requires applicants to be in the upper two thirds of their class. A minimum GPA of 2.0 is required. The SAT I or ACT is required. Graduation from an accredited secondary school is required; a GED will be accepted. Applicants must have completed the following academic credits with a minimum GPA of 2.0: 4 years of English, 3 of social studies, 2 each of mathematics and science, and 1/2 year each of fine arts and computer science. AP and CLEP credits are accepted.

Procedure: Freshmen are admitted to all sessions. Entrance exams should be taken during senior year in high school. Application deadlines are open. The application fee is $15. Notification is sent on a rolling basis. There is an early admissions plan.

Transfer: Some 419 transfer students enrolled in 1993–94. Transfer students must supply transcripts from all previous schools attended, high school and college, and must have maintained a minimum college GPA of 2.0. A total of 32 credits out of 128 must be completed at Black Hills State University.

Visiting: There are regularly scheduled orientations for prospective students. There are guides for informal visits and visitors may sit in on classes and stay overnight at the school. To arrange for a visit, contact the Admissions Office at (605) 642–6343 or (800) 255–2478.

Financial Aid: In 1993–94 70% of all current freshmen and 60% of continuing students received some form of financial aid. About 79% of freshmen and 65% of continuing students received need-based aid. The average freshman award was $2768. Of that total, scholarships or need-based grants averaged $772 ($2400 maximum); loans averaged $950 ($2625 maximum); and work contracts averaged $916 ($1400 maximum). Five percent of undergraduate students work part-time. Average earnings from campus work for the school year are $916. The average financial indebtedness of the 1992–93 graduate was $9928. The FAF or FFS and the PHEAA are required. The deadline for financial aid applications is April 1.

International Students: There are currently 11 international students enrolled. They must take the TOEFL and achieve a minimum score of 520.

Computers: The college provides computer facilities for student use. The mainframe is an IBM. More than 200 microcomputer terminals are available in residence halls, the main classroom building, and the library. All students may access the system. It may be used during laboratory and library hours. There are no time limits on using the system and no fees.

Graduates: In a recent year, 339 bachelor's degrees were awarded. The most popular majors among graduates were education (42%), business (26%), and social sciences (9%). Within an average freshman class, 20% graduate in 4 years, 45% in 5 years, and 15% in 6 years.

Admissions Contact: Office of Admissions and Records.

DAKOTA STATE UNIVERSITY

E-3

Madison, SD 57042   (605) 256–5139; (800) 952–3230 (out-of-state)

Full-time: 419 men, 545 women	Faculty: 56
Part-time: 134 men, 465 women	Ph.D.s: 41%
Graduate: none	Student/Faculty: 17 to 1
Year: semesters, summer session	Tuition: $2014 ($3476)
Application Deadline: open	Room & Board: $2360
Freshman Class: 313 applied, 290 accepted, 185 enrolled	
ACT: 20	LESS COMPETITIVE

Dakota State University, founded in 1881, is a public, coeducational institution offering undergraduate programs through the School of Education and the colleges of Business and Information Systems, Science and Mathematics, and Liberal Arts. There are 4 undergraduate schools. In addition to regional accreditation, DSU has baccalaureate program accreditation with AHEA. The library contains 100,000 volumes and 4000 microform items, and subscribes to 644 periodicals. Computerized library sources and services include the card catalog, interlibrary loans, and database searching. Special learning facilities include a learning resource center and natural history museum. The 40-acre campus is in a small town 45 miles northwest of Sioux Falls. Including residence halls, there are 17 buildings on campus.

Student Life: About 94% of undergraduates are from South Dakota. Students come from 38 states, 20 foreign countries, and Canada. Ninety-four percent are from public schools; 6% from private. Ninety-eight percent are white.

Housing: A total of 630 students can be accommodated in college housing. College-sponsored living facilities include single-sex and coed dormitories. On-campus housing is guaranteed for the freshman year only, is available on a first-come, first-served basis, and is available on a lottery system for upperclassmen. Sixty-five percent of students commute. Alcohol is not permitted. All students may keep cars on campus.

Activities: There are no fraternities or sororities on campus. There are many groups and organizations on campus, including art, band, cheerleading, choir, chorale, chorus, computers, drama, ethnic, honors, international, literary magazine, musical theater, newspaper, pep band, political, religious, student government, and yearbook. Popular campus events include Homecoming, Spring Classic Week, and Discover DSU Days.

Sports: There are 8 intercollegiate sports for men and 7 for women, and 20 intramural sports for men and 20 for women. Athletic and recreation facilities include courts for basketball and racquetball, a football field, a weight room, and a swimming pool.

Disabled Students: Seventy-seven percent of the campus is accessible to disabled students. The following facilities are available: elevators, special parking, specially equipped rest rooms, special class scheduling, and lowered drinking fountains.

Services: In addition to many counseling and information services, tutoring is available in every subject. There is also remedial math, reading, and writing.

Campus Safety and Security: Campus safety and security measures include pamphlets, posters, and films, lighted pathways and sidewalks, and a foot patrol.

Programs of Study: DSU awards the B.S., B.B.A., B.S.Ed., and associate degrees. Bachelor's degrees are awarded in BIOLOGICAL SCIENCE (biology/biological science), BUSINESS (business administration and management), COMMUNICATIONS AND THE ARTS (English, fine arts, and music), COMPUTER AND PHYSICAL SCIENCE (chemistry, computer programming, computer science, information sciences and systems, mathematics, and physics), EDUCATION (art, business, elementary, health, music, and secondary), HEALTH PROFESSIONS (medical laboratory technology, premedicine, and respiratory therapy). Business administration and information systems are the strongest academically. Business administration and information systems have the largest enrollments.

Required: To graduate, students must complete 128 semester hours, of which 12 must be in the major and 16 at the 300–400 course level. A 2.0 GPA and 43 hours of general education are also required. Students must take the Computer Concepts and Health courses. All candidates for graduation must apply formally to the Registration and Academic Records Office.

Special: The university offers co-op programs with South Dakota State University, internships, study abroad in London, and on-campus work-study programs. Also available are the general studies degree, credit for life, military, and work experience, nondegree study, and pass/fail options. There is a freshman honors program on campus, as well as 2 national honor societies.

Faculty/Classroom: Sixty-two percent of faculty are male; 38%, female. The average class size in an introductory lecture is 40; in a laboratory, 25; and in a regular course offering, 20.

Admissions: About 93% of the 1993–94 applicants were accepted. The ACT scores for the 1993–94 freshman class were as follows: 58% below 21, 25% between 21 and 23, 11% between 24 and 26, 4% between 27 and 28, and 1% above 28. About 15% of the current freshmen were in the top fifth of their class; 40% were in the top two fifths. About 3 freshmen graduated first in their class.

Requirements: DSU requires applicants to be in the upper 67% of their class. A minimum GPA of 2.0 is required. The SAT I or ACT is required, with a minimum composite score of 20 on the ACT. In addition, applicants must be graduates of an accredited secondary school or have a GED certificate, and have completed 4 years of English, 2 or 3 years each of mathematics and science, 3 years of social studies, and 1/2 year of computer science. CLEP credit is accepted.

Procedure: Freshmen are admitted to all sessions. Entrance exams should be taken before students register for classes. Application deadlines are open and the application fee is $15. Notification is sent on a rolling basis.

Transfer: About 279 transfer students enrolled in an earlier year. Transfer applicants must have a minimum 2.0 GPA. A total of 32 credits out of 128 must be completed at DSU.

Visiting: There are regularly scheduled orientations for prospective students. There are guides for informal visits and visitors may sit in on classes and stay overnight at the school. To arrange for a visit, contact the Admissions Office at (605) 256–5139.

Financial Aid: In 1993–94, 90% of all current freshmen and 90% of continuing students received some form of financial aid. About 84% of freshmen and 74% of continuing students received need-based aid. The average freshman award was $3499. Of that total, scholarships or need-based grants averaged $475 ($2000 maximum); loans averaged $2000 ($2625 maximum); and work contracts averaged $1700 ($1700 maximum). Seventy-five percent of undergraduate students work part-time. Average earnings from campus work for the school year are $1700. The average financial indebtedness of the 1992–93 graduate was $5697. The FAF, FFS or SFS and the EAC-PHEA is required. The deadline for financial aid applications is March 1.

International Students: There are currently 21 international students enrolled. They must take the TOEFL and achieve a minimum score of 550.

Computers: The college provides computer facilities for student use. The mainframe is an IBM 4361. There are 11 computer laboratories on campus, plus an additional 4 in residence halls. All the mainframe dump terminals are located in 1 laboratory. All laboratories are networked allowing all students to access the system. There are no time limits on using the system and no fees.

Graduates: In a prior year 120 bachelor's degrees were awarded. The most popular majors among graduates were business administration (46%), education (22%), and computer and information systems

(11%). Recently some 16 companies recruited on campus. In the 1992 graduating class, 85% of the men and 85% of the women had found employment within 6 months of graduation.

Admissions Contact: Mark Weiss, Director of Admissions.

DAKOTA WESLEYAN UNIVERSITY E-3

Mitchell, SD 57301   (605) 995-2650; (800) 333-8506 (out-of-state)

Full-time: 236 men, 286 women	**Faculty:** 40; IIB, --$
Part-time: 35 men, 111 women	**Ph.D.s:** 38%
Graduate: 2 women	**Student/Faculty:** 13 to 1
Year: semesters, summer session	**Tuition:** $7110
Application Deadline: August 26	**Room & Board:** $2660
Freshman Class: 496 applied, 421 accepted, 204 enrolled	
ACT: 20	**LESS COMPETITIVE**

Dakota Wesleyan University, founded in 1885, is a private, coeducational, liberal arts institution affiliated with the United Methodist Church. There is one undergraduate and one graduate school. In addition to regional accreditation, DWU has baccalaureate program accreditation with NLN. The library contains 65,000 volumes, 12,000 microform items, and 7360 audiovisual forms, and subscribes to 3500 periodicals. Computerized library sources and services include the card catalog and database searching. The 40-acre campus is in a small town 65 miles west of Sioux Falls. Including residence halls, there are 10 buildings on campus.

Student Life: About 87% of undergraduates are from South Dakota. Students come from 11 states and 4 foreign countries. Ninety-nine percent are from public schools. Ninety-one percent are white. Fifty-eight percent are Protestant; 31% Catholic; 11% claim no religious affiliation. The average age of freshmen is 19; all undergraduates, 24. Thirty-five percent drop out by the end of their first year; 42% remain to graduate.

Housing: A total of 325 students can be accommodated in college housing. College-sponsored living facilities include single-sex dormitories and off-campus apartments. On-campus housing is guaranteed for the freshman year only and is available on a first-come, first-served basis. Sixty-eight percent of students commute. Alcohol is not permitted. All students may keep cars on campus.

Activities: There are no fraternities or sororities on campus. There are 16 groups on campus, including cheerleading, choir, chorale, chorus, drama, honors, international, literary magazine, musical theater, newspaper, pep band, professional, religious, social, social service, student government, and yearbook. Popular campus events include Homecoming, Prom, Spring Week, theatrical productions, dances, Stark Lecture Series, and Family Life Conference.

Sports: There are 5 intercollegiate sports for men and 4 for women, and 5 intramural sports for men and 4 for women. Athletic and recreation facilities include a wellness center, a 500-seat stadium, and a 3500-seat auditorium/arena.

Disabled Students: Twenty percent of the campus is accessible to disabled students. The following facilities are available: wheelchair ramps, elevators, special parking, and specially equipped rest rooms.

Services: In addition to many counseling and information services, tutoring is available in every subject. In addition, there is a reader service for the blind, and remedial math, reading, and writing.

Campus Safety and Security: Campus safety and security measures include 24-hour foot and vehicle patrol, escort service, informal discussions, and pamphlets, posters, and films. In addition, there are emergency telephones and lighted pathways and sidewalks.

Programs of Study: DWU awards the B.A. degree. Associate and master's degrees also are awarded. Bachelor's degrees are awarded in BIOLOGICAL SCIENCE (biology/biological science), BUSINESS (accounting and business administration and management), COMMUNICATIONS AND THE ARTS (English and fine arts), COMPUTER AND PHYSICAL SCIENCE (mathematics), EDUCATION (elementary and secondary), HEALTH PROFESSIONS (predentistry and premedicine), SOCIAL SCIENCE (history, philosophy, prelaw, psychology, religion, and sociology). Business and education are the strongest academically. Business, education, and human services have the largest enrollments.

Required: To graduate, students must complete a total of 128 credit hours, with 29 to 45 hours in the major, 39 hours in general education, and at least 48 hours of upper-level credit. A minimum 2.0 GPA is required.

Special: The university offers internships, co-op programs, work-study programs, a general studies degree, credit for experience, and pass/fail options. There is a freshman honors program on campus, as well as 4 national honor societies, including Phi Beta Kappa. Two departments have honors programs.

Faculty/Classroom: Sixty-five percent of faculty are male; 35%, female. All teach undergraduates. No introductory courses are taught by graduate students. The average class size in an introductory lecture is 32; in a laboratory, 20; and in a regular course offering, 21.

Admissions: About 85% of the 1993-94 applicants were accepted. The ACT scores for the 1993-94 freshman class were as follows: 63% below 21, 19% between 21 and 23, 13% between 24 and 26, 1% between 27 and 28, and 4% above 28. About 32% of the current freshmen were in the top fifth of their class; 47% were in the top two fifths. One freshman graduated first in her class.

Requirements: A minimum GPA of 2.0 is required. The SAT I or ACT is required. Applicants must be graduates of an accredited secondary school or have a GED certificate. An interview is recommended. AP and CLEP credits are accepted.

Procedure: Freshmen are admitted to all sessions. Entrance exams should be taken during the senior year of high school. Applications should be filed by August 26 for fall entry, January 13 for spring entry, and June 4 for summer entry, along with an application fee of $15. Notification is sent on a rolling basis.

Transfer: Eighty-six transfer students enrolled in 1993-94. DWU will accept all credits from accredited institutions, but half the credits for the student's major must be completed at DWU. The last 32 semester hours out of 128 must be completed at DWU.

Visiting: There are regularly scheduled orientations for prospective students, including campus tours and meetings with faculty and students. There are guides for informal visits and visitors may sit in on classes and stay overnight at the school. To arrange for a visit, contact the Admission Office at (800) 333-8506.

Financial Aid: In 1993-94, 88% of all current freshmen and 79% of continuing students received some form of financial aid. About 76% of freshmen and 75% of continuing students received need-based aid. The average freshman award was $7564. Of that total, scholarships or need-based grants averaged $3229 ($7000 maximum); loans averaged $3980 ($9060 maximum); and work contracts averaged $1010 ($1440 maximum). Sixty percent of undergraduate students work part-time. Average earnings from campus work for the school year are $1025. The average financial indebtedness of the 1992-93 graduate was $10,903. DWU is a member of CSS. The FAF or FFS and the EAC - Preference are required. The deadline for financial aid applications is August 15.

International Students: The school actively recruits these students. They must take the TOEFL and achieve a minimum score of 500. The student must also take the SAT I or the ACT.

Computers: The college provides computer facilities for student use. The mainframe is an IBM System/36. There are 65 IBM and Apple microcomputers available for student use in laboratories, residence halls, and the library. All students may access the system. There are no fees.

Graduates: In 1992-93, 83 bachelor's degrees were awarded. The most popular majors among graduates were business (31%), education (18%), and human services (10%). Within an average freshman class, 44% graduate in 4 years, 15% in 5 years, and 2% in 6 years.

Admissions Contact: Melinda Larson, Director of Admission.

HURON UNIVERSITY E-2

Huron, SD 57350-2798   (605) 352-8721; (800) 942-5826

Full-time: 207 men, 192 women	**Faculty:** 36
Part-time: 27 men, 51 women	**Ph.D.s:** 25%
Graduate: 16 men, 12 women	**Student/Faculty:** 11 to 1
Year: semesters, summer session	**Tuition:** $6850
Application Deadline: open	**Room & Board:** $2940
Freshman Class: 850 applied, 518 accepted, 168 enrolled	
ACT: 18	**COMPETITIVE**

Huron University, established as Huron College in 1883, is a private institution offering career-oriented programs in the arts and sciences, nursing, and professional studies. There are 4 undergraduate schools and 1 graduate school. The library contains 62,000 volumes, and subscribes to 300 periodicals. Special learning facilities include a learning resource center. The 15-acre campus is in a small town 120 miles northwest of Sioux Falls. Including residence halls, there are 7 buildings on campus.

Student Life: About 70% of undergraduates are from South Dakota. Students come from 26 states, 14 foreign countries, and Canada. Sixty-eight percent are white. The average age of all undergraduates is 23.

Housing: A total of 300 students can be accommodated in college housing. College-sponsored living facilities include coed dormitories and on-campus apartments. On-campus housing is guaranteed for all 4 years. Fifty percent of students live on campus; of those, 85% remain on campus on weekends. Alcohol is not permitted. All students may keep cars on campus.

Activities: There are no fraternities or sororities on campus. There are 15 groups on campus, including cheerleading, computers, ethnic, honors, international, newspaper, pep band, professional, religious, social, social service, and student government. Popular campus events include Pow Wow Days, Paddle Days, Homecoming, and International Student Day.

Sports: There are 6 intercollegiate sports for men and 5 for women, and 15 intramural sports for men and 14 for women. Athletic and recreation facilities include saunas, an exercise room, a 2800-seat recreation center, and a 5000-seat arena.

Disabled Students: Seventy-five percent of the campus is accessible to disabled students. The following facilities are available: wheelchair ramps, special parking, specially equipped rest rooms, special class scheduling, lowered drinking fountains, and a portable chair lift.

Services: In addition to many counseling and information services, tutoring is available in every subject. There is also remedial math, reading, and writing.

Campus Safety and Security: Campus safety and security measures include informal discussions, pamphlets, posters, and films, lighted pathways and sidewalks, and a night watchman.

Programs of Study: The university awards the B.A. and B.S. degrees. Associate and master's degrees also are awarded. Bachelor's degrees are awarded in BUSINESS (business administration and management, hotel/motel and restaurant management, and management science), COMMUNICATIONS AND THE ARTS (communications), COMPUTER AND PHYSICAL SCIENCE (computer science), EDUCATION (business, elementary, and secondary), ENGINEERING AND ENVIRONMENTAL DESIGN (preengineering), HEALTH PROFESSIONS (predentistry and premedicine), SOCIAL SCIENCE (criminal justice, history, prelaw, psychology, social science, and social work). Nursing is the strongest academically. Business administration has the largest enrollment.

Required: To graduate, students must complete at least 120 to 128 credit hours with a minimum GPA of 2.0. Required courses include an introduction to higher education, computers, career planning, and other general education classes.

Special: The university offers cooperative programs, cross-registration, internships, study abroad, work-study programs, general studies and B.A.-B.S. degrees, dual majors, credit for life experience, nondegree study, and pass/fail options. There are 5 national honor societies on campus. Five departments have honors programs.

Faculty/Classroom: Fifty percent of faculty are male; 50%, female. The average class size in an introductory lecture is 30; in a laboratory, 15; and in a regular course offering, 20.

Admissions: About 61% of the 1993–94 applicants were accepted. The ACT scores for the 1993–94 freshman class were as follows: 76% below 21, 19% between 21 and 23, 4% between 24 and 26, and 1% between 27 and 28.

Requirements: The university requires applicants to be in the upper 75% of their class. A minimum GPA of 2.0 is required. The ACT, with a minimum composite score of 15, or the SAT I, with a minimum score of 700, is required. Applicants must be graduates of an accredited secondary school or have a GED certificate. An interview is recommended. CLEP credit is accepted. Important factors used in the admissions decision are leadership record, advanced placement or honor courses, recommendations by school officials, parents or siblings attending the school, and extracurricular activities record.

Procedure: Freshmen are admitted to all sessions. Entrance exams should be taken during the senior year. Application deadlines are open. Notification is sent on a rolling basis.

Transfer: Some 79 transfer students enrolled in 1993–94. A total of 32 credits out of 120 to 128 must be completed at the university.

Visiting: There are regularly scheduled orientations for prospective students. There are guides for informal visits and visitors may sit in on classes and stay overnight at the school. To arrange for a visit, contact Robert West, Director of Admissions, at (605) 352–8721 or (800) 942–5826.

Financial Aid: In a recent year, 95% of all students received some form of financial aid. About 75% of all students received need-based aid. The average freshman award was $6025. Of that total, scholarships or need-based grants averaged $2500 ($3950 maximum); loans averaged $2625 (maximum); and work contracts averaged $900 ($1200 maximum). Sixty-five percent of undergraduate students worked part-time. Average earnings from campus work for the school year were $1200. The average financial indebtedness of a recent graduate was $3313. The FAF or FFS, and the PHEAA are required.

International Students: There are currently 28 international students enrolled. The school actively recruits these students. They must take the TOEFL and achieve a minimum score of 500. The student must also take the SAT I or the ACT.

Computers: The college provides computer facilities for student use. There are 30 IBM PCs available in the computer laboratory in the library. There are no time limits on using the system and no fees.

Graduates: In 1992–93 69 bachelor's degrees were awarded. The most popular majors among graduates were business (41%), education (24%), and nursing (16%). Some 15 companies recruited on campus in 1992–93. In the 1992 graduating class, 2% of the men and 5% of the women were enrolled in graduate school within 6 months of graduation; 97% of the men and 95% of the women had found em-

ployment.

Admissions Contact: Robert West, Director of Admissions.

MOUNT MARTY COLLEGE
C-4
Yankton, SD 57078 (800) 658–4552

Full-time: 196 men, 446 women	Faculty: 59; IIB, --$
Part-time: 99 men, 311 women	Ph.D.s: 80%
Graduate: 22 men, 23 women	Student/Faculty: 11 to 1
Year: 4–1–4, summer session	Tuition: $7470
Application Deadline: August 15	Room & Board: $2980
Freshman Class: 280 applied, 276 accepted, 126 enrolled	
ACT: 22	**NONCOMPETITIVE**

Mount Marty College is a private, Catholic, liberal arts institution that was founded in 1936 by the Sisters of Saint Benedict. There is one graduate school. In addition to regional accreditation, Mount Marty has baccalaureate program accreditation with ADA and NLN. The library contains 76,000 volumes, 8000 microform items, and 6500 audiovisual forms, and subscribes to 600 periodicals. Computerized library sources and services include the card catalog, interlibrary loans, and database searching. Special learning facilities include a learning resource center, art gallery, and radio station. The 80-acre campus is in a small town 60 miles northwest of Sioux City, Iowa, and 80 miles southwest of Sioux Falls. Including residence halls, there are 11 buildings on campus.

Student Life: About 60% of undergraduates are from South Dakota. Students come from 28 states, 5 foreign countries, and Canada. Eighty percent are from public schools; 20% from private. Ninety-eight percent are white. Most are Catholic. The average age of freshmen is 20; all undergraduates, 23. Twelve percent drop out by the end of their first year; 65% remain to graduate.

Housing: A total of 380 students can be accommodated in college housing. College-sponsored living facilities include single-sex dormitories. On-campus housing is guaranteed for all 4 years. Seventy-five percent of students live on campus; of those, 70% remain on campus on weekends. Alcohol is not permitted. All students may keep cars on campus.

Activities: There are no fraternities or sororities on campus. There are 15 groups on campus, including band, cheerleading, choir, chorus, drill team, honors, literary magazine, newspaper, orchestra, photography, political, radio and TV, religious, and student government. Popular campus events include Parents Weekend, Oktoberfest, and Pig Roast.

Sports: There are 4 intercollegiate sports for men and 4 for women, and 10 intramural sports for men and 10 for women. Athletic and recreation facilities include volleyball and basketball courts, a jogging track, 2 racquetball courts, weight and training rooms, a 2220-seat stadium, a 1500-seat indoor gymnasium, and a 700-seat auditorium.

Disabled Students: The entire campus is accessible to disabled students. The following facilities are available: wheelchair ramps, elevators, special parking, specially equipped rest rooms, special class scheduling, and lowered drinking fountains.

Services: In addition to many counseling and information services, tutoring is available in most subjects. There is also remedial math, reading, and writing.

Campus Safety and Security: Campus safety and security measures include 24-hour foot and vehicle patrol, informal discussions, emergency telephones, and lighted pathways and sidewalks.

Programs of Study: Mount Marty awards the B.A. and B.S. degrees. Associate and master's degrees also are awarded. Bachelor's degrees are awarded in BIOLOGICAL SCIENCE (biology/biological science), BUSINESS (accounting), COMMUNICATIONS AND THE ARTS (communications, English, and music), COMPUTER AND PHYSICAL SCIENCE (chemistry and mathematics), EDUCATION (elementary, middle school, music, science, secondary, and special), HEALTH PROFESSIONS (medical laboratory technology and nursing), SOCIAL SCIENCE (religion and social science). Nursing, business, teacher education, and biology are the strongest academically. Business, nursing, and teacher education have the largest enrollments.

Required: To graduate, all students must complete at least 128 credit hours and 8 interim credits, with a minimum 2.0 GPA. Students are required to complete 10 credit hours in Values, Beliefs, and Thinking and Aesthetics and Culture, 9 in Communication and Socialization and Culture, and 8 in Order and Quantification.

Special: Mount Marty offers cross-registration with the Colleges of Middle America, co-op programs, a 3–2 engineering degree with Georgia Institute of Technology, internships, student-designed majors in selected studies, multi- and interdisciplinary majors, including health, physical education, and recreation, and nutrition and food science, credit for work, life, and military experience, and pass/fail options. There is a freshman honors program on campus, as well as 5 national honor societies. Five departments have honors programs.

Faculty/Classroom: No introductory courses are taught by graduate students. The average class size in an introductory lecture is 30 and in a laboratory, 30.

Admissions: About 99% of the 1993–94 applicants were accepted. The ACT scores for the 1993–94 freshman class were as follows: 19% below 21, 42% between 21 and 23, 23% between 24 and 26, 12% between 27 and 28, and 4% above 28.

Requirements: The SAT I or ACT is required. Applicants must be graduates of an accredited secondary school or have a GED certificate. An audition and an interview are recommended. AP and CLEP credits are accepted.

Procedure: Freshmen are admitted fall, spring, and summer. Entrance exams should be taken by October of the senior year. Applications should be filed by August 15 for fall entry, January 15 for winter entry, February 1 for spring entry, and May 15 for summer entry, along with an application fee of $10. Notification is sent on a rolling basis. There are early decision and deferred admissions plans. Ten early decision candidates were accepted for the 1993–94 class.

Transfer: Some 70 transfer students enrolled in 1993–94. Transfer students with fewer than 28 semester hours must submit high school and college transcripts. A minimum 2.0 GPA and at least 64 credit hours are required. An interview is recommended. A total of 32 credits out of 128 must be completed at Mount Marty.

Visiting: There are regularly scheduled orientations for prospective students. There are guides for informal visits and visitors may sit in on classes and stay overnight at the school. To arrange for a visit, contact the Director of Admissions at (800) 658–4552.

Financial Aid: In 1993–94 90% of all current freshmen and 95% of continuing students received some form of financial aid. The average freshman award was $6800. Of that total, scholarships or need-based grants averaged $900 ($2480 maximum); loans averaged $2100 ($2625 maximum); and work contracts averaged $555 ($1000 maximum). Average earnings from campus work for the school year are $870. The average financial indebtedness of the 1992–93 graduate was $9900. The FAF, FFS, or SFS is required. The deadline for financial aid applications is March.

International Students: There are currently 8 international students enrolled. The school actively recruits these students. They must take the TOEFL and achieve a minimum score of 500.

Computers: The college provides computer facilities for student use. The mainframe is a DEC PDP 11/44. There are also 30 Apple IIe, IBM PC, and Epson Equity 1 + microcomputers available in an academic building and the library. All students may access the system. It may be used 24 hours a day, 7 days per week. There are no time limits on using the system. The fees are $50 per semester.

Graduates: In 1992–93 98 bachelor's degrees were awarded. Some 26 companies recruited on campus in 1992–93. In the 1992 graduating class, 3% of the men and 5% of the women were enrolled in graduate school within 6 months of graduation; 95% of the men and 98% of the women had found employment.

Admissions Contact: Paula Tacke, Admissions Director.

NATIONAL COLLEGE

Rapid City, SD 57709–1780

B-3

(605) 394–4827

(800) 843–8892 (out-of-state)

Full-time: 226 men and women	**Faculty:** 26
Part-time: 37 men and women	**Ph.D.s:** 5%
Graduate: none	**Student/Faculty:** 9 to 1
Year: quarters, summer session	**Tuition:** $5875
Application Deadline: open	**Room & Board:** $3180
Freshman Class: 200 applied, 200 accepted, 100 enrolled	
ACT: required	**NONCOMPETITIVE**

National College, founded in 1941, is a private institution that offers undergraduate programs in business administration, travel, allied health, and computer information systems. The college has branch campuses in Sioux Falls and at Ellsworth Air Force Base, South Dakota; Albuquerque, New Mexico; St. Paul, Minnesota; Kansas City, Missouri; and Pueblo, Colorado Springs, and Denver, Colorado. There are 4 undergraduate schools. In addition to regional accreditation, National has baccalaureate program accreditation with CAHEA. The library contains 32,500 volumes, 15,894 microform items, and 1494 audiovisual forms, and subscribes to 435 periodicals. Computerized library sources and services include interlibrary loans and database searching. Special learning facilities include a learning resource center. The Animal Health Care Center and Medical Assisting Room are instructional facilities set up as doctors' offices. The 8-acre campus is in a small city. Including residence halls, there are 7 buildings on campus.

Student Life: About 53% of undergraduates are from South Dakota. Students come from 25 states and 6 foreign countries. Eighty percent are white; 15% Native American/Eskimo.

Housing: A total of 260 students can be accommodated in college housing. College-sponsored living facilities include dormitories. On-campus housing is guaranteed for all 4 years. Seventy-one percent of students commute. Alcohol is not permitted. All students may keep cars on campus.

Activities: There are 2 local and 1 national fraternities and 2 local and 1 national sororities. There are 16 groups on campus, including cheerleading, choir, computers, ethnic, international, political, professional, social, social service, and student government. Popular campus events include Maverick Day, spring and fall picnics, dances, concerts, rodeo, Miss National College, and fashion shows.

Sports: There are 2 intercollegiate sports for men and 3 for women, and 12 intramural sports for men and 11 for women. Athletic and recreation facilities include an 11,000-seat auditorium/arena, volleyball, basketball, and tennis courts, a 500-seat gymnasium, a weight room, and golf, rodeo, bowling, and table tennis facilities. The Student Senate pays half the cost of a YMCA membership for students.

Disabled Students: Virtually the entire campus is accessible to disabled students. The following facilities are available: wheelchair ramps, elevators, special parking, and lowered drinking fountains.

Services: In addition to many counseling and information services, tutoring is available in most subjects. There is also remedial math, reading, and writing. Some technical classes are tutored by instructors.

Programs of Study: National awards the B.S. degree. Associate degrees also are awarded. Bachelor's degrees are awarded in BUSINESS (accounting, business administration and management, and management science), COMPUTER AND PHYSICAL SCIENCE (computer programming), SOCIAL SCIENCE (paralegal studies). Accounting, paralegal studies, and business administration are the strongest programs academically. Business administration, management, accounting, and paralegal studies have the largest enrollments.

Required: To graduate, students must complete 192 quarter credit hours with a 2.0 GPA. Students are required to take 76 hours of general education courses, including 12 hours each of communications, mathematics, social science, and humanities, 8 hours of science, 4 hours of speech, and 16 hours of electives.

Special: National offers internships in travel and paralegal studies, study abroad in France and Switzerland, work-study programs on campus and with nonprofit organizations, accelerated degree programs in all majors, B.A.-B.S. degrees in accounting, computer information systems, business administration, paralegal studies, and applied management, and dual majors in accounting/computer information systems. A general studies degree, credit for life experience, nondegree study, and pass/fail options are also available. Operation Bootstrap allows qualified U.S. Air Force personnel to complete their college degrees on an accelerated basis.

Faculty/Classroom: Sixty-one percent of faculty are male; 39%, female. All teach undergraduates. The average class size in an introductory lecture is 30; in a laboratory, 10; and in a regular course offering, 25.

Admissions: All of the 1993–94 applicants were accepted.

Requirements: The ACT is required. Applicants must be graduates of an accredited secondary school or have the GED. An interview is recommended. CLEP credit is accepted.

Procedure: Freshmen are admitted to all sessions. Entrance exams should be taken before the end of the first quarter. Application deadlines are open. The application fee is $25. The college accepts all applicants. Notification is sent on a rolling basis.

Transfer: About 193 transfer students enrolled in an earlier year. Applicants must submit transcripts of all previous college work. Grades of C or better transfer for credit. A total of 48 quarter credit hours out of 192 must be completed at National.

Visiting: There are regularly scheduled orientations for prospective students. There are guides for informal visits and visitors may sit in on classes and stay overnight at the school. To arrange for a visit, contact the Admissions Office at (605) 394–4827.

Financial Aid: In an earlier year, 78% of all freshmen and 86% of continuing students received some form of financial aid. Scholarships or need-based grants averaged $600 ($1200 maximum); loans averaged $2625 ($3525 maximum); and work contracts averaged $1800 ($2400 maximum). The average financial indebtedness of a recent graduate was $8424. National is a member of CSS. The FAF, FFS, or SFS is required.

International Students: The school actively recruits international students. They must take the TOEFL and achieve a minimum score of 490.

Computers: The college provides computer facilities for student use. The mainframe is an NCR 9300. There are also 18 Commodore Colts, Sperry, IBM, and Tandy 1000 PCs available for student use. The facilities may be used from 7 A.M. to 8 P.M. Students may access the system 90 minutes, if another student is waiting. There are no fees.

Graduates: In an earlier class, 74 bachelor's degrees were awarded. Some 12 companies recruited on campus in an earlier year. In an earlier graduating class, 3% of all students were enrolled in graduate school within 6 months of graduation; 85% had found employment.

Admissions Contact: Polly J. Thomas, Administrative Secretary, Admissions Department.

NORTHERN STATE UNIVERSITY

D-1

Aberdeen, SD 57401   (605) 622-2544; (800) 678-5330 (out-of-state)

Full-time: 978 men, 1223 women	Faculty: 128; IIA, --$
Part-time: 205 men, 350 women	Ph.D.s: 80%
Graduate: 70 men, 145 women	Student/Faculty: 17 to 1
Year: semesters, summer session	Tuition: $2120 ($3792)
Application Deadline: August 15	Room & Board: $2066
Freshman Class: 1050 applied, 1022 accepted, 671 enrolled	
ACT: 20	LESS COMPETITIVE

Northern State University, established in 1901, is a state-supported institution offering undergraduate and graduate programs in the liberal arts and sciences, business, and education. There are 4 undergraduate schools and one graduate school. In addition to regional accreditation, Northern State has baccalaureate program accreditation with AACSB, NASM, and NCATE. The library contains 1,520,750 volumes and 87,640 microform items, and subscribes to 939 periodicals. Computerized library sources and services include the card catalog, interlibrary loans, and database searching. Special learning facilities include a learning resource center, art gallery, radio station, TV station, and fine arts center. The 52-acre campus is in an urban area one-half mile south of Aberdeen. Including residence halls, there are 21 buildings on campus.

Student Life: About 35% of undergraduates are from South Dakota. Students come from Canada. Ninety-six percent are white. The average age of freshmen is 18; all undergraduates, 22. About 50% of freshmen remain to graduate.

Housing: A total of 930 students can be accommodated in college housing. College-sponsored living facilities include single-sex and coed dormitories. On-campus housing is guaranteed for all 4 years. Seventy percent of students commute. Alcohol is not permitted. All students may keep cars on campus.

Activities: There are no fraternities or sororities on campus. There are 100 groups on campus, including art, band, cheerleading, chess, choir, chorus, computers, dance, drama, drill team, honors, international, jazz band, marching band, musical theater, newspaper, orchestra, photography, political, radio and TV, religious, social, social service, student government, symphony, and yearbook. Popular campus events include Gypsy Day, Gypsy Week, and I Hate Winter Weekend.

Sports: Athletic and recreation facilities include a sports complex, which houses a football stadium and an all-weather track, and a physical education building, which houses a 160-meter track, an Olympic-size pool, a weight room, 3 racquetball courts, a human performance laboratory, 2 basketball courts, and an 8300-seat arena.

Disabled Students: Ninety percent of the campus is accessible to disabled students. The following facilities are available: wheelchair ramps, elevators, special parking, specially equipped rest rooms, lowered drinking fountains, lowered telephones, and curb cuts.

Services: In addition to many counseling and information services, tutoring is available in most subjects. In addition, there is remedial math, reading, and writing. There is an educational media center, a mathematics laboratory, reading and writing centers, and a speech, language, and hearing clinic.

Campus Safety and Security: Campus safety and security measures include self defense education, informal discussions, pamphlets, posters, and films, and lighted pathways and sidewalks.

Programs of Study: Northern State awards the B.A., B.S., B.M.E., and B.S.Ed. degrees. Associate and master's degrees also are awarded. Bachelor's degrees are awarded in BIOLOGICAL SCIENCE (biology/biological science), BUSINESS (accounting, banking and finance, business administration and management, business economics, international business management, marketing/retailing/merchandising, and personnel management), COMMUNICATIONS AND THE ARTS (English, fine arts, French, German, music, and Spanish), COMPUTER AND PHYSICAL SCIENCE (chemistry and mathematics), EDUCATION (art, business, early childhood, elementary, foreign languages, health, industrial arts, middle school, music, physical, science, secondary, and special), ENGINEERING AND ENVIRONMENTAL DESIGN (environmental science, industrial administration/management, and industrial engineering technology), HEALTH PROFESSIONS (medical laboratory technology, predentistry, and premedicine), SOCIAL SCIENCE (community services, criminal justice, economics, history, political science/government, prelaw, psychology, social science, and sociology). Business education has the largest enrollment.

Required: Students must complete a minimum of 128 semester hours, with 51 in the major, and must maintain a 2.0 minimum GPA. The core curriculum consists of courses in English, history, fine arts, science, physical education, and psychology. In addition, there are specific course requirements. All students must pass a comprehensive exam.

Special: Opportunities are provided for internships, a Washington semester, work-study programs, a B.A.-B.S. degree, dual majors, a general studies degree, credit by examination, and nondegree study. There is a freshman and university-wide honors program on campus.

Faculty/Classroom: No introductory courses are taught by graduate students. The average class size in an introductory lecture is 28 and in a laboratory, 20.

Admissions: About 97% of the 1993–94 applicants were accepted.

Requirements: A minimum GPA of 2.0 is required. The ACT is required with a minimum composite score of 20. Graduation from an accredited secondary school is required; a GED will be accepted. Applicants should submit a minimum academic record distributed as follows: 4 years of English, 2 or 3 each of mathematics and science, 3 of social studies, and one-half year each of music and computer studies. AP and CLEP credits are accepted. Important factors used in the admissions decision are evidence of special talent, advanced placement or honor courses, extracurricular activities record, leadership record, and ability to finance college education.

Procedure: Freshmen are admitted fall, spring, and summer. Entrance exams should be taken during the summer before the senior year. Applications should be filed by August 15 for fall entry, along with an application fee of $15. Notification is sent on a rolling basis. There is a deferred admissions plan.

Transfer: About 110 transfer students enrolled in 1993–94. Applicants for transfer must submit official transcripts from all previous colleges attended. D grades do not transfer. If the applicant has not maintained a C average, an ACT score that places the applicant in the upper 50% of college-bound freshmen may be submitted for consideration.

Visiting: There are regularly scheduled orientations for prospective students, consisting of a welcome presentation, registration, refreshments, an academic visit, a campus tour, lunch, a financial aid presentation, student panel, and a cost and scholarship presentation. There are guides for informal visits and visitors may sit in on classes and stay overnight at the school. To arrange for a visit, contact the Admissions Office at (605) 622–2544 or (800) 678–5330.

Financial Aid: In 1993–94, 79% of all current freshmen and 79% of continuing students received some form of financial aid. About 66% of freshmen and 66% of continuing students received need-based aid. The average freshman award was $3585. Of that total, scholarships or need-based grants averaged $1637 ($2900 maximum); loans averaged $2603 ($6625 maximum); and work contracts averaged $1127 ($1200 maximum). One-hundred percent of undergraduate students work part-time. Average earnings from campus work for the school year are $1200. The average financial indebtedness of the 1992–93 graduate was $8316. The FAF, FFS or SFS is required. The deadline for financial aid applications is March 1.

International Students: There are currently 33 international students enrolled. They must take the TOEFL and achieve a minimum score of 500. The student must also take the ACT.

Computers: The college provides computer facilities for student use. The mainframe is an IBM System 36. There are 45 terminals connected to the mainframe, with additional work-processing, graphics, report-generation, and software capabilities. In addition, there are 475 microcomputers in 12 computer laboratories, classrooms, and offices. There are no time limits on using the system and no fees.

Admissions Contact: Steve Ochsner, Director of Admissions.

OGLALA LAKOTA COLLEGE

B-3

Kyle, SD 57752   (605) 455–2321

Full-time: 1100 men and women	Faculty: 42
Part-time: none	Ph.D.s: n/av
Graduate: none	Student/Faculty: 9 to 1
Year: semesters	Tuition: n/av
Application Deadline: open	Room & Board: n/app
Freshman Class: n/av	
SAT I or ACT: not required	NONCOMPETITIVE

Oglala Lakota College was founded in 1971 by the Oglala Sioux Tribal Council to provide academic, tribal, and cultural resources for the Pine Ridge Reservation community, offering programs in business, teaching, and human services. There are ten regional centers in addition to the central campus. Special learning facilities include a learning resource center, archives, an American Indian collection, and an audio video studio. The campus is in a rural area spread over the 5,000 square miles of the Pine Ridge Indian Reservation in the state's Southwest corner. There are 5 buildings on campus.

Housing: There are no residence halls; all students commute and may keep cars on campus.

Activities: There are some groups and organizations on campus, including student government. Popular campus events include Wounded Knee Run, Native People Film Festival, Homecoming, and the Wazi Paha Oyate Festival.

Services: In addition to many counseling and information services, tutoring is available in every subject. There is also remedial math, reading, and writing.

Programs of Study: OLC awards the B.S. degree. Associate degrees are also awarded. Bachelor's degrees are awarded in BUSINESS (business administration and management), EDUCATION (elementary), SOCIAL SCIENCE (history and human services).

Required: A core curriculum of 22 credit hours in English, speech, humanities, mathematics, and natural and social sciences and 15 credit hours in Lakota studies, including at least 1 course in the language, are required. A GPA of at least 2.0 and 128 credit hours are needed to graduate.

Special: OLC offers work-study, independent study, noncredit classes, and nondegree study.

Requirements: The SAT I or ACT is not required. Applicants should be high school graduates or have the GED. Certification of degree of Indian blood from the tribal census office is required.

Procedure: Application deadlines are open. Notification is sent on a rolling basis.

Transfer: A total of 30 credits out of 128 must be completed at OLC.

Visiting: Visitors may sit in on classes.

Financial Aid: The FFS is required.

Admissions Contact: Rosalie Janis, Acting Registrar.

PRESENTATION COLLEGE
D-1
Aberdeen, SD 57401

(605) 229-8492

(800) 437-6060, ext. 24 (out-of-state)

Full-time: 51 men, 216 women	Faculty: 31
Part-time: 31 men, 137 women	Ph.D.s: 10%
Graduate: none	Student/Faculty: 9 to 1
Year: semesters, summer session	Tuition: $6536
Application Deadline: open	Room & Board: $2580

Freshman Class: 109 applied, 107 accepted, 89 enrolled

SAT I or ACT: required **Noncompetitive**

Presentation College, founded in 1922 as Notre Dame Junior College, is an independent Catholic, coeducational institution offering undergraduate degrees in nursing and allied health service management. In addition to regional accreditation, Presentation has baccalaureate program accreditation with AHEA. The library contains 33,725 volumes, and subscribes to 221 periodicals. Computerized library sources and services include the card catalog and interlibrary loans. Special learning facilities include a learning resource center. The 100-acre campus is in a small town in Aberdeen.

Housing: College-sponsored housing is single-sex. On-campus housing is available on a first-come, first-served basis. Alcohol is not permitted. All students may keep cars on campus.

Activities: There are no fraternities or sororities on campus. There are some groups and organizations on campus, including chorus, ethnic, newspaper, professional, religious, and student government. Popular campus events include an Tostal Day, spring fling, and Snow Queen contest.

Sports: There is no sports program at Presentation.

Services: In addition to many counseling and information services, tutoring is available in some subjects.

Programs of Study: Presentation awards the B.S. and B.S.N. degrees. Associate degrees also are awarded. Bachelor's degrees are awarded in HEALTH PROFESSIONS (health care administration and nursing), SOCIAL SCIENCE (social work).

Required: Students must complete 128 semester hours, with 48 in upper-division courses and 36 in the major. The core curriculum consists of 18 hours of humanities and fine arts, 12 of social and behavioral sciences, 11 of natural sciences and mathematics, and 10 of religious studies and philosophy.

Special: Certificate programs are available in phlebotomy, surgical technology, administrative assistance, business/accounting, and computer operating. An external degree program offers an accelerated schedule for working adults. Limited credit for experiential learning is possible. There is one national honor society on campus.

Faculty/Classroom: Ten percent of faculty are male; 90%, female.

Admissions: About 98% of the 1993–94 applicants were accepted.

Requirements: A minimum GPA of 2.0 is required. The SAT I or ACT is required. In addition, prospective students must graduate high school or hold a GED, and a GPA of 2.0 is recommended. AP and CLEP credits are accepted.

Procedure: Freshmen are admitted in the fall. Application deadlines are open. Application fee is $10. The college accepts all applicants.

Transfer: In addition, a 2.0 GPA on previous college work is recommended. A total of 32 credits out of 128 must be completed at Presentation.

Visiting: To arrange for a visit, contact the Admissions Office at (605) 229-8492.

Financial Aid: The FFS is required.

International Students: They must take the TOEFL and achieve a minimum score of 450.

Computers: The college provides computer facilities for student use. Computer students may access the system.

Admissions Contact: Kathy Gerdes, Director of Admissions.

SINTE GLESKA COLLEGE
(See Sinte Gleska University)

SINTE GLESKA UNIVERSITY
E-3
(Formerly Sinte Gleska College)
Rosebud, SD 57570

(605) 747-2263

Full-time: 128 men, 242 women	Faculty: 23
Part-time: 94 men, 213 women	Ph.D.s: n/av
Graduate: 22 men, 41 women	Student/Faculty: 16 to 1
Year: semesters, summer session	Tuition: $1580
Application Deadline: September 1	Room & Board: n/app

Freshman Class: 151 applied, 151 accepted, 151 enrolled

SAT I or ACT: not required **NONCOMPETITIVE**

Sinte Gleska University, founded in 1970, is an independent, coeducational institution offering undergraduate programs in business, fine arts, professional training, and technical studies. There is one graduate school. The library contains 85,000 volumes. The 52-acre campus is in a rural area east of Mission. There are 7 buildings on campus.

Student Life: About 92% of undergraduates are from South Dakota. All are from public schools. Eighty-five percent are Native American/Eskimo; 15% white. The average age of all undergraduates is 31. Ten percent drop out by the end of their first year; 90% remain to graduate.

Housing: There are no residence halls. One-hundred percent of students commute. Alcohol is not permitted.

Activities: There are no fraternities or sororities on campus. There are some groups and organizations on campus, including newspaper and photography. Popular campus events include Founders Day.

Sports: There are 4 intramural sports for men and 3 for women.

Disabled Students: All of the campus is accessible to disabled students. The following facilities are available: wheelchair ramps, special parking, specially equipped rest rooms, and lowered drinking fountains.

Services: In addition to many counseling and information services, tutoring is available in every subject.

Campus Safety and Security: Campus safety and security measures include shuttle buses, informal discussions, and an evening security guard.

Programs of Study: Sinte Gleska awards the B.A. and B.S. degrees. Associate and master's degrees also are awarded. Bachelor's degrees are awarded in COMMUNICATIONS AND THE ARTS (art), EDUCATION (early childhood and elementary), HEALTH PROFESSIONS (mental health/human services), SOCIAL SCIENCE (human services). Education and human services are the strongest academically and have the largest enrollments.

Required: To graduate, students must complete at least 128 credits with a GPA of 2.0; education majors must have a 2.5. All students must fulfill the core curriculum requirements.

Special: The college offers work-study programs, accelerated degree programs, a general studies degree, and pass/fail options.

Admissions: All of the 1993–94 applicants were accepted.

Requirements: Applicants must be graduates of accredited secondary schools or have earned a GED. Ability to finance college education is an important factor used in the admissions decision.

Procedure: Freshmen are admitted to all sessions. Entrance exams should be taken before admission. Applications should be filed by September 1 for fall entry, January 15 for spring entry, and June 1 for summer entry, along with an application fee of $10. The college accepts all applicants. Notification is sent on a rolling basis.

Transfer: Two transfer students enrolled in 1993–94. Transfer applicants must submit their official transcript from their previous college. A total of 68 credits out of 128 must be completed at Sinte Gleska.

Visiting: There are regularly scheduled orientations for prospective students. There are guides for informal visits and visitors may stay overnight at the school. To arrange for a visit, contact Cheryl Crazy Bull, Vice President, at (605) 747-2263, ext. 52.

Financial Aid: In a recent year, 100% of all current freshmen received some form of financial aid. The SFS is required.

Computers: The college provides computer facilities for student use. Students may access the system for up to 3 laboratory hours. The fees are $45.

Graduates: In a recent year, 12 bachelor's degrees were awarded. In the 1992 graduating class, 20% of the men and 50% of the women were enrolled in graduate school within 6 months of graduation; 20% of the men and 30% of the women had found employment.

Admissions Contact: Michelle Zephier, Registrar.

SIOUX FALLS COLLEGE

F-3

Sioux Falls, SD 57105

(605) 331-6600; (800) 888-1047

Full-time: 271 men, 343 women	Faculty: 37; IIB, --$
Part-time: 104 men, 167 women	Ph.Ds: 65%
Graduate: 20 men, 46 women	Student/Faculty: 17 to 1
Year: 4-1-4, summer session	Tuition: $8450
Application Deadline: open	Room & Board: $3090
Freshman Class: 437 applied, 400 accepted, 250 enrolled	
ACT: 21	COMPETITIVE

Sioux Falls College, founded in 1883, is a private, coeducational, liberal arts institution affiliated with the American Baptist Churches. In addition to regional accreditation, SFC has baccalaureate program accreditation with CSWE and NCATE. The library contains 75,000 volumes and 4600 audiovisual forms, and subscribes to 450 periodicals. Computerized library sources and services include the card catalog, interlibrary loans, and database searching. Special learning facilities include a learning resource center, radio station, and TV station. The 22-acre campus is in a suburban area in Sioux Falls. Including residence halls, there are 13 buildings on campus.

Student Life: About 72% of undergraduates are from South Dakota. Students come from 19 states, 3 foreign countries, and Canada. Ninety-five percent are from public schools; 5% from private. Ninety-seven percent are white. Seventy-three percent are Protestant; 14% Catholic; 13% claim no religious affiliation. The average age of freshmen is 18; all undergraduates, 21. Forty-seven percent drop out by the end of their first year; 53% remain to graduate.

Housing: A total of 350 students can be accommodated in college housing. College-sponsored living facilities include single-sex and coed dormitories, on-campus apartments, and married-student housing. On-campus housing is guaranteed for the freshman year only, is available on a first-come, first-served basis, and is available on a lottery system for upperclassmen. Priority is given to out-of-town students. Sixty-one percent of students commute. Alcohol is not permitted. All students may keep cars on campus.

Activities: There are no fraternities or sororities on campus. There are 35 groups on campus, including art, band, cheerleading, choir, chorale, chorus, computers, drama, ethnic, honors, international, jazz band, musical theater, newspaper, pep band, photography, professional, radio and TV, religious, social, social service, student government, and yearbook. Popular campus events include Homecoming, TWIRP, Spring Formal, Staley Lectures, and Madrigals.

Sports: There are 5 intercollegiate sports for men and 5 for women, and 6 intramural sports for men and 6 for women. Athletic and recreation facilities include a student lounge, 4 racquetball courts, a 160-meter running track, volleyball, tennis, badminton, and basketball courts, facilities for aerobics, exercise machines, a whirlpool, a 700-seat indoor gymnasium, and an 850-seat auditorium/arena.

Disabled Students: Five percent of the campus is accessible to disabled students. The following facilities are available: wheelchair ramps, special parking, specially equipped rest rooms, and special class scheduling.

Services: In addition to counseling and information services, there is remedial math and reading.

Campus Safety and Security: Campus safety and security measures include self-defense education, escort service, informal discussions, and pamphlets, posters, and films. In addition, there are emergency telephones and lighted pathways and sidewalks.

Programs of Study: SFC awards the B.A. and B.S. degrees. Associate and master's degrees also are awarded. Bachelor's degrees are awarded in BIOLOGICAL SCIENCE (biology/biological science), BUSINESS (accounting, business administration and management, business economics, and marketing/retailing/merchandising), COMMUNICATIONS AND THE ARTS (communications, English, music, and speech/debate/rhetoric), COMPUTER AND PHYSICAL SCIENCE (chemistry, computer science, and mathematics), EDUCATION (art, early childhood, elementary, middle school, music, science, and secondary), HEALTH PROFESSIONS (medical laboratory technology and premedicine), SOCIAL SCIENCE (history, philosophy, political science/government, prelaw, psychology, religion, social work, and sociology). Business and elementary education are the strongest academically and have the largest enrollments.

Required: To graduate, all students must complete a minimum of 128 credit hours, with 64 hours in the major. Required courses include physical education, computer science, religion, history, English, science, economics, political science, psychology, social science, cross-cultural, speech, and fine arts. A writing proficiency test and a minimum 2.0 GPA are also required.

Special: The college offers co-op programs with Augustana College, Dakota State University, and the North American Baptist Seminary, internships, study abroad in Japan, Central America, and China, an American Studies Program in Washington, D.C., and a January interim. Also available are on-campus work-study programs, B.A.-B.S. degrees, dual and student-designed interdisciplinary majors, a general studies degree, a 3-2 engineering degree, credit for life and work experience, and pass/fail options. There is a freshman honors program on campus, as well as 3 national honor societies. Two departments have honors programs.

Faculty/Classroom: Seventy-eight percent of faculty are male; 22%, female. All teach undergraduates and 60% do research. Graduate students teach 1% of introductory courses. The average class size in an introductory lecture is 40; in a laboratory, 15; and in a regular course offering, 20.

Admissions: About 92% of the 1993-94 applicants were accepted. The ACT scores for the 1993-94 freshman class were as follows: 26% between 21 and 23, 48% between 24 and 26, 15% between 27 and 28, and 11% above 28. About 44% of the current freshmen were in the top fifth of their class; 78% were in the top two fifths. There was 1 National Merit finalist and 1 semifinalist. Twelve freshmen graduated first in their class.

Requirements: SFC requires applicants to be in the upper 50% of their class. A minimum GPA of 2.0 is required. The SAT I or ACT is required. The minimum required composite score on the SAT I is 800, and on the ACT, 19. Applicants must be graduates of an accredited secondary school or have a GED certificate. Students should have completed 4 years each of English and mathematics and 2 years each of foreign language, science, and social studies. AP and CLEP credits are accepted. Important factors used in the admissions decision are advanced placement or honor courses, evidence of special talent, leadership record, personality, intangible qualities, and recommendations by school officials.

Procedure: Freshmen are admitted to all sessions. Entrance exams should be taken during the junior or senior year of high school. Application deadlines are open. The application fee is $20. Notification is sent on a rolling basis. There is an early admissions plan.

Transfer: Some 72 transfer students enrolled in 1993-94. Transfer students must meet freshman admission requirements and have completed at least 24 hours of college courses with a minimum 2.0 GPA. The SAT I or ACT and an interview are recommended. A total of 30 credits out of 128 must be completed at SFC.

Visiting: There are regularly scheduled orientations for prospective students, including meetings with faculty and staff, class visits, a campus tour, and a financial aid session. There are guides for informal visits and visitors may sit in on classes and stay overnight at the school. To arrange for a visit, contact the Admissions Office at (800) 888-1047.

Financial Aid: In 1993-94 71% of all current freshmen and 94% of continuing students received some form of financial aid. About 83% of freshmen and 85% of continuing students received need-based aid. The average freshman award was $7168. Of that total, scholarships or need-based grants averaged $2213 ($10,750 maximum); loans averaged $3260 ($11,166 maximum); work contracts averaged $1330 ($1445 maximum); and PELL and SEOG grants averaged $1370 ($7605 maximum). Twenty-three percent of undergraduate students work part-time. Average earnings from campus work for the school year are $1156. The average financial indebtedness of the 1992-93 graduate was $12,600. SFC is a member of CSS. The FAF, FFS, or SFS and FAFSA are required. The deadline for financial aid applications is April 1.

International Students: There are currently 12 international students enrolled. The school actively recruits these students. They must take the TOEFL and achieve a minimum score of 550. The student must also take the SAT I or ACT if the exam is available to them; minimum required composite scores are 800 on the SAT I or 19 on the ACT.

Computers: The college provides computer facilities for student use. Students have access to 42 PCs in 3 publicly accessible laboratories. File space, letter-quality printers, and a laser printer are provided. IBM computer laboratories are part of the campus network. All students may access the system. It may be used 8 A.M. to 11 P.M. There are no time limits on using the system and no fees.

Graduates: In 1992-93 152 bachelor's degrees were awarded. The most popular majors among graduates were buisness administration (40%), education (17%), and social science/psychology (15%). Some 20 companies recruited on campus in 1992-93. In the 1992 graduating class, 2% of the men and 3% of the women were enrolled in graduate school within 6 months of graduation; 97% of all students had found employment.

Admissions Contact: Director of Admissions.

SOUTH DAKOTA SCHOOL OF MINES AND TECHNOLOGY
B-3
Rapid City, SD 57701–3995

(605) 394-2400
(800) 544-8162, ext. 2400

Full-time: 1241 men, 450 women	Faculty: 114; IIA, -$
Part-time: 241 men, 316 women	Ph.D.s: 78%
Graduate: 213 men, 33 women	Student/Faculty: 15 to 1
Year: semesters, summer session	Tuition: $2709 ($4794)
Application Deadline: August 15	Room & Board: $2620
Freshman Class: 704 applied, 530 accepted, 437 enrolled	
SAT I or ACT: required	COMPETITIVE

South Dakota School of Mines and Technology, founded in 1885, is a public university offering undergraduate and graduate programs in engineering, science, and mathematics. There is one graduate school. In addition to regional accreditation, SDSM&T has baccalaureate program accreditation with ABET. The library contains 155,886 volumes and 194,614 microform items, and subscribes to 959 periodicals. Computerized library sources and services include the card catalog and interlibrary loans. Special learning facilities include a learning resource center, art gallery, natural history museum, planetarium, radio station, and a geology museum. The 118-acre campus is in a suburban area 350 miles northeast of Denver. Including residence halls, there are 18 buildings on campus.

Student Life: About 66% of undergraduates are from South Dakota. Students come from 38 states, 29 foreign countries, and Canada. Eighty-four percent are white; 10% foreign nationals. Fifty-two percent are Protestant; 25% claim no religious affiliation; 22% are Catholic. The average age of freshmen is 22; all undergraduates, 24. Thirty percent drop out by the end of their first year; 54% remain to graduate.

Housing: A total of 542 students can be accommodated in college housing. College-sponsored living facilities include single-sex dormitories, fraternity houses, and sorority houses. On-campus housing is guaranteed for the freshman year only and is available on a first-come, first-served basis. Sixty-eight percent of students commute. Alcohol is not permitted. All students may keep cars on campus.

Activities: About 11% of men belong to 4 national fraternities; about 10% of women belong to 2 national sororities. There are 24 groups on campus, including art, band, cheerleading, choir, chorale, chorus, computers, drama, drill team, international, jazz band, marching band, newspaper, orchestra, pep band, political, professional, radio and TV, religious, social, student government, and yearbook. Popular campus events include M-Week (Homecoming).

Sports: There are 4 intercollegiate sports for men and 4 for women, and a varying number of intramural sports. Athletic and recreation facilities include a football field, track, and 700-seat gymnasium.

Disabled Students: Sixty percent of the campus is accessible to disabled students. The following facilities are available: wheelchair ramps, elevators, special parking, specially equipped rest rooms, and special class scheduling.

Services: In addition to many counseling and information services, tutoring is available in most subjects. There is also remedial math.

Campus Safety and Security: Campus safety and security measures include 24-hour foot and vehicle patrol, informal discussions, pamphlets, posters, and films, and lighted pathways and sidewalks.

Programs of Study: SDSM&T awards the B.S. degree. Master's and doctoral degrees also are awarded. Bachelor's degrees are awarded in COMPUTER AND PHYSICAL SCIENCE (chemistry, computer programming, computer science, geology, mathematics, and physics), ENGINEERING AND ENVIRONMENTAL DESIGN (chemical engineering, civil engineering, computer engineering, electrical/electronics engineering, geological engineering, industrial engineering, mechanical engineering, metallurgical engineering, and mining and mineral engineering). Engineering is the strongest academically. Mechanical engineering has the largest enrollment.

Required: Students must successfully complete 128 credits for science majors or 136 credits for engineering majors, and maintain a minimum GPA of 2.0. Included in these requirements are 16 credit hours each of mathematics, science, and humanities or social science. Additional requirements include courses in calculus, differential equations, English composition, chemistry, physics, physical education, and FORTRAN programming.

Special: Opportunities are provided for work-study programs, dual majors, an interdisciplinary science major, credit by examination, and nondegree study. There is a chapter of Phi Beta Kappa on campus.

Faculty/Classroom: Ninety percent of faculty are male; 10%, female. Ninety-five percent teach undergraduates, 20% do research, and 90% do both. Graduate students teach 4% of introductory courses. The average class size in an introductory lecture is 60; in a laboratory, 18; and in a regular course offering, 25.

Admissions: About 75% of the 1993–94 applicants were accepted. The ACT scores for the 1993–94 freshman class were as follows: 11% below 21, 30% between 21 and 23, 36% between 24 and 26, 15%

between 27 and 28, and 8% above 28. About 44% of the current freshmen were in the top fifth of their class; 74% were in the top two fifths. There were 3 National Merit finalists and 5 semifinalists.

Requirements: A minimum GPA of 2.0 is required. The SAT I, with a minimum composite score 920 (420 verbal and 500 mathematics), or the ACT, with a minimum composite score of 23, must be taken. Graduation from an accredited secondary school is required. A GED will be accepted. Applicants must submit high school credits distributed as follows: 4 years of English, 3 each of mathematics, laboratory science, and social studies, and a 1/2 year each of fine arts and computer science. AP and CLEP credits are accepted.

Procedure: Freshmen are admitted fall and spring. Entrance exams should be taken before application to the college. Applications should be filed by August 15 for fall entry, December 20 for spring entry, and June 5 for summer entry, along with an application fee of $15. Notification is sent on a rolling basis. There are early decision and early admissions plans.

Transfer: Some 216 transfer students enrolled in 1993–94. Transfer students must submit an official transcript from the previous college and must have maintained a minimum GPA of 2.0, with 2.5 recommended. A total of 32 credits out of 128 or 136, depending on the major, must be completed at SDSM&T.

Visiting: There are guides for informal visits and visitors may sit in on classes. To arrange for a visit, contact the Office of Admissions at (800) 742–8606, ext. 244 (in-state) or (800) 544–8162 (out-of-state).

Financial Aid: In 1993–94 68% of all current freshmen and 83% of continuing students received some form of financial aid. About 56% of freshmen and 52% of continuing students received need-based aid. The average freshman award was $4703. Of that total, scholarships or need-based grants averaged $600 ($8000 maximum); loans averaged $3025 ($8125 maximum); and work contracts averaged $1500 ($1600 maximum). Twenty-eight percent of undergraduate students work part-time. Average earnings from campus work for the school year are $1500. The average financial indebtedness of the 1992–93 graduate was $6793. SDSM&T is a member of CSS. The FAF, FFS, or SFS is required. The deadline for financial aid applications is April 15.

International Students: There are currently 246 international students enrolled. They must take the TOEFL and achieve a minimum score of 530.

Computers: The college provides computer facilities for student use. The mainframe is a CDC CYBER. There are also approximately 290 terminals in 15 different locations on campus. All students may access the system. It may be used 24 hours per day. There are no time limits on using the system and no fees.

Graduates: In 1992–93 246 bachelor's degrees were awarded. The most popular majors among graduates were mechanical engineering (28%), electrical engineering (13%), and civil engineering/computer science (11% each). Within an average freshman class, 54% graduate in 4 years, 29% in 5 years, and 17% in 6 years. Some 113 companies recruited on campus in 1992–93. In the 1992 graduating class, 8% of the men and 9% of the women were enrolled in graduate school within 6 months of graduation; 92% of all students had found employment.

Admissions Contact: Office of Admissions.

SOUTH DAKOTA STATE UNIVERSITY
F-3
Brookings, SD 57007   (605) 688-4121; (800) 952-3541 (in-state)

Full-time: 3708 men, 3292 women	Faculty: 510; IIA, --$
Part-time: 356 men, 747 women	Ph.D.s: 70%
Graduate: 663 men, 770 women	Student/Faculty: 14 to 1
Year: semesters, summer session	Tuition: $3060 ($4897)
Application Deadline: August 30	Room & Board: $1502
Freshman Class: 4186 applied, 2888 accepted, 1701 enrolled	
ACT: 23	COMPETITIVE

South Dakota State University, founded in 1881, is a public, land-grant institution offering undergraduate programs in agriculture and biological sciences, arts and science, engineering, home economics, nursing, pharmacy, education and counseling, and general registration. There are 8 undergraduate schools and one graduate school. In addition to regional accreditation, SDSU has baccalaureate program accreditation with ABET, ACEJMC, ACPE, ADA, AHEA, NASM, NCATE, and NLN. The library contains 463,008 volumes, 558,101 microform items, and 334 audiovisual forms, and subscribes to 3305 periodicals. Computerized library sources and services include the card catalog and interlibrary loans. Special learning facilities include a learning resource center, an art gallery, a radio station, a TV station, an arboretum, and an agricultural heritage museum. The 260-acre campus is in a rural area 50 miles north of Sioux Falls. Including residence halls, there are 58 buildings on campus.

Student Life: About 75% of undergraduates are from South Dakota. Students come from 46 states, 44 foreign countries, and Canada. Ninety-five percent are from public schools; 5% from private. Ninety-eight percent are white. The average age of freshmen is 18; all under-

graduates, 19. Twenty percent drop out by the end of their first year; 80% remain to graduate.

Housing: A total of 3200 students can be accommodated in college housing. College-sponsored living facilities include coed dormitories, on-campus apartments, and married-student housing. In addition there are special interest houses, including intensive study and 1 floor for engineering students. On-campus housing is available on a first-come, first-served basis. Alcohol is not permitted. All students may keep cars on campus.

Activities: About 4% of men belong to 5 national fraternities; about 3% of women belong to 3 national sororities. There are 180 groups on campus, including art, band, cheerleading, chess, choir, chorale, chorus, computers, dance, drama, ethnic, film, gay, honors, international, jazz band, literary magazine, marching band, musical theater, newspaper, opera, orchestra, pep band, photography, political, professional, radio and TV, religious, social, social service, student government, symphony, and yearbook. Popular campus events include Homecoming, Hobo Day, Family Day, Little International, and Home Economics Exposition.

Sports: There are 10 intercollegiate sports for men and 9 for women, and 35 intramural sports for men and 35 for women. Athletic and recreation facilities include a physical education complex, an intramural building, an outdoor track, lighted tennis courts, a wellness center, and intramural football and softball fields.

Disabled Students: Twenty-two percent of the campus is accessible to disabled students. The following facilities are available: wheelchair ramps, elevators, special parking, specially equipped rest rooms, special class scheduling, lowered drinking fountains, and lowered telephones.

Services: In addition to many counseling and information services, tutoring is available in most subjects. In addition, there is a reader service for the blind.

Campus Safety and Security: Campus safety and security measures include 24-hour foot and vehicle patrol, self-defense education, escort service, and informal discussions. In addition, there are pamphlets, posters, and films and lighted pathways and sidewalks.

Programs of Study: SDSU awards the B.A., B.S., B.Mus.Ed., and B.S.N. degrees. Associate, master's, and doctoral degrees also are awarded. Bachelor's degrees are awarded in AGRICULTURE (agricultural business management, agronomy, animal science, dairy science, horticulture, and range/farm management), BIOLOGICAL SCIENCE (biochemistry, biology/biological science, botany, and microbiology), BUSINESS (apparel and accessories marketing, business economics, and hotel/motel and restaurant management), COMMUNICATIONS AND THE ARTS (broadcasting, communications, design, English, fine arts, German, graphic design, journalism, music, music business management, Spanish, and speech/debate/rhetoric), COMPUTER AND PHYSICAL SCIENCE (chemistry, computer science, mathematics, and physics), EDUCATION (agricultural, art, business, early childhood, foreign languages, health, home economics, middle school, music, science, and secondary), ENGINEERING AND ENVIRONMENTAL DESIGN (agricultural engineering, agricultural engineering technology, civil engineering, electrical/electronics engineering, engineering technology, interior design, landscape architecture/design, mechanical engineering, and printing technology), HEALTH PROFESSIONS (medical laboratory science, medical laboratory technology, nursing, pharmacy, and speech pathology/audiology), SOCIAL SCIENCE (consumer services, dietetics, economics, food production/management/services, food science, geography, history, home economics, human services, liberal arts/general studies, parks and recreation management, political science/government, psychology, and sociology). Pharmacy, engineering, and nursing are the strongest academically. Nursing, economics, electrical engineering, and agricultural business have the largest enrollments.

Required: Students must complete 128 credits (136 for engineering and nursing), with at least 32 in the major, and must maintain a 2.0 minimum GPA. Additional requirements for graduation are 9 to 14 credits in social science, 8 to 13 in natural science, 6 to 11 in humanities, 3 each in mathematics and speech, and 2 in physical education.

Special: A co-op program in elementary education, internships, B.A.-B.S. degrees, and interdisciplinary majors including agricultural journalism, agricultural extension, environmental management, and wildlife and fisheries science, are available. Opportunities are provided for dual majors, credit by examination, student-designed majors, credit for military experience, nondegree study, a general studies degree, and pass/fail options. There is a freshman honors program on campus, as well as 27 national honor societies.

Faculty/Classroom: Seventy percent of faculty are male; 30%, female. Seventy percent teach undergraduates and 30% do research. Graduate students teach 5% of introductory courses. The average class size in an introductory lecture is 50; in a laboratory, 30; and in a regular course offering, 30.

Admissions: About 69% of the 1993–94 applicants were accepted. The ACT scores for the 1993–94 freshman class were as follows: 39% below 21, 31% between 21 and 23, 18% between 24 and 26, 8% between 27 and 28, and 4% above 28. Sixty-two freshmen graduated first in their class.

Requirements: The ACT is required. Graduation from an accredited secondary school is required. A GED will be accepted. Applicants must submit 4 years of English, 1/2 year each of computer science and art or music, 3 years of social studies, and 2 to 3 years each of mathematics and science. Students who have not scored acceptable grades in the above courses may be accepted if they are in the top half of their high school graduating class, or if they submit a minimum ACT composite score of 22 for in-state and Minnesota students, and 23 for out-of-state students. AP and CLEP credits are accepted. Important factors used in the admissions decision are advanced placement or honor courses, evidence of special talent, extracurricular activities record, recommendations by school officials, and recommendations by alumni.

Procedure: Freshmen are admitted fall, spring, and summer. Entrance exams should be taken by spring of the junior year. Applications should be filed by August 30 for fall entry and December 30 for spring entry, along with an application fee of $15. Notification is sent on a rolling basis. There is an early decision plan.

Transfer: About 640 transfer students enrolled in 1993–94. To be eligible for transfer, students must have been in good standing at the previous college and must have maintained a minimum GPA of 2.0 to 2.5, depending on the student's major. A total of 32 credits out of 128 to 136 must be completed at SDSU.

Visiting: There are regularly scheduled orientations for prospective students. There are guides for informal visits and visitors may sit in on classes and stay overnight at the school. To arrange for a visit, contact the High School Relations Office at (605) 688–4121 or (800) 952–3541 (in-state).

Financial Aid: In 1993–94, 74% of all current freshmen and 82% of continuing students received some form of financial aid. About 60% of freshmen and 72% of continuing students received need-based aid. The average freshman award was $3950. Of that total, scholarships or need-based grants averaged $1650 ($2880 maximum); loans averaged $2420 ($4220 maximum); and work contracts averaged $1100 ($1800 maximum). Eighty percent of undergraduate students work part-time. Average earnings from campus work for the school year are $1500. The average financial indebtedness of the 1992–93 graduate was $9100. The FAF, FFS, or SFS and the FAFSA are required.

International Students: There are currently 261 international students enrolled. They must take the TOEFL or the University of Michigan Language Test and achieve a minimum score on the TOEFL of 500.

Computers: The college provides computer facilities for student use. The mainframes are an IBM 4381 and a Prime 4050. Students have access to microcomputer laboratories in the library, residence halls, and the administration building. All students may access the system. There are no time limits on using the system and no fees.

Graduates: In 1992–93, 1235 bachelor's degrees were awarded. The most popular majors among graduates were nursing (11%), sociology (6%), and economics (6%). Some 196 companies recruited on campus in 1992–93. In the 1992 graduating class, 4% of the men and 6% of the women were enrolled in graduate school within 6 months of graduation; 86% of all graduates had found employment.

Admissions Contact: Kelly Bittner, Admissions Counselor.

UNIVERSITY OF SOUTH DAKOTA F-4
Vermillion, SD 57069 (605) 677-5434

Full-time: 2584 men, 3278 women	Faculty: I, --$
Part-time: 36 men, 54 women	Ph.D.s: 77%
Graduate: 764 men, 991 women	Student/Faculty: 13 to 1
Year: semesters, summer session	Tuition: $2294 ($4256)
Application Deadline: open	Room & Board: $2428
Freshman Class: 2160 applied, 2031 accepted, 1268 enrolled	
ACT: 22	COMPETITIVE

The University of South Dakota, founded in 1862, is a public, nonsectarian, coeducational institution with undergraduate programs in arts and sciences, education, fine arts, and business, and professional schools of law and medicine. There are 4 undergraduate schools and one graduate school. In addition to regional accreditation, USD has baccalaureate program accreditation with AACSB, CSWE, NASAD, NASM, NCATE, and NLN. Computerized library sources and services include the card catalog, interlibrary loans, and database searching. Special learning facilities include an art gallery, natural history museum, radio station, TV station, and The Institute of American Indian Studies, the Shrine to Music Museum, a speech and hearing center, an archaeology laboratory, South Dakota geological survey, a business research bureau, a governmental research bureau, an international studies center, a psychological services center, an early child-

hood center, a telecommunications center, a South Dakota Fine Arts Resource Center, a Center for the Study of the History of Musical Instruments, a institute of public affairs, a social science service, and an educational media center. The 216-acre campus is in a rural area. Including residence halls, there are 60 buildings on campus.

Student Life: About 74% of undergraduates are from South Dakota. Students come from 47 states and Canada. Ninety-three percent are white.

Housing: A total of 2122 students can be accommodated in college housing. College-sponsored living facilities include single-sex and coed dormitories, married-student housing, fraternity houses, and sorority houses. On-campus housing is available on a first-come, first-served basis. Seventy-three percent of students commute. Alcohol is not permitted. All students may keep cars on campus.

Activities: About 15% of men belong to 8 national fraternities; about 15% of women belong to 5 national sororities. There are 108 groups on campus, including art, band, cheerleading, choir, chorale, chorus, computers, dance, drama, drill team, ethnic, gay, honors, international, jazz band, literary magazine, marching band, musical theater, newspaper, opera, orchestra, pep band, photography, political, professional, radio and TV, religious, social, social service, student government, symphony, and yearbook. Popular campus events include Dakota Day (Homecoming), Strollers (variety production), and Rockfest.

Sports: Athletic and recreation facilities include an indoor football field, 5 basketball courts, a 25-meter swimming pool, an 8-lane 200-meter track, and handball, volleyball, and tennis courts.

Disabled Students: The following facilities are available: wheelchair ramps, special parking, specially equipped rest rooms, and special class scheduling.

Services: In addition to many counseling and information services, tutoring is available in most subjects. In addition, there is a reader service for the blind. A student counseling center, Trio Programs (Student Support Services, Upward Bound, and Talent Search), and an academic advising/testing center are available.

Campus Safety and Security: Campus safety and security measures include 24-hour foot and vehicle patrol, escort service, informal discussions, and pamphlets, posters, and films. In addition, there are emergency telephones and lighted pathways and sidewalks.

Programs of Study: USD awards the B.A., B.S., B.F.A., B.L.S., B.M., B.S.A.H. and B.S.H.A. degrees. Associate, master's, and doctoral degrees also are awarded. Bachelor's degrees are awarded in BIOLOGICAL SCIENCE (biology/biological science), BUSINESS (accounting, management science, and recreation and leisure services), COMMUNICATIONS AND THE ARTS (applied music, art, classics, communications, dramatic arts, English, French, German, Greek, Latin, music, Spanish, and speech/debate/rhetoric), COMPUTER AND PHYSICAL SCIENCE (chemistry, computer science, earth science, mathematics, physics, and statistics), EDUCATION (art, elementary, music, physical, secondary, and special), HEALTH PROFESSIONS (anesthesiology, dental hygiene, health care administration, medical laboratory technology, medical science, and speech pathology/audiology), SOCIAL SCIENCE (anthropology, criminal justice, economics, history, humanities, liberal arts/general studies, philosophy, political science/government, psychology, social work, and sociology). Business, biology, and psychology have the largest enrollments.

Required: To graduate, students must complete 128 semester hours with a minimum GPA of 2.0. Core curriculum requirements include 12 hours each in humanities/fine arts, social sciences, natural sciences/mathematics and 6 hours of composition. Students must pass an exit test in the major.

Special: USD offers internships, study abroad in France and Germany, and work-study programs. B.A.-B.S. degrees in 24 majors, a general studies degree, dual and student-designed majors, nondegree study, and pass/fail options are available. The Arts Outreach program provides arts activities and noncredit classes. There is a freshman honors program on campus.

Faculty/Classroom: Sixty-five percent of faculty are male; 35%, female. The average class size in a regular course offering is 32.

Admissions: About 94% of the 1993-94 applicants were accepted. The ACT scores for the 1993-94 freshman class were as follows: 40% below 21, 28% between 21 and 23, 19% between 24 and 26, 8% between 27 and 28, and 5% above 28. There were 7 National Merit finalists and 21 semifinalists. About 63 freshmen graduated first in their class.

Requirements: A minimum GPA of 2.0 is required. The SAT I or the ACT is required. Applicants who have earned a 2.0 in the following courses will be admitted regardless of ACT scores or class rank: 4 years of English; 3 years of laboratory science and 2 years of mathematics or 2 years of laboratory science and 3 years of mathematics; 3 years of social studies; 1 semester of fine art; and 1 semester of computer science. Students who do not meet these requirements should be in the top half of their graduation class, or have an ACT score of 22 for South Dakota and Minnesota applicants or 23 for other applicants. AP and CLEP credits are accepted.

Procedure: Freshmen are admitted to all sessions. Entrance exams should be taken prior to enrollment. Application deadlines are open, and the application fee is $15. Notification is sent on a rolling basis. There are early admissions and deferred admissions plans.

Transfer: About 469 transfer students enrolled in 1993-94. Applicants should have a minimum college GPA of 2.0 and be in good standing at their previous school. A total of 30 credits out of 128 must be completed at USD.

Visiting: There are regularly scheduled orientations for prospective students, including a genteral session, academic department visits, complimentary lunch, a session with USD students, and a campus tour. There are guides for informal visits and visitors may sit in on classes and stay overnight at the school. To arrange for a visit, contact the Admissions Office at (605) 677-5434.

Financial Aid: In 1993-94, 81% of all current freshmen and 81% of continuing students received some form of financial aid. About 81% of freshmen and 81% of continuing students received need-based aid. The average freshman award was $4925. Of that total, scholarships or need-based grants averaged $500; loans averaged $2625; and work contracts averaged $800. Sixty-five percent of undergraduate students work part-time. Average earnings from campus work for the school year are $740. The average financial indebtedness of the 1992-93 graduate was $13,000. USD is a member of CSS. The FAF or FFS and the FAFSA are required. The deadline for financial aid applications is February 15.

International Students: The school actively recruits these students. They must take the TOEFL and achieve a minimum score of 550.

Computers: The college provides computer facilities for student use. The mainframe is an MVS 9000 (l/av). Students have access to laboratories for statistical analysis and to professors who have links to the mainframe system. All students may access the system. It may be used 24 hours a day. There are no time limits on using the system and no fees.

Graduates: Some 100 companies recruited on campus in 1992-93.

Admissions Contact: David Lorenz, Associate Dean of Students and Director of Admissions.

TENNESSEE

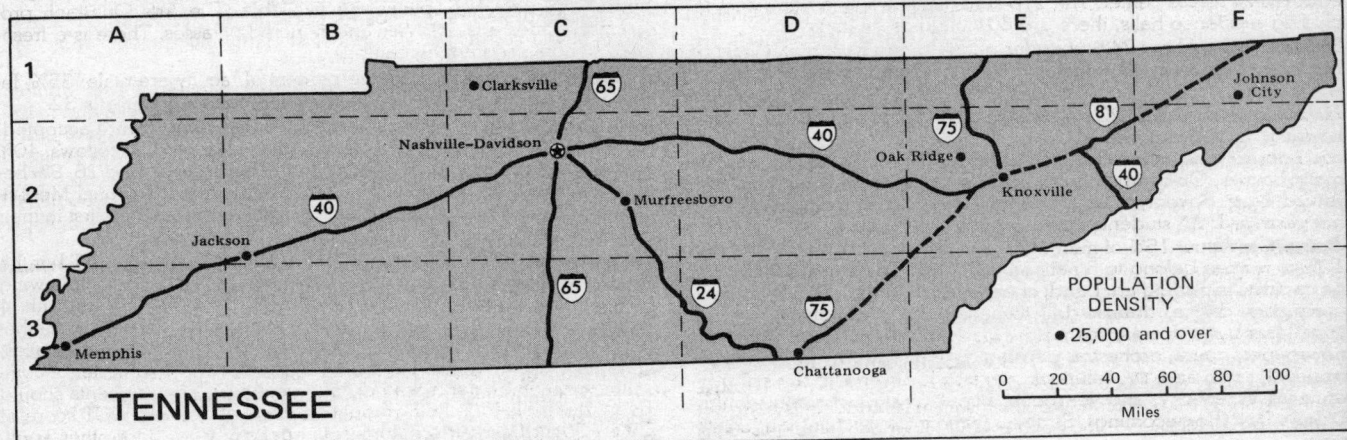

AMERICAN TECHNICAL INSTITUTE
A-3

Brunswick, TN 38014

(901) 382–5857

Part-time: 1625 men, 352 women

Graduate: none

Year: terms

Application Deadline: open

Faculty: 10

Ph.D.s: n/av

Student/Faculty: n/av

Tuition: $100 per credit hour

Room & Board: n/app

Freshman Class: n/av

ACT: required

SPECIAL

The American Technical Institute, founded in 1985 as an independent nonprofit educational institution, offers undergraduate programs in technology for industry. The institute's College of Nuclear Science offers a bachelor of science degree in nuclear engineering technology for employees of nuclear power plants. In addition to regional accreditation, the institute has baccalaureate program accreditation with ABET. The library contains 650 volumes, and subscribes to 8 periodicals. The Brunswick campus, located 15 miles east of Memphis, provides classroom and office space, but the program is generally carried out through on-site instruction at the power plants.

Housing: There are no residence halls.

Sports: There is no sports program at the institute.

Programs of Study: The institute awards the B.S. degree. Bachelor's degrees are awarded in ENGINEERING AND ENVIRONMENTAL DESIGN (nuclear engineering and nuclear engineering technology).

Required: To graduate, all students must have completed at least 132 credit hours with a minimum 2.0 GPA overall and a 2.5 in the major program. Students must complete 30 credits in general education and a minimum of 39 in upper-division work, plus satisfy degree program requirements. Other industrial requirements may apply.

Special: The institute offers co-op programs with local colleges and schools to provide general education courses. Credit is given for military and industrial training experience. Students may request challenge examinations for credit in courses where prerequisites have been met.

Requirements: The ACT is required unless the student has evidence of comparable educational achievement or training in either industrial or military programs. Applicants must be graduates of an accredited secondary school or have a GED certificate, with an average score of 45. AP and CLEP credits are accepted.

Procedure: Application deadlines are open. The application fee is $25.

Transfer: Transfer students must have a college record and be eligible to return to the last college attended. A minimum 2.0 GPA is required. Other industrial requirements may apply.

Computers: The college provides computer facilities for student use. Tandy 1000 microcomputers are available in each branch campus.

Graduates: In a recent year, 6 bachelor's degrees were awarded.

Admissions Contact: Donald Brady, Dean of Admissions.

AUSTIN PEAY STATE UNIVERSITY
C-2

Clarksville, TN 37044

(615) 648–7661

Full-time: 1455 men, 2285 women

Part-time: 1330 men, 1280 women

Graduate: 75 men, 300 women

Year: semesters, summer session

Application Deadline: August 19

Freshman Class: 1380 applied, 1160 accepted, 784 enrolled

ACT: required

Faculty: 204; IIA, --$

Ph.D.s: n/av

Student/Faculty: 18 to 1

Tuition: $1800 ($5582)

Room & Board: $2550

COMPETITIVE

Austin Peay State University, established in 1927, is a public institution offering undergraduate degrees in the liberal arts and sciences and professional preparation. In addition to regional accreditation, APSU has baccalaureate program accreditation with NASM, NCATE, and NLN. The library contains 264,630 volumes, 388,074 microform items, and 7407 audiovisual forms, and subscribes to 1266 periodicals. Special learning facilities include a learning resource center, art gallery, and radio station. The 150-acre campus is in an urban area 47 miles from Nashville. Including residence halls, there are 42 buildings on campus.

Student Life: About 95% of undergraduates are from Tennessee. The average age of freshmen is 20; all undergraduates, 23. Twenty percent drop out by the end of their first year; 50% remain to graduate.

Housing: A total of 1000 students can be accommodated in college housing. College-sponsored living facilities include single-sex and coed dormitories, on-campus apartments, and married-student housing. In addition there are honors houses. Alcohol is not permitted. All students may keep cars on campus.

Activities: There are 7 national fraternities and 7 national sororities. There are 80 groups on campus, including art, cheerleading, chorus, drama, honors, international, jazz band, literary magazine, newspaper, professional, social, social service, student government, and yearbook.

Sports: There are 6 intercollegiate sports for men and 6 for women, and 11 intramural sports for men and 11 for women. Athletic and recreation facilities include a gymnasium, an exercise room, and a jogging fitness trail.

Disabled Students: Ninety-five percent of the campus is accessible to disabled students. The following facilities are available: wheelchair ramps, elevators, special parking, specially equipped rest rooms, special class scheduling, and lowered drinking fountains.

Services: The university provides help with academic, learning, and test-taking problems.

Campus Safety and Security: Campus safety and security measures include shuttle buses, lighted pathways and sidewalks, and vehicle patrol.

Programs of Study: APSU awards the B.A., B.S., B.B.A., B.F.A., B.S.Ed., and B.S.N. degrees. Associate and master's degrees also are awarded. Bachelor's degrees are awarded in AGRICULTURE (agriculture and forestry and related sciences), BIOLOGICAL SCIENCE (biology/biological science and microbiology), BUSINESS (accounting, banking and finance, business administration and management, management science, marketing/retailing/merchandising, and recreation and leisure services), COMMUNICATIONS AND THE ARTS (communications, English, fine arts, French, German, languages, Latin, music, and Spanish), COMPUTER AND PHYSICAL SCIENCE (chemistry, earth science, geology, mathematics, physics, and radio-

logical technology), EDUCATION (business, elementary, health, physical, and special), ENGINEERING AND ENVIRONMENTAL DESIGN (engineering technology and food services technology), HEALTH PROFESSIONS (health care administration, medical laboratory technology, nursing, optometry, physical therapy, predentistry, premedicine, and prepharmacy), SOCIAL SCIENCE (economics, geography, history, philosophy, political science/government, prelaw, psychology, social work, and sociology).

Required: To graduate, students must complete a general education core consisting of courses in communications/English composition, health and personal development, history, foreign language/humanities, science/mathematics, and social science. Students must complete a total of 128 credits, at least 45 of which must be upper divisional, and have a minimum 2.0 GPA. Courses in physical education and computer literacy are required.

Special: APSU offers cooperative programs in nuclear medicine and radiological technology with Vanderbilt University. Work-study programs and dual majors are available. Credit may be granted for military experience. Pass/fail grading options are available. There is a freshman honors program on campus

Admissions: About 84% of the 1993–94 applicants were accepted.

Requirements: A minimum GPA of 2.8 or an ACT score of 19 is required. The ACT is required. Applicants must be graduates of an accredited secondary school or have a GED. Fourteen academic units are required, including 4 units of English, 2 units each of algebra, natural science, and a foreign language, and 1 unit each of visual and/or performing arts, geometry, social studies, and U.S. history. Applicants who do not meet these requirements may be considered for admission. AP and CLEP credits are accepted.

Procedure: Freshmen are admitted to all sessions. Applications should be filed by August 19 for fall entry, December 1 for spring entry, and May 1 for summer entry, along with an application fee of $5. Notification is sent on a rolling basis. There is an early admissions plan.

Transfer: Applicants must have a 2.0 GPA. Grades of D or better will transfer for credit. Application deadlines are the same as those for freshmen. A total of 24 credits out of 128 must be completed at APSU.

Visiting: There are regularly scheduled orientations for prospective students. There are guides for informal visits. To arrange for a visit, contact the Admissions Office at (615) 648–7661.

Financial Aid: Scholarships or need-based grants averaged $475; loans averaged $1050; and work contracts averaged $585. Twenty-five percent of undergraduate students work part-time. The FFS is required and Tennessee residents should submit the Tennessee Edition of the FFS.

International Students: They must take the TOEFL and achieve a minimum score of 500.

Computers: The college provides computer facilities for student use. The mainframe is a DEC VAX. All students may access the system. There are no time limits on using the system and no fees.

Admissions Contact: Charles McCorkle, Director of Admissions.

BELMONT UNIVERSITY
C-2
Nashville, TN 37212-3757 (615) 385-6785

Full-time: 851 men, 1113 women	Faculty: 158; IIA, --$
Part-time: 224 men, 399 women	Ph.D.s: 69%
Graduate: 284 men and women	Student/Faculty: 12 to 1
Year: semesters, summer session	Tuition: $7100
Application Deadline: August 1	Room & Board: $3440
Freshman Class: 1069 applied, 832 accepted, 536 enrolled	
SAT I Verbal/Math: 479/501	ACT: 23 COMPETITIVE

Belmont University, founded in 1951, is a private Christian liberal arts university affiliated with the Tennessee Baptist Convention. There are 6 undergraduate and 2 graduate schools. In addition to regional accreditation, Belmont has baccalaureate program accreditation with NASM and NLN. The library contains 150,176 volumes, 8755 microform items, and 12,788 audiovisual forms, and subscribes to 876 periodicals. Computerized library sources and services include the card catalog, interlibrary loans, and database searching. Special learning facilities include a learning resource center and art gallery. The 55-acre campus is in an urban area. Including residence halls, there are 22 buildings on campus.

Student Life: About 72% of undergraduates are from Tennessee. Students come from 46 states, 42 foreign countries, and Canada. Ninety-three percent are white. Eighty percent are Protestant; 10% claim no religious affiliation. The average age of freshmen is 21; all undergraduates, 23. Thirty percent drop out by the end of their first year; 42% remain to graduate.

Housing: A total of 762 students can be accommodated in college housing. College-sponsored living facilities include single-sex dormitories and married-student housing. On-campus housing is guaranteed for all 4 years. Sixty-five percent of students commute. Alcohol is not permitted. All students may keep cars on campus.

Activities: There are 2 local fraternities and 2 local sororities. There are 24 groups on campus, including art, band, cheerleading, choir, chorale, chorus, computers, dance, drama, drill team, ethnic, film, honors, international, jazz band, literary magazine, musical theater, newspaper, orchestra, pep band, photography, political, professional, religious, social, social service, student government, and yearbook.

Sports: There are 6 intercollegiate sports for men and 4 for women, and 4 intramural sports for men and 4 for women. Athletic and recreation facilities include a student center, which contains a pool and a racquetball court, and a separate gymnasium and wellness center.

Disabled Students: Fifty percent of the campus is accessible to disabled students. The following facilities are available: wheelchair ramps, elevators, special parking, specially equipped rest rooms, special class scheduling, and lowered drinking fountains.

Services: In addition to many counseling and information services, tutoring is available in some subjects. There is also remedial math, reading, and writing.

Campus Safety and Security: Campus safety and security measures include 24-hour foot and vehicle patrol, self-defense education, escort service, and shuttle buses. In addition, there are informal discussions, pamphlets, posters, and films, and lighted pathways and sidewalks.

Programs of Study: Belmont awards the B.A., B.S., B.B.A., B.M., and B.S.N. degrees. Master's degrees also are awarded. Bachelor's degrees are awarded in BIOLOGICAL SCIENCE (biology/biological science), BUSINESS (accounting, hotel/motel and restaurant management, management science, and marketing/retailing/merchandising), COMMUNICATIONS AND THE ARTS (communications, English, French, languages, music, and music performance), COMPUTER AND PHYSICAL SCIENCE (chemistry, computer science, mathematics, and physics), EDUCATION (elementary, physical, and science), ENGINEERING AND ENVIRONMENTAL DESIGN (preengineering), HEALTH PROFESSIONS (nursing, predentistry, premedicine, and prepharmacy), SOCIAL SCIENCE (criminal justice, economics, history, philosophy, political science/government, psychology, religion, and social work). Music, business, and humanities are the strongest academically. Business and music have the largest enrollments.

Required: All students must complete at least 128 hours with a C average, including 22 to 24 hours in the major field. B.A. candidates are required to pursue a minor field. All programs except the B.B.A. require a core curriculum, which includes courses in language and literature, humanities, including religion, social sciences, science, mathematics, and physical education.

Special: Dual degree programs are available with Auburn University of Tennessee at Knoxville and Georgia Institute of Technology for majors in mathematics, physics, or chemistry. Various 3–2 engineering programs are also available through Georgia Institute of Technology. A cooperative degree in fashion merchandising and design or interior design is offered with O'More College of Design in Franklin. A 3 + 1 program leading to the B.S. in biology and the B.S. in pharmacy is offered with Samford University in Alabama. Study abroad is possible for a summer or an academic year. There is a freshman honors program on campus, as well as 2 national honor societies. Three departments have honors programs.

Faculty/Classroom: Sixty-four percent of faculty are male; 36%, female. All teach undergraduates and 100% both teach and do research. No introductory courses are taught by graduate students. The average class size in an introductory lecture is 25 and in a laboratory, 24.

Admissions: About 78% of the 1993–94 applicants were accepted. The SAT scores for the 1993–94 freshman class were as follows: Verbal—46% below 500, 41% between 500 and 599, and 13% between 600 and 700; Math—45% below 500, 39% between 500 and 599, 16% between 600 and 700, and 1% above 700. The ACT scores were 21% below 21, 35% between 21 and 23, 21% between 24 and 26, 14% between 27 and 28, and 9% above 28. About 35% of the current freshmen were in the top fifth of their class; 80% were in the top two fifths.

Requirements: Belmont requires applicants to be in the upper 50% of their class. A minimum GPA of 2.0 is required. The ACT is preferred, but the SAT I is accepted. The college expects a composite score of at least 20 on the ACT. Applicants should be high school graduates or hold the GED. Secondary preparation should include 4 units of English, 3 of mathematics, and 2 each of a foreign language, history, science, and social studies. Potential music majors must audition. AP and CLEP credits are accepted. Ability to finance college education is an important factor used in the admissions decision.

Procedure: Freshmen are admitted fall, spring, and summer. Entrance exams should be taken during the junior or senior year. Applications should be filed by August 1 for fall entry and January 1 for spring entry, along with an application fee of $25. Notification is sent on a rolling basis. There is an early admissions plan.

Transfer: About 640 transfer students enrolled in 1993–94. Transfer applicants should present at least a 2.0 GPA in previous college work and be able to meet freshman entrance requirements. Those with fewer than 30 credit hours must also submit SAT I or ACT scores. A total of 32 credits out of 128 must be completed at Belmont.

Visiting: There are regularly scheduled orientations for prospective students. There are guides for informal visits and visitors may sit in on classes and stay overnight at the school. To arrange for a visit, contact the Admissions Office at (615) 385–6785.

Financial Aid: In 1993–94, 75% of all current freshmen and 75% of continuing students received some form of financial aid. Belmont is a member of CSS. The FAF and the college's own financial statement are required. The deadline for financial aid applications is April 15.

International Students: There are currently 151 international students enrolled. They must take the TOEFL and achieve a minimum score of 500.

Computers: The college provides computer facilities for student use. The mainframe is a DEC VAX 8350. There are also 175 AT&T, Sperry, Zenith, Apple, and Apple Macintosh microcomputers available in student laboratories and faculty offices. All students may access the system. There are no time limits on using the system and no fees.

Graduates: In an earlier year, 401 bachelor's degrees were awarded. Some 62 companies recruited on campus in an earlier year.

Admissions Contact: Kathryn H. Baugher, Dean of Admissions.

BETHEL COLLEGE
B-3

McKenzie, TN 38201

(901) 352–1000; (800) 441–4940

Full-time: 336 men and women	Faculty: 26; IIB, --$
Part-time: 64 men and women	Ph.D.s: 75%
Graduate: 15 men and women	Student/Faculty: 13 to 1
Year: semesters, summer session	Tuition: $6636
Application Deadline: September 15	Room & Board: $3100
Freshman Class: 567 applied, 500 accepted, 133 enrolled	
SAT I or ACT: required	**LESS COMPETITIVE**

Bethel College, established in 1842, is a private coeducational institution affiliated with the Cumberland Presbyterian Church and offers undergraduate degrees through its divisions of humanities, natural sciences, social sciences, education, and health science. The library contains 65,000 volumes, and subscribes to 305 periodicals. Special learning facilities include a learning resource center. The 100-acre campus is in a rural area 120 miles northeast of Memphis. Including residence halls, there are 9 buildings on campus.

Student Life: About 72% of undergraduates are from Tennessee. Eighty-five percent are white; 13% African American. The average age of freshmen is 18; all undergraduates, 20. Twenty-five percent drop out by the end of their first year; 25% remain to graduate.

Housing: A total of 230 students can be accommodated in college housing. College-sponsored living facilities include single-sex dormitories. On-campus housing is guaranteed for the freshman year only. Fifty percent of students live on campus. Alcohol is not permitted. All students may keep cars on campus.

Activities: About 50% of men and women belong to 4 local fraternities and sororities. There are some groups and organizations on campus, including cheerleading, choir, drama, newspaper, political, professional, religious, social, student government, and yearbook. Popular campus events include Homecoming.

Sports: There are 4 intercollegiate sports for men and 2 for women, and 5 intramural sports each for men and women. Athletic and recreation facilities include a gymnasium with a heated indoor pool and weight room; a field house; and a student center with pool tables, ping-pong tables, and other recreational equipment.

Disabled Students: Seventy-five percent of the campus is accessible to disabled students. The following facilities are available: wheelchair ramps, special parking, specially equipped rest rooms, special class scheduling, lowered drinking fountains, and lowered telephones.

Services: Tutoring is available free of charge to students.

Programs of Study: Bethel awards the B.A. and B.S. degrees. Master's degrees are also awarded. Bachelor's degrees are awarded in AGRICULTURE (soil science), BIOLOGICAL SCIENCE (biology/biological science), BUSINESS (accounting and business administration and management), COMMUNICATIONS AND THE ARTS (English and music), COMPUTER AND PHYSICAL SCIENCE (applied mathematics and chemistry), EDUCATION (elementary, health, and physical), SOCIAL SCIENCE (history, psychology, religion, and social science).

Required: Students must prove proficiency in mathematics, English, and reading. Distribution requirements include 57 to 60 credits in English, philosophy, religion, foreign language, mathematics, science, social sciences, history, and health. Students must complete 128 hours, 2 in physical education and at least 39 at the upper-division level, with a minimum GPA of 2.0. They must fulfill the requirements of a major and minor, with no grade below C in the major and a minimum GPA of 2.0 in the minor.

Special: Bethel offers evening classes for adults, in-service training for teachers, off-site classes, student-designed and dual majors, a 3–2 engineering program with Tennessee Technical University, a B.A.-B.S. degree, internships, work-study, nondegree study, a pass/fail option, and credit for prior learning equivalent to that which could be gained in the classroom. There is a freshman honors program on campus, as well as 3 national honor societies.

Faculty/Classroom: Seventy-two percent of faculty are male; 28%, female.

Admissions: About 88% of the 1993–94 applicants were accepted. The ACT scores for the 1993–94 freshman class were as follows: 65% below 21, 19% between 21 and 23, 8% between 24 and 26, 5% between 27 and 28, and 3% above 28.

Requirements: A minimum GPA of 2.0 is required. The SAT I or ACT is required. Applicants must graduate from an accredited secondary school. Those ranking in the upper half of their class, or scoring at least 16 on the ACT or 800 on the SAT I are granted regular acceptance. Other applicants may be admitted conditionally. Other factors in the admission procedure are standardized test scores, an interview, and evidence of special talent. AP and CLEP credits are accepted.

Procedure: Applications should be filed by September 15 for fall entry, December 15 for winter entry, March 15 for spring entry, and June 5 for summer entry, along with an application fee of $10. Notification is sent on a rolling basis. There is an early admissions plan.

Transfer: Transfer applicants must have a minimum GPA of 2.0. Up to 64 semester hours may be transferred toward the degree. Students with less than 12 semester hours must submit high school transcripts and ACT or SAT I scores, and take Bethel's placement test. A total of 36 credits out of 128 must be completed at Bethel.

Visiting: There are regularly scheduled orientations for prospective students. There are guides for informal visits and visitors may sit in on classes and stay overnight at the school. To arrange for a visit, contact the Admissions Office at (800) 441–4940.

Financial Aid: In 1993–94, 90% of all students received some form of financial aid. Twenty-five percent of undergraduate students work part-time. The FAF or FFS is required.

International Students: Students must take the TOEFL and achieve a minimum score of 475.

Computers: The college provides computer facilities for student use. Many PCs are available in the Academic Skills Center, the science building, and the business department. There are no time limits on using the system and no fees.

Admissions Contact: Joe Rigell, Assistant to the President for Admissions and Financial Aid.

BRYAN COLLEGE
D-3
(Formerly William Jennings Bryan College)
Dayton, TN 37321–7000

(615) 775–2041
(800) 277–9522 (out-of-state)

Full-time: 193 men, 217 women	Faculty: 26
Part-time: 10 men, 9 women	Ph.D.s: 69%
Graduate: none	Student/Faculty: 16 to 1
Year: semesters, summer session	Tuition: $7515
Application Deadline: July 31	Room & Board: $3950
Freshman Class: 279 applied, 271 accepted, 99 enrolled	
SAT I Verbal/Math: 453/471	ACT: 23 **COMPETITIVE**

Bryan College, founded in 1930, is a private, nonprofit, Christian institution that is evangelical and interdenominational. Its emphases are on the liberal arts, business, engineering, health science, fine arts, Bible and religious studies, music, and teacher preparation. The library contains 82,577 volumes, 13,489 microform items, and 3015 audiovisual forms, and subscribes to 435 periodicals. Computerized library sources and services include interlibrary loans and database searching. Special learning facilities include a museum of natural science. The 130-acre campus is in a small town 40 miles north of Chattanooga. Including residence halls, there are 28 buildings on campus.

Student Life: About 65% of undergraduates are from out-of-state, mostly the South. Students come from 33 states, 22 foreign countries, and Canada. Forty percent are from public schools; 60% from private. Ninety-four percent are white. Most are Protestant. The average age of freshmen is 18; all undergraduates, 20. Thirty-two percent drop out by the end of their first year; 55% remain to graduate.

Housing: A total of 551 students can be accommodated in college housing. College-sponsored living facilities include single-sex dormitories and married-student housing. On-campus housing is guaranteed for all 4 years. Eighty percent of students live on campus; of those, 75% remain on campus on weekends. Alcohol is not permitted. All students may keep cars on campus.

Activities: There are no fraternities or sororities on campus. There are 10 groups on campus, including cheerleading, choir, chorale, computers, drama, honors, international, literary magazine, newspaper, orchestra, pep band, photography, religious, social, social service, student government, and yearbook. Popular campus events include Homecoming and 4 fine arts series.

Sports: There are 3 intercollegiate sports for men and 3 for women, and 6 intramural sports for men and 6 for women. Athletic and recreation facilities include a 1200-seat gymnasium, a soccer and a softball field, an outdoor swimming pool, and 4 tennis courts.

Disabled Students: All of the campus is accessible to disabled students. The following facilities are available: wheelchair ramps, elevators, special parking, and specially equipped rest rooms.

Services: In addition to many counseling and information services, tutoring is available in some subjects, including mathematics and English. There is also remedial math, reading, and writing.

Campus Safety and Security: Campus safety and security measures include self-defense education, informal discussions, pamphlets, posters, and films, and a night security patrol.

Programs of Study: Bryan awards the B.A. and B.S degrees. Associate degrees also are awarded. Bachelor's degrees are awarded in BIOLOGICAL SCIENCE (biology/biological science), BUSINESS (accounting and business administration and management), COMMUNICATIONS AND THE ARTS (communications, English, and music), COMPUTER AND PHYSICAL SCIENCE (mathematics), EDUCATION (elementary and science), SOCIAL SCIENCE (Christian studies, history, psychology, and religion). Elementary education and biology are the strongest academically. Liberal arts and elementary licensure, business, and psychology have the largest enrollments.

Required: To graduate, students must complete 124 semester hours, with a minimum of 30 in the major, and maintain a GPA of at least 2.0. Distribution requirements include 16 semester hours in the Bible, 9 in communications, 7 each in personal development and natural science, and 6 each in the humanities and social science. Specific courses that must be taken include 7 semester hours in science, 6 hours each in freshman English, a foreign language, and history of Western civilization, 3 each in speech, general psychology, introduction to literature, fine arts, and physical education activity, and 1 semester hour in concepts of physical education. In addition, mathematics and English proficiency exams must be passed, as well as a comprehensive exam in the major.

Special: Special academic programs include practicums in business, accounting, and psychology, and psychology internships. An American Studies Program in Washington and a study-abroad Latin American Studies Program are offered through the Christian College coalition. A dual major in Christian education and church music is available. Student-designed majors are possible and 4 hours of physical education credits may be granted for basic training in the military.

Faculty/Classroom: Sixty-four percent of faculty are male; 36%, female. All teach undergraduates. The average class size in an introductory lecture is 27; in a laboratory, 13; and in a regular course offering, 16.

Admissions: About 97% of the 1993–94 applicants were accepted. The SAT scores for the 1993–94 freshman class were as follows: Verbal—69% below 500, 25% between 500 and 599, and 6% between 600 and 700; Math—59% below 500, 31% between 500 and 599, and 10% between 600 and 700. The ACT scores were 30% below 21, 31% between 21 and 23, 20% between 24 and 26, 14% between 27 and 28, and 5% above 28.

Requirements: A minimum GPA of 2.5 is required. The ACT is required with a minimum composite score of 20. An SAT I composite score of 800 may be substituted. Other admissions requirements include graduation from an approved secondary school with 20 academic credits, including a recommended distribution of 4 units of English, 3 each of mathematics, science, history, and social studies, and 2 of a foreign language. The GED is also accepted. References are required and an interview is recommended. AP and CLEP credits are accepted. Important factors used in the admissions decision are parents or siblings attending the school, recommendations by alumni, recommendations by school officials, leadership record, and personality, intangible qualities.

Procedure: Freshmen are admitted fall and spring. Entrance exams should be taken before the fall of the senior year in high school. Applications should be filed by July 31 for fall entry and December 1 for spring entry, along with an application fee of $20. Notification is sent on a rolling basis. There are early admissions and deferred admissions plans.

Transfer: Twenty-three transfer students enrolled in 1993–94. Transfer students need a minimum GPA of 2.0. A total of 30 credits out of 124 must be completed at Bryan.

Visiting: There are regularly scheduled orientations for prospective students, including a tour of the campus, sitting in on classes and chapel, meeting with professors in area of academic interest, staying with current students in residence halls, and eating meals in the dining room. There are guides for informal visits, and visitors may sit in on classes and stay overnight at the school. To arrange for a visit, contact Thomas A. Shaw, Director of Admissions, at (615) 775–2041, ext. 204, or (800) 277–9522.

Financial Aid: In 1993–94, 85% of all current freshmen and 90% of continuing students received some form of financial aid. About 67% of freshmen and 68% of continuing students received need-based aid. The average freshman award was $7684. Of that total, scholarships or need-based grants averaged $4000 ($7300 maximum); loans averaged $3000 ($5000 maximum); and work contracts averaged $850 ($1300 maximum). Eighty percent of undergraduate students work part-time. Average earnings from campus work for the school year are $850. The average financial indebtedness of the 1992–93 graduate was $6000. Bryan is a member of CSS. The FAFSA financial statement is required. The deadline for financial aid applications is May 1.

International Students: There are currently 14 international students enrolled. They must take the TOEFL and achieve a minimum score of 500. The student must also take the ACT.

Computers: The college provides computer facilities for student use. There are 46 microcomputers available in 5 computer laboratories in both residence halls and academic areas. Residence hall rooms have campus network hookups available. All students may access the system. It may be used at all times. There are no time limits on using the system. The fees are $125 per semester.

Graduates: In 1992–93, 69 bachelor's degrees were awarded. The most popular majors among graduates were English (16%), elementary education (13%), and psychology (12%). Within an average freshman class, 43% graduate in 4 years, 4% in 5 years, and 8% in 6 years.

Admissions Contact: Thomas A. Shaw, Director of Admissions.

CARSON-NEWMAN COLLEGE

E-2

Jefferson City, TN 37760

(615) 475-9061
(800) 678-9061 (out-of-state)

Full-time: 786 men, 990 women	**Faculty:** 115; IIB, --$
Part-time: 60 men, 179 women	**Ph.D.s:** 60%
Graduate: 22 men, 89 women	**Student/Faculty:** 15 to 1
Year: semesters, summer session	**Tuition:** $8250
Application Deadline: May 1	**Room & Board:** $3000
Freshman Class: 1143 applied, 961 accepted, 464 enrolled	
ACT: 23	**COMPETITIVE**

Carson-Newman College, founded in 1851, is a private, coeducational, liberal arts college affiliated with the Tennessee Baptist Convention. There is one undergraduate and one graduate school. In addition to regional accreditation, Carson-Newman has baccalaureate program accreditation with ADA, AHEA, NASAD, NCATE, and NLN. The library contains 180,000 volumes and 183,999 microform items, and subscribes to 1000 periodicals. Computerized library sources and services include database searching. Special learning facilities include a learning resource center, art gallery, natural history museum, and TV station. The 100-acre campus is in a small town 27 miles northeast of Knoxville. Including residence halls, there are 25 buildings on campus.

Student Life: About 70% of undergraduates are from Tennessee. Students come from 40 states, 9 foreign countries, and Canada. Ninety-five percent are from public schools; 5% from private. Ninety-five percent are white. Most are Protestant. The average age of freshmen is 18; all undergraduates, 21. Twenty-eight percent drop out by the end of their first year; 55% remain to graduate.

Housing: A total of 1430 students can be accommodated in college housing. College-sponsored living facilities include single-sex dormitories, on-campus apartments, and married-student housing. In addition there are honors houses. On-campus housing is guaranteed for all 4 years. Fifty-three percent of students live on campus; of those, 50% remain on campus on weekends. Alcohol is not permitted. All students may keep cars on campus.

Activities: About 30% of men belong to 2 local fraternities; about 35% of women belong to 2 local sororities. There are 55 groups on campus, including art, band, cheerleading, chess, choir, chorale, chorus, computers, drama, drill team, ethnic, film, honors, international, jazz band, literary magazine, marching band, musical theater, newspaper, orchestra, pep band, photography, political, professional, radio and TV, religious, social, social service, student government, and yearbook. Popular campus events include Homecoming, Spring Fest, Fall Formal, Honors Convocational, and Mud Ball Tournament.

Sports: There are 9 intercollegiate sports for men and 7 for women, and 20 intramural sports for men and 20 for women. Athletic and recreation facilities include a gymnasium, a football stadium, soccer, baseball, and softball fields, a pool, and a new student center with 3 racquetball courts, 3 gymnasiums, a weight room, an Olympic-size pool, a Jacuzzi, and an outdoor cafe.

Disabled Students: Three percent of the campus is accessible to disabled students. The following facilities are available: wheelchair ramps, elevators, and special parking.

Services: In addition to many counseling and information services, tutoring is available in most subjects, including English and mathematics. In addition, there is remedial math, reading, and writing.

Campus Safety and Security: Campus safety and security measures include 24-hour foot and vehicle patrol, informal discussions, pamphlets, posters, and films, and lighted pathways and sidewalks.

Programs of Study: Carson-Newman awards the B.A., B.S., B.S.M., and B.S.N. degrees. Associate and master's degrees also are awarded. Bachelor's degrees are awarded in BIOLOGICAL SCIENCE (biology/biological science), BUSINESS (accounting, business administration and management, and business economics), COMMUNICATIONS AND THE ARTS (communications, English, fine arts, French, German, languages, music, and Spanish), EDUCATION (art, early childhood, elementary, foreign languages, health, home economics, middle school, music, science, and secondary), HEALTH PROFESSIONS (nursing and physical therapy), SOCIAL SCIENCE (economics, history, philosophy, psychology, religion, social science, and sociology). Premedicine, nursing, and history are the strongest academically. Communication arts, psychology, business accounting, general business, and education have the largest enrollments.

Required: All students must complete 128 credit hours, including Composition I and II, Survey of Old Testament, Survey of New Testament, 15 hours in English and communications, 9 in social sciences, 6 each in religion, humanities, and science, and 3 each in history and literature. The major requires 40 to 48 hours. Students must achieve a minimum GPA of 2.0.

Special: The college offers co-op programs, internships, study in England, France, and Spain, a Washington semester, on-campus work-study programs, B.A.-B.S. degrees, various dual majors, a general studies degree, student-designed majors, a 3–2 engineering degree with the University of Tennessee and the University of Georgia, and pass/fail options. Students may receive credit for life, military, or work experience. There is a freshman honors program on campus, as well as one national honor society.

Faculty/Classroom: Sixty-five percent of faculty are male; 35%, female. All teach undergraduates and 35% do research. No introductory courses are taught by graduate students. The average class size in an introductory lecture is 30 and in a regular course offering, 20.

Admissions: About 84% of the 1993–94 applicants were accepted. The ACT scores for the 1993–94 freshman class were as follows: 42% below 21, 23% between 21 and 23, 20% between 24 and 26, 4% between 27 and 28, and 11% above 28. There was 1 National Merit finalist and 3 semifinalists. About 18 freshmen graduated first in their class.

Requirements: Carson-Newman requires applicants to be in the upper 50% of their class. A minimum GPA of 2.0 is required. The ACT, with a minimum composite score of 19, or the SAT I, with a minimum composite score of 800, is required. Applicants should be graduates of an accredited secondary school. The GED is accepted. Twenty academic credits are required. Students should have 4 units of English and 2 units each of history, mathematics, science, and social studies. An essay, a portfolio, an audition, and an interview are all recommended. AP and CLEP credits are accepted. Important factors used in the admissions decision are advanced placement or honor courses, leadership record, personality, intangible qualities, evidence of special talent, and recommendations by school officials.

Procedure: Freshmen are admitted fall, spring, and summer. Entrance exams should be taken in the fall. Applications should be filed by May 1 for fall entry, December 1 for spring entry, and April 1 for summer entry, along with an application fee of $25. Notification is sent on a rolling basis. There is an early admissions plan.

Transfer: About 220 transfer students enrolled in 1993–94. Transfer students should have a minimum GPA of 2.0. Either the SAT I or the ACT is required if the student has fewer than 24 hours. An interview is recommended. A total of 32 credits out of 128 must be completed at Carson-Newman.

Visiting: There are regularly scheduled orientations for prospective students, including information sessions, meetings with advisers, and preregistration. There are guides for informal visits, and visitors may sit in on classes and stay overnight at the school. To arrange for a visit, contact the Admissions Office at (800) 678–9061.

Financial Aid: In 1993–94, 78% of all current freshmen and 82% of continuing students received some form of financial aid. About 60% of freshmen and 80% of continuing students received need-based aid. The average freshman award was $2300. Of that total, scholarships and/or need-based grants averaged $2000 ($5000 maximum); loans averaged $2000 ($4000 maximum); and work contracts averaged $1000 ($2000 maximum). Thirty percent of undergraduate students work part-time. Average earnings from campus work for the school year are $850. Carson-Newman is a member of CSS. The FAF, the college's own financial statement, and the FAFSA are required. The deadline for financial aid applications is April 1.

International Students: There are currently 8 international students enrolled. They must take the TOEFL and achieve a minimum score of 500. The student must also take the SAT I or the ACT.

Computers: The college provides computer facilities for student use. The mainframe is a DEC MicroVAX 3600. Carson-Newman also has a word-processing laboratory for composition I and II students, an Apple Macintosh laboratory with 20 terminals, and a CIS laboratory with 20 terminals. There is a campuswide network and all residence hall rooms are wired for microcomputer hookup. All students may access the system. It may be used until the laboratory closes at 11 P.M. There are no time limits on using the system. The fees are $250 per year.

Graduates: In a recent year, 388 bachelor's degrees were awarded. The most popular majors among graduates were educaton (12%), management (11%), and psychology (9%). Within an average freshman class, 40% graduate in 4 years and 55% in 5 years. Some 28 companies recruited on campus in a recent year.

Admissions Contact: Sheryl M. Gray, Director of Admissions.

CHRISTIAN BROTHERS UNIVERSITY
Memphis, TN 38104–5581

A-4

(901) 722–0205

(800) 288–7576 (out-of-state)

Full-time: 509 men, 424 women	**Faculty:** 106
Part-time: 168 men, 206 women	**Ph.D.s:** 75%
Graduate: 133 men, 63 women	**Student/Faculty:** 8 to 1
Year: semesters, summer session	**Tuition:** $8940
Application Deadline: August 1	**Room & Board:** $3180
Freshman Class: 667 applied, 638 accepted, 225 enrolled	
SAT I Verbal/Math: 462/530	**ACT:** 24 **VERY COMPETITIVE**

Christian Brothers University, founded in 1871, is a nonprofit, private, comprehensive coeducational institution affiliated with the Roman Catholic Church. Its undergraduate and graduate programs emphasize the liberal arts and sciences, business, engineering and engineering management, health science, telecommunications management, and teacher preparation. There are 4 undergraduate and 3 graduate schools. In addition to regional accreditation, CBU has baccalaureate program accreditation with ABET. The library contains 91,830 volumes, 4000 microform items, and 300 audiovisual forms, and subscribes to 582 periodicals. Computerized library sources and services include the card catalog, interlibrary loans, and database searching. Special learning facilities include a learning resource center. The 70-acre campus is in an urban area in Memphis. Including residence halls, there are 18 buildings on campus.

Student Life: About 77% of undergraduates are from Tennessee. Students come from 33 states and 19 foreign countries. Sixty-eight percent are from public schools; 32% from private. Seventy-nine percent are white; 17% African American. Sixty-four percent are Protestant; 32% Catholic. The average age of freshmen is 19; all undergraduates, 24. Twenty-seven percent drop out by the end of their first year; 46% remain to graduate.

Housing: A total of 511 students can be accommodated in college housing. College-sponsored living facilities include single-sex and coed dormitories and on-campus apartments. On-campus housing is guaranteed for the freshman year only. Sixty-nine percent of students commute. Alcohol is not permitted. All students may keep cars on campus.

Activities: About 24% of men belong to 4 local and 4 national fraternities; about 20% of women belong to 3 local and 3 national sororities. There are more than 40 groups on campus, including cheerleading, chess, chorale, chorus, computers, drama, ethnic, honors, international, literary magazine, musical theater, newspaper, political, professional, religious, social, student government, and yearbook. Popular campus events include the Riverboat Dance, Spring Formal, and Homecoming.

Sports: There are 4 intercollegiate sports for men and 3 for women, and 14 intramural sports for men and 8 for women. Athletic and recreation facilities include an outdoor pool, a 2500-seat gymnasium, a 718-seat arena, basketball/volleyball and handball/racquetball courts, baseball and soccer fields, tennis courts, a batting cage, an outdoor track, and weight-training facilities.

Disabled Students: Ten percent of the campus is accessible to disabled students. The following facilities are available: wheelchair ramps, elevators, special parking, and specially equipped rest rooms.

Services: In addition to many counseling and information services, tutoring is available in most subjects, including mathematics, languages, reading, and writing. CBU also has centers for mathematics, language, and writing.

Campus Safety and Security: Campus safety and security measures include a 24-hour foot and vehicle patrol, self defense education, pamphlets, posters, films, emergency telephones and lighted pathways and sidewalks.

Programs of Study: CBU awards the B.A. and B.S. degrees. Master's degrees also are awarded. Bachelor's degrees are awarded in BIOLOGICAL SCIENCE (biology/biological science), BUSINESS (accounting, business administration and management, business economics, management science, and marketing/retailing/merchandising), COMMUNICATIONS AND THE ARTS (dramatic

arts, English, and journalism), COMPUTER AND PHYSICAL SCIENCE (chemistry, computer science, information sciences and systems, mathematics, and physics), EDUCATION (elementary and secondary), ENGINEERING AND ENVIRONMENTAL DESIGN (chemical engineering, civil engineering, electrical/electronics engineering, engineering physics, and mechanical engineering), HEALTH PROFESSIONS (medical laboratory technology, medical technology, predentistry, premedicine, and prepharmacy), SOCIAL SCIENCE (history, humanities, prelaw, and psychology). Engineering, accounting, and business are the strongest programs academically. Electrical engineering, accounting, and biology have the largest enrollments.

Required: To graduate, students must complete at least 128 semester hours, with a varying number of hours in the major, and maintain a minimum GPA of 2.0. General education requirements, totaling 38 to 40 semester hours, consist of 6 hours each of communication skills, mathematics, and social sciences, 12 hours of humanities, 4 hours of natural and physical sciences, 2 to 4 hours of business/technology, and 2 hours of health/physical education. Individual schools may vary in their core requirements.

Special: Special academic programs include on-campus work-study and internships that are arranged through the Career Center for all juniors and seniors. There is cross-registration with Memphis College of Art, Memphis Theological Seminary, and LeMoyne-Owen College. An accelerated degree program is available to all business majors through the evening program, and a general studies degree is offered. Up to 36 hours of nondegree study is possible, as are dual majors and pass/fail options. The B.S. degree in telecommunications and informations systems management and the executive master's degree in telecommunications management are also offered. There is a freshman honors program on campus, as well as 4 national honor societies.

Faculty/Classroom: Seventy percent of faculty are male; 30%, female. Ninety-five percent teach undergraduates. No introductory courses are taught by graduate students. The average class size in an introductory lecture is 22; in a laboratory, 15; and in a regular course offering, 16.

Admissions: About 96% of the 1993–94 applicants were accepted. The SAT scores for the 1993–94 freshman class were as follows: Verbal—63% below 500 and 38% between 500 and 599; Math—42% below 500, 25% between 500 and 599, and 33% between 600 and 700. The ACT scores were 24% below 21, 28% between 21 and 23, 20% between 24 and 26, 14% between 27 and 28, and 15% above 28. About 54% of the current freshmen were in the top fifth of their class; 74% were in the top two fifths. There were 6 National Merit semifinalists.

Requirements: CBU recommends applicants to be in the upper 50% of their class. A minimum GPA of 2.3 is required. The SAT I or ACT is required. The SAT I score should be 830, 415 verbal and 415 math; the ACT score should be 20. Other admissions requirements include graduation from an accredited secondary school, with a college-preparatory curriculum recommended. The GED is also accepted. An interview is advised. AP and CLEP credits are accepted. Important factors used in the admissions decision are advanced placement or honor courses, recommendations by school officials, recommendations by alumni, leadership record, and extracurricular activities record.

Procedure: Freshmen are admitted to all sessions. Entrance exams should be taken by the end of the junior year. Applications should be filed by August 1 for fall entry (May 1 preferred), January 1 for spring entry, and May 15 for summer entry, along with an application fee of $25. Notification is sent on a rolling basis. There is a deferred admissions plan.

Transfer: About 83 transfer students enrolled in a recent year. Transfer students should have a minimum GPA of 2.5 and be in good academic and disciplinary standing. An SAT I score of at least 830 is recommended, as is a minimum ACT score of 20. An interview is advised. A total of 35 semester hours out of 128 must be completed at CBU.

Visiting: There are regularly scheduled orientations for prospective students, including attendance at classes, meetings with professors and students, a campus tour, and meetings with admissions and financial aid representatives. There are guides for informal visits and visitors may sit in on classes and stay overnight at the school. To arrange for a visit, contact Gregory K. Miller, Dean of Admissions, at (901) 722–0205 or (800) 288–7576.

Financial Aid: In a recent year, 97% of all freshmen and 73% of continuing students received some form of financial aid. About 65% of freshmen and 62% of continuing students received need-based aid. The average freshman award was $6043. Of that total, scholarships or need-based grants averaged $2766 ($7940 maximum); loans averaged $1500 ($3625 maximum); and work contracts averaged $800 ($1200 maximum). Ninety percent of undergraduate students work part-time. Average earnings from campus work for the school year are $800. The average financial indebtedness of a recent

graduate was $10,500. CBU is a member of CSS. The FAF or FFS is required. The deadline for financial aid applications is April 1.

International Students: There are currently 50 international students enrolled. The school actively recruits these students. They must take the TOEFL and achieve a minimum score of 500. The student must also take the SAT I with a composite score of 800 or the ACT with a score of 20.

Computers: The college provides computer facilities for student use. The mainframe is a DEC VAX 6000–410. There are also 190 microcomputers and terminals available for student use in computer centers and academic buildings, including DEC VAXstation 3100 workstations, IBM PC, PC-AT, and PS/2, Sharp PC-compatible, AST PC-compatible, Apple IIe, DEC VT420 and VT320, Springvale PC-compatible, and Tektronix, among others. There is a campuswide, fiber-optic-based LAN, and software for word processing, spreadsheets, databases, engineering, accounting, calculus, mathematics, writing, chemistry, physics, and biology. All students may access the system during the 91 hours per week of computer center operation; 24-hour dial-in phone access is available. There are no time limits and no fees.

Graduates: In a recent year, 283 bachelor's degrees were awarded. The most popular majors among graduates were accounting (18%), electrical engineering (10%), and management (10%). Within an average freshman class, 46% graduate in 5 years. Some 60 companies recruited on campus in a recent year.

Admissions Contact: Gregory K. Miller, Dean of Admissions.

CRICHTON COLLEGE
A-3
Memphis, TN 38175–7830 (901) 367–9800
(800) 524–5554, ext. 6722 (out-of-state)

Full-time: 94 men, 116 women	**Faculty:** 16
Part-time: 64 men, 80 women	**Ph.D.s:** 44%
Graduate: none	**Student/Faculty:** 15 to 1
Year: semester, five evening sessions	**Tuition:** $4780
Application Deadline: open	**Room & Board:** $1767
Freshman Class: 202 applied, 190 accepted, 103 enrolled	
ACT: 18	**NONCOMPETITIVE**

Crichton College, founded in 1944, is a small, private, coeducational college offering programs in liberal arts, Bible, business, health science, music, religion, and teacher preparation. There are 5 undergraduate schools. The library contains 41,000 volumes, 1212 microform items, and 315 audiovisual forms, and subscribes to 355 periodicals. The 58-acre campus is in a suburban area 1 mile southeast of Memphis. Including residence halls, there are 3 buildings on campus.

Student Life: Students come from 5 states and 6 foreign countries. Ninety-five percent are from public schools; 5% from private. Seventy-two percent are white; 27% African American. Most are Protestant. The average age of freshmen is 18; all undergraduates, 27.

Housing: A total of 32 students can be accommodated in college housing. College-sponsored living facilities include dormitories and off-campus apartments. On-campus housing is guaranteed for all 4 years. Ninety percent of students commute. Alcohol is not permitted. All students may keep cars on campus.

Activities: There are no fraternities or sororities on campus. There are 4 groups on campus, including cheerleading, choir, chorale, and yearbook. Popular campus events include Spirit Week, Spring Fling, and Bible conferences.

Sports: There is 1 intercollegiate sport for men, and 7 intramural sports for men and 5 for women. Athletic and recreation facilities include an athletic building and a baseball field.

Disabled Students: All of the campus is accessible to disabled students. The following facilities are available: wheelchair ramps, elevators, special parking, specially equipped rest rooms, and lowered drinking fountains.

Services: There is remedial math, reading, and writing.

Programs of Study: Crichton awards the B.A., B.S., and B.M.E. degrees. Bachelor's degrees are awarded in BUSINESS (business administration and management), EDUCATION (business, elementary, music, and secondary), SOCIAL SCIENCE (ministries and psychology). Psychology and business are the strongest academically. Education, business, and psychology have the largest enrollments.

Required: Students must complete a minimum of 128 credit hours, and some disciplines require more. The number of hours for the major varies, but all students must take 18 hours of Bible studies. The minimum GPA required is 2.0, and for teacher education students, 2.5.

Special: The college offers B.A.-B.S. degrees, dual majors, and limited nondegree study.

Faculty/Classroom: Sixty-four percent of faculty are male; 36%, female. Ninety-seven percent teach undergraduates and 3% do research. The average class size in an introductory lecture is 34; in a laboratory, 15; and in a regular course offering, 12.

Admissions: About 94% of the 1993–94 applicants were accepted. The ACT scores for the 1993–94 freshman class were as follows: 49% below 21, 30% between 21 and 23, 15% between 24 and 26, 4% between 27 and 28, and 2% above 28. About 25% of the current freshmen were in the top fifth of their class; 40% were in the top two fifths.

Requirements: A minimum GPA of 2.0 is required. The ACT is required, with a minimum composite score of 16. Students must have a high school diploma, or the GED is accepted. An essay and an interview are required. AP and CLEP credits are accepted. Important factors used in the admissions decision are advanced placement or honor courses, evidence of special talent, leadership record, personality, intangible qualities, and extracurricular activities record.

Procedure: Freshmen are admitted fall, winter, spring, and summer. Entrance exams should be taken during orientation. Application deadlines are open. The application fee is $25. The college accepts all applicants. There is a deferred admissions plan.

Transfer: Transfer students must have a minimum GPA of 2.0 and an ACT score of 16. An interview is required. A total of 30 credits out of 128 must be completed at Crichton.

Visiting: There are guides for informal visits, and visitors may sit in on classes and stay overnight at the school. To arrange for a visit, contact the Admissions Office at (800) 524–5554, ext. 6722.

Financial Aid: The FAF is required. The deadline for financial aid applications is August 1.

International Students: There are currently 3 international students enrolled. They must take the TOEFL and achieve a minimum score of 500. The student must also take the ACT.

Computers: The college provides computer facilities for student use. There are 15 AT&T 6300 microcomputers available for student use in computer laboratories. All students may access the system. There are no time limits on using the system and no fees.

Graduates: In 1992–93, 32 bachelor's degrees were awarded.

Admissions Contact: Mr. Lee Ferguson, Director of Admissions.

CUMBERLAND UNIVERSITY
C-2

Lebanon, TN 37087   (615) 444–2562; (800) 467–0562 (out-of-state)

Full-time: 705 men and women	Faculty: 60
Part-time: 296 men and women	Ph.D.s: 60%
Graduate: 44 men and women	Student/Faculty: 12 to 1
Year: semesters, summer session	Tuition: $5700
Application Deadline: open	Room & Board: $2950
Freshman Class: 412 applied, 384 accepted, 261 enrolled	
ACT: 21	COMPETITIVE

Cumberland University, founded in 1842, is a private institution offering undergraduate and graduate degrees in business, education, and social sciences. There is one graduate school. The library contains 50,000 volumes and 1100 audiovisual forms, and subscribes to 500 periodicals. Computerized library sources and services include the card catalog, interlibrary loans, and database searching. Special learning facilities include a learning resource center, natural history museum, planetarium, and radio station. The 44-acre campus is in a small town 28 miles east of Nashville. Including residence halls, there are 11 buildings on campus.

Student Life: Students come from 27 states, 5 foreign countries, and Canada. Eighty-seven percent are white; 12% African American. The average age of freshmen is 19; all undergraduates, 21.

Housing: A total of 263 students can be accommodated in college housing. College-sponsored living facilities include single-sex dormitories and off-campus apartments. On-campus housing is available on a first-come, first-served basis. Seventy-five percent of students commute. Alcohol is not permitted. All students may keep cars on campus.

Activities: About 8% of men belong to 1 national fraternity; about 9% of women belong to 1 local sorority. There are 15 groups on campus, including cheerleading, choir, computers, drama, honors, newspaper, professional, religious, social, student government, and yearbook. Popular campus events include Octoberfest, Fall Festival, Homecoming, Springfest, and Wonderful Wednesdays.

Sports: There are 5 intercollegiate sports for men and 4 for women, and 5 intramural sports for men and 5 for women. Athletic and recreation facilities include a gymnasium, a field house, a weight room, baseball and soccer fields, as well as tennis courts and outdoor volleyball courts.

Disabled Students: The following facilities are available: wheelchair ramps, special parking, and lowered telephones.

Services: In addition to many counseling and information services, tutoring is available in most subjects. In addition, there is remedial math, reading, and writing.

Campus Safety and Security: Campus safety and security measures include 24-hour foot and vehicle patrol, informal discussions, lighted pathways and sidewalks, and the outside entrances of the dormitories are always secured; only residents have keys.

Programs of Study: Cumberland awards the B.A., B.S., B.B.A., B.S.Bus., B.S.Ed., and B.S.N. degrees. Associate and master's degrees also are awarded. Bachelor's degrees are awarded in BUSINESS (business administration and management), EDUCATION (elementary, health, middle school, and secondary), HEALTH PROFESSIONS (nursing and premedicine), SOCIAL SCIENCE (prelaw and social science). Business and education have the largest enrollments.

Special: Students may cross-register for lower-level courses at Aquinas Junior College. Cooperative programs with local businesses and internships in the state legislature are available. Nondegree study and pass/fail options are offered. There is a freshman honors program on campus, as well as 2 national honor societies. One department has an honors program.

Admissions: About 93% of the 1993–94 applicants were accepted. The ACT scores for the 1993–94 freshman class were as follows: 46% below 21, 27% between 21 and 23, 20% between 24 and 26, 8% between 27 and 28, and 2% above 28. There was 1 National Merit finalist. Nine freshmen graduated first in their class.

Requirements: Cumberland requires applicants to be in the upper 75% of their class. A minimum GPA of 2.0 is required. The SAT I or ACT is recommended. A minimum composite ACT score of 17 is expected. Applicants must be high school graduates or have earned the GED with a composite 50 score. AP and CLEP credits are accepted.

Procedure: Freshmen are admitted to all sessions. Entrance exams should be taken during the senior year in high school. Application deadlines are open. The application fee is $25. Notification is sent on a rolling basis. There is an early decision plan.

Transfer: About 100 transfer students enrolled in 1993–94. Transfer applicants should have completed at least 15 college credits with a GPA of at least 2.0. A total of 30 credits must be completed at Cumberland.

Visiting: There are regularly scheduled orientations for prospective students, consisting of campus tours, testing, information sessions pertaining to college life, and academic advising. A 'parent orientation' is provided in conjunction with student orientation programs. There are guides for informal visits and visitors may sit in on classes. To arrange for a visit, contact the Admissions Office at (615) 444–2562 or (800) 467–0562.

Financial Aid: In a recent year, 85% of all current freshmen and 85% of continuing students received some form of financial aid. Cumberland is a member of CSS. The FFS is required. The deadline for financial aid applications is March 1.

International Students: There are currently 10 international students enrolled. They must take the TOEFL or the University of Michigan Language Test and achieve a minimum score on the TOEFL of 500. The student must also take the SAT I or the ACT.

Computers: The college provides computer facilities for student use. Microcomputers are available in the computer laboratory. All students may access the system. There are no time limits on using the system and no fees.

Graduates: In 1992–93, 97 bachelor's degrees were awarded.

Admissions Contact: Charles W. Gregory, Dean of Admissions.

DAVID LIPSCOMB UNIVERSITY
C-3

Nashville, TN 37204–3951   (615) 269–1776
                     (800) 333–4358 (out-of-state)

Full-time: 928 men, 1005 women	Faculty: 97; IIB, -$
Part-time: 193 men, 209 women	Ph.D.s: 75%
Graduate: 61 men, 11 women	Student/Faculty: 20 to 1
Year: semesters, summer session	Tuition: $6270
Application Deadline: May 15	Room & Board: $1595
Freshman Class: 1239 applied, 872 accepted, 611 enrolled	
ACT: 23	VERY COMPETITIVE

David Lipscomb University, founded in 1891, is a private, coeducational, liberal arts university affiliated with the Church of Christ. There are 17 undergraduate and 2 graduate schools. In addition to regional accreditation, DLU has baccalaureate program accreditation with ADA, CSWE, NASM, and NCATE. The library contains 184,509 volumes, 93,779 microform items, and 6400 audiovisual forms, and subscribes to 940 periodicals. Computerized library sources and services include the card catalog. Special learning facilities include a learning resource center, art gallery, radio station, and TV station. The 65-acre campus is in a suburban area 2 miles south of Nashville. Including residence halls, there are 16 buildings on campus.

Student Life: About 58% of undergraduates are from Tennessee. Students come from 42 states, 17 foreign countries, and Canada. Forty-one percent are from public schools; 59% from private. Ninety percent are white and most are Protestant. The average age of freshmen is 19; all undergraduates, 20. Twenty percent drop out by the end of their first year; 62% remain to graduate.

Housing: A total of 1450 students can be accommodated in college housing. College-sponsored living facilities include single-sex residence halls. On-campus housing is guaranteed for all 4 years. Sixty

percent of students live on campus. Alcohol is not permitted. All students may keep cars on campus.

Activities: About 19% of men belong to 8 local fraternities; about 17% of women belong to 8 local sororities. There are 54 groups on campus, including art, band, cheerleading, chorale, chorus, computers, drama, ethnic, honors, international, jazz band, musical theater, newspaper, orchestra, photography, political, professional, radio and TV, social, social service, student government, and yearbook. Popular campus events include University Days, Sing-a-rama, Tau Phi Cowboy Show, Delta Na Na Na, and Homecoming.

Sports: There are 6 intercollegiate sports for men and 3 for women, and 7 intramural sports for men and 6 for women. Athletic and recreation facilities include a gymnasium with a basketball court and a pool, and a student activity center with 2 full-size basketball courts, 5 racquetball courts, a jogging course and weight, aerobics, and recreation rooms.

Disabled Students: Ninety-five percent of the campus is accessible to disabled students. The following facilities are available: wheelchair ramps, elevators, special parking, and specially equipped rest rooms.

Services: In addition to many counseling and information services, tutoring is available in some subjects. There is also remedial math, reading, and writing.

Campus Safety and Security: Campus safety and security measures include 24-hour foot and vehicle patrol, escort service, pamphlets, posters, and films, and emergency telephones. In addition, there are lighted pathways and sidewalks and residence hall security systems.

Programs of Study: DLU awards the B.A. and B.S. degrees. Master's degrees are also awarded. Bachelor's degrees are awarded in BIOLOGICAL SCIENCE (biochemistry and biology/biological science), BUSINESS (accounting, banking and finance, business administration and management, fashion merchandising, marketing/retailing/merchandising, and office supervision and management), COMMUNICATIONS AND THE ARTS (communications, English, French, German, languages, music, public relations, Spanish, and speech/debate/rhetoric), COMPUTER AND PHYSICAL SCIENCE (chemistry, computer science, mathematics, and physics), EDUCATION (art, business, elementary, foreign languages, music, physical, and science), ENGINEERING AND ENVIRONMENTAL DESIGN (engineering and preengineering), HEALTH PROFESSIONS (predentistry, premedicine, and prepharmacy), SOCIAL SCIENCE (American studies, biblical languages, dietetics, food production/management/services, history, home economics, political science/government, prelaw, psychology, religion, social work, sociology, and urban studies). Chemistry, biology, accounting, and mathematics are the strongest academically. Business, medicine, and education have the largest enrollments.

Required: All full-time students must take and pass a Bible class meeting each day the student has any classes. Other general education requirements involve 9 semester hours in communication, 6 each in humanities, science, history, and social science, 3 in mathematics, and 2 in physical education. Students must complete a total of 132 semester hours and have a minimum GPA of 2.0.

Special: DLU offers co-op programs in nursing and engineering, internships, and 3–2 engineering degrees with University of Tennessee at Knoxville, Georgia Institute of Technology, and Auburn, Vanderbilt, and Tennessee Technological universities. An adult credit and noncredit studies program and pass/fail options for physical education activity courses are available. There is a freshman honors program on campus, as well as one national honor society. Seventeen departments have honors programs.

Faculty/Classroom: Seventy-four percent of faculty are male; 20%, female. All teach undergraduates. No introductory courses are taught by graduate students. The average class size in an introductory lecture is 40; in a laboratory, 20; and in a regular course offering, 22.

Admissions: About 70% of the 1993–94 applicants were accepted. The SAT scores for the 1993–94 freshman class were as follows: Verbal—52% below 500, 28% between 500 and 599, 18% between 600 and 700, and 2% above 700; Math—30% below 500, 36% between 500 and 599, 30% between 600 and 700, and 4% above 700. The ACT scores were 28% below 21, 16% between 21 and 23, 22% between 24 and 26, 18% between 27 and 28, and 16% above 28. About 40% of the current freshmen were in the top fifth of their class; 80% were in the top two fifths. There were 8 National Merit finalists and 8 semifinalists.

Requirements: A minimum GPA of 2.3 is required. The SAT I or ACT is required. Candidates for admission should be graduates of accredited secondary schools. The GED is accepted. Fourteen academic units are required. Students should have completed 4 units of English, and 2 units each of history, mathematics, and science, and 2 units of a foreign language are highly recommended. Two additional units from the areas of English, foreign language, history, mathematics, science, and social studies are also required. AP and CLEP credits are accepted. Important factors used in the admissions decision are advanced placement or honor courses, personality, intangible quali-

ties, leadership record, evidence of special talent, and extracurricular activities record.

Procedure: Freshmen are admitted to all sessions. Early decision applications should be filed by November 15; regular applications, by May 15 for fall entry, along with an application fee of $25. Notification of early decision is sent January 1. There are early decision and early admissions plans. A waiting list is an active part of the admissions procedure, with about 5% of applicants on the list.

Transfer: About 234 transfer students enrolled in 1993–94. Students must be in good standing at their previous institution.

Visiting: There are regularly scheduled orientations for prospective students. There are guides for informal visits and visitors may sit in on classes and stay overnight at the school. To arrange for a visit, contact the Office of Undergraduate Admissions at (800) 333-4358 or (615) 269-1776.

Financial Aid: In 1993–94, 74% of all current freshmen received some form of financial aid. About 45% of freshmen received need-based aid. The average freshman award was $3600. Of that total, scholarships or need-based grants averaged $1031 ($5000 maximum). Fifty-eight percent of undergraduate students work part-time. Average earnings from campus work for the school year are $800. DLU is a member of CSS. The FAF and the FAFSA are required. The deadline for financial aid applications is April 15.

International Students: There are currently 38 international students enrolled. The school actively recruits these students. They must take the TOEFL or the University of Michigan Language Test and achieve a minimum score on the TOEFL of 500. The student must also take the SAT I or the ACT and achieve an SAT I score of 810 and an ACT 19.

Computers: The college provides computer facilities for student use. The mainframe is a DEC VAX 11/780. There are computer laboratories in every building on campus, including residence halls. There are computer hook-ups in every dorm room. All students may access the system. It may be used 24 hours per day, 7 days per week. There are no time limits on using the system and no fees.

Graduates: In a recent year 437 bachelor's degrees were awarded. The most popular majors among graduates were business (19%), medicine (14%), and education (12%). Within an average freshman class, 2% graduate in 3 years, 60% in 4 years, 36% in 5 years, and 2% in 6 years. More than 500 companies recruited on campus in 1992–93.

Admissions Contact: Wade Sandrell, Director of Admissions and Retention.

EAST TENNESSEE STATE UNIVERSITY F-2
Johnson City, TN 37614 (615) 929-4213

Full-time: 3185 men, 4172 women	Faculty: 250; IIA, -$
Part-time: 730 men, 1371 women	Ph.D.s: 80%
Graduate: 725 men, 1089 women	Student/Faculty: 29 to 1
Year: semesters, summer session	Tuition: $1606 ($5388)
Application Deadline: July 1	Room & Board: $2800
Freshman Class: 3330 applied, 2730 accepted, 1313 enrolled	
SAT I Verbal/Math: 400/450	ACT: 20 COMPETITIVE

East Tennessee State University, founded in 1911, is a public, coeducational institution that is part of the State University and Community College System of Tennessee. ETSU's undergraduate and graduate programs stress the liberal arts, business, art, fine arts, professional training, music, teacher preparation, technical studies, and health science. There are 7 undergraduate and 2 graduate schools. In addition to regional accreditation, ETSU has baccalaureate program accreditation with AACSB, ABET, ACEJMC, ADA, CAHEA, CSWE, NASAD, NASM, and NLN. The 3 libraries contain 536,000 volumes, 1.4 million microform items, and 17,060 audiovisual forms, and subscribe to 3400 periodicals. Computerized library sources and services include the card catalog, interlibrary loans, and database searching. Special learning facilities include a learning resource center, an art gallery, a planetarium, a radio station, a TV station, and a regional art and history museum. The 366-acre campus is in a small town 100 miles east of Knoxville. Including residence halls, there are 64 buildings on campus.

Student Life: About 86% of undergraduates are from Tennessee. Students come from 38 states, 40 foreign countries, and Canada. Ninety-seven percent are from public schools; 3% from private. Ninety-three percent are white. The average age of freshmen is 20.1; all undergraduates, 26.2. Twenty-two percent drop out by the end of their first year; 34% remain to graduate.

Housing: A total of 2415 students can be accommodated in college housing. College-sponsored living facilities include single-sex dormitories, on-campus apartments, and married-student housing. On-campus housing is guaranteed for all 4 years. Seventy-seven percent of students commute. Alcohol is not permitted. All students may keep cars on campus.

Activities: About 10% of men belong to 9 national fraternities; about 10% of women belong to 5 national sororities. There are 197 groups on campus, including art, band, cheerleading, choir, chorale, chorus, computers, dance, drama, drill team, ethnic, gay, honors, international, jazz band, literary magazine, marching band, newspaper, pep band, photography, political, professional, radio and TV, religious, social, social service, student government, and yearbook. Popular campus events include Homecoming, Preview, Leadership Conference, National Clean Up for Hunger, VIP Day, Winter Cruise, Into the Streets, Greek Rush, Wellness Programs, Women's Leadership Series, and National Volunteer Week.

Sports: There are 8 intercollegiate sports for men and 7 for women, and 20 intramural sports for men and 20 for women. Athletic and recreation facilities include a 4000-seat gymnasium and a domed stadium seating 12,000, which also includes a basketball arena, tennis and handball/racquetball courts, a track, and weight and training rooms.

Disabled Students: Fifty-seven percent of the campus is accessible to disabled students. The following facilities are available: wheelchair ramps, elevators, special parking, specially equipped rest rooms, special class scheduling, lowered drinking fountains, and lowered telephones.

Services: In addition to many counseling and information services, tutoring is available in most subjects. There is an office for students with disabilities. In addition, there is remedial math, reading, and writing.

Campus Safety and Security: Campus safety and security measures include 24-hour foot and vehicle patrol, self-defense education, escort service, and shuttle buses. In addition, there are informal discussions, pamphlets, posters, and films, emergency telephones, lighted pathways and sidewalks, and engravers available to identify personal property.

Programs of Study: ETSU awards the B.A., B.S., B.B.A., B.F.A., B.G.S., B.M., B.S.E.H., B.S.Ed., B.S.M.T., B.S.N., B.S.P.T., and B.S.W. degrees. Associate, master's, and doctoral degrees also are awarded. Bachelor's degrees are awarded in BIOLOGICAL SCIENCE (biology/biological science and microbiology), BUSINESS (accounting, banking and finance, business economics, and marketing/retailing/merchandising), COMMUNICATIONS AND THE ARTS (broadcasting, communications, design, dramatic arts, English, fine arts, journalism, music, photography, and speech/debate/rhetoric), COMPUTER AND PHYSICAL SCIENCE (chemistry, computer programming, computer science, geology, information sciences and systems, mathematics, and physics), EDUCATION (art, early childhood, elementary, foreign languages, health, home economics, middle school, music, science, secondary, and special), ENGINEERING AND ENVIRONMENTAL DESIGN (engineering technology), HEALTH PROFESSIONS (nursing, physical therapy, public health, and speech pathology/audiology), SOCIAL SCIENCE (criminal justice, dietetics, economics, geography, history, philosophy, political science/government, psychology, social science, social work, and sociology). Nursing, engineering technology, criminal justice, and education have the largest enrollments.

Required: All students must complete 128 semester hours, with 30 to 60 in the major, and maintain a minimum GPA of 2.0. Distribution requirements, which total 46 semester hours, include English, American history, physical education, natural science, social and behavioral science, the humanities, analysis, and a 3-hour computer literacy course. An exit examination is also required.

Special: Special academic programs include cooperative education programs, cross-registration with Milligan College, internships in political science, applied human sciences, and management, study abroad in Scotland, England, France, and Spain, and B.A.-B.S. degrees in all undergraduate majors. A general studies degree is offered. Credit for military experience may be granted, and nondegree study and pass/fail options are possible. There is a freshman honors program on campus, as well as 31 national honor societies.

Faculty/Classroom: Sixty-six percent of faculty are male; 34%, female. Seventy percent teach undergraduates and 33% do research. Graduate students teach 8% of introductory courses. The average class size in an introductory lecture is 36; in a laboratory, 22; and in a regular course offering, 21.

Admissions: About 82% of the 1993–94 applicants were accepted. The ACT scores for the 1993–94 freshman class were as follows: 40% below 21, 20% between 21 and 23, 24% between 24 and 26, 14% between 27 and 28, and 2% above 28. About 38% of the current freshmen were in the top fifth of their class; 57% were in the top two fifths. About 60 freshmen graduated first in their class.

Requirements: A minimum GPA of 2.3 is required. The SAT I, with a minimum composite score of 800 (400 verbal and 400 mathematics), or the enhanced ACT, with a minimum score of 19, is required. Other admissions requirements include graduation from an accredited secondary school, with 20 Carnegie units and 14 academic credits, including 4 of English, 3 of mathematics, 2 each of a foreign language and science, and 1 each of history, social studies, and art. In-state students who take the Tennessee State Proficiency Test are eligible to apply for admission, and if their ACT/SAT I is below a certain score, they must complete the Academic Assessment Placement Program (AAPP) test battery before registration for classes. The GED is also accepted. AP and CLEP credits are accepted.

Procedure: Freshmen are admitted to all sessions. Entrance exams should be taken during the junior year. Applications should be filed by July 1 for fall entry, November 1 for spring entry, and April 1 for summer entry, along with an application fee of $5. Notification is sent on a rolling basis. There is an early admissions plan.

Transfer: About 750 transfer students enrolled in 1993–94. Transfer students must have a minimum GPA of 2.0 in 12 or more credit hours of course work from a regionally accredited institution. Transfer students must also satisfy high school unit requirements if they graduated high school after 1988. A total of 34 credits out of 128 must be completed at ETSU.

Visiting: There are regularly scheduled orientations for prospective students, including 5 2-day orientation programs held during spring and summer for admitted new students to fall term. There are guides for informal visits and visitors may sit in on classes and stay overnight at the school. To arrange for a visit, contact the Admissions Office at (615) 929–4213.

Financial Aid: In 1993–94, 62% of all current freshmen and 58% of continuing students received some form of financial aid. About 55% of freshmen and 48% of continuing students received need-based aid. The average freshman award was $1418. Of that total, scholarships or need-based grants averaged $1177 ($7300 maximum); loans averaged $2072 ($5000 maximum); and work contracts averaged $998 ($1600 maximum). Fifteen percent of undergraduate students work part-time. Average earnings from campus work for the school year are $1043. The average financial indebtedness of the 1992–93 graduate was $9205. The FAFSA financial statement is required. The deadline for financial aid applications is July 1.

International Students: There are currently 155 international students enrolled. They must take the TOEFL and achieve a minimum score of 500. The student must also take the SAT I or the ACT.

Computers: The college provides computer facilities for student use. The mainframe is an IBM ES 9000–190. There are 120 microcomputers available for student use in computer laboratories in several buildings on campus. All students may access the system. It may be used 24 hours per day. There are no time limits on using the system. The fees are $15.

Graduates: In 1992–93, 1390 bachelor's degrees were awarded. The most popular majors among graduates were elementary education (9%), nursing (8%), and engineering technology (7%). Within an average freshman class, 11% graduate in 4 years, 29% in 5 years, and 34% in 6 years. Some 183 companies recruited on campus in 1992–93. In the 1992 graduating class, 9% of the graduates were enrolled in graduate school within 6 months of graduation; 92% had found employment.

Admissions Contact: Dr. Nancy Dishner, Dean of Admissions and Enrollment Management.

FISK UNIVERSITY

C-2

Nashville, TN 37208–3051   (615) 329–8665

Full-time: 350 men, 550 women	**Faculty:** 60
Part-time: none	**Ph.Ds:** 60%
Graduate: 25 men, 15 women	**Student/Faculty:** 15 to 1
Year: semesters	**Tuition:** n/av
Application Deadline: June 15	**Room & Board:** n/app
Freshman Class: n/av	
SAT I or ACT: recommended	**LESS COMPETITIVE**

Fisk University, founded in 1866, is a private, nonsectarian, liberal arts institution affiliated with the American Missionary Association of the United Congregational Church. Established as a college for African Americans, Fisk has always accepted students regardless of race. The library contains 186,000 volumes and 4000 microform items, and subscribes to 600 periodicals. Special learning facilities include an art gallery and a radio station. The 40-acre campus is in an urban area Nashville. Including residence halls, there are 21 buildings on campus.

Student Life: About 88% of undergraduates are from out-of-state, mostly the Midwest. Students come from 33 states, 5 foreign countries, and Canada. Seventy percent are from public schools; 25% from private. Ninety-five percent are African American. Most are Protestant. The average age of freshmen is 18; all undergraduates, 20. Twenty percent drop out by the end of their first year; 60% remain to graduate.

Housing: A total of 1030 students can be accommodated in college housing. College-sponsored living facilities include single-sex dormitories. On-campus housing is guaranteed for all 4 years. Ninety percent of students live on campus; of those, 90% remain on campus on weekends. Alcohol is not permitted. All students may keep cars on campus.

Activities: About 25% of men belong to 4 national fraternities; about 20% of women belong to 4 national sororities. There are some groups and organizations on campus, including cheerleading, choir, dance, drama, honors, literary magazine, newspaper, religious, student government, and yearbook.

Sports: Athletic and recreation facilities include a gymnasium and a student center.

Disabled Students: Eighty percent of the campus is accessible to disabled students. Specially equipped elevators are available.

Services: In addition to many counseling and information services, tutoring is available in some subjects. There is also remedial math, reading, and writing.

Campus Safety and Security: Campus safety and security measures include a 24-hour foot and vehicle patrol and lighted pathways and sidewalks.

Programs of Study: Fisk awards the B.A., B.S., and B.M. degrees. Master's degrees also are awarded. Bachelor's degrees are awarded in BIOLOGICAL SCIENCE (biology/biological science), BUSINESS (business administration and management), COMMUNICATIONS AND THE ARTS (dramatic arts, English, fine arts, French, music, Spanish, and speech/debate/rhetoric), COMPUTER AND PHYSICAL SCIENCE (chemistry, mathematics, and physics), EDUCATION (art and music), ENGINEERING AND ENVIRONMENTAL DESIGN (preengineering), HEALTH PROFESSIONS (predentistry, premedicine, and prepharmacy), SOCIAL SCIENCE (economics, history, philosophy, political science/government, prelaw, psychology, religion, and sociology). Engineering, biology, chemistry, and physics are the strongest programs academically. Business administration has the largest enrollment.

Required: To graduate, students must complete 120 credits, including a 36-credit core curriculum in communications, creative arts, humanistic experience and thought, natural sciences or mathematics, social sciences, and world civilization.

Special: Fisk offers cross-registration with Vanderbilt University, study abroad in 3 countries, dual majors in engineering and pharmacy, student-designed majors, and campus work-study. Students may take a 5-year B.S.-B.E. program with Vanderbilt University, Florida A&M, or the University of Alabama/Huntsville, or a combined B.S.-M.B.A. program with Vanderbilt. There are 8 national honor societies on campus, including Phi Beta Kappa.

Faculty/Classroom: Sixty-seven percent of faculty are male; 33%, female. All teach undergraduates, and 17% also do research. No introductory courses are taught by graduate students. The average class size in an introductory lecture is 30; in a laboratory, 15; and in a regular course offering, 19.

Requirements: The SAT I or ACT is recommended. Applicants should be high school graduates with 14 academic credits. AP credits are accepted. Important factors used in the admissions decision are advanced placement or honor courses, leadership record, and evidence of special talent.

Procedure: Freshmen are admitted in the fall and spring. Applications should be filed by June 15 for fall entry and November 1 for winter entry, along with an application fee of $15. Notification is sent on a rolling basis. There is an early admissions plan.

Transfer: Applicants for transfer should have a minimum college GPA of 2.0.

Visiting: There are guides for informal visits and visitors may sit in on classes and stay overnight at the school. To arrange for a visit, contact the Admissions Office at (615) 329-8666.

Financial Aid: In a recent year, 31% of all freshmen and 54% of continuing students received some form of financial aid. About 25% of freshmen and 60% of continuing students received need-based aid. The average freshman award was $6200. Of that total, scholarships or need-based grants averaged $5200 ($8950 maximum); loans averaged $2625 ($4125 maximum); and work contracts averaged $1000 ($1000 maximum). Thirty-one percent of undergraduate students work part-time. Average earnings from campus work for the school year are $1200. The average financial indebtedness of a recent graduate was $10,000. Fisk is a member of CSS. The FAF and the college's own financial statement are required. The deadline for financial aid applications is April 20.

International Students: International students must take the TOEFL and achieve a minimum score of 550.

Computers: The college provides computer facilities for student use. The mainframe is a DEC VAX 11/750. There are also TRS80 and Apple microcomputers available across campus. All students may access the system. There are no time limits.

Graduates: In a recent year, 113 bachelor's degrees were awarded. The most popular majors among graduates were psychology (24%), political science (21%), and biology (17%). Within an average freshman class, 37% graduate in 4 years, 16% in 5 years, and 5% in 6 years. In a recent graduating class, 14% of the men and 28% of the women were enrolled in graduate school within 6 months of graduation; 14% of the men and 28% of the women had found employment.

Admissions Contact: Director of Admissions.

FREED-HARDEMAN UNIVERSITY

B-3

Henderson, TN 38340   (901) 989-6651; (800) FHU-FHU1

Full-time: 520 men, 600 women	Faculty: 69; IIB, -$
Part-time: 25 men, 35 women	Ph.D.s: 65%
Graduate: 35 men, 30 women	Student/Faculty: 16 to 1
Year: semesters, 2 summer sessions	Tuition: $5565
Application Deadline: open	Room & Board: $3020
Freshman Class: 895 applied, 548 accepted, 313 enrolled	
SAT I Verbal/Math: 480/540	ACT: 23 **VERY COMPETITIVE**

Freed-Hardeman University, founded in 1869, is a private, coeducational liberal arts institution affiliated with the Church of Christ. There are 4 undergraduate and 2 graduate schools. In addition to regional accreditation, F-HU has baccalaureate program accreditation with CSWE and NCATE. The library contains 131,486 volumes, 5279 microform items, and 37,800 audiovisual forms, and subscribes to 864 periodicals. Computerized library sources and services include interlibrary loans and database searching. Special learning facilities include a learning resource center, an art gallery, a radio station, and a TV station. The 95-acre campus is in a rural area 85 miles east of Memphis. Including residence halls, there are 25 buildings on campus.

Student Life: About 53% of undergraduates are from out-of-state, mostly the South. Students come from 32 states and 14 foreign countries. Seventy-five percent are from public schools; 25% from private. Ninety-two percent are white. Most are Protestant. The average age of freshmen is 18; all undergraduates, 20. Thirty-four percent drop out by the end of their first year; 41% remain to graduate.

Housing: A total of 1200 students can be accommodated in college housing. College-sponsored living facilities include single-sex dormitories. On-campus housing is guaranteed for all 4 years. Seventy-three percent of students live on campus; of those, 55% remain on campus on weekends. Alcohol is not permitted. All students may keep cars on campus.

Activities: There are no fraternities or sororities on campus. There are 45 groups on campus, including art, band, cheerleading, chorus, computers, drama, honors, international, jazz band, musical theater, newspaper, pep band, photography, political, professional, radio and TV, religious, social, social service, student government, and yearbook. Popular campus events include Homecoming, and Makin' Music.

Sports: There are 4 intercollegiate sports for men and 4 for women, and 5 intramural sports for men and 5 for women. Athletic and recreation facilities include a gymnasium, a playing field, tennis courts, a student activities center, and a 5-hole golf course.

Disabled Students: Seventy percent of the campus is accessible to disabled students. The following facilities are available: wheelchair ramps, elevators, special parking, specially equipped rest rooms, special class scheduling, and lowered drinking fountains.

Services: In addition to many counseling and information services, tutoring is available in most subjects. In addition, there is remedial math, reading, and writing.

Campus Safety and Security: Campus safety and security measures include 24-hour foot and vehicle patrol, informal discussions, and lighted pathways and sidewalks.

Programs of Study: F-HU awards the B.A., B.S., B.B.A., and B.S.W. degrees. Master's degrees also are awarded. Bachelor's degrees are awarded in AGRICULTURE (agricultural business management), BIOLOGICAL SCIENCE (biology/biological science), BUSINESS (accounting, banking and finance, business administration and management, and marketing/retailing/merchandising), COMMUNICATIONS AND THE ARTS (broadcasting, communications, dramatic arts, English, fine arts, public relations, and speech/debate/rhetoric), COMPUTER AND PHYSICAL SCIENCE (chemistry, computer programming, computer science, information sciences and systems, and mathematics), EDUCATION (art, early childhood, elementary, health, middle school, music, science, and secondary), ENGINEERING AND ENVIRONMENTAL DESIGN (preengineering), HEALTH PROFESSIONS (medical laboratory technology, predentistry, and premedicine), SOCIAL SCIENCE (history, psychology, religion, and social work). Premedicine, preengineering, business, and Bible are the strongest academically. Business, Bible, and elementary education have the largest enrollments.

Required: To graduate, students must complete 132 semester hours, including 44 in upper-division courses in Bible, skills, humanities, and science, plus 3 hours of speech communication and 2 hours of physical education. The major requires a minimum of 30 semester hours, including 15 upper-division courses. Students must maintain a GPA of 2.0.

Special: F-HU offers cross-registration with Lambuth University and Union University, study abroad in Florence, a B.A.-B.S. degree in Bible and psychology, co-op programs, student-designed majors, 3-2 engineering degrees with 7 colleges, and nondegree study. There is

a freshman honors program on campus, as well as 4 national honor societies. Twelve departments have honors programs.

Faculty/Classroom: Seventy-three percent of faculty are male; 27%, female. All teach undergraduates. No introductory courses are taught by graduate students. The average class size in an introductory lecture is 25; in a laboratory, 18; and in a regular course offering, 20.

Admissions: About 61% of the 1993–94 applicants were accepted. The SAT I scores for the 1993–94 freshman class were as follows: Verbal—53% below 500, 32% between 500 and 599, and 15% between 600 and 700; Math—39% below 500, 39% between 500 and 599, and 22% between 600 and 700. The ACT scores were 38% below 21, 25% between 21 and 23, 19% between 24 and 26, 9% between 27 and 28, and 9% above 28. About 54% of the current freshmen were in the top fifth of their class; 88% were in the top two fifths. There were 3 National Merit finalists and 5 semifinalists. Ten freshmen graduated first in their class.

Requirements: A minimum GPA of 2.3 is required. The ACT is required, with a minimum composite score of 19. Candidate for admission should be graduate of an accredited secondary school with a GPA of 2.3. An interview is recommended. AP and CLEP credits are accepted. Important factors used in the admissions decision are personality, intangible qualities, recommendations by school officials, leadership record, advanced placement or honor courses, and extracurricular activities record.

Procedure: Freshmen are admitted to all sessions. Application deadlines are open. Notification is sent on a rolling basis. There is an early admissions plan.

Transfer: About 150 transfer students enrolled in 1993–94. Applicants should have a minimum college GPA of 2.0. Those with fewer than 30 college credits must submit a high school transcript and ACT or SAT I scores. A total of 33 credits out of 132 must be completed at F-HU.

Visiting: There are regularly scheduled orientations for prospective students, including an orientation during the 5 days prior to classes beginning in the fall. There are guides for informal visits and visitors may sit in on classes and stay overnight at the school. To arrange for a visit, contact Paul Pinckley at (901) 989–6651 or (800) FHU-FHU1.

Financial Aid: In a recent year, 87% of all current freshmen and 85% of continuing students received some form of financial aid. About 87% of freshmen and 85% of continuing students received need-based aid. The average freshman award was $4500. Of that total, scholarships or need-based grants averaged $500 ($7880 maximum); loans averaged $1800 ($4000 maximum); and work contracts averaged $1000 ($2000 maximum). Forty percent of undergraduate students work part-time. Average earnings from campus work for the school year are $1000. The average financial indebtedness of the 1992–93 graduate was $7500. F-HU is a member of CSS. The FAF, FFS or SFS is required. The deadline for financial aid applications is April 1.

International Students: There are currently 29 international students enrolled. They must take the TOEFL and achieve a minimum score of 500. The student must also take the ACT.

Computers: The college provides computer facilities for student use. The mainframe is a DEC VAX 11/750. Apple and Macintosh microcomputers are available in student laboratories and other locations, and each residence hall room has access. All students may access the system. There are no time limits on using the system. The fees are $45 per student using residence hall access.

Graduates: In 1992–93, 200 bachelor's degrees were awarded. The most popular majors among graduates were elementary education (14%), business administration (12%), and Bible (10%). Within an average freshman class, 1% graduate in 3 years, 30% in 4 years, 43% in 5 years, and 46% in 6 years. Some 20 companies recruited on campus in 1992–93.

Admissions Contact: Paul E. Pinckley Sr., Director of Admissions.

KING COLLEGE

F-2

Bristol, TN 37620–2699

(615) 652–4861
(800) 362–0014 (out-of-state)

Full-time: 233 men, 276 women	Faculty: 33; IIB, --$
Part-time: 9 men, 43 women	Ph.D.s: 73%
Graduate: none	Student/Faculty: 15 to 1
Year: semesters, summer session	Tuition: $8250
Application Deadline: open	Room & Board: $3250
Freshman Class: 355 applied, 300 accepted, 142 enrolled	
SAT I Verbal/Math: 450/500	ACT: 23 COMPETITIVE

King College, founded in 1867, is a private, coeducational liberal arts college affiliated with the Presbyterian Church. The library contains 96,000 volumes, 63,000 microform items, and 1800 audiovisual forms, and subscribes to 630 periodicals. Computerized library sources and services include interlibrary loans and database searching. Special learning facilities include a learning resource center and an observatory. The 135-acre campus is in a suburban area 2 miles east

of Bristol. Including residence halls, there are 16 buildings on campus.

Student Life: About 62% of undergraduates are from out-of-state, mostly the South. Students come from 26 states, 10 foreign countries, and Canada. Ninety-five percent are from public schools; 5% from private. Ninety percent are white. Eighty-five percent are Protestant; 13% claim no religious affiliation. The average age of freshmen is 18; all undergraduates, 20. One percent drop out by the end of their first year; 85% remain to graduate.

Housing: A total of 438 students can be accommodated in college housing. College-sponsored living facilities include single-sex dormitories. On-campus housing is guaranteed for all 4 years. Sixty-six percent of students live on campus; of those, 60% remain on campus on weekends. Alcohol is not permitted. All students may keep cars on campus.

Activities: There are no fraternities or sororities on campus. There are 29 groups on campus, including art, cheerleading, choir, chorale, chorus, dance, drama, honors, international, literary magazine, musical theater, newspaper, pep band, photography, professional, religious, student government, and yearbook. Popular campus events include Oval Day, Fall Ball, and Dogwood Festival.

Sports: There are 5 intercollegiate sports for men and 4 for women, and 13 intramural sports for men and women. Athletic and recreation facilities include a gymnasium, soccer and baseball fields, an indoor swimming pool, and a fitness trail.

Disabled Students: Eighty percent of the campus is accessible to disabled students. The following facilities are available: wheelchair ramps, elevators, special parking, and specially equipped rest rooms.

Services: In addition to many counseling and information services, tutoring is available in most subjects. In addition, there is remedial reading and writing.

Campus Safety and Security: Campus safety and security measures include escort service, informal discussions, emergency telephones, and lighted pathways and sidewalks. In addition, there are 24-hour foot and vehicle patrol on weekends, and 12-hour patrol Monday through Friday.

Programs of Study: King awards the B.A., B.S., and B.S. Med.Tech. degrees. Bachelor's degrees are awarded in BIOLOGICAL SCIENCE (biology/biological science), BUSINESS (business administration and management), COMMUNICATIONS AND THE ARTS (English, fine arts, French, modern language, and Spanish), COMPUTER AND PHYSICAL SCIENCE (applied mathematics, chemistry, mathematics, and physics), EDUCATION (foreign languages), HEALTH PROFESSIONS (medical laboratory technology), SOCIAL SCIENCE (behavioral science, biblical studies, history, political science/government, psychology, and religion). English, history, natural science, political sciences, and psychology are the strongest academically. Economics/business, psychology, political science, and English have the largest enrollments.

Required: Students must complete a minimum of 124 semester hours with 27 to 42 in the major. The 65 semester hours of core curriculum include courses in English, history, mathematics, Bible, humanities, science, social science, and physical education. Students must have a minimum GPA of 2.0. A comprehensive exam in the student's major area of concentration is required.

Special: King offers co-op programs, cross-registration with Virginia Intermont College, internships, study abroad in 7 countries, a Washington semester, work-study programs, and B.A.-B.S. degrees. There are 3-2 engineering degrees available with Georgia Institute of Technology, University of Maryland, and University of Tennessee. Nondegree study and pass/fail options for special students are also available. There is a freshman honors program on campus, as well as 5 national honor societies. Fourteen departments have honors programs.

Faculty/Classroom: Seventy-one percent of faculty are male; 29%, female. All teach undergraduates, 45% do research, and 45% do both. The average class size in an introductory lecture is 30; in a laboratory, 30; and in a regular course offering, 15.

Admissions: About 85% of the 1993–94 applicants were accepted. The SAT scores for the 1993–94 freshman class were as follows: Verbal—60% below 500, 31% between 500 and 599, 8% between 600 and 700, and 1% above 700; Math—42% below 500, 31% between 500 and 599, 24% between 600 and 700, and 3% above 700. The ACT scores were 11% below 21, 42% between 21 and 23, 27% between 24 and 26, 16% between 27 and 28, and 5% above 28. About 57% of the current freshmen were in the top fifth of their class; 83% were in the top two fifths. There were 3 National Merit semifinalists. Four freshmen graduated first in their class.

Requirements: King requires applicants to be in the upper 50% of their class. A minimum GPA of 2.4 is required. The SAT I or ACT is required. Candidates for admission should be graduates of accredited secondary schools. The GED is accepted. Students are required to have 16 academic credits, including 5 each in a foreign language, history, and social studies, 4 each in English and science, 2 in mathematics, and 1 in geometry. An essay is required. An audition and in-

terview are recommended. AP and CLEP credits are accepted. Important factors used in the admissions decision are advanced placement or honor courses, evidence of special talent, leadership record, recommendations by school officials, and extracurricular activities record.

Procedure: Freshmen are admitted to all sessions. Entrance exams should be taken before May 1. Application deadlines are open. Notification is sent on a rolling basis.

Transfer: About 40 transfer students enrolled in 1993–94. Transfer applicants should have a minimum 2.0 GPA and 30 semester hours completed. If fewer than 30 semester hours have been completed, a 2.4 high school GPA and a minimum ACT composite score of 22 or SAT I composite score of 900, are required. A total of 50 credits out of 124 must be completed at King.

Visiting: There are regularly scheduled orientations for prospective students, including a campus tour, a financial aid seminar, faculty sessions, an overnight visit in a dorm, and admissions counseling. There are guides for informal visits and visitors may sit in on classes. To arrange for a visit, contact The Admissions Office at (800) 362–0014.

Financial Aid: In 1993–94, 90% of all current freshmen and 90% of continuing students received some form of financial aid. About 81% of freshmen and 80% of continuing students received need-based aid. The average freshman award was $8594. Of that total, scholarships or need-based grants averaged $4334 ($7500 maximum); loans averaged $3174 ($4000 maximum); and work contracts averaged $1086 ($1200 maximum). Fifty percent of undergraduate students work part-time. Average earnings from campus work for the school year are $850. The average financial indebtedness of the 1992–93 graduate was $7600. King is a member of CSS. The college's own financial statement and FAFSA are required. The deadline for financial aid applications is March 1.

International Students: There are currently 35 international students enrolled. The school actively recruits these students.

Computers: The college provides computer facilities for student use. The mainframe is a DEC MicroVAX 3400. A campuswide Window-based network connects 52 80386-DX, 80486-DX, and Macintosh microcomputers located in 3 laboratories on the campus. Students can access the network from all dormitories with their personal computers. All students may access the system. There are no time limits on using the system and no fees.

Graduates: In a recent year, 92 bachelor's degrees were awarded. The most popular majors among graduates were economics/business (30%), English (16%), and elementary education (11%). Within an average freshman class, 80% graduate in 4 years and 30% in 5 years. In a recent graduating class, 5% of the men and 3% of the women were enrolled in graduate school within 6 months of graduation; 75% of the men and 65% of the women had found employment.

Admissions Contact: Roger Kieffer, Vice-President for Enrollment.

KNOXVILLE COLLEGE
Knoxville, TN 37921
E-3
(615) 524–6525

Full-time: 501 men, 275 women	Faculty: 58
Part-time: 45 men, 23 women	Ph.D.s: 52%
Graduate: none	Student/Faculty: 13 to 1
Year: semesters	Tuition: $5470
	Room & Board: $2850

Freshman Class: 395 applied, 337 accepted, 257 enrolled
SAT I: 550/440   ACT: 13   **LESS COMPETITIVE**

Knoxville College, founded in 1875, is a small, private liberal arts institution affiliated with the United Presbyterian Church. The library contains 78,455 volumes and 11,001 microform items, and subscribes to 450 periodicals. The 39-acre campus is in an urban area in Knoxville. Including residence halls, there are 22 buildings on campus.

Student Life: About 25% of undergraduates are from Tennessee. Ninety-five percent are from public schools. About 50% of freshmen remain to graduate.

Housing: Eighty percent of students live on campus.

Activities: There are some groups on campus, including band, chorus, drama, honors, newspaper, religious, social service, and student government.

Services: In addition to many counseling and information services, there is remedial math, reading, and writing.

Programs of Study: Knoxville awards the B.A., B.S., B.S.Ed., B.S.M.T., and B.S. in Tourism, Food, and Lodging Administration. degrees. Associate degrees also are awarded. Bachelor's degrees are awarded in BIOLOGICAL SCIENCE (biology/biological science), BUSINESS (accounting and business administration and management), COMMUNICATIONS AND THE ARTS (English and music), COMPUTER AND PHYSICAL SCIENCE (chemistry), EDUCATION (business, early childhood, elementary, health, mathematics, music, physical, recreation, and science), HEALTH PROFESSIONS (health care administration and medical laboratory technology), SOCIAL SCIENCE (political science/government, psychology, and sociology).

Required: To graduate, all students must complete 124 semester hours with at least a 2.0 GPA. Sixty-six hours in a core curriculum are required, including courses in English, speech, history, mathematics, natural and social sciences, religion, philosophy, humanities and the arts, computer science, health, and physical education. Between 26 and 40 hours are required in the major.

Special: A 3–2 engineering degree is offered with the University of Tennessee. Students seeking degrees in tourism, food, and lodging administration or recreation leadership may take some courses at the University of Tennessee. Cooperative programs, nondegree study, internships, and dual majors are possible. There is a freshman honors program on campus

Admissions: About 85% of the 1993–94 applicants were accepted. The SAT scores for the 1993–94 freshman class were as follows: Verbal—15% below 500, 50% between 500 and 599, 30% between 600 and 700, and 5% above 700. Four percent of the current freshmen were in the top two fifths of their class.

Requirements: Knoxville requires applicants to be in the upper 50% of their class. A minimum GPA of 2.0 is required. The SAT I or ACT is recommended. SAT I or ACT scores should be submitted for placement purposes. Applicants should be graduates of an accredited high school or have earned the GED. Secondary preparation should include a total of 15 Carnegie units. Music program applicants must audition. Culturally disadvantaged students may be admitted under a special program.

Procedure: Applications should be submitted by the deadlines, with an application fee of $15. Notification is sent on a rolling basis.

Transfer: Applicants with fewer than 15 college credits must submit a high school transcript. A total of 30 semester hours out of 124 must be completed at Knoxville.

Visiting: There are guides for informal visits. To arrange for a visit, contact Earl Nash, Director of Admissions/Financial Aid, at (615) 524–6525.

Financial Aid: The FAF, FFS or SFS and the college's own financial statement are required. The deadline for financial aid applications is April 15.

International Students: International students must take the TOEFL and achieve a minimum score of 475.

Computers: The college provides computer facilities for student use. All students may access the system.

Admissions Contact: Earl Nash, Director of Admissions/Financial Aid.

LAMBUTH UNIVERSITY
Jackson, TN 38301
B-3
(901) 425–2500; (800) 526–2884

Full-time: 435 men, 405 women	Faculty: 41; IIB, --$
Part-time: 123 men, 202 women	Ph.D.s: 60%
Graduate: none	Student/Faculty: 20 to 1
Year: semesters, summer session	Tuition: $5075
Application Deadline: open	Room & Board: $3320

Freshman Class: 881 applied, 538 accepted, 224 enrolled
ACT: 22   **COMPETITIVE**

Lambuth University, founded in 1843, is a private, coeducational liberal arts and sciences institution affiliated with the United Methodist Church. There are 4 undergraduate schools. The library contains 169,000 volumes, 45,326 microform items, and 1822 audiovisual forms, and subscribes to 397 periodicals. Computerized library sources and services include interlibrary loans and database searching. Special learning facilities include a learning resource center, planetarium, radio station, and and video studio. The 50-acre campus is in an urban area 75 miles northeast of Memphis. Including residence halls, there are 16 buildings on campus.

Student Life: About 85% of undergraduates are from Tennessee. Students come from 23 states, 6 foreign countries, and Canada. Eighty-two percent are white; 13% African American. Eighty percent are Protestant; 15% claim no religious affiliation. The average age of freshmen is 18; all undergraduates, 23. Thirty-five percent drop out by the end of their first year; 44% remain to graduate.

Housing: A total of 542 students can be accommodated in college housing. College-sponsored living facilities include single-sex dormitories, on-campus apartments, and fraternity houses. In addition, there is an international students' house. On-campus housing is guaranteed for all 4 years. Fifty-four percent of students live on campus. Alcohol is not permitted. All students may keep cars on campus.

Activities: About 35% of men belong to 3 national fraternities; about 24% of women belong to 4 national sororities. There are 26 groups on campus, including art, band, cheerleading, chess, choir, drama, ethnic, honors, international, jazz band, literary magazine, musical theater, newspaper, pep band, political, professional, radio and TV, religious, social, social service, student government, and yearbook. Popular campus events include Homecoming, Hawaiian Bash, FOCUS, Christmas Candlelight Service, weekly movies, Miss Lambuth Pageant, and All-Sing.

Sports: There are 6 intercollegiate sports for men and 3 for women, and 12 intramural sports for men and 7 for women. Athletic and recreation facilities include an indoor swimming pool, racquetball and tennis courts, a weight room, a gymnasium, and football, baseball, and soccer fields.

Disabled Students: Seventy-five percent of the campus is accessible to disabled students. The following facilities are available: wheelchair ramps, elevators, special parking, and special class scheduling.

Services: In addition to many counseling and information services, tutoring is available in most subjects.

Campus Safety and Security: Campus safety and security measures include 24-hour foot and vehicle patrol, self-defense education, escort service, and informal discussions. In addition, there are pamphlets, posters, films, emergency telephones, and lighted pathways and sidewalks.

Programs of Study: Lambuth awards the B.A., B.S., B.B.A., and B.M. degrees. Bachelor's degrees are awarded in BIOLOGICAL SCIENCE (biology/biological science), BUSINESS (accounting, business administration and management, and marketing/retailing/merchandising), COMMUNICATIONS AND THE ARTS (communications, design, English, fine arts, French, music, and Spanish), COMPUTER AND PHYSICAL SCIENCE (chemistry, computer science, mathematics, and physics), EDUCATION (elementary, health, home economics, music, secondary, and special), SOCIAL SCIENCE (economics, international relations, political science/government, psychology, religion, and sociology). Biological science, art, and business are the strongest academically. Business, education, and biology have the largest enrollments.

Required: All students must complete a minimum of 128 semester hours, including 3 semesters in English, 1 each in speech, computer science, and mathematics, and 2 each in physical education, religion, biological/physical sciences, writing courses, and interdisciplinary courses. Students must have a minimum GPA of 2.0.

Special: Lambuth offers cross-registration, internships in several disciplines, study abroad, a Washington semester, work-study programs, dual majors in all areas, student-designed majors in most areas, a 3–2 engineering degree, nondegree study, and pass/fail options. There are 5 national honor societies on campus.

Faculty/Classroom: Sixty-eight percent of faculty are male; 32%, female. All teach undergraduates. The average class size is 23.

Admissions: About 61% of the 1993–94 applicants were accepted. The ACT scores for the 1993–94 freshman class were as follows: 20% below 21, 28% between 21 and 23, 36% between 24 and 26, 8% between 27 and 28, and 8% above 28. About 20% of the current freshmen were in the top fifth of their class; 50% were in the top two fifths.

Requirements: Lambuth requires applicants to be in the upper 50% of their class. A minimum GPA of 2.0 is required. The SAT I or ACT is required. The minimum acceptable composite score for the SAT I is 750; for the ACT, 18. Candidates for admission should be graduates of accredited secondary schools. The GED is accepted. It is preferred that students have completed 4 courses each in English, history, mathematics, science, and social studies, and 2 each in foreign language, art, and music. An essay and interview are recommended. AP and CLEP credits are accepted. Important factors used in the admissions decision are advanced placement or honor courses, leadership record, recommendations by school officials, evidence of special talent, and extracurricular activities record.

Procedure: Freshmen are admitted to all sessions. Entrance exams should be taken by February of the senior year. Application deadlines are open. Application fee is $10. Notification is sent on a rolling basis. There is a deferred admissions plan.

Transfer: About 120 transfer students enrolled in a recent year. A minimum 2.0 GPA in courses taken, transcripts from all colleges attended, and a statement of honorable dismissal are required. An associate degree usually guarantees admission. A minimum of 12 successfully completed credit hours is recommended. A total of 32 semester hours out of 128 must be completed at Lambuth.

Visiting: There are regularly scheduled orientations for prospective students. There are guides for informal visits and visitors may sit in on classes and stay overnight at the school. To arrange for a visit, contact the Office of Admissions at (901) 425–2500 or (800) 526–2884.

Financial Aid: In a recent year, 75% of all students received some form of financial aid. About 38% of freshmen and 42% of continuing students received need-based aid. The average freshman award was $4800. Of that total, scholarships or need-based grants averaged $1800 ($4000 maximum); loans averaged $2000 ($4875 maximum); and work contracts averaged $1000 ($1500 maximum). Eighty-three percent of undergraduate students work part-time. Average earnings from campus work for the school year are $875. The average financial indebtedness of a recent graduate was $6000. Lambuth is a member of CSS. The FAF or FFS and the college's own financial statement are required. The deadline for financial aid applications is March 15.

International Students: There are currently 33 international students enrolled. The school actively recruits these students. They must take the TOEFL and achieve a minimum score of 500.

Computers: The college provides computer facilities for student use. The mainframe is an IBM AS400 C25. There are also 17 microcomputers available in the computer center. All students may access the system. It may be used 8 A.M. to 10 P.M. when classes are not in session. There are no time limits on using the system. The fees are $25 for some courses.

Graduates: In a recent year, 136 bachelor's degrees were awarded. The most popular majors among graduates were business (25%), education (23%), and social studies (17%). Within an average freshman class, 30% graduate in 4 years, 40% in 5 years, and 30% in 6 years. Some 15 companies recruited on campus in a recent year.

Admissions Contact: Nancy Callis, Director of Admissions.

LANE COLLEGE
B-3

Jackson, TN 38301   (901) 426–7533; (800) 960–7533 (out-of-state)

Full-time: 397 men, 347 women	**Faculty:** 35; IIB, --$
Part-time: none	**Ph.Ds:** n/av
Graduate: none	**Student/Faculty:** 21 to 1
Year: semesters, summer session	**Tuition:** $4766
Application Deadline: August 1	**Room & Board:** $2862
Freshman Class: 446 applied, 442 accepted, 260 enrolled	
ACT: 16	**LESS COMPETITIVE**

Lane College, founded in 1882, is a private liberal arts institution affiliated with the Christian Methodist Episcopal Church. The library contains 95,000 volumes, 7000 microform items, and 1800 audiovisual forms, and subscribes to 100 periodicals. Special learning facilities include a media center and a computer laboratory for teacher education students. The 17-acre campus is in a small town 79 miles from Memphis. Including residence halls, there are 14 buildings on campus.

Housing: On-campus housing is guaranteed for all 4 years and is available on a first-come, first-served basis. Seventy percent of students live on campus.

Activities: There are 4 national fraternities and 4 national sororities. There are some groups and organizations on campus, including newspaper and yearbook.

Sports: Athletic and recreation facilities include an Olympic-size swimming pool, a multipurpose room, and a gymnasium.

Disabled Students: Special parking is available.

Services: The Center for Academic Skills Development provides tutoring in reading, writing, mathematics, computer literacy, and test-taking and study skills.

Programs of Study: Lane awards the B.A. and B.S. degrees. Bachelor's degrees are awarded in BIOLOGICAL SCIENCE (biology/biological science), BUSINESS (business administration and management), COMMUNICATIONS AND THE ARTS (communications, English, and music), COMPUTER AND PHYSICAL SCIENCE (chemistry, computer science, and mathematics), EDUCATION (business and elementary), ENGINEERING AND ENVIRONMENTAL DESIGN (civil engineering and electrical/electronics engineering), HEALTH PROFESSIONS (nursing, predentistry, and premedicine), SOCIAL SCIENCE (history, prelaw, religion, and sociology).

Required: Students must complete a minimum of 124 semester hours with a 2.0 GPA. Fifty-six to 58 hours are required in the general studies curriculum, which includes courses in world cultures, art, music, foreign language, speech, composition, literature, history, sociology, mathematics, physical science, biology, computer literacy, and physical education.

Special: Cooperative programs are available in computer science with Jackson State University in Mississippi, and in engineering with Tennessee State University School of Engineering and Technology. The college also offers dual majors, student-designed majors, and nondegree study. There is a freshman honors program on campus.

Admissions: Nearly all of the 1993–94 applicants were accepted. The ACT scores for the 1993–94 freshman class were as follows: 90% below 21, 7% between 21 and 23, and 1% between 24 and 26. About 23% of the current freshmen were in the top two fifths of their class.

Requirements: A minimum GPA of 2.0 is required. The SAT I or ACT is required, with a minimum composite score of 13 on the ACT recommended. Graduation from an accredited secondary school is required; a GED will be accepted. Applicants' academic record must include 16 credits, including 4 credits in English, and 2 credits each in mathematics, science, and social studies. An additional 2 credits in a foreign language is recommended. An interview is recommended. AP and CLEP credits are accepted.

Procedure: Entrance exams should be taken by October of the senior year. Applications should be filed by August 1 for fall entry, December 15 for spring entry, and May 1 for summer entry, along with an application fee of $25.

Transfer: Applicants must submit transcripts from previous colleges attended and be in good standing at the time of application. Students having an associate degree will be given credit for a maximum of 68 semester hours in general education courses with a grade of C or higher. A total of 31 credits out of 124 must be completed at Lane.

Visiting: There are regularly scheduled orientations for prospective students. Visitors may stay overnight at the school. To arrange for a visit, contact the Office of Recruitment/Admissions at (901) 424–4600.

Financial Aid: The FAF, FFS or SFS is required. The deadline for financial aid applications is May 31.

International Students: International students must take the TOEFL.

Admissions Contact: Karen R. Winston, Director of Admissions.

LEE COLLEGE D-4

Cleveland, TN 37311 (615) 478–7327; (800) 533–9930 (out-of-state)

Full-time: 844 men, 1075 women	Faculty: 88; IIB, --$
Part-time: 40 men, 52 women	Ph.D.s: 50%
Graduate: none	Student/Faculty: 22 to 1
Year: semesters, summer session	Tuition: $4734
Application Deadline: open	Room & Board: $3160
Freshman Class: n/av	
SAT I or ACT: required	**LESS COMPETITIVE**

Lee College, founded in 1918, is a private, coeducational, liberal arts college affiliated with the Church of God. In addition to regional accreditation, Lee has baccalaureate program accreditation with NASM. The library contains 130,096 volumes, 14,880 microform items, and 7011 audiovisual forms, and subscribes to 800 periodicals. Computerized library sources and services include the card catalog, interlibrary loans, and database searching. Special learning facilities include a learning resource center, a natural history museum, and an audio/visual center. The 40-acre campus is in a suburban area 25 miles north of Chattanooga. Including residence halls, there are 32 buildings on campus.

Student Life: About 83% of undergraduates are from out-of-state, mostly the South. Students come from 46 states, 27 foreign countries, and Canada. Seventy-eight percent are from public schools; 22% from private. Eighty-six percent are white. Most are Protestant. The average age of freshmen is 20; all undergraduates, 22. Ten percent drop out by the end of their first year; 22% remain to graduate.

Housing: A total of 1050 students can be accommodated in college housing. College-sponsored living facilities include single-sex dormitories, on-campus apartments, and married-student housing. On-campus housing is guaranteed for all 4 years. Sixty-five percent of students live on campus; of those, 70% remain on campus on weekends. Alcohol is not permitted. All students may keep cars on campus.

Activities: Twenty percent of men belong to 4 local fraternities; about 20% of women belong to 4 local sororities. There are 48 groups on campus, including art, band, cheerleading, choir, chorale, chorus, computers, drama, ethnic, film, honors, international, jazz band, literary magazine, musical theater, newspaper, opera, orchestra, pep band, photography, political, professional, radio and TV, religious, social, social service, student government, symphony, and yearbook. Popular campus events include Homecoming, College Day, Parade of Favorites, and Frontline.

Sports: There are 4 intercollegiate sports for men and women, and 7 intramural sports for men and 5 for women. Athletic and recreation facilities include an arena, a recreation complex, a playing field, a tennis center, and a soccer field.

Disabled Students: Thirty-five percent of the campus is accessible to disabled students. The following facilities are available: wheelchair ramps, elevators, special parking, specially equipped rest rooms, special class scheduling, and lowered drinking fountains.

Services: In addition to many counseling and information services, tutoring is available in every subject. There is also a reader service for the blind, and remedial math, reading, and writing.

Campus Safety and Security: Campus safety and security measures include a 24-hour foot and vehicle patrol, informal discussions, pamphlets, posters, and films, and lighted pathways and sidewalks.

Programs of Study: Lee awards the B.A. and B.S. degrees. Bachelor's degrees are awarded in BIOLOGICAL SCIENCE (biology/biological science), BUSINESS (accounting and business administration and management), COMMUNICATIONS AND THE ARTS (communications, English, French, German, music, and Spanish), COMPUTER AND PHYSICAL SCIENCE (chemistry, computer programming, mathematics, and science), EDUCATION (elementary, music, and physical), HEALTH PROFESSIONS (medical laboratory technology), SOCIAL SCIENCE (crosscultural studies, history, psychology, religious education, social science, and sociology). Premedicine and communications are the strongest programs academically. Business, Bible, and teacher education have the largest enrollments.

Required: All students must complete a minimum of 130 credit hours including 8 hours in laboratory science, 6 each in history, English composition, Bible, theology, and religion electives, 4 in literature, 3 each in general psychology, general sociology, and mathematics, and 2 each in fine arts and physical activity. A minimum of 30 hours in the major is required. Students must have a minimum GPA of 2.0.

Special: The college offers internships, cross-registration with the Christian College Coalition, study abroad, a Washington semester, numerous work-study programs, B.A.-B.S. degrees, dual and student-designed majors, nondegree study, and limited pass/fail options. Every student completes a minor in religion. There is a freshman honors program on campus, as well as one national honor society. One department has an honors program.

Faculty/Classroom: Sixty-five percent of faculty are male; 35%, female. All teach undergraduates, and 20% also do research. The average class size in an introductory lecture is 45; in a laboratory, 22; and in a regular course offering, 25.

Requirements: A minimum GPA of 2.0 is required. The SAT I or ACT is required, with a composite score of 745 on the SAT I (375 verbal and 375 mathematics) or a composite score on the ACT of 17. Students must be graduates of accredited secondary schools. The GED is accepted. A portfolio is recommended. AP and CLEP credits are accepted. Important factors used in the admissions decision are recommendations by school officials, recommendations by alumni, ability to finance college education, parents or siblings attending the school, and advanced placement or honor courses.

Procedure: Freshmen are admitted to all sessions. Entrance exams should be taken prior to registration. Application deadlines are open. The application fee is $25. Notification is sent when the student's file is completed. There is an early admissions plan.

Transfer: About 237 transfer students enrolled in a recent year. Transfer students must take the SAT I, scoring 745, or the ACT, scoring 17, unless they have 16 credit hours with a GPA of 2.0 or better. A total of 30 credits out of 130 must be completed at Lee.

Visiting: There are regularly scheduled orientations for prospective students. There are guides for informal visits and visitors may sit in on classes. To arrange for a visit, contact the Recruitment Office at (615) 478–7326 or (800) 533–9930.

Financial Aid: In a recent year, 80% of all students received some form of financial aid. About 80% of freshmen received need-based aid. Scholarships or need-based grants averaged $1730 ($3460 maximum); loans averaged $2625 ($3875 maximum); and work contracts averaged $1072 ($1600 maximum). Ten percent of undergraduate students work part-time. The average financial indebtedness of a recent graduate was $6500. The FFS and the college's own financial statement are required. The deadline for financial aid applications is April 15.

International Students: There are currently 60 international students enrolled. The school actively recruits these students. They must take the TOEFL and achieve a minimum score of 450. The student must also take the SAT I or the ACT.

Computers: The college provides computer facilities for student use. The mainframe is an IBM AS/400. There are microcomputers available for student use in the computer laboratory. All students may access the system. There are no time limits on using the system. The fees are $25 per semester.

Graduates: In a recent year, 252 bachelor's degrees were awarded. Some 35 companies recruited on campus in a recent year.

Admissions Contact: Gary T. Ray, Director of Admissions.

LEMOYNE-OWEN COLLEGE A-4

Memphis, TN 38126 (901) 942–7302

Full-time: 1321 men and women	Faculty: 53
Part-time: none	Ph.D.s: 70%
Graduate: none	Student/Faculty: 19 to 1
Year: semesters, summer session	Tuition: $4500
Application Deadline: June 15	Room & Board: n/app
Freshman Class: n/av	
ACT: 18	**LESS COMPETITIVE**

LeMoyne-Owen College, established in 1870, is a private, coeducational commuter institution affiliated with the United Church of Christ and the Tennessee Baptist and Education Convention, offering degrees in the liberal arts and sciences and business administration. The library contains 90,000 volumes. Special learning facilities include a learning resource center and art gallery. The 15-acre campus is in an urban area. There are 10 buildings on campus.

Student Life: About 90% of undergraduates are from Tennessee. Students come from 13 states and 3 foreign countries. Ninety-two percent are from public schools; 8% from private. Ninety-eight percent are African American. Most are Protestant. The average age of freshmen is 19; all undergraduates, 23. Twenty percent drop out by the end of their first year; 48% remain to graduate.

Housing: There are no residence halls but about 200 students can be accommodated in off-campus apartments sponsored by the college. All students commute and may keep cars on campus. Alcohol is not permitted.

Activities: About 55% of men belong to 4 local and 4 national fraternities; about 35% of women belong to 4 local and 4 national sororities. There are 15 groups on campus, including cheerleading, choir, computers, drama, ethnic, newspaper, photography, professional, religious, social service, student government, and yearbook. Popular campus events include Heritage Day and Homecoming Week.

Sports: There are 3 intercollegiate sports for men, and 8 intramural sports each for men and women. Athletic and recreation facilities include a gymnasium, a pool, and other physical education installations.

Disabled Students: Ten percent of the campus is accessible to disabled students. Wheelchair ramps and elevators are available.

Services: In addition to many counseling and information services, tutoring is available in every subject. In addition, there is remedial math, reading, and writing.

Campus Safety and Security: Campus safety and security measures include escort service, lighted pathways and sidewalks, and a 24-hour foot patrol.

Programs of Study: LOC awards the B.A., B.S., and B.B.A. degrees. Bachelor's degrees are awarded in BIOLOGICAL SCIENCE (biology/biological science), BUSINESS (accounting and business administration and management), COMMUNICATIONS AND THE ARTS (art, English, and fine arts), COMPUTER AND PHYSICAL SCIENCE (chemistry, mathematics, and natural sciences), EDUCATION (education, elementary, health, and physical), ENGINEERING AND ENVIRONMENTAL DESIGN (engineering), SOCIAL SCIENCE (African American studies, economics, history, humanities, political science/government, social science, social work, and sociology). Business, science, and computer science are the strongest academically. Business has the largest enrollment.

Required: To graduate, students must satisfy 48 hours of core requirements in communication, mathematics, natural and computer sciences, literature and the humanities, African and African American history, social and behavioral sciences, and physical fitness. They must have a minimum GPA of 2.0 and grades of C or better in all major courses. The college requires 130 credits for graduation, including at least 45 in upper-division courses. All recent high school graduates must participate in the Freshman Year Experience Program.

Special: Students may cross-register with the Greater Memphis Consortium and Southern Illinois University. The college offers a work-study program. Dual and student-designed majors, internships, non-degree study, a 3–2 engineering degree with Southern Illinois University, and a pass/fail grading option are available. There is a freshman honors program on campus, as well as one national honor society. Two departments have honors programs.

Faculty/Classroom: Fifty percent of faculty are male; 50%, female. All teach undergraduates and 40% both teach and do research. The average class size in an introductory lecture is 20; in a laboratory, 20; and in a regular course offering, 25.

Requirements: The SAT I or ACT is required. Applicants must graduate from an accredited secondary school, having completed 20 high school units. Students 23 or older may be admitted to the division of lifelong learning, which accepts the GED. The college recommends 4 years of English, 2 each of mathematics, science, and social studies, and 1 of a foreign language. AP and CLEP credits are accepted.

Procedure: Freshmen are admitted to all sessions. Entrance exams should be taken in the spring of the junior year. Early decision applications should be filed by April 15; regular applications, by June 15 for fall entry, November 15 for spring entry, and March 1 for summer entry, along with an application fee of $25. Notification of early decision is sent April 30; regular decision, July 1. There are early decision and early admissions plans. About 13 early decision candidates were accepted for the 1993–94 class.

Transfer: About 160 transfer students enrolled in a recent year. Transfer applicants should have a GPA of 2.0. A total of 30 credits out of 130 must be completed at LOC.

Visiting: There are regularly scheduled orientations for prospective students. There are guides for informal visits and visitors may sit in on classes. To arrange for a visit, contact Dr. Marie Milam at (901) 942-7302.

Financial Aid: In a recent year, 85% of all students received some form of financial aid. About 85% of freshmen received need-based aid. The average freshman award was $6764. Of that total, scholarships or need-based grants averaged $3964; loans averaged $2000; and work contracts averaged $800. Sixty percent of undergraduate students work part-time. Average earnings from campus work for the school year are $3000. LOC is a member of CSS. The FAF or FFS is required. The deadline for financial aid applications is June 1.

International Students: There are currently 14 international students enrolled. The student must take the ACT.

Computers: The college provides computer facilities for student use. The mainframe is a DEC VAX 11/750. There are also 25 microcomputers and 5 mainframe systems with networking available for student use. All students may access the system. There are no time limits on using the system and no fees.

Graduates: In a recent year, 104 bachelor's degrees were awarded. The most popular majors among graduates were business (57%), science and mathematics (34%), and teacher education (9%). Within an average freshman class, 2% graduate in 3 years, 30% in 4 years, 20% in 5 years, and 10% in 6 years. Some 87 companies recruited on campus in a recent year. In the 1992 graduating class, 14% of all graduates were enrolled in graduate school within 6 months of graduation; 90% had found employment.

Admissions Contact: June Chinn-Jones, Director of Admissions.

LINCOLN MEMORIAL UNIVERSITY   E-2
Harrogate, TN 37752-0901   (615) 869-3611
(800) 325-2506 (out-of-state)

Full-time: 382 men, 543 women	**Faculty:** 66
Part-time: 120 men, 485 women	**Ph.D.s:** 68%
Graduate: 111 men, 263 women	**Student/Faculty:** 14 to 1
Year: semesters, summer session	**Tuition:** $5530
Application Deadline: open	**Room & Board:** $2688
Freshman Class: 787 applied, 562 accepted, 363 enrolled	
ACT: 22	**COMPETITIVE**

Lincoln Memorial University, founded in 1897, is an independent, co-educational, liberal arts university. In addition to regional accreditation, LMU has baccalaureate program accreditation with CAHEA and NLN. The library contains 126,000 volumes and 60,000 microform items, and subscribes to 600 periodicals. Computerized library sources and services include database searching. Special learning facilities include a learning resource center, radio and TV stations, and the Lincoln Museum. The 1000-acre campus is in a rural area 55 miles north of Knoxville. Including residence halls, there are 32 buildings on campus.

Student Life: About 57% of undergraduates are from Tennessee. Students come from 29 states, 16 foreign countries, and Canada. Eighty-seven percent are from public schools; 13% from private. Ninety-one percent are white. The average age of freshmen is 19; all undergraduates, 23. Fifteen percent drop out by the end of their first year; 42% remain to graduate.

Housing: A total of 500 students can be accommodated in college housing. College-sponsored living facilities include single-sex and coed dormitories and on-campus apartments. On-campus housing is guaranteed for the freshman year only and is available on a first-come, first-served basis. Priority is given to out-of-town students. Seventy-two percent of students commute. Alcohol is not permitted. All students may keep cars on campus.

Activities: About 10% of men belong to 3 local fraternities; about 7% of women belong to 2 local sororities. There are 26 groups on campus, including art, cheerleading, choir, computers, drama, drill team, honors, international, literary magazine, newspaper, pep band, photography, radio and TV, religious, student government, and yearbook. Popular campus events include Lincoln Day.

Sports: There are 6 intercollegiate sports for men and 5 for women, and 4 intramural sports for men and 4 for women. Athletic and recreation facilities include a 6000-seat arena, a baseball field, a playing field, a 5500-seat gymnasium, and a natatorium.

Disabled Students: Sixty percent of the campus is accessible to disabled students. The following facilities are available: wheelchair ramps, elevators, special parking, and special class scheduling.

Services: In addition to many counseling and information services, tutoring is available in most subjects. In addition, there is remedial math, reading, and writing.

Campus Safety and Security: Campus safety and security measures include 24-hour foot and vehicle patrol, informal discussions, pamphlets, posters, and films, and lighted pathways and sidewalks.

Programs of Study: LMU awards the B.A., B.S., B.S.N., and B.B.A. degrees. Associate and master's degrees also are awarded. Bachelor's degrees are awarded in AGRICULTURE (wildlife management), BIOLOGICAL SCIENCE (biology/biological science), BUSINESS (accounting, banking and finance, business administration and management, business economics, marketing/retailing/merchandising, and sports management), COMMUNICATIONS AND THE ARTS (broadcasting, communications, English, and fine arts), COMPUTER AND PHYSICAL SCIENCE (chemistry, information sciences and systems, and mathematics), EDUCATION (athletic training, business, early childhood, elementary, health, middle school, science, and secondary), ENGINEERING AND ENVIRONMENTAL DESIGN (environmental science), HEALTH PROFESSIONS (medical laboratory technology, nursing, predentistry, premedicine, and veterinary science), SOCIAL SCIENCE (history, prelaw, psychology, social science, and social work). Health professions are the strongest programs academically and have the largest enrollments.

Required: To graduate, all students must complete at least 128 semester credit hours, including the general studies requirements of the declared major and a minimum of 42 semester credit hours of upper-level courses. Students must achieve a minimum GPA of 2.0.

Special: The university offers pass/fail options and credit for life, military, and work experience. There is a freshman honors program on campus

Faculty/Classroom: Forty-nine percent of faculty are male; 51%, female. All teach undergraduates. No introductory courses are taught by graduate students. The average class size in a laboratory is 20 and in a regular course offering, 15.

Admissions: About 71% of the 1993–94 applicants were accepted. The ACT scores for the 1993–94 freshman class were as follows: 35% below 21, 31% between 21 and 23, 17% between 24 and 26, 6% between 27 and 28, and 11% above 28. About 41% of the current freshmen were in the top fifth of their class; 68% were in the top two fifths. About 25 freshmen graduated first in their class.

Requirements: A minimum GPA of 2.3 is required. The SAT I or ACT is required, with minimum scores of 17 on the ACT. Candidates for admission should be graduates of accredited secondary schools or have the GED. Students should have completed 4 years of English, 2 each of mathematics and science, and 1 each of history and social studies. AP and CLEP credits are accepted. Important factors used in the admissions decision are recommendations by school officials, personality, intangible qualities, leadership record, evidence of special talent, and recommendations by alumni.

Procedure: Freshmen are admitted fall, spring, and summer. Entrance exams should be taken in the spring of the junior year. Application deadlines are open. Notification of early decision is sent February 15; regular decision, on a rolling basis. There is a deferred admissions plan.

Transfer: About 163 transfer students enrolled in 1993–94. A total of 30 credits out of 128 must be completed at LMU.

Visiting: There are regularly scheduled orientations for prospective students. There are guides for informal visits and visitors may sit in on classes. To arrange for a visit, contact the Office of Admissions and Recruitment at (615) 869-6280.

Financial Aid: In 1993–94 65% of all current freshmen and 70% of continuing students received some form of financial aid. About 60% of freshmen and 65% of continuing students received need-based aid. Fifteen percent of undergraduate students work part-time. Average earnings from campus work for the school year are $1500. The average financial indebtedness of the 1992–93 graduate was $4000. LMU is a member of CSS. The FAF, FFS or SFS is required. The deadline for financial aid applications is June 1.

International Students: There are currently 81 international students enrolled. They must take the TOEFL, the University of Michigan Language Test, the Comprehensive English Language Test, or the college's own test.

Computers: The college provides computer facilities for student use. The mainframe is a DEC VAX 11/780. There are also 40 IBM Model 30 and Five Star 286 microcomputers available in the student center. All students may access the system. There are no time limits on using the system. There are no fees.

Graduates: In 1992–93 152 bachelor's degrees were awarded. The most popular majors among graduates were nursing (23%), elementary education (19%), and business (12%). Within an average freshman class, 5% graduate in 3 years, 32% in 4 years, 5% in 5 years, and 2% in 6 years. Some 40 companies recruited on campus in 1992–93. In the 1992 graduating class, 15% of the students were enrolled in graduate school within 6 months of graduation; 75% of the men and 60% of the women had found employment.

Admissions Contact: Conrad Daniels, Dean of Admissions.

MARYVILLE COLLEGE
E-3

Maryville, TN 37801 (615) 981-8092; (800) 597-2687 (out-of-state)

Full-time: 313 men, 310 women	Faculty: 50; IIB, -$
Part-time: 43 men, 86 women	Ph.D.s: 92%
Graduate: none	Student/Faculty: 12 to 1
Year: 4-1-4, summer session	Tuition: $10,428
Application Deadline: open	Room & Board: $4046
Freshman Class: 1094 applied, 888 accepted, 177 enrolled	
SAT I Verbal/Math: 440/500	ACT: 22 COMPETITIVE

Maryville College, founded in 1819, is a private, coeducational liberal arts college affiliated with the Presbyterian Church, USA. In addition to regional accreditation, Maryville has baccalaureate program accreditation with NASM. The library contains 108,500 volumes and 3426 microform items, and subscribes to 625 periodicals. Special learning facilities include an art gallery. The 370-acre campus is in a suburban area 15 miles south of Knoxville. Including residence halls, there are 20 buildings on campus.

Student Life: About 64% of undergraduates are from Tennessee. Students come from 28 states, 18 foreign countries, and Canada. Ninety percent are from public schools; 8% from private. Eighty-seven percent are white. Sixty-nine percent are Protestant; 19% claim no religious affiliation. The average age of freshmen is 18; all undergraduates, 23. Thirty-eight percent drop out by the end of their first year; 34% remain to graduate.

Housing: A total of 648 students can be accommodated in college housing. College-sponsored living facilities include single-sex and coed dormitories and on-campus apartments. In addition there are special interest houses and and an international house. On-campus housing is guaranteed for all 4 years. Seventy percent of students live on campus; of those, 80% remain on campus on weekends. Alcohol is not permitted. All students may keep cars on campus.

Activities: There are no fraternities or sororities on campus. There are 46 groups on campus, including art, band, cheerleading, choir, computers, dance, drama, ethnic, honors, international, jazz band, literary magazine, musical theater, newspaper, orchestra, pep band, photography, political, professional, religious, social service, student government, and yearbook. Popular campus events include Homecoming, Dogwood Arts Festival, and May Madness.

Sports: There are 4 intercollegiate sports for men and 4 for women, and 6 intramural sports for men and 6 for women. Athletic and recreation facilities include a physical education building with an indoor pool, racquetball and tennis courts, a weight room, and football, soccer, and baseball fields.

Disabled Students: Twenty percent of the campus is accessible to disabled students. The following facilities are available: wheelchair ramps, elevators, and special class scheduling.

Services: In addition to many counseling and information services, tutoring is available in some subjects. In addition, there is a reader service for the blind and tutors with knowledge of sign language.

Campus Safety and Security: Campus safety and security measures include 24-hour foot and vehicle patrol, informal discussions, and lighted pathways and sidewalks.

Programs of Study: Maryville awards the B.A., B.Mus., and B.S.N. degrees. Bachelor's degrees are awarded in BIOLOGICAL SCIENCE (biology/biological science), BUSINESS (business administration and management, management information systems, and management science), COMMUNICATIONS AND THE ARTS (English, fine arts, journalism, music, Spanish, and speech/debate/rhetoric), COMPUTER AND PHYSICAL SCIENCE (chemistry, computer science, and mathematics), EDUCATION (art, elementary, music, science, and secondary), ENGINEERING AND ENVIRONMENTAL DESIGN (preengineering), HEALTH PROFESSIONS (health science, nursing, physical therapy, predentistry, and premedicine), SOCIAL SCIENCE (economics, history, international relations, interpreter for the deaf, political science/government, prelaw, psychology, religion, and social science). Biology and chemistry are the strongest academically. Business has the largest enrollment.

Required: Each degree has its own general education requirements, which include humanities and a foreign language. Students must complete at least 128 total credit hours, including 48 in the majors, and must maintain a minimum 2.0 GPA. A freshman inquiry seminar and orientation are required in addition to a senior thesis in all majors and senior comprehensive exams.

Special: Maryville offers a co-op program in nursing, cross-registration, internships, study abroad in 5 countries, a Washington semester, accelerated degree programs, a B.A.-B.S. degree, and dual and student-designed majors. There are 3–2 engineering degrees offered with Georgia Institute of Technology and the University of Tennessee. Nondegree study and pass/fail options are possible. There is a freshman honors program on campus

Faculty/Classroom: Forty-seven percent of faculty are male; 53%, female. Ninety-three percent teach undergraduates. The average class size in a laboratory is 15 and in a regular course offering, 18.

Admissions: About 81% of the 1993–94 applicants were accepted. The SAT scores for the 1993–94 freshman class were as follows: Verbal—71% below 500, 21% between 500 and 599, and 8% between 600 and 700; Math—49% below 500, 30% between 500 and 599, 20% between 600 and 700, and 1% above 700. The ACT scores were 27% below 21, 35% between 21 and 23, 22% between 24 and 26, 10% between 27 and 28, and 6% above 28. About 48% of the current freshmen were in the top fifth of their class; 76% were in the top two fifths. Three freshmen graduated first in their class.

Requirements: Maryville requires applicants to be in the upper 50% of their class. A minimum GPA of 2.5 is required. The SAT I, with a minimum composite score of 850, or the ACT, with a minimum composite score of 18, is required. Candidates should be graduates of accredited secondary schools or have the GED. They should also have 4 years of English, 2 each of mathematics and science, and 1 of history. An essay, portfolio, audition, and interview are all recommended. AP and CLEP credits are accepted. Important factors used in the admissions decision are advanced placement or honor courses, recommendations by school officials, leadership record, extracurricular activities record, and personality, intangible qualities.

Procedure: Freshmen are admitted fall and spring. Entrance exams should be taken in December of the senior year. Application deadlines are open. Application fee is $25. Notification is sent on a rolling basis. There are early admissions and deferred admissions plans.

Transfer: About 45 transfer students enrolled in 1993–94. Transfer applicants must have a minimum GPA of 2.0 and a recommended 15 credit hours earned. An interview is also recommended. A total of 32 credits out of 128 must be completed at Maryville.

Visiting: There are regularly scheduled orientations for prospective students. There are guides for informal visits and visitors may sit in on classes and stay overnight at the school. To arrange for a visit, contact the Admissions Office at (800) 597–2687.

Financial Aid: In 1993–94, 97% of all current freshmen and 84% of continuing students received some form of financial aid. About 88% of freshmen and 75% of continuing students received need-based aid. The average freshman award was $11,269. Of that total, scholarships or need-based grants averaged $5352 ($10,278 maximum); loans averaged $4289 ($5625 maximum); and work contracts averaged $1000 ($1200 maximum). Sixty percent of undergraduate students work part-time. Average earnings from campus work for the school year are $1000. The average financial indebtedness of the 1992–93 graduate was $13,250. Maryville is a member of CSS. The FAF, FFS or SFS is required. The deadline for financial aid applications is April 1.

International Students: There are currently 44 international students enrolled. The school actively recruits these students. They must take the TOEFL, the University of Michigan Language Test, the Comprehensive English Language Test, or the college's own test.

Computers: The college provides computer facilities for student use. There are 40 Tandy, Hyundai, and IBM-compatible microcomputers available in student laboratories. All students may access the system. It may be used 7 days a week, 16 hours a day. There are no time limits on using the system and no fees.

Graduates: In 1992–93, 154 bachelor's degrees were awarded. The most popular majors among graduates were management (19%), business (15%), and child development and learning (12%). Some 26 companies recruited on campus in 1992–93. In the 1992 graduating class, 20% of all graduates were enrolled in graduate school within 6 months of graduation; 80% had found employment.

Admissions Contact: Donna F. Davis, Vice President of Admissions/Enrollment.

MEMPHIS COLLEGE OF ART
A-4

Memphis, TN 38104 — (901) 726–4085; (800) 727–1088

Full-time: 111 men, 80 women	Faculty: 14
Part-time: 11 men, 14 women	Ph.D.s: n/av
Graduate: 8 men, 19 women	Student/Faculty: 14 to 1
Year: semesters, summer session	Tuition: $8990
Application Deadline: open	Room & Board: $4150

Freshman Class: 134 applied, 133 accepted, 45 enrolled
SAT I: 426/433 — **ACT:** 19 — **SPECIAL**

Memphis College of Art, established in 1936, is a nonprofit, private, independent coeducational institution whose undergraduate and graduate instruction is in art, fine art, and design arts, including studio art, fiber/surface design, and computer arts. There are 3 graduate schools. In addition to regional accreditation, MCA has baccalaureate program accreditation with NASAD. The library contains 18,000 volumes, and subscribes to 120 periodicals. Computerized library sources and services include interlibrary loans. Special learning facilities include a learning resource center and an art gallery. The 200-acre campus is in an urban area in Memphis. Including residence halls, there are 4 buildings on campus.

Student Life: About 60% of undergraduates are from Tennessee. Students come from 26 states, 11 foreign countries, and Canada. Sixty-nine percent are from public schools; 31% from private. Seventy-five percent are white; 16% African American. Forty-six percent are Protestant; 35% Catholic; 12% claim no religious affiliation. The average age of freshmen is 23; all undergraduates, 26. Ten percent drop out by the end of their first year; 65% remain to graduate.

Housing: A total of 26 students can be accommodated in college housing. College-sponsored living facilities include coed on-campus apartments and off-campus apartments. On-campus housing is available on a first-come, first-served basis. Priority is given to out-of-town students. Alcohol is not permitted. All students may keep cars on campus.

Activities: There are no fraternities or sororities on campus. There are 2 groups on campus, including art and student government. Popular campus events include Holiday Bazaar, weekend workshops, gallery openings, and international dinners.

Sports: There is no sports program at MCA. Athletic and recreation facilities include those provided by the 200-acre city park on which MCA is located; there is an adjacent public golf course, playing fields, and a volleyball court. Regular Saturday football, soccer, and bicycling are popular activities.

Disabled Students: The entire campus is accessible to disabled students. The following facilities are available: wheelchair ramps, elevators, special parking, specially equipped rest rooms, lowered drinking fountains, and lowered telephones.

Services: In addition to many counseling and information services, tutoring is available in some subjects, including liberal studies classes.

Campus Safety and Security: Campus safety and security measures include informal discussions, pamphlets, posters, films, and lighted pathways and sidewalks. There are security guards in the buildings in the evening, and on weekends.

Programs of Study: MCA awards the B.F.A. degree. Master's degrees are also awarded. Bachelor's degrees are awarded in COMMUNICATIONS AND THE ARTS (design and fine arts). Graphic design, painting, and illustration are the strongest programs academically and have the largest enrollments.

Required: Students must complete 129 credit hours, with 33 in the major, and maintain a minimum GPA of 2.0. Distribution requirements include 33 credit hours in liberal studies, 12 in art history, and 84 in studio art. Eighteen hours in foundation classes, including drawing, design, and color theory, are necessary as well.

Special: Special academic programs include off-campus internships for juniors in advertising agencies, design firms, or other educational situations; on-campus work-study, including an in-house student advertising agency where students can get paid work experience dealing with clients; and study abroad in Europe, Canada, or Japan. There are co-op programs with Rhodes, Lemoyne-Owen, and Christian Brothers Colleges as well as with Memphis Theological Seminary, and there is cross-registration with the Alliance in Independent Colleges of Art and Design. Accelerated degree programs in all areas, a dual major in painting and illustration, student-designed majors, and credit for life and work experience are available. Nondegree study is offered as are pass/fail options for the workshop weeks.

Faculty/Classroom: Seventy-five percent of faculty are male; 25%, female. Ninety-three percent teach undergraduates. Graduate students teach 10% of introductory courses. The average class size in an introductory lecture is 20 and in a regular course offering, 15.

Admissions: About 99% of the 1993–94 applicants were accepted. The SAT scores for the 1993–94 freshman class were as follows: Verbal—63% below 500, 27% between 500 and 599, and 10% between 600 and 700; Math—61% below 500, 27% between 500 and 599, 10% between 600 and 700, and 2% above 700. The ACT scores were 66% below 21, 23% between 21 and 23, 7% between 24 and 26, and 3% between 27 and 28.

Requirements: The SAT I or ACT is required. Test scores are used for admissions and placement purposes. Other admissions requirements include graduation from an accredited secondary school, with a varying number of academic credits required. A portfolio must be presented, and the score on it is based on the application, essay, letters of recommendation, transcripts, and the portfolio itself, which is used for acceptance and scholarships. An essay and an interview are advised. The GED is also accepted. AP and CLEP credits are accepted. Important factors used in the admissions decision are evidence of special talent, advanced placement or honor courses, recommendations by school officials, leadership record, and extracurricular activities record.

Procedure: Freshmen are admitted in the fall and spring. Application deadlines are open. Application fee is $25. Notification is sent on a rolling basis. There is an early admissions plan.

Transfer: About 30 transfer students enrolled in 1993–94. A total of 48 credits out of 129 must be completed at MCA.

Visiting: There are regularly scheduled orientations for prospective students. There are guides for informal visits and visitors may sit in on classes. To arrange for a visit, contact the Admissions Office at (800) 727–1088.

Financial Aid: In a recent year, 90% of all current freshmen and 80% of continuing students received some form of financial aid. Scholarships or need-based grants averaged $1000; loans averaged $3000 ($6625 maximum); and work contracts averaged $1000 ($1500 maximum). The average financial indebtedness of the 1992–93 graduate was $10,000. MCA is a member of CSS. The FFS and the college's own financial statement are required. The deadline for financial aid applications is March 31.

International Students: There are currently 15 international students enrolled. The school actively recruits these students. They must take the TOEFL and achieve a minimum score of 500.

Computers: The college provides computer facilities for student use. There are also 50 Amiga and Apple Macintosh microcomputers available in the foundation, design arts, and weaving departments. All students may access the system. There are no time limits on using the system and no fees.

Graduates: In 1992–93, 36 bachelor's degrees were awarded. The most popular majors among graduates were design arts (50%) and fine arts (50%). Some 6 companies recruited on campus in 1992–93. In the 1992 graduating class, 30% of all students were enrolled in graduate school within 6 months of graduation; 70% had found em-

ployment.

Admissions Contact: Susan Miller, Director of Admissions.

MEMPHIS STATE UNIVERSITY
(See University of Memphis)

MIDDLE TENNESSEE STATE UNIVERSITY   C-3
Murfreesboro, TN 37132

(803) 898-2111
(800) 331-MTSU (in-state)

Full-time: 5959 men, 6582 women	Faculty: 612; IIA, --$
Part-time: 1336 men, 1549 women	Ph.D.s: 64%
Graduate: 805 men, 1152 women	Student/Faculty: 20 to 1
Year: semesters, summer session	Tuition: $1671 ($5453)
Application Deadline: July 1	Room & Board: $2186
Freshman Class: 4587 applied, 3423 accepted, 2132 enrolled	
ACT: 20	COMPETITIVE

Middle Tennessee State University, founded in 1911, is a public co-educational institution offering programs in liberal and fine arts, agriculture and technical studies, aviation, business, health science, professional training, teacher preparation, and mass communications. There are 5 undergraduate schools and one graduate school. In addition to regional accreditation, MTSU has baccalaureate program accreditation with AACSB, AHEA, CSWE, NASM, NCATE, NLN, and NRPA. The library contains 518,000 volumes and 842,000 microform items, and subscribes to 3600 periodicals. Computerized library sources and services include the card catalog, interlibrary loans, and database searching. Special learning facilities include a learning resource center, an art gallery, a radio station, and a TV station. The 500-acre campus is in a suburban area 32 miles southeast of Nashville. Including residence halls, there are 81 buildings on campus.

Student Life: About 95% of undergraduates are from Tennessee. Students come from 39 states, 43 foreign countries, and Canada. Eighty-eight percent are white. Sixty-two percent are Protestant; 27% claim no religious affiliation. The average age of all undergraduates is 23.

Housing: A total of 3478 students can be accommodated in college housing. College-sponsored living facilities include single-sex dormitories, on-campus apartments, and married-student housing. On-campus housing is available on a first-come, first-served basis. Seventy-five percent of students commute. All students may keep cars on campus. Alcohol is not permitted.

Activities: One percent of men belong to 13 national fraternities; about 1% of women belong to 9 national sororities. There are 135 groups on campus, including art, band, cheerleading, chess, choir, chorale, chorus, computers, dance, drama, drill team, ethnic, film, gay, honors, international, jazz band, literary magazine, marching band, musical theater, newspaper, opera, orchestra, pep band, photography, political, professional, radio and TV, religious, social, social service, student government, symphony, and yearbook. Popular campus events include Founders Day, and Uncle Dave and Macon Days.

Sports: There are 7 intercollegiate sports for men and 5 for women, and 27 intramural sports for men and women. Athletic and recreation facilities include an athletic center, a gymnasium, a stadium, tennis and racquetball courts, and indoor and outdoor tracks.

Disabled Students: The entire campus is accessible to disabled students. The following facilities are available: wheelchair ramps, elevators, special parking, specially equipped rest rooms, special class scheduling, lowered drinking fountains, and lowered telephones.

Services: In addition to many counseling and information services, tutoring is available in most subjects. There is also a reader service for the blind, and remedial math, reading, and writing.

Campus Safety and Security: Campus safety and security measures include a 24-hour foot and vehicle patrol, an escort service, shuttle buses, and pamphlets, posters, and films. In addition, there are emergency telephones and lighted pathways and sidewalks.

Programs of Study: MTSU awards the B.A., B.S., B.F.A., B.Mus., B.S.B.A., B.S.N., B.S.W., and B.U.S. degrees. Associate, master's, and doctoral degrees also are awarded. Bachelor's degrees are awarded in AGRICULTURE (agricultural business management, animal science, and horticulture), BIOLOGICAL SCIENCE (biology/biological science), BUSINESS (accounting, banking and finance, business administration and management, business economics, insurance, marketing/retailing/merchandising, and personnel management), COMMUNICATIONS AND THE ARTS (advertising, broadcasting, communications, design, dramatic arts, English, French, German, journalism, music, photography, Spanish, and speech/debate/rhetoric), COMPUTER AND PHYSICAL SCIENCE (actuarial science, chemistry, computer science, earth science, geology, information sciences and systems, mathematics, and physics), EDUCATION (art, business, early childhood, elementary, guidance, home economics, industrial arts, music, science, and secondary), ENGINEERING AND ENVIRONMENTAL DESIGN (aeronautical engineering and industrial administration/management), HEALTH PROFESSIONS (medical lab-

oratory technology, nursing, predentistry, premedicine, prepharmacy, and speech pathology/audiology), SOCIAL SCIENCE (anthropology, criminal justice, dietetics, economics, geography, history, international relations, philosophy, political science/government, prelaw, psychology, public administration, social science, social work, sociology, and urban studies). Aerospace is the strongest program academically. Mass communication has the largest enrollment.

Required: A total of at least 132 hours is needed to graduate with a minimum overall GPA of 2.0. All students must complete the general requirements, including 4 hours of physical education. Requirements for the major vary.

Special: MTSU offers co-op programs, cross-registration with Tennessee State University, a general studies degree, student-designed majors, nondegree study, and pass/fail options. Credit for life, military, and work experience may be granted. There is a freshman honors program on campus, as well as 5 national honor societies.

Faculty/Classroom: The average class size in an introductory lecture is 35; in a laboratory, 25; and in a regular course offering, 30.

Admissions: About 75% of the 1993–94 applicants were accepted. There was 1 National Merit finalist.

Requirements: A minimum GPA of 2.8 is required. The SAT I or the ACT is required, with a minimum composite score of 20 on the ACT. Applicants must be graduates of an accredited secondary school. The GED is accepted. The number of academic credits required is 14, including 4 years of English, 3 of mathematics, 2 each of a foreign language and science, and 1 each of social studies, history, and visual and/or performance arts. AP and CLEP credits are accepted.

Procedure: Freshmen are admitted to all sessions. Applications should be filed by July 1 for fall entry and December 1 for spring entry, along with an application fee of $5. Notification is sent on a rolling basis. There are early decision and early admissions plans.

Transfer: About 1759 transfer students enrolled in 1993–94. Transfer students with 60 or more hours attempted must have a minimum 2.0 GPA. A total of 60 credits out of 132 must be completed at MTSU.

Visiting: There are regularly scheduled orientations for prospective students, including a 2-day orientation for students and parents that takes place in July and August. There are guides for informal visits and visitors may sit in on classes and stay overnight at the school. To arrange for a visit, contact the Office of Admissions at (803) 898-2111 or (800) 331-MTSU (in-state).

Financial Aid: In a recent year, 50% of all students received some form of financial aid. Scholarships or need-based grants averaged $650 ($1900 maximum); loans averaged $1250 ($4000 maximum); and work contracts averaged $1072 ($2034 maximum). The average financial indebtedness of a recent graduate was $6000. The FFS is required. The deadline for financial aid applications is May 15.

International Students: There are currently 352 international students enrolled. They must take the TOEFL and achieve a minimum score of 500. The SAT I or the ACT is also required.

Computers: The college provides computer facilities for student use. The mainframes are a Bull HN, a Gould, and a DEC VAX cluster. There are about 150 microcomputers available that can access the network. All students may access the system. It may be used every day. There are no time limits on using the system and no fees.

Admissions Contact: Cliff Gillespie, Dean of Admissions and Records.

MILLIGAN COLLEGE   F-2
Milligan College, TN 37682

(615) 461-8730
(800) 262-8337 (out-of-state)

Full-time: 257 men, 381 women	Faculty: 46; IIB, --$
Part-time: 10 men, 15 women	Ph.D.s: 61%
Graduate: 11 men, 28 women	Student/Faculty: 14 to 1
Year: semesters, summer session	Tuition: $7590
Application Deadline: open	Room & Board: $3100
Freshman Class: 610 applied, 461 accepted, 189 enrolled	
SAT I Verbal/Math: 500/500	ACT: 23 COMPETITIVE

Milligan College, founded in 1881, is a private coeducational institution affiliated with the Christian Churches and Churches of Christ. Its undergraduate and graduate programs stress the liberal arts and biblical studies. There is one undergraduate and one graduate school. In addition to regional accreditation, Milligan has baccalaureate program accreditation with NCATE. The library contains 154,908 volumes, 66,803 microform items, and 2468 audiovisual forms, and subscribes to 450 periodicals. Special learning facilities include a learning resource center, radio station, and radio and TV studios, editing rooms, and a darkroom. The 135-acre campus is in a suburban area 4 miles south of Johnson City. Including residence halls, there are 23 buildings on campus.

Student Life: About 71% of undergraduates are from out-of-state, mostly the Midwest. Students come from 35 states and 5 foreign countries. Ninety-five percent are from public schools; 5% from private.

Ninety-six percent are white. Most are Protestant. Thirty-three percent drop out by the end of their first year; 42% remain to graduate.

Housing: A total of 632 students can be accommodated in college housing. College-sponsored living facilities include single-sex dormitories and married-student housing. On-campus housing is guaranteed for all 4 years. Eighty percent of students live on campus; of those, 80% remain on campus on weekends. Alcohol is not permitted. All students may keep cars on campus.

Activities: There are no fraternities or sororities on campus. There are 18 groups on campus, including art, cheerleading, choir, chorus, drama, honors, literary magazine, newspaper, orchestra, photography, political, professional, radio and TV, religious, social, social service, student government, symphony, and yearbook. Popular campus events include Christmas Madrigals and Wonderful Wednesday.

Sports: There are 5 intercollegiate sports for men and 4 for women, and 11 intramural sports for men and 10 for women. Athletic and recreation facilities include a field house with a 25-meter swimming pool and a basketball court, a 500-seat stadium, a 1500-seat gym, a baseball field, tennis courts, and softball and soccer fields.

Disabled Students: Eighty percent of the campus is accessible to disabled students. The following facilities are available: wheelchair ramps, elevators, special parking, specially equipped rest rooms, and lowered drinking fountains.

Services: In addition to many counseling and information services, tutoring is available in most subjects. There is also remedial math, reading, and writing.

Campus Safety and Security: Campus safety and security measures include self defense education, informal discussions, pamphlets, posters, and films, and lighted pathways and sidewalks.

Programs of Study: Milligan awards the B.A. and B.S. degrees. Associate and master's degrees also are awarded. Bachelor's degrees are awarded in BIOLOGICAL SCIENCE (biology/biological science), BUSINESS (accounting and business administration and management), COMMUNICATIONS AND THE ARTS (communications, English, and music), COMPUTER AND PHYSICAL SCIENCE (computer science), EDUCATION (elementary, music, and secondary), HEALTH PROFESSIONS (medical laboratory technology, nursing, predentistry, and premedicine), SOCIAL SCIENCE (history, prelaw, psychology, religion, and sociology). Premedical and nursing are the strongest academically. Business, education, and communications have the largest enrollments.

Required: Students must complete 128 semester hours, a varying number (usually about 30) in the major, with a minimum GPA of 2.0. Required disciplines include courses in English, history, the Bible, humanities, social studies, laboratory science, mathematics, and physical education.

Special: Milligan offers a Washington semester, study abroad in Birmingham, England, internships in sociology, psychology, business, and Christian education, dual degrees, cross-registration in any area, a 3-2 engineering degree with Georgia Institute of Technology, credit for life, military, or work experience, work-study, and nondegree study. An ROTC program with East Tennessee State University is possible. Six credits are offered for students participating in the annual summer tour of Europe. There are 2 national honor societies on campus.

Faculty/Classroom: Sixty-seven percent of faculty are male; 33%, female. No introductory courses are taught by graduate students. The average class size in an introductory lecture is 75; in a laboratory, 24; and in a regular course offering, 15.

Admissions: About 76% of the 1993–94 applicants were accepted. Five freshmen graduated first in their class.

Requirements: Milligan requires applicants to be in the upper 50% of their class. A minimum GPA of 2.5 is required. The SAT I or ACT is required. Students must be graduates of an accredited secondary school, with 18 Carnegie units and 18 academic credits, including 4 years of English, 3 of mathematics, 2 of science, and 1 each of history and social studies. An interview is advised and music students must audition. The GED is accepted. Other factors in the admission decision include character, ability, preparation, and Christian commitment. AP and CLEP credits are accepted.

Procedure: Application deadlines are open. Application fee is $20. Notification is sent on a rolling basis. There are early admissions and deferred admissions plans. A waiting list is an active part of the admissions procedure, with about 5% of applicants on the list.

Transfer: About 65 transfer students enrolled in 1993–94. Transfer students must have a minimum GPA of 2.0 and submit a letter of good standing from the previous institution as well as transcripts of all previous college work. A total of 30 credits out of 128 must be completed at Milligan.

Visiting: There are guides for informal visits and visitors may sit in on classes and stay overnight at the school. To arrange for a visit, contact the Admissions Office at (800) 262-8337.

Financial Aid: In 1993–94, 90% of all current freshmen and 70% of continuing students received some form of financial aid. About 90% of freshmen and 70% of continuing students received need-based aid. Milligan is a member of CSS. The FAF, FFS or SFS and the college's own financial statement are required.

International Students: There are currently 5 international students enrolled. They must take the TOEFL or the University of Michigan Language Test and achieve a minimum score on the TOEFL of 550. The student must also take the SAT I or ACT. The test, used for placement rather than admission, may be taken after the student arrives.

Computers: The college provides computer facilities for student use. The mainframe is an IBM S/36 (5360). There are also 33 IBM and Apple PCs in the science building and 2 computer laboratories plus 2 in the library. All students may access the system. There are no time limits on using the system and no fees.

Graduates: In a recent year, 102 bachelor's degrees were awarded. Within an average freshman class, 40% graduate in 5 years.

Admissions Contact: Michael A. Johnson, Director of Admissions.

RHODES COLLEGE

A-3

Memphis, TN 38112 (901) 726-3700; (800) 844-5969 (out-of-state)

Full-time: 605 men, 731 women	Faculty: 115; IIB, +$
Part-time: 19 men, 48 women	Ph.D.s: 99%
Graduate: 6 men	Student/Faculty: 12 to 1
Year: semesters, summer session	Tuition: $14,916
Application Deadline: February 1	Room & Board: $4708
Freshman Class: 2302 applied, 1831 accepted, 391 enrolled	
SAT I or ACT: required	**HIGHLY COMPETITIVE**

Rhodes College, founded in 1848, is a nonprofit, private, coeducational liberal arts institution affiliated with the Presbyterian Church. There is one graduate school. The 3 libraries contain 230,000 volumes, 35,000 microform items, and 57,000 audiovisual forms, and subscribe to 1160 periodicals. Computerized library sources and services include the card catalog, interlibrary loans, and database searching. Special learning facilities include an art gallery and the Human Relations Area Files, containing 2 million pages of human behavior resource materials on microfiche, 2 electron microscopes, a 0.8-meter infrared optimized telescope, and a cell culture laboratory. The 100-acre campus is in a suburban area in Memphis. Including residence halls, there are 43 buildings on campus.

Student Life: About 64% of undergraduates are from out-of-state, mostly the South. Students come from 42 states, 16 foreign countries, and Canada. Sixty-five percent are from public schools; 35% from private. Ninety-two percent are white. Seventy-seven percent are Protestant; 15% Catholic. The average age of freshmen is 19; all undergraduates, 20.5. Thirteen percent drop out by the end of their first year; 73% remain to graduate.

Housing: A total of 1090 students can be accommodated in college housing. College-sponsored living facilities include single-sex dormitories and special interest townhouses. On-campus housing is guaranteed for the freshman year only. Seventy-seven percent of students live on campus; of those, 90% remain on campus on weekends. All students may keep cars on campus.

Activities: About 58% of men belong to 6 national fraternities; about 57% of women belong to 7 national sororities. There are 60 groups on campus, including art, band, cheerleading, chorale, chorus, computers, dance, drama, ethnic, honors, international, literary magazine, musical theater, newspaper, pep band, photography, political, professional, religious, social, social service, student government, and yearbook. Popular campus events include the Rites of Spring, McCoy Theater performances, Homecoming, Fall Fest, Jazz Fest, and All-Sing.

Sports: There are 11 intercollegiate sports for men and 7 for women, and 9 intramural sports for men and women. Athletic and recreation facilities include 2 gymnasiums, an outdoor pool, 8 tennis courts, 2 soccer fields, a football field, an outdoor track, weight and dance rooms, and intramural fields.

Disabled Students: Ninety percent of the campus is accessible to disabled students. The following facilities are available: wheelchair ramps, elevators, special parking, specially equipped rest rooms, special class scheduling, and lowered drinking fountains.

Services: In addition to many counseling and information services, tutoring is available in some subjects, including mathematics, writing, and study skills. There is also a reader service for the blind.

Campus Safety and Security: Campus safety and security measures include a 24-hour foot and vehicle patrol, self defense education, an escort service, pamphlets, posters, and films. In addition, there are emergency telephones and lighted pathways and sidewalks.

Programs of Study: Rhodes awards the B.A. and B.S degrees. Master's degrees also are awarded. Bachelor's degrees are awarded in BIOLOGICAL SCIENCE (biochemistry and biology/biological science), BUSINESS (business administration and management), COMMUNICATIONS AND THE ARTS (art, classics, dramatic arts, English, French, German, languages, music, and Spanish), COMPUTER AND PHYSICAL SCIENCE (chemistry, mathematics, and physics), SOCIAL SCIENCE (anthropology, economics, history, international stud-

ies, Latin American studies, philosophy, political science/government, psychology, religion, Russian and Slavic studies, and urban studies). International studies, foreign languages, economics and business administration, political science, and the sciences (biology, chemistry, physics). are the strongest programs academically. English, psychology, biology, business administration, history, international studies, and religious studies have the largest enrollments.

Required: Students must complete 112 credit hours, with a variable number of hours in the major, and maintain a minimum GPA of 2.0. General degree requirements include a basic requirement in humanities; communication skills, a foreign language at the intermediate level, and area distribution requirements, which are comprised of 3 courses each in humanities, natural science, and social science, and 2 courses in fine arts. English 151 and 3 noncredit half-semester courses in physical education are also needed. A senior seminar is required.

Special: One half of Rhodes students have an internship experience, in which off-campus work and significant academic work are combined for credit. Study abroad in 7 countries, a Washington semester, cross-registration with Memphis College of Art, and a science semester at Oak Ridge National Laboratory are offered. The B.A.-B.S. degree and dual majors are offered in any combination, and student-designed majors can be arranged. Nondegree study and pass/fail options are also possible. There is a freshman honors program on campus, as well as 11 national honor societies, including Phi Beta Kappa. All departments have honors programs.

Faculty/Classroom: Sixty-seven percent of faculty are male; 33%, female. All teach undergraduates, and also do research. No introductory courses are taught by graduate students. The average class size in a laboratory is 18 and in a regular course offering, 18.

Admissions: Eighty percent of the 1993–94 applicants were accepted. The SAT scores for the 1993–94 freshman class were as follows: Verbal—14% below 500, 45% between 500 and 599, 34% between 600 and 700, and 7% above 700; Math—6% below 500, 33% between 500 and 599, 43% between 600 and 700, and 18% above 700. The ACT scores were 7% between 21 and 23, 15% between 24 and 25, 46% between 26 and 29, and 32% above 30. About 77% of the current freshmen were in the top fifth of their class; 93% were in the top two fifths. There were 17 National Merit finalists and 14 semifinalists. Thirty freshmen graduated first in their class.

Requirements: The SAT I or ACT is required. Graduation from an accredited secondary school is required, with 16 or more academic credits, including 4 years of English, 3 of mathematics, 2 of a foreign language, and 2 years each of science and social studies/history are strongly recommended. The GED is accepted. An essay is required; an interview, recommended. AP credits are accepted. Important factors used in the admissions decision are advanced placement or honor courses, recommendations by school officials, extracurricular activities record, leadership record, personality, and intangible qualities.

Procedure: Freshmen are admitted in the fall and spring. Entrance exams should be taken prior to December of the senior year. Early decision applications should be filed by November 15; regular applications, by February 1 for fall entry and December 1 for spring entry, along with an application fee of $35. Notification of early decision is sent December 15; regular decision, April 1. There are early decision, early admissions, and deferred admissions plans. About 38 early decision candidates were accepted for the 1993–94 class. A waiting list is an active part of the admissions procedure, with about 7% of applicants on the list.

Transfer: Twenty-two transfer students enrolled in 1993–94. Transfer applicants must submit all high school and college transcripts, as well as SAT I or ACT scores, and must be in good standing at the last institution they attended. A total of 56 credits out of 112 must be completed at Rhodes.

Visiting: There are regularly scheduled orientations for prospective students, including class visits, meetings with students, meetings with faculty, tours, and an overnight stay with students if desired. Interviews also are available. There are guides for informal visits and visitors may sit in on classes and stay overnight at the school. To arrange for a visit, contact the Office of Admissions at (901) 726–3700 or (800) 844–5969.

Financial Aid: In 1993–94, 79% of all current freshmen and 70% of continuing students received some form of financial aid. About 43% of freshmen and 46% of continuing students received need-based aid. The average freshman award was $10,465. Of that total, scholarships or need-based grants averaged $7789 ($23,574 maximum); loans averaged $3043 ($9625 maximum); and work contracts averaged $1018 ($1100 maximum). Thirty-eight percent of undergraduate students work part-time. Average earnings from campus work for the school year are $1055. The average financial indebtedness of the 1992–93 graduate was $10,900. Rhodes is a member of CSS. The FAF, the college's own financial statement and the FAFSA are required. The deadline for financial aid applications is March 1.

International Students: There are currently 45 international students enrolled. The school actively recruits these students. They must take the TOEFL and achieve a minimum score of 550. The SAT I or the ACT is also required.

Computers: The college provides computer facilities for student use. The mainframe is a DEC VAX 6320. There are also 75 Apple Macintosh microcomputers available in 3 computer laboratories. Letter-quality and laser printers are also available. Other computer facilities are in the mathematics and natural science buildings. All students may access the system 24 hours per day. There are no time limits on using the system and no fees.

Graduates: In 1992–93, 329 bachelor's degrees were awarded. The most popular majors among graduates were psychology (13%), English (12%), and international studies, business administration, and biology, (10%). Within an average freshman class, 72% graduate in 4 years, 73% in 5 years, and 75% in 6 years. Some 56 companies recruited on campus in 1992–93. In the 1992 graduating class, 34% of the graduates were enrolled in graduate school within 6 months of graduation.

Admissions Contact: David J. Wottle, Dean of Admissions and Financial Aid.

SOUTHERN COLLEGE OF SEVENTH-DAY ADVENTISTS

D-4

Collegedale, TN 37315

(615) 238–2844
(800) SOUTHERN (out-of-state)

Full-time: 577 men, 691 women	**Faculty:** 95; IIB, --$
Part-time: 78 men, 181 women	**Ph.D.s:** 43%
Graduate: none	**Student/Faculty:** 13 to 1
Year: semesters, summer session	**Tuition:** $7988
Application Deadline: open	**Room & Board:** $3360
Freshman Class: 790 applied, 768 accepted, 403 enrolled	
ACT: required	**NONCOMPETITIVE**

The Southern College of Seventh-day Adventists, founded in 1892, is a private, coeducational, liberal arts institution affiliated with the Seventh-day Adventist Church. In addition to regional accreditation, Southern College has baccalaureate program accreditation with NASM, NCATE, and NLN. The library contains 99,868 volumes, 81,454 microform items, and 1178 audiovisual forms, and subscribes to 947 periodicals. Special learning facilities include an art gallery and radio station. The 1000-acre campus is in a small town 18 miles southeast of Chattanooga. Including residence halls, there are 17 buildings on campus.

Student Life: About 80% of undergraduates are from out-of-state, mostly the South. Students come from 42 states, 18 foreign countries, and Canada. Twenty percent are from public schools; 80% from private. Eighty percent are white. Most are Protestant. The average age of freshmen is 19; all undergraduates, 22. One percent drop out by the end of their first year.

Housing: A total of 1000 students can be accommodated in college housing. College-sponsored living facilities include single-sex dormitories, on-campus apartments, and married-student housing. On-campus housing is guaranteed for all 4 years. Eighty percent of students live on campus; of those, 70% remain on campus on weekends. Alcohol is not permitted. All students may keep cars on campus.

Activities: There are no fraternities or sororities on campus. There are 13 groups on campus, including band, choir, chorus, drama, honors, international, newspaper, orchestra, radio, religious, student government, symphony, and yearbook. Popular campus events include Alumni Weekend and Weekly Spiritual Emphasis.

Sports: There are 10 intramural sports for men and 10 for women. Athletic and recreation facilities include 8 tennis courts, 2 athletic fields, a field house, a pool, 6 racquetball courts, a track, soccer fields, and a 3000-seat gymnasium.

Disabled Students: Fifty percent of the campus is accessible to disabled students. The following facilities are available: wheelchair ramps, elevators, special parking, and specially equipped rest rooms.

Services: In addition to many counseling and information services, tutoring is available in most subjects. There is also remedial math, reading, and writing.

Campus Safety and Security: Campus safety and security measures include 24-hour foot and vehicle patrol, escort service, informal discussions, and lighted pathways and sidewalks.

Programs of Study: Southern College awards the B.A., B.S., and B.B.A. degrees. Associate degrees also are awarded. Bachelor's degrees are awarded in BIOLOGICAL SCIENCE (biology/biological science), BUSINESS (accounting, business administration and management, and marketing/retailing/merchandising), COMMUNICATIONS AND THE ARTS (broadcasting, communications, English, French, German, journalism, music, and Spanish), COMPUTER AND PHYSICAL SCIENCE (chemistry, computer science, mathematics, and physics), EDUCATION (elementary and music), HEALTH PROFESSIONS (medical laboratory technology, nursing, predentistry,

and premedicine), SOCIAL SCIENCE (history, international relations, prelaw, psychology, religion, and social work). Business, nursing, education, and religion are the strongest academically. Nursing has the largest enrollment.

Required: Students must complete 124 semester hours, with at least 30 in the major, and maintain a minimum GPA of 2.0. General education requirements include 6 to 9 semester hours of English and up to 3 of mathematics, depending on the ACT score; 12 of religion; 6 each of history and activity skills; 3 of political and economic systems; 9 of language, literature, and fine arts; 6 to 9 of natural science; and 5 of behavioral, family, and health science.

Special: Internships in long-term life care, journalism, and social work practicum, and study abroad in Austria, Spain, and France are offered. The B.A.-B.S. degree and dual majors in any combination are available. Credit may be granted for 4 years of military experience. Pass/fail options are possible only for physical education activity classes. There is a freshman honors program on campus

Faculty/Classroom: Fifty-six percent of faculty are male; 44%, female. All teach undergraduates and 7% do research.

Admissions: About 97% of the 1993–94 applicants were accepted. There were 3 National Merit finalists and 2 semifinalists.

Requirements: A minimum GPA of 2.0 is required. The ACT is required, with a minimum composite score of 18. Students must graduate from an accredited secondary school with 14 academic credits, including 4 units of English, and 2 each of a foreign language, mathematics, science, social studies, and history. The GED is accepted. An essay must be submitted, and an interview is advised. AP and CLEP credits are accepted. Important factors used in the admissions decision are advanced placement or honor courses, ability to finance college education, evidence of special talent, recommendations by school officials, and leadership record.

Procedure: Freshmen are admitted fall and spring. The application deadlines are open. Application fee is $20. The college accepts all applicants. Notification is sent on a rolling basis. There are early admissions and deferred admissions plans.

Transfer: About 125 transfer students enrolled in 1993–94. Transfer applicants must have a cumulative GPA of at least 2.0, and a minimum ACT composite score of 18. Two letters of recommendation are also required. A total of 30 credits out of 124 must be completed at Southern College.

Visiting: There are guides for informal visits and visitors may sit in on classes and stay overnight at the school. To arrange for a visit, contact the Admissions Office at (615) 238–2844.

Financial Aid: In a recent year, 70% of all current freshmen and 62% of continuing students received some form of financial aid. The average freshman award was $1200. Of that total, scholarships or need-based grants averaged $1730; loans averaged $2653; and work contracts averaged $1954. Ninety percent of undergraduate students work part-time. Average earnings from campus work for the school year are $1500. The average financial indebtedness of a recent graduate was $4196. Southern College is a member of CSS. The FAF or FFS and the college's own financial statement are required. The deadline for financial aid applications is May 1.

International Students: There are currently 110 international students enrolled. The school actively recruits these students. They must take the TOEFL or the University of Michigan Language Test and achieve a minimum score on the TOEFL of 500. The student must also take the ACT.

Computers: The college provides computer facilities for student use. The mainframe is an HP 3000/Series III. There are also 25 IBM and IBM-compatible microcomputers in 3 student laboratories. Students who apply may use the mainframe. It may be used 23 hours per day. There are no time limits on using the system and no fees.

Graduates: In 1992–93, 205 bachelor's degrees were awarded. The most popular majors among graduates were business (30%), nursing (15%), and biology (8%). Within an average freshman class, 40% graduate in 6 years.

Admissions Contact: Ronald M. Barrow, Vice President for Admissions and College Relations.

STATE UNIVERSITY AND COMMUNITY COLLEGE SYSTEM OF TENNESSEE

The State University and Community College system of Tennessee, established in 1972, is a public system. It is governed by the Tennessee Board of Regents, whose chief administrator is the chancellor. The primary goal of the system is teaching, research, and public service. The main priorities are to provide quality programs accessible to state residents with equal opportunity in education and employment. Four-year campuses are located in Nashville, Cookeville, Clarksville, Memphis, Johnson City, and Murfreesboro. The total enrollment in fall 1993 of the 6 4-year university campuses, 14 2-year institutions, and 26 area vocational schools was 165,000; there were 4900 faculty members. Altogether there are 370 baccalaureate, 215 master's, 17 specialist, and 29 doctoral programs offered in State University and

Community College System of Tennessee. Four-year campuses are located in Nashville, Cookeville, Clarksville, Memphis, Johnson City, and Murfreesboro. Profiles of the 4-year campuses are included in this chapter in alphabetical order with other Tennessee schools.

TENNESSEE STATE UNIVERSITY   C-3
Nashville, TN 37209–1561   (615) 320–3420

Full-time: 1928 men, 2855 women	**Faculty:** 323; IIA, --$
Part-time: 702 men, 1132 women	**Ph.D.s:** 65%
Graduate: 426 men, 808 women	**Student/Faculty:** 15 to 1
Year: semesters, summer session	**Tuition:** $1706 ($5488)
Application Deadline: August 1	**Room & Board:** $2920
Freshman Class: 2127 applied, 971 accepted, 783 enrolled	
ACT: 19	**COMPETITIVE +**

Tennessee State University, founded in 1912, is a state-supported land-grant institution offering undergraduate and graduate programs in arts and sciences, agriculture, health professions, business, education, engineering and technology, and nursing. There are 7 undergraduate schools and one graduate school. In addition to regional accreditation, TSU has baccalaureate program accreditation with ABET, AHEA, NASM, NCATE, and NLN. The 2 libraries contain 342,632 volumes, 643,432 microform items, and 2152 audiovisual forms, and subscribe to 1259 periodicals. Computerized library sources and services include the card catalog, interlibrary loans, and database searching. Special learning facilities include a learning resource center and radio station. The 450-acre campus is in an urban area in Nashville. Including residence halls, there are 66 buildings on campus.

Student Life: About 79% of undergraduates are from Tennessee. Students come from 36 states, several foreign countries, and Canada. Ninety percent are from public schools; 10% from private. Sixty-two percent are African American; 35% white.

Housing: A total of 2027 students can be accommodated in college housing. College-sponsored living facilities include single-sex dormitories. On-campus housing is guaranteed for all 4 years. Seventy-five percent of students commute. Alcohol is not permitted. All students may keep cars on campus.

Activities: There are 4 national fraternities and 4 national sororities. There are 60 groups on campus, including band, cheerleading, choir, chorale, computers, dance, drama, honors, jazz band, literary magazine, marching band, newspaper, pep band, professional, radio and TV, religious, social, social service, student government, and yearbook. Popular campus events include Miss TSU Pageant and Inauguration, SGA Officers' Inauguration, Greek Show, Homecoming Week, Christmas Tree Lighting Ceremony, Martin Luther King, Jr., Birthday, Founders Day, and Academic and Co-Curricular Awards Days.

Sports: Athletic and recreation facilities include a major convocation and athletic center housing intramural sports, swimming, handball, and intercollegiate basketball. A new campus center that will provide extensive recreational facilities is under construction.

Disabled Students: The following facilities are available: wheelchair ramps, elevators, special parking, specially equipped rest rooms, lowered drinking fountains, and a campus improvement program under way will make all new and renovated buildings accessible by 1995.

Services: In addition to many counseling and information services, tutoring is available in some subjects, including all general education courses and many major-field courses. There is a reader service for the blind, and remedial math, reading, and writing. A writing clinic, mathematics laboratory, and reading center provide individualized assistance.

Campus Safety and Security: Campus safety and security measures include 24-hour foot and vehicle patrol, shuttle buses, informal discussions, pamphlets, posters, and films. In addition, there are lighted pathways and sidewalks.

Programs of Study: TSU awards the B.A., B.S., B.B.A., B.S.F., and B.S.N. degrees. Associate, master's, and doctoral degrees also are awarded. Bachelor's degrees are awarded in AGRICULTURE (agriculture and animal science), BIOLOGICAL SCIENCE (biology/biological science), BUSINESS (accounting, business administration and management, business economics, and hotel/motel and restaurant management), COMMUNICATIONS AND THE ARTS (communications, English, music, and speech/debate/rhetoric), COMPUTER AND PHYSICAL SCIENCE (chemistry, computer science, mathematics, and physics), EDUCATION (art, business, early childhood, home economics, music, and special), ENGINEERING AND ENVIRONMENTAL DESIGN (aeronautical technology, architectural engineering, civil engineering, electrical/electronics engineering, and mechanical engineering), HEALTH PROFESSIONS (dental hygiene, medical laboratory technology, nursing, occupational therapy, physical therapy, respiratory therapy, and speech pathology/audiology), SOCIAL SCIENCE (African studies, criminal justice, history, political science/government, psychology, social work, and sociology). Engineering, allied health professions, nursing, and business administration are the

strongest academically. Allied Health, nursing, engineering, and computer science have the largest enrollments.

Required: Students must complete at least 132 semester hours, with 24 in the major, and maintain a minimum GPA of 2.0. Additional requirements include demonstration of proficiency in English composition, a senior project, and courses in physical education, English, mathematics, social sciences, American history, humanities, and natural sciences.

Special: Opportunities are provided for co-op programs in business and engineering, cross-registration with Middle Tennessee State University and Meharry Medical College, a B.A.-B.S. degree in interdisciplinary studies, credit by examination, and nondegree study. There is a freshman honors program on campus.

Faculty/Classroom: Fifty-eight percent of faculty are male; 42%, female. No introductory courses are taught by graduate students. The average class size in an introductory lecture is 30; in a laboratory, 35; and in a regular course offering, 30.

Admissions: About 46% of the 1993–94 applicants were accepted. The ACT scores for the 1993–94 freshman class were as follows: 67% below 21, 21% between 21 and 23, 10% between 24 and 26, 1% between 27 and 28, and 1% above 28.

Requirements: A minimum GPA of 2.5 is required. The SAT I or ACT is required, with minimum composite scores of 720 on the SAT I or 19 on the ACT. Graduation from an accredited secondary school is required; the GED is accepted. Applicants should present an academic record with 4 credits in English, 2 each in science and a foreign language, 3 in mathematics, and 1 each in history, social studies, and art. AP and CLEP credits are accepted.

Procedure: Freshmen are admitted to all sessions. Entrance exams should be taken in the junior year. Applications should be filed by August 1 for fall entry, December 1 for spring entry, and May 1 for summer entry, along with an application fee of $5. There is an early admissions plan.

Transfer: Transfer students must submit official transcripts from all previous colleges attended. Applicants from other than Tennessee colleges must have maintained a minimum GPA of 2.0. The GPA requirements for students transferring from Tennessee colleges vary according to the number of semester hours being submitted for transfer credit.

Visiting: There are guides for informal visits and visitors may sit in on classes and stay overnight at the school. To arrange for a visit, contact the recruiting staff at (615) 320-3420.

Financial Aid: The FAF is required. The deadline for financial aid applications is April 1.

International Students: There are currently 211 international students enrolled. They must take the TOEFL and achieve a minimum score of 500. The student must also take the SAT I or the ACT.

Computers: The college provides computer facilities for student use. Numerous computer laboratories are available. There are no time limits on using the system and no fees.

Admissions Contact: Dean of Admissions and Records.

TENNESSEE TECHNOLOGICAL UNIVERSITY D-3
Cookeville, TN 38505 (615) 372-3888
(800) 255-8881 (out-of-state)

Full-time: 3547 men, 2914 women	Faculty: 379; IIA, -$
Part-time: 471 men, 439 women	Ph.D.s: 84%
Graduate: 449 men, 521 women	Student/Faculty: 17 to 1
Year: semesters, summer session	Tuition: $1710 ($5492)
Application Deadline: July 21	Room & Board: $3480
Freshman Class: 2594 applied, 2417 accepted, 1329 enrolled	
ACT: 22	**COMPETITIVE**

Tennessee Technological University, founded in 1915 and a member of the state university and community college system of Tennessee, is a public, coeducational institution offering undergraduate and graduate programs in the liberal arts, business, engineering, agriculture studies, art and fine arts, music, professional training, teacher preparation, nursing, home economics, and crafts. There are 8 undergraduate and 4 graduate schools. In addition to regional accreditation, Tennessee Tech has baccalaureate program accreditation with AACSB, ABET, NASM, NCATE, and NLN. The library contains 282,875 volumes, 1,069,000 microform items, and 18,000 audiovisual forms, and subscribes to 3050 periodicals. Computerized library sources and services include the card catalog, interlibrary loans, and database searching. Special learning facilities include a learning resource center, art gallery, radio station, and TV station. The 235-acre campus is in a small town 78 miles east of Nashville. Including residence halls, there are 98 buildings on campus.

Student Life: About 94% of undergraduates are from Tennessee. Students come from 39 states, 52 foreign countries, and Canada. Ninety-three percent are white. Fifty-five percent claim no religious affiliation; 37% Protestant. The average age of freshmen is 19; all undergraduates, 22. Thirty-seven percent drop out by the end of their first year; 55% remain to graduate.

Housing: A total of 3594 students can be accommodated in college housing. College-sponsored living facilities include single-sex dormitories, on-campus apartments, off-campus apartments, married-student housing, and fraternity houses. On-campus housing is guaranteed for all 4 years. Sixty-five percent of students commute. Alcohol is not permitted. All students may keep cars on campus.

Activities: About 18% of men belong to 16 national fraternities; about 12% of women belong to 6 national sororities. There are 166 groups on campus, including art, band, cheerleading, chess, choir, chorale, chorus, computers, dance, drama, drill team, ethnic, honors, international, jazz band, literary magazine, marching band, newspaper, pep band, photography, political, professional, radio and TV, religious, social, social service, student government, and yearbook. Popular campus events include intramural events, Homecoming, and Greek Week.

Sports: There are 6 intercollegiate sports for men and 7 for women, and 10 intramural sports for men and 4 for women. Athletic and recreation facilities include 2 gymnasiums seating 10,500 and 4,000, a 16,500-seat stadium with track facilities, an indoor pool, indoor and outdoor tennis courts, handball and basketball courts, baseball, softball, and football fields, a track, a rifle range, apparatus rooms, and a health and wellness center with an indoor track, 8 racquetball courts, a weight room, an aerobics classroom, a pool, and basketball/volleyball courts.

Disabled Students: Ninety percent of the campus is accessible to disabled students. The following facilities are available: wheelchair ramps, elevators, special parking, specially equipped rest rooms, special class scheduling, and lowered drinking fountains.

Services: In addition to many counseling and information services, tutoring is available in some subjects, including English and lower levels of mathematics. There is a reader service for the blind, and remedial math, reading, and writing.

Campus Safety and Security: Campus safety and security measures include 24-hour foot and vehicle patrol, escort service, informal discussions, and emergency telephones. In addition, there are lighted pathways and sidewalks and a student safety organization.

Programs of Study: Tennessee Tech awards the B.A., B.S., B.S.Agr., B.S.B.A., B.S.Ch., B.S.Ch.E., B.S.E., B.S.E.E., B.S.I.E., B.S.Ind.Tech., B.S.M.E., B.S.in Civil Eng., and B.S.N. degrees. Associate, master's, and doctoral degrees also are awarded. Bachelor's degrees are awarded in AGRICULTURE (agricultural economics, animal science, plant science, soil science, and wildlife management), BIOLOGICAL SCIENCE (biochemistry and biology/biological science), BUSINESS (accounting, business administration and management, management science, and marketing/retailing/merchandising), COMMUNICATIONS AND THE ARTS (English, fine arts, French, German, journalism, Spanish, and technical and business writing), COMPUTER AND PHYSICAL SCIENCE (chemistry, computer science, geology, mathematics, and physics), EDUCATION (agricultural, early childhood, elementary, home economics, music, physical, secondary, and special), ENGINEERING AND ENVIRONMENTAL DESIGN (chemical engineering, civil engineering, electrical/electronics engineering, engineering, industrial engineering, industrial engineering technology, and mechanical engineering), HEALTH PROFESSIONS (music therapy and nursing), SOCIAL SCIENCE (economics, history, political science/government, psychology, and sociology). Engineering and business are the strongest academically. Engineering has the largest enrollment.

Required: Students must complete 132 semester hours, with a variable number of hours in the major, and maintain a minimum GPA of 2.0. Twelve semester hours of English, 8 of a laboratory science, 6 of American history, and 2 of physical education are required.

Special: Co-op programs in most academic areas, internships in community-based programs, study abroad, a Washington semester, and work-study programs are available. Accelerated degree programs are offered in all specified majors with 3 calendar years of continuous studies. A B.A.-B.S. degree is available, as are dual majors in all areas. Credit may be granted for military experience, and nondegree study and pass/fail options are offered. There is a freshman honors program on campus, as well as 29 national honor societies.

Faculty/Classroom: Sixty-six percent of faculty are male; 34%, female. Graduate students teach 10% of introductory courses. The average class size in an introductory lecture is 60; in a laboratory, 25; and in a regular course offering, 40.

Admissions: About 93% of the 1993–94 applicants were accepted. The ACT scores for the 1993–94 freshman class were as follows: 35% below 21, 26% between 21 and 23, 21% between 24 and 26, 11% between 27 and 28, and 7% above 28. About 25% of the current freshmen were in the top fifth of their class; 45% were in the top two fifths. About 62 freshmen graduated first in their class.

Requirements: A minimum GPA of 2.35 is required. The ACT is recommended, with a minimum composite score of 19. Other admissions requirements include graduation from an accredited secondary school with 14 academic credits, including 4 of English, 3 of mathematics, 2 each in science and a foreign language, and 1 each in histo-

ry, social studies, and music/art. The GED is also accepted. AP and CLEP credits are accepted.

Procedure: Freshmen are admitted to all sessions. Entrance exams should be taken during the senior year. Applications should be filed by July 21 for fall entry, December 8 for spring entry, and May 4 for summer entry, along with an application fee of $5. Notification is sent on a rolling basis. There is an early admissions plan.

Transfer: A total of 612 transfer students enrolled in 1993–94. Transfer students should have a minimum of 24 credit hours earned; the minimum GPA depends on the number of credit hours accumulated. Official transcripts must be submitted, and the ACT is required. If an applicant has fewer than the 24 credit hours, admissions requirements are the same as for freshmen. A total of 30 credits out of 132 must be completed at Tennessee Tech.

Visiting: There are guides for informal visits and visitors may sit in on classes and stay overnight at the school. To arrange for a visit, contact the Admissions Office at (615) 372–3888 or (800) 255–8881.

Financial Aid: In a recent year 75% of all current freshmen and 60% of continuing students received some form of financial aid. Scholarships or need-based grants averaged $1100 ($5000 maximum); loans averaged $1900 ($2625 maximum); and work contracts averaged $1150 ($1600 maximum). Fifteen percent of undergraduate students work part-time. Average earnings from campus work for the school year are $1150. The average financial indebtedness of a recent graduate was $8000. The FFS is required. The deadline for financial aid applications is March 15.

International Students: There are currently 238 international students enrolled. The school actively recruits these students. They must take the TOEFL, the University of Michigan Language Test, or the college's own test and achieve a minimum score on the TOEFL of 500.

Computers: The college provides computer facilities for student use. The mainframes are a DEC VAX 11/785, 8800, and 11/750. VAV, AVAX, Gemini, IBM-compatible, Apple, and Macintosh microcomputers are available for student use in numerous buildings across campus. All students may access the system 24 hours a day. There are no time limits on using the system. There are no fees.

Graduates: In 1992–93, 1393 bachelor's degrees were awarded. The most popular majors among graduates were mechanical engineering (4%), civil engineering (3%), and electrical engineering (3%). Within an average freshman class, 10% graduate in 4 years, 45% in 5 years, and 40% in 6 years. Some 200 companies recruited on campus in 1992–93.

Admissions Contact: James Perry, Director of Admissions.

TENNESSEE WESLEYAN COLLEGE D-3
Athens, TN 37301–0040 (615) 745–7504

Full-time: 227 men, 175 women	Faculty: 34; IIB, --$
Part-time: 73 men, 164 women	Ph.D.s: 59%
Graduate: none	Student/Faculty: 12 to 1
Year: semesters, summer session	Tuition: $6520
Application Deadline: July 31	Room & Board: $3540
Freshman Class: 228 applied, 182 accepted, 99 enrolled	
ACT: 20	COMPETITIVE

Tennessee Wesleyan College, founded in 1857, is a nonprofit, private, coeducational institution affiliated with the United Methodist Church. Its undergraduate programs stress the liberal arts and teacher preparation. The library contains 87,827 volumes, 6392 microform items, and 10,998 audiovisual forms, and subscribes to 381 periodicals. Computerized library sources and services include interlibrary loans and database searching. The 40-acre campus is in an urban area 55 miles south of Knoxville. Including residence halls, there are 15 buildings on campus.

Student Life: About 77% of undergraduates are from Tennessee. Students come from 16 states and 7 foreign countries. Ninety-eight percent are from public schools; 2% from private. Eighty-three percent are white; 11% African American. Eighty-two percent are Protestant; 15% claim no religious affiliation. The average age of all undergraduates is 24.

Housing: A total of 336 students can be accommodated in college housing. College-sponsored living facilities include single-sex dormitories. On-campus housing is guaranteed for all 4 years. Fifty-two percent of students commute. Alcohol is not permitted. All students may keep cars on campus.

Activities: About 20% of women belong to 1 local and 1 national sorority. There are no fraternities on campus. There are 15 groups on campus, including cheerleading, choir, chorale, computers, drama, ethnic, honors, international, literary magazine, musical theater, newspaper, professional, religious, student government, and yearbook. Popular campus events include Literature Festival, Halloween Arts Carnival, Spirit Week, and Black History Emphasis Week.

Sports: There are 5 intercollegiate sports for men and 4 for women, and 5 intramural sports for men and 5 for women. Athletic and recreation facilities include a 2000-seat stadium, an 1800-seat gym, and a

YMCA adjacent to campus with an indoor/outdoor swimming pool available on a scheduled basis to students.

Disabled Students: Seventy percent of the campus is accessible to disabled students. The following facilities are available: wheelchair ramps, elevators, special parking, specially equipped rest rooms, and special class scheduling.

Services: In addition to many counseling and information services, tutoring is available in some subjects, including English and mathematics. In addition, there is remedial math and writing.

Campus Safety and Security: Campus safety and security measures include informal discussions and lighted pathways and sidewalks.

Programs of Study: TWC awards the B.A., B.S., B.Applied Sc., and B.Mus.Ed. degrees. Bachelor's degrees are awarded in BIOLOGICAL SCIENCE (biology/biological science), BUSINESS (business administration and management), COMMUNICATIONS AND THE ARTS (English and music), COMPUTER AND PHYSICAL SCIENCE (mathematics), EDUCATION (elementary, music, physical, science, and secondary), SOCIAL SCIENCE (history, psychology, religious education, social science, and social work). Business, education, history, and preprofessional fields are the strongest academically. Business and education have the largest enrollments.

Required: Students must complete 128 semester hours, fulfilling the requirements of the major and taking 28 semester hours at the upper-division level, and maintain a minimum GPA of 2.0 (2.5 for education majors). Distribution requirements include 12 semester hours of the humanities, 6 each of mathematics and English composition, 9 of social and behavioral sciences, 8 of science, and 3 each of speech and fine arts. Two semester hours of physical education are also needed. Internships are required for human services students, and all students must take an exit examination.

Special: Special academic programs include internships in some majors, study abroad in Japan and England, dual majors in several areas, student-designed majors, and nondegree study. There is one national honor society on campus.

Faculty/Classroom: Sixty-two percent of faculty are male; 38%, female. All teach undergraduates and 40% both teach and do research. The average class size in an introductory lecture is 22; in a laboratory, 13; and in a regular course offering, 12.

Admissions: About 80% of the 1993–94 applicants were accepted. The ACT scores for the 1993–94 freshman class were as follows: 73% below 21, 12% between 21 and 23, 12% between 24 and 26, 1% between 27 and 28, and 1% above 28. About 25% of the current freshmen were in the top fifth of their class; 70% were in the top two fifths.

Requirements: TWC requires applicants to be in the upper 75% of their class. A minimum GPA of 2.0 is required. The SAT I or ACT is required. Other admission requirements include graduation from an accredited secondary school, with 16 academic credits, including 4 units in English, 2 each in mathematics and science, and 1 each in social studies and history. Foreign language is recommended. The GED is also accepted. AP and CLEP credits are accepted. Important factors used in the admissions decision are leadership record, recommendations by school officials, extracurricular activities record, personality, intangible qualities, and evidence of special talent.

Procedure: Freshmen are admitted to all sessions. Entrance exams should be taken in the fall of the senior year. Applications should be filed by July 31 for fall entry, November 30 for spring entry, and March 31 for summer entry, along with an application fee of $25. Notification is sent on a rolling basis.

Transfer: About 170 transfer students enrolled in 1993–94. Transfer students must have a minimum GPA of 2.0; an associate degree is recommended. A total of 30 credits out of 128 must be completed at TWC.

Visiting: There are regularly scheduled orientations for prospective students. There are guides for informal visits and visitors may sit in on classes and stay overnight at the school. To arrange for a visit, contact Lynne Henderson, Director of Admissions at (615) 745–7504.

Financial Aid: In 1993–94, 80% of all current freshmen and 72% of continuing students received some form of financial aid. About 70% of freshmen and 60% of continuing students received need-based aid. The average freshman award was $4800. Of that total, scholarships or need-based grants averaged $1500 ($3000 maximum); loans averaged $2700 ($5500 maximum); and work contracts averaged $750. Twenty-five percent of undergraduate students work part-time. Average earnings from campus work for the school year are $750. TWC is a member of CSS. The FAF, the college's own financial statement, and the FAFSA are required. The priority deadline for financial aid applications is April 15.

International Students: There are currently 35 international students enrolled. The school actively recruits these students. They must take the TOEFL or the college's own test and achieve a minimum score on the TOEFL of 500.

Computers: The college provides computer facilities for student use. Students have access to 40 microcomputers located in 3 different laboratories on campus. All students may access the system. It may be

used during laboratory hours, generally 8:30 A.M. to 9 P.M. There are no time limits on using the system and no fees.

Graduates: In a recent year, 124 bachelor's degrees were awarded. The most popular majors among graduates were business (46%), education (14%), and interdisciplinary (10%).

Admissions Contact: Lynne Henderson, Director of Admissions.

TREVECCA NAZARENE COLLEGE C-3
Nashville, TN 37210-2877 (615) 248-1320
(800) 210-4TNC (out-of-state)

Full-time: 343 men, 418 women	Faculty: 60
Part-time: 78 men, 93 women	Ph.D.s: 50%
Graduate: 126 men, 248 women	Student/Faculty: 13 to 1
Year: semesters, summer session	Tuition: $6656
Application Deadline: open	Room & Board: $3170
Freshman Class: 235 applied, 235 accepted, 156 enrolled	
ACT: 21	NONCOMPETITIVE

Trevecca Nazarene College, founded in 1901, is a small private institution affiliated with the Church of the Nazarene offering programs in liberal arts and teacher education. There are 2 graduate schools. In addition to regional accreditation, TNC has baccalaureate program accreditation with CAHEA and NASM. The library contains 265,694 volumes and 157,833 microform items, and subscribes to 656 periodicals. Computerized library sources and services include the card catalog, interlibrary loans, and database searching. Special learning facilities include a radio station and a curriculum library. The 80-acre campus is in an urban area. Including residence halls, there are 21 buildings on campus.

Student Life: About 63% of undergraduates are from Tennessee. Students come from 35 states and Canada. Seventy-eight percent are white; 20% African American. Most are Protestant. The average age of freshmen is 19. Twenty-nine percent drop out by the end of their first year; 36% remain to graduate.

Housing: A total of 583 students can be accommodated in college housing. College-sponsored living facilities include single-sex dormitories, on-campus apartments, off-campus apartments, and married-student housing. On-campus housing is guaranteed for all 4 years. Sixty-two percent of students live on campus. Alcohol is not permitted. All students may keep cars on campus.

Activities: There are no fraternities or sororities on campus. There are many groups on campus, including band, cheerleading, choir, chorus, drama, honors, jazz band, literary magazine, marching band, newspaper, orchestra, pep band, professional, religious, social service, student government, and yearbook. Popular campus events include Homecoming, Thanksgiving Gala, Valentine's Banquet, Junior-Senior Banquets, Lyceum Programs, Wachtel Lecture Series, and Youth and Mission.

Sports: There are 4 intercollegiate sports for men and 3 for women, and 6 intramural sports for men and 5 for women. Athletic and recreation facilities include a gymnasium, a pool, a jogging track, handball and tennis courts, exercise and weight rooms, and playing fields.

Disabled Students: Seventy-five percent of the campus is accessible to disabled students. The following facilities are available: wheelchair ramps, elevators, special parking, specially equipped rest rooms, and special class scheduling.

Services: In addition to many counseling and information services, tutoring is available in every subject. There is also remedial math, reading, and writing. An academic enrichment program for students scoring below 19 on the ACT provides tutoring in mathematics, reading, writing, and study skills.

Campus Safety and Security: Campus safety and security measures include informal discussions, lighted pathways and sidewalks, and weekend and evening foot and vehicle patrol.

Programs of Study: TNC awards the B.A. and B.S. degrees. Associate and master's degrees also are awarded. Bachelor's degrees are awarded in BIOLOGICAL SCIENCE (biology/biological science), BUSINESS (accounting and business administration and management), COMMUNICATIONS AND THE ARTS (communications, dramatic arts, English, music, music business management, and speech/debate/rhetoric), COMPUTER AND PHYSICAL SCIENCE (chemistry, information sciences and systems, mathematics, and science), EDUCATION (early childhood, elementary, English, health, mathematics, music, and physical), HEALTH PROFESSIONS (allied health, medical laboratory technology, and physician's assistant), SOCIAL SCIENCE (behavioral science, crosscultural studies, history, ministries, philosophy, prelaw, psychology, religion, religious education, religious music, and social work). Management and human relations has the largest enrollment.

Required: To graduate, students must complete at least 128 semester hours with a minimum 2.0 GPA. The required 55-hour general education curriculum includes courses in English, communications, religion and philosophy, fine arts, history and social science (including foreign language), science and mathematics, and physical education.

Special: There are work-study programs, internships, and nondegree study. The B.S. in Management and Human Relations is offered for adult learners over age 25, with a minimum of 64 credit hours completed; a 3-2 nursing program is offered with Vanderbilt University, leading to the combined B.A.-M.S. degree; and there are 2-2 nursing programs with Belmont and Mid-America Nazarene Colleges. Dual majors, an accelerated degree program in management and human relations, and a Washington seminar are available. Study abroad is possible. There is a freshman honors program on campus.

Admissions: One hundred percent of the 1993-94 applicants were accepted. The ACT scores for the 1993-94 freshman class were as follows: 22% below 21, 31% between 21 and 23, 36% between 24 and 26, 10% between 27 and 28, and 1% above 28. About 30% of the current freshmen were in the top fifth of their class; 40% were in the top two fifths. Five freshmen graduated first in their class.

Requirements: TNC requires applicants to be in the upper 50% of their class. A minimum GPA of 2.0 is required. The SAT I or ACT is required. The ACT is preferred, with a composite score of at least 19. Candidates should have completed at least 15 academic secondary credits, including 4 units in English, 2 each in mathematics, foreign language, and social science, and 1 in natural science. A GED of at least 45 is also accepted. The physician assistant, medical technology, and teacher education programs have special admission requirements. AP and CLEP credits are accepted.

Procedure: Freshmen are admitted to all sessions. Entrance exams should be taken in the junior or senior years. Application deadlines are open. The application fee is $25. The college accepts all applicants. Notification is sent on a rolling basis. There are early admissions and deferred admissions plans.

Transfer: Transfer applicants must present official transcripts and recommendations.

Visiting: There are regularly scheduled orientations for prospective students, including a tour and meetings with admissions and financial aid personnel and faculty. There are guides for informal visits and visitors may sit in on classes and stay overnight at the school. To arrange for a visit, contact the Admissions Office at (615) 248-1320 or (800) 210-4TNC.

Financial Aid: In a recent year, 90% of all students received some form of financial aid. About 85% of students received need-based aid. The average freshman award was $6890. Of that total, scholarships or need-based grants averaged $750; loans averaged $2600; and work contracts averaged $1200. Seventy-two percent of undergraduate students work part-time. Average earnings from campus work for a recent year were $1200. The average financial indebtedness of a recent graduate was $15,000. TNC is a member of CSS. The FAF or FFS is required. The deadline for financial aid applications is April 15.

International Students: International students must take the SAT I or the ACT.

Computers: The college provides computer facilities for student use. The mainframe is a DEC VAX 750. An Ethernet fiber optics network connects all buildings on the campus to the 2 clustered VAX/VMS mainframe computers. TNC is part of the Vanderbilt Gateway, linking the school to the Internet and NSFnet national computing networks. Students can access the computer via modem 24 hours a day. The Academic Computing Laboratory, open from 7 A.M. to 10:30 P.M., Monday through Saturday, is available to all students. There are no time limits and no sign-up times. There are 16 VT320 terminals in the Academic Computing Laboratory, 8 line printers, and 2 laserjet printers. There are also 40 PCs in this laboratory and in the instructional PC classroom, along with 20 printers. All students may access the system. There are no time limits on using the system and no fees.

Graduates: Within an average freshman class, 4% graduate in 3 years, 19% in 4 years, 9% in 5 years, and 2% in 6 years. Some 42 companies recruited on campus a recent year.

Admissions Contact: Jan R. Forman, Dean of Enrollment Services.

TUSCULUM COLLEGE F-3
Greeneville, TN 37743 (615) 636-7312
(800) 729-0256 (out-of-state)

Full-time: 478 men, 505 women	Faculty: 70; IIB, --$
Part-time: 16 men, 24 women	Ph.D.s: 70%
Graduate: 53 men, 68 women	Student/Faculty: 14 to 1
Year: semesters, summer session	Tuition: $7100
Application Deadline: May 1	Room & Board: $3300
Freshman Class: 438 applied, 372 accepted, 145 enrolled	
SAT I Verbal/Math: 370/420	ACT: 18 LESS COMPETITIVE

Tusculum College, a small liberal arts institution chartered in 1794, is the oldest college in Tennessee, and the oldest coeducational college affiliated with the Presbyterian Church USA. The 2 libraries contain 70,500 volumes, 141,613 microform items, and 841 audiovisual forms, and subscribe to 500 periodicals. Computerized library sources and services include the card catalog, interlibrary loans, and database searching. Special learning facilities include a learning resource

center, an art gallery, and a radio station. The 142-acre campus is in a suburban area 30 miles south of Johnson City, in the foothills of the Great Smoky Mountains. Including residence halls, there are 21 buildings on campus.

Student Life: About 76% of undergraduates are from Tennessee. Students come from 20 states and 6 foreign countries. Ninety-eight percent are from public schools; 2% from private. Ninety-one percent are white. Sixty-one percent are Protestant; 15% claim no religious affiliation; 10% Catholic. The average age of freshmen is 18; all undergraduates, 29. Twenty percent drop out by the end of their first year; 43% remain to graduate.

Housing: A total of 386 students can be accommodated in college housing. College-sponsored living facilities include single-sex dormitories. On-campus housing is guaranteed for all 4 years. Alcohol is not permitted. All students may keep cars on campus.

Activities: There are no fraternities or sororities on campus. There are 21 groups on campus, including art, cheerleading, choir, chorale, dance, drama, ethnic, honors, newspaper, photography, professional, radio and TV, religious, student government, and yearbook. Popular campus events include McCormick Day, Homecoming, Opening Convocation, Awards Convocation, Parents Weekend, and Professional Studies Day.

Sports: There are 7 intercollegiate sports for men and 6 for women, and 12 intramural sports for men and 13 for women. Athletic and recreation facilities include a gymnasium-pool complex, tennis courts, and various playing fields, including a new football field.

Disabled Students: Fifty percent of the campus is accessible to disabled students. The following facilities are available: wheelchair ramps, special parking, special class scheduling, and classes and activities scheduled in accessible areas.

Services: In addition to many counseling and information services, tutoring is available in some subjects, including mathematics, English, and foreign language.

Campus Safety and Security: Campus safety and security measures include 24-hour foot and vehicle patrol, informal discussions, emergency telephones, and lighted pathways and sidewalks.

Programs of Study: Tusculum awards the B.A. and B.S. degrees. Master's degrees also are awarded. Bachelor's degrees are awarded in BIOLOGICAL SCIENCE (biology/biological science), BUSINESS (management science and sports management), COMMUNICATIONS AND THE ARTS (English and fine arts), COMPUTER AND PHYSICAL SCIENCE (computer science), EDUCATION (elementary, museum studies, physical, and special), ENGINEERING AND ENVIRONMENTAL DESIGN (environmental science), HEALTH PROFESSIONS (medical laboratory technology), SOCIAL SCIENCE (human development, psychology, and social studies). Management, education, and biology are the strongest academically. Management and education have the largest enrollments.

Required: All students must complete at least 128 hours with an overall minimum GPA of 2.0 and 2.3 in the major field. Specific degree programs have specific requirements. B.S. candidates must take a core curriculum consisting of courses in English, art, music, sociology, economics, and psychology. B.A. candidates must complete a set of interdisciplinary courses, validate 15 competencies, complete a civic arts project, and fulfill the requirements of a major.

Special: Internships, practice, and student-teaching opportunities are offered in business administration, professional and special education, social services, psychology, biology, chemistry, medical technology, and prenursing. The B.S. in applied organizational management is designed for adult transfer students with previous training and work experience. The medical technology program is offered in cooperation with a medical center in Kingsport. An independent major, nondegree study, and pass/fail options are available. There is an accelerated evening program for working adults. There is one national honor society on campus.

Faculty/Classroom: Seventy percent of faculty are male; 30%, female. All teach undergraduates. No introductory courses are taught by graduate students. The average class size in an introductory lecture is 25; in a laboratory, 20; and in a regular course offering, 15.

Admissions: About 85% of the 1993–94 applicants were accepted. The SAT scores for the 1993–94 freshman class were as follows: Verbal—93% below 500, 6% between 500 and 599, and 1% between 600 and 700; Math—78% below 500, 19% between 500 and 599, and 3% between 600 and 700. The ACT scores were 72% below 21, 22% between 21 and 23, 3% between 24 and 26, and 2% between 27 and 28. About 25% of the current freshmen were in the top fifth of their class; 46% were in the top two fifths. One freshman graduated first in his class.

Requirements: Tusculum requires applicants to be in the upper 50% of their class. A minimum GPA of 2.0 is required. The SAT I or ACT is required. The recommended composite score is 800 on the SAT I or 18 on the ACT. Applicants should be high school graduates or have the GED. Secondary school preparation should include 4 units of English, 2 units each of foreign language, mathematics, and science, and 1 unit of history. A personal essay is also required. AP

and CLEP credits are accepted. Important factors used in the admissions decision are advanced placement or honor courses, evidence of special talent, leadership record, personality, intangible qualities, and parents or siblings attending the school.

Procedure: Freshmen are admitted to all sessions. Entrance exams should be taken in spring of the junior year. Applications should be filed by May 1 for fall entry and November 1 for spring entry. Notification is sent on a rolling basis. There is an early admissions plan.

Transfer: About 40 transfer students enrolled in 1993–94. Transfer applicants should present at least a 2.0 GPA in previous college work. Tusculum recommends that applicants also submit SAT I or ACT scores. A total of 32 credits out of 128 must be completed at Tusculum.

Visiting: There are guides for informal visits and visitors may sit in on classes and stay overnight at the school. To arrange for a visit, contact the Admissions Office at (615) 636-7312.

Financial Aid: In 1993–94, 83% of all current freshmen and 94% of continuing students received some form of financial aid. About 84% of freshmen and 78% of continuing students received need-based aid. The average freshman award was $7402. Of that total, scholarships or need-based grants averaged $4084 ($10,400 maximum); loans averaged $3937 ($12,050 maximum); and work contracts averaged $750 ($1000 maximum). Sixty percent of undergraduate students work part-time. Average earnings from campus work for the school year are $700. The average financial indebtedness of the 1992–93 graduate was $6335. Tusculum is a member of CSS. The college's own financial statement and FAFSA are required. The deadline for financial aid applications is open.

International Students: There are currently 9 international students enrolled. They must take the TOEFL and achieve a minimum score of 550. The student must also take the SAT I or the ACT and achieve a minimum score of 800 on the SAT I or 18 on the ACT.

Computers: The college provides computer facilities for student use. A laboratory with 17 IBM/PS 2s is available. All students may access the system. It may be used from 1 P.M. to 12 A.M., Sunday through Friday, and from 1 P.M. to 4 P.M. on Saturday. There are no time limits on using the system and no fees.

Graduates: In 1992–93, 242 bachelor's degrees were awarded. The most popular majors among graduates were management (82%), education (6%), and biology (3%). Within an average freshman class, 66% graduate in 5 years. Some 25 companies recruited on campus in 1992–93.

Admissions Contact: Laura Bryant, Director of Admissions.

UNION UNIVERSITY
Jackson, TN 38305

B-3
(901) 668-1818

Full-time: 568 men, 987 women	Faculty: 93; IIB, --$
Part-time: 98 men, 260 women	Ph.D.s: 42%
Graduate: 15 men, 74 women	Student/Faculty: 17 to 1
Year: 4-1-4, summer session	Tuition: $5380
Application Deadline: open	Room & Board: $2500
Freshman Class: 846 applied, 752 accepted, 406 enrolled	
ACT: 24	COMPETITIVE +

Union University, founded in 1823, is a private, nonprofit, coeducational institution affiliated with the Southern Baptist Convention. The university offers programs in arts and sciences, education, business, and nursing. There are 4 undergraduate schools and one graduate school. In addition to regional accreditation, Union has baccalaureate program accreditation with AACSB, NASM, NCATE, and NLN. The library contains 177,642 volumes, 273,921 microform items, and 21,040 audiovisual forms, and subscribes to 1200 periodicals. Computerized library sources and services include the card catalog and database searching. Special learning facilities include a learning resource center, an art gallery, and a TV station. The 230-acre campus is in a suburban area 75 miles east of Memphis. Including residence halls, there are 5 buildings on campus.

Student Life: About 78% of undergraduates are from Tennessee. Students come from 32 states, 9 foreign countries, and Canada. Ninety-three percent are white. Most are Protestant. The average age of all undergraduates is 21.

Housing: A total of 1000 students can be accommodated in college housing. College-sponsored living facilities include single-sex on-campus apartments and married-student housing. On-campus housing is available on a first-come, first-served basis. Fifty percent of students live on campus; of those, 40% remain on campus on weekends. Alcohol is not permitted. All students may keep cars on campus.

Activities: About 26% of men belong to 3 national fraternities; about 27% of women belong to 3 national sororities. There are 73 groups on campus, including art, band, cheerleading, choir, chorus, computers, drama, honors, jazz band, literary magazine, newspaper, orchestra, pep band, photography, political, professional, radio and TV, religious, student government, symphony, and yearbook. Popular campus events include Campus Day, Greek Week, All Sing, Spring Splash, and Homecoming.

Sports: There are 4 intercollegiate sports for men and 2 for women, and 30 intramural sports for men and 27 for women. Athletic and recreation facilities include tennis and racquetball courts, a student recreation center, an indoor swimming pool, a 1200-seat auditorium, and 2 gymnasiums, one seating 3000.

Disabled Students: Ninety-eight percent of the campus is accessible to disabled students. The following facilities are available: wheelchair ramps, special parking, specially equipped rest rooms, special class scheduling, and apartments.

Services: In addition to many counseling and information services, tutoring is available in every subject.

Campus Safety and Security: Campus safety and security measures include 24-hour foot and vehicle patrol, informal discussions, pamphlets, posters, and films, and emergency telephones. In addition, there are lighted pathways and sidewalks.

Programs of Study: Union awards the B.A., B.S., B.M., B.S.B.A., and B.S.N. degrees. Master's degrees also are awarded. Bachelor's degrees are awarded in BIOLOGICAL SCIENCE (biology/biological science), BUSINESS (accounting and marketing management), COMMUNICATIONS AND THE ARTS (communications, English, French, journalism, music, and Spanish), COMPUTER AND PHYSICAL SCIENCE (chemistry, computer science, mathematics, physical sciences, and physics), EDUCATION (elementary, music, and physical), HEALTH PROFESSIONS (medical laboratory technology, nursing, predentistry, and premedicine), SOCIAL SCIENCE (economics, history, ministries, prelaw, psychology, religion, religious music, social studies, and sociology). Business, nursing, and education have the largest enrollments.

Required: All students must complete 128 credit hours, with at least 30 in the major, and maintain a minimum overall GPA of 2.0. The general core requirements are 12 credit hours of English, 8 of natural sciences, 6 each of history, social sciences, and religion, 3 each of mathematics and fine arts, and 2 of physical education.

Special: Cross-registration with Lambuth and Free-Hardeman Colleges, internships, and cooperative and work-study programs are available. Union also offers dual and student-designed majors, 3–2 engineering degrees, and nondegree study. There is a freshman honors program on campus, as well as 11 national honor societies, including Phi Beta Kappa.

Faculty/Classroom: Forty-eight percent of faculty are male; 37%, female. All teach undergraduates. The average class size in an introductory lecture is 35; in a laboratory, 24; and in a regular course offering, 30.

Admissions: About 89% of the 1993–94 applicants were accepted. The ACT scores for the 1993–94 freshman class were as follows: 28% below 21, 19% between 21 and 23, 28% between 24 and 26, 15% between 27 and 28, and 10% above 28. About 20 freshmen graduated first in their class.

Requirements: A minimum GPA of 2.5 is required. The SAT I or ACT is required; the ACT is preferred. A minimum composite score of 20 on the ACT or 820 on the SAT I is recommended. Candidates must be graduates of an accredited secondary school or have the GED. A minimum of 18 academic credits is required, including at least 14 in English, mathematics, foreign language, and social and natural sciences. An interview is also recommended. AP and CLEP credits are accepted. Important factors used in the admissions decision are personality, intangible qualities, recommendations by school officials, recommendations by alumni, evidence of special talent, and parents or siblings attending the school.

Procedure: Freshmen are admitted to all sessions. Entrance exams should be taken in the spring of the junior year or fall of the senior year. Application deadlines are open; the fee is $10. Notification is sent on a rolling basis.

Transfer: About 270 transfer students enrolled in 1993–94. Candidates must have a minimum GPA of 2.0 in more than 12 semester hours and submit a social transfer form from the last institution attended. A total of 32 credits out of 128 must be completed at Union.

Visiting: There are guides for informal visits and visitors may sit in on classes and stay overnight at the school. To arrange for a visit, contact Carroll W. Griffin, Director of Admissions at (901) 668–1818.

Financial Aid: In 1993–94, 82% of all current freshmen and 78% of continuing students received some form of financial aid. About 70% of freshmen and 71% of continuing students received need-based aid. The average freshman award was $3900. Of that total, scholarships or need-based grants averaged $1450 ($4190 maximum); loans averaged $1400 ($2625 maximum); and work contracts averaged $1000 ($2000 maximum). Thirty-five percent of undergraduate students work part-time. Average earnings from campus work for the school year are $1000. The average financial indebtedness of the 1992–93 graduate was $6000. The FFS is required. The deadline for financial aid applications is August 24.

International Students: There are currently 20 international students enrolled. They must take the TOEFL and achieve a minimum score of 525 or take the ACT or SAT I.

Computers: The college provides computer facilities for student use. The mainframe is an HP 3000/Series 935. There are 5 microcomputer laboratories available on campus. It may be used during laboratory hours. There are no time limits on using the system and no fees.

Graduates: In 1992–93, 310 bachelor's degrees were awarded. The most popular majors among graduates were nursing (32%), elementary education (19%), and management/marketing (16%). Some 47 companies recruited on campus in 1992–93.

Admissions Contact: Carroll W. Griffin, Director of Admissions.

UNIVERSITY OF MEMPHIS   A-4
(Formerly Memphis State University)
Memphis, TN 38152   (901) 678–2169; (800) 669–2678 (out-of-state)

Full-time: 4955 men, 5666 women	Faculty: 730; I, --$
Part-time: 2073 men, 2791 women	Ph.D.s: 75%
Graduate: 2135 men, 2753 women	Student/Faculty: 15 to 1
Year: semesters, summer session	Tuition: $1858 ($5640)
Application Deadline: August 1	Room: $1618
Freshman Class: 2921 applied, 2557 accepted, 1691 enrolled	
ACT: 22	**COMPETITIVE**

The University of Memphis, founded in 1912, is a public, coeducational liberal arts and sciences institution and part of the Tennessee Board of Regents system. There are 6 undergraduate schools and one graduate school. The 6 libraries contain 1 million volumes, 3 million microform items, and 5000 audiovisual forms, and subscribe to 15,000 periodicals. Computerized library sources and services include the card catalog, interlibrary loans, and database searching. Special learning facilities include a learning resource center, an art gallery, a radio station, a TV station, an earthquake research center, a center for electron microscopy, Chucalissa Indian Village and Museum, and a speech and hearing center. The 1159-acre campus is in an urban area. Including residence halls, there are 92 buildings on campus.

Student Life: About 88% of undergraduates are from Tennessee. Students come from 50 states, 80 foreign countries, and Canada. Eighty percent are white; 17% African American. The average age of all undergraduates is 23.

Housing: A total of 2483 students can be accommodated in college housing. College-sponsored living facilities include single-sex dormitories and married-student housing. In addition, there is an athletic dormitory and family housing. On-campus housing is available on a first-come, first-served basis. Priority is given to out-of-town students. Alcohol is not permitted. All students may keep cars on campus.

Activities: About 7% of men belong to 16 national fraternities; about 6% of women belong to 12 national sororities. There are 165 groups on campus, including band, cheerleading, chess, choir, chorale, chorus, computers, dance, drama, drill team, ethnic, film, gay, honors, international, jazz band, literary magazine, marching band, musical theater, newspaper, opera, orchestra, pep band, photography, political, professional, radio and TV, religious, social, social service, student government, symphony, and yearbook.

Sports: There are 7 intercollegiate sports for men and 5 for women, and 12 intramural sports for men and 11 for women. Athletic and recreation facilities include a gymnasium, a football stadium, a baseball field, swimming pools, a track, a weight room, and tennis, handball, and racquetball courts.

Disabled Students: Ninety-five percent of the campus is accessible to disabled students. The following facilities are available: wheelchair ramps, elevators, special parking, specially equipped rest rooms, special class scheduling, lowered drinking fountains, lowered telephones, modified housing, and a transportation service.

Services: In addition to many counseling and information services, tutoring is available in most subjects. In addition, there is a reader service for the blind, and remedial math, reading, and writing.

Campus Safety and Security: Campus safety and security measures include 24-hour foot and vehicle patrol, escort service, informal discussions, and emergency telephones. In addition, there are lighted pathways and sidewalks.

Programs of Study: The university awards the B.A., B.S., B.B.A., B.F.A., B.L.S., B.M., B.P.S., B.S.C.E., B.S.Ed., B.S.E.E., B.S.E.T., B.S.H.E., B.S.M.E., B.S.M.T., and B.S.N. degrees. Master's and doctoral degrees also are awarded. Bachelor's degrees are awarded in BIOLOGICAL SCIENCE (biology/biological science), BUSINESS (accounting, banking and finance, business economics, insurance and risk management, management information systems, marketing/retailing/merchandising, real estate, and transportation management), COMMUNICATIONS AND THE ARTS (art history and appreciation, communications, dramatic arts, English, fine arts, French, German, journalism, Latin, music, Russian, and Spanish), COMPUTER AND PHYSICAL SCIENCE (chemistry, computer science, earth science, information sciences and systems, mathematics, physics, and statistics), EDUCATION (early childhood, health, home economics, physical, and special), ENGINEERING AND ENVIRONMENTAL DESIGN (architectural technology, civil engineering, computer technol-

ogy, electrical/electronics engineering, electrical/electronics engineering technology, engineering technology, manufacturing technology, and mechanical engineering), HEALTH PROFESSIONS (medical laboratory technology, nursing, predentistry, and premedicine), SOCIAL SCIENCE (anthropology, criminal justice, economics, geography, history, international relations, paralegal studies, parks and recreation management, philosophy, political science/government, prelaw, psychology, social work, and sociology). Business, engineering, and preprofessional studies have the largest enrollments.

Required: To graduate, students must complete a minimum of 132 credit hours with a GPA of 2.0, and demonstrate proficiency in computer skills. Distribution requirements include 6 hours each of English composition, social science, natural science, and U.S. history; 3 to 6 hours of mathematics; 4 hours of physical education; and 3 hours each of communication, fine arts, literature, history/philosophy, computation, intensive writing, and thematic and integrative courses.

Special: The university offers co-op programs, cross-registration, internships, study abroad in England and Spain, B.A.-B.S. degrees, dual and student-designed majors, nondegree study, and pass/fail options. Students may receive credit for life, military, and work experience. A B.M.-B.F.A. degree in commercial music is available. There is a freshman honors program on campus.

Faculty/Classroom: Seventy-five percent of faculty are male; 25%, female.

Admissions: About 88% of the 1993–94 applicants were accepted. The ACT scores for the 1993–94 freshman class were as follows: 36% below 21, 30% between 21 and 23, 18% between 24 and 26, 9% between 27 and 28, and 7% above 28.

Requirements: A minimum GPA of 2.0 is required. The SAT I or ACT is required. For the ACT, the minimum acceptable composite score is 20. Candidates for admission should be graduates of an accredited secondary school and have 14 academic credits and 20 Carnegie units. The GED is accepted. Academic preparation should include 4 units in English, 3 in mathematics, 2 each in science, social studies, and foreign language, and 1 in visual and performing arts. An audition is required for music majors. AP and CLEP credits are accepted. Important factors used in the admissions decision are recommendations by school officials, evidence of special talent, advanced placement or honor courses, recommendations by alumni, and personality and other intangible qualities.

Procedure: Freshmen are admitted to all sessions. Entrance exams should be taken in the spring of the junior year or October of the senior year. Applications should be filed by August 1 for fall entry, December 1 for spring entry, and May 1 for summer entry, along with an application fee of $5. Notification is sent on a rolling basis.

Transfer: About 1360 transfer students enrolled in a recent year. For guaranteed admission, applicants should have a GPA of 2.0 and be eligible to return to the last college of regular enrollment. A total of 33 credits out of 132 must be completed at the university.

Visiting: There are regularly scheduled orientations for accepted students throughout July and August. There are guides for informal visits and visitors may sit in on classes and stay overnight at the school. To arrange for a visit, contact June M. Armitage, Director of Admissions/Student Relations, at (800) 669–2678 or (901) 678–2169.

Financial Aid: In a recent year, 42% of all current freshmen and 32% of continuing students received some form of financial aid. Scholarships or need-based grants averaged $1400 ($5000 maximum); loans averaged $2450 ($6625 maximum); and work contracts averaged $1500 ($2200 maximum). The university is a member of CSS. The FAF or FFS (preferred) is required. The deadline for financial aid applications is April 1.

International Students: There are currently 700 international students enrolled. The school actively recruits these students. They must take the TOEFL. The student must also take the SAT I or ACT, and the minimum test score is tied to the applicant's GPA.

Computers: The college provides computer facilities for student use. The mainframes are a DEC VAX 8820 and Sperry Univac. Residence halls have computer sites with mainframe access and Apple Macintosh and IBM microcomputers. There is a PC hookup in all residence hall rooms. Other computer sites include learning laboratories spread throughout the campus. The DEC VAX system is accessible only to graduates and computer students. The fees vary.

Graduates: In a recent year, 1842 bachelor's degrees were awarded.

Admissions Contact: William Akey, Assistant Director of Admissions/Student Relations.

UNIVERSITY OF TENNESSEE SYSTEM

The University of Tennessee system, established in 1794, is a land-grant system. It is governed by a board of trustees, whose chief administrator is president. The primary goals of the system are to provide quality learning, research, and public service opportunities for students from Tennessee and throughout the country. The total enrollment in fall 1993 of all 4 campuses was 42,383; there were 3106 faculty members. Altogether there are 209 baccalaureate, 132 master's, and 67 doctoral programs offered in the University of Tennessee system. Profiles of the 4-year campuses are included in this chapter in alphabetical order with other Tennessee schools.

UNIVERSITY OF TENNESSEE AT CHATTANOOGA

D-4

Chattanooga, TN 37403   (615) 755–4662; (800) UTC-6627 (in-state)

Full-time: 2511 men, 2848 women	Faculty: 285; IIA, -$
Part-time: 763 men, 995 women	Ph.D.s: 78%
Graduate: 544 men, 664 women	Student/Faculty: 19 to 1
Year: semesters, summer session	Tuition: $1770 ($5550)
Application Deadline: August 15	Room & Board: $3605
Freshman Class: 2091 applied, 1338 accepted, 979 enrolled	
SAT I or ACT: required	COMPETITIVE

The University of Tennessee at Chattanooga, founded in 1886, is a public, coeducational institution. Part of the state's university system, it offers programs in liberal and fine arts, business, engineering, health science, military science, and teacher preparation. There are 5 undergraduate and 5 graduate schools. In addition to regional accreditation, UTC has baccalaureate program accreditation with AACSB, ABET, AHEA, APTA, CSWE, NASAD, NASM, NCATE, and NLN. The library contains 424,272 volumes, 1,083,505 microform items, and 5200 audiovisual forms, and subscribes to 3018 periodicals. Computerized library sources and services include the card catalog and interlibrary loans. Special learning facilities include a radio station and an observatory. The 101-acre campus is in an urban area. Including residence halls, there are 60 buildings on campus.

Student Life: About 89% of undergraduates are from Tennessee. Students come from 38 states, 44 foreign countries, and Canada. Eighty-five percent are white; 10% African American. The average age of freshmen is 20.2; all undergraduates, 24.3. Twenty-six percent drop out by the end of their first year; 33% remain to graduate.

Housing: A total of 1306 students can be accommodated in college housing. College-sponsored living facilities include single-sex and coed dormitories, on-campus apartments, and fraternity houses. On-campus housing is available on a first-come, first-served basis. Eighty-four percent of students commute. Alcohol is not permitted. All students may keep cars on campus.

Activities: About 6% of men belong to 6 national fraternities; about 6% of women belong to 6 national sororities. There are 130 groups on campus, including band, cheerleading, chess, choir, chorale, chorus, computers, drama, drill team, ethnic, gay, honors, international, jazz band, literary magazine, marching band, newspaper, orchestra, pep band, photography, political, professional, radio and TV, religious, social, social service, student government, symphony, and yearbook. Popular campus events include Homecoming Week.

Sports: There are 10 intercollegiate sports for men and 6 for women, and 12 intramural sports for men and 7 for women. Athletic and recreation facilities include a gymnasium, an arena, a tennis and racquet center, a swimming pool, and 2 fields, including a soccer field.

Disabled Students: The following facilities are available: wheelchair ramps, elevators, special parking, specially equipped rest rooms, special class scheduling, lowered drinking fountains, and lowered telephones.

Services: In addition to many counseling and information services, tutoring is available in most subjects. There is also a reader service for the blind, and remedial math, reading, and writing.

Campus Safety and Security: Campus safety and security measures include escort service, informal discussions, pamphlets, posters, films, and emergency telephones. In addition, there are lighted pathways and sidewalks and 24-hour vehicle patrol.

Programs of Study: UTC awards the B.A., B.S., B.F.A., B.M., B.S.E., B.S.N., B.S.P.T., and B.S.W. degrees. Master's degrees also are awarded. Bachelor's degrees are awarded in BIOLOGICAL SCIENCE (biology/biological science), BUSINESS (business administration and management and recreation and leisure services), COMMUNICATIONS AND THE ARTS (communications, English, fine arts, French, Greek, Latin, music, and Spanish), COMPUTER AND PHYSICAL SCIENCE (applied mathematics, chemistry, computer science, geology, mathematics, and physics), EDUCATION (art, early childhood, elementary, music, secondary, and special), ENGINEERING AND ENVIRONMENTAL DESIGN (engineering, engineering management, and environmental science), HEALTH PROFESSIONS (medical laboratory technology, nursing, and physical therapy), SOCIAL SCIENCE (American studies, criminal justice, economics, history, home economics, human services, humanities, philosophy, physical fitness/movement, political science/government, psychology, social work, and sociology). Engineering and business are the strongest academically. Business has the largest enrollment.

Required: All students must complete at least 128 semester hours and maintain a minimum GPA of 2.0. General education requirements include 6 hours each in written communication in English and behavioral and social sciences, 9 hours in humanities and fine arts, 4 hours in physical and natural sciences, and 3 hours each in mathematics, and perspectives. A health and physical education course is required in the first year, and another physical education activity course must be taken before graduation. Requirements vary by major.

Special: Cooperative programs are offered in accounting, business systems, chemistry, communications, engineering, environmental studies, nursing, and psychology. UTC offers internships, study abroad in England, work-study and accelerated degree programs, B.A.-B.S. degrees, dual majors, interdisciplinary majors, including theater and speech, 3-2 engineering degrees, and nondegree study. Credit is given for life, military, or work experience. There is a freshman honors program on campus, as well as 30 national honor societies. Twenty-five departments have honors programs.

Faculty/Classroom: Seventy-two percent of faculty are male; 28%, female. The average class size in an introductory lecture is 25.

Admissions: About 64% of the 1993–94 applicants were accepted.

Requirements: A minimum GPA of 2.0 is required. The SAT I or the ACT is required. Secondary school credits should include 4 in English, 3 in mathematics, and 2 each in science, social studies, and a foreign language. The GED is accepted. AP and CLEP credits are accepted. Important factors used in the admissions decision are recommendations by school officials, advanced placement or honor courses, evidence of special talent, extracurricular activities record, and leadership record.

Procedure: Freshmen are admitted to all sessions. Entrance exams should be taken in spring of the junior year. Applications should be filed by August 15 for fall entry and December 15 for spring entry, along with an application fee of $15. Notification is sent on a rolling basis. There is an early admissions plan.

Transfer: About 733 transfer students enrolled in 1993–94. A minimum GPA of 2.0 is required. A total of 30 credits out of 128 must be completed at UTC.

Visiting: There are regularly scheduled orientations for prospective students. There are guides for informal visits and visitors may sit in on classes and stay overnight at the school. To arrange for a visit, contact the Admissions Office at (615) 755–4662 or (800) UTC-6627 (in-state).

Financial Aid: In 1993–94 58% of all current freshmen and 63% of continuing students received some form of financial aid. About 41% of freshmen and 57% of continuing students received need-based aid. The average freshman award was $2100. Of that total, scholarships or need-based grants averaged $1075 ($3656 maximum); loans averaged $1000 ($2625 maximum); and work contracts averaged $800 ($1546 maximum). Seventy-seven percent of undergraduate students work part-time. Average earnings from campus work for the school year are $1650. The average financial indebtedness of the 1992–93 graduate was $5800. The FAFSA financial statement is required. The deadline for financial aid applications is June 1.

International Students: There are currently 164 international students enrolled. The school actively recruits these students. They must take the TOEFL and achieve a minimum score of 500. The student must also take the SAT I or ACT, if available in the student's country.

Computers: The college provides computer facilities for student use. The mainframe is an HP 3000/Series 950. There are no time limits and no fees.

Graduates: In 1992–93 1053 bachelor's degrees were awarded. The most popular majors among graduates were business administration (26%), engineering (7%), and secondary education (7%). Within an average freshman class, 8% graduate in 4 years, 26% in 5 years, and 38% in 6 years. Some 100 companies recruited on campus in a recent year.

Admissions Contact: Patsy Reynolds, Director of Admissions.

UNIVERSITY OF TENNESSEE AT KNOXVILLE
(See University of Tennessee/Knoxville)

UNIVERSITY OF TENNESSEE AT MARTIN   B-2

Martin, TN 38238   (901) 587-7020; (800) 443-UTMI (out-of-state)

Full-time: 2123 men, 2546 women	Faculty: 236; IIA, --$
Part-time: 239 men, 436 women	Ph.D.s: 75%
Graduate: 57 men, 145 women	Student/Faculty: 20 to 1
Year: semesters, summer session	Tuition: $1810 ($5590)
Application Deadline: August 1	Room & Board: $2740
Freshman Class: 1770 applied, 1361 accepted, 1123 enrolled	
ACT: 22	COMPETITIVE

The University of Tennessee at Martin, founded in 1927, is a land-grant, coeducational institution. Part of the state's university system, it

offers programs in liberal and fine arts, agriculture, aviation, business, health science, engineering, military science, professional training, technical studies, teacher preparation, and home economics. There are 5 undergraduate and 3 graduate schools. In addition to regional accreditation, UTM has baccalaureate program accreditation with ABET, ADA, AHEA, CAHEA, CSWE, NASM, NCATE, and NLN. The library contains 350,000 volumes, 143,496 microform items, and 5683 audiovisual forms, and subscribes to 1639 periodicals. Computerized library sources and services include the card catalog. Special learning facilities include a learning resource center, natural history museum, radio station, and TV station. The 200-acre campus is in a small town 100 miles north of Memphis. Including residence halls, there are 38 buildings on campus.

Student Life: About 90% of undergraduates are from Tennessee. Students come from 36 states and 35 foreign countries. Ninety-three percent are from public schools; 8% from private. Eighty-four percent are white; 15% African American. Most are Protestant. The average age of freshmen is 18; all undergraduates, 24. Thirty-six percent drop out by the end of their first year; 40% remain to graduate.

Housing: A total of 2800 students can be accommodated in college housing. College-sponsored living facilities include single-sex and coed dormitories, off-campus apartments, married-student housing, and fraternity houses. In addition there are honors houses. On-campus housing is guaranteed for all 4 years. Sixty-five percent of students live on campus; of those, 65% remain on campus on weekends. Alcohol is not permitted. All students may keep cars on campus.

Activities: About 15% of men belong to 12 national fraternities; about 17% of women belong to 9 national sororities. There are 95 groups on campus, including art, band, cheerleading, choir, chorale, chorus, computers, dance, drama, ethnic, film, honors, international, jazz band, literary magazine, marching band, musical theater, newspaper, opera, orchestra, pep band, photography, professional, radio and TV, religious, social, social service, student government, and yearbook. Popular campus events include Daytona Beach Days, Greekfest, UTM Rodeo-N-Roundup Days, and All-Niter.

Sports: There are 7 intercollegiate sports for men and 7 for women, and 5 intramural sports for men and 4 for women. Athletic and recreation facilities include a physical convocation center, a pavilion, a football stadium, a fitness trail, and a swimming pool.

Disabled Students: The entire campus is accessible to disabled students. The following facilities are available: wheelchair ramps, elevators, special parking, specially equipped rest rooms, special class scheduling, lowered drinking fountains, and lowered telephones.

Services: In addition to many counseling and information services, tutoring is available in every subject, including English, mathematics, accounting, writing, and reading. There is also remedial math, reading, and writing.

Campus Safety and Security: Campus safety and security measures include 24-hour foot and vehicle patrol, self defense education, escort service, and informal discussions. In addition, there are pamphlets, posters, films, emergency telephones, and lighted pathways and sidewalks.

Programs of Study: UTM awards the B.A., B.S., B.A.Mus., B.F.A., B.M.Mus.Ed., B.S.Ag., B.S.B.A., B.S.Chem., B.S.C.J., B.S.Ed., B.S.Eng.Tech., B.S.H.E., B.S.Mus., B.S.N., B.S.NRM., B.S.P.Adm., and B.S.S.W. degrees. Master's degrees also are awarded. Bachelor's degrees are awarded in AGRICULTURE (agricultural business management, agriculture, and animal science), BIOLOGICAL SCIENCE (biology/biological science), BUSINESS (accounting, banking and finance, business administration and management, business economics, international business management, marketing/retailing/merchandising, and personnel management), COMMUNICATIONS AND THE ARTS (communications, English, fine arts, French, music, and Spanish), COMPUTER AND PHYSICAL SCIENCE (chemistry, computer science, geology, and mathematics), EDUCATION (agricultural, art, business, early childhood, elementary, foreign languages, health, home economics, music, science, and secondary), ENGINEERING AND ENVIRONMENTAL DESIGN (civil engineering, civil engineering technology, electrical/electronics engineering technology, engineering technology, and mechanical engineering technology), HEALTH PROFESSIONS (nursing, predentistry, premedicine, and prepharmacy), SOCIAL SCIENCE (criminal justice, dietetics, economics, geography, history, parks and recreation management, political science/government, prelaw, psychology, public administration, social work, and sociology). Engineering technology, computer science, health science, accounting, and chemistry are the strongest academically. Business, accounting, health sciences, nursing, agriculture, and human learning have the largest enrollments.

Required: The total number of credit hours required is at least 130. All students must have at least a 2.0 GPA overall and in the last 30 semester hours. Specific courses and major requirements vary by the program selected.

Special: UTM offers co-op programs, internships, work-study programs, study abroad, B.A.-B.S. degrees, dual and student-designed majors, and pass/fail options. Credit is given for life, military, and

work experience. There is a freshman honors program on campus, as well as 6 national honor societies. Three departments have honors programs.

Faculty/Classroom: Seventy-one percent of faculty are male; 9%, female. All teach undergraduates. No introductory courses are taught by graduate students. The average class size in an introductory lecture is 31; in a laboratory, 16; and in a regular course offering, 25.

Admissions: About 77% of the 1993–94 applicants were accepted. The ACT scores for the 1993–94 freshman class were as follows: 39% below 21, 31% between 21 and 23, 24% between 24 and 26, and 6% between 27 and 28. There were 3 National Merit finalists and 12 semifinalists. Twenty-one freshmen graduated first in their class.

Requirements: The ACT is recommended. Students should have a minimum composite score of 19 on the ACT with a 2.25 GPA or 16 on the ACT with a 2.6 GPA. Candidates for admissions should be graduates of an accredited secondary school with 14 academic credits. The GED is accepted with a 50 score. Secondary school units should include 4 of English, 2 of a foreign language, 3 of mathematics, and 1 each of science, history, social studies, and fine and performing arts. AP and CLEP credits are accepted. Important factors used in the admissions decision are advanced placement or honor courses, recommendations by school officials, evidence of special talent, extracurricular activities record, and recommendations by alumni.

Procedure: Freshmen are admitted to all sessions. Entrance exams should be taken early in the senior year. Applications should be filed by August 1 for fall entry, December 15 for spring entry, and April 1 for summer entry, along with an application fee of $15. Notification is sent on a rolling basis. There are early admissions and deferred admissions plans.

Transfer: About 412 transfer students enrolled in 1993–94. Transfer students should have a minimum GPA of 2.0. An interview is recommended. A total of 30 semester hours out of 130 must be completed at UTM.

Visiting: There are regularly scheduled orientations for prospective students, including a freshman studies week, one week prior to the start of classes. There are guides for informal visits and visitors may sit in on classes and stay overnight at the school. To arrange for a visit, contact the Admissions Office at (800) 829–8861.

Financial Aid: In a recent year, 60% of all students received some form of financial aid. About 55% of freshmen and 65% of continuing students received need-based aid. The average freshman award was $2300. Of that total, scholarships or need-based grants averaged $1250 ($2500 maximum); loans averaged $2000 ($2625 maximum); and work contracts averaged $1800 (maximum). Thirty percent of undergraduate students work part-time. Average earnings from campus work for the school year are $1700. The average financial indebtedness of the 1992–93 graduate was $2500. UTM is a member of CSS. The FAFSA financial statement is required. The priority deadline for financial aid applications is March 1.

International Students: There are currently 301 international students enrolled. The school actively recruits these students. They must take the TOEFL and achieve a minimum score of 500.

Computers: The college provides computer facilities for student use. The mainframes are a DEC PDP 11/70 and an IBM 4361. There are also 56 IBM PS/2s and IBM PCs as well as Apple Macintosh microcomputers available in student laboratories. All students may access the system. It may be used during laboratory hours. There are no time limits and no fees.

Graduates: In 1992–93 742 bachelor's degrees were awarded. The most popular majors among graduates were elementary education (12%), economics (9%), and secondary education (6%). Within an average freshman class, 2% graduate in 3 years, 18% in 4 years, 38% in 5 years, and 45% in 6 years. Some 114 companies recruited on campus in a recent year. In the 1992 graduating class, 20% of all graduates were enrolled in graduate school within 6 months of graduation; 73% had found employment.

Admissions Contact: Paul Kelley, Executive Director of Admissions.

UNIVERSITY OF TENNESSEE KNOXVILLE   E-2

(Formerly University of Tennessee at Knoxville)
Knoxville, TN 37919–0230   (615) 974–2184
                                        (800) 221-VOLS (in-state)

Full-time: 8270 men, 7481 women	Faculty: 1152; I, --$
Part-time: 1500 men, 1737 women	Ph.D.s: 86%
Graduate: 3387 men, 3515 women	Student/Faculty: 14 to 1
Year: semesters, summer session	Tuition: $1982 ($5762)
Application Deadline: July 1	Room & Board: $3686
Freshman Class: 7473 applied, 5372 accepted, 3013 enrolled	
SAT I Verbal/Math: 468/525	ACT: 23 COMPETITIVE

The University of Tennessee/Knoxville, founded in 1794, and the original campus of the state university system, is now a large public institution offering more than 300 graduate and undergraduate programs through 16 schools and colleges. There are 10 undergraduate and 14 graduate schools. In addition to regional accreditation, UT Knoxville has baccalaureate program accreditation with AACSB, ABET, ACEJMC, ADA, AHEA, ASLA, CSWE, FIDER, NAAB, NASAD, NASM, NCATE, NLN, NRPA, and SAF. The 4 libraries contain 2,104,865 volumes, 1,956,384 microform items, and 29,227 audiovisual forms, and subscribe to 14,037 periodicals. Computerized library sources and services include the card catalog, interlibrary loans, and database searching. Special learning facilities include a learning resource center, art gallery, natural history museum, radio station, and TV station. The 526-acre campus is in an urban area 178 miles east of Nashville. Including residence halls, there are 234 buildings on campus.

Student Life: About 88% of undergraduates are from Tennessee. Students come from 50 states, 68 foreign countries, and Canada. Ninety-two percent are white. The average age of all undergraduates is 22.7. Twenty-one percent drop out by the end of their first year; 55% remain to graduate.

Housing: A total of 7728 students can be accommodated in college housing. College-sponsored living facilities include single-sex and coed dormitories, on-campus apartments, married-student housing, and fraternity houses. In addition, there are language houses, special interest houses, sorority housing within a residence hall, and volunteer community and EXCEL, 2 specialized housing programs for freshmen. On-campus housing is available on a first-come, first-served basis. Sixty-five percent of students commute. Alcohol is not permitted. All students may keep cars on campus.

Activities: About 11% of men belong to 26 national fraternities; about 14% of women belong to 18 national sororities. There are 300 groups on campus, including art, band, cheerleading, chess, choir, chorale, chorus, computers, dance, drama, ethnic, film, gay, honors, international, jazz band, literary magazine, marching band, musical theater, newspaper, opera, orchestra, pep band, photography, political, professional, radio and TV, religious, social, student government, symphony, and yearbook. Popular campus events include Homecoming, All-Sing, Carnicus, Torch Night, and International Festival.

Sports: There are 9 intercollegiate sports for men and 8 for women, and 24 intramural sports for men and 24 for women. Athletic and recreation facilities include a 25,000-seat basketball arena, stadium facilities, an Olympic track, Olympic indoor and outdoor pools, and various outdoor facilities.

Disabled Students: Ninety-five percent of the campus is accessible to disabled students. The following facilities are available: wheelchair ramps, elevators, special parking, specially equipped rest rooms, special class scheduling, lowered drinking fountains, and lowered telephones.

Services: In addition to many counseling and information services, tutoring is available in some subjects. In addition, there is a reader service for the blind. Tutoring in mathematics, English, and most lower-division courses can be arranged.

Campus Safety and Security: Campus safety and security measures include 24-hour foot and vehicle patrol, self defense education, escort service, and shuttle buses. In addition, there are informal discussions, pamphlets, posters, and films, emergency telephones, lighted pathways and sidewalks, and campus safety educational programs.

Programs of Study: UT Knoxville awards the B.A., B.S., B.Arch., B.F.A., B.M., and specialized B.S. degrees in 25 fields, including business administration, nursing, and social work. Master's and doctoral degrees also are awarded. Bachelor's degrees are awarded in AGRICULTURE (agricultural economics, agriculture, animal science, fishing and fisheries, forestry and related sciences, and horticulture), BIOLOGICAL SCIENCE (biochemistry, biology/biological science, botany, microbiology, nutrition, and zoology), BUSINESS (accounting, banking and finance, business administration and management, business economics, hotel/motel and restaurant management, management science, marketing/retailing/merchandising, and transportation management), COMMUNICATIONS AND THE ARTS (advertising, art history and appreciation, broadcasting, classics, comparative literature, dramatic arts, English, film arts, fine arts, French, German, graphic design, Italian, journalism, linguistics, music, Russian, Spanish, speech/debate/rhetoric, and studio art), COMPUTER AND PHYSICAL SCIENCE (chemistry, computer science, geology, mathematics, physics, and statistics), EDUCATION (agricultural, art, business, elementary, health, home economics, industrial arts, marketing and distribution, music, physical, recreation, and special), ENGINEERING AND ENVIRONMENTAL DESIGN (aeronautical engineering, agricultural engineering, architecture, chemical engineering, civil engineering, electrical/electronics engineering, engineering, engineering physics, interior design, materials engineering, materials science, mechanical engineering, and nuclear engineering), HEALTH PROFESSIONS (health science, medical laboratory technology, medical records administration/services, nursing, physical therapy, predentistry, premedicine, preveterinary science,

and speech pathology/audiology), SOCIAL SCIENCE (African American studies, American studies, anthropology, Asian/Oriental studies, child care/child and family studies, classical/ancient civilization, economics, food science, geography, history, human services, Latin American studies, medieval studies, philosophy, political science/government, psychology, public administration, religion, Russian and Slavic studies, social work, sociology, textiles and clothing, urban studies, and women's studies). Engineering, physical sciences, English, and physical anthropology are the strongest academically. Business administration has the largest enrollment.

Required: All students must complete at least 120 credits with a minimum 2.0 GPA. Many degree programs require higher credit totals and GPAs. All students take 2 English composition courses and a core curriculum including 2 courses each in mathematical sciences, humanities and the arts, history, social sciences, natural sciences, and foreign language or integrative studies.

Special: Cooperative programs are offered in engineering, communications, liberal arts, and business. Cross-registration is possible through the Academic Common Market, a Southern 14-state consortium, in any of 11 programs. Internships are available in social work, education, and architecture, and there are a number of work-study programs. Study abroad, mostly in Western Europe, is possible. Dual and student-designed majors, accelerated study, nondegree study, and pass/fail options are offered. There is a freshman honors program on campus, as well as 53 national honor societies, including Phi Beta Kappa. Four departments have honors programs.

Faculty/Classroom: Seventy-seven percent of faculty are male; 23%, female. Sixty-seven percent teach undergraduates and 67% both teach and do research. Graduate students teach 28% of introductory courses.

Admissions: About 72% of the 1993–94 applicants were accepted. The SAT scores for the 1993–94 freshman class were as follows: Verbal—63% below 500, 28% between 500 and 599, 8% between 600 and 700, and 1% above 700; Math—38% below 500, 39% between 500 and 599, 18% between 600 and 700, and 5% above 700. The ACT scores were 26% below 21, 49% between 21 and 25, 20% between 26 and 29, and 6% between 30 and 36. About 47% of the current freshmen were in the top fifth of their class; 75% were in the top two fifths. There were 32 National Merit finalists and 32 semifinalists. Nineteen freshmen graduated first in their class.

Requirements: A minimum GPA of 2.0 is required. The SAT I or ACT is required; most applicants take the ACT. Applicants should be high school graduates or have the GED. Required secondary school courses include 4 credits in English, 3 in mathematics, 2 each in science and a single foreign language, and 1 each in history and world history or world geography, and 1 unit of visual/performing arts. AP and CLEP credits are accepted. Important factors used in the admissions decision are advanced placement or honor courses, parents or siblings attending the school, leadership record, geographic diversity, and extracurricular activities record.

Procedure: Freshmen are admitted to all sessions. Entrance exams should be taken in spring of the junior year or fall of the senior year. Applications should be filed by July 1 for fall entry, November 1 for spring entry, and April 1 for summer entry, along with an application fee of $15. Notification is sent on a rolling basis. There is an early admissions plan.

Transfer: About 1500 transfer students enrolled in 1993–94. Transfer applicants should present a minimum 2.0 GPA in previous college work, although many specific programs have higher requirements. A total of 30 credits out of 120 must be completed at UT Knoxville.

Visiting: There are regularly scheduled orientations for prospective students, including 2 open houses yearly where prospective students can meet with faculty, administrators, and students to discuss admissions, housing, financial aid, student activities, academic colleges and departments, and organizations. There are guides for informal visits and visitors may sit in on classes. To arrange for a visit, contact Undergraduate Admissions at (615) 974–2184.

Financial Aid: In 1993–94, 52% of all current freshmen and 88% of continuing students received some form of financial aid, including need-based aid. The average freshman award was $3872. Of that total, scholarships or need-based grants averaged $1000 ($7500 maximum); loans averaged $1637 ($2625 maximum); and work contracts averaged $1276 ($200 maximum). Average earnings from campus work for the school year are $2000. UT Knoxville is a member of CSS. The FAF or FFS is required. The deadline for financial aid applications is April 1.

International Students: There are currently 806 international students enrolled. They must take the TOEFL and achieve a minimum score of 525. The student must also take the SAT I or the ACT.

Computers: The university provides computer facilities for student use. The mainframes are an IBM 3090, 200E, and 3081D, and a DEC VAX cluster. There are also Apple Macintosh, IBM, and DEC microcomputers available throughout the campus. Students can access the library mainframe from apartment or dormitory rooms via modem. Those students enrolled in specific courses with computing accounts

may access the system. The amount of course-related use permitted is determined by department. The fees vary.

Graduates: In 1992–93, 3308 bachelor's degrees were awarded. The most popular majors among graduates were psychology (6%), accounting (5%), and logistics and transportation (4%). Within an average freshman class, 17% graduate in 4 years, 43% in 5 years, and 55% in 6 years. Some 360 companies recruited on campus in 1992–93.

Admissions Contact: Gordon E. Stanley, Director of Admissions.

UNIVERSITY OF THE SOUTH D-4
Sewanee, TN 37375–1000 (615) 598–1238
(800) 522–2234 (out-of-state)

Full-time: 577 men, 552 women	Faculty: 101; IIB, +$
Part-time: 11 men, 13 women	Ph.D.s: 93%
Graduate: 49 men, 28 women	Student/Faculty: 11 to 1
Year: semesters, summer session	Tuition: $14,910
Application Deadline: February 1	Room & Board: $3920
Freshman Class: 1445 applied, 966 accepted, 326 enrolled	
SAT I Verbal/Math: 557/601	ACT: 27 HIGHLY COMPETITIVE

University of the South, founded in 1857, is an independent, coeducational, liberal arts university affiliated with the Episcopal Church. There is one graduate school. The library contains 433,820 volumes, 199,683 microform items, and 8448 audiovisual forms, and subscribes to 2724 periodicals. Computerized library sources and services include the card catalog, interlibrary loans, and database searching. Special learning facilities include a learning resource center, art gallery, and radio station. The 10,000-acre campus is in a small town 45 miles west of Chattanooga and 90 miles southeast of Nashville. Including residence halls, there are 42 buildings on campus.

Student Life: About 78% of undergraduates are from out-of-state, mostly the South. Students come from 45 states, 17 foreign countries, and Canada. Fifty-four percent are from public schools; 46% from private. Ninety-six percent are white. Most are Protestant. The average age of freshmen is 18; all undergraduates, 20. Two percent drop out by the end of their first year; 87% remain to graduate.

Housing: A total of 1061 students can be accommodated in college housing. College-sponsored living facilities include single-sex and coed dormitories, on-campus apartments, and married-student housing. In addition there are language houses. On-campus housing is guaranteed for all 4 years and is available on a lottery system for upperclassmen. Ninety-eight percent of students live on campus; of those, 90% remain on campus on weekends. All students may keep cars on campus.

Activities: About 62% of men belong to 11 national fraternities; about 65% of women belong to 6 local sororities. There are 110 groups on campus, including art, BACCHUS, Big Brother/Big Sister, cheerleading, Community building Community, choir, chorale, chorus, computers, dance, drama, ethnic, gay, honors, international, literary magazine, musical theater, newspaper, orchestra, photography, political, professional, radio and TV, religious, social, social service, student government, and yearbook. Popular campus events include Homecoming, Spring Festival Weekend, BACCHUS Challenge, SAMS, and Rock-A-Like.

Sports: There are 15 intercollegiate sports for men and 13 for women, and 17 intramural sports for men and 13 for women. Athletic and recreation facilities include an indoor pool, indoor and outdoor tennis, racquetball, squash and basketball courts, a multiweather track, an equestrian center and stables, softball, soccer, and baseball fields, a lake and areas for rappelling, caving, hiking, and rock climbing.

Disabled Students: Seventy-five percent of the campus is accessible to disabled students. The following facilities are available: wheelchair ramps, elevators, special parking, specially equipped rest rooms, special class scheduling, special administrative services, and a telecommunications device for the deaf, which is available to both students and visitors.

Services: In addition to many counseling and information services, tutoring is available in most subjects. Study skills training is also offered.

Campus Safety and Security: Campus safety and security measures include 24-hour foot and vehicle patrol, self defense education, escort service, and shuttle buses. In addition, there are informal discussions, pamphlets, posters, films, and lighted pathways and sidewalks.

Programs of Study: Sewanee awards the B.A. and B.S. degrees. Master's and doctoral degrees also are awarded. Bachelor's degrees are awarded in AGRICULTURE (natural resource management), BIOLOGICAL SCIENCE (biology/biological science), COMMUNICATIONS AND THE ARTS (comparative literature, English, fine arts, French, German, Greek, Latin, music, performing arts, Russian, and Spanish), COMPUTER AND PHYSICAL SCIENCE (chemistry, computer science, geology, mathematics, and physics), SOCIAL SCI-

ENCE (American studies, anthropology, economics, German area studies, history, medieval studies, philosophy, political science/government, psychology, religion, Russian and Slavic studies, social science, and Third World studies). English and premedical preparation are the strongest academically. English, economics, history, political science, psychology, and natural resources have the largest enrollments.

Required: All students must complete at least 123 semester hours, 81 of which must be outside the major, with a minimum GPA of 2.0. Students must take a core curriculum including 2 courses each in English, physical education, and philosophy and religion, 4 in social science, 3 in mathematics and science, and 1 each in fine arts and a foreign language at the 300 level. The total number of hours in the major varies. Comprehensive exams in the major field of study are required.

Special: The university offers internships in economics and public affairs, study abroad in 13 countries, a Washington semester, and student-designed majors. Teacher certification and Peace Corps, medical, law, and veterinary preparation are available. A 3–2 engineering degree is offered with Columbia, Washington, and Vanderbilt Universities, Georgia Institute of Technology, and Rensselaer Polytechnic Institute. Pass/fail options are possible. There is a freshman honors program on campus, as well as 10 national honor societies, including Phi Beta Kappa. Twenty-eight departments have honors programs.

Faculty/Classroom: Seventy-seven percent of faculty are male; 23%, female. All teach undergraduates, 90% do research, and 90% do both. No introductory courses are taught by graduate students. The average class size in an introductory lecture is 20; in a laboratory, 16; and in a regular course offering, 12.

Admissions: About 67% of the 1993–94 applicants were accepted. The SAT scores for the 1993–94 freshman class were as follows: Verbal—24% below 500, 45% between 500 and 599, 28% between 600 and 700, and 3% above 700; Math—4% below 500, 46% between 500 and 599, 41% between 600 and 700, and 9% above 700. The ACT scores were 10% between 21 and 23, 35% between 24 and 26, 25% between 27 and 28, and 30% above 28. About 75% of the current freshmen were in the top fifth of their class; 96% were in the top two fifths.

Requirements: The SAT I or ACT is required. Candidates for admission should have 15 secondary school academic credits, 4 years of English, 3 years of mathematics, including algebra I and II and geometry, and 2 years of science, a foreign language, and history or social science. An essay is required and an interview is recommended. AP credits are accepted. Important factors used in the admissions decision are advanced placement or honor courses, leadership record, evidence of special talent, recommendations by school officials, and extracurricular activities record.

Procedure: Freshmen are admitted to all sessions. Entrance exams should be taken by December of the senior year. Early decision applications should be filed by November 15; regular applications, by February 1 for fall entry and December 1 for winter entry, along with an application fee of $35. Notification of early decision is sent December 15; regular decision, April 1. There are early decision, early admissions, and deferred admissions plans. About 74 early decision candidates were accepted for the 1993–94 class. A waiting list is an active part of the admissions procedure, with about 7% of applicants on the list.

Transfer: About 25 transfer students enrolled in 1993–94. Transfer students should have a minimum GPA of 3.0, and take the SAT I or ACT. They must be eligible to continue in their present university. An interview is recommended. A total of 64 credits out of 123 must be completed at Sewanee.

Visiting: There are regularly scheduled orientations for prospective students, including a tour, interview, class visits, and a meeting with a counselor. There are guides for informal visits and visitors may sit in on classes and stay overnight at the school. To arrange for a visit, contact Delores Snowden at (615) 598-1238 or (800) 522-2234.

Financial Aid: In 1993–94 55% of all current freshmen and 57% of continuing students received some form of financial aid. About 39% of freshmen and 44% of continuing students received need-based aid. The average freshman award was $11,136. Of that total, scholarships or need-based grants averaged $8157 (maximim); loans averaged $2328 ($4000 maximum); and work contracts averaged $651 ($1000 maximum). Thirty-seven percent of undergraduate students work part-time. Average earnings from campus work for the school year are $1000. Sewanee is a member of CSS. The FAF, FFS or SFS, and the college's own financial statement are required. The deadline for financial aid applications is March 1.

International Students: There are currently 29 international students enrolled. The school actively recruits these students. They must take the TOEFL and achieve a minimum score of 550. The student must also take the SAT I or the ACT.

Computers: The college provides computer facilities for student use. The mainframes are an HP 3000/947 and an HP 3000/937. There are 65 Apple computers in 7 laboratories for student use. The academic system is networked with all offices and dormitory rooms and can be accessed on or off campus (by modem). All students may access the system. It may be used 24 hours a day. There are no time limits and no fees.

Graduates: In 1992–93, 277 bachelor's degrees were awarded. The most popular majors among graduates were English (17%), psychology (12%), and political science (12%). Within an average freshman class, 1% graduate in 3 years, 87% in 4 years, 88% in 5 years, and 88% in 6 years. Some 40 companies recruited on campus in an earlier year. In an earlier graduating class, 23% of all graduates were enrolled in graduate school within 6 months of graduation; 55% had found employment.

Admissions Contact: Robert M. Hedrick, Director of Admission.

VANDERBILT UNIVERSITY
C-2

Nashville, TN 37212 (615) 322-2561

Full-time: 2953 men, 2609 women	Faculty: 616; I, +$
Part-time: 52 men, 38 women	Ph.D.s: 98%
Graduate: 2196 men, 2005 women	Student/Faculty: 9 to 1
Year: semesters, summer session	Tuition: $17,202
Application Deadline: January 15	Room & Board: $6220
Freshman Class: 7791 applied, 4690 accepted, 1499 enrolled	
SAT I Verbal/Math: 559/640	ACT: 28 HIGHLY COMPETITIVE +

Vanderbilt University, founded in 1873, is a private coeducational university offering programs in liberal and fine arts, business, engineering, health science, military science, religion, law, music, and teacher preparation. There are 4 undergraduate and 6 graduate schools. In addition to regional accreditation, Vanderbilt has baccalaureate program accreditation with AACSB, ABET, CAHEA, and NCATE. The 8 libraries contain 2,085,652 volumes, 150,064 microform items, and 20,731 audiovisual forms, and subscribe to 16,357 periodicals. Computerized library sources and services include the card catalog, interlibrary loans, and database searching. Special learning facilities include a learning resource center, art gallery, radio station, 2 observatories, TV station, and TV news archive. The 330-acre campus is in an urban area less than a mile and a half from downtown Nashville. Including residence halls, there are 140 buildings on campus.

Student Life: About 86% of undergraduates are from out-of-state, mostly the South. Students come from 50 states, 45 foreign countries, and Canada. Sixty percent are from public schools; 40% from private. Eighty-two percent are white. The average age of freshmen is 18; all undergraduates, 20. Eleven percent drop out by the end of their first year; 81% remain to graduate.

Housing: A total of 4617 students can be accommodated in college housing. College-sponsored living facilities include single-sex and coed dormitories, on-campus apartments, and married-student housing. In addition there are language houses and special interest houses. On-campus housing is guaranteed for the freshman year only, is available on a first-come, first-served basis, and is available on a lottery system for upperclassmen. Priority is given to out-of-town students. Eighty-six percent of students live on campus. Upperclassmen may keep cars on campus.

Activities: About 36% of men belong to 17 national fraternities; about 54% of women belong to 12 national sororities. There are 264 groups on campus, including art, band, cheerleading, chess, choir, chorale, chorus, computers, dance, drama, drill team, ethnic, film, gay, honors, international, jazz band, literary magazine, marching band, musical theater, newspaper, opera, orchestra, pep band, photography, political, professional, radio and TV, religious, social, social service, student government, symphony, and yearbook. Popular campus events include Rites of Spring, Blues Fest, IMPACT Speakers Series, Alternative Spring Break, and Homecoming.

Sports: There are 7 intercollegiate sports for men and 6 for women, and 41 intramural sports for men and 40 for women. Athletic and recreation facilities include a gymnasium, a tennis center, a pool, a football field, intramural fields, a new student recreation center, basketball and racquetball courts, a suspended indoor track, and a climbing wall.

Disabled Students: Ninety percent of the campus is accessible to disabled students. The following facilities are available: wheelchair ramps, elevators, special parking, specially equipped rest rooms, special class scheduling, lowered drinking fountains, and lowered telephones.

Services: In addition to many counseling and information services, tutoring is available in most subjects. In addition, there is a reader service for the blind.

Campus Safety and Security: Campus safety and security measures include 24-hour foot and vehicle patrol, escort service, shuttle buses, and informal discussions. In addition, there are pamphlets,

posters, and films, emergency telephones, lighted pathways and sidewalks, a bicycle patrol, and student dorm monitors.

Programs of Study: Vanderbilt awards the B.A., B.S., B.Eng., and B.M. degrees. Master's and doctoral degrees also are awarded. Bachelor's degrees are awarded in BIOLOGICAL SCIENCE (biology/biological science), COMMUNICATIONS AND THE ARTS (classical languages, classics, dramatic arts, English, fine arts, French, German, music, music performance, music theory and composition, Portuguese, Russian, and Spanish), COMPUTER AND PHYSICAL SCIENCE (astronomy, chemistry, computer science, geology, mathematics, and physics), EDUCATION (early childhood, elementary, secondary, and special), ENGINEERING AND ENVIRONMENTAL DESIGN (biomedical engineering, chemical engineering, civil engineering, electrical/electronics engineering, engineering, environmental engineering, and mechanical engineering), SOCIAL SCIENCE (anthropology, cognitive science, economics, history, human development, philosophy, political science/government, psychology, religion, and sociology). Social science, engineering, and English have the largest enrollments.

Required: All students must take at least 120 total credit hours. General requirements vary, as do specific major requirements, depending on the chosen program. A minimum GPA of 2.0 is usually needed. There is a mandatory writing requirement. Students majoring in human development complete an internship in the fall semester of the senior year.

Special: Vanderbilt offers cross-registration with Fisk and Howard universities and Meharry Medical College, study abroad in 8 countries, a Washington semester, B.A.-B.S. degrees, dual and student-designed majors, nondegree study, and pass/fail options. Internships, required for human development majors, are available in human service agencies, city and state government, and businesses. A 3-2 engineering degree is offered with Fisk University. The school belongs to NASA's Tennessee Space Grant Consortium, the Intercollegiate Center for Classical Studies in Rome, the Tennessee Transportation Technology Coalition (research, development, and evaluation of transportation-related initiatives), and the Southeastern Consortium of University Transportation Centers. There is a freshman honors program on campus, as well as 19 national honor societies, including Phi Beta Kappa. Twenty-one departments have honors programs.

Faculty/Classroom: Seventy-five percent of faculty are male; 25%, female. Ninety percent both teach undergraduates and do research. Graduate students teach 10% of introductory courses. The average class size in an introductory lecture is 29; in a laboratory, 29; and in a regular course offering, 22.

Admissions: About 60% of the 1993-94 applicants were accepted. The SAT scores for the 1993-94 freshman class were as follows: Verbal—19% below 500, 50% between 500 and 599, 27% between 600 and 700, and 4% above 700; Math—3% below 500, 23% between 500 and 599, 52% between 600 and 700, and 22% above 700. The ACT scores were 2% between 17 and 20, 22% between 21 and 25, and 76% above 26. About 87% of the current freshmen were in the top fifth of their class; 98% were in the top two fifths. There were 85 National Merit finalists. About 100 freshmen graduated first in their class.

Requirements: The SAT I or ACT is required. SAT II: Subject tests are required in mathematics level I, II or IIc, writing, and 1 other area. Admission requirements vary by school. Candidates should be graduates of an accredited secondary school with 15 academic credits. The GED is accepted. Arts and science programs require 4 years of English, 3 years of mathematics, 3 of a foreign language, and recommend 2 of history and 1 of social studies. An essay is required. An audition is required when appropriate. AP credits are accepted. Important factors used in the admissions decision are advanced placement or honor courses, recommendations by school officials, evidence of special talent, extracurricular activities record, and personality, intangible qualities.

Procedure: Freshmen are admitted in the fall. Entrance exams should be taken in the spring of the junior year or the fall of the senior year. Early decision applications should be filed by November 1; regular applications, by January 15 for fall entry, along with an application fee of $50. Notification of early decision is sent December 15; regular decision, April 1. There are early decision, early admissions, and deferred admissions plans. About 150 early decision candidates were accepted for the 1993-94 class. A waiting list is an active part of the admissions procedure.

Transfer: About 80 transfer students enrolled in 1993-94. Transfers must take the SAT I or ACT. A minimum of 24 hours of college credits must have been earned. Students must meet all freshman requirements and be in good standing at the previous institution attended. A total of 60 credits out of 120 must be completed at Vanderbilt.

Visiting: There are regularly scheduled orientations for prospective students. Group information sessions are available Monday through Saturday. Campus tours are given daily. There are guides for informal visits and visitors may sit in on classes and stay overnight at the school. To arrange for a visit, contact the Office of Undergraduate Admissions at (615) 322-2561.

Financial Aid: In 1993-94, 55% of all current freshmen and 47% of continuing students received some form of financial aid. About 38% of freshmen and 33% of continuing students received need-based aid. The average freshman award was $17,489. Of that total, scholarships or need-based grants averaged $12,020 ($23,730 maximum); loans averaged $3979 ($6000 maximum); and work contracts averaged $1556 ($1600 maximum). Twenty-eight percent of undergraduate students work part-time. Average earnings from campus work for the school year are $1239. The average financial indebtedness of the 1992-93 graduate was $11,135. Vanderbilt is a member of CSS. The college's own financial statement, tax return information, and FAFSA are required. The deadline for financial aid applications is February 15.

International Students: There are currently 607 international students enrolled. The school actively recruits these students. They must take the TOEFL and achieve a minimum score of 570. The student must also take the SAT I or the ACT. Students must take SAT II: Subject tests in writing, mathematics, and 1 other subject.

Computers: The university provides computer facilities for student use. The mainframe is a DEC VAX 8800. About 400 computer terminal/PCs are located in the computer center, laboratories, libraries, and dormitories. They are networked through Bitnet and Internet (WAN), and include DOS and Appletalk (LAN). Six computer languages and 48 software packages are available. All students may access the system more than 80 hours per week. There are no time limits on using the system. Fees for using the system vary.

Graduates: In 1992-93, 1207 bachelor's degrees were awarded. The most popular majors among graduates were human development (11%), economics (10%), and English (10%). Within an average freshman class, 1% graduate in 3 years, 73% in 4 years, 80% in 5 years, and 81% in 6 years. Some 206 companies recruited on campus in a recent year.

Admissions Contact: Neill Sanders, Dean of Undergraduate Admissions.

WILLIAM JENNINGS BRYAN COLLEGE
(See Bryan College)

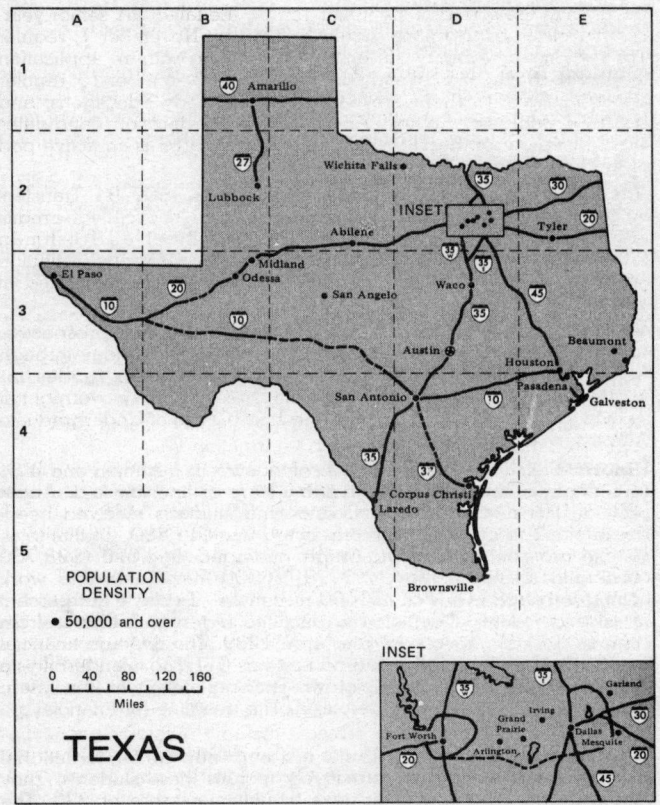

POPULATION DENSITY

● 50,000 and over

0 40 80 120 160
Miles

TEXAS

INSET

ABILENE CHRISTIAN UNIVERSITY   C-2

Abilene, TX 79699   (915) 674-2650; (800) 888-0228 (out-of-state)

Full-time: 1439 men, 1450 women	**Faculty:** 157; IIA, --$
Part-time: 242 men, 254 women	**Ph.D.s:** 76%
Graduate: 406 men, 278 women	**Student/Faculty:** 18 to 1
Year: semesters, summer session	**Tuition:** $7370
Application Deadline: open	**Room & Board:** $3090

Freshman Class: 1381 applied, 1379 accepted, 856 enrolled
SAT I Verbal/Math: 430/490   **ACT:** 21   **NONCOMPETITIVE**

Abilene Christian University, founded in 1906, is a private nonprofit, coeducational institution affiliated with the Church of Christ. The university offers programs in biblical studies, business, liberal and fine arts, professional studies, and natural and applied science. There are 3 undergraduate schools and one graduate school. In addition to regional accreditation, Abilene Christian has baccalaureate program accreditation with CSWE, NASM, and NLN. The library contains 493,387 volumes, 785,266 microform items, and 37,997 audiovisual forms, and subscribes to 2347 periodicals. Computerized library sources and services include the card catalog, interlibrary loans, and database searching. Special learning facilities include a learning resource center, art gallery, planetarium, radio station, and TV station. The 208-acre campus is in a suburban area 150 miles west of the Dallas-Forth Worth metroplex. Including residence halls, there are 45 buildings on campus.

Student Life: About 68% of undergraduates are from Texas. Students come from 50 states, 52 foreign countries, and Canada. Ninety-two percent are from public schools; 8% from private. Eighty-three percent are white. Most are Protestant. The average age of freshmen is 19; all undergraduates, 23. Fifteen percent drop out by the end of their first year; 46% remain to graduate.

Housing: A total of 2163 students can be accommodated in college housing. College-sponsored living facilities include single-sex dormitories, on-campus apartments, and married-student housing. On-campus housing is guaranteed for all 4 years. Alcohol is not permitted. All students may keep cars on campus.

Activities: There are no fraternities or sororities on campus. There are 75 groups on campus, including art, band, cheerleading, choir, chorale, chorus, computers, drama, ethnic, film, honors, international, jazz band, literary magazine, marching band, musical theater, newspaper, opera, orchestra, pep band, photography, political, professional, radio and TV, religious, social, social service, student govern-

ment, symphony, and yearbook. Popular campus events include Sing Song Festival, Bible lectures, Homecoming Musical, Freshman Follies, and Parents Day.

Sports: There are 6 intercollegiate sports for men and 4 for women, and 42 intramural sports for men and 41 for women. Athletic and recreation facilities include a coliseum, 2 stadiums (one of them for track), tennis, racquetball and handball courts, soccer and baseball fields, an indoor swimming pool, and gymnasiums.

Disabled Students: The entire campus is accessible to disabled students. The following facilities are available: wheelchair ramps, elevators, special parking, specially equipped rest rooms, special class scheduling, lowered drinking fountains, and lowered telephones.

Services: In addition to many counseling and information services, tutoring is available in every subject. There is also a reader service for the blind, and remedial math, reading, and writing.

Campus Safety and Security: Campus safety and security measures include 24-hour foot and vehicle patrol, self defense education, escort service, and informal discussions. In addition, there are pamphlets, posters, films, emergency telephones, and lighted pathways and sidewalks. Fire safety discussions are also held.

Programs of Study: Abilene Christian awards the B.A., B.S., B.B.A., B.F.A., B.M., B.S.H.E., and B.S.N. degrees. Associate, master's, and doctoral degrees also are awarded. Bachelor's degrees are awarded in AGRICULTURE (animal science), BIOLOGICAL SCIENCE (biochemistry, biology/biological science, and microbiology), BUSINESS (accounting, banking and finance, management science, and marketing/retailing/merchandising), COMMUNICATIONS AND THE ARTS (advertising, broadcasting, communications, design, dramatic arts, English, fine arts, French, German, Greek, journalism, music, Spanish, and speech/debate/rhetoric), COMPUTER AND PHYSICAL SCIENCE (chemistry, computer science, information sciences and systems, mathematics, and physics), EDUCATION (art, business, early childhood, elementary, foreign languages, home economics, industrial arts, middle school, music, science, secondary, and teaching English as a second language/foreign language), HEALTH PROFESSIONS (nursing, predentistry, premedicine, and speech pathology/audiology), SOCIAL SCIENCE (criminal justice, history, international relations, political science/government, prelaw, psychology, religion, social science, and social work). Education, business, communication, Bible, and physical sciences are the strongest programs academically and have the largest enrollments.

Required: To graduate, students must complete courses in Bible, science, English, history, behavioral science, communication, physical education (4 hours), fine arts, and mathematics. Thirty-three semester hours of advanced work must be taken and a minimum 2.0 GPA maintained. A minimum of 128 credit hours is needed, more in some programs, plus 30 to 64 hours in the major, 18 of which must be upper division.

Special: The university offers cross-registration with Hardin-Simmons, McMurry, and Texas Tech Universities, study abroad in England, France, and Spain, and work-study programs with Dow Chemical. Dual majors and credit for military training are available. Parallel internships are possible in business and communications, as are B.A.-B.S. degrees in Bible, biology, chemistry, communication, computer science, and mathematics. A 3-2 engineering degree is offered with the University of Texas at Dallas. Student-designed majors (interdisciplinary studies) are available. There is a freshman honors program on campus, as well as 8 national honor societies. Twenty-five departments have honors programs.

Faculty/Classroom: Seventy-eight percent of faculty are male; 22%, female. Thirty percent teach undergraduates, 2% do research, and 68% do both. Graduate students teach 1% of introductory courses. The average class size in an introductory lecture is 25; in a laboratory, 14; and in a regular course offering, 21.

Admissions: Nearly all of the 1993-94 applicants were accepted. The SAT scores for the 1993-94 freshman class were as follows: Verbal—71% below 500, 20% between 500 and 599, 8% between 600 and 700, and 1% above 700; Math—48% below 500, 32% between 500 and 599, 16% between 600 and 700, and 4% above 700. The ACT scores were 45% below 21, 27% between 21 and 23, 15% between 24 and 26, 6% between 27 and 28, and 7% above 28. About 39% of the current freshmen were in the top fifth of their class; 59% were in the top two fifths. There were 10 National Merit finalists and 10 semifinalists. About 10 freshmen graduated first in their class.

Requirements: Abilene Christian requires applicants to be in the upper 75% of their class. The SAT I or ACT is required with a minimum composite score of 19 on the ACT. SAT II: Subject tests in English composition and essay, mathematics level II, and foreign language (French, German, Spanish, or Latin) are required. Applicants must be graduates of an accredited secondary school or have the GED and have completed 22 academic credits, including 4 in En-

glish, 2 each in mathematics and science, and 1 each in history and social studies. Two years of the same foreign language are required. Art majors need to submit a portfolio, and music majors must audition. AP and CLEP credits are accepted. Important factors used in the admissions decision are evidence of special talent, leadership record, personality, intangible qualities, recommendations by school officials, and extracurricular activities record.

Procedure: Freshmen are admitted to all sessions. Entrance exams should be taken in October of the senior year. Application deadlines are open. The application fee is $25. Notification is sent on a rolling basis. There is a deferred admissions plan. A waiting list is an active part of the admissions procedure, with about 15% of applicants on the list.

Transfer: About 200 transfer students enrolled in 1993–94. Transfer students must be in good standing at previously attended universities/colleges and have a minimum 2.0 GPA. A minimum composite ACT score of 19 is required for students with fewer than 64 semester hours. A maximum of 64 semester hours from community or junior colleges will be accepted. An interview is recommended. A total of 24 credits out of 128 must be completed at Abilene Christian.

Visiting: There are regularly scheduled orientations for prospective students, including tours and interviews with faculty, administrators, and admissions/financial aid counselors. There are guides for informal visits and visitors may sit in on classes and stay overnight at the school. To arrange for a visit, contact Elaine Roberson, Coordinator of Welcome Center at (915) 674–2650.

Financial Aid: In 1993–94 69% of all current freshmen and 60% of continuing students received some form of financial aid. About 47% of freshmen and 40% of continuing students received need-based aid. The average freshman award was $7278. Of that total, scholarships or need-based grants averaged $3832 ($11,200 maximum); loans averaged $3681 ($7500 maximum); and work contracts averaged $1840 ($2400 maximum). Twenty percent of undergraduate students work part-time. Average earnings from campus work for the school year are $1526. The average financial indebtedness of the 1992–93 graduate was $12,500. Abilene Christian is a member of CSS. The FAF, FFS or SFS, and any federally approved financial statement are accepted. The deadline for financial aid applications is March 1.

International Students: There are currently 152 international students enrolled. The school actively recruits these students. They must take the TOEFL or the college's own test and achieve a minimum score on the TOEFL of 525. The student must also take the SAT I or the ACT and achieve a minimum composite score on the SAT I of 800 or the ACT 19.

Computers: The college provides computer facilities for student use. The mainframes are a DEC VAX 11/785 4000/500 and 4000/200. Students have access to more than 400 terminals and PCs in both open and departmental laboratories. IBM PC access is primarily through business, communication, and computer science departmental laboratories. Apple Macintosh laboratories are available through education, English, art, journalism and mass communication, foreign language, music, home economics, family studies departments, and a Learning Enhancement Center. Mainframe access is through the computer science department laboratory and an open laboratory. All students may access the system. Some students have 24-hour-a-day access; all others may use the system from 9 A.M. to 11 P.M. Monday through Friday, 9 A.M. to 4 P.M. Saturday, and 2 P.M. to 5 P.M. Sunday. There are no time limits and no fees.

Graduates: In an earlier year, bachelor's degrees were awarded. The most popular majors among graduates were elementary education (13%), human communication (9%), and accounting (8%). Within an average freshman class, 5% graduate in 3 years, 30% in 4 years, 45% in 5 years, and 46% in 6 years. Some 100 companies recruited on campus in an earlier year. In the 1992 graduating class, 60% of the men and 40% of the women were enrolled in graduate school within 6 months of graduation; all graduates had found employment.

Admissions Contact: Don King, Director of Field Recruiting.

AMBASSADOR COLLEGE
Big Sandy, TX 75755
Recognized candidate for accreditation

E-2

(903) 636–2190

Full-time: 528 men, 559 women	Faculty: 72
Part-time: 14 men, 9 women	Ph.D.s: 22%
Graduate: none	Student/Faculty: 15 to 1
Year: semesters, summer session	Tuition: $2716
Application Deadline: February 1	Room & Board: $1375

Freshman Class: 682 applied, 381 accepted, 342 enrolled
SAT I Verbal/Math: 490/520

COMPETITIVE

Ambassador College, founded in 1947, is a private institution affiliated with the Worldwide Church of God, offering undergraduate degree programs in business administration, management information systems, home economics, English, and liberal studies. The library contains 144,490 volumes, 49,300 microform items, and 5652 audio-

visual forms, and subscribes to 1300 periodicals. Computerized library sources and services include the card catalog and database searching. Special learning facilities include a radio station and archaeology exhibits. The 347-acre campus is in a rural area 23 miles north of Tyler and 100 miles east of Dallas. Including residence halls, there are 321 buildings on campus.

Student Life: About 88% of undergraduates are from out-of-state. Students come from 47 states, 42 foreign countries, and Canada. Seventy-four percent are white; 20% foreign nationals. Most are members of the school's denomination. The average age of freshmen is 19; all undergraduates, 21.4.

Housing: A total of 1077 students can be accommodated in college housing. College-sponsored living facilities include single-sex dormitories and married-student housing. On-campus housing is guaranteed for all 4 years. Ninety-four percent of students live on campus; of those, all remain on campus on weekends. Alcohol is not permitted. All students may keep cars on campus.

Activities: There are no fraternities or sororities on campus. There are 11 groups on campus, including band, cheerleading, chorale, international, jazz band, literary magazine, newspaper, orchestra, pep band, radio and TV, social, student government, and yearbook. Popular campus events include Charter Day (homecoming), Senior Dinner, Alumni Homecoming, Thanksgiving Ball, Freshamn Reception, Speech Banquet, Barn Dance, and Graduation Ball.

Sports: There are 7 intercollegiate sports for men and 5 for women, and 5 intramural sports for men and 4 for women. Athletic and recreation facilities include 3 softball diamonds, a soccer field, tennis and racquetball courts, 2 gymnasiums, and a running track. Lake Lona, a 9-hole golf course, a driving range, and a shooting range are adjacent to the campus.

Disabled Students: Fourteen percent of the campus is accessible to disabled students. The following facilities are available: wheelchair ramps, elevators, special parking, specially equipped rest rooms, lowered drinking fountains, lowered telephones for the hearing impaired, and Braille markings for elevators.

Services: In addition to many counseling and information services, tutoring is available in some subjects, including biology, accounting, business, and mathematics. There is also remedial math and writing.

Campus Safety and Security: Campus safety and security measures include 24-hour foot and vehicle patrol, self defense education, escort service, and shuttle buses. In addition, there are informal discussions, pamphlets, posters, films, emergency telephones, lighted pathways and sidewalks, an evacuation plan, fire drills, and forums on safety.

Programs of Study: AC awards the B.A. and B.S. degrees. Associate degrees also are awarded. Bachelor's degrees are awarded in BUSINESS (business administration and management and management information systems), COMMUNICATIONS AND THE ARTS (English), SOCIAL SCIENCE (home economics and liberal arts/general studies). Liberal studies and business administration have the largest enrollments.

Required: General education requirements include 24 units in theology, 14 in humanities and fine arts, 8 in communications, 6 in natural sciences and mathematics, 5 in social/behavioral sciences, and 4 in physical education. Students must demonstrate proficiency in computer skills through examination or coursework, complete capstone courses in the major (or a senior thesis for English majors), and pass a comprehensive examination. To graduate, students must complete 128 credit hours including 24 in upper-division courses in the major, with a minimum GPA of 2.0.

Special: Internships are available for business majors.

Faculty/Classroom: Seventy-seven percent of faculty are male; 23%, female. Ninety percent teach undergraduates and 10% both teach and do research. The average class size in an introductory lecture is 149; in a laboratory, 14; and in a regular course offering, 30.

Admissions: About 56% of the 1993–94 applicants were accepted. The SAT scores for the 1993–94 freshman class were as follows: Verbal—58% below 500, 30% between 500 and 599, 11% between 600 and 700, and 1% above 700; Math—42% below 500, 36% between 500 and 599, 20% between 600 and 700, and 2% above 700. About 10 freshmen graduated first in their class.

Requirements: The SAT I is required. In addition, students must submit a high school transcript or GED results and a personal essay. An academic counselor's evaluation is recommended, and an interview is required. AP and CLEP credits are accepted. Important factors used in the admissions decision are leadership record, evidence of special talent, personality, intangible qualities, ability to finance college education, and advanced placement or honor courses.

Procedure: Freshmen are admitted in the fall. Entrance exams should be taken by the end of January of the senior year. Applications should be filed by February 1 for fall entry, November 1 for spring entry, and May 1 for summer entry, along with an application fee of $35. Notification is sent on a rolling basis. A waiting list is an active part of the admissions procedure, with about 7% of applicants on the list.

Transfer: About 80 transfer students enrolled in 1993–94. A total of 30 credits out of 128 must be completed at AC.

Visiting: There are regularly scheduled orientations for prospective students. There are guides for informal visits and visitors may sit in on classes and stay overnight at the school. To arrange for a visit, contact the Student Services Department at (903) 636–2000.

Financial Aid: Ninety-five percent of undergraduate students work part-time. Average earnings from campus work for the school year are $2975. The FAFSA financial statement is required.

International Students: There are currently 253 international students enrolled. They must take the TOEFL and achieve a minimum score of 480.

Computers: The college provides computer facilities for student use. The mainframe is an IBM AS400. There are 100 microcomputers distributed among 3 computer laboratories, with additional microcomputers located in offices throughout the campus, all connected via Novell Netware. All students may access the system for 2-hour blocks during computer laboratory hours of 8 A.M. to 11 P.M. The fees are $20 per student per semester.

Graduates: In 1992–93, 247 bachelor's degrees were awarded. The most popular majors among graduates were theology (45%), business administration (27%), and home economics (11%). In the 1992 graduating class, 22% of the men were enrolled in graduate school within 6 months of graduation.

Admissions Contact: H. Jnay Marlett, Associate Director of Admissions.

ANGELO STATE UNIVERSITY

C-3

San Angelo, TX 76909   (915) 942–2041

Full-time: 1942 men, 2248 women	Faculty: 202; IIB, av$
Part-time: 659 men, 853 women	Ph.D.s: 67%
Graduate: 169 men, 229 women	Student/Faculty: 21 to 1
Year: semesters	Tuition: $1584 ($5664)
Application Deadline: August 5	Room & Board: $3592
Freshman Class: 3540 applied, 2001 accepted, 1016 enrolled	
SAT I: 439/507	ACT: 22 COMPETITIVE

Angelo State University, founded in 1928, and part of the Texas State University System, offers degrees through the colleges of liberal and fine arts, professional studies, and sciences. There are 3 undergraduate schools and one graduate school. In addition to regional accreditation, ASU has baccalaureate program accreditation with NASM and NLN. The library contains 440,098 volumes, 502,815 microform items, and 3835 audiovisual forms, and subscribes to 2018 periodicals. Special learning facilities include a planetarium. The 268-acre campus is in a small town 200 miles west of Austin. Including residence halls, there are 48 buildings on campus.

Student Life: About 94% of undergraduates are from Texas. Students come from 45 states, 27 foreign countries, and Canada. Ninety-eight percent are from public schools; 2% from private. Eighty percent are white; 14% Hispanic. The average age of freshmen is 19; all undergraduates, 24. About 73% of freshmen remain to graduate.

Housing: A total of 1608 students can be accommodated in college housing. College-sponsored living facilities include single-sex dormitories, on-campus apartments, and married-student housing. On-campus housing is guaranteed for all 4 years and is available on a first-come, first-served basis. Seventy-two percent of students commute. Alcohol is not permitted. All students may keep cars on campus.

Activities: About 3% of men belong to 3 national fraternities; about 1% of women belong to 3 national sororities. There are 75 groups on campus, including art, band, cheerleading, choir, chorale, computers, dance, drama, drill team, ethnic, film, honors, international, jazz band, marching band, musical theater, newspaper, opera, pep band, political, professional, radio and TV, religious, social, student government, and yearbook. Popular campus events include Homecoming.

Sports: There are 4 intercollegiate sports each for men and women, and 12 intramural sports each for men and women. Athletic and recreation facilities include a gymnasium, a multipurpose sports complex, racquetball, basketball, volleyball, badminton, and tennis courts, and a 25-meter Olympic-size pool. The campus stadium seats 17,500, and the indoor gymnasium 4000.

Disabled Students: Nearly all of the campus is accessible to disabled students. The following facilities are available: wheelchair ramps, elevators, special parking, specially equipped rest rooms, special class scheduling, lowered drinking fountains, and lowered telephones.

Services: In addition to many counseling and information services, tutoring is available in some subjects, including mathematics and English. There is also remedial math, reading, and writing.

Campus Safety and Security: Campus safety and security measures include 24-hour foot and vehicle patrol and lighted pathways and sidewalks.

Programs of Study: ASU awards the B.A., B.S., B.A.M., B.B.A., and B.S.N. degrees. Associate and master's degrees also are awarded. Bachelor's degrees are awarded in AGRICULTURE (animal science), BIOLOGICAL SCIENCE (biology/biological science), BUSINESS (accounting, banking and finance, business administration and management, business economics, management science, and marketing/retailing/merchandising), COMMUNICATIONS AND THE ARTS (communications, dramatic arts, English, fine arts, French, journalism, music, Spanish, and speech/debate/rhetoric), COMPUTER AND PHYSICAL SCIENCE (chemistry, computer science, geology, mathematics, and physics), EDUCATION (art, business, early childhood, elementary, foreign languages, guidance, middle school, music, science, secondary, and special), HEALTH PROFESSIONS (medical laboratory technology, nursing, predentistry, and premedicine), SOCIAL SCIENCE (criminal justice, economics, history, interdisciplinary studies, political science/government, psychology, religion, and sociology). Business-related programs has the largest enrollment.

Required: To graduate, students must complete a total of 130 semester hours with a minimum GPA of 2.0 (2.5 for all programs leading to teacher certification). Between 30 and 36 hours are required in the major. General education core courses must be taken in English, government, history, modern language, and physical education. Students must also fulfill distributional requirements of 6 to 8 credits each in art, communication, drama, journalism, music, and philosophy; economics, geography, linguistics, psychology, sociology; and laboratory science.

Special: ASU offers co-op programs with the University of Texas at El Paso; internships in psychology, public administration, and journalism; work-study programs; and a 3–2 engineering degree. There are 8 national honor societies on campus. One department has an honors program.

Faculty/Classroom: Sixty-three percent of faculty are male; 37%, female. All teach undergraduates. Graduate students teach 3% of introductory courses. The average class size in an introductory lecture is 28; in a laboratory, 16; and in a regular course offering, 24.

Admissions: About 57% of the 1993–94 applicants were accepted. The SAT scores for the 1993–94 freshman class were as follows: Verbal—74% below 500, 19% between 500 and 599, 6% between 600 and 700, and 1% above 700; Math—46% below 500, 34% between 500 and 599, 18% between 600 and 700, and 2% above 700. The ACT scores were 43% below 21, 28% between 21 and 23, 17% between 24 and 26, 5% between 27 and 28, and 7% above 28. About 54% of the current freshmen were in the top fifth of their class; 89% were in the top two fifths.

Requirements: The SAT I or ACT is required. Applicants must be graduates of an accredited secondary school or have the GED. AP and CLEP credits are accepted. Important factors used in the admissions decision are advanced placement or honor courses, extracurricular activities record, recommendations by school officials, leadership record, personality, and intangible qualities.

Procedure: Freshmen are admitted to all sessions. Entrance exams should be taken during the spring of the junior year or fall of the senior year. Applications should be filed by August 5 for fall entry, January 2 for spring entry, and May for summer entry. Notification is sent on a rolling basis. There are early decision and early admissions plans.

Transfer: About 393 transfer students enrolled in 1993–94. Transfer students must have a minimum 2.0 GPA; those with fewer than 18 hours must meet high school admission requirements. A total of 30 semester hours out of 130 must be completed at ASU.

Visiting: There are regularly scheduled orientations for prospective students. There are guides for informal visits and visitors may sit in on classes and stay overnight at the school. To arrange for a visit, contact the Office of University Affairs at (915) 942–2117.

Financial Aid: In 1993–94, 80% of all current freshmen and 46% of continuing students received some form of financial aid. About 80% of freshmen and 46% of continuing students received need-based aid. Scholarships or need-based grants averaged $1954 ($4500 maximum); loans averaged $2718 ($3000 maximum); and work contracts averaged $1600. Six percent of undergraduate students work part-time. ASU is a member of CSS. The FFS is required. The deadline for financial aid applications is July 15.

International Students: There are currently 81 international students enrolled. They must take the TOEFL and achieve a minimum score of 550. The student must also take the SAT I or the ACT.

Computers: The college provides computer facilities for student use. The mainframes are an IBM 4381 and 4341. Students may access 200 microcomputers located in 6 microcomputer laboratories on campus. The microcomputers include IBM PC and PS/2, Tandy, HP, Apple, and Apple Macintosh systems. All students may access the system. There are no time limits on using the system. The fees are $3 per semester credit hour.

Graduates: In 1992–93, 632 bachelor's degrees were awarded. The most popular majors among graduates were business (22%), social sciences (13%), and teacher education (10%). Within an average

freshman class, 20% graduate in 4 years, 25% in 5 years, and 28% in 6 years. Some 25 companies recruited on campus in 1992–93.

Admissions Contact: Manuel R. Lujan, Dean of Admissions and Registrar.

AUSTIN COLLEGE
D-2

Sherman, TX 75090 (903) 813–2387; (800) 442–5363 (out-of-state)

Full-time: 543 men, 578 women	Faculty: 84; IIB, +$
Part-time: 5 men, 9 women	Ph.D.s: 95%
Graduate: 7 men, 29 women	Student/Faculty: 13 to 1
Year: 4–1-4, summer session	Tuition: $10,865
Application Deadline: December 1, February 1, and March 1	Room & Board: $4134

Freshman Class: 948 applied, 798 accepted, 295 enrolled

SAT I Verbal/Math: 498/554   ACT: 24   **VERY COMPETITIVE**

Austin College, founded in 1849, is a private liberal arts institution affiliated with the Presbyterian Church USA, offering programs in business, liberal arts, and health. There is one graduate school. The library contains 385,005 volumes, 134,040 microform items, and 2831 audiovisual forms, and subscribes to 943 periodicals. Computerized library sources and services include the card catalog, interlibrary loans, and database searching. Special learning facilities include a learning resource center, a social science laboratory, television studios for media instruction, and televised instruction through a network of universities and colleges. The 65-acre campus is in a suburban area 60 miles north of Dallas. Including residence halls, there are 28 buildings on campus.

Student Life: About 90% of undergraduates are from Texas. Students come from 28 states and 16 foreign countries. Ninety percent are from public schools; 10% from private. Seventy-eight percent are white. Sixty percent are Protestant; 17% Catholic. The average age of freshmen is 18; all undergraduates, 20. Seventeen percent drop out by the end of their first year; 70% remain to graduate.

Housing: A total of 957 students can be accommodated in college housing. College-sponsored living facilities include single-sex and coed dormitories and on-campus apartments. In addition there are language houses. On-campus housing is guaranteed for all 4 years. Sixty-seven percent of students live on campus; of those, 60% remain on campus on weekends. All students may keep cars on campus.

Activities: About 19% of men belong to 9 local fraternities; about 21% of women belong to 6 local sororities. There are 35 groups on campus, including art, cheerleading, choir, drama, ethnic, film, honors, international, jazz band, literary magazine, musical theater, newspaper, pep band, photography, political, professional, radio and TV, religious, social, social service, student government, symphony, and yearbook. Popular campus events include Spring Fest Weekend, Christmas Pops, Oktoberfest, Film Series, Christmas Dance (Alpha Ski Lodge), and All Greek Dance.

Sports: There are 8 intercollegiate sports for men and 5 for women, and 5 intramural sports for men and 5 for women. Athletic and recreation facilities include an 1100-seat gymnasium, athletic center, athletic field, 2000-seat auditorium, indoor swimming pool, and 2 stadiums, one for tennis and the other seating 2100.

Disabled Students: Ninety-nine percent of the campus is accessible to disabled students. The following facilities are available: wheelchair ramps, elevators, special parking, specially equipped rest rooms, special class scheduling, and lowered drinking fountains.

Services: In addition to many counseling and information services, tutoring is available in some subjects.

Campus Safety and Security: Campus safety and security measures include 24-hour foot and vehicle patrol, self defense education, escort service, and informal discussions. In addition, there are pamphlets, posters, films, emergency telephones, and lighted pathways and sidewalks.

Programs of Study: AC awards the B.A. degree. Master's degrees also are awarded. Bachelor's degrees are awarded in BIOLOGICAL SCIENCE (biology/biological science), BUSINESS (business administration and management), COMMUNICATIONS AND THE ARTS (classics, communications, English, fine arts, French, German, music, and Spanish), COMPUTER AND PHYSICAL SCIENCE (chemistry, mathematics, and physics), EDUCATION (physical), SOCIAL SCIENCE (American studies, economics, history, interdisciplinary studies, international studies, Latin American studies, philosophy, political science/government, psychology, religion, and sociology). Chemistry, biology, international studies, and psychology are the strongest academically. Business administration, psychology, biology, political science, and English have the largest enrollments.

Required: Core requirements for graduation include Freshman Communication Inquiry and 3 Heritage of Western Culture courses, 8 courses distributed among the arts, social sciences, natural sciences, meaning and values, formal reasoning, language and written expression, historical/social perspective, and social policy/values/ decision making. Students must have a minimum 2.0 GPA and a total of 34 course credits (136 semester hours), with 7 to 11 credit hours

in the major. Students must complete a physical profile and activity course and at least 8 of the last 11 course credits at AC.

Special: AC offers co-op programs with Central College and the Institute for European Studies, internships during the January and summer terms through academic departments and the Individual Study Off-Campus Program, study abroad in 10 countries, and a Washington summer seminar. Work-study, accelerated degree programs in all majors, B.A.-B.S. degrees, and dual and student-designed majors are available. The 3–2 engineering degree program is in conjunction with the University of Texas at Dallas, Washington University in St. Louis, and Texas A&M University. Nondegree study, pass/fail options, language-house, preprofessional, teacher education programs, and a January term with experimental and off-campus opportunities are offered. There are 11 national honor societies on campus.

Faculty/Classroom: Eighty-one percent of faculty are male; 19%, female. All both teach and do research. No introductory courses are taught by graduate students. The average class size in an introductory lecture is 35; in a laboratory, 30; and in a regular course offering, 20.

Admissions: About 84% of the 1993–94 applicants were accepted. The SAT scores for the 1993–94 freshman class were as follows: Verbal—51% below 500, 35% between 500 and 599, 12% between 600 and 700, and 2% above 700; Math—24% below 500, 45% between 500 and 599, 23% between 600 and 700, and 8% above 700. The ACT scores were 15% below 21, 28% between 21 and 23, 29% between 24 and 26, 19% between 27 and 28, and 9% above 28. About 62% of the current freshmen were in the top fifth of their class; 89% were in the top two fifths. There were 4 National Merit finalists and 1 semifinalist.

Requirements: AC requires applicants to be in the upper 50% of their class. The SAT I or ACT is required. Applicants must be graduates of an accredited secondary school or have a GED. The recommended academic requirements are 1 credit in art/music/theater, 2 each in social studies and foreign language, 3 each in mathematics and science, and 4 in English. An essay is required and an interview is recommended. AP and CLEP credits are accepted. Important factors used in the admissions decision are advanced placement or honor courses, leadership record, recommendations by school officials, evidence of special talent, and extracurricular activities record.

Procedure: Freshmen are admitted fall, spring, and summer. Entrance exams should be taken in the junior year or the fall of the senior year. The application fee is $25. There are early admissions and deferred admissions plans.

Transfer: About 59 transfer students enrolled in 1993–94. Transfer students must have a minimum 2.0 GPA, submit SAT I scores and 2 recommendations, and be in good standing at previously attended colleges and universities. A total of 17 course credits out of 34 must be completed at AC.

Visiting: There are regularly scheduled orientations for prospective students. Four overnight (Sunday to Monday) preview programs are held for high school juniors and seniors and parents. There are guides for informal visits and visitors may sit in on classes and stay overnight at the school. To arrange for a visit, contact the Admissions Office at (800) 442–5363.

Financial Aid: In 1993–94 90% of all current freshmen and 85% of continuing students received some form of financial aid. About 53% of freshmen and 55% of continuing students received need-based aid. The average freshman award was $9171. Of that total, scholarships or need-based grants averaged $5328 (maximum); loans averaged $3053 ($4125 maximum); and work contracts averaged $790 ($1300 maximum). Thirty percent of undergraduate students work part-time. Average earnings from campus work for the school year are $1200. The average financial indebtedness of the 1992–93 graduate was $15,000. AC is a member of CSS. The FAF and the college's own financial statement are required. The deadline for financial aid applications is April 15.

International Students: There are currently 30 international students enrolled. The school actively recruits these students. They must take the TOEFL and achieve a minimum score of 550.

Computers: The college provides computer facilities for student use. The mainframe is a DEC 5000 Model 260. Students may use the 26 IBM PCs in the library and the 20 Macintosh and 4 NEXT terminals in the new numeric and graphic computing facility. All students may access the system. It may be used 10 hours daily; 24 hours in some locations. There are no time limits and no fees.

Graduates: In 1992–93 237 bachelor's degrees were awarded. The most popular majors among graduates were psychology (19%), biology (18%), and business management (14%). Within an average freshman class, 1% graduate in 3 years, 62% in 4 years, 70% in 5 years, and 71% in 6 years. In the 1992 graduating class, 35% of all graduates were enrolled in graduate school within 6 months of graduation; 42% had found employment.

Admissions Contact: Admissions Office.

BAYLOR UNIVERSITY
D-3

Waco, TX 76798 (817) 755–1811

Full-time: 4446 men, 5473 women
Part-time: 189 men, 295 women
Graduate: 998 men, 793 women
Year: semesters, summer session
Application Deadline: open
Freshman Class: 2433 enrolled

Faculty: 598; I, --$
Ph.D.s: n/av
Student/Faculty: 17 to 1
Tuition: $7070
Room & Board: $3920

COMPETITIVE +

Baylor University, founded in 1845, is an independent, coeducational institution offering undergraduate programs in liberal arts and sciences, business, education, music, and nursing. There are 6 undergraduate and 9 graduate schools. In addition to regional accreditation, Baylor has baccalaureate program accreditation with AACSB, ABET, ACCE, AHEA, APTA, CAHEA, CSWE, NASM, NCATE, and NLN. The 9 libraries contain 1,510,561 volumes, 1,013,639 microform items, and 62,621 audiovisual forms, and subscribe to 9171 periodicals. Computerized library sources and services include the card catalog, interlibrary loans, and database searching. Special learning facilities include a learning resource center, art gallery, natural history museum, and radio station. The 428-acre campus is in an urban area 100 miles south of Dallas/Fort Worth. Including residence halls, there are 74 buildings on campus.

Student Life: About 78% of undergraduates are from Texas. Students come from 50 states, 60 foreign countries, and Canada. Eighty-two percent are white. Most are Protestant. The average age of freshmen is 19; all undergraduates, 21. Fifteen percent drop out by the end of their first year; 70% remain to graduate.

Housing: A total of 3467 students can be accommodated in college housing. College-sponsored living facilities include single-sex dormitories, on-campus apartments, and married-student housing. On-campus housing is guaranteed for all 4 years. Alcohol is not permitted. All students may keep cars on campus.

Activities: About 20% of men belong to 3 local and 14 national fraternities; about 26% of women belong to 1 local and 12 national sororities. There are 232 groups on campus, including art, band, cheerleading, choir, chorale, chorus, computers, drama, ethnic, film, honors, international, jazz band, marching band, musical theater, newspaper, opera, orchestra, pep band, photography, political, professional, radio and TV, religious, social, social service, student government, symphony, and yearbook. Popular campus events include Dia del Oso (Day of the Bear), Campus Sing, Pigskin Review, Welcome Week, and Homecoming.

Sports: There are 12 intercollegiate sports for men and 9 for women, and 17 intramural sports for men and 17 for women. Athletic and recreation facilities include a 48,000-seat stadium, gymnasiums, intramural fields, tennis courts, a swimming pool, a marina, and a center which seats 10,030.

Disabled Students: Ninety-five percent of the campus is accessible to disabled students. The following facilities are available: wheelchair ramps, elevators, special parking, specially equipped rest rooms, and lowered drinking fountains.

Services: In addition to many counseling and information services, tutoring is available in every subject. There is also a reader service for the blind and remedial reading and writing.

Campus Safety and Security: Campus safety and security measures include 24-hour foot and vehicle patrol, escort service, shuttle buses, and informal discussions. In addition, there are pamphlets, posters, films, emergency telephones, and lighted pathways and sidewalks.

Programs of Study: Baylor awards the B.A., B.S., B.B.A., B.F.A., B.M., B.M.E., B.S.Av.Sc., B.S.E., B.S.Ed., B.S.H.E., and B.S.N. degrees. Master's and doctoral degrees also are awarded. Bachelor's degrees are awarded in BIOLOGICAL SCIENCE (biology/biological science), BUSINESS (accounting, banking and finance, business administration and management, business economics, business law, international business management, marketing/retailing/merchandising, and personnel management), COMMUNICATIONS AND THE ARTS (broadcasting, communications, design, dramatic arts, English, film arts, fine arts, French, German, journalism, languages, Latin, music, Russian, Spanish, and speech/debate/rhetoric), COMPUTER AND PHYSICAL SCIENCE (chemistry, computer programming, computer science, earth science, geology, information sciences and systems, mathematics, physics, and statistics), EDUCATION (art, business, early childhood, elementary, foreign languages, health, home economics, science, secondary, and special), ENGINEERING AND ENVIRONMENTAL DESIGN (computer engineering, electrical/electronics engineering, engineering, and mechanical engineering), HEALTH PROFESSIONS (medical laboratory technology, nursing, predentistry, premedicine, and speech pathology/audiology), SOCIAL SCIENCE (anthropology, dietetics, economics, history, philosophy, political science/government, prelaw, psychology, religion, social work, sociology, and urban studies). Biology, business, education, and psychology have the largest enrollments.

Required: All degree programs include distributed education requirements based upon the specific degree. Basic requirements for the B.A. degree are 12 semester hours of English and science, 18 semester hours of social science, 6 to 9 hours of fine arts, 3 to 16 hours of foreign language, 3 hours of mathematics, 4 hours of physical education, and 2 semesters of chapel forum. Requirments for other degrees vary.

Special: Baylor offers internships in each school, study abroad and student exchange in more than 8 countries, and pass/fail options. There are also honors and university scholars programs and faculty exchange with 4 schools in China, 1 in Japan, 1 in Thailand, and 1 in Russia. There is a freshman honors program on campus, as well as 39 national honor societies, including Phi Beta Kappa.

Faculty/Classroom: The average class size in a regular course offering is 35.

Admissions: There were 47 National Merit finalists.

Requirements: The SAT I or the ACT is required. The recommended minimum composite score is 1000 on the SAT I or 25 on the ACT. Applicants must be graduates of an accredited secondary school. An interview is recommended. AP and CLEP credits are accepted. Important factors used in the admissions decision are parents or siblings attending the school, advanced placement or honor courses, leadership record, evidence of special talent, and recommendations by school officials.

Procedure: Freshmen are admitted to all sessions. Entrance exams should be taken in spring of the junior year or fall of the senior year. Application deadlines are open. The application fee is $20. Notification is sent on a rolling basis. There is an early admissions plan.

Transfer: About 417 transfer students enrolled in 1993–94. Transfer students should begin studies no later than the end of the sophomore year, because of the 60-hour semester hour residence requirement for a bachelor's degree. A minimum 2.5 GPA is required. Students with fewer than 30 credit hours earned must meet the entrance requirements for freshmen. A total of 60 credits out of 124 must be completed at Baylor.

Visiting: There are regularly scheduled orientations for prospective students. There are guides for informal visits and visitors may sit in on classes and stay overnight at the school. To arrange for a visit, contact the Office of Admissions at (817) 755–1811.

Financial Aid: In 1993–94 62% of all current freshmen and 68% of continuing students received some form of financial aid. About 36% of freshmen and 39% of continuing students received need-based aid. Twenty-two percent of undergraduate students work part-time. Average earnings from campus work for the school year are $1037. The average financial indebtedness of the 1992–93 graduate was $11,244. Baylor is a member of CSS. The FAFSA financial statement is required. The deadline for financial aid applications is May 1.

International Students: There are currently 302 international students enrolled. The school actively recruits these students. They must take the TOEFL and achieve a minimum score of 540.

Computers: The college provides computer facilities for student use. The mainframes are a DEC VAX cluster 6510 and 8700, and IBM 4381 computers. Apple Macintoshes and Apple IIe microcomputers are also available throughout the campus for academic use. All students may access the system. There are no time limits and no fees.

Graduates: In 1992–93 2196 bachelor's degrees were awarded. Within an average freshman class, 50% graduate in 4 years, 67% in 5 years, and 70% in 6 years. Some 265 companies recruited on campus in an earlier year.

Admissions Contact: Diana M. Ramey, Director of Undergraduate Admissions.

CONCORDIA LUTHERAN COLLEGE
D-3

Austin, TX 78705 (512) 452–7661; (800) 285–4252 (in-state)

Full-time: 202 men, 299 women
Part-time: 101 men, 104 women
Graduate: none
Year: semesters, summer session
Application Deadline: August 15
Freshman Class: 233 applied, 230 accepted, 111 enrolled
SAT I Verbal/Math: 410/475

Faculty: 31
Ph.D.s: 50%
Student/Faculty: 16 to 1
Tuition: $6760
Room & Board: $3500

ACT: 20 **COMPETITIVE +**

Concordia Lutheran College, founded in 1926, is a private college affiliated with the Lutheran Church-Missouri Synod. It offers undergraduate programs in liberal arts, behavioral science, business, communication, education, environmental science, and church music. The library contains 86,827 volumes, 4952 microform items, and 2655 audiovisual forms, and subscribes to 682 periodicals. Special learning facilities include a TV station. The 20-acre campus is in an urban area. Including residence halls, there are 16 buildings on campus.

Student Life: About 90% of undergraduates are from Texas. Students come from 26 states. Eighty-four percent are white. Seventy-six percent are Protestant; 11% Catholic. The average age of freshmen is 19.

Housing: A total of 222 students can be accommodated in college housing. College-sponsored living facilities include dormitories. On-campus housing is guaranteed for the freshman year only and is available on a first-come, first-served basis. Sixty-seven percent of students commute. Alcohol is not permitted. All students may keep cars on campus.

Activities: There are no fraternities or sororities on campus. There are some groups and organizations on campus, including cheerleading, choir, drama, religious, social, and student government. Popular campus events include Fall Festival Weekend, Parents Day, Founders Day, Homecoming, and Field Day.

Sports: There are 4 intercollegiate sports for men and 3 for women, and 10 intramural sports for men and 9 for women. Athletic and recreation facilities include an activities center, a 1600-seat gymnasium, and a 250-seat auditorium.

Disabled Students: Seventy-five percent of the campus is accessible to disabled students. The following facilities are available: wheelchair ramps, elevators, special parking, specially equipped rest rooms, and lowered drinking fountains.

Services: In addition to many counseling and information services, tutoring is available in most subjects.

Campus Safety and Security: Campus safety and security measures include 24-hour foot and vehicle patrol, escort service, informal discussions, and pamphlets, posters, and films. In addition, there are lighted pathways and sidewalks.

Programs of Study: Concordia awards the B.A. degree. Associate degrees also are awarded. Bachelor's degrees are awarded in BUSINESS (accounting and business administration and management), COMMUNICATIONS AND THE ARTS (communications, English, music, and Spanish), EDUCATION (elementary and secondary), ENGINEERING AND ENVIRONMENTAL DESIGN (environmental science), SOCIAL SCIENCE (behavioral science, liberal arts/general studies, and Mexican-American/Chicano studies). Business administration, accounting, elementary education, and communication have the largest enrollments.

Required: To graduate, all students must complete 12 hours each of English, social/behavioral science, and religion, 6 to 8 hours of natural science, and 3 hours each of fine arts, mathematics, physical education, and speech. Students must earn 96 semester hours, 39 upper-level hours, and 33 to 48 hours in the major. A minimum 2.0 GPA is required.

Special: Concordia offers internships in communications, environmental science, and Mexican-American studies, study abroad in Mexico, credit for experience, nondegree study, pass/fail options, and a preseminary program. There is one national honor society on campus.

Faculty/Classroom: Seventy-five percent of faculty are male; 25%, female.

Admissions: About 99% of the 1993–94 applicants were accepted. The SAT scores for the 1993–94 freshman class were as follows: Verbal—84% below 500, 14% between 500 and 599, and 2% between 600 and 700; Math—63% below 500, 22% between 500 and 599, 14% between 600 and 700, and 1% above 700. The ACT scores were 57% below 21, 25% between 21 and 23, 13% between 24 and 26, 2% between 27 and 28, and 3% above 28. About 20% of the current freshmen were in the top fifth of their class; 60% were in the top two fifths. Two freshmen graduated first in their class.

Requirements: Concordia requires applicants to be in the upper 60% of their class. A minimum GPA of 2.5 is required. The SAT I or ACT is required. The recommended minimum composite score is 750 on the SAT I or 14 on the ACT. Applicants must be graduates of an accredited secondary school or have the GED. AP and CLEP credits are accepted.

Procedure: Freshmen are admitted fall and spring. Applications should be filed by August 15 for fall entry, December 15 for spring entry, and May 15 for summer entry, along with an application fee of $25. Notification is sent on a rolling basis. There are early decision and early admissions plans.

Transfer: About 134 transfer students enrolled in a recent year. Transfer students with fewer than 18 hours earned must meet freshmen admissions requirements and submit high school and college transcripts; those with 18 or more hours earned must be in good standing at the previously attended college with a minimum 2.0 GPA. A total of 30 credits out of 96 must be completed at Concordia.

Visiting: There are regularly scheduled orientations for prospective students. There are guides for informal visits and visitors may sit in on classes. To arrange for a visit, contact Terry Small, Director of Admissions at (800) 285–4252 or (512) 452–7661.

Financial Aid: In an earlier year, 75% of all current freshmen and 70% of continuing students received some form of financial aid. Scholarships or need-based grants averaged $1200 ($4500 maximum); loans averaged $2500 ($2625 maximum); and work contracts averaged $1500 ($2000 maximum). Eighty percent of undergraduate students work part-time. The average financial indebtedness of an

earlier graduate was $5000. The FFS is required. The deadline for financial aid applications is July 1.

International Students: There are currently 3 international students enrolled. They must take the TOEFL and achieve a minimum score of 550.

Computers: The college provides computer facilities for student use. There are 200 Apple IIe and American Research Company Microcomputers available for academic use in the computer laboratories. Students enrolled in computer courses may access the system. There are no time limits and no fees.

Graduates: In an earlier year, 61 bachelor's degrees were awarded.

Admissions Contact: Rachel Meissner, Associate Director of Admissions.

DALLAS BAPTIST UNIVERSITY
Dallas, TX 75211–9800   (214) 333–5360

Full-time: 430 men, 418 women	Faculty: 64
Part-time: 670 men, 872 women	Ph.D.s: 48%
Graduate: 235 men, 178 women	Student/Faculty: 13 to 1
Year: 4–1–4, summer session	Tuition: $6460
Application Deadline: open	Room & Board: $3160
Freshman Class: 360 applied, 314 accepted, 155 enrolled	
SAT I Verbal/Math: 435/495	ACT: 22 **LESS COMPETITIVE**

Dallas Baptist University, established in 1965, is a private institution affiliated with the Baptist General Convention of Texas. The university offers undergraduate degrees in the arts, sciences, music, and business while emphasizing Christian fundamentalist principles. There are 7 undergraduate and 5 graduate schools. In addition to regional accreditation, DBU has baccalaureate program accreditation with AACSB. The library contains 523,993 volumes, 314,602 microform items, and 1832 audiovisual forms, and subscribes to 496 periodicals. Computerized library sources and services include interlibrary loans and database searching. Special learning facilities include a Corrie ten Boom collection. The 200-acre campus is in an urban area 13 miles from downtown Dallas and 19 miles from Fort Worth. Including residence halls, there are 14 buildings on campus.

Student Life: About 98% of undergraduates are from Texas. Students come from 28 states, 49 foreign countries, and Canada. Sixty-one percent are white; 17% African American. Eighty-one percent are Protestant; 10% Jehovah's Witnesses, Mormon, Seventh-day Adventist, Disciples of Christ, undeclared, and unknown.

Housing: A total of 472 students can be accommodated in college housing. College-sponsored living facilities include coed dormitories. On-campus housing is available on a first-come, first-served basis. Eighty-five percent of students commute. Alcohol is not permitted. All students may keep cars on campus.

Activities: There are no fraternities or sororities on campus. There are 32 groups on campus, including art, band, choir, chorale, drama, honors, international, musical theater, professional, religious, social, social service, student government, and yearbook. Popular campus events include Homecoming, Jog-a-rama, Parents Weekend, Graduates' Candlelighting Service, and Spiritual Emphasis Week.

Sports: There are 2 intercollegiate sports for men and 1 for women, and 11 intramural sports for men and 11 for women. Athletic and recreation facilities include a gymnasium, an 8-lane track, tennis courts, a baseball diamond, and soccer and football fields.

Disabled Students: The entire campus is accessible to disabled students. The following facilities are available: elevators, special parking, special class scheduling, lowered drinking fountains, and lowered telephones.

Services: Student counseling is available.

Campus Safety and Security: Campus safety and security measures include 24-hour foot and vehicle patrol, shuttle buses, emergency telephones, and lighted pathways and sidewalks.

Programs of Study: DBU awards the B.A., B.S., B.A.A.S., B.A.B.A., B.B.A., B.C.M., and B.M. degrees. Associate and master's degrees also are awarded. Bachelor's degrees are awarded in BIOLOGICAL SCIENCE (biology/biological science), BUSINESS (accounting, banking and finance, business administration and management, and marketing/retailing/merchandising), COMMUNICATIONS AND THE ARTS (applied music, communications, English, fine arts, music, and music performance), COMPUTER AND PHYSICAL SCIENCE (computer science and mathematics), EDUCATION (physical), ENGINEERING AND ENVIRONMENTAL DESIGN (aviation administration/management), HEALTH PROFESSIONS (allied health), SOCIAL SCIENCE (biblical studies, counseling psychology, criminal justice, economics, history, interdisciplinary studies, pastoral studies, philosophy, psychology, public administration, religious education, and sociology).

Required: To graduate, students must have a minimum GPA of 2.0 and complete 126 credit hours, including 24 hours in the major and 42 hours that are upper divisional. Students must also take 61 hours of general studies courses, including computer science, English, fine arts, foreign language, history, mathematics, natural science, physical

education, religion, speech, and social science. Chapel attendance is required for all students. All freshmen must take 2 semesters of an orientation course.

Special: Work-study programs, study abroad, and a Washington semester are available. There are 2 national honor societies on campus.

Faculty/Classroom: Sixty-two percent of faculty are male; 38%, female.

Admissions: About 87% of the 1993-94 applicants were accepted. The SAT scores for the 1993-94 freshman class were as follows: Verbal—70% below 500, 27% between 500 and 599, and 3% between 600 and 700; Math—51% below 500, 31% between 500 and 599, 15% between 600 and 700, and 3% above 700. About 31% of the current freshmen were in the top fifth of their class; 56% were in the top two fifths. About five freshmen graduated first in their class.

Requirements: DBU requires applicants to be in the upper 50% of their class. A minimum GPA of 2.0 is required. The SAT I or ACT is required. Applicants must be graduates of an accredited secondary school or have a GED and meet one of the following criteria: a composite SAT I score of at least 800; a composite ACT score of at least 18; or a high school average no lower than B-. High school courses should include 4 years of English, 3 years each of mathematics and social studies, 2 to 3 years of a foreign language, and 2 years each of history and science. An essay is required and an interview is recommended. AP and CLEP credits are accepted. Important factors used in the admissions decision are personality, intangible qualities, leadership record, evidence of special talent, recommendations by school officials, and recommendations by alumni.

Procedure: Freshmen are admitted to all sessions. Entrance exams should be taken during the spring of junior year and fall of senior year. Application deadlines are open. The application fee is $25. Notification is sent on a rolling basis.

Transfer: About 134 transfer students enrolled in 1993-94. Applicants must submit an essay and transcripts of all previous college work. Students with fewer than 30 hours must furnish high school transcripts and ACT or SAT I scores. A total of 30 credits out of 126 must be completed at DBU.

Visiting: There are regularly scheduled orientations for prospective students, including a Preview Weekend conducted each fall and spring semester to provide information on financial aid and admissions. There are guides for informal visits and visitors may sit in on classes. To arrange for a visit, contact the Admissions Office at (214) 333-5360.

Financial Aid: In 1993-94 80% of all current freshmen received some form of financial aid. About 45% of freshmen received need-based aid. The average freshman award was $6103. Of that total, scholarships or need-based grants averaged $3865 ($7520 maximum); loans averaged $1778 ($4875 maximum); and work contracts averaged $1882 ($2040 maximum). Five percent of undergraduate students work part-time. Average earnings from campus work for the school year are $1230. The average financial indebtedness of the 1992-93 graduate was $8509. DBU is a member of CSS. The FAF or FFS is required. The Federal Financial Aid Application may be submitted for PELL grants only. A financial statement is required. The deadline for financial aid applications is May 15.

International Students: There are currently 160 international students enrolled. They must take the TOEFL and achieve a minimum score of 525. The student must also take the SAT I or the ACT.

Computers: The college provides computer facilities for student use. The Center for Computer Literacy provides microcomputers and software packages that students can use for class assignments. All students may access the system. There are no time limits and no fees.

Graduates: In 1992-93 537 bachelor's degrees were awarded. The most popular majors among graduates were business (53%), liberal arts/general studies (12%), and computer science/analysis (8%).

Admissions Contact: Office of Admissions.

DEVRY INSTITUTE OF TECHNOLOGY DALLAS
D-2

Irving, TX 75063-2440 (214) 258-6330

Full-time: 1149 men, 265 women	Faculty: 55
Part-time: 421 men, 198 women	Ph.D.s: n/av
Graduate: none	Student/Faculty: 26 to 1
Year: trimesters, summer session	Tuition: $5609
Application Deadline: open	Room & Board: n/app
Freshman Class: 1038 applied, 963 accepted, 568 enrolled	
SAT I or ACT: see profile	**LESS COMPETITIVE**

The DeVry Institute of Technology/Dallas is a private institution that opened in 1969; there are 10 other DeVry Institutes in the United States and Canada that are owned by Keller Graduate School of Management. The school offers undergraduate technology-based programs in accounting, business operations, electronics, and computer information systems. In addition to regional accreditation, DeVry has baccalaureate program accreditation with ABET. The library

contains 7286 volumes, 159 microform items, and 84 audiovisual forms, and subscribes to 184 periodicals. Computerized library sources and services include the card catalog, interlibrary loans, and database searching. Special learning facilities include a learning resource center and electronics and other laboratories. The 13-acre campus is in a suburban area 12 miles northwest of Dallas. There is one building on campus.

Student Life: About 84% of undergraduates are from Texas. Students come from 20 foreign countries and Canada. Fifty-four percent are white; 24% African American; 14% Hispanic. The average age of all undergraduates is 27. Fifty-two percent drop out by the end of their first year; 32% remain to graduate.

Housing: There are no residence halls. College-sponsored living facilities include off-campus apartments. All students commute. Alcohol is not permitted. All students may keep cars on campus.

Activities: There are no fraternities or sororities on campus. There are 10 groups on campus, including ethnic, honors, newspaper, professional, and religious. Popular campus events include Club Fair Day, Welcome Weekend, Pool Party, Casino Night, Talent and Fashion Show, Career Expo Cookout, Ski Trip, Trivial Pursuit Contest, Black Student Month, and Blood Drive.

Sports: There are 4 intramural sports for men and 4 for women.

Disabled Students: Ninety percent of the campus is accessible to disabled students. The following facilities are available: wheelchair ramps, elevators, special parking, specially equipped rest rooms, and lowered drinking fountains.

Services: In addition to many counseling and information services, tutoring is available in every subject.

Campus Safety and Security: Campus safety and security measures include informal discussions, pamphlets, posters, and films, emergency telephones, and lighted pathways and sidewalks. Buildings are monitored after hours by a bonded security company with door entry switches and sound-activated sensors.

Programs of Study: DeVry awards the B.S. degree. Associate degrees also are awarded. Bachelor's degrees are awarded in BUSINESS (accounting and business administration and management), COMPUTER AND PHYSICAL SCIENCE (information sciences and systems), ENGINEERING AND ENVIRONMENTAL DESIGN (electrical/electronics engineering technology). Electronics has the largest enrollment.

Required: In order to graduate, students must complete between 143 and 158 credit hours with a 2.0 minimum GPA. Course requirements vary according to program. All first-semester students take courses in business organization, computer applications, algebra, psychology, and student success strategies.

Special: Nondegree study and evening classes are possible. There is one national honor society on campus.

Faculty/Classroom: Seventy-eight percent of faculty are male; 22%, female. All teach undergraduates. The average class size in an introductory lecture is 30; in a laboratory, 30; and in a regular course offering, 30.

Admissions: About 93% of the 1993-94 applicants were accepted.

Requirements: Admissions requirements include graduation from a secondary school; the GED is also accepted. Applicants must pass the DeVry entrance exam or present satisfactory ACT, SAT I, or WPCT scores. CLEP credit is accepted.

Procedure: Freshmen are admitted to all sessions. Application deadlines are open. Application fee is $25. Notification is sent on a rolling basis. There are early decision and deferred admissions plans.

Transfer: Transfer students must take the DeVry entrance exam. It is recommended that applicants have math scores of at least 23 on the ACT or 480 on the SAT I. A total of 50 credits out of 143 to 158 must be completed at DeVry.

Visiting: There are regularly scheduled orientations for prospective students. There are guides for informal visits and visitors may sit in on classes. To arrange for a visit, contact Deidre Leslie, New Student Coordinator at (214) 258-6770.

Financial Aid: In 1993-94, 79% of all students received some form of financial aid. About 79% of students received need-based aid. DeVry is a member of CSS. The FAFSA financial statement is required.

International Students: International students must take the TOEFL and achieve a minimum score of 550. The ACT, SAT I, or WPCT may be accepted in lieu of the DeVry entrance exam.

Computers: The college provides computer facilities for student use. The mainframe is an IBM 3081K. Laboratory facilities include IBM and IBM-compatible PCs in stand-alone and network configurations, with access to the mainframe. LANs provide access to a wide range of applications software. Hard copy from the mainframe is provided through a local minicomputer and medium- and high-speed printers. Students enrolled in the computer information program may access the system during laboratory hours. There are no fees.

Graduates: In 1992-93, 236 bachelor's degrees were awarded. The most popular majors among graduates were electronics technology (71%), business administration and management (14%), and computer information systems and sciences (14%). Within an average fresh-

man class, 32% graduate in 5 years. Some 100 companies recruited on campus in 1992–93. In the 1992 graduating class, 83% of the men and women had found employment within 6 months of graduation.

Admissions Contact: Danny Millan, Director of Admissions.

EAST TEXAS BAPTIST UNIVERSITY E-2
Marshall, TX 75670–1498 (214) 935–7963, ext. 225

Full-time: 445 men, 604 women	Faculty: 55; IIB, --$
Part-time: 53 men, 100 women	Ph.D.s: 62%
Graduate: 13 men, 38 women	Student/Faculty: 19 to 1
Year: 4-1-4, summer session	Tuition: $5100
Application Deadline: open	Room & Board: $2640
Freshman Class: 612 applied, 591 accepted, 451 enrolled	
ACT: required	COMPETITIVE

East Texas Baptist University, founded in 1912, is affiliated with the Baptist General Convention of Texas. The private liberal arts university offers undergraduate programs in the arts and sciences and professional areas, such as business, teacher education, nursing, and Christian ministry. In addition to regional accreditation, ETBU has baccalaureate program accreditation with NASM. The library contains 106,942 volumes, 9250 microform items, and 350 audiovisual forms, and subscribes to 609 periodicals. The 193-acre campus is in a small town 35 miles west of Shreveport, Louisana. Including residence halls, there are 20 buildings on campus.

Student Life: About 78% of undergraduates are from Texas. Students come from 22 states, 14 foreign countries, and Canada. Eighty-one percent are white; 11% African American. Most are Protestant.

Housing: A total of 563 students can be accommodated in college housing. College-sponsored living facilities include single-sex dormitories, on-campus apartments, off-campus apartments, and married-student housing. On-campus housing is available on a first-come, first-served basis. Sixty-one percent of students live on campus; of those, 40% remain on campus on weekends. Alcohol is not permitted. All students may keep cars on campus.

Activities: About 9% of men belong to 1 local fraternity; about 6% of women belong to 1 local sorority. There are 19 groups on campus, including band, cheerleading, choir, chorale, chorus, computers, drama, honors, international, jazz band, literary magazine, newspaper, pep band, professional, religious, social, social service, student government, and yearbook. Popular campus events include theater productions, Miss ETBU Pageant, and choral and band concerts.

Sports: There are 3 intercollegiate sports for men and 2 for women, and 7 intramural sports for men and 7 for women. Athletic and recreation facilities include a baseball field, tennis courts, a weight room, and a 1500-seat gymnasium.

Disabled Students: The following facilities are available: wheelchair ramps, special parking, specially equipped rest rooms, and special class scheduling.

Services: In addition to many counseling and information services, tutoring is available in some subjects, including mathematics. In addition, there is remedial math and writing.

Campus Safety and Security: Campus safety and security measures include 24-hour foot and vehicle patrol, self defense education, and lighted pathways and sidewalks.

Programs of Study: ETBU awards the B.A., B.S., B.A.S., B.B.A., B.M., B.S.E., and B.S.N. degrees. Associate and master's degrees also are awarded. Bachelor's degrees are awarded in BIOLOGICAL SCIENCE (biology/biological science), BUSINESS (accounting and business administration and management), COMMUNICATIONS AND THE ARTS (dramatic arts, English, music, Spanish, and speech/debate/rhetoric), COMPUTER AND PHYSICAL SCIENCE (chemistry, information sciences and systems, and mathematics), EDUCATION (business, elementary, English, mathematics, middle school, music, physical, science, and secondary), HEALTH PROFESSIONS (medical laboratory technology and nursing), SOCIAL SCIENCE (behavioral science, history, psychology, religion, and sociology). Teacher education and music are the strongest academically. Religion, business, teacher education, and mathematics/computer science have the largest enrollments.

Required: To graduate, students must complete general distribution requirements, ranging from 34 hours for B.M. degrees to 60 hours for B.A. and B.S. degrees, and have a minimum 2.0 GPA. A total of 128 semester hours, with at least 30 in the major, is required, including 4 hours of physical activity, 3 religion courses, 12 hours of English, 6 hours of history, 3 to 6 hours of mathematics, and at least 1 laboratory science course.

Special: Internships are available, as well as dual majors in church-related fields. There is a freshman honors program on campus, as well as 6 national honor societies.

Faculty/Classroom: Seventy-one percent of faculty are male; 29%, female. All teach undergraduates and 20% both teach and do research. No introductory courses are taught by graduate students. The

average class size in an introductory lecture is 28; in a laboratory, 14; and in a regular course offering, 22.

Admissions: About 97% of the 1993–94 applicants were accepted. There were 2 National Merit semifinalists.

Requirements: ETBU requires applicants to be in the upper 50% of their class. A minimum GPA of 2.0 is required. The ACT is required (minimum composite score 18). SAT I scores will be accepted, but students must take the ACT prior to enrolling or during orientation. Applicants must be graduates of an accredited secondary school or have the GED. Students not meeting these requirements may be admitted conditionally for 1 term or semester. The Texas Academic Skills Program Test and an essay are required for all students. AP and CLEP credits are accepted.

Procedure: Freshmen are admitted to all sessions. Entrance exams should be taken in the first semester of the senior year. Application deadlines are open. Application fee is $25. Notification is sent on a rolling basis. There is a deferred admissions plan.

Transfer: Transfer students must have a minimum 2.0 GPA and be eligible to return to the last college attended. A total of at least 36 credits out of 128 must be completed at ETBU.

Visiting: There are regularly scheduled orientations for prospective students. There are guides for informal visits and visitors may sit in on classes and stay overnight at the school. To arrange for a visit, contact the Director of Admissions at (214) 935–7963, ext. 225.

Financial Aid: In 1993–94, 86% of all students received some form of financial aid. About 55% of students received need-based aid. The average freshman award was $5690. Of that total, scholarships or need-based grants averaged $3383 ($6000 maximum); loans averaged $1950 ($2625 maximum); and work contracts averaged $357 ($1400 maximum). Twenty-two percent of undergraduate students work part-time. Average earnings from campus work for the school year are $1432. The average financial indebtedness of the 1992–93 graduate was $10,047. The FAF, FFS, SFS, or the FAFSA the college's own financial statement are required. The deadline for financial aid applications is June 1.

International Students: There are currently 71 international students enrolled. The school actively recruits these students. They must take the TOEFL or the University of Michigan Language Test and achieve a minimum score on the TOEFL of 500. The student must also take the ACT (and achieve a score of 18), and the Texas Academic Skills Program Test.

Computers: The university provides computer facilities for student use. The mainframe is a DEC 5000/200. There are also 21 Apple Macintoshes and 20 IBM PCs available in the business and computer laboratories. All students may access the system from 8 A.M. to 9 P.M. Monday through Thursday and from 8 A.M. to 4:30 P.M. Friday and Saturday. There are no time limits on using the system and no fees.

Graduates: In 1992–93, 179 bachelor's degrees were awarded. The most popular majors among graduates were teacher education (34%) and business (25%).

Admissions Contact: Director of Admissions.

EAST TEXAS STATE UNIVERSITY E-2
Commerce, TX 75429 (903) 886–5101

Full-time: 4129 men and women	Faculty: 218; IIA, --$
Part-time: 1343 men and women	Ph.D.s: 81%
Graduate: 2673 men and women	Student/Faculty: 19 to 1
Year: semesters, summer session	Tuition: $1332 ($4596)
Application Deadline: August 10	Room & Board: $3240
Freshman Class: 1441 accepted, 719 enrolled	
SAT I or ACT: required	LESS COMPETITIVE

East Texas State University, founded in 1889, is part of the East Texas State University Complex and offers undergraduate and graduate programs in business and technology, arts and sciences, and education. There are 3 undergraduate schools and one graduate school. In addition to regional accreditation, ETSU has baccalaureate program accreditation with AACSB, CSWE, NASM, and NCATE. The library contains 994,503 volumes, 435,323 microform items, and 5571 audiovisual forms, and subscribes to 2154 periodicals. Computerized library sources and services include interlibrary loans and database searching. Special learning facilities include a radio station, a TV station, a performing arts center, and a farm. The 140-acre campus is in a small town 65 miles northeast of Dallas. Including residence halls, there are 77 buildings on campus.

Student Life: About 98% of undergraduates are from Texas. Students come from 41 states, 28 foreign countries, and Canada. Ninety percent are from public schools; 10% from private. Eighty-one percent are white; 10% African American. The average age of freshmen is 19; all undergraduates, 27. Twenty percent drop out by the end of their first year; 50% remain to graduate.

Housing: A total of 2750 students can be accommodated in college housing. College-sponsored living facilities include single-sex and coed dormitories, on-campus apartments, married-student housing, fraternity houses, and sorority houses. In addition, there are honors

houses and special interest houses. On-campus housing is available on a first-come, first-served basis. All students may keep cars on campus.

Activities: About 15% of men belong to 9 national fraternities; about 12% of women belong to 7 national sororities. There are 96 groups on campus, including art, band, cheerleading, chorale, chorus, drama, honors, international, jazz band, literary magazine, marching band, musical theater, newspaper, pep band, photography, political, professional, radio and TV, religious, and yearbook. Popular campus events include Sam Rayburn Symposium and Christmas Feast of Carols.

Sports: There are 7 intramural sports each for men and women. Athletic and recreation facilities include a 1700-seat auditorium, a 10,000-seat stadium, a gymnasium, handball and racquetball courts, a bowling alley, a swimming pool, a weight room, tennis courts, a field house, and outdoor intramural fields.

Disabled Students: Fifty percent of the campus is accessible to disabled students. The following facilities are available: wheelchair ramps, elevators, special parking, and specially equipped rest rooms.

Services: In addition to many counseling and information services, tutoring is available in some subjects, including mathematics and writing. In addition, there is remedial math, reading, and writing.

Campus Safety and Security: Campus safety and security measures include 24-hour foot and vehicle patrol, self-defense education, informal discussions, and pamphlets, posters, and films. In addition, there are lighted pathways and sidewalks and a police service for special and social events, crime and date-rape prevention presentations, and motorist assistance.

Programs of Study: ETSU awards the B.A., B.S., B.A.C.J., B.B.A., B.F.A., B.G.S., B.M., B.M.Ed., B.S.C.J., B.S.Lib.Sci., and B.S.W. degrees. Master's and doctoral degrees also are awarded. Bachelor's degrees are awarded in AGRICULTURE (agricultural economics, agriculture, animal science, and wildlife management), BIOLOGICAL SCIENCE (biology/biological science and botany), BUSINESS (accounting, banking and finance, business administration and management, marketing/retailing/merchandising, and personnel management), COMMUNICATIONS AND THE ARTS (advertising, broadcasting, dramatic arts, English, fine arts, French, German, journalism, languages, music, photography, printmaking, and Spanish), COMPUTER AND PHYSICAL SCIENCE (chemistry, computer science, earth science, geology, mathematics, and physics), EDUCATION (agricultural, business, early childhood, elementary, guidance, health, industrial arts, music, science, and secondary), ENGINEERING AND ENVIRONMENTAL DESIGN (engineering technology and preengineering), HEALTH PROFESSIONS (dental hygiene, medical laboratory technology, medical records administration/services, nursing, optometry, physician's assistant, predentistry, premedicine, prepharmacy, and veterinary science), SOCIAL SCIENCE (anthropology, criminal justice, economics, geography, history, political science/government, prelaw, psychology, religion, social work, and sociology). Education, computer science, and business administration are the strongest programs academically and have the largest enrollments.

Required: To graduate, all students must earn a GPA of 2.0 while taking at least 126 semester hours, including 24 hours in the major. Distribution requirements include 24 hours in culture courses such as American history and foreign languages, 12 in English composition, mathematics, and speech skills, 8 in sciences, 6 hours in upper-division courses, and 4 in physical education.

Special: ETSU offers co-op programs with E-Systems Inc. and numerous other firms, cross-registration by independent arrangement, study abroad in England, and work-study programs. B.A.-B.S. degrees, second degrees, a general studies degree, credit for life experience, nondegree study, and pass/fail options are also available. There is a freshman honors program on campus, as well as 18 national honor societies.

Faculty/Classroom: Seventy-three percent of faculty are male; 27%, female. Ninety-six percent teach undergraduates, 62% do research, and 62% do both. Graduate students teach 40% of introductory courses. The average class size in an introductory lecture is 30; in a laboratory, 20; and in a regular course offering, 25.

Admissions: The ACT scores for the 1993–94 freshman class were as follows: 50% below 21, 26% between 21 and 23, 18% between 24 and 26, 3% between 27 and 28, and 3% above 28.

Requirements: The SAT I, with a minimum recommended composite score of 800, or the ACT, with a minimum recommended score of 20, is required. Applicants need not be graduates of an accredited secondary school, although high school graduation is required. The GED is also accepted. AP and CLEP credits are accepted.

Procedure: Freshmen are admitted to all sessions. Entrance exams should be taken prior to enrollment. Applications should be filed by August 10 for fall entry, January 6 for spring entry, and May 25 for summer entry. Notification is sent on a rolling basis. There are early decision, early admissions, and deferred admissions plans.

Transfer: About 470 transfer students enrolled in an earlier year. Transfer students must have a college GPA of 2.0 with a minimum of 21 credit hours. The SAT I or ACT is not required. A total of 30 semester hours out of 126 must be completed at ETSU.

Visiting: There are regularly scheduled orientations for prospective students. There are guides for informal visits and visitors may sit in on classes. To arrange for a visit, contact the Office of School Relations at (903) 886–5081.

Financial Aid: In 1993–94, 34% of all current freshmen received need-based financial aid. The average freshman award was $3409. Of that total, scholarships or need-based grants averaged $1664 ($4300 maximum); loans averaged $1962 ($6625 maximum); and work contracts averaged $1023 ($6465 maximum). Two-hundred-sixty-two percent of undergraduate students work part-time. Average earnings from campus work for the school year are $1216. The FFS and the college's own financial statement is required. The deadline for financial aid applications is October 1.

International Students: There are currently 200 international students enrolled. They must take the TOEFL and achieve a minimum score of 500. The student must also take the SAT I or the ACT and score a minimum composite score of 800 on the SAT I or 20 on the ACT. Minimum scores are also required on SAT II: Subject tests.

Computers: The college provides computer facilities for student use. The mainframe is an IBM 9370 Model 60. There are also IBM, Apple Macintosh, and Packard Bell microcomputers available in the library and business administration building. All students may access the system. It may be used 24 hours daily, except holidays, during the academic term. There are no time limits on using the system and no fees.

Graduates: In a recent year, 1047 bachelor's degrees were awarded.

Admissions Contact: Director of Admissions.

HARDIN-SIMMONS UNIVERSITY   C-2

Abilene, TX 79698   (915) 670–1206; (800) 568–2692 (out-of-state)

Full-time: 649 men, 716 women	Faculty: 101; IIA, --$
Part-time: 133 men, 201 women	Ph.D.s: 76%
Graduate: 93 men, 182 women	Student/Faculty: 14 to 1
Year: semesters, summer session	Tuition: $6480
Application Deadline: open	Room & Board: $2600
Freshman Class: 467 applied, 424 accepted, 350 enrolled	
SAT I Verbal/Math: 470/510	ACT: 22 COMPETITIVE

Hardin-Simmons University, founded in 1891, is a private liberal arts institution affiliated with the Baptist General Convention of Texas. There are 6 undergraduate schools and one graduate school. In addition to regional accreditation, HSU has baccalaureate program accreditation with CSWE, NASM, and NLN. The 2 libraries contain 411,025 volumes, 18,061 microform items, and 9575 audiovisual forms, and subscribe to 986 periodicals. Special learning facilities include an art gallery and an observatory. The 40-acre campus is in an urban area 150 miles west of Fort Worth. Including residence halls, there are 29 buildings on campus.

Student Life: About 92% of undergraduates are from Texas. Students come from 31 states and 10 foreign countries. Eighty-four percent are white. Seventeen percent are other unknown or no response; 6% Protestant. The average age of freshmen is 21; all undergraduates, 23. Sixty-seven percent drop out by the end of their first year; 33% remain to graduate.

Housing: A total of 942 students can be accommodated in college housing. College-sponsored living facilities include single-sex dormitories and married-student housing. On-campus housing is guaranteed for the freshman year only and is available on a first-come, first-served basis. Fifty-nine percent of students live on campus. Alcohol is not permitted. All students may keep cars on campus.

Activities: About 14% of men belong to 4 local and 1 national fraternities; about 14% of women belong to 4 local and 1 national sororities. There are more than 50 groups on campus, including band, choir, chorale, computers, drama, ethnic, honors, international, literary magazine, marching band, musical theater, newspaper, orchestra, pep band, political, professional, religious, social, social service, student government, symphony, and yearbook. Popular campus events include Homecoming, Sing, theater productions, opera, chorale fall concert, Christmas tree lighting, all school Christmas party, Cowboy Band barbeque, Black History Week, choir tour, rodeo, Western Heritage Day, and pops concert.

Sports: There are 6 intercollegiate sports for men and 5 for women, and 15 intramural sports for men and 15 for women. Athletic and recreation facilities include a rodeo arena, 2 running ovals, a practice field, soccer amd baseball fields, outdoor and indoor swimming pools, 6 bowling alleys, a fitness course, 4 basketball, 4 racquetball, 8 tennis, and 8 badminton/paddleball courts and a Nautilus weight lifting room.

Disabled Students: The following facilities are available: wheelchair ramps, elevators, special parking, specially equipped rest rooms, and lowered drinking fountains.

Services: In addition to many counseling and information services, tutoring is available in most subjects. There are also free counseling services for students through the Family Ministry program.

Campus Safety and Security: Campus safety and security measures include 24-hour foot and vehicle patrol, informal discussions, pamphlets, posters, films, and emergency telephones. In addition, there are lighted pathways and sidewalks.

Programs of Study: HSU awards the B.A., B.S., B.B.A., B.F.A., B.Mus., B.S.N., and B.Behavioral Science degrees. Associate and master's degrees also are awarded. Bachelor's degrees are awarded in BIOLOGICAL SCIENCE (biology/biological science), BUSINESS (accounting, banking and finance, business administration and management, and marketing/retailing/merchandising), COMMUNICATIONS AND THE ARTS (applied music, communications, English, French, German, music, Spanish, and theater management), COMPUTER AND PHYSICAL SCIENCE (chemistry, computer science, geology, mathematics, and physics), EDUCATION (art, business, early childhood, elementary, foreign languages, health, music, physical, reading, science, and secondary), HEALTH PROFESSIONS (medical laboratory technology, nursing, physical therapy, and speech pathology/audiology), SOCIAL SCIENCE (criminal justice, history, law enforcement and corrections, ministries, philosophy, physical fitness/movement, political science/government, psychology, religion, social science, social work, sociology, and theological studies). Elementary education is the strongest academically.

Required: To graduate, students must complete a minimum of 124 semester hours with a 2.0 GPA. At least 18 hours are required in the major and 42 hours in upper-division courses. Forty-nine hours of core courses must be taken, including 12 of social science, 9 of English, 7 of natural science, 6 each of Bible and humanities, 4 hours of physical education, 3 hours each of mathematics and oral communication, and 2 of computer science. All students must satisfy chapel attendance requirements and must demonstrate proficiency in written English.

Special: Cross-registration may be arranged with Abilene Christian University, McMurry University and Howard Payne University. The college offers cooperative programs, internships, dual majors, credit by examination, nondegree study, and pass/fail options in certain courses. Students may study abroad in England, Uzbekistan, and Israel, where HSU is involved in an ongoing archaeological excavation of Early Christian sites.

Faculty/Classroom: Seventy-four percent of faculty are male; 26%, female. All teach undergraduates. No introductory courses are taught by graduate students. The average class size in an introductory lecture is 25; in a laboratory, 16; and in a regular course offering, 18.

Admissions: About 91% of the 1993–94 applicants were accepted. The SAT scores for the 1993–94 freshman class were as follows: Verbal—65% below 500, 25% between 500 and 599, 9% between 600 and 700, and 1% above 700; Math—46% below 500, 32% between 500 and 599, 19% between 600 and 700, and 2% above 700. The ACT scores were 38% below 21, 23% between 21 and 23, 23% between 24 and 26, 9% between 27 and 28, and 7% above 28. About 39% of the current freshmen were in the top fifth of their class; 87% were in the top two fifths. Twelve freshmen graduated first in their class.

Requirements: HSU requires applicants to be in the upper 50% of their class. The SAT I or ACT is required. Graduation from an accredited secondary school is required; a GED will be accepted. Applicants should submit an academic record of at least 16 units, distributed as follows: 3 units of English, 2 units each of mathematics, science, and social studies, and 7 units of electives. AP and CLEP credits are accepted.

Procedure: Application deadlines are open. The application fee is $25. There are early decision and early admissions plans. About 4 early decision candidates were accepted for the 1993–94 class.

Transfer: About 148 transfer students enrolled in 1993–94. Applicants must submit official transcripts from all previous colleges. Grades of D do not transfer; however, a student may petition to transfer up to 2 D grades if the overall GPA is 2.0 or higher. Students transferring from a two-year college may receive credit for up to 66 semester hours of transferable courses. Applicants with fewer than 30 hours must submit a high school transcript and official report of ACT or SAT I scores. Students ineligible to continue at another istitution are not eligible for regular admission to HSU. A total of 30 credits out of 124 must be completed at HSU.

Visiting: There are regularly scheduled orientations for prospective students. There are guides for informal visits and visitors may sit in on classes and stay overnight at the school. To arrange for a visit, contact the Admissions Office, Drawer M, HSU Station, Abilene, TX 79698 or call (915) 670-1206.

Financial Aid: In 1993–94 89% of all students received some form of financial aid. About 61% of all students received need-based aid. The average freshman award was $6367. Of that total, scholarships or need-based grants averaged $2325 ($12,000 maximum); loans averaged $2978 ($12,000 maximum); and work contracts averaged

$383 ($3000 maximum). Forty-five percent of undergraduate students work part-time. The average financial indebtedness of the 1992–93 graduate was $13,000. The FAF, FFS, or SFS is required.

International Students: There are currently 12 international students enrolled. They must take the TOEFL and achieve a minimum score of 550. The student must also take the SAT I or the ACT.

Computers: The college provides computer facilities for student use. The mainframe is an IBM 4361. There are also microcomputers in laboratories available for student use. All students may access the system. There are no time limits and no fees.

Graduates: In 1992–93 227 bachelor's degrees were awarded. The most popular majors among graduates were physical education (7%), nursing (7%), and psychology (7%). Within an average freshman class, 21% graduate in 4 years, 5% in 5 years, and 2% in 6 years.

Admissions Contact: Laura Moore, Director of Admissions.

HOUSTON BAPTIST UNIVERSITY
E-3
Houston, TX 77074–3298

(713) 995–3210
(800) 969–3210 (in-state)

Full-time: 479 men, 794 women	Faculty: 108
Part-time: 113 men, 317 women	Ph.D.s: 71%
Graduate: 186 men, 302 women	Student/Faculty: 12 to 1
Year: quarters, summer session	Tuition: $8175
Application Deadline: open	Room & Board: $2880
Freshman Class: 378 applied, 223 accepted, 219 enrolled	
SAT I: 420/500	ACT: 21 COMPETITIVE

Houston Baptist University, founded in 1960, is a private institution affiliated with the Baptist General Convention of Texas and offering undergraduate programs in nursing, arts and science, music, and business administration. There are 7 undergraduate and 3 graduate schools. In addition to regional accreditation, HBU has baccalaureate program accreditation with NLN. The library contains 157,119 volumes, 303,238 microform items, and 4100 audiovisual forms, and subscribes to 1003 periodicals. Computerized library sources and services include the card catalog, interlibrary loans, and database searching. Special learning facilities include a learning resource center and a TV station. The 100-acre campus is in an urban area in southwest Houston. Including residence halls, there are 16 buildings on campus.

Student Life: About 97% of undergraduates are from Texas. Students come from 19 states, 31 foreign countries, and Canada. Fifty-nine percent are white; 18% Asian American; 11% African American; 10% Hispanic. Thirty-four percent are Catholic. The average age of all undergraduates is 23.

Housing: A total of 450 students can be accommodated in college housing. College-sponsored living facilities include single-sex dormitories and off-campus apartments. On-campus housing is guaranteed for all 4 years and is available on a first-come, first-served basis. Seventy percent of students commute. Alcohol is not permitted. All students may keep cars on campus.

Activities: There are 2 local fraternities and 1 national fraternity; about 18% of women belong to 2 local and 1 national sororities. There are 23 groups on campus, including art, band, cheerleading, choir, chorus, computers, ethnic, honors, international, jazz band, newspaper, opera, orchestra, photography, political, professional, religious, student government, and yearbook. Popular campus events include Ornogah Beauty Pageant, Husky Revue, and Homecoming Events.

Sports: There are 9 intramural sports each for men and women. Athletic and recreation facilities include volleyball, basketball, and tennis courts, an indoor track, areas for track and field and soccer, and a gymnastics center.

Disabled Students: Eighty percent of the campus is accessible to disabled students. The following facilities are available: wheelchair ramps, elevators, special parking, and specially equipped rest rooms.

Campus Safety and Security: Campus safety and security measures include a 24-hour foot and vehicle patrol, an escort service, emergency telephones, and lighted pathways and sidewalks.

Programs of Study: HBU awards the B.A., B.S., B.B.A., B.M., and B.S.N. degrees. Associate and master's degrees also are awarded. Bachelor's degrees are awarded in BIOLOGICAL SCIENCE (biology/biological science), BUSINESS (accounting, banking and finance, business economics, and marketing/retailing/merchandising), COMMUNICATIONS AND THE ARTS (communications, English, fine arts, French, music, Spanish, and speech/debate/rhetoric), COMPUTER AND PHYSICAL SCIENCE (chemistry and mathematics), EDUCATION (art, early childhood, elementary, foreign languages, music, science, secondary, special, and teaching English as a second language/foreign language), HEALTH PROFESSIONS (medical laboratory technology, nursing, predentistry, and premedicine), SOCIAL SCIENCE (history, psychology, and sociology). Biology and chemistry (premedicine) are the strongest programs academically.

Required: To graduate, students must complete a minimum of 130 semester hours, satisfy a residence requirement of 32 semester hours including at least 12 hours of upper-level courses in the major and courses in Christianity, language and literature, and biology, chemistry, or physics or a foreign language and mathematics. Also required are a minimum 2.0 GPA, completion of the English Proficiency Examination, and 12 hours of senior seminars. Other requirements vary by program.

Special: HBU offers internships through its academic colleges, study abroad in 1 country, B.A.-B.S. degrees and dual majors in most areas, a 3–2 engineering degree with the University of Houston, work-study programs, credit for military experience, and pass/fail options.

Faculty/Classroom: No introductory courses are taught by graduate students. The average class size in an introductory lecture and a regular course offering is 17.

Admissions: About 59% of the 1993–94 applicants were accepted. The SAT scores for the 1993–94 freshman class were as follows: Verbal—82% below 500, 14% between 500 and 599, and 4% between 600 and 700; Math—50% below 500, 37% between 500 and 599, 9% between 600 and 700, and 4% above 700. The ACT scores were 40% below 21, 31% between 21 and 23, 18% between 24 and 26, 6% between 27 and 28, and 4% above 28. Six freshmen graduated first in their class.

Requirements: HBU requires applicants to be in the upper 50% of their class. The SAT I or ACT is required, with recommended minimum composite scores of 900 or 20, respectively. Applicants must be graduates of an accredited secondary school or have the GED. AP and CLEP credits are accepted. Important factors used in the admissions decision are recommendations by school officials, personality, intangible qualities, advanced placement or honor courses, extracurricular activities record, and leadership record.

Procedure: Freshmen are admitted to all sessions. Entrance exams should be taken in the fall of the senior year. Application deadlines are open. The application fee is $25. Notification is sent on a rolling basis. There are early decision and early admissions plans. Three early decision candidates were accepted for the 1993–94 class.

Transfer: Transfer students with fewer than 30 semester hours earned must submit high school and college transcripts and SAT I or ACT scores. All students must have a minimum 2.0 GPA. A total of 32 semester hours out of 130 must be completed at HBU.

Visiting: There are guides for informal visits and visitors may sit in on classes and stay overnight at the school. To arrange for a visit, contact the Office of Admissions at (800) 969–3210 or (713) 995–3210.

Financial Aid: In 1993–94 70% of all current freshmen received some form of financial aid. HBU is a member of CSS. The FAF, the college's own financial statement, and the FAFSA are required. The deadline for financial aid applications to ensure priority consideration is May 1.

International Students: There are currently 42 international students enrolled. They must take the TOEFL and achieve a minimum score of 600. The student must also take the SAT I or ACT.

Computers: The college provides computer facilities for student use. There are 18 IBM PCs available to students. All students may access the system from 8 A.M. to 10 P.M. There are no time limits and no fees.

Graduates: In 1992–93, 280 bachelor's degrees were awarded. Some 21 companies recruited on campus in 1992–93.

Admissions Contact: Estelle S. Jeu, Director of Admissions.

HOWARD PAYNE UNIVERSITY
C-3

Brownwood, TX 76801-2794

(915) 643-7809
(800) 880-4478 (out-of-state)

Full-time: 649 men, 561 women	Faculty: 84
Part-time: 138 men, 119 women	Ph.D.s: 59%
Graduate: none	Student/Faculty: 14 to 1
Year: semesters, summer session	Tuition: $5070
Application Deadline: August 15	Room & Board: $2982
Freshman Class: 516 applied, 454 accepted, 322 enrolled	
SAT I Verbal/Math: 405/458	ACT: 20 COMPETITIVE

Howard Payne University, founded in 1889 and affiliated with the Baptist General Convention of Texas, is a coeducational institution offering undergraduate programs in the arts and sciences, business administration, education, Christianity, music, and social sciences. There are 6 undergraduate schools. In addition to regional accreditation, HPU has baccalaureate program accreditation with NASM. The library contains 120,000 volumes, 28,600 microform items, and 3500 audiovisual forms, and subscribes to 862 periodicals. Computerized library sources and services include interlibrary loans and database searching. Special learning facilities include a children's literature center, an audio production facility, a TV production studio, and a video editing facility. The 29-acre campus is in a small town 120 miles southwest of Dallas/Forth Worth. Including residence halls, there are 21 buildings on campus.

Student Life: About 97% of undergraduates are from Texas. Students come from 19 states, 8 foreign countries, and Canada. Ninety-five percent are from public schools; 5% from private. Eighty-three percent are white. Eighty-three percent are Protestant; 16% are unknown or claim no religious affiliation. The average age of freshmen is 18.5; all undergraduates, 23.8. Thirty-four percent drop out by the end of their first year; 30% remain to graduate.

Housing: A total of 686 students can be accommodated in college housing. College-sponsored living facilities include single-sex dormitories and married-student housing. On-campus housing is guaranteed for all 4 years. Fifty-six percent of students commute. Alcohol is not permitted. All students may keep cars on campus.

Activities: About 12% of men belong to 8 local fraternities; about 18% of women belong to 4 local sororities. There are 36 groups on campus, including art, band, cheerleading, choir, chorus, computers, drama, ethnic, honors, jazz band, literary magazine, marching band, musical theater, newspaper, photography, professional, radio and TV, religious, social, social service, student government, and yearbook. Popular campus events include Homecoming, Christian Concerts, and College Preview Weekends.

Sports: There are 6 intercollegiate sports for men and 4 for women, and 4 intramural sports for men and 4 for women. Athletic and recreation facilities include basketball and volleyball courts, a gymnasium, a weight room, a practice field, a swimming pool, and a student union. The stadium seats 8000, and the largest auditorium/arena, 1500.

Disabled Students: The entire campus is accessible to disabled students. The following facilities are available: wheelchair ramps, elevators, special parking, specially equipped rest rooms, special class scheduling, and lowered drinking fountains.

Services: In addition to many counseling and information services, tutoring is available in some subjects. There is also remedial math, reading, and writing. A writing laboratory and computer laboratory are available for mathematics, computer science, and English.

Campus Safety and Security: Campus safety and security measures include informal discussions, pamphlets, posters, films, emergency telephones, and lighted pathways and sidewalks. In addition, there are 12-hour foot patrols, monthly dormitory meetings, 2 security seminars for the entire campus, and 24-hour telephone availability with on-duty officers carrying cellular phones.

Programs of Study: HPU awards the B.A., B.S., B.A.A.S, B.B.A., and B.M. degrees. Bachelor's degrees are awarded in BIOLOGICAL SCIENCE (biology/biological science), BUSINESS (accounting and business administration and management), COMMUNICATIONS AND THE ARTS (communications, dramatic arts, English, fine arts, music, and Spanish), COMPUTER AND PHYSICAL SCIENCE (chemistry, computer science, and mathematics), EDUCATION (art, business, early childhood, elementary, foreign languages, music, science, and secondary), ENGINEERING AND ENVIRONMENTAL DESIGN (environmental science), HEALTH PROFESSIONS (premedicine), SOCIAL SCIENCE (history, philosophy, political science/government, prelaw, psychology, religion, social science, social work, and sociology). Biology, chemistry, political science, sociology, and psychology are the strongest academically. Business management, elementary education, and physical education have the largest enrollments.

Required: To graduate, students must complete a minimum of 128 credit hours, 49 in general education courses, 30 to 36 in the major, and 18 to 24 in a minor, plus electives. A minimum 2.0 GPA is required. Students must take Bible, English, social science, computer science, fine arts, physical education, laboratory science, and mathematics courses. Requirement for students not obtaining the B.A. or B.S. vary.

Special: Cross-registration is offered with Howard County Community College and Hardin-Simmons University and internships are possible in social work and practice theology. HPU offers credit for experience for B.A.A.S. candidates only, and pass/fail options. Special programs include the Douglas MacArthur Academy of Freedom, an interdisciplinary honors program in the social sciences; a chemistry honors program; and a provisional program for underprepared students. There are 4 national honor societies on campus, including Phi Beta Kappa. Two departments have honors programs.

Faculty/Classroom: Seventy-two percent of faculty are male; 28%, female. All teach undergraduates. The average class size in an introductory lecture is 26; in a laboratory, 18; and in a regular course offering, 16.

Admissions: About 88% of the 1993–94 applicants were accepted. The SAT scores for the 1993–94 freshman class were as follows: Verbal—84% below 500, 12% between 500 and 599, 3% between 600 and 700, and 1% above 700; Math—62% below 500, 25% between 500 and 599, 12% between 600 and 700, and 1% above 700. The ACT scores were 54% below 21, 25% between 21 and 23, 12% between 24 and 26, 5% between 27 and 28, and 4% above 28. About 28% of the current freshmen were in the top fifth of their class; 61%

were in the top two fifths. There was 1 National Merit finalist. Five freshmen graduated first in their class.

Requirements: HPU requires applicants to be in the upper 50% of their class. A minimum GPA of 3.0 is required for unconditional admission. The SAT I or ACT is required. Applicants must be graduates of an accredited secondary school or have a GED and have completed 3 credits of English, 2 of science or mathematics, 1 in social science, and the remaining from courses approved by the Texas Education Agency. Graduates of high schools or home study programs that are not accredited by a regional or state accrediting agency will have their work reviewed by the admissions committee on an individual basis. AP and CLEP credits are accepted. Important factors used in the admissions decision are recommendations by school officials, leadership record, personality, intangible qualities, advanced placement or honor courses, and extracurricular activities record.

Procedure: Freshmen are admitted to all sessions. Entrance exams should be taken during the senior year. Applications should be filed by August 15 for fall entry and January 1 for spring entry, along with an application fee of $25. Notification is sent on a rolling basis. There is an early admissions plan.

Transfer: About 106 transfer students enrolled in 1993-94. Transfer students must be able to return to the university they are leaving and submit official transcripts from all previously attended colleges/universities. Students younger than 21 with fewer than 12 semester hours must submit SAT I or ACT scores. The same GPA per number of hours attempted is required of transfers as for continuing HPU students. A total of 32 credits out of 128 must be completed at HPU.

Visiting: There are regularly scheduled orientations for prospective students, including college preview weekends in the fall and spring. There are guides for informal visits and visitors may sit in on classes and stay overnight at the school. To arrange for a visit, contact the Recruiting Office at (800) 880-4478.

Financial Aid: In a recent year, 75% of all current freshmen and 85% of continuing students received some form of financial aid. About 55% of all students received need-based aid. The average freshman award was $5000. Of that total, scholarships or need-based grants averaged $1000 ($3000 maximum); loans averaged $2625 ($7500 maximum); and work contracts averaged $1200 ($2000 maximum). Sixty percent of undergraduate students work part-time. Average earnings from campus work for the school year are $1700. The average financial indebtedness of the 1992-93 graduate was $10,000. The FFS is required. The deadline for financial aid applications is May 1.

International Students: There are currently 7 international students enrolled. The school actively recruits these students. They must take the TOEFL and achieve a minimum score of 550. The student must also take the SAT I or ACT. Students must score 19 on the ACT or 830 on the SAT I for unconditional admission; otherwise, a provisional program may be available.

Computers: The college provides computer facilities for student use. Two computer laboratories are available to all students, one with 35 computers on a 286 Novell Local Area Network, and the other with 28 computers. Laboratory hours are 8 A.M. to 10 P.M., Monday through Friday. There are no time limits and no fees.

Graduates: In 1992-93 201 bachelor's degrees were awarded. The most popular majors among graduates were elementary education (13%), physical education (11%), and business management (11%). Within an average freshman class, 2% graduate in 3 years, 13% in 4 years, 25% in 5 years, and 27% in 6 years. Some 7 companies recruited on campus in an earlier year. In an earlier year's graduating class, 15% of the men and 10% of the women were enrolled in graduate school within 6 months of graduation; 80% of the men and 75% of the women had found employment.

Admissions Contact: Cheryl Mangrum, Admissions Officer.

HUSTON-TILLOTSON COLLEGE   D-3
Austin, TX 78702   (512) 505-3027

Full-time: 213 men, 242 women	Faculty: 41
Part-time: 36 men, 48 women	Ph.D.s: 42%
Graduate: none	Student/Faculty: 11 to 1
Year: 4-1-4, summer session	Tuition: $5040
Application Deadline: March 1	Room & Board: $3450
Freshman Class: 306 applied, 276 accepted, 206 enrolled	
ACT: 16	COMPETITIVE

Huston-Tillotson College, formed in 1952 by the merger of Tillotson College and Samuel Huston College, both founded in the mid-1870s, is a private liberal arts institution affiliated with the United Church of Christ and the United Methodist Church. The library contains 74,491 volumes, 52,476 microform items, and 3212 audiovisual forms, and subscribes to 320 periodicals. The 23-acre campus is in an urban area 78 miles north of San Antonio. Including residence halls, there are 12 buildings on campus.

Student Life: About 74% of undergraduates are from Texas. Students come from 20 states and 15 foreign countries. Seventy percent are from public schools; 30% from private. Seventy-eight percent are African American. Seventy-three percent are Protestant; 17% claim no religious affiliation; 10% Catholic. The average age of freshmen is 19. One percent drop out by the end of their first year.

Housing: A total of 386 students can be accommodated in college housing. College-sponsored living facilities include single-sex and coed dormitories. On-campus housing is available on a first-come, first-served basis. Priority is given to out-of-town students. Sixty-three percent of students commute. Alcohol is not permitted. All students may keep cars on campus.

Activities: There are 4 local and 4 national fraternities and 4 local and 4 national sororities. There are 7 groups on campus, including cheerleading, choir, chorus, drill team, honors, international, jazz band, newspaper, professional, religious, social, social service, student government, and yearbook.

Sports: There are 2 intercollegiate sports for men and 2 for women, and 2 intramural sports for men and 2 for women. Athletic and recreation facilities include an 800-seat gymnasium and a baseball field.

Disabled Students: The following facilities are available: wheelchair ramps, elevators, and special parking.

Services: In addition to many counseling and information services, tutoring is available in every subject. There is also remedial math, reading, and writing.

Campus Safety and Security: Campus safety and security measures include 24-hour foot and vehicle patrol and lighted pathways and sidewalks.

Programs of Study: The college awards the B.A. and B.S. degrees. Bachelor's degrees are awarded in BIOLOGICAL SCIENCE (biology/biological science), BUSINESS (accounting, business administration and management, hotel/motel and restaurant management, and marketing/retailing/merchandising), COMMUNICATIONS AND THE ARTS (communications, English, and music), COMPUTER AND PHYSICAL SCIENCE (chemistry, computer science, and mathematics), EDUCATION (education, elementary, and physical), SOCIAL SCIENCE (political science/government and sociology). Biology, computer science, and early childhood education are the strongest academically. Business administration, computer science, education, mass communication, accounting, and biology have the largest enrollments.

Required: All students must complete 120 credit hours, including 54 in the general education required curriculum, 30 in the major, plus elective courses and must earn a minimum 2.0 GPA. Core requirements include 18 hours of English and foreign languages, 9 each of mathematics/computer science and social sciences, 8 of natural science, 6 of physical education and health, 3 of philosophy, and 1 of psychology.

Special: The college offers co-op programs with area businesses and industry, internships, work-study programs, a B.A.-B.S. degree in hotel restaurant management, dual majors, a 3-2 engineering degree with Prairie View A&M University, and nondegree study. There is a freshman honors program on campus, as well as 4 national honor societies. One department has an honors program.

Faculty/Classroom: Fifty percent of faculty are male; 50%, female. All teach undergraduates and 4% do research. The average class size in an introductory lecture is 30; in a laboratory, 20; and in a regular course offering, 28.

Admissions: About 90% of the 1993-94 applicants were accepted. The ACT scores for the 1993-94 freshman class were as follows: 97% below 21 and 3% between 21 and 23. About 36% of the current freshmen were in the top fifth of their class; 51% were in the top two fifths. There was 1 National Merit semifinalist.

Requirements: The college requires applicants to be in the upper 50% of their class. A minimum GPA of 2.5 is required. The SAT I or ACT is required, with a minimum composite score of 700 on the SAT I or 15 on the ACT. Applicants should be high school graduates with 18 academic credits, including 4 in English, 3 in mathematics, 2 each in science and social studies, and 1 in physical education. AP and CLEP credits are accepted. Important factors used in the admissions decision are advanced placement or honor courses, parents or siblings attending the school, personality, intangible qualities, evidence of special talent, and recommendations by school officials.

Procedure: Freshmen are admitted fall, spring, and summer. Applications should be filed by March 1 for fall, spring, or summer entry, along with an application fee of $15. Notification is sent on a rolling basis. There is an early admissions plan.

Transfer: About 52 transfer students enrolled in 1993-94. Transfer applicants must submit transcripts from all colleges or universities attended and must have an overall G.P.A. of 2.0. Students with fewer than 15 credit hours must meet freshman entrance requirements. A total of 30 credits out of 120 must be completed at the college.

Visiting: There are regularly scheduled orientations for prospective students. There are guides for informal visits and visitors may sit in on classes and stay overnight at the school. To arrange for a visit, contact the Director of Admission at (512) 505-3027.

Financial Aid: In a recent year, 95% of all current freshmen and 89% of continuing students received some form of financial aid. The average freshman award was $6200. Of that total, scholarships or need-based grants averaged $5040 ($8490 maximum); loans averaged $2125 ($2625 maximum); and work contracts averaged $1375 ($1680 maximum). The average financial indebtedness of a recent year's graduate was $8500. The college is a member of CSS. The FAF, FFS or SFS are required. The deadline for financial aid applications is March 1.

International Students: There are currently 86 international students enrolled. They must take the TOEFL and achieve a minimum score of 500. The student must also take the SAT I or the ACT.

Computers: The college provides computer facilities for student use. The mainframe is a Tandem Non-Stop II. PCs are also available. All students may access the system. It may be used during laboratory hours. There are no time limits on using the system. The fee is $15.

Graduates: In a recent year, 52 bachelor's degrees were awarded. The most popular majors among graduates were business administration (30%), accounting (13%), and mass communication (9%). Some 80 companies recruited on campus in 1992-93.

Admissions Contact: Donnie J. Scott, Director of Admission.

INCARNATE WORD COLLEGE

D-4

San Antonio, TX 78209-6397

(210) 829-6005

Full-time: 486 men, 1199 women	Faculty: 138
Part-time: 127 men, 429 women	Ph.D.s: 64%
Graduate: 217 men, 349 women	Student/Faculty: 12 to 1
Year: semesters, summer session	Tuition: $8250
Application Deadline: open	Room & Board: $4057
Freshman Class: 1380 applied, 1106 accepted, 472 enrolled	
SAT I Verbal/Math: 441/480	ACT: 21 COMPETITIVE

Incarnate Word College, founded in 1881, is a liberal arts college affiliated with the Catholic Church that offers undergraduate programs in art, business, health science, education, music, religious studies, nursing, and fine arts. There are 3 undergraduate and 14 graduate schools. In addition to regional accreditation, IWC has baccalaureate program accreditation with AHEA, CAHEA, NCATE, and NLN. The 2 libraries contain 170,000 volumes, and subscribe to 700 periodicals. Computerized library sources and services include database searching. Special learning facilities include an art gallery and a media service center. The 56-acre campus is in an urban area 2 miles north of downtown San Antonio. Including residence halls, there are 17 buildings on campus.

Student Life: About 98% of undergraduates are from Texas. Students come from 19 states and 4 foreign countries. Eighty percent are from public schools; 20% from private. Forty-seven percent are Hispanic; 41% white. Most are Catholic. The average age of freshmen is 21.3; all undergraduates, 25.2. Nineteen percent drop out by the end of their first year; 72% remain to graduate.

Housing: A total of 526 students can be accommodated in college housing. College-sponsored living facilities include single-sex and coed dormitories and on-campus apartments. On-campus housing is guaranteed for all 4 years. Priority is given to out-of-town students. Eighty percent of students commute. All students may keep cars on campus.

Activities: There are many groups and organizations on campus, including cheerleading, choir, chorale, drama, drill team, honors, international, jazz band, literary magazine, newspaper, orchestra, pep band, political, religious, social, and student government. Popular campus events include Run for Brainpower, O'Fair Shenanigan's, Fashion Show, Incarnate Word Day, Weekend on Broadway, and Higher Education Week.

Sports: There are 6 intercollegiate sports for men and 5 for women, and 23 intramural sports for men and 23 for women. Athletic and recreation facilities include a convocation center, a field house, 8 tennis courts, 2 soccer fields, softball and baseball fields, a 1/4-mile track, a 3/4-mile jogging trail, gymnasium, basketball courts, and a swimming pool.

Disabled Students: Eighty-five percent of the campus is accessible to disabled students. The following facilities are available: wheelchair ramps, elevators, special parking, and specially equipped rest rooms.

Services: In addition to many counseling and information services, tutoring is available in most subjects. There is also remedial math, reading, and writing.

Campus Safety and Security: Campus safety and security measures include a professional security force on campus.

Programs of Study: IWC awards the B.A., B.S., B.B.A., and B.M. degrees. Master's degrees also are awarded. Bachelor's degrees are awarded in BIOLOGICAL SCIENCE (biology/biological science), BUSINESS (accounting, banking and finance, business administration

and management, hotel/motel and restaurant management, international business management, and marketing/retailing/merchandising), COMMUNICATIONS AND THE ARTS (communications, dance, dramatic arts, English, music, music business management, Spanish, and speech/debate/rhetoric), COMPUTER AND PHYSICAL SCIENCE (chemistry, information sciences and systems, and mathematics), EDUCATION (art, business, early childhood, elementary, middle school, music, science, secondary, and special), ENGINEERING AND ENVIRONMENTAL DESIGN (environmental science), HEALTH PROFESSIONS (medical laboratory technology, nuclear medical technology, nursing, predentistry, and premedicine), SOCIAL SCIENCE (dietetics, fashion design and technology, history, philosophy, political science/government, prelaw, psychology, religion, and sociology). Nursing and nutrition are the strongest academically. Business has the largest enrollment.

Required: To graduate, students must complete at least 128 credit hours, 36 to 51 in the major, with a minimum GPA of 2.0. Core curriculum requirements, include physical education, philosophy and theology, computer literacy, and Senior Synthesis, a course incorporating community service. Most majors require a minor or focus.

Special: IWC offers co-op programs with San Antonio, Palo Alto, and St. Phillip's Colleges, cross-registration with Our Lady of the Lake and St. Mary's Universities and Oblate School of Theology. Also available are internships in business and social sciences, study abroad in England, France, Mexico, Spain, Greece, Italy, Japan, and Central and South America, work-study, B.A.-B.S. degrees in fashion design, interior design, and fashion merchandising, dual majors, credit for experience or by exam, nondegree study, and pass/fail options. There is a freshman honors program on campus.

Faculty/Classroom: Forty-one percent of faculty are male; 59%, female. All teach undergraduates. The average class size in an introductory lecture is 40; in a laboratory, 24; and in a regular course offering, 30.

Admissions: About 80% of the 1993-94 applicants were accepted. About 48% of the current freshmen were in the top fifth of their class; 82% were in the top two fifths. About 6 freshmen graduated first in their class.

Requirements: IWC requires applicants to be in the upper 50% of their class. A minimum GPA of 2.0 is required. The SAT I or ACT is required, with minimum composite scores of 800 on the SAT I or 18 on the ACT. Applicants must be graduates of an accredited secondary school or have the GED and have completed 16 Carnegie units, including at least 4 units of English, 3 of social studies and history, 2 each of mathematics, science, and foreign language, and 1 of fine arts. In some cases, IWC may administer its own assessment tests for placement and require an interview. AP and CLEP credits are accepted. Important factors used in the admissions decision are advanced placement or honor courses, leadership record, extracurricular activities record, recommendations by school officials, and personality, intangible qualities.

Procedure: Freshmen are admitted to all sessions. Entrance exams should be taken in the junior or senior year of high school. Application deadlines are open. The application fee is $15. Notification is sent on a rolling basis. There are early decision, early admissions, and deferred admissions plans.

Transfer: About 115 transfer students enrolled in 1993-94. Transfer students must have a minimum 2.5 GPA if they have at least 30 transferable hours. Other students may have to take an academic assessment test and/or be individually reviewed, and submit high school and college records and SAT I or ACT scores. A total of 36 credits out of 128 must be completed at IWC.

Visiting: There are regularly scheduled orientations for prospective students. There are guides for informal visits and visitors may sit in on classes and stay overnight at the school. To arrange for a visit, contact the Office of Admissions at (210) 829-6005.

Financial Aid: In 1993-94 65% of all current freshmen and 63% of continuing students received some form of financial aid. About 62% of freshmen received need-based aid. The average freshman award was $3141. Of that total, scholarships or need-based grants averaged $1639 ($4195 maximum); loans averaged $1627 ($3125 maximum); and institutional grants averaged $1123 ($3125 maximum). Forty percent of undergraduate students work part-time. Average earnings from campus work for the school year are $2400. The average financial indebtedness of the 1992-93 graduate was $14,625. IWC is a member of CSS. The FAF is required. The deadline for financial aid applications is March 31.

International Students: There are currently 76 international students enrolled. They must take the TOEFL or the college's own test and achieve a minimum score on the TOEFL of 550.

Computers: The college provides computer facilities for student use. The mainframe is an HP9000. There are also more than 50 IBM PCs and compatibles in the academic computer laboratory. All students may access the system. It may be used 8 A.M. to 10 P.M. Monday through Thursday, 8 A.M. to 4 P.M. Friday, and 1 P.M. to 7 P.M. Sunday. There are no time limits on using the system. The fees are

$10 to $30 only if in a classroom setting. No fees are charged for individual use.

Graduates: In 1992–93 324 bachelor's degrees were awarded. The most popular majors among graduates were business (34%), nursing (13%), and communication arts (7%). Within an average freshman class, 72% graduate in 5 years. More than 20 companies recruited on campus in 1992–93. In the 1992 graduating class, 20% of all graduates were enrolled in graduate school within 6 months of graduation.

Admissions Contact: Sister Sally Mitchell, Dean of Enrollment.

JARVIS CHRISTIAN COLLEGE   E-2
Hawkins, TX 75765   (903) 769-5733

Full-time: 201 men, 277 women	Faculty: 54; IIB, --$
Part-time: 7 men, 11 women	Ph.D.s: 27%
Graduate: none	Student/Faculty: 9 to 1
Year: semesters, summer session	Tuition: $4110
Application Deadline: August 8	Room & Board: $3060
Freshman Class: 186 accepted, 131 enrolled	
SAT I: 307/361	ACT: 14 **LESS COMPETITIVE**

Jarvis Christian College, founded in 1913, is a private, liberal arts institution affiliated with the Disciples of Christ Church. The library contains 64,000 volumes and 1700 microform items, and subscribes to 400 periodicals. Special learning facilities include a learning resource center and TV studio. The 243-acre campus is in a rural area 100 miles southeast of Dallas.

Student Life: About 64% of undergraduates are from Texas. The average age of freshmen is 18; all undergraduates, 19. Forty-two percent drop out by the end of their first year; 40% remain to graduate.

Housing: College-sponsored living facilities include single-sex dormitories. Alcohol is not permitted. All students may keep cars on campus.

Activities: About 30% of men belong to fraternities; about 30% of women belong to sororities. There are some on campus, including chorus, drama, newspaper, professional, religious, student government, and yearbook.

Sports: Athletic and recreation facilities include a physical fitness laboratory, training rooms, an Olympic-size pool, a 2432-seat gymnasium, an auxiliary gymnasium, a dance studio, and playing and track fields.

Services: In addition to many counseling and information services, tutoring is available in most subjects. There is remedial math, reading, and writing.

Programs of Study: Jarvis awards the B.A., B.S., and B.B.A. degrees. Bachelor's degrees are awarded in BIOLOGICAL SCIENCE (biology/biological science), BUSINESS (accounting, management science, and marketing/retailing/merchandising), COMMUNICATIONS AND THE ARTS (English), COMPUTER AND PHYSICAL SCIENCE (chemistry, computer science, and mathematics), EDUCATION (elementary, music, reading, secondary, and special), HEALTH PROFESSIONS (premedicine), SOCIAL SCIENCE (criminal justice, history, political science/government, religion, and sociology).

Required: A 64-credit general education requirement includes courses in English, literature, mathematics, religion, science, history, speech, political and social sciences, health, and physical education. Other graduation requirements include a minimum 2.0 GPA, at least 124 credit hours, mathematics and writing proficiencies, and satisfactory scores on the sophomore comprehensive examination and on the GRE.

Special: Jarvis offers co-op and work-study programs, internships, study abroad, student-designed majors, a general studies degree, and a pass/fail option. Also available are the Brookhaven National Laboratory Semester Program, the UNCF Premedical Summer Program with Fisk University, the Biomedical Sciences Program with Meharry Medical College, and a joint degree program with St. John's University Law School. There is a freshman honors program on campus, as well as 3 national honor societies.

Admissions: The SAT scores for the 1993–94 freshman class were as follows: Verbal—all below 500; Math—all below 500. The ACT scores were 99% below 21 and 1% between 21 and 23.

Requirements: The SAT I or ACT is required. Applicants should graduate from an accredited secondary school with 16 academic credits, including 3 each in English and social science, 2 in mathematics, and 1 in science. The GED is accepted. Graduates of nonaccredited high schools are given conditional admission. AP and CLEP credits are accepted.

Procedure: Freshmen are admitted to all sessions. Entrance exams should be taken before entrance or during orientation week. Applications should be filed by August 8 for fall entry and December 1 for winter entry, along with an application fee of $15. The college accepts all applicants. Notification is sent on a rolling basis. There is an early admissions plan.

Transfer: Applicants must submit official transcripts from all schools of higher education attended and provide proof of honorable dismissal from the most recent one.

Financial Aid: In an earlier year, 97% of all current freshmen received some form of financial aid. Scholarships or need-based grants averaged $1000; loans averaged $1500; and work contracts averaged $1000. Jarvis is a member of CSS. The FFS and the college's own financial statement are required.

International Students: The school actively recruits international students. They must take the TOEFL (with a minimum required score of 500) and the ACT.

Computers: The college provides computer facilities for student use. The computer laboratory is on the first floor of the library. Students enrolled in computer-relevant courses may access the system.

Admissions Contact: Anetha D. Francis, Recruitment and Admissions Coorindator.

LAMAR UNIVERSITY   E-3
Beaumont, TX 77710   (409) 880-8888; (800) 458-7558

Full-time: 2331 men, 2661 women	Faculty: 428; IIA, --$
Part-time: 1554 men, 2278 women	Ph.D.s: 61%
Graduate: none	Student/Faculty: 12 to 1
Year: semesters, summer session	Tuition: $1298 ($4418)
Application Deadline: August 10	Room & Board: $2500
Freshman Class: 1971 applied, 1339 accepted, 863 enrolled	
SAT I Verbal/Math: 413/459	**COMPETITIVE**

Lamar University-Beaumont, founded in 1923, is part of the Lamar University System. The university offers undergraduate degrees in arts and sciences, business, education, engineering, fine arts, communications, health and behavioral science, and technical arts. There are 7 undergraduate and 5 graduate schools. In addition to regional accreditation, Lamar has baccalaureate program accreditation with AACSB, ABET, CSWE, NASM, and NCATE. The library contains 900,000 volumes, and subscribes to 2800 periodicals. Computerized library sources and services include the card catalog, interlibrary loans, and database searching. Special learning facilities include a learning resource center, art gallery, and radio station. The 200-acre campus is in an urban area 90 miles east of Houston. Including residence halls, there are 90 buildings on campus.

Student Life: About 96% of undergraduates are from Texas. Students come from 39 states, 61 foreign countries, and Canada. Ninety-five percent are from public schools; 5% from private. Seventy-nine percent are white; 16% African American. The average age of freshmen is 19; all undergraduates, 25. Forty percent drop out by the end of their first year; 19% remain to graduate.

Housing: A total of 1700 students can be accommodated in college housing. College-sponsored living facilities include dormitories, on-campus apartments, fraternity houses, and sorority houses. In addition there are special interest houses. On-campus housing is guaranteed for all 4 years. Ninety-one percent of students commute. Alcohol is not permitted. All students may keep cars on campus.

Activities: About 5% of men belong to 11 national fraternities; about 5% of women belong to 7 national sororities. There are 120 groups on campus, including art, band, cheerleading, choir, chorale, chorus, computers, dance, drama, ethnic, film, honors, international, jazz band, literary magazine, marching band, musical theater, newspaper, opera, orchestra, pep band, photography, political, professional, radio and TV, religious, social, social service, student government, and symphony. Popular campus events include Springfest, Birdfeed, Love Lamar Week, and Honors Brunch.

Sports: There are 7 intercollegiate sports for men and 6 for women, and 15 intramural sports for men and 15 for women. Athletic and recreation facilities include a 10,000-seat multipurpose facility for basketball and other sports; a student center with games areas and a video lounge; a gymnasium; an indoor/outdoor pool; a track; and a 17,000-seat stadium.

Disabled Students: The entire campus is accessible to disabled students. The following facilities are available: wheelchair ramps, elevators, special parking, specially equipped rest rooms, special class scheduling, lowered drinking fountains, and lowered telephones.

Services: In addition to many counseling and information services, tutoring is available in some subjects, including mathematics and English. In addition, there is a reader service for the blind, and remedial math, reading, and writing.

Campus Safety and Security: Campus safety and security measures include 24-hour foot and vehicle patrol, self defense education, informal discussions, and pamphlets, posters, and films. In addition, there are lighted pathways and sidewalks.

Programs of Study: Lamar awards the B.A., B.S., B.A.A.S., B.B.A., B.F.A., B.G.S., and B.S.W. degrees. Associate, master's, and doctoral degrees also are awarded. Bachelor's degrees are awarded in BIOLOGICAL SCIENCE (biology/biological science), BUSINESS (accounting, business administration and management, business economics, business law, marketing/retailing/merchandising, and personnel management), COMMUNICATIONS AND THE ARTS (advertising, communications, design, dramatic arts, English, fine arts, French, music, Spanish, and speech/debate/rhetoric), COMPUTER

AND PHYSICAL SCIENCE (chemistry, computer programming, computer science, geology, information sciences and systems, mathematics, and physics), EDUCATION (art, early childhood, elementary, foreign languages, health, home economics, music, science, secondary, and special), ENGINEERING AND ENVIRONMENTAL DESIGN (chemical engineering, civil engineering, electrical/electronics engineering, industrial engineering, industrial engineering technology, and mechanical engineering), HEALTH PROFESSIONS (medical laboratory technology, nursing, occupational therapy, pharmacy, physical therapy, predentistry, premedicine, and speech pathology/audiology), SOCIAL SCIENCE (criminal justice, economics, history, political science/government, prelaw, psychology, public administration, social science, social work, and sociology). Engineering is the strongest academically. Arts and sciences have the largest enrollments.

Required: To graduate, all students must complete 124 to 132 total credit hours, with 30 hours in the major. Required courses include 6 hours each of electives, political science, and American history, 12 hours of English, and 4 hours each of laboratory science or mathematics and physical activity and/or marching band and/or ROTC. Students must have a minimum 2.0 GPA.

Special: The university offers internships in social work, work-study programs, B.A.-B.S. degrees, dual majors in biochemistry, the general studies degree, credit for experience, nondegree study, and pass/fail options. There is a freshman honors program on campus, as well as 2 national honor societies, including Phi Beta Kappa.

Faculty/Classroom: Fifty-eight percent of faculty are male; 42%, female. All teach undergraduates. The average class size in an introductory lecture is 50; in a laboratory, 25; and in a regular course offering, 24.

Admissions: About 68% of the 1993–94 applicants were accepted.

Requirements: A minimum GPA of 2.0 is required. The SAT I or ACT is required, with a minimum composite score of 850 on the SAT I or 20 on the ACT. SAT II: Subject tests in mathematics are required for engineering and physical science majors. Applicants must be graduates of an accredited secondary school or have a GED certificate, and must have completed 4 credits of English, 3 of mathematics, 2 of science, and 2 1/2 of history. AP and CLEP credits are accepted. Important factors used in the admissions decision are advanced placement or honor courses, evidence of special talent, leadership record, recommendations by school officials, and parents or siblings attending the school.

Procedure: Freshmen are admitted to all sessions. Entrance exams should be taken in the fall of the senior year. Applications should be filed by August 10 for fall entry, December 1 for spring entry, and May 1 for summer entry. Notification is sent on a rolling basis.

Transfer: A total of 467 transfer students enrolled in a recent year. Transfer students must have a minimum 2.0 GPA and at least 18 credit hours earned. A total of 30 credits out of 124 to 132 must be completed at Lamar.

Visiting: There are regularly scheduled orientations for prospective students. There are guides for informal visits. To arrange for a visit, contact the Admissions Office at (800) 458–7558.

Financial Aid: In an earlier year, 58% of all freshmen and 34% of continuing students received some form of financial aid. Scholarships or need-based grants averaged $1089 ($2550 maximum); loans averaged $1368 ($2625 maximum); and work contracts averaged $1070 ($2600 maximum). Sixty-three percent of undergraduate students work part-time. The average financial indebtedness of an earlier year's graduate was $3427. Lamar is a member of CSS. The FAF and the college's own financial statement are required. The deadline for financial aid applications is April 1.

International Students: There are currently 375 international students enrolled. They must take the TOEFL and achieve a minimum score of 500. The student must also take the SAT I or the ACT, and achieve a minimum composite score of 800 on the SAT I or 18 on the ACT.

Computers: The university provides computer facilities for student use. The mainframe is a Honeywell DPS 8/49. There are also 300 AT&T, IBM, Compaq, Sperry, and Apple PCs available throughout the campus. All students may access the system. There are no time limits on using the system. The fees are $30 per semester.

Graduates: In an earlier year, 1010 bachelor's degrees were awarded.

Admissions Contact: Director of Admissions.

LE TOURNEAU UNIVERSITY

E-2

Longview, TX 75607   (903) 753–0231; (800) 759–8811 (in-state)

Full-time: 1498 men and women	Faculty: 49; IIB, -$
Part-time: 113 men and women	Ph.D.s: 65%
Graduate: 134 men and women	Student/Faculty: 31 to 1
Year: semesters, summer session	Tuition: $8340
Application Deadline: August 15	Room & Board: $4040
Freshman Class: 683 applied, 661 accepted, 298 enrolled	
SAT I Verbal/Math: 491/552	ACT: 24 COMPETITIVE +

Le Tourneau University, founded in 1946, is a private, interdenominational Christian university offering programs in aviation, business administration, engineering, education, liberal arts, and technology. There are 7 undergraduate schools and one graduate school. In addition to regional accreditation, Le Tourneau has baccalaureate program accreditation with ABET. The library contains 98,650 volumes, 38,520 microform items, and 468 audiovisual forms, and subscribes to 495 periodicals. Computerized library sources and services include the card catalog, interlibrary loans, and database searching. Special learning facilities include a learning resource center. The 163-acre campus is in an urban area 60 miles east of Shreveport, Louisiana. Including residence halls, there are 52 buildings on campus.

Student Life: About 55% of undergraduates are from out-of-state, mostly the Northeast. Students come from 45 states, 27 foreign countries, and Canada. Fifty-nine percent are from public schools; 41% from private. Eighty-nine percent are white. Most are Protestant. The average age of freshmen is 19. Twenty-eight percent drop out by the end of their first year; 55% remain to graduate.

Housing: A total of 727 students can be accommodated in college housing. College-sponsored living facilities include single-sex dormitories, married-student housing, and fraternity houses. In addition there are society houses for men. On-campus housing is guaranteed for all 4 years. Sixty-eight percent of students live on campus; of those, 95% remain on campus on weekends. Alcohol is not permitted. All students may keep cars on campus.

Activities: There are no fraternities or sororities on campus. There are 25 groups on campus, including choir, chorale, chorus, computers, drama, honors, international, jazz band, newspaper, pep band, photography, political, professional, religious, social, social service, student government, and yearbook. Popular campus events include Spiritual Emphasis Week, Fall Retreat, athletic tournaments, Fall Fest Week, Frontier Week, and Missions Emphasis Week.

Sports: There are 4 intercollegiate sports for men and 2 for women, and 22 intramural sports for men and 6 for women. Athletic and recreation facilities include soccer, baseball, and intramural fields, a 1000-seat gymnasium, a 1000-seat arena/auditorium, and a games area.

Disabled Students: Ninety percent of the campus is accessible to disabled students. The following facilities are available: wheelchair ramps, elevators, special parking, and specially equipped rest rooms.

Services: In addition to many counseling and information services, tutoring is available in most subjects.

Campus Safety and Security: Campus safety and security measures include 24-hour foot and vehicle patrol, informal discussions, pamphlets, posters, films, and lighted pathways and sidewalks.

Programs of Study: Le Tourneau awards the B.A. and B.S. degrees. Associate and master's degrees also are awarded. Bachelor's degrees are awarded in BIOLOGICAL SCIENCE (biology/biological science), BUSINESS (accounting, business administration and management, and marketing/retailing/merchandising), COMMUNICATIONS AND THE ARTS (English), COMPUTER AND PHYSICAL SCIENCE (chemistry, computer science, and mathematics), EDUCATION (business, physical, science, and secondary), ENGINEERING AND ENVIRONMENTAL DESIGN (aviation computer technology, electrical/electronics engineering, engineering, engineering technology, industrial administration/management, mechanical engineering, and welding engineering), HEALTH PROFESSIONS (medical laboratory technology), SOCIAL SCIENCE (history, public administration, and religion). Engineering, computer science, and mathematics are the strongest academically. Engineering and aviation have the largest enrollments.

Required: All students must fulfill general curricula requirements, including 12 hours of biblical studies, 9 of English, 8 of laboratory science, and 6 of humanities and social science, as well as 4 of physical education and 1 of computer science. A total of at least 124 semester credit hours with a minimum GPA of 2.0 is required in order to graduate.

Special: Le Tourneau offers co-op programs in engineering, business, and accounting, internships through business and liberal arts programs, an American studies program with the Christian College Coalition, and credit for experience. There is a freshman honors program on campus

Faculty/Classroom: Eighty-five percent of faculty are male; 15%, female. All teach undergraduates. The average class size in an introductory lecture is 30; in a laboratory, 15; and in a regular course offering, 15.

Admissions: About 97% of the 1993–94 applicants were accepted. The SAT scores for the 1993–94 freshman class were as follows: Verbal—51% below 500, 32% between 500 and 599, 15% between 600 and 700, and 2% above 700; Math—31% below 500, 26% between 500 and 599, 30% between 600 and 700, and 12% above 700. The ACT scores were 29% below 21, 23% between 21 and 23, 27% between 24 and 26, 11% between 27 and 28, and 10% above 28. There was 1 National Merit finalist. Ten freshmen graduated first in their class.

Requirements: Le Tourneau requires applicants to be in the upper 50% of their class. A minimum GPA of 2.0 is required. The SAT I, with a recommended minimum composite score of 800, or the ACT, with a recommended minimum score of 20, is required. Applicants must be graduates of an accredited secondary school or have the GED and have completed 16 academic credits, including 4 in English, 2 each in mathematics and social studies, 1 in natural science, and 7 in electives. An essay is required. AP and CLEP credits are accepted. Important factors used in the admissions decision are extracurricular activities record, leadership record, personality, intangible qualities, evidence of special talent, and recommendations by school officials.

Procedure: Freshmen are admitted to all sessions. Entrance exams should be taken by the fall of the senior year. Applications should be filed by August 15 for fall entry and December 1 for spring entry, along with an application fee of $20. Notification is sent on a rolling basis.

Transfer: About 83 transfer students enrolled in a recent year. Transfer students with at least 26 semester hours must have a minimum 2.0 GPA. Other students must satisfy freshman entrance requirements. A total of 30 credits out of 124 must be completed at Le Tourneau.

Visiting: There are regularly scheduled orientations for prospective students. Visits are individualized and may include a tour, attendance of classes, special events, or chapel, meeting with faculty and financial aid personnel, and staying in a dormitory. There are guides for informal visits and visitors may sit in on classes and stay overnight at the school. To arrange for a visit, contact the Visitor Coordinator at (800) 759–8811 (in-state) or (903) 753–0231.

Financial Aid: In an earlier year, 80% of all current freshmen and 82% of continuing students received some form of financial aid. About 76% of freshmen and 85% of continuing students received need-based aid. The average freshman award was $6000. Of that total, scholarships or need-based grants averaged $1000 ($6056 maximum); loans averaged $2500 ($3800 maximum); and work contracts averaged $940 ($2000 maximum). Fifty-five percent of undergraduate students work part-time. Average earnings from campus work for the school year are $940. The average financial indebtedness of a recent year's graduate was $11,904. Le Tourneau is a member of CSS. The FAF and FFS or SFS are required. The FAFSA is preferred. is required. The deadline for financial aid applications is February 15.

International Students: There are currently 51 international students enrolled. They must take the TOEFL and achieve a minimum score of 500. The student must also take the SAT I or the ACT and achieve a minimum composite score of 800 on the SAT I or 20 on the ACT.

Computers: The college provides computer facilities for student use. The mainframe is a MicroVAX. There are 5 computers in the library and 5 in the CAD laboratory. All students may access the system. There are no time limits and no fees.

Graduates: In a recent year, 151 bachelor's degrees were awarded. The most popular majors among graduates were engineering (51%), business and management (36%), and computer science (7%). Some 20 companies recruited on campus in a recent year.

Admissions Contact: Howard Wilson, Dean of Enrollment.

LUBBOCK CHRISTIAN UNIVERSITY B-2
Lubbock, TX 79407

(806) 796–8800, ext. 260
(800) 933–7601 (in-state)

Full-time: 386 men, 482 women	Faculty: 50; IIB, --$
Part-time: 95 men, 135 women	Ph.D.s: 60%
Graduate: 17 men, 1 woman	Student/Faculty: 17 to 1
Year: semesters, summer session	Tuition: $7040
Application Deadline: open	Room & Board: $2800
Freshman Class: n/av	
ACT: 21	NONCOMPETITIVE

Lubbock Christian University, founded in 1957 in affiliation with the Churches of Christ, offers undergraduate degrees in liberal arts and professional studies. There are 2 undergraduate schools and one graduate school. The library contains 93,700 volumes and 68,072 microform items, and subscribes to 593 periodicals. Special learning facilities include an art gallery. The 20-acre campus is in a suburban area. Including residence halls, there are 19 buildings on campus.

Student Life: About 66% of undergraduates are from Texas. Students come from 38 states, 15 foreign countries, and Canada. Eighty-five percent are white. The average age of freshmen is 20; all undergraduates, 23.

Housing: A total of 650 students can be accommodated in college housing. College-sponsored living facilities include single-sex dormitories, on-campus apartments, and married-student housing. On-campus housing is guaranteed for all 4 years. Sixty percent of students live on campus. Alcohol is not permitted. All students may keep cars on campus.

Activities: There are no fraternities or sororities on campus. There are 20 groups on campus, including cheerleading, chorus, computers, drama, honors, jazz band, musical theater, newspaper, pep band, professional, religious, social, student government, and yearbook. Popular campus events include High School Days, Super-Son-sational, Encore, Twirp Week, and Winter Fest.

Sports: There are 3 intercollegiate sports for men and 3 for women, and 20 intramural sports for men and 20 for women. Athletic and recreation facilities include a field house, a stadium, an intramural field, Chap Stadium, and game rooms.

Disabled Students: The following facilities are available: wheelchair ramps, elevators, special parking, specially equipped rest rooms, and special class scheduling.

Services: In addition to many counseling and information services, tutoring is available in every subject. There is also a reader service for the blind, and remedial math, reading, and writing.

Campus Safety and Security: Campus safety and security measures include 24-hour foot and vehicle patrol and lighted pathways and sidewalks.

Programs of Study: Lubbock Christian awards the B.A., B.S., and B.S.Ed. degrees. Associate and master's degrees also are awarded. Bachelor's degrees are awarded in AGRICULTURE (agricultural business management and animal science), BIOLOGICAL SCIENCE (biology/biological science), BUSINESS (accounting, banking and finance, and business administration and management), COMMUNICATIONS AND THE ARTS (art, communications, English, fine arts, journalism, music, Spanish, and speech/debate/rhetoric), COMPUTER AND PHYSICAL SCIENCE (chemistry and mathematics), EDUCATION (art, business, elementary, home economics, middle school, music, physical, science, and secondary), HEALTH PROFESSIONS (predentistry and premedicine), SOCIAL SCIENCE (history, prelaw, psychology, religion, social work, and sociology). Education is the strongest academically. Business has the largest enrollment.

Required: To graduate, students must complete 132 credit hours, including at least 44 upper-division courses and 30 to 33 hours in the major, with a minimum GPA of 2.0 overall and 2.25 in the major. All students must fulfill general education and biblical studies course requirements.

Special: Lubbock Christian offers co-op programs in engineering and computer sciences, internships in biblical studies, psychology, and social work, and cross-registration with Texas Tech University and its School of Allied Health. A general studies degree, a 3–2 engineering degree, student-designed majors, nondegree study, and pass/fail options are also available.

Admissions: There was 1 National Merit finalist.

Requirements: The SAT I or ACT is required. Applicants must be graduates of an accredited secondary school or have a GED certificate. A portfolio or audition (in applicable majors) and an interview are recommended. AP credits are accepted. Important factors used in the admissions decision are ability to finance college education, advanced placement or honor courses, parents or siblings attending the school, evidence of special talent, and leadership record.

Procedure: Freshmen are admitted to all sessions. Entrance exams should be taken before registration. Application deadlines are open. Application fee is $10. Notification is sent on a rolling basis. A waiting list is an active part of the admissions procedure.

Transfer: About 80 transfer students enrolled in a recent year. Transfer students with fewer than 16 hours of college credit must meet freshman admission requirements, submit an official transcript from previously attended colleges or universities, and have a minimum GPA of 2.0. A total of 30 credits out of 132 must be completed at Lubbock Christian.

Visiting: There are regularly scheduled orientations for prospective students. There are guides for informal visits and visitors may sit in on classes and stay overnight at the school. To arrange for a visit, contact Steve German, Director of Recruiting at (806) 792–3221.

Financial Aid: In an earlier year, 95% of all students received some form of financial aid. The FFS is required. The deadline for financial aid applications is July 15.

International Students: There are currently 47 international students enrolled. They must take the TOEFL and achieve a minimum score of 500.

Computers: The college provides computer facilities for student use. The mainframe is a DEC MicroVax. There are also 14 IBM-compatible microcomputers available in the computer laboratory, 10 computers in the English laboratory, 6 in the science laboratory, and 20 in the Sucess 2000 laboratory. All students may access the system. There are no time limits on using the system. The fees are $25.

Graduates: In 1992–93, 160 bachelor's degrees were awarded.

Admissions Contact: Steve German, Dean of Admissions.

MCMURRY UNIVERSITY

Abilene, TX 79697

C-2

(915) 691-6402

Full-time: 388 men, 492 women
Part-time: 247 men, 230 women
Graduate: none
Year: semesters, summer session
Application Deadline: August 15
Freshman Class: 578 applied, 411 accepted, 187 enrolled
SAT I Verbal/Math: 410/500

Faculty: 70
Ph.D.s: 66%
Student/Faculty: 13 to 1
Tuition: $6648
Room & Board: $3452

ACT: 21

COMPETITIVE

McMurry University, chartered in 1923, is a private liberal arts institution affiliated with the United Methodist Church. There are 4 undergraduate schools. In addition to regional accreditation, McMurry has baccalaureate program accreditation with NLN. The library contains 137,010 volumes, 410 microform items, and 991 audiovisual forms, and subscribes to 615 periodicals. Computerized library sources and services include the card catalog, interlibrary loans, and database searching. Special learning facilities include a learning resource center and art gallery. The 41-acre campus is in a suburban area 180 miles west of Dallas. Including residence halls, there are 19 buildings on campus.

Student Life: About 94% of undergraduates are from Texas. Students come from 18 states and 2 foreign countries. Ninety-six percent are from public schools; 4% from private. Seventy-nine percent are white; 10% African American. Seventy-four percent are Protestant; 13% claim no religious affiliation; 13% Catholic. The average age of freshmen is 19; all undergraduates, 24. Thirty-nine percent drop out by the end of their first year; 29% remain to graduate.

Housing: A total of 574 students can be accommodated in college housing. College-sponsored living facilities include single-sex dormitories. On-campus housing is available on a first-come, first-served basis. Fifty-one percent of students commute. Alcohol is not permitted. All students may keep cars on campus.

Activities: About 30% of men belong to 7 local fraternities; about 23% of women belong to 6 local sororities. There are 31 groups on campus, including art, band, cheerleading, choir, chorale, computers, dance, drama, ethnic, honors, jazz band, literary magazine, marching band, musical theater, newspaper, political, professional, religious, social, social service, student government, and yearbook. Popular campus events include Homecoming, Parents Weekend, Black History Week, Women's History Week, and Spring fling.

Sports: There are 4 intercollegiate sports for men and 3 for women, and 15 intramural sports for men and 13 for women. Athletic and recreation facilities include a 4500-seat stadium, an intramural and a 2200-seat gymnasium, a 1500-seat auditorium, a swimming pool and diving area, 2 racquetball courts, and basketball, volleyball, and badminton courts.

Disabled Students: Seventy percent of the campus is accessible to disabled students. The following facilities are available: wheelchair ramps, elevators, special parking, specially equipped rest rooms, and lowered drinking fountains.

Services: In addition to many counseling and information services, tutoring is available in some subjects, including algebra, calculus, chemistry, physics, accounting, Spanish, computer science, study skills, English, and writing across the disciplines. There is also remedial math, reading, and writing.

Campus Safety and Security: Campus safety and security measures include 24-hour foot and vehicle patrol, emergency telephones, and lighted pathways and sidewalks.

Programs of Study: McMurry awards the B.A., B.S., B.B.A., B.F.A., B.Mus., and B.Mus.Ed. degrees. Associate degrees also are awarded. Bachelor's degrees are awarded in BIOLOGICAL SCIENCE (biology/biological science), BUSINESS (accounting, banking and finance, business administration and management, business economics, and marketing/retailing/merchandising), COMMUNICATIONS AND THE ARTS (ceramic art and design, communications, dramatic arts, English, music, and Spanish), COMPUTER AND PHYSICAL SCIENCE (chemistry, computer programming, computer science, mathematics, and natural sciences), EDUCATION (elementary, music, physical, and secondary), HEALTH PROFESSIONS (medical laboratory technology, nursing, predentistry, and premedicine), SOCIAL SCIENCE (economics, history, paralegal studies, philosophy, political science/government, prelaw, psychology, religion, social science, and sociology). Education, biology, chemistry, English, history, and nursing are the strongest academically. Education, business, biology,

sociology, psychology, nursing, and English have the largest enrollments.

Required: Students must complete 126 semester hours, including 27 in the major, with a GPA of at least 2.0. Distribution requirements vary with the degree but include courses in English, ethics, humanities, fine arts, mathematics, social science, religion, political science, sociology, history, science, foreign language, and health fitness.

Special: McMurry offers internships in business and sociology, co-op programs, and cross-registration with Abilene Christian and Hardin-Simmons Universities. There are work-study programs with the college and area businesses for seniors. B.A.-B.S. degrees in business administration, accounting, banking and finance, biology, chemistry, multidisciplinary studies, nursing, and computer science and dual majors in mathematics/computer science, church music, and chemistry-business administration are available. There is a freshman honors program on campus, as well as 15 national honor societies. Eleven departments have honors programs.

Faculty/Classroom: Seventy-five percent of faculty are male; 25%, female. All teach undergraduates and 32% both teach and do research. The average class size in an introductory lecture is 16; in a laboratory, 12; and in a regular course offering, 10.

Admissions: About 71% of the 1993–94 applicants were accepted. The SAT scores for the 1993–94 freshman class were as follows: Verbal—82% below 500, 16% between 500 and 599, and 2% between 600 and 700; Math—50% below 500, 27% between 500 and 599, 15% between 600 and 700, and 8% above 700. The ACT scores were 42% below 21, 31% between 21 and 23, 17% between 24 and 26, 6% between 27 and 28, and 5% above 28. About 43% of the current freshmen were in the top fifth of their class; 76% were in the top two fifths. Six freshmen graduated first in their class.

Requirements: McMurry requires applicants to be in the upper 50% of their class. A minimum GPA of 2.0 is required. The SAT I or ACT is required, with a minimum composite score of 780 on the SAT I or 19 on the ACT. Those making the minimum score must rank in the top 40% of their high school class. Applicants need 16 academic credits, including 4 units of English, 3 each in mathematics and social studies, and 2 each in foreign language and science. An essay and interview are recommended. The GED is accepted. AP and CLEP credits are accepted. Important factors used in the admissions decision are advanced placement or honor courses, leadership record, extracurricular activities record, evidence of special talent, and recommendations by school officials.

Procedure: Freshmen are admitted fall and spring. Entrance exams should be taken in the junior year. Applications should be filed by August 15 for fall entry and December 15 for spring entry, along with an application fee of $20. Notification is sent on a rolling basis. There is a deferred admissions plan.

Transfer: About 112 transfer students enrolled in 1993–94. All transfer students must have a GPA of at least 2.0. Those with fewer than 15 credit hours must submit high school transcripts and SAT I or ACT scores; those with fewer than 30 hours need only the high school transcripts. A total of 30 credits out of 126 must be completed at McMurry.

Visiting: There are regularly scheduled orientations for prospective students. There are guides for informal visits and visitors may sit in on classes and stay overnight at the school. To arrange for a visit, contact the Admissions Office at (915) 691-6402 or (800) 477-0077.

Financial Aid: In 1993–94 90% of all current freshmen and 87% of continuing students received some form of financial aid. About 67% of freshmen and 51% of continuing students received need-based aid. The average freshman award was $7503. Of that total, scholarships or need-based grants averaged $4673 ($8675 maximum); loans averaged $2206 ($6625 maximum); and work contracts averaged $624 ($1000 maximum). Fifty percent of undergraduate students work part-time. Average earnings from campus work for the school year are $1000. The average financial indebtedness of the 1992–93 graduate was $8600. McMurry is a member of CSS. The FAFSA financial statement is required. The deadline for financial aid applications is March 15.

International Students: There are currently 4 international students enrolled. The school actively recruits these students. They must take the TOEFL and achieve a minimum score of 500. The student must also take the SAT I or the ACT and achieve a minimum score of 780 on the SAT I or 19 on the ACT.

Computers: The college provides computer facilities for student use. The mainframe is a DEC VAX. There are also 102 PCs available, including 8 in the learning center, 20 in the library, 48 in computer laboratories for biology, computer science, education, and psychology, and 26 in the writing classroom. PCs are accessible to all students; the mainframe is accessible to only those students who have paid a $37 computer science laboratory fee. It may be used Monday to Thursday 8 A.M. to 9:30 P.M.; Friday 8 A.M. to 5 P.M. There are no time limits on using the system.

Graduates: In 1992–93 208 bachelor's degrees were awarded. The most popular majors among graduates were education (33%), business (24%), and sociology (9%). Within an average freshman class, 1% graduate in 3 years, 23% in 4 years, 29% in 5 years, and 29% in 6 years. In the 1992 graduating class, 15% of the men and 11% of the women were enrolled in graduate school within 6 months of graduation; 82% of all graduates had found employment.

Admissions Contact: Becki Bryant, Director of Admissions.

MIDWESTERN STATE UNIVERSITY D-2
Wichita Falls, TX 76308 (817) 689-4321

Full-time: 1568 men, 1836 women	Faculty: 169; IIA, -$
Part-time: 806 men, 928 women	Ph.Ds: 67%
Graduate: 330 men, 378 women	Student/Faculty: 20 to 1
Year: semesters, summer session	Tuition: $1422 ($5562)
Application Deadline: August 7	Room & Board: $3120
Freshman Class: 1597 applied, 1125 accepted, 751 enrolled	
SAT I or ACT: required	**LESS COMPETITIVE**

Midwestern State University, founded in 1922, is a public liberal arts institution offering courses in the areas of business administration, education, fine arts, health sciences, humanities, mathematics and science, political science and public administration, and social and behavioral sciences. There are 9 undergraduate and 7 graduate schools. In addition to regional accreditation, Midwestern has baccalaureate program accreditation with ABET, ADA, NASM, NCATE, and NLN. The library contains 241,000 volumes, 158,000 microform items, and 6757 audiovisual forms, and subscribes to 1100 periodicals. Special learning facilities include an art gallery, planetarium, and TV station. The 172-acre campus is in an urban area 135 miles northwest of Dallas. Including residence halls, there are 31 buildings on campus.

Student Life: About 93% of undergraduates are from Texas. Students come from 42 foreign countries and Canada. Eighty-five percent are white. The average age of all undergraduates is 24. Thirty-seven percent drop out by the end of their first year; 26% remain to graduate.

Housing: A total of 600 students can be accommodated in college housing. College-sponsored living facilities include single-sex and coed dormitories, off-campus apartments, and married-student housing. On-campus housing is available on a first-come, first-served basis. Ninety percent of students commute. Alcohol is not permitted. All students may keep cars on campus.

Activities: About 10% of men belong to 5 national fraternities; about 10% of women belong to 4 national sororities. There are 90 groups on campus, including art, band, cheerleading, choir, chorale, computers, drama, ethnic, honors, international, literary magazine, marching band, newspaper, political, professional, radio and TV, religious, social, social service, student government, symphony, and yearbook. Popular campus events include Burns Fantasy of Lights, Greatest College Weekend, Spirit Days, and Homecoming.

Sports: There are 6 intercollegiate sports for men and 4 for women, and 13 intramural sports for men and 10 for women. Athletic and recreation facilities include a 5000-seat gymnasium, a soccer stadium, and tennis courts.

Disabled Students: Ninety-nine percent of the campus is accessible to disabled students. The following facilities are available: wheelchair ramps, elevators, special parking, specially equipped rest rooms, special class scheduling, and lowered drinking fountains.

Services: In addition to many counseling and information services, tutoring is available in some subjects. There is also a reader service for the blind, and remedial math, reading, and writing.

Campus Safety and Security: Campus safety and security measures include informal discussions, pamphlets, posters, films, and lighted pathways and sidewalks.

Programs of Study: Midwestern awards the B.A., B.S., B.A.A.S., B.B.A., B.F.A., B.M., B.S.C.J., B.S.M.T., B.S.N., and B.S.R.T. degrees. Associate and master's degrees also are awarded. Bachelor's degrees are awarded in BIOLOGICAL SCIENCE (biology/biological science and wildlife biology), BUSINESS (accounting, banking and finance, business administration and management, business economics, management science, and marketing/retailing/merchandising), COMMUNICATIONS AND THE ARTS (communications, dramatic arts, English, fine arts, music, Spanish, and speech/debate/rhetoric), COMPUTER AND PHYSICAL SCIENCE (chemical technology, chemistry, computer science, geology, mathematics, physical sciences, and physics), EDUCATION (music and physical), ENGINEERING AND ENVIRONMENTAL DESIGN (electrical/electronics engineering technology, engineering technology, and preengineering), HEALTH PROFESSIONS (dental hygiene, medical laboratory technology, nursing, predentistry, premedicine, prepharmacy, preveterinary science, and radiological science), SOCIAL SCIENCE (criminal justice, economics, history, humanities, interdisciplinary studies, political science/government, prelaw, psychology, social work, and sociol-

ogy). Physical science is the strongest academically. Business and nursing have the largest enrollments.

Required: All students must earn a minimum GPA of 2.0 while taking 120 semester hours, 24 in the major. Distribution requirements include 6 hours from a list of humanities classes, 6 from social science, 7 to 10 hours from natural science, and additional physical education requirements.

Special: Co-op programs with Collin County Community College, an exchange program with Monterrey Institute of Technology, cross-registration with the University of Texas at Arlington, internships with local firms and agencies, and study abroad in London are available. Dual majors, a general studies degree, credit for military experience, and nondegree study up to 12 hours are also offered. There is a freshman honors program on campus, as well as one national honor society.

Faculty/Classroom: Sixty-seven percent of faculty are male; 33% female. All teach undergraduates. Graduate students teach 10% of introductory courses. The average class size in an introductory lecture is 25; in a laboratory, 20; and in a regular course offering, 25.

Admissions: About 70% of the 1993–94 applicants were accepted.

Requirements: Midwestern requires applicants to be in the upper 60% of their class. The SAT I or ACT is required, with a minimum recommended composite score of 800 on the SAT I or 20 on the ACT. High school credits should include 4 years of English and 2 years of mathematics. The GED is accepted. AP and CLEP credits are accepted.

Procedure: Freshmen are admitted to all sessions. Entrance exams should be taken before applying for admission. Applications should be filed by August 7 for fall entry, December 15 for spring entry, and May 15 for summer entry. Notification is sent on a rolling basis. There are early decision and early admissions plans.

Transfer: About 560 transfer students enrolled in 1993–94. Transfer students with fewer than 18 semester hours must meet beginning freshmen criteria. All transfers must be eligible to re-enroll in all previous schools. A total of 24 credits out of 120 must be completed at Midwestern.

Visiting: There are guides for informal visits and visitors may sit in on classes and stay overnight at the school. To arrange for a visit, contact the Office of School Relations at (817) 689-4334.

Financial Aid: In an earlier year, 23% of all current freshmen and 33% of continuing students received some form of financial aid. Midwestern is a member of CSS. The FAF, FFS, or SFS is required. The deadline for financial aid applications is May 1.

International Students: There are currently 95 international students enrolled. The school actively recruits these students. They must take the TOEFL and achieve a minimum score of 500. The student must also take the SAT I or the ACT and achieve a minimum score of 800 on SAT I or 20 on the ACT.

Computers: The college provides computer facilities for student use. The mainframe is an IBM 4381 VSE operating system. There are also 145 IBM-compatibles and Apple IIe's in classrooms. Students enrolled in computer courses may access the system. The usage hours generally coincide with building access hours. There are no time limits on using the system.

Graduates: In 1992–93 589 bachelor's degrees were awarded. The most popular majors among graduates were applied arts and sciences (10%), accounting (8%), and nursing (8%). Within an average freshman class, 26% graduate in 6 years.

Admissions Contact: Judy Smelser, Director of Admissions.

OUR LADY OF THE LAKE UNIVERSITY OF SAN ANTONIO
San Antonio, TX 78207-4689 D-4
(210) 434-6711

Full-time: 290 men, 912 women	Faculty: 92; IIA, --$
Part-time: 247 men, 695 women	Ph.Ds: 57%
Graduate: 302 men, 657 women	Student/Faculty: 13 to 1
Year: semesters, summer session	Tuition: $7584
Application Deadline: open	Room & Board: $3496
Freshman Class: 2308 applied, 1336 accepted, 295 enrolled	
SAT I Verbal/Math: 415/420	**COMPETITIVE**

Our Lady of the Lake, founded as a private Catholic institution in 1911 by the Sisters of Divine Providence, offers programs in the arts and sciences, business, education, and social service. There are 4 undergraduate and 4 graduate schools. In addition to regional accreditation, the Lake has baccalaureate program accreditation with ASLA and CSWE. The library contains 128,000 volumes and 6100 audiovisual forms, and subscribes to 24,000 periodicals. Computerized library sources and services include database searching. Special learning facilities include a demonstration school (early childhood to grade 8) and a communication/learning disorders center. The 75-acre campus is in an urban area.

Student Life: About 99% of undergraduates are from Texas. Students come from 24 states and 9 foreign countries. Forty-nine percent are Hispanic; 40% white. Most are Catholic. The average age of freshmen is 19; all undergraduates, 29. Forty percent drop out by the end of their first year; 32% remain to graduate.

Housing: A total of 400 students can be accommodated in college housing. College-sponsored living facilities include coed dormitories, honors houses, and quiet and nonsmoking housing. On-campus housing is guaranteed for all 4 years. Eighty-three percent of students commute. All students may keep cars on campus.

Activities: There are no fraternities or sororities on campus. There are some groups and organizations on campus, including art, computers, honors, literary magazine, newspaper, political, professional, religious, social service, and student government. Popular campus events include Spirit Week.

Sports: Athletic and recreation facilities include playing fields, tennis courts, indoor and outdoor pools, and a gymnasium equipped for weight lifting, aerobics, and other indoor sports.

Disabled Students: Ninety-five percent of the campus is accessible to disabled students. The following facilities are available: wheelchair ramps, elevators, special parking, specially equipped rest rooms, and special class scheduling.

Services: In addition to many counseling and information services, tutoring is available in some subjects. There is also a reader service for the blind, and remedial math, reading, and writing.

Campus Safety and Security: Campus safety and security measures include 24-hour foot and vehicle patrol and lighted pathways and sidewalks.

Programs of Study: The Lake awards the B.A., B.S., B.A.S., B.B.A., and B.S.W. degrees. Master's and doctoral degrees also are awarded. Bachelor's degrees are awarded in BIOLOGICAL SCIENCE (biology/biological science), BUSINESS (accounting, human resources, and management science), COMMUNICATIONS AND THE ARTS (communications, English, fine arts, music, Spanish, and speech/debate/rhetoric), COMPUTER AND PHYSICAL SCIENCE (chemistry, information sciences and systems, and mathematics), EDUCATION (art and elementary), SOCIAL SCIENCE (American studies, philosophy, psychology, public administration, religion, social studies, social work, and sociology). Biology and chemistry are the strongest academically. Management (business administration) has the largest enrollment.

Required: A general education requirement includes competencies in English, mathematics, natural, social, and behavioral sciences, religion, philosophy, literature, art, history, and physical education. Other graduation requirements are a minimum 2.0 GPA, 128 credit hours, requirements specific to the major, and satisfactory scores on the COMP/ACT.

Special: There is cross-registration with Incarnate Word College, Oblate School of Theology, and Saint Mary's University. Dual majors are possible in the B.A.-B.B.A. programs. A 3–2 engineering degree is offered with Texas Tech and Washington Universities. Credit by examination and for life/work/military experience is available, as is a special degree program for working adults/nontraditional students through the Weekend College.

Faculty/Classroom: Fifty-four percent of faculty are male; 46%, female.

Admissions: About 58% of the 1993–94 applicants were accepted. The SAT scores for the 1993–94 freshman class were as follows: Verbal—83% below 500, 14% between 500 and 599, and 3% between 600 and 700; Math—84% below 500, 13% between 500 and 599, and 3% between 600 and 700.

Requirements: The SAT I or the ACT is recommended. Applicants should graduate from an accredited secondary school with 16 academic credits, including 4 in English, 3 in social studies, and 2 each in mathematics and laboratory science. A combination of SAT I or ACT scores and high school GPA or class rank determines admission. A GED with an average minimum score of 45 on each of the 5 tests and a satisfactory SAT I or ACT score are also acceptable. Mature students returning to school may waive the SAT I/ACT requirement for the college's own testing. AP and CLEP credits are accepted.

Procedure: Freshmen are admitted to all sessions. Application deadlines are open. Application fee is $15. Notification is sent on a rolling basis. There is an early admissions plan.

Transfer: About 176 transfer students enrolled in 1993–94. Transfer applicants with 30 or more credit hours and a minimum 2.0 GPA are accepted. Others are evaluated by the same criteria as freshmen applicants. A total of 30 credits out of 128 must be completed at the Lake.

Visiting: There are regularly scheduled orientations for prospective students. There are guides for informal visits and visitors may sit in on classes and stay overnight at the school. To arrange for a visit, contact the Admissions Office at (210) 434-6711, ext. 314.

Financial Aid: In a recent year, 65% of all current freshmen received some form of financial aid. Twenty-three percent of undergraduate students work part-time. The Lake is a member of CSS. The FAF or FFS is required. The deadline for financial aid applications is July 15.

International Students: There are currently 39 international students enrolled. The school actively recruits these students. They must take the TOEFL and achieve a minimum score of 525.

Computers: The college provides computer facilities for student use. The mainframe is a generic 486 PC. A UNIX server and a Novell PC network serve 3 different computer laboratories, which house a total of about 110 PCs/terminals for student use. All students may access the system. There are no time limits and no fees.

Graduates: In 1992–93 330 bachelor's degrees were awarded. The most popular majors among graduates were business/public administration (31%), liberal studies (10%), and social services (6%). Within an average freshman class, 15% graduate in 4 years, 10% in 5 years, and 6% in 6 years.

Admissions Contact: Loretta A. Schlegel, Registrar.

PAUL QUINN COLLEGE

D-3

Dallas, TX 75241-4398 (214) 302-3575 or 302-3520

Full-time: 300 men, 300 women	Faculty: 96
Part-time: 20 men, 50 women	Ph.D.s: n/av
Graduate: none	Student/Faculty: 6 to 1
Year: semesters, summer session	Tuition: $4140
Application Deadline: August 1	Room & Board: $2950
Freshman Class: 400 applied, 300 accepted, 290 enrolled	
SAT I or ACT: required	LESS COMPETITIVE

Paul Quinn College, founded in 1872, is a coeducational liberal arts college affiliated with the African Methodist Episcopal Church. In addition to regional accreditation, PQC has baccalaureate program accreditation with CSWE. The library contains 88,187 volumes and 30,550 microform items, and subscribes to 131 periodicals. Special learning facilities include a learning resource center. The 130-acre campus is in a residential urban area.

Student Life: About 72% of undergraduates are from Texas. All are from public schools. The average age of freshmen is 18; all undergraduates, 20.

Housing: College-sponsored living facilities include single-sex dormitories. On-campus housing is guaranteed for all 4 years. Alcohol is not permitted. All students may keep cars on campus.

Activities: There are some groups on campus, including band, chorale, dance, drama, international, newspaper, religious, social service, student government, and yearbook. Popular campus events include Honors Day and Founders Day.

Sports: There are 3 intercollegiate sports each for men and women, and 5 intramural sports each for men and women.

Services: In addition to counseling and information services, there is remedial math, reading, and writing.

Programs of Study: PQC awards the B.A., B.S., B.Applied Sci., and B.S.Ed. degrees. Bachelor's degrees are awarded in BIOLOGICAL SCIENCE (biology/biological science), BUSINESS (accounting and business administration and management), COMMUNICATIONS AND THE ARTS (English and music), COMPUTER AND PHYSICAL SCIENCE (computer science and mathematics), EDUCATION (physical and secondary), SOCIAL SCIENCE (history, religion, social work, and sociology).

Required: To graduate, students must complete at least 128 credit hours, including a core curriculum, internship, and health and physical education.

Special: PQC offers co-op and work-study programs, a B.A.-B.S. degree, a general studies degree, and nondegree study. A parallel degree program is available with Texas State Technical Institute.

Admissions: About 75% of the 1993–94 applicants were accepted. About 25% of the current freshmen were in the top fifth of their class; 50% were in the top two fifths.

Requirements: The SAT I or ACT is required and high school transcripts must be submitted. CLEP credit is accepted.

Procedure: Applications should be filed by August 1 for fall entry, November 15 for spring entry, and April 15 for summer entry, along with an application fee of $15.

Transfer: Applicants must meet the basic admissions requirements. A total of 30 of the last 36 credits out of at least 128 must be completed at PQC.

Visiting: There are regularly scheduled orientations for prospective students. There are guides for informal visits and visitors may sit in on classes and stay overnight at the school. To arrange for a visit, contact the Dean of Student Life.

Financial Aid: Scholarships or need-based grants averaged $4000 in a recent year. PQC is a member of CSS. The FAF and the previous year's student/parent tax forms are required. The deadline for financial aid applications is June 1.

International Students: International students must take the TOEFL and achieve a minimum score of 550. They must also take the SAT I or the ACT.

Computers: The college provides computer facilities for student use. The mainframe is an IBM 3400. All students may access the system. There are no fees.

Admissions Contact: Ralph Spencer, Jr., Admissions Officer.

PRAIRIE VIEW A&M UNIVERSITY
E-3

Prairie View, TX 77446 (409) 857-2690

Full-time, part-time: 5419 men and women	Faculty: 267; IIA, --$
	Ph.D.s: 43%
Graduate: 747 men and women	Student/Faculty: n/av
Year: semesters, summer session	Tuition: $1440 ($5620)
Application Deadline: open	Room & Board: $3300
Freshman Class: 3650 applied, 2691 accepted, 1050 enrolled	
SAT I Verbal/Math: 335/380	ACT: 19 **LESS COMPETITIVE**

Prairie View A&M University, established in 1878, is a comprehensive unit of the Texas A&M University system, offering undergraduate and graduate degree programs in applied sciences and engineering technology, business, engineering, nursing, arts and sciences, and education. There are 7 undergraduate and 5 graduate schools. In addition to regional accreditation, PVAMU has baccalaureate program accreditation with ABET, CSWE, NCATE, and NLN. The library contains 240,117 volumes, 261,318 microform items, and 101,212 audiovisual forms, and subscribes to 1600 periodicals. Computerized library sources and services include the card catalog, interlibrary loans, and database searching. Special learning facilities include a learning resource center and radio station. The 1440-acre campus is in a small town 40 miles northwest of Houston. Including residence halls, there are 36 buildings on campus.

Student Life: About 87% of undergraduates are from Texas. Students come from 40 states and 44 foreign countries. Eighty-five percent are African American. The average age of freshmen is 18; all undergraduates, 19. Twenty percent drop out by the end of their first year; 60% remain to graduate.

Housing: A total of 3347 students can be accommodated in college housing. College-sponsored living facilities include single-sex dormitories. On-campus housing is available on a first-come, first-served basis. Seventy-five percent of students live on campus; of those, 25% remain on campus on weekends. Alcohol is not permitted. All students may keep cars on campus.

Activities: About 8% of men belong to 4 national fraternities; about 8% of women belong to 4 national sororities. There are 30 groups on campus, including band, cheerleading, choir, chorus, dance, drama, drill team, ethnic, honors, international, jazz band, marching band, newspaper, orchestra, photography, political, professional, radio and TV, religious, social, social service, student government, and yearbook. Popular campus events include Homecoming, Honors Week, and Family Day.

Sports: There are 7 intercollegiate sports for men and 5 for women, and 6 intramural sports for men and 4 for women. Athletic and recreation facilities include a large complex and a 5000-seat stadium.

Disabled Students: Five percent of the campus is accessible to disabled students. The following facilities are available: wheelchair ramps, elevators, special parking, and specially equipped rest rooms.

Services: In addition to many counseling and information services, tutoring is available in some subjects. There is a reader service for the blind, and remedial math, reading, and writing.

Campus Safety and Security: Campus safety and security measures include 24-hour foot and vehicle patrol, informal discussions, pamphlets, posters, films, and emergency telephones. In addition, there are lighted pathways and sidewalks and a 24-hour department of traffic and security.

Programs of Study: PVAMU awards the B.A., B.S., B.Arch., B.A.S.W., B.B.A., B.Mus., B.S.Ag., B.S.C.E., B.S.C.E.T., B.S.Ed., B.S.H.E., B.S.L.E., B.S.M.E., and B.S.N. degrees. Master's degrees also are awarded. Bachelor's degrees are awarded in BIOLOGICAL SCIENCE (biology/biological science), BUSINESS (accounting, banking and finance, business administration and management, business economics, and marketing/retailing/merchandising), COMMUNICATIONS AND THE ARTS (broadcasting, communications, dramatic arts, English, journalism, music, Spanish, and speech/debate/rhetoric), COMPUTER AND PHYSICAL SCIENCE (chemistry, computer science, mathematics, and physics), ENGINEERING AND ENVIRONMENTAL DESIGN (architectural engineering, chemical engineering, civil engineering, computer engineering, electrical/electronics engineering, engineering technology, industrial engineering technology, and mechanical engineering), HEALTH PROFESSIONS (medical laboratory technology and nursing), SOCIAL SCIENCE (criminal justice, geography, history, political science/government, psychology, social work, and sociology). Engineering and biology are the strongest programs academically. Engineering,

business, nursing, communications, and biology have the largest enrollments.

Required: All students must complete 120 semester hours, including at least 45 in the major, with a minimum 2.0 GPA.

Special: Cooperative programs and internships in various majors, work-study programs, and combined B.A.-B.S. degrees in chemistry, biology, mathematics, and computer science are offered. There is a freshman honors program on campus as well as 24 national honor societies, including Phi Beta Kappa.

Faculty/Classroom: Sixty percent of faculty are male; 40%, female. Graduate students teach 1% of introductory courses. The average class size in an introductory lecture is 70; in a laboratory, 15; and in a regular course offering, 35.

Admissions: About 74% of the 1993-94 applicants were accepted.

Requirements: A GPA of at least 2.0 is necessary for financial aid eligibility. The SAT I or ACT is required. The minimum composite score must be 700 on the SAT I or 15 on the ACT. Applicants should be graduates of accredited high schools or have earned the GED. Secondary school preparation should include 4 years each of English and academic electives, 3 each of mathematics and social studies, and 2 of science. AP and CLEP credits are accepted. Important factors used in the admissions decision are leadership record, advanced placement or honor courses, recommendations by school officials, recommendations by alumni, and parents or siblings attending the school.

Procedure: Freshmen are admitted to all sessions. Entrance exams should be taken before enrollment. Application deadlines are open. The application fee is $10. Notification is sent on a rolling basis. There are early decision, early admissions, and deferred admissions plans.

Transfer: About 230 transfer students enrolled in a recent year. Transfer applicants must present at least a 2.0 GPA in a minimum of 3 previous college courses. A total of 36 semester hours out of 120 must be completed at PVAMU.

Visiting: There are regularly scheduled orientations for prospective students. Orientation is held 2 days prior to registration. There are guides for informal visits and visitors may sit in on classes and stay overnight at the school. To arrange for a visit, contact the Office of Admissions and Records at (409) 857-2618/2626.

Financial Aid: In a recent year, 76% of all current freshmen and 68% of continuing students received some form of financial aid. About 75% of freshmen and 69% of continuing students received need-based aid. The average freshman award was $4000. Of that total, scholarships or need-based grants averaged $1500 ($4500 maximum); and loans averaged $2625 ($7500 maximum). Fifty percent of undergraduate students work part-time. Average earnings from campus work for the school year are $3040. The average financial indebtedness of a recent graduate was $5250. PVAMU is a member of CSS. The FAF is required. The deadline for financial aid applications is April 1.

International Students: There are currently 330 international students enrolled. They must take the TOEFL and achieve a minimum score of 500. The student must also take the SAT I (minimum composite score 700) or the ACT (minimum composite score 18).

Computers: The university provides computer facilities for student use. The mainframe is an IBM 4361. A student computer center is available, as are IBM and AT&T PCs in the library. Students enrolled in computer courses may access the system. There are no fees.

Graduates: In a recent year, 518 bachelor's degrees were awarded. Some 110 companies recruited on campus.

Admissions Contact: Mary E. Gooch, Admissions Coordinator.

RICE UNIVERSITY
E-3

Houston, TX 77251 (713) 527-4036; (800) 527-OWLS

Full-time: 1584 men, 1090 women	Faculty: 523; I, +$
Part-time: none	Ph.D.s: 90%
Graduate: 954 men, 495 women	Student/Faculty: 5 to 1
Year: semesters, summer session	Tuition: $9650
Application Deadline: January 3	Room & Board: $5460
Freshman Class: 7935 applied, 1514 accepted, 633 enrolled	
SAT I: required	**MOST COMPETITIVE**

Rice University, founded in 1912, is a private institution offering undergraduate and graduate programs in engineering, natural sciences, humanities, social sciences, music, architecture, and administrative sciences. There are 6 undergraduate schools and one graduate school. In addition to regional accreditation, Rice has baccalaureate program accreditation with ABET and NAAB. The library contains 1.5 million volumes, 2.2 million microform items, and 3000 audiovisual forms, and subscribes to 14,000 periodicals. Computerized library sources and services include the card catalog and database searching. Special learning facilities include an art gallery, a radio station, and a media center. The 300-acre campus is in a suburban area 3 miles southwest of downtown Houston. Including residence halls, there are 40 buildings on campus.

Student Life: About 55% of undergraduates are from out-of-state, mostly the Southwest. Students come from 45 states, 30 foreign countries, and Canada. Ninety percent are from public schools; 10% from private. Eighty percent are white. The average age of freshmen is 17; all undergraduates, 20. Five percent drop out by the end of their first year; 88% remain to graduate.

Housing: A total of 1720 students can be accommodated in college housing. College-sponsored living facilities include coed dormitories. On-campus housing is available on a lottery system for upperclassmen. Sixty-five percent of students live on campus; of those, 95% remain on campus on weekends. All students may keep cars on campus.

Activities: There are no fraternities or sororities on campus. There are 200 groups on campus, including art, band, cheerleading, chess, choir, chorale, chorus, computers, dance, drama, ethnic, film, gay, honors, international, jazz band, literary magazine, marching band, musical theater, newspaper, orchestra, pep band, photography, political, professional, religious, social, social service, student government, symphony, and yearbook. Popular campus events include Baker Shakespeare Festival, an annual biking relay race, and Archi Arts, a costume ball.

Sports: There are 8 intercollegiate sports for men and 6 for women, and 12 intramural sports each for men and women. Athletic and recreation facilities include a 5000-seat gymnasium; a pool; a track stadium; fields for soccer, lacrosse, and rugby; courts for tennis, squash, racquetball, volleyball, and basketball; and a 70,000-seat stadium.

Disabled Students: Fifty percent of the campus is accessible to disabled students. The following facilities are available: wheelchair ramps, elevators, special parking, specially equipped rest rooms, special class scheduling, lowered drinking fountains and telephones, and a stair lift.

Services: In addition to many counseling and information services, tutoring is available in every subject.

Campus Safety and Security: Campus safety and security measures include a campus police department.

Programs of Study: Rice awards the B.A., B.S., B.Arch., B.F.A., and B.Mus. degrees. Master's and doctoral degrees also are awarded. Bachelor's degrees are awarded in BIOLOGICAL SCIENCE (biochemistry and biology/biological science), BUSINESS (management science), COMMUNICATIONS AND THE ARTS (classics, English, fine arts, French, German, linguistics, music, and Spanish), COMPUTER AND PHYSICAL SCIENCE (chemistry, computer science, geology, geophysics and seismology, mathematics, physics, and statistics), ENGINEERING AND ENVIRONMENTAL DESIGN (architectural engineering, chemical engineering, civil engineering, computer engineering, electrical/electronics engineering, environmental science, materials science, and mechanical engineering), SOCIAL SCIENCE (anthropology, behavioral science, cognitive science, economics, history, philosophy, physical fitness/movement, political science/government, psychology, public affairs, religion, Russian and Slavic studies, and sociology). Engineering has the largest enrollment.

Required: All students must complete at least 120 credits with a 1.67 overall GPA and a 2.0 GPA in the major field. Core requirements include 1 to 3 courses in natural sciences, social sciences, or humanities, depending on the major, and additional courses in these fields to meet distribution requirements. All students take 2 semesters of physical education. At least 48 semester hours in upper-level courses are required.

Special: Cross-registration at other colleges, internships, a semester studying deep-water oceanography in Massachusetts and the Caribbean or maritime culture and commerce on a sailing vessel off the North American coastline, study abroad in a number of countries, dual and student-designed majors, nondegree study, and limited pass/fail options are offered. There are 10 national honor societies on campus, including Phi Beta Kappa. Nine departments have honors programs.

Faculty/Classroom: The average class size in a regular course offering is 18.

Admissions: About 19% of the 1993-94 applicants were accepted. The SAT scores for the 1993-94 freshman class were as follows: Verbal—7% below 500, 17% between 500 and 599, 51% between 600 and 700, and 25% above 700; Math—3% below 500, 9% between 500 and 599, 28% between 600 and 700, and 60% above 700. About 98% of the current freshmen were in the top fifth of their class; all were in the top two fifths.

Requirements: The SAT I is required. Three SAT II: Subject tests also are required, including the writing test; potential engineering and natural science majors should also take mathematics I or II and either chemistry or physics. Applicants should be high school graduates or have earned the GED. Secondary preparation should include 4 years of English, 3 each of mathematics and academic electives, and 2 each of a foreign language, science, and social studies. An interview is recommended and a personal essay is required; architecture majors should submit a portfolio, and music majors should audition. Candidates must submit evaluations from a counselor and a

teacher. AP and CLEP credits are accepted. Important factors used in the admissions decision are advanced placement or honor courses, extracurricular activities record, personality, intangible qualities, evidence of special talent, and leadership record.

Procedure: Freshmen are admitted in the fall. Entrance exams should be taken between October and January of the senior year, depending on the decision plan. Early decision applications should be filed by November 1; early action, by December 1; and regular applications, by January 3 for fall entry, along with an application fee of $25. Notification of early decision is sent December 1; regular decision, April 1. There is an early decision plan. About 55 early decision candidates were accepted for a recent class. A waiting list is an active part of the admissions procedure.

Transfer: About 60 transfer students enrolled in a recent class. Transfer applicants should present a 3.2 GPA in previous college work, SAT I scores, 2 college teacher recommendations, and high school and college transcripts. A total of 60 credits out of 120 must be completed at Rice.

Visiting: There are regularly scheduled orientations for prospective students. There are guides for informal visits and visitors may sit in on classes and stay overnight at the school. To arrange for a visit, contact the Office of Admissions at (800) 527-OWLS.

Financial Aid: In a recent year, 80% of all current freshmen and 85% of continuing students received some form of financial aid. Scholarships or need-based grants averaged $7250 ($11,650 maximum); and loans averaged $1800 (maximum). The average financial indebtedness of a recent graduate was $2239. Rice is a member of CSS. The college's own financial statement, FAFSA, and parent and student tax returns are required. The deadline for financial aid applications is June 1.

International Students: There were recently 62 international students enrolled. They must take the TOEFL (minimum score 550) and the SAT I. Students must take SAT II: Subject tests in writing and 2 others, depending on the potential major.

Computers: The university provides computer facilities for student use. The mainframes are an NAS AS/9000 and an IBM 3081. There are also Apple Macintosh and IBM microcomputers available in the computing center, the library, and academic laboratories. All students may access the system. There are no time limits and no fees.

Graduates: In a recent class, 835 bachelor's degrees were awarded. Some 225 companies recruited on campus.

Admissions Contact: Julie M. Browning, Director of Admission.

SAINT EDWARD'S UNIVERSITY

D-3

Austin, TX 78704 (512) 448-8500

Full-time: 730 men, 1002 women	Faculty: 83; IIB, -$
Part-time: 398 men, 538 women	Ph.D.s: 47%
Graduate: 237 men, 202 women	Student/Faculty: 21 to 1
Year: semesters, summer session	Tuition: $8902
Application Deadline: August 1	Room & Board: $3734
Freshman Class: 1272 applied, 1012 accepted, 375 enrolled	
SAT I Verbal/Math: 430/480	ACT: 22 COMPETITIVE

Saint Edward's University, founded in 1885, is an independent Catholic institution offering undergraduate and graduate courses in liberal arts, human service, business administration, and computer science. There are 5 undergraduate and 2 graduate schools. In addition to regional accreditation, SEU has baccalaureate program accreditation with AACSB. The library contains 145,000 volumes, 4500 microform items, and 1400 audiovisual forms, and subscribes to 1100 periodicals. Computerized library sources and services include the card catalog, interlibrary loans, and database searching. Special learning facilities include a learning resource center and a photography laboratory. The 180-acre campus is in an urban area in Austin. Including residence halls, there are 24 buildings on campus.

Student Life: About 91% of undergraduates are from Texas. Students come from 37 states, 45 foreign countries, and Canada. Seventy-eight percent are from public schools; 22% from private. Sixty-two percent are white; 25% Hispanic. Fifty-seven percent are Catholic; 38% Protestant. The average age of freshmen is 18; all undergraduates, 24. Eight percent drop out by the end of their first year; 40% remain to graduate.

Housing: A total of 550 students can be accommodated in college housing. College-sponsored living facilities include single-sex and coed dormitories. On-campus housing is guaranteed for all 4 years. Eighty-three percent of students commute. All students may keep cars on campus.

Activities: There are no fraternities or sororities on campus. There are 36 groups on campus, including art, choir, chorale, computers, dance, drama, ethnic, gay, honors, international, jazz band, literary magazine, musical theater, newspaper, photography, political, professional, religious, social service, and student government. Popular campus events include Beach Bash, Festival of Lights, Spring Fling, and Hillstock Music Fest.

Sports: There are 5 intercollegiate sports for men and 5 for women, and 15 intramural sports for men and 13 for women. Athletic and recreation facilities include 2 gymnasiums, baseball and softball fields, 2 soccer fields, an indoor/outdoor pool, a weight room, aerobic/dance studios, a track, and tennis, basketball, racquetball/handball, and volleyball courts.

Disabled Students: Ninety percent of the campus is accessible to disabled students. The following facilities are available: wheelchair ramps, elevators, special parking, specially equipped rest rooms, and lowered drinking fountains.

Services: In addition to many counseling and information services, tutoring is available in every subject. In addition, there is remedial math, reading, and writing. There are also listening laboratories and a Strategies for Learning course.

Campus Safety and Security: Campus safety and security measures include 24-hour foot and vehicle patrol, self defense education, informal discussions, pamphlets, posters, and films. In addition, there are emergency telephones and lighted pathways and sidewalks. The outside doors of residence halls are locked at all times; only residents are issued keys.

Programs of Study: SEU awards the B.A., B.S., B.A.A.S., B.B.A., and B.L.S. degrees. Master's degrees also are awarded. Bachelor's degrees are awarded in BIOLOGICAL SCIENCE (biology/biological science), BUSINESS (accounting, banking and finance, business administration and management, international business management, marketing/retailing/merchandising, and sports management), COMMUNICATIONS AND THE ARTS (communications, dramatic arts, English, English literature, fine arts, photography, and Spanish), COMPUTER AND PHYSICAL SCIENCE (chemistry, computer science, and mathematics), EDUCATION (bilingual/bicultural, elementary, and secondary), ENGINEERING AND ENVIRONMENTAL DESIGN (preengineering), HEALTH PROFESSIONS (premedicine), SOCIAL SCIENCE (criminal justice, economics, history, international studies, liberal arts/general studies, philosophy, political science/government, prelaw, psychology, religion, social work, and sociology). Liberal arts, business, and computer science are the strongest academically. Biology, criminal justice, psychology, business, and computer science have the largest enrollments.

Required: All students must maintain a minimum GPA of 2.0 while taking 120 semester hours, including 31 to 75 in the major. The core curriculum includes courses from foundational skills, cultural foundations, and foundations for values and decisions. In the required capstone class, seniors identify a problem in society, research it, and present their solutions in an extensive final paper.

Special: Co-op programs in business and computer science, cross-registration with Saint Norbert College in Wisconsin, internships in many majors, and study abroad in a variety of countries through the ISEP are available. Dual majors in Spanish/international business, a general studies degree, credit for life experience, nondegree study, and pass/fail options also are possible. SEU also offers the New College, a flexible program for working adults. There are 6 national honor societies on campus. There is a university-wide honors program.

Faculty/Classroom: Fifty-nine percent of faculty are male; 41%, female. Ninety-five percent teach undergraduates and 95% both teach and do research. No introductory courses are taught by graduate students. The average class size in an introductory lecture is 30; in a laboratory, 20; and in a regular course offering, 25.

Admissions: About 80% of the 1993–94 applicants were accepted. The SAT scores for the 1993–94 freshman class were as follows: Verbal—76% below 500, 22% between 500 and 599, and 2% between 600 and 700; Math—58% below 500, 32% between 500 and 599, and 10% between 600 and 700. The ACT scores were 39% below 21, 30% between 21 and 23, 24% between 24 and 26, 6% between 27 and 28, and 1% above 28. About 37% of the current freshmen were in the top fifth of their class; 70% were in the top two fifths. Three freshmen graduated first in their class.

Requirements: A minimum GPA of 2.0 is required. The SAT I or ACT is required. In addition, applicants must be graduates of an accredited secondary school; the GED is accepted. An interview is recommended. AP and CLEP credits are accepted. Important factors used in the admissions decision are advanced placement or honor courses, evidence of special talent, leadership record, recommendations by school officials, and extracurricular activities record.

Procedure: Freshmen are admitted fall and spring. Entrance exams should be taken the summer before the senior year. Applications should be filed by August 1 for fall entry and December 1 for spring entry, along with an application fee of $25. Notification is sent on a rolling basis. There are early admissions and deferred admissions plans.

Transfer: About 250 transfer students enrolled in 1993–94. Transfer applicants must have a minimum GPA of 2.0. A total of 30 credits out of 120 must be completed at SEU.

Visiting: There are regularly scheduled orientations for prospective students, including a tour, financial aid session, academic session, class visits, entertainment, and an overnight stay in a residence hall.

There are guides for informal visits and visitors may sit in on classes and stay overnight at the school. To arrange for a visit, contact the Admissions Office at (512) 448–8500.

Financial Aid: In 1993–94, 71% of all students received some form of financial aid. About 65% of freshmen and 47% of continuing students received need-based aid. The average freshman award was $5773. Of that total, scholarships or need-based grants averaged $2500 ($5000 maximum); loans averaged $2200 ($2625 maximum); and work contracts averaged $1500 ($1800 maximum). Eighty percent of undergraduate students work part-time. The average financial indebtedness of the 1992–93 graduate was $12,500. SEU is a member of CSS. The FAFSA financial statement is required. The deadline for financial aid applications is March 1.

International Students: There are currently 123 international students enrolled. The school actively recruits these students. They must take the TOEFL and achieve a minimum score of 500.

Computers: The university provides computer facilities for student use. The mainframe is an HP 9000/835s. Students use the multiuser system for computer science assignments and electronic mail. All students may access the system 70 hours per week. Dial-up is available 24 hours every day. There are no time limits on using the system. There is a $40 laboratory fee for computer science courses.

Graduates: In 1992–93, 489 bachelor's degrees were awarded. The most popular majors among graduates were marketing (6%), management (6%), and communications (5%). Within an average freshman class, 1% graduate in 3 years, 21% in 4 years, 38% in 5 years, and 35% in 6 years. Some 75 companies recruited on campus in 1992–93.

Admissions Contact: Megan Murphy, Director of Admissions.

SAINT MARY'S UNIVERSITY

San Antonio, TX 78228-8503

D-4

(210) 436–3126; (800) FOR-STMU

Full-time: 917 men, 1232 women	**Faculty:** 159; IIA, +$
Part-time: 178 men, 240 women	**Ph.D.s:** 76%
Graduate: 809 men, 753 women	**Student/Faculty:** 14 to 1
Year: semesters, summer session	**Tuition:** $8626
Application Deadline: August 15	**Room & Board:** $3438
Freshman Class: 1243 applied, 1020 accepted, 412 enrolled	
SAT I or ACT: required	COMPETITIVE

Saint Mary's University, established in 1852, is a private Roman Catholic institution in the Marianist tradition, offering undergraduate programs in humanities and social sciences, business and administration, and science, engineering, and technology. There are 3 undergraduate and 2 graduate schools. In addition to regional accreditation, Saint Mary's has baccalaureate program accreditation with ABET and NASM. The 2 libraries contain 335,000 volumes, 60,000 microform items, and 6000 audiovisual forms, and subscribe to 1320 periodicals. Computerized library sources and services include the card catalog, interlibrary loans, and database searching. Special learning facilities include a learning resource center and the Learning Assistance Center. The 135-acre campus is in a suburban area 5 miles northwest of San Antonio. Including residence halls, there are 32 buildings on campus.

Student Life: About 89% of undergraduates are from Texas. Students come from 30 states, 33 foreign countries, and Canada. Eighty-six percent are from public schools; 14% from private. Forty-five percent are Hispanic; 44% white. Seventy-four percent are Catholic. The average age of freshmen is 18; all undergraduates, 20. Seven percent drop out by the end of their first year; 64% remain to graduate.

Housing: A total of 1200 students can be accommodated in college housing. College-sponsored living facilities include single-sex and coed dormitories. On-campus housing is guaranteed for the freshman year only and is available on a first-come, first-served basis. Priority is given to out-of-town students. Fifty-six percent of students commute. Alcohol is not permitted. All students may keep cars on campus.

Activities: About 14% of men belong to 1 local and 4 national fraternities; about 16% of women belong to 1 international and 3 national sororities. There are 55 groups on campus, including art, band, cheerleading, choir, chorale, dance, drama, ethnic, honors, international, jazz band, newspaper, pep band, photography, political, professional, religious, social, social service, and student government. Popular campus events include Campus Ministry Retreat, Hunger Awareness Week, and Fiesta Oyster Bake.

Sports: There are 5 intercollegiate sports for men and 5 for women, and 28 intramural sports for men and 28 for women. Athletic and recreation facilities include a gymnasium, weight room, various playing fields, and tennis, handball, and basketball courts.

Disabled Students: Eighty percent of the campus is accessible to disabled students. The following facilities are available: wheelchair ramps, elevators, special parking, specially equipped rest rooms, special class scheduling, and specially designed rooms in designated residence halls.

Services: In addition to many counseling and information services, tutoring is available in every subject. In addition, there is remedial math, reading, and writing.

Campus Safety and Security: Campus safety and security measures include 24-hour foot and vehicle patrol, escort service, informal discussions, and pamphlets, posters, and films. In addition, there are emergency telephones, lighted pathways and sidewalks, and a crime prevention awareness program each semester.

Programs of Study: Saint Mary's awards the B.A., B.S., B.A.S., B.A.T., and B.B.A. degrees. Master's and doctoral degrees also are awarded. Bachelor's degrees are awarded in BIOLOGICAL SCIENCE (biochemistry and biology/biological science), BUSINESS (accounting, banking and finance, business administration and management, human resources, international business management, and marketing/retailing/merchandising), COMMUNICATIONS AND THE ARTS (communications, English, French, German, music, Spanish, and speech/debate/rhetoric), COMPUTER AND PHYSICAL SCIENCE (chemistry, computer science, earth science, mathematics, and physics), EDUCATION (business, elementary, science, and secondary), ENGINEERING AND ENVIRONMENTAL DESIGN (computer engineering, electrical/electronics engineering, engineering, and industrial engineering), HEALTH PROFESSIONS (predentistry and premedicine), SOCIAL SCIENCE (criminal justice, economics, history, international relations, international studies, Latin American studies, philosophy, political science/government, prelaw, psychology, sociology, and theological studies). Premedical, predental, accounting, prelaw, psychology, English, communications, and industrial engineering are the strongest academically. Electrical engineering, biology, accounting, psychology, and political science have the largest enrollments.

Required: All students must complete at least 129 semester hours, 24 to 30 in the major, with a minimum 2.5 GPA. Core curriculum requirements include courses in fine arts, English, foreign language, speech, natural science, mathematics, social science, philosophy, and theology. Students must also take computer science and demonstrate computer literacy and take interdisciplinary electives.

Special: Saint Mary's offers cooperative programs and internships in all majors, depending on the student's needs. Students may cross-register at any of the United Colleges of San Antonio, spend a semester in Washington, D.C., or study in England, Austria, or Mexico. Dual majors are possible in computer science and engineering and public justice and political science, psychology, or sociology. Accelerated degree programs are offered in law (JD/MBA), and dentistry (B.A. in combined science and dental degree). Required theology courses may be taken on a pass/fail basis. There is a freshman honors program on campus, as well as 3 national honor societies.

Faculty/Classroom: Seventy-three percent of faculty are male; 27% female. All teach undergraduates. No introductory courses are taught by graduate students. The average class size in an introductory lecture is 40; in a laboratory, 70; and in a regular course offering, 35.

Admissions: About 82% of the 1993–94 applicants were accepted. About 62% of the current freshmen were in the top fifth of their class; 85% were in the top two fifths. Twelve freshmen graduated first in their class.

Requirements: Saint Mary's requires applicants to be in the upper 50% of their class. A minimum GPA of 2.0 is required. The SAT I or ACT is required. All applicants must be high school graduates or have the GED, and score in the 50th percentile on the SAT I or ACT. Secondary school preparation should include 4 units of English, 3 units each of mathematics and academic electives, and 2 units each of social science, natural science, and foreign language. Potential science and engineering majors should have 4 units of mathematics and 3 units of laboratory science, including chemistry or physics. AP and CLEP credits are accepted. Important factors used in the admissions decision are leadership record, advanced placement or honor courses, personality, intangible qualities, extracurricular activities record, and evidence of special talent.

Procedure: Freshmen are admitted to all sessions. Entrance exams should be taken by fall of the senior year. Applications should be filed by August 15 for fall entry, November 15 for spring entry, and April 15 for summer entry, along with an application fee of $15. Notification is sent on a rolling basis. There are early admissions and deferred admissions plans.

Transfer: About 200 transfer students enrolled in 1993–94. Transfer applicants must present at least a 2.0 GPA in previous college work, which should include 3 hours of English composition. Saint Mary's also recommends that applicants submit SAT I or ACT scores and schedule an interview. A total of 30 credits out of 129 must be completed at Saint Mary's.

Visiting: There are regularly scheduled orientations for prospective students, including a tour, an admissions/financial aid session, an overnight stay, and class visits. There are guides for informal visits and visitors may sit in on classes and stay overnight at the school. To arrange for a visit, contact the Undergraduate Admissions Office at (210) 436-3126.

Financial Aid: In 1993–94, 79% of all students received some form of financial aid. About 59% of students received need-based aid. The average freshman award was $6900. Of that total, scholarships or need-based grants averaged $3500 ($6500 maximum); loans averaged $2100 ($4100 maximum); and work contracts averaged $1250 ($1750 maximum). Fifty-five percent of undergraduate students work part-time. Average earnings from campus work for the school year are $1750. The average financial indebtedness of the 1992–93 graduate was $9200. Saint Mary's is a member of CSS. The FAF is required. The deadline for financial aid applications is April 1.

International Students: There are currently 127 international students enrolled. The school actively recruits these students. They must take the TOEFL and achieve a minimum score of 550.

Computers: The university provides computer facilities for student use. The mainframes are a DEC VAX 6000 Model 510, MicroVAX II, and Super Mini Alliant FX40. Students have access to 36 PCs in the academic library during library hours. They can also check out software to use with the library's computers. Mainframe systems are available to students on a restricted basis, either by faculty approval or course requirement. There are no time limits on using the system. The fees are $15 for systems other than the library PCs.

Graduates: In a recent year, 470 bachelor's degrees were awarded. The most popular majors among graduates were biology (12%), political science (9%), and finance (8%). Some 105 companies recruited on campus in a recent year.

Admissions Contact: Richard Castillo, Director of Undergraduate Admissions.

SAM HOUSTON STATE UNIVERSITY — E-3
Huntsville, TX 77341 — (409) 294-1056

Full-time: 4216 men, 4682 women	Faculty: 335; IIA, --$
Part-time: 1116 men, 1126 women	Ph.D.s: 68%
Graduate: 591 men, 1069 women	Student/Faculty: 27 to 1
Year: semesters, summer session	Tuition: $1536 ($5616)
Application Deadline: open	Room & Board: $2970
Freshman Class: 4839 applied, 3549 accepted, 1677 enrolled	
ACT: 20	COMPETITIVE

Sam Houston University, founded in 1879, is a public institution offering programs in arts and sciences, business administration, criminal justice, education, and applied science. There are 4 undergraduate and 4 graduate schools. In addition to regional accreditation, Sam Houston State has baccalaureate program accreditation with NASM and NCATE. The library contains 766,350 volumes, 864,379 microform items, and 11,147 audiovisual forms, and subscribes to 3111 periodicals. Computerized library sources and services include the card catalog, interlibrary loans, and database searching. Special learning facilities include a learning resource center, planetarium, radio station, TV station, and the Sam Houston Museum. The 1678-acre campus is in a small town 70 miles north of Houston. Including residence halls, there are 191 buildings on campus.

Student Life: About 98% of undergraduates are from Texas. Students come from 43 states, 41 foreign countries, and Canada. Eighty percent are white; 11% African American. The average age of freshmen is 19; all undergraduates, 22.6. About 34% of freshmen remain to graduate.

Housing: A total of 3344 students can be accommodated in college housing. College-sponsored living facilities include single-sex and coed dormitories, on-campus apartments, married-student housing, and sorority houses. In addition, there are honors houses and special interest houses. On-campus housing is guaranteed for all 4 years. Seventy-four percent of students commute. Alcohol is not permitted. All students may keep cars on campus.

Activities: About 7% of men belong to 14 local fraternities. There are 143 groups on campus, including art, band, cheerleading, choir, chorale, chorus, computers, dance, drama, drill team, ethnic, film, gay, honors, international, jazz band, marching band, musical theater, newspaper, orchestra, pep band, photography, political, professional, radio and TV, religious, social, social service, student government, symphony, and yearbook. Popular campus events include Organization Fair, Greek Week, and Spring Fling.

Sports: There are 7 intercollegiate sports for men and 7 for women, and 14 intramural sports for men and 14 for women. Athletic and recreation facilities include a 14,000-seat stadium, a 5200-seat gymnasium, 4 basketball courts, 10 racquetball courts, 3 swimming pools, and 2 weight rooms.

Disabled Students: Ninety percent of the campus is accessible to disabled students. The following facilities are available: wheelchair ramps, elevators, special parking, specially equipped rest rooms, and lowered drinking fountains.

Services: In addition to many counseling and information services, tutoring is available in every subject. There is also a reader service for the blind, and remedial math, reading, and writing.

Campus Safety and Security: Campus safety and security measures include 24-hour foot and vehicle patrol, escort service, informal discussions, and pamphlets, posters, and films. In addition, there are lighted pathways and sidewalks.

Programs of Study: Sam Houston State awards the B.A., B.S., B.A.A.S., B.A.T., B.B.A., B.F.A., B.M., B.M.Ed., and B.S.W. degrees. Master's and doctoral degrees also are awarded. Bachelor's degrees are awarded in AGRICULTURE (agriculture, animal science, and horticulture), BIOLOGICAL SCIENCE (biology/biological science), BUSINESS (accounting, banking and finance, business economics, international business management, and marketing/retailing/merchandising), COMMUNICATIONS AND THE ARTS (applied art, dance, dramatic arts, English, French, German, graphic design, journalism, music, music theory and composition, photography, and speech/debate/rhetoric), COMPUTER AND PHYSICAL SCIENCE (chemistry, computer science, geology, mathematics, and physics), EDUCATION (physical), ENGINEERING AND ENVIRONMENTAL DESIGN (environmental science), HEALTH PROFESSIONS (music therapy), SOCIAL SCIENCE (criminal justice, geography, history, home economics, humanities, law enforcement and corrections, philosophy, political science/government, psychology, and sociology). Criminal justice is the strongest academically. Criminal justice and general business have the largest enrollments.

Required: All students must maintain a GPA of 2.0 while taking 128 semester hours, including 30 in the major. Distribution requirements include 12 hours of English courses, 12 hours of history and political science, 6 hours of mathematics or statistics, 8 hours of sciences, 3 hours of fine arts, 9 hours of such courses as geography and psychology, and 2 to 4 hours of physical education.

Special: Work-study programs with the university, second degrees, and B.A.-B.S. degrees are available. There is a freshman honors program on campus, as well as one national honor society. There is also a university-wide honors program.

Faculty/Classroom: Sixty-six percent of faculty are male; 34%, female. All teach undergraduates, 15% do research, and 15% do both. Graduate students teach 4% of introductory courses. The average class size in a regular course offering is 22.

Admissions: About 73% of the 1993–94 applicants were accepted. The ACT scores for the 1993–94 freshman class were as follows: 58% below 21, 28% between 21 and 23, 10% between 24 and 26, 3% between 27 and 28, and 1% above 28. About 41% of the current freshmen were in the top fifth of their class.

Requirements: Sam Houston State requires applicants to be in the upper 50% of their class. The SAT I or ACT is required, with a minimum required composite score of 900 on the SAT I or 21 on the ACT. Applicants must have secondary school credits as follows: 4 of English, 2 each of mathematics, history, and science, and a half credit each of social studies, physical education, and health education. The GED is accepted. AP and CLEP credits are accepted.

Procedure: Freshmen are admitted to all sessions. Application deadlines are open. There is an early admissions plan.

Transfer: About 1466 transfer students enrolled in 1993–94. Transfer applicants must present a 2.0 GPA on all previous college work.

Visiting: There are regularly scheduled orientations for prospective students and guides for informal visits. To arrange for a visit, contact the Recruitment Office at (409) 294-1056.

Financial Aid: Ten percent of undergraduate students work part-time. Sam Houston State is a member of CSS. The FAF is required. The deadline for financial aid applications is March 1.

International Students: There are currently 285 international students enrolled. They must take the TOEFL and achieve a minimum score of 550.

Computers: The college provides computer facilities for student use. The mainframes are a DEC VAX 8650, 785, 750, 6320 and DEC MicroVAX II 3400. There are also 161 IBM and Apple Macintosh PCs available in laboratories and class buildings. All students may access the system. There are no time limits on using the system. The fees are $30 per semester.

Graduates: In 1992–93 1835 bachelor's degrees were awarded. The most popular majors among graduates were general business (8%), law enforcement and police science (6%), and psychology (6%). Within an average freshman class, 34% graduate in 6 years. Some 148 companies recruited on campus in an earlier year.

Admissions Contact: Joey Chandler, Director of Undergraduate Admissions.

SCHREINER COLLEGE
Kerrville, TX 78028   (210) 896–5411; (800) 343–4919   D-4

Full-time: 256 men, 265 women	Faculty: 44; IIB, --$
Part-time: 30 men, 69 women	Ph.D.s: 63%
Graduate: none	Student/Faculty: 12 to 1
Year: 4-1-4, summer session	Tuition: $8650
Application Deadline: August 15	Room & Board: $5670
Freshman Class: 558 applied, 435 accepted, 111 enrolled	
SAT I Verbal/Math: 400/460	ACT: 21 COMPETITIVE

Schreiner College, founded in 1917, is an independent liberal arts college affiliated with the Presbyterian Church U.S.A. The library contains 70,000 volumes, 1700 microform items, and 1690 audiovisual forms, and subscribes to 400 periodicals. Computerized library sources and services include the card catalog. Special learning facilities include a learning resource center. The 175-acre campus is in a small town 50 miles north of San Antonio. Including residence halls, there are 18 buildings on campus.

Student Life: About 84% of undergraduates are from Texas. Students come from 14 states, 10 foreign countries, and Canada. Ninety percent are from public schools; 10% from private. Seventy-eight percent are white; 12% Hispanic. The average age of freshmen is 19; all undergraduates, 21. Ten percent drop out by the end of their first year; 20% remain to graduate.

Housing: A total of 360 students can be accommodated in college housing. College-sponsored living facilities include single-sex and coed dormitories and off-campus apartments. On-campus housing is guaranteed for all 4 years. Sixty-five percent of students live on campus; of those, 80% remain on campus on weekends. All students may keep cars on campus.

Activities: There are no fraternities or sororities on campus. There are 20 groups on campus, including art, cheerleading, chorale, drama, honors, international, literary magazine, newspaper, photography, political, professional, religious, social, and student government. Popular campus events include the annual softball tournament, Halloween Dance, Schreiner Speaker Series, Parents Weekend, Homecoming, winter and spring formals, and Trull Casino Night.

Sports: There are 5 intercollegiate sports for men and 5 for women, and 6 intramural sports for men and 5 for women. Athletic and recreation facilities include a basketball court, a baseball diamond, 3 handball/racquetball courts, a track, 8 tennis courts, a swimming pool, soccer fields, a softball diamond, and intramural fields.

Disabled Students: Ninety-five percent of the campus is accessible to disabled students. The following facilities are available: wheelchair ramps, elevators, special parking, specially equipped rest rooms, special class scheduling, lowered drinking fountains, and lowered telephones.

Services: In addition to many counseling and information services, tutoring is available in every subject, including introductory-level courses. In addition, there is remedial math, reading, and writing. Other tutoring services include a certified peer-tutoring program, workshops, a mathematics laboratory, a self-management orientation course, and computer-assisted instruction for learning skills.

Campus Safety and Security: Campus safety and security measures include informal discussions, pamphlets, posters, and films, emergency telephones, and a night vehicle patrol.

Programs of Study: Schreiner awards the B.A., B.B.A., and B.G.S. degrees. Associate degrees also are awarded. Bachelor's degrees are awarded in BIOLOGICAL SCIENCE (biochemistry and biology/biological science), BUSINESS (accounting, business administration and management, marketing/retailing/merchandising, and real estate), COMMUNICATIONS AND THE ARTS (English, fine arts, and Spanish), COMPUTER AND PHYSICAL SCIENCE (mathematics), EDUCATION (art, elementary, and secondary), HEALTH PROFESSIONS (predentistry and premedicine), SOCIAL SCIENCE (history, humanities, philosophy, prelaw, psychology, and religion). History, English, exercise science, psychology, biology, and mathematics are the strongest academically. Business administration, exercise science, and psychology have the largest enrollments.

Required: All students must have a minimum GPA of 2.0 for 128 semester hours, including 24 in the major. The 64-hour core curriculum includes courses from English composition, oral communication, foreign language, history, natural science, mathematics, philosophy or religion, business data systems, government, business administration, literature, social science, and health, physical education, and recreation.

Special: Internships are offered as a necessary part of the B.B.A. degree. Study abroad in Japan and work-study with the college also are available. In addition, Schreiner offers second majors, a general studies degree, a 3–2 engineering degree with the University of Texas and Texas A&M University, credit for life experience, and nondegree study. There is a freshman honors program on campus, as well as one national honor society.

Faculty/Classroom: Seventy-one percent of faculty are male; 29%, female. All teach undergraduates. The average class size in an introductory lecture is 25; in a laboratory, 15; and in a regular course offering, 20.

Admissions: About 78% of the 1993–94 applicants were accepted. Seven freshmen graduated first in their class.

Requirements: A minimum GPA of 2.0 is required. The SAT I, with a composite score of 800, or the ACT, with a score of 20, is recommended. Applicants need 20 secondary-school academic credits. The college strongly recommends that those credits include 4 years of English, 3 of mathematics, and 2 each in history, science, and social studies. An interview is advised. The GED is accepted. AP and CLEP credits are accepted. Important factors used in the admissions decision are advanced placement or honor courses, leadership record, evidence of special talent, extracurricular activities record, and recommendations by school officials.

Procedure: Freshmen are admitted to all sessions. Entrance exams should be taken in the spring of the junior year. Applications should be filed by August 15 for fall entry, December 15 for winter entry, January 15 for spring entry, and June 1 for summer entry, along with an application fee of $20. Notification is sent on a rolling basis. There is a deferred admissions plan.

Transfer: A total of 62 transfer students enrolled in a recent year. Transfer applicants with fewer than 15 credit hours must meet freshman admission requirements. For those with more, the SAT I or ACT is not required. A 2.0 minimum GPA is necessary. A total of 30 credits out of 128 must be completed at Schreiner.

Visiting: There are regularly scheduled orientations for prospective students. The structured program includes guides, financial aid information, and faculty and student discussions. There are guides for informal visits and visitors may sit in on classes and stay overnight at the school. To arrange for a visit, contact the Admissions Office at (800) 343-4919.

Financial Aid: In 1993–94, 75% of all students received some form of financial aid. About 60% received need-based aid. The average freshman award was $7400. Of that total, scholarships or need-based grants averaged $1500 ($10,200 maximum); loans averaged $2050 ($2625 maximum); and work contracts averaged $1000 (maximum). Twenty percent of undergraduate students work part-time. Average earnings from campus work for the school year are $1000. The average financial indebtedness of a recent year's graduate was $6231. Schreiner is a member of CSS. The FAF, FFS, or SFS is required. The deadline for financial aid applications is August 1.

International Students: There are currently 25 international students enrolled. The school actively recruits these students. They must take the TOEFL, the University of Michigan Language Test, the Comprehensive English Language Test, or the college's own test.

Computers: The college provides computer facilities for student use. Twenty IBM and Apple PCs are available in the computer laboratory. All students may access the system.

Graduates: In a recent year, 53 bachelor's degrees were awarded. The most popular majors among graduates were business and management (28%), mathematics (15%), and psychology (13%). Five companies recruited on campus in a recent year. In a recent graduating class, 2% of the men and 5% of the women were enrolled in graduate school within 6 months of graduation; 90% had found employment.

Admissions Contact: Sandy Speed, Director of Admission.

SOUTHERN METHODIST UNIVERSITY   D-2
Dallas, TX 75275   **(214) SMU-2058; (800) 323-0672 (out-of-state)**

Full-time: 2356 men, 2536 women	Faculty: 483; I, -$
Part-time: 144 men, 243 women	Ph.D.s: 85%
Graduate: 2298 men, 1354 women	Student/Faculty: 10 to 1
Year: semesters, summer session	Tuition: $13,580
Application Deadline: January 15	Room & Board: $4940
Freshman Class: 4301 applied, 3455 accepted, 1166 enrolled	
SAT I or ACT: required	**VERY COMPETITIVE**

Southern Methodist University, founded in 1911, is a private nonsectarian institution affiliated with the United Methodist Church. SMU offers undergraduate and graduate programs in humanities and sciences, business, arts, and engineering and applied sciences. Graduate and professional programs are also offered in law and theology. There are 4 undergraduate and 6 graduate schools. In addition to regional accreditation, SMU has baccalaureate program accreditation with AACSB, ABA, ABET, ACS, ATS, NASD, and NASM. The 8 libraries contain 2,800,507 volumes, 1,388,495 microform items, and 26,112 audiovisual forms, and subscribe to 5727 periodicals. Computerized library sources and services include the card catalog, interlibrary loans, and database searching. Special learning facilities include a learning resource center, art gallery, natural history museum, radio station, TV station and studio, research laboratories, and several performing arts theaters, including Classical Thrust Stage. The 163-

acre campus is in a suburban area 5 miles north of downtown Dallas. Including residence halls, there are 75 buildings on campus.

Student Life: About 58% of undergraduates are from Texas. Students come from 50 states, 57 foreign countries, and Canada. Sixty-eight percent are from public schools; 32% from private. Seventy-nine percent are white. Fifty-five percent are Protestant; 22% Catholic. The average age of freshmen is 18; all undergraduates, 20. Eighteen percent drop out by the end of their first year; 67% remain to graduate.

Housing: A total of 2262 students can be accommodated in college housing. College-sponsored living facilities include single-sex and coed dormitories, on-campus apartments, off-campus apartments, married-student housing, fraternity houses, and sorority houses. In addition, there are honors houses, special interest houses, wellness floors, an international floor, and some floors catering to particular disciplines. On-campus housing is guaranteed for all 4 years. All students may keep cars on campus; 55% commute.

Activities: About 44% of men belong to 15 national fraternities; about 51% of women belong to 11 national sororities. There are 151 groups on campus, including art, band, cheerleading, choir, chorale, chorus, computers, dance, ethnic, gay, honors, international, jazz band, literary magazine, marching band, musical theater, newspaper, opera, orchestra, pep band, photography, political, professional, radio and TV, religious, social, social service, student government, symphony, and yearbook. Popular campus events include Homecoming, Pigskin Review, Celebration of Lights, Parents Weekend, Community Service Day, Peruna's Birthday, Rotunda Passage, Commencement, and Literary Festival.

Sports: There are 8 intercollegiate sports for men and 7 for women, and 20 intramural sports for men and 19 for women. Athletic and recreation facilities include gymnastic and weight rooms, basketball, volleyball, tennis, badminton, and racquetball courts, a dance studio, indoor and outdoor jogging tracks, an indoor and outdoor pool, and a 2400-seat outdoor and a 6500-seat indoor stadium.

Disabled Students: Ninety-five percent of the campus is accessible to disabled students. The following facilities are available: wheelchair ramps, elevators, special parking, specially equipped rest rooms, special class scheduling, and lowered drinking fountains. An ongoing renovation aims to make the campus completely accessible.

Services: In addition to many counseling and information services, tutoring is available in most subjects. There is also a reader service for the blind. The Learning Enhancement Center provides study skills workshops, notetaking techniques, and time management skills seminars.

Campus Safety and Security: Campus safety and security measures include 24-hour foot and vehicle patrol, self defense education, escort service, and informal discussions. In addition, there are pamphlets, posters, films, emergency telephones, and lighted pathways and sidewalks. Card-key devices, issued to all students living in residence halls, must be used to enter these buildings.

Programs of Study: SMU awards the B.A., B.S., B.B.A., B.F.A., B.Hum., B.M., B.S.C.E., B.S.Comp.Eng., B.S.E.E., B.S.M.E., and B.Soc.Sci. degrees. Master's and doctoral degrees also are awarded. Bachelor's degrees are awarded in BIOLOGICAL SCIENCE (biochemistry and biology/biological science), BUSINESS (accounting, business administration and management, management information systems, management science, marketing/retailing/merchandising, organizational behavior, and real estate), COMMUNICATIONS AND THE ARTS (advertising, art history and appreciation, broadcasting, creative writing, dance, dramatic arts, English, film arts, French, German, journalism, languages, media arts, music performance, music theory and composition, piano/organ, public relations, Russian, and Spanish), COMPUTER AND PHYSICAL SCIENCE (chemistry, computer science, geology, geophysics and seismology, mathematics, physics, and statistics), EDUCATION (music), ENGINEERING AND ENVIRONMENTAL DESIGN (computer engineering, electrical/electronics engineering, and mechanical engineering), HEALTH PROFESSIONS (music therapy), SOCIAL SCIENCE (African American studies, anthropology, economics, history, humanities, international studies, Latin American studies, liberal arts/general studies, Mexican-American/Chicano studies, philosophy, political science/government, psychology, religion, Russian and Slavic studies, social science, and sociology). Electrical engineering, theater, business, history, economics, chemistry, psychology, anthropology, dance, biology, fine arts, geological sciences, and computer science are the strongest academically. General business, psychology, advertising, history, and political science have the largest enrollments.

Required: Basic requirements consist of 122 semester hours, including a general education requirement of 32 hours distributed across writing, mathematics, arts and humanities, social and natural sciences, intercultural and non-Western co-requirements, a major, and a minor. All students (except those in performing arts) must have a major or minor concentration in a liberal arts discipline. There is also a 2-credit-hour wellness education requirement. Students must maintain a GPA of 2.0.

Special: SMU offers a co-op program in engineering, study abroad in 10 countries, dual majors in any combination, interdisciplinary majors, including economics with finance applications, and economics with systems analysis, student-designed majors, and numerous internships. A 3–2 M.B.A. is available, as are evening degree programs in humanities and social sciences, and teacher certification programs. There is a freshman honors program on campus, as well as 17 national honor societies, including Phi Beta Kappa.

Faculty/Classroom: Seventy-seven percent of faculty are male; 23%, female. All teach undergraduates and do research. Graduate students teach 6% of introductory courses.

Admissions: About 80% of the 1993–94 applicants were accepted. About 61% of the current freshmen were in the top fifth of their class; 85% were in the top two fifths. There were 16 National Merit finalists.

Requirements: The SAT I or ACT is required. In addition, applicants should graduate from an accredited high school with 15 academic credits: 4 in English, 3 in higher mathematics, including Algebra I, II and plane geometry, 3 each in natural science and social science, and 2 in the same foreign language. Home School Certificate applicants may qualify with the SAT I or ACT and 6 SAT II: Subject tests, including writing and mathematics. Performing arts majors must audition. Interviews are not required. AP and CLEP credits are accepted.

Procedure: Freshmen are admitted to all sessions. Entrance exams should be taken by December of senior year. Early decision applications should be filed by November 1; regular applications, by January 15 for fall entry, December 1 for spring, and April 1 for summer, along with an application fee of $40. Notification of early decision is sent December 30; rolling after March 15. There are early decision and deferred admissions plans. About 15 early decision candidates were accepted for the 1993–94 class. A waiting list is an active part of the admissions procedure, with about 3% of applicants on the list.

Transfer: About 311 transfer students enrolled in 1993–94. A minimum 2.5 GPA is generally required for transfer, but requirements vary according to the program for which the student seeks admission. Candidates must demonstrate math proficiency and meet a foreign language requirement as indicated through high school or college work. A total of 60 credits out of 122 must be completed at SMU.

Visiting: There are regularly scheduled orientations for prospective students, including information about academic studies, financial aid information sessions, discussions with current students, lunch with faculty and students, and a tour of the campus. There is also a Spring Fest visitation in April for juniors. There are guides for informal visits and visitors may sit in on classes and stay overnight at the school. To arrange for a visit, contact the Undergraduate Admission Office at (214) SMU-2058 or (800) 323-0672.

Financial Aid: In 1993–94 79% of all current freshmen and 66% of continuing students received some form of financial aid. About 42% of freshmen and 36% of continuing students received need-based aid. The average freshman award was $12,181. Of that total, scholarships or need-based grants averaged $2900 ($15,000 maximum); loans averaged $8000 ($12,000 maximum); and work contracts averaged $1900 (maximum). Average earnings from campus work for the school year are $1858. The average financial indebtedness of the 1992–93 graduate was $13,000. SMU is a member of CSS. The FAF is required. The deadline for financial aid applications is February 1.

International Students: There are currently 137 international undergraduate students enrolled. The school actively recruits these students. They must take the TOEFL and achieve a minimum score of 550. The student must also take the SAT I or the ACT.

Computers: The college provides computer facilities for student use. The mainframes are an IBM RS 6000 980 B running AIX and a SUN 4/490 server running SUN 05. Access to the mainframe and other campus computers is available from any campus location. Several hundred microcomputers and terminals are available for student use around the campus, including in dormitories. A student computing laboratory is located in a campus library. All students may access the system. It may be used 24 hours a day. There are no time limits and no fees.

Graduates: In 1992–93, 1344 bachelor's degrees were awarded. The most popular majors among graduates were psychology (9%), history and political science (6%), and advertising (6%). Within an average freshman class, 1% graduate in 3 years, 59% in 4 years, 67% in 5 years, and 73% in 6 years. Some 123 companies recruited on campus in 1992–93.

Admissions Contact: Ron W. Moss, Director of Admissions and Enrollment Management.

SOUTHWEST TEXAS STATE UNIVERSITY
San Marcos, TX 78666

D-4
(512) 245-2803

Full-time: 7042 men, 7508 women	Faculty: 662; IIA, --$
Part-time: 1910 men, 2037 women	Ph.D.s: 49%
Graduate: 913 men, 1071 women	Student/Faculty: 22 to 1
Year: semesters, summer session	Tuition: $1624 ($5704)
Application Deadline: August 1	Room & Board: $3500
Freshman Class: 13,761 applied, 8532 accepted, 4437 enrolled	
ACT: 22	COMPETITIVE

Southwest Texas State University, founded in 1899, is part of the Texas State University System and offers programs in general studies, applied arts and technology, business, education, fine arts, health professions, liberal arts, and science. There are 8 undergraduate schools and one graduate school. In addition to regional accreditation, SWT has baccalaureate program accreditation with AHEA, ASLA, CSWE, NASM, and NCATE. The library contains 932,869 volumes, 1,295,433 microform items, and 17,023 audiovisual forms, and subscribes to 5847 periodicals. Computerized library sources and services include the card catalog. Special learning facilities include a learning resource center, art gallery, and radio station. The 364-acre campus is in a small town 30 miles south of Austin and 50 miles north of San Antonio. Including residence halls, there are 100 buildings on campus.

Student Life: About 97% of undergraduates are from Texas. Students come from 38 states, 62 foreign countries, and Canada. Ninety-eight percent are from public schools; 2% from private. Seventy-five percent are white; 17% Hispanic. The average age of freshmen is 18; all undergraduates, 23. Thirty-six percent drop out by the end of their first year.

Housing: A total of 5000 students can be accommodated in college housing. College-sponsored living facilities include single-sex and coed dormitories, on-campus apartments, and married-student housing. In addition there are honors houses, language houses, and special interest houses. On-campus housing is guaranteed for all 4 years. Seventy-five percent of students commute. Alcohol is not permitted. All students may keep cars on campus.

Activities: About 4% of men belong to 19 national fraternities; about 4% of women belong to 7 national sororities. There are 153 groups on campus, including art, band, cheerleading, chess, choir, chorale, chorus, computers, dance, drama, drill team, ethnic, gay, honors, international, jazz band, literary magazine, marching band, musical theater, newspaper, opera, orchestra, political, professional, radio and TV, religious, social, social service, student government, symphony, and yearbook. Popular campus events include Homecoming, Roanoak Street Festival, Greek Week, International Food Fair, Celebration of Song, Monster Concerts, Springfest, and Christmas on the Quad.

Sports: Athletic and recreation facilities include a 14,104-seat stadium, a 7200-seat gymnasium, tennis courts, a spring-fed pool, an aquatic sports center, and basketball and volleyball courts.

Disabled Students: The following facilities are available: wheelchair ramps, elevators, special parking, specially equipped rest rooms, special class scheduling, lowered drinking fountains, and lowered telephones.

Services: In addition to many counseling and information services, tutoring is available in most subjects. There is also a reader service for the blind, and remedial math, reading, and writing.

Campus Safety and Security: Campus safety and security measures include 24-hour foot and vehicle patrol, self defense education, escort service, and shuttle buses. In addition, there are informal discussions, pamphlets, posters, films, emergency telephones, and lighted pathways and sidewalks.

Programs of Study: SWT awards the B.A., B.S., B.A.A.S., B.B.A., B.F.A., B.M., and B.S.W. degrees. Associate and master's degrees also are awarded. Bachelor's degrees are awarded in AGRICULTURE (agricultural business management, agricultural mechanics, agriculture, animal science, fishing and fisheries, and horticulture), BIOLOGICAL SCIENCE (biology/biological science, botany, marine biology, microbiology, physiology, wildlife biology, and zoology), BUSINESS (accounting, banking and finance, business administration and management, business economics, fashion merchandising, marketing/retailing/merchandising, personnel management, and recreation and leisure services), COMMUNICATIONS AND THE ARTS (advertising, applied art, broadcasting, communications, dance, dramatic arts, English, fine arts, French, German, journalism, music, music performance, Spanish, speech/debate/rhetoric, and studio art), COMPUTER AND PHYSICAL SCIENCE (chemistry, computer science, earth science, information sciences and systems, mathematics, and physics), EDUCATION (agricultural, art, business, early childhood, elementary, foreign languages, health, home economics, industrial arts, middle school, music, physical, reading, science, secondary, special, and vocational), ENGINEERING AND ENVIRONMENTAL DESIGN (cartography, city/community/regional planning,

commercial art, environmental science, industrial administration/management, industrial engineering technology, and interior design), HEALTH PROFESSIONS (medical laboratory technology, medical records administration/services, predentistry, premedicine, respiratory therapy, and speech pathology/audiology), SOCIAL SCIENCE (anthropology, Asian/Oriental studies, child care/child and family studies, consumer services, corrections, criminal justice, economics, European studies, food science, geography, history, home economics, international relations, international studies, law enforcement and corrections, Middle Eastern studies, philosophy, physical fitness/movement, political science/government, psychology, social science, social work, and sociology). Geography, theater, education, business, and biology are the strongest academically. Prebusiness has the largest enrollment.

Required: All students must earn a minimum GPA of 2.0 while taking at least 128 semester hours, including 30 in the major. The general studies core includes courses from the categories of basic skills, history and politics, natural science, social science, philosophy, international perspectives, literature, fine arts, and physical fitness. Two physical education credits are required.

Special: Co-op programs with the University of Texas at Austin and Texas A&M University in engineering and with A&M in marine biology, internships in many departments, study abroad in England, Germany, France, Japan, Spain, and Mexico, and Washington semesters are available. Dual majors, credit for life experience, and nondegree study also are possible. There is a freshman honors program on campus, as well as 2 national honor societies. One department has an honors program.

Faculty/Classroom: Sixty-five percent of faculty are male; 35%, female. Eighty percent teach undergraduates, 10% do research, and 10% do both. Graduate students teach 1% of introductory courses. The average class sizes in an introductory lecture and in a regular course offering are 33.

Admissions: About 62% of the 1993–94 applicants were accepted. The ACT scores for the 1993–94 freshman class were as follows: 31% below 21, 40% between 21 and 23, 22% between 24 and 26, 5% between 27 and 28, and 2% above 28. About 35% of the current freshmen were in the top fifth of their class; 90% were in the top two fifths. Twenty-six freshmen graduated first in their class.

Requirements: A minimum GPA of 2.0 is required. The SAT I or ACT is required, with minimum scores determined by high school class rank. Applicants need 14 academic credits, including 4 units in English, 3 in mathematics and social science, and 2 in laboratory science. The GED is accepted; applicants with a GED are treated as though they were ranked in the 4th quarter. AP and CLEP credits are accepted. Important factors used in the admissions decision are advanced placement or honor courses, leadership record, extracurricular activities record, evidence of special talent, and recommendations by alumni.

Procedure: Freshmen are admitted to all sessions. Entrance exams should be taken at the end of the junior year. Applications should be filed by August 1 for fall entry, December 1 for spring entry, and May 1 for summer entry. Notification is sent on a rolling basis 2 weeks after receipt of all credentials.

Transfer: About 1825 transfer students enrolled in 1993–94. Transfer students with 29 or fewer credits must meet freshman requirements; those with 30 or more credits must submit official transcripts to verify a minimum 2.3 GPA. A total of 30 credits out of 128 must be completed at SWT.

Visiting: There are regularly scheduled orientations for prospective students. There are guides for informal visits and visitors may sit in on classes. To arrange for a visit, contact the Admissions and Visitors Center at (512) 245-2364.

Financial Aid: Scholarships or need-based grants averaged $500 ($2000 maximum); loans $2625 (maximum). Twenty percent of undergraduate students work part-time. SWT is a member of CSS. The FAF or FFS is required and the FFS is preferred. The deadline for financial aid applications is April 1.

International Students: There are currently 263 international students enrolled. They must take the TOEFL and achieve a minimum score of 550.

Computers: The college provides computer facilities for student use. The mainframe is a DEC VAX 8650. There are also IBM, IBM-compatible, Macintosh, and Apple II PCs available for student use throughout the campus. Those students taking computer classes or with faculty members sponsorship may access the system. It may be used 24 hours daily. There are no time limits on using the system. The fees are $25.

Graduates: In 1992–93 2694 bachelor's degrees were awarded. The most popular majors among graduates were elementary education (9%), marketing (6%), and occupational education (5%). Some 540 companies recruited on campus in an earlier year.

Admissions Contact: Fernando Yarrito, Director of Admissions.

SOUTHWESTERN ADVENTIST COLLEGE   D-2

Keene, TX 76059   (817) 645-3921; (800) 433-2240

Full-time: 371 men, 440 women	Faculty: 48
Part-time: 30 men, 72 women	Ph.Ds: 48%
Graduate: 1 man, 8 women	Student/Faculty: 17 to 1
Year: semesters, summer session	Tuition: $7064
Application Deadline: open	Room & Board: $3466

Freshman Class: 318 accepted, 186 enrolled

SAT I Verbal/Math: 390/410   ACT: 22   NONCOMPETITIVE

Southwestern Adventist College, founded in 1893, is a small, coeducational, Seventh-day Adventist institution offering liberal arts and professional degree programs. There is one graduate school. In addition to regional accreditation, SAC has baccalaureate program accreditation with NLN. The library contains 98,570 volumes, 338,729 microform items, and 6280 audiovisual forms, and subscribes to 452 periodicals. Computerized library sources and services include the card catalog and database searching. Special learning facilities include a learning resource center, natural history museum, radio station, and an observatory. The 150-acre campus is in a rural area 35 miles south of Fort Worth. Including residence halls, there are 25 buildings on campus.

Student Life: About 67% of undergraduates are from out-of-state, mostly the Southwest. Students come from 44 states, 32 foreign countries, and Canada. Twenty percent are from public schools; 80% from private. Sixty-six percent are white; 14% Hispanic; 10% African American. Most are Protestant. The average age of freshmen is 19; all undergraduates, 26. Thirty-one percent drop out by the end of their first year; 69% remain to graduate.

Housing: A total of 373 students can be accommodated in college housing. College-sponsored living facilities include single-sex dormitories, off-campus apartments, and married-student housing. On-campus housing is guaranteed for all 4 years. Sixty-three percent of students commute. Alcohol is not permitted. All students may keep cars on campus.

Activities: There are no fraternities or sororities on campus. There are 20 groups on campus, including art, band, choir, chorale, computers, drama, ethnic, film, international, newspaper, orchestra, pep band, photography, radio and TV, religious, social, social service, student government, symphony, and yearbook. Popular campus events include Founders Day, Fall Holiday, and Memosa Memories.

Sports: There are 2 intercollegiate sports for men and 1 for women, and 4 intramural sports for men and 4 for women. Athletic and recreation facilities include jogging and fitness tracks, weight and aerobics rooms, courts for tennis, racquetball, and basketball, and fields for football and baseball.

Disabled Students: The following facilities are available: wheelchair ramps, elevators, specially equipped rest rooms, and lowered drinking fountains.

Services: In addition to many counseling and information services, tutoring is available in some subjects, including accounting, biology, chemistry, English, Greek, mathematics, nursing and Spanish. In addition, there is remedial math and writing.

Campus Safety and Security: Campus safety and security measures include informal discussions, pamphlets, posters, and films, and lighted pathways and sidewalks.

Programs of Study: SAC awards the B.A., B.S., B.B.A., and B.S.W. degrees. Associate and master's degrees also are awarded. Bachelor's degrees are awarded in BIOLOGICAL SCIENCE (biology/biological science and biometrics and biostatistics), BUSINESS (accounting, business administration and management, and office supervision and management), COMMUNICATIONS AND THE ARTS (broadcasting, communications, English, and journalism), COMPUTER AND PHYSICAL SCIENCE (chemistry, computer science, information sciences and systems, mathematics, and physics), EDUCATION (elementary), HEALTH PROFESSIONS (health, health care administration, medical laboratory technology, and nursing), SOCIAL SCIENCE (history, international relations, psychology, religion, social science, social work, and theological studies). Nursing, biology, religion, and business are the strongest academically. Education, nursing, and business have the largest enrollments.

Required: All students must take at least 128 hours, including 40 hours in upper-division courses. An overall 2.0 GPA is required for graduation, with a 2.3 in upper-division courses in the major field. General education requirements include courses in English, health and physical education, mathematics and science, religion, social science and humanities, and, in some cases, foreign language.

Special: Cooperative programs in medical technology are available with several area hospitals. Internships are arranged on an individual basis. Students may study abroad in Germany, France, or Spain. Student-designed majors, interdisciplinary majors, including mathematical physics, a 3–2 engineering degree with Walla Walla College and Andrew University, and an adult degree program are offered. There is a campuswide honors program.

Faculty/Classroom: Sixty-three percent of faculty are male; 37%, female. All teach undergraduates. No introductory courses are taught by graduate students. The average class size in an introductory lecture is 30; in a laboratory, 15; and in a regular course offering, 20.
Admissions: The SAT scores for the 1993–94 freshman class were as follows: Verbal—79% below 500, 18% between 500 and 599, 3% between 600 and 700, and 1% above 700; Math—75% below 500, 20% between 500 and 599, 5% between 600 and 700, and 1% above 700. The ACT scores were 45% below 21, 26% between 21 and 23, 14% between 24 and 26, 9% between 27 and 28, and 6% above 28. There were 2 National Merit finalists. Nine freshmen graduated first in their class.
Requirements: The SAT I or ACT is required. Applicants should be high school graduates or hold the GED. Secondary preparation is expected to include 12 academic credits in English, foreign language, mathematics, natural or physical science, and social science. Potential nursing or education majors and Seventh-day Adventist ministers must meet additional requirements. CLEP credit is accepted.
Procedure: Freshmen are admitted to all sessions. Entrance exams should be taken before registration. Application deadlines are open. The college accepts all applicants. Notification is sent on a rolling basis.
Transfer: About 120 transfer students enrolled in 1993–94. An official transcript from each college or university the student has attended must be mailed directly to SAC's Enrollment Office. Transfer students with less than a C average may be accepted on a probationary basis. Nursing, education, and theology majors have additional requirements. A total of 30 credits out of 128 must be completed at SAC.
Visiting: There are regularly scheduled orientations for prospective students. There are guides for informal visits and visitors may sit in on classes and stay overnight at the school. To arrange for a visit, contact the Enrollment Office at (800) 433–2240.
Financial Aid: In 1993–94, 58% of all current freshmen and 50% of continuing students received some form of financial aid. About 38% of freshmen and 41% of continuing students received need-based aid. The average freshman award was $4880. Of that total, scholarships or need-based grants averaged $1200 ($2400 maximum); loans averaged $2625; and work contracts averaged $1500 ($2000 maximum). The average financial indebtedness of the 1992–93 graduate was $4000. SAC is a member of CSS. The FAF and the college's own financial statement are required.
International Students: There are currently 71 international students enrolled. They must take the TOEFL or the University of Michigan Language Test and achieve a minimum score on the TOEFL of 520.
Computers: The college provides computer facilities for student use. The mainframe is a DEC 4000 Model 200. Microcomputers are available in faculty offices and academic departments. All students may access the system 24 hours per day. There are no time limits on using the system and no fees.
Graduates: In 1992–93, 140 bachelor's degrees were awarded. Within an average freshman class, 24% graduate in 6 years.
Admissions Contact: Victor Brown, Enrollment Vice President.

SOUTHWESTERN CHRISTIAN COLLEGE   D-2
Terrell, TX 75160   (214) 563-3341, ext. 142

Full-time: 128 men, 98 women	Faculty: 16
Part-time: 19 men, 9 women	Ph.Ds: 19%
Graduate: none	Student/Faculty: 14 to 1
Year: semesters	Tuition: $4386
Application Deadline: July 31	Room & Board: $2647
Freshman Class: n/av	
SAT I or ACT: required	**NONCOMPETITIVE**

Southwestern Christian College, chartered in 1949, is a private coeducational institution affiliated with the Church of Christ, offering bachelor's degrees in Bible and religious education. The library contains 23,702 volumes and 2457 audiovisual forms. Special learning facilities include a learning resource center and a sound recording studio. The 25-acre campus is in a rural area 32 miles east of Dallas. Including residence halls, there are 15 buildings on campus.
Student Life: About 47% of undergraduates are from out-of-state, mostly the Northeast. Students come from 27 states and 8 foreign countries. Ninety-five percent are from public schools. Eighty-five percent are African American. Most are Protestant. The average age of freshmen is 20; all undergraduates, 21.
Housing: A total of 192 students can be accommodated in college housing. College-sponsored living facilities include single-sex dormitories. On-campus housing is guaranteed for all 4 years. Eighty-five percent of students live on campus. All students may keep cars on campus.
Activities: There are no fraternities or sororities on campus. There are 19 groups on campus, including cheerleading, chorus, drama, international, jazz band, newspaper, religious, student government, and

yearbook. Popular campus events include Annual College Lectureship, Homecoming, and High School Day.
Sports: Athletic and recreation facilities include a gymnasium, a weight room, handball courts, 2 tennis courts, a game room, and a 1500-seat auditorium.
Services: In addition to many counseling and information services, tutoring is available in some subjects. There is remedial math, reading, and writing.
Programs of Study: SwCC awards the B.A. in Bible and B.S. in religious education degrees. Associate degrees also are awarded. Religious education is the strongest program academically and has the largest enrollment.
Required: Students must complete 124 to 133 semester hours with a 2.25 GPA. Required courses include physical education, computer literacy, Bible, English, foreign language or science, history, humanities, mathematics, and freshman orientation. Students must attend daily chapel and various other church services and activities, and agree to maintain the high moral standards required by SwCC.
Special: SwCC offers work-study, a ministerial internship, a B.A.-B.S. degree in Bible and religious education, credit by examination, and nondegree study.
Faculty/Classroom: Sixty-two percent of faculty are male; 37%, female.
Requirements: The SAT I or ACT is required. Applicants should be high school graduates or have the GED. Secondary school preparation should include a minimum of 15 units in academic courses, including at least 3 in English. A campus tour and an interview are strongly recommended.
Procedure: Freshmen are admitted to all sessions. Entrance exams should be taken prior to registration. Applications should be filed by July 31 for fall entry and December 15 for spring entry, along with an application fee of $10. The college accepts all applicants. Notification is sent on a rolling basis.
Transfer: About 16 transfer students enrolled in an earlier year. A GPA of 2.0 is recommended. Transcripts and a letter of recommendation should be submitted 60 days before enrollment. A total of 32 semester hours out of 124 to 133 must be completed at SwCC.
Visiting: There are regularly scheduled orientations for prospective students. There are guides for informal visits and visitors may sit in on classes and stay overnight at the school. To arrange for a visit, contact Jacob McClinton, Admissions Counselor, at (903) 563–3341, ext. 155.
Financial Aid: Scholarships, loans, and grants are available. In a recent year, freshmen with a high school GPA of 3.7 were eligible for an annual renewable scholarship of $800; $600 for those with a GPA of 3.3. SwCC is a member of CSS. The FAF and the college's own financial statement are required.
International Students: They must take the TOEFL and achieve a minimum score of 500. The student must also take the college's own entrance exam and a full course load of 12 semester hours.
Computers: The college provides computer facilities for student use. The mainframe is an IBM/34. There are computer laboratories in the library. All students may access the system during regular school hours. There are no time limits on using the system and no fees.
Graduates: In a recent year, 5 bachelor's degrees were awarded.
Admissions Contact: John Edmerson, Director of Admissions.

SOUTHWESTERN UNIVERSITY   D-3
Georgetown, TX 78626   (512) 863-1200; (800) 252-3166

Full-time: 508 men, 669 women	Faculty: 87; IIB, +$
Part-time: 13 men, 30 women	Ph.Ds: 89%
Graduate: none	Student/Faculty: 14 to 1
Year: semesters, summer session	Tuition: $11,000
Application Deadline: February 15	Room & Board: $4484
Freshman Class: 1244 applied, 912 accepted, 351 enrolled	
SAT I Verbal/Math: 526/577	ACT: 25 **HIGHLY COMPETITIVE**

Southwestern University, founded in 1840, is a private liberal arts institution affiliated with the United Methodist Church. In addition to regional accreditation, Southwestern has baccalaureate program accreditation with NASM. The library contains 243,833 volumes, 27,244 microform items, and 1272 audiovisual forms, and subscribes to 1292 periodicals. Computerized library sources and services include the card catalog, interlibrary loans, and database searching. Special learning facilities include a learning resource center. The 500-acre campus is in a small town 28 miles north of Austin. Including residence halls, there are 25 buildings on campus.
Student Life: About 89% of undergraduates are from Texas. Students come from 32 states, 14 foreign countries, and Canada. Eighty-six percent are from public schools; 14% from private. Seventy-eight percent are white; 13% African American. Sixty-four percent are Protestant; 24% Catholic; 10% claim no religious affiliation. The average age of freshmen is 18; all undergraduates, 20. Fourteen percent drop out by the end of their first year; 71% remain to graduate.

Housing: A total of 885 students can be accommodated in college housing. College-sponsored living facilities include single-sex and coed dormitories and fraternity houses. On-campus housing is guaranteed for the freshman year only, is available on a first-come, first-served basis, and is available on a lottery system for upperclassmen. Seventy-seven percent of students live on campus; of those, 55% remain on campus on weekends. Alcohol is not permitted. All students may keep cars on campus.

Activities: About 41% of men belong to 4 national fraternities; about 42% of women belong to 3 national sororities. There are 70 groups on campus, including art, band, cheerleading, choir, chorale, chorus, computers, dance, drama, ethnic, gay, honors, international, jazz band, literary magazine, musical theater, newspaper, opera, orchestra, pep band, political, professional, religious, social, social service, student government, and yearbook. Popular campus events include Homecoming Sing, Mall Ball, and Brown Symposium (a 2- to 3-day intellectual experience each spring).

Sports: There are 6 intercollegiate sports for men and 5 for women, and 9 intramural sports for men and 9 for women. Athletic and recreation facilities include a physical education center, a 2000-seat gymnasium, and a 9-hole golf course.

Disabled Students: Ninety percent of the campus is accessible to disabled students. The following facilities are available: wheelchair ramps, elevators, special parking, specially equipped rest rooms, lowered drinking fountains, and lowered telephones.

Services: In addition to many counseling and information services, tutoring is available in most subjects, including mathematics, computer science, and sciences.

Campus Safety and Security: Campus safety and security measures include 24-hour foot and vehicle patrol, escort service, pamphlets, posters, and films, and emergency telephones. In addition, there are lighted pathways and sidewalks.

Programs of Study: Southwestern awards the B.A., B.S., B.F.A., and B.Mus. degrees. Bachelor's degrees are awarded in AGRICULTURE (animal science), BIOLOGICAL SCIENCE (biology/biological science), BUSINESS (accounting and business administration and management), COMMUNICATIONS AND THE ARTS (art, classics, communications, dramatic arts, English, French, German, Latin, music, and Spanish), COMPUTER AND PHYSICAL SCIENCE (chemistry, computer science, mathematics, and physics), SOCIAL SCIENCE (American studies, child psychology/development, economics, history, international studies, philosophy, physical fitness/movement, political science/government, psychology, religion, sociology, and women's studies). Psychology, chemistry, music, history, biology, business, and sociology are the strongest academically. Business, biology, English, history, psychology, communications, and international studies have the largest enrollments.

Required: All students must complete at least 122 credits with a 2.0 GPA and satisfy distribution requirements in the arts, humanities, social science, and natural science. The total number of hours required in most majors is 30. A freshman symposium and mathematics course are required. All students must take 1 semester of English composition and must demonstrate computer literacy. Seniors must complete a capstone requirement in their major.

Special: Students may study abroad in England, France, Mexico, Korea, and other countries. The university offers a semester in Washington, D.C., dual, student-designed and an independent major, and internships in government, psychology, and science. A 3-2 engineering program may be arranged with Washington, Texas A&M, and Arizona State universities, and the University of Texas at Austin. Some pass/fail options are available. There are 6 national honor societies on campus.

Faculty/Classroom: Sixty-seven percent of faculty are male; 33%, female. All teach undergraduates. The average class size in an introductory lecture is 31; in a laboratory, 20; and in a regular course offering, 22.

Admissions: About 73% of the 1993–94 applicants were accepted. The SAT scores for the 1993–94 freshman class were as follows: Verbal—38% below 500, 42% between 500 and 599, 18% between 600 and 700, and 2% above 700; Math—14% below 500, 43% between 500 and 599, 33% between 600 and 700, and 9% above 700. The ACT scores were 4% below 21, 27% between 21 and 23, 33% between 24 and 26, 17% between 27 and 28, and 19% above 28. About 69% of the current freshmen were in the top fifth of their class; 88% were in the top two fifths. There were 8 National Merit finalists and 8 semifinalists. Eleven freshmen graduated first in their class.

Requirements: The SAT I or ACT is required. Applicant should be a graduate of an accredited high school or have the GED. Secondary preparation should include 4 years each of English and mathematics, 3 years each of science and social science or history, 2 years of a foreign language, and 1 year of an academic elective. There is no minimun score required on the SAT I or ACT. An essay is required and an interview is recommmended. AP and CLEP credits are accepted. Important factors used in the admissions decision are advanced placement or honor courses, recommendations by school officials, ex-

tracurricular activities record, leadership record, and evidence of special talent.

Procedure: Freshmen are admitted fall and spring. Entrance exams should be taken in the fall of the senior year. Early decision applications should be filed by November 1 (Round I) and January 1 (Round II); regular applications, by February 15 for fall entry and December 1 for spring entry, along with an application fee of $25. Notification of early decision is sent December 1 (Round I) and February 1 (Round II); regular decision, March 31. There are early decision, early admissions, and deferred admissions plans. About 130 early decision candidates were accepted for the 1993–94 class. A waiting list is an active part of the admissions procedure, with about 8% of applicants on the list.

Transfer: A total of 34 transfer students enrolled in 1993–94. Preference is given to students having a 3.0 GPA in all college work. A total of 30 credits out of 122 must be completed at Southwestern.

Visiting: There are regularly scheduled orientations for prospective students, including 2 or 3 group overnight options and a Saturday open house in the fall. There are guides for informal visits and visitors may sit in on classes and stay overnight at the school. To arrange for a visit, contact the Admission Office at (800) 252–3166.

Financial Aid: In 1993–94, 66% of all current freshmen and 68% of continuing students received some form of financial aid. About 57% of freshmen and 59% of continuing students received need-based aid. The average freshman award was $10,472. Of that total, scholarships or need-based grants averaged $7672 ($11,334 maximum); loans averaged $2029 ($4000 maximum); and work contracts averaged $771 ($1500 maximum). Fifty-two percent of undergraduate students work part-time. Average earnings from campus work for the school year are $1008. The average financial indebtedness of the 1992–93 graduate was $10,200. Southwestern is a member of CSS. The college's own financial statement and FAFSA are required. The deadline for financial aid applications is March 1.

International Students: There are currently 23 international students enrolled. The school actively recruits these students. They must take the TOEFL and achieve a minimum score of 550. The student must also take the SAT I or the ACT.

Computers: The university provides computer facilities for student use. The mainframes are a Burroughs and a Sequent 9000. There are approximately 170 microcomputers located throughout the campus for student use. Students may also use the facilities in 2 computer laboratories where there is access to the mainframe and to the Computation Center at the University of Texas. All students may access the system anytime. There are no time limits on using the system and no fees.

Graduates: In 1992–93, 272 bachelor's degrees were awarded. The most popular majors among graduates were biology (13%), communication (10%), and business (10%). Within an average freshman class, 1% graduate in 3 years, 58% in 4 years, 69% in 5 years, and 72% in 6 years. Some 53 companies recruited on campus in 1992–93. In the 1992 graduating class, 42% of the men and 21% of the women were enrolled in graduate school within 6 months of graduation; 54% of the men and 76% of the women had found employment.

Admissions Contact: John W. Lind, Vice President for Enrollment Management.

STEPHEN F. AUSTIN STATE UNIVERSITY   E-3
Nacogdoches, TX 75962   (409) 568-2504

Full-time: 4499 men, 5352 women	Faculty: 412; IIA, --$
Part-time: 646 men, 643 women	Ph.D.s: 75%
Graduate: 627 men, 726 women	Student/Faculty: 24 to 1
Year: semesters, summer session	Tuition: $1515 ($5595)
Application Deadline: open	Room & Board: $3602
Freshman Class: 5964 applied, 4457 accepted, 2267 enrolled	
SAT I Verbal/Math: 430/470	ACT: 21 COMPETITIVE

Stephen F. Austin State University, founded in 1923, is a public regional university offering undergraduate and graduate degree programs through 7 undergraduate schools and one graduate school. In addition to regional accreditation, SFA has baccalaureate program accreditation with AACSB, CSWE, FIDER, NASM, NCATE, NLN, and SAF. The library contains 821,857 volumes, 674,088 microform items, and 17,544 audiovisual forms, and subscribes to 3993 periodicals. Computerized library sources and services include the card catalog, interlibrary loans, and database searching. Special learning facilities include a learning resource center, art gallery, planetarium, radio station, and TV station. The 401-acre campus is in a small town 140 miles northeast of Houston. Including residence halls, there are 75 buildings on campus.

Student Life: About 99% of undergraduates are from Texas. Students come from 34 states, 18 foreign countries, and Canada. Ninety-nine percent are from public schools. Ninety percent are white. The average age of freshmen is 19; all undergraduates, 21. Thirty-five percent drop out by the end of their first year; 42% remain to graduate.

Housing: A total of 5000 students can be accommodated in college housing. College-sponsored living facilities include single-sex and coed dormitories, on-campus apartments, and married-student housing. In addition there are honors houses. On-campus housing is guaranteed for all 4 years. Sixty percent of students commute. Alcohol is not permitted. All students may keep cars on campus.

Activities: About 11% of men belong to 16 national fraternities; about 10% of women belong to 10 national sororities. There are 160 groups on campus, including art, band, cheerleading, choir, chorale, chorus, dance, drama, ethnic, honors, international, marching band, musical theater, newspaper, orchestra, pep band, photography, political, radio and TV, religious, social, social service, student government, symphony, and yearbook. Popular campus events include Parents Weekend, Midnight Yell, Homecoming, and Watermelon Bash.

Sports: There are 7 intercollegiate sports for men and 6 for women, and 27 intramural sports for men and 27 for women. Athletic and recreation facilities include 2 gymnasiums, courts for handball, tennis, and racquetball, weight and gymnastics rooms, and various playing fields.

Disabled Students: The entire campus is accessible to disabled students. The following facilities are available: wheelchair ramps, elevators, special parking, specially equipped rest rooms, special class scheduling, lowered drinking fountains, and lowered telephones.

Services: In addition to many counseling and information services, tutoring is available in most subjects. In addition, there is a reader service for the blind, and remedial math, reading, and writing.

Campus Safety and Security: Campus safety and security measures include 24-hour foot and vehicle patrol, self defense education, escort service, and shuttle buses. In addition, there are informal discussions, pamphlets, posters, and films, emergency telephones, and lighted pathways and sidewalks.

Programs of Study: SFA awards the B.A., B.S., B.A.A.S., B.B.A., B.F.A., B.M., B.S.Ag., B.S.F., B.S.H.E., B.S.N., and B.S.W. degrees. Master's and doctoral degrees also are awarded. Bachelor's degrees are awarded in AGRICULTURE (agricultural business management, agriculture, animal science, forestry production and processing, and horticulture), BIOLOGICAL SCIENCE (biology/biological science), BUSINESS (accounting, banking and finance, business administration and management, business economics, fashion merchandising, management science, marketing/retailing/merchandising, and office supervision and management), COMMUNICATIONS AND THE ARTS (broadcasting, communications, dramatic arts, English, fine arts, French, journalism, music, Spanish, and speech/debate/rhetoric), COMPUTER AND PHYSICAL SCIENCE (chemistry, computer programming, computer science, geology, mathematics, and physics), EDUCATION (agricultural, early childhood, education of the deaf and hearing impaired, education of the visually handicapped, health, and home economics), ENGINEERING AND ENVIRONMENTAL DESIGN (environmental science, interior design, and preengineering), HEALTH PROFESSIONS (health science, medical laboratory technology, nursing, and rehabilitation therapy), SOCIAL SCIENCE (child psychology/development, criminal justice, dietetics, food production/management/services, geography, gerontology, history, home economics, humanities, interdisciplinary studies, political science/government, psychology, public administration, social work, and sociology). Accounting, computer science, and natural science are the strongest academically. Business has the largest enrollment.

Required: All students must complete at least 130 hours with a 2.0 GPA. General education requirements vary by degree program. For example, the B.A. program requires courses in communication skills, mathematics and natural science, humanities, social science, and physical activity.

Special: Internships, dual majors, and dual degrees are possible in some programs. Preengineering and 3–2 engineering programs are offered, as are preprofessional programs and a general studies degree. There are 15 national honor societies on campus.

Faculty/Classroom: Sixty-seven percent of faculty are male; 33%, female. Ninety-five percent teach undergraduates. Graduate students teach 5% of introductory courses. The average class size in an introductory lecture is 45; in a laboratory, 40; and in a regular course offering, 28.

Admissions: About 75% of the 1993–94 applicants were accepted. The SAT scores for the 1993–94 freshman class were as follows: Verbal—85% below 500, 12% between 500 and 599, and 2% between 600 and 700; Math—62% below 500, 31% between 500 and 599, 6% between 600 and 700, and 1% above 700. The ACT scores were 49% below 21, 39% between 21 and 23, 6% between 24 and 26, 4% between 27 and 28, and 2% above 28. About 59% of the current freshmen were in the top two fifths of their class.

Requirements: A minimum GPA of 2.0 is required. The SAT I or ACT is required. For clear admission, students graduating from accredited schools who are in the top 50% of their high school class with an SAT I greater than or equal to 800 (math and verbal combined) or an ACT composite greater than or equal to 19 will be offered admission. Also, students graduating from accredited schools

who are in the top 60% of their high school class with an SAT I greater than or equal to 900 (math and verbal combined) or an ACT composite greater than or equal to 21 will be offered admission. AP credits are accepted.

Procedure: Freshmen are admitted to all sessions. Entrance exams should be taken during the junior year. Application deadlines are open. There are early decision and early admissions plans.

Transfer: A total of 1777 transfer students enrolled in 1993–94. Applicants with fewer than 15 hours of college work must meet freshmen admission requirements. Those with more than 15 hours must have at least a 2.0 GPA. Those with GPAs lower than 2.0 may be admitted to the summer school on probation. A total of 42 credits out of 130 must be completed at SFA.

Visiting: There are regularly scheduled orientations for prospective students. There are guides for informal visits and visitors may stay overnight at the school. To arrange for a visit, contact the Admissions Office at (409) 568–2504.

Financial Aid: In 1993–94, 55% of all current freshmen and 65% of continuing students received some form of financial aid. About 30% of freshmen and 40% of continuing students received need-based aid. The average freshman award was $4000. Of that total, scholarships or need-based grants averaged $1600 ($2650 maximum); loans averaged $1150 ($2625 maximum); and work contracts averaged $1000 ($2800 maximum). Twenty percent of undergraduate students work part-time. Average earnings from campus work for the school year are $1400. SFA is a member of CSS. The FFS is required. The deadline for financial aid applications is June 1.

International Students: There are currently 36 international students enrolled. They must take the TOEFL.

Computers: The university provides computer facilities for student use. The mainframes are a Honeywell CP6 and a DEC VAX. Several microcomputer laboratories are strategically located around campus. All students may access the system. There are no time limits on using the system.

Graduates: In a recent year, 1828 bachelor's degrees were awarded. The most popular majors among graduates were elementary education (21%), marketing (8%), and accounting (5%). Within an average freshman class, 42% graduate in 5 years.

Admissions Contact: Dennis Jones, Senior Associate for Admissions and Records.

SUL ROSS STATE UNIVERSITY　　B-3
Alpine, TX 79832　　(915) 837–8053

Full-time: 783 men, 649 women	Faculty: 78; IIB, --$
Part-time: 70 men, 72 women	Ph.D.s: 74%
Graduate: 273 men, 335 women	Student/Faculty: 18 to 1
Year: semesters, summer session	Tuition: $1224 ($4488)
Application Deadline: open	Room & Board: $2920
Freshman Class: 363 applied, 353 accepted, 322 enrolled	
SAT I Verbal/Math: 340/390	ACT: 17　NONCOMPETITIVE

Sul Ross State University, founded in 1917, is a public institution offering programs in the liberal arts and sciences, fine arts and music, range animal science, business, and education. In addition, an upper-level and graduate center at Uralde offers courses in Uralde, Del Rio, and Eagle Pass, Texas. There are 3 undergraduate schools and one graduate school. The library contains 248,598 volumes, 444,950 microform items, and 13,011 audiovisual forms, and subscribes to 1951 periodicals. Computerized library sources and services include the card catalog, interlibrary loans, and database searching. Special learning facilities include a learning resource center, an art gallery, a natural history museum, a planetarium, a radio station, and extensive geology/chemistry laboratory equipment, including a scanning electron microscope. The 600-acre campus is in a rural area 165 miles from Odessa. Including residence halls, there are 22 buildings on campus.

Student Life: About 97% of undergraduates are from Texas. Students come from 18 states and 7 foreign countries. Ninety-eight percent are from public schools; 2% from private. Fifty-five percent are white; 41% Hispanic. Fifty-one percent are Catholic; 48% Protestant. The average age of freshmen is 19.7; all undergraduates, 24.2. Fifty-five percent drop out by the end of their first year; 20% remain to graduate.

Housing: A total of 769 students can be accommodated in college housing. College-sponsored living facilities include single-sex and coed dormitories, on-campus apartments, and married-student housing. On-campus housing is guaranteed for the freshman year only and is available on a first-come, first-served basis. Sixty-seven percent of students commute. Alcohol is not permitted. All students may keep cars on campus.

Activities: There are no fraternities or sororities on campus. There are 41 groups on campus, including art, cheerleading, choir, drama, ethnic, honors, international, literary magazine, newspaper, pep band, political, professional, religious, student government, and year-

book. Popular campus events include dances, cultural events, Fall on the Mall, Honors Day, and NIRA Rodeo.

Sports: There are 5 intercollegiate sports for men and 4 for women, and 5 intramural sports for men and 4 for women. Athletic and recreation facilities include a gymnasium.

Disabled Students: Ninety percent of the campus is accessible to disabled students. The following facilities are available: wheelchair ramps, elevators, special parking, specially equipped rest rooms, special class scheduling, and lowered drinking fountains.

Services: In addition to many counseling and information services, tutoring is available in some subjects, including mathematics, reading, and English.

Campus Safety and Security: Campus safety and security measures include 24-hour foot and vehicle patrol, informal discussions, pamphlets, posters, and films, and lighted pathways and sidewalks.

Programs of Study: Sully awards the B.A., B.S., B.B.A., and B.F.A. degrees. Associate and master's degrees also are awarded. Bachelor's degrees are awarded in AGRICULTURE (animal science and wildlife management), BIOLOGICAL SCIENCE (biology/biological science), BUSINESS (accounting, business administration and management, business economics, marketing management, and office supervision and management), COMMUNICATIONS AND THE ARTS (applied music, communications, dramatic arts, English, and Spanish), COMPUTER AND PHYSICAL SCIENCE (chemistry, geology, and mathematics), EDUCATION (art, business, elementary, industrial arts, and music), ENGINEERING AND ENVIRONMENTAL DESIGN (industrial engineering technology), SOCIAL SCIENCE (criminal justice, history, political science/government, psychology, and social science). Behavioral and social sciences, education, fine arts and communication, range animal science, and languages and literature are the strongest programs academically. Physical education, criminal justice, education, and psychology have the largest enrollments.

Required: All students must complete a general education requirement of 53 to 57 hours, including courses in English, history, foreign language, political science, mathematics, the arts, social science, and natural science. A minimum 2.0 GPA and 130 credit hours are required to graduate. There are additional requirements for some degree programs. All students must take 2 courses in physical education and 1 in computer science. The total number of hours required in the major varies.

Special: Sully offers unpaid internships in several departments, including psychology and criminal justice, as well as work-study programs, and nondegree study. There is a freshman honors program on campus, as well as 8 national honor societies.

Faculty/Classroom: Sixty-nine percent of faculty are male; 31%, female. Ninety-five percent teach undergraduates and 85% both teach and do research. No introductory courses are taught by graduate students. The average class size in an introductory lecture is 42; in a laboratory, 15; and in a regular course offering, 21.

Admissions: About 97% of the 1993–94 applicants were accepted. The SAT scores for the 1993–94 freshman class were as follows: Verbal—94% below 500, 6% between 500 and 599, and 1% between 600 and 700; Math—85% below 500, 14% between 500 and 599, and 1% between 600 and 700. The ACT scores were 88% below 21, 11% between 21 and 23, and 2% between 24 and 26. About 16% of the current freshmen were in the top fifth of their class; 40% were in the top two fifths. Three freshmen graduated first in their class.

Requirements: Sully requires applicants to be in the upper 50% of their class. The SAT I or ACT is required. Applicants should be graduates of an accredited secondary school and have a minimum of 14 credits, including 4 in English, 3 in mathematics, 2 each in science, history, and physical education/health, and 1 in government/economics. Applicants must meet one of the following criteria for full admission: present a minimum composite score of 20 on the ACT or 800 on the SAT I; or graduate in the upper half of their class. Probationary admission is possible for students who do not meet the admissions standards. AP and CLEP credits are accepted.

Procedure: Freshmen are admitted to all sessions. Preferably, entrance exams should be taken early in the senior year. Application deadlines are open. The college accepts all applicants. Notification is sent on a rolling basis. There is an early admissions plan.

Transfer: About 159 transfer students enrolled in 1993–94. The GPA required for transfer students varies according to the number of college credits completed. A total of 30 credits out of 130 must be completed at Sully.

Visiting: There are regularly scheduled orientations for prospective students, consisting of 1 1/2-day programs in January, June, July, and late August. There are guides for informal visits and visitors may sit in on classes and stay overnight at the school. To arrange for a visit, contact the Office of Admissions at (915) 837–8059.

Financial Aid: About 75% of undergraduates receive some form of aid, most of it need-based. Seven percent of undergraduate students work part-time. Average earnings from campus work for the school year are $2000. Sully is a member of CSS. The FAF is required. The deadline for financial aid applications is June 1.

International Students: There are currently 43 international students enrolled. They must take the TOEFL and achieve a minimum score of 520. The student must also take the SAT I or the ACT.

Computers: The college provides computer facilities for student use. The mainframe is an IBM AS 400. Microcomputers are available for academic use. All students may access the system. There are no time limits on using the system. The fees are $2 per semester credit hour.

Graduates: In 1992–93, 229 bachelor's degrees were awarded. The most popular majors among graduates were education (21%), physical education (16%), and criminal justice (13%). Within an average freshman class, 8% graduate in 4 years, 16% in 5 years, and 20% in 6 years. Some 50 companies recruited on campus in 1992–93. In the 1992 graduating class, 2% of all graduates were enrolled in graduate school within 6 months of graduation; 83% had found employment.

Admissions Contact: Dorothy M. Leavitt, Dean of Admissions and Records.

TARLETON STATE UNIVERSITY D-2
Stephenville, TX 76402 (817) 968-9125

Full-time: 2487 men, 2369 women	Faculty: 216; IIA, --$
Part-time: 281 men, 443 women	Ph.D.s: 86%
Graduate: 361 men, 514 women	Student/Faculty: 22 to 1
Year: semesters, summer session	Tuition: $1420 ($5500)
Application Deadline: August 7	Room & Board: $2662
Freshman Class: 1195 applied, 1095 accepted, 966 enrolled	
SAT I Verbal/Math: 391/441	ACT: 20 LESS COMPETITIVE

Tarleton State University, founded in 1899, is a public institution offering undergraduate and graduate programs in agriculture and technology, arts and sciences, business, and education and fine arts. There are 4 undergraduate schools and one graduate school. In addition to regional accreditation, Tarleton has baccalaureate program accreditation with AACSB, CSWE, NASM, and NCATE. The library contains 250,000 volumes, 700,000 microform items, and 15,000 audiovisual forms, and subscribes to 2000 periodicals. Computerized library sources and services include database searching. Special learning facilities include a learning resource center, art gallery, a 600-acre farm, a 1200-acre ranch, and an equine center. The 123-acre campus is in a small town 67 miles south of Fort Worth. Including residence halls, there are 82 buildings on campus.

Student Life: About 99% of undergraduates are from Texas. Students come from 30 states, 8 foreign countries, and Canada. Ninety-five percent are from public schools; 5% from private. Ninety-two percent are white. The average age of freshmen is 18; all undergraduates, 20. Thirty-nine percent drop out by the end of their first year; 33% remain to graduate.

Housing: A total of 1209 students can be accommodated in college housing. College-sponsored living facilities include single-sex and coed dormitories, on-campus apartments, off-campus apartments, and married-student housing. On-campus housing is guaranteed for the freshman year only and is available on a first-come, first-served basis. All students may keep cars on campus.

Activities: About 7% of men belong to 5 national fraternities; about 5% of women belong to 3 national sororities. There are 95 groups on campus, including art, band, cheerleading, choir, computers, drama, drill team, ethnic, honors, international, jazz band, marching band, musical theater, newspaper, political, professional, religious, social, social service, student government, and yearbook. Popular campus events include Howdy Week, Homecoming, Spring Fest, Tarleton Christmans, and Halloween Carnival and Haunted House.

Sports: There are 7 intercollegiate sports for men and 5 for women, and 19 intramural sports for men and 19 for women. Athletic and recreation facilities include a fully equipped complex with a heated pool, track, courts for basketball, volleyball, tennis and racquetball, and various playing fields. There is also a 5500-seat stadium, a 3300-seat gymnasium, and a fully lighted, 550-seat baseball stadium.

Disabled Students: Eighty percent of the campus is accessible to disabled students. The following facilities are available: wheelchair ramps, elevators, special parking, specially equipped rest rooms, special class scheduling, lowered drinking fountains, and lowered telephones.

Services: In addition to many counseling and information services, tutoring is available in most subjects, including mathematics, science, English, and social studies.

Campus Safety and Security: Campus safety and security measures include 24-hour foot and vehicle patrol, self defense education, escort service, and shuttle buses. In addition, there are informal discussions, pamphlets, posters, and films, emergency telephones, and lighted pathways and sidewalks.

Programs of Study: Tarleton awards the B.A., B.S., B.A.A.S., B.B.A., B.F.A., B.M., and B.S.W. degrees. Associate and master's degrees also are awarded. Bachelor's degrees are awarded in AGRICULTURE (agricultural business management, agricultural economics, agricultural mechanics, agriculture, animal science, horticulture, plant science, and range/farm management), BIOLOGICAL SCIENCE

(biology/biological science), BUSINESS (accounting, banking and finance, business administration and management, fashion merchandising, human resources, management science, marketing and distribution, marketing/retailing/merchandising, office supervision and management, and personnel management), COMMUNICATIONS AND THE ARTS (art, dramatic arts, English, fine arts, music, Spanish, and speech/debate/rhetoric), COMPUTER AND PHYSICAL SCIENCE (chemistry, computer programming, earth science, geology, information sciences and systems, mathematics, and physics), EDUCATION (agricultural, art, business, home economics, industrial arts, and physical), ENGINEERING AND ENVIRONMENTAL DESIGN (industrial engineering technology), HEALTH PROFESSIONS (health, medical laboratory technology, nursing, physical therapy, predentistry, premedicine, prepharmacy, and preveterinary science), SOCIAL SCIENCE (criminal justice, economics, history, home economics, interdisciplinary studies, law enforcement and corrections, physical fitness/movement, political science/government, prelaw, social work, sociology, theological studies, and water resources). Science and business are the strongest academically. Agriculture and education have the largest enrollments.

Required: All students must complete at least 128 hours, including 24 hours in the major, with a 2.0 GPA. The 57-hour required core curriculum includes courses in English, U.S. and Texas government, U.S. history, laboratory science, computer information systems, and physical education. There are also distributional requirements that must be met in humanities and social sciences and a writing proficiency examination.

Special: Tarleton offers work-study programs, internships, limited nondegree study, and cross-registration. There is a 3–2 engineering degree available with Texas A&M University. Special degree programs may be designed to meet unusual requirements. There is a freshman honors program on campus, as well as 11 national honor societies. Nine departments have honors programs.

Faculty/Classroom: Sixty percent of faculty are male; 40%, female. Ninety-five percent teach undergraduates, and 4% both teach and do research. No introductory courses are taught by graduate students. The average class size in an introductory lecture is 35; in a laboratory, 24; and in a regular course offering, 31.

Admissions: About 92% of the 1993–94 applicants were accepted. The SAT scores for the 1993–94 freshman class were as follows: Verbal—90% below 500, 9% between 500 and 599, and 1% between 600 and 700; Math—74% below 500, 20% between 500 and 599, 6% between 600 and 700, and 1% above 700. The ACT scores were 66% below 21, 23% between 21 and 23, 8% between 24 and 26, 2% between 27 and 28, and 1% above 28. About 34% of the current freshmen were in the top fifth of their class; 76% were in the top two fifths.

Requirements: Tarleton requires applicants to be in the upper 50% of their class. The SAT I, with a minimum composite score of 800, or the ACT, with a minimum composite score of 19, is required. Applicant be a graduate of an accredited secondary school, or advanced high school program, or rank in top half of graduating class. Secondary preparation should include 3 years of English and 1 year of Algebra I. A GED will be considered equivalent to a high school diploma, provided the average standard score is at least 55 or subscore is less than 50. AP and CLEP credits are accepted.

Procedure: Freshmen are admitted to all sessions. Applications should be filed by August 7 for fall entry, January 3 for spring entry, and May 25 for summer entry, along with an application fee of $20. Notification is sent on a rolling basis. There are early decision, early admissions, and deferred admissions plans.

Transfer: A total of 735 transfer students enrolled in 1993–94. Applicants with 46 or more credits must present a 2.0 GPA, those with 30 to 45 credits must present a 1.75 GPA. Applicants with 15 to 29 credits may be admitted if they have at least a 2.8 GPA and are in good standing, and if they meet freshman admission requirements. A GPA of 1.75 to 2.79 may be admitted provided transfers also meet regular admisssion standards of first-time freshman applicants. Applicants with fewer than 15 credits may be admitted if they have at least a 1.75 GPA and meet regular admission standards of first-time freshman. A total of 30 credits out of 128 must be completed at Tarleton.

Visiting: There are regularly scheduled orientations for prospective students, including a tour of the campus. There are guides for informal visits and visitors may sit in on classes. To arrange for a visit, contact the Office of School Relations, Tarleton Center, at (817) 968-9256.

Financial Aid: In 1993–94, 57% of all students received some form of financial aid. About 57% of received need-based aid. The average freshman award was $4267. Of that total, scholarships or need-based grants averaged $1642 ($2300 maximum); loans averaged $2625; and work contracts averaged $2840. Eleven percent of undergraduate students work part-time. Average earnings from campus work for the school year are $1235. The average financial indebtedness of the 1992–93 graduate was $12,000. Tarleton is a member of CSS. The FFS is required. The deadline for financial aid applications is June 1.

International Students: There are currently 20 international students enrolled in Texas. They must take the TOEFL and achieve a minimum score of 540.

Computers: The university provides computer facilities for student use. The mainframe is a CDC 180/860. Microcomputers are available in student laboratories and faculty offices. All students may access the system. There are no time limits on using the system. The fee is $3 per semester hour.

Graduates: In 1992–93, 925 bachelor's degrees were awarded. The most popular majors among graduates were interdisiplinary studies (11%), exercise and sport studies (10%), and general business (8%). Within an average freshman class, 13% graduate in 4 years, 30% in 5 years, and 32% in 6 years. Some 200 companies recruited on campus in 1992–93.

Admissions Contact: Gail Mayfield, Director of Admissions.

TEXAS A & M UNIVERSITY SYSTEM

The Texas A & M University system, established in 1876, is a public system in Texas. It is governed by a 9-member board of regents, whose chief administrator is the System Chancellor. The primary mission of the A & M System's 7 universities and 8 state agencies is education, leadership development, research, and service. Four-year campuses are located in College Station, Corpus Christi, Galveston, Prairie View, Kingsville, and Stephenville. The total enrollment in fall 1993 of all 8 campuses was 75,416; there were approximately 19,000 faculty and staff members. Altogether there are approximately 500 baccalaureate, 350 master's, and 100 doctoral programs offered in the Texas A & M University System. Profiles of the 4-year campuses are included in this chapter in alphabetical order with other Texas schools.

TEXAS A&I UNIVERSITY
(See Texas A&M University at Kingsville)

TEXAS A&M UNIVERSITY   D-3
College Station, TX 77843   (409) 845-3741

Full-time: 17,627 men, 14,016 women	Faculty: 1985; I, -$
Part-time: 1622 men, 1176 women	Ph.D.s: 87%
Graduate: 5298 men, 2785 women	Student/Faculty: 16 to 1
Year: semesters, summer session	Tuition: $1526 ($5606)
Application Deadline: March 1	Room & Board: $3856
Freshman Class: 14,474 applied, 10,519 accepted, 6392 enrolled	
SAT I Verbal/Math: 490/580	ACT: 24 **VERY COMPETITIVE**

Texas A&M University, founded in 1876, is part of the Texas A&M University System. Undergraduate degrees are offered in agriculture and life sciences, architecture, business administration, education, engineering, geosciences, maritime studies, liberal arts, medicine, science, and veterinary medicine. There are 10 undergraduate schools and one graduate school. In addition to regional accreditation, Texas A&M has baccalaureate program accreditation with AACSB, ABET, ACCE, ACEJMC, ADA, ASLA, NAAB, NCATE, and SAF. The 2 libraries contain 2.2 million volumes, 4.3 million microform items, and 9500 audiovisual forms, and subscribe to 13,000 periodicals. Computerized library sources and services include the card catalog, interlibrary loans, and database searching. Special learning facilities include a learning resource center, art gallery, radio station, TV station, weather station, and observatory. The 5200-acre campus is in a small town 90 miles northwest of Houston. Including residence halls, there are 750 buildings on campus.

Student Life: About 94% of undergraduates are from Texas. Students come from 50 states, 115 foreign countries, and Canada. Ninety-six percent are from public schools; 4% from private. Eighty-two percent are white. Sixty-six percent are Protestant; 28% Catholic. The average age of freshmen is 18; all undergraduates, 21. Twelve percent drop out by the end of their first year; 66% remain to graduate.

Housing: A total of 11,081 students can be accommodated in college housing. College-sponsored living facilities include single-sex and coed dormitories, on-campus apartments, and married-student housing. In addition there are honors houses. On-campus housing is guaranteed for all 4 years. All students may keep cars on campus.

Activities: About 8% of men belong to 1 local fraternity and 27 national fraternities; about 12% of women belong to 11 national sororities. There are 700 groups on campus, including art, band, cheerleading, chess, choir, chorale, chorus, computers, dance, drama, drill team, drum and bugle corps, ethnic, film, gay, honors, international, jazz band, literary magazine, marching band, musical theater, newspaper, opera, orchestra, photography, political, professional, radio and TV, religious, social, social service, student government, symphony, and yearbook. Popular campus events include Aggie Bonfire, Parents Weekend, Aggie Muster, the Big Event, Fish Camp, Ring Dance, Silver Taps, Elephant Walk, Final Review, T-Camp, ExCel (Excellence uniting Culture, Education, and Leadership), SBSLC (South-

western Black Student Leadership Conference), Hispanic Heritage Month, SCONA (Student Conference on National Affairs), Native American Week, OPAS (Opera and Performing Arts Series), RHA Casino, International Week, and Whoopstock (a celebration of unity through diversity).

Sports: There are 10 intercollegiate sports for men and 10 for women, and 80 intramural sports for men and 79 for women. Athletic and recreation facilities include a coliseum, a track and field complex, a tennis center, a natatorium, 11 basketball/volleyball courts, 27 handball/racquetball courts, badminton, weight and activity rooms, jogging trails, 36 tennis courts, a squash court, a 72,387-seat stadium, an 8,000-seat indoor gymnasium, and a 2,500-seat auditorium/arena. Also available are an 18-hole golf course, driving range, flag football fields, 4 soccer fields, 4 outdoor basketball courts, 5 walking trails, and a baseball field.

Disabled Students: Ninety-five percent of the campus is accessible to disabled students. The following facilities are available: wheelchair ramps, elevators, special parking, specially equipped rest rooms, special class scheduling, lowered drinking fountains, and lowered telephones. There is an office of support services for students with disabilities.

Services: In addition to many counseling and information services, tutoring is available in most subjects. In addition, there is a reader service for the blind, and remedial math, reading, and writing. Workshops in time management, basic study techniques, and test-taking skills are available.

Campus Safety and Security: Campus safety and security measures include 24-hour foot and vehicle patrol, self defense education, escort service, and shuttle buses. In addition, there are informal discussions, pamphlets, posters, and films, emergency telephones, lighted pathways and sidewalks, a security awareness committee, and crime-watch and safety-tip lines.

Programs of Study: Texas A&M awards the B.A., B.S., B.B.A., B.E.D., and B.L.A. degrees. Master's and doctoral degrees also are awarded. Bachelor's degrees are awarded in AGRICULTURE (agricultural business management, agricultural economics, animal science, dairy science, fish and game management, fishing and fisheries, forestry and related sciences, horticulture, poultry science, and range/farm management), BIOLOGICAL SCIENCE (biochemistry, biology/biological science, botany, entomology, genetics, microbiology, and zoology), BUSINESS (accounting, banking and finance, business systems analysis, marketing/retailing/merchandising, and personnel management), COMMUNICATIONS AND THE ARTS (English, French, German, journalism, Russian, Spanish, and speech/debate/rhetoric), COMPUTER AND PHYSICAL SCIENCE (atmospheric sciences and meteorology, chemistry, computer science, geology, geophysics and seismology, mathematics, and physics), EDUCATION (elementary, health, physical, and secondary), ENGINEERING AND ENVIRONMENTAL DESIGN (aeronautical engineering, agricultural engineering, bioengineering, chemical engineering, civil engineering, computer engineering, construction engineering, electrical/electronics engineering, engineering technology, environmental design, environmental science, industrial engineering technology, landscape architecture/design, mechanical engineering, nuclear engineering, and petroleum/natural gas engineering), HEALTH PROFESSIONS (biomedical science), SOCIAL SCIENCE (anthropology, economics, history, international studies, parks and recreation management, philosophy, political science/government, psychology, and sociology). Engineering and business administration are the strongest academically. Engineering, business administration, and liberal arts have the largest enrollments.

Required: In order to graduate, students must complete at least 128 credit hours, including 30 to 33 in the major. A minimum 2.0 GPA is required. Students must complete courses in American and Texan history and government, physical education, computers, foreign language, speech and language writing skills, mathematics/logical reasoning, science, humanities, social science, and citizenship. Requirements in the major vary.

Special: The university offers co-op programs, internships on and off campus, and study abroad in 12 countries. An accelerated degree program in premedicine, B.A.-B.S. degrees, credit for military experience, nondegree study, dual majors, and pass/fail options are available. A 5-year MBA/liberal arts program is offered, as well as a 3–2 engineering degree with Sam Houston State University. There is a freshman honors program on campus, as well as 41 national honor societies.

Faculty/Classroom: Eighty-three percent of faculty are male; 17%, female. Ninety-six percent teach undergraduates, 80% do research, and 75% do both. Graduate students teach 19% of introductory courses. The average class size in an introductory lecture is 82; in a laboratory, 30; and in a regular course offering, 37.

Admissions: About 73% of the 1993–94 applicants were accepted. The SAT scores for the 1993–94 freshman class were as follows: Verbal—74% below 500, 20% between 500 and 599, 5% between 600 and 700, and 1% above 700; Math—37% below 500, 39% between 500 and 599, 21% between 600 and 700, and 3% above 700. The ACT scores were 12% below 21, 28% between 21 and 23, 29% between 24 and 26, 16% between 27 and 28, and 15% above 28. About 77% of the current freshmen were in the top fifth of their class; 95% were in the top two fifths. There were 174 National Merit finalists and 200 semifinalists. A total of 194 freshmen graduated first in their class.

Requirements: The SAT I or ACT is required. Applicant must be a graduate of a secondary school. Required high school courses include 4 credits in English, 3 1/2 credits in mathematics, 2 credits in science (from biology, chemistry, or physics), and 6 1/2 academic electives. AP and CLEP credits are accepted. Important factors used in the admissions decision are advanced placement or honor courses, evidence of special talent, leadership record, extracurricular activities record, and recommendations by school officials.

Procedure: Freshmen are admitted to all sessions. Entrance exams should be taken during the spring of the junior year or by December of the senior year. Applications should be filed by March 1 for fall entry, November 1 for spring entry, and March 1 for summer entry, along with an application fee of $25. Notification is sent on a rolling basis. There are early admissions and deferred admissions plans. A waiting list is an active part of the admissions procedure.

Transfer: A total of 3134 transfer students enrolled in 1993–94. Applicants must submit transcripts from previously attended colleges. Requirements vary, depending on how many semester hours were attempted and whether the student is a Texas resident. Students with fewer than 30 semester hours must submit high school transcripts and SAT I or ACT scores. A total of 30 credits out of 128 must be completed at Texas A&M.

Visiting: There are regularly scheduled orientations for prospective students. There are guides for informal visits and visitors may sit in on classes and stay overnight at the school. To arrange for a visit, contact Aggieland Visitor Center at (409) 845–5851.

Financial Aid: In 1993–94, 63% of all current freshmen and 66% of continuing students received some form of financial aid. About 28% of freshmen and 30% of continuing students received need-based aid. The average freshman award was $4025. Of that total, scholarships or need-based grants averaged $2815 ($12,500 maximum); loans averaged $3037 ($8100 maximum); and work contracts averaged $1105 ($2500 maximum). Twenty-three percent of undergraduate students work part-time. Average earnings from campus work for the school year are $1700. The average financial indebtedness of the 1992–93 graduate was $6100. Texas A&M is a member of CSS. The FAFSA financial statement is required. The deadline for financial aid applications is April 15.

International Students: There are currently 686 international students enrolled. They must take the TOEFL and achieve a minimum score of 550. The SAT I or ACT is required for graduates of U.S. high schools only.

Computers: The university computer facilities for student use. The mainframes are an IBM 3090–600E, an Amdahl 5860, and DEC VAXs 880, 8650, and 9000–210V. Approximately 2000 IBM and Apple Macintosh microcomputers are available throughout campus. All students may access the system at any time. The fees are $3 per credit hour.

Graduates: In a recent year, 6896 bachelor's degrees were awarded. The most popular majors among graduates were psychology (6%), accounting (6%), and curriculum and instruction (5%). Within an average freshman class, 66% graduate in 6 years.

Admissions Contact: Admissions Counselor.

TEXAS A&M UNIVERSITY AT GALVESTON   E-4

Galveston, TX 77553–1675   (409) 740–4415

Full-time: 567 men, 461 women	Faculty: 61
Part-time: 72 men, 66 women	Ph.D.s: 82%
Graduate: none	Student/Faculty: 17 to 1
Year: semesters, summer session	Tuition: $1496 ($5576)
Application Deadline: open	Room & Board: $3378
Freshman Class: 481 accepted, 243 enrolled	
SAT I or ACT: required	LESS COMPETITIVE

Texas A&M University at Galveston, founded in 1962, is a public institution that offers marine and maritime-related programs. Part of the Texas A&M University system, it is a branch of Texas A&M University College of Geosciences and Maritime Studies. There are 2 undergraduate schools. In addition to regional accreditation, TAMUG has baccalaureate program accreditation with ABET. The library contains 43,000 volumes and 52,984 microform items, and subscribes to 800 periodicals. Computerized library sources and services include the card catalog, interlibrary loans, and database searching. Special learning facilities include a learning resource center and a training ship, the T/S Texas Clipper, used for an annual summer training cruise. The 100-acre campus is in a suburban area 50 miles south of Houston. Including residence halls, there are 11 buildings on campus.

Student Life: About 70% of undergraduates are from Texas. Students come from 43 states, 10 foreign countries, and Canada. Eighty-eight percent are white. The average age of freshmen is 18; all undergraduates, 20.

Housing: A total of 624 students can be accommodated in college housing. College-sponsored living facilities include coed dormitories. On-campus housing is available on a first-come, first-served basis. Fifty-one percent of students live on campus. Alcohol is not permitted. All students may keep cars on campus.

Activities: There are no fraternities or sororities on campus. There are 20 groups on campus, including drama, literary magazine, newspaper, pep band, professional, social, social service, student government, and yearbook. Popular campus events include Springfest, Mardi Gras, and the departure and arrival of the T/S Texas Clipper.

Sports: There are 2 intercollegiate sports for men and 1 for women, and 6 intramural sports for men and 2 for women. Athletic and recreation facilities include tennis, volleyball, and basketball courts, and a swimming pool.

Disabled Students: Eighty percent of the campus is accessible to disabled students. The following facilities are available: wheelchair ramps, elevators, special parking, and specially equipped rest rooms.

Services: In addition to many counseling and information services, tutoring is available in some subjects, including mathematics and science. There is remedial math, reading, and writing.

Campus Safety and Security: Campus safety and security measures include an escort service, shuttle buses, and lighted pathways and sidewalks.

Programs of Study: TAMUG awards the B.S. degree. Bachelor's degrees are awarded in AGRICULTURE (fishing and fisheries), BIOLOGICAL SCIENCE (marine biology and marine science), ENGINEERING AND ENVIRONMENTAL DESIGN (marine engineering and systems engineering). Marine science is the strongest program academically. Marine biology has the largest enrollment.

Required: Depending on the major, students must complete 130 to 160 credit hours with a GPA of 2.0 overall and in the major. The required core curriculum includes courses in mathematics, political science, American history, and macroeconomics. Distribution requirements include 12 credits in citizenship, 8 in science, and 6 each in English, calculus, humanities, and social sciences. Students must also complete a 2-semester sequence of a foreign language and 1 computer language course.

Special: TAMUG offers dual majors in all majors, dual degrees, and credit for military service. Students may challenge any course for credit by examination. A pass/fail option is available for electives taken by juniors or seniors who have a minimum 2.5 GPA. Selected majors may earn a ship's officer license with a degree program.

Faculty/Classroom: Seventy-nine percent of faculty are male; 21%, female. All teach undergraduates. The average class size in an introductory lecture is 61; in a laboratory, 18; and in a regular course offering, 26.

Admissions: There were 2 National Merit semifinalists in a recent year.

Requirements: The SAT I or ACT is required. Acceptable test scores depend on high school rank, with minimum composite scores of 1000 on the SAT I and 24 on the ACT required. Applicants must be graduates of an accredited high school or hold a GED. A minimum of 16 academic credits is required, including 4 units of English, 3.5 of mathematics, 2.5 of either history or social studies, 2 each of a foreign language and science, and the rest in electives. AP and CLEP credits are accepted.

Procedure: Freshmen are admitted to all sessions. Entrance exams should be taken late in the junior year or early in the senior year. Application deadlines are open, but it is suggested that applications be filed by March 1 for summer and fall enty and November 1 for spring entry. Application fee is $25. Notification is sent on a rolling basis. There are early decision, early admissions, and deferred admissions plans. About 2 early decision candidates were accepted for a recent class.

Transfer: About 220 transfer students enrolled in a recent year. Applicants must have a cumulative 2.0 GPA in a minimum of 18 completed credit hours as well as a 2.0 GPA in each of the last 2 terms attended. A total of 30 credits out of 130 to 160 must be completed at TAMUG.

Visiting: There are regularly scheduled orientations for prospective students, including campus tours conducted Monday and Friday at 10 A.M. There are guides for informal visits and visitors may sit in on classes. To arrange for a visit, contact the University Information Office at (409) 740-4422.

Financial Aid: In a recent year, 50% of all current freshmen and 40% of continuing students received some form of financial aid. Scholarships or need-based grants averaged $500 ($3200 maximum); loans averaged $1200 ($3500 maximum); and work contracts averaged $1500 ($2000 maximum). Sixty-five percent of undergraduate students work part-time. Average earnings from campus work for the school year are $1200. The average financial indebtedness of a recent graduate was $6000. The FAF and the college's own financial statement are required. The deadline for financial aid applications is April 1.

International Students: There are currently 12 international students enrolled. They must take the TOEFL or the college's own test and achieve a minimum score on the TOEFL of 550. The student must also take the SAT I (minimum composite score 1000) or the ACT (minimum composite score 24).

Computers: The university provides computer facilities for student use. The mainframe is a Prime 9655. A DEC VAX 3100 is available to students. There are 80 terminals located in the Learning Resource Center, 4 laboratories, and other campus locations. All students may access the system with no time limits. The fee is $10.

Graduates: In a recent year, 74 bachelor's degrees were awarded.

Admissions Contact: Donna C. Lang, Admissions and Records Officer.

TEXAS A&M UNIVERSITY AT KINGSVILLE   D-5
(Formerly Texas A&I University)
Kingsville, TX 78363   (512) 595-2811

Full-time: 2315 men, 2134 women	Faculty: 226; IIA, --$
Part-time: 429 men, 524 women	Ph.D.s: 85%
Graduate: 565 men, 609 women	Student/Faculty: 20 to 1
Year: semesters, summer session	Tuition: $1184 ($3776)
Application Deadline: open	Room & Board: $2624
Freshman Class: 1500 applied, 1350 accepted, 960 enrolled	
SAT I or ACT: required	LESS COMPETITIVE

Texas A&M University at Kingsville, founded in 1925 as South Texas Teachers College, is a comprehensive university and part of the Texas A&M University System. Graduate and undergraduate programs are offered through colleges of agriculture and home economics, arts and sciences, business administration, education, and engineering. There are 5 undergraduate and 5 graduate schools. In addition to regional accreditation, Texas A&M University at Kingsville has baccalaureate program accreditation with ABET, NASM, and NCATE. The library contains 461,408 volumes, 2400 microform items, and 15,000 audiovisual forms, and subscribes to 2400 periodicals. Computerized library sources and services include the card catalog, interlibrary loans, and database searching. Special learning facilities include a learning resource center, an art gallery, a natural history museum, planetarium, a radio station, a TV station, and and wildlife and citrus research facilities. The 246-acre campus is in a small town 40 miles southwest of Corpus Christi. Including residence halls, there are 82 buildings on campus.

Student Life: Most undergraduates are from Texas. Students come from 32 states, 54 foreign countries, and Canada. Ninety-eight percent are from public schools; 2% from private. Sixty-two percent are Hispanic; 29% white. The average age of freshmen is 19; all undergraduates, 23. Forty percent drop out by the end of their first year; 35% remain to graduate.

Housing: A total of 1200 students can be accommodated in college housing. College-sponsored living facilities include single-sex and coed dormitories and married-student housing. On-campus housing is guaranteed for all 4 years. Seventy percent of students commute. All students may keep cars on campus.

Activities: There are many groups and organizations on campus, including art, band, cheerleading, choir, chorus, computers, dance, drama, drill team, ethnic, honors, international, jazz band, marching band, newspaper, orchestra, political, professional, radio and TV, religious, social, and student government. Popular campus events include Fall Carnival.

Sports: There are 3 intercollegiate sports each for men and women, and 2 intramural sports each. Athletic and recreation facilities include 2 gymnasiums, an Olympic pool, courts for tennis and racquetball, an all-weather track, and various playing fields. Recreational facilities are available for archery, golf, fencing, weight training, and jogging.

Disabled Students: Ninety percent of the campus is accessible to disabled students. The following facilities are available: wheelchair ramps, elevators, special parking, specially equipped rest rooms, and lowered drinking fountains and telephones.

Services: In addition to many counseling and information services, tutoring is available in every subject. There is a reader service for the blind, and remedial math, reading, and writing.

Campus Safety and Security: Campus safety and security measures include 24-hour foot and vehicle patrol, escort service, informal discussions, and pamphlets, posters, and films. In addition, there are emergency telephones and lighted pathways and sidewalks.

Programs of Study: Texas A&M University at Kingsville awards the B.A., B.S., B.A.A.S., B.B.A., B.F.A., and B.M. degrees. Master's and doctoral degrees also are awarded. Bachelor's degrees are awarded in AGRICULTURE (agricultural business management, animal science, plant science, range/farm management, and soil science), BIOLOGICAL SCIENCE (biology/biological science), BUSINESS (accounting, banking and finance, business administration and

management, business economics, management science, marketing/retailing/merchandising, and real estate), COMMUNICATIONS AND THE ARTS (communications, dramatic arts, English, fine arts, music, and Spanish), COMPUTER AND PHYSICAL SCIENCE (chemistry, computer science, geology, mathematics, and physics), EDUCATION (agricultural, elementary, health, music, physical, and secondary), ENGINEERING AND ENVIRONMENTAL DESIGN (chemical engineering, civil engineering, electrical/electronics engineering, engineering management, industrial engineering technology, mechanical engineering, and petroleum/natural gas engineering), HEALTH PROFESSIONS (medical laboratory technology, nursing, predentistry, premedicine, prepharmacy, preveterinary science, and speech pathology/audiology), SOCIAL SCIENCE (geography, history, home economics, political science/government, prelaw, psychology, public administration, and sociology). Engineering is the strongest academically. Education has the largest enrollment.

Required: All students must complete 120 to 135 hours with at least a 2.0 GPA. General education requirements include courses in oral and written communication, mathematics and reasoning, U.S. and Texas government, social sciences, American and world history, laboratory sciences, fine arts, and physical education. An additional 24 to 36 hours are required in the major.

Special: A nontraditional Bachelor of Applied Arts and Sciences program is offered to students with vocational or technical training or experience. The Center for Continuing Education offers noncredit enrichment courses in a variety of subjects, a professional development program in organizational management, and a number of seminars and short courses that are held abroad. The college also offers a work-study program and the College I Freshman program. There are 10 national honor societies on campus. Twenty departments have honors programs.

Faculty/Classroom: Sixty-six percent of faculty are male; 34%, female. The average class size in an introductory lecture is 30; in a laboratory, 20; and in a regular course offering, 25.

Admissions: About 90% of the 1993–94 applicants were accepted. Ten freshmen graduated first in their class.

Requirements: The SAT I or ACT is required. Applicant should be a high school graduate or have a GED. Secondary preparation must include 3 units of English, 2 each in mathematics, including algebra, and in a foreign language or natural science, 1 each in history and another social science, and 7 of electives, no more than 4 of which may be in vocational subjects. The university sets minimum admissible scores each year. An interview is encouraged. AP and CLEP credits are accepted.

Procedure: Freshmen are admitted to all sessions. Entrance exams should be taken varies. Application deadlines are open. The application fee is $25 for international students. Notification is sent on a rolling basis.

Transfer: About 530 transfer students enrolled in 1993–94. All applicants must present a GPA of at least 2.0. A total of 30 credits out of 120 to 135 must be completed at Texas A&M University at Kingsville.

Visiting: There are regularly scheduled orientations for prospective students, including advisement, tours, stays in dormitories, entertainment, registration, and financial information. There are guides for informal visits and visitors may sit in on classes and stay overnight at the school. To arrange for a visit, contact the Office of School Relations at (512) 595–3907.

Financial Aid: In 1993–94, 80% of all current freshmen and 60% of continuing students received some form of financial aid. Texas A&M University at Kingsville is a member of CSS. The FAF or FFS, the college's own financial statement, and FAFSA are required. The deadline for financial aid applications is May 15.

International Students: There are currently 324 international students enrolled. They must take the TOEFL or the college's own test and achieve a minimum score on the TOEFL of 500. The student must also take the SAT I or the ACT.

Computers: The university provides computer facilities for student use. The mainframe is an IBM 9370. There are 400 microcomputers located in the library and in the business, engineering, agriculture, and education buildings as well as other sites on campus. All students may access the system. There are no time limits on using the system. The fees are $5 per student.

Graduates: In 1992–93, 532 bachelor's degrees were awarded. The most popular majors among graduates were education (36%), engineering (19%), and business (15%). Within an average freshman class, 31% graduate in 6 years. Some 120 companies recruited on campus in 1992–93.

Admissions Contact: Joe Estrada, Registrar and Director of Admissions.

TEXAS CHRISTIAN UNIVERSITY

D-2

Fort Worth, TX 76129   (817) 921–7490; (800) TCU-3764

Full-time: 2103 men, 2961 women   Faculty: 322; I, -$
Part-time: 234 men, 426 women   Ph.D.s: 93%
Graduate: 575 men, 523 women   Student/Faculty: 16 to 1
Year: semesters, summer session   Tuition: $8970
Application Deadline: February 15   Room & Board: $3210
Freshman Class: 4095 applied, 3079 accepted, 1195 enrolled
SAT I: required   **COMPETITIVE**

Texas Christian University, founded in 1873, is a private, coeducational university affiliated with the Christian Church (Disciples of Christ). TCU is a teaching and research institution offering undergraduate programs in arts, sciences, business, education, fine arts, communications, nursing, and engineering. There are 5 undergraduate and 5 graduate schools. In addition to regional accreditation, TCU has baccalaureate program accreditation with AACSB, ACEJ-MC, ADA, CSWE, FIDER, and NLN. The library contains 1,562,014 volumes, 415,426 microform items, and 14,376 audiovisual forms, and subscribes to 3748 periodicals. Computerized library sources and services include the card catalog, interlibrary loans, and database searching. Special learning facilities include a learning resource center, art gallery, radio station, TV station, an observatory, and a speech and hearing clinic. The 237-acre campus is in a suburban area 3 miles southwest of downtown Fort Worth. Including residence halls, there are 67 buildings on campus.

Student Life: About 70% of undergraduates are from Texas. Students come from 50 states, 63 foreign countries, and Canada. Eighty-eight percent are from public schools; 12% from private. Eighty-five percent are white. Forty-seven percent are Protestant; 29% claim no religious affiliation; 14% Catholic. The average age of freshmen is 18; all undergraduates, 21. Twenty-one percent drop out by the end of their first year; 66% remain to graduate.

Housing: A total of 3064 students can be accommodated in college housing. College-sponsored living facilities include single-sex and coed dormitories, fraternity houses, and sorority houses. In addition there are special interest houses. On-campus housing is guaranteed for all 4 years. Fifty-two percent of students live on campus; of those, 90% remain on campus on weekends. Alcohol is not permitted. All students may keep cars on campus.

Activities: About 29% of men belong to 2 local and 8 national fraternities; about 38% of women belong to 2 local and 10 national sororities. There are 150 groups on campus, including art, band, cheerleading, chorale, chorus, computers, dance, drama, drill team, ethnic, film, honors, international, jazz band, literary magazine, marching band, musical theater, newspaper, opera, orchestra, pep band, photography, political, professional, radio and TV, religious, social, social service, student government, symphony, and yearbook. Popular campus events include Parents Weekend, Homecoming, Howdy Rush Week, Christmas Lighting, Carols by Candlelight, National Hunger Week, and International Week.

Sports: There are 10 intercollegiate sports for men and 9 for women, and 18 intramural sports for men and 18 for women. Athletic and recreation facilities include indoor and outdoor tennis facilities, a 46,000-seat stadium, a 1200-seat auditorium, a 7,200-seat coliseum, and a building for health, physical education, and recreation, which houses an indoor NCAA regulation swimming pool, a diving well, 3 gymnasiums, 1 of which seats 7000, handball and racquetball courts, and 2 rooms for body conditioning and weight training.

Disabled Students: Sixty-three percent of the campus is accessible to disabled students. The following facilities are available: wheelchair ramps, elevators, special parking, specially equipped rest rooms, special class scheduling, lowered drinking fountains, and lowered telephones. For visually impaired and hearing-impaired students, there are flashing lights and vibrators on beds in case of fire. Hearing-assisted devices are also available.

Services: In addition to many counseling and information services, tutoring is available in most subjects. In addition, there is a reader service for the blind.

Campus Safety and Security: Campus safety and security measures include 24-hour foot and vehicle patrol, escort service, informal discussions, and pamphlets, posters, and films. In addition, there are emergency telephones and lighted pathways and sidewalks.

Programs of Study: TCU awards the B.A., B.S., B.B.A., B.F.A., B.G.S., B.Mus., B.Med., B.S.Ed., and B.S.N., degrees. Master's and doctoral degrees also are awarded. Bachelor's degrees are awarded in BIOLOGICAL SCIENCE (biology/biological science, neurosciences, and nutrition), BUSINESS (accounting, banking and finance, fashion merchandising, management science, and marketing/retailing/merchandising), COMMUNICATIONS AND THE ARTS (advertising, art history and appreciation, broadcasting, communications, dance, design, dramatic arts, English, film arts, fine arts, French, graphic design, journalism, music, music performance, music theory and composition, Spanish, and studio art), COMPUTER AND PHYSI-

CAL SCIENCE (astronomy, chemistry, computer science, geology, mathematics, and physics), EDUCATION (art, education of the deaf and hearing impaired, elementary, health, music, physical, recreation, secondary, and special), ENGINEERING AND ENVIRONMENTAL DESIGN (commercial art, engineering, environmental science, and interior design), HEALTH PROFESSIONS (medical laboratory technology, nursing, and speech pathology/audiology), SOCIAL SCIENCE (criminal justice, economics, fashion design and technology, history, Latin American studies, philosophy, physical fitness/movement, political science/government, psychology, religion, social work, and sociology). Natural sciences and business are the strongest academically. Business, education, journalism, political science, natural science, radio-TV-film, psychology, and nursing have the largest enrollments.

Required: All students must satisfy the TCU liberal arts and science core, about 40% of a typical degree, which includes 6 hours each of natural sciences, social sciences, and either foreign language or oral communication/literature; 3 hours each of fine arts, critical inquiry, religion studies, historical studies, and mathematics; and 2 hours of physical education/health concepts. There is also a writing requirement. To graduate, candidates must complete at least 124 semester hours, which includes 24 to 36 in the major, earning a minimum GPA of 2.0.

Special: A 3–2 engineering degree, a general studies degree, and a combined B.A.-B.S. degree in numerous majors are offered. Student-designed majors, dual majors, nondegree study, and pass/no credit options are available. TCU also accepts credit by examination and credit for life, military, and work experience. There is a cooperative program in medical technology with a local hospital, and internships in social work, criminal justice, nutrition and dietetics, speech, political science, and theater. The university also offers a Washington semester and study abroad in Japan, Singapore, and 8 European cities. There is a freshman honors program on campus, as well as 4 national honor societies, including Phi Beta Kappa. Twenty-four departments have honors programs.

Faculty/Classroom: Sixty-seven percent of faculty are male; 33%, female. All teach undergraduates and do research.

Admissions: About 75% of the 1993–94 applicants were accepted. About 55% of the current freshmen were in the top fifth of their class; 83% were in the top two fifths. There were 11 National Merit finalists. About 35 freshmen graduated first in their class.

Requirements: The SAT I is required. Candidates should be graduates of an accredited secondary school and have completed 2 years of academic electives and 15 Carnegie units, including 4 years of English, 3 years each of mathematics, science, and social studies, and 2 of the same foreign language. TCU also recommends an interview and requires an essay and counselor's recommendation. AP and CLEP credits are accepted. Important factors used in the admissions decision are advanced placement or honor courses, leadership record, evidence of special talent, recommendations by school officials, and extracurricular activities record.

Procedure: Freshmen are admitted to all sessions. Entrance exams should be taken during or before the fall semester of the senior year. Early decision applications should be filed by November 15; regular applications, by February 15 for fall entry and December 1 for spring entry, along with an application fee of $30. Notification of early decision is sent January 1; regular decision, April 1. There are early decision, early admissions, and deferred admissions plans. About 740 early decision candidates were accepted for the 1993–94 class. A waiting list is an active part of the admissions procedure, with about 3% of applicants on the list.

Transfer: A total of 356 transfer students enrolled in 1993–94. A minimum GPA of 2.0 is required. Applicants must complete an application form and submit official transcripts for each college attended as well as a secondary school transcript. If fewer than 24 semester hours of transferable work have been completed at the time of application, SAT I or ACT scores are required, and secondary school credentials are considered. A total of 63 credits out of 124 must be completed at TCU.

Visiting: There are regularly scheduled orientations for prospective students, student-led campus tours, and optional personal interviews and departmental visits. There are guides for informal visits and visitors may sit in on classes and stay overnight at the school. To arrange for a visit, contact the Admissions Office at (800) TCU-3764.

Financial Aid: In a recent year, 64% of all current freshmen and 52% of continuing students received some form of financial aid. About 35% of freshmen and 33% of continuing students received need-based aid. Scholarships or need-based grants averaged $3000 ($8576 maximum); loans averaged $1500 ($14,500 maximum); and work contracts averaged $1300 ($1500 maximum). Fourteen percent of undergraduate students work part-time. Average earnings from campus work for the school year are $1500. TCU is a member of CSS. The FAFSA and parent's and student's tax returns are required. The deadline for financial aid applications is May.

International Students: There are currently 218 international students enrolled. The school actively recruits these students. They must take the TOEFL and achieve a minimum score of 550.

Computers: The university provides computer facilities for student use. The mainframes are an IBM 4381/P13, an IBM 9370/Mod 60, a DEC VAX 4000, and a DEC VAX 6310. There are also 1269 microcomputers available for student use in 5 DOS-based PC laboratories, 1 Apple Macintosh laboratory, 2 open mainframe terminal laboratories, and 3 additional mainframe laboratories for computer science and business students; any PC equipped with a modem may also access the mainframe. All students may access the system anytime. There are no time limits on using the system and no fees.

Graduates: In 1992–93, 1100 bachelor's degrees were awarded. The most popular majors among graduates were psychology (7%), marketing (6%), and advertising/public relations (5%). Within an average freshman class, 2% graduate in 3 years, 55% in 4 years, 64% in 5 years, and 65% in 6 years. Some 85 companies recruited on campus in 1992–93.

Admissions Contact: Leo Munson, Dean of Admissions.

TEXAS COLLEGE
E-2
Tyler, TX 75702-2404

(903) 593-8311, ext. 236
(800) 952-2127 (in-state)

Full-time: 239 men, 179 women	Faculty: 25
Part-time: 10 men, 24 women	Ph.D.s: 25%
Graduate: none	Student/Faculty: 17 to 1
Year: semesters, summer session	Tuition: $3500
Application Deadline: May 15	Room & Board: $2430
Freshman Class: 174 applied, 174 accepted, 115 enrolled	
ACT: 15	NONCOMPETITITVE

Texas College, founded in 1894, is a private, coeducational, liberal arts college affiliated with the Christian Methodist Episcopal Church. The library contains 82,875 volumes, 24,513 microform items, and 4961 audiovisual forms, and subscribes to 130 periodicals. Special learning facilities include a learning resource center. The 66-acre campus is in an urban area 89 miles east of Dallas.

Student Life: About 45% of undergraduates are from Texas. Ninety-five percent are African American. The average age of freshmen is 18; all undergraduates, 21. Twenty-five percent drop out by the end of their first year; 39% remain to graduate.

Housing: College-sponsored housing is single-sex and coed. On-campus housing is guaranteed for all 4 years. Alcohol is not permitted.

Activities: About 5% of men belong to 4 local fraternities; about 10% of women belong to 3 local sororities. There are some groups on campus, including cheerleading, choir, drama, drill team, marching band, newspaper, professional, social service, student government, and yearbook.

Sports: There are 2 intercollegiate sports for men, and several intramural sports both for men and women.

Disabled Students: Special parking is available for disabled students.

Programs of Study: TC awards the B.A. and B.S. degrees. Bachelor's degrees are awarded in BIOLOGICAL SCIENCE (biology/biological science), BUSINESS (business administration and management), COMMUNICATIONS AND THE ARTS (English, music, and studio art), COMPUTER AND PHYSICAL SCIENCE (chemistry, computer science, and mathematics), EDUCATION (art, business, early childhood, elementary, music, physical, and secondary), SOCIAL SCIENCE (economics, history, international relations, political science/government, prelaw, social science, social work, and sociology).

Required: Students must complete a minimum of 124 semester hours and must maintain a minimum overall GPA of 2.0. A grade of C or better must be achieved in all courses in the student's major and minor.

Special: Opportunities are provided for work-study programs, a B.A.-B.S. degree, and nondegree study. There are 3 national honor societies on campus.

Admissions: All of the 1993–94 applicants were accepted.

Requirements: The SAT I or ACT is strongly recommended. The Pre TASP is required. Graduation from an accredited secondary school is required; a GED will be accepted. Applicants should submit 16 academic credits, distributed as follows: 4 credits in English, 2 each in history, mathematics, and science, and 6 in additional academic electives.

Procedure: Entrance exams should be taken prior to registration. Applications should be filed by May 15 (priority) for fall entry, along with an application fee of $5. The college accepts all applicants. There is an early admissions plan.

Visiting: There are regularly scheduled orientations for prospective students. There are guides for informal visits and visitors may stay overnight at the school. To arrange for a visit, contact L. V. Nauls, Vice President for Student Affairs, at (903) 593-8311, ext. 268.

Financial Aid: The FAF is required. The deadline for financial aid applications is March 31.
International Students: Students must take the TOEFL and achieve a minimum score of 500. They must also take the ACT or the college's own entrance exam.
Admissions Contact: Varetta Rider, Director of Admissions.

TEXAS LUTHERAN COLLEGE   D-4

Seguin, TX 78155	(512) 372-8050; (800) 771-8521
Full-time: 357 men, 538 women	Faculty: 61; IIB, -$
Part-time: 31 men, 97 women	Ph.D.s: 68%
Graduate: none	Student/Faculty: 15 to 1
Year: semesters, summer session	Tuition: $7460
Application Deadline: August 1	Room & Board: $3250
Freshman Class: 533 applied, 460 accepted, 215 enrolled	
SAT I Verbal/Math: 435/498	ACT: 22 COMPETITIVE

Texas Lutheran College, founded in 1891, is a private liberal arts institution affiliated with the Evangelical Lutheran Church of America. The library contains 146,986 volumes, 72,655 microform items, and 5419 audiovisual forms, and subscribes to 718 periodicals. Computerized library sources and services include interlibrary loans and database searching. Special learning facilities include a geological museum. The 161-acre campus is in a small town 37 miles east of San Antonio. Including residence halls, there are 32 buildings on campus.
Student Life: About 87% of undergraduates are from Texas. Students come from 30 states, 10 foreign countries, and Canada. Eighty-eight percent are from public schools; 12% from private. Seventy-six percent are white; 13% Hispanic. Seventy-one percent are Protestant; 19% Catholic. The average age of freshmen is 18.9; all undergraduates, 21.5. About 41% of freshmen remain to graduate.
Housing: A total of 830 students can be accommodated in college housing. College-sponsored living facilities include single-sex dormitories, on-campus apartments, and married-student housing. On-campus housing is guaranteed for all 4 years. Sixty-four percent of students live on campus; of those, 60% remain on campus on weekends. All students may keep cars on campus.
Activities: About 19% of men belong to 5 local fraternities; about 17% of women belong to 4 local sororities. There are 43 groups on campus, including art, band, cheerleading, choir, computers, dance, drama, ethnic, honors, international, jazz band, literary magazine, musical theater, newspaper, opera, pep band, political, professional, religious, social, social service, student government, symphony, and yearbook. Popular campus events include Christmas Vespers, Krost Symposium, Homecoming, and Parents Weekend.
Sports: There are 5 intercollegiate sports for men and 5 for women, and 10 intramural sports for men and 10 for women. Athletic and recreation facilities include a 2200-seat gymnasium, an 8-lane swimming pool, playing areas for intramural sports, and softball, baseball, and soccer fields.
Disabled Students: Ninety percent of the campus is accessible to disabled students. The following facilities are available: wheelchair ramps, elevators, special parking, specially equipped rest rooms, special class scheduling, and lowered drinking fountains.
Services: In addition to many counseling and information services, tutoring is available in most subjects, including mathematics and computer science. Assistance with writing assignments is available.
Campus Safety and Security: Campus safety and security measures include self defense education, escort service, informal discussions, and pamphlets, posters, and films. In addition, there are lighted pathways and sidewalks, evening foot and vehicle patrol, and coded locks in residence halls.
Programs of Study: TLC awards the B.A., B.S., and B.B.A. degrees. Associate degrees also are awarded. Bachelor's degrees are awarded in BIOLOGICAL SCIENCE (biology/biological science), BUSINESS (business administration and management and business economics), COMMUNICATIONS AND THE ARTS (communications, English, German, music, and Spanish), COMPUTER AND PHYSICAL SCIENCE (chemistry, computer management, computer science, and mathematics), SOCIAL SCIENCE (economics, history, philosophy, political science/government, psychology, social work, sociology, and theological studies). Biology, chemistry, and business are the strongest academically and have the largest enrollments.
Required: All students must complete 124 semester hours, including 24 to 54 in their major, with a 2.0 GPA. Between 45 and 49 hours of distribution courses are required. A senior seminar, project, or concert is required in most majors.
Special: Internships are available in most majors. Study abroad in all countries affiliated with ISEP, a Washington semester with American University, and work-study programs are available. The college offers student-designed majors, B.A.-B.S. degree options in biology, chemistry, and mathematics, and dual majors. There is a freshman honors program on campus, as well as 8 national honor societies. Eight departments have honors programs.

Faculty/Classroom: Sixty-seven percent of faculty are male; 33%, female. All teach undergraduates. The average class size in an introductory lecture is 30; in a laboratory, 25; and in a regular course offering, 22.
Admissions: About 86% of the 1993-94 applicants were accepted. The SAT scores for the 1993-94 freshman class were as follows: Verbal—75% below 500, 20% between 500 and 599, 4% between 600 and 700, and 2% above 700; Math—50% below 500, 33% between 500 and 599, 14% between 600 and 700, and 3% above 700. The ACT scores were 35% below 21, 26% between 21 and 23, 21% between 24 and 26, 14% between 27 and 28, and 4% above 28. About 47% of the current freshmen were in the top fifth of their class; 73% were in the top two fifths. There were 2 National Merit semifinalists. Eight freshmen graduated first in their class.
Requirements: TLC requires applicants to be in the upper 50% of their class. The SAT I or ACT is required. Applicant must have 16 Carnegie units, including a recommended 4 years in English, 3 each of social studies, mathematics and science, and 2 in foreign language. A minimum score of 800 on the SAT I, or 18 on the ACT is recommended. The GED is accepted. AP and CLEP credits are accepted. Important factors used in the admissions decision are advanced placement or honor courses, leadership record, recommendations by school officials, personality, intangible qualities, and extracurricular activities record.
Procedure: Freshmen are admitted to all sessions. Entrance exams should be taken in the spring of the junior year or the summer before the senior year. Applications should be filed by August 1 for fall entry, December 1 for spring entry, and May 1 for summer entry, along with an application fee of $20. There is a deferred admissions plan.
Transfer: A total of 55 transfer students enrolled in 1993-94. Applicants for transfer must have a GPA of at least 2.0 and be in good academic standing. A total of 30 credits out of 124 must be completed at TLC.
Visiting: There are regularly scheduled orientations for prospective students. There are guides for informal visits and visitors may sit in on classes and stay overnight at the school. To arrange for a visit, contact the Admissions Office at (800) 771-8521.
Financial Aid: In 1993-94, 80% of all current freshmen and 89% of continuing students received some form of financial aid. About 57% of freshmen and 56% of continuing students received need-based aid. The average freshman award was $7195. Of that total, scholarships or need-based grants averaged $3805 ($10,740 maximum); loans averaged $2870 ($8110 maximum); and work contracts averaged $520 ($800 maximum). Thirty percent of undergraduate students work part-time. Average earnings from campus work for the school year are $750. The average financial indebtedness of the 1992-93 graduate was $14,400. TLC is a member of CSS. The FFS, the college's own financial statement, and the FAFSA are required. The deadline for financial aid applications is April 1.
International Students: There are currently 44 international students enrolled. They must take the TOEFL and achieve a minimum score of 550.
Computers: The college provides computer facilities for student use. The mainframes are a DEC MicroVAX II and a DEC Alpha 3000 VAX. The computer laboratory houses 12 terminals. Three additional terminals are located in the library, and 4 more are in residence halls. Students can also have 24-hour access to the VAX system via a modem if they own a computer. Primary uses include programming languages, statistical applications, mail, and word processing. All students may access the system about 80 hours per week. There are no time limits on using the system and no fees.
Graduates: In 1992-93, 193 bachelor's degrees were awarded. The most popular majors among graduates were business administration (32%), natural sciences (23%), and education (9%). Within an average freshman class, 1% graduate in 3 years, 28% in 4 years, 38% in 5 years, and 40% in 6 years. In a recent graduating class, 33% of the men and 30% of the women were enrolled in graduate school within 6 months of graduation.
Admissions Contact: Jennifer Brewer Ehlers, Director of Admissions.

TEXAS SOUTHERN UNIVERSITY   E-3

Houston, TX 77004	(713) 527-7070
Full-time: 2143 men, 3441 women	Faculty: 424
Part-time: 1170 men, 1931 women	Ph.D.s: 50%
Graduate: 888 men, 1066 women	Student/Faculty: 13 to 1
Year: semesters, summer session	Tuition: $1180 ($5324)
Application Deadline: August 5	Room & Board: $3320
Freshman Class: 2357 applied, 2357 accepted, 1624 enrolled	
ACT: 16	NONCOMPETITIVE

Texas Southern University, founded in 1947, is a state-supported institution offering undergraduate programs in the arts and sciences, education and behavioral sciences, pharmacy and health science, business, and technology. There are 5 undergraduate and 3 graduate

schools. In addition to regional accreditation, TSU has baccalaureate program accreditation with NCATE. The 3 libraries contain 900,000 volumes and 180,000 microform items, and subscribe to 4500 periodicals. Special learning facilities include a learning resource center, art gallery, radio station, and TV station. The 131-acre campus is in an urban area 3 miles southeast of downtown Houston. Including residence halls, there are 45 buildings on campus.

Student Life: About 80% of undergraduates are from Texas. Students come from 48 states and 56 foreign countries. Ninety-seven percent are from public schools; 3% from private. Eighty percent are African American. Ninety percent are Protestant. The average age of freshmen is 19; all undergraduates, 27.

Housing: A total of 1000 students can be accommodated in college housing. College-sponsored living facilities include single-sex dormitories and off-campus apartments. On-campus housing is available on a first-come, first-served basis. Priority is given to out-of-town students. Ninety percent of students commute. Alcohol is not permitted. Upperclassmen may keep cars on campus.

Activities: About 30% of men belong to 4 national fraternities; about 35% of women belong to 4 national sororities. There are 29 groups on campus, including art, band, cheerleading, choir, chorus, computers, dance, drama, ethnic, film, honors, international, jazz band, marching band, newspaper, orchestra, photography, political, professional, radio and TV, religious, social, social service, student government, symphony, and yearbook. Popular campus events include Homecoming, Senior Day, Christmas Tree Lighting, Christmas Musicale, Fall Greek Show, and New Student Convocation.

Sports: There are 6 intercollegiate sports for men and 3 for women, and 12 intramural sports for men and 6 for women. Athletic and recreation facilities include a health and physical education complex, a 7000-seat football stadium, and 2 gymnasiums, the largest seating 1000.

Disabled Students: Sixty percent of the campus is accessible to disabled students. The following facilities are available: wheelchair ramps, elevators, special parking, specially equipped rest rooms, lowered drinking fountains, and lowered telephones.

Services: In addition to many counseling and information services, tutoring is available in most subjects. In addition, there is remedial math, reading, and writing.

Campus Safety and Security: Campus safety and security measures include 24-hour foot and vehicle patrol, self defense education, informal discussions, and pamphlets, posters, and films. In addition, there are emergency telephones and lighted pathways and sidewalks.

Programs of Study: TSU awards the B.A., B.S., and B.B.A. degrees. Master's and doctoral degrees also are awarded. Bachelor's degrees are awarded in BIOLOGICAL SCIENCE (biology/biological science), BUSINESS (accounting, business administration and management, and marketing/retailing/merchandising), COMMUNICATIONS AND THE ARTS (communications, English, fine arts, French, journalism, music, Spanish, and speech/debate/rhetoric), COMPUTER AND PHYSICAL SCIENCE (chemistry, computer programming, computer science, mathematics, and physics), EDUCATION (art, early childhood, elementary, guidance, health, home economics, industrial arts, music, science, secondary, and special), ENGINEERING AND ENVIRONMENTAL DESIGN (engineering technology), HEALTH PROFESSIONS (medical laboratory technology, pharmacy, premedicine, and public health), SOCIAL SCIENCE (criminal justice, economics, history, political science/government, psychology, public administration, social work, and sociology). Pharmacy is the strongest academically. General business has the largest enrollment.

Required: Students must complete between 136 and 148 semester hours, depending on the student's major. A minimum of 30 hours is required in the major. A course in physical education is also required.

Special: Special academic programs include cross-registration in military science with the University of Houston and study abroad in Africa. There is a freshman honors program on campus. Thirty departments have honors programs.

Faculty/Classroom: The average class size in an introductory lecture is 22.

Admissions: All of the 1993–94 applicants were accepted. The SAT scores for the 1993–94 freshman class were as follows: Verbal—100% below 500; Math—100% below 500. The ACT scores were 100% below 21.

Requirements: The SAT I or ACT is required. Candidates should be graduates of an accredited secondary school or have the GED.

Procedure: Freshmen are admitted fall, spring, and summer. Entrance exams should be taken by January. Applications should be filed by August 5 for fall entry, December 16 for spring entry, May 20 for first term summer entry, and July 1 for second term entry, along with an application fee of $10. Notification is sent on a rolling basis.

Transfer: The applicant must be a student in good standing. The SAT I or ACT is required. A total of 15 semester hours out of 136 to 148 must be completed at TSU.

Visiting: There are guides for informal visits and visitors may stay overnight at the school. To arrange for a visit, contact the Office of Recruitment and Admissions at (713) 527-7070.

Financial Aid: In a recent year, 85% of all students received some form of financial aid. TSU is a member of CSS. The FAF, FFS, SFS, or the college's own financial statement must be filed. The deadline for financial aid applications is April 1.

International Students: There are currently 1000 international students enrolled. They must take the TOEFL and achieve a minimum score of 500. The student must also take the SAT I, ACT, or the college's own entrance exam, and scores must meet TSU's requirements.

Computers: The college provides computer facilities for student use. The mainframe is a DEC. There are microcomputers available. Computer science students may access the system. It may be used by appointment and during assigned periods. Students may access the system 4 hours at a time. There are no fees.

Graduates: In a recent year, 617 bachelor's degrees were awarded. The most popular majors among graduates were education (30%) and pharmacy and health sciences (27%). Within an average freshman class, 5% graduate in 4 years, 40% in 5 years, and 75% in 6 years. Some 54 companies recruited on campus. In the 1992 graduating class, 35% of the men and 45% of the women were enrolled in graduate school within 6 months of graduation; 65% of the men and 70% of the women had found employment.

Admissions Contact: Director of Recruitment and Admissions.

TEXAS STATE UNIVERSITY SYSTEM

The Texas State University system, established in 1911, is a public system. It is governed by a 9-member board of regents, whose chief administrator is the chancellor. The primary goal of the system is teaching. The main priorities are teacher education, business, and liberal arts. The total enrollment of all 5 campuses is approximately 43,000, with about 1400 faculty members. Altogether, there are 325 baccalaureate and 200 master's programs, along with one doctoral program offered within the Texas State University system. Four-year campuses are located in San Angelo, Huntsville, San Marcos, and Alpine. Profiles of the 4-year campuses are included in this chapter in alphabetical order with other Texas schools.

TEXAS TECH UNIVERSITY
Lubbock, TX 79409–5015

B-2

(806) 742–3654

Full-time: 9148 men, 7637 women	**Faculty:** 695; I, --$
Part-time: 1375 men, 1405 women	**Ph.D.s:** 91%
Graduate: 2520 men, 1922 women	**Student/Faculty:** 24 to 1
Year: semesters, summer session	**Tuition:** $2320 ($6400)
Application Deadline: July 15	**Room & Board:** $3688
Freshman Class: 6334 applied, 5051 accepted, 2957 enrolled	
SAT I Verbal/Math: 439/507	**ACT:** 22 COMPETITIVE

Texas Tech University, founded in 1923, is a large, comprehensive public university offering undergraduate and graduate programs in a variety of professional and vocational fields. There are 7 undergraduate and 2 graduate schools. In addition to regional accreditation, Texas Tech has baccalaureate program accreditation with AACSB, ADA, ASLA, CSWE, FIDER, NAAB, NASAD, NASM, and NCATE. The 3 libraries contain 1.2 million volumes and 800,000 microform items, and subscribe to 8000 periodicals. Computerized library sources and services include the card catalog, interlibrary loans, and database searching. Special learning facilities include a learning resource center, art gallery, natural history museum, planetarium, radio station, TV station, and a ranching heritage center. The 1839-acre campus is in an urban area in Lubbock. Including residence halls, there are 171 buildings on campus.

Student Life: About 92% of undergraduates are from Texas. Students come from 50 states, 92 foreign countries, and Canada. Eighty-three percent are white. The average age of freshmen is 19; all undergraduates, 21. Twenty-four percent drop out by the end of their first year; 38% remain to graduate.

Housing: A total of 7000 students can be accommodated in college housing. College-sponsored living facilities include single-sex and coed dormitories and on-campus apartments. On-campus housing is guaranteed for the freshman year only and is available on a first-come, first-served basis. Seventy percent of students commute. Alcohol is not permitted. All students may keep cars on campus.

Activities: About 16% of men belong to 1 local fraternity and 25 national fraternities; about 18% of women belong to 1 local sorority and 14 national sororities. There are 300 groups on campus, including art, band, cheerleading, chess, choir, chorale, chorus, computers, dance, drama, drill team, ethnic, film, gay, honors, international, jazz band, literary magazine, marching band, musical theater, newspaper, opera, orchestra, pep band, photography, political, professional, radio and TV, religious, social, social service, student government, symphony, and yearbook. Popular campus events include Homecoming, Parents Day, Carol of the Lights, and Madrigal Dinner.

Sports: There are 8 intercollegiate sports for men and 7 for women, and 34 intramural sports for men and 34 for women. Athletic and recreation facilities include an athletic training center and 2 student recreation centers.

Disabled Students: Seventy-five percent of the campus is accessible to disabled students. The following facilities are available: wheelchair ramps, elevators, special parking, specially equipped rest rooms, lowered drinking fountains, lowered telephones, and dormitory rooms accessible to the handicapped.

Services: In addition to many counseling and information services, tutoring is available in every subject. In addition, there is a reader service for the blind, and remedial math, reading, and writing. An attorney is available for students to obtain legal advice and guidance.

Campus Safety and Security: Campus safety and security measures include 24-hour foot and vehicle patrol, shuttle buses, pamphlets, posters, and films, and emergency telephones. In addition, there are lighted pathways and sidewalks.

Programs of Study: Texas Tech awards the B.A., B.S., B.Arch., B.B.A., B.F.A., B.I.D., B.Land.Arch., B.M., B.S.Ag.E., B.S.C.E., B.S.Ch.E., B.S. in E., B.S. in Eco., B.S.E.E., B.S. in Engineering Physics, B.S.H.E., B.S.I.E., B.S.M.E., B.S. in Petroleum Engineering, B.S. in Restaurant, Hotel, and Institutional Management, B.S.Tech., B.S. in Textile Engineering, B.S. in Textile Technology Management, and B.G.S. degrees. Master's and doctoral degrees also are awarded. Bachelor's degrees are awarded in AGRICULTURE (agricultural business management, agricultural economics, agricultural mechanics, animal science, horticulture, range/farm management, soil science, and wildlife management), BIOLOGICAL SCIENCE (biochemistry, biology/biological science, cell biology, entomology, microbiology, and zoology), BUSINESS (accounting, banking and finance, business administration and management, business economics, hotel/motel and restaurant management, international business management, management information systems, marketing/retailing/merchandising, and recreation and leisure services), COMMUNICATIONS AND THE ARTS (advertising, art history and appreciation, broadcasting, dance, dramatic arts, English, fine arts, French, German, journalism, Latin, music, music performance, music theory and composition, photography, public relations, Spanish, speech/debate/rhetoric, studio art, and telecommunications), COMPUTER AND PHYSICAL SCIENCE (chemistry, computer science, geology, geophysics and seismology, geoscience, mathematics, and physics), EDUCATION (agricultural, art, business, early childhood, education, elementary, home economics, music, and physical), ENGINEERING AND ENVIRONMENTAL DESIGN (agricultural engineering, architectural engineering, chemical engineering, civil engineering, construction technology, electrical/electronics engineering, electrical/electronics engineering technology, engineering, engineering physics, environmental engineering, industrial engineering technology, interior design, landscape architecture/design, mechanical engineering, mechanical engineering technology, petroleum/natural gas engineering, textile engineering, and textile technology), HEALTH PROFESSIONS (medical laboratory technology), SOCIAL SCIENCE (anthropology, child care/child and family studies, clothing and textiles management/production/services, dietetics, economics, family/consumer resource management, fashion design and technology, food production/management/services, food science, geography, history, home economics, Latin American studies, parks and recreation management, philosophy, physical fitness/movement, political science/government, prelaw, psychology, Russian and Slavic studies, social work, and sociology). Business, engineering, communications, education, psychology, and human development and family studies have the largest enrollments.

Required: All students must meet the requirements of the core curriculum, including courses in science and technology, mathematics, English, history, and political science. Total credits required for graduation vary from 125 to 174, depending on the degree program. A minimum GPA of 2.0 is required.

Special: There are many work-study programs and internships, and students may study in Mexico, England, Italy, or Malaysia. The college also offers an accelerated degree program, dual degrees, dual majors, a general studies degree, a 3–2 engineering program, nondegree study, and pass/fail options. There is a freshman honors program on campus, as well as 7 national honor societies.

Faculty/Classroom: Sixty-nine percent of faculty are male; 31%, female. The average class size in an introductory lecture is 44; in a laboratory, 24; and in a regular course offering, 40.

Admissions: About 80% of the 1993–94 applicants were accepted. The SAT scores for the 1993–94 freshman class were as follows: Verbal—78% below 500, 18% between 500 and 599, and 4% between 600 and 700; Math—46% below 500, 37% between 500 and 599, 14% between 600 and 700, and 3% above 700. The ACT scores were 31% below 21, 35% between 21 and 23, 21% between 24 and 26, 8% between 27 and 28, and 5% above 28. About 46% of the current freshmen were in the top fifth of their class; 79% were in the top two fifths.

Requirements: The SAT I or ACT is required. Applicants should be graduates of an accredited high school or have the GED. The university requires 19 credits of academic work in high school, including 4 credits in English, 3 credits in mathematics, 2.5 in social studies, 2 credits in science, and 3.5 credits in academic electives. The university admits all students scoring 1200 (composite) on the SAT I or 29 on the ACT. Special circumstances may allow those not fulfilling the above requirements to be admitted. AP and CLEP credits are accepted.

Procedure: Freshmen are admitted to all sessions. Entrance exams should be taken before July 1. Applications should be filed by July 15 for fall entry and December 5 for spring entry, along with an application fee of $25. Notification is sent on a rolling basis. There is an early admissions plan.

Transfer: About 1900 transfer students enrolled in 1993–94. Applicants should present at least a C average in previous college work. Those with fewer than 12 college credits must also submit ACT or SAT I scores. A total of 30 credits out of 125 to 174 must be completed at Texas Tech.

Visiting: There are regularly scheduled orientations for prospective students. There are guides for informal visits and visitors may sit in on classes and stay overnight at the school. To arrange for a visit, contact the New Student Relations Office at (806) 742–1482.

Financial Aid: In 1993–94, 48% of all current freshmen and 43% of continuing students received some form of financial aid. About 48% of freshmen and 42% of continuing students received need-based aid. The average freshman award was $3538. Of that total, scholarships or need-based grants averaged $937 ($9430 maximum); loans averaged $2712 ($5975 maximum); and work contracts averaged $1988 ($2400 maximum). Eight percent of undergraduate students work part-time. The FFS is required. The deadline for financial aid applications is April 15.

International Students: There are currently 726 international students enrolled. They must take the TOEFL and achieve a minimum score of 550. The student must also take the SAT I or the ACT.

Computers: The university provides computer facilities for student use. The mainframes are an IBM 3090, a DEC VAX 8650, a DEC VAX 6520, and various departmental systems. There are also Macintosh, IBM, Zenith, SUN, and other microcomputers available in the Advanced Technology Learning Center and in academic departments. All students may access the system 152 hours a week or more. There are no time limits on using the system. The fees are $3 per semester credit hour.

Graduates: In 1992–93, 3354 bachelor's degrees were awarded. The most popular majors among graduates were education-multidisciplinary studies (8%), restaurant/hotel and institutional management (5%), and marketing (5%). Within an average freshman class, 14% graduate in 4 years, 32% in 5 years, and 38% in 6 years.

Admissions Contact: Dale Grusing, Director of Undergraduate Admissions.

TEXAS WESLEYAN UNIVERSITY   D-2
Fort Worth, TX 76105-1536

(817) 531-4422
(800) 580-8980 (in-state)

Full-time: 470 men, 734 women	Faculty: 85; IIB, av$
Part-time: 144 men, 248 women	Ph.Ds: 77%
Graduate: 437 men, 404 women	Student/Faculty: 14 to 1
Year: semesters, summer session	Tuition: $6150
Application Deadline: open	Room & Board: $3230
Freshman Class: 592 applied, 501 accepted, 279 enrolled	
SAT I Verbal/Math: 430/460	ACT: 20 LESS COMPETITIVE

Texas Wesleyan University, founded in 1891, is a liberal arts institution affiliated with the United Methodist Church. There are 4 undergraduate and 2 graduate schools. In addition to regional accreditation, Texas Wesleyan has baccalaureate program accreditation with NASM. The library contains 205,000 volumes, 314,000 microform items, and 3724 audiovisual forms, and subscribes to 1511 periodicals. Computerized library sources and services include the card catalog. Special learning facilities include an art gallery. The 79-acre campus is in an urban area 7 miles east of Fort Worth. Including residence halls, there are 22 buildings on campus.

Student Life: About 94% of undergraduates are from Texas. Students come from 21 states, 20 foreign countries, and Canada. Seventy-two percent are white; 13% African American; 12% Hispanic. Forty-nine percent are Protestant; 15% Catholic; 11% claim no religious affiliation. The average age of freshmen is 18; all undergraduates, 26. Eight percent drop out by the end of their first year; 43% remain to graduate.

Housing: A total of 350 students can be accommodated in college housing. College-sponsored living facilities include single-sex and coed dormitories and on-campus apartments. In addition there are honors houses. On-campus housing is guaranteed for all 4 years. Seventy-nine percent of students commute. Alcohol is not permitted. All students may keep cars on campus.

Activities: About 10% of men belong to 2 national fraternities; about 9% of women belong to 3 national sororities. There are 57 groups on campus, including art, band, cheerleading, choir, chorale, chorus, computers, drama, ethnic, honors, international, jazz band, literary magazine, musical theater, newspaper, opera, orchestra, pep band, political, professional, radio and TV, religious, social, social service, student government, and yearbook. Popular campus events include Sig Ep Air Band Jam, Oktoberfest, and the Wilson lectures.

Sports: There are 5 intercollegiate sports for men and 4 for women, and 11 intramural sports each. Athletic and recreation facilities include an activities center and tennis courts.

Disabled Students: The entire campus is accessible to disabled students. The following facilities are available: wheelchair ramps, elevators, special parking, specially equipped rest rooms, and special class scheduling.

Services: In addition to many counseling and information services, tutoring is available in most subjects. In addition, there is remedial math, reading, and writing.

Campus Safety and Security: Campus safety and security measures include 24-hour foot and vehicle patrol, escort service, pamphlets, posters, and films, and lighted pathways and sidewalks.

Programs of Study: Texas Wesleyan awards the B.A., B.S., B.B.A., and B.M. degrees. Master's degrees also are awarded. Bachelor's degrees are awarded in BIOLOGICAL SCIENCE (biology/biological science), BUSINESS (accounting, banking and finance, business administration and management, business economics, international business management, and marketing/retailing/merchandising), COMMUNICATIONS AND THE ARTS (communications, dramatic arts, English, fine arts, music, and Spanish), COMPUTER AND PHYSICAL SCIENCE (chemistry, computer science, earth science, information sciences and systems, mathematics, and physical sciences), EDUCATION (early childhood, elementary, middle school, music, physical, reading, secondary, and teaching English as a second language/foreign language), SOCIAL SCIENCE (applied legal science, Christian studies, criminal justice, economics, history, humanities, political science/government, psychology, religion, and social science). Accounting is the strongest academically. Business administration has the largest enrollment.

Required: A minimum GPA of 2.0 and 124 credit hours are required in order to graduate. All students must complete a general education requirement of 51 credits, including courses in writing, literature, religion, laboratory science, history, mathematics, political or economic systems, fine arts, humanities, physical education, and social science, philosophy, or psychology.

Special: Study abroad is offered in 2 countries. A 3–2 engineering degree is offered in conjunction with a number of universities. Pass/fail options are available. There is one national honor society on campus, Phi Beta Kappa. Eight departments have honors programs.

Faculty/Classroom: Seventy-two percent of faculty are male; 28%, female. Eighty-eight percent teach undergraduates. No introductory courses are taught by graduate students. The average class size in an introductory lecture is 30 and in a laboratory, 30.

Admissions: About 85% of the 1993–94 applicants were accepted. The SAT scores for the freshman class were as follows: Verbal—79% below 500, 16% between 500 and 599, and 5% between 600 and 700; Math—65% below 500, 25% between 500 and 599, and 10% between 600 and 700. The ACT scores were 64% below 21, 20% between 21 and 23, 10% between 24 and 26, 5% between 27 and 28, and 1% above 28. About 41% of the current freshmen were in the top fifth of their class; 72% were in the top two fifths. Three freshmen graduated first in their class.

Requirements: Texas Wesleyan requires applicants to be in the upper 50% of their class. A minimum GPA of 2.0 is required. Either the SAT I, with a minimum composite score of 800, or the ACT, with a minimum score of 19, is required. Applicant must be a graduate of an accredited secondary school or have a GED equivalent. An interview is recommended. AP and CLEP credits are accepted. Important factors used in the admissions decision are leadership record, extracurricular activities record, recommendations by alumni, recommendations by school officials, personality, and intangible qualities.

Procedure: Freshmen are admitted to all sessions. Entrance exams should be taken as early as possible. Application deadlines are open. The application fee is $20. Notification is sent on a rolling basis. There is an early admissions plan.

Transfer: About 300 transfer students enrolled in 1993–94. Applicants with fewer than 30 credit hours must submit a high school transcript and the results of either the SAT I (with a minimum composite score of 800) or the ACT (with a minimum score of 19). A minimum GPA of 2.0 is required. A total of 30 credits out of 124 must be completed at Texas Wesleyan.

Visiting: There are regularly scheduled orientations for prospective students. There are guides for informal visits and visitors may sit in on classes and stay overnight at the school. To arrange for a visit, contact the Office of Admissions at (817) 531–4422 or (800) 580–8980 (in-state).

Financial Aid: In 1993–94, 89% of all current freshmen and 79% of continuing students received some form of financial aid. About 46% of freshmen and 40% of continuing students received need-based aid. The average freshman award was $4150. Of that total, scholarships or need-based grants averaged $2637 ($10,000 maximum); loans averaged $2000 ($2625 maximum); and work contracts averaged $2000 ($3400 maximum). Twenty percent of undergraduate students work part-time. Average earnings from campus work for the school year are $2000. The average financial indebtedness of the 1992–93 graduate was $2257. Texas Wesleyan is a member of CSS. The college's own financial statement and SASFA are required. The deadline for financial aid applications is April 15.

International Students: There are currently 58 international students enrolled. They must take the TOEFL and achieve a minimum score of 550.

Computers: The university provides computer facilities for student use. The mainframes are a Data General MV/10000 and a DEC VAX 4000/300. There are 9 Data General terminals for instruction, 15 Macintosh, and 65 IBM, in 5 minicomputer laboratories; 27 IBMs are in a networked minicomputer laboratory. All students may access the system 9 A.M. to 9 P.M. Monday through Thursday, 9 A.M. to 5 P.M. Friday, and 9 A.M. to 1 P.M. weekends. There are no time limits on using the system and no fees.

Graduates: In 1992–93, 272 bachelor's degrees were awarded. The most popular majors among graduates were business (32%), education (21%), and psychology (8%). Within an average freshman class, 33% graduate in 4 years, 14% in 5 years, and 2% in 6 years. Some 20 companies recruited on campus in 1992–93. In a recent graduating class, 6% of the men and 9% of the women were enrolled in graduate school within 6 months of graduation; 92% of the students found employment.

Admissions Contact: Dave Voskuil, Vice President for Enrollment Management.

TEXAS WOMAN'S UNIVERSITY

D-2

Denton, TX 76204-0547 (817) 898-3040

Full-time: 161 men, 3631 women	Faculty: 401; I, --$
Part-time: 104 men, 1861 women	Ph.D.s: 69%
Graduate: 529 men, 3416 women	Student/Faculty: 9 to 1
Year: semesters, summer session	Tuition: $1450 ($5530)
Application Deadline: July 15	Room & Board: $2942
Freshman Class: 772 applied, 496 accepted, 473 enrolled	
SAT I or ACT: required	COMPETITIVE

Texas Woman's University, founded in 1901, is a comprehensive public university primarily for women, offering degree programs in the liberal arts, education, music and fine arts, and the business and health professions. There are 6 undergraduate and 7 graduate schools. In addition to regional accreditation, TWU has baccalaureate program accreditation with ADA, APTA, CSWE, NASM, and NLN. The 2 libraries contain 774,985 volumes, 640,735 microform items, and 11,658 audiovisual forms, and subscribe to 3072 periodicals. Computerized library sources and services include the card catalog and database searching. Special learning facilities include a learning resource center, art gallery, medical centers and clinics, radio and TV studios, and a nursery school. The 270-acre Denton campus is in an urban area 38 miles north of Dallas. Including residence halls, there are 46 buildings on campus.

Student Life: About 95% of undergraduates are from Texas. Students come from 38 states, 55 foreign countries, and Canada. Seventy-seven percent are white; 11% African American. The average age of freshmen is 22; all undergraduates, 27.

Housing: A total of 2300 students can be accommodated in college housing. College-sponsored living facilities include single-sex and coed dormitories, on-campus apartments, and married-student housing. On-campus housing is guaranteed for the freshman year only and is available on a first-come, first-served basis. Eighty-four percent of students commute. All students may keep cars on campus.

Activities: About 5% of women belong to 2 local and 6 national sororities. There are no fraternities on campus. There are 100 groups on campus, including art, choir, chorale, chorus, dance, drama, ethnic, gay, honors, international, jazz band, newspaper, political, professional, radio and TV, social, social service, and student government. Popular campus events include Black Awareness Week, Mexican Festival, and dance programs.

Sports: There are 4 intercollegiate sports for women, and 16 intramural sports for men and 16 for women. Athletic and recreation facilities include a wellness center, indoor and outdoor pools, weight-training and fitness rooms, tennis courts, and a golf course.

Disabled Students: Ninety-five percent of the campus is accessible to disabled students. The following facilities are available: wheelchair ramps, elevators, special parking, specially equipped rest rooms, lowered drinking fountains, lowered telephones, and lowered library equipment. There is an office to assist students with disabilities.

Services: In addition to many counseling and information services, tutoring is available in some subjects, including science and mathematics. In addition, there is remedial math, reading, and writing.

Campus Safety and Security: Campus safety and security measures include 24-hour foot and vehicle patrol, self defense education, escort service, and informal discussions. In addition, there are pamphlets, posters, and films, emergency telephones, and lighted pathways and sidewalks.

Programs of Study: TWU awards the B.A., B.S., B.B.A., B.F.A., and B.S.W. degrees. Master's and doctoral degrees also are awarded. Bachelor's degrees are awarded in BIOLOGICAL SCIENCE (biology/biological science), BUSINESS (accounting, business administration and management, marketing/retailing/merchandising, and personnel management), COMMUNICATIONS AND THE ARTS (advertising, communications, dance, design, dramatic arts, English, fine arts, music, photography, and Spanish), COMPUTER AND PHYSICAL SCIENCE (chemistry, computer science, and mathematics), HEALTH PROFESSIONS (nursing and occupational therapy), SOCIAL SCIENCE (child psychology/development, criminal justice, dietetics, economics, history, interdisciplinary studies, kinesiology, political science/government, social work, and sociology). Nursing has the largest enrollment.

Required: General education requirements vary according to the degree. All degree programs require 12 hours of English, 6 of American history, 3 of sociology or economics, 6 of government, 4 of kinesiology, and either foreign language or mathematics or science. A 2.0 GPA, successful completion of the Texas-mandated examination in reading, writing, and mathematics, and a minimum of 124 hours are needed to graduate.

Special: Co-op programs in most majors and internships are available. Study abroad is offered in many different degree programs. Cross-registration is possible with the University of North Texas and East Texas State University. A 3-2 engineering program exists with the University of Texas at Dallas. Dual majors, nondegree study, and work-study programs are available. There is a freshman honors program on campus, as well as 28 national honor societies.

Faculty/Classroom: Twenty-seven percent of faculty are male; 73%, female.

Admissions: About 64% of the 1993-94 applicants were accepted.

Requirements: A minimum GPA of 2.0 is required. The SAT I or ACT is required. A minimum combined score of 630 is required on the SAT I, or a score of 14 on the ACT. Applicants should be graduates of an accredited secondary school or have a GED certificate and have completed 3 secondary school units in English, 2 each in mathematics, social studies, and science, and 6 in academic electives. AP credits are accepted.

Procedure: Freshmen are admitted to all sessions. Entrance exams should be taken during the junior or the senior year of high school. Applications should be filed by July 15 for fall entry and December 1 for spring entry, along with an application fee of $25. Notification is sent on a rolling basis. There are early admissions and deferred admissions plans.

Transfer: About 950 transfer students enrolled in 1993-94. Transfer students must possess at least a 2.0 GPA and be in good standing at all previously attended institutions. A total of 30 credits out of 124 must be completed at TWU.

Visiting: There are regularly scheduled orientations for prospective students, including admissions and financial aid sessions and a campus tour. There are guides for informal visits and visitors may sit in on classes and stay overnight at the school. To arrange for a visit, contact the Office of Admissions at (817) 898-3040.

Financial Aid: In a recent year, 46% of all current freshmen and 56% of continuing students received some form of financial aid. About 41% of freshmen and 53% of continuing students received need-based aid. The average freshman award was $3895. Of that total, scholarships or need-based grants averaged $1810 ($4000 maximum); loans averaged $2105 ($2625 maximum); and work contracts averaged $1950 (maximum). Thirteen percent of undergraduate students work part-time. Average earnings from campus work for the school year are $1950. The average financial indebtedness of the 1992-93 graduate was $8100. TWU is a member of CSS. The FFS and FAFSA is required. The deadline for financial aid applications is April 1.

International Students: There are currently 229 international students enrolled. The school actively recruits these students. They must take the TOEFL and achieve a minimum score of 550.

Computers: The university provides computer facilities for student use. The mainframe is a DEC VAX 6330. There are more than 200 microcomputers and terminals available to TWU students in academic computing laboratories, libraries, and residence halls. Those who have applied for a computer account may access the system. There are no time limits on using the system. The fees are $15-50 per semester.

Graduates: In 1992-93, 1147 bachelor's degrees were awarded. The most popular majors among graduates were nursing (21%), interdisciplinary studies (11%), and occupational therapy (9%). Within an average freshman class, 1% graduate in 3 years, 15% in 4 years, 27% in 5 years, and 32% in 6 years.

Admissions Contact: Cynthia B. Johnson, Director of Undergraduate Admissions.

TRINITY UNIVERSITY D-4
San Antonio, TX 78712-7200 (210) 736-7207
(800) TRINITY (out-of-state)

Full-time: 1032 men, 1075 women	Faculty: 224; IIA, +$
Part-time: 47 men, 54 women	Ph.D.s: 96%
Graduate: 107 men, 150 women	Student/Faculty: 9 to 1
Year: semesters, summer session	Tuition: $11,720
Application Deadline: February 1	Room & Board: $4950
Freshman Class: 2425 applied, 1818 accepted, 601 enrolled	
SAT I Verbal/Math: 575/635	ACT: 28 HIGHLY COMPETITIVE

Trinity University, founded in 1869, is a liberal arts and sciences institution affiliated with the Presbyterian Church (U.S.A.). There is one graduate school. In addition to regional accreditation, Trinity has baccalaureate program accreditation with ABET, NASM, and NCATE. The library contains 740,388 volumes, 258,839 microform items, and 17,072 audiovisual forms, and subscribes to 2464 periodicals. Computerized library sources and services include the card catalog and database searching. Special learning facilities include a radio station. The 113-acre campus is in an urban area 4 miles north of San Antonio. Including residence halls, there are 40 buildings on campus.

Student Life: About 63% of undergraduates are from Texas. Students come from 50 states, 22 foreign countries, and Canada. Eighty percent are from public schools; 20% from private. Seventy-nine percent are white. Fifty-eight percent are Protestant; 27% Catholic; 16% claim no religious affiliation. The average age of freshmen is 18; all undergraduates, 20. Twelve percent drop out by the end of their first year; 75% remain to graduate.

Housing: A total of 1900 students can be accommodated in college housing. College-sponsored living facilities include single-sex and coed dormitories. In addition there are language houses. On-campus housing is guaranteed for all 4 years. Seventy-five percent of students live on campus. All students may keep cars on campus.

Activities: About 30% of men belong to 6 local fraternities; about 33% of women belong to 6 local sororities. There are 80 groups on campus, including art, cheerleading, choir, chorus, computers, dance, drama, ethnic, film, gay, honors, international, jazz band, literary magazine, newspaper, orchestra, photography, political, professional, radio and TV, religious, social, social service, student government, symphony, and yearbook. Popular campus events include Parents Weekend and Tigerfest.

Sports: There are 9 intercollegiate sports for men and 8 for women, and 23 intramural sports for men and 25 for women. Athletic and recreation facilities include the 2000-seat Bell Center, an indoor Olympic pool and diving center, a 5000-seat stadium and a 3000-seat auditorium/arena.

Disabled Students: Ninety-nine percent of the campus is accessible to disabled students. The following facilities are available: wheelchair ramps, elevators, special parking, specially equipped rest rooms, lowered drinking fountains, and lowered telephones.

Services: In addition to many counseling and information services, tutoring is available in most subjects.

Campus Safety and Security: Campus safety and security measures include 24-hour foot and vehicle patrol, escort service, pamphlets, posters, and films, and emergency telephones. In addition, there are lighted pathways and sidewalks.

Programs of Study: Trinity awards the B.A., B.S., and B.M. degrees. Master's degrees also are awarded. Bachelor's degrees are awarded in BIOLOGICAL SCIENCE (biochemistry and biology/biological science), BUSINESS (accounting, business administration and management, and business economics), COMMUNICATIONS AND THE ARTS (communications, dramatic arts, English, French, German, journalism, music, Russian, Spanish, and speech/debate/rhetoric), COMPUTER AND PHYSICAL SCIENCE (chemistry, computer science, earth science, geology, mathematics, and physics), EDUCATION (art, foreign languages, and science), ENGINEERING AND ENVIRONMENTAL DESIGN (engineering and applied science), HEALTH PROFESSIONS (predentistry, premedicine, and preveterinary science), SOCIAL SCIENCE (anthropology, economics, history, international relations, philosophy, political science/government, prelaw, psychology, religion, sociology, and urban studies). Economics, business, and English are the strongest academically. Business and communications have the largest enrollments.

Required: In order to graduate, all students must satisfy the common curriculum and residency requirements and complete a minimum of 124 credit hours (129 for a B.S. in engineering science and 141 for a B.M. in performance and composition). Students must take at least

60 hours outside the major and 36 hours in upper-division courses. A minimum 2.0 GPA is required.

Special: The university offers study abroad in Europe, the former Soviet Union, Mexico, South America, China, Japan, Africa, and Israel. A Washington semester, dual majors, and pass/fail options are also available, as is Air Force ROTC in conjunction with the University of Texas at San Antonio. There are 5 national honor societies on campus, including Phi Beta Kappa. Six departments have honors programs.

Faculty/Classroom: Seventy-nine percent of faculty are male; 21%, female. All teach undergraduates and 90% both teach and do research. No introductory courses are taught by graduate students. The average class size in an introductory lecture is 15; in a laboratory, 25; and in a regular course offering, 20.

Admissions: About 75% of the 1993–94 applicants were accepted. The SAT scores for the 1993–94 freshman class were as follows: Verbal—17% below 500, 48% between 500 and 599, 32% between 600 and 700, and 3% above 700; Math—4% below 500, 31% between 500 and 599, 35% between 600 and 700, and 20% above 700. The ACT scores were 1% below 21, 10% between 21 and 23, 27% between 24 and 26, 40% between 27 and 28, and 22% above 28. About 86% of the current freshmen were in the top fifth of their class; 98% were in the top two fifths. There were 36 National Merit finalists.

Requirements: Trinity requires applicants to be in the upper 40% of their class. The SAT I or ACT is required. Applicants should have completed, upon high school graduation, 4 years of English, 3 of mathematics, 2 of laboratory science, 2 of social studies, and 2 of a single foreign language. AP credits are accepted. Important factors used in the admissions decision are leadership record, evidence of special talent, personality, intangible qualities, extracurricular activities record, and parents or siblings attending the school.

Procedure: Freshmen are admitted to all sessions. Entrance exams should be taken late in the junior year or early in the senior year of high school. Early decision applications should be filed by November 15; regular applications, by February 1 for fall entry and December 1 for spring entry, along with an application fee of $25. Notification of early decision is sent December 15; regular decision, April 1. There are early decision and deferred admissions plans. About 110 early decision candidates were accepted for a recent class. A waiting list is an active part of the admissions procedure, with about 5% of applicants on the list.

Transfer: A total of 26 transfer students enrolled in 1993–94. A total of 60 credits out of 124 must be completed at Trinity.

Visiting: There are regularly scheduled orientations for prospective students. There are guides for informal visits and visitors may sit in on classes and stay overnight at the school. To arrange for a visit, contact the Admissions Office at (210) 736–7207 or (800) TRINITY (out-of-state).

Financial Aid: In 1993–94, 75% of all current freshmen and 72% of continuing students received some form of financial aid. About 43% of freshmen and 40% of continuing students received need-based aid. The average freshman award was $9500. Of that total, scholarships or need-based grants averaged $4500; loans averaged $3500; and work contracts averaged $1300. Ten percent of undergraduate students work part-time. Average earnings from campus work for the school year are $1500. Trinity is a member of CSS. The FAF is required. The deadline for financial aid applications is February 1.

International Students: There are currently 35 international students enrolled. The school actively recruits these students. They must take the TOEFL. The student must also take the SAT I or the ACT.

Computers: The university provides computer facilities for student use. The mainframe is an IBM 4381. Students may obtain an account on the mainframe. All students may access the system 24 hours per day. There are no time limits on using the system and no fees.

Graduates: In 1992–93, 537 bachelor's degrees were awarded. The most popular majors among graduates were business (14%), communication (8%), and English (7%). Within an average freshman class, 1% graduate in 3 years, 65% in 4 years, 75% in 5 years, and 76% in 6 years. Some 100 companies recruited on campus in a recent year. In a recent graduating class, 50% of the men and women were enrolled in graduate school within 6 months of graduation.

Admissions Contact: Dr. George Boyd, Director of Admissions.

UNIVERSITY OF DALLAS
D-2

Irving, TX 75062-4799   (214) 721–5266; (800) 628–6999

Full-time: 494 men, 564 women	Faculty: 109; IIA, --$
Part-time: 28 men, 45 women	Ph.D.s: 95%
Graduate: 1082 men, 688 women	Student/Faculty: 10 to 1
Year: semesters, summer session	Tuition: $10,200
Application Deadline: February 1	Room & Board: $4783
Freshman Class: 680 applied, 585 accepted, 246 enrolled	
SAT I Verbal/Math: 530/580	ACT: 26 **VERY COMPETITIVE**

The University of Dallas, founded in 1955, is a private liberal arts institution affiliated with the Roman Catholic Church. Programs are offered through the Constantin College of Liberal Arts, a collegiate seminary, and 2 graduate schools. A second campus is located in Rome, Italy. The library contains 288,566 volumes, 75,416 microform items, and 1100 audiovisual forms, and subscribes to 1022 periodicals. Computerized library sources and services include the card catalog, interlibrary loans, and database searching. Special learning facilities include an art gallery and planetarium. The 750-acre campus is in a suburban area 12 miles west of Dallas. Including residence halls, there are 28 buildings on campus.

Student Life: About 61% of undergraduates are from Texas. Students come from 48 states and 22 foreign countries. Seventy-one percent are white; 13% Hispanic; 10% Asian American. Sixty-eight percent are Catholic; 15% claim no religious affiliation; 13% Protestant. The average age of freshmen is 18; all undergraduates, 21. Sixteen percent drop out by the end of their first year; 65% remain to graduate.

Housing: A total of 705 students can be accommodated in college housing. College-sponsored living facilities include single-sex and coed dormitories and on-campus apartments. On-campus housing is guaranteed for all 4 years. Sixty-one percent of students live on campus; of those, 70% remain on campus on weekends. All students may keep cars on campus.

Activities: There are no fraternities or sororities on campus. There are 43 groups on campus, including cheerleading, chess, choir, chorale, chorus, computers, dance, drama, ethnic, honors, international, literary magazine, musical theater, newspaper, pep band, political, professional, religious, social, social service, student government, and yearbook. Popular campus events include Charity Week, Oktoberfest, Christmas Progressive Dinner, Sunday Night Fights (debate), Spring Musical, fall and spring drama productions, and Spring Formal.

Sports: There are 3 intercollegiate sports for men and 3 for women, and 13 intramural sports for men and 13 for women. Athletic and recreation facilities include rugby, soccer, baseball, and all-purpose fields; basketball, tennis, and volleyball courts; and a 1500-seat indoor gymnasium.

Disabled Students: Sixty-six percent of the campus is accessible to disabled students. The following facilities are available: wheelchair ramps, elevators, special parking, specially equipped rest rooms, and lowered drinking fountains.

Services: In addition to many counseling and information services, tutoring is available in every subject. In addition, there is remedial math and writing.

Campus Safety and Security: Campus safety and security measures include 24-hour foot and vehicle patrol, self defense education, escort service, and informal discussions. In addition, there are pamphlets, posters, and films, emergency telephones, and lighted pathways and sidewalks.

Programs of Study: The university awards the B.A. and B.S. degrees. Master's and doctoral degrees also are awarded. Bachelor's degrees are awarded in BIOLOGICAL SCIENCE (biochemistry and biology/biological science), COMMUNICATIONS AND THE ARTS (classics, dramatic arts, English, fine arts, French, German, and Spanish), COMPUTER AND PHYSICAL SCIENCE (chemistry, mathematics, and physics), EDUCATION (art, elementary, and secondary), SOCIAL SCIENCE (economics, history, philosophy, political science/government, psychology, and theological studies). English, politics, biochemistry, and classics are the strongest academically. Biology, English, psychology, and politics have the largest enrollments.

Required: In order to graduate, all students must satisfy the requirements of the core curriculum and their major, and pass a comprehensive examination during the senior year. Students must complete at least 120 credit hours, including 36 hours in the major, with a minimum 2.0 GPA. Core curriculum includes English, philosophy, mathematics/fine arts, science, foreign language, American and Western civilizations, politics, economics, and theology.

Special: The university offers Air Force and Army ROTC cross-registration with the University of North Texas, internships in field experience or off-campus research, study abroad in Rome, a Washington semester, on-campus work-study programs, and an accelerated MBA degree program. Dual and student-designed majors are available through the Constantin Scholars Program. A 3–2 engineering

degree may be arranged with Washington University in St. Louis and the University of Texas at Dallas. There is a chapter of Phi Beta Kappa on campus.

Faculty/Classroom: Seventy-six percent of faculty are male; 24%, female. All teach undergraduates. No introductory courses are taught by graduate students. The average class size in an introductory lecture is 35; in a laboratory, 15; and in a regular course offering, 20.

Admissions: About 86% of the 1993–94 applicants were accepted. The SAT scores for the 1993–94 freshman class were as follows: Verbal—26% below 500, 49% between 500 and 599, 22% between 600 and 700, and 3% above 700; Math—16% below 500, 41% between 500 and 599, 36% between 600 and 700, and 7% above 700. The ACT scores were 3% below 21, 21% between 21 and 23, 30% between 24 and 26, 22% between 27 and 28, and 24% above 28. About 65% of the current freshmen were in the top fifth of their class; 89% were in the top two fifths. There were 8 National Merit finalists and 9 semifinalists. Thirteen freshmen graduated first in their class.

Requirements: The university requires applicants to be in the upper 50% of their class. The SAT I or ACT is required. Applicant must be a graduate of an accredited secondary school or have a GED certificate. Sixteen academic or Carnegie credits are required, including courses in English, social studies, mathematics, science, and a foreign language. An interview is recommended and an essay is required. AP credits are accepted. Important factors used in the admissions decision are advanced placement or honor courses, leadership record, personality, intangible qualities, recommendations by school officials, and evidence of special talent.

Procedure: Freshmen are admitted fall and spring. Entrance exams should be taken during the junior year or by the fall of the senior year of high school. Early action applications should be filed by December 1; regular applications, by February 1 for fall entry and December 1 for spring entry, along with an application fee of $30. Notification of early action is sent January 15; regular decision, March 15. There are early admissions and deferred admissions plans.

Transfer: A total of 85 transfer students enrolled in 1993–94. Applicants must have a minimum 2.5 GPA from an accredited college or university. The SAT I or ACT, an associate degree, and an interview are recommended. A total of 30 credits out of 120 must be completed at the university.

Visiting: There are regularly scheduled orientations for prospective students. There are guides for informal visits and visitors may sit in on classes and stay overnight at the school. To arrange for a visit, contact the Admissions Office at (214) 721–5266 or (800) 628–6999.

Financial Aid: In 1993–94, 92% of all current freshmen and 84% of continuing students received some form of financial aid. About 72% of freshmen and 65% of continuing students received need-based aid. The average freshman award was $12,891. Of that total, scholarships or need-based grants averaged $6969 ($10,150 maximum); loans averaged $3878 ($4625 maximum); and work contracts averaged $1487 ($1910 maximum). Thirty-seven percent of undergraduate students work part-time. Average earnings from campus work for the school year were $1120. The average financial indebtedness of the 1992–93 graduate was $10,800. The college's own financial statement and FAFSA are required. The deadline for financial aid applications is March 1.

International Students: There are currently 338 international students enrolled. The school actively recruits these students. They must take the TOEFL and achieve a minimum score of 550.

Computers: The university provides computer facilities for student use. The mainframe is an IBM RISC 6000. The university is currently upgrading academic computing to a network of IBM RISC 6000s that will serve all university students. There will be 4 computer laboratories available for student use on campus, as well as individual workstations in the library, the foreign language and mathematics departments, and at various other sites throughout campus. All students may access the system. There are no time limits on using the system. The fees are $10 per semester.

Graduates: In 1992–93, 212 bachelor's degrees were awarded. The most popular majors among graduates were politics (13%), biology (13%), and English (11%). Within an average freshman class, 3% graduate in 3 years, 53% in 4 years, and 65% in 5 years. Some 25 companies recruited on campus in a recent year.

Admissions Contact: Office of Admissions.

UNIVERSITY OF HOUSTON SYSTEM

The University of Houston system, established in 1977, is a public system in Texas. It is governed by a 9-member board of regents, whose chief administrator is the chancellor. The primary goal of the system is overall coordination of teaching, research, and service. The main priorities are long-range planning, governmental and private representation, and overall executive management. The total student enrollment of all 4 campuses is usually about 49,000, with more than 3000 faculty members. Altogether, there are 180 baccalaureate, 163 master's, and 51 doctoral programs offered within the system. Profiles of the 4-year campuses are included in this chapter.

UNIVERSITY OF HOUSTON
Houston, TX 77204–2161

E-3

(713) 743–1010

Full-time: 14,999 men and women	**Faculty:** 907; I, -$
Part-time: 7387 men and women	**Ph.D.s:** n/av
Graduate: 7432 men and women	**Student/Faculty:** 17 to 1
Year: semesters	**Tuition:** $1015 ($4007)
Application Deadline: July 15	**Room & Board:** $4200

Freshman Class: 6530 applied, 3918 accepted, 2350 enrolled
SAT I or ACT: required

COMPETITIVE

The University of Houston, established in 1929, is a public, coeducational institution, with programs in arts and sciences, business, education, engineering, and health professions. In addition to regional accreditation, UH has baccalaureate program accreditation with AACSB, ABET, ACPE, ADA, CSWE, NAAB, NASM, and NCATE. The 4 libraries contain 1,562,001 volumes and 3,001,026 microform items, and subscribe to 19,942 periodicals. Computerized library sources and services include the card catalog, interlibrary loans, and database searching. Special learning facilities include a learning resource center, an art gallery, a radio station, a TV station, and an observatory. The 540-acre campus is in an urban area 3 miles from the Houston business district. Including residence halls, there are 75 buildings on campus.

Student Life: About 85% of undergraduates are from Texas. Students come from 80 states. Sixty-seven percent are white. The average age of freshmen is 19; all undergraduates, 26. Eighteen percent drop out by the end of their first year; 23% remain to graduate.

Housing: A total of 2210 students can be accommodated in college housing. College-sponsored living facilities include coed dormitories, on-campus apartments, and married-student housing. In addition, there are honors houses and special interest houses. On-campus housing is available on a first-come, first-served basis. Ninety percent of students commute. All students may keep cars on campus.

Activities: About 4% of men belong to 3 local and 18 national fraternities; about 3% of women belong to 16 national sororities. There are 200 groups on campus, including band, cheerleading, chess, choir, chorale, computers, dance, drama, drill team, ethnic, film, gay, honors, international, jazz band, marching band, musical theater, newspaper, opera, photography, political, professional, radio and TV, religious, social, social service, student government, symphony, and yearbook. Popular campus events include Homecoming, Chicano Week, Spring Fair, Greek Week, and International Food Fair.

Sports: There are 6 intercollegiate sports for men and 7 for women, and 12 intramural sports for men and 10 for women. Athletic and recreation facilities include the 25,000-seat Robertson Stadium, racquetball and handball courts, 12 tennis courts, a weight room, a concourse for indoor running, an outdoor track, saunas, and indoor and outdoor pools.

Disabled Students: The following facilities are available: wheelchair ramps, elevators, special parking, specially equipped rest rooms, special class scheduling, lowered drinking fountains, lowered telephones, and automatic doors.

Services: In addition to many counseling and information services, tutoring is available in most subjects, including core requirements. In addition, there is remedial math, reading, and writing.

Campus Safety and Security: Campus safety and security measures include 24-hour foot and vehicle patrol, self-defense education, escort service, and shuttle buses. In addition, there are pamphlets, posters, and films, emergency telephones, and lighted pathways and sidewalks.

Programs of Study: UH awards the B.A., B.S., B.Acc., B.Arch., B.B.A., B.F.A., B.M., B.S.C.E., B.S.Ch.E., B.S.Ed., B.S.E.E., B.S.I.E., B.S.M.E., B.S.Pharm., and B.S.Tech. degrees. Master's and doctoral degrees also are awarded. Bachelor's degrees are awarded in BIOLOGICAL SCIENCE (biochemistry and biology/biological science), BUSINESS (accounting, banking and finance, business administration and management, hotel/motel and restaurant management, marketing/retailing/merchandising, and personnel management), COMMUNICATIONS AND THE ARTS (broadcasting, classical languages, communications, dramatic arts, English, fine arts, French, German, journalism, music, Spanish, and speech/debate/rhetoric), COMPUTER AND PHYSICAL SCIENCE (chemistry, computer science, geology, information sciences and systems, mathematics, physics, and statistics), EDUCATION (art, business, early childhood, elementary, health, music, physical, science, secondary, special, teaching English as a second language/foreign language, and trade and industrial), ENGINEERING AND ENVIRONMENTAL DESIGN (architectural engineering, chemical engineering, civil engineering, computer technology, construction technology, drafting and design technology, electrical/electronics engineering, industrial engineering, industrial engineering technology, manufacturing technology, mechanical engineering, and surveying engineering), HEALTH PRO-

FESSIONS (optometry, predentistry, premedicine, prepharmacy, and preveterinary science), SOCIAL SCIENCE (anthropology, economics, history, philosophy, political science/government, prelaw, psychology, social science, and sociology). Chemical engineering is the strongest academically. Psychology has the largest enrollment.

Required: To graduate, students must complete 122 credits, with a minimum GPA of 2.0. The core curriculum requirements include 4 semesters of English and 2 each of political science, natural science, history, mathematics, and cultural heritage. All students must take 2 hours of physical education, and complete TASP and exit examinations and a writing proficiency test.

Special: UH offers cross-registration with the University of Texas and Texas Wesleyan University, internships in engineering and political science, co-op programs in 7 majors, study abroad in London, and work-study programs. There are programs in Mexican-American studies, as well as the Houston Inter-University African Studies Program for students interested in Africa, and the Mickey Leland Internship in Washington, D.C. B.A.-B.S. degrees and dual majors in all offered areas of study, nondegree study, and pass/fail options are available. There is a freshman honors program on campus, as well as 10 national honor societies. Thirteen departments have honors programs.

Admissions: About 60% of the 1993–94 applicants are accepted.

Requirements: The SAT I or ACT is required. A minimum composite score of 800 (400 verbal and 400 mathematics) on the SAT I or 19 on the ACT is required if the student is in the top 10% of his high school class. Lower ranks require higher scores. Applicants must be graduates of an accredited secondary school or have the GED. Students should complete the following high school courses: English, 4 credits; mathematics and social studies, 3 credits each; and laboratory science, 2 credits. There are special requirements for the College of Engineering and the School of Music. An audition is necessary for applicants to the School of Music. AP and CLEP credits are accepted. Important factors used in the admissions decision are evidence of special talent, advanced placement or honor courses, recommendations by school officials, leadership record, and extracurricular activities record.

Procedure: Freshmen are admitted to all sessions. Entrance exams should be taken at the end of the junior year. Applications should be filed by July 15 for fall entry, November 15 for spring entry, and May 1 for summer entry, along with an application fee of $25. There is an early admissions plan.

Transfer: About 2610 transfer students enrolled in a recent year. Applicants must be eligible to return to their last college. Application deadlines are the same as for freshmen.

Visiting: There are regularly scheduled orientations for prospective students, including a Cougar Preview held during fall and spring semesters. There are guides for informal visits and visitors may stay overnight at the school. To arrange for a visit, contact the Admissions Office at (713) 743–1010.

Financial Aid: UH is a member of CSS. The FAF or FFS is required. The deadline for financial aid applications is April 1.

International Students: Students must take the TOEFL and achieve a minimum score of 550. The student must also take the SAT I or the ACT.

Computers: The college provides computer facilities for student use. The mainframe is an NAS AS-9000. Registered students have access to computer facilities that are located throughout the campus, including the library and a 24-hour site. In addition, individual departments, the honors program, and the residence hall also have their own computer facilities. All students may access the system. There are no time limits on using the system. The fees are $30.

Graduates: In a recent year, 3128 bachelor's degrees were awarded. Within an average freshman class, 7% graduate in 4 years and 20% in 5 years.

Admissions Contact: Admissions Counselors.

UNIVERSITY OF HOUSTON-DOWNTOWN

E-3

Houston, TX 77002 (713) 221–8533

Full-time, part time: 3982 men, 4071 women	Faculty: IIB, -$
	Ph.D.s: 67%
Graduate: none	Student/Faculty: 21 to 1
Year: semesters, summer sessions	Tuition: $1143 ($4860)
Application Deadline: see profile	Room & Board: n/app
Freshman Class: n/av	
SAT I or ACT: recommended	NONCOMPETITIVE

University of Houston-Downtown, founded in 1974, is part of the University of Houston System. The commuter university offers programs through the colleges of business, mathematics, engineering, technology and natural sciences, and humanities and social studies. There are 4 undergraduate schools. In addition to regional accreditation, UH-Downtown has baccalaureate program accreditation with ABET. The library contains 181,000 volumes, 20,000 microform items, and 4200 audiovisual forms, and subscribes to 1300 periodicals. Computerized library sources and services include the card catalog and

database searching. Special learning facilities include an art gallery. The campus is in an urban area in the central business district of Houston. There are 2 buildings on campus.

Student Life: About 95% of undergraduates are from Texas. Students come from 20 states and 79 foreign countries. Ninety-six percent are from public schools; 4% from private. Thirty-six percent are white; 24% Hispanic; 23% African American; 12% Asian American. The average age of all undergraduates is 26.

Housing: There are no residence halls; all students commute and may keep cars on campus.

Activities: There is 1 national sorority but no fraternities. There are 35 groups on campus, including choir, computers, drama, ethnic, honors, international, literary magazine, newspaper, political, professional, social, social service, and student government. Popular campus events include Spring Festival, Awards Gala, Chinese New Year, Casino Nite, Oktoberfest, Fiestas Patrias, CSA Mid-Autumn Festival, and Red Rose Ball.

Sports: Athletic and recreation facilities include a game room, a basketball court goal, and a swimming pool. The largest auditorium seats 300. Students involved in intramural sports may use the facilities at the University of Houston main campus.

Disabled Students: The entire campus is accessible to disabled students. The following facilities are available: wheelchair ramps, elevators, special parking, specially equipped rest rooms, lowered drinking fountains and lowered telephones. Braille materials are available.

Services: In addition to many counseling and information services, tutoring is available in some subjects, including science. There is also a reader service for the blind, and remedial math, reading, and writing.

Campus Safety and Security: Campus safety and security measures include 24-hour foot and vehicle patrol, escort service, shuttle buses, and emergency telephones.

Programs of Study: UH-Downtown awards the B.A., B.S. and B.G.S. degrees. Bachelor's degrees are awarded in BIOLOGICAL SCIENCE (microbiology), BUSINESS (accounting, banking and finance, business administration and management, business data processing, office supervision and management, purchasing/inventory management, and real estate), COMMUNICATIONS AND THE ARTS (communications and journalism), COMPUTER AND PHYSICAL SCIENCE (applied mathematics, chemistry, computer management, computer science, natural sciences, physics, and quantitative methods), ENGINEERING AND ENVIRONMENTAL DESIGN (electrical/electronics engineering, industrial engineering, engineering technology, and petroleum/natural gas engineering), HEALTH PROFESSIONS (medical laboratory technology, nursing, occupational therapy, optometry, physical therapy, physician's assistant, predentistry, premedicine, prepharmacy, respiratory therapy, and veterinary science), SOCIAL SCIENCE (criminal justice, humanities, liberal arts/general studies, and social science). The College of Business has the largest enrollment.

Required: In order to graduate, students must complete 44 core hours and a total of 120 to 136 hours. Courses in writing skills, mathematics, and computers, enhancement courses, and a junior year writing proficiency examination are required. Students must maintain a minimum 2.0 GPA.

Special: The university offers co-op programs with Baylor College of Medicine and the University of Texas Health Science Center, cross-registration with the University of Houston System campuses, internships, and work-study programs. An interdisciplinary degree in biological and physical sciences; general studies degrees in applied mathematics, natural sciences, arts and humanities, and social sciences; nondegree study in the language institute; and pass/fail options in selected courses are available.

Faculty/Classroom: Sixty-one percent of faculty are male; 39%, female. All teach undergraduates and 40% do research. The average class size in an introductory lecture is 33; in a laboratory, 25; and in a regular course offering, 30.

Requirements: The SAT I or ACT is recommended. Applicant must be a graduate of and provide an official transcript from an accredited secondary school, or have a GED certificate. They must meet state testing requirements and comply with the Texas academic skills program, including high school courses in English, mathematics, science, and social studies. AP and CLEP credits are accepted.

Procedure: Freshmen are admitted to all sessions. Applications should be filed August 6 for early fall decision, August 20 for late fall decision, January 4 for spring entry, and May 5 for summer entry. The application fee is $10. There are early admissions and deferred admissions plans.

Transfer: About 1200 transfer students enrolled in a recent year. Transfer students must have completed a minimum of 15 credit hours. The SAT I or ACT is recommended. The final 30 credits must be completed at UH-Downtown.

Visiting: There are regularly scheduled new student orientations for prospective students in the fall and spring. There are guides for informal visits and visitors may sit in on classes. To arrange for a visit, con-

tact Diana Talley, Admissions Counselor/Recruiter, at (713) 221-8040.

Financial Aid: In a recent year, 40% of all current freshmen and 23% of continuing students received some form of financial aid. Scholarships or need-based grants averaged $1000 ($2000 maximum); loans averaged $2625 ($1400 maximum); and work contracts averaged $2000 ($2400 maximum). The average financial indebtedness of a recent graduate was $6000. The FFS is required.

International Students: There were recently 260 international students enrolled. The school actively recruits these students. They must take the TOEFL and achieve a minimum score of 550.

Computers: The college provides computer facilities for student use. The mainframe is a DEC VAX 8550. There are also IBM and Macintosh microcomputers available in various locations on campus. All students may access the system. It may be used during the more-than-70 laboratory hours available Monday through Saturday. There are no individual time limits on using the system. The fee is $30.

Admissions Contact: Rosa Cruz, Admissions Counselor/Recruiter.

UNIVERSITY OF MARY HARDIN-BAYLOR D-3
Belton, TX 76513   (817) 939-8642 or (817) 698-8642
(800) 727-8642

Full-time: 497 men, 990 women	Faculty: 86
Part-time: 141 men, 258 women	Ph.D.s: 55%
Graduate: 74 men, 182 women	Student/Faculty: 17 to 1
Year: semesters, summer session	Tuition: $5250
Application Deadline: open	Room & Board: $2870
Freshman Class: 309 applied, 304 accepted, 259 enrolled	
SAT I Verbal/Math: 424/462	ACT: 21 NONCOMPETITIVE

The University of Mary Hardin-Baylor, founded in 1845, is a Southern Baptist institution offering undergraduate and graduate degrees in liberal arts, fine arts, music, business, and education. There are 3 graduate schools. In addition to regional accreditation, UMHB has baccalaureate program accreditation with NLN. The library contains 115,000 volumes, and subscribes to 650 periodicals. Special learning facilities include a learning resource center. The 90-acre campus is in a small town 40 miles south of Waco. Including residence halls, there are 19 buildings on campus.

Student Life: About 83% of undergraduates are from Texas. Students come from 12 states, 30 foreign countries, and Canada. Ninety-three percent are from public schools; 7% from private. Seventy-seven percent are white. Seventy percent are Protestant; 20% Catholic; 10% claim no religious affiliation. The average age of freshmen is 19; all undergraduates, 27. Three percent drop out by the end of their first year; 60% remain to graduate.

Housing: A total of 700 students can be accommodated in college housing. College-sponsored living facilities include single-sex dormitories. On-campus housing is guaranteed for the freshman year only and is available on a first-come, first-served basis. Seventy-five percent of students commute. Alcohol is not permitted. All students may keep cars on campus.

Activities: There are no fraternities or sororities on campus. There are many groups and organizations on campus, including art, band, cheerleading, chess, choir, chorus, computers, drama, ethnic, honors, international, literary magazine, musical theater, newspaper, photography, professional, religious, social service, student government, and yearbook. Popular campus events include Miss UMHB Pageant, Homecoming, Play Day, Easter Pageant, and Mr. UMHB Pageant.

Sports: There are 5 intercollegiate sports for men and 5 for women, and 17 intramural sports for men and 17 for women. Athletic and recreation facilities include a gymnasium, a weight room, 2 pools, a sauna, a steam bath, and soccer and baseball fields.

Disabled Students: Fifty percent of the campus is accessible to disabled students. The following facilities are available: wheelchair ramps, elevators, special parking, and specially equipped rest rooms.

Services: In addition to many counseling and information services, tutoring is available in most subjects. In addition, there is remedial math, reading, and writing.

Campus Safety and Security: Campus safety and security measures include a security service on campus.

Programs of Study: UMHB awards the B.A., B.S., B.B.A., B.F.A., B.M., B.S.N., B.G.Technology, and B.G.S. degrees. Master's degrees are also awarded. Bachelor's degrees are awarded in BIOLOGICAL SCIENCE (biology/biological science), BUSINESS (accounting, banking and finance, business administration and management, business economics, marketing/retailing/merchandising, and personnel management), COMMUNICATIONS AND THE ARTS (communications, English, fine arts, music, Spanish, and speech/debate/rhetoric), COMPUTER AND PHYSICAL SCIENCE (chemistry, computer science, information sciences and systems, and mathematics), EDUCATION (art, business, early childhood, elementary, foreign languages, health, home economics, middle school, music, science, secondary, and special), HEALTH PROFESSIONS (medical laboratory technology, nursing, and premedicine), SOCIAL SCIENCE (community ser-

vices, criminal justice, economics, history, parks and recreation management, political science/government, prelaw, psychology, religion, social science, social work, and sociology). Education, business, and nursing are the strongest academically. Education has the largest enrollment.

Required: All students must complete 124 credits, including at least 24 in the major field and at least 36 upper-level credits, with a 2.0 GPA. Requirements include 6 credits each in English, social sciences, and religion, 6 to 8 in mathematics, laboratory science, or foreign language, 2 in physical education, 6 in electives, and 3 in humanities. There is a chapel attendance requirement.

Special: Combined B.A.-B.S. degrees in most areas, a work-study program, dual majors, a general studies degree, and nondegree study are offered. There is one national honor society on campus.

Faculty/Classroom: Fifty-two percent of faculty are male; 48%, female. The average class size in an introductory lecture is 35; in a laboratory, 25; and in a regular course offering, 30.

Admissions: About 98% of the 1993–94 applicants were accepted. The SAT scores for the 1993–94 freshman class were as follows: Verbal—84% below 500, 14% between 500 and 599, and 2% between 600 and 700; Math—61% below 500, 32% between 500 and 599, and 6% between 600 and 700. The ACT scores were 48% below 21, 25% between 21 and 23, 16% between 24 and 26, 8% between 27 and 28, and 4% above 28. About 30% of the current freshmen were in the top fifth of their class; 59% were in the top two fifths. Eight freshmen graduated first in their class.

Requirements: UMHB requires applicants to be in the upper 50% of their class. The SAT I or ACT is required. UMHB requires a minimum composite SAT I score of 740 or minimum ACT score of 18. Applicants should be graduates of an accredited high school or have earned the GED. Students should have completed 15 academics, including 3 in English and 2 each in social science and mathematics. AP and CLEP credits are accepted.

Procedure: Entrance exams should be taken by the fall of the senior year of high school. Application deadlines are open. Application fee is $35. The college accepts all applicants. Notification is sent on a rolling basis. There is an early admissions plan.

Transfer: A total of 453 transfer students enrolled in 1993–94. Transfer applicants must present at least a 2.0 GPA in a minimum of 30 college credits, be in good standing at their previous institutions, and submit all college transcripts. Those with fewer than 30 credits must also meet freshman requirements. A total of 31 credits out of 124 must be completed at UMHB.

Visiting: There are regularly scheduled orientations for prospective students. There are guides for informal visits and visitors may sit in on classes and stay overnight at the school. To arrange for a visit, contact the Recruiting Office at (817) 939–4520.

Financial Aid: In a recent year, 75% of continuing students received some form of financial aid. Fifty percent of undergraduate students work part-time. UMHB is a member of CSS. The FAF or FFS is required. The deadline for financial aid applications is June 1.

International Students: There are currently 84 international students enrolled. The school actively recruits these students.

Computers: The university provides computer facilities for student use. The mainframe is a DEC VAX unit. There are also 7 IBM-compatible microcomputers available for academic use. Those students enrolled in computer classes may access the system anytime. There are no time limits on using the system and no fees.

Graduates: In a recent year, 242 bachelor's degrees were awarded.

Admissions Contact: Bobby Johnson, Director of Admissions.

UNIVERSITY OF NORTH TEXAS D-2
Denton, TX 76203   (817) 565-2681

Full-time: 6827 men, 7220 women	Faculty: 763; I, --$
Part-time: 2634 men, 2500 women	Ph.D.s: 87%
Graduate: 2935 men, 3643 women	Student/Faculty: 18 to 1
Year: semesters, summer session	Tuition: $1274 ($4538)
Application Deadline: June 15	Room & Board: $3579
Freshman Class: 4418 applied, 2737 accepted, 2009 enrolled	
SAT I Verbal/Math: 467/526	ACT: 23 COMPETITIVE

The University of North Texas, founded in 1890, is a public institution offering programs through its colleges of arts and sciences, education, business administration, community services, library and information sciences, music, and merchandising and hospitality management. There are 8 undergraduate schools and one graduate school. In addition to regional accreditation, UNT has baccalaureate program accreditation with AACSB, ACEJMC, CSWE, FIDER, and NASM. The 4 libraries contain 1,055,717 volumes, 2,675,957 microform items, and 50,402 audiovisual forms, and subscribe to 10,525 periodicals. Computerized library sources and services include the card catalog, interlibrary loans, and database searching. Special learning facilities include a learning resource center, art gallery, radio station, observatory, and TV and film production unit. The 425-acre

campus is in an urban area 35 miles north of Dallas/Fort Worth. Including residence halls, there are 90 buildings on campus.

Student Life: About 90% of undergraduates are from Texas. Students come from 50 states, 97 foreign countries, and Canada. Eighty-one percent are white. The average age of all undergraduates is 21. Thirty-two percent drop out by the end of their first year.

Housing: A total of 4000 students can be accommodated in college housing. College-sponsored living facilities include single-sex and coed dormitories and off-campus apartments. Eighty-five percent of students commute. All students may keep cars on campus.

Activities: About 3% of men belong to 16 national fraternities; about 3% of women belong to 10 national sororities. There are 214 groups on campus, including band, cheerleading, chess, choir, chorale, chorus, computers, dance, drama, ethnic, film, gay, honors, international, jazz band, literary magazine, marching band, musical theater, newspaper, opera, orchestra, pep band, photography, political, professional, radio and TV, religious, social, social service, student government, symphony, and yearbook. Popular campus events include Homecoming, Honors Convocation, Silver Christmas Ball, Howdy Week, Taste of North Texas, and Union Day.

Sports: There are 6 intercollegiate sports for men and 5 for women, and 36 intramural sports for men and 36 for women. Athletic and recreation facilities include a 20,000-seat stadium, an 18-hole golf course, a weight-training building, tennis courts, swimming pools, 3 gymnasiums, handball and racquetball courts, and gymnastics equipment.

Disabled Students: The following facilities are available: wheelchair ramps, elevators, special parking, specially equipped rest rooms, special class scheduling, lowered drinking fountains, and lowered telephones. Nine dorm rooms have been adapted for disabled students.

Services: In addition to many counseling and information services, tutoring is available in numerous subjects. There is a reader service for the blind, and remedial math, reading, and writing.

Campus Safety and Security: Campus safety and security measures include 24-hour foot and vehicle patrol, self defense education, escort service, and shuttle buses. In addition, there are informal discussions, pamphlets, posters, films, emergency telephones, lighted pathways and sidewalks, a crime prevention program, sexual assault information services, and a full-time crime prevention officer on duty.

Programs of Study: UNT awards the B.A., B.S., B.A.A.S., B.B.A., B.F.A., B.M., B.S.B.C., B.S.Bio, B.S.Chem., B.S.Ed., B.S.E.T., B.S.I.T., B.S.MTH, B.S.M.T., B.S.PHY, and B.S.W. degrees. Master's and doctoral degrees also are awarded. Bachelor's degrees are awarded in BIOLOGICAL SCIENCE (biochemistry, biology/biological science, and molecular biology), BUSINESS (accounting, banking and finance, business administration and management, business economics, hotel/motel and restaurant management, human resources, insurance, management information systems, management science, marketing/retailing/merchandising, personnel management, real estate, recreation and leisure services, and small business management), COMMUNICATIONS AND THE ARTS (advertising, applied art, art, art history and appreciation, broadcasting, ceramic art and design, communications, crafts, dance, dramatic arts, drawing, English, fiber/textiles/weaving, film arts, fine arts, French, German, jazz, journalism, metal/jewelry, music, music history and appreciation, music performance, music theory and composition, painting, photography, piano/organ, printmaking, radio/television technology, sculpture, Spanish, and visual and performing arts), COMPUTER AND PHYSICAL SCIENCE (chemistry, computer science, earth science, information sciences and systems, mathematics, and physics), EDUCATION (business, early childhood, elementary, health, library science, music, physical, and vocational), ENGINEERING AND ENVIRONMENTAL DESIGN (emergency/disaster science, engineering technology, industrial administration/management, interior design, and preengineering), HEALTH PROFESSIONS (cytotechnology, medical laboratory technology, predentistry, premedicine, rehabilitation therapy, and speech pathology/audiology), SOCIAL SCIENCE (anthropology, child psychology/development, clothing and textiles management/production/services, counseling psychology, criminal justice, economics, fashion design and technology, geography, gerontology, history, home furnishings and equipment management/production/services, interdisciplinary studies, liberal arts/general studies, philosophy, physical fitness/movement, political science/government, psychology, social science, social work, and sociology). Biology and radio/tv/film have the largest enrollments.

Required: All students must complete at least 124 semester hours, including a minimum of 24 hours in the major, with a 2.0 GPA. Distribution requirements include 12 hours of English, 6 hours each in science, American history, federal and state constitution, science, social sciences, and humanities, and 4 hours in physical education.

Special: UNT offers co-op programs in 34 majors, internships, and work-study programs with the university. Students may study abroad in the United Kingdom, France, Germany, Mexico, and Australia. An accelerated degree program in mathematics and science allows Texas high school students to obtain 2 years of college credit during their

last 2 years in high school. Dual degrees, a general studies degree, and pass/fail options are also offered. There is a freshman honors program on campus, as well as 3 national honor societies. One department has an honors program.

Faculty/Classroom: Seventy-three percent of faculty are male; 27%, female. All both teach and do research. Graduate students teach 44% of introductory courses. The average class size in an introductory lecture is 35 and in a regular course offering, 36.

Admissions: About 62% of the 1993–94 applicants were accepted. About 37% of the current freshmen were in the top fifth of their class; 71% were in the top two fifths. There were 10 National Merit finalists.

Requirements: The SAT I or ACT is required. Applicants must be graduates of an accredited high school, and submit a high school transcript. The required minimum score for entrance exams is determined by high school class rank. AP and CLEP credits are accepted.

Procedure: Freshmen are admitted to all sessions. Entrance exams should be taken at least 2 months before admissions deadlines. Applications should be filed by June 15 for fall entry, December 15 for spring entry, and May 15 and July 1 for summer entry, along with an application fee of $25. Notification is sent on a rolling basis. There are early admissions and deferred admissions plans.

Transfer: A total of 2581 transfer students enrolled in 1993–94. Applicants with fewer than 30 hours from an accredited college must have a 2.5 GPA and must meet freshman entrance requirements. Applicants with at least 30 but no more than 44 transferable hours must have a 2.3 GPA; those with more than 44 hours must have a 2.0 GPA. A total of 30 credits out of 124 must be completed at UNT.

Visiting: There are regularly scheduled orientations for prospective students, including UNT Previews held one Saturday in the fall and one in the spring. The agenda includes a campus tour, presentations by academic and student service offices, and question-and-answer sessions. There are guides for informal visits and visitors may sit in on classes, with permission of the instructor, and stay overnight at the school. To arrange for a visit, contact the information desk assistant at (817) 565–2108 or (817) 565–2000.

Financial Aid: In a recent year, 30% of all students received some form of financial aid, including need-based aid. Scholarships or need-based grants averaged $1400 ($1600 maximum); loans averaged $2200 ($2625 maximum); and work contracts averaged $2200 ($2500 maximum). The average financial indebtedness of a recent year's graduate was $8800. UNT is a member of CSS. The deadline for financial aid applications is June 1.

International Students: There are currently 1591 international students enrolled. They must take the TOEFL and achieve a minimum score of 550. Graduates of U.S. high schools may substitute the SAT I or ACT.

Computers: The university provides computer facilities for student use. The mainframes are an HDS-80–83, a Solbourne SE/904, a DEC VAX cluster, an NBIV16S, an NAS8000, and an IBM 43004. There are no time limits on using the system. Fees are $5 to $10.

Graduates: In a recent year, 2773 bachelor's degrees were awarded. The most popular majors among graduates were marketing (11%), management (10%), and finance/insurance/real estate/law (9%). Within an average freshman class, 10% graduate in 4 years, 24% in 5 years, and 30% in 6 years. Some 152 companies recruited on campus in a recent year.

Admissions Contact: Don Palermo, Director of Admissions and School Relations.

UNIVERSITY OF SAINT THOMAS
E-3
Houston, TX 77006   **(713) 522–7911**

Full-time: 339 men, 656 women	Faculty: 85; IIA, --$
Part-time: 161 men, 247 women	Ph.D.s: 75%
Graduate: 471 men, 410 women	Student/Faculty: 12 to 1
Year: semesters, summer session	Tuition: $8046
Application Deadline: open	Room & Board: $3630
Freshman Class: 347 applied, 328 accepted, 192 enrolled	
SAT I Verbal/Math: 500/560	ACT: 25 **COMPETITIVE +**

University of Saint Thomas, founded in 1947, is a private, nonprofit coeducational institution affiliated with the Catholic Church, offering programs in business, arts and sciences, and education. There are 4 undergraduate and 5 graduate schools. The 4 libraries contain 155,868 volumes, 400,967 microform items, and 3279 audiovisual forms, and subscribe to 792 periodicals. Computerized library sources and services include the card catalog, interlibrary loans, and database searching. Special learning facilities include a learning resource center and art gallery. The 20-acre campus is in an urban area in Houston. Including residence halls, there are 32 buildings on campus.

Student Life: About 90% of undergraduates are from Texas. Students come from 22 states, 52 foreign countries, and Canada. Sixty-three percent are white; 17% Hispanic. Fifty-seven percent are Catholic; 26% Protestant. The average age of freshmen is 19; all under-

graduates; 25. Thirty-one percent drop out by the end of their first year; 50% remain to graduate.

Housing: A total of 216 students can be accommodated in college housing. College-sponsored living facilities include coed dormitories and on-campus apartments. On-campus housing is available on a first-come, first-served basis. Priority is given to out-of-town students. Eighty-six percent of students commute. Alcohol is not permitted. All students may keep cars on campus.

Activities: There are no fraternities or sororities on campus. There are 30 groups on campus, including chess, choir, drama, ethnic, honors, international, jazz band, literary magazine, musical theater, newspaper, photography, political, professional, radio and TV, religious, social, social service, student government, and yearbook. Popular campus events include Nee Wollah Ball, fall and spring formals, guest speakers on cultural events, jazz ensembles, and plays.

Sports: There are 12 intramural sports for men and 12 for women. Athletic and recreation facilities include a 1000-seat gymnasium, racquetball and tennis courts, a weight-training room, a swimming pool, and a multipurpose area.

Disabled Students: The entire campus is accessible to disabled students. The following facilities are available: wheelchair ramps, elevators, special parking, specially equipped rest rooms, and special class scheduling.

Services: In addition to many counseling and information services, tutoring is available in every subject. In addition, there is remedial math, reading, and writing.

Campus Safety and Security: Campus safety and security measures include 24-hour foot and vehicle patrol, self defense education, escort service, and informal discussions. In addition, there are pamphlets, posters, and films, emergency telephones, and lighted pathways and sidewalks.

Programs of Study: UST awards the B.A. and B.S. degrees. Master's and doctoral degrees also are awarded. Bachelor's degrees are awarded in BIOLOGICAL SCIENCE (biology/biological science), BUSINESS (accounting, business administration and management, management information systems, and marketing/retailing/merchandising), COMMUNICATIONS AND THE ARTS (communications, dramatic arts, English, fine arts, and music), COMPUTER AND PHYSICAL SCIENCE (chemistry and mathematics), EDUCATION (elementary and secondary), HEALTH PROFESSIONS (predentistry), SOCIAL SCIENCE (economics, history, international relations, philosophy, political science/government, prelaw, psychology, and religion). Accounting, biology, business administration, communications, education, and international studies are the strongest academically. Psychology, political science (prelaw), biology, and international studies have the largest enrollments.

Required: To graduate, students must complete a combined total of 24 hours of theology and philosophy, 12 hours of English, and 6 to 8 hours of a foreign language, and a minimum 126 credit hours, with 36 in the major. Also required are 6 hours each of history and/or humanities and social studies, 8 hours of laboratory science, and 3 hours of mathematics. Students must have a minimum 2.0 GPA.

Special: The university offers co-op programs in mathematics, preengineering, and business administration; cross-registration with the universities of Houston and Notre Dame, and Rice and Texas Southern universities; internships; and study abroad in more than 14 countries. The general studies and B.A.-B.S. degrees are available, and 3-2 engineering degrees with the universities of Notre Dame and Houston can be pursued. Nondegree study, dual majors, and a NASA Cooperative Program are available. There is a freshman honors program on campus, as well as 14 national honor societies. One department has an honors program.

Faculty/Classroom: Sixty-one percent of faculty are male; 39%, female. All teach undergraduates. No introductory courses are taught by graduate students. The average class size in an introductory lecture is 30; in a laboratory, 20; and in a regular course offering, 15.

Admissions: About 95% of the 1993–94 applicants were accepted. The SAT scores for the 1993–94 freshman class were as follows: Verbal—53% below 500, 36% between 500 and 599, and 11% between 600 and 700; Math—27% below 500, 49% between 500 and 599, 22% between 600 and 700, and 2% above 700. The ACT scores were 16% below 21, 22% between 21 and 23, 28% between 24 and 26, 9% between 27 and 28, and 25% above 28. There were 3 National Merit finalists. Five freshmen graduated first in their class.

Requirements: UST requires applicants to be in the upper 50% of their class. A minimum GPA of 2.0 is required. The SAT I or ACT is required, with a minimum composite score of 900 on the SAT I or 21 on the ACT. Applicants must be graduates of an accredited secondary school or have a GED certificate and have 16 academic credits, 4 years of English, 3 years of mathematics, 2 years each of foreign language, science, and social studies, and 1 year of history. AP and CLEP credits are accepted. Important factors used in the admissions decision are advanced placement or honor courses, evidence of special talent, recommendations by school officials, leadership record, and extracurricular activities record.

Procedure: Freshmen are admitted to all sessions. Entrance exams should be taken as early as possible. Application deadlines are open. Application fee is $25. Notification is sent on a rolling basis. There is a deferred admissions plan.

Transfer: About 240 transfer students enrolled in 1993–94. Transfer students must have a minimum 2.0 GPA. A total of 36 credits out of 126 must be completed at UST.

Visiting: There are regularly scheduled orientations for prospective students, including tours, special sessions for class registration, introductions to faculty and administrative members, and financial aid sessions. There are guides for informal visits and visitors may sit in on classes and stay overnight at the school. To arrange for a visit, contact an Admissions Counselor at (713) 522–7911, ext. 500.

Financial Aid: In 1993–94, 75% of all current freshmen and 65% of continuing students received some form of financial aid. About 60% of freshmen and 50% of continuing students received need-based aid. The average freshman award was $8000. Of that total, scholarships or need-based grants averaged $3000 ($11,660 maximum); loans averaged $2500 ($2600 maximum); and work contracts averaged $1850 ($5000 maximum). Twelve percent of undergraduate students work part-time. Average earnings from campus work for the school year are $2000. The average financial indebtedness of the 1992–93 graduate was $10,000. UST is a member of CSS. The college's own financial statement and the FAFSA and income tax forms are required. The deadline for financial aid applications is March 1.

International Students: There are currently 118 international students enrolled. The school actively recruits these students. They must take the TOEFL and achieve a minimum score of 550. The student must also take the SAT I or the ACT.

Computers: The university provides computer facilities for student use. The mainframe is a Prime 9755. There are more than 100 microcomputers located in the dormitory and throughout the campus. All students may access the system. There are no time limits on using the system and no fees.

Graduates: In 1992–93, 394 bachelor's degrees were awarded. The most popular majors among graduates were psychology (11%), elementary education (9%), and business administration (8%). Within an average freshman class, 1% graduate in 3 years, 22% in 4 years, 15% in 5 years, and 2% in 6 years. Some 5 companies recruited on campus in 1992–93.

Admissions Contact: Director of Admissions.

UNIVERSITY OF TEXAS SYSTEM

The University of Texas system, established in 1950, is a public system. It is governed by a board of regents, whose chief administrator is the chancellor. The primary goals of the system are to provide instruction, research, and public service throughout the state. The main priorities are undergraduate education, social and economic development of Texas, and professional training in and effective management of health care. The total enrollment usually approaches 150,000, with nearly 10,000 faculty members. Altogether, there are 388 baccalaureate, 309 master's, and 148 doctoral programs offered in the system. Four-year campuses are located in Arlington, Austin, El Paso, and San Antonio. Profiles of the 4-year campuses are included in this chapter in alphabetical order with other Texas schools.

UNIVERSITY OF TEXAS AT ARLINGTON   D-2
Arlington, TX 76019-0088   (817) 273-2119

Full-time: 5704 men, 5261 women	Faculty: 565; I, --$
Part-time: 4278 men, 4153 women	Ph.D.s: 55%
Graduate: 2502 men, 1851 women	Student/Faculty: 19 to 1
Year: semesters, summer session	Tuition: $1374 ($5454)
Application Deadline: August 1	Room & Board: $4175
Freshman Class: 2752 applied, 2411 accepted, 1474 enrolled	
SAT I Math: 486	LESS COMPETITIVE

The University of Texas at Arlington, founded in 1895, is part of the University of Texas System and is organized into colleges and schools covering business administration, engineering, liberal arts, science, architecture, nursing, social work, graduate studies, urban studies, and teacher education. There are 10 undergraduate schools and one graduate school. In addition to regional accreditation, UTA has baccalaureate program accreditation with AACSB, ABET, CSWE, NAAB, NASM, and NLN. The libraries subscribe to 5500 periodicals. Computerized library sources and services include the card catalog, interlibrary loans, and database searching. Special learning facilities include a learning resource center, art gallery, planetarium, radio station, and TV station. The 383-acre campus is in a suburban area 15 miles west of Dallas. Including residence halls, there are 46 buildings on campus.

Student Life: About 90% of undergraduates are from Texas. Students come from 45 states, 65 foreign countries, and Canada. Ninety-five percent are from public schools; 5% from private. Seventy-three percent are white. The average age of freshmen is 19; all undergrad-

uates, 26. Thirty-three percent drop out by the end of their first year; 30% remain to graduate.

Housing: A total of 2300 students can be accommodated in college housing. College-sponsored living facilities include coed dormitories, on-campus apartments, off-campus apartments, married-student housing, fraternity houses, and sorority houses. On-campus housing is available on a first-come, first-served basis. Seventy-five percent of students commute. Alcohol is not permitted. All students may keep cars on campus.

Activities: About 5% of men belong to 17 national fraternities; about 5% of women belong to 8 national sororities. There are 228 groups on campus, including art, band, cheerleading, chess, choir, chorale, chorus, computers, drama, drill team, drum and bugle corps, ethnic, gay, honors, international, jazz band, marching band, musical theater, newspaper, opera, orchestra, photography, political, professional, radio and TV, religious, social, social service, student government, and symphony. Popular campus events include art shows, Homecoming, International Week, Ethnic Week, Hispanic Week, and Panhellenic Week.

Sports: There are 6 intercollegiate sports for men and 7 for women, and 9 intramural sports for men and 7 for women. Athletic and recreation facilities include racquetball, handball, and volleyball courts, 16 lighted tennis courts, an inside track, 2 Olympic-size pools (1 indoors), a weight room, a 17,000-seat stadium, and a 3000-seat gymnasium.

Disabled Students: Eighty percent of the campus is accessible to disabled students. The following facilities are available: wheelchair ramps, elevators, special parking, specially equipped rest rooms, special class scheduling, and lowered drinking fountains.

Services: In addition to many counseling and information services, tutoring is available in most subjects, including English, mathematics, and computer science. In addition, there is a reader service for the blind, and remedial math, reading, and writing.

Campus Safety and Security: Campus safety and security measures include 24-hour foot and vehicle patrol, shuttle buses, pamphlets, posters, and films, and emergency telephones. In addition, there are lighted pathways and sidewalks.

Programs of Study: UTA awards the B.A., B.S., B.B.A., B.F.A., B.M., and B.S.W. degrees. Master's and doctoral degrees also are awarded. Bachelor's degrees are awarded in BIOLOGICAL SCIENCE (biochemistry, biology/biological science, microbiology, and physiology), BUSINESS (accounting, banking and finance, business administration and management, business economics, management science, marketing/retailing/merchandising, personnel management, and real estate), COMMUNICATIONS AND THE ARTS (advertising, art history and appreciation, broadcasting, communications, English, fine arts, French, German, journalism, music, public relations, Russian, Spanish, speech/debate/rhetoric, and studio art), COMPUTER AND PHYSICAL SCIENCE (chemistry, computer science, geology, information sciences and systems, mathematics, and physics), EDUCATION (art, elementary, health, music, physical, reading, science, secondary, and teaching English as a second language/foreign language), ENGINEERING AND ENVIRONMENTAL DESIGN (aeronautical engineering, architectural engineering, architecture, civil engineering, computer engineering, electrical/electronics engineering, industrial engineering technology, interior design, landscape architecture/design, and mechanical engineering), HEALTH PROFESSIONS (medical laboratory technology, nursing, predentistry, and premedicine), SOCIAL SCIENCE (anthropology, criminal justice, economics, history, interdisciplinary studies, liberal arts/general studies, philosophy, political science/government, prelaw, psychology, social work, sociology, and urban studies). Engineering, business, architecture, nursing, social work, music, and physical science are the strongest academically. Liberal arts, business, and engineering have the largest enrollments.

Required: All students must earn a GPA of 2.0 while taking at least 124 semester hours, including 30 in their major. Distribution requirements include 12 hours of English, 6 hours each of U.S. history and mathematics, 11 hours of laboratory science, and 3 hours each of fine arts, social science, U.S. government, and Texas government.

Special: Cooperative education programs provide opportunities to gain experience in local business through the colleges of engineering and business. Cross-registration with the Summer Institute of Linguistics and the University of Texas Health Science Center as well as with other members of the University of Texas System are available. Study abroad in China, England, France, Russia, and Mexico, work-study at the University, B.A.-B.S. degrees, dual majors, a general studies degree, credit for military experience, and pass/fail options are also offered. There is a freshman honors program on campus, as well as 25 national honor societies, including Phi Beta Kappa.

Faculty/Classroom: Eighty percent of faculty are male; 20%, female.

Admissions: About 88% of the 1993–94 applicants were accepted. There were 2 National Merit finalists and 3 semifinalists.

Requirements: The SAT I, with a minimum composite score of 700, 350 verbal and 350 mathematics, or the ACT, with a score of 18, is required. The GED is not accepted. Applicants must have 20 academic credits, including 4 units of English, 2 each in mathematics, science, foreign language, and social studies, and 1 in history. AP and CLEP credits are accepted. Important factors used in the admissions decision are leadership record, advanced placement or honor courses, recommendations by school officials, personality, intangible qualities, and extracurricular activities record.

Procedure: Freshmen are admitted to all sessions. Entrance exams should be taken during the fall of the senior year. Applications should be filed by August 1 for fall entry, December 1 for spring entry, and May 1 for summer entry. Notification is sent on a rolling basis. There are early decision and early admissions plans.

Transfer: About 8000 transfer students enrolled in a recent year. Transfer students need a 2.0 GPA. A total of 30 credits out of 124 must be completed at UTA.

Visiting: There are guides for informal visits. To arrange for a visit, contact the Admissions Office at (817) 273-3275.

Financial Aid: In a recent year, 30% of all current freshmen and 35% of continuing students received some form of financial aid. The average financial indebtedness of the 1992–93 graduate was $1500. UTA is a member of CSS. The FAF or FFS is required. The deadline for financial aid applications is June 1.

International Students: There are currently 1300 international students enrolled. They must take the TOEFL and achieve a minimum score of 550. The student must also take the SAT I.

Computers: The university provides computer facilities for student use. The mainframes are an IBM 4381, IBM 4341, and DEC VAX 8820. In addition, there are some 450 microcomputers available for academic use throughout the campus.

Graduates: In a recent year, 2745 bachelor's degrees were awarded. The most popular majors among graduates were business administration (23%), accounting (8%), and electrical engineering (5%). Within an average freshman class, 1% graduate in 3 years, 6% in 4 years, 19% in 5 years, and 26% in 6 years.

Admissions Contact: Glenn A. Read, Admissions Evaluator.

UNIVERSITY OF TEXAS AT AUSTIN
D-3
Austin, TX 78712 (512) 471-7601

Full-time: 15,770 men, 14,247 women	Faculty: 2161; I, av$
Part-time: 2739 men, 2450 women	Ph.D.s: 92%
Graduate: 7559 men, 5790 women	Student/Faculty: 14 to 1
Year: semesters, summer session	Tuition: $1460 ($4990)
Application Deadline: March 1	Room & Board: $3700
Freshman Class: 14,772 applied, 9572 accepted, 5329 enrolled	
SAT I Verbal/Math: 523/603	ACT: 25 **VERY COMPETITIVE**

The University of Texas at Austin, founded in 1883, is part of the University of Texas System and provides a wide range of programs through 11 undergraduate schools and colleges ranging from pharmacy to engineering. There are 14 graduate schools. In addition to regional accreditation, UT has baccalaureate program accreditation with AACSB, ABET, ACEJMC, ACPE, ADA, CSWE, NAAB, NASM, NCATE, and NLN. The 17 libraries contain 6.8 million volumes, 4.9 million microform items, and 91,167 audiovisual forms, and subscribe to 51,338 periodicals. Special learning facilities include an art gallery, natural history museum, radio station, McDonald Observatory, the University of Texas Marine Science Institute, Lyndon Baines Johnson Library and Museum, and a fusion reactor. The 350-acre campus is in an urban area near downtown Austin, just off the interstate. Including residence halls, there are 93 buildings on campus.

Student Life: About 91% of undergraduates are from Texas. Students come from 50 states, 111 foreign countries, and Canada. Sixty-seven percent are white; 12% Hispanic. The average age of freshmen is 18; all undergraduates, 21.5. Seventeen percent drop out by the end of their first year; 62% remain to graduate.

Housing: A total of 5315 students can be accommodated in college housing. College-sponsored living facilities include single-sex and coed dormitories, off-campus apartments, and married-student housing. In addition there are honors houses. On-campus housing is guaranteed for all 4 years. Eighty-nine percent of students commute. Alcohol is not permitted. All students may keep cars on campus.

Activities: About 14% of men belong to 28 national fraternities; about 14% of women belong to 15 national sororities. There are 650 groups on campus, including art, band, cheerleading, chess, choir, chorale, chorus, computers, dance, drama, ethnic, film, gay, honors, international, jazz band, literary magazine, marching band, musical theater, newspaper, opera, orchestra, pep band, photography, political, professional, radio and TV, religious, social, social service, student government, symphony, and yearbook. Popular campus events include Texas Roundup, Cinco de Mayo, Texas-Oklahoma Weekend, Texas Independence Day, Parents Weekend, Black History Month, and Honors Day.

Sports: There are 8 intercollegiate sports for men and 8 for women, and 30 intramural sports for men and 30 for women. Athletic and recreation facilities include a 77,809-seat football stadium, a 16,231-seat basketball center, a 2,000-seat volleyball arena, a 6,000-seat baseball stadium, a 3,000-seat Olympic swimming facility, 6 multipurpose indoor recreational/athletic facilities of various sizes available for basketball, volleyball, racquetball, swimming, weight training, and related activities, and 3 outdoor facilities covering nearly 40 acres available for tennis, basketball, racquetball, and various field sports.

Disabled Students: Ninety percent of the campus is accessible to disabled students. The following facilities are available: wheelchair ramps, elevators, special parking, specially equipped rest rooms, lowered drinking fountains, lowered telephones, specially equipped reading rooms, a speech and hearing center, academic accomodations specific to the student's disability, interpreters for the hearing impaired, and wheelchair maintenace and repair.

Services: In addition to many counseling and information services, tutoring is available in most subjects. In addition, there is a reader service for the blind, and remedial math, reading, and writing.

Campus Safety and Security: Campus safety and security measures include 24-hour foot and vehicle patrol, self defense education, escort service, and shuttle buses. In addition, there are informal discussions, pamphlets, posters, and films, emergency telephones, and lighted pathways and sidewalks. There is also a crime prevention unit and closed-circuit TV covering some park areas and offices.

Programs of Study: UT awards the B.A., B.S., B.Arch., B.B.A., B.F.A., B.M., B.J., and B.S.W. among more than 30 specific degrees. Master's and doctoral degrees also are awarded. Bachelor's degrees are awarded in BIOLOGICAL SCIENCE (biochemistry, biology/biological science, botany, microbiology, nutrition, and zoology), BUSINESS (accounting, business administration and management, international business management, management information systems, management science, and marketing/retailing/merchandising), COMMUNICATIONS AND THE ARTS (advertising, African languages, applied music, art history and appreciation, classics, communications, dance, design, dramatic arts, English, French, German, Greek, Hebrew, Italian, journalism, Latin, linguistics, music, music history and appreciation, music theory and composition, Portuguese, Russian, Scandinavian languages, Slavic languages, Spanish, speech/debate/rhetoric, studio art, and visual and performing arts), COMPUTER AND PHYSICAL SCIENCE (astronomy, chemistry, computer science, geology, mathematics, and physics), ENGINEERING AND ENVIRONMENTAL DESIGN (aeronautical engineering, architectural engineering, architecture, chemical engineering, civil engineering, electrical/electronics engineering, interior design, mechanical engineering, and petroleum/natural gas engineering), HEALTH PROFESSIONS (medical technology, nursing, and pharmacy), SOCIAL SCIENCE (African studies, American studies, anthropology, archeology, Asian/Oriental studies, child care/child and family studies, child psychology/development, community services, economics, ethnic studies, geography, history, home economics, humanities, Latin American studies, liberal arts/general studies, Middle Eastern studies, philosophy, physical fitness/movement, political science/government, psychology, Russian and Slavic studies, sociology, and textiles and clothing). Architecture, business, engineering, and liberal arts are the strongest academically. Liberal arts, business administration, and natural sciences have the largest enrollments.

Required: All students must maintin a GPA of 2.0 while satisfactorily completing 120 to 167 semester hours. Distribution requirements include 6 hours each in American government, American history, and science, 3 hours each in mathematics, social science, and humanities/fine arts, 2 semesters of foreign language, and 2 writing courses.

Special: Cooperative programs are available in all engineering courses, microbiology, chemistry, computer science, geology, and actuarial studies. Cross-registration is provided in pharmacy with the University of Texas at San Antonio. Internships, study abroad, B.A.-B.S. degrees in sciences and mathematics, dual majors in architecture, student-designed majors for humanities students, and pass/fail options are offered. There is a freshman honors program on campus, as well as 3 national honor societies, including Phi Beta Kappa. All departments have honors programs.

Faculty/Classroom: Seventy-two percent of faculty are male; 28%, female. All both teach and do research.

Admissions: About 65% of the 1993–94 applicants were accepted. The SAT scores for the 1993–94 freshman class were as follows: Verbal—39% below 500, 39% between 500 and 599, 19% between 600 and 700, and 3% above 700; Math—11% below 500, 36% between 500 and 599, 36% between 600 and 700, and 17% above 700. The ACT scores were 7% below 21, 21% between 21 and 23, 36% between 24 and 26, 15% between 27 and 28, and 20% above 28. About 2500 of the current freshmen were in the top 10% of their class; 83% were in the top 25%. There were 184 National Merit finalists.

Requirements: The SAT I or ACT is required. The minimum scores are determined by a scale balancing high school class rank and course work. For graduates of a nonaccredited high school, scores of 1100 in the SAT I and 27 in the ACT, plus 500 on the SAT II: Subject tests in writing, mathematics level I or II, and a third test are needed. In addition, applicants need 15 1/2 academic credits, including 4 in English, 3 each in mathematics and social studies, 2 each in science and foreign language, and 1 1/2 in electives. An essay is recommended for all, while an audition is required for applied music majors. The GED is accepted, with supportive information. AP and CLEP credits are accepted. Important factors used in the admissions decision are advanced placement or honor courses, leadership record, extracurricular activities record, recommendations by school officials, and geographic diversity.

Procedure: Freshmen are admitted to all sessions. Entrance exams should be taken early in the senior year. Early decision applications should be filed by February 1; regular applications, by March 1 for fall and summer entry, and October 1 for spring entry, along with an application fee of $35. Notification is sent on a rolling basis. There are early decision and deferred admissions plans.

Transfer: About 1900 transfer students enrolled in 1993–94. Transfer students must have 30 transferable hours and a transfer GPA of 3.0. A total of 30 credits out of 120 to 167 must be completed at UT.

Visiting: There are regularly scheduled orientations for prospective students. There are guides for informal visits and visitors may sit in on classes. To arrange for a visit, contact Office of Admissions, Freshman Admissions Center at (512) 471-7601.

Financial Aid: In 1993–94, 52% of all current freshmen and 55% of continuing students received some form of financial aid. About 30% of freshmen and 35% of continuing students received need-based aid. The average freshman award was $3500. Of that total, scholarships or need-based grants averaged $2100 ($5000 maximum); loans averaged $2400 ($3000 maximum); and work contracts averaged $1450 ($1800 maximum). Eighteen percent of undergraduate students work part-time. Average earnings from campus work for the school year are $1950. The average financial indebtedness of the 1992–93 graduate was $7000. UT is a member of CSS. The FAFSA financial statement is required. The deadline for financial aid applications is April 1.

International Students: There are currently 4024 international students enrolled. They must take the TOEFL and achieve a minimum score of 550. The student must also take the SAT I or the ACT and achieve a composite SAT I score of 1000 or ACT score of 28.

Computers: The university provides computer facilities for student use. The mainframes are a DEC 6000–430 operating in a cluster with 10 VAX 4000VLC workstations, a DEC 5820 Ultrix system, an Encore MultiMax system, a Sun SparcServer 10, an IBM 3081 KX48, and a cluster of 22 Sun SPARCstations. A Cray Y-MP 8/864 at the University of Texas System Center for High Performance Computing is also available for use by all UT System component institutions. Students have access to the mainframe computers through classes that require computer use, or through individually funded computer user numbers. A 200-seat microcomputer laboratory includes Macintosh and DOS-compatible microcomputers, and is available to all students. The 10 VAXstations and 10 of the SPARCstations are in a public facility for hands-on access, and are also available through remote log-in. Some 57 campus buildings, and thousands of computers and microcomputers, are on the campuswide network, which in turn provides access to the worldwide Internet. All students may access the system 24 hours a day. There are no time limits on using the system. The fees are $6 per semester hour.

Graduates: In 1992–93, 7708 bachelor's degrees were awarded. The most popular majors among graduates were liberal arts (34%), business (19%), and natural sciences (12%). Within an average freshman class, 2% graduate in 3 years, 31% in 4 years, 56% in 5 years, and 64% in 6 years.

Admissions Contact: Freshman Admissions Center.

UNIVERSITY OF TEXAS AT DALLAS   D-2
Richardson, TX 75083-0688   (214) 690-2341

Full-time: 1065 men, 991 women	Faculty: 205; I, -$
Part-time: 1260 men, 1410 women	Ph.D.s: 96%
Graduate: 2276 men, 1638 women	Student/Faculty: 10 to 1
Year: semesters, summer session	Tuition: $1222 ($4486)
Application Deadline: March 1	Room & Board: n/app
Freshman Class: 1089 applied, 780 accepted, 423 enrolled	
SAT I: 553/631	ACT: 27 VERY COMPETITIVE +

The University of Texas at Dallas, founded in 1969 as part of the University of Texas system, offers undergraduate programs in the liberal arts and sciences, business, and engineering. There are 8 undergraduate and 8 graduate schools. In addition to regional accreditation, UTD has baccalaureate program accreditation with ABET and ASLA. The library contains 454,488 volumes, 1,504,824 microform items, and 3314 audiovisual forms, and subscribes to 2745 periodicals.

Computerized library sources and services include the card catalog, interlibrary loans, and database searching. Special learning facilities include a learning resource center and the Callier Center for Communications Disorders. The 455-acre campus is in a suburban area 18 miles north of Dallas. There are 40 buildings on campus. There are no residence halls.

Student Life: About 97% of undergraduates are from Texas. Students come from 30 states, 33 foreign countries, and Canada. Seventy-nine percent are white. The average age of freshmen is 18; all undergraduates, 29.

Housing: There are no residence halls. College-sponsored housing is single-sex and coed. In addition there are privately owned campus apartments. All students may keep cars on campus.

Activities: There is 1 national fraternity and 1 national sorority. There are 45 groups on campus, including ethnic, honors, international, newspaper, professional, religious, social, and student government. Popular campus events include Messiah Sing, and Community July 4 Celebration.

Sports: There are 12 intramural sports for men and 12 for women. Athletic and recreation facilities include 4 racquetball courts, 3 squash courts, saunas, 10 lighted tennis courts, an outdoor basketball court, a sand volleyball court, a 1-mile gravel track, 4 soccer fields, and 2 softball fields.

Disabled Students: All of the campus is accessible to disabled students. The following facilities are available: wheelchair ramps, elevators, special parking, specially equipped rest rooms, and lowered drinking fountains.

Services: In addition to many counseling and information services, tutoring is available in some subjects, including calculus, linear algebra, computer science, operations research, statistics, writing, and production management. There is a reader service for the blind, and remedial math, reading, and writing.

Campus Safety and Security: Campus safety and security measures include 24-hour foot and vehicle patrol, escort service, informal discussions, and pamphlets, posters, and films. In addition, there are emergency telephones and lighted pathways and sidewalks.

Programs of Study: UTD awards the B.A., B.S., and B.S.E.E. degrees. Master's and doctoral degrees also are awarded. Bachelor's degrees are awarded in BIOLOGICAL SCIENCE (biology/biological science), BUSINESS (accounting and business administration and management), COMMUNICATIONS AND THE ARTS (literature and telecommunications), COMPUTER AND PHYSICAL SCIENCE (applied mathematics, chemistry, computer science, mathematics, physics, and statistics), ENGINEERING AND ENVIRONMENTAL DESIGN (electrical/electronics engineering), HEALTH PROFESSIONS (speech pathology/audiology), SOCIAL SCIENCE (American studies, economics, history, interdisciplinary studies, political science/government, psychology, public administration, and sociology). Business administration, interdisciplinary studies, psychology, accounting, computer science, and electrical engineering have the largest enrollments.

Required: To graduate, students must complete at least 120 credit hours, including 36 in the major and 60 in upper-division courses, with a minimum GPA of 2.0. Students must take 6 credits each in English, U.S./Texas government, and American history along with required core courses in rhetoric, mathematics, arts and humanities, ethics, laboratory science, and world civilization.

Special: Cross-registration is available with other University of Texas campuses. Accelerated degree programs and B.A.-B.S. degrees are offered in several majors, as is a 3–2 engineering degree with Austin College, Texas Women's University, or Abilene Christian University. Dual and student-designed majors are possible. There are 3 national honor societies on campus.

Faculty/Classroom: Eighty-nine percent of faculty are male; 11%, female. All teach and do research. No introductory courses are taught by graduate students.

Admissions: About 72% of the 1993–94 applicants were accepted.

Requirements: The SAT I or the ACT is required. Applicants should graduate in the upper 50% of their class at an accredited secondary school. AP and CLEP credits are accepted.

Procedure: Freshmen are admitted in the fall. Entrance exams should be taken at the end of the junior year or beginning of the senior year. Applications should be filed by March 1 for fall entry, along with an application fee of $15. Notification is sent on a rolling basis.

Transfer: About 4860 transfer students enrolled in 1993–94. Sophomore applicants must present a GPA of 3.0 and 12 credits in the general education core. Upper-division applicants should have a GPA of 2.3 (2.5 for engineering and computer science majors) with 19 credits in the general core and at least 54 lower-division credits.

Visiting: There are regularly scheduled orientations for prospective students, including meetings with faculty and an admissions counselor and a campus tour. There are guides for informal visits and visitors may sit in on classes. To arrange for a visit, contact the Office of Admissions at (214) 690-2341.

Financial Aid: In 1993–94 20% of all current freshmen and 21% of continuing students received some form of financial aid, including need-based aid. The average freshman award was $2163. Of that total, scholarships or need-based grants averaged $468 ($2300 maximum); loans averaged $1081 ($2000 maximum); and work contracts averaged $614 ($2600 maximum). Sixty-five percent of undergraduate students work part-time. Average earnings from campus work for the school year are $1412. UTD is a member of CSS. The FAF and the college's own financial statement is required. The deadline for financial aid applications is May 1.

International Students: There are currently 484 international students enrolled. They must take the TOEFL and achieve a minimum score of 550. The student must also take the SAT I or the ACT.

Computers: The college provides computer facilities for student use. The mainframe is a Convex 3220, an IBM 4381, and a SUN with a Novell server. Student facilities include 49 terminals, 123 Macintosh microcomputers, and 24 work stations. All students may access the system. It may be used 8 A.M. to 12 midnight in laboratories; 24 hours a day from remote locatons via modem. There are no time limits on using the system. The fees are $35 per semester.

Graduates: In 1992–93 1163 bachelor's degrees were awarded. The most popular majors among graduates were business administration (22%), interdisciplinary studies (18%), and accounting (12%). Some 215 companies recruited on campus in 1992–93.

Admissions Contact: Barry Samsula, Director of Admissions.

UNIVERSITY OF TEXAS AT EL PASO   A-3
El Paso, TX 79968   (915) 747-5576

Full-time: 9570 men and women	Faculty: 372; IIA, --$
Part-time: 4933 men and women	Ph.D.s: 90%
Graduate: 2498 men and women	Student/Faculty: 26 to 1
Year: semesters, summer session	Tuition: $1300 ($4550)
Application Deadline: May 1	Room: $1860
Freshman Class: 3000 applied, 2941 accepted, 2073 enrolled	
SAT I or ACT: required	**LESS COMPETITIVE**

The University of Texas at El Paso, founded in 1913 and the second oldest academic member of the University of Texas System, was originally called the Texas School of Mines and Metallurgy. It now offers a wide variety of classes through the schools and colleges of business, education, engineering, liberal arts, nursing and allied health, and science. There are 6 undergraduate schools and one graduate school. In addition to regional accreditation, UTEP has baccalaureate program accreditation with ABET. The library contains 797,180 volumes, 4000 microform items, and 2122 audiovisual forms, and subscribes to 4057 periodicals. Computerized library sources and services include the card catalog, interlibrary loans, and database searching. Special learning facilities include a learning resource center, an art gallery, a natural history museum, a radio station, a TV station, a seismic observatory, and the El Paso Centennial Museum. The 366-acre campus is in an urban area. Including residence halls, there are 76 buildings on campus.

Student Life: About 88% of undergraduates are from Texas. Students come from 50 states and 64 foreign countries. Ninety-five percent are from public schools; 5% from private. Fifty-nine percent are Hispanic; 28% white. The average age of freshmen is 19; all undergraduates, 24. Thirty-three percent drop out by the end of their first year.

Housing: A total of 870 students can be accommodated in college housing. College-sponsored living facilities include coed dormitories and on-campus apartments. On-campus housing is available on a first-come, first-served basis. Ninety-eight percent of students commute. Alcohol is not permitted. All students may keep cars on campus.

Activities: There are 100 groups on campus, including art, band, cheerleading, chess, choir, chorale, computers, dance, drama, drill team, drum and bugle corps, ethnic, film, honors, international, jazz band, literary magazine, marching band, musical theater, newspaper, opera, orchestra, pep band, photography, political, professional, radio and TV, religious, social, social service, student government, symphony, and yearbook. Popular campus events include Women's History, Hispanic Cultural Week, and St. Patrick's Engineering Initiation.

Sports: There are 6 intercollegiate sports for men and 5 for women, and a number of intramural sports for men and women. Athletic and recreation facilities include basketball, volleyball, badminton, racquetball, and tennis courts; grass fields for multiple use; an Outdoor Adventure Program with backpacking, bicycling, rafting, and ski trips; a 52,000-seat football stadium; a 12,222-seat basketball gymnasium; a swimming pool; a bowling alley; and a weight room.

Disabled Students: The following facilities are available: wheelchair ramps, elevators, special parking, specially equipped rest rooms, special class scheduling, and lowered drinking fountains.

Services: In addition to many counseling and information services, tutoring is available in every subject. In addition, there is a reader service for the blind, and remedial math, reading, and writing.

Campus Safety and Security: Campus safety and security measures include shuttle buses and lighted pathways and sidewalks.

Programs of Study: UTEP awards the B.A., B.S., B.B.A., B.F.A., B.I.S., B.M., B.S.C.E., B.S.Ed., B.S.E.E., B.S.I.E., B.S.MeT.E., B.S.N. and B.S.W. degrees. Master's and doctoral degrees also are awarded. Bachelor's degrees are awarded in BIOLOGICAL SCIENCE (biology/biological science, botany, microbiology, and zoology), BUSINESS (accounting, banking and finance, business administration and management, business economics, marketing/retailing/merchandising, and real estate), COMMUNICATIONS AND THE ARTS (communications, dance, dramatic arts, drawing, English, fine arts, French, graphic design, journalism, languages, metal/jewelry, music, painting, printmaking, sculpture, Spanish, and speech/debate/rhetoric), COMPUTER AND PHYSICAL SCIENCE (chemistry, computer science, geology, geophysics and seismology, mathematics, physics, and statistics), EDUCATION (art, early childhood, elementary, health, music, physical, and secondary), ENGINEERING AND ENVIRONMENTAL DESIGN (civil engineering, electrical/electronics engineering, industrial engineering technology, mechanical engineering, and metallurgical engineering), HEALTH PROFESSIONS (allied health, medical laboratory technology, and nursing), SOCIAL SCIENCE (anthropology, criminal justice, economics, history, Latin American studies, Mexican-American/Chicano studies, philosophy, political science/government, psychology, social work, and sociology). Business, nursing, and engineering are the strongest academically. Criminal justice, psychology, and biology have the largest enrollments.

Required: All students must have a minimum GPA of 2.0 while taking 125 to 130 semester hours. Students also must complete a distribution of courses through the general foundation program.

Special: Internships, mainly at the graduate level, study abroad in London and Hildesheim, Germany, work-study programs, nondegree study, and pass/fail options are available. There also is the Inter-American Sciences and Humanities Program for students from Spanish-speaking countries whose English is less than adequate for normal study in the United States. The Center for Inter-American and Border Studies also promotes teaching, research, and outreach programs to further the understanding of Latin America. Similar studies are offered through the Cross-Cultural Southwest Ethnic Study Center. There is a freshman honors program on campus

Faculty/Classroom: Seventy-eight percent of faculty are male; 22%, female. The average class size in an introductory lecture is 25; in a laboratory, 15; and in a regular course offering, 22.

Admissions: Almost all of the 1993–94 applicants were accepted.

Requirements: A minimum GPA of 2.0 is required. For citizens or permanent residents of the United States who have graduated within the past 5 years, the SAT I, with a score of 700 for those ranking in the second quarter of their class, or the ACT, with a score of 15, is required. UTEP recommends high school preparation that includes 4 years of English, 3 to 3.5 of mathematics, 3 each of natural science and social studies, and 2 of foreign language. The GED is accepted. AP and CLEP credits are accepted.

Procedure: Applications should be filed by May 1 for fall entry, October 1 for spring entry, and March 1 for summer entry. Notification is sent on a rolling basis. There is an early admissions plan.

Transfer: About 950 transfer students enrolled in a recent year. Transfer applicants must have at least a C average and must be eligible to return to all previous institutions attended. A total of 30 credits out of 125 must be completed at UTEP.

Visiting: There are regularly scheduled orientations for prospective students, including preenrollment counseling and campus tours. There are guides for informal visits and visitors may sit in on classes and stay overnight at the school. To arrange for a visit, contact Beto Lopez, Recruiting Office, at (915) 747–5430.

Financial Aid: In a recent year, 50% of all students received some form of financial aid. Seventy-five percent of undergraduate students work part-time. UTEP is a member of CSS. The FFS is required. The deadline for financial aid applications is April 1.

International Students: There are currently 1099 international students enrolled. The school actively recruits these students. They must take the TOEFL and achieve a minimum score of 500. The student must also take the SAT I or ACT, with the minimum score required depending on high school rank.

Computers: The college provides computer facilities for student use. The mainframe is an IBM 3270. Students use terminals to access the mainframe from various sites on campus. All computing facilities are interconnected by a campuswide data communication network. Those students enrolled in computer courses or with department permission may access the system. There are no time limits on using the system. The fees are $10.

Graduates: In a recent class, 1551 bachelor's degrees were awarded. The most popular majors among graduates were nursing (5%), criminal justice (4%), and accounting (4%). Some 542 companies recruited on campus in 1992–93.

Admissions Contact: Diana Guerrero, Director of Admissions.

UNIVERSITY OF TEXAS AT SAN ANTONIO D-4

San Antonio, TX 78249

(512) 691–4530; (800) 669–0919

Full-time: 4472 men, 4903 women	Faculty: 275; IIA, -$
Part-time: 2426 men, 3031 women	Ph.D.s: 99%
Graduate: 1093 men, 1172 women	Student/Faculty: 34 to 1
Year: semesters, summer session	Tuition: $1340 ($4604)
Application Deadline: July 1	Room & Board: $5080
Freshman Class: 3993 applied, 3106 accepted, 1656 enrolled	
SAT I Verbal/Math: 416/475	ACT: 20 COMPETITIVE

University of Texas at San Antonio was established as part of the state university system in 1969, and is now a large, comprehensive institution offering undergraduate programs in arts, business, engineering, music, health science, and education. There are 4 undergraduate and 15 graduate schools. In addition to regional accreditation, UTSA has baccalaureate program accreditation with AACSB, ABET, and NASM. The library contains 379,140 volumes and 381,788 microform items, and subscribes to 3716 periodicals. Computerized library sources and services include the card catalog, interlibrary loans, and database searching. Special learning facilities include a learning resource center, an art gallery, and the Institute of Texan Culture. The 600-acre campus is in a suburban area. Including residence halls, there are 18 buildings on campus.

Student Life: Almost all undergraduates are from Texas. Students come from 45 states, 60 foreign countries, and Canada. Eighty-four percent are from public schools. Fifty-seven percent are white; 35% Hispanic. The average age of freshmen is 18; all undergraduates, 25.4.

Housing: A total of 1500 students can be accommodated in college housing. College-sponsored living facilities include coed dormitories and on-campus apartments. On-campus housing is available on a first-come, first-served basis. Ninety-two percent of students commute. All students may keep cars on campus.

Activities: About 3% of men belong to 9 national fraternities; about 1% of women belong to 3 national sororities. There are 98 groups on campus, including art, band, cheerleading, chess, choir, chorale, chorus, computers, drama, ethnic, gay, honors, international, jazz band, newspaper, orchestra, pep band, political, professional, religious, social, social service, student government, symphony, and yearbook. Popular campus events include Fiesta UTSA, Best Fest, and Homecoming.

Sports: Athletic and recreation facilities include gymnasiums, weight machines, a jogging path and a 400-meter track, a tennis center, an indoor pool, various playing fields, and courts for basketball, volleyball, badminton, and shuffleboard.

Disabled Students: The entire campus is accessible to disabled students. The following facilities are available: wheelchair ramps, elevators, special parking, specially equipped rest rooms, special class scheduling, and lowered drinking fountains.

Services: In addition to many counseling and information services, tutoring is available in every subject. There is also a reader service for the blind, and remedial math; reading, and writing.

Campus Safety and Security: Campus safety and security measures include 24-hour foot and vehicle patrol, escort service, shuttle buses, and informal discussions. In addition, there are pamphlets, posters, and films, emergency telephones, and lighted pathways and sidewalks.

Programs of Study: UTSA awards the B.A., B.S., B.B.A, B.F.A, B.M., and B.M.E. degrees. Master's and doctoral degrees also are awarded. Bachelor's degrees are awarded in BIOLOGICAL SCIENCE (biology/biological science), BUSINESS (accounting, banking and finance, business economics, management information systems, management science, marketing/retailing/merchandising, and personnel management), COMMUNICATIONS AND THE ARTS (English, fine arts, French, German, music, and Spanish), COMPUTER AND PHYSICAL SCIENCE (chemistry, computer science, geology, mathematics, physics, and statistics), EDUCATION (early childhood, elementary, health, and physical), ENGINEERING AND ENVIRONMENTAL DESIGN (architectural engineering, civil engineering, electrical/electronics engineering, interior design, and mechanical engineering), HEALTH PROFESSIONS (medical laboratory technology, occupational therapy, and physical therapy), SOCIAL SCIENCE (American studies, anthropology, criminal justice, economics, geography, history, humanities, political science/government, psychology, and sociology). Business has the largest enrollment.

Required: All students must complete at least 120 credit hours with a 2.0 GPA for graduation. General education requirements total 42 credits, and include courses in fine arts, composition, computer science or logic, economics, foreign language, American and Texas history, social science, literacy studies, mathematics, U.S. and Texas constitutions, and natural science.

Special: UTSA offers cooperative programs in occupational therapy, physical therapy, and medical technology with the University of Texas Health Science Center, study abroad, and a B.A.-B.S. degree. In-

ternships and work-study, dual majors, nondegree study, and pass/fail options are available. There is a freshman honors program on campus, as well as 2 national honor societies. One department has an honors program.

Faculty/Classroom: Sixty-six percent of faculty are male; 34%, female. The average class size in a regular course offering is 29.

Admissions: About 78% of the 1993–94 applicants were accepted.

Requirements: Admission is based on a formula derived from class rank and SAT I or ACT scores. Applicants must be graduates of accredited high schools or have earned the GED. UTSA recommends that high school preparation include 4 units of English, at least 3 of mathematics, at least 2 each of a foreign language, natural science, and social science, and at least 1 of fine arts. AP and CLEP credits are accepted.

Procedure: Freshmen are admitted to all sessions. Entrance exams should be taken in the spring of the junior year. Applications should be filed by July 1 for fall entry, December 1 for spring entry, and May 1 for summer entry, along with an application fee of $20. Notification is sent on a rolling basis. There is an early admissions plan.

Transfer: A total of 1919 transfer students enrolled in 1993–94. Applicants with at least 30 hours of college credit must present a C average in all college work attempted and evidence of good standing. Those with fewer than 30 hours must meet freshman admission standards and present a C average in college work attempted. A total of 30 credits out of a minimum of 120 must be completed at UTSA.

Visiting: There are regularly scheduled orientations for prospective students. There are guides for informal visits and visitors may sit in on classes. To arrange for a visit, contact the Admissions and Registrar's Office at (512) 691–4530.

Financial Aid: In a recent year, 54% of all current freshmen and 60% of continuing students received some form of financial aid. About 51% of freshmen and 55% of continuing students received need-based aid. The average freshman award was $2578. Of that total, scholarships or need-based grants averaged $965 ($1550 maximum); loans averaged $1000 ($2625 maximum); and work contracts averaged $613 ($2031 maximum). Twenty-seven percent of undergraduate students work part-time. Average earnings from campus work for the school year are $1850. The average financial indebtedness of the 1992–93 graduate was $10,000. UTSA is a member of CSS. The college's own financial statement and the Singlefile Form are preferred. The deadline for financial aid applications is March 31.

International Students: There are currently 537 international students enrolled. The school actively recruits these students. They must take the TOEFL and achieve a minimum score of 550. The student must also take the SAT I or the ACT.

Computers: The university provides computer facilities for student use. The mainframe is an IBM 4341. A large computer laboratory is available with 200 IBM and Macintosh PCs used with a variety of software options. Specialty computer laboratories are also available, such as for engineering applications. The system may be used 24 hours a day. There are no time limits. The fees are $3 per semester hour.

Graduates: In a recent year, 1817 bachelor's degrees were awarded. Some 359 companies recruited on campus.

Admissions Contact: John H. Brown, Director of Admissions and Registrar.

UNIVERSITY OF TEXAS-PAN AMERICAN   D-5
Edinburg, TX 78539-2999   (210) 381-2209

Full-time: 3045 men, 3981 women	Faculty: IIA, --$
Part-time: 2399 men, 3339 women	Ph.D.s: n/av
Graduate: 337 men, 594 women	Student/Faculty: n/av
Year: semesters, summer session	Tuition: $1182 ($4446)
Application Deadline: August 7	Room & Board: $2010
Freshman Class: 4724 applied, 4724 accepted, 2118 enrolled	
ACT: 16	NONCOMPETITIVE

University of Texas-Pan American, founded in 1927, is a state-supported institution offering programs in the arts and sciences, education, business, and health-related professions. It is part of the University of Texas system. There are 3 graduate schools. In addition to regional accreditation, UT Pan American has baccalaureate program accreditation with AACSB, ADA, CAHEA, CSWE, NCATE, and NLN. The library contains 18,700 volumes and 106,000 microform items, and subscribes to 2800 periodicals. The 200-acre campus is in a small town close to the Mexican border and the Gulf of Mexico. Including residence halls, there are 23 buildings on campus.

Student Life: About 97% of undergraduates are from Texas.

Housing: A total of 380 students can be accommodated in college housing. College-sponsored living facilities include dormitories.

Activities: There are many groups on campus, including art, international, professional, religious, social, social service, and student government.

Sports: There are 5 intercollegiate sports for men and 4 for women and 7 intramural sports for women.

Services: In addition to many counseling and information services, tutoring is available in most subjects, including biology, chemistry, history, and Spanish. There is also remedial math, reading, and writing. The Learning Assistance Center provides small-group and individual tutoring and computer-aided instruction.

Campus Safety and Security: Campus safety and security measures include a university police department.

Programs of Study: UT Pan American awards the B.A., B.S., B.A.A.S., B.B.A., B.S.C.J., B.F.A., B.G.S., B.S.N., and B.S.W. degrees. Associate and master's degrees also are awarded. Bachelor's degrees are awarded in BUSINESS (accounting, banking and finance, business administration and management, business economics, management information systems, management science, and marketing/retailing/merchandising), COMMUNICATIONS AND THE ARTS (communications, English, fine arts, and Spanish), EDUCATION (elementary, health, and secondary), HEALTH PROFESSIONS (medical laboratory technology, nursing, and physical therapy), SOCIAL SCIENCE (dietetics, history, philosophy, physical fitness/movement, psychology, and sociology).

Required: To graduate, students must complete 124 semester hours with a 2.0 GPA. At least 30 hours are required in the major. Students must also fulfill a general education requirement of 60 hours by taking 24 hours in humanities (including English and a foreign language); 18 of social science (including U.S. history and Texas government), 8 of laboratory science, 4 of physical education, and 3 of computer science. Other requirements vary according to degree.

Special: Internships, co-op programs, work-study programs, and nondegree study are available. The American Humanics Program, a national program based on 15 university campuses, provides internships and career preparation for students interested in youth agency administration. There is a freshman honors program on campus, as well as 3 national honor societies.

Admissions: All of the 1993–94 applicants were accepted. The ACT scores for the 1993–94 freshman class were as follows: 90% below 21, 7% between 21 and 23, 2% between 24 and 26, 1% between 27 and 28, and 1% above 28. About 31% of the current freshmen were in the top quarter of their class; 67% were in the top half.

Requirements: A minimum GPA of 2.0 is required. The SAT I or ACT is required; the ACT is preferred. Applicants must be graduates of an accredited high school or have the GED. Twenty-one academic units are required, including 4 of English; 3 of mathematics, at least 1 of which must be algebra; 2 of science; 1 each in world history and U.S. history; and 1/2 unit each in U.S. government, economics, physical education, and health education. An additional 7 units may be taken in electives.

Procedure: Freshmen are admitted to all sessions. Applications should be filed by August 7 for fall entry, December 4 for spring entry, and April 23 for summer entry. The college accepts all applicants. Notification is sent on a rolling basis.

Transfer: Transfer applicants must meet the same criteria as entering freshmen.

Visiting: There are regularly scheduled orientations for prospective students. There are guides for informal visits and visitors may sit in on classes. To arrange for a visit, contact the Admissions Office at (210) 381-2209.

Financial Aid: The deadline for financial aid applications is May 1.

International Students: They must take the TOEFL and achieve a minimum score of 500.

Computers: The mainframe is a DEC VAX 10. All students may access the system.

Admissions Contact: David R. Zuniga, Director of Admissions and Registrar.

WAYLAND BAPTIST UNIVERSITY   B-2
Plainview, TX 79072   (806) 296-4709; (800) 999-1928 (in-state)

Full-time: 477 men, 507 women	Faculty: 46
Part-time: 1217 men, 687 women	Ph.D.s: 53%
Graduate: 75 men, 85 women	Student/Faculty: 21 to 1
Year: 4-1-4, summer session	Tuition: $4970
Application Deadline: open	Room & Board: $2841
Freshman Class: 243 applied, 243 accepted, 189 enrolled	
ACT: 20	NONCOMPETITIVE

Wayland Baptist University, founded in 1908, is a private liberal arts school affiliated with the Baptist General Convention of Texas (Southern Baptist). There is one graduate school. The library contains 96,122 volumes, 111,098 microform items, and 23,551 audiovisual forms, and subscribes to 522 periodicals. Computerized library sources and services include interlibrary loans. Special learning facilities include a learning resource center, a natural history museum, a radio station, and a TV station. The 80-acre campus is in a small town 45 miles north of Lubbock. Including residence halls, there are 41 buildings on campus.

Housing: A total of 548 students can be accommodated in college housing. College-sponsored living facilities include single-sex dormitories, on-campus apartments, off-campus apartments, and married-student housing. Alcohol is not permitted. All students may keep cars on campus.

Activities: There are no fraternities or sororities on campus. There are many groups and organizations on campus, including band, cheerleading, choir, chorale, chorus, computers, ethnic, honors, international, literary magazine, newspaper, photography, political, professional, radio and TV, religious, social, social service, student government, and yearbook. Popular campus events include Homecoming.

Sports: There are 4 intercollegiate sports each for men and women, and 6 intramural sports each for men and women. Athletic and recreation facilities include a 2500-seat gymnasium and basketball, racquetball, and tennis courts.

Disabled Students: The following facilities are available: wheelchair ramps, elevators, special parking, and special class scheduling.

Services: In addition to many counseling and information services, tutoring is available in every subject. There is remedial math, reading, and writing.

Campus Safety and Security: Campus safety and security measures include a security service on campus.

Programs of Study: Wayland awards the B.A., B.S., B.B.A., B.M., and B.S.O.E. degrees. Associate and master's degrees also are awarded. Bachelor's degrees are awarded in BIOLOGICAL SCIENCE (biology/biological science and life science), BUSINESS (business administration and management), COMMUNICATIONS AND THE ARTS (communications, dramatic arts, English, fine arts, and music), COMPUTER AND PHYSICAL SCIENCE (chemistry, mathematics, physics, and science), EDUCATION (music, physical, science, and vocational), ENGINEERING AND ENVIRONMENTAL DESIGN (industrial administration/management), HEALTH PROFESSIONS (predentistry and premedicine), SOCIAL SCIENCE (Christian studies, history, human services, interdisciplinary studies, philosophy, political science/government, psychology, religion, religious education, religious music, and social science). Biology, education, Bible, history, and psychology are the strongest programs academically. Education, business, and psychology have the largest enrollments.

Required: All students must earn a GPA of at least 2.0 while taking 124 semester hours, with 30 in their major and at least 42 in upper-level courses. Distribution requirements include 12 hours of English; 8 to 16 in science; 6 each in Bible study, history, and humanities; up to 6 in foreign language; 4 in physical education; 3 to 6 in mathematics; and 3 in computer science and sociology or psychology. Satisfactory scores on the GRE also are required. There is a chapel attendance requirement.

Special: A cooperative education program with Texas Tech University, internships in education and social work, and work-study plans through the Social Security Administration are available. In addition, credit for life experience and nondegree study in the lifelong learning program are offered. There is a freshman honors program on campus, as well as 3 national honor societies.

Faculty/Classroom: Seventy percent of faculty are male; 30%, female. The average class size in an introductory lecture is 25.

Admissions: All of the 1993–94 applicants were accepted.

Requirements: Wayland requires applicants to be in the upper 70% of their class. The SAT I or ACT is required. Wayland requires graduation from an accredited secondary school with 4 or fewer years in vocational courses, 3 of English, 2 each of mathematics and social science, and 1 of science for unconditional acceptance. The GED is accepted. AP and CLEP credits are accepted.

Procedure: Application deadlines are open. Application fee is $35. The college accepts all applicants. Notification is sent on a rolling basis.

Transfer: Transfer students need a minimum GPA of 2.0 and must be able to re-enter all colleges previously attended. A total of 30 credits out of 124 must be completed at Wayland.

Visiting: There are regularly scheduled orientations for prospective students. There are guides for informal visits and visitors may sit in on classes and stay overnight at the school. To arrange for a visit, contact D. Claude Lusk, Director of Admissions, at (806) 296–4709.

Financial Aid: In an earlier year, 68% of continuing students received some form of financial aid. Scholarships or need-based grants averaged $1567 ($2940 maximum); loans averaged $2651 ($4875 maximum); and work contracts averaged $1500 ($2500 maximum). The average financial indebtedness of an earlier graduate was $10,601. Wayland is a member of CSS. The FAF, FFS, or SFS is required. The deadline for financial aid applications is May 1.

International Students: There are currently 13 international students enrolled. The school actively recruits these students. They must take the University of Michigan Language Test and the ACT.

Computers: The university provides computer facilities for student use. Those students enrolled in computer courses may access the system.

Graduates: In an earlier class, 435 bachelor's degrees were awarded.

Admissions Contact: D. Claude Lusk, Director of Admissions.

WEST TEXAS A&M UNIVERSITY B-1
(Formerly West Texas State University)
Canyon, TX 79016   (806) 656–2020; (800) 99-WTAMU (out-of-state)

Full-time: 2294 men, 2476 women	**Faculty:** 207; IIA, --$
Part-time: 316 men, 323 women	**Ph.D.s:** 54%
Graduate: 456 men, 702 women	**Student/Faculty:** 23 to 1
Year: semesters, summer session	**Tuition:** $1224 ($4700)
Application Deadline: open	**Room & Board:** $3000
Freshman Class: 1673 applied, 1407 accepted, 1014 enrolled	
SAT I Verbal/Math: 450/426	**ACT:** 22 **COMPETITIVE**

West Texas A&M University, founded in 1909, is a public institution offering programs in the liberal arts and sciences, fine arts, agriculture, nursing, and education. There are 4 undergraduate and 4 graduate schools. In addition to regional accreditation, WTAMU has baccalaureate program accreditation with AACSB, CSWE, NASM, NCATE, and NLN. The library contains 270,610 volumes, 26,801 microform items, and 468 audiovisual forms, and subscribes to 244 periodicals. Computerized library sources and services include the card catalog, interlibrary loans, and database searching. Special learning facilities include a learning resource center, art gallery, natural history museum, radio station, and an alternative energy institute. The 135-acre campus is in a small town 17 miles south of Amarillo. Including residence halls, there are 42 buildings on campus.

Student Life: About 94% of undergraduates are from Texas. Students come from Canada. Eighty-nine percent are from public schools. Eighty-four percent are white. The average age of freshmen is 19; all undergraduates, 22. Thirty-three percent drop out by the end of their first year; 36% remain to graduate.

Housing: A total of 1800 students can be accommodated in college housing. College-sponsored living facilities include single-sex and coed dormitories. In addition there are special interest houses and sorority and fraternity units within the residence halls and areas with 24-hour quiet hours. On-campus housing is guaranteed for all 4 years. Sixty-five percent of students commute. Alcohol is not permitted. All students may keep cars on campus.

Activities: About 6% of men belong to 5 national fraternities; about 5% of women belong to 3 national sororities. There are 120 groups on campus, including art, band, cheerleading, choir, chorale, chorus, computers, dance, drama, ethnic, film, honors, international, jazz band, literary magazine, marching band, musical theater, newspaper, orchestra, political, professional, radio and TV, religious, social, social service, student government, and symphony. Popular campus events include the Bea and Boone Pickens Distinguished Lecture Series, Homecoming, Christmas Daze, Workathon, and the RHA Mud Pull.

Sports: There are 6 intercollegiate sports for men and 4 for women, and 20 intramural sports for men and 20 for women. Athletic and recreation facilities include an Olympic-size pool; handball, racquetball, tennis, basketball, and volleyball courts; 8-lane bowling alley; weight-training rooms; and a 20,000-seat stadium.

Disabled Students: The entire campus is accessible to disabled students. The following facilities are available: wheelchair ramps, elevators, special parking, specially equipped rest rooms, special class scheduling, lowered drinking fountains, and lowered telephones.

Services: In addition to many counseling and information services, tutoring is available in every subject. In addition, there is remedial math, reading, and writing.

Campus Safety and Security: Campus safety and security measures include 24-hour foot and vehicle patrol, self defense education, escort service, and shuttle buses. In addition, there are informal discussions, pamphlets, posters, and films, emergency telephones, and lighted pathways and sidewalks.

Programs of Study: WTAMU awards the B.A., B.S., B.A.A.S., B.B.A., B.B.E., B.F.A., B.M., B.M.E., B.S.M.T., B.S.N., and B.G.S. degrees. Master's degrees also are awarded. Bachelor's degrees are awarded in AGRICULTURE (agriculture, animal science, and plant science), BIOLOGICAL SCIENCE (biology/biological science), BUSINESS (accounting, banking and finance, business administration and management, business economics, management science, and marketing/retailing/merchandising), COMMUNICATIONS AND THE ARTS (broadcasting, dance, graphic design, journalism, music business management, music performance, Spanish, speech/debate/rhetoric, and studio art), COMPUTER AND PHYSICAL SCIENCE (chemistry, computer science, geology, mathematics, and physics), EDUCATION (art, business, elementary, health, music, physical, secondary, and social studies), ENGINEERING AND ENVIRONMENTAL DESIGN (construction management and engineering technology), HEALTH PROFESSIONS (biomedical science, music therapy, nursing, predentistry, and premedicine), SOCIAL SCIENCE (criminal justice, geography, history, political science/government, psychology, public administration, social science, social work, and sociology). Ed-

ucation, music, preprofessional programs, agriculture, and business are the strongest academically. Education has the largest enrollment.

Required: A general education requirement of 60 hours includes courses in analytic reasoning and communication skills, cultural heritage, English, science, history, political science, humanities, and physical education. Additional core requirements vary according to major. A 2.0 GPA and 130 credit hours are required to graduate.

Special: Work-study programs, internships, and credit by examination are available. Dual and student-designed majors, a general studies degree, nondegree study, and pass/fail options are offered. There are 16 national honor societies on campus. Thirteen departments have honors programs.

Faculty/Classroom: Ninety-seven percent of faculty teach undergraduates and 70% both teach and do research. Graduate students teach 12% of introductory courses. The average class size in a regular course offering is 26.

Admissions: About 84% of the 1993–94 applicants were accepted. About 30% of the current freshmen were in the top fifth of their class; 80% were in the top two fifths. About 20 freshmen graduated first in their class.

Requirements: The SAT I or ACT is required. Applicants should graduate from an accredited secondary school or have a GED. Admission requires graduation in the top 50% of the student's high school class or a minimum composite score of 20 on the ACT or 800 on the SAT I. AP and CLEP credits are accepted.

Procedure: Freshmen are admitted to all sessions. Entrance exams should be taken in the fall of the senior year. Application deadlines are open. Notification is sent on a rolling basis.

Transfer: About 820 transfer students enrolled in 1993–94. A 2.0 GPA is generally required for transfer students. A total of 30 credits out of 130 must be completed at WTAMU.

Visiting: There are regularly scheduled orientations for prospective students. There are guides for informal visits and visitors may sit in on classes and stay overnight at the school. To arrange for a visit, contact the Admissions Office at (806) 656–2020 or (800) 99-WTAMU (out-of-state).

Financial Aid: In a recent year, 25% of all students received some form of financial aid. About 20% of students received need-based aid. The average freshman award was $4000. Of that total, scholarships or need-based grants averaged $1800; loans averaged $1500; and work contracts averaged $700. Three percent of undergraduate students work part-time. Average earnings from campus work for the school year are $1800. The average financial indebtedness of a recent graduate was $12,000. The FFS and the Institutional Packet are required. The deadline for financial aid applications is June 30.

International Students: There are currently 185 international students enrolled. The school actively recruits these students. They must take the TOEFL and achieve a minimum score of 550. The student must also take the SAT I or the ACT.

Computers: The university provides computer facilities for student use. The mainframes are a 3 Prime computers. Some 500 microcomputers are available, in classrooms, residence halls, and laboratories. All students may access the system. There are no time limits on using the system. The fees are $27 per semester.

Graduates: In a recent year, 895 bachelor's degrees were awarded. Some 442 companies recruited on campus.

Admissions Contact: Lila Vars, Director of Admissions.

WEST TEXAS STATE UNIVERSITY
(See West Texas A&M University)

WILEY COLLEGE
Marshall, TX 75670

E-2
(214) 938–8341

Full-time: 160 men, 230 women	**Faculty:** 28
Part-time: 10 men, 10 women	**Ph.D.s:** 67%
Graduate: none	**Student/Faculty:** 14 to 1
Year: semesters, summer session	**Tuition:** n/av
Application Deadline: June 1	**Room & Board:** n/app
Freshman Class: n/av	
SAT I or ACT: recommended	**NONCOMPETITIVE**

Wiley College, founded in 1873 as a college for blacks, is affiliated with the United Methodist Church. The college offers programs in the liberal arts, sciences, and teacher training. The library contains 80,000 volumes, and subscribes to 298 periodicals. The 58-acre campus is in a small town 35 miles west of Shreveport.

Student Life: About 80% of undergraduates are from Texas.

Housing: College-sponsored living facilities include dormitories. Seventy-five percent of students live on campus.

Activities: There are 8 national fraternities and 8 national sororities.

Sports: There are 3 intercollegiate sports each for men and women, and 4 intramural sports each for men and women. There is a student union on campus.

Programs of Study: Wiley awards the B.A., B.S., and B.B.A. degrees. Bachelor's degrees are awarded in BIOLOGICAL SCIENCE (biology/biological science), BUSINESS (business administration and management, hotel/motel and restaurant management, and office supervision and management), COMMUNICATIONS AND THE ARTS (communications, English, music, and music performance), COMPUTER AND PHYSICAL SCIENCE (chemistry, computer science, mathematics, and physics), EDUCATION (business, elementary, English, mathematics, music, physical, secondary, social science, and special), SOCIAL SCIENCE (history, liberal arts/general studies, philosophy, religion, social science, and sociology).

Required: Core requirements include courses in education, English, humanities, history, religion, science, and mathematics. Two credits in physical education and 3 in computer science are required. A 2.0 GPA and 124 semester hours are needed to graduate.

Requirements: Applicants must be graduates of an accredited secondary school or have scored at least 40 on the GED. The SAT I or ACT is recommended. A letter of recommendation from a high school counselor or teacher is required.

Procedure: Applications should be filed by June 1 for fall entry, December 10 for spring entry, and May 10 for summer entry, along with an application fee of $10. There is an early admissions plan.

Transfer: Transfer applicants must be in good standing at their last college. A total of 30 credits out of 124 must be completed at Wiley.

International Students: They must take the TOEFL and achieve a minimum score of 400.

Computers: The college provides computer facilities for student use. The mainframes are an IBM System 36 and a DEC Dolphin. All students may access the system.

Admissions Contact: Dr. Warren Hawkins, Director of Institutional Research.

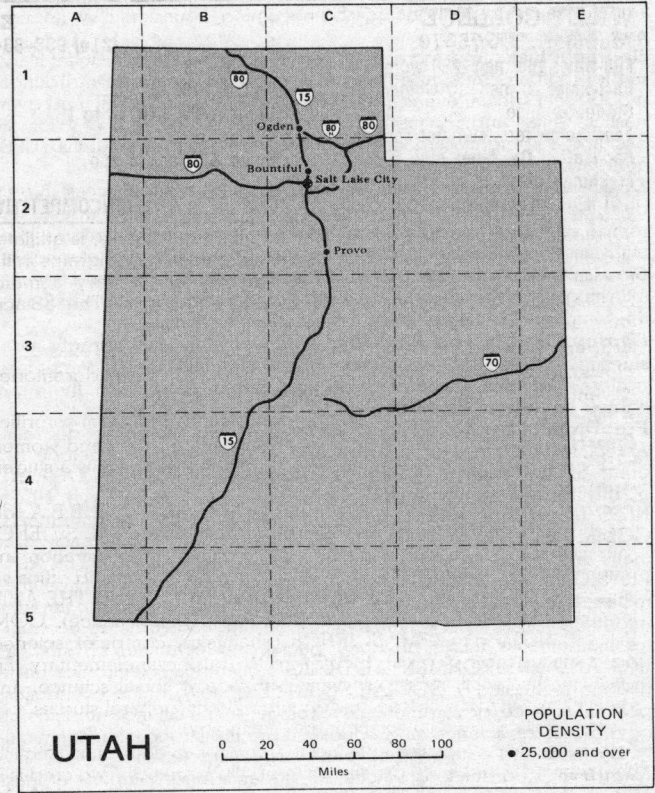

UTAH

POPULATION
DENSITY
● 25,000 and over

0 20 40 60 80 100
Miles

BRIGHAM YOUNG UNIVERSITY
Provo, UT 84602

C-2

(801) 378-2507

Full-time: 13,062 men, 13,316 women	Faculty: 1335
Part-time: 616 men, 637 women	Ph.D.s: 77%
Graduate: 1833 men, 1083 women	Student/Faculty: 20 to 1
Year: 4-4-2-2	Tuition: $2200
Application Deadline: February 15	Room & Board: $3425
Freshman Class: 7316 applied, 5152 accepted, 4298 enrolled	
ACT: 27	**HIGHLY COMPETITIVE**

Brigham Young University, founded in 1875, is a private, coeducational university affiliated with the Church of Jesus Christ of Latter-Day Saints. There are 12 undergraduate and 5 graduate schools. In addition to regional accreditation, Brigham Young has baccalaureate program accreditation with AACSB, ABET, ACEJMC, ADA, ASLA, CSWE, NASM, and NCATE. The 3 libraries contain 2,278,729 volumes, 1,003,710 microform items, and 45,703 audiovisual forms, and subscribe to 18,048 periodicals. Computerized library sources and services include the card catalog, interlibrary loans, and database searching. Special learning facilities include a learning resource center, an art gallery, a natural history museum, a planetarium, a radio station, a TV station, an archaeological museum, an earth science museum, reading and writing laboratories, and mathematics and computer laboratories. The 638-acre campus is in a suburban area 45 miles south of Salt Lake City. Including residence halls, there are 481 buildings on campus.

Student Life: About 70% of undergraduates are from out-of-state, mostly the West. Students come from 51 states, 110 foreign countries, and Canada. Eighty-six percent are white. Most are Protestant. The average age of freshmen is 19; all undergraduates, 25. Twenty percent drop out by the end of their first year; 44% remain to graduate.

Housing: A total of 6281 students can be accommodated in college housing. College-sponsored living facilities include single-sex dormitories, on-campus apartments, and married-student housing. In addition, there are honors houses and language houses. On-campus housing is available on a first-come, first-served basis. Alcohol is not permitted. All students may keep cars on campus.

Activities: There are no fraternities or sororities on campus. There are 225 groups on campus, including art band, cheerleading, chess, choir, chorus, computers, dance, drama, drill team, ethnic, film, honors, international, jazz band, literary magazine, marching band, musical theater, newspaper, opera, orchestra, pep band, photography, political, professional, radio and TV, religious, social, social service,

student government, and symphony. Popular campus events include Club Week, Homecoming, Preference, Fine Arts Ball, New Student Orientation, and Y-Days.

Sports: There are 10 intercollegiate sports for men and 9 for women, and 30 intramural sports each for men and women. Athletic and recreation facilities include pools, tennis courts, racquetball courts, gymnasiums, tracks, fields, and weight rooms.

Disabled Students: Most of the campus is accessible to disabled students. The following facilities are available: wheelchair ramps, elevators, special parking, specially equipped rest rooms, special class scheduling, and lowered drinking fountains and telephones.

Services: In addition to many counseling and information services, tutoring is available in most subjects. There is also a reader service for the blind, and remedial math, reading, and writing.

Campus Safety and Security: Campus safety and security measures include 24-hour foot and vehicle patrol, self defense education, informal discussions, pamphlets, posters, and films. In addition, there are emergency telephones and lighted pathways and sidewalks.

Programs of Study: Brigham Young awards the B.A., B.S., B.F.A., B.Mus., and B.Independent Studies degrees. Associate, master's, and doctoral degrees also are awarded. Bachelor's degrees are awarded in AGRICULTURE (agricultural economics, agriculture, animal science, horticulture, natural resource management, and wildlife management), BIOLOGICAL SCIENCE (biochemistry, biology/biological science, botany, entomology, microbiology, nutrition, and zoology), BUSINESS (accounting, banking and finance, business administration and management, fashion merchandising, human resources, management information systems, sports management, and tourism), COMMUNICATIONS AND THE ARTS (advertising, art history and appreciation, broadcasting, Chinese, communications, comparative literature, dance, design, dramatic arts, English, film arts, fine arts, French, German, graphic design, Greek, illustration, industrial design, Italian, Japanese, journalism, Korean, Latin, linguistics, music, painting, performing arts, photography, Portuguese, printmaking, public relations, Russian, sculpture, Spanish, and speech/debate/rhetoric), COMPUTER AND PHYSICAL SCIENCE (chemistry, computer science, geology, mathematics, physics, and statistics), EDUCATION (art, business, early childhood, elementary, foreign languages, home economics, industrial arts, middle school, music, physical, science, secondary, special, and teaching English as a second language/foreign language), ENGINEERING AND ENVIRONMENTAL DESIGN (cartography, ceramic science, chemical engineering, civil engineering, computer engineering, construction management, electrical/electronics engineering, electrical/electronics engineering technology, engineering, engineering technology, geological engineering, industrial administration/management, interior design, manufacturing technology, and mechanical engineering), HEALTH PROFESSIONS (health science, medical laboratory technology, nursing, and speech pathology/audiology), SOCIAL SCIENCE (American studies, anthropology, Asian/Oriental studies, Canadian studies, clothing and textiles management/production/services, community services, dietetics, economics, European studies, family/consumer studies, fashion design and technology, food science, geography, history, human development, humanities, international relations, Latin American studies, Near Eastern studies, philosophy, political science/government, psychology, public affairs, social work, and sociology). Engineering, accounting, business, and languages are the strongest programs academically. Business, elementary education, communications, and English have the largest enrollments.

Required: To graduate, students must complete 128 semester hours. All students must take a total of 14 semester hours of religion and 2 hours of physical education. There are general education requirements in English, advanced writing, foreign language or mathematics, arts and letters, natural sciences, and social sciences.

Special: The college offers cooperative programs, internships, study abroad in 8 countries, and a Washington semester. B.A.-B.S. degrees, dual majors, student-designed majors, nondegree study, and credit for life and work experience are available. There is a freshman honors program on campus. All departments have honors programs.

Faculty/Classroom: Eighty-three percent of faculty are male; 17%, female. The average class size in an introductory lecture is 45; in a laboratory, 17; and in a regular course offering, 41.

Admissions: About 70% of the 1993–94 applicants were accepted. The ACT scores for the freshman class were as follows: 3% below 21, 10% between 21 and 23, 26% between 24 and 26, 21% between 27 and 28, and 39% above 28. About 81% of the current freshmen were in the top fifth of their class; 96% were in the top two fifths. There were 110 National Merit finalists.

Requirements: The ACT is required. Applicants must be graduates of an accredited secondary school. The GED is accepted. The school recommends that applicants complete 4 years of English, 2 of mathe-

matics beyond algebra, and courses in foreign language, science, history, and social studies. Essays and letters of recommendation are required with the application. AP and CLEP credits are accepted. Important factors used in the admissions decision are advanced placement or honor courses, recommendations by school officials, evidence of special talent, extracurricular activities record, and geographic diversity.

Procedure: Freshmen are admitted to all sessions. Entrance exams should be taken by December of the senior year. Applications should be filed by February 15 for fall entry, November 1 for winter entry, February 15 for spring entry, and February 15 for summer entry, along with an application fee of $25. Notification is sent on a rolling basis. There is an early admissions plan.

Transfer: About 1200 transfer students enrolled in 1993–94. For transfer applicants, primary consideration for admission will be given to basic general education subjects (English, mathematics, history, and foreign languages) and major subjects. The GPA from those subjects must be near 3.0 to be competitive for admission. A total of 30 credits out of 128 must be completed at Brigham Young.

Visiting: There are regularly scheduled orientations for prospective students, including a campus tour, visits with department advisement center for prospective major, an interview with preadmissions counselor, and a campus dance or other weekend activity (including football games). There are guides for informal visits, and visitors may sit in on classes. To arrange for a visit, contact Markay Brown at (801) 378-4431.

Financial Aid: In 1993–94, 65% of all current freshmen and 45% of continuing students received some form of financial aid. About 35% of freshmen and 45% of continuing students received need-based aid. The average freshman award was $3550. Of that total, scholarships or need-based grants averaged $1400 ($2700 maximum); and loans averaged $500 ($2625 maximum). The average financial indebtedness of the 1992–93 graduate was $3500. Brigham Young is a member of CSS. The FFS is required. The deadline for financial aid applications is March 1.

International Students: There are currently 1668 international students enrolled. The school actively recruits these students. They must take the TOEFL and achieve a minimum score of 500. The student must also take the ACT.

Computers: The college provides computer facilities for student use. The mainframe is an IBM 3090. Microcomputers are available in departments and computer laboratories throughout the campus. Those who have an account on the system may access it anytime. There are no time limits on using the system.

Graduates: In 1992–93, 5802 bachelor's degrees were awarded. The most popular majors among graduates were communications (6%), English (6%), and elementary education (6%). Within an average freshman class, 53% graduate in 6 years. Some 450 companies recruited on campus in an earlier year.

Admissions Contact: Jeffery M. Tanner, Admissions Office.

SOUTHERN UTAH UNIVERSITY   B-4
Cedar City, UT 84720   **(801) 586-7740**

Full-time: 1604 men, 1828 women	Faculty: 157; IIB, --$
Part-time: 228 men, 388 women	Ph.D.s: 65%
Graduate: 6 men, 5 women	Student/Faculty: 22 to 1
Year: quarters, summer session	Tuition: $1599 ($4740)
Application Deadline: July 1	Room & Board: $2505
Freshman Class: 1685 applied, 1649 accepted, 856 enrolled	
ACT: 21	**LESS COMPETITIVE**

Southern Utah University, founded in 1897, is part of the Utah System of Higher Education. The university offers undergraduate degrees in arts and letters, science, education, and business. There are 4 undergraduate and 2 graduate schools. The library contains 195,324 volumes, 549,046 microform items, and 15,677 audiovisual forms, and subscribes to 1191 periodicals. Special learning facilities include a learning resource center, an art gallery, a natural history museum, a planetarium, a radio station, and a TV station. The 113-acre campus is in a rural area 170 miles north of Las Vegas, Nevada. Including residence halls, there are 62 buildings on campus.

Student Life: About 95% of undergraduates are from Utah. Students come from 20 states, 5 foreign countries, and Canada. Ninety-eight percent are from public schools; 2% from private. Ninety-five percent are white. The average age of freshmen is 19; all undergraduates, 23. Forty percent drop out by the end of their first year; 60% remain to graduate.

Housing: A total of 660 students can be accommodated in college housing. College-sponsored living facilities include dormitories, on-campus apartments, married-student housing, and fraternity houses. On-campus housing is guaranteed for all 4 years. Alcohol is not permitted. All students may keep cars on campus.

Activities: About 3% of men belong to 2 national fraternities; about 3% of women belong to 1 local sorority. There are 45 groups on campus, including art, bagpipe band, band, cheerleading, choir, chorale,

chorus, computers, dance, drama, drill team, ethnic, film, honors, international, jazz band, marching band, musical theater, newspaper, opera, orchestra, pep band, political, professional, radio and TV, religious, social, social service, student government, and symphony. Popular campus events include Homecoming, Founders Day, dances, and service programs.

Sports: Athletic and recreation facilities include a 10,000-seat stadium for football, track, and field; a baseball field; recreation grounds; a 5300-seat special events facility for basketball, volleyball, and gymnastics; tennis and racquetball courts; large, all-weather practice areas; and a skiing classroom. The college owns and operates a 1000-acre farm and a 3700-acre ranch.

Disabled Students: Ninety percent of the campus is accessible to disabled students. The following facilities are available: wheelchair ramps, elevators, special parking, specially equipped rest rooms, special class scheduling, and lowered drinking fountains and telephones.

Services: In addition to many counseling and information services, tutoring is available in most subjects. There is also a reader service for the blind, and remedial math, reading, and writing.

Campus Safety and Security: Campus safety and security measures include self-defense education, informal discussions, pamphlets, posters, and films, and emergency telephones. In addition, there are lighted pathways and sidewalks.

Programs of Study: SUU awards the B.A., B.S., and B.I.S. degrees. Associate and master's degrees also are awarded. Bachelor's degrees are awarded in AGRICULTURE (agriculture), BIOLOGICAL SCIENCE (biology/biological science, botany, and zoology), BUSINESS (accounting and business administration and management), COMMUNICATIONS AND THE ARTS (communications, dance, dramatic arts, English, German, music, and Spanish), COMPUTER AND PHYSICAL SCIENCE (chemistry, computer science, geology, mathematics, and physical sciences), EDUCATION (art, business/computer information systems, elementary, foreign languages, home economics, mathematics, music, physical, special, and technical), ENGINEERING AND ENVIRONMENTAL DESIGN (electrical/electronics engineering technology), SOCIAL SCIENCE (history, home economics, political science/government, psychology, social science, and sociology). Business, science, and education are the strongest academically. Business and education have the largest enrollments.

Required: In order to graduate, all students must complete at least 183 credit hours, with 45 to 70 in the major, and a minimum 2.0 GPA. Students must satisfy general education, major and minor, and basic skills requirements, including 4 courses each in social and physical sciences, 2 each in English, fine arts, and humanities, 1 each in mathematics, physical education, and communications, and introductory courses in either history, political science, or economics.

Special: The college offers co-op programs with Weber State University, work-study programs, and internships with government officials in Washington, D.C. There is a chapter of Phi Beta Kappa on campus.

Faculty/Classroom: Seventy percent of faculty are male; 30%, female. All teach undergraduates and 65% do research. No introductory courses are taught by graduate students. The average class size in an introductory lecture and regular course offering is 25; in a laboratory, 20.

Admissions: About 98% of the 1993–94 applicants were accepted.

Requirements: A minimum GPA of 2.0 is required. The SAT I or ACT is required. In addition, applicants should be graduates of an accredited secondary school or have a GED certificate, and have completed the following: 4 years each of English and electives, 3 of mathematics, and 2 each of biological/physical sciences and social studies. AP and CLEP credits are accepted.

Procedure: Freshmen are admitted to all sessions. Applications should be filed by July 1 for fall entry, December 1 for winter entry, and March 1 for spring entry, along with an application fee of $25. Notification is sent on a rolling basis. There is an early admissions plan.

Transfer: About 600 transfer students enrolled in an earlier class. Transfer students must submit transcripts from previously attended colleges or universities and have a minimum 2.3 GPA. ACT scores are required from students who have not completed English or mathematics courses at another institution or who have not completed a minimum of 45 credit hours at an institution of higher education. A total of 30 quarter credits out of 183 must be completed at SUU.

Visiting: There are regularly scheduled orientations for prospective students, including campus tours, which can be arranged by appointment. There are guides for informal visits and visitors may sit in on classes and stay overnight at the school. To arrange for a visit, contact Jake Shewmake, Coordinator of School Relations, at (801) 586-7740.

Financial Aid: In 1993–94, 68% of all current freshmen and 61% of continuing students received some form of financial aid. About 38% of freshmen and 48% of continuing students received need-based aid. The average freshman award was $2906. Of that total, scholarships or need-based grants averaged $1949 ($5000 maximum); loans averaged $2420 ($4090 maximum); and work contracts averaged $1800 ($2000 maximum). Fifty-seven percent of under-

graduate students work part-time. Average earnings from campus work for the school year are $1293. SUU is a member of CSS. The FAF, FFS, or SFS is required.

International Students: There are currently 35 international students enrolled. The school actively recruits these students. They must take the TOEFL and achieve a minimum score of 500. The student must also take the SAT I or the ACT.

Computers: The college provides computer facilities for student use. The mainframe is a DEC VAX 6420. All students may access the system. There are no time limits on using the system. The fees are $10 per quarter.

Graduates: In 1992–93, 531 bachelor's degrees were awarded. The most popular majors among graduates were elementary education (21%), business administration (10%), and accounting (9%). Some 29 companies recruited on campus in 1992–93. In the 1992 graduating class, 13% of all students were enrolled in graduate school within 6 months of graduation; 78% had found employment.

Admissions Contact: Marlynn Smith, Admissions Office.

UNIVERSITY OF UTAH

Salt Lake City, UT 84112   C-2
      (801) 581-7281

Full-time: 7801 men, 6040 women	Faculty: 1463; I, --$
Part-time: 4073 men, 3278 women	Ph.D.s: 95%
Graduate: 2883 men, 1907 women	Student/Faculty: 9 to 1
Year: quarters, summer session	Tuition: $2298 ($6795)
Application Deadline: July 1	Room & Board: $3677

Freshman Class: 4856 applied, 4353 accepted, 2394 enrolled
SAT I Verbal/Math: 480/550   ACT: 23   **COMPETITIVE**

The University of Utah, founded in 1850, is a part of the Utah System of Higher Education. The university offers undergraduate degrees in architecture, business, education, engineering, fine arts, health, humanities, nursing, medicine, mines and earth sciences, pharmacy, science, and social and behavioral science. There are 13 undergraduate and 14 graduate schools. In addition to regional accreditation, the university has baccalaureate program accreditation with AACSB, ABET, ACPE, ADA, APTA, ASLA, CSWE, NAAB, NASM, NCATE, NLN, and NRPA. The 3 libraries contain 2,277,387 volumes, 3,096,495 microform items, and 39,674 audiovisual forms, and subscribe to 20,500 periodicals. Computerized library sources and services include the card catalog, interlibrary loans, and database searching. Special learning facilities include a learning resource center, an art gallery, a natural history museum, a radio station, a TV station, and an arboretum. The 1535-acre campus is in Salt Lake City. Including residence halls, there are 280 buildings on campus.

Student Life: About 92% of undergraduates are from Utah. Students come from 50 states, 99 foreign countries, and Canada. Ninety-five percent are from public schools; 5% from private. Eighty-seven percent are white. Forty-seven percent belong to the Church of Jesus Christ of Latter-day Saints; 21% claim no religious affiliation; 10% are Catholic. The average age of freshmen is 19; all undergraduates, 24.8. Thirty-eight percent drop out by the end of their first year; 44% remain to graduate.

Housing: A total of 2300 students can be accommodated in college housing. College-sponsored living facilities include single-sex dormitories, on-campus apartments, off-campus apartments, married-student housing, fraternity houses, and sorority houses. In addition, there are honors houses and special interest houses. On-campus housing is available on a first-come, first-served basis. Ninety-four percent of students commute. Alcohol is not permitted. All students may keep cars on campus.

Activities: About 7% of men belong to 12 national fraternities; about 6% of women belong to 7 national sororities. There are 250 groups on campus, including art, band, cheerleading, chess, choir, chorale, chorus, computers, dance, drama, drill team, drum and bugle corps, ethnic, film, gay, honors, international, jazz band, marching band, musical theater, newspaper, orchestra, pep band, photography, political, professional, radio and TV, religious, social, social service, student government, and symphony. Popular campus events include Mayfest and Autumn Openings.

Sports: There are 10 intercollegiate sports each for men and women, and 68 intramural sports for men and 61 for women. Athletic and recreation facilities include a 35,000-seat stadium, a 15,500-seat basketball arena, 6 indoor gymnasiums, 13 indoor and 22 outdoor tennis courts, 3 indoor swimming pools, a gymnastics room, 5 weight rooms, 19 handball/racquetball/squash courts, a 9-hole golf course, 3 outdoor playing fields, a 10-lane bowling alley, a movie theater, video games, and a big-screen TV.

Disabled Students: Ninety percent of the campus is accessible to disabled students. The following facilities are available: wheelchair ramps, elevators, special parking, specially equipped rest rooms, special class scheduling, and lowered drinking fountains and telephones.

Services: In addition to many counseling and information services, tutoring is available in most subjects. There is also a reader service for the blind and remedial math and writing.

Campus Safety and Security: Campus safety and security measures include 24-hour foot and vehicle patrol, self-defense education, escort service, and shuttle buses. In addition, there are informal discussions, pamphlets, posters, films, emergency telephones, and lighted pathways and sidewalks.

Programs of Study: The university awards the B.A., B.S., B.F.A., and B.U.S. degrees. Master's and doctoral degrees also are awarded. Bachelor's degrees are awarded in BIOLOGICAL SCIENCE (biology/biological science), BUSINESS (accounting, banking and finance, management science, marketing/retailing/merchandising, and recreation and leisure services), COMMUNICATIONS AND THE ARTS (art history and appreciation, classics, communications, dance, dramatic arts, English, film arts, French, German, linguistics, music, Russian, Spanish, and speech/debate/rhetoric), COMPUTER AND PHYSICAL SCIENCE (atmospheric sciences and meteorology, chemistry, computer science, geology, geophysics and seismology, mathematics, and physics), EDUCATION (art, early childhood, elementary, health, home economics, and special), ENGINEERING AND ENVIRONMENTAL DESIGN (chemical engineering, civil engineering, computer engineering, electrical/electronics engineering, geological engineering, materials engineering, mechanical engineering, metallurgical engineering, mining and mineral engineering, and urban planning technology), HEALTH PROFESSIONS (medical laboratory technology, nursing, pharmacy, physical therapy, and speech pathology/audiology), SOCIAL SCIENCE (anthropology, child care/child and family studies, economics, family/consumer studies, geography, history, Middle Eastern studies, philosophy, physical fitness/movement, political science/government, psychology, social science, and sociology).

Required: To graduate, all students must satisfy requirements in the Liberal Education program, writing proficiency, and American Institutions. The core curriculum consists of 1 course each in 3 of the following 4 areas: science, humanities, fine arts, and social/behavioral science. Distribution requirements include 2 courses in each of 3 of the following 4 areas, excluding the major area: science, humanities, fine arts, and social science. Students must complete at least 183 credit hours, with 45 to 60 in the major. A minimum 2.0 GPA is required.

Special: The university offers numerous opportunities for cooperative programs, cross-registration, study abroad, internships, work-study and accelerated degree programs, and B.A.-B.S. degrees. Also available are a general studies degree, a Washington semester, student-designed and dual majors, credit for telecourses and military experience, nondegree study, and pass/fail options. There is a freshman honors program on campus as well as 32 national honor societies, including Phi Beta Kappa. One department has an honors program.

Faculty/Classroom: Eighty percent of faculty are male; 20%, female. The average class size in an introductory lecture is 41 and in a laboratory, 20.

Admissions: About 90% of the 1993–94 applicants were accepted. The SAT scores for the 1993–94 freshman class were as follows: Verbal—55% below 500, 28% between 500 and 599, 15% between 600 and 700, and 2% above 700; Math—34% below 500, 32% between 500 and 599, 26% between 600 and 700, and 8% above 700. The ACT scores were 26% below 21, 23% between 21 and 23, 26% between 24 and 26, 10% between 27 and 28, and 15% above 28. There were 27 National Merit finalists and 37 semifinalists.

Requirements: A minimum GPA of 2.0 is required. The SAT I or ACT is required. The ACT, with a minimum composite score of 20, is preferred, while the SAT I, with a minimum composite score of 880, is accepted. In addition, applicants must be graduates of an accredited secondary school or have the GED. Fifteen academic credits are required, including 4 years each of English and electives, 2 each of foreign language, mathematics, and science/laboratory, and 1 of U.S. history. AP and CLEP credits are accepted.

Procedure: Freshmen are admitted to all sessions. Entrance exams should be taken in the junior year of high school. Applications should be filed by July 1 for fall entry, November 15 for winter entry, February 15 for spring entry, and May 15 for summer entry, along with an application fee of $30. Notification is sent 2 to 3 weeks after the application is received. There are early admissions and deferred admissions plans. A waiting list is an active part of the admissions procedure.

Transfer: About 1881 transfer students enrolled in 1993–94. Transfer students must have completed at least 45 quarter hours with a minimum 2.5 GPA. A total of 45 quarter hours out of 183 must be completed at the university.

Visiting: There are regularly scheduled orientations for prospective students, including course selection and a campus tour. There are guides for informal visits and visitors may sit in on classes and stay overnight at the school. To arrange for a visit, contact the Office of High School and Prospective Student Services at (801) 581-8761.

Financial Aid: In 1993–94, 35% of all current freshmen and 43% of continuing students received some form of financial aid. About 30% of freshmen and 37% of continuing students received need-based aid. The average freshman award was $6463. Of that total,

scholarships or need-based grants averaged $1450 ($6000 maximum); loans averaged $2000 ($5000 maximum); and work contracts averaged $1563 ($4000 maximum). The average financial indebtedness of the 1992–93 graduate was $10,000. The university is a member of CSS. The FAFSA financial statement is required. The deadline for financial aid applications is February 15.

International Students: There are currently 1677 international students enrolled. They must take the TOEFL and achieve a minimum score of 500. The student must also take the SAT I and score 830 or the ACT and score 20. However, the ACT is required if the student graduated from a U.S. high school.

Computers: The college provides computer facilities for student use. The mainframe is an IBM 3090. There are 800 microcomputers for student use located in the library, engineering, business, student housing, student union, and mathematics buildings. Other facilities include an IBM 9090 Model 600-S supercomputer, 25 mainframes, 75 minicomputers, and 125 workstation computers. All students may access the system 24 hours a day. There are no time limits on using the system and no fees.

Graduates: In 1992–93, 3137 bachelor's degrees were awarded. The most popular majors among graduates were political science (7%), psychology (7%), and accounting (5%). Within an average freshman class, 14% graduate in 4 years, 26% in 5 years, and 34% in 6 years. Some 470 companies recruited on campus in 1992–93.

Admissions Contact: Staynes Landward, Director of Admissions.

UTAH STATE UNIVERSITY
C-1
Logan, UT 84322 (801) 750-1094

Full-time: 6614 men, 5411 women	Faculty: 765; I, --$
Part-time: 920 men, 667 women	Ph.D.s: 81%
Graduate: 1638 men, 1152 women	Student/Faculty: 16 to 1
Year: quarters, summer session	Tuition: $1878 ($5523)
Application Deadline: July 1	Room & Board: $2805
Freshman Class: 4281 applied, 3825 accepted, 2420 enrolled	
ACT: 22	COMPETITIVE

Utah State University, founded in 1888 as a land-grant institution, offers degree programs in the liberal arts and sciences, agriculture and natural resources, engineering, business, education, fine arts, music, and family life. There are 8 undergraduate schools and one graduate school. In addition to regional accreditation, USU has baccalaureate program accreditation with AACSB, ABET, AHEA, ASLA, CSWE, NASM, NCATE, and SAF. The library contains 801,067 volumes, 897,751 microform items, and 3781 audiovisual forms. Computerized library sources and services include the card catalog, interlibrary loans, and database searching. Special learning facilities include a learning resource center, an art gallery, a radio station, a TV station, a laboratory school, a historical farm, a fine arts center, and a developmental center for handicapped persons. The 332-acre campus is in a small town 96 miles north of Salt Lake City. Including residence halls, there are 104 buildings on campus.

Student Life: About 86% of undergraduates are from Utah. Students come from 47 states, 79 foreign countries, and Canada. Ninety-seven percent are from public schools; 3% from private. Eighty percent are white. The average age of freshmen is 19; all undergraduates, 24. Thirty-three percent drop out by the end of their first year; 54% remain to graduate.

Housing: A total of 2595 students can be accommodated in college housing. College-sponsored living facilities include single-sex dormitories, on-campus apartments, married-student housing, fraternity houses, and sorority houses. In addition, there are honors houses and special interest houses. On-campus housing is available on a first-come, first-served basis. Eighty percent of students commute. Alcohol is not permitted. All students may keep cars on campus.

Activities: About 2% of men belong to 1 local fraternity and 6 national fraternities; about 1% of women belong to 1 local sorority and 3 national sororities. There are 137 groups on campus, including art, band, cheerleading, choir, chorale, chorus, computers, dance, drama, drill team, ethnic, film, gay, honors, international, jazz band, literary magazine, marching band, musical theater, newspaper, opera, orchestra, pep band, photography, political, professional, radio and TV, religious, social, social service, student government, symphony, and yearbook. Popular campus events include Festival of the American West, Homecoming, Founders Day, Christmas Dinner at the Manor House, and Mother's Day Weekend.

Sports: There are 5 intercollegiate sports for men and 7 for women, and 23 intramural sports each for men and women. Athletic and recreation facilities include 5 gymnasiums, indoor and outdoor tennis courts, 2 swimming pools, 40 acres of grass for outdoor sports, a field house, and golf and skiing areas. The campus stadium seats 30,257 and the largest auditorium seats 10,000.

Disabled Students: Ninety percent of the campus is accessible to disabled students. The following facilities are available: wheelchair ramps, elevators, special parking, specially equipped rest rooms, special class scheduling, lowered drinking fountains and telephones,

special phones to receive calls from the deaf, and a disability resource center.

Services: In addition to many counseling and information services, tutoring is available in every subject. There is also a reader service for the blind and remedial math and reading, as well as a writing laboratory and a tutor room.

Campus Safety and Security: Campus safety and security measures include 24-hour foot and vehicle patrol, escort service, shuttle buses, and informal discussions. In addition, there are pamphlets, posters, films, emergency telephones, lighted pathways and sidewalks, and campus police.

Programs of Study: USU awards the B.A., B.S., B.F.A., B.L.A., and B.M. degrees. Associate, master's, and doctoral degrees also are awarded. Bachelor's degrees are awarded in AGRICULTURE (agricultural business management, agricultural economics, animal science, dairy science, forestry and related sciences, international agriculture, natural resource management, plant science, range/farm management, soil science, and wildlife management), BIOLOGICAL SCIENCE (biochemistry, biology/biological science, and microbiology), BUSINESS (accounting, banking and finance, business administration and management, business economics, fashion merchandising, international business management, management information systems, marketing/retailing/merchandising, and personnel management), COMMUNICATIONS AND THE ARTS (dance, dramatic arts, English, fine arts, French, German, journalism, music, and Spanish), COMPUTER AND PHYSICAL SCIENCE (chemistry, computer science, earth science, geology, information sciences and systems, mathematics, physics, and statistics), EDUCATION (agricultural, art, business, early childhood, elementary, foreign languages, health, home economics, industrial arts, music, physical, science, secondary, and special), ENGINEERING AND ENVIRONMENTAL DESIGN (agricultural engineering, civil engineering, electrical/electronics engineering, engineering, environmental science, industrial engineering, industrial engineering technology, interior design, landscape architecture/design, and mechanical engineering), HEALTH PROFESSIONS (medical laboratory technology, music therapy, predentistry, premedicine, public health, speech pathology/audiology, and veterinary science), SOCIAL SCIENCE (American studies, child care/child and family studies, economics, food science, geography, history, home economics, human development, international relations, liberal arts/general studies, parks and recreation management, philosophy, political science/government, prelaw, psychology, social work, and sociology). Natural resources, engineering, special education, art, agriculture, and landscape architecture are the strongest academically. Humanities, arts, and social science have the largest enrollments.

Required: A total of 46 quarter hours of general education courses, including at least 6 of writing, and completion of 186 quarter hours, with a GPA of 2.5 in the major, are required in order to graduate. Other requirements vary according to the college.

Special: Internships are available in most departments through the Cooperative Education Program. The National Student Exchange Program allows students to cross-register in designated institutions and programs and the International Student Exchange Program enables students to study abroad. A general studies degree and student-designed majors are available. Study via Comnet satellite is an option. Nondegree study, pass/fail options, and credit for military experience are offered. There is a freshman honors program on campus as well as 22 national honor societies. Six departments have honors programs.

Faculty/Classroom: Eighty-one percent of faculty are male; 19%, female. Graduate students teach 7% of introductory courses. The average class size in an introductory lecture is 100; in a laboratory, 24; and in a regular course offering, 39.

Admissions: About 89% of the 1993–94 applicants were accepted. The ACT scores for the 1993–94 freshman class were as follows: 35% below 21, 29% between 21 and 23, 16% between 24 and 26, 9% between 27 and 28, and 11% above 28. About 47% of the current freshmen were in the top fifth of their class; 80% were in the top two fifths. There were 25 National Merit finalists.

Requirements: USU requires applicants to be in the upper 60% of their class. A minimum GPA of 2.2 is required. The SAT I or ACT is required, with the ACT preferred. In addition, students should graduate from an accredited secondary school with 15 academic units, including 4 in English, 3 each in social sciences and mathematics, and 2 in science. GED equivalency is accepted, provided ACT scores are 19 or higher. Students not meeting entrance requirements may be considered for admission on a provisional basis. AP and CLEP credits are accepted. Important factors used in the admissions decision are recommendations by school officials, recommendations by alumni, parents or siblings attending the school, evidence of special talent, and leadership record.

Procedure: Freshmen are admitted to all sessions. Entrance exams should be taken in the spring of the junior year of high school. Applications should be filed by July 1 for fall entry, November 1 for winter

entry, February 1 for spring entry, and May 1 for summer entry, along with an application fee of $25. Notification is sent on a rolling basis. There are early decision, early admissions, and deferred admissions plans.

Transfer: A total of 1552 transfer students enrolled in 1993–94. A minimum 2.2 GPA, higher for some majors, is required for transfer students. Those transfer applicants with less than 45 credits must also submit ACT scores. A total of 45 quarter hours out of 186 must be completed at USU.

Visiting: There are regularly scheduled orientations for prospective students. There are guides for informal visits and visitors may sit in on classes and stay overnight at the school. To arrange for a visit, contact Mark Tenhoeve at (801) 750–1129.

Financial Aid: In 1993–94, 65% of all current freshmen and 75% of continuing students received some form of financial aid. About 60% of freshmen and 65% of continuing students received need-based aid. The average freshman award was $4800. Of that total, scholarships or need-based grants averaged $1200 ($4500 maximum); loans averaged $2100 ($4200 maximum); and work contracts averaged $1500 ($2100 maximum). Some 50% of undergraduate students work part-time. Average earnings from campus work for the school year are $2295. The FAF, FFS, or SFS is required. The deadline for financial aid applications is February 10.

International Students: There are currently 1200 international students enrolled. They must take the TOEFL or the University of Michigan Language Test and achieve a minimum score on the TOEFL of 500.

Computers: The college provides computer facilities for student use. The mainframes are an IBM 4381 and a DEC VAX 8650. Microcomputers are available in laboratories throughout the campus. All students may access the system 24 hours a day, 7 days a week. There are no time limits on using the system. The fees are $2 for each credit hour per quarter.

Graduates: In 1992–93, 1548 bachelor's degrees were awarded. Within an average freshman class, 51% graduate in 5 years and 66% in 6 years. Some 61 companies recruited on campus in 1992–93.

Admissions Contact: J. Rodney Clark, Director of Admissions.

UTAH SYSTEM OF HIGHER EDUCATION

The Utah System of Higher Education, established in 1969, is a public system in Utah. It is governed by a state board of regents, whose chief administrator is a commissioner of higher education. The primary goal of the system is teaching, research, and public service. The main priorities are to provide a high-quality, efficient, and economical public system of higher education, to coordinate, consolidate, and avoid unnecessary duplication, and to systematically develop the role of each institution within the system. The total enrollment in a recent year of all 9 campuses was 95,823; there were 2575 faculty members. Four-year campuses are located in Salt Lake City, Logan, Ogden, and Cedar City. Profiles of those campuses are included in this chapter in alphabetical order with other Utah schools.

WEBER STATE UNIVERSITY

C-1

Ogden, UT 84408–1015   (801) 626–6046

Full-time: 4107 men, 4502 women	**Faculty:** 433; IIB, av$
Part-time: 2685 men, 2995 women	**Ph.D.s:** 60%
Graduate: 158 men and women	**Student/Faculty:** 20 to 1
Year: quarters, summer session	**Tuition:** $1638 ($4866)
Application Deadline: July 1	**Room & Board:** $2760
Freshman Class: 3241 applied, 3110 accepted, 2041 enrolled	
ACT: 21	**COMPETITIVE**

Weber State University, founded in 1889, is a public, primarily commuter institution offering undergraduate degrees in allied health sciences, arts and humanities, business and economics, education, natural sciences, social sciences, and technology, and graduate degrees in education and professional accountancy. There are 7 undergraduate and 2 graduate schools. In addition to regional accreditation, WSU has baccalaureate program accreditation with ADA, CAHEA, CSWE, NASM, NCATE, and NLN. The library contains 324,823 volumes, 461,456 microform items, and 7164 audiovisual forms, and subscribes to 2788 periodicals. Computerized library sources and services include the card catalog. Special learning facilities include a learning resource center, an art gallery, a planetarium, a radio station, an observatory, a working crime laboratory, and a science museum. The 400-acre campus is in an urban area 35 miles north of Salt Lake City. Including residence halls, there are 57 buildings on campus.

Student Life: About 95% of undergraduates are from Utah. Students come from 43 states, 32 foreign countries, and Canada. Ninety percent are from public schools; 10% from private. Ninety-two percent are white. The average age of freshmen is 19; all undergraduates, 26. Forty percent drop out by the end of their first year.

Housing: A total of 576 students can be accommodated in college housing. College-sponsored living facilities include single-sex and coed dormitories and on-campus apartments. On-campus housing is guaranteed for all 4 years. Ninety-six percent of students commute. Alcohol is not permitted. All students may keep cars on campus.

Activities: About 1% of men belong to 5 national fraternities; about 1% of women belong to 4 local sororities and 1 national sorority. There are 80 groups on campus, including art, band, cheerleading, choir, chorale, chorus, computers, dance, drama, drill team, drum and bugle corps, ethnic, honors, international, jazz band, literary magazine, marching band, musical theater, newspaper, opera, orchestra, pep band, photography, professional, radio and TV, religious, social, social service, student government, and symphony. Popular campus events include SunFest, WinterFest, Homecoming, and Crystal Crest.

Sports: There are 5 intercollegiate sports each for men and women, and 36 intramural sports each for men and women. Athletic and recreation facilities include a physical education center with an indoor track, complete strength-training equipment, and 3 indoor basketball courts; a swimming pool; racquetball and tennis courts; a 17,000-seat stadium; an 11,515-seat gymnasium; a 7800-seat auditorium/arena; an events center; a playing field; an exercise conditioning room; and a 1-mile jogging trail.

Disabled Students: The entire campus is accessible to disabled students. The following facilities are available: wheelchair ramps, elevators, special parking, specially equipped rest rooms, special class scheduling, and lowered drinking fountains and telephones.

Services: In addition to many counseling and information services, tutoring is available in every subject. There is a reader service for the blind, translators for the hearing impaired, and remedial math, reading, and writing.

Campus Safety and Security: Campus safety and security measures include 24-hour foot and vehicle patrol, self-defense education, escort service, shuttle buses, emergency telephones, and lighted pathways and sidewalks.

Programs of Study: WSU awards the B.A., B.S., B.F.A., and B.I.S. degrees. Associate and master's degrees also are awarded. Bachelor's degrees are awarded in BIOLOGICAL SCIENCE (biology/biological science, botany, microbiology, and zoology), BUSINESS (accounting, business administration and management, business economics, marketing management, and personnel management), COMMUNICATIONS AND THE ARTS (communications, design, dramatic arts, English, fine arts, French, German, music, Spanish, and speech/debate/rhetoric), COMPUTER AND PHYSICAL SCIENCE (chemistry, computer programming, computer science, earth science, geology, mathematics, physical sciences, and physics), EDUCATION (art, business, early childhood, elementary, foreign languages, health, home economics, middle school, music, physical, science, and secondary), ENGINEERING AND ENVIRONMENTAL DESIGN (automotive technology, engineering technology, manufacturing technology, and mechanical engineering), HEALTH PROFESSIONS (clinical science, nursing, predentistry, and premedicine), SOCIAL SCIENCE (child psychology/development, criminal justice, economics, family/consumer studies, geography, gerontology, history, political science/government, psychology, social science, social work, and sociology).

Required: To graduate, students must demonstrate mathematics competency and complete courses in government/history, English, humanities, mathematics, biological/physical sciences, and social sciences. At least 183 quarter credit hours, with 60 at the upper-division level, and a minimum 2.0 GPA are required. Hours in the major and distribution requirements vary with the degree.

Special: WSU offers co-op programs and internships in many majors, a Washington semester, study abroad in Mexico and England, work-study programs with WSU and community businesses, B.A.-B.S. degrees, dual majors in any combination, student-designed majors resulting in a B.I.S. degree, a general studies degree, credit for military experience, nondegree study, and pass/fail options. There is a freshman honors program on campus, as well as one national honor society, Phi Beta Kappa.

Faculty/Classroom: Sixty-six percent of faculty are male; 34%, female.

Admissions: About 96% of the 1993–94 applicants were accepted. The ACT scores for the 1993–94 freshman class were as follows: 46% below 21, 26% between 21 and 23, 19% between 24 and 26, 7% between 27 and 28, and 3% above 28.

Requirements: A minimum GPA of 2.0 is required. The ACT is required. In addition, applicants must be graduates of an accredited secondary school or have a GED. Other requirements vary by department. Nonresidents must have a minimum 2.0 high school GPA. AP and CLEP credits are accepted.

Procedure: Freshmen are admitted to all sessions. Entrance exams should be taken in the junior or senior year. Applications should be filed by July 1 for fall entry, along with an application fee of $20. Notification is sent on a rolling basis. There are early admissions and deferred admissions plans.

Transfer: Transfer students must submit official transcripts from previously attended colleges or universities and have a minimum 2.0 GPA. A total of 45 quarter credits out of 183 must be completed at WSU.

Visiting: There are regularly scheduled orientations for prospective students and visits can be arranged by appointment. There are guides for informal visits and visitors may sit in on classes and stay overnight at the school. To arrange for a visit, contact the Admissions Advisors at (801) 626-6046.

Financial Aid: In a recent year, 50% of all current freshmen received some form of financial aid. The AFSA financial statement is required. The deadline for financial aid applications is May 1.

International Students: There are currently 296 international students enrolled. They must take the TOEFL or the college's own test and achieve a minimum score on the TOEFL of 500.

Computers: WSU provides computer facilities for student use. The mainframes are a DEC VAX 9000 and 8700. All students may access the system. There are no time limits on using the system and no fees.

Graduates: In an earlier class, 1100 bachelor's degrees were awarded.

Admissions Contact: Winslow Horst, Director of Admissions.

WESTMINSTER COLLEGE OF SALT LAKE CITY

C-2

Salt Lake City, UT 84105	(801) 488-4200
Full-time: 335 men, 671 women	Faculty: 92; IIB, -$
Part-time: 270 men, 483 women	Ph.D.s: 83%
Graduate: 201 men, 193 women	Student/Faculty: 11 to 1
Year: 4-4-1, summer session	Tuition: $8220
Application Deadline: open	Room & Board: $3880
Freshman Class: 917 applied, 720 accepted, 213 enrolled	
SAT I: 500/570	ACT: 23 COMPETITIVE

Westminster College of Salt Lake City, founded in 1875, is a private, coeducational institution offering undergraduate programs in business, nursing and health sciences, and arts and sciences. There are 3 undergraduate and 2 graduate schools. In addition to regional accreditation, Westminster has baccalaureate program accreditation with NLN. The library contains 74,500 volumes and 2400 audiovisual forms, and subscribes to 350 periodicals. The 27-acre campus is in an urban area 2 miles southeast of Salt Lake City. Including residence halls, there are 14 buildings on campus.

Student Life: About 92% of undergraduates are from Utah. Students come from 24 states, 15 foreign countries, and Canada. Ninety-five percent are from public schools; 5% from private. Ninety-one percent are white. Twenty-six percent are Protestant; 24% Catholic. The average age of freshmen is 18; all undergraduates, 29. Twenty-five percent drop out by the end of their first year; 25% remain to graduate.

Housing: A total of 110 students can be accommodated in college housing. College-sponsored living facilities include coed dormitories. On-campus housing is guaranteed for the freshman year only and is available on a first-come, first-served basis. Priority is given to out-of-town students. Ninety-five percent of students commute. All students may keep cars on campus.

Activities: There are no fraternities or sororities on campus. There are a number of groups on campus, including art, band, choir, computers, drama, ethnic, gay, international, literary magazine, newspaper, political, professional, religious, and student government.

Sports: There is 1 intercollegiate sport for men, and 5 intramural sports each for men and women. Athletic and recreation facilities include a soccer field, tennis courts, an athletic stadium, and a gymnasium.

Disabled Students: All of the campus is accessible to disabled students. The following facilities are available: wheelchair ramps, elevators, special parking, specially equipped rest rooms, and lowered drinking fountains.

Services: In addition to many counseling and information services, tutoring is available in every subject. There is also a reader service for the blind, and remedial math, reading, and writing.

Campus Safety and Security: Campus safety and security measures include 24-hour foot and vehicle patrol, self-defense education, escort service, and informal discussions. In addition, there are pamphlets, posters, films, emergency telephones, and lighted pathways and sidewalks.

Programs of Study: Westminster awards the B.A., B.S., and B.S.N. degrees. Master's degrees also are awarded. Bachelor's degrees are awarded in BIOLOGICAL SCIENCE (biology/biological science), BUSINESS (accounting, business administration and management, and marketing/retailing/merchandising), COMMUNICATIONS AND THE ARTS (communications, dramatic arts, English, and fine arts), COMPUTER AND PHYSICAL SCIENCE (chemistry, computer science, mathematics, and physics), EDUCATION (early childhood, elementary, and secondary), ENGINEERING AND ENVIRONMENTAL DESIGN (aviation administration/management), HEALTH PROFESSIONS (nursing), SOCIAL SCIENCE (economics, history, human development, philosophy, psychology, social science, and sociology). Nursing and education are the strongest academically. Business has the largest enrollment.

Required: In order to graduate, all students must complete at least 124 credit hours, with 40 to 80 in the major and a minimum 2.25 GPA.

Special: The college offers internships, study abroad in England, dual and student-designed majors, credit for life/military/work experience, and pass/fail options. There is a freshman honors program on campus as well as one national honor society, Phi Beta Kappa. One department has an honors program.

Faculty/Classroom: Forty-nine percent of faculty are male; 51%, female. The average class size in an introductory lecture is 25; in a laboratory, 5; and in a regular course offering, 16.

Admissions: About 79% of the 1993-94 applicants were accepted. The SAT scores for the 1993-94 freshman class were as follows: Verbal—47% below 500, 47% between 500 and 599, and 6% between 600 and 700; Math—37% below 500, 30% between 500 and 599, 30% between 600 and 700, and 3% above 700. The ACT scores were 29% below 21, 27% between 21 and 23, 31% between 24 and 26, 9% between 27 and 28, and 4% above 28. About 48% of the current freshmen were in the top fifth of their class; 85% were in the top two fifths.

Requirements: A minimum GPA of 2.0 is required. The SAT I or ACT is required. In addition, applicants must be graduates of an accredited secondary school or have a GED certificate. An interview is recommended. AP and CLEP credits are accepted.

Procedure: Freshmen are admitted to all sessions. Entrance exams should be taken in the senior year of high school. Application deadlines are open. Notification is sent on a rolling basis. There are early admissions and deferred admissions plans.

Transfer: A total of 276 transfer students enrolled in 1993-94. Transfer students must have a minimum 2.2 GPA and be in good standing at the previously attended college. A total of 30 credits out of 124 must be completed at Westminster.

Visiting: There are regularly scheduled orientations for prospective students. There are guides for informal visits and visitors may sit in on classes and stay overnight at the school. To arrange for a visit, contact Terry Overturf, Associate Director of Admissions, at (801) 488-4200.

Financial Aid: In 1993-94, 56% of all current freshmen and 72% of continuing students received some form of financial aid. About 40% of freshmen received need-based aid. The average freshman award was $6630. About 5% of undergraduate students work part-time. Average earnings from campus work for the school year are $1750. Westminster is a member of CSS. The FAF, FFS, or SFS is required.

International Students: There are currently 35 international students enrolled. The school actively recruits these students. They must take the TOEFL or the University of Michigan Language Test and achieve a minimum score on the TOEFL of 500.

Computers: The college provides computer facilities for student use. The mainframe is a Data General 8002. A number of microcomputers are available in the student union. All students may access the system from 7 A.M. to 11 P.M. There are no time limits on using the system and no fees.

Graduates: In 1992-93, 310 bachelor's degrees were awarded.

Admissions Contact: Beverly Levy, Associate Director of Admissions.

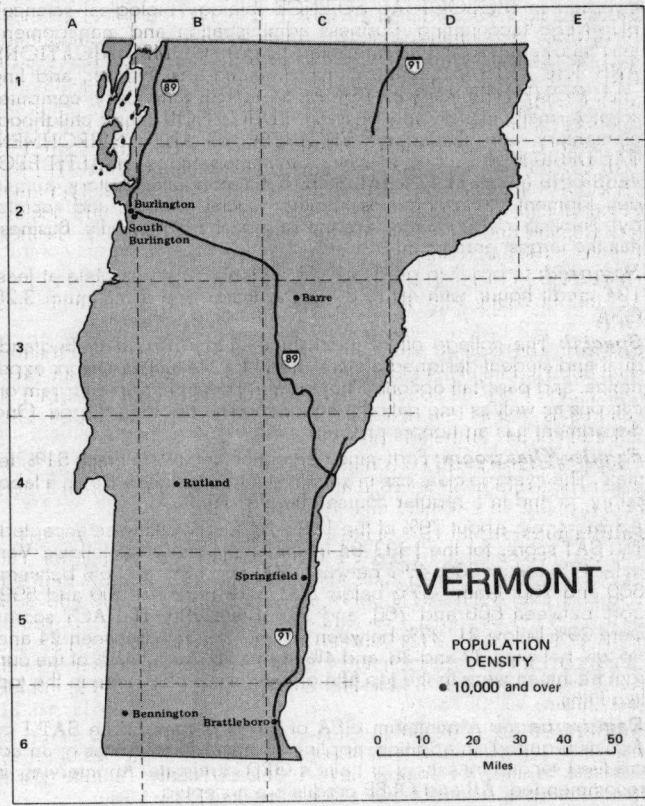

VERMONT

POPULATION
DENSITY

● 10,000 and over

```
0    10    20    30    40    50
            Miles
```

BENNINGTON COLLEGE

A-6

Bennington, VT 05201   (802) 442–6349; (800) 833–6845 (in-state)

Full-time: 171 men, 286 women   Faculty: 56; IIB, av$
Part-time: 1 man, 1 woman   Ph.D.s: 38%
Graduate: 34 men, 33 women   Student/Faculty: 8 to 1
Year: 4–1–4   Tuition, Room &
Application Deadline: January 1   Board: $24,850
Freshman Class: 589 applied, 365 accepted, 141 enrolled
SAT I: 601/551   ACT: 25   **VERY COMPETITIVE +**

Bennington College, founded in 1932, is a private, coeducational liberal arts school where students design their own programs in consultation with faculty. There are 4 graduate schools. The 3 libraries contain 114,689 volumes, 6075 microform items, and 1015 audiovisual forms, and subscribe to 580 periodicals. Computerized library sources and services include the card catalog, interlibrary loans, and database searching. Special learning facilities include an art gallery, dance archives, a script library, photography darkrooms, an observatory, music practice rooms, a greenhouse, and a pond for biological studies. The 550-acre campus is in a small town 45 miles east of Albany, New York. Including residence halls, there are 59 buildings on campus.

Student Life: About 94% of undergraduates are from out-of-state, mostly the Northeast. Students come from 39 states, 15 foreign countries, and Canada. Seventy-two percent are white; 12% foreign nationals. The average age of freshmen is 17; all undergraduates, 20. Fifteen percent drop out by the end of their first year; 62% remain to graduate.

Housing: A total of 600 students can be accommodated in college housing. College-sponsored living facilities include coed dormitories and off-campus apartments. In addition there are quiet study houses. On-campus housing is guaranteed for all 4 years. Ninety-eight percent of students live on campus; of those, 95% remain on campus on weekends. All students may keep cars on campus.

Activities: There are no fraternities or sororities on campus. There are 20 groups on campus, including art, band, chorus, dance, drama, ethnic, film, gay, international, jazz band, literary magazine, musical theater, newspaper, orchestra, photography, political, social, social service, student government, and symphony. Popular campus events include Sun Fest, faculty concerts, Sunday night faculty seminars, Swing into Spring, theme parties, dance concerts, films, lectures, and theater productions.

Sports: There are 4 intramural sports each for men and women. Athletic and recreation facilities include soccer and other playing fields, outdoor clay tennis courts, a basketball court, a karate studio, a weight room, and hiking and biking areas.

Disabled Students: The following facilities are available: wheelchair ramps, special parking, special fire alarms in houses, and amplifiers on phones.

Campus Safety and Security: Campus safety and security measures include 24-hour foot and vehicle patrol, escort service, informal discussions, pamphlets, posters, and films. In addition, there are emergency telephones and lighted pathways and sidewalks.

Programs of Study: Bennington awards the B.A. degree. Master's degrees also are awarded. Bachelor's degrees are awarded in BIOLOGICAL SCIENCE (biology/biological science), COMMUNICATIONS AND THE ARTS (art history and appreciation, Chinese, creative writing, dance, dramatic arts, English, fine arts, French, German, languages, literature, music, photography, and Spanish), COMPUTER AND PHYSICAL SCIENCE (chemistry, computer science, mathematics, and physics), EDUCATION (early childhood), ENGINEERING AND ENVIRONMENTAL DESIGN (architecture), SOCIAL SCIENCE (anthropology, economics, history, philosophy, political science/government, and psychology). Literature and languages, visual arts, drama, social sciences, and interdivisional programs have the largest enrollments.

Required: A minimum of 128 credit hours is required to graduate. By the end of their second year, all students must take courses from 4 of 7 divisions in addition to classes beyond the introduction level in 2 fields outside their major. Before the end of the second year, students also must write a tentative academic plan. A thesis or final project is required of all majors.

Special: Eight-week work/internships are required all four years (during January and February). Cross-registration with Southern Vermont College is possible. A cooperative program with the Bank Street College of Education in New York City offers a joint B.A.-M.S. degree in education. In addition, study abroad in numerous countries, an individually arranged Washington semester, B.A.-B.S. degrees, and dual and student-designed majors are offered. Grading is pass/fail with extensive written evaluation.

Faculty/Classroom: Seventy percent of faculty are male; 30%, female. All teach undergraduates and also do research. Graduate students teach 1% of introductory courses. The average class size in an introductory lecture is 12; in a laboratory, 8; and in a regular course offering, 9.

Admissions: About 62% of the 1993–94 applicants were accepted. About 47% of the current freshmen were in the top fifth of their class; 85% were in the top two fifths. There were 5 National Merit finalists and 7 semifinalists. Four freshmen graduated first in their class.

Requirements: The SAT I or ACT is required. Applicants should have 16 credits including 4 units in English, 3 each in mathematics, science, and social studies, 2 or 3 in foreign language, and 2 in history. Art and music courses are highly recommended. An essay and interview are required and a portfolio is recommended for certain majors. The GED is accepted.

Procedure: Freshmen are admitted in the fall and spring. Entrance exams should be taken during the spring of the junior or fall of the senior year. There are early decision, early admissions, and deferred admissions plans. Early decision applications should be filed by November 15; regular applications, by January 1 for fall entry and January 1 for spring entry, along with an application fee of $45. Notification of early decision is sent January 1; regular decision, on a rolling basis. About 16 early decision candidates were accepted for the 1993–94 class. A waiting list is an active part of the admissions procedure.

Transfer: About 52 transfer students enrolled in 1993–94. Two-year transfers must have a faculty interview. All transfers must submit secondary school reports, college transcripts, and recommendations from 2 faculty members. They must also submit SAT I or ACT scores and interview with a member of the admissions staff. A total of 64 credits out of 128 must be completed at Bennington.

Visiting: There are regularly scheduled orientations for prospective students, including faculty and student panels, dinner and socializing, class visitation, and interviews. There are guides for informal visits and visitors may stay overnight at the school. To arrange for a visit, contact the Admissions Office at (802) 442–6349 or (800) 833–6845 (in-state).

Financial Aid: In 1993–94, 70% of all current freshmen and 83% of continuing students received some form of financial aid. About 70% of freshmen and 83% of continuing students received need-based aid. The average freshman award was $17,000. Of that total, scholarships or need-based grants averaged $13,460; loans averaged $2440 ($2705 maximum); and work contracts averaged $1100

($1580 maximum). Average earnings from campus work for the school year are $1200. The average financial indebtedness of the 1992–93 graduate was $11,200. Bennington is a member of CSS. The FAF, the college's own financial statement, and the FAFSA are required. The deadline for financial aid applications is March 1.

International Students: There are currently 37 international students enrolled. The school actively recruits these students. They must take the TOEFL and achieve a minimum score of 550. The student must also take the SAT I or the ACT.

Computers: The college provides computer facilities for student use. The mainframe is a Dual 83–80. Microcomputers are available in the science building. Students in classes that require use may access the system 3 hours per day when college is in session. There are no fees.

Graduates: In a recent year, 130 bachelor's degrees were awarded. The most popular majors among graduates were interdivisional (24%), literature and languages (22%), and visual arts (13%). Within an average freshman class, 65% graduate in 5 years.

Admissions Contact: Karen Kristoff, Director of Admissions.

BURLINGTON COLLEGE
Burlington, VT 05401

A-2

(802) 862–9616

Full-time: 28 men, 43 women	Faculty: n/av
Part-time: 35 men, 55 women	Ph.D.s: 20%
Graduate: none	Student/Faculty: 2 to 1
Year: semesters, summer session	Tuition: $6150
Application Deadline: see profile	Room & Board: n/app
Freshman Class: n/av	
ACT: required	NONCOMPETITIVE

Burlington College, founded in 1972, is a private coeducational institution offering a small, flexible liberal arts program, residential and nonresidential, geared toward the adult learner. The library contains 45,000 volumes and subscribes to 350 periodicals. Computerized library sources and services include interlibrary loans and database searching. Special learning facilities include a learning resource center and an art gallery. The 1-acre campus is in Burlington. There is one building on campus.

Student Life: About 90% of undergraduates are from Vermont. Students come from 8 states, 4 foreign countries, and Canada. Ninety-five percent are from public schools; 5% from private. Eighty-seven percent are white. The average age of freshmen is 30; all undergraduates, 34.

Housing: There are no residence halls. All students commute. Alcohol is not permitted. All students may keep cars on campus.

Activities: There are no fraternities or sororities on campus. There are some groups and organizations on campus, including newspaper, student government, and a support group for low income students. Popular campus events include coffeehouses, Christmas party, an evening video series, and the archetype series.

Sports: There is no sports program at Burlington College.

Disabled Students: Sixty percent of the campus is accessible to disabled students. The following facilities are available: wheelchair ramps, special parking, specially equipped rest rooms, special class scheduling, and lowered drinking fountains and telephones.

Services: In addition to many counseling and information services, tutoring is available in every subject. There is also remedial math, reading, and writing.

Programs of Study: Burlington College awards the B.A. degree. Associate degrees also are awarded. Bachelor's degrees are awarded in COMMUNICATIONS AND THE ARTS (fine arts), SOCIAL SCIENCE (human services, humanities, psychology, and women's studies). Psychology, transpersonal psychology, and individualized (self-designed) programs have the largest enrollments.

Required: All students are required to complete at least 120 semester credits, including 36 upper level credits in their major. Distribution requirements include 9 credits each in the following divisions: personal vision, human community, and natural environment. Specific course requirements include 3 credits each in writing and mathematics. Students are also required to take a 3-credit practicum within their areas of concentration.

Special: Cross-registration is available with the University of Vermont, St. Michael's Trinity College, Champlain College, and the Community College of Vermont; internships through various organizations and work-study programs with nonprofit organizations are also available. The college offers dual majors, interdisciplinary majors, including transpersonal psychology, individualized majors, independent study, a non-residential degree program, credit for life experience, and pass/fail options.

Faculty/Classroom: Forty-eight percent of faculty are male; 52%, female. All teach undergraduates. The average class size in a regular course offering is 8.

Requirements: The ACT is required. Burlington also requires a high school diploma or the GED and a successful interview with the Director of Admissions. CLEP credit is accepted. Personality and intangible qualities are an important factor used in the admission decision.

Procedure: Freshmen are admitted to all sessions. Applications should be submitted 2 weeks prior to the start of the semester of entry, along with an application fee of $30. The college accepts all applicants. Notification is sent on a rolling basis. There are early admissions and deferred admissions plans.

Transfer: About 23 transfer students enrolled in a recent year. A total of 30 credits out of 120 must be completed at Burlington College.

Visiting: There are guides for informal visits and visitors may sit in on classes. To arrange for a visit, contact the Admissions Office at (802) 862–9616.

Financial Aid: In a recent year, 80% of all students received some form of financial aid. About 80% of students received need-based aid. The average freshman award that year was $5560. Of that total, scholarships or need-based grants averaged $3100 ($6250 maximum); loans averaged $3400 ($8025 maximum); and work contracts averaged $1235 ($1500 maximum). Seventy-two percent of undergraduate students work part-time. Average earnings from campus work for the school year are $1500. Burlington College is a member of CSS. The FAF and the college's own financial statement are required. The deadline for financial aid applications is July 1.

International Students: There are currently 4 international students enrolled.

Computers: The college provides computer facilities for student use. There are 10 stand-alone PCs and 1 Macintosh available for student use, all in the student computer room. All students may access the system 80 hours per week. There are no time limits on using the system and no fees.

Graduates: In a recent year, 34 bachelor's degrees were awarded. The most popular majors among recent graduates were psychology (44%), education (19%), and fine arts (14%). About half of graduates continue their education at the graduate level.

Admissions Contact: Nancy Wilson, Director of Admissions.

CASTLETON STATE COLLEGE
Castleton, VT 05735

B-4

(802) 468–5611, ext. 213

Full-time: 758 men, 808 women	Faculty: 88; IIB, -$
Part-time: 101 men, 202 women	Ph.D.s: 80%
Graduate: 66 men, 154 women	Student/Faculty: 18 to 1
Year: semesters, summer session	Tuition: $3738 ($7890)
Application Deadline: open	Room & Board: $4640
Freshman Class: 1104 applied, 893 accepted, 382 enrolled	
SAT I Verbal/Math: 416/459	ACT: 21 LESS COMPETITIVE

Castleton State College, founded in 1787, is the oldest institution of higher learning in Vermont. As part of the Vermont State Colleges system, it offers a state-supported undergraduate and graduate program that includes liberal arts, teacher preparation, and professional programs. There is one graduate school. In addition to regional accreditation, Castleton has baccalaureate program accreditation with CSWE and NLN. The library contains 110,000 volumes, 400,000 microform items, and 1750 audiovisual forms, and subscribes to 657 periodicals. Computerized library sources and services include the card catalog, interlibrary loans, and database searching. Special learning facilities include a learning resource center, an art gallery, a radio station, a TV studio, an observatory, and a theater. The 130-acre campus is in a rural area 11 miles west of Rutland. Including residence halls, there are 24 buildings on campus.

Student Life: About 65% of undergraduates are from Vermont. Students come from 28 states, 4 foreign countries, and Canada. Eighty percent are from public schools; 20% from private. Ninety-eight percent are white. The average age of freshmen is 18. Twenty-nine percent drop out by the end of their first year; 65% remain to graduate.

Housing: A total of 734 students can be accommodated in college housing. College-sponsored living facilities include single-sex and coed dormitories. In addition, there are honors houses. On-campus housing is guaranteed for the freshman year only and is available on a lottery system for upperclassmen. Fifty percent of students live on campus; of those, 85% remain on campus on weekends. All students may keep cars on campus.

Activities: There are no fraternities or sororities on campus. There are 48 groups on campus, including art, band, cheerleading, choir, chorale, chorus, computers, dance, drama, film, honors, international, jazz band, literary magazine, musical theater, newspaper, photography, political, professional, radio and TV, religious, social, social service, student government, and yearbook. Popular campus events include Spring and Winter Weekends, Alumni Weekend, and Martin Luther King Week.

Sports: There are 6 intercollegiate sports each for men and women, and 4 intramural sports each for men and women. Athletic and recreation facilities include a 6-lane swimming pool, 2 racquetball courts, a recreation gymnasium, and the nearby 2,000-acre Pond Hill Ranch with more than 70 miles of trails, swimming, sailing, fishing, and golf facilities.

Disabled Students: Ninety percent of the campus is accessible to disabled students. The following facilities are available: wheelchair ramps, elevators, special parking, specially equipped rest rooms, special class scheduling, and lowered drinking fountains and telephones.
Services: In addition to many counseling and information services, tutoring is available in most subjects. There is also remedial math, reading, and writing.
Campus Safety and Security: Campus safety and security measures include 24-hour foot and vehicle patrol, self-defense education, escort service, and shuttle buses. In addition, there are informal discussions, pamphlets, posters, films, emergency telephones, and lighted pathways and sidewalks.
Programs of Study: Castleton awards the B.A., B.S., and B.S.W. degrees. Associate and master's degrees also are awarded. Bachelor's degrees are awarded in BUSINESS (business administration and management), COMMUNICATIONS AND THE ARTS (communications, dramatic arts, fine arts, languages, literature, music, and Spanish), COMPUTER AND PHYSICAL SCIENCE (information sciences and systems, mathematics, and natural sciences), EDUCATION (business, elementary, foreign languages, mathematics, physical, science, and secondary), SOCIAL SCIENCE (criminal justice, history, psychology, social science, social work, and sociology). Nursing, athletic training, and science are the strongest academically. Business and education have the largest enrollments.
Required: All students must maintain a GPA of 2.0 while taking 128 semester hours, including 30 to 84 in their major. Distribution requirements include 1 course each in foreign cultures, history, philosophy and psychology, and social analysis, 3 in literature and the arts, and 2 each in mathematics and natural sciences. Specific courses include computers, communication, and an introduction to liberal arts.
Special: Cooperative programs with Clarkson University, internships, study abroad in 14 countries, and many work-study programs are available. In addition, B.A.-B.S. degrees, dual majors, student-designed majors in business and secondary and elementary education, a 3-2 engineering degree with Clarkson University, a 2-3 pharmacy degree with Albany College of Pharmacy, credit for life experience, nondegree study, and pass/fail options are offered. There are 2 national honor societies on campus. Four departments have honors programs.
Faculty/Classroom: Sixty-eight percent of faculty are male; 32%, female. All teach undergraduates. No introductory courses are taught by graduate students. The average class size in an introductory lecture, and a regular course offering is 18; in a laboratory, 15.
Admissions: About 81% of the 1993–94 applicants were accepted. About 18% of the current freshmen were in the top fifth of their class; 41% were in the top two fifths. Four freshmen graduated first in their class.
Requirements: The SAT I or ACT is required. The college recommends that candidates have 4 years of English, 3 each of mathematics, social studies, or history, 2 each of foreign language and science, and 2 to 4 of electives. An essay is required and an interview is recommended. The GED is accepted. AP and CLEP credits are accepted. Important factors used in the admissions decision are advanced placement or honor courses, leadership record, recommendations by school officials, extracurricular activities record, and personality.
Procedure: Freshmen are admitted in the fall and spring. Entrance exams should be taken during the spring of the junior year or the fall of the senior year. Application deadlines are open. Application fee is $40. Notification is sent on a rolling basis. There are early admissions and deferred admissions plans. A waiting list is an active part of the admissions procedure, with about 10% of applicants on the list.
Transfer: About 180 transfer students enrolled in 1993–94. Transfer applicants must have a 2.0 GPA. An associate degree, 15 credit hours, and an interview are recommended. A total of 30 credits out of 128 must be completed at Castleton.
Visiting: There are regularly scheduled orientations for prospective students, including meetings with admissions counselors, faculty, and coaches as well as a campus tour. Visitors may sit in on classes and stay overnight at the school. To arrange for a visit, contact the Admissions Office at (802) 468–5611, ext. 213.
Financial Aid: In 1993–94, 75% of all students received some form of financial aid. Twenty-five percent of undergraduate students work part-time. Castleton is a member of CSS. The FAFSA financial statement is required. The deadline for financial aid applications is March 15.
International Students: There are currently 6 international students enrolled. They must take the TOEFL and achieve a minimum score of 500.
Computers: The college provides computer facilities for student use. The mainframes are a DEC VAX 11/750 and a DEC VAX 11/785. More than 180 terminals and microcomputers are available for student use at the academic computing center, the business department, and the education department, as well as several smaller areas. All students may access the system. There are no time limits on using the system and no fees.

Graduates: In an earlier class, 186 bachelor's degrees were awarded.
Admissions Contact: Gary Fallis, Director of Admissions.

CHAMPLAIN COLLEGE
A-2
Burlington, VT 05402–0670   (802) 860–2727

Full-time: 504 men, 743 women	Faculty: 61; III, -$
Part-time: 328 men, 472 women	Ph.Ds: 2%
Graduate: none	Student/Faculty: 20 to 1
Year: semesters, summer session	Tuition: $8020
Application Deadline: open	Room & Board: $5617
Freshman Class: n/av	
SAT Verbal/Math: 369/407	LESS COMPETITIVE

Champlain College, founded in 1878, is a private, coeducational institution offering '2 plus 2' bachelor's degree programs in accounting and in business management through the Walter Cerf School of Business. The library contains 33,187 volumes, 1100 microform items, and 1350 audiovisual forms, and subscribes to 1100 periodicals. Computerized library sources and services include the card catalog, interlibrary loans, and database searching. Special learning facilities include a learning resource center, video production studio, and child-care center. The 18-acre campus is in a suburban area in the Hill Section of Burlington. Including residence halls, there are 26 buildings on campus.
Student Life: About 80% of undergraduates are from Vermont. Students come from 19 states, 15 foreign countries, and Canada. Ninety-six percent are white. The average age of all undergraduates is 20. Thirty percent drop out by the end of their first year; 67% remain to graduate.
Housing: A total of 525 students can be accommodated in college housing. College-sponsored living facilities include single-sex dormitories. On-campus housing is available on a first-come, first-served basis. Sixty-four percent of students commute. Alcohol is not permitted.
Activities: There are no fraternities or sororities on campus. There are 10 groups on campus, including cheerleading, computers, drama, international, photography, social service, student government, and yearbook. Popular campus events include Family Day, Senior Week, basketball tournaments, skiing trips, outing club trips, and seasonal dances.
Sports: There are 4 intercollegiate sports for men and 4 for women, and 8 intramural sports for men and 8 for women. Athletic and recreation facilities are offered through the community YMCA and a local tennis club, park, and ski resort.
Disabled Students: The following facilities are available: wheelchair ramps, elevators, special parking, specially equipped rest rooms, special class scheduling, lowered drinking fountains, and lowered telephones.
Services: In addition to many counseling and information services, peer tutoring is available in most subjects. Other support services include supplementary classes, a writing assistance laboratory, a mathematics laboratory, foreign language (ESL) tutors, and note-taking services.
Campus Safety and Security: Campus safety and security measures include 24-hour foot and vehicle patrol, self-defense education, escort service, and shuttle buses. In addition, there are informal discussions, pamphlets, posters, films, emergency telephones, and lighted pathways and sidewalks.
Programs of Study: Champlain awards the B.S. degree. Associate degrees also are awarded. Bachelor's degrees are awarded in BUSINESS (accounting and business administration and management). Accounting and business management are the strongest academically.
Required: A minimum GPA of 2.0 and 120 credits are required for the B.S. degree.
Faculty/Classroom: Forty-nine percent of faculty are male; 51%, female. All teach undergraduates. The average class size in an introductory lecture is 35; in a laboratory, 15; and in a regular course offering, 25.
Admissions: About 21% of the current freshmen were in the top fifth of their class; 45% were in the top two fifths.
Requirements: Champlain requires applicants to be in the upper 67% of their class. The SAT I or the ACT is recommended. Applicants should be graduates of an accredited high school or the equivalent, with a minimum GPA of 2.0. AP and CLEP credits are accepted. Important factors used in the admissions decision are advanced placement or honor courses, recommendations by school officials, leadership record, personality, intangible qualities, and evidence of special talent.
Procedure: Freshmen are admitted to all sessions. Application deadlines are open. Application fee is $25. Notification is sent on a rolling basis. There are early decision, early admissions, and deferred admissions plans. Five early decision candidates were accepted for the 1993–94 class. A waiting list is an active part of the admissions procedure.

Transfer: About 280 transfer students enrolled in a recent year. High school and college transcripts are required. At least 60 credits out of 120 must be completed at Champlain.

Visiting: There are regularly scheduled orientations for prospective students, including an open house, a guided campus tour, and a personal interview. There are guides for informal visits, and visitors may sit in on classes. To arrange for a visit, contact the Admissions Office at (802) 860-2727.

Financial Aid: In 1993-94, 96% of all current freshmen and 82% of continuing students received some form of financial aid. About 75% of all students received need-based aid. The average freshman award was $10,000. Of that total, scholarships or need-based grants averaged $5100 ($7200 maximum); loans averaged $3800 ($4425 maximum); and work contracts averaged $1700 ($2100 maximum). Twenty percent of undergraduate students work part-time. Average earnings from campus work for the school year are $1800. The average financial indebtedness of the 1992-93 graduate was $6191. Champlain is a member of CSS. The FAF, the college's own financial statement, and the FAFSA are required. The deadline for financial aid applications is May 1.

International Students: There are currently 30 international students enrolled. The school actively recruits these students. They must take the TOEFL and achieve a minimum score of 500.

Computers: The college provides computer facilities for student use. The mainframe is an IBM AS/400. Champlain provides more than 100 IBM personal computers for students. Three supervised computer laboratories are open 7 days a week for programming, word processing, database management, accounting, desktop publishing, and other functions. All students may access the system. There are no time limits on using the system and no fees.

Graduates: In 1992-93, 42 bachelor's degrees were awarded.

Admissions Contact: Josephine Churchill, Director of Admissions.

COLLEGE OF SAINT JOSEPH
B-4

Rutland, VT 05701-3899   (802) 773-5905

Full-time: 75 men, 125 women	Faculty: 15
Part-time: 64 men, 131 women	Ph.D.s: 86%
Graduate: 28 men, 85 women	Student/Faculty: 13 to 1
Year: semesters, summer session	Tuition: $8000
Application Deadline: open	Room & Board: $4650
Freshman Class: 132 applied, 127 accepted, 42 enrolled	
SAT I Verbal/Math: 370/390	LESS COMPETITIVE

The College of St. Joseph, founded in 1954, is a private, coeducational Catholic institution offering undergraduate programs in the arts and sciences, business, education, and human services. The college serves a primarily commuter student body. There are 2 graduate schools. The library contains 44,547 volumes, 59,644 microform items, and 6006 audiovisual forms, and subscribes to 224 periodicals. Computerized library sources and services include interlibrary loans and database searching. Special learning facilities include a learning resource center. The 99-acre campus is in a rural area 1 mile west of Rutland. Including residence halls, there are 4 buildings on campus.

Student Life: About 81% of undergraduates are from Vermont. Students come from 10 states and 3 foreign countries. Ninety-five percent are white. Thirty-two percent drop out by the end of their first year; 52% remain to graduate.

Housing: A total of 160 students can be accommodated in college housing. College-sponsored living facilities include single-sex dormitories. On-campus housing is guaranteed for all 4 years. Seventy-five percent of students commute. Alcohol is not permitted. All students may keep cars on campus.

Activities: There are no fraternities or sororities on campus. There are 13 groups on campus, including chorus, drama, honors, literary magazine, newspaper, professional, social, social service, student government, and yearbook. Popular campus events include Spring Fling, cultural event series (year round), Fright Night, Fall Classic Semiformal Dance, Parents Weekend, Annual Sno-Ball, Choral Christmas Concert, Student Leadership-Academic Awards Dinner, and Fall/Spring Academic Convocation.

Sports: There are 2 intercollegiate sports for men and 3 for women, and 1 intramural sport for both men and women. Athletic and recreation facilities include a 200-seat gymnasium, a weight room, a cross-country skiing/running trail, a softball diamond, and a soccer field.

Disabled Students: All of the campus is accessible to disabled students. The following facilities are available: wheelchair ramps, special parking, specially equipped rest rooms, special class scheduling, and lowered drinking fountains and telephones.

Services: In addition to many counseling and information services, tutoring is available in every subject. There is also remedial math, reading, and writing, and personal growth and spiritual counseling.

Campus Safety and Security: Campus safety and security measures include shuttle buses, informal discussions, pamphlets, posters, films, and emergency telephones. In addition, there are lighted pathways and sidewalks.

Programs of Study: St. Joseph's awards the B.A. and B.S. degrees. Associate and master's degrees also are awarded. Bachelor's degrees are awarded in BUSINESS (accounting and business administration and management), COMMUNICATIONS AND THE ARTS (English), COMPUTER AND PHYSICAL SCIENCE (computer science), EDUCATION (early childhood, elementary, secondary, and special), SOCIAL SCIENCE (American studies, history, human services, political science/government, prelaw, psychology, and social science). Education is the strongest academically. Arts and sciences have the largest enrollments.

Required: To graduate, students must complete 127 credit hours with a minimum GPA of 2.0, including 15 credits in English/speech, 12 in social/behavioral sciences, 9 each in mathematics/computer and philosophy/religious studies, 6 in natural sciences, and 3 in fine arts. Human services majors must complete 2 internships.

Special: The college offers internships in Rutland County businesses, human service agencies, and elementary and secondary schools. In addition, a B.A.-B.S. degree, dual majors, and independent and directed study options are available. There are 2 national honor societies on campus. One department has an honors program.

Faculty/Classroom: Fifty-eight percent of faculty are male; 42%, female. All teach undergraduates. No introductory courses are taught by graduate students. The average class size in an introductory lecture is 20 and in a regular course offering, 14.

Admissions: About 96% of the 1993-94 applicants were accepted. The SAT scores for the 1993-94 freshman class were as follows: Verbal—92% below 500 and 7% between 500 and 599; Math—82% below 500, 15% between 500 and 599, and 3% between 600 and 700. About 20% of the current freshmen were in the top fifth of their class; 41% were in the top two fifths.

Requirements: St. Joseph's requires applicants to be in the upper 50% of their class. A minimum GPA of 2.0 is required. The SAT I or ACT is required. In addition, applicants should be graduates of accredited secondary schools or have earned a GED. College preparatory study must include 4 years of English, 3 of mathematics, 2 each of science and social studies, and 5 other academic electives. The college prefers that students rank in the upper half of their graduating class. An essay is required and an interview is recommended. AP and CLEP credits are accepted. Important factors used in the admissions decision are advanced placement or honor courses, leadership record, extracurricular activities record, personality, intangible qualities, and parents or siblings attending the school.

Procedure: Freshmen are admitted to all sessions. Entrance exams should be taken by December of the senior year. Application deadlines are open. Application fee is $25. There is an early decision plan. Notification of early decision is sent November 15; regular decision, on a rolling basis.

Transfer: About 15 transfer students enrolled in 1993-94. Transfers must present a minimum GPA of 2.0. A total of 30 credits out of 127 must be completed at St. Joseph's.

Visiting: There are regularly scheduled orientations for prospective students, including a campus tour, admissions interview, and visits to classes. There are guides for informal visits and visitors may stay overnight at the school. To arrange for a visit, contact Admissions Office at (802) 773-5905.

Financial Aid: In 1993-94, 79% of all current freshmen and 80% of continuing students received some form of financial aid. The average freshman award was $5077. Of that total, scholarships or need-based grants averaged $3345 ($5000 maximum); loans averaged $3243 ($5500 maximum); and work contracts averaged $225 ($1200 maximum). Thirteen percent of undergraduate students work part-time. Average earnings from campus work for the school year are $850. The average financial indebtedness of the 1992-93 graduate was $11,017. St. Joseph's is a member of CSS. The FAF is required. The deadline for financial aid applications is March 1.

International Students: There are currently 4 international students enrolled. They must take the TOEFL and achieve a minimum score of 550.

Computers: The college provides computer facilities for student use. The mainframe is a DEC PDP 11/84. A network of 14 microcomputers is also available for academic use. All students may access the system. There are no time limits on using the system and no fees.

Graduates: In 1992-93, 50 bachelor's degrees were awarded. The most popular majors among graduates were business (40%), liberal studies (31%), and education (27%). Within an average freshman class, 52% graduate in 4 years.

Admissions Contact: Dean of Admissions.

GODDARD COLLEGE

C-2

Plainfield, VT 05667   (802) 454-8311; (800) 468-4888 (out-of-state)

Full-time: 50 men, 75 women	Faculty: 16
Part-time: 40 men, 60 women	Ph.D.s: 75%
Graduate: 100 men, 125 women	Student/Faculty: 8 to 1
Year: semesters	Tuition: $13,470
Application Deadline: open	Room & Board: $4520
Freshman Class: 94 applied, 82 accepted, 49 enrolled	
SAT I Verbal/Math: 473/464	**LESS COMPETITIVE**

Goddard College, founded in 1938, is a private coeducational college that stresses progressive, individualized education for personal and community transformation, based on John Dewey's learning by involvement theory. There is one graduate school. The library contains 75,000 volumes and subscribes to 225 periodicals. Computerized library sources and services include interlibrary loans and database searching. Special learning facilities include a learning resource center, a radio station, a holograph laboratory, and a video/photo studio. The 200-acre campus is in a rural area 10 miles from Montpelier.

Student Life: About 82% of undergraduates are from out-of-state, mostly the Northeast. Students come from 18 states, 2 foreign countries, and Canada. Ninety percent are from public schools; 10% from private. Some 90% are white. The average age of freshmen is 19; all undergraduates, 22. Three percent drop out by the end of their first year; 60% remain to graduate.

Housing: A total of 125 students can be accommodated in college housing. College-sponsored living facilities include single-sex and coed dormitories and married-student housing. In addition, there are special interest houses and single-parent houses. On-campus housing is guaranteed for all 4 years. Eighty-five percent of students live on campus. All students may keep cars on campus.

Activities: There are no fraternities or sororities on campus. There are a number of groups on campus, including art, drama, gay, jazz band, literary magazine, newspaper, radio and TV, and student government.

Sports: There is no sports program at Goddard.

Disabled Students: Wheelchair ramps are available for these students.

Services: Advisor system requires 1-hour weekly meeting with faculty advisor.

Campus Safety and Security: Campus safety and security measures include informal discussions, lighted pathways and sidewalks, and an evening security guard.

Programs of Study: Goddard awards the B.A. degree. Master's degrees also are awarded. Bachelor's degrees are awarded in COMMUNICATIONS AND THE ARTS (creative writing, media arts, and visual and performing arts), EDUCATION (education), ENGINEERING AND ENVIRONMENTAL DESIGN (environmental science), SOCIAL SCIENCE (counseling psychology, crosscultural studies, interdisciplinary studies, social science, and women's studies).

Required: All students spend 4 hours in a work program that contributes to the college and 4 hours in basic labor for the community each week. No grades are assigned; faculty and students write evaluations, and a student either passes or fails a semester's work. Each semester is worth 15 credit hours and a total of 120 is needed to graduate. All students must attend a 9-day meeting at the beginning of each semester. A senior study project is required in the final semester.

Special: Students and faculty design all curriculum; there are no prescribed courses. Learning takes the form of group or independent studies, workshops, action projects, research, field trips, seminars, and performances. There are a number of away-from-campus study options, including a field semester involving an internship, apprenticeship, or study-travel and a semester-abroad program offered in 20 countries.

Faculty/Classroom: Fifty percent of faculty are male; 50%, female. Graduate students teach 1% of introductory courses. The average class size in an introductory lecture is 8 and in a regular course offering, 10.

Admissions: About 87% of the 1993-94 applicants were accepted.

Requirements: Goddard admits students who can contribute to its learning community and who will thrive in a self-directed study program. The admission decision is based on the student's application, which includes several essays, letters of recommendation and transcripts, and samples of the student's work. A personal interview, and SAT I or ACT scores, while not required, are also considered when submitted. AP and CLEP credits are accepted. Important factors used in the admissions decision are personality, intangible qualities, writing ability, advanced placement or honor courses, evidence of special talent, leadership record, and recommendations by school officials.

Procedure: Freshmen are admitted to all sessions. Application fee is $35. Notification is sent on a rolling basis. There are early admissions and deferred admissions plans.

Transfer: About 25 transfer students enrolled in 1993-94. College transcripts must be submitted by transfer applicants. A total of 30 credits out of 120 must be completed at Goddard.

Visiting: There are regularly scheduled orientations for prospective students, including Discover Goddard Days held in the fall and spring and individual tours and interviews. There are guides for informal visits and visitors may sit in on classes and stay overnight at the school. To arrange for a visit, contact the Admissions Office at (802) 454-8311 or (800) 468-4888.

Financial Aid: In 1993-94, 80% of all students received some form of financial aid. About 80% of students received need-based aid. All undergraduate students work part-time. Average earnings from campus work for the school year are $900. The FAF or FFS is required.

International Students: There is currently 1 international student enrolled. International students must take the TOEFL and achieve a minimum score of 550.

Computers: The college provides computer facilities for student use. The mainframes are an IBM 5/34 and an AS400. Many types of microcomputers are available for student use in the computer center. All students may access the system. There are no time limits and no fees.

Admissions Contact: Peter S. Burns, Director of Admissions.

GREEN MOUNTAIN COLLEGE

A-4

Poultney, VT 05764

(802) 287-9313, ext. 208
(800) 776-6675 (out-of-state)

Full-time: 268 men, 293 women	Faculty: 35; IIB, --$
Part-time: 11 men, 20 women	Ph.D.s: 80%
Graduate: none	Student/Faculty: 16 to 1
Year: semesters	Tuition: $11,200
Application Deadline: see profile	Room & Board: $2880
Freshman Class: 900 applied, 700 accepted, 198 enrolled	
SAT I Verbal/Math: 460/440	**COMPETITIVE**

Green Mountain College, established in 1834, is a private, nonprofit liberal arts institution. The library contains 60,000 volumes, 10,000 microform items, and 2000 audiovisual forms, and subscribes to 300 periodicals. Computerized library sources and services include database searching. Special learning facilities include a writing clinic and a skills advancement center. The 155-acre campus is in a small town 20 miles southwest of Rutland. Including residence halls, there are 26 buildings on campus.

Student Life: About 90% of undergraduates are from out-of-state, mostly the Northeast. Students come from 26 states and 13 foreign countries. Seventy percent are from public schools; 30% from private. Ninety-seven percent are white. The average age of freshmen is 18; all undergraduates, 21. Fifteen percent drop out by the end of their first year; 70% remain to graduate.

Housing: A total of 600 students can be accommodated in college housing. College-sponsored living facilities include coed dormitories. On-campus housing is guaranteed for all 4 years. Ninety-five percent of students live on campus; of those, 80% remain on campus on weekends. All students may keep cars on campus.

Activities: There are no fraternities or sororities on campus. There are 30 groups on campus, including art, cheerleading, chorus, dance, drama, international, newspaper, professional, social, social service, student government, and yearbook. Popular campus events include Parents Weekend, fall and spring formals, Winter Carnival, Homecoming, and Honors Banquet.

Sports: There are 4 intercollegiate sports for men and 5 for women, and 8 intramural sports for men and 7 for women. Athletic and recreation facilities include a gymnasium with an indoor pool, a dance studio, a weight room, playing fields, tennis courts, a par course, and a fitness trail.

Disabled Students: Seventy percent of the campus is accessible to disabled students. The following facilities are available: wheelchair ramps, elevators, special parking, specially equipped rest rooms, special class scheduling, and lowered drinking fountains.

Services: In addition to many counseling and information services, tutoring is available in every subject. There is also remedial math, reading, and writing.

Campus Safety and Security: Campus safety and security measures include 24-hour foot and vehicle patrol and lighted pathways and sidewalks.

Programs of Study: Green Mountain awards the B.A., B.S., and B.F.A. degrees. Bachelor's degrees are awarded in BUSINESS (business administration and management, recreation and leisure services, and recreational facilities management), COMMUNICATIONS AND THE ARTS (English and fine arts), EDUCATION (elementary and special), HEALTH PROFESSIONS (recreation therapy), SOCIAL SCIENCE (behavioral science and liberal arts/general studies). Elementary education and recreation are the strongest academically. Elementary education, special education, and fine arts have the largest enrollments.

Required: In order to graduate, students must complete 39 semester hours in general education, including 2 courses each in human culture, language, and expression, and 3 courses each in scientific endeavor, individual and social worlds, and health and well-being. A minimum GPA of 2.0 is required. Students must complete 120 to 130 hours, with 80 to 90 credits in the major. Some programs require prescribed computer science course work.

Special: Semester-long internships are required in all majors. Students may study abroad in England, Spain, Italy, France, and Japan. Work-study programs are available. Students may pursue a dual major in education and a general studies degree, which may be pursued alone or in conjunction with a concentrated area of study. There are 2 national honor societies on campus, including Phi Beta Kappa.

Faculty/Classroom: Sixty-three percent of faculty are male; 37%, female. All teach undergraduates. The average class size in an introductory lecture, laboratory, and regular course offering, is 14.

Admissions: About 78% of the 1993–94 applicants were accepted. The SAT scores for the 1993–94 freshman class were as follows: Verbal—68% below 500, 24% between 500 and 599, 5% between 600 and 700, and 3% above 700; Math—75% below 500, 18% between 500 and 599, 6% between 600 and 700, and 1% above 700. The ACT scores were 25% below 21, 45% between 21 and 23, 18% between 24 and 26, 10% between 27 and 28, and 2% above 28.

Requirements: A minimum GPA of 2.0 is required. The SAT I is required. Applicants must graduate from an accredited secondary school or have a GED. Sixteen academic credits are required. Students must complete 4 years in English, 3 in mathematics, 2 to 3 in science, and 2 each in history and social studies. An essay is required. Interviews are recommended. Where appropriate, portfolios are also recommended. AP and CLEP credits are accepted. Important factors used in the admissions decision are personality, intangible qualities, advanced placement or honor courses, evidence of special talent, extracurricular activities record, and leadership record.

Procedure: Freshmen are admitted to all sessions. Entrance exams should be taken in the fall of the senior year of high school. There are early decision, early admissions, and deferred admissions plans. Early decision applications should be filed by November 1; regular applications are open for fall entry, January 1 for winter entry, and December 1 for spring entry, along with an application fee of $20. Notification of early decision is sent December 1; regular decision, on a rolling basis. About 23 early decision candidates were accepted for the 1993–94 class.

Transfer: A total of 25 transfer students enrolled in 1993–94. Transfer students are required to have a GPA of 2.0. They must have earned a minimum of 12 credits and are required to submit an essay. The SAT I or ACT is required. A total of 30 credits out of 120 to 130 must be completed at Green Mountain.

Visiting: There are regularly scheduled orientations for prospective students. There are guides for informal visits and visitors may sit in on classes and stay overnight at the school. To arrange for a visit, contact Lori Patten, Campus Visit Coordinator, at (802) 287–9313, ext. 208.

Financial Aid: In 1993–94, 48% of all current freshmen and 52% of continuing students received some form of financial aid. About 43% of freshmen and 41% of continuing students received need-based aid. The average freshman award was $7500. Of that total, scholarships or need-based grants averaged $4000 ($13,900 maximum); loans averaged $2625 ($4225 maximum); and work contracts averaged $1000 ($2500 maximum). Forty percent of undergraduate students work part-time. Average earnings from campus work for the school year are $1000. The average financial indebtedness of the 1992–93 graduate was $14,000. Green Mountain is a member of CSS. The FFS is required. The deadline for financial aid applications is February 15.

International Students: There are currently 28 international students enrolled. The school actively recruits these students. They must take the TOEFL and achieve a minimum score of 450.

Computers: The college provides computer facilities for student use. Personal computers are available for student use in the computer center. All students may access the system. There are no time limits and no fees.

Graduates: In 1992–93, 98 bachelor's degrees were awarded. The most popular majors among graduates were elementary education (22%), business management (21%), and recreation (16%). Some 50 companies recruited on campus in 1992–93.

Admissions Contact: Kevin M.R. Mayne, Vice President for External Affairs and Admissions.

JOHNSON STATE COLLEGE C-2

Johnson, VT 05656   (802) 635–2356; (800) 635–2356 (out-of-state)

Full-time: 639 men, 587 women	**Faculty:** 64; IIB, --$
Part-time: 137 men, 259 women	**Ph.D.s:** 80%
Graduate: 33 men, 61 women	**Student/Faculty:** 19 to 1
Year: semesters, summer session	**Tuition:** $3753 ($7905)
Application Deadline: open	**Room & Board:** $4640
Freshman Class: 833 applied, 669 accepted, 277 enrolled	
SAT I Verbal/Math: 390/410	**LESS COMPETITIVE**

Johnson State College, founded in 1828, is a public, coeducational liberal arts and teacher preparation college. There is one graduate school. The library contains 83,000 volumes, 31,000 microform items, and 850 audiovisual forms, and subscribes to 496 periodicals. Computerized library sources and services include the card catalog, interlibrary loans, and database searching. Special learning facilities include a learning resource center, an art gallery, and a radio station. The 500-acre campus is in a rural area 45 miles northeast of Burlington. Including residence halls, there are 15 buildings on campus.

Student Life: About 71% of undergraduates are from Vermont. Students come from 18 states, 11 foreign countries, and Canada. Ninety-four percent are white.

Housing: A total of 600 students can be accommodated in college housing. College-sponsored living facilities include single-sex and coed dormitories, on-campus apartments, and married-student housing. In addition, there are special interest houses, an alcohol-free residence hall, and an international house. On-campus housing is available on a first-come, first-served basis and is available on a lottery system for upperclassmen. Fifty percent of students live on campus. All students may keep cars on campus.

Activities: There are no fraternities or sororities on campus. There are 30 groups on campus, including art, band, chorus, dance, drama, film, gay, honors, international, jazz band, literary magazine, musical theater, newspaper, orchestra, photography, political, radio and TV, religious, social, social service, student government, and yearbook. Popular campus events include Spring and Winter Weekends, Parents Weekends, and alumni athletic competitions.

Sports: There are 6 intercollegiate sports each for men and women, and 22 intramural sports each. Athletic and recreation facilities include a gymnasium, 3 athletic fields, 4 tennis courts, a pool, racquetball and basketball courts, weight training, a fitness center, and a climbing wall.

Disabled Students: Sixty percent of the campus is accessible to disabled students. The following facilities are available: wheelchair ramps, elevators, special parking, specially equipped rest rooms, special class scheduling, lowered drinking fountains, and a swimming pool with access.

Services: In addition to many counseling and information services, tutoring is available in most subjects. There is also a reader service for the blind and remedial math, reading, and writing. Other services include provisions for the learning-disabled, casework, and academic and personal growth workshops.

Campus Safety and Security: Campus safety and security measures include 24-hour foot and vehicle patrol, self-defense education, informal discussions, pamphlets, posters, and films. In addition, there are lighted pathways and sidewalks.

Programs of Study: The college awards the B.A., B.S., and B.F.A. degrees. Associate and master's degrees also are awarded. Bachelor's degrees are awarded in BIOLOGICAL SCIENCE (biology/biological science), BUSINESS (business administration and management and hospitality management services), COMMUNICATIONS AND THE ARTS (art, English, fine arts, literature, music, performing arts, and studio art), COMPUTER AND PHYSICAL SCIENCE (mathematics), EDUCATION (elementary), ENGINEERING AND ENVIRONMENTAL DESIGN (environmental science), HEALTH PROFESSIONS (health science), SOCIAL SCIENCE (anthropology, history, political science/government, and psychology). Teaching certification programs and hotel/hospitality management are the strongest academically. Environmental science, sports medicine, and business management have the largest enrollments.

Required: Candidates for the bachelor's degree must complete at least 120 semester credits including 40 in upper-level courses. Requirements for the major vary. Students must earn a certification of writing competency. General education requirements include 13 disciplinary credits in arts/humanities, science, and social science, 12 interdisciplinary credits, and 6 credits each in writing and mathematics. Students should achieve a minimum GPA of 2.0.

Special: The college offers nondegree study, a semester in London or Quebec, cooperative programs, a B.A.-B.S degree, pass/fail options, a general studies degree, internships, student-designed and dual majors, and work-study programs.

Faculty/Classroom: Thirty-eight percent of faculty are male; 42%, female. No introductory courses are taught by graduate students. The average class size in an introductory lecture is 28; in a laboratory, 16; and in a regular course offering, 15.

Admissions: About 80% of the 1993–94 applicants were accepted. The SAT scores for the freshman class were as follows: Verbal—89% below 500, 10% between 500 and 599, and 1% between 600 and 700; Math—77% below 500, 21% between 500 and 599, and 2% between 600 and 700. About 6% of the current freshmen were in the top fifth of their class; 25% were in the top two fifths.

Requirements: The SAT I or ACT is required. Students should have completed a college preparatory program including 4 years of English, at least 3 of mathematics, including algebra, and 2 of science. Students should have at least a C average. AP and CLEP credits are accepted. Important factors used in the admissions decision are advanced placement or honor courses, extracurricular activities record, and recommendations by school officials.

Procedure: Freshmen are admitted in the fall and spring. Application deadlines are open. The application fee is $40. Notification is sent on a rolling basis. There is a deferred admissions plan.

Transfer: About 85 transfer students enrolled in 1993–94. Transfer students should submit transcripts from each institution previously attended and a recommendation from their academic advisor. A GPA of at least 2.0 is required. A total of 30 credits out of 120 must be completed at the college.

Visiting: There are regularly scheduled orientations for prospective students, including a campus video, a campus tour, and an admission interview. There are guides for informal visits, and visitors may sit in on classes and stay overnight at the school. To arrange for a visit, contact the Admissions Office at (802) 635-2356 or (800) 635-2356 (CT, ME, RI, NH, NJ, NY).

Financial Aid: In 1993–94, 67% of all current freshmen received some form of financial aid. Average earnings from campus work for the school year are $1300. The average financial indebtedness of a recent graduate was $8000. The college is a member of CSS. The FAF, FFS, or SFS is required. The deadline for financial aid applications is March 1.

International Students: There are currently 18 international students enrolled. The school actively recruits these students. They must take the TOEFL and achieve a minimum score of 475.

Computers: The college provides computer facilities for student use. The mainframe is a DEC VAX 11/780. There are also 100 IBM-compatible microcomputers available in 6 laboratories. All students may access the system. There are no time limits and no fees.

Graduates: In a recent year, 234 bachelor's degrees were awarded. The most popular majors among graduates were education (16%), business (12%), and psychology (10%). Five companies recruited on campus.

Admissions Contact: Jonathan H. Henry, Director of Admissions.

LYNDON STATE COLLEGE

Lyndonville, VT 05851

D-2

(802) 626-9371, ext. 113
(800) 225-1998 (out-of-state)

Full-time: 500 men, 430 women	**Faculty:** 55; IIB, -$
Part-time: 40 men, 80 women	**Ph.D.s:** 49%
Graduate: 30 men, 70 women	**Student/Faculty:** 17 to 1
Year: semesters, summer session	**Tuition:** $3754 ($7906)
Application Deadline: open	**Room & Board:** $4640

Freshman Class: 778 applied, 702 accepted, 367 enrolled

SAT I: required

LESS COMPETITITVE

Lyndon State College, founded in 1911 as a teacher's college, became a liberal arts school in 1962, offering undergraduate and graduate courses. There is one graduate school. In addition to regional accreditation, LSC has baccalaureate program accreditation with NRPA. The library contains 70,000 volumes, 10,000 microform items, and 1483 audiovisual forms, and subscribes to 500 periodicals. Computerized library sources and services include the card catalog, interlibrary loans, and database searching. Special learning facilities include an art gallery, a radio station, a TV station, the founder's museum, and a meteorology laboratory. The 175-acre campus is in a small town 184 miles north of Boston. Including residence halls, there are 17 buildings on campus.

Student Life: About 57% of undergraduates are from Vermont. Students come from 19 states, 5 foreign countries, and Canada. Ninety-nine percent are white. The average age of freshmen is 18; all undergraduates, 20. Thirty-two percent drop out by the end of their first year; 47% remain to graduate.

Housing: A total of 500 students can be accommodated in college housing. College-sponsored living facilities include coed dormitories. On-campus housing is guaranteed for all 4 years. Fifty percent of students live on campus; of those, 75% remain on campus on weekends. Alcohol is not permitted. All students may keep cars on campus.

Activities: There are no fraternities or sororities on campus. There are 22 groups on campus, including cheerleading, choir, chorale, chorus, drama, film, honors, international, jazz band, literary magazine, newspaper, photography, political, professional, radio and TV, social, social service, student government, and yearbook. Popular campus events include Family Weekend, Alumni Weekend, Winter and Spring Weekends, and the Kingdom Concert series.

Sports: There are 5 intercollegiate sports each for men and women, and 12 intramural sports each for men and women. Athletic and recreation facilities include a gymnasium complex with a weight room, squash, handball, and racquetball courts, an auxiliary gymnasium, and an Olympic-size pool; outdoor tennis courts; fields for hockey, softball, and soccer; cross-country ski trails and running trails; and access to an ice rink, nearby mountains, and a ski resort.

Disabled Students: Seventy percent of the campus is accessible to disabled students. The following facilities are available: wheelchair ramps, elevators, special parking, specially equipped rest rooms, and lowered drinking fountains.

Services: In addition to many counseling and information services, tutoring is available in every subject. There is also remedial math, reading, and writing. A mathematics laboratory and a writing center are available for student use.

Campus Safety and Security: Campus safety and security measures include 24-hour foot and vehicle patrol, escort service, lighted pathways and sidewalks, a security and safety service on campus, and a 24-hour emergency rescue squad.

Programs of Study: LSC awards the B.A. and B.S. degrees. Associate and master's degrees also are awarded. Bachelor's degrees are awarded in BUSINESS (accounting, business administration and management, recreation and leisure services, and sports management), COMMUNICATIONS AND THE ARTS (communications, English, and journalism), COMPUTER AND PHYSICAL SCIENCE (atmospheric sciences and meteorology, computer science, mathematics, and natural sciences), EDUCATION (early childhood, elementary, English, physical, recreation, and science), SOCIAL SCIENCE (human services, interdisciplinary studies, psychology, and social science). Meteorology, natural science, mathematics, and computer science are the strongest academically. Education, communications, and business have the largest enrollments.

Required: All students must maintain a minimum GPA of 2.0 while taking 122 semester hours. The number required within each major field of study varies. Distribution requirements include 12 credits in arts and humanities, 7 in mathematics and science, and 6 in social and behavioral sciences. Specific required courses include freshman English, composition and literature, and elementary functions in mathematics.

Special: Cooperative programs in a variety of businesses, including local ski areas, social agencies, and radio and TV stations, internships in recreation programs and communications, and study abroad in Nova Scotia and England are available. B.A.-B.S. degrees, work-study, a general studies degree, dual and student-designed majors, a 3–2 engineering degree with Norwich University in Vermont, credit for life experience, nondegree study, and pass/fail options also are offered.

Faculty/Classroom: Sixty-nine percent of faculty are male; 31%, female. All teach undergraduates. No introductory courses are taught by graduate students. The average class size in an introductory lecture is 25; in a laboratory and regular course offering, 16.

Admissions: About 90% of the 1993–94 applicants were accepted.

Requirements: The SAT I is required. LSC recommends that applicants have 4 years of English and 2 years each of mathematics, foreign language, history, and science. An essay also is needed, as is a recommendation from the high school principal or guidance counselor. An interview is recommended. The GED is accepted. AP and CLEP credits are accepted. Important factors used in the admissions decision are advanced placement or honor courses, recommendations by school officials, leadership record, parents or siblings attending the school, and recommendations by alumni.

Procedure: Freshmen are admitted in the fall and spring. Application deadlines are open. The application fee is $40. Notification is sent on a rolling basis. There is a deferred admissions plan.

Transfer: About 80 transfer students enrolled in an earlier year. Interviews are recommended for transfer students. An official transcript from each college attended is required. A total of 30 credits out of 122 must be completed at LSC.

Visiting: There are guides for informal visits, and visitors may sit in on classes and stay overnight at the school. To arrange for a visit, contact the Admissions Office at (802) 626-9371, ext. 113.

Financial Aid: In an earlier class, 55% of all current freshmen and 42% of continuing students received some form of financial aid. Scholarships or need-based grants averaged $1200 ($4500 maximum); loans averaged $1500 ($8875 maximum); and work contracts averaged $1200 ($4000 maximum). The average financial indebtedness of an earlier graduate was $5000. LSC is a member of CSS.

The FAF or FFS, parent and student income tax forms, and FAFSA are required. The deadline for financial aid applications is March 15.
International Students: There are currently 10 international students enrolled. They must take the TOEFL and achieve a minimum score of 500.
Computers: The college provides computer facilities for student use. The mainframe is a DEC VAX 11/785. There are also PCs and Apple Macintosh microcomputers available. All students may access the system. There are no time limits on using the system. There is a $10 laboratory fee.
Graduates: In an earlier year, 96 bachelor's degrees were awarded.
Admissions Contact: R. Joseph Bellavance, Jr., Director of College Recruitment.

MARLBORO COLLEGE   B-6
Marlboro, VT 05344   **(802) 257-4333; (800) 343-0049 (out-of-state)**

Full-time: 127 men, 131 women	Faculty: 32; IIB, --$
Part-time: 3 men, 10 women	Ph.D.s: 60%
Graduate: none	Student/Faculty: 8 to 1
Year: semesters, summer session	Tuition: $17,625
Application Deadline: August 1	Room & Board: $5680
Freshman Class: 257 applied, 225 accepted, 93 enrolled	
SAT I Verbal/Math: 580/530	COMPETITIVE +

Marlboro College, established in 1946, is a private institution offering degrees in the liberal and fine arts and humanities, and employing self-designed programs of study that include one-on-one tutorials and oral examinations. The library contains 59,000 volumes and 6555 microform items, and subscribes to 189 periodicals. Computerized library sources and services include interlibrary loans. Special learning facilities include an art gallery and a planetarium. The 350-acre campus is in a rural area 9 miles west of Brattleboro. Including residence halls, there are 34 buildings on campus.
Student Life: Students come from 22 states, 6 foreign countries, and Canada. Seventy percent are from public schools; 30% from private. Ninety percent are white. Forty percent claim no religious affiliation; 20% Catholic; 10% Protestant. The average age of freshmen is 19. Seventeen percent drop out by the end of their first year; 55% remain to graduate.
Housing: A total of 210 students can be accommodated in college housing. College-sponsored living facilities include single-sex and coed dormitories, on-campus apartments, and married-student housing. In addition, there is an alcohol-free dormitory. On-campus housing is guaranteed for the freshman year only and is available on a first-come, first-served basis. Seventy-five percent of students live on campus; of those, 90% remain on campus on weekends. All students may keep cars on campus.
Activities: There are no fraternities or sororities on campus. There are a number of groups on campus, including art, chess, choir, chorus, computers, dance, drama, film, gay, jazz band, literary magazine, musical theater, newspaper, photography, political, social, social service, and student government. Popular campus events include Green-up Day, Cabaret, Fall Rites, Spring Rites, Town Meeting, Work Day, cross-country skiing, Dick Judd Triathalon, and trip to London.
Sports: Athletic and recreation facilities include a soccer field, a volleyball field, cross-country trails, a basketball court, a weight room, a climbing wall, and field trips for canoeing, white-water rafting, skiing, and skydiving.
Disabled Students: Almost all of the campus is accessible to disabled students. Wheelchair ramps, special parking, and specially equipped rest rooms are available.
Services: In addition to many counseling and information services, tutoring is available in some subjects, including writing and languages.
Campus Safety and Security: Campus safety and security measures include self-defense education, informal discussions, pamphlets, posters, films, and lighted pathways and sidewalks. In addition, there is a buddy system.
Programs of Study: Marlboro awards the B.A., B.S., B.A. in World Studies degrees. Master's degrees also are awarded. Bachel s degrees are awarded in BIOLOGICAL SCIENCE (bioche istry, biology/biological science, botany, and microbiology), COM MUNI-CATIONS AND THE ARTS (creative writing, dance, dramatic ts, English, fine arts, French, German, Greek, Italian, Latin, linguistics, music, Russian, and Spanish), COMPUTER AND PHYSICAL SCIENCE (chemistry, computer science, mathematics, physics, and statistics), HEALTH PROFESSIONS (premedicine), SOCIAL SCIENCE (anthropology, economics, history, interdisciplinary studies, international relations, philosophy, political science/government, prelaw, psychology, social science, and sociology). Sciences, environmental studies, humanities, writing, theater, and art are the strongest academically. Humanities has the largest enrollment.
Required: In order to graduate, students must complete a core curriculum and a writing requirement. A minimum GPA of 2.0 is required. Students must earn 120 credits, with 50 credits in the major.

Special: The college offers cross-registration with the School for International Training, a variety of internships, and study abroad in many countries. Accelerated and B.A.-B.S. degree programs are available. Students may pursue dual majors. Majors reflect an integrated course of study designed by students and their faculty advisors during the junior year.
Faculty/Classroom: Sixty-five percent of faculty are male; 35%, female. All teach undergraduates. The average class size in an introductory lecture is 10; in a laboratory and regular course offering, 8.
Admissions: About 88% of the 1993-94 applicants were accepted. About 40% of the current freshmen were in the top fifth of their class; 35% were in the top two fifths. One freshman graduated first in her class.
Requirements: Marlboro requires applicants to be in the upper 40% of their class. A minimum GPA of 3.0 is required. The SAT I is required. Applicants must graduate from an accredited secondary school or have a GED. They must earn 16 Carnegie units and complete 4 years of English and 3 each of mathematics, science, history, and a foreign language. SAT II: Subject tests are recommended. Essays and interviews are required. Auditions and portfolios are recommended in appropriate cases. AP and CLEP credits are accepted. Important factors used in the admissions decision are advanced placement or honor courses, evidence of special talent, leadership record, and recommendations by school officials.
Procedure: Freshmen are admitted in the fall and spring. Entrance exams should be taken by October before entry. There are early decision, early admissions, and deferred admissions plans. Early decision applications should be filed by December 1; regular applications, by August 1 for fall entry and January 1 for spring entry, along with an application fee of $30. Notification of early decision is sent December 15; regular decision, on a rolling basis. Seven early decision candidates were accepted for an earlier class.
Transfer: About 20 transfer students enrolled in 1993-94. Transfers must have a minimum GPA of 2.0. A total of 30 credits out of 120 must be completed at Marlboro.
Visiting: There are regularly scheduled orientations for prospective students, including camping trips and testing. There are guides for informal visits, and visitors may sit in on classes and stay overnight at the school. To arrange for a visit, contact Dora Poulos at (800) 343-0049.
Financial Aid: In 1993-94, 65% of all current freshmen and 60% of continuing students received some form of financial aid. About 65% of freshmen and 60% of continuing students received need-based aid. The average freshman award was $12,000. Of that total, scholarships or need-based grants averaged $8000 ($14,000 maximum); loans averaged $3000 ($5500 maximum); and work contracts averaged $1400 (maximum). Sixty-five percent of undergraduate students work part-time. Average earnings from campus work for the school year are $2600. The average financial indebtedness of the 1992-93 graduate was $12,000. Marlboro is a member of CSS. The FAF, the college's own financial statement, and FAFSA are required. The deadline for financial aid applications is April 1.
International Students: There are 18 international students enrolled. The school actively recruits these students. They must take the TOEFL and achieve a minimum score of 550. The student must also take the SAT I.
Computers: The college provides computer facilities for student use. Apple Macintoshes are available in a computer laboratory. All students may access the system 24 hours a day. There are no time limits on using the system and no fees.
Graduates: In an earlier class, 54 bachelor's degrees were awarded. The most popular majors among graduates were literature (30%), sociology (11%), and history (11%).
Admissions Contact: Wayne R. Wood, Director of Admissions.

MIDDLEBURY COLLEGE   A-3
Middlebury, VT 05753   **(802) 388-3711, ext. 5153**

Full-time: 980 men, 980 women	Faculty: IIB, + +$
Part-time: none	Ph.D.s: 80%
Graduate: none	Student/Faculty: n/av
Year: 4-1-4	Tuition: $24,400
Application Deadline: see profile	Room & Board: see profile
Freshman Class: 3456 applied, 1171 accepted, 451 enrolled	
SAT I or ACT: see profile	MOST COMPETITIVE

Middlebury College, founded in 1800, is a small, independent, coeducational liberal arts institution offering degree programs in languages, humanities, and social and natural sciences. The $24,400 tuition includes room and board. There are 2 graduate schools. The library contains 703,500 volumes, 70,098 microform items, and 19,721 audiovisual forms, and subscribes to 1950 periodicals. Computerized library sources and services include the card catalog, interlibrary loans, and database searching. Special learning facilities include a learning resource center, an art gallery, and a radio station.

The 350-acre campus is in a small town 35 miles south of Burlington. Including residence halls, there are 61 buildings on campus.

Student Life: About 96% of undergraduates are from out-of-state, mostly the Northeast. Students come from 49 states, 64 foreign countries, and Canada. Fifty-five percent are from public schools; 45% from private. Eighty percent are white. The average age of freshmen is 18; all undergraduates, 20. Three percent drop out by the end of their first year; 93% remain to graduate.

Housing: A total of 1960 students can be accommodated in college housing. College-sponsored living facilities include single-sex and coed dormitories. In addition, there are language and special interest houses. On-campus housing is guaranteed for all 4 years. Nearly all students live on campus; of those, 90% remain on campus on weekends. All students may keep cars on campus.

Activities: There are no fraternities or sororities on campus. There are 96 groups on campus, including art, band, chess, choir, chorus, computers, dance, drama, ethnic, film, gay, honors, international, jazz band, literary magazine, newspaper, orchestra, pep band, photography, political, professional, radio and TV, religious, social, social service, student government, symphony, and yearbook. Popular campus events include Winter Carnival, May Day, Student Concert Series, and Martin Luther King Weekend.

Sports: There are 12 intercollegiate sports each for men and women, and 15 intramural sports each for men and women. Athletic and recreation facilities include 2 field houses, gymnasiums, a swimming pool, a fitness center, tennis courts, playing fields, an 18-hole golf course, alpine and nordic ski areas, and a 3000-seat campus stadium.

Disabled Students: The following facilities are available: wheelchair ramps, elevators, special parking, specially equipped rest rooms, special class scheduling, and lowered drinking fountains.

Services: In addition to many counseling and information services, tutoring is available in every subject. There is a reader service for the blind and remedial math, reading, and writing.

Campus Safety and Security: Campus safety and security measures include 24-hour foot and vehicle patrol, escort service, informal discussions, pamphlets, posters, and films. In addition, there are lighted pathways and sidewalks.

Programs of Study: ÖMiddlebury awards the A.B. degree. Master's and doctoral degrees also are awarded. Bachelor's degrees are awarded in BIOLOGICAL SCIENCE (biochemistry, biology/biological science, and molecular biology), BUSINESS (international economics), COMMUNICATIONS AND THE ARTS (American literature, art, Chinese, classics, dance, dramatic arts, English, film arts, French, German, Italian, literature, music, Russian, and Spanish), COMPUTER AND PHYSICAL SCIENCE (chemistry, computer science, geology, mathematics, and physics), ENGINEERING AND ENVIRONMENTAL DESIGN (environmental science), HEALTH PROFESSIONS (predentistry, premedicine, and preveterinary science), SOCIAL SCIENCE (American studies, anthropology, classical/ancient civilization, East Asian studies, economics, geography, history, international relations, philosophy, political science/government, psychology, religion, Russian and Slavic studies, sociology, and women's studies). Foreign languages, international relations, science, and literature are the strongest programs academically. English, political science, history, economics, art, and biology have the largest enrollments.

Required: Students must complete 36 courses, including winter-term courses. Freshmen must take a freshman seminar and a writing course, and all students must take physical education. A major normally requires 12 courses; most students can fulfill the distribution requirement and the cultures and civilization requirement by taking 6 to 8 courses outside of their major. Students may also elect to complete a minor.

Special: Off-campus opportunities include an international major program at one of the Middlebury College schools abroad; exchange programs with Berea, St. Mary's, and Swarthmore colleges; a junior year abroad; study through the American Collegiate Consortium for East-West Cultural and Academic Exchange; a 1-year program at Lincoln and Worcester Colleges, Oxford; a Washington, D.C. semester; and a maritime studies program with Williams College at Mystic Seaport. Middlebury also offers an independent scholar program, joint and double majors, various professional programs, dual degrees in business management, forestry/environmental studies, engineering, and nursing, and an early assurance premed program with Dartmouth, Rochester, Tufts, and the Medical College of Pennsylvania, which assures medical school acceptance by the end of the sophomore year. There is a chapter of Phi Beta Kappa on campus. All departments have honors programs.

Faculty/Classroom: Seventy percent of faculty are male; 30%, female. All teach undergraduates. The average class size in a regular course offering is 15.

Admissions: About 34% of the 1993–94 applicants were accepted. The SAT scores for the 1993–94 freshman class were as follows: Verbal—7% below 500, 31% between 500 and 599, 55% between 600 and 700, and 7% above 700; Math—2% below 500, 16% between

500 and 599, 55% between 600 and 700, and 28% above 700. About 84% of the current freshmen were in the top fifth of their class; 98% were in the top two fifths.

Requirements: Standardized test scores are accepted as follows: the SAT I and 3 SAT II: Subject tests (including 1 in writing), 5 SAT II: Subject tests (including 1 in writing), or the ACT. AP exams may be substituted for achievement tests. Applicants should be high school graduates or have earned the GED. A recommended secondary program includes 4 years each of English, a foreign language, and mathematics and/or computer science, 2 or more each of laboratory sciences and history, and some courses in music, art, or drama. AP credit is accepted. Important factors used in the admissions decision are advanced placement or honor courses, recommendations by school officials, evidence of special talent, leadership record, and personality, intangible qualities.

Procedure: Freshmen are admitted in the fall and spring. Entrance exams should be taken by January 31 of the senior year. There are early decision and deferred admission plans. Early decision applications should be filed by November 15; regular applications, by December 15 for Part 1 and January 1 for Part 2;, along with an application fee of $50. Notification of early decision is sent December 15; regular decision, by April 5. About 134 early decision candidates were accepted for the 1993–94 class. A waiting list is an active part of the admissions procedure, with about 15% of applicants on the list.

Transfer: Four transfer students enrolled in 1993–94. Transfer students must have the strongest academic record possible. A total of 18 courses out of 36 must be completed at Middlebury.

Visiting: There are regularly scheduled orientations for prospective students, including campus tours and a group or individual interview. There are guides for informal visits and visitors may sit in on classes and stay overnight at the school.

Financial Aid: In 1993–94, 38% of all current freshmen received some form of financial aid. All freshmen received need-based aid. The average freshman award in an earlier year was $11,683. Sixty percent of undergraduate students work part-time. Average earnings from campus work for the school year are $650. The FAF, the college's own financial statement, the federal tax form, and FAFSA are required. The deadline for financial aid applications is January 15.

International Students: There are currently 173 international students enrolled. The school actively recruits these students. They must take the TOEFL and achieve the same standardized test requirements as freshman applicants.

Computers: The college provides computer facilities for student use. The mainframe is a DEC VAX/VMS. Individual student rooms are wired to the mainframe. More than half of the students have their own personal computers, and there are more than 150 public microcomputers easily available in 7 buildings on campus. There are connections to Internet and Bitnet and a variety of software is available. All students may access the system 24 hours a day. There are no time limits and no fees.

Graduates: In an earlier year, 375 bachelor's degrees were awarded. Within an average freshman class, 95% graduate in 4 years. Some 32 companies recruited on campus in 1992–93.

Admissions Contact: Geoffrey R. Smith, Director of Admissions.

NORWICH UNIVERSITY
C-3

Northfield, VT 05663 (802) 485-2001; (800) 468-6679 (out-of-state)

Full-time: 1256 men, 606 women	Faculty: 110; IIA, --$
Part-time: 80 men, 302 women	Ph.D.s: 85%
Graduate: 141 men, 302 women	Student/Faculty: 17 to 1
Year: semesters, summer session	Tuition: $13,460
Application Deadline: open	Room & Board: $5270
Freshman Class: n/av	
SAT I Verbal/Math: 465/510	ACT: 23 COMPETITIVE

Norwich University, founded in 1819, offers coeducational programs in arts and sciences, engineering, and education, and in the military, health science, and business professions. There is one graduate school. In addition to regional accreditation, Norwich has baccalaureate program accreditation with ABET and NLN. The library contains 230,000 volumes, 75,000 microform items, and 4487 audiovisual forms, and subscribes to 1364 periodicals. Special learning facilities include a learning resource center, an art gallery, and a radio station. The 1125-acre campus is in a small town 11 miles south of Montpelier. Including residence halls, there are 34 buildings on campus.

Student Life: About 80% of undergraduates are from out-of-state, mostly the Northeast. Students come from 48 states, 29 foreign countries, and Canada. Seventy-five percent are from public schools; 25% from private. Ninety-four percent are white. The average age of freshmen is 18; all undergraduates, 20. Twenty-five percent drop out by the end of their first year; 62% remain to graduate.

Housing: A total of 1725 students can be accommodated in college housing. College-sponsored living facilities include single-sex and coed dormitories. On-campus housing is guaranteed for all 4 years. Eighty-two percent of students live on campus; of those, 65% remain

on campus on weekends. Alcohol is not permitted. Upperclassmen may keep cars on campus.

Activities: There are no fraternities or sororities on campus. There are 50 groups on campus, including band, cheerleading, choir, chorus, drama, drill team, international, jazz band, marching band, musical theater, newspaper, orchestra, pep band, political, professional, radio and TV, religious, social service, student government, and yearbook. Popular campus events include Regimental Ball, Winter Carnival, Junior Weekend, Homecoming/Alumni Weekend, and Parents and Family Weekend.

Sports: There are 15 intercollegiate sports for men and 10 for women, and 17 intramural sports for men and 12 for women. Athletic and recreation facilities include an ice hockey arena, a field house with an indoor track, an indoor swimming pool, weight and wrestling rooms, playing fields, an outdoor track, a 1200-seat basketball arena, and a 1000-seat stadium.

Disabled Students: The following facilities are available: wheelchair ramps, elevators, special parking, and specially equipped rest rooms.

Services: In addition to many counseling and information services, tutoring is available in most subjects. There is also remedial math, reading, and writing.

Campus Safety and Security: Campus safety and security measures include 24-hour foot and vehicle patrol and lighted pathways and sidewalks.

Programs of Study: Norwich awards the B.A., B.S., B.Arch. degrees. Associate and master's degrees also are awarded. Bachelor's degrees are awarded in BIOLOGICAL SCIENCE (biology/biological science), BUSINESS (accounting, business administration and management, and business economics), COMMUNICATIONS AND THE ARTS (communications, English, and Russian), COMPUTER AND PHYSICAL SCIENCE (chemistry, earth science, information sciences and systems, mathematics, and physics), EDUCATION (physical and secondary), ENGINEERING AND ENVIRONMENTAL DESIGN (architecture, civil engineering, computer engineering, electrical engineering, engineering, engineering technology, environmental science, and mechanical engineering), HEALTH PROFESSIONS (medical laboratory technology, nursing, predentistry, premedicine, and sports medicine), SOCIAL SCIENCE (criminal justice, history, international studies, political science/government, prelaw, psychology, and religion). Engineering is the strongest program academically. Engineering has the largest enrollment.

Required: The total number of required credits and courses vary by program. All students are required to complete 3 credit hours in history and 2 semesters in physical education. A 2.0 GPA is required to graduate.

Special: Many internships are available. Study abroad through other schools and through the Vermont Overseas Studies Program is accepted. The B.A.-B.S. degree, a general studies degree, pass/fail options, and student-designed majors are possible. There is a special Adult Degree Program. The Russian School offers a special intensive summer session. There are 5 national honor societies on campus, including Phi Beta Kappa.

Faculty/Classroom: Eighty-five percent teach undergraduates. No introductory courses are taught by graduate students. The average class size in an introductory lecture is 28; in a laboratory, 15; and in a regular course offering, 20.

Admissions: The SAT scores for the 1993–94 freshman class were as follows: Verbal—73% below 500, 20% between 500 and 599, 6% between 600 and 700, and 1% above 700; Math—53% below 500, 36% between 500 and 599, 10% between 600 and 700, and 1% above 700. The ACT scores were 16% below 21, 49% between 21 and 25, 31% between 26 and 29, and 4% above 30. About 25% of the current freshmen were in the top fifth of their class; 70% were in the top two fifths. Ten freshmen graduated first in their class.

Requirements: Norwich requires applicants to be in the upper 50% of their class. A minimum GPA of 2.5 is required. The SAT I or ACT is required. Applicants should graduate from an accredited secondary school with 18 academic credits or achieve the GED equivalent. AP and CLEP credits are accepted. Important factors used in the admissions decision are leadership record, recommendations by school officials, extracurricular activities record, advanced placement or honor courses, and evidence of special talent.

Procedure: Freshmen are admitted in the fall and spring. Entrance exams should be taken beginning in the spring of the junior year. Application deadlines are open. The application fee is $25. Notification is sent on a rolling basis. There is an early decision plan. About 25 early decision candidates were accepted for the 1993–94 class.

Transfer: About 25 transfer students enrolled in 1993–94. Transfer students should present a 2.0 GPA and meet all standards for entering freshmen.

Visiting: There are regularly scheduled orientations for prospective students. There are guides for informal visits and visitors may sit in on classes and stay overnight at the school. To arrange for a visit, contact Admissions, Main Office at (800) 468-6679.

Financial Aid: In a recent year, 53% of all current freshmen and 58% of continuing students received some form of financial aid. The average freshman award was $11,000. Norwich is a member of CSS. The FAF and FAFSA are required.

International Students: There are currently 32 international students enrolled. The school actively recruits these students. They must take the TOEFL and achieve a minimum score of 500.

Computers: The university provides computer facilities for student use. The mainframes are a DEC VAX 11/780 and a DEC VAX 11/785. All students may access the system 20 hours per day. There are no time limits and no fees.

Graduates: In an earlier year, 298 bachelor's degrees were awarded. Some 25 companies recruited on campus.

Admissions Contact: Frank E. Griffis, Director of Admissions and Marketing.

SAINT MICHAEL'S COLLEGE
A-2
Colchester, VT 05439

(802) 654-3000
(800) 762-8000 (out-of-state)

Full-time: 795 men, 888 women	Faculty: 121; IIB, av$
Part-time: 16 men, 20 women	Ph.D.s: 87%
Graduate: 220 men, 444 women	Student/Faculty: 14 to 1
Year: semesters, summer session	Tuition: $12,430
Application Deadline: February 15	Room & Board: $5500
Freshman Class: 1910 applied, 1380 accepted, 463 enrolled	
SAT I Verbal/Math: 487/540	COMPETITIVE

St. Michael's College, established in 1904, is a nonprofit, liberal arts and sciences institution affiliated with the Roman Catholic Church. There are 5 graduate schools. The library contains 160,000 volumes, 25,000 microform items, and 9630 audiovisual forms, and subscribes to 1000 periodicals. Computerized library sources and services include interlibrary loans and database searching. Special learning facilities include a radio station and an observatory. The 400-acre campus is in a suburban area 2 miles east of Burlington. Including residence halls, there are 56 buildings on campus.

Student Life: About 82% of undergraduates are from out-of-state, mostly the Northeast. Students come from 28 states, 25 foreign countries, and Canada. Sixty-nine percent are from public schools; 31% from private. Ninety-two percent are white. Eighty-five percent are Catholic; 10% Protestant. The average age of freshmen is 18; all undergraduates, 21. Twelve percent drop out by the end of their first year; 75% remain to graduate.

Housing: A total of 1500 students can be accommodated in college housing. College-sponsored living facilities include single-sex and coed dormitories and on-campus apartments. In addition, there are small homes on the campus periphery accommodating many special interests and themes, including substance-free housing. On-campus housing is guaranteed for all 4 years. Eighty-seven percent of students live on campus; of those, 95% remain on campus on weekends. Upperclassmen may keep cars on campus.

Activities: There are no fraternities or sororities on campus. There are 45 groups on campus, including band, cheerleading, choir, chorale, dance, drama, ethnic, gay, honors, international, jazz band, literary magazine, musical theater, newspaper, photography, political, professional, radio, religious, social, social service, student government, and yearbook. Popular campus events include Dorm Daze, Homecoming, Winter Weekend, Friday Night Dry, Spring Weekend, Parents Weekend, Academic Convocation, and a variety of seminars and symposia.

Sports: There are 10 intercollegiate sports each for men and women, and 7 intramural sports for men and 5 for women. Athletic and recreation facilities include a 2100-seat gymnasium with basketball, volleyball, badminton, and tennis courts; a 6-lane swimming pool; weight, exercise, and training rooms; soccer, field hockey, lacrosse, and softball fields; and outdoor tennis courts.

Disabled Students: Half of the campus is accessible to disabled students. The following facilities are available: wheelchair ramps, elevators, special parking, specially equipped rest rooms, special class scheduling, lowered drinking fountains and telephones, and specially equipped residential space.

Services: In addition to many counseling and information services, tutoring is available in some subjects, including mathematics, accounting, science, and writing.

Campus Safety and Security: Campus safety and security measures include 24-hour foot and vehicle patrol, shuttle buses, informal discussions, pamphlets, posters, and films. In addition, there are emergency telephones, lighted pathways and sidewalks, and a campus fire and rescue squad.

Programs of Study: St. Michael's awards the B.A. and B.S. degrees. Master's degrees also are awarded. Bachelor's degrees are awarded in BIOLOGICAL SCIENCE (biochemistry and biology/biological science), BUSINESS (accounting and business administration and management), COMMUNICATIONS AND THE ARTS (dramatic arts, English, fine arts, French, journalism, music, and Spanish), COMPUTER

AND PHYSICAL SCIENCE (chemistry, computer science, mathematics, and physics), EDUCATION (art, elementary, foreign languages, science, and secondary), ENGINEERING AND ENVIRONMENTAL DESIGN (environmental science), HEALTH PROFESSIONS (predentistry and premedicine), SOCIAL SCIENCE (anthropology, economics, history, philosophy, political science/government, prelaw, psychology, religion, and sociology). Business administration, psychology, English literature, and political science have the largest enrollments.

Required: To graduate, students must complete 9 credits in humanities, 6 each in communications, religious studies, philosophy, science, mathematics, and social sciences, and 3 each in global perspectives and interdisciplinary studies. They must have a GPA of 2.0. The college requires a minimum of 124 credits and a minimum of 34 different courses for graduation. A maximum of 52 credits may be taken in the major.

Special: Students may cross-register with Trinity College or Xavier University of Louisiana. A variety of internships are available. There is a Washington semester with American University and study abroad in 20 countries. Student-designed majors may be pursued. The college offers a 3–2 engineering degree program in cooperation with Clarkson University and 4–1 with University of Vermont. Nondegree study and pass/fail grading options are offered on a limited basis. There is a freshman honors program on campus, as well as one national honor society. One department has an honors program.

Faculty/Classroom: Seventy-one percent of faculty are male; 29%, female. All faculty teach and do research. The average class size in an introductory lecture is 30; in a laboratory, 15; and in a regular course offering, 20.

Admissions: About 72% of the 1993–94 applicants were accepted. The SAT scores for the 1993–94 freshman class were as follows: Verbal—65% below 500, 31% between 500 and 599, and 4% between 600 and 700; Math—36% below 500, 48% between 500 and 599, 15% between 600 and 700, and 1% above 700. About 35% of the current freshmen were in the top fifth of their class; 82% were in the top two fifths. Eight freshmen graduated first in their class.

Requirements: St. Michael's requires applicants to be in the upper 50% of their class. The SAT I of ACT is required. Applicants must graduate from an accredited secondary school or have a GED. They must complete 16 Carnegie units. The college requires 4 credits in English, 3 to 4 in mathematics, 2 to 4 in science, and 2 to 3 each in history, social studies, and a foreign language. An essay is required and an interview is recommended. AP and CLEP credits are accepted. Important factors used in the admissions decision are advanced placement or honor courses, evidence of special talent, recommendations by school officials, geographic diversity, and parents or siblings attending the school.

Procedure: Freshmen are admitted in the fall. Entrance exams should be taken in the fall of the senior year. There are early decision and deferred admissions plans. Early decision applications should be filed by November 15; regular applications, by February 15 for fall entry and November 11 for winter entry, along with an application fee of $35. Notification of early decision is sent January 1; regular decision, April 1. About 125 early decision candidates were accepted for the 1993–94 class. A waiting list is an active part of the admissions procedure, with about 7% of applicants on the list.

Transfer: Transfer applicants must have a minimum GPA of 2.5; generally, those admitted have a GPA of at least 3.3. The SAT I is required. An interview is recommended. A total of 30 credits out of 124 must be completed at St. Michael's.

Visiting: There are regularly scheduled orientations for prospective students, including a group information session, a video about the school, and a review of admissions criteria. There are guides for informal visits and visitors may sit in on classes and stay overnight at the school. To arrange for a visit, contact the Admissions Office at (802) 654-3000.

Financial Aid: In 1993–94, 74% of all current freshmen and 61% of continuing students received some form of financial aid. About 65% of freshmen and 49% of continuing students received need-based aid. The average freshman award was $11,345. Of that total, scholarships or need-based grants averaged $6350 ($12,000 maximum); loans averaged $3625 ($5125 maximum); and work contracts averaged $850 ($2000 maximum). Thirty-six percent of undergraduate students work part-time. Average earnings from campus work for the school year are $900. The average financial indebtedness of the 1992–93 graduate was $11,200. St. Michael's is a member of CSS. Both student and parent federal tax forms and the FAFSA financial statement are required. The deadline for financial aid applications is March 15.

International Students: There are currently 65 international students enrolled. The school actively recruits these students. They must take the TOEFL or the college's own test and achieve a minimum score on the TOEFL of 550. The student must also take the SAT I, or ACT. If possible, St. Michael's will consider the TOEFL in place of the SAT I.

Computers: The college provides computer facilities for student use. The mainframes are 2 DEC VAX 3400s and 4000s, and a DEC MicroVAX II. There are 8 microcomputer laboratories available for student use, 6 of them connected to the campus network (Mikenet). The seventh laboratory supports undergraduate and graduate education programs and the eighth is an Apple Macintosh laboratory. All students may access the system. There are no time limits on using the system and no fees.

Graduates: In 1992–93, 437 bachelor's degrees were awarded. The most popular majors among graduates were business administration (24%), psychology (14%), and English literature (11%). Within an average freshman class, 1% graduate in 3 years, 74% in 4 years, and 75% in 5 years. Some 40 companies recruited on campus in a recent year.

Admissions Contact: Jerry E. Flanagan, Dean of Admission and Enrollment Management.

SOUTHERN VERMONT COLLEGE A-6
Bennington, VT 05201 (802) 442-5427

Full-time: 212 men, 206 women	Faculty: 27; IIB, --$
Part-time: 62 men, 221 women	Ph.D.s: 13%
Graduate: none	Student/Faculty: 15 to 1
Year: semesters, summer session	Tuition: $8670
Application Deadline: open	Room & Board: $4304
Freshman Class: 329 applied, 223 accepted, 186 enrolled	
SAT I or ACT: nor required	COMPETITIVE

Southern Vermont College, established in 1926, is a private institution offering undergraduate degrees in liberal arts, professional training, and business, and through a weekend program that accommodates adult students. The library contains 25,000 volumes and 3 microform items, and subscribes to 270 periodicals. Computerized library sources and services include interlibrary loans and database searching. Special learning facilities include a learning resource center and an art gallery. The 371-acre campus is in a small town 40 miles east of Albany, New York. Including residence halls, there are 10 buildings on campus.

Student Life: About 58% of undergraduates are from out-of-state, mostly the Northeast. Students come from 20 states, 5 foreign countries, and Canada. Eighty-five percent are from public schools. Ninety-five percent are white. The average age of freshmen is 19; all undergraduates, 20. Twenty-one percent drop out by the end of their first year; 79% remain to graduate.

Housing: A total of 250 students can be accommodated in college housing. College-sponsored living facilities include coed dormitories. In addition, college-sponsored off-campus housing, and quiet, nonsmoking, and fitness residence halls are available. On-campus housing is guaranteed for all 4 years. Sixty-five percent of students commute. Alcohol is not permitted. All students may keep cars on campus.

Activities: There are no fraternities or sororities on campus. There are 20 groups on campus, including drama, ethnic, gay, honors, international, literary magazine, newspaper, professional, social, social service, student government, and yearbook. Popular campus events include Octoberfest, Spree Day, Superstars Weekend, and Family Weekend.

Sports: There are 4 intercollegiate sports each for men and women, and 5 intramural sports each for men and women. Athletic and recreation facilities include a multipurpose field for softball, baseball, and soccer, a gymnasium and health education facility, and putting greens.

Disabled Students: Fifty percent of the campus is accessible to disabled students. Wheelchair ramps and special parking are available.

Services: In addition to many counseling and information services, tutoring is available in every subject. In addition, there is remedial math, reading, and writing. Skills workshops, a freshman seminar, and a program to assist students with basic college skills are also available.

Campus Safety and Security: Campus safety and security measures include 24-hour foot and vehicle patrol, escort service, shuttle buses, and informal discussions. In addition, there are pamphlets, posters, films, emergency telephones, lighted pathways and sidewalks, 2-way radios, fire drills, and safe rides on weekends from where alcohol is served.

Programs of Study: SVC awards the B.A., B.S., and B.S.N. degrees. Associate degrees also are awarded. Bachelor's degrees are awarded in BUSINESS (accounting, business administration and management, and hotel/motel and restaurant management), COMMUNICATIONS AND THE ARTS (communications and English), ENGINEERING AND ENVIRONMENTAL DESIGN (environmental science), HEALTH PROFESSIONS (nursing), SOCIAL SCIENCE (child psychology/development, criminal justice, gerontology, human services, liberal arts/general studies, and social work). English, environmental studies, and accounting are the strongest programs ac-

ademically. Business, criminal justice, and liberal arts have the largest enrollments.

Required: To graduate, students must complete a 48-credit core requirement consisting of course work in economics, English, environmental studies, government, history, cultural arts, mathematics (including computer science), natural sciences, philosophy, psychology, and sociology. Management students must take courses in accounting, writing, management, organizational behavior, marketing, supervision, and management ethics, and they must take a management decision-making course or complete an internship. Students who do not pursue the management program must complete a minor in addition to the major. A minimum GPA of 2.0 is required. Students must earn a minimum of 120 credits.

Special: The college offers internships, work-study, and cooperative programs in criminal justice and environmental studies. Students may study abroad in Oxford, England. Individualized degree programs and dual majors may be pursued. There is an accelerated degree program, and credit for life, military, and work experience may be granted. Nondegree study and a pass/fail grading option are also offered. There is a freshman honors program on campus, as well as campuswide honors program.

Faculty/Classroom: Forty-six percent of faculty are male; 54%, female. All teach undergraduates. The average class size in an introductory lecture is 25 and in a regular course offering, 18.

Admissions: About 68% of the 1993–94 applicants were accepted.

Requirements: A minimum GPA of 2.0 is required. The SAT I or ACT is not required. Applicants must graduate from an accredited secondary school or have a GED. The college requires 3 years of English and 2 years of mathematics. AP and CLEP credits are accepted. Important factors used in the admissions decision are recommendations by school officials, leadership record, evidence of special talent, and extracurricular activities record.

Procedure: Freshmen are admitted in the fall and spring. Application deadlines are open. The application fee is $25. Notification is sent on a rolling basis. There are early admissions and deferred admissions plans.

Transfer: About 50 transfer students enrolled in a recent year. Transfer applicants must have a GPA of 2.0 and be in good standing. Interviews are recommended. A total of 30 credits out of 120 must be completed at SVC.

Visiting: There are guides for informal visits and visitors may sit in on classes and stay overnight at the school. To arrange for a visit, contact Admissions at (802) 442–5427, ext. 150.

Financial Aid: In 1993–94, 92% of all current freshmen and 65% of continuing students received some form of financial aid. About 89% of freshmen and 65% of continuing students received need-based aid. The average freshman award was $5825. Of that total, scholarships or need-based grants averaged $3545 ($12,500 maximum); loans averaged $3154 ($5500 maximum); and work contracts averaged $1500 (maximum). Twenty percent of undergraduate students work part-time. Average earnings from campus work for the school year was $1500. The average financial indebtedness of the 1992–93 graduate was $13,250. SVC is a member of CSS. The FAF and FAFSA are required. The deadline for financial aid applications is May 1.

International Students: There are currently 5 international students enrolled. They must take the TOEFL and achieve a minimum score of 500.

Computers: The college provides computer facilities for student use and word processors for academic use. All students may access the system. There are no time limits and no fees.

Graduates: In a recent year, 70 bachelor's degrees were awarded. The most popular majors among graduates were business and management (47%), parks/recreation, protective services, and public affairs (31%), and letters/literature (9%). Within an average freshman class, 22% graduate in 4 years and 40% in 5 years. In the 1992 graduating class, 3% of all graduate were enrolled in graduate school within 6 months of graduation; 51% had found employment.

Admissions Contact: Mary G. Van Arsdale, Director of Admissions.

TRINITY COLLEGE OF VERMONT
Burlington, VT 05401

A-2
(802) 658-0337

Full-time: 24 men, 472 women	Faculty: 45; IIB, --$
Part-time: 135 men, 385 women	Ph.Ds: 78%
Graduate: none	Student/Faculty: 11 to 1
Year: semesters, summer session	Tuition: $10,945
Application Deadline: open	Room & Board: $5070
Freshman Class: 233 applied, 216 accepted, 90 enrolled	
SAT I Verbal/Math: 410/420	LESS COMPETITIVE

Trinity College of Vermont, established in 1925, is a nonprofit, private, primarily women's liberal arts institution operated by the Sisters of Mercy of the Roman Catholic Church. Its traditional admissions program accepts qualified women who have been graduates from high school for less than 4 years. Trinity's nontraditional program provides motivated adults, both women and men, an opportunity to begin or resume college careers. There is one graduate school. In addition to regional accreditation, Trinity has baccalaureate program accreditation with CSWE. The library contains 50,000 volumes, 43,000 microform items, and 1200 audiovisual forms, and subscribes to 378 periodicals. Computerized library sources and services include interlibrary loans and database searching. Special learning facilities include a learning resource center. The 20-acre campus is in a small urban area on Lake Champlain. Including residence halls, there are 12 buildings on campus.

Student Life: About 86% of undergraduates are from Vermont. Students come from 18 states, 3 foreign countries, and Canada. Seventy-six percent are from public schools; 24% from private. Nearly all are white. Fifty percent are Catholic. The average age of freshmen is 18. Thirty percent drop out by the end of their first year; 50% remain to graduate.

Housing: A total of 315 students can be accommodated in college housing. College-sponsored living facilities include single-sex dormitories. On-campus housing is guaranteed for all 4 years. Sixty-five percent of students live on campus; of those, 70% remain on campus on weekends. Upperclassmen may keep cars on campus.

Activities: There are no fraternities or sororities on campus. There are 13 groups on campus, including choir, chorale, drama, honors, international, musical theater, newspaper, political, religious, social service, student government, and yearbook.

Sports: There are 2 intercollegiate sports and 3 intramural sports. Athletic and recreation facilities include a fitness center and a gymnasium plus an agreement with St. Michael's College in nearby Colchester that permits use of its facilities.

Disabled Students: Ninety-two percent of the campus is accessible to disabled students. The following facilities are available: wheelchair ramps, elevators, special parking, specially equipped rest rooms, and lowered drinking fountains.

Services: In addition to many counseling and information services, tutoring is available in most subjects. There is also remedial math and writing.

Campus Safety and Security: Campus safety and security measures include 24-hour foot and vehicle patrol, self-defense education, escort service, and informal discussions. In addition, there are pamphlets, posters, films, and lighted pathways and sidewalks.

Programs of Study: Trinity awards the B.A. and B.S. degrees. Associate and master's degrees also are awarded. Bachelor's degrees are awarded in BIOLOGICAL SCIENCE (biology/biological science), BUSINESS (accounting, banking and finance, business administration and management, management information systems, and marketing/retailing/merchandising), COMMUNICATIONS AND THE ARTS (communications, English, French, modern language, and Spanish), COMPUTER AND PHYSICAL SCIENCE (chemistry and mathematics), EDUCATION (business, early childhood, elementary, science, secondary, and special), ENGINEERING AND ENVIRONMENTAL DESIGN (environmental science), HEALTH PROFESSIONS (medical laboratory technology), SOCIAL SCIENCE (criminal justice, crosscultural studies, economics, history, human services, interdisciplinary studies, philosophy, psychology, and social work). Education, business, biology, and chemistry are the strongest programs academically. Business, psychology, and education have the largest enrollments.

Required: Students must complete 120 credits, with 30 to 45 in the major, and maintain a minimum GPA of 2.0. The general education program is comprised of 39 credits, with 6 credits required in each of humanities, social sciences, and natural sciences/mathematics. Writing, speaking, quantitative, and computing competencies must be completed as well. A first-year advising seminar is also required.

Special: Special academic programs include on-campus work-study, internships, which are strongly encouraged in each major, and study-abroad opportunities available through a networking program in Bath, England. There is cross-registration with St. Michael's College. Dual majors are offered, and interdisciplinary degree programs include those in communication, U.S.-Canadian cultural studies, mathematics and science in elementary schools, computer programming, and business. Student-designed majors are an option, as is nondegree study. There are 3 national honor societies on campus.

Faculty/Classroom: Thirty-seven percent of faculty are male; 63%, female. All teach undergraduates. The average class size in an introductory lecture is 25; in a laboratory, 15; and in a regular course offering, 10.

Admissions: About 93% of the 1993–94 applicants were accepted. The SAT scores for the 1993–94 freshman class were as follows: Verbal—88% below 500, 10% between 500 and 599, and 2% between 600 and 700; Math—80% below 500, 18% between 500 and 599, and 2% between 600 and 700. About 31% of the current freshmen were in the top fifth of their class; 62% were in the top two fifths.

Requirements: A minimum GPA of 2.0 is required. The SAT I is required. Other admissions requirements include graduation from an accredited secondary school with 16 Carnegie units. Strongly recommended are 4 years of English, 2 each of a foreign language, mathe-

matics, science, social studies, and history, and 1 of a laboratory science. An essay must be submitted and an interview is advised. The GED is also accepted. AP and CLEP credits are accepted. Important factors used in the admissions decision are advanced placement or honor courses, leadership record, personality, intangible qualities, extracurricular activities record, and recommendations by school officials.

Procedure: Freshmen are admitted to all sessions. Entrance exams should be taken by the fall of the senior year. Application deadlines are open. The application fee is $30. Notification is sent on a rolling basis. There are early admissions and deferred admissions plans.

Transfer: About 25 transfer students enrolled in 1993–94. The criteria for transfer students is the same as for freshmen if they have earned fewer than 12 credits. Otherwise, applicants should have a minimum GPA of 2.0 and schedule an interview; each student is reviewed individually, taking into account the previous academic record. A total of 30 credits out of 120 must be completed at Trinity.

Visiting: There are regularly scheduled orientations for prospective students, including campus tours, visits to classes, and panel discussions. There are guides for informal visits, and visitors may stay overnight at the school. To arrange for a visit, contact the Admissions Office at (802) 658–0337.

Financial Aid: In 1993–94, 90% of all current freshmen and 78% of continuing students received some form of financial aid. About 86% of freshmen and 78% of continuing students received need-based aid. The average freshman award was $11,000. Of that total, scholarships or need-based grants averaged $7650 ($10,900 maximum); loans averaged $2678 ($3125 maximum); and work contracts averaged $996 ($1000 maximum). Forty-seven percent of undergraduate students work part-time. Average earnings from campus work for the school year are $1150. The average financial indebtedness of the 1992–93 graduate was $15,000. Trinity is a member of CSS. The FFS, the college's own financial statement, and the FAFSA are required. The deadline for financial aid applications is May 1.

International Students: There are currently 6 international students enrolled. They must take the TOEFL and achieve a minimum score of 500.

Computers: The college provides computer facilities for student use. The mainframe is an IBM AS 400. IBM microcomputers are available in the computer laboratory. There are no time limits on using the system and no fees.

Graduates: In 1992–93, 199 bachelor's degrees were awarded. The most popular majors among graduates were business (33%), elementary education (18%), and psychology (13%). In the 1992 graduating class, 10% of the graduates were enrolled in graduate school within 6 months of graduation; 85% had found employment.

Admissions Contact: Pamela Chisholm, Director of Admissions and Financial Aid.

UNIVERSITY OF VERMONT

A-2

Burlington, VT 05405
(802) 656–3370

Full-time: 3433 men, 3822 women	Faculty: 864; I, --$
Part-time: 199 men, 297 women	Ph.D.s: 87%
Graduate: 545 men, 670 women	Student/Faculty: 8 to 1
Year: semesters, summer session	Tuition: $6400 ($15,344)
Application Deadline: February 1	Room & Board: $4376

Freshman Class: 7663 applied, 6008 accepted, 1735 enrolled
SAT I Verbal/Math: 480/550
COMPETITIVE +

The University of Vermont, established in 1791, is a public, land-grant, comprehensive coeducational institution. Its undergraduate and graduate programs stress the liberal arts, business administration, engineering, mathematics, natural resources, agricultural studies, fine arts, professional training, teacher preparation, social services, environmental studies, and health science, including nursing. There are 8 undergraduate schools and one graduate school. In addition to regional accreditation, UVM has baccalaureate program accreditation with AACSB, ABET, ADA, APTA, ASLA, CAHEA, CSWE, NASM, NCATE, NLN, and SAF. The 5 libraries contain 1.3 million volumes, 1.2 million microform items, and 18,647 audiovisual forms, and subscribe to 10,318 periodicals. Computerized library sources and services include database searching. Special learning facilities include a learning resource center, an art gallery, and a radio station. In addition, the Medical Center Hospital of Vermont, the largest research hospital in the state, is located on the campus. The 425-acre campus is in a small town 90 miles south of Montreal and 200 miles north of Boston. Including residence halls, there are 90 buildings on campus.

Student Life: About 56% of undergraduates are from out-of-state, mostly the Northeast. Students come from 46 states, 40 foreign countries, and Canada. Seventy percent are from public schools; 30% from private. Ninety-five percent are white. The average age of freshmen is 18; all undergraduates, 21. Six percent drop out by the end of their first year; 75% remain to graduate.

Housing: A total of 3800 students can be accommodated in college housing. College-sponsored living facilities include coed dormitories, on-campus apartments, off-campus apartments, married-student housing, fraternity houses, and sorority houses. In addition, there are environmental halls and language and special interest suites/floors. On-campus housing is available on a lottery system for upperclassmen. Fifty-four percent of students commute. Upperclassmen may keep cars on campus.

Activities: About 16% of men belong to 14 national fraternities; about 14% of women belong to 6 national sororities. There are 100 groups on campus, including art, band, cheerleading, choir, chorus, computers, dance, drama, ethnic, gay, international, jazz band, literary magazine, musical theater, newspaper, orchestra, pep band, photography, political, radio and TV, social service, student government, and yearbook. Popular campus events include Octoberfest.

Sports: There are 12 intercollegiate sports each for men and women, and 30 intramural sports each for men and women. Athletic and recreation facilities include a 3228-seat gymnasium, a 4000-seat stadium, a field house, and Centennial Field.

Disabled Students: Eighty-seven percent of the campus is accessible to disabled students. The following facilities are available: wheelchair ramps, elevators, special parking, specially equipped rest rooms, special class scheduling, and lowered drinking fountains.

Services: In addition to many counseling and information services, tutoring is available in most subjects. There are also supplemental instruction, note-taking and test-taking seminars, and writing tutors, as well as support for ESL students. In addition, there is a reader service for the blind.

Campus Safety and Security: Campus safety and security measures include 24-hour foot and vehicle patrol, self-defense education, escort service, and shuttle buses. In addition, there are informal discussions, pamphlets, posters, films, emergency telephones, and lighted pathways and sidewalks.

Programs of Study: UVM awards the B.A., B.S., and B.M. degrees. Associate, master's, and doctoral degrees also are awarded. Bachelor's degrees are awarded in AGRICULTURE (animal science), BIOLOGICAL SCIENCE (biochemistry, biology/biological science, botany, microbiology, and zoology), BUSINESS (business administration and management and marketing/retailing/merchandising), COMMUNICATIONS AND THE ARTS (classics, dramatic arts, English, French, German, Greek, Latin, music, Russian, and Spanish), COMPUTER AND PHYSICAL SCIENCE (chemistry, computer science, geology, mathematics, physics, and statistics), EDUCATION (art, early childhood, elementary, foreign languages, health, music, secondary, and special), ENGINEERING AND ENVIRONMENTAL DESIGN (civil engineering, electrical/electronics engineering, engineering management, environmental science, and mechanical engineering), HEALTH PROFESSIONS (medical laboratory technology, nursing, and physical therapy), SOCIAL SCIENCE (anthropology, dietetics, economics, food science, geography, history, parks and recreation management, philosophy, political science/government, psychology, religion, social work, and sociology). Physical therapy, chemistry, and environmental studies are the strongest programs academically. Political science and psychology have the largest enrollments.

Required: Degree requirements vary among the individual colleges, but all require at least a 2.0 GPA and 2 semesters of physical education. For a B.A., the College of Arts and Sciences requires a minimum of 122 semester hours, completion of general requirements, including a foreign language, mathematics, and non-European cultures, and distribution requirements comprised of fine arts, literature, humanities, social sciences, and natural sciences.

Special: Special academic programs include internships, study abroad, a Washington semester, work-study, and cooperative programs in business and engineering. Dual and student-designed majors are available. Nondegree study and pass/fail options are possible. A special feature of the school is the Living/Learning Center, an integrated academic and student-support unit with a 588-student residence; it sponsors 30 to 35 year-long programs, each including course work, independent study, seminars, and field trips that support a particular theme. There are 17 national honor societies on campus, including Phi Beta Kappa. All departments have honors programs.

Faculty/Classroom: Seventy-one percent of faculty are male; 29%, female. Graduate students teach less than 5% of introductory courses. The average class size in a regular course offering is 23.

Admissions: About 78% of the 1993–94 applicants were accepted. The SAT scores for the 1993–94 freshman class were as follows: Verbal—55% below 500, 37% between 500 and 599, 8% between 600 and 700, and 1% above 700; Math—24% below 500, 45% between 500 and 599, 28% between 600 and 700, and 3% above 700. About 43% of the current freshmen were in the top fifth of their class; 81% were in the top two fifths.

Requirements: The SAT I is required. Other admissions requirements include graduation from an accredited secondary school, with 16 Carnegie units. Required high school course work includes 4 years of English, 3 of mathematics, including algebra I and II and ge-

ometry, and 2 each of a foreign language, science, and social studies. An essay must be submitted. The GED is also accepted. AP and CLEP credits are accepted. Important factors used in the admissions decision are advanced placement or honor courses, recommendations by school officials, leadership record, evidence of special talent, and parents or siblings attending the school.

Procedure: Freshmen are admitted in the fall and spring. Entrance exams should be taken by November of the senior year. There are early decision, early admissions, and deferred admissions plans. Early decision applications should be filed by November 1; regular applications, by February 1 for fall entry and November 1 for spring entry. The application fee is $30 for in-state students and $45 for out-of-state. Notification of early decision is sent December 15; regular decision, March 16. A waiting list is an active part of the admissions procedure.

Transfer: About 330 transfer students enrolled in 1993–94. Transfer students must have a minimum GPA of 2.5 in credited courses and meet the same criteria as freshmen. Considerations include the college and high school records, the major indicated, SAT I or ACT scores, and availabiltiy of space at UVM. A total of 30 credits out of 122 must be completed at UVM.

Visiting: There are regularly scheduled orientations for prospective students. There are guides for informal visits, and visitors may sit in on classes and stay overnight at the school. To arrange for a visit, contact the Admissions Office at (802) 656–3370.

Financial Aid: In 1993–94, 46% of all current freshmen and 44% of continuing students received some form of financial aid. About 46% of freshmen and 44% of continuing students received need-based aid. The average freshman award was $7808. All undergraduate students work part-time. UVM is a member of CSS. The FAF and FAFSA are required. The deadline for financial aid applications is March 1.

International Students: There are currently 229 international students enrolled. The school actively recruits these students. They must take the TOEFL and achieve a minimum score of 550. The student must also take the SAT I or the ACT.

Computers: The university provides computer facilities for student use. The mainframes are an IBM 4381 and a DEC VAX 8600. There are also microcomputers located in laboratories throughout the campus. All students may access the system. There are no time limits and no fees. It is recommended that students in all business and engineering majors have personal computers.

Graduates: In 1992–93, 1718 bachelor's degrees were awarded. The most popular majors among graduates were business (11%), political science (10%), and psychology (7%). Within an average freshman class, 60% graduate in 4 years, 73% in 5 years, and 77% in 6 years. More than 200 companies recruited on campus in 1992–93. In the 1992 graduating class, 17% of all students were enrolled in graduate school within 1 year of graduation; 76% found employment.

Admissions Contact: Carol Cotman Hogan, Director of Admissions.

VERMONT STATE COLLEGES

Vermont State Colleges, established in 1962, is a public system. It is governed by a board of trustees, whose chief administrator is the chancellor. The primary goal of the system is teaching. The main priorities are to insure that Vermonters and others have access to higher education, to provide educational programs that permit individuals to lead more productive and responsible lives, and to maintain a high quality of cultural, social, and economic life in Vermont. The total enrollment of all campuses is about 9000, with some 250 faculty members. Altogether, there are 60 baccalaureate and 5 master's programs offered by the Vermont State Colleges. Profiles of the 4-year campuses, located in Castleton, Johnson, and Lyndonville, are included in this chapter.

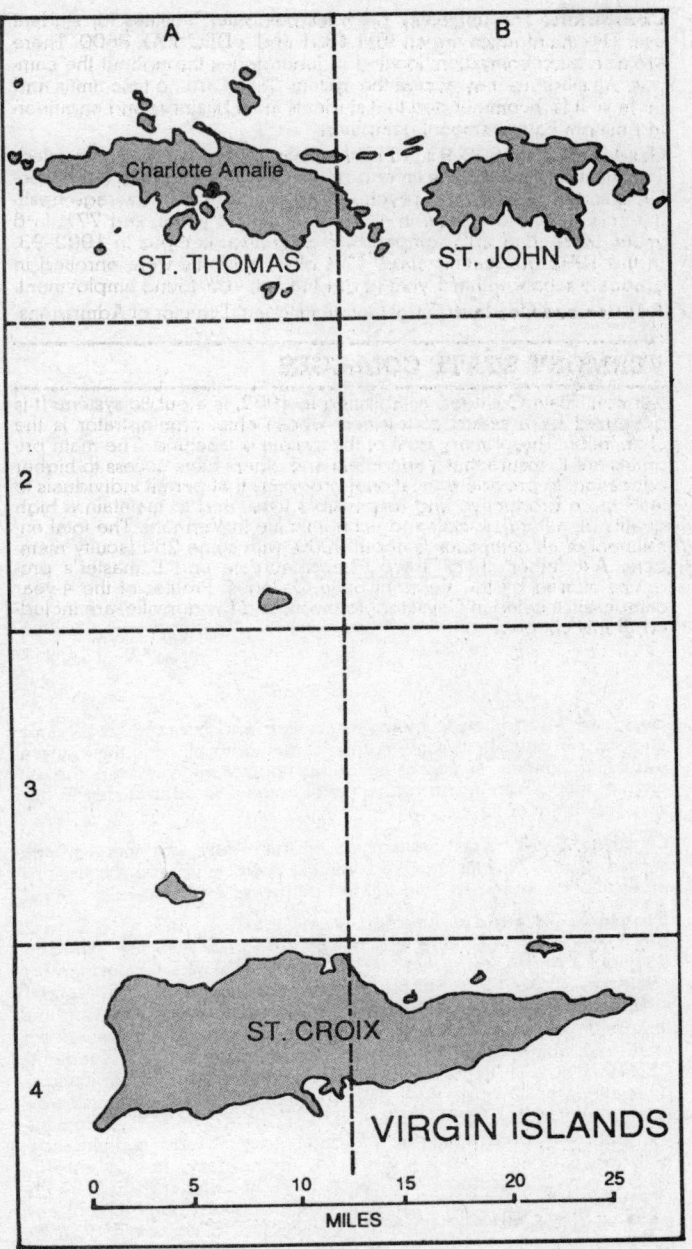

UNIVERSITY OF THE VIRGIN ISLANDS
St Thomas, VI 00802

A-1
(809) 776-9200

Full-time: 295 men, 851 women
Part-time: 407 men, 1115 women
Graduate: 56 men, 200 women
Year: semesters, summer session
Application Deadline: April 15
Freshman Class: 711 applied, 551 accepted, 321 enrolled
SAT I: required

Faculty: 112
Ph.D.s: 56%
Student/Faculty: 10 to 1
Tuition: $1596 ($4596)
Room & Board: $4300

The University of the Virgin Islands, founded in 1962, is a public, co-educational liberal arts university. There are 6 undergraduate and 3 graduate schools. In addition to regional accreditation, UVI has baccalaureate program accreditation with NLN. The 2 libraries contain 101,000 volumes, 850,000 microform items, and 2000 audiovisual forms, and subscribe to 1014 periodicals. The 175-acre campus is in a suburban area 3 miles west of Charlotte Amalie. Including residence halls, there are 45 buildings on campus.

Student Life: Most undergraduates are from the Virgin Islands. Students come from 14 states, 19 foreign countries, and Canada. Seventy-nine percent are African American.

Housing: A total of 238 students can be accommodated in college housing. College-sponsored living facilities include coed dormitories. On-campus housing is available on a first-come, first-served basis. Seventy-five percent of students commute. Alcohol is not permitted. All students may keep cars on campus.

Activities: There are no fraternities or sororities on campus. There are a number of groups on campus, including art, band, choir, computers, drama, honors, jazz band, newspaper, political, religious, social, student government, and yearbook.

Sports: There are 13 intramural sports for men and 12 for women. Athletic and recreation facilities include netball, volleyball, and basketball courts, a softball diamond, and tennis courts.

Disabled Students: Seventy-five percent of the campus is accessible to disabled students. The following facilities are available: wheelchair ramps, special parking, special class scheduling, and lowered telephones.

Services: In addition to many counseling and information services, tutoring is available in most subjects, including mathematics, English, and sciences. There is remedial math, reading, and writing.

Campus Safety and Security: Campus safety and security measures include 24-hour foot and vehicle patrol, informal discussions, pamphlets, posters, films, and lighted pathways and sidewalks.

Programs of Study: UVI awards the B.A. and B.S.C. degrees. Associate and master's degrees also are awarded. Bachelor's degrees are awarded in BIOLOGICAL SCIENCE (biology/biological science and marine biology), BUSINESS (accounting and business administration and management), COMMUNICATIONS AND THE ARTS (English and Spanish), COMPUTER AND PHYSICAL SCIENCE (chemistry and mathematics), EDUCATION (elementary, music, and vocational), HEALTH PROFESSIONS (nursing), SOCIAL SCIENCE (Caribbean studies, humanities, psychology, social science, and social work). Education and business are the strongest programs academically and have the largest enrollments.

Required: Graduation requirements vary by major selected. Most students will need to take courses in humanities, mathematics, social sciences, and physical education. A minimum of 120 credits must be earned, a 2.0 GPA must be achieved, and an English proficiency exam is required.

Special: The program in marine biology is augmented by work at the Marine Research Center on the island of St. John. UVI also offers dual majors, interdisciplinary majors, including chemistry with physics and speech communication and theater, and nondegree study.

Faculty/Classroom: Fifty-eight percent of faculty are male; 42%, female. No introductory courses are taught by graduate students.

Admissions: About 77% of the 1993–94 applicants were accepted. There were 2 National Merit semifinalists.

Requirements: A minimum GPA of 2.0 is required. The SAT I is required. Candidates for admission need not be graduates of an accredited secondary school. The GED is accepted. An essay is required. A candidate must have achieved a 2.0 GPA by the end of the junior year and maintained it during the senior year. The usual college preparatory courses are preferred, including 4 years of English, 2 of a foreign language, and 2 of algebra, or one of algebra and 2 of plane geometry. CLEP credit is accepted.

Procedure: Freshmen are admitted in the fall and spring. Entrance exams should be taken by May. Applications should be filed by April 15 for fall entry and November 15 for spring entry, along with an application fee of $20. Notification is sent on a rolling basis. There are early admissions and deferred admissions plans.

Transfer: Transfers must have completed at least 12 semester credits and have maintained at least a C or 2.0 cumulative average at the college(s) attended, plus all information required by a regular applicant. A total of 30 credits out of 120 must be completed at UVI.

Visiting: There are regularly scheduled orientations for prospective students. There are guides for informal visits and visitors may sit in on classes. To arrange for a visit, contact Student Affairs at (809) 776-9200.

Financial Aid: The FAF and FAFSA are required. The deadline for financial aid applications is April 15.

International Students: There are currently 137 international students enrolled. They must take the TOEFL and achieve a minimum score of 550.

Computers: The university provides computer facilities for student use. There are several computer laboratories equipped with IBM-PC compatibles and Macintosh PCs. All students may access the system with no time limits. The fees are $20.

Graduates: In 1992–93, 174 bachelor's degrees were awarded. The most popular majors among graduates were business administration (36%), accounting (16%), and education (12%).

Admissions Contact: Judith W. Edwin, Director of Admissions.

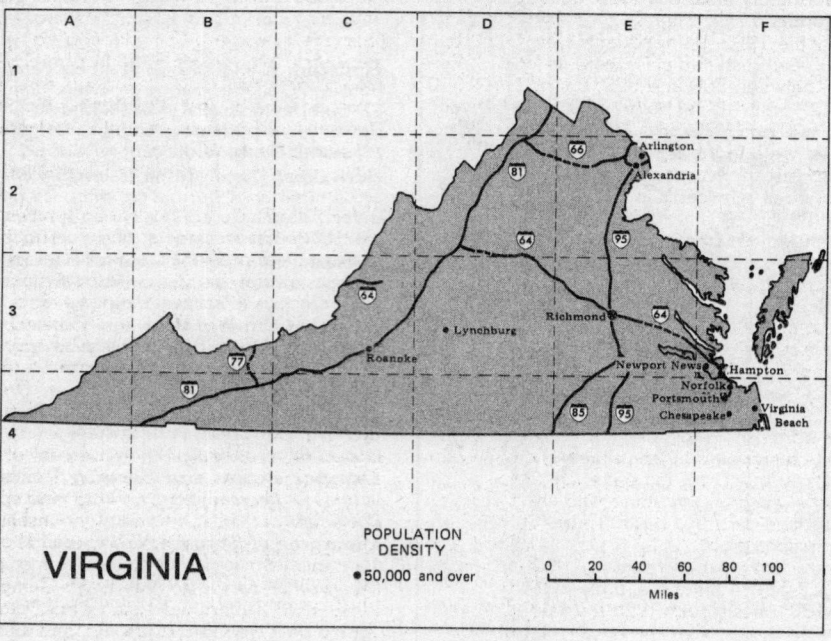

VIRGINIA

POPULATION
DENSITY
● 50,000 and over

0 20 40 60 80 100
Miles

AVERETT COLLEGE
D-4
Danville, VA 24541

(804) 791-5660
(800) AVERETT (283-7388) (out-of-state)

Full-time: 334 men, 443 women
Part-time: 294 men, 294 women
Graduate: 446 men, 213 women
Year: semesters, summer session
Application Deadline: August 1
Freshman Class: 851 applied, 745 accepted, 295 enrolled
SAT I Verbal/Math: 432/465

Faculty: 55; IIB, --$
Ph.D.s: 77%
Student/Faculty: 14 to 1
Tuition: $9710
Room & Board: $3900

LESS COMPETITIVE

Averett College, founded in 1859, is a small, private coeducational institution affiliated with the Baptist General Association of Virginia, offering undergraduate and graduate programs in liberal arts, business administration, and teacher education. In addition to regional accreditation, Averett has baccalaureate program accreditation with CSWE. The 2 libraries contain 126,450 volumes and 29,130 microform items, and subscribe to 417 periodicals. Computerized library sources and services include the card catalog, interlibrary loans, and database searching. The 25-acre campus is in a suburban area 45 miles from Greensboro, North Carolina and 140 miles from Richmond. Including residence halls, there are 15 buildings on campus.

Student Life: About 76% of undergraduates are from Virginia. Students come from 28 states, 12 foreign countries, and Canada. Eighty percent are from public schools; 20% from private. Eighty-one percent are white; 12% African American. Fifty-eight percent are Protestant; 13% Catholic. The average age of freshmen is 18; all undergraduates, 20. Forty percent drop out by the end of their first year; 37% remain to graduate.

Housing: A total of 500 students can be accommodated in college housing. College-sponsored living facilities include coed dormitories. On-campus housing is guaranteed for all 4 years. Fifty-six percent of students commute. Alcohol is not permitted. All students may keep cars on campus.

Activities: About 15% of men belong to 2 national fraternities; about 12% of women belong to 1 national sorority. There are 22 groups on campus, including art, cheerleading, choir, chorale, chorus, drama, honors, international, literary magazine, newspaper, political, professional, religious, social, social service, student government, and yearbook. Popular campus events include Homecoming and Spring Weekend.

Sports: There are 5 intercollegiate sports for men and 5 for women, and 6 intramural sports for men and 6 for women. Athletic and recreation facilities include a gymnasium, tennis courts, facilities for intramural sports, and a new 80-acre equestrian center. A 75-acre sports and convocation complex is in development.

Disabled Students: Fifty-eight percent of the campus is accessible to disabled students. The following facilities are available: wheelchair ramps, elevators, special parking, and specially equipped rest rooms.

Services: In addition to many counseling and information services, tutoring is available in some subjects, including all required general education courses, as well as academic courses in equestrian and aviation studies. Tutoring in higher level courses is offered depending on availability of tutors.

Campus Safety and Security: Campus safety and security measures include 24-hour foot and vehicle patrol, informal discussions, emergency telephones, and lighted pathways and sidewalks.

Programs of Study: Averett awards the B.A., B.A.S., B.S., and B.B.A. degrees. Associate and master's degrees also are awarded. Bachelor's degrees are awarded in AGRICULTURE (equestrian science), BIOLOGICAL SCIENCE (biochemistry, biology/biological science, botany, and zoology), BUSINESS (accounting, banking and finance, business administration and management, management science, marketing/retailing/merchandising, and sports management), COMMUNICATIONS AND THE ARTS (advertising, communications, dramatic arts, English, fine arts, journalism, music, and speech/debate/rhetoric), COMPUTER AND PHYSICAL SCIENCE (chemistry, computer programming, computer science, and mathematics), EDUCATION (art, early childhood, elementary, health, middle school, physical, science, and secondary), ENGINEERING AND ENVIRONMENTAL DESIGN (aviation administration/management and environmental science), HEALTH PROFESSIONS (medical laboratory technology, predentistry, premedicine, and sports medicine), SOCIAL SCIENCE (criminal justice, history, liberal arts/general studies, ministries, parks and recreation management, political science/government, prelaw, psychology, religion, social work, and sociology). Business administration, education, and aviation have the largest enrollments.

Required: All students must complete at least 123 hours with a minimum 2.0 GPA and attend commencement exercises in order to graduate. Core requirements include 15 hours of history or social science, 9 of English, and 6 each of fine arts, religion, and philosophy. Freshmen must take a 3-hour seminar; B.A. students need an additional 6 to 8 hours of mathematics or natural science and 6 to 14 hours in a foreign language, depending on proficiency; B.S. students need an additional 6 hours in mathematics and 8 hours in natural science.

Special: Students may design their own majors, select dual majors, or pursue a combined B.A.-B.S. degree. A general studies degree and nondegree study are offered, as are up to 5 pass/fail options. Senior equestrian studies majors may spend a semester or summer in England preparing for the British Horse Society A.I. certificate; religion majors may spend a summer on an archaelogical dig in the Middle East. Altogether, study abroad is available in 8 countries. Accelerated degrees are available in all majors. There is a freshman honors program on campus, as well as 3 national honor societies. All departments have honors programs.

Faculty/Classroom: Sixty-eight percent of faculty are male; 32%, female. All teach undergraduates and 15% both teach and do research. No introductory courses are taught by graduate students. The average class size in an introductory lecture is 17; in a laboratory, 15; and in a regular course offering, 13.

Admissions: About 88% of the 1993–94 applicants were accepted. The SAT scores for the 1993–94 freshman class were as follows: Verbal—72% below 500, 20% between 500 and 599, 6% between 600 and 700, and 2% above 700; Math—58% below 500, 32% between 500 and 599, 8% between 600 and 700, and 2% above 700. About 35% of the current freshmen were in the top fifth of their class; 57% were in the top two fifths. Five freshmen graduated first in their class.

Requirements: Averett requires applicants to be in the upper 60% of their class. A minimum GPA of 2.0 is required. The SAT I or ACT is required, with a recommended composite score of 850 for the SAT I or 18 for the ACT. Applicants should be high school graduates or have earned the GED. Recommended secondary preparation should include 4 units in English, 3 each in mathematics and social science, and 2 each in foreign language and science. AP and CLEP credits are accepted. Important factors used in the admissions decision are advanced placement or honor courses, evidence of special talent, extracurricular activities record, leadership record, and personality, intangible qualities.

Procedure: Freshmen are admitted to all sessions. Entrance exams should be taken spring of the junior year or fall of the senior year. Applications should be filed by August 1 for fall entry, December 1 for spring entry, and April 4 for summer entry, along with an application fee of $20. Notification is sent on a rolling basis. There are early admissions and deferred admissions plans.

Transfer: About 115 transfer students enrolled in 1993–94. Applicants must present at least a 2.0 GPA and be eligible to return to their previous college. A total of 30 credits out of 123 must be completed at Averett.

Visiting: There are regularly scheduled orientations for prospective students. There are spring and fall open houses, a Virginia Visitors Day, and special visit days for selected majors. There are guides for informal visits and visitors may sit in on classes and stay overnight at the school. To arrange for a visit, contact the Admissions Office at (804) 791–5660 or (800) AVERETT (283–7388).

Financial Aid: In 1993–94, 87% of all current freshmen and 82% of continuing students received some form of financial aid. About 68% of freshmen and 65% of continuing students received need-based aid. The average freshman award was $8000. Of that total, scholarships or need-based grants averaged $5400 ($8000 maximum); loans averaged $3000 ($5600 maximum); and work contracts averaged $1200 ($1500 maximum). Forty-five percent of undergraduate students work part-time. Average earnings from campus work for the school year are $1200. The average financial indebtedness of the 1992–93 graduate was $9000. Averett is a member of CSS. The FAF, the college's own financial statement, and the FAFSA are required. The deadline for financial aid applications is April 1.

International Students: There are currently 90 international students enrolled. The school actively recruits these students. They must take the TOEFL and achieve a minimum score of 500.

Computers: The college provides computer facilities for student use. Over 60 PCs are available for student use in 3 separate computer laboratories; a separate computer laboratory is maintained for the psychology department; computers are also available in the library. All students may access the system. It may be used 15 hours per day. There are no time limits on using the system and no fees.

Graduates: In 1992–93, 246 bachelor's degrees were awarded. The most popular majors among graduates were business administration (30%), social sciences (20%), and education (10%). Within an average freshman class, 33% graduate in 4 years and 12% in 5 years. Some 35 companies recruited on campus in 1992–93.

Admissions Contact: Gary Sherman, Dean of Enrollment Management.

BLUEFIELD COLLEGE   B–

Bluefield, VA 24605   (703) 326–4214; (800) 872–0175 (out-of-state)

Full-time, Part-time: 341 men, 424 women	**Faculty:** 33
	Ph.D.s: 65%
Graduate: none	**Student/Faculty:** 20 to 1
Year: semesters, summer session	**Tuition:** $6500
Application Deadline: open	**Room & Board:** $4100
Freshman Class: 379 applied, 357 accepted, 179 enrolled	
ACT: 21	**COMPETITIVE**

Bluefield College, founded in 1922, is a private, liberal arts institution affiliated with the Southern Baptist Church. The library contains 40,000 volumes, 95 microform items, and 1858 audiovisual forms, and subscribes to 158 periodicals. Computerized library sources and services include interlibrary loans and database searching. Special learning facilities include a learning resource center. The 85-acre campus is in a small town 100 miles west of Roanoke on the Virginia-

West Virginia state line. Including residence halls, there are 9 buildings on campus.

Student Life: About 77% of undergraduates are from Virginia. Students come from 11 states, 4 foreign countries, and Canada. About 95% are from public schools; 5% from private. Almost all are white. Most are Protestant. The average age of freshmen is 18; all undergraduates, 26. Almost 35% drop out by the end of their first year.

Housing: A total of 272 students can be accommodated in college housing. College-sponsored living facilities include single-sex dormitories, on-campus apartments, and married-student housing. On-campus housing is guaranteed for all 4 years. Sixty percent of students commute. Alcohol is not permitted. All students may keep cars on campus.

Activities: There are 3 local fraternities and 3 local sororities. There are 15 groups on campus, including cheerleading, choir, chorale, chorus, dance, drama, honors, literary magazine, musical theater, newspaper, pep band, political, religious, social, student government, and yearbook. Popular campus events include Homecoming, Octoberfest, Spring Weekend, and Christmas Banquet.

Sports: There are 5 intercollegiate sports for men and 4 for women, and 6 intramural sports for men and 5 for women. Athletic and recreation facilities include the Golden Dome gymnasium, with game courts and weight rooms, a student activities center, a game room, and tennis courts.

Disabled Students: Ninety percent of the campus is accessible to disabled students. The following facilities are available: wheelchair ramps, elevators, special parking, and specially equipped rest rooms.

Services: In addition to many counseling and information services, tutoring is available in most subjects. There is also a reader service for the blind, and remedial math, reading, and writing.

Campus Safety and Security: Campus safety and security measures include informal discussions, pamphlets, posters, and films, lighted pathways and sidewalks, and and foot and vehicle patrol from 11 P.M. to 6 A.M.

Programs of Study: BC awards the B.A. and B.S. degrees. Associate degrees also are awarded. Bachelor's degrees are awarded in BIOLOGICAL SCIENCE (biology/biological science), BUSINESS (business administration and management and human resources), COMMUNICATIONS AND THE ARTS (communications, English, fine arts, and music), COMPUTER AND PHYSICAL SCIENCE (chemistry, computer science, and mathematics), EDUCATION (middle school, physical, and secondary), SOCIAL SCIENCE (criminal justice, history, interdisciplinary studies, psychology, religion, and social studies). Business, teacher education, and biology are the strongest programs academically. Business, teacher education, health, physical education and recreation, and management of human resources have the largest enrollments.

Required: In order to graduate, students must have completed a minimum 126 semester hours including a liberal arts requirement of 51 to 53 hours, with 30 to 45 hours in the major, and a minimum 2.0 GPA. Other requirements vary per program.

Special: The college offers credit for life/military/work experience, nondegree study through the Fine Arts Community School, an accelerated degree program in management of human resources, and internships in criminal justice, psychology, and recreation. There is a freshman honors program on campus, as well as 1 national honor society.

Faculty/Classroom: Seventy-nine percent of faculty are male; 21%, female. All teach undergraduates and 10% both teach and do research. The average class size in an introductory lecture is 40; in a laboratory, 12; and in a regular course offering, 18.

Admissions: About 94% of the 1993–94 applicants were accepted. About 44% of the current freshmen were in the top quarter of their class; 30% were in the top half. Four freshmen graduated first in their class.

Requirements: A minimum GPA of 2.0 is required. The SAT I or ACT is not required. Applicants must be graduates of an accredited secondary school or have a GED certificate, and have completed 4 years of English, 2 years of social sciences, 1 year of science, and 5 years of electives. AP and CLEP credits are accepted. Important factors used in the admissions decision are leadership record, advanced placement or honor courses, recommendations by school officials, recommendations by alumni, and extracurricular activities record.

Procedure: Freshmen are admitted to all sessions. Entrance exams should be taken early in the senior year. Application deadlines are open. Application fee is $15. Notification is sent on a rolling basis. There are early admissions and deferred admissions plans.

Transfer: About 51 transfer students enrolled in 1993–94. Prospective students must submit transcripts of all academic work, financial aid transcript, and SAT I or ACT scores. A total of 24 credits out of 126 must be completed at BC.

Visiting: There are regularly scheduled orientations for prospective students, including campus tours, and a chance to develop class schedules and attend financial aid workshops. There are guides for informal visits and visitors may sit in on classes and stay overnight at

the school. To arrange for a visit, contact the Admissions Office at (703) 326–4214 or (800) 872–0175.

Financial Aid: In 1993–94, 77% of all current freshmen and 90% of continuing students received some form of financial aid. The average freshman award was $5261. Of that total, scholarships or need-based grants averaged $2738 ($6400 maximum); loans averaged $2345 ($3300 maximum); and work contracts averaged $178 ($700 maximum). About 3% of undergraduate students work part-time. Average earnings from campus work for the school year are $700. The average financial indebtedness of the 1992–93 graduate was $3380. BC is a member of CSS. The FAF, the college's own financial statement, and the FAFSA are required. The deadline for financial aid applications is March 15.

International Students: There are currently 10 international students enrolled. The school actively recruits these students. They must take the TOEFL and achieve a minimum score of 500.

Computers: The college provides computer facilities for student use. Students may use the 64 microcomputers in laboratories. There are no time limits on using the system and no fees.

Graduates: In 1992–93, 127 bachelor's degrees were awarded. The most popular majors among graduates were management of human resources (37%), business management (13%), criminal justice and education (11%). Some 7 companies recruited on campus.

Admissions Contact: Admissions Office.

BRIDGEWATER COLLEGE   D-2
Bridgewater, VA 22812   (703) 828–2501

Full-time: 405 men, 476 women	Faculty: 62; IIB, av$
Part-time: 18 men, 36 women	Ph.D.s: 66%
Graduate: none	Student/Faculty: 14 to 1
Year: 3–3–1–3, summer session	Tuition: $10,770
Application Deadline: June 1	Room & Board: $4530
Freshman Class: 838 applied, 673 accepted, 292 enrolled	
SAT I or ACT: required	**COMPETITIVE**

Bridgewater College, founded in 1880, is a coeducational liberal arts institution affiliated with the Church of the Brethren. In addition to regional accreditation, the college has baccalaureate program accreditation with ACBSP. The library contains 150,419 volumes, 42,285 microform items, and 5963 audiovisual forms, and subscribes to 553 periodicals. Computerized library sources and services include inter-library loans and database searching. Special learning facilities include a learning resource center, radio station, and general museum of Shenandoah Valley and Church of the Brethren. The 190-acre campus is in a small town 8 miles south of Harrisonburg. Including residence halls, there are 24 buildings on campus.

Student Life: About 71% of undergraduates are from Virginia. Students come from 18 states, 9 foreign countries, and Canada. Ninety-five percent are white. Eighty percent are Protestant; 10% claim no religious affiliation. The average age of freshmen is 18; all undergraduates, 20. Nine percent drop out by the end of their first year; 57% remain to graduate.

Housing: A total of 1024 students can be accommodated in college housing. College-sponsored living facilities include single-sex dormitories. On-campus housing is guaranteed for all 4 years. Seventy-four percent of students live on campus; of those, 70% remain on campus on weekends. Alcohol is not permitted. All students may keep cars on campus.

Activities: There are no fraternities or sororities on campus. There are 41 groups on campus, including art, band, cheerleading, choir, chorale, chorus, drama, honors, international, jazz band, literary magazine, musical theater, newspaper, pep band, photography, political, professional, radio and TV, religious, social, social service, student government, and yearbook. Popular campus events include Homecoming, May Day, and endowed lectureships.

Sports: There are 8 intercollegiate sports for men and 7 for women, and 19 intramural sports for men and 17 for women. Athletic and recreation facilities include a gymnasium, a swimming pool, a weight room, handball and racquetball courts, and playing fields for baseball, softball, football, field hockey, and soccer.

Disabled Students: Ninety percent of the campus is accessible to disabled students. The following facilities are available: wheelchair ramps, elevators, special parking, specially equipped rest rooms, and lowered drinking fountains.

Services: In addition to many counseling and information services, tutoring is available in every subject. In addition, there is a reader service for the blind, and remedial math, reading, and writing. The counseling and career services center provides personal counseling services.

Campus Safety and Security: Campus safety and security measures include 24-hour foot and vehicle patrol, self defense education, informal discussions, and pamphlets, posters, and films. In addition, there are lighted pathways and sidewalks.

Programs of Study: Bridgewater awards the B.A., B.S., and B.G.S. degrees. Bachelor's degrees are awarded in BIOLOGICAL SCIENCE (biology/biological science), BUSINESS (business administration and management), COMMUNICATIONS AND THE ARTS (art, English, French, German, music, and Spanish), COMPUTER AND PHYSICAL SCIENCE (chemistry, computer programming, mathematics, physical sciences, physics, and science), EDUCATION (physical), HEALTH PROFESSIONS (health science and medical laboratory technology), SOCIAL SCIENCE (economics, history, home economics, international studies, philosophy, political science/government, psychology, and sociology). Sciences, foreign languages, and computer science are the strongest academically. Business administration has the largest enrollment.

Required: To graduate, all students must fulfill general education requirements and complete a minimum 123 credit hours, with 30 to 48 hours in the major. A minimum 2.0 GPA is required, and all seniors must pass a comprehensive exam.

Special: Bridgewater offers internships to junior and seniors, study abroad in Ecuador, England, France, Germany, Greece, Spain, China, and Japan, Washington interterm opportunities, B.A.-B.S. and general studies degrees, a 3–2 engineering degree with Pennsylvania State University, a 3–2 forestry degree with Duke University, and a dual degree program in veterinary science with Virginia Polytechnic Institute. Interdisciplinary majors available include computer science and mathematics, history and political science, and physics and mathematics. The college's 3-3-1-3 calendar enables students to concentrate on 3 courses during the 10-week terms and 1 course in the interterm. There are 5 national honor societies on campus. All departments have honors programs.

Faculty/Classroom: Eighty-one percent of faculty are male; 19%, female. All teach undergraduates and 50% both teach and do research. The average class size in an introductory lecture is 22; in a laboratory, 18; and in a regular course offering, 18.

Admissions: About 80% of the 1993–94 applicants were accepted. About 39% of the current freshmen were in the top fifth of their class; 72% were in the top two fifths. There was 1 National Merit finalist and 2 semifinalists. Seven freshmen graduated first in their class.

Requirements: Bridgewater requires applicants to be in the upper 50% of their class. A minimum GPA of 2.0 is required. The SAT I or ACT is required. Achievement tests in English composition and in intermediate or advanced mathematics and an interview are recommended. Applicants must be graduates of an accredited secondary school or have a GED certificate, and have completed 18 units, including 4 in English, 2 each in foreign language, mathematics, science, history, and social studies, and 4 in electives. AP credits are accepted. Important factors used in the admissions decision are recommendations by school officials, advanced placement or honor courses, recommendations by alumni, evidence of special talent, and leadership record.

Procedure: Freshmen are admitted to all sessions. Entrance exams should be taken fall of the senior year in high school. Applications should be filed by June 1 for fall entry, September 1 for winter entry, January 15 for spring entry, and May 1 for summer entry, along with an application fee of $15. Notification is sent on a rolling basis. There is a deferred admissions plan.

Transfer: About 40 transfer students enrolled in 1993–94. A total of 27 credits out of 123 must be completed at Bridgewater.

Visiting: There are regularly scheduled orientations for prospective students. There are guides for informal visits and visitors may sit in on classes and stay overnight at the school. To arrange for a visit, contact Dean Brian C. Hildebrand at (703) 828–2501, ext. 400.

Financial Aid: In 1993–94, 99% of all current freshmen and 97% of continuing students received some form of financial aid. About 75% of freshmen and 69% of continuing students received need-based aid. The average freshman award was $11,427. Of that total, scholarships or need-based grants averaged $7625 ($13,500 maximum); loans averaged $3986 ($5625 maximum); and work contracts averaged $1451 ($2375 maximum). Twenty-eight percent of undergraduate students work part-time. Average earnings from campus work for the school year are $776. The average financial indebtedness of the 1992–93 graduate was $12,004. Bridgewater is a member of CSS. The FAF is required. The deadline for financial aid applications is March 15.

International Students: There are currently 23 international students enrolled. They must take the TOEFL and achieve a minimum score of 500. The student must also take the SAT I or the ACT.

Computers: The college provides computer facilities for student use. The mainframe is a Prime 6150. There are 3 computer laboratories in Bowman Hall containing a computer network consisting of 18 IBM-compatible computers, 6 terminals to the Prime 6150 mainframe computer, and 9 Apple IIGS computers. Also, there is a network of 10 IBM-compatible computers in the Chemistry Department and a network of 5 IBM-compatible computers in the Sociology Department. Access to the Prime 6150 and to Internet is available through the networks. All students may access the system. It may be used 8 A.M. to

11 P.M. Monday through Thursday, 8 A.M. to 5 P.M. Friday and Saturday, and 1 to 11 P.M. Sunday. There are no time limits on using the system and no fees.

Graduates: In 1992–93, 199 bachelor's degrees were awarded. The most popular majors among graduates were business administration (30%), biology (13%), and psychology (9%). Within an average freshman class, 52% graduate in 4 years, 53% in 5 years, and 57% in 6 years. Some 10 companies recruited on campus in 1992–93.

Admissions Contact: Dean Brian C. Hildebrand, Dean for Enrollment Management.

CHRISTENDOM COLLEGE   D-2
Front Royal, VA 22630   (703) 636–2900
                                              (800) 877–5456 (out-of-state)

Full-time: 60 men, 82 women	Faculty: 12; IIB, --$
Part-time: 2 men, 1 woman	Ph.D.s: 75%
Graduate: none	Student/Faculty: 12 to 1
Year: semesters	Tuition: $8350
Application Deadline: April 1	Room & Board: $3400
Freshman Class: 96 applied, 85 accepted, 51 enrolled	
SAT I Verbal/Math: 575/550	ACT: 21 **VERY COMPETITIVE**

Christendom College, founded in 1977, is a coeducational liberal arts institution affiliated with the Roman Catholic Church. The library contains 39,172 volumes, 704 microform items, and 407 audiovisual forms, and subscribes to 274 periodicals. Computerized library sources and services include interlibrary loans and database searching. Special learning facilities include a writing center. The 150-acre campus is in a rural area 65 miles west of Washington, D.C. Including residence halls, there are 17 buildings on campus.

Student Life: About 70% of undergraduates are from out-of-state, mostly the Middle Atlantic. Students come from 33 states, 2 foreign countries, and Canada. Most are Catholic. The average age of freshmen is 18; all undergraduates, 20. Fifteen percent drop out by the end of their first year; 60% remain to graduate.

Housing: A total of 180 students can be accommodated in college housing. College-sponsored living facilities include single-sex dormitories and on-campus apartments. On-campus housing is guaranteed for all 4 years. Ninety-eight percent of students live on campus; of those, all remain on campus on weekends. Alcohol is not permitted. All students may keep cars on campus.

Activities: There are no fraternities or sororities on campus. There are 15 groups on campus, including choir, chorale, drama, musical theater, newspaper, photography, political, religious, social service, student government, and yearbook. Popular campus events include Octoberfest, St. Patrick's Day Coffee House, St. Cecilia Festival, and Spring Formal.

Sports: There is 1 intercollegiate sport for men and 1 for women. There are 9 intramural sports for men and 9 for women. Athletic and recreation facilities include basketball and volleyball courts, playing fields, table games, a recreation center, and a swimming pool.

Disabled Students: Seventy percent of the campus is accessible to disabled students. The following facilities are available: wheelchair ramps, special parking, and specially equipped rest rooms.

Campus Safety and Security: Campus safety and security measures include 24-hour foot and vehicle patrol, escort service, emergency telephones, and lighted pathways and sidewalks.

Programs of Study: Christendom awards the B.A. degree. Associate degrees also are awarded. Bachelor's degrees are awarded in COMMUNICATIONS AND THE ARTS (English and French), SOCIAL SCIENCE (history, philosophy, political science/government, religion, and theological studies). History has the largest enrollment.

Required: To graduate, all students must complete a total of 120 credit hours, a 30 hour major, and an 81 credit core curriculum including 18 hours each in theology and philosophy. A thesis and a minimum 2.0 GPA are required.

Special: Christiandom offers summer internships in Washington, D.C. for political science students, and also sponsors summer programs in Rome, Italy and in Dublin, Ireland.

Faculty/Classroom: Seventy-eight percent of faculty are male; 22% female. All teach undergraduates. The average class size in an introductory lecture is 35; in a laboratory, 5; and in a regular course offering, 15.

Admissions: About 89% of the 1993–94 applicants were accepted. The SAT scores for the 1993–94 freshman class were as follows: Verbal—27% below 500, 27% between 500 and 599, 36% between 600 and 700, and 10% above 700; Math—28% below 500, 36% between 500 and 599, 24% between 600 and 700, and 12% above 700. The ACT scores were 45% below 21, 20% between 21 and 23, 14% between 24 and 26, 7% between 27 and 28, and 14% above 28. About 53% of the current freshmen were in the top fifth of their class; 86% were in the top two fifths. There was 1 National Merit finalist and 5 semifinalists. Two freshmen graduated first in their class.

Requirements: Christendom requires applicants to be in the upper 50% of their class. A minimum GPA of 3.0 is required. The SAT I or the ACT is required, but the SAT I is preferred. A minimum composite score of 950 on the SAT I and 20 on the ACT is required. Applicants need not be graduates of an accredited secondary school. GED certificates are accepted. Students should have completed 4 years of English, 2 years each of foreign language, mathematics, history, and science, and 1 year of social studies. Essays are required. Interviews are recommended. AP credits are accepted. Important factors used in the admissions decision are leadership record, evidence of special talent, advanced placement or honor courses, recommendations by school officials, and parents or siblings attending the school.

Procedure: Freshmen are admitted to all sessions. Entrance exams should be taken during orientation weekend. Early decision applications should be filed by December 31; regular applications, by April 1 for fall entry and January 1 for spring entry, along with an application fee of $25. Notification is sent January 15. There are early decision and early admissions plans. Two early decision candidates were accepted for the 1993–94 class. A waiting list is an active part of the admissions procedure.

Transfer: Eleven transfer students enrolled in 1993–94. Transfer students must have a minimum 2.0 GPA and meet all other applicable requirements of standard Application for Admission. The SAT I or ACT is recommended. A total of 30 credits out of 120 must be completed at Christendom.

Visiting: There are guides for informal visits and visitors may sit in on classes and stay overnight at the school. To arrange for a visit, contact the Admissions Counselor at (800) 877–5456.

Financial Aid: In 1993–94, 80% of all current freshmen and 74% of continuing students received some form of financial aid. About 53% of freshmen and 52% of continuing students received need-based aid. The average freshman award was $5815. Of that total, scholarships or need-based grants averaged $646 ($900 maximum); loans averaged $3492 ($5000 maximum); and work contracts averaged $2416 ($2300 maximum). Forty percent of undergraduate students work part-time. Average earnings from campus work for the school year are $2284. The average financial indebtedness of the 1992–93 graduate was $6761. Christendom is a member of CSS. The FAF and the college's own financial statement are required. The deadline for financial aid applications is April 1.

International Students: There are currently 3 international students enrolled.

Computers: The college provides computer facilities for student use. There is a network of personal computers for student use. All students may access the system. Students may access the system 150 on-line hours per semester. The fees are $25.

Graduates: In 1992–93, 39 bachelor's degrees were awarded. Within an average freshman class, 2% graduate in 3 years, 95% in 4 years, and 3% in 5 years. In the 1992 graduating class, 34% of all graduates were enrolled in graduate school within 6 months of graduation.

Admissions Contact: John F. Ciskanik, Director of Admissions.

CHRISTOPHER NEWPORT COLLEGE
(See Christopher Newport University)

CHRISTOPHER NEWPORT UNIVERSITY   F-3
(Formerly Christopher Newport College)
Newport News, VA 23606–2998   (804) 594–7015

Full-time: 1135 men, 1775 women	Faculty: 165; IIB, av$
Part-time: 759 men, 990 women	Ph.D.s: 80%
Graduate: 33 men, 64 women	Student/Faculty: 18 to 1
Year: semesters, summer session	Tuition: $3196 ($7860)
Application Deadline: August 1	Room & Board: n/app
Freshman Class: 920 applied, 793 accepted, 556 enrolled	
SAT I Verbal/Math: 415/445	**LESS COMPETITIVE**

Christopher Newport University, founded in 1960, is a public, comprehensive, liberal arts institution offering undergraduate programs in business and economics, arts and humanities, social science and professional studies, and science and technology. The library contains 300,000 volumes, 152,800 microform items, and 6858 audiovisual forms, and subscribes to 1350 periodicals. Computerized library sources and services include the card catalog and database searching. Special learning facilities include an art gallery. The 75-acre campus is in a suburban area 30 miles west of Norfolk. There are 11 buildings on campus.

Student Life: About 91% of undergraduates are from Virginia. Students come from 14 foreign countries and Canada. Eighty percent are white; 13% African American. The average age of freshmen is 18; all undergraduates, 26.

Housing: A total of 433 students can be accommodated in college housing. College-sponsored living facilities include a coed dormitory. On-campus housing is guaranteed for all 4 years. Ninety percent of students commute and all students may keep cars on campus.

Activities: About 2% of men belong to 4 national fraternities; about 2% of women belong to 3 national sororities. There are 50 groups on campus, including cheerleading, chorale, computers, drama, ethnic, honors, international, literary magazine, newspaper, orchestra, political, professional, religious, social, social service, and student government.

Sports: There are 9 intercollegiate sports for men and 8 for women, and 13 intramural sports each for men and women. Athletic and recreation facilities include a 1000-seat gymnasium, which houses 2 basketball courts, weight training and Nautilus equipment, and physical activities rooms.

Disabled Students: All of the campus is accessible to disabled students. The following facilities are available: wheelchair ramps, elevators, special parking, specially equipped rest rooms, special class scheduling, and lowered drinking fountains.

Services: In addition to many counseling and information services, tutoring is available in most subjects. There is remedial math, reading, and writing.

Campus Safety and Security: Campus safety and security measures include 24-hour foot and vehicle patrol, emergency telephones, lighted pathways and sidewalks, and a campus police department.

Programs of Study: CNU awards the B.A., B.S., B.M., B.S.A., B.S.B.A., B.S.G.A., B.S.I.S., and B.S.N. degrees. Master's degrees also are awarded. Bachelor's degrees are awarded in AGRICULTURE (horticulture), BIOLOGICAL SCIENCE (biology/biological science), BUSINESS (accounting, banking and finance, business administration and management, business economics, international business management, marketing/retailing/merchandising, and real estate), COMMUNICATIONS AND THE ARTS (English, fine arts, French, German, journalism, music, and Spanish), COMPUTER AND PHYSICAL SCIENCE (computer science, information sciences and systems, mathematics, and physics), EDUCATION (foreign languages, middle school, music, science, and secondary), HEALTH PROFESSIONS (nursing, predentistry, and premedicine), SOCIAL SCIENCE (criminal justice, economics, history, parks and recreation management, philosophy, political science/government, prelaw, psychology, public administration, religion, social work, and sociology). Business, education, psychology, and computer science have the largest enrollments.

Required: To graduate, all students must fulfill distribution requirements in composition, mathematics, humanities, social studies, natural science, and degree studies, plus 1 semester of physical education. A minimum 120 semester hours, with 58 to 66 hours in the major and in elective studies, are required. Students must have a 2.0 GPA.

Special: CNU offers cross-registration with Thomas Nelson Community College, Hampton University, and Old Dominion University; dual majors; various B.A.-B.S. degrees; and a student-designed, interdisciplinary studies major. There is a freshman honors program on campus, as well as 3 national honor societies.

Faculty/Classroom: Sixty-six percent of faculty are male; 34%, female. All teach undergraduates and 55% also do research. No introductory courses are taught by graduate students.

Admissions: About 86% of the 1993–94 applicants were accepted. The SAT scores for the 1993–94 freshman class were as follows: Verbal—88% below 500, 11% between 500 and 599, and 2% between 600 and 700; Math—75% below 500, 19% between 500 and 599, 6% between 600 and 700, and 1% above 700. About 31% of the current freshmen were in the top fifth of their class; 80% were in the top two fifths.

Requirements: CNU requires applicants to be in the upper 50% of their class. A minimum GPA of 2.0 is required. SAT I, with a minimum composite score of 800, is required. The ACT is accepted. Applicants must be graduates of an accredited secondary school or have a GED certificate. A total of 23 academic credits is required, including 4 units of English, 3 each in social science, mathematics, and science, and either 3 units in 1 foreign language or 2 years of 2 foreign languages. An essay and interview are recommended. AP and CLEP credits are accepted. Advanced placement or honor courses is an important factor used in the admission decision.

Procedure: Freshmen are admitted fall and spring. Entrance exams should be taken in the junior year. Applications should be filed by August 1 for fall entry and December 15 for spring entry, along with an application fee of $25. Notification is sent on a rolling basis. There is an early admissions plan.

Transfer: About 1350 transfer students enrolled in a recent year. Transfer students must have earned at least 24 semester hours with a 2.0 GPA, and be eligible to return to the most recently attended college or university. Students with fewer than 24 semester hours must submit official transcripts from their secondary school and all colleges attended. A total of 30 credits out of 120 must be completed at CNU.

Visiting: There are regularly scheduled orientations for prospective students, including admission presentations and guided campus tours. There are guides for informal visits and visitors may sit in on classes. To arrange for a visit, contact the Office of Admissions at (804) 594–7015.

Financial Aid: In 1993–94, 15% of all students received some form of financial aid. Scholarships or need-based grants averaged $2000 ($9330 maximum); loans averaged $2500 ($9330 maximum); and work contracts averaged $1600 ($9330 maximum). CNU is a member of CSS. The FAF, the college's own financial statement, and FAFSA are required. The deadline for financial aid applications is April 1.

International Students: There are currently 20 international students enrolled. They must take the TOEFL (with a minimum score of 500) and SAT I (composite score of 800).

Computers: The college provides computer facilities for student use. The mainframe is a Prime 9955. The Prime student laboratory contains 20 terminals. In addition, there are 2 general purpose computer laboratories with 30 IBM-compatible, 20 Apple IIe, and 5 Apple Macintosh microcomputers available for word processing, spreadsheets, and course-specific instruction. Those in classes requiring mainframe access may access the system, which is available 158 hours per week. There are no time limits and no fees.

Admissions Contact: Admissions Office.

CLINCH VALLEY COLLEGE
UNIVERSITY OF VIRGINIA
C-2
Wise, VA 24293–0016
(703) 328–0103
(800) 468–3412 (out-of-state)

Full-time: 564 men, 561 women	**Faculty:** 58; IIB, -$
Part-time: 120 men, 302 women	**Ph.D.s:** 71%
Graduate: none	**Student/Faculty:** 19 to 1
Year: semesters, summer session	**Tuition:** $2988 ($6826)
Application Deadline: August 15	**Room & Board:** $3376
Freshman Class: 689 applied, 561 accepted, 250 enrolled	
SAT I or ACT: required	**COMPETITIVE**

University of Virginia/Clinch Valley College, founded in 1954, offers undergraduate programs through the departments of business studies, education, languages and literature, behavioral and social sciences, natural sciences, mathematics and computer science, history and philosophy, visual and performing arts, and nursing. The library contains 140,000 volumes, 51,295 microform items, and 6975 audiovisual forms, and subscribes to 1254 periodicals. Computerized library sources and services include database searching. The 350-acre campus is in a small town 60 miles northwest of Bristol. Including residence halls, there are 26 buildings on campus.

Student Life: About 90% of undergraduates are from Virginia. Students come from Canada. Nearly all are from public schools. Ninety-four percent are white. Twenty-two percent are Protestant; 18% Catholic. The average age of freshmen is 18; all undergraduates, 22. Seventeen percent drop out by the end of their first year; 42% remain to graduate.

Housing: A total of 500 students can be accommodated in college housing. College-sponsored living facilities include single-sex and coed dormitories and on-campus apartments. In addition there are honors houses. On-campus housing is guaranteed for the freshman year only and is available on a first-come, first-served basis. Seventy-two percent of students commute. All students may keep cars on campus.

Activities: About 15% of men belong to 1 local and 3 national fraternities; about 15% of women belong to 5 local sororities. There are 31 groups on campus, including cheerleading, choir, chorus, computers, dance, drama, ethnic, honors, international, newspaper, pep band, political, professional, religious, social, student government, and yearbook. Popular campus events include Christmas Around the World, International Arts Festival, organizational games, and Founders Day.

Sports: There are 6 intercollegiate sports for men and 4 for women, and 5 intramural sports each for men and women. Athletic and recreation facilities include a baseball field, gymnasium, tennis courts, a swimming pool, and 2 practice football fields.

Disabled Students: Ninety percent of the campus is accessible to disabled students. The following facilities are available: wheelchair ramps, elevators, special parking, specially equipped rest rooms, special class scheduling, and lowered drinking fountains and telephones.

Services: In addition to many counseling and information services, tutoring is available in most subjects. There is remedial math, reading, and writing. Students can also access the services of the Virginia Department of Deaf and Hard of Hearing, the Virginia departments for the Visually Handicapped, and the Virginia Department of Rehabilitation Services.

Campus Safety and Security: Campus safety and security measures include 24-hour foot and vehicle patrol, escort service, informal discussions, and emergency telephones. In addition, there are lighted pathways and sidewalks.

Programs of Study: CVC awards the B.A. and B.S. degrees. Bachelor's degrees are awarded in BIOLOGICAL SCIENCE (biology/biological science), BUSINESS (accounting and business administration and management), COMMUNICATIONS AND THE ARTS (communications, dramatic arts, and English), COMPUTER AND PHYSICAL SCIENCE (chemistry, information sciences and systems, and mathematics), ENGINEERING AND ENVIRONMENTAL DESIGN (environmental science), HEALTH PROFESSIONS (medical laboratory technology and nursing), SOCIAL SCIENCE (economics, history, political science/government, and social science). Natural science is the strongest academically. Business administration and education have the largest enrollments.

Required: To graduate, all students must satisfy course and general education requirements and complete at least 124 credit hours, with a minimum 15 hours of upper-level courses in the major. A minimum 2.0 GPA is required.

Special: The college offers co-op programs in all majors with area businesses, internships in student teaching and social sciences, on-campus work-study programs, the B.A.-B.S. degrees in all majors, dual and student-designed majors, and pass/fail options for classes not required for the major. There is a freshman honors program and all departments have honors programs.

Faculty/Classroom: Sixty-six percent of faculty are male; 34%, female. All teach undergraduates, and 10% also do research. The average class size in an introductory lecture is 35; in a laboratory, 22; and in a regular course offering, 16.

Admissions: About 81% of the 1993–94 applicants were accepted. The SAT scores for the 1993–94 freshman class were as follows: Verbal—85% below 500, 12% between 500 and 599, and 3% between 600 and 700; Math—74% below 500, 20% between 500 and 599, 5% between 600 and 700, and 1% above 700. Seven freshmen graduated first in their class.

Requirements: CVC requires applicants to be in the upper 50% of their class. A minimum GPA of 2.5 is required. The SAT I or ACT is required. A minimum composite score of 800 for SAT I or 18 for the ACT is required. Applicants must be graduates of an accredited secondary school or have a GED certificate. The required number of Carnegie units is 22. Students should have completed 4 years of English, 3 each of mathematics and science, and 2 each of foreign language and history. AP credits are accepted.

Procedure: Freshmen are admitted to all sessions. Applications should be filed by August 15 for fall entry and January 5 for spring entry, along with an application fee of $15. Notification is sent on a rolling basis.

Transfer: About 130 transfer students enrolled in 1993–94. Transfer students must meet all general admissions requirements and submit secondary school transcripts or GED results and transcripts of all previous college work. A minimum 2.0 GPA is required. Students who have a minimum of 54 semester hours of college work, or an associate degree, or are at least 25 years old, need not submit SAT I or ACT scores. For others, SAT I (minimum score 800), or the ACT (minimum score 15) is recommended. A total of 30 credits out of 124 must be completed at CVC.

Visiting: There are regularly scheduled orientations for prospective students. There are guides for informal visits and visitors may sit in on classes. To arrange for a visit, contact the Admissions Office at (703) 328–0103 or (800) 468–3412.

Financial Aid: In 1993–94, 72% of all current freshmen and 67% of continuing students received some form of financial aid. About 55% of all students received need-based aid. The average freshman award was $3264. Of that total, scholarships or need-based grants averaged $1219 ($4300 maximum); loans averaged $1461; and work contracts averaged $584 ($4000 maximum). Thirteen percent of undergraduate students work part-time. Average earnings from campus work for the school year are $963. The average financial indebtedness of the 1992–93 graduate was $9403. The FAFSA financial statement is required. The deadline for financial aid applications is April 1.

International Students: There are currently 4 international students enrolled. The student must take the SAT I or the ACT.

Computers: The college provides computer facilities for student use. The mainframe is an HP 3000/Series 925. There are three computer laboratories, and access is also provided in residence halls if students have their own machines. All students may access the system 24 hours per day. There are no time limits and no fees.

Graduates: In 1992–93, 185 bachelor's degrees were awarded. The most popular majors among graduates were business administration (33%), social sciences (20%), and history (14%). Within an average freshman class, 1% graduate in 3 years, 20% in 4 years, 27% in 5 years, and 42% in 6 years. Five companies recruited on campus in 1992–93. In the 1992 graduating class, 5% of the men and 2% of the

women were enrolled in graduate school within 6 months of graduation.

Admissions Contact: Doyle Bickers, Director of Admissions and Financial Aid.

COLLEGE OF WILLIAM AND MARY
Williamsburg, VA 23187–8795

E-3

(804) 221–4223

Full-time: 2307 men, 2873 women
Part-time: 65 men, 75 women
Graduate: 1058 men, 1208 women
Year: semesters, summer session
Application Deadline: January 15
Freshman Class: 7117 applied, 3106 accepted, 1217 enrolled
SAT I Verbal/Math: 600/640

Faculty: 416; I, -$
Ph.D.s: 92%
Student/Faculty: 10 to 1
Tuition: $4414 ($12,604)
Room & Board: $4188

MOST COMPETITIVE

College of William and Mary, founded in 1693, is the second-oldest college in the United States. The public institution offers undergraduate degrees in the College of Arts and Sciences. The campus also contains the Marshall-Wythe School of Law, School of Business, School of Education, Graduate Arts and Sciences, and the Virginia Institute of Marine Science. There are 3 undergraduate and 5 graduate schools. In addition to regional accreditation, William and Mary has baccalaureate program accreditation with AACSB and NCATE. The 10 libraries contain 1,203,718 volumes, 1,717,093 microform items, and 6465 audiovisual forms, and subscribe to 10,133 periodicals. Computerized library sources and services include the card catalog, interlibrary loans, and database searching. Special learning facilities include a learning resource center, an art gallery, a radio station, a TV station, an anthropology museum, and an art studio. The 2000-acre campus is in a small town 50 miles east of Richmond. Including residence halls, there are 165 buildings on campus.

Student Life: About 65% of undergraduates are from Virginia. Students come from 50 states, 47 foreign countries, and Canada. Eighty-two percent are from public schools; 18% from private. Eighty-four percent are white. The average age of freshmen is 19; all undergraduates, 20. Seven percent drop out by the end of their first year; 85% remain to graduate.

Housing: A total of 4320 students can be accommodated in college housing. College-sponsored living facilities include single-sex and coed dormitories, on-campus apartments, off-campus apartments, married-student housing, fraternity houses, and sorority houses. In addition there are honors houses, language houses, special interest houses, and an honors dormitory. On-campus housing is guaranteed for the freshman year only and is available on a lottery system for upperclassmen. Seventy-eight percent of students live on campus. Upperclassmen may keep cars on campus.

Activities: About 40% of men belong to 16 national fraternities; about 45% of women belong to 13 national sororities. There are 212 groups on campus, including art, band, cheerleading, chess, choir, chorale, chorus, computers, dance, drama, drill team, ethnic, gay, honors, international, jazz band, literary magazine, marching band, musical theater, newspaper, opera, orchestra, pep band, photography, political, professional, radio and TV, religious, social, social service, student government, and yearbook. Popular campus events include Black Student Leadership Development Conference, Charter Day Convocation, Homecoming, Occasion for the Arts, Yule Log Ceremony, Opening Convocation, Black History Month, Multicultural Awareness Month, Voices Only Concert, 2 concert series programs, William and Mary Theater series, Student Association Lecture Program, and film series.

Sports: There are 13 intercollegiate sports for men and 12 for women, and 48 intramural sports for men and 44 for women. Athletic and recreation facilities include William and Mary Hall, a gymnasium, and a student recreation sports center. These house a swimming pool, an indoor track, gymnastic, weight and wrestling rooms, racquetball, badminton, and 14 lighted tennis courts, and playing fields. The campus stadium seats 14,500, the basketball arena, 11,000.

Disabled Students: The following facilities are available: wheelchair ramps, elevators, special parking, specially equipped rest rooms, special class scheduling, lowered drinking fountains, and modified recreational facilities.

Services: In addition to many counseling and information services, tutoring is available in most subjects. In addition, there is a reader service for the blind. There are reasonable in-class accomodations for learning disabled students and hearing impaired students and diagnostic services for learning disabilities.

Campus Safety and Security: Campus safety and security measures include 24-hour foot and vehicle patrol, self-defense education, escort service, and shuttle buses. In addition, there are informal discussions, pamphlets, posters, and films, emergency telephones, and lighted pathways and sidewalks.

Programs of Study: William and Mary awards the B.A., B.S., and B.B.A. degrees. Master's and doctoral degrees also are awarded. Bachelor's degrees are awarded in BIOLOGICAL SCIENCE (biology/biological science), BUSINESS (business administration and

management), COMMUNICATIONS AND THE ARTS (classics, English, fine arts, French, German, music, Spanish, and speech/debate/rhetoric), COMPUTER AND PHYSICAL SCIENCE (chemistry, computer science, geology, mathematics, and physics), EDUCATION (physical), SOCIAL SCIENCE (American studies, anthropology, economics, history, interdisciplinary studies, international relations, international studies, philosophy, political science/government, psychology, religion, and sociology). Government, English, economics, psychology, and biology have the largest enrollments.

Required: In order to graduate, all students must fulfill area/sequence requirements and demonstrate proficiency in physical education, writing, and foreign language. Students must complete 124 credit hours, with 33 to 48 in the major, and a minimum 2.0 GPA.

Special: William and Mary offers 3-2 programs with Rensselaer Polytechnic Institute, Columbia University, Case Western Reserve University, Washington University in St. Louis, and a forestry/environmental science program with Duke University. Departmental internships and study abroad in France, Scotland, Germany, the United Kingdom, Denmark, Italy, Spain, Switzerland, the Netherland Antilles, and China, are possible. Also available are dual and student-designed majors, internships, a Washington semester, nondegree study, and pass/fail options. There is a freshman honors program on campus, as well as 3 national honor societies, including Phi Beta Kappa. Nineteen departments have honors programs.

Faculty/Classroom: Seventy-three percent of faculty are male; 27%, female. The average class size in a laboratory is 17 and in a regular course offering, 23.

Admissions: About 44% of the 1993-94 applicants were accepted. The SAT scores for the 1993-94 freshman class were as follows: Verbal—13% below 500, 35% between 500 and 599, 44% between 600 and 700, and 8% above 700; Math—4% below 500, 22% between 500 and 599, 48% between 600 and 700, and 27% above 700. About 91% of the current freshmen were in the top fifth of their class; 98% were in the top two fifths. There were 55 National Merit finalists and 39 semifinalists. About 130 freshmen graduated first in their class.

Requirements: The SAT I or ACT and an essay are required. SAT II: Subject tests in writing, mathematics, and foreign language are recommended. AP credits are accepted. Important factors used in the admissions decision are advanced placement or honor courses, evidence of special talent, extracurricular activities record, personality, intangible qualities, and leadership record.

Procedure: Freshmen are admitted fall and spring. Entrance exams should be taken in the spring of the junior year or in the fall of the senior year. Early decision applications should be filed by November 1; regular applications, by January 15 for fall entry and November 1 for spring entry, along with an application fee of $40. Notification of early decision is sent December 1; regular decision, April 1. There are early decision, early admissions, and deferred admissions plans. About 320 early decision candidates were accepted for the 1993-94 class. A waiting list is an active part of the admissions procedure, with about 15% of applicants on the list.

Transfer: About 130 transfer students enrolled in 1993-94. Transfer students must have at least 15 credit hours earned. A minimum 3.0 GPA is recommended. Emphasis is placed on the individual's college records. SAT I scores are recommended. A total of 60 credits out of 124 must be completed at William and Mary.

Visiting: There are regularly scheduled orientations for prospective students, consisting of a group information session followed by a student-led tour. Visitors may sit in on classes. To arrange for a visit, contact the Office of Admissions at (804) 221-3999.

Financial Aid: In 1993-94, 45% of all current freshmen and 40% of continuing students received some form of financial aid. About 36% of freshmen and 25% of continuing students received need-based aid. The average freshman award was $6000. Of that total, scholarships or need-based grants averaged $3909 ($9500 maximum); loans averaged $1800 ($3625 maximum); and work contracts averaged $343 ($1200 maximum). Forty percent of undergraduate students work part-time. Average earnings from campus work for the school year are $1000. William and Mary is a member of CSS. The FAF or FFS is required. The deadline for financial aid applications is February 15.

International Students: There are currently 184 international students enrolled. The school actively recruits these students. They must take the TOEFL and achieve a minimum score of 580. The student must also take the SAT I or the ACT.

Computers: The college provides computer facilities for student use. The mainframe is an IBM 4381 Model T24 HDS 6660. There are 200 microcomputers located in about a dozen locations around campus. All students may access the system. There are no time limits on using the system and no fees.

Graduates: In 1992-93, 1378 bachelor's degrees were awarded. The most popular majors among graduates were business (13%), psychology (10%), and English (10%). Within an average freshman class, 85% graduate in 5 years. Some 196 companies recruited on campus in 1992-93. In the 1992 graduating class, 40% of all graduates were enrolled in graduate school within 6 months of graduation; 58% had found employment.

Admissions Contact: Office of Admissions.

EASTERN MENNONITE COLLEGE D-2
Harrisonburg, VA 22801 (703) 432-4118
(800) 368-2665 (out-of-state)

Full-time: 375 men, 528 women	Faculty: 68; IIB, --$
Part-time: 24 men, 35 women	Ph.D.s: 56%
Graduate: 83 men, 59 women	Student/Faculty: 13 to 1
Year: semesters, summer session	Tuition: $9100
Application Deadline: see profile	Room & Board: $3600
Freshman Class: 486 applied, 440 accepted, 227 enrolled	
SAT I Verbal/Math: 468/510	ACT: 22 COMPETITIVE

Eastern Mennonite College, founded in 1917, is affiliated with the Mennonite Church. The private coeducational college offers programs in the arts and sciences. The Pennsylvania Extension Education Program is offered in Lancaster, Pennsylvania. There are 2 graduate schools. In addition to regional accreditation, EMC has baccalaureate program accreditation with ADA, CSWE, NCATE, and NLN. The library contains 135,070 volumes, 47,660 microform items, and 9360 audiovisual forms, and subscribes to 1070 periodicals. Computerized library sources and services include interlibrary loans and database searching. Special learning facilities include a learning resource center, art gallery, natural history museum, planetarium, and radio station. The 90-acre campus is in a small town 100 miles southwest of Washington, D.C. Including residence halls, there are 37 buildings on campus.

Student Life: About 66% of undergraduates are from out-of-state, mostly the Middle Atlantic. Students come from 34 states, 11 foreign countries, and Canada. Ninety-two percent are white. Most are Protestant. The average age of freshmen is 19; all undergraduates, 21. Twenty-five percent drop out by the end of their first year; 55% remain to graduate.

Housing: A total of 550 students can be accommodated in college housing. College-sponsored living facilities include single-sex dormitories, on-campus apartments, off-campus apartments, and married-student housing. In addition there are 2 intentional communities. On-campus housing is guaranteed for all 4 years. Fifty-six percent of students live on campus; of those, 75% remain on campus on weekends. Alcohol is not permitted. All students may keep cars on campus.

Activities: There are no fraternities or sororities on campus. There are 28 groups on campus, including chess, choir, chorale, chorus, dance, drama, ethnic, film, honors, international, jazz band, literary magazine, musical theater, newspaper, orchestra, pep band, political, professional, radio and TV, religious, social, social service, student government, and yearbook. Popular campus events include Spring Arts Festival, Fall Festival, Mission and Service Week, and Spiritual Emphasis Week.

Sports: There are 7 intercollegiate sports for men and 6 for women, and 10 intramural sports for men and 9 for women. Athletic and recreation facilities include an 800-seat gymnasium, a lighted artificial turf playing field, lighted tennis courts, a weight room, a rubberized track, baseball, softball, and soccer fields, and outdoor basketball and sand volleyball courts. The largest auditorium seats 1100.

Disabled Students: Seventy-five percent of the campus is accessible to disabled students. The following facilities are available: wheelchair ramps, elevators, special parking, specially equipped rest rooms, special class scheduling, and lowered drinking fountains.

Services: In addition to many counseling and information services, tutoring is available in every subject. In addition, there is a reader service for the blind, and remedial math, reading, and writing.

Campus Safety and Security: Campus safety and security measures include self-defense education, informal discussions, pamphlets, posters, films, and emergency telephones. In addition, there are lighted pathways and sidewalks and a 12-hour foot watchman.

Programs of Study: EMC awards the B.A. and B.S. degrees. Associate and master's degrees also are awarded. Bachelor's degrees are awarded in AGRICULTURE (international agriculture), BIOLOGICAL SCIENCE (biology/biological science and nutrition), BUSINESS (accounting and business administration and management), COMMUNICATIONS AND THE ARTS (English, fine arts, French, German, music, and Spanish), COMPUTER AND PHYSICAL SCIENCE (chemistry, computer management, computer science, and mathematics), EDUCATION (early childhood, elementary, physical, secondary, and special), HEALTH PROFESSIONS (medical laboratory technology and nursing), SOCIAL SCIENCE (biblical studies, dietetics, food production/management/services, history, liberal arts/general studies, ministries, psychology, religion, social science, social work, sociology, and youth ministry). Biology, nursing, and education are the strongest academically, and have the largest enrollments.

Required: In order to graduate, all students must complete general education courses, courses in the major, electives, and 2 hours of physical education for a minimum of 128 credit hours. Cross-cultural study is required. Hours in the major vary. A minimum 2.0 GPA is required.

Special: EMC offers study-abroad programs with Brethren Colleges. There are also internships in a variety of majors, a Washington study-service year, B.A.-B.S. degrees, dual majors, a general studies degree, and a nondegree study certificate program. The college also offers a cross-cultural program and a hands-on learning in education block program. There is a freshman honors program on campus.

Faculty/Classroom: Sixty-two percent of faculty are male; 38%, female. All teach undergraduates, and 13% both teach and do research. The average class size in an introductory lecture is 70; in a laboratory, 20; and in a regular course offering, 30.

Admissions: About 91% of the 1993–94 applicants were accepted. The SAT scores for the 1993–94 freshman class were as follows: Verbal—55% below 500, 28% between 500 and 599, 15% between 600 and 700, and 3% above 700; Math—40% below 500, 32% between 500 and 599, 21% between 600 and 700, and 6% above 700. The ACT scores were 39% below 21, 15% between 21 and 23, 24% between 24 and 26, 15% between 27 and 28, and 7% above 28. About 34% of the current freshmen were in the top fifth of their class; 67% were in the top two fifths. There were 6 National Merit semifinalists. Six freshmen graduated first in their class.

Requirements: EMC requires applicants to be in the upper 50% of their class. A minimum GPA of 2.0 is required. The SAT I or ACT is required, with a minimum composite score of 750 on the SAT I or 19 on the ACT. Applicants must be graduates of an accredited secondary school or have a GED certificate. The college recommends that students have completed 4 credits of English, 3 each of mathematics and social studies, 2 or more of foreign language, and chemistry for nursing majors. An essay is required, and an interview is recommended. AP and CLEP credits are accepted. Important factors used in the admissions decision are advanced placement or honor courses, recommendations by school officials, leadership record, parents or siblings attending the school, and extracurricular activities record.

Procedure: Freshmen are admitted in the fall and spring. Entrance exams should be taken in the spring of the junior year and/or the fall of the senior year. Applications should be filed by 30 days prior to the beginning of the semester. Notification is sent on a rolling basis. There are early admissions and deferred admissions plans.

Transfer: Seventy-four transfer students enrolled in 1993–94. Transfer students must have a minimum 2.0 transfer and high school GPA and either the SAT I, minimum composite score 750, or the ACT, minimum composite score 19. At least 30 credits out of 128 must be completed at EMC.

Visiting: There are regularly scheduled orientations for prospective students, including a financial aid seminar; a review of general education; attendance at an assembly; the opportunity to sit in on classes, meet with professors and admissions representatives, sleep in dormitories, and eat in the cafeteria; attendance at special campus events; and a banquet with the president. There are guides for informal visits, and visitors may sit in on classes and stay overnight at the school. To arrange for a visit, contact the Admissions Office at (703) 432–4118 or (800) 368–2665 (out-of-state).

Financial Aid: In 1993–94, 97% of all current freshmen and 98% of continuing students received some form of financial aid. About 75% of freshmen and 76% of continuing students received need-based aid. The average freshman award was $8930. Of that total, scholarships or need-based grants averaged $4769 ($10,635 maximum); loans averaged $3667 ($6500 maximum); and work contracts averaged $1280 ($1500 maximum). Fifty percent of undergraduate students work part-time. Average earnings from campus work for the school year are $1000. The average financial indebtedness of the 1992–93 graduate was $11,500. EMC is a member of CSS. The FAF is required. The deadline for financial aid applications is May 15.

International Students: There are currently 32 international students enrolled. The school actively recruits these students. They must take the TOEFL and achieve a minimum score of 550.

Computers: The college provides computer facilities for student use. There are 13 networked microcomputers in the science center, and 20 microcomputers networked in the business department, with 32 additional microcomputers, not networked, in the library, nursing and biology departments, and the science center computer room. All students may access the system day and evening. There are no time limits on using the system and no fees.

Graduates: In 1992–93, 243 bachelor's degrees were awarded. The most popular majors among graduates were education (20%), liberal arts (17%), and business (11%). Within an average freshman class, 55% graduate in 5 years. Some 6 companies recruited on campus in 1992–93. In the 1992 graduating class, 8% of all students enrolled in graduate school within 6 months of graduation; 97% had found employment.

Admissions Contact: Admissions Office.

EMORY AND HENRY COLLEGE

B-4

Emory, VA 24327–0947

(703) 944–4121, ext. 3133
(800) 848–5493 (in-state)

Full-time: 407 men, 402 women	**Faculty:** 55; IIB, -$
Part-time: 13 men, 19 women	**Ph.D.s:** 89%
Graduate: none	**Student/Faculty:** 15 to 1
Year: semesters, summer session	**Tuition:** $8546
Application Deadline: open	**Room & Board:** $4230
Freshman Class: 765 applied, 598 accepted, 226 enrolled	
SAT I Verbal/Math: 443/485	**ACT:** 23 COMPETITIVE

Emory and Henry College, founded in 1836, is a private liberal arts institution affiliated with the United Methodist Church. The library contains 240,328 volumes, 10,073 microform items, and 3238 audiovisual forms, and subscribes to 1063 periodicals. Computerized library sources and services include interlibrary loans and database searching. Special learning facilities include a learning resource center, an art gallery, and a radio station. The 150-acre campus is in a rural area in southwest Virginia. Including residence halls, there are 20 buildings on campus.

Student Life: About 77% of undergraduates are from Virginia. Students come from 14 states and 3 foreign countries. Ninety percent are from public schools; 10% from private. Ninety-six percent are white. Most are Protestant. The average age of freshmen is 18; all undergraduates, 20. Fifteen percent drop out by the end of their first year; 60% remain to graduate.

Housing: A total of 600 students can be accommodated in college housing. College-sponsored living facilities include single-sex dormitories. In addition there are honors houses. On-campus housing is guaranteed for all 4 years. Seventy percent of students live on campus; of those, 50% remain on campus on weekends. Alcohol is not permitted. All students may keep cars on campus.

Activities: About 20% of men belong to 6 local fraternities; about 31% of women belong to 5 local sororities. There are 30 groups on campus, including cheerleading, choir, computers, dance, drama, ethnic, literary magazine, newspaper, opera, orchestra, pep band, photography, political, professional, radio, religious, social, social service, student government, and yearbook. Popular campus events include Parents Day, Homecoming, Alumni Weekend, the Staley Lectures, and the R.J. Reynolds Lectures.

Sports: There are 7 intercollegiate sports for men and 5 for women, and 11 intramural sports for men and 11 for women. Athletic and recreation facilities include a gymnasium, a pool, a racquetball court, outdoor volleyball courts, tennis courts, a weight room, a dance room, golf courses, baseball and football fields, and a horseshoes area.

Disabled Students: Fifty percent of the campus is accessible to disabled students. The following facilities are available: wheelchair ramps, elevators, special parking, and specially equipped rest rooms.

Services: In addition to many counseling and information services, tutoring is available in most subjects. In addition, there is a reader service for the blind and remedial writing.

Campus Safety and Security: Campus safety and security measures include 24-hour foot and vehicle patrol, informal discussions, and lighted pathways and sidewalks.

Programs of Study: The College awards the B.A. and B.S. degrees. Bachelor's degrees are awarded in BIOLOGICAL SCIENCE (biology/biological science), BUSINESS (accounting and business administration and management), COMMUNICATIONS AND THE ARTS (classics, communications, creative writing, French, German, journalism, literature, music performance, music theory and composition, and Spanish), COMPUTER AND PHYSICAL SCIENCE (chemistry, computer science, mathematics, and physics), EDUCATION (art, early childhood, middle school, physical, recreation, science, and secondary), HEALTH PROFESSIONS (medical laboratory technology and premedicine), SOCIAL SCIENCE (crosscultural studies, economics, geography, history, philosophy, political science/government, prelaw, psychology, religious music, social science, and sociology).

Required: All students complete a general studies curriculum covering western traditions, Great Books, religion, values inquiry and global studies. Specific courses include 1 each from 3 disciplines, including social science, humanities, and natural sciences, and according to major, either a foreign language or quantitative methods. A total of 116 semester hours for a B.A., or 124 for a B.S. with a GPA of 2.0, is required for graduation.

Special: The college offers study abroad, cooperative programs in engineering with Tulane and North Carolina State Universities, and forestry with Duke University. Dual and student-designed majors, combined B.A.-B.S. degrees, internships, work-study, nondegree study, and pass/fail options are also available. There are 4 national honor societies on campus.

Faculty/Classroom: Seventy-six percent of faculty are male; 24%, female. All teach undergraduates. The average class size in an introductory lecture is 25; in a laboratory, 13; and in a regular course offering, 30.

Admissions: About 78% of the 1993–94 applicants were accepted. About 53% of the current freshmen were in the top fifth of their class; 85% were in the top two fifths. About 12 freshmen graduated first in their class.

Requirements: The College requires applicants to be in the upper 50% of their class. A minimum GPA of 2.3 is required. The SAT I or ACT is required. Applicants should be high school graduates. High school courses required include 4 years of English, 3 or more units of mathematics including Algebra I, Algebra II, and geometry, 2 or more units of laboratory science, 2 units of a single foreign language and 2 or more units of social studies and history. One additional unit in fine arts is strongly recommended. A personal essay is required, and an interview is strongly recommended. AP and CLEP credits are accepted. Important factors used in the admissions decision are advanced placement or honor courses, leadership record, personality, intangible qualities, extracurricular activities record, and evidence of special talent.

Procedure: Freshmen are admitted fall and spring. Entrance exams should be taken in November of high school senior year. Application deadlines are open. Application fee is $25. Notification is sent on a rolling basis. There is an early admissions plan.

Transfer: About 75 transfer students enrolled in 1993–94. Transfers must have at least a 2.0 GPA in previous college work. Those with at least 30 credits may be admitted without high school data; those with fewer than 30 credits must meet freshman admission standards. A total of 62 credits out of 116 to 124 must be completed at the College.

Visiting: There are regularly scheduled orientations for prospective students, including a program for students to meet faculty and staff and to attend education sessions on college life. There are guides for informal visits and visitors may sit in on classes and stay overnight at the school. To arrange for a visit, contact the Admissions Office at (800) 848–5493 (in-state) or (703) 944–4121, ext. 3133.

Financial Aid: In 1993–94, 90% of all current freshmen and 76% of continuing students received some form of financial aid. About 66% of freshmen and 51% of continuing students received need-based aid. The average freshman award was $6000. Of that total, scholarships or need-based grants averaged $3750 ($8201 maximum); loans averaged $1905 ($3625 maximum); and work contracts averaged $600 ($1000 maximum). Forty percent of undergraduate students work part-time. Average earnings from campus work for the school year are $650. The average financial indebtedness of the 1992–93 graduate was $5552. The College is a member of CSS. The FAF or FFS and the college's own financial statement are required. The deadline for financial aid applications is February 15.

International Students: There are currently 5 international students enrolled. The school actively recruits these students. They must take the TOEFL and achieve a minimum score of 550.

Computers: The college provides computer facilities for student use. The mainframe is an IBM/36. There are 52 terminals available for student use in the library, the computer laboratory, and the writing center. All students may access the system. There are no time limits on using the system and no fees.

Graduates: In 1992–93, 187 bachelor's degrees were awarded. The most popular majors among graduates were economics and business (20%), interdisciplinary English (13%), and history (9%). Within an average freshman class, 51% graduate in 4 years and 62% in 5 years.

Admissions Contact: Jean M. Luce, Ed.D., Dean of Admissions and Financial Aid.

FERRUM COLLEGE
C-3

Ferrum, VA 24088   (703) 365–4290; (800) 868–9797 (out-of-state)

Full-time: 642 men, 408 women	Faculty: 77; IIB, --$
Part-time: 27 men, 51 women	Ph.D.s: 63%
Graduate: none	Student/Faculty: 14 to 1
Year: semesters, summer session	Tuition: $8800
Application Deadline: open	Room & Board: $4000
Freshman Class: 1339 applied, 1108 accepted, 336 enrolled	
SAT I Verbal/Math: 387/433	**LESS COMPETITIVE**

Ferrum College, founded in 1913, is a private, coeducational, liberal arts institution affiliated with the United Methodist Church. In addition to regional accreditation, The college has baccalaureate program accreditation with NRPA. The library contains 98,000 volumes, 5000 microform items, and 1212 audiovisual forms, and subscribes to 525 periodicals. Computerized library sources and services include the card catalog, interlibrary loans, and database searching. Special learning facilities include a learning resource center, art gallery, radio station, and folk art museum. The 880-acre campus is in a rural area 35 miles south of Roanoke. Including residence halls, there are 27 buildings on campus.

Student Life: About 89% of undergraduates are from Virginia. Students come from 21 states and 10 foreign countries. Most are from public schools. Eighty-five percent are white; 11% African American. Fifty-nine percent are Protestant; 26% claim no religious affiliation; 14% Catholic. The average age of freshmen is 19.4; all undergraduates, 21.1. Thirty-nine percent drop out by the end of their first year; 66% remain to graduate.

Housing: A total of 1174 students can be accommodated in college housing. College-sponsored living facilities include single-sex and coed dormitories, on-campus apartments, and married-student housing. In addition there are honors houses and special interest houses. On-campus housing is guaranteed for all 4 years and is available on a first-come, first-served basis. Seventy-five percent of students live on campus; of those, 50% remain on campus on weekends. All students may keep cars on campus.

Activities: There are no fraternities or sororities on campus. There are 60 groups on campus, including art, cheerleading, choir, chorale, chorus, computers, dance, drama, ethnic, film, honors, international, jazz band, literary magazine, musical theater, newspaper, photography, political, radio and TV, religious, social, social service, student government, and yearbook. Popular campus events include Spring Fling, Homecoming, and Blue Ridge Festival.

Sports: There are 6 intercollegiate sports each for men and women, and 5 for both, and 6 intramural sports each for men and women. Athletic and recreation facilities include a gymnasium, field house, tennis courts, weight room, indoor pool, outdoor volleyball court, football stadium, and a recreation center with indoor basketball courts, racquetball courts, and universal weights.

Disabled Students: Ninety-five percent of the campus is accessible to disabled students. The following facilities are available: wheelchair ramps, elevators, special parking, specially equipped rest rooms, and special class scheduling.

Services: In addition to many counseling and information services, tutoring is available in most subjects. There are also college skill classes and individual assistance for study strategies.

Campus Safety and Security: Campus safety and security measures include 24-hour foot and vehicle patrol, self-defense education, escort service, and informal discussions. In addition, there are pamphlets, posters, films, emergency telephones, lighted pathways and sidewalks, and sexual assault awareness information.

Programs of Study: The college awards the B.A., B.S., and B.S.W. degrees. Bachelor's degrees are awarded in AGRICULTURE (agriculture), BIOLOGICAL SCIENCE (biology/biological science), BUSINESS (accounting, banking and finance, business administration and management, management information systems, marketing/retailing/merchandising, and recreation and leisure services), COMMUNICATIONS AND THE ARTS (art, dramatic arts, English, fine arts, French, Russian, and Spanish), COMPUTER AND PHYSICAL SCIENCE (chemistry, computer science, mathematics, and science), EDUCATION (education and physical), ENGINEERING AND ENVIRONMENTAL DESIGN (environmental science), HEALTH PROFESSIONS (medical laboratory technology), SOCIAL SCIENCE (history, interdisciplinary studies, international studies, liberal arts/general studies, philosophy, political science/government, psychology, religion, social studies, and social work). Environmental science, biology, English, history, and international studies are the strongest academically. Business administration, psychology, and teacher education have the largest enrollments.

Required: To graduate, students must complete at least 127 semester hours with a minimum GPA of 2.0. There are 55 hours of distribution requirements, including 12 in social sciences, 8 in natural sciences, 6 each in English, religion and philosophy, mathematics, and degree cognates, 3 in fine arts, and 2 in physical education. A major may require up to 57 semester hours, and 30 hours of the total must be in courses at the 300 or 400 level.

Special: The college offers internships, work-study programs, an accelerated degree program in social work, and B.A.-B.S. degrees. A liberal studies degree and nondegree study are available. There is a freshman honors program on campus, as well as one national honor society. Two departments have honors programs.

Faculty/Classroom: All teach undergraduates and half do research. The average class size in an introductory lecture is 22; in a laboratory, 22; and in a regular course offering, 19.

Admissions: About 83% of the 1993–94 applicants were accepted. The SAT scores for the 1993–94 freshman class were as follows: Verbal—93% below 500, 6% between 500 and 599, and 1% between 600 and 700; Math—82% below 500, 15% between 500 and 599, and 3% between 600 and 700.

Requirements: The SAT, with a minimum score of 700 composite (350 verbal and 350 mathematics) or the ACT is required. Applicants must be graduates of an accredited secondary school; the GED is accepted. Applicants should complete 18 high school academic credits. AP and CLEP credits are accepted. Important factors used in the admissions decision are advanced placement or honor courses, leadership record, evidence of special talent, extracurricular activities record, and recommendations by school officials.

Procedure: Freshmen are admitted to all sessions. Application deadlines are open. The application fee is $20. Notification is sent on a rolling basis.

Transfer: About 66 transfer students enrolled in 1993–94. Applicants for transfer must be in good academic standing at their current school. A total of 32 credits out of 127 must be completed at the college.

Visiting: There are regularly scheduled orientations for prospective students, including faculty information sessions, parent-to-parent and student-to-student sessions, and tours of the campus and residence halls. There are guides for informal visits and visitors may sit in on classes and stay overnight at the school. To arrange for a visit, contact the Director of Admissions at (703) 365–4290 or (800) 868–9797 (out-of-state).

Financial Aid: In 1993–94, 92% of all current freshmen and 95% of continuing students received some form of financial aid. About 62% of freshmen and 64% of continuing students received need-based aid. Scholarships or need-based grants averaged $4500 ($8800 maximum); loans averaged $2080 ($3800 maximum); and work contracts averaged $900 ($1500 maximum). Thirty-five percent of undergraduate students work part-time. Average earnings from campus work for the school year are $998. The average financial indebtedness of the 1992–93 graduate was $6000. The college is a member of CSS. The college's own financial statement and FAFSA are required. The deadline for financial aid applications is May 1.

International Students: There are currently 14 international students enrolled. They must take the TOEFL and achieve a minimum score of 550. The student must also take the SAT I or the ACT.

Computers: The college provides computer facilities for student use. The mainframe is an IBM 400 and a Data General. There are 83 microcomputers in laboratories for all students in the library, the student computer center, and the business department. Computer science majors may access the system at all times. There are no time limits and no fees.

Graduates: In 1992–93 245 bachelor's degrees were awarded. Within an average freshman class, 20% graduate in 4 years, 30% in 5 years, and 1% in 6 years. Fifteen companies recruited on campus in 1992–93.

Admissions Contact: Robert H. Bailey, Jr., Director of Admissions.

GEORGE MASON UNIVERSITY
E-2

Fairfax, VA 22030–4444   (703) 993–2400

Full-time: 4318 men, 5210 women	Faculty: 459; I, -$
Part-time: 1625 men, 2198 women	Ph.D.s: 87%
Graduate: 3875 men, 4074 women	Student/Faculty: 21 to 1
Year: semesters, summer session	Tuition: $3888 ($10,056)
Application Deadline: February 1	Room & Board: $4840
Freshman Class: 5645 applied, 4621 accepted, 1727 enrolled	
SAT I or ACT: required	**COMPETITIVE**

George Mason University, founded in 1957, offers undergraduate and graduate degrees in arts and sciences, business administration, information technology and engineering, nursing and health science, and education. A second campus in Arlington houses a professional center, the School of Law, and the International Institute. There are 4 undergraduate and 5 graduate schools. In addition to regional accreditation, GMU has baccalaureate program accreditation with AACSB, ABET, CSWE, NCATE, and NLN. The 2 libraries contain 682,557 volumes, 1,417,866 microform items, and 10,641 audiovisual forms, and subscribe to 8205 periodicals. Computerized library sources and services include the card catalog, interlibrary loans, and database searching. Special learning facilities include a radio station and TV station. The 682-acre campus is in a suburban area 18 miles southwest of Washington, D.C. Including residence halls, there are 92 buildings on campus.

Student Life: About 91% of undergraduates are from Virginia. Students come from 28 states, 83 foreign countries, and Canada. Ninety-five percent are from public schools; 5% from private. Seventy-two percent are white; 13% Asian American. The average age of freshmen is 18.8; all undergraduates, 24. Twenty-two percent drop out by the end of their first year; 44% remain to graduate.

Housing: A total of 3006 students can be accommodated in college housing. College-sponsored living facilities include single-sex and coed dormitories, on-campus apartments, and off-campus apartments. In addition there are honors houses and blocks of student housing rooms for fraternities and sororities. On-campus housing is guaranteed for all 4 years. Eighty-one percent of students commute. Alcohol is not permitted. All students may keep cars on campus.

Activities: About 15% of men belong to 19 national fraternities; about 12% of women belong to 10 national sororities. There are 200 groups on campus, including band, cheerleading, chess, choir, chorale, chorus, computers, dance, drama, ethnic, film, gay, honors, international, jazz band, literary magazine, musical theater, newspaper, orchestra, pep band, photography, political, professional, radio and TV, religious, social, social service, student government, symphony, and yearbook. Popular campus events include Mason Day and Patriot Day.

Sports: There are 11 intercollegiate sports for men and 10 for women, and 13 intramural sports for men and 13 for women. Athletic and recreation facilities include a 10,000-seat arena for basketball, indoor soccer, and concerts; a sports and recreation complex, which includes a 200-meter track, basketball, handball/racquetball, tennis, and volleyball courts, baseball and softball diamonds, batting cages, a weight room, saunas, and a golf and archery net; a 400-meter outdoor track; and playing fields.

Disabled Students: Eighty-five percent of the campus is accessible to disabled students. The following facilities are available: wheelchair ramps, elevators, special parking, specially equipped rest rooms, special class scheduling, lowered drinking fountains, and lowered telephones. Special arrangements can be made for testing, readers, notetakers, and interpreters.

Services: In addition to many counseling and information services, tutoring is available in most subjects. In addition, there is a reader service for the blind. Tutoring is available for a fee.

Campus Safety and Security: Campus safety and security measures include 24-hour foot and vehicle patrol, self defense education, escort service, and informal discussions. In addition, there are pamphlets, posters, and films, emergency telephones, lighted pathways and sidewalks, and 33 security call boxes located throughout campus.

Programs of Study: GMU awards the B.A., B.S., B.F.A., B.I.S., B.M., B.S.E., and B.S.N. degrees. Master's and doctoral degrees also are awarded. Bachelor's degrees are awarded in BIOLOGICAL SCIENCE (biology/biological science), BUSINESS (accounting, banking and finance, business administration and management, and marketing/retailing/merchandising), COMMUNICATIONS AND THE ARTS (classics, communications, dance, dramatic arts, English, fine arts, French, German, journalism, music, Spanish, and speech/debate/rhetoric), COMPUTER AND PHYSICAL SCIENCE (chemistry, computer science, geology, information sciences and systems, mathematics, and physics), EDUCATION (foreign languages, health, industrial arts, and teaching English as a second language/foreign language), HEALTH PROFESSIONS (premedicine, preveterinary science, and public health), SOCIAL SCIENCE (anthropology, economics, geography, history, international relations, parks and recreation management, philosophy, political science/government, prelaw, psychology, public administration, social work, and sociology). Economics, public affairs, English, and information technology are the strongest academically. Business, psychology, and English have the largest enrollments.

Required: To graduate, all students must complete a core of study that includes 6 semester hours each of English composition, humanities, mathematics/science, and social sciences, courses in communication, analytical reasoning, social science, natural science, and non-Western culture, and at least 45 hours of upper-division work. Hours in the major vary. A minimum 2.0 GPA is required and a total of 120 to 133 credit hours must be completed. Education majors must complete a 4-year major in a chosen area and then must complete a fifth year for certification.

Special: GMU offers co-op programs in all majors with Shenendoah University, Virginia Polytechnic Institute and State University, Old Dominion University, and the University of Virginia, cross registration with the Washington Consortium of Universities, internships through academic departments, study abroad in 9 countries, and on-campus work-study programs. Also available are dual and student-designed majors, nondegree study, and pass/fail options. The Program for Alternative General Education (PAGE) is an interdisciplinary program for freshmen and sophomores. There is a freshman honors program on campus, as well as 2 national honor societies. Eight departments have honors programs.

Faculty/Classroom: Sixty-three percent of faculty are male; 37%, female. Seventy percent teach undergraduates, 14% do research, and 3% do both. Graduate students teach 16% of introductory courses. The average class size in an introductory lecture is 44; in a laboratory, 19; and in a regular course offering, 31.

Admissions: About 82% of the 1993–94 applicants were accepted. There were 10 National Merit finalists. About 25 freshmen graduated first in their class.

Requirements: GMU requires applicants to be in the upper 50% of their class. A minimum GPA of 2.5 is required. The SAT I, with a minimum composite score of 1000, and 3 SAT II: Subject tests in mathematics, writing, foreign language, or science, or the ACT is required. Applicants must be graduates of an accredited secondary school or have a GED certificate. A minimum of 16 credits are required, including 4 years of English, 3 years each of mathematics, social studies, and electives, and 2 years each of foreign language and science. An essay is recommended. AP and CLEP credits are accepted. Important factors used in the admissions decision are advanced placement or honor courses, evidence of special talent, leadership record, personality, intangible qualities, and parents or siblings attending the school.

Procedure: Freshmen are admitted fall and spring. Entrance exams should be taken during the spring of the junior year. Early decision applications should be filed by December 1; regular applications, by February 1 for fall entry and November 1 for spring entry, along with an application fee of $25. Notification is sent April 1 for regular decision, and on a rolling basis for early decision. There are early decision and early admissions plans. About 800 early decision candidates were accepted for the 1993–94 class. A waiting list is an active part of the admissions procedure, with about 5% of applicants on the list.

Transfer: About 1800 transfer students enrolled in 1993–94. Transfer students must have a minimum 2.0 GPA and at least 24 credit hours earned. Computer science, engineering, and mathematics majors must have a minimum 2.5 GPA. Other requirements vary by program. A total of 30 credits out of 120 to 133 must be completed at GMU.

Visiting: There are regularly scheduled orientations for prospective students. There are guides for informal visits and visitors may sit in on classes and stay overnight at the school. To arrange for a visit, contact the Admissions Office at (703) 993–2400.

Financial Aid: In 1993–94, 48% of all current freshmen and 37% of continuing students received some form of financial aid. About 39% of freshmen and 35% of continuing students received need-based aid. The average freshman award was $4499. Of that total, scholarships or need-based grants averaged $3206 ($17,886 maximum); loans averaged $2471 ($7000 maximum); and work contracts averaged $1787 ($3000 maximum). Eighty-two percent of undergraduate students work part-time. Average earnings from campus work for the school year are $1800. GMU is a member of CSS. The FAFSA financial statement is required. The deadline for financial aid applications is March 1.

International Students: There are currently 495 international students enrolled. They must take the TOEFL and achieve a minimum score of 570. The student must also take the SAT I or the ACT.

Computers: The college provides computer facilities for student use. The mainframes are a DEC VAX 8820 and an 8530. Approximately 510 terminals are located in public student laboratories, the libraries, dormitories, and academic departments. Those students taking computer-related courses or courses requiring computer access may access the system. It may be used 24 hours per day. There are no time limits on using the system and no fees.

Graduates: In 1992–93, 3054 bachelor's degrees were awarded. The most popular majors among graduates were business (9%), psychology (7%), and English (6%). Within an average freshman class, 20% graduate in 4 years, 40% in 5 years, and 44% in 6 years. Some 142 companies recruited on campus in 1992–93. In the 1992 graduating class, 23% of all graduates were enrolled in graduate school within 6 months of graduation; 91% had found employment.

Admissions Contact: Dr. Patricia Riordan, Dean of Admissions.

HAMPDEN-SYDNEY COLLEGE
Hampden-Sydney, VA 23943

D-3

(804) 223–6120
(800) 755–0733 (out-of-state)

Full-time: 946 men	Faculty: 60; IIB, +$
Part-time: none	Ph.D.s: 87%
Graduate: none	Student/Faculty: 16 to 1
Year: semesters, summer session	Tuition: $12,974
Application Deadline: March 1	Room & Board: $4398
Freshman Class: 817 applied, 644 accepted, 307 enrolled	
SAT I Verbal/Math: 510/560	COMPETITIVE +

Hampden-Sydney College, founded in 1776, is a private men's liberal arts institution affiliated with the Presbyterian Church. The library contains 190,000 volumes, 33,300 microform items, and 10,300 audiovisual forms, and subscribes to 798 periodicals. Computerized library sources and services include interlibrary loans and database searching. Special learning facilities include a learning resource center, radio station, international communications center, and museum. The 820-acre campus is in a rural area 60 miles southwest of Richmond. Including residence halls, there are 60 buildings on campus.

Student Life: About 53% of undergraduates are from Virginia. Students come from 30 states and 4 foreign countries. Fifty-four percent are from public schools; 46% from private. Ninety-five percent are white. Seventy-seven percent are Protestant; 14% Catholic. The average age of freshmen is 18; all undergraduates, 20. Fifteen percent drop out by the end of their first year; 67% remain to graduate.

Housing: A total of 922 students can be accommodated in college housing. College-sponsored living facilities include dormitories, on-campus apartments, married-student housing, and fraternity houses. In addition there are special interest houses and and a house for students interested in environmental concerns. On-campus housing is guaranteed for all 4 years. Ninety-five percent of students live on campus; of those, 75% remain on campus on weekends. All students may keep cars on campus.

Activities: About 50% of men belong to 12 national fraternities. There are 28 groups on campus, including chorale, chorus, computers, drama, ethnic, honors, international, literary magazine, radio, newspaper, pep band, photography, political, professional, religious, social, social service, student government, and yearbook. Popular campus events include athletic events, lectures and dances, Homecoming, Greek Weekend, Macon Week, Midwinters CAC events, Outsiders Club events, and Fall Symposium.

Sports: Athletic and recreation facilities include a field house with 3 basketball courts, 5 racquetball/handball courts, indoor track, pool, squash courts, weight room, gymnasium, tennis courts, and many playing fields.

Disabled Students: Eighty percent of the campus is accessible to disabled students. The following facilities are available: wheelchair ramps, elevators, special parking, specially equipped rest rooms, special class scheduling, and lowered telephones.

Services: In addition to many counseling and information services, tutoring is available in every subject.

Campus Safety and Security: Campus safety and security measures include informal discussions, pamphlets, posters, films, and lighted pathways and sidewalks. Campus security is on call at all times. There also is a fire department on campus, and a 'first responder' unit for emergency medical assistance. The dormitory phone lines are hooked into 911.

Programs of Study: Hampden-Sydney awards the B.A. and B.S. degrees. Bachelor's degrees are awarded in BIOLOGICAL SCIENCE (biochemistry, biology/biological science, and biophysics), BUSINESS (business economics), COMMUNICATIONS AND THE ARTS (classics, English, French, German, Greek, Latin, and Spanish), COMPUTER AND PHYSICAL SCIENCE (chemistry, computer science, mathematics, physical chemistry, and physics), SOCIAL SCIENCE (economics, history, humanities, philosophy, political science/government, psychology, and religion). Economics and history have the largest enrollments.

Required: To graduate, students must complete 120 credit hours with a minimum GPA of 2.0. Distribution requirements include 7 courses in humanities, 4 in mathematics and natural sciences, and 3 courses in social sciences. All students must also take rhetoric and foreign language, and pass a rhetoric examination.

Special: The college offers co-op programs with Longwood, Washington and Lee, Randolph-Macon, Randolph-Macon Women's, Sweet Briar, Hollins, and Mary Baldwin colleges. Cross-registration with Longwood College, internships, study abroad, a 3–2 engineering program, a Washington semester, work-study programs, B.A.-B.S. degrees, and dual majors are available. There is a freshman honors program on campus, as well as 13 national honor societies, including Phi Beta Kappa. All departments have honors programs.

Faculty/Classroom: Eighty-two percent of faculty are male; 18%, female. All teach and do research. The average class size in an introductory lecture is 20; in a laboratory, 15; and in a regular course offering, 20.

Admissions: About 79% of the 1993–94 applicants were accepted. The SAT scores for the 1993–94 freshman class were as follows: Verbal—42% below 500, 41% between 500 and 599, 16% between 600 and 700, and 1% above 700; Math—18% below 500, 47% between 500 and 599, 27% between 600 and 700, and 8% above 700. About 33% of the current freshmen were in the top fifth of their class; 66% were in the top two fifths. There were 5 National Merit semifinalists. Four freshmen graduated first in their class.

Requirements: The SAT I or ACT is required. The school recommends SAT II: Subject tests in writing, mathematics, and another subject of the student's choice. Applicants must be graduates of an accredited secondary school. Applicants should complete 18 high school academic credits, including 4 credits of English, 3 credits of mathematics, 2 credits each of foreign language and science, and 1 credit of social studies. An essay is required and an interview is recommended. The GED is accepted. AP credits are accepted. Important factors used in the admissions decision are advanced placement or honor courses, recommendations by school officials, leadership record, extracurricular activities record, and personality, intangible qualities.

Procedure: Freshmen are admitted in the fall and spring. Entrance exams should be taken during the junior or senior year of high school. Early decision applications should be filed by November 15; regular applications, by March 1 for fall entry and December 1 for spring entry, along with an application fee of $30. Notification of early decision is sent December 15; regular decision, by April. There are early decision and early admissions plans. Eighty-nine early decision candidates were accepted for the 1993–94 class. A waiting list is an active part of the admissions procedure, with about 7% of applicants on the list.

Transfer: A total of 13 transfer students enrolled in 1993–94. Applicants for transfer must have a minimum GPA of 2.5 and must take either the SAT I or the ACT. An interview is recommended. At least 60 credits out of 120 must be completed at Hampden-Sydney.

Visiting: There are regularly scheduled orientations for prospective students, consisting of lectures, information sessions, tours, lunch, and an athletic event. There are guides for informal visits, and visitors may sit in on classes and stay overnight at the school. To arrange for a visit, contact the Admissions Office at (804) 223-6120 or (800) 755-0733.

Financial Aid: In 1993–94, 80% of all current freshmen and 72% of continuing students received some form of financial aid. About 62% of freshmen and 34% of continuing students received need-based aid. The average freshman award was $11,361. Of that total, scholarships or need-based grants averaged $6054 ($17,377 maximum); loans averaged $2200 ($2625 maximum); and work contracts averaged $1231 ($1300 maximum). Eighteen percent of undergraduate students work part-time. Average earnings from campus work for the school year are $750. The average financial indebtedness of the 1992–93 graduate was $10,000. Hampden-Sydney is a member of CSS. The FAF and FAFSA are required. The deadline for financial aid applications is March 1.

International Students: There are currently 4 international students enrolled. The school actively recruits these students. They must take the TOEFL and achieve a minimum score of 570 and must also take the SAT I or the ACT.

Computers: The college provides computer facilities for student use. The mainframe is a DEC VAX 4000. Students may use the mainframe computer during computer center hours by accessing terminals in the center. Students may access the mainframe through microcomputers in their dormitory rooms, which can be hooked up through the phone system. All students may access the system during daily computing center hours. There are no time limits on using the system and no fees.

Graduates: In 1992–93, 194 bachelor's degrees were awarded. The most popular majors among graduates were economics (26%), history (17%), and biology (11%). Within an average freshman class, 61% graduate in 4 years and 67% in 5 years. Some 25 companies recruited on campus in 1992–93. In the 1992 graduating class, 10% of all students were enrolled in graduate school within 6 months of graduation; 70% had found employment.

Admissions Contact: Anita H. Garland, Director of Admissions.

HAMPTON UNIVERSITY

F-3

Hampton, VA 23668

(804) 727-5328; (800) 624-3328

Full-time: 4557 men and women
Part-time: 183 men and women
Graduate: 396 men and women
Year: semesters, summer session
Application Deadline: March 15
Freshman Class: 1428 enrolled
SAT I: 925 (composite)

Faculty: 299; IIA, --$
Ph.D.s: 47%
Student/Faculty: 15 to 1
Tuition: $7356
Room & Board: $3350

COMPETITIVE

Hampton University, founded in 1868, is a private, coeducational, liberal arts institution. There are 4 undergraduate schools and one graduate school. In addition to regional accreditation, The university has baccalaureate program accreditation with ASLA, NAAB, NASM, NCATE, and NLN. The library contains 335,000 volumes and 476,000 microform items, and subscribes to 1438 periodicals. Computerized library sources and services include the card catalog, interlibrary loans, and database searching. Special learning facilities include a learning resource center, an art gallery, a natural history museum, a radio station, and a TV station. The 204-acre campus is in an urban area 15 miles west of Norfolk. Including residence halls, there are 125 buildings on campus.

Student Life: About 67% of undergraduates are from out-of-state, mostly the Middle Atlantic. Students come from 35 states, 5 foreign countries, and Canada. Ninety percent are from public schools. Ninety-five percent are African American. The average age of freshmen is 18; all undergraduates, 20. About 65% of freshmen remain to graduate.

Housing: A total of 2800 students can be accommodated in college housing. College-sponsored living facilities include single-sex and coed dormitories and on-campus apartments. In addition, there are honors houses and special interest houses. On-campus housing is available on a first-come, first-served basis and is available on a lottery system for upperclassmen. Sixty-five percent of students live on campus; of those, 95% remain on campus on weekends. Alcohol is not permitted. Upperclassmen may keep cars on campus.

Activities: There are 5 national fraternities and 4 national sororities. There are many groups on campus, including art, band, cheerleading, choir, chorale, chorus, dance, drama, drill team, ethnic, honors, international, jazz band, marching band, newspaper, orchestra, pep band, photography, political, radio and TV, religious, social service, student government, symphony, and yearbook. Popular campus events include Homecoming, Career Day, High School Day, Black Family/Parents Weekend, Founders Weekend.

Sports: There are 5 intercollegiate sports for men and 4 for women, and 2 intramural sports for men and 1 for women.

Disabled Students: The following facilities are available: wheelchair ramps, elevators, special parking, specially equipped rest rooms, and lowered drinking fountains and telephones.

Services: In addition to many counseling and information services, tutoring is available in most subjects. There is remedial math, reading, and writing.

Campus Safety and Security: Campus safety and security measures include 24-hour foot and vehicle patrol, informal discussions, pamphlets, posters, films, emergency telephones, and lighted pathways and sidewalks.

Programs of Study: The university awards the B.A., B.S., and B.S.N. degrees. Master's degrees also are awarded. Bachelor's degrees are awarded in BIOLOGICAL SCIENCE (biology/biological science and nutrition), BUSINESS (accounting, banking and finance, business administration and management, and marketing/retailing/merchandising), COMMUNICATIONS AND THE ARTS (art, communications, dramatic arts, English, and music), COMPUTER AND PHYSICAL SCIENCE (chemistry, computer science, information sciences and systems, mathematics, and physics), EDUCATION (early childhood, elementary, physical, and special), ENGINEERING AND ENVIRONMENTAL DESIGN (aeronautical science, architectural engineering, architecture, chemical engineering, construction technology, electrical/electronics engineering, interior design, and maritime science), HEALTH PROFESSIONS (health, nursing, and speech pathology/audiology), SOCIAL SCIENCE (dietetics, economics, gerontology, history, political science/government, psychology, social work, and sociology). Architecture, biology, chemistry, and mass media are the strongest programs academically. Business has the largest enrollment.

Required: To graduate, students must complete 120 credit hours, with 74 hours in the major, related subjects, and free electives, and a GPA of 2.0. There is a 46 to 48 hour distribution requirement in freshman studies, history, language, arts and humanities, English, social sciences, mathematics, pure and applied sciences, speech, and physical and health education.

Special: The university offers co-op programs in business and mass media, cross-registration with six schools, internships, and student-designed majors. Students may receive credit for life, military, and work experience. There are pass/fail options. There is a freshman honors program on campus, as well as 14 national honor societies. Four departments have honors programs.

Faculty/Classroom: Forty-eight percent of faculty are male; 52%, female. All teach undergraduates and 25% both teach and do research. No introductory courses are taught by graduate students. The average class size in an introductory lecture is 150; in a laboratory 24; and in a regular course offering, 35.

Requirements: The university requires applicants to be in the upper 50% of their class. A minimum GPA of 2.0 is required. The SAT I or ACT is required, with a composite score of 800 required on the SAT I. Applicants must be graduates of an accredited secondary school; the GED is accepted. Students should complete 17 Carnegie units, including 6 academic electives, 4 units of English, 3 of mathematics (Algebra I and II and geometry), and 2 of science (chemistry and biology) and social studies. An interview is recommended. AP and CLEP credits are accepted. Important factors used in the admissions decision are advanced placement or honor courses, recommendations by school officials, recommendations by alumni, leadership record, and evidence of special talent.

Procedure: Freshmen are admitted to all sessions. Entrance exams should be taken during the junior year or in the fall of the senior year. Applications should be filed by March 15 for fall entry and December 15 for spring entry, along with an application fee of $15. Notification is sent on a rolling basis. There are early decision, early admissions, and deferred admissions plans. A waiting list is an active part of the admissions procedure, with about 2% of applicants on the list.

Transfer: About 125 transfer students enrolled in a recent year. Applicants for transfer must have a minimum GPA of 2.3 and 15 transferable hours. Students must have at least 60 semester or 90 quarter hours in order to be exempt from submitting their high school record and SAT I or ACT scores. An interview is recommended. A total of 30 credits out of 120 must be completed at Hampton.

Visiting: There are regularly scheduled orientations for prospective students. There are guides for informal visits and visitors may sit in on classes. To arrange for a visit, contact the Office of Admissions at (804) 727-5328 or (800) 624-3328.

Financial Aid: In an earlier year, 64% of all current freshmen and 66% of continuing students received some form of financial aid. Scholarships or need-based grants averaged $1000; loans averaged $500 ($2000 maximum); and work contracts averaged $1200 (maximum). The average financial indebtedness of an earlier graduate was $4500. The university is a member of CSS. The FAF and the college's own financial statement are required. The deadline for financial aid applications is March 31.

International Students: They must take the TOEFL and achieve a minimum score of 600. The student must also take the SAT I or the ACT.

Computers: Hampton provides computer facilities for student use.

Admissions Contact: Ollie M. Bowman, Dean of Admissions.

HOLLINS COLLEGE

C-3

Roanoke, VA 24020   (703) 362-6401; (800) 456-9595 (out-of-state)

Full-time: 779 women	Faculty: 78; IIB, av$
Part-time: 63 women	Ph.D.s: 90%
Graduate: 44 men, 115 women	Student/Faculty: 10 to 1
Year: 4-1-4	Tuition: $13,184
Application Deadline: February 15	Room & Board: $5300
Freshman Class: 583 applied, 498 accepted, 215 enrolled	
SAT I: 505/502	ACT: 22 COMPETITIVE

Hollins College, founded in 1842 as Virginia's first chartered women's college, is a private, independent institution providing a broad liberal arts curriculum. There are 3 graduate schools. The library contains 146,000 volumes, 193,293 microform items, and 3150 audiovisual forms, and subscribes to 823 periodicals. Computerized library sources and services include interlibrary loans and database searching. Special learning facilities include an art gallery, a TV station, and an astronomy tower. The 475-acre campus is in a suburban area in Roanoke. Including residence halls, there are 31 buildings on campus.

Student Life: About 68% of undergraduates are from out-of-state, mostly the South. Students come from 38 states and 12 foreign countries. Seventy-three percent are from public schools; 27% from private. Ninety-one percent are white. Forty-six percent are Protestant; 33% claim no religious affiliation; 17% Catholic. The average age of freshmen is 18; all undergraduates, 20. Fifteen percent drop out by the end of their first year; 67% remain to graduate.

Housing: A total of 742 students can be accommodated in college housing. College-sponsored living facilities include single-sex dormitories and on-campus apartments. In addition there are language houses and special interest houses. On-campus housing is guaranteed for all 4 years. Almost all students live on campus; 77% remain on campus on weekends. All students may keep cars on campus.

Activities: There are no fraternities. There are 32 groups on campus, including art, choir, chorale, computers, dance, drama, ethnic, film, gay, honors, international, literary magazine, newspaper, photography, political, professional, radio and TV, religious, social, social service, student government, and yearbook. Popular campus events include Literary Festival, Phi Beta Kappa visiting lecturers, French and German film festivals, Classics Symposium, Founders' Day, Fall Weekend, Spring Cotillion, and White Gift Service.

Sports: Athletic and recreation facilities include a swimming center, a fitness center, a gymnasium, an equestrian center, a ropes course, a jogging and exercise trail, tennis courts, 2 playing fields, and a driving range and putting green.

Disabled Students: Forty-six percent of the campus is accessible to disabled students. The following facilities are available: wheelchair ramps, elevators, special parking, specially equipped rest rooms, special class scheduling, and lowered drinking fountains.

Services: In addition to many counseling and information services, tutoring is available in most subjects. There is a reader service for the blind.

Campus Safety and Security: Campus safety and security measures include 24-hour foot and vehicle patrol, self-defense education, informal discussions, pamphlets, posters, and films. In addition, there are emergency telephones, lighted pathways and sidewalks, and emergency buttons located along walkways and in laboratories.

Programs of Study: The college awards the B.A. degree. Master's degrees also are awarded. Bachelor's degrees are awarded in BIOLOGICAL SCIENCE (biology/biological science), BUSINESS (business economics), COMMUNICATIONS AND THE ARTS (art, art history and appreciation, classics, communications, dramatic arts, English, fine arts, French, German, music, performing arts, and Spanish), COMPUTER AND PHYSICAL SCIENCE (chemistry, computer science, mathematics, and physics), SOCIAL SCIENCE (American studies, history, philosophy, political science/government, psychology, religion, and sociology). English, creative writing, psychology, political science, art history, and economics are the strongest academically. English, creative writing, psychology, political science, economics, art, and history have the largest enrollments.

Required: To graduate, students must complete 128 credits of academic work and 16 short-term credits. At least 32 hours in the major and a 2.0 GPA are required. Distribution requirements include 8 credits each in the humanities, social sciences, natural sciences and mathematics, and fine arts. All students must also take one course that emphasizes the development of writing ability and two semesters of physical education or varsity sport participation.

Special: The college offers internships during the January term, dual majors, accelerated degrees, study abroad in England, France, Russia, and Japan, and a Washington semester with American University. The B.A.-B.S. degree is awarded in 25 majors, and a 3-2 engineering degree is possible with Washington University in St. Louis and Virginia Polytechnic Institute and State University. There is cross-registration with Seven Colleges Exchange and Mills College in California and a 3-2 nursing program with the University of Virginia. There is a freshman honors program on campus, as well as 11 national honor societies, including Phi Beta Kappa. Twenty-one departments have honors programs.

Faculty/Classroom: Fifty-five percent of faculty are male; 45%, female. All teach undergraduates, 95% do research, and 95% do both. No introductory courses are taught by graduate students. The average class size in an introductory lecture is 15; in a laboratory, 12; and in a regular course offering, 15.

Admissions: About 85% of the 1993-94 applicants were accepted. The SAT scores for the 1993-94 freshman class were as follows: Verbal—50% below 500, 34% between 500 and 599, 15% between 600 and 700, and 1% above 700; Math—50% below 500, 37% between 500 and 599, 12% between 600 and 700, and 1% above 700. The ACT scores were 27% below 21, 38% between 21 and 23, 25% between 24 and 26, and 10% between 27 and 28. About 50% of the current freshmen were in the top fifth of their class; 77% were in the top two fifths. Five freshmen graduated first in their class.

Requirements: The SAT I or ACT is required. Applicants must be graduates of an accredited secondary school. The GED is accepted. Applicants should complete 16 high school academic credits, including 4 credits of English and 3 each of foreign language, mathematics, science, and social studies. SAT II: Subject tests in writing plus 2 others of the student's choice are recommended. An essay is required and an interview is recommended. AP credits are accepted. Important factors used in the admissions decision are advanced placement or honor courses, recommendations by school officials, extracurricular activities record, leadership record, and evidence of special talent.

Procedure: Freshmen are admitted in the fall and spring. Entrance exams should be taken by January of the senior year. Early decision applications should be filed by December 1, and regular applications by February 15 for fall entry and December 1 for spring entry, along with an application fee of $25. Notification of early decision is sent December 15; regular decision, on a rolling basis. There are early decision, early admissions, and deferred admissions plans. More than 60 early decision candidates were accepted for the 1993-94 class. A waiting list is an active part of the admissions procedure, with about 4% of applicants on the list.

Transfer: About 20 transfer students enrolled in 1993-94. Applicants for transfer should have a minimum GPA of 2.5. Other criteria are the same as for entering freshmen. A total of 68 credits out of 128 must be completed at The college.

Visiting: There are regularly scheduled orientations for prospective students, including 2 programs for seniors offered in October and November, and 1 for juniors and sophomores in March. There are guides for informal visits and visitors may sit in on classes and stay overnight at the school. To arrange for a visit, contact Admissions Office at (703) 362-6401 or (800) 456-9595 (out-of-state).

Financial Aid: In 1993-94, 79% of all current freshmen and 51% of continuing students received some form of financial aid. About 62% of freshmen and 49% of continuing students received need-based aid. The average freshman award was $14,802. Of that total, scholarships or need-based grants averaged $10,140 ($12,000 maximum); loans averaged $2630 ($5500 maximum); and work contracts averaged $1900 ($1950 maximum). Forty-five percent of undergraduate students work part-time. Average earnings from campus work for the school year are $1700. The average financial indebtedness of the 1992-93 graduate was $10,452. The college is a member of CSS. The college's own financial statement, parents/student tax returns, and FAFSA are required. The deadline for financial aid applications is March 1.

International Students: There are currently 10 international students enrolled. The school actively recruits these students. They must take the TOEFL and achieve a minimum score of 550. The SAT I or ACT will be accepted in place of the TOEFL.

Computers: The college provides computer facilities for student use. The mainframes are a DEC VAX cluster, MicroVAX 3900, MicroVAX II, and VAX Station 3100. There are 70 terminals for student use located throughout the campus. All students may access the system at any hour, every day of the week. There are no time limits. The fees are $15 per year.

Graduates: In 1992-93, 201 bachelor's degrees were awarded. The most popular majors among graduates were English/creative writing (23%), psychology (12%), and economics (business) and math (10%). Within an average freshman class, 68% graduate in 4 years, 69% in 5 years, and 69% in 6 years. More than 20 companies recruited on campus. In the 1992 graduating class, 36% of the women were enrolled in graduate school and 57% had found employment within a

year of graduation.

Admissions Contact: Stuart Trinkle, Director of Admissions.

JAMES MADISON UNIVERSITY

D-2

Harrisonburg, VA 22807

(703) 568–6147

Full-time: 4243 men, 5302 women

Faculty: 508; IIA, -$

Part-time: 224 men, 158 women

Ph.D.s: 81%

Graduate: 287 men, 524 women

Student/Faculty: 19 to 1

Year: semesters, summer session

Tuition: $3798 ($7650)

Application Deadline: January 15

Room & Board: $4400

Freshman Class: 11,512 applied, 5328 accepted, 2082 enrolled

SAT I Verbal/Math: 521/587

HIGHLY COMPETITIVE

James Madison University, founded in 1908, is a public, coeducational institution with programs in letters and sciences, business, education and psychology, fine arts and communication, health and human services, and integrated science and technology. There are 6 undergraduate schools and one graduate school. In addition to regional accreditation, the university has baccalaureate program accreditation with AACSB, AHEA, CSWE, NASAD, NASM, NCATE, and NLN. The library contains 333,085 volumes and 1,318,910 microform items, and subscribes to 2328 periodicals. Computerized library sources and services include the card catalog and interlibrary loans. Special learning facilities include a learning resource center, art gallery, planetarium, radio station, TV station, arboretum, and music library. The 472-acre campus is in a small town 120 miles southwest of Washington, D.C. Including residence halls, there are 84 buildings on campus.

Student Life: About 74% of undergraduates are from Virginia. Students come from 43 states, 60 foreign countries, and Canada. Ninety-five percent are from public schools; 5% from private. Eighty-seven percent are white. Thirty-seven percent are Protestant; 27% Catholic; 17% claim no religious affiliation. The average age of freshmen is 18; all undergraduates, 20. Nine percent drop out by the end of their first year; 81% remain to graduate.

Housing: A total of 4727 students can be accommodated in college housing. College-sponsored living facilities include single-sex and coed dormitories, fraternity houses, and sorority houses. On-campus housing is guaranteed for all 4 years. Fifty-nine percent of students commute. Upperclassmen may keep cars on campus.

Activities: About 16% of men belong to 17 national fraternities; about 20% of women belong to 12 national sororities. There are 215 groups on campus, including art, band, cheerleading, choir, chorale, chorus, computers, dance, drama, ethnic, honors, international, jazz band, literary magazine, marching band, musical theater, newspaper, opera, pep band, photography, political, professional, radio and TV, religious, social, social service, student government, symphony, and yearbook. Popular campus events include Parents Weekend, Homecoming, Founders Day, Festival of the Arts, Arts and Sciences Symposium, Graduation, and Masterpiece Series.

Sports: Athletic and recreation facilities include a 12,800-seat stadium, convocation center, all-weather track, gymnasium, natatorium, and tennis courts.

Disabled Students: Eighty-five percent of the campus is accessible to disabled students. The following facilities are available: wheelchair ramps, elevators, special parking, specially equipped rest rooms, special class scheduling, lowered drinking fountains, lowered telephones, and automated doors in 2 buildings.

Services: In addition to many counseling and information services, tutoring is available in every subject. There is a reader service for the blind as well as a reading and writing support laboratory.

Campus Safety and Security: Campus safety and security measures include 24-hour foot and vehicle patrol, self-defense education, escort service, and informal discussions. In addition, there are pamphlets, posters, films, emergency telephones, lighted pathways and sidewalks, and public bus transportation routes through the campus.

Programs of Study: The university awards the B.A., B.S., B.B.A., B.F.A., B.M., B.S.N., B.S.W., and B.G.S. degrees. Master's degrees also are awarded. Bachelor's degrees are awarded in BIOLOGICAL SCIENCE (biology/biological science and life science), BUSINESS (accounting, banking and finance, business administration and management, business economics, fashion merchandising, hotel/motel and restaurant management, international business management, management science, marketing/retailing/merchandising, and office supervision and management), COMMUNICATIONS AND THE ARTS (art history and appreciation, communications, dance, dramatic arts, English, fine arts, French, German, modern language, music, Russian, and Spanish), COMPUTER AND PHYSICAL SCIENCE (chemistry, computer management, computer science, geology, mathematics, physics, and science technology), EDUCATION (marketing and distribution and trade and industrial), HEALTH PROFESSIONS (health science, medical laboratory technology, nursing, and speech pathology/audiology), SOCIAL SCIENCE (anthropology, dietetics, economics, geography, history, international studies, liberal arts/general studies, philosophy, physical fitness/movement, political

science/government, psychology, public administration, religion, social science, social work, and sociology). Biology, business, communications, and music are the strongest academically. Psychology, English, biology, accounting, political science, mass communications, marketing, finance, music, and health sciences have the largest enrollments.

Required: To graduate, students must complete a minimum of 128 credit hours, with a GPA of at least 2.0. Liberal studies requirements include freshman seminar, composition, fine arts/aesthetics, history/civilization, literature, mathematics, natural science, oral communication, philosophy/religion, physical education/dance, social science, and U.S. and global culture.

Special: The college offers internships and study abroad in London, Paris, Florence, and Salamanca. A general studies degree, nondegree study, pass/fail options, and credit for life, military, and work experience are available. There is a freshman honors program on campus, as well as 28 national honor societies. Thirty-seven departments have honors programs.

Faculty/Classroom: Seventy percent of faculty are male; 30%, female. All teach undergraduates and do research. Graduate students teach 10% of introductory courses. The average class size in an introductory lecture is 100; in a laboratory, 25; and in a regular course offering, 48.

Admissions: About 46% of the 1993–94 applicants were accepted. The SAT scores for the 1993–94 freshman class were as follows: Verbal—41% below 500, 47% between 500 and 599, 11% between 600 and 700, and 1% above 700; Math—13% below 500, 44% between 500 and 599, 38% between 600 and 700, and 5% above 700. About 63% of the current freshmen were in the top fifth of their class; 87% were in the top two fifths.

Requirements: The SAT I is required. Applicants must be graduates of an accredited secondary school. Applicants must show solid achievement in each of the four high school years, including courses in English, foreign language, mathematics, science, and social studies. A personal statement is required. Art students must present a portfolio; dance, theater, and music students must audition. AP credits are accepted. Important factors used in the admissions decision are advanced placement or honor courses, evidence of special talent, leadership record, parents or siblings attending the school, and geographic diversity.

Procedure: Freshmen are admitted in the fall. Entrance exams should be taken in the spring of the junior year and the fall of the senior year. There is an early action plan. Early action applications should be filed by December 1; regular applications, by January 15 for fall entry, along with an application fee of $25. Notification of early action is sent January 15; regular decision, April 1. A waiting list is an active part of the admissions procedure, with about 11% of applicants on the list.

Transfer: A total of 485 transfer students enrolled in 1993–94. Applicants for transfer must have a minimum GPA of 2.0. Applicants who have not completed a full year of college must submit their SAT I scores. At least 32 credits out of 128 must be completed at the university.

Visiting: There are regularly scheduled orientations for prospective students, including daily campus tours at 10 A.M. and 1 P.M. during the week and 10 A.M. Saturdays, and group conferences following the tours. There are guides for informal visits. To arrange for a visit, contact the Admissions Office at (703) 568–6147.

Financial Aid: In 1993–94, 48% of all current freshmen and 54% of continuing students received some form of financial aid. About 40% of freshmen and 43% of continuing students received need-based aid. The average freshman award was $2600. Of that total, scholarships or need-based grants averaged $2008 ($3798 maximum); loans averaged $2625 ($5500 maximum); and work contracts averaged $1190 ($1785 maximum). Twenty-eight percent of undergraduate students work part-time. Average earnings from campus work for the school year are $1190. The average financial indebtedness of the 1992–93 graduate was $5467. The university is a member of CSS. The FAFSA financial statement is required. The deadline for financial aid applications is February 15.

International Students: There are currently 112 international students enrolled. The school actively recruits these students. They must take the TOEFL with a minimum score of 550 and must also take SAT I.

Computers: The college provides computer facilities for student use. The mainframe is a DEC VAX 4000. Computers are located in classrooms, computer laboratories, residence halls, academic buildings, the library, and the computer center. All students may access the system 23 hours a day. There are no time limits on using the system and no fees.

Graduates: In 1992–93, 2158 bachelor's degrees were awarded. The most popular majors among graduates were psychology (10%), English (8%), and political science (7%). Within an average freshman class, 58% graduate in 4 years, 80% in 5 years, and 81% in 6 years.

Some 186 companies recruited on campus in 1992–93.
Admissions Contact: Alan L. Cerveny, Associate Vice President.

LIBERTY UNIVERSITY   D-3
Lynchberg, VA 24506–8001   (804) 582–2158; (800) 652–4488

Full-time: 2186 men, 2123 women	Faculty: 156; IIA, --$
Part-time: 168 men, 164 women	Ph.D.s: 55%
Graduate: 186 men, 52 women	Student/Faculty: 28 to 1
Year: semesters, summer session	Tuition: $6900
Application Deadline: August 1	Room & Board: $4600
Freshman Class: n/av	
SAT I or ACT: required	**LESS COMPETITIVE**

Liberty University, founded in 1971, is a private, nondenominational Christian liberal arts institution. There are 7 undergraduate and 2 graduate schools. The library contains 191,679 volumes, 32,440 microform items, and 6080 audiovisual forms, and subscribes to 1100 periodicals. Computerized library sources and services include the card catalog, interlibrary loans, and database searching. Special learning facilities include a learning resource center, a radio station, a TV station, and a creation science museum. The 160-acre campus is in a suburban area 45 miles east of Roanoke. Including residence halls, there are 64 buildings on campus.
Student Life: About 83% of undergraduates are from out-of-state, mostly the Middle Atlantic. Students come from 50 states, 48 foreign countries, and Canada. Ninety percent are white. Most are Protestant. The average age of freshmen is 18; all undergraduates, 20.
Housing: A total of 3496 students can be accommodated in college housing. College-sponsored living facilities include single-sex dormitories. On-campus housing is guaranteed for all 4 years. Seventy percent of students live on campus. Alcohol is not permitted. All students may keep cars on campus.
Activities: There are no fraternities or sororities on campus. There are 66 groups on campus, including band, cheerleading, choir, chorale, chorus, drama, ethnic, marching band, musical theater, newspaper, opera, orchestra, pep band, political, professional, radio and TV, religious, social service, student government, and yearbook. Popular campus events include Homecoming.
Sports: There are 12 intercollegiate sports for men and 5 for women, and 11 intramural sports for men and 5 for women. Athletic and recreation facilities include an 11,000-seat football stadium, an 8000-seat basketball arena/convention center, baseball and soccer fields, a track, and an athletic center.
Disabled Students: Ninety percent of the campus is accessible to disabled students. The following facilities are available: wheelchair ramps, special parking, specially equipped rest rooms, special class scheduling, and lowered drinking fountains and telephones.
Services: In addition to many counseling and information services, tutoring is available in every subject. There is remedial math, reading, and writing.
Campus Safety and Security: Campus safety and security measures include 24-hour foot and vehicle patrol, self-defense education, escort service, informal discussions, pamphlets, posters, films, and lighted pathways and sidewalks.
Programs of Study: Liberty awards the B.A., B.S., and B.S.N. degrees. Associate, master's, and doctoral degrees also are awarded. Bachelor's degrees are awarded in BIOLOGICAL SCIENCE (biology/biological science), BUSINESS (accounting, banking and finance, business administration and management, business economics, fashion merchandising, management information systems, marketing/retailing/merchandising, recreation and leisure services, and sports management), COMMUNICATIONS AND THE ARTS (broadcasting, dramatic arts, English, French, journalism, linguistics, modern language, music, music performance, Spanish, speech/debate/rhetoric, and telecommunications), COMPUTER AND PHYSICAL SCIENCE (actuarial science, chemistry, computer programming, computer science, and mathematics), EDUCATION (elementary, health, and physical), HEALTH PROFESSIONS (nursing and public health), SOCIAL SCIENCE (biblical studies, criminal justice, family and community services, history, human ecology, interdisciplinary studies, ministries, missions, pastoral studies, philosophy, physical fitness/movement, political science/government, prelaw, psychology, public administration, religious music, and social science). Business, psychology, and education have the largest enrollments.
Required: Students must complete 120 to 123 credit hours to graduate, with a minimum GPA of 2.0. With few exceptions by major, all must complete 18 hours of foundational studies in English, mathematics, speech communications, general education, and physical education. An additional 42 credits of investigative studies are required; these vary according to the degree sought, but include English, natural sciences, history, arts, music, languages, government, social sciences, philosophy, theology, Bible studies, and integrated studies.
Special: Liberty offers individually designed co-op programs and internships, a Washington semester, and student-designed majors in interdisciplinary and general studies. There is a freshman honors program on campus, as well as 9 national honor societies. In addition, there is a university-wide honors program.
Faculty/Classroom: Sixty-six percent of faculty are male; 34%, female. Nearly all teach undergraduates. No introductory courses are taught by graduate students. The average class size in an introductory lecture is 50; in a laboratory, 20; and in a regular course offering, 30.
Requirements: The SAT I or ACT is required. Applicants for transfer must complete 16 high school academic credits or the GED is accepted. An essay is required. AP and CLEP credits are accepted. Important factors used in the admissions decision are ability to finance college education, recommendations by school officials, advanced placement or honor courses, leadership record, and extracurricular activities record.
Procedure: Freshmen are admitted to all sessions. Entrance exams should be taken during the junior year. Applications should be filed by August 1 for fall entry and January 1 for spring entry, along with an application fee of $35. Notification is sent on a rolling basis. There are early admissions and deferred admissions plans.
Transfer: About 360 transfer students enrolled in 1992–93. Applicants for transfer must have a GPA of 2.0. If transferring fewer than 30 hours, high school transcript and test scores are required. A total of 32 credits out of 120 to 123 must be completed at Liberty.
Visiting: There are regularly scheduled orientations for prospective students. Liberty offers 'College for a Weekend', a 2-day program offering a chance to attend classes and special meetings. There are guides for informal visits and visitors may sit in on classes and stay overnight at the school. To arrange for informal visits, contact the Visitor's Center at (804) 582–2064; for the College for a Weekend, call the Admissions Office at (804) 532–2158.
Financial Aid: In 1992–93 85% of all students received some form of financial aid. About 45% of freshmen received need-based aid. The average freshman award was $4625. Of that total, scholarships or need-based grants averaged $2000; and loans averaged $2625. Average earnings from campus work for the school year are $2000. Liberty is a member of CSS. The FAF and Single file (preferred) are required. The deadline for financial aid applications is April 15.
International Students: There are currently 228 international students enrolled. They must take the TOEFL and achieve a minimum score of 500.
Computers: Some 150 microcomputers are located in laboratories. All students may access the system Monday through Friday 8 A.M. to 11 P.M. and certain weekend hours. There are no time limits on using the system. The fees vary by class.
Graduates: In arecent year, the most popular majors among graduates were business and management (28%), psychology (13%), and education (11%). Some 119 companies recruited on campus.
Admissions Contact: Shaun Redgate, Associate Director of Admissions.

LONGWOOD COLLEGE   D-3
Farmville, VA 23909   (804) 395–2060; (800) 281–4677 (out-of-state)

Full-time: 941 men, 1933 women	Faculty: 153; IIB, av$
Part-time: 43 men, 75 women	Ph.D.s: 92%
Graduate: 85 men, 283 women	Student/Faculty: 19 to 1
Year: semesters, summer session	Tuition: $4106 ($9190)
Application Deadline: March 1	Room & Board: $3694
Freshman Class: 2747 applied, 1870 accepted, 724 enrolled	
SAT I Verbal/Math: 450/490	**COMPETITIVE**

Longwood College, founded in 1839, is a state-supported, coeducational institution with programs in liberal arts, business, and teacher preparation. There are 3 undergraduate schools and one graduate school. In addition to regional accreditation, Longwood has baccalaureate program accreditation with CSWE, NASM, NCATE, and NRPA. The library contains 884,329 volumes, 549,936 microform items, and 33,946 audiovisual forms, and subscribes to 1645 periodicals. Computerized library sources and services include the card catalog, interlibrary loans, and database searching. Special learning facilities include a learning resource center, an art gallery, a radio station, a TV station, a greenhouse, a language laboratory, 6 computer laboratories, and a psychology laboratory. The 154-acre campus is in a small town 60 miles west of Richmond and 60 miles south of Charlottesville. Including residence halls, there are 49 buildings on campus.
Student Life: Most undergraduates are from Virginia. Students come from 21 states, 8 foreign countries, and Canada. Ninety-four percent are from public schools; 6% from private. Eighty-nine percent are white. Fifty-one percent are Protestant; 27% claim no religious affiliation; 16% are Catholic. The average age of freshmen is 18; all undergraduates, 20. Twenty percent drop out by the end of their first year; 55% remain to graduate.
Housing: A total of 2206 students can be accommodated in college housing. College-sponsored living facilities include single-sex and coed dormitories. In addition, there are honors houses, language houses, special interest houses, an international studies floor,

fraternity/sorority floors, and an ecology floor. On-campus housing is guaranteed for all 4 years. Eighty-three percent of students live on campus; of those, 66% remain on campus on weekends. Upperclassmen may keep cars on campus.

Activities: About 22% of men belong to 7 national fraternities; about 27% of women belong to 12 national sororities. There are 101 groups on campus, including art, band, cheerleading, choir, chorus, computers, dance, drama, drill team, ethnic, gay, honors, international, jazz band, literary magazine, musical theater, newspaper, political, professional, radio and TV, religious, social, social service, student government, and yearbook. Popular campus events include Spring Weekend and Oktoberfest.

Sports: There are 7 intercollegiate sports for men and 8 for women, and 33 intramural sports each for men and women. Athletic and recreation facilities include a 9-hole golf course, a weight training facility, 2 gymnasiums, racquetball courts, 11 lighted tennis courts, 2 pools, a bowling alley, 3 outdoor sand volleyball courts, a 10-station fitness trail, a frisbee golf course, outdoor basketball courts, and playing fields.

Disabled Students: Eighty-five percent of the campus is accessible to disabled students. The following facilities are available: wheelchair ramps, elevators, special parking, special class scheduling, and lowered drinking fountains and telephones. The campus is being made fully accessible; until then, classes can be scheduled in accessible buildings.

Services: In addition to many counseling and information services, tutoring is available in most subjects. There is also remedial math, reading, and writing, assistance in study skills, learning strategies, advocacy training, and compensatory strategy instruction available.

Campus Safety and Security: Campus safety and security measures include 24-hour foot and vehicle patrol, self-defense education, escort service, and shuttle buses. In addition, there are informal discussions, pamphlets, posters, films, emergency telephones, and lighted pathways and sidewalks.

Programs of Study: Longwood awards the B.A., B.S., B.F.A., B.M., and B.S.B.A. degrees. Master's degrees are also awarded. Bachelor's degrees are awarded in BIOLOGICAL SCIENCE (biology/biological science), BUSINESS (business administration and management), COMMUNICATIONS AND THE ARTS (dramatic arts, English, French, German, music, Spanish, and visual and performing arts), COMPUTER AND PHYSICAL SCIENCE (chemistry, computer science, mathematics, and physics), EDUCATION (art, elementary, music, physical, secondary, and special), ENGINEERING AND ENVIRONMENTAL DESIGN (preengineering), HEALTH PROFESSIONS (premedicine, recreation therapy, and speech pathology/audiology), SOCIAL SCIENCE (anthropology, economics, history, liberal arts/general studies, political science/government, psychology, social work, and sociology). Sciences, English, business, education, history, and mathematics are the strongest academically. Business, psychology, and education have the largest enrollments.

Required: To graduate, students must complete 126 to 128 credits, with a minimum GPA of 2.0 overall and in the major. A 33-hour general education core curriculum, 2 intensive writing courses, a physical education course, and 30 upper-level credit hours are also required.

Special: Longwood offers internships in political science, social work, business, education, art, and therapeutic recreation, study abroad in 5 countries, a dual major in psychology and special education, and a student-designed general studies major for adults. B.A.-B.S. degrees are offered in 11 majors. Cross-registration is possible with Hampden-Sydney College, as are 3-2 engineering degrees with Old Dominion University, the University of Virginia, and Georgia Institute of Technology. Also, there are 2-2 preprofessional programs in nursing, dentistry, medicine, and physical therapy with UVA, Old Dominion, and Georgia Tech. There is a freshman honors program on campus, as well as 3 national honor societies. Twenty-one departments have honors programs.

Faculty/Classroom: Sixty-seven percent of faculty are male; 33%, female. All teach undergraduates and half also do research. Graduate students teach 1% of introductory courses. The average class size in an introductory lecture is 30; in a laboratory, 22; and in a regular course offering, 25.

Admissions: About 68% of the 1993-94 applicants were accepted. The SAT scores for the freshman class were as follows: Verbal—72% below 500, 26% between 500 and 599, and 2% between 600 and 700; Math—50% below 500, 43% between 500 and 599, 5% between 600 and 700, and 2% above 700. About 20% of the current freshmen were in the top fifth of their class; 36% were in the top two fifths.

Requirements: Longwood requires applicants to be in the upper 50% of their class. A minimum GPA of 2.5 is required. The SAT I is required. Applicants must be graduates of an accredited secondary school or have a GED. Students should complete 4 years of high school English, 3 of science, including 2 laboratory courses, 2 each of history and foreign languages, and algebra I and II and geometry. An essay is required. A portfolio is recommended for art students and

an audition is required for music students. AP and CLEP credits are accepted. Important factors used in the admissions decision are advanced placement or honor courses, evidence of special talent, leadership record, parents or siblings attending the school, and recommendations by alumni.

Procedure: Freshmen are admitted to all sessions. Entrance exams should be taken in the fall of the senior year. There are early action, early admissions, and deferred admissions plans. Early action applications should be filed by November 15; regular applications, by March 1 for fall entry and November 15 for spring entry, along with an application fee of $25. Notification of early action is sent January 6; regular decision, on a rolling basis. About 159 early decision candidates were accepted for the 1993-94 class. A waiting list is an active part of the admissions procedure, with about 10% of the applicants on the list.

Transfer: About 210 transfer students enrolled in 1993-94. Applicants for transfer must have a GPA of at least 2.2 in all college course work attempted. Other criteria are the same as for entering freshmen. A total of 30 credits out of 126 must be completed at Longwood.

Visiting: There are regularly scheduled orientations for prospective students, including informational and tour programs, and open houses in October, February, and March. There are guides for informal visits and visitors may sit in on classes and stay overnight at the school. To arrange for a visit, contact the Admissions Office at (804) 395-2060 or (800) 281-4677.

Financial Aid: In 1993-94, 60% of all students received some form of financial aid; 50% received need-based aid. The average freshman award was $6220. Of that total, scholarships or need-based grants averaged $1000 ($10,000 maximum); loans averaged $2000 ($4000 maximum); and work contracts averaged $1350 ($2000 maximum). Twenty-one percent of undergraduate students work part-time. Average earnings from campus work for the school year are $1600. The average financial indebtedness of the 1992-93 graduate was $13,250. Longwood is a member of CSS. The FAF, the college's own financial statement, and FAFSA are required. The deadline for financial aid applications is March 1.

International Students: There are currently 31 international students enrolled. The school actively recruits these students. They must take the TOEFL and achieve a minimum score of 550.

Computers: The college provides computer facilities for student use. The mainframes are an IBM 4341 and an HP 3000 Series 70. There are a total of 185 networked microcomputers, including IBM-compatible and Apple. Two student computer laboratories are open 9 A.M. to 10 P.M. daily. Software packages available include Wordstar 5, WordPerfect 5.1, dBase 3+, Turbo Pascal 5.5, FORTRAN, COBOL, and Harvard Graphics 3.0. All students may access the system. There are no time limits and no fees.

Graduates: In 1992-93, 676 bachelor's degrees were awarded. The most popular majors among graduates were business administration (25%), elementary education (20%), and psychology (12%). Within an average freshman class, 43% graduate in 4 years, 50% in 5 years, and 54% in 6 years. Some 56 companies recruited on campus. In the 1992 graduating class, 14% of all seniors were enrolled in graduate school within 6 months of graduation and 95% of the others had found employment

Admissions Contact: Robert J. Chonko, Dean of Admissions and Enrollment Management.

LYNCHBURG COLLEGE D-3
Lynchburg, VA 24501　　　　　　　　　　　　　(804) 522-8300
　　　　　　　　　　　　　　　　　　　　(800) 426-8101 (out-of-state)

Full-time: 619 men, 970 women	Faculty: 144; IIA, --$
Part-time: 105 men, 175 women	Ph.D.s: 67%
Graduate: 172 men, 338 women	Student/Faculty: 11 to 1
Year: semesters, summer session	Tuition: $11,600
Application Deadline: June 1	Room & Board: $5400
Freshman Class: 1750 applied, 1400 accepted, 418 enrolled	
SAT I or ACT: required	COMPETITIVE

Lynchburg College, established in 1903, is a private, nonprofit institution affiliated with the Christian Church (Disciples of Christ) offering bachelor's degrees in liberal arts. There are 2 graduate schools. In addition to regional accreditation, L.C. has baccalaureate program accreditation with NLN. The library contains 264,800 volumes, 19,200 microform items, and 22,630 audiovisual forms, and subscribes to 740 periodicals. Computerized library sources and services include the card catalog, interlibrary loans, and database searching. Special learning facilities include an art gallery and radio station. The 214-acre campus is in a suburban area 180 miles southwest of Washington, D.C. Including residence halls, there are 26 buildings on campus.

Student Life: About 52% of undergraduates are from out-of-state, mostly the Middle Atlantic. Students come from 30 states and 22 foreign countries. Seventy percent are from public schools; 30% from private. Eighty-nine percent are white. Fifty percent are Protestant;

30% Catholic. The average age of freshmen is 18; all undergraduates, 20. Twenty percent drop out by the end of their first year; 60% remain to graduate.

Housing: A total of 1100 students can be accommodated in college housing. College-sponsored living facilities include single-sex and coed dormitories and on-campus apartments. In addition there are honors houses, language houses, and special interest houses. On-campus housing is guaranteed for all 4 years. Seventy-five percent of students live on campus; of those, 80% remain on campus on weekends. Upperclassmen may keep cars on campus.

Activities: About 13% of men belong to 1 local and 5 national fraternities; about 9% of women belong to 3 national sororities. There are 45 groups on campus, including art, band, cheerleading, choir, computers, ethnic, film, honors, international, jazz band, literary magazine, musical theater, newspaper, photography, political, professional, radio and TV, religious, social, social service, student government, and yearbook. Popular campus events include new student convocation, Parents Weekend, Homecoming, Academic Awards Banquet, Leadership Appreciation Night, Octoberfest, Duckfest, and Day in Dell.

Sports: There are 11 intercollegiate sports each for men and women, and 20 intramural sports for men and 17 for women. Athletic and recreation facilities include a gymnasium, a field house, an indoor pool, athletic fields, and a ropes course.

Disabled Students: Seventy percent of the campus is accessible to disabled students. The following facilities are available: wheelchair ramps, elevators, special parking, specially equipped rest rooms, special class scheduling, and lowered drinking fountains and telephones.

Services: In addition to many counseling and information services, tutoring is available in most freshman and sophomore subjects, some upperclass subjects, and in mathematics and writing. The college also has a writing laboratory.

Campus Safety and Security: Campus safety and security measures include 24-hour foot and vehicle patrol, escort service, shuttle buses, and informal discussions. In addition, there are pamphlets, posters, and films, emergency telephones, and lighted pathways and sidewalks.

Programs of Study: L.C. awards the B.A. and B.S. degrees. Master's degrees also are awarded. Bachelor's degrees are awarded in BIOLOGICAL SCIENCE (biology/biological science), BUSINESS (accounting, international business management, and marketing/retailing/merchandising), COMMUNICATIONS AND THE ARTS (communications, English, French, German, music, Spanish, and theater design), COMPUTER AND PHYSICAL SCIENCE (chemistry, computer science, information sciences and systems, mathematics, and physics), EDUCATION (early childhood, middle school, and special), ENGINEERING AND ENVIRONMENTAL DESIGN (environmental science), HEALTH PROFESSIONS (medical laboratory technology and nursing), SOCIAL SCIENCE (American studies, economics, European studies, history, international relations, philosophy, political science/government, psychology, religion, and sociology). Management, communication, and psychology have the largest enrollments.

Required: To graduate, students must complete a 15- to 18-hour basic skills requirement, which includes English, a foreign language, mathematics, and health/movement science/recreation. Students must also complete 15 to 21 hours in the humanities (history, literature, philosophy, and religion), 6 hours each in fine arts and social sciences, 6 to 16 hours in physical sciences, and a 2-hour senior symposium. The minimum GPA is 2.0. Students must earn 124 credits, with 24 to 62 in the major.

Special: Students may cross-register with Sweet Briar and Randolph-Macon Colleges, and they may study abroad in several countries. There is a Washington semester available, internships, and a work-study program. Dual majors may be pursued in business and a foreign language. Three-two engineering degrees are available in cooperation with the Georgia Institute of Technology and Old Dominion University. Nondegree study and a pass/fail grading option are also available. There is a freshman honors program on campus, as well as 2 national honor societies. Forty-six departments have honors programs.

Faculty/Classroom: All teach undergraduates and 80% also do research. The average class size in an introductory lecture is 25; in a laboratory, 16; and in a regular course offering, 25.

Admissions: About 80% of the 1993–94 applicants were accepted. There were 5 National Merit semifinalists. Three freshmen graduated first in their class.

Requirements: L.C. requires applicants to be in the upper 50% of their class. A minimum GPA of 2.5 is required. The SAT I or ACT is required and SAT II: Subject tests are recommended. Applicants must graduate from an accredited secondary school. They must have earned 15 academic credits, with 4 credits in English, 3 each in mathematics and social studies, and 2 each in science and a foreign language. AP and CLEP credits are accepted. Important factors used in the admissions decision are advanced placement or honor courses, leadership record, recommendations by school officials, evidence of special talent, and parents or siblings attending the school.

Procedure: Freshmen are admitted to all sessions. Entrance exams should be taken in the junior year and first semester of the senior year. Applications should be filed by June 1 for fall entry, December-1 for spring entry, and May 1 for summer entry, along with an application fee of $20. Notification is sent on a rolling basis. There are early admissions and deferred admissions plans. A waiting list is an active part of the admissions procedure, with about 5% of applicants on the list.

Transfer: About 100 transfer students enrolled in 1993–94. Transfer students must have a minimum GPA of 2.0 to be considered, and must be in good academic and social standing. SAT I or the ACT and the intercollegiate request form are required. An interview is recommended. A total of 48 credits out of 124 must be completed at L.C.

Visiting: There are regularly scheduled orientations for prospective students, and individual appointments are available. There are guides for informal visits and visitors may sit in on classes and stay overnight at the school. To arrange for a visit, contact the Admissions Office at (804) 522–8300 or (800) 426–8101 (out-of-state).

Financial Aid: In 1993–94, 83% of all current freshmen and 67% of continuing students received some form of financial aid; 53% of freshmen and 44% of continuing students received need-based aid. The average freshman award was $10,420. Of that total, scholarships or need-based grants averaged $5620 ($11,600 maximum); loans averaged $3200 ($3625 maximum); and work contracts averaged $1600. Thirty-two percent of undergraduate students work part-time. Average earnings from campus work for the school year are $1036. The average financial indebtedness of the 1992–93 graduate was $9904. L.C. is a member of CSS. The FAF, the college's own financial statement, and the FAFSA are required. The deadline for financial aid applications is April 1.

International Students: There are currently 39 international students enrolled. The school actively recruits these students. They must take the TOEFL and achieve a minimum score of 550.

Computers: The college provides computer facilities for student use. The mainframe is a DEC VAX 4000/200. Student computing is primarily PC-based, with some access to mainframe facilities. One hundred microcomputers are located in laboratories and classrooms across campus. Students with their own computers in their rooms number about 700. It is recommended that students in all programs have personal computers. A DOS computer with 286 or 386 chip technology is recommended. All students may access the main system. It may be used 8 A.M. to 12 A.M. Monday through Thursday, 8 A.M. to 5 P.M. Friday, 12 P.M. to 12 A.M. Saturday and Sunday. There are no time limits and no fees.

Graduates: In 1992–93, 422 bachelor's degrees were awarded. The most popular majors among graduates were communication (11%), management (8%), and nursing (8%). Within an average freshman class, 1% graduate in 3 years, 57% in 4 years, and 63% in 5 years. Some 84 companies recruited on campus in 1992–93. In the 1992 graduating class, 18% of the seniors were enrolled in graduate school within 6 months of graduation; 65% found employment.

Admissions Contact: Dee Hubble, Director of Admissions.

MARY BALDWIN COLLEGE

D-2

Staunton, VA 24401　　　　(703) 887–7019; 826–0154 **(out-of-state)**

Full-time: 52 men, 774 women	**Faculty:** 74; IIB, -$
Part-time: 27 men, 316 women	**Ph.D.s:** 72%
Graduate: 9 men, 47 women	**Student/Faculty:** 11 to 1
Year: 4-4-1	**Tuition:** $10,654
Application Deadline: April 15	**Room & Board:** $7046
Freshman Class: 449 applied, 411 accepted, 174 enrolled	
SAT I or ACT: required	**LESS COMPETITIVE**

Mary Baldwin College, established in 1842, is a private college for women affiliated with the Presbyterian Church offering undergraduate liberal arts degrees. The college sponsors a program for exceptionally gifted young women who have completed the eighth grade or higher. There is one graduate school. The library contains 180,000 volumes, and subscribes to 600 periodicals. Special learning facilities include a learning resource center, art gallery, radio station, and TV station. The 54-acre campus is in a small town 100 miles west of Richmond. Including residence halls, there are 30 buildings on campus.

Student Life: Half of the undergraduates are from out-of-state, mostly the Middle Atlantic. Students come from 30 states and 10 foreign countries. Seventy percent are from public schools; 30% from private. Ninety percent are white. Sixty percent are Protestant; 10% Catholic. The average age of freshmen is 18. Twenty percent drop out by the end of their first year; 60% remain to graduate.

Housing: College-sponsored living facilities include dormitories and on-campus apartments. In addition, there are honors houses, language houses, special interest houses, and a community service house for students who do volunteer work. On-campus housing is guaranteed for all 4 years. Ninety-two percent of students live on campus; of those, 75% remain on campus on weekends. All students may keep cars on campus.

Activities: There are no fraternities. There are 22 groups on campus, including art, cheerleading, chess, choir, computers, dance, drama, ethnic, film, honors, international, literary magazine, musical theater, newspaper, orchestra, photography, political, professional, radio and TV, religious, social, social service, student government, and yearbook. Popular campus events include Apple Day, Junior Dads Weekend, Charter Day, Founders Day, Senior Day, and theatrical productions.

Sports: Athletic and recreation facilities include a gymnasium, a swimming pool, a Universal gym room, a room for dance and fencing, basketball and racquetball courts, sauna, whirlpool steamroom, and Nautilus equipment.

Disabled Students: Forty percent of the campus is accessible to disabled students. The following facilities are available: wheelchair ramps, elevators, special parking, and specially equipped rest rooms.

Services: In addition to many counseling and information services, tutoring is available in every subject.

Campus Safety and Security: Campus safety and security measures include 24-hour foot and vehicle patrol, self defense education, escort service, and informal discussions. In addition, there are pamphlets, posters, films, emergency telephones, lighted pathways and sidewalks, and 24-hour locked residence halls.

Programs of Study: Mary Baldwin awards the B.A. degree. Master's degrees also are awarded. Bachelor's degrees are awarded in BIOLOGICAL SCIENCE (biology/biological science), BUSINESS (business administration and management and business economics), COMMUNICATIONS AND THE ARTS (arts administration/management, communications, dramatic arts, English, fine arts, French, and Spanish), COMPUTER AND PHYSICAL SCIENCE (chemistry, computer mathematics, and mathematics), EDUCATION (art, early childhood, English, foreign languages, mathematics, middle school, science, secondary, and social studies), HEALTH PROFESSIONS (medical laboratory technology), SOCIAL SCIENCE (international relations, philosophy, political science/government, psychology, social work, and sociology). Psychology, art, and business have the largest enrollments.

Required: To graduate, students must complete 9 hours each in natural sciences, social sciences, arts, and humanities, 6 each of writing courses, international education (foreign language, cross-cultural studies, and/or study abroad), and 3 each of mathematics and women's studies. A minimum GPA of 2.0 is required. Students must earn 132 credits, with at least 33 credits in the major. There is a 2-hour physical education requirement and a 3-hour experiential education requirement. Most disciplines require senior projects consisting of some type of original research, a thesis, or something similar.

Special: There are cooperative programs with Randolph-Macon, Sweet Briar, and Hampden-Sydney colleges, and Washington and Lee universities. Internships and work-study programs are available. Students may study abroad in Japan, Italy, England, France, Spain, and Germany. There is a Washington semester. The college offers an accelerated degree program. Dual and student-designed majors may be pursued. There are 3-2 programs are available in engineering with Washington University in St. Louis, and in nursing with Vanderbilt University. Credit for life, military, and work experience may be granted through the adult degree program only. Nondegree study and a pass/fail grading option are available. There is a freshman honors program on campus, as well as 9 national honor societies, including Phi Beta Kappa.

Faculty/Classroom: Forty-five percent of faculty are male; 55%, female. All teach undergraduates. The average class size in an introductory lecture is 19; in a laboratory, 13; and in a regular course offering, 16.

Admissions: About 92% of the 1993–94 applicants were accepted.

Requirements: The SAT I or ACT is required. SAT II: Subject tests are recommended. Applicants must graduate from an accredited secondary school or have a GED. A minimum of 16 academic units are required, including 4 units in English, 2 to 3 in social studies, 3 in mathematics, and 2 each in a foreign language and science. Essays are required and interviews are recommended. AP credits are accepted. Important factors used in the admissions decision are advanced placement or honor courses, recommendations by school officials, leadership record, extracurricular activities record, and evidence of special talent.

Procedure: Freshmen are admitted fall and spring. Entrance exams should be taken in the junior or senior years. There are early decision, early admissions, and deferred admissions plans. Early decision applications should be filed by November 15; regular applications, by April 15 for fall entry and November 15 for spring entry, along with an application fee of $25. Notification of early decision is sent December 15; regular decision, on a rolling basis. About 25 early decision candidates were accepted for the 1993–94 class.

Transfer: About 53 transfer students enrolled in 1993–94. A total of 66 credits out of 132 must be completed at Mary Baldwin.

Visiting: There are regularly scheduled orientations for prospective students. There are guides for informal visits and visitors may sit in on classes and stay overnight at the school. To arrange for a visit, contact Director of Admissions at (800) 468–2262 (in-state) or (800) 826–0154.

Financial Aid: In a recent year, 74% of all current freshmen and 70% of continuing students received some form of financial aid. About 55% of freshmen and 45% of continuing students received need-based aid. The average freshman award was $963. Of that total, scholarships or need-based grants averaged $6038 ($9000 maximum); loans averaged $2625 ($5500 maximum); and work contracts averaged $1300. Forty-five percent of undergraduate students work part-time. Average earnings from campus work for the school year are $1300. The average financial indebtedness of a recent graduate was $10,000. Mary Baldwin is a member of CSS. The FFS is required. The deadline for financial aid applications is April 15.

International Students: There are currently 32 international students enrolled. The school actively recruits these students. They must take the TOEFL and achieve a minimum score of 500.

Computers: The college provides computer facilities for student use. The mainframe is an IBM/400. Some 90 microcomputers are spread throughout the campus, there are public workstations in every classroom building, and 40 terminals are networked to the main computer center. All students may access the system. There are no time limits and no fees.

Graduates: In 1992–93, 276 bachelor's degrees were awarded. The most popular majors among graduates were business administration (16%), self-designed majors (14%), and psychology (11%). Within an average freshman class, 4% graduate in 3 years, 55% in 4 years, and 60% in 5 years. Some 45 companies recruited on campus in 1992–93.

Admissions Contact: Patricia N. LeDonne, Director of Admissions.

MARY WASHINGTON COLLEGE
E-2
Fredericksburg, VA 22401-5358

(703) 899–4681
(800) 468–5614 (out-of-state)

Full-time: 1069 men, 1928 women	Faculty: 163; IIB, av$
Part-time: 221 men, 515 women	Ph.D.s: 88%
Graduate: 23 men, 35 women	Student/Faculty: 18 to 1
Year: semesters, summer session	Tuition: $3066 ($7136)
Application Deadline: February 1	Room & Board: $4844
Freshman Class: 4350 applied, 2178 accepted, 756 enrolled	
SAT I: required	**HIGHLY COMPETITIVE**

Mary Washington College, founded in 1908, is a public, coeducational, liberal arts institution. There is one graduate school. In addition to regional accreditation, The college has baccalaureate program accreditation with NASM. The library contains 338,000 volumes and 104,200 microform items, and subscribes to 1700 periodicals. Computerized library sources and services include the card catalog and database searching. Special learning facilities include an art gallery, radio station, and center for historic preservation. The 176-acre campus is in a small town 50 miles south of Washington, D.C. Including residence halls, there are 36 buildings on campus.

Student Life: About 75% of undergraduates are from Virginia. Students come from 36 states, 15 foreign countries, and Canada. Eighty-three percent are from public schools; 17% from private. Ninety percent are white. The average age of freshmen is 18; all undergraduates, 20. Nine percent drop out by the end of their first year; 73% remain to graduate.

Housing: A total of 2130 students can be accommodated in college housing. College-sponsored living facilities include single-sex and coed dormitories. In addition there are honors houses, language houses, and special interest houses. On-campus housing is guaranteed for all 4 years and is available on a first-come, first-served basis. Some 75 to 80% of all students live on campus; of those, more than 80% remain on campus on weekends. All students may keep cars on campus.

Activities: There are no fraternities or sororities. There are 82 groups on campus, including art, cheerleading, choir, chorale, chorus, computers, dance, drama, drill team, ethnic, gay, honors, international, jazz band, literary magazine, musical theater, newspaper, orchestra, political, professional, radio and TV, religious, social service, student government, and yearbook. Popular campus events include Halloween, Grill on the Hill, Devil Goat Day, Westock, homecoming, commencement, and a Multicultural International Festival.

Sports: There are 9 intercollegiate sports for men and 11 for women, and 17 intramural sports each. Athletic and recreation facilities include an indoor pool, basketball and volleyball courts, a weight room, batting cages, training rooms, playing fields for all outdoor sports, a running course, handball/racquetball courts, and an 8-lane, 400-meter track.

Disabled Students: Sixty-five percent of the campus is accessible to disabled students. The following facilities are available: wheelchair ramps, elevators, special parking, specially equipped rest rooms, and lowered drinking fountains and telephones.

Services: There is a writing center and a center for the visually impaired.

Campus Safety and Security: Campus safety and security measures include 24-hour foot and vehicle patrol, escort service, informal discussions, and pamphlets, posters, and films. In addition, there are emergency telephones and lighted pathways and sidewalks.

Programs of Study: The college awards the B.A., B.S., and B.L.S degrees. Master's degrees are also awarded. Bachelor's degrees are awarded in BIOLOGICAL SCIENCE (biology/biological science), BUSINESS (business administration and management), COMMUNICATIONS AND THE ARTS (classics, dance, dramatic arts, English, French, German, languages, Latin, music, and Spanish), COMPUTER AND PHYSICAL SCIENCE (chemistry, computer science, geology, mathematics, and physics), ENGINEERING AND ENVIRONMENTAL DESIGN (environmental science), HEALTH PROFESSIONS (predentistry, premedicine, and preveterinary science), SOCIAL SCIENCE (economics, geography, history, international relations, philosophy, political science/government, prelaw, psychology, religion, and sociology). Business administration, psychology, and English have the largest enrollments.

Required: To graduate, students must complete 122 credit hours, with 30 to 40 hours in the major and a minimum GPA of 2.0. Distribution requirements include 9 credits each in Intellectual Frameworks, Modes of Creativity, and Human World, 8 in Natural World, and 6 in Abstract Thought. Specific courses required include 5 classes in Writing Intensive and foreign language competency, 2 classes in laboratory science, 1 class in mathematics, and 2 in physical education.

Special: Study abroad, a Washington semester, and credit for off-campus work experience are available. The college offers a cooperative program in computer science, dual majors, student-designed majors, and pass/fail options. Many internships are also available. There are 10 national honor societies on campus, including Phi Beta Kappa.

Faculty/Classroom: Sixty-seven percent of faculty are male; 33%, female. No introductory courses are taught by graduate students. The average class size in an introductory lecture is 38; in a laboratory, 25; and in a regular course offering, 18.

Admissions: About 50% of the 1993–94 applicants were accepted. The SAT scores for the 1993–94 freshman class were as follows: Verbal—31% below 500, 51% between 500 and 599, and 18% between 600 and 700; Math—15% below 500, 48% between 500 and 599, and 37% between 600 and 700. About 70% of the current freshmen were in the top fifth of their class; 94% were in the top two fifths. There were 6 National Merit semi-finalists and 1 finalist. Fourteen freshmen graduated first in their class.

Requirements: SAT I is required and the SAT II: Writing test is recommended. Applicants must be graduates of an accredited secondary school or hold the GED. Students should complete 16 high school academic credits, including 4 of English, 3–4 of foreign language, and 3 each of mathematics, science, and social studies. AP and CLEP credits are accepted. Important factors used in the admissions decision are advanced placement or honor courses, evidence of special talent, recommendations by school officials, leadership record, and extracurricular activities record.

Procedure: Freshmen are admitted fall and spring. Entrance exams should be taken by January of the senior year. There are early decision and early admissions plans. Early decision applications should be filed by November 1; regular applications, by February 1 for fall entry and November 1 for spring entry, along with an application fee of $25. Notification is sent April 1. About 145 early decision candidates were accepted for the 1993–94 class. A waiting list is an active part of the admissions procedure, with about 10% of applicants on the list.

Transfer: About 155 transfer students enrolled in 1993–94. The college recommends that applicants for transfer have a minimum GPA of 2.5, an associate degree, and a minimum of 30 college credits. The SAT and high school transcripts are required. A total of 30 credits out of 122 must be completed at the college.

Visiting: There are regularly scheduled orientations for prospective students, including information sessions, available Monday through Friday at 10:30 A.M. and 2 P.M. and most Saturdays at 9:30 A.M. and 10:30 A.M., followed by a student-guided tour. Visitors may sit in on classes and stay overnight at the school. To arrange for a visit, contact the Office of Admissions at (703) 899–4681 or (800) 468–5614.

Financial Aid: In 1993–94, half of all students received some form of financial aid. Fifty percent received need-based aid. The average freshman award was $4790. Of that total, scholarships or need-based grants averaged $1500 ($1700 maximum); loans averaged $2100 ($2625 maximum); and work contracts averaged $1250 ($1900 maximum). Twenty percent of undergraduate students work part-time. Average earnings from campus work for the school year are $1250. The

average financial indebtedness of the 1992–93 graduate was $5200. The college is a member of CSS. The FAFSA financial statement is required. The deadline for financial aid applications is March 1.

International Students: There are currently 20 international students enrolled. The school actively recruits these students. They must take the TOEFL and achieve a minimum score of 570.

Computers: The college provides computer facilities for student use. The mainframe is an HP 850. All students may access the system. There are no time limits and no fees.

Graduates: In 1992–93, 679 bachelor's degrees were awarded. The most popular majors among graduates were business administration (20%), English (10%), and psychology (10%). Within an average freshman class, 1% graduate in 3 years, 65% in 4 years, 8% in 5 years, and 2% in 6 years. Some 105 companies recruited on campus. In the 1992 graduating class, 20% of the seniors were enrolled in graduate school within a year of graduation; 78% found employment.

Admissions Contact: Vice President for Admissions and Financial Aid.

MARYMOUNT UNIVERSITY E-2
Arlington, VA 22207-4299 (703) 284–1500
(800) 548–7638 (out-of-state)

Full-time: 309 men, 938 women	**Faculty:** 91; IIA, -$
Part-time: 198 men, 653 women	**Ph.D.s:** 82%
Graduate: 717 men, 1150 women	**Student/Faculty:** 14 to 1
Year: semesters, summer session	**Tuition:** $10,804
Application Deadline: open	**Room & Board:** $5126
Freshman Class: 941 applied, 772 accepted, 214 enrolled	
SAT I Verbal/Math: 440/467	**COMPETITIVE**

Marymount University, established in 1950, is an independent, comprehensive university related to the Catholic Church offering undergraduate and graduate programs in arts and sciences, business administration, education and human services, and nursing. There are 4 undergraduate and 4 graduate schools. In addition to regional accreditation, Marymount has baccalaureate program accreditation with FIDER, NCATE, and NLN. The library contains 123,574 volumes, 213,249 microform items, and 3441 audiovisual forms, and subscribes to 1158 periodicals. Computerized library sources and services include the card catalog, interlibrary loans, and database searching. Special learning facilities include a learning resource center and art gallery. The 26-acre campus is in a suburban area 2 miles southwest of Washington, D.C. Including residence halls, there are 10 buildings on campus.

Student Life: About 69% of undergraduates are from Virginia. Students come from 33 states, 64 foreign countries, and Canada. Sixty-two percent are from public schools; 38% from private. Sixty-six percent are white; 12% African American; 11% foreign nationals. Forty-two percent are Catholic, 13% are Protestant, and 22% claim no religious affiliation. The average age of freshmen is 20; all undergraduates, 25. Twenty-eight percent drop out by the end of their first year; 47% remain to graduate.

Housing: A total of 660 students can be accommodated in college housing. College-sponsored living facilities include single-sex and coed dormitories. Seventy-four percent of students commute. All students may keep cars on campus.

Activities: There are no fraternities or sororities. There are 27 groups on campus, including computers, drama, ethnic, honors, international, literary magazine, newspaper, photography, political, professional, religious, social, social service, student government, and yearbook. Popular campus events include Festival of the Arts, Career Fair, Student-Faculty Picnic, retreats, Octoberfest, Springfest, and Thanksgiving and Christmas celebrations.

Sports: There are 6 intercollegiate sports for men and 5 for women, and 5 intramural sports for men and 4 for women. Athletic and recreation facilities include a gymnasium with seating for 750, a pool, exercise rooms, a bowling alley, and a practice field.

Disabled Students: Seventy percent of the campus is accessible to disabled students. The following facilities are available: wheelchair ramps, elevators, special parking, specially equipped rest rooms, special class scheduling, and lowered drinking fountains and telephones.

Services: In addition to many counseling and information services, tutoring is available in most subjects.

Campus Safety and Security: Campus safety and security measures include 24-hour foot and vehicle patrol, escort service, shuttle buses, and informal discussions. In addition, there are lighted pathways and sidewalks.

Programs of Study: Marymount awards the B.A., B.S., B.S.N., B.B.A. degrees. Associate and master's degrees also are awarded. Bachelor's degrees are awarded in BIOLOGICAL SCIENCE (biology/biological science), BUSINESS (accounting, banking and finance, business administration and management, business economics, business law, fashion merchandising, international business management, management science, marketing/retailing/merchandising, and personnel management), COMMUNICATIONS AND THE ARTS

(communications, English, and graphic design), COMPUTER AND PHYSICAL SCIENCE (computer science and mathematics), EDUCATION (mathematics), ENGINEERING AND ENVIRONMENTAL DESIGN (environmental science and interior design), HEALTH PROFESSIONS (health care administration and nursing), SOCIAL SCIENCE (criminal justice, fashion design and technology, history, liberal arts/general studies, paralegal studies, philosophy, physical fitness/movement, political science/government, and psychology). Psychology, business administration/management, nursing and design programs are the strongest academically. Business administration, nursing, psychology, and interior design have the largest enrollments.

Required: In order to graduate, students must complete core curriculum requirements in communications, humanities, mathematics, science, and social studies. Specific required courses include English Composition I and II, General Psychology, and Introduction to Physical Education. They must earn 120 credits, with 39 to 60 credits in the major.

Special: Students may cross-register with the Consortium of Universities of the Washington Metropolitan Area and the Consortium of Continuing Education in Northern Virginia. They are required to complete an internship in Washington or London. Marymount offers a work-study program, dual majors, an accelerated nursing degree, and non-degree study. There is a freshman honors program on campus, as well as 4 national honor societies.

Faculty/Classroom: Thirty-nine percent of faculty are male; 61%, female. Eighty percent teach undergraduates. No introductory courses are taught by graduate students. The average class size in an introductory lecture and in a laboratory, 20; and in a regular course offering, 17.

Admissions: About 82% of the 1993–94 applicants were accepted. The SAT scores for the 1993–94 freshman class were as follows: Verbal—73% below 500 and 27% between 500 and 599; Math—62% below 500, 32% between 500 and 599, and 6% between 600 and 700. About 20% of the current freshmen were in the top fifth of their class; 40% were in the top two fifths.

Requirements: A minimum GPA of 2.0 is required. The SAT I or ACT is required. Applicants must graduate from an accredited secondary school or have a GED. Marymount requires 16 academic credits and 16 Carnegie units, and strongly recommends biology and chemistry for nursing candidates. Essays are required and interviews are recommended. AP and CLEP credits are accepted. Important factors used in the admissions decision are advanced placement or honor courses, evidence of special talent, personality, intangible qualities, leadership record, and recommendations by school officials.

Procedure: Freshmen are admitted to all sessions. Application deadlines are open. The application fee is $30. Notification is sent on a rolling basis.

Transfer: About 315 transfer students enrolled in 1993–94. Transfer applicants with 30 or more credits must have a minimum GPA of 2.0. Those with less than 30 must also meet freshman requirements. A total of 36 credits out of 120 must be completed at Marymount.

Visiting: There are regularly scheduled orientations for prospective students, including campus visit days, overnight visits, and information nights. There are guides for informal visits and visitors may sit in on classes and stay overnight at the school. To arrange for a visit, contact Charles Coe, Director of Admissions at (703) 284–1500 or (800) 548–7638.

Financial Aid: In 1993–94, 55% of all current freshmen and 53% of continuing students received some form of financial aid. About 42% of freshmen and 35% of continuing students received need-based aid. The average freshman award was $11,296. Of that total, scholarships or need-based grants averaged $8751 ($16,524 maximum); loans averaged $1432 ($2625 maximum); and work contracts averaged $1113 ($1500 maximum). Thirty-five percent of undergraduate students work part-time. Average earnings from campus work for the school year are $1113. The average financial indebtedness of the 1992–93 graduate was $10,000. Marymount is a member of CSS. The college's own financial statement, the family's federal income tax return, and FAFSA are required. The recommended deadline for financial aid applications is March 1.

International Students: There are currently 223 international students enrolled. The school actively recruits these students. They must take the TOEFL and achieve a minimum score of 500. If the TOEFL score is between 500 and 550, additional English ability assessment is required through the university's Learning Resource Center.

Computers: The college provides computer facilities for student use. There are 165 Novell-networked microcomputers available at computer center laboratories throughout campus. A RISC architecture minicomputer and a graphic design (CAD) laboratory are also available. All residence halls have PCs on each floor. All students may access the system and there are no time limits or fees.

Graduates: In 1992–93, 400 bachelor's degrees were awarded. The most popular majors among graduates were nursing (9%), psychology (9%), and interior design (9%). Within an average freshman class,

37% graduate in 4 years, 44% in 5 years, and 47% in 6 years.
Admissions Contact: Mr. Charles Coe, Director of Admissions.

NORFOLK STATE UNIVERSITY F-4
Norfolk, VA 23504 (804) 683–8600

Full-time: 2597 men, 4043 women	Faculty: 350; IIA, -$
Part-time: 353 men, 619 women	Ph.D.s: 53%
Graduate: 218 men, 822 women	Student/Faculty: 19 to 1
Year: semesters, summer session	Tuition: $2745 ($6025)
Application Deadline: August 1	Room & Board: $3600
Freshman Class: 3628 applied, 3517 accepted, 1395 enrolled	
SAT I or ACT: required	LESS COMPETITIVE

Norfolk State University, founded in 1935, is an independent coeducational institution offering undergraduate and graduate programs in liberal arts and sciences, business education, health-related professions, and vocational, technical, and professional training. In addition to regional accreditation, NSU has baccalaureate program accreditation with ADA, CAHEA, NASM, NCATE, and NLN. The library contains 330,000 volumes and 17,500 microform items, and subscribes to 2300 periodicals. Computerized library sources and services include the card catalog. Special learning facilities include a learning resource center and planetarium. The campus is in an urban area in the port city of Norfolk.

Student Life: Eighty percent are African American.

Housing: A total of 1366 students can be accommodated in college housing. College-sponsored living facilities include single-sex dormitories and honors houses.

Activities: There are some groups on campus, including honors, newspaper, professional, student government, and yearbook.

Sports: Athletic and recreation facilities include tennis courts, a baseball field, a practice field, and the adjacent Brambleton Recreation Center.

Disabled Students: The following facilities are available: wheelchair ramps, elevators, and special parking.

Services: In addition to many counseling and information services, tutoring is available in some subjects. There is remedial math, reading, and writing.

Programs of Study: NSU awards the B.A., B.S., B.M., and B.S.W. degrees. Associate and master's degrees also are awarded. Bachelor's degrees are awarded in BIOLOGICAL SCIENCE (biology/biological science), BUSINESS (accounting, banking and finance, business administration and management, hotel/motel and restaurant management, and marketing/retailing/merchandising), COMMUNICATIONS AND THE ARTS (communications, English, fine arts, journalism, languages, and music), COMPUTER AND PHYSICAL SCIENCE (chemistry, computer science, and mathematics), EDUCATION (business, early childhood, health, home economics, industrial arts, music, physical, secondary, and special), ENGINEERING AND ENVIRONMENTAL DESIGN (city/community/regional planning, construction technology, and electrical/electronics engineering technology), HEALTH PROFESSIONS (allied health, medical laboratory technology, medical records administration/services, and nursing), SOCIAL SCIENCE (child care/child and family studies, consumer services, economics, geography, history, home economics, political science/government, prelaw, psychology, social science, social work, and sociology).

Required: Students must complete at least 126 semester hours with a minimum 2.0 GPA, including general education courses such as communication, humanities, social science, natural science, health education, physical education, and computer literacy.

Special: NSU offers cross-registration with other institutions in the Tidewater Consortium, a student-exchange program with Old Dominion University, co-op education, a second baccalaureate degree with a minimum of 30 additional semester hours earned, a B.A.-B.S. degree, and a general studies degree. Credit for military experience is possible. There is a freshman honors program on campus.

Admissions: About 97% of the 1993–94 applicants were accepted.

Requirements: The SAT I or ACT is required. In addition, applicants should be graduates of an accredited secondary school or have the GED equivalent and have completed 20 to 22 academic units, including 7 to 9 in electives, 4 in English, 3 in history/social studies, and 2 each in mathematics, science, and health/physical education. Nursing applicants must meet additional requirements. AP and CLEP credits are accepted.

Procedure: Freshmen are admitted to all sessions. Entrance exams should be taken by March of the senior year. Applications should be filed by August 1 for fall entry and December 1 for spring entry, along with an application fee of $20. Notification is sent on a rolling basis. There is an early admissions plan.

Transfer: Transfers must meet freshman admissions criteria. A total of 30 credits out of 126 must be completed at NSU.

Visiting: There are guides for informal visits. To arrange for a visit, contact the Admissions Office at (804) 683–8600.

Financial Aid: NSU is a member of CSS. The FAF is required. The deadline for financial aid applications is April 1.

International Students: They must take the TOEFL and achieve a minimum score of 500. The student must also take the SAT I or the ACT.

Computers: NSU provides computer facilities for student use. The mainframe is a DEC VAX 11/785. There are 96 terminals in the academic center and at satellite locations campuswide for faculty and students, and system software is available. All students may access the system.

Admissions Contact: Frank W. Cool, Director of Admissions.

OLD DOMINION UNIVERSITY
F-4
Norfolk, VA 23529-0050

(804) 683-4609
(800) 348-7926 (out-of-state)

Full-time: 4820 men, 4805 women	Faculty: 494; I, --$
Part-time: 999 men, 1000 women	Ph.D.s: 86%
Graduate: 2407 men, 2768 women	Student/Faculty: 19 to 1
Year: semesters, summer session	Tuition: $3817 ($9427)
Application Deadline: May 1	Room & Board: $4500
Freshman Class: 4569 applied, 3562 accepted, 1300 enrolled	
SAT I Verbal/Math: 430/490	COMPETITIVE

Old Dominion University, founded in 1930, is a public, coeducational institution with programs in arts and letters, business and public administration, engineering, education, sciences, and health sciences. There are 6 undergraduate and 6 graduate schools. In addition to regional accreditation, Old Dominion has baccalaureate program accreditation with AACSB, ABET, APTA, NCATE, and NLN. The library contains 513,379 volumes, 953,058 microform items, and 38,265 audiovisual forms, and subscribes to 4647 periodicals. Special learning facilities include an art gallery, planetarium, radio station, and a music library. The 146-acre campus is in a suburban area in Norfolk. Including residence halls, there are 68 buildings on campus.

Student Life: About 86% of undergraduates are from Virginia. Students come from 81 foreign countries and Canada. Eighty-two percent are white; 11% African American. The average age of freshmen is 19; all undergraduates, 23. Twenty-seven percent drop out by the end of their first year; 45% remain to graduate.

Housing: A total of 2260 students can be accommodated in college housing. College-sponsored living facilities include coed dormitories and on-campus apartments. In addition, there are honors and special interest houses, as well as international, coeducational, and quiet-study floors. On-campus housing is guaranteed for all 4 years. Alcohol is not permitted. All students may keep cars on campus.

Activities: About 9% of men belong to 15 national fraternities; about 9% of women belong to 9 national sororities. There are 180 groups on campus, including art, cheerleading, chess, choir, chorale, computers, dance, drama, ethnic, gay, honors, international, jazz band, literary magazine, musical theater, newspaper, orchestra, pep band, political, professional, radio and TV, religious, social, student government, and yearbook. Popular campus events include Literary Festival, Glennan Lecture Series, Every Woman's Festival, Model U.N., Unity Week, Black History Month, Exam Jam, and Mainstreet.

Sports: There are 8 intercollegiate sports each for men and women, and 21 intramural sports each. Athletic and recreation facilities include an arena, a playing field, a baseball complex, 2 pools, intramural fields, a soccer stadium, and a sailing center.

Disabled Students: Most of the campus is accessible to disabled students. The following facilities are available: wheelchair ramps, elevators, special parking, specially equipped rest rooms, special class scheduling, lowered drinking fountains and telephones, and services for the learning disabled.

Services: In addition to many counseling and information services, tutoring is available in most subjects, including English, mathematics, writing, reading, and sciences. There is also a reader service for the blind, and remedial math, reading, and writing.

Campus Safety and Security: Campus safety and security measures include 24-hour foot and vehicle patrol, self defense education, escort service, and shuttle buses. In addition, there are informal discussions, pamphlets, posters, films, emergency telephones, lighted pathways and sidewalks, and a bicycle patrol.

Programs of Study: Old Dominion awards the B.A., B.S., and B.F.A. degrees. Master's and doctoral degrees also are awarded. Bachelor's degrees are awarded in BIOLOGICAL SCIENCE (biochemistry and biology/biological science), BUSINESS (accounting, banking and finance, business administration and management, and marketing/retailing/merchandising), COMMUNICATIONS AND THE ARTS (dance, dramatic arts, English, fine arts, French, German, journalism, music, Russian, Spanish, and speech/debate/rhetoric), COMPUTER AND PHYSICAL SCIENCE (chemistry, computer science, geology, mathematics, and physics), EDUCATION (early childhood, elementary, middle school, secondary, and teaching English as a second language/foreign language), ENGINEERING AND ENVIRONMENTAL DESIGN (civil engineering, computer engineering, electrical/

electronics engineering, engineering technology, and mechanical engineering), HEALTH PROFESSIONS (medical laboratory technology, nursing, premedicine, public health, and speech pathology/audiology), SOCIAL SCIENCE (anthropology, criminal justice, economics, geography, history, international relations, philosophy, political science/government, psychology, public administration, religion, social science, sociology, and women's studies). Business, engineering, biology, and psychology have the largest enrollments.

Required: To graduate, students must complete at least 120 credits, with a minimum GPA of 2.0. Students must take courses in English, mathematics, philosophy, foreign language, and history. English composition is a required course, and students must pass a writing proficiency exam.

Special: Old Dominion offers cross-registration with schools in the Tidewater Consortium program. There are co-op programs, internships, study abroad in 8 countries, and a work-study program. Students may take a B.A.-B.S. degree in engineering and liberal arts. An interdisciplinary program, dual majors, a 3–2 engineering degree, nondegree study, pass/fail options, and credit for military experience are available. There is a freshman honors program on campus, as well as one national honor society. Thirteen departments have honors programs.

Faculty/Classroom: Sixty-three percent of faculty are male; 37%, female. Eighty-five percent teach undergraduates. The average class size in an introductory lecture is 30; in a laboratory, 20; and in a regular course offering, 23.

Admissions: About 78% of the 1993–94 applicants were accepted. The SAT scores for the 1993–94 freshman class were as follows: Verbal—75% below 500, 20% between 500 and 599, 4% between 600 and 700, and 1% above 700; Math—60% below 500, 30% between 500 and 599, 7% between 600 and 700, and 3% above 700. About 35% of the current freshmen were in the top fifth of their class; 67% were in the top two fifths. There were 15 National Merit finalists. Thirteen freshmen graduated first in their class.

Requirements: Old Dominion requires applicants to be in the upper 50% of their class. A minimum GPA of 2.0 is required. The SAT I, with a minimum combined score of 850 (minimum 400 on each part), or the ACT is required. Applicants must be graduates of an accredited secondary school. The GED is accepted. Applicants should have completed 4 years of mathematics and 3 each of English, foreign languages, science, and social science. An essay and an interview are recommended. AP and CLEP credits are accepted. Important factors in the admissions decision are advanced placement or honor courses, recommendations by school officials, extracurricular activities record, evidence of special talent, and leadership record.

Procedure: Freshmen are admitted to all sessions. Entrance exams should be taken in May of the junior year or November/December of the senior year. Applications should be filed by May 1 for fall entry, December 1 for winter entry, and April 15 for summer entry, along with an application fee of $30. Notification is sent on a rolling basis. There is a deferred admissions plan.

Transfer: Applicants for transfer must have a minimum GPA of 2.0 and must have at least 24 semester hour credits. Applicants with fewer semester hours must meet the same requirements as freshmen. A total of 30 credits out of 120 must be completed at Old Dominion.

Visiting: There are regularly scheduled orientations for prospective students. There are guides for informal visits. To arrange for a visit, contact the Admissions Office at (800) 348-7926 or (804) 683-4609.

Financial Aid: In 1993–94, 64% of all current freshmen and 64% of continuing students received some form of financial aid. About 39% of freshmen and 53% of continuing students received need-based aid. The average freshman award was $4487. Of that total, scholarships or need-based grants averaged $4761 ($10,512 maximum); loans averaged $2474 ($8625 maximum); and work contracts averaged $1834 ($2000 maximum). Six percent of undergraduate students work part-time. Average earnings from campus work for the school year are $2000. The average financial indebtedness of the 1992–93 graduate was $6210. Old Dominion is a member of CSS. The FAFSA financial statement is required. The deadline for financial aid applications is May 2.

International Students: There are currently 483 international students enrolled. The school actively recruits these students. They must take the TOEFL and achieve a minimum score of 550.

Computers: The college provides computer facilities for student use. The mainframe is an IBM 3090. All students may access the system 24 hours a day. There are no time limits and no fees.

Graduates: In 1992–93 2175 bachelor's degrees were awarded. The most popular majors among graduates were psychology (8%), elementary education (7%), and financial management (5%). Within an average freshman class, 14% graduate in 4 years, 38% in 5 years, and 44% in 6 years.

Admissions Contact: Sara L. Marchello, Associate Director.

RADFORD UNIVERSITY

C-3

Radford, VA 24142

(703) 831-5371

Full-time: 3413 men, 4697 women
Part-time: 191 men, 226 women
Graduate: 276 men, 577 women
Year: semesters, summer session
Application Deadline: April 1
Freshman Class: 5702 applied, 4894 accepted, 1743 enrolled
SAT I Verbal/Math: 417/453

Faculty: 420; IIA, --$
Ph.D.s: 76%
Student/Faculty: 19 to 1
Tuition: $2924 ($6684)
Room & Board: $4110

ACT: 21   **LESS COMPETITIVE**

Radford University, founded in 1910, is a public, coeducational institution with programs in arts and sciences, business and economics, education and human development, nursing and health services, and visual and performing arts. There are 5 undergraduate schools and one graduate school. In addition to regional accreditation, RU has baccalaureate program accreditation with AACSB, ADA, CSWE, NASM, NCATE, and NLN. The library contains 284,778 volumes, 1,214,264 microform items, and 11,370 audiovisual forms, and subscribes to 3110 periodicals. Special learning facilities include a learning resource center, an art gallery, a planetarium, a radio station, a TV station, and a 386-acre conservancy used for studies in ecology, botany, geology, resource management, and history. The 177-acre campus is in a small town 45 miles southwest of Roanoke. Including residence halls, there are 35 buildings on campus.

Student Life: About 84% of undergraduates are from Virginia. Students come from 48 states, 57 foreign countries, and Canada. Ninety percent are from public schools. Ninety-one percent are white. The average age of freshmen is 18; all undergraduates, 20. Twenty-three percent drop out by the end of their first year; 83% remain to graduate.

Housing: A total of 3200 students can be accommodated in college housing. College-sponsored living facilities include single-sex and coed dormitories. In addition there are special interest houses. On-campus housing is guaranteed for the freshman year only and is available on a lottery system for upperclassmen. Sixty-five percent of students commute. All students may keep cars on campus.

Activities: About 18% of men belong to 13 national fraternities; about 19% of women belong to 10 national sororities. There are 150 groups on campus, including art, band, cheerleading, choir, chorale, chorus, computers, dance, drama, ethnic, gay, honors, international, jazz band, literary magazine, musical theater, newspaper, opera, orchestra, pep band, political, professional, radio and TV, religious, social, social service, student government, and yearbook. Popular campus events include Club Fair, Greek Week, Christmas Luminaries, Family FunFest Weekend, and Homecoming.

Sports: There are 8 intercollegiate sports for men and 9 for women, and 10 intramural sports for men and 10 for women. Athletic and recreation facilities include a 5000-seat recreation and convocation complex housing a natatorium with an 8-lane swimming pool, basketball, volleyball, handball, and racquetball courts, areas for free exercise, a weight room, steam rooms, and a 1/6-mile jogging track. Outdoor facilities include a jogging trail, 12 tennis courts, and areas for baseball, soccer, lacrosse, softball, and intramural football.

Disabled Students: Eighty-five percent of the campus is accessible to disabled students. The following facilities are available: wheelchair ramps, elevators, special parking, specially equipped rest rooms, special class scheduling, lowered drinking fountains, and lowered telephones.

Services: In addition to many counseling and information services, tutoring is available in most subjects. In addition, there is a reader service for the blind. There are writing and reading centers and a center to teach students study and time-management skills. There is a coordinator for disabled students.

Campus Safety and Security: Campus safety and security measures include 24-hour foot and vehicle patrol, self-defense education, escort service, and shuttle buses. In addition, there are informal discussions, pamphlets, posters, and films, emergency telephones, and lighted pathways and sidewalks.

Programs of Study: RU awards the B.A., B.S., B.B.A., B.F.A., and B.G.S. degrees. Master's degrees also are awarded. Bachelor's degrees are awarded in BIOLOGICAL SCIENCE (biology/biological science), BUSINESS (accounting, banking and finance, business administration and management, business economics, marketing/retailing/merchandising, and personnel management), COMMUNICATIONS AND THE ARTS (broadcasting, communications, dance, design, dramatic arts, English, fine arts, journalism, languages, music, and speech/debate/rhetoric), COMPUTER AND PHYSICAL SCIENCE (chemistry, computer science, geology, information sciences and systems, mathematics, physical sciences, and statistics), EDUCATION (art, foreign languages, music, physical, and science), HEALTH PROFESSIONS (medical laboratory technology, nursing, and speech pathology/audiology), SOCIAL SCIENCE (anthropology, criminal justice, economics, food science, geography, history, human development, interdisciplinary studies, liberal arts/general studies, parks and

recreation management, philosophy, political science/government, psychology, religion, social science, social work, and sociology). Nursing, education, geography, and medical technology are the strongest academically. Business, education, psychology, and criminal justice have the largest enrollments.

Required: To graduate, students must complete at least 126 credit hours, including 30 to 90 in the major, with a 2.0 GPA. There are general education requirements in English, foreign language, speech, fine arts, philosophy/religion, laboratory science, mathematics/statistics/computer science, history, psychology, social science, and health/physical education.

Special: RU offers internships, dual majors in any subject, study abroad in 5 countries, a general studies degree, and pass/fail options. On-campus work-study is available. There is a freshman honors program on campus, as well as 29 national honor societies, including Phi Beta Kappa. Twenty departments have honors programs.

Faculty/Classroom: Fifty-nine percent of faculty are male; 41%, female. All teach undergraduates. Graduate students teach 4% of introductory courses. The average class size in an introductory lecture is 35.

Admissions: About 86% of the 1993-94 applicants were accepted. The SAT scores for the 1993-94 freshman class were as follows: Verbal—87% below 500, 12% between 500 and 599, and 1% between 600 and 700; Math—72% below 500, 24% between 500 and 599, and 4% between 600 and 700. About 29% of the current freshmen were in the top fifth of their class; 60% were in the top two fifths. Six freshmen graduated first in their class.

Requirements: A minimum GPA of 2.0 is required. The SAT I or ACT is required. Applicants must be graduates of an accredited secondary school. The GED is accepted. Applicants should complete 21 high school academic credits, including 4 courses in English, 3 in mathematics, and 2 each in sciences, foreign language, and social studies (including 1 in history). AP and CLEP credits are accepted. Important factors used in the admissions decision are advanced placement or honor courses, extracurricular activities record, recommendations by school officials, personality, intangible qualities, and leadership record.

Procedure: Freshmen are admitted to all sessions. Entrance exams should be taken between April of the junior year and December of the senior year. Applications should be filed by April 1 for fall entry and December 1 for spring entry, along with an application fee of $15. Notification is sent on a rolling basis. There is a deferred admissions plan. A waiting list is an active part of the admissions procedure, with about 4% of applicants on the list.

Transfer: About 840 transfer students enrolled in 1993-94. Applicants for transfer must have a minimum GPA of 2.0. Those with fewer than 30 semester hours of college work must submit their high school record.

Visiting: There are regularly scheduled orientations for prospective students, consisting of an open house in the fall. There are guides for informal visits and visitors may sit in on classes. To arrange for a visit, contact the Office of Admissions at (703) 831-5371.

Financial Aid: In 1993-94, 54% of all current freshmen and 48% of continuing students received some form of financial aid. About 38% of freshmen and 34% of continuing students received need-based aid. The average freshman award was $4881. Of that total, scholarships or need-based grants averaged $2462 ($10,794 maximum); loans averaged $2807 ($10,019 maximum); and work contracts averaged $1275. Thirteen percent of undergraduate students work part-time. Average earnings from campus work for the school year are $1275. The average financial indebtedness of the 1992-93 graduate was $7815. RU is a member of CSS. The FAFSA financial statement is required. The deadline for financial aid applications is March 1.

International Students: There are currently 251 international students enrolled. The school actively recruits these students. They must take the TOEFL and achieve a minimum score of 520, or take the SAT I or ACT.

Computers: The college provides computer facilities for student use. The mainframe is a Sun. Terminals are located in several academic buildings. There are also 9 PC-equipped laboratories in academic departments and residence halls. Available software includes programming languages, databases, graphics, mathematics, simulation languages, statistics, spreadsheets, and word processing. All students may access the system. There are no time limits on using the system and no fees.

Graduates: In 1992-93, 1710 bachelor's degrees were awarded. The most popular majors among graduates were education (10%), management (8%), and marketing (7%). Within an average freshman class, 25% graduate in 4 years, 47% in 5 years, and 52% in 6 years. Some 160 companies recruited on campus in 1992-93. In the 1992 graduating class, 22% of all graduates were enrolled in graduate school within 6 months of graduation; 71% had found employment.

Admissions Contact: Admissions Officer.

RANDOLPH-MACON COLLEGE
Ashland, VA 23005

D-3

(804) 752-7305; (800) 888-1762 (in-state)

Full-time: 549 men, 543 women	Faculty: 96; IIB, av$
Part-time: 10 men, 17 women	Ph.D.s: 82%
Graduate: none	Student/Faculty: 11 to 1
Year: 4-1-4, summer session	Tuition: $12,230
Application Deadline: March 1	Room & Board: $4750
Freshman Class: 1771 applied, 1325 accepted, 306 enrolled	
SAT I or ACT: required	COMPETITIVE

Randolph-Macon College, established in 1830, is a private, coeducational, liberal arts college historically affiliated with the United Methodist Church. The library contains 143,551 volumes, 56,457 microform items, and 3747 audiovisual forms, and subscribes to 889 periodicals. Computerized library sources and services include interlibrary loans and database searching. Special learning facilities include a learning resource center, an art gallery, an observatory with a 12-inch reflecting telescope, a fully equipped darkroom, and a greenhouse. The 111-acre campus is in a small town 15 miles north of Richmond. Including residence halls, there are 50 buildings on campus.

Student Life: About 55% of undergraduates are from Virginia. Students come from 32 states, 12 foreign countries, and Canada. Sixty-five percent are from public schools; 35% from private. Ninety-two percent are white. Fifty-six percent are Protestant; 23% Catholic. The average age of freshmen is 18; all undergraduates, 20. Fifteen percent drop out by the end of their first year; 76% remain to graduate.

Housing: A total of 950 students can be accommodated in college housing. College-sponsored living facilities include single-sex and coed dormitories, on-campus apartments, married-student housing, fraternity houses, and sorority houses. In addition there are honors houses, language houses, special interest houses, and several college-owned houses are also used for students. On-campus housing is guaranteed for all 4 years. Eighty percent of students live on campus; of those, 65% remain on campus on weekends. All students may keep cars on campus.

Activities: About 40% of men belong to 7 national fraternities; about 39% of women belong to 4 national sororities. There are 67 groups on campus, including art, cheerleading, chess, choir, chorale, computers, dance, drama, ethnic, honors, international, literary magazine, musical theater, newspaper, photography, political, professional, religious, social, social service, student government, and yearbook. Popular campus events include Spring Fling, Blackwell Cultural Arts Series, Blackwell Lectures, and Earth Day.

Sports: There are 8 intercollegiate sports for men and 6 for women, and 7 intramural sports for men and 6 for women. Athletic and recreation facilities include 10 tennis courts, several playing fields, 2 gymnasiums, an indoor track, an indoor pool, a football field, a weight room, and an exercise room.

Disabled Students: Fifty percent of the campus is accessible to disabled students. The following facilities are available: wheelchair ramps, elevators, special parking, specially equipped rest rooms, special class scheduling, and specialist advisors for learning disabled students.

Services: In addition to many counseling and information services, tutoring is available in every subject. There is a reader service for the blind, and remedial math, reading, and writing. There is also a summer collaborative writing program for all entering students taught by upper-class peer tutors.

Campus Safety and Security: Campus safety and security measures include 24-hour foot and vehicle patrol, self-defense education, escort service, and informal discussions. In addition, there are pamphlets, posters, and films, emergency telephones, and lighted pathways and sidewalks.

Programs of Study: Randolph-Macon awards the B.A. and B.S. degrees. Bachelor's degrees are awarded in BIOLOGICAL SCIENCE (biology/biological science), BUSINESS (business economics), COMMUNICATIONS AND THE ARTS (art history and appreciation, arts administration/management, classics, dramatic arts, English, fine arts, French, German, Greek, Latin, music, Spanish, and studio art), COMPUTER AND PHYSICAL SCIENCE (chemistry, computer science, mathematics, and physics), ENGINEERING AND ENVIRONMENTAL DESIGN (environmental science), SOCIAL SCIENCE (economics, history, international relations, international studies, philosophy, political science/government, psychology, religion, and sociology). Biological and physical sciences, psychology, political science, history, English economics/business, and computer science are the strongest academically. Economics/business, psychology, political science, English, and history have the largest enrollments.

Required: To graduate, students must complete 112 to 115 credit hours, with 30 hours in the major and a minimum GPA of 2.0. All students must take 2 courses each in mathematics, social science, laboratory science, literature, philosophy/theology, and physical education; 1 course in fine arts, and enough foreign language to show proficien-

cy. Specific courses required are English composition and European history. There is also a computer proficiency and oral communication requirement.

Special: The college offers cooperative programs in engineering with Washington University in St. Louis, Columbia University, and the University of Virginia; in forestry with Duke University; and in accounting with Virginia Commonwealth University. There is cross-registration with Hollins, Sweet Briar, Randolph-Macon Women's College, Hampden-Sydney, Washington and Lee, and Mary Baldwin. Internships, dual majors, and a Washington semester are available. Students in all majors may take part in an accelerated degree program. Study abroad programs are offered in England, France, Spain, Germany, Italy, Japan, and Korea. There is a freshman honors program on campus, as well as 12 national honor societies, including Phi Beta Kappa. All departments have honors programs.

Faculty/Classroom: Sixty-seven percent of faculty are male; 33%, female. All teach undergraduates and do research. The average class size in an introductory lecture is 25; in a laboratory, 15; and in a regular course offering, 17.

Admissions: About 75% of the 1993-94 applicants were accepted. About 36% of the current freshmen were in the top fifth of their class; 66% were in the top two fifths. There was 1 National Merit semifinalist. Two freshmen graduated first in their class.

Requirements: The SAT I or ACT is required. SAT II: Subject tests are recommended in writing, mathematics, and foreign language. Applicants must be graduates of an accredited secondary school. The GED is accepted. Applicants should complete a minimum of 16 high school academic credits, including 4 years of English; 3 to 4 years each of mathematics and science; 2 to 3 years of foreign language; 2 years of history; and 1 to 2 years of social studies. An essay is required and an interview is recommended. AP and CLEP credits are accepted. Important factors used in the admissions decision are advanced placement or honor courses, recommendations by school officials, leadership record, evidence of special talent, and parents or siblings attending the school.

Procedure: Freshmen are admitted fall and spring. Entrance exams should be taken by November of senior year. Early decision applications should be filed by December 1; regular applications, by March 1 for fall entry and December 1 for spring entry, along with an application fee of $30. Notification of early decision is sent December 20; regular decision, April 1. There are early decision, early admissions, and deferred admissions plans. About 26 early decision candidates were accepted for the 1993-94 class. A waiting list is an active part of the admissions procedure, with about 5% of applicants on the list.

Transfer: About 30 transfer students enrolled in 1993-94. Applicants for transfer must have a minimum GPA of 2.0 and must be eligible to return to their previous institution. They must submit high school and college transcripts and SAT I scores. At least 37 credits, including one half of the major program, out of 112 to 115 must be completed at Randolph-Macon.

Visiting: There are regularly scheduled orientations for prospective students, including interviews and tours at specific hours Monday through Saturday, October through April. Also, there are several open houses each year. There are guides for informal visits and visitors may sit in on classes and stay overnight at the school. To arrange for a visit, contact the Office of Admissions at (804) 752-7305 or (800) 888-1762 (in-state).

Financial Aid: In 1993-94, 82% of all current freshmen and 72% of continuing students received some form of financial aid. About 47% of freshmen and 33% of continuing students received need-based aid. The average freshman award was $9880. Of that total, scholarships or need-based grants averaged $5845 ($18,130 maximum); loans averaged $3235; and work contracts averaged $800. Twenty-six percent of undergraduate students work part-time. Average earnings from campus work for the school year are $800. The average financial indebtedness of the 1992-93 graduate was $10,697. Randolph-Macon is a member of CSS. The FAF, FFS or SFS, the college's own financial statement, and the FAFSA are required. The deadline for financial aid applications is March 1.

International Students: There are currently 22 international students enrolled. The school actively recruits these students. They must take the TOEFL and achieve a minimum score of 550.

Computers: The college provides computer facilities for student use. The mainframes are a Perkin-Elmer 3230 super minicomputer and a DEC VAX 4500. Students have direct access to the mainframe, and to more than 250 microcomputers located throughout the campus. All dormitory rooms are also wired with computer hook-ups. All students may access the system. It may be used 8 A.M. to 1 A.M. There are no time limits on using the system and no fees.

Graduates: In 1992-93, 242 bachelor's degrees were awarded. The most popular majors among graduates were economics/business (21%), English (17%), and psychology (16%). Within an average freshman class, 1% graduate in 3 years, 69% in 4 years, 4% in 5 years, and 2% in 6 years. Some 40 companies recruited on campus in 1992-93. In the 1992 graduating class, 29% of all graduates were

enrolled in graduate school within 6 months of graduation; 80% had found employment.

Admissions Contact: John C. Conkright, Dean of Admissions and Financial Aid.

RANDOLPH-MACON WOMAN'S COLLEGE D-3
Lynchburg, VA 24503

(804) 947-8100
(800) 745-7692 (out-of-state)

Full-time: 653 women	Faculty: 66; IIB, av$
Part-time: 2 men, 54 women	Ph.D.s: 95%
Graduate: none	Student/Faculty: 10 to 1
Year: semesters, summer session	Tuition: $13,320
Application Deadline: March 1	Room & Board: $5780
Freshman Class: 701 applied, 621 accepted, 171 enrolled	
SAT I: 502/517 (mean)	ACT: 25	COMPETITIVE

Randolph-Macon Woman's College, founded in 1891, is an independent, liberal arts institution affiliated with the United Methodist Church. Male students are enrolled as special students and cannot earn bachelor's degrees. The library contains 164,000 volumes, 10,000 microform items, and 1000 audiovisual forms, and subscribes to 840 periodicals. Computerized library sources and services include the card catalog, interlibrary loans, and database searching. Special learning facilities include a learning resource center, art gallery, radio station, an observatory, an art museum, 2 theaters, and 3 nature preserves. The 100-acre campus is in a suburban area in Lynchburg, in the foothills of the Blue Ridge Mountains. Including residence halls, there are 18 buildings on campus.

Student Life: About 61% of undergraduates are from out-of-state, mostly the South. Students come from 44 states and 18 foreign countries. Sixty-eight percent are from public schools; 32% from private. Eighty-four percent are white. Sixty-one percent are Protestant; 18% Catholic; 11% claim no religious affiliation. The average age of freshmen is 18; all undergraduates, 20. Twenty percent drop out by the end of their first year; 66% remain to graduate.

Housing: A total of 717 students can be accommodated in college housing. College-sponsored living facilities include dormitories. In addition there is a special senior dormitory. On-campus housing is guaranteed for all 4 years. Eighty-three percent of students live on campus. All students may keep cars on campus.

Activities: There are no sororities on campus. There are 35 groups on campus, including art, chorale, chorus, dance, drama, ethnic, gay, international, literary magazine, newspaper, political, professional, religious, social, social service, student government, and yearbook. Popular campus events include lectures, serenades, Skeller sings, the Daisy Chain, Pumpkin Parade, concerts, film series, and trips.

Sports: Athletic and recreation facilities include 2 gymnasiums, a regulation-size swimming pool, dance studios, aerobic and weight rooms, tennis courts, athletic fields, a 100-acre riding center with teaching and amphitheater show rings and indoor and outdoor arenas, and a 900-seat auditorium.

Disabled Students: Fifty percent of the campus is accessible to disabled students. The following facilities are available: wheelchair ramps, elevators, special parking, and specially equipped rest rooms.

Services: In addition to many counseling and information services, tutoring is available in every subject. There is a writing center with peer tutors and a faculty director.

Campus Safety and Security: Campus safety and security measures include 24-hour foot and vehicle patrol, self defense education, escort service, and informal discussions. In addition, there are pamphlets, posters, and films, emergency telephones, and lighted pathways and sidewalks.

Programs of Study: R-MWC awards the A.B. degree. Bachelor's degrees are awarded in BIOLOGICAL SCIENCE (biology/biological science), COMMUNICATIONS AND THE ARTS (art, classics, communications, dance, dramatic arts, English, French, German, music, and Spanish), COMPUTER AND PHYSICAL SCIENCE (chemistry, mathematics, and physics), SOCIAL SCIENCE (economics, history, international relations, philosophy, political science/government, psychology, religion, Russian and Slavic studies, and sociology). English, sciences, art, politics, and psychology have the largest enrollments.

Required: To graduate, all students must complete at least 124 credit hours with a minimum GPA of 2.0. Students must satisfy the requirements for the general education and major programs.

Special: R-MWC offers a junior year spring semester American Culture Program, as well as study abroad at the University of Reading in England, the American School of Classical Studies at Athens, the Intercollegiate Center for Classical Studies in Rome, and the Kansai University of Foreign Studies in Japan. A Washington semester at American University is available, as is the Tri-College Consortium with Sweet Briar and Lynchburg Colleges, and the Seven-College Exchange Program with Hampden-Sydney, Hollins, Mary Baldwin, and Sweet Briar Colleges, and Washington and Lee University. There are 3-2 engineering programs with Duke, Vanderbilt, and Washington

universities, dual degree programs in mathematics, physics, or chemistry with the University of Virginia, 3-2 nursing programs with Johns Hopkins and Vanderbilt universities, a B.A.-B.S. program in occupational therapy with Washington University School of Medicine, and an accelerated program in public health with the University of Rochester School of Medicine and Dentistry. Interdepartmental majors are offered in economics and mathematics and political economy. There are 4 national honor societies on campus, including Phi Beta Kappa.

Faculty/Classroom: Fifty-two percent of faculty are male; 48%, female. All teach undergraduates. The average class size in an introductory lecture is 18 and in a regular course offering, 14.

Admissions: About 89% of the 1993-94 applicants were accepted. The SAT scores for the 1993-94 freshman class were as follows: Verbal—50% below 500, 32% between 500 and 599, 17% between 600 and 700, and 1% above 700; Math—38% below 500, 46% between 500 and 599, 15% between 600 and 700, and 2% above 700. The ACT scores were 14% below 21, 30% between 21 and 23, 22% between 24 and 26, 16% between 27 and 28, and 18% above 28. About 58% of the current freshmen were in the top fifth of their class; 83% were in the top two fifths. About 9 freshmen graduated first in their class.

Requirements: The SAT I or ACT is required. In addition, applicants must be graduates of an accredited secondary school with at least 16 academic credits, including 4 units in English, 3 to 4 in a foreign language, 3 in mathematics, 2 in biology, chemistry, or physics with laboratory work, and 1 to 2 in electives from other academic study. An interview is strongly recommended. AP and CLEP credits are accepted.

Procedure: Freshmen are admitted fall and spring. Entrance exams should be taken in the junior or senior year. Early decision applications should be filed by November 15; regular applications, by March 1 for fall entry, along with an application fee of $25. Notification of early decision is sent December 15. There are early decision and early admissions plans. About 47 early decision candidates were accepted for the 1993-94 class.

Transfer: About 34 transfer students enrolled in 1993-94. Transfer students must have a minimum GPA of 2.0 and submit college and high school transcripts, 3 letters of recommendation, a copy of their current college's catalog, and SAT I or ACT scores. An interview is recommended if possible. Seniors may not transfer in. A total of 62 credits out of 124 must be completed at R-MWC.

Visiting: There are regularly scheduled orientations for prospective students. There are guides for informal visits and visitors may sit in on classes and stay overnight at the school. To arrange for a visit, contact the Admissions Office at (804) 846-9680 or (800) 745-7692.

Financial Aid: In 1993-94, 69% of all students received some form of financial aid. About 52% of freshmen and 49% of continuing students received need-based aid. The average freshman award was $14,013. Of that total, scholarships or need-based grants averaged $7306 ($12,000 maximum); loans averaged $3469 ($4125 maximum); and work contracts averaged $1503 ($1550 maximum). Fifty-five percent of undergraduate students work part-time. Average earnings from campus work for the school year are $960. The average financial indebtedness of the 1992-93 graduate was $16,500. R-MWC is a member of CSS. The college's own financial statement and the FAFSA are required. The deadline for financial aid applications is March 1.

International Students: There are currently 39 international students enrolled. The school actively recruits these students. They must take the TOEFL and achieve a minimum score of 550.

Computers: The college provides computer facilities for student use. The mainframe is an IBM AS/400 D45. Students may access 67 microcomputers, 49 of which are networked, in several campus locations. In addition, there are Macintosh and PC-compatible machines in computer laboratories in academic buildings, with word processing, spreadsheet, database, and academic application. Access to E-mail is also available. All students may access the system. There are no time limits on using the system and no fees.

Graduates: In 1992-93, 154 bachelor's degrees were awarded. The most popular majors among graduates were sciences (16%), politics (14%), and psychology (13%). Within an average freshman class, 64% graduate in 4 years and 66% in 5 years. In the 1992 graduating class, 25% of the women were enrolled in graduate school within 6 months of graduation; 80% of the women had found employment.

Admissions Contact: Admissions Officer.

ROANOKE COLLEGE

C-3

Salem, VA 24153

(703) 375-2270

Full-time: 579 men, 881 women
Part-time: 108 men, 131 women
Graduate: none
Year: semesters, summer session
Application Deadline: March 1
Freshman Class: 2227 applied, 1790 accepted, 437 enrolled
SAT I Verbal/Math: 480/530

Faculty: 98; IIB, av$
Ph.D.s: 88%
Student/Faculty: 15 to 1
Tuition: $12,625
Room & Board: $4350

COMPETITIVE

Roanoke College, founded in 1842, is a private, coeducational institution affiliated with the Evangelical Lutheran Church in America. The college offers undergraduate programs in the arts and sciences and business administration. The library contains 168,000 volumes, 145,000 microform items, and 2500 audiovisual forms, and subscribes to 935 periodicals. Computerized library sources and services include the card catalog, interlibrary loans, and database searching. Special learning facilities include a learning resource center, art gallery, media classroom, and TV production facility. The 70-acre campus is in a suburban area 5 miles west of Roanoke. Including residence halls, there are 40 buildings on campus.

Student Life: About 56% of undergraduates are from Virginia. Students come from 37 states, 14 foreign countries, and Canada. Seventy-nine percent are from public schools; 21% from private. Ninety-six percent are white. Sixty-three percent are Protestant; 21% Catholic; 14% claim no religious affiliation. The average age of freshmen is 18; all undergraduates, 21. Ten percent drop out by the end of their first year; 57% remain to graduate.

Housing: A total of 955 students can be accommodated in college housing. College-sponsored living facilities include single-sex and coed dormitories and fraternity houses. In addition there are honors houses and and freshman residence halls. On-campus housing is guaranteed for all 4 years. Fifty-six percent of students live on campus; of those, 98% remain on campus on weekends. All students may keep cars on campus.

Activities: About 31% of men belong to 4 national fraternities; about 29% of women belong to 3 national sororities. There are 65 groups on campus, including art, cheerleading, choir, chorale, chorus, computers, dance, drama, ethnic, honors, international, jazz band, literary magazine, musical theater, newspaper, pep band, photography, political, professional, religious, social, social service, student government, and yearbook. Popular campus events include Parents Weekend, Alumni Weekend, the Fowler Public Policy Series, Fall Ball, and Fridays-on-the-Quad.

Sports: There are 7 intercollegiate sports for men and 7 for women, and 11 intramural sports for men and 11 for women. Athletic and recreation facilities include a 2400-seat gymnasium, a 400-seat arena, athletic fields, an all-weather track, practice and playing fields, tennis and racquetball courts, a swimming pool, and a fitness center with weight training and physical conditioning equipment.

Disabled Students: Seventy-five percent of the campus is accessible to disabled students. The following facilities are available: wheelchair ramps, elevators, special parking, specially equipped rest rooms, and special class scheduling.

Services: In addition to many counseling and information services, tutoring is available in most subjects.

Campus Safety and Security: Campus safety and security measures include 24-hour foot and vehicle patrol, self defense education, escort service, and informal discussions. In addition, there are pamphlets, posters, and films, emergency telephones, lighted pathways and sidewalks, and security/safety services are provided in-house, not contracted out.

Programs of Study: Roanoke awards the B.A., B.S., and B.B.A. degrees. Bachelor's degrees are awarded in BIOLOGICAL SCIENCE (biology/biological science), BUSINESS (business administration and management), COMMUNICATIONS AND THE ARTS (dramatic arts, English, fine arts, French, music, and Spanish), COMPUTER AND PHYSICAL SCIENCE (chemistry, computer science, information sciences and systems, mathematics, and physics), EDUCATION (physical), HEALTH PROFESSIONS (medical laboratory technology), SOCIAL SCIENCE (criminal justice, economics, history, international relations, philosophy, political science/government, psychology, religion, and sociology). Psychology, English, biology, and chemistry are the strongest academically. Business, psychology, sociology, and English have the largest enrollments.

Required: Requirements for graduation include completion of 36 courses, including about 12 in a major. Specific course requirements include 2 courses each in mathematics, laboratory science, social science, and physical education, a 3-course sequence in civilization, a freshman-year writing course, a values course, and a senior reading course. All students must attain a 2.0 GPA and be able to demonstrate competency in a foreign language.

Special: There is cross-registration with Hollins College and study abroad in 8 countries. A dual major is offered in religion/philosophy. Roanoke also offers internships, a Washington semester, the Virginia at Oxford Program, combined B.A.-B.S. degrees in chemistry, biology, and physics, a 3-2 engineering degree with Virginia Polytechnic Institute and State University and Washington University in St. Louis, credit by exam, and pass/fail options. Nondegree study is available to those students admitted with special status. There is a freshman honors program on campus, as well as 21 national honor societies.

Faculty/Classroom: Sixty-one percent of faculty are male; 39%, female. Fifty percent teach undergraduates and 50% both teach and do research. The average class size in an introductory lecture is 24; in a laboratory, 20; and in a regular course offering, 17.

Admissions: About 80% of the 1993-94 applicants were accepted. The SAT scores for the 1993-94 freshman class were as follows: Verbal—57% below 500, 34% between 500 and 599, and 9% between 600 and 700; Math—31% below 500, 47% between 500 and 599, 19% between 600 and 700, and 3% above 700. About 48% of the current freshmen were in the top fifth of their class; 72% were in the top two fifths. There were 2 National Merit finalists and 1 semifinalist. About 10 freshmen graduated first in their class.

Requirements: The SAT I or ACT is required, but the SAT I is preferred. SAT II: Subject tests, an essay, and an interview are recommended. Applicants must be graduates of accredited secondary schools or have earned a GED. The college requires 17 academic units, based on 4 years of English, 3 courses in mathematics, and 2 courses each in foreign language, science, and social studies. An audition is also recommended for performing arts majors. AP and CLEP credits are accepted. Important factors used in the admissions decision are advanced placement or honor courses, evidence of special talent, leadership record, extracurricular activities record, and recommendations by school officials.

Procedure: Freshmen are admitted fall and spring. Entrance exams should be taken no later than November of the senior year. Early decision applications should be filed by November 15; regular applications, by March 1 for fall entry, along with an application fee of $30. Notification of early decision is sent November 30; regular decision, April 1. There are early decision, early admissions, and deferred admissions plans. About 77 early decision candidates were accepted for the 1993-94 class. A waiting list is an active part of the admissions procedure, with about 5% of applicants on the list.

Transfer: About 83 transfer students enrolled in 1993-94. Transfers must have already earned at least 27 credit hours with a minimum GPA of 2.2. SAT I scores and an interview are recommended. A total of 16 courses out of 36 must be completed at Roanoke.

Visiting: There are regularly scheduled orientations for prospective students, consisting of open houses that provide a sampling of college life at Roanoke. There are guides for informal visits and visitors may sit in on classes and stay overnight at the school. To arrange for a visit, contact the Admissions Office at (703) 375-2270.

Financial Aid: In 1993-94, 86% of all current freshmen and 80% of continuing students received some form of financial aid. About 58% of freshmen and 49% of continuing students received need-based aid. The average freshman award was $9276. Of that total, scholarships or need-based grants averaged $4000 ($16,975 maximum); loans averaged $3625; and work contracts averaged $1300. Twenty-five percent of undergraduate students work part-time. Average earnings from campus work for the school year are $1300. The average financial indebtedness of the 1992-93 graduate was $12,000. Roanoke is a member of CSS. The FAF or FFS and the FAFSA are required. The deadline for financial aid applications is March 1.

International Students: There are currently 18 international students enrolled. The school actively recruits these students. They must take the TOEFL and achieve a minimum score of 500. The student must also take the SAT I or ACT and SAT II: Subject tests are recommended.

Computers: The college provides computer facilities for student use. The mainframe is a DEC VAX 4000-300. Approximately 350 PCs, 80 terminals, and 70 printers support students, faculty, and staff in the academic division. There are 7 computer laboratories distributed across campus, including the library, which has an on-line catalog. From any connected PC or terminal, students have access to word processing, spreadsheets, databases, electronic mail, Internet, programming languages, and programs for specific classes. All students may access the system. It may be used at least 18 hours a day. There are no time limits on using the system and no fees.

Graduates: In 1992-93, 352 bachelor's degrees were awarded. The most popular majors among graduates were business administration (18%), psychology (15%), and sociology (13%). Within an average freshman class, 51% graduate in 4 years, 55% in 5 years, and 57% in 6 years. Some 30 companies recruited on campus in 1992-93.

Admissions Contact: Rita Detwiler, Director of Admissions.

SAINT PAUL'S COLLEGE

Lawrenceville, VA 23868

E-4

(804) 848-3984

(800) 678-7071 (out-of-state)

Full-time: 246 men, 307 women	Faculty: 37; IIB, --$
Part-time: 14 men, 42 women	Ph.D.s: 49%
Graduate: none	Student/Faculty: 15 to 1
Year: semesters, summer session	Tuition: $5521
Application Deadline: open	Room & Board: $3650
Freshman Class: 600 applied, 400 accepted, 240 enrolled	
SAT I: required	**COMPETITIVE**

Saint Paul's College, founded in 1888, is a small, private, coeducational liberal arts college affiliated with the Protestant Episcopal Church, offering undergraduate programs in arts and sciences, business, and education. The library contains 70,000 volumes, 32,903 microform items, and 4529 audiovisual forms, and subscribes to 225 periodicals. Computerized library sources and services include interlibrary loans and database searching. Special learning facilities include a learning resource center. The 75-acre campus is in a rural area 75 miles from Richmond. Including residence halls, there are 18 buildings on campus.

Student Life: About 74% of undergraduates are from Virginia. Students come from 16 states and 3 foreign countries. Ninety-nine percent are from public schools; 1% from private. Ninety-three percent are African American. Forty-two percent are Protestant; 20% claim no religious affiliation. The average age of freshmen is 18.5; all undergraduates, 20.5. Thirty-seven percent drop out by the end of their first year; 31% remain to graduate.

Housing: A total of 431 students can be accommodated in college housing. College-sponsored living facilities include single-sex dormitories and on-campus apartments. In addition there are honors houses, special interest houses, and the Single Parent Support System (SPSS). On-campus housing is guaranteed for the freshman year only and is available on a lottery system for upperclassmen. Sixty-six percent of students live on campus; of those, 50% remain on campus on weekends. Alcohol is not permitted. All students may keep cars on campus.

Activities: About 7% of men belong to 4 national fraternities; about 5% of women belong to 4 national sororities. There are 25 groups on campus, including art, cheerleading, chess, choir, dance, drama, ethnic, honors, jazz band, newspaper, pep band, political, religious, social service, student government, and yearbook. Popular campus events include a lecture and concert series, College for a Day, Homecoming, and Founders Day.

Sports: There are 5 intercollegiate sports for men and 4 for women, and 2 intramural sports for men and 2 for women. Athletic and recreation facilities include a gymnasium, a football field, practice fields, and tennis courts.

Disabled Students: Twenty-five percent of the campus is accessible to disabled students. The following facilities are available: wheelchair ramps, elevators, special parking, and specially equipped rest rooms.

Services: In addition to many counseling and information services, tutoring is available in most subjects. There is remedial math, reading, and writing.

Campus Safety and Security: Campus safety and security measures include 24-hour foot and vehicle patrol, shuttle buses, informal discussions, and pamphlets, posters, and films. In addition, there are emergency telephones and lighted pathways and sidewalks.

Programs of Study: Saint Paul's awards the B.A., B.S., and B.S.Ed. degrees. Bachelor's degrees are awarded in BIOLOGICAL SCIENCE (biology/biological science), BUSINESS (business administration and management), COMMUNICATIONS AND THE ARTS (English), COMPUTER AND PHYSICAL SCIENCE (mathematics), EDUCATION (business, elementary, and secondary), ENGINEERING AND ENVIRONMENTAL DESIGN (environmental science), SOCIAL SCIENCE (law enforcement and corrections, political science/government, social science, and sociology). Business administration and management are the strongest academically. Business administration has the largest enrollment.

Required: All students must complete 42 semester hours of general education requirements, including courses in humanities, natural science and mathematics, social sciences, health and physical education, and computer information systems. A minimum of 120 hours, including at least 30 in the major, with at least a 2.0 GPA is required in order to graduate.

Special: Minors are offered in accounting, biology, chemistry, communications, computer information systems, English, history, management, marketing, mathematics, political science, and sociology. Nonmajor preprofessional programs are available in law, ministry, and the health professions. Endorsements in early childhood, middle, and secondary education are available in appropriate majors. A general studies degree and work-study programs are available. Nondegree study is possible. There is a freshman honors program on campus, as well as 2 national honor societies. Three departments have honors programs.

Faculty/Classroom: Fifty-one percent of faculty are male; 49%, female. All teach undergraduates, 6% do research, and 6% do both. The average class size in an introductory lecture is 10; in a laboratory, 8; and in a regular course offering, 23.

Admissions: About 67% of the 1993–94 applicants were accepted. One freshman graduated first in her class.

Requirements: Saint Paul's requires applicants to be in the upper 50% of their class. A minimum GPA of 2.0 is required. The SAT I is required. In addition, applicants should be graduates of an accredited secondary school and have completed 16 academic units, including English, mathematics, science, and social sciences. CLEP credit is accepted. Important factors used in the admissions decision are recommendations by school officials, leadership record, evidence of special talent, extracurricular activities record, and recommendations by alumni.

Procedure: Freshmen are admitted fall and spring. Entrance exams should be taken during the senior year. Application deadlines are open. The application fee is $15. Notification is sent on a rolling basis. There are early decision and early admissions plans. About 5 early decision candidates were accepted for the 1993–94 class.

Transfer: About 51 transfer students enrolled in 1993–94. Transfer applicants must supply all former official high school and college transcripts, as well as a background form which must be completed by the former college. A total of 30 credits out of 120 must be completed at Saint Paul's.

Visiting: There are regularly scheduled orientations for prospective students. Options include Homecoming, Open House, College for a Day, Honors Convocation, and Pre-Orientation. There are guides for informal visits and visitors may sit in on classes and stay overnight at the school. To arrange for a visit, contact the Director of Admission and Recruitment at (804) 848-3984.

Financial Aid: In a recent year 88% of all students received some form of financial aid. About 85% of freshmen and 83% of continuing students received need-based aid. Average earnings from campus work for the school year are $1500. Saint Paul's is a member of CSS. The FAF is required. The deadline for financial aid applications is July 1.

International Students: There are currently 9 international students enrolled. The school actively recruits these students. The student must take the SAT I.

Computers: The college provides computer facilities for student use. The mainframe is an HP 3000 Series 300. Students enrolled in FORTRAN, BASIC, and COBOL laboratory classes may access the system. It may be used Monday through Friday from 3 A.M. to 6 P.M. There are no time limits on using the system. The fees is $20.

Graduates: In a recent year 83 bachelor's degrees were awarded. The most popular majors among graduates were sociology (22%), business administration and management (15%), and business administration accounting (12%). Within an average freshman class, 17% graduate in 4 years, 30% in 5 years, and 32% in 6 years.

Admissions Contact: Director of Admissions and Recruitment.

SHENANDOAH COLLEGE AND CONSERVATORY

(See Shenandoah University)

SHENANDOAH UNIVERSITY

D-1

(Formerly Shenandoah College and Conservatory)

Winchester, VA 22601

(703) 665-4581

(800) 432-2266 (out-of-state)

Full-time: 345 men, 525 women	Faculty: 82; IIB, -$
Part-time: 97 men, 213 women	Ph.D.s: 67%
Graduate: 187 men, 297 women	Student/Faculty: 11 to 1
Year: semesters, summer session	Tuition: $9800
Application Deadline: open	Room & Board: $1950–2200
Freshman Class: 820 applied, 616 accepted, 212 enrolled	
SAT I Verbal/Math: 438/477	**COMPETITIVE**

Shenandoah University, founded in 1875, is a private, coeducational university, affiliated with the United Methodist Church and offers programs in arts and sciences, nursing and health professions, business, music, theater, and dance. There are 4 undergraduate and 4 graduate schools. In addition to regional accreditation, Shenandoah has baccalaureate program accreditation with AACSB, NASM, and NLN. The library contains 104,024 volumes, 47,871 microform items, and 14,572 audiovisual forms, and subscribes to 644 periodicals. Computerized library sources and services include the card catalog and interlibrary loans. Special learning facilities include a radio station. The 70-acre campus is in a small town 72 miles west of Washington, D.C. Including residence halls, there are 14 buildings on campus.

Student Life: About 65% of undergraduates are from Virginia. Students come from 33 states, 27 foreign countries, and Canada. Eighty-seven percent are white. Fifty-four percent are Protestant; 27% claim no religious affiliation; 16% Catholic. The average age of freshmen is 19.2; all undergraduates, 24. Thirty-four percent drop out by the end of their first year; 72% remain to graduate.

Housing: A total of 450 students can be accommodated in college housing. College-sponsored living facilities include single-sex and coed dormitories. On-campus housing is guaranteed for all 4 years. Seventy-two percent of students commute. All students may keep cars on campus.

Activities: There are no fraternities or sororities on campus. There are 25 groups on campus, including choir, chorale, chorus, dance, drama, ethnic, honors, international, jazz band, musical theater, newspaper, opera, orchestra, professional, radio and TV, religious, social service, student government, symphony, and yearbook. Popular campus events include Fall and Spring Formals, conservatory productions, International Days, and Spring Fling.

Sports: There are 6 intercollegiate sports for men and 5 for women, and 2 intramural sports for men and 2 for women. Athletic and recreation facilities include a soccer field, a gymnasium with basketball and volleyball courts, a weight room, a track, and a lacrosse field.

Disabled Students: Ninety percent of the campus is accessible to disabled students. The following facilities are available: wheelchair ramps, elevators, special parking, specially equipped rest rooms, special class scheduling, lowered drinking fountains, and lowered telephones.

Services: In addition to many counseling and information services, tutoring is available in some subjects. There is also a reader service for the blind, and remedial math, reading, and writing.

Campus Safety and Security: Campus safety and security measures include a 24-hour foot and vehicle patrol, self defense education, an escort service, and informal discussions. In addition, there are pamphlets, posters, films, emergency telephones, and lighted pathways and sidewalks.

Programs of Study: Shenandoah awards the B.A., B.S., B.B.A., B.F.A., B.M., and B.M.T. degrees. Associate and master's degrees also are awarded. Bachelor's degrees are awarded in BIOLOGICAL SCIENCE (biology/biological science), BUSINESS (accounting, business administration and management, international business management, and marketing/retailing/merchandising), COMMUNICATIONS AND THE ARTS (communications, dance, dramatic arts, English, fine arts, music, and theater design), COMPUTER AND PHYSICAL SCIENCE (chemistry, computer science, and mathematics), EDUCATION (elementary, music, physical, and secondary), HEALTH PROFESSIONS (nursing and respiratory therapy), SOCIAL SCIENCE (history, psychology, and religion). Physical therapy, occupational therapy, and nursing are the strongest academically. Nursing, business administration, and music education have the largest enrollments.

Required: To graduate, all students must have taken 1 religion/philosophy courses and 2 physical education courses. Students must complete at least 120 credit hours with a minimum 2.0 GPA. Other requirements vary depending on the program of study.

Special: A B.A.-B.S. degree program, internships, dual majors, and work-study programs are available. Nondegree study is possible. There is a freshman honors program on campus, as well as one national honor society. One department has an honors program.

Faculty/Classroom: Forty-eight percent of faculty are male; 52%, female. Ninety percent teach undergraduates. No introductory courses are taught by graduate students. The average class size in an introductory lecture is 15; in a laboratory, 10; and in a regular course offering, 20.

Admissions: About 75% of the 1993–94 applicants were accepted. The SAT scores for the 1993–94 freshman class were as follows: Verbal—72% below 500, 23% between 500 and 599, and 5% between 600 and 700; Math—57% below 500, 27% between 500 and 599, 14% between 600 and 700, and 2% above 700.

Requirements: The SAT I or ACT, with a minimum composite score of 850 on the SAT I or 19 on the ACT is required. Applicants must be graduates of an accredited secondary school. The GED is accepted. Students should complete 15 high school academic credits, including 4 years of English, 3 years of mathematics, and 2 years each of foreign language, science, and social studies. A minimum GPA of 2.5 is required. An audition is required for music, theater, and dance. AP and CLEP credits are accepted. Important factors used in the admissions decision are advanced placement or honor courses, evidence of special talent, extracurricular activities record, leadership record, and recommendations by school officials.

Procedure: Freshmen are admitted to all sessions. Entrance exams should be taken early in the senior year. Application deadlines are open. The application fee is $30. Notification is sent on a rolling basis. There are early decision, early admissions, and deferred admissions plans.

Transfer: About 234 transfer students enrolled in 1993–94. Transfer applicants must have a GPA of 2.0. An audition is required for music, dance, and theater. Official transcripts for all previous college work must be submitted. A total of 24 credits out of 120 must be completed at Shenandoah.

Visiting: There are regularly scheduled orientations for prospective students. The agenda is invidually designed for each student. There are guides for informal visits and visitors may sit in on classes and stay overnight at the school. To arrange for a visit, contact the Admissions Office at (800) 432–2266.

Financial Aid: In 1993–94, 85% of all current freshmen and 79% of continuing students received some form of financial aid. About 53% of all students received need-based aid. The average freshman award was $6666. Of that total, scholarships or need-based grants averaged $2800 ($9800 maximum); loans averaged $2625 ($4625 maximum); and work contracts averaged $1275 ($1350 maximum). Twenty-two percent of undergraduate students work part-time. Average earnings from campus work for the school year are $1300. The average financial indebtedness of the 1992–93 graduate was $13,250. The college's own financial statement, the State aid form, and FAFSA are required. The deadline for financial aid applications is March 15.

International Students: There are currently 110 international students enrolled. The school actively recruits these students. They must take the TOEFL or the college's own test and achieve a minimum score on the TOEFL of 450.

Computers: The college provides computer facilities for student use. There are approximately 70 Macintosh and IBM microcomputers and workstations located in computer laboratories throughout the campus. All students may access the system. It may be used during scheduled hours. There are no time limits on using the system and no fees.

Graduates: In 1992–93 97 bachelor's degrees were awarded. The most popular majors among graduates were nursing (34%), business administration (11%), and psychology (10%). Within an average freshman class, 33% graduate in 4 years, 15% in 5 years, and 2% in 6 years.

Admissions Contact: Patricia A. Coyle, Director of Admissions.

SWEET BRIAR COLLEGE D-3
Sweet Briar, VA 24595 (804) 381–6142
(800) 947–4300 (out-of-state)

Full-time: 2 men, 525 women	Faculty: 64; IIB, +$
Part-time: 9 men, 32 women	Ph.D.s: 95%
Graduate: none	Student/Faculty: 8 to 1
Year: 4-1-4	Tuition: $14,015
Application Deadline: February 15	Room & Board: $5755
Freshman Class: 462 applied, 402 accepted, 146 enrolled	
SAT I or ACT: required	COMPETITIVE

Sweet Briar College, founded in 1901, is a private independent, liberal arts, women's institution. Men may be admitted as special students but may not receive a degree from Sweet Briar. The 4 libraries contain 217,032 volumes, 289,156 microform items, and 4074 audiovisual forms, and subscribe to 968 periodicals. Computerized library sources and services include the card catalog, interlibrary loans, and database searching. Special learning facilities include a learning resource center, an art gallery, a radio station, and a college museum. The 3300-acre campus is in a small town 50 miles southwest of Charlottesville and 150 miles southwest of Washington, D.C. Including residence halls, there are 38 buildings on campus.

Student Life: About 67% of undergraduates are from out-of-state, mostly the South. Students come from 43 states and 18 foreign countries. Sixty-nine percent are from public schools; 31% from private. Eighty-seven percent are white. The average age of freshmen is 18; all undergraduates, 20. Twenty percent drop out by the end of their first year; 61% remain to graduate.

Housing: A total of 545 students can be accommodated in college housing. College-sponsored living facilities include dormitories. In addition there is a language hall. On-campus housing is guaranteed for all 4 years. Eighty-three percent of students live on campus; of those, 65% remain on campus on weekends. All students may keep cars on campus.

Activities: There are no sororities on campus. There are 41 groups on campus, including art, choir, chorus, computers, dance, drama, ethnic, film, honors, international, literary magazine, musical theater, newspaper, photography, political, professional, religious, social, social service, student government, and yearbook. Popular campus events include Stepsinging, Dell Parties, Founder's Day, Fall Weekend, Spring Weekend, Black History Month, Babcock Season performances, Ewald Scholars Program, Lyman Lectures, and Winter Forums.

Sports: There are 4 club intercollegiate sports. Athletic and recreation facilities include a natatorium, a gymnasium, a Nautilus center, a weight room, trails for walking, biking, and riding, 14 tennis courts,

a riding center, soccer/lacrosse/field hockey fields, a fitness circuit, and 2 lakes.

Disabled Students: Eighty percent of the campus is accessible to disabled students. The following facilities are available: wheelchair ramps, elevators, special parking, specially equipped rest rooms, and lowered telephones.

Services: In addition to many counseling and information services, tutoring is available in most subjects.

Campus Safety and Security: Campus safety and security measures include 24-hour foot and vehicle patrol, self defense education, escort service, and shuttle buses. In addition, there are informal discussions, pamphlets, posters, and films, lighted pathways and sidewalks, locked gates from 8 P.M. to 8 A.M., and locked dormitories with student key access.

Programs of Study: Sweet Briar awards the A.B. and B.S. degrees. Bachelor's degrees are awarded in BIOLOGICAL SCIENCE (biochemistry, biology/biological science, and molecular biology), COMMUNICATIONS AND THE ARTS (dance, English, and languages), COMPUTER AND PHYSICAL SCIENCE (chemistry, computer science, mathematics, and physics), SOCIAL SCIENCE (anthropology, economics, history, international relations, philosophy, political science/government, psychology, religion, social science, and sociology). International affairs, English, art, biology, and chemistry are the strongest academically. Psychology, government, and English have the largest enrollments.

Required: To graduate, students must complete 120 credits, of which 60 must be earned at Sweet Briar, with a minimum GPA of 2.0. In addition to major requirements, there are specific degree requirements, including English 1, proficiency in a foreign language, 6 hours of literature or the arts, 3 hours in biology, environmental studies, or psychology, 3 hours in chemistry, mathematical sciences, or physics, 3 hours in social sciences, 3 hours in classical or European civilization, history, philosophy or religion, 3 hours in non-Western studies, and 2 hours of physical education.

Special: The college offers a coordinate program in general business management, public administration, and arts management, internships, study abroad in 7 countries, an environmental junior year program with 6 universities, and a Washington semester with American University. B.A.-B.S. degrees, student-designed and interdisciplinary majors, accelerated degree programs, and 3–2 engineering degrees with Georgia Institute of Technology are available. Cross-registration with Lynchburg and Randolph-Macon Woman's colleges (the Tri-College Consortium) and the Seven College Exchange is also possible. There is a freshman honors program on campus, as well as 2 national honor societies, including Phi Beta Kappa.

Faculty/Classroom: Forty-eight percent of faculty are male; 52%, female. All teach undergraduates and do research. The average class size in an introductory lecture is 15; in a laboratory, 7; and in a regular course offering, 12.

Admissions: About 87% of the 1993–94 applicants were accepted. About 55% of the current freshmen were in the top fifth of their class; 82% were in the top two fifths. There were 2 National Merit semifinalists. About 2 freshmen graduated first in their class.

Requirements: Sweet Briar recommends applicants to be in the upper 50% of their class. A minimum GPA of 2.8 is recommended. The SAT I or ACT is required. If the SAT I is submitted, it is strongly recommended that the applicant also take SAT II: Subject tests in writing, mathematics, and a foreign language. Applicants must be graduates of an accredited secondary school. The GED is accepted. Applicants should complete at least 16 high school academic credits, including 4 years of English and 3 each of mathematics, social studies, foreign language, science, and history. The college requires an essay and recommends an interview. AP credits are accepted. Important factors used in the admissions decision are advanced placement or honor courses, recommendations by school officials, leadership record, evidence of special talent, and personality, intangible qualities.

Procedure: Freshmen are admitted in the fall. Entrance exams should be taken by January of the year of application; SAT II: Subject tests can be taken in the spring of the senior year. Early decision applications should be filed by November 15; regular applications, by February 15 for fall entry and November 15 for spring entry, along with an application fee of $25. Notification of early decision is sent December 15; regular decision, April 15. There are early decision, early admissions, and deferred admissions plans. About 57 early decision candidates were accepted for the 1993–94 class.

Transfer: About 7 transfer students enrolled in 1993–94. Transfer applicants must submit official transcripts from high school and college, test scores, a college catalog, and recommendations from a previous dean and professor. A total of 60 credits out of 120 must be completed at Sweet Briar.

Visiting: There are regularly scheduled orientations for prospective students, consisting of attendance at classes, meetings with faculty and coaches, attendance at campus events, an overnight stay in a dorm, a campus tour, and an interview. There are guides for informal visits. To arrange for a visit, contact Nancy E. Church, Director, Admissions Office at (800) 947–4300 (out-of-state) or (804) 381–6142.

Financial Aid: In 1993–94, 83% of all current freshmen and 56% of continuing students received some form of financial aid. About 57% of freshmen and 47% of continuing students received need-based aid. The average freshman award was $12,647. Of that total, scholarships or need-based grants averaged $8644 ($14,250 maximum); loans averaged $3169 ($5625 maximum); and work contracts averaged $834 ($1000 maximum). Fifty-eight percent of undergraduate students work part-time. Average earnings from campus work for the school year are $775. The average financial indebtedness of the 1992–93 graduate was $7940. Sweet Briar is a member of CSS. The FAF, FFS, or SFS is required. The priority deadline for financial aid applications for meeting 100% or need is March 1.

International Students: There are currently 17 international students enrolled. The school actively recruits these students. They must take the TOEFL and achieve a minimum score of 550.

Computers: The college provides computer facilities for student use. The mainframe is a DEC VAX 4100. There are 92 computers for student use located across campus in 24-hour study laboratories, the libraries, study rooms, and academic buildings. The computer-student ratio is 1:6.5. Networks to the mainframes exist in academic buildings. The college is connected to Internet. All students may access the system. It may be used 24 hours a day. There are no time limits on using the system and no fees.

Graduates: In 1992–93, 145 bachelor's degrees were awarded. The most popular majors among graduates were psychology (15%), English (11%), and economics, government, and international affairs (9%). Within an average freshman class, 61% graduate in 4 years and 63% in 6 years. Some 5 companies recruited on campus in 1992–93. In the 1992 graduating class, 21% of the women were enrolled in graduate school within 6 months of graduation; 44% of the women had found employment.

Admissions Contact: Nancy E. Church, Director of Admissions and Financial Aid.

UNIVERSITY OF RICHMOND   E-3
University of Richmond, VA 23173   (804) 289–8640

Full-time: 1449 men, 1427 women	**Faculty:** 265; IIA, +$
Part-time: 201 men, 388 women	**Ph.D.s:** 92%
Graduate: 445 men, 417 women	**Student/Faculty:** 11 to 1
Year: semesters, summer session	**Tuition:** $13,540
Application Deadline: February 1	**Room & Board:** $3160
Freshman Class: 5894 applied, 2713 accepted, 759 enrolled	
SAT I or ACT: required	**HIGHLY COMPETITIVE**

The University of Richmond, founded in 1830, is a private, coeducational, independent institution affiliated with the Baptist General Association of Virginia, offering programs in arts and sciences, business, and leadership studies. There are 4 undergraduate and 2 graduate schools. In addition to regional accreditation, UR has baccalaureate program accreditation with AACSB and NASM. The 4 libraries contain 615,975 volumes, 49,041 microform items, and 464,161 audiovisual forms, and subscribe to 7132 periodicals. Computerized library sources and services include the card catalog, interlibrary loans, and database searching. Special learning facilities include a learning resource center, art gallery, and radio station. The 350-acre campus is in a suburban area 6 miles west of Richmond. Including residence halls, there are 50 buildings on campus.

Student Life: About 80% of undergraduates are from out-of-state, mostly the Middle Atlantic. Students come from 45 states, 27 foreign countries, and Canada. Seventy-one percent are from public schools; 29% from private. Ninety-two percent are white. Fifty-four percent are Protestant; 33% Catholic; 10% claim no religious affiliation. The average age of freshmen is 18; all undergraduates, 20. Eight percent drop out by their first year; 83% remain to graduate.

Housing: A total of 2700 students can be accommodated in college housing. College-sponsored living facilities include single-sex and coed dormitories and on-campus apartments. In addition there are language houses and special interest houses. On-campus housing is guaranteed for the freshman year only, is available on a first-come, first-served basis, and is available on a lottery system for upperclassmen. Ninety-two percent of students live on campus; of those, 90% remain on campus on weekends. All students may keep cars on campus.

Activities: About 50% of men belong to 10 national fraternities; about 60% of women belong to 8 national sororities. There are 185 groups on campus, including band, cheerleading, choir, chorus, computers, dance, drama, drill team, ethnic, gay, honors, international, jazz band, literary magazine, musical theater, newspaper, orchestra, pep band, political, professional, religious, social, social service, student government, and yearbook. Popular campus events include UR Century Bike Race, Homecoming Week, Greek Theater Parties, Ring Dance, Proclamation Night, Black History Month, Inter-

national Film Festival, Campus Activities Board events, Awareness Week, and Midnight Expressions.

Sports: There are 11 intercollegiate sports for men and 9 for women, and 24 intramural sports for men and 23 for women. Athletic and recreation facilities include a 10,000-seat gymnasium, a stadium, a soccer/track complex, lighted intramural fields, tennis courts, and 2 intramural gymnasiums.

Disabled Students: Eighty percent of the campus is accessible to disabled students. The following facilities are available: wheelchair ramps, elevators, special parking, specially equipped rest rooms, and lowered drinking fountains.

Services: In addition to many counseling and information services, tutoring is available in most subjects.

Campus Safety and Security: Campus safety and security measures include a 24-hour foot and vehicle patrol, self defense education, an escort service, and shuttle buses. In addition, there are informal discussions, pamphlets, posters, films, emergency telephones, lighted pathways and sidewalks, and card-access systems in women's residence halls, vehicle assistance, emergency first aid service, fingerprinting, firearm storage, and personal property engraving and identification.

Programs of Study: UR awards the B.A., B.S., B.M., and B.S.B.A. degrees. Master's degrees also are awarded. Bachelor's degrees are awarded in BIOLOGICAL SCIENCE (biology/biological science), BUSINESS (accounting, banking and finance, business administration and management, business economics, and marketing/retailing/merchandising), COMMUNICATIONS AND THE ARTS (English, French, German, journalism, music, Russian, Spanish, and speech/debate/rhetoric), COMPUTER AND PHYSICAL SCIENCE (chemistry, computer science, mathematics, and physics), EDUCATION (art, early childhood, health, middle school, music, science, and secondary), SOCIAL SCIENCE (criminal justice, economics, history, international relations, philosophy, political science/government, psychology, religion, sociology, and urban studies). Business, social sciences, natural sciences, and humanities have the largest enrollments.

Required: To graduate, students must complete 122 credits with a minimum GPA of 2.0. There are specific requirements in English composition, mathematics and computer science, Western civilization or an interdisciplinary core course, foreign language, social sciences, natural sciences, physical education, humanities and fine arts, and languages and literatures.

Special: Internships in nearly every major, study abroad in 13 countries, and a Washington semester with American University are available. The university offers work-study programs, accelerated degree programs, B.A.-B.S. degrees, dual majors, student-designed majors, and a general studies degree through University College. There is a 3–2 program with Duke University in forestry and environmental management, and a marine biology study option with the Marine Sciences Laboratory at Duke University. There is a freshman honors program on campus, as well as 32 national honor societies, including Phi Beta Kappa. Ten departments have honors programs.

Faculty/Classroom: Sixty-eight percent of faculty are male; 32%, female. All teach undergraduates. No introductory courses are taught by graduate students. The average class size in an introductory lecture is 23 and in a regular course offering, 20.

Admissions: About 46% of the 1993–94 applicants were accepted. The SAT I scores for the 1993–94 freshman class were as follows: Verbal—14% below 500, 50% between 500 and 599, 32% between 600 and 700, and 4% above 700; Math—3% below 500, 24% between 500 and 599, 53% between 600 and 700, and 20% above 700. The ACT scores were 8% below 21, 9% between 21 and 23, 21% between 24 and 26, 18% between 27 and 28, and 43% above 28. About 72% of the current freshmen were in the top fifth of their class; 97% were in the top two fifths. There were 26 National Merit finalists and 33 semifinalists. About 29 freshmen graduated first in their class.

Requirements: The SAT I or ACT is required. In addition, SAT II: Subject tests are required in writing, mathematics I or II, and another subject of the student's choice. Applicants must be graduates of an accredited secondary school. The GED is accepted. Applicants must complete 16 high school academic credits, including 4 years of English, 3 each of mathematics and foreign language, and 2 each of history and science. An essay, counselor recommendation, and auditions for music scholarships are required. AP and CLEP credits are accepted. Important factors used in the admissions decision are advanced placement or honor courses, leadership record, evidence of special talent, extracurricular activities record, and recommendations by school officials.

Procedure: Freshmen are admitted in the fall. Entrance exams should be taken by February 1 of the senior year. Early decision applications should be filed by November 1; regular applications, by February 1 for fall entry, along with an application fee of $40. Notification of early decision is sent November 15; regular decision, April 1. There are early decision, early admissions, and deferred admissions plans.

About 90 early decision candidates were accepted for the 1993–94 class. A waiting list is an active part of the admissions procedure.

Transfer: About 21 transfer students enrolled in 1993–94. Applicants for transfer must have earned a minimum of 24 credit hours in transferable courses. A minimum GPA of 2.0 is required; however, to be competitive an applicant needs about a 3.3 GPA. A total of 60 credits out of 122 must be completed at UR.

Visiting: There are regularly scheduled orientations for prospective students, consisting of conferences and tours offered Monday through Friday. Visitors may sit in on classes. To arrange for a visit, contact the Admissions Office at (804) 289–8640.

Financial Aid: In 1993–94, 60% of all current freshmen and 56% of continuing students received some form of financial aid. About 30% of freshmen and 24% of continuing students received need-based aid. The average freshman award was $8654. Of that total, scholarships or need-based grants averaged $7265 ($16,700 maximum); loans averaged $3078 ($4600 maximum); and work contracts averaged $1200 ($2000 maximum). Twenty-five percent of undergraduate students work part-time. Average earnings from campus work for the school year are $735. The average financial indebtedness of the 1992–93 graduate was $10,525. UR is a member of CSS. The college's own financial statement and FAFSA are required. The deadline for financial aid applications is February 25.

International Students: There are currently 54 international students enrolled. The school actively recruits these students. They must take the TOEFL and achieve a minimum score of 550. Nonnative English speakers must take the TOEFL and SAT II: Subject tests in writing, math, and one other. Native English speakers must also take the SAT I.

Computers: The college provides computer facilities for student use. The mainframe is a DEC VAX 11/750 and 11/785. All students have access to laboratories housing Macintosh, NeXT, IBM-compatible, UNIX, and DEC VAX equipment. Bitnet and Internet networks are also available. All students may access the system. There are no time limits on using the system and no fees.

Graduates: In a recent year, 760 bachelor's degrees were awarded. The most popular majors among graduates were business administration (15%), English (10%), and political science (9%). Within an average freshman class, 78% graduate in 4 years and 83% in 5 years. Some 355 companies recruited on campus in a recent year. In the 1992 graduating class, 23% of all students were enrolled in graduate school within 6 months of graduation; 59% had found employment.

Admissions Contact: Pamela W. Spence, Dean of Admissions.

UNIVERSITY OF VIRGINIA   D-3
Charlottesville, VA 22906   (804) 982-3200

Full-time: 5492 men, 5759 women	Faculty: 905; I, av$
Part-time: 45 men, 75 women	Ph.D.s: 90%
Graduate: 3443 men, 2790 women	Student/Faculty: 12 to 1
Year: semesters, summer session	Tuition: $4350 ($12,254)
Application Deadline: January 2	Room & Board: $3614
Freshman Class: 15,848 applied, 5383 accepted, 2675 enrolled	
SAT I Verbal/Math: 570/650	MOST COMPETITIVE

The University of Virginia, founded in 1819, is a public, coeducational institution with undergraduate programs in architecture, arts and sciences, commerce, education, engineering and applied science, and nursing. There are 6 undergraduate and 8 graduate schools. In addition to regional accreditation, UVA has baccalaureate program accreditation with AACSB, ABET, NASM, NCATE, and NLN. The 17 libraries contain 3,948,504 volumes, 4,105,665 microform items, and 466,310 audiovisual forms, and subscribe to 36,716 periodicals. Computerized library sources and services include the card catalog, interlibrary loans, and database searching. Special learning facilities include a learning resource center, an art gallery, a radio station, a TV station, and an art museum. The 1094-acre campus is in a suburban area 70 miles northwest of Richmond. Including residence halls, there are 557 buildings on campus.

Student Life: About 65% of undergraduates are from Virginia. Students come from 49 states, 85 foreign countries, and Canada. Seventy-nine percent are from public schools; 21% from private. Seventy-six percent are white; 12% African American. Forty-seven percent are Protestant; 23% Catholic; 20% claim no religious affiliation. The average age of freshmen is 17.8; all undergraduates, 19.7. Three percent drop out by the end of their first year; 92% remain to graduate.

Housing: A total of 6767 students can be accommodated in college housing. College-sponsored living facilities include coed dormitories, on-campus apartments, and married-student housing. In addition there are honors houses and language houses. On-campus housing is guaranteed for the freshman year only and is available on a lottery system for upperclassmen. Fifty-two percent of students live on campus. All students may keep cars on campus.

Activities: About 28% of men belong to 39 national fraternities; about 30% of women belong to 22 national sororities. There are 300 groups on campus, including art, band, cheerleading, chess, choir, chorale, chorus, computers, dance, drama, ethnic, film, gay, honors, international, jazz band, literary magazine, musical theater, newspaper, orchestra, pep band, photography, political, professional, radio and TV, religious, social, social service, student government, symphony, and yearbook. Popular campus events include Culturefest, Parents Weekend, Homecoming, Foxfield Races, Commonwealth Ball, and the Virginia Film Festival.

Sports: There are 12 intercollegiate sports for men and 11 for women, and 30 intramural sports for men and 30 for women. Athletic and recreation facilities include a 44,000-seat stadium, a 9000-seat gymnasium, a recreation center, and a recreation building.

Disabled Students: The entire campus is accessible to disabled students. The following facilities are available: wheelchair ramps, elevators, special parking, specially equipped rest rooms, special class scheduling, lowered drinking fountains, lowered telephones, and curb cuts, voice synthesizers, braille printers, and large-screen monitors.

Services: In addition to many counseling and information services, tutoring is available in every subject. There is also a reader service for the blind, transcribers, note takers, and taped readings for disabled students.

Campus Safety and Security: Campus safety and security measures include a 24-hour foot and vehicle patrol, self defense education, an escort service, and shuttle buses. In addition, there are informal discussions, pamphlets, posters, films, emergency telephones, and lighted pathways and sidewalks.

Programs of Study: UVA awards the B.A., B.S., B.A.R.H., B.C.P., B.S.C., B.S.Ed., and B.S.N. degrees. Master's and doctoral degrees also are awarded. Bachelor's degrees are awarded in BIOLOGICAL SCIENCE (biology/biological science), BUSINESS (business economics), COMMUNICATIONS AND THE ARTS (art, classics, communications, dramatic arts, English, French, German, Italian, literature, music, Slavic languages, and Spanish), COMPUTER AND PHYSICAL SCIENCE (applied mathematics, astronomy, chemistry, computer science, mathematics, and physics), EDUCATION (health), ENGINEERING AND ENVIRONMENTAL DESIGN (Aerospace Studies, architectural technology, architecture, chemical engineering, city/community/regional planning, civil engineering, electrical/electronics engineering, engineering, environmental science, mechanical engineering, and systems engineering), HEALTH PROFESSIONS (nursing and speech pathology/audiology), SOCIAL SCIENCE (African American studies, anthropology, economics, ethnic studies, history, interdisciplinary studies, international relations, philosophy, political science/government, psychology, religion, and sociology). English, history, biology, and foreign languages are the strongest programs academically. English, government and foreign affairs, and psychology have the largest enrollments.

Required: To graduate, students must complete 120 credit hours, with 24 to 42 hours in the major and a minimum GPA of 2.0. Distribution requirements include 9 to 12 hours of mathematics and science, 6 hours each of humanities and social sciences, 4 semesters of foreign languages, and 3 to 6 hours of composition.

Special: The college offers internships, study abroad in 3 countries, accelerated degree programs, B.A.-B.S. degrees in chemistry and physics, and nondegree study. Dual majors in most arts and sciences programs, student-designed majors, and pass/fail options are available. There is a freshman honors program on campus, as well as 2 national honor societies, including Phi Beta Kappa. Five departments have honors programs.

Faculty/Classroom: Seventy-eight percent of faculty are male; 22% female. Fifty-four percent teach undergraduates, 100% do research, and 54% do both. Graduate students teach 49% of introductory courses. The average class size in an introductory lecture is 44 and in a laboratory, 58.

Admissions: About 34% of the 1993–94 applicants were accepted. The SAT scores for the 1993–94 freshman class were as follows: Verbal—17% below 500, 42% between 500 and 599, 36% between 600 and 700, and 5% above 700; Math—5% below 500, 21% between 500 and 599, 48% between 600 and 700, and 26% above 700. About 92% of the current freshmen were in the top fifth of their class; 99% were in the top two fifths. There were 172 National Merit finalists. About 186 freshmen graduated first in their class.

Requirements: The SAT I is required. In addition, SAT II: Subject tests in writing, mathematics I or II, and a choice of foreign language, history, or science are required. With few exceptions, candidates graduate from accredited secondary schools. While the GED is accepted, it is rare for candidates for first-year admission who have this credential to be competitive in the admissions process. Applicants should complete 16 high school academic courses, including 4 courses of English, 4 courses of mathematics, beginning with Algebra I, 2 courses of physics, biology, or chemistry (3 if applying to engineering), and 2 years of foreign language. An essay is also required.

AP credits are accepted. Important factors used in the admissions decision are advanced placement or honor courses, recommendations by school officials, parents or siblings attending the school, geographic diversity, and leadership record.

Procedure: Freshmen are admitted in the fall. Entrance exams should be taken by January of the senior year. Early decision applications should be filed by November 1; regular applications, by January 2 for fall entry, along with an application fee of $40. Notification of early decision is sent December 1; regular decision during the first week of April. There is an early decision plan. About 565 early decision candidates were accepted for the 1993–94 class. A waiting list is an active part of the admissions procedure, with about 19% of applicants on the list.

Transfer: About 454 transfer students enrolled in 1993–94. Applicants for transfer must have a minimum GPA of 3.0, submit SAT I scores, and meet prerequisite courses. A total of 54 credits out of 120 must be completed at UVA.

Visiting: There are regularly scheduled orientations for prospective students, consisting of comprehensive information sessions and campus tours. There are guides for informal visits and visitors may sit in on classes and stay overnight at the school. To arrange for a visit, contact the Monroe Society at (804) 924–3321.

Financial Aid: In 1993–94, 39% of all current freshmen and 35% of continuing students received some form of financial aid. About 27% of all students received need-based aid. The average freshman award was $6780. Of that total, scholarships or need-based grants averaged $5345 ($16,500 maximum); loans averaged $3390 ($4850 maximum); and work contracts averaged $1400 ($1500 maximum). Thirty percent of undergraduate students work part-time. Average earnings from campus work for the school year are $1200. The average financial indebtedness of the 1992–93 graduate was $7400. UVA is a member of CSS. The FAF and the college's own financial statement are required for returning students only. The FAFSA is required for all applicants. The deadline for financial aid applications is March 1.

International Students: There are currently 202 international students enrolled. The school actively recruits these students. They must take the TOEFL. International students must take the same tests as all other entering students.

Computers: The college provides computer facilities for student use. The Academic Computer Center provides a large variety of computer resources, including mainframes, minicomputers, microcomputers, a network of printers, and other hardware. Numerous mainframe terminals and PCs are available to students in many locations on the grounds. All students may access the system 24 hours a day. There are no time limits on using the system and no fees.

Graduates: In 1992–93, 2949 bachelor's degrees were awarded. The most popular majors among graduates were commerce (11%), English (9%), and psychology (7%). Within an average freshman class, 1% graduate in 3 years, 78% in 4 years, 90% in 5 years, and 92% in 6 years. Some 500 companies recruited on campus in a recent year.

Admissions Contact: John A. Blackburn, Dean of Admissions.

VIRGINIA COMMONWEALTH UNIVERSITY   E-3
Richmond, VA 23284   (804) 367–1190
(800) 841–3638 (out-of-state)

Full-time: 4277 men, 5955 women	Faculty: 578; I, --$
Part-time: 2227 men, 2870 women	Ph.D.s: 87%
Graduate: 2409 men, 4116 women	Student/Faculty: 18 to 1
Year: semesters, summer session	Tuition: $3747 ($10,304)
Application Deadline: February 1	Room & Board: $4162
Freshman Class: 4963 applied, 3497 accepted, 1567 enrolled	
SAT I Verbal/Math: 485/525	COMPETITIVE

Virginia Commonwealth University, founded in 1838, is a public coeducational institution. There are 10 undergraduate and 10 graduate schools. In addition to regional accreditation, VCU has baccalaureate program accreditation with AACSB, ACEJMC, ACPE, APTA, CAHEA, CSWE, FIDER, NASAD, NCATE and NLN. The 2 libraries contain 641,000 volumes, and subscribe to 1138 periodicals. Computerized library sources and services include the card catalog, interlibrary loans, and database searching. Special learning facilities include a learning resource center, an art gallery, a radio station, and a TV station. The 60-acre campus is in an urban area 2 miles west of downtown Richmond. Including residence halls, there are 122 buildings on campus.

Student Life: About 94% of undergraduates are from Virginia. Students come from 46 states, 74 foreign countries, and Canada. Seventy-six percent are white; 15% African American. Eighty percent are Protestant; 10% Catholic. The average age of freshmen is 18.2; all undergraduates, 23.5. Twenty-three percent drop out by the end of their first year; 43% remain to graduate.

Housing: A total of 3357 students can be accommodated in college housing. College-sponsored living facilities include coed dormitories, on-campus apartments, and off-campus apartments. In addition there are honors houses and honors and special interest floors. On-campus housing is guaranteed for the freshman year only and is available on a first-come, first-served basis. All students may keep cars on campus.

Activities: There are 15 national fraternities and 9 national sororities. There are 150 groups on campus, including art, band, cheerleading, chess, choir, chorale, chorus, computers, dance, drama, ethnic, gay, honors, international, jazz band, literary magazine, musical theater, newspaper, orchestra, pep band, photography, political, professional, radio and TV, religious, social, social service, student government, symphony, and yearbook. Popular campus events include Black History Month, College Bowl, Kwanzaa Leadership, Service Awards Ceremony, Organizational Fair, Panhellenic Rush, Poor Starving Artist Festival, and Spring Fling.

Sports: Athletic and recreation facilities include a recreation complex with sports clubs and a fitness program, a gymnasium, a swimming pool, and an outdoor adventure program.

Disabled Students: The following facilities are available: wheelchair ramps, elevators, special parking, specially equipped rest rooms, special class scheduling, lowered drinking fountains, and lowered telephones.

Services: In addition to many counseling and information services, tutoring is available in most subjects. In addition, there is a reader service for the blind, and remedial math, reading, and writing.

Campus Safety and Security: Campus safety and security measures include a 24-hour foot and vehicle patrol, self defense education, an escort service, and shuttle buses. In addition, there are informal discussions, pamphlets, posters, films, emergency telephones, and lighted pathways and sidewalks.

Programs of Study: VCU awards the B.A., B.S., B.F.A., B.G.S., B.Mus., B.Mus.Ed., B.S.N., and B.S.W. degrees. Associate, master's, and doctoral degrees also are awarded. Bachelor's degrees are awarded in BIOLOGICAL SCIENCE (biology/biological science), BUSINESS (accounting, business administration and management, business economics, and marketing/retailing/merchandising), COMMUNICATIONS AND THE ARTS (communications, dance, design, dramatic arts, English, fine arts, languages, and music), COMPUTER AND PHYSICAL SCIENCE (chemistry, computer science, information sciences and systems, mathematics, and physics), EDUCATION (art, elementary, and health), HEALTH PROFESSIONS (nursing, occupational therapy, pharmacy, physical therapy, predentistry, and premedicine), SOCIAL SCIENCE (anthropology, criminal justice, economics, history, political science/government, psychology, religion, social work, and urban studies).

Required: The total number of credit hours required for graduation varies with the major. Students must achieve a minimum GPA of 2.0.

Special: Internships are available for seniors with government agencies, banking and finance centers, private industry, media, and community service agencies. Co-op programs in all majors, work-study programs on campus and with state agencies in the city, study abroad in 6 countries, general studies degrees, and B.A.-B.S. degrees in psychology and economics are offered. Students may take a 3-2 engineering degree with Old Dominion, George Washington, and Auburn Universities. Student-designed majors through a nontraditional studies program, nondegree study, and credit for life, military, and work experience are possible. There is a freshman honors program on campus, as well as 8 national honor societies, including Phi Beta Kappa. Twenty-seven departments have honors programs.

Faculty/Classroom: Seventy percent of faculty are male; 30%, female. Sixty-four percent teach undergraduates and 100% do research. Graduate students teach 5% of introductory courses. The average class size in an introductory lecture is 42; in a laboratory, 22; and in a regular course offering, 34.

Admissions: About 70% of the 1993-94 applicants were accepted. The SAT scores for the 1993-94 freshman class were as follows: Verbal—60% below 500, 30% between 500 and 599, and 10% between 600 and 700; Math—39% below 500, 42% between 500 and 599, 16% between 600 and 700, and 3% above 700. About 45% of the current freshmen were in the top fifth of their class; 77% were in the top two fifths. About 14 freshmen graduated first in their class.

Requirements: A minimum GPA of 2.2 is required. The SAT I is required, with a minimum composite score of 800 (400 M recommended and 350 V required). Applicants must be graduates of an accredited secondary school. The GED is accepted. Applicants should complete 20 high school academic credits, including 4 credits of English, 3 of mathematics (including Algebra I and II and geometry), 2 each for foreign language, history, and science (including a laboratory science), and 1 of social studies. Applicants for the School of the Arts must audition or submit a portfolio. An essay and an interview are recommended. AP and CLEP credits are accepted. Important factors used in the admissions decision are evidence of special talent, advanced placement or honor courses, recommendations by school officials, recommendations by alumni, and leadership record.

Procedure: Freshmen are admitted fall and spring. Early decision applications should be filed by November 1; regular applications, by February 1 for fall entry and December 1 for spring entry, along with an application fee of $20. Notification of early decision is sent December 1; regular decision, April 1. There are early decision, early admissions, and deferred admissions plans. About 43 early decision candidates were accepted for the 1993-94 class. A waiting list is an active part of the admissions procedure, with about 5% of applicants on the list.

Transfer: About 1672 transfer students enrolled in 1993-94. Transfer students with 30 semester hours or more must have a 2.3 GPA or better; those with fewer hours and who are under the age of 22 must submit SAT I scores. An associate degree and interview are advised. A total of 30 credits must be completed at VCU.

Visiting: There are regularly scheduled orientations for prospective students, including an information session with a counselor followed by a student-led tour. Visitors may sit in on classes. To arrange for a visit, contact the Office of Admissions at (800) 841-3638 or (804) 367-1190.

Financial Aid: In 1993-94, 70% of all current freshmen and 65% of continuing students received some form of financial aid. About 65% of all students received need-based aid. The average freshman award was $4274. Of that total, scholarships or need-based grants averaged $2500 ($7500 maximum); loans averaged $3000 ($5500 maximum); and work contracts averaged $2100. Average earnings from campus work for the school year are $1700. The average financial indebtedness of the 1992-93 graduate was $10,000. VCU is a member of CSS. The Singlefile Form financial statement is required. The deadline for financial aid applications is March 15.

International Students: There are currently 460 international students enrolled. The school actively recruits these students. They must take the TOEFL or the college's own test and achieve a minimum score on the TOEFL of 550.

Computers: The mainframe is an IBM 3081K. IBM and Apple PCs are available in academic buildings. All students may access the system. There are no time limits on using the system and no fees.

Graduates: In 1992-93, 2480 bachelor's degrees were awarded. The most popular majors among graduates were psychology (9%), nursing (7%), and mass communications (5%). Within an average freshman class, 17% graduate in 4 years, 36% in 5 years, and 43% in 6 years.

Admissions Contact: Delores T. Taylor, Associate Director of Admissions.

VIRGINIA INTERMONT COLLEGE
B-4

Bristol, VA 24201-4298   (703) 669-6101; (800) 451-1842

Full-time: 190 men, 460 women	**Faculty:** 36; IIB, --$
Part-time: 16 men, 52 women	**Ph.D.s:** 75%
Graduate: none	**Student/Faculty:** 18 to 1
Year: semesters, summer session	**Tuition:** $8270
Application Deadline: open	**Room & Board:** $3980
Freshman Class: n/av	
SAT I or ACT: required	**LESS COMPETITIVE**

Virginia Intermont College, founded in 1884, is a private, coeducational institution affiliated with the Baptist General Association of Virginia. In addition to regional accreditation, the college has baccalaureate program accreditation with CSWE. The library contains 60,000 volumes, 27,000 microform items, and 12,000 audiovisual forms, and subscribes to 300 periodicals. Computerized library sources and services include interlibrary loans and database searching. Special learning facilities include an art gallery, an equestrian center, a ballet center, and a film laboratory. The 16-acre campus is in an urban area 110 miles southwest of Roanoke. Including residence halls, there are 16 buildings on campus.

Student Life: About 63% of undergraduates are from Virginia. Students come from 35 states, 8 foreign countries, and Canada. Ninety-three percent are white. Fifty-nine percent are Protestant; 17% claim no religious affiliation. The average age of freshmen is 18; all undergraduates, 20. Thirty-three percent drop out by the end of their first year; 55% remain to graduate.

Housing: A total of 488 students can be accommodated in college housing. College-sponsored living facilities include single-sex dormitories. On-campus housing is guaranteed for all 4 years. Fifty-nine percent of students commute. Alcohol is not permitted. All students may keep cars on campus.

Activities: There are no fraternities or sororities on campus. There are a number of groups on campus, including art, cheerleading, choir, dance, drama, international, literary magazine, newspaper, photography, political, religious, social service, student government, and yearbook. Popular campus events include Environmental Awareness Week, Cultural Awareness Week, Spring Fling, May Day, and Family Weekend.

Sports: There are 3 intercollegiate sports for men and 2 for women, and 9 intramural sports each for men and women. Athletic and recreation facilities include a gymnasium, a 1200-seat amphitheater, lighted tennis courts, a swimming pool, and a weight room.

Disabled Students: Twenty-five percent of the campus is accessible to disabled students. The following facilities are available: wheelchair ramps, special parking, and special class scheduling.

Services: In addition to many counseling and information services, tutoring is available in every subject. There is remedial math, reading, and writing.

Campus Safety and Security: Campus safety and security measures include self defense education and lighted pathways and sidewalks.

Programs of Study: The college awards the B.A., B.S., B.F.A., and B.S.W. degrees. Associate degrees also are awarded. Bachelor's degrees are awarded in AGRICULTURE (equestrian science), BIOLOGICAL SCIENCE (biology/biological science), BUSINESS (business administration and management, marketing/retailing/merchandising, and office supervision and management), COMMUNICATIONS AND THE ARTS (dance, English, fine arts, music, and photography), EDUCATION (art, early childhood, elementary, middle school, music, and secondary), HEALTH PROFESSIONS (medical laboratory technology, predentistry, and premedicine), SOCIAL SCIENCE (history, paralegal studies, political science/government, prelaw, psychology, religion, and social work). Education is the strongest program academically. Horsemanship has the largest enrollment.

Required: To graduate, students must complete 124 credits with a minimum GPA of 2.0. Specific core courses required are English, world history, computer fundamentals, college mathematics, natural science, performing arts, visual arts, psychology or sociology, economics or political science, philosophy or religion, speech, and physical education.

Special: The school offers cross-registration with King College and internships in paralegal studies, social work, and merchandising. Dual majors, study abroad in Germany or Great Britain, a general studies degree, nondegree study, and pass/fail options are available. There are 3 national honor societies on campus.

Faculty/Classroom: Fifty-two percent of faculty are male; 48%, female. All teach undergraduates. The average class size in an introductory lecture is 26 and in a laboratory, 15.

Requirements: A minimum GPA of 2.0 is required. The SAT I or ACT is required, with a minimum composite score of 650 required on the SAT I, or 15 on the ACT. Applicants must be graduates of an accredited secondary school. The GED is accepted. Applicants should complete 15 academic credits, including 4 credits of English, 2 each of social science and mathematics, 1 of a laboratory science, and 6 electives. An essay is required of students not meeting the normal admissions requirements. An audition or portfolio for music and art students is needed. AP and CLEP credits are accepted.

Procedure: Freshmen are admitted to all sessions. Entrance exams should be taken during orientation. Application deadlines are open. Application fee is $15. Notification is sent on a rolling basis. There are early decision, early admissions, and deferred admissions plans. Five early decision candidates were accepted for a recent class.

Transfer: About 70 transfer students enrolled in a recent year. Applicants for transfer should have a minimum GPA of 2.0. An interview is recommended. A total of 30 credits out of 124 must be completed at the college.

Visiting: There are regularly scheduled orientations for prospective students. There are guides for informal visits and visitors may sit in on classes and stay overnight at the school. To arrange for a visit, contact the Admissions Office at (800) 451-1842.

Financial Aid: In a recent year, 76% of all current freshmen and 62% of continuing students received some form of financial aid. Scholarships or need-based grants averaged $1000 ($5400 maximum); loans averaged $800 ($2625 maximum); and work contracts averaged $1000 ($2000 maximum). The average financial indebtedness of a recent graduate was $12,000. The college is a member of CSS. The FAF, FFS, or SFS and the college's own financial statement are required. The deadline for financial aid applications is August 1.

International Students: There are currently 15 international students enrolled. They must take the TOEFL and achieve a minimum score of 400, or the SAT I or ACT.

Computers: The college provides computer facilities for student use. There are IBM, Apple Macintosh, Epson, and Leading Edge microcomputers available in the computer center in the science hall. All students may access the system 8 A.M. to 10 P.M. There are no fees.

Graduates: In a recent year, 69 bachelor's degrees were awarded. Some 68 companies recruited on campus. In a recent graduating class, 84% of the men and 87% of the women had found employment within 6 months of graduation.

Admissions Contact: Lawton Blandford, Dean of Admissions.

VIRGINIA MILITARY INSTITUTE   D-3

Lexington, VA 24450   (703) 464-7211; (800) 767-4207 (out-of-state)

Full-time: 1191 men	Faculty: 96; IIB, +$
Part-time: none	Ph.D.s: 84%
Graduate: none	Student/Faculty: 12 to 1
Year: semesters, summer session	Tuition: $4940 ($10,780)
Application Deadline: April 1	Room & Board: $3690
Freshman Class: 904 applied, 683 accepted, 349 enrolled	
SAT I: 484/543	ACT: 22 COMPETITIVE

Virginia Military Institute, established in 1839, is a public men's institution offering programs in military science, liberal arts, engineering, and sciences. All students are members of the Corps of Cadets, live in barracks, eat together in the mess hall, and wear uniforms. In addition to regional accreditation, VMI has baccalaureate program accreditation with ABET and ACS. The 2 libraries contain 240,959 volumes, 3156 microform items, and 548 audiovisual forms, and subscribe to 959 periodicals. Computerized library sources and services include the card catalog, interlibrary loans, and database searching. Special learning facilities include a learning resource center, planetarium, radio station, and observatory. The 134-acre campus is in a small town 50 miles north of Roanoke. Including residence halls, there are 63 buildings on campus.

Student Life: About 63% of undergraduates are from Virginia. Students come from 42 states, 12 foreign countries, and Canada. Seventy-one percent are from public schools; 15% from private. Eighty-four percent are white. Thirty percent are Catholic; 26% Episcopal. The average age of freshmen is 18; all undergraduates, 20. Twenty-nine percent drop out by the end of their first year; 64% remain to graduate.

Housing: A total of 1300 students can be accommodated in college housing. College-sponsored living facilities include dormitories. On-campus housing is guaranteed for all 4 years. All students live on campus; of those, 75% remain on campus on weekends. Alcohol is not permitted. Upperclassmen may keep cars on campus.

Activities: There are no fraternities on campus. There are 70 groups on campus, including band, cheerleading, choir, chorus, drama, ethnic, film, international, jazz band, literary magazine, marching band, musical theater, newspaper, pep band, political, professional, religious, social, social service, student government, and yearbook. Popular campus events include Hop Weekend, Ring Figure, Parents Weekend, Homecoming, various sports activities, Virginia Transportation Conference, and Environment Virginia Conference.

Sports: Athletic and recreation facilities include fields for lacrosse, football, baseball, and soccer, basketball, racquetball, and tennis courts, a swimming pool, a rifle range, indoor and outdoor running tracks, and access to a golf course.

Disabled Students: The entire campus is accessible to disabled students. The following facilities are available: wheelchair ramps, elevators, special parking, and specially equipped rest rooms.

Services: In addition to many counseling and information services, tutoring is available in some subjects, including French, Spanish, German, chemistry, mathematics, and physics.

Campus Safety and Security: Campus safety and security measures include 24-hour foot and vehicle patrol, informal discussions, emergency telephones, and lighted pathways and sidewalks. In addition, there is a 24-hour student guard team.

Programs of Study: VMI awards the B.A. and B.S. degrees. Bachelor's degrees are awarded in BIOLOGICAL SCIENCE (biology/biological science), BUSINESS (business economics), COMMUNICATIONS AND THE ARTS (English and modern language), COMPUTER AND PHYSICAL SCIENCE (chemistry, computer science, mathematics, and physics), ENGINEERING AND ENVIRONMENTAL DESIGN (civil engineering, electrical/electronics engineering, and mechanical engineering), SOCIAL SCIENCE (economics, history, and international studies). Engineering (civil, electrical, and mechanical) and sciences are the strongest academically. History, business/economics, and civil engineering have the largest enrollments.

Required: To graduate, students must complete 136 to 144 semester hours, with a GPA of 2.0. Students must take chemistry, English, history, mathematics, physical education, ROTC, and computer classes. In addition, all cadets must take swimming, boxing, and wrestling.

Special: Cross-registration, study abroad in 5 countries, and work-study programs are available. VMI offers dual majors in any combination and B.A.-B.S. degrees in liberal arts, physical sciences, and engineering. There is a freshman honors program on campus, as well as 9 national honor societies. Three departments have honors programs.

Faculty/Classroom: Ninety-three percent of faculty are male; 7%, female. All teach undergraduates and 60% do research. The average class size in an introductory lecture is 19; in a laboratory, 15; and in a regular course offering, 16.

Admissions: About 76% of the 1993–94 applicants were accepted. About 40% of the current freshmen were in the top fifth of their class; 77% were in the top two fifths.

Requirements: VMI requires applicants to be in the upper 50% of their class. A minimum GPA of 2.8 is required. The SAT I or ACT is required. In addition, applicants must be graduates of an accredited secondary school. Applicants should complete 19 to 20 high school academic units, including 4 years of English and mathematics, 3 of science, history, and foreign language, and 2 of social studies. An essay is required and an interview is recommended. AP credits are accepted. Important factors used in the admissions decision are recommendations by school officials, recommendations by alumni, personality, intangible qualities, parents or siblings attending the school, and leadership record.

Procedure: Freshmen are admitted in the fall. Early decision applications should be filed by November 15; regular applications, by April 1 for fall entry, along with an application fee of $25. Notification of early decision is sent December 15; regular decision, on a rolling basis. There is an early decision plan. About 79 early decision candidates were accepted for the 1993-94 class.

Transfer: About 48 transfer students enrolled in 1993-94. Applicants for transfer must have a minimum GPA of 2.0 and a satisfactory high school record. Either the SAT I or ACT is required.

Visiting: There are regularly scheduled orientations for prospective students, consisting of tours, conferences with academic instructors and ROTC instructors, and overnight stays. There are guides for informal visits and visitors may sit in on classes. To arrange for a visit, contact Admissions at (703) 464-7211 or (800) 767-4207.

Financial Aid: In 1993-94, 57% of all current freshmen and 63% of continuing students received some form of financial aid. About 40% of freshmen and 37% of continuing students received need-based aid. The average freshman award was $4500. Of that total, scholarships or need-based grants averaged $2000 ($14,470 maximum); and loans averaged $2500 ($5625 maximum). Eighteen percent of undergraduate students work part-time. Freshman are not permitted to work. Average earnings from campus work for the school year are $964. The average financial indebtedness of the 1992-93 graduate was $10,500. VMI is a member of CSS. The FAF, FFS or SFS, the college's own financial statement and tax returns are required. The deadline for financial aid applications is March 1.

International Students: There are currently 36 international students enrolled. They must take the TOEFL and achieve a minimum score of 500. The student must also take the SAT I or the ACT and receive a 700 on the SAT I or a 17 on the ACT.

Computers: The college provides computer facilities for student use. The mainframe is a Unisys A6. The Unisys mainframe is for administrative use only. Students can use the DEC VAX 4300 available in the library. There are 110 computers in laboratories, 74 of which are networked and can access the local area network and the VAX. All students may access the system. There are no time limits on using the system and no fees.

Graduates: In 1992-93, 270 bachelor's degrees were awarded. The most popular majors among graduates were history (28%), economics (15%), and civil engineering (13%). Within an average freshman class, 54% graduate in 4 years, 62% in 5 years, and 64% in 6 years. Some 32 companies recruited on campus. In the 1992 graduating class, 7% of the students were enrolled in graduate school within 6 months of graduation; 85% found employment.

Admissions Contact: LTC Daniel A. Troppoli, Director of Admissions.

VIRGINIA POLYTECHNIC INSTITUTE AND STATE UNIVERSITY

Blacksburg, VA 24061-0202   C-3
                                                  (703) 231-6267

Full-time: 10,965 men, 7546 women	**Faculty:** 1444; I, -$
Part-time: 336 men, 268 women	**Ph.D.s:** 87%
Graduate: 2814 men, 1619 women	**Student/Faculty:** 13 to 1
Year: semesters, summer session	**Tuition:** $3812 ($9680)
Application Deadline: February 1	**Room & Board:** $3016
Freshman Class: 15,712 applied, 11,719 accepted, 4277 enrolled	
SAT I or ACT: required	**COMPETITIVE**

Virginia Polytechnic Institute and State University, founded in 1872, is a public, land-grant, coeducational institution. There are 7 undergraduate and 2 graduate schools. In addition to regional accreditation, Virginia Tech has baccalaureate program accreditation with AACSB, ABET, ADA, AHEA, ASLA, FIDER, and SAF. The 5 libraries contain 1.7 million volumes, 5.2 million microform items, and 11,700 audiovisual forms, and subscribe to 13,000 periodicals. Computerized library sources and services include the card catalog, interlibrary loans, and database searching. Special learning facilities include a learning resource center, an art gallery, a natural history museum, a radio station, a TV station, an airport, wind tunnels, agricultural stations, CAD/CAM labs, radio/visual observatories, and a satellite uplink station. The 2600-acre campus is in a rural area 40 miles southwest of Roanoke. Including residence halls, there are 100 buildings on campus.

Student Life: About 77% of undergraduates are from Virginia. Students come from 50 states, 58 foreign countries, and Canada. Eighty-seven percent are white. The average age of freshmen is 18; all undergraduates, 20. Twelve percent drop out by the end of their first year; 67% remain to graduate.

Housing: A total of 8500 students can be accommodated in college housing. College-sponsored living facilities include single-sex and coed dormitories, fraternity houses, and sorority houses. In addition, there are language houses and special interest houses. On-campus housing is guaranteed for the freshman year only and is available on a lottery system for upperclassmen. Fifty-six percent of students commute. All students may keep cars on campus.

Activities: About 15% of men belong to 2 local and 31 national fraternities; about 20% of women belong to 16 national sororities. There are about 400 groups on campus, including art, band, cheerleading, chess, choir, chorale, chorus, computers, dance, drama, drill team, drum and bugle corps, ethnic, film, gay, honors, international, jazz band, literary magazine, marching band, musical theater, newspaper, orchestra, pep band, photography, political, professional, radio and TV, religious, social, social service, student government, symphony, and yearbook. Popular campus events include Homecoming, Parents Weekend, Spring Fling, Quad Jams, Broadway series, and a film series.

Sports: There are 11 intercollegiate sports for men and 7 for women, and 25 intramural sports for men and 24 for women. Athletic and recreation facilities include a football stadium; a basketball coliseum; a field house; an indoor tennis pavilion; an 18-hole golf course; soccer and baseball fields; a swimming pool; a diving well; tennis, basketball, volleyball, racquetball, handball and squash courts; a gymnastics room; a weight-lifting room; lighted multipurpose recreation fields; and a pond for ice skating.

Disabled Students: Sixty percent of the campus is accessible to disabled students. The following facilities are available: wheelchair ramps, elevators, special parking, specially equipped rest rooms, special class scheduling, lowered drinking fountains and telephones, and a special services library room for the visually impaired.

Services: In addition to many counseling and information services, tutoring is available in most subjects. There is a reader service for the blind and remedial reading.

Campus Safety and Security: Campus safety and security measures include 24-hour foot and vehicle patrol, self-defense education, escort service, shuttle buses, informal discussions, pamphlets, posters, films, and lighted pathways and sidewalks.

Programs of Study: Virginia Tech awards the B.A., B.S., B.Arch., B.F.A., B.Land.Arch., B.S.Bus., B.S.E., and B.S.Ed. degrees. Associate, master's, and doctoral degrees also are awarded. Bachelor's degrees are awarded in AGRICULTURE (agricultural economics, agriculture, animal science, dairy science, forestry and related sciences, horticulture, poultry science, and soil science), BIOLOGICAL SCIENCE (biochemistry and biology/biological science), BUSINESS (accounting, banking and finance, business economics, hotel/motel and restaurant management, management science, and marketing/retailing/merchandising), COMMUNICATIONS AND THE ARTS (communications, dramatic arts, dramatic arts, English, fine arts, French, German, music, and Spanish), COMPUTER AND PHYSICAL SCIENCE (chemistry, computer science, geology, geophysics and seismology, mathematics, physics, and statistics), EDUCATION (agricultural, business, early childhood, health, home economics, marketing and distribution, physical, technical, and vocational), ENGINEERING AND ENVIRONMENTAL DESIGN (agricultural engineering, architecture, chemical engineering, civil engineering, computer engineering, construction management, electrical/electronics engineering, environmental science, interior design, landscape architecture/design, materials engineering, mechanical engineering, mining and mineral engineering, and ocean engineering), HEALTH PROFESSIONS (premedicine and preveterinary science), SOCIAL SCIENCE (child care/child and family studies, economics, food science, geography, history, international studies, liberal arts/general studies, philosophy, political science/government, prelaw, psychology, public administration, sociology, textiles and clothing, and urban studies). Engineering, architecture, business, science, computer science, and theater arts are the strongest program academically. Biology, accounting, architecture, electrical engineering, and mechanical engineering have the largest enrollments.

Required: To graduate, students must complete between 126 and 156 credit hours (depending on the major), with a minimum GPA of 2.0. There is a required core curriculum that includes 8 hours of science and 6 hours each of humanities, social science, mathematics, and writing and discourse. Students must also meet a foreign language requirement.

Special: Students may cross-register with Miami University in Ohio, Oxford Polytechnic Institute, California Polytechnic Institute, and Florida A&M. Study abroad, a Washington semester, and a wide range of work-study programs are available, including co-ops in 48 majors. There are honors options for most majors, B.A.-B.S. degrees, dual and

student-designed majors, credit for independent study or research, nondegree study, and pass/fail options. The Corps of Cadets, a militarily structured organization, is open to men and women. There is a freshman honors program on campus, as well as 13 national honor societies, including Phi Beta Kappa. Fifty-four departments have honors programs.

Faculty/Classroom: Eighty percent of faculty are male; 20%, female. Graduate students teach 12% of introductory courses. The average class size in an introductory lecture is 46 and in a laboratory, 30.

Admissions: About 75% of the 1993–94 applicants were accepted. The SAT scores for the 1993–94 freshman class were as follows: Verbal—51% below 500, 37% between 500 and 599, 11% between 600 and 700, and 1% above 700; Math—17% below 500, 40% between 500 and 599, 34% between 600 and 700, and 9% above 700. About 57% of the current freshmen were in the top fifth of their class.

Requirements: A minimum GPA of 2.0 is required. The SAT I or ACT is required. Students must also take SAT II: Subject tests in writing and mathematics. Applicants must be graduates of an accredited secondary school; the GED is accepted. Applicants should complete 18 high school academic credits, including 4 years of English, 3 of mathematics, including algebra II and geometry, 2 of laboratory science, to be chosen from biology, chemistry, or physics, and 1 each of history and social studies. An additional 3 years from college preparatory courses and 4 years from any credit course offerings are required. There is also a language study requirement. A portfolio and audition are required for art and music students. AP credits are accepted. Important factors used in the admissions decision are advanced placement or honor courses, recommendations by school officials, personality, intangible qualities, parents or siblings attending the school, and leadership record.

Procedure: Freshmen are admitted to all sessions. Entrance exams should be taken by January 1 of the senior year. Early decision applications should be filed by November 1; regular applications, by February 1 for fall entry, October 1 for spring entry, and April 22 for summer entry, along with an application fee of $10 for residents and $20 for nonresidents. Notification of early decision is sent December 15; regular decision, on a rolling basis. There are early decision, early admissions, and deferred admissions plans. About 800 early decision candidates were accepted for a recent class. A waiting list is an active part of the admissions procedure, with about 4% of applicants on the list.

Transfer: About 570 transfer students enrolled in a recent year. Applicants for transfer must have a minimum GPA of 2.0. They must specify a major. A total of 30 credits out of 126 to 156 must be completed at Virginia Tech.

Visiting: There are regularly scheduled orientations for prospective students. A Fall Open House Series consists of half-day on-campus programs that include presentations, tours, and question and answer sessions. There are guides for informal visits and visitors may sit in on classes. To arrange for a visit, contact the Office of Undergraduate Admissions at (703) 231–6267; Cadet candidates: Office of the Commandant at (703) 231–6858.

Financial Aid: In a recent year, 55% of all current freshmen and 45% of continuing students received some form of financial aid. About 45% of freshmen and 35% of continuing students received need-based aid. The average freshman award was $5700. Of that total, scholarships or need-based grants averaged $2634; loans averaged $2125 ($3500 maximum); and work contracts averaged $900 ($1200 maximum). Thirty percent of undergraduate students work part-time. Average earnings from campus work for the school year are $1500. The average financial indebtedness of a recent graduate was $8500. Virginia Tech is a member of CSS. The FAF is required. The deadline for financial aid applications is March 15.

International Students: There are currently 1400 international students enrolled. The school actively recruits these students. They must take the TOEFL and achieve a minimum score of 550. The student must also take the SAT I and SAT II: Subject tests in writing, and mathematics I or II.

Computers: Virginia Tech provides computer facilities for student use. The mainframes are an IBM-3090, an IBM 3084, and a DEC VAX 8800. Undergraduates receive guidance on using the mainframe or PCs from their professors. They may access the mainframe or use PCs in any one of many computer laboratories on campus, or from their dormitory rooms if they have their own PCs. Dormitory rooms are wired for data, voice, and video transmission. All students may access the system any time. A charge back system controls usage. There are no fees. It is recommended that students in engineering, computer science, and statistics provide their own computers. The College of Business requires access, not ownership.

Graduates: In a recent year, 3781 bachelor's degrees were awarded. The most popular majors among graduates were electrical engineering (6%), marketing (5%), and mechanical engineering (5%). Within an average freshman class, 67% graduate in 5 years. Some 600 companies recruited on campus in a recent year.

Admissions Contact: Office of Undergraduate Admissions.

VIRGINIA STATE UNIVERSITY

E-3

Petersburg, VA 23803 (804) 524–5902

Full-time: 1260 men, 1800 women — Faculty: IIA, --$
Part-time: 100 men, 140 women — Ph.D.s: 57%
Graduate: 85 men, 180 women — Student/Faculty: 16 to 1
Year: semesters, summer session — Tuition: $2913 ($6315)
Application Deadline: May 1 — Room & Board: $4127
Freshman Class: n/av
SAT I or ACT: required — **LESS COMPETITIVE**

Virginia State University, established in 1882, is a public land-grant institution whose mission is to provide higher education for black students. There are 6 undergraduate schools and one graduate school. In addition to regional accreditation, VSU has baccalaureate program accreditation with ABET, ADA, CSWE, NASM, and NCATE. The library contains 232,357 volumes, 476,690 microform items, and 54,251 audiovisual forms, and subscribes to 1220 periodicals. Computerized library sources and services include the card catalog, interlibrary loans, and database searching. Special learning facilities include an art gallery and radio station. The 652-acre campus is in a suburban area 25 miles south of Richmond. Including residence halls, there are 52 buildings on campus.

Student Life: About 57% of undergraduates are from Virginia. Students come from 40 states and 5 foreign countries. Ninety-six percent are from public schools; 4% from private. Ninety-three percent are African American. The average age of freshmen is 18; all undergraduates, 21. Forty percent drop out by the end of their first year; 18% remain to graduate.

Housing: A total of 2050 students can be accommodated in college housing. College-sponsored living facilities include single-sex dormitories. In addition, there are honors houses. On-campus housing is available on a first-come, first-served basis. Priority is given to out-of-town students. Fifty-seven percent of students live on campus; of those, 55% remain on campus on weekends. Alcohol is not permitted. All students may keep cars on campus.

Activities: About 28% of men belong to 4 national fraternities; about 31% of women belong to 4 national sororities. There are 44 groups on campus, including band, cheerleading, chess, choir, chorus, computers, dance, drama, drill team, ethnic, honors, international, marching band, musical theater, newspaper, orchestra, photography, political, professional, radio and TV, religious, student government, and yearbook. Popular campus events include High School Day and VSU Day.

Sports: There are 6 intercollegiate sports for men and 5 for women, and 5 intramural sports for men and 6 for women. Athletic and recreation facilities include a gymnasium, an Olympic-size pool, a dance studio, tennis courts, and a track field.

Disabled Students: Twenty-five percent of the campus is accessible to disabled students. The following facilities are available: wheelchair ramps, elevators, special parking, specially equipped rest rooms, special class scheduling, lowered drinking fountains, and lowered telephones.

Services: In addition to many counseling and information services, tutoring is available in most subjects. In addition, there is a reader service for the blind, and remedial math, reading, and writing.

Programs of Study: VSU awards the B.A., B.S., B.F.A., B.I.S., and B.Mus. degrees. Master's degrees are also awarded. Bachelor's degrees are awarded in AGRICULTURE (agricultural business management and agriculture), BIOLOGICAL SCIENCE (biology/biological science), BUSINESS (accounting, business administration and management, business economics, hotel/motel and restaurant management, and marketing management), COMMUNICATIONS AND THE ARTS (English, languages, and music), COMPUTER AND PHYSICAL SCIENCE (chemistry, earth science, geology, mathematics, and physics), EDUCATION (art, elementary, home economics, industrial arts, music, physical, and special), ENGINEERING AND ENVIRONMENTAL DESIGN (engineering technology), SOCIAL SCIENCE (history, international relations, political science/government, psychology, public administration, social work, and sociology). Business administration, accounting, business information systems, psychology, and public administration have the largest enrollments.

Required: To graduate, students must have a minimum GPA of 2.0 overall and 2.2 in the major. They must earn at least 120 credits, with 60 in the major. Requirements include those in physical education, freshman writing, mathematics, biology, social or physical science, history, and psychology. Freshman orientation must also be completed.

Special: VSU offers dual majors, a general studies degree, a 3–2 engineering degree program, nondegree study, and a pass/fail grading option. There is a freshman honors program on campus, as well as 10 national honor societies, including Phi Beta Kappa. Seven departments have honors programs.

Faculty/Classroom: Sixty-seven percent of faculty are male; 33%, female. Graduate students teach 2% of introductory courses.

Admissions: There was 1 National Merit semifinalist. One freshman graduated first in his class.

Requirements: The SAT I or ACT is required. Applicants must graduate from an accredited secondary school, having earned 16 academic credits and 12 Carnegie units, or have a GED. Students must take 4 years of English, 2 each of a foreign language, mathematics, and science, and 1 each of history and social studies. Essays, 2 letters of recommendation, evidence of physical condition, interviews, and, if appropriate, auditions are required. AP and CLEP credits are accepted. Important factors used in the admissions decision are advanced placement or honor courses, recommendations by school officials, leadership record, recommendations by alumni, and extracurricular activities record.

Procedure: Freshmen are admitted fall and spring. Applications should be filed by May 1 for fall entry and October 1 for spring entry, along with an application fee of $10. Notification is sent on a rolling basis. There is a deferred admissions plan.

Transfer: About 170 transfer students enrolled in a recent year. Transfer applicants must have a minimum GPA of 2.0. Those transferring fewer than 25 semester hours must meet freshman standards. A total of 30 credits out of 120 must be completed at VSU.

Visiting: There are guides for informal visits and visitors may sit in on classes. To arrange for a visit, contact Admissions at (804) 524–5902.

Financial Aid: In a recent year, 83% of all current freshmen and 74% of continuing students received some form of financial aid. Scholarships or need-based grants averaged $1500 ($3100 maximum); loans averaged $2500 ($2625 maximum); and work contracts averaged $1600 ($1980 maximum). The average financial indebtedness of the recent graduate was $5500. VSU is a member of CSS. The FAF and the college's own financial statement is required. The deadline for financial aid applications is March 31.

International Students: There are currently 19 international students enrolled. They must take the TOEFL and achieve a minimum score of 500. The student must also take the SAT I.

Computers: The college provides computer facilities for student use. The mainframe is an IBM 4361. There are also 150 IBM-compatible PCs available in computer laboratories and in various units on campus. All students may access the system 8 A.M. to 10 P.M. Monday through Friday and 8 A.M. to 4 P.M. Saturdays. There are no fees.

Graduates: In a recent year, 369 bachelor's degrees were awarded. Some 75 companies recruited on campus that year.

Admissions Contact: Director of Admissions.

VIRGINIA UNION UNIVERSITY
Richmond, VA 23220
C-3
(804) 257–5600

Full-time: 563 men, 735 women	Faculty: 79; IIB, --$
Part-time: 22 men, 45 women	Ph.Ds: n/av
Graduate: 144 men, 40 women	Student/Faculty: 16 to 1
Year: semesters, summer session	Tuition: $7061
Application Deadline: open	Room & Board: $3494
Freshman Class: 1752 applied, 1501 accepted, 439 enrolled	
SAT I Verbal/Math: 317/343	LESS COMPETITIVE

Virginia Union University, established in 1865 and affiliated with the Baptist Church, is a private coeducational institution offering undergraduate programs in education and psychology, business, humanities, natural science and mathematics, and social sciences. In addition to regional accreditation, VUU has baccalaureate program accreditation with AACSB and CSWE. The library contains 131,000 volumes and 11,000 microform items, and subscribes to 600 periodicals. Computerized library sources and services include database searching. The 72-acre campus is in an urban area located in central Richmond. Including residence halls, there are 18 buildings on campus.

Student Life: About 55% of undergraduates are from Virginia. Eighty-five percent are from public schools. Ninety-eight percent are African American. The average age of freshmen is 18. Forty percent drop out by the end of their first year; 55% remain to graduate.

Housing: College-sponsored living facilities include single-sex dormitories. Fifty percent of students live on campus. All students may keep cars on campus.

Activities: There are 4 national fraternities and 4 national sororities. There are 45 groups on campus, including drama, international, newspaper, religious, student government, and yearbook. Popular campus events include films, lectures, concerts, social events, Homecoming Weekend, and Founders Day.

Sports: There are 7 intercollegiate sports for men and 6 for women, and 3 intramural sports for men and 2 for women. Athletic and recreation facilities include a gymnasium-auditorium and a 10,000-seat stadium.

Services: In addition to many counseling and information services, tutoring is available in every subject. There is also remedial math, reading, and writing.

Campus Safety and Security: There is a safety and security service on campus.

Programs of Study: VUU awards the B.A. and B.S. degrees. Master's and doctoral degrees also are awarded. Bachelor's degrees are awarded in BIOLOGICAL SCIENCE (biology/biological science), BUSINESS (accounting, banking and finance, and business administration and management), COMMUNICATIONS AND THE ARTS (English, French, journalism, and music), COMPUTER AND PHYSICAL SCIENCE (chemistry and mathematics), EDUCATION (business, early childhood, elementary, music, recreation, secondary, and special), SOCIAL SCIENCE (history, philosophy, political science/government, psychology, religion, social work, and sociology).

Required: To graduate, all students must complete at least 124 credit hours with a GPA of at least 2.0. Courses in religion, English, mathematics, science, social science, a foreign language, and physical education are required. There are also chapel and VUU events attendance requirements. All students must take the English Essay Examination, usually by the end of the junior year.

Special: The university offers internships, co-op programs, work-study programs, a general studies degree, a joint law degree with St. John's University School of Law in New York, a dual degree in engineering with the University of Michigan and Iowa and Howard universities, and exchange programs. There are 2 national honor societies on campus.

Admissions: About 86% of the 1993–94 applicants were accepted. About 8% of the current freshmen were in the top fifth of their class; 13% were in the top two fifths.

Requirements: VUU requires applicants to be in the upper 50% of their class. The SAT I or ACT is required. In addition, graduation from an accredited secondary school is required; the GED is accepted. Sixteen academic units are required, including 4 of English, 3 each of mathematics and academic electives, and 2 each of foreign language, social science, and natural science. Special consideration is given to disadvantaged students. Children of alumni are given some preference. AP and CLEP credits are accepted.

Procedure: Freshmen are admitted fall and spring. Entrance exams should be taken between March of the junior year and March of the senior year. Application deadlines are open. Application fee is $15. Notification is sent on a rolling basis. There are early admissions and deferred admissions plans.

Transfer: Transfer students must be in good standing at their previous institutions and must submit all college transcripts. A total of 30 credits out of 124 must be completed at VUU.

Financial Aid: In an earlier year, 96% of continuing students received some form of financial aid. Scholarships or need-based grants averaged $1000; loans averaged $2300; and work contracts averaged $1100. VUU is a member of CSS. The FAF is required. The deadline for financial aid applications is June 1.

International Students: They must take the TOEFL and achieve a minimum score of 500.

Computers: The mainframe is a DEC PDP 11. Microcomputers also are available, and there is an Apple computer laboratory for the teacher training program. All students may access the system. It may be used whenever the terminal room is open. There are no time limits on using the system.

Admissions Contact: Gil Powell, Director of Admissions.

VIRGINIA WESLEYAN COLLEGE
Norfolk/Virginia Beach, VA 23502
F-4
(804) 455–3208

Full-time: 456 men, 684 women	Faculty: 70; IIB, av$
Part-time: 143 men, 264 women	Ph.Ds: 85%
Graduate: none	Student/Faculty: 16 to 1
Year: 4–1–4, summer session	Tuition: $10,150
Application Deadline: March 1	Room & Board: $4800
Freshman Class: 1463 applied, 880 accepted, 288 enrolled	
SAT I: required	VERY COMPETITIVE

Virginia Wesleyan College, established in 1961, is a private coeducational institution affiliated with the United Methodist Church offering undergraduate degrees in the humanities, the social sciences, the natural sciences, and mathematics. In addition to regional accreditation, Virginia Wesleyan has baccalaureate program accreditation with NRPA. The library contains 103,369 volumes, 12,553 microform items, and 2879 audiovisual forms, and subscribes to 569 periodicals. Computerized library sources and services include interlibrary loans and database searching. Special learning facilities include a learning resource center, a radio station, and a greenhouse. The 300-acre campus is in an urban area 10 miles west of Virginia Beach and 8 miles east of downtown Norfolk. Including residence halls, there are 26 buildings on campus.

Student Life: About 65% of undergraduates are from Virginia. Students come from 34 states and 23 foreign countries. Sixty percent are from public schools; 40% from private. Eighty-seven percent are white. Fifty-four percent are Protestant; 27% Catholic; 12% claim no religious affiliation. The average age of freshmen is 18; all undergraduates, 21. Fifteen percent drop out by the end of their first year; 62% remain to graduate.

Housing: A total of 600 students can be accommodated in college housing. College-sponsored living facilities include coed dormitories and on-campus apartments. In addition there are international studies, fraternity, sorority, honors, speical interest, and religious life halls. On-campus housing is guaranteed for all 4 years. Priority is given to out-of-town students. Fifty-five percent of students live on campus; of those, 90% remain on campus on weekends. All students may keep cars on campus.

Activities: About 15% of men belong to 3 national fraternities; about 10% of women belong to 3 national sororities. There are 56 groups on campus, including art, cheerleading, choir, chorus, computers, dance, drama, ethnic, honors, international, literary magazine, musical theater, newspaper, political, professional, radio and TV, religious, social, social service, student government, and yearbook. Popular campus events include Casino Night, Toga Party, Air Band, Spring Formal, Spring Fling, Seafood Party in the Dell, and Homecoming Dance.

Sports: There are 6 intercollegiate sports for men and 5 for women, and 15 intramural sports for men and 15 for women. Athletic and recreation facilities include a gymnasium, a health fitness center, baseball, softball, lacrosse, field hockey, and soccer fields, and 6 tennis courts.

Disabled Students: Ninety percent of the campus is accessible to disabled students. The following facilities are available: wheelchair ramps, elevators, special parking, and specially equipped rest rooms.

Services: In addition to many counseling and information services, tutoring is available in every subject. There is also remedial math, reading, and writing.

Campus Safety and Security: Campus safety and security measures include a 24-hour foot and vehicle patrol, self defense education, an escort service, and shuttle buses. In addition, there are informal discussions, pamphlets, posters, films, emergency telephones, and lighted pathways and sidewalks.

Programs of Study: Virginia Wesleyan awards the B.A. degree. Bachelor's degrees are awarded in BIOLOGICAL SCIENCE (biochemistry and biology/biological science), BUSINESS (accounting, business administration and management, business economics, international business management, marketing/retailing/merchandising, and personnel management), COMMUNICATIONS AND THE ARTS (broadcasting, communications, dramatic arts, English, fine arts, French, journalism, music, and Spanish), COMPUTER AND PHYSICAL SCIENCE (chemistry, computer science, mathematics, and physics), EDUCATION (art, elementary, foreign languages, middle school, music, science, and secondary), HEALTH PROFESSIONS (predentistry, premedicine, and recreation therapy), SOCIAL SCIENCE (community services, economics, history, international relations, parks and recreation management, philosophy, political science/government, prelaw, psychology, religion, social science, social work, sociology, and western civilization/culture). Natural sciences, political science, and English are the strongest programs academically. Communication, education, and business have the largest enrollments.

Required: To graduate, students must complete a general studies requirement, which includes course work in Empirical Knowledge, Aesthetic Understanding and Activity, Ethical Values, World Views, and Faith Perspectives, the Historical Perspective, Communications, and Institutional and Cultural Systems. Students must earn 120 credits, including at least 40 in the major, with a minimum 2.0 GPA. Students must complete 3 credits designated to fulfill a Senior Integrative Experience requirement. They must also complete 2 January term projects, each involving an intensive, 2-week course of study in a single subject. Students must be enrolled in at least 1 writing course each semester and must demonstrate a proficiency in 1 foreign language. A freshman seminar is also required.

Special: Students may cross-register with Old Dominion University, the College of William and Mary, or Norfolk State University through the Virginia Tidewater Consortium. Internships are available and are usually completed during the senior year. The college offers study-abroad programs in 5 countries. Dual majors, individualized majors, and interdisciplinary majors, such as social ecology, are available. Work-study programs with Virginia Wesleyan are offered. Credit may be granted for life, military, and work experience. Nondegree study and a pass/fail grading option are also available. There is a freshman honors program on campus, as well as 8 national honor societies.

Faculty/Classroom: Sixty percent of faculty are male; 40%, female. Ninety-six percent teach undergraduates. The average class size in an introductory lecture is 25; in a laboratory, 10; and in a regular course offering, 15.

Admissions: About 60% of the 1993–94 applicants were accepted. The SAT scores for the 1993–94 freshman class were as follows: Verbal—34% below 500, 35% between 500 and 599, 26% between 600 and 700, and 5% above 700; Math—27% below 500, 37% between 500 and 599, 31% between 600 and 700, and 5% above 700. About 35% of the current freshmen were in the top fifth of their class; 60% were in the top two fifths. There was 1 National Merit finalist and 12 semifinalists. About 8 freshmen graduated first in their class.

Requirements: The SAT I is required. In addition, applicants must graduate from an accredited secondary school or have a GED. The college recommends 14 academic credits. Students should complete 4 years of English, 3 of mathematics and science, and 2 each of history, social studies, and a foreign language. Essays are required and interviews are recommended. AP and CLEP credits are accepted. Important factors used in the admissions decision are advanced placement or honor courses, leadership record, parents or siblings attending the school, evidence of special talent, and personality, intangible qualities.

Procedure: Freshmen are admitted fall and spring. Entrance exams should be taken in the spring of the junior year and the fall of the senior year. Early decision applications should be filed by December 1; regular applications, by March 1 for fall entry and December 1 for spring entry, along with an application fee of $25. Notification of early decision is sent December 15; regular decision, April 1. There are early decision, early admissions, and deferred admissions plans. About 33 early decision candidates were accepted for the 1993–94 class. A waiting list is an active part of the admissions procedure.

Transfer: About 140 transfer students enrolled in 1993–94. Transfer applicants must have a minimum GPA of 2.5 in courses to be transferred, and they must have earned at least 12 credits. A total of 30 credits out of 120 must be completed at Virginia Wesleyan.

Visiting: There are regularly scheduled orientations for prospective students, consisting of 2 Open House Days on Saturdays for prospective students to meet faculty and current students and to tour the campus. There are guides for informal visits and visitors may sit in on classes. To arrange for a visit, contact the Admission Office at (804) 455-3208.

Financial Aid: In 1993–94, 79% of all students received some form of financial aid. About 70% of all students received need-based aid. The average freshman award was $7200. Of that total, scholarships or need-based grants averaged $3500 ($10,150 maximum); loans averaged $2600 ($3600 maximum); and work contracts averaged $1000 ($1500 maximum). Ten percent of undergraduate students work part-time. Average earnings from campus work for the school year are $1300. The average financial indebtedness of the 1992–93 graduate was $11,000. Virginia Wesleyan is a member of CSS. The FAF and FAFSA are required. The deadline for financial aid applications is March 1.

International Students: There are currently 46 international students enrolled. They must take the TOEFL and achieve a minimum score of 550.

Computers: The college provides computer facilities for student use. The mainframe is a Prime 750. There are also 35 terminals with WordPerfect in the computer laboratory in the library and 20 terminals connected to the mainframe in the science building. All students may access the system. There are no time limits on using the system and no fees.

Graduates: In a recent year, 266 bachelor's degrees were awarded. The most popular majors among graduates were business (10%), communications (8%), and education (5%). Within an average freshman class, 3% graduate in 3 years, 58% in 4 years, and 5% in 5 years. Some 65 companies recruited on campus in 1992–93. In a recent graduating class, 15% of the men and 20% of the women were enrolled in graduate school within 6 months of graduation; 78% of the men and 75% of the women had found employment.

Admissions Contact: Admission Officer.

WASHINGTON AND LEE UNIVERSITY   D-3
Lexington, VA 24450   (703) 463-8710

Full-time: 947 men, 636 women	Faculty: 141; IIB, + +$
Part-time: 1 man, 3 women	Ph.D.s: 93%
Graduate: 215 men, 143 women	Student/Faculty: 11 to 1
Year: 12–12–6	Tuition: $13,235
Application Deadline: February 15	Room & Board: $4500
Freshman Class: 3318 applied, 1092 accepted, 441 enrolled	
SAT I: 600/650	ACT: 29 MOST COMPETITIVE

Washington and Lee University, established in 1749, is a private institution offering undergraduate liberal arts degrees. There are 2 undergraduate schools and one graduate school. In addition to regional accreditation, Washington and Lee has baccalaureate program accreditation with AACSB and ACEJMC. The 2 libraries contain 415,480 volumes, 117,261 microform items, and 4306 audiovisual forms, and subscribe to 1578 periodicals. Computerized library sources and services include the card catalog, interlibrary loans, and database searching. Special learning facilities include an art gallery, a radio station, a TV station, an observatory, and a performing arts center. The 322-acre campus is in a small town 50 miles northeast of Roanoke. Including residence halls, there are 38 buildings on campus.

Student Life: About 86% of undergraduates are from out-of-state, mostly the South. Students come from 48 states, 21 foreign countries, and Canada. Sixty-eight percent are from public schools; 32% from

private. Ninety-four percent are white. Fifty-three percent are Protestant; 24% claim no religious affiliation; 21% Catholic. The average age of freshmen is 18; all undergraduates, 20. Seven percent drop out by the end of their first year; 91% remain to graduate.

Housing: A total of 880 students can be accommodated in college housing. College-sponsored living facilities include coed dormitories, on-campus apartments, and fraternity houses. In addition there are special interest houses. On-campus housing is guaranteed for all 4 years. Fifty-eight percent of students live on campus; of those, 95% remain on campus on weekends. All students may keep cars on campus.

Activities: About 80% of men belong to 16 national fraternities; about 65% of women belong to 4 national sororities. There are 30 groups on campus, including art, band, choir, chorale, chorus, dance, drama, ethnic, film, gay, honors, international, jazz band, literary magazine, musical theater, newspaper, orchestra, pep band, photography, political, radio and TV, religious, social, social service, student government, and yearbook. Popular campus events include the Presidential Mock Convention and a fancy-dress ball.

Sports: There are 13 intercollegiate sports for men and 9 for women, and 18 intramural sports for men and 11 for women. Athletic and recreation facilities include a gymnasium, a 2400-seat arena, a 7000-seat stadium, a pool with a 500-seat gallery; weight, training, and exercise rooms; handball, racquetball, squash, and tennis courts; an outdoor track, and baseball and practice fields.

Disabled Students: Eighty percent of the campus is accessible to disabled students. The following facilities are available: wheelchair ramps, elevators, special parking, and specially equipped rest rooms.

Services: In addition to many counseling and information services, tutoring is available in every subject.

Campus Safety and Security: Campus safety and security measures include a 24-hour foot and vehicle patrol, an escort service, shuttle buses, and informal discussions. In addition, there are pamphlets, posters, films, emergency telephones, lighted pathways and sidewalks, and required safety programs for freshmen.

Programs of Study: Washington and Lee awards the B.A. and B.S. degrees. Bachelor's degrees are awarded in AGRICULTURE (forestry and related sciences), BIOLOGICAL SCIENCE (biology/biological science and neurosciences), BUSINESS (business administration and management), COMMUNICATIONS AND THE ARTS (art, classics, dramatic arts, English, fine arts, French, German, journalism, music, romance languages, and Spanish), COMPUTER AND PHYSICAL SCIENCE (chemistry, computer science, geology, geophysics and seismology, mathematics, and physics), ENGINEERING AND ENVIRONMENTAL DESIGN (engineering and engineering physics); SOCIAL SCIENCE (anthropology, archeology, cognitive science, East Asian studies, economics, history, philosophy, political science/government, public administration, religion, and sociology). The preprofessional program in commerce, journalism, and mass media, psychology, history, and English are the strongest programs academically. Economics, history, English, biology, and journalism have the largest enrollments.

Required: To graduate, students must achieve proficiency in a foreign language and English composition, and complete 6 credits in literature, 12 in fine arts, 10 in science and mathematics, and 9 in social sciences. A total of 121 credits, with a minimum GPA of 1.9 overall and 2.0 in the major, is required. All students must take 5 courses in physical education.

Special: Government internships and journalism and mass communications internships are available. Study-abroad programs are offered in several countries. There is a 3-3 law program, a 3-2 engineering degree with Rensselaer Polytechnic Institute and Columbia University, and a 3-2 program in forestry or environmental management with Duke University. Washington and Lee also offers interdisciplinary majors, including chemistry-engineering and natural science and mathematics, and student-designed majors. There is a freshman honors program on campus, as well as 9 national honor societies, including Phi Beta Kappa. Twenty-five departments have honors programs.

Faculty/Classroom: Eighty percent of faculty are male; 20%, female. All teach undergraduates and also do research. No introductory courses are taught by graduate students. The average

class size in an introductory lecture is 25; in a laboratory, 15; and in a regular course offering, 15.

Admissions: About 33% of the 1993–94 applicants were accepted. About 88% of the current freshmen were in the top fifth of their class; 99% were in the top two fifths. There were 29 National Merit finalists. About 33 freshmen graduated first in their class.

Requirements: Applicants must take the SAT I and 3 SAT II: Subject tests or the ACT. Applicants must graduate from an accredited secondary school. They must earn 16 units, including 4 units in English, 3 in mathematics, 2 in a foreign language, and 1 each in history and natural science. Course work in social sciences is also required. Essays are required, and interviews are recommended. AP credits are accepted. Important factors used in the admissions decision are advanced placement or honor courses, recommendations by school officials, evidence of special talent, extracurricular activities record, and leadership record.

Procedure: Freshmen are admitted in the fall. Entrance exams should be taken between March of the junior year and January of the senior year. Early decision applications should be filed by December 1; regular applications, by February 15 for fall entry, along with an application fee of $40. Notification of early decision is sent December 20; regular decision, April 1. There are early decision and deferred admissions plans. About 141 early decision candidates were accepted for the 1993–94 class. A waiting list is an active part of the admissions procedure, with about 12% of applicants on the list.

Transfer: About 8 transfer students enrolled in 1993–94. In addition, transfer applicants must have a GPA of at least 3.0; no more than 87 credits will transfer. There is a two-year residency requirement. A total of 34 credits out of 121 must be completed at Washington and Lee.

Visiting: There are regularly scheduled orientations for prospective students. There are guides for informal visits and visitors may sit in on classes and stay overnight at the school. To arrange for a visit, contact the Admissions Office at (703) 463-8710.

Financial Aid: In 1993–94, 55% of all current freshmen and 47% of continuing students received some form of financial aid. About 30% of freshmen and 27% of continuing students received need-based aid. The average freshman award was $8760. Of that total, scholarships or need-based grants averaged $8360 ($17,745 maximum); loans averaged $2740 ($5625 maximum); and work contracts averaged $700. Twenty-two percent of undergraduate students work part-time. Average earnings from campus work for the school year are $1000. The average financial indebtedness of the 1992–93 graduate was $7920. Washington and Lee is a member of CSS. The college's own financial statement, the CSS Divorced/Separated Parents Form and the CSS Business/Farm Supplement, if applicable, and FAFSA are required. The deadline for financial aid applications is February 1.

International Students: There are currently 31 international students enrolled. The school actively recruits these students. They must take the TOEFL and achieve a minimum score of 600. The student must also take the SAT I or 3 SAT II: Subject tests or the ACT.

Computers: The college provides computer facilities for student use. The mainframe is a Prime 9955. There are also 135 microcomputers in 10 locations throughout academic buildings, 40 networked terminals and 29 networked microcomputers providing access to the mainframe, and dial-up access to the mainframe from off campus. All students may access the system. There are no time limits on using the system and no fees.

Graduates: In 1992–93, 390 bachelor's degrees were awarded. Within an average freshman class, 89% graduate in 4 years, 92% in 5 years, and 92% in 6 years. Some 115 companies recruited on campus in 1992–93. In the 1992 graduating class, 25% of all students were enrolled in graduate school within 6 months of graduation; 51% had found employment.

Admissions Contact: William M. Hartog, Dean of Admissions and Financial Aid.

WILLIAM AND MARY
(See College of William and Mary)

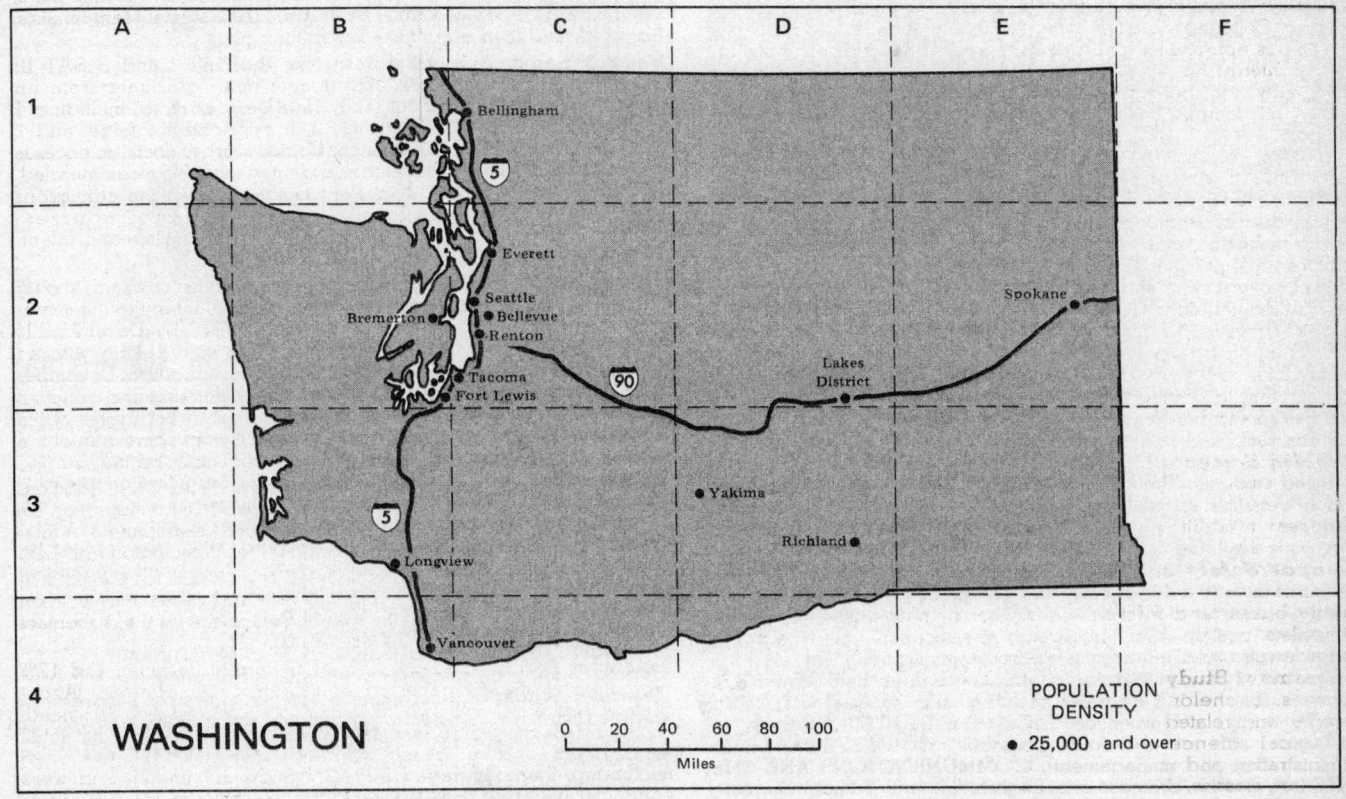

WASHINGTON

POPULATION DENSITY

● 25,000 and over

0 20 40 60 80 100

Miles

CENTRAL WASHINGTON UNIVERSITY D-2

Ellensburg, WA 98926 (509) 963-3001

Full-time: 3417 men, 3403 women Faculty: 344; IIA, -$
Part-time: 606 men, 696 women Ph.D.s: n/av
Graduate: 124 men, 174 women Student/Faculty: 20 to 1
Year: quarters, summer session Tuition: $2046 ($7023)
Application Deadline: March 1 Room & Board: $3598
Freshman Class: 2963 applied, 2254 accepted, 1047 enrolled
SAT I Verbal/Math: 414/463 COMPETITIVE

Central Washington University, founded in 1891, is a public, coeducational institution offering undergraduate programs in the arts and sciences, business administration, education, and professional training. There are 4 undergraduate schools and one graduate school. In addition to regional accreditation, CWU has baccalaureate program accreditation with ABET, ACCE, NASM, and NRPA. The library contains 485,417 volumes, 868,435 microform items, and 31,107 audiovisual forms, and subscribes to 1907 periodicals. Computerized library sources and services include database searching. Special learning facilities include a learning resource center, an art gallery, a natural history museum, a planetarium, a radio station, a TV station, an anthropology museum, a botanical greenhouse, and a chimpanzee laboratory. The 380-acre campus is in a small town 100 miles east of Seattle. Including residence halls, there are 74 buildings on campus.

Student Life: About 96% of undergraduates are from Washington. Students come from 36 states, 35 foreign countries, and Canada. Eighty-eight percent are white. The average age of freshmen is 19; all undergraduates, 24. Fifteen percent drop out by the end of their first year; 42% remain to graduate.

Housing: A total of 2447 students can be accommodated in college housing. College-sponsored living facilities include coed dormitories, on-campus apartments, off-campus apartments, and married-student housing. In addition there are special interest houses and a freshman-only enrichment house, a tobacco- and alcohol-free hall, and a residence hall for transfers and upper-classmen only. On-campus housing is guaranteed for the freshman year only and is available on a first-come, first-served basis. All students may keep cars on campus.

Activities: There are no fraternities or sororities on campus. There are 65 groups on campus, including art, band, cheerleading, chess, choir, chorale, chorus, computers, dance, drama, ethnic, film, gay, honors, international, jazz band, literary magazine, marching band, musical theater, newspaper, opera, orchestra, pep band, photogra-

phy, political, professional, radio and TV, religious, social, social service, student government, and symphony. Popular campus events include Homecoming, Lipsync Contest, Tower Theater productions, and Jazz Night.

Sports: There are 10 intercollegiate sports for men and 8 for women, and 7 intramural sports for men and 6 for women. Athletic and recreation facilities include a 3500-seat stadium, a swimming pool, an arena, a weight training room, an athletic field, and 3 gymnasiums.

Disabled Students: Nearly all of the campus is accessible to disabled students. The following facilities are available: wheelchair ramps, elevators, special parking, specially equipped rest rooms, special class scheduling, lowered drinking fountains, and lowered telephones.

Services: In addition to many counseling and information services, tutoring is available in most subjects. There is also a reader service for the blind, and remedial math, reading, and writing.

Campus Safety and Security: Campus safety and security measures include a 24-hour foot and vehicle patrol, an escort service, shuttle buses, and informal discussions. In addition, there are pamphlets, posters, films, emergency telephones, lighted pathways and sidewalks, and controlled-entry residence halls.

Programs of Study: CWU awards the B.A., B.S., B.A.Ed., and B.M. degrees. Master's degrees also are awarded. Bachelor's degrees are awarded in BIOLOGICAL SCIENCE (biology/biological science and zoology), BUSINESS (accounting, banking and finance, business administration and management, business economics, international business management, marketing/retailing/merchandising, and recreation and leisure services), COMMUNICATIONS AND THE ARTS (broadcasting, communications, dramatic arts, English, fine arts, French, German, journalism, music, Spanish, and speech/debate/rhetoric), COMPUTER AND PHYSICAL SCIENCE (actuarial science, chemistry, computer programming, computer science, earth science, geology, information sciences and systems, mathematics, and physics), EDUCATION (art, business, early childhood, elementary, foreign languages, health, home economics, industrial arts, middle school, music, science, secondary, and special), ENGINEERING AND ENVIRONMENTAL DESIGN (electrical/electronics engineering, engineering technology, and mechanical engineering), HEALTH PROFESSIONS (public health), SOCIAL SCIENCE (anthropology, criminal justice, economics, food science, geography, history, parks and recreation management, philosophy, political science/government, psychology, public administration, social science, social work, sociology, and urban studies). Accounting, education, music, business adminis-

tration, and engineering technologies are the strongest programs academically. Business and education have the largest enrollments.

Required: Students must complete a minimum of 180 quarter credits, including 60 in upper-division courses and a minimum of 45 in the major plus a minor or 60 in the major. Core curriculum requirements include 61 credits of basic and breadth courses, including 15 credits each in arts and humanities, social and behavioral sciences, and natural science, 9 credits of English composition, and 2 credits of physical education, a philosophy logic or finite mathematics course. Students must maintain a 2.3 GPA in the major and 2.0 GPA overall. A comprehensive examination in reading comprehension, sentence skills, and mathematics is required.

Special: Students may study abroad in 7 countries. There are 3–2 engineering degree programs in conjunction with the University of Puget Sound, the University of Washington, and Washington State University. CWU also offers co-op programs, cross-registration, internships, work-study programs, an accelerated degree program, credit/no credit options, dual and student-designed majors, and credit for military experience. Nondegree study is offered through adult/continuing education programs. There is a freshman honors program on campus, as well as 11 national honor societies, including Phi Beta Kappa. Twelve departments have honors programs.

Faculty/Classroom: Seventy-nine percent of faculty are male; 21%, female. The average class size in an introductory lecture is 40; in a laboratory, 20; and in a regular course offering, 40.

Admissions: About 76% of the 1993–94 applicants were accepted. The SAT scores for the 1993–94 freshman class were as follows: Verbal—84% below 500, 14% between 500 and 599, and 2% between 600 and 700; Math—66% below 500, 25% between 500 and 599, 8% between 600 and 700, and 1% above 700. About 25% of the current freshmen were in the top fifth of their class; 57% were in the top two fifths. There was 1 National Merit finalist and 11 semifinalists. Thirty freshmen graduated first in their class.

Requirements: A minimum GPA of 2.0 is required. The SAT I or ACT is required. Test scores and GPA are considered in combination according to a sliding scale. Applicants must be graduates of accredited secondary schools or have earned a GED. The university requires 15 academic credits or Carnegie units, based on 4 years of English, 1 of performing arts or an academic elective, 2 of the same foreign language, 2 of science, and 3 each of mathematics and social studies. AP credits are accepted. Important factors used in the admissions decision are leadership record, recommendations by school officials, recommendations by alumni, extracurricular activities record, and advanced placement or honor courses.

Procedure: Freshmen are admitted to all sessions. Entrance exams should be taken before the fall of the senior year. Early decision applications should be filed by June 30; regular applications, by March 1 for fall entry, October 1 for winter entry, January 1 for spring entry, and June 1 for summer entry, along with an application fee of $35. Notification of early decision is sent July 31; regular decision, on a rolling basis. There are early decision, early admissions, and deferred admissions plans.

Transfer: Some 1474 transfer students enrolled in 1993–94. Transfers must have earned at least 40 credits at another institution. Students presenting an associate degree need a minimum GPA of 2.0; those with more than 90 credits, a 2.2; those with 60 to 89 credits, a 2.3; and those with 59 or fewer credits, a 2.5. A total of 45 quarter credits out of 180 must be completed at CWU.

Visiting: There are regularly scheduled orientations for prospective students, consisting of the 2-day Central Sampler, which includes dinner with Sampler hosts, an information session, a tour of residence halls, a tour of the campus, prearranged appointments with faculty, and a financial aid presentation. There are guides for informal visits and visitors may sit in on classes and stay overnight at the school. To arrange for a visit, contact the Admissions Office at (509) 963–3001.

Financial Aid: In 1993–94, 48% of all current freshmen and 45% of continuing students received some form of financial aid. About 36% of freshmen and 37% of continuing students received need-based aid. The average freshman award was $3678. Of that total, scholarships or need-based grants averaged $1060 ($2000 maximum); loans averaged $2330 ($2625 maximum); and work contracts averaged $288 ($1950 maximum). Thirty-one percent of undergraduate students work part-time. The average financial indebtedness of the 1992–93 graduate was $4392. CWU is a member of CSS. The FAFSA financial statement is required. The deadline for financial aid applications is March 15.

International Students: There are currently 120 international students enrolled. The school actively recruits these students. They must take the TOEFL and achieve a minimum score of 525. The student must also take the SAT I or the ACT.

Computers: The college provides computer facilities for student use. The mainframe is a 6 DEC VAX models. There are also 1200 IBM PC, Macintosh, Apple, AT&T, Zenith, and Rainbow microcomputers available in various buildings. All students may access the system 24 hours a day. There are no time limits on using the system. The fee is $18 per quarter.

Graduates: In a recent year, 1810 bachelor's degrees were awarded. The most popular majors among graduates were business administration (19%), accounting (12%), and elementary education (6%). Within an average freshman class, 2% graduate in 3 years, 20% in 4 years, 37% in 5 years, and 42% in 6 years. Some 124 companies recruited on campus in 1992–93.

Admissions Contact: William Swain, Director of Admissions and Academic Advising Services.

CITY UNIVERSITY C-2
Bellevue, WA 98004 (206) 624–1688; (800) 422–4898 (out-of-state)

Full-time: 98 men, 117 women	Faculty: 31; IIB, --$
Part-time: 723 men, 1011 women	Ph.D.s: n/av
Graduate: 1241 men, 4387 women	Student/Faculty: 7 to 1
Year: quarters, summer session	Tuition: $6400
Application Deadline: open	Room & Board: n/app
Freshman Class: n/av	
SAT I or ACT: not required	NONCOMPETITIVE

City University, established in 1973, is a private nonresidential institution offering undergraduate and graduate programs at a variety of instructional sites in addition to the Bellevue campus, including locations in Washington, Oregon, California, British Columbia, Europe, and Asia. There are 2 undergraduate and 2 graduate schools. The library contains 10,000 volumes and 110 microform items, and subscribes to 280 periodicals. Computerized library sources and services include interlibrary loans and database searching. Special learning facilities include a learning resource center. The 10-acre campus is in a suburban area 12 miles east of Seattle.

Student Life: Eighty percent are white.

Housing: There are no residence halls. Alcohol is not permitted.

Activities: There are no fraternities or sororities on campus.

Sports: There is no sports program at City University.

Disabled Students: Ninety percent of the campus is accessible to disabled students. The following facilities are available: wheelchair ramps, elevators, special parking, and specially equipped rest rooms.

Services: Tutoring is available.

Programs of Study: City University awards the B.S. degree. Associate and master's degrees also are awarded. Bachelor's degrees are awarded in BUSINESS (accounting, banking and finance, business administration and management, and marketing/retailing/merchandising), COMMUNICATIONS AND THE ARTS (telecommunications), COMPUTER AND PHYSICAL SCIENCE (computer programming and computer science), EDUCATION (elementary, middle school, and teaching English as a second language/foreign language), HEALTH PROFESSIONS (health care administration), SOCIAL SCIENCE (behavioral science, criminal justice, liberal arts/general studies, and public administration). Business administration has the largest enrollment.

Required: Students are required to complete 180 quarter credits, with a minimum of 45 of these credits taken at City University, and maintain a minimum GPA of 2.0. Thirty credits are required in the major. All students must also complete 55 general education credits, which include courses in the humanities, social sciences, natural sciences, and mathematics.

Special: Opportunities are provided for cooperative programs with other schools, internships, study abroad, work-study programs, dual majors, student-designed majors, and accelerated degree programs. A general studies degree, pass/fail options, independent study and weekend programs, and credit for military service schools attended are offered.

Requirements: Graduation from an accredited secondary school is not required; a GED will be accepted. An interview is recommended. CLEP credit is accepted.

Procedure: Freshmen are admitted to all sessions. Application deadlines are open. The application fee is $50. The college accepts all applicants. Notification is sent on a rolling basis.

Transfer: Students applying for transfer must submit official transcripts from all colleges previously attended. Applicants may transfer up to 135 quarter credits from accredited 4-year colleges, with at least 45 of these credits in upper-level courses. Up to 90 quarter credits may be transferred from 2-year colleges. A total of 45 credits out of 180 must be completed at City University.

Visiting: To arrange for a visit, contact Student Services at (206) 643–2000 or (800) 422–4898.

Financial Aid: The college's own financial statement and AFSA are required. The deadline for financial aid applications is July 9.

International Students: There are currently 258 international students enrolled. They must take the TOEFL and achieve a minimum score of 540.

Computers: The college provides computer facilities for student use. All students may access the system. There are no time limits on using the system and no fees.

Graduates: In 1992–93, 391 bachelor's degrees were awarded.
Admissions Contact: Student Services/Admissions.

COGSWELL COLLEGE NORTH

C-2

Kirkland, WA 98033
Recognized candidate for accreditation   (206) 822–3137

Full-time: 7 men, 2 women	Faculty: 8
Part-time: 200 men, 10 women	Ph.D.s: 50%
Graduate: none	Student/Faculty: 5 to 1
Year: quarters, summer session	Tuition: $7200
Application Deadline: open	Room & Board: n/app
Freshman Class: 5 applied, 5 accepted, 3 enrolled	
SAT I or ACT: not required	**NONCOMPETITIVE**

Cogswell College North, established in 1979, is a private, coeducational institution with evening-only programs in engineering and computer science. The library contains 3500 volumes. The 1-acre campus is in a suburban area 10 miles east of Seattle. There are 3 buildings on campus.

Student Life: Nearly all undergraduates are from Washington. Ninety-five percent are from public schools; 5% from private. Ninety-five percent are white. The average age of freshmen is 30; all undergraduates, 35. One percent drop out by the end of their first year; 99% remain to graduate.

Housing: There are no residence halls. All students commute.

Activities: There are no fraternities or sororities on campus.

Sports: There is no sports program at CCN.

Disabled Students: Seventy percent of the campus is accessible to disabled students. The following facilities are available: wheelchair ramps, special parking, and specially equipped rest rooms.

Services: In addition to many counseling and information services, tutoring is available in some subjects.

Campus Safety and Security: Campus safety and security measures include pamphlets, posters, films, and lighted pathways and sidewalks.

Programs of Study: CCN awards the B.S.E.E., and B.S.E.T. degrees. Associate degrees also are awarded. Bachelor's degrees are awarded in ENGINEERING AND ENVIRONMENTAL DESIGN (electrical/electronics engineering, electrical/electronics engineering technology, manufacturing technology, and mechanical engineering technology). Electrical engineering is the strongest program academically. Mechanical engineering technology has the largest enrollment.

Required: Students must complete a minimum of 194 quarter hours, 74 in the major, and maintain a minimum 2.0 GPA. The core curriculum includes 30 credits in humanities and social sciences, 3 classes each in written and oral communication and physics, and classes in mathematics, chemistry, and moral and ethical problems. A senior thesis or project is required.

Faculty/Classroom: Ninety-one percent of faculty are male; 9%, female. All teach undergraduates. The average class size in an introductory lecture, a laboratory, and a regular course offering is 10.

Admissions: All of the 1993–94 applicants were accepted.

Requirements: A high school diploma or GED is required. AP and CLEP credits are accepted.

Procedure: Freshmen are admitted to all sessions. Entrance exams should be taken prior to registration. Application deadlines are open. Application fee is $50. The college accepts all applicants. Notification is sent on a rolling basis.

Transfer: Nineteen transfer students enrolled in 1993–94. Transferring students must forward all transcripts from previously attended schools. A total of 48 quarter hours out of 194 must be completed at CCN.

Visiting: There are guides for informal visits and visitors may sit in on classes. To arrange for a visit, contact Jacqueline Juras, Director of Admissions, at (206) 822–3137.

Financial Aid: In 1993–94, 2% of all current freshmen and 6% of continuing students received some form of financial aid. About 2% of freshmen and 6% of continuing students received need-based aid. The average freshman award was $6642. Of that total, scholarships or need-based grants had a $2050 cap; loans averaged $6625 (maximum). Nearly all of undergraduate students work part-time. The average financial indebtedness of the 1992–93 graduate was $8861. CCN is a member of CSS. The FAF, FFS, or SFS and the college's own financial statement are required. The deadline for financial aid applications is September 1.

International Students: There is currently 1 international student enrolled. The school actively recruits international students. They must take the TOEFL and achieve a minimum score of 550.

Computers: The college provides computer facilities for student use. The mainframe is a MicroVAX AS/400. A PC laboratory and main computer laboratory are available. All students may access the system. There are no time limits on using the system and no fees.

Graduates: In 1992–93, 30 bachelor's degrees were awarded. The most popular majors among graduates were mechanical engineering technology (41%), electronics engineering technology (37%), and electrical engineering (22%). Within an average freshman class, 30% graduate in 6 years. In the 1992 graduating class, 5% of all students were enrolled in graduate school within 6 months of graduation.

Admissions Contact: Jacqueline B. Juras, Director, Admissions/Registrar.

CORNISH COLLEGE OF THE ARTS

C-2

Seattle, WA 98102   (206) 323–1400, ext. 205
(800) 726-ARTS (out-of-state)

Full-time: 211 men, 274 women	Faculty: 27; IIB, --$
Part-time: 44 men, 78 women	Ph.D.s: 56%
Graduate: none	Student/Faculty: 18 to 1
Year: semesters, summer session	Tuition: $9300
Application Deadline: August 15	Room & Board: n/app
Freshman Class: 574 applied, 407 accepted, 237 enrolled	
SAT I or ACT: required	**SPECIAL**

Cornish College of the Arts, founded in 1914, is an independent commuter institution offering undergraduate programs in the fine arts, dance, design, music, theater, and performance production. The library contains 12,000 volumes, 2895 audiovisual forms, and subscribes to 88 periodicals. Special learning facilities include an art gallery. The 4-acre campus is in an urban area in the Capitol Hill neighborhood of Seattle. There are 8 buildings on campus.

Student Life: About 71% of undergraduates are from Washington. Students come from 28 states, 10 foreign countries, and Canada. Seventy-eight percent are white. The average age of freshmen is 24; all undergraduates, 25. Twenty percent drop out by the end of their first year; 50% remain to graduate.

Housing: There are no residence halls; all students commute and may keep cars on campus. Alcohol is not permitted.

Activities: There are no fraternities or sororities on campus. There are several groups on campus, including art, band, choir, chorale, chorus, dance, drama, jazz band, newspaper, opera, orchestra, professional, and student government. Popular campus events include Spring Arts Festival, noon lectures, concerts, theatrical performances, and gallery showings.

Sports: There is no sports program at Cornish.

Disabled Students: Half of the campus is accessible to disabled students. The following facilities are available: wheelchair ramps, elevators, special parking, specially equipped rest rooms, and lowered drinking fountains and telephones.

Services: In addition to many counseling and information services, tutoring is available in every subject. There is a reader service for the blind and remedial writing. There are also books on tape.

Campus Safety and Security: Campus safety and security measures include 24-hour foot and vehicle patrol.

Programs of Study: Cornish awards the B.A.A., B.F.A., and B.M. degrees. Bachelor's degrees are awarded in COMMUNICATIONS AND THE ARTS (dance, design, dramatic arts, fine arts, music, performing arts, and theater design). Design is the strongest academically. Fine arts has the largest enrollment.

Required: General education requirements include 30 semester hours in the humanities and sciences, as well as 6 to 8 in arts electives. To graduate, students must complete at least 130 semester hours, including 94 in their specific discipline, and maintain a minimum GPA of 2.5 during their senior year.

Special: Cornish offers a premajor first year of study to those music students who initially need more fundamental training. Internships are available to upperclassmen majoring in design, theater, or performance production. Students may earn credit by examination in humanities and science courses, as well as credit for life experience in all majors where appropriate. Work-study programs and nondegree study are also offered.

Faculty/Classroom: All teach undergraduates. The average class size in an introductory lecture is 25 and in a regular course offering, 15.

Admissions: About 71% of the 1993–94 applicants were accepted.

Requirements: A minimum GPA of 2.0 is required. The SAT I or ACT is required. The required audition or portfolio review is the single most important criterion in the admissions decision. Applicants should be graduates of accredited secondary schools or have earned a GED. In addition to providing evidence of their artistic talent, students must submit an essay and arrange for an interview. AP and CLEP credits are accepted. Important factors used in the admissions decision are evidence of special talent, personality, intangible qualities, recommendations by school officials, recommendations by alumni, and extracurricular activities record.

Procedure: Freshmen are admitted in the fall. Applications should be filed by August 15 for fall entry and December 15 for spring entry, along with an application fee of $30. Notification is sent on a rolling basis. There is a deferred admissions plan.

Transfer: A total of 48 credits out of 130 must be completed at Cornish.

Visiting: There are regularly scheduled orientations for prospective students, consisting of Preview Days during which applicants can attend classes, interact with students and faculty, and experience campus life. There are guides for informal visits and visitors may sit in on classes. To arrange for a visit, contact the Admissions Office at (206) 323-1400, ext. 205.

Financial Aid: Cornish is a member of CSS. The FAF, the college's own financial statement, and the FAFSA are required. The deadline for financial aid applications is March 31.

International Students: There are currently 24 international students enrolled. They must take the TOEFL and achieve a minimum score of 525.

Computers: The college provides computer facilities for student use. There are 11 Apple Macintosh and Apple IIe microcomputers available in the design department. Design students may access the system. There are no time limits and no fees.

Graduates: In 1992-93, 90 bachelor's degrees were awarded. The most popular majors among graduates were art (31%), theater (24%), and dance/design (16%). Within an average freshman class, 50% graduate in 4 years.

Admissions Contact: Jane Buckman, Director of Admissions and Financial Aid.

EASTERN WASHINGTON UNIVERSITY
E-2
Cheney, WA 99004-2496 (509) 359-2397

Full-time: 3093 men, 3842 women	Faculty: 396; IIA, -$
Part-time: 347 men, 455 women	Ph.D.s: 64%
Graduate: 287 men, 407 women	Student/Faculty: 18 to 1
Year: quarters, summer session	Tuition: $2091 ($7068)
Application Deadline: February 15	Room & Board: $3348
Freshman Class: n/av	
SAT I or ACT: required	LESS COMPETITIVE

Eastern Washington University, founded in 1882, is a comprehensive public university that provides programs in the arts and sciences, business, health sciences and nursing, and technology. There are 6 undergraduate schools and one graduate school. In addition to regional accreditation, EWU has baccalaureate program accreditation with AACSB, ABET, ADA, APTA, CSWE, NASM, NCATE, NLN, and NRPA. The library contains 671,068 volumes, 1,260,290 microform items, and 29,302 audiovisual forms, and subscribes to 5439 periodicals. Computerized library sources and services include the card catalog, interlibrary loans, and database searching. Special learning facilities include a learning resource center, art gallery, natural history museum, planetarium, radio station, and TV station. The 35-acre campus is in a small town 18 miles southwest of Spokane. Including residence halls, there are 32 buildings on campus.

Student Life: About 93% of undergraduates are from Washington. Students come from 43 states, 53 foreign countries, and Canada. Ninety-eight percent are from public schools. Eighty-one percent are white. The average age of freshmen is 18.7; all undergraduates, 24.6. Twenty-four percent drop out by the end of their first year; 40% remain to graduate.

Housing: A total of 2066 students can be accommodated in college housing. College-sponsored living facilities include single-sex and coed dormitories, on-campus apartments, and married-student housing. In addition, there are older-student floors available in dormitories. On-campus housing is guaranteed for all 4 years. Fifty-two percent of students commute. All students may keep cars on campus.

Activities: About 6% of men belong to 6 national fraternities; about 3% of women belong to 1 local and 3 national sororities. There are 86 groups on campus, including art, band, cheerleading, chess, choir, chorale, chorus, computers, dance, drama, ethnic, film, gay, honors, international, jazz band, literary magazine, marching band, musical theater, newspaper, orchestra, pep band, photography, political, professional, radio and TV, religious, social, social service, student government, and symphony. Popular campus events include Mayfest, Homecoming, Reno Day, Street Dance, Parents Weekend, Winter and Spring Formals, Indian Awareness Week, Black Education Week, Fall Family Weekend, Welcome Back Week, International Night, and Togo-Winter Formal.

Sports: There are 6 intercollegiate sports each for men and women, and 16 intramural sports for men and 14 for women. Athletic and recreation facilities include a 200-meter indoor track, 12 racquetball courts, an indoor swimming pool, wrestling rooms, a dance studio, a 7000-seat stadium, a 5800-seat indoor gymnasium, a fitness studio, and volleyball, baseball, and basketball courts.

Disabled Students: Ninety percent of the campus is accessible to disabled students. The following facilities are available: wheelchair ramps, elevators, special parking, specially equipped rest rooms, special class scheduling, lowered drinking fountains, lowered telephones, and specially designed campus apartments.

Services: In addition to many counseling and information services, tutoring is available in every subject. There is a reader service for the blind, and remedial math, reading, and writing.

Campus Safety and Security: Campus safety and security measures include 24-hour foot and vehicle patrol, escort service, informal discussions, and pamphlets, posters, and films. In addition, there are lighted pathways and sidewalks and emergency telephones and crisis lines.

Programs of Study: EWU awards the B.A., B.S., B.A.B., B.A.E., B.D.H., B.F.A., B.Mu., and B.S.N. degrees. Master's degrees also are awarded. Bachelor's degrees are awarded in BIOLOGICAL SCIENCE (biochemistry, biology/biological science, botany, microbiology, and zoology), BUSINESS (accounting, banking and finance, business administration and management, business economics, management science, marketing/retailing/merchandising, personnel management, and recreation and leisure services), COMMUNICATIONS AND THE ARTS (art, art history and appreciation, broadcasting, communications, creative writing, dance, dramatic arts, English, French, German, graphic design, journalism, literature, music, music business management, music performance, photography, Spanish, speech/debate/rhetoric, and studio art), COMPUTER AND PHYSICAL SCIENCE (chemistry, computer science, geology, information sciences and systems, mathematics, physics, and statistics), EDUCATION (art, business, computer, elementary, foreign languages, guidance, health, marketing and distribution, mathematics, middle school, music, physical, recreation, science, secondary, and social science), ENGINEERING AND ENVIRONMENTAL DESIGN (computer technology, mechanical engineering technology, and military science), HEALTH PROFESSIONS (dental hygiene, health care administration, medical laboratory technology, nursing, physical therapy, predentistry, premedicine, preveterinary science, recreation therapy, and speech pathology/audiology), SOCIAL SCIENCE (anthropology, criminal justice, economics, geography, history, humanities, international relations, parks and recreation management, philosophy, political science/government, prelaw, psychology, public administration, social science, social work, sociology, and urban studies). Health sciences, biology, computer science, education, and business are the strongest academically. Technology and business, education, and general studies have the largest enrollments.

Required: All students must complete 180 quarter credits, including 60 to 110 in their major, while earning a minimum GPA of 2.0. Specific requirements include English composition and mathematics courses to demonstrate competency. Distribution requirements include 11 total courses from 3 breadth areas: humanities, natural sciences and mathematics, and social sciences.

Special: Cooperative programs with Whitworth College and Washington State University, cross-registration with the Intercollegiate School of Nursing, internships with area businesses, and work-study based on federal financial aid are available. B.A.-B.S. degrees, dual majors in any subject, study abroad in 12 countries, 3 types of general studies degrees, student-designed majors, and a 3-2 engineering degree with Washington State University are offered. Credit for military experience, nondegree study, and pass/fail options for nonmajor or nonminor courses also are possible. There is a freshman honors program on campus, as well as 8 national honor societies, including Phi Beta Kappa. Ten departments have honors programs.

Faculty/Classroom: Seventy-one percent of faculty are male; 29%, female.

Requirements: The SAT I or ACT is required. Admission is determined by an index coordinating the GPA with entrance exam scores. The GED is accepted. EWU requires 4 years of English, 3 each of mathematics and social science, 2 each of science (including a laboratory science) and a single foreign language (ASL accepted), and 1 of fine arts or academic electives. AP credits are accepted. Important factors used in the admissions decision are recommendations by school officials, advanced placement or honor courses, evidence of special talent, geographic diversity, and extracurricular activities record.

Procedure: Freshmen are admitted to all sessions. Entrance exams should be taken during the spring of the junior year or fall of the senior year. Applications should be filed by February 15 for fall entry, October 15 for winter entry, and February 1 for spring entry, along with an application fee of $35. Notification is sent on a rolling basis. A waiting list is an active part of the admissions procedure.

Transfer: About 1640 transfer students enrolled in 1993-94. Applicants with fewer than 40 credits must submit high school and college transcripts and test scores; those with more than 40 credits acceptable by Eastern or who have earned an associate degree from a Washington community college must submit a college transcript. A total of 45 quarter credits out of 180 must be completed at EWU.

Visiting: There are regularly scheduled orientations for prospective students, consisting of overnight programs for students and parents that present informational sessions on campus life and academic survival skills, academic advising, course registration, and social functions. There are guides for informal visits and visitors may sit in on classes. To arrange for a visit, contact the Admissions Office at (509) 359-6555.

Financial Aid: In 1993–94, 38% of all current freshmen and 43% of continuing students received some form of financial aid. About 50% of freshmen and 43% of continuing students received need-based aid. The average freshman award was $4400. Of that total, scholarships or need-based grants averaged $1000 ($5000 maximum); loans averaged $2163 ($7500 maximum); and work contracts averaged $2000 ($7500 maximum). Fourteen percent of undergraduate students work part-time. Average earnings from campus work for the school year are $1800. The average financial indebtedness of the 1992–93 graduate was $12,200. EWU is a member of CSS. The FAF and FAFSA are required. The deadline for financial aid applications is February 15.

International Students: There are currently 590 international students enrolled. The school actively recruits these students. They must take the TOEFL and achieve a minimum score of 525.

Computers: The college provides computer facilities for student use. The mainframe is a DEC VAX 6510 minicomputer. Students need an account number, available through classes. Five computer laboratories and 5 specialized department laboratories are available. All students may access the system. It may be used throughout the workday, plus evenings and weekends. There are no time limits on using the system and no fees.

Graduates: In 1992–93, 1372 bachelor's degrees were awarded. The most popular majors among graduates were business administration (20%), English (6%), and general studies (6%). Some 60 companies recruited on campus in 1992–93. In the 1992 graduating class, 14% were enrolled in graduate school within 6 months of graduation; 66% had found employment.

Admissions Contact: Roger Pugh, Assistant Vice Provost for Enrollment Management and Director of Admissions.

EVERGREEN STATE COLLEGE   B-3

Olympia, WA 98505   **(206) 866–6000, ext. 6170**

Full-time: 1366 men, 1669 women	Faculty: 144; IIB, +$
Part-time: 164 men, 199 women	Ph.D.s: 74%
Graduate: 123 men, 151 women	Student/Faculty: 21 to 1
Year: quarters, summer session	Tuition: $2352 ($8070)
Application Deadline: March 1	Room & Board: $3954
Freshman Class: 1801 applied, 1108 accepted, 438 enrolled	
SAT I or ACT: required	**COMPETITIVE**

Evergreen State College, founded in 1971, is a public, coeducational liberal arts college offering team-taught, interdisciplinary studies that culminate with written evaluations. There are 3 graduate schools. The library contains 254,646 volumes and 120,000 microform items, and subscribes to 1558 periodicals. Computerized library sources and services include the card catalog, interlibrary loans, and database searching. Special learning facilities include a learning resource center, art gallery, radio station, and a communications laboratory. The 1000-acre campus is in a small town 7 miles west of Olympia. Including residence halls, there are 51 buildings on campus.

Student Life: About 76% of undergraduates are from Washington. Students come from 30 states, 15 foreign countries, and Canada. Eighty-eight percent are white. The average age of all undergraduates is 24. Twenty-six percent drop out by the end of their first year.

Housing: A total of 1100 students can be accommodated in college housing. College-sponsored living facilities include coed on-campus apartments. In addition there is drug- and alcohol-free housing. On-campus housing is guaranteed for the freshman year only and is available on a first-come, first-served basis. Sixty-seven percent of students commute. Alcohol is not permitted. All students may keep cars on campus.

Activities: There are no fraternities or sororities on campus. There are some groups and organizations on campus, including chorale, ethnic, gay, literary magazine, newspaper, political, radio and TV, social, and student government. Popular campus events include Super Saturday, Tribute to Japan Festival, and Evergreen Expressions Series.

Sports: There are 3 intercollegiate sports each for men and women, and 10 intramural sports each. Athletic and recreation facilities include a recreation center, which houses an 11-lane swimming pool, a diving well, exercise and weight training rooms, and 5 racquetball courts. There is a 3100-seat gymnasium, a covered pavilion, 4 tennis courts, and 5 playing fields.

Disabled Students: The following facilities are available: wheelchair ramps, elevators, special parking, specially equipped rest rooms, lowered drinking fountains, and lowered telephones.

Services: In addition to many counseling and information services, tutoring is available in most subjects. There is a reader service for the blind, and remedial math, reading, and writing.

Campus Safety and Security: Campus safety and security measures include 24-hour foot and vehicle patrol, self defense education, escort service, and informal discussions. In addition, there are pamphlets, posters, and films, emergency telephones, and lighted pathways and sidewalks.

Programs of Study: Evergreen awards the B.A. and B.S. degrees. Master's degrees also are awarded. Bachelor's degrees are awarded in BIOLOGICAL SCIENCE (biochemistry, biology/biological science, botany, and zoology), BUSINESS (marketing/retailing/merchandising), COMMUNICATIONS AND THE ARTS (broadcasting, communications, dance, dramatic arts, English, film arts, fine arts, French, Greek, Japanese, journalism, Latin, music, photography, Russian, Spanish, speech/debate/rhetoric, and telecommunications), COMPUTER AND PHYSICAL SCIENCE (chemistry, computer programming, computer science, earth science, geology, mathematics, and physics), EDUCATION (art, foreign languages, and science), HEALTH PROFESSIONS (premedicine and public health), SOCIAL SCIENCE (anthropology, community services, economics, history, international relations, parks and recreation management, philosophy, political science/government, prelaw, psychology, public administration, social science, social work, sociology, and urban studies). Liberal arts, particularly environmental studies, media, human services, and teaching are the strongest academically and have the largest enrollments.

Required: Students must earn a minimum of 180 quarter hours of credit to receive a bachelor's degree. There are no other requirements.

Special: All work at the college is interdisciplinary, and the programs of study change annually. The college's credit-generating options include the comprehensive Coordinated Study Program, which allows students and faculty to work together intensively. Credits may be earned through cooperative programs, work-study programs, internships, or from prior learning and military experience. All majors are student-designed. A B.A.-B.S. combined degree is possible in liberal arts or teacher education. Study abroad is possible in France, Japan, Russia, and Central America.

Faculty/Classroom: Sixty-three percent of faculty are male; 37%, female. All teach undergraduates. No introductory courses are taught by graduate students.

Admissions: About 62% of the 1993–94 applicants were accepted. About 40% of the current freshmen were in the top fifth of their class; 80% were in the top two fifths.

Requirements: Evergreen requires applicants to be in the upper 50% of their class. A minimum GPA of 2.0 is required. The SAT I or ACT is required. In addition, candidates should be graduates of an accredited secondary school and have completed 15 academic credits, consisting of 4 in English, 2 each in foreign language and science, 3 each in mathematics and social studies, and 1 in fine or performing arts. A GED certificate is acceptable. AP and CLEP credits are accepted.

Procedure: Freshmen are admitted in the fall. Entrance exams should be taken during the junior year. Applications should be filed by March 1 for fall entry, October 1 for winter entry, and December 1 for spring entry, along with an application fee of $35. Notification is sent by April 1.

Transfer: About 785 transfer students enrolled in 1993–94. Applicants with fewer than 40 credits must submit SAT I or ACT scores and a high school transcript. A 2.0 minimum GPA is required. An associate degree is recommended. All applicants must submit all college transcripts. A total of 45 quarter credits out of 180 must be completed at Evergreen.

Visiting: There are regularly scheduled orientations for prospective students, including an admissions session, a class visit, and a tour. There are guides for informal visits and visitors may sit in on classes. To arrange for a visit, contact the Campus Visitation Program, Office of Admissions, at (206) 866–6000, ext. 6170.

Financial Aid: In 1993–94, 52% of all students received some form of financial aid. The average freshman award was $5618. Of that total, scholarships or need-based grants averaged $2000 ($2500 maximum); loans averaged $750 ($2500 maximum); and work contracts averaged $1600 ($1800 maximum). The average financial indebtedness of the 1992–93 graduate was $3400. Evergreen is a member of CSS. The FAFSA financial statement is required. The deadline for financial aid applications is February 15.

International Students: There are currently 41 international students enrolled. They must take the TOEFL and achieve a minimum score of 525.

Computers: The college provides computer facilities for student use. The mainframe is a DEC VAX Cluster. There are also 90 AT&T and Apple Macintosh II microcomputers in a computer center and laboratories. All students may access the system 24 hours per day. There are no time limits and no fees.

Graduates: In an earlier year, 659 bachelor's degrees were awarded. The most popular majors among graduates were human services (18%), education (10%), and environmental studies (7%). Some 52 companies recruited on campus in 1992–93. In the 1992 graduating class, 17% of all students were enrolled in graduate school within 6 months of graduation; 68% found employment.

Admissions Contact: Doug Scrima, Assistant to the Dean.

GONZAGA UNIVERSITY
Spokane, WA 99258-0001

E-2

(509) 484-6484
(800) 523-9712 (out-of-state)

Full-time: 1251 men, 1353 women	Faculty: 192; IIA, --$
Part-time: 105 men, 226 women	Ph.D.s: 88%
Graduate: 586 men, 845 women	Student/Faculty: 14 to 1
Year: semesters, summer session	Tuition: $12,200
Application Deadline: April 1	Room & Board: $4150
Freshman Class: 1886 applied, 1524 accepted, 526 enrolled	
SAT I Verbal/Math: 499/548	ACT: 25 VERY COMPETITIVE

Gonzaga University, founded in 1887, is a private, coeducational, liberal arts institution affiliated with the Roman Catholic Church and the Society of Jesus (Jesuits). The university offers undergraduate and graduate degrees in arts and sciences, business, education, engineering, and professional studies. There are 5 undergraduate and 5 graduate schools. In addition to regional accreditation, Gonzaga has baccalaureate program accreditation with AACSB, ABET, NCATE, and NLN. The 2 libraries contain 723,994 volumes, 801,384 microform items, and 782 audiovisual forms, and subscribe to 3849 periodicals. Computerized library sources and services include the card catalog, interlibrary loans, and database searching. Special learning facilities include an art gallery, a radio station, and a television production center. The 83-acre campus is in an urban area near downtown Spokane. Including residence halls, there are 60 buildings on campus.

Student Life: About 51% of undergraduates are from Washington. Students come from 44 states, 46 foreign countries, and Canada. Sixty-eight percent are from public schools; 32% from private. Eighty percent are white. Sixty-two percent are Catholic; 14% claim no religious affiliation; 13% Protestant. The average age of freshmen is 18; all undergraduates, 21. Sixteen percent drop out by the end of their first year; 57% remain to graduate.

Housing: A total of 1160 students can be accommodated in college housing. College-sponsored living facilities include single-sex and coed dormitories, on-campus apartments, and off-campus apartments. On-campus housing is available on a first-come, first-served basis and is available on a lottery system for upperclassmen. Priority is given to out-of-town students. Fifty-three percent of students commute. Alcohol is not permitted. All students may keep cars on campus.

Activities: There are no fraternities or sororities on campus. There are 41 groups on campus, including art, band, cheerleading, chess, choir, chorale, chorus, computers, dance, drama, ethnic, honors, international, jazz band, literary magazine, musical theater, newspaper, orchestra, pep band, photography, political, professional, radio and TV, religious, social, social service, student government, and yearbook. Popular campus events include Search, Aprilfest, Octoberfest, Charity Ball, a speaker series, and a rodeo.

Sports: There are 7 intercollegiate sports each for men and women, and 8 intramural sports each for men and women. Athletic and recreation facilities include an athletic center with an indoor running track, a full-sized pool, a weight room, a dance studio, 6 basketball/volleyball courts, and 8 racquetball courts.

Disabled Students: Forty-seven percent of the campus is accessible to disabled students. The following facilities are available: wheelchair ramps, elevators, special parking, specially equipped rest rooms, special class scheduling, lowered drinking fountains, and lowered telephones.

Services: In addition to many counseling and information services, informal peer tutoring in English, mathematics, and computer science is available. There is also a reader service for the blind, and remedial math, reading, and writing.

Campus Safety and Security: Campus safety and security measures include a 24-hour foot and vehicle patrol, an escort service, informal discussions, pamphlets, posters, and films. In addition, there are emergency telephones and lighted pathways and sidewalks.

Programs of Study: Gonzaga awards the B.A., B.S., B.B.A., B.E., and B.G.S. degrees. Master's and doctoral degrees are also awarded. Bachelor's degrees are awarded in BIOLOGICAL SCIENCE (biology/biological science), BUSINESS (accounting, banking and finance, business administration and management, international business management, and marketing/retailing/merchandising), COMMUNICATIONS AND THE ARTS (broadcasting, classics, dramatic arts, English, fine arts, French, German, Germanic languages and literature, Greek, Italian, journalism, Latin, literature, music performance, public relations, Spanish, and speech/debate/rhetoric), COMPUTER AND PHYSICAL SCIENCE (chemistry, computer management, computer science, information sciences and systems, mathematics, physics, and science), EDUCATION (music, physical, and special), ENGINEERING AND ENVIRONMENTAL DESIGN (civil engineering, electrical/electronics engineering, and mechanical engineering), HEALTH PROFESSIONS (nursing, predentistry, and premedicine), SOCIAL SCIENCE (classical/ancient civilization, criminal justice, economics, history, interdisciplinary studies, liberal arts/general studies, philosophy, political science/government, prelaw, psychology, religion, and sociology). Engineering and business administration are the strongest programs academically. Political science, business, and communications have the largest enrollments.

Required: All students must complete 128 credit hours with a minimum 2.0 GPA. The major requirements are 18 hours in upper-division courses and supporting courses required by the major department. Students must complete 9 credits each of philosophy and religious studies, 7 credits in English, speech, and philosophy, and 3 credits in mathematics and English literature.

Special: Cross-registration with Whitworth College, internships, study abroad in 5 countries, a Washington semester, and on- and off-campus work-study programs are offered. High school seniors may take 6 credits per semester. There is a limited pass/fail option, and a general studies degree, student-designed majors, and dual majors are possible. There is a freshman honors program on campus, as well as 9 national honor societies.

Faculty/Classroom: Seventy-one percent of faculty are male; 29%, female. Eighty-one percent teach undergraduates and 17% do research. The average class size in an introductory lecture is 30 to 80; in a laboratory, 14; and in a regular course offering, 21.

Admissions: About 81% of the 1993-94 applicants were accepted. The SAT scores for the 1993-94 freshman class were as follows: Verbal—53% below 500, 36% between 500 and 599, 10% between 600 and 700, and 1% above 700; Math—27% below 500, 45% between 500 and 599, 22% between 600 and 700, and 6% above 700. The ACT scores were 11% below 21, 44% between 21 and 25, 35% between 27 and 28, and 10% above 28. About 59% of the current freshmen were in the top fifth of their class; 83% were in the top two fifths. There were 11 National Merit finalists and 5 semifinalists. Twenty-two freshmen graduated first in their class.

Requirements: A minimum GPA of 2.8 is required. The SAT I or ACT is required. Applicants should be graduates of an accredited secondary school or hold a GED certificate. They must have completed 17 academic credits consisting of 4 years of English, 3 of mathematics, 2 of a foreign language, 1 each of history and science, and 6 years of electives, 4 of which must be from the above subjects and the arts. An essay and letters of recommendation are required. An interview is recommended. AP and CLEP credits are accepted. Important factors used in the admissions decision are advanced placement or honor courses, leadership record, extracurricular activities record, evidence of special talent, and personality, intangible qualities.

Procedure: Freshmen are admitted to all sessions. Entrance exams should be taken by May of the junior year. Applications should be filed by April 1 for fall entry and December 15 for spring entry, along with an application fee of $30. Notification is sent on a rolling basis. There is a deferred admissions plan. A waiting list is an active part of the admissions procedure.

Transfer: About 273 transfer students enrolled in 1993-94. A minimum GPA of 2.5 is required. Students younger than 21 must submit test scores for the SAT I or ACT. An interview is recommended. A total of 30 credits out of 128 must be completed at Gonzaga.

Visiting: There are regularly scheduled orientations for prospective students. Day visits are permitted Monday through Friday; overnight visits, Sunday through Thursday (except for holiday periods). There are guides for informal visits and visitors may sit in on classes and stay overnight at the school. To arrange for a visit, contact the Admissions Office Visitation Coordinator at (800) 572-9658 (in-state) or (800) 523-9712 (out-of-state).

Financial Aid: In 1993-94, 78% of all current freshmen and 75% of continuing students received some form of financial aid. About 65% of all students received need-based aid. The average freshman award was $12,300. Of that total, scholarships or need-based grants averaged $5275 ($12,300 maximum); loans averaged $5125 ($9125 maximum); and work contracts averaged $1,900. All undergraduate students work part-time. Average earnings from campus work for the school year are $1650. The average financial indebtedness of the 1992-93 graduate was $16,000. Gonzaga is a member of CSS. The FAF is required. The deadline for financial aid applications is February 1.

International Students: There are currently 473 international students enrolled. The school actively recruits these students. They must take the TOEFL or the University of Michigan Language Test and achieve a minimum score on the TOEFL of 520.

Computers: The college provides computer facilities for student use. The mainframes are a DEC VAX 6000/40 and a Dec MicroVAX II. Students may access the mainframes from 15 stations in the microcomputer laboratory in the administration building; 48 terminals in the engineering building; and 52 stations in the computer laboratory in the business building. All students may access the system 24 hours per day. There are no time limits and no fees.

Graduates: In 1992-93, 490 bachelor's degrees were awarded. The most popular majors among graduates were business and management (25%), communication arts (10%), and engineering (10%). Within an average freshman class, 1% graduate in 3 years, 54% in 4 years, 57% in 5 years, and 57% in 6 years. Some 70 companies re-

cruited on campus in 1992–93. In the 1992 graduating class, 27% of the students were enrolled in graduate school within 6 months of graduation; 32% had found employment.
Admissions Contact: Philip Ballinger, Dean of Admissions.

HERITAGE COLLEGE   D-3
Toppenish, WA 98948   **(509) 865-2244**

Full-time: 88 men, 233 women	Faculty: 34; IIB, --$
Part-time: 51 men, 147 women	Ph.D.s: 100%
Graduate: 138 men, 370 women	Student/Faculty: 9 to 1
Year: semesters, summer session	Tuition: $5540
Application Deadline: open	Room & Board: n/app
Freshman Class: n/av	
SAT I or ACT: recommended	**NONCOMPETITIVE**

Heritage College, founded in 1982, is a private, coeducational, non-profit commuter college offering undergraduate and graduate programs in liberal arts and teacher education, half of which are given on evenings and weekends. There is one graduate school. The library contains 40,000 volumes, 4850 microform items, and 70 audiovisual forms, and subscribes to 190 periodicals. Special learning facilities include a learning resource center. The 12-acre campus is in a rural area 20 miles south of Yakima. There are 15 buildings on campus.
Student Life: About 98% of undergraduates are from Washington. Students come from 2 states and 2 foreign countries. Forty-six percent are white; 32% Hispanic; 20% Native American/Eskimo. The average age of freshmen is 35; all undergraduates, 35.
Housing: There are no residence halls. All students commute. Alcohol is not permitted. All students may keep cars on campus.
Activities: There are no fraternities or sororities on campus. There are many groups on campus, including computers, ethnic, literary magazine, newspaper, and student government.
Disabled Students: The entire campus is accessible to disabled students. The following facilities are available: wheelchair ramps, special parking, specially equipped rest rooms, special class scheduling, and lowered drinking fountains.
Services: In addition to many counseling and information services, tutoring is available in most subjects. There is also remedial math, reading, and writing.
Campus Safety and Security: Campus safety and security measures include lighted pathways and sidewalks.
Programs of Study: Heritage awards the B.A., B.S., and B.A.Ed. degrees. Master's degrees also are awarded. Bachelor's degrees are awarded in BUSINESS (business administration and management), COMMUNICATIONS AND THE ARTS (English and Spanish), COMPUTER AND PHYSICAL SCIENCE (computer science, mathematics, and science), EDUCATION (elementary, science, secondary, and social studies), ENGINEERING AND ENVIRONMENTAL DESIGN (environmental science), SOCIAL SCIENCE (interdisciplinary studies, psychology, public administration, and sociology). Education has the largest enrollment.
Required: All students must complete 40 credits of general college requirements, which include 12 credits each in arts and letters, 10 credits in science and mathematics, 9 credits in social sciences, and 1 year of English and computer science. At least 126 semester credit hours must be completed, with at least 48 upper-division credits. The education major must have a minimum GPA of 2.5; others must have a 2.0.
Special: Heritage provides individualized assistance. Credit by examination is available in many courses, and credit may be given for work experience. The college also has cooperative programs with 3 school districts and internships in local businesses and social service agencies. Pass/fail options are possible for some courses.
Faculty/Classroom: Forty-seven percent of faculty are male; 53%, female. No introductory courses are taught by graduate students. The average class size in an introductory lecture is 20; in a laboratory, 16; and in a regular course offering, 20.
Requirements: The SAT I or ACT is recommended, but entrance exams are not required. Applicants must have graduated from an accredited secondary school or hold a GED certificate. An interview is recommended. Assessment for placement in English and mathematics courses is required. AP and CLEP credits are accepted.
Procedure: Freshmen are admitted to all sessions. Application deadlines are open. The college accepts all applicants. Notification is sent on a rolling basis.
Transfer: A total of 32 credits out of 126 must be completed at Heritage.
Visiting: There are regularly scheduled orientations for prospective students, consisting of a day and an evening fall orientation. There are guides for informal visits and visitors may sit in on classes. To arrange for a visit, contact Bertha Ortega, Dean of Students at (509) 865-2244.
Financial Aid: In a recent year, 60% of all students received some form of financial aid. About 58% of all students received need-based aid. The average freshman award was $6500. Of that total, scholar-

ships or need-based grants averaged $2275 ($4500 maximum); loans averaged $500 ($4875 maximum); and work contracts averaged $2000 ($5000 maximum). Forty-five percent of undergraduate students work part-time. Average earnings from campus work for the school year are $3000. The average financial indebtedness of the 1992–93 graduate was $2500. Heritage is a member of CSS. The FAF, the college's own financial statement, financial aid transcripts from colleges previously attended, and a copy of income tax returns are required. The deadline for financial aid applications is April 1.
International Students: There are currently 2 international students enrolled. They must take the TOEFL and achieve a minimum score of 500.
Computers: The college provides computer facilities for student use. The mainframes are a VT420 and a DEC VAX for administrative use. There are 150 networked terminals; 26 are always available for student use. Others are available when classes are not scheduled in the rooms. All students may access the system. There are no time limits on using the system.
Graduates: In 1992–93, 74 bachelor's degrees were awarded. The most popular majors among graduates were education (30%), special science/social work (24%), and business (11%).
Admissions Contact: Winona Zack, Director of Admissions.

NORTHWEST COLLEGE   C-2
(Formerly Northwest College of the Assemblies of God)
Kirkland, WA 98033   **(206) 889-5210; (800) 6-NWEST-1**

Full-time: 339 men, 365 women	Faculty: 34; IIB, --$
Part-time: 26 men, 27 women	Ph.D.s: 50%
Graduate: none	Student/Faculty: 21 to 1
Year: semesters, summer session	Tuition: $6647
Application Deadline: August 1	Room & Board: $3250
Freshman Class: 201 applied, 199 accepted, 167 enrolled	
SAT I Verbal/Math: 470/440	ACT: 21 **LESS COMPETITIVE**

Northwest College, founded in 1934, is a private coeducational, Christian institution affiliated with the Assemblies of God. It offers undergraduate programs in religion, ministerial studies, liberal arts, and professional studies. The library contains 92,000 volumes, and subscribes to 600 periodicals. Computerized library sources and services include database searching. Special learning facilities include a radio station. The 60-acre campus is in a suburban area in Kirkland, 10 miles east of Seattle. Including residence halls, there are 19 buildings on campus.
Student Life: About 71% of undergraduates are from Washington. Students come from 20 states, 8 foreign countries, and Canada. Eighty-eight percent are white. Most are Protestant. The average age of freshmen is 20; all undergraduates, 22.7. Thirty-five percent drop out by the end of their first year.
Housing: A total of 510 students can be accommodated in college housing. College-sponsored living facilities include single-sex dormitories, on-campus apartments, and married-student housing. On-campus housing is guaranteed for all 4 years. Fifty-eight percent of students live on campus; of those, 50% remain on campus on weekends. Alcohol is not permitted. All students may keep cars on campus.
Activities: There are no fraternities or sororities on campus. There are 15 groups on campus, including cheerleading, choir, chorale, chorus, drama, international, musical theater, newspaper, pep band, professional, radio, religious, social, social service, student government, and yearbook. Popular campus events include Harvest Time Social, Homecoming, and All-School Banquet.
Sports: There are 2 intercollegiate sports for men and 2 for women, and 2 intramural sports for men and 2 for women. Athletic and recreation facilities include a gymnasium pavilion, outdoor tennis courts, a practice field for soccer and intramural football, and access to the Seattle Seahawks' fields.
Disabled Students: Fifty-five percent of the campus is accessible to disabled students. The following facilities are available: wheelchair ramps, special parking, and specially equipped rest rooms.
Services: There is a reader service for the blind. Tutoring assistance is available.
Campus Safety and Security: Campus safety and security measures include 24-hour foot and vehicle patrol, informal discussions, pamphlets, posters, films, and emergency telephones. In addition, there are lighted pathways and sidewalks.
Programs of Study: Northwest awards the B.A. degree. Associate degrees also are awarded. Bachelor's degrees are awarded in BUSINESS (business administration and management), EDUCATION (education), SOCIAL SCIENCE (behavioral science, biblical studies, interdisciplinary studies, ministries, religion, and religious music). Behavioral science and teacher education are the strongest academically. Teacher education, church ministries, behavioral science, and business management and administration have the largest enrollments.

Required: Students must complete 17 credits in humanities, 10 in science and mathematics, 12 in social science, and 10 in religion. At least 124 semester credits (up to 139 for teacher education), with a minimum GPA of 2.0, are required. The number of semester credits needed in the major varies from 36 to 50.

Special: Northwest offers study abroad in 3 countries through the Christian College Coalition, dual majors in all areas, and a student-designed interdisciplinary studies major.

Faculty/Classroom: Sixty-eight percent of faculty are male; 32%, female. All teach undergraduates.

Admissions: About 99% of the 1993–94 applicants were accepted.

Requirements: Northwest requires applicants to be in the upper 50% of their class. A minimum GPA of 2.0 is required. The SAT I or ACT is required. AP and CLEP credits are accepted. Important factors used in the admissions decision are personality, intangible qualities, leadership record, recommendations by alumni, recommendations by school officials, and parents or siblings attending the school.

Procedure: Freshmen are admitted to all sessions. Entrance exams should be taken in the spring of the junior year. There are early decision and deferred admissions plans. Early decision applications should be filed by November 15; regular applications, by August 1 for fall entry, December 15 for spring entry, and April 15 for summer entry, along with an application fee of $20. Notification of early decision is sent December 1; regular decision, on a rolling basis. About 20 early decision candidates were accepted for the 1993–94 class.

Transfer: About 140 transfer students enrolled in 1993–94. Transfers must have a minimum 2.0 GPA from high school and college and must submit SAT I or ACT scores, an essay, and 2 letters of reference. At least 30 semester credits out of 124 to 139 must be completed at Northwest.

Visiting: There are regularly scheduled orientations for prospective students, including Northwest Fridays during the fall semester and a Campus Days weekend each spring with class visits and special events. There are guides for informal visits and visitors may sit in on classes and stay overnight (when space allows) at the school. To arrange for a visit, contact Sharon Gerard at (206) 889–5210 or (800) 6-NWEST-1.

Financial Aid: In 1993–94, 75% of all current freshmen and 80% of continuing students received some form of financial aid. About 70% of freshmen and 75% of continuing students received need-based aid. The average freshman award was $6540. Of that total, scholarships or need-based grants averaged $2485; loans averaged $3859; and work contracts averaged $196. Eighty percent of undergraduate students work part-time. Average earnings from campus work for the school year are $2385. Northwest is a member of CSS. The college's own financial statement and FAFSA are required. The deadline for financial aid applications is March 1.

International Students: There are currently 23 international students enrolled. They must take the TOEFL and achieve a minimum score of 500. They must also take the SAT I or the ACT.

Computers: There are 18 IBMs and 4 Apple Macintosh computers in the computer center and the library. All students may access the system evenings and weekends when computer classes are not in session. There are no time limits on using the system. The fees are $30 per semester for students not enrolled in a computer class.

Graduates: In 1992–93, 109 bachelor's degrees were awarded. The most popular majors among graduates were biblical literature (22%), behavioral science (21%), and elementary education (19%). Within an average freshman class, 25% graduate in 5 years.

Admissions Contact: Calvin L. White, Director, Enrollment Services.

NORTHWEST COLLEGE OF THE ASSEMBLIES OF GOD
(See Northwest College)

PACIFIC LUTHERAN UNIVERSITY   C-2
Tacoma, WA 98447   (206) 535–7151; (800) 247–6758 (in-state)

Full-time: 1076 men, 1504 women	Faculty: 225; IIA, -$
Part-time: 104 men, 198 women	Ph.D.s: 79%
Graduate: 170 men, 297 women	Student/Faculty: 12 to 1
Year: 4–1–4, summer session	Tuition: $11,968
Application Deadline: March 1	Room & Board: $4030
Freshman Class: 1463 applied, 1170 accepted, 508 enrolled	
SAT I Verbal/Math: 460/510	**VERY COMPETITIVE**

Pacific Lutheran University, founded in 1890, is an independent, nonprofit, coeducational institution affiliated with the Evangelical Lutheran Church of America. It offers programs in arts and sciences, business administration, education, nursing, music, and physical education. There are 6 undergraduate schools and one graduate school. In addition to regional accreditation, PLU has baccalaureate program accreditation with AACSB, CSWE, NASM, NCATE, and NLN. The library contains 332,950 volumes and 54,101 microform items, and subscribes to 2105 periodicals. Computerized library sources and services include the card catalog, interlibrary loans, and database searching. Special learning facilities include a learning resource center, an art gallery, a radio station, a TV station, an herbarium, invertebrate and vertebrate museums, a biology field station, Northwest history collections, and the Scandinavian history collection. The 133-acre campus is in a suburban area 7 miles south of Tacoma. Including residence halls, there are 39 buildings on campus.

Student Life: About 68% of undergraduates are from Washington. Students come from 39 states, 27 foreign countries, and Canada. Ninety-seven percent are from public schools; 3% from private. Eighty-three percent are white. Sixty-six percent are Protestant; 23% claim no religious affiliation. The average age of freshmen is 19; all undergraduates, 24. Eighteen percent drop out by the end of their first year; 65% remain to graduate.

Housing: A total of 1795 students can be accommodated in college housing. College-sponsored living facilities include single-sex and coed dormitories, off-campus apartments, and married-student housing. On-campus housing is guaranteed for all 4 years. Fifty-five percent of students live on campus. Alcohol is not permitted. All students may keep cars on campus.

Activities: There are no fraternities or sororities on campus. There are 45 groups on campus, including art, band, cheerleading, choir, chorale, chorus, computers, dance, drama, ethnic, honors, international, jazz band, literary magazine, musical theater, newspaper, opera, orchestra, pep band, photography, political, professional, radio and TV, religious, social, social service, student government, symphony, and yearbook. Popular campus events include an opening convocation, a Christmas concert, a presidential forum, and the Lucia Bride Festival.

Sports: There are 10 intercollegiate sports each for men and women, and 13 intramural sports each for men and women. Athletic and recreation facilities include a fitness center with an all-weather track, a 9-hole golf course, a swimming pool, and racquetball, squash, and tennis courts. The campus indoor gymnasium seats 4000, and the Olsen auditorium seats 4000.

Disabled Students: Ninety percent of the campus is accessible to disabled students. The following facilities are available: wheelchair ramps, elevators, special parking, specially equipped rest rooms, special class scheduling, lowered drinking fountains, and lowered telephones.

Services: In addition to many counseling and information services, tutoring is available in most subjects.

Campus Safety and Security: Campus safety and security measures include 24-hour foot and vehicle patrol, self-defense education, escort service, and informal discussions. In addition, there are pamphlets, posters, films, emergency telephones, and lighted pathways and sidewalks.

Programs of Study: PLU awards the B.A., B.S., B.A. Ed., B.A.P.E., B.A.Rec., B.B.A., B.F.A., B.M., B.M.Arts, B.M.Ed., B.S.N., and B.S.P.E. degrees. Master's degrees are also awarded. Bachelor's degrees are awarded in BIOLOGICAL SCIENCE (biology/biological science), BUSINESS (business administration and management), COMMUNICATIONS AND THE ARTS (classics, communications, English, fine arts, French, German, music, music performance, music theory and composition, piano/organ, Scandinavian languages, Spanish, and voice), COMPUTER AND PHYSICAL SCIENCE (chemistry, computer programming, computer science, earth science, geology, mathematics, and physics), EDUCATION (music and physical), ENGINEERING AND ENVIRONMENTAL DESIGN (computer engineering, electrical/electronics engineering, and engineering physics), HEALTH PROFESSIONS (nursing), SOCIAL SCIENCE (anthropology, economics, history, international studies, law, philosophy, political science/government, psychology, religion, Scandinavian studies, social work, and sociology). Business administration and education have the largest enrollments.

Required: All students must complete 128 credit hours, with a maximum of 40 in the major. Candidates for degrees in nursing, business administration, and education need a cumulative 2.5 GPA; all others must have a 2.0 GPA. The required curriculum is 36 credit hours of distributive core consisting of 8 each in arts/literature, natural sciences/mathematics, philosophy, religious studies, and social sciences, and 28 credit hours of interdisciplinary courses that explore a central theme.

Special: PLU offers 2 different bachelor's degrees simultaneously; 3-2 engineering degrees with Washington University in St. Louis and Columbia University, and accelerated degree programs in most majors. Dual majors and student-designed majors can be arranged. There are 40 study-abroad programs in 20 countries, extensive internships with local businesses, and work-study programs. Credit is given by examination and through the AURA Program for adults 30 years of age or older. Nondegree study and pass/fail options are also available. There are 7 national honor societies on campus. Six departments have honors programs.

Faculty/Classroom: Sixty-one percent of faculty are male; 39%, female. The average class size in an introductory lecture is 24 and in a regular course offering, 19.

Admissions: About 80% of the 1993–94 applicants were accepted. The SAT scores for the 1993–94 freshman class were as follows: Verbal—65% below 500, 26% between 500 and 599, and 9% between 600 and 700; Math—43% below 500, 36% between 500 and 599, 17% between 600 and 700, and 4% above 700. About 61% of the current freshmen were in the top fifth of their class; 86% were in the top two fifths. There were 5 National Merit finalists.

Requirements: PLU requires applicants to be in the upper 50% of their class. A minimum GPA of 2.5 is required. The SAT I is required and the ACT is recommended. PLU prefers graduates of accredited secondary schools, although GED certificates are accepted. The university requires 2 years each of college-preparatory mathematics and a foreign language, and recommends 4 years of English, 2 each of history, social studies, laboratory science, and music, and 1 each of computer science and art. An essay is required; an audition and an interview recommended. AP and CLEP credits are accepted. Important factors used in the admissions decision are advanced placement or honor courses, evidence of special talent, leadership record, extracurricular activities record, and recommendations by alumni.

Procedure: Freshmen are admitted fall and spring. Entrance exams should be taken by January of the senior year. Early decision applications should be filed by November 15; regular applications, by March 1 for fall entry and January 1 for spring entry, along with an application fee of $35. Notification is sent on a rolling basis. There are early decision, early admissions, and deferred admissions plans. About 246 early decision candidates were accepted for an earlier class. A waiting list is an active part of the admissions procedure, with about 5% of applicants on the list.

Transfer: About 360 transfer students enrolled in an earlier year. Candidates must have acceptable records in other colleges and universities attended. Test scores are not required if at least 1 year of acceptable work totaling 30 semester credits is presented. A PLU-supplied clearance form must be completed by the most recently attended institution. A total of 32 credits out of 128 must be completed at PLU.

Visiting: There are guides for informal visits and visitors may sit in on classes and stay overnight at the school. To arrange for a visit, contact David E. Gunovich, Director of Admissions at (800) 247–6758 or (206) 535–7151.

Financial Aid: In an earlier year, 73% of all current freshmen and 72% of continuing students received some form of financial aid. Scholarships or need-based grants averaged $2500 ($9000 maximum); loans averaged $1500 ($4000 maximum); and work contracts averaged $1000 ($2000 maximum). The average financial indebtedness of a recent graduate was $5000. PLU is a member of CSS. The FAF is required. The deadline for financial aid applications is March 1.

International Students: There were 140 international students enrolled in a recent year. The school actively recruits these students. They must take the TOEFL and achieve a minimum score of 550.

Computers: The college provides computer facilities for student use. The mainframe is a DEC VAX 6210–6220 cluster. There are 3 campus computer laboratories. All students may access the system. It may be used 18 hours per day, 24 hours with a modem. There are no time limits on using the system and no fees.

Graduates: In an earlier year, 839 bachelor's degrees were awarded. Some 120 companies recruited on campus that year.

Admissions Contact: David E. Gunovich, Director of Admissions.

SAINT MARTIN'S COLLEGE B-3
Lacey, WA 98503   (206) 438–4311; (800) 368–8803 (out-of-state)

Full-time: 201 men, 288 women	Faculty: 53; IIB, --$
Part-time: 261 men, 321 women	Ph.D.s: 66%
Graduate: 134 men, 154 women	Student/Faculty: 9 to 1
Year: semesters, summer session	Tuition: $10,905
Application Deadline: open	Room & Board: $4060
Freshman Class: 190 applied, 165 accepted, 63 enrolled	
SAT I Verbal/Math: 460/480	ACT: 21 COMPETITIVE

St. Martin's College, founded in 1895, is a small, coeducational, Roman Catholic institution conducted by the Benedictine order, offering undergraduate and graduate programs in liberal arts and sciences, business, engineering, nursing, and preprofessional areas. There are 6 undergraduate and 4 graduate schools. In addition to regional accreditation, St. Martin's has baccalaureate program accreditation with ABET and NLN. The library contains 88,956 volumes and 18,000 microform items, and subscribes to 450 periodicals. Special learning facilities include a learning resource center, an art gallery, and a natural history museum. The 400-acre campus is in a suburban area 3 miles from Olympia and 60 miles south of Seattle. Including residence halls, there are 9 buildings on campus.

Student Life: About 80% of undergraduates are from Washington. Students come from 10 states, 9 foreign countries, and Canada. Seventy percent are from public schools; 30% from private. Eighty-four percent are white. Fifty percent are Catholic. The average age of freshmen is 19; all undergraduates, 31. Six percent drop out by the end of their first year; 75% remain to graduate.

Housing: A total of 175 students can be accommodated in college housing. College-sponsored living facilities include coed dormitories. On-campus housing is guaranteed for all 4 years. Eighty-five percent of students commute. Alcohol is not permitted. All students may keep cars on campus.

Activities: About 2% of men belong to 2 local fraternities; about 2% of women belong to 1 national and 1 local sorority. There are 40 groups on campus, including cheerleading, computers, drama, ethnic, international, newspaper, professional, religious, social, social service, student government, and yearbook. Popular campus events include Homecoming, Hawaiian Luau, Parents Weekend, Career Fair, and theater productions.

Sports: There are 2 intercollegiate sports for men and 3 for women, and 9 intramural sports each for men and women. Athletic and recreation facilities include a 5300-seat multipurpose pavillion, a student union, athletic fields, tennis courts, and nearby golf courses, lakes, and mountains.

Disabled Students: Ninety percent of the campus is accessible to disabled students. The following facilities are available: elevators, special parking, and specially equipped rest rooms.

Services: St. Martin's provides career, military, personal, and psychological counseling and information services.

Campus Safety and Security: Campus safety and security measures include an escort service, pamphlets, posters, films, lighted pathways and sidewalks, and security patrol from dark to dawn.

Programs of Study: St. Martin's awards the B.A., B.S., B.S.C.E., and B.S.N. degrees. Associate and master's degrees also are awarded. Bachelor's degrees are awarded in BIOLOGICAL SCIENCE (biology/biological science), BUSINESS (accounting, banking and finance, international business management, management science, and marketing/retailing/merchandising), COMMUNICATIONS AND THE ARTS (English), COMPUTER AND PHYSICAL SCIENCE (chemistry, computer science, and mathematics), EDUCATION (computer, elementary, social studies, and special), ENGINEERING AND ENVIRONMENTAL DESIGN (aviation administration/management, civil engineering, and mechanical engineering), HEALTH PROFESSIONS (nursing, predentistry, premedicine, prepharmacy, and preveterinary science), SOCIAL SCIENCE (community services, criminal justice, economics, history, humanities, political science/government, prelaw, psychology, and religion). Education is the strongest program academically and has the largest enrollment.

Required: All students must complete freshman composition and general education requirements, including 1 course each in literature, philosophy, religious studies, natural science with laboratory, mathematics (pre-calculus), computer science, U.S. history, and non-U.S. history, as well as 2 courses in social sciences, 1 in the arts, and 2 credits of physical education. Students must pass an English proficiency examination. A total of 120 to 130 semester credits with a 2.0 GPA (2.5 in nursing major courses) is required. One year of foreign language is required if the student did not take 2 years of a single foreign language in high school.

Special: Double majors, work-study with the state of Washington and Saint Martin's, internships in all disciplines, a Washington semester with American University, and pass/fail options are offered. The FOCUS program offers credit for job experience. Nondegree study is possible.

Faculty/Classroom: Sixty-eight percent of faculty are male; 32%, female. All teach undergraduates and 70% do research. No introductory courses are taught by graduate students. The average class size in an introductory lecture is 25; in a laboratory, 12; and in a regular course offering, 17.

Admissions: About 87% of the 1993–94 applicants were accepted. The SAT scores for the 1993–94 freshman class were as follows: Verbal—60% below 500, 30% between 500 and 599, and 10% between 600 and 700; Math—70% below 500, 25% between 500 and 599, and 5% between 600 and 700. The ACT scores were 10% below 21, 40% between 21 and 23, 30% between 24 and 26, 10% between 27 and 28, and 10% above 28. About 20% of the current freshmen were in the top fifth of their class; 40% were in the top two fifths. Four freshmen graduated first in their class.

Requirements: A minimum GPA of 2.5 is required. The SAT I or ACT is required. Applicants must be graduates of an accredited secondary school or have a GED, with a minimum of 16 academic units, including 4 in English, 2 or 3 in mathematics, 2 in history/social science, 1 or 2 each in foreign language and laboratory science, and 7 in electives. Class standing also is considered. An essay and recommendation from a teacher or counselor are required. AP and CLEP credits are accepted. Important factors used in the admissions decision are advanced placement or honor courses, recommendations by

school officials, personality, intangible qualities, geographic diversity, and leadership record.

Procedure: Freshmen are admitted to all sessions. Application deadlines are open. The application fee is $25. Notification is sent on a rolling basis.

Transfer: About 173 transfer students enrolled in 1993–94. Transfer applicants must submit transcripts from all colleges previously attended. A total of 30 credits out of 120 to 130 must be completed at St. Martin's.

Visiting: There are regularly scheduled orientations for prospective students, including a campus tour and faculty, student service, and financial aid presentations. There are guides for informal visits and visitors may sit in on classes and stay overnight at the school. To arrange for a visit, contact the Admissions Office at (206) 438-4311 or (800) 368-8803.

Financial Aid: In 1993–94, all current freshmen and 69% of continuing students received some form of financial aid. About 96% of freshmen and 57% of continuing students received need-based aid. The average freshman award was $6887. Of that total, scholarships or need-based grants averaged $3752 ($10,740 maximum); loans averaged $3811 ($4125 maximum); and work contracts averaged $2430 ($3400 maximum). All undergraduate students work part-time. The average financial indebtedness of the 1992–93 graduate was $8100. St. Martin's is a member of CSS. The FAF is required. The deadline for financial aid applications is March 1.

International Students: There are currently 45 international students enrolled. They must take the TOEFL and achieve a minimum score of 525. The student must also take the SAT I or the ACT.

Computers: The college provides computer facilities for student use. IBM PC and Macintosh microcomputers are available in the computer center. All students may access the system.

Graduates: In 1992–93, 232 bachelor's degrees were awarded. The most popular majors among graduates were accounting (18%), elementary education (17%), and psychology (13%). Within an average freshman class, 1% graduate in 3 years, 22% in 4 years, and 27% in 5 years. Some 80 companies recruited on campus in 1992–93. In the 1992 graduating class, 90% of all graduates were enrolled in graduate school within 6 months of graduation or had found employment.

Admissions Contact: Rob Kvidt, Director of Admissions.

SEATTLE PACIFIC UNIVERSITY

C-2

Seattle, WA 98119   (206) 281-2021; (800) 366-3344 (in-state)

Full-time: 653 men, 1244 women	**Faculty:** 145; IIA, --$
Part-time: 158 men, 217 women	**Ph.D.s:** 83%
Graduate: 404 men, 761 women	**Student/Faculty:** 13 to 1
Year: quarters, summer session	**Tuition:** $11,979
Application Deadline: September 1	**Room & Board:** $4524

Freshman Class: 1183 applied, 1016 accepted, 407 enrolled

SAT I Verbal/Math: 467/506   **COMPETITIVE**

Seattle Pacific University, founded in 1891, is a private, coeducational, nonprofit institution affiliated with the Free Methodist Church. It offers programs in business and economics, education, fine and performing arts, health science, humanities, natural and mathematical sciences, physical education and athletics, religion, and social and behavioral sciences. There are 9 undergraduate and 6 graduate schools. In addition to regional accreditation, SPU has baccalaureate program accreditation with ABET, ADA, NASM, NCATE, and NLN. The library contains 170,000 volumes, 380,000 microform items, and 3800 audiovisual forms, and subscribes to 1500 periodicals. Computerized library sources and services include database searching. Special learning facilities include a learning resource center, an art gallery, a science center, and a performing arts theater. The 35-acre campus is in an urban area. Including residence halls, there are 94 buildings on campus.

Student Life: About 69% of undergraduates are from Washington. Students come from 38 states, 45 foreign countries, and Canada. Eighty-six percent are white. Seventy-five percent are Protestant; 17% claim no religious affiliation. The average age of freshmen is 18; all undergraduates, 21. Twenty-eight percent drop out by the end of their first year; 41% remain to graduate.

Housing: A total of 1206 students can be accommodated in college housing. College-sponsored living facilities include single-sex and coed dormitories, on-campus apartments, and married-student housing. On-campus housing is available on a first-come, first-served basis and is available on a lottery system for upperclassmen. Fifty-three percent of students commute. Alcohol is not permitted. All students may keep cars on campus.

Activities: There are no fraternities or sororities on campus. There are 50 groups on campus, including art, cheerleading, chess, choir, drama, ethnic, honors, international, jazz band, literary magazine, newspaper, orchestra, pep band, political, professional, religious, social, social service, student government, and yearbook. Popular campus events include Christmas Tradition celebration, Family Weekend,

Homecoming, Talent Show, spring picnic, and Ivy Cutting at Graduation.

Sports: There are 5 intercollegiate sports for men and 6 for women, and 22 intramural sports each for men and women. Athletic and recreation facilities include a soccer field, an oval track, tennis and basketball courts, a gymnasium and crew house, a crew dock, a 2600-seat indoor gymnasium, and an 800-seat campus auditorium.

Disabled Students: Seventy percent of the campus is accessible to disabled students. The following facilities are available: wheelchair ramps, elevators, special parking, specially equipped rest rooms, and special class scheduling.

Services: In addition to many counseling and information services, tutoring is available in most subjects. There is also a reader service for the blind, remedial math and writing, and priority registration for disabled students.

Campus Safety and Security: Campus safety and security measures include a 24-hour foot and vehicle patrol, an escort service, pamphlets, posters, films, emergency telephones, and lighted pathways and sidewalks.

Programs of Study: SPU awards the B.A. and B.S. degrees. Master's and doctoral degrees also are awarded. Bachelor's degrees are awarded in BIOLOGICAL SCIENCE (biology/biological science), BUSINESS (accounting, business administration and management, and recreation and leisure services), COMMUNICATIONS AND THE ARTS (classics, communications, dramatic arts, English, fine arts, music, and visual and performing arts), COMPUTER AND PHYSICAL SCIENCE (chemistry, computer science, mathematics, physics, and science), EDUCATION (Christian Education, mathematics, music, physical, social science, and special), ENGINEERING AND ENVIRONMENTAL DESIGN (electrical/electronics engineering and engineering and applied science), HEALTH PROFESSIONS (nursing), SOCIAL SCIENCE (biblical studies, clothing and textiles management/production/services, economics, European studies, family/consumer studies, food science, history, liberal arts/general studies, philosophy, physical fitness/movement, political science/government, psychology, religion, sociology, and theological studies). Business administration, nursing, and education have the largest enrollments.

Required: All students must demonstrate competency in mathematics and English. Students must complete 15 credits in Christian heritage and values, 56 in general education, plus up to 15 credits of foreign language competency, and at least 45 to 60 in the major, depending on the major. A minimum of 180 credits is needed for the bachelor's degree, with a 2.0 GPA overall. At least 60 credits must be earned in 3000-level courses or higher.

Special: There is a cooperative program with Fashion Institute of Technology in New York City, Fashion Institute of Design and Merchandising in Los Angeles, and Han Nam University in Korea, cross-registration with the Christian College Consortium and Christian College Coalition, and a Washington semester in American studies through the Christian College Coalition. SPU offers internships, study abroad in Costa Rica, Europe, and Korea, work-study programs, student-designed majors, interdisciplinary majors such as language arts, and a liberal studies major for associate degree graduates. A general studies degree, pass/no credit options, and nondegree study are available. There is a freshman honors program on campus, as well as 5 national honor societies. There is a university-wide honors program.

Faculty/Classroom: Sixty-four percent of faculty are male; 36%, female. All teach undergraduates. No introductory courses are taught by graduate students. The average class size in a regular course offering is 18.

Admissions: About 86% of the 1993–94 applicants were accepted. The SAT scores for the 1993–94 freshman class were as follows: Verbal—62% below 500, 29% between 500 and 599, 8% between 600 and 700, and 1% above 700; Math—50% below 500, 29% between 500 and 599, 17% between 600 and 700, and 4% above 700. About 70% of the current freshmen were in the top fifth of their class; 86% were in the top two fifths. There were 3 National Merit finalists. Thirty-one freshmen graduated first in their class.

Requirements: A minimum GPA of 2.5 is required. The SAT I is required, with a minimum required composite score of 950. Candidates should be graduates of an accredited secondary school or hold a GED certificate. An interview is recommended. AP and CLEP credits are accepted. Important factors used in the admissions decision are advanced placement or honor courses, leadership record, extracurricular activities record, evidence of special talent, and personality, intangible qualities.

Procedure: Freshmen are admitted to all sessions. Entrance exams should be taken before January of the senior year. Applications should be filed by September 1 for fall entry, December 1 for winter entry, March 1 for spring entry, and May 1 for summer entry, along with an application fee of $35. Notification is sent on a rolling basis. There are early decision and early admissions plans. About 230 early decision candidates were accepted for the 1993–94 class.

Transfer: About 301 transfer students enrolled in 1993–94. A minimum 2.5 GPA is required, and an interview is recommended. Transcripts from all previous colleges attended and from high school are required. Evidence of honorable dismissal from the previous school is also required. Students with at least 30 credits earned are not required to take the SAT I or ACT. A total of 45 quarter credits out of 180 must be completed at SPU.

Visiting: There are regularly scheduled orientations for prospective students. There are guides for informal visits and visitors may sit in on classes and stay overnight at the school. To arrange for a visit, contact Jennifer Feddern, Admissions Counselor, at (206) 281–2021 or (800) 366–3344.

Financial Aid: In 1993–94, 65% of all students received some form of financial aid. About 62% of freshmen and 61% of continuing students received need-based aid. The average freshman award was $12,457. Of that total, scholarships or need-based grants averaged $6658 ($11,453 maximum); loans averaged $3916 ($4700 maximum); and work contracts averaged $1883 ($2500 maximum). Seventy-five percent of undergraduate students work part-time. Average earnings from campus work for the school year are $1629. The average financial indebtedness of the 1992–93 graduate was $14,000. SPU is a member of CSS. The FAFSA financial statement is required. There is no deadline for financial aid applications.

International Students: There are currently 197 international students enrolled. The school actively recruits these students. They must take the TOEFL or the University of Michigan Language Test and achieve a minimum score on the TOEFL of 550.

Computers: The college provides computer facilities for student use. The mainframe is a DEC VAX 4600. There are also 140 microcomputers in 2 computer laboratories. Students have access to minicomputers through a network; all students may use the microcomputers. Some dormitory rooms are wired to the mainframe for E-Mail. Computers may be used during laboratory hours, Monday through Saturday during the academic year. There are no fees.

Graduates: In 1992–93, 438 bachelor's degrees were awarded. The most popular majors among graduates were teacher certification (19%), nursing (8%), and computer science (7%). Within an average freshman class, 42% graduate in 4 years and 35% in 5 years. Some 45 companies recruited on campus in a recent year. In the 1992 graduating class, 10% of students were enrolled in graduate school within 6 months of graduation; 75% had found employment.

Admissions Contact: Ken Cornell, Director of Admissions.

SEATTLE UNIVERSITY
C-2

Seattle, WA 98122   (206) 296–5800; (800) 426–7123 (out-of-state)

Full-time: 1141 men, 1388 women | Faculty: 279; IIA, av$
Part-time: 376 men, 435 women | Ph.Ds: 84%
Graduate: 830 men, 890 women | Student/Faculty: 9 to 1
Year: quarters, summer session | Tuition: $12,150
Application Deadline: June 1 | Room & Board: $4440
Freshman Class: 1861 applied, 1431 accepted, 497 enrolled
SAT I Verbal/Math: 457/533   **COMPETITIVE**

Seattle University, founded in 1891, is a private, comprehensive, co-educational institution affiliated with the Roman Catholic Church and operated by the Jesuit Fathers. The emphasis of the undergraduate and graduate programs is on the liberal arts and sciences, business, engineering, health science, teacher preparation, and theological studies. There are 5 undergraduate and 6 graduate schools. In addition to regional accreditation, SU has baccalaureate program accreditation with AACSB, ABET, CAHEA, NCATE, and NLN. The library contains 233,000 volumes, and subscribes to 1450 periodicals. Special learning facilities include a learning resource center and an art gallery. The 58-acre campus is in an urban area close to downtown Seattle. Including residence halls, there are 27 buildings on campus.

Student Life: About 58% of undergraduates are from Washington. Students come from 39 states, 71 foreign countries, and Canada. Fifty-five percent are from public schools; 45% from private. Seventy-three percent are white; 13% Asian American. Forty percent are Catholic. The average age of freshmen is 18; all undergraduates, 25.5. Twenty-four percent drop out by the end of their first year; 57% remain to graduate.

Housing: A total of 1000 students can be accommodated in college housing. College-sponsored living facilities include single-sex and coed dormitories. On-campus housing is guaranteed for all 4 years. Sixty-one percent of students commute. All students may keep cars on campus.

Activities: There are no fraternities or sororities on campus. There are 60 groups on campus, including art, cheerleading, chorale, dance, drama, ethnic, gay, honors, international, literary magazine, newspaper, photography, political, professional, radio and TV, religious, social, social service, and student government. Popular campus events include Homecoming, Hawaiian Luau, and Quad Stock.

Sports: There are 5 intercollegiate sports for men and 5 for women, and 12 intramural sports for men and 10 for women. Athletic and recreation facilities include a center with 2 swimming pools, 5 racquetball, 2 squash, and 3 basketball courts; a fitness/weight room; and an Astroturf gymnasium seating 1200.

Disabled Students: Nearly all of the campus is accessible to disabled students. The following facilities are available: wheelchair ramps, elevators, special parking, specially equipped rest rooms, special class scheduling, lowered drinking fountains, and lowered telephones.

Services: In addition to many counseling and information services, tutoring is available in most subjects, including mathematics, English, accounting, language, and science. There is also a reader service for the blind, and remedial math, reading, and writing.

Campus Safety and Security: Campus safety and security measures include a 24-hour foot and vehicle patrol, self defense education, an escort service, and shuttle buses. In addition, there are informal discussions, pamphlets, posters, films, emergency telephones, and lighted pathways and sidewalks.

Programs of Study: SU awards the B.A. and B.S. degrees. Master's and doctoral degrees also are awarded. Bachelor's degrees are awarded in BUSINESS (accounting, banking and finance, business administration and management, business economics, international business management, and marketing/retailing/merchandising), COMMUNICATIONS AND THE ARTS (communications, dramatic arts, English, fine arts, French, German, journalism, and Spanish), COMPUTER AND PHYSICAL SCIENCE (chemistry, computer science, mathematics, and physics), ENGINEERING AND ENVIRONMENTAL DESIGN (civil engineering, electrical/electronics engineering, and mechanical engineering), HEALTH PROFESSIONS (nursing, predentistry, and premedicine), SOCIAL SCIENCE (criminal justice, economics, history, liberal arts/general studies, philosophy, political science/government, prelaw, psychology, public administration, religion, and sociology). Engineering, accounting, nursing, business, and psychology are the strongest programs academically and have the largest enrollments.

Required: Students must complete 180 to 192 quarter hours, depending on the degree, with 70 to 90 in the major, and maintain a minimum GPA of 2.25 to 2.5. Core curriculum requirements total 78 quarter hours, and 10 quarter hours in religious studies must be taken as well. All students must take courses in English, mathematics, science, philosophy, social studies, and fine arts.

Special: Special academic programs include internships in several disciplines, study abroad in 6 countries, and both on- and off-campus work-study through the Washington State Work-Study Program. A B.A.-B.S. degree in economics and psychology, a liberal studies degree, and an accelerated degree program in business and education are offered. Pass/fail options are possible. There is a freshman honors program on campus. Two departments have honors programs.

Faculty/Classroom: No introductory courses are taught by graduate students. The average class size in a regular course offering is 20.

Admissions: About 77% of the 1993–94 applicants were accepted. The SAT scores for the 1993–94 freshman class were as follows: Verbal—56% below 500, 37% between 500 and 599, 6% between 600 and 700, and 1% above 700; Math—35% below 500, 38% between 500 and 599, 22% between 600 and 700, and 5% above 700. About 45% of the current freshmen were in the top fifth of their class; 90% were in the top two fifths. There were 3 National Merit semifinalists. About 22 freshmen graduated first in their class.

Requirements: SU requires applicants to be in the upper 50% of their class. A minimum GPA of 2.5 is required. The SAT I or ACT is required. The minimum SAT I score should be 850, 425 verbal and 425 math. Other admissions requirements include graduation from an accredited secondary school, with 16 academic credits, including 4 years of English, 2 each of mathematics, 1 each of science and history, and 9 academic electives; 2 years of a foreign language are needed by arts and science majors, 3 years of mathematics are required of science and engineering students, and 2 years of laboratory science are needed by nursing students. The GED is also accepted. AP and CLEP credits are accepted. Important factors used in the admissions decision are recommendations by school officials, leadership record, advanced placement or honor courses, recommendations by alumni, and geographic diversity.

Procedure: Freshmen are admitted to all sessions. Entrance exams should be taken during the fall of the senior year. Applications should be filed by June 1 for fall entry, December 6 for winter entry, April 30 for spring entry, and May 12 for summer entry, along with an application fee of $35. Notification is sent on a rolling basis beginning December 1. There are early decision, early admissions, and deferred admissions plans.

Transfer: About 422 transfer students enrolled in 1993–94. Transfer students should have a GPA of at least 2.5. An associate degree is recommended. A total of 45 quarter hours out of 180 to 192 must be completed at SU.

Visiting: There are regularly scheduled orientations for prospective students. There are guides for informal visits and visitors may sit in on classes and stay overnight at the school. To arrange for a visit, contact the Office of Admissions/Campus Assistance Center at (206) 296-5800.

Financial Aid: In 1993-94, 84% of all current freshmen and 75% of continuing students received some form of financial aid. The average freshman award was $13,220. Forty percent of undergraduate students work part-time. Average earnings from campus work for the school year was $2400. The FAFSA financial statement is required. The deadline for financial aid applications is March 1.

International Students: There are currently 489 international students enrolled. The school actively recruits these students. They must take the TOEFL and achieve a minimum score of 520.

Computers: The college provides computer facilities for student use. The mainframe is an HP Series 44. There are also 230 Apple Macintosh II and Epson microcomputers available for student use. All students may access the system during posted hours. There are no time limits on using the system and no fees.

Graduates: In 1992-93, 717 bachelor's degrees were awarded. Within an average freshman class, 65% graduate in 5 years. Some 175 companies recruited on campus in 1992-93.

Admissions Contact: Lee K. Gerig, Dean of Admissions.

UNIVERSITY OF PUGET SOUND
C-2

Tacoma, WA 98416

(206) 756-3211

Full-time: 1132 men, 1606 women	Faculty: 202; IIA, +$
Part-time: 44 men, 73 women	Ph.D.s: 80%
Graduate: 84 men, 231 women	Student/Faculty: 14 to 1
Year: semesters, summer session	Tuition: $15,220
Application Deadline: March 1	Room & Board: $4300
Freshman Class: 3881 applied, 2826 accepted, 688 enrolled	
SAT I: 520/581	ACT: 25 **HIGHLY COMPETITIVE**

The University of Puget Sound, established in 1888, is a nonprofit, private, coeducational institution with an historical affiliation with the Methodist Church. The emphasis of its undergraduate and graduate programs is on the liberal arts and sciences, business and public administration, music, occupational and physical therapy, law, and education. There are 4 undergraduate and 3 graduate schools. In addition to regional accreditation, Puget Sound has baccalaureate program accreditation with APTA, CAHEA, NASM, and NCATE. The 3 libraries contain 346,533 volumes, 146,320 microform items, and 8586 audiovisual forms, and subscribe to 1933 periodicals. Computerized library sources and services include interlibrary loans and database searching. Special learning facilities include a learning resource center, art gallery, natural history museum, radio station, and student science laboratories. The 95-acre campus is in a suburban area 35 miles south of Seattle. Including residence halls, there are 44 buildings on campus.

Student Life: About 54% of undergraduates are from out-of-state, mostly the West. Students come from 43 states, 14 foreign countries, and Canada. Eighty-five percent are white. Forty-five percent claim no religious affiliation; 36% Protestant; 15% Catholic. The average age of freshmen is 18; all undergraduates, 20.4. Fourteen percent drop out by the end of their first year; 64% remain to graduate.

Housing: A total of 1700 students can be accommodated in college housing. College-sponsored living facilities include single-sex and coed dormitories, on-campus houses, fraternity houses, and sorority houses. In addition there are honors houses, language houses, special interest and theme houses. On-campus housing is guaranteed for the freshman year only on a first-come, first-served basis. It is also available on a lottery system for upperclassmen. Sixty percent of students live on campus; of those, 70% remain on campus on weekends. All students may keep cars on campus.

Activities: About 33% of men belong to 6 national fraternities; about 33% of women belong to 6 national sororities. There are 38 groups on campus, including art, band, cheerleading, choir, chorale, chorus, computers, dance, drama, ethnic, gay, honors, international, jazz band, literary magazine, musical theater, newspaper, opera, orchestra, pep band, photography, political, professional, radio and TV, religious, social, social service, student government, symphony, and yearbook. Popular campus events include Homecoming, Foolish Pleasures, (student film festival), Mistletoast Holiday, Spring Weekend, Logger Days, and Songfest.

Sports: There are 11 intercollegiate sports for men and 10 for women, and 24 intramural sports for men and 21 for women. Athletic and recreation facilities include a 3000-seat basketball and volleyball gymnasium, a pool, a 2488-seat football and soccer stadium, 4 indoor tennis courts, 4 outdoor tennis courts, a weight room, an aerobics exercise area, a dance studio, a track, a baseball field, and an auxiliary gymnasium for intramurals and recreation.

Disabled Students: Seventy-five percent of the campus is accessible to disabled students. The following facilities are available: wheelchair ramps, elevators, special parking, specially equipped rest rooms, special class scheduling, lowered drinking fountains, and lowered telephones.

Services: In addition to many counseling and information services, tutoring is available in some subjects. There is a reader service for the blind.

Campus Safety and Security: Campus safety and security measures include 24-hour foot and vehicle patrol, escort service, informal discussions, pamphlets, posters, and films. In addition, there are emergency telephones, lighted pathways and sidewalks, and vehicle escort within 3 miles of campus. Residence halls are always locked.

Programs of Study: Puget Sound awards the B.A., B.S., and B.M. degrees. Master's degrees also are awarded. Bachelor's degrees are awarded in BIOLOGICAL SCIENCE (biology/biological science), BUSINESS (accounting and business administration and management), COMMUNICATIONS AND THE ARTS (communications, dramatic arts, English, fine arts, French, German, music, music performance, and Spanish), COMPUTER AND PHYSICAL SCIENCE (chemistry, computer science, geology, mathematics, natural sciences, and physics), EDUCATION (physical), HEALTH PROFESSIONS (occupational therapy), SOCIAL SCIENCE (Asian/Oriental studies, economics, history, international affairs, philosophy, political science/government, psychology, public administration, religion, religious music, social science, and sociology). Foreign language, biology, English, economics, and Asian studies are the strongest academically. English, psychology, communication and theater arts, politics and government, occupational therapy, and business have the largest enrollments.

Required: Students must complete 32 units of course work, with 8 to 14 in the major, and maintain a minimum GPA of 2.0. Core requirements include 1 unit each of written communication, oral communication, mathematical reasoning, historical perspective, humanistic perspective, fine arts, comparative values, society, international studies, and science in context, and 2 units of the natural world.

Special: Special academic programs include on- and off-campus work-study, paid and unpaid internships in the community in conjunction with an internship seminar, and study abroad in several countries. There are 3-2 engineering degrees with Washington University at St. Louis, Columbia, Boston, and Duke universities, and the University of Southern California. Dual majors and pass/fail options are possible. Two special features of the curriculum are the intensive 4-year study of the classics of Western civilization and the Business Leadership Program, combining traditional business and liberal arts study. There is a freshman honors program on campus, as well as 12 national honor societies, including Phi Beta Kappa.

Faculty/Classroom: Sixty percent of faculty are male; 40%, female. All teach undergraduates. No introductory courses are taught by graduate students. The average class size in an introductory lecture is 35; in a laboratory, 19; and in a regular course offering, 19.

Admissions: About 73% of the 1993-94 applicants were accepted. The SAT scores for the 1993-94 freshman class were as follows: Verbal—40% below 500, 41% between 500 and 599, 17% between 600 and 700, and 2% above 700; Math—16% below 500, 39% between 500 and 599, 37% between 600 and 700, and 8% above 700. The ACT scores were 9% below 21, 18% between 21 and 23, 34% between 24 and 26, 19% between 27 and 28, and 20% above 28. About 70% of the current freshmen were in the top fifth of their class; 88% were in the top two fifths. There were 24 National Merit finalists. About 59 freshmen graduated first in their class.

Requirements: The SAT I or ACT is required. The SAT I is preferred. Other admissions requirements include graduation from an accredited secondary school, with a recommended 4 years each of English and mathematics, 3 to 4 years of natural/physical laboratory science, 3 years of social studies/history, 2 to 3 years of foreign language, and 1 year of fine/visual/performing arts. Also required is a letter of personal recommendation from a teacher and counselor; 2 are preferred. An essay must be submitted, and an interview is recommended. It is recommended that art students present a portfolio and that music students audition. The GED is also accepted. AP credits are accepted. Important factors used in the admissions decision are advanced placement or honor courses, evidence of special talent, leadership record, personality, intangible qualities, and extracurricular activities record.

Procedure: Freshmen are admitted to all sessions. Entrance exams should be taken during the fall of the senior year. Early decision applications should be filed by November 15; regular applications, by March 1 for fall entry and November 1 for spring entry, along with an application fee of $35. Notification of early decision is sent December 5; regular decision, on a rolling basis beginning January 20. There are early decision, early admissions, and deferred admissions plans. About 104 early decision candidates were accepted for the 1993-94 class. A waiting list is an active part of the admissions procedure, with about 9% of applicants on the list.

Transfer: About 240 transfer students enrolled in 1993-94. Transfer applicants must have an honorable dismissal from the institution(s) previously attended and good academic standing, with a minimum

GPA of 2.5. All college transcripts and the rigor of prior course work and resulting grades are evaluated. The SAT I is recommended, as is an interview. An essay or a copy of a graded paper is required of all undergraduate transfers. A total of 16 course units, including the last 8, out of 32 must be completed at Puget Sound.

Visiting: There are regularly scheduled orientations for prospective students, consisting of campus days and individual visits. There are guides for informal visits and visitors may sit in on classes and stay overnight at the school. To arrange for a visit, contact the Campus Visit Coordinator, Office of Admission at (206) 756-3211.

Financial Aid: In 1993-94, 75% of all students received some form of financial aid. About 65% of all students received need-based aid. The average freshman award was $12,200. Of that total, scholarships or need-based grants averaged $7300 ($12,200 maximum); loans averaged $3400 ($5125 maximum); and work contracts averaged $1500 ($1900 maximum). Seventy percent of undergraduate students work part-time. Average earnings from campus work for the school year are $1800. The average financial indebtedness of the 1992-93 graduate was $15,535. Puget Sound is a member of CSS. The FAF and FAFSA are required. The deadline for financial aid applications is February 15.

International Students: There are currently 33 international students enrolled. The school actively recruits these students. They must take the TOEFL and achieve a minimum score of 550.

Computers: The college provides computer facilities for student use. The mainframe is a DEC VAX 4000 series. The mainframe can be reached by on-campus terminals or through dial-up lines. There are also 3 large Apple Macintosh and 2 IBM-compatible laboratories, additional satellite laboratories in departments, and a network of Apollo workstations. All students may access the system. There are no time limits on using the system and no fees.

Graduates: In 1992-93, 667 bachelor's degrees were awarded. The most popular majors among graduates were business administration (15%), English (12%), and psychology (8%). Within an average freshman class, 1% graduate in 3 years, 55% in 4 years, 64% in 5 years, and 59% in 6 years. Some 39 companies recruited on campus. In the 1992 graduating class, 4% of the men and 5% of the women were enrolled in graduate school within 6 months of graduation; 23% of the men and 41% of the women had found employment.

Admissions Contact: George H. Mills, Jr., Dean of Admission and Enrollment.

UNIVERSITY OF WASHINGTON

C-2

Seattle, WA 98195   (206) 543-9686

Full-time, part-time: 12,339 men, 12,599 women	Faculty: 3213; I, -$
	Ph.D.s: 85%
Graduate: 4739 men, 4269 women	Student/Faculty: 7 to 1
Year: quarters, summer session	Tuition: $2532 ($7134)
Application Deadline: February 1	Room & Board: $4086
Freshman Class: 12,749 applied, 7025 accepted, 3343 enrolled	
SAT I or ACT: required	**VERY COMPETITIVE**

The University of Washington, founded in 1861, is a state-controlled institution comprised of 16 undergraduate and graduate schools and colleges. There are 13 undergraduate schools. In addition to regional accreditation, the University of Washington has baccalaureate program accreditation with AACSB, ABET, NCATE, and NLN. The 21 libraries contain 5.1 million volumes and 5 million microform items. Computerized library sources and services include the card catalog, interlibrary loans, and database searching. Special learning facilities include a learning resource center, an art gallery, a natural history museum, a planetarium, a radio station, a state museum, a full teaching hospital, a marine science laboratory, a 200-acre arboretum, and a field-research forest. The 690-acre campus is in an urban area 10 miles from downtown Seattle. Including residence halls, there are 128 buildings on campus.

Student Life: About 90% of undergraduates are from Washington. Students come from 52 states, 59 foreign countries, and Canada. Eighteen percent are Asian American. The average age of freshmen is 18; all undergraduates, 21. Ten percent drop out by the end of their first year; 56% remain to graduate.

Housing: A total of 5200 students can be accommodated in college housing. College-sponsored living facilities include coed dormitories, on-campus apartments, married-student housing, fraternity houses, and sorority houses. In addition, there are language houses, special interest houses, and a freshman house. On-campus housing is guaranteed for all 4 years. Alcohol is not permitted. All students may keep cars on campus.

Activities: About 17% of men belong to 31 national fraternities; about 16% of women belong to 19 national sororities. There are 300 groups on campus, including band, cheerleading, choir, chorale, chorus, computers, dance, drama, ethnic, film, gay, honors, international, jazz band, literary magazine, marching band, musical theater, newspaper, opera, orchestra, pep band, political, professional, radio and TV, religious, social, social service, student government, sympho-

ny, and yearbook. Popular campus events include Homecoming, Four Bands for 4 Bucks (concert), Opening Day (of boating/crew season), and Convocation.

Sports: Athletic and recreation facilities include a 72,500-seat football stadium, a baseball field, a track and field complex, lakeside facilities, tennis courts, the intramurals building, a golf driving range, and a swimming pool.

Disabled Students: Eighty-five percent of the campus is accessible to disabled students. The following facilities are available: wheelchair ramps, elevators, special parking, specially equipped rest rooms, special class scheduling, lowered drinking fountains, and lowered telephones.

Services: In addition to many counseling and information services, tutoring is available in every subject. There is a reader service for the blind, and remedial math, reading, and writing.

Campus Safety and Security: Campus safety and security measures include 24-hour foot and vehicle patrol, escort service, shuttle buses, and informal discussions. In addition, there are pamphlets, posters, and films, emergency telephones, lighted pathways and sidewalks, and emergency telephone numbers.

Programs of Study: The University of Washington awards the B.A., B.S., B.A.B.A., B.C.H.S., B.L.Arch., B.Mus., B.S.A.&A., B.S.B.C., B.S.Cer.E., B.S.Comp.E., B.S.F., B.S.Fish., B.S.I.E., B.S.M.E., B.S.Med.Tech., B.S.Met.E., B.S.Nur., B.S.Occ.Therapy, B.S.Pharmacy, and B.S.Phys.Therapy degrees. Master's and doctoral degrees also are awarded. Bachelor's degrees are awarded in AGRICULTURE (fishing and fisheries, forest engineering, forestry production and processing, and wood science), BIOLOGICAL SCIENCE (biochemistry, biology/biological science, botany, microbiology, and zoology), BUSINESS (accounting, banking and finance, business administration and management, business economics, international business management, marketing/retailing/merchandising, and personnel management), COMMUNICATIONS AND THE ARTS (art history and appreciation, classics, communications, comparative literature, dance, dramatic arts, English, fiber/textiles/weaving, French, Germanic languages and literature, graphic design, industrial design, Italian, Japanese, jazz, metal/jewelry, music history and appreciation, music performance, painting, photography, printmaking, Scandinavian languages, sculpture, Slavic languages, Spanish, speech/debate/rhetoric, studio art, and technical and business writing), COMPUTER AND PHYSICAL SCIENCE (astronomy, atmospheric sciences and meteorology, computer science, geology, information sciences and systems, mathematics, oceanography, physics, quantitative methods, and statistics), EDUCATION (music), ENGINEERING AND ENVIRONMENTAL DESIGN (aeronautical engineering, ceramic engineering, ceramic science, chemical engineering, civil engineering, computer engineering, construction engineering, electrical/electronics engineering, engineering, environmental science, industrial engineering technology, landscape architecture/design, materials science, ocean engineering, and paper and pulp science), HEALTH PROFESSIONS (dental hygiene, environmental health science, health care administration, medical laboratory technology, nursing, occupational therapy, pharmacy, physical therapy, and speech pathology/audiology), SOCIAL SCIENCE (African American studies, anthropology, Asian/American studies, Asian/Oriental studies, Canadian studies, economics, ethnic studies, food science, geography, history, international relations, Judaic studies, liberal arts/general studies, Near Eastern studies, peace studies, philosophy, political science/government, psychology, religion, Russian and Slavic studies, social work, sociology, South Asian studies, and women's studies). Biological and life sciences, computer science and engineering, physics, psychology, nursing, international studies, and creative writing are the strongest academically. Business, English, art, psychology, and political science have the largest enrollments.

Required: All students must maintain a GPA of 2.0 while taking 180 academic credits, with 45 in the major. Distribution requirements include courses from the humanities, social sciences, and natural sciences.

Special: A wide variety of internships, including those for minority students in engineering, concurrent dual majors, study abroad in 21 countries, a Washington semester, a general studies degree, and co-op programs are available. Work-study programs, credit/no credit options, student-designed majors, and accelerated degree programs, nondegree study, and a 5-year B.A.-B.S. degree also are offered. There is a freshman honors program on campus, as well as 20 national honor societies, including Phi Beta Kappa. Thirty-six departments have honors programs.

Faculty/Classroom: Seventy-one percent of faculty are male; 29%, female. One percent teach undergraduates, 14% do research, and 85% do both. Graduate students teach 40% of introductory courses. The average class size in an introductory lecture is 80; in a laboratory, 20; and in a regular course offering, 20.

Admissions: About 55% of the 1993-94 applicants were accepted. The SAT scores for the 1993-94 freshman class were as follows: Verbal—58% below 500, 27% between 500 and 599, 13% between

600 and 700, and 2% above 700; Math—25% below 500, 35% between 500 and 599, 30% between 600 and 700, and 10% above 700.

Requirements: A minimum GPA of 2.0 is required. The SAT I or ACT is required. Applicants must have completed 15 academic units including 4 years of English, 2 each of foreign language and science, 3 each of mathematics and social sciences, and 1/2 year each in fine/visual performing arts and electives. Admission is based on an indexing system. AP credits are accepted.

Procedure: Freshmen are admitted to all sessions. Entrance exams should be taken by December of the senior year. Applications should be filed by February 1 for fall entry, November 1 for winter entry, February 1 for spring entry, and February 1 for summer entry, along with an application fee of $25. Notification is sent March 15. There is an early admissions plan.

Transfer: About 2060 transfer students enrolled in 1993–94. The school has a special direct transfer agreement with Washington community colleges. Admission is based on an indexing system. A total of 45 quarter credits out of 180 must be completed at the University of Washington.

Visiting: There are regularly scheduled orientations for prospective students, including attendance at class, lunch, a meeting with an admissions counselor, and an overnight stay. To arrange for a visit, contact the Student Visitation Program at (206) 543-5429.

Financial Aid: In a recent year, 33% of all current freshmen and 31% of continuing students received some form of financial aid. About 30% of all students received need-based aid. The average freshman award was $4714. Of that total, scholarships or need-based grants averaged $1605; loans averaged $2414; and work contracts averaged $295. The University of Washington is a member of CSS. The FAF is required. The deadline for financial aid applications is February 28.

International Students: There are currently 1827 international students enrolled. They must take the TOEFL or the University of Michigan Language Test and achieve a minimum score on the TOEFL of 500.

Computers: The college provides computer facilities for student use. The mainframes are an IBM 3090, several DEC VAX Systems, and a Sequent. There are several public laboratories containing 10,000 IBM PC, Macintosh, SUN, DEC, and NeXT microcomputers and terminals. Dial-up is also used because most students live off campus. All students may access the system. It may be used 24 hours daily. There are no time limits on using the system and no fees.

Graduates: In 1992–93 5450 bachelor's degrees were awarded. The most popular majors among graduates were business (14%), English (10%), and psychology (7%). Within an average freshman class, 29% graduate in 4 years, 56% in 5 years, and 63% in 6 years. Some 600 companies recruited on campus in a recent year.

Admissions Contact: Wilbur W. Washburn, Executive Director.

WALLA WALLA COLLEGE

College Place, WA 99324-1198   E-3

Full-time: 1620 men and women	(509) 527-2327; (800) 541-8900
Part-time: none	Faculty: 120; IIB, --$
Graduate: 151 men and women	Ph.D.s: n/av
Year: quarters, summer session	Student/Faculty: 14 to 1
Application Deadline: August 1	Tuition: $10,080
Freshman Class: n/av	Room & Board: $3135
ACT: required	**COMPETITIVE**

Walla Walla College, founded in 1892, is a private, comprehensive, coeducational institution affiliated with the Seventh-Day Adventist Church. There are 3 undergraduate and 3 graduate schools. In addition to regional accreditation, WWC has baccalaureate program accreditation with ABET, CSWE, NASM, and NLN. The 3 libraries contain 204,168 volumes and 7532 microform items, and subscribe to 1042 periodicals. Computerized library sources and services include the card catalog, interlibrary loans, and database searching. Special learning facilities include a learning resource center, art gallery, and radio station. The 55-acre campus is in a small town 120 miles southsouthwest of Spokane. Including residence halls, there are 28 buildings on campus.

Student Life: About 70% of undergraduates are from out-of-state, mostly the West. Students come from 40 states, 48 foreign countries, and Canada. Twenty percent are from public schools; 80% from private. Eighty-one percent are white. Most are Protestant. The average age of freshmen is 17.5; all undergraduates, 21. Seven percent drop out by the end of their first year.

Housing: A total of 1500 students can be accommodated in college housing. College-sponsored living facilities include single-sex dormitories, on-campus apartments, off-campus apartments, and marriedstudent housing. On-campus housing is guaranteed for all 4 years. Sixty-six percent of students live on campus; of those, 90% remain on campus on weekends. Alcohol is not permitted. All students may keep cars on campus.

Activities: There are no fraternities or sororities on campus. There are 30 groups on campus, including art, band, choir, chorale, drama, ethnic, honors, international, literary magazine, newspaper, photography, professional, radio and TV, religious, social service, student government, symphony, and yearbook. Popular campus events include The Mud Bowl football game, and the Sonneberg Series basketball tournament.

Sports: There are 5 intercollegiate sports each for men and women, and 6 intramural sports each. Athletic and recreation facilities include an Olympic pool, a track, tennis courts, gymnastics sports gymnasium, a gymnasium, weight rooms, and residence hall health spas.

Disabled Students: The following facilities are available: wheelchair ramps, elevators, special parking, and special class scheduling.

Services: In addition to many counseling and information services, tutoring is available in some subjects, including mathematics, languages, and science. In addition, there is remedial math, reading, and writing.

Campus Safety and Security: Campus safety and security measures include 24-hour foot and vehicle patrol, informal discussions, and lighted pathways and sidewalks.

Programs of Study: WWC awards the B.A., B.S., B.Mus., B.S.B.A., B.S.E., and B.S.W. degrees. Associate and master's degrees are also awarded. Bachelor's degrees are awarded in BIOLOGICAL SCIENCE (biology/biological science), BUSINESS (business administration and management), COMMUNICATIONS AND THE ARTS (communications, English, fine arts, French, German, music, Spanish, and speech/debate/rhetoric), COMPUTER AND PHYSICAL SCIENCE (chemistry, computer science, mathematics, and physics), EDUCATION (business, elementary, health, industrial arts, music, and physical), ENGINEERING AND ENVIRONMENTAL DESIGN (bioengineering and engineering), HEALTH PROFESSIONS (medical laboratory technology, nursing, predentistry, and premedicine), SOCIAL SCIENCE (history, prelaw, psychology, religion, social work, and sociology). Engineering and nursing are the strongest academically. Engineering has the largest enrollment.

Required: Students must successfully complete 192 quarter hours, with at least 45 in the major and 60 in upper-level work, and a minimum GPA of 2.0. Grades below C- will not apply toward the major. Students must also meet a general studies requirement that includes courses in the areas of applied arts, health and physical education, history and social studies, humanities, language arts, mathematics and natural science, and religion and theology. A comprehensive exam is required, as is attendance at chapel and assemblies.

Special: Opportunities are provided for internships, study abroad in 2 countries, work-study programs, a B.A.-B.S. degree, dual majors, credit by examination, and nondegree study. There is a freshman honors program on campus. Five departments have honors programs.

Admissions: There were 3 National Merit finalists and 9 semifinalists.

Requirements: A minimum GPA of 2.0 is required. The ACT is required. Scores are used for placement and academic advisement. Graduation from an accredited secondary school is required; a GED will be accepted. Applicants should submit an academic record distributed as follows: 4 years of English, 2 of history, 2 of science, and 2 of mathematics, which must include algebra and geometry. AP and CLEP credits are accepted. Important factors used in the admissions decision are advanced placement or honor courses, recommendations by school officials, leadership record, recommendations by alumni, and extracurricular activities record.

Procedure: Freshmen are admitted to all sessions. Entrance exams should be taken the junior or senior year. Applications should be filed by August 1 for fall entry, October 1 for winter entry, January 1 for spring entry, and June 1 for summer entry, along with an application fee of $20. The college accepts all applicants. Notification is sent on a rolling basis. There are early decision, early admissions, and deferred admissions plans.

Transfer: Transfer applicants should have a 2.0 minimum GPA and must submit all college transcripts. A total of 36 credits out of 192 must be completed at WWC.

Visiting: Visitors may sit in on classes. To arrange for a visit, contact the Admissions and Marketing Office at (509) 527-2327.

Financial Aid: The FAF and the college's own financial statement is required. The deadline for financial aid applications is April 1.

International Students: There were recently 85 international students enrolled. The school actively recruits these students. They must take the TOEFL and achieve a minimum score of 500.

Computers: The college provides computer facilities for student use. The mainframes are an HP 3000 Series 935, a DEC MicroVAX, and an HP 9000. There are 3 general purpose PC laboratories housing 39 microcomputers, and subject-specific computer laboratories for chemistry, engineering, and physics. All students may access the system. It may be used 6:00 A.M. to 11:00 P.M., Sunday through Friday. There are no time limits on using the system and no fees.

Admissions Contact: Gary Wisbey, Vice President for Admissions and Marketing.

WASHINGTON STATE UNIVERSITY

E-3

Pullman, WA 99164–1046

(509) 335–5586

Full-time: 7590 men, 6573 women
Part-time: 662 men, 887 women
Graduate: 1710 men, 1318 women
Year: early semesters, summer session
Application Deadline: May 1
Freshman Class: 6540 applied, 5839 accepted, 2440 enrolled
SAT I or ACT: required

Faculty: 965; I, --$
Ph.D.s: 98%
Student/Faculty: 15 to 1
Tuition: $2532 ($7134)
Room & Board: $3832

COMPETITIVE

Washington State University, founded in 1890, is a public, land-grant, comprehensive coeducational institution. Its undergraduate and graduate programs stress the liberal arts, business, economics, art and fine arts, engineering, architecture, agricultural and technical studies, home economics, music, teacher preparation, and health sciences, including nursing, pharmacy, and veterinary medicine. There are 8 undergraduate schools and one graduate school. In addition to regional accreditation, WSU has baccalaureate program accreditation with AACSB, ACCE, ACPE, ADA, ASLA, FIDER, NAAB, NASM, NCATE, NLN, NRPA, and SAF. The 5 libraries contain 1,717,764 volumes, 2,899,011 microform items, and 36,577 audiovisual forms, and subscribe to 24,038 periodicals. Computerized library sources and services include the card catalog, interlibrary loans, and database searching. Special learning facilities include a learning resource center, art gallery, planetarium, radio station, TV station, observatory, electron microscopy center, and nuclear radiation center. The 656-acre campus is in a small town 80 miles south of Spokane. Including residence halls, there are 175 buildings on campus.

Student Life: About 84% of undergraduates are from Washington. Students come from 50 states, 89 foreign countries, and Canada. Eighty-four percent are white. The average age of freshmen is 18.2; all undergraduates, 22.1. Sixteen percent drop out by the end of their first year; 56% remain to graduate.

Housing: A total of 6061 students can be accommodated in college housing. College-sponsored living facilities include single-sex and coed dormitories, off-campus apartments, married-student housing, fraternity houses, and sorority houses. In addition there are language houses. On-campus housing is guaranteed for all 4 years. Fifty-seven percent of students commute. Alcohol is not permitted. All students may keep cars on campus.

Activities: About 8% of men belong to 25 national fraternities; about 11% of women belong to 14 national sororities. There are 133 groups on campus, including band, cheerleading, chess, choir, dance, drama, ethnic, gay, honors, international, jazz band, literary magazine, marching band, musical theater, newspaper, opera, orchestra, photography, political, professional, radio and TV, religious, social, social service, student government, symphony, and yearbook. Popular campus events include Dad's Weekend, Mom's Weekend, Homecoming, Graduation, and Land Grant Days.

Sports: There are 7 intercollegiate sports for men and 8 for women, and 22 intramural sports for men and 17 for women. Athletic and recreation facilities include a 40,000-seat stadium, a 12,000-seat arena, an indoor track and tennis courts, a weight/aerobic facility, a golf course, bowling lanes, and an outdoor area for activities.

Disabled Students: Eighty-five percent of the campus is accessible to disabled students. The following facilities are available: wheelchair ramps, elevators, special parking, specially equipped rest rooms, special class scheduling, lowered drinking fountains, and lowered telephones.

Services: In addition to many counseling and information services, tutoring is available in most subjects. In addition, there is a reader service for the blind and remedial math and writing. There is also a reading and study-skills course.

Campus Safety and Security: Campus safety and security measures include 24-hour foot and vehicle patrol, self defense education, escort service, and informal discussions. There are pamphlets, posters, and films, emergency telephones, lighted pathways and sidewalks, lighting surveys, and a women's transit service.

Programs of Study: WSU awards the B.A., B.S., B.Arch., B.F.A., B.M., and B.Pharm. degrees. Master's and doctoral degrees also are awarded. Bachelor's degrees are awarded in AGRICULTURE (animal science, horticulture, and soil science), BIOLOGICAL SCIENCE (biochemistry, biology/biological science, entomology, microbiology, wildlife biology, and zoology), BUSINESS (banking and finance, business administration and management, business economics, hotel/motel and restaurant management, international business management, marketing/retailing/merchandising, and personnel management), COMMUNICATIONS AND THE ARTS (advertising, broadcasting, communications, dramatic arts, English, fine arts, French, German, journalism, music, Russian, Spanish, and speech/debate/rhetoric), COMPUTER AND PHYSICAL SCIENCE (chemistry, computer science, geology, mathematics, and physics), EDUCATION

(early childhood, elementary, foreign languages, home economics, secondary, and special), ENGINEERING AND ENVIRONMENTAL DESIGN (agricultural engineering, chemical engineering, civil engineering, construction management, electrical/electronics engineering, and mechanical engineering), HEALTH PROFESSIONS (nursing, pharmacy, predentistry, premedicine, speech pathology/audiology, and veterinary science), SOCIAL SCIENCE (anthropology, criminal justice, dietetics, food science, history, parks and recreation management, philosophy, political science/government, prelaw, psychology, social science, and sociology). Communications, veterinary medicine, and hotel/restaurant administration are the strongest academically. Business has the largest enrollment.

Required: Students must complete 120 semester hours, with fulfillment of a major and 40 hours of upper-division work, and maintain a minimum GPA of 2.0. Specific disciplines to be taken vary within majors. The curriculum must include the general university requirements, including 3 hours of intercultural studies, 9 hours of arts and humanities, and social science, 3 hours of communications proficiency, 10 hours of science, and 6 hours of world civilization. Students must complete a writing portfolio and pass a writing qualifying examination prior to graduation.

Special: Special academic programs include internships through the Professional Experience Program, study abroad in over 80 countries from Europe to the Orient, and work-study with numerous employers. There is a co-op program with the University of Idaho. Students may attend the Intercollegiate Center for Nursing Education, which is a consortium of WSU, Eastern Washington University, and Whitworth College. Dual majors are available, as is a general studies degree. Credit may be granted for military service, and nondegree and pass/fail options are possible. Special features of the school include opportunity for undergraduates to become involved in research and honors programs. There is a freshman honors program on campus, as well as one national honor society, Phi Beta Kappa.

Faculty/Classroom: Seventy-one percent of faculty are male; 29%, female. The average class size in a regular course offering is 25.

Admissions: About 89% of the 1993–94 applicants were accepted. The SAT scores for the freshman class were as follows: Verbal—78% below 500, 19% between 500 and 599, and 3% between 600 and 700; Math—50% below 500, 33% between 500 and 599, 15% between 600 and 700, and 2% above 700. About 55% of the current freshmen were in the top fifth of their class; 90% were in the top two fifths. There was 1 National Merit finalist.

Requirements: The SAT I or ACT is required. Other admissions requirements include graduation from an accredited secondary school, with 4 years of English, 3 years each of mathematics and social studies/history, and 2 years each of a foreign language and science. A combination of the high school GPA and test scores is considered. The GED is also accepted. AP and CLEP credits are accepted. Important factors used in the admissions decision are recommendations by school officials, extracurricular activities record, leadership record, personality, intangible qualities, and evidence of special talent.

Procedure: Freshmen are admitted fall and spring. Entrance exams should be taken during the spring of the junior year or fall of the senior year. Priority application deadlines are May 1 for fall entry, and December 15 for spring entry. The application fee is $35. Notification is sent on a rolling basis.

Transfer: About 2350 transfer students enrolled in 1993–94. Transfer students must have at least 27 semester hours, or 40 quarter hours, with a GPA of at least 2.0. If they have fewer hours, the criteria are the same as for freshmen. A total of 30 credits out of 120 must be completed at WSU.

Visiting: There are guides for informal visits and visitors may sit in on classes and stay overnight at the school. To arrange for a visit, contact the Office of Admissions at (509) 335–5586.

Financial Aid: In 1993–94, 41% of all students received some form of financial aid. About 10% of freshmen and 14% of continuing students received need-based aid. The average freshman award was $5280. Of that total, scholarships or need-based grants averaged $1612; loans averaged $2047; and work contracts averaged $1663. Nine percent of undergraduate students work part-time. Average earnings from campus work for the school year are $2500. WSU is a member of CSS. The FAF is required. The deadline for financial aid applications is March 1.

International Students: There are currently 1257 international students enrolled. They must take the TOEFL or the University of Michigan Language Test and achieve a minimum score on the TOEFL of 520.

Computers: The college provides computer facilities for student use. The mainframe is an IBM 3090. There are also IBM PS/2 and Apple Macintosh microcomputers available in each department. All students may access the system. It may be used 24 hours a day. There are no time limits on using the system and no fees.

Graduates: The most popular majors among graduates were business administration (21%), communications (8%), and psychology (5%). Within an average freshman class, 23% graduate in 4 years,

26% in 5 years, and 7% in 6 years. Some 125 companies recruited on campus in 1992–93.

Admissions Contact: Terry Flynn, Director of Admissions.

WESTERN WASHINGTON UNIVERSITY
Bellingham, WA 98225–9009

C-1

(206) 650–3440

Full-time: 3996 men, 4913 women	Faculty: 408; IIA, av$
Part-time: 240 men, 263 women	Ph.D.s: 87%
Graduate: 254 men, 407 women	Student/Faculty: 22 to 1
Year: quarters, summer session	Tuition: $2121 ($7110)
Application Deadline: March 1	Room & Board: $3956
Freshman Class: 5548 applied, 3563 accepted, 1557 enrolled	
SAT I: 470/530	ACT: 24 **VERY COMPETITIVE**

Western Washington University, founded in 1893, is a nonprofit, public, comprehensive coeducational institution whose emphasis is on the liberal arts and sciences, business and business administration and economics, art, fine arts, and performing arts, music, teacher preparation, interdisciplinary learning, and environmental studies. There are 6 undergraduate and 30 graduate schools. In addition to regional accreditation, WWU has baccalaureate program accreditation with AACSB, ABET, ASLA, NASM, NCATE, and NRPA. The library contains 600,000 volumes, 1.5 million microform items, and 16,331 audiovisual forms, and subscribes to 5600 periodicals. Computerized library sources and services include interlibrary loans and database searching. Special learning facilities include a learning resource center, art gallery, planetarium, radio station, TV station, marine laboratory, neutron generator laboratory, motor vehicle research laboratory, wind tunnel, air pollution laboratory, electronic music studio, and performing arts center. The 190-acre campus is in a small town 60 miles south of Vancouver, British Columbia, and 90 miles north of Seattle. Including residence halls, there are 78 buildings on campus.

Student Life: Most undergraduates are from Washington. Students come from 45 states, 35 foreign countries, and Canada. Ninety percent are from public schools; 10% from private. Eighty-three percent are white. The average age of freshmen is 18; all undergraduates, 20.6. Twenty percent drop out by the end of their first year; 50% remain to graduate.

Housing: A total of 3606 students can be accommodated in college housing. College-sponsored living facilities include coed dormitories, on-campus apartments, off-campus apartments, and married-student housing. In addition there is a fitness/wellness hall. On-campus housing is available on a first-come, first-served basis. Sixty-eight percent of students commute. All students may keep cars on campus.

Activities: There are no fraternities or sororities on campus. There are 99 groups on campus, including art, band, cheerleading, chess, choir, chorale, chorus, computers, dance, drama, ethnic, film, gay, honors, international, jazz band, literary magazine, musical theater, newspaper, orchestra, photography, political, professional, radio and TV, religious, social, social service, student government, and symphony. Popular campus events include the Western Jam Talent Show, Casino Night, Cinco de Mayo, Pow/Wow, Homecoming, Asian Pacific Islander Heritage, Black History Month, Lesbian/Gay Pride Month, and International Women's Week.

Sports: There are 8 intercollegiate sports for men and 8 for women, and 17 intramural sports for men and 16 for women. Athletic and recreation facilities include a 3000-seat gymnasium, playing fields, 8 tennis courts, a 6000-seat stadium, a golf course, salt/freshwater recreational facilities and equipment, and a student-run outdoor center (equipment and excursions).

Disabled Students: The entire campus is accessible to disabled students. The following facilities are available: wheelchair ramps, elevators, special parking, specially equipped rest rooms, special class scheduling, lowered drinking fountains, and lowered telephones.

Services: In addition to many counseling and information services, tutoring is available in most subjects, including English, humanities, social sciences, and mathematics and natural sciences. There is also a reader service for the blind.

Campus Safety and Security: Campus safety and security measures include 24-hour foot and vehicle patrol, self defense education, escort service, and shuttle buses. In addition, there are informal discussions, pamphlets, posters, and films, emergency telephones, and lighted pathways and sidewalks.

Programs of Study: WWU awards the B.A., B.S., B.A.E., B.F.A., and B.M. degrees. Master's degrees also are awarded. Bachelor's degrees are awarded in BIOLOGICAL SCIENCE (biochemistry and biology/biological science), BUSINESS (accounting, business administration and management, international business management, and marketing/retailing/merchandising), COMMUNICATIONS AND THE ARTS (classical languages, communications, dramatic arts, English, fine arts, French, German, journalism, music, Spanish, and speech/debate/rhetoric), COMPUTER AND PHYSICAL SCIENCE (chemistry, computer science, geology, mathematics, and physics), EDUCATION (art, early childhood, elementary, foreign languages,

health, music, science, and secondary), ENGINEERING AND ENVIRONMENTAL DESIGN (electrical/electronics engineering technology, engineering technology, and manufacturing technology), HEALTH PROFESSIONS (premedicine and speech pathology/audiology), SOCIAL SCIENCE (anthropology, Canadian studies, East Asian studies, economics, geography, history, parks and recreation management, philosophy, political science/government, prelaw, psychology, sociology, and urban studies). Computer science, business, technology, fine arts, and environmental studies are the strongest academically. Psychology, environmental studies, education, and business have the largest enrollments.

Required: Students must complete at least 180 quarter hours, with fulfillment of a major and at least 60 credits in upper-division study, and maintain at least a 2.0 GPA or that prescribed by departments/divisions. General university requirements include 70 to 75 credits, and students must satisfy writing proficiency requirements as well. Fairhaven College has a seperate, interdisciplinary core program.

Special: Special academic programs include internships through various academic departments and study abroad in 40 countries. Dual majors are available through various departments. There is a general studies degree and a B.A. in humanities. A 3–2 engineering degree is possible with the University of Washington. Student-designed majors are offered through the liberal studies department in the College of Arts and Sciences and through Fairhaven College, which affords an unusual degree of student involvement in the structure and contents of their own programs, and which uses faculty narrative for students' academic evaluations. In addition, Huxley College of Environmental Studies provides specialized education and research. Up to 30 credits of electives may be granted for military service, and nondegree study and pass/fail options are possible. There is a freshman honors program on campus, as well as one national honor society. One department has an honors program.

Faculty/Classroom: Seventy percent of faculty are male; 30%, female. All teach undergraduates, and 90% also do research. Graduate students teach 4% of introductory courses. The average class size in an introductory lecture is 85; in a laboratory, 25; and in a regular course offering, 30.

Admissions: About 64% of the 1993–94 applicants were accepted. The SAT scores for the 1993–94 freshman class were as follows: Verbal—63% below 500, 29% between 500 and 599, and 8% between 600 and 700; Math—34% below 500, 44% between 500 and 599, 20% between 600 and 700, and 2% above 700. About 58% of the current freshmen were in the top fifth of their class; 89% were in the top two fifths. There were 8 National Merit finalists.

Requirements: A minimum GPA of 2.5 is required. The SAT I or the ACT is required. Other admissions requirements include graduation from an accredited secondary school, with 15 academic credits, comprised of 4 years of college preparatory English composition and literature courses; 3 years of college preparatory mathematics, including 2 years of algebra; 2 years of science, including 1 year of a chemistry or physics course having an algebra prerequisite; 2 years of the same foreign language; 3 years of social studies/history; 1 semester plus 1 semester in other academic field, and 1 year of fine or performing arts. Freshman applicants meeting minimum GPA and subject requirements are ranked by an index combining the GPA and a standardized test score. The GED is also accepted. Other factors taken into consideration include talent, learning disability, ethnicity, and other forms of diversity, grade trends, nature and difficulty of courses, and personal circumstances. AP credits are accepted.

Procedure: Freshmen are admitted to all sessions. Entrance exams should be taken by fall of the senior year. Applications should be filed by March 1 for fall entry, October 15 for winter entry, January 15 for spring entry, and March 1 for summer entry, along with an application fee of $35. Notification is sent January through April. A waiting list is an active part of the admissions procedure, with about 3% of applicants on the list.

Transfer: About 1354 transfer students enrolled in 1993–94. Transfer applicants with fewer than 40 quarter credits are eligible for admission consideration if they have completed the last term before transferring with a GPA of at least 2.0 and if they satisfy the requirements for freshman admission. Those with 40 or more transferable quarter credits are eligible if they have achieved a cumulative GPA of at least 2.0. Admission is selective. A total of 45 quarter credits out of 180 must be completed at WWU.

Visiting: There are regularly scheduled orientations for prospective students, including tours, class visits, and advisement. There are guides for informal visits and visitors may sit in on classes. To arrange for a visit, contact the Student-to-Student Program at (206) 650–3861.

Financial Aid: In 1993–94, 65% of all current freshmen and 68% of continuing students received some form of financial aid. About 31% of freshmen received need-based aid. The average freshman award was $5342. Of that total, scholarships or need-based grants averaged $1053 ($3906 maximum). Twenty-five percent of undergraduate students work part-time. Average earnings from campus work for the school year are $1400. WWU is a member of CSS. The

FAFSA financial statement is required. The deadline for financial aid applications is February 28.

International Students: There are currently 112 international students enrolled. They must take the TOEFL and achieve a minimum score of 565.

Computers: The college provides computer facilities for student use. The mainframes are a DEC VAX 8650, VMS, and a VAX 780 UNIX. There are also 1000 Apple and IBM-compatible microcomputers available in the administrative offices, computer center, and residence halls. All students may access the system. There are no time limits on using the system and no fees.

Graduates: In 1992–93, 2221 bachelor's degrees were awarded. The most popular majors among graduates were business and management (17%), social sciences (14%), and parks and recreation (11%). Within an average freshman class, 15% graduate in 4 years, 41% in 5 years, and 50% in 6 years. Some 80 companies recruited on campus in 1992–93. In the 1992 graduating class, 20% of the graduates were enrolled in graduate school within 6 months of graduation; 80% found employment.

Admissions Contact: Karen G. Copetas, Director of Admission.

WHITMAN COLLEGE   E-3
Walla Walla, WA 99362   (509) 527-5176

Full-time: 570 men, 650 women	Faculty: 100; IIB, +$
Part-time: 29 men, 17 women	Ph.D.s: 93%
Graduate: none	Student/Faculty: 12 to 1
Year: semesters	Tuition: $15,805
Application Deadline: February 15	Room & Board: $4790
Freshman Class: 1860 applied, 1131 accepted, 403 enrolled	
SAT I Verbal/Math: 550/600	ACT: 28 HIGHLY COMPETITIVE

Whitman College, founded in 1859, is a nonprofit, private, coeducational liberal arts institution. In addition to regional accreditation, Whitman has baccalaureate program accreditation with NCATE. The library contains 320,000 volumes, 10,000 microform items, and 900 audiovisual forms, and subscribes to 1950 periodicals. Computerized library sources and services include the card catalog, interlibrary loans, and database searching. Special learning facilities include an art gallery, natural history museum, planetarium, radio station, and an electron microscope laboratory. The 45-acre campus is in a small town 170 miles south of Spokane, 260 miles southeast of Seattle, and 235 miles east of Portland. Including residence halls, there are 30 buildings on campus.

Student Life: About 53% of undergraduates are from out-of-state, mostly the West. Students come from 37 states, 22 foreign countries, and Canada. Eighty-five percent are from public schools; 15% from private. Eighty-one percent are white. The average age of freshmen is 18; all undergraduates, 19. Five percent drop out by the end of their first year; 75% remain to graduate.

Housing: A total of 759 students can be accommodated in college housing. College-sponsored living facilities include single-sex and coed dormitories, off-campus apartments, and fraternity houses. In addition there are language houses and special interest houses. On-campus housing is guaranteed for all 4 years. Eighty percent of students live on campus; of those, 95% remain on campus on weekends. All students may keep cars on campus.

Activities: About 47% of men belong to 5 national fraternities; about 42% of women belong to 1 local and 4 national sororities. There are more than 100 groups on campus, including art, band, choir, chorale, chorus, drama, ethnic, gay, international, jazz band, literary magazine, musical theater, newspaper, orchestra, photography, political, professional, religious, social service, student government, and yearbook. Popular campus events include Black History Month, Renaissance Fair, Homecoming, Cinco de Mayo, International Days, Choral Contest, Asian Awareness Month, Interim, Freshman Scrambles, and Earth Day.

Sports: There are 9 intercollegiate sports for men and 8 for women, and 6 intramural sports each. Athletic and recreation facilities include a stadium, a center with a 3000-seat gymnasium, squash and handball courts, saunas, a pool, an indoor climbing wall, a small gymnasium, a weights/Nautilus room, 4 tennis courts, and a soccer field.

Disabled Students: Ninety percent of the campus is accessible to disabled students. The following facilities are available: wheelchair ramps, elevators, special parking, and specially equipped rest rooms.

Services: In addition to many counseling and information services, tutoring is available in most subjects. In addition, there is a reader service for the blind. There are also centers for study skills and writing.

Campus Safety and Security: Campus safety and security measures include escort service, informal discussions, pamphlets, posters, and films, and lighted pathways and sidewalks.

Programs of Study: Whitman awards the B.A. degree. Bachelor's degrees are awarded in BIOLOGICAL SCIENCE (biology/biological science), COMMUNICATIONS AND THE ARTS (dramatic arts, English, fine arts, French, German, music, and Spanish), COMPUTER AND PHYSICAL SCIENCE (chemistry, computer science, ge-

ology, mathematics, and physics), SOCIAL SCIENCE (anthropology, economics, history, philosophy, political science/government, prelaw, psychology, and sociology). English, history, politics, psychology, biology, and economics have the largest enrollments.

Required: Students must complete 124 credits, with 32 to 36 in the major, and maintain a minimum GPA of 2.0. Distribution requirements must be followed, and freshman core and senior colloquium must be taken as well. Written and oral tests are also required.

Special: Special academic programs include more than 500 internships, study abroad in many cities in 9 countries, and a Washington semester. Dual majors are available in any area, and student-designed majors are offered. There is a business management program with the University of Chicago, a 3–2 environmental management and forestry program with Duke University, a 3–2 engineering program with California Institute of Technology and Columbia and Duke universities, and a 3–3 law program with Columbia University. Certification is offered for elementary and secondary education. A pass-D-fail option is available. A special feature of the curriculum is the integrated general studies program for freshmen. There is a freshman honors program on campus, as well as 5 national honor societies, including Phi Beta Kappa.

Faculty/Classroom: Seventy-seven percent of faculty are male; 23%, female. All faculty both teach and do research. The average class size in an introductory lecture is 25; in a laboratory, 21; and in a regular course offering, 14.

Admissions: About 61% of the 1993–94 applicants were accepted. The SAT scores for the freshman class were as follows: Verbal—26% below 500, 42% between 500 and 599, 25% between 600 and 700, and 8% above 700; Math—11% below 500, 35% between 500 and 599, 41% between 600 and 700, and 13% above 700. About 68% of the current freshmen were in the top fifth of their class; 91% were in the top two fifths. There were 8 National Merit finalists. About 41 freshmen graduated first in their class.

Requirements: The SAT I or ACT is required. The GED is accepted. An essay must be submitted, and an interview is recommended. Credit by challenge examination is accepted. AP credits are accepted. Important factors used in the admissions decision are leadership record, evidence of special talent, advanced placement or honor courses, personality, intangible qualities, and extracurricular activities record.

Procedure: Freshmen are admitted fall and spring. Entrance exams should be taken by February of the senior year. Early decision applications should be filed by December 1; regular applications, by February 15 for fall entry and December 15 for spring entry, along with an application fee of $45. Notification of early decision is sent January 31; regular decision, April 1. There are early decision, early admissions, and deferred admissions plans. About 93 early decision candidates were accepted for the 1993–94 class. A waiting list is an active part of the admissions procedure, with about 5% of applicants on the list.

Transfer: About 46 transfer students enrolled in 1993–94. Transfer applicants must submit the common application, a personal supplement, a teacher/counselor recommendation, their high school and college transcripts, and SAT I or ACT scores. A total of 54 credits out of 124 must be completed at Whitman.

Visiting: There are regularly scheduled orientations for prospective students, including Fall and Spring Visitors' Days. There are guides for informal visits and visitors may sit in on classes and stay overnight at the school. To arrange for a visit, contact the Admission Office at (509) 527-5176.

Financial Aid: In 1993–94, 89% of all current freshmen and 82% of continuing students received some form of financial aid. About 64% of freshmen and 62% of continuing students received need-based aid. The average freshman award was $13,237. Of that total, scholarships or need-based grants averaged $8454 ($19,500 maximum); loans averaged $3300 ($5000 maximum); and work contracts averaged $667 ($2000 maximum). Fifty percent of undergraduate students work part-time. Average earnings from campus work for the school year are $850. The average financial indebtedness of the 1992–93 graduate was $9864. Whitman is a member of CSS. The FAF and FAFSA are required. The deadline for financial aid applications is February 15.

International Students: There are currently 60 international students enrolled. The school actively recruits these students. They must take the TOEFL and achieve a minimum score of 560. The student must also take the SAT I or the ACT.

Computers: The college provides computer facilities for student use. The mainframe is a DEC VAX 6310. Programming languages include Pascal, C, FORTRAN, BASIC, Modulad, Macsyma, SAS, and SPSS-X. There are 3 microcomputer laboratories on campus that are generally used for word processing. Another site has 18 PCs, 1 laserjet printer, and 2 dot-matrix printers, and another has 25 PCs, 1 laserjet printer, and 4 dot-matrix printers. The library has 5 PCs and 2 dot-matrix printers. Other laboratories on campus have a total of 25 PCs, 4 Apple Macintoshes, 3 laserjet printers, and 3 dot-matrix printers. All stu-

dents may access the system 24 hours a day. There are no time limits and no fees.

Graduates: In a recent year, 306 bachelor's degrees were awarded. The most popular majors among graduates were English (13%), economics (11%), and politics (11%). Within an average freshman class, 1% graduate in 3 years, 75% in 4 years, and 77% in 5 years. Some 32 companies recruited on campus in 1992–93.

Admissions Contact: Madeleine R. Eagon, Director of Admissions.

WHITWORTH COLLEGE
Spokane, WA 99251

C-2

(509) 466–3212; (800) 533–4668 (in-state)

Full-time: 538 men, 732 women	Faculty: 79; IIB, -$
Part-time: 51 men, 109 women	Ph.D.s: 80%
Graduate: 128 men, 280 women	Student/Faculty: 16 to 1
Year: 4-1-4, summer session	Tuition: $11,965
Application Deadline: March 1	Room & Board: $4300
Freshman Class: 1132 applied, 941 accepted, 363 enrolled	
SAT I or ACT: required	**COMPETITIVE**

Whitworth College, founded in 1890, is a nonprofit, independent, comprehensive coeducational institution affiliated with the Presbyterian Church, USA. The emphasis of its undergraduate and graduate programs is on the liberal arts, business, art and fine arts, music, religious studies, and teacher preparation. There is one undergraduate and one graduate school. In addition to regional accreditation, Whitworth has baccalaureate program accreditation with NASM and NCATE. The library contains 141,000 volumes, 54,250 microform items, and 1528 audiovisual forms, and subscribes to 810 periodicals. Special learning facilities include an art gallery and radio station. The 200-acre campus is in a suburban area 7 miles north of Spokane. Including residence halls, there are 40 buildings on campus.

Student Life: About 55% of undergraduates are from Washington. Students come from 29 states, 25 foreign countries, and Canada. Ninety-five percent are from public schools; 5% from private. Eighty-six percent are white. Seventy-six percent are Protestant; 10% claim no religious affiliation. The average age of freshmen is 19; all undergraduates, 22. Twenty percent drop out by the end of their first year; 60% remain to graduate.

Housing: A total of 850 students can be accommodated in college housing. College-sponsored living facilities include single-sex and coed dormitories and on-campus apartments. In addition there are language houses and special interest houses. On-campus housing is guaranteed for all 4 years. Sixty-six percent of students live on campus; of those, 90% remain on campus on weekends. Alcohol is not permitted. All students may keep cars on campus.

Activities: There are no fraternities or sororities on campus. There are 22 groups on campus, including band, cheerleading, choir, chorale, chorus, dance, drama, ethnic, honors, international, jazz band, literary magazine, newspaper, political, radio and TV, religious, social, social service, student government, and yearbook. Popular campus events include athletic events, movies, and theme weeks.

Sports: There are 8 intercollegiate sports for men and 7 for women, and 10 intramural sports for men and 8 for women. Athletic and recreation facilities include a 2000-seat stadium, a 1200-seat gymnasium, a field house, an aquatic center, and playing fields.

Disabled Students: Seventy percent of the campus is accessible to disabled students. The following facilities are available: wheelchair ramps, elevators, special parking, specially equipped rest rooms, and lowered drinking fountains.

Services: In addition to many counseling and information services, tutoring is available in most subjects, including biology, chemistry, computer science, French, German, Spanish, mathematics, physics, and writing.

Campus Safety and Security: Campus safety and security measures include 24-hour foot and vehicle patrol, informal discussions, emergency telephones, and lighted pathways and sidewalks.

Programs of Study: Whitworth awards the B.A. and B.S. degrees. Master's degrees also are awarded. Bachelor's degrees are awarded in BIOLOGICAL SCIENCE (biology/biological science), BUSINESS (accounting, business administration and management, and international business management), COMMUNICATIONS AND THE ARTS (communications, English, fine arts, French, journalism, music, Spanish, and speech/debate/rhetoric), COMPUTER AND PHYSICAL SCIENCE (chemistry, computer science, mathematics, and physics), EDUCATION (art, elementary, English, foreign languages, mathematics, music, science, secondary, and social studies), HEALTH PROFESSIONS (nursing, predentistry, and premedicine), SOCIAL SCIENCE (economics, history, international relations, international studies, philosophy, political science/government, prelaw, psychology, religion, and sociology). English, history, and chemistry are the strongest academically. Education, business, and history/political studies have the largest enrollments.

Required: Students must complete 130 credit hours, with 42 in the major, and maintain a GPA of at least 2.0. The curriculum includes 3 core courses on religious, rationalist, and scientific traditions; distribution requirements are comprised of 1 course each in biblical literature, oral communication, fine arts, social science, and humanities, and 2 each in a foreign language and science/mathematics. Additionally, an other-culture course or experience must be fulfilled, and 4 physical education activity courses are needed.

Special: Special academic programs include many work-study opportunities, 1 to 3 internship course credits that may be earned by juniors and seniors, and a January Washington term. Study abroad is available in 12 countries. There is cross-registration with the Intercollegiate Language Study Consortium. Accelerated degree programs are possible, and students may choose to specialize in an area of concentration in lieu of a major. Credit may be granted for life, military, or work experience. Nondegree study is possible for those auditing or in seminars, and there is 1 pass/fail option allowed per year. A special feature of the school is the modified semester calendar, which affords unusual opportunities for internships, study tours, and other activities. There is a freshman honors program on campus

Faculty/Classroom: Seventy percent of faculty are male; 30%, female. All teach undergraduates, and do research. No introductory courses are taught by graduate students. The average class size in an introductory lecture is 30; in a laboratory, 15; and in a regular course offering, 19.

Admissions: About 83% of the 1993–94 applicants were accepted. There were 3 National Merit finalists. About 28 freshmen graduated first in their class.

Requirements: Whitworth requires applicants to be in the upper 50% of their class. A minimum GPA of 2.7 is required. The SAT I or ACT is required. Suggested scores are 1000 for the SAT I, 500 verbal and 500 mathematics, and 22 for the ACT. Other admissions criteria include 4 high school credits in English, 2 of a foreign language, and 3 each in mathematics, science, and history/social studies. An essay must be submitted, and an interview is recommended. Music students are advised to audition. AP and CLEP credits are accepted. Important factors used in the admissions decision are advanced placement or honor courses, extracurricular activities record, leadership record, recommendations by school officials, and recommendations by alumni.

Procedure: Freshmen are admitted fall, winter, and spring. Entrance exams should be taken by the fall of the senior year, though the spring of the junior year is preferred. Early decision applications should be filed by November 30. March 1 is the preferred application deadline for fall entry. Notification of early decision is sent December 15; regular decision, March 1. There are early decision and deferred admissions plans. About 100 early decision candidates were accepted for the 1993–94 class. A waiting list is an active part of the admissions procedure, with about 10% of applicants on the list.

Transfer: About 141 transfer students enrolled in a recent year. Transfer students must have a GPA of at least 2.25 and a recommended 45 quarter credits earned. The SAT I or ACT is recommended; the SAT I composite score should be 1000 and the ACT score 22. A total of 32 credits out of 130 must be completed at Whitworth.

Visiting: There are regularly scheduled orientations for prospective students. There are guides for informal visits and visitors may sit in on classes and stay overnight at the school. To arrange for a visit, contact the Campus Visit Coordinator at (800) 533–4668.

Financial Aid: In 1993–94, 90% of all current freshmen and 88% of continuing students received some form of financial aid. The average freshman award was $10,951. Of that total, scholarships or need-based grants averaged $5617; loans averaged $2669 ($4000 maximum); and work contracts averaged $1559 ($2500 maximum). All undergraduate students work part-time. Average earnings from campus work for the school year are $1402. Whitworth is a member of CSS. The FAF, or FFS, or SFS is required. The FAF is preferred. The priority deadline for financial aid applications is March 1.

International Students: There are currently 43 international students enrolled. The school actively recruits these students. They must take the TOEFL and achieve a minimum score of 460.

Computers: The college provides computer facilities for student use. The mainframe is a DEC MicroVAX 3500. There are also microcomputer laboratories available for student use. All students may access the system. It may be used anytime during library hours. There are no time limits on using the system. The fees are $10 per term.

Graduates: In 1992–93, 292 bachelor's degrees were awarded. Within an average freshman class, 57% graduate in 4 years and 66% in 5 years. Some 35 companies recruited on campus in 1992–93.

Admissions Contact: Ken Moyer, Director of Admissions.

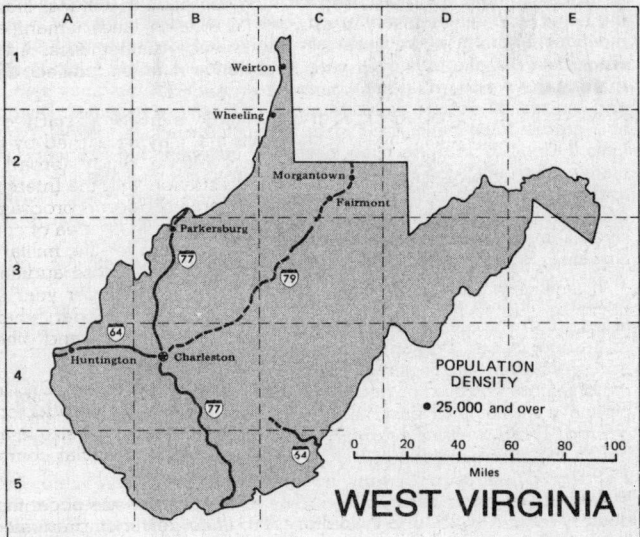

POPULATION
DENSITY
● 25,000 and over

0 20 40 60 80 100
Miles

WEST VIRGINIA

ALDERSON-BROADDUS COLLEGE
Philippi, WV 26416

C-3

(304) 457-1700

Full-time: 339 men, 460 women
Part-time: 20 men, 58 women
Graduate: 18 men, 16 women
Year: semesters, summer session
Application Deadline: open
Freshman Class: 1026 applied, 819 accepted, 282 enrolled
SAT I or ACT: required

Faculty: 63; IIB, --$
Ph.D.s: 50%
Student/Faculty: 13 to 1
Tuition: $9200
Room & Board: $3000

COMPETITIVE

Alderson-Broaddus College is a private institution, founded in 1871 and affiliated with American Baptist Churches, USA, offering a liberal arts program along with teacher preparation and professional, music, business, religion, art, and science studies. There is one graduate school. In addition to regional accreditation, Alderson-Broaddus has baccalaureate program accreditation with CAHEA and NLN. The library contains 100,000 volumes, 8000 microform items, and 5000 audiovisual forms, and subscribes to 670 periodicals. Computerized library sources and services include the card catalog, interlibrary loans, and database searching. Special learning facilities include a learning resource center, art gallery, planetarium, radio station, and TV station. The 170-acre campus is in a small town 100 miles south of Pittsburgh. Including residence halls, there are 15 buildings on campus.

Student Life: About 61% of undergraduates are from West Virginia. Students come from 37 states, 7 foreign countries, and Canada. Ninety percent are from public schools; 10% from private. Ninety percent are white. Seventy-seven percent are Protestant; 13% claim no religious affiliation; 10% Catholic. The average age of freshmen is 18.5; all undergraduates, 20.5. Twenty-six percent drop out by the end of their first year; 44% remain to graduate.

Housing: A total of 700 students can be accommodated in college housing. College-sponsored living facilities include single-sex dormitories, off-campus apartments, and married-student housing. On-campus housing is guaranteed for all 4 years. Fifty percent of students live on campus; of those, 60% remain on campus on weekends. Alcohol is not permitted. All students may keep cars on campus.

Activities: There are 4 local fraternities and 3 local sororities . There are 40 groups on campus, including art, band, cheerleading, choir, chorale, chorus, computers, drama, ethnic, film, honors, international, jazz band, musical theater, newspaper, pep band, photography, political, professional, radio and TV, religious, social, social service, student government, and yearbook. Popular campus events include Homecoming, open houses, plays, Spring Weekend, music recitals, and Christmas programs.

Sports: There are 4 intercollegiate sports each for men and women, and 10 intramural sports each. Athletic and recreation facilities include several playing fields near the main campus, a swimming pool, a weight room, handball courts, auxiliary gymnasiums, an archery range, a batting cage, and horse-riding trails at a nearby school of horsemanship.

Disabled Students: Seventy-five percent of the campus is accessible to disabled students. The following facilities are available: wheelchair ramps, elevators, special parking, specially equipped rest rooms, and special class scheduling.

Services: In addition to many counseling and information services, tutoring is available in every subject. There is remedial math, reading, and writing.

Campus Safety and Security: Campus safety and security measures include informal discussions, pamphlets, posters, and films, lighted pathways and sidewalks, and security guard patrol from 4 P.M. to 4 A.M.

Programs of Study: Alderson-Broaddus awards the B.A. and B.S. degrees. Associate and master's degrees also are awarded. Bachelor's degrees are awarded in BIOLOGICAL SCIENCE (biology/biological science), BUSINESS (accounting, business administration and management, and management information systems), COMMUNICATIONS AND THE ARTS (broadcasting, creative writing, English, music, speech/debate/rhetoric, and technical and business writing), COMPUTER AND PHYSICAL SCIENCE (chemistry, computer science, and mathematics), EDUCATION (elementary, middle school, music, recreation, and secondary), HEALTH PROFESSIONS (cytotechnology, medical laboratory technology, medical science, nursing, predentistry, premedicine, preveterinary science, radiograph medical technology, and sports medicine), SOCIAL SCIENCE (Christian studies, history, humanities, liberal arts/general studies, political science/government, prelaw, psychology, and sociology). Health, natural sciences, and music are the strongest academically. Health has the largest enrollment.

Required: All students must maintain a GPA of 2.0 while taking 128 semester hours. Distribution requirements are built around the core program, which prescribes freshman English, English, religion, philosophy, history, and 4 credits from 2 of the following areas: speech, physical education, and fine arts. Necessary upper-division courses stem from the liberal studies minor and the Nine-Hour Block, which require courses from humanities, natural sciences, and social sciences.

Special: Internships, co-op programs, cross-registration with the Mountain State Association of Colleges, study abroad through the college's programs in Austria and England or through the Junior Year Abroad program in conjunction with other schools, and work scholarships at the college are available. In addition, the college offers dual and student-designed majors, a general studies degree, an accelerated degree program in organizational management, the B.A.-B.S. degree, nondegree study, and pass/fail options. There is a freshman honors program on campus

Faculty/Classroom: Sixty percent of faculty are male; 40%, female. All teach undergraduates. No introductory courses are taught by graduate students. The average class size in an introductory lecture is 40; in a laboratory, 30; and in a regular course offering, 20.

Admissions: About 80% of the 1993–94 applicants were accepted. There were 3 National Merit finalists. About 6 freshmen graduated first in their class.

Requirements: A minimum GPA of 2.0 is required. The SAT I or ACT is required. The recommended composite score for the SAT I is 800; for the ACT, 20. Applicants who are graduates of secondary schools or have passed the GED are considered for admission. An audition for certain majors and an interview are recommended. AP and CLEP credits are accepted. Important factors used in the admissions decision are advanced placement or honor courses, leadership record, recommendations by school officials, recommendations by alumni, and personality, intangible qualities.

Procedure: Freshmen are admitted to all sessions. Entrance exams should be taken as early as possible. Application deadlines are open. The application fee is $10. Notification is sent on a rolling basis. There are early decision and early admissions plans.

Transfer: About 110 transfer students enrolled in 1993–94. Transfer applicants must have a minimum 2.0 GPA. If they have fewer than 29 transfer credit hours, ACT or SAT I results and a high school diploma are required. A total of 60 credits out of 128 must be completed at Alderson-Broaddus.

Visiting: There are regularly scheduled orientations for prospective students. There are guides for informal visits and visitors may sit in on classes and stay overnight at the school. To arrange for a visit, contact the Admissions Office at (304) 457-1700.

Financial Aid: In 1993–94 97% of all current freshmen and 95% of continuing students received some form of financial aid. About 79% of freshmen and 75% of continuing students received need-based aid. The average freshman award was $9469. Of that total, scholarships or need-based grants averaged $2150 ($13,500 maximum); loans averaged $3500 ($15,500 maximum); and work contracts averaged $1200 ($3000 maximum). Forty-eight percent of undergraduate students work part-time. Average earnings from campus work for

the school year are $1200. The average financial indebtedness of the 1992–93 graduate was $12,000. Alderson-Broaddus is a member of CSS. The college's own financial statement and and FAFSA are required. The deadline for financial aid applications is August 1.

International Students: There are currently 18 international students enrolled. The school actively recruits these students. They must take the TOEFL and achieve a minimum score of 500. The student must also take the SAT I or the ACT.

Computers: The college provides computer facilities for student use. The mainframe is a DEC VAX. All students have access to mainframe and personal computer laboratories. There are no fees. It is recommended that students in computer science have personal computers. An IBM-compatible personal computer or an Apple Macintosh is recommended.

Graduates: In a recent year, 123 bachelor's degrees were awarded. The most popular majors among graduates were medical science (30%), teacher education (14%), and nursing (10%).

Admissions Contact: Craig Gould, Director of Admissions.

BETHANY COLLEGE

C-1

Bethany, WV 26032	(304) 829–7611; (800) 922–7611 (in-state)
Full-time: 372 men, 365 women	Faculty: 57; IIB, --$
Part-time: 26 men, 14 women	Ph.D.s: 85%
Graduate: none	Student/Faculty: 13 to 1
Year: 4-1-4	Tuition: $13,600
Application Deadline: August 15	Room & Board: $4700
Freshman Class: 664 applied, 535 accepted, 210 enrolled	
SAT or ACT: required	COMPETITIVE +

Bethany College, founded in 1840, is a coeducational liberal arts institution affiliated with the Christian Church (Disciples of Christ). In addition to regional accreditation, Bethany has baccalaureate program accreditation with CSWE and NCATE. The library contains 201,930 volumes, 3600 microform items, and 4293 audiovisual forms, and subscribes to 585 periodicals. Computerized library sources and services include the card catalog, interlibrary loans, and database searching. Special learning facilities include a learning resource center, radio station, and TV station. The 300-acre campus is in a small town 14 miles north of Wheeling. Including residence halls, there are 33 buildings on campus.

Student Life: About 80% of undergraduates are from out-of-state, mostly the Middle Atlantic. Students come from 38 states, 16 foreign countries, and Canada. Seventy percent are from public schools; 30% from private. Ninety percent are white. Forty percent are Protestant; 33% Catholic; 19% claim no religious affiliation. The average age of freshmen is 18; all undergraduates, 20. Twelve percent drop out by the end of their first year; 67% remain to graduate.

Housing: A total of 786 students can be accommodated in college housing. College-sponsored living facilities include single-sex dormitories, off-campus apartments, fraternity houses, and sorority houses. In addition, there are honors houses. On-campus housing is guaranteed for all 4 years. Ninety percent of students live on campus; of those, 87% remain on campus on weekends. Alcohol is not permitted. All students may keep cars on campus.

Activities: About 50% of men belong to 6 national fraternities; about 50% of women belong to 4 national sororities. There are 38 groups on campus, including art, cheerleading, chess, choir, chorale, chorus, computers, dance, drama, ethnic, honors, international, literary magazine, newspaper, pep band, photography, political, professional, radio and TV, religious, social, social service, student government, and yearbook. Popular campus events include Spring Weekend, Mid-Term Break, and Snow Carnival.

Sports: There are 9 intercollegiate sports for men and 9 for women, and 4 intramural sports for men and 4 for women. Athletic and recreation facilities include a 2000-seat stadium, a 1000-seat gymnasium, a natatorium, and football, soccer, and field hockey fields.

Disabled Students: Twenty percent of the campus is accessible to disabled students. The following facilities are available: wheelchair ramps, elevators, special parking, and specially equipped rest rooms.

Services: In addition to many counseling and information services, tutoring is available in every subject. There is also a center for academic success, where guidance is provided for students needing special assistance.

Campus Safety and Security: Campus safety and security measures include 24-hour foot and vehicle patrol, escort service, informal discussions, and pamphlets, posters, and films. In addition, there are lighted pathways and sidewalks.

Programs of Study: Bethany awards the B.A. and B.S. degrees. Bachelor's degrees are awarded in BIOLOGICAL SCIENCE (biochemistry and biology/biological science), BUSINESS (accounting and business economics), COMMUNICATIONS AND THE ARTS (communications, English, fine arts, French, German, journalism, languages, and Spanish), COMPUTER AND PHYSICAL SCIENCE (chemistry, computer science, mathematics, and physics), EDUCATION (early childhood, elementary, English, foreign languages, phys-

ical, science, secondary, and special), HEALTH PROFESSIONS (predentistry and premedicine), SOCIAL SCIENCE (economics, history, philosophy, political science/government, prelaw, psychology, public administration, religion, and social work). Communications, premedicine, and biochemistry are the strongest academically. Communications, economics, and education have the largest enrollments.

Required: All students must earn 128 semester hours, including 24 to 48 in the major, while maintaining a 2.0 GPA. A freshman seminar and 'origins of modern world thought' courses are required. Distribution credits must be earned in historical foundations, global awareness, Judeo-Christian tradition, aesthetic judgment, life science, quantitative reasoning, social institutions, human personality and behavior, and physical science. Students must complete 4 practicums, a writing proficiency requirement, a senior project, and a senior comprehensive examination in order to graduate.

Special: Bethany offers a 3–2 engineering degree with Columbia, Washington (at St. Louis), and Case Western Reserve Universities, cross-registration with West Liberty State and Wheeling Jesuit Colleges, internships which are required with many majors, study abroad in France, Spain, England, and Germany, a Washington semester, and work-study programs. B.A.-B.S. degrees and dual majors in all majors, a general studies degree, student-designed majors in interdisciplinary studies and pass/fail options in nonmajor courses also are offered. There is also a voluntary January term. There are 15 national honor societies on campus.

Faculty/Classroom: Seventy-five percent of faculty are male; 25%, female. All teach undergraduates. The average class size in an introductory lecture is 25; in a laboratory, 15; and in a regular course offering, 15.

Admissions: About 81% of the 1993–94 applicants were accepted. The SAT I scores for the 1993–94 freshman class were as follows: Verbal—58% below 500, 33% between 500 and 599, 8% between 600 and 700, and 1% above 700; Math—48% below 500, 37% between 500 and 599, 12% between 600 and 700, and 3% above 700. The ACT scores were 16% below 21, 39% between 21 and 23, 30% between 24 and 26, 11% between 27 and 28, and 4% above 28. About 35% of the current freshmen were in the top fifth of their class; 71% were in the top two fifths. Eight freshmen graduated first in their class.

Requirements: The SAT I or ACT is required. Applicants must have 15 Carnegie units, which should include 4 years of English, 3 years each in mathematics and science, and 2 years each in foreign language, history, and social studies. An essay, an interview, a portfolio, and an audition are recommended, depending on the major. The GED is accepted. AP and CLEP credits are accepted. Important factors used in the admissions decision are advanced placement or honor courses, extracurricular activities record, recommendations by school officials, leadership record, and recommendations by alumni.

Procedure: Freshmen are admitted fall and spring. Entrance exams should be taken during the junior year. Early decision applications should be filed by November 15; regular applications, by August 15 for fall entry and January 15 for spring entry, along with an application fee of $20. Notification of early decision is sent December 15; regular decision, on a rolling basis. There are early decision and deferred admissions plans. About 35 early decision candidates were accepted for the 1993–94 class.

Transfer: Seventeen transfer students enrolled in 1993–94. Transfer students must have a minimum GPA of 2.0. A total of 32 credits out of 128 must be completed at Bethany.

Visiting: There are regularly scheduled orientations for prospective students, including a tour and meetings with faculty, coaches, and financial aid and admission personnel. There are guides for informal visits and visitors may sit in on classes and stay overnight at the school. To arrange for a visit, contact the Admissions Office at (800) 922–7611.

Financial Aid: In 1993–94, 70% of all current freshmen and 79% of continuing students received some form of financial aid. About 48% of freshmen and 43% of continuing students received need-based aid. The average freshman award was $9650. Of that total, scholarships or need-based grants averaged $9450 ($13,660 maximum); loans averaged $2650 ($5100 maximum); and work contracts averaged $1000 ($1500 maximum). Seventy-nine percent of undergraduate students work part-time. Average earnings from campus work for the school year are $400. Bethany is a member of CSS. The FAF is required. The deadline for financial aid applications for fall entry is April 1, and for spring entry, December 15.

International Students: There are currently 38 international students enrolled. The school actively recruits these students. They must take the TOEFL and achieve a minimum score of 500.

Computers: The college provides computer facilities for student use. The mainframe is a Prime. There are 20 terminals for the mainframe in the computer center. There is also a Macintosh computer center with 8 student laboratories. In addition, there are computer laboratories for English, economics, communications, biology, chemistry, education, and social sciences, with about 200 microcomputers avail-

able. All students may access the system. It may be used 24 hours daily. There are no time limits on using the system. There are no fees.

Graduates: In 1992–93, 143 bachelor's degrees were awarded. The most popular majors among graduates were communications (21%), psychology (16%), and economics (9%). Within an average freshman class, 3% graduate in 3 years, 64% in 4 years, 3% in 5 years, and 1% in 6 years. Some 20 companies recruited on campus in 1992–93.

Admissions Contact: Sheryl Reddy, Director of Admissions.

BLUEFIELD STATE COLLEGE   B-5
Bluefield, WV 24701   (304) 327–4067; (800) 654–7798 (out-of-state)

Full-time: 704 men, 759 women	Faculty: 91; IIB, --$
Part-time: 407 men, 743 women	Ph.D.s: 27%
Graduate: none	Student/Faculty: 16 to 1
Year: semesters, summer session	Tuition: $1832 ($4202)
Application Deadline: open	Room & Board: n/app
Freshman Class: 1046 applied, 832 accepted, 518 enrolled	
SAT I: 390/410	ACT: 18 LESS COMPETITIVE

Bluefield State College, founded in 1895, is a state-supported commuter college offering programs in engineering technologies, business, teacher education, arts and sciences, health science professions, and a variety of career fields. The college also offers a wide variety of off-campus courses. In addition to regional accreditation, Bluefield State has baccalaureate program accreditation with ABET. The library contains 78,000 volumes, 110,000 microform items, and 50,000 audiovisual forms, and subscribes to 450 periodicals. Computerized library sources and services include the card catalog, interlibrary loans, and database searching. Special learning facilities include a learning resource center and art gallery. The 40-acre campus is in a small town 90 miles south of Charleston. There are 9 buildings on campus.

Student Life: About 93% of undergraduates are from West Virginia. Students come from 8 states, 9 foreign countries, and Canada. Almost all are from public schools. Ninety-one percent are white. The average age of freshmen is 23.1; all undergraduates, 26.9. Thirty-four percent drop out by the end of their first year; 52% remain to graduate.

Housing: There are no residence halls. All students commute. Alcohol is not permitted. All students may keep cars on campus.

Activities: About 3% of men belong to 3 local and 3 national fraternities; about 1% of women belong to 3 local and 1 national sororities. There are 42 groups on campus, including cheerleading, choir, international, jazz band, newspaper, student government, and yearbook. Popular campus events include Homecoming, dances, and sports events.

Sports: There are 5 intercollegiate sports for men and 4 for women, and 20 intramural sports for men and 15 for women. Athletic and recreation facilities include a gymnasium, a pool, tennis courts, an athletic field, and physical fitness and aerobics rooms.

Disabled Students: Most of the campus is accessible to disabled students. The following facilities are available: wheelchair ramps, elevators, special parking, specially equipped rest rooms, and lowered drinking fountains.

Services: In addition to many counseling and information services, tutoring is available in most subjects. There is remedial math, reading, and writing.

Campus Safety and Security: Campus safety and security measures include 24-hour foot and vehicle patrol, self defense education, pamphlets, posters, and films, and emergency telephones. In addition, there are lighted pathways and sidewalks.

Programs of Study: Bluefield State awards the B.A., B.S., B.S.E.T., and B.S.N. degrees. Associate degrees also are awarded. Bachelor's degrees are awarded in BIOLOGICAL SCIENCE (biology/biological science), BUSINESS (accounting and business administration and management), COMPUTER AND PHYSICAL SCIENCE (computer science and mathematics), EDUCATION (elementary, middle school, physical, science, secondary, and special), ENGINEERING AND ENVIRONMENTAL DESIGN (engineering technology), HEALTH PROFESSIONS (nursing), SOCIAL SCIENCE (criminal justice, humanities, and social science). Engineering technology and health science are the strongest academically. Business has the largest enrollment.

Required: The minimum requirement for graduation is a 2.0 GPA overall and in the student's major and minor, and 128 semester hours. All graduating students must have completed the general program specific to their degree.

Special: A general studies degree and life experience credentials are offered through the Regents Bachelor of Arts Degree Program, designed for adults. Nondegree study is offered. There is a freshman honors program on campus, as well as 2 national honor societies. One department has an honors program.

Faculty/Classroom: Sixty-two percent of faculty are male; 38%, female. All teach undergraduates. The average class size in an introductory lecture is 40; in a laboratory, 25; and in a regular course offering, 25.

Admissions: About 80% of the 1993–94 applicants were accepted. The SAT scores for the 1993–94 freshman class were as follows: Verbal—91% below 500, 8% between 500 and 599, and 1% between 600 and 700; Math—92% below 500, 7% between 500 and 599, and 1% between 600 and 700. The ACT scores were 62% below 21, 31% between 21 and 23, 4% between 24 and 26, 2% between 27 and 28, and 1% above 28. About 18% of the current freshmen were in the top fifth of their class; 52% were in the top two fifths. About 12 freshmen graduated first in their class.

Requirements: A minimum GPA of 2.0 is required. The SAT I or ACT is required. Students meeting GED requirements or having a high school diploma, with an overall 2.0 GPA or a composite score of at least 17 on the ACT or at least 680 on the SAT I, and having successfully completed minimum high school curricular unit requirements consisting of 4 units in English, 3 in social studies, 2 in mathematics (Algebra I and higher), and 2 in laboratory science are given regular admission. Other students not meeting these requirements may be admitted on a conditional basis. AP and CLEP credits are accepted.

Procedure: Freshmen are admitted to all sessions. Entrance exams should be taken before enrolling. Application deadlines are open. Notification is sent on a rolling basis. There are early admissions and deferred admissions plans.

Transfer: About 143 transfer students enrolled in 1993–94. Transfer applicants must be in good standing at the institution from which they are transferring. A total of 32 credits out of 128 must be completed at Bluefield State.

Visiting: There are regularly scheduled orientations for prospective students. There are guides for informal visits and visitors may sit in on classes. To arrange for a visit, contact the Admissions Office at (304) 327–4065.

Financial Aid: In 1993–94, 45% of all students received some form of financial aid. About 76% of all students received need-based aid. The average freshman award was $2000. Seventy percent of undergraduate students work part-time. Average earnings from campus work for the school year are $1000. Bluefield State is a member of CSS. The college's own financial statement and FAFSA are required. The deadline for financial aid applications is March 15.

International Students: There are currently 14 international students enrolled. They must take the TOEFL and achieve a minimum score of 550. The student must also take the ACT.

Computers: The college provides computer facilities for student use. The mainframe is a DEC 4000; WVNET computer systems are accessed through telecommunications. There are also 5 computer laboratories available on campus for student use. All students may access the system. It may be used during class and laboratory hours. There are no time limits on using the system and no fees.

Graduates: In 1992–93, 365 bachelor's degrees were awarded. The most popular majors among graduates were business administration (30%), engineering technology (30%), and teacher education (15%). Within an average freshman class, 42% graduate in 4 years, 51% in 5 years, and 4% in 6 years. Some 72 companies recruited on campus in 1992–93. In the 1992 graduating class, 5% of the graduates were enrolled in graduate school within 6 months of graduation; 80% found employment.

Admissions Contact: John C. Cardwell, Director of Admissions and Enrollment Management.

CONCORD COLLEGE   B-5
Athens, WV 24712   (304) 384–5248; (800) 344–6679 (in-state)

Full-time: 890 men, 1236 women	Faculty: 88; IIB, --$
Part-time: 283 men, 551 women	Ph.D.s: 51%
Graduate: none	Student/Faculty: 24 to 1
Year: semesters, summer session	Tuition: $1936 ($4106)
Application Deadline: open	Room & Board: $3168
Freshman Class: 1671 applied, 1634 accepted, 957 enrolled	
SAT I or ACT: required	NONCOMPETITIVE

Concord College, founded in 1872, is a public liberal arts and professional training college. In addition to regional accreditation, Concord has baccalaureate program accreditation with CSWE and NCATE. The library contains 145,000 volumes, 35,430 microform items, and 4091 audiovisual forms, and subscribes to 600 periodicals. Computerized library sources and services include interlibrary loans and database searching. Special learning facilities include a learning resource center, art gallery, radio station, and TV station. The 97-acre campus is in a small town 85 miles south of Charleston. Including residence halls, there are 19 buildings on campus.

Student Life: About 80% of undergraduates are from West Virginia. Students come from 16 states and 11 foreign countries. Ninety-eight percent are from public schools; 2% from private. Ninety-five percent

are white. The average age of freshmen is 19.5; all undergraduates, 25. Twenty-five percent drop out by the end of their first year; 60% remain to graduate.

Housing: A total of 1158 students can be accommodated in college housing. College-sponsored living facilities include single-sex dormitories and married-student housing. On-campus housing is guaranteed for all 4 years. Sixty percent of students commute. All students may keep cars on campus.

Activities: About 20% of men belong to 2 local and 6 national fraternities; about 20% of women belong to 4 national sororities. There are 60 groups on campus, including art, cheerleading, choir, computers, drama, honors, international, jazz band, literary magazine, marching band, musical theater, newspaper, pep band, political, professional, radio and TV, religious, social, social service, student government, and yearbook. Popular campus events include big name concerts, Alumni Day, faculty and student plays, and musicals.

Sports: There are 6 intercollegiate sports for men and 4 for women, and 15 intramural sports each. Athletic and recreation facilities include 5 tennis courts, 4 racquetball courts, 2 gymnasiums, a Nautilus fitness room, a pool, a dance studio, and various outdoor fields. The campus stadium seats 4000, the larger gymnasium 2700, and the largest auditorium, 900.

Disabled Students: Ninety percent of the campus is accessible to disabled students. The following facilities are available: wheelchair ramps, elevators, special parking, and special class scheduling.

Services: In addition to many counseling and information services, tutoring is available in every subject. There is a reader service for the blind, and remedial math, reading, and writing.

Campus Safety and Security: Campus safety and security measures include informal discussions, pamphlets, posters, and films, emergency telephones, and lighted pathways and sidewalks. In addition, foot and vehicle patrol is available 24 hours Monday through Friday and is on call Saturday and Sunday.

Programs of Study: Concord awards the B.A., B.S., B.B.A., B.S.C.I.S., B.S.Ed., B.S.Med.Tech., B.S.W., and B.A./B.S.I.S. degrees. Associate degrees also are awarded. Bachelor's degrees are awarded in BIOLOGICAL SCIENCE (biology/biological science), BUSINESS (accounting, banking and finance, business administration and management, hotel/motel and restaurant management, marketing/retailing/merchandising, office supervision and management, and small business management), COMMUNICATIONS AND THE ARTS (broadcasting, communications, and English), COMPUTER AND PHYSICAL SCIENCE (chemistry, computer programming, computer science, information sciences and systems, and mathematics), EDUCATION (art, business, early childhood, elementary, middle school, music, science, secondary, and special), HEALTH PROFESSIONS (medical laboratory technology, predentistry, premedicine, and prepharmacy), SOCIAL SCIENCE (community services, geography, history, parks and recreation management, political science/government, prelaw, psychology, social science, social work, and sociology). Teacher education, business, mathematics, and science are the strongest academically. Teacher education, business, and travel industry management have the largest enrollments.

Required: To graduate, students must earn 128 credit hours with a minimum GPA of 2.0, and complete the college's general studies curriculum. Required courses include 14 to 15 semester hours of mathematics and science, 12 of English and literature, 12 of social studies, 6 of fine arts, 3 of speech, and 2 of physical education.

Special: Students may serve internships in medical technology, social work, travel industry management, commercial art/advertising, and communications arts, as well as a Washington semester through the political science department. The college has cross-registration with Bluefield State College. Dual majors, interdisciplinary student-designed majors, and nondegree study are available. Credit for life, military, and work experience is granted to adult students through the Regents Bachelor of Arts Degree Program. There are 4 national honor societies on campus.

Faculty/Classroom: Sixty-four percent of faculty are male; 36%, female. All teach undergraduates. The average class size in an introductory lecture is 35; in a laboratory, 20; and in a regular course offering, 35.

Admissions: Most of the 1993–94 applicants were accepted. There were 5 National Merit semifinalists.

Requirements: A minimum GPA of 2.0 is required. The SAT I or ACT is required. In addition, applicants must be high school graduates or hold a GED. Students should have earned 17 academic credits, including 4 in English, 3 in social studies, 2 each in mathematics and science, 1 in history, as well as 1 in health/physical education. An interview is recommended and, where appropriate, also a portfolio or audition. AP and CLEP credits are accepted. Important factors used in the admissions decision are advanced placement or honor courses, personality, intangible qualities, recommendations by school officials, extracurricular activities record, and leadership record.

Procedure: Freshmen are admitted to all sessions. Entrance exams should be taken in the junior year or preferably early in the senior year. Application deadlines are open. Notification is sent on a rolling basis.

Transfer: About 314 transfer students enrolled in an earlier year. Transfer applicants must have a GPA of at least 2.0. The college recommends a minimum of 15 credit hours of college work completed and an interview. A total of 32 credits out of 128 must be completed at Concord.

Visiting: There are guides for informal visits and visitors may sit in on classes and stay overnight at the school. To arrange for a visit, contact the Admissions Office at (304) 384-5248.

Financial Aid: In 1993–94, 64% of all current freshmen and 50% of continuing students received some form of financial aid. About 53% of freshmen and 49% of continuing students received need-based aid. The average freshman award was $3413. Of that total, loans averaged $1450 ($2650 maximum); and work contracts averaged $1359 ($2144 maximum). Twenty-three percent of undergraduate students work part-time. Average earnings from campus work for the school year are $1800. The average financial indebtedness of the 1992–93 graduate was $10,000. Concord is a member of CSS. The FAF is required. The deadline for financial aid applications is April 15.

International Students: There are currently 22 international students enrolled. The school actively recruits these students. They must take the TOEFL and achieve a minimum score of 500. The student must also take the SAT I or the ACT.

Computers: The college provides computer facilities for student use. Concord is a participant in the statewide WVNET computer network systems. Programming languages and statistical packages are run from the central mainframe, a DEC MicroVAX 3900. There are also 60 Apple and IBM-compatible microcomputers available in computer laboratories and faculty offices. All students may access the system. There are no time limits on using the system and no fees.

Graduates: In an earlier year, 260 bachelor's degrees were awarded. The most popular majors among graduates were education (42%), business (28%), and travel industry management (6%). Within an average freshman class, 60% graduate in 4 years. Some 100 companies recruited on campus. In the 1992 graduating class, 15% of all students were enrolled in graduate school within 6 months of graduation; 60% found employment.

Admissions Contact: Dale Dickens, Director of Admissions.

DAVIS AND ELKINS COLLEGE
C-3

Elkins, WV 26241   (304) 636–1900; (800) 624–3157 (out-of-state)

Full-time: 311 men, 443 women	Faculty: 58; IIB, --$
Part-time: 91 men, 96 women	Ph.D.s: 62%
Graduate: none	Student/Faculty: 13 to 1
Year: semesters, summer session	Tuition: $8980
Application Deadline: open	Room & Board: $4250
Freshman Class: 585 applied, 501 accepted, 183 enrolled	
SAT I Verbal/Math: 396/426	LESS COMPETITIVE

Davis and Elkins College, founded in 1904 and affiliated with the Presbyterian Church, USA, offers programs in the liberal arts, business, professional training, teacher preparation, nursing, and recreation management. The library contains 225,000 volumes, 300,000 microform items, and 14,000 audiovisual forms, and subscribes to 410 periodicals. Computerized library sources and services include the card catalog. Special learning facilities include a learning resource center, an art gallery, a planetarium, and a radio station. The 170-acre campus is in a small town 200 miles west of Washington, D.C. Including residence halls, there are 20 buildings on campus.

Student Life: About 60% of undergraduates are from West Virginia. Students come from 30 states, 12 foreign countries, and Canada. Ninety percent are white. The average age of all undergraduates is 22. Thirty-five percent drop out by the end of their first year; 65% remain to graduate.

Housing: A total of 740 students can be accommodated in college housing. College-sponsored living facilities include single-sex and coed dormitories. On-campus housing is guaranteed for all 4 years. Sixty percent of students live on campus; of those, 75% remain on campus on weekends. All students may keep cars on campus.

Activities: About 20% of men belong to 3 national fraternities; about 20% of women belong to 2 national sororities. There are 33 groups on campus, including art, cheerleading, choir, computers, drama, honors, international, jazz band, literary magazine, musical theater, newspaper, photography, political, professional, radio and TV, religious, social, social service, student government, and yearbook. Popular campus events include Parents Weekend, Homecoming, and Deja Vu.

Sports: There are 6 intercollegiate sports for men and 5 for women, and 10 intramural sports each. Athletic and recreation facilities include a 2000-seat gymnasium, a 1300-seat arena, fields, a fitness cen-

ter and fitness trails, a tennis court, a pool, and a nearby national forest.

Disabled Students: Sixty percent of the campus is accessible to disabled students. The following facilities are available: wheelchair ramps, elevators, special parking, specially equipped rest rooms, special class scheduling, and lowered drinking fountains and telephones.

Services: In addition to many counseling and information services, tutoring is available in every subject. There is alsp remedial math, reading, and writing. Learning disabilities services also are available.

Campus Safety and Security: Campus safety and security measures include lighted pathways and sidewalks. The campus security service is on duty from 5 P.M. to 4 A.M.

Programs of Study: D&E awards the B.A., B.S., B.S.N. and associate degrees. Bachelor's degrees are awarded in BIOLOGICAL SCIENCE (biology/biological science), BUSINESS (accounting, business administration and management, hotel/motel and restaurant management, international business management, marketing/retailing/merchandising, office supervision and management, and recreation and leisure services), COMMUNICATIONS AND THE ARTS (communications, dramatic arts, English, fine arts, French, journalism, languages, literature, music, Spanish, and theater design), COMPUTER AND PHYSICAL SCIENCE (chemistry, computer science, mathematics, and physics), EDUCATION (art, business, elementary, health, middle school, science, and secondary), ENGINEERING AND ENVIRONMENTAL DESIGN (engineering and environmental science), HEALTH PROFESSIONS (health care administration, medical laboratory technology, nursing, occupational therapy, predentistry, premedicine, and prepharmacy), SOCIAL SCIENCE (economics, fashion design and technology, history, philosophy, political science/government, prelaw, psychology, religion, and sociology). Natural science and psychology are the strongest academically. Business and nursing have the largest enrollments.

Required: To graduate, students must complete 124 credit hours, including 30 to 40 in the major, with a GPA of 2.0. General education requirements include 7 hours of natural science, 6 each of history, social science, English composition, philosophy, religion, literature, and mathematics, 5 of fine arts, and 2 of physical education, as well as a course in computer literacy.

Special: Students may study abroad in London or take a Washington semester. The college offers co-op programs with Washington, Duke, Syracuse, and Boston universities, as well as internships in business and recreation management. Students may take dual majors in psychology/human services, biology/environmental sciences, and history/political science, and student-designed majors are permitted through a contract degree program. The college has a 3–2 engineering degree program and awards credit for life, military, and work experience. Nondegree study is allowed, and pass/fail options are open. The college's mentor-assisted degree-completion program allows adults to earn degrees through credit for life experience and off-campus study. There is a freshman honors program on campus, as well as 6 national honor societies. Five departments have honors programs.

Faculty/Classroom: Fifty-seven percent of faculty are male; 43%, female and all teach undergraduates. The average class size in an introductory lecture is 23; in a laboratory, 16; and in a regular course offering, 14.

Admissions: About 86% of the 1993–94 applicants were accepted. The SAT scores for the freshman class were as follows: Verbal—88% below 500, 9% between 500 and 599, and 3% between 600 and 700; Math—74% below 500, 20% between 500 and 599, 5% between 600 and 700, and 1% above 700. The ACT scores were 72% below 21, 19% between 21 and 23, 7% between 24 and 26, 1% between 27 and 28, and 1% above 28. About 23% of the current freshmen were in the top fifth of their class; 49% were in the top two fifths. There was 1 National Merit finalist. About 2 freshmen graduated first in their class.

Requirements: D&E requires applicants to be in the upper 50% of their class. A minimum GPA of 2.0 is required. The SAT I or ACT is required, with a minimum composite score of 800 on the SAT I or 18 on the ACT. Students must meet 2 out of the 3 above requirements to be admitted. Applicants should be high school graduates or hold a GED. Students should have earned 16 academic credits, including 4 in English, 3 in social studies, 2 in mathematics, including algebra I minimum, and 2 in natural science, inlcuding a laboratory course. Two years of foreign language is recommended. AP and CLEP credits are accepted. Important factors used in the admissions decision are advanced placement or honor courses, recommendations by school officials, leadership record, extracurricular activities record, and evidence of special talent.

Procedure: Freshmen are admitted to all sessions. Entrance exams should be taken during the fall of the senior year. Application deadlines are open. The application fee is $25. Notification is sent on a rolling basis. There are early decision, early admissions, and deferred admissions plans.

Transfer: About 75 transfer students enrolled in 1993–94. Transfer applicants should have earned 62 credit hours, with a GPA of 2.0. An associate degree is recommended. A total of 28 credits out of 124 must be completed at D&E.

Visiting: There are regularly scheduled orientations for prospective students. There are guides for informal visits and visitors may sit in on classes and stay overnight at the school. To arrange for a visit, contact the Admissions Office at (304) 636-5850 or (800) 624-3157.

Financial Aid: In 1993–94, 65% of all current freshmen and 65% of continuing students received some form of financial aid. About 75% of freshmen and 70% of continuing students received need-based aid. The average freshman award was $6700. Of that total, scholarships or need-based grants averaged $1000 ($3500 maximum); loans averaged $3000 ($4000 maximum); and work contracts averaged $1200 ($2000 maximum). Forty-one percent of undergraduate students work part-time. Average earnings from campus work for the school year are $1200. The average financial indebtedness of the 1992–93 graduate was $12,000. D&E is a member of CSS. The FAF and FAFSA are required. The deadline for financial aid applications is May 1.

International Students: There are currently 19 international students enrolled. They must take the TOEFL or the University of Michigan Language Test and achieve a minimum score on the TOEFL of 450.

Computers: The college provides computer facilities for student use. The mainframe is a DEC VAX 4300. There are 72 Apple IIe, Macintosh Plus, and AT&T microcomputers available in 2 laboratories. Students in courses requiring its use may access the system. There are no time limits and no fees.

Graduates: In 1992–93, 121 bachelor's degrees were awarded. The most popular majors among graduates were business (36%), education (12%), and psychology (10%). Some 5 companies recruited on campus in 1992–93.

Admissions Contact: Kevin D. Chenoweth, Director of Admissions.

FAIRMONT STATE COLLEGE
C-2

Fairmont, WV 26554   (304) 367-4141; (800) 641-5678 (out-of-state)

Full-time: 1982 men, 2422 women	Faculty: 173; IIB, -$
Part-time: 867 men, 1058 women	Ph.D.s: 40%
Graduate: none	Student/Faculty: 25 to 1
Year: semesters, summer session	Tuition: $1800 ($4238)
Application Deadline: June 15	Room & Board: $2840
Freshman Class: 1997 accepted, 1537 enrolled	
SAT or ACT: required	**LESS COMPETITIVE**

Fairmont State College, founded in 1865, is a public, coeducational institution offering programs in business, education, and engineering technology. In addition to regional accreditation, Fairmont State has baccalaureate program accreditation with ABET, NCATE, and NLN. The library contains 215,000 volumes, 31,559 microform items, and 6955 audiovisual forms, and subscribes to 834 periodicals. Special learning facilities include a learning resource center. The 80-acre campus is in a suburban area 75 miles south of Pittsburgh, Pennsylvania. Including residence halls, there are 16 buildings on campus.

Student Life: Most undergraduates are from West Virginia. Students come from 20 states, 5 foreign countries, and Canada. Almost all are from public schools. Ninety-four percent are white. Forty-five percent claim no religious affiliation; 35% Protestant; 20% Catholic. The average age of freshmen is 22; all undergraduates, 24. Thirty percent drop out by the end of their first year; 40% remain to graduate.

Housing: A total of 450 students can be accommodated in college housing. College-sponsored living facilities include single-sex dormitories. On-campus housing is available on a first-come, first-served basis. Most students commute. Alcohol is not permitted. All students may keep cars on campus.

Activities: About 4% of men belong to 3 national fraternities; about 4% of women belong to 3 national sororities. There are 45 groups on campus, including art, band, cheerleading, choir, chorus, drama, jazz band, marching band, musical theater, newspaper, photography, political, professional, religious, social, student government, symphony, and yearbook.

Sports: There are 7 intercollegiate sports for men and 5 for women, and 24 intramural sports each. Athletic and recreation facilities include a physical education center, a 5000-seat stadium, a 4000-seat basketball arena, and playing fields.

Disabled Students: Sixty-five percent of the campus is accessible to disabled students. The following facilities are available: wheelchair ramps, elevators, special parking, specially equipped rest rooms, special class scheduling, and lowered drinking fountains and telephones.

Services: In addition to many counseling and information services, tutoring is available in most subjects.

Campus Safety and Security: Campus safety and security measures include 24-hour foot and vehicle patrol, emergency telephones, and lighted pathways and sidewalks.

Programs of Study: Fairmont State awards the B.A., B.S., B.A.E., and B.E.T. degrees. Associate degrees also are awarded. Bachelor's degrees are awarded in BIOLOGICAL SCIENCE (biology/biological science), BUSINESS (accounting, banking and finance, business administration and management, business economics, and marketing/retailing/merchandising), COMMUNICATIONS AND THE ARTS (communications, English, French, and speech/debate/rhetoric), COMPUTER AND PHYSICAL SCIENCE (chemistry, computer science, and mathematics), EDUCATION (art, business, early childhood, elementary, foreign languages, health, home economics, middle school, music, science, and secondary), ENGINEERING AND ENVIRONMENTAL DESIGN (architectural technology, civil engineering technology, electrical/electronics engineering technology, engineering technology, manufacturing technology, and mechanical engineering technology), SOCIAL SCIENCE (criminal justice, history, political science/government, psychology, and sociology). Biology, engineering, technology, education, and business are the strongest academically. Business has the largest enrollment.

Required: To graduate, students must complete 128 hours with a GPA of 2.0. Students must complete 50 core curriculum hours for the B.S. degree or 56 hours for the B.A. All students must take 1 hour of physical education. Course and distribution requirements vary according to the program.

Special: The college offers internships in teacher education, retailing, and psychology, and awards a B.S.-B.S. degree in chemistry/mathematics. There is a freshman honors program on campus one department has an honors program.

Faculty/Classroom: Sixty-nine percent of faculty are male; 31%, female. All teach undergraduates. The average class size in an introductory lecture is 35; in a laboratory, 20; and in a regular course offering, 38.

Admissions: There was 1 National Merit finalist and 3 semifinalists. About 12 freshmen graduated first in their class.

Requirements: A minimum GPA of 2.3 is required. The SAT I or ACT is required. The minimum composite score required is 730 on the SAT I or 19 on the ACT. In addition, applicants must be high school graduates or hold a GED. The college requires 4 credits in English, 3 in history (1 in U.S. history), and 2 each in mathematics (algebra I and higher) and laboratory science. The college no longer requires ACT or SAT scores from students who have graduated from high school or completed GED requirements more than 5 years prior to seeking admission. AP and CLEP credits are accepted.

Procedure: Freshmen are admitted to all sessions. Entrance exams should be taken during the fall of the senior year. Applications should be filed by June 15 for fall entry, December 24 for winter entry, and May 1 for summer entry. Notification is sent on a rolling basis. There are early decision and early admissions plans. About 950 early decision candidates were accepted for the 1993-94 class.

Transfer: About 295 transfer students enrolled in 1993-94. Transfer applicants must have a GPA of 2.0. A total of 32 credits out of 128 must be completed at Fairmont State.

Visiting: Visitors may sit in on classes. To arrange for a visit, contact the Student Affairs Office at (304) 367-4216.

Financial Aid: In 1993-94, 68% of all current freshmen and 64% of continuing students received some form of financial aid. About 66% of freshmen and 64% of continuing students received need-based aid. The average freshman award was $900. Of that total, scholarships or need-based grants averaged $300; loans averaged $320; and work contracts averaged $250. Thirty-five percent of undergraduate students work part-time. Average earnings from campus work for the school year are $1800. The average financial indebtedness of the 1992-93 graduate was $6000. Fairmont State is a member of CSS. The FAFSA financial statement is required. The deadline for financial aid applications is March 1.

International Students: There are currently 53 international students enrolled. They must take the TOEFL and achieve a minimum score of 500.

Computers: The college provides computer facilities for student use. The mainframe is a DEC VAX 8250. There are also 500 IBM PCs available for student use. Those students with accounts may access the system. It may be used 8 A.M. to 11 P.M., 4 days per week. There are no time limits and no fees.

Graduates: Recently, 825 bachelor's degrees were awarded. The most popular majors among graduates were business (25%), education (24%), and technology (23%). Within an average freshman class, 30% graduate in 4 years, 40% in 5 years, and 3% in 6 years. Some 35 companies recruited on campus. In an earlier graduating class, 2% of the seniors were enrolled in graduate school within 6 months of graduation; 65% found employment.

Admissions Contact: John G. Conway, Director of Admissions.

GLENVILLE STATE COLLEGE

C-3

Glenville, WV 26351   (304) 462-7361; (800) 924-2010 (in-state)

Full-time: 832 men, 891 women	**Faculty:** 72; IIB, --$
Part-time: 169 men, 402 women	**Ph.Ds:** 28%
Graduate: none	**Student/Faculty:** 24 to 1
Year: semesters, summer session	**Tuition:** $1730 ($3944)
Application Deadline: open	**Room & Board:** $3080
Freshman Class: 1244 applied, 1202 accepted, 553 enrolled	
SAT I or ACT: required	**LESS COMPETITIVE**

Glenville State College, founded in 1872, is a public, coeducational college offering programs in education, the arts and sciences, and business. In addition to regional accreditation, Glenville State has baccalaureate program accreditation with NCATE and NLN. The library contains 205,000 volumes, 395,000 microform items, and 20,000 audiovisual forms, and subscribes to 73 periodicals. Computerized library sources and services include the card catalog. Special learning facilities include a learning resource center and an art gallery. The 160-acre campus is in a rural area 90 miles northeast of Charleston. Including residence halls, there are 16 buildings on campus.

Student Life: About 92% of undergraduates are from West Virginia. Students come from 18 states, 6 foreign countries, and Canada. Ninety-eight percent are from public schools; 2% from private. Ninety-six percent are white. Most are Protestant. The average age of freshmen is 19.1; all undergraduates, 26.5. Twenty-four percent drop out by the end of their first year; 40% remain to graduate.

Housing: A total of 640 students can be accommodated in college housing. College-sponsored living facilities include single-sex dormitories and married-student housing. On-campus housing is guaranteed for all 4 years. Sixty-three percent of students commute. Alcohol is not permitted. All students may keep cars on campus.

Activities: About 6% of men belong to 2 national fraternities; about 6% of women belong to 2 national sororities. There are 41 groups on campus, including band, cheerleading, choir, chorus, drama, honors, international, jazz band, literary magazine, marching band, musical theater, newspaper, religious, student government, and yearbook. Popular campus events include Homecoming in October and GSC Week (a campus celebration) in April.

Sports: There are 5 intercollegiate sports for men and 4 for women, and 5 intramural sports each. Athletic and recreation facilities include a field house, a 5000-seat football stadium, a running track, tennis courts, a 700-seat gymnasium, a swimming pool, and a bowling alley.

Disabled Students: Ten percent of the campus is accessible to disabled students. The following facilities are available: wheelchair ramps, elevators, and special parking.

Services: In addition to many counseling and information services, tutoring is available in most subjects. In addition, there is remedial math, reading, and writing.

Campus Safety and Security: Campus safety and security measures include 24-hour foot and vehicle patrol and lighted pathways and sidewalks.

Programs of Study: Glenville State awards the B.A. and B.S. degrees. Associate degrees also are awarded. Bachelor's degrees are awarded in BIOLOGICAL SCIENCE (biology/biological science), BUSINESS (accounting, business administration and management, and marketing/retailing/merchandising), COMMUNICATIONS AND THE ARTS (English), COMPUTER AND PHYSICAL SCIENCE (chemistry and computer science), EDUCATION (art, business, early childhood, elementary, middle school, music, physical, science, secondary, and special), HEALTH PROFESSIONS (nursing), SOCIAL SCIENCE (history). Chemistry is the strongest academically. Education has the largest enrollment.

Required: All students must take the general studies program, consisting of 44 hours in English, mathematics, science, the social sciences, humanities, and physical education. Computer science is also required. To graduate, students must complete 128 credit hours, with 42 in the major. Noneducation majors must maintain a 2.0 GPA; education majors, a 2.5.

Special: The college offers B.A.-B.S. degrees in numerous majors, credit by examination, and pass/fail options. There is a freshman honors program on campus, as well as 2 national honor societies. Four departments have honors programs.

Faculty/Classroom: Sixty-eight percent of faculty are male; 32%, female and all teach undergraduates. The average class size in an introductory lecture is 40; in a laboratory, 20; and in a regular course offering, 25.

Admissions: Almost all of the 1993-94 applicants were accepted. There were 3 National Merit semifinalists. About 21 freshmen graduated first in their class.

Requirements: A minimum GPA of 2.0 is required. The SAT I or ACT is required, with a minimum composite score of 17 on the ACT or 680 on the SAT I. Applicants should be graduates of an accredited secondary school and have taken 4 courses in English, 2 each in

higher mathematics and laboratory sciences, and 3 in social studies. GED admission is also possible. A limited number of students are accepted for conditional admission. AP and CLEP credits are accepted. Important factors used in the admissions decision are evidence of special talent, recommendations by school officials, advanced placement or honor courses, recommendations by alumni, and personality, intangible qualities.

Procedure: Freshmen are admitted to all sessions. Entrance exams should be taken at the end of the junior year. Application deadlines are open. Notification is sent on a rolling basis.

Transfer: About 64 transfer students enrolled in 1993–94. Transfer applicants must have a 2.0 GPA in 28 or more hours of college completed. A total of 32 credits out of 128 must be completed at Glenville State.

Visiting: There are regularly scheduled orientations for prospective students, including meetings with an admissions officer and a division officer and a campus tour. There are guides for informal visits and visitors may sit in on classes. To arrange for a visit, contact the Office of Admissions at (304) 462–7361.

Financial Aid: In 1993–94, 55% of all current freshmen and 60% of continuing students received some form of financial aid. About 61% of freshmen and 67% of continuing students received need-based aid. The average freshman award was $2300. Of that total, scholarships or need-based grants averaged $1350 ($2300 maximum); loans averaged $1890 ($2625 maximum); and work contracts averaged $800 ($800 maximum). Twelve percent of undergraduate students work part-time. Average earnings from campus work for the school year are $800. The average financial indebtedness of the 1992–93 graduate was $3970. Glenville State is a member of CSS. The SAR financial statement is required. The deadline for financial aid applications is March 1.

International Students: There are currently 58 international students enrolled. They must take the TOEFL and achieve a minimum score of 550. The student must also take the ACT.

Computers: The college provides computer facilities for student use. The mainframe is a DEC MicroVAX 3900 that accesses an IBM 3081 and VAX cluster. There are 52 terminals located throughout campus. All students may access the system. There are no time limits on using the system and no fees.

Graduates: Recently, bachelor's degrees were awarded. The most popular majors among graduates were education (53%), business (32%), and biology (4%). Within an average freshman class, 28% graduate in 4 years, 34% in 5 years, and 38% in 6 years. In a prior graduating class, 1% of the seniors were enrolled in graduate school within 6 months of graduation.

Admissions Contact: Mack Samples, Dean of Records and Admissions.

MARSHALL UNIVERSITY
Huntington, WV 25705   (304) 696–3160; (800) 642–3463 (in-state)

Full-time: 3581 men, 4122 women	**Faculty:** 404; IIA, --$
Part-time: 1121 men, 1218 women	**Ph.Ds:** 70%
Graduate: 774 men, 1696 women	**Student/Faculty:** 19 to 1
Year: semesters, summer session	**Tuition:** $1882 ($5146)
Application Deadline: September 1	**Room & Board:** $3880
Freshman Class: 3723 applied, 3712 accepted, 1980 enrolled	
SAT I: 480/450	**ACT:** 21 **LESS COMPETITIVE**

Marshall University, founded in 1837 and part of the University of West Virginia system, is a comprehensive, public institution offering programs in liberal arts and sciences, business, education, fine arts, and nursing. There are 7 undergraduate and 2 graduate schools. In addition to regional accreditation, Marshall has baccalaureate program accreditation with ACEJMC, CAHEA, CSWE, NASM, NCATE, NLN, and NRPA. The 3 libraries contain 418,467 volumes, 184,851 microform items, and 17,634 audiovisual forms, and subscribe to 2756 periodicals. Computerized library sources and services include interlibrary loans and database searching. Special learning facilities include a learning resource center, an art gallery, a natural history museum, a radio station, a TV station, and a greenhouse. The 55-acre campus is in an urban area 126 miles east of Lexington, Kentucky. Including residence halls, there are 28 buildings on campus.

Student Life: About 87% of undergraduates are from West Virginia. Students come from 38 states, 30 foreign countries, and Canada. Ninety-four percent are white. The average age of freshmen is 19.5; all undergraduates, 24. Thirty-two percent drop out by the end of their first year; 51% remain to graduate.

Housing: A total of 2500 students can be accommodated in college housing. College-sponsored living facilities include single-sex and coed dormitories, married-student housing, and sorority houses. In addition, there are honors and quiet study floors. On-campus housing is guaranteed for all 4 years. Eighty percent of students commute. Alcohol is not permitted. All students may keep cars on campus.

Activities: About 3% of men belong to 8 national fraternities; about 3% of women belong to 5 national sororities. There are 120 groups on campus, including art, band, cheerleading, choir, chorale, chorus, computers, dance, drama, ethnic, gay, honors, international, jazz band, literary magazine, marching band, musical theater, newspaper, opera, orchestra, pep band, photography, political, professional, radio and TV, religious, social, social service, student government, and yearbook. Popular campus events include Parents Day, Springfest, Homecoming, and International Festival.

Sports: There are 7 intercollegiate sports for men and 6 for women, and 19 intramural sports each. Athletic and recreation facilities include a 10,500-seat basketball arena, a 28,000-seat football stadium, tennis courts, a baseball field, 2 Olympic-size pools, 3 auxiliary gymnasiums, Nautilus/free weight rooms, racquetball courts, and a fitness laboratory.

Disabled Students: Ninety percent of the campus is accessible to disabled students. The following facilities are available: wheelchair ramps, elevators, special parking, specially equipped rest rooms, special class scheduling, lowered drinking fountains and telephones, and an accessible van transportation, and an attendant care program.

Services: In addition to many counseling and information services, tutoring is available in most subjects, including all lower-division courses. There is a reader service for the blind, and remedial math, reading, and writing, study skills courses, and other services for all disabilities.

Campus Safety and Security: Campus safety and security measures include 24-hour foot and vehicle patrol, self defense education, escort service, and informal discussions. In addition, there are pamphlets, posters, films, emergency telephones, and lighted pathways and sidewalks.

Programs of Study: Marshall awards the B.A., B.S., B.B.A., B.F.A., B.S.M.T., B.S.N., and B.S.W. degrees. Associate, master's, and doctoral degrees also are awarded. Bachelor's degrees are awarded in BIOLOGICAL SCIENCE (biology/biological science), BUSINESS (accounting, banking and finance, business economics, fashion merchandising, marketing/retailing/merchandising, and sports management), COMMUNICATIONS AND THE ARTS (advertising, broadcasting, classics, communications, dramatic arts, English, fine arts, French, German, journalism, music, and Spanish), COMPUTER AND PHYSICAL SCIENCE (chemistry, computer programming, computer science, geology, information sciences and systems, mathematics, and physics), EDUCATION (art, business, early childhood, elementary, foreign languages, guidance, health, home economics, middle school, music, science, and special), HEALTH PROFESSIONS (health care administration, medical laboratory technology, nursing, predentistry, premedicine, and preveterinary science), SOCIAL SCIENCE (criminal justice, dietetics, economics, geography, history, humanities, international relations, parks and recreation management, philosophy, physical fitness/movement, political science/government, prelaw, psychology, religion, safety and security technology, social work, and sociology). Biological sciences, psychology, journalism, and education are the strongest academically. Elementary education, accounting, management, and liberal arts have the largest enrollments.

Required: All students take a core curriculum including English, speech, humanities, fine arts, natural sciences, mathematics, and social science. A minimum GPA of 2.5 in the College of Education and 2.0 in all others and 128 credit hours, with 40 to 65 in the major, are required to graduate.

Special: Internships are available in business and journalism. There are co-op programs in business, radiology, journalism, electronics, and aviation technologies. Students may study abroad in 20 countries. Work-study programs, nondegree study, credit for life experience, and credit/no credit options are offered. There is a freshman honors program on campus, as well as 16 national honor societies, including Phi Beta Kappa.

Faculty/Classroom: Sixty-four percent of faculty are male; 36%, female. The average class size in an introductory lecture is 34; in a laboratory, 25; and in a regular course offering, 21.

Admissions: All of the 1993–94 applicants were accepted. The ACT scores for the freshman class were as follows: 53% below 21, 26% between 21 and 23, 13% between 24 and 26, 5% between 27 and 28, and 3% above 28. There were 6 National Merit finalists and 19 semifinalists. About 57 freshmen graduated first in their class.

Requirements: A minimum GPA of 2.0 is required. The SAT I or ACT is required. Regular admission is open to all students who have graduated from a secondary school with the required units of study and a 2.0 GPA or with a minimum composite score of 17 on the ACT or 700 on the SAT I. Required study is 4 years in English, 3 in social studies, and 2 each in higher mathematics and laboratory science. Two years of a foreign language is strongly recommended. The GED is also accepted. Students not meeting university requirements are admitted to the Community and Technical College component of the university in a transition program. AP and CLEP credits are accepted. Important factors used in the admissions decision are advanced

placement or honor courses, evidence of special talent, recommendations by school officials, leadership record, and geographic diversity.

Procedure: Freshmen are admitted to all sessions. Entrance exams should be taken during the junior year or early in the senior year. Early decision applications should be filed by September 15; regular applications, by September 1 for fall entry, January 1 for spring entry, and June 1 for summer entry, along with an application fee of $10 for in-state students (25% for out-of-state). Notification is sent on a rolling basis. There are early decision, early admissions, and deferred admissions plans. About 1100 early decision candidates were accepted for the 1993–94 class.

Transfer: About 550 transfer students enrolled in 1993–94. A 2.0 GPA on all previous college work is generally required of transfer applicants. A total of 36 credits out of 128 must be completed at Marshall.

Visiting: There are regularly scheduled orientations for prospective students. There are guides for informal visits and visitors may sit in on classes and stay overnight at the school. To arrange for a visit, contact the recruitment secretary at (800) 642–3463 (in-state).

Financial Aid: Recently, 55% of all current freshmen and 45% of continuing students received some form of financial aid. About 57% of freshmen and 47% of continuing students received need-based aid. Scholarships or need-based grants averaged $900 ($1200 maximum); loans averaged $2050 ($2625 maximum); and work contracts averaged $1000 ($2000 maximum). Forty percent of undergraduate students work part-time. Average earnings from campus work for the school year are $2500. The average financial indebtedness of the 1992–93 graduate was $2400. Marshall is a member of CSS. The FAF, FFS or SFS is required. The deadline for financial aid applications is February 1.

International Students: There are currently 103 international students enrolled. The school actively recruits these students. They must take the TOEFL or the University of Michigan Language Test and achieve a minimum score on the TOEFL of 525. The student must also take the SAT I or the ACT and acheive an SAT I score of 680 and ACT of 17.

Computers: The college provides computer facilities for student use. There are microcomputers available for student use in the computer laboratory in the business building. All students may access the system. It may be used during scheduled hours Monday through Saturday. There are no time limits on using the system and no fees.

Graduates: In a prior year, 1157 bachelor's degrees were awarded. The most popular majors among graduates were education (25%), liberal arts (24%), and business (24%). About 275 companies recruited on campus.

Admissions Contact: Dr. James W. Harless, Director of Admissions.

OHIO VALLEY COLLEGE

B-3

Parkersburg, WV 26101   (304) 485-7384, ext. 32

Full-time: 138 men, 144 women	Faculty: 12; III, --$
Part-time: 4 men, 3 women	Ph.D.s: 17%
Graduate: none	Student/Faculty: 24 to 1
Year: semesters, summer session	Tuition: $5730
Application Deadline: open	Room & Board: $3050
Freshman Class: 289 applied, 262 accepted, 134 enrolled	
ACT: 20	**LESS COMPETITIVE**

Ohio Valley College, founded in 1960, is a liberal arts institution affiliated with the Church of Christ. The library contains 21,250 volumes, 1550 microform items, and 4500 audiovisual forms, and subscribes to 190 periodicals. Special learning facilities include a learning resource center and a mass communications studio facility for the production of broadcast-quality videotapes. The 125-acre campus is in a suburban area 120 miles southwest of Pittsburgh, Pennsylvania. Including residence halls, there are 8 buildings on campus.

Student Life: About 61% of undergraduates are from out-of-state, mostly the Midwest. Students come from 9 states and 2 foreign countries. Ninety-nine percent are from public schools; 1% from private. Ninety-one percent are white. Most are Protestant. The average age of freshmen is 18; all undergraduates, 19. Fifty-five percent drop out by the end of their first year; 25% remain to graduate.

Housing: A total of 233 students can be accommodated in college housing. College-sponsored living facilities include dormitories. On-campus housing is guaranteed for all 4 years. Alcohol is not permitted.

Activities: There are no fraternities or sororities on campus. There are 16 groups on campus, including band, cheerleading, choir, chorale, chorus, drama, newspaper, religious, social, student government, and yearbook. Popular campus events include Expressions, a schoolwide musical review.

Sports: There are 2 intercollegiate sports for men, and 7 intramural sports each for men and women. Athletic and recreation facilities include a weight room, a student union with recreation facilities, an activity center, and a gymnasium.

Disabled Students: Thirty percent of the campus is accessible to disabled students. The following facilities are available: wheelchair ramps, special parking, specially equipped rest rooms, special class scheduling, and lowered telephones.

Services: There are remedial math and writing services.

Campus Safety and Security: Campus safety and security measures include 12-hour foot and vehicle patrol.

Programs of Study: Ohio Valley awards the B.A. and B.S. degrees in Bible and religion. Associate degrees also are awarded. Bachelor's degrees are awarded in SOCIAL SCIENCE (Bible and religion).

Required: To graduate, students must complete 128 credit hours, including 53 to 60 in the major, with a minimum GPA of 2.0. General requirements include 4 courses of Bible studies, 2 of English composition, 1 to 2 of history, and 1 each of speech, computer literacy, mathematics, and social science. There is also a physical education requirement. Students must attend chapel daily and take 1 Bible class each semester.

Special: Ohio Valley offers internships with churches for student ministers. One department has an honors program.

Faculty/Classroom: Seventy-eight percent of faculty are male; 22%, female. The average class size in an introductory lecture is 30; in a laboratory, 20; and in a regular course offering, 15.

Admissions: About 91% of the 1993–94 applicants were accepted. There was 1 National Merit finalist and 2 semifinalists.

Requirements: Ohio Valley requires applicants to be in the upper half of their class. The ACT is required. Applicants should be graduates of an accredited secondary school or have earned a GED. AP and CLEP credits are accepted. Important factors used in the admissions decision are recommendations by school officials, personality, intangible qualities, leadership record, extracurricular activities record, and evidence of special talent.

Procedure: Freshmen are admitted fall and winter. Entrance exams should be taken during the senior year. Application deadlines are open. The application fee is $10. There is an early admissions plan.

Transfer: About 11 transfer students enrolled in a recent year. A total of 32 credits out of 128 must be completed at Ohio Valley.

Visiting: There are guides for informal visits and visitors may sit in on classes and stay overnight at the school. To arrange for a visit, contact Glen Laird at (304) 485–7384, ext. 32.

Financial Aid: In a prior year, 86% of all current freshmen and 86% of continuing students received some form of financial aid. Scholarships or need-based grants averaged $400 ($4224 maximum); loans averaged $2600 ($4000 maximum); and work contracts averaged $1000 ($1500 maximum). The average financial indebtedness of the 1992–93 graduate was $5200. Ohio Valley is a member of CSS. The FAF and FAFSA are required. The deadline for financial aid applications is August 15.

International Students: There are currently 7 international students enrolled. The school actively recruits these students. They must take the TOEFL and achieve a minimum score of 420. The student must also take the ACT.

Computers: The college provides computer facilities for student use. The mainframe is a DEC VAX 11/730. There are also Apple II, IBM PC, Ohio Scientific, and DEC Rainbow microcomputers available in the learning assistance center and the computer science laboratory. All students may access the system. There are no time limits on using the system and no fees.

Graduates: In an earlier year, 4 bachelor's degrees were awarded. In the 1992 graduating class, 75% of the men were enrolled in graduate school within 6 months of graduation; 25% of the men had found employment.

Admissions Contact: Bob Crum, Admissions Officer.

SALEM-TEIKYO UNIVERSITY

C-3

Salem, WV 26426   (304) 782-5336; (800) 283-4562

Full-time: 502 men, 209 women	Faculty: 46; IIB, --$
Part-time: 35 men, 21 women	Ph.D.s: 33%
Graduate: 12 men, 8 women	Student/Faculty: 15 to 1
Year: 12 month-long modules	Tuition: $10,575
Application Deadline: open	Room & Board: $3952
Freshman Class: 489 applied, 384 accepted, 147 enrolled	
ACT: 22	**COMPETITIVE**

Salem-Teikyo University, founded in 1888, is a private coeducational institution offering both liberal arts and career-oriented degree programs including business, health science, education, technical fields, and aviation. There is one graduate school. The library contains 110,000 volumes and 200,000 microform items, and subscribes to 400 periodicals. Special learning facilities include a radio station and Fort New Salem, an 1800s settlement, and an equestrian center. The 100-acre campus is in a rural area 100 miles south of Pittsburgh, Pennsylvania. Including residence halls, there are 15 buildings on campus.

Student Life: Students come from 28 states, 10 foreign countries, and Canada. Forty-six percent are foreign nationals. The average age of freshmen is 18. Twenty-five percent drop out by the end of their first year; 40% remain to graduate.

Housing: A total of 1000 students can be accommodated in college housing. College-sponsored living facilities include single-sex and coed dormitories. On-campus housing is guaranteed for all 4 years. All students may keep cars on campus.

Activities: About 30% of men belong to 2 local and 3 national fraternities; about 30% of women belong to 3 local sororities. There are 13 groups on campus, including cheerleading, computers, ethnic, honors, international, newspaper, radio and TV, social, social service, student government, and yearbook.

Sports: There are 5 intercollegiate sports for men and 4 for women, and 10 intramural sports for men and 9 for women. Athletic and recreation facilities include a gymnasium, a pool, a weight room, tennis courts, a football/soccer stadium, and a fitness trail.

Disabled Students: Fifty percent of the campus is accessible to disabled students. The following facilities are available: wheelchair ramps, elevators, special parking, and special class scheduling.

Services: In addition to many counseling and information services, tutoring is available in most subjects. In addition, there is a reader service for the blind, and remedial math, reading, and writing.

Campus Safety and Security: Campus safety and security measures include 24-hour foot and vehicle patrol.

Programs of Study: S-TU awards the B.A., B.S., and B.Eqe.Ed. degrees. Associate and master's degrees are also awarded. Bachelor's degrees are awarded in AGRICULTURE (equestrian science), BIOLOGICAL SCIENCE (biology/biological science), BUSINESS (accounting, business administration and management, and marketing/retailing/merchandising), COMMUNICATIONS AND THE ARTS (broadcasting and communications), COMPUTER AND PHYSICAL SCIENCE (computer science and mathematics), EDUCATION (elementary and secondary), ENGINEERING AND ENVIRONMENTAL DESIGN (aeronautical science, engineering technology, and industrial engineering technology), HEALTH PROFESSIONS (medical laboratory technology), SOCIAL SCIENCE (criminal justice). Education is the strongest academically. Business management and career aviation have the largest enrollments.

Required: All students must take 57 hours in the core curriculum, including courses in communication skills, humanities, science/mathematics, social studies, psychology, and health and physical education. A minimum 2.0 GPA overall, with a minimum 2.25 GPA in the major, and 128 credit hours are required to graduate.

Special: A student may cross-register with another college within the Mountain State Association of Colleges. Many internships are available. Study abroad is offered in 3 countries. Dual majors, credit by examination, and credit for life experience may be arranged. There is one national honor society on campus.

Faculty/Classroom: Fifty-nine percent of faculty are male; 41%, female. The average class size in an introductory lecture is 25; in a laboratory, 10; and in a regular course offering, 15.

Admissions: About 79% of the 1993–94 applicants were accepted. The SAT scores for the 1993–94 freshman class were as follows: Verbal—63% below 500, 26% between 500 and 599, 6% between 600 and 700, and 5% above 700; Math—59% below 500, 25% between 500 and 599, 14% between 600 and 700, and 2% above 700. The ACT scores were 54% below 21, 15% between 21 and 23, 15% between 24 and 26, 13% between 27 and 28, and 3% above 28. One freshman graduated first in his class.

Requirements: A minimum GPA of 2.0 is required. The SAT I or ACT is required. Applicants should be graduates of an accredited secondary school with 15 academic courses, including 4 in English, 3 each in mathematics, science, and social studies, and 2 in a foreign language. AP and CLEP credits are accepted. Important factors used in the admissions decision are leadership record, personality, intangible qualities, recommendations by school officials, advanced placement or honor courses, and evidence of special talent.

Procedure: Freshmen are admitted fall, winter, and spring. Application deadlines are open. Application fee is $25. Notification is sent on a rolling basis. There is a deferred admissions plan.

Transfer: About 40 transfer students enrolled in a recent year. A minimum GPA of 2.5 is required for acceptance as a transfer student. A total of 32 credits out of 128 must be completed at S-TU.

Visiting: There are regularly scheduled orientations for prospective students. There are guides for informal visits and visitors may sit in on classes and stay overnight at the school. To arrange for a visit, contact the Admissions Office at (800) 283–4562.

Financial Aid: S-TU is a member of CSS. The FAF (preferred), FFS, or SFS is required. The deadline for financial aid applications is July 15.

International Students: There were recently 274 international students enrolled. The school actively recruits these students. They must take the TOEFL and achieve a minimum score of 500.

Computers: The college provides computer facilities for student use. The mainframe is a DEC VAX 11/750. Approximately 25 computers are available for use. Those enrolled in a computer course may access the system. It may be used any time. There are no time limits on using the system and no fees.

Graduates: In a recent year, 63 bachelor's degrees were awarded. The most popular majors among graduates were management (19%), biology/natural science (10%), and aviation (8%).

Admissions Contact: Dr. Paul Dauphinais, Assistant Director of Admissions.

SHEPHERD COLLEGE E-2
Shepherdstown, WV 25443

(304) 876–2511
(800) 344–5231 (out-of-state)

Full-time: 2453	Faculty: 115; IIB, --$
Part-time: 1113	Ph.D.s: 70%
Graduate: none	Student/Faculty: 21 to 1
Year: semesters, summer session	Tuition: $2040 ($4670)
Application Deadline: February 1	Room & Board: $3500
Freshman Class: 1544 applied, 1239 accepted, 606 enrolled	
SAT I or ACT: required	COMPETITIVE

Shepherd College, founded in 1871, is a state-supported institution offering programs encompassing the liberal and creative arts, business administration, teacher education, the social and natural sciences, health, and other career-oriented areas. There are 3 undergraduate schools. In addition to regional accreditation, Shepherd has baccalaureate program accreditation with CSWE, NASM, NCATE, and NLN. The library contains 255,336 volumes, 47,285 microform items, and 7588 audiovisual forms, and subscribes to 958 periodicals. Computerized library sources and services include the card catalog, interlibrary loans, and database searching. Special learning facilities include a learning resource center, an art gallery, a radio station, a nursery school, a wellness center, and 3 theaters. The 320-acre campus is in a small town 70 miles northwest of Washington, DC, and Baltimore. Including residence halls, there are 29 buildings on campus.

Student Life: About 66% of undergraduates are from West Virginia. Students come from 30 states, 10 foreign countries, and Canada. Seventy-five percent are from public schools; 25% from private. Ninety percent are white. Eighty percent are Protestant; 17% Catholic. The average age of freshmen is 19; all undergraduates, 21. Twenty percent drop out by the end of their first year; 68% remain to graduate.

Housing: A total of 1000 students can be accommodated in college housing. College-sponsored living facilities include coed dormitories, on-campus apartments, and fraternity houses. In addition there are honors houses and special interest houses. On-campus housing is guaranteed for all 4 years. All students may keep cars on campus.

Activities: About 20% of men belong to 2 local and 3 national fraternities; about 20% of women belong to 5 national sororities. There are 70 groups on campus, including art, band, cheerleading, choir, chorale, chorus, computers, drama, drill team, ethnic, honors, international, jazz band, literary magazine, marching band, musical theater, newspaper, orchestra, pep band, political, professional, religious, social, social service, student government, and yearbook. Popular campus events include Homecoming, Parents Day, Winter Carnival, Spring Weekend, and Greek Week.

Sports: There are 7 intercollegiate sports each for men and women, and 23 intramural sports for men and 18 for women. Athletic and recreation facilities include a 7000-seat football stadium, baseball and softball fields, tennis and handball courts, a 5000-seat gymnasium, 2 indoor tennis courts, a fitness/wellness center, and a swimming pool.

Disabled Students: Ninety percent of the campus is accessible to disabled students. The following facilities are available: wheelchair ramps, elevators, special parking, specially equipped rest rooms, special class scheduling, and lowered drinking fountains and telephones.

Services: In addition to many counseling and information services, tutoring is available in most subjects. There is a reader service for the blind, and remedial math, reading, and writing.

Campus Safety and Security: Campus safety and security measures include 24-hour foot and vehicle patrol, self defense education, escort service, and shuttle buses. In addition, there are informal discussions, pamphlets, posters, films, emergency telephones, and lighted pathways and sidewalks.

Programs of Study: Shepherd awards the B.A., B.S., and B.F.A degrees. Associate degrees also are awarded. Bachelor's degrees are awarded in BIOLOGICAL SCIENCE (biology/biological science), BUSINESS (accounting, business administration and management, business economics, hotel/motel and restaurant management, marketing/retailing/merchandising, and sports management), COMMUNICATIONS AND THE ARTS (broadcasting, communications, design, dramatic arts, English, fine arts, music, photography, and speech/debate/rhetoric), COMPUTER AND PHYSICAL SCIENCE (chemistry, computer programming, computer science, earth science, information sciences and systems, and mathematics), EDUCATION

(art, business, early childhood, elementary, health, home economics, middle school, music, science, and secondary), ENGINEERING AND ENVIRONMENTAL DESIGN (engineering), HEALTH PROFESSIONS (nursing, physical therapy, predentistry, premedicine, preveterinary science, recreation therapy, and sports medicine), SOCIAL SCIENCE (anthropology, economics, geography, history, parks and recreation management, political science/government, prelaw, psychology, social science, social work, and sociology). Business, science, art, music, English, and history are the strongest academically. Business and education have the largest enrollments.

Required: All students take a general studies core of 47 hours in art, music, English, speech, literature, science, mathematics, history, economics, sociology, political science, foreign language, and physical education. A 2.0 GPA overall, a 2.5 GPA in the student's major, and 128 semester hours are required to graduate.

Special: Internships are available in most departments. Dual majors are offered in 18 fields. Credit by exam, life experience credentialing through the Regents degree, nondegree study, and pass/fail options for electives are offered. There is a freshman honors program on campus, as well as 28 national honor societies. One department has an honors program.

Faculty/Classroom: Fifty-five percent of faculty are male; 45%, female. All teach undergraduates, 25% do research, and 25% do both. The average class size in an introductory lecture is 30; in a laboratory, 24; and in a regular course offering, 35.

Admissions: About 80% of the 1993–94 applicants were accepted. There were 10 National Merit semifinalists. About 55 freshmen graduated first in their class.

Requirements: A minimum GPA of 2.5 is required. The SAT I or ACT is required, with composite scores of 900 on the SAT I or 21 on the ACT. Applicants should be graduates of an accredited secondary school with 21 academic credits, including 4 in English, 3 each in higher mathematics, laboratory science, and history or social studies, 2 in foreign language, and 6 in computer and academic electives. The GED is accepted. AP and CLEP credits are accepted. Important factors used in the admissions decision are advanced placement or honor courses, leadership record, extracurricular activities record, personality, intangible qualities, and evidence of special talent.

Procedure: Freshmen are admitted to all sessions. Entrance exams should be taken during the junior year. Applications should be filed by February 1 for fall entry, November 1 for spring entry, and February 1 for summer entry, along with an application fee of $20. Notification of early action is sent December 15; regular decision, March 1. There are early admissions and deferred admissions plans. A waiting list is an active part of the admissions procedure, with about 20% of applicants on the list.

Transfer: About 345 transfer students enrolled in 1993–94. Transfer applicants must have a 2.5 GPA in all previous college work and a minimum of 15 semester hours completed. A total of 32 credits out of 128 must be completed at Shepherd.

Visiting: There are regularly scheduled orientations for prospective students, consisting of Fall Open Houses, Spring Information Saturdays, and weekday information sessions and campus tours by appointment. There are guides for informal visits and visitors may sit in on classes. To arrange for a visit, contact the Admissions Office at (800) 344–5231 or (304) 876–2511, ext. 212, 213.

Financial Aid: In 1993–94, 27% of all current freshmen and 29% of continuing students received some form of financial aid. About 18% of freshmen and 19% of continuing students received need-based aid. The average freshman award was $3446. Of that total, scholarships or need-based grants averaged $1553 ($4600 maximum); loans averaged $1422 ($3725 maximum); and work contracts averaged $1063 ($1600 maximum). Thirty percent of undergraduate students work part-time. Average earnings from campus work for the school year are $600. The average financial indebtedness of the 1992–93 graduate was $2500. Shepherd is a member of CSS. The FAF, the college's own financial statement and the FAFSA are required. The deadline for financial aid applications is March 1.

International Students: There are currently 11 international students enrolled. The school actively recruits these students. They must take the TOEFL and achieve a minimum score of 550. The student must also take the SAT I or the ACT and achieve a composite SAT I score of 900 and 21 on the ACT.

Computers: The college provides computer facilities for student use. The mainframes are a DEC VAX 11/780, a DEC VAX 3900 and 4000, and an Amdahl 470/V7A. There are also 150 IBM PCs in business and general use laboratories, and separate education, engineering, and English writing computer laboratories. Business and mathematics or computer majors may access the system. It may be used weekdays from 7 A.M. to 2 A.M. There are no time limits on using the system and no fees.

Graduates: In 1992–93, 435 bachelor's degrees were awarded. The most popular majors among graduates were business (25%), education (20%), and nursing (10%). Within an average freshman class, 5% graduate in 3 years, 70% in 4 years, 20% in 5 years, and 5% in 6

years. Some 110 companies recruited on campus in 1992–93. In the 1992 graduating class, 50% of the seniors were enrolled in graduate school within 6 months of graduation; 45% found employment.

Admissions Contact: Karl L. Wolf, Director of Admissions.

UNIVERSITY OF CHARLESTON
Charleston, WV 25304

B-4
(304) 357-4750
(800) 995-4682 (out-of-state)

Full-time: 246 men, 525 women	Faculty: 72; IIB, --$
Part-time: 179 men, 432 women	Ph.D.s: 60%
Graduate: 27 men, 25 women	Student/Faculty: 11 to 1
Year: semesters, summer session	Tuition: $9250
Application Deadline: open	Room & Board: $3500
Freshman Class: 758 applied, 582 accepted, 201 enrolled	
SAT I: 443/505	ACT: 21 COMPETITIVE

The University of Charleston, founded in 1888, is an independent private university offering programs in interior design, teacher education, sports medicine, environmental science, nursing, radiologic technology, political science, respiratory care, and business. There are 3 undergraduate schools and one graduate school. In addition to regional accreditation, UC has baccalaureate program accreditation with AACSB, CAHEA, NCATE, and NLN. The library contains 94,959 volumes, 91,416 microform items, and 664 audiovisual forms, and subscribes to 580 periodicals. Computerized library sources and services include the card catalog, interlibrary loans, and database searching. Special learning facilities include a learning resource center and an art gallery. The 40-acre campus is in an urban area in Charleston. Including residence halls, there are 7 buildings on campus.

Student Life: About 87% of undergraduates are from West Virginia. Students come from 23 states, 16 foreign countries, and Canada. Most are white. Thirty-two percent are Protestant. Twenty-three percent drop out by the end of their first year; 77% remain to graduate.

Housing: A total of 450 students can be accommodated in college housing. College-sponsored living facilities include coed dormitories. On-campus housing is guaranteed for all 4 years. Sixty-three percent of students commute. All students may keep cars on campus.

Activities: About 31% of men belong to 3 national fraternities; about 17% of women belong to 2 national sororities. There are 30 groups on campus, including art, cheerleading, choir, chorus, drama, honors, international, literary magazine, newspaper, political, professional, radio and TV, religious, social, social service, student government, and yearbook. Popular campus events include sporting events, plays, concerts, hot air balloon races, the Christmas Convocation, and Awards Convocation.

Sports: There are 6 intercollegiate sports each for men and women, and 5 intramural each. Athletic and recreation facilities include a gymnasium, soccer, softball, and baseball fields; a Nautilus center; racquetball, volleyball, and tennis courts; a game room; and an indoor pool.

Disabled Students: Forty-five percent of the campus is accessible to disabled students. The following facilities are available: wheelchair ramps, elevators, special parking, specially equipped rest rooms, and lowered telephones.

Services: In addition to many counseling and information services, tutoring is available in some subjects, including mathematics, English, and sciences. There is remedial math, reading, and writing.

Campus Safety and Security: Campus safety and security measures include 24-hour foot and vehicle patrol, self defense education, escort service, and informal discussions. In addition, there are pamphlets, posters, and films, emergency telephones, lighted pathways and sidewalks, burglar alarms in dormitories, and safety and date-rape seminars.

Programs of Study: UC awards the B.A., B.S., and B.S.N. degrees. Associate and master's degrees also are awarded. Bachelor's degrees are awarded in BIOLOGICAL SCIENCE (biology/biological science), BUSINESS (accounting, banking and finance, business administration and management, management science, and marketing/retailing/merchandising), COMMUNICATIONS AND THE ARTS (arts administration/management, communications, English, music, and music business management), COMPUTER AND PHYSICAL SCIENCE (chemistry, information sciences and systems, and mathematics), EDUCATION (art, elementary, mathematics, music, physical, science, secondary, and social studies), ENGINEERING AND ENVIRONMENTAL DESIGN (environmental science, interior design, and military science), HEALTH PROFESSIONS (nursing, predentistry, premedicine, radiological science, respiratory therapy, and sports medicine), SOCIAL SCIENCE (history, humanities, liberal arts/general studies, political science/government, prelaw, psychology, religion, and social science). Environmental science, sports medicine, interior design, business, education, political science, and health sciences are the strongest academically. Business and health sciences have the largest enrollments.

Required: All students must fulfill the general education program requirements, which include 48 hours of courses in English, computer systems, social sciences, humanities, natural science, health or physical education, and elective options. A total of 120 to 128 credit hours and a GPA of 2.0 are required for graduation. A comprehensive examination also is required.

Special: The university offers credit by examination and credit for prior learning. A general studies degree, student-designed majors, nondegree study, and pass-fail options are available. Internships, on-campus work-study, hospital clinical experience in qualified programs, a co-op program in political science, a Washington semester, and study abroad in Japan are offered. There is a freshman honors program on campus, as well as 6 national honor societies.

Faculty/Classroom: Forty percent of faculty are male; 60%, female. All teach undergraduates and 20% both teach and do research. No introductory courses are taught by graduate students. The average class size in an introductory lecture is 17; in a laboratory, 23; and in a regular course offering, 15.

Admissions: About 77% of the 1993–94 applicants were accepted. The SAT scores for the 1993–94 freshman class were as follows: Verbal—76% below 500, 15% between 500 and 599, and 9% between 600 and 700; Math—51% below 500, 31% between 500 and 599, 9% between 600 and 700, and 9% above 700. The ACT scores were 47% below 21, 31% between 21 and 23, 15% between 24 and 26, 4% between 27 and 28, and 3% above 28. About 48% of the current freshmen were in the top fifth of their class; 74% were in the top two fifths.

Requirements: UC requires applicants to be in the upper 50% of their class. A minimum GPA of 2.3 is required. The SAT I or ACT is required. Applicants should have a minimum GPA of 2.25 and be in the upper 50% of their class, with a minimum composite score of 800 on the SAT I or 18 on the ACT for automatic admission. Applicants should be graduates of an accredited secondary school or have the GED and have taken 16 academic courses. AP and CLEP credits are accepted. Important factors used in the admissions decision are advanced placement or honor courses, leadership record, personality, intangible qualities, extracurricular activities record, and recommendations by school officials.

Procedure: Freshmen are admitted to all sessions. Entrance exams should be taken by December of the senior year. The application deadlines are open. Application fee is $20. Notification of early decision is sent January 31; regular decision, on a rolling basis. There is an early decision plan. About 48 early decision candidates were accepted for the 1993–94 class.

Transfer: About 196 transfer students enrolled in 1993–94. Applicants for transfer should have a minimum GPA of 2.0. A total of 30 credits out of 120 to 128 must be completed at UC.

Visiting: There are regularly scheduled orientations for prospective students, including meetings with faculty, financial aid and student life information sessions, a campus tour, and lunch. There are guides for informal visits and visitors may sit in on classes and stay overnight at the school. To arrange for a visit, contact Rhonda Dorsey at (304) 357-4750 or (800) 995-4682.

Financial Aid: In a prior year, 70% of all current freshmen and 68% of continuing students received some form of financial aid. About 62% of freshmen and 61% of continuing students received need-based aid. The average freshman award was $8200. Of that total, scholarships or need-based grants averaged $3660 ($13,130 maximum); loans averaged $4460 ($6850 maximum); and work contracts averaged $890 ($900 maximum). Twelve percent of undergraduate students work part-time. Average earnings from campus work for the school year are $680. The average financial indebtedness of a recent graduate was $12,500. UC is a member of CSS. The college's own financial statement and FAFSA and income tax returns are required. The deadline for financial aid applications is March 1.

International Students: They must take the TOEFL and achieve a minimum score of 500. The SAT I or ACT is required of students from English-speaking countries.

Computers: The mainframe is a Prime 4150. There are 100 Apple Macintosh, Apple, IBM PC, and IBM PS/2 microcomputers available in computer laboratories for student use.

Graduates: In 1992–93, 128 bachelor's degrees were awarded. The most popular majors among graduates were business administration (20%), nursing (18%), and accounting (7%). Within an average freshman class, 38% graduate in 3 years, 51% in 4 years, 52% in 5 years, and 54% in 6 years. Some 5 companies recruited on campus. In the 1992 graduating class, 62% of all graduates found employment within 6 months of graduation.

Admissions Contact: Alan Liebrecht, Director of Admissions.

WEST LIBERTY STATE COLLEGE
West Liberty, WV 26074

C-1

(304) 336-8076
(800) 732-6204 (out-of-state)

Full-time: 1040 men, 1105 women	**Faculty:** 130; IIB, --$
Part-time: 106 men, 126 women	**Ph.D.s:** 31%
Graduate: none	**Student/Faculty:** 17 to 1
Year: semesters, summer session	**Tuition:** $1800 ($3870)
Application Deadline: August 1	**Room & Board:** $2890
Freshman Class: 1063 applied, 970 accepted, 495 enrolled	
ACT: 19	**LESS COMPETITIVE**

West Liberty State College, founded in 1837, is a state-supported college offering programs in teacher education, liberal and fine arts, sciences, business, and preprofessional and technical fields. There are 4 undergraduate schools. In addition to regional accreditation, West Liberty has baccalaureate program accreditation with AHEA, NASM, and NCATE. The library contains 207,000 volumes, 70,000 microform items, and 10,000 audiovisual forms, and subscribes to 800 periodicals. Computerized library sources and services include interlibrary loans and database searching. Special learning facilities include a learning resource center, radio station, TV station, and and a publication area. The 290-acre campus is in a rural area 10 miles north of Wheeling. Including residence halls, there are 22 buildings on campus.

Student Life: About 68% of undergraduates are from West Virginia. Students come from 17 states, 11 foreign countries, and Canada. Ninety percent are from public schools; 10% from private. Ninety-six percent are white, sixty-two percent are Catholic, and 32% Protestant. The average age of freshmen is 18.1; all undergraduates, 19.6. Twenty-nine percent drop out by the end of their first year; 49% remain to graduate.

Housing: A total of 1337 students can be accommodated in college housing. College-sponsored living facilities include single-sex dormitories and married-student housing. In addition there is an honors floor located in Krise Hall. On-campus housing is guaranteed for all 4 years. Fifty-seven percent of students live on campus; of those, 46% remain on campus on weekends. Alcohol is not permitted. All students may keep cars on campus.

Activities: About 11% of men and about 2% of women belong to 5 local and 3 national fraternities; about 10% of women belong to 1 local and 2 national sororities. There are 50 groups on campus, including band, cheerleading, choir, chorus, drama, honors, international, jazz band, literary magazine, musical theater, newspaper, photography, political, professional, radio and TV, religious, social, social service, and student government. Popular campus events include Multi-Cultural Day, Greek Week, Homecoming, Band Blast, and Parents Day.

Sports: There are 7 intercollegiate sports for men and 5 for women, and 6 intramural sports for men and 7 for women. Athletic and recreation facilities include a field house with basketball, indoor tennis, volleyball, handball, and racquetball courts and locker and training rooms. Another athletic building features large and small gymnasiums and an indoor swimming pool. There is also a 4-lane bowling alley, a game area with pool tables and table tennis, and 8 all-weather surface tennis courts.

Disabled Students: Sixty percent of the campus is accessible to disabled students. The following facilities are available: wheelchair ramps, elevators, special parking, and specially equipped rest rooms.

Services: In addition to many counseling and information services, tutoring is available in every subject. In addition, there is remedial math and writing.

Campus Safety and Security: Campus safety and security measures include 24-hour foot and vehicle patrol, informal discussions, pamphlets, posters, and films, and emergency telephones. In addition, there are lighted pathways and sidewalks.

Programs of Study: West Liberty awards the B.A. and B.S. degrees. Associate degrees also are awarded. Bachelor's degrees are awarded in BIOLOGICAL SCIENCE (biology/biological science), BUSINESS (accounting, banking and finance, business administration and management, business economics, management science, marketing/retailing/merchandising, and office supervision and management), COMMUNICATIONS AND THE ARTS (communications, English, fine arts, graphic design, and music), COMPUTER AND PHYSICAL SCIENCE (chemistry, computer programming, and mathematics), EDUCATION (art, business, early childhood, elementary, foreign languages, middle school, music, science, secondary, and special), ENGINEERING AND ENVIRONMENTAL DESIGN (preengineering), HEALTH PROFESSIONS (dental hygiene, medical laboratory technology, nursing, predentistry, premedicine, and prepharmacy), SOCIAL SCIENCE (criminal justice, economics, geography, history, interdisciplinary studies, political science/government, prelaw, psychology, public administration, social science, and sociology). Business, natural science, dental hygiene, and music are the strongest academically. Business has the largest enrollment.

Required: The required core curriculum varies for B.A. and B.S. candidates, but both include courses in communications, fine arts and humanities, natural science and mathematics, social science and history, and physical education and health. A minimum GPA of 2.0 and 128 credit hours are required to graduate.

Special: A work-study program with the Internal Revenue Service is possible. Students may cross-register with the Four-College Consortium. Internships are available in fashion marketing, communications, medical technology, physical education, and nursing and are required in criminal justice, energy management, and science of exercise. Student-designed majors in interdisciplinary studies, dual majors, and a B.A.-B.S. degree in psychology, biology, chemistry, and mathematics are available. Credit for life experience is given through the Board of Regents degree. A general studies degree, credit by examination, nondegree study, and pass/fail options are possible. There is a freshman honors program on campus, as well as 3 national honor societies. Five departments have honors programs.

Faculty/Classroom: Sixty-six percent of faculty are male; 34%, female. All teach undergraduates. The average class size in an introductory lecture is 25; in a laboratory, 20; and in a regular course offering, 20.

Admissions: About 91% of the 1993–94 applicants were accepted. The ACT scores for the 1993–94 freshman class were as follows: 69% below 21, 21% between 21 and 23, 4% between 24 and 26, 4% between 27 and 28, and 2% above 28. About 60% of the current freshmen were in the top two fifths of their class. One freshman graduated first in the class.

Requirements: A minimum GPA of 2.0 is required. The SAT I or ACT is required. In addition, applicants must graduate from an accredited secondary school with a minimum GPA of 2.0, or have a composite minimum score of 14 on the ACT or 680 on the SAT I. Students must have completed 4 years in English, 2 each in higher mathematics, laboratory science, and history, and 1 in social studies. The GED is accepted. AP and CLEP credits are accepted.

Procedure: Freshmen are admitted to all sessions. Entrance exams should be taken in time so that all admissions credentials, including test scores, are received 2 weeks prior to the beginning of the term. Applications should be filed by August 1 for fall entry and December 1 for spring entry. Notification is sent on a rolling basis. There are early decision and deferred admissions plans. About 8 early decision candidates were accepted for the 1993–94 class.

Transfer: About 226 transfer students enrolled in 1993–94. Students must be eligible to return to the institution from which they wish to transfer. An official college transcript and a minimum GPA of 2.0 overall are required. Admissions criteria are the same as for freshmen if the student has completed fewer than 28 hours of college-level course work. A total of 36 credits out of 128 must be completed at West Liberty.

Visiting: There are guides for informal visits and visitors may sit in on classes and stay overnight at the school. To arrange for a visit, contact the Office of Admissions at (304) 336–8076 or (800) 732–6204.

Financial Aid: In 1993–94, 70% of all current freshmen and 60% of continuing students received some form of financial aid. About 50% of freshmen and 50% of continuing students received need-based aid. The average freshman award was $3000. Of that total, scholarships or need-based grants averaged $1500 ($3050 maximum); loans averaged $1000 ($2625 maximum); and work contracts averaged $400 ($800 maximum). Twenty-nine percent of undergraduate students work part-time. Average earnings from campus work for the school year are $800. The average financial indebtedness of the 1992–93 graduate was $5000. The college's own financial statement and FAFSA are required. The deadline for financial aid applications is March 1.

International Students: There are currently 21 international students enrolled. They must take the TOEFL and achieve a minimum score of 500. The student must also take the SAT I or the ACT.

Computers: The college provides computer facilities for student use. The mainframes are a DEC VAX 3900, a DEC VAX cluster, an IBM 3081 KX, and an IBM 3081 D. There are also 140 IBM and Apple microcomputers available throughout the campus. All students may access the system. There are no time limits on using the system and no fees.

Graduates: In 1992–93, 416 bachelor's degrees were awarded. The most popular majors among graduates were business administration (29%), elementary education (14%), and secondary education (11%). Within an average freshman class, 6% graduate in 3 years, 28% in 4 years, 11% in 5 years, and 4% in 6 years.

Admissions Contact: Paul B. Milam, Admissions Director.

WEST VIRGINIA INSTITUTE OF TECHNOLOGY

Montgomery, WV 25136

B-4
(304) 442–3151

Full-time: 1514 men, 746 women	Faculty: 146; IIB, --$
Part-time: 248 men, 316 women	Ph.D.s: 46%
Graduate: 34 men, 1 women	Student/Faculty: 15 to 1
Year: semesters, summer session	Tuition: $1998 ($4490)
Application Deadline: August 1	Room & Board: $3860
Freshman Class: 1638 applied, 1615 accepted, 617 enrolled	
ACT: 20	LESS COMPETITIVE

West Virginia Institute of Technology, founded in 1895, is a coeducational, public institution offering programs in business and economics, arts and sciences, community and technical fields, and engineering. There are 4 undergraduate schools and one graduate school. In addition to regional accreditation, West Virginia Tech has baccalaureate program accreditation with ABET, ADA, and NCATE. The library contains 151,122 volumes and 360,000 microform items, and subscribes to 740 periodicals. Computerized library sources and services include the card catalog, interlibrary loans, and database searching. Special learning facilities include a learning resource center and art gallery. The 112-acre campus is in a small town 30 miles east of Charleston. Including residence halls, there are 15 buildings on campus.

Student Life: About 86% of undergraduates are from West Virginia. Students come from 15 foreign countries. Ninety-five percent are from public schools; 5% from private. Eighty-nine percent are white. The average age of freshmen is 18; all undergraduates, 22. Twenty-five percent drop out by the end of their first year; 70% remain to graduate.

Housing: A total of 1075 students can be accommodated in college housing. College-sponsored living facilities include single-sex and coed dormitories. On-campus housing is guaranteed for all 4 years. Sixty-nine percent of students commute. All students may keep cars on campus.

Activities: About 9% of men belong to 8 national fraternities; about 8% of women belong to 4 national sororities. There are 30 groups on campus, including art, band, cheerleading, choir, computers, drama, drill team, ethnic, honors, international, jazz band, marching band, newspaper, photography, political, professional, religious, social, student government, and yearbook. Popular campus events include comedy and film series, Homecoming, Black History Month, Orientation Week, and Greek Week.

Sports: There are 4 intercollegiate sports for men and 3 for women, and 8 intramural sports for men and 8 for women. Athletic and recreation facilities include two gymnasiums, a weightroom, tennis and handball courts, a student union, a football field, a swimming pool, and game rooms.

Disabled Students: Sixty percent of the campus is accessible to disabled students. The following facilities are available: wheelchair ramps, elevators, special parking, specially equipped rest rooms, special class scheduling, and lowered drinking fountains.

Services: In addition to many counseling and information services, tutoring is available in most subjects. There is also remedial math, reading, and writing.

Campus Safety and Security: Campus safety and security measures include 24-hour foot and vehicle patrol, self defense education, escort service, pamphlets, posters, and films. In addition, there are lighted pathways and sidewalks.

Programs of Study: West Virginia Tech awards the B.A., B.S., B.E.T., B.M.E.T., B.S.C.E., B.S.E., and B.S.E.E. degrees. Associate and master's degrees also are awarded. Bachelor's degrees are awarded in BIOLOGICAL SCIENCE (biology/biological science), BUSINESS (accounting, banking and finance, and business administration and management), COMMUNICATIONS AND THE ARTS (English, music, and music business management), COMPUTER AND PHYSICAL SCIENCE (chemistry, computer programming, computer science, and physics), EDUCATION (business, health, industrial arts, middle school, music, science, and secondary), ENGINEERING AND ENVIRONMENTAL DESIGN (chemical engineering, city/community/regional planning, civil engineering, electrical/electronics engineering, electrical/electronics engineering technology, engineering technology, industrial administration/management, industrial engineering technology, mechanical engineering, and paper and pulp science), HEALTH PROFESSIONS (health care administration and nursing), SOCIAL SCIENCE (history and public administration). Engineering is the strongest academically.

Required: Core curriculum requirements include humanities and social studies for all students, but other requirements vary according to degree sought. A minimum 2.0 GPA overall and in the major, and 128 semester hours are required to graduate.

Special: An extensive co-op program is offered in all areas as well as a number of internships in public service and industrial relations. Credit for armed service experience and credit by departmental ex-

amination are available. There is a freshman honors program on campus

Faculty/Classroom: Seventy-five percent of faculty are male; 25%, female. Graduate students teach 1% of introductory courses. The average class size in a laboratory is 10 and in a regular course offering, 22.

Admissions: About 99% of the 1993–94 applicants were accepted. The ACT scores for the 1993–94 freshman class were as follows: 21% between 21 and 23, 13% between 24 and 26, 5% between 27 and 28, and 2% above 28.

Requirements: The SAT I or the ACT is required. Applicants should be graduates from an accredited secondary school or have qualifying scores on the GED. AP and CLEP credits are accepted.

Procedure: Freshmen are admitted to all sessions. Entrance exams should be taken in sufficient time for the scores to reach the institute by the application deadline. Applications should be filed by August 1 for fall entry, December 15 for winter entry, December 15 for spring entry, and May 1 for summer entry. Notification is sent on a rolling basis.

Transfer: About 114 transfer students enrolled in a recent year. Criteria for transfer admission vary according to the college. A total of 30 credits out of 128 must be completed at West Virginia Tech.

Visiting: There are regularly scheduled orientations for prospective students. There are guides for informal visits and visitors may sit in on classes and stay overnight at the school. To arrange for a visit, contact the Admissions Office at (304) 442–3151.

Financial Aid: In 1993–94, 51% of all current freshmen and 41% of continuing students received some form of financial aid. About 38% of freshmen and 31% of continuing students received need-based aid. The average freshman award was $3174. Sixteen percent of undergraduate students work part-time. West Virginia Tech is a member of CSS. The FAF and the college's own financial statement is required. The deadline for financial aid applications is April 1.

International Students: There are currently 120 international students enrolled. They must take the TOEFL and achieve a minimum score of 500.

Computers: The college provides computer facilities for student use. The mainframe is a DEC PDP 11/44 with access to an IBM 3081D and a DEC VAX 780 through WVNET. Student in computer courses may access the system. It may be used 24 hours a day. There are no time limits on using the system and no fees. Microcomputers are also available.

Graduates: In an earlier year, 317 bachelor's degrees were awarded. Recently some 50 companies recruited on campus.

Admissions Contact: Robert P. Scholl, Enrollment Manager/Registrar.

WEST VIRGINIA STATE COLLEGE
B-4

Institute, WV 25112–1000

(304) 766-3221

Full-time: 1390 men, 1427 women	Faculty: 139; IIB, --$
Part-time: 764 men, 1175 women	Ph.D.s: 26%
Graduate: none	Student/Faculty: 20 to 1
Year: early semesters, summer session	Tuition: $1894 ($4294)
	Room & Board: $3150
Application Deadline: August 10	
Freshman Class: 2276 enrolled	
ACT: 18	LESS COMPETITIVE

West Virginia State College, founded in 1891, is a state-supported institution offering broad programs in the arts and sciences and in professional studies, including business and education. It also offers a comprehensive evening class schedule. In addition to regional accreditation, State College has baccalaureate program accreditation with ABET, CSWE, NCATE, and NRPA. The library contains 28,295 volumes, 500,000 microform items, and 6184 audiovisual forms, and subscribes to 630 periodicals. Computerized library sources and services include the card catalog, interlibrary loans, and database searching. Special learning facilities include a learning resource center, an art gallery, and a TV station. The 88-acre campus is in a suburban area 8 miles west of Charleston. Including residence halls, there are 40 buildings on campus.

Student Life: About 95% of undergraduates are from West Virginia. Students come from 34 states, 7 foreign countries, and Canada. Ninety-nine percent are from public schools; 1% from private. Eighty-seven percent are white; 12% African American. The average age of freshmen is 26; all undergraduates, 27. Thirty percent drop out by the end of their first year; 64% remain to graduate.

Housing: A total of 794 students can be accommodated in college housing. College-sponsored living facilities include single-sex dormitories, on-campus apartments, and married-student housing. Ninety-three percent of students commute. Alcohol is not permitted. All students may keep cars on campus.

Activities: About 1% of men belong to 1 local and 4 national fraternities; about 1% of women belong to 3 national sororities. There are 42 groups on campus, including art, band, cheerleading, choir, chorale,

---

chorus, drama, drill team, ethnic, film, honors, international, jazz band, literary magazine, newspaper, orchestra, pep band, photography, political, radio and TV, religious, social, social service, student government, and yearbook. Popular campus events include movies, comedy shows, plays, concerts, galleries, convocations, and ensembles.

Sports: There are 5 intercollegiate sports for men and 4 for women, and 8 intramural sports for men and 7 for women. Athletic and recreation facilities include a 6000-seat stadium, a pool, a sports center, a 1500-seat gymnasium, the student union, and a student mall/plaza.

Disabled Students: All of the campus is accessible to disabled students. The following facilities are available: wheelchair ramps, elevators, special parking, specially equipped rest rooms, special class scheduling, and lowered drinking fountains.

Services: In addition to many counseling and information services, tutoring is available in most subjects, including economics, political science, upper-division mathematics, and accounting. There is also remedial math, reading, and writing.

Campus Safety and Security: Campus safety and security measures include 24-hour foot and vehicle patrol, informal discussions, pamphlets, posters, films, and lighted pathways and sidewalks. In addition, there are formal educational sessions held in the dormitories each semester.

Programs of Study: State College awards the B.A., B.S., and B.S.Ed. degrees. Associate degrees are also awarded. Bachelor's degrees are awarded in BIOLOGICAL SCIENCE (biology/biological science), BUSINESS (accounting, banking and finance, business administration and management, and marketing/retailing/merchandising), COMMUNICATIONS AND THE ARTS (communications, English, and fine arts), COMPUTER AND PHYSICAL SCIENCE (applied mathematics, chemistry, and mathematics), EDUCATION (art, early childhood, elementary, and secondary), HEALTH PROFESSIONS (recreation therapy), SOCIAL SCIENCE (criminal justice, economics, history, political science/government, psychology, social work, and sociology). Biology is the strongest academically. Education and business have the largest enrollments.

Required: Bachelor candidates must take 52 to 53 semester credits of general studies courses, including freshman seminar, English, mathematics, natural science, literature, fine arts, history, and cultural studies. A 2.0 GPA (cumulative and in the major) is required to graduate. Students must complete 121 to 128 credits depending on the major.

Special: Internships, a Washington semester, and work-study programs are offered. The B.A.-B.S. degree in communications, psychology, and biology may be pursued. Credit by examination and for life/military/work experience are available. Nondegree study and pass/fail options are possible. There is a freshman honors program on campus, as well as 7 national honor societies. Seven departments have honors programs.

Faculty/Classroom: Fifty-six percent of faculty are male; 44%, female. The average class size in a regular course offering is 25.

Requirements: A minimum GPA of 2.0 is required. The ACT is required and the SAT I is recommended. A minimum composite score on the ACT of 14.3 or a 2.0 GPA is required for regular admission. Applicants should be graduates of an accredited secondary school with a minimum of 4 years in English, 3 in social studies, 2 each in mathematics and science, and 4 in academic electives. The GED is accepted. AP and CLEP credits are accepted. Important factors used in the admissions decision are evidence of special talent, leadership record, advanced placement or honor courses, personality, intangible qualities, and extracurricular activities record.

Procedure: Freshmen are admitted to all sessions. There is an early decision plan. Entrance exams should be taken 6 months prior to entry. Early decision applications should be filed by March 10; regular applications, by August 10 for fall entry, November 10 for spring entry, and March 10 for summer entry. Notification is sent on a rolling basis.

Transfer: About 330 transfer students enrolled in 1993–94. Transfer applicants must submit ACT scores and high school transcripts, and must have a 2.5 GPA. A total of 30 credits out of 121 must be completed at State College.

Visiting: There are regularly scheduled orientations for prospective students, including both academic and social acitivties. There are guides for informal visits and visitors may sit in on classes and stay overnight at the school. To arrange for a visit, contact John L. Fuller at (304) 766–3144.

Financial Aid: In a recent year, 55% of all freshmen and 44% of continuing students received some form of financial aid. State College is a member of CSS. The FAF is required. The deadline for financial aid applications is March 1.

International Students: There were recently 6 international students enrolled. They must take the TOEFL and achieve a minimum score of 500. The student must also take the ACT.

Computers: The college provides computer facilities for student use. The mainframe is a DEC MicroVAX 3900. There are more than 90 terminals and more than 400 computers at different facilities on campus. All students may access the system and it is available more than 60 hours a week. Each student is allocated $200 of use per semester. There are no fees.

Graduates: In a recent year, 348 bachelor's degrees were awarded.

Admissions Contact: Robin Green, Assistant Director, Admissions.

WEST VIRGINIA UNIVERSITY
Morgantown, WV 26506-6009

C-2

(304) 293-2121
(800) 344-9881 (in-state)

Full-time: 7939 men, 6585 women
Part-time: 460 men, 593 women
Graduate: 3080 men, 4423 women
Year: semesters, summer session
Application Deadline: open
Freshman Class: n/av
SAT I Verbal/Math: 430/500

Faculty: 1388; I, --$
Ph.D.s: 82%
Student/Faculty: 10 to 1
Tuition: $1928 ($5486)
Room & Board: $3846

COMPETITIVE

West Virginia University, founded in 1867, is a comprehensive, public land-grant research university offering over 100 undergraduate degrees in liberal arts and sciences, health science and professional training. There are 14 undergraduate and 15 graduate and professional schools. In addition to regional accreditation, WVU has baccalaureate program accreditation with AACSB, ABET, ACEJMC, ACPE, ADA, APTA, ASLA, CAHEA, CSWE, NASAD, NASM, NCATE, NLN, NRPA, and SAF. The 10 libraries contain 1,706,768 volumes, 2,386,690 microform items, and 22,391 audiovisual forms, and subscribe to 11,099 periodicals. Computerized library sources and services include the card catalog, interlibrary loans, and database searching. Special learning facilities include a learning resource center, an art gallery, a planetarium, a radio and TV station, a laboratory for inventors, a coal, mining, and minerals history museum, and a pharmacy museum. The 541-acre campus is in a small town 75 miles south of Pittsburgh and 200 miles west of Baltimore and Washington, D.C. Including residence halls, there are 136 buildings on campus.

Student Life: About 55% of undergraduates are from West Virginia. Students come from 49 states, 76 foreign countries, and Canada. Ninety-one percent are white. The average age of freshmen is 18; all undergraduates, 21. About 21% do not return for their sophomore year; 49% remain to graduate.

Housing: A total of 3500 students can be accommodated in college housing. College-sponsored living facilities include single-sex and coed dormitories, on-campus apartments, and married-student housing. In addition there are honors houses, language houses, special interest houses, and sections within residence halls designated for special programming. On-campus housing is available on a first-come, first-served basis. Most students live on campus. Alcohol is not permitted. All students may keep cars on campus.

Activities: About 20% of men belong to 23 national fraternities; about 23% of women belong to 13 national sororities. There are more than 240 groups on campus, including art, band, cheerleading, chess, choir, chorale, chorus, computers, dance, drama, ethnic, film, gay, honors, international, jazz band, literary magazine, marching band, newspaper, opera, orchestra, pep band, photography, political, professional, radio and TV, religious, social, social service, student government, symphony, and yearbook. Popular campus events include Homecoming, Mountaineer Week, Parents Weekend, Spring Week, and Greek Week.

Sports: There are 10 intercollegiate sports for men and 8 for women, and 22 intramural sports for men and 20 for women. Athletic and recreation facilities include a natatorium with swimming and diving pools, tennis courts, weight room, in/outdoor tracks, racquetball and squash courts, bowling alley, lacrosse, baseball and soccer fields, a 63,500-seat stadium, and a 14,000-seat gymnasium.

Disabled Students: Ninety percent of the campus is accessible to disabled students. The following facilities are available: wheelchair ramps, elevators, special parking, specially equipped rest rooms, special class scheduling, and lowered drinking fountains and telephones. Academic programs are made accessible by transferring classes to an architecturally accessible facility. Other facilities include tactile signage, specially designed laboratory facilities and portable laboratory stations, a Kurzweil reading machine, special apartments for hearing and mobility impaired students, and a specially equipped van for inner-city transportation. All coordination is done through the Office of Disability Services.

Services: In addition to many counseling and information services, tutoring is available in most subjects. There is also a reader service for the blind, and remedial math, reading, and writing.

Campus Safety and Security: Campus safety and security measures include 24-hour foot and vehicle patrol, self defense education, escort service, and shuttle buses. In addition, there are informal discussions, pamphlets, posters, films, emergency telephones, lighted pathways and sidewalks, neighborhood watch programs, and sexual assault prevention booths staffed by city and university police.

Programs of Study: WVU awards the B.A., B.S., B.F.A., B.M., B.S.A.E., B.S.Agr., B.S.B.Ad., B.S.C.E., B.S.Ch.E., B.S.Cp.E., B.S.E.E., B.S.E.Ed., B.S.E.M., B.S.F., B.S. Fam. Res., B.S.I.E., B.S.J., B.S.L.A., B.S.M.E., B.S.N., B.S.P.Ed., B.S.Pet.E., B.S.Pharm., B.S.R., B.S.S.Ed., and B.S.W. degrees. Master's and doctoral degrees also are awarded. Bachelor's degrees are awarded in AGRICULTURE (agricultural business management, agronomy, animal and veterinary science, fishing and fisheries, forestry and related sciences, horticulture, natural resource management, plant science, soil science, and wood science), BIOLOGICAL SCIENCE (biology/biological science, nutrition, and wildlife biology), BUSINESS (accounting, banking and finance, business administration and management, fashion merchandising, marketing and distribution, and sports management), COMMUNICATIONS AND THE ARTS (advertising, broadcasting, communications, dramatic arts, English, journalism, foreign languages, music, public relations, and visual and performing arts), COMPUTER AND PHYSICAL SCIENCE (chemistry, computer science, geology, mathematics, physics, science, and statistics), EDUCATION (agricultural, elementary, home economics, physical, and secondary), ENGINEERING AND ENVIRONMENTAL DESIGN (aerospace engineering, chemical engineering, civil engineering, computer engineering, electrical/electronics engineering, environmental science, industrial engineering, interior design, landscape architecture/design, mechanical engineering, mining and mineral engineering, mining and petroleum technology, and petroleum/natural gas engineering), HEALTH PROFESSIONS (dental hygiene, medical technology, nursing, pharmacy, physical therapy, and speech pathology/audiology), SOCIAL SCIENCE (anthropology and sociology, child care/child and family studies, economics, family/consumer resource management, geography, history, interdisciplinary studies, international studies, liberal arts/general studies, parks and recreation management, philosophy, physical fitness/movement, political science/government, psychology, social work, sociology, and textiles and clothing). Engineering, psychology, political science, international studies, and pharmacy are the strongest programs academically. Business, engineering, health sciences, education, and arts and sciences have the largest enrollments.

Required: All students are required to take 12 credit hours in each of 3 areas: humanities and fine arts, social and behavioral sciences, and natural sciences and mathematics. The 36 credit hours must include international/minority/gender studies, mathematics, composition, and an advanced course emphasizing writing skills. A minimum 2.0 GPA and at least 128 credit hours are required to graduate.

Special: Cross-registration with schools in the Southern Regional Education Board through the Academic Common Market is possible. Internships, study abroad in 12 countries, a Washington semester, a dual major in business and foreign language, and B.A.-B.S. degrees in economics, chemistry, physics, and geology are available. A liberal studies degree, credit by examination, credit for life experience, nondegree study, and pass/fail options are also offered. There is a freshman honors program on campus, as well as 40 national honor societies, including Phi Beta Kappa. Five departments have honors programs.

Faculty/Classroom: Seventy-four percent of faculty are male; 26%, female. All teach undergraduates, 74% also do research.

Admissions: There were 13 National Merit finalists.

Requirements: A minimum GPA of 2.0 is required. The SAT I or ACT is required. In-state students need a minimum composite score of 770 on the SAT, or 19 on the ACT. Out-of-state students need scores of 820 or 20 respectively. Applicants should graduate from an accredited school no sooner than their junior year, after completing 4 years of English, 3 of social studies including U.S. history, 2 years of laboratory sciences, and 2 years of mathematics. An additonal year of mathematics and 2 years of foreign language are recommended. Music students must audition, and art applicants must submit a portfolio. AP and CLEP credits are accepted. Important factors used in the admissions decision are personality, intangible qualities, parents or siblings attending the school, leadership record, evidence of special talent, and advanced placement or honor courses.

Procedure: Freshmen are admitted to all sessions. Entrance exams should be taken by spring of the junior year. Application deadlines are open. The application fee is $10 for residents; $25 for nonresidents. Notification is sent on a rolling basis. There are early admissions and deferred admissions plans. A waiting list is an active part of the admissions procedure, with about 4% of applicants on the list.

Transfer: About 804 transfer students enrolled in 1993–94. Minimum college GPA of 2.0 is required of transfers; all applicants must submit college transcripts. Students having fewer than 29 transferable credit hours are subject to freshman admission criteria and must submit SAT I or ACT scores and high school transcripts. A total of 30 credits out of 128 must be completed at WVU.

Visiting: There are regularly scheduled orientations for prospective students, consisting of 2-day sessions with campus tours, placement testing, academic and advisement meetings, parent/student orientation discussions, and transitional meetings. There are guides for informal visits and visitors may sit in on classes. To arrange for a visit, contact the Admissions and Records Tour Office at (800) 344-9881.

Financial Aid: In 1993-94, 55% of all current freshmen and 53% of continuing students received some form of financial aid. About 43% of freshmen and 44% of continuing students received need-based aid. The average freshman award was $1638. Of that total, scholarships or need-based grants averaged $1310 ($8650 maximum); loans averaged $2270 ($6625 maximum); and work contracts averaged $1000 ($2000 maximum). Thirty-six percent of undergraduate students work part-time. Average earnings from campus work for the school year are $1225. The average financial indebtedness of the 1992-93 graduate was $9000. WVU is a member of CSS. The FAFSA financial statement is required. The deadline for financial aid applications is March 1; January 15 for freshman scholarships.

International Students: There are currently 970 international students enrolled. They must take the TOEFL and achieve a minimum score of 550. The student must also take the SAT I or the ACT.

Computers: The college provides computer facilities for student use. The mainframes are an IBM 3090-300E running VM/XA and MVS/XA and a DEC VAX 8650, VAX 8550, and VAX 8250 in a VAX cluster running VMS. Students who are required to use the mainframe for class projects are issued an individual account by their instructor. Several colleges operate their own laboratories containing both microcomputers and providing mainframe access. Public sites with consultants provide additional access to training and facilities. IBM-compatible and Apple equipment is available throughout the campus, as is access to the VAX cluster. All students may access the system. It may be used 24 hours a day seven days a week. There are no time limits on using the system and no fees.

Graduates: In 1992-93, 2989 bachelor's degrees were awarded. The most popular majors among graduates were business and management (19%), engineering (9%), and health sciences (8%). Within an average freshman class, 25% graduate in 4 years and 49% in 5 years. Some 735 companies recruited on campus in 1992-93. In the 1992 graduating class, 3% of the men and 2% of the women were enrolled in graduate school within 6 months of graduation; 87% of the men and 89% of the women had found employment.

Admissions Contact: Dr. Glenn G. Carter, Admissions and Records.

WEST VIRGINIA WESLEYAN COLLEGE C-3
Buckhannon, WV 26201 (304) 473-8510
(800) 722-9933 (out-of-state)

Full-time: 744 men, 765 women	Faculty: 77; IIB, av$
Part-time: 53 men, 117 women	Ph.D.s: 62%
Graduate: 54 men, 22 women	Student/Faculty: 20 to 1
Year: 4-1-4, summer session	Tuition: $13,400
Application Deadline: open	Room & Board: $3500

Freshman Class: 1710 applied, 1395 accepted, 478 enrolled
SAT I or ACT: required **COMPETITIVE**

West Virginia Wesleyan College, founded in 1890, is an independent liberal and applied arts college affiliated with the United Methodist Church. There is one graduate school. In addition to regional accreditation, WVWC has baccalaureate program accreditation with NASM and NLN. The 2 libraries contain 149,085 volumes, 6479 microform items, and 1734 audiovisual forms, and subscribe to 674 periodicals. Special learning facilities include a learning resource center, art gallery, planetarium, and radio station. The 80-acre campus is in a small town in the Appalachian foothills, 135 miles south of Pittsburgh, Pennsylvania. Including residence halls, there are 23 buildings on campus.

Student Life: About 55% of undergraduates are from out-of-state, mostly the Middle Atlantic. Students come from 34 states, 22 foreign countries, and Canada. Eighty-five percent are from public schools; 15% from private. Eighty-nine percent are white. Forty-seven percent are Protestant; 21% Catholic. The average age of freshmen is 18; all undergraduates, 19. Twenty-four percent drop out by the end of their first year; 53% remain to graduate.

Housing: A total of 1321 students can be accommodated in college housing. College-sponsored living facilities include single-sex and coed dormitories and on-campus apartments. In addition, there are quiet study living areas. On-campus housing is guaranteed for all 4 years. Eighty percent of students live on campus; of those, 90% remain on campus on weekends. All students may keep cars on campus.

Activities: About 26% of men belong to 6 national fraternities; about 26% of women belong to 4 national sororities. There are 75 groups on campus, including band, cheerleading, choir, chorale, chorus, computers, drama, ethnic, honors, international, jazz band, literary magazine, musical theater, newspaper, political, professional, radio

and TV, religious, social, social service, student government, and yearbook. Popular campus events include Homecoming, Founders Day, Festivals of Lessons and Carols, and Spring Sing.

Sports: There are 9 intercollegiate sports for men and 8 for women, and 9 intramural sports for men and 8 for women. Athletic and recreation facilities include baseball and football fields with seating for 3500, as well as a physical education center with a 3800-seat intercollegiate basketball court, 2 intramural practice courts, 4 handball courts, an auxiliary gymnasium, indoor tennis courts, volleyball courts, golf and wrestling practice areas, sauna baths, a dance studio, and gymnastics and weight rooms. A state park is near the campus.

Disabled Students: Seventy-five percent of the campus is accessible to disabled students. The following facilities are available: wheelchair ramps, elevators, special parking, specially equipped rest rooms, special class scheduling, and lowered drinking fountains.

Services: In addition to many counseling and information services, tutoring is available in every subject. There is also a reader service for the blind, and remedial math, reading, and writing.

Campus Safety and Security: Campus safety and security measures include 24-hour foot and vehicle patrol, self defense education, escort service, and informal discussions. In addition, there are pamphlets, posters, films, lighted pathways and sidewalks, and rape awareness educational programs, and appropriate training for residence hall staff.

Programs of Study: WVWC awards the B.A., B.S., B.M.E., and B.S.N. degrees. Master's degrees also are awarded. Bachelor's degrees are awarded in BIOLOGICAL SCIENCE (biology/biological science and nutrition), BUSINESS (accounting, business administration and management, fashion merchandising, management information systems, and marketing/retailing/merchandising), COMMUNICATIONS AND THE ARTS (dramatic arts, English, music, public relations, and speech/debate/rhetoric), COMPUTER AND PHYSICAL SCIENCE (chemistry, computer science, mathematics, and physics), EDUCATION (art, elementary, music, physical, and secondary), ENGINEERING AND ENVIRONMENTAL DESIGN (engineering physics), HEALTH PROFESSIONS (nursing and rehabilitation therapy), SOCIAL SCIENCE (economics, history, international studies, philosophy, political science/government, psychology, public administration, religion, religious education, social science, and sociology). Physical and natural sciences and accounting are the strongest programs academically. Business, biology, education, and psychology have the largest enrollments.

Required: To graduate, students must earn 128 semester hours with a minimum GPA of 2.0; 24 to 51 hours must be in the major, 49 to 51 in general studies, and 15 in the minor. Required disciplines are international studies, natural science and mathematics, social sciences, health and physical education, religion, philosophy, fine arts and literature, and communications. Composition, fundamentals of speech, and 2 hours of physical education activities are also needed.

Special: WVWC offers cross-registration with the Mountain State Association of Colleges, a 3-2 engineering degree with the University of Pennsylvania, a 3-2 degree in forestry or environmental studies with Duke University, and a 4-1 aeronautical engineering degree with NASA Langley Research Center. Students may participate in a wide variety of internships, including a Washington Center Internship and work-study and study-abroad programs; there are exchange agreements with 2 Korean universities. Nondegree and pass/fail study, dual, student-designed, and contract majors, and credit for life, military, and work experience are available. The optional January term offers special courses and travel opportunities, including a program in Bulgaria. There is a freshman honors program on campus.

Faculty/Classroom: Fifty-nine percent of faculty are male; 41%, female. All teach undergraduates. The average class size in an introductory lecture is 30; in a laboratory, 20; and in a regular course offering, 19.

Admissions: About 82% of the 1993-94 applicants were accepted. The SAT scores for the freshman class were as follows: Verbal—75% below 500, 20% between 500 and 599, and 5% between 600 and 700; Math—54% below 500, 31% between 500 and 599, 11% between 600 and 700, and 4% above 700. The ACT scores were 27% below 21, 25% between 21 and 23, 25% between 24 and 26, 11% between 27 and 28, and 12% above 28. There were 2 National Merit finalists and 5 semifinalists. About 14 freshmen graduated first in their class.

Requirements: WVWC requires applicants to be in the upper 50% of their class. A minimum GPA of 2.0 is required. The SAT I or ACT is required. The minimum composite score needed is 800 on the SAT I, 420 verbal and 380 mathematics, or 18 on the ACT. In addition, applicants must be high school graduates, or hold a GED. Students should have earned 16 academic credits, consisting of 4 in English, 3 each in mathematics and social studies, and 2 each in foreign language, laboratory science, and electives. An essay and an interview are recommended. AP and CLEP credits are accepted. Important factors used in the admissions decision are extracurricular activities rec-

ord, recommendations by school officials, leadership record, evidence of special talent, and advanced placement or honor courses.

Procedure: Freshmen are admitted fall and spring. Entrance exams should be taken in fall of the senior year. The application deadlines are open. Application fee is $25. Notification is sent on a rolling basis. There is an early admissions plan.

Transfer: About 69 transfer students enrolled in a recent year. Transfer applicants must supply a high school transcript if their GPA for college work is less than 2.5. An associate degree and an interview are recommended. A total of 32 credits out of 128 must be completed at WVWC.

Visiting: There are regularly scheduled orientations for prospective students. There are guides for informal visits and visitors may sit in on classes and stay overnight at the school. To arrange for a visit, contact Robert Skinner, Director of Admission at (304) 473–8510 or (800) 722–9933.

Financial Aid: In 1993–94, 82% of all current freshmen and 77% of continuing students received some form of financial aid. About 84% of continuing students received need-based aid. The average freshman award was $10,533. Of that total, scholarships or need-based grants averaged $7392 ($15,080 maximum); loans averaged $3141 ($4125 maximum); and work contracts averaged $800 ($1000 maximum). The average financial indebtedness of the 1992–93 graduate was $5245. WVWC is a member of CSS. The FAF and the college's own financial statement are required. The deadline for financial aid applications is March 1.

International Students: There are currently 64 international students enrolled. They must take the TOEFL and achieve a minimum score of 500. They also take the SAT I or ACT if they are seeking scholarships.

Computers: The college provides computer facilities for student use. The mainframe is a DEC MicroVAX 3900. The mainframe can be accessed through PC networks. There are 150 terminals in the computer center, 4 computer laboratories, and in academic departments. All students may access the system. There are no time limits on using the system and no fees.

Graduates: In 1992–93, 276 bachelor's degrees were awarded. Within an average freshman class, 53% graduate in 5 years. In a recent graduating class, 7% of the men and 9% of the women were enrolled in graduate school within 6 months of graduation; 93% of the men and 91% of the women had found employment.

Admissions Contact: Robert N. Skinner II, Director of Admission.

WHEELING JESUIT COLLEGE
C-2

Wheeling, WV 26003 (304) 243–2359; (800) 624–6992 (out-of-state)

Full-time: 420 men, 551 women	Faculty: 70; IIB, --$
Part-time: 60 men, 246 women	Ph.D.s: 71%
Graduate: 98 men, 65 women	Student/Faculty: 14 to 1
Year: semesters, summer session	Tuition: $10,000
Application Deadline: May 15	Room & Board: $4370
Freshman Class: 820 applied, 755 accepted, 213 enrolled	
SAT I Verbal/Math: 433/479	ACT: 22 **COMPETITIVE**

Wheeling Jesuit College, founded in 1954, is an independent, coeducational college affiliated with the Society of Jesus, offering undergraduate programs in the liberal arts and sciences, nursing, allied health, and business, and graduate programs in business administration and applied theology. There are 3 graduate schools. In addition to regional accreditation, Wheeling Jesuit has baccalaureate program accreditation with CAHEA and NLN. The library contains 126,000 volumes, 84,000 microform items, and 1200 audiovisual forms, and subscribes to 550 periodicals. Special learning facilities include a learning resource center. The 70-acre campus is in a suburban area 60 miles southwest of Pittsburgh, Pennsylvania. Including residence halls, there are 15 buildings on campus.

Student Life: About 56% of undergraduates are from out-of-state, mostly the Middle Atlantic. Students come from 20 states, 10 foreign countries, and Canada. Half are from public schools; half from private. Ninety-two percent are white. Sixty-five percent are Catholic; 30% Protestant. The average age of freshmen is 18; all undergraduates, 22. Twenty-five percent drop out by the end of their first year; 62% remain to graduate.

Housing: A total of 630 students can be accommodated in college housing. College-sponsored living facilities include single-sex and coed dormitories. On-campus housing is guaranteed for all 4 years. Sixty percent of students live on campus; of those, 75% remain on campus on weekends. All students may keep cars on campus.

Activities: There are no fraternities or sororities. There are 20 groups on campus, including cheerleading, choir, chorus, drama, honors, international, literary magazine, newspaper, pep band, professional, religious, social, social service, student government, and yearbook. Popular campus events include Homecoming, Week of the Person, rock concerts, Day of Diversity, Honors Convocation, and Coffee House.

Sports: There are 4 intercollegiate sports each for men and women, and 6 intramural sports for men and 5 for women. Athletic and recreation facilities include a recreation center with a swimming pool, 2 gymnasiums, racquetball courts, complete Nautilus equipment, and an indoor jogging track. There are also 3 fields as well as game rooms.

Disabled Students: Eighty percent of the campus is accessible to disabled students. The following facilities are available: wheelchair ramps, elevators, special parking, specially equipped rest rooms, lowered drinking fountains, and lowered telephones.

Services: In addition to many counseling and information services, tutoring is available in most subjects. There is also a reader service for the blind, and remedial math, reading, and writing.

Campus Safety and Security: Campus safety and security measures include 24-hour foot and vehicle patrol, self defense education, informal discussions, and pamphlets, posters, and films. In addition, there are lighted pathways and sidewalks and a student intern campus patrol.

Programs of Study: Wheeling Jesuit awards the B.A., B.S., and B.S.N. degrees. Master's degrees also are awarded. Bachelor's degrees are awarded in BIOLOGICAL SCIENCE (biology/biological science), BUSINESS (accounting, management science, and marketing/retailing/merchandising), COMMUNICATIONS AND THE ARTS (English, French, romance languages, Spanish, and technical and business writing), COMPUTER AND PHYSICAL SCIENCE (chemistry, computer science, mathematics, physics, and science), ENGINEERING AND ENVIRONMENTAL DESIGN (industrial engineering and technology and public affairs), HEALTH PROFESSIONS (nuclear medical technology, nursing, and respiratory therapy), SOCIAL SCIENCE (criminal justice, ethics, politics, and social policy, history, international relations, philosophy, political science/government, psychology, and religion). Biology, psychology, nursing, respiratory therapy, accounting, and nuclear medicine technology are the strongest programs academically. Accounting, psychology, nursing, and biology have the largest enrollments.

Required: To graduate, students must complete 120 credit hours, with a GPA of 2.0. The core curriculum consists of 51 specified credits in English composition, mathematics, modern languages, literature, history, social science, natural science, philosophy, theology, and 1 course in either ethics or Christian morality, as well as 1 additional mathematics or science course. Students are also required to complete 2 units in each of the dimensions of the school's Wellness Program.

Special: The college offers internships with many businesses and institutions, as well as a Washington semester and study abroad. Students may obtain a B.A./M.B.A. degree, as well as a 3–2 engineering degree with Case Western Reserve University. The college permits dual and student-designed majors. Credit for life, military, and work experience may be granted to adult students. Pass/fail options are open in some courses. There is a freshman honors program on campus, as well as 5 national honor societies. Four departments have honors programs.

Faculty/Classroom: Sixty-four percent of faculty are male; 36%, female. All teach undergraduates and do research. The average class size in an introductory lecture is 28; in a laboratory, 10; and in a regular course offering, 20.

Admissions: About 92% of the 1993–94 applicants were accepted. The SAT scores for the freshman class were as follows: Verbal—79% below 500, 19% between 500 and 599, and 2% between 600 and 700; Math—61% below 500, 28% between 500 and 599, 10% between 600 and 700, and 1% above 700. The ACT scores were 46% below 21, 28% between 21 and 23, 19% between 24 and 26, 4% between 27 and 28, and 3% above 28. About 32% of the current freshmen were in the top fifth of their class; 62% were in the top two fifths. There were 2 National Merit semifinalists. Two freshmen graduated first in their class.

Requirements: Wheeling Jesuit recommends applicants to be in the upper 50% of their class. A minimum GPA of 2.5 is required. The SAT I or ACT is required, with a minimum composite score of 850 on the SAT I or 18 on the ACT. In addition, applicants must be high school graduates or hold a GED. Students should have earned 15 academic credits, consisting of 4 in English, 2 each in mathematics and history or social science, 1 in laboratory science (2 are recommended for science majors), and 6 in academic electives, with a foreign language recommended. Students entering programs in the natural sciences should have taken 1 course each of chemistry and biology. Exceptions are made, especially if the high school GPA is 3.0 or better. An interview is recommended. AP and CLEP credits are accepted. Important factors used in the admissions decision are leadership record, recommendations by school officials, extracurricular activities record, personality, intangible qualities, and evidence of special talent.

Procedure: Freshmen are admitted to all sessions. Applications should be filed by May 15 for fall entry and December 1 for spring entry, along with an application fee of $25. Notification is sent on a

rolling basis and there are early admissions and deferred admissions plans.

Transfer: About 45 transfer students enrolled in 1993–94. Transfer applicants must have a GPA of 2.0 for college work, or supply high school transcripts if entering at the freshman level. The SAT I or ACT is required if the student has less than 1 year of college work; otherwise, it is still recommended, as is an interview. Transfer students must take placement tests given by the college. A total of 30 credits out of 120 must be completed at Wheeling Jesuit.

Visiting: There are regularly scheduled orientations for prospective students, including meetings with faculty, discussions by students and parents, meals, and campus tours. There are guides for informal visits and visitors may sit in on classes and stay overnight at the school. To arrange for a visit, contact Dennis Soberl, Director of Recruitment at (800) 624–6992.

Financial Aid: In 1993–94, 88% of all current freshmen and 75% of continuing students received some form of financial aid. About 76% of freshmen and 75% of continuing students received need-based aid. The average freshman award was $9552. Of that total, scholarships or need-based grants averaged $6062 ($15,470 maximum); loans averaged $3185 ($4000 maximum); and work contracts averaged $1311 ($2040 maximum). Fifty percent of undergraduate students work part-time. Average earnings from campus work for the school year are $1210. The average financial indebtedness of the 1992–93 graduate was $13,100. Wheeling Jesuit is a member of CSS. The FAF, FFS, or SFS are required; the FAF is preferred. The deadline for first priority financial aid applications is April 1.

International Students: There are currently 33 international students enrolled. The school actively recruits these students. They must take the TOEFL and achieve a minimum score of 550.

Computers: The college provides computer facilities for student use. The mainframe is an AT&T Star group LAN with 6386 WGS. There are also 40 IBM PS/2, AT&T 6300, and NCR microcomputers available in the computer center, and in the academic resource center. All students may access the system. There are no time limits on using the system and no fees.

Graduates: In 1992–93, 230 bachelor's degrees were awarded. The most popular majors among graduates were management (12%), nursing (11%), and psychology (9%). Within an average freshman class, 1% graduate in 3 years, 57% in 4 years, 62% in 5 years, and 62% in 6 years. Some 20 companies recruited on campus in 1992–93. In the 1992 graduating class, 25% of the men and 35% of the women were enrolled in graduate school within 6 months of graduation; 60% found employment.

Admissions Contact: Dennis J. Soberl, Director of Admissions.

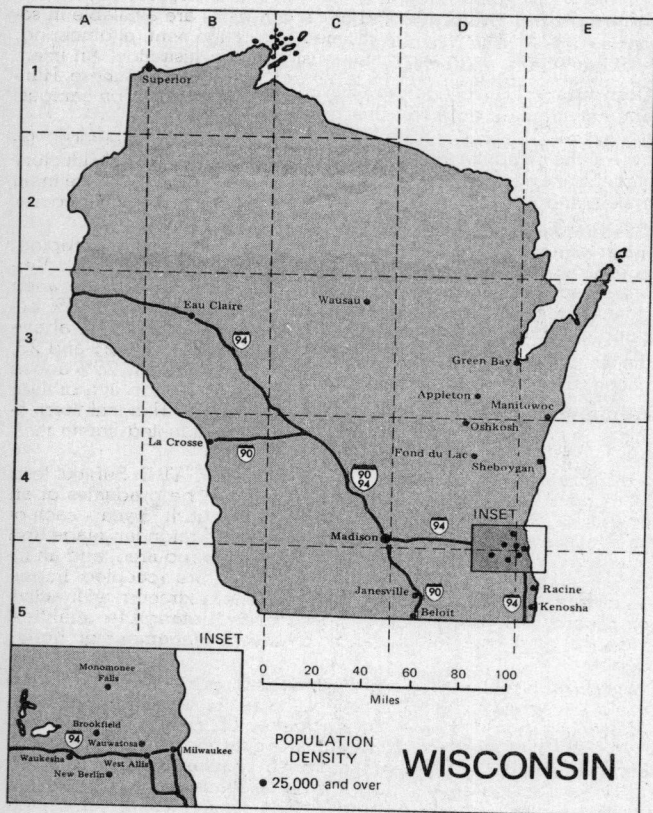

POPULATION
DENSITY
● 25,000 and over

WISCONSIN

0 20 40 60 80 100
Miles

INSET

ALVERNO COLLEGE

Milwaukee, WI 53234-3922

E-4

(414) 382-6100
(800) 933-3401 (out-of-state)

Full-time: 1317 women
Part-time: 1235 women
Graduate: none
Year: semesters, summer session
Application Deadline: August 1
Freshman Class: 966 applied, 529 accepted, 267 enrolled
ACT: 20

Faculty: 118; IIB, --$
Ph.D.s: 81%
Student/Faculty: 11 to 1
Tuition: $7884
Room & Board: $3460

COMPETITIVE

Alverno College, founded in 1887, is a Roman Catholic, women's liberal arts institution. In addition to regional accreditation, Alverno has baccalaureate program accreditation with NASM, NCATE, and NLN. The library contains 114,037 volumes, 198,851 microform items, and 12,475 audiovisual forms, and subscribes to 1541 periodicals. Computerized library sources and services include database searching. Special learning facilities include a learning resource center and art gallery. The 52-acre campus is in a suburban area on the southwest edge of Milwaukee. Including residence halls, there are 9 buildings on campus.

Student Life: Most undergraduates are from Wisconsin. Students come from 12 states and 11 foreign countries. Seventy-five percent are white; 15% African American. Forty-six percent are Catholic; 24% Protestant. The average age of freshmen is 19; all undergraduates, 24. Ten percent drop out by the end of their first year; 88% remain to graduate.

Housing: A total of 250 students can be accommodated in college housing. On-campus housing is guaranteed for all 4 years. Eighty-nine percent of students commute. All students may keep cars on campus.

Activities: There are no fraternities. There are 31 groups on campus, including art, choir, chorale, dance, drama, ethnic, honors, international, literary magazine, musical theater, newspaper, orchestra, political, professional, religious, social, social service, and student government. Popular campus events include fine arts performances.

Sports: Athletic and recreation facilities include a gymnasium, a fitness center, a 1.2-mile par course, and indoor and outdoor volleyball and basketball courts.

Disabled Students: Seventy-five percent of the campus is accessible to disabled students. The following facilities are available: wheelchair ramps, elevators, special parking, specially equipped rest rooms, special class scheduling, and lowered telephones.

Services: In addition to many counseling and information services, tutoring is available in most subjects. There is also remedial math, reading, and writing.

Campus Safety and Security: Campus safety and security measures include 24-hour foot and vehicle patrol, self defense education, escort service, and informal discussions. In addition, there are pamphlets, posters, films, and lighted pathways and sidewalks.

Programs of Study: Alverno awards the B.A., B.Mus., B.S.Educ., B.S.N., and B.S.T. degrees. Bachelor's degrees are awarded in BIOLOGICAL SCIENCE (biology/biological science), BUSINESS (business administration and management), COMMUNICATIONS AND THE ARTS (communications, English, fine arts, and music), COMPUTER AND PHYSICAL SCIENCE (chemistry and mathematics), EDUCATION (art, early childhood, elementary, music, science, secondary, and social studies), HEALTH PROFESSIONS (music therapy, nuclear medical technology, nursing, predentistry, and premedicine), SOCIAL SCIENCE (history, philosophy, political science/government, prelaw, psychology, religious music, and social science). Interdisciplinary humanities, psychology, nursing, business management, and science and teacher education are the strongest programs academically. Business management, education, nursing, and professional communication have the largest enrollments.

Required: General education requirements include mastery in a range of liberal arts courses as well as demonstrated ability in 8 broad areas: communications, analysis, problem solving, values in decision making, social interaction, global perspectives, effective citizenship, and aesthetic responsiveness. In addition, students must complete course requirements as set forth by their major and minor departments. A varying number of total credit hours is needed, depending on the curriculum. At least 1 internship is required.

Special: Alverno offers cross-registration with the Milwaukee School of Engineering and the Milwaukee Institute of Art and Design. Internships, study abroad in England and Japan, dual majors, and nondegree study are possible. The school's interactive curriculum is outcome oriented and performance-based. There are 2 national honor societies on campus. One department has an honors program.

Faculty/Classroom: Twenty-nine percent of faculty are male; 71%, female. All teach undergraduates and do research. The average class size in an introductory lecture is 26; in a laboratory, 24; and in a regular course offering, 28.

Admissions: About 55% of the 1993-94 applicants were accepted.

Requirements: A minimum GPA of 2.0 is required. The SAT I or ACT is recommended. Applicants must be graduates of an accredited secondary school, having completed 17 academic credits with college preparatory courses. The GED is accepted. An interview is recommended. AP and CLEP credits are accepted.

Procedure: Freshmen are admitted fall and spring. Entrance exams should be taken as early as possible. Applications should be filed by August 1 for fall entry and January 1 for spring entry, along with an application fee of $10. Notification is sent on a rolling basis.

Transfer: About 110 transfer students enrolled in 1993-94. Most transfer students are evaluated on the basis of their performance. Transfers should have a minimum GPA of 2.0.

Visiting: There are regularly scheduled orientations for prospective students, including open houses and overnight events. There are guides for informal visits and visitors may sit in on classes and stay overnight at the school. To arrange for a visit, contact the Admissions Office at (414) 382-6100 or (800) 933-3401.

Financial Aid: In 1993-94, 79% of all current freshmen and 73% of continuing students received some form of financial aid. About 79% of freshmen and 73% of continuing students received need-based aid. The average freshman award was $4742. Of that total, scholarships or need-based grants averaged $3000 ($5500 maximum); loans averaged $2625; and work contracts averaged $1200 ($2500 maximum). Forty percent of undergraduate students work part-time. Average earnings from campus work for the school year are $1200. The average financial indebtedness of the 1992-93 graduate was $11,032. Alverno is a member of CSS. The FAF and the college's own financial statement are required. The deadline for financial aid applications is August 1.

International Students: There are currently 16 international students enrolled. They must take the TOEFL and achieve a minimum score of 500.

Computers: The college provides computer facilities for student use. Students have access to 88 microcomputers on campus, including Apple IIe, Macintosh, and IBM-compatible PCs. The computer center may be accessed by all students. There are no time limits on using the system and no fees.

Graduates: In 1992-93, 334 bachelor's degrees were awarded. The most popular majors among graduates were business (33%), professional communication (20%), and nursing (19%). Within an average freshman class, 52% graduate in 4 years. Some 68 companies recruited on campus in 1992-93. In the 1992 graduating class, 1% of the

women were enrolled in graduate school within 6 months of graduation; 92% found employment.

Admissions Contact: Colleen K. Hayes, Director of Admissions.

BELOIT COLLEGE

D-5

Beloit, WI 53511 (608) 363-2500; (800) 356-0751 (out-of-state)

Full-time: 485 men, 638 women	Faculty: 86; IIB, +$
Part-time: 27 men, 56 women	Ph.D.s: 94%
Graduate: 4 men, 1 woman	Student/Faculty: 13 to 1
Year: semesters	Tuition: $15,430
Application Deadline: March 15	Room & Board: $3520

Freshman Class: 1230 applied, 943 accepted, 284 enrolled

SAT I Verbal/Math: 550/580 ACT: 26 **VERY COMPETITIVE +**

Beloit College, founded in 1846, is an independent, coeducational, liberal arts institute. The library contains 229,433 volumes, 140,976 microform items, and 1846 audiovisual forms, and subscribes to 928 periodicals. Computerized library sources and services include the card catalog, interlibrary loans, and database searching. Special learning facilities include a learning resource center, art gallery, natural history museum, planetarium, radio station, TV station, a comprehensive language laboratory, and a theater complex. The 40-acre campus is in a small town 50 miles south of Madison and 90 miles northwest of Chicago, Illinois. Including residence halls, there are 50 buildings on campus.

Student Life: About 78% of undergraduates are from out-of-state, mostly the Midwest. Students come from 49 states, 42 foreign countries, and Canada. Eighty percent are from public schools; 20% from private. Eighty-two percent are white. Thirty percent are Protestant; 20% Catholic; 10% Jewish. The average age of freshmen is 18; all undergraduates, 20. Three percent drop out by the end of their first year; 68% remain to graduate.

Housing: A total of 982 students can be accommodated in college housing. College-sponsored living facilities include single-sex and coed dormitories, fraternity houses, and sorority houses. In addition, there are language houses and special interest houses. On-campus housing is guaranteed for all 4 years and is available on a lottery system for upperclassmen. Ninety-two percent of students live on campus; of those, 100% remain on campus on weekends. All students may keep cars on campus.

Activities: About 10% of men belong to 4 national fraternities; about 5% of women belong to 2 local sororities. There are 87 groups on campus, including art, band, choir, chorus, computers, dance, drama, ethnic, film, gay, honors, international, jazz band, literary magazine, musical theater, newspaper, orchestra, pep band, photography, political, radio and TV, religious, social, social service, student government, symphony, and yearbook. Popular campus events include Great Lecture Series, Folk and Blues Weekend, Spring Day, and Student Symposium Day.

Sports: There are 11 intercollegiate sports for men and 10 for women, and 15 intramural sports for men and 13 for women. Athletic and recreation facilities include a new $6 million sports center, racquetball and indoor tennis courts, a dance room, a fitness center, a batting/pitching cage, an all-weather track, a football stadium, and many outdoor playing fields.

Disabled Students: Twenty percent of the campus is accessible to disabled students. The following facilities are available: wheelchair ramps, elevators, special parking, and specially equipped rest rooms.

Services: In addition to many counseling and information services, tutoring is available in most subjects, including most introductory and some advanced courses.

Campus Safety and Security: Campus safety and security measures include 24-hour foot and vehicle patrol, escort service, informal discussions, and pamphlets, posters, and films. In addition, there are emergency telephones and lighted pathways and sidewalks.

Programs of Study: The College awards the B.A. and B.S. degrees. Master's degrees also are awarded. Bachelor's degrees are awarded in BIOLOGICAL SCIENCE (biochemistry and biology/biological science), BUSINESS (business administration and management), COMMUNICATIONS AND THE ARTS (art history and appreciation, English, French, German, languages, music, Russian, Spanish, and studio art), COMPUTER AND PHYSICAL SCIENCE (chemistry, computer science, geology, mathematics, and physics), EDUCATION (art, elementary, science, and secondary), SOCIAL SCIENCE (anthropology, economics, history, international relations, philosophy, political science/government, psychology, religion, and sociology). Anthropology, English, geology, and economics management are the strongest programs academically. Economics management, English, and psychology have the largest enrollments.

Required: To graduate, students must complete 31 units or 124 credit hours, with 8 to 13 units in the major, and a minimum GPA of 2.0. Distribution requirements include 2 courses each from natural sciences and mathematics, social sciences, and arts and humanities. A writing requirement, submission of a comprehensive academic plan, and an interdisciplinary minor, second major, teaching certification, or 3-2, 2-2, or 4-2 cooperative program are also needed.

Special: The college offers cross-registration with the University of Wisconsin/Madison, internships, study abroad in 29 countries, and a Washington semester. Dual majors, student-designed and interdiscipli-

nary majors, and nondegree study are available. Students may take a 3-2 M.B.A. program with the University of Chicago and Washington University, and a 2-2 nursing program and a 3-2 medical technology program with Rush University. A 3-2 engineering degree is offered with 9 institutions, and co-op programs are available in social services, forestry and environmental management, engineering, nursing, medical technology, and business administration. An intensive summer language program is offered in Chinese, Japanese, Hungarian, and Russian. There are 6 national honor societies on campus, including Phi Beta Kappa.

Faculty/Classroom: Seventy percent of faculty are male; 30%, female. All teach undergraduates, and do research. No introductory courses are taught by graduate students. The average class size in an introductory lecture is 17; in a laboratory, 16; and in a regular course offering, 13.

Admissions: About 77% of the 1993-94 applicants were accepted. The SAT scores for the 1993-94 freshman class were as follows: Verbal—25% below 500, 42% between 500 and 599, 30% between 600 and 700, and 3% above 700; Math—15% below 500, 44% between 500 and 599, 30% between 600 and 700, and 11% above 700. The ACT scores were 10% below 21, 18% between 21 and 23, 26% between 24 and 26, 22% between 27 and 28, and 25% above 28. About 43% of the current freshmen were in the top fifth of their class; 80% were in the top two fifths. There were 5 National Merit finalists and 11 semifinalists. Eleven freshmen graduated first in their class.

Requirements: The SAT I or ACT is required. SAT II: Subject tests are recommended. In addition, applicants must be graduates of an accredited secondary school, with 4 years of English, 3 years each of mathematics and science, and 2 years each of foreign language and social studies. The GED is accepted. An essay is required, and an interview is recommended. AP and CLEP credits are accepted. Important factors used in the admissions decision are extracurricular activities record, leadership record, personality, intangible qualities, evidence of special talent, and advanced placement or honor courses.

Procedure: Freshmen are admitted fall and spring. Entrance exams should be taken before Christmas of the senior year. Early decision applications should be filed by December 15; regular applications, by March 15 for fall entry, along with an application fee of $25. Notification of early decision is sent January 15; regular decision, on a rolling basis. There are early decision, early admissions, and deferred admissions plans. About 24 early decision candidates were accepted for the 1993-94 class.

Transfer: About 40 transfer students enrolled in 1993-94. Applicants for transfer must have a minimum GPA of 2.0. The SAT I or ACT is required, and an interview is recommended. A total of 16 credits out of 31 must be completed at the College.

Visiting: There are regularly scheduled orientations for prospective students, including a tour, class visits, and meeting with professors, including an interview. There are guides for informal visits and visitors may sit in on classes and stay overnight at the school. To arrange for a visit, contact the Admissions Office at (608) 363-2500 or (800) 356-0751 (out-of-state).

Financial Aid: In 1993-94, 83% of all current freshmen and 84% of continuing students received some form of financial aid. About 73% of freshmen and 71% of continuing students received need-based aid. The average freshman award was $11,996. Of that total, scholarships or need-based grants averaged $9138 ($16,550 maximum); loans averaged $1761 ($2625 maximum); and work contracts averaged $1097 ($1350 maximum). Seventy-five percent of undergraduate students work part-time. Average earnings from campus work for the school year are $856. The average financial indebtedness of the 1992-93 graduate was $8130. The College is a member of CSS. The FAF, or FFS, or SFS, or the college's own financial statement, and the FAFSA are required. The FAF is preferred. The deadline for financial aid applications is April 15.

International Students: There are currently 122 international students enrolled. The school actively recruits these students. They must take the TOEFL and achieve a minimum score of 525. The student must also take the SAT I and a school leaving exam/certificate from selected countries.

Computers: The college provides computer facilities for student use. The mainframes are IBM RISC/6000's Models H340 and H320. Students can use the networked computers for E-mail purposes, class programming purposes, which include Logic, FORTRAN, Pascal, and statistical packages, and specific departmental programs. Students can access the networks via more than 27 terminal servers and PCs throughout the campus; there are numerous computer laboratories. All students may access the system at any time. There are no time limits and no fees.

Graduates: In 1992-93, 222 bachelor's degrees were awarded. The most popular majors among graduates were economics and management (13%), anthropology (11%), and literary studies (9%). Within an average freshman class, 56% graduate in 4 years, 64% in 5 years, and 68% in 6 years. Some 81 companies recruited on campus in 1992-93. In a recent graduating class, 30% of the students were enrolled in graduate school within 6 months of graduation; 53% of the men and 44% of the women had found employment.

Admissions Contact: James Zielinski, Director of School and College Relations.

CARDINAL STRITCH COLLEGE

E-4

Milwaukee, WI 53217-3985

(414) 351-7504

(800) 347-8822 (out-of-state)

Full-time: 938 men, 1465 women	Faculty: 65; IIB, -$
Part-time: 106 men, 255 women	Ph.Ds: 50%
Graduate: 742 men, 2133 women	Student/Faculty: 37 to 1
Year: semesters, summer session	Tuition: $7772
Application Deadline: August 15	Room & Board: $3480
Freshman Class: 343 applied, 272 accepted, 172 enrolled	
ACT: 21	**COMPETITIVE**

Cardinal Stritch College, founded in 1937, is a private, Catholic, co-educational institution sponsored by the Sisters of St. Francis. There is one graduate school. In addition to regional accreditation, Stritch has baccalaureate program accreditation with NCATE and NLN. The library contains 113,391 volumes, 97,383 microform items, and 8419 audiovisual forms, and subscribes to 1114 periodicals. Computerized library sources and services include the card catalog, interlibrary loans, and database searching. Special learning facilities include a learning resource center and art gallery. The 40-acre campus is in a suburban area 10 miles north of Milwaukee. Including residence halls, there are 9 buildings on campus.

Student Life: About 78% of undergraduates are from Wisconsin. Students come from 15 states and 6 foreign countries. Sixty percent are from public schools; 40% from private. Ninety-one percent are white. Sixty-five percent are Catholic; 25% Protestant. The average age of freshmen is 21; all undergraduates, 33. Twenty percent drop out by the end of their first year; 55% remain to graduate.

Housing: A total of 300 students can be accommodated in college housing. College-sponsored living facilities include coed dormitories. On-campus housing is available on a first-come, first-served basis. Ninety percent of students commute and all students may keep cars on campus.

Activities: There are no fraternities or sororities. There are 50 groups on campus, including art, cheerleading, choir, computers, drama, international, newspaper, photography, political, professional, religious, social, social service, student government, and yearbook. Popular campus events include Thursday night events and weekly activities, such as sporting events, plays, or other activities.

Sports: There are 3 intercollegiate sports each for men and women, and 7 intramural sports for each. Athletic and recreation facilities include basketball and volleyball courts, a batting cage, an indoor track, a weight and exercise room, and an area for table tennis and billiards.

Disabled Students: Eighty percent of the campus is accessible to disabled students. The following facilities are available: elevators, special parking, specially equipped rest rooms, special class scheduling, and lowered telephones.

Services: In addition to many counseling and information services, tutoring is available in every subject. There is also remedial math, reading, and writing.

Campus Safety and Security: Campus safety and security measures include 24-hour foot and vehicle patrol, informal discussions, pamphlets, posters, and films, and lighted pathways and sidewalks.

Programs of Study: Stritch awards the B.A., B.S. and B.F.A. degrees. Associate and master's degrees also are awarded. Bachelor's degrees are awarded in BIOLOGICAL SCIENCE (biology/biological science), BUSINESS (accounting, business administration and management, and international business management), COMMUNICATIONS AND THE ARTS (art, communications, dramatic arts, English, fine arts, French, and Spanish), COMPUTER AND PHYSICAL SCIENCE (chemistry, computer science, and mathematics), EDUCATION (early childhood, elementary, middle school, secondary, and special), HEALTH PROFESSIONS (nursing and premedicine), SOCIAL SCIENCE (history, prelaw, psychology, religion, social science, and sociology). Education in general and special education in particular are the strongest programs academically. Business has the largest enrollment.

Required: To graduate, students must complete 128 credits, 34 to 72 in the major, with a GPA of at least 2.0. Required disiciplines include history, foreign language, literature, written communication, and communication arts. Five courses are required in humanities, 3 in social/behavioral sciences, 2 each in communication arts and written communication, and 1 each in mathematics and natural science. An English proficiency examination must be taken.

Special: Students may participate in a variety of internships with Milwaukee business and organizations. Stritch offers an accelerated degree program and a B.A.-B.S. degree in business, dual majors, a general studies degree, and nondegree study. There is study abroad, work-study programs, pass/fail options, and credit for life, military, and work experience. An accelerated evening program and a management program are offered for working adults.

Faculty/Classroom: Thirty percent of faculty are male; 70%, female. All teach undergraduates and do research. No introductory courses are taught by graduate students. The average class size in an introductory lecture is 20; in a laboratory, 10; and in a regular course offering, 14.

Admissions: About 79% of the 1993-94 applicants were accepted. The ACT scores for the 1993-94 freshman class were as follows: 33% below 21, 35% between 21 and 23, 20% between 24 and 26, 7% between 27 and 28, and 6% above 28. About 29% of the current freshmen were in the top fifth of their class; 53% were in the top two fifths. There was 1 National Merit finalist. Two freshmen graduated first in their class.

Requirements: Stritch requires applicants to be in the upper 50% of their class. A minimum GPA of 2.0 is required. The SAT I or ACT is required, with the recommended minimum composite score of 18 on the ACT or 780 on the SAT I. Applicants must be graduates of an accredited secondary school, with 16 academic credits, including 4 years of English and 2 years each of mathematics and social studies. The GED is accepted. Stritch requires an essay and recommends an interview. AP and CLEP credits are accepted. Important factors used in the admissions decision are leadership record, evidence of special talent, recommendations by school officials, advanced placement or honor courses, and extracurricular activities record.

Procedure: Freshmen are admitted to all sessions. Entrance exams should be taken as early as possible. Applications should be filed by August 15 for fall entry, along with an application fee of $20. Notification is sent on a rolling basis. There are early decision, early admissions, and deferred admissions plans.

Transfer: About 250 transfer students enrolled in a recent year. Applicants for transfer should have a minimum GPA of 2.0. A total of 32 credits out of 128 must be completed at Stritch.

Visiting: There are regularly scheduled orientations for prospective students. There are guides for informal visits and visitors may sit in on classes and stay overnight at the school. To arrange for a visit, contact the Admissions Office at (414) 351-7504.

Financial Aid: In a recent year, 79% of all current freshmen and 75% of continuing students received some form of financial aid. About 70% of freshmen and 65% of continuing students received need-based aid. The average freshman award was $6328. Of that total, scholarships or need-based grants averaged $4091 ($9960 maximum); loans averaged $1857 ($2625 maximum); and work contracts averaged $380 ($1500 maximum). About 90% of undergraduate students work part-time. Average earnings from campus work for the school year are $850. The average financial indebtedness of a recent graduate was $1500. Stritch is a member of CSS. The FAF is required. The deadline for financial aid applications is August 1.

International Students: There are currently 22 international students enrolled. They must take the TOEFL and achieve a minimum score of 600. The student must also take the SAT I, ACT, or the college's own entrance exam and achieve a minimum score of 780 on the SAT I or 18 on the ACT.

Computers: The college provides computer facilities for student use. Students have free and unlimited use of about 50 microcomputers on campus, including IBM, Macintosh, and Apple varieties. There are no time limits on using the system and no fees.

Graduates: In a recent year, 510 bachelor's degrees were awarded. The most popular majors among graduates were business (60%), education (9%), and nursing (8%). Within an average freshman class, 55% graduate in 5 years. Some 10 companies recruited on campus in a recent year. In the graduating class, 8% of the men and women were enrolled in graduate school within 6 months of graduation; 92% found employment.

Admissions Contact: David Wegener, Director of Admissions.

CARROLL COLLEGE

D-5

Waukesha, WI 53186

(414) 524-7220

(800) CARROLL (out-of-state)

Full-time: 485 men, 872 women	Faculty: 71
Part-time: 225 men, 512 women	Ph.Ds: 77%
Graduate: 12 men, 48 women	Student/Faculty: 19 to 1
Year: 4-1-4, summer session	Tuition: $11,790
Application Deadline: open	Room & Board: $3700
Freshman Class: 1160 applied, 991 accepted, 352 enrolled	
ACT: 23	**COMPETITIVE**

Carroll College, founded in 1846, is an independent, coeducational, liberal arts institution affiliated with the Presbyterian Church. There is one graduate school. The library contains 184,590 volumes, 15,650 microform items, and 300 audiovisual forms, and subscribes to 570 periodicals. Computerized library sources and services include the card catalog and interlibrary loans. Special learning facilities include a learning resource center, art gallery, radio station, studio theater, and a recital hall. The 52-acre campus is in a suburban area 15 miles west of Milwaukee. Including residence halls, there are 29 buildings on campus.

Student Life: About 90% of undergraduates are from Wisconsin. Students come from 14 states and 6 foreign countries. Eighty-nine percent are from public schools; 11% from private. Eighty-nine percent are white. Forty-six percent are Protestant; 43% Catholic; 12% claim no religious affiliation. The average age of freshmen is 18; all

undergraduates, 20. Twenty-five percent drop out by the end of their first year; 67% remain to graduate.

Housing: A total of 943 students can be accommodated in college housing. College-sponsored living facilities include single-sex and coed dormitories, on-campus apartments, off-campus apartments, and fraternity houses. On-campus housing is guaranteed for all 4 years. Fifty-eight percent of students live on campus. All students may keep cars on campus.

Activities: About 16% of men belong to 1 local and 3 national fraternities; about 16% of women belong to 4 national sororities. There are 59 groups on campus, including art, band, cheerleading, choir, chorale, chorus, computers, drama, ethnic, honors, international, jazz band, literary magazine, musical theater, newspaper, orchestra, photography, political, professional, radio and TV, religious, social, social service, student government, symphony, and yearbook. Popular campus events include Homecoming, Black History Month, International Folk Fair, Cinco de Mayo, Madrigal Dinner, Confrontation Lecture Series, Parents Weekend, and Spring Fling.

Sports: There are 10 intercollegiate sports for men and 8 for women, and 10 intramural sports each. Athletic and recreation facilities include a campus center, 2 sand volleyball courts, 1 all-purpose field house, 1 small gymnasium, 3 tennis courts, a 6-lane pool, a football field, a practice field, pool tables, a dart machine, and video games.

Disabled Students: Twenty percent of the campus is accessible to disabled students. The following facilities are available: wheelchair ramps, elevators, special parking, and specially equipped rest rooms.

Services: In addition to many counseling and information services, tutoring is available in most subjects. There is also remedial math, reading, and writing.

Campus Safety and Security: Campus safety and security measures include 24-hour foot and vehicle patrol, escort service, emergency telephones, and lighted pathways and sidewalks.

Programs of Study: Carroll awards the B.A., B.S., B.S.M.T., and B.S.N. degrees. Master's degrees also are awarded. Bachelor's degrees are awarded in BIOLOGICAL SCIENCE (biology/biological science), BUSINESS (accounting, business administration and management, business economics, marketing/retailing/merchandising, and personnel management), COMMUNICATIONS AND THE ARTS (communications, dramatic arts, English, fine arts, French, German, journalism, languages, music, and Spanish), COMPUTER AND PHYSICAL SCIENCE (chemistry, computer science, mathematics, and physics), EDUCATION (art, early childhood, elementary, foreign languages, music, science, and secondary), ENGINEERING AND ENVIRONMENTAL DESIGN (engineering), HEALTH PROFESSIONS (nursing, predentistry, and premedicine), SOCIAL SCIENCE (cognitive science, criminal justice, economics, geography, history, international relations, philosophy, physical fitness/movement, political science/government, prelaw, psychology, religion, social work, and sociology). Sciences, business, computer science, and psychology are the strongest programs academically. Business and communication have the largest enrollments.

Required: To graduate, students must complete 128 credit hours, 32 to 40 in the major, with a minimum GPA of 2.0. Students must take 2 courses each in natural science, social science, and humanities, and 1 each in fine arts, language skills, and religion. A 2-part Common Course is required of all students during the January term of their first 2 years. Two credit computer science courses and a mathematics course are needed for the B.S.; 2 years of foreign language is needed for the B.A.

Special: Internships may be taken during January or regular terms in the junior and senior years. Study abroad in Cannes, France or Nottingham, England is available for the junior year. A Washington semester at American University and a United Nations semester are offered, as are some accelerated degree programs, B.A.-B.S. degrees, dual and individually designed majors, and a self-determined curriculum. Students may take a 3-2 engineering degree with Marquette University. Under the New Cultural Experience Program, juniors and seniors travel during the January term to places that are culturally different from their own, such as Latin America, Africa, or Asia. There is a freshman honors program on campus, as well as 5 national honor societies.

Faculty/Classroom: Seventy-three percent of faculty are male; 27%, female. Ninety-eight percent teach undergraduates and do research. No introductory courses are taught by graduate students. The average class size in an introductory lecture is 25; in a laboratory, 18; and in a regular course offering, 20.

Admissions: About 85% of the 1993–94 applicants were accepted. The ACT scores for the 1993–94 freshman class were as follows: 36% below 21, 33% between 21 and 23, 20% between 24 and 26, 6% between 27 and 28, and 5% above 28. About 46% of the current freshmen were in the top fifth of their class; 75% were in the top two fifths. There were 2 National Merit finalists. Seven freshmen graduated first in their class.

Requirements: Carroll requires applicants to be in the upper 50% of their class. A minimum GPA of 2.0 is required. The SAT I or ACT is required. In addition, applicants must be graduates of an accredited secondary school. The GED is accepted. An essay and interview are recommended for all students, and a portfolio or audition is advised for art and music students, respectively. AP and CLEP credits

are accepted. Important factors used in the admissions decision are advanced placement or honor courses, personality, intangible qualities, evidence of special talent, leadership record, and extracurricular activities record.

Procedure: Freshmen are admitted to all sessions. Entrance exams should be taken during the junior year. Application deadlines are open. Notification is sent on a rolling basis. There is a deferred admissions plan.

Transfer: About 164 transfer students enrolled in 1993–94. Applicants for transfer must have a minimum GPA of 2.0. An interview is recommended. A total of 32 credits out of 128 must be completed at Carroll.

Visiting: There are regularly scheduled orientations for prospective students. There are guides for informal visits and visitors may sit in on classes and stay overnight at the school. To arrange for a visit, contact the Office of Admissions at (414) 524–7220.

Financial Aid: In 1993–94, 90% of all current freshmen and 88% of continuing students received some form of financial aid. About 88% of freshmen and 80% of continuing students received need-based aid. The average freshman award was $11,734. Of that total, scholarships or need-based grants averaged $8545 ($16,000 maximum); loans averaged $2594 ($2625 maximum); and work contracts averaged $595 ($1000 maximum). Forty-one percent of undergraduate students work part-time. Average earnings from campus work for the school year are $875. The average financial indebtedness of the 1992–93 graduate was $7200. Carroll is a member of CSS. The college's own financial statement, FAFSA, and federal tax forms are required. The deadline for financial aid applications is April 1.

International Students: There are currently 18 international students enrolled. They must take the TOEFL and achieve a minimum score of 550.

Computers: The college provides computer facilities for student use. The mainframe is an HP 9000. There are also 175 Apple Macintosh, IBM-compatible PCs, and work stations located throughout the campus on a campuswide Ethernet. All students may access the system. It may be used 24 hours every day. There are no time limits on using the system and no fees.

Graduates: In a recent year, 371 bachelor's degrees were awarded. The most popular majors among graduates were business (22%), nursing (13%), and communication/education (8%). Some 12 companies recruited on campus in 1992–93. In the 1992 graduating class, 24% of the men and 76% of the women were enrolled in graduate school within 6 months of graduation; 18% of the men and 82% of the women had found employment.

Admissions Contact: Debra Morgan, Director of Admission, Traditional Students.

CARTHAGE COLLEGE
E-5
Kenosha, WI 53140   (800) 351–4058 (out-of-state)

Full-time: 642 men, 762 women	Faculty: 85; IIB, -$
Part-time: 179 men, 391 women	Ph.D.s: 89%
Graduate: 11 men, 47 women	Student/Faculty: 17 to 1
Year: 4-1-4, summer session	Tuition: $12,400
Application Deadline: May 1	Room & Board: $3595
Freshman Class: 1583 applied, 1430 accepted, 438 enrolled	
ACT: 22	COMPETITIVE

Carthage College, founded in 1847, is an independent, liberal arts institution affiliated with the Evangelical Lutheran Church in America. In addition to regional accreditation, Carthage has baccalaureate program accreditation with CSWE and NASM. The library contains 208,539 volumes, 21,352 microform items, and 662 audiovisual forms, and subscribes to 1081 periodicals. Computerized library sources and services include database searching. Special learning facilities include a learning resource center and art gallery. The 75-acre campus is in a suburban area 30 miles south of Milwaukee and 1 hour north of Chicago, Illinois, on the shore of Lake Michigan. Including residence halls, there are 12 buildings on campus.

Student Life: About 64% of undergraduates are from Wisconsin. Students come from 24 states, 7 foreign countries, and Canada. Eighty percent are from public schools; 20% from private. Ninety-one percent are white. Fifty-eight percent are Protestant; 27% Catholic. The average age of freshmen is 18. Twenty-eight percent drop out by the end of their first year; 60% remain to graduate.

Housing: A total of 1188 students can be accommodated in college housing. College-sponsored living facilities include single-sex and coed dormitories. In addition, there are study-intensive floors. On-campus housing is guaranteed for all 4 years. Eighty percent of students live on campus; of those, 65% remain on campus on weekends. Alcohol is not permitted. All students may keep cars on campus.

Activities: About 18% of men belong to 5 local and 3 national fraternities; about 25% of women belong to 4 local sororities. There are 60 groups on campus, including art, band, cheerleading, choir, drama, ethnic, honors, international, jazz band, literary magazine, newspaper, orchestra, pep band, political, professional, religious, social, social service, student government, and yearbook. Popular campus events include May Madness, Casino Night, and Jestures.

Sports: There are 9 intercollegiate sports for men and 8 for women, and 13 intramural sports for men and 12 for women. Athletic and recreation facilities include a physical education center, a 3000-seat stadium, a 3500-seat gymnasium, tennis courts, and a natatorium.

Disabled Students: About 90% of the campus is accessible to disabled students. The following facilities are available: wheelchair ramps, elevators, special parking, specially equipped rest rooms, special class scheduling, lowered drinking fountains, and TDD phones.

Services: In addition to many counseling and information services, tutoring is available in most subjects.

Campus Safety and Security: Campus safety and security measures include 24-hour foot and vehicle patrol, self defense education, escort service, and informal discussions. In addition, there are pamphlets, posters, and films, emergency telephones, lighted pathways and sidewalks, and electronic exit locks on residence halls.

Programs of Study: Carthage awards the B.A. degree. Master's degrees also are awarded. Bachelor's degrees are awarded in BIOLOGICAL SCIENCE (biology/biological science), BUSINESS (accounting, business administration and management, international business management, marketing/retailing/merchandising, and sports management), COMMUNICATIONS AND THE ARTS (design, dramatic arts, English, fine arts, French, German, languages, music, Spanish, and visual and performing arts), COMPUTER AND PHYSICAL SCIENCE (chemistry, mathematics, natural sciences, and physics), EDUCATION (art, elementary, foreign languages, middle school, music, physical, science, secondary, and social studies), ENGINEERING AND ENVIRONMENTAL DESIGN (preengineering), HEALTH PROFESSIONS (medical laboratory technology, occupational therapy, physical therapy, predentistry, premedicine, and prepharmacy), SOCIAL SCIENCE (criminal justice, economics, geography, history, philosophy, political science/government, prelaw, psychology, religion, social science, social work, and sociology). Education, business, and sciences are the strongest programs academically. Business and education have the largest enrollments.

Required: To graduate, students must complete 136 credits, with 60 in the major, and a minimum GPA of 2.0. Students must complete 48 credits in liberal arts studies, including the Heritage Seminar Series, which includes 4 courses that cover history, philosophy, literature, and communication in depth.

Special: Internships are available during the January term or, in some cases, for a semester. Carthage offers study abroad, a general studies degree, and dual and student-designed majors. Students may take a 3–2 engineering degree with Case Western Reserve and Washington universities and the University of Wisconsin/Madison. There are pass/fail options and credit for life, military, and work experience. There is a freshman honors program on campus, as well as 2 national honor societies. Seventeen departments have honors programs.

Faculty/Classroom: Seventy-one percent of faculty are male; 29%, female. No introductory courses are taught by graduate students. The average class size in an introductory lecture is 25; in a laboratory, 12; and in a regular course offering, 15.

Admissions: About 90% of the 1993–94 applicants were accepted. The ACT scores for the freshman class were as follows: 40% below 21, 23% between 21 and 23, 20% between 24 and 26, 12% between 27 and 28, and 5% above 28. About 34% of the current freshmen were in the top fifth of their class; 62% were in the top two fifths.

Requirements: A minimum GPA of 2.0 is required. The SAT I or ACT is required. In addition, applicants should be graduates of an accredited secondary school, having earned 14 academic credits, including 4 years of English and 2 years each of history, mathematics, science, and social studies. The GED is accepted. An interview is recommended. AP and CLEP credits are accepted. Important factors used in the admissions decision are advanced placement or honor courses, evidence of special talent, leadership record, personality, intangible qualities, and extracurricular activities record.

Procedure: Freshmen are admitted to all sessions. Entrance exams should be taken in spring of the junior year or fall of the senior year. Early decision applications should be filed by October 1; regular applications, by May 1 for fall entry, December 15 for spring entry, and June 1 for summer entry, along with an application fee of $25. Notification of early decision is sent on a rolling basis after October 1. There are early decision, early admissions, and deferred admissions plans.

Transfer: About 100 transfer students enrolled in a recent year. Transfer students are accepted based on academic performance at their previous school; they should have a GPA greater than 2.0. If they have fewer than 12 credits, the high school record is considered. Either the SAT I or ACT, and an interview are recommended. A total of 32 credits out of 136 must be completed at Carthage.

Visiting: There are regularly scheduled orientations for prospective students. There are guides for informal visits and visitors may sit in on classes and stay overnight at the school. To arrange for a visit, contact the Office of Admissions at (800) 351-4058.

Financial Aid: In 1993–94, 95% of all current freshmen and 81% of continuing students received some form of financial aid. About 69% of freshmen and 74% of continuing students received need-based aid. The average freshman award was $10,100. Of that total, scholarships or need-based grants averaged $3700 ($15,995 maxi-

mum); loans averaged $2426 ($2625 maximum); and work contracts averaged $1200 ($1500 maximum). Forty-seven percent of undergraduate students work part-time. Average earnings from campus work for the school year are $1236. Carthage is a member of CSS. The college's own financial statement and FAFSA are required. The deadline for financial aid applications is February 15.

International Students: There are currently 20 international students enrolled. The school actively recruits these students. They must take the TOEFL and achieve a minimum score of 500.

Computers: The college provides computer facilities for student use. The mainframe is an IBM AS400. There are also 66 Apple II, Apple Macintosh, and IBM PS/2 PCs available in academic buildings. All students may access the system. It may be used 24 hours. There are no time limits on using the system and no fees.

Graduates: In 1992–93, 277 bachelor's degrees were awarded. The most popular majors among graduates were business (30%), education (15%), and social sciences (10%). Within an average freshman class, 50% graduate in 4 years and 60% in 5 years. Some 25 companies recruited on campus in 1992–93. In the 1992 graduating class, 19% of the men and 16% of the women were enrolled in graduate school within 6 months of graduation; 87% of the men and 93% of the women had found employment.

Admissions Contact: Brenda A. Porter, Vice President for Enrollment.

COLUMBIA COLLEGE OF NURSING D-5
Milwaukee, WI 53211 (414) 524-7225

Full-time: 15 men, 218 women	Faculty: 114
Part-time: 16 men, 137 women	Ph.D.s: n/av
Graduate: none	Student/Faculty: n/av
Year: 4-1-4, summer session	Tuition: $11,940
Application Deadline: open	Room & Board: $3260
Freshman Class: 152 applied, 112 accepted, 91 enrolled	
ACT: 20	**COMPETITIVE**

Columbia College of Nursing is a private institution that offers an intercollegiate program in nursing with Carroll College, the nursing degree being granted jointly by both schools. In addition to regional accreditation, CCN has baccalaureate program accreditation with NLN. The library contains 177,491 volumes and 8285 microform items, and subscribes to 572 periodicals. Special learning facilities include a learning resource center. The campus is in an urban area on Milwaukee's east side, 30 minutes from the Carroll College campus in Waukesha. There is 1 building on campus.

Student Life: About 90% of undergraduates are from Wisconsin. Students come from 5 states and 2 foreign countries. Seventy percent are from public schools; 30% from private. Eighty-nine percent are white. Fifty percent are Protestant; 50% Catholic. About 68% of freshmen remain to graduate.

Housing: A total of 75 students can be accommodated in college housing. College-sponsored living facilities include coed dormitories for upper-level students. Eighty-five percent of students live on campus; of those, 50% remain on campus on weekends. Alcohol is not permitted. All students may keep cars on campus.

Activities: About 33% of men belong to 2 local and 2 national fraternities; about 33% of women belong to 4 national sororities. There are 60 groups on campus, including band, cheerleading, choir, chorale, chorus, drama, drill team, international, jazz band, marching band, musical theater, newspaper, orchestra, pep band, political, professional, religious, social, student government, symphony, and yearbook. Popular campus events include Homecoming, International Multicultural Day, and Black History Week.

Sports: There are 8 intercollegiate sports for men and 5 for women, and 4 intramural sports each for men and women. Athletic and recreation facilities include a natatorium, a gymnasium, a field house, tennis courts, and a weight room.

Disabled Students: The following facilities are available: elevators, special parking, specially equipped rest rooms, and lowered drinking fountains.

Services: In addition to many counseling and information services, tutoring is available in every subject. The learning resource center works one-on-one with students.

Programs of Study: CCN awards the B.S.N. degree. Bachelor's degrees are awarded in HEALTH PROFESSIONS (nursing).

Required: Students must complete a minimum of 130 credits, with 56 of these credits in the nursing major, and must maintain a minimum GPA of 2.0. All students must also complete the general education requirements, which include courses in English, religion, computational skills, fine arts, humanities, physical education, science, and social science.

Special: Opportunities are provided for work-study programs, credit by examination, and pass/fail options.

Faculty/Classroom: The average class size in an introductory lecture is 25; in a laboratory, 20; and in a regular course offering, 25.

Admissions: About 74% of the 1993–94 applicants were accepted. About 30% of the current freshmen were in the top fifth of their class; 68% were in the top two fifths. There was 1 National Merit finalist and 2 semifinalists. Two freshmen graduated first in their class.

Requirements: The SAT I or ACT is required, as well as graduation from an accredited secondary school; a GED will be accepted. Applicants should submit an academic record indicating preparation in algebra, chemistry, and biology. An essay and an interview are recommended. AP and CLEP credits are accepted. Important factors used in the admissions decision are evidence of special talent, advanced placement or honor courses, leadership record, personality, intangible qualities, and extracurricular activities record.

Procedure: Freshmen are admitted to all sessions. Application deadlines are open. Notification is sent on a rolling basis.

Transfer: Twelve transfer students enrolled in 1993–94. Transfers to Carroll/Columbia nursing programs are expected to demonstrate high school preparation in algebra, chemistry, and biology and have a minimum of 2.0 in transferable work. SAT I or ACT scores are not required of transfer students. Students are judged on the basis of transferable college work. A total of 32 credits out of 130 must be completed at CCN.

Visiting: There are regularly scheduled orientations for prospective students. There are guides for informal visits and visitors may sit in on classes and stay overnight at the school. To arrange for a visit, contact the Admissions Office at (414) 524–7220 or (800) 547–1233 (out-of-state).

Financial Aid: In a recent year, 90% of all current freshmen and 90% of continuing students received some form of financial aid. CCN is a member of CSS. The FAF or FFS, the college's own financial statement, and copies of tax returns are required. The deadline for financial aid applications is March 15.

International Students: There is currently 1 international student enrolled. Students must take the TOEFL and achieve a minimum score of 500.

Computers: The college provides computer facilities for student use. Microcomputers are available in computer centers at both Carroll and Columbia. All students may access the system. There are no time limits on using the system and no fees.

Graduates: In an earlier year, 106 bachelor's degrees were awarded. Some 25 companies recruited on campus that year. All graduates of that class had found employment within 6 months of graduation.

Admissions Contact: Debra L. Morgan, Director of Traditional Admission, Carroll College.

CONCORDIA UNIVERSITY WISCONSIN
Mequon, WI 53097

E-4
(414) 243–4300

Full-time: 665 men, 925 women	Faculty: 67; IIB, -$
Part-time: 160 men, 220 women	Ph.D.s: 48%
Graduate: 40 men, 70 women	Student/Faculty: 24 to 1
Year: 4–1–4, summer session	Tuition: $8740
Application Deadline: August 1	Room & Board: $3400
Freshman Class: 1105 applied, 892 accepted, 230 enrolled	
SAT I or ACT: required	COMPETITIVE

Concordia University Wisconsin, established in 1881, is a private coeducational institution affiliated with the Lutheran Church-Missouri Synod. There are 4 undergraduate schools and one graduate school. In addition to regional accreditation, Concordia has baccalaureate program accreditation with NLN. The library contains 80,000 volumes, 135,000 microform items, and 2150 audiovisual forms, and subscribes to 750 periodicals. Computerized library sources and services include the card catalog, interlibrary loans, and database searching. Special learning facilities include a learning resource center, art gallery, radio station, and and a curriculum library for education students. The 126-acre campus is in a suburban area 15 miles north of Milwaukee. Including residence halls, there are 14 buildings on campus.

Student Life: About 60% of undergraduates are from Wisconsin. Students come from 19 states and 25 foreign countries. Eighty-six percent are white. Eighty percent are Protestant; 13% Catholic. The average age of freshmen is 18; all undergraduates, 21. Twenty-five percent drop out by the end of their first year; 42% remain to graduate.

Housing: A total of 650 students can be accommodated in college housing. College-sponsored living facilities include single-sex dormitories. On-campus housing is guaranteed for all 4 years and is available on a lottery system for upperclassmen. Fifty-seven percent of students live on campus; of those, 50% remain on campus on weekends. Alcohol is not permitted. All students may keep cars on campus.

Activities: There are no fraternities or sororities on campus. There are 16 groups on campus, including art, band, cheerleading, choir, chorale, drama, ethnic, honors, international, jazz band, literary magazine, musical theater, newspaper, pep band, political, professional, radio and TV, religious, student government, and yearbook. Popular campus events include Homecoming, Winterfest, and Springfest.

Sports: There are 9 intercollegiate sports for men and 7 for women, and 10 intramural sports for men and 9 for women. Athletic and recreation facilities include a field house, a stadium, and a gymnasium.

Disabled Students: Eighty percent of the campus is accessible to disabled students. The following facilities are available: wheelchair ramps, elevators, special parking, and specially equipped rest rooms.

Services: In addition to many counseling and information services, tutoring is available in every subject. There is also a reader service for the blind, and remedial math, reading, and writing.

Campus Safety and Security: Campus safety and security measures include security guards on staff from 4 P.M. to 8 A.M. on weekdays, and 24 hours a day on weekends.

Programs of Study: Concordia awards the B.A., B.S., and B.S.N. degrees. Associate and master's degrees also are awarded. Bachelor's degrees are awarded in AGRICULTURE (agricultural business management), BIOLOGICAL SCIENCE (biology/biological science), BUSINESS (accounting, court reporting, and management science), COMMUNICATIONS AND THE ARTS (communications, English, and music), COMPUTER AND PHYSICAL SCIENCE (mathematics), EDUCATION (art, business, elementary, and secondary), ENGINEERING AND ENVIRONMENTAL DESIGN (electrical/electronics engineering and interior design), HEALTH PROFESSIONS (nursing and occupational therapy), SOCIAL SCIENCE (biblical languages, history, humanities, ministries, paralegal studies, psychology, religion, social science, and social work). Education, business, and nursing are the strongest programs academically. Education and business have the largest enrollments.

Required: To graduate, students must complete 126 credits, at least 30 in the major, with a minimum GPA of 2.0. The 44 1/2 credit core curriculum includes theology/philosophy, humanities, cross culture, social science, natural science, communication, mathematics, and physical education. Incoming students must take Higher Education: A New Experience.

Special: Internships, study abroad, pass/fail options, and credit for life, military, and work experience are available. Concordia offers a general studies degree, dual, student-designed, and interdisciplinary majors, including justice and public policy, a 3–2 engineering degree, and nondegree study. There is 1 national honor society on campus.

Faculty/Classroom: Sixty-nine percent of faculty are male; 31%, female. All teach undergraduates and 40% both teach and do research. No introductory courses are taught by graduate students. The average class size in an introductory lecture is 30; in a laboratory, 24; and in a regular course offering, 25.

Admissions: About 81% of the 1993–94 applicants were accepted. The ACT scores for the 1993–94 freshman class were as follows: 55% below 21, 23% between 21 and 23, 13% between 24 and 26, 5% between 27 and 28, and 5% above 28. About 21% of the current freshmen were in the top fifth of their class; 44% were in the top two fifths. About 5 freshmen graduated first in their class.

Requirements: A minimum GPA of 2.3 is required. Either the SAT I with a minimum composite score of 730, or the ACT, with a minimum composite score of 16, is required. Applicants must be graduates of an accredited secondary school, having completed 16 academic credits, including 3 of English and 2 each of mathematics, science, and social studies. The GED is accepted. AP and CLEP credits are accepted. Important factors used in the admissions decision are personality, intangible qualities, advanced placement or honor courses, recommendations by school officials, evidence of special talent, and extracurricular activities record.

Procedure: Freshmen are admitted to all sessions. Entrance exams should be taken in the junior year. Applications should be filed by August 1 for fall entry, along with an application fee of $25. Notification is sent on a rolling basis.

Transfer: Applicants for transfer must have a minimum GPA of 2.0 and meet the same entrance exam criteria as entering freshmen. A total of 36 credits out of 126 must be completed at Concordia.

Visiting: There are regularly scheduled orientations for prospective students, including a tour and financial aid and academic information sessions. There are guides for informal visits and visitors may sit in on classes and stay overnight at the school. To arrange for a visit, contact the Admission Office at (414) 243–4300.

Financial Aid: In a recent year, 90% of all current freshmen and 89% of continuing students received some form of financial aid. Scholarships or need-based grants averaged $900 ($6800 maximum); loans averaged $1500 ($2625 maximum); and work contracts averaged $600 ($1400 maximum). The average financial indebtedness of the 1992–93 graduate was $7035. The FAF, the college's own financial statement and income tax forms are required. The deadline for financial aid applications is May 1.

International Students: There are currently 85 international students enrolled. The school actively recruits these students. They must take the TOEFL and achieve a minimum score of 500.

Computers: The college provides computer facilities for student use. There are HP Vectra, IBM, and Apple microcomputers available to all students throughout the campus. All students may access the system. There are no limits or fees.

Graduates: In a recent year, 175 bachelor's degrees were awarded. Within an average freshman class, 42% graduate in 4 years and 75% in 5 years.

Admissions Contact: Dawn Cochran, Admission Counselor.

EDGEWOOD COLLEGE
C-4
Madison, WI 53711   (608) 257–4861; (800) 444–4861 (out-of-state)

Full-time: 224 men, 603 women	Faculty: 53
Part-time: 153 men, 412 women	Ph.D.s: 68%
Graduate: 174 men, 223 women	Student/Faculty: 16 to 1
Year: 4–1-4, summer session	Tuition: $8100
Application Deadline: August 1	Room & Board: $3600
Freshman Class: 375 applied, 311 accepted, 173 enrolled	
ACT: 21	COMPETITIVE

Edgewood College, established in 1927, is a private Catholic institution sponsored by the Sinsinawa Dominican Sisters. There are 27 undergraduate and 3 graduate schools. In addition to regional accreditation, Edgewood has baccalaureate program accreditation with AACSB and NCATE. The library contains 60,794 volumes, 81,224 microform items, 3391 audiovisual forms, and subscribes to 470 periodicals. Computerized library sources and services include the card catalog and database searching. Special learning facilities include a learning resource center and art gallery. The 55-acre campus is in a suburban area 5 miles southwest of Madison. Including residence halls, there are 8 buildings on campus.

Student Life: About 85% of undergraduates are from Wisconsin. Students come from 13 foreign countries and Canada. Seventy-five percent are from public schools; 25% from private. Seventy-eight percent are white. Forty-four percent are Catholic; 29% claim no religious affiliation; 17% Protestant. The average age of freshmen is 18. Twenty-two percent drop out by the end of their first year; 45% remain to graduate.

Housing: A total of 275 students can be accommodated in college housing. College-sponsored living facilities include single-sex and coed dormitories and on-campus apartments. On-campus housing is guaranteed for all 4 years. Seventy-five percent of students commute. Alcohol is not permitted. All students may keep cars on campus.

Activities: There are no fraternities or sororities. There are 20 groups on campus, including art, band, cheerleading, choir, chorale, chorus, drama, ethnic, honors, international, musical theater, newspaper, political, religious, social service, and student government. Popular campus events include Springfest and Amnesty International Day.

Sports: There are 5 intercollegiate sports each for men and women, and 2 intramural sports each. Athletic and recreation facilities include a 1000-seat gymnasium.

Disabled Students: Eighty percent of the campus is accessible to disabled students. The following facilities are available: elevators, special parking, specially equipped rest rooms, automated doors in the library, activities center, and residence halls.

Services: In addition to many counseling and information services, tutoring is available in some subjects, including most sciences, introductory mathematics courses, and Spanish. There is a reader service for the blind, and remedial math, reading, and writing.

Campus Safety and Security: Campus safety and security measures include escort service, shuttle buses, informal discussions, and pamphlets, posters, and films. In addition, there are lighted pathways and sidewalks. Residence halls have alarms, and campus security guards are on duty 24 hours a day weekends and 8 P.M. to 4 A.M. weekdays.

Programs of Study: Edgewood awards the B.A. and B.S. degrees. Associate and master's degrees also are awarded. Bachelor's degrees are awarded in BIOLOGICAL SCIENCE (biology/biological science), BUSINESS (accounting, business administration and management, and marketing/retailing/merchandising), COMMUNICATIONS AND THE ARTS (English, fine arts, French, music, performing arts, and Spanish), COMPUTER AND PHYSICAL SCIENCE (chemistry, computer science, information sciences and systems, mathematics, and natural sciences), EDUCATION (art, early childhood, elementary, and middle school), HEALTH PROFESSIONS (art therapy, cytotechnology, medical laboratory technology, and nursing), SOCIAL SCIENCE (child psychology/development, criminal justice, economics, history, political science/government, psychology, public administration, religion, and sociology). Business, education, and nursing are the strongest programs academically and have the largest enrollments.

Required: To graduate, students must complete 120 credit hours with a minimum GPA of 2.0. There are general education requirements, and each student must complete a human issues study.

Special: Students may cross-register with the University of Wisconsin/Madison. Internships, study abroad, B.A.-B.S. degrees, dual and student-designed majors, nondegree study, pass/fail options, and credit for life, military, and work experience are available. There is a weekend degree program. There is a freshman honors program on campus, as well as 5 national honor societies. The honors program is college wide.

Faculty/Classroom: Fifty-one percent of faculty are male; 49%, female. Ninety-two percent teach undergraduates and 6% both teach and do research. No introductory courses are taught by graduate students. The average class size in an introductory lecture is 22; in a laboratory, 15; and in a regular course offering, 17.

Admissions: About 83% of the 1993–94 applicants were accepted. The ACT scores for the 1993–94 freshman class were as follows: 4% below 21, 27% between 21 and 23, 17% between 24 and 26, 5% between 27 and 28, and 3% above 28. Three freshmen graduated first in their class.

Requirements: Edgewood requires applicants to be in the upper 60% of their class. A minimum GPA of 2.0 is required. The ACT or SAT I is required, with a minimum composite score of 17 on the ACT recommended. Applicants should complete 16 Carnegie units, including 4 of English, 3 each of mathematics and electives, and 2 each of foreign language, science, and social studies. The GED is accepted. AP and CLEP credits are accepted. Important factors used in the admissions decision are leadership record, advanced placement or honor courses, extracurricular activities record, recommendations by school officials, and evidence of special talent.

Procedure: Freshmen are admitted to all sessions. Entrance exams should be taken by the senior year. Applications should be filed by August 1 for fall entry and December 15 for spring entry, along with an application fee of $25. Notification is sent on a rolling basis.

Transfer: About 190 transfer students enrolled in 1993–94. Applicants for transfer must have a minimum GPA of 2.0. A total of 32 credits out of 120 must be completed at Edgewood.

Visiting: There are regularly scheduled orientations for prospective students, including 2 open houses per year. There are guides for informal visits and visitors may sit in on classes and stay overnight at the school. To arrange for a visit, contact the Admissions Office at (608) 257–4861 or (800) 444–4861.

Financial Aid: In 1993–94, 85% of all current freshmen and 80% of continuing students received some form of financial aid. About 72% of freshmen and 68% of continuing students received need-based aid. The average freshman award was $7593. Of that total, scholarships or need-based grants averaged $4700 ($8000 maximum); loans averaged $2500 ($4000 maximum); and work contracts averaged $1400 ($2000 maximum). Twenty-five percent of undergraduate students work part-time. Average earnings from campus work for the school year are $1360. The average financial indebtedness of the 1992–93 graduate was $10,500. Edgewood is a member of CSS. The FAF, the college's own financial statement and a tax return are required. The deadline for financial aid applications is April 1.

International Students: There are currently 58 international students enrolled. The school actively recruits these students. They must take the TOEFL or the University of Michigan Language Test and achieve a minimum score on the TOEFL of 525.

Computers: The college provides IBM and Apple computer facilites for student use. The computer center in Regina Hall houses 30 computers. All students may access the system. It may be used 8 A.M. to 10 P.M. There are no time limits on using the system and no fees.

Graduates: In 1992–93, 94 bachelor's degrees were awarded. The most popular majors among graduates were business (33%), nursing (16%), and education (14%). Within an average freshman class, 33% graduate in 4 years, 43% in 5 years, and 45% in 6 years. Some 45 companies recruited on campus in 1992–93. In the 1992 graduating class, 20% were enrolled in graduate school within 6 months of graduation.

Admissions Contact: Kevin C. Kucera, Director of Admissions and Financial Aid.

LAKELAND COLLEGE
E-4
Sheboygan, WI 53082–0359
(414) 565–1217
(800) 242–3347 (in-state)

Full-time: 310 men, 378 women	Faculty: 52; IIB, -$
Part-time: 24 men, 29 women	Ph.D.s: 62%
Graduate: 6 men, 26 women	Student/Faculty: 13 to 1
Year: 4–1-4	Tuition: $9145
Application Deadline: August 15	Room & Board: $3700
Freshman Class: 278 applied, 253 accepted, 129 enrolled	
ACT: 20	LESS COMPETITIVE

Lakeland College, established in 1862, is a private, coeducational institution affiliated with the United Church of Christ. The library contains 62,047 volumes, 25,283 microform items, and 489 audiovisual forms, and subscribes to 284 periodicals. Computerized library sources and services include interlibrary loans and database searching. Special learning facilities include a learning resource center, an art gallery, and a radio station. The 240-acre campus is in a rural area 10 miles northwest of Sheboygan. Including residence halls, there are 16 buildings on campus.

Student Life: About 90% of undergraduates are from Wisconsin. Students come from 13 states and 8 foreign countries. Ninety percent are from public schools; 10% from private. Ninety-two percent are white. Thirty-two percent are Protestant; 29% Catholic; 25% claim no religious affiliation. Thirty percent drop out by the end of their first year; 50% remain to graduate.

Housing: A total of 480 students can be accommodated in college housing. College-sponsored living facilities include single-sex and coed dormitories and on-campus apartments. In addition, there are honors and language houses and suites. On-campus housing is guar-

anteed for all 4 years. Sixty percent of students live on campus; of those, 60% remain on campus on weekends. All students may keep cars on campus.

Activities: About 12% of men belong to 3 local fraternities; about 5% of women belong to 2 local sororities. There are 25 groups on campus, including art, band, cheerleading, choir, chorale, chorus, computers, drama, ethnic, honors, international, jazz band, literary magazine, newspaper, pep band, political, professional, radio and TV, religious, social, social service, student government, and yearbook. Popular campus events include Homecoming, Orientation, Winter Beach Blow Out, Family Day, Winter Carnival, May Celebration, Christmas at Lakeland, Black History Month, Martin Luther King Celebration, and Women's Awareness.

Sports: There are 8 intercollegiate sports for men and 6 for women, and 14 intramural sports each for men and women. Athletic and recreation facilities include a $4 million sports complex, a fitness laboratory, numerous locker rooms for students and staff, 3 full-size basketball courts, a weight room, indoor and outdoor tennis courts, softball, baseball, football, soccer, and practice fields, and indoor pitching and batting facilities.

Disabled Students: Fifty percent of the campus is accessible to disabled students. The following facilities are available: wheelchair ramps, elevators, special parking, specially equipped rest rooms, and lowered drinking fountains.

Services: In addition to many counseling and information services, tutoring is available in every subject. There is also a reader service for the blind, and remedial math, reading, and writing.

Campus Safety and Security: Campus safety and security measures include shuttle buses, informal discussions, pamphlets, posters, films, and emergency telephones. In addition, there are lighted pathways and sidewalks and foot patrol on weekends and evenings.

Programs of Study: Lakeland awards the B.A. degree. Master's degrees also are awarded. Bachelor's degrees are awarded in BUSINESS (accounting, business administration and management, business economics, and hospitality management services), COMMUNICATIONS AND THE ARTS (creative writing, English, German, and music), COMPUTER AND PHYSICAL SCIENCE (chemistry, computer science, and mathematics), EDUCATION (early childhood, elementary, foreign languages, music, and secondary), ENGINEERING AND ENVIRONMENTAL DESIGN (agricultural engineering, chemical engineering, civil engineering, electrical/electronics engineering, geological engineering, industrial engineering, materials engineering, mechanical engineering, and nuclear engineering), SOCIAL SCIENCE (economics, history, philosophy, psychology, public administration, religion, social work, and sociology). Business, education, accounting, writing, and sciences are the strongest programs academically. Business, accounting, and computer science have the largest enrollments.

Required: To graduate, students must complete 136 semester hours, with at least 32 in the major and a minimum 2.0 GPA. There are requirements in history, humanities, natural sciences, social sciences, and religion. Students must take a course each year in the Critical Thinking Curriculum.

Special: Internships in all majors, study abroad in Germany and Japan, a Washington semester, and work-study programs are available. There are B.A.-B.S. degrees in all areas, some dual majors, a general studies degree, a 3–2 engineering degree with the University of Wisconsin/Madison, and nondegree study. There is a freshman honors program on campus. Ten departments have honors programs.

Faculty/Classroom: Sixty-four percent of faculty are male; 36%, female. All faculty teach and do research. No introductory courses are taught by graduate students. The average class size in an introductory lecture is 25; in a laboratory, 5; and in a regular course offering, 20.

Admissions: About 91% of the 1993–94 applicants were accepted. The ACT scores for the 1993–94 freshman class were as follows: 51% below 21, 28% between 21 and 23, 14% between 24 and 26, 4% between 27 and 28, and 3% above 28. About 31% of the current freshmen were in the top fifth of their class; 57% were in the top two fifths. Four freshmen graduated first in their class.

Requirements: Lakeland requires applicants to be in the upper 50% of their class. A minimum GPA of 2.0 is required. The SAT I or ACT is required; the ACT is recommended, with a minimum composite score of 19 needed. Applicants must be graduates of an accredited secondary school or have the GED. An interview is recommended. AP and CLEP credits are accepted. Important factors used in the admissions decision are advanced placement or honor courses, leadership record, evidence of special talent, extracurricular activities record, personality, and intangible qualities.

Procedure: Freshmen are admitted in the fall, winter, and spring. Entrance exams should be taken after the enrollment deposit is paid. Applications should be filed by August 15 for fall entry, January 1 for winter entry, and January 15 for spring entry, along with an application fee of $20. Notification is sent on a rolling basis.

Transfer: About 93 transfer students enrolled in a recent year. Applicants for transfer should have a GPA of at least 2.0. Lakeland recommends the ACT, with a minimum score of 19, and an interview. A total of 40 semester hours out of 136 must be completed at Lakeland.

Visiting: There are regularly scheduled orientations for prospective students, consisting of a 2-day agenda. There are guides for informal visits and visitors may sit in on classes and stay overnight at the school. To arrange for a visit, contact the Admissions Office at (414) 565–1217 or (800) 242–3347.

Financial Aid: In 1993–94, 95% of all current freshmen and 92% of continuing students received some form of financial aid. About 90% of all students received need-based aid. The average freshman award was $9061. Of that total, scholarships or need-based grants averaged $5830 ($9145 maximum); loans averaged $2131 ($2625 maximum); and work contracts averaged $1100 (maximum). Forty percent of undergraduate students work part-time. Average earnings from campus work for the school year are $1200. The FAF is required. The deadline for financial aid applications is July 1.

International Students: There are currently 25 international students enrolled. The school actively recruits these students. They must take the TOEFL and achieve a minimum score of 500. The student must also take the SAT I or ACT, and 3 placement tests in writing, reading, or mathematics.

Computers: The college provides computer facilities for student use. The mainframe is a DEC VAX 11/730. The VAX laboratory has 8 terminals available 7 days a week and has dial-in access. The library houses 6 Apple IIes, and the microcomputer laboratory houses 6 Apple IIes and 12 IBM-compatibles. All students may access the system during the hours posted. There are no time limits and no fees.

Graduates: The most popular majors among graduates were business administration (23%), psychology (11%), and accounting (10%). Within an average freshman class, 5% graduate in 3 years, 40% in 4 years, 42% in 5 years, and 13% in 6 years. In the 1992 graduating class, 9% of the men and 7% of the women were enrolled in graduate school within 6 months of graduation.

Admissions Contact: Leo Gavrilos, Director of Admissions.

LAWRENCE UNIVERSITY D-3

Appleton, WI 54912   (414) 832–6500; (800) 227–0982 (out-of-state)

Full-time: 548 men, 614 women	Faculty: 105; IIB, +$
Part-time: 19 men, 30 women	Ph.D.s: 92%
Graduate: none	Student/Faculty: 11 to 1
Year: terms	Tuition: $16,431
Application Deadline: February 1	Room & Board: $3555

Freshman Class: 1242 applied, 947 accepted, 324 enrolled
SAT I: 540/610   **ACT:** 28   **HIGHLY COMPETITIVE +**

Lawrence University, founded in 1847, is an independent liberal arts institution with a conservatory of music. In addition to regional accreditation, Lawrence has baccalaureate program accreditation with NASM. The library contains 326,135 volumes, 102,011 microform items, and 15,922 audiovisual forms, and subscribes to 1297 periodicals. Computerized library sources and services include the card catalog, interlibrary loans, and database searching. Special learning facilities include a learning resource center, art gallery, natural history museum, and radio station. The 84-acre campus is in an urban area 100 miles north of Milwaukee. Including residence halls, there are 38 buildings on campus.

Student Life: About 58% of undergraduates are from out-of-state, mostly the Midwest. Students come from 46 states, 44 foreign countries, and Canada. Seventy-nine percent are from public schools; 21% from private. Eighty-two percent are white; 10% foreign nationals. The average age of freshmen is 18; all undergraduates, 20. Ten percent drop out by the end of their first year; 76% remain to graduate.

Housing: A total of 1220 students can be accommodated in college housing. College-sponsored living facilities include single-sex and coed dormitories, on-campus apartments, married-student housing, and fraternity houses. In addition, there are language houses and special interest houses. On-campus housing is guaranteed for all 4 years. Ninety-seven percent of students live on campus; most remain on campus on weekends. All students may keep cars on campus.

Activities: About 42% of men belong to 5 national fraternities; about 24% of women belong to 3 national sororities. There are 120 groups on campus, including art, band, cheerleading, choir, chorale, chorus, computers, dance, drama, ethnic, film, gay, honors, international, jazz band, literary magazine, musical theater, newspaper, opera, orchestra, photography, political, professional, religious, social, social service, student government, symphony, and yearbook. Popular campus events include Octoberfest, Celebrate! Spring Festival of the Arts, and Annual Midwest Trivia Contest.

Sports: There are 13 intercollegiate sports for men and 10 for women, and 28 intramural sports each. Athletic and recreation facilities include a 5255-seat football stadium; 8-lane all-weather and 4-lane indoor tracks; baseball, soccer, practice fields; 9 tennis, 2 squash, and 3 racquetball/handball courts; a gymnasium for basketball, volleyball, and badminton; 2 batting cages; an 8-lane swimming pool with diving well; weight, exercise, and sauna rooms; and a dance studio.

Disabled Students: Eighty percent of the campus is accessible to disabled students. The following facilities are available: wheelchair ramps, elevators, special parking, specially equipped rest rooms, and special class scheduling.

Services: In addition to many counseling and information services, tutoring is available in every subject. There is also a reader service for the blind and remedial math and writing.

Campus Safety and Security: Campus safety and security measures include 24-hour foot and vehicle patrol, self defense education, escort service, and informal discussions. In addition, there are pamphlets, posters, and films, emergency telephones, lighted pathways and sidewalks, and the Whistle Stop Program.

Programs of Study: Lawrence awards the B.A. and B.Mus. degrees. Bachelor's degrees are awarded in BIOLOGICAL SCIENCE (biology/biological science and neurosciences), COMMUNICATIONS AND THE ARTS (art history and appreciation, classics, dramatic arts, English, French, German, linguistics, music performance, music theory and composition, Slavic languages, Spanish, and studio art), COMPUTER AND PHYSICAL SCIENCE (chemistry, computer science, geology, mathematics, and physics), EDUCATION (art, music, and secondary), ENGINEERING AND ENVIRONMENTAL DESIGN (environmental science), SOCIAL SCIENCE (anthropology, East Asian studies, economics, history, international relations, philosophy, political science/government, psychology, and religion). Biology, English, psychology, economics, government, history, and music have the largest enrollments.

Required: Students must complete 36 term course credits, including 7 to 12 in the major, with a minimum GPA of 2.0. The B.A. requires 5 course credits from the areas of language, humanities, and arts and 5 from the social sciences, mathematics, and natural sciences. The B.Mus. requires that two thirds of courses are in the conservatory and that one third are in subjects other than music. All students must take Freshman Studies, a 2-course sequence described as a microcosm of the liberal arts.

Special: Lawrence offers cooperative programs with Duke University in forestry and environmental studies and with the University of Chicago in social services administration. Also available are Chicago-based programs in urban studies, urban education, and the arts, and a science internship at Oak Ridge National Laboratory and a biological field station in Minnesota. There are study-abroad programs in 13 countries, a Washington semester, limited pass/fail options, student-designed majors, and nondegree study. Students may take a 3–2 engineering degree with Columbia or Washington universities, Rensselaer Polytechnic Institute, or the University of Michigan. A 5-year B.A.-B.Mus. degree is offered. There are 8 national honor societies on campus, including Phi Beta Kappa. Twenty-one departments have honors programs.

Faculty/Classroom: Seventy-three percent of faculty are male; 27%, female. All teach undergraduates. The average class size in an introductory lecture is 29; in a laboratory, 14; and in a regular course offering, 14.

Admissions: About 76% of the 1993–94 applicants were accepted. The SAT scores for the 1993–94 freshman class were as follows: Verbal—28% below 500, 36% between 500 and 599, 32% between 600 and 700, and 4% above 700; Math—16% below 500, 30% between 500 and 599, 38% between 600 and 700, and 16% above 700. The ACT scores were 5% below 21, 17% between 21 and 23, 18% between 24 and 26, 17% between 27 and 28, and 44% above 28. About 70% of the current freshmen were in the top fifth of their class; 91% were in the top two fifths. There were 12 National Merit finalists. About 28 freshmen graduated first in their class.

Requirements: The SAT I or ACT is required. In addition, applicants should complete 16 high school academic credits. Lawrence requires an essay, reports from a teacher and counselor, and, for music majors, an audition. The school recommends the SAT II: English with an essay, an interview, and, for art majors, a portfolio. AP credits are accepted. Important factors used in the admissions decision are advanced placement or honor courses, evidence of special talent, leadership record, personality, intangible qualities, and extracurricular activities record.

Procedure: Freshmen are admitted in the fall. Entrance exams should be taken in the spring of the junior year or fall of the senior year. Early decision applications should be filed by November 15 and January 1; regular applications, by February 1 for fall entry, along with an application fee of $25. Notification of early decision is sent December 1 and January 15; regular decision, April 1. There are early decision, early admissions, and deferred admissions plans. About 74 early decision candidates were accepted for the 1993–94 class. A waiting list is an active part of the admissions procedure, with about 6% of applicants on the list.

Transfer: About 18 transfer students enrolled in 1993–94. Applicants must present official transcripts of their college and secondary school work, SAT I or ACT scores, and the recommendation of a college professor. Typically, candidates with a college GPA of 2.75 or higher will receive serious consideration. A total of 18 course credits out of 36 must be completed at Lawrence.

Visiting: There are guides for informal visits and visitors may sit in on classes and stay overnight at the school. To arrange for a visit, contact the Office of Admissions at (800) 227-0982.

Financial Aid: In 1993–94, 87% of all current freshmen and 85% of continuing students received some form of financial aid. About 65% of freshmen and 61% of continuing students received need-based aid. The average freshman award was $15,484. Of that total,

scholarships or need-based grants averaged $9901 ($16,566 maximum); loans averaged $2385 ($5625 maximum); and work contracts averaged $1082 ($1400 maximum). Seventy percent of undergraduate students work part-time. Average earnings from campus work for the school year are $1200. The average financial indebtedness of the 1992–93 graduate was $11,500. Lawrence is a member of CSS. The college's own financial statement and the FAFSA are required. The deadline for financial aid applications is March 15.

International Students: There are currently 104 international students enrolled. The school actively recruits these students. They must take the TOEFL and achieve a minimum score of 575. The student must also take the SAT I or the ACT.

Computers: The college provides computer facilities for student use. The mainframe is a DEC VAX 6210. There are also about 60 terminals and 60 PCs distributed around the campus in residence halls and academic buildings. Each residence hall room has PC access to the mainframe, computerized library services, Bitnet, and Internet. All students may access the system. It may be used 24 hours a day. There are no time limits on using the system and no fees.

Graduates: In 1992–93, 234 bachelor's degrees were awarded. The most popular majors among graduates were biology (12%), English (9%), and psychology (7%). Within an average freshman class, 65% graduate in 4 years, 73% in 5 years, and 75% in 6 years. Some 24 companies recruited on campus in 1992–93. In the 1992 graduating class, 27% of the men and women were enrolled in graduate school within 6 months of graduation; 70% found employment.

Admissions Contact: Susan Dean, Director of Admissions.

MARIAN COLLEGE OF FOND DU LAC   D-4
Fond du Lac, WI 54935   (414) 923-7650

(800) 2-MARIAN (in-state)

Full-time: 422 men, 744 women	**Faculty:** 78; IIB, --$
Part-time: 261 men, 392 women	**Ph.D.s:** 37%
Graduate: 216 men, 434 women	**Student/Faculty:** 15 to 1
Year: semesters, summer session	**Tuition:** $8650
Application Deadline: open	**Room & Board:** $3600
Freshman Class: 700 applied, 670 accepted, 338 enrolled	
ACT: 20	**COMPETITIVE**

Marian College, founded in 1936, is a private Roman Catholic institution offering degree programs in the arts and sciences, business, education, and health fields. There are 2 graduate schools. In addition to regional accreditation, Marian has baccalaureate program accreditation with CSWE, NCATE, and NLN. The library contains 95,000 volumes and 5629 microform items, and subscribes to 690 periodicals. Computerized library sources and services include the card catalog, interlibrary loans, and database searching. Special learning facilities include a learning resource center. The 50-acre campus is in a small town 60 miles north of Milwaukee. Including residence halls, there are 14 buildings on campus.

Student Life: About 90% of undergraduates are from Wisconsin. Students come from 12 states, 4 foreign countries, and Canada. Some 70% are from public schools; 30% from private. Nearly 95% are white. About 60% are Catholic; 40% Protestant. The average age of freshmen is 18. Nearly 16% drop out by the end of their first year; 59% remain to graduate.

Housing: A total of 420 students can be accommodated in college housing. College-sponsored living facilities include single-sex and coed dormitories, on-campus apartments, and fraternity houses. On-campus housing is guaranteed for all 4 years. About 55% of students live on campus; of those, 70% remain on campus on weekends. All students may keep cars on campus.

Activities: About 1% of men belong to 1 national fraternity; about 1% of women belong to 1 national sorority. There are 15 groups on campus, including band, cheerleading, choir, chorus, drama, ethnic, honors, international, jazz band, literary magazine, newspaper, orchestra, photography, professional, religious, social, social service, student government, symphony, and yearbook. Popular campus events include Heritage Festival of Arts, Fine Arts Series, Germanfest, Sabre Show, Jazz/Swing Choir, and business and industry events.

Sports: There are 6 intercollegiate sports for men and 6 for women, and 5 intramural sports for men and 5 for women. Athletic and recreation facilities include a soccer field, a softball field, a gymnasium, tennis courts, a game room, a hockey rink, and a weight room.

Disabled Students: About 90% of the campus is accessible to disabled students. The following facilities are available: wheelchair ramps, elevators, special parking, specially equipped rest rooms, special class scheduling, lowered drinking fountains, and lowered telephones.

Services: In addition to many counseling and information services, tutoring is available in every subject. There is also a reader service for the blind, and remedial math, reading, and writing.

Campus Safety and Security: Campus safety and security measures include escort service, informal discussions, pamphlets, posters, and films, and emergency telephones. In addition, there are lighted pathways and sidewalks.

Programs of Study: Marian awards the B.A., B.S., B.B.A., B.S.B.A., B.S.Ed., B.S.M.T., B.S.N., B.S.R.T., and B.S.W. degrees. Master's degrees also are awarded. Bachelor's degrees are awarded in BIOLOGICAL SCIENCE (biology/biological science), BUSINESS (accounting, business administration and management, management science, marketing/retailing/merchandising, and sports management), COMMUNICATIONS AND THE ARTS (art, communications, English, and music), COMPUTER AND PHYSICAL SCIENCE (chemistry, mathematics, and radiological technology), EDUCATION (art, business, early childhood, elementary, middle school, music, and secondary), HEALTH PROFESSIONS (cytotechnology, medical laboratory technology, and nursing), SOCIAL SCIENCE (criminal justice, history, human services, psychology, social work, and theological studies). Nursing, education, and business are the strongest programs academically. Nursing, education, and business have the largest enrollments.

Required: To graduate, students must complete 128 credits with a minimum GPA of 2.0. Core requirements include 24 credits in arts and humanities, 12 to 13 in social behavioral science, and 12 in mathematics and natural science, as well as a freshman seminar.

Special: Internships are offered in most areas of study, cooperative programs in all majors, and accelerated-degree programs in nursing, business administration, quality management, and operation management. Student-designed and dual majors, credit for prior learning, work-study, nondegree study, and cooperative education (paid work experience) are available. Study abroad at Harlexton College, England, is possible. There are evening degree completion programs for working adults. There is 1 national honor society on campus.

Faculty/Classroom: About 40% of faculty are male; 60%, female. All teach undergraduates. No introductory courses are taught by graduate students. The average class size in an introductory lecture is 25; in a laboratory, 20; and in a regular course offering, 25.

Admissions: About 96% of the 1993–94 applicants were accepted. The ACT scores for the 1993–94 freshman class were as follows: 39% below 21, 53% between 21 and 23, and 8% between 24 and 26. About 20% of the current freshmen were in the top fifth of their class; 45% were in the top two fifths. Five freshmen graduated first in their class.

Requirements: Marian requires applicants to be in the upper 50% of their class. A minimum GPA of 2.0 is required. The ACT is required, with a minimum composite score of 18. Applicants must be graduates of an accredited secondary school or have earned a GED. An interview is recommended. AP and CLEP credits are accepted. Important factors used in the admissions decision are evidence of special talent, advanced placement or honor courses, leadership record, personality, intangible qualities, and recommendations by school officials.

Procedure: Freshmen are admitted to all sessions. Entrance exams should be taken in the junior year. Application deadlines are open. Application fee is $15. Notification is sent on a rolling basis. There are early admissions and deferred admissions plans.

Transfer: About 150 transfer students enrolled in 1993–94. The school recommends a minimum GPA of 2.0, the SAT I or ACT, and an interview. A total of 32 credits out of 128 must be completed at Marian.

Visiting: There are regularly scheduled orientations for accepted students, consisting of sessions in April, May, June, and July for course selection and meeting with advisors. There are guides for informal visits and visitors may sit in on classes and stay overnight at the school. To arrange for a visit, contact the Admissions Office at (414) 923-7650.

Financial Aid: In 1993–94, 85% of all current freshmen and continuing students received some form of financial aid. Marian is a member of CSS. The college's own financial statement and the FAFSA are required. The deadline for financial aid applications is March 15.

International Students: There are currently 5 international students enrolled. They must take the TOEFL and achieve a minimum score of 525. The student must also take a standardized entrance exam, preferably the ACT.

Computers: The college provides computer facilities for student use. The mainframe is an IBM. There are 75 IBM and Apple microcomputers available, as well as word-processing equipment. Those students enrolled in computer-related courses may access the system. There are no time limits on using the system and no fees.

Graduates: In a recent year, 251 bachelor's degrees were awarded. The most popular majors among graduates were business (38%), nursing (34%), and education (30%). Within an average freshman class, 62% graduate in 4 years.

Admissions Contact: Carol Reichenberger, Vice President for Enrollment Services.

MARQUETTE UNIVERSITY
E-4

Milwaukee, WI 53233–9981

(414) 288–7302

(800) 222–6544 (out-of-state)

Full-time: 3409 men, 3620 women	**Faculty:** 490; I, -$
Part-time: 410 men, 381 women	**Ph.D.s:** 94%
Graduate: 1722 men, 1222 women	**Student/Faculty:** 14 to 1
Year: semesters, summer session	**Tuition:** $10,884
Application Deadline: open	**Room & Board:** $5230
Freshman Class: 5152 applied, 4600 accepted, 1685 enrolled	
SAT I: 490/560	**ACT:** 25 **VERY COMPETITIVE**

Marquette University, established in 1881, is a private Roman Catholic, coeducational institution. There are 7 undergraduate and 4 graduate schools. In addition to regional accreditation, Marquette has baccalaureate program accreditation with AACSB, ABET, ACEJMC, ADA, APTA, ASLA, CSWE, NCATE, and NLN. The 3 libraries contain 971,791 volumes, 362,178 microform items, and 3898 audiovisual forms, and subscribe to 9689 periodicals. Computerized library sources and services include the card catalog, interlibrary loans, and database searching. Special learning facilities include a learning resource center, art gallery, radio station, and TV station. The 80-acre campus is in an urban area 70 miles north of Chicago. Including residence halls, there are 48 buildings on campus.

Student Life: About 53% of undergraduates are from Wisconsin. Students come from 50 states, 64 foreign countries, and Canada. About 55% are from public schools; 46% from private. Some 84% are white. Nearly 63% are Catholic; 19% Protestant. The average age of freshmen is 18; all undergraduates, 21. Some 15% drop out by the end of their first year; 75% remain to graduate.

Housing: A total of 3800 students can be accommodated in college housing. College-sponsored living facilities include single-sex and coed dormitories, on-campus apartments, and married-student housing. In addition, there are honors houses. On-campus housing is guaranteed for all 4 years and is available on a lottery system for upperclassmen. About 55% of students commute. All students may keep cars on campus.

Activities: About 7% of men belong to 10 national fraternities; about 7% of women belong to 8 national sororities. There are 156 groups on campus, including art, band, cheerleading, chess, choir, chorale, chorus, computers, dance, drama, drill team, ethnic, honors, international, jazz band, literary magazine, musical theater, newspaper, orchestra, pep band, photography, political, professional, radio and TV, religious, social, social service, student government, and yearbook. Popular campus events include Homecoming, basketball games, Spring Thaw, Student Organization Fest, Senior Week, Labor Day Festival, P.A.R.T.Y. Week, Freshman Orientation, and Greek Olympics.

Sports: There are 8 intercollegiate sports for men and 7 for women, and 30 intramural sports for men and 30 for women. Athletic and recreation facilities include a multirecreation center.

Disabled Students: About 80% of the campus is accessible to disabled students. The following facilities are available: wheelchair ramps, elevators, special parking, specially equipped rest rooms, special class scheduling, lowered drinking fountains, and lowered telephones. Book-taping and note-taking are also available.

Services: In addition to many counseling and information services, tutoring is available in most subjects. There is also a reader service for the blind, and remedial math, reading, and writing.

Campus Safety and Security: Campus safety and security measures include 24-hour foot and vehicle patrol, self defense education, escort service, and shuttle buses. In addition, there are informal discussions, pamphlets, posters, and films, emergency telephones, lighted pathways and sidewalks, and closed-circuit cameras in selected parking lots.

Programs of Study: Marquette awards the B.A., B.S., and B.S.N. degrees. Associate, master's, and doctoral degrees also are awarded. Bachelor's degrees are awarded in BIOLOGICAL SCIENCE (biochemistry, biology/biological science, and molecular biology), BUSINESS (accounting, banking and finance, business administration and management, business economics, human resources, international business management, management information systems, management science, marketing/retailing/merchandising, and personnel management), COMMUNICATIONS AND THE ARTS (advertising, broadcasting, communications, dramatic arts, English, French, German, journalism, public relations, Spanish, and speech/debate/rhetoric), COMPUTER AND PHYSICAL SCIENCE (chemistry, computer science, information sciences and systems, mathematics, physics, and statistics), EDUCATION (elementary, secondary, social foundations, and social science), ENGINEERING AND ENVIRONMENTAL DESIGN (biomedical engineering, civil engineering, computer engineering, electrical/electronics engineering, engineering, environmental engineering, industrial engineering technology, and mechanical engineering), HEALTH PROFESSIONS (dental hygiene, medical laboratory technology, nursing, physical therapy, and speech pathology/audiology), SOCIAL SCIENCE (anthropology, criminal justice, criminology, economics, history, interdisciplinary studies, international relations, philosophy, political science/government, psychology, religion/theology, social science, social work, and sociolo-

gy). Mechanical engineering, accounting, electrical engineering, nursing, and psychology have the largest enrollments.

Required: Depending on the field of study, undergraduates complete 50 to 75 semester hours in general education requirements distributed among various academic areas, including English composition, history, mathematics, foreign languages, natural sciences, philosophy and the fine arts. To graduate, students must complete 126 to 136 credits.

Special: Marquette offers internships, study abroad, a Washington summer term, and work-study programs. Dual and student-designed majors, nondegree study, and pass/fail options are available. The Freshman Frontier Program is an academic support program for selected entering freshmen who do not meet regular admission requirements but show potential for success. The Educational Opportunity Program affords students from minority groups and low-income families the opportunity to attend the school. There is a freshman honors program on campus, as well as 13 national honor societies, including Phi Beta Kappa.

Faculty/Classroom: About 72% of faculty are male; 28%, female. All teach undergraduates, 94% do research, and 94% do both.

Admissions: About 89% of the 1993–94 applicants were accepted. The SAT scores for the 1993–94 freshman class were as follows: Verbal—59% below 500, 32% between 500 and 599, 8% between 600 and 700, and 1% above 700; Math—28% below 500, 41% between 500 and 599, 25% between 600 and 700, and 6% above 700. The ACT scores were 6% below 21, 24% between 21 and 23, 32% between 24 and 26, 19% between 27 and 28, and 17% above 28. About 60% of the current freshmen were in the top fifth of their class; 89% were in the top two fifths. There were 8 National Merit finalists. About 68 freshmen graduated first in their class.

Requirements: The SAT I or ACT is required, with a recommended minimum composite scores of 800 (400 verbal and 400 math) on the SAT I or 21 on the enhanced ACT. Applicants must be graduates of an accredited secondary school, having completed 16 academic credits, including 4 years of English, 2 to 4 years of mathematics and science, 2 to 3 years of social studies, 2 years of foreign language, and 2 to 5 years of additional academic subjects. Students should rank in the upper quarter of their high school class. The GED is accepted. Applicants must demonstrate ability, preparation, and motivation. An interview is recommended for the student's information. AP and CLEP credits are accepted. Important factors used in the admissions decision are advanced placement or honor courses, recommendations by school officials, leadership record, extracurricular activities record, and evidence of special talent.

Procedure: Freshmen are admitted to all sessions. Entrance exams should be taken in the junior or senior year. Application deadlines are open. Application fee is $25. Notification is sent on a rolling basis. A waiting list is an active part of the admissions procedure, with about 1% of applicants on the list.

Transfer: About 280 transfer students enrolled in 1993–94. Applicants for transfer must have a minimum GPA of 2.0; some programs require a higher average. The SAT I or ACT is required if the applicant has completed fewer than 12 hours of college-level work. A total of 30 credits out of 126 to 136 must be completed at Marquette.

Visiting: There are regularly scheduled orientations for prospective students. The agenda for visits varies according to the specific program; open houses are available on scheduled weekends throughout the academic year. There are guides for informal visits and visitors may sit in on classes and stay overnight at the school. To arrange for a visit, contact the Office of Admissions at (414) 288-7302 or (800) 222-6544.

Financial Aid: In 1993–94, 95% of all current freshmen and 80% of continuing students received some form of financial aid. About 64% of freshmen and 65% of continuing students received need-based aid. The average freshman award was $11,050. Of that total, scholarships or need-based grants averaged $4760 ($10,700 maximum); loans averaged $3750 ($5125 maximum); and work contracts averaged $2000. Some 75% of undergraduate students work part-time. Average earnings from campus work for the school year are $1200. Marquette is a member of CSS. The FAFSA financial statement is required. The deadline for financial aid applications is March 1.

International Students: There are currently 501 international students enrolled. The school actively recruits these students. They must take the TOEFL and achieve a minimum score of 500, the University of Michigan Language Test, the Comprehensive English Language Test, the college's own test, or successfully complete the WESLI English program (Madison, Wisconsin). The school requires success in final external secondary exams according to the student's country of education.

Computers: The college provides computer facilities for student use. The mainframes are various models of DEC VAX in a VAX Cluster configuration. There are also more than 800 time-sharing terminals and PCs in residence halls, libraries, and academic facilities. Students can also use word-processing facilities in the library or computing center. In addition, both IBM-DOS and Macintosh PCs are available in various buildings for student and faculty use. All students may access the system. It may be used 24 hours a day during the semester. There are no time limits on using the system and no fees.

Graduates: In 1992–93, 1847 bachelor's degrees were awarded. Within an average freshman class, 21% graduate in 3 years, 53% in 4 years, 72% in 5 years, and 74% in 6 years. Some 118 companies recruited on campus in 1992–93.

Admissions Contact: Raymond A. Brown, Dean of Admissions.

MILWAUKEE INSTITUTE OF ART AND DESIGN

E-4

Milwaukee, WI 53202–6003 (414) 291–8070

Full-time: 251 men, 171 women	Faculty: 25
Part-time: 41 men, 42 women	Ph.D.s: 82%
Graduate: none	Student/Faculty: 17 to 1
Year: semesters, summer session	Tuition: $9800
Application Deadline: April 1	Room & Board: n/app
Freshman Class: 365 applied, 309 accepted, 165 enrolled	
SAT I or ACT: not required	**SPECIAL**

Milwaukee Institute of Art and Design, founded in 1974, is a private, coeducational, 4-year professional college of art and design. In addition to regional accreditation, MIAD has baccalaureate program accreditation with NASAD. The library contains 19,600 volumes, 20,000 microform items, and 200 audiovisual forms, and subscribes to 55 periodicals. Special learning facilities include an art gallery. The campus is in an urban area in downtown Milwaukee. There is one building on campus. There are no residence halls.

Student Life: About 80% of undergraduates are from Wisconsin. Students come from 10 states, 5 foreign countries, and Canada. About 80% are from public schools; 20% from private. Some 87% are white. The average age of freshmen is 19; all undergraduates, 22. About 19% drop out by the end of their first year; 58% remain to graduate.

Housing: There are no residence halls. All students commute. Alcohol is not permitted. All students may keep cars on campus.

Activities: There are no fraternities or sororities. There are some groups and organizations on campus, including art, literary magazine, newspaper, photography, professional, and student government. Popular campus events include visiting artist lectures and workshops, gallery openings, and school picnics in fall and spring.

Sports: There is no sports program at MIAD.

Disabled Students: The entire campus is accessible to disabled students. The following facilities are available: wheelchair ramps, elevators, specially equipped rest rooms, lowered drinking fountains, and lowered telephones.

Services: There is a program in developmental freshman English as well as student tutoring, and a writing center.

Campus Safety and Security: Campus safety and security measures include shuttle buses, informal discussions, pamphlets, posters, and films, and emergency telephones. In addition, there are lighted pathways and sidewalks.

Programs of Study: MIAD awards the B.F.A. degree. Bachelor's degrees are awarded in COMMUNICATIONS AND THE ARTS (drawing, fine arts, graphic design, illustration, industrial design, painting, photography, printmaking, and sculpture), ENGINEERING AND ENVIRONMENTAL DESIGN (interior design). Graphic design, illustration, and industrial design have the largest enrollments.

Required: About 66% of the graduation credits are in studio courses. Students must complete 123 credits, with 81 studio credits and a minimum GPA of 2.0. MIAD requires 12 credits in art history and at least 12 credits in English/writing and 18 credits in the humanities and sciences.

Special: Students may cross-register with Marquette University, Alverno College, and 29 other nationally accredited art colleges. Study abroad in Japan and Canada, a semester at New York Artists Studio, and internships in all design fields and photography are available. Nondegree study and credit for life, military, and work experience are possible.

Faculty/Classroom: About 60% of faculty are male; 40%, female. All teach undergraduates. The average class size in an introductory lecture is 18.

Admissions: About 85% of the 1993–94 applicants were accepted.

Requirements: The SAT I or ACT is not required. Applicants must be graduates of an accredited secondary school. The GED is accepted. A portfolio review and an interview are required. AP and CLEP credits are accepted. Important factors used in the admissions decision are evidence of special talent, leadership record, advanced placement or honor courses, recommendations by school officials, and personality, intangible qualities.

Procedure: Freshmen are admitted in the fall and spring. Applications should be filed by April 1 for fall entry, along with an application fee of $25. Notification is sent on a rolling basis. There is a deferred admissions plan.

Transfer: About 28 transfer students enrolled in 1993–94. A transfer portfolio evaluation is done. Transcripts are reviewed for comparable courses to MIAD's programs. A grade of C or better is required for transfer. A total of 30 credits out of 123 must be completed at MIAD.

Visiting: There are guides for informal visits and visitors may sit in on classes. To arrange for a visit, contact the Admissions Office at (414) 291–8070.

Financial Aid: In 1993–94, 69% of all current freshmen and 93% of continuing students received some form of financial aid. About 65% of freshmen and 72% of continuing students received need-based aid. The average freshman award was $7723. Of that total, scholarships or need-based grants averaged $3725 ($11,222 maximum); loans averaged $3888 ($13,625 maximum); and work contracts averaged $110 ($1200 maximum). About 15% of undergraduate students work part-time. Average earnings from campus work for the school year are $810. The average financial indebtedness of the 1992–93 graduate was $12,500. MIAD is a member of CSS. The FAF, FFS or SFS, the college's own financial statement, and the FAFSA are required. The deadline for financial aid applications is March 1.

International Students: There are currently 5 international students enrolled. They must take the TOEFL and achieve a minimum score of 550.

Computers: The college provides computer facilities for student use. All students may access the system. There are no fees.

Graduates: In 1992–93, 72 bachelor's degrees were awarded. The most popular majors among graduates were graphic design (22%), drawing (19%), and industrial design (15%).

Admissions Contact: Mary Strupp-Schopp, Executive Director of Enrollment Services.

MILWAUKEE SCHOOL OF ENGINEERING
Milwaukee, WI 53201-0644

E-4

(414) 277-7200
(800) 332-6763 (out-of-state)

Full-time: 1574 men, 270 women	Faculty: 110
Part-time: 699 men, 91 women	Ph.D.s: 40%
Graduate: 208 men and women	Student/Faculty: 17 to 1
Year: quarters, summer session	Tuition: $10,600
Application Deadline: open	Room & Board: $3500
Freshman Class: 1217 applied, 1088 accepted, 497 enrolled	
ACT: required	COMPETITIVE

Milwaukee School of Engineering, established in 1903, is a private institution with programs in engineering, engineering technology, and business. There are 3 undergraduate schools and one graduate school. In addition to regional accreditation, MSOE has baccalaureate program accreditation with ABET. The library contains 60,000 volumes and 11,000 microform items, and subscribes to 675 periodicals. Computerized library sources and services include the card catalog, interlibrary loans, and database searching. Special learning facilities include a learning resource center and radio station. The campus is in an urban area. Including residence halls, there are 9 buildings on campus.

Student Life: About 78% of undergraduates are from Wisconsin. Students come from 22 states and 23 foreign countries. Some 85% are from public schools; 15% from private. About 89% are white. Nearly 45% are Catholic; 32% Protestant; 13% claim no religious affiliation. The average age of freshmen is 18; all undergraduates, 21. About 26% drop out by the end of their first year; 50% remain to graduate.

Housing: A total of 750 students can be accommodated in college housing. College-sponsored living facilities include coed dormitories. In addition, there are suites for upperclassmen with kitchens, bathrooms, and living rooms. On-campus housing is guaranteed for all 4 years. About 65% of students live on campus; of those, 80% remain on campus on weekends. All students may keep cars on campus.

Activities: About 10% of men belong to 1 local and 4 national fraternities; about 5% of women belong to 2 local sororities. There are 55 groups on campus, including band, chess, computers, drama, ethnic, honors, international, jazz band, newspaper, pep band, photography, political, professional, radio and TV, religious, social, social service, student government, and yearbook. Popular campus events include Homecoming, Wellness Week, St. Patrick's Week, and Leadership.

Sports: There are 8 intercollegiate sports for men and 5 for women, and 5 intramural sports for men and 4 for women. Athletic and recreation facilities include a gymnasium, health club, and weight-lifting room.

Disabled Students: About 75% of the campus is accessible to disabled students. The following facilities are available: wheelchair ramps, elevators, special parking, specially equipped rest rooms, special class scheduling, and lowered drinking fountains.

Services: In addition to many counseling and information services, tutoring is available in every subject. There is also a reader service for the blind, and remedial math, reading, and writing.

Campus Safety and Security: Campus safety and security measures include 24-hour foot and vehicle patrol, escort service, shuttle buses, and pamphlets, posters, and films. In addition, there are lighted pathways and sidewalks.

Programs of Study: MSOE awards the B.A. and B.S. degrees. Associate and master's degrees also are awarded. Bachelor's degrees are awarded in BUSINESS (business administration and management), COMMUNICATIONS AND THE ARTS (technical and business writing), COMPUTER AND PHYSICAL SCIENCE (computer science), ENGINEERING AND ENVIRONMENTAL DESIGN (architectural engineering, biomedical engineering, computer engineering, electrical/

electronics engineering, engineering technology, industrial engineering, and mechanical engineering). Architectural and mechanical engineering have the largest enrollments.

Required: To graduate, students must complete 205 quarter credits with a minimum GPA of 2.0. There are requirements in speech, composition, computer programming, and ethics.

Special: MSOE offers summer internships in the student's discipline, study abroad at Sunderland Polytechnic Institute in England, on-campus work-study programs, and nondegree study. A 4-year engineering degree and a dual degree in engineering and business are available. There is 1 national honor society on campus.

Faculty/Classroom: About 88% of faculty are male; 12%, female. All teach undergraduates. The average class size in an introductory lecture is 30 and in a laboratory, 20.

Admissions: About 89% of the 1993–94 applicants were accepted. There were 2 National Merit finalists. Nine freshmen graduated first in their class.

Requirements: A minimum GPA of 3.2 is required. MSOE requires the ACT, though the SAT I is acceptable. In addition, applicants must be graduates of an accredited secondary school, having completed 15 academic credits, including 4 units of English, 2 units each of science and mathematics, and 1 unit each of social studies and history. More units in mathematics, science, and English are strongly advised; 1 unit in computer science is helpful. The GED is accepted. An essay is required, and an interview is recommended. AP and CLEP credits are accepted. Important factors used in the admissions decision are advanced placement or honor courses, leadership record, personality, intangible qualities, recommendations by school officials, and extracurricular activities record.

Procedure: Freshmen are admitted to all sessions. Entrance exams should be taken in fall of the senior year. Application deadlines are open. Application fee is $20. Notification is sent on a rolling basis.

Transfer: About 122 transfer students enrolled in 1993–94. Applicants for transfer should have a minimum GPA of 2.5. The ACT and an interview are recommended. At least half of the 205 quarter credits required for graduation must be taken at MSOE.

Visiting: There are regularly scheduled orientations for prospective students. There are guides for informal visits and visitors may sit in on classes and stay overnight at the school. To arrange for a visit, contact the Admission Office at (800) 332-6763.

Financial Aid: In 1993–94, 90% of all current freshmen and 74% of continuing students received some form of financial aid. About 74% of freshmen and 83% of continuing students received need-based aid. The average freshman award was $9150. Of that total, scholarships or need-based grants averaged $5738; loans averaged $3324; and work contracts averaged $1500 ($1800 maximum). Some 50% of undergraduate students work part-time. Average earnings from campus work for the school year are $1500. The average financial indebtedness of the 1992–93 graduate was $13,000. MSOE is a member of CSS. The FAF or FFS is required. The deadline for financial aid applications is April 1.

International Students: There are currently 65 international students enrolled. The school actively recruits these students. They must take the TOEFL and achieve a minimum score of 500.

Computers: The college provides computer facilities for student use. The mainframe is a DEC VAX. More than 150 PCs and terminals are located throughout the library, science building, and student center for student use. Students can also dial up the main computer center over the phone lines to access computer service. All students may access the system. There are no time limits on using the system and no fees.

Graduates: In a recent year, 339 bachelor's degrees were awarded. Within an average freshman class, 30% graduate in 4 years and 95% in 5 years. Some 130 companies recruited on campus in a recent year. In the 1992 graduating class, 8% of the men and women were enrolled in graduate school within 6 months of graduation; 94% of the men and 95% of the women had found employment.

Admissions Contact: Owen Smith, Dean of Admission.

MOUNT MARY COLLEGE
Milwaukee, WI 53222

E-4

(414) 259-9220
(800) 321-6265 (out-of-state)

Full-time: 932 women	Faculty: 73; IIB, --$
Part-time: 14 men, 487 women	Ph.D.s: 50%
Graduate: 2 men, 87 women	Student/Faculty: 13 to 1
Year: semesters, summer session	Tuition: $8100
Application Deadline: August 15	Room & Board: $2820
Freshman Class: 235 applied, 217 accepted, 121 enrolled	
SAT I Verbal/Math: 510/520	COMPETITIVE

Mount Mary College, founded in 1913, is a private, women's liberal arts institution affiliated with the Roman Catholic Church. In addition to regional accreditation, The college has baccalaureate program accreditation with ADA, CAHEA, CSWE, FIDER, and NCATE. The library contains 103,406 volumes, 27,545 microform items, and 21,881 audiovisual forms, and subscribes to 818 periodicals. Special learning facilities include a learning resource center and art gallery. The 80-acre campus is in a suburban area 7 miles west of downtown

Milwaukee. Including residence halls, there are 7 buildings on campus.

Student Life: About 96% of undergraduates are from Wisconsin. Students come from 14 states, 10 foreign countries, and Canada. Nearly 77% are from public schools; 23% from private. Almost 89% are white. About 61% are Catholic; 34% Protestant. The average age of freshmen is 18; all undergraduates, 25. About 10% drop out by the end of their first year; 64% remain to graduate.

Housing: A total of 280 students can be accommodated in college housing. On-campus housing is available on a first-come, first-served basis and on a lottery system for upperclassmen. Priority is given to out-of-town students. Some 78% of students commute. Alcohol is not permitted. All students may keep cars on campus.

Activities: There are no fraternities or sororities. There are 32 groups on campus, including art, choir, chorale, chorus, dance, drama, ethnic, honors, international, literary magazine, newspaper, political, professional, religious, social, social service, student government, and yearbook. Popular campus events include Freshman Investiture, Madrigal Dinner, All-School Christmas Dinner, All-School Picnic, Father-Daughter Dinner-Dance, and Mother-Daughter Luncheon.

Sports: There are 6 intercollegiate sports for women and 3 intramural sports for women. Athletic and recreation facilities include a gymnasium, swimming pool, a weight room, a soccer field, and large recreational grounds.

Disabled Students: The entire campus is accessible to disabled students. The following facilities are available: wheelchair ramps, elevators, special parking, specially equipped rest rooms, lowered drinking fountains, and lowered telephones.

Services: In addition to many counseling and information services, tutoring is available in most subjects. A tutoring language laboratory is available. There is also a reader service for the blind, and remedial math, reading, and writing.

Campus Safety and Security: Campus safety and security measures include 24-hour foot and vehicle patrol, escort service, informal discussions, and pamphlets, posters, and films. In addition, there are emergency telephones and lighted pathways and sidewalks.

Programs of Study: The college awards the B.A. and B.S. degrees. Master's degrees also are awarded. Bachelor's degrees are awarded in BIOLOGICAL SCIENCE (biology/biological science), BUSINESS (accounting, business administration and management, and hotel/motel and restaurant management), COMMUNICATIONS AND THE ARTS (communications, English, fine arts, French, German, music, and Spanish), COMPUTER AND PHYSICAL SCIENCE (chemistry, computer science, and mathematics), EDUCATION (art, bilingual/bicultural, business, early childhood, elementary, foreign languages, home economics, music, science, and secondary), ENGINEERING AND ENVIRONMENTAL DESIGN (food services technology), HEALTH PROFESSIONS (art therapy, occupational therapy, predentistry, and premedicine), SOCIAL SCIENCE (behavioral science, dietetics, history, philosophy, prelaw, social work, and theological studies). Occupational therapy is the strongest program academically. Business administration has the largest enrollment.

Required: To graduate, students must complete 128 credit hours, including 24 in the major, with a GPA of at least 2.0, though most majors specify 2.5 and above. A 48-credit liberal arts core curriculum and demonstrated mathematics competency are required.

Special: Mount Mary College offers internships, a Washington semester, and an accelerated degree program in business administration. Student-designed majors, pass/fail options, and credit for life, military, and work experience are available. There is a freshman honors program on campus, as well as 8 national honor societies.

Faculty/Classroom: About 20% of faculty are male; 80%, female. Nearly 97% teach undergraduates. No introductory courses are taught by graduate students. The average class size in an introductory lecture is 25; in a laboratory, 13; and in a regular course offering, 18 to 20.

Admissions: About 92% of the 1993–94 applicants were accepted. About 32% of the current freshmen were in the top fifth of their class; 64% were in the top two fifths. One freshman graduated first in her class.

Requirements: The college requires applicants to be in the upper 50% of their class. A minimum GPA of 2.3 is required. The SAT I is required. Applicants must be graduates of an accredited secondary school. The GED is accepted. Students should have completed 16 credits, including 4 each in history, social sciences, or foreign language, 3 in English, and 2 each in mathematics and science. An interview is recommended. AP and CLEP credits are accepted. Important factors used in the admissions decision are advanced placement or honor courses, recommendations by school officials, leadership record, evidence of special talent, and extracurricular activities record.

Procedure: Freshmen are admitted in the fall and spring. Entrance exams should be taken in the junior year or fall of the senior year. Applications should be filed by August 15 for fall entry and December 15 for spring entry, along with an application fee of $15. Notification is sent on a rolling basis. There are early decision and deferred admissions plans.

Transfer: About 85 transfer students enrolled in 1993–94. Applicants for transfer should have a minimum GPA of 2.0, though each department has its own admission requirements. The school recom-

mends either the SAT I or ACT, and an interview. A total of 32 credits out of 128 must be completed at the college.

Visiting: There are regularly scheduled orientations for prospective students. There are guides for informal visits and visitors may sit in on classes and stay overnight at the school. To arrange for a visit, contact the Admission Office at (800) 321–6265 or (414) 259–9220.

Financial Aid: In 1993–94, 78% of all current freshmen and 61% of continuing students received some form of financial aid. About 74% of freshmen and 60% of continuing students received need-based aid. The average freshman award was $8400. Of that total, scholarships or need-based grants averaged $4075 ($8000 maximum); loans averaged $2625; and work contracts averaged $1700 ($1800 maximum). About 15% of undergraduate students work part-time. Average earnings from campus work for the school year are $1500. The average financial indebtedness of the 1992–93 graduate was $8486. The college is a member of CSS. The college's own financial statement and FAFSA are required. The deadline for financial aid applications is March 15.

International Students: There are currently 14 international students enrolled. The school actively recruits these students. They must take the TOEFL and achieve a minimum score of 500.

Computers: The college provides computer facilities for student use. The computer center has 52 PCs that are available to students. In addition, a CAD classroom can accommodate 10 students. All students may access the system. There are no time limits on using the system and no fees.

Graduates: In 1992–93, 262 bachelor's degrees were awarded. The most popular majors among graduates were business administration (32%), occupational therapy (20%), and teacher education (10%). Within an average freshman class, 50% graduate in 5 years and 62% in 6 years. In the 1992 graduating class, 6% of the women were enrolled in graduate school within 6 months of graduation; 91% of the women had found employment.

Admissions Contact: Mary Jane Reilly, Director of Admission.

MOUNT SENARIO COLLEGE   B-2
Ladysmith, WI 54848   (715) 532–5511, ext. 322

Full-time: 254 men, 208 women	**Faculty:** 31
Part-time: 489 men, 211 women	**Ph.D.s:** 35%
Graduate: none	**Student/Faculty:** 15 to 1
Year: semesters, summer session	**Tuition:** $7720
Application Deadline: open	**Room & Board:** $3250
Freshman Class: 288 applied, 204 accepted, 96 enrolled	
ACT: required	**COMPETITIVE**

Mount Senario College, established in 1962, is a private liberal arts college offering undergraduate programs in the arts and sciences, business, education, science, and social sciences. The 2 libraries contain 48,508 volumes and 7833 microform items, and subscribe to 276 periodicals. Special learning facilities include an art gallery. The 120-acre campus is in a rural area 65 miles north of Eau Claire. Including residence halls, there are 3 buildings on campus.

Student Life: About 90% of undergraduates are from Wisconsin. Students come from 15 states and 3 foreign countries. About 59% are white; 29% Native American/Eskimo; 11% Asian American. The average age of freshmen is 20; all undergraduates, 25.

Housing: A total of 180 students can be accommodated in college housing. College-sponsored living facilities include coed dormitories. On-campus housing is guaranteed for all 4 years. Half of all students live on campus; of those, 25% remain on campus on weekends. Alcohol is not permitted. All students may keep cars on campus.

Activities: There are no fraternities or sororities. There are 12 groups on campus, including art, cheerleading, choir, chorale, dance, drama, international, newspaper, photography, social service, student government, and yearbook. Popular campus events include Homecoming, Winter Carnival, ski trips, and MSC Day.

Sports: There are 3 intercollegiate sports for men and 3 for women, and 5 intramural sports for men and 5 for women. Athletic and recreation facilities include football and baseball fields, tennis courts, and community golf and bowling.

Disabled Students: Half of the campus is accessible to disabled students. Elevators are available for these students.

Services: In addition to many counseling and information services, tutoring is available in every subject. There is also remedial math, reading, and writing.

Campus Safety and Security: Campus safety and security measures include informal discussions, pamphlets, posters, and films, and lighted pathways and sidewalks.

Programs of Study: MSC awards the B.A., B.S., and B.F.A. degrees. Associate degrees also are awarded. Bachelor's degrees are awarded in BIOLOGICAL SCIENCE (biology/biological science), BUSINESS (accounting and business administration and management), COMMUNICATIONS AND THE ARTS (design, English, fine arts, and music), EDUCATION (art, early childhood, elementary, music, science, and secondary), SOCIAL SCIENCE (criminal justice, history, psychology, social science, and social work). Criminal justice is the strongest program academically. Business has the largest enrollment.

Required: Students must complete 128 credits with a varying number in the major, and must maintain a minimum GPA of 2.0, with 2.5 in the major. There are physical education and general education requirements.

Special: MSC offers a cooperative program with Michigan Technological University, internships, dual majors, and B.A.-B.S. degrees. Study abroad is available through HECUA; the country varies with the semester. Credit for life experience and pass/fail options are possible. There is 1 national honor society on campus.

Faculty/Classroom: About 70% of faculty are male; 30%, female. All teach undergraduates. The average class size in an introductory lecture is 20 and in a laboratory, 10.

Admissions: About 71% of the 1993-94 applicants were accepted.

Requirements: A minimum GPA of 2.0 is required. The ACT is required with a minimum composite score of 15 needed. Graduation from an accredited secondary school is required; the GED is accepted. Applicants must submit 16 academic credits, including 4 years of English, 2 of mathematics, and 1 of science. An essay, portfolio and audition, where appropriate, and interview are recommended. AP and CLEP credits are accepted. Important factors used in the admissions decision are recommendations by school officials, advanced placement or honor courses, leadership record, extracurricular activities record, and evidence of special talent.

Procedure: Freshmen are admitted to all sessions. Application deadlines are open. Application fee is $10. Notification is sent on a rolling basis.

Transfer: Transfer students must have maintained a minimum GPA of 2.0 in courses totaling 30 credits, and must submit 2 letters of recommendation. A total of 32 credits out of 128 must be completed at MSC.

Visiting: There are regularly scheduled orientations for prospective students. There are guides for informal visits and visitors may sit in on classes. To arrange for a visit, contact Joan Seversen, Campus Visit Counselor at (715) 532-5511.

Financial Aid: In a recent year, 80% of all current freshmen and 96% of continuing students received some form of financial aid. About 86% of freshmen and 95% of continuing students received need-based aid. The average freshman award was $4942. Of that total, scholarships or need-based grants averaged $1446 ($2200 maximum); loans averaged $1997 ($2625 maximum); and work contracts averaged $800 ($2300 maximum). About 75% of undergraduate students work part-time. Average earnings from campus work for the school year are $800. The average financial indebtedness of a recent graduate was $8700. MSC is a member of CSS. The FAF, FFS, or SFS is required. The deadline for financial aid applications is May 15.

International Students: There are currently 15 international students enrolled. The school actively recruits these students. They must take the TOEFL or the University of Michigan Language Test and achieve a minimum score on the TOEFL of 500.

Computers: The college provides computer facilities for student use. The mainframe is an AT&T 3B2/400. There are also 13 IBM-compatible, IBM PS/2 30286, Apple IIe, and Apple V65 PCs available in the computer center and McLaughlin Hall. All students may access the system. It may be used 8 A.M. to 9 P.M. Monday through Thursday and 8 A.M. to 4 P.M. Friday. There are no time limits on using the system and no fees.

Graduates: In a recent year, 133 bachelor's degrees were awarded. Some 15 companies recruited on campus in a recent year.

Admissions Contact: Max M. Waits, Admissions Consultant.

NORTHLAND COLLEGE

B-1

Ashland, WI 54806   (715) 682-1224

Full-time: 346 men, 337 women	Faculty: 42; IIB, --$
Part-time: 21 men, 34 women	Ph.D.s: 58%
Graduate: none	Student/Faculty: 16 to 1
Year: 4-4-1, summer session	Tuition: $9800
Application Deadline: August 1	Room & Board: $3750

Freshman Class: 917 applied, 883 accepted, 196 enrolled
SAT I: 495/510   ACT: 23   **LESS COMPETITIVE**

Northland College, founded in 1892, is an independent liberal arts institution affiliated with the United Church of Christ and offers undergraduate programs in the arts and sciences, business, education, health professions, and social sciences. The library contains 83,000 volumes and 9300 microform items, and subscribes to 350 periodicals. Computerized library sources and services include the card catalog, interlibrary loans, and database searching. Special learning facilities include a learning resource center, art gallery, natural history museum, and environmental research acreage. The 80-acre campus is in a small town 70 miles east of Duluth, Minnesota. Including residence halls, there are 20 buildings on campus.

Student Life: About 62% of undergraduates are from out-of-state, mostly the Midwest. Students come from 41 states, 7 foreign countries, and Canada. Nearly 90% are from public schools; 10% from private. About 88% are white. The average age of freshmen is 19; all undergraduates, 21. Some 34% drop out by the end of their first year; 42% remain to graduate.

Housing: A total of 460 students can be accommodated in college housing. College-sponsored living facilities include single-sex and coed dormitories and on-campus apartments. In addition, there are special interest houses. On-campus housing is guaranteed for all 4 years. About 60% of students live on campus; of those, 80% remain on campus on weekends. All students may keep cars on campus.

Activities: About 7% of men belong to 1 local and 1 national fraternity; about 8% of women belong to 2 local sororities. There are 20 groups on campus, including art, band, cheerleading, choir, chorale, chorus, computers, drama, gay, honors, international, jazz band, literary magazine, newspaper, orchestra, photography, political, professional, religious, social, social service, student government, symphony, and yearbook. Popular campus events include Snow Festival, Parents Weekend, and Spring Fling.

Sports: There are 4 intercollegiate sports for men and 4 for women, and 11 intramural sports for men and 11 for women. Athletic and recreation facilities include an Olympic pool, a weight-lifting room, tennis and racquetball courts, and an outdoor recreation program.

Disabled Students: About 75% of the campus is accessible to disabled students. The following facilities are available: wheelchair ramps, elevators, special parking, specially equipped rest rooms, and special class scheduling.

Services: In addition to many counseling and information services, tutoring is available in every subject. There is also a reader service for the blind, and remedial math, reading, and writing.

Campus Safety and Security: Campus safety and security measures include escort service, informal discussions, pamphlets, posters, and films, and lighted pathways and sidewalks.

Programs of Study: Northland awards the B.A. and B.S. degrees. Bachelor's degrees are awarded in BIOLOGICAL SCIENCE (biology/biological science), BUSINESS (accounting, business administration and management, and business economics), COMMUNICATIONS AND THE ARTS (English and music), COMPUTER AND PHYSICAL SCIENCE (chemistry, computer programming, computer science, earth science, geology, information sciences and systems, mathematics, and physics), EDUCATION (art, business, early childhood, elementary, middle school, music, science, and secondary), HEALTH PROFESSIONS (occupational therapy, predentistry, and premedicine), SOCIAL SCIENCE (economics, history, parks and recreation management, prelaw, psychology, public administration, religion, social science, and sociology). Biology, chemistry, and environmental studies are the strongest programs academically. Biology, business, teacher education, outdoor education, and business have the largest enrollments.

Required: Students must complete 124 credits, including 35 to 55 in the major, with a minimum GPA of 2.0. All students must meet requirements that include courses in English composition, literature, history, philosophy, social and natural sciences, physical science, fine arts, physical education, and studies of other cultures.

Special: Opportunities are provided for cooperative programs in many majors and with other schools, internships, work-study programs with state and federal agencies, student-designed majors, credit for life experience, pass/fail options, and study abroad in 5 countries. Cross-registration is offered with Spring Term Consortium Schools. A 3-2 engineering degree is available in conjunction with Michigan Technological University. Other 3-2 degree programs are in forestry, natural resources management, and occupational therapy. There is a freshman honors program on campus, as well as 2 national honor societies.

Faculty/Classroom: About 76% of faculty are male; 24%, female. The average class size in an introductory lecture is 30; in a laboratory, 25; and in a regular course offering, 28.

Admissions: About 96% of the 1993-94 applicants were accepted. About 39% of the current freshmen were in the top fifth of their class; 74% were in the top two fifths. There were 2 National Merit finalists and 8 semifinalists. Three freshmen graduated first in their class.

Requirements: The SAT I or ACT is recommended. Graduation from an accredited secondary school is required; the GED is accepted. An essay and interview are recommended. AP and CLEP credits are accepted. Important factors used in the admissions decision are advanced placement or honor courses, extracurricular activities record, recommendations by school officials, evidence of special talent, and leadership record.

Procedure: Freshmen are admitted in the fall and winter. Entrance exams should be taken in the fall. Early decision applications should be filed by November 22; regular applications, by August 1 for fall entry and December 1 for winter entry. Notification is sent on a rolling basis. There are early decision, early admissions, and deferred admissions plans. About 11 early decision candidates were accepted for the 1993-94 class.

Transfer: About 71 transfer students enrolled in a recent year. Transfer students must have maintained a minimum GPA of 2.0 in previously attended colleges. A total of 30 credits out of 124 must be completed at Northland.

Visiting: There are regularly scheduled orientations for prospective students, including an interview, tour, class visits, and an overnight stay in a dorm. There are guides for informal visits and visitors may sit in on classes and stay overnight at the school. To arrange for a visit, contact the Admissions Office at (715) 682-1224.

Financial Aid: Northland is a member of CSS. The FAF, FFS, or SFS is required. The deadline for financial aid applications is September 1.

International Students: There are currently 13 international students enrolled. The school actively recruits these students. They must take the TOEFL or the University of Michigan Language Test and achieve a minimum score on the TOEFL of 500.

Computers: The college provides computer facilities for student use. The mainframe is a Prime and a DEC VAX. Students have nearly unlimited use of the Prime and PCs. PCs are located in classrooms, laboratories, the computer center, and some residence halls. All students may access the system. There are no time limits on using the system and no fees.

Graduates: In a recent year, 112 bachelor's degrees were awarded. The most popular majors among graduates were biology (30%), business (16%), and teacher education (13%). Within an average freshman class, 2% graduate in 3 years, 38% in 4 years, and 4% in 5 years.

Admissions Contact: James L. Miller, Dean of Student Development and Enrollment.

NORTHWESTERN COLLEGE

D-4

Watertown, WI 53094   (414) 261-4352, ext. 120

Full-time: 185 men	Faculty: 23
Part-time: 2 men	Student/Faculty: 8 to 1
Graduate: none	Tuition: $3428
Year: semesters	Room & Board: $1790
Application Deadline: August 1	
Freshman Class: 46 applied, 45 accepted, 37 enrolled	
ACT: required	COMPETITIVE

Northwestern College, founded in 1865, is a private, men's liberal arts college affiliated with the Lutheran-Wisconsin Synod. It stresses preparation of students for Wisconsin Lutheran Seminary. The library contains 50,000 volumes, 25 microform items, and 180 audiovisual forms, and subscribes to 187 periodicals. The 38-acre campus is in a small town 50 miles west of Milwaukee. Including residence halls, there are 8 buildings on campus.

Student Life: About 50% of undergraduates are from out-of-state, mostly the Midwest. Students come from 22 states, 4 foreign countries, and Canada. About 10% are from public schools; 90% from private. Nearly 98% are white. Most are Protestant. The average age of freshmen is 18; all undergraduates, 20. About 15% drop out by the end of their first year; 30% remain to graduate.

Housing: A total of 288 students can be accommodated in college housing. College-sponsored living facilities include dormitories. On-campus housing is guaranteed for all 4 years. Almost 95% of students live on campus; of those, 75% remain on campus on weekends. Alcohol is not permitted. All students may keep cars on campus.

Activities: There are many groups and organizations on campus, including band, choir, chorus, computers, drama, jazz band, literary magazine, newspaper, pep band, religious, student government, and yearbook. Popular campus events include Homecoming, Winter Carnival, and concerts.

Sports: Athletic and recreation facilities include a 1500-seat gymnasium with basketball courts, a weight-lifting room, athletic fields, and a stadium.

Services: In addition to many counseling and information services, tutoring is available in every subject.

Programs of Study: Northwestern awards the B.A. degree. Bachelor's degrees are awarded in SOCIAL SCIENCE (ministries).

Required: To graduate, students must maintain a minimum 2.0 GPA and complete 134 credit hours. Required courses include 20 hours of religion, 15 of Greek, 14 of Hebrew, 11 of history, 10 of English, 9 each of German and Latin, 6 of mathematics, 4 of psychology, 3 hours each of music and philosophy, 1 hour of physical education, and 1 semester of typing.

Special: A seminary certification program is offered.

Faculty/Classroom: The entire faculty is male. All teach undergraduates. The average class size in an introductory lecture is 20; in a laboratory, 20; and in a regular course offering, 20.

Admissions: About 98% of the 1993–94 applicants were accepted. The ACT scores for the 1993–94 freshman class were as follows: 22% below 21, 30% between 21 and 23, 22% between 24 and 26, 14% between 27 and 28, and 14% above 28.

Requirements: A minimum GPA of 2.0 is required. The ACT is required, with a minimum composite score of 18. Applicants must be graduates of an accredited secondary school, having earned 11 academic credits, including 3 of English, 2 of social science, 2 electives, and 2 each of mathematics and science. The GED is accepted. Recommendations from the applicant's pastor and school counselor are required. AP and CLEP credits are accepted.

Procedure: Freshmen are admitted in the fall and winter. Applications should be filed by August 1 for fall entry and December 1 for winter entry, along with an application fee of $25. Notification is sent on a rolling basis.

Transfer: About 11 transfer students enrolled in a recent year. Applicants for transfer should have a GPA of 2.0. All 134 credits must be completed at Northwestern.

Visiting: There are regularly scheduled orientations for prospective students. There are guides for informal visits and visitors may sit in on classes and stay overnight at the school. To arrange for a visit, contact John A. Braun, Director of Admissions at (414) 261–4352.

Financial Aid: In a recent year, 91% of all current freshmen and 93% of continuing students received some form of financial aid. About 75% of freshmen and 69% of continuing students received need-based aid. The average freshman award was $2391. Of that total, scholarships or need-based grants averaged $2105 ($2400 maximum); and work contracts averaged $81 ($1970 maximum). The average financial indebtedness of a recent graduate was $710. Northwestern is a member of CSS. The FAF, the college's own financial statement, and FAFSA are required. The deadline for financial aid applications is May 1.

Computers: The college provides computer facilities for student use. There are 20 IBM PCs available throughout the campus. There are no time limits on using the system and no fees.

Graduates: In a recent year, 29 bachelor's degrees were awarded. In a recent graduating class, 83% of the men were enrolled in graduate school within 6 months of graduation.

Admissions Contact: Philip Hirsch, Director of Admissions.

RIPON COLLEGE

D-4

Ripon, WI 54971   (414) 748–8102; (800) 94-RIPON (out-of-state)

Full-time: 380 men, 356 women	Faculty: 74; IIB, av$
Part-time: 12 men, 20 women	Ph.D.s: 91%
Graduate: none	Student/Faculty: 10 to 1
Year: semesters	Tuition: $14,510
Application Deadline: March 15	Room & Board: $3810
Freshman Class: 587 applied, 501 accepted, 227 enrolled	
SAT I: 513/557	ACT: 24 COMPETITIVE +

Ripon College, established in 1851, is a private, coeducational, residential, liberal arts institution. The library contains 146,000 volumes, 17,000 microform items, and 6000 audiovisual forms, and subscribes to 710 periodicals. Computerized library sources and services include the card catalog, interlibrary loans, and database searching. Special learning facilities include a learning resource center, art gallery, radio station, music library, art slide library, and college archives. The 250-acre campus is in a small town 80 miles north of Milwaukee. Including residence halls, there are 28 buildings on campus.

Student Life: About 55% of undergraduates are from Wisconsin. Students come from 39 states and 19 foreign countries. Some 57% are from public schools; 43% from private. Nearly 90% are white. The average age of freshmen is 18; all undergraduates, 20. About 7% drop out by the end of their first year; 75% remain to graduate.

Housing: A total of 940 students can be accommodated in college housing. College-sponsored living facilities include single-sex and coed dormitories and fraternity houses. Theme and interest groups may form living areas in the residence halls. On-campus housing is guaranteed for all 4 years and is available on a lottery system for upperclassmen. Nearly 97% of students live on campus; of those, 98% remain on campus on weekends. All students may keep cars on campus.

Activities: About 55% of men belong to 2 local and 3 national fraternities; about 33% of women belong to 1 local and 2 national sororities. There are 80 groups on campus, including art, cheerleading, chess, choir, chorale, chorus, computers, dance, drama, drill team, ethnic, gay, honors, international, jazz band, literary magazine, musical theater, newspaper, orchestra, photography, political, professional, radio and TV, religious, social, social service, student government, and yearbook. Popular campus events include Spring and Winter Festivals, Homecoming, Milwaukee Symphony concerts, theater events, and a chamber music series.

Sports: There are 10 intercollegiate sports for men and 8 for women, and 19 intramural sports for men and 17 for women. Athletic and recreation facilities include a physical education center, 2 fields, tennis courts, a recreation center, and an exercise room. The campus is within 5 miles of lakes and cross-country skiing opportunities.

Disabled Students: Half of the campus is accessible to disabled students. The following facilities are available: wheelchair ramps, elevators, special parking, specially equipped rest rooms, special class scheduling, and lowered drinking fountains.

Services: In addition to many counseling and information services, tutoring is available in every subject. Tutoring and services are also available for learning-disabled students.

Campus Safety and Security: Campus safety and security measures include 24-hour foot and vehicle patrol, escort service, informal discussions, and pamphlets, posters, and films. In addition, there are emergency telephones, lighted pathways and sidewalks, and a paging system.

Programs of Study: Ripon College awards the B.A. degree. Bachelor's degrees are awarded in BIOLOGICAL SCIENCE (biochemistry and biology/biological science), COMMUNICATIONS AND THE ARTS (English, French, German, music, Spanish, and speech/

debate/rhetoric), COMPUTER AND PHYSICAL SCIENCE (chemistry, computer science, mathematics, and physics), EDUCATION (early childhood, elementary, middle school, and secondary), SOCIAL SCIENCE (anthropology, economics, history, international relations, philosophy, political science/government, psychology, religion, and sociology). Biology, chemistry, physics, philosophy, and history are the strongest programs academically. Economics, history, business management, English, and psychology have the largest enrollments.

Required: To graduate, students must complete 124 credit hours, including usually 24 in the major, with a minimum GPA of 2.0. Students must take 6 credits each in behavioral and social sciences, fine arts, humanities, and natural sciences/mathematics. Also required are a third-semester competency in a foreign language, English literature and composition, a writing-intensive course in any department, and 2 credits in physical education. A thesis is required or recommended for certain majors. There is a senior seminar with a research project and presentation of results.

Special: Students may cross-register with the Associated Colleges of the Midwest. Internships, study abroad in 13 countries and study through 7 domestic programs, and a Washington semester are available. The college offers dual and student-designed majors and pass/fail options. A 3-2 engineering degree is available with Rensselaer Polytechnic Institute, Washington University, and University of Minnesota; other 3-2 programs are in environmental studies and in forestry with Duke University and in social welfare with the University of Chicago. A 2-2 nursing program is possible with Rush University. There is a freshman honors program on campus, as well as 11 national honor societies, including Phi Beta Kappa.

Faculty/Classroom: About 72% of faculty are male; 28%, female. All teach undergraduates. The average class size in an introductory lecture is 15; in a laboratory, 15; and in a regular course offering, 12.

Admissions: About 85% of the 1993-94 applicants were accepted. The SAT scores for the 1993-94 freshman class were as follows: Verbal—34% below 500, 47% between 500 and 599, 16% between 600 and 700, and 2% above 700; Math—24% below 500, 35% between 500 and 599, 35% between 600 and 700, and 6% above 700. The ACT scores were 23% below 21, 27% between 21 and 23, 30% between 24 and 26, 10% between 27 and 28, and 11% above 28. About 43% of the current freshmen were in the top fifth of their class; 71% were in the top two fifths. There were 4 National Merit finalists. Nine freshmen graduated first in their class.

Requirements: Ripon College requires applicants to be in the upper 50% of their class. A minimum GPA of 2.0 is required. The SAT I or ACT is required. In addition, applicants must be graduates of an accredited secondary school. The GED is accepted. Applicants should complete 15 Carnegie units. An essay is required, and an interview is recommended. AP and CLEP credits are accepted. Important factors used in the admissions decision are advanced placement or honor courses, recommendations by school officials, extracurricular activities record, personality, intangible qualities, and evidence of special talent.

Procedure: Freshmen are admitted in the fall and spring. Entrance exams should be taken in the junior year or fall of the senior year. Early decision applications should be filed by December 1; regular applications, by March 15 for fall entry and December 15 for spring entry, along with an application fee of $20. Notification of early decision is sent December 15; regular decision, beginning January 15 and every 2 weeks thereafter. There are early decision, early admissions, and deferred admissions plans. About 67 early decision candidates were accepted for the 1993-94 class.

Transfer: About 22 transfer students enrolled in 1993-94. Transfer applicants must have a minimum 2.0 GPA and be in good standing at their previous college. The SAT I or ACT and an interview are recommended. A total of 32 credits out of 124 must be completed at Ripon College.

Visiting: There are regularly scheduled orientations for prospective students, including a tour, interview, meetings with professors and coaches, class visits, and overnight stay. There are guides for informal visits and visitors may sit in on classes and stay overnight at the school. To arrange for a visit, contact the Admission Office at (800) 94-RIPON.

Financial Aid: In 1993-94, 82% of all current freshmen and 73% of continuing students received some form of financial aid. About 75% of freshmen and 70% of continuing students received need-based aid. Scholarships or need-based grants averaged $1886 ($14,340 maximum); loans averaged $2079; and work contracts averaged $695 ($890 maximum). About 45% of undergraduate students work part-time. Average earnings from campus work for the school year are $650. The average financial indebtedness of the 1992-93 graduate was $10,094. Ripon College is a member of CSS. The FAFSA financial statement is required. The deadline for financial aid applications is March 15.

International Students: There are currently 39 international students enrolled. The school actively recruits these students. They must take the TOEFL and achieve a minimum score of 600. The student must also take the SAT I, if available.

Computers: The college provides computer facilities for student use. The mainframes are 2 DEC VAX 11/750 machines. The mainframes and Apple Macintosh microcomputers are in the computer center; the many terminals allow for easy access. A second computer resource center is on the second floor of Lane Library. VAX terminals are located in several buildings. Macintosh and IBM PCs are supported through laboratories in the economics, mathematics, computer science, and natural sciences departments. All students may access the system. There are no time limits in using the system and no fees.

Graduates: In 1992-93, 183 bachelor's degrees were awarded. The most popular majors among graduates were English (15%), history (15%), and biology/economics (9%). Within an average freshman class, 5% graduate in 3 years, 60% in 4 years, 67% in 5 years, and 68% in 6 years. Some 40 companies recruited on campus in 1992-93. In the 1992 graduating class, 31% of the men and women were enrolled in graduate school within 6 months of graduation; 68% of the men and 64% of the women in an earlier year had found employment.

Admissions Contact: Paul J. Weeks, Dean of Admission.

SAINT NORBERT COLLEGE   D-3
De Pere, WI 54115   (414) 337-3005; (800) 236-4878 (out-of-state)

Full-time: 837 men, 1109 women	Faculty: 119; IIB, av$
Part-time: 30 men, 65 women	Ph.D.s: 78%
Graduate: 3 men, 15 women	Student/Faculty: 16 to 1
Year: semesters, summer session	Tuition: $11,465
Application Deadline: open	Room & Board: $4245
Freshman Class: 1334 applied, 1243 accepted, 568 enrolled	
ACT: 24	**VERY COMPETITIVE**

Saint Norbert College, founded in 1898, is a private, coeducational, undergraduate institution affiliated with the Roman Catholic Church (Norbertine Order). It offers bachelor's degrees in the arts, the sciences, music, and business administration. The library contains 167,562 volumes, 24,304 microform items, and 5745 audiovisual forms, and subscribes to 871 periodicals. Computerized library sources and services include the card catalog, interlibrary loans, and database searching. Special learning facilities include a learning resource center, art gallery, radio station, TV station, language laboratories, media center with satellite hookup, observatory, transmission electron microscope, and 2 theaters. The 72-acre campus is in a suburban area 5 miles south of Green Bay. Including residence halls, there are 30 buildings on campus.

Student Life: About 71% of undergraduates are from Wisconsin. Students come from 29 states, 7 foreign countries, and Canada. About 60% are from public schools; 40% from private. Nearly 95% are white. Most are Catholic. The average age of freshmen is 18; all undergraduates, 20. Almost 16% drop out by the end of their first year; 71% remain to graduate.

Housing: A total of 1383 students can be accommodated in college housing. College-sponsored living facilities include single-sex and coed dormitories and on-campus apartments. In addition, there are language houses, special interest houses, and a townhouse complex. On-campus housing is guaranteed for all 4 years. Nearly 85% of students live on campus; of those, 75% remain on campus on weekends. All students may keep cars on campus.

Activities: About 11% of men belong to 2 local and 3 national fraternities; about 3% of women belong to 3 local and 1 national sororities. There are 70 groups on campus, including art, band, cheerleading, choir, chorale, chorus, computers, drama, drill team, ethnic, honors, international, jazz band, literary magazine, musical theater, newspaper, orchestra, pep band, photography, political, professional, radio and TV, religious, social, social service, student government, symphony, and yearbook. Popular campus events include Homecoming, Winter Carnival, Big Bash on Campus, Economic Summit, Global Ecology Summit, Fine Arts Series (includes the Milwaukee Symphony), and Killeen Chair of Theology and Philosophy Series.

Sports: There are 9 intercollegiate sports for men and 7 for women, and 10 intramural sports for men and 10 for women. Athletic and recreation facilities include a 3000-seat stadium, a sports complex, and a sports center.

Disabled Students: Some 80% of the campus is accessible to disabled students. The following facilities are available: wheelchair ramps, elevators, special parking, specially equipped rest rooms, special class scheduling, lowered drinking fountains, lowered telephones, special residence hall rooms, and on-campus apartments.

Services: Tutoring is available in nearly every major. In addition, there is a reader service for the blind, and remedial math, reading, and writing.

Campus Safety and Security: Campus safety and security measures include 24-hour foot and vehicle patrol, escort service, informal discussions, and pamphlets, posters, and films. There are also emergency telephones and lighted pathways and sidewalks.

Programs of Study: St. Norbert awards the B.A., B.S., B.B.A., and B.Mus. degrees. Master's degrees also are awarded. Bachelor's degrees are awarded in BIOLOGICAL SCIENCE (biology/biological science), BUSINESS (accounting, business administration and management, international business management, and international economics), COMMUNICATIONS AND THE ARTS (art, communications, English, fine arts, French, German, music, Spanish, and visual and performing arts), COMPUTER AND PHYSICAL SCIENCE (chemistry, computer science, information sciences and systems, mathemat-

ics, and physics), EDUCATION (art, elementary, music, and secondary), ENGINEERING AND ENVIRONMENTAL DESIGN (environmental policy studies, environmental science), HEALTH PROFESSIONS (medical laboratory technology, predentistry, premedicine, prepharmacy, and preveterinary science), SOCIAL SCIENCE (anthropology, economics, history, human ecology, humanities, international studies, philosophy, political science/government, prelaw, psychology, religion, and sociology). International studies, environmental science, humanities, international business and language area studies, mathematics, and chemistry are the strongest programs academically. Business administration, communications, and elementary education have the largest enrollments.

Required: To graduate, students must complete 128 credits with at least a 2.0 GPA. There are general education requirements in the areas of religious heritage, human nature, human relationships, natural world, creative expression, American heritage, foreign heritages, quantitative skills, verbal skills, Western tradition, global society, and Senior Colloquium.

Special: There is cross-registration with St. Edward's University in Austin, Texas. Internships, study abroad, a Washington semester, and work-study programs are available. Students may obtain a B.A.-B.S. in international business and language area studies. The college offers dual and student-designed majors, a 3–2 engineering degree, nondegree study, and limited credit for life, military, and work experience. The LEAD (Leadership Experience and Development) program helps students improve their leadership abilities through courses and activities. There is a freshman honors program on campus, as well as 5 national honor societies.

Faculty/Classroom: About 70% of faculty are male; 30%, female. All teach undergraduates, 60% do research, and 60% do both. No introductory courses are taught by graduate students. The average class size in an introductory lecture is 35; in a laboratory, 24; and in a regular course offering, 30.

Admissions: About 93% of the 1993–94 applicants were accepted. The ACT scores for the 1993–94 freshman class were as follows: 24% below 21, 29% between 21 and 23, 22% between 24 and 26, 14% between 27 and 28, and 11% above 28. About 48% of the current freshmen were in the top fifth of their class; 76% were in the top two fifths. There were 2 National Merit finalists and 2 semifinalists.

Requirements: St. Norbert requires applicants to be in the upper 50% of their class. A minimum GPA of 2.5 is required. The SAT I or ACT is required. The recommended minimum composite score for the SAT I is 900 (450 verbal, 450 math) and for the ACT, 19. Applicants must be graduates of an accredited secondary school. The GED is accepted. Students should complete 4 years of high school English, 3 years of mathematics, 2 years each of history, social studies, and natural science, and 2 years recommended of foreign language. The school requires an essay and a recommendation, and recommends an interview. AP and CLEP credits are accepted. Important factors used in the admissions decision are extracurricular activities record, leadership record, evidence of special talent, parents or siblings attending the school, and recommendations by alumni.

Procedure: Freshmen are admitted to all sessions. It is recommended that entrance exams be taken by the end of the junior year. Application deadlines are open. Application fee is $25. Notification is sent 2 to 3 weeks after the receipt of all admissions materials. There is a deferred admissions plan.

Transfer: About 70 transfer students enrolled in 1993–94. Applicants for transfer should have a minimum GPA of 2.5 and must submit college transcripts. They must also be in good academic standing at their previous college. A total of 48 credits out of 128 must be completed at St. Norbert.

Visiting: There are regularly scheduled orientations for prospective students, including preregistration, meetings with advisors, and meetings regarding programming and activities, housing, and student life. There are guides for informal visits and visitors may sit in on classes and stay overnight at the school. To arrange for a visit, contact the Office of Admissions at (414) 337-3005 or (800) 236-4878.

Financial Aid: In 1993–94, 92% of all current freshmen and 87% of continuing students received some form of financial aid. About 67% of freshmen and 60% of continuing students received need-based aid. The average freshman award was $9585. Of that total, scholarships or need-based grants averaged $5110; loans averaged $3660; and work contracts averaged $1332. About 55% of undergraduate students work part-time. Average earnings from campus work for the school year was $970. The average financial indebtedness of the 1992–93 graduate was $7425. St. Norbert is a member of CSS. The FAF and FAFSA are required. The preferred deadline for financial aid applications is March 1.

International Students: There are currently 19 international students enrolled. The school actively recruits these students. They must take the TOEFL and achieve a minimum score of 550.

Computers: The college provides computer facilities for student use. The mainframes are 3 DEC station 5000 systems. Four laboratories containing 75 IBM-compatible and 15 Apple Macintosh microcomputers are available for student use. The laboratories are connected to the campus network, which provides access to a wide variety of software, high-quality laser printing, and the central computing facilities and library automation system. Dial-up access is available to the

central computing facilities 24 hours per day. Several classrooms and auditoriums are connected to the campus network and have access to campuswide video service. The college is a member of WiscNet, a statewide educational and research computer network that is a part of the Internet. All students may access the system. It may be used during the semester as needed or as required by the instructor. There are no time limits on using the system and no fees.

Graduates: In 1991–92, 416 bachelor's degrees were awarded. The most popular majors among graduates were business administration (20%), communications, media, and theater (14%), and elementary education (8%). Within an average freshman class, 71% graduate in 4 years. Some 55 companies recruited on campus in 1992–93. In the 1992 graduating class, 19% of the men and women were enrolled in graduate school within 6 months of graduation; 76% of the men and women had found employment.

Admissions Contact: Craig S. Wesley, Dean of Admission.

SILVER LAKE COLLEGE E-3

Manitowoc, WI 54220   (414) 684-5955; (800) 236-4752 (in-state)

Full-time: 108 men, 285 women	**Faculty:** 40
Part-time: 170 men, 266 women	**Ph.D.s:** 25%
Graduate: 46 men, 73 women	**Student/Faculty:** 10 to 1
Year: semesters, summer session	**Tuition:** $8280
Application Deadline: open	**Room & Board:** n/app
Freshman Class: 82 applied, 75 accepted, 34 enrolled	
ACT: 19	**NONCOMPETITIVE**

Silver Lake College, founded in 1869, is a private Catholic, coeducational, liberal arts institution. In addition to regional accreditation, Silver Lake has baccalaureate program accreditation with NASM, NCATE, and NLN. The library contains 60,293 volumes, 1812 microform items, and 23,522 audiovisual forms, and subscribes to 362 periodicals. Special learning facilities include a learning resource center. The 30-acre campus is 4 miles west of Manitowoc. There is one building on campus. There are no residence halls.

Student Life: About 98% of undergraduates are from Wisconsin. Students come from 7 states and 2 foreign countries. Nearly 94% are from public schools; 6% from private. Almost 97% are white. The average age of freshmen is 20. About 18% drop out by the end of their first year; 63% remain to graduate.

Housing: There are no residence halls. All students commute. Alcohol is not permitted. All students may keep cars on campus.

Activities: There are no fraternities or sororities. There are 14 groups on campus, including art, band, cheerleading, choir, chorus, computers, drama, honors, jazz band, literary magazine, newspaper, orchestra, religious, and student government. Popular campus events include Fine Arts Series, Wildlife Series, and campus ministry programs.

Sports: There are 3 intercollegiate sports for women, and 3 intramural sports for men and 2 for women. Athletic and recreation facilities include a YMCA and Two Rivers and Manitowac Recreation Department.

Disabled Students: About 90% of the campus is accessible to disabled students. The following facilities are available: wheelchair ramps, elevators, special parking, and special class scheduling.

Services: In addition to many counseling and information services, tutoring is available in every subject, including study groups and academic tutoring as needed. There is also a reader service for the blind.

Campus Safety and Security: Campus safety and security measures include self defense education, informal discussions, pamphlets, posters, and films, and emergency telephones. In addition, there are lighted pathways and sidewalks.

Programs of Study: Silver Lake awards the B.A., B.S., B.B.A, and B.M. degrees. Associate and master's degrees also are awarded. Bachelor's degrees are awarded in BIOLOGICAL SCIENCE (biology/biological science), BUSINESS (accounting, business administration and management, and personnel management), COMMUNICATIONS AND THE ARTS (English, fine arts, and music), COMPUTER AND PHYSICAL SCIENCE (mathematics), EDUCATION (art, early childhood, elementary, music, and secondary), SOCIAL SCIENCE (history, religion, and social science). Elementary education is the strongest program academically. Business administration and management have the largest enrollments.

Required: To graduate, students must complete at least 128 credit hours, with a minimum GPA of 2.0. A core of liberal arts courses must be taken.

Special: Silver Lake offers cross-registration with Lake Shore Technical Colleges, internships, B.A.-B.S. degrees, and dual and student-designed majors. Nondegree study, pass/fail options, and credit for life, military, and work experience are available. An accelerated degree program in business is offered through a career-directed program for adults.

Faculty/Classroom: About 25% of faculty are male; 75%, female. Nearly 99% teach undergraduates and 4% both teach and do research. No introductory courses are taught by graduate students. The average class size in an introductory lecture is 25; in a laboratory, 15; and in a regular course offering, 15.

Admissions: About 91% of the 1993-94 applicants were accepted. The ACT scores for the 1993-94 freshman class were as follows: 56% below 21, 22% between 21 and 23, 13% between 24 and 26, and 9% above 28. About 21% of the current freshmen were in the top fifth of their class; 39% were in the top two fifths.

Requirements: A minimum GPA of 2.0 is required. The ACT is required, with a minimum composite score of 16. Applicants must be graduates of an accredited secondary school. The GED is accepted. Applicants should complete 3 years of high school English, and 2 years each of mathematics and history or social studies. CLEP credit is accepted. Important factors used in the admissions decision are evidence of special talent, leadership record, recommendations by school officials, personality, intangible qualities, and extracurricular activities record.

Procedure: Freshmen are admitted to all sessions. Application deadlines are open. Application fee is $15. The college accepts all applicants. Notification is sent on a rolling basis.

Transfer: About 105 transfer students enrolled in 1993-94. Transfer applicants who have 30 acceptable credits must have a minimum GPA of 2.0; those with fewer credits must meet the requirements for entering freshmen, except that the ACT is not required. A total of 30 credits out of 128 must be completed at Silver Lake.

Visiting: There are regularly scheduled orientations for prospective students, including a tour and meetings with an admissions counselor, an advisor, the Financial Aid Department, and the Housing Director. There are guides for informal visits. To arrange for a visit, contact the Admissions Office at (414) 684-5955.

Financial Aid: In 1993-94, 88% of all current freshmen and 75% of continuing students received some form of financial aid. About 76% of freshmen and 89% of continuing students received need-based aid. The average freshman award was $7395. Of that total, scholarships or need-based grants averaged $4505 ($9280 maximum); loans averaged $2693 ($6625 maximum); and work contracts averaged $647 ($1000 maximum). About 9% of undergraduate students work part-time. Average earnings from campus work for the school year are $683. The average financial indebtedness of the 1992-93 graduate was $10,306. Silver Lake is a member of CSS. The FAF and tax returns are required. The deadline for financial aid applications is March 15.

International Students: There are currently 2 international students enrolled. They must take the TOEFL and achieve a minimum score of 550.

Computers: The college provides computer facilities for student use. There are no time limits on using the system and no fees.

Graduates: In 1992-93, 137 bachelor's degrees were awarded. The most popular majors among graduates were management (50%), accounting (10%), and education (10%). Within an average freshman class, 8% graduate in 4 years, 63% in 5 years, and 63% in 6 years. Some 10 companies recruited on campus in 1992-93. In the 1992 graduating class, 20% of the men and women were enrolled in graduate school within 6 months of graduation; 83% of the men and women had found employment.

Admissions Contact: Sandra O. Schwartz, Director of Admissions.

UNIVERSITY OF WISCONSIN SYSTEM

The University of Wisconsin System, established in 1971, is a public system in Wisconsin. It is governed by a 17-member appointed board of regents, whose chief administrator is president. The primary goal of the system is teaching, research, and public service. The main priorities are to develop human resources;, to discover and disseminate knowledge; and, and to extend kwowledge and its application. The total enrollment in a recent year of all 26 campuses was 161,000; there were 7200 faculty members. Altogether there are 670 baccalaureate, more than 350 master's, and nearly 140 doctoral programs offered in the University of Wisconsin System. Profiles of the 4-year campuses are included in this chapter in alphabetical order with other Wisconsin schools.

UNIVERSITY OF WISCONSIN
EAU CLAIRE   B-3
Eau Claire, WI 54701   (715) 836-5415

Full-time: 3395 men, 5121 women	Faculty: 511; IIA, -$
Part-time: 442 men, 822 women	Ph.D.s: 68%
Graduate: 153 men, 412 women	Student/Faculty: 17 to 1
Year: semesters, summer session	Tuition: $2172 ($6620)
Application Deadline: March 1	Room & Board: $2475
Freshman Class: 5729 applied, 4520 accepted, 1957 enrolled	
SAT I Verbal/Math: 455/520	ACT: 22 COMPETITIVE

The University of Wisconsin/Eau Claire, founded in 1916, is a public institution offering programs in the liberal arts and sciences, business, teacher education, nursing, music, and the fine arts. There are 4 undergraduate schools and one graduate school. In addition to regional accreditation, UW-Eau Claire has baccalaureate program accreditation with CSWE, NASM, and NLN. The library contains 541,501 volumes, 1,327,893 microform items, and 47,310 audiovisual forms, and subscribes to 1143 periodicals. Computerized library sources and services include the card catalog, interlibrary loans, and database searching. Special learning facilities include a learning resource center, an art gallery, a planetarium, a radio station, a TV station, a geographic research center, a bird museum, and an observatory. The 333-acre campus is in an urban area 95 miles east of Minneapolis, Minnesota. Including residence halls, there are 26 buildings on campus.

Student Life: About 82% of undergraduates are from Wisconsin. Students come from 23 states, 42 foreign countries, and Canada. Nearly 95% are from public schools; 5% from private. Almost 95% are white. The average age of freshmen is 19; all undergraduates, 22. About 21% drop out by the end of their first year; 49% remain to graduate.

Housing: A total of 3600 students can be accommodated in college housing. College-sponsored living facilities include single-sex and coed dormitories. On-campus housing is available on a first-come, first-served basis. About 65% of students commute. All students may keep cars on campus.

Activities: About 1% of men and women belong to 4 national fraternities and sororities. There are 100 groups on campus, including art, band, cheerleading, chess, choir, chorus, computers, dance, drama, ethnic, gay, honors, international, jazz band, literary magazine, marching band, musical theater, newspaper, orchestra, political, professional, radio and TV, religious, social, social service, student government, symphony, and yearbook. Popular campus events include Viennese Ball, Homecoming, Artsfest, Winter Carnival, Springfest, Cabaret, and International Folk Fair.

Sports: There are 10 intercollegiate sports for men and 9 for women, and 40 intramural sports for men and 40 for women. Athletic and recreation facilities include a gymnasium, a pool, 30 acres of intramural and recreation fields, a game room, bowling and billards, a Nautilus fitness center, racquetball courts, a weight room, and a 3212-seat stadium.

Disabled Students: About 80% of the campus is accessible to disabled students. The following facilities are available: wheelchair ramps, elevators, special parking, specially equipped rest rooms, special class scheduling, lowered drinking fountains, and lowered telephones.

Services: In addition to many counseling and information services, tutoring is available in some subjects. There is also a reader service for the blind, remedial math, reading, and writing, and entry-level courses in the areas of foreign languages, humanities, and social and physical sciences.

Campus Safety and Security: Campus safety and security measures include 24-hour foot and vehicle patrol, self-defense education, escort service, and informal discussions. In addition, there are pamphlets, posters, films, and lighted pathways and sidewalks.

Programs of Study: UW-Eau Claire awards the B.A., B.S., B.B.A., B.F.A., B.M., B.M.E., B.S.E.Ph., B.S.H.C.A., B.S.M.T., B.S.N., and B.S.W. degrees. Associate and master's degrees also are awarded. Bachelor's degrees are awarded in BIOLOGICAL SCIENCE (biochemistry, biology/biological science, botany, and zoology), BUSINESS (accounting, banking and finance, business administration and management, business economics, marketing/retailing/merchandising, and secretarial studies/office management), COMMUNICATIONS AND THE ARTS (advertising, art, broadcasting, communications, dramatic arts, English, fine arts, French, German, journalism, music, photography, Spanish, speech/debate/rhetoric, and telecommunications), COMPUTER AND PHYSICAL SCIENCE (chemistry, computer programming, computer science, geology, information sciences and systems, mathematics, physical sciences, physics, and statistics), EDUCATION (art, business, elementary, foreign languages, music, physical, science, secondary, and special), HEALTH PROFESSIONS (health care administration, medical laboratory technology, music therapy, nursing, public health, and speech pathology/audiology), SOCIAL SCIENCE (criminal justice, economics, geography, history, Latin American studies, philosophy, political science/government, psychology, religion, social science, social work, and sociology). Elementary education, nursing, and accounting have the largest enrollments.

Required: All students must take 4 to 5 credits in English, 2 in physical education, and 39 in general education, including 12 each in social sciences and humanities, 9 in natural sciences, and 6 in communications. All students must also complete a minimum of two courses that contain significant content dealing with race and ethnicity. A minimum 2.0 GPA and 128 credit hours, including 60 in the major, are required to graduate.

Special: Numerous internships, work-study programs, and study abroad in 14 countries are offered. Dual majors and interdisciplinary majors, including communication, theater arts, and communication arts, are possible. Credit by exam, nondegree study, and pass/fail options are offered. There is a freshman honors program on campus, as well as 25 national honor societies. Eleven departments have honors programs.

Faculty/Classroom: About 62% of faculty are male; 38%, female. Some 77% teach undergraduates, and 44% also do research. No introductory courses are taught by graduate students. The average class size in an introductory lecture is 31 and in a laboratory, 19.

Admissions: About 79% of the 1993-94 applicants were accepted. The SAT scores for the 1993-94 freshman class were as follows: Verbal—69% below 500, 20% between 500 and 599, 7% between 600 and 700, and 4% above 700; Math—38% below 500, 39% between 500 and 599, 17% between 600 and 700, and 6% above 700. The ACT scores were 26% below 21, 36% between 21 and 23, 24% between 24 and 26, 8% between 27 and 28, and 6% above 28. About 41% of the current freshmen were in the top fifth of their class; 79% were in the top two fifths. There were 7 National Merit finalists and 70 semifinalists. Forty freshmen graduated first in their class.

Requirements: UW-Eau Claire requires applicants to be in the upper 50% of their class. The SAT I or ACT is required. Applicants should graduate from an accredited secondary school or present its equivalent, with 17 academic credits; including 4 in English, 3 each in social studies, college preparatory mathematics, and science. Students must graduate in the upper 50% of their class or present a minimum composite score of 1000 on the SAT I or 22 on the ACT. Probationary admission is sometimes offered for the spring semester. Music majors or minors must audition. AP and CLEP credits are accepted. Important factors used in the admissions decision are advanced placement or honor courses, recommendations by school officials, leadership record, extracurricular activities record, and evidence of special talent.

Procedure: Freshmen are admitted to all sessions. Entrance exams should be taken by October. Early decision applications should be filed by December 1; regular applications, by March 1 for fall entry, December 1 for spring entry, and March 1 for summer entry, along with an application fee of $25. Notification of early decision is sent January 1; regular decision, on a rolling basis. There is an early admissions plan. A waiting list is an active part of the admissions procedure, with about 2% of applicants on the list.

Transfer: About 516 transfer students enrolled in 1993-94. Transfer applicants' previous academic record must qualify them as students in acceptable standing, having completed 24 semester credits with a 2.5 GPA. Preference is given to transfers who have completed the equivalent of freshman composition and college algebra. A total of 32 credits out of 128 must be completed at UW-Eau Claire.

Visiting: There are regularly scheduled orientations for prospective students, including tours at 11 A.M. and 2 P.M. on school days and appointments with counselors throughout the day. There are guides for informal visits and visitors may sit in on classes and stay overnight at the school. To arrange for a visit, contact the Admissions Office at (715) 836-5415.

Financial Aid: In 1993-94, 53% of all current freshmen and 49% of continuing students received some form of financial aid. About 45% of freshmen and 40% of continuing students received need-based aid. The average freshman award was $4005. Of that total, scholarships or need-based grants averaged $2065 ($4000 maximum); loans averaged $2133 ($2625 maximum); and work contracts averaged $1685 ($3700 maximum). About 90% of undergraduate students work part-time. Average earnings from campus work for the school year are $1800. The average financial indebtedness of the 1992-93 graduate was $5970. The FAFSA financial statement is required. The deadline for financial aid applications is February 28.

International Students: There are currently 190 international students enrolled. The school actively recruits these students. They must take the TOEFL or the University of Michigan Language Test and achieve a minimum score on the TOEFL of 525.

Computers: The college provides computer facilities for student use. The mainframe is a DEC VAX 6440. Students may use computer facilities for purposes of classroom assignments, research, network access to other resources, and mail. Terminals and PCs are located across campus. There are 14 supported laboratories plus laboratories in housing and the library. Dial-in access is offered. All students may access the system. It may be used 24 hours a day, 7 days per week. There are no time limits on using the system and no fees.

Graduates: In 1992-93, 1695 bachelor's degrees were awarded. The most popular majors among graduates were accounting (7%), elementary education (7%), and nursing (6%). Within an average freshman class, 1% graduate in 3 years, 13% in 4 years, 44% in 5 years, and 49% in 6 years. Some 255 companies recruited on campus in 1992-93. In the 1992 graduating class, 1% of the men and 4% of the women were enrolled in graduate school within 6 months of graduation; 74% of the men and women had found employment.

Admissions Contact: Roger Groene Wold, Director of Admissions.

UNIVERSITY OF WISCONSIN
GREEN BAY
D-3

Green Bay, WI 54302 (414) 465-2111

Full-time: 1520 men, 2302 women   **Faculty:** 175; IIA, -$
Part-time: 428 men, 918 women   **Ph.D.s:** 97%
Graduate: 122 men, 115 women   **Student/Faculty:** 22 to 1
Year: semesters, summer session   **Tuition:** $2104 ($6552)
Application Deadline: February 1   **Room & Board:** $2800
Freshman Class: 2409 applied, 1939 accepted, 759 enrolled
ACT: 22   COMPETITIVE

The University of Wisconsin/Green Bay, founded in 1968, is a public institution offering programs in humanities and fine arts, natural sciences, social sciences, business, education, health, and preprofessional areas. There is one graduate school. In addition to regional accreditation, UWGB has baccalaureate program accreditation with ADA, CSWE, NASM, and NLN. The library contains 290,000 volumes, 410,000 microform items, and 2500 audiovisual forms, and subscribes to 1890 periodicals. Computerized library sources and services include the card catalog, interlibrary loans, and database searching. Special learning facilities include a learning resource center, an art gallery, a natural history museum, a radio station, and a TV station. The 700-acre campus is in a rural area 111 miles north of Milwaukee. Including residence halls, there are 36 buildings on campus.

Student Life: About 95% of undergraduates are from Wisconsin. Students come from 27 states, 30 foreign countries, and Canada. Eighty-six percent are from public schools; 14% from private. Ninety-five percent are white. Forty-five percent are Protestant; 43% Catholic. The average age of freshmen is 19; all undergraduates, 22. Twenty-four percent drop out by the end of their first year; 36% remain to graduate.

Housing: A total of 1120 students can be accommodated in college housing. College-sponsored living facilities include coed dormitories and on-campus apartments. On-campus housing is available on a first-come, first-served basis. Eighty percent of students commute. All students may keep cars on campus.

Activities: About 1% of men belong to 1 national fraternity; about 1% of women belong to 2 national sororities. There are 80 groups on campus, including art, band, cheerleading, chess, choir, chorus, dance, drama, ethnic, honors, international, jazz band, literary magazine, musical theater, newspaper, pep band, photography, political, professional, radio and tv, religious, social, social service, and student government. Popular campus events include Welcome Month, Homecoming, Spring Screamer, and Black History Awareness Month.

Sports: There are 7 intercollegiate sports for men and 7 for women, and 5 intramural sports for men and 5 for women. Athletic and recreation facilities include a sports center housing a swimming pool, racquetball courts, a weight room, and a 2000-seat gymnasium, intramural fields, a soccer field, a golf course, an outing center, a 5600-seat arena, a 2500-seat stadium, and student recreation facilities in the student union.

Disabled Students: All of the campus is accessible to disabled students. The following facilities are available: wheelchair ramps, elevators, special parking, specially equipped rest rooms, lowered drinking fountains, and lowered telephones.

Services: In addition to many counseling and information services, tutoring is available in most subjects. There is also a reader service for the blind, and remedial math, reading, and writing. There is an academic support office, language and writing centers, student health services, and individual counseling.

Campus Safety and Security: Campus safety and security measures include 24-hour foot and vehicle patrol, escort service, informal discussions, and pamphlets, posters, and films. In addition, there are emergency telephones and lighted pathways and sidewalks.

Programs of Study: UWGB awards the B.A., B.S., B.G.S., B.S.N., and B.S.W. degrees. Associate and master's degrees also are awarded. Bachelor's degrees are awarded in BIOLOGICAL SCIENCE (biology/biological science and nutrition), BUSINESS (accounting and business administration and management), COMMUNICATIONS AND THE ARTS (communications, dramatic arts, English, fine arts, French, German, music, and Spanish), COMPUTER AND PHYSICAL SCIENCE (chemistry, earth science, information sciences and systems, mathematics, and physics), ENGINEERING AND ENVIRONMENTAL DESIGN (environmental design and environmental science), HEALTH PROFESSIONS (nursing), SOCIAL SCIENCE (dietetics, economics, geography, history, human development, humanities, philosophy, political science/government, psychology, public administration, social work, sociology, and urban studies). Information and computing science, accounting, and music are the strongest academically. Business and communications have the largest enrollments.

Required: All students must complete at least 124 semester hours, including an average of 36 in the major, with a minimum GPA of 2.0 or higher, depending on the major. A 27-credit requirement in general education consists of 9 credits each in humanities and fine arts, social sciences, and natural sciences. Students must declare an interdisciplinary minor or major and must complete at least 30 credits in the discipline. A Senior Seminar, Other Culture Studies, and Ethnic Studies are needed; other course requirements vary by major.

Special: UWGB offers cross-registration with Bellin College of Nursing, and the Universities of Wisconsin at Milwaukee and Oshkosh. There are study-abroad programs in Mexico, Sweden, Denmark, Germany, France, and Ukraine. Students can receive credit by exam or for life, military, or work experience. Internships in social work, business, and other fields; dual, interdisciplinary, including communication and the arts, human biology, and regional planning, and student-designed majors; work-study, B.A.-B.S. degrees in most areas; nondegree study; a general studies degree; and pass/fail options are available. The Extended Degree Program, largely off campus, provides for individual study. There is one national honor society on campus.

Faculty/Classroom: Seventy-five percent of faculty are male; 25%, female. Ninety-five percent teach undergraduates and 95% both teach and do research. No introductory courses are taught by graduate students. The average class size in an introductory lecture is 85; in a laboratory, 20; and in a regular course offering, 25.

Admissions: About 80% of the 1993–94 applicants were accepted. The ACT scores for the 1993–94 freshman class were as follows: 32% below 21, 34% between 21 and 23, 24% between 24 and 26, 7% between 27 and 28, and 3% above 28. About 38% of the current freshmen were in the top fifth of their class; 80% were in the top two fifths. There were 3 National Merit semifinalists. Ten freshmen graduated first in their class.

Requirements: UWGB requires applicants to be in the upper 50% of their class. A minimum GPA of 2.5 is required. The ACT is required. Candidates must be graduates of an accredited secondary school or hold a GED certificate. They must have completed 17 academic credits consisting of 4 in English, 3 in social sciences, 3 each in science and mathematics, 2 in any of the above areas or a foreign language, and 2 other electives. AP and CLEP credits are accepted. Important factors used in the admissions decision are recommendations by school officials, evidence of special talent, advanced placement or honor courses, leadership record, and extracurricular activities record.

Procedure: Freshmen are admitted to all sessions. Entrance exams should be taken between the junior and senior years. Applications should be filed by February 1 for fall entry and December 15 for spring entry, along with an application fee of $25. Notification is sent on a rolling basis. There are early admissions and deferred admissions plans. A waiting list is an active part of the admissions procedure, with about 15% of applicants on the list.

Transfer: About 500 transfer students enrolled in 1993–94. Transfer students must submit ACT scores and have a minimum GPA of 2.0 based on at least 15 transferable credits; priority for admission is given to students with 24 credits and a 2.5 GPA. A total of 52 credits out of 124 must be completed at UWGB.

Visiting: There are regularly scheduled orientations for prospective students, including Campus Preview Days which consist of information sessions, academic area workshops, and campus tours. There are guides for informal visits and visitors may sit in on classes. To arrange for a visit, contact Myron Van deVen, Director of Admissions and Enrollment Services at (414) 465–2111.

Financial Aid: In a recent year, 52% of all current freshmen and 46% of continuing students received some form of financial aid. About 50% of freshmen and 45% of continuing students received need-based aid. The average freshman award was $2400. Of that total, scholarships or need-based grants averaged $2380 ($5000 maximum); loans averaged $2180 ($5000 maximum); and work contracts averaged $1700 ($3000 maximum). Sixty percent of undergraduate students work part-time. Average earnings from campus work for the school year are $1500. The average financial indebtedness of the 1992–93 graduate was $5000. UWGB is a member of CSS. The FAF, FFS, and other forms as requested are required. The deadline for financial aid applications is April 15.

International Students: There are currently 83 international students enrolled. The school actively recruits these students. They must take the TOEFL and achieve a minimum score of 500. The student must also take placement tests in mathematics and English as a second language.

Computers: The college provides computer facilities for student use. The mainframes are a DEC VAX 8530, and a Telefile T85. A computer account for mainframe access is available to students for $10 per semester. PC and networked terminals are widely available in computer laboratories, classrooms, and the Residence Community Center. All students may access the system. It may be used 7 A.M. to 12 A.M. There are no time limits on using the system.

Graduates: In 1992–93, 584 bachelor's degrees were awarded. The most popular majors among graduates were business administration (24%), human development (16%), and communications (6%). Within an average freshman class, 4% graduate in 3 years, 14% in 4 years, 32% in 5 years, and 36% in 6 years. Some 40 companies recruited on campus in 1992–93. In the 1992 graduating class, 11% of all graduates were enrolled in graduate school within 6 months of graduation; 89% had found employment.

Admissions Contact: Myron Van deVen, Director of Admissions and Enrollment Services.

UNIVERSITY OF WISCONSIN
LA CROSSE
La Crosse, WI 54601

B-4

(608) 785–8067

Full-time: 7306 men and women	**Faculty:** 365; IIA, -$
Part-time: 164 men and women	**Ph.D.s:** 78%
Graduate: 210 men, 436 women	**Student/Faculty:** 20 to 1
Year: semesters, summer session	**Tuition:** $2217 ($6665)
Application Deadline: September 15	**Room & Board:** $2270

Freshman Class: 4868 applied, 2877 accepted, 1727 enrolled
ACT: 22

COMPETITIVE

The University of Wisconsin/La Crosse, founded in 1909, is a public institution offering undergraduate and graduate studies in arts and sciences, health and human services, business administration, education, physical education and recreation, professional development, and educational administration. There are 5 undergraduate and 5 graduate schools. In addition to regional accreditation, UW/L has baccalaureate program accreditation with AACSB, APTA, CSWE, NASM, and NCATE. The library contains 524,269 volumes, 845,070 microform items, and 6994 audiovisual forms, and subscribes to 1900 periodicals. Computerized library sources and services include database searching. Special learning facilities include a learning resource center, an art gallery, a planetarium, a radio station, and a TV station. The 119-acre campus is in a small town 140 miles west of Madison. Including residence halls, there are 29 buildings on campus.

Student Life: About 85% of undergraduates are from Wisconsin. Students come from 33 states, 37 foreign countries, and Canada. Ninety percent are from public schools. Ninety-five percent are white. The average age of freshmen is 19; all undergraduates, 21. Twenty-five percent drop out by the end of their first year; 50% remain to graduate.

Housing: A total of 2836 students can be accommodated in college housing. College-sponsored living facilities include single-sex and coed dormitories. In addition there are special interest houses and a residence hall for international students and students 21 years or older. On-campus housing is available on a first-come, first-served basis and is available on a lottery system for upperclassmen. All students may keep cars on campus.

Activities: About 1% of men and women belong to 3 national fraternities; about 1% of women belong to 2 national sororities. There are 132 groups on campus, including art, band, cheerleading, chess, choir, chorale, chorus, computers, dance, drama, ethnic, gay, honors, international, jazz band, literary magazine, marching band, musical theater, newspaper, orchestra, pep band, photography, political, professional, radio and TV, religious, social, social service, student government, and symphony. Popular campus events include Homecoming, Parents Weekend, Big Chill, Coon Creek Canoe Races, a community-sponsored Oktoberfest, and various cultural events.

Sports: There are 10 intercollegiate sports for men and 9 for women, and 15 intramural sports for men and 13 for women. Athletic and recreation facilities include 3 regulation basketball courts, a wrestling room, an indoor track, an Olympic-size swimming pool, a strength-training room, a dance studio, racquetball courts, a 4363-seat stadium, a 2880-seat gymnasium, and an 880-seat auditorium.

Disabled Students: The entire campus is accessible to disabled students. The following facilities are available: wheelchair ramps, elevators, special parking, specially equipped rest rooms, special class scheduling, lowered drinking fountains, and lowered telephones.

Services: In addition to many counseling and information services, tutoring is available in most subjects. There is also a reader service for the blind and remedial math and writing. There is also a counseling and testing center and a writing laboratory.

Campus Safety and Security: Campus safety and security measures include 24-hour foot and vehicle patrol, self-defense education, escort service, and informal discussions. In addition, there are pamphlets, posters, films, emergency telephones, and lighted pathways and sidewalks.

Programs of Study: UW/L awards the B.A. and B.S. degrees. Associate and master's degrees also are awarded. Bachelor's degrees are awarded in BIOLOGICAL SCIENCE (biology/biological science and microbiology), BUSINESS (accounting, banking and finance, business administration and management, and marketing/retailing/merchandising), COMMUNICATIONS AND THE ARTS (communications, dramatic arts, English, fine arts, French, music, Spanish, and speech/debate/rhetoric), COMPUTER AND PHYSICAL SCIENCE (chemistry, computer science, mathematics, and physics), EDUCATION (elementary, health, physical, secondary, and social studies), HEALTH PROFESSIONS (medical laboratory technology, nuclear medical technology, physical therapy, and recreation therapy), SOCIAL SCIENCE (archeology, economics, geography, history, parks and recreation management, philosophy, political science/government, psychology, public administration, social work, and sociology). Physical therapy, microbiology, nuclear medicine technology, education, and business are the strongest academically. Business administration, elementary education, and physical therapy have the largest enrollments.

Required: To graduate, students must earn 128 semester credits, including 68 in subjects outside the major and at least 40 in 300- or 400-level courses. The minimum GPA is 2.0, though it is considerably higher for some programs. Distribution requirements include 30 to 40 credits in liberal studies and 13 to 19 credits in skill courses.

Special: Cooperative programs and cross-registration are available with Viterbo College. There are study-abroad programs in 8 countries, and an international student exchange program. UW/L also offers work-study programs, internships, nondegree study, credit by exam, and pass/fail options. There is a freshman honors program on campus, as well as 9 national honor societies. Eight departments have honors programs.

Faculty/Classroom: No introductory courses are taught by graduate students. The average class size in an introductory lecture is 45; in a laboratory, 27; and in a regular course offering, 30.

Admissions: About 59% of the 1993–94 applicants were accepted. The ACT scores for the 1993–94 freshman class were as follows: 27% below 21, 39% between 21 and 23, 23% between 24 and 26, 8% between 27 and 28, and 3% above 28. About 39% of the current freshmen were in the top fifth of their class; 82% were in the top two fifths. Thirty freshmen graduated first in their class.

Requirements: UW/L requires applicants to be in the upper 35% of their class. The ACT is required. Candidates must be graduates of an accredited secondary school or hold a GED certificate. They must have completed 16 academic credits, including 4 courses in English, 3 in social studies, 2 in science, 1 each in algebra and geometry, and 5 other academic courses. Students must rank in the top 35% of their high school graduating class or score a 23 or higher on the ACT. AP and CLEP credits are accepted. Important factors used in the admissions decision are recommendations by school officials, advanced placement or honor courses, leadership record, extracurricular activities record, and evidence of special talent.

Procedure: Freshmen are admitted to all sessions. Entrance exams should be taken toward the end of the junior year or at the beginning of the senior year. Applications should be filed by September 15 for fall entry and January 1 for spring entry, along with an application fee of $25. Notification is sent on a rolling basis. A waiting list is an active part of the admissions procedure, with about 1% of applicants on the list.

Transfer: About 320 transfer students enrolled in 1993–94. A minimum GPA of 2.8 overall is required. Acceptance is determined entirely from the college transcript. A total of 32 credits out of 128 must be completed at UW/L.

Visiting: There are regularly scheduled orientations for prospective students, including attendance at two academic sessions, a parent panel, a UW/L student panel, and a tour of the campus on 6 campus close-up programs. There are guides for informal visits and visitors may sit in on classes and stay overnight at the school. To arrange for a visit, contact the Admissions Office at (608) 785–8067.

Financial Aid: About 58% of freshmen received need-based aid. Scholarships or need-based grants averaged $1983 ($3500 maximum); loans averaged $2040 ($2625 maximum); and work contracts averaged $980 ($1400 maximum). Eight percent of undergraduate students work part-time. Average earnings from campus work for the school year are $980. The average financial indebtedness of the 1992–93 graduate was $7400. UW/L is a member of CSS. The FAF is required. The deadline for financial aid applications is March 15.

International Students: There are currently 110 international students enrolled. They must take the TOEFL and achieve a minimum score of 500.

Computers: The college provides computer facilities for student use. The mainframe is a DEC VAX 11/780. There are also 200 PCs, primarily IBM PC, Zenith-compatible, and Apple Macintosh, available in open laboratories and residence halls. All students may access the system. It may be used 24 hours a day. There are no time limits on using the system and no fees.

Graduates: In 1992–93, 1265 bachelor's degrees were awarded.

Admissions Contact: Timothy R. Lewis, Associate Director of Admissions.

UNIVERSITY OF WISCONSIN MADISON

Madison, WI 53706   C-4
                                              (608) 262–3961

Full-time: 24,280 men and women	Faculty: 2021; I, av$
Part-time: 2358 men and women	Ph.D.s: 95%
Graduate: 11,918 men and women	Student/Faculty: 12 to 1
Year: semesters, summer session	Tuition: $2400 ($8400)
Application Deadline: February 1	Room & Board: $4000
Freshman Class: 14,901 applied, 10,932 accepted, 4632 enrolled	
SAT I or ACT: required	**HIGHLY COMPETITIVE**

The University of Wisconsin/Madison, founded in 1849, is a public, land-grant institution offering undergraduate and graduate study in almost every major field. There are 9 undergraduate and 4 graduate schools. In addition to regional accreditation, Wisconsin has baccalaureate program accreditation with AACSB, ABET, ACEJMC, AHEA, ASLA, CSWE, NASAD, NASM, NCATE, and NLN. The 40 libraries contain 5.8 million volumes and 1.3 million microform items, and sub-

scribe to 51,000 periodicals. Computerized library sources and services include the card catalog. Special learning facilities include a learning resource center, art gallery, natural history museum, planetarium, radio station, and TV station. The 900-acre campus is in an urban area 75 miles west of Milwaukee and 150 miles north of Chicago. Including residence halls, there are 192 buildings on campus.

Student Life: About 65% of undergraduates are from Wisconsin. Students come from 50 states, 72 foreign countries, and Canada. About 70% are from public schools; 30% from private. Nearly 91% are white. The average age of freshmen is 18; all undergraduates, 21. Some 4% drop out by the end of their first year; 85% remain to graduate.

Housing: A total of 7975 students can be accommodated in college housing. College-sponsored living facilities include single-sex and coed dormitories, on-campus apartments, off-campus apartments, married-student housing, fraternity houses, and sorority houses. In addition, there are honors houses and language houses. On-campus housing is guaranteed for all 4 years. About 95% of students live on campus; of those, 90% remain on campus on weekends. All students may keep cars on campus.

Activities: About 10% of men belong to 27 national fraternities; about 10% of women belong to 10 national sororities. There are more than 900 groups on campus, including art, band, cheerleading, chess, choir, chorale, chorus, computers, dance, drama, ethnic, film, gay, honors, international, jazz band, literary magazine, marching band, musical theater, newspaper, opera, orchestra, pep band, photography, political, professional, radio and TV, religious, social, social service, student government, symphony, and yearbook. Popular campus events include Homecoming, football weekends, Parents Weekend, alumni reunions, and an annual band concert.

Sports: There are 11 intercollegiate sports for men and 9 for women, and 29 intramural sports for men and 24 for women. Athletic and recreation facilities include several gymnasiums (one seating 12,000), pools, a field house, 2 stadiums, one for tennis and the other seating 77,000, and a 12,000-seat arena.

Disabled Students: Almost 95% of the campus is accessible to disabled students. The following facilities are available: wheelchair ramps, elevators, special parking, specially equipped rest rooms, special class scheduling, lowered drinking fountains, and lowered telephones.

Services: In addition to many counseling and information services, tutoring is available in most subjects. There is also a reader service for the blind, and remedial math, reading, and writing.

Campus Safety and Security: Campus safety and security measures include 24-hour foot and vehicle patrol, self defense education, escort service, and shuttle buses. In addition, there are informal discussions, pamphlets, posters, films, emergency telephones, and lighted pathways and sidewalks.

Programs of Study: Wisconsin awards the B.A., B.S., B.Art Ed., B.B.A., B.F.A., B.M., B.S.Ch., B.S.E., and B.S.P. degrees. Master's and doctoral degrees also are awarded. Bachelor's degrees are awarded in AGRICULTURE (agricultural business management, agricultural economics, agricultural mechanics, animal science, dairy science, forestry and related sciences, horticulture, poultry science, and soil science), BIOLOGICAL SCIENCE (bacteriology, biochemistry, botany, entomology, genetics, microbiology, molecular biology, nutrition, plant pathology, toxicology, wildlife biology, and zoology), BUSINESS (accounting, banking and finance, business administration and management, insurance and risk management, marketing/retailing/merchandising, real estate, recreation and leisure services, and retailing), COMMUNICATIONS AND THE ARTS (African languages, art history and appreciation, Chinese, classics, communications, comparative literature, dramatic arts, English, French, German, Greek, Italian, Japanese, journalism, Latin, linguistics, music, Portuguese, Russian, and Spanish), COMPUTER AND PHYSICAL SCIENCE (actuarial science, applied mathematics, astronomy, atmospheric sciences and meteorology, chemistry, computer science, geology, information sciences and systems, mathematics, physics, quantitative methods, and statistics), EDUCATION (agricultural, art, elementary, physical, and secondary), ENGINEERING AND ENVIRONMENTAL DESIGN (agricultural engineering, cartography, chemical engineering, civil engineering, construction management, electrical/electronics engineering, engineering mechanics, engineering physics, geological engineering, industrial engineering, interior design, landscape architecture/design, mechanical engineering, metallurgical engineering, nuclear engineering, and textile technology), HEALTH PROFESSIONS (medical laboratory technology, medical science, nursing, occupational therapy, pharmacy, physical therapy, physician's assistant, and speech pathology/audiology), SOCIAL SCIENCE (anthropology, Asian/Oriental studies, behavioral science, child care/child and family studies, consumer services, dietetics, economics, family/consumer studies, food science, geography, history, history of science, humanities, international relations, Judaic studies, philosophy, political science/government, psychology, rural sociology, Scandinavian studies, social work, sociology, South Asian studies, textiles and clothing, and women's studies). Political science, psychology, and English have the largest enrollments.

Required: Required courses vary with individual programs. A total of 120 to 130 credit hours, with at least 30 in the major, and a cumulative GPA of 2.0 are minimum requirements for graduation.

Special: Co-op programs in engineering, internships in political science in Washington, D.C., and the state capital are possible. Study abroad is offered in more than 40 countries in Europe, Asia, and South America. Work-study programs, credit by exam, and pass/fail options are available. Students in the College of Letters and Science may select dual or self-designed majors, or an integrated liberal studies program. There is a freshman honors program on campus, as well as 24 national honor societies, including Phi Beta Kappa.

Faculty/Classroom: About 84% of faculty are male; 16%, female. All do research and 95% teach undergraduates. The average class size in an introductory lecture is 75; in a laboratory, 15; and in a regular course offering, 30.

Admissions: About 73% of the 1993–94 applicants were accepted. The SAT scores for the 1993–94 freshman class were as follows: Verbal—35% below 500, 39% between 500 and 599, 20% between 600 and 700, and 6% above 700; Math—14% below 500, 33% between 500 and 599, 35% between 600 and 700, and 18% above 700. The ACT scores were 2% below 21, 24% between 21 and 23, 33% between 24 and 26, 20% between 27 and 28, and 21% above 28. About 67% of the current freshmen were in the top fifth of their class; 96% were in the top two fifths. There were 150 National Merit finalists. Seventy-eight freshmen graduated first in their class.

Requirements: The ACT is required for in-state students, and either the ACT or the SAT I for out-of-state students. Candidates should be graduates of an accredited secondary school or hold a GED certificate. They must have completed 16 academic credits, including 4 in English, and 3 each in mathematics, history, social studies, a foreign language, science, and college-preparatory electives. Grades, rank in class, and scores, as well as rigor of senior class course selection are considered. AP and CLEP credits are accepted. Important factors used in the admissions decision are advanced placement or honor courses, evidence of special talent, parents or siblings attending the school, geographic diversity, and recommendations by school officials.

Procedure: Freshmen are admitted to all sessions. Entrance exams should be taken in the junior year, preferably. Applications should be filed by February 1 for fall entry, November 15 for spring entry, and February 1 for summer entry, along with an application fee of $25. Notification is sent on a rolling basis. There are early admissions and deferred admissions plans. A waiting list is an active part of the admissions procedure, with about 5% of applicants on the list.

Transfer: About 1378 transfer students enrolled in a recent year. Admission is competitive and varies by program. Generally, applicants must have at least sophomore standing and a GPA of 3.2 or higher. A total of 30 credits, including at least half in the major field, out of 120 to 130 must be completed at Wisconsin.

Visiting: There are regularly scheduled orientations for prospective students, including an admission information session, a tour, and class visits. There are guides for informal visits and visitors may sit in on classes and stay overnight at the school. To arrange for a visit, contact the Tour Coordinator, Office of Admissions at (608) 262-3318.

Financial Aid: In 1993–94, 45% of all current freshmen and 37% of continuing students received some form of financial aid. About 30% of freshmen and 31% of continuing students received need-based aid. The average freshman award was $4400. Of that total, scholarships or need-based grants averaged $1365 ($4250 maximum); loans averaged $1650 ($3825 maximum); and work contracts averaged $1300 ($1700 maximum). The average financial indebtedness of the 1992–93 graduate was $8369. Wisconsin is a member of CSS. The FAF or FFS, the college's own financial statement, and a federal income tax return are required. The deadline for financial aid applications is March 1.

International Students: There are currently 3628 international students enrolled. They must take the TOEFL or the University of Michigan Language Test. The student must also take the SAT I or the ACT.

Computers: The college provides computer facilities for student use. The mainframes are a DEC VAX 8600, 6300, and 6200. There are also 1,000 IBM PS/2 and Apple Macintosh PCs available in 15 open laboratories and dormitories. All students may access the system. There are no time limits on using the system and no fees.

Graduates: In a recent year, 3177 bachelor's degrees were awarded. The most popular majors among graduates were political science (7%), English (5%), and psychology (5%). Within an average freshman class, 10% graduate in 3 years, 33% in 4 years, 82% in 5 years, and 85% in 6 years. Some 900 companies recruited on campus in a recent year.

Admissions Contact: Millard Storey, Director of Admissions.

UNIVERSITY OF WISCONSIN MILWAUKEE
E-4

Milwaukee, WI 53201 (414) 229-6164

Full-time: 5738 men, 5781 women	Faculty: 868; I, --$
Part-time: 3292 men, 4305 women	Ph.D.s: 90%
Graduate: 2010 men, 2668 women	Student/Faculty: 13 to 1
Year: semesters, summer session	Tuition: $2725 ($8721)
Application Deadline: June 30	Room & Board: $3440
Freshman Class: 5141 applied, 3760 accepted, 1930 enrolled	
ACT: 22	COMPETITIVE

The University of Wisconsin/Milwaukee, founded in 1885, offers undergraduate and graduate degrees in arts and sciences, fine arts, business, education, engineering and applied sciences, architecture and urban planning, social welfare, and health fields. There are 15 undergraduate schools and one graduate school. The library contains 1.4 million volumes, 1 million microform items, and 18,500 audiovisual forms, and subscribes to 10,400 periodicals. Computerized library sources and services include database searching. Special learning facilities include a learning resource center, an art gallery, a planetarium, a TV station, and a geological museum. The 93-acre campus is in an urban area 90 miles north of Chicago. Including residence halls, there are 41 buildings on campus.

Student Life: About 94% of undergraduates are from Wisconsin. Students come from 40 states, 69 foreign countries, and Canada. Eighty-four percent are white. The average age of freshmen is 20; all undergraduates, 23.

Housing: A total of 1950 students can be accommodated in college housing. College-sponsored living facilities include coed dormitories. On-campus housing is available on a first-come, first-served basis. Ninety-two percent of students commute. All students may keep cars on campus.

Activities: About 3% of men belong to 1 local and 6 national fraternities; about 3% of women belong to 6 national sororities. There are 250 groups on campus, including art, band, cheerleading, chorale, computers, dance, drama, ethnic, film, gay, honors, international, literary magazine, musical theater, newspaper, orchestra, pep band, photography, political, professional, radio and TV, religious, social, social service, student government, and symphony. Popular campus events include concerts, art exhibitions, dance performances, and films.

Sports: There are 9 intercollegiate sports for men and 8 for women, and 15 intramural sports for men and 13 for women. Athletic and recreation facilities include a center for physical education, a gymnasium, a field, courts, and a 3000-seat auditorium.

Disabled Students: Ninety percent of the campus is accessible to disabled students. The following facilities are available: wheelchair ramps, elevators, special parking, specially equipped rest rooms, special class scheduling, lowered drinking fountains, lowered telephones, and special library facilities.

Services: In addition to many counseling and information services, tutoring is available in some subjects, including English composition, mathematics, science, business, reading, and study skills. There is also a reader service for the blind, and remedial math, reading, and writing.

Campus Safety and Security: Campus safety and security measures include shuttle buses, pamphlets, posters, films, emergency telephones, and lighted pathways and sidewalks.

Programs of Study: UWM awards the B.A., B.S., B.B.A., B.F.A., B.S. Applied S., and B.S.E. degrees. Associate, master's, and doctoral degrees also are awarded. Bachelor's degrees are awarded in AGRICULTURE (conservation and regulation), BIOLOGICAL SCIENCE (biochemistry, biology/biological science, botany, microbiology, and zoology), BUSINESS (accounting, banking and finance, business administration and management, management information systems, marketing/retailing/merchandising, real estate, and recreation and leisure services), COMMUNICATIONS AND THE ARTS (art history and appreciation, classics, communications, comparative literature, dance, dramatic arts, English, film arts, fine arts, French, German, Hebrew, Italian, linguistics, music, Russian, and Spanish), COMPUTER AND PHYSICAL SCIENCE (applied mathematics, chemistry, computer science, geology, geoscience, mathematics, and physics), EDUCATION (art, education, music, and social science), ENGINEERING AND ENVIRONMENTAL DESIGN (architecture, civil engineering, electrical/electronics engineering, engineering, industrial administration/management, industrial engineering, materials engineering, and mechanical engineering), HEALTH PROFESSIONS (clinical science, health care administration, health science, medical science, nursing, occupational therapy, pharmacy, predentistry, premedicine, and speech pathology/audiology), SOCIAL SCIENCE (African American studies, anthropology, criminal justice, economics, geography, history, law, philosophy, political science/government, prelaw, psychology, religion, social work, and sociology). Architecture and engineering are the strongest academically.

Required: English composition and mathematics proficiency examinations must be passed with satisfactory scores. Distribution requirements include 6 credits each in humanities, natural sciences, and social sciences and 3 credits each in the arts and cultural diversity. All students must complete a minimum of 120 credits.

Special: UWM offers cooperative programs in engineering, cross-registration with UW/Parkside, study abroad in Europe and Asia, internships, a Washington semester, and work-study programs. Students may select an accelerated degree program, dual majors, a general studies degree, and student-designed majors. Credit/no credit options, nondegree study, credit by examination, and credit for life, military, and work experience are also available. There is a freshman honors program on campus, as well as one national honor society, Phi Beta Kappa. Two departments have honors programs.

Faculty/Classroom: Seventy-one percent of faculty are male; 29%, female. All teach undergraduates. The average class size in an introductory lecture is 48; in a laboratory, 15; and in a regular course offering, 27.

Admissions: About 73% of the 1993–94 applicants were accepted. The ACT scores for the 1993–94 freshman class were as follows: 35% below 21, 35% between 21 and 23, 19% between 24 and 26, 6% between 27 and 28, and 5% above 28. About 25% of the current freshmen were in the top fifth of their class; 56% were in the top two fifths. Thirteen freshmen graduated first in their class.

Requirements: UWM requires applicants to be in the upper 50% of their class. The SAT I or ACT is required. A minimum score of 21 on the ACT is required of all Wisconsin residents. Out-of-state students may substitute the SAT I with a minimum composite score of 920. Candidates must have graduated from an accredited secondary school with 16 Carnegie units consisting of at least 4 in English, 3 in history/social science, 1 each in algebra, geometry, biology or chemistry laboratory, and an additional science, and the remainder in academic electives. A GED certificate is accepted. Music and theater majors must audition. AP and CLEP credits are accepted. Important factors used in the admissions decision are geographic diversity, advanced placement or honor courses, evidence of special talent, extracurricular activities record, and leadership record.

Procedure: Freshmen are admitted to all sessions. Applications should be filed by June 30 for fall entry and November 15 for spring entry, along with an application fee of $25. Notification is sent on a rolling basis.

Transfer: About 1400 transfer students enrolled in 1993–94. Transfer applicants must have earned a minimum of 12 credit hours and have at least a 2.0 GPA. A total of 30 credits out of 120 must be completed at UWM.

Visiting: There are regularly scheduled orientations for prospective students. Visitors may stay overnight at the school. To arrange for a visit, contact the Student Visitor Center at (414) 229–4397.

Financial Aid: In 1993–94, 54% of all current freshmen and 33% of continuing students received some form of financial aid. The average freshman award was $1300. Of that total, scholarships or need-based grants averaged $1001; loans averaged $1937 ($3825 maximum); and work contracts averaged $1468 ($2000 maximum). The average financial indebtedness of the 1992–93 graduate was $8000. UWM is a member of CSS. The FAF or FFS is required. The deadline for financial aid applications is March 1.

International Students: There are currently 254 international students enrolled. They must take the TOEFL, the University of Michigan Language Test, the Comprehensive English Language Test, or the college's own test.

Computers: The college provides computer facilities for student use. The mainframe is a Convex C220 and a Unisys Unix. Microcomputers are available in the library, residence halls, and the student union. All students may access the system. It may be used any time. There are no time limits on using the system and no fees.

Graduates: In 1992–93, 2678 bachelor's degrees were awarded. The most popular majors among graduates were marketing (6%), education (6%), and accounting (6%). Within an average freshman class, 10% graduate in 4 years, 26% in 5 years, and 35% in 6 years. Some 166 companies recruited on campus in 1992–93.

Admissions Contact: Beth Weckmueller, Director of Admissions.

UNIVERSITY OF WISCONSIN OSHKOSH

Oshkosh, WI 54901   **D-4**

(414) 424–0202; (800) 624–4266 (in-state)

Full-time: 3357 men, 4504 women	Faculty: 418; IIA, -$
Part-time: 553 men, 867 women	Ph.D.s: 77%
Graduate: 552 men, 920 women	Student/Faculty: 19 to 1
Year: semesters, summer session	Tuition: $2040 ($6500)
Application Deadline: open	Room & Board: $2200
Freshman Class: 4800 applied, 3000 accepted, 1517 enrolled	
ACT: required	COMPETITIVE

The University of Wisconsin/Oshkosh, founded in 1871, is a public institution offering undergraduate and graduate programs in education, business, the arts and sciences, and health fields. There are 4 undergraduate and 5 graduate schools. In addition to regional accreditation, UW/Oshkosh has baccalaureate program accreditation with AACSB, ACEJMC, CSWE, NASM, NCATE, and NLN. The library contains 439,614 volumes, 1,523,260 microform items, and 15,692 audiovisual forms, and subscribes to 1787 periodicals. Computerized library sources and services include the card catalog, interlibrary loans, and database searching. Special learning facilities include a

learning resource center, an art gallery, a planetarium, a radio station, and a TV station. The 192-acre campus is in an urban area 90 miles north of Milwaukee. Including residence halls, there are 36 buildings on campus.

Student Life: About 96% of undergraduates are from Wisconsin. Students come from 30 states, 32 foreign countries, and Canada. Ninety-five percent are white. The average age of freshmen is 18; all undergraduates, 23. Twenty-five percent drop out by the end of their first year; 50% remain to graduate.

Housing: A total of 4278 students can be accommodated in college housing. College-sponsored living facilities include single-sex and coed dormitories. On-campus housing is guaranteed for all 4 years. Sixty-two percent of students commute. All students may keep cars on campus.

Activities: About 2% of men belong to 8 national fraternities; about 3% of women belong to 1 local and 7 national sororities. There are 150 groups on campus, including art, band, cheerleading, chess, choir, computers, dance, ethnic, gay, honors, international, jazz band, musical theater, newspaper, pep band, political, professional, radio and TV, religious, social, social service, student government, and symphony. Popular campus events include Homecoming, Winter Carnival, and the University Speakers series.

Sports: There are 9 intercollegiate sports for men and 9 for women, and 15 intramural sports for men and 15 for women. Athletic and recreation facilities include a hall for basketball, swimming and volleyball; a sports center for basketball, tennis, and indoor track; a 10400-seat stadium for football and outdoor track; a 2500-seat indoor gymnasium; and a 5808-seat arena.

Disabled Students: All of the campus is accessible to disabled students. The following facilities are available: wheelchair ramps, elevators, special parking, specially equipped rest rooms, special class scheduling, lowered drinking fountains, and lowered telephones.

Services: In addition to many counseling and information services, tutoring is available in most subjects. There is also a reader service for the blind, and remedial math, reading, and writing. There is a writing laboratory.

Campus Safety and Security: Campus safety and security measures include escort service, informal discussions, pamphlets, posters, films, and lighted pathways and sidewalks.

Programs of Study: UW/Oshkosh awards the B.A., B.S., B.Art Ed., B.B.A., B.F.A., B.L.S., B.M., B.M.E., B.S.N., and B.S.W. degrees. Associate and master's degrees also are awarded. Bachelor's degrees are awarded in BIOLOGICAL SCIENCE (biology/biological science and microbiology), BUSINESS (business administration and management), COMMUNICATIONS AND THE ARTS (broadcasting, English, fine arts, French, German, journalism, music, Spanish, and speech/debate/rhetoric), COMPUTER AND PHYSICAL SCIENCE (chemistry, computer science, geology, mathematics, and physics), EDUCATION (art, elementary, music, physical, secondary, social science, and special), HEALTH PROFESSIONS (medical laboratory technology, music therapy, nursing, and speech pathology/audiology), SOCIAL SCIENCE (anthropology, criminal justice, economics, geography, history, human services, international studies, liberal arts/general studies, philosophy, political science/government, psychology, religion, social work, sociology, and urban studies). Business, education, and nursing have the largest enrollments.

Required: All students must complete a minimum of 128 credit hours with at least a 2.0 GPA overall. A minimum of 42 credits in general education requirements includes 9 credits each in humanities and social science, 8 in natural science, 6 in English composition, 3 each in mathematics or logic, non-Western culture, and speech, and 2 in physical education.

Special: UW/Oshkosh offers internships, study abroad options, and a Washington semester. Credit by exam and for life, military, and work experience are possible. Nondegree study and pass/fail options are also offered. There is a freshman honors program on campus, as well as 14 national honor societies.

Faculty/Classroom: Sixty-one percent of faculty are male; 39%, female. The average class size in an introductory lecture is 36 and in a laboratory, 21.

Admissions: About 63% of the 1993–94 applicants were accepted. The ACT scores for the 1993–94 freshman class were as follows: 42% below 21, 31% between 21 and 23, 18% between 24 and 26, 6% between 27 and 28, and 3% above 28. About 36% of the current freshmen were in the top fifth of their class; 77% were in the top two fifths. There were 6 National Merit finalists. Twenty freshmen graduated first in their class.

Requirements: UW/Oshkosh requires applicants to be in the upper 50% of their class. The ACT is required, with a minimum required score of 23. Students must graduate in the upper 50% of an accredited secondary school. They should have completed 17 academic credits, including 4 in English, 3 each in mathematics and social sciences (with 1 in history), 2 in science, and 4 in electives, preferably in a foreign language or fine arts/humanities. AP and CLEP credits are accepted.

Procedure: Freshmen are admitted to all sessions. Entrance exams should be taken in June or October. Application deadlines are open. Application fee is $25. Notification is sent on a rolling basis. There is

a deferred admissions plan. A waiting list is an active part of the admissions procedure, with about 10% of applicants on the list.

Transfer: About 816 transfer students enrolled in 1993–94. Candidates should have completed 30 or more semester credits; if not, high school transcripts are reviewed. Preference is given to students with at least a 2.5 GPA overall. Admission may be offered to those with a 2.0 to 2.4 GPA on a space-available basis. A total of 30 credits out of 128 must be completed at UW/Oshkosh.

Visiting: There are regularly scheduled orientations for prospective students, preview days are held 4 times a year. Tours are given at 10:30 A.M. and 2:00 P.M. There are guides for informal visits and visitors may sit in on classes and stay overnight at the school. To arrange for a visit, contact the Admissions and Gruenhagen Conference Center at (800) 624–1466.

Financial Aid: In 1993–94, 52% of all students received some form of financial aid. About 47% received need-based aid. The average freshman award was $2375. Of that total, scholarships or need-based grants averaged $950; loans averaged $1650; and work contracts averaged $600. Ninety-two percent of undergraduate students work part-time. Average earnings from campus work for the school year are $900. The FAF, FFS or SFS is required. The deadline for financial aid applications is March 15.

International Students: There are currently 100 international students enrolled. They must take the TOEFL and achieve a minimum score of 500.

Computers: The college provides computer facilities for student use. The mainframes are a DEC VAX 11/780 and 8250. There are also 125 Apple IIe, IBM PC and IBM PS/2 Model 50Z microcomputers. All students may access the system. It may be used 24 hours, 7 days a week. There are no time limits on using the system and no fees.

Graduates: In 1992–93, 1666 bachelor's degrees were awarded. The most popular majors among graduates were marketing (9%), elementary education (9%), and nursing (8%). Within an average freshman class, 50% graduate in 6 years. Some 271 companies recruited on campus in 1992–93.

Admissions Contact: Richard M. Hillman, Assistant Director of Admissions.

UNIVERSITY OF WISCONSIN
PARKSIDE
E-5

Kenosha, WI 53141–2000   (414) 595–2345

Full-time undergraduate and graduate: 3004 men and women	Faculty: IIA, -$
	Ph.D.s: 86%
Part-time undergraduate and graduate: 1979 men and women	Student/Faculty: 17 to 1
	Tuition: $2137 ($6585)
Year: semesters, summer session	Room & Board: $3110

Application Deadline: August 14
Freshman Class: 1965 applied, 1340 accepted, 779 enrolled
ACT: 20

COMPETITIVE

The University of Wisconsin/Parkside, founded in 1968, offers undergraduate programs in liberal arts, business, education, and science and technology. There are 4 undergraduate and 3 graduate schools. The library contains 350,000 volumes, 150,000 microform items, and 10,200 audiovisual forms, and subscribes to 1500 periodicals. Computerized library sources and services include the card catalog. Special learning facilities include a learning resource center, an art gallery, and a radio station. The 700-acre campus is in a suburban area 30 miles south of Milwaukee. Including residence halls, there are 11 buildings on campus.

Student Life: About 95% of undergraduates are from Wisconsin. Ninety-one percent are white. Twenty-two percent drop out by the end of their first year; 60% remain to graduate.

Housing: A total of 400 students can be accommodated in college housing. College-sponsored living facilities include coed on-campus apartments and off-campus apartments. In addition, there are special interest houses. On-campus housing is guaranteed for all 4 years. Fifty-two percent of students commute. All students may keep cars on campus.

Activities: There are no fraternities or sororities on campus. There are 60 groups on campus, including art, band, cheerleading, choir, chorale, chorus, computers, drama, ethnic, gay, honors, international, jazz band, literary magazine, musical theater, newspaper, orchestra, political, professional, religious, social, social service, student government, and yearbook. Popular campus events include Cinco de Mayo, Winter Carnival, Homecoming, Welcome Week, Hispanic Heritage Week, Black History Month, and Daytona Beach Spring Fling.

Sports: Athletic and recreation facilities include a national/cross-country course, tennis courts, playing fields, and an all-purpose physical education building with a 3000-seat auditorium for athletic events and concerts.

Disabled Students: All of the campus is accessible to disabled students. The following facilities are available: wheelchair ramps, elevators, special parking, specially equipped rest rooms, lowered drinking fountains, and lowered telephones.

Services: In addition to many counseling and information services, tutoring is available in every subject. There is a reader service for the blind, and remedial math, reading, and writing.

Campus Safety and Security: Campus safety and security measures include shuttle buses, pamphlets, posters, films, emergency telephones, and lighted pathways and sidewalks.

Programs of Study: UW/Parkside awards the B.A. and B.S. degrees. Master's degrees are also awarded. Bachelor's degrees are awarded in BIOLOGICAL SCIENCE (biology/biological science), BUSINESS (business administration and management), COMMUNICATIONS AND THE ARTS (communications, dramatic arts, English, fine arts, French, German, music, and Spanish), COMPUTER AND PHYSICAL SCIENCE (chemistry, computer science, geology, mathematics, physics, and science), EDUCATION (education), ENGINEERING AND ENVIRONMENTAL DESIGN (industrial administration/management), SOCIAL SCIENCE (economics, geography, history, humanities, international studies, philosophy, political science/government, psychology, and sociology). Social sciences and physical sciences are the strongest academically. Business has the largest enrollment.

Required: A total of 120 credits with at least 30 in the major and a GPA of 2.0 are required for graduation. Students must complete a minimum of 12 credits in humanities and the arts, 12 in social and behavioral sciences, and 9 in natural sciences. Nonengineering majors with fewer than 2 units of foreign language in high school must also fulfill a foreign language requirement.

Special: UW/Parkside offers on-campus work-study programs, internships, study abroad, student-designed majors, and an accelerated premedicine program. Nondegree study and credit by exam are possible. There is a freshman honors program on campus.

Faculty/Classroom: No introductory courses are taught by graduate students. The average class size in an introductory lecture is 150; in a laboratory, 50; and in a regular course offering, 30.

Admissions: About 68% of the 1993–94 applicants were accepted. Five freshmen graduated first in their class.

Requirements: UW/Parkside requires applicants to be in the upper 50% of their class. The ACT is required for in-state students; either the ACT or SAT I for out-of-state students. A minimum score of 21 is required on the ACT. Students may use a lower ACT score in combination with class rank to gain admission. Candidates must be graduates of an accredited secondary school or hold a GED diploma. At least 16 academic credits are required, including 4 in English, 3 in social sciences, 2 in natural sciences, and 1 each in algebra and plane geometry. AP and CLEP credits are accepted. Important factors used in the admissions decision are recommendations by school officials, advanced placement or honor courses, leadership record, parents or siblings attending the school, and personality and other intangible qualities.

Procedure: Freshmen are admitted fall and spring. Entrance exams should be taken by the fall of the senior year. Applications should be filed by August 14 for fall entry and January 10 for spring entry, along with an application fee of $25. Notification is sent on a rolling basis. There are early admissions and deferred admissions plans.

Transfer: About 400 transfer students enrolled in a recent year. Students must have a GPA of 2.0 and be in good standing with the previous institution attended. A total of 30 credits out of 120 must be completed at UW/Parkside.

Visiting: There are regularly scheduled orientations for prospective students, including open houses and campus tours. There are guides for informal visits and visitors may sit in on classes. To arrange for a visit, contact Student Enrollment Services at (414) 595–2355.

Financial Aid: In a recent year, 34% of all current freshmen and 30% of continuing students received some form of financial aid. The FAF or FFS and the college's own financial statement are required. The deadline for financial aid applications is April 15.

International Students: There were recently 27 international students enrolled. They must take the TOEFL and achieve a minimum score of 525.

Computers: The college provides computer facilities for student use. The mainframe is an IBM 4381. There are also 50 IBM, Apple Macintosh, Zenith, and Apple IIe microcomputers available in the library/learning center. Two general-purpose laboratories are available to all students. There are no time limits on using the system and no fees.

Graduates: In a recent year, 415 bachelor's degrees were awarded.

Admissions Contact: Charles Murphy, Admissions Director.

UNIVERSITY OF WISCONSIN
PLATTEVILLE
C-5

Platteville, WI 53818–3099   (608) 342–1125
            (800) 362–5515 (in-state)

Full-time: 3290 men, 1620 women	Faculty: 226; IIA, -$
Part-time: none	Ph.D.s: 65%
Graduate: 76 men, 148 women	Student/Faculty: 22 to 1
Year: semesters, summer session	Tuition: $2208 ($6271)
Application Deadline: January 1	Room & Board: $2622

Freshman Class: 2715 applied, 2000 accepted, 917 enrolled
ACT: 23

COMPETITIVE

The University of Wisconsin/Platteville, founded in 1866, offers undergraduate programs in arts and sciences, agriculture, education, engineering, communication, business, and industry. There are 5 un-

dergraduate schools and one graduate school. In addition to regional accreditation, UW/Platteville has baccalaureate program accreditation with ABET, ABFSE, and NASM. The library contains 265,126 volumes, 731,921 microform items, and 8184 audiovisual forms, and subscribes to 1770 periodicals. Special learning facilities include a learning resource center, an art gallery, a radio station, and a TV station. The 340-acre campus is in a small town 20 miles northeast of Dubuque, Iowa and 75 miles southwest of Madison. Including residence halls, there are 65 buildings on campus.

Student Life: About 93% of undergraduates are from Wisconsin. Ninety percent are from public schools; 10% from private. Ninety-five percent are white. Sixty percent are Protestant; 30% Catholic. The average age of freshmen is 18.2. Twenty-two percent drop out by the end of their first year; 49% remain to graduate.

Housing: A total of 2306 students can be accommodated in college housing. College-sponsored living facilities include single-sex and coed dormitories and fraternity houses. In addition there are intensive-study quiet floors, an engineering hall, and a computing technology hall. On-campus housing is guaranteed for all 4 years and is available on a first-come, first-served basis. All students may keep cars on campus.

Activities: About 2% of men and about 1% of women belong to 1 local and 9 national fraternities; about 5% of women belong to 1 local and 3 national sororities. There are 92 groups on campus, including art, band, cheerleading, chess, choir, chorale, chorus, computers, drama, drill team, ethnic, film, gay, honors, international, jazz band, literary magazine, marching band, musical theater, newspaper, opera, orchestra, pep band, photography, political, professional, radio and TV, religious, social, social service, student government, symphony, and yearbook. Popular campus events include Family Weekend, Music and Art Festival, Shakespeare Festival, Black History Week, Homecoming, international student dinners, Madrigal, Residence Hall Week, Welcome Week, Celebrate Diversity Week, February Follies, and Student Appreciation Day.

Sports: There are 7 intercollegiate sports for men and 6 for women, and 17 intramural sports for men and 16 for women. Athletic and recreation facilities include a 2000-seat gymnasium, a 10,000-seat stadium, a 200-meter indoor track, a 400-meter outdoor track, 7 basketball courts, 7 volleyball, 6 tennis, and 4 racquetball courts, a weight room, a swimming pool, a baseball diamond, and soccer fields.

Disabled Students: Ninety-five percent of the campus is accessible to disabled students. The following facilities are available: wheelchair ramps, elevators, special parking, specially equipped rest rooms, special class scheduling, lowered drinking fountains, and lowered telephones.

Services: In addition to many counseling and information services, tutoring is available in most subjects. There is a reader service for the blind, and remedial math, reading, and writing.

Campus Safety and Security: Campus safety and security measures include 24-hour foot and vehicle patrol, escort service, informal discussions, and pamphlets, posters, and films. In addition, there are emergency telephones, lighted pathways and sidewalks, and locked residence halls.

Programs of Study: UW/Platteville awards the B.A. and B.S. degrees. Associate and master's degrees are also awarded. Bachelor's degrees are awarded in AGRICULTURE (agricultural business management, agricultural economics, animal science, and soil science), BIOLOGICAL SCIENCE (biology/biological science), BUSINESS (accounting, business administration and management, business economics, and management science), COMMUNICATIONS AND THE ARTS (English, fine arts, French, German, music, Spanish, and speech/debate/rhetoric), COMPUTER AND PHYSICAL SCIENCE (chemistry, computer science, mathematics, physical sciences, physics, and science), EDUCATION (agricultural, art, elementary, middle school, music, physical, science, secondary, and technical), ENGINEERING AND ENVIRONMENTAL DESIGN (agricultural engineering technology, civil engineering, electrical/electronics engineering, engineering, industrial engineering, industrial engineering technology, land use management and reclamation, and mechanical engineering), SOCIAL SCIENCE (criminal justice, economics, geography, history, international studies, philosophy, political science/government, psychology, and social science). Engineering, middle school education, technology management, criminal justice and agriculture are the strongest academically. Engineering has the largest enrollment.

Required: To graduate, students must complete a minimum of 128 credit hours, with a minimum GPA of 2.0 overall and within the major. Course requirements include 12 credits in humanities and fine arts, 9 each in social sciences and natural sciences, 4 in ethnic and gender studies, and 3 in international education. Other competency requirements include 6 in English composition, 3 in mathematics, and 2 each in speech and physical education.

Special: UW/Platteville offers internships in business, industry, and communication, a co-op program in engineering, and study abroad in 12 countries. Credit by exam, credit for life, military, and work experience, work-study programs, student-designed majors, nondegree study, and pass/fail options are also available. There is a freshman honors program on campus, as well as 12 national honor societies. Four departments have honors programs.

Faculty/Classroom: Eighty percent of faculty are male; 20%, female. Ninety-nine percent teach undergraduates. No introductory courses are taught by graduate students. The average class size in an introductory lecture is 30; in a laboratory, 20; and in a regular course offering, 22.

Admissions: About 74% of the 1993–94 applicants were accepted. About 38% of the current freshmen were in the top fifth of their class; 80% were in the top two fifths. There were 2 National Merit finalists. Twenty-five freshmen graduated first in their class.

Requirements: UW/Platteville requires applicants to be in the upper 65% of their class. The ACT is required, with a minimum score of 22 or a class rank in the upper 40%. Applicants must be graduates of an accredited secondary school or hold the GED certificate. Special permission may be granted from the dean for nontraditional students. Academic preparation should include 4 credits in English, 3 in social sciences, 2 each in mathematics and natural sciences, 3 in any of the above or in a foreign language, and 2 in other academic areas. AP and CLEP subject credits are accepted. Important factors used in the admissions decision are ability to finance college education, recommendations by school officials, advanced placement or honor courses, evidence of special talent, and leadership record.

Procedure: Freshmen are admitted to all sessions. Entrance exams should be taken in April or June of the junior year. Applications should be filed by January 1 for fall entry, along with an application fee of $25. Notification is sent on a rolling basis. There is a deferred admissions plan. A waiting list is an active part of the admissions procedure, with about 16% of applicants on the list.

Transfer: About 190 transfer students enrolled in 1993–94. Out-of-state applicants must have a college GPA of 3.0 and be in good standing at their current or previous institution. Wisconsin residents should have a GPA of 2.5 and a minimum of 14 college credits. All transfer students must have completed 6 semester credits of UW/Platteville's English requirement, and 3 semester credits of public speaking. A total of 32 credits out of 128 must be completed at UW/Platteville.

Visiting: There are regularly scheduled orientations for prospective students. The Pioneer Previews, held on 4 or 5 dates each year, include group tours, an admissions briefing, and visits to specific colleges and departments. There are guides for informal visits and visitors may sit in on classes. To arrange for a visit, contact Richard Schumacher, Dean of Admissions and Enrollment Management, at (608) 342–1125 or (800) 362–5515 (in-state).

Financial Aid: In 1993–94, 76% of all current freshmen and 74% of continuing students received some form of financial aid. About 65% of all students received need-based aid. The average freshman award was $2776. Of that total, scholarships or need-based grants averaged $1527 ($2300 maximum); loans averaged $1401 ($2625 maximum); and work contracts averaged $800 ($2000 maximum). Thirty percent of undergraduate students work part-time. Average earnings from campus work for the school year are $1021. The average financial indebtedness of the 1992–93 graduate was $7500. UW/Platteville is a member of CSS. The FFS is required. The deadline for financial aid applications is March 15.

International Students: There are currently 42 international students enrolled. They must take the TOEFL and achieve a minimum score of 550. The student must also take the ACT, or the Wisconsin English and mathematics placement exam.

Computers: The college provides computer facilities for student use. The mainframes are DEC VAX 4000 series servers and an IBM 9375. There are 80 networked (Intel and Macintosh) microcomputers and 37 terminals available to students in general-access laboratories across campus. All students may access the system. There are no time limits on using the system and no fees.

Graduates: In 1992–93, 838 bachelor's degrees were awarded. The most popular majors among graduates were business administration (15%), mechanical engineering (8%), and civil engineering (8%). Within an average freshman class, 48% graduate in 6 years.

Admissions Contact: Richard R. Schumacher, Dean of Admissions and Enrollment Management.

UNIVERSITY OF WISCONSIN RIVER FALLS

A-3

River Falls, WI 54022 — (715) 425–3500

Full-time: 2292 men, 2971 women	Faculty: 275; IIA, -$
Part-time: none	Ph.D.s: 68%
Graduate: 443 men and women	Student/Faculty: 19 to 1
Year: semesters, summer session	Tuition: $2145 ($6593)
Application Deadline: January 1	Room & Board: $2510
Freshman Class: 2157 applied, 1596 accepted, 846 enrolled	
ACT: 22	COMPETITIVE

The University of Wisconsin/River Falls, founded in 1874, is a public coeducational institution offering undergraduate programs in arts and sciences, education, and agriculture. There are 3 undergraduate schools and one graduate school. In addition to regional accreditation, UW/River Falls has baccalaureate program accreditation with ACEJMC, ASLA, NASM, and NCATE. The library contains 200,000 volumes, 450,000 microform items, and 50,000 audiovisual forms,

and subscribes to 1500 periodicals. Computerized library sources and services include the card catalog and database searching. Special learning facilities include a learning resource center, an art gallery, a planetarium, a radio station, a TV station, a greenhouse, a climbing wall, a communicative disorders laboratory, an educational technology center, and food science and meat facilities. The 200-acre campus is in a small town 29 miles east of Minneapolis-St. Paul, Minnesota. Including residence halls, there are 26 buildings on campus.

Student Life: About 54% of undergraduates are from Wisconsin. Students come from 29 states, 22 foreign countries, and Canada. Ninety-five percent are from public schools; 5% from private. Ninety-six percent are white. The average age of freshmen is 18; all undergraduates, 21. Twenty-five percent drop out by the end of their first year; 50% remain to graduate.

Housing: A total of 1844 students can be accommodated in college housing. College-sponsored living facilities include single-sex and coed dormitories and fraternity houses. In addition, there is a dorm for upperclassmen and students over 21. On-campus housing is available on a first-come, first-served basis. All students may keep cars on campus.

Activities: About 3% of men belong to 5 national fraternities; about 1% of women belong to 3 national sororities. There are 110 groups on campus, including art, band, cheerleading, choir, chorus, dance, drama, ethnic, honors, international, jazz band, literary magazine, musical theater, newspaper, opera, orchestra, pep band, political, professional, radio and TV, religious, social, student government, and yearbook. Popular campus events include Homecoming, Winter Carnival, Annual Rodeo, and Parents Weekend.

Sports: There are 10 intercollegiate sports for men and 8 for women, and 17 intramural sports each. Athletic and recreation facilities include an ice arena, a 4550-seat stadium, 2 multipurpose physical education centers, a swimming pool, a 2600-seat gymnasium and a smaller gymnasium, handball courts, a field house, an indoor track, and basketball, tennis, and volleyball courts.

Disabled Students: Ninety-five percent of the campus is accessible to disabled students. The following facilities are available: wheelchair ramps, elevators, special parking, specially equipped rest rooms, special class scheduling, and lowered drinking fountains.

Services: In addition to many counseling and information services, tutoring is available in every subject. There is also a reader service for the blind, and remedial math, reading, and writing.

Campus Safety and Security: Campus safety and security measures include 24-hour foot and vehicle patrol, self-defense education, escort service, and shuttle buses. In addition, there are informal discussions, pamphlets, posters, films, emergency telephones, and lighted pathways and sidewalks.

Programs of Study: UW/River Falls awards the B.A., B.S., B.F.A, B.M.E., and B.S.W. degrees. Associate and master's degrees are also awarded. Bachelor's degrees are awarded in AGRICULTURE (agricultural business management, agricultural economics, agriculture, animal science, conservation and regulation, horticulture, range/farm management, and soil science), BIOLOGICAL SCIENCE (biology/biological science), BUSINESS (accounting and business administration and management), COMMUNICATIONS AND THE ARTS (English, fine arts, French, German, journalism, music, and speech/debate/rhetoric), COMPUTER AND PHYSICAL SCIENCE (chemistry, computer programming, geology, mathematics, physical sciences, and physics), EDUCATION (agricultural, art, early childhood, elementary, foreign languages, middle school, music, physical, science, and secondary), ENGINEERING AND ENVIRONMENTAL DESIGN (agricultural engineering and land use management and reclamation), HEALTH PROFESSIONS (predentistry, premedicine, prepharmacy, and speech pathology/audiology), SOCIAL SCIENCE (American studies, economics, food science, geography, history, political science/government, prelaw, psychology, social studies, sociology, and urban studies). Physics, chemistry, elementary education, agriculture, journalism, and art are the strongest academically. Business, elementary education, and animal science have the largest enrollments.

Required: To graduate, students must complete 128 semester hours, including 34 to 36 in the major, with a GPA of 2.0 overall and 2.25 in the major field. General education requirements include 39 semester hours in English composition, speech and humanities, natural and social sciences, mathematics, and physical education.

Special: Co-op programs in agriculture, work-study progams, and accelerated degree programs in several preprofessional areas are available. UW/RF also offers internships, student-designed majors, credit by exam, nondegree study, and pass/fail options. Study abroad is available through the National Student Exchange and the International Student Exchange Program. There is a freshman honors program on campus, as well as 14 national honor societies.

Faculty/Classroom: Seventy percent of faculty are male; 30%, female. All teach undergraduates. No introductory courses are taught by graduate students. The average class size in an introductory lecture is 30; in a laboratory, 24; and in a regular course offering, 20.

Admissions: About 74% of the 1993–94 applicants were accepted. The ACT scores for the 1993–94 freshman class were as follows: 35% below 21, 35% between 21 and 23, 20% between 24 and 26, 7% between 27 and 28, and 3% above 28. About 39% of the current fresh-

men were in the top fifth of their class; 78% were in the top two fifths. Twenty freshmen graduated first in their class.

Requirements: UW/River Falls requires applicants to be in the upper 40% of their class. The ACT is required, with a minimum composite score of 21. Candidates must be graduates of an accredited secondary school and have completed at least 16 academic credits, including 4 in English, 3 in social sciences, and 2 each in mathematics and science. A GED certificate is acceptable. AP and CLEP credits are accepted.

Procedure: Freshmen are admitted to all sessions. Entrance exams should be taken in the spring of the junior year. Applications should be filed by January 1 for fall entry and June 1 for spring entry, along with an application fee of $25. Notification is sent on a rolling basis. There are early admissions and deferred admissions plans. A waiting list is an active part of the admissions procedure.

Transfer: About 420 transfer students enrolled in a recent year. Priority admission is given to students with a college GPA of 2.6 or higher. Students with a GPA of 2.0 to 2.6 are placed on a waiting list. A total of 32 credits out of 128 must be completed at UW/River Falls.

Visiting: There are regularly scheduled orientations for prospective students. There are guides for informal visits and visitors may sit in on classes. To arrange for a visit, contact the Admissions Office at (715) 425–3500.

Financial Aid: In an earlier year, 72% of all current freshmen and 78% of continuing students received some form of financial aid. Scholarships or need-based grants averaged $300; loans averaged $996; and work contracts averaged $472. The average financial indebtedness of an earlier graduate was $7500. UW/River Falls is a member of CSS. The FAF or FFS is required. The deadline for financial aid applications is March 18.

International Students: There were recently 66 international students enrolled. They must take the TOEFL and achieve a minimum score of 500. The SAT I or ACT is also recommended.

Computers: The college provides computer facilities for student use. The mainframe is a DEC VAX 11/780. The mainframe laboratory has 18 terminals. There are also more than 150 Apple and IBM microcomputers available in laboratories, offices, and residence halls across campus. All students may access the system. It may be used more than 80 hours per week, and by telephone request when laboratories are closed. There are no time limits on using the system and no fees.

Graduates: In a recent year, 1027 bachelor's degrees were awarded. The most popular majors among graduates were business administration (18%), elementary education (16%), and animal science (7%). Some 88 companies recruited on campus in a recent year. In the 1992 graduating class, 4% of the men and 5% of the women were enrolled in graduate school within 6 months of graduation; 95% of the men and 92% of the women had found employment.

Admissions Contact: Alan J. Tuchtenhagen, Admissions Director.

UNIVERSITY OF WISCONSIN STEVENS POINT
C-3
Stevens Point, WI 54481–3897　　　　(715) 346-2441

Full-time: 3583 men, 3733 women	Faculty: 392; IIA, -$
Part-time: 300 men, 443 women	Ph.D.s: 76%
Graduate: 151 men, 405 women	Student/Faculty: 19 to 1
Year: 4-1-4, summer session	Tuition: $2147 ($6595)
Application Deadline: open	Room & Board: $2900
Freshman Class: 4191 applied, 2555 accepted, 1375 enrolled	
ACT: 24	COMPETITIVE +

The University of Wisconsin/Stevens Point, founded in 1894, offers undergraduate programs in natural resources, education, business, arts and sciences, and professional studies. There are 4 undergraduate schools and one graduate school. In addition to regional accreditation, UW/Stevens Point has baccalaureate program accreditation with ASLA, NASAD, NASM, and SAF. The library contains 326,714 volumes and 543,824 microform items, and subscribes to 2003 periodicals. Special learning facilities include a learning resource center, an art gallery, a natural history museum, a planetarium, a radio station, an observatory, a map center, a 200-acre nature preserve, a groundwater center, and a wellness institute. The 335-acre campus is in a small town 110 miles north of Madison. Including residence halls, there are 35 buildings on campus.

Student Life: About 90% of undergraduates are from Wisconsin. Ninety-seven percent are white. The average age of all undergraduates is 23.5. About 30% of freshmen remain to graduate.

Housing: A total of 3152 students can be accommodated in college housing. College-sponsored living facilities include single-sex and coed dormitories, fraternity houses, and sorority houses. In addition, there are privately owned off-campus apartments. On-campus housing is guaranteed for all 4 years. All students may keep cars on campus.

Activities: About 2% of men belong to 3 national fraternities; about 2% of women belong to 1 national and 3 local sororities. There are 145 groups on campus, including art, band, cheerleading, choir, chorale, chorus, computers, dance, drama, ethnic, film, honors, international, jazz band, literary magazine, marching band, musical thea-

ter, newspaper, orchestra, photography, political, professional, religious, social, social service, student government, symphony, and yearbook.

Sports: There are 10 intercollegiate sports for men and 9 for women, and 14 intramural sports for men and 12 for women. Athletic and recreation facilities include the physical education building and the University Center. The campus stadium seats 5500, the indoor gymnasium 3500; and there is a 391-seat auditorium.

Disabled Students: All of the campus is accessible to disabled students. The following facilities are available: wheelchair ramps, elevators, special parking, specially equipped rest rooms, special class scheduling, lowered drinking fountains, and lowered telephones.

Services: In addition to many counseling and information services, tutoring is available in most subjects. In addition, there is a reader service for the blind, and remedial math, reading, and writing. Notetaking services and talking books are also available for the hearing and visually impaired.

Programs of Study: UW/Stevens Point awards the B.A., B.S., B.F.A, and B.M. degrees. Associate and master's degrees are also awarded. Bachelor's degrees are awarded in AGRICULTURE (forestry and related sciences, natural resource management, and soil science), BIOLOGICAL SCIENCE (biology/biological science and wildlife biology), BUSINESS (business administration and management, fashion merchandising, and management science), COMMUNICATIONS AND THE ARTS (arts administration/management, communications, dance, dramatic arts, English, fine arts, French, German, music, and Spanish), COMPUTER AND PHYSICAL SCIENCE (chemistry, mathematics, natural sciences, and physics), EDUCATION (art, education of the exceptional child, elementary, home economics, music, and physical), ENGINEERING AND ENVIRONMENTAL DESIGN (interior design and paper and pulp science), HEALTH PROFESSIONS (medical laboratory technology, medical technology, nursing, predentistry, premedicine, and speech pathology/audiology), SOCIAL SCIENCE (dietetics, economics, food production/management/services, geography, history, international studies, philosophy, political science/government, psychology, public administration, social science, sociology, and water resources). Busines administration, elementary education, and communication have the largest enrollments.

Required: To graduate, students must complete 124 credit hours, with a minimum GPA of 2.0. Core curriculum requirements must also be fulfilled, along with 4 credits in physical education.

Special: A co-op program in nursing is offered with UW/Eau Claire and St. Joseph's Hospital. Internships, study abroad in 7 countries, work-study programs, dual and student-designed majors, independent study, and pass/fail options are also available. Credit is given for military, life, and work experience. There is a freshman honors program on campus, as well as 9 national honor societies.

Faculty/Classroom: Graduate students teach 1% of introductory courses. The average class size in an introductory lecture is 43; in a laboratory, 21; and in a regular course offering, 29.

Admissions: About 61% of the 1993-94 applicants were accepted. About 37% of the current freshmen were in the top fifth of their class; 74% were in the top two fifths. There was 1 National Merit finalist.

Requirements: UW/Stevens Point requires applicants to be in the upper 65% of their class. The ACT is required, with a minimum score of 22 and/or graduation in the upper 65% of the class at an accredited secondary school. The GED is accepted. Required academic preparation includes 4 units of English, 3 of social studies, and 2 each of mathematics and laboratory science, along with 5 electives. Two units of foreign language are recommended. An interview is suggested. AP and CLEP credits are accepted. Evidence of special talent is an important factor used in the admission decision.

Procedure: Freshmen are admitted fall and spring. Entrance exams should be taken by February of the senior year. Application deadlines are open. Application fee is $25. Notification is sent on a rolling basis.

Transfer: About 480 transfer students enrolled in a recent year. Applicants must submit high school and college transcripts. A college GPA of 2.75 is required. A total of 30 credits out of 124 must be completed at UW/Stevens Point.

Visiting: There are regularly scheduled orientations for prospective students.

Financial Aid: In a recent year, 46% of continuing students received some form of financial aid. About 32% of freshmen received need-based aid. Average earnings from campus work for the school year are $915. The FFS is required. The deadline for financial aid applications is June 15.

International Students: There were recently 23 international students enrolled.

Computers: The college provides computer facilities for student use. There are 1500 networked IBM or IBM-compatible microcomputers on campus, utilizing more than 200 computer languages and software packages. Both stand-alone and networked PCs are available in residence halls. There are no time limits on using the system and no fees.

Graduates: In a recent year, 1389 bachelor's degrees were awarded. Within an average freshman class, 10% graduate in 4 years and 35% in 5 years.

Admissions Contact: Dr. John A. Larson, Director of Admissions.

UNIVERSITY OF WISCONSIN STOUT

B-3

Menomonie, WI 54751 (715) 232-1411

Full-time: 3203 men, 3019 women	Faculty: 330; IIA, --$
Part-time: 289 men, 292 women	Ph.D.s: 75%
Graduate: 261 men, 279 women	Student/Faculty: 19 to 1
Year: semesters, summer session	Tuition: $2175 ($6623)
Application Deadline: open	Room & Board: $2544
Freshman Class: 2590 applied, 1966 accepted, 1032 enrolled	
ACT: 21	COMPETITIVE

The University of Wisconsin/Stout, founded in 1891, offers undergraduate programs in Liberal studies, home economics, industry and technology, education, and human services. There are 4 undergraduate schools and one graduate school. In addition to regional accreditation, UW/Stout has baccalaureate program accreditation with ADA, NASAD, and NCATE. The library contains 214,540 volumes, 928,201 microform items, and 12,372 audiovisual forms, and subscribes to 1516 periodicals. Computerized library sources and services include the card catalog, interlibrary loans, and database searching. Special learning facilities include a learning resource center, an art gallery, and a radio station. The 120-acre campus is in a rural area 60 miles east of Minneapolis/St. Paul, Minnesota. Including residence halls, there are 28 buildings on campus.

Student Life: About 70% of undergraduates are from Wisconsin. Students come from 30 states, 28 foreign countries, and Canada. Ninety-five percent are white. The average age of freshmen is 20; all undergraduates, 22. Thirteen percent drop out by the end of their first year; 50% remain to graduate.

Housing: A total of 2900 students can be accommodated in college housing. College-sponsored living facilities include coed dormitories and off-campus apartments. On-campus housing is available on a first-come, first-served basis. All students may keep cars on campus.

Activities: About 2% of men belong to 4 local and 2 national fraternities; about 3% of women belong to 1 local and 3 national sororities. There are 112 groups on campus, including art, band, cheerleading, choir, chorale, chorus, computers, dance, drama, ethnic, film, gay, honors, international, jazz band, literary magazine, marching band, musical theater, newspaper, orchestra, pep band, photography, political, professional, radio and TV, religious, social, social service, student government, and yearbook. Popular campus events include Haute Cuisine, Homecoming, and Winter Carnival.

Sports: There are 9 intercollegiate sports for men and 7 for women, and 31 intramural sports for men and 28 for women. Athletic and recreation facilities include baseball, soccer, and football fields, indoor and outdoor tracks, and a field house with racquetball courts, volleyball courts, a pool, weight and gymnastics rooms, basketball courts, and indoor and outdoor tennis courts.

Disabled Students: Ninety percent of the campus is accessible to disabled students. The following facilities are available: wheelchair ramps, elevators, special parking, specially equipped rest rooms, special class scheduling, lowered drinking fountains, and lowered telephones.

Services: In addition to many counseling and information services, tutoring is available in most subjects. There is also a reader service for the blind, and remedial math, reading, and writing.

Campus Safety and Security: Campus safety and security measures include 24-hour foot and vehicle patrol, informal discussions, pamphlets, posters, films, and lighted pathways and sidewalks. In addition, there are training sessions.

Programs of Study: UW/Stout awards the B.A., B.S., and B.F.A. degrees. Master's degrees also are awarded. Bachelor's degrees are awarded in BUSINESS (business administration and management, fashion merchandising, hospitality management services, and retailing), COMMUNICATIONS AND THE ARTS (fine arts), COMPUTER AND PHYSICAL SCIENCE (applied mathematics), EDUCATION (art, early childhood, home economics, marketing and distribution, technical, and vocational), ENGINEERING AND ENVIRONMENTAL DESIGN (construction technology, engineering, industrial engineering technology, and manufacturing engineering), HEALTH PROFESSIONS (rehabilitation therapy), SOCIAL SCIENCE (child care/child and family studies, dietetics, fashion design and technology, food production/management/services, and psychology). Industrial engineering technology and hospitality and tourism management have the largest enrollments.

Required: Students must complete a minimum of 124 credits. All students must complete a general education component. Some degree programs have specific general education courses that must be taken in order to satisfy certification, accreditation or prerequisite standards. Students must also fulfill an ethnic studies requirement.

Special: UW/Stout offers business and industry internships, cooperative programs, work-study programs, and study abroad in London. Dual majors, credit by exam, credit for life, military, and work experience, nondegree study, and pass/fail options are also available. There is one national honor society on campus.

Faculty/Classroom: Seventy-three percent of faculty are male; 27% female. One-hundred percent both teach and do research. Graduate students teach 2% of introductory courses. The average

class size in an introductory lecture is 32; in a laboratory, 18; and in a regular course offering, 20.

Admissions: About 76% of the 1993–94 applicants were accepted. The ACT scores for the 1993–94 freshman class were as follows: 46% below 21, 37% between 21 and 23, 13% between 24 and 26, 3% between 27 and 28, and 1% above 28. About 22% of the current freshmen were in the top fifth of their class; 56% were in the top two fifths. There was 1 National Merit finalist and 1 semifinalist. Nine freshmen graduated first in their class.

Requirements: UW/Stout requires applicants to be in the upper 50% of their class. The ACT is required for Wisconsin residents, with a minimum composite score of 21. Out-of-state residents may substitute the SAT I, with a minimum composite score of 900. Applicants should graduate in the upper 50% of their class at an accredited secondary school. The GED is accepted. Secondary school preparation should include academic credits, consisting of 4 in English, 3 in social studies, 2 each in mathematics and science, and 5 in electives. Minimum test scores are waived if the student meets the high school requirements. AP and CLEP credits are accepted.

Procedure: Freshmen are admitted to all sessions. Entrance exams should be taken in June of the junior year. Application deadlines are open. Application fee is $25. Notification is sent on a rolling basis. A waiting list is an active part of the admissions procedure, with about 11% of applicants on the list.

Transfer: About 615 transfer students enrolled in a recent year. A minimum college GPA of 2.0 is required. A total of 32 credits out of 124 must be completed at UW/Stout.

Visiting: There are regularly scheduled orientations for prospective students, including an interview with an admissions counselor and a campus tour. There are guides for informal visits and visitors may sit in on classes. To arrange for a visit, contact Shirley Severtson at (800) HI-STOUT.

Financial Aid: In 1993–94, 54% of all current freshmen and 64% of continuing students received some form of financial aid. About 52% of freshmen and 49% of continuing students received need-based aid. The average freshman award was $3475. Of that total, scholarships or need-based grants averaged $1838 ($2300 maximum); loans averaged $2300 ($2625 maximum); and work contracts averaged $1000 ($1400 maximum). Forty percent of undergraduate students work part-time. Average earnings from campus work for the school year are $1000. The average financial indebtedness of the 1992–93 graduate was $9831. UW/Stout is a member of CSS. The FAFSA financial statement is required. The deadline for financial aid applications is April 1.

International Students: There are currently 139 international students enrolled. They must take the TOEFL and achieve a minimum score of 500. The student must also take the college's own entrance exam.

Computers: The college provides computer facilities for student use. The mainframe is a DEC VAX 6410. Students can access the mainframe form over 200 microcomputers in computer laboratories and residence halls. Other laboratories are equipped with networked microcomputers that do not access the mainframe. All students may access the system. It may be used 24 hours a day, 7 days a week. There are no time limits on using the system and no fees.

Graduates: In 1992–93, 1167 bachelor's degrees were awarded. The most popular majors among graduates were hotel and restaurant management (17%), business administration (13%), and industrial technology (10%). Within an average freshman class, 46% graduate in 6 years. Some 250 companies recruited on campus in 1992–93.

Admissions Contact: Charles Kell, Director of School Relations.

UNIVERSITY OF WISCONSIN SUPERIOR

A-1

Superior, WI 54880   (715) 394-8230

Full-time: 1675 men and women	Faculty: 115; IIA, -$
Part-time: 510 men and women	Ph.D.s: 75%
Graduate: 550 men and women	Student/Faculty: 15 to 1
Year: semesters, summer session	Tuition: $2036 ($6484)
Application Deadline: May 1	Room & Board: $2300
Freshman Class: 920 applied, 840 accepted, 364 enrolled	
ACT: 21	**COMPETITIVE**

The University of Wisconsin/Superior, founded in 1893, offers undergraduate programs in the liberal arts and sciences, business, education, fine arts, and applied arts. There are 5 undergraduate schools and one graduate school. The library contains 300,000 volumes, and subscribes to 1000 periodicals. Computerized library sources and services include the card catalog, interlibrary loans, and database searching. Special learning facilities include a learning resource center, an art gallery, a planetarium, an aquatic laboratory, a color television studio, and an FM radio station. The 230-acre campus is in a small town 150 miles north of Minneapolis/St. Paul, Minnesota. Including residence halls, there are 17 buildings on campus.

Student Life: About 58% of undergraduates are from Wisconsin. Students come from 21 states, 11 foreign countries, and Canada. Ninety percent are from public schools; 10% from private. Ninety-five percent are white. The average age of freshmen is 18; all undergrad-

uates, 23. Fifteen percent drop out by the end of their first year; 40% remain to graduate.

Housing: A total of 620 students can be accommodated in college housing. College-sponsored living facilities include single-sex and coed dormitories. On-campus housing is guaranteed for all 4 years. Seventy-seven percent of students commute. All students may keep cars on campus.

Activities: There are no fraternities or sororities on campus. There are 25 groups on campus, including art, band, cheerleading, choir, chorus, computers, dance, drama, ethnic, honors, international, jazz band, musical theater, newspaper, orchestra, pep band, photography, political, professional, radio and TV, religious, social, social service, student government, and symphony. Popular campus events include Snow Week, sports events, and social dances.

Sports: There are 5 intercollegiate sports for men and 5 for women, and 5 intramural sports for men for women. Athletic and recreation facilities include a 4000-seat stadium, a 3000-seat gymnasium, an ice arena, a swimming pool, a weight training room, a dance studio, an all-weather track, and softball and baseball fields.

Disabled Students: Ninety-five percent of the campus is accessible to disabled students. The following facilities are available: wheelchair ramps, elevators, special parking, specially equipped rest rooms, special class scheduling, lowered drinking fountains, and lowered telephones.

Services: In addition to many counseling and information services, tutoring is available in every subject. There is also remedial math and writing.

Campus Safety and Security: Campus safety and security measures include 24-hour foot and vehicle patrol, self-defense education, informal discussions, and pamphlets, posters, and films. In addition, there are emergency telephones and lighted pathways and sidewalks.

Programs of Study: UW/Superior awards the B.A., B.S., B.F.A., B.M., and B.M.E. degrees. Associate and master's degrees also are awarded. Bachelor's degrees are awarded in BIOLOGICAL SCIENCE (biology/biological science), BUSINESS (accounting, business administration and management, and business economics), COMMUNICATIONS AND THE ARTS (advertising, communications, design, dramatic arts, English, fine arts, music, photography, and speech/debate/rhetoric), COMPUTER AND PHYSICAL SCIENCE (chemistry, computer science, information sciences and systems, and mathematics), EDUCATION (art, elementary, music, physical, science, and secondary), HEALTH PROFESSIONS (medical laboratory technology), SOCIAL SCIENCE (criminal justice, history, political science/government, psychology, social studies, social work, and sociology). Business and education are the strongest academically. Business has the largest enrollment.

Required: To graduate, students must complete 128 credit hours, including 34 in the major, with a GPA of 2.5. The required core curriculum includes 55 credits in communications, English, mathematics, physical education, world culture, contemporary society, aesthetic experience, natural science, and human behavior. A comprehensive exam and a senior project are required.

Special: UW/Superior offers co-op programs in business and internships in social work, business, and criminal justice. There is a comprehensive program of student-designed majors, along with a cooperative program in marine studies with Texas A&M University, and 3-2 engineering and forestry programs with Michigan Technological University. Students may cross-register for 2 classes per semester at the University of Minnesota/Duluth, the College of St. Scholastica, or Northland College. An extended degree is offered. Credit for life experience and pass/fail options are available. There is a freshman honors program on campus.

Faculty/Classroom: Sixty percent of faculty are male; 40%, female. All teach undergraduates and 100% both teach and do research. No introductory courses are taught by graduate students. The average class size in an introductory lecture is 40 and in a laboratory, 20.

Admissions: About 91% of the 1993–94 applicants were accepted. The ACT scores for the 1993–94 freshman class were as follows: 6% below 21, 65% between 21 and 23, 21% between 24 and 26, 6% between 27 and 28, and 2% above 28. About 21% of the current freshmen were in the top fifth of their class; 76% were in the top two fifths. There were 5 National Merit semifinalists. Twelve freshmen graduated first in their class.

Requirements: UW/Superior requires applicants to be in the upper 50% of their class. The ACT is required. Out-of-state residents may submit SAT I scores instead. Applicants must graduate from an accredited secondary school or the equivalent. They must rank in the upper 50% of their graduating class or achieve a minimum composite score of 20 on the ACT. AP and CLEP credits are accepted. Important factors used in the admissions decision are ability to finance college education, extracurricular activities record, parents or siblings attending the school, personality, intangible qualities, and recommendations by alumni.

Procedure: Freshmen are admitted to all sessions. Entrance exams should be taken before admission. Applications should be filed by May 1 for fall entry and November 1 for spring entry, along with an application fee of $25. Notification is sent on a rolling basis. There are early admissions and deferred admissions plans.

Transfer: About 270 transfer students enrolled in 1993–94. A college GPA of 2.3 is required. A total of 32 credits out of 128 must be completed at UW/Superior.

Visiting: There are regularly scheduled orientations for prospective students, consisting of a day and a half of social and educational programs. There are guides for informal visits and visitors may sit in on classes and stay overnight at the school. To arrange for a visit, contact the Admissions Office at (715) 394–8230.

Financial Aid: In a recent year, 79% of all current freshmen and 61% of continuing students received some form of financial aid. About 80% of freshmen and 68% of continuing students received need-based aid. Twenty-one percent of undergraduate students work part-time. Average earnings from campus work for the school year are $800. The average financial indebtedness of the 1992–93 graduate was $4500. UW/Superior is a member of CSS. The FAF, FFS or SFS and the college's own financial statement are required. The deadline for financial aid applications is May 1.

International Students: There are currently 48 international students enrolled. The school actively recruits these students. They must take the TOEFL and achieve a minimum score of 525. The student must also take the ACT or SAT I.

Computers: The college provides computer facilities for student use. The mainframe is an HP 9000. There are also 75 IBM PCs available in the main hall, the library, and dormitories. All students may access the system. It may be used 24 hours a day. There are no time limits on using the system and no fees.

Graduates: In 1992–93, 380 bachelor's degrees were awarded. The most popular majors among graduates were education (27%), business (27%), and fine and applied arts (2%). Within an average freshman class, 30% graduate in 4 years and 40% in 5 years. Some 125 companies recruited on campus in 1992–93.

Admissions Contact: Admissions Counselor.

UNIVERSITY OF WISCONSIN WHITEWATER
D-5
Whitewater, WI 53190
(414) 472–1440

Full-time: 3574 men, 4088 women	Faculty: 347; IIA, -$
Part-time: 766 men, 868 women	Ph.D.s: 78%
Graduate: 453 men, 764 women	Student/Faculty: 22 to 1
Year: semesters, summer session	Tuition: $2200 ($6700)
Application Deadline: open	Room & Board: $2500

Freshman Class: 4300 applied, 3719 accepted, 1846 enrolled
ACT: 22
COMPETITIVE

The University of Wisconsin/Whitewater, founded in 1868, offers programs in teacher education, business, liberal arts, preprofessional studies, fine arts, and music. There are 4 undergraduate schools and one graduate school. In addition to regional accreditation, UW/Whitewater has baccalaureate program accreditation with AACSB, CSWE, NASM, and NCATE. The library contains 348,238 volumes, 1,015,730 microform items, and 81,193 audiovisual forms, and subscribes to 2382 periodicals. Computerized library sources and services include the card catalog, interlibrary loans, and database searching. Special learning facilities include a learning resource center, an art gallery, a radio station, a TV station, and an observatory. The 385-acre campus is in a small town 50 miles southwest of Milwaukee. Including residence halls, there are 45 buildings on campus.

Student Life: About 94% of undergraduates are from Wisconsin. Students come from 31 states, 33 foreign countries, and Canada. Eighty-five percent are from public schools; 15% from private. Ninety-three percent are white. The average age of all undergraduates is 21.5. Twenty-two percent drop out by the end of their first year; 55% remain to graduate.

Housing: A total of 4141 students can be accommodated in college housing. College-sponsored living facilities include single-sex and coed dormitories. On-campus housing is guaranteed for all 4 years. Fifty percent of students live on campus; of those, 50% remain on campus on weekends. All students may keep cars on campus.

Activities: About 5% of men belong to 1 local and 7 national fraternities; about 5% of women belong to 1 local and 4 national sororities. There are 130 groups on campus, including art, band, cheerleading, choir, chorus, computers, dance, drama, drill team, ethnic, film, gay, honors, international, marching band, musical theater, newspaper, orchestra, pep band, photography, political, professional, radio and TV, religious, social, social service, student government, symphony, and yearbook. Popular campus events include Homecoming, Job Fair, Performing Arts Series, and athletic contests.

Sports: There are 9 intercollegiate sports for men and 8 for women, and 12 intramural sports for men and 12 for women. Athletic and recreation facilities include tennis courts, pools, playing fields, a 13,000-seat stadium, and a 3500-seat gymnasium.

Disabled Students: All of the campus is accessible to disabled students. The following facilities are available: wheelchair ramps, elevators, special parking, specially equipped rest rooms, special class scheduling, lowered drinking fountains, lowered telephones, vans for mobility, and a wide variety of services and programs.

Services: In addition to many counseling and information services, tutoring is available in most subjects. There is also a reader service for the blind, remedial math, reading, and writing and help with study skills.

Campus Safety and Security: Campus safety and security measures include 24-hour foot and vehicle patrol, self-defense education, escort service, and shuttle buses. In addition, there are informal discussions, pamphlets, posters, films, emergency telephones, and lighted pathways and sidewalks.

Programs of Study: UW/Whitewater awards the B.A., B.S., B.B.A., B.F.A., B.S.Ed., and B.M. degrees. Associate and master's degrees also are awarded. Bachelor's degrees are awarded in BIOLOGICAL SCIENCE (biology/biological science), BUSINESS (accounting, banking and finance, business administration and management, business economics, marketing/retailing/merchandising, office supervision and management, and personnel management), COMMUNICATIONS AND THE ARTS (art history and appreciation, communications, dramatic arts, English, French, German, journalism, music, public relations, Spanish, and speech/debate/rhetoric), COMPUTER AND PHYSICAL SCIENCE (chemistry, computer programming, mathematics, and physics), EDUCATION (art, business, early childhood, elementary, foreign languages, middle school, music, physical, science, secondary, social studies, and special), SOCIAL SCIENCE (economics, geography, history, international studies, political science/government, prelaw, psychology, public administration, safety and security technology, social work, sociology, and women's studies). Accounting, computer science, education, arts, and public relations are the strongest academically. Business/Accounting and education have the largest enrollments.

Required: Students must complete 42 credits of general studies, a writing competency requirement, and 3 credits in minority issues. A GPA of 2.0 and 120 hours are required to graduate.

Special: Internships, student-designed majors, and a general studies degree are available. Credit by exam, credit for life experience, non-degree study, and pass/fail options are also offered. There is a freshman honors program on campus, as well as 14 national honor societies. Seven departments have honors programs.

Faculty/Classroom: Seventy-one percent of faculty are male; 29%, female. All teach undergraduates. The average class size in a regular course offering is 26.

Admissions: About 86% of the 1993–94 applicants were accepted. About 25% of the current freshmen were in the top fifth of their class; 74% were in the top two fifths. Twenty freshmen graduated first in their class.

Requirements: UW/Whitewater requires applicants to be in the upper 50% of their class. The SAT I or ACT is recommended. Applicants should graduate from an accredited secondary school or with 14 academic units, including 4 in English, 3 in social studies, and 2 each in mathematics and science. The GED may be accepted. Applicants should rank in the upper 50% of their graduating class or achieve a combined class rank and ACT or SAT I test percentile that totals 100% or more. AP and CLEP credits are accepted. Important factors used in the admissions decision are advanced placement or honor courses, evidence of special talent, extracurricular activities record, leadership record, and personality.

Procedure: Freshmen are admitted to all sessions. Application deadlines are open. Application fee is $25. Notification is sent on a rolling basis. A waiting list is an active part of the admissions procedure, with about 10% of applicants on the list.

Transfer: About 425 transfer students enrolled in 1993–94. Applicants should have a minimum college GPA of 2.5. Other requirements vary by specific program. A total of 30 credits out of 120 must be completed at UW/Whitewater.

Visiting: There are regularly scheduled orientations for prospective students. There are guides for informal visits and visitors may sit in on classes. To arrange for a visit, contact the Admissions Office at (414) 472–1440.

Financial Aid: UW/Whitewater is a member of CSS. The FFS is required. The deadline for financial aid applications is April 15.

International Students: There are currently 180 international students enrolled. The school actively recruits these students. They must take the TOEFL and achieve a minimum score of 500.

Computers: The college provides computer facilities for student use. The mainframes are an IBM 4341 and a DEC VAX 11/780. There are also 115 Zenith 286 and AT&T (IBM-compatible) microcomputers available in McGraw Hall. All students may access the system. It may be used 24 hours if they have their own terminal or 8 A.M. to 11 P.M., Monday through Thursday and varied Friday and weekend hours in the general laboratory. There are no time limits on using the system and no fees.

Graduates: In a recent year, 1594 bachelor's degrees were awarded. Within an average freshman class, 46% graduate in 5 years. Some 420 companies recruited on campus in 1992–93. In the 1992 graduating class, 75% of the men and 81% of the women had found employment within 6 months of graduation.

Admissions Contact: I. A. Madsen, Director of Admissions.

VITERBO COLLEGE
B-4

LaCrosse, WI 54601   (608) 791-0420; (800) 542-5652 (in-state)

Full-time: 257 men, 757 women   **Faculty:** 70; IIB, -$
Part-time: 74 men, 313 women   **Ph.Ds:** 55%
Graduate: 43 men, 71 women   **Student/Faculty:** 14 to 1
Year: semesters, summer session   **Tuition:** $8770
Application Deadline: August 15   **Room & Board:** $3900
Freshman Class: 732 applied, 625 accepted, 378 enrolled
ACT: 22   **COMPETITIVE**

Viterbo College, founded in 1931, is a private, coeducational, Catholic college offering undergraduate programs in liberal arts and sciences, music, education, and health sciences. There are 5 undergraduate schools and one graduate school. In addition to regional accreditation, Viterbo has baccalaureate program accreditation with ADA, NASM, NCATE, and NLN. The 2 libraries contain 70,000 volumes and 1000 audiovisual forms, and subscribe to 500 periodicals. Special learning facilities include a learning resource center and an art gallery. The 5-acre campus is in a small town 140 miles from Minneapolis/St. Paul. Including residence halls, there are 9 buildings on campus.

Student Life: About 80% of undergraduates are from Wisconsin. Students come from 7 states, 6 foreign countries, and Canada. Eighty-four percent are from public schools; 16% from private. Ninety-three percent are white. Fifty percent are Catholic; 45% Protestant. The average age of freshmen is 18; all undergraduates, 21. Twenty-five percent drop out by the end of their first year; 55% remain to graduate.

Housing: A total of 400 students can be accommodated in college housing. College-sponsored living facilities include coed dormitories and on-campus apartments. On-campus housing is guaranteed for all 4 years. Sixty percent of students live on campus; of those, 90% remain on campus on weekends. All students may keep cars on campus.

Activities: There are no fraternities or sororities on campus. There are 30 groups on campus, including art, band, cheerleading, choir, chorale, dance, drama, ethnic, international, literary magazine, musical theater, newspaper, opera, orchestra, photography, religious, social, social service, student government, and yearbook. Popular campus events include Hog Wild, Survival Weekend, Homecoming, Courtyard Carni, Humanities Symposium, and Roommate Game.

Sports: There are 3 intercollegiate sports for men and 3 for women, and 5 intramural sports for men and 5 for women. Athletic and recreation facilities include a student center with training and fitness rooms and courts for basketball, volleyball, and racquetball. The nearby Mississippi River and Mt. LaCrosse provide additional recreational opportunities.

Disabled Students: Eighty-five percent of the campus is accessible to disabled students. The following facilities are available: elevators, special parking, specially equipped rest rooms, and lowered telephones.

Services: In addition to many counseling and information services, tutoring is available in every subject. In addition, there is a reader service for the blind, and remedial math, reading, and writing.

Campus Safety and Security: Campus safety and security measures include emergency telephones and lighted pathways and sidewalks.

Programs of Study: Viterbo awards the B.A. B.Art.Ed., B.L.S., B.M., B.S., B.S.Ed., B.S. Community-Medical Dietetics., and B.S.N. degrees. Master's degrees also are awarded. Bachelor's degrees are awarded in BIOLOGICAL SCIENCE (biology/biological science and nutrition), BUSINESS (accounting, business administration and management, marketing/retailing/merchandising, and personnel management), COMMUNICATIONS AND THE ARTS (applied music, arts administration/management, dramatic arts, English, fine arts, and music), COMPUTER AND PHYSICAL SCIENCE (chemistry, computer programming, computer science, and mathematics), EDUCATION (art, business, early childhood, elementary, and music), HEALTH PROFESSIONS (health care administration, medical laboratory technology, and nursing), SOCIAL SCIENCE (dietetics, human services, ministries, psychology, religion, religious music, and sociology).

Required: All students must complete at least 128 semester hours, at least 43 of which must be in upper-level courses, with a 2.0 GPA. A core curriculum totals 45 hours, including courses in English, religious studies, philosophy, history, social and natural science, and fine arts. All students must pass a competency exam in English composition. B.A. students must complete the equivalent of 14 hours in one foreign language; B.S. students must take 3 hours of natural science beyond the core requirements.

Special: Students may cross-register at the University of Wisconsin/LaCrosse, enroll for independent study, or earn a dual degree. Double majors, student-designed majors, work-study, internships, credit by examination, and credit/no credit options are available.

Faculty/Classroom: Forty-two percent of faculty are male; 58%, female. All teach undergraduates. The average class size in an introductory lecture is 30; in a laboratory, 25; and in a regular course offering, 14.

Admissions: About 85% of the 1993-94 applicants were accepted. About 22% of the current freshmen were in the top fifth of their class; 73% were in the top two fifths.

Requirements: Viterbo requires applicants to be in the upper 50% of their class. A minimum GPA of 2.0 is required. The SAT I or the ACT is required, but the ACT is preferred. Graduation from an accredited secondary school is required; the GED is accepted. Secondary preparation should include 16 credits, with 3 or 4 in English and 2 each in mathematics, natural science, and social science or history. Art students may be required to audition or submit a portfolio. AP and CLEP credits are accepted.

Procedure: Freshmen are admitted to all sessions. Entrance exams should be taken in spring of the junior year or fall of the senior year. Applications should be filed by August 15 for fall entry and January 2 for spring entry, along with an application fee of $15. Notification is sent on a rolling basis. There are early decision and early admissions plans.

Transfer: About 100 transfer students enrolled in 1993-94. Applicants should present at least a 2.0 GPA in previous college work; in addition, freshman admission standards must be met. All college transcripts must be submitted. A total of 30 credits out of 128 must be completed at Viterbo.

Visiting: There are regularly scheduled orientations for prospective students, a meeting with an Admissions staff member, a tour of the campus, and optional meetings with a Financial Aid officer and faculty members. Visitors may stay overnight at the school. To arrange for a visit, contact the Admissions Office at (608) 791-0420 or (800) 542-5652 (in-state).

Financial Aid: About 56% of freshmen received need-based aid. The average freshman award was $8500. Of that total, scholarships or need-based grants averaged $2500 ($6000 maximum); loans averaged $2625; and work contracts averaged $1000. Average earnings from campus work for the school year are $1000. The average financial indebtedness of the 1992-93 graduate was $13,500. Viterbo is a member of CSS. The FAF or FFS, and the college's own financial statement, the student's and parents' income tax returns, and the FAFSA are required. The deadline for financial aid applications is March 1.

International Students: There are currently 6 international students enrolled. They must take the TOEFL or the college's own test and achieve a minimum score on the TOEFL of 500.

Computers: The college provides computer facilities for student use. The mainframe is a DEC VAX 8200 minicomputer. There are terminals for the mainframe as well as IBM PC and Apple Macintosh microcomputers available in the computer center. All students may access the system. It may be used 8 A.M. to 11 P.M., Monday through Thursday; until 6 P.M. on Friday; and for about 5 hours on weekends. There are no time limits on using the system and no fees.

Graduates: In 1992-93, 125 bachelor's degrees were awarded. The most popular majors among graduates were nursing (37%), business (14%), and education (9%). Within an average freshman class, 83% graduate in 4 years, 13% in 5 years, and 4% in 6 years. Some 15 companies recruited on campus in 1992-93. In the 1992 graduating class, 15% of all graduates were enrolled in graduate school within 6 months of graduation; 98% had found employment.

Admissions Contact: Dr. Roland W. Nelson, Director of Admissions.

WISCONSIN LUTHERAN COLLEGE
E-4

Milwaukee, WI 53226   (414) 774-8620

Full-time: 103 men, 179 women   **Faculty:** 31
Part-time: 6 men, 16 women   **Ph.Ds:** 42%
Graduate: 7 men, 10 women   **Student/Faculty:** 9 to 1
Year: semesters, summer session   **Tuition:** $8680
Application Deadline: April 1   **Room & Board:** $3500
Freshman Class: 144 applied, 138 accepted, 85 enrolled
ACT: 22   **COMPETITIVE**

Wisconsin Lutheran College, founded in 1973 in affiliation with the Wisconsin Evangelical Lutheran Synod, offers higher education in the arts and sciences taught within the framework of Christian doctrine. The library contains 75,000 volumes, 6703 microform items, and 3780 audiovisual forms, and subscribes to 300 periodicals. Computerized library sources and services include the card catalog, interlibrary loans, and database searching. Special learning facilities include a sound studio. The 12-acre campus is in a suburban area 5 miles west of Milwaukee. Including residence halls, there are 3 buildings on campus.

Student Life: About 84% of undergraduates are from Wisconsin. Students come from 18 states and 2 foreign countries. Thirty-one percent are from public schools; 69% from private. Ninety-five percent are white. Most are Protestant. The average age of freshmen is 18; all undergraduates, 20. Twenty percent drop out by the end of their first year; 58% remain to graduate.

Housing: A total of 280 students can be accommodated in college housing. College-sponsored living facilities include single-sex dormitories and off-campus apartments. On-campus housing is guaranteed for all 4 years. Sixty-three percent of students live on campus. Alcohol is not permitted. All students may keep cars on campus.

Activities: There are no fraternities or sororities on campus. There are 20 groups on campus, including art, band, cheerleading, choir, drama, ethnic, musical theater, newspaper, pep band, photography, student government, and yearbook. Popular campus events include Heritage Week, Kris Kringle Week, and Winter Fest.

Sports: There are 5 intercollegiate sports for men and 4 for women, and 4 intramural sports for men and 4 for women. Athletic and recreation facilities include three full basketball courts, a 2600-seat gymnasium, a weight room, a fitness center, training and therapy rooms, and a walking/running track.

Disabled Students: The following facilities are available: wheelchair ramps, elevators, special parking, specially equipped rest rooms, and lowered telephones.

Services: In addition to many counseling and information services, tutoring is available in some subjects. In addition, there is remedial math and writing.

Campus Safety and Security: Campus safety and security measures include self-defense education, escort service, informal discussions, and pamphlets, posters, and films. In addition, there are lighted pathways and sidewalks and a security service.

Programs of Study: Wisconsin Lutheran awards the B.A., B.S., and B.B.A. degrees. Bachelor's degrees are awarded in BUSINESS (business administration and management), COMMUNICATIONS AND THE ARTS (communications and English), COMPUTER AND PHYSICAL SCIENCE (chemistry and mathematics), SOCIAL SCIENCE (psychology and theological studies). Chemistry, English, mathematics, and education are the strongest academically. Business, psychology, and communication have the largest enrollments.

Required: Composition, mathematics, library skills, and foreign language competencies are required. All students must complete a core curriculum that includes 3 credits each in communication, computer science, and deductive reasoning, 3 per year in theology, and 1 in physical education/lifetime sport. A student's course selections must also include 12 credits each in humanities and social science, and 10 to 16 in natural science, depending on the degree sought. A minimum overall GPA of 2.0 and 2.5 in the major plus 128 credit hours are required to graduate.

Special: Cross-registration is possible with the Wisconsin Conservatory of Music. Internships are available in public relations, psychological counseling, and museum work. Nondegree study for adults is available. There is one national honor society on campus.

Faculty/Classroom: Seventy-four percent of faculty are male; 26%, female. The average class size in an introductory lecture is 24; in a laboratory, 12; and in a regular course offering, 16.

Admissions: About 96% of the 1993–94 applicants were accepted. The ACT scores for the 1993–94 freshman class were as follows: 36% below 21, 19% between 21 and 23, 23% between 24 and 26, 15% between 27 and 28, and 7% above 28. About 38% of the current freshmen were in the top fifth of their class; 58% were in the top two fifths. One freshman graduated first in his class.

Requirements: Wisconsin Lutheran requires applicants to be in the upper 50% of their class. A minimum GPA of 2.5 is required. The SAT I or ACT is required, with a minimum composite score of 875 on

the SAT I or 20 on the ACT. Students should be graduates of an accredited high school or its equivalent with a minimum of 16 high school units, including 3 in English, 2 in mathematics, 4 in science/foreign language/social studies, and 7 in academic electives. Students must rank in the upper half of their graduating class or have a minimum GPA of 2.5. The Academic Recommendation Form must be submitted. An essay for journalism and leadership grants, a portfolio for art grants, and an audition for music and drama grants are required. AP and CLEP credits are accepted. Important factors used in the admissions decision are personality, intangible qualities, leadership record, evidence of special talent, advanced placement or honor courses, and recommendations by school officials.

Procedure: Freshmen are admitted to all sessions. Entrance exams should be taken in the spring of the junior year or October of the senior year. Applications should be filed by April 1 for fall entry, December 1 for spring entry, and June 1 for summer entry, along with an application fee of $15 ($25 for international students). Notification is sent on a rolling basis.

Transfer: About 20 transfer students enrolled in 1993–94. Students should have a GPA of at least 2.0 for transfer credit. The Transfer Recommendation Form is required. A total of 30 credits out of 128 must be completed at Wisconsin Lutheran.

Visiting: There are regularly scheduled orientations for prospective students. There are guides for informal visits and visitors may sit in on classes and stay overnight at the school. To arrange for a visit, contact Admissions Office at (414) 774–8620.

Financial Aid: In 1993–94, 92% of all current freshmen and 86% of continuing students received some form of financial aid. The average freshman award was $8065. Of that total, scholarships or need-based grants averaged $4868 ($8872 maximum); loans averaged $2455 ($2625 maximum); and work contracts averaged $1195 ($1200 maximum). Thirty-two percent of undergraduate students work part-time. Average earnings from campus work for the school year are $1200. The college's own financial statement and the FAFSA are required. The deadline for financial aid applications is April 1.

International Students: There are currently 2 international students enrolled. They must take the TOEFL and achieve a minimum score of 550. The student must also take the SAT I or the ACT.

Computers: The college provides computer facilities for student use. There are 24 Zenith 286, 3 Apple Macintosh, and 2 Apple IIgs microcomputers available in instructional, study, and education laboratories. There are no time limits on using the system and no fees.

Graduates: In 1992–93, 43 bachelor's degrees were awarded. The most popular majors among graduates were communication (30%), psychology (23%), and business administration (18%). Within an average freshman class, 31% graduate in 4 years and 57% in 5 years. Some 15 companies recruited on campus in 1992–93. In the 1992 graduating class, 30% of the men and 25% of the women were enrolled in graduate school within 6 months of graduation; 70% had found employment.

Admissions Contact: Joel P. Mischke, Director of Admissions.

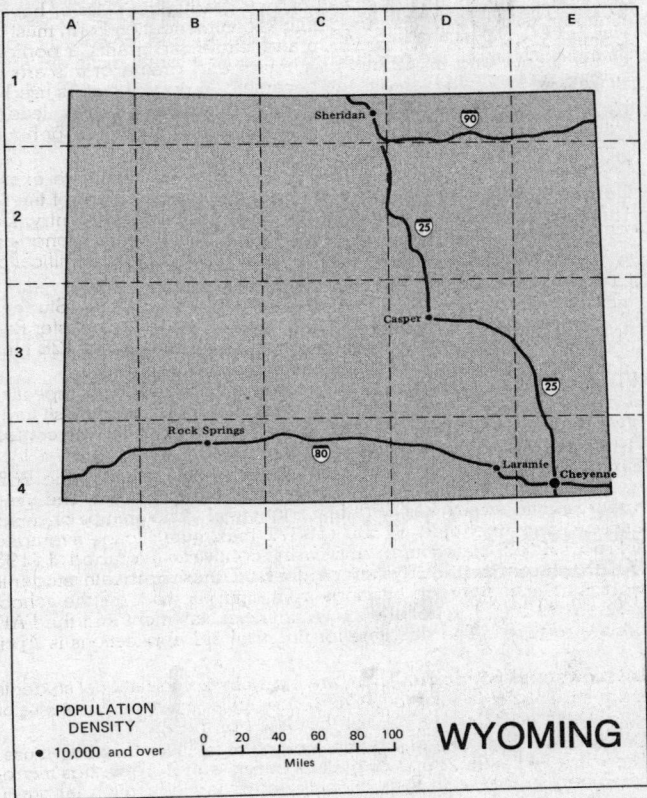

POPULATION DENSITY
• 10,000 and over

0   20   40   60   80   100
Miles

WYOMING

UNIVERSITY OF WYOMING
D-4

Laramie, WY 82071   (307) 766–5160; (800) DIAL-WYO (in-state)

Full-time: 4098 men, 3793 women
Part-time: 601 men, 801 women
Graduate: 1297 men, 1462 women
Year: semesters, 2 summer sessions
Application Deadline: August 10
Freshman Class: 2085 applied, 1716 accepted, 1309 enrolled
ACT: 23

Faculty: 600; I, --$
Ph.D.s: 93%
Student/Faculty: 13 to 1
Tuition: $1648 ($5182)
Room & Board: $3343

NONCOMPETITIVE

The University of Wyoming, founded in 1886, is a public, nonprofit institution offering programs in agriculture, arts and sciences, business, education, engineering, and health science. There are 6 undergraduate schools and one graduate school. In addition to regional accreditation, UW has baccalaureate program accreditation with AACSB, ABET, ACPE, CSWE, NASM, NCATE, and NLN. The 7 libraries contain 1,096,703 volumes, 2,375,560 microform items, and 6741 audiovisual forms, and subscribe to 11,486 periodicals. Computerized library sources and services include the card catalog, interlibrary loans, and database searching. Special learning facilities include a learning resource center, art gallery, natural history museum, planetarium, radio station, TV station, and American Heritage Center. The 785-acre campus is in a small town 128 miles north of Denver, Colorado. Including residence halls, there are 82 buildings on campus.

Student Life: About 70% of undergraduates are from Wyoming. Students come from 50 states, 66 foreign countries, and Canada. About 84% are white. The average age of freshmen is 20; all undergraduates, 23.7. Some 29% drop out by the end of their first year; 47% remain to graduate.

Housing: A total of 4000 students can be accommodated in college housing. College-sponsored living facilities include coed dormitories, on-campus apartments, married-student housing, fraternity houses, and sorority houses. In addition, there are language floors in the residence halls. On-campus housing is available on a first-come, first-served basis. About 67% of students commute. All students may keep cars on campus.

Activities: About 10% of men belong to 11 national fraternities; about 9% of women belong to 4 national sororities. There are 128 groups on campus, including art, band, cheerleading, chess, choir, chorale, chorus, computers, dance, drama, drill team, ethnic, gay, honors, international, jazz band, literary magazine, marching band,

musical theater, newspaper, opera, orchestra, pep band, political, professional, radio and TV, religious, social, social service, student government, and symphony. Popular campus events include President's Welcome, Parents Weekend, Homecoming, Holiday Festival, Spring Daze, cultural ceremonies and ethnic events, health awareness activities, and honorary and recognition ceremonies.

Sports: There are 9 intercollegiate sports for men and 7 for women, and 21 intramural sports for men and 17 for women. Athletic and recreation facilities include a 33,000-seat stadium, a 15,000-seat indoor gymnasium, and a 15,000-seat arena, basketball, volleyball, and racquetball courts, running tracks, 2 pools, weight rooms, and an indoor tennis complex.

Disabled Students: About 90% of the campus is accessible to disabled students. The following facilities are available: wheelchair ramps, elevators, special parking, specially equipped rest rooms, special class scheduling, lowered drinking fountains, and lowered telephones.

Services: In addition to many counseling and information services, tutoring is available in most subjects. There are also a reader service for the blind, note-taking services, tape recorders, and interpreters for the hearing-impaired. Remedial tutoring is available through a local community college.

Campus Safety and Security: Campus safety and security measures include 24-hour foot and vehicle patrol, escort service, shuttle buses, and informal discussions. In addition, there are pamphlets, posters, and films, emergency telephones, and lighted pathways and sidewalks.

Programs of Study: UW awards the B.A., B.S., B.F.A., B.M., B.S.Ag.E., B.S.Ch.E., B.S.C.E., B.S.D.H., B.S.E.E., B.S.H.E., B.S.M.E., B.S.N., B.S.P.E., B.S.Petr.E., and B.S.W. degrees. Master's and doctoral degrees also are awarded. Bachelor's degrees are awarded in AGRICULTURE (agricultural business management, agriculture, animal science, international agriculture, range/farm management, soil science, and wildlife management), BIOLOGICAL SCIENCE (biology/biological science, botany, entomology, molecular biology, physiology, and zoology), BUSINESS (accounting, banking and finance, business administration and management, business economics, management information systems, marketing/retailing/merchandising, and small business management), COMMUNICATIONS AND THE ARTS (broadcasting, communications, dramatic arts, English, fine arts, French, German, journalism, music, music performance, music theory and composition, Russian, and Spanish), COMPUTER AND PHYSICAL SCIENCE (applied mathematics, astronomy, chemistry, computer science, geology, geophysics and seismology, mathematics, natural sciences, physics, and statistics), EDUCATION (agricultural, art, business, elementary, health, home economics, industrial arts, music, physical, secondary, special, and trade and industrial), ENGINEERING AND ENVIRONMENTAL DESIGN (architectural engineering, bioengineering, chemical engineering, civil engineering, computer engineering, electrical/electronics engineering, mechanical engineering, and petroleum/natural gas engineering), HEALTH PROFESSIONS (dental hygiene, medical laboratory technology, nursing, pharmacy, and speech pathology/audiology), SOCIAL SCIENCE (American studies, anthropology, criminal justice, economics, food science, geography, history, humanities, international studies, parks and recreation management, political science/government, psychology, social work, and sociology). Elementary education, psychology, and nursing have the largest enrollments.

Required: To graduate, students must complete 120 to 146 credit hours including 35 in the major, with a GPA of 2.0. Required courses include 6 semester hours of English, 2 of physical education, and a course in Wyoming and national constitutions. Entering freshmen must complete the University Studies Program.

Special: Cross-registration is available with local community colleges. The university offers co-op programs, internships, study abroad, Washington and U.N. semesters, work-study programs, dual majors, interdisciplinary majors, including agroecology, pass/fail options, credit by exam, and credit for life, military, and work experience. There is a freshman honors program on campus, as well as 20 national honor societies, including Phi Beta Kappa.

Faculty/Classroom: About 79% of faculty are male; 21%, female. No introductory courses are taught by graduate students. The average class size in an introductory lecture is 37 and in a regular course offering, 22.

Admissions: About 82% of the 1993–94 applicants were accepted. The ACT scores for the 1993–94 freshman class were as follows: 31% below 21, 24% between 21 and 23, 24% between 24 and 26, 10% between 27 and 28, and 11% above 28. About 35% of the current freshmen were in the top fifth of their class; 60% were in the top two

fifths. There were 11 National Merit finalists and 7 semifinalists. About 47 freshmen graduated first in their class.

Requirements: A minimum GPA of 2.5 is required for out-of-state applicants; there is no minimum GPA required of in-state applicants. The SAT I or the ACT is required, but the ACT is preferred. Applicants must be graduates of an accredited secondary school or hold a GED certificate. Secondary preparation should include 18 academic credits consisting of 4 years of English, 3 each of mathematics, science, and social studies, and 1 each of art or music, speech, and computer science. Two years of a foreign language are strongly recommended. A visit is suggested. AP and CLEP credits are accepted. Important factors used in the admissions decision are recommendations by alumni, personality, intangible qualities, recommendations by school officials, leadership record, and geographic diversity.

Procedure: Freshmen are admitted to all sessions. Entrance exams should be taken in the fall of the senior year or spring of junior year. Applications should be filed by August 10 for fall entry, along with an application fee of $20. The college accepts all in-state residents who apply. Notification is sent on a rolling basis. There are early admissions and deferred admissions plans.

Transfer: About 973 transfer students enrolled in 1992–93. A minimum college GPA of 2.3 is required. A total of 30 credits out of 120 to 146 must be completed at UW.

Visiting: There are guides for informal visits and visitors may sit in on classes and stay overnight at the school. To arrange for a visit, contact the Admissions Office at (307) 766–5160.

Financial Aid: In 1993–94, 58% of all current freshmen and 68% of continuing students received some form of financial aid. About 51% of freshmen and 48% of continuing students received need-based aid. The average freshman award in 1992–93 was $3427. Of that total, scholarships or need-based grants averaged $1000 ($4555 maximum); loans averaged $1000 ($3625 maximum); and work contracts averaged $1000. Half of undergraduate students work part-time. Average earnings from campus work for the school year are $1100. The average financial indebtedness of the 1992–93 graduate was $9000. UW is a member of CSS. The FAF and the college's own financial statement are required. The deadline for financial aid applications is March 1.

International Students: There are currently 502 international students enrolled. The school actively recruits these students. They must take the TOEFL and achieve a minimum score of 525.

Computers: The college provides computer facilities for student use. The mainframes are a DEC VAX 7620 and an IBM 9121. Students are assigned computer accounts and user names on the DEC 7620 system, which may be accessed from computer laboratories across campus or via modem. The Novell network can be accessed only via the arts and sciences laboratory. More than 475 microcomputers are available to students in departmental laboratories, campus libraries, and residence halls. All students may access the system. It is available more than 120 hours a week, with no individual time limits on using the system, and no fees.

Graduates: In 1992–93, 1856 bachelor's degrees were awarded. The most popular majors among graduates were elementary education (11%), business administration (4%), and psychology (4%). Within an average freshman class, 16% graduate in 4 years, 36% in 5 years, and 44% in 6 years. Some 100 companies recruited on campus in 1992–93.

Admissions Contact: Richard A. Davis, Director of Admissions.

ENROLLMENT IN CANADIAN SCHOOLS

About five percent of all students enrolled in Canadian colleges and universities come from the United States and other foreign countries. Most Canadian universities admit international students—although some have a quota on the number they will accept—and will give interested students information on how their academic qualifications are equated with Canadian requirements.

The Association of Universities and Colleges of Canada (AUCC) represents 89 universities and university-level colleges. These institutions account for almost 99% of the total university enrollment in Canada. Almost all Canadian colleges are coeducational. Of the 89, eighteen use French as the language of instruction, six use both French and English, and the rest primarily use English. This section contains individual profiles for those English-language universities that enroll more than 10,000 students.

Affiliated with each of these universities are a number of general, theological, or residential colleges, which also have been listed here. The names and addresses of the three French-speaking colleges with enrollments of more than 10,000 may be found at the end of this introduction.

Admissions Requirements

Admissions requirements vary much more among Canadian universities than among American schools, and the amount of time it takes to earn degrees also varies more widely.

Each Canadian province has its own pattern of elementary and secondary education; provinces may require 11, 12, or 13 years of schooling. Universities usually base general admissions requirements on the educational pattern of the province in which they are located. Therefore, international students may have to complete a year or more of college-level work before some universities will consider their applications.

Some universities require American students to submit SAT I and SAT II: Subject tests scores, but most rely primarily on high school performance in determining admission. Students from British Commonwealth countries may have to pass appropriate A- or O-level exams. Students whose native language is not English generally are required to take the TOEFL, the University of Michigan English Language Test, the University of Cambridge Certificate of Proficiency in English, or some other test of competency in English. Some universities also require English-speaking students to take English tests at the start of their freshman year to determine whether a student needs remedial instruction.

Universities also usually ask international students to submit, along with their high school records, a notarized translation of those records into English or French. However, no Canadian university requires students to be fluent in both languages.

Admissions Procedure

After being accepted, the applicant must obtain a student visa from a Canadian diplomatic mission in his or her home country. The mission will ask the student to provide evidence of university admission and proof of adequate funds to pay all expenses in Canada as well as the cost of the journey home. Visas are good only for a specific program at a specific institution for a specific period of time, and cannot be changed once the student is in Canada. Revisions have recently been made to Canada's employment regulations as they pertain to international students at the post-secondary level. The changes affect the following categories: on-campus employment; spouses of students; education related work with industry following graduation (for periods up to 12 months); and expanded access to employment opportunities for students holding Canadian International Development Agency (CIDA) Awards. International students should consult the immigration officer at a Canadian post in their home country for detailed information on current employment regulations.

All students in Canada, including those from other countries, must be covered by a public or private hospital and medical insurance program.

Degrees Offered

Canadian universities, like those in the United States, grant three levels of degrees: bachelor's and first professional, master's, and doctoral as well as undergraduate certificates and diplomas and graduate diploma programs.

Earning the first degree can take three to five years. A general, or unspecialized, program leading to a Bachelor of Arts or Bachelor of Science usually can be completed in three years. An honors degree, earned in a specialized program, usually requires four years. Students must meet more rigorous requirements to enter an honors-degree program and must maintain high grades to remain in it. First professional degrees in some fields may take more than four years to earn, and students may be required to undertake two or three years of university study before enrolling in the professional program. Students who enter graduate programs with a general degree usually must study a year longer than those with honors degrees. Undergraduate diplomas and certificates may be from one to three years' duration and may (although not necessarily) be used as a basis for entry to a degree program. A graduate diploma may be considered as conferring a qualification that is intermediate between the bachelor's (or first professional degree) and master's degree. It may be completed in as little as two or as long as three academic years.

Organizations

Virtually all universities have organizations for international students, and sponsor international student centers and advisers. There also are national organizations that aid international students, including the World University Service of Canada and the Canadian Bureau for International Education, which arranges for representatives to meet international students arriving at Canadian airports.

Tuition, Fees, and Aid

Universities and colleges are heavily subsidized by provincial and federal governments, and tuition fees actually cover less than 15% of university operating costs. Canadian institutions charge different fees for different programs, unlike American institutions, which charge the same tuition regardless of the program of study. Each profile in this book lists the range of tuitions, which may or may not include student fees. Some universities have higher fees for international students, and where that is the case, the profile includes just the international fees. All costs are given in Canadian dollars. In all cases, you should check with the university in which you are interested to obtain the most up-to-date information about tuition and room-and-board charges.

Most awards available to international students through Canadian universities or from the Canadian government are restricted to graduate and post graduate studies. Some of the scholarship programs for international students to study in Canada include the Commonwealth Scholarship and Fellowship Plan, the Canadian International Development Agency awards and the Government of Canada awards program of cultural exchanges. Students interested in applying for aid should contact a Canadian diplomatic mission in their home countries and, for information on cultural exchange programs, their own nation's education department or ministry.

Additional Information

Students interested in more information on studying in Canada can write to the following sources:

Association of Universities and Colleges of Canada
151 Slater Street
Ottawa, Ontario, Canada K1P 5N1
(publications include Canada's Universities: *International Student Guide* and *Directory of Canadian Universities*)

Canadian Bureau for International Education
85 Albert Street, Suite 1400
Ottawa, Ontario, Canada K1P 6A3
(publications include *Guide to Foreign Student Authorizations for Canada, Statistics on Foreign Students, Existing Institutional Policies and Practices Regarding Foreign Students,* 'Information Canada,' and others)

Canadian Consulate General
1251 Avenue of the Americas
16th Floor (Library)
New York, New York 10020
(212) 586-2400

Employment and Immigration Canada
Ottawa, Ontario, Canada K1A 0J9
(publications include *Studying in Canada: Facts for Foreign Students)*

Canadian International Development Agency
Place du Centre 200, Promenade du Portage
Hull (Quebec), Canada K1A 0G4

Social Sciences and Humanities Research Council of Canada
255 Albert Street
P.O. Box 1610
Ottawa, Ontario, Canada K1P 6G4

Statistics Canada
Education, Science, and Culture Division
R.H. Coats Building, 16th Floor
Tunneys Pasture
Ottawa, Ontario, Canada K1A 0T6
(publications include *Tuition and Living Costs at Canadian Universities,* updated annually)

World University Service of Canada
P.O. Box 3000
Station C
Ottawa, Ontario, Canada K1Y 4M8

MEXICAN SCHOOL ENROLLMENT

The Mexican school presented in this book is one of three accredited by a regional accrediting association in the United States. It is accredited by the Southern Association of Colleges and Schools. Costs are given in U.S. dollars. For information on applying to Mexican schools and on immigration regulations, American students can write or call:

Mexican Consulate
8 East 41st Street
New York, New York 10017
(212) 689-0456

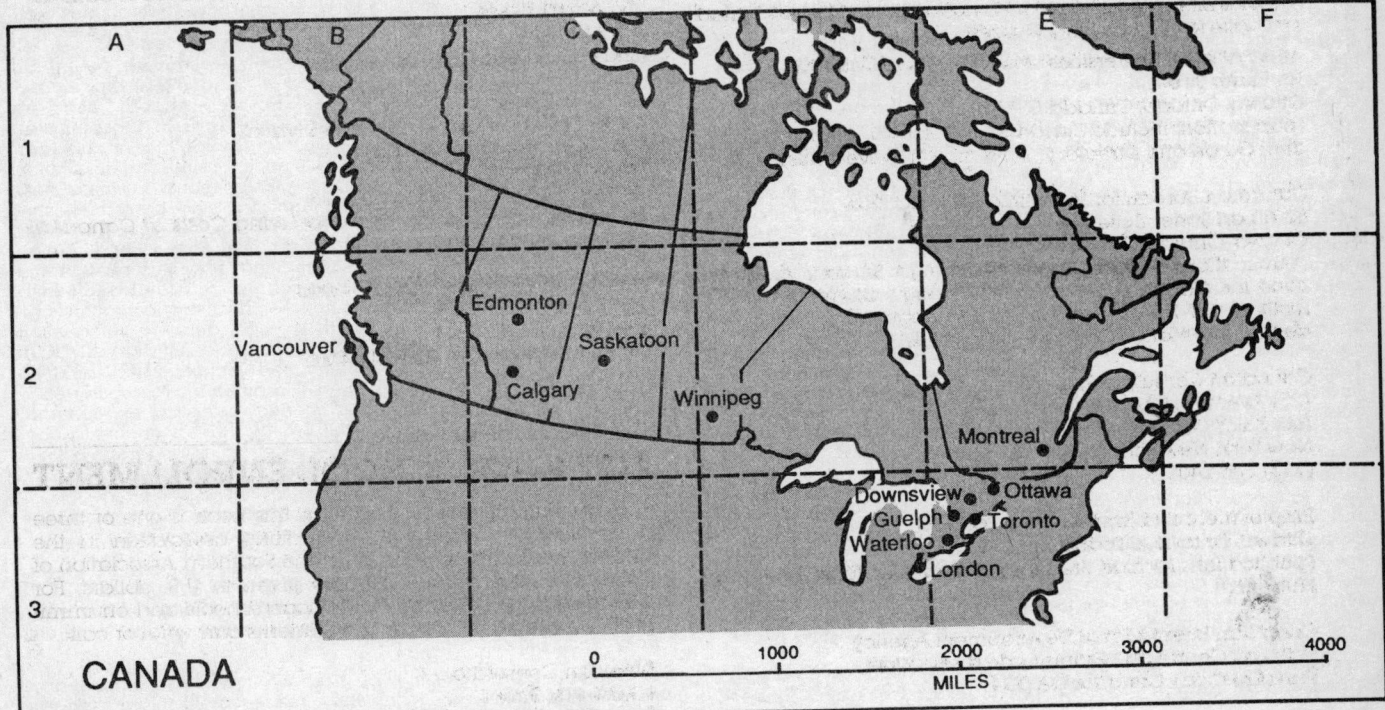

CANADA

CARLETON UNIVERSITY
Ottawa, ON, Canada K1S 5B6

E-3

(613) 788-3663
(800) 267-7366 (Ontario and Quebec)

Full-time: 8173 men, 6826 women
Part-time: 2281 men, 2565 women
Graduate: 1390 men, 1177 women
Year: semesters, summer session
Application Deadline: June 1

Faculty: 691
Ph.D.s: n/av
Student/Faculty: 22 to 1
Tuition: $2373–2561
    ($7986–12,815)
Room & Board: $4723

Freshman Class: 13,000 applied, 10,000 accepted, 4900 enrolled
SAT I: required

Carleton University, founded in 1942, is a public, coeducational institution operated by the province of Ontario. There are 11 undergraduate and 37 graduate degree programs offered. The library contains 1,518,937 volumes, 916,973 microform items, and 19,591 audiovisual forms, and subscribes to 12,903 periodicals. Computerized library sources and services include the card catalog, interlibrary loans, and database searching. Special learning facilities include a learning resource center, art gallery, radio station, and an environmental biology laboratories annex. The 152-acre campus is in an urban area. Including residence halls, there are 27 buildings on campus.

Student Life: Students come from 100 foreign countries. The average age of freshmen is 20.

Housing: A total of 1666 students can be accommodated in college housing. College-sponsored living facilities include single-sex and coed dormitories. On-campus housing is available on a lottery system for upperclassmen. Priority is given to out-of-town students. About 89% of students commute; all remain on campus on weekends. All students may keep cars on campus.

Activities: There are no fraternities or sororities. There are 80 groups on campus, including chess, computers, drama, ethnic, gay, international, newspaper, pep band, photography, political, radio and TV, religious, and student government. Popular campus events include Orientation and Homecoming.

Sports: There are 8 intercollegiate sports for men and 9 for women, and 11 intramural sports for men and 7 for women. Athletic and recreation facilities include a physical recreation center with an Olympic-size pool, squash courts, Nautilus and fitness centers, and a double gymnasium. Outdoor tennis courts and playing fields are also available.

Disabled Students: Nearly 98% of the campus is accessible to disabled students. The following facilities are available: wheelchair ramps, elevators, special parking, specially equipped rest rooms, lowered drinking fountains, and lowered telephones. There are also automatic doors in some buildings, tactile control panels in elevators, tunnels connecting buildings, specially equipped residence rooms, and attendant services.

Services: In addition to many counseling and information services, tutoring is available in most subjects. There are also a reader service for the blind, study skills workshops in essay writing and preparation and writing of examinations, special exam scheduling, and a study center for disabled students.

Campus Safety and Security: Campus safety and security measures include 24-hour foot and vehicle patrol, escort service, pamphlets, posters, and films, and emergency telephones. In addition, there are lighted pathways and sidewalks and electronic access to residences.

Programs of Study: Carleton University awards the B.A., B.Sc., B.Arch., B.Comm., B.C.S., B.Eng., B.I.D., B.J., B.Mus., B.P.A., and B.S.W. degrees. Master's and doctoral degrees also are awarded. Bachelor's degrees are awarded in BIOLOGICAL SCIENCE (biochemistry, biology/biological science, and biotechnology), BUSINESS (accounting, business economics, human resources, international business management, marketing and distribution, marketing/retailing/merchandising, and operations research), COMMUNICATIONS AND THE ARTS (art history and appreciation, classics, communications, English, film arts, French, German, industrial design, Italian, journalism, linguistics, music, Russian, and Spanish), COMPUTER AND PHYSICAL SCIENCE (chemistry, computer science, earth science, information sciences and systems, mathematics, physical sciences, physics, and statistics), EDUCATION (teaching English as a second language/foreign language), ENGINEERING AND ENVIRONMENTAL DESIGN (aeronautical engineering, architecture, civil engineering, electrical/electronics engineering, engineering, environmental engineering, environmental science, mechanical engineering, and systems engineering), SOCIAL SCIENCE (anthropology, Canadian studies, classical/ancient civilization, cognitive science, criminology, Eastern European studies, economics, geography, German area studies, history, human ecology, interdisciplinary studies, law, philosophy, political science/government, psychology, public administration, religion, social work, sociology, and women's studies). Arts, engineering, science, and commerce have the largest enrollments.

Required: Requirements for graduation vary according to programs.

Special: The university offers co-op programs in computer science and public administration, and an exchange program with the University of Ottawa. Study abroad, internships in industrial design, dual and student-designed majors, accelerated degree programs, and interdisciplinary programs are available. The university also utilizes instructional television.

Faculty/Classroom: About 77% of faculty are male; 23%, female. The average class size in an introductory lecture is 107 and in a regular course offering, 58.

Admissions: About 77% of the 1993–94 applicants were accepted. All of the current freshmen were in the top fifth of their class.

Requirements: Carleton University requires applicants to be in the upper 25% of their class. The SAT I is required, with a minimum composite score of 1100 (550 verbal and 550 mathematics). Applicants must be graduates of an accredited secondary school. Architecture and industrial design students must present a portfolio; social work students should submit a personal information form; music students must audition. AP and CLEP credits are accepted.

Procedure: Freshmen are admitted in the fall. Applications should be filed by June 1 for fall entry, February 1 for Architecture and Social Work, and May 1 for Journalism, along with an application fee of $50 (domestic) or $60 (international). Notification is sent from March on. There are early decision, early admissions, and deferred admissions plans. A waiting list is an active part of the admissions procedure, with about 2% of applicants on the list.

Transfer: Applicants are evaluated on individual merits. A total of 5 credits must be completed at Carleton University.

Visiting: There are regularly scheduled orientations for prospective students, including welcome sessions in July and August. There are guides for informal visits and visitors may sit in on classes and stay overnight at the school. To arrange for a visit, contact Student Liaison and Publication Services at (613) 788-3663.

International Students: There are currently 900 international students enrolled. They must take the TOEFL or the college's own test and achieve a minimum score on the TOEFL of 580.

Computers: The college provides computer facilities for student use. The mainframe is a Honeywell CP6. Students have access to computers through their courses. PCs are available at a number of sites. Students who have an account for the mainframe may access the system. It may be used at any time. There are no time limits on using the system and no fees.

Graduates: In 1992–93, 2631 bachelor's degrees were awarded.

Admissions Contact: Victor Chapman, Director of Admissions.

CONCORDIA UNIVERSITY

Montreal, PQ, Canada H3G IM8

E-2

(514) 848-4971

Full-time: 6142 men, 6093 women
Part-time: 4616 men, 5550 women
Graduate: 2004 men, 1579 women
Year: semesters, summer session
Application Deadline: March 1
Freshman Class: 16,000 applied, 7000 accepted, 4000 enrolled
SAT I or ACT: not required

Faculty: 823
Ph.D.s: 82%
Student/Faculty: 15 to 1
Tuition: $1842 ($7754)
Room & Board: $4200

Concordia University, established in 1974, is a public, coeducational institution operated by the province of Quebec. There are 4 undergraduate schools and one graduate school. The 4 libraries contain 1.5 million volumes, 75,000 microform items, and 2000 audiovisual forms, and subscribe to 5500 periodicals. Computerized library sources and services include the card catalog, interlibrary loans, and database searching. Special learning facilities include a learning resource center, art gallery, radio station, TV station, greenhouse, an audiovisual instruction service, and a specialized research center. The campus is in a suburban area in Loyola and an urban area of Montreal. Including residence halls, there are 80 buildings on campus.

Student Life: About 87% of undergraduates are from Quebec. Students come from 18 states and 117 foreign countries. The average age of freshmen is 21; all undergraduates, 22. About 11% drop out by the end of their first year.

Housing: A total of 250 students can be accommodated in college housing. College-sponsored living facilities include single-sex and coed dormitories, off-campus apartments, fraternity houses, and sorority houses. On-campus housing is available on a first-come, first-served basis. Priority is given to out-of-town students. Nearly 98% of students commute. All students may keep cars on campus.

Activities: About 1% of men belong to 3 national fraternities; about 1% of women belong to 2 national sororities. There are 37 groups on campus, including art, choir, chorale, chorus, computers, dance, drama, ethnic, film, gay, honors, international, jazz band, literary magazine, musical theater, newspaper, orchestra, photography, political, professional, radio and TV, religious, social, social service, student government, symphony, and yearbook.

Sports: There are 8 intercollegiate sports for men and 6 for women, and 16 intramural sports for men and 12 for women. Athletic and recreation facilities include an arena, a gymnasium, and a football stadium.

Disabled Students: About 75% of the campus is accessible to disabled students. The following facilities are available: wheelchair ramps, elevators, special parking, specially equipped rest rooms, special class scheduling, lowered drinking fountains, and lowered telephones.

Services: In addition to many counseling and information services, tutoring is available in most subjects. There is also a reader service for the blind, and remedial math, reading, and writing.

Campus Safety and Security: Campus safety and security measures include 24-hour foot and vehicle patrol, self defense education, escort service, and shuttle buses. In addition, there are informal discussions, pamphlets, posters, and films, emergency telephones, and lighted pathways and sidewalks.

Programs of Study: Concordia University awards the B.A., B.S., B.Admin., B.Comm., B.Ed., B.Eng., B.F.A., and B.S.Comp.Sci. degrees. Master's and doctoral degrees also are awarded. Bachelor's degrees are awarded in BIOLOGICAL SCIENCE (biochemistry, biology/biological science, botany, microbiology, and zoology), BUSINESS (accounting, banking and finance, business administration and management, business economics, international business management, marketing/retailing/merchandising, and personnel management), COMMUNICATIONS AND THE ARTS (communications, dance, design, dramatic arts, English, English as a second/foreign language, film arts, fine arts, journalism, language interpretation and translation, languages, music, and photography), COMPUTER AND PHYSICAL SCIENCE (actuarial science, chemistry, computer programming, computer science, earth science, geology, information sciences and systems, mathematics, physics, and statistics), EDUCATION (art, early childhood, elementary, and science), ENGINEERING AND ENVIRONMENTAL DESIGN (civil engineering, computer engineering, electrical/electronics engineering, industrial engineering, and mechanical engineering), SOCIAL SCIENCE (anthropology, community services, East Asian studies, economics, geography, history, human ecology, philosophy, political science/government, psychology, Russian and Slavic studies, social science, sociology, and urban studies). Computer engineering, accounting, communication studies, and psychology are the strongest programs academically.

Required: In order to graduate, students must complete 90 credits (in province) or 120 credits (out-of-province), with a minimum GPA of 2.0. Between 48 and 54 credits are required in the major. All students must fulfill the requirements of the core curriculum and take the university writing test.

Special: Co-op programs may be arranged in building, engineering, chemistry/biochemistry, accountancy, management information systems, economics, mathematics, physics, computer science, and translation. The university offers programs in many majors with the Institute for Co-operative Education, internships, and study abroad in 12 countries. There are accelerated degree programs, B.A.-B.S. degrees, dual majors, a general studies degree, and student-designed majors. There is a chapter of Phi Beta Kappa on campus. Some 21 departments have honors programs.

Faculty/Classroom: About 82% of faculty are male; 18%, female. No introductory courses are taught by graduate students. The average class size in an introductory lecture is 50; in a laboratory, 50; and in a regular course offering, 50.

Admissions: About 44% of the 1993–94 applicants were accepted.

Requirements: Concordia University requires applicants to be in the upper 30% of their class. A minimum GPA of 2.5 is required. The SAT I or ACT is not required. Applicants must be graduates of an accredited secondary school. The GED is accepted. An essay, interview, portfolio, or audition may be required for some programs. AP and CLEP credits are accepted.

Procedure: Freshmen are admitted to all sessions. Applications should be filed by March 1 for fall entry, November 1 for winter entry, and April 15 for summer entry, along with an application fee of $15. The college accepts all in-state residents who apply. Notification is sent on a rolling basis. There are early decision and early admissions plans. A waiting list is an active part of the admissions procedure.

Transfer: Applicants must have a minimum GPA of 2.2. A total of 45 credits out of 90 (in-province) or 120 (out-of-province) must be completed at Concordia University.

Visiting: There are regularly scheduled orientations for prospective students. There are guides for informal visits and visitors may sit in on classes. To arrange for a visit, contact the Liaison Office at (514) 848-4970.

Financial Aid: Scholarships or need-based grants averaged $1000 ($2000 maximum).

International Students: The school actively recruits these students. They must take the TOEFL, the University of Michigan Language Test, or the college's own test and achieve a minimum score on the TOEFL of 550.

Computers: The college provides computer facilities for student use. The mainframe is a CYBER 835. There are also IBM microcomputers. All students may access the system. It may be used 8:30 A.M. to 11:30 P.M. There are no time limits on using the system and no fees.

Graduates: In 1992–93, 4201 bachelor's degrees were awarded. The most popular majors among graduates were arts and science (55%), commerce and administration (25%), and fine arts (10%). Some 325 companies recruited on campus in an earlier year.

Admissions Contact: Pete Regimbald, Director, Liaison Office.

DALHOUSIE UNIVERSITY
E-2
Halifax, NS, Canada B3H 4H6   (902) 494–2450

Full-time: 7549 men and women   **Faculty:** 920
Part-time: 1096 men and women   **Ph.D.s:** 85%
Graduate: 2311 men and women   **Student/Faculty:** 8 to 1
Year: terms, summer session   **Tuition:** $2900 ($4600)
Application Deadline: June 1   **Room & Board:** $4700
Freshman Class: 5741 applied, 3767 accepted, 1897 enrolled
SAT I: required

Dalhousie University, founded in 1818, is a public, nonsectarian institution offering undergraduate, graduate, and professional programs. There are 7 undergraduate schools and one graduate school. The 3 libraries contain 1,270,000 volumes, 340,000 microform items, and 13,800 audiovisual forms, and subscribe to 8182 periodicals. Computerized library sources and services include the card catalog and interlibrary loans. Special learning facilities include a learning resource center, an art gallery, a natural history museum, a radio station, a science museum, an aquatron, a slowpoke nuclear reactor, and a super computer. The 64-acre campus is in an urban area in Halifax. Including residence halls, there are 85 buildings on campus.

Student Life: About 75% of undergraduates are from Nova Scotia. Students come from 72 foreign countries. The average age of freshmen is 19; all undergraduates, 24. About 17% drop out by the end of their first year.

Housing: A total of 1100 students can be accommodated in college housing. College-sponsored living facilities include single-sex and coed dormitories, on-campus apartments, off-campus apartments, fraternity houses, and sorority houses. In addition, there are language houses, special interest houses, and graduate houses. On-campus housing is available on a first-come, first-served basis. Priority is given to out-of-town students. About 80% of students commute. All students may keep cars on campus.

Activities: There are 8 national fraternities and 1 national sorority. There are 70 groups on campus, including chorale, computers, drama, ethnic, gay, international, musical theater, newspaper, photography, political, professional, radio and TV, religious, social, student government, and yearbook. Popular campus events include Frosh Week and Winter Carnival.

Sports: There are 8 intercollegiate sports for men and 6 for women, and 10 intramural sports for men and 10 for women. Athletic and recreation facilities include an athletic center, an arena, indoor and outdoor tennis courts, a track, a playing field, an Olympic-size swimming pool, and squash and volleyball courts.

Disabled Students: Almost 70% of the campus is accessible to disabled students. The following facilities are available: wheelchair ramps, elevators, special parking, specially equipped rest rooms, special class scheduling, lowered drinking fountains, and lowered telephones. The office of the vice president of student services is available to provide assistance on an individual basis.

Services: In addition to many counseling and information services, tutoring is available in most subjects. There is also a reader service for the blind and remedial math and writing.

Campus Safety and Security: Campus safety and security measures include 24-hour foot and vehicle patrol, self defense education, escort service, and informal discussions. In addition, there are pamphlets, posters, and films, lighted pathways and sidewalks, and a student-organized campus patrol program.

Programs of Study: Dalhousie awards the B.A., B.Sc, B.Comm., B.Ed., B.Laws, B.Mus., B.Recreation, Physical and Health Ed., B.S.C.Kinesiology, B.S.N., B.S.O.T., B.S.Pharm., B.S.Physiotherapy, and B.S.W. degrees. Master's and doctoral degrees also are awarded. Bachelor's degrees are awarded in BIOLOGICAL SCIENCE (biochemistry, biology/biological science, marine biology, microbiology, and neurosciences), BUSINESS (business economics and recreation and leisure services), COMMUNICATIONS AND THE ARTS (classics, dramatic arts, English, French, German, music, Russian, and Spanish), COMPUTER AND PHYSICAL SCIENCE (chemistry, computer science, earth science, mathematics, physics, and statistics), EDUCATION (education, health, music, and physical), HEALTH PROFESSIONS (dental hygiene, nursing, occupational therapy, pharmacy, predentistry, and premedicine), SOCIAL SCIENCE (African studies, anthropology, economics, history, international studies, law, philosophy, political science/government, psychology, religion, social work, sociology, and women's studies). Science, health science, arts, and commerce are the strongest programs academically. Arts, science, and commerce have the largest enrollments.

Required: To graduate, most students must complete a minimum of 15 full-year courses, including at least 5 in the major. Most students are required to take some classes outside their area of study. Programs vary in requirements.

Special: Co-op programs may be arranged in mathematics, biochemistry, statistics, computer science, marine biology, earth sciences, physics, and commerce. The university offers cross-registration with Mount St. Vincent, Saint Mary's, and N.S.A.C., study abroad in 5 countries, and accelerated degree programs. Student-designed majors are available. The honors programs provide an extra year of advanced study to qualified students. A 2–3 engineering degree is of-

fered with the Technical University of Nova Scotia. The Science Foundation Year uses an integrated approach to teach a variety of first-year sciences. There is a freshman honors program on campus. Some 26 departments have honors programs.

Faculty/Classroom: About 60% of faculty are male; 40%, female. The average class size in an introductory lecture is 65; in a laboratory, 30; and in a regular course offering, 40.

Admissions: About 66% of the 1993–94 applicants were accepted.

Requirements: The SAT I is required, with a minimum composite score of 1100. At least 2 traditional high school academic courses are required in history, mathematics, and science. Grade 12 credit in English is required and a foreign language is preferred. An audition is necessary for music and theater students. AP credits are accepted. Important factors used in the admissions decision are advanced placement or honor courses, leadership record, recommendations by school officials, extracurricular activities record, and evidence of special talent.

Procedure: Freshmen are admitted to all sessions. There are early decision, early admissions, and deferred admissions plans. Early decision applications should be filed by March 1; regular applications, by June 1 for fall entry, November 15 for winter entry, April for spring entry, and June for summer entry, along with an application fee of $30. Notification of early decision is sent March 1; regular decision, on a rolling basis. More than 500 early decision applicants were admitted in 1992–93.

Transfer: Applicants are assessed on an individual basis. They should have grades of C or 65% and higher from a recognized university. A total of 8 course credits out of 15 must be completed at Dalhousie.

Visiting: There are regularly scheduled orientations for prospective students, including a mixture of social events and workshops. There are guides for informal visits and visitors may sit in on classes and stay overnight at the school. To arrange for a visit, contact the Admissions Secretary at (902) 494–2148.

Financial Aid: In 1993–94, about 17% of all current students received some form of financial aid. The average freshman award was $500. Of that total, scholarships or need-based grants averaged $1700 ($5000 maximum); and loans averaged $500 ($3500 maximum). About 65% of undergraduate students work part-time. The deadline for financial aid applications is April 1.

International Students: There are currently 548 international students enrolled. The school actively recruits these students. They must take the TOEFL and achieve a minimum score of 580. The student must also take the SAT I and achieve a minimum composite score of 1100.

Computers: The college provides computer facilities for student use. The mainframes are a VAX 8800 (VMS operation system), an IBM 4381, and an Alliant 6400. There are a number of Sun workstations (UNIX-based) and high-end graphics workstations. Several microcomputer laboratories are available to students in Killam Library and there are other laboratories throughout the campus, most connected in a local area network. All students may access the system. It may be used anytime. There are no time limits on using the system and no fees.

Graduates: In 1992–93, 1797 bachelor's degrees were awarded. The most popular majors among graduates were biology (12%), psychology (9%), and commerce (9%).

Admissions Contact: Director of Admissions.

LAVAL UNIVERSITY
E-2
Ste-Foy, PQ, Canada G1K 7P4   (418) 656–3080

Full-time: 9321 men, 11,605 women   **Faculty:** 1700
Part-time: 2889 men, 5383 women   **Ph.D.s:** 81%
Graduate: 3684 men, 3265 women   **Student/Faculty:** 12 to 1
Year: trimesters, summer session   **Tuition:** $1758 ($7546)
Application Deadline: March 1   **Room:** $1685
Freshman Class: 16,229 applied, 12,984 accepted, 6713 enrolled
SAT I or ACT: not required

Laval University, founded in 1852, is the oldest French-language university in North America. It offers undergraduate and graduate programs through 9 schools and 14 faculties. There are 23 undergraduate and 23 graduate school and 1 advanced studies facility. The 2 libraries contain 1,990,000 volumes, 49,400 microform items, and 17,900 audiovisual forms, and subscribe to 16,975 periodicals. Computerized library sources and services include the card catalog, interlibrary loans, and database searching. Special learning facilities include a learning resource center, an art gallery, and a natural history museum. The 465-acre campus is in an urban area 2 miles west of Quebec City. Including residence halls, there are 32 buildings on campus.

Student Life: Nearly all of undergraduates are from Canada. The average age of freshmen is 26.1; all undergraduates, 24. About 50% of freshmen remain to graduate.

Housing: A total of 2303 students can be accommodated in college housing. College-sponsored living facilities include single-sex and coed fraternity houses and sorority houses. On-campus housing is guaranteed for all 4 years. All students may keep cars on campus.

Activities: There are 90 groups on campus, including art, band, chorale, computers, dance, drama, ethnic, film, gay, international, jazz band, literary magazine, musical theater, newspaper, opera, orchestra, photography, political, radio and TV, religious, social, social service, and student government. Popular campus events include Thematic Weeks, Salon de L'Etudiant, Student Festival, Carrefour de L'Emploi, and Athletes' Gala.

Sports: There are 7 intercollegiate sports for men and women, and 7 intramural sports for men and women. Athletic and recreation facilities include a covered stadium with a 200-meter running track, 4 tennis courts, a 50-meter swimming pool with a 10-meter diving tower, a double ice arena, 1 triple and 2 single gymnasiums, 4 squash courts, 4 handball and racquetball courts, judo, karate, and self-defense rooms, a dance studio, an open-air stadium with a 400 meter running track, soft, touch football, and soccer fields, 9 outdoor tennis courts, 3 physical training rooms, and a golf driving range.

Disabled Students: Ninety-five percent of the campus is accessible to disabled students. The following facilities are available: wheelchair ramps, elevators, special parking, specially equipped rest rooms, special class scheduling, lowered drinking fountains, lowered telephones, teletype machines for the deaf, computerized classrooms for the visually disabled, electric doors, sidewalks adjusted for handicapped people, a spoken newspaper, and elevators equipped with speaking devices (for the blind).

Services: There is a reader service for the blind and remedial math and writing (French grammar).

Campus Safety and Security: Campus safety and security measures include a 24-hour foot and vehicle patrol, an escort service, informal discussions, pamphlets, posters, and films, emergency telephones, and lighted pathways and sidewalks. Other services include 24-hour camera surveillance in pedestrian tunnels and trained evacuating teams in all buildings. Security training for social events is offered to all student associations.

Programs of Study: Laval University awards the B.A., B.Sc., B.A.A., B.Arch., B.A.V., B.Ed., B.Mus., B.Pharm., B.Sc.A., B.Th., and LL.B. degrees. Master's and doctoral degrees also are awarded. Bachelor's degrees are awarded in BIOLOGICAL SCIENCE (biochemistry, biology/biological science, and microbiology), COMMUNICATIONS AND THE ARTS (art history and appreciation, communications, dramatic arts, English, French, German, language interpretation and translation, Latin, linguistics, and Spanish), COMPUTER AND PHYSICAL SCIENCE (actuarial science, chemistry, geology, physics, and statistics), EDUCATION (education), ENGINEERING AND ENVIRONMENTAL DESIGN (industrial administration/management), HEALTH PROFESSIONS (nursing), SOCIAL SCIENCE (anthropology, archeology, classical/ancient civilization, crosscultural studies, geography, history, philosophy, political science/government, rural economics, sociology, and theological studies). Sciences, business administration, and social sciences have the largest enrollments.

Required: The requirements for graduation vary according to the program. A minimum GPA of 2.5 out of 5 is required per 30 credits.

Special: The university offers work-study programs in metallurgy and mining and forestry. Students may study abroad in the United States, France, Switzerland, and Great Britain.

Faculty/Classroom: Eighty-five percent of faculty are male; 15%, female. Graduate students teach 10% of introductory courses.

Admissions: About 80% of the 1993–94 applicants were accepted.

Requirements: The SAT I or ACT is not required. The only general requirement is the D.E.C. (13 years of scholarity) or the equivalent. Some programs have specific requirements.

Procedure: Freshmen are admitted to all sessions. Applications should be filed by March 1 for fall entry, September 1 for winter entry, and February 1 for summer entry, along with an application fee of $55.

Transfer: About 683 transfer students enrolled in 1993–94. Applicants must have the D.E.C. or the equivalent. A total of 60 credits out of 90 must be completed at Laval University.

Visiting: There are regularly scheduled orientations for prospective students, by reservation only. There are guides for informal visits. To arrange for a visit, contact Carolle Pelletier at (418) 656–3333.

Financial Aid: Financial aid is available only to Canadian residents.

International Students: There are currently 1419 international students enrolled.

Computers: The college provides computer facilities for student use. The mainframes are a are a Convex C-220, a DEC VAX 6610 and 6410, an IBM 9121–320 and 4381–24, and a MASPAR MP-1102. Access is provided by telecommunications. Microcmputers and terminals are available in all buildings. All students may access the system 24 hours a day. There are no time limits on using the system and no fees.

Graduates: In 1992–93, 6802 bachelor's degrees were awarded.

Admissions Contact: Bureau du Registraire, Director of Admissions.

MCGILL UNIVERSITY E-2
Montreal, PQ, Canada H3A 2T5 (514) 398–3910

Full-time: 6200 men, 7700 women	Faculty: 1040
Part-time: 3900 men, 5700 women	Ph.D.s: 75%
Graduate: 3400 men, 2600 women	Student/Faculty: 13 to 1
Year: semesters, summer session	Tuition: $1691 ($6479)
Application Deadline: January 15	Room & Board: $5316
Freshman Class: n/av	
SAT I: required	

McGill University, founded in 1829, is a public, coeducational institution that grants undergraduate, graduate, and professional degrees. There are 10 undergraduate and 17 graduate schools. In addition to regional accreditation, McGill has baccalaureate program accreditation with APTA. The 18 libraries contain 3 million volumes, 990,099 microform items, and 100,000 audiovisual forms, and subscribe to 20,000 periodicals. Computerized library sources and services include the card catalog, interlibrary loans, and database searching. Special learning facilities include a learning resource center, a natural history museum, a radio station, and The McCord Museum of Canadian History, Mont St. Hilaire Nature Conservation Center, an herbarium, an arboretum, a subarctic research station, the Institute of Air and Space Law, and the Institute of Islamic Studies. The 80-acre campus is in an urban area in Montreal. Including residence halls, there are 75 buildings on campus.

Housing: A total of 1400 students can be accommodated in college housing. College-sponsored living facilities include single-sex and coed off-campus apartments and married-student housing. In addition, there are off-campus residences. Priority for on-campus housing is given to out-of-town students.

Activities: About 10% of men belong to 1 local and 13 national fraternities; about 3% of women belong to 4 national sororities. There are 250 groups on campus, including band, cheerleading, chess, choir, chorale, chorus, computers, dance, drama, ethnic, film, gay, honors, international, jazz band, literary magazine, musical theater, newspaper, opera, orchestra, photography, political, radio and TV, religious, social, student government, symphony, and yearbook. Popular campus events include Open House, Orientation Week, Winter Carnival, Multi-Cultural Festival.

Sports: There are 14 intercollegiate sports for men and 15 for women, and 24 intramural sports for men and 16 for women. Athletic and recreation facilities include a 16000-seat stadium, gymnasiums, basketball, volleyball, badminton and squash courts, a weight training room, dance and martial arts studios, a pool, tennis courts, a gymnastics facility, and an Olympic-size track.

Disabled Students: Sixty percent of the campus is accessible to disabled students. The following facilities are available: wheelchair ramps, elevators, special parking, specially equipped rest rooms, special class scheduling, lowered telephones, a Braille variable speed tape recorder, and a talking calculator.

Services: In addition to many counseling and information services, tutoring is available in every subject. There are also a reader service for the blind and remedial math, reading, and writing.

Programs of Study: McGill awards the B.A., B.Arch., B.C.L., B.Eng., B.Mus., B.Sc.Agr., B.Sc.AgrEng., B.ScArch., B.Sc.F.Sc., B.Sc.N., B.Sc.Nutri.Sc., B.S.W., B.Th., LL.B., B.Sc., B.Ed., B.Com., B.Sc.Occ.Ther., and B.Sc.Phys.Ther. degrees. Master's and doctoral degrees are also awarded. Bachelor's degrees are awarded in AGRICULTURE (agriculture), BIOLOGICAL SCIENCE (anatomy, biochemistry, biology/biological science, microbiology, nutrition, and physiology), BUSINESS (accounting, banking and finance, international business management, labor studies, management information systems, management science, marketing management, and organizational behavior), COMMUNICATIONS AND THE ARTS (art history and appreciation, classics, English, French, German, Italian, jazz, linguistics, modern language, music history and appreciation, music performance, music theory and composition, Russian, and Spanish), COMPUTER AND PHYSICAL SCIENCE (chemistry, computer science, geology, geophysics and seismology, mathematics, and physics), EDUCATION (art, elementary, music, physical, secondary, and vocational), ENGINEERING AND ENVIRONMENTAL DESIGN (agricultural engineering, architecture, chemical engineering, civil engineering, electrical/electronics engineering, mechanical engineering, and mining and mineral engineering), HEALTH PROFESSIONS (nursing, occupational therapy, and physical therapy), SOCIAL SCIENCE (anthropology, Canadian studies, East Asian studies, economics, geography, history, Judaic studies, Latin American studies, law, Middle Eastern studies, philosophy, political science/government, psychology, religion, social work, and sociology). Faculty of arts has the largest enrollment.

Required: To graduate, students must successfully complete a required number of approved credits, usually between 90 and 120. Students must also be in satisfactory standing, with a minimum cumulative GPA of 2.0.

Special: There is cross-registration with area universities. Study abroad, dual majors, and student-designed majors are available.

Faculty/Classroom: Eighty-three percent of faculty are male; 17%, female.

Admissions: About 55% of a recent year's applicants were accepted.

Requirements: The SAT I is required. A score of 3 or better on appropriate AP tests, which are required, is recommended. Important factors used in the admissions decision are advanced placement or honor courses, recommendations by school officials, evidence of special talent, leadership record, and extracurricular activities record.

Procedure: Freshmen are admitted fall and winter. Entrance exams should be taken spring of the junior year and/or fall of the senior year. Applications should be filed by January 15 for fall entry and September 1 for winter entry, along with an application fee of $25. Notification is sent on a rolling basis. There is a deferred admissions plan.

Transfer: About 444 transfer students enrolled in an earlier year. Requirements for transfer students vary with faculty. A total of 60 credits out of 90 must be completed at McGill.

Visiting: There are guides for informal visits and visitors may sit in on classes. To arrange for a visit, contact the Admissions Office at (514) 398-3910.

International Students: There are currently 2950 international students enrolled. The school actively recruits these students. They must take the TOEFL or the University of Michigan Language Test and achieve a minimum score on the TOEFL of 550.

Computers: The college provides computer facilities for student use. The mainframes are an IBM 3090-180 and an IBM 4381. The 3090 operates under the MVS/XA operating system, the 4381 under the VM/HPO and MUSIC (Multi User System for Interactive Competing). Microcomputer laboratories, LAN's, and terminals throughout the campus are connected to the mainframe through a high speed fiber optics network, or wide-band communications transmission and data switching systems. Specialized department systems in the network include SUN, DEC, and NEXT. All students may access the system. There are no limits or fees.

Graduates: In an earlier year, 3668 bachelor's degrees were awarded.

Admissions Contact: Mariela Johansen, Director Admissions Office.

MCMASTER UNIVERSITY
E-3

Hamilton, ON, Canada L85 4L8   (905) 525-4600

Full-time: 11,886 men and women   **Faculty:** 1025
Part-time: 3071 men and women   **Ph.D.s:** n/av
Graduate: 2291 men and women   **Student/Faculty:** 12 to 1
Year: Canadian standard year, summer   **Tuition:** $2351-2580
session   ($7560-12,225)
Application Deadline: June 30   **Room & Board:** $4675
Freshman Class: n/av
SAT I or ACT: not required

McMaster University is a private, nonsectarian institution, offering programs in the arts and sciences, business, engineering, health sciences, kinesiology, and social work. There is one graduate school. The 5 libraries contain 1,600,000 volumes, 1,200,000 microform items, and 19,500 audiovisual forms, and subscribe to 13,657 periodicals. Special learning facilities include an art gallery, planetarium, radio station, nuclear reactor, tandem accelerator, greenhouses, hospital, communication research laboratory, and Bertrand Russell archives. The 300-acre campus is in an urban area 60 miles southwest of Toronto. Including residence halls, there are 44 buildings on campus.

Student Life: About 95% of undergraduates are from Ontario. Students come from 12 states and 60 countries. The average age of freshmen is 20; all undergraduates, 22. One percent drop out by the end of their first year.

Housing: A total of 2765 students can be accommodated in college housing. College-sponsored living facilities include single-sex and coed dormitories and on-campus apartments. In addition, there are language houses, La Maison Francaise, an international house, and a quiet house. On-campus housing is guaranteed for the freshman year only and is available on a lottery system for upperclassmen. Priority is given to out-of-town students. Seventy-seven percent of students commute. All students may keep cars on campus.

Activities: There are no fraternities or sororities on campus. There are 120 groups on campus, including art, band, cheerleading, choir, computers, drama, ethnic, gay, international, jazz band, musical theater, newspaper, photography, political, radio and TV, religious, social, student government, and yearbook. Popular campus events include Homecoming and Marauder Weekend.

Sports: There are 17 intercollegiate sports for men and 14 for women, and 14 intramural sports for men and 12 for women. Athletic and recreation facilities include a combatives gymnasium, an outdoor track and field, gymnastics facilities, a weight room, a swimming pool, cross-country trails, rugby, soccer, and football fields, and tennis, squash, and handball courts.

Disabled Students: Fifty percent of the campus is accessible to disabled students. The following facilities are available: wheelchair ramps, elevators, special parking, specially equipped rest rooms, special class scheduling, lowered telephones, and basement-level and above-ground tunnels with connecting walkways.

Services: In addition to many counseling and information services, tutoring is available in some subjects. There is also a reader service for the blind.

Campus Safety and Security: Campus safety and security measures include 24-hour foot and vehicle patrol, escort service, shuttle buses, and informal discussions. In addition, there are pamphlets, posters, films, emergency telephones, lighted pathways and sidewalks, the Emergency First-Response Team, a campus watch program, a prevention programs officer, and video monitoring in some parking areas.

Programs of Study: McMaster University awards the B.A., B.S., B.A.S, B.A./B.S.W., B.C., B.Eng., B.Eng. and Management, B.Eng. and Society, B.H.S., B.Kinesiology, B.Mus., and B.S.N. degrees. Master's and doctoral degrees also are awarded. Bachelor's degrees are awarded in BIOLOGICAL SCIENCE (biochemistry, biology/biological science, biotechnology, and life science), BUSINESS (business economics and labor studies), COMMUNICATIONS AND THE ARTS (art, art history and appreciation, classics, comparative literature, dramatic arts, English, French, German, linguistics, modern language, and music), COMPUTER AND PHYSICAL SCIENCE (applied physics, chemistry, computer science, earth science, geology, mathematics, physical sciences, physics, science, and statistics), ENGINEERING AND ENVIRONMENTAL DESIGN (ceramic engineering, chemical engineering, civil engineering, computer engineering, electrical/electronics engineering, engineering physics, environmental science, manufacturing engineering, materials engineering, materials science, mechanical engineering, and metallurgical engineering), HEALTH PROFESSIONS (medical laboratory technology, medical science, nursing, occupational therapy, and physical therapy), SOCIAL SCIENCE (anthropology, economics, geography, gerontology, history, interdisciplinary studies, Japanese Studies, philosophy, physical fitness/movement, political science/government, psychology, religion, social work, and sociology).

Required: Requirements for graduation vary according to the program of study. A minimum 2.5 GPA in 90 to 150 units is required for most programs.

Special: Many opportunities exist to combine 2 subjects of study within one faculty, or between 2 faculties. All honors students have the option of taking a minor in a second subject area. Nondegree study is possible through the Center for Continuing Education. Students may repeat failed courses provided they are eligible to continue in the program. Forty-one departments have honors programs.

Faculty/Classroom: Seventy-seven percent of faculty are male; 23%, female. All teach undergraduates and do research.

Requirements: The SAT I or ACT is not required. Applicants must be graduates of an accredited secondary school. The required high school courses should include 5 years each of English and mathematics. A portfolio is required for art students and an audition for music students. A supplementary application form is required for some programs. Offers of admission are made based on academic standing and audition/portfolio requirements where necessary.

Procedure: Freshmen are admitted in the fall. Applications should be filed by June 30, along with an application fee of $50. Notification is sent as early as possible. There is an early decision plan. A waiting list is an active part of the admissions procedure.

Transfer: Transfer students are considered on an individual basis. Review of high school, college, and/or university work determines admission status.

Visiting: There are regularly scheduled orientations for prospective students. There are guides for informal visits, and visitors may sit in on classes. To arrange for a visit, contact the Tour Coordinator, Division of Student Liaison, at (905) 525-4600.

Financial Aid: In 1993-94, 25% of all current freshmen received some form of financial aid. The deadline for financial aid applications is July 15.

International Students: They must take the TOEFL with a minimum score of 580, the University of Michigan Language Test, or the college's own test.

Computers: The college provides computer facilities for student use. The mainframes are a DEC VAX 6420, 8530, and 11/785, an IBM 4381 Q03, and a Multiflow Trace 14/300. The mainframes and DOS network (NFS-based) may be accessed from approximately 280 microcomputers at 4 building locations across campus. The microcomputers are IBM-PC and compatibles networked via an Ethernet LAN. The mainframes may also be accessed off campus through a modem pool. Students in specific courses may access the system anytime. There are no time limits on using the system and no fees.

Graduates: In 1992-93, 2955 bachelor's degrees were awarded.

Admissions Contact: Associate Registrar (Liaison and Admissions).

MEMORIAL UNIVERSITY OF NEWFOUNDLAND

F-2

St. John's, NF, Canada A1C 5S7   (709) 737-3200

Full-time: 6151 men, 7600 women
Part-time: 1954 men, 2927 women
Graduate: 1179 men and women
Year: trimesters, summer session
Application Deadline: April 1
Freshman Class: n/av
SAT I or ACT: not required

Faculty: n/av
Ph.D.s: n/av
Student/Faculty: n/av
Tuition: $2210 ($4210)
Room & Board: $3394

Memorial University of Newfoundland, founded in 1925, is a public liberal arts institution. The 3 libraries contain 2.5 million volumes, and subscribe to more than 700 periodicals. Computerized library sources and services include the card catalog, interlibrary loans, and database searching. Special learning facilities include a learning resource center, an art gallery, and a radio station. The 220-acre campus is in an urban area within St. John's. Including residence halls, there are 40 buildings on campus.

Housing: A total of 1750 students can be accommodated in college housing. College-sponsored living facilities include single-sex and coed dormitories, on-campus apartments, and off-campus apartments. On-campus housing is available on a first-come, first-served basis. Priority is given to out-of-town students. All students may keep cars on campus.

Activities: There are no fraternities or sororities on campus. There are many groups and organizations on campus, including band, chess, choir, computers, drama, gay, international, literary magazine, newspaper, photography, political, radio and TV, student government, and yearbook. Popular campus events include Winter Carnival.

Sports: Athletic and recreation facilities include a swimming pool, a gymnasium, squash courts, a rifle range, a weight room, and a soccer field.

Disabled Students: Almost all of the campus is accessible to disabled students. The following facilities are available: wheelchair ramps, elevators, special parking, specially equipped rest rooms, lowered drinking fountains, and lowered telephones.

Services: In addition to many counseling and information services, tutoring is available in some subjects, including mathematics and languages. There is also remedial math and writing.

Campus Safety and Security: Campus safety and security measures include a 24-hour foot and vehicle patrol, an escort service, informal discussions, pamphlets, posters, and films, and lighted pathways and sidewalks.

Programs of Study: MUN awards the B.A., B.Sc., B.Comm.(Gen.), B.Comm.(co-op.), B.Ed., B.Eng., B.F.A., B.N., B.Mus., B.Mus.Ed., B.Med.Sc., B.Sc.(Pharm.)., B.P.E., B.S.W., B.Spec.Ed., and B.Voc.Ed. degrees. Master's and doctoral degrees also are awarded. Bachelor's degrees are awarded in BUSINESS (business administration and management), COMMUNICATIONS AND THE ARTS (fine arts), COMPUTER AND PHYSICAL SCIENCE (science), EDUCATION (education), ENGINEERING AND ENVIRONMENTAL DESIGN (engineering), HEALTH PROFESSIONS (medical science and nursing), SOCIAL SCIENCE (liberal arts/general studies and social work).

Required: Students must complete 40 to 50 credits to graduate.

Special: The college offers co-op programs in commerce, physical education, and engineering. Internships are available in education and nursing. Study abroad may be arranged in 3 countries.

Requirements: A minimum GPA of 60.0 is required. The SAT I or ACT is not required. AP credits are accepted.

Procedure: Freshmen are admitted to all sessions. Applications should be filed by April 1 for fall entry, October 1 for winter entry, and February 1 for spring entry, along with an application fee of $30. There is an early decision plan.

Transfer: Transfer applicants must be in good academic standing at the previous institution. At least 10 credits out of 40 to 50 must be completed at MUN.

Visiting: There are regularly scheduled orientations for prospective students.

International Students: International students must take the TOEFL or the University of Michigan Language Test and achieve a minimum score on the TOEFL of 550.

Computers: The college provides computer facilities for student use. The mainframe is a VAX/SUN cluster. About 175 PCs/terminals are available for student use. All students may access the system. There are no time limits on using the system and no fees.

Admissions Contact: Joseph Byrne, Manager of Admissions.

QUEEN'S UNIVERSITY AT KINGSTON

E-3

Kingston, ON, Canada K7L 3N6   (613) 545-2218

Full-time: 11,150 men and women
Part-time: 4561 men and women
Graduate: 2778 men and women
Year: semesters, summer session
Application Deadline: May 13
Freshman Class: n/av
SAT I or ACT: not required

Faculty: 1010
Ph.D.s: n/av
Student/Faculty: 11 to 1
Tuition: $2396 ($7664)
Room & Board: $5325

Queen's University, founded in 1841, is a public institution offering undergraduate and graduate programs in the arts and sciences, business, engineering, health sciences, and teacher education. There are 10 undergraduate and 5 graduate schools. The 20 libraries contain 1,838,616 volumes, 2,000,000 microform items, and 7000 audiovisual forms, and subscribe to 15,000 periodicals. Computerized library sources and services include the card catalog, interlibrary loans, and database searching. Special learning facilities include a learning resource center, an art gallery, a radio station, a TV station, a geology museum, and an observatory. The 160-acre campus is in an urban area 150 miles east of Toronto. Including residence halls, there are 89 buildings on campus.

Student Life: About 85% of undergraduates are from Ontario. Students come from 80 foreign countries and Canada.

Housing: A total of 2500 students can be accommodated in college housing. College-sponsored living facilities include single-sex and coed dormitories, on-campus apartments, and off-campus apartments. In addition, there are language houses, special-interest houses, study floors, and nonsmoking floors. On-campus housing is guaranteed for the freshman year only and is available on a first-come, first-served basis thereafter. All students may keep cars on campus.

Activities: There are no fraternities or sororities on campus. There are 190 groups on campus, including art, bagpipe band, band, cheerleading, chess, choir, chorale, computers, dance, drama, ethnic, film, gay, international, jazz band, literary magazine, musical theater, newspaper, orchestra, photography, political, professional, radio and TV, religious, social, social service, student government, symphony, and yearbook. Popular campus events include Orientation Week and Alumni Weekend.

Sports: There are 20 intercollegiate sports for men and 20 for women, and 30 intramural sports for men and 30 for women. Athletic and recreation facilities include a pool, an indoor track, a hockey arena, tennis, squash, and racquetball courts, a weight room, a dance studio, and a projectile range. There is also a 5000-seat indoor gymnasium and a 12,000-seat football stadium.

Disabled Students: Eighty percent of the campus is accessible to disabled students. The following facilities are available: wheelchair ramps, elevators, special parking, specially equipped rest rooms, special class scheduling, lowered drinking fountains, and lowered telephones.

Services: In addition to many counseling and information services, tutoring is available in most subjects. There is also a reader service for the blind, and remedial math, reading, and writing.

Campus Safety and Security: Campus safety and security measures include a 24-hour foot and vehicle patrol, self-defense education, an escort service, and shuttle buses. In addition, there are informal discussions, pamphlets, posters, films, emergency telephones, and lighted pathways and sidewalks.

Programs of Study: Queen's awards the B.A., B.Sc., B.A./B.Ed., B.Sc./B.Ed., B.F.A., B.Mus., B.A./B.Phe., B.N.Sc., B.Phe., B.Comm., B.S.C.E., B.Sc.O.T., and B.Sc.P.T. degrees. Master's and doctoral degrees also are awarded. Bachelor's degrees are awarded in BIOLOGICAL SCIENCE (biochemistry and biology/biological science), COMMUNICATIONS AND THE ARTS (communications, dramatic arts, English, film arts, fine arts, French, German, Greek, Italian, Latin, music, and Spanish), COMPUTER AND PHYSICAL SCIENCE (chemistry, computer science, geology, mathematics, physics, and statistics), EDUCATION (elementary, middle school, and secondary), ENGINEERING AND ENVIRONMENTAL DESIGN (chemical engineering, civil engineering, electrical/electronics engineering, engineering physics, geological engineering, and mechanical engineering), HEALTH PROFESSIONS (nursing, occupational therapy, and physical therapy), SOCIAL SCIENCE (economics, geography, history, philosophy, political science/government, psychology, and sociology). Arts, science, and engineering have the largest enrollments.

Special: Internships are available in life science, commerce, and engineering. Students may study abroad in 25 countries. Dual majors are available. There is a freshman honors program on campus. Twenty departments have honors programs.

Faculty/Classroom: The average class size in a laboratory is 40.

Requirements: The SAT I or ACT is not required. Candidates for admission are required to submit a school profile. Important factors used in the admissions decision are leadership record, extracurricular activities record, and evidence of special talent.

Procedure: Freshmen are admitted in the fall. Applications should be filed by May 13, along with an application fee of $50. Notification is sent June 16. There are early admissions and deferred admissions plans. A waiting list is an active part of the admissions procedure.

Transfer: About 90 transfer students enrolled in 1993–94. At least 10 credits out of 19 must be completed at Queen's.

Visiting: There are regularly scheduled orientations for prospective students, consisting of a short briefing session and an hour-long walking tour. Visitors may sit in on classes and stay overnight at the school. To arrange for a visit, contact the Liaison Office at (613) 545–2217.

Financial Aid: The deadline for financial aid applications is May 13 (April 15 for those not from Ontario).

International Students: There are currently 812 international students enrolled. The school actively recruits these students. They must take the TOEFL with a minimum score of 580, or the University of Michigan Language Test. U.S. students must also take the SAT I.

Computers: The college provides computer facilities for student use. There are 4 computer centers on campus. All students are issued a special ID to access the system 24 hours a day. There are no time limits on using the system and no fees.

Graduates: In 1992–93, 3469 bachelor's degrees were awarded. The most popular majors among graduates were arts (39%), education (20%), and science (13%).

Admissions Contact: Assistant Registrar (Admissions).

RYERSON POLYTECHNIC INSTITUTE

E-3

Toronto, ON, Canada M5B 2K3   (416) 979–5304

Full-time/part-time: 13,541 men and women	Faculty: 562
	Ph.D.s: 28%
Graduate: none	Student/Faculty: 17 to 1
Year: semesters	Tuition: $2563 ($7808)
Application Deadline: see profile	Room & Board: $5455
Freshman Class: 26,417 applied, 7782 accepted, 4396 enrolled	
SAT I or ACT: not required	

Ryerson Polytechnic University, founded in 1948, is a public institution offering undergraduate programs in arts, applied arts, business, community services, and engineering and applied science. There are 29 undergraduate schools. In addition to regional accreditation, Ryerson has baccalaureate program accreditation with FIDER. The library contains 320,898 volumes, 400 microform items, and 6283 audiovisual forms, and subscribes to 3239 periodicals. Computerized library sources and services include the card catalog, interlibrary loans, and database searching. Special learning facilities include a learning resource center, a radio station, a TV station, and a film and photography gallery. The 20-acre campus is in an urban area in downtown Toronto. Including residence halls, there are 27 buildings on campus.

Student Life: About 88% of undergraduates are from Ontario. Twenty-four percent drop out by the end of their first year. Seventy-five percent remain to graduate for 3-year programs and 68% remain for four-year programs.

Housing: A total of 858 students can be accommodated in college housing. College-sponsored living facilities include coed dormitories, language houses, and special interest houses. On-campus housing is available on a first-come, first-served basis. Priority is given to out-of-town students. Ninety-four percent of students commute. All students may keep cars on campus.

Activities: There are no fraternities or sororities on campus. There are 55 groups on campus (26 extracurricular and 29 course union), including choir, chorale, ethnic, film, gay, international, literary magazine, newspaper, political, professional, radio and TV, religious, social, student government, and yearbook. Popular campus events include Orientation, Island Picnic, and Winter Carnival.

Sports: There are 8 intercollegiate sports for men and 7 for women, and 7 intramural sports for men and 6 for women. Athletic and recreation facilities include a recreation and athletics center, 7 squash courts, a fitness training center that includes an indoor running track and weight-training equipment, a rehabilitation center, a 25-yard pool, saunas, 3 studios, and 6 gyms.

Disabled Students: The following facilities are available: wheelchair ramps, elevators, special parking, specially equipped rest rooms, special class scheduling, and lowered telephones. The Access Center on campus offers information, seminars, and workshops, test and examination adaptations, computer-equipped exam and study rooms, assistive listening devices for personal use and for use in auditorium settings, advocacy services, individual needs assessment, and access to a wide range of technical devices.

Services: There are a reader service for the blind, remedial math, reading, and writing, and a study skills development workshop available.

Campus Safety and Security: Campus safety and security measures include a 24-hour foot and vehicle patrol, self-defense education, an escort service, informal discussions, pamphlets, posters, and films, emergency telephones, and lighted pathways and sidewalks. Other services include sexual assault training, harassment prevention and crime prevention programs, and community policing programs.

Programs of Study: Ryerson awards the B.A.A., B.B.M., B.Eng., B.H.Sc., B.S.W., and B.Tech. degrees. Bachelor's degrees are awarded in BUSINESS (business administration and management, hospitality management services, and management information systems), COMMUNICATIONS AND THE ARTS (broadcasting, journalism, and photography), COMPUTER AND PHYSICAL SCIENCE (chemi-

cal technology and computer programming), EDUCATION (early childhood), ENGINEERING AND ENVIRONMENTAL DESIGN (aeronautical engineering, architecture, chemical engineering, civil engineering, electrical/electronics engineering, graphic and printing production, industrial engineering, interior design, mechanical engineering, surveying engineering, and urban planning technology), HEALTH PROFESSIONS (environmental health science and nursing), SOCIAL SCIENCE (child care/child and family studies, family/consumer studies, fashion design and technology, geography, public administration, and social work). Business management, electrical engineering, and administration and information management have the largest enrollments.

Required: Students must have a 2.0 GPA and complete the requirements of their program of study.

Special: The university offers co-op programs in applied chemistry and biology, chemical engineering, and midwifery. Accelerated degree programs are available in journalism and nursing, and many programs have a work-study component.

Faculty/Classroom: All teach undergraduates. The average class size in a regular course offering is 30.

Admissions: About 29% of the 1993–94 applicants were accepted.

Requirements: Ryerson requires applicants to be in the upper 60% of their class. The SAT I or ACT is not required. Requirements vary for each program.

Procedure: Freshmen are admitted in the fall. The application deadlines are March 15 for selective programs and June 1 for all others. The application fee is $50. Notification is sent June 15. A waiting list is an active part of the admissions procedure, which varies by program.

Transfer: Transfer applicants must have completed 1 year at the college level. Acceptance of transfer credits is at the discretion of the Office of Admissions/Liaison. Half of the required credits for a particular degree program must be completed at Ryerson.

Visiting: There are regularly scheduled orientations for prospective students, including a half-day tour and discussion session featuring campus tours and visits to specific schools and departments. There are guides for informal visits and visitors may sit in on classes. To arrange for a visit, contact the Liaison Office at (416) 979–5030 or (416) 979–5221 (FAX).

Financial Aid: Scholarships or need-based grants averaged $500; and loans averaged $550. Nonneed-based scholarships/grants average $450. Ryerson is a member of CSS. Forms applicable to Ontario government requirements are needed. The deadline for financial aid applications is September 30.

International Students: There are currently 542 international students enrolled. They must take the TOEFL, the University of Michigan Language Test, or the college's own test and achieve a minimum score on the TOEFL of 550.

Computers: The college provides computer facilities for student use. The mainframe is an IBM RISC 6000. Most major buildings have clusters of PCs that are networked to the backbone network. There are also clusters of IBM terminals, which allow access to the mainframe and more than 300 workstations on networks. There are more than 400 mainframe terminals, although this number is changing as PCs are replacing the terminals. All students may access the system according to their program. There are no fees.

Graduates: In 1992–93, 3000 bachelor's degrees were awarded. Twenty-five hundred companies recruited on campus in 1992–93.

Admissions Contact: Eugene Logel, Director of Admissions.

SIMON FRASER UNIVERSITY

B-2

Burnaby, BC V5A 1S6   (604) 291–3111

Full-time: 3427 men, 4060 women	Faculty: 599
Part-time: 2972 men, 4382 women	Ph.D.s: 90%
Graduate: 1210 men, 1051 women	Student/Faculty: 12 to 1
Year: trimesters, summer session	Tuition: $2125 CDN ($6205 CDN)
Application Deadline: July 15	Room & Board: n/app
Freshman Class: 6587 applied, 3907 accepted, 1382 enrolled	
SAT I or ACT: recommended	COMPETITIVE

Simon Fraser University, established in 1963, is a public institution offering undergraduate and graduate programs in the arts and sciences, business, education, and applied science. In addition to its main campus, the university maintains the Harbour Centre campus in downtown Vancouver to provide mid-career education to the urban population. There are 5 undergraduate schools. The library contains 902,430 volumes and 7389 microform items, and subscribes to 9822 periodicals. Computerized library sources and services include the card catalog, interlibrary loans, and database searching. Special learning facilities include a learning resource center, an art gallery, a radio station, an archaeology museum, special literature and map collections, a fine and performing arts theater, a hypo/hyperbaric chamber, a back test unit, a rock climbing wall, and an apiary. The 1235-acre campus is in a suburban area 9 miles east of Vancouver. Including residence halls, there are more than 25 buildings on campus.

Student Life: About 85% of undergraduates are from British Columbia. Students come from 64 foreign countries and Canada. Ninety-two percent are from public schools; 8% from private. The average age of freshmen is 20; all undergraduates, 25.

Housing: A total of 1025 students can be accommodated in college housing. College-sponsored living facilities include single-sex and coed dormitories, on-campus apartments, and married-student housing. In addition there are some handicapped/disabled suites. Priority for on-campus housing is given to out-of-town students. Eighty-eight percent of students commute. All students may keep cars on campus.

Activities: There are no fraternities or sororities on campus. There are 40 groups on campus, including bagpipe band, chess, ethnic, gay, newspaper, political, professional, religious, social, and student government. Popular campus events include Convocation, Clubs Day, and United Way Campaign.

Sports: There are 8 intercollegiate sports each for men and women, and 4 intramural sports for men and 2 for women. Athletic and recreation facilities include 2 gymnasiums, a swimming and diving pool, a running track, weight rooms, saunas, playing fields, a combative room, and tennis, squash, and racquetball courts.

Disabled Students: Ninety percent of the campus is accessible to disabled students. The following facilities are available: wheelchair ramps, elevators, special parking, specially equipped rest rooms, lowered drinking fountains, and telephones, and some specially equipped on-campus housing.

Services: There are taped library books, a braille typewriter, and a Visualtek machine for disabled students. Some lectures are taped.

Campus Safety and Security: Campus safety and security measures include 24-hour foot and vehicle patrol, escort service, emergency telephones, and lighted pathways and sidewalks. In addition, there are safe-walk stations, student patrols, and individual dormitory room security.

Programs of Study: Simon Fraser awards the B.A., B.Sc., B.B.A., B.Ed., B.F.A., and B.G.S. degrees. Master's and doctoral degrees also are awarded. Bachelor's degrees are awarded in BIOLOGICAL SCIENCE (biochemistry and biology/biological science), BUSINESS (business administration and management), COMMUNICATIONS AND THE ARTS (art, art history and appreciation, communications, dance, dramatic arts, English, film arts, fine arts, French, linguistics, music, Spanish, and visual and performing arts), COMPUTER AND PHYSICAL SCIENCE (applied mathematics, applied physics, chemistry, computer science, mathematics, physical chemistry, physics, science, and statistics), EDUCATION (education and reading), ENGINEERING AND ENVIRONMENTAL DESIGN (engineering and applied science), HEALTH PROFESSIONS (health), SOCIAL SCIENCE (anthropology, archeology, cognitive science, criminology, economics, ethnic studies, geography, gerontology, history, Latin American studies, philosophy, physical fitness/movement, political science/government, psychology, sociology, and systems science).

Required: General bachelor's degrees require completion of 120 semester hours over 8 semesters; honors degrees, 132 hours.

Special: Simon Fraser offers cooperative education in most areas of study, dual majors, B.A.-B.S. degrees, and a variety of continuing education programs, including nondegree and evening study. There is a freshman honors program. Thirty-three departments have honors programs.

Faculty/Classroom: Seventy-seven percent of faculty are male; 23%, female. All teach undergraduates and do research. Graduate students teach 4% of introductory courses.

Admissions: About 60% of the 1993–94 applicants were accepted.

Requirements: A minimum GPA of 2.5 is required. The SAT I or ACT is recommended. Applicants must be graduates of an accredited secondary school and have a minimum grade average of 75.

Procedure: Freshmen are admitted to all sessions. Applications should be filed by July 15 for fall entry, November 15 for spring entry, and March 15 for summer entry, along with an application fee of $20.

Transfer: Applicants must have a minimum GPA of 2.4 and be in good standing at their previous school.

Visiting: There are regularly scheduled 1-day campus orientations for prospective students. There are guides for informal visits, and visitors may stay overnight at the school. To arrange for a visit, contact the Residence and Housing Office at (604) 291–4503.

Financial Aid: Average earnings from campus work for the school year are $800. The FAFSA financial statement is required. The deadline for financial aid applications is July 1.

International Students: They must take the TOEFL or the University of Michigan Language Test.

Computers: The college provides computer facilities for student use. There are IBM, Sun, and SGI host computers. The Word Stations contain IBM and Apple Macintosh computers and printers for student word processing needs. All students may access the system. There are no time limits and no fees.

Graduates: In 1992–93, 2529 bachelor's degrees were awarded. The most popular majors among graduates were General Studies (13%), Business (13%), and Psychology (10%). Within an average freshman class, 80% graduate in 5 years.

Admissions Contact: Nick Heath, Director of Admissions.

UNIVERSITY OF ALBERTA
C-2
Edmonton, AB , Canada T6G 2M7 (403) 492–3283

Full-time: 10,503 men, 12,244 women	Faculty: 1988
Part-time: 1016 men, 2067 women	Ph.D.s: 77%
Graduate: 2437 men, 2227 women	Student/Faculty: 11 to 1
Year: terms, summer session	Tuition: $2338 ($4676)
Application Deadline: May 1	Room & Board: $4257
Freshman Class: n/av	
SAT I or ACT: not required	

The University of Alberta, founded in 1906, is a publicly supported institution offering undergraduate and graduate programs in arts and science, agriculture, forestry, home economics, business, education, engineering, law, medicine, medical laboratory science, dentistry, nursing, pharmaceutical sciences, physical education and recreation, rehabilitation medicine, and native studies. There are 16 undergraduate schools and one graduate school. The 6 libraries contain 3,400,000 volumes and 2,800,000 microform items, and subscribe to 18,900 periodicals. Computerized library sources and services include the card catalog, interlibrary loans, and database searching. Special learning facilities include a learning resource center, art gallery, radio station, agricultural meteorological research station, ecological sanctuary, botanical garden, and a Japanese garden farm. The 155-acre campus is in an urban area 2 miles southwest of downtown Edmonton. Including residence halls, there are 90 buildings on campus.

Student Life: Students come from 10 provinces and 110 countries.

Housing: A total of 4900 students can be accommodated in college housing. College-sponsored living facilities include single-sex and coed dormitories, on-campus apartments, off-campus apartments, and married-student housing. In addition, there are honors houses. On-campus housing is guaranteed for all 4 years. All students may keep cars on campus.

Activities: There are 7 national fraternities and 3 national sororities. There are 200 groups on campus, including art, band, cheerleading, chess, choir, chorale, chorus, computers, dance, drama, ethnic, gay, international, jazz band, musical theater, newspaper, opera, orchestra, pep band, photography, political, radio and TV, religious, social, social service, student government, and symphony.

Sports: There are 9 intercollegiate sports for men and 6 for women, and 60 intramural sports for men and 45 for women. Athletic and recreation facilities include a stadium, swimming pools, gymnasiums, combatives and weight rooms, ballet/fencing and aerobics studios, a 400-meter outdoor track, an ice arena, racquetball and squash courts, a wrestling gymnasium, an indoor field house, a sports medicine clinic, and a training center for handicapped athletes.

Disabled Students: Ninety-eight percent of the campus is accessible to disabled students. The following facilities are available: wheelchair ramps, elevators, special parking, specially equipped rest rooms, special class scheduling, lowered drinking fountains, lowered telephones, and automatic doors.

Services: In addition to many counseling and information services, tutoring is available in some subjects. There is also a reader service for the blind, and remedial math, reading, and writing.

Campus Safety and Security: Campus safety and security measures include 24-hour foot and vehicle patrol, escort service, pamphlets, posters, films, and emergency telephones. In addition, there are lighted pathways and sidewalks.

Programs of Study: U of A awards the B.A., B.S., B.Comm., B.Ed., B.F.A., B.Mus., and B.P.E. degrees. Master's and doctoral degrees also are awarded. Bachelor's degrees are awarded in AGRICULTURE (agricultural economics, agriculture, animal science, plant science, and soil science), BIOLOGICAL SCIENCE (biochemistry, biology/biological science, botany, cell biology, entomology, genetics, marine science, microbiology, physiology, and zoology), BUSINESS (accounting, management science, marketing/retailing/merchandising, organizational behavior, recreation and leisure services, recreational facilities management, and sports management), COMMUNICATIONS AND THE ARTS (classics, comparative literature, dance, dramatic arts, English, film arts, French, Germanic languages and literature, linguistics, music, romance languages, and Slavic languages), COMPUTER AND PHYSICAL SCIENCE (applied mathematics, chemistry, computer science, earth science, geology, geophysics and seismology, mathematics, paleontology, physical sciences, physics, and statistics), EDUCATION (early childhood, education of the deaf and hearing impaired, education of the multiply handicapped, elementary, industrial arts, physical, secondary, special, and vocational), ENGINEERING AND ENVIRONMENTAL DESIGN (chemical engineering technology, civil engineering, computer engineering, construction engineering, electrical/electronics engineering, engineering physics, mechanical engineering, metallurgical engineering, mining and mineral engineering, and petroleum/natural gas engineering), HEALTH PROFESSIONS (medical laboratory science, nursing, occupational therapy, pharmacy, and physical therapy), SOCIAL SCIENCE (anthropology, Canadian studies, clothing and textiles management/production/services, criminology, East Asian studies, Eastern European studies, economics, family/consumer studies, geography, history, law, philosophy, political science/

government, psychology, rural sociology, sociology, and women's studies). Arts, science, education, engineering, and business have the largest enrollments.

Special: The university offers cooperative work experience/study programs in business and engineering. Opportunities for study abroad in 25 countries, internships, dual majors, bilingual classes in French and English, credit by examination (special assessment), and pass/fail options are also available.

Faculty/Classroom: Eighty-three percent of faculty are male; 17%, female. All teach undergraduates and also do research.

Requirements: The SAT I or ACT is not required. Graduation from an accredited secondary school is required. A minimum average of 65% or 70% program dependent is required in all courses submitted for academic credit. Depending on the program selected by the student, an essay, portfolio, audition, or interview may be required. AP credits are accepted.

Procedure: Freshmen are admitted to all sessions. There is an early decision plan. Early decision applications should be filed by April 1; regular applications, by May 1 for fall entry, March 1 for spring entry, and March 1 for summer entry, along with an application fee of $50. Notification of early decision is sent in May; regular decision, July. A waiting list is an active part of the admissions procedure.

Transfer: About 1820 transfer students enrolled in 1993–94. Applicants must meet minimum matriculation requirements or complete 24 credits of transferable work (most facilities) with satisfactory standing. At least 60 credits out of 120 must be completed at U of A.

Visiting: There are regularly scheduled orientations for prospective students. There are guides for informal visits and visitors may sit in on classes. To arrange for a visit, contact Donna Guest at (403) 492–1956.

Financial Aid: In an earlier year, 53% of all freshmen and 60% of continuing students received some form of financial aid. Scholarships or need-based grants averaged $1000 ($5000 maximum); and loans averaged $3500 ($5500 maximum). The deadline for financial aid applications is June 1.

International Students: There are currently 1559 international students enrolled. They must take the TOEFL with a minimum score of 580, or the University of Michigan Language Test.

Computers: The college provides computer facilities for student use. The mainframe is an Amdahl 5870. There are also 370 IBM, Apple, Zenith, and SUN PCs available in various locations on campus. All students may access the system 24 hours a day. There are no time limits on using the system. The fees vary by amount of CPU usage.

Graduates: In 1992–93, 5302 bachelor's degrees were awarded.

Admissions Contact: Bonnie Newman, Director of Admissions.

UNIVERSITY OF BRITISH COLUMBIA
B-2
Vancouver, B.C., Canada V6T 1Z1   (604) 822–3014

Full-time: 19,500 men and women	Faculty: 1870
Part-time: 7200 men and women	Ph.D.s: n/av
Graduate: 5700 men and women	Student/Faculty: 10 to 1
Year: see profile	Tuition: $2208 ($5520)
Application Deadline: see profile	Room & Board: $5400
Freshman Class: n/av	
SAT I or ACT: not required	

The University of British Columbia, established in 1908, is a province-supported institution offering undergraduate and graduate programs in the arts, sciences, and various professions. The winter session lasts from early September through April; some courses extend into May. Summer session begins in May and goes to mid-August, and consists of 2 terms. There are 18 undergraduate schools. The 990-acre campus is in an urban area of Vancouver. Including residence halls, there are 475 buildings on campus.

Student Life: About 80% of undergraduates are from British Columbia. The average age of all undergraduates is 20. Thirty-three percent drop out by the end of their first year.

Housing: College-sponsored living facilities include on-campus apartments and married-student housing. All students may keep cars on campus.

Activities: There are some groups and organizations on campus, including international, newspaper, political, radio and TV, religious, social service, and student government.

Disabled Students: The following facilities are available: wheelchair ramps, elevators, special parking, specially equipped rest rooms, and special living facilities.

Services: In addition, there is remedial reading and writing.

Campus Safety and Security: Campus safety and security measures include 24-hour foot and vehicle patrol, escort service, shuttle buses, and informal discussions. In addition, a Royal Canadian mounted police detachment is on campus; campus security provides awareness programs on theft and personal safety lectures for women.

Programs of Study: UBC awards the B.A., B.S., B.A.Sc., B.Com., B.F.A., B.H.E., B.P.E., B.S.A., B.S.F., B.S.N., and B.S.W. degrees. Master's and doctoral degrees are also awarded. Bachelor's degrees are awarded in AGRICULTURE (agricultural economics, animal science, forestry and related sciences, plant science, range/farm management, soil science, and wildlife management), BIOLOGICAL SCI-

ENCE (nutrition), BUSINESS (accounting, international business management, management information systems, and marketing/retailing/merchandising), COMMUNICATIONS AND THE ARTS (classics, creative writing, dramatic arts, English, fine arts, French, German, Italian, linguistics, music, Polish, Portuguese, Russian, and Spanish), COMPUTER AND PHYSICAL SCIENCE (mathematics), EDUCATION (elementary, secondary, and special), ENGINEERING AND ENVIRONMENTAL DESIGN (architecture, bioengineering, chemical engineering, civil engineering, electrical/electronics engineering, engineering physics, geological engineering, industrial administration/management, landscape architecture/design, mechanical engineering, and mining and mineral engineering), HEALTH PROFESSIONS (preveterinary science), SOCIAL SCIENCE (anthropology, Asian/Oriental studies, dietetics, economics, food science, geography, history, home economics, philosophy, political science/government, psychology, and sociology).

Required: Graduation requirements vary according to the degree sought. B.A. candidates must complete coursework in English composition, science, literature, and a foreign language.

Faculty/Classroom: Eighty-one percent of faculty are male; 19%, female.

Requirements: The SAT I or ACT is not required. Graduation from a secondary school is mandatory, with a minimum average of C+. Courses should include 4 years of English and at least 3 of mathematics. International students must have completed course work equivalent to that of British Columbia secondary schools. Specific secondary school requirements vary by program.

Procedure: Application deadlines vary by program, and the earliest deadline for regular winter term decision is Fegruary 1 for law. The application fee is $15. There is an early admissions plan.

Visiting: There are regularly scheduled orientations for prospective students.

International Students: Students with English as a second language must take the TOEFL and achieve a minimum score of 570 (580 for arts).

Computers: The college provides computer facilities for student use. The mainframe is an Amdahl 5860. Those students requiring computers in their course work may access the system 24 hours per day. Time limits vary.

Graduates: In a recent year, 3994 bachelor's degrees were awarded. Within an average freshman class, 60% graduate in 4 years.

Admissions Contact: Office of the Registrar.

UNIVERSITY OF CALGARY
C-2
Calgary, AB, Canada T2N 1N4   (403) 220–6673

Full-time: 7525 men, 8653 women	Faculty: 1365
Part-time: 1394 men, 2257 women	Ph.D.s: n/av
Graduate: 1465 men, 1301 women	Student/Faculty: 12 to 1
Year: semesters, summer session	Tuition: $2400 ($4464)
Application Deadline: June 1	Room & Board: $3310 ($4120)
Freshman Class: n/av	
SAT I: required	

The University of Calgary, founded in 1945, is a public institution offering undergraduate programs in numerous liberal arts and professional fields. There are 14 undergraduate and 2 graduate faculties. The library contains 1,900,000 volumes, 2,600,000 microform items, and 1,300,000 audiovisual forms, and subscribes to 13,600 periodicals. Computerized library sources and services include the card catalog, interlibrary loans, and database searching. Special learning facilities include student radio and TV stations, an arts museum, an environmental research center, an observatory, and human performance and theater laboratories. The 304-acre campus is in an urban area in northwest Calgary. Including residence halls, there are 30 buildings on campus.

Housing: A total of 1400 students can be accommodated in college housing. College-sponsored living facilities include coed dormitories, on-campus apartments, and married-student housing. On-campus housing is available on a first-come, first-served basis. Priority is given to out-of-town students. All students may keep cars on campus.

Activities: There are no fraternities or sororities on campus. There are many groups and organizations on campus, including band, choir, drama, newspaper, orchestra, political, radio and TV, religious, social, student government, and yearbook.

Sports: There are 8 intercollegiate sports for men and 7 for women, and 20 intramural sports for men and 18 for women. Athletic and recreation facilities include 3 gymnasiums, a 50-meter swimming pool, a 200-meter indoor track, a 3-story climbing wall, an indoor speed-skating arena, and an outdoor stadium; rooms for weight training, aerobics, and combatives; and squash, tennis, racquetball courts. There is also a 200-seat lecture theater, a games area, and an outdoor recreation center.

Disabled Students: The entire campus is accessible to disabled students. The following facilities are available: wheelchair ramps, elevators, special parking, specially equipped rest rooms, lowered drinking fountains, and lowered telephones.

Services: In addition to many counseling and information services, tutoring is available in most subjects. There is also a reader service for the blind and remedial writing.

Campus Safety and Security: Campus safety and security measures include escort service, informal discussions, emergency telephones, and lighted pathways and sidewalks.

Programs of Study: U of C awards the B.A., B.Comm., B.Ed., B.F.A., B.Mus., B.N., B.P.E., B.Sc., B.Sc. (Eng.), B.S.W., and LL.B. degrees. Master's and doctoral degrees also are awarded. Bachelor's degrees are awarded in BIOLOGICAL SCIENCE (biochemistry, biology/biological science, botany, cell biology, ecology, and zoology), BUSINESS (accounting, business administration and management, marketing/retailing/merchandising, and tourism), COMMUNICATIONS AND THE ARTS (art history and appreciation, communications, dramatic arts, English, fine arts, French, German, Greek, Latin, linguistics, music, music history and appreciation, music performance, music theory and composition, Russian, and Spanish), COMPUTER AND PHYSICAL SCIENCE (actuarial science, applied mathematics, astrophysics, chemistry, computer science, geology, geophysics and seismology, mathematics, physics, science technology, and statistics), EDUCATION (art, early childhood, elementary, mathematics, music, physical, science, secondary, social studies, and special), ENGINEERING AND ENVIRONMENTAL DESIGN (chemical engineering, civil engineering, electrical/electronics engineering, mechanical engineering, and surveying engineering), HEALTH PROFESSIONS (nursing), SOCIAL SCIENCE (anthropology, archeology, Canadian studies, classical/ancient civilization, economics, geography, history, law, peace studies, philosophy, political science/government, psychology, religion, social work, sociology, urban studies, and women's studies). Engineering is the strongest program academically. Psychology and education have the largest enrollments.

Required: In order to graduate, all students must satisfy the required courses, course sequences, and credit distribution in their particular program. Students must maintain a minimum 2.0 GPA and complete 7 to 10 full-course equivalents in the major field.

Special: The university offers cooperative education programs in engineering, science, business, and many other fields. Internships in engineering, a combined B.Comm./B.Sc. degree in actuarial sciences, study abroad in the People's Republic of China, work-study programs, and double majors are also available. Students may cross-register with any of 8 member colleges in the Big Country Education Consortium. The university sponsors or is affiliated with 20 research institutes and groups.

Faculty/Classroom: The average class size in an introductory lecture is 60 and in a laboratory, 24.

Requirements: The SAT I is required. U.S. applicants must be graduates of a secondary school and submit SAT I and 3 SAT II: Subject test scores, as required by the individual faculties. A minimum score of 400 on each part of the SAT I and an overall average of 500 or above on the 5 tests is required. Due to controlled admission, an average test score of only 500 will not guarantee admission. AP credits are accepted.

Procedure: Freshmen are admitted in the fall. Applications should be filed by June 1, along with an application fee of $50. There is an early admissions plan.

Transfer: Applicants must have a minimum GPA of 2.0 on all transfer and nontransfer courses. At least 2 years out of 4 must be completed at U of C.

Visiting: There are regularly scheduled orientations for prospective students, ranging from 1 day to 1 week. There are guides for informal visits. To arrange for a visit, contact the Student Resource Center at (403) 220–6920.

International Students: There are currently 945 international students enrolled. They must take the TOEFL and achieve a minimum score of 580.

Computers: The college provides computer facilities for student use. The mainframe is an IBM RISC 6000 Model 950. There are a number of PC, Apple Macintosh, and UNIX workstation laboratories on campus. Students enrolled in certain courses may access the systems. 800 terminals are available 24 hours a day. There are no time limits on using the system and no fees.

Graduates: In 1992–93, 3194 bachelor's degrees were awarded.

Admissions Contact: Assistant Registrar and Director of Admissions.

UNIVERSITY OF GUELPH
Guelph, ON, Canada N1G 2WI

E-3

(519) 824–4120

Full-time: 11,360 men and women	**Faculty:** 778
Part-time: 2241 men and women	**Ph.D.s:** 81%
Graduate: 1731 men and women	**Student/Faculty:** 15 to 1
Year: trimesters, summer session	**Tuition:** $2226 ($7302)
Application Deadline: August 1	**Room & Board:** $2576
Freshman Class: 16,504 applied, 5914 accepted, 2567 enrolled	
SAT I or ACT: not required	

The University of Guelph, founded in 1964, is a public institution offering programs in arts and sciences, agriculture, engineering, commerce, landscape architecture, veterinary medicine, and applied science. There are 7 undergraduate schools. The 2 libraries contain 2,500,000 volumes. Computerized library sources and services include interlibrary loans and database searching. Special learning facilities include a learning resource center. The 1200-acre campus is in a suburban area 2 miles south of the center of Guelph. Including residence halls, there are 80 buildings on campus.

Student Life: About 85% of undergraduates are from Ontario. Students come from 10 states and 90 countries. Ninety-five percent are from public schools; 5% from private. The average age of freshmen is 18; all undergraduates, 20. Twenty-three percent drop out by the end of their first year.

Housing: A total of 4000 students can be accommodated in college housing. College-sponsored living facilities include single-sex and coed dormitories, on-campus apartments, and married-student housing. In addition, there are language houses, special-interest houses, an international house, La Maison Francaise, and an arts house. On-campus housing is guaranteed for the freshman year only, and is available on a first-come, first-served basis and lottery system for upperclassmen. Sixty-seven percent of students commute. All students may keep cars on campus.

Activities: There are no fraternities or sororities on campus. There are 100 groups on campus, including cheerleading, chess, choir, chorale, computers, dance, drama, gay, international, jazz band, newspaper, political, professional, radio and TV, religious, social, social service, and student government. Popular campus events include College Royal Open House in March.

Sports: Athletic and recreation facilities include a twin-pad arena, 7 squash courts, a fitness gymnasium, weight-training rooms, a 6-lane swimming pool, an Olympic-size pool, a fitness circuit, and 3 gymnasiums. Outdoor facilities include 4 tennis courts, a running track, lighted football, field hockey, soccer, rugby, and fastball fields, jogging trails, and multipurpose fields.

Disabled Students: Ninety percent of the campus is accessible to disabled students. The following facilities are available: wheelchair ramps, elevators, special parking, and specially equipped rest rooms.

Services: In addition to many counseling and information services, tutoring is available in some subjects, including mathematics and sciences. There is also a reader service for the blind.

Campus Safety and Security: Campus safety and security measures include escort service, pamphlets, posters, films, emergency telephones, and lighted pathways and sidewalks. In addition, there is a campus police patrol.

Programs of Study: U of G awards the B.A., B.A.Sc., B.Comm., B.L.A., B.Sc., B.Sc.Agr., B.Sc.Eng., and B.Sc.Env. degrees. Associate, master's, and doctoral degrees also are awarded. Bachelor's degrees are awarded in AGRICULTURE (agriculture), BIOLOGICAL SCIENCE (biology/biological science), COMPUTER AND PHYSICAL SCIENCE (physical sciences), ENGINEERING AND ENVIRONMENTAL DESIGN (engineering, environmental science, and landscape architecture/design), HEALTH PROFESSIONS (veterinary science), SOCIAL SCIENCE (social science). Biological/physical sciences and veterinary medicine are the strongest academically. Biological/physical sciences, arts, and social sciences have the largest enrollments.

Required: To graduate, students must complete 30 credits (half courses) for a general degree and 40 credits (half courses) for an honors degree. The university requires a minimum of 10 credits in the major.

Special: The school offers co-op programs, study abroad in 3 countries, and work-study with numerous companies. Accelerated degree programs, B.A.-B.S. degrees, dual majors, a general studies degree, and nondegree study are available. There is a freshman honors program on campus.

Faculty/Classroom: The average class size in an introductory lecture is 300 and in a laboratory, 25.

Admissions: About 36% of the 1993–94 applicants were accepted. About 48% of the current freshmen were in the top fifth of their class.

Requirements: Test scores are not considered in the admissions decision. Ontario applicants must have a minimum overall average of 60% on 6 Ontario Academic Course (Grade 13) credits. Higher averages may be required for admission to individual programs. U.S. applicants should rank in the upper quarter of their high school class and have a B minimum average. Some programs require an essay or interview.

Procedure: Freshmen are admitted fall, winter, and spring. Applications should be filed by August 1 for fall entry, December 1 for winter entry, and April 1 for spring entry, along with an application fee of $30. There are early decision and early admissions plans.

Transfer: A total of 10 half-course credits out of 30 to 40 must be completed at U of G.

Visiting: There are regularly scheduled orientations for prospective students, including a tour of the campus. There are guides for informal visits, and visitors may sit in on classes. To arrange for a visit, contact the Admissions Office at (519) 824–4120, ext. 8712.

Financial Aid: In a recent year, 40% of all freshmen received some form of financial aid. The deadline for financial aid applications is January 30.

International Students: There are currently 600 international students enrolled. The school actively recruits these students. They must take the TOEFL and achieve a minimum score of 575.

Computers: The college provides computer facilities for student use. The mainframe is an IBM/3084Q. There are also 500 IBM, IBM-compatible, and Macintosh computers available throughout campus. The schedule and time limits vary by department and program. There are no fees.

Graduates: Some 200 companies recruited on campus in a recent year. In a recent graduating class, 41% of the graduates were enrolled in graduate school within 6 months of graduation.

Admissions Contact: Starr Ellis, Assistant Registrar, Admissions.

UNIVERSITY OF MONTREAL
E-2
Montreal, PQ, Canada H3C 3J7   (514) 343-7076

Full-time: 9695 men, 11,821 women	Faculty: 1518
Part-time: 6748 men, 12,436 women	Ph.D.s: 81%
Graduate: 5524 men, 5313 women	Student/Faculty: 14 to 1
Year: trimesters, summer session	Tuition: n/app
Application Deadline: March 1	Room: $1400
Freshman Class: n/av	
SAT I or ACT: not required	

The University of Montreal, founded in 1878, is the largest French-language university in North America, with 13 faculties, 2 affiled schools, 63 teaching departments, and 108 research units. There are 16 undergraduate and 5 graduate schools. The 25 libraries contain 4,170,307 volumes and 148,760 audiovisual forms, and subscribe to 16,993 periodicals. Computerized library sources and services include the card catalog, interlibrary loans, and database searching. Special learning facilities include a learning resource center, an art gallery, and a radio station. The 150-acre campus is in an urban area in Montreal. Including residence halls, there are 34 buildings on campus.

Student Life: Students come from 104 foreign countries. The average age of freshmen is 25; all undergraduates, 29. Thirty-two percent drop out by the end of their first year; 55% remain to graduate.

Housing: A total of 1130 students can be accommodated in college housing. College-sponsored living facilities include coed off-campus apartments. On-campus housing is guaranteed for all 4 years. Ninety-nine percent of students commute. All students may keep cars on campus.

Activities: There are no fraternities or sororities on campus. There are 50 groups on campus, including art, choir, chorale, computers, dance, drama, ethnic, film, gay, international, jazz band, literary magazine, newspaper, orchestra, photography, radio and TV, religious, social, social service, student government, and yearbook.

Sports: There are 3 intercollegiate sports for men and women, and 12 intramural sports for men and women. Athletic and recreation facilities include a skating rink, a football field, a gymnasium, a squash field, a racquetball field, an Olympic-size pool, and a diving pool.

Disabled Students: Ninety-five percent of the campus is accessible to disabled students. The following facilities are available: wheelchair ramps, elevators, special parking, specially equipped rest rooms, lowered drinking fountains, and lowered telephones. There is also a specialized equipment center for students with disabilities.

Services: In addition to many counseling and information services, tutoring is available in some subjects, including mathematics and French. There is also a reader service for the blind, and remedial math, reading, and writing.

Campus Safety and Security: Campus safety and security measures include a 24-hour foot and vehicle patrol, an escort service, shuttle buses, informal discussions, pamphlets, posters, and films, emergency telephones, and lighted pathways and sidewalks.

Programs of Study: U. de M.L. awards the B.A., B.Sc., B.A.A., B.Arch., B.A.P., B.D.I., B.Ing., B.Mus., B.Pharm., and B.Th. degrees. Master's and doctoral degrees also are awarded. Bachelor's degrees are awarded in BIOLOGICAL SCIENCE (biochemistry, biology/biological science, and nutrition), BUSINESS (business administration and management), COMMUNICATIONS AND THE ARTS (art history and appreciation, classics, English, film arts, French, German, industrial design, language interpretation and translation, linguistics, and music), COMPUTER AND PHYSICAL SCIENCE (chemistry, computer science, geology, mathematics, and physics), EDUCATION (education, physical, and psychology), ENGINEERING AND ENVIRONMENTAL DESIGN (architecture, engineering, industrial administration/management, and landscape architecture/design), HEALTH PROFESSIONS (dental hygiene, nursing, occupational therapy, pharmacy, physical therapy, physiotherapy, and speech pathology/audiology), SOCIAL SCIENCE (anthropology, biblical studies, criminology, East Asian studies, economics, geography, Hispanic American studies, history, law, philosophy, political science/government, psychology, social work, sociology, Spanish Studies, theological studies, and urban studies). Arts and Science have the largest enrollments.

Required: Students must have a GPA of 2.0 on a 0 to 4.3 scale. The total number of credit hours required in most programs is 90. Professional programs, particularly those in health-related fields, require more hours.

Special: The university offers co-op programs in mining and engineering, internships in medicine, and work-study programs in hospitals and businesses in Quebec. B.A.-B.S. degrees, dual majors in mathematics and science, and 3-2 engineering degrees may also be arranged.

Faculty/Classroom: Sixty-six percent of faculty are male; 34%, female. The average class size in an introductory lecture is 45; in a laboratory, 17; and in a regular course offering, 38.

Requirements: The SAT I or ACT is not required. Applicants in certain limited enrollment programs must take the university's admissions tests. An interview is also required in some of these programs.

Procedure: Freshmen are admitted in the fall and winter. Entrance exams should be taken. The university's admissions tests are administered at the end of March and the beginning of April. Applications should be filed by March 1 for fall entry and October 15 for winter entry, along with an application fee of $55. A waiting list is an active part of the admissions procedure for some programs.

Financial Aid: Financial aid is available only for Canadian students. U de M is a member of CSS.

International Students: There are currently 1534 international students enrolled.

Computers: The college provides computer facilities for student use. The mainframes are a 6 SGI 4d/380, 6 SGI Challenge, and 3 SGI 4d/280 models. Students have access to 2600 PCs and 300 workstations located in 6 computer laboratories on campus. Graduate and undergraduate students in related programs may access the system 24 hours per day. There are no time limits on using the system and no fees.

Graduates: In 1992-93, 5339 bachelor's degrees were awarded. Some 79 companies recruited on campus in 1992-93. In the 1992 graduating class, 40% of the men and were enrolled in graduate school within 6 months of graduation; 91% had found employment.

Admissions Contact: Fernand Boucher, Director of Admissions.

UNIVERSITY OF OTTAWA
E-3
Ottawa, ON, Canada K1N 6N5   (613) 564-3928

Full-time: 5800 men, 8000 women	Faculty: 1190
Part-time: 2600 men, 4900 women	Ph.D.s: n/av
Graduate: 1850 men, 1880 women	Student/Faculty: 12 to 1
Year: semesters, summer session	Tuition: $2040 ($6770)
Application Deadline: see profile	Room & Board: $1950
Freshman Class: n/av	
SAT I: required	

The University of Ottawa, founded in 1848, is a bilingual (French/English) institution offering undergraduate and graduate degrees in administration, arts, law, health sciences, medicine, science, engineering, social sciences and education. There are 9 undergraduate and 9 graduate schools. The library contains 2 million volumes, 390,355 microform items, and 10,800 audiovisual forms, and subscribes to 13,500 periodicals. The 70-acre campus is in an urban area. Including residence halls, there are 31 buildings on campus.

Student Life: About 78% of undergraduates are from Ontario. Students come from 10 states and 4 foreign countries.

Housing: A total of 2132 students can be accommodated in college housing. College-sponsored living facilities include dormitories, off-campus apartments, and married-student housing. On-campus housing is available on a lottery system for upperclassmen. Eighty-four percent of students commute. All students may keep cars on campus.

Activities: There are no fraternities or sororities on campus. There are 50 groups on campus, including art, band, chess, choir, chorale, computers, drama, ethnic, gay, international, jazz band, newspaper, orchestra, photography, political, professional, radio and TV, religious, social, social service, student government, and symphony. Popular campus events include Ottawa Day, Panda football game, Orientation Week, International Week, and Careers Week.

Sports: There are 8 intercollegiate sports for men and 6 for women, and 6 intramural sports each for men and women. Athletic and recreation facilities include weight training and combat rooms, a 50-meter swimming pool, gymnasiums, racquetball and squash courts, billiards and Ping-Pong tables, an indoor arena, and a sports field.

Disabled Students: Seventy-five percent of the campus is accessible to disabled students. The following facilities are available: wheelchair ramps, elevators, special parking, specially equipped rest rooms, special class scheduling, lowered drinking fountains, lowered telephones, and automatic doors and specialized equipment.

Services: In addition to many counseling and information services, tutoring is available in most subjects. There are also a reader service for the blind and remedial math, reading, and writing.

Campus Safety and Security: Campus safety and security measures include 24-hour foot and vehicle patrol, self-defense education, escort service, and shuttle buses. In addition, there are informal discussions, pamphlets, posters, films, lighted pathways and sidewalks, and the university participates in a community crime-stoppers program.

Programs of Study: UO awards the B.A., B.Ad., B.A.Sc., B.Com., B.Ed., B.Soc.Sc., B.Sc., B.F.A., B.Mus., and B.Sc.N. degrees. Master's and doctoral degrees also are awarded. Bachelor's degrees are

awarded in BIOLOGICAL SCIENCE (biochemistry, biology/biological science, biotechnology, and physiology), BUSINESS (accounting, banking and finance, business administration and management, human resources, management information systems, management science, and marketing/retailing/merchandising), COMMUNICATIONS AND THE ARTS (art history and appreciation, communications, dramatic arts, English, French, German, Italian, Latin, linguistics, music, photography, Spanish, and visual and performing arts), COMPUTER AND PHYSICAL SCIENCE (chemistry, computer science, geology, mathematics, and physics), EDUCATION (education), ENGINEERING AND ENVIRONMENTAL DESIGN (chemical engineering, civil engineering, computer engineering, electrical/electronics engineering, environmental engineering, and mechanical engineering), HEALTH PROFESSIONS (nursing and occupational therapy), SOCIAL SCIENCE (Canadian studies, criminology, economics, geography, history, law, medieval studies, philosophy, political science/government, psychology, public administration, religion, Russian and Slavic studies, sociology, and women's studies). Law, medicine, education, chemistry, biology, lettres francaises, political science, and criminology are the strongest academically. Arts, social sciences, and science have the largest enrollments.

Required: Students must maintain a GPA of 3.5 out of 10 for all courses, including those in major. Students must also complete a second langauge requirement: French for English students, and English for French students.

Special: Opportunities are provided for cooperative programs, study abroad in France and England, a general studies degree in arts and in sciences, and combined programs in all fields in arts and in social sciences. Forty departments have honors programs.

Faculty/Classroom: Seventy-six percent of faculty are male; 24%, female. The average class size in an introductory lecture is 60; in a laboratory, 30; and in a regular course offering, 30.

Admissions: About 56% of a recent year's applicants were accepted.

Requirements: The SAT I is required, with a minimum composite score of 1000 (500 verbal and 500 math). Graduation from an accredited secondary school is required. Those students planning to major in occupational or physical therapy must speak French. A portfolio is required for fine arts students, and an audition for music students. AP credits are accepted.

Procedure: Freshmen are admitted in the fall. Application deadlines vary by program, and the earliest deadline is February 1 for common law. The application fee is $28. Notification is sent on a rolling basis. A waiting list is an active part of the admissions procedure.

Transfer: Admissions requirements vary according to program. A total of 30 credits must be completed at UO.

Visiting: There are regularly scheduled orientations for prospective students. There are guides for informal visits and visitors may sit in on classes. To arrange for a visit, contact the Liaison Office at (613) 564–3937.

International Students: There are currently 650 international students enrolled. They must take the TOEFL, the University of Michigan Language Test, the Comprehensive English Language Test, or the college's own test.

Computers: The college provides computer facilities for student use. The mainframe is an Amdahl 5880. Students have access to IBM and Macintosh microcomputers in several computer laboratories on campus. All students may access the system. It may be used 8 A.M. to 10 P.M., 6 days a week. There are no time limits on using the system and no fees.

Graduates: In an earlier year, 3535 bachelor's degrees were awarded.

Admissions Contact: Andre-Pierre Lepage, Director of Admissions and Associate Registrar.

UNIVERSITY OF SASKATCHEWAN   C-2
Saskatoon, SK, Canada S7N 0W0   (306) 966-6746

Full-time: 6122 men, 7111 women	Faculty: 1047
Part-time: 953 men, 1977 women	Ph.D.s: 62%
Graduate: 1170 men, 712 women	Student/Faculty: 13 to 1
Year: terms, summer session	Tuition: $2355
Application Deadline: May 15	Room & Board: $3600
Freshman Class: 7210 applied, 3967 accepted, 3243 enrolled	
SAT I or ACT: not required	

The University of Saskatchewan, founded in 1907, is a public coeducational institution offering programs in business, agriculture, arts and sciences, education, engineering, and health professions. There are 14 undergraduate schools and one graduate school. The 8 libraries contain 1,410,000 volumes, 2,000,000 microform items, and 27,600 audiovisual forms, and subscribe to 10,000 periodicals. Computerized library sources and services include the card catalog and interlibrary loans. Special learning facilities include an art gallery, natural history museum, and planetarium. The 363-acre campus is in an urban area in Saskatoon. Including residence halls, there are 50 buildings on campus.

Student Life: About 92% of undergraduates are from Saskatchewan. Students come from 67 countries. The average age of all undergraduates is 21. Fifteen percent drop out by the end of their first year.

Housing: College-sponsored living facilities include dormitories, off-campus apartments, and married-student housing. On-campus housing is available on a first-come, first-served basis. All students may keep cars on campus.

Activities: There are no fraternities or sororities on campus. There are many groups and organizations on campus, including band, choir, chorale, chorus, computers, drama, ethnic, international, newspaper, orchestra, political, professional, religious, social, social service, and student government.

Sports: There are 9 intramural sports for men and 5 for women.

Disabled Students: Ninety-nine percent of the campus is accessible to disabled students. The following facilities are available: wheelchair ramps, elevators, special parking, specially equipped rest rooms, special class scheduling, lowered drinking fountains, lowered telephones. There is also a coordinator of disabled student services, special funding application assistance, and special exam scheduling.

Services: In addition to many counseling and information services, tutoring is available in most subjects.

Campus Safety and Security: Campus safety and security measures include 24-hour foot and vehicle patrol and escort service.

Programs of Study: University of Saskatchewan awards the B.A., B.Sc., B.Comm., B.E., B.Ed., B.F.A., B.Mus., B.Mus.Ed., B.S.A., B.Sc.(Nutr.), B.S.N., B.S.P., B.S.P.E., B.Sc.(P.T.), and L.L.B. degrees. Master's and doctoral degrees also are awarded. Bachelor's degrees are awarded in AGRICULTURE (agricultural economics, agricultural mechanics, agronomy, animal science, horticulture, plant science, poultry science, and soil science), BIOLOGICAL SCIENCE (anatomy, biochemistry, biology/biological science, botany, ecology, microbiology, nutrition, physiology, and zoology), BUSINESS (accounting, banking and finance, business administration and management, business economics, human resources, marketing/retailing/merchandising, and recreation and leisure services), COMMUNICATIONS AND THE ARTS (art history and appreciation, dramatic arts, English, English as a second/foreign language, fine arts, French, German, Greek, Hebrew, Latin, linguistics, music, Russian, Slavic languages, Spanish, and studio art), COMPUTER AND PHYSICAL SCIENCE (actuarial science, chemistry, computer science, geology, geophysics and seismology, mathematics, paleontology, physics, and quantitative methods), EDUCATION (art, elementary, home economics, industrial arts, mathematics, music, physical, reading, science, secondary, social studies, and vocational), ENGINEERING AND ENVIRONMENTAL DESIGN (agricultural engineering, chemical engineering, civil engineering, electrical/electronics engineering, engineering, engineering physics, geological engineering, geophysical engineering, land use management and reclamation, mechanical engineering, petroleum/natural gas engineering, and urban design), HEALTH PROFESSIONS (medical science, medical technology, nursing, pharmacy, physical therapy, predentistry, premedicine, public health, and veterinary science), SOCIAL SCIENCE (anthropology, classical/ancient civilization, dietetics, economics, food science, geography, history, international relations, law, Native American studies, Near Eastern studies, philosophy, political science/government, prelaw, psychology, public administration, religion, religious education, Russian and Slavic studies, and sociology).

Required: Requirements for graduation vary according to the program of study.

Special: The University of Saskatchewan offers interdisciplinary majors, including agricultural biology, agricultural chemistry, agricultural and bioresource engineering, agricultural extension, and anthropology and archaeology.

Faculty/Classroom: Eighty-four percent of faculty are male; 16%, female. The average class size in an introductory lecture is 67 and in a regular course offering, 40.

Admissions: About 55% of the 1993–94 applicants were accepted.

Requirements: A minimum GPA of 65% is required. The SAT I or ACT is not required. Applicants must be graduates of an accredited secondary school. In direct-entry programs, priority is given to Saskatchewan residents. AP credits are accepted.

Procedure: Freshmen are admitted in the fall. Applications should be filed by May 15, along with an application fee of $35. There are early decision and early admissions plans.

Transfer: Applicants must meet promotion levels for college to which transfer is sought; they must in most cases be Saskatchewan residents.

Visiting: There are regularly scheduled orientations for prospective students. To arrange for a visit, contact the Student's Union at (306) 966-6963.

Financial Aid: The deadline for financial aid applications is April 1.

International Students: There are currently 539 international students enrolled. They must take the TOEFL with a minimum score of 550, or the University of Michigan Language Test.

Computers: The college provides computer facilities for student use. The mainframe is a DEC VAX 6300. Computer science students may access the system. The fees vary.

Graduates: In 1992–93, 3159 bachelor's degrees were awarded.

Admissions Contact: Alison Pickrell, Admissions Counsellor.

UNIVERSITY OF SHERBROOKE
E-2

Sherbrooke, PQ, Canada J1H 1B9   (819) 821-7687
(800) 267-8337 (out-of-state)

Full-time: 3902 men, 4445 women   **Faculty:** 630
Part-time: 2310 men, 3920 women   **Ph.D.s:** 55%
Graduate: 1915 men, 1961 women   **Student/Faculty:** 14 to 1
Year: trimesters, summer session   **Tuition:** $1820 ($7608)
Application Deadline: March 1   **Room & Board:** n/av
Freshman Class: n/av
SAT I or ACT: not required

The University of Sherbrooke, founded in 1954, is a private liberal arts institution affiliated with the Roman Catholic Church. The college offers undergraduate and graduate programs through 10 schools and colleges. The teaching language of the university is French. There are 10 undergraduate and 9 graduate schools. The 4 libraries contain 1 million volumes and 50,000 audiovisual forms, and subscribe to 5800 periodicals. Computerized library sources and services include the card catalog, interlibrary loans, and database searching. Special learning facilities include an art gallery. The 350-acre campus is in an urban area 100 miles east of Montreal. Including residence halls, there are 21 buildings on campus.

Student Life: About 96% of undergraduates are from Quebec. Students come from 10 Canadian provinces and 64 foreign countries.

Housing: A total of 1200 students can be accommodated in college housing. College-sponsored living facilities include coed dormitories. On-campus housing is available on a first-come, first-served basis. Eighty-five percent of students commute. All students may keep cars on campus.

Activities: There are 10 local fraternities. There are 20 groups on campus, including ethnic, international, newspaper, photography, political, radio and TV, religious, social service, and yearbook. Popular campus events include Welcome Week and Winter Carnival.

Sports: There are 8 intercollegiate sports each for men and women, and 20 intramural sports each. Athletic and recreation facilities include an Olympic-size pool, a 200-meter indoor track, a field house, a 400-meter outdoor track and field, squash and racquetball courts, and a double gymnasium.

Disabled Students: The entire campus is accessible to disabled students. The following facilities are available: wheelchair ramps, elevators, special parking, specially equipped rest rooms, lowered drinking fountains, lowered telephones, and special library facilities.

Services: In addition to counseling and information services, there is a reader service for the blind.

Campus Safety and Security: Campus safety and security measures include 24-hour foot and vehicle patrol, pamphlets, posters, films, emergency telephones, and lighted pathways and sidewalks.

Programs of Study: The university awards the B.A., B.A.A., B.Ed., B.Eng., B.Sc., and B.Th. degrees. Master's and doctoral degrees are also awarded. Bachelor's degrees are awarded in BIOLOGICAL SCIENCE (biochemistry and biology/biological science), BUSINESS (business administration and management), COMMUNICATIONS AND THE ARTS (English, French, and music), COMPUTER AND PHYSICAL SCIENCE (chemistry, computer science, mathematics, and physics), EDUCATION (education, physical, and vocational), ENGINEERING AND ENVIRONMENTAL DESIGN (chemical engineering, civil engineering, electrical/electronics engineering, and mechanical engineering), HEALTH PROFESSIONS (nursing), SOCIAL SCIENCE (economics, geography, history, law, philosophy, psychology, social work, and theological studies). Business administration, fiscal studies, chemistry, microbiology, pharmacology, remote sensing, and microelectronics are the strongest academically. Fiscal studies, business administration, school administration, teaching, and theology have the largest enrollments.

Required: In order to graduate, students must complete a total of 90 credits. Engineering student must complete 120 credits and have sufficient knowledge of French.

Special: The college offers co-op programs in business administration, vocational studies, physical education, economics, geography, writing, mathematics, physics, and engineering. Internships may be arranged in family medicine and all medical specialties.

Admissions: About 54% of the 1993–94 applicants were accepted.

Procedure: Freshmen are admitted fall and winter. Applications should be filed by March 1 for fall entry and October 15 for winter entry, along with an application fee of $15. Notification is sent May 15. A waiting list is an active part of the admissions procedure.

Transfer: About 440 transfer students enrolled in a recent year. Admission is based on an applicant's academic record.

Visiting: There are guides for informal visits. To arrange for a visit, contact Pierre Cabana at (819) 821-7687 or (800) 267-8337.

Financial Aid: In a recent year, 75% of all current freshmen received some form of financial aid. The average freshman award was $5600. Of that total, scholarships or need-based grants averaged $3219 ($10,995 maximum); and loans averaged $2439 ($3655 maximum).

International Students: In a recent year, 430 international students were enrolled. Applicants must take the TURBO French proficiency test and obtain a minimum score of 45%.

Computers: The college provides computer facilities for student use. The mainframes are an IBM 4381 and an IBM 9000. There are 300 terminals available in microcomputer laboratories located in different schools on campus. All students may access the system. It may be used 24 hours a day. There are no time limits and no fees.

Graduates: In a recent year, 2103 bachelor's degrees were awarded. The most popular majors among graduates were business administration (15%), education (13%), and engineering (10%). Some 300 companies recruited on campus that year.

Admissions Contact: Michel Laval and Pierre Cabana, Directors of Admissions.

UNIVERSITY OF TORONTO
E-3

Toronto, ON, Canada M5S 1A3   (416) 978-2190

Full-time: 15,462 men, 16,338 women   **Faculty:** n/av
Part-time: 5175 men, 8165 women   **Ph.D.s:** n/av
Graduate: 5263 men, 5515 women   **Student/Faculty:** n/av
Year: terms, summer session   **Tuition:** $2000 ($7000)
Application Deadline: April 1   **Room & Board:** n/app
Freshman Class: 27,942 applied, 14,768 accepted, 8994 enrolled
SAT I or ACT: see profile

The University of Toronto, founded in 1827, is a public institution offering undergraduate programs in applied science and engineering, arts and science, architecture, forestry, landscape architecture, music, nursing, pharmacy, physical and health education, physical therapy, and occupational therapy. There are 9 undergraduate schools and one graduate school. The 40 libraries contain 7,300,000 volumes and 3,400,000 microform items, and subscribe to 4000 periodicals. Computerized library sources and services include the card catalog, interlibrary loans, and database searching. Special learning facilities include a learning resource center, art gallery, radio station, and observatory. The campus is in an urban area.

Housing: College-sponsored living facilities include single-sex and coed dormitories, on-campus apartments, and off-campus apartments. On-campus housing is available on a first-come, first-served basis. Priority is given to out-of-town students. Eighty percent of students commute.

Activities: There are no fraternities or sororities on campus. There are 200 groups on campus, including art, chess, choir, chorus, computers, dance, drama, ethnic, film, gay, international, jazz band, literary magazine, musical theater, newspaper, opera, orchestra, photography, political, radio and TV, religious, social, student government, symphony, and yearbook. Popular campus events include Homecoming, U of T Day, concerts, theater productions, films, lectures, and seasonal activities.

Sports: There are 23 intercollegiate sports for men and 23 for women, and 23 intramural sports for men and 23 for women. Athletic and recreation facilities include swimming pools, an outdoor hockey rink, weight and exercise rooms, gymnasiums, squash and multipurpose courts, a rifle range, dance studios, playing fields, a stadium, an arena, and a 200-meter indoor running track.

Disabled Students: The following facilities are available: wheelchair ramps, elevators, special parking, specially equipped rest rooms, lowered drinking fountains, and lowered telephones.

Services: In addition to many counseling and information services, tutoring is available in every subject. In addition, there is a reader service for the blind.

Programs of Study: U of T awards the B.A., B.Arch., B.A.Sc., B.Com., B.Ed., B.Sc., B.Sc.F., B.Sc.N., B.Sc.(OT), B.Sc.Phm., B.Sc.(P.T.), B.S.P.H.E., and Mus.Bac. degrees. Master's and doctoral degrees also are awarded. Bachelor's degrees are awarded in AGRICULTURE (forestry and related sciences), BIOLOGICAL SCIENCE (biochemistry, biology/biological science, botany, microbiology, and zoology), BUSINESS (banking and finance), COMMUNICATIONS AND THE ARTS (classics, dramatic arts, English, fine arts, French, German, Italian, linguistics, literature, music, Portuguese, Slavic languages, and Spanish), COMPUTER AND PHYSICAL SCIENCE (applied mathematics, astronomy, chemistry, computer science, geology, mathematics, and physics), EDUCATION (health and physical), ENGINEERING AND ENVIRONMENTAL DESIGN (architecture, chemical engineering, civil engineering, electrical/electronics engineering, engineering and applied science, geological engineering, industrial engineering, materials science, mechanical engineering, and metallurgical engineering), HEALTH PROFESSIONS (nursing, occupational therapy, pharmacy, and physical therapy), SOCIAL SCIENCE (American studies, Canadian studies, Celtic studies, criminology, economics, geography, political science/government, sociology, urban studies, and women's studies).

Required: Arts and science majors must satisfy a breadth requirement, which includes 3 courses from outside major. Students must complete 15 credits for a 3-year degree or 20 credits for a 4-year degree, plus prerequisite subjects.

Special: The university offers co-op programs in administration, arts administration, computer science and physics, and international development studies. Interdisciplinary programs and various work-study programs are also available.

Admissions: About 53% of the 1993–94 applicants were accepted.

Requirements: The faculty of Arts and Science will consider U.S. applicants who have graduated from an accredited secondary school with a minimum 3.0 GPA and who have scored an average of at least 550 on each part of the SAT I and 500 on each of 3 SAT II: Subject tests. Some divisions require first-year university standing. Other requirements may apply. Architecture students must submit a questionnaire and a portfolio. Music students must audition.

Procedure: Application fee is $50. There is an early admissions plan.

Visiting: There are regularly scheduled orientations for prospective students. Visitors may sit in on classes. To arrange for a visit, contact Admissions and Awards.

Financial Aid: In 1993–94 10% of all current freshmen received some form of financial aid.

International Students: They must take the TOEFL, the University of Michigan Language Test, the Comprehensive English Language Test, or the college's own test.

Computers: The college provides computer facilities for student use. The university provides IBM-compatible PCs for academic use. There are no time limits on using the system and no fees.

Admissions Contact: Admissions Counselor.

UNIVERSITY OF VICTORIA
B-2
Victoria, B.C., Canada V8W 3P2   (604) 721-8119

Full-time: 8154 men and women	Faculty: n/av
Part-time: 5002 men and women	Ph.D.s: n/av
Graduate: 1803 men and women	Student/Faculty: n/av
Year: terms, summer session	Tuition: $2095 ($5130)
Application Deadline: see profile	Room & Board: $3636
Freshman Class: n/av	
SAT I or ACT: not required	

The University of Victoria, founded in 1903 as Victoria College, is a public, coeducational institution operated by the province of British Columbia. It offers undergraduate and graduate programs in arts and sciences, education, engineering, fine arts, human and social development, and law. There are 5 undergraduate schools and one graduate school. The 4 libraries contain 1,373,000 volumes, 1,556,000 microform items, and 177,000 audiovisual forms, and subscribe to 8000 periodicals. Computerized library sources and services include the card catalog, interlibrary loans, and database searching. Special learning facilities include a learning resource center and a radio station. The 385-acre campus is in an urban area in Victoria. Including residence halls, there are 66 buildings on campus.

Student Life: About 90% of undergraduates are from British Columbia.

Housing: A total of 1200 students can be accommodated in college housing. College-sponsored living facilities include single-sex and coed dormitories. In addition, there is an off-campus housing registry service. On-campus housing is available on a first-come, first-served basis.

Activities: There are some groups and organizations on campus, including chorus, jazz band, newspaper, orchestra, political, social service, student government, symphony, and yearbook.

Sports: There are 2 intercollegiate sports for men and 3 for women, and 6 intramural sports for men and 5 for women. Athletic and recreation facilities include a gymnasium, a dance studio, a weight training room, a pool, squash courts, playing fields, an outdoor stadium, tennis courts, a sailing compound, and jogging trails.

Disabled Students: Speech synthesizers and Arkenstone reading computers are available.

Services: In addition to counseling and information services, there is remedial reading and writing.

Programs of Study: UVIC awards the B.A., B.S., B.Com., B.Ed., B.Eng., B.F.A., B.Mus., B.S.N., B.S.W., B.Sc., and L.L.B. degrees. Master's and doctoral degrees are also awarded. Bachelor's degrees are awarded in BIOLOGICAL SCIENCE (biology/biological science), BUSINESS (recreation and leisure services), COMMUNICATIONS AND THE ARTS (art history and appreciation, classics, creative writing, dramatic arts, English, French, Germanic languages and literature, linguistics, music, and visual and performing arts), COMPUTER AND PHYSICAL SCIENCE (astronomy, chemistry, computer science, mathematics, and physics), EDUCATION (elementary, physical, and secondary), ENGINEERING AND ENVIRONMENTAL DESIGN (electrical/electronics engineering and mechanical engineering), HEALTH PROFESSIONS (nursing), SOCIAL SCIENCE (anthropology, child care/child and family studies, economics, geography, history, Pacific area studies, philosophy, political science/government, psychology, social work, and sociology).

Required: To graduate, students must complete the university English requirement, complete a minimum of 60 units above the 100 level, at least 21 of which must be upper level, and have a 2.0 GPA.

Special: A number of co-op and internship programs are available in specific disciplines as are many dual majors. Work study is possible on a limited basis at the university for Canadian students only.

Requirements: Application requirements include high school graduation with a minimum 3.24 GPA for B.C. applicants and a 3.5 for out-of-province applicants, 4 semesters of English, and 2 each of so-

cial science, mathematics, science, and language. AP credits are accepted.

Procedure: Applications should be filed May through August for fall entry and January through July for spring or summer entry, along with an application fee of $20 for Canadian students and $60 for other students.

Transfer: Requirements vary with program and individual. A total of 30 credits must be completed at UVIC.

Visiting: There are guides for informal visits and visitors may sit in on classes and stay overnight at the school. To arrange for a visit, contact the Advising Center of the individual school at (604) 721-7211.

Financial Aid: Financial aid is available only to Canadian students.

International Students: The school actively recruits these students. They must take the TOEFL and achieve a minimum score of 575.

Computers: The mainframes are an IBM 3090-150S, a Sun 3/280S, and a Pyramid 98Xe. Access to the mainframes are by wideband and Ethernet networks to microcomputers and terminals throughout campus. The Sun and Pyramid systems utilize UNIX operating systems. Microcomputer equipment includes IBM, Apple, and DEC VAX models. All students may access the system 24 hours a day.

Graduates: In a recent year, 1779 bachelor's degrees were awarded.

Admissions Contact: Dr. E. Keith Clamp, Director of Admissions Services.

UNIVERSITY OF WATERLOO
E-3
Waterloo, ON, Canada N2L 3G1   (519) 885-1211, ext. 2268

Full-time: 9030 men, 7108 women	Faculty: 833
Part-time: 2936 men, 5122 women	Ph.D.s: 91%
Graduate: 2210 men and women	Student/Faculty: 19 to 1
Year: terms, summer session	Tuition: $3004 ($8618)
Application Deadline: May 1	Room & Board: $4604
Freshman Class: 20,810 applied, 8676 accepted, 3395 enrolled	
SAT I or ACT: recommeded	

The University of Waterloo, founded in 1957, is a public institution that offers undergraduate and graduate studies through the faculties of applied health sciences, arts, engineering, environmental studies, mathematics, and science. There are 4 church-related colleges on campus. There are 6 undergraduate and graduate faculties. The 4 libraries contain 2,400,000 volumes, 895,000 microform items, and 4400 audiovisual forms, and subscribe to 10,000 periodicals. Computerized library sources and services include the card catalog, interlibrary loans, and database searching. Special learning facilities include a learning resource center, art gallery, radio station, 3 museums, and 2 theaters. The 900-acre campus is in a suburban area 60 miles southwest of Toronto. Including residence halls, there are 41 buildings on campus.

Student Life: About 91% of undergraduates are from Ontario. Students come from 58 countries. Ten percent drop out by the end of their first year.

Housing: A total of 5000 students can be accommodated in college housing. College-sponsored living facilities include coed dormitories, on-campus apartments, off-campus apartments, and married-student housing. In addition, there are special-interest houses. On-campus housing is available on a lottery system for upperclassmen. Priority is given to out-of-town students. Seventy-eight percent of students commute. All students may keep cars on campus.

Activities: There are no fraternities or sororities on campus. There are many groups and organizations on campus, including band, cheerleading, chess, choir, computers, drama, drill team, ethnic, gay, honors, international, literary magazine, marching band, musical theater, newspaper, political, professional, religious, social, social service, and student government. Popular campus events include Oktoberfest, Canada Day, and Homecoming.

Sports: There are 16 intercollegiate sports for men and 15 for women, and 10 intramural sports for men and 10 for women. Athletic and recreation facilities include a golf course, outdoor playing fields, an ice arena, a swimming pool, a diving tank, squash courts, weight rooms, 2 gymnasiums, a dance studio, tennis courts, and activity areas.

Disabled Students: The entire campus is accessible to disabled students. The following facilities are available: wheelchair ramps, elevators, special parking, specially equipped rest rooms, special class scheduling, lowered drinking fountains, lowered telephones, and up-to-date technical equipment for the visually and hearing impaired.

Services: In addition to many counseling and information services, tutoring is available in most subjects. There is also a reader service for the blind, and remedial math, reading, and writing.

Campus Safety and Security: Campus safety and security measures include 24-hour foot and vehicle patrol, self-defense education, escort service, and shuttle buses. In addition, there are informal discussions, pamphlets, posters, films, emergency telephones, and lighted pathways and sidewalks.

Programs of Study: UW awards the B.A., B.Sc., B.Arch., B.A.S.C., B.E.S., B.I.S. and B.Math. degrees. Master's and doctoral degrees also are awarded. Bachelor's degrees are awarded in BIOLOGICAL SCIENCE (biochemistry, biology/biological science, and biotechnol-

ogy), BUSINESS (accounting, management science, operations research, and recreation and leisure services), COMMUNICATIONS AND THE ARTS (classics, dance, English, fine arts, French, German, Greek, Latin, music, Russian, and Spanish), COMPUTER AND PHYSICAL SCIENCE (actuarial science, applied mathematics, chemistry, computer science, earth science, mathematics, physics, science, and statistics), ENGINEERING AND ENVIRONMENTAL DESIGN (architecture, chemical engineering, city/community/regional planning, civil engineering, computer engineering, electrical/electronics engineering, geological engineering, mechanical engineering, and systems engineering), HEALTH PROFESSIONS (health and optometry), SOCIAL SCIENCE (anthropology, Canadian studies, economics, geography, gerontology, history, international studies, Latin American studies, medieval studies, philosophy, political science/government, psychology, and sociology). Engineering, accounting, and mathematics are the strongest academically. The arts program has the largest enrollment.

Required: To graduate, all students must satisfy specific program requirements.

Special: Students may cross-register with Wilfred Laurier University, the University of Guelph, and the University of Western Ontario. UW offers study abroad in 20 countries, dual and student-designed studies, and noncredit courses. Students may study under the regular or cooperative system, which allows off-campus work terms in education, professional organizations and agencies, business, industry, or government for students with permanent resident status.

Faculty/Classroom: Eighty-seven percent of faculty are male; 13%, female. All both teach and do research.

Admissions: About 42% of the 1993–94 applicants were accepted.

Requirements: The SAT I or ACT is recommended. Candidates from the United States must have a high school diploma with exceptionally high standing and AP exams in prerequisite subjects or first-year university standing in acceptable subjects from an accredited university. An audition, portfolio, and/or interview are required for certain programs. Important factors used in the admissions decision are advanced placement or honor courses, recommendations by school officials, extracurricular activities record, leadership record, and recommendations by alumni.

Procedure: Freshmen are admitted in the fall. There is an early decision plan. Applications should be filed by May 1, along with an application fee of $60. Notification of early decision is sent mid-June; regular decision, on a rolling basis.

Transfer: Transfer applicants are considered on an individual basis. At least half the required courses must be completed at UW.

Visiting: There are regularly scheduled orientations for prospective students, including tours and individual and group information sessions. There are guides for informal visits, and visitors may sit in on classes and stay overnight at the school. To arrange for a visit, contact the Visitors Reception Center at (519) 885–1211, ext. 3614.

Financial Aid: In a recent year, 24% of all students received need-based aid. UW is a member of CSS. The FAF is required. The deadline for financial aid applications is July 31.

International Students: There are currently 897 international students enrolled. They must take the TOEFL and achieve a minimum score of 600.

Computers: The college provides computer facilities for student use. There are more than 300 multiuser computing systems and 2000 access terminals campuswide. Students must obtain an account. Rules vary by department. All students may access the system. There are no time limits on using the system and no fees.

Graduates: In a recent year, 3301 bachelor's degrees were awarded. Within an average freshman class, 35% graduate in 3 years and 65% in 4 years. Some 200 companies recruited on campus in a recent year.

Admissions Contact: Registrar's Office.

UNIVERSITY OF WESTERN ONTARIO
D-3
London, ON, Canada N6A 5B8   **(519) 661–2120**

Full-time: 9759 men, 10,372 women	**Faculty:** 1564
Part-time: 1870 men, 3750 women	**Ph.D.s:** n/av
Graduate: 1646 men, 1186 women	**Student/Faculty:** 13 to 1
Year: semesters, summer session	**Tuition:** $2680 ($8293)
Application Deadline: June 1	**Room & Board:** $4603
Freshman Class: n/av	
SAT I or ACT: not required	

The University of Western Ontario, chartered in 1878, is a coeducational, public institution offering daytime, evening, and correspondence programs in the liberal arts and sciences, fine arts and music, engineering, education, health services, and business. There are 14 undergraduate and 4 graduate schools. The 7 libraries contain 2,100,000 volumes, 2,860,000 microform items, and 31,000 audiovisual forms, and subscribe to 17,300 periodicals. Computerized library sources and services include the card catalog, interlibrary loans, and database searching. Special learning facilities include a learning resource center, art gallery, and planetarium. The 402-acre campus is in an urban area 120 miles northwest of Detroit, Michigan. Including residence halls, there are 70 buildings on campus.

Student Life: Students come from 80 countries. The average age of freshmen is 19.7; all undergraduates, 22.

Housing: A total of 3550 students can be accommodated in college housing. College-sponsored living facilities include single-sex and coed dormitories, on-campus apartments, and married-student housing. In addition, there are language houses, special-interest houses, an international house, and quiet floors. On-campus housing is available on a lottery system for upperclassmen. Priority is given to out-of-town students. Sixty percent of students commute. All students may keep cars on campus.

Activities: About 9% of men belong to 19 national fraternities; about 3% of women belong to 6 national sororities. There are 100 groups on campus, including art, cheerleading, chess, choir, computers, drama, ethnic, gay, international, jazz band, marching band, musical theater, newspaper, political, professional, religious, social, social service, and student government. Popular campus events include Homecoming, Orientation Week, Student for a Day, and Parents Day.

Sports: There are 23 intercollegiate sports for men and 19 for women, and 17 intramural sports for men and 13 for women. Athletic and recreation facilities include skating rinks, weight rooms, pools, gymnasiums, and numerous outdoor facilities.

Disabled Students: Eighty percent of the campus is accessible to disabled students. The following facilities are available: wheelchair ramps, elevators, special parking, specially equipped rest rooms, special class scheduling, and lowered telephones.

Services: In addition to many counseling and information services, tutoring is available in most subjects. There is also a reader service for the blind, and remedial math, reading, and writing.

Campus Safety and Security: Campus safety and security measures include escort service, emergency telephones, and lighted pathways and sidewalks.

Programs of Study: Western awards the B.A., B.Ed., B.E.Sc., B.F.A., B.Mus., B.Mus.A., B.S.W., B.Sc., B.Sc.N., B.Sc.H.Ec., B.Sc.O.T., B.Sc.P.T., and L.L.B. degrees. Master's and doctoral degrees also are awarded. Bachelor's degrees are awarded in AGRICULTURE (plant science), BIOLOGICAL SCIENCE (biochemistry, biology/biological science, biophysics, cell biology, ecology and evolution, genetics, microbiology and immunology, physiology, and zoology), BUSINESS (business administration and management), COMMUNICATIONS AND THE ARTS (classics, English, film arts, French, German, Greek, Latin, music, Russian, Spanish, and visual and performing arts), COMPUTER AND PHYSICAL SCIENCE (actuarial science, applied mathematics, astronomy, chemistry, computer science, geology, geophysics and seismology, mathematics, physics, and statistics), EDUCATION (elementary, mathematics, middle school, music, and secondary), ENGINEERING AND ENVIRONMENTAL DESIGN (chemical engineering, civil engineering, electrical/electronics engineering, materials engineering, and mechanical engineering), HEALTH PROFESSIONS (nursing, occupational therapy, pharmacy, and physical therapy), SOCIAL SCIENCE (anthropology, economics, geography, history, history of science, law, philosophy, physical fitness/movement, political science/government, psychology, sociology, western civilization/culture, and women's studies). Bachelor of arts programs has the largest enrollment.

Required: All students are required to take 2 essay courses and courses in the arts, science, and social science; other distribution and course requirements vary by major. A 60% overall average and 15 courses are the minimum requirements for a bachelor's degree. Many degrees have additional requirements.

Special: There are many 3-year bachelor's degree programs. Dual majors are possible in most subjects. Study abroad is available in France, Australia, Scotland, and Denmark. Pass/fail options are available in some courses. The faculty of Part-Time and Continuing Education offers off-campus mediated learning courses and several diploma and certificate programs.

Faculty/Classroom: Eighty-three percent of faculty are male; 17%, female.

Requirements: U.S. applicants must be graduates of an accredited secondary school with 4 academic course credits in their senior year, and in the top 15% of their class in order to apply for admission their first year. (Canadian students complete the Ontario secondary school diploma.) First-year admissions are limited. Admission to the music program requires an audition. Advanced placement or honor courses is an important factor used in the admission decision.

Procedure: Freshmen are admitted in the fall and winter. Applications should be filed by June 1 for fall entry, along with an application fee of $60. Notification is sent in March and April. There are early decision, early admissions, and deferred admissions plans.

Transfer: A minimum overall average of 60% is required to transfer. At least 5 full senior courses must be completed at Western.

Visiting: There are regularly scheduled orientations for prospective students. Visitors may sit in on classes. To arrange for a visit, contact the Department of Liaison Services at (519) 661–2026.

Financial Aid: In 1993–94, 70% of all current freshmen and 25% of continuing students received some form of financial aid. The average financial indebtedness of a recent graduate was $8600. Western is a member of CSS. The deadline for financial aid applications is January 31.

International Students: There are currently 783 international students enrolled. The school actively recruits these students. They must take the TOEFL with a minimum score or 550, or the University of Michigan Language Test.

Computers: The college provides computer facilities for student use. The mainframes are a DEC VAX 6230, a CDC Cyber 930, and an ETA-10. There are hundreds of access terminals in campus buildings. All students may access the system. There are no time limits on using the system and no fees.

Graduates: In 1992–93, 5543 bachelor's degrees were awarded.

Admissions Contact: Robert J. Tiffin, Director, Office of the Registrar.

UNIVERSITY OF WINDSOR
Windsor, ON, Canada N9B, 3P4

E-2
(519) 973-7014

Full-time: 5148 men, 5578 women	Faculty: 600
Part-time: 2448 men, 2614 women	Ph.D.s: 80%
Graduate: 541 men, 361 women	Student/Faculty: 17 to 1
Year: trimesters, summer session	Tuition: $2200–2400
Application Deadline: May 1	($7800–12,700)
	Room & Board: $5400–6000

Freshman Class: n/av
SAT I or ACT: required

The University of Windsor, founded in 1857, is a public liberal arts institution offering undergraduate programs through 8 faculties and 6 schools. There are 8 undergraduate schools and one graduate school. The 2 libraries contain 1.6 million volumes, 160,000 microform items, and 2000 audiovisual forms, and subscribe to 15,000 periodicals. Computerized library sources and services include the card catalog, interlibrary loans, and database searching. Special learning facilities include a learning resource center, an art gallery, a natural history museum, and a radio station. The 71-acre campus is in an urban area. Including residence halls, there are 50 buildings on campus.

Student Life: About 90% of undergraduates are from Ontario. Students come from 10 Canadian provinces and 38 foreign countries. Ninety-five percent are from public schools; 5% from private. The average age of freshmen is 19; all undergraduates, 22. Ten percent drop out by the end of their first year.

Housing: A total of 1800 students can be accommodated in college housing. College-sponsored living facilities include single-sex and coed dormitories, on-campus apartments, and married-student housing. On-campus housing is guaranteed for the freshman year only and is available on a lottery system for upperclassmen. Priority is given to out-of-town students. Eighty percent of students commute. All students may keep cars on campus.

Activities: About 2% of men belong to 4 national fraternities; about 1% of women belong to 1 national sorority. There are 50 groups on campus, including cheerleading, chess, choir, drama, ethnic, honors, international, jazz band, literary magazine, musical theater, newspaper, orchestra, political, professional, radio and TV, religious, social, and student government. Popular campus events include Homecoming.

Sports: There are 10 intramural sports for men and 8 for women. Athletic and recreation facilities include a 6-lane, 200-meter track, a multiuse gymnasium, a field house, a stadium, an indoor pool, and weight rooms.

Disabled Students: Ninety percent of the campus is accessible to disabled students. The following facilities are available: wheelchair ramps, elevators, special parking, specially equipped rest rooms, special class scheduling, lowered drinking fountains, and lowered telephones.

Services: In addition to many counseling and information services, tutoring is available in some subjects, including mathematics and physical sciences. In addition, there is a reader service for the blind, and remedial math, reading, and writing.

Campus Safety and Security: Campus safety and security measures include 24-hour foot and vehicle patrol, self-defense education, escort service, and informal discussions. In addition, there are pamphlets, posters, films, emergency telephones, and lighted pathways and sidewalks.

Programs of Study: U of W awards the B.A., B.Sc., B.A.Sc., B.Comm., B.C.S., B.Ed., B.F.A., B.H.K., B.Mus., B.Mus.Th., B.P.A., B.Sc.N., B.S.W., and L.L.B. degrees. Master's and doctoral degrees also are awarded. Bachelor's degrees are awarded in BIOLOGICAL SCIENCE (biochemistry and biology/biological science), BUSINESS (business administration and management), COMMUNICATIONS AND THE ARTS (classics, communications, dramatic arts, English, French, music, and visual and performing arts), COMPUTER AND PHYSICAL SCIENCE (chemistry, computer science, geology, mathematics, physics, science, and statistics), EDUCATION (education), ENGINEERING AND ENVIRONMENTAL DESIGN (engineering), HEALTH PROFESSIONS (music therapy and nursing), SOCIAL SCIENCE (anthropology, Asian/Oriental studies, Canadian studies, criminology, economics, family/consumer studies, geography, history, international relations, law, philosophy, political science/government,

psychology, public administration, social work, sociology, and urban studies).

Required: In order to graduate, students must complete a total of 90 credit hours, including 30 in major, with a C average. Honors students must complete 120 hours, including 60 in major, with a B average. All students must fulfill the requirements of the core curriculum.

Special: The college offers a variety of co-op programs and internships. Cross registration may be arranged with the University of Detroit, University of Michigan, Wayne State University, and University of Central Florida. Students may study abroad in the United States, France, and Japan.

Faculty/Classroom: Eighty percent of faculty are male; 20%, female. All faculty both teach undergraduates and do research.

Admissions: About 65% of the 1993–94 applicants were accepted.

Requirements: A minimum grade average of 68 is required. U.S. students are required to take the SAT I or ACT. AP credits are accepted.

Procedure: Freshmen are admitted to all sessions. Entrance exams should be taken as early as possible. Applications should be filed by May 1 for fall entry, December 1 for winter entry, April 1 for spring entry, and June 1 for summer entry, along with an application fee of $50. Notification is sent on a rolling basis. There are early decision and early admissions plans. About 200 early decision candidates were accepted for a recent class. A waiting list is an active part of the admissions procedure, with about 10% of applicants on the list.

Transfer: Applicants must present an official transcript and be in good academic standing. A total of 10 senior credits out of 30 must be completed at U of W.

Visiting: There are regularly scheduled orientations for prospective students, including a tour, counseling, and classes. There are guides for informal visits and visitors may sit in on classes. To arrange for a visit, contact the Director, Secondary School Liaison, at (800) 567-7014 (Ontario and Quebec) or (519) 973-7014.

International Students: In a recent year, 6 international students were enrolled. The school actively recruits these students. They must take the TOEFL (and achieve a minimum score of 550), the University of Michigan Language Test, the Comprehensive English Language Test, or the college's own test.

Computers: The college provides computer facilities for student use. The mainframes are an IBM 4381 and an SGI. Students have access to a parallel processing fileserver linked to graphics X-terminals through a campus-wide fiber optic network. There is also a CAD-CAM teaching laboratory with 30 network terminals, 60 microcomputers in a DEC network, and numerous other academic local networks. All students may access the system. There are no time limits on using the system and no fees.

Graduates: In a recent year, 3000 bachelor's degrees were awarded. The most popular majors among graduates were education (12%), business (10%), and law (6%). Some 100 companies recruited on campus that year.

Admissions Contact: Director of Admissions.

YORK UNIVERSITY
North York, ON, Canada M3J 1P3

E-3
(416) 736-5100

Full-time: 10,548 men, 14,787 women	Faculty: 1240
Part-time: 4549 men, 9853 women	Ph.D.s: n/av
Graduate: 1995 men, 1503 women	Student/Faculty: 20 to 1
Year: terms, summer session	Tuition: $2484 ($8097)
Application Deadline: March 1	Room & Board: $4230

Freshman Class: n/av
SAT I or ACT: required

York University, founded in 1959, is a public institution offering programs in science, environmental studies, fine arts, liberal arts, teacher preparation, administrative studies, nursing, and social work. There are 8 undergraduate and 2 graduate schools. The 5 libraries contain 1,000,000 volumes and more than 5000 audiovisual forms. Computerized library sources and services include interlibrary loans and database searching. Special learning facilities include a learning resource center, art gallery, radio station, and TV station. The 650-acre Keele campus is in the northwest section of Toronto, and the 85-acre Glendon campus is also located in Toronto. Including residence halls, there are 50 buildings on the 2 campuses.

Student Life: The average age of freshmen is 19; all undergraduates, 22.

Housing: A total of 2550 students can be accommodated in college housing. College-sponsored living facilities include single-sex and coed dormitories, on-campus apartments, and married-student housing. In addition, there are language houses, special-interest houses, and co-op housing. On-campus housing is available on a first-come, first-served basis and is available on a lottery system for upperclassmen. Priority is given to out-of-town students. Ninety-three percent of students commute. All students may keep cars on campus.

Activities: There are no fraternities or sororities on campus. There are 130 groups on campus, including art, band, cheerleading, chess, choir, computers, dance, drama, ethnic, film, gay, international, jazz band, literary magazine, musical theater, newspaper, orchestra, photography, political, professional, radio and TV, religious, social, social

service, and student government. Popular campus events include the Blue Bowl (football) and Orientation Week.

Sports: There are 12 intercollegiate sports for men and 12 for women, and 20 intramural sports for men and women. Athletic and recreation facilities include a track and field center, 2 25-meter pools, 26 indoor and outdoor tennis courts, an ice arena, 16 squash courts, 6 gymnasiums, 2 fitness centers, 2 dance/aerobics studios, a combative room, 7 playing fields, 5 softball diamonds, a cricket pitch, 3 teaching laboratories, 2 fitness-training areas, 3 strength-training areas, and 2 sports therapy clinics.

Disabled Students: Sixty-five percent of the campus is accessible to disabled students. The following facilities are available: wheelchair ramps, elevators, special parking, specially equipped rest rooms, special class scheduling, lowered drinking fountains, and lowered telephones. The Office for Persons with Disabilities offers a variety of additional services.

Services: In addition to many counseling and information services, tutoring is available in most subjects. There are centers for mathematics and writing, as well as a reader service for the blind.

Campus Safety and Security: Campus safety and security measures include 24-hour foot and vehicle patrol, self-defense education, escort service, and shuttle buses. In addition, there are pamphlets, posters, films, emergency telephones, and lighted pathways and sidewalks. There is also a bicycle patrol team system monitoring the campuses.

Programs of Study: York awards the B.A., B.A.S., B.B.A., B.E.S., B.Ed., B.F.A., B.S.W., B.Sc., B.Sc.N., and L.L.B. degrees. Master's and doctoral degrees also are awarded. Bachelor's degrees are awarded in BIOLOGICAL SCIENCE (biology/biological science), BUSINESS (accounting, business administration and management, business economics, business statistics, and labor studies), COMMUNICATIONS AND THE ARTS (classics, communications, creative writing, dance, dramatic arts, English, film arts, fine arts, French, German, Greek, Italian, Latin, music, photography, Russian, Spanish, and visual and performing arts), COMPUTER AND PHYSICAL SCIENCE (applied mathematics, atmospheric sciences and meteorology, chemistry, computer science, mathematics, physics, and statistics), EDUCATION (early childhood, education of the deaf and hearing impaired, elementary, and physical), ENGINEERING AND ENVIRONMENTAL DESIGN (environmental science), HEALTH PROFESSIONS (nursing and rehabilitation therapy), SOCIAL SCIENCE (African studies, anthropology, Canadian studies, East Asian studies, economics, French studies, geography, Hispanic American studies, history, humanities, international studies, Judaic studies, Latin American studies, law, law enforcement and corrections, philosophy, political science/government, psychology, public administration, religion, social science, social work, sociology, Third World studies, urban studies, and women's studies). Psychology has the largest enrollment.

Required: Students must maintain at least a C average in 90 credits to receive an ordinary degree and a C + in 120 credits to receive an honors degree. Requirements for graduation vary according to program.

Special: Cross-registration with Seneca, Centennial, and Humber colleges, study abroad in 8 countries and work-study are available. York offers B.A.-B.S. degrees and dual, student-designed, and multi- and interdisciplinary majors, including atmospheric chemistry, physics and astronomy; science, technology, culture, and society; social and political thought; space and communication sciences; and translation. Independent study and nondegree study are also possible. There is a freshman honors program on campus, and all departments have honors programs.

Faculty/Classroom: Seventy percent of faculty are male; 30%, female. Sixty percent both teach and do research.

Requirements: York requires applicants to be in the upper 25% of their class. A minimum GPA of 2.5 is required. The SAT I or ACT is required. U.S. applicants are required to present evidence of superior academic achievement. Secondary school record, letter of recommendation, SAT I and/or ACT scores, and ranking in class (if available) will be taken into consideration. In addition, applicants to a fine arts program are required to pass an audition/evaluation, and business administration and environmental studies applicants are required to submit a supplementary application. Admissions averages and course prerequisites vary by faculty. AP credits are accepted.

Procedure: Freshmen are admitted in the fall. Applications should be filed by March 1, along with an application fee of $60. Notification is sent on a rolling basis. There is an early admissions plan for Ontario residents.

Visiting: There are guides for informal visits and visitors may sit in on classes and stay overnight at the school. To arrange for a visit, contact the Admissions Liaison Office at (416) 736–5100.

International Students: There are currently 1661 international students enrolled. Applicants whose first language is not English or French must take the TOEFL, the University of Michigan Language Test, the Comprehensive English Language Test, or the college's own test. They must also take the SAT I or the ACT.

Computers: The college provides computer facilities for student use. The mainframes are an IBM 3090, and 4381; a MAS 6650; a DEC VAX 8600, 6230, 11/78x, 11/750, and 11/730; and a UNIX. There are 30 IBM microcomputers and 25 Macintosh SE/30 available. Students enrolled in computer courses will be given first priority in the computer laboratories. Students must make arrangements with professors. It may be used 24 hours per day. There are no time limits on using the system and no fees.

Graduates: In a recent year, 6653 bachelor's degrees were awarded. The most popular majors among graduates were administrative studies (15%), psychology (11%), and sociology (7%).

Admissions Contact: Tom Myers, Director of Admissions.

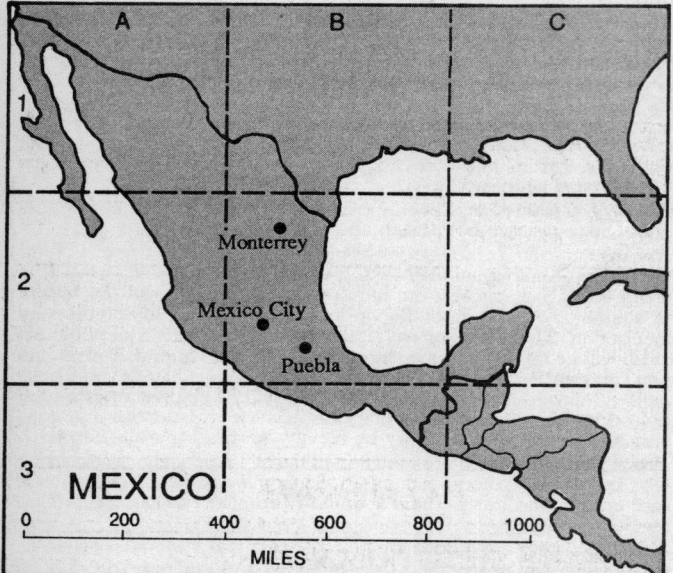

MEXICO

0   200   400   600   800   1000
MILES

Monterrey

Mexico City

Puebla

UNIVERSIDAD DE LAS AMERICAS, A.C.   B-2
Mexico City, D.F., Mexico 06700   (52) (5) 208-02-47, ext. 210
Full-time: 466 men, 826 women   Faculty: 20
Part-time: 23 men, 34 women   Ph.D.s: 65%
Graduate: 132 men, 112 women   Student/Faculty: 65 to 1
Year: semesters, summer session   Tuition: $8000
Application Deadline: August   Room & Board: n/app
Freshman Class: n/av
SAT I: recommended

The Universidad de las Americas, founded in 1940, is an independent university offering undergraduate, graduate, and professional degrees in administrative sciences, economics, education and psychology, human communication, and inter-American studies. There are 3 undergraduate schools and one graduate school. The library contains 30,000 volumes, 3424 microform items, and 520 audiovisual forms, and subscribes to 150 periodicals. Computerized library sources and services include the card catalog, interlibrary loans, and database searching. Special learning facilities include a learning resource center and an off-campus museum of Zapotecan Art. The campus is in an urban area. There are 3 buildings on campus.
Student Life: About 88% of undergraduates are from Mexico. Students come from 13 states and 23 countries. Ten percent are from public schools; 90% from private. The average age of freshmen is 18; all undergraduates, 23. One percent drop out by the end of their first year; 99% remain to graduate.
Housing: There are no residence halls. College-sponsored living facilities include off-campus apartments. The university helps students find lodgings with Mexican families. All students may keep cars on campus.
Activities: There are no fraternities or sororities on campus. There are some groups and organizations on campus, including art, computers, drama, international, musical theater, newspaper, professional, social, social service, and student government. Popular campus events include October 12.
Sports: There are 2 intercollegiate sports for men and 1 for women, and 6 intramural sports for men and 3 for women. The university has arrangements with several athletic clubs in the area to provide athletic facilities for students.
Services: There is remedial math, reading, and writing.

Programs of Study: Universidad de las Americas, A.C. awards the B.A. and B.B.A. degrees. Master's degrees also are awarded. Bachelor's degrees are awarded in BUSINESS (business administration and management), COMPUTER AND PHYSICAL SCIENCE (computer science), EDUCATION (education), SOCIAL SCIENCE (international relations and psychology). Business administration and international relations are the strongest academically.
Required: To graduate, all students must be Spanish-English bilingual and have completed a core of courses in Anglo-Saxon and Latin American cultures. A computer course is required. Students must complete at least 40 courses, depending on the degree, with a minimum GPA of 2.0.
Special: The university offers field study courses in Meso-American culture and archaeology, study in the United States, and nondegree study. B.A.-B.S. degrees are available in business administration, international political studies, education, psychology, human communication, computer systems, and law.
Faculty/Classroom: Seventy-six percent of faculty are male; 24%, female. Sixty-seven percent teach undergraduates, 20% do research, and 13% do both. No introductory courses are taught by graduate students.
Requirements: The SAT I is recommended. Applicants must rank in the upper half of their graduating class. The university administers placement examinations in written and oral Spanish, English, and mathematics. An interview is required. Students who do not meet minimum proficiences may take noncredit courses to work toward meeting admission standards. CLEP credit is accepted. Important factors used in the admissions decision are evidence of special talent, personality, intangible qualities, recommendations by school officials, leadership record, and parents or siblings attending the school.
Procedure: Freshmen are admitted to all sessions. The college's own entrance exams must be taken 30 days before classes begin. Applications should be filed by August for fall entry and April for spring entry, along with an application fee of 200 pesos ($70 U.S.). Notification is sent on a rolling basis. There are early admissions and deferred admissions plans.
Transfer: About 15 transfer students enrolled in a recent year. At least 150 credits out of 300 must be completed at Universidad de las Americas, A.C.
Visiting: To arrange for a visit, contact Margarita Guitart at 208-36-65.
Financial Aid: In 1993–94, 10% of all current freshmen received some form of financial aid. About 5% of freshmen received need-based aid. The average freshman award was $2000. Of that total, scholarships or need-based grants averaged $2000 ($3000 maximum). The deadline for financial aid applications is August 15.
International Students: There are currently 54 international students enrolled. They must take the TOEFL with a minimum score of 550, or the Comprehensive English Language Test. They must also take the college's own entrance exam.
Computers: The college provides computer facilities for student use. The university has an IBM RS/6000 minicomputer. Students have access to 20 computers in each of 2 computer classrooms, 40 in a common use area, and 20 in the Multimedia Resource Center, all connected in a local area network. All students may access the system Monday to Friday 7 A.M. to 10 P.M., and Saturday 8 A.M. to 6 P.M. There are no time limits on using the system and no fees.
Graduates: In a recent year, 66 bachelor's degrees were awarded. The most popular majors among graduates were administration (53%), psychology (42%), and education (5%). Within an average freshman class, 9% graduate in 3 years, 89% in 4 years, 1% in 5 years, and 1% in 6 years. Some 25 companies recruited on campus in a recent year. In a recent graduating class, 23% of the men and 77% of the women were enrolled in graduate school within 6 months of graduation.
Admissions Contact: Marcelo Rivas Hernandez, Registrar, Admissions Office.

RELIGIOUS COLLEGES

ALABAMA

SOUTHERN CHRISTIAN UNIVERSITY
C-4
Montgomery, AL 36117-3553   (205) 277-2277

Full-time: 130 men	Faculty: 7
Part-time: 15 women	Tuition: $3740
Graduate: 100 men	Room & Board: n/app
SAT I, ACT: not required	

Southern Christian University, founded in 1967, is nondenominational. Its mission is the educational development of ministers, leaders, teachers, and scholars for the churches of Christ, who will use their gifts and knowledge in the proclamation of the gospel and in Christian service. Southern Christian University awards the B.A. and B.S. in religion. The school also awards master's and doctorate degrees.

ARIZONA

AMERICAN INDIAN BIBLE COLLEGE
C-4
Phoenix, AZ 85021   (602) 944-3335

Full-time: 40 men, 54 women	Faculty: 25
Part-time: 1 woman	Tuition: $3012
Application Deadline: 2 weeks after classes start	Room & Board: $2800
SAT I or ACT: not required	

American Indian Bible College, founded in 1957, is affiliated with Assemblies of God. Its mission is to provide education as developmental growth, specifically spiritual, intellectual, social, and physical. The Word of God is the heart, spirit, and final authority in all courses taught. American Indian Bible College awards the B.A. in ministerial studies, Christian education, and elementary education. The school also awards associate and bachelor's degrees.

ARIZONA COLLEGE OF THE BIBLE
C-4
Phoenix, AZ 85021   (602) 995-2670 or (800) 847-2138

Full-time: 53 men, 39 women	Faculty: 9
Part-time: 22 men, 16 women	Tuition: $4370
Application Deadline: open	Room & Board: $1420
SAT I or ACT: required	

Arizona College of the Bible, founded in 1971, is nondenominational. Its mission is to prepare men and women for Christian living, church ministries, and related professional vocation. ACB specializes in Bible and Christian doctrine. In addition to regional accreditation, the college is accredited by AABC. Arizona College of the Bible awards the B.A. in Bible, church ministries, cross-cultural studies, elementary education, music, pastoral ministry, youth ministry, and specialized studies. The school also awards associate degrees.

SOUTHWESTERN CONSERVATIVE BAPTIST BIBLE COLLEGE
C-4
Phoenix, AZ 85032   (602) 992-6101 or (800) 247-2697

Full-time: 65 men, 71 women	Faculty: 10
Part-time: 9 men, 9 women	Tuition: $5240
Application Deadline: August 10	Room & Board: $2350
SAT I Verbal/Math: 460/450	ACT: 21

Southwestern Conservative Baptist Bible College, founded in 1960, is affiliated with the Sun Valley Conservative Baptist Association/Arizona Baptist Convention. Its mission is to prepare students for vocational and lay ministries. In addition to regional accreditation, the college is accredited by AABC. Southwestern Conservative Baptist Bible College awards the B.A. and B.S. in elementary education, general Bible studies, and Christian ministries.

ARKANSAS

CENTRAL BAPTIST COLLEGE
C-3
Conway, AR 72032   (501) 329-6872

Full-time: 138 men, 110 women	Faculty: 11
Part-time: 9 men, 16 women	Tuition: $2630
Application Deadline: August 15	Room & Board: $2152
ACT: 18	

Central Baptist College, founded in 1952, is affiliated with the Baptist Missionary Association of Arkansas. It offers undergraduate degrees in Bible studies and religious education. In addition to regional accreditation, the college is accredited by AABC. Central Baptist College awards the B.A. and B.S. in Bible studies, Christian missions, church music, pastoral ministry, and religious education. The school also awards associate degrees.

CALIFORNIA

BETHANY BIBLE COLLEGE
(See Bethany College)

BETHANY COLLEGE
B-3
(Formerly Bethany Bible College)
Scotts Valley, CA 95066   (408) 438-3800 or (800) 843-9410

Full-time: 187 men, 261 women	Faculty: 22
Part-time: 74 men, 95 women	Tuition: $6941
Application Deadline: July 15	Room & Board: $3340
SAT I Verbal/Math: 428/546	ACT: 20

Bethany College, founded in 1919, is affiliated with Assemblies of God. Its mission is to prepare students for leadership in the church and society. Bethany College awards the B.A. in church leadership, English, communication arts, music, preseminary, psychology, Christian education, social sciences, business administration, biblical and theological studies, cross-cultural communication, cross-cultural ministries, general ministries, addiction counseling and studies, early childhood development, intercultural child development, integrated studies, and applied professional studies. The school also awards associate degrees.

PATTEN COLLEGE
B-3
Oakland, CA 94601   (510) 533-8306

Full-time: 76 men, 55 women	Faculty: 10
Part-time: 431 men, 162 women	Tuition: $4780
Application Deadline: July 15	Room & Board: $5076
SAT I or ACT: not required	

Patten College, founded in 1944, is affiliated with the Christian Evangelical Churches of America. Its mission is to offer a balanced liberal arts education with a strong biblical studies emphasis and to help students prepare for a life of Christian service. Patten College awards the B.A. in biblical studies, Christian education, liberal studies, pastoral studies, preseminary studies, and sacred music. The school also awards associate degrees.

SAINT JOHN'S SEMINARY COLLEGE
C-4
Camarillo, CA 93010   (805) 482-2755, ext. 202

Full-time: 108 men	Faculty: 25
Application Deadline: July 1	Tuition: $5500
	Room & Board: n/app
SAT I: required	

Saint John's Seminary College, founded in 1927, is affiliated with the Roman Catholic Church. Its mission is to provide a liberal arts education for young men interested in becoming priests for the Archdiocese of Los Angeles. Saint John's Seminary College awards the B.A. in philosophy, English, Spanish, liberal studies, and theology.

CONNECTICUT

HOLY APOSTLES COLLEGE AND SEMINARY   C-2
Cromwell, CT 06416   (203) 632-3000

Full-time: 9 men	Faculty: n/av
Part-time: 2 men, 8 women	Tuition: $4000
Graduate: 157 men, 25 women	Room & Board: $5950
Application Deadline: open	

Holy Apostles College and Seminary, founded in 1956, is affiliated with the Roman Catholic Church. Its mission is to provide adult men training for the Catholic priesthood with an academic and seminary environment suited to their age and background. Holy Apostles College and Seminary awards the B.A. in humanities, philosophy, religious studies, and social sciences. The school also awards associate, bachelor's, and master's degrees.

FLORIDA

FLORIDA BAPTIST THEOLOGICAL COLLEGE   B-1
Graceville, FL 32440   (904) 263-3261

Full-time: 355 men, 84 women	Faculty: 17
Part-time: 36 men, 22 women	Tuition: $2054
Application Deadline: open	Room & Board: $1700-1800
SAT I: required	

Florida Baptist Theological College, founded in 1943, is affiliated with the Florida Baptist Convention. Its mission is to promote, provide for, operate, and control a program of education and training for ministers and other religious workers. Florida Baptist Theological College awards the B.A. in music ministry, religious education, religious education/music, and theology. The school also awards associate degrees.

SAINT JOHN VIANNEY COLLEGE SEMINARY   E-5
Miami, FL 33165   (305) 223-4561

Full-time: 49 men, 1 woman	Faculty: 11
Part-time: 6 men, 2 women	Tuition: $6600
Application Deadline: July	Room & Board: $3500
SAT I or ACT: not required	

Saint John Vianney College Seminary, founded in 1959, is affiliated with the Roman Catholic Church. Its mission is to provide an undergraduate education preparatory for students whose stated objective is to serve the Catholic Church in the priesthood, and to provide spiritual and intellectual formation within an Anglo-Hispanic bilingual, bicultural setting. Saint John Vianney College Seminary awards the B.A. in philosophy.

WARNER SOUTHERN COLLEGE   D-4
Lake Wales, FL 33853   (813) 638-2109

Full-time: 200 men, 245 women	Faculty: 25
Part-time: 10 men, 30 women	Tuition: $5640
Application Deadline: open	Room & Board: $3100
SAT I or ACT: required	

Warner Southern College, founded in 1968, is affiliated with the Church of God. Its mission is to provide a quality program of higher education within an evagelical Christian perspective in the Wesleyan tradition. Warner Southern College awards the B.A. in biblical studies, business administration, church ministries, communication arts, missions, physical education, social services, and teacher education. The school also awards associate and bachelor's degrees.

GEORGIA

ATLANTA CHRISTIAN COLLEGE   B-2
East Point, GA 30344   (404) 761-8861

Full-time: 112 men, 104 women	Faculty: 16
Part-time: 32 men, 14 women	Tuition: $4384
Application Deadline: August 1	Room & Board: $2830
SAT I or ACT: required	

Atlanta Christian College, founded in 1928, is affiliated with Christian Churches and Churches of Christ. It's mission is to provide education in biblical studies, the arts and sciences, and professional studies to equip men and women for Christian service. The college is accredited by AABC. Atlanta Christian College awards the B.A. and B.S. in Christian education in the church, Christian education in the school, missions, music, and preaching ministry. The school also awards associate degrees.

ILLINOIS

LINCOLN CHRISTIAN COLLEGE   D3
Lincoln, IL 62656   (217) 732-3168

Full-time: 231 men, 215 women	Faculty: n/av
Part-time: 24 men, 48 women	Tuition: $381
Graduate: 184 men, 46 women	Room & Board: $1408
Application Deadline: open	
ACT: required	

Lincoln Christian College, founded in 1942, is affiliated with the Christian Church/Church of Christ. Its mission is to educate and train preachers, Christian teachers, and other Christian workers. In addition to regional accreditation, the college is accredited by AABC. Lincoln Christian College awards the B.A. and B.S. in ministry, Christian education, missions, Christian business administration, and music. The school also awards associate and master's degrees.

MOODY BIBLE INSTITUTE   E-2
Chicago, IL 60610   (312) 329-4265

Full-time: 840 men, 565 women	Faculty: 74
Part-time: 29 men, 26 women	Tuition: $1161
Graduate: 49 men, 36 women	Room & Board: $4060
Application Deadline: May 1	
ACT: 22	

Moody Bible Institute, founded in 1886, is affiliated with the Evangelical Protestant Church. Its mission is to educate and train individuals to proclaim the gospel of the Lord Jesus Christ, to promote evangelism, and to serve the evangelical Christian church vocationally and/or avocationally in its worldwide ministry. In addition to regional accreditation, the college is accredited by AABC. Moody Bible Institute awards the B.A. and B.S. in aviation technology, biblical studies, communication, world missions, pastoral studies, religious education, sacred music, theology, and applied linguistics. The school also awards master's degrees.

IOWA

DIVINE WORD COLLEGE   E-2
Epworth, IA 52045   (319) 876-3353, ext. 249

Full-time: 60 men	Tuition: $6000
Part-time: 3 men, 3 women	Room & Board: $1200
Application Deadline: July 15	

Divine Word College, founded in 1912, is affiliated with the Roman Catholic Church. Its mission is excellence in combining a liberal arts education with a cross-cultural program of missionary formation for Divine Word Missionaries and other leaders in the Roman Catholic Church. Divine Word College awards the B.A. and B.S. in English, general science, philosophy, sociology, mathematics/science, and humanites, with concentrations in English, art, or music. The school also awards associate and bachelor's degrees.

FAITH BAPTIST BIBLE COLLEGE AND SEMINARY   C-3
Ankeny, IA 50021   (800) 352-0147

Full-time: 94 men, 92 women	Faculty: n/av
Part-time: 16 men, 23 women	Tuition: $4892
Graduate: 24 men, 1 woman	Room & Board: $1519
Application Deadline: August 1	
ACT: 21	

Faith Baptist Bible College and Seminary, founded in 1921, is affiliated with General Association of Regular Baptist Churches. It provides an intensive biblical and vocational education to prepare students for Christian leadership positions in fundamental Baptist churches and organizations. The college is accredited by AABC. Faith Baptist Bible College and Seminary awards the B.A. and B.S. in Bible and theology, assistant pastor, Christian education, Christian school, missions, music ministries, and secretarial training. The school also awards associate and master's degrees.

KENTUCKY

MID-CONTINENT BAPTIST BIBLE COLLEGE A-4
Mayfield, KY 42066-0357 (502) 247-8521
Full-time: 53 men, 17 women | Faculty: 6
Part-time: 34 men, 12 women | Tuition: $1730
Application Deadline: August 15 | Room & Board: $2832
SAT I or ACT: required

Mid-Continent Baptist Bible College, founded in 1949, is affiliated with the Baptist Church. Its mission is to prepare pastors and workers for service in Baptist churches and institutions and to provide general education and theological courses to the community. Mid-Continent Baptist Bible College awards the B.A. and B.S. in Bible study and religious education.

LOUISIANA

JIMMY SWAGGART BIBLE COLLEGE AND SEMINARY C-4
Baton Rouge, LA 70828-8000 (504) 769-3820
Full-time: 200 men, 175 women | Faculty: 44
Part-time: 40 men, 30 women | Tuition: $2920
Graduate: 20 men, 10 women | Room & Board: n/app
Application Deadline: August 1
ACT: required

Jimmy Swaggart Bible College and Seminary was founded in 1984. The college awards the B.A. and B.S. in Bible studies, elementary education, middle school education, missionary studies, music performance, religious education, religious music, and secondary education. The school also awards associate and master's degrees.

SAINT JOSEPH SEMINARY COLLEGE D-3
St. Benedict, LA 70457 (504) 982-1800
Full-time: 60 men | Faculty: 37 total
Application Deadline: open | Tuition: $5530
 | Room & Board: $4400
ACT: 20

Saint Joseph Seminary College, founded in 1891, is affiliated with the Roman Catholic Church. Its mission is the education and training of men for the priesthood in the Roman Catholic Church. Saint Joseph Seminary College awards the B.A. in liberal arts.

MARYLAND

BALTIMORE HEBREW UNIVERSITY D-2
Baltimore, MD 21215-3996
Full-time: 10 men, 60 women | Faculty: 34 total
Part-time: 2 men, 280 women | Ph.D.s: n/av
Graduate: 50 men, 80 women | Student/Faculty: n/av
Year: semesters, summer session | Tuition: $3400
Application Deadline: open | Room & Board: n/app
Freshman Class: n/av

Baltimore Hebrew University was founded in 1919. Its mission is to provide students with the broadest understanding of the civilization of the Jews through programs leading to the B.A., M.A., and Ph.D. degrees in Jewish studies; to train professionals in all fields of Jewish communal service; to offer courses for students choosing study for its own sake; to provide services to the general community such as the Library, lectures, conferences, and other activities.

MASSACHUSETTS

SAINT HYACINTH COLLEGE SEMINARY B-3
Granby, MA 01033 (413) 467-7191
Full-time: 14 men | Faculty: 12
Part-time: 14 men, 21 women | Tuition: $3795
Application Deadline: open | Room & Board: $4500
SAT I Verbal/Math: 470/500

Saint Hyacinth College Seminary, founded in 1927, is affiliated with the Roman Catholic Church. Its mission is to educate and form men who are responding to a call to serve God and neighbor as Franciscan priests and brothers and to provide qualified studies with a sound liberal arts education. Saint Hyacinth College Seminary awards the B.A. in philosophy. The school also awards associate degrees.

SAINT JOHN'S SEMINARY COLLEGE E-2
Brighton, MA 02135
Recognized candidate for accreditation (617) 254-2610
Full-time: 30 men | Faculty: 24 total
Part-time: 8 men | Tuition: $3600
Application Deadline: open | Room & Board: $3000
SAT I: required

Saint John's Seminary College, founded in 1884, is affiliated with the Roman Catholic Church. Its mission is to assist college-level seminarians to grow in Christian maturity as liberally educated persons committed to the service of the Church. Saint John's Seminary College awards the B.A. in philosophy. The school also awards associate and bachelor's degrees.

MICHIGAN

GRACE BIBLE COLLEGE D-4
Grand Rapids, MI 49509 (616) 538-2330
Full-time: 59 men, 54 women | Faculty: 8
Part-time: 12 men, 8 women | Tuition: $4725
Application Deadline: open | Room & Board: $3100
ACT: 19

Grace Bible College, founded in 1939, is affiliated with the Grace Gospel Fellowship. Its mission is to emphasize Bible, business, music, and human service studies, and provide training for the professional ministries. In addition to regional accreditation, the college is accredited by AABC. Grace Bible College awards the B.R.E. and B.Th. in business administration, Christian education, church music, early childhood education, educational ministries, human services, pastoral ministry, youth ministry, and Christian music industry. The school also awards associate degrees.

SACRED HEART MAJOR SEMINARY E-5
Detroit, MI 48206 (313) 883-8552
Full-time: 31 men, 1 woman | Faculty: 24
Part-time: 80 men, 61 women | Tuition: $4130
Graduate: 53 men, 13 women | Room & Board: $4100
Application Deadline: open
ACT: 18

Sacred Heart Major Seminary, founded in 1924, is affiliated with the Roman Catholic Church. Its mission is to provide spiritual formation and a liberal arts education for candidates preparing for the Roman Catholic priesthood in Detroit and for students preparing for other ministries within the Church. Sacred Heart Major Seminary awards the A.B. in philosophy. The school also awards associate and master's degrees.

MINNESOTA

CROWN COLLEGE C-4
Saint Bonifacius, MN 55375 (612) 446-4132
Full-time: 209 men, 207 women | Faculty: 22
Part-time: 18 men, 84 women | Tuition: $7554
Application Deadline: open | Room & Board: $3590
ACT: 20

Crown College, founded in 1916, is affiliated with the Christian and Missionary Alliance. Its mission is to provide a biblically-based education for Christian leadership in the Christian and Missionary Alliance, the church-at-large, and the world. In addition to regional accreditation, the college is accredited by AABC. Crown College awards the B.A., B.S., and B.Mus.Ed. in biblical and theological studies, business administration/sports fitness management, business administration, Christian education, church music, church music and ministries, elementary education, family and child development, history, history precounseling, history preseminary, history/secondary education, music education, pastoral ministries, social science/secondary education, world mission, youth, psychology, English, English education, physical education/coaching, psychology/early childhood education, and linguistics. The school also awards associate degrees.

DR. MARTIN LUTHER COLLEGE C-4
New Ulm, MN 56073 (507) 354-8221
Full-time: 188 men, 371 women | Faculty: 60
Part-time: 3 men, 8 women | Tuition: $3600
Application Deadline: July 20 | Room & Board: $1790
ACT: 22

Dr. Martin Luther College, founded in 1884, is affiliated with WELS Lutheran Church. Its mission is to enable its graduates to teach and

serve in the schools and congregations of the Wisconsin Evangelical Lutheran Synod. Dr. Martin Luther College awards the B.S.Ed. in elementary and secondary education.

music education, church education, elementary education, missionary aviation, music, and pastoral. The school also awards the bachelor's degree.

MISSISSIPPI

MAGNOLIA BIBLE COLLEGE D-3
Kosciusko, MS 39090   (601) 289-2896

Full-time: 16 men, 4 women	Faculty: 5
Part-time: 19 men, 4 women	Tuition: $2580
Application Deadline: open	Room & Board: $1400
ACT: 17	

Magnolia Bible College, founded in 1976, is affiliated with Churches of Christ. Its mission is to enable students to acquire a college-level educational in general, biblical, and professional studies that will enable them to serve as preachers, missionaries, directors of Christian education, Bible chair directors, campus evangelists, and other Christian workers. In addition to regional accreditation, the college is accredited by AABC. Magnolia Bible College awards the B.A. in Bible and theology.

MISSOURI

CONCEPTION SEMINARY COLLEGE A-1
Conception, MO 64433   (816) 944-2218

Full-time: 7 men	Faculty: 18
Part-time: 7 men, 4 women	Tuition: $5504
Application Deadline: July 1	Room & Board: $2974
ACT: 19	

Conception Seminary College, founded in 1886, is affiliated with the Roman Catholic Church. Its mission is the formation of young men wishing to discover their calling to the priesthood by providing a liberal arts education aimed at integrating academic, spiritual, personal, and social growth. Conception Seminary College awards the B.A. in philosophy, pretheology, psychology, and religion.

NEW YORK

WADHAMS HALL SEMINARY COLLEGE C-2
Ogdensburg, NY 13669   (315) 393-4231

Full-time: 25 men, 2 women	Faculty: 12
Part-time: 9 men, 29 women	Tuition: $3650
Application Deadline: August 15	Room & Board: $3400
SAT I or ACT: required	

Wadhams Hall Seminary College, founded in 1924, is affiliated with the Roman Catholic Church. Its mission is to prepare men at the college level for further studies leading to priesthood in the Catholic church, and to prepare other students for leadership in the Catholic church. Wadhams Hall Seminary College awards the B.A. in philosophy and religious studies.

NORTH CAROLINA

EAST COAST BIBLE COLLEGE C-3
Charlotte, NC 28214   (704) 394-2307

Full-time: 100 men, 64 women	Faculty: 12
Part-time: 106 men, 126 women	Tuition: $4140
Application Deadline: August 1	Room & Board: $2400
ACT: required	

East Coast Bible College, founded in 1976, is affiliated with the Church of God. Its mission is to prepare workers for Christian ministries and emphasize Biblical content in all of its programs. In addition to regional accreditation, the college is accredited by AABC. East Coast Bible College awards the B.A. and B.S. in Bible studies, Christian education, church music, and elementary education. The school also awards associate degrees.

PIEDMONT BIBLE COLLEGE C-2
Winston-Salem, NC 27101
Recognized candidate for accreditation   (919) 725-8344

Full-time: 160 men, 75 women	Tuition: $4090
Part-time: 25 men, 25 women	Room & Board: $2600
Application Deadline: open	

Piedmont Bible College, founded in 1945, is affiliated with Independent Baptist. Its mission is to train people in full-time Christian vocations. The college is accredited by AABC. Piedmont Bible College awards the B.A., B.S., and B.Th. in biblical studies, Christian school,

NORTH DAKOTA

TRINITY BIBLE COLLEGE E-4
Ellendale, ND 58436   (701) 349-3621

Full-time: 190 men, 156 women	Faculty: 16
Part-time: 9 men, 11 women	Tuition: $4734
Application Deadline: open	Room & Board: $2994
ACT: required	

Trinity Bible College, founded in 1948, is affiliated with the Assemblies of God Church. In addition to regional accreditation, the college is accredited by AABC. Trinity Bible College awards the B.A. in Biblical studies, business, Christian education, elementary education, ministerial studies, missions, and precounseling. The school also awards associate degrees.

OHIO

CINCINNATI BIBLE COLLEGE AND SEMINARY
A-5
Cincinnati, OH 45204-3200   (513) 244-8141 or (800) 949-4CBC

Full-time: 285 men, 223 women	Faculty: 43
Part-time: 51 men, 62 women	Tuition: $5203
Graduate: 242 men, 58 women	Room & Board: $3400
Application Deadline: August 10	
ACT: 21	

Cincinnati Bible College and Seminary, founded in 1924, is affiliated with the nondemominational Christian/Church of Christ. Its mission is to prepare students for Christian service. In addition to regional accreditation, the college is accredited by AABC. Cincinnati Bible College and Seminary awards the B.A., B.S., and B.Church Mus. in biblical studies, Christian education, Christmas ministries, church music, and missions. The school also awards associate and master's degrees.

PONTIFICAL COLLEGE JOSEPHINUM C-3
Columbus, OH 43235   (614) 885-5585

Full-time: 50 men, 2 women	Faculty: 51 total
Part-time: 2 men, 3 women	Tuition: $5152
Graduate: 80 men, 10 women	Room & Board: $3532
Application Deadline: July 15	
SAT I or ACT: required	

Pontifical College Josephinum was founded in 1888. Its mission is to prepare young men for the priesthood. Pontifical College Josephinum awards the B.A. in English, history, Latin American studies, philosophy, and psychology. The school also awards master's degrees.

OKLAHOMA

MID-AMERICAN BIBLE COLLEGE D-3
Oklahoma City, OK 73170   (405) 691-3800

Full-time: 177 men, 125 women	Faculty: 17
Part-time: 56 men, 55 women	Tuition: $4172
Application Deadline: open	Room & Board: $2596
ACT: required	

Mid-American Bible College, founded in 1953, is affiliated with the Church of God-Anderson, Indiana. Its mission is to train and prepare men and women for the Christian ministry. In addition to regional accreditation, the college is accredited by AABC. Mid-American Bible College awards the B.A. and B.S. in behavioral science, elementary education, English, music, pastoral ministry, secondary education, and specialized ministries.

SOUTHWESTERN COLLEGE OF CHRISTIAN MINISTRIES D-3
Bethany, OK 73008   (405) 789-7661

Full-time: 107 men, 50 women	Faculty: 9
Part-time: 13 men, 7 women	Tuition: $3450
Application Deadline: open	Room & Board: $2500
ACT: 15	

Southwestern College of Christian Ministries, founded in 1946, is affiliated with Pentecostal Holiness. Its mission is the education and training for Christian service leading toward professional competence in the practice of various ministry forms. Southwestern College of

Christian Ministries awards the B.A. and B.S. in biblical studies, Christian elementary education, Christian ministry/pastoral studies, and religion. The school also awards associate degrees.

OREGON

MOUNT ANGEL SEMINARY
B-2
St. Benedict, OR 97373 (503) 845-3951
Full-time: 39 men
Graduate: 65 men, 48 women
Application Deadline: July 15
SAT, ACT: not required

Faculty: 11
Tuition: $4650
Room & Board: $3500

Mount Angel Seminary, founded in 1889, is affiliated with the Roman Catholic Church. Its mission is to prepare students for the Roman Catholic priesthood for religious orders and dioceses. Mount Angel Seminary awards the B.A. in philosophy and religious studies.

NORTHWEST CHRISTIAN COLLEGE
B-2
Eugene, OR 97401 (503) 343-1641
Full-time: 113 men, 113 women
Part-time: 42 men, 32 women
Graduate: 23 men, 28 women
Application Deadline: open
SAT I Verbal/Math: 439/481

Faculty: 11
Tuition: $7600
Room & Board: $3690

Northwest Christian College, founded in 1895, is affiliated with the Christian Church/Church of Christ. Its mission is to provide education in biblical studies, arts and sciences, and selected professions in an environment that fosters Christian faith, self-understanding and participation in community, and encourages service in the church and in the world. Northwest Christian College awards the B.A., B.S., B.C.M., B.Sac.Mus., and B.Th. in biblical languages and interpretation, cross-cultural ministry, educational ministry, intercultural studies, interdisciplinary studies, management communication, music ministry, organizational management, pastoral ministry, preseminary, speech communication, and youth ministry. The school also awards associate and master's degrees.

PENNSYLVANIA

BAPTIST BIBLE COLLEGE OF PENNSYLVANIA
E-2
Clarks Summit, PA 18411 (717) 587-1172, ext. 376
Full-time: 231 men, 261 women
Part-time: 30 men, 48 women
Graduate: 2 men, 2 women
Application Deadline: August 15
SAT I Verbal/Math: 450/450

Faculty: 22
Tuition: $6061
Room & Board: $3660

ACT: 19

Baptist Bible College of Pennsylvania, founded in 1932, is affiliated with the General Association of Regular Baptist Churches. Its mission is to prepare men and women for service in selected Christian ministries as pastors, missionaries, Christian education workers, teachers for Christian schools, counselors, church musicians, and secretaries for Christian organizations. In addition to regional accreditation, the college is accredited by AABC. Baptist Bible College of Pennsylvania awards the B.S in Bible and B.S.M. in church music, elementary education, general missions, local church ministries, music education, outreach and evangelism pastor, pastoral ministry, pastor of Christian education, preseminary, secondary education, secretarial ministries, youth pastor, precounseling, general ministries, and women's ministries. The school also awards associate and master's degrees.

LANCASTER BIBLE COLLEGE
E-3
Lancaster, PA 17601 (717) 560-8271 or (800) 544-7335
Full-time: 165 men, 180 women
Part-time: 81 men, 81 women

Faculty: 21
Tuition: $7410
Room & Board: $3300

SAT I, ACT: not required

Lancaster Bible College, founded in 1933, is nondenominational. Its mission is educating Christian men and women to live according to a biblical world view and to serve through professional Christian ministries. In addition to regional accreditation, the college is accredited by AABC. Lancaster Bible College awards the B.S. in Bible, Christian education, computers in ministry, missions, music, pastoral studies, preseminary, youth ministries, counseling, teacher education, and early childhood. The school also awards associate degrees.

SAINT CHARLES BORROMEO SEMINARY
F-3
Overbrook, PA 19096 (215) 667-3394
Full-time: 80 men
Part-time: 34 men, 82 women
Graduate: 207 men, 66 women
Application Deadline: July 1
SAT I or ACT: required

Faculty: 42
Tuition: $5525
Room & Board: $3500

Saint Charles Borromeo Seminary, founded in 1832, is affiliated with the Roman Catholic Church. Its mission is to prepare and educate men studying for the Roman Catholic priesthood and men and women who wish to pursue theological studies. Saint Charles Borromeo Seminary awards the B.A. in philosophy. The school also awards master's degrees.

SOUTH CAROLINA

BIBLE COLLEGE AND SEMINARY
(See Columbia International University)

COLUMBIA INTERNATIONAL UNIVERSITY
C-3
Columbia Bible College and Seminary
Columbia, SC 29230 (803) 754-4100
Full-time: 214 men, 172 women
Part-time: 26 men, 25 women
Graduate: 10 men, 38 women
Application Deadline: open
SAT I Verbal/Math: 450/480

Faculty: 23
Tuition: $6210
Room & Board: $3262

ACT: 21

Columbia International University, founded in 1923, is multidenominational. Its mission is to prepare students to grow in spiritual maturity, Bible knowledge, and ministry skills in preparation for vocational or lay Christian ministry. In addition to regional accreditation, the college is accredited by AABC. Columbia International University awards the B.A. and B.S. in Bible, elementary education, and intercultural studies, psychology, biblical languages, music, Bible teaching, youth ministry, humanities, and pastoral ministries. The school also awards associate, master's, and doctoral degrees.

TENNESSEE

JOHNSON BIBLE COLLEGE
E-3
Knoxville, TN 37998 (615) 573-4517
Full-time: 233 men, 172 women
Part-time: 11 men, 12 women
Graduate: 54 men, 1 woman
Application Deadline: August 1
ACT: 21

Faculty: 18
Tuition: $4250
Room & Board: $3030

Johnson Bible College, founded in 1893, is affiliated with the Christian faith. Its mission is to educate students for specialized Christian ministries. In addition to regional accreditation, the college is accredited by AABC. Johnson Bible College awards the B.A. and B.S. in Bible, Bible and nursing, teacher education and Bible, and music and Bible. The school also awards associate and master's degrees.

TEXAS

BAPTIST MISSIONARY THEOLOGICAL SEMINARY
E-2
Jacksonville, TX 75766 (903) 586-2501
Full-time: 17 men, 1 woman
Part-time: 19 men, 5 women
Graduate: 37 men, 3 women
Application Deadline: open
SAT I, ACT: not required

Faculty: 8
Tuition: $1260
Room & Board: $1800

Baptist Missionary Theological Seminary, founded in 1955, is affiliated with the Baptist Missionary Association. Its mission is to train individuals for Christian ministry. Baptist Missionary Theological Seminary awards the B.A.R. in religion. The school also awards associate and master's degrees.

CRISWELL COLLEGE
D-2
Dallas, TX 75246
(214) 821–5433

Full-time: 130 men, 25 women	Faculty: 10
Part-time: 100 men, 20 women	Tuition: $2650
Graduate: 60 men, 2 women	Room & Board: n/app
Application Deadline: open	

Criswell College, founded in 1970, is affiliated with the Baptist Church. Its mission is to educate and train laymen and full-time Christian workers in biblical, theological, and professional studies so they can serve effectively in evangelistic, educational, pastoral, and missionary vocations of the Christian Church. Criswell College awards the B.A. in biblical studies, counseling, missions, and evangelism. The school also awards associate and master's degrees.

INSTITUTE FOR CHRISTIAN STUDIES
D-4
Austin, TX 78705
(512) 476–2772

Full-time: 20 men, 4 women	Faculty: 6
Part-time: 29 men, 29 women	Tuition: $30 p/c
Application Deadline: June 1 (recommended)	Room & Board: $2000
SAT I or ACT: required	

The Institute for Christian Studies, founded in 1917, is affiliated with the Church of Christ. Its mission is to educate ministers and other Christian leaders in biblical studies. The Institute for Christian Studies awards the B.A. and B.S. in biblical studies.

SOUTHWESTERN ASSEMBLIES OF GOD COLLEGE
D-2
Waxahachie, TX 75165
Recognized candidate for accreditation
(214) 937–4010

Full-time: 260 men, 220 women	Faculty: 18
Part-time: 75 men, 40 women	Tuition: $2900
Application Deadline: open	Room & Board: $2762
ACT: required	

Southwestern Assemblies of God College, founded in 1927, is affiliated with the Assemblies of God Church. Its mission is the training of Christian individuals to carry the gospel to the ends of the earth or to fill any other divinely approved place in the Kingdom of God. In addition to regional accreditation, the college is accredited by AABC. Southwestern Assemblies of God College awards the B.A., B.S., and B. Career Arts in business, church ministries, and interdisciplinary studies for elementary teachers. The school also awards associate and bachelor's degrees.

WASHINGTON

LUTHERAN BIBLE INSTITUTE OF SEATTLE
C-2
Issaquah, WA 98027
(800) 843–5659

Full-time: 70 men, 62 women	Faculty: 10 part-time
Part-time: 12 men, 19 women	Tuition: $2840
Application Deadline: August 15	Room & Board: $3600
SAT I or ACT: required	

Lutheran Bible Institute of Seattle, founded in 1944, is affiliated with the Lutheran Church. Its mission is to train students for professional ministry. Lutheran Bible Institute of Seattle awards the B.A. in biblical studies, Christian education, youth and family ministry, urban missions, and global missions. The school also awards associate degrees.

WISCONSIN

MARANTHA BAPTIST BIBLE COLLEGE
D-4
Watertown, WI 53094
(414) 261–9300, ext. 308

Full-time: 186 men, 244 women	Faculty: 32
Part-time: 39 men, 27 women	Tuition: $4280
Graduate: 21 men	Room & Board: $1350
Application Deadline: open	
ACT: required	

Marantha Baptist Bible College, founded in 1968, is affiliated with the Baptist Church. Its mission is to train men and women for effective gospel ministry in the local church through a post-secondary program of biblical, general, and professional studies. Marantha Baptist Bible College awards the B.A. and B.S. in Bible, church ministries, education, general studies, fine arts, business, and nursing. The school also awards associate and master's degrees.

FURTHER READING

Two other Barron's books present more detailed information on selected schools. *Barron's Top Fifty*, edited by Tom Fischgrund, features lengthy pieces written by recent graduates of some of the nation's most prestigious colleges. *Barron's Best Buys* by Lucia Solórzano features some 300 colleges and universities that are perceived to give the best bargains in higher educations. These essays are written by the author, with input from deans and students from each of the schools.

College students considering application to a graduate professional school will find relevant information in *Barron's Guide to Medical and Dental Schools*, *Barron's Guide to Law Schools*, and *Barron's Guide to Graduate Business Schools*.

Further information on entrance examinations and other aspects of college can be found in the following Barron's publications, all of which are available from Barron's Educational Series, 250 Wireless Boulevard, Hauppauge, New York 11788.

ACT — How to Prepare for the ACT
ACT — Computer Study Program for the ACT
ACT — Pass Key to the ACT
AP — How to Prepare for the Advanced Placement
   Examinations:
   Biology
   English
   European History
   Mathematics
   U.S. History
Barron's Top 50: An Inside Look at America's Best Colleges
Barron's Best Buys in College Education
Complete College Financing Guide
ELM — How to Prepare for the California Entry Level
   Mathematics Exams
EZ — 101 Study Keys:
   Accounting
   American History to 1877
   American History 1877 to Present
   American Literature
   Art History
   Biology
   Chemistry
   Computer Science
   English Literature
   Finance
   Macroeconomics
   Management
   Microeconomics
   Physics
   Sociology
   Statistics

How to Prepare for the California State University Writing
   Proficiency Exams
How to Prepare for the Michigan Test Battery
How to Beat Test Anxiety (and Score Higher on the SAT
   and All Other Tests)
Keys to Financing a College Education
Making the Grade in College
MAT — How to Prepare for the Miller Analogy Test
Pocket Guide to Study Tips: How to Study Effectively
   and Get Better Grades
PSAT-NMSQT — How to Prepare for the Preliminary
   SAT/National Merit Scholarship Qualifying Test
PSAT-NMSQT — Pass Key to the PSAT-NMSQT
SAT I — Computer Study Program for SAT I
SAT I — 14 Days to Higher SAT I Scores
SAT I — Hot Words for SAT I
SAT I — How to Prepare for SAT I
SAT I — Mathematics Workbook
SAT I — Pass Key to SAT I
SAT I — Verbal Workbook
SAT II — How to Prepare for SAT II:
   American History and Social Studies
   Biology
   Chemistry
   English
   European History
   French
   Latin
   Mathematics Level I
   Mathematics Level II
   Physics
   Spanish
   Writing
Student Success Secrets
Student's New Concise Encyclopedia
Study Tactics
TASP — How to Prepare for the Texas Academic Skills
   Program Test
TOEFL — Classroom TOEFL
TOEFL — How to Prepare for the Test of English as a Foreign
   Language
TOEFL — Pass Key to the TOEFL
TOEFL — Practice Exercises for the Test of English as a
   Foreign Language
TOEFL — TOEFL Strategies
Writing a Successful College Application Essay
You Can Succeed! The Ultimate Study Guide for Students

INDEX